SCIENTIFIC AND TECHNICAL
BOOKS AND SERIALS
IN PRINT
1986

This Edition of SCIENTIFIC AND TECHNICAL
BOOKS AND SERIALS IN PRINT 1986
is prepared by the R.R. Bowker
Company's Data Services Division in collaboration
with the Publication Systems Department

Staff of the Data Services Division includes:
Peter Simon, Vice President, Data Services Division;
Scott D. MacFarland, Managing Editor, Databases, Serials/Reference Books;
Dean Hollister, Senior Product Manager;
Andrew Grabois, Product Manager;
Kathy Berger, Editorial Coordinator;
James Cason, Michael Edmund, Melissa Kapustey, and Helen Murray, Assistant Editors;
Chris Andrews, Joshua Cabat, Lisa Dierbeck and Meera Kothari, Editorial Assistants;
William Garbe and Kenneth Goodman, Contributing Editors.

Senior staff of the Serials Bibliography Department includes:
Leigh Carol Yuster, Senior Product Manager, Serials Bibliography;
Richard H. Oosterom, Project Coordinator, Subject Bibliographies, Serials Bibliography;
Jacqueline Mullikin, Project Coordinator, Serials Bibliography;
Sharon R. Argov, Data Sources Coordinator, Serials Bibliography.

Senior Staff of Publisher Address Databases/Associations Department includes:
Brenda Sutton-McElroy, Manager;
Keith Schiffman, Product Manager;
Jane Tiarsmith, Product Manager.

Bernard Kideckel, Manager, Computer Systems and Development;
Michael Gold, Manager, Systems Development.
Betty Birdsell, Data Processing Manager
Jack Murphy, Computer Operations Coordinator

SCIENTIFIC
AND TECHNICAL
BOOKS AND SERIALS
IN PRINT
1986

VOLUME 1
BOOKS—SUBJECT INDEX

R.R. BOWKER COMPANY

Published by R. R. Bowker Division of Reed Publishing USA
205 East Forty-Second Street, New York, N.Y. 10017
Copyright © 1985 by Reed Publishing USA, a division of Reed Holdings, Inc.

International Standard Book Number Set: 0-8352-2083-4
Vol. 1 0-8352-2084-2, Vol. 2 0-8352-2085-0, Vol. 3 0-8352-2086-9
International Standard Serial Number 0000-054X
Library of Congress Catalog Card Number: 78-640940

Printed and bound in the United States of America

CONTENTS

ISBN
INTERNATIONAL STANDARD
BOOK NUMBER

The 1986 SCIENTIFIC AND TECHNICAL BOOKS AND SERIALS IN PRINT lists each title or edition of a title in the book indexes with an ISBN. All publishers were notified and requested to submit the ISBN for their titles.

During the past decade, the majority of the publishers complied with requirements of the standard and implemented the ISBN. At present, approximately 97% of all new titles and all new editions are submitted for listing with a valid ISBN.

To fulfill the responsibility of accomplishing total book numbering, the ISBN Agency allocated the ISBN prefixes 0-317, 0-318, 0-685 and 0-686 to number their titles in the SUBJECT GUIDE TO BOOKS IN PRINT database without an ISBN. Titles not having an ISBN at the closing date of this publication were assigned an ISBN with one of these prefixes by the International Standard Book Numbering Agency.

Titles numbered within the prefixes 0-317, 0-318, 0-685 and 0-686 are:
—Publishers who did not assign ISBN to their titles.
—Distributors with titles published and imported from countries not in the ISBN system, or not receiving the ISBN from the originating publisher.
—Errors from transposition and transcription which occurred in transmitting the ISBN to the BOOKS IN PRINT database.

All the ISBN listed in SUBJECT GUIDE TO BOOKS IN PRINT are validated by using the check digit control, and only valid ISBN are listed in the database.

All publishers participating in the ISBN system having titles numbered within the prefixes 0-317, 0-318, 0-685 and 0-686 will receive a computer printout, requesting them to submit the correct ISBN.

Publishers not participating in the ISBN system may request from the ISBN Agency the assignment of an ISBN Publisher Prefix, and start numbering their titles.

The Book Industry System Advisory Committee (BISAC) developed a standard format for data transmission, and many companies are already accepting orders transmitted on magnetic tape using the ISBN. Another standard format by BISAC for title updating is under development.

The ISBN Agency and the Data Services Division of the Bowker Company wish to express their appreciation to all publishers who collaborated in making the ISBN system the standard of the publishing industry.

For additional information related to the ISBN total numbering, please refer to Emery Koltay, Director of the ISBN/SAN Agency.

PREFACE

The R. R. Bowker Company first published *Scientific And Technical Books In Print* in 1974. Our aim then, as now, was to provide a comprehensive subject selection of Bowker's bibliographic data base that would provide our users with current bibliographic and ordering information for in-print titles published or exclusively distributed in the United States. Recognizing the importance of serials in science and technology. Bowker expanded its bibliography in 1978 to include serials and changed the name to *Scientific and Technical Books And Serials In Print* to reflect this expanded scope. A special mailing to associations was also done for that edition to increase our coverage of monographs from these sources. The 1978 edition also included an article by Ellis Mount titled "Scientific and Technological Information: Its Sources and Availability" which describes the various types of publications and nonprint materials available in this field. For this edition, Mr. Mount has brought all this material up-to-date, in an article entitled "Informational Sources For Science and Technology."

While Bowker has expanded *Scientific and Technical Books And Serials In Print* to include additional types of publications and added new subject areas as they emerged as important to the field, no major changes have been made to the original subject scope of this bibliography. As in earlier editions, the selection of titles for *Scientific and Technical Books And Serials In Print 1986* was intended to meet the needs of professionals in scientific and technical fields as well as laymen and young adults with interests in these areas. All aspects of physical and biological sciences and their applications are included as well as engineering and what can be generally called technology. Specifically, titles in the field of industry were selected for their treatment of technological problems rather than economic, marketing, or management aspects. In architecture the emphasis was on materials and structure rather than design and social considerations.

Material pertaining to hobbies is limited; more emphasis is given to "technical" hobbies than those considered "artistic" pastimes. Therefore, there is little on gardening and cooking for the layman, but botanical descriptions and treatises are included, as are books on food technology and professional food preparation. Business and economics are generally excluded; they are covered in Bowker's *Business And Economics Books And Serials In Print*. Medicine and psychology, except for animal behavior, were considered outside the scope of this volume but are completely covered in Bowker's annual *Medical Books And Serials In Print*. In order to provide a wider background for contemporary technology and science, relevant biographies and philosophic works as well as dealing with historic technologies were included.

Scientific And Technical Books And Serials In Print excerpts from the data bases of the R.R. Bowker Company's Data Services Division titles which fall within this subject and audience scope. This edition was produced from records stored on magnetic tape, edited by computer programs, and set in type by computer-controlled photocomposition.

In order to produce the Books section, which includes subject, author, and title indexes, we have examined the data base used to produce *Books In Print, Books In Print Supplement, Forthcoming Books, Subject Guide To Books In Print, Subject Guide To Forthcoming Books* and other bibliographies in the "In Print" line. This data base contains titles which have been or will be published or exclusively distributed in the United States. The data base was updated to conform with the latest information received from publishers for the production of *Books In Print 1985-1986* and *Subject Guide To Books In Print 1985-1986* and includes information on titles to be published through January 1986. This information will be updated and supplemented by bi-monthly issues of *Forthcoming Books* and *Subject Guide To Forthcoming Books* and by *Books In Print Supplement 1985-1986* to be published in April 1986. At present, we have included only titles that are priced at least 25 cents and are available to the trade and to the general public. In the future, the data base may be expanded to include free or member-only materials.

The author and title indexes include over 114,168 titles available from some 4,385 publishers. The subject index to books follows the headings assigned by the Library of Congress. Titles were searched in the catalogs and MARC tapes of the Library of Congress to determine the headings to be assigned. To some books LC assigned a single heading and to others it assigned two or more headings; some books, therefore, appear two or more times. Actually, the 114,168 titles appear about 145,540 times under some 12,965 headings with 15,913 references.

The Serials section, which contains subject and title indexes, lists almost 17,642 titles published by the United Nations or the European Communities or in the following countries: Australia, Austria, Belgium, Canada, Denmark, France, West Germany, Ireland, Israel, Italy, Japan, Luxembourg, Netherlands, Norway, New Zealand, Portugal, South Africa, Spain, Sweden, Switzerland, United Kingdom or the United States. The large volume of serial publications in scientific and technical areas prohibits our including publications from all countries. We recognize the importance of publications from the Soviet Union; however, the difficulty of obtaining complete bibliographic information prohibits our covering them directly. We have attempted to provide access to this material through our coverage of translations of Soviet serials.

We have included serial publications issued by governments or by the United Nations or the European Communities. These serial publications include indexes to monographic or serial government publications. The volume or monographic government publications in this area prohibits our listing them individually.

Entries for the Serials section were selected from the Bowker International Serials Database and provide the latest information included in and received since the publication of *Ulrich's International Periodicals Directory,* 24th edition, *Irregular Serials And Annuals,* 11th Edition, and *Ulrich's Quarterly,* Vol. 9, No. 3. Some titles appear two or more times in the subject index. Actually, some 17,642 titles appear about 23,894 times under some 486 subject headings with 500 cross-references.

The R. R. Bowker Company has used its best efforts in collecting and preparing material for inclusion in *Scientific And Technical Books And Serials In Print 1986* but does not assume, and hereby disclaims, any liability to any party for any loss or damage caused by errors or omissions in *Scientific And Technical Books And Serials In Print 1986* whether such errors or omissions resulted from negligence, accident, or any other cause. The participation of our users in correcting such errors in future editions will be welcomed and appreciated.

Scott D. MacFarland
Managing Editor,
Databases

Dean Hollister
Senior Product Manager,
Data Services Division

Andrew Grabois
Product Manager,
Data Services Division

Leigh Carol Yuster
Senior Product Manager,
Serials Bibliography

INFORMATIONAL SOURCES FOR SCIENCE AND TECHNOLOGY

There are several aspects of informational sources for science and technology (or engineering) which are not widely known outside the circle of those who work regularly with such data, as in libraries or information centers dealing with such subjects. One fact not generally known is that there is a very wide range of materials available for all levels of comprehension. At one extreme would be very complex works written for a small group of experts in some narrow field, generally incomprehensible to all others. A larger group of materials, covering the middle ground of a spectrum of comprehension, would be data written for college students and practitioners in beginning level positions. Nearer the other extreme would be materials presented for adult laypeople, not particularly trained in technical matters. At the far end of the spectrum would be materials aimed at children and young adults. Thus there are informational sources suitable for all levels of society, contrary to the belief of many people that science and engineering publications are prepared almost exclusively for the professionals in those fields.

Another aspect of informational materials of a sci-tech nature of which many people are not aware is the availability of a rich body of reference tools aimed at aiding readers in the understanding and the location of suitable technical data. The use of such tools simplifies and speeds one's work with sci-tech materials. Hundreds of titles exist, representing all sorts of reference works and covering all aspects of science and technology; these tools rival, and in many cases surpass, the reference aids available for the social sciences and the humanities.

The purpose of this article is to describe the nature and the uses of more than twenty types of sci-tech informational sources, including print and nonprint materials. It is hoped this brief description of sources will prove to be a useful supplement to *Scientific and Technical Books and Serials in Print,* which provides an annual index to sci-tech books and serials currently available. Its author, title and subject approach to more than 114,168 books and its title and subject indexes for nearly 17,642 serials make it a convenient tool for identifying books and serials in all aspects of science and technology.

Those desiring more information about reference tools are urged to make use of any of several current guides to sci-tech literature. One which describes hundreds of reference works in all branches of technology and science, including brief annotations for each, is the book by H. Robert Malinowsky entitled *Science and engineering literature: a guide to reference sources* (3d ed., Littleton, CO; Libraries Unlimited; 1980). Other guides of a general sci-tech nature are available, as are those aimed at detailed coverage of sources for one particular discipline.

BASIC SOURCES

Probably the two best known informational sources in any discipline are books and serials; science and technology are no exception to this general rule.

Books — Broadly speaking, this category consists of *texts* and *monographs.* The former category covers works that range from elementary accounts to advanced tutorial materials suitable for graduate colleges. In general, little of a research nature is ever included in these books, and the style is consistently tutorial in nature, as befits the category. Monographs, on the other hand, often treat a narrow topic, many times presenting new findings and advanced concepts. Data about the quantity and average cost of such books may be found each year in one of the February issues of *Publishers Weekly.*

Serials—This category consists of annuals, periodicals (or journals) and other publications issued in parts on a regular basis. Journals constitute one of the most important types of literature in sci-tech circles. One reason is the fact that they can present very recent information, sometimes barely a few weeks old. Another is that their articles can be very specific, concerned with some minute aspects of science or technology. Journals, like books, have their levels of complexity. Most of them are written for practicing scientists or engineers, usually of little aid to the neophyte. A few are aimed at the general public, and a very few are written for pre-college age students. The rising costs of journals constitute a real problem in sci-tech libraries, often resulting in reductions in book purchases in order to keep important serials in the collection. Many sci-tech libraries seek journals from foreign sources, needed because of the important contributions made by scientists and engineers in other countries. Data on the costs of sci-tech journals can be found in an annual article in *Library Journal,* usually in a mid-year issue.

Other sources — There are several other informational sources which present basic information and bear sim-

ilarities to books or journals. One of these is *conference papers,* which often contain the first public presentation of new data. The papers may be combined into a set of papers given at a given meeting and bound together; others are subsequently printed in appropriate journals. Some are never published.

Another source related to this category is *annual reviews,* which consist usually of long articles concerned with either one particular segment of the year's activities in a branch of sci-tech disciplines or else with a serious account of some project or development unrelated to the previous year's developments. They are often excellent sources of citations to important literature on the topic.

Dissertations and *master's essays* — They present, in varied degree, new information on particular aspects of science and technology. They are generally unbiased, refereed and well monitored.

Technical reports — These publications are generally issued on a non-commercial basis by companies, government agencies and research institutes. Written for people in the field, they are of little value to the person new to a particular field, and many times their distribution is carefully controlled in accordance with company or government security regulations. They are essential for the carrying out of ongoing projects or the proposal of new ones. Tens of thousands are issued each year.

Patents — The issuance of patents guarantees companies or individuals the right to control the manufacture or preparation of certain products and gives them an opportunity to profit from their inventions. They are usually written in complex legal style, making them mysterious and arcane to all but those engaged in similar fields. Not all countries are important in their patent output, but many foreign patents are extremely valuable.

Geological fieldtrip guides — To the geologist a fieldtrip guide provides detailed knowledge of the geological features of some small section, written in a fashion that allows the reader to trace out the features by walking in the area described. There are hundreds of them, issued by various sources, such as local geological societies, larger geology groups and formal earth science agencies in research circles.

Standards — These publications are designed at regularizing the production of objects or the carrying out of a process, ranging from a standard for the correct way to mix strong concrete to the preparation of bibliographic references. They are issued by government agencies, professional societies, private organizations, corporations and other sources. They do not make for stimulating reading, but they accomplish an important task—the making of better quality products, or safer products or less expensive products. Thousands of standards, sometimes called specifications, are in existence, continually being updated or superseded by newer efforts.

Trade catalogs — These may be called manufacturers' brochures or sales literature, the latter indicating more directly the essentially commercial nature of these items. They are designed for one primary purpose—the increase of sales of the products of a particular commercial firm. While many governmental regulations are in existence to reduce inaccuracies or fraudulent statements in trade catalogs, one must be aware of the bias inherent in these publications and act accordingly. On the other hand some are models of accuracy and often present detailed technical information that can be found in no other source. Probably hundreds of thousands of catalogs are produced annually.

REFERENCE TOOLS

This section will describe a number of works designed to aid the reader to understand sci-tech materials or to locate needed information in an efficient manner. Some are very expensive, some are not. Some have a relatively long useful life, others are soon outdated. But collectively they are essential to the proper utilization of sci-tech materials.

Bibliographies — These organized lists of publications, arranged perhaps by subject, or author, or title, or sometimes all three, provide access to various types of informational sources whether they be books, serial titles, technical reports, patents or any other basic source. Some are issued as frequently as weekly, others appear annually and some are issued as hard-bound books, never subsequently updated. Some are annotated, others bear no abstracts of the individual items.

Literature-searches — Similar in nature to bibliographies, literature searches may be described as very thorough, all-encompassing bibliographies, in which the topic being searched is covered in great depth. For example, where appropriate a literature search may cover not only U.S. patents but also foreign ones as well. The expense of producing them precludes this becoming a widely-used source, but when done they tend to be quite useful for those concerned with their topics.

Guides to the literature — As previously mentioned, this type of source aims at reviewing and describing important reference tools and basic sources for either all of science and technology or else for one discipline or group of disciplines. The most helpful ones have annotations for all items plus general comments on the importance and uses of major types of informational sources.

Encyclopedias — Sci-tech versions of these familiar reference tools are similar to their general purpose counterparts known to most people. Their main value is as a fast, easily used tool, which presents basic information. Some works cover all of science and technology, while others may be restricted to one discipline or even one small topic within a discipline. Because of costs they are not updated frequently, although at least one sci-tech set of distinction uses annual yearbooks for this purpose.

Handbooks — Although there are many disparate types of reference tools labeled as handbooks, in general they can be described as edited works with tersely written chapters prepared by experts in the field. They usually present important formulas, tables and factual material. They are written for experienced people in the field, having little value for a newcomer to the topic. Because of the basic nature of their contents, they tend to have a long life.

Dictionaries — In general sci-tech dictionaries are written in the English language, providing not only definitions but sometimes illustrations also of the terms. They may cover broad topics, such as all of chemistry, or cover a field as narrow as computers. In addition there are a number of foreign language bilingual dictionaries,

which may involve English also; in a few instances sci-tech multilingual dictionaries may be found, giving no more than the equivalent terms in other languages. They are not updated frequently, but their useful life tends to be long.

Indexing Services — These cover a variety of basic sources, particularly periodical articles, technical reports and conference papers. Most provide annotations of some sort. They are absolutely necessary in order to retrieve information from the huge quantities of journal articles or reports; some also include patents. Many have spawned the creation of computerized versions, which are dealt with in another section. Some cover all of the sci-tech disciplines, but more commonly they are restricted to one topic, such as physics, metals, pollution and the like.

Directories — These publications provide detailed, current data about people, institutions and/or products. They are easily outdated, so frequent updating is necessary, generally at least annually. They are easy to use in almost every instance. As in the case of other types of literature, their scope varies greatly. For example, they might cover all research laboratories in the U.S. or biographical data for all engineers in the country; on the other hand, they might be restricted to facts about metals or the names of environmental research agencies.

NONPRINT MATERIALS

In recent years nonprint materials have played an increasingly greater role in sci-tech informational circles. They range from motion pictures to color slides, from video cassettes to film strips. The funding made available to the life and health sciences from government grants and projects have made those disciplines outstanding in the use of nonprint media. Large quantities are used in college and university programs. The historic benefits provided by nonprint materials have carried over to sci-tech applications, where clarity, dramatic impact and imaginative approaches are as important as they were over the years in the humanities and the social sciences.

Relatively recently the emergence of computerized data bases has made a quick impact on the sci-tech field. Many of the data bases were originally inhouse versions of printed abstracting and indexing services, then the availability of the proper technology made it possible for individuals and libraries to search distant data bases using their own terminals. The speed of searching, the complexity of questions which can be handled and the wide range of materials indexed all combine to make the use of computerized data bases important to the operation of sci-tech information organizations. Some data bases include all aspects of science and technology, while others may be restricted to narrow topics (such as energy sources or a particular metal) or be limited to particular formats (such as government documents or patents).

Depending upon one's definition of nonprint materials, one could include here maps and atlases, graphic tools of great importance in many types of sci-tech projects and research. Government agencies issue a large proportion of all sci-tech maps, such as those related to meteorology geology, or oceanographic charting of hazards. There are not many ways to retrieve or locate individual maps outside of the catalogs of large map libraries, such as can be found at many universities, or the use of indexes prepared by the various agencies which produce maps.

No doubt during the years ahead more and more nonprint materials will find their way into sci-tech libraries and information centers, as well as into university classrooms and special training institutes.

ELLIS MOUNT
Assistant Professor, School of Library Service, Columbia University

How To Use
SCIENTIFIC AND TECHNICAL
BOOKS AND SERIALS
IN PRINT
1986

BOOK INDEXES

GENERAL EDITORIAL POLICIES

In order to insure that the essential information in these listings is uniform, complete, and easy to find, the following editorial policies have been maintained:

If more than two authors are responsible for a certain publication, only the name of the first is given followed by *et al.*

Every effort is made by most contributing publishers to prepare their material with consideration for its accuracy throughout the life of this edition of *Scientific and Technical Books and Serials in Print.* Most publishers anticipate price changes when they revise their material, list forthcoming books even if publication dates and prices are not set, and for the most part, try not to list books that may shortly become unavailable before the new edition is published. All prices are subject to change without notice.

Most prices are list prices. Lack of uniformity in the individual catalogs prohibits indicating trade discounts. A lower case "t" indicates a tentative price; "x" indicates a short discount 20 percent or less. Short discount (20% or less) information is generally supplied by publishers to Bowker for each publication. However, all publishers do not uniformly supply this information, and Bowker can only make its best efforts to transmit this information when it is provided.

An "i" following the price indicates an invoice price. Specific policies for such titles should be obtained from individual publishers.

Publishers' and distributors' names are abbreviated. A key to these abbreviations will be found in the *Key to Publishers' & Distributors' Abbreviations* at the end of volume two. Entries in this "Key" are arranged alphabetically by the abbreviations used in the bibliographic entries. The full name, ISBN prefix, editorial address, telephone number, ordering address (if different from the editorial address), and imprints follow the abbreviation SAN (Standard Address Number) is a unique identification code for each address of each organization in or served by the book industry.

For example:

Bowker, *(Bowker, R. R. Co.; 0-8352)*
205 E. 42nd St., New York, NY 10017 Tel 212-916-1600, (SAN 214-1191); Orders to: P.O. Box 1807, Ann Arbor, MI 48106 (SAN 214-1205).

If an entry contains a "Pub by" note after the price, the title should be ordered from the company whose abbreviation appears at the end of the entry. For example, an entry for a book published by Melbourne University Press but distributed by International Scholarly Book Services, Inc., will convey this information in the form "Pub by Melbourne U Pr" after the price with "Intl Schl Bk Serv" at the end of the entry.

ALPHABETICAL ARRANGEMENT OF ENTRIES

Each entry is filed alphabetically by word, with the following exceptions:

M', Mc and *Mac* are filed as if they were spelled *Mac* and are interfiled with other names beginning with *Mac:* for example, Macan, McAnally, Macardle, McAree, McArthur, Macartney, M'Aulay, Macaulay. Within a specific name grouping *Mc* and *Mac* are interfiled according to the given name of the author: for example, Macdonald, Agnes; MacDonald, Alexander; McDonald, Annie L.; MacDonald, Austin F.; MacDonald, Betty. In the *Books—Author Index,* compound names are listed under the first part of the name and cross-references appear under the last part of the name.

Entries beginning with initial letters (whether authors' given names or titles) are filed first: Smith, H.C. comes before Smith, Harold A.; *J.B. Priestley: The Man and His Ideas* comes before *Jade.*

Numerals, including year dates, are written out in most cases and are filed alphabetically:

SEVEN CORPORATIONS
SEVENTEEN
SEVENTEEN FAMOUS INVENTIONS
SEVENTEEN-FIFTEEN TO THE PRESENT
SEVENTEEN PAST YEARS
SEVENTEEN READER
SEVENTEENTH CENTURY

INFORMATION INCLUDED IN ENTRIES

Entries include the following bibliographic information, when available: author, co-author, editor, co-editor, translator, co-translator, title, number of volumes, edition, Library of Congress number, series, whether or not illustrated, year of publication, price with type of binding if other than cloth over boards, publisher's order number, International Standard Book Number, and publisher's name. (Information on the International Standard Book Numbering System in the United States and other English-speaking countries is available from the R. R. Bowker Co.)

BOOKS—SUBJECT INDEX

Entries are arranged alphabetically by author within subject. If no author is given, the entry is filed alphabetically by title within the author arrangement.

Headings and cross-references were updated to conform to the ninth edition of *Library of Congress Subject Headings* and its supplements.

Whenever official LC classification was unavailable, headings were assigned provisionally. Among these fall most of the titles now in preparation or to be published sometime in 1986. As LC headings for such books become available, the provisional headings will be verified or changed in future editions of *Scientific and Technical Books and Serials in Print.*

ALPHABETICAL ARRANGEMENT OF SUBJECT HEADINGS

Subject headings are arranged alphabetically:

BIRDS
BODY FLUIDS
BOTANY
BUILDING-ACCIDENTS

Many of the main headings are broken down still further:

SCIENCE
SCIENCE—BIBLIOGRAPHY
SCIENCE—DATA PROCESSING
SCIENCE—DICTIONARIES
SCIENCE—HISTORY

There are also many cross-references:

BY-PRODUCTS
    see WASTE PRODUCTS
ELECTROCHEMISTRY, INDUSTRIAL
    see also ELECTROSTATIC PRECIPITATION

Headings, patterned after those used in the card catalog in the Library of Congress, are explicit rather than general. Thus books on Geochemistry are under GEOCHEMISTRY not under CHEMISTRY.

When looking for the books on Astronautics, search past the main entry to the various subheadings:

ASTRONAUTICS
ASTRONAUTICS—HISTORY
ASTRONAUTICS—SYSTEMS ENGINEERINGS
ASTRONAUTICS—RUSSIA
ASTRONAUTICS, MILITARY
ASTRONAUTICS IN GEOLOGY
ASTRONAUTICS IN NAVIGATION

Note the sequence of the above cited headings and subheadings. The editors of this book took as a guideline the *Filing Rules for the Dictionary Catalogs of the Library of Congress* as prepared by the Processing Department of the Library of Congress.

Other typical examples of the sequence used are:

LIGHT
LIGHT—SCATTERING
LIGH, WAVE THEORY OF
PHOTOGRAPHY
PHOTOGRAPHY—COPYING
PHOTOGRAPHY—FILMS
PHOTOGRAPHY—PROCESSING
PHOTOGRAPHY, AERIAL
PHOTOGRAPHY, INDUSTRIAL
PHOTOGRAPHY, NIGHT
PHOTOGRAPHY IN GEOLOGY

Although a constant effort is made to maintain consistency and to avoid splitting entries on a given subject among several headings, a certain amount is inevitable. The Library of Congress updates its subject headings constantly but cannot make such updating retroactive to cards and catalogs previously issued. For example, LC recently added the subject heading KIRLIAN PHOTOGRAPHY. If previously published titles which appeared under the heading PHOTOGRAPHY did not indicate by their titles that they should have been moved to KIRLIAN PHOTOGRAPHY, they may have been left under PHOTOGRAPHY.

SERIAL INDEXES

SERIALS—SUBJECT INDEX

Entries with bibliographic and buying information for selected, current serials which are published periodically or

irregularly are arranged alphabetically by title within subject category. The complete entry is listed under one subject heading. If a serial covers more than one subject, cross-references direct the user from related subjects to the subject under which the complete entry is listed. Subheadings on "Abstracting, Bibliographies & Statistics" are also included in 62 subject categories.

Adding to the usefulness of this directory is the expansion of the subject heading "Computer Technology," accomplished for the 22nd edition of *Ulrich's International Periodicals Directory* and other Bowker International Serials Database publications, and now a continuing feature of *Scientific and Technical Books and Serials in Print.* In this edition of *Scientific and Technical Books and Serials in Print,* there are some 32 subject headings defining major segments of this subject area, as well as 24 subject headings specific to computer applications in such fields as Aeronautics and Space Flight, Engineering, and Sciences: Comprehensive Works. In today's information explosion, serials will continue to be a major source of current information in all areas of computers and their use.

SERIALS—TITLE INDEX

Title Index entries include the following: title, ISSN and country code, name of issuing body if main entry title contains only the initials of the issuing body. Cross-references for variant titles, parallel language titles, and former titles are included. The page number where the complete entry appears is printed in italic type; page numbers in roman type indicate pages of related subject listings.

INFORMATION INCLUDED IN MAIN ENTRIES

Basic Information. The following items are mandatory for listing: title, frequency of publication, publisher name and address, country of publication code, Dewey Decimal Classification number.

Title Information. Main entry title: ISSN; subtitle; key title (entered only if different from main entry title); parallel language title, variant title, title variation note, former title and ISSN; original title of translation and ISSN; translated edition title and ISSN; and "issued with" title and ISSN (ISSN given only when available).

Buying and Ordering Information. Publisher name and address and, when applicable, subscription address and/or distributor name and address; subscription price in currency of country of publication and U.S. rates for foreign publications when supplied by the publisher; price per issue if subscription rate is not applicable; the designation ‡ for a title not available from a subscription agency (printed after price information); the micropublisher if not the same as the publisher (following notation on microform edition).

Abstracting and Indexing Information. Services which index the listed title on a regular basis are given in abbreviated form.

Author and Editor Information. Name of corporate author if corporate author is not also the publisher, name of editor or the abbreviation Ed.Bd. which indicates editorship by three or more persons (usually advanced degrees and titles have been omitted with the exception of medical, military, and clerical titles; absence of a title does not mean that the editor has none).

Bibliographic Notes. Year first published or year of first known issue; frequency of publication; year and number of latest issue if frequency is irregular; language notation if text is in language other than official language of country of publication; special features contained in the serial (such as book reviews, illustrations, charts, statistics); availability of cumulative indexes; availability of microform and other alternative formats; subject annotation; additional bibliographic notations, such as title of main series in cases of subseries entry, or irregularities in volume numbering.

RULES FOR MAIN ENTRY

Whenever possible, main entry cataloging is done from a sample title page of the most recent issue, according to the following rules:

Serials with distinctive titles are usually entered under title. For example:

> *Scientific American*

If the title consists only of the name of the issuing body and a generic term, or if the name of the issuing body clarifies the content of the publication, entry is under the name of the issuing body. For example:

> *Journal of the American Chemical Society*
> is entered as
> *American Chemical Society. Journal*

A title is considered nondistinctive if it consists of a subject modified generic term and the name of the issuing body and is entered under the name of the issuing body. For example:

> *Scientific Papers of the Institute of Physical and Chemical Research*
> is entered as
> *Institute of Physical and Chemical Research. Scientific Papers.*

Government publications with nondistinctive titles are usually entered under the name of the government jurisdiction of the issuing body; distinctive titles of government issuing bodies are entered under title. For example:

> *France. Ministere de l'Agriculture. Bulletin Technique d'Information*
> but
> *Monthly Abstract of Meteorological Observations of Malaysia*

Multilingual titles are entered under the first title given on the title page (or first title as reported by publisher if title page is not available). Titles in other languages are entered directly after the main entry title.

Titles which begin with the initials of the issuing body are entered under the initials of the issuing body. Cross references from the full name of issuing body to initials in main entry are given in the *Serials—Title Index.*

FILING RULES

Articles at the beginning of titles have been omitted; articles and prepositions within titles are alphabetized as words:

> *Advances in Research and Technology of Seeds*
> precedes
> *Advances in the Astronautical Sciences.*

Hyphenated words are treated as separate words:
Druck-Print
precedes
Druckindustrie

Titles entered under corporate author or government jurisdiction are sequenced before distinctive titles which begin with the same words:

Alaska. Division of Geological and
Geophysical Surveys. Geologic/Professional Report
will precede
Alaska Construction and Oil.

Acronyms and initials are treated as such and are listed at the beginning of each letter of the alphabet with the exception of the abbreviations U.N. (United Nations), U.S. (United States), Gt. Britain (Great Britain), and St. (Saint) which are filed as words:

U.P. Irrigation Research Institute.
Technical Memorandum.
Underwater Naturalist.
U.S. Nuclear Regulatory Commission.
Operating Units Status Report.

KEYS TO ABBREVIATIONS

GENERAL

a	after price, specially priced library edition available
a	annual
abr.	abridged
abstr.	abstracts
adpt.	adapted
adv.	advertising
Amer.	American
annot.	annotation(s), annotated
ans.	answer(s)
app.	appendix
approx.	approximately
assn.	association
auth.	author
Ave.	Avenue
bd.	bound
bdg.	binding
bds.	boards
bi-m.	every two months
bib(s).	bibliography (ies)
bk(s).	book, books
bk. rev.	book reviews
bklet(s)	booklets
Blvd.	Boulevard
Bro.	Brother
c/o	care of
charts	charts (diagrams, graphs, tables)
circ.	circulation
coll.	college
comm.	commission, committee
co.	company
comp(s)	compiler(s)
cond.	condensed
contr.	controlled
corp.	corporation
cum. ind.	cumulative index
Cy.	county
d.	daily
dept.	department
diag(s).	diagram(s)
dir.	director
dist.	distributor
Div.	Division
doz.	dozen
Dr.	Drive
ea.	each
ed.	editor, edited, edition
Ed. Bd.	Editorial Board
ed., eds.	editions, editors, editor
educ.	education
elem.	elementary
ency.	encyclopedia
Eng.	English
enl.	enlarged
exp.	expurgated
fac.	facsimile
fasc.	fascicle
fict.	fiction
fig(s).	figures(s)
film rev.	film reviews
for.	foreign
fortn.	fortnightly
Fr.	French
frwd.	foreword
g	after price, guaranteed juvenile binding
gen.	general

Ger.	German
Gr.	greek
gr.	grade, grades
hdbk.	handbook
Heb.	Hebrew
i.	invoice price
i.t.a.	initial teaching alphabet
Illus	Illustrated, Illustration(s), illustrator(s)
in prep.	in preparation
incl.	includes, including
inst.	institute
intro.	introduction
ISSN	International Standard Serial Number
irreg.	irregular
It.	Italian
Jr.	Junior
Jt. auth.	joint author
jt. ed.	joint editor
k	kindergarten audience level
l.p.	long playing
ltd. ed.	limited edition
lab.	laboratory
lang(s).	language(s)
Lat.	Latin
lea.	leather
lib.	library
lit.	literature, literary
m.	monthly
math.	mathematics
mkt.	market prices
mod.	modern
mor.	morocco
MS, MSS	manuscript, manuscripts
music rev.	music reviews
N.S.	New Series
natl.	national
no., nos.	number, numbers
o.p.	out of print
orig.	original text, not a reprint
pap.	paper
pat.	patents
photos	photographs, photographer
play rev.	play reviews (theatre reviews)
PLB	publisher's library binding
P.O.	Post Office
Pol.	Polish
pop. ed.	popular edition
Port.	Portuguese
prep.	preparation
probs.	problems
Prof.	Professor
prog. bk.	programmed book
ps	preschool audience level
pseud.	pseudonym
pt(s).	part, parts
pub.	published, publisher, publishing
pubn.	publication
Pubns	Publications
q.	quarterly
record rev.	record reviews
ref(s).	reference(s)
repr.	reprint
reprod(s)	reproduction(s)
rev.	revised

rpm.	revolution per minute (photo records)		t	after price, tentative price
Rus.	Russian		tech.	technical
s-a.	twice annually		tele. rev.	television reviews
s-m.	twice monthly		text ed.	text edition
s-w.	twice weekly		3/m	3 times a month
s.p.	school price		3/yr.	3 times a year
sec.	section		tr.	translator, translated translation
sel.	selected			
ser.	series		tr. lit.	trade literature (manufacturers' catalogues, etc.)
s & l	signed & limited			
sep	single copy, direct to the consumer price			
			tr. mk.	trade marks
Soc.	Society		univ.	university
sols.	solutions		vol(s).	volume, volumes
Span.	Spanish		w.	weekly
Sr. (after given name)	Senior		wkbk.	workbook
			x	after price, short discount (20% or less)
Sr. (before given name)	Sister		YA	young adult audience level
St.	Saint, Street		yrbk.	yearbook
stat.	statistics		‡	not available from a subscription agency
subs.	subsidiary			
subscr.	subscription		x	short discount
suppl.	supplement		*	not updated

COUNTRY OF PUBLICATION CODE

AT	Australia	IE	Ireland	PO	Portugal
AU	Austria	IS	Israel	SA	South Africa
BE	Belgium	IT	Italy	SP	Spain
CN	Canada	JA	Japan	SW	Sweden
DK	Denmark	LU	Luxembourg	SZ	Switzerland
EI	European Communities	NE	Netherlands	UK	United Kingdom
FR	France	NO	Norway	UN	United Nations
GW	Germany, West	NZ	New Zealand	US	United States

MICROPUBLISHERS

AMS   AMS Press, Inc., 56 E. 13th St., New York, NY 10003

BLH   Bell & Howell Micro Photo Division, Old Mansfield Rd., Wooster, OH 44691

BLI   Balch Institute, 18 South 7th St., Philadelphia, PA 19106

CLA   Canadian Library Association, Microfilm Project, 151 Sparks St., Ottawa, Ont. K1P SE3, Canada

EDR   Eric Document Reproduction Service, Box 190, Arlington, VA 22210

FCM   Fairchild Microfilms, Visual Division, Fairchild Publications, Inc., 7 East 12th St., New York, NY 10003

GMC   General Microfilm Co., 70 Coolidge Hill Rd., Watertown, MA 02172

HPL   Harvester Press Microfilm Publications Ltd., 17 Ship St. Brighton, Sussex BN1 1AD, England

IDC   Inter Documentation Co., AG., Poststrasse 14, 6300 Zurich, Switzerland

ISI   Institute for Scientific Information, University City Science Center, 3501 Market St., Philadelphia, PA 19104

JAI   JAI Press, Inc. (formerly Johnson Associates, Inc.), 36 Sherwood Pl., P.O. Box 1678, 165 W. Putnam Ave., Greenwich, CT 06830

JOH   Johnson Reprint Microeditions, 111 Fifth Ave., New York, NY 10003

JRC   Johnson Research Corp. Moved, no forwarding address

JSC   J.S. Canner & Co., 49-65 Lansdowne St., Boston, MA 02110

KTO   KTO Microform, Division of Kraus-Thomson Organization, Ltd., Route 100, Millwood, NY 10546

LCP   The Library of Congress, Photoduplication Service, 10 First St., S.E., Washington, DC 20540

LIB   Library Microfilms, 737 Loma Verde Ave., Palo Alto, CA 94303

MCA   Microfilming Corporation of America, 200 Park Ave., New York, NY 10166

MCE   Professional Data Services (formerly Microcard Editions), c/o Congressional Information Services, 450 East-West Hwy, Suite 800, Bethesda, MD 20814

MIM   Microforms International Marketing Co. (Subsidiary of Pergamon Press, Inc.), Maxwell House, Fairview Park, Elmsford, NY 10523

MML   Micromedia Limited, 144 Front St. W., P.O. Box 502, Station S., Toronto, Ontario M5J 2L7, Canada

MMP   McLaren Micropublishing, P.O. Box 972, Station F, Toronto, Ontario, Canada M4Y 2N9

NBI   Newsbank, Inc., 58 Pine St., New Canaan, CT 06840

NTI   National Technical Information Service, 5285 Port Royal Rd., Springfield, VA 22161

NYT   New York Times Information Bank, 229 West 43rd St., New York, NY 10036

OMP   Oxford Microform Publications Ltd. (Subsidiary of Pergamon Press, Inc.), Maxwell House, Fairview Park, Elmsford, NY 10523

PMC   Princeton Microfilm Corp., P.O. Box 2073, Princeton, NJ 08540

RRI   Rothman, Fred B & Co., 10368 W. Centennial Rd., Littleton, CO 80127

TMI   Tennessee Microfilms, P.O. Box 1096, Nashville, TN 37202

UMI   University Microfilms International, 300 North Zeeb Rd., Ann Arbor, MI 48106 (University Microfilms International Ltd., 30-32 Mortimer St., London W1N 7RA, England)

UNM   University of Michigan Library, Interlibrary Lending, Circulation Dept. Harlan Hatcher Graduate Library, Ann Arbor, MI 48104

UNW   University of Wisconsin Library, Interlibrary Loan Dept., 728 State St., Madison, WI 53706

WDS   Dawson Microfiche, Cannon House, Parkfarm Road, Folkestone, Kent CT30 1RR, England

WMP   World Microfilm Publications Ltd., 62 Queen's Grove, London NW8 6ER, England

MONEY SYMBOLS

SYMBOL	UNIT	COUNTRY
Aus.$	dollars	Australia
Can.$	dollars	Canada
DM.	marks	West Germany
$	dollars; pesos	various
Esc.	escudos	Portugal
F.	francs	France
fl.	florins or guilders	The Netherlands, Surinam
Fr.	francs	Belgium, Switzerland
IS	shekels	Israel
Kr.	kroner; kronor	Scandinavian countries
L.	lempira; lira	Honduras, Italy
$m.n.	moneda nacional	various
N.Z.$	dollars	New Zealand
P.	pesos	various
£	pounds	Great Britain
ptas.	pesetas	Spain
R.	rands	South Africa
S.	schillings	Austria

ABSTRACTING AND INDEXING SERVICES

A.A.P.P.Abstr.	Amino Acids, Peptide & Protein Abstracts
A.B.C.Pol.Sci.	Advance Bibliography of Contents, Political Science & Government
ABTICS	Abstracts and Book Title Index
A.I.C.P.	Anthropological Index to Current Periodicals in the Library of the Museum of Mankind (Royal Anthropological Institute)
A.S.& T.Ind.	Applied Science & Technology Index
ASCA	Automatic Subject Citation Alert
Abr.R.G.	Abridged Reader's Guide to Periodical Literature
Abstr. Anthropol.	Abstracts in Anthropology
Abstr.Bk.Rev. Curr.Leg.Per.	Abstracts of Book Reviews in Current Legal Periodicals
Abstr.Bull.Inst. Pap. Chem.	Abstract Bulletin of the Institute of Paper Chemistry
Abstr.Comput. Lit.	Abstracts of Computer Literature (Ceased)
Abstr.Engl.Stud.	Abstracts of English Studies
Abstr.Folk.Stud.	Abstracts of Folklore Studies
Abstr.J.Earthq. Eng.	Abstract Journal in Earthquake Engineering
Abstr.Muslim. Rel.	Abstracts: European Muslims and Christian-Muslim Relations
Abstr.N.Amer. Geol.	Abstracts of North American Geology
Abstr.Pop.Cult.	Abstracts of Popular Culture
Abstr.Trop. Agri.	Abstracts on Tropical Agriculture
Abstrax	Abstrax
Access	Access: the Supplementary Index to Periodicals
Acoust.Abstr.	Acoustics Abstracts
Adol.Ment. Health Abstr.	Adolescent Mental Health Abstracts
Agri.Eng.Abstr.	Agricultural Engineering Abstracts
Agri.Ind.	Agriculture Index (Now: Biological & Agricultural Index)
Agrindex	Agrindex
Air Un.Lib.Ind.	Air University Library Index to Military Periodicals
Alt.Press Ind.	Alternative Press Index
Amer.Hist.& Life	America: History & Life
Amer.Hum.Ind.	American Humanities Index
Amer.Stat.Ind.	American Statistics Index
Anal.Abstr.	Analytical Abstracts
Anbar	Anbar Publications Ltd.
	Accounting & Data Processing Abstracts
	Marketing & Distribution Abstracts
	Personnel & Training Abstracts
	Top Management Abstracts
	Work Study & O and M Abstracts
Anim.Behav. Abstr.	Animal Behavior Abstracts
Anim.Breed. Abstr.	Animal Breeding Abstracts
Ap.Ind.	Apple Index
Apic.Abstr.	Apicultural Abstracts
Appl.Ecol. Abstr.	Applied Ecology Abstracts
Appl.Mech.Rev.	Applied Mechanics Review
Aqua.Sci.& Fish.Abstr.	Aquatic Sciences & Fisheries Abstracts
Arct.Bibl.	Arctic Bibliography
Art Ind.	Art Index
Arts & Hum. Cit.Ind.	Arts & Humanities Citation Index
Ash.G.Bot.Per.	Asher's Guide to Botanical Periodicals
Astron.& Astrophys. Abstr.	Astronomy and Astrophysics Abstracts
Astron. Jahresber.	Astronomischer Jahresbericht
Aus.Educ.Ind.	Australian Education Index
Aus.P.A.I.S.	Australian Public Affairs Information Service
Aus.Sci.Ind.	Australian Science Index
Aus.Speleo Abstr.	Australian Speleo Abstracts
Avery Ind. Archit.Per.	Avery Index to Architectural Periodicals
B.C.I.R.A	B.C.I.R.A. Abstracts of Foundry Literature
B.P.I.	Business Periodicals Index
B.P.I.A.	Business Publications Index and Abstracts
Behav.Abstr.	Behavioural Abstracts
Ber.Biochem. Biol.	Berichte Biochemie und Biologie
Bibl.Agri.	Bibliography of Agriculture
Bibl.& Ind. Geol.	Bibliography & Index to Geology
Bibl.Ind.	Bibliographic Index
Bibl.Pflanz.	Bibliographie der Pflanzenschutzliteratur
Bibl.Repro.	Bibliography of Reproduction
Bioeng.Abstr.	Bioengineering Abstracts
Biog.Ind.	Biography Index
Biol.Abstr.	Biological Abstracts
Biol.& Agri. Ind.	Biological & Agricultural Index (Formerly: Agricultural Index)
Biol.Dig.	Biology Digest
Bk.Rev.Dig.	Book Review Digest
Bk.Rev.Ind.	Book Review Index
Br.Archaeol. Abstr.	British Archaeological Abstracts
Br.Ceram.Abstr.	British Ceramic Abstracts
Br.Educ.Ind.	British Education Index
Br.Hum.Ind.	British Humanities Index
Br.Tech.Ind.	British Technology Index
Bull.Inst. Pasteur	Bulletin de l'Institute Pasteur

Bull.Signal.	Bulletin Signaletique (Now: PASCAL)
Bus.Comput. Ind.	Business Computer Index
Bus.Educ.Ind.	Business Education Index
Bus.Ind.	Business Index
CALL	Current Awareness—Library Literature
C.C.L.P.	Contents of Current Legal Periodicals (Now: Legal Contents)
C.C.M.J.	Contents of Contemporary Mathematical Journals
C.I.J.E.	Current Index to Journals in Education
CINAHL (also C.I.N.L.)	Cumulative Index to Nursing and Allied Health Literature
C.I.S.Abstr.	C.I.S. Abstracts on Cards
C.I.S. Ind.	Congressional Information Service Index
CJPI	Criminal Justice Periodical Index
C.L.I.	Current Law Index
C.P.I.	Current Physics Index
C.R.E.J.	Contents of Recent Economic Journals
Cab.Vid.Ind.	Cable-Video-Index
Can.B.P.I.	Canadian Business Periodical Index (Now: Canadian Business Index)
Can.Educ.Ind.	Canadian Education Index
Can.Ind.	Canadian Periodical Index
Can.Ind.Geosci. Data	Canadian Index to Geoscience Data
Canon Law Abstr.	Canon Law Abstracts
Cath.Ind.	Catholic Periodical & Literature Index (Formerly: Catholic Periodical Index)
Ceram.Abstr.	Ceramic Abstracts
Chem.Abstr.	Chemical Abstracts
Chem.Titles	Chemical Titles
Child Devel. Abstr.	Child Development Abstracts
Child.Mag.Gd.	Children's Magazine Guide (Formerly: Subject Index to Children's Magazines)
Chr.Per.Ind.	Christian Periodical Index
Commer.Fish. Abstr.	Commercial Fisheries Abstracts
Commun.Abstr.	Communication Abstracts
Comput.& Info. Sys.	Computer and Information Systems
Comput.Abstr.	Computer Abstracts
Comput.& Contr.Abstr.	Computer & Control Abstracts (See: Science Abstracts)
Comput.Bus.	Computer Business
Comput.Cont.	Computer Contents
Comput.Lit.Ind.	Computer Literature Index (Formerly: Quarterly Bibliography of Computers and Data Processing)
Comput.Rev.	Computing Reviews
Consum.Ind.	Consumer's Index
Copper Abstr.	Copper Abstracts
Corros.Abstr.	Corrosion Abstracts
Cum.Comput. Abstr.	Cumulative Computer Abstracts

Curr.Adv.Plant Sci.	Current Advances in Plant Science
Curr.Antarc. Lit.	Current Antarctic Literature
Curr.Chem. React.	Current Chemical Reactions
Curr.Cont.	Current Contents
Curr.Ind.Stat.	Current Index to Statistics
Cur.Tit. Electrochem.	Current Titles in Electrochemistry
DM & T	Defense Markets & Technology
DSH Abstr.	DSH Abstracts
Diary Sci.Abstr.	Dairy Science Abstracts
Data Process. Dig.	Data Processing Digest
Deep Sea Res.& Oceanogr. Abstr.	Deep Sea Research & Oceanographic Abstracts
Dent.Ind.	Index to Dental Literature
Dok.Str.	Dokumentation Strasse
Dok.Wasser	Dokumentation Wasser
ERIC	Eric Clearinghouse (See also C.I.J.E.)
Ecol.Abstr.	Ecological Abstracts
Econ.Abstr.	Economic Abstracts (Now: Key to Economic Science)
Educ.Admin. Abstr.	Educational Administration Abstracts
Educ.Ind.	Education Index
Elec.& Electron. Abstr.	Electrical & Electronic Abstracts
Elec.Eng.Abstr.	Electrical Engineering Abstracts (See: Science Abstracts)
Electroanal. Abstr.	Electroanalytical Abstracts
Electron.& Communic. Abstr.J.	Electronics and Communications Abstracts Journal (Formerly: Electronics Abstracts Journal)
Energy Ind.	Energy Index
Energy Info. Abstr.	Energy Information Abstracts
Energy Res. Abstr.	Energy Research Abstracts
Eng.Ind.	Engineering Index
Entomol.Abstr.	Entomology Abstracts
Environ.Abstr.	Environmental Abstracts
Environ.Per. Bibl.	Environmental Periodicals Bibliography
Ergon.Abstr.	Ergonomics Abstracts
Except.Child Educ.Abstr.	Exceptional Child Education Abstracts
Excerp.Bot.	Excerpta Botanica
Excerp.Med.	Excerpta Medica
Exec.Sci.Inst.	Executive Sciences Institute Operations Research/Management Science Abstract Services Quality Control and Applied Statistics

F.A.C.T.	Fuel Abstracts & Current Titles (Now: Fuel & Energy Abstracts)
Farm & Garden Ind.	Farm & Garden Index
Fert.Abstr.	Fertilizer Abstracts
Field Crop Abstr.	Field Crop Abstracts
Film Lit.Ind.	Film Literature Index
Food Sci.& Tech.Abstr.	Food Science and Technology Abstracts
Forest.Abstr.	Forestry Abstracts
Fuel & Energy Abstr.	Fuel & Energy Abstracts Formerly: Fuel Abstracts & Current Titles)
Fut.Surv.	Future Survey
G.Soc.Sci.& Rel.Per.Lit.	Guide to Social Science and Religion in Periodical Literature
Gas Abstr.	Gas Abstracts
Gdlns.	Guidelines
Geneal.Per.Ind.	Genealogical Periodical Annual Index
Genet.Abstr.	Genetics Abstracts
Geo.Abstr.	Geographical Abstracts
Geophys.Abstr.	Geophysical Abstracts
GeoRef	GeoRef Information System
Geosci.Doc.	Geoscience Documentation
Geotech.Abstr.	Geotechnical Abstracts
Helminthol. Abstr.	Helminthological Abstracts
Herb.Abstr.	Herbage Abstracts
Hist.Abstr.	Historical Abstracts
Hort.Abstr.	Horticultural Abstracts
Hosp.Lit.Ind.	Hospital Literature Index
Hum.Ind.	Humanities Index
Human Resour. Abstr.	Human Resources Abstracts (Formerly: Poverty & Human Resources Abstracts)
Hwy.Res.Abstr.	Highway Research Abstracts (Now: Transportation Research Abstracts)
IBM PC Ind.	IBM PC Index
I.M.M.Abstr.	I M M Abstracts (Institute of Mining & Metallurgy)
INIS Atomind.	INIS Atomindex
INSPEC	Information Services for the Physics and Engineering Communities, The Institution of Electrical Engineers (See: Science Abstracts)
I.P.A.	International Pharmaceutical Abstracts
Ind.Chem.	Current Abstracts of Chemistry and Index Chemicus (Formerly: Index Chemicus)
Ind.Child.Mag.	Subject Index to Children's Magazines (Now: Children's Magazine Guide)
Ind.Econ.J.	Index of Economic Journals
Ind.Heb.Per.	Index to Hebrew Periodicals
Ind.Hyg.Dig.	Industrial Hygiene Digest
Ind.Med.	Index Medicus

Ind.N.Z.Per.	Index to New Zealand Periodicals
Ind.Per.Art. Relat.Law	Index to Periodical Articles Related to Law
Ind.S.A.Per.	Index to South African Periodicals
Ind.Sci.Rev.	Index to Scientific Reviews
Ind.U.S.Gov. Per.	Index to U.S. Government Periodicals
Ind.Vet.	Index Veterinarius
Indian Sci. Abstr.	Indian Science Abstracts
Inform.Process. J.	Information Processing Journal
Inform.Sci. Abstr.	Information Science Abstracts (Formerly: Documentation Abstracts)
Int.Abstr.Biol. Sci.	International Abstracts of Biological Sciences
Int.Abstr.Oper. Res.	International Abstracts In Operations Research
Int.Aerosp. Abstr.	International Aerospace Abstracts
Int.Build. Serv.Abstr.	International Building Services Abstracts (Formerly: Thermal Abstracts)
Int.Ind.	International Index (Now: Social Sciences Index and Humanities Index)
Int.Nurs.Ind.	International Nursing Index
Int.Polit.Sci. Abstr.	International Political Science Abstracts
JAMA	Journal of the American Medical Association
J.Curr.Laser Abstr.	Journal of Current Laser Abstracts
J.of Econ.Abstr.	Journal of Economic Abstracts
J.of Econ.Lit.	Journal of Economic Literature
Jap.Per.Ind.	Japanese Periodicals Index
Key to Econ.Sci.	Key to Economic Science
Key Word Ind. Wildl.Res.	Key Word Index to Wildlife Research
LAMP	Literature Analysis of Microcomputer Publications
LCR	Literary Criticism Register
LHTN	Library High Tech News
LISA	Library & Information Science Abstracts (Formerly: Library Science Abstracts)
L.R.I.	Legal Resource Index
Lang.& Lang. Behav.Abstr.	Language & Language Behavior Abstracts
Lead Abstr.	Lead Abstracts
Left Ind.	Left Index
Leg.Per.	Index to Legal Periodicals
Lib.Lit.	Library Literature
Lib.Sci.Abstr.	Library Science Abstracts (Now: Library & Information Science Abstracts)

Lit.Automat.	New Literature on Automation	P.I.R.A	P.I.R.A Marketing Abstracts
		P.M.I.	Photography Magazine Index
		PMR	Popular Magazine Review
MELSA	Metropolitan Library Service	PROMT	Predicasts Overview of Markets and Technology
M.L.A.	Modern Language Abstracts		
M.M.R.I.	Multi-Media Reviews Index (Now: Media Review Digest)	Periodex	Periodex (Now: Point de Repere)
Mag.Ind.	Magazine Index	Petrol.Abstr.	Petroleum Abstracts
Manage.Cont.	Management Contents	Petrol.Energy B.N.I.	Petroleum/Energy Business News Index
Mar.Sci.Cont. Tab.	Marine Science Contents Tables (Ceased)	Pharmcog.Tit.	Pharmacognosy Titles (Ceased)
Math.R.	Mathematical Reviews	Phil.Ind.	Philosopher's Index
Med.Care Rev.	Medical Care Review	Photo.Abstr.	Photographic Abstracts
Media Rev. Dig.	Media Review Digest (Formerly: Multi-Media Reviews Index)	Photo.Ind.	Photography Index
		Phys.Abstr.	Physics Abstracts (See: Science Abstracts)
Met.Abstr.	Metal Abstracts (Formed by the merger of: ASM Review of Metal Literature & Metallurgical Abstracts)	Phys.Ber.	Physikalische Berichte
		Plant Breed. Abstr.	Plant Breeding Abstracts
Met.Finish. Abstr.	Metal Finishing Abstracts	Pollut.Abstr.	Pollution Abstracts
		Psychol.Abstr.	Psychological Abstracts
Meteor.& Geo- astrophys. Abstr.	Meteorological & Geoastro- physical Abstracts	Psychol.R.G.	Psychological Reader's Guide
		Pt.de.Repere	Point de Repere (Formed by the merger of: Periodex & RADAR)
Microbiol. Abstr.	Microbiological Abstracts		
Microcomp.Ind.	Microcomputer Index	Qual.Contr. Appl.Stat.	Quality Control and Applied Statistics (See: Executive Sciences Institute)
Microgr.Ind.	Micrographics Index		
Mineral.Abstr.	Mineralogical Abstracts	RADAR	Repertoire Analytique d'Articles des Revues de Quebec (Now: Point de Repere)
Music Artic. Guide	Music Article Guide		
Music Ind.	Music Index		
Mycol.Abstr.	Mycological Abstracts	RAPRA	Rubber & Plastics Research Association of Great Britain
		R.G.	Readers' Guide to Periodical Literature
New Per.Ind.	New Periodicals Index	RILA	RILA (International Repertory of the Literature of Art)
Noise Pollut. Publ.Abstr.	Noise Pollution Publications Abstracts		
Nucl.Sci.Abstr.	Nuclear Science Abstracts (Superseded by: INIS Atomindex)	RILM	RILM Abstracts of Music Literature
		Ref.Zh.	Referativnyi Zhurnal
Nutr.Abstr.	Nutrition Abstracts & Reviews	Rel.& Theol. Abstr.	Religious & Theological Abstracts
Ocean.Abstr.	Oceanic Abstracts (Formerly: Oceanic Index)	Rel.Ind.One	Religion Index One: Periodicals (Formerly: Index to Religious Periodicals)
Ocean.Abstr. Bibl.	Oceanic Abstracts and Bibliography		
Ocean.Ind.	Oceanic Index (Now: Oceanic Abstracts)	Res.High.Educ. Abstr.	Research into Higher Education Abstracts
		Resour.Ctr.Ind.	Resource Center Index
Oper.Res. Manage.Sci.	Operations Research/Manage- ment Science (Sec: Executive Sciences Institute)	Rev.Appl. Entomol.	Review of Applied Entomology
		Rev.Appl. Mycol.	Review of Applied Mycology
Ophthal.Lit.	Ophthalmic Literature	Rev.Plant Path.	Review of Plant Pathology
		Rheol.Abstr.	Rheology Abstracts
P.A.I.S.	Public Affairs Information Service	Risk Abstr.	Risk Abstracts
		Robomat.	Robomatix Reporter
P.A.I.S.For. Lang.Ind.	P.A.I.S. Foreign Language Index	Rural Recreat. Tour.Abstr.	Rural Recreational and Tourism Abstracts
PASCAL	Plan de Classement PASCAL		
PC Abstr.	PC Abstracts		
PHRA	Poverty & Human Resources Abstracts (Now: Human Resources Abstracts)	S.A.Waterabstr.	S.A. (South Africa) Waterabstracts

SSCI	Social Science Citation Index
Saf.Sci.Abstr.	Safety Science Abstracts Journal
Sage Urb.Stud. Abstr.	Sage Urban Studies Abstracts
Sci.Abstr.	Science Abstracts
	A. Physics Abstracts
	B. Electrical Engineering Abstracts
	C. Computer & Control Abstracts
Sci.& Tech. Aerosp.Rep.	Science & Technical Aerospace Reports
Sci.Cit.Ind.	Science Citation Index
Sci.Res.Abstr.	Science Research Abstracts
Sel.Water Res. Abstr.	Selected Water Resources Abstracts
Soc.Sci.Ind.	Social Science Index
Sociol.Abstr.	Sociological Abstracts
Sociol.Educ. Abstr.	Sociology of Education Abstracts
Soils & Fert.	Soils & Fertilizers
Solid St.Abstr.	Solid State Abstracts
Speleol.Abstr.	Speleological Abstracts
Stat.Theor. Meth.Abstr.	Statistical Theory and Method Abstracts
T.C.E.A.	Theoretical Chemical Engineering Abstracts
Tech.Educ. Abstr.	Technical Education Abstracts
Tech.Zentralbl.	Technisches Zentralblatt
Text.Tech.Dig.	Textile Technology Digest
Therm.Abstr.	Thermal Abstracts (Now: International Building Services Abstracts)
Tr.& Indus.Ind.	Trade & Industry Index
Trans.Res. Abstr.	Transportation Research Abstracts (Formerly: Highway Research Abstracts) (Ceased)

Trop.Abstr.	Tropical Abstracts
Trop.Dis.Bull.	Tropical Disease Bulletin
Urb.Aff.Abstr.	Urban Affairs Abstracts
Vert.File Ind.	Vertical File Index
Vet.Bull.	Veterinary Bulletin
Virol.Abstr.	Virology Abstracts
Vis.Ind.	Vision Index (Ceased)
W.R.C.Inf.	W.R.C. Information (Water Research Centre) (Formerly: Water Pollution Abstracts)
Water Pollut. Abstr.	Water Pollution Abstracts (Now: W.R.C. Information)
Water Resour. Abstr.	Water Resources Abstracts
Weed Abstr.	Weed Abstracts
Wild Life Rev.	Wild Life Review
Wom.Stud. Abstr.	Women's Studies Abstracts
Work Rel.Abstr.	Work Related Abstracts (Formerly: Employment Related Abstracts)
World Agri. Econ.& Rural Sociol.Abstr.	World Agricultural Economics and Rural Sociology Abstracts
World Alum. Abstr.	World Aluminum Abstracts
World Surf. Coat.	World Surface Coatings Abstracts
Zent.Math.	Zentralblatt fuer Mathematik und ihre Grenzgebiete
Zoo.Rec.	Zoological Record

BOOKS
SUBJECT INDEX

A

A-C CARRIER CONTROL SYSTEMS
see *Carrier Control Systems*
A-THIRTY-SIX (FIGHTER-BOMBER PLANES)
see *Mustang (Fighter Planes)*
ABACUS
Cotter, Joan A. Activities for the Abacus: A Hands-On Approach to Learning Arithmetic. (Illus.). 90p. (Orig.). 1982. pap. text ed. 8.95 (ISBN 0-9609636-1-8). Aids Learning.
Kojima, Takashi. Advanced Abacus: Japanese Theory & Practice. LC 62-15064. (Illus.). 160p. 1963. pap. 5.50 (ISBN 0-8048-0003-0). C E Tuttle.
Moon, Larry. The Abacus. LC 72-143627. (Illus.). 188p. 1971. 57.75x (ISBN 0-677-01960-2). Gordon.
ABATTOIRS
see *Slaughtering and Slaughter-Houses*
ABBREVIATIONS, CHEMICAL
see *Chemistry–Abbreviations*
ABDOMEN
see also *Intestines; Kidneys; Liver*
Gerrick, David J. Surface Anatomy: Abdomen. (Illus.). 1978. 20.00 (ISBN 0-916750-57-4). Dayton Labs.
Raymond, Howard W. Fundamentals of Abdominal Sonography: A Teaching Approach. 208p. 1979. 45.50 (ISBN 0-8089-1144-9, 793526). Grune.
Weill, F. S. & Le Mouel, A. Exercises in Diagnostic Ultrasonography of the Abdomen. (Illus.). 125p. 1983. pap. 19.00 (ISBN 0-387-12228-1). Springer-Verlag.
ABELIAN GROUPS
see also *Homology Theory*
Accola, R. D. Riemann Surfaces, Theta Functions, & Abelian Automorphisms Groups. LC 75-25928. (Lecture Notes in Mathematics: Vol. 483). iii, 105p. 1975. pap. text ed. 13.00 (ISBN 0-387-07398-1). Springer-Verlag.
Argabright, Loren & De Lamadrid, Jesus G. Fourier Analysis of Unbounded Measures on Locally Compact Abelian Groups. LC 74-6499. (Memoirs: No. 145). 53p. 1974. 10.00 (ISBN 0-8218-1845-7, MEMO-145). Am Math.
Armacost. The Structure of Locally Compact Abelian Groups. 152p. 1981. 45.00 (ISBN 0-8247-1507-1). Dekker.
Arnold, D. M., et al, eds. Abelian Group Theory: Proceedings of the 2nd New Mexico State University Bicentennial Conference on Abelian Group, Held at Las Cruces, New Mexico, Dec. 9-12 1976. (Lecture Notes in Mathematics: Vol. 616). 1977. pap. text ed. 26.00 (ISBN 0-387-08447-9). Springer-Verlag.

Berg, C. & Forst, G. Potential Theory on Locally Compact Abelian Groups. (Ergebnisse der Mathematik und Ihrer Grenzgebiete Ser.: Vol. 87). 240p. 1975. 37.00 (ISBN 0-387-07249-7). Springer-Verlag.
Bures, Donald. Abelian Subalgebras of Von Neumann Algebras. LC 52-42839. (Memoirs: No. 110). 127p. 1971. pap. text ed. 9.00 (ISBN 0-8218-1810-4, MEMO-110). Am Math.
Fossum, R. M., et al. Trivial Extensions of Abelian Categories: Homological Algebra of Trivial Extensions of Abelian Categories with Applications to Ring Theory. (Lecture Notes in Mathematics Ser.: Vol. 456). xi, 122p. (Orig.). 1975. pap. 13.00 (ISBN 0-387-07159-8). Springer-Verlag.
Fuchs, L. Infinite Abelian Groups, 2 vols. (Pure & Applied Mathematics Ser.: Vol. 36). Vol. 1 1970. 59.50 (ISBN 0-12-269601-8); Vol. 2 1973. 69.50 (ISBN 0-12-269602-6). Acad Pr.
Gobel, R., et al, eds. Abelian Groups & Modules. (CISM International Centre for Mechanical Sciences Ser.: Vol. 287). (Illus.). xii, 531p. pap. 40.60 (ISBN 0-387-81847-2). Springer-Verlag.
Goebel, R. & Walker, E., eds. Abelian Group Theory: Proceedings. (Lecture Notes in Mathematics Ser.: Vol. 874). 447p. 1981. pap. 27.00 (ISBN 0-387-10855-6). Springer-Verlag.
Goebel, R., et al, eds. Abelian Group Theory. (Lecture Notes in Mathematics Ser.: Vol. 1006). 771p. 1983. 32.00 (ISBN 0-387-12335-0). Springer-Verlag.
Griffith, Phillip A. Infinite Abelian Group Theory. LC 70-124398. (Chicago Lectures in Mathematics Ser) 1970. pap. text ed. 7.00x (ISBN 0-226-30870-7). U of Chicago Pr.
Igusa, J. Theta Functions. LC 74-183900. (Die Grundlehren der Mathematischen Wissenschaften: Vol. 194). 232p. 1972. 35.00 (ISBN 0-387-05699-8). Springer-Verlag.
Kaplansky, Irving. Infinite Abelian Groups. LC 54-62893. (University of Michigan Publications in Mathematics Ser.: No. 2). pap. 24.50 (ISBN 0-317-08467-4, 2051051). Bks Demand UMI.
Knight, James T. Commutative Algebra. LC 76-152625. (London Mathematical Society Lecture Notes Ser.: No. 5). (Illus.). 1971. pap. 16.95 (ISBN 0-521-08193-9). Cambridge U Pr.
Kraft, H. Kommutative Algebraische Gruppen und Ringe. (Lecture Notes in Mathematics: Vol. 455). 163p. 1975. pap. 10.70 (ISBN 0-387-07158-X). Springer-Verlag.
Larsen, Max D. & McCarthy, Paul J. Multiplicative Theory of Ideals. (Pure & Applied Mathematics Ser.: Vol. 43). 1971. 68.00 (ISBN 0-12-436850-6). Acad Pr.
Mazur, W. & Messing, W. Universal Extensions & One Dimensional Crystalline Cohomology. (Lecture Notes in Mathematics: Vol. 370). vii, 134p. 1974. pap. 12.00 (ISBN 0-387-06659-4). Springer-Verlag.

Misina, A. P. & Skornjakov, L. A. Abelian Groups & Modules. LC 76-22560. (Translations Ser.: No. 2, Vol. 107). 1976. 36.00 (ISBN 0-8218-3057-0, TRANS 2-107). Am Math.
Morris, S. A. Pontryagin Duality & the Structure of Locally Compact Abelian Groups. LC 76-53519. (London Mathematical Society Lecture Note Ser.: No. 29). 1977. 22.95x (ISBN 0-521-21543-9). Cambridge U Pr.
Oort, F. Commutative Group Schemes. (Lecture Notes in Mathematics: Vol. 15). (Orig.). 1966. pap. 10.70 (ISBN 0-387-03598-2). Springer-Verlag.
Popescu, N. Abelian Categories with Applications to Rings & Modules. (London Mathematical Society Symposium Ser.). 1973. 75.00 (ISBN 0-12-561550-7). Acad Pr.
Williamson, J. H. Algebras in Analysis. (London Mathematical Society Symposium Ser.). 1975. 59.50 (ISBN 0-12-757150-7). Acad Pr.
ABERDEEN-ANGUS CATTLE
Christians, Charles J. Aberdeen Angus Bloodlines. LC 60-63767. 140p. 1958. 5.00 (ISBN 0-911042-03-2). N Dak Inst.
ABERRATION, CHROMATIC AND SPHERICAL
see *Lenses; Mirrors; Optical Instruments*
ABIOGENESIS
see *Life–Origin; Spontaneous Generation*
ABNORMALITIES (ANIMALS)
Berry, C. L. & Poswillo, D., eds. Teratology: Trends & Applications. (Illus.). 260p. 1975. 48.00 (ISBN 0-387-07333-7). Springer-Verlag.
Persaud, T. V., et al. Basic Concepts in Teratology. LC 84-27762. 200p. 1985. 38.00 (ISBN 0-8451-0241-9). A R Liss.
Wilson, James G. & Warkany, Josef, eds. Teratology: Principles & Techniques. LC 65-14432. 1965. 15.00x (ISBN 0-226-90049-5). U of Chicago Pr.
ABRASIVES
Coes, L. Abrasives. LC 78-153451. (Applied Minerology: Vol. 1). (Illus.). 1971. 31.00 (ISBN 0-387-80968-6). Springer-Verlag.
Collie, M. J., ed. Industrial Abrasive Materials & Compositions. LC 81-38326. (Chem. Tech. Rev. Ser. 190). (Illus.). 351p. 1981. 45.00 (ISBN 0-8155-0851-4). Noyes.
Farago, Francis T. Abrasive Methods Engineering, Vol. 2. LC 76-14970. (Illus.). 508p. 1980. 55.00 (ISBN 0-8311-1134-8). Indus Pr.
McKee, Richard L. Machining with Abrasives. 320p. 1981. 22.95 (ISBN 0-442-25281-1). Van Nos Reinhold.
Pinkstone, William G. The Abrasive Ages. LC 74-23797. (Illus.). 136p. 1975. 10.00 (ISBN 0-915010-01-1). Sutter House.
Society of Manufacturing Engineers. Superabrasives 1985: Proceedings. 1985. 58.00 (ISBN 0-87263-183-4). SME.

ABSCISSION (BOTANY)
Addicott, Frederick T. Abscission. LC 81-4065. (Illus.). 376p. 1982. 50.00x (ISBN 0-520-04288-3). U of Cal Pr.
Kozlowski, T. T., ed. Shedding of Plant Parts. (Physiological Ecology Ser.). 1973. 85.00 (ISBN 0-12-424250-2). Acad Pr.
ABSOLUTE DIFFERENTIAL CALCULUS
see *Calculus of Tensors*
ABSORPTION
see also *Gases–Absorption and Adsorption*
Chatterjee, P. K., ed. Absorbency: Textile Science & Technology, Vol. 7. 334p. 1985. 85.25 (ISBN 0-444-42377-X). Elsevier.
Chattoraj, D. K. & Birdi, K. S. Adsorption & the Gibbs Surface Excess. 441p. 1984. 59.50x (ISBN 0-306-41334-5, Plenum Pr). Plenum Pub.
Clark, Alfred. Theory of Adsorption & Catalysis. (Physical Chemistry Ser.: Vol. 18). 1970. 78.00 (ISBN 0-12-175450-2). Acad Pr.
Goddard, E. D. & Vincent, B., eds. Polymer Adsorption & Dispersion Stability. LC 83-25787. (ACS Symposium Ser.: No. 240). 477p. 1984. lib. bdg. 79.95 (ISBN 0-8412-0820-4). Am Chemical.
Maddox, R. N. Process Engineer's Absorption Pocket Handbook. LC 85-852. (Illus.). 96p. 1985. 13.95x (ISBN 0-87201-016-3). Gulf Pub.
Maloiy, G. M., ed. Comparative Physiology of Osmoregulation in Animals, Vol. I. 1979. 97.50 (ISBN 0-12-467001-6). Acad Pr.
Pajonk, G. M., et al, eds. Spillover of Adsorbed Species. (Studies in Surface Science & Catalysis: Vol. 17). 320p. 1983. 74.50 (ISBN 0-444-42224-2, I-271-83). Elsevier.
Rachinskii, Vladimir V. The General Theory of Sorption Dynamics & Chromatography. LC 65-15004. 107p. 1965. 25.00x (ISBN 0-306-10711-2, Consultants). Plenum Pub.
ABSORPTION (HEAT)
see *Heat–Radiation and Absorption*
ABSORPTION (PHYSIOLOGY)
Bickel, H. & Schutz, Y., eds. Digestion & Absorption of Nutrients. (International Journal for Vitamin & Nutrition Research, Supplement: No. 25). (Illus.). 94p. (Orig.). 1983. pap. 15.00 (ISBN 3-456-81335-X, Pub. by Hans Huber). J K Burgess.
Brandav, R. & Lippold, H. Dermal & Transdermal Absorption. (First International Symposium from 12-14 Jnauary, 1981, Munich). 257p. 1982. 49.00 (ISBN 0-9909000-0-2, Pub. by Wissenschaftliche W Germany). Heyden.
Creutzfeldt, Werner & Flosch, Doz U. Delaying Absorption as a Therapeutic Principle in Metabolic Disease. (Illus.). 159p. 1983. text ed. 27.00 (ISBN 0-86577-158-8). Thieme Stratton.
Rolih, Susan & Albietz, Carol, eds. Enzymes, Inhibitions & Absorptions. (Illus.). 72p. 1981. 10.40 (ISBN 0-914404-67-9). Am Assn Blood.

Solomons, Noel W. & Rosenberg, Irwin H. Absorption & Malabsorption of Mineral Nutrients. LC 84-15513. (Current Topics in Nutrition & Diseases Ser.: Vol. 12). 324p. 1984. 66.00 (ISBN 0-8451-1611-8). A R Liss.

ABSORPTION, ATMOSPHERIC
see Solar Radiation

ABSORPTION IN SOILS
see Soil Absorption and Adsorption

ABSORPTION OF GASES
see Gases–Absorption and Adsorption

ABSORPTION OF SOUND
see also Architectural Acoustics; Soundproofing
Bhatia, A. B. Ultrasonic Absorption: An Introduction to the Theory of Sound Absorption & Dispersion in Gases, Liquids & Solids. 440p. 1985. pap. 8.95 (ISBN 0-486-64917-2). Dover.

ABSORPTION SPECTRA
see also Astronomical Spectroscopy; Heat–Radiation and Absorption; Molecular Spectra; Spectrum Analysis
also subdivision Spectra under subjects, e.g. Stars–Spectra
Blass, William E. & Halsey, George. Deconvolution of Absorption Spectra. LC 81-12667. 1981. 29.50 (ISBN 0-12-104650-8). Acad Pr.
Burgess, C. & Knowles, A. Standards in Absorption Spectrometry. (Techniques in Visible & Ultraviolet Spectrometry Ser.) 1981. 22.00x (ISBN 0-412-22470-4, 2230, Pub. by Chapman & Hall). Methuen Inc.
Cole, Howard, ed. Tables of Wavenumbers for the Calibration of Infrared Spectrometers, Vol. 9. 2nd ed. 1977. text ed. 44.00 (ISBN 0-08-021247-6). Pergamon.
Ebdon, L. An Introduction to Atomic Absorption Spectroscopy: A Self Teaching Approach. 1981. pap. text ed. 24.95x (ISBN 0-471-26194-7). Wiley.
Elwell, W. T. & Gidley, J. A. Atomic Absorption Spectrophotometry. 2nd ed. 1966. 21.00 (ISBN 0-08-012063-6). Pergamon.
Fikhtegol'ts, V. S., et al. Ultraviolet Spectra of Elastomers & Rubber Chemicals. LC 66-12889. 170p. 1966. 49.50x (ISBN 0-306-65119-X, IFI Plenum). Plenum Pub.
Hershenson, Herbert M. Infrared Absorption Spectra, 2 vols. Incl. Index for 1945-57. 1959. 43.50 (ISBN 0-12-343250-2). Acad Pr.
--Ultraviolet & Visible Absorption Spectra, 3 vols. Incl. Index for 1930-1954. 1956. 46.50 (ISBN 0-12-343265-0). Acad Pr.
Hirayama, Kenzo. Handbook of Ultraviolet & Visible Absorption Spectra of Organic Compounds. LC 66-24948. 645p. 1967. 75.00x (ISBN 0-306-65123-8, IFI Plenum). Plenum Pub.
Katz, Sidney A. & Jenniss, Stephen W. Regulatory Compliance Monitoring by Atomic Absorption Spectroscopy. (Illus.). 278p. 1983. 37.50x (ISBN 0-89573-114-2). VCH Pubs.
Knowles, A. & Burgess, C., eds. Practical Absorption Spectrometry. (Techniques in Ultraviolet Spectrometry Ser.: Vol. 3). 300p. 1984. 39.95x (ISBN 0-412-24390-3, NO. 6850). Methuen Inc.
Lang. Absorption Spectra, Vols. 18 & 19. 1974. Vol. 18. 86.50 (ISBN 0-12-436318-0); Vol. 19. 86.50 (ISBN 0-12-436319-9). Acad Pr.
Lang, L., ed. Absorption Spectra in the Ultraviolet & Visible Region. Incl. Vols. 3-4. 86.50 ea. Vol. 3, 1963 (ISBN 0-12-436303-2). Vol. 4, 1963 (ISBN 0-12-436304-0); Vol. 5. 1965. 86.50 (ISBN 0-12-436305-9); Vols. 6-12. 86.50 ea. Vol. 6, 1966 (ISBN 0-12-436306-7). Vol. 7, 1967 (ISBN 0-12-436307-5). Vol. 8, 1967 (ISBN 0-12-436308-3). Vol. 9, 1968 (ISBN 0-12-436309-1). Vol. 10, 1968 (ISBN 0-12-436310-5). Vol. 11,1969. (ISBN 0-12-436311-3); Vol. 12, 1970. (ISBN 0-12-436312-1); Index to Volumes. 1969. 47.50 (ISBN 0-12-436356-3); Vols. 13-15. 1970. 86.50 ea. Vol. 13 (ISBN 0-12-436313-X). Vol. 14,1971 (ISBN 0-12-436314-8). Vol. 15 (ISBN 0-12-436315-6); Index to Volumes 11-15. 1971. 47.50 (ISBN 0-12-436357-1); Vols. 16-17. 1972-73. 86.50 ea. Vol. 17 (ISBN 0-12-436317-2). Acad Pr.
Lenoble, Jacqueline, ed. Radiative Transfer in Scattering & Absorbing Atmospheres: Standard Computational Procedures. 1985. write for info. (ISBN 0-937194-05-0). A Deepak Pub.
Ottaway, J. M. & Ure, A. M. Practical Atomic Absorption Spectrometry. 1987. 30.01 (ISBN 0-08-023800-9). Pergamon.
Parikh, V. M. Absorption Spectroscopy of Organic Molecules. LC 72-3460. 1974. pap. text ed. 24.95 (ISBN 0-201-05708-5). Addison-Wesley.
Pestemer, M. Correlation Tables for the Structural Determination of Organic Compounds by Ultraviolet Light Absorptiometry. 163p. 1975. 57.70x (ISBN 3-527-25531-1). VCH Pubs.
Phillips, John P. Spectra-Structure Correlation. (Illus.). 1964. 47.50 (ISBN 0-12-553450-7). Acad Pr.

Slavin, W., ed. Graphite Furnace Technology & Atomic Absorption Spectroscopy: Commemorating the 25th Anniversary of the Publication of the First Paper by B. V. L'vov. 400p. 1984. pap. 55.00 (ISBN 0-08-031405-8). Pergamon.
Uehara, K. & Sasada, H. High Resolution Spectral Atlas of Nitrogen Dioxide 559-597 nm. (Springer Series in Chemical Physics: Vol. 41). (Illus.). 230p. 1985. 37.00 (ISBN 0-387-15027-7). Springer-Verlag.
Velluz, L., et al. Optical Circular Dichroism: Principles Measurements, & Applications. (Illus.). 1969. 34.20x (ISBN 3-527-25289-4). VCH Pubs.
Welz, B., ed. Atomic Absorption Spectrometry. 2nd ed. Skegg, Chistopher, tr. (Illus.). 305p. 1985. lib. bdg. 47.50 (ISBN 0-89573-418-4). VCH Pubs.
Welz, Bernhard. Atomic Absorption Spectroscopy. (Illus.). 267p. 1976. 40.00x (ISBN 3-527-25680-6). VCH Pubs.

ABSTRACT ALGEBRA
see Algebra, Abstract

ABSTRACT AUTOMATA
see Machine Theory

ABSTRACT MACHINES
see Machine Theory

ABSTRACT METRICS
see Distance Geometry

ABSTRACTING
Abstracting & Indexing Career Guide. 1983. 12.00 (ISBN 0-942308-16-6). NFAIS.
INIS: Instructions for Submitting Abstracts. (INIS Reference Ser.: No. 4). pap. 5.50 (ISBN 92-0-178171-7, IN4/R1, IAEA). Unipub.

ABSTRACTION
Brownell, William A. Arithmetical Abstractions: The Movement Toward Conceptual Maturity under Differing Systems of Instructions. LC 67-65751. (University of California Publications in Education Ser.: Vol. 17). pap. 58.00 (ISBN 0-317-11014-4, 2021359). Bks Demand UMI.
Narens, Louis. Abstract Measurement Theory. 400p. 1985. text ed. 40.00x (ISBN 0-262-14037-3). MIT Pr.
Zimmer, J. A. Abstraction for Programmers. 288p. 1985. 17.95 (ISBN 0-07-072832-1). McGraw.

ABYSSAL ZONE
see also Ocean Bottom
Heezen, B. C. Influence of Abyssal Circulation on Sedimentary Accumulations in Space & Time. (Developments in Sedimentology Ser.: Vol. 23). 216p. 1977. 53.25 (ISBN 0-444-41569-6). Elsevier.
Menzies, Robert J., et al. Abyssal Environment & Ecology of the World Oceans. LC 72-8780. 488p. 1973. 37.50 (ISBN 0-686-65289-4, Pub. by Wiley). Krieger.

ACANTHOCEPHALA
Crompton, D. W. & Nickol, B. B., eds. Biology of Acanthocephala. (Illus.). 512p. Date not set. 89.50 (ISBN 0-521-24674-1). Cambridge U Pr.

ACARI
see Mites

ACARINA
see Ticks

ACCELERATION (MECHANICS)
see also Mechanics; Motion; Speed
Cooper, G. R. & McGillem, C. D. Modern Communications & Spread Spectrum. 544p. 1985. 51.95 (ISBN 0-07-012951-7). McGraw.
Eighth Aerodynamic Decelerator & Balloon Technology. 50.00 (ISBN 0-317-06652-8). AIAA.
Newman, Wolfgang S., ed. Eleventh International Conference on High-Energy Accelerators: Geneva 1980. (Experientia Supplimentia: 40). 940p. 1980. text ed. 129.95x (ISBN 0-8176-1215-7). Birkhauser.
Newton, Robert R. Ancient Astronomical Observations & the Accelerations of the Earth & Moon. LC 70-122011. (Illus.). Repr. of 1970 ed. 62.60 (ISBN 0-8357-9264-1, 2013730). Bks Demand UMI.
Reiser, M. & Rostoker, N., eds. Collective Methods of Acceleration. (Accelerators & Storage Rings: Vol. 2). 752p. 1979. lib. bdg. 61.50 (ISBN 3-7186-0005-6). Harwood Academic.

ACCELERATORS, ELECTRON
see Particle Accelerators

ACCELERATORS, LINEAR
see Linear Accelerators

ACCIDENTS, AIRCRAFT
see Aeronautics–Accidents

ACCIDENTS, SPACECRAFT
see Astronautics–Accidents

ACCLIMATIZATION
see also Altitude, Influence Of; Animal Introduction
Heath, Donald & Williams, David R. Man at High Altitude: The Pathophysiology of Acclimatization & Adaptation. 2nd ed. (Illus.). 1981. text ed. 65.00 (ISBN 0-443-02081-7). Churchill.

Van Matre, Steve. Acclimatization. (Illus.). 138p. 1972. pap. 5.50 (ISBN 0-87603-007-X). Am Camping.

ACCLIMATIZATION (PLANTS)
see Botany–Ecology; Plant Introduction

ACCOUNTING–DATA PROCESSING
Accounting Software Controls. 1983. 16.00x (ISBN 0-85012-430-1). Intl Pubns Serv.
Anderson, Donald L. & Raun, Donald L. Information Analysis in Management Accounting. LC 77-14938. (Wiley Series in Accounting & Information Systems). 706p. 1978. 46.50x (ISBN 0-471-02815-0). Wiley.
Anderson, Kenneth, ed. Computer Applications in Property Management Accounting. 4th ed. 64p. 1983. pap. text ed. 16.50 (ISBN 0-912104-71-6, 990). Inst Real Estate.
Anthony, Robert N. Teach Yourself Essentials of Accounting on the IBM PC. 80p. 1983. write for info. (ISBN 0-201-15329-7); write for info. incl. disk (ISBN 0-201-15328-9); write for info. incl. disk (ISBN 0-201-15331-9). Addison-Wesley.
Arkin, H. & Arkin, R. Statistical Sampling Software for Auditing & Accounting. 160p. 1985. 275.00 (ISBN 0-07-079119-8). McGraw.
Ashton, Robert H. Human Information Processing in Accounting, Vol. 17. (Studies in Accounting Research). 215p. 1982. 9.00 (ISBN 0-86539-038-X); members 6.00. Am Accounting.
Bodnar, George. Accounting Information Systems. 2nd ed. 520p. 1983. text ed. 37.14 (ISBN 0-205-07929-6, 057929). Allyn.
Bower, James B., et al. Computer-Oriented Accounting Systems. 1985. text ed. 22.35 (ISBN 0-538-01740-6, A74). SW Pub.
British Computer Society. Buying Financial Accounting Software. (Software Package Buyer's Guides Ser.). 48p. 1985. pap. 8.95 (ISBN 0-521-31781-9). Cambridge U Pr.
Brown, Gary D. & Sefton, Donald. Surviving with Financial Application Packages for the Computer. 233p. 1983. 24.50 (ISBN 0-471-87065-X, Pub. by Wiley-Interscience). Wiley.
Carlson, Arthur E., et al. Boyds Clothiers: Automated Accounting for the Microcomputer. 1983. 8.00 (ISBN 0-538-01150-5, A15). SW PUb.
Carr, J. G. Information Technology & the Accountant: An Accountancy Sector Study Jointly Sponsored by the Chartered Association of Certified Accountants & the Department of Industry. 318p. 1985. pap. text ed. 89.95x set (ISBN 0-566-02568-X). Gower Pub Co.
Charles, Thomas W. & Stiner, Frederic M., Jr. Your Name Company: Accounting Practice Set for the Computer. 144p. 1985. pap. write for info. (ISBN 0-534-04506-5). Kent Pub Co.
Clay, Susan & Brooks, JoeAnn. Software Primer: Computer Accounting. Harper, Larry D., ed. LC 83-82214. (Software Primer Ser.). 180p. 1984. binder cancelled (ISBN 0-913871-04-4). JNZ.
Computer Strategies. The Contractor's Computer Handbook. 150p. 1983. looseleaf 45.00x (ISBN 0-9603584-9-8). Computer Strat.
--The CPA Computer Handbook. 150p. 1983. 45.00x (ISBN 0-913505-06-4). Computer Strat.
Continental Software. The Home Accountant - Apple. (Orig.). 1985. pap. 9.95 manual (ISBN 0-538-01010-X, AO11). SW Pub.
--The Home Accountant - IBM PC. 1985. manual 9.95 (ISBN 0-538-01012-6, A013). SW Pub.
--The Home Accountant - TRS 80. 1985. manual 9.95 (ISBN 0-538-01011-8, A012). SW Pub.
Cushing, Barry E. Accounting Information Systems & Business Organizations. 3rd ed. LC 81-2411. (Accounting Ser.). (Illus.). 808p. 1981. text ed. 36.95 (ISBN 0-201-10111-4); instrs' manual 21.95 (ISBN 0-201-10112-2). Addison-Wesley.
Davis, James R. & Cushing, Barry E. Accounting Information Systems: A Book of Readings. LC 78-74681. pap. 17.95 (ISBN 0-201-01099-2). Addison-Wesley.
Edwards, Donald E. & Kettering, Ronald C. Computer Assisted Practice Set in Financial Accounting: Cook's Solar Energy Systems. LC 82-83660. 96p. 1983. 11.95 (ISBN 0-395-33492-6); instr's manual 2.00 (ISBN 0-395-33493-4). HM.
Eliason, Alan & Kitts, Kent D. Business Computer Systems & Applications. 2nd ed. LC 78-18447. 384p. 1979. 16.95 (ISBN 0-574-21215-9, 13-4215); instr's guide 2.25 (ISBN 0-574-21216-7, 13-4216). SRA.
Elliott, Patrica C. A Practical Guide to the Computer for Tax Practitioners. 1976. pap. 11.50 1983 supplement (ISBN 0-88450-504-9, 1701-B). Lawyers & Judges.
Forrest, Arthur T. Microcomputers for the Professional Accountant. 108p. (Orig.). 1983. pap. 38.50x (ISBN 0-566-03441-7). Gower Pub Co.

GLAS: General Ledger Accounting System for VisiCalc. (Key-By-Key Ser.). (Illus.). 240p. 1983. pap. write for info. (ISBN 0-534-02881-0); write for info. Wadsworth Pub.
Golding, Steve & Kormann, Chris. The Home Accountant Desk Reference. Date not set. pap. write for info (ISBN 0-912003-48-0). Bk Co.
Goodman & Mason. Experiencing Accounting: A Study Guide for Personal Computing. (Pt. 1). 1985. 12.86 (ISBN 0-205-08221-1, 058221). Allyn.
Greynolds, Elbert B. Financial Analysis Using Calculators. (Calculating & Computing Bks.). 472p. 1980. pap. 20.95 (ISBN 0-317-27321-3, LCB4531). Tex Instr Inc.
Greynolds, Elbert B., Jr. Time Sharing: Computer Programs & Applications in Accounting. (Research Monograph: No. 57). 1974. spiral bdg. 30.00 (ISBN 0-88406-021-7). Ga St U Busn Pub.
Guidelines to Assess Computerized General Ledger & Financial Reporting Systems for Use in CPA Firms. (Computer Services Guidelines Ser.). 47p. 1979. pap. 7.50 (ISBN 0-686-70233-6). Am Inst CPA.
Guidelines to Assess Computerized Time & Billing Systems for Use in CPA Firms. (Computer Services Guidelines Ser.). 55p. 1980. pap. 7.50 (ISBN 0-686-70234-4). Am Inst CPA.
Halligan, Joseph. Accounting-SOFTWHERE. Halligan, Joseph & Winther, Richard P., eds. (SOFTWHERE Software Directories Ser.: Vol. 1). (Orig.). 1984. pap. 49.95 (ISBN 0-918451-00-0). Moore Data.
Hamilton, S. S. Accounting Applications for the Microcomputer. (Microcomputer Software Program Ser.). 1983. 9.65 (ISBN 0-07-025736-1). McGraw.
Hamilton, S. S., et al. Microcomputer Accounting Applications. (Microcomputer Software Program Ser.). 128p. 1982. text ed. 6.84 (ISBN 0-07-025818-X). McGraw.
Hicks, James O., Jr. & Leininger, Wayne E. Accounting Information Systems. 608p. 1981. text ed. 28.95 (ISBN 0-8299-0384-4). West Pub.
Hicks, Sam A. & Safter, Donald V. Microcomputers in Accounting. (Illus.). Date not set. pap. text ed. price not set (ISBN 0-314-87265-5). West Pub.
Hixson, Amanda C. A Buyer's Guide to Microcomputer Business Software: Accounting & Spreadsheets. 1918p. 1984. pap. 19.95 (ISBN 0-201-11065-2). Addison-Wesley.
Hoskin, Robert E. & Labbe, R. A. Financial Accounting with Lotus 1-2-3. (Illus.). 288p. 1986. pap. text ed. 19.95 (ISBN 0-13-315870-5). P-H.
International Computer Programs Staff. ICP Software Directory, Vol. 2: General Accounting Systems. Hamilton, Dennis L., ed. 1985. pap. 95.00 (ISBN 0-88094-043-3). Intl Computer.
Keeling, B. Lewis, et al. Payroll Accounting for Microcomputers. 1986. text ed. 8.00 wkbk. (ISBN 0-538-01470-9, A47). SW Pub.
Kelley. An Accounting Experience with the Apple II Microcomputer: A Service Firm. 1983. pap. 16.95t (ISBN 0-256-02955-5). Business Pubns.
--An Accounting Experience with the IBM Microcomputer: A Service Firm. 2nd ed. 1985. pap. 16.95x (ISBN 0-256-03437-0). Business Pubns.
Kieso, D. E. Computer-Assisted Practice Set & Problems for Intermediate Accounting - Apple II. 4th ed. 1985. incl. disk 30.95 (ISBN 0-471-80475-4). Wiley.
Klooster, Dale H. & Allen, Warren W. Automated Accounting for the Microcomputer. 1982. text ed. 7.55 wkbk. (ISBN 0-538-02398-8, B398). SW Pub.
--Automated (Micro Computer) Accounting Practice: Midtown Electronic Simulation. 1983. 7.85 (ISBN 0-538-01090-8, A09). SW Pub.
Lauderdale, Leslie. The Home Accountant Plus: A Handholding Guide for IBM-PC Users. 1985. pap. write for info (ISBN 0-912003-44-8). Bk Co.
Leitch, Robert A. & Davis, K. Roscoe. Accounting Information Systems. (Illus.). 720p. 1983. 37.95 (ISBN 0-13-002949-1). P-H.
Li, David H. Accounting Information Systems: A Control Emphasis. 1983. 31.95x (ISBN 0-256-02909-1). Irwin.
Lindhe, Richard & Grossman, Steven D. Accounting Information Systems. 500p. 1980. text ed. 31.95x (ISBN 0-931920-23-X). Dame Pubns.
Louvau, Gordon E. & Carvajal, Arnold J. Systems Specifications for a Micro or Mini Computer Based Accountant's Client Write-Up Systems. (Accounting Ser.). (Illus.). 135p. 1982. 32.50 (ISBN 0-534-01227-2). Lifetime Learn.

Louvau, Gordon E. & Jackson, Marjorie E. Computers in Accountants' Offices. (Accounting Ser.). (Illus.). 132p. 1982. 25.00 (ISBN 0-534-97967-X). Lifetime Learn.

Louvau, Gordon E., et al. Systems Specifications for a Micro-or Mini-Computer Based Accountant's Client Write-up System. 128p. 1983. pap. 32.50 (ISBN 0-534-01227-2). Van Nos Reinhold.

McNairn, William N. The Accountant's & Consultant's Guide to Computer. (Illus.). 236p. (Orig.). 1985. wkbk. 34.95 (ISBN 0-932621-00-7). Quotamus Pr.

McRae, T. W. Computer & Accounting. LC 75-6793. 167p. 1976. 32.95x (ISBN 0-471-58985-3, Pub. by Wiley-Interscience). Wiley.

Monroe, J. Spreadsheet Applications in Accounting Information Systems: Includes SuperCalc 3 Educational Version. 24.95 (ISBN 0-471-82255-8). Wiley.

Morgan, James. Computer Power for Your Accounting Firm. LC 84-51244. 250p. 1984. pap. 9.95 (ISBN 0-89588-164-0). SYBEX.

Moscove, Stephen A. & Simkin, Mark G. Accounting Information Systems: Concepts & Practice for Effective Decision Making. 2nd ed. LC 83-16842. 721p. 1984. 35.45 (ISBN 0-471-88354-9); tchr's manual avail. (ISBN 0-471-88124-4); test bank avail. (ISBN 0-471-81098-3). Wiley.

Murdick, Robert, et al. Accounting Information Systems. (Illus.). 1978. ref. ed. 36.95 (ISBN 0-13-002014-1). P-H.

Nash, John F. & Roberts, Martin B. Accounting Information Systems. 704p. 1984. text ed. write for info. (ISBN 0-02-386050-2). Macmillan.

Needleman, Theodore. Microcomputers for Accountants. (Illus.). 186p. 1983. 24.95 (ISBN 0-13-580696-8, Spec); pap. 14.95 (ISBN 0-13-580688-7). P-H.

Newman, Maurice S. Accounting Estimates by Computer Sampling. 2nd ed. LC 81-12955. 279p. 1982. 36.95x (ISBN 0-471-09147-2, Pub. by Ronald Pr). Wiley.

Ochi, Kaz & Hughes, Pat. Accounting with Lotus 1-2-3. 200p. 1983. pap. write for info (ISBN 0-534-03038-6). Wadsworth Pub.

Page & Hooper. Accounting & Information Systems. 2nd ed. 1982. text ed. 30.95 (ISBN 0-8359-0090-8); practice case 8.95 (ISBN 0-8359-0092-4); instr's. manual free (ISBN 0-8359-0091-6). Reston.

Page, John & Hooper, Paul. Accounting & Information Systems. 3rd ed. 1985. text ed. 29.95 (ISBN 0-8359-9121-0). Reston.

--Microcomputer Accounting & Information Systems. 1985. pap. text ed. 18.95 (ISBN 0-8359-4408-5); instr's. manual avail. (ISBN 0-8359-9122-9). Reston.

Parker, Alan & Stewart, John. Accountant's BASIC Programming for the Apple II. 1983. 16.95 (ISBN 0-8359-0047-9). Reston.

Perry, William E. The Accountants' Guide to Computer Systems. (Modern Accounting Perspectives & Practice Ser.). 286p. 1982. text ed. 45.00x (ISBN 0-471-08992-3, Pub. by Ronald Pr). Wiley.

--Data Processors' Survival Guide to Accounting. 336p. 1985. 34.95 (ISBN 0-471-88178-3). Wiley.

Philips, Sheldon W. & King, Brian L. GLAS: General Ledger Accounting System for SuperCalc. LC 83-10413. (Key-By-Key Ser.). (Illus.). 240p. 1983. pap. write for info. (ISBN 0-534-02851-9); write for info. Wadsworth Pub.

--OSGLAS: General Ledger Accounting System for Osborne Computers. (Key-By-Key Ser.). (Illus.). 240p. (Orig.). 1983. pap. write for info. (ISBN 0-534-02872-1); write for info. templates on disk. Wadsworth Pub.

--OSGLAS: Payroll for Osborne Computers. (Key-By-Key Ser.). (Illus.). 150p. 1983. pap. write for info. (ISBN 0-534-02874-8); write for info. Wadsworth Pub.

Pillsbury, Wilbur F. Computer Augmented Accounting. 1979. text ed. 6.70 (ISBN 0-538-01357-5, A357). SW Pub.

Pillsbury, Wilbur F. & Ripperger, William. Microcomputer Augmented Accounting. 1983. text ed. 9.50 wkbk. (ISBN 0-538-01660-4, A66). SW Pub.

--Microcomputer-Oriented Accounting: A CAI Approach. 1983. text ed. 6.95 wkbk. (ISBN 0-538-02355-4, B355). SW Pub.

Romney, Marshall B., et al. Casebook in Accounting Information Systems. 112p. pap. text ed. 10.95x (ISBN 0-471-81445-8); solutions manual avail. Wiley.

Scorgie, Michael & Magnus, Anne. Accounting on Your IBM PC. 224p. 1984. pap. 18.95 (ISBN 0-8359-0025-8). Reston.

Shaffer & Shaffer Applied Research & Development, Inc. VisiCalc Programming: No Experience Necessary: A Self Instructional Disk & Book for Use with the Apple II Plus Computer. 256p. 1983. disk & manual in slipcase 59.95 (ISBN 0-316-78239-4). Little.

Sharifi, Mohsen & Farah, Badie. Integrated Case Studies in Accounting Information Systems. 1985. pap. text ed. 16.95 (ISBN 0-8359-3205-2); tchr's. manual avail. (ISBN 0-8359-3206-0). Reston.

Simon, Gary. Choosing Accounting Software for Your Micro. (Illus.). 160p. 1985. pap. 17.95 (ISBN 0-00-383006-3, Pub. by Collins England). Sheridan.

Small Business Accounting Software Guide. 340p. 1984. 19.95 (ISBN 0-317-04404-4). Micro Info.

Small Business Software Guide & Handbook Including Vertical Market & Accounting Programs. 1985. Master Volume. 19.95 (ISBN 0-912603-33-X); Apple Volume. 16.95 (ISBN 0-912603-42-9); IBM Volume. 16.95 (ISBN 0-912603-19-4). Micro Info.

Smith. Electronic Spreadsheet Applications for Financial Accounting. 1986. pap. text ed. price not set (ISBN 0-538-40182-6, O7A1). SW Pub.

Stewart, William E., et al. Accountant's Guide to Desktop Computers. (Illus.). 224p. 18.95 (ISBN 0-8359-0011-8). Reston.

Towles, Martin F. & Towles, Michael T. Handbook of Applied Accounting Mathematics. 332p. 1982. 34.95 (ISBN 0-13-372490-5). P-H.

Tyran, Michael R. Computerized Accounting Methods & Controls. 2nd ed. (Illus.). 250p. 1978. 39.95 (ISBN 0-13-165761-5, Busn). P-H.

--Computerized Financial Forecasting & Performance Reporting. 384p. 1980. 50.00 (ISBN 0-13-166173-6). P-H.

Weaver, D. Microcomputer Testing Program for Accounting: Systems & Procedures. 4th ed. 175.00 (ISBN 0-07-009053-X). McGraw.

Weis, Rick. Epson Printers for Accountants. 1985. pap. 19.95 (ISBN 0-8359-1748-7). Reston.

--Epson Printers for CPA's. 1985. pap. 19.95 (ISBN 0-8359-1748-7). Reston.

Weis, Stephen, ed. Computer Systems Guide for Accountants. 1984. text ed. 29.95 (ISBN 0-8359-0851-8); pap. text ed. 17.95 (ISBN 0-8359-0850-X). Reston.

Wilkinson, Joseph W. Accounting & Information Systems. LC 81-13153. (Wiley Series in Accounting & Information Systems). 845p. 1982. text ed. 37.50 (ISBN 0-471-04986-7); tchr's manual avail. (ISBN 0-471-04987-5). Wiley.

--Accounting with the Computer: A Practice Case & Simulation. 3rd ed. 1975. pap. 14.95x (ISBN 0-256-01659-3). Irwin.

Wu, Frederick H. Accounting Information Systems: Theory & Practice. (Illus.). 608p. 1983. text ed. 34.95 (ISBN 0-07-072121-1). McGraw.

ACCOUNTING–MACHINE METHODS

see Machine Accounting

ACCOUNTING–PROGRAMMED INSTRUCTION

Dixon, R. L. The McGraw-Hill Thirty-Six Hour Accounting Course. 2nd ed. 1982. 34.50 (ISBN 0-07-017091-6). McGraw.

ACCOUNTING MACHINES

Rudman, Jack. Electric Accounting Machine Operator. (Career Examination Ser.: C-238). (Cloth bdg. avail. on request). pap. 10.00 (ISBN 0-8373-0238-2). Natl Learning.

--Senior Accounting Machine Operator. (Career Examination Ser.: C-2203). (Cloth bdg. avail. on request). pap. 10.00 (ISBN 0-686-53447-6). Natl Learning.

ACCUMULATORS

see Storage Batteries

ACE

see Automatic Checkout Equipment

ACEPHALIA

see Lamellibranchiata

ACETABULARIA

Brachet, Jean & Bonotto, S., eds. Biology of Acetabularia: Proceedings. 1970. 55.00 (ISBN 0-12-123360-X). Acad Pr.

Woodcock, C. L., ed. Progress in Acetabularia Research. 1977. 45.00 (ISBN 0-12-763750-8). Acad Pr.

ACETAL RESINS

Sittig, Marshall. Polyacetal Resins. LC 63-1271. 152p. 1963. 6.95x (ISBN 0-87201-722-2). Gulf Pub.

ACETATE SILK

see Rayon

ACETIC ACID

Hartman, Guido R., ed. Die Aktivierte Essigsaure: Festschrift Fur Feodor Lynen. 1976. 30.00x (ISBN 3-11-006824-9). De Gruyter.

ACETYLENE

Acetylene Cylinder Charging Plants. (Fifty Ser). 1974. pap. 2.00 (ISBN 0-685-58090-3, 51A). Natl Fire Prot.

Viehe, H. G., ed. Chemistry of Acetylenes. 1969. 225.00 (ISBN 0-8247-1675-2). Dekker.

ACETYLENE BLACK

see Carbon-Black

ACETYLENE COMPOUNDS

Bohlmann, F., et al. Naturally Occurring Acetylenes. 1973. 98.00 (ISBN 0-12-111150-4). Acad Pr.

Bradsma, L. & Verkruijsse, H. D. Synthesis of Acetylenes, Allenes & Cumulenes: A Laboratory Manual. (Studies in Organic Chemistry: Vol. 8). 276p. 1981. 70.25 (ISBN 0-444-42009-6). Elsevier.

Merrill, Gary F. & Weiss, Harvey R., eds. CA 2t Entry Blockers, Adenosine, & Neurohumors. LC 82-17591. (Illus.). 345p. 1983. pap. 38.00 (ISBN 0-8067-1271-6). Urban & S.

Tedeschi, Robert J. Acetelyne Based Chemicals from Coal & Other Natural Sources. (Chemical Industries Ser.: Vol. 6). (Illus.). 232p. 1982. 45.00 (ISBN 0-8247-1358-3). Dekker.

ACID BASE EQUILIBRIUM

Cohen, Jordan J. & Kassirer, Jerome P. Acid-Base. 1982. text ed. 49.95 (ISBN 0-316-15011-8). Little.

Davenport, Horace W. ABC of Acid-Base Chemistry: The Elements of Physiological Blood-Gas Chemistry for Medical Students & Physicians. 6th rev. ed. LC 79-88230. 1974. 10.00x (ISBN 0-226-13705-8); pap. text ed. 5.95x (ISBN 0-226-13703-1). U of Chicago Pr.

Finston, Harmon L. & Rychtman, Allen C. A New View of Current Acid-Base Theories. LC 81-16030. 216p. 1982. 58.00 (ISBN 0-471-08472-7, Pub. by Wiley-Interscience). Wiley.

Gamble, James L., Jr. Acid-Base Physiology: A Direct Approach. 144p. 1982. text ed. 15.00x (ISBN 0-8018-2629-2). Johns Hopkins.

Hand, Clifford W. Acid Base Chemistry. 1986. pap. text ed. price not set (ISBN 0-02-349910-9). Macmillan.

Kildeberg, Poul. Quantitative Acid-Base Physiology. LC 81-80908. (Illus.). 142p. 1981. 27.50 (ISBN 0-89640-048-4). Igaku-Shoin.

Quintero, Jorge A. Acid Base Balance: A Manual for Clinicians. 2nd ed. LC 77-81798. 1981. 12.50 (ISBN 0-87527-148-0). Green.

Schwartz, Allan B. & Lyons, Harvey, eds. Acid-Base & Electrolyte Balance: Normal Regulation & Clinical Disorders. (Illus.). 320p. 1977. 34.50 (ISBN 0-8089-0991-6, 793927). Grune.

STewart. How to Understand Acid-Base: A Quantitative Acid-Base Primer for Biology & Medicine. 186p. 1981. 29.00 (ISBN 0-444-00406-8, Biomedical Pr). Elsevier.

ACID PRECIPITATION (METEOROLOGY)

see Acid Rain

ACID PROTEINASE

see Pepsin

ACID RAIN

Bhumralker, Chandrakant & Teasley, John I., eds. Meteorological Aspects of Acid Rain. (Acid Precipitation Ser.: Vol. 1). 256p. 1984. text ed. 32.50 (ISBN 0-250-40566-0). Butterworth.

Boyle, Robert H. & Boyle, R. Alexander. Acid Rain. LC 82-21410. 128p. (Orig.). 1983. 14.95 (ISBN 0-8052-3854-9); pap. 8.95 (ISBN 0-8052-0746-5). Schocken.

Bricker, Owen P. & Teasley, John I., eds. Geological Effects of Acid Deposition. (Acid Percipitation Ser.: Vol. 7). 160p. 1984. text ed. 32.50 (ISBN 0-250-40572-5). Butterworth.

Bubenick, David V. Acid Rain Information Book. 2nd ed. LC 83-21986. (Illus.). 397p. 1984. 39.00 (ISBN 0-8155-0967-7). Noyes.

Calvert, Jack G. & Teasley, John I., eds. SO2, No, & NO2 Oxidation Mechanisms: Atmospheric Considerations. (Acid Precipitation Ser.: Vol. 3). 272p. 1984. text ed. 32.50 (ISBN 0-250-40568-7). Butterworth.

Canter, L. W. Acid Precipitation & Dry Deposition. (Illus.). 400p. 1985. 49.95 (ISBN 0-87371-016-9). Lewis Pubs Inc.

Carroll, John E. Acid Rain: An Issue in Canadian-American Relations. LC 82-82205. (Canadian-American Committee). 98p. (Orig.). 1982. pap. 6.00 (ISBN 0-89068-064-7). Natl Planning.

Committee on Transport & Chemical Transformation in Acid Precipitation, Nation Research Council. Acid Deposition: Atmospheric Process in Eastern North America. 1983. pap. text ed. 16.50 (ISBN 0-309-03389-6). Natl Acad Pr.

Crocker, Thomas D. & Teasley, John I., eds. Economic Perspectives on Acid Deposition Control. (Acid Percipitation Ser.: Vol. 8). 208p. 1984. text ed. 32.50 (ISBN 0-250-40573-3). Butterworth.

Curtis, Carolyn, ed. Before the Rainbow: What We Know about Acid Rain. (Decisionmakers Bookshelf Ser.: Vol. 9). (Illus.). 102p. (Orig.). 1980. pap. 2.50 (ISBN 0-931032-09-1). Edison Electric.

DOE Technical Information Center. Acid Precipitation: A Compilation of Worldwide Literature-A Bibliography. 732p. 1983. pap. 30.00 (ISBN 0-87079-500-7, DOE/TIC-3399); microfiche 4.50 (ISBN 0-87079-501-5, DOE/TIC-3399). DOE.

Durham, Jack L. & Teasley, John I., eds. Chemistry of Particles, Fogs & Rains. (Acid Precipitation Ser.: Vol. 2). 288p. 1984. text ed. 32.50 (ISBN 0-250-40567-9). Butterworth.

Elliott, Thomas C. & Schwieger, Robert G., eds. The Acid Rain Sourcebook. (Illus.). 296p. 1984. 44.95 (ISBN 0-07-606540-5). McGraw.

Elsworth, Steve. Acid Rain: In the UK & Europe. 54p. (Orig.). 1984. pap. 5.95 (ISBN 0-86104-791-5, Pub. by Pluto Pr). Longwood Pub Group.

Fluoride: The Missing Link in Acid Rain. pap. 2.00 (ISBN 0-318-04802-7). Top-Ecol Pr.

Gould, Roy R. Going Sour: Science & Politics of Acid Rain. LC 84-21700. 200p. 1985. 11.95 (ISBN 0-8176-3251-4). Birkhauser.

Gray, Charles, Jr. & Alson, Jeff. Methanol: The Transportation Fuel of the Future (The Optimal Solution to the Acid Rain & Energy Problems) 300p. 1985. text ed. 25.00x (ISBN 0-472-10071-8); pap. text ed. 12.50x (ISBN 0-472-08063-6). U of Mich Pr.

Hendray, George & Teasley, John I., eds. Early Biotic Responses to Advancing Lake Acidification. (Acid Precipitation Ser.: Vol. 6). 192p. 1984. text ed. 32.50 (ISBN 0-250-40571-7). Butterworth.

Hicks, Bruce B. & Teasley, John I., eds. Deposition Both Wet & Dry. (Acid Precipitation Ser.: Vol.4). 224p. 1984. text ed. 32.50 (ISBN 0-250-40569-5). Butterworth.

Howard, Ross & Perley, Michael. Acid Rain. (Paperback Ser.). (Illus.). 208p. 1982. pap. 6.95 (ISBN 0-07-030546-3). McGraw.

Hutchinson, T. C. & Havas, M., eds. Effects of Acid Precipitation on Terrestial Ecosystems. LC 79-21816. (NATO Conference Ser. I, Ecolocy: Vol. 4). 666p. 1980. 85.00x (ISBN 0-306-40309-9, Plenum Pr). Plenum Pub.

Inform Inc. & Cannon, James S. Acid Rain & Energy: A Challenge for New Jersey. LC 84-81446. pap. text ed. 3.50 (ISBN 0-918780-29-2). Inform.

Kundell, James E. Acid Rain: The Georgia Situation. 20p. (Orig.). 1984. pap. 4.50 (ISBN 0-89854-097-6). U of Ga Inst Govt.

Linthurst, Rick A. & Teasley, John I., eds. Direct & Indirect Effects of Acidic Deposition on Vegetation, 9 vols. (Acid Precipitation Ser.: Vol. 5). 128p. 1984. text ed. 32.50 (ISBN 0-250-40570-9). Butterworth.

Long-Range Transport of Sulphur in the Atmosphere & Acid Rain: Lectures Presented at the Thirty-third Session of the WMO Executive Committee. 53p. 1983. pap. text ed. 8.00 (ISBN 92-63-10603-7, W560, WMO). Unipub.

Luoma, Jon R. Troubled Skies, Troubled Waters: The Story of Acid Rain. LC 83-47927. 155p. 1984. 12.95 (ISBN 0-670-73263-X). Viking.

Miletich, John J. Acid Rain in Canada: A Selected Bibliography. LC 83-15159. (CPL Bibliography Ser.: No. 124). 1983. 6.00 (ISBN 0-86602-124-8). CPL Biblios.

Ostmann, Robert, Jr. Acid Rain: A Plague upon the Waters. (Illus.). 208p. 1982. 12.95 (ISBN 0-87518-224-0). Dillon.

Pawlick, Thomas. A Killing Rain: The Global Threat of Acid Precipitation. LC 84-5367. 224p. 1984. 15.95 (ISBN 0-87156-823-3). Sierra.

Postel, Sandra. Air Pollution, Acid Rain, & the Future of Forests. LC 84-50653. (Worldwatch Papers). 1984. pap. 4.00 (ISBN 0-916468-57-7). Worldwatch Inst.

Roth, Philip, et al. The American West's Acid Rain Test. 56p. (Orig.). 1985. pap. text ed. 4.50 (ISBN 0-915825-06-6). World Resources Inst.

Schnoor, Jerold L. & Teasley, John I., eds. Modeling of Total Acid Percipitation Impacts. (Acid Precipitation Ser.: Vol. 9). 224p. 1984. text ed. 32.50 (ISBN 0-250-40574-1). Butterworth.

Schwieger, R. G. & Elliott, T. C. Acid Rain Sourcebook. 320p. 1984. 37.50 (ISBN 0-07-055738-1). McGraw.

Stopp, G. Harry, Jr. Acid Rain: A Bibliography of Research Annotated for Easy Access. LC 85-10858. 192p. 1985. 16.00 (ISBN 0-8108-1822-1). Scarecrow.

University of Florida. Acid Deposition: Causes & Effects. LC 83-82073. (Illus.). 316p. 1983. pap. text ed. 38.00 (ISBN 0-86587-060-8). Gov Insts.

Westone, Gregory & Rosencranz, Armin. Acid Rain in Europe & North America: National Responses to an International Problem - Final Report. LC 83-1466. 1983. 14.00 (ISBN 0-911937-01-3). Environ Law Inst.

Yanarella, Ernest J. & Ihara, Randal H., eds. The Acid Rain Debate: Scientific, Economic & Political Dimensions. (WVSS in Science, Technology & Public Policy Ser.). 200p. 1985. pap. text ed. 17.95x (ISBN 0-8133-7065-5). Westview.

Zimmer, Michael J. & Thompson, James A., Jr. Acid Rain: Planning for the Eighties. (Illus.). 311p. 1983. 3-ring binder 85.00 (ISBN 0-86587-118-3). Gov Insts.

ACIDS
see also names of acids, Sulphuric Acid
Graf, Ernst, ed. Phytic Acid: Chemistry & Applications. (Illus.). 350p. 1986. 46.50 (ISBN 0-9614915-0-7). Pilatus Pr.
Halter, F., ed. Antacids in the Eighties. (Illus.). 160p. 1982. text ed. 22.00 (ISBN 0-8067-0831-X). Urban & S.
Imelik, B. Catalysis by Acids & Bases. (Studies in Surface Science & Catalysis: Vol. 20). 1985. 94.50 (ISBN 0-444-42449-0). Elsevier.
Jensen, William B. The Lewis Acid-Base Concepts: An Overview. LC 79-15561. 364p. 1980. 53.50x (ISBN 0-471-03902-0, Pub. by Wiley-Interscience). Wiley.
Kehl, H. Chemistry & Biology of Hydroxamic Acids. xii, 192p. 1982. 101.50 (ISBN 3-8055-3453-1). S Karger.
Kirwan, Richard. Essay on Phlogiston & the Constitution of Acids. 322p. 1968. Repr. of 1789 ed. 35.00x (ISBN 0-7146-1603-6, BHA-01603, F Cass Co). Biblio Dist.
Murray. A Colour Atlas of Acid Etch. 1985. 28.50 (ISBN 0-88416-544-2). PSG Pub Co.
Newman, Stephen A., ed. Acid & Sour Gas Treating Processes. LC 84-25339. 820p. 1985. 42.95x (ISBN 0-87201-839-3). Gulf Pub.
Olah, George A., et al. Superacid Chemistry. 384p. 1985. 57.95 (ISBN 0-471-88469-3). Wiley.
Pearson, R. G., ed. Hard & Soft Acids & Bases. LC 72-93262. (Benchmark Paprs in Inorganic Chemistry Ser). 496p. 1973. 55.00 (ISBN 0-87933-021-X). Van Nos Reinhold.
Reutov, O. A., et al. CH-Acids. LC 77-30618. (Illus.). 1979. 48.00 (ISBN 0-08-021610-2). Pergamon.
Reutter, Werner, ed. Orotic Acid. 1981. lib. bdg. 25.00 (ISBN 0-85200-294-7, Pub. by MTP Pr England). Kluwer Academic.
Tanabe, Kozo. Solid Acids & Bases: Their Catalytic Properties. 1971. 47.00 (ISBN 0-12-683250-1). Acad Pr.
Tang, Jordan, ed. Acid Proteases: Structure, Function & Biology. (Advances in Experimental Medicine & Biology Ser.: Vol. 95). 365p. 1977. 49.50x (ISBN 0-306-32695-7, Plenum Pr). Plenum Pub.
Walser, M. & Williamson, J. R., eds. Metabolism & Clinical Implications of Branched Chain Amino & Ketoacids. (Developments in Biochemistry Ser.: Vol. 18). 632p. 109.00 (ISBN 0-444-00622-2, Biomedical Pr). Elsevier.

ACIDS, FATTY
Ackman, R. G. & Metcalfe, L. D., eds. Analysis of Fatty Acids & Their Esters by Chromatographic Methods. 1976. 25.00 (ISBN 0-912474-07-6). Preston Pubns.
Barlow, S. M. & Stansby, M. E., eds. Nutritional Evaluation of Long-Chain Fatty Acids in Fish Oil. 1982. 45.00 (ISBN 0-12-078920-5). Acad Pr.
Galli, C. & Avogaro, P., eds. Polyunsaturated Fatty Acids in Nutrition: Proceedings of a Round Table in Polyunsaturated Fatty Acids in Nutrition, Milan, Italy, April 1979. (Progress in Food & Nutrition Sciences Ser.: Vol. 4, No. 5). (Illus.). 80p. 1980. pap. 29.00 (ISBN 0-08-027362-9). Pergamon.
Holmes, W. L. & Bortz, W. M., eds. Biochemistry & Pharmacology of Free Fatty Acids. (Progress in Biochemical Pharmacology: Vol. 6). 1971. 41.50 (ISBN 3-8055-1211-2). S Karger.
Markley, Klare S. Fatty Acids: Their Chemistry, Properties, Production & Uses, 5 pts. 2nd ed. LC 82-8934. 1983. Set. lib. bdg. 312.50. Krieger.
Mead, James F. & Fulco, Armand J. Unsaturated & Polyunsaturated Fatty Acid in Health & Disease. (Illus.). 208p. 1976. 27.50x (ISBN 0-398-03413-3). C C Thomas.
Numa, S., ed. Fatty Acid Metabolism & Its Regulation. (New Comprehensive Biochemistry Ser.: Vol. 7). 216p. 1984. 49.75 (ISBN 0-444-80528-1, I-020-84). Elsevier.
Pattison, E. Scott, ed. Fatty Acids & their Industrial Applications. LC 68-12437. (Illus.). pap. 100.50 (ISBN 0-317-07984-0, 2055004). Bks Demand UMI.
Preston, Seaton T., Jr. A Guide to the Analysis of Fatty Acids and Their Esters by Gas Chromatography. 1971. spiral bdg 25.00 (ISBN 0-913106-08-9). PolyScience.

ACIDS, ORGANIC
Addison, G. M., et al, eds. Organic Acidureas. 1984. lib. bdg. 37.50 (ISBN 0-85200-875-9, Pub. by MTP Pr England). Kluwer Academic.
Chalmers, R. A. & Lawson, A. M. Organic Acids in Man. LC 81-11342. 1982. 68.00x (ISBN 0-412-14890-0, NO. 6573, Pub. by Chapman & Hall). Methuen Inc.
Hegyeli, Ruth J., ed. Arachidonic Acid Metabolites. (Atherosclerosis Reviews Ser.: Vol. 13). 1985. text ed. price not set (ISBN 0-88167-131-2). Raven.
Hilderbrand, Richard L., ed. The Role of Phosphonates in Living Systems. 216p. 1983. 65.00 (ISBN 0-8493-5724-1). CRC Pr.
Lawrence, A. A. Food Acid Manufacture-Recent Developments. LC 74-75899. (Chemical Technology Review Ser: No. 31). 302p. 1974. 36.00 (ISBN 0-8155-0531-0). Noyes.
Serjeant, E. P. & Dempsey, B., eds. Ionization Constants of Organic Acids in Aqueous Solution. (Chemical Data Ser.: Vol. 23). (Illus.). 1979. text ed. 200.00 (ISBN 0-08-022339-7). Pergamon.
Stichting ILRA International Research Association. Lactic Acid: Properties & Chemistry of Lactic Acid & Derivatives. LC 76-163974. (Illus.). 594p. 1971. 79.50x (ISBN 3-527-25344-0). VCH Pubs.
Walker, John M. Pharmacology of Naturally Occurring Polypeptides & Lipid Soluble Acids, Vol. VI. 320p. 1972. text ed. 61.00 (ISBN 0-08-016347-5). Pergamon.

ACOUSTIC ENGINEERING
see Acoustical Engineering

ACOUSTIC HOLOGRAPHY
Aldridge, E. E. Acoustical Holography. 46p. 1971. 39.00x (ISBN 0-900541-16-4, Pub. by Meadowfield Pr England). State Mutual Bk.
Ash, Eric A. & Hill, C. R., eds. Acoustical Imaging, Vol. 12. LC 69-12533. 790p. 1983. 110.00x (ISBN 0-306-41247-0, Plenum Press). Plenum Pub.
Booth, N., ed. Acoustical Holography, Vol. 6. LC 69-12533. 771p. 1975. 95.00x (ISBN 0-306-37726-8, Plenum Pr). Plenum Pub.
Camatini, E., ed. Optical & Acoustical Holography. LC 74-188923. 435p. 1972. 59.50x (ISBN 0-306-30584-4, Plenum Pr). Plenum Pub.
Green, Philip S., ed. Acoustical Holography, Vol. 5. LC 69-12533. 752p. 1974. 95.00x (ISBN 0-306-37725-X, Plenum Pr). Plenum Pub.
Hildebrand, B. P. & Brenden, B. B. An Introduction to Acoustical Holography. LC 70-179756. 224p. 1972. 37.50x (ISBN 0-306-30561-5, Plenum Pr); pap. 8.95 (ISBN 0-306-20005-8). Plenum Pub.
Hildebrand, B. Percy & Brenden, Byron B. An Introduction to Acoustical Holography. 224p. 1974. pap. 8.95x (ISBN 0-306-20005-8, Plenum Pr). Plenum Pub.
Kessler, L. W., ed. Acoustical Holography, Vol. 7. LC 69-12533. 667p. 1977. 89.50x (ISBN 0-306-37727-6, Plenum Pr). Plenum Pub.
Luescher, E., et al. Photoacoustic Effect: Principles & Applications. LC 83-10233. 183p. 1984. 48.00 (ISBN 3-528-08573-8). Heyden.
Metherell, A. F., ed. Acoustical Holography, Vol. 3. LC 69-12533. 414p. 1971. 69.50x (ISBN 0-306-37723-3, Plenum Pr). Plenum Pub.
--Acoustical Imaging, Vol. 8. LC 69-12533. 801p. 1980. 110.00x (ISBN 0-306-40171-1, Plenum Pr). Plenum Pub.
Metherell, A. F. & Larmore, L., eds. Acoustical Holography, Vol. 2. LC 69-12533. 391p. 1970. 59.50x (ISBN 0-306-37722-5, Plenum Pr). Plenum Pub.
Metherell, A. F., et al, eds. Acoustical Holography, Vol. 1. LC 69-12533. (Illus.). 312p. 1969. 55.00x (ISBN 0-306-37721-7, Plenum Pr). Plenum Pub.
Powers, John P., ed. Acoustical Imaging, Vol. 11. LC 69-12533. 1982. 89.50x (ISBN 0-306-40988-7, Plenum Pr). Plenum Pub.
Sanders, Roger C. Clinical Sonography: A Practical Guide. 396p. 1984. pap. text ed. 27.95 (ISBN 0-316-77010-8). Little.
Wade, Glen, ed. Acoustic Imaging: Cameras, Microscopes, Phased Arrays & Holographic Systems. LC 76-21. 325p. 1976. 52.50x (ISBN 0-306-30914-9, Plenum Pr). Plenum Pub.
--Acoustical Holography, Vol. 4. LC 69-12533. 752p. 1972. 95.00x (ISBN 0-306-37724-1, Plenum Pr). Plenum Pub.
Wang, Keith, ed. Acoustical Imaging, Vol. 9. LC 69-12533. 850p. 1980. 115.00x (ISBN 0-306-40477-X, Plenum Pr). Plenum Pub.

ACOUSTIC IMAGING (HOLOGRAPHY)
see Acoustic Holography

ACOUSTIC NERVE
see also Vestibular Nuclei
Beagley, H. A., ed. Auditory Investigation: The Scientific & Technological Basis. (Illus.). 1979. text ed. 95.00x (ISBN 0-19-857526-2). Oxford U Pr.
Hammer, Gunnar. A Quantitative Cytochemical Study of Shock Wave Effects on Spiral Ganglion Cells. 1956. 12.00 (ISBN 0-384-21250-6). Johnson Repr.
House & Luetje, C. Acoustic Tumors: Diagnosis & Management. 318p. 1979. Vol. I (Diagnosis) text ed. 37.00 (ISBN 0-8391-1314-5); Vol. II (Management) 296 pp. text ed. 37.00 (ISBN 0-8391-1346-3). Univ Park.
Naunton, Ralph F., ed. Evoked Electrical Activity in the Auditory Nervous System. 1978. 53.50 (ISBN 0-12-514960-3). Acad Pr.
Pool, J. Lawrence, et al. Acoustic Nerve Tumors: Early Diagnosis & Treatment. 2nd ed. (Illus.). 252p. 1970. photocopy 26.50x (ISBN 0-398-01507-4). C C Thomas.
Rasmussen, Grant L. & Windle, William F. Neural Mechanisms of the Auditory & Vestibular Systems. (Illus.). 436p. 1965. photocopy ed. 43.50x (ISBN 0-398-01554-6). C C Thomas.
Taylor, I. G. & Markides, Andreas, eds. Disorders of Auditory Function, III. 1981. 49.00 (ISBN 0-12-684780-0). Acad Pr.
Wersall, Jan. Studies in the Structure & Innervation of the Sensory Epithelium of the Cristae Ampullares in the Guinea Pig. Repr. of 1956 ed. 12.00 (ISBN 0-384-66900-X). Johnson Repr.

ACOUSTIC PHENOMENA IN NATURE
see also Echo; Thunderstorms
Hardy, H. Reginald, Jr. First Conference on Acoustic Emission (Microseismic Activity) in Geologic Structures & Materials. new ed. (Illus.). 500p. 1977. text ed. 40.00x (ISBN 0-87849-017-5). Trans Tech.

ACOUSTIC PRESSURE
see Sound Pressure

ACOUSTIC TUMORS
see Acoustic Nerve

ACOUSTICAL ENGINEERING
see also Architectural Acoustics; Electro-Acoustics; Music–Acoustics and Physics; Noise; Noise Control; Soundproofing; Telecommunication; Ultrasonic Waves–Industrial Applications; Underwater Acoustics
Accoustical Manual: Apartment & Home. 78p. 1978. pap. 11.00 (ISBN 0-317-12690-3). Natl Assn Home.
Acoustic Emission - STP 505. 337p. 1972. 22.50 (ISBN 0-8031-0116-3, 04-505000-22). ASTM.
Acoustic Emission Monitoring of Pressurized Systems - STP 697. 228p. 1979. 26.50x (ISBN 0-8031-0271-2, 04-697000-22). ASTM.
Acoustics Testing Facility Survey of the United States: 1975. 2.50 (ISBN 0-686-96262-1). Inst Environ Sci.
Alais, Pierre & Metherell, Alexander F., eds. Acoustical Imaging, Vol. 10. LC 69-12533. 842p. 1981. 115.00x (ISBN 0-306-40725-6, Plenum Pr). Plenum Pub.
Albers, Vernon M. Acoustical Society of America Suggested Experiments for Laboratory Courses in Acoustics & Vibrations. 2nd ed. LC 75-165357. 175p. 1973. text ed. 24.95x (ISBN 0-271-01104-1). Pa St U Pr.
Ando, Y. Concert Hall Acoustics. (Springer Series in Electrophysics: Vol. 17). (Illus.). 170p. 1985. 41.50 (ISBN 0-387-13505-7). Springer-Verlag.
Applied Technical Dictionary: Acoustics. 50.00x (ISBN 0-569-08535-7, Pub. by Collets). State Mutual Bk.
Ballou, Glen. Handbook for Sound Engineers. Date not set. 44.95 (ISBN 0-672-21983-2, 21983). Sams.
Bar Code Technology & Applications. 1984. 3-ring bdg. 110.00 (ISBN 0-317-20439-4). Optosonic Pr.
Beyer, Robert T., ed. Nonlinear Acoustics in Fluids. 416p. 1984. 59.50 (ISBN 0-442-21182-1). Van Nos Reinhold.
Blake, Michael P. & Mitchell, William S., eds. Vibration & Acoustic Measurement Handbook. (Illus.). 1972. 34.50 (ISBN 0-8104-9195-8). Hayden.
Clason, W. E. Elsevier's Dictionary of Cinema, Sound & Music. (Eng., Fr., Span., Ital., Dutch, & Ger.). 948p. (Polyglot). 1956. 127.75 (ISBN 0-444-40117-2). Elsevier.
Datta, Supriyo. Surface Acoustic Wave Devices. (Illus.). 208p. 1986. text ed. 42.95 (ISBN 0-13-877911-2). P-H.
Educational Research Council of America. Sound Engineer. Ferris, Theodore N. & Marchak, John P., eds. (Real People at Work Ser.: R). (Illus.). 36p. 1977. 2.70 (ISBN 0-89247-132-8, 9623). Changing Times.
Everest, F. Alton. Acoustic Techniques for Home & Studio. 2nd ed. (Illus.). 352p. 1984. 19.95 (ISBN 0-8306-0696-3, 1696); pap. 15.50 (ISBN 0-8306-1696-9). TAB Bks.
--The Master Handbook of Acoustics. (Illus.). 352p. 1983. 18.95 (ISBN 0-8306-0008-6); pap. 13.50 (ISBN 0-8306-1296-3, 1296). TAB Bks.
Filippi, P., ed. Theoretical Acoustics & Numerical Techniques. (CISM International Centre for Mechanical Sciences, Courses & Lectures Ser.: No. 277). xiv, 348p. 1983. pap. 23.20 (ISBN 0-387-81786-7). Springer-Verlag.
German Society of Metallurgy, ed. Acoustic Emission: Proceedings of the Symposium, held in Bad Nauheim, West Germany, 1979. Nicoll, A. R., tr. (Illus.). 385p. 1980. lib. bdg. 63.00 (ISBN 3-88355-030-2, Pub. by DGM Metallurgy Germany). IR Pubns.
Groves, Ivor D., Jr., ed. Acoustic Transducers. LC 81-4113. (Benchmark Papers in Acoustics Ser.: Vol. 14). 391p. 1981. 53.95 (ISBN 0-87933-387-1). Van Nos Reinhold.
Hardy, H. R., Jr. & Leighton, F. W., eds. Acoustic Emission & Microseismic Activity in Geologic Structures & Materials. LC 83-81165. 680p. 1984. 50.00x (ISBN 0-87201-546-7). Gulf Pub.
Helfrich, Hede. Satzmelodie und Sprachwahrnehmung: Psycholinguistische Untersuchungen zur Grundfrequenz. (Grundlagen der Kommunikation - Bibliotheksausgabe Ser.). (Ger.). xviii, 400p. 1985. 67.20x (ISBN 3-11-009918-7). De Gruyter.
Herrick, Clyde N. Audio Systems. LC 74-9696. 1974. 24.95 (ISBN 0-87909-049-9). Reston.
International Symposium on Acoustical Imaging, et al. Acoustical Imaging: Proceedings of the International Symposium on Acoustical Imaging, 13th, Minneapolis, Minn., Oct. 26-28, 1984, Vol. 13. Kaveh, M., et al, eds. 576p. 1984. 89.50x (ISBN 0-306-41717-0, Plenum Pr). Plenum Pub.
Jordan, V. L. Acoustical Design of Concert Halls & Theatres. (Illus.). xiv, 225p. 1980. 44.50 (ISBN 0-85334-853-7, Pub. by Elsevier Applied Sci England). Elsevier.
Kamal, M. M. & Wolf, J. A., Jr., eds. Finite Element Applications in Acoustics. 126p. 1981. 25.00 (ISBN 0-686-34486-3, I00143). ASME.
Kana, D. D. & Butler, T. G., eds. Reliability Design for Vibroacoustic Environments: AMD, Vol. 9. 1974. pap. 18.00 (ISBN 0-685-77460-0, I00047). ASME.
Lindsay, R. Bruce. Physical Acoustics. LC 73-12619. (Benchmark Papers in Acoustics Ser.: Vol. 4). 480p. 1974. 58.95 (ISBN 0-87933-040-6). Van Nos Reinhold.
Lindsay, R. Bruce, ed. Acoustics. LC 72-90974. (Benchmark Papers in Acoustics Ser.: Vol. 2). 465p. 1973. 57.95 (ISBN 0-87933-015-5). Van Nos Reinhold.
Liquid Crystal Display Devices. 1984. 3 ring bdg. 150.00 (ISBN 0-317-20430-0). Optosonic Pr.
Magnetic Bubble Domain Devices. 1984. 3 ring bdg. 100.00 (ISBN 0-317-20436-X). Optosonic Pr.
Matthews, James R., ed. Acoustic Emission. LC 82-20928. (Nondestructive Testing Monographs & Tracts: Vol. 2). (Illus.). 175p. 1983. 39.50 (ISBN 0-677-16490-4). Gordon.
Meyer, Erwin & Neumann, Ernst-Georg. Physical & Applied Acoustics: An Introduction. 1972. 29.50 (ISBN 0-12-493150-2). Acad Pr.
Miller, H. B., ed. Acoustical Measurements: Methods & Instrumentation. LC 81-7175. (Benchmark Papers in Acoustics: Vol. 16). 407p. 1982. 54.95 (ISBN 0-87933-415-0). Van Nos Reinhold.
Miller, Richard K. & Montone, Wayne V. Handbook of Acoustical Enclosures & Barriers. 29.95 (ISBN 0-915586-06-1). Fairmont Pr.
Piraux, Henri. Diccionario General De Acustica y Electro Acustica. (Espn.). 374p. 1967. 14.95 (ISBN 84-283-0153-0, S-50237). French & Eur.
Porges, G. Applied Acoustics. LC 77-18250. 180p. 1977. pap. 26.95x (ISBN 0-470-26748-8). Halsted Pr.
Reichardt, W. Acoustics Dictionary. Date not set. lib. bdg. 28.50 (ISBN 90-247-2707-3, Pub. by Martinus Nijhoff Netherlands). Kluwer Academic.
Rettinger, M. Acoustic Design & Noise Control, 2 vols. 1977. Vol. 1. 24.50 (ISBN 0-8206-0203-5); Vol. 2. 28.50 (ISBN 0-8206-0204-3). Chem Pub.
Reynolds, Douglas D. Engineering Principles of Acoustics: Noise & Vibration Control. 640p. 1981. text ed. 38.20 (ISBN 0-205-07271-2, 327271). Allyn.
Ristic, Velimir M. Principles of Acoustic Devices. LC 82-20278. 359p. 1983. 44.95 (ISBN 0-471-09153-7, Pub. by Wiley-Interscience). Wiley.
Robin, Christopher. How to Build Your Own Stereo Speakers: Construction, Applications, Circuits & Characteristics. (Illus.). 1978. ref. ed. 21.95 (ISBN 0-87909-374-9); pap. 12.95 (ISBN 0-8359-2936-1). Reston.
Schaudinischky, L. H. Sound, Man & Building. (Illus.). 415p. 1976. 55.50 (ISBN 0-85334-655-0, Pub. by Elsevier Applied Sci England). Elsevier.
Surface Acoustic Wave Devices. 1984. 3 ring bdg. 130.00 (ISBN 0-317-20434-3). Optosonic Pr.
Temkin, Samuel. Elements of Acoustics. LC 80-24416. 515p. 1981. text ed. 45.50 (ISBN 0-471-05990-0). Wiley.
Templeton, Duncan & Lord, Peter. Detailing for Acoustics. (Illus.). 96p. 1983. 35.00 (ISBN 0-89397-161-8). Nichols Pub.
White, R. G., et al. Noise & Vibration. 866p. 1983. 124.95x (ISBN 0-470-27553-7). Halsted Pr.
Williams, Royson V. Acoustic Emission. 140p. 1980. 29.00 (ISBN 0-9960020-0-6, Pub. by A Hilger England). Heyden.
Winder, Alan A. & Loda, Charles J. Space Time Information Processing. (Illus.). 200p. 1980. Repr. of 1962 ed. 17.95 (ISBN 0-932146-04-X). Peninsula CA.

ACOUSTICAL HOLOGRAPHY
see Acoustic Holography

ACOUSTICS
see Architectural Acoustics; Hearing; Molecular Acoustics; Music–Acoustics and Physics; Sound; Underwater Acoustics

ACRASIALES
Farr, M. L. How to Know the True Slime Molds. (Picture Key Nature Ser.). 200p. 1981. write for info. wire coil (ISBN 0-697-04779-2). Wm C Brown.
Fullmer, E. L. The Slime Molds of Ohio. 1921. 1.50 (ISBN 0-86727-010-1). Ohio Bio Survey.
Raper, Kenneth B. & Rahn, Ann W. The Dictyostelids. LC 83-43089. (Illus.). 448p. 1984. 75.00x (ISBN 0-691-08345-2). Princeton U Pr.

ACRIDINE
Weissberger, Arnold & Acheson, R. M., eds. Acridines: Pyridine & Its Derivatives. (Chemistry of Heterocyclic Compounds Ser.: Vol. 9). 892p. Repr. of 1973 ed. cancelled 0.00 (ISBN 0-89874-604-3). Krieger.

ACROGENS
see Cryptogams; Ferns; Mosses

ACTH
ACTH & Related Peptides: Structure, Regulation, & Action, Vol. 297. (Annals of the New York Academy of Sciences). 664p. 1977. 60.00x (ISBN 0-89072-043-6). NY Acad Sci.
Frigrjesi, T. Corticothalamic Projections & Sensorimotor Activities. 1972. 36.50 (ISBN 0-7204-7029-3). Elsevier.

ACTINIDE ELEMENTS
see also names of specific elements, e.g. Uranium
The Chemical Thermodynamics of Actinide Elements & Compounds, 2 vols. (Illus.). 1977. Vol. 1: Actinide Elements. pap. 13.00 (ISBN 92-0-149076-3, ISP424-1, IAEA); Vol. 2: The ActinideAqueous Ions. pap. 9.25 (ISBN 92-0-149176-X, ISP424-2). Unipub.
The Chemical Thermodynamics of Actinide Elements & Compounds, Part 5: The Actinide Binary Alloys. (Illus.). 277p. 1982. pap. 35.50 (ISBN 92-0-149081-X, ISP424/5, IAEA). Unipub.
Edelstein, N. M., ed. Actinides in Perspective: Proceedings of the Conference Held at Pacific Grove, CA, USA, Sept. 10-15, 1981. (Illus.). 620p. 1982. 83.00 (ISBN 0-08-029193-7). Pergamon.
Erdos, Paul & Robinson, John M. The Physics of Actinide Compounds. (Physics of Solids & Liquids). 225p. 1983. 39.50x (ISBN 0-306-41150-4, Plenum Press). Plenum Pub.
Evaluation of Actinide Partitioning & Transmutation: Final Report of a Co-ordinated Research Programme on Environmental Evaluation and Hazard Assessment of the Separation for Actinides from Nuclear Wastes Followed by Either Transmutation or Separate Disposal. (Technical Reports Ser.: No. 214). (Illus.). 124p. 1982. pap. 19.25 (ISBN 92-0-125182-3, IDC214, IAEA). Unipub.
Fields, Paul R. & Moeller, Therald, eds. Lanthanide-Actinide Chemistry. LC 67-31656. (Advances in Chemistry Ser: No. 71). 1967. 29.95 (ISBN 0-8412-0072-6). Am Chemical.
Freeman, A. J. & Lander, G. Handbook on the Physics & Chemistry of the Actinides, Pt. 1: Physics, Vol. 2. 504p. 1985. 111.00 (ISBN 0-444-86907-7, North-Holland). Elsevier.
Freeman, A. J. & Darby, J. B., eds. The Actinides: Electronic Structure & Related Properties, 2 vols. Vol. 1. 1974. 75.00 (ISBN 0-12-266701-8); Vol. 2. 1974. 75.00 (ISBN 0-12-266702-6). Acad Pr.
Freeman, A. J. & Lander, G. H., eds. Handbook on the Physics & Chemistry of the Actinides, Vol. 1. 530p. 1984. 115.50 (ISBN 0-444-86903-4, North-Holland). Elsevier.
Fuger, J. & Parker, V. B. The Chemical Thrmodynamics of Actinide Elements & Compounds: Part 8, the Actinide Halides. 267p. 1984. pap. 45.00 (ISBN 92-0-149183-2, ISP424-8, IAEA). Unipub.
Hellwege, K. H., ed. Magnetic & Other Properties of Oxides & Related Compounds: Hexagonal Ferrites. Special Lanthanide & Actinide Compounds. (Landolt-Boernstein Ser.: Group III, Vol. 12, Pt. C). (Illus.). 650p. 1983. 405.20 (ISBN 0-387-10137-3). Springer-Verlag.
Holley, C. E., Jr. & Rand, M. H. The Chemical Thermodynamics of Actinide Elements & Compounds: The Actinide Carbides, Pt. 6. 101p. 1984. pap. 18.50 (ISBN 92-0-149184-0, ISP424/6 5071, IAEA). Unipub.
Manes, L., ed. Actinides: Chemistry & Physical Properties. (Structure & Bonding Ser.: Vol. 59-60). (Illus.). 250p. 1985. 57.50 (ISBN 0-387-13752-1). Springer-Verlag.
Navratil, James D. & Schulz, Wallace W., eds. Actinide Separations. LC 79-23956. (ACS Symposium Ser.: No. 117). 1980. 54.95 (ISBN 0-8412-0527-2). Am Chemical.
Techniques for Identifying Transuranic Speciation in Aquatic Environments: Proceedings of a Technical Committee Meeting, Italy, 24-28 March 1980, Jointly Organized by IAEA and the Commission of European Communities. (Panel Proceedings Ser.). 290p. 1982. pap. 32.00 (ISBN 92-0-021081-3, ISP613, IAEA). Unipub.
Thermodynamics of Actinide Elements and Compounds (IAEA). Unipub.

ACTINOMYCETES
Farrell, George E. Actinomycosis of the Thorax. (Illus.). 144p. 1981. 22.50 (ISBN 0-87527-205-3). Green.
Goodfellow, M., ed. The Biology of the Nocardiae. 1976. 82.50 (ISBN 0-12-289650-5). Acad Pr.
Goodfellow, Michael, et al. The Biology of the Actinomycetes. 1984. 95.00 (ISBN 0-12-289670-X). Acad Pr.
Juhasz, Stephen E. & Plummer, Gordon. Host-Virus Relationships in Mycobacterium, Nocardia & Actinomyces: Proceedings. (Illus.). 248p. 1970. photocopy ed. 24.75x (ISBN 0-398-00953-8). C C Thomas.
McGinnis, Michael R. & D'Amoto, Richard F. Pictorial Handbook of Medically Important Fungi & Aerobic Actinomycetes. LC 81-5306. (Illus.). 172p. 1981. pap. 22.95 (ISBN 0-03-058364-0). Praeger.
Ortiz-Ortiz, Librado, et al, eds. Actinomycetes Biology. 1984. 49.50 (ISBN 0-12-528620-1). Acad Pr.
Sykes, G. & Skinner, F. A., eds. Actinomycetales: Characteristics & Practical Importance. (Society for Applied Bacteriology Symposium Ser.: No. 2). 1973. 59.00 (ISBN 0-12-679950-4). Acad Pr.

ACTIVATED CARBON
see Carbon, Activated

ACTIVATION ANALYSIS
see Radioactivation Analysis

ACTIVE TRANSPORT
see Biological Transport

ACTIVITY COEFFICIENTS
Kardos. Problem of the Regulation of Activity. 44.00 (ISBN 0-9960070-4-0). Heyden.

ACTIVITY THEORY
see Activity Coefficients

ACULEATA
see Ants; Bees; Wasps

ACYLATION
Schaffner, Kenneth F. Three-Acylcyclopentenes & Five-Acylbiyclo (2.1.0) Pentanes: Photochemical & Thermal Isomerizations. 1976. pap. text ed. 14.00 (ISBN 0-08-020476-7). Pergamon.

ADA (COMPUTER PROGRAM LANGUAGE)
Amoroso, S. & Ingargiola, G. Ada: An Introduction to Program Design & Coding. 368p. 1985. text ed. 32.50 (ISBN 0-273-01818-3). Pitman Pub MA.
APL. (Alfred's Language Bks.). 1981. pap. 3.50 (ISBN 0-317-04680-2). Alfred Pub.
Barnes. Programming in Ada. 300p. (Orig.). 1983. pap. 21.95 (ISBN 0-201-13799-2). Addison-Wesley.
Barnes, J. G. & Fisher, G., eds. Ada in Use: Proceedings of the ADA International Conference, Paris. (Ada Companion Ser.). 350p. 1985. 49.50 (ISBN 0-521-30968-9). Cambridge U Pr.
Bjorner, B. & Oest, O. N., eds. Towards a Formal Description of Ada. (Lecture Notes in Computer Science: Vol. 98). 630p. 1980. pap. 31.00 (ISBN 0-387-10283-3). Springer-Verlag.
Bryant, Ry & Vaget, Brian W., eds. Simulation in Strongly Typed Languages: Ada, Pascal, Simula... (SCS Simulation Ser.: Vol. 13, No. 2). 1984. 30.00 (ISBN 0-317-05019-2). Soc Computer Sim.
Buhr, Raymond. Systems Design with Ada. (Illus.). 288p. 1984. text ed. 33.00 (ISBN 0-13-881623-9). P-H.
Burns, A. Concurrent Programming in Ada. 250p. Date not set. price not set. Cambridge U Pr.
Caverly, Philip W. & Goldstein, Philip. Introduction to Ada: A Top-Down Approach for Programmers. 250p. 1986. pap. text ed. 12.00 (ISBN 0-534-05820-5). Brooks-Cole.
Cherry, George. Parallel Programming in ANSI Standard Ada. 1984. text ed. 21.95 (ISBN 0-8359-5434-X). Reston.
Chirlian, Paul. Introduction to Ada. Morrice, Nancy, ed. LC 84-15456. 300p. 1985. pap. 19.95 (ISBN 0-916460-42-8). Matrix Pub.
Chirlian, Paul M. Introduction to Ada. 224p. 1984. pap. 19.95 (ISBN 0-916460-42-8). Dilithium Pr.
Clark, Robert G. Programming in Ada: A First Course. 350p. 1985. 39.50 (ISBN 0-521-25728-X); pap. 17.95 (ISBN 0-521-27675-6). Cambridge U Pr.
Cohen, Norman. Ada as a Second Language. 1984. pap. 26.95 (ISBN 0-07-011589-3). McGraw.
Feuer, Alan & Gehani, Narain. Comparing & Assessing Programming Languages: Ada, C & Pascal. (Software Ser.). (Illus.). 256p. 1984. text ed. 18.95; pap. text ed. write for info. (ISBN 0-13-154840-9). P-H.
Freedman, Roy S. Programming Concepts with the Ada Reference Manual. (Illus.). 128p. 1982. pap. text ed. 12.00 (ISBN 0-89433-190-6). Petrocelli.
Gehani, Narain. ADA: An Advanced Introduction Including Reference Manual for the Ada Programming Language. (Illus.). 672p. 1984. text ed. 32.95 (ISBN 0-13-003997-7). P-H.
--Ada: Concurrent Programming. (Illus.). 272p. 1984. pap. 26.95 (ISBN 0-13-004011-8). P-H.
Gilpin, Geoff. Ada: A Guided Tour & Tutorial. 352p. 1985. 22.95 (ISBN 0-13-004045-2); pap. 16.95 (ISBN 0-13-003914-4). P-H.
Goldsack, S. J. Ada for Specification: Possibilities & Limitations. (Ada Companion Ser.). (Illus.). 280p. 1985. 37.50 (ISBN 0-521-30853-4). Cambridge U Pr.
Goos, G., et al, eds. Diana: An Intermediate Language for Ada. 201p. 1983. pap. 14.00 (ISBN 0-387-12695-3). Springer Verlag.
Habermann, A. Nico. Ada for Experienced Programmers. Perry, Dewayne E., ed. LC 82-20757. (Computer Science Ser.). (Illus.). 496p. 1983. pap. 21.95 (ISBN 0-201-11481-X). Addison-Wesley.
Hibbard, Peter, et al. Studies in Ada Style. 2nd ed. (Illus.). 111p. 1983. pap. 14.00 (ISBN 0-387-90816-1). Springer-Verlag.
Introduction to Ada. 19.95 (ISBN 0-317-26567-9). Merl Miller Assoc.
Katzan, Harry, Jr. Invitation to Ada. (Illus.). 184p. 1984. pap. 14.95 (ISBN 0-89433-239-2). Petrocelli.
--Invitation to Ada & the Ada Reference Manual. (Illus.). 400p. 1982. 32.95 (ISBN 0-89433-132-9). Petrocelli.
--Invitation to Ada: Condensed Edition. (Illus.). 173p. 1984. pap. 14.95 (ISBN 0-89433-239-2). Van Nos Reinhold.
Ledgard, H. Ada: An Introduction. 2nd ed. (Illus.). 135p. 1983. pap. text ed. 18.00 (ISBN 0-387-90814-5). Springer-Verlag.
Lewis. Problem-Solving Principles for Ada Programmers: Applied Logic, Psychology, & Grit. 1983. 10.95 (ISBN 0-8104-5211-1, 5211). Hayden.
McDermid, John A. & Ripken, Knut. Life Cycle Support in the Ada Environment. LC 83-18911. (Ada Companion Ser.). 247p. 1984. 24.95 (ISBN 0-521-26042-6). Cambridge U Pr.
McGettrick, Andrew D. Program Verification Using Ada. LC 81-12276. (Cambridge Computer Science Texts: No. 13). (Illus.). 350p. 1982. 44.50 (ISBN 0-521-24215-0); pap. 19.95 (ISBN 0-521-28531-3). Cambridge U Pr.
Mayoh, Brian H. Problem Solving with Ada. LC 81-14675. 233p. 1982. 26.95 (ISBN 0-471-10025-0). Wiley.
Nissen, J. C. & Wallis, P. J. Portability & Style in Ada. LC 83-26237. (Ada Companion Ser.). 255p. 1984. 24.95 (ISBN 0-521-26482-0). Cambridge U Pr.
Olsen, Eric W. Ada for Programmers. pap. 20.95 (ISBN 0-8359-0149-1). Reston.
Pokrass, David. Understanding Ada: A Software Engineering Approach. Bray, Gary, ed. 384p. 1984. pap. text ed. 16.95 (ISBN 0-471-87833-2, Pub. by Wiley). Wiley.
Price, David. Introduction to Ada. 1983. text ed. 24.95 (ISBN 0-13-477653-4); pap. text ed. 17.95 (ISBN 0-13-477646-1). P-H.
The Programming Language Ada: A Reference Manual. Proposed Standard Document US Department of Defence. (Lecture Notes in Computer Sciences Ser.: Vol. 106). 243p. 1981. pap. 19.00 (ISBN 0-387-10693-6). Springer-Verlag.
The Programming Language Ada Reference Manual. (Lecture Notes in Computer Science Ser.: Vol. 155). 331p. 1983. pap. 16.50 (ISBN 0-387-12328-8). Springer-Verlag.
Pyle. The Ada Programming Language. 1981. pap. 23.95 (ISBN 0-13-003921-7). P-H.
Pyle, Ian. The Ada Programming Language. 2nd. ed. LC 84-17817. (Illus.). 336p. (Orig.). 1985. pap. text ed. 19.95 (ISBN 0-13-003906-3). P-H.
Reference Manual for the Ada Programming Language. 331p. 1983. pap. 13.50 (ISBN 0-387-90887-0). Springer-Verlag.
Reference Manual for the Ada Programming Language. (MIL STD 1815A 1983 Ser.). 344p. (Orig.). 1983. pap. 8.00 (ISBN 0-318-11823-8). Gov Printing Office.
Rogers, M. W., ed. Ada: Language, Compilers & Bibliography. LC 84-7688. (Ada Companion Ser.). 1984. 17.95 (ISBN 0-521-26464-2). Cambridge U Pr.
Saib, Sabina. Introduction to Programming in Ada. 1985. text ed. 26.95 (ISBN 0-03-059487-1). HR&W.
Saib, Sabina H. & Fritz, Robert E. The Ada Programming Language. (Tutorial Texts Ser.). 538p. 1983. 36.00 (ISBN 0-8186-0456-5, Q456). IEEE Comp Soc.
Shumate, Ken. Understanding Ada. 352p. 1984. pap. text ed. 18.22 (ISBN 0-06-046133-0, HarpC). Har-Row.
Smedema, C. H., et al. The Programming Languages: Pascal, Modula, Chill, & Ada. 160p. 1983. 16.95. P-H.
Stratford-Collins, M. J. ADA: A Programmer's Conversion Course. (Computers & Their Applications Ser.). 170p. 1982. 52.95 (ISBN 0-470-27332-1). Halsted Pr.
Teller, Joachim, ed. Proceedings of the Third Joint Ada Europe & Ada Tec Conference. (Ada Companion Ser.). 350p. 1985. 39.50. Cambridge U Pr.
Uhl, J., et al. An Attribute Grammar for the Semantic Analysis of Ada. (Lecture Notes in Computer Science Ser.: Vol. 139). 511p. 1982. pap. 24.00 (ISBN 0-387-11571-4). Springer-Verlag.
Wallis, P. J., ed. Ada Software Tools Interfaces. (Lecture Notes in Computer Science Ser.: Vol. 180). iii, 164p. 1984. pap. 13.00 (ISBN 0-387-13878-1). Springer-Verlag.
Wegner, P. Programming with Ada: An Introduction by Means of Graduated Examples. 1980. 27.50 (ISBN 0-13-730697-0). P-H.
Wiener, Richard & Sincovec, Richard. Programming in Ada. 345p. 1983. 29.50 (ISBN 0-471-87089-7). Wiley.
Young. An Introduction to Ada. 2nd, rev. ed. (Computers & Their Applications Ser.). 1984. pap. 29.95 (ISBN 0-470-20112-6). Wiley.
Young, S. J. An Introduction to Ada. LC 82-15547. (Computers & Their Applications Ser.: No.1403). 400p. 1983. 69.95x (ISBN 0-470-27551-0); pap. 29.95x (ISBN 0-470-27350-X). Halsted Pr.

ADAM (COMPUTER)
Abikoff, William & Cornell, Gary. The BASIC Adam. LC 84-7532. (Series 1-999). 524p. 1984. pap. 14.95 (ISBN 0-471-80807-5, Pub. by Wiley Pr). Wiley.
Alden, Carole. Word Processing with Your Coleco Adam. LC 84-51243. 127p. 1984. pap. 5.95 (ISBN 0-89588-182-9). SYBEX.
Banse, Timothy P. Home Applications & Games for the Coleco Adam. 132p. 1985. lib. bdg. 15.95 (ISBN 0-934523-00-2); pap. 14.95 (ISBN 0-934523-01-0). Version One Point-Zero.
Bell, A. J. & Bell, E. Q. Adam User's Guide. 336p. 1984. 7.95 (ISBN 0-89303-300-6). Brady Comm.
Benson, Ramsey J. & Rochester, Jack B. The Adam's Companion. 400p. 1984. pap. 9.95 (ISBN 0-380-87650-7, 87650-7). Avon.
Berg, Eric N. & Smith, Alan. Adam: The Home Computing System. 272p. 1984. pap. 14.95 (ISBN 0-88693-066-9). Banbury Bks.
Blackadar, Thomas. The Easy Guide to Your Coleco Adam. LC 84-50364. 175p. 1984. pap. 9.95 (ISBN 0-89588-181-0). SYBEX.
Claflin, Edward B. & Heil, John A. Programming Adam: Home Applications in the BASIC Language. 320p. 1984. pap. 14.95 (ISBN 0-88693-034-0). Banbury Bks.
The Coleco Adam User's Encyclopedia. 1984. 14.95 (ISBN 0-317-05838-X). Bk Co.
Dent, Arthur. The First Book of Adam the Computer. (Illus.). 208p. (Orig.). 1984. 14.95 (ISBN 0-8306-0720-X, 1720); pap. 9.95 (ISBN 0-8306-1720-5). TAB Bks.
Dusthimer, David & Buchholz, Ted. Coleco Adam. LC 84-71059. (Tool Kit Ser.). 9.95 (ISBN 0-672-22312-0). Sams.
Goldstein, Larry J. The Adam Home Computer: An Introduction to SmartBASIC & Applications. (Illus.). 240p. 1985. pap. 7.95 (ISBN 0-89303-296-4). Brady Comm.
Haskell, Richard E. Coleco Adam BASIC. 230p. 1985. pap. 10.95 (ISBN 0-13-140450-4). P-H.
Knight, Timothy O. Basic BASIC Programs for the Adam. (Illus.). 144p. 1984. 12.95 (ISBN 0-8306-0116-3, 01008897X); pap. 8.25 (ISBN 0-8306-0716-1). TAB Bks.
--Using & Programming the Adam: Including Ready-to-Run Programs. (Illus.). 128p. (Orig.). 1984. 14.95 (ISBN 0-8306-0706-4); pap. 7.95 (ISBN 0-8306-1706-X, 1706). TAB Bks.
Miastkowski, Stan. Getting the Most from Your Coleco Adam. 256p. (Orig.). cancelled (ISBN 0-88134-129-0). Osborne-McGraw.
Mullish, Henry & Wiesenthal, Robert. The Coleco Adam. 256p. (Orig.). pap. cancelled (ISBN 0-916688-78-X, 78-X). Creative Comp.
Reymann, Joseph. How to Use the Coleco Adam. (Handy Guide Ser.). 64p. (Orig.). 1984. pap. 2.95 (ISBN 0-88284-274-9). Alfred Pub.
Roth, Pam. The First Book of Adam: Using & Programming the Coleco Adam. 227p. 1984. pap. text ed. 12.95 (ISBN 0-88022-063-5, 110). Que Corp.
--The Second Book of Adam: Using SmartWriter. 260p. 1984. pap. 10.95 (ISBN 0-88022-066-X, 111). Que Corp.

Rugg, Tom & Feldman, Phil. Thirty-Two BASIC Programs for the Coleco Adam. 288p. 1984. pap. 19.95 (ISBN 0-88056-141-6); incl. disk 39.95 (ISBN 0-88056-201-3). Dilithium Pr.
Sawyer, Brian. The Coleco Adam Entertainer. 150p. (Orig.). 1984. 12.95 (ISBN 0-07-881134-1, 134-1). Osborne-McGraw.
Scharf, Peter. Learning Together with Adam. 224p. 1985. 9.95 (ISBN 0-07-055169-3). McGraw.
Searle, W. & Jones, D. Smart BASIC for the Adam. (Illus.). 384p. 1984. pap. 12.95 (ISBN 0-89303-846-6). Brady Comm.
Softsync & West, Gary. Joy of BASIC for the Adam. (Illus.). 352p. pap. cancelled (ISBN 0-89303-589-0). Brady Comm.
Spear, Barbara. Word Processing with Your Adam. (Illus.). 160p. (Orig.). 1984. 15.95 (ISBN 0-8306-0766-8); pap. 9.25 (ISBN 0-8306-1766-3, 1766). TAB Bks.
Swadley, Richard & Wikert, Joseph. Using Your Coleco Adam: Beginning BASIC & Applications. 300p. 1985. pap. 11.95 (ISBN 0-13-937368-3); incl. tape 24.95 (ISBN 0-13-939018-9). P-H.
Talcott Mountain Science Center. Discovering Science on Your ADAM, with 25 Programs. (Illus.). 176p. (Orig.). 1984. 15.95 (ISBN 0-8306-0780-3); pap. 9.95 (ISBN 0-8306-1780-9, 1780). TAB Bks.
Titus, Christopher & Titus, Jonathan. Coleco Adam Starter Book. LC 84-51347. 384p. 1984. 16.95 (ISBN 0-672-22380-5, 22380). Sams.
Uston, Ken. Ken Uston's Illustrated Guide to the Adam. (Illustrated Guides Ser.). 1984. 12.95 (ISBN 0-13-514647-X). P-H.
Weber Systems, Inc. Staff. Coleco Adam for Students. 280p. 1984. pap. 13.95 student edition (ISBN 0-938862-42-1); pap. cancelled parent-teacher edition (ISBN 0-938862-43-X). Weber Systems.
Weber Systems Staff. Coleco Adam User's Handbook. (Orig.). 1984. 9.95 (ISBN 0-345-31839-0). Ballantine.
Willis, Jerry. How to Use the Coleco Adam. 100p. 1984. pap. 5.95 (ISBN 0-88056-149-1). Dilithium Pr.
Willis, Jerry, et al. Things to Do with Your Coleco Adam Computer. 1984. pap. 3.95 (ISBN 0-451-13182-7, Sig). NAL.
--Things to Do with Your Colecovision Adam. pap. cancelled (ISBN 0-451-13182-7). Dilithium Pr.
Wolenik, Robert. The Practical Adam: A Family Guidebook. 14.95 (ISBN 0-8359-5583-4). Reston.

ADAPTATION (BIOLOGY)

see also Genetics; Man–Influence of Environment; Origin of Species

Berry, R. J. Inheritance & Natural History. (The New Natural Ser.). (Illus.). 1978. 14.95 (ISBN 0-8008-4195-6). Taplinger.
Boucher, Doug A., ed. The Biology of Mutualism: Ecology & Evolution. 400p. 1985. 49.95 (ISBN 0-19-520483-2). Oxford U Pr.
Calhoun, John B., ed. Environment & Population: Problems of Adaptation. (Illus.). 508p. 1983. 71.00 (ISBN 0-03-063337-0). Praeger.
Cloudsley-Thompson, J. L. Animal Conflict & Adaptation. LC 65-26318. (Illus.). 1965. 13.95 (ISBN 0-8023-1026-5). Dufour.
--Dietary Adaptions in Animals. 76p. 1976. 39.00x (ISBN 0-686-96990-1, Pub. by Meadowfield Pr England). State Mutual Bk.
--Form & Function in Animals. 92p. 1979. 39.00x (ISBN 0-900541-90-3, Pub. by Meadowfield Pr England). State Mutual Bk.
Conrad, Michael. Adaptability: The Significance of Variability from Molecule to Ecosystem. LC 82-24558. 408p. 1983. 45.00x (ISBN 0-306-41223-3, Plenum Pr). Plenum Pub.
DeBeer, Gavin. Adaptation. rev ed. Head, J. J., ed. LC 77-88028. (Carolina Biology Readers Ser.). (Illus.). 16p. 1978. pap. 1.60 (ISBN 0-89278-222-6, 45-9622). Carolina Biological.
Dubos, Rene. Man Adapting. enl. ed. LC 80-16492. (Silliman Lectures Ser.). (Illus.). 527p. 1980. 36.00x (ISBN 0-300-02580-7); pap. 9.95 (ISBN 0-300-02581-5, Y-197). Yale U Pr.
Eisenberg, John F. The Mammalian Radiations: An Analysis of Trends in Evolution, Adaption & Behavior. LC 80-27940. (Illus.). 640p. 1983. pap. 22.00x (ISBN 0-226-19538-4). U of Chicago Pr.
Florkin, Marcel & Schoffeniels, Ernest. A Molecular Approaches to Ecology. 1969. 49.00 (ISBN 0-12-261046-6). Acad Pr.
Hainsworth, F. Reed. Animal Physiology: Adaptations in Function. (Life Sciences Ser.). (Illus.). 600p. 1981. text ed. 36.95 (ISBN 0-201-03401-8). Addison-Wesley.
Hecht, Max K., et al, eds. Evolutionary Biology, Vol. 17. 338p. 1984. 42.50x (ISBN 0-306-41651-4, Plenum Pr). Plenum Pub.
Hitching, Francis. The Neck of the Giraffe: Darwin, Evolution, & the New Biology. 1983. pap. 4.95 (ISBN 0-451-62434-3, Ment). NAL.
Hochachka, Peter W. & Somero, George N. Biochemical Adaptation. LC 83-43076. (Illus.). 480p. 1984. 60.00x (ISBN 0-691-08343-6); pap. 19.50x (ISBN 0-691-08344-4). Princeton U Pr.
Holland, John H. Adaptation in Natural & Artificial Systems: An Introductory Analysis with Applications to Biology, Control & Artificial Intelligence. LC 74-78988. (Illus.). 1975. 14.95x (ISBN 0-472-08460-7). U of Mich Pr.
Hooke, J. M. Historical Change in Physical Environment. 256p. 1982. text ed. 69.95. Butterworth.
Horvath, S. M., et al, eds. Comparative Studies on Humar. Adaptability of Japanese, Caucasians & Japanese Americans, Vol. 1. (Japan International Biological Program Synthesis Ser.). 184p. 1975. 24.00 (ISBN 0-86008-211-3, Pub. by U of Tokyo Japan). Columbia U Pr.
Ingram, D. L. & Mount, L. E. Man & Animals in Hot Environments. (Topics in Environmental Physiology & Medicine Ser.). (Illus.). x, 190p. 1975. 49.00 (ISBN 0-387-06865-1). Springer-Verlag.
Jamison, P. L. & Zegura, S. L., eds. The Eskimo of Northwestern Alaska: A Biological Perspective. LC 77-18941. (US-IBP Synthesis Ser.: Vol. 8). 319p. 1978. 47.95 (ISBN 0-87933-319-7). Van nos Reinhold.
Kavaler, Lucy. A Matter of Degree: Heat Life & Death. LC 80-8789. 224p. 1981. 15.34i (ISBN 0-06-014854-3, HarpT). Har-Row.
Kellogg, William W. & Schware, Robert. Climate Change & Society: Consequences of Increasing Atmospheric Carbon Dioxide. (Special Study Ser.). 170p. (Orig.). 1981. 21.50x (ISBN 0-86531-179-X); pap. 9.50x (ISBN 0-86531-180-3). Westview.
Little, Colin. The Colonisation of Land: Origins & Adaptations of Terrestrial Animals. LC 83-1787. (Illus.). 480p. 1984. 99.50 (ISBN 0-521-25218-0). Cambridge U Pr.
Llano, George, ed. Adaptions Within Antarctic Ecosystems: Proceedings of the Third SCAR Symposium on Antarctic Biology. LC 76-21500. 1296p. 1977. 19.95x (ISBN 0-87201-000-7). Gulf Pub.
Margaris, N. S., et al, eds. Plant, Animal, & Microbial Adaptations to Terrestial Environment. 275p. 1983. 39.50x (ISBN 0-306-41468-6, Plenum Pr). Plenum Pub.
Marler, P. & Terrace, H. S., eds. The Biology of Learning. (Dahlem Workshop Reports Ser.: Vol. 29). (Illus.). 750p. 1984. 31.00 (ISBN 0-387-13923-0). Springer-Verlag.
Messel, H., ed. The Biological Manipulation of Life. (Illus.). 352p. 1981. text ed. 34.00 (ISBN 0-08-024825-X); pap. 20.00 (ISBN 0-08-024824-1). Pergamon.
Miller, Alan S. A Planet to Choose. 192p. (Orig.). 1978. pap. 6.95 (ISBN 0-8298-0348-3). Pilgrim NY.
Napier, J. R. Primates & Their Adaptations. rev. ed. Head, J. J., ed. LC 76-29380. (Carolina Biology Readers Ser.). (Illus.). 16p. 1977. pap. 1.60 (ISBN 0-89278-228-5, 45-9628). Carolina Biological.
Ortner, Donald J., ed. How Humans Adapt: A Biocultural Odyssey. LC 82-600233. (Illus.). 560p. 1983. text ed. 19.95x (ISBN 0-87474-726-0); pap. text ed. 9.95x (ISBN 0-87474-725-2). Smithsonian.
Piaget, Jean. Adaptation & Intelligence: Organic Selection & Phenocopy. Eames, Steward, tr. LC 79-25592. 130p. 1980. 11.00x (ISBN 0-226-66777-4). U of Chicago Pr.
Rebach, Steve & Dunham, David W., eds. Studies in Adaptation: The Behavior of Higher Crustacea. LC 82-13501. 282p. 1983. text ed. 45.50x (ISBN 0-471-89823-6, Pub. by Wiley Interscience). Wiley.
Reynolds, V., ed. Human Behavior & Adaptation. (Symposia of the Society for the Study of Human Biology Ser.: Vol. 18). 314p. 1978. cancelled (ISBN 0-85066-137-4). Taylor & Francis.
Rohwer, Sievert. Specific Distinctness & Adaptive Differences in Southwestern Meadowlarks. (Occasional Papers: No. 44). 14p. 1976. pap. 1.25 (ISBN 0-317-04634-9). U of KS Mus Nat Hist.
The Size of Animals. 64p. 1977. 39.00x (ISBN 0-900541-80-6, Pub. by Meadowfield Pr England). State Mutual Bk.
Steegman, A. Theodore, Jr., ed. Boreal Forest Adaptations: The Northern Algonkians. 355p. 1983. 49.50x (ISBN 0-306-41238-1, Plenum Pr). Plenum Pub.
Steele, E. J. Somatic Selection & Adaptive Evolution: On the Inheritance of Acquired Characters. rev. ed. LC 81-11419. (Illus.). 1981. lib. bdg. 18.00x (ISBN 0-226-77162-8); pap. 5.95X (ISBN 0-226-77163-6). U of Chicago Pr.
Sychev, Y. The Individual & the Microenvironment. 165p. 1978. 6.45 (ISBN 0-8285-3302-4, Pub. by Progress Pubs USSR). Imported Pubns.
Symposium Held in Honor of David B. Dill, April, 1971. Physiological Adaptations: Desert & Mountain. Yousef, Mohamed K., et al, eds. (Environmental Science: An Interdisciplinary Monograph Ser). 1972. 55.00 (ISBN 0-12-774650-1). Acad Pr.
Thorpe, Malcolm R., ed. Organic Adaptation to Environment. 1924. 49.50x (ISBN 0-685-69877-7). Elliots Bks.
Tributsch, Helmut. How Life Learned to Live: Adaptation in Nature. (Illus.). 232p. 1985. pap. 7.95 (ISBN 0-262-70028-X). MIT Pr.
Turner, N. C. & Kramer, P. J. Adaptation of Plants to Water & High Temperature Stress. LC 79-24428. 482p. 1980. text ed. 56.50x (ISBN 0-471-05372-4, Pub. by Wiley-Interscience). Wiley.
Wallace, Bruce & Srb, Adrian M. Adaption. LC 77-18812. (Foundations of Modern Biology Ser.). 1978. Repr. of 1964 ed. lib. bdg. 19.75x (ISBN 0-313-20212-5, WAAD). Greenwood.
Weiner, J. S., et al, eds. Human Adaptability: A Historical & Compendium of Research for the International Biological Programme. 368p. cancelled (ISBN 0-85066-087-4). Taylor & Francis.
Wessells, Norman K., intro. by. Vertebrates: Adaptation: Readings from Scientific American. LC 80-188. (Illus.). 256p. 1980. text ed. 23.95x (ISBN 0-7167-1167-2); pap. text ed. 12.95x (ISBN 0-7167-1168-0). W H Freeman.
Williams, George C. Adaptation & Natural Selection: A Critique of Some Current Evolutionary Thought. 1966. pap. 9.95x (ISBN 0-691-02357-3). Princeton U Pr.
Witcombe, John R. & Erskine, William, eds. Genetic Resources & Their Exploitation - Chickpeas, Faba Beans, & Lentils. (Advances Agricultural Biotechnology Ser.). 1984. lib. bdg. 36.50 (ISBN 90-247-2939-4, Pub. by Martinus Nijhoff Netherlands). Kluwer-Academic.
The Zodiac Symposium on Adaption: Proceedings. 1978. pap. 24.00 (ISBN 90-220-0680-8, PDC131, PUDOC). Unipub.

ADAPTATION (PHYSIOLOGY)

Adolfson, John A. & Berghage, Thomas E. Perception & Performance Underwater. LC 73-23009. 380p. 1974. 24.50 (ISBN 0-471-00900-8, Pub. by Wiley). Krieger.
Assenmacherm, I. & Farner, D. S., eds. Environmental Endocrinology: Proceedings of an International Symposium Held in Montpellier (France), July 11-15, 1977. (Proceedings in Life Sciences). (Illus.). 1978. 45.00 (ISBN 0-387-08809-1). Springer-Verlag.
Carroll, Charles & Miller, Dean. Health: The Science of Human Adaptation. 3rd ed. 720p. 1982. pap. text ed. write for info. (ISBN 0-697-07393-9); instructor's manual avail. (ISBN 0-697-07394-7); transparencies avail. (ISBN 0-697-07395-5). Wm C Brown.
Cooper, Wendy & Smith, Tim. Beyond Our Limits: What Ordinary Humans Can Do in Extremis. LC 81-48443. 224p. 1982. 14.95 (ISBN 0-8128-2867-4). Stein & Day.
Dyson-Hudson, Rada & Little, Michael A. Rethinking Human Adaptation. (Special Study). 200p. 1982. 23.00x (ISBN 0-86531-511-6). Westview.
European Society for Comparative Physiology & Biochemistry, 1st Conference, Liege, Belgium, 1979. Animals & Environment Fitness; Physiological & Biochemical Aspects of Adaptations & Ecology: Proceedings, 2 vols. Gilles, R., ed. (Illus.). 638p. 1980. Vol. 1. 125.00 (ISBN 0-08-024938-8); Vol. 2. 54.00 (ISBN 0-08-024939-6). Pergamon.
Geist, V. Life Strategies, Human Evolution, Environmental Design: Toward a Biological Theory of Health, Vol. I. LC 78-10807. (Illus.). 1978. 39.50 (ISBN 0-387-90363-1). Springer-Verlag.
Hiernaux, Jean. Man in the Heat, High Altitude, & Society. (Illus.). 130p. 1982. 24.75x (ISBN 0-398-04644-1). C C Thomas.
Hill, Richard W. Comparative Physiology of Animals: An Enviromental Approach. (Illus.). 672p. 1976. text ed. 35.50 scp (ISBN 0-06-042827-9, HarpC). Har-Row.
Meerson, F. Z. Adaptation, Stress & Prophylaxis. (Illus.). 340p. 1984. 47.00 (ISBN 0-387-12363-6). Springer-Verlag.
Moberg, Gary P. Animal Stress. 332p. 1985. 42.50 (ISBN 0-683-06101-1). Waverly Pr.
Selye, Hans. The Stress of Life. 2nd ed. (McGraw Hill Paperbacks). 1978. pap. 6.95 (ISBN 0-07-056212-1). McGraw.
Snow, David. The Web of Adaptation: Bird Studies in the American Tropics. LC 85-7890. 192p. (Orig.). 1985. pap. text ed. 7.95x (ISBN 0-8014-9316-1). Cornell U Pr.
Stini, William A., ed. Physiological & Morphological Adaptation & Evolution. (World Anthropology Ser.). 1979. text ed. 37.60x (ISBN 90-279-7710-0). Mouton.
Thiele, H. U. Carabid Beetles in Their Environments: A Study on Habit Selection by Adaptations in Physiology & Behaviour. LC 77-9924. (Zoophysiology & Ecology: Vol. 10). (Illus.). 1977. 63.00 (ISBN 0-387-08306-5). Springer-Verlag.
West, John B., ed. High Altitude Physiology. (Benchmark Papers in Human Physiology: Vol. 15). 480p. 1981. 55.00 (ISBN 0-87933-388-X). Van Nos Reinhold.
Wood & Lenfant. Evolution of Respiratory Processes. LC 79-4051. (Lung Biology in Health & Disease Ser.: Vol. 13). 1979. 69.75 (ISBN 0-8247-6793-4). Dekker.

ADAPTIVE CONTROL SYSTEMS

see also Feedback Control Systems

Anderson, B. D. & Ljung, L., eds. Adaptive Control. 232p. 1984. pap. 40.00 (ISBN 0-08-031660-3). Pergamon.
Davies, W. D. System Identification for Self-Adaptive Control. LC 70-128756. pap. 98.50 (ISBN 0-317-08013-X, 2022540). Bks Demand UMI.
Gaertner, Wolfgang, ed. Adaptive Electronics. LC 71-189397. (Illus.). 370p. 1973. pap. 14.00x (ISBN 0-89006-013-4). Artech Hse.
Harris, C. J. & Billings, S. A. Self Tuning & Adaptive Control: Theory & Applications. (IEE Control Engineering Ser.: No. 15). 352p. 1981. 50.00 (ISBN 0-906048-62-1, CE015). Inst Elect Eng.
IFAC Workshop, San Francisco, Calif., June 1983 & Landau, I. D. Adaptive Systems in Control & Signal Processing 1983: Proceedings. (IFAC Proceedings Ser.). 420p. 1984. 94.00 (ISBN 0-08-030565-2). Pergamon.
Ioannou, P. A. & Kokotovic, P. V. Adaptive Systems with Reduced Models. (Lecture Notes in Control & Information Sciences Ser.: Vol. 47). 164p. 1983. pap. 12.00 (ISBN 0-387-12150-1). Springer-Verlag.
Lee, E. Stanley. Quasilinearization & Invariant Imbedding. (Mathematics in Science & Engineering Ser.,: Vol. 41). 1968. 70.00 (ISBN 0-12-440250-X). Acad Pr.
Narendra, Kumpati & Monopoli, Richard, eds. Applications of Adaptive Control. 1980. 55.00 (ISBN 0-12-514060-6). Acad Pr.
Pervozvanskii, A. A. Random Processes in Nonlinear Control Systems. (Mathematics in Science & Engineering Ser.: Vol. 15). 1965. 77.00 (ISBN 0-12-551650-9). Acad Pr.
Sawaragi, Yoshikazu, et al. Statistical Decision Theory in Adaptive Control Systems. (Mathematics in Science & Engineering Ser: Vol. 39). 1967. 60.00 (ISBN 0-12-620350-4). Acad Pr.
Sworder, David D. Optimal Adaptive Control Systems. (Mathematics in Science & Engineering Ser.: Vol. 25). 1966. 49.50 (ISBN 0-12-679550-9). Acad Pr.
Tsypkin, Ya. Z. Adaptation & Learning in Automatic Systems. Nikolic, S. J., tr. LC 78-129017. (Mathematics in Science & Engineering Ser.: Vol. 73). 1971. 70.00 (ISBN 0-12-702050-0). Acad Pr.
Weiss, David J. New Horizons in Testing: Latent Trait Test & Computerized Adaptive Testing. 1983. 38.00 (ISBN 0-12-742780-5). Acad Pr.

ADAPTIVE CONTROL SYSTEMS–MATHEMATICAL MODELS

Anderson, B. D. & Ljung, L., eds. Adaptive Control. 232p. 1984. pap. 40.00 (ISBN 0-08-031660-3). Pergamon.
Unbehauen, H., ed. Methods in Adaptive Control: Proceedings. (Lecture Notes in Control & Information Sciences: Vol. 24). (Illus.). 309p. 1980. pap. 26.00 (ISBN 0-387-10226-4). Springer-Verlag.

ADDING MACHINES

see Calculating-Machines

ADDITION

The Arithmetic Classroom: Addition, 3 pts. (Courses by Computers Ser.). Apple. 49.95 (ISBN 0-88408-196-6); IBM-PC, PCjr. 49.95 (ISBN 0-88408-284-9); Acom. 49.95 (ISBN 0-88408-340-3). Sterling Swift.
Lutgendorf, Philip. Addition & Subtraction. LC 79-730038. (Illus.). 1978. pap. text ed. 135.00 (ISBN 0-89290-092-X, A508-SATC). Soc for Visual.
SLAM-Addition, 30 wkbks. Set. 15.95 (ISBN 0-86624-031-4, LWB6536TB). Bilingual Ed Serv.

ADDITIVE PROCESS (PROBABILITY THEORY)

see Random Walks (Mathematics)

ADDITIVES, FOOD

see Food Additives

Hunter, Beatrice. Food Additives: The Mirage of Safety. 322p. 9.95 (ISBN 0-318-15658-X). Natl Health Fed.

ADENOHYPOPHYSIS

Costoff, Allen. Ultrastructure of Rat Adenohypophysis: Correlation with Function. 1973. 49.00 (ISBN 0-12-191550-6). Acad Pr.

Jutisz, Marian & McKerns, Kenneth W., eds. Synthesis & Release of Adenohypophyseal Hormones. LC 80-96. (Biochemical Endocrinology Ser.). (Illus.). 821p. 1980. 89.50x (ISBN 0-306-40247-5, Plenum Pr). Plenum Pub.

Tixier-Vidal, A. & Farquhar, Marilyn G., eds. The Anterior Pituitary. 1975. 73.00 (ISBN 0-12-692050-8). Acad Pr.

ADENOSINEMONOPHOSPHATE

Berne, Robert M., et al, eds. The Regulatory Function of Adenosine. 1983. lib. bdg. 93.50 (ISBN 90-247-2779-0, Pub. by Martinus Nijhoff Netherlands). Kluwer Academic.

ADENOSINETRIPHOSPHATE

Bridger, William A. & Hendessen, J. Frank. Cell ATP. LC 82-24797. (Transport in Life Science Ser.). 170p. 1983. 59.95 (ISBN 0-471-08507-3, Pub. by Wiley-Interscience). Wiley.

Cooper, Dermot M. F. & Seamon, Kenneth B., eds. Dual Regulation of Adenylate Cyclase. (Advances in Cyclic Nucleotide & Protein Phosphorylation Research Ser.: Vol. 19). (Illus.). 352p. 1985. text ed. 59.00 (ISBN 0-88167-079-0). Raven.

ADHESION

see also Cohesion

Adhesion Measurement of Thin Films, Thick Films & Bulk Coatings. 410p. 1978. 39.25 (ISBN 0-8031-0272-0, 04-640000-25). ASTM.

Allen, K. W., ed. Adhesion, Vols. 1-5. 1977-81. Vol. 1. 48.00 (ISBN 0-85334-735-2, Pub. by Elsevier Applied Sci England); Vol. 2. 44.50 (ISBN 0-85334-743-3); Vol. 3. 48.00 (ISBN 0-85334-808-1); Vol. 4. 48.00 (ISBN 0-85334-861-8); Vol. 5. 48.00 (ISBN 0-85334-929-0). Elsevier.

--Adhesion, Vol. 6. (Illus.). x, 210p. 1983. 64.75 (ISBN 0-85334-106-0, Pub. by Elsevier Applied Sci England). Elsevier.

--Adhesion, Vol. 8. (Illus.). 220p. 1984. 64.75 (ISBN 0-85334-252-0, I-518-83, Pub. by Elsevier Applied Sci England). Elsevier.

--Adhesion: Papers from the Annual Conference on Adhesion & Adhesives, 22nd, City University, London, UK, Vol. 9. 198p. 1985. 52.50 (ISBN 0-85334-328-4, Pub. by Elsevier Applied Sci England). Elsevier.

Bikales, Norbert M., ed. Adhesion & Bonding. LC 78-172950. 220p. 1971. 16.00 (ISBN 0-471-07230-3). Krieger.

Contact Angle, Wettability & Adhesion. LC 63-14481. (Advances in Chemistry Ser: No. 43). 1964. 39.95 (ISBN 0-8412-0044-0). Am Chemical.

Dunitz, J. D., et al, eds. Coordinative Interactions. Incl. Metal Complexes of Chelating Olefin-Group V Ligands. Williams, R. J., et al.; Structural Radii, Electron-Cloud Radii, Ionic Radii & Solvation. Baughan, E. C; Quantitative Evaluation & Prediction of Donor-Acceptor Interactions. Drago, R. S; Redox Properties: Changes Affected by Coordination. Gutmann, V; Thermodynamics of the Stepwise Formation of Metal-Ion Complexes in Aqueous Solution. Ahrland, S. (Structure & Bonding Ser.: Vol. 15). (Illus.). 189p. 1973. pap. 40.00 (ISBN 0-387-06410-9). Springer-Verlag.

Houwink, Roelof, ed. Adhesion & Adhesives, 2 vols. 2nd ed. Incl. Vol. 1. Adhesives. 548p. 1965. 98.00 (ISBN 0-444-40300-0); Vol. 2. Applications. 590p. 1967. 98.00 (ISBN 0-444-40301-9). Set. 159.75. Elsevier.

Lee, Lieng-Huang. Adhesion Science & Technology. Incl. Pt. A. 470p (ISBN 0-306-36493-X); Pt. B. 455p (ISBN 0-306-36494-8). LC 75-35744. (Polymer Science & Technology Ser.: Vols. 9A & 9B). 1975. 69.50 ea. (Plenum Pr). Plenum Pub.

Lee, Lieng-Huang, ed. Recent Advances in Adhesion. LC 73-86915. 568p. 1973. 123.75 (ISBN 0-677-12190-3). Gordon.

Manly, Richard S., ed. Adhesion in Biological Systems. 1970. 60.00 (ISBN 0-12-469050-5). Acad Pr.

Ministry Of Technology. U. K. Adhesion Fundamentals & Practice U. K. 322p. 1971. 80.95x (ISBN 0-677-61430-6). Gordon.

Oliver, John F., ed. Adhesion in Cellulosic & Wood-Based Composites. LC 81-11983. (NATO Conference Series VI--Material Science: Vol. 3). 268p. 1981. 49.50x (ISBN 0-306-40812-0, Plenum Pr). Plenum Pub.

Patrick. Treatise on Adhesion & Adhesives, Vol. 5. 416p. 1981. 65.00 (ISBN 0-8247-1399-0). Dekker.

Patrick, R. L., ed. Treatise on Adhesion & Adhesives, Vols. 1 & 2. Incl. Vol. 1. Theory. 1967. soft cover 89.75 (ISBN 0-8247-7037-4); Vol. 2. Materials. 1969. Dekker.

Wake, W. C. Adhesion & the Formulation of Adhesives. 2nd ed. (Illus.). 326p. 1982. 48.00 (ISBN 0-85334-134-6, Pub. by Elsevier Applied Sci England). Elsevier.

Zimon, A. D. Adhesion of Dust & Powder. LC 69-12547. 424p. 1969. 47.50x (ISBN 0-306-30391-4, Plenum Pr). Plenum Pub.

Zimon, Anatolii D., ed. Adhesion of Dust & Powder. 2nd ed. Johnston, Robert K., tr. from Rus. LC 80-16154. 449p. 1982. 72.50x (ISBN 0-306-10962-X, Consultants). Plenum Pub.

ADHESIVES

see also Cement; Glue

Adhesive Age Magazine. The Adhesives Redbook: Adhesives Age Directory. 32.50 (ISBN 0-686-48218-2, 0501). T-C Pubns CA.

Adhesive Bonding of Composites Materials, 1970-Jan. 1983. 124p. 1983. 78.00 (ISBN 0-686-48264-6, LS102). T-C Pubns CA.

Adhesive Properties, Preparation, & Applications, 1982-May 1983. 235p. 1983. 78.00 (ISBN 0-686-48262-X, LS101). T-C Pubns CA.

Adhesives & Sealants. 1982. 475.00 (ISBN 0-318-00507-7). Busn Trend.

Adhesives & Sealants. 1985. 595.00. Busn Trend.

Adhesives for Industry: Proceedings of a Conference, March 1976, El Segundo, California. 116p. 32.50 (ISBN 0-686-48227-1, 0101). T-C Pubns CA.

Adhesives for Industry: Proceedings of a Special Conference, June 1980, Los Angeles, California. (Illus.). 293p. 38.00 (ISBN 0-938648-04-7, 0103). T-C Pubns CA.

Adhesives Used on Building Materials, 1970-April 1982. 71p. 1982. 78.00 (ISBN 0-686-48269-7, LS104). T-C Pubns CA.

Adhesivs-Structural: Formulations & Applications. 145p. 1983. 78.00 (ISBN 0-686-48265-4, LS103). T-C Pubns CA.

Ash, M. & Ash, I. Formulary of Adhesives & Sealants. Date not set. 35.00 (ISBN 0-8206-0297-3). Chem Pub.

Bruno, E. J., ed. Adhesives in Modern Manufacturing. LC 79-93212. (Manufacturing Data Ser). (Illus., Orig.). 1970. pap. 11.50x (ISBN 0-87263-017-X). SME.

Buonocore, Michael G. The Use of Adhesives in Dentistry. (Illus.). 472p. 1975. photocopy ed. 54.50x (ISBN 0-398-03367-6). C C Thomas.

Business Communications Staff. Structural & Adhesives Specialty. 1984. 1500.00 (ISBN 0-89336-108-9, C-009N). BCC.

Cagle, Charles V. Handbook of Adhesive Bonding. Lee, Henry & Neville, Kris, eds. 754p. 1982. Repr. of 1973 ed. 64.50 (ISBN 0-07-009588-4). McGraw.

De Lollis, Nicholas J. Adhesives: Adherends, Adhesion. LC 79-1371. 352p. 1980. lib. bdg. 29.50 (ISBN 0-88275-981-7). Krieger.

Deryagin, B. V., et al. Adhesion of Solids. LC 78-1843. (Studies in Soviet Science--Physical Sciences Ser.). (Illus.). 473p. 1978. 72.50x (ISBN 0-306-10941-7, Consultants). Plenum Pub.

Flick, Ernest W. Adhesive & Sealant Compound Formulations. 2nd ed. LC 83-22016. 366p. 1984. 48.00 (ISBN 0-8155-0966-9). Noyes.

--Handbook of Adhesive Raw Materials. LC 82-2251. (Illus.). 303p. 1982. 45.00 (ISBN 0-8155-0897-2). Noyes.

Haviland. Handbook of Machinery Adhesives. (Mechanical Engineering Ser.). 336p. 1985. price not set (ISBN 0-8247-7467-1). Dekker.

Herman, B. S. Adhesives-Recent Developments. LC 76-2195. (Chemical Review Ser.: No. 65). (Illus.). 302p. 1976. 32.00 (ISBN 0-8155-0613-9). Noyes.

Hot Melt Adhesives & Coatings: Course Notes. 100p. 1981. soft cover 39.95 (ISBN 0-686-98539-7, 01-06-1681). TAPPI.

Houwink, Roelof, ed. Adhesion & Adhesives, 2 vols. 2nd ed. Incl. Vol. 1. Adhesives. 548p. 1965. 98.00 (ISBN 0-444-40300-0); Vol. 2. Applications. 590p. 1967. 98.00 (ISBN 0-444-40301-9). Set. 159.75. Elsevier.

International Plastics Selector, Inc. The Adhesives Desk-Top Data Bank. 95.00 (ISBN 0-686-48215-8, 0301). T-C Pubns CA.

--Specifications for Adhesives. 55.00 (ISBN 0-686-48216-6, 0308). T-C Pubns CA.

Jones, Peter. Fasteners, Joints & Adhesives: A Guide to Engineering Solid Constructions. 416p. 1983. 24.95 (ISBN 0-13-307694-6); pap. 14.95 (ISBN 0-13-307686-5). P-H.

Kinloch, A. J. Developments in Adhesives, Vol. 2. (Applied Science Ser.). (Illus.). 419p. 1981. 72.25 (ISBN 0-85334-958-4, Pub. by Elsevier Applied Sci England). Elsevier.

Kinloch, A. J., ed. Durability of Structural Adhesives. (Illus.). 352p. 1983. 74.00 (ISBN 0-85334-214-8, Pub. by Elsevier Applied Sci England). Elsevier.

Lee, H., ed. Cyanoacrylate Resins: The Instant Adhesives. 241p. 1981. 50.00 (ISBN 0-938648-14-4). T-C Pubns CA.

Lees, W. A. Adhesives in Engineering Design. 155p. 1985. 28.00 (ISBN 0-387-15024-2). Springer-Verlag.

Ministry Of Technology. U. K. Adhesion Fundamentals & Practice U. K. 322p. 1971. 80.95x (ISBN 0-677-61430-6). Gordon.

Padday, J. F., ed. Wetting, Spreading & Adhesion. 1978. 87.00 (ISBN 0-12-544350-1). Acad Pr.

Patrick. Treatise on Adhesion & Adhesives, Vol. 5. 416p. 1981. 65.00 (ISBN 0-8247-1399-0). Dekker.

Pizzi. Wood Adhesives Chemistry & Technology. 304p. 1983. 65.00 (ISBN 0-8247-1579-9). Dekker.

Reinforced Plastics-Composites, Adhesives & Thermosets: SPE PACTEC 81. 17.50 (ISBN 0-686-48232-8, 1507). T-C Pubns CA.

Satas, Donastas, ed. Handbook of Pressure-Sensitive Adhesive Technology. 680p. 1982. 37.50 (ISBN 0-442-25724-4). Van Nos Reinhold.

Satas, Donatas, ed. Handbook of Pressure-Sensitive Adhesive Technology. (Illus.). 636p. 1982. 37.50 (ISBN 0-686-48211-5, 0214). T-C Pubns CA.

Satriana, M. J., ed. Adhesives Technology Annual, Vol. 1. LC 77-94229. (Illus.). 1978. 40.00 (ISBN 0-8155-0697-X). Noyes.

Schneberger. Adhesives in Manufacturing. (Manufacturing Engineering & Materials Processes Ser.). 728p. 1983. 95.00 (ISBN 0-8247-1894-1). Dekker.

Sellers. Plywood & Adhesive Technology. 840p. 1985. write for info. (ISBN 0-8247-7407-8). Dekker.

Shields, J. Adhesives Handbook. 3rd ed. 348p. 1984. text ed. 79.95 (ISBN 0-408-01356-7). Butterworth.

Skeist, Irving. The Handbook of Adhesives. 2nd ed. (Illus.). 939p. 1977. 49.50 (ISBN 0-686-48206-9, 0201). T-C Pubns CA.

Skeist, Irving, ed. Handbook of Adhesives. 2nd ed. LC 76-18057. 1977. 49.50 (ISBN 0-442-27634-6). Van Nos Reinhold.

Structural Adhesives & Bonding: Proceedings of a Special Conference, March 1979, El Segundo, California. (Illus.). 426p. 46.50 (ISBN 0-938648-07-1, 0111). T-C Pubns CA.

Technical Association of the Pulp & Paper Industry. Testing of Adhesives: A Project of the Adhesives Testing Committee. Meese, R. Gregory, ed. LC 73-88201. (TAPPI Monograph Ser.: No. 35). pap. 56.00 (ISBN 0-317-28875-X, 2020303). Bks Demand UMI.

Thrall & Shannon. Adhesive Bonding of Aluminum Alloys. 1985. 79.95 (ISBN 0-8247-7405-1). Dekker.

Torrey, S., ed. Adhesive Technology: Developments Since 1977. LC 79-25936. (Chemical Technology Review Ser.: No. 148). (Illus.). 500p. 1980. 54.00 (ISBN 0-8155-0787-9). Noyes.

Wake, W. C., ed. Developments in Adhesives, Vol. 1. (Illus.). 318p. 1977. 55.50 (ISBN 0-85334-749-2, Pub. by Elsevier Applied Sci England). Elsevier.

Weiner, Jack & Roth, Lillian. Adhesives. Incl. Vol. 1. General Applications, Theory, & Testing, Supplement 2. (Bibliographic Ser.: No. 205). 20.00 (ISBN 0-87010-023-8); Vol. 2. Paper, Supplement 2. (Bibliograpghic Ser.: No. 206). 12.00 (ISBN 0-87010-024-6); Vol. 3. Board, Plastics, Textiles, & Supplement. (Bibliographic Ser.: No. 207). 15.00 (ISBN 0-87010-025-4); Vol. 4. Tapes & Machinery, Supplement 2. LC 64-13319. (Bibliographic Ser.: No. 208). 14.00 (ISBN 0-87010-026-2). (Bibliographic Ser.). 1974. Inst Paper Chem.

Weyher, Douglas F. Adhesives in Modern Manufacturing. Bruno, E. J., ed. LC 79-93212. (Manufacturing Data Ser.). pap. 49.50 (ISBN 0-317-29881-X, 201600). Bks Demand UMI.

Wood Adhesives: Present & Future. pap. price not set (ISBN 0-471-81334-6). Wiley.

ADIPOSE TISSUES

Allen, Philip W. Tumors & Proliferations of Adipose Tissue: A Clinicopathologic Approach. LC 80-28916. (Masson Monographs in Diagnostic Pathology: Vol. 1). 200p. 1981. text ed. 45.50x (ISBN 0-89352-057-8). Masson Pub.

Bonnet, F. P. Adipose Tissue in Childhood. 192p. 1981. 69.00 (ISBN 0-8493-5771-3). CRC Pr.

Kinsell, Laurance W. Adipose Tissue as an Organ: Proceedings of the Duel Conference on Lipids. (Illus.). 292p. 1962. photocopy ed. 27.75x (ISBN 0-398-04311-6). C C Thomas.

Reynolds, E. L. Distribution of Subcutaneous Fat in Childhood & Adolescence. (SRCD: Vol. 15, No. 2). 1950. 15.00 (ISBN 0-527-01551-2). Kraus Repr.

ADOBE CONSTRUCTION

see Building, Adobe

ADRENALIN

Fuxe, Kjell, et al, eds. Central Adrenaline Neurons: Basic Aspects & Their Role in Cardiovascular Disease: Proceedings of an International Symposium 27-28 August 1979, Wenner-Gren Center, Stockholm. (Wenner-Gren Ser.: Vol. 33). (Illus.). 356p. 1980. 63.00 (ISBN 0-08-025927-8). Pergamon.

ADSORPTION

see also Adhesion; Carbon, Activated; Ion Exchange; Permeability; Porosity; Wetting Agents

Application of Adsorption to Wastewater Treatment. (Illus.). 1981. text ed. 40.00 (ISBN 0-937976-03-2). Enviro Pr.

Dash, J. G. Films on Solid Surfaces. 1975. 59.50 (ISBN 0-12-203350-7). Acad Pr.

Flank, William H., ed. Adsorption & Ion Exchange with Synthetic Zeolites. LC 80-18916. (ACS Symposium Ser.: No. 135). 1980. 34.95 (ISBN 0-8412-0582-5). Am Chemical.

Gileadi, Eliezer, ed. Electrosorption. LC 67-15143. 221p. 1967. 35.00x (ISBN 0-306-30283-7, Plenum Pr). Plenum Pub.

Giordano, Carmelo, ed. Sorbents & Their Clinical Applications. 1980. 67.50 (ISBN 0-12-285250-8). Acad Pr.

Interdisciplinary Surface Science Conference, 2nd, England, 1975. Adsorption at Solid Surfaces: Proceedings. Brundle, C. R. & Todd, C. J., eds. 1976. 95.75 (ISBN 0-444-11071-2, North-Holland). Elsevier.

King, D. A. & Woodruff, D. P., eds. Adsorption at Solid Surface. (Chemical Physics of Solid Surface & Heterogeneous Catalysis Ser.: Vol. 2A). 386p. 1983. 119.25 (ISBN 0-444-42026-6). Elsevier.

Kiselev, V. F. & Krylov, O. V. Adsorption Processes on Semiconductor & Dielectric Surfaces I. (Springer Series in Chemical Physics: Vol. 32). (Illus.). 295p. Date not set. 43.50 (ISBN 0-387-12416-0). Springer-Verlag.

Ma, Y. H. & Ausikaitis, J. P., eds. Recent Advances in Adsorption & Ion Exchange. LC 82-24424. (AIChE Symposium). pap. 34.00 (ISBN 0-8169-0243-7, S-219); pap. 17.00 members (ISBN 0-686-47551-9). Am Inst Chem Eng.

Ma, Y. H., et al, eds. Adsorption & Ion Exchange, 1983. (AIChE Symposium Ser.: Vol. 79, No. 230). 85p. 1983. 30.00 (ISBN 0-8169-0267-4). Am Inst Chem Eng.

Misra, D. N., ed. Adsorption on & Surface Chemistry of Hydroxyapatite. 188p. 1984. 39.50x (ISBN 0-306-41516-X, Plenum Pr). Plenum Pub.

Mittal, K. L., ed. Adsorption at Interface: Papers from a Symposium Honoring Robert D. Vold & Majorie J. Vold. LC 74-32040. (American Chemical Society Symposium Ser.: No. 8). pap. 76.00 (ISBN 0-317-08993-5, 2015232). Bks Demand UMI.

Myers, Alan L. & Belfort, Georges, eds. Fundamentals of Adsorption: International Conference on Fundamentals of Adsorption, Schloss Elmau, Bavaria, West Germany, May 6-11, 1983. 1984. text ed. 60.00 (ISBN 0-8169-0265-8); Member. text ed. 45.00. Am Inst Chem Eng.

Nicholson, D. & Parsonage, N. G. Computer Simulation & the Statiscal Mechanics of Adsorption. 1983. 59.00 (ISBN 0-12-518060-8). Acad Pr.

Oscik, J. Adsorption. (Ellis Horwood Series in Physical Chemistry). 206p. 1982. 74.95 (ISBN 0-470-27218-X). Halsted Pr.

Ottewill, R. H., ed. Adsorption from Solution. 1983. 33.00 (ISBN 0-12-530980-5). Acad Pr.

Rachinskii, Vladimir V. The General Theory of Sorption Dynamics & Chromatography. LC 65-15004. 107p. 1965. 25.00x (ISBN 0-306-10711-2, Consultants). Plenum Pub.

Rouquerol, J. & Sing, K. S., eds. Adsorption at the Gas-Solid Interface: Proceedings of the International Symposium at Auxen - Provence, Sept. 1981. (Studies in Surface Science & Catalysis: Vol. 10). 512p. 1982. 93.75 (ISBN 0-444-42087-8). Elsevier.

Ruthven, D. M. Principles of Adsorption & Adsorption Processes. LC 83-16904. 433p. 1984. 49.50x (ISBN 0-471-86606-7, Pub. by Wiley-Interscience). Wiley.

Ruthven, Douglas M. Principles of Adsorption & Adsorption Processes. 433p. 1984. 49.50 (ISBN 0-471-90028-1). Wiley.

Segal, E. Mathematical Cosmology & Extragalactic Astronomy. (Pure & Applied Mathematics Ser.: Vol. 68). 1976. 29.50 (ISBN 0-12-635250-X). Acad Pr.

Selwood, Pierce W. Adsorption & Collective Paramagnetism. 1962. 49.00 (ISBN 0-12-636550-4). Acad Pr.

Sherman, John, ed. Adsorption & Ion Exchange-Progress & Future Prospects. LC 84-11020. (AIChE Symposium Ser.: Vol 80, No. 233). 124p. 1984. pap. 36.00 (ISBN 0-8169-0318-2). Am Inst Chem Eng.

Slejko, Frank. Applied Adsorption Technology. (Chemical Industries Ser.). 256p. 1985. 55.00 (ISBN 0-8247-7285-7). Dekker.

Smith, J. R., ed. Theory of Chemisorption. (Topics in Current Physics Ser.: Vol. 19). (Illus.). 280p. 1980. 40.00 (ISBN 0-387-09891-7). Springer-Verlag.

Tewari, P. H., ed. Adsorption from Aqueous Solutions. LC 81-10708. 256p. 1981. 45.00x (ISBN 0-306-40747-7, Plenum Pr). Plenum Pub.

Weber, Walter J., Jr. & Matijevic, Egon, eds. Adsorption from Aqueous Solution. LC 68-59407. (Advances in Chemistry Ser: No. 79). 1968. 19.95 (ISBN 0-8412-0080-7). Am Chemical.

ADSORPTION IN SOILS

see Soil Absorption and Adsorption

ADSORPTION OF GASES

see Gases–Absorption and Adsorption

ADVENTURE AND BEAGLE EXPEDITION, 1826-1830

Fitz-Roy, Robert, et al. Narrative of the Surveying Voyages of His Majesty's Ships Adventure & Beagle, 3 Vols. in 4 Pts. Repr. of 1839 ed. Set. 295.00 (ISBN 0-404-09900-9). Vol. 1 (ISBN 0-404-09901-7). Vol. 2 Pt. 1 (ISBN 0-404-09902-5). Vol. 2 Pt. 2 (ISBN 0-404-09903-3). Vol. 3 (ISBN 0-404-09904-1). AMS Pr.

AERIAL BOMBS

see Bombs

AERIAL NAVIGATION

see Navigation (Aeronautics)

AERIAL PHOTOGRAPH READING

see Photographic Interpretation

AERIAL PHOTOGRAPHY

see Photography, Aerial

AERIAL PHOTOGRAPHY IN ANTHROPOLOGY

see also Aerial Photography in Archaeology

Vogt, Evon Z., ed. Aerial Photography in Anthropological Research. LC 73-90850. (Illus.). 224p. 1974. text ed. 20.00x (ISBN 0-674-00626-7). Harvard U Pr.

AERIAL PHOTOGRAPHY IN ARCHAEOLOGY

Norman, E. R. & St Joseph, J. K. Early Development of Irish Society: The Evidence of Aerial Photography. LC 71-85734. (Air Surveys Ser.: No. 3). (Illus.). 1969. 39.50 (ISBN 0-521-07471-1). Cambridge U Pr.

AERIAL PHOTOGRAPHY IN GEOGRAPHY

Campell, James B. Mapping the Land: Ariel Imagery for Land Use Information. Knight, C. Gregory, ed. 85p. (Orig.). 1983. pap. 5.00 (ISBN 0-89291-167-0). Assn Am Geographers.

Dickinson, G. C. Maps & Air Photographs: Images of Earth. 2nd ed. LC 78-31287. 348p. 1979. pap. 17.95 (ISBN 0-470-26641-4). Halsted Pr.

El-Ashry, Mohamed T., ed. Air Photography & Coastal Problems. (Benchmark Papers in Geology: Vol. 38). 1977. 69.50 (ISBN 0-12-786410-5). Acad Pr.

Lo, C. P. Geographical Applications of Aerial Photography. LC 75-37401. 336p. 1976. 27.50x (ISBN 0-8448-0872-5). Crane-Russak Co.

Way, Douglas S. Terrain Analysis: A Guide to Site Selection Using Aerial Photographic Interpretation. 2nd ed. (Community Development Ser.: Vol. 1). (Illus.). 1978. 48.95 (ISBN 0-87933-318-9). Van Nos Reinhold.

AERIAL PHOTOGRAPHY IN GEOLOGY

Allum, J. A. Photogeology & Regional Mapping. 1966. 25.00 (ISBN 0-08-012033-4); pap. 9.95 (ISBN 0-08-012032-6). Pergamon.

Pandey. Principles & Applications of Photogeology. 1985. 29.95 (ISBN 0-470-20126-6). Wiley.

Strandberg, Carl H. Aerial Discovery Manual. LC 67-19945. (Photographic Science & Technology & the Graphic Arts Ser.). 249p. 1967. pap. 42.95x (ISBN 0-471-83170-0, Pub. by Wiley-Interscience). Wiley.

AERIAL PROPELLERS

see Propellers, Aerial

AERIAL ROCKETS

see Rockets (Aeronautics); Rockets (Ordnance)

AEROBIOLOGY

see Air–Microbiology

AERODROMES

see Airports

AERODYNAMIC FORCES

see Drag (Aerodynamics)

AERODYNAMIC HEATING

see also Space Vehicles–Atmospheric Entry

Daubert, T. E. Chemical Engineering Thermodynamics. (Chemical Engineering Ser.). 496p. 1985. 40.00 (ISBN 0-07-015413-9). McGraw.

Predvoditelev, A. S., ed. Physics of Heat Exchange & Gas Dynamics. LC 62-12858. 99p. 1963. 25.00x (ISBN 0-306-10574-8, Consultants). Plenum Pub.

AERODYNAMICS

see also Aerodynamics, Supersonic; Aerodynamics, Transonic; Aeroelasticity; Aeronautics; Boundary Layer; Drag (Aerodynamics); Gas Flow; Turbulence; Wind Tunnels

Abbott, Ira H. & Von Doenhoff, Albert E. Theory of Wing Sections: Including a Summary of Airfoil Data. (Illus.). 1949. pap. 9.95 (ISBN 0-486-60586-8). Dover.

Advances in Road Vehicle Aerodynamics. 1973. pap. 38.00x (ISBN 0-900983-26-4, Dist. by Air Science Co.). BHRA Fluid.

Aerodynamic Decelerator & Balloon Technology Conference: Proceedings, 8th, Hyannis MA, April 1984. (Illus.). 266p. 1984. 50.00 (ISBN 0-317-36864-8, CP843); members 40.00 (ISBN 0-317-36865-6). AIAA.

Aerodynamik der Reinen Unterschallstromung. (Flugtechnische Reihe: No. 1). (Ger., Illus.). 324p. 1979. 48.95x (ISBN 0-8176-1073-1). Birkhauser.

Aeronautique, Astronautique, Aerodynamique. Anglais Technique. (Fr. & Eng.). 268p. (Technical English: Aeronautics, Astronauts, Aerodynamics). 1976. pap. 32.50 (ISBN 0-686-56754-4, M-6000). French & Eur.

Aerothermodynamics of Gas Turbine & Rocket Propulsion. LC 84-11152. (Illus.). 412p. 1984. 45.00 (ISBN 0-915928-87-6). AIAA.

AIAA Thirteenth Aerodynamic Testing Conference. (Illus.). 342p. 1984. 65.00 (ISBN 0-317-36850-8, CP841); members 50.00 (ISBN 0-317-36851-6). AIAA.

Allen, John E. Aerodynamics: The Science of Fluid in Motion. 2nd ed. (Illus.). 205p. 1982. 27.50 (ISBN 0-07-001074-9). McGraw.

Ashley, Holt & Landahl, Marten. Aerodynamics of Wings & Bodies. 288p. 1985. pap. 6.95 (ISBN 0-486-64899-0). Dover.

Automobile Aerodynamics: Wakes, Wind Effect, Vehicle Development. 136p. 1984. 18.00 (ISBN 0-89883-340-X, SP569). Soc Auto Engineers.

Aynsley, R. M., et al. Architectural Aerodynamics. (Illus.). 254p. 1977. 40.75 (ISBN 0-85334-698-4, Pub. by Elsevier Applied Sci England). Elsevier.

Beer, J. M. & Chigier, N. A. Combustion Aerodynamics. LC 82-13084. 274p. 1982. Repr. of 1972 ed. lib. bdg. 19.50 (ISBN 0-89874-545-4). Krieger.

Bertin, John J. & Smith, Michael L. Aerodynamics for Engineers. (Illus.). 1979. text ed. 38.95 (ISBN 0-13-018234-6). P-H.

Bollinger, L. E. & Goldsmith, M., eds. Liquid Rockets & Propellants. LC 60-16913. (Illus.). 682p. 1970. 34.00 (ISBN 0-317-36836-2); members 17.50 (ISBN 0-317-36837-0). AIAA.

Bonney, E. A. Aerodynamics, Propulsion, Structures, & Design Practice. LC 56-9727. 595p. 1956. 29.50 (ISBN 0-442-00896-1, Pub. by Van Nos Reinhold). Krieger.

Bouhuys, Arend, ed. Airway Dynamics: Physiology & Pharmacology. (Illus.). 360p. 1970. photocopy ed. 54.50x (ISBN 0-398-00200-2). C C Thomas.

Bridge Aerodynamics. 140p. 1981. 90.00x (ISBN 0-7277-0135-5, Pub. by Tech Pr). State Mutual Bk.

Cebeci, T., ed. Numerical & Physical Aspects of Aerodynamic Flows, Pt. II. (Illus.). 500p. 1964. 64.00 (ISBN 0-387-12659-7). Springer-Verlag.

--Numerical & Physical Aspects of Aerodynamic Flows, California State University 1981: Proceedings. (Illus.). 636p. 1983. 84.00 (ISBN 0-387-11044-5). Springer-Verlag.

Clancy, Laurence J. Aerodynamics. LC 73-15266. 610p. 1975. text ed. 34.95x (ISBN 0-470-15837-9). Halsted Pr.

Danenshyar, M. One-Dimensional Compressible Flow. 1977. text ed. 35.00 (ISBN 0-08-020414-7); pap. text ed. 11.75 (ISBN 0-08-020413-9). Pergamon.

Dictionary of Aerodynamics. (Eng. & Chinese.). 250p. 1974. pap. 5.95 (ISBN 0-686-92380-4, M-9595). French & Eur.

Dole, Charles E. Flight Theory & Aerodynamcs: A Practical Guide for Operational Safety. LC 81-3009. 299p. 1981. 42.95x (ISBN 0-471-09152-9, Pub. by Wiley-Interscience). Wiley.

Dumas, R. & Fulachier, L., eds. Structure of Complex Turbulent Shear Flow: Marseille, France, 1982, Proceedings. (IUTLM Symposium). (Illus.). 444p. 1983. 42.00 (ISBN 0-387-12156-0). Springer-Verlag.

Durand, W. Fredrick, ed. Aerodynamic Theory: A General View of Progress, 6 vols. Incl. Vol. 1. Mathematical Aids, Fluid Mechanics, Historical Sketch. 16.00 (ISBN 0-8446-0603-0); Vol. 2. General Aerodynamic Theory, Perfect Fluids. 16.00 (ISBN 0-8446-0604-9); Vol. 3. Theory of Single Burbling, Mechanics of Viscous Fluids, Etc. 16.00 (ISBN 0-8446-0605-7); Vol. 4. Applied Airfoil Theory, Airplane Body Drag & Influence, Etc. 16.00 (ISBN 0-8446-0606-5); Vol. 5. Dynamics of the Airplane, Airplane Performance. 16.00 (ISBN 0-8446-0607-3); Vol. 6. Airplanes As a Whole, Aerodynamics of Airships, Etc. 16.00 (ISBN 0-8446-0739-8). Set. 96.00 (ISBN 0-8446-0602-2). Peter Smith.

Etkin, Bernard. Dynamics of Atmospheric Flight. LC 73-165946. (Illus.). 579p. 1972. text ed. 49.00x (ISBN 0-471-24620-4). Wiley.

General Aviation Aircraft Aerodynamics. 1985. 18.00 (ISBN 0-89883-842-8, SP621). Soc Auto Engineers.

Gessow, Alfred & Myers, Garry C., Jr. Aerodynamics of the Helicopter. LC 67-26126. 1967. 28.00 (ISBN 0-8044-4275-4). Ungar.

Gostelow, J. P. Cascade Aerodynamics. (Thermodynamics & Fluid Mechanics for Mechanical Engineers Ser.). 300p. 1983. 50.00 (ISBN 0-08-020428-7); pap. 22.50 (ISBN 0-08-020427-9). Pergamon.

Hedrick, J. Karl, ed. The Dynamics of Vehicles on Roads & On Tracks: Proceedings of 8th IAVSD Symposium held at Massachusetts Institute of Technology, Cambridge, MA, August 15-19, 1983. x, 704p. 1984. pap. text ed. 45.00x (ISBN 90-265-0461-6, Pub. by Swets Pub Serv Holland). Swets North Am.

Houghton, E. I. & Carruthers, N. B. Aerodynamics for Engineering Students. 3rd ed. 704p. 1982. pap. text ed. 39.50 (ISBN 0-7131-3433-X). E Arnold.

Hurt, H. H., Jr. Aerodynamics for Naval Aviators. (Illus.). 1965. pap. 12.95 (ISBN 0-939158-00-0, Pub. by Flightshop). Aviation.

--Aerodynamics for Naval Aviators. rev. ed. 416p. 1965. pap. text ed. 9.95 (ISBN 0-939158-00-0). Flightshops.

International Symposium on the Aerodynamics & Ventilation of Vehicle Tunnels, 1st. Proceedings. 1973. text ed. 47.00x (ISBN 0-900983-28-0, Dist. by Air Science Co.). BHRA Fluid.

International Union of Theoretical & Applied Mechanics Symposium, Freiberg 1957. Boundary Layer Research. Goertler, H., ed. (Illus.). 1958. 67.90 (ISBN 0-387-02273-2). Springer-Verlag.

Kuchemann, D. The Aerodynamic Design of Aircraft: In SI/Metric Units. 1978. text ed. 89.00 (ISBN 0-08-020515-1); pap. text ed. 32.00 (ISBN 0-08-020514-3). Pergamon.

Kuethe, Arnold M. & Chow, Chuen-Yen. Foundations of Aerodynamics: Bases of Aerodynamic Design. 3rd ed. LC 76-20761. 527p. 1976. 46.45x (ISBN 0-471-50953-1). Wiley.

Landa, Henry C. Automotive Aerodynamics Handbook. 5th ed. (Illus.). 1983. 14.00 (ISBN 0-931974-11-9). FICOA.

Langewiesche, Wolfgang. Stick & Rudder. (Illus.). 1944. 16.95 (ISBN 0-07-036240-8). McGraw.

Liepmann, Hans W. & Roshko, A. Elements of Gasdynamics. LC 56-9823. 439p. 1957. text ed. 50.45 (ISBN 0-471-53460-9). Wiley.

Lin, Chia-Ch'iao, ed. Turbulent Flows & Heat Transfer. LC 58-50928. (High Speed Aerodynamics & Jet Propulsion: Vol. 5). pap. 142.30 (ISBN 0-317-09274-X, 2001132). Bks Demand UMI.

McCormick, Barnes W. Aerodynamics, Aeronautics, & Flight Mechanics. LC 79-11073. 652p. 1979. text ed. 47.45x (ISBN 0-471-03032-5). Wiley.

McRuer, Duane, et al. Aircraft Dynamics & Automatic Control. LC 73-134350. 624p. 1974. 80.00x (ISBN 0-691-08083-6). Princeton U Pr.

Milne-Thompson, L. M. Theoretical Aerodynamics. 430p. 1973. pap. text ed. 8.50 (ISBN 0-486-61980-X). Dover.

Moran, Jack. An Introduction to Theorectical & Computational Aerodynamics. LC 84-7243. 464p. 1984. 36.95 (ISBN 0-471-87491-4); write for info tchr's solution manual (ISBN 0-471-80130-5). Wiley.

Morel, T. & Miller, J., eds. Aerodynamics of Transportation II. 89p. 1983. pap. text ed. 24.00 (ISBN 0-317-03525-8, H00282); member 12.00. ASME.

Perkins, Courtland D. & Hage, R. E. Airplane Performance, Stability & Control. 493p. 1949. 47.45 (ISBN 0-471-68046-X). Wiley.

Plate, Erich J. Aerodynamic Characteristics of Atmospheric Boundary Layers. LC 70-611329. (AEC Critical Review Ser.). 191p. 1971. pap. 12.75 (ISBN 0-87079-132-X, TID-25465); microfiche 4.50 (ISBN 0-87079-133-8, TID-25465). DOE.

Prandtl, Ludwig & Tietjens, O. G. Applied Hydro & Aeromechanics. Den Hartog, Jacob P., ed. (Illus.). 1934. pap. text ed. 7.00 (ISBN 0-486-60375-X). Dover.

--Fundamentals of Hydro & Aeromechanics. Rosenhead, L., tr. (Illus.). pap. text ed. 5.50 (ISBN 0-486-60374-1). Dover.

Reed, Robert. The Streamline Era. LC 75-12995. (Illus.). 300p. 1975. 32.95 (ISBN 0-87095-053-3). Golden West.

Roed, Aage. Flight Safety Aerodynamics. 158p. 1982. 30.00x (ISBN 0-9504543-5-4, Pub. by Airlife England). State Mutual Bk.

Schafer, Joseph. Aircraft Weight & Balance. (Aviation Technician Training Course Ser.). (Illus.). 104p. 1979. pap. text ed. 5.95 (ISBN 0-89100-096-8, EA-BAL). Aviation Maintenance.

Scibor-Rylski, A. J. Road Vehicle Aerodynamics. 2nd ed. 260p. 1984. text ed. 29.95x (ISBN 0-470-20097-9). Halsted Pr.

Scorer, R. S. Environmental Aerodynamics. LC 77-23909. (Mathematics & Its Applications Ser.). 488p. 1978. 94.95x (ISBN 0-470-99270-0). Halsted Pr.

Seddon, J. & Goldsmith, E. L. Intake Aerodynamics. 256p. 1985. 60.00x (ISBN 0-00-383048-9, Pub. by Collins England). Sheridan.

Society of Automotive Engineers. Automotive Aerodynamics. LC 78-57059. 282p. 1978. Eighteen papers. 38.00 (ISBN 0-89883-104-0, PT 16). Soc Auto Engineers.

State of California, Office of Appropriate Technology. Common Sense Wind Energy. 128p. (Orig.). 1983. pap. 8.95 (ISBN 0-931790-38-7). Brick Hse Pub.

Streamline Era. 29.95 (ISBN 0-685-83399-2). Chatham Pub CA.

Symposium on Aerodynamic Noise. Aerodynamic Noise: Proceedings of AFOSR-UTIAS Symposium, Held at Toronto, 1968. LC 70-443978. pap. 113.50 (ISBN 0-317-28227-1, 2014382). Bks Demand UMI.

Symposium on Computers in Aerodynamics at the Aerodynamics Laboratories Polytechnic Institute of New York, 1979. Computers in Aerodynamics. Rubin, S. G. & Bloom, M. H., eds. 130p. 1980. 42.00 (ISBN 0-08-025426-8). Pergamon.

Thirteenth Aerodynamic Testing. 65.00 (ISBN 0-317-06651-X). AIAA.

Transonic Aerodynamics. LC 82-4027. (Illus.). 669p. 1982. 75.00 (ISBN 0-317-36808-7); members 45.00 (ISBN 0-317-36809-5). AIAA.

Truitt, Robert W. Hypersonic Aerodynamics. LC 59-8392. (Illus.). pap. 118.50 (ISBN 0-317-10423-3, 2012443). Bks Demand UMI.

Twelfth Aerodynamic Testing. 40.00 (ISBN 0-317-06665-X). AIAA.

Von Mises, Richard. Theory of Flight. 17.00 (ISBN 0-8446-2599-X). Peter Smith.

Wallis, Raymond A. Axial Flow Fans & Ducts. LC 83-3540. 431p. 1983. 52.50 (ISBN 0-471-87086-2, Pub. by Wiley-Interscience). Wiley.

Ward-Smith, A. J. Biophysical Aerodynamics & the Natural Environment. 172p. 1984. 38.95 (ISBN 0-471-90436-8). Wiley.

Wickens, A. H., ed. The Dynamics of Vehicles on Roads & On Tracks: Proceedings of the 7th IAVSD Symposium held at the University of Cambridge, UK, September 1981. x, 568p. 1982. pap. text ed. 40.00 (ISBN 90-265-0392-X, Pub. by Swets Pub Serv Holland). Swets North Am.

Wilson, R. F. & Lissaman, P. B. Aerodynamics of Wind Turbines. (Industrial Aerodynamics Ser.: Vol. 1). Date not set. price not set. Elsevier.

Woods, Leslie C. The Theory of Subsonic Plane Flow. LC 61-4283. (Cambridge Aeronautical Ser.: No. 3). pap. 154.00 (ISBN 0-317-08679-0, 2051464). Bks Demand UMI.

AERODYNAMICS, HYPERSONIC

Chernyi, G. G. Introduction to Hypersonic Flow. Probstein, Ronald F., ed. 1961. 59.50 (ISBN 0-12-170650-8). Acad Pr.

Hayes, Wallace D. & Probstein, Ronald F., eds. Hypersonic Flow Theory, Vol. 1: Inviscid Flows. 2nd ed. (Applied Mechanics & Mathematics Ser.: Vol. 5). 1966. 85.00 (ISBN 0-12-334361-5). Acad Pr.

Riddell, Frederick R., ed. Hypersonic Flow Research. LC 62-11318. (Illus.). 758p. 1962. 38.00 (ISBN 0-317-36830-3); members 19.00 (ISBN 0-317-36831-1). AIAA.

AERODYNAMICS, SUBSONIC

see Aerodynamics

AERODYNAMICS, SUPERSONIC

see also Aerodynamics, Hypersonic; Aerothermodynamics; Shock Waves; Supersonic Planes

Carafoli, E. Wing Theory in Supersonic Flow. 1969. 105.00 (ISBN 0-08-012330-9). Pergamon.

Miles, John W. The Potential Theory of Unsteady Supersonic Flow. LC 59-564. (Cambridge Monographs on Mechanics & Mathematics). pap. 58.50 (ISBN 0-317-10245-1, 2050772). Bks Demand UMI.

Predvoditelev, A. S., ed. Physics of Heat Exchange & Gas Dynamics. LC 62-12858. 99p. 1963. 25.00x (ISBN 0-306-10574-8, Consultants). Plenum Pub.

Sears, William R., ed. General Theory of High Speed Aerodynamics. LC 54-13128. (High Speed Aerodynamics & Jet Propulsion Ser.: Vol. 6). pap. 160.00 (ISBN 0-317-09241-3, 2000699). Bks Demand UMI.

AERODYNAMICS, TRANSONIC

see also Aerothermodynamics

Ferrari, Carlo & Tricomi, Francesco. Transonic Aerodynamics. Cramer, R. H., tr. LC 67-23156. 1968. 94.00 (ISBN 0-12-253950-8). Acad Pr.

Nixon, David, ed. Transonic Aerodynamics. 55.00 (ISBN 0-915928-65-5). AIAA.

Oswatitsch, K. & Rues, D., eds. Symposium Transsonicum 2. (International Union of Theoretical & Applied Mechanics). 1976. 63.80 (ISBN 0-387-07526-7). Springer-Verlag.

Symposium Transsonicum, Aachen, 1962. Proceedings. Oswatitisch, K., ed. (Eng, Ger. & Fr.). 1964. 77.90 (ISBN 0-387-03223-1). Springer-Verlag.

Trevor, H. Moulden. Fundamentals of Transonic Flow. LC 84-7381. 332p. 1984. 46.95x (ISBN 0-471-04661-2, Pub. by Wiley Interscience). Wiley.

--Pilot's Bahamas Aviation Guide, 1981. (Illus.). 480p. 1980. ring binding 12.95 (ISBN 0-686-31872-2). Pilot Pubns.

--Pilot's Bahamas Aviation Guide, 1982. (Illus.). 494p. 1981. ring binding 19.95 (ISBN 0-686-31873-0). Pilot Pubns.

--Pilot's Bahamas Aviation Guide, 1983. (Illus.). 494p. 1982. ring binding 19.95 (ISBN 0-686-40511-0). Pilot Pubns.

Cameron, Don. Ballooning Handbook. (Illus.). 174p. 1981. 15.95 (ISBN 0-7207-1220-3, Pub. by Michael Joseph). Merrimack Pub Cir.

Campbell, R. D. & Jones, J. The Microlight Flying Manual. 240p. (Orig.). 1982. pap. text ed. 21.95x (ISBN 0-246-11914-4, Pub. by Granada England). Brookfield Pub Co.

Collins, Richard L. & Bradley, Patrick E. Instrument Flying Refresher. rev. ed. (An Eleanor Friede Bk.). 304p. 1984. 17.95 (ISBN 0-02-527160-1). Macmillan.

Crane, Dale. ITP General Textbook. 542p. (Orig.). 1981. pap. 19.95 (ISBN 0-89100-241-3, ITP-GB); wkbk. 8.95 (ISBN 0-89100-242-1, ITP-GW-B); study guide 6.95 (ISBN 0-89100-201-4, ITP-GSG-B). Aviation Maintenance.

Crane, Dale, et al. ITP Powerplant Textbook. 563p. (Orig.). 1983. pap. 19.95 (ISBN 0-89100-251-0, ITP-P); wkbk. 8.95 (ISBN 0-89100-252-9, ITP-PW); study guide 6.95 (ISBN 0-89100-253-7, ITP-PSG). Aviation Maintenance.

Dickson, Ron R. Weather & Flight: An Introduction to Meteorology for Pilots. 186p. 1982. 16.95 (ISBN 0-13-947119-7); pap. 7.95 (ISBN 0-13-947101-4). P-H.

F-51 D Mustang Pilot Handbook. 3rd ed. (Illus.). pap. 9.95 (ISBN 0-912470-13-5). Flying Ent.

Federal Aviation Administration. Airframe & Powerplant Mechanics Airframe Handbook: AC 65-15A. 601p. pap. 13.00x (ISBN 0-89100-080-1). Aviation Maintenance.

--Airframe & Powerplant Mechanics Certification Guide: AC 65-2D. pap. 4.00x (ISBN 0-685-46348-6). Aviation.

--Airframe & Powerplant Mechanics General Handbook: AC 65-9A. 549p. pap. 13.00x (ISBN 0-89100-078-X). Aviation Maintenance.

--Airframe & Powerplant Mechanics Powerplant Handbook: AC 65-12A. 500p. pap. 12.00x (ISBN 0-89100-079-8). Aviation Maintenance.

--Airman's Information Manual, 1985. 20th ed. Winner, Walter P., ed. LC 70-164372. (Illus.). 312p. 1985. pap. 6.75 (ISBN 0-916413-00-4). Aviation.

--Basic Helicopter Handbook: Ac 61-13b. pap. 5.50 (ISBN 0-86677-003-8, Pub. by Cooper). Aviation.

--Flight Training Handbook: Ac 61-21a. pap. 9.00 (ISBN 0-86677-004-6, Pub. by Cooper). Aviation.

--Instrument Flying Handbook: Ac 61-27c. 1980. pap. 8.50 (ISBN 0-86677-005-4, Pub. by Cooper). Aviation.

--Pilot's Handbook of Aeronautical Knowledge: Ac 61-23b. pap. 11.00 (ISBN 0-86677-012-7, Pub. by Cooper). Aviation.

--Pilots Weight & Balance Handbook: FAA AC 91-23A. (Illus.). 1977. pap. 5.00 (ISBN 0-939158-22-1, Pub. by Cooper). Aviation.

Fletcher Aircraft Company Staff. Standard Aircraft Workers' Manual. spiral bdg. 7.50x (ISBN 0-911721-29-0, Pub. by Fletcher). Aviation.

Guerny, Gene & Skiera, Joseph A. Pilot's Handbook of Weather. 2nd ed. Reithmaier, Lawrence W., ed. LC 74-77535. (Illus.). 1974. pap. 10.95 (ISBN 0-8168-7355-0). Aero.

Haldon Books. Visualized Flight Maneuvers Handbook for Instructors & Students. (Illus.). 172p. 1980. ringbound softcover 15.00 (ISBN 0-940766-05-1, Pub. by Haldon). Aviation.

Kershner, William K. Instrument Flight Manual. 3rd ed. (Illus.). 1977. pap. 14.95 (ISBN 0-8138-0839-1). Iowa St U Pr.

--The Student Pilot's Flight Manual. 5th ed. (Illus.). 1979. pap. 16.95 (ISBN 0-8138-1610-6). Iowa St U Pr.

Kershner, William K. & O'Kelley, Genie R. The Student Pilot's Study Guide. (Illus.). 104p. 1983. pap. 17.95 (ISBN 0-8138-0821-9). Iowa St U Pr.

Kohn, Leo J., ed. Pilot's Handbook for Grumman Wildcat. (Illus.). 1979. pap. 10.95 (ISBN 0-87994-099-9, Pub. by AvPubns). Aviation.

--Pilot's Manual for B-25 Mitchell. (Illus.). 1979. pap. 10.95 (ISBN 0-87994-004-2, Pub. by AvPubns). Aviation.

Lambie, Jack. Ultralight Airmanship: How to Master the Air in an Ultralight. Markowski, Michael A., ed. LC 81-71888. (Ultralight Aviation Ser.: No. 2). (Illus., Orig.). 1984. 17.95 (ISBN 0-938716-03-4); pap. 10.95 (ISBN 0-938716-02-6). Ultralight Pubns.

Markowski, Michael A. Ultralight Aircraft: The Basic Handbook of Ultralight Aviation. 3rd, rev. ed. LC 81-60021. (Ultralight Aviation Ser.: No. 1). 320p. 1983. pap. 15.95 (ISBN 0-938716-16-6). Ultralight Pubns.

--Ultralight Aircraft: The Basic Handbook of Ultralight Aviation. 3rd, rev. ed. LC 83-50244. (Ultralight Aviation Ser.: No. 1). (Illus., Orig.). 1983. pap. 15.95 (ISBN 0-938716-16-6). Ultralight Pubns.

--Ultralight Flight: The Pilot's Handbook of Ultralight Knowledge. LC 81-71889. (Ultralight Aviation Ser.: No. 3). (Illus.). 206p. (Orig.). 1984. 20.95 (ISBN 0-938716-07-7); pap. 13.95 (ISBN 0-938716-06-9). Ultralight Pubns.

Oliver, Robert. Pilots Handbook of Mexico & Central America. 1978. ring bnd. 18.50 (ISBN 0-911721-25-8, Pub. by G &O Pubs). Aviation.

Pan American Navigation Service Staff, ed. Airline Transport Pilot. 4th rev. & exp. ed. LC 63-11061. (The Zweng Manuals). (Illus.). 564p. 1981. soft bdg. 18.95 (ISBN 0-87219-004-8). Pan Am Nav.

Reithmaier, Larry, ed. Aviation Mechanics Certification Guide. LC 80-11630. (Illus.). 1980. 6.95 (ISBN 0-932882-01-3). Palomar Bks.

Rice, Michael S., ed. Instruction Manual for Ford Trimotor Airplane. pap. 7.95 (ISBN 0-87994-023-9). Aviation.

Robertson, Bruce. Aviation Enthusiasts Data Book. (Illus.). 1984. pap. 9.95 (ISBN 0-8253-0208-0). Beaufort Bks NY.

Sendak, Maurice. Ten Little Rabbits. pap. 2.50 (ISBN 0-939084-09-0, Pub. by Rosenbach Mus & Lib). U Pr of Va.

Welch, John F., ed. Van Sickle's Modern Airmanship. 5th ed. 896p. 1980. 26.95 (ISBN 0-442-25793-7). Van Nos Reinhold.

AERONAUTICS–HISTORY

Adams, Harry B. Propjet 1984. (Illus.). 142p. 1984. pap. 5.95 (ISBN 0-941024-08-3). Avcom Intl.

Aeroplane (or Flying Machine) Scrap Book: Amazing Developments in American Aeronautics 1911-1939. pap. 4.50 (ISBN 0-87505-215-0). Borden.

Air Force Colors: Nineteen Twenty-Six to Nineteen Forty-Two. 1980. pap. 7.95 (ISBN 0-89747-091-5). Squad Sig Pubns.

Bilstein, Roger. Flight Patterns: Trends of Aeronautical Development in the United States, 1918-1929. (Illus.). 248p. 18.50 (ISBN 0-8203-0670-3). U of Ga Pr.

Bowen, Ezra. Knights of the Air. Time-Life Books, ed. (Epic of Flight Ser.). (Illus.). 1980. 14.95 (ISBN 0-8094-3250-1). Time-Life.

Brown, Warren J. Florida's Aviation History. 1980. pap. 6.95 (ISBN 0-912522-70-4). Aero-Medical.

Bruno, Harry. Wings Over America: The Inside Story of American Aviation. 1942. 30.00 (ISBN 0-932062-21-0). Sharon Hill.

Bryan, C. D. National Air & Space Museum. (Illus.). 1979. 60.00 (ISBN 0-8109-0666-X). Abrams.

Callahan, Neal & Young, David. Fill the Heavens with Commerce: Chicago Aviation 1855 to 1926. (Illus.). 250p. 1981. 15.00 (ISBN 0-914090-99-2). Chicago Review.

Christy, Joe. Illustrated Handbook of Aviation & Aerospace Facts. (Illus.). 720p. (Orig.). 1984. pap. 29.50 (ISBN 0-8306-2397-3, 2397). TAB Bks.

Clouston, A. E. The Dangerous Skies. Gilbert, James, ed. LC 79-7240. (Flight: Its First Seventy-Five Years Ser.). (Illus.). 1979. Repr. of 1954 ed. 17.00x (ISBN 0-405-12155-5). Ayer Co Pubs.

Compton, Joy B. A Decade of Glory. (Illus.). 64p. 1983. 10.50 (ISBN 0-89962-322-0). Todd & Honeywell.

Corlett, John. Aviation in Ulster. (Illus.). 148p. 1981. pap. 8.95 (ISBN 0-85640-252-4, Pub. by Blackstaff Pr). Longwood Pub Group.

Cottam, K. J., ed. & tr. In the Sky Above the Front. (Illus.). 270p. 1984. pap. text ed. 31.00x (ISBN 0-89126-126-5). MA-AH Pub.

Crouch, Thomas. The Giant Leap: A Chronology of Ohio Aerospace Events & Personalities, 1915-1969. (Illus.). 77p. 1971. pap. 0.50 (ISBN 0-318-00826-2). Ohio Hist Soc.

Crouch, Tom D. A Dream of Wings: Americans & the Airplane, Eighteen Seventy-Five to Nineteen Hundred Five. (Illus.). 1981. 15.95 (ISBN 0-393-01385-5). Norton.

Dollfus, Charles & Bouche, Henri. Histoire de l'Aeronautique: The History of Aeronautics. Gilbert, James, ed. LC 79-7246. (Flight: Its First Seventy-Five Years Ser.). (Fr., Illus.). 1979. Repr. of 1942 ed. lib. bdg. 229.00x (ISBN 0-405-12158-X). Ayer Co Pubs.

Emme, E. M., ed. Two Hundred Years of Flight in America: A Bicentennial Survey. 326p. 35.00 (ISBN 0-317-26100-2, Pub. by Am Astro Soc); pap. 25.00 (ISBN 0-317-26101-0). Univelt Inc.

Emme, Eugene M., ed. Two Hundred Years of Flight in America. (AAS History Ser.: Vol. 1). (Illus.). 1979. softcover 25.00x (Pub. by Am Astronaut); text ed. 35.00x. Univelt Inc.

--Two Hundred Years of Flight in America. 2nd ed. (AAS History Ser.: Vol. 1). (Illus.). 1977. lib. bdg. 35.00x (ISBN 0-87703-091-X); soft cover 25.00x (ISBN 0-87703-101-0). Univelt Inc.

The Explorers. LC 82-19551. (Epic of Flight Ser.). 1983. lib. bdg. 21.27 (ISBN 0-8094-3367-2, Pub. by Time-Life). Silver.

Foulois, Benjamin D. & Glines, Carroll V. From the Wright Brothers to the Astronauts: The Memoirs of Major General Benjamin D. Foulois. Gilbert, James, ed. LC 79-2191. (Flight: Its First Seventy-Five Years Ser.). (Illus.). 1979. Repr. of 1968 ed. lib. bdg. 27.50x (ISBN 0-405-12211-X). Ayer Co Pubs.

Gilbert, James, ed. Flight: Its First Seventy-Five Years, 57 bks, Vols. 1-12. (Illus.). 1979. Set. lib. bdg. 2238.50x (ISBN 0-405-12146-6). Ayer Co Pubs.

--Literature & History of Aviation Ser, 35 bks. 1972. Repr. Set. 953.00 (ISBN 0-405-03789-9). Ayer Co Pubs.

Gillispie, Charles C. The Montgolfier Brothers & the Invention of Aviation, 1783-1784: With a Word on the Importance of Ballooning for the Science of Heat & for the Art of Building Railroads. LC 82-61363. (Illus.). 272p. 1983. 35.00 (ISBN 0-691-08321-5). Princeton U Pr.

Grosser, Morton. Gossamer Odyssey: The Triumph of Human-Powered Flight. (Illus.). 288p. 1981. 14.95 (ISBN 0-395-30531-4). HM.

Hart, Clive. The Prehistory of Flight. LC 84-8677. 1985. 35.00 (ISBN 0-520-05213-7). U of Cal Pr.

Haydon, Frederick S. Aeronautics in the Union & Confederate Armies: With a Survey of Military Aeronautics Prior to 1861, Vol. I. Gilbert, James, ed. LC 79-7271. (Flight: Its First Seventy-Five Years Ser.). (Illus.). 1979. Repr. of 1941 ed. lib. bdg. 44.00x (ISBN 0-405-12181-4). Ayer Co Pubs.

Historical Aviation Album, Vol. 17. LC 84-16736. (Illus.). 96p. 1984. pap. 10.00 (ISBN 0-911852-16-6). Hist Aviation.

Hudson, Kenneth & Pettifer, Julian. Diamonds in the Sky: A Social History of Air Travel. 240p. 1981. 19.95 (ISBN 0-370-30162-5, Pub. by the Bodley Head). Merrimack Pub Cir.

Hunsaker, Jerome C. Aeronautics at the Mid-Century. 1952. 39.50x (ISBN 0-685-89732-X). Elliots Bks.

Huttig, Jack. Nineteen Twenty-Seven: Summer of Eagles. LC 79-16462. (Illus.). 160p. 1980. 28.95x (ISBN 0-88229-525-X). Nelson-Hall.

Ingells, Douglas J. L-Ten Eleven-Tristar & the Lockheed Story. LC 73-83065. (Illus.). 256p. 1973. o. p. 13.95 (ISBN 0-8168-6650-3); pap. 10.95 (ISBN 0-8168-6651-1). Aero.

Jablonski, E. America in the Air War. LC 82-5539. (Epic of Flight Ser.). lib. bdg. 21.27 (ISBN 0-8094-3342-7, Pub. by Time-Life). Silver.

Jackson, Donald. The Explorers. (The Epic of Flight Ser.). (Illus.). 176p. 1983. 14.95 (ISBN 0-8094-3366-4). Time Life.

--Flying the Mail. (Epic of Flight Ser.). 1982. 14.95 (ISBN 0-8094-3329-X). Time-Life.

Jackson, Donald D. Flying the Mail. LC 82-2020. (Epic of Flight Ser.). lib. bdg. 21.27 (ISBN 0-8094-3330-3, Pub. by Time-Life). Silver.

Johnson, Clarence L. & Smith, Maggie. Kelly: More Than My Share of It All. Geary, Leo, intro. by. LC 84-600316. (Illus.). 210p. 1985. 17.50 (ISBN 0-87474-564-0, JOKM). Smithsonian.

Kohn, Leo J. Story of the AT-6 Texan. 1975. pap. 6.95 (ISBN 0-87994-034-4, Pub. by AvPubns). Aviation.

Lambert, W. C. Barnstorming & Girls. 1980. pap. text ed. 15.00x (ISBN 0-89745-010-8). Sunflower U Pr.

LePage, W. Lawrence. Growing up with Aviation. 212p. 1981. 12.00 (ISBN 0-8059-2801-4). Dorrance.

Lewis, Cecil. Farewell to Wings. Gibert, James, ed. LC 79-7279. (Flight: Its First Seventy-Five Years Ser.). (Illus.). 1979. Repr. of 1964 ed. lib. bdg. 12.00x (ISBN 0-405-12188-1). Ayer Co Pubs.

Lewis, Peter. British Bomber Since Nineteen Fourteen. rev., 3rd ed. (Putnam Aeronautical Bks.). (Illus.). 432p. 1980. 21.95 (ISBN 0-370-30265-6, Pub. by the Bodley Head). Merrimack Pub Cir.

--British Fighter Since Nineteen Twelve. 4th ed. (Putnam Aeronautical Bks.). (Illus.). 416p. 1980. 21.95 (ISBN 0-370-30250-8, Pub. by the Bodley Head). Merrimack Pub Cir.

Magoun, F. A. & Hodgins, Eric. History of Aircraft. LC 70-169431. (Literature & History of Aviation Ser). 1972. Repr. of 1931 ed. 31.00 (ISBN 0-405-03774-0). Ayer Co Pubs.

Maloney, Edward. Boeing P-26 Peashooter. LC 72-85152. (Aero Ser.: Vol. 22). (Illus.). 1973. pap. 3.95 (ISBN 0-8168-0584-9). Aero.

Matt, Paul R. Historical Aviation Album, Vol.15. Rust, Kenn C. & Foxworth, Thomas G., eds. (All American Collector's Ser.). (Illus.). 1977. pap. 7.50 (ISBN 0-911852-14-X, Pub. by Hist Aviation). Aviation.

Messimer, Dwight R. No Margin for Error: The U. S. Navy's Transpacific Flight of 1925. LC 80-84063. (Illus.). 176p. 1981. 15.95 (ISBN 0-87021-497-7). Naval Inst Pr.

Meyers, John. Airways to Airlines: 50 Year History of Commercial Aviation. (Illus.). 1975. pap. 4.95 (ISBN 0-911720-95-2, Pub. by Allicraft). Aviation.

Miller, Ronald E. & Sawers, David. The Technical Development of Modern Aviation. (Airlines History Project Ser.). Date not set. Repr. of 1968 ed. 42.50 (ISBN 0-404-19328-5). AMS Pr.

Mondey, David & Taylor, Michael. Milestones of Flight. (Illus.). 320p. 1983. pap. 10.95 (ISBN 0-86720-666-7). Jane's Pub Inc.

Moolman, Valerie. The Road to Kitty Hawk. Time-Life Books, ed. (Epic of Flight Ser.). (Illus.). 176p. 1980. 14.95 (ISBN 0-8094-3258-7). Time-Life.

Morrow, John H., Jr. German Airpower in World War I. LC 81-11588. (Illus.). xiv, 275p. 1982. 21.50x (ISBN 0-8032-3076-1). U of Nebr Pr.

Mudge, Robert W. Adventures of a Yellowbird. (Airlines History Project Ser.). Date not set. Repr. of 1969 ed. 39.50 (ISBN 0-404-19329-3). AMS Pr.

Newton, Wesley P. The Perilous Sky: Evolution of United States Aviation Diplomacy Toward Latin America, 1919-1931. LC 77-84781. (Illus.). 1978. text ed. 20.00 (ISBN 0-87024-298-9). U of Miami Pr.

Ogilvy, David. The Shuttleworth Collection. 1982. 42.00x (ISBN 0-906393-18-3, Pub. by Airlife England). State Mutual Bk.

O'Neil, Paul. Barnstormers & Speed Kings. Time-Life Bks. Eds., ed. (The Epic of Flight Ser.). (Illus.). 176p. 1981. 14.95 (ISBN 0-8094-3275-7). Time-Life.

Penrose, Harald. British Aviation: The Adventuring Years Nineteen Twenty to Nineteen Twenty-Nine. (Putnam Aeronautical Books). (Illus.). 734p. 1979. 31.95 (ISBN 0-370-10016-6, Pub. by the Bodley Head). Merrimack Pub Cir.

Prendergast, Curt. The First Aviators. (The Epic of Flight). (Illus.). 176p. (Orig.). 1981. 14.95 (ISBN 0-8094-3262-5). Time-Life.

Rausa, Rosario. The Blue Angels: An Illustrated History. (Illus.). 1979. 14.50 (ISBN 0-911721-82-7, Pub. by Moran). Aviation.

Reinhold, Ruth M. Sky Pioneering: Arizona in Aviation History. LC 81-11514. (Illus.). 232p. 1982. 22.50 (ISBN 0-8165-0737-6); pap. 10.95 (ISBN 0-8165-0757-0). U of Ariz Pr.

Rosenberry, C. R. The Challenging Skies: The Colorful Story of Aviation's Most Exciting Years, 1919-1939. Gilbert, James, ed. LC 79-7294. (Flight: Its First Seventy-Five Years Ser.). (Illus.). 1979. Repr. of 1966 ed. lib. bdg. 73.50x (ISBN 0-405-12201-2). Ayer Co Pubs.

Rowe, Basil. Under My Wings. (Airlines History Project Ser.). Date not set. Repr. of 1946 ed. 30.00 (ISBN 0-404-19333-1). AMS Pr.

Rust, Kenn C. Twelfth Air Force Story. (Illus.). 64p. 1975. pap. 7.95 (ISBN 0-911852-77-8, Pub. by Hist Aviation). Aviation.

Seagrave, Sterling. The Bush Pilots. LC 82-19155. (Epic of Flight Ser.). 1983. lib. bdg. 21.27 (ISBN 0-8094-3309-5, Pub. by Time-Life). Silver.

Seven Decades of Progress: History of G. E. Engine Group. LC 79-6349. 238p. 1980. 29.95 (ISBN 0-8168-8355-6). Aero.

Sims, Edward H. Fighter Tactics & Strategy Nineteen Fourteen to Nineteen Seventy. 2nd ed. LC 80-68106. (Illus.). 266p. 1980. 12.95 (ISBN 0-8168-8795-0). Aero.

Smith, Henry L. Airways Abroad: The Story of American World Air Routes. (Airlines History Project Ser.). Date not set. Repr. of 1950 ed. 40.00 (ISBN 0-404-19336-6). AMS Pr.

Smith, Myron J., Jr. Air War Bibliography, 1939-1945: English Language Sources, Vol. 4, Pt. 6-the Aircraft. (Illus.). 265p. 1978. pap. text ed. 30.00x (ISBN 0-89126-056-0). MA-AH Pub.

Stoewer, H. & Bainum, P. M., eds. From Spacelab to Space Station: Fifth DGLR-AAS Symposium, Oct. 3-5, 1984, Hamburg, Gemany. (Advances in the Astronautical Sciences Ser.: Vol. 56). 270p. 1984. 50.00 (ISBN 0-317-27273-X); pap. 40.00 (ISBN 0-317-27274-8). Univelt Inc.

Stoewer, H. & Bainum, Peter M., eds. From Spacelab to Space Station. (Advances in the Astronautical Sciences Ser.: Vol. 56). (Illus.). 270p. (Orig.). 1985. lib. bdg. 50.00 (ISBN 0-87703-209-2, Pub by Am Astro Soc); pap. text ed. 40.00 (ISBN 0-87703-210-6). Univelt Inc.

Taylor, Michael. Fantastic Flying Machines. (Illus.). 144p. 1982. 12.95 (ISBN 0-86720-552-0). Jane's Pub Inc.

Taylor, Michael & Mondey, David. Giants in the Sky. (Illus.). 216p. 1982. 17.95 (ISBN 0-86720-626-8). Jane's Pub Inc.

Titler, Dalem. Wings of Mystery: True Stories of Aviation History. rev. ed. LC 81-810. (Illus.). 1981. 10.95 (ISBN 0-396-07826-5). Dodd.

Trimble, William F. High Frontier: A History of Aeronautics in Pennsylvania. LC 81-70218. (Illus.). 392p. (Orig.). 1982. pap. 12.95 (ISBN 0-8229-5340-4). U of Pittsburgh Pr.

Turner, C. C. Old Flying Days. LC 74-169440. (Literature & History of Aviation Ser). 1971. Repr. of 1927 ed. 30.00 (ISBN 0-405-03783-X). Ayer Co Pubs.

Verdon-Roe, Alliott. The World of Wings & Things. Gilbert, James, ed. LC 79-7293. (Flight: Its First Seventy-Five Years Ser.). (Illus.). 1979. Repr. of 1939 ed. lib. bdg. 23.00x (ISBN 0-405-12200-4). Ayer Co Pubs.

Vergnano, Piero. Origin of Aviation in Italy, 1783-1918. (Illus.). 1964. 15.00 (ISBN 0-913076-19-8). Beachcomber Bks.

Wagner, Ray. The Story of the PBY Catalina Flying Boat. pap. 3.50 (ISBN 0-911721-30-4, Pub. by FC). Aviation.

Wise, John. Through the Air: A Narrative of Forty Years' Experience As an Aeronaut. LC 79-169444. (Literature & History of Aviation Ser). 1971. Repr. of 1873 ed. 40.00 (ISBN 0-405-03787-2). Ayer Co Pubs.

Wooldridge, E. T. Winged Wonders: The Story of the Flying Wings. (Illus.). 230p. 1983. 25.00 (ISBN 0-87474-966-2); pap. 14.95 (ISBN 0-87474-967-0). Smithsonian.

Wragg, David W. Speed in the Air: A History of Aviation. (Illus.). 192p. 1974. 15.95x (ISBN 0-8464-0879-1). Beekman Pubs.

AERONAUTICS–LAW AND LEGISLATION

Department of Aviation Education. Federal Aviation Regulations. 3rd. ed. LC 80-67616. 1982. pap. 3.95 (ISBN 0-912682-32-9). Aero Products.

Doberstein, Dick. Regulations Made Easy for Commercial Pilots. 1984. pap. text ed. 5.95 (ISBN 0-9607866-0-0). Simplified Reg.

--Regulations Made Easy for Instrument Pilots. 1984. pap. text ed. 5.95 (ISBN 0-9607866-1-9). Simplified Reg.

--Regulations Made Easy for Private Pilots. 1984. pap. text ed. 5.95 (ISBN 0-9607866-4-3). Simplified Reg.

Enga, John. Aircraft Inspection & Maintenance Records. (Aviation Technician Training Course Ser.). 92p. (Orig.). 1979. pap. text ed. 5.95 (ISBN 0-89100-094-1, EA-IAR). Aviation Maintenance.

Federal Aviation Administration Staff. Federal Aviation Regulations for Pilots, 1985. 9th ed. Winner, Walter P., ed. 216p. 1985. pap. 4.95 (ISBN 0-911721-99-1). Aviation.

Ground Training for the Private Pilot Licence, No. 1: Air Legislation, Aviation Law, Flight Rules & Procedure. 182p. 1985. pap. 20.00x (ISBN 0-00-383112-4, Pub. by collins England). Sheridan.

Haanappel, P. P. Pricing & Capacity Determination in International Air Transport. 1984. pap. text ed. 38.40 (ISBN 90-6544-154-9, Pub. by Kluwer Law Netherlands). Kluwer Academic.

Heere, Wybo P. International Bibliography of Air Law: Supplement 1977-1980. 394p. 1981. lib. bdg. 69.50 (ISBN 90-247-2555-0, Pub. by Martinus Nijhoff Netherlands). Kluwer Academic.

Kean, A. Essays in Air Law. 1982. lib. bdg. 74.00 (ISBN 90-247-2543-7, Pub. by Martinus Nijhoff Netherlands). Kluwer Academic.

Knauth, Christopher R. & Leuzzi, J. P., eds. U. S. Aviation Reports. 1974. Vols. 47, 1928-1967. lib. bdg. 50.00 ea.; Vols. 32, 1968-1981. lib. bdg. 45.00 ea. (ISBN 0-379-14100-0); Cumulative Digest, 4th, 4 vols. lib. bdg. 100.00 ea.; Set 83 vols. lib. bdg. 3560.00. Oceana.

Pucci, Gerard. Aviation Law: Fundamental Cases. 4th ed. 1981. pap. text ed. 15.95 (ISBN 0-8403-2535-5). Kendall Hunt.

White, Irvin L. Decision-Making for Space: Law & Politics in Air, Sea, & Outer Space. LC 77-109153. 304p. 1970. 6.50 (ISBN 0-911198-24-5). Purdue U Pr.

White, Jay C. Pilots & Aircraft Owners Legal Guide. 4th ed. 125p. 1984. pap. 9.95 (ISBN 0-939426-01-3). Aviation.

AERONAUTICS–NAVIGATION

see Navigation (Aeronautics)

AERONAUTICS–PICTORIAL WORKS

James, Derek N. Schneider Trophy Aircraft Nineteen Thirteen to Nineteen Thirty-One. (Putnam Aeronautical). (Illus.). 200p. 1981. 38.00 (ISBN 0-370-30328-8, Pub. by the Bodley Head). Merrimack Pub Cir.

Seo, Hiroshi. Civil Aircraft of the World. (Illus.). 96p. 1982. 12.95 (ISBN 0-86720-558-X). Jane's Pub Inc.

Skogsberg, Bertil. Wings on the Screen. Bisset, George, tr. from Swedish. LC 81-4790. (Illus.). 192p. cancelled (ISBN 0-498-02495-4). A S Barnes.

Stevenson, J. Northrop F-Eighteen Hornet. (Aero Ser.). 104p. pap. write for info (ISBN 0-8168-0608-X). Aero.

Taylor, Michael & Mondey, David. Giants in the Sky. (Illus.). 216p. 1982. 17.95 (ISBN 0-86720-626-8). Jane's Pub Inc.

Xaudaro, J. Perils of Flight. LC 78-24054. (Illus.). 1979. Repr. of 1911 ed. 8.95 (ISBN 0-8317-6810-X, Mayflower Bks). Smith Pubs.

AERONAUTICS–RESEARCH

see Aeronautical Research

AERONAUTICS–SAFETY MEASURES

see also Air Traffic Control

Aircraft Electrical Systems Maintenance Operations. (Four Hundred Ser). 1968. pap. 2.00 (ISBN 0-685-58061-X, 410A). Natl Fire Prot.

Aircraft Hand Fire Extinguishers. (Four Hundred Ser.). 1973. pap. 2.00 (ISBN 0-685-58062-8, 408). Natl Fire Prot.

Aircraft Interior Fire Protection Systems. (Four Hundred Ser.). 1973. pap. 2.00 (ISBN 0-685-58219-1, 421). Natl Fire Prot.

Anderson, Eric. Plane Safety & Survival. LC 78-8247. 1978. 7.95 (ISBN 0-8168-7508-1); pap. 5.95 (ISBN 0-8168-7510-3). Aero.

Aviation Ground Operation Safety Handbook. 3rd ed. LC 77-74161. 132p. 1977. 24.25 (ISBN 0-87912-028-2, 129.62). Natl Safety Coun.

Bellomo, Chas & Lynch, John. Crash, Fire & Rescue Handbook. (Pilot Training Ser.). 94p. (Orig.). 1984. pap. text ed. 8.95 (ISBN 0-89100-250-2, EA-250-2). Aviation Maintenance.

Birch, N. H. & Bramson, A. E. The Pilot's Guide to Flight Emergency Procedures. LC 77-91556. (Illus.). 1978. 7.95 (ISBN 0-385-13544-0). Doubleday.

Corporate Aviation Safety Seminar. Managing Corporate Aviation Safety: Proceedings, 27th Annual Meeting, April 4-6, 1982, Houston Texas. pap. 41.00 (ISBN 0-317-29060-6, 2017828). Bks Demand UMI.

--Safety in the Terminal Environment: Proceedings, 23rd Annual Meeting, April 9-12, 1978, Arlington Va. pap. 33.50 (ISBN 0-317-10145-5, 2010339). Bks Demand UMI.

Delp, Frank. Commercial Pilot Question Book Including Answers, Explanations, & References. rev. ed. (Pilot Training Ser.). 475p. 1985. pap. text ed. 12.95 (ISBN 0-89100-261-8, EA-FAA-T-8080-2C). Aviation Maintenance.

Enga, John. Aircraft Inspection & Maintenance Records. (Aviation Technician Training Course Ser.). 92p. (Orig.). 1979. pap. text ed. 5.95 (ISBN 0-89100-094-1, EA-IAR). Aviation Maintenance.

Federal Aviation Administration. Aircraft Inspection, Repair & Alterations: AC 43.13-1A & 43.13-2a. 449p. pap. 11.50 (ISBN 0-89100-081-X). Aviation Maintenance.

Flight Safety Foundation. What Is Safe: Corporate Aviation Safety Seminar Proceedings, 28th Annual Meeting, April 17-19, 1983, Fairmont Hotel, New Orleans, Louisiana. pap. 53.00 (ISBN 0-317-29629-9, 2021549). Bks Demand UMI.

General Aviation Ground Operation Safety Handbook. LC 82-81228. 78p. 27.50 (ISBN 0-87912-027-4, 129.60). Natl Safety Coun.

Ground Training for the Private Pilot Licence, No. 4: Specific Aircraft Type, Fire, First Aid & Safety Equipment, Aeromedical Facts. 1982. 18.00x (ISBN 0-246-11704-4, Pub. by Granada England). Sheridan.

Heller, William. Airline Safety: A View from the Cockpit. 120p. 1984. 11.95 (ISBN 0-917613-00-7); pap. 8.95 (ISBN 0-917613-01-5). Rulorca.

Hurst, Leslie & Hurst, Ronald, eds. Fly & Survive: Safety in General Aviation. (Illus.). 208p. 1985. 26.50x (ISBN 0-00-383029-2, Pub. by Collins England). Sheridan.

IFSTA Committee. Aircraft Fire Protection & Rescue Procedures: 206. 2nd ed. Williams, Connie & Laughlin, Jerry, eds. LC 78-52898. (Illus.). 244p. 1978. pap. text ed. 10.00 (ISBN 0-87939-025-5). Intl Fire Serv.

International Air Safety Seminar. Human Factors in Managing Aviation Safety: Proceedings of the 37th Annual Meeting. pap. 70.00 (ISBN 0-317-26167-3, 2025190). Bks Demand UMI.

International Air Safety Seminar Staff. Safety Needs in the Terminal Environment: Proceedings of the 30th Annual International Air Safety Seminar, Ottawa, 1977. pap. 58.00 (ISBN 0-317-10944-8, 2006140). Bks Demand UMI.

International Air Safety Seminar, 1983. Meeting Aviation's Safety Challenges: Proceedings of the 36th Annual Meeting. pap. 79.00 (ISBN 0-317-20513-7, 2022874). Bks Demand UMI.

Johnson, Daniel A. Just in Case: A Passenger's Guide to Airplane Safety & Survival. 300p. 1984. (full discount avail.) 16.95 (ISBN 0-306-41576-3, Plenum Pr). Plenum Pub.

Knauth, Percy. Safety in the Skies. (Illus.). 166p. 1982. pap. 9.95 (ISBN 0-8306-2341-8, 2341). TAB Bks.

Low-Altitude Wind Shear & Its Hazard to Aviation Committee, National Research Council. Low-Altitude Wind Shear & Its Hazard to Aviation. 1983. pap. text ed. 12.50 (ISBN 0-309-03432-9). Natl Acad Pr.

Norris, William. The Unsafe Sky. 224p. 1982. 14.95 (ISBN 0-393-01596-3). Norton.

Roed, Aage. Flight Safety Aerodynamics. 158p. 1982. 30.00x (ISBN 0-9504543-5-4, Pub. by Airlife England). State Mutual Bk.

Stich, Rodney, ed. The Unfriendly Skies: An Aviation Watergate. 2nd, rev. ed. LC 79-52680. 1980. pap. 15.95 (ISBN 0-932438-02-4). Diablo West Pr.

Stoffel, Robert & LaValle, Patrick. Survival Sense for Pilots. LC 80-70906. (Illus.). 160p. 1980. pap. 7.95 (ISBN 0-913724-24-6, Pub. by Emergency Response). Aviation.

AERONAUTICS–STUDY AND TEACHING

see also Aeronautical Research; Flight Training

Crane, Dale. Technical Instruction. 209p. 1981. pap. text ed. 12.95 (ISBN 0-89100-183-2, EA-183-2). Aviation Maintenance.

Department of Aviation Education. Flight Training Manual. LC 80-70568. 1981. pap. 9.95 (ISBN 0-912682-28-0). Aero Products.

FAA Department of Transportation. Aviation Instructor's Handbook (AC 60.14) (Illus.). 124p. (Orig.). 1977. pap. text ed. 6.00 (ISBN 0-941272-02-8). Astro Pubs.

FAA, Department of Transportation. Fundamentals of Instructing Flight & Ground Instructors. (Illus.). 112p. 1979. pap. text ed. 8.95 (ISBN 0-941272-12-5, AP 490). Astro Pubs.

Federal Aviation Administration. Aviation Instructors Handbook. rev. ed. 123p. 1977. pap. text ed. 3.50 (ISBN 0-939158-03-5). Flightshops.

--Flight Training Handbook: Ac 61-21a. pap. 9.00 (ISBN 0-86677-004-6, Pub. by Cooper). Aviation.

Kershner, William K. & O'Kelley, Genie R. The Student Pilot's Study Guide. (Illus.). 104p. 1983. pap. 17.95 (ISBN 0-8138-0821-9). Iowa St U Pr.

Maher, Gay D. The Joy of Learning to Fly. 1983. 9.95 (ISBN 0-02-579320-9). Macmillan.

AERONAUTICS–TERMINOLOGY

Aviation Language School Inc. Intermediate Aeronautical Language Manual. 124p. 1978. pap. text ed. 15.95 (ISBN 0-941456-01-3). Aviation Lang Sch.

--Primary Aeronautical Language Manual. 201p. 1980. pap. text ed. 29.95 (ISBN 0-941456-00-5). Aviation Lang Sch.

Balter, Deborah J. Intermediate Aeronautical Language Manual. 1978. pap. 14.95 (ISBN 0-941456-01-3). Aviation.

--Primary Aeronautical Language Manual. 1980. pap. 30.95 (ISBN 0-941456-00-5). Aviation.

AERONAUTICS–VOCATIONAL GUIDANCE

Educational Research Council of America. Airplane Machinist. Ferris, Theodore N. & Marchak, John P., eds. (Real People at Work Ser.: R). (Illus.). 36p. 1977. 2.70 (ISBN 0-89247-136-0, 9627). Changing Times.

AERONAUTICS–YEARBOOKS

Jane's All the World's Aircraft, 1979-1980. 109.95 (ISBN 0-531-03915-3). Key Bk Serv.

Jensen, Harmon. Aviation Quarterly. 1984. 19.95 (ISBN 0-686-32715-2). Aviation Quarterly.

Taylor, Michael, ed. Jane's Aviation Review. 4th ed. (Jane's Reviews Ser.). (Illus.). 160p. 1985. 14.95 (ISBN 0-7106-0333-9). Jane's Pub Inc.

AERONAUTICS–ALASKA

Helmericks, Harmon. Last of the Bush Pilots. (Illus.). 1969. 15.95 (ISBN 0-394-43241-X). Knopf.

Stirling, Dale. A Bibliography of Alaskan Aviation, 1940-1984. LC 84-80776. (Orig.). pap. 3.00 (ISBN 0-913905-00-3). Heritage N Pr.

AERONAUTICS–AUSTRALIA

Joy, William. The Aviators. (Historical Ser.). (Illus.). 211p. Repr. of 1965 ed. 17.50x (ISBN 0-85558-011-9, ABC). Sportshelf.

Proceedings of the Nineteen Seventy-Nine Australian Astronautics Convention. 1981. Pt. I, 176p. pap. 20.00 (ISBN 0-317-26092-8, Pub by Astronautical Soc W Australia); Pt. II, 168p. pap. 20.00 (ISBN 0-317-26093-6). Univelt Inc.

AERONAUTICS–CANADA

Ellis, Frank H. Canada's Flying Heritage. 1980. pap. 16.95 (ISBN 0-8020-6417-5). U of Toronto Pr.

Molson, Taylor. Canadian Aircraft Since Nineteen Hundred Nine. 448p. 49.95 (ISBN 0-370-30095-5, Pub. by the Bodley Head). Merrimack Pub Cir.

AERONAUTICS–FRANCE

Feldman, Elliot J. Concorde & Dissent: Explaining High Technology Project Failures in Britain & France. (Illus.). 192p. 1985. 34.50 (ISBN 0-521-30519-5). Cambridge U Pr.

Kennett & Christienn. French Military Aviation. 1985. lib. bdg. 45.00 (ISBN 0-8240-8985-5). Garland Pub.

AERONAUTICS–GERMANY

Morrow, John H., Jr. German Airpower in World War I. LC 81-11588. (Illus.). xiv, 275p. 1982. 21.50x (ISBN 0-8032-3076-1). U of Nebr Pr.

Smith, J. R. & Kay, Antony. German Aircraft of the Second World War. (Putnam Aeronautical Bks.). (Illus.). 760p. 1979. 32.95 (ISBN 0-370-00024-2, Pub. by the Bodley Head). Merrimack Pub Cir.

AERONAUTICS–GREAT BRITAIN

Airlife Publishing Ltd., ed. Pooley's Flight Guide: United Kingdom & Ireland. 400p. 1982. 59.00x (ISBN 0-902037-07-2, Pub. by Airlife England). State Mutual Bk.

Baxter, R. E. & Phillips, C. Ports, Inland Waterways & Civil Aviation. Maunder, W. F., ed. 1979. text ed. 65.00 (ISBN 0-08-022460-1). Pergamon.

Feldman, Elliot J. Concorde & Dissent: Explaining High Technology Project Failures in Britain & France. (Illus.). 192p. 1985. 34.50 (ISBN 0-521-30519-5). Cambridge U Pr.

Kinsey, Gordon. Aviation. (Illus.). 1979. 25.00 (ISBN 0-900963-29-8, Pub. by Terence Dalton England). State Mutual Bk.

Lewis, Peter. British Bomber Since Nineteen Fourteen. rev., 3rd ed. (Putnam Aeronautical Bks.). (Illus.). 432p. 1980. 21.95 (ISBN 0-370-30265-6, Pub. by the Bodley Head). Merrimack Pub Cir.

--British Fighter Since Nineteen Twelve. 4th ed. (Putnam Aeronautical Bks.). (Illus.). 416p. 1980. 21.95 (ISBN 0-370-30250-8, Pub. by the Bodley Head). Merrimack Pub Cir.

Mason, Francis K. Harrier. 2nd ed. LC 82-62644. 201p. 1983. 19.95 (ISBN 0-87021-829-8). Naval Inst Pr.

Penrose, Harald. British Aviation: The Adventuring Years Nineteen Twenty to Nineteen Twenty-Nine. (Putnam Aeronautical Books). (Illus.). 734p. 1979. 31.95 (ISBN 0-370-10016-6, Pub. by the Bodley Head). Merrimack Pub Cir.

Sharp, Martin. The History of De-Havillands. 1982. 79.00x (ISBN 0-906393-20-5, Pub. by Airlife England). State Mutual Bk.

AERONAUTICS–ITALY

Vergnano, Piero. Origin of Aviation in Italy, 1783-1918. (Illus.). 1964. 15.00 (ISBN 0-913076-19-8). Beachcomber Bks.

AERONAUTICS–SOVIET UNION

Hardesty, Von. Red Phoenix: The Rise of Soviet Air Power 1941-1945. LC 82-600153. (Illus.). 288p. 1982. 22.50 (ISBN 0-87474-510-1). Smithsonian.

AERONAUTICS, COMMERCIAL

see also Heliports; Transport Planes

Baxter, R. E. & Phillips, C. Ports, Inland Waterways & Civil Aviation. Maunder, W. F., ed. 1979. text ed. 65.00 (ISBN 0-08-022460-1). Pergamon.

Biederman, Paul. The U. S. Airline Industry: End of an Era. LC 81-17845. 222p. 1982. 29.95 (ISBN 0-03-060324-2). Praeger.

Branch, Melville C. Urban Air Traffic & City Planning: Case Study of Los Angeles County. LC 73-1090. (Special Studies in U.S. Economic, Social & Political Issues). 1973. 49.50x (ISBN 0-275-28701-7). Irvington.

Cahiers de l'Institut de Science Economique Appliquee; Propagation du Progres Technique: Industrie Chimique et Aeronautique. (Economies et Societes Serie AI: No. 1). 1962. 19.00 (ISBN 0-317-16521-6). Kraus Repr.

Dangerous Goods Panel of Air Navigation Commission of ICAO. Technical Instructions for the Safe Transport of Dangerous Goods by Air, 1985. 510p. 1984. write for info. (ISBN 0-940394-13-8). Intereg.

Davies, R. E. Airlines of Latin America Since Nineteen-Nineteen. (Illus.). 704p. 1984. 47.50x (ISBN 0-87474-358-3, DALA). Smithsonian.

Frederick, John H. Commercial Air Transportation. 5th ed. LC 54-42. pap. 127.30 (ISBN 0-317-09208-1, 2000127). Bks Demand UMI.

Grey, Jerry. Aerospace Technology & Commercial Nuclear Power. 19.50 (ISBN 0-915928-69-8). AIAA.

Hudson, Kenneth & Pettifer, Julian. Diamonds in the Sky: A Social History of Air Travel. 240p. 1981. 19.95 (ISBN 0-370-30162-5, Pub. by the Bodley Head). Merrimack Pub Cir.

Kean, A. Essays in Air Law. 1982. lib. bdg. 74.00 (ISBN 90-247-2543-7, Pub. by Martinus Nijhoff Netherlands). Kluwer Academic.

Moore, Kenneth C. Airport, Aircraft & Airline Security. LC 76-45104. (Illus.). 1976. 29.95 (ISBN 0-913708-26-7). Butterworth.

Munson, Ken. U. S. Commercial Aircraft. (Illus.). 192p. 1982. 19.95 (ISBN 0-86720-628-4). Jane's Pub Inc.

National Academy of Engineering. State of the Nation's Air Transportation System. LC 76-47852. 1976. pap. 6.95 (ISBN 0-309-02534-6). Natl Acad Pr.

Newhouse, John. The Sporty Game. LC 81-48123. 1982. 19.95 (ISBN 0-394-51447-5). Knopf.

Reeves, Earl. Aviation's Place in Tomorrow's Business. (Airlines History Project Ser.). Date not set. Repr. of 1930 ed. 35.00 (ISBN 0-404-19331-5). AMS Pr.

Richardson, J. D. Essentials of Aviation Management. LC 76-44189. (Illus.). 1977. pap. text ed. 18.95 (ISBN 0-8403-2430-8, 40243002). Kendall-Hunt.

Smith, Henry L. Airways: The History of Commercial Aviation in the United States. (Airlines History Project Ser.). (Illus.). Date not set. Repr. of 1942 ed. 52.50 (ISBN 0-404-19335-8). AMS Pr.

Stevenson, Arthur J. The New York-Newark Air Freight System. LC 82-160111. (Research Papers: Nos. 199-200). (Illus.). 440p. 1982. pap. 20.00x (ISBN 0-89065-106-X). U Chicago Dept Geog.

Stroud, John. Annals of British & Commonwealth Air Transport, 1919-1960. (Airlines History Project Ser.). (Illus.). Date not set. Repr. of 1962 ed. 110.00 (ISBN 0-404-19337-4). AMS Pr.

--Soviet Transport Aircraft Since 1945. (Putnam Aeronautical Bks.). (Illus.). 318p. 1979. 19.95 (ISBN 0-370-00126-5, Pub. by the Bodley Head). Merrimack Pub Cir.

Wassenbergh, H. A. & Van Fenema, H. P., eds. International Air Transport in the Eighties. 260p. 1982. 40.00 (ISBN 90-65-44026-7, Pub. by Kluwer Law Netherlands). Kluwer Academic.

Webb, Jim. Fly the Wing. 1971. pap. 15.50 (ISBN 0-8138-0545-7). Iowa St U Pr.

AERONAUTICS, ELECTRONICS IN

see Electronics in Aeronautics

AERONAUTICS, HIGH-SPEED

see High-Speed Aeronautics

AERONAUTICS, MILITARY

see also Air Power; Aircraft Carriers; Airplanes, Military

also subdivision Aerial Operations under names of wars, e.g. World War, 1939-45–Aerial Operations

Christienne, Charles & Lissarrague, Pierre. A History of French Military Aviation. Kianka, Frances, tr. from Fr. LC 85-600032. (Illus.). 400p. 1985. 39.95 (ISBN 0-87474-310-9, CHHF). Smithsonian.

Freney, Michael A. & Townsend, James J. The Future of Military Aviation, Vol. VI. (Significant Issues Ser.: No. 14). 51p. 1984. 8.95 (ISBN 0-89206-065-4). CSI Studies.

Ginter, Steve. Chance Vought F7U Cutlass. (Naval Fighter Ser.: No. 6). 106p. 1982. pap. 13.95 (ISBN 0-942612-06-X). Aviation.

Gunston, Bill. An Illustrated Guide to Military Helicopters. LC 81-67084. (Illus.). 160p. 1981. 9.95 (ISBN 0-668-05345-3, 5345). Arco.

Hirst, Mike. Airborne Early Warning: Design Development & Operations. (Illus.). 192p. 29.95 (ISBN 0-85045-532-4, Pub. by Osprey England). Motorbooks Intl.

Jablonski, Edward. Flying Fortress. LC 65-19886. (Illus.). 1965. 22.95 (ISBN 0-385-03855-0). Doubleday.

Jordan, John. An Illustrated Guide to Modern Naval Aviation & Aircraft Carriers. LC 83-2761. (Illustrated Military Guides Ser.). (Illus.). 160p. 1983. 9.95 (ISBN 0-668-05824-2, 5824). Arco.

Layman, R. D. To Ascend from a Floating Base: Shipboard Aeronautics & Aviation, 1783-1914. LC 77-89782. (Illus.). 272p. 1979. 26.50 (ISBN 0-8386-2078-7). Fairleigh Dickinson.

Lee, Asher, ed. The Soviet Air & Rocket Forces. LC 75-27682. (Illus.). 311p. 1976. Repr. of 1959 ed. lib. bdg. 35.00x (ISBN 0-8371-8456-8, LESAR). Greenwood.

Levine, Isaac D. Mitchell, Pioneer of Air Power. LC 71-169426. (Literature & History of Aviation Ser). 1971. Repr. of 1943 ed. 25.00 (ISBN 0-405-03777-5). Ayer Co Pubs.

Military Helicopters. (Illus.). 9.95 (ISBN 0-668-05345-3). Arco.

Mitchell, William. Winged Defense. LC 75-137977. (American History & Culture in the Twentieth Century Ser.). 1971. Repr. of 1925 ed. 26.50x (ISBN 0-8046-1432-6, Pub. by Kennikat). Assoc Faculty Pr.

Modern Naval Aviation & Aircraft Carriers. (Illus.). 9.95 (ISBN 0-668-05824-2). Arco.

Momyer, William W. Airpower in Three Wars. new ed. Gilbert, James, ed. LC 79-7287. (Flight: Its First Seventy-Five Years Ser.). (Illus.). 1979. lib. bdg. 28.50x (ISBN 0-405-12196-2). Ayer Co Pubs.

Morrow, John H. Building German Airpower, 1909-1914. LC 76-15287. pap. 41.00 (ISBN 0-317-20106-9, 2023171). Bks Demand UMI.

Morrow, John H., Jr. German Airpower in World War I. LC 81-11588. (Illus.). xiv, 275p. 1982. 21.50x (ISBN 0-8032-3076-1). U of Nebr Pr.

Nevin, David. Architects of Air Power. (The Epic of Flight Ser.). (Illus.). 175p. 1981. 14.95 (ISBN 0-8094-3279-X). Time-Life.

Piercey, Stephen. Sky Truck. (Illus.). 128p. 1984. 11.95 (ISBN 0-85045-552-9, Pub. by Osprey England). Motorbooks Intl.

Rausa, Rosano. Gold Wings, Blue Sea: A Naval Aviator's Story. LC 80-26954. (Illus.). 216p. 1981. 16.95 (ISBN 0-87021-219-2). Naval Inst Pr.

Swanborough, Gordon & Bowers, Peter M. United States Navy Aircraft Since 1911. LC 76-12910. 518p. 1977. 19.95 (ISBN 0-87021-968-5). Naval Inst Pr.

Toliver, Raymond & Constable, Trevor. Fighter Aces of the U. S. A. LC 79-53300. (Illus.). 1979. 24.95 (ISBN 0-8168-5792-X). Aero.

Trotti, John. Marine Air: First to Fight. (Presidio Press Air Power Ser.). (Illus.). 192p. (Orig.). 1986. pap. 12.95 (ISBN 0-89141-190-9). Presidio Pr.

U. S. Air Force. Wings at War Series, 6 vols. in one, No. 1-6. Gilbert, James, ed. LC 79-7301. (Flight: Its First Seventy-Five Years Ser.). (Illus.). 1979. Repr. of 1945 ed. lib. bdg. 34.50x (ISBN 0-405-12207-1). Ayer Co Pubs.

Wagner, Ray. American Combat Planes. 3rd & enl. ed. LC 77-16952. (Illus.). 608p. 1982. 29.95 (ISBN 0-385-13120-8). Doubleday.

Wykeham, Peter. Fighter Command: A Study of Air Defence 1914-1960. Gilbert, James, ed. LC 79-7303. (Flight: Its First Seventy-Five Years Ser.). (Illus.). 1979. Repr. of 1960 ed. lib. bdg. 27.50x (ISBN 0-405-12209-8). Ayer Co Pubs.

AERONAUTICS, NAVAL

see Aeronautics, Military

AERONAUTICS, RADIO IN

see Radio in Aeronautics

AERONAUTICS IN AGRICULTURE

Akesson, N. B. & Yates, W. E. The Use of Aircraft in Agriculture. (Agricultural Development Papers: No. 94). (Illus.). 217p. 1974. pap. 12.25 (ISBN 92-5-100067-0, F488, FAO). Unipub.

Quantick, H. R. Aviation in Crop Protection, Pollution & Insect Control. (Illus.). 450p. 1985. text ed. 45.00x (ISBN 0-00-383049-7, Pub. by Collins England). Sheridan.

Sinclair, Donna M. The Pastor's Wife Today. LC 80-26076. (Creative Leadership Ser.). 128p. (Orig.). 1981. pap. 5.95 (ISBN 0-687-30269-2). Abingdon.

Techno-Economic Trends in Airborne Equipment for Agriculture & Other Selected Areas: Proceedings of a Seminar Organized by the United Nations Economic Commission for Europe, Warsaw, Poland, 18-22 September 1978. (ECE Seminars & Symposia). (Illus.). 294p. 1980. 50.00 (ISBN 0-08-022425-3). Pergamon.

AERONAUTICS IN FORESTRY

Techno-Economic Trends in Airborne Equipment for Agriculture & Other Selected Areas: Proceedings of a Seminar Organized by the United Nations Economic Commission for Europe, Warsaw, Poland, 18-22 September 1978. (ECE Seminars & Symposia). (Illus.). 294p. 1980. 50.00 (ISBN 0-08-022425-3). Pergamon.

AERONAUTICS IN METEOROLOGY

see also Atmosphere, Upper–Rocket Observations; Meteorology in Aeronautics

Climatic Impact Committee. Environmental Impact of Stratospheric Flight. 1975. pap. 12.00 (ISBN 0-309-02346-7). Natl Acad Pr.

FAA, Dept. of Transportation. Aviation Weather Services. (Illus.). 132p. 1981. pap. text ed. 6.00 (ISBN 0-941272-09-5, AC 0045B). Astro Pubs.

Federal Aviation Administration. Aviation Weather: Ac 00-6A. pap. 8.50 (ISBN 0-86677-000-3, Pub. by Cooper). Aviation.

Multidisciplinary Studies of the Social, Economic, & Political Impact Resulting from Recent Advances in Satellite Meteorology, 6 vols. 1975. Vol. 1. pap. 15.00x (ISBN 0-299-97035-3); Vol. 2. pap. 15.00x (ISBN 0-299-97036-1); Vol. 3. pap. 10.00x (ISBN 0-299-97046-9); Vol. 4. pap. 10.00x (ISBN 0-299-97047-7); Vol. 5. pap. 10.00x (ISBN 0-299-97051-5); Vol. 6. pap. 10.00x (ISBN 0-299-97057-4). U of Wis Pr.

Oppenheim, A. K. Impact of Aerospace Technology on Studies of the Earth's Atmosphere. LC 74-5410. 1974. text ed. 28.00 (ISBN 0-08-018131-7). Pergamon.

Vinnichenko, N. K. & Gorelik, A. G., eds. Advances in Satellite Meteorology, Vol. 2. Levi, M., tr. from Rus. 148p. 1974. text ed. 39.95x (ISBN 0-470-90836-X). Halsted Pr.

AEROPLANES

see Airplanes

AEROSOL THERAPY

Dautrebande, L. Microaerosols: Physiology, Pharmacology, Therapeutics. 1962. 76.00 (ISBN 0-12-204350-2). Acad Pr.

Marlow, W. H., ed. Aerosol Microphysics I: Particle Interactions. (Topics in Current Physics: Vol. 16). (Illus.). 180p. 1980. 37.00 (ISBN 0-387-09866-6). Springer-Verlag.

Zuev, V. E., et al. High-Power Laser Radiation in Atmospheric Aerosols. 1985. lib. bdg. 59.00 (ISBN 90-277-1736-2, Pub. by Reidel Holland). Kluwer Academic.

AEROSOLS

see also Aerosol Therapy; Fume Control

Bolle, H. J., ed. Radiation in the Atmosphere: Proceedings. LC 77-5205. (Illus.). 1977. lib. bdg. 62.00 (ISBN 0-89500-002-4). Sci Pr.

Clayton, P. The Filtration Efficiency of a Range of Filter Media for Sub-Micrometre Aerosols, 1978. 1981. 50.00x (ISBN 0-686-97079-9, Pub. by W Spring England). State Mutual Bk.

Dautrebande, L. Microaerosols: Physiology, Pharmacology, Therapeutics. 1962. 76.00 (ISBN 0-12-204350-2). Acad Pr.

Davies, Charles N., ed. Aerosol Science. 1967. 74.00 (ISBN 0-12-205650-7). Acad Pr.

Dennis, Richard, ed. Handbook on Aerosols. ERDA Technical Information Center. LC 75-33965. 148p. 1976. pap. 11.75 (ISBN 0-87079-024-2, TID-26608); microfiche 4.50 (ISBN 0-87079-237-7, TID-26608). DOE.

Fissan, H., ed. Aerosols in Science, Medicine & Technology: Proceedings of the Tenth Annual Conference of the Association for Aerosol Research (Gesellschaft fur Aerosolforschung), Bologna, Italy, 14-17 September 1982. 225p. 1983. pap. 29.50 (ISBN 0-08-030260-2). Pergamon.

Friedlander, S. K. Smoke, Dust & Haze: Fundamentals of Aerosol Behavior. LC 76-26928. 317p. 1977. 46.50x (ISBN 0-471-01468-0, Pub. by Wiley Interscience). Wiley.

Gerber, Hermann E. & Deepak, Adarsh, eds. Aerosols & Their Climatic Effects. LC 85-1651. (Illus.). 300p. 1984. 45.00 (ISBN 0-937194-06-9). A Deepak Pub.

Gerber, Hermann E. & Hindman, Edward E., eds. Light Absorption by Aerosol Particles. LC 82-80728. (Illus.). 1982. 47.50 (ISBN 0-937194-00-X). A Deepak Pub.

Hidy, G. H., ed. Aerosols & Atmospheric Chemistry. 1972. 50.50 (ISBN 0-12-347250-4). Acad Pr.

Hidy, G. M. & Brock, J., eds. International Reviews in Aerosol Physics & Chemistry, 3 vols. Incl. Vol. 1. The Dynamics of Aerocolloidal Systems. 1971. 67.50 (ISBN 0-08-006613-5); Vol. 2. Topics in Current Aerosol Research, Pt. 1. 1972. 45.00 (ISBN 0-08-016674-1); Vol. 3. Topics in Current Aerosol Research, Pt. 2. 1973. 47.50 (ISBN 0-08-016809-4). Pergamon.

Hidy, George M. Aerosols: An Industrial & Environmental Science (Monograph) 1984. 89.00 (ISBN 0-12-347260-1). Acad Pr.

Hidy, George M., et al, eds. The Character & Origins of Smog Aerosols: A Digest of Results from the California Aerosol Characterization Experiment (ACHEX, Vol. 9. LC 79-4585. (Advances in Environmental Science & Technology Ser.). 776p. 1980. 95.50 (ISBN 0-471-04899-2, Pub. by Wiley-Interscience). Wiley.

Hinds, William C. Aerosol Technology: Properties, Behavior, & Measurement of Airborne Particles. LC 82-1889. 424p. 1982. text ed. 47.00 (ISBN 0-471-08726-2, Pub. by Wiley-Interscience). Wiley.

Johnsen, Montfort A. Aerosol Handbook. 2nd ed. 1982. 62.50x (ISBN 0-9603250-3-4). Dorland Pub Co.

Kneip, Theo J. & Lioy, Paul J., eds. Aerosols: Anthropogenic & Natural, Sources & Transport. LC 80-12891. (Annals of New York Academy of Sciences: Vol. 338). 618p. 1980. 110.00x (ISBN 0-89766-064-1); pap. 108.00x (ISBN 0-89766-065-X). NY Acad Sci.

Lee, S. D., et al. Aerosols. (Illus.). 900p. 1985. 79.95 (ISBN 0-87371-051-7). Lewis Pubs Inc.

Liu, B., et al. Aerosols: Science, Technology & Industrial Applications of Airborne Particles. 1984. 95.00 (ISBN 0-444-00947-7). Elsevier.

Lundgren, Dale A., et al, eds. Aerosol Measurement. LC 78-15424. 1979. 45.00 (ISBN 0-8130-0603-1). U Presses Fla.

McCormick, M. P. & Lovill, J. E., eds. Space Observations of Aerosols & Ozone: Proceedings of the Topical Meeting of the COSPAR Interdisciplinary Scientific Commission A (Meetings A1 & A2) of the COSPAR 24th Plenary Meeting held in Ottawa, Canada, 16 May-2 June, 1982, Vol. 2/5. (Illus.). 120p. 1983. pap. 45.00 (ISBN 0-08-030427-3). Pergamon.

Macias, Edward S. & Hopke, Phillip K., eds. Atmospheric Aerosol: Source-Air Quality Relationships. LC 81-10960. (ACS Symposium Ser.: No. 167). 1981. 39.95 (ISBN 0-8412-0646-5). Am Chemical.

Malissa, Hanns, ed. Analysis of Airborne Particles by Physical Methods. (Uniscience Ser.). 320p. 1978. 85.00 (ISBN 0-8493-5275-4). CRC Pr.

Marlow, W. H. Aerosol Microphysics II: Chemical Physics of Microparticles. (Topics in Current Physics: Vol. 29). (Illus.). 189p. 1982. 32.00 (ISBN 0-387-11400-9). Springer-Verlag.

Mednikov, Evgenii P. Acoustic Coagulation & Precipitation of Aerosols. LC 64-23251. 180p. 1965. 32.50x (ISBN 0-306-10718-X, Consultants). Plenum Pub.

Mercer, Thomas T. Aerosol Technology in Hazard Evaluation. (U. S. Atomic Energy Commission Monograph Ser.). 1973. 39.50 (ISBN 0-12-491150-1). Acad Pr.

Morgan-Grampian Books, ed. Aerosol Review, 1985. 120p. 1980. 125.00 (ISBN 0-686-75509-X, Pub. by Morgan-Grampian Bk). State Mutual Bk.

Phalen, Robert F. Inhalation Studies: Foundations & Techniques. 288p. 1984. 89.00 (ISBN 0-8493-5469-2). CRC Pr.

Reist, Parker C. Introduction to Aerosol Science. 1984. 34.95 (ISBN 0-02-949600-4). Macmillan.

Ruhnke, Lothar H. & Deepak, A., eds. Hygroscopic Aerosols. LC 84-9529. (Illus.). 390p. 1984. 45.00 (ISBN 0-937194-02-6). A Deepak Pub.

Sanders, Paul A. Handbook of Aerosol Technology. 2nd. ed. LC 78-18428. 540p. 1979. 34.50 (ISBN 0-442-27348-7). Krieger.

Shaw, David T., ed. Fundamentals of Aerosol Science. LC 77-19331. 372p. 1978. 75.00 (ISBN 0-471-02949-1, Pub. by Wiley-Interscience). Wiley.

Spurny, Kvetoslav. Aerosols. 944p. 1965. 180.50x (ISBN 0-677-10730-7). Gordon.

Trautlein, J., ed. Aerosols, Airways & Asthma. 121p. 1981. text ed. 20.00 (ISBN 0-89335-058-3). SP Med & Sci Bks.

Twomey, S. Atmospheric Aerosols. (Developments in Atmospheric Science Ser.: Vol. 7). 302p. 1977. 81.00 (ISBN 0-444-41527-0). Elsevier.

AEROSPACE INDUSTRIES

see also Aircraft Industry

Advances in Aerospace Propulsion. 168p. 1985. 30.00 (ISBN 0-89883-815-0, SP594). Soc Auto Engineers.

Aerospace Fluid Power & Control Systems, 8 papers. 112p. 1983. pap. 22.00 (ISBN 0-89883-325-6, SP554). Soc Auto Engineers.

Aerospace Testing Seminar: Proceedings of the 8th Seminar Sponsored by the Aerospace Corp. & IES, March 1984. 237p. (Orig.). 1984. pap. text ed. 25.00 (ISBN 0-915414-73-2). Inst Environ Sci.

Airey, T., et al, eds. Aircraft Erecting. (Engineering Craftsmen: No. H34). (Illus.). 1977. spiral bdg. 39.95x (ISBN 0-85083-413-9). Trans-Atlantic.

Applying Robotics in the Aerospace Industry, 17 papers. 59.50 (ISBN 0-317-07143-2, 815). SME.

AWS Conference on Welding for the Aerospace Industry, October 1980. Welding Technology for the Aerospace Industry: Proceedings. (Welding Technology Ser.). 176p. 1981. 25.00 (ISBN 0-686-95643-5). Am Welding.

Beer, T. The Aerospace Environment. (Wykeham Science Ser.: No. 36). 170p. 1975. pap. cancelled (ISBN 0-85109-021-4). Taylor & Francis.

Bright, Charles D. The Jet Makers: The Aerospace Industry from 1945 to 1972. LC 78-2377. (Illus.). 1978. 22.50x (ISBN 0-7006-0172-4). U Pr of KS.

Clark, Douglas A. Aerospace Historian: Cumulative Index by Author, Book Review, Title & Subject 1974-1983. 122p. 1985. pap. text ed. 17.50 (ISBN 0-89126-124-9). MA-AH Pub.

Crouch, Thomas. The Giant Leap: A Chronology of Ohio Aerospace Events & Personalities, 1915-1969. (Illus.). 77p. 1971. pap. 0.50 (ISBN 0-318-00826-2). Ohio Hist Soc.

Hanle, Paul A., ed. High Technology on Earth: Studies in Using Aerospace Systems & Methods. LC 78-14329. (Smithsonian Studies in Air & Space: No. 3). pap. 20.00 (ISBN 0-317-09477-7, 2011429). Bks Demand UMI.

Institution of Civil Engineers Staff, compiled by. Aircraft Pavement Design. 119p. 1971. 40.25x (ISBN 0-901948-04-7). Am Soc Civil Eng.

Instrumentation in the Aerospace Industry & Advances in Test Measurement, Vol. 29 & Vol. 21. LC 69-59467. 676p. 1983. pap. text ed. 75.00x (ISBN 0-87664-754-9). Instru Soc.

International Instrumentation Symposium. Fundamentals of Aerospace Instrumentation & Fundamentals of Test Measurement: Tutorial Proceedings of the 29th International Instrumentation Symposium, Vol. 14 & Vol. 9. LC 68-59468. 112p. 1983. pap. text ed. 25.00x (ISBN 0-87664-757-3). Instru Soc.

--Fundamentals of Aerospace Instrumentation, Vol. 15 & Fundamentals of Test Measurement, Vol. 10: Tutorial Proceedings of the 30th International Instrumentation Symposium. LC 68-59468. 32p. 1984. pap. text ed. 12.00x (ISBN 0-87664-807-3). Instru Soc.

ISA Aerospace & Test Measurement Proceedings Index, 1980. Aerospace & Test Measurement Proceedings Index: Index of Proceedings from Instrumentation in the Aerospace Industry, Vols. 1-24, Fundamentals of Aerospace Instrumentation, Vols. 1-10 & Advances in Test Measurement, Vols. 11-15. LC 79-52762. 198p. 1980. pap. text ed. 30.00x (ISBN 0-87664-445-0). Instru Soc.

Laurenson, R. M. & Yuceoglu, U., eds. Advances in Aerospace Structures & Materials, 1982. (AD-03). 1982. 30.00 (H00240). ASME.

Manufacturing in Space. (PED Ser.: Vol. 11). 224p. 1983. pap. text ed. 40.00 (ISBN 0-317-02629-1, H00286). ASME.

May, Clayton A., ed. Resins for Aerospace. LC 80-15342. (ACS Symposium Ser.: No. 132). 1980. 49.95 (ISBN 0-8412-0567-1). Am Chemical.

The Military & Aerospace Computer Market (U. S.) 1981. 1200.00 (ISBN 0-86621-009-1, A959). Frost & Sullivan.

The Military & Aerospace Display Market in the U. S. 1981. 1200.00 (ISBN 0-86621-010-5, A923). Frost & Sullivan.

Military & Aerospace Power Supply Market. 271p. 1982. 1200.00 (ISBN 0-86621-011-3, A1080). Frost & Sullivan.

National Air & Space Museum Library Staff, ed. The International Handbook of Aerospace Awards & Trophies. LC 77-25053. (Illus.). 252p. 1978. pap. text ed. 17.50x (ISBN 0-87474-670-1). Smithsonian.

Sixth Aerospace Testing Seminar: Proceedings. LC 62-38584. (Illus.). 221p. (Orig.). 1981. pap. text ed. 25.00 (ISBN 0-915414-65-1). Inst Environ Sci.

Symposium on Newer Structural Materials for Aerospace Vehicles. LC 65-16809. (American Society for Testing & Materials: No. 379). pap. 31.30 (ISBN 0-317-09248-0, 2000735). Bks Demand UMI.

Ung, Monte, ed. Aerospace Simulation. 1984. 30.00. Soc Computer Sim.

Wang, S. S. & Renton, W. J., eds. Nineteen Eighty-One Advances in Aerospace Structures & Materials (AD-01) (No. H00194). 311p. 1981. 40.00 (ISBN 0-686-34472-3). ASME.

Yuceoglu, U., et al. Advances in Aerospace Structures, Materials, & Dynamics: A Symposium on Composites. 1983. pap. text ed. 40.00 (ISBN 0-317-02538-4, H00272). ASME.

AEROTHERMODYNAMICS

see also Aerodynamic Heating

Oates, Gordon C. Aerothermodynamics of Gas Turbines & Rocket Propulsion. LC 84-11152. (Illus.). 412p. 1984. 45.00 (ISBN 0-915928-87-6). AIAA.

Steltz, W. E. & Donaldson, A. M., eds. Aero-Thermodynamics of Steam Turbines. 1981. 24.00 (ISBN 0-686-34474-X, H00203). ASME.

AFFINE GEOMETRY

see Geometry, Affine

AFFINITY, CHEMICAL

see Chemical Affinity

AFGHAN (DOG)

see Dogs–Breeds–Afghan Hounds

AFLATOXINS

Castegnaro, M., et al, eds. Laboratory Decontamination & Destruction of Aflatoxins, B1, B2, G1, G2 in Laboratory Wastes. (IARC Ser.). (Illus.). 68p. 1980. pap. 9.95x (ISBN 0-19-723037-7). Oxford U Pr.

Heathcote, J. G. & Hibbert, J. R. Aflatoxins: Chemical & Biological Aspects. (Developments in Food Science Ser.: Vol. 1). 212p. 1978. 55.50 (ISBN 0-444-41686-2). Elsevier.

AFRICAN OIL-PALM

see Oil-Palm

AFRICAN VIOLETS

African-Violets & Relatives. 2.25 (ISBN 0-686-21147-2). Bklyn Botanic.

Free, Montague. All about African Violets: The Complete Guide to Success with America's Favorite House Plant. rev. ed. LC 78-60289. (Illus.). 1979. 12.95 (ISBN 0-385-14521-7). Doubleday.

James, Theodore, Jr. African Violets & Other Gesneriads: How to Select & Grow. (Illus.). 144p. 1983. pap. 7.95 (ISBN 0-89586-222-0). H P Bks.

Sunset Editors. African Violets. 5th ed. LC 76-46656. (Illus.). 80p. 1977. pap. 4.95 (ISBN 0-376-03058-5, Sunset Bks). Sunset-Lane.

Top Rated African Violets. (Golden Gardening Ser.). (Illus.). 64p. 1984. pap. 3.95 (ISBN 0-307-46643-4, Golden Pr). Western Pub.

Wilson, Helen V. Helen Van Pelt Wilson's African Violet Book. (Illus.). 1970. 11.95 (ISBN 0-8015-3852-1, Hawthorn); pap. 9.95 (ISBN 0-8015-3858-0, 0966-290, Hawthorn). Dutton.

AGAR

Stewart, Joyce A. Methods of Media Preparation for the Biological Sciences. (Illus.). 108p. 1974. 14.75x (ISBN 0-398-02990-3). C C Thomas.

AGARICACEAE

Donk, M. A. The Generic Names Proposed for Agaricaceae. 1962. pap. 35.00 (ISBN 3-7682-5405-4). Lubrecht & Cramer.

Fayod, V. Prodrome D'Une Histoire Naturelle Des Agaricinees. 1968. Repr. of 1889 ed. 14.00 (ISBN 90-6123-064-0). Lubrecht & Cramer.

Kauffman, Calvin H. The Agaricaceae of Michigan, 2 Vols. (Illus.). 1918. 75.00 (ISBN 0-384-28780-8). Johnson Repr.

Moser, Meinhard. The Polypores, Boletes & Agarica. Kibby, G. & Rayner, R., trs. from Ger. (Illus.). 355p. 1983. text ed. 33.95x (ISBN 0-916422-43-7). Mad River.

AGARICALES

Baroni, T. J. A Revision of the Genus Rhodocybe Maire: Agaricales. (Nova Hedwigia Beiheft: No. 67). (Illus.). 300p. 1981. lib. bdg. 42.00x (ISBN 3-7682-5467-4). Lubrecht & Cramer.

Bresinsky, A. & Huber, J. Schluessel Fuer Die Ggattung Hygrophorus Nach Exsikkatenmerkmalen. (Illus.). 1967. 6.00 (ISBN 3-7682-0536-3). Lubrecht & Cramer.

Dennis, R. W., et al. New Check List of British Agarics & Boleti. 1974. Repr. of 1960 ed. 14.00 (ISBN 3-7682-0935-0). Lubrecht & Cramer.

Horak, E. Entoloma (Agaricales) in Indo-Malaysia & Australasia. (Nova Hedwigia Beiheft Ser.: No. 65). (Illus.). 1980. lib. bdg. 52.50 (ISBN 3-7682-5465-8). Lubrecht & Cramer.

Pegler, D. N. & Young, T. W. Basidiospore Morphology in the Agaricales. (Illus.). 1971. 56.00 (ISBN 3-7682-5435-6). Lubrecht & Cramer.

Singer, R. The Agaricales in Modern Taxonomy. 4th & rev. ed. 1985. 90.00 (ISBN 3-7682-0143-0). Lubrecht & Cramer.

AGASSIZ, LOUIS, 1807-1873

Agassiz, Louis. Geological Sketches. 229p. 1985. Repr. of 1885 ed. 29.00 (ISBN 0-932051-24-3). Am Repr Serv.

--The Intelligence of Louis Agassiz: A Specimen Book of Scientific Writings; Selected, with an Introduction & Notes. Davenport, Guy, ed. LC 83-18504. x, 237p. 1983. Repr. of 1963 ed. lib. bdg. 42.50x (ISBN 0-313-24249-6, AGIN). Greenwood.

Lurie, Edward. Louis Agassiz: A Life in Science. abr. ed. LC 60-11623. 1967. pap. 3.95x (ISBN 0-226-49704-6, P248, Phoen). U of Chicago Pr.

Paton, Lucy A. Elizabeth Cary Agassiz: A Biography. LC 74-3969. (Women in America Ser). (Illus.). 454p. 1974. Repr. of 1919 ed. 32.00x (ISBN 0-405-06117-X). Ayer Co Pubs.

Robinson, Mabel L. Runner of the Mountain Tops: The Life of Louis Agassiz. LC 73-167139. 1971. Repr. of 1939 ed. 40.00x (ISBN 0-8103-3806-8). Gale.

Tiner, John H. The Ghost Lake: The True Story of Louis Agassiz. (Voyager Ser.). 96p. (Orig.). 1983. pap. 3.95 (ISBN 0-8010-8870-4). Baker Bk.

AGATHA (INSECTS)

see May-Flies

AGAVE

Gentry, Howard S. The Agaves of Continental North America. LC 82-6896. (Illus.). 670p. 1982. 49.50x (ISBN 0-8165-0775-9). U of Ariz Pr.

AGE HARDENING

see Precipitation Hardening

AGE OF ROCKS

see Geological Time; Geology, Stratigraphic

AGGLUTINANTS

see Adhesives

AGGREGATES

see Set Theory

AGING

Adelman, Richard, et al, eds. Neural Regulatory Mechanisms During Aging. LC 80-26333. (Modern Aging Ser.: Vol. 1). 246p. 1980. 25.00 (ISBN 0-8451-2300-9). A R Liss.

Adelman, Richard C. & Roth, George S., eds. Altered Proteins & Aging. 192p. 1983. 49.50 (ISBN 0-8493-5812-4). CRC Pr.

Ageing & Reproduction. 122p. 1970. 35.00x (ISBN 0-686-45131-7, Pub. by Biochemical England). State Mutual Bk.

Alder, William H. & Nordin, Albert A. Immunological Techniques Applied to Aging Research. 256p. 1981. 77.00 (ISBN 0-8493-5809-4). CRC Pr.

Alter, Joseph D. Life after Fifty: Your Guide to Health & Happiness. (Illus.). 144p. 1983. 10.95 (ISBN 0-89313-060-5). G F Stickley.

American College of Sports Medicine. Exercise & Aging: The Scientific Basis. Smith, Everett L. & Serfass, Robert C., eds. LC 80-24700. (Illus.). 191p. 1981. text ed. 17.95x (ISBN 0-89490-042-0). Enslow Pubs.

Andersen, A. C., et al. Dogs & Other Large Mammals in Aging Research, Vol. 1. LC 74-8039. 168p. 1974. text ed. 21.50x (ISBN 0-8422-7226-7). Irvington.

Andrew, Warren. Anatomy of Aging in Man & Animals. LC 73-92018. (Illus.). 259p. 1971. 71.50 (ISBN 0-8089-0640-2, 790101). Grune.

Bakerman, Seymour. Aging Life Processes. (Illus.). 204p. 1969. 17.50x (ISBN 0-398-00083-2). C C Thomas.

Balazs, Andras, et al. Reproduction & Aging. 331p. 1974. text ed. 29.50x (ISBN 0-8422-7159-7). Irvington.

Beall, C. M., ed. Cross-Cultural Studies of Biological Aging. 100p. 1982. 19.50 (ISBN 0-08-028946-0). Pergamon.

Behnke, John A., et al, eds. The Biology of Aging. LC 78-19012. (Illus.). 400p. 1978. 18.95x (ISBN 0-306-31139-9, Plenum Pr). Plenum Pub.

Birren, J. E., ed. Aging: A Challenge to Science & Society; Vol. 3, Behavioral Sciences & Conclusions. (Illus.). 1983. text ed. 74.00x (ISBN 0-19-261256-5). Oxford U Pr.

Birren, James E. Psychology of Aging. 1964. text ed. 27.95 (ISBN 0-13-733428-1). P-H.

Bittles, A. H. & Collins, K. J., eds. The Biology of Human Ageing. (Illus.). 350p. Date not set. price not set (ISBN 0-521-30485-7). Cambridge U Pr.

Bowden, Douglas M. Aging in Nonhuman Primates. (Primate Behavior & Development Ser.). 1979. 32.50 (ISBN 0-442-20734-4). Van Nos Reinhold.

Breckenridge, Mary B. Age, Time & Fertility: Applications of Exploratory Data Analysis. (Studies in Population Ser.). 1983. 39.50 (ISBN 0-12-128750-5). Acad Pr.

Burnet, F. Macfarlane. Endurance of Life. LC 78-54323. (Illus.). 1978. 32.50 (ISBN 0-521-22114-5). Cambridge U Pr.

Carlisle, Anthony. An Essay on the Disorders of Old Age, & on the Means for Prolonging Human Life. Kastenbaum, Robert, ed. LC 78-22183. (Aging & Old Age Ser.). 1979. Repr. of 1818 ed. lib. bdg. 12.00x (ISBN 0-405-11802-3). Ayer Co Pubs.

Cherkin, Arthur, et al, eds. Physiology & Cell Biology of Aging. LC 77-94148. (Aging Ser.: Vol. 8). 245p. 1979. text ed. 37.50 (ISBN 0-89004-283-7). Raven.

Clark, Arnold M., et al. Aging in Insects. (Aging Ser.). 201p. 1976. text ed. 24.50x (ISBN 0-8422-7269-0). Irvington.

Cohen, Elias & Singal, Dharam P. Non-HLA Antigens in Health, Aging, & Malignancy. LC 83-13533. (Progress in Clinical & Biological Research Ser.: Vol. 133). 288p. 1983. 44.00 (ISBN 0-8451-0133-1). A R Liss.

Comfort, A. The Biology of Senescence. 3rd ed. 414p. 1979. 31.50 (ISBN 0-444-00266-9, Biomedical Pr). Elsevier.

Conference Held at Jackson Laboratory, Bar Harbor, Maine, Sept. 1976. Genetic Effects on Aging: Proceedings. Harrison, David E. & Bergsma, Daniel, eds. LC 77-20249. (Birth Defects Original Article Ser.: Vol. 14, No. 1). 550p. 1978. 70.00x (ISBN 0-8451-1016-0). A R Liss.

Cooper, Edwin & Brazier, Mary. Developmental Immunology: Clinical Problems & Aging. LC 82-4035. (UCLA Forum in Medical Sciences Ser.: No. 25). 1982. 35.00 (ISBN 0-12-188040-0). Acad Pr.

Corso, John F. Aging Sensory Systems & Perception. LC 80-39579. 302p. 1981. 42.95x (ISBN 0-03-058957-6). Praeger.

Cowdry, E. V. & Kastenbaum, Robert, eds. Problems of Aging: Biological & Medical Aspects. LC 78-22196. (Aging & Old Age Ser.). (Illus.). 1979. Repr. of 1939 ed. lib. bdg. 53.50x (ISBN 0-405-11813-9). Ayer Co Pubs.

Craik, Fergus & Trehub, Sandra, eds. Aging & Cognitive Processes. (Advances in the Study of Communications & Affect: Vol. 8). 395p. 1982. 39.50 (ISBN 0-306-40946-1, Plenum Pr). Plenum Pub.

Danon, D., ed. Aging: A Challenge to Science & Society--Vol. 1, Biology. (Illus.). 1981. 68.50x (ISBN 0-19-261254-9). Oxford U Pr.

Davis, Bernard B. & Wood, W. Gibson, eds. Homeostatic Function & Aging. (Aging Ser.: Vol. 30). 1985. text ed. write for info. (ISBN 0-88167-139-8). Raven.

Davis, Roger T. & Leathers, Charles W. Behavior & Pathology of Aging in Rhesus Monkeys. LC 85-5255. (MP Ser.: Vol. 8). 326p. 1985. write for info. (ISBN 0-8451-3407-8). A R Liss.

Didactic Systems. Understanding Aging & Human Needs. 72p. 1978. 14.95 (ISBN 0-686-85781-X). Van Nos Reinhold.

Dietz, A. A. & Grannis, G. F., eds. Aging - Its Chemistry: Proceedings of the Third Arnold O. Beckman Conference in Clinical Chemistry. LC 80-65825. 448p. 1980. AACC members 25.00 (ISBN 0-915274-10-8); non-members 35.00. Am Assn Clinical Chem.

Dingley, Fay, et al. Fidelity of Protein Synthesis & Transfer RNA During Aging. LC 74-5496. 174p. 1975. text ed. 34.50x (ISBN 0-8422-7220-8). Irvington.

Dismukes, Key & Sekular, Robert. Aging & Human Visual Functions. LC 82-7172. (Modern Aging Research Ser.: Vol. 2). 366p. 1982. 54.00 (ISBN 0-8451-2301-7). A R Liss.

Elias, Merrill F., et al, eds. Special Review of Experimental Aging Research: Progress in Biology. LC 77-23262. 1976. 24.00 (ISBN 0-933786-00-X); professional individual discount 10.00 (ISBN 0-686-67622-X). Beech Hill.

Engle, Earl T. & Pincus, Gregory, eds. Hormones & the Aging Process. 1956. 55.00 (ISBN 0-12-239050-4). Acad Pr.

Florini, James R., ed. Handbook of Biochemistry in Aging. 320p. 1981. 59.00 (ISBN 0-8493-3141-2). CRC Pr.

Florini, James R., et al, eds. Rates of Protein Synthesis During Aging. 253p. 1974. text ed. 34.50x (ISBN 0-8422-7221-6). Irvington.

Frankel & Richard. Be Alive As Long As You Live: The Older Person's Guide to Exercise for Joyful Living. 1980. 14.37i (ISBN 0-690-01892-4). Har-Row.

Frolkis, V. V. Aging & Life-Prolonging Processes. (Illus.). 380p. 1982. 41.50 (ISBN 0-387-81685-2). Springer-Verlag.

Frolkis, V. V., ed. Physiology of Cell Aging. (Interdisciplinary Topics in Gerontology: Vol. 18). (Illus.). viii, 208p. 1984. 70.00 (ISBN 3-8055-3866-9). S Karger.

Gey, H. F., et al. Structure & Chemistry of the Aging Heart. 238p. 1974. text ed. 24.00x (ISBN 0-8422-7168-6). Irvington.

Gurland, Barry J., et al. The Mind & Mood of Aging: Mental Health Problems of the Community Elderly in New York & London. LC 83-294. 192p. 1983. text ed. 32.95 (ISBN 0-917724-28-3, B28). Haworth Pr.

Hall, David A. Elastolysis & Ageing. (Illus.). 176p. 1964. 16.75x (ISBN 0-398-00756-X). C C Thomas.

Harris, Diana K. & Cole, William E. Sociology of Aging. LC 79-89741. (Illus.). 1980. text ed. 25.50 (ISBN 0-395-28528-3); instr's. manual 1.00 (ISBN 0-395-28529-1). HM.

Hickey, Tom. Health & Aging. LC 79-25033. (Social Gerontology Ser.). 1980. pap. text ed. 8.00 pub net (ISBN 0-8185-0374-2). Brooks-Cole.

Ho, Betty Y. Living Function of Sleep, Life & Aging. LC 79-13810. (Illus., Orig.). 1967. pap. 3.50 (ISBN 0-9600148-0-2). Juvenescent.

Hoffer, Abram & Walker, Morton. Nutrients to Age Without Senility. LC 79-93428. 265p. 1980. pap. 3.50 (ISBN 0-87983-218-5). Keats.

Holeckova, E. & Cristofalo, V. J. Aging in Cell & Tissue Culture. LC 70-110800. 163p. 1970. 27.50x (ISBN 0-306-30470-8, Plenum Pr). Plenum Pub.

Jameson, Thomas. Essays on the Changes of the Human Body at Its Different Ages. Kastenbaum, Robert, ed. LC 78-22203. (Aging & Old Age Ser.). 1979. Repr. of 1811 ed. lib. bdg. 27.50x (ISBN 0-405-11818-X). Ayer Co Pubs.

Janicki, Matthew P. & Wisniewski, Henryk M., eds. Aging & Developmental Disabilities: Issues & Approaches. LC 84-29304. (Illus.). 446p. 1985. text ed. 35.95 (ISBN 0-933716-46-X, 46X). P H Brookes.

Johnson, John E., Jr., ed. Aging & Cell Function. 300p. 1984. 42.50x (ISBN 0-306-41420-1, Plenum Pr). Plenum Pub.

--Aging & Cell Structure, Vol. 1. LC 81-17886. 401p. 1981. 59.50 (ISBN 0-306-40695-0, Plenum Pr). Plenum Pub.

Kahn, Carol. Beyond the Helix: DNA & the Quest for Longevity. LC 85-40343. 288p. 1985. 16.95 (ISBN 0-8129-1153-9). Times Bks.

Kanungo, M. S. Biochemistry of Aging. LC 79-41522. 1980. 55.00 (ISBN 0-12-396450-4). Acad Pr.

Katzman, Robert & Terry, Robert D. The Neurology of Aging. LC 82-14921. (Contemporary Neurology Ser.: No. 22). (Illus.). 249p. 1983. text ed. 41.00x (ISBN 0-8036-5231-3). Davis Co.

Kenney. Physiology of Aging: A Synopsis. 1982. 17.95 (ISBN 0-8151-5016-4). Year Bk Med.

Kohn, Robert R. Principles of Mammalian Aging. 2nd ed. (Illus.). 1978. 28.95 (ISBN 0-13-709352-7). P-H.

Korenman, S. G., ed. Endocrine Aspects of Aging. (Current Endocrinology Ser.: Vol. 6). 276p. 1982. 47.25 (ISBN 0-444-00681-8, Biomedical Pr). Elsevier.

Lambert, Gillies. Conquest of Age: Niehans Cellular Therapy. 1981. 9.95x (ISBN 0-686-76730-6). B Of A.

Lesnoff-Caravaglia, Gari, ed. Aging & the Human Condition. LC 81-6630. (Frontiers in Aging Ser.: Vol. II). 160p. 1982. 19.95 (ISBN 0-89885-029-0). Human Sci Pr.

Lindop, Patricia J. & Sacher, G. A., eds. Radiation & Aging. 1966. 32.50x (ISBN 0-89563-020-6). Intl Ideas.

Lints, F. A. Genetics & Ageing. (Interdisciplinary Topics in Gerontology: Vol. 14). (Illus.). 1978. pap. 25.25 (ISBN 3-8055-2891-4). S Karger.

Lints, F. A., et al. Aging in Drosophila. (Aging Ser.). 179p. 1977. text ed. 24.50x (ISBN 0-8422-7244-5). Irvington.

McKee, Patrick L., ed. Philosophical Foundations of Gerontology. LC 81-2922. 352p. 1982. 34.95x (ISBN 0-89885-040-1); pap. 16.95x (ISBN 0-89885-041-X). Human Sci Pr.

Makinodan, Takashi & Kay, Marguerite M., eds. CRC Handbook of Immunology of Aging. (Series in Aging). 328p. 1981. 62.00 (ISBN 0-8493-3144-7). CRC Pr.

March, James & McGaugh, James, eds. Aging: Biology & Behavior. 1981. 40.00 (ISBN 0-12-040001-4); pap. 20.00 (ISBN 0-12-040021-9). Acad Pr.

Meites, Joseph, ed. Neuroendocrinology of Aging. 376p. 1983. 45.00x (ISBN 0-306-41310-8, Plenum Pr). Plenum Pub.

Mortimer, James & Pirozzolo, Francis J., eds. The Aging Motor System. LC 82-598. (Vol. 3). 270p. 1982. 34.95x (ISBN 0-03-059283-6). Praeger.

National Research Council Assembly of Mathematical & Physical Sciences. Aging & the Geochemical Environment. 141p. 1981. pap. 10.00 (ISBN 0-309-03184-2). Natl Acad Pr.

Oota, Kunio, et al, eds. Aging Phenomena: Relationships Among Different Levels of Organization. LC 80-16223. (Advances in Experimental Medicine & Biology Ser.: Vol. 129). 330p. 1980. 45.00x (ISBN 0-306-40460-5, Plenum Pr). Plenum Pub.

Ordy, J. Mark & Brizzee, Kenneth, eds. Sensory Systems & Communication in the Elderly. LC 79-65426. (Aging Ser.: Vol. 10). 334p. 1979. text ed. 46.00 (ISBN 0-89004-235-7). Raven.

Pearson, Durk & Shaw, Sandy. Life Extension: Adding Years to Your Life & Life to Your Years: A Practical Scientific Approach. LC 80-27589. (Illus.). 600p. (Orig.). 1982. pap. 22.50 (ISBN 0-446-51272-9); pap. 10.95 (ISBN 0-446-87990-8). Warner Bks.

Peiffer, Jurgen. Brain Aging: Human Destiny-Human Disease. (Illus.). 52p. 1981. pap. text ed. 9.00 (ISBN 3-456-81039-3, Pub. by Hans Huber Pubs). J K Burgess.

Roberts, Jay, et al, eds. Pharmacological Intervention in the Aging Process. LC 78-1288. (Advances in Experimental Medicine & Biology Ser.: Vol. 97). 347p. 1978. 49.50x (ISBN 0-306-32697-3, Plenum Pr). Plenum Pub.

Rockstein, Morris & Sussman, Marvin. Biology of Aging. 1979. pap. text ed. write for info (ISBN 0-534-00687-6). Wadsworth Pub.

Rosenbloom, Alfred A. & Morgan, Meredith. Vision & Aging: General & Clinical Perspectives. 1985. 60.00 (ISBN 0-87873-045-1). Prof Press.

Rossman, Isadore, ed. Clinical Geriatrics. 2nd ed. LC 79-1274. 1979. text ed. 57.50x (ISBN 0-397-50411-X, 65-03874, Lippincott Medical). Lippincott.

Samis, H. V. & Capobianco, S., eds. Aging & Biological Rhythms. LC 78-18448. (Advances in Experimental Medicine & Biology Ser.: Vol. 108). 354p. 1978. 47.50x (ISBN 0-306-40031-6, Plenum Pr). Plenum Pub.

Sauer, H. W., ed. Cellular Ageing. (Monographs in Developmental Biology: Vol. 17). (Illus.). x, 278p. 1984. 63.00 (ISBN 3-8055-3860-X). S Karger.

Schaie, K. Warner & Geiwitz, James. Adult Development & Aging. 1982. text ed. 28.95 (ISBN 0-316-77271-2); tchrs.' manual avail. (ISBN 0-316-77273-9). Little.

Scheff, Steven W., ed. Aging & Recovery of Function in the Central Nervous System. 236p. 1984. 35.00x (ISBN 0-306-41525-9, Plenum Pr). Plenum Pub.

Schneider, E. L., ed. The Genetics of Aging. LC 78-28. (Illus.). 440p. 1978. 45.00x (ISBN 0-306-31100-3, Plenum Pr). Plenum Pub.

Sinex, F. Marott. Biochemistry of Aging. Date not set. price not set (ISBN 0-89004-172-5). Raven.

Smith, Kendric C., ed. Aging, Carcinogenesis & Radiation Biology: The Role of Nucleic Acid Addition Reactions. LC 75-42528. 574p. 1976. 65.00x (ISBN 0-306-30911-4, Plenum Pr). Plenum Pub.

Sohal, R. S., et al, eds. Molecular Biology of Aging: Gene Stability & Gene Expression. (Aging Ser.: Vol. 29). 1985. text ed. write for info. (ISBN 0-88167-140-1). Raven.

Stein, D. G. Psychobiology of Aging. 446p. 1980. 66.00 (ISBN 0-444-00391-6, Biomedical Pr). Elsevier.

Sweetser, William. Human Life: Considered in Its Present Condition & Future Developments. Kastenbaum, Robert, ed. LC 78-22219. (Aging & Old Age Ser.). 1979. Repr. of 1867 ed. lib. bdg. 25.50x (ISBN 0-405-11832-5). Ayer Co Pubs.

Theory Development in Environment & Aging. 294p. 1974. 4.00 (ISBN 0-318-02259-1). Gerontological Soc.

Verndakis, A. Hormones in Development & Aging. 718p. 1981. text ed. 75.00 (ISBN 0-89335-140-7). SP Med & Sci Bks.

Wantz, Molly S. & Gay, John E. The Aging Process: A Health Perspective. (Orig., 8c). 1981. pap. text ed. 11.95 (ISBN 0-316-92156-4). Little.

Wells, Thelma. Aging & Health Promotion. LC 81-12734. 232p. 1981. text ed. 34.00 (ISBN 0-89443-398-9). Aspen Systems.

Wolff, Kurt. The Biological, Sociological, & Psychological Aspects of Aging. LC 78-6601. 1978. Repr. of 1959 ed. lib. bdg. 15.00x (ISBN 0-8371-9057-6, WOBS). Greenwood.

Wood, W. Gibson & Elias, Merrill F., eds. Alcoholism & Aging: Current Advances in Research. 240p. 1982. 66.00 (ISBN 0-8493-5832-9). CRC Pr.

Woodruff, Diana S. & Birren, James E. Aging: Scientific Perspectives & Social Issues. 2nd ed. LC 82-19768. (Psychology Ser.). 448p. 1983. text ed. 24.00 pub net (ISBN 0-534-01253-1). Brooks-Cole.

AGING–PSYCHOLOGICAL ASPECTS

see Genetic Psychology

AGING–RESEARCH

Adelman, Richard C., et al. Enzyme Induction in Aging & Protein Synthesis. LC 74-6131. 172p. 1974. text ed. 21.50x (ISBN 0-8422-7222-4). Irvington.

The Aging of Fish. (Illus.). 234p. 1975. pap. 36.00 (ISBN 0-9502121-1-3, UBL1, FAO). Unipub.

The Aging Process: Therapeutic Implications. Bearn, Alexander G., ed. (MEDAC 1984). 352p. 1984. text ed. 49.50 (ISBN 0-88167-065-0). Raven.

Baltes, Margaret M. & Baltes, Paul B., eds. The Psychology of Aging & Control. 496p. 1985. text ed. 49.95 (ISBN 0-89859-701-3). L Erlbaum Assocs.

Beauchene, Roy E., et al. Enzyme Activities & Aging. LC 74-5496. 208p. 1974. text ed. 34.50x (ISBN 0-8422-7217-8). Irvington.

Buchanan, James W., et al. Dogs & Other Large Mammals in Aging Research, Vol. 2. LC 74-8039. 194p. 1974. text ed. 29.50x (ISBN 0-8422-7227-5). Irvington.

Cristofalo, V. J., et al, eds. Explorations in Aging. LC 75-20442. (Advances in Experimental Medicine & Biology Ser.: Vol. 61). 316p. 1975. 39.50x (ISBN 0-306-39061-2, Plenum Pr). Plenum Pub.

Curtis, Howard J. Biological Mechanisms of Aging. (Illus.). 148p. 1966. 14.75x (ISBN 0-398-00384-X). C C Thomas.

Fabris, N. Immunology & Ageing. 1982. lib. bdg. 37.50 (ISBN 90-247-2640-9, Pub. by Martinus Nijhoff Netherlands). Kluwer Academic.

Gaitz, C. M., ed. Aging & the Brain. LC 72-77227. (Advances in Behavioral Biology Ser.: Vol. 3). 231p. 1972. 32.50x (ISBN 0-306-37903-1, Plenum Pr). Plenum Pub.

Hultsch, David F. & Deutsch, Francine. Adult Development & Aging. (Illus.). 448p. 1980. 30.95 (ISBN 0-07-031156-0). McGraw.

Institute of Laboratory Animals Resources, National Research Council. Mammalian Models for Research on Aging. 1981. pap. text ed. 19.95 (ISBN 0-309-03094-3). Natl Acad Pr.

Knight, Pamela. Television Looks at Aging. Briller, Bert R. & Miller, Steven, eds. LC 85-51255. (Illus.). 116p. (Orig.). 1985. pap. 6.95 (ISBN 0-317-26078-2). TV Info Off.

Lints, F. A., ed. Non-Mammalian Models for Research on Ageing. (Interdisciplinary Topics in Gerontology: Vol. 21). (Illus.). viii, 288p. 1985. 84.25 (ISBN 3-8055-4019-1). S Karger.

Lockett, Betty A. Aging, Politics & Research: Setting the Federal Agenda for Research on Aging. 224p. 1983. text ed. 25.95 (ISBN 0-8261-4430-6). Springer Pub.

Masoro, Edward J., ed. CRC Handbook of Physiology in Aging. (Series in Clinical Laboratory Science). 520p. 1981. 80.00 (ISBN 0-8493-3143-9). CRC Pr.

Medvedev, Zhores A. Protein Biosynthesis & Problems of Heredity Development & Aging. LC 67-71423. pap. 151.50 (ISBN 0-317-28826-1, 2020702). Bks Demand UMI.

Meier-Ruge, W., ed. CNS Aging & Its Neuropharmacology: Experimental & Clinical Aspects. (Interdisciplinary Topics in Gerontology: Vol. 15). (Illus.). 1979. pap. 37.50 (ISBN 3-8055-2980-5). S Karger.

Mizruchi, Ephraim H., et al. Time & Aging: Conceptualization & Application in Sociological & Gerontological Research. LC 82-80240. 186p. (Orig.). 1982. lib. bdg. 25.95x (ISBN 0-930390-41-5); pap. text ed. 12.95x (ISBN 0-930390-40-7). Gen Hall.

Moment, Gairdner B. Nutritional Approaches to Aging Research. 280p. 1982. 83.50 (ISBN 0-8493-5831-0). CRC Pr.

Ordy, J. M. & Brizzee, K. R., eds. Neurobiology of Aging: An Interdisciplinary Life-Span Approach. LC 75-19441. (Advances in Behavioral Biology Ser.: Vol. 16). 599p. 1975. 65.00x (ISBN 0-306-37916-3, Plenum Pr). Plenum Pub.

Osterbind, Carter C. & Bell, William G., eds. Data Based Planning in the Field of Aging. x, 159p. (Orig.). 1983. pap. 8.50 (ISBN 0-8130-0765-8). U Presses Fla.

Reed, Robert D. How & Where to Research & Find Information on Aging in America. LC 82-60572. 50p. (Orig.). 1984. pap. 4.50 (ISBN 0-88247-698-X). R & E Pubs.

Robinson, Pauline K., et al, eds. Aging & Technological Advances. (NATO Conference Series III-Human Advances: Vol. 24). 480p. 1985. 69.50x (ISBN 0-306-41822-3, Plenum Pr). Plenum Pub.

Rothstein, Morton. Biochemical Approaches to Aging. 1982. 44.50 (ISBN 0-12-598780-3). Acad Pr.

--Review of Biological Research in Aging, Vol. 1. 424p. 1983. 64.00 (ISBN 0-8451-3500-7). A R Liss.

--Review of Biological Research in Aging, Vol. 2. 572p. 1985. 96.00 (ISBN 0-8451-3501-5). A R Liss.

Thorbecke, Gertruida J., ed. Biology of Aging & Development. LC 75-34295. (Illus.). 350p. 1976. 39.50x (ISBN 0-306-34503-X, Plenum Pr). Plenum Pub.

AGITATORS (MACHINERY)

see Mixing Machinery

AGRICULTURAL BOTANY

see Botany, Economic

AGRICULTURAL CHEMICALS

see also Fertilizers and Manures; Fungicides; Growth Promoting Substances; Herbicides; Insecticides; Pesticides; Seeds–Disinfection; Trace Elements

Agrochemicals: Fate in Food & the Environment. (Proceedings Ser.). (Illus.). 363p. 1983. pap. 42.25 (ISBN 92-0-010382-0, ISP623, IAEA). Unipub.

Atrazine, Simazine, Propazine, Prometryn, Methopropotryn, Terbutryn. (Specifications for Plant Protection Products: No. 27). 1975. pap. 7.50 (F2012, FAO). Unipub.

Azinphos-Methyl & Azinphos-Ethyl. (Specifications for Plant Protection Products: No. 9). 1978. Repr. of 1971 ed. pap. 7.50 (F1994, FAO). Unipub.

Business Communications Staff. Specialty Agricultural Chemicals. 1982. 950.00 (ISBN 0-89336-225-5, GA-035R). BCC.

Captan. (Specifications for Plant Protection Products: No. 23). 1975. Repr. of 1973 ed. pap. 7.50 (F2008, FAO). Unipub.

Carbaryl. (Specifications for Plant Protection Products: No. 21). 1975. Repr. of 1973 ed. pap. 7.50 (F2006, FAO). Unipub.

Chlorbenside. (Specifications for Plant Protection Products: No. 22). 1973. pap. 7.50 (F2007, FAO). Unipub.

Chlorfenvinphos. (Specifications for Plant Protection Products: No. 32). 1977. pap. 7.50 (F2015, FAO). Unipub.

Chlorthiamid. (Specifications for Plant Protection Products: No. 33). 1977. pap. 7.50 (F2016, FAO). Unipub.

DDP & Camphachlor. (Specifications for Plant Protection Products: No. 34). 1977. pap. 7.50 (F2017, FAO). Unipub.

Diazinon. (Specifications for Plant Protection Products: No. 20). 1975. Repr. of 1973 ed. pap. 7.50 (F2005, FAO). Unipub.

Dicamba. (Specifications for Plant Protection Products: No. 25). 1973. pap. 7.50 (F2010, FAO). Unipub.

Dichlorodiphenyltrichloroethane. (Specifications for Plant Protection Products: No. 5). 1978. Repr. of 1973 ed. pap. 7.50 (F1990, FAO). Unipub.

Dichlorophenosyacetic Acid-2,4. (Specifications for Plant Protection Products: No. 8). 1975. pap. 7.50 (F1993, FAO). Unipub.

Endrin. (Specifications for Plant Protection Products: No. 14). 1978. pap. 7.50 (F1999, FAO). Unipub.

Gamma-BHC (Lindane Grade) Incl. F1996. (Specifications for Plant Protection Products: No. 11). 1978. pap. 7.50 (F1996, FAO). (Specifications for Plant Protection Products: No. 3). 1976. pap. 7.50 (F1988, FAO). Unipub.

HEOD (Dieldrin Products) (Specifications for Plant Protection Products: No. 4). 1978. pap. 7.50 (F1989, FAO). Unipub.

Heptachlor. (Specifications for Plant Protection Products: No. 15). 1973. pap. 7.50 (F2000, FAO). Unipub.

HHDN (Aldrin Products) (Specifications for Plant Protection Products: No. 6). 1978. Repr. of 1971 ed. pap. 7.50 (F1991, FAO). Unipub.

Hilton, James L. Agricultural Chemicals of the Future (BARC VIII) (Illus.). 480p. 1985. text ed. 53.00x (ISBN 0-86598-138-8). Rowman & Allanheld.

McLaren. Chemical Manipulation of Crop Growth. 1982. text ed. 99.95 (ISBN 0-408-10767-7). Butterworth.

MCPA. (Specifications for Plant Protection Products: No. 16). 1978. pap. 7.50 (F2001, FAO). Unipub.

Opportunities for Chemical Plant Growth Regulation. 222p. 1978. 42.00x (ISBN 0-686-45037-X, Pub. by BCPC Pubns England). State Mutual Bk.

Parathion, 2 vols. (Specifications for Plant Protection Products: No. 1 & 2). Repr. of 1971 ed. pap. 7.50, 1978 (F1986, FAO); pap. 7.50, 1975 (F1987). Unipub.

Pyrethrin & Piperonyl Butoxide. (Specifications for Plant Protection Products: No. 7). 1978. Repr. of 1971 ed. pap. 7.50 (F1992, FAO). Unipub.

Sodium Chlorate & Dalapon Sodium Salt or 2, 2-Dichloropropionic Acid. (Specifications for Plant Protection Products: No. 41). 1977. pap. 7.50 (ISBN 92-5-100550-8, F2019, FAO). Unipub.

Soil Chemistry, Soil Fertility & Soil Clay Mineralogy Commissions of the International Society of Soil Science, 13-18 July 1976, Jerusalem. Agrochemicals in Soils: Selected Papers. Banin, A. & Kafkafi, U., eds. LC 79-41750. 500p. 1980. 94.00 (ISBN 0-08-025914-6). Pergamon.

Soils & Crop Protection Chemicals. (Monograph Ser.: No. 27). 200p. (Orig.). 1984. pap. 32.00x (ISBN 0-901436-80-1, Pub. by B C P C England). Intl Spec Bk.

Thomson, W. T. Agricultural Chemicals, Book I: Insecticides. rev. ed. 260p. 1985. pap. 14.50 (ISBN 0-913702-31-5). Thomson Pub Ca.

--Agricultural Chemicals-Book, IV: Fungicides, 1985. LC 64-24795. 185p. 1984. pap. 14.50 (ISBN 0-913702-29-3). Thomson Pub CA.

--Agricultural Chemicals, Book 3: Miscellaneous Chemicals. Rev. ed. LC 80-52106. 190p. 1983. 13.50 (ISBN 0-913702-21-8). Thomson Pub CA.

--Agricultural Chemicals: Herbicides 1983-84, Bk. II. rev. ed. 285p. 1983. pap. 13.50 (ISBN 0-913702-23-4). Thomson Pub CA.

Trichlorophenoxyacetic Acid-2,4,5. (Specifications for Plant Protection Products: No. 13). 1975. Repr. of 1972 ed. pap. 7.50 (F1998, FAO). Unipub.

Van Keulen, H. & Van Heemst, H. D. J. Crop Response to the Supply of Macronutrients. (Agricultural Research Reports: No. 916). 52p. 1982. pap. 6.75 (ISBN 90-220-0807-X, PDC247, PUDOC). Unipub.

Wagner, Sheldon L. Clinical Toxicology of Agricultural Chemicals. LC 82-14421. (Illus.). 306p. 1983. 28.00 (ISBN 0-8155-0930-8). Noyes.

What Future for Agrichemicals? GA-031. 125p. 1981. 750.00 (ISBN 0-89336-157-7). BCC.

AGRICULTURAL CHEMISTRY

see also Agricultural Chemicals; Chemurgy; Dairy Products–Analysis and Examination; Fertilizers and Manures; Plants–Chemical Analysis; Soil Chemistry; Soils; Wood–Chemistry

Bolt, G. H., ed. Soil Chemistry, Pt. B: Physico-Chemical Models. 2nd, rev. ed. (Developments in Soil Science Ser.: Vol. 5B). 538p. 1982. 76.75 (ISBN 0-444-42060-6). Elsevier.

Burns, R. G., ed. Soil Enzymes. 1978. 69.50 (ISBN 0-12-145850-4). Acad Pr.

Business Communications Staff. Markets for Bugs & Enzymes, C-008: C-008. 1982. 1250.00 (ISBN 0-89336-101-1). BCC.

Calbally, E. I. & Freney, J. R., eds. The Cycling of Carbon, Nitrogen, Sulfur, & Phosphorus in Terrestrial & Aquatic Ecosystems. 230p. 1982. 28.00 (ISBN 0-387-11272-3). Springer-Verlag.

Goring, Cleve A. & Hamaker, John W., eds. Organic Chemicals in the Soil Environment. LC 71-179384. (Books in Soils & the Environment Ser.: Vol. 1). pap. 114.00 (ISBN 0-317-28661-7, 2055084). Bks Demand UMI.

Harmsen, K. Behavior of Heavy Metals in Soil. (Agricultural Research Reports: No. 866). (Illus.). 1977. pap. 13.25 (ISBN 90-220-0635-2, PDC17, PUDOC). Unipub.

Hay, Robert K. Chemistry for Agriculture & Ecology. (Illus.). 240p. 1981. pap. text ed. 13.95 (ISBN 0-632-00699-4, B 2114-3). Mosby.

Hesse, P. R. A Textbook of Soil Chemical Analysis. 1972. 50.00 (ISBN 0-8206-0242-6). Chem Pub.

International IUPAC Congress-2nd. Pesticide Chemistry: Proceedings of the International IUPAC Congress, 2nd Congress, 6 vols. Tahori, A. S., ed. Set. 443.75x (ISBN 0-677-12120-2); Vol. 1, 506p., 1972. 101.25x (ISBN 0-677-12130-X); Vol. 2, 310p., 1971. 69.50x (ISBN 0-677-12140-7); Vol. 3, 236p., 1971. 62.50x (ISBN 0-677-12150-4); Vol. 4, 618p., 1971. 129.50x (ISBN 0-677-12160-1); Vol. 5, 578p., 1972. 123.75x (ISBN 0-677-12170-9); Vol. 6, 584p., 1972. 121.50x (ISBN 0-677-12180-6). Gordon.

Kanwar, J. S., et al, eds. Fertilizer Sulfur & Food Production: Research & Policy Implications for Tropical Countries. (IFDC Technical Bulletin Ser.: T-27). (Illus.). 1983. pap. text ed. 4.00 (ISBN 0-88090-047-4). Intl Fertilizer.

Kilmer, V. J., et al, eds. The Role of Potassium in Agriculture. (Illus.). 1968. 7.50 (ISBN 0-89118-003-6). Am Soc Agron.

L'Annunziata, Michael. Radiotracers Im Agricultural Chemistry. 1979. 78.50 (ISBN 0-12-436250-8). Acad Pr.

Liebig, Justus Von. The Natural Laws of Husbandry. LC 72-2852. (Use & Abuse of America's Natural Resources Ser). 392p. 1972. Repr. of 1863 ed. 25.50 (ISBN 0-405-04541-7). Ayer Co Pubs.

Lindsay, Willard L. Chemical Equilibria in Soils. LC 79-12151. 449p. 1979. 40.50x (ISBN 0-471-02704-9, Pub. by Wiley-Interscience). Wiley.

Plimmer, Jack R., ed. Pesticide Chemistry in the Twentieth Century. LC 76-51748. (ACS Symposium Ser: No. 37). 1977. 19.95 (ISBN 0-8412-0532-9). Am Chemical.

Rossiter, Margaret W. The Emergence of Agricultural Science: Justus Liebig & the Americans, 1840-1880. LC 74-29737. (Studies in the History of Science & Medicine Ser.: No. 9). 288p. 1975. 27.00x (ISBN 0-300-01721-9). Yale U Pr.

Sauchelli, Vincent. Phosphates in Agriculture. LC 65-27055. 228p. 1965. 15.50 (ISBN 0-442-15040-7, Pub. by Van Nos Reinhold). Krieger.

Slack, A. V., ed. Phosphoric Acid, 2 pts. (Fertilizer Science & Technology Ser.: Vol.1). 1968. Pt. 1. 115.00 (ISBN 0-8247-1628-0). Dekker.

Teranishi, Roy. Agricultural & Food Chemistry: Past, Present, Future. (Illus.). 1978. lib. bdg. 49.50 (ISBN 0-87055-231-7). AVI.

Uehara, Goro & Gillman, Gavin P. The Mineralogy, Chemistry, & Physics of Tropical Soils with Variable Charge Clays. (Tropical Agriculture Ser.). 1981. 36.50x (ISBN 0-89158-484-6). Westview.

Unsworth. Effects of Gaseous Air Pollution in Agriculture & Horticulture. 1982. text ed. 99.95 (ISBN 0-408-10705-7). Butterworth.

Woodbine, M., ed. Antimicrobials & Agriculture. (Agricultural & Food Sciences Studies). 520p. 1984. text ed. 130.00 (ISBN 0-408-11155-0). Butterworth.

Zweig, Gunter, ed. Analytical Methods for Pesticides, Plant Growth Regulators & Food Additives, 11 vols. Incl. Vol. 1. Principles, Methods & General Applications. 1963. 86.50 (ISBN 0-12-784301-9); Vol. 2. Insecticides. 1964.. 86.50 (ISBN 0-12-784302-7); Vol. 3. Fungicides, Nematocides & Soil Fumigants, Rodenticides, & Food & Feed Additives. 1964; Vol. 4. Herbicides (Plant Growth Regulators) 1964. 50.50 (ISBN 0-12-784304-3); Vol. 5. 1967. 82.50 (ISBN 0-12-784305-1); Vol. 6. 1970. 89.50 (ISBN 0-12-784306-X); Vol. 7. Thin-Layer & Liquid Chromatography & Analysis of Pesticides of International Importance. 1973. 89.50 (ISBN 0-12-784307-8); Vol. 8. Government Regulations, Pheromone Analyses, Additional Pesticides. Zweig, Gunter & Sharma, Joseph, eds. 1976. 86.50 (ISBN 0-12-784308-6); Vol. 10. Newer & Updated Methods. Zweig, Gunter & Sharma, Joseph, eds. 1978. 73.50 (ISBN 0-12-784310-8); Vol. 11. 1980. 66.00 (ISBN 0-12-784311-6). Acad Pr.

AGRICULTURAL CHEMISTRY–BIBLIOGRAPHY

Browne, Charles A. A Source Book of Agricultural Chemistry. Egerton, Frank N., 3rd, ed. LC 77-74205. (History of Ecology Ser.). 1978. Repr. of 1944 ed. lib. bdg. 23.50x (ISBN 0-405-10375-1). Ayer Co Pubs.

AGRICULTURAL CLIMATOLOGY

see Crops and Climate

AGRICULTURAL COLLEGES

see also Agricultural Education; Agricultural Extension Work

Boukli, Noureddine. Mostaganem Institute of Agricultural Technology: An Educational Innovation. (Experiments & Innovations in Education Ser.: No. 19). 46p. 1975. pap. 5.00 (ISBN 92-3-101309-2, U391, UNESCO). Unipub.

AGRICULTURAL COMMODITIES

see Farm Produce

AGRICULTURAL EDUCATION

see also Agricultural Colleges; Agricultural Extension Work; Agriculture–Study and Teaching; Forestry Schools and Education

American Association Of Teacher Educators In Agriculture. Summaries of Studies in Agricultural Education 1963-1965. 1968. pap. 3.00x (ISBN 0-8134-1070-3, 1070). Interstate.

--Summaries of Studies in Agricultural Education 1965-1967. 1970. pap. text ed. 4.00x (ISBN 0-8134-1134-3, 1134). Interstate.

Bail, Joe P. Agricultural Education: Renewal & Rebirth. 10p. 1973. pap. text ed. 1.00x (ISBN 0-8134-1622-1, 1622). Interstate.

Blauch, Lloyd E. Federal Cooperation in Agricultural Extension Work, Vocational Education, & Vocational Rehabilitation. LC 76-89150. (American Education: Its Men, Institutions & Ideas, Ser. 1). 1969. Repr. of 1935 ed. 15.00 (ISBN 0-405-01388-4). Ayer Co Pubs.

Boukli, Noureddine. Mostaganem Institute of Agricultural Technology: An Educational Innovation. (Experiments & Innovations in Education Ser.: No. 19). 46p. 1975. pap. 5.00 (ISBN 92-3-101309-2, U391, UNESCO). Unipub.

Brown, Mary, et al. Agricultural Education in a Technical Society: An Annotated Bibliography of Resources. LC 72-7501. pap. 60.00 (ISBN 0-317-26603-9, 2024189). Bks Demand UMI.

Burlingham, H. H. & Juergenson, Elwood M. Selected Lessons for Teaching Off-Farm Agricultural Occupations. LC 66-19257. (Illus.). 1967. text ed. 7.95x (ISBN 0-8134-0899-7, 899). Interstate.

Byram, Harold M. Guidance in Agricultural Education. LC 65-25513. (Illus.). 298p. 1966. text ed. 7.95x (ISBN 0-8134-0521-1, 521). Interstate.

Chang, C. W. Increasing Food Production Through Education, Research & Extension. (Freedom from Hunger Campaign Basic Studies: No. 9). 78p. (Orig., 2nd Printing 1965). 1962. pap. 5.25 (ISBN 92-5-101637-2, F240, FAO). Unipub.

Convention of Friends of Agricultural Education, Chicago. Early View of the Land-Grant Colleges. LC 67-20999. 162p. 1967. 15.95x (ISBN 0-252-72463-1). U of Ill Pr.

Goldstein, Amy J. & Ready, Barbara C., eds. Graduate Programs in the Biological, Agricultural, & Health Sciences 1986. 20th ed. (Annual Guides to Graduate Study Ser.). 2050p. (Orig.). 1985. pap. 28.95 (ISBN 0-87866-344-4). Petersons Guides.

Haines, Michael. Introduction to Farming Systems. (Illus.). 1983. pap. text ed. 14.95x (ISBN 0-582-45081-0). Longman.

Hamlin, Herbert M. Public School Education in Agriculture. LC 62-12038. 1962. text ed. 5.75x (ISBN 0-8134-0067-8, 67). Interstate.

Hardin, Charles M. Freedom in Agricultural Education. LC 75-27640. (World Food Supply Ser). 1976. Repr. of 1955 ed. 28.50x (ISBN 0-405-07780-7). Ayer Co Pubs.

Higher Education for Crop Protection. 139p. 1974. 39.00x (ISBN 0-901436-36-4, Pub. by CAB Bks England). State Mutual Bk.

Howell, David L., et al. Elements of the Structure of Agricultural Education in the United States of America. (Structure & Terminology of Agricultural Education Ser.). (Illus.). 72p. 1984. pap. text ed. 13.25 (ISBN 92-3-102056-0, U1309, UNESCO). Unipub.

Loften, W. Travis. New Horizons, Challenge to Agricultural Education. 1967. pap. text ed. 1.00x (ISBN 0-8134-1008-8, 1008). Interstate.

McClay, David R. Agricultural Education: Some Concerns & Comforts. 10p. 1970. pap. text ed. 1.00x (ISBN 0-8134-1226-9, 1226). Interstate.

Martin, W. Howard. Agricultural Education: Image & Substance. 12p. 1969. pap. text ed. 1.00x (ISBN 0-8134-1139-4, 1139). Interstate.

Peterson, Milo J. Agricultural Education: Some Issues & Some Reactions. 18p. 1968. pap. text ed. 1.00x (ISBN 0-8134-1075-4, 1075). Interstate.

Phipps, Lloyd J. Handbook on Agricultural Education in Public Schools. (Illus.). 599p. 1980. text ed. 17.50x (ISBN 0-8134-2094-6, 2094). Interstate.

Population Concepts in Agricultural Training Curricula. 1979. pap. 7.50 (ISBN 92-5-100600-8, F1516, FAO). Unipub.

Report of the Second International Training Course in Remote Sensing Applications for Agriculture: Rome, 1977. (Miscellaneous Documents Ser.). 93p. 1978. pap. 7.50 (ISBN 92-5-100425-0, F1316, FAO). Unipub.

Robbins, Jerry H. & Williams, Stirling B., Jr. Administrator's Manual of School Plant Administration. 380p. 1970. pap. text ed. 3.95x (ISBN 0-8134-1130-0, 1130). Interstate.

Schmidt, Gustavus A. Vocational Education in Agriculture in Federally-Aided Secondary Schools: A Study of Its Instructional & Training Phases. LC 75-177802. (Columbia University. Teachers College. Contributions to Education: No. 534). Repr. of 1932 ed. 22.50 (ISBN 0-404-55534-9). AMS Pr.

Slay, Ronald J. Development of the Teaching of Agriculture in Mississippi with Special Emphasis on Agriculture As a Part of School Curricula. LC 78-177780. (Columbia University. Teachers College. Contributions to Education: No. 310). Repr. of 1928 ed. 22.50 (ISBN 0-404-55310-9). AMS Pr.

Training for Agriculture & Rural Development, 1976. (Economic & Social Development Papers: No. 2). (Illus.). 144p. (2nd Printing 1977). 1976. pap. 12.25 (ISBN 92-5-100164-2, F465, FAO). Unipub.

True, Alfred C. History of Agricultural Education in the United States 1785-1925. LC 76-89248. (American Education: Its Men, Institutions & Ideas, Series 1). 1969. Repr. of 1929 ed. 19.00 (ISBN 0-405-01485-6). Ayer Co Pubs.

AGRICULTURAL ENGINEERING

see also Agricultural Machinery; Drainage; Electricity in Agriculture; Farm Buildings; Farm Equipment; Irrigation

Advances in Infiltration. LC 83-73061. 385p. 1984. pap. 27.50 (ISBN 0-916150-58-5). Am Soc Ag Eng.

Agricultural Electronics: Nineteen-Eighty Three & Beyond, 2 Vols. 1984. Set. 47.50 (ISBN 0-317-06782-6); Vol. 1, 343 pp. 24.50 (ISBN 0-916150-63-1); Vol. 2, 458 pp. 28.50 (ISBN 0-916150-64-X). Am Soc Ag Eng.

Agricultural Engineering 1945-1971. pap. 7.50 (F955, FAO). Unipub.

Boumans, G. Grain Handling & Storage. (Developments in Agricultural Engineering Ser.: Vol. 4). 442p. 1985. 94.50 (ISBN 0-444-42439-3). Elsevier.

Bowers, W., et al. Engineering Applications in Agriculture. 1980. pap. 9.80x (ISBN 0-87563-186-X). Stipes.

Business Communications Staff. Biotechnology in Agriculture. 1985. pap. 1750.00 (ISBN 0-89336-440-1, GA-051R). BCC.

Csaki, C. Simulation & Systems Analysis in Agriculture. (Developments in Agricultural Engineering Ser.: Vol. 2). 1985. 55.75 (ISBN 0-444-99622-2). Elsevier.

Curtis, Paul E., et al. Here's How: On-Job-Training, Agricultural Mechanics. 157p. 1972. pap. text ed. 4.00x (ISBN 0-8134-1433-4, 1433). Interstate.

Davis, Gene. Agriculture & Automotive Diesel Mechanics. (Illus.). 256p. 1983. 20.95 (ISBN 0-13-018838-7). P-H.

Dictionnaire Technique de la Mecanisation Agricole. (Fr., Eng., Ger., Span. & Ital., Technical Dictionary of Agricultural Mechanics). 1968-70. pap. 59.95 (ISBN 0-686-56723-4, M-6155). French & Eur.

Dole, D. J., intro. by. Agricultural Engineering, 1980: Agricultural Conferences. 290p. (Orig.). 1980. pap. text ed. 45.00x (ISBN 0-85825-138-8, Pub. by Inst Engineering Australia). Brookfield Pub Co.

Dubois, P. & Brighton, C. A. Plastics in Agriculture. (Illus.). 1978. text ed. 20.50 (ISBN 0-85334-776-X, Pub. by Elsevier Applied Sci England). Elsevier.

Energy Management & Membrane Technology in Food & Dairy Processing. LC 83-72936. 128p. 1983. pap. 15.50 (ISBN 0-916150-57-7). Am Soc Ag Eng.

Esmay, Merle L. & Dixon, John E. Environmental Control for Agricultural Buildings. (Illus.). 1985. text ed. 45.00 pre-pub (ISBN 0-87055-469-7). AVI.

Farrall, Arthur W. & Basselman, James A. Dictionary of Agricultural & Food Engineering. LC 78-71856. 450p. 1979. 24.35 (ISBN 0-8134-2023-7, 2023); text ed. 18.25x. Interstate.

Fruit, Nut, & Vegetable Harvesting Mechanization. 424p. 1984. 38.50 (ISBN 0-317-06789-3). Am Soc Ag Eng.

A Guide for Instructors in Organizing & Conducting Agricultural Engineering Training Courses. (Agricultural Services Bulletins: No. 12). (Eng., Fr. & Span., Illus.). 100p. (2nd Printing 1975). 1971. pap. 7.50 (ISBN 92-5-101881-2, F707, FAO). Unipub.

Hellickson & Walker, eds. Ventilation of Agricultural Structures. LC 83-72691. 374p. 1983. 32.00 (ISBN 0-916150-56-9). Am Soc Ag Eng.

Howes, K. M. & Rummery, R. A. Energy & Agriculture. 308p. 1982. 40.00x (ISBN 0-643-02654-1, Pub. by CSIRO Australia). State Mutual Bk.

Hudson, Norman. Field Engineering for Agricultural Development. (Oxford Tropical Handbooks). (Illus.). 1975. 32.50x (ISBN 0-19-859442-9). Oxford U Pr.

International Conference on Economic Analysis in the Design of New Technology for Small Farmers. Economics & the Design of Small-Farmer Technology. Valdes, Alberto, et al, eds. LC 78-18917. pap. 55.80 (ISBN 0-317-30427-5, 2024933). Bks Demand UMI.

International Directory of Agricultural Engineering Institutions. 537p. (Orig.). 1973. pap. 18.50 (F242, FAO). Unipub.

International Directory of Agricultural Engineering Institutions. (Eng., Fr & Span.). 487p. 1983. pap. text ed. 35.50 (ISBN 92-5-001397-3, F2522, FAO). Unipub.

Kader, Adel A., ed. Postharvest Technology of Horticultural Crops. LC 85-70729. (Illus.). 212p. (Orig.). 1985. pap. 20.00 (ISBN 0-931876-72-9, 3311). Ag & Nat Res.

Kalman, R. & Martinez, J. Computer Applications in Food Production & Agricultural Engineering. 334p. 1982. 42.75 (ISBN 0-444-86382-6, North-Holland). Elsevier.

Karafiath, L. L. & Nowatzki, E. A. Soil Mechanics for Off-Road Vehicle Engineering. (Rock & Soil Mechanics Ser.). (Illus.). 1978. 58.00 (ISBN 0-87849-020-5). Trans Tech.

Leschber, R., et al, eds. Chemical Methods for Assessing Bio-Available Metals in Sludges & Soils: Proceedings of a CEC Seminar Held at the Josef-Konig Institute, Munster, West Germany, 11-13 April 1984. 104p. 1985. 30.00 (ISBN 0-85334-359-4, Pub. by Elsevier Applied Sci England). Elsevier.

Magnien, E. & De Nettancourt, D., eds. Genetic Engineering of Plants & Micro-Organisms Important for Agriculture. (Advances in Agricultural Biotechnology Ser.). 1985. lib. bdg. 36.00 (ISBN 90-247-3131-3, Pub. by Martinus Nijhoff Netherlands). Kluwer Academic.

Michael, A. M. & Ojha, T. P. Principles of Agriculture Engineering, 2 vols. 532p. 1982. Vol. I 60.00x (ISBN 0-7069-1733-2, Pub. by Garlandfold England); pap. 50.00x Vol. I (ISBN 0-7069-1734-0); Vol. II 60.00x (ISBN 0-7069-1735-9); pap. 50.00x Vol. II (ISBN 0-7069-1736-7). State Mutual Bk.

Midwest Plan Service Engineers. Dairy Housing & Equipment Handbook. 4th ed. Midwest Plan Service Staff, ed. LC 84-1195. (Illus.). 110p. 1985. pap. 6.00 (ISBN 0-89373-062-9, MWPS-7). Midwest Plan Serv.

--Livestock Waste Facilities Handbook. 2nd ed. Midwest Plan Service Staff, ed. LC 84-9687. (Illus.). 112p. 1985. pap. 6.00 (ISBN 0-89373-063-7, MWPS-18). Midwest Plan Serv.

O'Shea, J. A., intro. by. Survey of Research & Investigations in Agricultural Engineering, 1978. 129p. (Orig.). 1978. pap. text ed. 20.25x (ISBN 0-85825-098-5, Pub. by Inst Engineering Australia). Brookfield Pub Co.

--Survey of Research & Investigations in Agricultural Engineering, 1982. 110p. (Orig.). 1982. pap. text ed. 18.00x (ISBN 0-85825-180-9, Pub. by Inst Engineering Australia). Brookfield Pub Co.

O'Shea, John A., intro. by. Agricultural Engineering: 1978. 325p. (Orig.). 1978. pap. text ed. 54.00x (ISBN 0-85825-097-7, Pub. by Inst Engineering Australia). Brookfield Pub Co.

Perrens, S. J., intro. by. Agricultural Engineering, 1982. (Agricultural Conferences Ser.). 225p. (Orig.). 1982. pap. text ed. 42.00x (ISBN 0-85825-176-0, Pub. by Inst Engineering Australia). Brookfield Pub Co.

Phipps, Lloyd J. Mechanics in Agriculture. 3rd ed. LC 76-24049. 1983. 25.00 (ISBN 0-8134-2260-4); text ed. 18.75x. Interstate.

--Mechanics in Agriculture Workbook, Pt. 1. 1983. pap. 4.95x (ISBN 0-8134-2315-5). Interstate.

--Mechanics in Agriculture Workbook, Pt. 2. 1983. pap. 4.95x (ISBN 0-8134-2316-3). Interstate.

Pimentel, David. Handbook of Energy: Utilization in Agriculture. 496p. 1980. 76.50 (ISBN 0-8493-2661-3). CRC Pr.

Planner, J. H., ed. Grain Handling. 246p. 1985. pap. text ed. 20.00x (ISBN 0-85825-241-4, Pub. by Inst Engineering Australia); microfiche 12.00 (ISBN 0-85825-237-6). Brookfield Pub Co.

Richey, C. B., et al. Agricultural Engineers' Handbook. 1961. 62.50 (ISBN 0-07-052617-6). McGraw.

Ripp, B. E., ed. Controlled Atmosphere & Fumigation in Grain Storages: Proceedings of an International Symposium Held from 11-12 April, 1983, in Perth, Western Australia. (Developments in Agricultural Engineering Ser.: No. 5). 798p. 1984. 105.75 (ISBN 0-444-42417-2). Elsevier.

Ritchie, James D. Sourcebook of Farm Energy Alternatives. 384p. 1983. 34.50 (ISBN 0-07-052951-5). McGraw.

Roth, L. O., et al. Introduction to Agricultural Engineering. (Illus.). 1975. pap. text ed. 24.50 (ISBN 0-87055-302-X). AVI.

Schultz, Theodore W. Transforming Traditional Agriculture. LC 75-26314. (World Food Supply Ser). (Illus.). 1976. Repr. of 1964 ed. 21.00x (ISBN 0-405-07792-0). Ayer Co Pubs.

Selected ASTM Standards for Agricultural Engineering Students. 264p. 1981. pap. 9.50 (ISBN 0-8031-0820-6, 03-000181-38). ASTM.

Selected Papers in Greenhouse & Nursery Engineering. 117p. 1984. 30.00 (ISBN 0-317-06801-6). Am Soc Ag Eng.

Selected Papers in Greenhouse & Nursery Mechanization Concepts. 112p. 1984. 27.00 (ISBN 0-317-06802-4). Am Soc Ag Eng.

Shinn, Glen C. & Weston, Curtis. Working in Agricultural Mechanics. Amberson, Max L., ed. (Illus.). 1978. pap. text ed. 14.80 (ISBN 0-07-000843-4). McGraw.

Shultz, Richard & Smith, Richard. Introduction to Electric Power Engineering. LC 84-4554. 264p. 1984. text ed. 35.50 scp (ISBN 0-06-046131-4, HarpC). Har-Row.

Sprinkler Irrigation: A Compilation of Papers. 214p. 1984. 25.00 (ISBN 0-317-06794-X). Am Soc Ag Eng.

Status of Harvest Mechanization of Horticultural Crops. 78p. 1984. 10.25 (ISBN 0-317-06793-1). Am Soc Ag Eng.

Storr, Eric D., ed. Agricultural Engineering Eighty-Four. 250p. pap. text ed. cancelled (ISBN 0-85825-204-X, Pub. by Inst Engineering Austrailia). Brookfield Pub Co.

Trickle Irrigation: A Compilation of Published Papers. 72p. 1984. 15.00 (ISBN 0-317-06795-8). Am Soc Ag Eng.

Wahed, Abd El. Agricultural Engineering Dictionary: English-French-German-Arabic. (Eng., Fr., Ger. & Arabic.). 446p. 1977. 45.00 (ISBN 0-686-92251-4, M-9761). French & Eur.

Jones, F. G. & Jones, Margaret G. Pests of Field Crops. 2nd ed. LC 74-75834. 448p. 1974. 35.00 (ISBN 0-312-60305-3). St Martin.

Judenko, E. Analytical Method for Assessing Yield Losses Caused by Pests on Cereal Crops with & Without Pesticides. 1973. 35.00x (ISBN 0-85135-061-5, Pub. by Centre Overseas Research). State Mutual Bk.

King, W. J. Cotton in the Gambia: Report on the Cotton Development Project 1975 to 1978. 1980. 35.00x (ISBN 0-85135-109-3, Pub. by Centre Overseas Research). State Mutual Bk.

Kranz, J., et al, eds. Diseases, Pests & Weeds in Tropical Crops. LC 78-6212. 666p. 1977. 110.95 (ISBN 0-471-99667-X, Pub. by Wiley-Interscience). Wiley.

Locust & Grasshopper Agricultural Manual. 1982. 195.00 (ISBN 0-85135-120-4, Pub. by Centre Overseas Research). State Mutual BK.

Merino-Rodriguez, Manuel, ed. Lexicon of Plant Pests & Diseases. (Elsevier Lexica Ser.: Vol. 7). (Eng., Lat., Fr., Span., Ital. & Ger.). 351p. (Polyglot). 1966. 74.50 (ISBN 0-444-40393-0). Elsevier.

Nault, L. R. & Rodriguez, J. G. The Leafhoppers & Planthoppers. 576p. 1985. 50.00 (ISBN 0-471-80611-0). Wiley.

Pimentel, David, ed. Handbook of Pest Management in Agriculture. 1981. vol. 1, 296 pgs., July 1981 76.00 (ISBN 0-8493-5855-8); vol. 2, 336 pgs., Aug. 1981 89.50 (ISBN 0-8493-3842-5); vol. 3, 672 pgs., Sept. 1981 89.50 (ISBN 0-8493-3843-3). CRC Pr.

Roberts, Daniel A. Fundamentals of Plant-Pest Control. LC 77-16135. (Illus.). 242p. 1978. text ed. 27.95x (ISBN 0-7167-0041-7). W H Freeman.

Service, M. W. Methods for Sampling Adult Simulidae, with Special Reference to the Simulium Damnosum Complex. 1977. 35.00x (ISBN 0-85135-087-9, Pub. by Centre Overseas Research). State Mutual Bk.

Singh, S. R., et al, eds. Pests of Grain Legumes: Ecology & Control. 1979. 55.00 (ISBN 0-12-646350-6). Acad Pr.

Thresh, J. M., ed. Pest, Pathogens & Vegetation: The Role of Weeds & Wild Plants in the Ecology of Crop Pests & Diseases. LC 80-27419. (Pitman International Ser. in Bioscience). 440p. 1981. text ed. 75.95 (ISBN 0-273-08498-4). Pitman Pub MA.

Tunstall, J. P. & King, W. J. The Gumbia Cotton Handbook. 1979. 40.00x (ISBN 0-85135-100-X, Pub. by Centre Overseas Research). State Mutual Bk.

Wright, E. N. & Inglis, I. Bird Problems in Agriculture. 210p. 1980. 60.00x (ISBN 0-901436-48-8, CAB Bks). State Mutual Bk.

AGRICULTURAL PHYSICS

see also Crops and Climate; Soil Physics

Mohsenin, Nuri N. Physical Properties of Food & Agricultural Materials: A Teaching Manual. 157p. 1981. 28.95 (ISBN 0-677-05630-3). Gordon.

AGRICULTURAL PROCESSING

see also Food Industry and Trade

Brockington, N. R. Computer Modeling in Agriculture. (Illus.). 1979. 35.00x (ISBN 0-19-854523-1). Oxford U Pr.

Hall, Carl W. & Davis, Denny C. Processing Equipment for Agricultural Products. 2nd ed. (Illus.). 1979. lib. bdg. 27.50 (ISBN 0-87055-270-8). AVI.

Henderson, S. M. & Perry, R. L. Agricultural Process Engineering. 3rd ed. (Illus.). 1976. text ed. 24.50 (ISBN 0-87055-300-3). AVI.

AGRICULTURAL PRODUCTION FUNCTIONS

see Agriculture–Economic Aspects–Mathematical Models; Farm Management–Mathematical Models

AGRICULTURAL PRODUCTS

see Farm Produce

AGRICULTURAL RESEARCH

see also Field Experiments; Forestry Research; Plant-Breeding; Range Research

Agricultural Research. (Sector Policy Paper). 110p. 1981. 5.00 (ISBN 0-686-36055-9, PP-8101-E). World Bank.

Agriculture Board, National Research Council. Genetic Engineering of Plants: Agricultural Research Opportunities & Policy Concerns. 1984. pap. text ed. 9.50 (ISBN 0-309-03434-5). Natl Acad Pr.

Analysis of an FAO Survey of Post-Harvest Crop Losses in Developing Countries. (Illus.). 1978. pap. 13.00 (ISBN 0-685-86537-1, F719, FAO). Unipub.

Andrew, Chris O. & Hildebrand, Peter E. Planning & Conducting Applied Agricultural Research. 96p. 1982. 13.00 (ISBN 0-86531-461-6); pap. text ed. 8.50x (ISBN 0-86531-460-8). Westview.

Arndt, Thomas M., et al, eds. Resource Allocation & Productivity in National & International Agricultural Research. LC 76-44064. (Illus.). 1977. 32.50x (ISBN 0-8166-0805-9). U of Minn Pr.

Arnold, M. H. Agricultural Research for Development. 368p. 1976. 67.50 (ISBN 0-521-21051-8). Cambridge U Pr.

Arnold, M. H., ed. Agricultural Research for Development: The Hamulonge Contribution. LC 75-31400. pap. 93.80 (ISBN 0-317-26071-5, 2024411). Bks Demand UMI.

Arnon, I. The Planning & Programming of Agricultural Research. 122p. (2nd Printing 1978). 1975. pap. 7.50 (ISBN 92-5-100850-7, F320, FAO). Unipub.

Arnon, Isaac. Organisation & Administration of Agricultural Research. 342p. 1971. 39.00 (ISBN 0-444-20028-2, Pub. by Elsevier Applied Sci England). Elsevier.

Aspects of Assimilation & Accumulation of Nitrate in Some Cultivated Plants. (Agricultural Research Reports: No. 843). 1975. pap. 10.25 (ISBN 90-220-0586-0, PDC199, PUDOC). Unipub.

Beardsley, Edward H. Harry L. Russell & Agricultural Science in Wisconsin. (Illus.). 252p. 1969. 25.00x (ISBN 0-299-05470-5). U of Wis Pr.

Blanchard, J. Richard & Farrell, Lois. Guide to Sources for Agricultural & Biological Research. 672p. 1981. 48.50x (ISBN 0-520-03226-8). U of Cal Pr.

Bofinger, V. J. & Wheeler, J. L. Developments in Field Experiment Design & Analysis: Proceedings of Symposium held at the University of New England, Armidale, New South Wales, 3-7 September, 1973. 196p. 1975. 42.00x (ISBN 0-85198-333-2, Pub. by CAB Bks England). State Mutual Bk.

Brady, N. C., ed. Advances in Agronomy, Vol. 34. 1981. 75.00 (ISBN 0-12-000734-7). Acad Pr.

Burkett, J., ed. Agricultural Research Index: A Guide to Agricultural Research Including Dairy Farming, Fisheries, Food, Forestry, Horticulture, & Veterinary Science, 2vols. 6th ed. LC 78-40700. 1020p. Set. 295.00x (ISBN 0-582-90000-X, Pub. by Longman). Gale.

CAB Books, ed. List of Research Workers. 658p. 1981. 89.00x (ISBN 0-85198-485-1, Pub. by CAB Bks England). State Mutual Bk.

Chang, C. W. Increasing Food Production Through Education, Research & Extension. (Freedom from Hunger Campaign Basic Studies: No. 9). 78p. (Orig., 2nd Printing 1965). 1962. pap. 5.25 (ISBN 92-5-101637-2, F240, FAO). Unipub.

Compton, J. Lin, ed. The Transformation of International Agricultural Research & Development. (Westview Special Studies in Agriculture Science & Policy). 275p. 1985. pap. 19.85x (ISBN 0-8133-0057-6). Westview.

Cooke, G. W. Agricultural Research Nineteen Thirty-One to Nineteen Eighty-One. 367p. 1981. 90.00x (ISBN 0-7084-0180-5, Pub. by CAB Bks England). State Mutual Bk.

Curso De Planificacion Del Desarrollo Agricola, 1967: Seleccion de Conferenias y Ejercicios. (Agricultural Planning Studies: No. 9). (Span.). 140p. 1968. pap. 9.50 (ISBN 92-5-301989-1, F692, FAO). Unipub.

Dahlberg, Kenneth A., ed. New Directions for Agriculture & Agricultural Research: Neglected Dimensions & Emerging Alternatives. 220p. 1985. 45.00x (ISBN 0-8476-7417-7). Rowman.

Daniels, D. & Nestel, B., eds. Resource Allocation to Agricultural Research: Proceedings of a Workshop Held in Singapore, 8-10 June 1981. (Eng. & Fr.). 180p. 1981. pap. 12.00 (ISBN 0-88936-314-5, IDRC182, IDRC). Unipub.

Davidson, B. R. Experimental Research & Farm Productions. 1969. pap. 8.00x (ISBN 0-85564-008-1, Pub. by U of W Austral Pr). Intl Spec Bk.

A Decade of Learning: International Development Research Centre, Agriculture, Food & NutritionSciences Division: The First Ten Years. (Eng., Fr. & Span.). 180p. 1981. pap. 9.00 (ISBN 0-88936-297-1, IDRC170, IDRC). Unipub.

Directory of Agricultural Research Institutions & Projects in West Africa: CARIS Pilot Project. 543p. 1975. pap. 39.50 (ISBN 0-685-57611-6, F1254, FAO). Unipub.

Evans, L. T., ed. Crop Physiology. LC 73-91816. (Illus.). 384p. 1975. 57.50 (ISBN 0-521-20422-4); pap. 20.95x (ISBN 0-521-29390-1). Cambridge U Pr.

Gomez, Kwanchai A. & Gomez, Arturo A. Statistical Procedures for Agricultural Research. 2nd ed. LC 83-14556. 680p. 1984. 39.95x (ISBN 0-471-87092-7, Wiley-Interscience). Wiley.

Hadwiger, Don F. The Politics of Agricultural Research. LC 81-24077. x, 230p. 1982. 18.95x (ISBN 0-8032-2322-6). U of Nebr Pr.

Hardin, Charles M. Freedom in Agricultural Education. LC 75-27640. (World Food Supply Ser). 1976. Repr. of 1955 ed. 28.50x (ISBN 0-405-07780-7). Ayer Co Pubs.

Horton, Douglas. Social Scientists in Agricultural Research: Lessons from the Mantaro Valley Project, Peru. 67p. 1984. pap. 11.00 (ISBN 0-88936-400-1, IDRC219, IDRC). Unipub.

Isotopes & Radiation in Agricultural Research in the Soviet Union. (Study Tour Reports: No. 15). (Illus.). 108p. (Orig.). 1974. pap. 10.75 (ISBN 92-0-117173-0, ISTR5, IAEA). Unipub.

Mead, R. & Curnow, R. N. Statistical Methods in Agriculture & Experimental Biology. 300p. 1983. 49.95 (ISBN 0-412-24230-3, NO. 6767); pap. 25.00 (ISBN 0-412-24240-0, NO. 6768). Methuen Inc.

Merrill, Richard, ed. Radical Agriculture. LC 76-23504. 1976. 30.00x (ISBN 0-8147-5414-7). NYU Pr.

Muchow, Russell C., ed. Agro-Research for the Semi-Arid Tropics: North-West Australia. LC 84-11979. (Illus.). 640p. 1985. text ed. 44.50x (ISBN 0-7022-1776-X). U of Queensland Pr.

Nemeth, K. Application of Electro-Ultrafiltration (EUF) in Agricultural Production. 1982. pap. text ed. 22.00 (ISBN 90-247-2641-7, Pub. by Martinus Nijhoff Netherlands). Kluwer Academic.

Norman, A. G., ed. Advances in Agronomy, 24 vols. Incl. Vol. 1. 1949. 75.00 (ISBN 0-12-000701-0); Vol. 2. 1950. 75.00 (ISBN 0-12-000702-9); Vol. 3. 1951. 75.00 (ISBN 0-12-000703-7); Vol. 4. 1952. 75.00 (ISBN 0-12-000704-5); Vol. 5. 1953. 75.00 (ISBN 0-12-000705-3); Vol. 6. 1954. 75.00 (ISBN 0-12-000706-1); Vol. 7. 1955. 70.00 (ISBN 0-12-000707-X); Vol. 8. 1956. 75.00 (ISBN 0-12-000708-8); Vol. 9. 1957. 75.00 (ISBN 0-12-000709-6); Vol. 10. 1959. 75.00 (ISBN 0-12-000710-X); Vol. 11. 1959. 75.00 (ISBN 0-12-000711-8); Vol. 12. 1960. 75.00 (ISBN 0-12-000712-6); Vol. 13. 1961. 75.00 (ISBN 0-12-000713-4); Vol. 14. 1962. 75.00 (ISBN 0-12-000714-2); Vol. 15. 1963 (ISBN 0-12-000715-0); Vol. 16. 1964. 75.00 (ISBN 0-12-000716-9); Vol. 17. 1965. 75.00 (ISBN 0-12-000717-7); Vol. 18. 1966. 75.00 (ISBN 0-12-000718-5); Vol. 19. 1967. 75.00 (ISBN 0-12-000719-3); Vol. 20 o.s. 1968. 75.00 (ISBN 0-12-000720-7); Vol. 21. Brady, N. C., ed. 1969. 75.00 (ISBN 0-12-000721-5); Vol. 22. 1970. 75.00 (ISBN 0-12-000722-3); Vol. 23. 1971. 75.00 (ISBN 0-12-000723-1); Vol. 24. 1972. 75.00 (ISBN 0-12-000724-X). Vols. 1-24. Acad Pr.

Occurence & Properties of Bacterial Pectate Lyases. (Agricultural Research Reports: No. 779). 1972. pap. 14.00 (ISBN 90-220-0411-2, PDC60, PUDOC). Unipub.

Pearson, C. J., ed. Control of Crop Productivity. 339p. 1984. 49.50 (ISBN 0-12-548280-9). Acad Pr.

Peterson, R. Experimental Designs for Agriculture Research in Developing Areas. pap. 5.75x (ISBN 0-88246-086-2). Oreg St U Bkstrs.

Report on the 1970 World Census of Agriculture: Results by Countries. (Census Bulletins: No. 19). 50p. 1979. pap. 7.50 (ISBN 0-686-59471-1, F1493, FAO). Unipub.

Research Guidelines for Field Action Projects to Promote Participation of the Poor in Rural Organizations. (Rural Organization Action Programmes). (Eng., Fr & Span.). 63p. 1979. pap. 9.00 (ISBN 92-5-100868-X, F1887, FAO). Unipub.

Rodgers, Andrew D., 3rd. Liberty Hyde Bailey: A Story of American Plant Sciences. LC 85-1100. (Illus.). 1965. Repr. of 1949 ed. 15.95x (ISBN 0-02-851100-X). Hafner.

Ruttan, Vernon W. Agricultural Research Policy. LC 81-16396. 382p. 1982. 32.50x (ISBN 0-8166-1101-7); pap. 13.95x (ISBN 0-8166-1102-5). U of Minn Pr.

St. John, Judy, ed. Frontiers of Membrane Research in Agriculture. (Beltsville Symposia in Agriculture Research Ser.: Vol. IX). (Illus.). 512p. 1985. text ed. 58.50x (ISBN 0-8476-7426-6). Rowman & Allanheld.

Scobie, Grant M. Investment in International Agricultural Research: Some Economic Dimensions. (Working Paper: No. 361). iv, 98p. 1979. 5.00 (ISBN 0-686-36067-2, WP-0361). World Bank.

Seedlings of Some Tropical Trees & Shrubs Mainly of South East Asia. 1972. pap. 35.00 (ISBN 90-220-0416-3, PDC81, PUDOC). Unipub.

Shaner, W. W. & Philipp, P. F., eds. Readings in Farming Systems Research & Development. (Special Studies in Agriculture-Aquaculture Science & Policy). 166p. 1982. lib. bdg. 22.00x (ISBN 0-86531-502-7). Westview.

Sironval, C. & Brouers, M., eds. Protochlorophyllide Reduction & Greening. (Advances in Agricultural Biotechnology Ser.). 1984. lib. bdg. 55.00 (ISBN 90-247-2954-8, Pub. by Martinus Nijhoff Netherlands). Kluwer-Academic.

Staples, R. C. & Kuhr, R. J., eds. Linking Research to Crop Production. LC 79-25737. 250p. 1980. 37.50x (ISBN 0-306-40331-5, Plenum Pr). Plenum Pub.

Stern, Norman J. & Gamble, H. Ray, eds. Hybridoma Technology in Agricultural & Veterinary Research. LC 84-17795. (Illus.). 354p. 1984. 52.50x (ISBN 0-8476-7362-6). Rowman & Allanheld.

Storer, Norman W. Science & Scientists in an Agricultural Research Organization: A Sociological Study. Zuckerman, Harriet & Merton, Robert K., eds. LC 79-9029. (Dissertations on Sociology Ser.). 1980. lib. bdg. 21.00x (ISBN 0-405-12996-3). Ayer Co Pubs.

Studies on the Influence of Some Auxin Herbicides on Grass-Seed Crops. 1960. pap. 4.00 (PDC156, PUDOC). Unipub.

Thorne, Marlowe D., ed. Agronomists & Food: Contributions & Challenges. 1977. pap. gratis (ISBN 0-89118-048-6). Am Soc Agron.

True, Alfred. Alfred True on Agricultural Experimentation & Research: An Original Anthology. Cohen, I. Bernard, ed. LC 79-8001. (Three Centuries of Science in America Ser.). (Illus.). 1980. lib. bdg. 64.50x (ISBN 0-405-12589-5). Ayer Co Pubs.

Westmaas Research Group on New Tillage Systems. Experiences with Three Tillage Systems on a Marine Loam Soil I: 1972-1975. (Agricultural Research Reports: No. 899). 104p. 1980. pap. 18.50 (ISBN 90-220-0741-3, PDC219, PUDOC). Unipub.

Whyte, William F. Participatory Approaches to Agricultural Research & Development: A State-of-the-Art Paper. (Special Series on Agriculture Research & Extension). 111p. (Orig.). 1981. pap. 8.15 (ISBN 0-86731-053-7). RDC Ctr Intl Stud.

Wind-Profile Measurements - Above a Maize. (Agricultural Research Reports: No. 882). 1978. pap. 16.00 (ISBN 90-220-0684-0, PDC134, PUDOC). Unipub.

Yaron, D. & Tapiero, C., eds. Operations Research in Agriculture & Water Resources. 586p. 1980. 85.00 (ISBN 0-444-86044-4, North-Holland). Elsevier.

AGRICULTURAL SCHOOLS

see Agricultural Colleges

AGRICULTURAL SUPPLIES

see Farm Equipment

AGRICULTURAL TOOLS

see Agricultural Implements

AGRICULTURAL WASTES

see also Compost

Agricultural Waste. (Guides to Information Sources: No. 34). pap. 4.00 (ISBN 0-686-93204-8, UNID230, UN). Unipub.

Grundy, Kevin. Tackling Farm Waste. (Illus.). 250p. 18.95 (ISBN 0-85236-103-3, Pub. by Farming Pr UK). Diamond Farm Bk.

Hobson, P. N., et al. Methane Production from Agricultural & Domestic Wastes. LC 81-5048. (Energy from Wastes Ser.). 269p. 1981. 54.95x (ISBN 0-470-27154-X). Halsted Pr.

Information Sources on Bioconversion of Agricultural Wastes. (UNIDO Guides to Information Sources: No.33). 84p. 1980. pap. 4.00 (ISBN 0-686-70500-9, UNID228, UN). Unipub.

Inglett, George E. Symposium: Processing Agricultural & Municipal Wastes. (Illus.). 1973. text ed. 50.00 (ISBN 0-87055-139-6). AVI.

Jenkins, S. H. The Agricultural Industry & its Effects on Water Quality Programme. flexi-cover 89.00x (ISBN 0-08-024889-6). Pergamon.

Keterlaars, E. H. & Iwema, S. Boer, eds. Animals as Waste Converters: Proceedings of an International Symposium, Wageningen, Netherlands, 30 November - 2 December 1983. 153p. 1984. pap. 17.50 (ISBN 90-220-0857-6, PDC271, Pudoc). Unipub.

Lee, Robert E., Jr. Air Pollution from Pesticides & Agricultural Processes. (Uniscience Ser.). 280p. 1976. 69.00 (ISBN 0-8493-5157-X). CRC Pr.

Loehr, Raymond. Agricultural Waste Management. 1974. 85.00 (ISBN 0-12-455250-1). Acad Pr.

Residue Utilization: Management of Agricultural & Agro-Industrial Wastes. 1978. pap. 7.50 (ISBN 92-5-100320-3, F1265, FAO). Unipub.

Schuler, Michael. The Utilization & Recycle of Agricultural Wastes & Residues. 304p. 1980. 82.00 (ISBN 0-8493-5569-9). CRC Pr.

The Worldwide Loss of Cropland. (Worldwatch Institute Papers: No. 24). 48p. 1978. pap. 2.95 (ISBN 0-686-94920-X, WW24, WW). Unipub.

AGRICULTURE

see also Aeronautics in Agriculture; Animal Industry; Aquaculture; Botany, Economic; Cattle; Chemurgy; Crop Yields; Dairying; Domestic Animals; Drainage; Electricity in Agriculture; Farm Buildings; Farm Management; Farm Produce; Farmers; Farms; Fertilizers and Manures; Field Crops; Floriculture; Food Industry and Trade; Forage Plants; Forests and Forestry; Fruit; Fruit-Culture; Grain; Grasses; Horticulture; Insects, Injurious and Beneficial; Irrigation; Irrigation Farming; Livestock; Organic Farming; Pastures; Plant-Breeding; Radioisotopes in Agriculture; Reclamation of Land; Seeds; Shifting Cultivation; Soil Science; Soil Surveys; Soils; Trees; Vegetable Gardening; Vegetables; Viticulture; Water-Supply, Agricultural also headings beginning with the word Agricultural, and names of agricultural products

Adams, George. Nature Ever New: Essays on the Renewal of Agriculture. 1979. pap. 6.50 (ISBN 0-916786-40-4). St George Bk Serv.

Agricultural Board - Division Of Biology And Agriculture. Guide to Environmental Research on Animals. LC 76-609948. (Illus., Orig.). 1971. pap. 12.75 (ISBN 0-309-01869-2). Natl Acad Pr.

Agricultural Credit. (Terminology Bulletins: No. 32). 1978. pap. 14.50 (ISBN 92-5-000521-0, F1485, FAO). Unipub.

Agricultural Development & Employment Performance & Planning: A Comparative Analysis. (Agricultural Planning Studies: No. 18). (Eng., Fr., & Span.). 144p. 1974. pap. 9.75 (ISBN 92-5-100816-7, F2062, FAO). Unipub.

Agricultural Feedstock & Waste Treatment & Engineering. (Advances in Biochemical Engineering-Biotechnology Ser.: Vol. 32). (Illus.). 280p. 1985. 46.50 (ISBN 0-387-15490-6). Springer-Verlag.

Agricultural Residues: Compendium of Technologies. (Agricultural Services Bulletins: No. 33). (Eng., Fr., & Span.). 376p. 1978. pap. 26.75 (ISBN 92-5-000554-7, F1427, FAO). Unipub.

Agricultural Residues: Compendium of Technologies. (Agricultural Services Bulletins: No. 33, Rev. 1). (Eng., Fr., & Span.). 632p. 1982. pap. text ed. 45.00 (ISBN 92-5-001249-7, F2378, FAO). Unipub.

Agriculture in the Planning & Management of Peri-Urban Areas, Vol. 1. 1979. 5.00x (ISBN 92-64-11892-6). OECD.

Agriculture in the Twentieth Century. facsimile ed. LC 77-90597. (Essay Index Reprint Ser). 1939. 21.00 (ISBN 0-8369-1268-3). Ayer Co Pubs.

Alexandratos, Nikos, et al. Agriculture from the Perspective of Population Growth: Some Results from "Agriculture Toward 2000". (Economic & Social Development Papers: No. 30). 100p. 1984. pap. 7.50 (ISBN 92-5-101365-9, F2484, FAO). Unipub.

Baden, John, ed. The Vanishing Farmland Crisis: Critical Views of the Movement to Preserve Agricultural Land. LC 84-2004. (Studies in Government & Public Policy). 184p. 1984. 19.95x (ISBN 0-7006-0253-4). U Pr of KS.

Bardach, Eugene & Angelides, Sotirios. Water Banking: How to Stop Wasting Agricultural Water. LC 78-50766. 56p. 1978. pap. 2.00 (ISBN 0-917616-26-X). ICS Pr.

Barlett. Agricultural Decision Making. 1984. 19.50 (ISBN 0-12-078882-9). Acad Pr.

Barlett, Peggy F., ed. Agricultural Decision Making: Anthropological Contributions to Rural Development. LC 80-513. (Studies in Anthropology Ser.). 1980. 37.50 (ISBN 0-12-078880-2). Acad Pr.

Barrau, Jacques. Subsistence Agriculture in Melanesia, 2 vols. (BMB). 1958-1961. Repr. of 1958 ed. Vol. 1. 15.00 (ISBN 0-527-02327-2); Vol. 2. 14.00 (ISBN 0-527-02331-0). Kraus Repr.

Basic Texts of the FAO, Vols. 1 & 2. 1978. Set. pap. 27.00 (ISBN 92-5-100568-0, F1556, FAO). Unipub.

Bayliss-Smith, T. P. The Ecology of Agricultural Systems. 2nd ed. LC 82-1132. (Cambridge Topics in Geography Ser.: No. 2). (Illus.). 96p. 1982. 14.95 (ISBN 0-521-23125-6); pap. 7.95 (ISBN 0-521-29829-6). Cambridge U Pr.

Berardi, Gigi M. & Geisler, Charles C., eds. The Social Consequences & Challenges of New Agricultural Technologies. (Rural Studies). 450p. 1985. pap. 29.50x softcover (ISBN 0-86531-666-X). Westview.

Berry, Wendell. The Unsettling of America: Culture & Agriculture. LC 77-3729. 238p. 1977. 14.95 (ISBN 0-87156-194-8). Sierra.

Bertin, Jacques, et al. Atlas of Food Crops. (Ecoles Practiques Des Hautes Etudes: Section 6). (Illus.). 41p. 1971. text ed. 40.80x (ISBN 90-2791-798-1). Mouton.

Bibliography of Agriculture: Annual Cumulative, Vol. 45. 1981. 350.00 (ISBN 0-912700-90-4). Oryx Pr.

Blake, C. D. Fundamentals of Modern Agriculture. 516p. 1974. (Pub. by Sydney U Pr); pap. 21.00x (ISBN 0-424-06930-X, Pub. by Sydney U Pr). Intl Spec Bk.

Borgstrom, G. Harvesting the Earth. (Illus.). 1973. 11.49i (ISBN 0-200-71974-2). Har-Row.

Brady, N. C., ed. Advances in Agronomy, Vol. 28. 1976. 75.00 (ISBN 0-12-000728-2). Acad Pr.

--Advances in Agronomy, Vol. 29. 1977. 75.00 (ISBN 0-12-000729-0). Acad Pr.

--Advances in Agronomy, Vol. 30. LC 50-5598. 1979. 65.00 (ISBN 0-12-000730-4). Acad Pr.

--Advances in Agronomy, Vol. 31. LC 50-5598. (Serial Publication Ser.). 1980. 60.00 (ISBN 0-12-000731-2). Acad Pr.

--Advances in Agronomy, Vol. 33. 1980. 65.00 (ISBN 0-12-000733-9). Acad Pr.

--Advances in Agronomy, Vol. 35. (Serial Publication Ser.). 1982. 50.00 (ISBN 0-12-000735-5). Acad Pr.

Brengle, Kenneth G. Principles & Practices of Dryland Farming. 1982. 15.00x (ISBN 0-87081-095-2). Colo Assoc.

Brewer, Robert N., et al. Solar Applications in Agriculture. 143p. 1981. 12.95 (ISBN 0-89168-034-9). L Erlbaum Assocs.

Brown, Lester R. The Worldwide Loss of Cropland. LC 78-64454. (Worldwatch Papers). 1978. pap. 2.00 (ISBN 0-916468-23-2). Worldwatch Inst.

Buck, Solon J. The Granger Movement: A Study of Agricultural Organization & Its Political, Economic, & Social Manifestations, 1870-1880. LC 63-9713. (Illus.). xii, 384p. 1963. pap. 6.50x (ISBN 0-8032-5027-4, BB 166, Bison). U of Nebr Pr.

Bunch, Roland. Two Ears of Corn: A Guide to People-Centered Agricultural Improvement. (Illus.). 250p. 1982. pap. 7.95 (ISBN 0-942716-03-5). World Neigh.

Busch, Lawerence & Lacy, William B. Science, Agriculture, & Government: The Politics of Research. LC 82-15923. (WVSS in Agriculture Aquaculture Science & Policy Ser.). (Illus.). 325p. (Orig.). 1982. lib. bdg. 32.00x (ISBN 0-86531-225-7); pap. text ed. 13.50x (ISBN 0-86531-230-3). Westview.

Busch, Lawrence, ed. Science & Agricultural Development. LC 81-65005. 198p. 1981. text ed. 31.50x (ISBN 0-86598-022-5). Allanheld.

Butterfield, R. M. & May, N. D. Muscles of the Ox. (Illus.). 1966. 25.00x (ISBN 0-7022-0400-5). U of Queensland Pr.

Byram, H. M. Occupations for Youth in Agriculture. text ed. 4.00x (ISBN 0-8134-0492-4, 492). Interstate.

Cannell, G. H., et al, eds. Agriculture in Semi-Arid Environments. (Ecological Studies: Vol. 34). (Illus.). 1979. 60.00 (ISBN 0-387-09414-8). Springer-Verlag.

Carman, Harry J., et al. Jesse Buel, Agricultural Reformer: Selections from His Writings. LC 72-2835. (Use & Abuse of America's Natural Resources Ser). 650p. 1972. Repr. of 1947 ed. 37.50 (ISBN 0-405-04503-4). Ayer Co Pubs.

Cato & Varro. On Agriculture. (Loeb Classical Library: No. 283). 12.50x (ISBN 0-674-99313-6). Harvard U Pr.

Cayre, Henri. Agriculture Plenty: A Monograph. 176p. 1980. 40.00x (ISBN 0-85614-070-8, Pub. by Gentry England). State Mutual Bk.

CERES: FAO Review on Agriculture and Development. pap. 15.00, per year (FAO). Unipub.

Chambers, J. D. & Mingay, G. E. The Agricultural Revolution. 1975. pap. 16.95 (ISBN 0-7134-1358-1, Pub. by Batsford England). David & Charles.

Charles-Edwards, D., ed. Physiological Determinants of Crop Growth. 1983. 37.00 (ISBN 0-12-169360-0). Acad Pr.

Chrispeels, Maarten J. & Sadava, David. Plants, Food, & People. LC 76-46498. (Illus.). 278p. 1977. text ed. 25.95 (ISBN 0-7167-0378-5); pap. text ed. 13.95 (ISBN 0-7167-0377-7). W H Freeman.

Cobbett, William. Year's Residence in the United States of America. LC 64-14796. (Centaur Classics Ser.). 338p. 1964. 19.50x (ISBN 0-8093-0149-0). S Ill U Pr.

Computer Strategies. The Agriculture Computer Handbook. 150p. 1983. looseleaf 45.00x. Computer Strat.

Cox, S. W. Microelectronics in Agriculture & Horticulture: Electronics & Computers In Farming. 240p. 1982. pap. text ed. 26.50x (ISBN 0-86598-087-X). Allanheld.

Crop Science. 65.00 (ISBN 0-686-40174-3); 13.00 ea.; indexes 3.00 (ISBN 0-686-40175-1). Crop Sci Soc Am.

Crunkilton, John R. & Krebs, Al H. Teaching Agriculture Through Problem Solving. 3rd ed. 1981. text ed. 13.50x (ISBN 0-8134-2199-3). Interstate.

Dahlberg, Kenneth A., ed. Beyond the Green Revolution: The Ecology & Politics of Global Agricultural Development. LC 78-11271. (Illus.). 270p. 1979. 25.00x (ISBN 0-306-40120-7, Plenum Pr). Plenum Pub.

--New Directions for Agriculture & Agricultural Research: Neglected Dimensions & Emerging Alternatives. 220p. 1985. 45.00x (ISBN 0-8476-7417-7). Rowman.

Dalton, G. E., ed. Study of Agricultural Systems. (Illus.). 1975. 61.00 (ISBN 0-85334-640-2, Pub. by Elsevier Applied Sci England). Elsevier.

Davidson, John & Lloyd, Richard, eds. Conservation & Agriculture. LC 77-697. 252p. 1978. 58.95x (ISBN 0-471-99502-9, Pub. by Wiley-Interscience). Wiley.

Day, Peter R., ed. The Genetic Basis of Epidemics in Agriculture, Vol. 287. (Annals of the New York Academy of Sciences). 400p. 1977. 37.00x (ISBN 0-89072-033-9). NY Acad Sci.

Demaree, Albert L. The American Agricultural Press: 1819-1860. LC 73-16296. (Perspectives in American History Ser.: No. 4). (Illus.). 430p. Repr. of 1941 ed. lib. bdg. 35.00x (ISBN 0-87991-331-2). Porcupine Pr.

Dempsey, James M. Fiber Crops. LC 74-4259. 1975. 18.50 (ISBN 0-8130-0449-7). U Presses Fla.

Dent, J. B. & Blackie, M. J. Systems Simulation in Agriculture. (Illus.). 180p. 1979. 31.50 (ISBN 0-85334-827-8, Pub. by Elsevier Applied Sci England). Elsevier.

Dethier, V. G. Man's Plague? Insects & Agriculture. LC 75-15216. (Illus.). 237p. (Orig.). 1976. 9.95 (ISBN 0-87850-026-X). Darwin Pr.

Development Planning & Research Associates, Inc., for U. S. Dept. of Agri., Manhattan, Kansas. Wind Energy Applications in Agriculture. 204p. 1982. pap. 29.50x (ISBN 0-89934-172-1, W064). Solar Energy Info.

De Wit, C. T. Simulation of Assimilation, Respiration & Transpiration of Crops. 148p. 1978. pap. 11.50 (ISBN 90-220-0601-8, PDC141, PUDOC). Unipub.

Dies, Edward J. Titans of the Soil: Great Builders of Agriculture. LC 76-49613. (Illus.). 1977. Repr. of 1949 ed. lib. bdg. 24.75x (ISBN 0-8371-9329-X, DITS). Greenwood.

D'Itri, Frank, et al, eds. Municipal Wastewater in Agriculture. 1982. 55.00 (ISBN 0-12-214880-0). Acad Pr.

Dover, Michael J. A Better Mousetrap: Innovative Technologies for Agricultural Pest Management, No. 4. Courrier, Kathleen, ed. (Illus., Orig.). Date not set. pap. text ed. 3.50 (ISBN 0-915825-09-0). World Resources Inst.

Drache, Hiram M. Beyond the Furrow: Some Keys to Successful Farming in the Twentieth Century. LC 76-29489. 560p. 1976. 14.95 (ISBN 0-8134-1858-5). Interstate.

Energy Cropping versus Food Production: Rome, June 1980. (Agricultural Services Bulletins: No. 46). (Eng., Fr. & Span.). 62p. 1981. pap. 7.50 (ISBN 92-5-101088-9, F2234, FAO). Unipub.

Farming with Animal Power. (Better Farming Ser.: No. 14). 57p. 1977. pap. 7.50 (ISBN 92-5-100157-X, F71, FAO). Unipub.

Fluck, Richard C. & Baird, C. Direlle. Agricultural Energetics. (Illus.). 1980. text ed. 22.50 (ISBN 0-87055-346-1). AVI.

Fuller, Anthony M. & Mage, Julius A. Part-Time Farming. (Rural Geography Ser.). 291p. 1980. pap. 13.80x (ISBN 0-902246-57-7, Pub. by GEO Abstracts England). State Mutual Bk.

Furuseth, Owen J. & Pierce, John T. Agricultural Land in an Urban Society. Knight, C. Gregory, ed. LC 82-18424. (Resource Publications in Geography Ser.). 89p. (Orig.). 1982. pap. 5.00 (ISBN 0-89291-149-2). Assn Am Geographers.

Goforth, Allene, ed. Energy & Agriculture: A Classified Title List to the Microfiche Collection. 116p. 1981. pap. text ed. 25.00 (ISBN 0-667-00666-4). Microfilming Corp.

Gorenflo, Louise, et al. Farm & Rural Energy Planning Manual. (Illus.). 120p. (Orig.). 1981. pap. 5.00 (ISBN 0-937786-04-7). Inst Ecological.

Gupta, U. S. Physiological Aspects of Dryland Farming. 392p. 1981. 80.00x (ISBN 0-686-76654-7, Pub. by Oxford & IBH India). State Mutual Bk.

Hannaway, David B., ed. Foothills for Food & Forests. (Illus.). 350p. (Orig.). 1983. pap. 34.95x (ISBN 0-917304-00-4). Timber.

Harper, F. Principles of Arable Crop Production. 352p. 1983. pap. 19.95x (ISBN 0-246-11741-9, Pub. by Granada England). Sheridan.

Hebblethwaite, P. D., et al, eds. Vicia Faba: Agronomy Physiology & Breeding. LC 84-4181. (World Crops: Production, Utilization & Description Ser.). 380p. 1984. 53.50 (ISBN 90-247-2964-5, Pub. by Martinus Nijhoff Netherlands). Kluwer Academic.

Hewitt, Edward & Brazier, David. Agricultural Science for Schools & Colleges. 2nd ed. 320p. 1986. pap. write for info. (ISBN 0-246-11355-3, Pub. by Granada England). Sheridan.

Hollaender, Alexander, ed. The Biosaline Concept: An Approach to the Utilization of Underexploited Resources. LC 79-18804. (Environmental Science Research Ser.: Vol. 14). 399p. 1979. 59.50x (ISBN 0-306-40295-5, Plenum Pr). Plenum Pub.

Howard, Albert. An Agricultural Testament. (Illus.). 272p. 1973. 14.95 (ISBN 0-87857-060-8). Rodale Pr Inc.

Howes, K. M. & Rummery, R. A. Integrating Agriculture & Forestry. 238p. 1981. 30.00x (ISBN 0-643-02431-X, Pub. by CSIRO Australia). State Mutual Bk.

Hunter, Albert S., ed. Advances in Agronomy: Vol. 32, Cumulative Index for Volumes 1-30. 1980. 50.00 (ISBN 0-12-000732-0). Acad Pr.

IDRC, Ottawa. Agriculture, Food & Nutrition Sciences Division: The First Five Years. 49p. 1977. pap. 5.00 (ISBN 0-88936-130-4, IDRC89, IDRC). Unipub.

Instituto Geografico De Agostini. World Atlas of Agriculture: Europe, U. S. S. R., Asia Minor; South & East Asia, Oceania; the Americas; & Africa, 5 Vols. LC 73-78857. (Illus.). 2248p. (Atlas, Vols. 1 & 3 published 1972; Vol. 2 1974; Vol. 4 August 1975). 1975. Set. 795.00 (ISBN 0-685-52999-1, IGA100, FAO). Unipub.

International Seminar on Energy Conservation & Use of Renewable Energies in the Bio-Industries, Trinity College, Oxford, UK, 2nd 6-10 Sept. 1982 & Vogt, F. Energy Conservation & Use of Renewable Energies in the Bio-Industries: Proceedings. (Illus.). 750p. 1982. 100.00 (ISBN 0-08-029781-1). Pergamon.

Irrigation Association Membership Directory & Buyers Guide 1984. Date not set. 50.00 (ISBN 0-935030-06-9). Irrigation.

Irrigation Technical Conference Proceedings 1983. LC 76-12209. (Illus.). 14.00 (ISBN 0-935030-04-2). Irrigation.

Jones & Socolofsky, eds. Science & Technology in Agriculture. 1980. cancelled (ISBN 0-87461-034-6). McNally.

Jones, E. L. Agriculture & the Industrial Revolution. LC 74-2400. 233p. 1975. 24.95x (ISBN 0-470-44870-9). Halsted Pr.

Kellogg, Charles E. Agricultural Development: Soil, Food, People, Work. (Illus.). 233p. 1975. 8.75 (ISBN 0-89118-763-4). Soil Sci Soc Am.

Keswani, C. L. & Ndunguru, B. J., eds. Intercropping: Proceedings of the Second Symposium on Intercropping in Semi-Arid Areas, Held at Morogoro, Tanzania 4-7 Aug. 1980. 168p. 1982. pap. 12.00 (ISBN 0-88936-318-8, IDRC186, IDRC). Unipub.

Knight, C. Gregory & Wilcox, R. Paul. Triumph or Triage? The World Food Problem in Geographical Persective. Natoli, Salvatore J., ed. LC 76-29265. (Resource Papers for College Geography Ser.). 1977. pap. text ed. 4.00 (ISBN 0-89291-115-8). Assn Am Geographers.

Koepf, Herbert H., et al. Bio-Dynamic Agriculture. 1976. 15.95 (ISBN 0-910142-73-4). Anthroposophic.

Konecci, E. B., ed. Environmental Control & Agri-Technology. (Science & Technology: Vol. 39). (Illus.). 1976. microfiche 30.00x (ISBN 0-87703-075-8, Pub. by Am Astronaut). Univelt Inc.

Lahiri, R. K. Family Farming in a Developing Economy. 1979. pap. text ed. 9.00x (ISBN 0-391-01851-5). Humanities.

Lambrick, George. Archaeology & Agriculture. 46p. 1977. pap. text ed. 7.45x (ISBN 0-900312-44-0, Pub. by Coun Brit Archaeology). Humanities.

L'Annunziata, Michael F. & Legg, Joe. Isotopes & Radiation in Agricultural Sciences: Soil-Plant-Water Relationships, Vol. 1. 1984. 65.00 (ISBN 0-12-436601-5). Acad Pr.

L'Annuziata, Michael F. & Legg, Joe, eds. Isotopes & Radiation in Agricultural Sciences: Animals, Plants, Food & the Environment, Vol. 2. 1984. 75.00 (ISBN 0-12-436602-3). Acad Pr.

Lawson, Roger H. National Work Conference on Microbial Collections of Major Importance to Agriculture. LC 81-66705. 52p. 1981. text ed. 6.50 (ISBN 0-89054-044-6). Am Phytopathol Soc.

Lendvay, Olga. Primer for Agricultural Libraries. 97p. 1980. pap. 7.50 (ISBN 90-220-0727-8, PDC165, PUDOC). Unipub.

Liebig, Justus Von. The Natural Laws of Husbandry. LC 72-2852. (Use & Abuse of America's Natural Resources Ser). 392p. 1972. Repr. of 1863 ed. 25.50 (ISBN 0-405-04541-7). Ayer Co Pubs.

Lionberger, Herbert F. Adoption of New Ideas & Practices. facsimile ed. (Illus.). 164p. 1961. pap. 9.45x (ISBN 0-8138-2200-9). Iowa St U Pr.

Living on a Few Acres: Yearbook of Agriculture, 1978. 432p. 1978. 13.00 (ISBN 0-318-11797-5). Gov Printing Office.

Lockeretz, William, ed. Environmentally Sound Agriculture. 444p. 1983. 39.95 (ISBN 0-03-062863-6). Praeger.

Lowrance, Richard, et al. Agricultural Ecosystems: Unifying Concepts. LC 83-23504. 233p. 1984. 39.95 (ISBN 0-471-87888-X, Pub. by Wiley-Interscience). Wiley.

McClure, Thomas A., ed. Resource Materials. Lipinsky, Edward S. (Handbook of Biosolar Resources Ser.: Vol. 2). 608p. 1981. 83.00 (ISBN 0-8493-3473-X). CRC Pr.

Maimondies. The Book of Agriculture. Klein, Isaac, ed. LC 49-9495. (Yale Judaica Ser.: No. 7). 1979. text ed. 65.00x (ISBN 0-300-02223-9). Yale U Pr.

Makkink, G. F. & Van Heemst, H. D. Simulation of the Water Balance of Arable Land & Pastures. (Illus.). 85p. 1975. pap. 12.00 (ISBN 90-220-0566-6, PDC87, PUDOC). Unipub.

Maltha, D. J. Agricultural Science: Wageningen in Focus. (Illus.). 92p. (11 drawings., 62 colour photographs, 76 b&w photos). 1981. pap. 11.75 (ISBN 90-220-0771-5, PDC243, Pudoc). Unipub.

Manassah, Jamal & Briskey, Ernest J., eds. Advances in Food Producing Systems for Arid & Semi-Arid Lands, 2 pts. 1981. Pt. A. 69.50 (ISBN 0-12-467301-5); Pt. B. 69.50 (ISBN 0-12-467302-3). Acad Pr.

Martins, Susanna W. A Great Estate at Work. LC 79-51827. (Illus.). 308p. 1980. 57.50 (ISBN 0-521-22696-1). Cambridge U Pr.

Matlon, P. & Cantrell, R., eds. Coming Full Circle: Farmers' Participation in the Development of Technology. (Illus.). 176p. 1984. pap. 15.00 (ISBN 0-88936-324-2, IDRC189E, IDRC). Unipub.

Mechanization of Irrigated Crop Production. (Agricultural Services Bulletins: No. 28). (Illus.). 413p. (2nd Printing 1979). 1977. pap. 24.75 (ISBN 92-5-100254-1, F717, FAO). Unipub.

Miller, Howard L. & Woodin, Ralph J. AGDEX: A System for Classifying, Indexing, & Filing Agricultural Publications. (Illus.). 50p. tchrs ed. 10.00 (ISBN 0-89514-030-6, 01081). Am Voc Assn.

Moen, Aaron N. Agriculture & Wildlife Management. LC 83-70990. (Illus.). xii, 367p. 1983. text ed. 39.00 (ISBN 0-913523-00-3); pap. text ed. 27.00 (ISBN 0-913523-01-1). CornerBrook Pr.

Mollison, Bill. Permaculture Two: Practical Design for Town & Country in Permanent Agriculture. (Illus.). 150p. (Orig.). 1979. pap. 10.95 (ISBN 0-908228-00-7). Intl Tree Crops.

Mussell, Harry & Staples, Richard C. Stress Physiology in Crop Plants. LC 78-27567. 510p. 1979. 54.95x (ISBN 0-471-03809-1, Pub. by Wiley-Interscience). Wiley.

National Academy Of Sciences. Prospects of the World Food Supply. 1966. pap. 1.50 (ISBN 0-309-00070-X). Natl Acad Pr.

National Agricultural Library Catalog: Indexes for 1971-1975, 2 vols. 1978. Set. 115.00x (ISBN 0-8476-6093-1). Rowman.

National Research Council. New Directions for Biosciences Research in Agriculture: High Reward Opportunities. 122p. 1985. pap. text ed. 9.95 (ISBN 0-309-03542-2). Natl Acad Pr.

New Protectionism & Attempts at Liberalization in Agricultural Trade. (Economic & Social Development Papers: No. 27). (Eng., Fr. & Span.). 100p. 1983. pap. text ed. 7.50 (ISBN 92-5-101312-8, F2432, FAO). Unipub.

New Technology & Agricultural Transformation: A Comparative Study of Punjab, India & Punjab, Pakistan. (Country Monographs). 113p. 1979. pap. 8.50 (ISBN 0-686-78244-5, CRD073, UNCRD). Unipub.

Newbury, P. A. R. A Geography of Agriculture. (Illus.). 336p. 1980. pap. text ed. 23.50x (ISBN 0-7121-0733-9). Trans-Atlantic.

Nichols, Mark. Young Farmers: Their Problems, Activities & Educational Program. (Illus.). 1952. text ed. 7.50x (ISBN 0-8134-0234-4, 234). Interstate.

Nicholson, Heather J. & Nicholson, Ralph L. Distant Hunger: Agriculture, Food, & Human Values. LC 78-60761. (Science & Society: A Purdue University Series in Science, Technology, & Human Values: Vol. 3). (Illus.). 240p. 1979. pap. 3.95 (ISBN 0-931682-00-2). Purdue Univ.

Nineteen-Seventy World Census of Agriculture: Analysis & International Comparison of Data. (Statistics Ser.: No. 37). 300p. 1981. pap. 26.25 (ISBN 92-5-101037-4, F2290, FAO). Unipub.

Norman, A. G., ed. Advances in Agronomy, 24 vols. Incl. Vol. 1. 1949. 75.00 (ISBN 0-12-000701-0); Vol. 2. 1950. 75.00 (ISBN 0-12-000702-9); Vol. 3. 1951. 75.00 (ISBN 0-12-000703-7); Vol. 4. 1952. 75.00 (ISBN 0-12-000704-5); Vol. 5. 1953. 75.00 (ISBN 0-12-000705-3); Vol. 6. 1954. 75.00 (ISBN 0-12-000706-1); Vol. 7. 1955. 70.00 (ISBN 0-12-000707-X); Vol. 8. 1956. 75.00 (ISBN 0-12-000708-8); Vol. 9. 1957. 75.00 (ISBN 0-12-000709-6); Vol. 10. 1959. 75.00 (ISBN 0-12-000710-X); Vol. 11. 1959. 75.00 (ISBN 0-12-000711-8); Vol. 12. 1960. 75.00 (ISBN 0-12-000712-6); Vol. 13. 1961. 75.00 (ISBN 0-12-000713-4); Vol. 14. 1962. 75.00 (ISBN 0-12-000714-2); Vol. 15. 1963 (ISBN 0-12-000715-0); Vol. 16. 1964. 75.00 (ISBN 0-12-000716-9); Vol. 17. 1965. 75.00 (ISBN 0-12-000717-7); Vol. 18. 1966. 75.00 (ISBN 0-12-000718-5); Vol. 19. 1967. 75.00 (ISBN 0-12-000719-3); Vol. 20 o.s. 1968. 75.00 (ISBN 0-12-000720-7); Vol. 21. Brady, N. C., ed. 1969. 75.00 (ISBN 0-12-000721-5); Vol. 22. 1970. 75.00 (ISBN 0-12-000722-3); Vol. 23. 1971. 75.00 (ISBN 0-12-000723-1); Vol. 24. 1972. 75.00 (ISBN 0-12-000724-X). Vols. 1-24. Acad Pr.

--Advances in Agronomy, Vol. 26. (Serial Publication Ser.). 1974. 75.00 (ISBN 0-12-000726-6). Acad Pr.

Palti, J. Cultural Practices & Infectious Crop Diseases. (Advanced Series in Agricultural Sciences: Vol. 9). (Illus.). 200p. 1981. 42.00 (ISBN 0-387-11047-X). Springer-Verlag.

Papavizas, George C., ed. Biological Control in Crop Production. LC 81-65017. (Beltsville Symposia in Agricultural Research Ser.: No. 5). 474p. 1982. text ed. 42.00x (ISBN 0-86598-037-3). Allanheld.

Park, R. D. & Eddowes, Maurice. Crop Husbandry. 2nd ed. (Illus.). 1975. 45.00x (ISBN 0-19-859443-7). Oxford U Pr.

Pearce, S. C. The Agricultural Field Experiment: A Statistical Examination of Theory & Practice. LC 82-13711. 335p. 1983. 44.95x (ISBN 0-471-10511-2, Pub. by Wiley-Interscience). Wiley.

Pearson, Frank A. & Harper, Floyd A. World's Hunger. LC 71-153235. 1971. Repr. of 1945 ed. 24.00x (ISBN 0-8046-1545-4, Pub. by Kennikat). Assoc Faculty Pr.

Penning de Vries, F. W. T. & Van Laar, H. H., eds. Simulation of Plant Growth & Crop Production. (Simulation Monographs). 308p. (20 papers, index). 1982. pap. 29.25 (ISBN 90-220-0809-6, PDC250, PUDOC). Unipub.

People for Open Space. Endangered Harvest: The Future of Bay Area Farmland. (Orig.). 1980. pap. 5.00 (ISBN 0-9605262-0-X). PFOS.

Perspectives in World Agriculture. 517p. 1980. 80.00x (ISBN 0-85198-458-4, Pub. by CAB Bks England). State Mutual Bk.

Phillips, Ronald E. No-Tillage Agriculture Principles. Phillips, Shirley H., ed. 320p. 1984. 34.50 (ISBN 0-442-27731-8). Van Nos Reinhold.

Pimentel, David. Food, Energy & Future of Society. 1980. pap. 3.50x (ISBN 0-87081-089-8). Colo Assoc.

Pond, Wilson G. & Mumpton, Frederick A., eds. Zeo-Agriculture: The Use of Natural Zeolites in Agriculture & Aquaculture. 450p. 1983. lib. bdg. 52.50x (ISBN 0-86531-602-3). Westview.

Price, D. Porter, et al. Modern Vocational Agriculture: Science, Production, Finance, & Economics. 1986. price not set (ISBN 0-9606246-6-X). SW Sci Pub.

Programme for the 1970 World Census of Agriculture. pap. 15.50 (F1037, FAO). Unipub.

Programming for Agricultural Development. (Agricultural Planning Studies: No. 1). (Eng., Fr. & Span.). 57p. (5th Printing 1976). 1963. pap. 7.50 (ISBN 92-5-100814-0, F2058, FAO). Unipub.

Raeburn, John R. Agriculture: Foundations, Principles & Development. LC 84-3619. 350p. 1984. text ed. 29.95 (ISBN 0-471-10308-X). Wiley.

Rajki, ed. Proceedings of a Workshop on Agricultural Potentiality Directed by Nutritional Needs. 1979. 24.50 (ISBN 0-9960014-4-1, Pub. by Akademiai Kaido Hungary). Heyden.

Regional Training Course in Agricultural Project Analysis Held at New Delhi, India 2-28 November 1970. pap. 7.50 (F697, FAO). Unipub.

Report of an FAO-UNFPA Seminar on Agricultural Planning & Population: Malta, 1974. (United Nations Funds-in-Trust Ser.). (Illus.). 162p. 1976. pap. 12.75 (ISBN 0-685-66312-4, F1139, FAO). Unipub.

Report of the Eighth Session of the Near East Commission on Agricultural Planning. (Illus.). 26p. 1978. pap. 7.50 (ISBN 92-5-100354-8, F1251, FAO). Unipub.

Report of the Eleventh FAO Regional Conference for Europe. 1979. pap. 7.50 (ISBN 92-5-100726-8, F1580, FAO). Unipub.

Report of the FAO Council: 78th Session, Rome, November 24 - December 4, 1980. (Eng., Fr. & Span.). 119p. 1980. pap. 8.75 (ISBN 92-5-101032-3, F2136, FAO). Unipub.

Report of the General Commemorative Conference of FAO: Rome, 16 Nov. 1970. 75p. pap. 4.50 (ISBN 92-5-101868-5, F1931, FAO). Unipub.

Report of the Regional Conference for Asia & the Far East. Incl. Twelfth, Tokyo, Japan, 17-27 Sept. 1974. 76p. 1976. pap. 7.50 (ISBN 0-685-66334-5, F1122); Third, Bandung, 1956. 94p. 1957. pap. 4.25 (ISBN 0-686-92902-0, F390). FAO). Unipub.

Report on the Ad Hoc Consultation on a Scheme for Agricultural Credit Development. (Development Documents: No. 31). (Eng., Fr. & Span.). 24p. 1976. pap. 7.50 (ISBN 92-5-100087-5, F1150, FAO). Unipub.

Report on the Agro-Ecological Zones Project: Methodology & Results for South & Central America, Vol. 3. (World Soil Resources Reports: No. 48-3). (Eng. & Span.). 251p. 1982. pap. 19.75 (ISBN 92-5-101081-1, F2225, FAO). Unipub.

Report on the 1950 World Census of Agriculture. (Census Bulletins: Vol. 2). 168p. 1958. pap. 10.00 (ISBN 0-686-93071-1, F1929, FAO). Unipub.

Report on the 1960 World Census of Agriculture: Analysis & International Comparison of Census, Vol. 5. 239p. 1971. pap. 18.25 (ISBN 92-5-101730-1, F395, FAO). Unipub.

Report on the 1960 World Census of Agriculture: Methodology, Vol. 3. 414p. 1969. pap. 26.00 (ISBN 92-5-101728-X, F392, FAO). Unipub.

Report on the 1960 World Census of Agriculture: Processing & Tabulation, Vol. 4. 147p. 1968. pap. 10.75 (ISBN 92-5-101729-8, F396, FAO). Unipub.

Report on the 1960 World Census of Agriculture: Programme, Concepts & Scope, Vol. 2. 186p. 1969. pap. 22.50 (ISBN 92-5-101727-1, F393, FAO). Unipub.

Report on the 1970 World Census of Agriculture - Jordan. (Census Bulletins: No. 23). 1979. pap. 7.50 (ISBN 0-685-96684-4, F1563, FAO). Unipub.

Report on the 1970 World Census of Agriculture. Incl. Botswana, Surinam. (No. 1). 1973 (F1051); Japan, Malta. (No. 2). 1973 (F1052); Czechoslovakia, Luxembourg. (No. 3). 1973 (F1053); Canada, Sweden. (No. 4). 1973 (F1054); Fiji, Norway, Portugal. (No. 5). 1974 (F1055); American Samoa, Guam, Pacific Islands (Trust Territory), Puerto Rico, Virgin Islands (U.S.) (No. 6). 1974 (F1056); Finland, USA. (No. 7). 1974 (F1057); Ghana, Iraq, Uruguay. (No. 8). 1974 (F1058); France, Lesotho, Malawi. (No. 9). 1975 (F1059); Costa Rica, Korea, Republic of Swaziland. (No. 10). 1975 (F1060); New Zealand, Zambia. (No. 11). 1975 (F1061); Greece, Jamaica. (No. 13). 1976 (F1079); Denmark, Netherlands, Switzerland. (No. 14). 1976 (F1080); Bahrain, Italy, Peru. (No. 16). 1977 (F1274); Saudi Arabia, Yugoslavia. (No. 17). 1977 (F1273). (Census Bulletin Ser.). pap. 7.50 each (FAO). Unipub.

Review of Agricultural Planning During the Second Postwar Decade. (Agricultural Planning Studies: No. 5). 31p. 1976. Repr. of 1966 ed. pap. 7.50 (ISBN 92-5-101111-7, F689, FAO). Unipub.

Ritchie, Gary A., ed. New Agricultural Crops. (AAAS Selected Symposium: No. 38). 1979. softcover 26.00 (ISBN 0-89158-473-0). Westview.

Robinson, D. H. Fream's Elements of Agriculture. 15th ed. 25.00 (ISBN 0-7195-2579-9). Transatlantic.

Rodale, Robert. Our Next Frontier: A Personal Guide for Tomorrow's Lifestyle. Stoner, Carol, ed. (Illus.). 252p. 1981. 14.95 (ISBN 0-87857-365-8). Rodale Pr Inc.

Romberger, John A. Virology in Agriculture. LC 76-42139. (Beltsville Symposia in Agricultural Reasearch Ser.: No. 1). 320p. 1977. text ed. 26.50x (ISBN 0-916672-14-X). Allanheld.

Rosenblum, John W., ed. Agriculture in the Twenty-First Century. LC 83-19847. 415p. 1983. 29.95x (ISBN 0-471-88538-X, Pub. by Wiley-Interscience). Wiley.

Rowat, R. Trained Manpower for Agricultural & Rural Development. (Economic & Social Development Papers: No. 10, suppl.). 26p. 1983. pap. 9.75 (ISBN 92-5-101387-X, F1963, FAO). Unipub.

Schultz, Theodore W., ed. Distortions of Agricultural Incentives: Papers Presented at a 1977 Three-Day Workshop Sponsored by the Midwest Center of the American Academy of Arts & Sciences. LC 78-3246. pap. 87.80 (ISBN 0-317-28580-7, 2055201). Bks Demand UMI.

Scientific American Editors. Food & Agriculture: A Scientific American Book. (Illus.). 154p. 1976. text ed. 20.95x (ISBN 0-7167-0382-3); pap. 10.95x (ISBN 0-7167-0381-5). W H Freeman.

Scrimshaw, Nevin S. & Behar, Moises, eds. Nutrition & Agricultural Development. LC 76-2043. (Basic Life Sciences Ser.: Vol. 7). (Illus.). 524p. 1976. 65.00x (ISBN 0-306-36507-3, Plenum Pr). Plenum Pub.

Seeds: Proceedings of the FAO/SIDA Technical Conference on Improved Seed Production, June 2-6, 1981. (Plant Production & Protection Papers: No. 39). 569p. 1983. pap. 41.75 (ISBN 92-5-001226-8, F2361, FAO). Unipub.

Septieme Cours Sur la Planification Agricole, 1974, Vol. 2. (Agricultural Planning Ser.: No. 19). (Fr.). 232p. 1974. pap. 19.00 (ISBN 92-5-201992-8, FAO). Unipub.

Silano, V., et al, eds. Improvement of Nutritional Quality of Food Crops: A State of the Art Report. Bansul, H. C. & Bozzini, A. (Plant Production & Protection Papers: No. 34). 96p. 1981. pap. 7.50 (ISBN 92-5-101166-4, F2298, FAO). Unipub.

Simmonds, N. W. Principles of Crop Improvement. LC 78-40726. (Illus.). 1979. pap. text ed. 22.00x (ISBN 0-582-44630-9). Longman.

Skerman, P. J. Tropical Forage Legumes. (Plant Production & Protection Papers: No. 2). 609p. 1977. 40.25 (ISBN 92-5-100163-4, F1401, FAO). Unipub.

Smaller Farmlands Can Yield More. pap. 4.50 (F422, FAO). Unipub.

Spedding, C. R. The Biology of Agricultural Systems. 1975. 49.00 (ISBN 0-12-656550-3). Acad Pr.

Spedding, C. R., et al. Biological Efficiency in Agriculture. 1981. 49.50 (ISBN 0-12-656560-0). Acad Pr.

Spedding, F. R., ed. Fream's Agriculture. 16th ed. (Illus.). 816p. 1984. 29.95 (ISBN 0-7195-4034-8, Pub. by Salem Hse Ltd). Merrimack Pub Cir.

Stanhill, G., ed. Energy & Agriculture. (Advanced Series in Agricultural Sciences: Vol. 14). (Illus.). 210p. 1984. 32.50 (ISBN 0-387-13476-X). Springer-Verlag.

The State of Food & Agriculture. annual Incl. 1957. pap. 4.25 (ISBN 0-685-48263-4, F441); 1963. 227p. pap. 14.25 (ISBN 92-5-101500-7, F1479, FAO); 1969. pap. 18.00 (ISBN 92-5-101500-7, F442); 1970. pap. 22.25 (ISBN 0-685-48266-9, F443); 1971. 23p. pap. 25.25 (ISBN 92-5-101507-4, F444); 1974. 196p. 1975. pap. 28.25 (ISBN 92-5-101509-0, F446); 1975. 150p. 1976. pap. 23.50 (ISBN 92-5-101510-4, F447); 1976. (No. 4). (Illus.). 157p. 1978. pap. 17.00 (ISBN 92-5-100181-2, F1224, FAO); 1977. 224p. 1979. pap. 17.00 (ISBN 92-5-100607-5, F1528); 1978. (No. 9). 162p. 1980. pap. 17.00 (ISBN 92-5-100737-3, F1850); 1979. (No. 10). 214p. 1981. pap. 21.75 (ISBN 92-5-100897-3, F2113, FAO); 1980. (No. 12). 181p. 1982. pap. 20.50 (ISBN 92-5-101043-9, F2214); 1981. (No. 14). 177p. 1983. pap. 32.50 (ISBN 92-5-101201-6, F2266, FAO). (Agricultural Ser.). (Illus., Orig., FAO). Unipub.

Statistics & Studies for Agricultural Development Planning: A Phased Programme. (Agricultural Planning Studies). (Eng. & Fr.). 32p. 1976. Repr. of 1968 ed. pap. 7.50 (ISBN 92-5-100004-2, F693, FAO). Unipub.

Stout, L. A. & Myers, C. A. Energy for World Agriculture. (Agricultural Ser.: No. 7). 286p. (2nd Printing 1981). 1979. pap. 16.25 (ISBN 92-5-100465-X, F1882, FAO). Unipub.

Subba Rao. Advances in Agriculture Microbiology. 1982. text ed. 99.95 (ISBN 0-408-10848-7). Butterworth.

Thorne, Marlowe D. & Thorne, D. Wynne. Soil, Water & Crop Production. (Illus.). 1979. text ed. 22.50 (ISBN 0-87055-281-3). AVI.

Thorne, Marlowe D., ed. Agronomists & Food: Contributions & Challenges. 1977. pap. gratis (ISBN 0-89118-048-6). Am Soc Agron.

Timmer, W. J. The Human Side of Agriculture: Theory & Practice of Agricultural Extension. LC 80-53419. 223p. 1982. 10.00 (ISBN 0-533-04849-4). Vantage.

Training for Agriculture & Rural Development, 1977. (Economic & Social Development Papers: No. 7). 122p. 1977. pap. 13.25 (ISBN 92-5-100365-3, F1458, FAO). Unipub.

Troller, John A. & Christian, J. H. Water Activity & Food. (Food Science & Technology Ser.). 1978. 39.50 (ISBN 0-12-700650-8). Acad Pr.

Tsunoda, S., et al, eds. Brassica Crops & Wild Allies. 360p. 1980. 38.00x (ISBN 0-89955-211-0, Pub. by Japan Sci Soc Japan). Intl Spec Bk.

U. S. Department of Energy. Solar Energy for Agriculture & Industrial Process Heat: Program Summary. 91p. 1979. pap. 14.95x (ISBN 0-930978-26-9, D-005). Solar Energy Info.

Uritani, Ikuzo & Reyes, Edilberto D., eds. Tropical Root Crops: Postharvest Physiology & Processing. (Illus.). 328p. (Orig.). 1984. pap. 26.00x (ISBN 4-7622-6358-3, Pub. by Japan Sci Soc Japan). Intl Spec Bk.

Iswaran, V. A Laboratory Handbook for Agricultural Analysts. (Methods & the Interpretation of Results Ser.). 368p. 1980. 30.00 (ISBN 0-88065-133-4, Pub. by Messers Today & Tomorrows Printers & Publishers India). Scholarly Pubns.

Jamison, Dean T. & Lau, Lawrence J. Farmer Education & Farm Efficiency. LC 81-47612. (World Bank Research Publication Ser.). 320p. (Orig.). 1982. text ed. 27.50x (ISBN 0-8018-2575-X). Johns Hopkins.

Lewandowski, Stephen, ed. Farmer's & Housekeepers's Cyclopaedia of 1888. LC 77-23827. 644p. 1978. 25.00 (ISBN 0-912278-91-9); pap. 12.95 (ISBN 0-686-71761-9). Crossing Pr.

Nearing, Helen & Nearing, Scott. Continuing the Good Life: Half a Century of Homesteading. LC 78-21151. (Illus.). 1979. 9.95 (ISBN 0-8052-3703-8); pap. 4.95 (ISBN 0-8052-0642-6). Schocken.

Robinette, Gary O. & Nehring, Richard, eds. Planting Details. 256p. 1983. text ed. 22.50 (ISBN 0-442-22345-5). Van Nos Reinhold.

Schaller, Frank W. & Bailey, George W., eds. Agricultural Management & Water Quality. (Illus.). 472p. 1983. text ed. 39.95 (ISBN 0-8138-0082-X). Iowa St U Pr.

Simmons, Glenn & Simmons, Kathleen. From the Ground Up, Vols. 1 & 2. (Illus.). 1976. (Pub by Glenn Simmons). Intl Spec Bk.

Vivian, John. Manual of Practical Homesteading. 1977. pap. 11.95 (ISBN 0-87857-154-X). Rodale Pr Inc.

Widtsoe, John A. Dry-Farming: A System of Agriculture for Countries Under a Low Rainfall. 1980. lib. bdg. 79.95 (ISBN 0-8490-3161-3). Gordon Pr.

Wolfe, I. A., ed. Handbook of Processing & Utilization in Agriculture. 672p. 1982. 99.50 (ISBN 0-8493-3871-9). CRC Pr.

AGRICULTURE–HISTORY

Agricultural Cooperation 1945-1971. pap. 7.50 (F957, FAO). Unipub.

Ardrey, Robert L. American Agricultural Implements, a Review of Invention & Development in the Agricultural Implement Industry of the United States: Pt. 1 - General History of Invention & Improvement, Pt. 2 - Pioneer Manufacturing Centers, 2 pts. LC 72-5028. (Technology & Society Ser.). (Illus.). 240p. 1972. Repr. of 1894 ed. 20.00 (ISBN 0-405-04681-2). Ayer Co Pubs.

Battelle Memorial Institute. Agriculture Two-Thousand: A Look at the Future. Bucher, Mary, ed. LC 82-25308. (Illus.). 183p. (Orig.). 1983. pap. 6.95 (ISBN 0-935470-15-8). Battelle.

--Agriculture Two Thousand: A Look at the Future. Bucher, Mary, ed. LC 82-25308. (Illus.). 199p. 1983. 17.00x (ISBN 0-935470-18-2). Battelle.

Berry, Wendell. The Gift of Good Land: Further Essays Cultural & Agricultural. LC 81-81507. 304p. 1981. 18.00 (ISBN 0-86547-051-0); pap. 9.50 (ISBN 0-86547-052-9). N Point Pr.

Bidwell, Percy & Falconer, John I. History of Agriculture in the Northern United States 1620-1860. LC 72-11914. Repr. of 1925 ed. 45.00x (ISBN 0-678-00956-2). Kelley.

Bidwell, Percy W. History of Agriculture in the Northern United States: 1620-1860. 19.00 (ISBN 0-8446-1075-5). Peter Smith.

Carrier, Lyman. Agriculture in Virginia, Sixteen Hundred Seven to Sixteen Ninety-Nine. (Illus.). 41p. 1974. pap. 2.95 (ISBN 0-8139-0138-3). U Pr of Va.

--Beginnings of Agriculture in America. (History of American Economy Ser). 1968. Repr. of 1923 ed. 24.00 (ISBN 0-384-07771-4). Johnson Repr.

Carter, Vernon G. & Dale, Tom. Topsoil & Civilization. rev. ed. (Illus.). 240p. 1974. 12.95 (ISBN 0-8061-0332-9); pap. 8.95x (ISBN 0-8061-1107-0). U of Okla Pr.

Clark, William H. Farms & Farmers. facsimile ed. LC 75-99625. (Essay Index Reprint Ser.). 1945. 32.00 (ISBN 0-8369-1560-7). Ayer Co Pubs.

Cohen, Mark N. The Food Crisis in Prehistory: Over Population & Origins of Agriculture. LC 76-41858. 1979. pap. 10.95x (ISBN 0-300-02351-0). Yale U Pr.

Craven, Avery O. Soil Exhaustion As a Factor in the Agricultural History of Virginia and Maryland, 1606-1860. 1926. 11.50 (ISBN 0-8446-1136-0). Peter Smith.

Danhof, Clarence H. Change in Agriculture: The Northern United States, 1820-1870. LC 70-75430. 1969. text ed. 22.50x (ISBN 0-674-10770-5). Harvard U Pr.

Demaree, Albert L. The American Agricultural Press: 1819-1860. LC 73-16296. (Perspectives in American History Ser.: No. 4). (Illus.). 430p. Repr. of 1941 ed. lib. bdg. 35.00x (ISBN 0-87991-331-2). Porcupine Pr.

Duby, Georges. Rural Economy & Country Life in the Medieval West. Postan, Cynthia, tr. LC 68-20530. Orig. Title: Economie Rurale et la Vie Des Campagnes Dans l'Occident Medieval. (Illus.). xvi, 612p. 1968. pap. 9.95x (ISBN 0-87249-347-4). U of SC Pr.

Edwards, Everett E. Bibliography of the History of Agriculture in the U. S. LC 66-27834. 1967. Repr. of 1930 ed. 40.00x (ISBN 0-8103-3102-0). Gale.

Fletcher, Stevenson W. Pennsylvania Agriculture & Country Life: 1840-1940. LC 50-9470. 630p. 1955. 9.50 (ISBN 0-911124-34-9). Pa Hist & Mus.

Food & Agricultural Industries 1945-1970. pap. 11.00 (F952, FAO). Unipub.

Fussell, G. E. The Classical Tradition in West European Farming. LC 77-181502. 237p. 1972. 18.50 (ISBN 0-8386-1090-0). Fairleigh Dickinson.

Gompertz, M. Corn from Egypt: The Beginning of Agriculture. 1979. Repr. of 1928 ed. lib. bdg. 15.00 (ISBN 0-8495-2036-3). Arden Lib.

Goody, Jack, ed. Production & Reproduction. LC 76-4238. (Cambridge Studies in Social Anthropology: No.17). (Illus.). 1977. 34.50 (ISBN 0-521-21294-4); pap. 10.95 (ISBN 0-521-29088-0). Cambridge U Pr.

Gras, Norman S. History of Agriculture in Europe & America. 2nd ed. (History of American Economy Ser.). 1968. Repr. of 1946 ed. 37.00 (ISBN 0-384-19710-8). Johnson Repr.

Gray, Lewis C. History of Agriculture in the Southern United States to 1860, 2 Vols. LC 72-13878. Repr. of 1933 ed. Set. 75.00x (ISBN 0-678-00957-0). Kelley.

--History of Agriculture in the Southern United States to 1860, 2 vols. Set. 36.00 (ISBN 0-8446-1206-5). Peter Smith.

Grigg, David. The Dynamics of Agricultural Change: The Historical Experience. LC 82-24034. (Illus.). 304p. 1983. 29.50x (ISBN 0-312-22316-1). St Martin.

Grigg, David B. The Agricultural Systems of the World. LC 73-82451. (Cambridge Geographical Studies). (Illus.). 348p. 1974. pap. 22.95 (ISBN 0-521-09843-2). Cambridge U Pr.

Haas, Peter J. & Neusner, Jacob. A History of the Mishnaic Law of Agriculture: Tractate Maaser Sheni. LC 80-25479. (Brown Judaic Studies). 1980. 15.00 (ISBN 0-89130-442-8, 14-00-18); pap. 10.50 (ISBN 0-89130-443-6). Scholars Pr GA.

Halley. Agricultural Note Book. 17th ed. 1982. text ed. 59.95 (ISBN 0-408-10701-4). Butterworth.

Harding, T. Swann. Two Blades of Grass: A History of Scientific Development in the U. S. Department of Agriculture. Cohen, I. Bernard, ed. LC 79-7966. (Three Centuries of Science in America Ser.). (Illus.). 1980. Repr. of 1947 ed. lib. bdg. 32.50x (ISBN 0-405-12547-X). Ayer Co Pubs.

Hedrick, Ulysses P. A History of Agriculture in the State of New York. 6.95 (ISBN 0-917334-06-X); pap. 2.45 (ISBN 0-917334-07-8). Fenimore Bk.

Jarchow, Merrill E. Earth Brought Forth: A History of Minnesota Agriculture to 1855. (History of American Economy Ser). 1970. Repr. of 1949 ed. 23.00 (ISBN 0-384-26865-X). Johnson Repr.

Karolevitz, Robert F. Old Time Agriculture in the Ads. LC 77-122596. (Illus.). 96p. 1970. pap. 2.95 (ISBN 0-87970-116-1). North Plains.

Kelsey, D. P., ed. Farming in the New Nation: American Agriculture 1790-1840. 1972. cancelled (ISBN 0-87461-045-1). McNally.

Killingray, Margaret. The Agricultural Revolution. Yapp, Malcolm & O'Connor, Edmund, eds. (World History Ser.). (Illus.). 32p. 1980. lib. bdg. 6.95 (ISBN 0-89908-131-2); pap. text ed. 2.45 (ISBN 0-89908-106-1). Greenhaven.

Peake, Harold. The Origins of Agriculture. 1979. Repr. of 1928 ed. lib. bdg. 12.50 (ISBN 0-8495-4376-2). Arden Lib.

Peake, Harold J. The Origins of Agriculture. LC 76-44776. Repr. of 1928 ed. 10.50 (ISBN 0-404-15960-5). AMS Pr.

Rindos, David. The Origins of Agriculture: A Evolutionary Perspective (Monograph) 1984. 32.50 (ISBN 0-12-589280-2). Acad Pr.

Robson, ed. Southern Agriculture Since the Civil War. cancelled (ISBN 0-87461-031-1). McNally.

Rowley, Trevor, ed. The Origins of Open Field Agriculture. (Illus.). 258p. 1981. 28.50x (ISBN 0-389-20102-2, 06876). B&N Imports.

Scott, Roy V. The Reluctant Farmer: The Rise of Agricultural Extension to 1914. LC 70-102023. pap. 93.50 (ISBN 0-317-28992-6, 2020235). Bks Demand UMI.

Shideler, ed. Agriculture in the Development of the Far West. 1975. cancelled (ISBN 0-87461-043-5). McNally.

Steensberg, Axel. New Guinea Gardens: A Study of Husbandry with Parallels in Prehistoric Europe. 1980. 33.00 (ISBN 0-12-664940-5). Acad Pr.

Stratton, John M. Agricultural Records, A. D. to Twenty to Nineteen Sixty-Five. Whitlock, Ralph, ed. LC 79-103163. (Illus.). 1969. 17.50x (ISBN 0-678-08009-7). Kelley.

Taylor, Henry C. Tarpleywick: A Century of Iowa Farming. LC 70-103840. (Illus.). 1970. 5.95 (ISBN 0-8138-1690-4). Iowa St U Pr.

Teranishi, Roy. Agricultural & Food Chemistry: Past, Present, Future. (Illus.). 1978. lib. bdg. 49.50 (ISBN 0-87055-231-7). AVI.

Watson, Andrew M. Agricultural Innovation in the Early Islamic World. LC 82-17773. (Cambridge Studies in Islamic Civilization). (Illus.). 228p. 1983. 44.50 (ISBN 0-521-24711-X). Cambridge U Pr.

Weller, John. History of the Farmstead: The Development of Energy Sources. (Illus.). 272p. 1982. 24.95 (ISBN 0-571-11804-6); pap. 14.95 (ISBN 0-571-11805-4). Faber & Faber.

Wessel, T. R., ed. Agriculture in the Great Plains, 1876-1936. 1977. cancelled (ISBN 0-87461-041-9). McNally.

Whitaker, J. W., ed. Farming in the Midwest 1840-1900. 1974. cancelled (ISBN 0-87461-044-3). McNally.

Wilson, Harold F. Hill Country of Northern New England: Its Social & Economic History 1790-1930. LC 79-182730. Repr. of 1936 ed. 21.50 (ISBN 0-404-06994-0). AMS Pr.

Wiser, V., ed. Two Centuries of American Agriculture. 1976. cancelled. McNally.

AGRICULTURE–INFORMATION SERVICES

see also Agricultural Extension Work

Koekebakker, F. A., ed. Agricode for Agricultural Libraries: Code for the Classification of Agricultural Literature, with Index. 1977. 17.50 (ISBN 90-220-0567-4, PDC1, Pub. by PUDOC). Unipub.

Uses of Soil Information Systems: Proceedings of the Australian Meeting of the ISSS Working Group on Soil Information Systems, Canbera, 2-4 March, 1976. Moore, Alan W. & Bie, Stein W., eds. 1978. pap. 14.00 (ISBN 90-220-0638-7, PDC98, Pub. by PUDOC). Unipub.

AGRICULTURE–LABORATORY MANUALS

Waldren, Richard P. & Ehler, Stanley W. Laboratory Manual of Crop Science. 2nd ed. 1981. 14.95x (ISBN 0-8087-3729-5). Burgess.

AGRICULTURE–MAPS

see also Soils–Maps

Report on the Agro-Ecological Zones Project, 2 vols. Incl. Vol. 1. Methodology & Results from Africa. (Eng. & Fr.). 85p. pap. 10.00 (ISBN 92-5-101172-9, F1877); Vol. 2. Results from Southwest Asia. 28p. pap. 6.00 (ISBN 92-5-100694-6, F1872). 1978 (FAO). Unipub.

AGRICULTURE–OUTLINES, SYLLABI, ETC.

Syllabuses & Course Content for Crop Protection Courses. 126p. 1977. 32.00x (ISBN 0-901436-51-8, Pub. by CAB Bks England). State Mutual Bk.

AGRICULTURE–PROBLEMS, EXERCISES, ETC.

France, J. & Thornley, J. H. Mathematical Models in Agriculture: A Quantitative Approach to Problems in Agriculture & Related Sciences. 352p. 1984. text ed. 79.95 (ISBN 0-408-10868-1). Butterworth.

AGRICULTURE–RESEARCH

see Agricultural Research

AGRICULTURE–SAFETY MEASURES

Guide to Health & Hygiene in Agricultural Work. xii, 309p. 1980. pap. 15.70 (ISBN 92-2-101974-8, ILO141, ILO). Unipub.

Guide to Safety in Agriculture. (Illus.). xiii, 247p. 1969. 6.85 (ISBN 92-2-100030-3). Intl Labour Office.

The Trouble with Temik: An Historical-Environmental Look at Long Island Agriculture & Pesticide Usage. 12.95 (ISBN 0-317-03376-X); pap. 7.95 (ISBN 0-317-03377-8). De Young Pr.

AGRICULTURE–STATISTICS

see also Crop Yields

Estimation of Crop Areas & Yields in Agricultural Statistics. (Economic & Social Development Papers: No. 22). (Eng., Fr. & Span.). 193p. 1982. pap. 14.00 (ISBN 92-5-101179-6, F2350, FAO). Unipub.

FAO Studies in Agricultural Economics & Statistics, 1952-1977. (Statistics Ser.: No. 20). 442p. 1978. 30.50 (ISBN 92-5-100649-0, F1559, FAO). Unipub.

Inman, A. H. Domesday & Feudal Statistics with a Chapter on Agriculture Statistics. LC 77-137948. (Economic Thought, History & Challenge Ser.). 1971. Repr. of 1900 ed. 26.50x (ISBN 0-8046-1450-4, Pub. by Kennikat). Assoc Faculty Pr.

Mead, R. & Curnow, R. N. Statistical Methods in Agriculture & Experimental Biology. 300p. 1983. 49.95 (ISBN 0-412-24230-3, NO. 6767); pap. 25.00 (ISBN 0-412-24240-0, NO. 6768). Methuen Inc.

Nineteen-Seventy World Census of Agriculture: Analysis & International Comparison of Data. (Statistics Ser.: No. 37). 300p. 1981. pap. 26.25 (ISBN 92-5-101037-4, F2290, FAO). Unipub.

Report of the 1960 World Census of Agriculture: Census Results by Countries. Vol. 1, pt. A. pap. 10.00 (F388, FAO); Vol. 1, pt. B. pap. 20.00 (F391); Vol. 1, pt. C. pap. 36.50 (F394). Unipub.

Report on the 1970 World Census of Agriculture. (Statistics Ser.: No. 10). (Illus.). 1977. pap. 17.00 (ISBN 92-5-100427-7, F1444, FAO). Unipub.

Report on the 1970 World Census of Agriculture. Incl. Botswana, Surinam. (No. 1). 1973 (F1051); Japan, Malta. (No. 2). 1973 (F1052); Czechoslovakia, Luxembourg. (No. 3). 1973 (F1053); Canada, Sweden. (No. 4). 1973 (F1054); Fiji, Norway, Portugal. (No. 5). 1974 (F1055); American Samoa, Guam, Pacific Islands (Trust Territory), Puerto Rico, Virgin Islands (U.S.) (No. 6). 1974 (F1056); Finland, USA. (No. 7). 1974 (F1057); Ghana, Iraq, Uruguay. (No. 8). 1974 (F1058); France, Lesotho, Malawi. (No. 9). 1975 (F1059); Costa Rica, Korea, Republic of Swaziland. (No. 10). 1975 (F1060); New Zealand, Zambia. (No. 11). 1975 (F1061); Greece, Jamaica. (No. 13). 1976 (F1079); Denmark, Netherlands, Switzerland. (No. 14). 1976 (F1080); Bahrain, Italy, Peru. (No. 16). 1977 (F1274); Saudi Arabia, Yugoslavia. (No. 17). 1977 (F1273). (Census Bulletin Ser.). pap. 7.50 each (FAO). Unipub.

Statistics 1945-1966. pap. 9.00 (F942, FAO). Unipub.

AGRICULTURE–STUDY AND TEACHING

see also Agricultural Colleges; Forestry Schools and Education

Agriculture Teacher's Plan Book. 96p. 1962. pap. text ed. 1.50x (ISBN 0-8134-0069-4, 69). Interstate.

Binkley, Harold R. & Tulloch, Rodney W. Teaching Vocational Agriculture-Agribusiness. (Illus.). 250p. 1981. pap. 9.95x (ISBN 0-8134-2153-5). Interstate.

Burlingham, H. H. & Juergenson, Elwood M. Selected Lessons for Teaching Off-Farm Agricultural Occupations. LC 66-19257. (Illus.). 1967. text ed. 7.95x (ISBN 0-8134-0899-7, 899). Interstate.

Clip Art: Agricultural Communicators in Education, Bk. 5. (Illus.). 192p. 1982. pap. text ed. 14.95x (ISBN 0-8134-2253-1). Interstate.

Commission On Education In Agriculture & Natural Resources. Undergraduate Education in the Plant & Soil Sciences. LC 71-600161. (Orig.). 1969. pap. 4.25 (ISBN 0-309-01704-1). Natl Acad Pr.

Curriculum Development for Bukora Institute of Agriculture. (Programmes for Better Family Living Reports: No. 12). pap. 8.50 (F1077, FAO). Unipub.

Curtis, Paul E., et al. Here's How: On-Job-Training, Agricultural Resources & Forestry. 159p. 1972. pap. text ed. 4.00x (ISBN 0-8134-1436-9, 1436). Interstate.

--Here's How: On-Job-Training, Agricultural Supplies & Services. 111p. 1972. pap. text ed. 4.00x (ISBN 0-8134-1432-6, 1432). Interstate.

Drawbaugh, Charles C. & Hull, William L. Agricultural Education: Approaches to Learning & Teaching. LC 71-132866. 1971. text ed. 23.95 (ISBN 0-675-09274-4). Merrill.

Eaton, Theodore H. Study of Organization & Method of the Course of Study in Agriculture in Secondary Schools. LC 78-176740. (Columbia University. Teachers College. Contributions to Education: No. 86). Repr. of 1917 ed. 12.50 (ISBN 0-404-55086-X). AMS Pr.

Everote, Warren P. Agricultural Science to Serve Youth: Outcomes of a Course in Experimental Science for Secondary-School Students. LC 72-176760. (Columbia University. Teachers College. Contributions to Education: No. 901). Repr. of 1943 ed. 22.50 (ISBN 0-404-55901-8). AMS Pr.

FAO-UNESCO-ILO World Directory of Distribution Sources of Educational Audio Visual Materials Relating to Agriculture & Food: Part 1: Africa, Asia, Oceania, Latin America. 1979. pap. 7.50 (ISBN 92-5-000638-1, F1504, FAO). Unipub.

Food, Nutrition & Agriculture Guidelines for Agriculture Training Curricula in Africa. (Food & Nutrition Papers: No. 22). (Eng. & Fr.). 205p. 1982. pap. 15.50 (ISBN 92-5-101176-1, F2293, FAO). Unipub.

Oberholtzer, Kenneth E. American Agricultural Problems in the Social Studies. LC 73-177125. (Columbia University. Teachers College. Contributions to Education: No. 718). Repr. of 1937 ed. 22.50 (ISBN 0-404-55718-X). AMS Pr.

Robison, Clarence H. Agricultural Instruction in the Public Schools of the United States. LC 75-177198. (Columbia University. Teachers College. Contributions to Education: No. 39). Repr. of 1911 ed. 22.50 (ISBN 0-404-55039-8). AMS Pr.

Rudman, Jack. Agriculture. (National Teachers Examination Ser.: NT-20). (Cloth bdg. avail. on request). pap. 11.95 (ISBN 0-8373-8430-3). Natl Learning.

Schmidt, Gustavus A. Vocational Education in Agriculture in Federally-Aided Secondary Schools: A Study of Its Instructional & Training Phases. LC 75-177802. (Columbia University. Teachers College. Contributions to Education: No. 534). Repr. of 1932 ed. 22.50 (ISBN 0-404-55534-9). AMS Pr.

Sheffield, James R., et al. Agriculture in Secondary Schools: Case Studies of Botswana, Kenya & Tanzania. LC 76-11330. 124p. (Orig.). 1976. pap. 2.75 (ISBN 0-686-66072-2). AAI.

Slay, Ronald J. Development of the Teaching of Agriculture in Mississippi with Special Emphasis on Agriculture As a Part of School Curricula. LC 78-177780. (Columbia University. Teachers College. Contributions to Education: No. 310). Repr. of 1928 ed. 22.50 (ISBN 0-404-55310-9). AMS Pr.

Training for Agriculture & Rural Development, 1979. (Economic & Social Development Papers: No. 19). 124p. 1980. pap. 24.50 (ISBN 92-5-100948-1, F2153, FAO). Unipub.

True, Alfred C. A History of Agricultural Experimentation & Research in the United States 1607-1925, Including a History of the United States Department of Agriculture. (History of American Economy Ser.). (Illus.). Repr. of 1937 ed. 28.00 (ISBN 0-384-61740-9). Johnson Repr.

AGRICULTURE–VOCATIONAL GUIDANCE

Agricultural Employment in Developing Countries. (Agricultural Planning Studies: No. 16). (Eng., Fr. & Span.). 48p. 1977. pap. 7.50 (ISBN 92-5-100252-5, F698, FAO). Unipub.

Bishop, Douglas D. Working in Plant Science. Amberson, Max L. & Chapman, Stephen, eds. (Illus.). 1978. pap. text ed. 13.72 (ISBN 0-07-000835-3). McGraw.

Byram, Harold M. Guidance in Agricultural Education. LC 65-25513. (Illus.). 298p. 1966. text ed. 7.95x (ISBN 0-8134-0521-1, 521). Interstate.

Conley, Diane & Ready, Barbara C., eds. Graduate Programs in the Biological, Agricultural, & Health Sciences 1985. 19th ed. (Annual Guides-Graduate Study Ser.). 2038p. (Orig.). 1984. pap. 25.95 (ISBN 0-87866-236-7). Petersons Guides.

Farrington, William, et al. Working with Plant Supplies & Services. (Illus.). 144p. 1980. pap. text ed. 10.24 (ISBN 0-07-019965-5). McGraw.

Hoover, Norman K. Handbook of Agricultural Occupations. 4th ed. LC 85-82064. (Illus.). 374p. 1985. 19.95 (ISBN 0-8134-2351-1, 2351); text ed. 14.95x. Interstate.

Peterson, Paul, et al. Working in Animal Science. Amberson, Max, ed. (Illus.). 1978. pap. text ed. 13.72 (ISBN 0-07-000839-6). McGraw.

Stone, Archie A., et al. Careers in Agribusiness & Industry. 3rd ed. LC 76-106341. (Illus.). 282p. 18.00 (ISBN 0-8134-2073-3); text ed. 13.50x. Interstate.

AGRICULTURE–AFRICA

Agroclimatology of the Highlands of Eastern Africa: Proceedings of the Technical Conference, Nairobi, 1-5 Oct.1973. 242p. (Orig.). 1974. pap. 40.00 (ISBN 92-63-10389-5, W160, WMO). Unipub.

Bates, Robert H. & Lofchie, Michael F. Agricultural Development in Africa: Issues of Public Policy. LC 79-24914. 464p. 1980. 53.95x (ISBN 0-03-056173-6). Praeger.

Beck, Walter G. Beitrage Zur Kulturgeschichte der Afrikanischen Feldarbeit. Repr. of 1943 ed. 19.00 (ISBN 0-384-03705-4). Johnson Repr.

Cocheme, J. & Franqiun, P. Agroclimatology Survey of a Semi-arid Area in Africa: South of the Sahara. (Illus.). 136p. 1967. pap. 15.00 (ISBN 0-685-57271-4, W54, WMO). Unipub.

Crop Ecological Survey in West Africa: Atlas, Vol. 2. pap. 13.25 (F121, FAO). Unipub.

Davis, Jackson. Africa Advancing: A Study of Rural Education & Agriculture in West Africa & Belgian Congo. LC 72-98717. (Illus.). Repr. of 1945 ed. 19.75x (ISBN 0-8371-2791-2, DAA&, Pub. by Negro U Pr). Greenwood.

Davy, E. J. & Mattei, F. An Evaluation of Climate & Water Resources for Development of Agriculture in the Sudano-Sahelian Zone of West Africa. (Special Environmental Reports: No. 9). (Eng. & Fr., Illus.). 289p. (Prepared in Co-operation with the United Nations Environment Programme). 1976. pap. 40.00 (ISBN 92-63-10459-X, W255, WMO). Unipub.

Diamond, R. B., et al. Etude sur les Engrais en Afrique de L'Ouest Vol. 5: Niger. (Technical Bulletin Ser.: TF-7). (Fr., Illus.). 51p. (Orig.). 1978. pap. 4.00 (ISBN 0-88090-035-0). Intl Fertilizer.

Ecological Management of Arid & Semi-Arid Rangeland II: Sudan, Vol. 8. 41p. 1979. pap. 7.50 (ISBN 92-5-100677-6, F1589, FAO). Unipub.

Food & Agriculture Organization. Drought in the Sahel: International Relief Operations, 1973-1975. 48p. 1976. pap. 7.50 (ISBN 0-685-66344-2, F751, FAO). Unipub.

Food, Nutrition & Agriculture Guidelines for Agriculture Training Curricula in Africa. (Food & Nutrition Papers: No. 22). (Eng. & Fr.). 205p. 1982. pap. 15.50 (ISBN 92-5-101176-1, F2293, FAO). Unipub.

Gilbert, Zoe. Fruit Growing in Southern Africa. 1980. 32.00x (ISBN 0-686-69982-3, Pub. by Bailey & Swinton South Africa). State Mutual Bk.

Githens, Thomas S. & Wood, Carroll E. Jr. Food Resources of Africa. (African Handbooks Ser.: Vol. 3). (Illus.). 105p. 1943. 7.50x (ISBN 0-686-24087-1). Univ Mus of U PA.

Lawani, S. M. & Alluri, F. M. Farming Systems in Africa: A Working Bibliography, 1930-1978. 1979. lib. bdg. 33.50 (ISBN 0-8161-8293-0, Hall Reference). G K Hall.

Levi, J. African Agriculture: Economic Action & Reaction in Sierra Leone. 428p. 1976. 50.00x (ISBN 0-85198-374-X, Pub. by CAB Bks England). State Mutual Bk.

May, Jacques M. & McLellan, Donna L., eds. Studies in Medical Geography, 14 vols. Incl. Vol. 2. Studies in Disease Ecology. (Illus.). 1961. 27.95x (ISBN 0-02-848980-2); Vol. 3. The Ecology of Malnutrition in the Far & Near East. (Illus.). 1961. 24.95x (ISBN 0-02-849010-X); Vol. 4. The Ecology of Malnutrition in Five Countries of Eastern & Central Europe: East Germany,Poland, Yugoslavia, Albania, Greece. (Illus.). 1964. 18.95x (ISBN 0-02-848970-5); Vol. 5. The Ecology of Malnutrition in Middle Africa: Ghana, Nigeria, Republic of the Congo, Rwanda & Burundi & the Former French Equatorial Africa. (Illus.). 1965. 16.95x (ISBN 0-02-848990-X); Vol. 6. The Ecology of Malnutrition in Central & Southern Europe: Austria, Hungary, Romania, Bulgaria & Czechoslovakia. (Illus.). 1966. 18.95x (ISBN 0-02-849000-2); Vol. 7. The Ecology of Malnutrition in Northern Africa: Libya, Tunisia, Algeria, Morocco, Spanish Sahara & Ifni, Mauretania. (Illus.). 1967. 18.95x (ISBN 0-02-848950-0); Vol. 8. The Ecology of Malnutrition in the French-Speaking Countries of West Africa & Madagascar: Senegal, Guinea, Ivory Coast, Togo, Dahomey, Cameroon, Niger, Mali, Upper Volta, & Madagascar. (Illus.). 1968. 21.95x (ISBN 0-02-848960-8); Vol. 9. The Ecology of Malnutrition in Eastern Africa: Equatorial Guinea, the Gambia, Liberia, Sierra Leone, Malawi, Rhodesia, Zambia, Kenya, Tanzania, Uganda, Ethiopia, the French Territory of the Atars & Issas, the Somali Republic & Sudan. 1970. 32.95x (ISBN 0-02-849020-7); Vol. 10. The Ecology of Malnutrition in Seven Countries of Southern Africa and in Portuguese Guinea: The/Republic of South Africa, South West Africa (Namibia), Botswana, Lesotho, Swaziland, Mozambique, Angola, Portuguese Guinea. 1971. 27.95x (ISBN 0-02-848940-3); Vol. 11. The Ecology of Malnutrition in Mexico & Central America. 1972. 24.95x (ISBN 0-02-848930-6); Vol. 12. The Ecology of Malnutrition in the Caribbean. 1973. 21.95x (ISBN 0-02-848920-9); Vol. 13. The Ecology of Malnutrition in Eastern South America. 1975. 41.95x (ISBN 0-02-849060-6); Vol. 14. The Ecology of Malnutrition in Western South America. 1975. 32.95x (ISBN 0-02-849070-3). Hafner.

Mondot-Bernard, J. & Labonne, M. Satisfaction of Food Requirements in Mali to 2000 A. D. 214p. (Orig.). 1982. pap. 15.00x (ISBN 92-64-12300-8). OECD.

Nair, Kusum. Transforming Traditionally: Land & Labor Use in Agriculture in Asia & Africa. LC 83-61217. (Perspectives on Asian & African Development Ser.: No. 1). 168p. 1983. 12.00 (ISBN 0-913215-00-7). Riverdale Co.

Organic Recycling in Africa: Papers Presented at the FAO-SIDA Workshop on the Use of Organic Materials as Fertilizers in Africa, Buea, Cameroon, Dec. 5-14, 1977. (Soils Bulletins: No. 43). 308p. 1980. pap. 22.00 (ISBN 92-5-100945-7, F2096, FAO). Unipub.

Outline Research Programme for the African Regional Aquaculture Centre: Report of a Task Force Sponsored by the FAO-UNDP Aquaculture Development & Coordination Programme, Port Harcourt, Rivers State, Nigeria, Feb. 3-19, 1980. 21p. 1980. pap. 7.50 (ISBN 92-5-101019-6, F2142, FAO). Unipub.

Porter, Philip W. Food & Development in the Semi-Arid Zone of East Africa. LC 79-20312. (Foreign & Comparative Studies Program, African Ser.: No. 32). (Illus.). 114p. 1979. pap. text ed. 7.50x (ISBN 0-915984-54-7). Syracuse U Foreign Comp.

Rainfed Agriculture in the Near East & North Africa: Proceedings of the FAO Regional Seminar, Amman, Jordan, May 5-10, 1979. 416p. 1980. pap. 28.75 (ISBN 92-5-101030-7, F2174, FAO). Unipub.

Rastyannikov, V. G. Food for Developing Countries in Asia & North Africa. Watts, George S., tr. LC 75-26311. (World Food Supply Ser). (Illus.). 1976. Repr. of 1969 ed. 12.00x (ISBN 0-405-07789-0). Ayer Co Pubs.

Remy, Gerard. Yobri: Etude Geographique Du Terroir D'un Village Gourmantche De Haute-Volta. (Atlas Des Structurews Agraires Au Sud Du Sahara: No. 1). (Illus.). 1967. pap. 14.00x (ISBN 90-2796-056-9). Mouton.

Rensburg, H. V. van. Management & Utilization of Pastures: East Africa: Pt. 1, Kenya; Pt. 2 Tanzania; Pt. 3 Uganda, 3 Pts. (Pasture & Fodder Crop Studies: No. 3). (Eng. & Fr.). 124p. (2nd Printing 1978). 1969. pap. 10.50 (ISBN 92-5-100420-X, F1970, FAO). Unipub.

Report of the FAO Regional Conference for Africa, Eighth, Rose Hill, Mauritius, August 1974. 23p. 1976. pap. 7.50 (ISBN 0-685-66324-8, F1110, FAO). Unipub.

Report of the Government Consultation on Crop & Post Harvest Protection Needs in the Sahel. (Illus.). 46p. 1978. pap. 7.50 (ISBN 92-5-100304-1, F1246, FAO). Unipub.

Report of the Ninth FAO Regional Conference for Africa: Freetown, Sierra Leone 2-12. pap. 7.50 (ISBN 92-5-100246-0, F1113, FAO). Unipub.

Report of the 11th Regional Conference for Africa. pap. 7.50 (ISBN 92-5-100996-1, F2098, FAO). Unipub.

Rice, R. P. & Rice, L. W. Fruit & Vegetable Production in Tropical Africa. LC 82-23698. 250p. 1985. 34.95 (ISBN 0-471-10362-4, Pub. by Wiley-Interscience); pap. write for info. (ISBN 0-471-90138-5). Wiley.

Schreiner, Olive. The Story of an African Farm. 12.00 (ISBN 0-8446-0247-7). Peter Smith.

Shantz, Homer L. & Marbut, Curtis F. Vegetation & Soils of Africa. LC 70-170848. Repr. of 1923 ed. 19.00 (ISBN 0-404-05953-8). AMS Pr.

Shifting Cultivation & Soil Conservation in Africa: Papers Presented at the FAO-SUDA-ARCN Regional Seminar Held in Ibadan, Nigeria, 2-21 July 1973. (Soils Bulletins: No. 24). (Eng., Fr. & Span.). 254p. 1974. pap. 18.50 (ISBN 92-5-100393-9, F1166, FAO). Unipub.

Sinha. Field Crop Production in Tropical Africa. Date not set. price not set (ISBN 0-471-90102-4). Wiley.

Strange, L. R. An Introduction to African Pastureland Production with Special Reference to Farm & Rangeland Environments of Eastern Africa. (Pasture & Fodder Crop Studies: No. 6). 204p. 1980. pap. 14.75 (ISBN 92-5-100872-8, F2075, FAO). Unipub.

Terry, E. R. & Oduro, K. A., eds. Tropical Root Crops - Research Strategies for the 1980's: Proceedings of the First Triennial Root Crops Symposium of the International Society of Root Crops, Africa Branch, 8-12 September 1980, Ibadan, Nigeria. (Eng. & Fr.). 280p. 1981. pap. 18.00 (ISBN 0-88936-285-8, IDRC163, IDRC). Unipub.

Tindall, H. D. & Sai, F. A. Fruits & Vegetables in West Africa. 259p. (Orig., 5th Printing 1983). 1965. pap. 11.00 (ISBN 92-5-100062-X, F201, FAO). Unipub.

Tinley, J. M. South African Food & Agriculture in World War II. (Illus.). 1954. 12.50x (ISBN 0-8047-0457-0). Stanford U Pr.

Westphal, E. Agricultural Systems in Ethiopia. (Agricultural Research Reports: No. 826). (Illus.). 278p. 1975. 34.00 (ISBN 90-220-0556-9, PDC15, PUDOC). Unipub.

A Zambian Handbook of Pasture & Fodder Crops. 148p. 1980. pap. 9.75 (ISBN 92-5-100730-6, F1866, FAO). Unipub.

AGRICULTURE–ALASKA

Roberts, Ann. Growing Vegetables in Alaska: & Other Far North Climates. (Illus.). 265p. 1984. 13.95 (ISBN 0-918270-08-1). That New Pub.

AGRICULTURE–AMERICA

Ardrey, Robert L. American Agricultural Implements, a Review of Invention & Development in the Agricultural Implement Industry of the United States: Pt. 1 - General History of Invention & Improvement, Pt. 2 - Pioneer Manufacturing Centers, 2 pts. LC 72-5028. (Technology & Society Ser.). (Illus.). 240p. 1972. Repr. of 1894 ed. 20.00 (ISBN 0-405-04681-2). Ayer Co Pubs.

Barger, Harold. American Agriculture, 1899-1939: A Study of Output, Employment & Productivity. LC 75-41017. (BCL Ser. II). Repr. of 1942 ed. 22.50 (ISBN 0-404-14640-6). AMS Pr.

Dunn, Finlay. American Farming & Food. 1980. lib. bdg. 75.00 (ISBN 0-8490-3185-0). Gordon Pr.

MacDonald, James. Food from the Far West. or, American Agriculture. 1980. lib. bdg. 69.95 (ISBN 0-8490-3187-7). Gordon Pr.

Scheuring, Ann F., ed. A Guidebook to California Agriculture. LC 82-2669. (Illus.). 544p. 1983. 32.50x (ISBN 0-520-04709-5). U of Cal Pr.

AGRICULTURE–ARGENTINE REPUBLIC

Scobie, James R. Revolution on the Pampas: A Social History of Argentine Wheat, 1860-1910. (Latin American Monograph: No. 1). 220p. 1964. 12.50x (ISBN 0-292-73352-6). U of Tex Pr.

AGRICULTURE–ASIA

Agricultural Growth in Japan, Taiwan, Korea, & the Philippines. 404p. 1979. 12.00 (ISBN 0-8248-0391-4, APO82, APO). Unipub.

Agricultural Mechanization in Selected Asian Countries. 176p. 1985. pap. 16.25 (ISBN 92-833-2024-7, APO155, APO). Unipub.

Anderson, Robert S., et al, eds. Science, Politics, & the Agricultural Revolution in Asia. (Selected Symposium Ser.: No. 70). 450p. 1982. lib. bdg. 36.50x (ISBN 0-86531-320-2). Westview.

Asian Development Bank. Asian Agricultural Survey. 795p. 1969. 50.00x (ISBN 0-295-97866-X); pap. 25.00x (ISBN 0-295-78585-3). U of Wash Pr.

FAO-UNDP International Expert Consultation on the Use of Improved Technology for Food Production in Rainfed Areas of Tropical Asia: Report, 3 Vols. Vol. 1. pap. 28.00 (F1089, FAO); Vol. 2. pap. 17.75; Vol. 3. pap. 23.75. Unipub.

Farm Mechanization in Asia. 510p. 1983. pap. text ed. 16.25 (ISBN 92-833-2003-4, APO137, APO). Unipub.

Gomez, A. A. & Gomez, K. A. Multiple Cropping in the Humid Tropics of Asia. 248p. 1983. pap. text ed. 15.00 (ISBN 0-88936-304-8, IDRC176, IDRC). Unipub.

Handelman, Howard, ed. The Politics of Agrarian Change in Asia & Latin America. LC 81-47565. (Illus.). 148p. 1981. 22.50x (ISBN 0-253-34548-0). Ind U Pr.

Herkiots, G. A. C. Vegetables in Southeast Asia. (Illus.). 1972. pap. 20.00x (ISBN 0-04-635008-X). Allen Unwin.

Johl, S. S. & De Clerq, C. Irrigation & Agricultural Development. LC 80-40435. (Illus.). 386p. 1980. 68.00 (ISBN 0-08-025675-9). Pergamon.

Nair, Kusum. Transforming Traditionally: Land & Labor Use in Agriculture in Asia & Africa. LC 83-61217. (Perspectives on Asian & African Development Ser.: No. 1). 168p. 1983. 12.00 (ISBN 0-913215-00-7). Riverdale Co.

Poehlam, J. M. & Borthakur, D. N. Breeding Asian Field Crops. 504p. 1981. 30.00x (ISBN 0-686-76626-1, Pub by Oxford & IBH India). State Mutual Bk.

Rastyannikov, V. G. Food for Developing Countries in Asia & North Africa. Watts, George S., tr. LC 75-26311. (World Food Supply Ser). (Illus.). 1976. Repr. of 1969 ed. 12.00x (ISBN 0-405-07789-0). Ayer Co Pubs.

Regional Cooperation in the Development of Coarse Grains, Pulses, Roots & Tuber (CGPRT) Crops in Asia & the Pacific. 242p. 1979. pap. 14.00 (ISBN 0-686-61477-1, UN78/2F7, UN). Unipub.

Report for the Thirteenth FAO Regional Conference for Asia & the Far East, Manila, Philippines 5-13 August, 1976. pap. 7.50 (F1119, FAO). Unipub.

Report of an FAO-UNDP International Expert Consultation on the Use of Improved Technology for Food Production in Rainfed Areas of Tropical Asia. 65p. 1976. pap. 7.50 (ISBN 0-685-66341-8, F1088, FAO). Unipub.

Report of the FAO-ECAFE Expert Group on Selected Aspects of Agricultural Planning in Asia & the Far East. (Agricultural Planning Studies: No. 2). (Eng. & Fr.). 62p. (5th Printing 1975). 1963. pap. 7.50 (ISBN 92-5-100003-4, F2059, FAO). Unipub.

Report of the Sixteenth Conference for Asia & the Pacific: Jakarta, 1-11 June 1982. (Eng., Fr. & Span.). 70p. 1982. pap. 7.50 (ISBN 92-5-101255-5, F2365, FAO). Unipub.

Report of the Tenth Session of the Plant Protection Committee for the Southeast Asia & Pacific Region Held in Canberra, Australia. pap. 7.50 (ISBN 92-5-100049-2, F1115, FAO). Unipub.

Spencer, J. E. Shifting Cultivation in Southeastern Asia. (California Library Reprint Ser.). 1978. 35.00x (ISBN 0-520-03517-8). U of Cal Pr.

Tan, Bock T. & Saho-er Ong, eds. Readings in Asian Farm Management. 362p. 1979. pap. 10.00x (ISBN 0-8214-0514-4, 82-93474, Pub. by Singapore U Pr). Ohio U Pr.

Technology Diffusion Among Asian Rice Farmers: Report of a Study Meeting. 171p. 1983. pap. 14.75 (ISBN 92-833-1475-1, APO103, APO). Unipub.

Ward, R. Gerard & Proctor, Andrew, eds. South Pacific Agriculture: Choices & Constraints. LC 79-56229. (South Pacific Agricultural Survey 1979). 525p. 1980. text ed. 21.00 (ISBN 0-7081-1944-1, 0532). Australia N U P.

Wong, John, ed. Group Farming in Asia: Experiences & Potentials. 312p. 1979. 20.00x (ISBN 0-8214-0518-7, 82-93516, Pub. by Singapore U Pr). Ohio U Pr.

AGRICULTURE–AUSTRALIA AND NEW ZEALAND

Alexander, D. M. Some Avocado Varieties for Australia. 1980. 20.00x (ISBN 0-643-02276-7, Pub. by CSIRO Australia). State Mutual Bk.

Anderson, Kym & George, Aurelia, eds. Australian Agriculture & Newly Industrialising Asia: Isssues for Research. LC 80-69631. (Australia-Japan Economic Relations Research Project-Monograph: No. 4). 462p. 1981. pap. text ed. 7.00 (ISBN 0-9596197-3-9, 0104, Pub. by ANUP Australia). Australia N U P.

Atkinson, James. An Account of the State of Agriculture & Grazing in New South Wales. (Illus.). 184p. 1975. Repr. of 1826 ed. 21.00x (ISBN 0-424-06960-1, Pub by Sydney U Pr). Intl Spec Bk.

Bauer, June B. & Mollah, W. S. Two North Australian Cropping Studies. (North Australia Research Bulletin: No. 7). 191p. 1981. pap. text ed. 8.00 (ISBN 0-909596-67-0, 0100, Pub. by ANUP Australia). Australia N U P.

Blake, C. D. Fundamentals of Modern Agriculture. 516p. 1974. (Pub. by Sydney U Pr); pap. 21.00x (ISBN 0-424-06930-X, Pub. by Sydney U Pr). Intl Spec Bk.

Bollard, Alan. Agricultural Project Design & Evaluation in an Island Community. (Development Studies Centre - Monograph: No. 15). (Illus., Orig.). 1980. pap. 8.00 (ISBN 0-7081-1071-1, 0537, Pub. by ANUP Australia). Australia N U P.

Burvill, G. H. Agriculture in Western Australia. 397p. 1980. 30.00x (ISBN 0-85564-154-1, Pub. by U of W Austral Pr). Intl Spec Bk.

Connell, John. Tiam Bilong Mani: The Evolution of Agriculture in a Solomon Is. Society. (Development Studies Monograph: No. 12). (Orig.). 1978. pap. text ed. 9.00x (ISBN 0-909150-66-4, 506, Pub. by ANUP Australia). Australia N U P.

CSIRO Published Papers: Subject Index (1916-1968) 1982. 100.00x (ISBN 0-643-02114-0, Pub. by CSIRO Australia); microfiche 40.00x (ISBN 0-686-73073-9). State Mutual Bk.

CSIRO Research Program 1980-1981. 591p. 1982. 40.00x (ISBN 0-686-73074-7, Pub. by CSIRO Australia). State Mutual Bk.

CSIRO Research Programs, 1980-1981. Incl. CSIRO Research Programs: 1979-80. 533p. 1980. pap. 18.00 (CD33, CSTRO). 591p. 1980. pap. 22.50 (ISBN 0-686-73420-3, C060, CSIRO). Unipub.

Currie, George & Graham, J. Origines of CSIRO. 216p. 1981. 29.00x (ISBN 0-643-02754-8, Pub. by CSIRO Australia). State Mutual Bk.

Ferns, G. K. Australian Wheat Varieties. 126p. 1982. 35.00x (ISBN 0-643-00143-3, Pub. by CSIRO Australia). State Mutual Bk.

Fitzsimmons, R. W. & Wrigley, C. W. Australian Barley. 62p. 1980. 20.00x (ISBN 0-643-00344-4, Pub. by CSIRO Australia). State Mutual Bk.

Gifford, Roger & Millington, R. J. Energetics of Agriculture & Food Production: With Special Emphasis on the Australian Situation. (Bulletin Ser.: No. 288). 29p. (2nd Printing 1977). 1975. pap. 6.00 (ISBN 0-643-00147-6, C042, CSIRO). Unipub.

Gifford, Roger M. Energetics of Agriculture & Food Production. (Illus.). 29p. 1977. pap. 2.25x (ISBN 0-643-00147-6, Pub. by CSIRO). Intl Spec Bk.

Gillison, A. N. & Anderson, D. J. Vegetation Classification in Australia. LC 81-68097. 229p. 1981. text ed. 13.50 (ISBN 0-7081-1309-5, 1077, Pub. by ANUP Australia). Australia N U P.

Gillison, A. N. & Anderson, D. J., eds. Vegetation Classification in Australia. 229p. 1983. (Pub. by CSIRO Australia). Intl Spec Bk.

Graetz, R. D. & Howes, K. M. Studies of the Australian Arid Zone: Chenopod Shrublands, Pt. 4. 202p. 1981. 40.00x (ISBN 0-643-00347-9, Pub. by CSIRo Australia). State Mutual Bk.

Hartley, W. Checklist of Economic Plants in Australia. 214p. 1979. pap. 9.00 (ISBN 0-643-02551-0, C004, CSIRO). Unipub.

--Checklist of Economic Plants in Australia. 214p. 1980. pap. 8.00x (ISBN 0-643-02551-0, Pub. by CSIRO Australia). Intl Spec Bk.

Howes, K. M. Studies of the Australian Arid Zone: Water in Rangelands, Pt. 3. 256p. 1981. 40.00x (ISBN 0-643-00289-8, Pub. by CSIRO Australia). State Mutual Bk.

The Impact of Climate on Australian Society & Economy. 238p. 1979. pap. 22.75 (ISBN 0-686-71834-8, C028, CSIRO). Unipub.

Lang, John D. Cooksland in North-Eastern Australia. LC 4-32563. 1971. Repr. of 1847 ed. 37.00 (ISBN 0-384-31300-0). Johnson Repr.

McLachlan, K. D. Sulphur in Australasian Agriculture. (Illus.). 256p. 1975. 36.00x (ISBN 0-424-06850-8, Pub by Sydney U Pr). Intl Spec Bk.

McLachlan, K. D., ed. Handbook on Sulphur in Australian Agriculture. (Illus.). 1977. pap. 2.25x (ISBN 0-643-00087-9, Pub. by CSIRO). Intl Spec Bk.

Marsden, J. S., et al. Returns on Australian Agricultural Research. 115p. 1981. 30.00x (ISBN 0-643-02723-8, Pub. by CSIRO Australia). State Mutual Bk.

Muchow, Russell C., ed. Agro-Research for the Semi-Arid Tropics: North-West Australia. LC 84-11979. (Illus.). 640p. 1985. text ed. 44.50x (ISBN 0-7022-1776-X). U of Queensland Pr.

Nalson, J. S. Manpower Training for Agriculture in Western Australia. 1966. pap. 3.00x (ISBN 0-85564-019-7, Pub. by U of W Austral Pr). Intl Spec Bk.

Report of the Tenth Session of the Plant Protection Committee for the Southeast Asia & Pacific Region Held in Canberra, Australia. pap. 7.50 (ISBN 92-5-100049-2, F1115, FAO). Unipub.

Stewart, G. A., et al. Potential for Production of 'Hydrocarbon' Fuels from Crops in Australia. (Illus.). 86p. (Orig.). 1983. pap. 4.95x (ISBN 0-643-02931-1, Pub. by CSIRO Australia). Intl Spec Bk.

AGRICULTURE–CANADA

Food Production in the Canadian Environment. (Perspectives Ser.: No. 3). 1978. pap. 4.25 (ISBN 0-660-00515-8, SSC90, SSC). Unipub.

Shirreff, Patrick. A Tour Through North America: Together with a Comprehensive View of the Canada & United States, As Adapted for Agricultural Emigration. LC 75-173121. Repr. of 1835 ed. 27.50 (ISBN 0-405-08970-8). Ayer Co Pubs.

Warley, T. K. Agriculture in an Interdependent World: U.S. & Canadian Perspectives. LC 77-73919. (Canadian-American Committee Ser.). 104p. 1977. 4.00 (ISBN 0-89068-040-X). Natl Planning.

AGRICULTURE–CHILE

McBride, George M. Chile: Land & Society. LC 71-154618. 1971. Repr. of 1936 ed. lib. bdg. 29.00x (ISBN 0-374-95429-1). Octagon.

AGRICULTURE–CHINA

Chang Pei-Kang. Agriculture & Industrialization. LC 69-13854. Repr. of 1949 ed. lib. bdg. 15.00x (ISBN 0-8371-1057-2, CHAI). Greenwood.

China: Development of Olive Production: Report of a Study Tour to the People's Republic of China, Sept. 25 - Oct, 19, 1979. (Plant Production & Protection Papers: No. 23). 163p. 1980. pap. 11.75 (ISBN 92-5-100995-3, F2097, FAO). Unipub.

China: Forestry Support for Agriculture: Report of an FAO-UNDP Study Tour to the People's Republic of China, Aug 11- Sept 30, 1977. (Forestry Papers: No. 12). 115p. 1978. pap. 8.50 (ISBN 92-5-100695-4, F1554, FAO). Unipub.

China: Multiple Cropping & Related Crop Production Technology: Report of an FAO-UNDP Study Tour to the People's Republic of China, June 25 - July 22, 1979. (Plant Production & Protection Papers: No. 22). 66p. 1980. pap. 11.75 (ISBN 92-5-100977-5, F2108, FAO). Unipub.

China: Post-Harvest Grain Technology: Report of a Study Group in the People's Republic of China September-October 1977. (Agricultural Services Bulletins: No. 50). 70p. 1982. pap. 7.50 (ISBN 92-5-101196-6, F2324, FAO). Unipub.

China: Recycling of Organic Wastes in Agriculture: Report of a FAO-UNDP Tour to the People's Republic of China, April 28 - May 24, 1981. (Soils Bulletins: No. 40). (Eng., Fr. & Span.). 122p. (3rd printing 1981). 1977. pap. 9.00 (ISBN 92-5-100524-9, F1405, FAO). Unipub.

China: Rural Processing Technology. (Agricultural Services Bulletins: No. 36). 63p. 1979. pap. 7.50 (ISBN 92-5-100728-4, F1553, FAO). Unipub.

China: Sericulture: Report on FAO-UNDP Study Tour to the People's Republic of China, 6 May - 4 June 1979. (Agricultural Services Bulletins: No. 42). 133p. 1980. pap. 8.50 (ISBN 92-5-100987-2, F2120, FAO). Unipub.

China: The Agricultural Training System: Report of an FAO-UNDP Study Tour to the People's Republic of China. (Economic & Social Development Papers: No. 11). (Illus.). 141p. 1980. pap. 10.00 (ISBN 92-5-100898-1, F1941, FAO). Unipub.

Hinton, William. Iron Oxen: A Documentary of Revolution in Chinese Farming. LC 70-105310. 1971. pap. 1.95 (ISBN 0-394-71328-1, Vin). Random.

Hsu, Cho-yun. Han Agriculture: The Formation of the Early Chinese Agrarian Economy. Dull, Jack, ed. LC 79-4920. (Illus.). 404p. (Includes material translated from Chinese). 1980. 27.50x (ISBN 0-295-95676-3). U of Wash Pr.

King, F. H. Farmers of Forty Centuries: Permanent Agriculture in China, Korea, & Japan. 1977. 59.95 (ISBN 0-8490-1806-4). Gordon Pr.

--Farmers of Forty Centuries: Permanent Agriculture in China, Korea & Japan. LC 72-90823. (Illus.). 546p. 1973. Repr. of 1911 ed. 15.95 (ISBN 0-87857-054-3). Rodale Pr Inc.

Kuo, Leslie T. The Technical Transformation of Agriculture in Communist China. LC 73-181867. (Special Studies in International Economics & Development). 1971. 39.50x (ISBN 0-275-28276-7). Irvington.

Learning from China: A Report on Agriculture & the Chinese's People's Communes. 1979. pap. 8.75 (ISBN 92-5-100616-4, F1527, FAO). Unipub.

Plucknett, Donald L. & Beemer, Halsey, eds. Vegetable Farming Systems in the People's Republica of China. (Westview Special Studies in Agricultural Science). 350p. 1981. 36.50x (ISBN 0-89158-999-6). Westview.

Sheridan, Mary. Peasant Innovation & Diffusion of Agricultural Technology in China. (Special Series on Agriculture Research & Extension). 83p. (Orig.). 1981. pap. 7.35 (ISBN 0-86731-051-0). RDC Ctr Intl Stud.

Tang, Anthony M. An Analytical & Empirical Investigation of Agriculture in Mainland China, 1952-1980. (Illus.). 248p. 1984. 25.00 (ISBN 0-295-96257-7). U of Wash Pr.

Tawney, Richard H. Land & Labour in China. 1964. lib. bdg. 18.50x (ISBN 0-374-97771-2). Octagon.

Van Buren, Ariane & Pyle, Leo, eds. A Chinese Biogas Manual. Crook, Michael, tr. from Chinese. (Illus.). 135p. (Orig.). 1979. pap. 11.50x (ISBN 0-903031-65-5, Pub. by Intermediate Tech England). Intermediate Tech.

AGRICULTURE–CONGO

Guillot, Bernard. La Terre Enkou: Recherches Sur les Structures Agraires Du Plateau Koukouya (Congo) (Atlas Des Structures Agraires Au Sud Du Sahara: No.8). 1973. pap. 22.40 (ISBN 0-686-21233-9). Mouton.

Management & the Use of Grasslands, Democratic Republic of the Congo. 152p. 1966. pap. 9.75 (ISBN 0-686-70623-4, F1918, FAO). Unipub.

AGRICULTURE–COSTA RICA

Alleger, Daniel E., ed. Fertile Lands of Friendship: The Florida-Costa Rican Experiment in International Agricultural Cooperation. LC 62-20773. 1962. 6.50 (ISBN 0-8130-0007-6). U Presses Fla.

AGRICULTURE–DENMARK

Wade, William W. Institutional Determinants of Technical Change & Agricultural Productivity Growth: Denmark, France, & Great Britain, 1870-1965. Bruchey, Stuart, ed. LC 80-2833. (Dissertations in European Economic History II). (Illus.). 1981. lib. bdg. 35.50x (ISBN 0-405-14017-7). Ayer Co Pubs.

AGRICULTURE–EGYPT

Richards, Alan. Egypt's Agricultural Development, 1800-1980: Technical & Social Change. (Replica Edition Ser.). 300p. 1981. softcover 31.00 (ISBN 0-86531-099-8). Westview.

AGRICULTURE–EUROPE

Agricultural Trade in Europe: Recent Developments, Nos. 12-20. Incl. No. 12. The European Market for Strawberries. (Prepared in 1974). pap. 6.00 (ISBN 0-686-93595-0, UN75/2E/8); No. 13. (Prepared in 1975). pap. 3.00 (ISBN 0-686-93596-9, UN76/2E10); No. 14. The European Market for Unmanufactured Tobacco. (Prepared in 1976). pap. 7.00 (ISBN 0-686-93597-7, UN77/2E9); No. 15. (Prepared in 1977). pap. 5.00 (ISBN 0-686-93598-5, UN78/2E11); No. 16. (Prepared 1978). pap. 5.00 (ISBN 0-686-93599-3, UN79/2E11); No. 17. (Prepared in 1979). pap. 6.00 (ISBN 0-686-93600-0, UN80 2E11); No. 18. (Prepared in 1980). pap. 6.00 (UN81/2E12); No. 19. (Prepared in 1981). pap. 5.00 (UN82/2E11); No. 20. Agricultural Trade in Europe, Recent Developments. 54p. 1983. pap. text ed. 8.50 (UN83/2E17, UN). UN). Unipub.

Banfield, Thomas C. Industry of the Rhine: Series 1-2, 2 Vols in 1. LC 68-55470. Repr. of 1848 ed. 45.00x (ISBN 0-678-00568-0). Kelley.

Broekhuizen, S. & Thran, P., eds. Atlas of Cereal Growing in Europe. (Agro-Ecological Atlas Ser.: Vol. 2). 156p. 1970. 159.50 (ISBN 0-444-40819-3). Elsevier.

Delisle, Leopold V. Etudes sur la Condition de la Classe Agricole et l'Etat de l'Agriculture en Normandie au Moyen Age. 1965. Repr. of 1906 ed. 45.00 (ISBN 0-8337-0820-1). B Franklin.

Dietl, Walter. Standortgemasse Verbesserung und Bewirtschaftung Von Alpenweiden. (Tierhaltung: No. 7). (Ger., Illus.). 67p. 1979. pap. 15.95x (ISBN 0-8176-1028-6). Birkhauser.

Fraas, Karl N. Geschichte Der Landbau-Und Forstwissenschaft. Repr. of 1865 ed. 50.00 (ISBN 0-384-16660-1). Johnson Repr.

Morgan, Ora S., ed. Agricultural Systems of Middle Europe: A Symposium. LC 72-94470. Repr. of 1933 ed. 21.50 (ISBN 0-404-04434-4). AMS Pr.

Report of the FAO Regional Conference for Europe: Ninth, Lauanne, Switzerland, 1974. 1976. pap. 7.50 (ISBN 0-685-66317-5, F1114, FAO). Unipub.

Report of the Twelfth FAO Regional Conference for Europe: Athens, Greece, 22-27 Sept. 1980. 50p. 1980. pap. 7.50 (ISBN 92-5-101013-7, F2165, FAO). Unipub.

Review of the Agricultural Situation in Europe at the End of 1981, 2 Vols. pap. 17.00 (UN82/2E8, UN). Unipub.

Thran, P. & Brockhuizen, S., eds. Agro-Climatic Atlas of Europe. (Agro-Ecological Atlas Ser.: Vol. 1). 294p. 1965. 202.25 (ISBN 0-444-40569-0). Elsevier.

Wadekin, Karl-Eugen, ed. Agriculture in Eastern Europe & the Soviet Union: Comparative Studies. LC 80-636. (Studies in East European & Soviet Russian Agrarian Policy: Vol. III). 450p. text ed. cancelled (ISBN 0-916672-42-5). Rowman & Allanheld.

Zadoks, J. C. & Rijsdijk, F. H. Atlas of Cereal Diseases & Pests in Europe. (Agro-ecological Atlas of Cereal Growing in Europe: Vol. 3). (Illus.). 169p. 1985. 30.50 (ISBN 90-220-0863-0, PDC281, Pudoc). Unipub.

AGRICULTURE–EUROPE–HISTORY

Abel, Wilhelm. Agricultural Fluctuations in Europe: From the Thirteenth to the Twentieth Centuries. Ordish, Olive, tr. LC 80-5072. 1980. 12.95 (ISBN 0-312-01465-1). St Martin.

Jarman, M. R, et al. Early European Agriculture: Its Foundations & Development. LC 81-17960. 280p. 1982. 47.50 (ISBN 0-521-24359-9). Cambridge U Pr.

Nasse, Erwin. On the Agricultural Community of the Middle Ages, & Inclosures of the 16th Century in England. Ouvray, H. A., tr. LC 79-1586. 1980. Repr. of 1872 ed. 11.50 (ISBN 0-88355-891-2). Hyperion Conn.

AGRICULTURE–FINLAND

Varjo, U. Finnish Farming Technology & Economics. 1977. 10.50 (ISBN 0-9960004-1-0, Pub. by Akademiai Kaido Hungary). Heyden.

AGRICULTURE–FRANCE

Clout, Hugh. Agriculture in France on the Eve of the Railway Age. (Illus.). 239p. 1980. 28.50x (ISBN 0-389-20017-4). B&N Imports.

Wade, William W. Institutional Determinants of Technical Change & Agricultural Productivity Growth: Denmark, France, & Great Britain, 1870-1965. Bruchey, Stuart, ed. LC 80-2833. (Dissertations in European Economic History II). (Illus.). 1981. lib. bdg. 35.50x (ISBN 0-405-14017-7). Ayer Co Pubs.

Young, Arthur. Travels During the Years 1787, 1788 & 1789, 2 Vols. 2nd ed. LC 79-115008. Repr. of 1794 ed. Set. 145.00 (ISBN 0-404-07068-X). AMS Pr.

AGRICULTURE–GERMANY

Farquharson, John E. The Plough & the Swastika: The NSDAP & Agriculture in Germany 1928-45. LC 74-31570. (Sage Studies in 20th Century History Ser.: Vol. 5). pap. 80.00 (ISBN 0-317-29682-5, 2021897). Bks Demand UMI.

Zimmermann, Josef. Bodenkultur und Landschaft der Erftniederung. 20.00 (ISBN 0-384-71010-7). Johnson Repr.

AGRICULTURE–GREAT BRITAIN

Agricultural Tribunal of Investigation. Final Report: Presented to Parliament by Command of His Majesty. LC 75-26316. (World Food Supply Ser.). (Illus.). 1976. Repr. of 1924 ed. 32.00x (ISBN 0-405-07793-9). Ayer Co Pubs.

Agriculture, 2 pts. Incl. Pt. 1. General, 32 vols. Set. 2538.00x (ISBN 0-7165-1433-8); Pt. 2. Animal Health, 4 vols. Set. 432.00x (ISBN 0-7165-1434-6). (British Parliamentary Papers Ser.). 1971 (Pub. by Irish Academic Pr Ireland). Biblio Dist.

Britton, Denis K., et al. Statistical Handbook of U. K. Agriculture. 20.00x (ISBN 0-686-79165-7, Pub. by Dominican Ireland). State Mutual Bk.

Caird, James. English Agriculture in Eighteen Fifty & Eighteen Fifty-One. LC 67-16347. Repr. of 1852 ed. 37.50x (ISBN 0-678-05033-3). Kelley.

--Landed Interest & the Supply of Food. 4th ed. LC 67-16346. Repr. of 1880 ed. 25.00x (ISBN 0-678-05034-1). Kelley.

Dahlman, C. J. The Open Field System & Beyond. LC 79-7658. 1980. 32.50 (ISBN 0-521-22881-6). Cambridge U Pr.

Davenport, Frances G. Economic Development of a Norfolk Manor, 1085-1585. LC 67-16349. (Illus.). Repr. of 1906 ed. 25.00x (ISBN 0-678-05041-4). Kelley.

Fowler, Peter. The Farming of Prehistoric Britain. LC 83-1808. 256p. 1983. pap. 15.95 (ISBN 0-521-27369-2). Cambridge U Pr.

Great Britain Board of Agriculture. Agriculture State of the Kingdom, 1816. LC 78-108849. Repr. of 1816 ed. lib. bdg. 37.50x (ISBN 0-678-07767-3). Kelley.

Holt, John. General View of the Agriculture of the County of Lancaster. LC 68-13155. (Illus.). Repr. of 1795 ed. 35.00x (ISBN 0-678-05602-1). Kelley.

Lockhart, J. A. & Wiseman, A. J. Introduction to Crop Husbandry. 5th ed. (Illus.). 300p. 1983. 40.00 (ISBN 0-08-029793-5); pap. 16.00 (ISBN 0-08-029792-7). Pergamon.

McDonald, Donald. Agricultural Writers from Sir Walter of Henley to Arthur Young 1200-1800. LC 68-56721. (Bibliography & Reference Ser: No. 217). (Illus.). 1968. Repr. of 1908 ed. 22.50 (ISBN 0-8337-2327-8). B Franklin.

Markham, Gervase. The Inrichment of the Weald of Kent: Or, a Direction to the Husbandman. LC 73-6151. (English Experience Ser.: No. 614). 24p. 1973. Repr. of 1625 ed. 3.50 (ISBN 90-221-0614-4). Walter J Johnson.

Marshall, William. Rural Economy of the West of England 2 Vols. LC 78-85333. Repr. of 1796 ed. Set. 76.50x (ISBN 0-678-05564-5). Kelley.

Riches, Naomi. Agricultural Revolution in Norfolk. LC 67-20814. (Illus.). Repr. of 1937 ed. 25.00x (ISBN 0-678-05082-1). Kelley.

Royal Society Study Group Report Staff. The Nitrogen Cycle of the United Kingdom: A Study Group Report. (RSL Study Group Report Ser.). (Illus.). 264p. 1984. pap. text ed. 28.00 (ISBN 0-85403-227-4, Pub. by Royal Soc London). Scholium Intl.

Slater, Gilbert. English Peasantry & the Enclosure of Common Fields. LC 68-27295. (Illus.). Repr. of 1907 ed. 32.50x (ISBN 0-678-00401-3). Kelley.

Spedding, C. R. & Diekmahns, E. C., eds. Grasses & Legumes in British Agriculture. 511p. 1972. 89.00x (ISBN 0-85198-016-3, Pub. by CAB Bks England). State Mutual Bk.

Stratton, John M. & Brown, Jack H. Agricultural Records in Britain, A. D. 200 to 1977. 2nd ed. Whitlock, Ralph, ed. 259p. 1979. 19.00 (ISBN 0-208-01818-2, Archon). Shoe String.

Vancouver, Charles. General View of the Agriculture of the County of Devon. LC 68-56062. (Illus.). Repr. 39.50x (ISBN 0-678-05639-0). Kelley.

Young, Arthur. General View of the Agriculture of Norfolk. LC 69-13757. (Illus.). Repr. of 1804 ed. 45.00x (ISBN 0-678-05648-X). Kelley.

--General View of the Agriculture of the County of Lincolnshire. LC 78-100414. (Illus.). Repr. of 1813 ed. lib. bdg. 39.50x (ISBN 0-678-05681-1). Kelley.

--General View of the Agriculture of the County of Oxfordshire. LC 74-91998. (Illus.). Repr. of 1813 ed. lib. bdg. 39.50x (ISBN 0-678-05543-2). Kelley.

--General View of the Agriculture of the County of Sussex. LC 71-100415. (Illus.). Repr. of 1813 ed. lib. bdg. 39.50x (ISBN 0-678-05680-3). Kelley.

--General View of the Agriculture of the County of Suffolk. LC 78-91999. (Illus.). Repr. of 1813 ed. lib. bdg. 39.50x (ISBN 0-678-05544-0). Kelley.

--Political Arithmetic. LC 67-29462. Repr. of 1774 ed. 37.50x (ISBN 0-678-00338-6). Kelley.

--Six Months Tour Through the North of England, 4 Vols. 2nd ed. LC 67-29461. Repr. of 1771 ed. 175.00x (ISBN 0-678-00332-7). Kelley.

AGRICULTURE–GREAT BRITAIN–HISTORY

Ault, Warren O. Open-Field Farming in Medieval England. (Historical Problems; Studies & Documents). 1972. text ed. 18.95x (ISBN 0-04-942104-2); pap. text ed. 8.95x (ISBN 0-04-942105-0). Allen Unwin.

Davenport, Frances G. A Classified List of Printed Original Materials for English Manorial & Agrarian History During the Middle Ages. (Radcliffe College Monographs: No. 6). 1964. Repr. of 1894 ed. 20.00 (ISBN 0-8337-0774-4). B Franklin.

Fussell, G. E. English Dairy Farmer: 1500-1900. (Illus.). 357p. 1966. 27.50x (ISBN 0-7146-1309-6, F Cass Co). Biblio Dist.

Grigg, David B. Agricultural Revolution in South Lincolnshire. (Cambridge Studies in Economic History). 1966. 42.50 (ISBN 0-521-05152-5). Cambridge U Pr.

Harvey, Nigel. The Industrial Archaeology of Farming in England & Wales. (Illus.). 224p. 1980. 32.00 (ISBN 0-7134-1845-1, Pub. by Batsford England). David & Charles.

Inman, A. H. Domesday & Feudal Statistics with a Chapter on Agriculture Statistics. LC 77-137948. (Economic Thought, History & Challenge Ser.). 1971. Repr. of 1900 ed. 26.50x (ISBN 0-8046-1450-4, Pub. by Kennikat). Assoc Faculty Pr.

Jones, E. L. Development of English Agriculture, 1815-1873. (Studies in Economic & Social History). (Illus.). 1968. pap. text ed. 3.25x (ISBN 0-333-04910-1). Humanities.

Marshall, William. Review & Abstract of the County Reports to the Board of Agriculture 5 Vols. LC 69-11853. Repr. of 1818 ed. 195.00x (ISBN 0-678-05613-7). Kelley.

Moore, Margaret F. Two Select Bibliographies of Medieval Historical Study. 1912. 21.00 (ISBN 0-8337-2452-5). B Franklin.

Nasse, Erwin. On the Agricultural Community of the Middle Ages, & Inclosures of the 16th Century in England. Ouvray, H. A., tr. LC 79-1586. 1980. Repr. of 1872 ed. 11.50 (ISBN 0-88355-891-2). Hyperion Conn.

Piggott, Stuart, ed. The Agrarian History of England & Wales, Vol. 1, Pt. 1: Prehistory. LC 66-19763. (Agrarian History of England & Wales Ser.). 1981. 69.50 (ISBN 0-521-08741-4). Cambridge U Pr.

Prothero, Rowland E. English Farming Past & Present. LC 72-83276. 519p. Repr. of 1917 ed. 27.50 (ISBN 0-405-08866-3, Pub. by Blom). Ayer Co Pubs.

Thirsk, J., ed. Agrarian History of England & Wales, Vol. 4: 1500-1640. 105.00 (ISBN 0-521-06617-4). Cambridge U Pr.

Wade, William W. Institutional Determinants of Technical Change & Agricultural Productivity Growth: Denmark, France, & Great Britain, 1870-1965. Bruchey, Stuart, ed. LC 80-2833. (Dissertations in European Economic History II). (Illus.). 1981. lib. bdg. 35.50x (ISBN 0-405-14017-7). Ayer Co Pubs.

AGRICULTURE–GREECE, MODERN

Brumfield, Allaire C. The Attic Festivals of Demeter & Their Relation to the Agricultural Year. Connor, W. R., ed. LC 80-2643. (Monographs in Classical Studies). 1981. lib. bdg. 29.00 (ISBN 0-405-14031-2). Ayer Co Pubs.

AGRICULTURE–GUATEMALA

Fletcher, Lehman B., et al. Guatemala's Economic Development: The Role of Agriculture. facsimile ed. LC 74-114800. (Orig.). 1970. pap. 8.20x (ISBN 0-8138-2240-8). Iowa St U Pr.

Mathewson, Kent. Irrigation Horticulture in Highland Guatemala: The Tablon System of Panajachel. (Replica Edition Ser.). 185p. 1983. softcover 20.50x (ISBN 0-86531-973-1). Westview.

AGRICULTURE–HAWAII

Lind, Andrew W. Island Community: Ecological Succession in Hawaii. LC 68-28639. 1968. Repr. of 1938 ed. lib. bdg. 22.75x (ISBN 0-8371-0538-2, LIIC). Greenwood.

AGRICULTURE–INDIA

Agarwal, Bina. Mechanization in Indian Agriculture: An Analytical Study Based on the Punjab. 1984. 24.00x (ISBN 0-8364-1168-4, Pub. by Allied India). South Asia Bks.

Agricultural Production Team. Report on India's Food Crisis & Steps to Meet It. LC 75-26294. (World Food Supply Ser). 1976. Repr. of 1959 ed. 21.00x (ISBN 0-405-07767-X). Ayer Co Pubs.

Ahmed, Iftikhar. Technological Change & Agrarian Structure: A Study of Bangladesh. International Labour Office, ed. xvi, 136p. (Orig.). 1981. pap. 8.55 (ISBN 92-2-102543-8). Intl Labour Office.

Aziz, Abdul. Organizing Agricultural Labourers in India. 1980. 7.50x (ISBN 0-8364-0651-6, Pub. by Minerva India). South Asia Bks.

Banga, Indu. Agrarian System of the Sikhs Seventeen Fifty-Nine to Eighteen Forty-Nine. 1979. 18.50x (ISBN 0-88386-758-3). South Asia Bks.

Bansil, P. C. Agricultural Problems of India. 2nd ed. 1977. 11.00x (ISBN 0-686-26275-1). Intl Bk Dist.

Bhattacharyya, Swapan K. Farmers Rituals, & Modernization in India: A Sociological Study. 1976. 12.50x (ISBN 0-88386-800-8). South Asia Bks.

Bumb, Balu. A Survey of the Fertilizer Sector in India. (Working Paper: No. 331). iv, 216p. 1979. 5.00 (ISBN 0-686-36189-X, WP-0331). World Bank.

Dasgupta, Sipra. Class Relations & Technological Change in Indian Agriculture. 1981. 16.00x (ISBN 0-8364-0676-1, Pub. by Macmillan India). South Asia Bks.

Famine Inquiry Commission of India. Report on Bengal. LC 75-26302. (World Food Supply Ser). 1976. Repr. of 1945 ed. 20.00x (ISBN 0-405-07781-5). Ayer Co Pubs.

FAO-UNDP International Expert Consultation on the Use of Improved Technology for Food Production in Rainfed Areas of Tropical Asia: Report, 3 Vols. Vol. 1. pap. 28.00 (F1089, FAO); Vol. 2. pap. 17.75; Vol. 3. pap. 23.75. Unipub.

Harriss, John. Capitalism & Peasant Farming: Agrarian Structure & Ideology in Northern Tamil Nadu. (Illus.). 1982. 27.50x (ISBN 0-19-561340-6). Oxford U Pr.

Husain, M. Crop Combinations in India. 200p. 1982. text ed. 22.00x (ISBN 0-391-02754-9, Pub. by Concept India). Humanities.

Islam, M. M. Bengal Agriculture Nineteen Twenty to Nineteen Forty-Six. LC 76-57098. (Cambridge South Asian Studies: No. 22). 1979. 52.50 (ISBN 0-521-21579-X). Cambridge U Pr.

Johnson, B. L. C. India: Resources & Development. LC 78-15402. (Illus.). 211p. 1979. text ed. 28.50x (ISBN 0-06-493348-2). B&N Imports.

Johnson, D. Gale, ed. Famine in India: An Original Anthology. LC 75-29759. (World Food Supply Ser). 1976. 20.00x (ISBN 0-405-07774-2). Ayer Co Pubs.

Leaf, Murray J. Song of Hope: The Green Revolution in a Panjab Village. 304p. 1984. text ed. 28.00 (ISBN 0-8135-1025-2). Rutgers U Pr.

Mohammad, Ali, ed. Dynamics of Agricultural Development in India. 1979. text ed. 21.00x (ISBN 0-391-01859-0). Humanities.

Nair, P. K. Intensive Multiple Cropping with Coconuts in India: Principles, Programmes & Prospects. (Advances in Agronomy & Crop Science Ser.: Vol. 6). (Illus.). 148p. (Orig.). 1979. pap. text ed. 28.00 (ISBN 3-489-71210-2). Parey Sci Pubs.

Pandit, Som N. Critical Study of Agricultural Productivity in Uttar Pradesh. 154p. 1983. text ed. 18.00x (ISBN 0-391-02887-1, Pub. by Concept India). Humanities.

Population & Agricultural Development: Selected Relationships & Possible Planning Uses, No. 5: Population Growth & Agricultural Development - A Case Study of Kerala. (Development Documents: No. 51). 99p. 1978. pap. 6.75 (ISBN 0-686-92855-5, F1643, FAO). Unipub.

Rao, V. M. Second India Studies: Food. 1975. text ed. 5.50x (ISBN 0-333-90116-9). South Asia Bks.

Seetharam, G. N. Strategy & Tactics of India's Agricultural Development. 1984. 12.00x (ISBN 0-8364-1134-X, Pub. by Ajanta). South Asia Bks.

Sen, Bandhudas. The Green Revolution in India: A Perspective. LC 74-11066. 118p. 1974. 19.95x (ISBN 0-470-77590-4). Halsted Pr.

Sharma, H. S. The Physiography of the Lower Chambal Valley & Its Agricultural Development. 1979. text ed. 16.25x (ISBN 0-391-01927-9). Humanities.

Shingi, P. M., et al. Rural Youth: Education, Occupation & Social Outlook. 1980. 10.00x (ISBN 0-8364-0663-X, Pub. by Abhinav India). South Asia Bks.

Thirumalai, S. Post-War Agricultural Problems & Policies in India. LC 75-30086. (Institute of Pacific Relations). Repr. of 1954 ed. 23.00 (ISBN 0-404-59567-7). AMS Pr.

AGRICULTURE–ISRAEL

Mandelbaum, Irving J. A History of the Mishnaic Law of Agriculture: Kilayim. Neusner, Jacob, ed. LC 81-1462. (Brown Judaic Studies Ser.: No. 26). 1981. pap. text ed. 18.00 (ISBN 0-89130-465-7, 14 00 26). Scholars Pr GA.

Weitz, R. & Rokach, A. Agricultural Development, Planning & Implementation: Israel Case Study. 404p. 1968. 37.00 (ISBN 90-277-0102-4). Kluwer Academic.

AGRICULTURE–JAPAN

Development of Local Culture & the Irrigation System of the Azusa Basin. (Human & Social Development Programme - Research Papers). 32p. 1980. pap. 5.00 (ISBN 92-808-0050-7, TUNU032, UNU). Unipub.

The Fertilization Technology Described in Historical Japanese Farm Manuals & That Utilized by Modern Farm Households. 65p. 1981. pap. 5.00 (ISBN 92-808-0259-3, TUNU143, UNU). Unipub.

Francks, Penelope. Technology & Agricultural Development in Pre-War Japan. LC 82-20306. 352p. 1984. 32.00x (ISBN 0-300-02927-6). Yale U Pr.

Havens, Thomas R. Farm & Nation in Modern Japan: Agrarian Nationalism, 1870-1949. LC 73-16774. pap. 92.80 (ISBN 0-317-27577-1, 2014874). Bks Demand UMI.

King, F. H. Farmers of Forty Centuries: Permanent Agriculture in China, Korea, & Japan. 1977. 59.95 (ISBN 0-8490-1806-4). Gordon Pr.

--Farmers of Forty Centuries: Permanent Agriculture in China, Korea & Japan. LC 72-90823. (Illus.). 546p. 1973. Repr. of 1911 ed. 15.95 (ISBN 0-87857-054-3). Rodale Pr Inc.

Land Improvement Investment & Agricultural Enterprises in Japan: As Seen in the Azusa River System. 36p. 1980. pap. 5.00 (ISBN 92-808-0088-4, TUNU059, UNU). Unipub.

McCune, Shannon. Geographical Aspects of Agricultural Changes in the Ryukyu Islands. LC 75-11729. (University of Florida Social Sciences Monographs: No. 54). 86p. 1975. pap. 3.50 (ISBN 0-8130-0487-X). U Presses Fla.

Nasu, Shiroshi. Aspects of Japanese Agriculture: A Preliminary Survey. LC 75-30073. (Institute of Pacific Relations). Repr. of 1941 ed. 24.50 (ISBN 0-404-59575-8). AMS Pr.

Numata, M., et al, eds. Studies in Conservation of Natural Terrestrial Ecosystems in Japan, Part II: Vegetation & Its Conservation, Vol. 8. (Japan International Biological Program Synthesis Ser.). 157p. 1975. 18.50x (ISBN 0-86008-218-0, Pub. by U of Tokyo Japan). Columbia U Pr.

--Studies in Conservation of Natural Terrestrial Ecosystems in Japan, Part II: Animal Communities, Vol. 9. (Japan International Biological Program Synthesis Ser.). 91p. 1975. 15.00x (ISBN 0-86008-219-9, Pub. by U of Tokyo Japan). Columbia U Pr.

Shidei, T. & Kira, T., eds. Primary Productivity of Japanese Forests, Productivity of Terrestrial Communities, Vol. 16. (Japan International Biological Program Synthesis Ser.). 289p. 1977. 32.50x (ISBN 0-86008-226-1, Pub. by U of Tokyo Japan). Columbia U Pr.

AGRICULTURE–KOREA

Keidel, Albert, 3rd. Korean Regional Farm Product & Income: 1910-1975. 267p. 1981. text ed. 15.00x (ISBN 0-8248-0758-8, Korea Devel Inst). UH Pr.

King, F. H. Farmers of Forty Centuries: Permanent Agriculture in China, Korea, & Japan. 1977. 59.95 (ISBN 0-8490-1806-4). Gordon Pr.

Wade, Robert. Irrigation & Agricultural Politics in South Korea. (Special Studies in Social, Political, & Economic Development Ser.). 160p. 1982. 26.00x (ISBN 0-86531-264-8). Westview.

AGRICULTURE–LATIN AMERICA

Actas Del Simposio Sobre Acuicultura En America Latina: Montevideo, Uruguay, 26 Noviembre-2 Diciembre de 1974, 3 Vols. Incl. Vol. 1. pap. 20.75 (F1501, FAO); Vol. 2. pap. 9.50 (F1502, FAO); Vol. 3. pap. 9.75 (F1503, FAO). 1974 (FAO). Unipub.

Agrarian Reform in Latin America: An Annotated Bibliography. LC 74-29076. (Land Economics Monograph Ser. No. 5). 684p. 1974. 40.00x (ISBN 0-299-95030-1); pap. 20.00x (ISBN 0-299-95034-4). U of Wis Pr.

Derecho Agrario y Desarrollo Agricola: Estado Actual y Perspectivas en America Latina: Informe Final del Groupo Regional de Asesores en Derecho Agrario. (Legislative Studies: No. 13). (Span.). pap. 14.50 (F1495, FAO). Unipub.

Handelman, Howard, ed. The Politics of Agrarian Change in Asia & Latin America. LC 81-47565. (Illus.). 148p. 1981. 22.50x (ISBN 0-253-34548-0). Ind U Pr.

Mabbutt, J. A., ed. Strategies for Improved Management of Latin American Drylands. Schneider, H. J., et al. 29p. 1981. pap. 5.00 (ISBN 92-808-0227-5, TUNU127, UNU). Unipub.

Mosher, Arthur T. Technical Co-Operation in Latin-American Agriculture. LC 75-26310. (World Food Supply Ser). (Illus.). 1976. Repr. of 1957 ed. 36.50x (ISBN 0-405-07788-2). Ayer Co Pubs.

Pineiro, Martin E. & Trigo, Eduardo J., eds. Technical Change & Social Conflict in Agriculture: Latin American Perspectives. 266p. 1983. pap. 35.00x (ISBN 0-86531-802-6). Westview.

Report of the FAO Regional Conference for Latin America: Thirteenth, Panama City, Panama, August 1974. 1976. pap. 7.50 (ISBN 0-685-66321-3, F1123, FAO). Unipub.

Report of the Fourteenth FAO Regional Conference for Latin America & the Latin American ECLA-FAO Food Conference. pap. 7.50 (F1126, FAO). Unipub.

Report of the Joint FAO-WHO Food Standards Regional Conference for Latin America. (Codex Alimentarius Commission Reports). 1979. pap. 13.00 (ISBN 92-5-100682-2, F1618, FAO). Unipub.

Report of the Meetings on Fertilizer Production, Distribution & Utilization in Latin America: Rio de Janeiro, 1951. (Agricultural Development Papers: No. 36). 52p. 1953. pap. 4.50 (ISBN 0-686-92856-3, F1919, FAO). Unipub.

Report of the Seventeenth FAO Regional Conference for Latin America: Managua, 30th Aug. to 10th Sept. 1982. (Eng., Fr. & Span.). 58p. 1983. pap. text ed. 7.50 (ISBN 92-5-101317-9, F2396, FAO). Unipub.

Report of the Sixteenth FAO Regional Conference for Latin America: Havana, 1-6 Sept. 1980. (Eng., Fr. & Span.). 109p. 1980. pap. 8.00 (ISBN 92-5-101039-0, F2148, FAO). Unipub.

Report on the Agro-Ecological Zones Project: Methodology & Results for South & Central America, Vol. 3. (World Soil Resources Reports: No. 48-3). (Eng. & Span.). 251p. 1982. pap. 19.75 (ISBN 92-5-101081-1, F2225, FAO). Unipub.

Wilson, Charles M., ed. New Crops for the New World. LC 73-138140. (Illus.). 1971. Repr. of 1945 ed. lib. bdg. 24.75x (ISBN 0-8371-5713-7, WINC). Greenwood.

Zanstra, H. & Swanberg, K. Caqueza: Living Rural Development. (Eng. & Span.). 321p. 1979. Casebound 18.00 (ISBN 0-88936-167-3, IDRC107, IDRC). Unipub.

AGRICULTURE–MEXICO

Cowgill, Ursula M. Soil Fertility & the Ancient Maya. (Connecticut Academy of Arts & Sciences Transactions Ser.: Vol. 42). 56p. 1961. 12.00 (ISBN 0-317-03798-6). Shoe String.

Cummings, Ronald G. Interbasin Water Transfers: A Case Study in Mexico. LC 74-6819. pap. 31.80 (ISBN 0-317-26457-5, 2023793). Bks Demand UMI.

Ewell, Peter T. & Poleman, Thomas T. Uxpanapa: Agricultural Development in the Mexican Tropics. LC 80-12208. (Pergamon Policy Studies). 220p. 1980. 30.00 (ISBN 0-08-025967-7). Pergamon.

Flannery, Kent V. Guila Naquitz: Arcahic Foraging & Early Agriculture in Oaxaca, Mexico. Date not set. price not set (ISBN 0-12-259830-X). Acad Pr.

Norton, Roger D. & Solis, Leopoldo M., eds. The Book of CHAC: Programming Studies for Mexican Agricultural Policy. (World Bank Ser.). 624p. 1983. 35.00x (ISBN 0-8018-2585-7). Johns Hopkins.

Tannenbaum, Frank. Mexican Agrarian Revolution. (Brookings Institution Reprint Ser). (Illus.). lib. bdg. 19.50x (ISBN 0-697-00172-5); pap. 6.95x (ISBN 0-89197-845-3). Irvington.

Yates, P. Lamartine. Mexico's Agricultural Dilemma. LC 81-10279. 291p. 1981. 19.95x (ISBN 0-8165-0734-1); pap. 8.95x (ISBN 0-8165-0733-3). U of Ariz Pr.

AGRICULTURE–NEAR EAST

McLackhlan, K. S., ed. The Developing Agriculture of the Middle East: Opportunities & Prospects. 74p. 1976. 43.00x (ISBN 0-86010-046-4, Pub. by Graham & Trotman England). State Mutual Bk.

Rainfed Agriculture in the Near East & North Africa: Proceedings of the FAO Regional Seminar, Amman, Jordan, May 5-10, 1979. 416p. 1980. pap. 28.75 (ISBN 92-5-101030-7, F2174, FAO). Unipub.

Regional Study on Rainfed Agriculture & Agro-Climatic Inventory of Eleven Countries in the Near East Region. (Illus.). 174p. 1982. pap. 18.00 (ISBN 92-5-101222-9, F2369, FAO). Unipub.

Report for the Thirteenth FAO Regional Conference for the Near East, Tunis, Tunisia, October 4-11, 1976. pap. 7.50 (F1124, FAO). Unipub.

Report of the Fourteenth FAO Regional Conference for the Near East. 1979. pap. 7.50 (ISBN 92-5-100688-1, F1555, FAO). Unipub.

Report of the Sixth Session of the Near East Plant Production Commission, 1976. pap. 8.25 (ISBN 92-5-100299-1, F1244, FAO). Unipub.

Ryan, John & Saad, Adib T., eds. Agricultural Education for Development in the Middle East. 1981. 20.00x (ISBN 0-8156-6057-X, Am U of Beirut). Syracuse U Pr.

Samarraie, Husam. Agriculture in Iraq During the Third Century. (Arab Background Ser.). 1972. 15.00x (ISBN 0-86685-026-0). Intl Bk Ctr.

Small-Scale Cash Crop Farming in South Asia: Seminar Proceedings, FAO-DANIDA, Colombo, Sri Lanka, 15-27 Oct. 1979. (Plant Production & Protection Papers: No. 27). 93p. 1981. pap. 7.50 (ISBN 92-5-101050-1, F2191, FAO). Unipub.

AGRICULTURE–NEW ZEALAND

Best, Elsdon. Maori Agriculture. LC 75-35232. Repr. of 1925 ed. 68.00 (ISBN 0-404-14409-8). AMS Pr.

Smith, H. C. & Wratt, G. S., eds. Plant Breeding in New Zealand. (Illus.). 300p. (Orig.). 1983. pap. 34.95 (ISBN 0-409-70137-8). Butterworth.

AGRICULTURE–NIGERIA

Bohannan, Paul. Tiv Farm & Settlement. pap. 10.00 (ISBN 0-384-04959-1). Johnson Repr.

Maiduguri Mill Project: Grain Milling & Utilization in West Africa. 15p. 1978. pap. 5.00 (ISBN 0-88936-085-5, IDRCTS2, IDRC). Unipub.

Oyenuga, V. A. Agriculture in Nigeria: An Introduction. 308p. 1967. pap. 13.25 (ISBN 92-5-101514-7, F16, FAO). Unipub.

AGRICULTURE–NORTH AMERICA

Aandahl, Andrew R. Soils of the Great Plains: Land Use, Crops, & Grasses. LC 81-7435. (Illus.). xvi, 282p. 1982. 28.50x (ISBN 0-8032-1011-6). U of Nebr Pr.

Wilson, Charles M., ed. New Crops for the New World. LC 73-138140. (Illus.). 1971. Repr. of 1945 ed. lib. bdg. 24.75x (ISBN 0-8371-5713-7, WINC). Greenwood.

AGRICULTURE–PAKISTAN

Nulty, Leslie. The Green Revolution in West Pakistan: Implications of Technological Change. LC 73-170471. (Special Studies in International Economics & Development). 1972. 29.50x (ISBN 0-89197-779-1). Irvington.

AGRICULTURE–PAPUA–NEW GUINEA (TERRITORY)

Bleeker, P. Explanatory Notes to the Land Limitation & Agricultural Land Use Potential Map of Papua New Guinea. (Land Research Ser.: No. 36). (Illus.). 1977. pap. 10.00x (ISBN 0-643-00164-6, Pub. by CSIRO). Intl SPEC Bk.

Paijmans, K. Explanatory Notes to the Vegetation Map of Papua New Guinea. (Land Research Ser.: No. 35). (Illus.). 46p. 1977. pap. 10.00x (ISBN 0-643-00138-7, Pub. by CSIRO). Intl Spec Bk.

Sillitoe, Paul. Roots of the Earth: Crops in the Highlands of Papua New Guinea. LC 82-62247. 278p. 1983. 35.00 (ISBN 0-7190-0874-3, Pub. by Manchester Univ Pr). Longwood Pub Group.

AGRICULTURE–PERU

Alberda, Th. Production & Water Use of Several Food & Fodder Crops Under Irrigation in the Desert Area of Southwestern Peru. (Agricultural Research Reports: No. 928). (Illus.). 50p. 1985. pap. 7.50 (ISBN 90-220-0869-X, PDC291, Pudoc). Unipub.

Horton, Douglas. Social Scientists in Agricultural Research: Lessons from the Mantaro Valley Project, Peru. 67p. 1984. pap. 11.00 (ISBN 0-88936-400-1, IDRC219, IDRC). Unipub.

AGRICULTURE–ROME

Cato The Censor. On Farming. Brehaut, Ernest, tr. 1968. lib. bdg. 16.50x (ISBN 0-374-90969-5). Octagon.

Clausing, Roth. Roman Colonate: The Theories of Its Origin. LC 70-78011. (Columbia University Studies in the Social Sciences: No. 260). 1969. Repr. of 1925 ed. 27.50 (ISBN 0-404-51260-7). AMS Pr.

Heitland, William E. Agricola: A Study of Agriculture & Rustic Life in the Greco-Roman World from the Point of View of Labour. Repr. of 1921 ed. lib. bdg. 37.00 (ISBN 0-8371-4088-9, HEAG). Greenwood.

Hoerle, Joseph. Catos Hausbuecher: Analyse Seiner Schrift de Agricultura. 1929. 22.00 (ISBN 0-384-23880-7). Johnson Repr.

White, K. D. Roman Farming. Scullard, H. H., ed. LC 77-119592. (Aspects of Greek & Roman Life). (Illus.). 536p. 1970. 34.50x (ISBN 0-8014-0575-0). Cornell U Pr.

AGRICULTURE–SOUTH AFRICA

Tinley, J. M. South African Food & Agriculture in World War II. (Illus.). 1954. 12.50x (ISBN 0-8047-0457-0). Stanford U Pr.

AGRICULTURE–SOVIET UNION

Antsiferov, Alexis N., et al. Russian Agriculture During the War: Rural Economy; The Land Settlement. (Economic & Social History of the World War, Russian Ser.). 1930. 19.50x (ISBN 0-317-27551-8). Elliots Bks.

Confino, Michael. Systemes Agraires & Progres Agricole - L'assolement Triennal En Russie Au XVIIIe-XIXe Siecles. (Etudes Sur L'histoire, L'economie & la Sociologie Des Pays Slaves: No. 14). 1970. pap. 34.40 (ISBN 90-2796-294-4). Mouton.

Gustafson, Thane. Reform in Soviet Politics: The Lessons of Recent Policies on Land & Water. LC 80-24286. (Illus.). 224p. 1981. 34.50 (ISBN 0-521-23377-1). Cambridge U Pr.

Jacobs, Everett M., ed. The Organization of Agriculture in the Soviet Union & Eastern Europe. LC 79-3807. (Studies in East European & Soviet Russian Agrarian Policy: Vol. 2). 500p. text ed. cancelled (ISBN 0-916672-41-7). Rowman & Allanheld.

Morozov, V. A. Soviet Agriculture. 220p. 1977. 3.95 (ISBN 0-8285-0280-3, Pub. by Progress Pubs USSR). Imported Pubns.

Volin, Lazar. Century of Russian Agriculture: From Alexander Second to Khrushchev. LC 72-119075. (Russian Research Center Studies: No. 63). 1970. 37.50x (ISBN 0-674-10621-0). Harvard U Pr.

Wadekin, Karl-Eugen, ed. Agriculture in Eastern Europe & the Soviet Union: Comparative Studies. LC 80-636. (Studies in East European & Soviet Russian Agrarian Policy: Vol. III). 450p. text ed. cancelled (ISBN 0-916672-42-5). Rowman & Allanheld.

AGRICULTURE–SPAIN

Young, Arthur. Travels During the Years 1787, 1788 & 1789, 2 Vols. 2nd ed. LC 79-115008. Repr. of 1794 ed. Set. 145.00 (ISBN 0-404-07068-X). AMS Pr.

AGRICULTURE–TANZANIA

Bohlen, E. Crop Pests in Tanzania & Their Control. 2nd rev. ed. (Illus.). 142p. 1978. lib. bdg. 34.00 (ISBN 3-489-65126-X). Parey Sci Pubs.

Glaeser, Bernhard. Ecodevelopment in Tanzania: An Empirical Contribution on Needs, Self-Sufficiency & Environmentally-Sound Agriculture on Peasant Farms. Antal, David, tr. LC 83-23736. xx, 229p. 1984. 25.20x (ISBN 3-11-009719-2). Mouton.

AGRICULTURE–THAILAND

Panayotou, Theodore, et al. The Economics of Catfish Farming in Central Thailand. (ICLARM Technical Reports: No. 4). (Illus.). 60p. (Orig.). 1983. pap. 10.00x (ISBN 0-89955-379-6, Pub. by ICLARM Philippines). Intl Spec Bk.

Suthasupa, Paiboon, et al. Protein Food Production in Thailand: An Evaluation of a Project in Two Lamphun Villages. 100p. (Orig.). pap. text ed. 15.00 (ISBN 9971-902-55-9, Pub. by Inst Southeast Asian Stud). Gower Pub Co.

AGRICULTURE–TROPICS

see also Tropical Crops

Ayanaba, A. & Dart, P. J., eds. Biological Nitrogen Fixation in Farming Systems of the Tropics. LC 77-1304. 377p. 1978. 86.95x (ISBN 0-471-99499-5, Pub. by Wiley-Interscience). Wiley.

Devendra, Canagasaby & Fuller, M. F. Pig Production in the Tropics. (Oxford Tropical Handbooks Ser.). (Illus.). 1979. text ed. 32.50x (ISBN 0-19-859474-7). Oxford U Pr.

FAO-UNDP International Expert Consultation on the Use of Improved Technology for Food Production in Rainfed Areas of Tropical Asia: Report, 3 Vols. Vol. 1. pap. 28.00 (F1089, FAO); Vol. 2. pap. 17.75; Vol. 3. pap. 23.75. Unipub.

Goerling, T. James. Tropical Root Crops & Rural Development. (Working Paper: No. 324). 85p. 1979. 5.00 (ISBN 0-686-36081-8, WP-0324). World Bank.

Greaves, Ida C. Modern Production Among Backward Peoples. LC 68-9759. Repr. of 1935 ed. 22.50x (ISBN 0-678-00419-6). Kelley.

Greenland, D. J. & Lal, R., eds. Soil Conservation & Management in the Humid Tropics. LC 76-8908. 283p. 1977. 84.95 (ISBN 0-471-99473-1, Pub. by Wiley-Interscience). Wiley.

Ilaco, B. V. Agricultural Compendium: For Rural Development in the Tropics & Subtropics. 740p. 1981. 42.75 (ISBN 0-444-41952-7). Elsevier.

Kahn, T. N. Winged Bean Production in the Tropics. (Plant Production & Protection Papers: No. 38). 223p. 1982. pap. 16.00 (ISBN 92-5-101230-X, F2366, FAO). Unipub.

Lal, R. & Greenland, D. J., eds. Soil Physical Properties & Crop Production in the Tropics. LC 79-40583. 551p. 1979. 137.95x (ISBN 0-471-99757-9, Pub. by Wiley-Interscience). Wiley.

Lal, R. & Russell, E. W., eds. Tropical Agricultural Hydrology: Watershed Management & Land Use. LC 80-41590. 482p. 1981. 74.95x (ISBN 0-471-27931-5, Pub. by Wiley-Interscience). Wiley.

McCune, Donald L. Fertilizers for Tropical & Subtropical Agriculture. Thompson, Marie K., ed. LC 82-11908. (Special Publication Ser.: Sp-2). (Illus.). 30p. (Orig.). pap. text ed. 4.00 (ISBN 0-88090-040-7). Intl Fertilizer.

Marten, Gerald G., ed. The Human Ecology of Traditional Agriculture in the Tropics. 275p. 1985. 27.50 (ISBN 0-8133-7026-4). Westview.

Martin, Franklin W. & Ruberte, Ruth. Patiofarming: A Compendium of Useful Tables. (Studies in Tropical Agriculture). 1980. lib. bdg. 69.95 (ISBN 0-8490-3075-7). Gordon Pr.

--The Round Garden: Plans for a Small Intensive Vegetable Garden for Year Round Production in the Tropics. (Studies in Tropical Agriculture). 1980. lib. bdg. 59.95 (ISBN 0-8490-3073-0). Gordon Pr.

Martin, Franklin W. & Ruberte, Ruth M. Edible Leaves of the Tropics. (Tropical Agriculture Ser.). 1980. lib. bdg. 75.00 (ISBN 0-8490-3069-2). Gordon Pr.

Martin, Franklin W., et al. Vegetables for the Hot, Humid Tropics. (Studies in Tropical Agriculture). 1980. lib. bdg. 59.95 (ISBN 0-8490-3071-4). Gordon Pr.

Mayaguez Institute of Tropical Agriculture. The Mayaguez Institute of Tropical Agriculture, Puerto Rico: A Bibliography of Publications. (Studies in Tropical Agriculture). 1980. lib. bdg. 59.95 (ISBN 0-8490-3072-2). Gordon Pr.

Munson, Robert D. Potassium, Calcium, & Magnesium in the Tropics & Subtropics. Brosheer, J. C., ed. LC 82-11944. (Technical Bulletins Ser.: T-23). (Illus.). 70p. (Orig.). pap. text ed. 8.00 (ISBN 0-88090-041-5). Intl Fertilizer.

On-Farm Maize Drying & Storage in the Humid Tropics. (Agricultural Services Bulletins: No. 40). 69p. 1980. pap. 7.50 (ISBN 92-5-100944-9, F2077, FAO). Unipub.

Report of an FAO-UNDP International Expert Consultation on the Use of Improved Technology for Food Production in Rainfed Areas of Tropical Asia. 65p. 1976. pap. 7.50 (ISBN 0-685-66341-8, F1088, FAO). Unipub.

Rice, R. P. & Rice, L. W. Fruit & Vegetable Production in Tropical Africa. LC 82-23698. 250p. 1985. 34.95 (ISBN 0-471-10362-4, Pub. by Wiley-Interscience); pap. write for info. (ISBN 0-471-90138-5). Wiley.

Sanchez, Pedro A. Properties & Management of Soils in the Tropics. LC 76-22761. 618p. 1976. 49.95x (ISBN 0-471-75200-2, Pub. by Wiley-Interscience). Wiley.

Tropical Grazing Land Ecosystems: A State-of-Knowledge Report. (Natural Resources Research Ser.: No. 16). (Illus.). 655p. 1979. 64.75 (ISBN 92-3-101625-3, U999, UNESCO) (ISBN 92-3-101611-3). Unipub.

Uehara, Goro & Gillman, Gavin P. The Mineralogy, Chemistry, & Physics of Tropical Soils with Variable Charge Clays. (Tropical Agriculture Ser.). 1981. 36.50x (ISBN 0-89158-484-6). Westview.

Van Loon, J. H. & Staudt, F. J., eds. Ergonomics in Tropical Agriculture & Forestry: Proceedings. 136p. 1979. pap. 14.00 (ISBN 0-686-93162-9, PDC148, Pudoc). Unipub.

Wilson, Charles M., ed. New Crops for the New World. LC 73-138140. (Illus.). 1971. Repr. of 1945 ed. lib. bdg. 24.75x (ISBN 0-8371-5713-7, WINC). Greenwood.

AGRICULTURE–UNITED STATES

Here are entered works on agriculture in the United States as a whole, as well as specific areas of the United States.

Adjustment Administration, U.S. Department of Agriculture. Agricultural Adjustment. LC 75-27634. (World Food Supply Ser). (Illus.). 1976. Repr. of 1934 ed. 32.00x (ISBN 0-405-07776-9). Ayer Co Pubs.

Alleger, Daniel E., ed. Fertile Lands of Friendship: The Florida-Costa Rican Experiment in International Agricultural Cooperation. LC 62-20773. 1962. 6.50 (ISBN 0-8130-0007-6). U Presses Fla.

Bailey, Joseph C. Seaman A. Knapp: Schoolmaster of American Agriculture. LC 73-165702. (American Education, Ser. 2). 1971. Repr. of 1945 ed. 17.00 (ISBN 0-405-03691-4). Ayer Co Pubs.

Barger, Harold & Landsberg, Hans H. American Agriculture, 1899-1939: A Study of Output, Employment, & Productivity. LC 75-19693. (National Bureau of Economic Research Ser.). (Illus.). 1975. Repr. of 1942 ed. 33.00x (ISBN 0-405-07574-X). Ayer Co Pubs.

Batie, Sandra S. & Healy, Robert G., eds. The Future of American Agriculture As a Strategic Resource. LC 80-70162. 294p. 1980. pap. 11.50 (ISBN 0-89164-064-9). Conservation Foun.

Bidwell, Percy W. Rural Economy in New England at the Beginning of the 19th Century. LC 68-55480. (Illus.). 1972. Repr. of 1916 ed. 25.00x (ISBN 0-678-00815-9). Kelley.

Board on Agriculture & Renewable Resources, National Research Council. Climate & Food: Climatic Fluctuation & U. S. Agricultural Production. LC 76-46195. 1976. pap. 9.25 (ISBN 0-309-02522-2). Natl Acad Pr.

Capper, Arthur. The Agricultural Bloc. LC 78-136848. 171p. 1972. Repr. of 1922 ed. lib. bdg. 15.00 (ISBN 0-8371-5282-8, CAAG). Greenwood.

Carrier, Lyman. The Beginnings of Agriculture in America. 1976. lib. bdg. 59.95 (ISBN 0-8490-1485-9). Gordon Pr.

Crosson, Pierre R. & Stout, Anthony T. Productivity Effects of Cropland Erosion in the United States. LC 83-19094. 152p. 1984. pap. text ed. 11.00x (ISBN 0-8018-3207-1). Johns Hopkins.

Dorothea Lange: Farm Security Administration Photographs, 1935 - 1939, 2 clothbound vols. LC 80-24201. (Illus., Vol. 1 236pp.; vol. 2 178 pp.). 1980. Vol.1, 732 Photos & Maps On 9 Black & White Fiches, Captions In Text, 236 Pages. 44.50x (ISBN 0-89969-000-9); Vol. 2, 622 Photos & Maps On 8 Black & White Fiches, Captions In Text, 178 Pages. 42.50x (ISBN 0-89969-001-7); Set. 87.00x (ISBN 0-89969-002-5). Text-Fiche.

Edwards, Everett E., ed. Jefferson & Agriculture: A Sourcebook. LC 75-27636. (World Food Supply Ser). 1976. Repr. of 1943 ed. 14.00x (ISBN 0-405-07778-5). Ayer Co Pubs.

Ethyl Corporation. Food for America's Future. LC 72-14156. (Essay Index Reprint Ser.). Repr. of 1960 ed. 15.25 (ISBN 0-518-10009-X). Ayer Co Pubs.

Fite, Gilbert C. American Farmers: The New Minority. LC 80-8843. (Illus.). 288p. 1981. 22.50x (ISBN 0-253-30182-3); pap. 7.95x (ISBN 0-253-20321-X, 321, MB). Ind U Pr.

Gardner, Bruce L. The Governing of Agriculture: Studies in Government & Public Policy. (Illus.). xii, 148p. 1981. pap. 9.95x (ISBN 0-7006-0215-1). U Pr of KS.

Johnson, D. Gale, ed. Developments in American Farming: An Original Anthology. LC 75-29760. (World Food Supply Ser). (Illus.). 1976. 16.00x (ISBN 0-405-07773-4). Ayer Co Pubs.

Kellar, H. A., ed. Solon Robinson, Pioneer & Agriculturalist, 2 Vols. LC 68-16242. (American Scene Ser). (Illus.). 1968. Repr. of 1936 ed. Set. lib. bdg. 95.00 (ISBN 0-306-71017-X). Da Capo.

Kolb, John H. Study of Rural Society. LC 70-136074. (Illus.). 1971. Repr. of 1952 ed. lib. bdg. 28.25x (ISBN 0-8371-5224-0, KORS). Greenwood.

Land Planning Committee, U.S. National Resources Board. Report of the Land Planning Committee, Pt. 2. LC 75-26322. (World Food Supply Ser). (Illus.). 1976. Repr. of 1934 ed. 18.00x (ISBN 0-405-07798-X). Ayer Co Pubs.

Moore, John H. Agriculture in Ante-Bellum Mississippi. 1971. lib. bdg. 18.50x (ISBN 0-374-95830-0). Octagon.

Petulla, Joseph M. American Environmental History: The Exploitation & Conservation of Natural Resources. LC 75-4870. (Illus.). 1977. 18.00x (ISBN 0-87835-058-6). Boyd & Fraser.

Pitt, W. General View of the Agriculture of the County of Worcester. LC 77-92000. (Illus.). Repr. of 1813 ed. 39.50x (ISBN 0-678-05545-9). Kelley.

Projections of United States Agricultural Production & Demand: An Original Anthology. LC 75-29757. (World Food Supply Ser). (Illus.). 1976. 25.00x (ISBN 0-405-07782-3). Ayer Co Pubs.

Radewald, John D. Nematode Diseases of Food & Fiber Crops of the Southwestern United States. LC 77-81143. 1978. pap. 6.00 (ISBN 0-931876-16-8, 4083). Ag & Nat Res.

Rasmussen, David W. Agriculture in the U. S. A Documentary History, 4 Vols. (Documentary Reference Collection Ser.). 1975. lib. bdg. 60.00 ea. Vol. 1 (ISBN 0-313-20148-X). Vol. 2 (ISBN 0-313-20149-8). Vol. 3 (ISBN 0-313-20150-1). Vol. 4 (ISBN 0-313-20151-X). Set. lib. bdg. 192.50 (ISBN 0-313-20147-1, RAAG/). Greenwood.

Robinson, Solon. Solon Robinson, Pioneer & Agriculturist. Kellar, Herbert A., ed. LC 74-145268. (Illus.). 1971. Repr. of 1936 ed. 59.00x (ISBN 0-403-01183-3). Scholarly.

Russell, Howard S. A Long, Deep Furrow: Three Centuries of Farming in New England. Abr. ed. Lapping, Mark, ed. & abridged by. LC 81-51605. (Illus.). 394p. 1982. pap. 15.95 (ISBN 0-87451-214-X). U Pr of New Eng.

Schapsmeier, Edward L. & Schapsmeier, Frederick H., eds. Agriculture in the West. 113p. 1980. pap. text ed. 9.95x (ISBN 0-89745-005-1). Sunflower U Pr.

Scheuring, Ann, et al. Agricultural Resources of California Counties. LC 82-71076. 136p. (Orig.). 1982. pap. text ed. 5.00x (ISBN 0-931876-57-5, 3275). Ag & Nat Res.

Schmidt, Hubert G. Rural Hunterdon: An Agricultural History. LC 77-139149. (Illus.). 331p. 1972. Repr. of 1945 ed. lib. bdg. 20.25x (ISBN 0-8371-5765-X, SCRH). Greenwood.

Shirreff, Patrick. A Tour Through North America: Together with a Comprehensive View of the Canada & United States, As Adapted for Agricultural Emigration. LC 75-173121. Repr. of 1835 ed. 27.50 (ISBN 0-405-08970-8). Ayer Co Pubs.

Voss, Ronald E. Onion Production in California. LC 79-55403. (Illus.). 1979. pap. 5.00 (ISBN 0-931876-35-4, 4097). Ag & Nat Res.

Warley, T. K. Agriculture in an Interdependent World: U.S. & Canadian Perspectives. LC 77-73919. (Canadian-American Committee Ser.). 104p. 1977. 4.00 (ISBN 0-89068-040-X). Natl Planning.

White, Philip L. Beekmantown, New York: Forest Frontier to Farm Community. (Illus.). 398p. 1979. text ed. 27.50x (ISBN 0-292-72428-4). U of Tex Pr.

Woodward, Carl R. Ploughs & Politicks: Charles Read of New Jersey & His Notes on Agriculture, 1715-1744. LC 73-16351. (Perspectives in American History Ser.: No. 24). (Illus.). 468p. 1974. Repr. of 1941 ed. lib. bdg. 35.00x (ISBN 0-87991-338-X). Porcupine Pr.

AGRICULTURE–UNITED STATES–HISTORY

Bailey, Liberty H., et al, eds. Cyclopedia of American Agriculture: A Popular Survey of Agricultural Conditions, Practices & Ideals in the United States & Canada - Vol. 2, Crops Fourth Edition. facsimile ed. LC 74-30617. (American Farmers & the Rise of Agribusiness Ser.). (Illus.). 1975. Repr. of 1912 ed. 65.00x (ISBN 0-405-06762-3). Ayer Co Pubs.

Beardsley, Edward H. Harry L. Russell & Agricultural Science in Wisconsin. LC 77-84950. pap. 67.30 (ISBN 0-317-28985-3, 2023728). Bks Demand UMI.

Childs, Marquis W. Yesterday, Today & Tomorrow: The Farmer Takes a Hand. rev. ed. LC 52-5629. 178p. 1980. pap. 2.25 (ISBN 0-686-28113-6). Natl Rural.

Cochrane, Willard W. The Development of American Agriculture: A Historical Analysis. (Illus.). 1979. pap. 12.95x (ISBN 0-8166-0929-2). U of Minn Pr.

Daniel, Pete. Breaking the Land: The Transformation of Cotton, Tobacco, & Rice Cultures since 1880. LC 84-197. (Illus.). 368p. 1985. 22.50x (ISBN 0-252-01147-3). U of Ill Pr.

Ebeling, Walter. The Fruited Plain: The Story of American Agriculture. LC 78-62837. 1980. 35.00x (ISBN 0-520-03751-0). U of Cal Pr.

Gibson, James R. Farming the Frontier: The Agricultural Opening of the Oregon Country, 1786-1846. (Illus.). 288p. 1985. 25.00 (ISBN 0-295-96297-6, Pub. by Univ British Columbia Pr). U of Wash Pr.

Herscher, Uri D. Jewish Agricultural Utopias in America, 1880-1910. LC 81-4620. (Illus.). 214p. 1981. 15.95 (ISBN 0-8143-1678-6). Wayne St U Pr.

Hewes, Leslie. The Suitcase Farming Frontier: A Study in the Historical Geography of the Central Great Plains. LC 72-85031. xviii, 281p. 1973. 21.50x (ISBN 0-8032-0825-1). U of Nebr Pr.

Hurt, R. Douglas. The Dust Bowl: An Agricultural & Social History. LC 81-4031. 240p. 1981. text ed. 22.95x (ISBN 0-88229-541-1); pap. 11.95x (ISBN 0-88229-789-9). Nelson-Hall.

Jarchow, Merrill E. Earth Brought Forth: A History of Minnesota Agriculture to 1855. (History of American Economy Ser). 1970. Repr. of 1949 ed. 23.00 (ISBN 0-384-26865-X). Johnson Repr.

John Vachon: Farm Security Administration Photographs, 1938-1942. 1983. write for info. Text-Fiche.

Peterson, Trudy H., ed. Farmers, Bureaucrats, & Middlemen: Historical Perspectives on American Agriculture. LC 80-14609. (National Archives Conference Ser.: Vol. 17). (Illus.). 350p. 1980. 19.95 (ISBN 0-88258-083-3). Howard U Pr.

Pirtle, Thomas R. History of the Dairy Industry. LC 72-89079. (Rural America Ser.). 1973. Repr. of 1926 ed. 39.00 (ISBN 0-8420-1494-2). Scholarly Res Inc.

Rasmussen, Wayne D., ed. The New American State Papers: Agriculture Subject Set, 19 vols. LC 72-95579. 1973. Set. lib. bdg. 1100.00 (ISBN 0-8420-1590-6). Scholarly Res Inc.

Rossiter, Margaret W. The Emergence of Agricultural Science: Justus Liebig & the Americans, 1840-1880. LC 74-29737. (Studies in the History of Science & Medicine Ser.: No. 9). 288p. 1975. 27.00x (ISBN 0-300-01721-9). Yale U Pr.

Saloutos, Theodore. The American Farmer & the New Deal. (Henry A. Wallace Series on Agricultural History & Studies: Vol. 1). 328p. 1982. text ed. 25.75x (ISBN 0-8138-1076-0). Iowa St U Pr.

Schapsmeier, Frederick H. & Schapsmeier, Edward L. Encyclopedia of American Agricultural History. LC 74-34563. 467p. (Orig.). 1975. lib. bdg. 39.95x (ISBN 0-8371-7958-0, SAA/). Greenwood.

Schmidt, Hubert G. Agriculture in New Jersey: A Three Hundred Year History. (Illus.). 352p. 1973. 30.00 (ISBN 0-8135-0756-1). Rutgers U Pr.

Shepard, Silas M. The Hog in America: Past & Present with Suggestions upon Farms, Pens, Breeds, Breeding. LC 72-89094. (Rural America Ser.). 1973. Repr. of 1839 ed. 26.00 (ISBN 0-8420-1498-5). Scholarly Res Inc.

Sidar, Jean. George Hamell Cook: A Life in Agriculture & Geology, 1818-1889. 1976. 20.00x (ISBN 0-8135-0827-4). Rutgers U Pr.

Spurrier, John. The Practical Farmer: Being a New & Compendious System of Husbandry, Adapted to the Different Soils & Climates of America. LC 72-89091. (Rural America Ser.). 1973. Repr. of 1793 ed. 30.00 (ISBN 0-8420-1499-3). Scholarly Res Inc.

AGRICULTURE–VENEZUELA

Ruddle, Kenneth. The Yukpa Cultivation System: A Study of Shifting Cultivation in Columbia & Venezuela. (Publications in Ibero-Americana Ser: Vol. 52). 1976. pap. 24.00x (ISBN 0-520-09497-2). U of Cal Pr.

AGRICULTURE–WEST INDIES

Frolander-Ulf, Monica & Lindenfeld, Frank. A New Earth: The Jamaican Sugar Worker's Cooperatives, 1975-1981. (Illus.). 240p. (Orig.). 1985. lib. bdg. 24.50 (ISBN 0-8191-4844-X); pap. text ed. 12.50 (ISBN 0-8191-4845-8). U Pr of Amer.

AGRICULTURE, SOILLESS

see Hydroponics

AGRICULTURE AND STATE

see also Agricultural Extension Work

Agricultural Policy Issues. 1978. pap. 8.00 (ISBN 0-918592-27-5). Policy Studies.

Bale, Malcolm. Agricultural Trade & Food Policy: The Experience of Five Developing Countries. (Staff Working Paper No. 724). 56p. 1985. 5.00 (ISBN 0-318-11959-5, WP 0724). World Bank.

Campbell, Keith O. Food for the Future: How Agriculture Can Meet the Challenge. LC 78-23982. xii, 178p. 1979. 15.95x (ISBN 0-8032-0965-7). U of Nebr Pr.

Chandler, Robert F., Jr. Rice in the Tropics: A Guide to Development of National Programs. (IADS Development-Oriented Literature Ser.). 1979. lib. bdg. 24.50x (ISBN 0-89158-361-0). Westview.

Douglas, J. Sholto & Hart, Robert A. Forest Farming: Towards a Solution to Problems of World Hunger & Conservation. 207p. 1985. pap. 15.95 (ISBN 0-8133-0331-1). Westview.

Haar, Charles M., et al. Transfer of Development Rights: A Primer. (Land Policy Roundtable: No. 206). 75p. 1981. pap. text ed. 6.00 (ISBN 0-686-30623-6). Lincoln Inst Land.

Halcrow, Harold G. Food Policy for America. (TBD Ser.). (Illus.). 1977. text ed. 37.95 (ISBN 0-07-025550-4). McGraw.

Hardin, Charles M. Freedom in Agricultural Education. LC 75-27640. (World Food Supply Ser). 1976. Repr. of 1955 ed. 28.50x (ISBN 0-405-07780-7). Ayer Co Pubs.

Levy, Maurice & Robinson, John L., eds. Energy & Agriculture: Their Interacting Futures Policy & Implications & Global Models. (Golbal Modelling & Applications Ser.: Vol. I). 384p. 1983. 78.00 (ISBN 3-7186-0187-7). Harwood Academic.

Meister, Anton D., et al. Quadratic Programming Models Applied to Agriculture Policies. (Illus.). 1978. text ed. 7.00x (ISBN 0-8138-1930-X). Iowa St U Pr.

Schickele, Rainer. Agricultural Policy, Farm Programs & National Welfare. 11.25 (ISBN 0-8446-2876-X). Peter Smith.

Schnidman, Frank. Agricultural Land Preservation: Serious Land Policy Concern or Latest "Public Interest" Ploy. (Lincoln Institute Monograph: No. 81-1). 1981. pap. text ed. 5.00 (ISBN 0-686-30620-1). Lincoln Inst Land.

Sein Lin & Wasim Zaman, eds. Land Management Issues & Development Strategies in Developing Countries, Vol. II. (Lincoln Institute Monograph: No. 81-2). 103p. 1981. pap. text ed. 5.00 (ISBN 0-686-30622-8). Lincoln Inst Land.

Steiner, Frederick R. & Theilacker, John. Protecting Farmlands. (Illus.). 1984. lib. bdg. 32.50 (ISBN 0-87055-452-2). AVI.

Sweeten, John & Humenik, Frank J., eds. Agriculture & the Environment: An Examination of Critical Issues for Food Policy. 128p. 1984. 65.00 (ISBN 0-916150-62-3). Am Soc Ag Eng.

Tweeten, Luther. Foundations of Farm Policy. 2nd, rev. ed. LC 78-23978. xiv, 567p. 1979. 19.50x (ISBN 0-8032-0972-X). U of Nebr Pr.

AGRICULTURISTS

see also Agriculture–Vocational Guidance; Farmers; Horticulturists

Gazley, John G. The Life of Arthur Young, Seventeen Forty-One to Eighteen Twenty. (Memoirs Ser.: Vol. 97). (Illus.). 1973. 12.50 (ISBN 0-87169-097-7). Am Philos.

Harris, Lement. Harold M. Ware (1890-1935) Agricultural Pioneer, U.S.A. & USSR. (Occasional Papers: No. 30). 1978. mimeo 1.75 (ISBN 0-89977-020-7). Am Inst Marxist.

AGRONOMISTS

see Agriculturists

AGRONOMY

see Agriculture

AGROSTOLOGY

see Grasses

AIDS TO AIR NAVIGATION

see also Electronics in Aeronautics; Meteorology in Aeronautics; Radio in Aeronautics

Givens, Bill. Flying with Loran C. (Illus.). 208p. (Orig.). 1985. pap. 15.95 (ISBN 0-8306-2370-1). TAB Bks.

Reithmaier, Larry. Computer Guide for Pilots. LC 78-94966. (Pilot Guides). pap. 2.95 (ISBN 0-8168-7200-7). Aero.

AIR

see also Aerodynamics; Atmosphere; Bubbles; Ventilation;

also headings beginning with the word Atmospheric

Ingelstedt, Sven. Studies on the Conditioning of Air in the Respiratory Tract. 1956. 12.00 (ISBN 0-384-25735-6). Johnson Repr.

Irvine, Thomas F., Jr. & Hartnett, James P. Steam & Air Tables, SI Units. LC 75-34007. (Illus.). 125p. 1976. pap. text ed. 16.95 (ISBN 0-89116-004-3). Hemisphere Pub.

Pascal, Blaise. Extraits des Traites de l'Equilibre des Liqueurs et de la Pesanteur de la Masse de l'A Ir. 64p. 1963. 5.95 (ISBN 0-686-54846-9). French & Eur.

--Physical Treatises of Pascal. Barry, Frederick, ed. 1969. lib. bdg. 20.50x (ISBN 0-374-90418-9). Octagon.

--Traite de l'Equilibre des Liqueurs et de la Pesanteur de la Masse de l'Aire. 106p. 1956. 22.50 (ISBN 0-686-54853-1). French & Eur.

WHO Expert Committee. Geneva, 1972. Air Quality Criteria & Guides for Urban Air Pollutants: Report. (Technical Report Ser.: No. 506). (Also avail. in French & Spanish). 1972. pap. 2.40 (ISBN 92-4-120506-7). World Health.

AIR–ANALYSIS

see also Argon

Banks, P. M. & Kockarts, G. Aeronomy. Incl. Pt. A. 1973. 66.00 (ISBN 0-12-077801-7); Pt. B. 1973. 67.50 (ISBN 0-12-077802-5). Acad Pr.

Katz, Morris, ed. Methods of Air Sampling & Analysis. 2nd ed. LC 77-6826. 984p. 1977. 45.00x (ISBN 0-87553-079-6, 040). Am Pub Health.

Oikawa, Kikuo. Trace Analysis of Atmospheric Samples. LC 77-3458. 158p. 1977. 39.95 (ISBN 0-470-99013-9). Halsted Pr.

Priestley, Joseph. Experiments & Observations on Different Kinds of Air, 3 vols. LC 71-125366. Repr. of 1790 ed. Set. 108.00 (ISBN 0-527-72710-5). Kraus Repr.

AIR–BACTERIOLOGY

see Air–Microbiology

AIR–MICROBIOLOGY

see also Airborne Infection

Edmonds, Robert L., ed. Aerobiology: The Ecological Systems Approach. LC 78-23769. (US-IBP Synthesis Ser.: Vol. 10). 386p. 1979. 36.00 (ISBN 0-87933-346-4). Van Nos Reinhold.

Liu, Ben & Siu-Hung Yu, Eden. Air Pollution Damage Functions & Regional Damage Estimates. LC 77-90376. 1977. 9.95x (ISBN 0-87762-247-7). Technomic.

Nilsson, S. T., ed. Atlas of Airborne Fungal Spores in Europe. (Illus.). 145p. 1983. 55.00 (ISBN 0-387-11900-0). Springer-Verlag.

Peagley, D. E. Weather & Airborne Organisms. (Technical Note Ser.: No. 173). 91p. 1980. pap. 12.00 (ISBN 92-63-10562-6, W487, WMO). Unipub.

Tyndall, John. Essays on the Floating-Matter of the Air in Relation to Putrefaction & Infection. Repr. of 1882 ed. 25.00 (ISBN 0-384-62270-4). Johnson Repr.

AIR–POLLUTION

see also Acid Rain; Air Quality; Automobiles–Motors–Exhaust Gas; Dust; Fume Control; Motor Vehicles–Pollution Control Devices; Radioactive Pollution of the Atmosphere; Smog

Ackerman, Bruce A. & Hassler, William T. Clean Coal: Dirty Air. LC 80-1089. (Illus.). 175p. 1981. 25.00x (ISBN 0-300-02628-5); pap. 7.95x (ISBN 0-300-02643-9). Yale U Pr.

Air Pollutants, Meteorology & Plant Injury. 73p. 1969. pap. 13.00 (ISBN 0-685-02471-7, W67, WMO). Unipub.

Air Pollution Measurement Techniques, Pts. 1 & 2. (Special Environmental Reports: No. 10). (Illus.). 1977. pap. 35.00 (ISBN 92-63-10460-3, W256, WMO). Unipub.

Air Pollution Studies. 265p. 19.00 (ISBN 0-317-18747-3, E.84.II.E.8). UN.

Air Resources Management Primer. 260p. 1973. pap. text ed. 16.75 (ISBN 0-87262-055-7). Am Soc Civil Eng.

Airborne Sulphur Pollution: Effects & Control: Report Prepared Within the Framework of the Convention on Long-Range Transboundary Air Pollution. (Illus.). 265p. 1985. pap. 19.00 (UN84/2E8, UN). Unipub.

Apling, A. J., et al. Air Pollution from Oxides of Nitrogen, Carbon Monoxide & Hydrocarbons, 1979. 1981. 59.00x (ISBN 0-686-97009-8, Pub. by W Spring England). State Mutual Bk.

--Air Pollution in Homes: Validation of Diffusion Tube Measurements of Nitrogen Dioxide, 1979. 1981. 40.00x (ISBN 0-686-97013-6, Pub. by W Spring England). State Mutual Bk.

Applegate, Howard G. & Bath, C. Richard, eds. Air Pollution along the United States-Mexico Border. LC 74-80108. 1974. 6.00 (ISBN 0-87404-051-5). Tex Western.

ASCE Conference, Urban Transportation Division, 1980. Transportation & the 1977 Clean Air Act Amendments. LC 80-66291. 440p. pap. 33.50x (ISBN 0-87262-242-8). Am Soc Civil Eng.

Bailey, D. L. & Clayton, P. The Measurement of Suspended Particulate & Carbon Concentrations in the Atmosphere Using Standard Smoke Shade Methods, 1980. 1982. 45.00x (ISBN 0-686-97112-4, Pub. by W Spring England). State Mutual Bk.

Bates, David. A Citizen's Guide to Air Pollution. (Environmental Damage & Control in Canada Ser.: Vol. 2). 250p. 1976. pap. 4.95 (ISBN 0-7735-0145-2). McGill-Queens U Pr.

Battan, Louis J. The Unclean Sky: A Meteorologist Looks at Air Pollution. LC 80-23434. (Selected Topics in the Atmospheric Sciences, Science Study Ser.). (Illus.). xii, 141p. 1980. Repr. of 1966 ed. lib. bdg. 24.75x (ISBN 0-313-22710-1, BAUS). Greenwood.

Benarie, M. M. Atmospheric Pollution, 1982. (Studies in Environmental Science: Vol. 20). 404p. 1982. 85.00 (ISBN 0-444-42083-5). Elsevier.

Benarie, M. M., ed. Atmospheric Pollution, 1980: Proceedings of the 14th International Colloqium, Paris, May 1980. (Studies in Environmental Science: Vol. 8). 440p. 1980. 85.00 (ISBN 0-444-41889-X). Elsevier.

Benarie, Michael M. Urban Air Pollution Modeling. (Illus.). 1980. text ed. 65.00x (ISBN 0-262-02140-4). MIT Pr.

Berlyand, M. E., ed. Air Pollution & Athmospheric Diffusion. LC 73-1982. 221p. 1973. Vol. 1. cloth 42.95x (ISBN 0-470-07034-X). Halsted Pr.

Bethea, Robert M. Air Pollution Control Technology. (Environmental Engineering Ser). 1978. 39.95 (ISBN 0-442-20715-8). Van Nos Reinhold.

Bibbero, Robert J. & Young, Irving G. Systems Approach to Air Pollution Control. LC 74-8905. pap. 135.50 (ISBN 0-317-11255-4, 2055157). Bks Demand UMI.

BNA's Environmental & Safety Information Services. Air Pollution. (BNA Policy & Practice Ser.). write for info. BNA.

Bowen, D. Michael, ed. Air Pollution. LC 72-97720. (ACS Reprint Collection). 1973. Repr. 9.95 (ISBN 0-8412-0160-9). Am Chemical.

Bragg, Gordon M. & Strauss, Jennifer. Strauss' Air Pollution Control, Vol. 4. LC 79-28773. (Environmental Science & Technology: A Wiley-Interscience Series of Texts & Monographs). 356p. 1981. 75.00x (ISBN 0-471-07957-X, Pub. by Wiley-Interscience). Wiley.

Brauer, H. & Varma, Y. B. Air Pollution Control Equipment. (Illus.). 388p. 1981. 105.00 (ISBN 0-387-10463-1). Springer-Verlag.

Brittin, Wesley E., et al. Air & Water Pollution. LC 72-165367. 1971. 19.50x (ISBN 0-87081-024-3); pap. 7.95x (ISBN 0-87081-040-5). Colo Assoc.

Brunner, Calvin R. Hazardous Air Emissions from Incineration. 250p. 1985. text ed. 35.00 (ISBN 0-412-00721-5, NO. 9093, Pub. by Chapman & Hall England). Methuen Inc.

Bryson, R. E. & Kutzbach, J. E., eds. Air Pollution. LC 68-54859. (CCG Resource Papers Ser.: No. 2). (Illus.). 1968. pap. text ed. 4.00 (ISBN 0-89291-049-6). Assn Am Geographers.

Building Research Advisory Board. Impact of Air-Pollution Regulations on Design Criteria for Boiler Plants at Federal Facilities. (Illus.). 62p. 1973. pap. 6.50 (ISBN 0-309-02107-3). Natl Acad Pr.

Burton, Ian & Kates, Robert W. The Environment As Hazard. (Illus.). 1978. pap. text ed. 12.95x (ISBN 0-19-502222-X). Oxford U Pr.

Butler, J. D. Air Pollution Chemistry. 1979. 69.50 (ISBN 0-12-147950-1). Acad Pr.

Calvert, Seymour & Englund, Harold M., eds. Handbook of Air Pollution Technology. LC 83-19797. 1066p. 1984. 84.95x (ISBN 0-471-08263-5, Pub. by Wiley-Interscience). Wiley.

Camagni, P. & Sandroni, S., eds. Optical Remote Sensing of Air Pollution: Lectures of a Course at the Joint Research Centre, Ispra, Italy, April 12-15,1983. 350p. 1984. 96.50 (ISBN 0-444-42343-5, I-186-84). Elsevier.

Carr, Donald E. The Sky Is Still Falling. 1982. 14.95 (ISBN 0-393-01508-4). Norton.

Committee on Biological Effects of Atmospheric Pollutants. Lead: Airborne Lead in Perspective. LC 71-186214. (Biological Effects of Atmospheric Pollutants Ser.). (Illus.). 1972. pap. 10.95 (ISBN 0-309-01941-9). Natl Acad Pr.

Committee on Impacts of Stratospheric Change, National Research Council. Halocarbons: Environmental Effects of Chlorofluoromethane Release. 125p. 1976. pap. 7.75 (ISBN 0-309-02529-X). Natl Acad Pr.

Critser, James R., Jr. Air Pollution Control: Internal Combustion Engines - Exhaust Treatment 1976. (Ser. 4IC-76). 1977. 115.00 (ISBN 0-914428-40-3). Lexington Data.

--Air Pollution Control-Processes, Equipment, Instrumentation. Incl. Indexes & Abstracts 1967-1971. 310.00 (ISBN 0-914428-08-X, 4-6771B). (Ser. 4-67713). Lexington Data Inc.

Cross, Framk L., Jr. & Forehand, David, eds. Air Pollution Emissions from Bulk Loading Facilities. LC 75-26079. (Environmental Monograph: Vol. 6). (Illus.). 22p. 1976. 3.95 (ISBN 0-87762-179-9). Technomic.

Cross, Frank L., Jr. & Forehand, David. Guidelines for Air Pollution Permit Review. LC 75-26078. (Environmental Monograph). (Illus.). 1976. 3.95 (ISBN 0-87762-188-8). Technomic.

Cross, Frank L., Jr. & Hesketh, Howard E. Handbook for the Operation & Maintenance of Air Pollution Control Equipment. LC 74-33843. 285p. 1975. pap. 14.95x (ISBN 0-87762-160-8). Technomic.

Cross, Frank L, Jr. & Forehand, David, eds. Air Pollution Meteorology. LC 75-26075. (Environmental Monograph: Vol. 2). (Illus.). 18p. 1976. 3.95 (ISBN 0-87762-177-2). Technomic.

Cross, Frank L., Jr. & Forehand, David, eds. The Evaluation of Air Pollution Complex Sources. LC 75-26076. (Environmental Monograph). (Illus.). 38p. 1976. 4.95x (ISBN 0-87762-178-0). Technomic.

De Wispelaere, C., ed. Air Pollution Modeling & Its Application, Part I. LC 81-12020. (NATO Challenges of Modern Society Ser.: Vol. 1). 762p. 1981. 95.00x (ISBN 0-306-40820-1, Plenum Pr). Plenum Pub.

--Air Pollution Modeling & Its Application, III. (NATO Challenges in Modern Society Ser.: Vol. 5). 750p. 1983. 95.00x (ISBN 0-306-41491-0, Plenum Pr). Plenum Pub.

--Air Pollution Modeling & Its Applications, No. IV. (NATO Challenges for Modern Society Ser.: Vol. 7). 806p. 1985. 110.00x (ISBN 0-306-41908-4, Plenum Pr). Plenum Pub.

--Air Pollution Modeling & Its Application, Part II. (NATO-Challenges of Modern Society Ser.: Vol. 3). 886p. 1983. 110.00 (ISBN 0-306-41115-6, Plenum Pr). Plenum Pub.

Dobbins, Richard A. Atmospheric Motion & Air Pollution: An Introduction for Students of Engineering & Science. LC 79-952. (Environmental Science & Technology: Texts & Monographs). 323p. 1979. 60.00 (ISBN 0-471-21675-5, Pub. by Wiley-Interscience). Wiley.

Effect of Cold Weather on Motor Vehicle Emissions. pap. 2.35 (SSC30, SSC). Unipub.

Ferry, B. W., et al, eds. Air Pollution & Lichens. (Illus.). 389p. 1973. 70.00 (ISBN 0-485-11140-3, Pub. by Athlone Pr Ltd). Longwood Pub Group.

Fisher, Anthony C. Economic Efficiency & Air Pollution Control. LC 81-17464. (East-West Environment & Policy Institute Research Report: No. 8). v, 74p. (Orig.). 1981. pap. text ed. 3.00 (ISBN 0-86638-030-2). E W Center HI.

Forsdyke, A. G. Meteorological Factors of Air Pollution. (Technical Note Ser.: No. 114). (Illus.). 32p. 1970. pap. 10.00 (ISBN 0-685-02472-5, W86, WMO). Unipub.

Friedlaender, Ann F., ed. Approaches to Controlling Air Pollution. LC 77-25484. (MIT Bicentennial Ser.: Vol. 3). 1978. 45.00x (ISBN 0-262-06064-7). MIT Pr.

Gardner, Murray B., et al. Physiological Effects of Air Pollution. 222p. 1973. text ed. 29.75x (ISBN 0-8422-7137-6). Irvington.

Gardon, J. L. & Prane, J. W., eds. Non-Polluting Coatings & Coating Processes. LC 72-97719. 272p. 1973. 42.50x (ISBN 0-306-30729-4, Plenum Pr). Plenum Pub.

Georgii, H. & Pankrath, J. Deposition of Atmospheric Pollutants. 1982. 37.00 (ISBN 90-277-1438-X, Pub. by Reidel Holland). Kluwer Academic.

Gilpin, Alan. Air Pollution. 2nd ed. (Austrailian Environment Ser.). (Illus.). 1978. pap. 9.95x (ISBN 0-7022-1178-8). U of Queensland Pr.

Goldstein, Elliot, et al. Air Pollution & the Politics of Control. 182p. 1973. text ed. 23.50x (ISBN 0-8422-7136-8). Irvington.

Gooriah, B. D. & Williams, F. P. The Investigation of Air Pollution: National Survey of Smoke & Sulphur Dioxide--Annual Summary Statistics for the Period 1963-4 to 1977-8, 1979. 1981. 60.00x (ISBN 0-686-97088-8, Pub. by W Spring England). State Mutual Bk.

Guderian, R. Air Pollution: Phytotoxicity of Acidic Gases & Its Significance in Air Pollution Control. LC 76-50626. (Ecological Studies: Vol. 22). 1977. 36.00 (ISBN 0-387-08030-9). Springer-Verlag.

Guderian, R., ed. Air Pollution by Photochemical Oxidants. (Ecological Studies, Analysis & Synthesis: Vol. 52). (Illus.). 380p. 1985. 55.50 (ISBN 0-387-13966-4). Springer-Verlag.

Hall, D. J. The Discharge of Fume Cupboard Effluents into the Atmosphere, 1979. 1981. 30.00x (ISBN 0-686-97058-6, Pub. by W Spring England). State Mutual Bk.

--Further Experiments on a Model of an Escape of Heavy Gas, 1979. 1981. 45.00x (ISBN 0-686-97083-7, Pub. by W Spring England). State Mutual Bk.

Halvorsen, Robert & Ruby, Michael G. Benefit-Cost Analysis of Air-Pollution Control. LC 78-19587. (Illus.). 288p. 1981. 31.50x (ISBN 0-669-02647-6). Lexington Bks.

Harrison, Paul R., et al. Analysis of Industrial Air Pollutants. (Air Pollution Ser: Vol. 3). 185p. 1974. text ed. 29.00x (ISBN 0-8422-7154-6). Irvington.

Hay, Alastair. The Chemical Scythe: The Lessons of 2, 4, 5-T & Dioxin. LC 82-12249. (Disaster Research in Practice Ser.). 278p. 1982. 27.50x (ISBN 0-306-40973-9, Plenum Pr). Plenum Pub.

Heidt, Volber. Flechtenkartierung und Die Beziehung zur Immissionsbelastung des sudlichen Munsterlands. (Biogeographica Ser.: No. 12). 1978. lib. bdg. 21.00 (ISBN 90-6193-213-0, Pub. by Junk Pubs. Netherlands). Kluwer Academic.

Henderson-Sellers, A. Pollution of Our Atmosphere. 276p. 1984. 23.00 (ISBN 0-9903000-5-6, Pub. by A Hilger England); pap. write for info. (ISBN 0-9903000-6-4). Heyden.

Hesketh, H. E., ed. Second Symposium on Integrated Environmental Controls for Coal Fired Power Plants. 139p. 1983. pap. text ed. 25.00 (ISBN 0-317-02646-1, H00252). ASME.

Hesketh, Howard E. Air Pollution Control. LC 78-71429. 1979. 49.95 (ISBN 0-250-40288-2). Butterworth.

Hidy, G. H., ed. Aerosols & Atmospheric Chemistry. 1972. 50.50 (ISBN 0-12-347250-4). Acad Pr.

Hidy, George M., et al, eds. The Character & Origins of Smog Aerosols: A Digest of Results from the California Aerosol Characterization Experiment (ACHEX, Vol. 9. LC 79-4585. (Advances in Environmental Science & Technology Ser.). 776p. 1980. 95.50 (ISBN 0-471-04899-2, Pub. by Wiley-Interscience). Wiley.

Hunt, et al, eds. Building Air Change Rate & Infiltration Measurements-STP 719. 195p. 1980. 21.00 (ISBN 0-8031-0607-6, 04-71900-10). ASTM.

International Advanced Course & Workshop on Thermal Effluent Disposal from Power Generation, Aug. 23-28, 1976, Dubrovnik, Yugoslavia. Thermal Effluent Disposal from Power Generation: Proceedings. Zaric, Z., ed. LC 77-28808. (Thermal & Fluids Engineering, International Centre for Heat & Mass Transfer Ser.). (Illus.). 375p. 1978. text ed. 74.50 (ISBN 0-89116-093-0). Hemisphere Pub.

International Clean Air Congress, 2nd. Proceedings. Englund, Harold M. & Beery, W. T., eds. 1971. 125.00 (ISBN 0-12-239450-X). Acad Pr.

International Operations Handbook for Measurement of Background Atmospheric Pollution. 1978. pap. 30.00 (ISBN 92-63-10491-3, W417, WMO). Unipub.

International Symposium, Dubrovnik, Yugoslavia, 7-14 Sept. 1977. Sulphur in the Atmosphere: Proceedings. Husar, R. B., et al, eds. 1978. text ed. 83.00 (ISBN 0-08-022932-8). Pergamon.

IUTAM. Atmospheric Dispersion in Heavy Gases & Small Particles: Symposium, Delft, the Netherlands, August 29 - September 2, 1983. Ooms, G. & Tennekes, H., eds. (International Union of Theoretical & Applied Mechanics). (Illus.). 450p. 1984. text ed. 38.50 (ISBN 0-387-13491-3). Springer-Verlag.

Izmerov, N. F. Control of Air Pollution in the USSR. (Public Health Paper: No. 54). 1973. pap. 3.60 (ISBN 92-4-130054-X). World Health.

Katz, M. Measurement of Air Pollutants: Guide to the Selection of Methods. 123p. 1969. pap. 9.20 (ISBN 92-4-154006-0, 71). World Health.

Keith, Lawrence H. Identification & Analysis of Organic Pollutants in the Air. 1983. text ed. 49.95 (ISBN 0-250-40575-X). Butterworth.

Kennedy, H. W., et al. Symposium on Air Pollution. LC 75-152831. (Symposia on Law & Society Ser). 1971. Repr. of 1968 ed. lib. bdg. 22.50 (ISBN 0-306-70143-X). Da Capo.

Klingbeil, Louis J. & Klingbeil, Reinhold L. Battle to Breathe. LC 76-170374. (Better Living Ser). (Illus.). 64p. 1971. pap. 0.99 (ISBN 0-8127-0059-7). Review & Herald.

Kohn, Robert E. A Linear Programming Model for Air Pollution Control. 1978. 40.00x (ISBN 0-262-11062-8). MIT Pr.

Koziol, Michael J. & Whatley, F. R., eds. Gaseous Air Pollutants & Plant Metabolism. 1984. text ed. 99.95 (ISBN 0-408-11152-6). Butterworth.

Lahaye, J. & Prado, G., eds. Soot in Combustion Systems & Its Toxic Properties. (NATO Conference Series IV, Materials Science: Vol. 7). 430p. 1983. 57.50x (ISBN 0-306-41245-4, Plenum Press). Plenum Pub.

Laszt, L. & Schaad, R. Luftverunreinigung und Herz-Kreislauf-System. (Illus.). viii, 140p. 1980. pap. 12.00 (ISBN 3-8055-3067-6). S Karger.

Ledbetter, J. O. Air Pollution, Pt. B: Prevention & Control. (Environmental Health Engineering Textbooks Ser.: Vol. 2). 300p. 1974. 29.75 (ISBN 0-8247-1406-7). Dekker.

Lee, Douglas H., ed. Environmental Factors in Respiratory Disease. (Environmental Science Ser.). 1972. 39.50 (ISBN 0-12-440655-6). Acad Pr.

Lee, Kaiman. Air Pollution: Its Effect on the Urban Man & His Adaptive Strategies. LC 74-182905. 52p. 1974. 12.00x (ISBN 0-915250-13-6). Environ Design.

Lee, Robert E., Jr. Air Pollution from Pesticides & Agricultural Processes. (Uniscience Ser.). 280p. 1976. 69.00 (ISBN 0-8493-5157-X). CRC Pr.

Licht, W. Air Pollution Control Engineering. (Pollution Engineering & Technology Ser.: Vol. 10). 1980. 45.00 (ISBN 0-8247-6846-9). Dekker.

Long-Range Transport of Sulphur in the Atmosphere & Acid Rain: Lectures Presented at the Thirty-third Session of the WMO Executive Committee. 53p. 1983. pap. text ed. 8.00 (ISBN 92-63-10603-7, W560, WMO). Unipub.

Lundgren, Dale A., et al. Airborne Pollutants: Characteristics & Detection. (Air Pollution Ser: Vol. 7). 153p. 1974. text ed. 24.00x (ISBN 0-8422-7158-9). Irvington.

Lundqvist, Lennart J. The Hare & the Tortoise: Clean Air Policy in the United States and Sweden. 248p. 1980. 15.00x (ISBN 0-472-09310-X). U of Mich Pr.

McCormac, B. M., ed. Introduction to the Scientific Study of Atmospheric Pollution. LC 70-170340. 169p. 1971. lib. bdg. 24.00 (ISBN 90-277-0215-2, Pub. by Reidel Holland); pap. 16.00 (ISBN 90-277-0243-8, Pub. by Reidel Holland). Kluwer Academic.

Mamantov, Gleb & Shults, W. D., eds. Determination of Air Quality. LC 72-182861. 200p. 1972. 32.50x (ISBN 0-306-30571-2, Plenum Pr). Plenum Pub.

Manning, W. J. & Feder, W. A. Biomonitoring Air Pollutants with Plants. (Pollution Monitoring Ser.: No. 2). (Illus.). 142p. 1980. 26.00 (ISBN 0-85334-916-9, Pub. by Elsevier Applied Sci England). Elsevier.

Marchello, Joseph M. & Kelley, John J., eds. Gas Cleaning for Air Quality Control: Industrial & Environmental Health & Safety Requirements. (Chemical Processing & Engineering: An International Ser., Vol. 2). 424p. 1975. 65.00 (ISBN 0-8247-6079-4). Dekker.

Medical Sciences Division. Manganese. LC 73-18174. (Medical & Biologic Effects of Environmental Pollutants Ser.). 192p. 1974. pap. 10.50 (ISBN 0-309-02143-X). Natl Acad Pr.

Meetham, A. R., et al. Atmospheric Pollution: Its History, Origins & Prevention. 4th ed. (Illus.). 288p. 1981. 42.00 (ISBN 0-08-024003-8); pap. 15.00 (ISBN 0-08-024002-X). Pergamon.

Mendelsohn, Robert O. Towards Efficient Regulation of Air Pollution from Coal-Fired Power Plants. LC 78-75020. (Outstanding Dissertations in Economics Ser.). 1979. lib. bdg. 29.00 (ISBN 0-8240-4055-4). Garland Pub.

Mercer, Thomas T. Aerosol Technology in Hazard Evaluation. (U. S. Atomic Energy Commission Monograph Ser.). 1973. 39.50 (ISBN 0-12-491150-1). Acad Pr.

Meteorological Aspects of Air Pollution. (Technical Note Ser.: No. 106). (Illus.). 69p. (Orig.). 1970. pap. 12.00 (ISBN 0-685-04917-5, W77, WMO). Unipub.

Meteorology & the Human Environment: Lectures Presented at the 29th Session of the WMO Executive Committee. (Special Environmental Reports: No. 13). (Illus.). 49p. 1979. pap. 25.00 (ISBN 92-63-10517-0, W425, WMO). Unipub.

Morton, J & Falla, N A. Analysis of Airborne Pollutants in Working Atmosphere. 192p. 1983. 30.00 (ISBN 0-85186-860-6, Pub. by Royal Soc Chem Uk). Heyden.

Nieuwstadt, F. T. & Van Dop, H., eds. Atmospheric Turbulence & Air Pollution. 384p. 1982. lib. bdg. 49.00 (ISBN 90-277-1365-0, Pub. by Reidel Holland); pap. 29.50 (ISBN 90-277-1807-5). Kluwer Academic.

Nieuwstadt, F. T. M. & Dop, D. van, eds. Atmospheric Turbulence & Air Pollution Modelling. rev. ed. 1984. lib. bdg. 49.00 (ISBN 0-318-01663-X, Pub. by Reidel Holland); pap. text ed. 29.50 (ISBN 90-277-1807-5). Kluwer Academic.

Occupational Exposure to Airborne Substances Harmful to Health. (Codes Of Practice Ser.). viii, 44p. 1980. pap. 5.70 (ISBN 92-2-102442-3, ILO152, ILO). Unipub.

Papers Presented at the WMO Symposium on Boundary Layer Physics Applied to Specific Problems of Air Pollution: Norrkiping, 19-23 June 1978. xii, 322p. 1978. pap. 35.00 (ISBN 92-63-10510-3, W395, WMO). Unipub.

Perkins, H. C. Air Pollution. (Illus.). 448p. 1974. text ed. 48.00 (ISBN 0-07-049302-2). McGraw.

Perry, Roger & Young, Robert J., eds. Handbook of Air Pollution Analysis. 1977. 69.95x (ISBN 0-412-12660-5, NO. 6220, Pub. by Chapman & Hall). Methuen Inc.

Postel, Sandra. Air Pollution, Acid Rain, & the Future of Forests. LC 84-50653. (Worldwatch Papers). 1984. pap. 4.00 (ISBN 0-916468-57-7). Worldwatch Inst.
Powals, Richard J., et al. Handbook of Stack Sampling & Analysis. LC 78-19914. (Illus.). 1978. pap. 45.00x (ISBN 0-87762-233-7). Technomic.
Public Interest Report: Fluoride Fallout from Factories Making Man the Endangered Species, No. 1. pap. 1.50 (ISBN 0-318-03955-9). Top Ecol Pr.
Public Interest Report, No. Two: Fluoride Industry's Phantom Air Pollutant Poisoning Animals, Farm & Forest. pap. 1.50 (ISBN 0-318-03956-7). Top Ecol Pr.
Rasool, S. I. Chemistry of the Lower Atmosphere. LC 72-90336. 335p. 1973. 45.00x (ISBN 0-306-30591-7, Plenum Pr). Plenum Pub.
Research into Environmental Pollution: A Report of 5 WHO Scientific Groups. (Technical Report Ser: No. 406). 83p. 1968. pap. 2.40 (ISBN 92-4-120406-0, 73). World Health.
Roahe, H. & Eliassen, A. Tropospheric Chemistry & Air Pollution. (Technical Note Ser.: No. 176). 141p. 1982. pap. 14.00 (ISBN 0-686-97567-7, W517, WMO). Unipub.
Ross, R. D. Air Pollution & Industry. LC 70-180160. 510p. 1972. 25.00 (ISBN 0-442-27052-6). Krieger.
Ross, Richard D. Air Pollution & Industry. (Environmental Engineering Ser.). 448p. 1972. 26.50 (ISBN 0-442-27052-6). Van Nos Reinhold.
Royal Society of London, Study Group on Pollution in the Atmosphere, 1977. Pathways of Pollutants in the Atmosphere. (Proceedings of the Royal Society). (Illus.). 170p. 1979. 37.00x (ISBN 0-85403-107-3, Pub by Royal Soc London). Scholium Intl.
Rudman, Jack. Air Pollution Control Chemist. (Career Examination Ser.: C-1084). (Cloth bdg. avail. on request). pap. 12.00 (ISBN 0-8373-1084-9). Natl Learning.
--Air Pollution Control Engineer. (Career Examination Ser.: C-76). (Cloth bdg. avail. on request). pap. 12.00 (ISBN 0-8373-0076-2). Natl Learning.
--Air Pollution Control Engineering Trainee. (Career Examination Ser.: C-1926). (Cloth bdg. avail. on request). pap. 10.00 (ISBN 0-8373-1926-9). Natl Learning.
--Air Pollution Control Technician. (Career Examination Ser.: C-1085). (Cloth bdg. avail. on request). pap. 12.00 (ISBN 0-8373-1085-7). Natl Learning.
--Air Pollution Inspector. (Career Examination Ser.: C-11). (Cloth bdg. avail. on request). pap. 12.00 (ISBN 0-8373-0011-8). Natl Learning.
--Air Pollution Laboratory Maintainer. (Career Examination Ser.: C-1086). (Cloth bdg. avail. on request). pap. 12.00 (ISBN 0-8373-1086-5). Natl Learning.
--Assistant Air Pollution Control Engineer. (Career Examination Ser.: C-1094). (Cloth bdg. avail on request). pap. 12.00 (ISBN 0-8373-1094-6). Natl Learning.
--Junior Air Pollution Control Engineer. (Career Examination Ser.: C-1334). (Cloth bdg. avail. on request). pap. 12.00 (ISBN 0-8373-1334-1). Natl Learning.
--Senior Air Pollution Inspector. (Career Examination Ser.: C-1469). (Cloth bdg. avail. on request). pap. 10.00 (ISBN 0-8373-1469-0). Natl Learning.
--Supervising Air Pollution Inspector. (Career Examination Ser.: C-1502). (Cloth bdg. avail. on request). pap. 10.00 (ISBN 0-8373-1502-6). Natl Learning.
Schneider, T., ed. Automatic Air Quality Monitoring Systems: Proceedings of the Conference Held in Bilthorn in 1973. 1974. 21.50 (ISBN 0-444-41202-6). Elsevier.
Schneider, T. & Grant, L., eds. Air Pollution by Nitrogen Oxides: Proceedings of the U. S.-Dutch International Symposium, Maastricht, May 24-28, 1982. (Studies in Environmental Science: No. 21). 1118p. 1983. 159.75 (ISBN 0-444-42127-0). Elsevier.
Schneider, T., et al, eds. Air Pollution Reference Measurement Methods & Systems: Proceedings of the International Workshop, Bilthoven, December 1977. (Studies in Environmental Science: Vol. 2). 168p. 1979. 51.00 (ISBN 0-444-41764-8). Elsevier.
Scorer, R. S. Air Pollution. 1968. pap. 14.50 (ISBN 0-08-012275-2). Pergamon.
Sheridan, Lillian B. Adverse Effects of Air Pollutants: Medical Subject Analysis & Research Bibliography. LC 84-45660. 150p. 1984. 29.95 (ISBN 0-88164-210-X); pap. 21.95 (ISBN 0-88164-211-8). ABBE Pubs Assn.
Sittig, M. Particulates & Fine Dust Removal: Processes & Equipment. LC 77-77018. (Pollution Technology Review Ser.: No. 34). (Illus.). 1977. 48.00 (ISBN 0-8155-0664-3). Noyes.
Smith, W. H. Air Pollution & Forests. (Springer Series on Environmental Management). (Illus.). 379p. 1981. 35.00 (ISBN 0-387-90501-4). Springer-Verlag.
Starkman, Ernest S., ed. Combustion-Generated Air Pollution. LC 73-155925. 335p. 1971. 49.50x (ISBN 0-306-30538-0, Plenum Pr). Plenum Pub.
Stern, Arthur. Air Pollution, Vol. 2. 3rd ed. (Environmental Sciences Ser). 1977. 89.50 (ISBN 0-12-666602-4). Acad Pr.
--Air Pollution, Vol. 5. 3rd ed. 1977. 75.00 (ISBN 0-12-666605-9). Acad Pr.
Stern, Arthur C. Air Pollution, Vol. 1: Air Pollutants, Their Transformation & Transport. (Environmental Sciences Ser.). 715p. 1976. 89.50 (ISBN 0-12-666601-6). Acad Pr.
--Air Pollution, Vol. 4: Engineering Control of Air Pollution. (Environmental Sciences Ser.). 946p. 1977. 93.00 (ISBN 0-12-666604-0). Acad Pr.
Stern, Arthur C., et al. Fundamentals of Air Pollution. 2nd ed. 1984. 39.50 (ISBN 0-12-666580-X). Acad Pr.
Stevenson, K. J., et al. Air Pollution in Homes III: Measurements of Carbon Monoxide & Nitrogen Oxides in Two Living Rooms, 1979. 1981. 39.00x (ISBN 0-686-97012-8, Pub. by W Spring England). State Mutual Bk.
Stoker, H. Stephen & Seager, Spencer L. Environmental Chemistry: Air & Water Pollution. 2nd ed. 1976. pap. 10.80 (ISBN 0-673-07978-3). Scott F.
Strauss, W. & Mainwaring, S. J. Air Pollution. 52p. 1984. pap. text ed. 12.95 (ISBN 0-7131-3493-3). E Arnold.
Suess, M. J. & Craxford, S. R., eds. Manual on Urban Air Quality Management. (WHO Regional Pub., European Ser.: No. 1). (Also avail. in French). 1976. pap. 14.40 (ISBN 0-686-16922-0). World Health.
Summer, W. Odour Pollution of Air: Causes & Control. 1972. 45.00x (ISBN 0-249-44022-9). Intl Ideas.
Symposium on Air-Pollution Measurement Methods. LC 63-21664. (American Society for Testing & Materials. Special Technical Publications Ser.: No. 352). pap. 21.00 (ISBN 0-317-10904-9, 2000117). Bks Demand UMI.
Techniques for Controlling Air Pollution from the Operation of Nuclear Facilities. (Safety Ser.: No. 17). (Illus.). 118p. 1966. pap. 9.75 (ISBN 92-0-123166-0, ISP121, IAEA). Unipub.
Theodore, Louis. Air Pollution Control for Hospitals & Medical Facilities. LC 80-19352. 336p. 1981. lib. bdg. 41.50 (ISBN 0-8240-7132-8). Garland Pub.
Theodore, Louis, et al. Particulate Air Pollution: Problems & Solutions. 112p. 1980. 42.00 (ISBN 0-8493-5541-9). CRC Pr.
Thomas, William A., ed. Indicators of Environmental Quality. LC 72-86142. (Environmental Science Research Ser.: Vol. 1). 285p. 1972. 45.00x (ISBN 0-306-36301-1, Plenum Pr); pap. 9.95 (ISBN 0-306-20011-2). Plenum Pub.
Treatment of Airborne Radioactive Wastes. (Proceedings Ser.). (Illus.). 818p. 1968. pap. 53.75 (ISBN 92-0-020068-0, ISP195, IAEA). Unipub.
Ulrich, B. & Pankrath, J. Effects of Accumulation of Air Pollutants in Forest Ecosystems. 1983. lib. bdg. 58.50 (ISBN 90-277-1476-2, Pub. by Reidel Holland). Kluwer Academic.
Verner, S., ed. Sampling & Analysis of Toxic Organics in the Atmosphere -STP 721. 192p. 1981. 19.75 (ISBN 0-8031-0604-1, 04-721000-19). ASTM.
Wadden, Richard A. & Scheff, Peter A. Indoor Air Pollution: Characterization, Prediction & Control. LC 82-11153. (Environmental Science & Technology: A Wiley Interscience Series of Texts & Monographs). 213p. 1982. 43.00 (ISBN 0-471-87673-9, 1-121, Pub. by Wiley-Interscience). Wiley.
Wark, Kenneth & Warner, Cecil F. Air Pollution: Its Origin & Control. 2nd ed. 526p. 1981. text ed. 35.95 scp (ISBN 0-7002-2534-X, HarpC). Har-Row.
Warner, Peter O. Analysis of Air Pollutants. LC 75-26685. (Environmental Science & Technology Ser.). pap. 64.60 (ISBN 0-317-11251-1, 2055094). Bks Demand UMI.
Weatherley, M. L. The National Survey of Smoke & Sulphur Dioxide: Quality Control & the Air Sampling Arrangements, 1979. 1981. 50.00x (ISBN 0-686-97121-3, Pub. by W Spring England). State Mutual Bk.
Webb, J. C., et al. Detection & Control of Air Pollution. (Air Pollution Ser.: Vol. 2). 1974. 32.50x (ISBN 0-8422-7153-8). Irvington.
Weber, Erich, ed. Air Pollution: Assessment Methodology & Modeling. LC 82-3546. (NATO Challenges of Modern Society Ser.: Vol. 2). 350p. 45.00x (ISBN 0-306-40997-6, Plenum Pr). Plenum Pub.
Weiner, Jack & Roth, Lillian. Air Pollution in the Pulp & Paper Industry. LC 73-82482. (Bibliographic Ser.: No. 237). supplement 1, 1970 8.00 (ISBN 0-87010-000-9); supplement 2, 1973 12.00 (ISBN 0-87010-001-7). Inst Paper Chem.
Westberg, Karl, et al. The Chemistry of Air Pollution. LC 73-11037. (Air Pollution Ser.: Vol. 1). 199p. 1974. text ed. 25.50x (ISBN 0-8422-7152-X). Irvington.
White, Warren, ed. Plumes & Visibility. (Illus.). 230p. 1983. pap. 66.00 (ISBN 0-08-028733-6); pap. 33.00 suppl. (ISBN 0-08-028741-7). Pergamon.
Whiteside, Thomas. Pendulum & the Toxic Cloud: The Dioxin Threat from Vietnam to Seveso. 1979. pap. 8.95x (ISBN 0-300-02283-2). Yale U Pr.
WHO Collaborating Centre on Air Pollution Control & WHO Collaborating Centre on Clinical & Epidemiological Aspects of Air Pollution. Selected Methods of Measuring Air Pollutants. (Offset Pub.: No. 24). (Also avail. in French & Spanish). 1976. pap. 8.00 (ISBN 92-4-170024-6). World Health.
WHO Expert Committee, Geneva, 1968. Urban Air Pollution: With Particular Reference to Motor Vehicles. (Technical Report Ser: No. 410). 53p. 1969. pap. 2.00 (ISBN 92-4-120410-9, 64). World Health.
WHO Expert Committee. Geneva, 1972. Air Quality Criteria & Guides for Urban Air Pollutants: Report. (Technical Report Ser.: No. 506). (Also avail. in French & Spanish). 1972. pap. 2.40 (ISBN 92-4-120506-7). World Health.
Woodwell, G. M., et al. Ecological & Biological Effects of Air Pollution. 1973. 37.50x (ISBN 0-8422-7138-4). Irvington.
Young & Cross. Specifying Air Pollution Control Equipment. (Pollution & Engineering Technology Series: Vol. 20). 320p. 1982. 38.50 (ISBN 0-8247-1696-5). Dekker.

AIR-POLLUTION-BIBLIOGRAPHY

An Annotated Bibliography of Canadian Air Pollution Literature. pap. 9.25 (SSC1, SSC). Unipub.
Library of Congress, Science & Technology Div., ed. Air Pollution Bibliography, Two Vols. in One, 2 vols. in 1. LC 57-60050. Repr. of 1957 ed. 42.00 (ISBN 0-527-00875-3). Kraus Repr.
Miller, E. Willard. Environmental Hazards-Air Pollution: A Bibliography. (Public Administration Ser.: Bibliography P-1611). 54p. 1985. pap. 8.25 (ISBN 0-89028-261-7). Vance Biblios.

AIR-POLLUTION-LAWS AND LEGISLATION

Air Pollution Control. (Policy & Practice Ser.). write for info. BNA.
Air Pollution Control: National & International Perspectives. 90p. 1980. pap. 6.00 (ISBN 0-686-47960-2). Amer Bar Assn.
ALI-ABA Committee on Continuing Professional Education & Environmental Law Institute. Water & Air Pollution: ALI-ABA Course of Study Materials. LC 83-169811. (Illus.). ciii, 539p. Date not set. 40.00. Am Law Inst.
Bromberg, J. Philip. Clean Air Act Handbook: "How to Comply with the Clean Air Act". LC 83-82074. 275p. 1983. pap. 48.00 (ISBN 0-86587-059-4). Gov Insts.
Crandall, Robert W. Controlling Industrial Pollution: The Economics & Politics of Clean Air. LC 82-45982. 220p. 1983. 26.95 (ISBN 0-8157-1604-4); pap. 9.95 (ISBN 0-8157-1603-6). Brookings.
Goldstein, Elliot, et al. Air Pollution & the Politics of Control. 182p. 1973. text ed. 23.50x (ISBN 0-8422-7136-8). Irvington.
Harrington, Winston. The Regulatory Approach to Air Quality Management: A Case Study of New Mexico. LC 81-81368. (RFF Research Papers, R25). 144p. 1981. pap. text ed. 7.50x (ISBN 0-8018-2700-0). Johns Hopkins.
Haskell, Elizabeth H. The Politics of Clean Air: EPA Standards for Coal Burning Power Plants. LC 81-13863. 224p. 1982. 29.95 (ISBN 0-03-059701-3). Praeger.
Krier, James E. & Ursin, Edmund. Pollution & Policy: A Case Essay on California & Federal Experience with Motor Vehicle Air Pollution, 1940-1975. LC 76-3881. 1978. 24.50x (ISBN 0-520-03204-7). U of Cal Pr.
Lave, Lester B. & Omenn, Gilbert S. Clearing the Air: Reforming the Clean Air Act. LC 81-70469. (Regulation of Economic Activity). 65p. 1981. pap. 6.95 (ISBN 0-8157-5159-1). Brookings.
Rowe, Robert D. & Chestnut, Lauraine G. The Value of Visibility: Economic Theory & Application of Air Pollution Control. LC 82-6862. 267p. 1983. 27.00 (ISBN 0-317-03150-3). Abt Bks.
White, Lawrence J. Regulation of Air Pollutant Emissions from Motor Vehicles. 1982. 13.95 (ISBN 0-8447-3492-6); pap. 4.95 (ISBN 0-8447-3487-X). Am Enterprise.

AIR-POLLUTION-LONDON

Dorling, T. A. & Sullivan, E. J. Airborne Particulate Lead Levels in Central London, 1980: Nineteen Seventy-Three to Seventy-Nine. 1981. 50.00x (ISBN 0-686-97019-5, Pub. by W Spring England). State Mutual Bk.
Royal Society of London, Study Group on Pollution in the Atmosphere, 1977. Pathways of Pollutants in the Atmosphere. (Proceedings of the Royal Society). (Illus.). 170p. 1979. 37.00x (ISBN 0-85403-107-3, Pub by Royal Soc London). Scholium Intl.

AIR-PURIFICATION

see also Air Conditioning

Ashby, Eric & Anderson, Mary. The Politics of Clean Air. (Monographs on Science, Technology, & Society). 1981. 36.50x (ISBN 0-19-858330-3). Oxford U Pr.
Mahalingam, R. & Engel, Alfred J., eds. Research Trends in Air Pollution Control: Scrubbing, Hot Gas Clean-up, Sampling & Analysis. (AIChe Symposium Ser.: Vol. 77). 94p. 1981. pap. 32.00 (ISBN 0-8169-0219-4, S-211); pap. 17.00 members (ISBN 0-686-47538-0). Am Inst Chem Eng.
NEA. Air Cleaning in Accident Situations. 126p. (Orig.). 1984. pap. 20.00x (ISBN 0-318-03889-7). OECD.
Solving Corrosion Problems in Air Pollution Control Equipment. LC 84-62370. 479p. 35.00 (ISBN 0-915567-07-5); member 28.00 (ISBN 0-317-18669-8). Natl Corrosion Eng.
Theodore, Louis & Buonicore, Anthony J., eds. Air Pollution Control Equipment: Selection, Design, Operation & Maintenance. (Illus.). 640p. 1982. text ed. 44.95 (ISBN 0-13-021154-0). P-H.

AIR-RADIOACTIVE POLLUTION

see Radioactive Pollution of the Atmosphere

AIR, IONIZED

see also Ionosphere

Soyka, Fred & Edmonds, Alan. The Ion Effect. 1978. pap. 3.95 (ISBN 0-553-34232-0). Bantam.

AIR, MOISTURE OF

see Humidity

AIR-BEARING VEHICLES

see Ground-Effect Machines

AIR BUILDINGS

see Air-Supported Structures

AIR CONDITIONING

see also Dampness in Buildings; Refrigeration and Refrigerating Machinery; Ventilation;
also specific subject with or without subdivision air-conditioning, e.g. Dwellings-Air conditioning

Air Conditioning & Refrigeration Institute. Refrigeration & Air Conditioning. (Illus.). 1979. 32.95 (ISBN 0-13-770164-0). P-H.
Air Conditioning & Ventilating Systems. (Eighty-Ninety Ser.). 1974. pap. 2.50 (ISBN 0-685-58161-6, 90A). Natl Fire Prot.
Althouse, Andrew & Turnquist, C. H. Modern Refrigeration & Air Conditioning. LC 81-20002. (Illus.). 1012p. 1982. text ed. 26.00x (ISBN 0-87006-340-5); lab manual 5.28x (ISBN 0-87006-422-3). Goodheart.
American Society of Mechanical Engineers. Energy Conservation in Building Heating & Air Conditioning Systems. Gopal, R., et al, eds. LC 78-60047. pap. 27.30 (ISBN 0-317-19849-1, 2023146). Bks Demand UMI.
Anderson, Edwin P. Air Conditioning: Home & Commercial. 2nd ed. LC 83-223476. 1984. 14.95 (ISBN 0-672-23397-5). Audel.
Application of Infrared Sensing Devices to the Assessment of Building Heat Loss Characteristics, ANSI-ASHRAE Standard 101-1981. (ASHRAE Standards Ser.). 1983. pap. text ed. 14.00 (ISBN 0-910110-27-1). Am Heat Ref & Air Eng.
Applied Technical Dictionary: Air Conditioning & Refrigeration. (Eng., Ger., Fr., Rus. & Slovak.). 69.00x (ISBN 0-569-08534-9, Pub. by Collets). State Mutual Bk.
Barding, LeRoy F. Air-Condition Handbook. 48p. (Orig.). 1981. pap. 3.00 (ISBN 0-9605848-0-3). Barding Pub.
Booth, K. M., ed. Dictionary of Refrigeration & Air Conditioning. 315p. 1971. 27.75 (ISBN 0-444-20069-X, Pub. by Elsevier Applied Sci England). Elsevier.
Brumbaugh, James. Heating, Ventilating, & Air Conditioning Library, 3 vols. 2nd ed. LC 83-7064. (Illus.). 1983. 14.95 ea. Vol. 1 (ISBN 0-672-23389-4, 23248). Vol. 2 (ISBN 0-672-23390-8, 23249). Vol. 3 (ISBN 0-672-23391-6, 23250). 41.95, set of 3 vols. (ISBN 0-672-23227-8). Audel.
Brumbaugh, James E. Heating, Ventilating & Air Conditions Library. (Audel). (Illus.). Set. 41.95 (ISBN 0-672-23388-6); Vol. 1. 14.95 (ISBN 0-672-23389-4); Vol. 2. 14.95 (ISBN 0-672-23390-8); Vol. 3. 14.95 (ISBN 0-672-23391-6); 41.95. G K Hall.
Carrier. Manual de Aire Acondicionado. (Espn.). 848p. 1977. 75.95 (ISBN 84-267-0115-9, S-30875). French & Eur.
Carrier Air Conditioning Co. Handbook of Air Conditioning System Design. 1965. 74.50 (ISBN 0-07-010090-X). McGraw.

Clifford, George. Heating, Ventilating & Air Conditioning. 1984. text ed. 39.95 (ISBN 0-8359-2812-8); sol. manual avail. (ISBN 0-8359-2813-6). Reston.
Crane, Dale, ed. Aircraft Air Conditioning Systems: Vapor Cycle. 2nd. ed. (Aviation Technician Training Ser.). (Illus.). 25p. 1975. pap. 3.95 (ISBN 0-89100-051-8, EA-AAC-1). Aviation Maint.
Croome, D. J. & Roberts, B. M. Air Conditioning & Ventilation of Buildings, Vol. 1. 2nd ed. LC 79-40965. (International Ser. in Heating, Ventilation & Refrigeration: Vol. 14). (Illus.). 575p. 1981. text ed. 66.00 (ISBN 0-08-024779-2). Pergamon.
Diamant, R. M. & Kut, David. District Heating & Cooling for Energy Conservation. LC 81-4110. 464p. 1981. 63.95x (ISBN 0-470-27182-5). Halsted Pr.
Doolin, James H. La Biblia Doolin Para el Tecnico Reparador. 500p. 1973. 35.00 (ISBN 0-914626-01-9). Doolco Inc.
--Doolin's Trouble Shooters Bible. 500p. 1963. 35.00 (ISBN 0-914626-00-0). Doolco Inc.
Down, P. G. Heating & Cooling Load Calculations. 1969. 31.00 (ISBN 0-08-013001-1). Pergamon.
Eastop, Thomas D. & Gasiorek, Janus M. Air Conditioning Through Worked Examples, with Chapters 7 & 8 on Duct Sizing & Fans. LC 73-441904. pap. 91.00 (ISBN 0-317-10833-6). Bks Demand UMI.
Ebeling, A. & Schweitzer, G. Basic Air Conditioning, 2 Vols. (Illus.). 1971. pap. 8.25 ea.; Vol. 1. (ISBN 0-8104-0791-4); Vol. 2. (ISBN 0-8104-0792-2); transparencies 239.00 (ISBN 0-685-03714-2, A001). Hayden.
Edwards, Harry J., Jr. Automatic Controls for Heating & Air Conditioning: Pneumatic-Electric Control Systems. (Illus.). 1980. 27.50 (ISBN 0-07-019046-1). McGraw.
European Heating & Ventilating Associations, ed. The International Dictionary of Heating, Ventilating, & Air Conditioning. LC 79-41714. 416p. 1982. 79.95x (ISBN 0-419-11650-8, NO. 6553, E&FN Spon England). Methuen Inc.
Gladstone, John. Air Conditioning & Mechanical Trades: Preparing for the Contractor's License Examination. LC 74-18258. (Illus.). 425p. 1980. pap. 19.95 (ISBN 0-930644-04-2). Engineers Pr.
--Air Conditioning Testing-Adjusting-Balancing: A Field Practice Manual. 2nd ed. 160p. 1981. 21.95 (ISBN 0-442-22714-0). Van Nos Reinhold.
Goings, Leslie F. Automotive Air Conditioning. LC 73-84847. pap. 49.00 (ISBN 0-317-10803-4, 2015779). Bks Demand UMI.
Gosling, C. T. Applied Air Conditioning & Refrigeration. 2nd ed. (Illus.). 410p. 1980. 44.50 (ISBN 0-85334-877-4, Pub. by Elsevier Applied Sci England). Elsevier.
Gupta, Vinod. Natural Cooling of Buildings. 31p. 1981. pap. 4.75x (ISBN 0-910661-00-6). Innovative Inform.
Harris, N. Modern Air Conditioning Practice. 3rd ed. 464p. 1983. 28.95 (ISBN 0-07-026833-9). McGraw.
Harris, Norman C. & Conde, D. F. Modern Air Conditioning Practice. 2nd ed. 27.95 (ISBN 0-07-026811-8). McGraw.
Havrella, Raymond. Heating, Ventilating & Air Conditioning Fundamentals. LC 80-17155. (Contemporary Construction Ser.). (Illus.). 288p. 1981. text ed. 23.72 (ISBN 0-07-027281-6). McGraw.
Heating, Air Conditioning & Refrigeration. 1984. 650.00 (ISBN 0-318-03908-7). Busn Trend.
Ingels, Margaret. Willis Haviland Carrier, Father of Air-Conditioning. LC 72-5056. (Technology & Society Ser.). (Illus.). 178p. 1972. Repr. of 1952 ed. 15.00 (ISBN 0-405-04708-8). Ayer Co Pubs.
Jennings, Burgess H. Environmental Engineering: Analysis & Practice. 765p. 1970. text ed. 34.75 scp (ISBN 0-7002-2259-6, HarpC); solution manual avail. Har-Row.
Jones, W. P. Air Conditioning Engineering. 3rd ed. 550p. 1985. text ed. 49.50 (ISBN 0-7131-3522-0). E Arnold.
Kimura, Ken-Ichi. Scientific Basis of Air Conditioning. (Illus.). 273p. 1977. 52.00 (ISBN 0-85334-732-8, Pub. by Elsevier Applied Sci England). Elsevier.
Kissell, Thomas. Motors, Controls & Circuits for Air Conditioning & Refrigeration Systems. 1984. text ed. 26.95 (ISBN 0-8359-4666-5). Reston.
Konzo, Seichi, et al. Summer Air Conditioning. pap. 138.50 (ISBN 0-317-10814-X, 2003090). Bks Demand UMI.
Lamere, Bernard. Guide to Home Air Conditioners & Refrigeration Equipment. (Illus., Orig.). 1963. pap. 6.50 (ISBN 0-8104-0294-7). Hayden.
Lang, V. Paul. Air Conditioning: Procedures & Installation. LC 80-70700. (Air Conditioning - Refrigeration Ser.). (Illus.). 112p. (Orig.). 1982. pap. text ed. 9.40 (ISBN 0-8273-1956-8). Delmar.
--Heating & Cooling Safety. LC 76-24983. 1977. pap. 7.40 (ISBN 0-8273-1011-0); instructor's guide o.p. 2.20 (ISBN 0-8273-1012-9). Delmar.
--Principles of Air Conditioning. LC 77-78900. (Air Conditioning, Refrigeration Ser.). 1979. pap. text ed. 17.00 (ISBN 0-8273-1009-9); instr's. guide 2.25 (ISBN 0-8273-1002-1). Delmar.
Langley, Billy. Air Conditioning & Refrigeration Trouble-Shooting Handbook. (Illus.). 650p. 1980. text ed. 35.95 (ISBN 0-8359-0204-8). Reston.
Langley, Billy C. Control Systems for Air Conditioning & Refrigeration. (Illus.). 192p. 1985. text ed. 24.95 (ISBN 0-13-171679-4). P-H.
--Electric Controls for Refrigeration & Air Conditioning. 1974. 29.95 (ISBN 0-13-247072-1); pap. 23.95 ref. ed. (ISBN 0-13-247064-0). P-H.
--Electricity for Refrigeration & Air Conditioning. text ed. 24.95 (ISBN 0-8359-1601-4); pap. text ed. 19.95 (ISBN 0-8359-1600-6); solutions manual avail. (ISBN 0-8359-1791-6). Reston.
--Estimating Air-Conditioning Systems. 1983. text ed. 24.95 (ISBN 0-8359-1790-8). Reston.
--Refrigeration & Air Conditioning. 2nd ed. 1982. text ed. 29.95 (ISBN 0-8359-6617-8); lab manual avail. (ISBN 0-8359-6619-4); instrs' avail. (ISBN 0-8359-6618-6). Reston.
Laube, Herbert L. How to Have Air-Conditioning & Still Be Comfortable. LC 73-172957. (Illus.). 254p. 12.95 (ISBN 0-912524-04-9). Busn News.
Long, Wayne. Refrigeration & Air Conditioning: Operation & Analysis Servicing. 832p. 1985. text ed. 31.95 scp (ISBN 0-672-97994-2); scp instr's guide 7.33 (ISBN 0-672-97995-0). Bobbs.
McQuiston, F. C. & Parker, J. D. Heating, Ventilating, & Air Conditioning: Analysis & Design. 2nd ed. 666p. 1982. 42.50 (ISBN 0-471-08259-7); write for info. solutions (ISBN 0-471-86657-1). Wiley.
Mahoney, Edward. Electricity for Air Conditioning & Refrigeration. (Illus.). 1980. text ed. 24.95 (ISBN 0-8359-1620-0); pap. text ed. 19.95 (ISBN 0-8359-1619-7); free instrs' manual (ISBN 0-8359-1621-9). Reston.
--Readings & Interpreting Diagrams in Air Conditioning & Refrigeration. 1983. text ed. 24.95 (ISBN 0-8359-6483-3); pap. text ed. 18.95 (ISBN 0-8359-6482-5); instr's. manual avail. (ISBN 0-8359-6484-1). Reston.
Miliaras, E. S. Power Plants with Air-Cooled Condensing Systems. (Monographs in Modern Electrical Technology). 240p. 1974. 32.50x (ISBN 0-262-13093-9). MIT Pr.
Miller, Rex. Refrigeration & Air-Conditioning Technology. 1983. text ed. 20.92 (ISBN 0-02-665540-3); student ed. 5.32 (ISBN 0-02-665560-8); tchr's. ed. 5.32 (ISBN 0-02-665550-0). Bennett IL.
Morris, Ralph C. Air Conditioning Cutter's Ready Reference. rev ed. LC 73-148571. (Illus.). 363p. 1971. 24.50 (ISBN 0-912524-02-2). Busn News.
Olivieri, Joseph B. How to Design Heating-Cooling Comfort Systems. 3rd ed. LC 75-84355. (Illus.). 1973. 24.00 (ISBN 0-912524-09-X). Busn News.
Palmquist, Roland. Refrigeration & Air Conditioning Library, 2 vols. (Illus.). 1977. Set. 21.95 (ISBN 0-672-23305-3); vol. I, air conditioning 10.95, home & commercial (ISBN 0-672-23288-X); vol. II refrigeration:home & commercial, 656pgs. 12.95 (ISBN 0-672-23286-3). Audel.
--Refrigeration & Air Conditioning Library, 2 vols. (Illus.). 1984. Set. 20.50 (ISBN 0-672-23411-4); Vol. 1, Air Conditioning: Home & Commercial. 14.95 (ISBN 0-672-23397-5); Vol. 2, Refrigeration: Home & Commercial. 16.95 (ISBN 0-672-23397-5). Audel.
Pita, Edward G. Air Conditioning Principles & Systems: An Energy Approach. LC 80-18958. 467p. 1981. text ed. 31.95x (ISBN 0-471-04214-5); tchrs.' manual 10.00 (ISBN 0-471-09636-9). Wiley.
Price, William & Price, James. Central Heating & Air Conditioning Repair Guide. 2nd ed. (Illus.). 320p. 1983. pap. 13.50 (ISBN 0-8306-1520-2). TAB Bks.
Rudman, Jack. Air Conditioning & Refrigeration. (Occupational Competency Examination Ser.: OCE-1). (Cloth bdg. avail. on request). pap. 13.95 (ISBN 0-8373-5701-2). Natl Learning.
--Assistant Supervisor (Air Conditioning, Rolling Stock) (Career Examination Ser.: C-2063). (Cloth bdg. avail. on request). 1977. pap. 12.00 (ISBN 0-8373-2063-1). Natl Learning.
Russell, Allen. Getting Started in Heating & Air Conditioning Service. 3rd ed. LC 77-13571. 1977. text ed. 24.50 (ISBN 0-912524-17-0). Busn News.
Schneider, Raymond K. HVAC Control Systems. LC 80-23588. 358p. 1981. text ed. 30.95 (ISBN 0-471-05180-2); avail. tchr's manual (ISBN 0-471-09274-6). Wiley.
Severns, William H. & Fellows, Julian R. Air Conditioning & Refrigeration. LC 58-7908. (Illus.). pap. 144.30 (ISBN 0-317-10907-3, 2019289). Bks Demand UMI.
Sherrat, A. F. Air Conditioning System Design for Buildings. 256p. 1983. write for info (ISBN 0-07-084591-3). McGraw.
Sherratt, A. F., ed. Air Conditioning & Energy Conservation. (Illus.). 287p. 1980. 69.50 (ISBN 0-89397-071-9, Pub. by Architectural Pr). Nichols Pub.
Shurcliff, W. A. Air-To-Air Heat Exchanges for Houses: How to Build Fresh Air into Your Home & Expel Polluted Air, While Recovering Valuable Heat. 224p. 1982. 29.95 (ISBN 0-471-88649-1). Wiley.
Solar Cooling & Heating Forum, Dec. 13-15, 1976, Miami Beach. Solar Cooling & Heating: Architectural, Engineering & Legal Aspects, Proceedings, 3 vols. new ed. Veziroglu, T. N., ed. LC 77-28813. (Illus.). 1066p. 1978. Set. text ed. 250.00 (ISBN 0-89116-165-1). Hemisphere Pub.
Stamper, Eugene & Koral, Richard L., eds. Handbook of Air Conditioning, Heating & Ventilating. 3rd ed. LC 78-71559. (Illus.). 1420p. 1979. 70.00 (ISBN 0-8311-1124-0). Indus Pr.
Stoecker, W. F. Using SI Units (Standard International Metric) in Heating, Air Conditioning, & Refrigeration. LC 74-26697. (Illus.). 1975. 7.50 (ISBN 0-912524-12-X). Busn News.
Stoecker, W. F. & Jones, J. W. Refrigeration & Air Conditioning. 2nd ed. 464p. 1982. 44.00x (ISBN 0-07-061619-1). McGraw.
Swenson, S. Don. Troubleshooting & Servicing Air Conditioning Equipment. 1985. pap. text ed. 23.00 (ISBN 0-534-04932-X, 77F6067). Breton Pubs.
Technical Dictionary: Refrigeration & Air Conditioning. (Eng., Fr., Ger. & Arabic.). 1979. 35.00x (ISBN 0-686-44746-8, Pub. by Collets). State Mutual Bk.
Technical Publications Staff. Air Conditioning Service Manual. 2nd ed. 60p. (Orig.). 1985. pap. 5.95 (ISBN 0-87288-183-0, ACS-2). Tech Pubns.
Trott, A. R. Refrigeration & Air Conditioning. 304p. 1981. 39.50 (ISBN 0-07-084543-3). McGraw.
Ward, Dan S., et al. How to Solve Materials & Design Problems in Solar Heating & Cooling. LC 81-18928. (Energy Technology Review: No. 77). (Illus.). 298p. 1982. 36.00 (ISBN 0-8155-0889-1). Noyes.
Warm Air Heating & Air Conditioning System. (Eighty-Ninety Ser). 1973. pap. 6.00 (ISBN 0-685-58162-4, 90B). Natl Fire Prot.
Zurick, Timothy. Air Conditioning, Heating & Refrigeration Dictionary. LC 77-10318. 1977. sewn lexotone 5.95 (ISBN 0-912524-16-2). Busn News.

AIR-CUSHION VEHICLES
see Ground-Effect Machines

AIR DUCTS
see also Air Conditioning; Ventilation
Interlaboratory Cooperative Study of the Precision of the Determination of Average Velocity in a Duct Using ASTM D 3154, DS 55-DS7. 1974. pap. 5.00 (ISBN 0-8031-0386-7, 05-055070-17). ASTM.
Wallis, Raymond A. Axial Flow Fans & Ducts. LC 83-3540. 431p. 1983. 52.50 (ISBN 0-471-87086-2, Pub. by Wiley-Interscience). Wiley.
Yingling, Ronald K., et al. Residential Duct Systems. (Illus.). 65p. 1981. 17.50 (ISBN 0-86718-000-5); pap. 13.00 members. Natl Assn Home.

AIR FLOW
see also Gas Flow; Permeability
The Airflow over Mountains: Research, 1958-1972. (Technical Note Ser.). (Illus.). 74p. (Orig.). 1974. pap. 27.00 (ISBN 0-685-40247-9, W134, WMO). Unipub.
Nevins, Ralph G. Air Diffusion Dynamics. 1976. 19.95 (ISBN 0-912524-14-6). Busn News.
Ower, Ernest & Pankhurst, F. C. Measurement of Air Flow: In SI-Metric Units. 5th ed. 1977. text ed. 45.00 (ISBN 0-08-021282-4); pap. text ed. 23.00 (ISBN 0-08-021281-6). Pergamon.

AIR FRAMES
see Airframes

AIR GUNS
Churchill, Bob & Davies, Granville. Modern Airweapon Shooting. (Illus.). 188p. 1981. 19.95 (ISBN 0-7153-8123-7). David & Charles.
Walter, John D. The Airgun Book. 3rd ed. 1984. 19.95 (ISBN 0-85368-675-0, Arms & Armour Pr). Sterling.

AIR NAVIGATION
see Aeronautics; Navigation (Aeronautics)

AIR PILOTS
see also Astronauts; Women in Aeronautics also subdivision Piloting under special types of aircraft, e.g. Airplanes–Piloting
Baker, E. C. Fighter Aces of the R. A. F., 1939-45. (Illus.). 1965. pap. 4.95 (ISBN 0-913076-00-7). Beachcomber Bks.
Barron, John. MIG Pilot: The Story of Viktor Belenko. 1980. 10.95 (ISBN 0-07-003850-3). McGraw.
Bellomo, Chas & Lynch, John. Crash, Fire & Rescue Handbook. (Pilot Training Ser.). 94p. (Orig.). 1984. pap. text ed. 8.95 (ISBN 0-89100-250-2, EA-250-2). Aviation Maintenance.
Bong, Carl & O'Conner, Mike. Rule the Air: The Story of Dick Bong, America's Ace of Aces. 1985. cancelled. Champlin Museum.
Canadian Private Pilot Manual. (Pilot Training Ser.). (Illus.). 428p. 1981. pap. text ed. 19.95 (ISBN 0-88487-074-X, JS314131). Jeppesen Sanderson.
Cass, Martin. The Pilot in Command. 220p. 1981. 35.00x (ISBN 0-906393-05-1, Pub. by Airlife England). State Mutual Bk.
Coleman, John E. Commercial Pilot Questions Answers Explanations. rev. ed. (Illus.). 312p. (Orig.). 1985. pap. text ed. 12.95x. Astro Pubs.
--Private Pilot Airplane: Questions-Answers-Explanations. (Illus.). 208p. 1984. pap. text ed. 10.95 (ISBN 0-317-18180-7, QAE 8080-1). Astro Pubs.
--Questions-Answers-Explanations: Private Pilot Airplane Written Test Guide. (Illus.). 168p. 1982. pap. text ed. 10.95 (ISBN 0-941272-10-9, QAE 32C). Astro Pubs.
--Questions-Answers-Explanations: Private Pilot Airplane Written Test Guide. rev. ed. (Illus.). 212p. 1984. pap. text ed. 11.95 (ISBN 0-941272-24-9, QAE-32C). Astro Pubs.
DeHaan, Warren V. The Optometrist's & Ophthalmologist's Guide to Pilot's Vision. LC 81-69431. 200p. 1982. 33.00 (ISBN 0-941388-00-X). Am Trend Pub.
Delp, Frank. Commercial Pilot Question Book Including Answers, Explanations, & References. rev. ed. (Pilot Training Ser.). 475p. 1985. pap. text ed. 12.95 (ISBN 0-89100-261-8, EA-FAA-T-8080-2C). Aviation Maintenance.
Downie, Don, rev. by. Flight Facts for Private Pilots. 2nd ed. Rodney, Morgan R. 1983. pap. 10.95 (ISBN 0-8168-5804-7). Aero.
Dunn, William R. Fighter Pilot: The First American Ace of World War II. LC 82-40172. (Illus.). 272p. 1982. 18.00 (ISBN 0-8131-1465-9). U Pr of Ky.
Educational Research Council of America. Commercial Airline Pilot. Ferris, Theodore N. & Marchak, John P., eds. (Real People at Work Ser.: Q). (Illus.). 36p. 1977. pap. 2.70 (ISBN 0-89247-121-2, 9612). Changing Times.
FAA Dept. of Transportation. Private Pilot Airplane Written Test Guide (With Answers) (Illus.). 156p. 1979. pap. text ed. 5.95 (ISBN 0-941272-13-3). Astro Pubs.
--Private Pilot Question Book (with Answers) (Illus.). 160p. 1984. pap. text ed. 5.00 (ISBN 0-317-18182-3). Astro Pubs.
Federal Aviation Administration. Advanced Ground Instructor Written Test Guide. 88p. 1980. pap. text ed. 4.50 (ISBN 0-939158-24-8). Flightshops.
--Airline Transport Pilot-Airplane Written Test Guide: Air Carrier. rev. ed. 189p. 1980. pap. text ed. 7.00 (ISBN 0-939158-16-7). Flightshops.
--Basic Ground Instructor Written Test Guide. 113p. 1980. pap. text ed. 4.75 (ISBN 0-939158-23-X). Flightshops.
--Commercial Pilot-Airplane Flight Test Guide. rev. ed. 70p. 1975. pap. text ed. 4.00 (ISBN 0-939158-10-8). Flightshops.
--Commercial Pilot-Airplane Written Test Guide. rev. ed. 141p. 1979. pap. text ed. 5.50 (ISBN 0-939158-14-0). Flightshops.
--Commercial Pilot Question Book. (Pilot Training Ser.). (Illus.). 228p. 1984. pap. 6.50 (ISBN 0-89100-260-X, EA-FAA-T-8080-2). Aviation Maintenance.
--Flight Instructor Airplane Written Test Guide. rev. ed. 138p. 1979. pap. text ed. 7.00 (ISBN 0-939158-15-9). Flightshops.
--Flight Instructor Instrument-Airplane Written Test Guide. rev. ed. 86p. 1980. pap. text ed. 4.00 (ISBN 0-939158-13-2). Flightshops.
--Flight Instructor Practical Test Guide. rev. ed. 17p. 1978. pap. text ed. 1.75 (ISBN 0-939158-12-4). Flightshops.
--Flight Instructor Question Book. (Pilot Training Ser.). (Illus.). 150p. 1984. pap. 5.50 (ISBN 0-89100-262-6, EA-FAA-T-8080-3). Aviation Maintenance.
--Flight Training Handbook. rev. ed. 325p. 1980. pap. text ed. 9.00 (ISBN 0-939158-06-X). Flightshops.
--Fundamentals of Instructing Flight & Ground Instructors Written Test Guide. 36p. 1979. pap. text ed. 2.25 (ISBN 0-939158-17-5). Flightshops.

--The Great Dirigibles, Their Triumphs & Disasters. Orig. Title: Ships in the Sky: the Story of the Great Dirigibles. (Illus.). 14.00 (ISBN 0-8446-4612-1). Peter Smith.
Ventry, Lord & Kolesnik, Eugene M. Airship Saga. 192p. 1983. 16.95 (ISBN 0-7137-1001-2, Pub. by Blandford Pr England). Sterling.

AIR-SUPPORTED STRUCTURES

American Society of Civil Engineers. State-of-the-Art Report on Air-Supported Structures. LC 79-125997. (Illus.). pap. 25.80 (ISBN 0-317-10911-1, 2019556). Bks Demand UMI.
International Conference on Practical Applications of Application of Air-Supported Structures: Proceedings. 220p. 1974. 35.00 (ISBN 0-318-01548-X, 20035). Indus Fabrics.
Otto, Frei. Tensile Structures. 490p. 1973. pap. 19.95x (ISBN 0-262-65005-3). MIT Pr.
Tents, Grandstands & Air Supported Structures. (One Hundred Ser.). 1972. pap. 2.00 (ISBN 0-685-58179-9, 102). Natl Fire Prot.

AIR TERMINALS

see Airports

AIR TRAFFIC CONTROL

see also Electronics in Aeronautics; Omnirange System

Borins, Sandford F. The Language of the Skies: The Bilingual Air Traffic Control Conflict in Canada. (Canadian Public Administration Series: IPAC). 352p. 1983. 30.00x (ISBN 0-7735-0402-8); pap. 12.95 (ISBN 0-7735-0403-6). McGill-Queens U Pr.
Borotto, A. V. Basic Flight Operations & Air Traffic Procedures for Pilots. LC 78-64346. 209p. 1978. pap. 9.95 (ISBN 0-87762-258-2). Technomic.
Carlson, Glenn E. Air Plane Talk. 276p. (Orig.). 1982. pap. 16.95 (ISBN 0-9611954-0-1). Watosh Pub.
Flax, Oriel. Rock the Tower. LC 84-90521. 107p. 1985. 10.95 (ISBN 0-533-06456-2). Vantage.
Gilbert, Glen A. Air Traffic Control: The Uncrowded Sky. LC 73-6005. (Illus.). 160p. 1973. 19.95x (ISBN 0-87474-140-8). Smithsonian.
Higham, Robin. Britain's Imperial Air Routes: 1918-1939. 395p. 1960. 15.00x (ISBN 0-89745-015-9). Sunflower U Pr.
Rudman, Jack. Air Traffic Control Specialist - ATCS. (Career Examination Ser.: C-68). (Cloth bdg. avail. on request). pap. 12.00 (ISBN 0-8373-0068-1). Natl Learning.

AIR-TURBINES

see also Rotors; Wind Power

Curtice, David & James Patton Systems Control, Inc. Handbook of the Operation of Small Wind Turbines on a Utility Distribution System. 2nd ed. (Illus.). 192p. 1984. pap. text ed. 49.50 (ISBN 0-88016-009-8). Windbks.
Hinrichsen, E. N. Control of Large Wind Turbine Generators Connected to Utility Networks. 96p. 1984. pap. 22.00 (ISBN 0-88016-033-0). Windbks.
Linscott, Bradford S. Large, Horizontal-Axis Wind Turbines. 68p. 1984. pap. 7.95X (W067). Solar Energy Info.
Pacific Northwest Laboratory. Siting Guide for Large Wind Turbines. 508p. 1982. pap. 49.50x (ISBN 0-89934-161-6). Solar Energy Info.
Sandia National Laboratory. Field Test Report of the Department of Energy's 100KW Vertical Axis Wind Turbine. 60p. 1985. pap. 14.95 (ISBN 0-317-18861-5, W-070). Solar Energy Info.
Schlueter, R. A., et al. Wind Turbine Arrays & Power Systems Operation. 1984. pap. 49.50 (ISBN 0-88016-020-9). Windbks.
Seiler, Farrell S., ed. Megawatt Wind Turbines. LC 84-51179. (Wind Energy Systems Ser.: Vol. 4 (of 4 vol. set). (Illus.). 300p. 1986. pap. 125.00 (ISBN 0-88016-025-X). Windbks.
Sixth International Symposium on Air Breathing Engines. 75.00 (ISBN 0-317-06657-9). AIAA.
Spera, David, ed. Wind Turbine Technology: Horizontal Axis Megawatt Wind Energy Systems. (Illus.). 450p. 1984. pap. 85.00 (ISBN 0-88016-043-8). Windbks.
University of Michigan, Ann Arbor, Department of Electrical & Computer Engineering. Electromagnetic Interference by Wind Turbine Generators. 163p. 1982. pap. 19.95x (ISBN 0-89934-171-3, W063). Solar Energy Info.
Wind Turbine Technology: Vertical Axis Wind Energy Systems. (Illus.). 1984. pap. 65.00 (ISBN 0-88016-007-1). Windbks.
Wortman. Introduction to Wind Turbine Engineering. 1983. text ed. 29.95 (ISBN 0-250-40562-8). Butterworth.

AIRBORNE INFECTION

Brooksby, J. B., ed. The Aerial Transmission of Disease. (Philosophical Transactions of the Royal Society: Ser. B, Vol. 302). (Illus.). 166p. 1984. Repr. text ed. 54.00x (ISBN 0-85403-214-2, Pub. by Royal Soc London). Scholium Intl.
Peagley, D. E. Weather & Airborne Organisms. (Technical Note Ser.: No. 173). 91p. 1980. pap. 12.00 (ISBN 92-63-10562-6, W487, WMO). Unipub.
Tice, Raymond R., et al, eds. Genotoxic Effects of Airborne Agents. LC 81-23497. (Environmental Science Research Ser.: Vol. 25). 672p. 1982. 75.00x (ISBN 0-306-40983-6, Plenum Pr). Plenum Pub.
Woodwell, G. M., et al. Ecological & Biological Effects of Air Pollution. 1973. 37.50x (ISBN 0-8422-7138-4). Irvington.

AIRCRAFT, FIXED WING

see Airplanes

AIRCRAFT ACCIDENTS

see Aeronautics–Accidents

AIRCRAFT CARRIERS

Bryan, Joseph, III. Aircraft Carrier. 1982. pap. 2.75 (ISBN 0-345-30486-1). Ballantine.
Friedman, Norman. Carrier Air Power. (Illus.). 176p. 1981. 30.00 (ISBN 0-8317-1192-2, Rutledge Pr). Smith Pubs.
--U. S. Aircraft Carriers: An Illustrated Design History. (Illus.). 488p. 1983. 46.95 (ISBN 0-87021-739-9). Naval Inst Pr.
Garrison, Paul. The Corporate Aircraft Owner's Handbook. (Illus.). 224p. 1982. 14.95 (ISBN 0-8306-9665-2); pap. 8.95 (ISBN 0-8306-2296-9, 2296). TAB Bks.
Hoyt, Edwin P. The Men of Gambier Bay. 296p. 1981. pap. 2.95 (ISBN 0-380-55806-8, 55806-8). Avon.
Jordan, John. An Illustrated Guide to Modern Naval Aviation & Aircraft Carriers. LC 83-2761. (Illustrated Military Guides Ser.). (Illus.). 160p. 1983. 9.95 (ISBN 0-668-05824-2, 5824). Arco.
Low, A. Lani & Muche, James F. U. S. Aircraft Carriers: A Bibliography. (Orig.). Date not set. pap. text ed. 15.00x (ISBN 0-910651-12-4). Fathom Eight.
Modern Naval Aviation & Aircraft Carriers. (Illus.). 9.95 (ISBN 0-668-05824-2). Arco.
Roberts, John. Anatomy of the Ship: The Aircraft Carrier Intrepid. LC 82-81105. (Illus.). 128p. 1982. text ed. 21.95 (ISBN 0-87021-901-4). Naval Inst Pr.
Terzibaschitcsch, Stefan. Aircraft Carriers of the U. S. Navy. (Illus.). 336p. 1980. 35.00 (ISBN 0-8317-0109-9, Mayflower Bks). Smith Pubs.

AIRCRAFT ENGINES

see Airplanes–Motors; Airplanes–Turbojet Engines

AIRCRAFT FUELS

see Airplanes–Fuel

AIRCRAFT GAS TURBINES

see also Airplanes–Turbojet Engines

Bent, R. & McKinley, J. Aircraft Powerplants. 5th ed. 608p. 1985. 28.95 (ISBN 0-07-004797-9). McGraw.

AIRCRAFT INDUSTRY

see also Airplanes

Aircraft-Airline Industries. (IES Committee Reports Ser.). 1975. 5.50 (ISBN 0-686-96209-5, CP-40); members 2.75 (ISBN 0-686-99733-6). Illum Eng.
Aircraft Loading Walkways. (Four Hundred Ser.). 1973. pap. 2.00 (ISBN 0-685-58236-1, 417). Natl Fire Prot.
Lighting for the Aircraft Airline Industries. 5.50 (ISBN 0-686-47878-9). Illum Eng.
Bluestone, Barry & Jordan, Peter. Aircraft Industry Dynamics. LC 81-2118. 208p. 1981. 24.95 (ISBN 0-86569-053-7). Auburn Hse.
Carpenter, Dorr & Mayborn, Mitch. Ryan Guidebook. rev., 2nd ed. LC 75-1687. (American Aircraft Ser: Bk. 3). (Illus.). 120p. 1975. 14.95 (ISBN 0-912470-23-2); pap. 9.95 (ISBN 0-912470-18-6). Flying Ent.
CNES & Chvidchenko, Ivan. Large Space Programs Management. (Illus.). 364p. 1971. 93.75 (ISBN 0-677-50670-8). Gordon.
Cohen, David. Fixed Base Operators: Management Handbook. Jones, David & Hurst, M. Dale, eds. (Aviation Management Ser.). 107p. 1980. pap. text ed. 8.95 (ISBN 0-89100-148-4, EA-148-4). Aviation Maintenance.
De Vries, John A. Eaglerock: The History of the Alexander Aircraft Company. Feitz, Leland, ed. (Illus.). 120p. 1984. 24.95 (ISBN 0-937080-17-9); pap. 19.95 (ISBN 0-937080-18-7). Century One.
Federal Aviation Administration. Non-Destructive Testing in Aircraft: AC 43-3. 38p. pap. 2.00x (ISBN 0-89100-083-6). Aviation Maint.
Gardner, Charles. British Aircraft Corporation: A History. (Illus.). 320p. 1981. 35.00 (ISBN 0-7134-3815-0, Pub. by Batsford England). David & Charles.
Goddard Memorial Symposium, 15th. Export of Aerospace Technology. Tross, Carl H., ed. (Science & Technology: Vol. 46). 1978. lib. bdg. 20.00x (ISBN 0-87703-093-6). Univelt Inc.
Harlan, N. E. Management Control in Airframe Subcontracting. 1956. 21.00 (ISBN 0-08-018741-2). Pergamon.
Hayward, Keith. Government & British Civil Aerospace: A Case Study in Post-War Technology Policy. LC 82-820857. 224p. 1983. 28.00 (ISBN 0-7190-0877-8, Pub. by Manchester Univ Pr). Longwood Pub Group.
Interavia ABC, 1982: World Directory of Aviation & Astronautics. 30th ed. LC 36-22039. 1400p. 1982. 120.00x (ISBN 0-8002-2987-8). Intl Pubns Serv.
Juptner, Joseph P. U. S. Civil Aircraft, 9 vols. Incl. Vol. 1. ATC 1-100. 1962 (ISBN 0-8168-9150-8); Vol. 2. ATC 101-200. 1964 (ISBN 0-8168-9154-0); Vol. 3. ATC 201-300. 1966 (ISBN 0-8168-9158-3); Vol. 4. ATC 301-400. 1967 (ISBN 0-8168-9162-1); Vol.5. ATC 401-500. 1971 (ISBN 0-8168-9166-4); Vol. 7. ATC 601-700. 1978 (ISBN 0-8168-9174-5); Vol. 8. ATC 801-817 & Series Index. 351p. 1980 (ISBN 0-8168-9178-8); Vol. 9. ATC 701-800. 240p. 1982 (ISBN 0-8168-9182-6); Vol. 6. ATC 501-600. (Illus.). 1974 (ISBN 0-8168-9170-2). LC 62-15967. 19.95 ea.; 159.95 set (ISBN 0-8168-9186-9). Aero.
Mayborn, Mitch. Grumman Guidebook: Nineteen Thirty-One Through Wildcat, Vol. 1. new ed. LC 74-3076. (American Aircraft Ser: Bk. 4). (Illus.). 112p. 1976. 14.95 (ISBN 0-912470-21-6); pap. 9.95 (ISBN 0-912470-16-X). Flying Ent.
Mondey, David. Planemakers: 2 Westland. (Planemakers Ser.). (Illus.). 160p. 1982. 15.95 (ISBN 0-86720-555-5). Jane's Pub Inc.
Morrow, John H. Building German Airpower, 1909-1914. LC 76-15287. pap. 41.00 (ISBN 0-317-20106-9, 2023171). Bks Demand UMI.
Phillips, Richard H. Building Big Is Beautiful. 3rd rev. ed. (Illus.). 146p. 1985. pap. 11.95 (ISBN 0-934575-00-2). Vip Aero Pubs.
Ramsden, J. M. The Safe Airline: How the Airline Industry Operates. (Illus.). 1976. 19.95x (ISBN 0-8464-0808-2). Beekman Pubs.
Sharp, Martin. The History of De-Havillands. 1982. 79.00x (ISBN 0-906393-20-5, Pub. by Airlife England). State Mutual Bk.
Simonson, G. R., ed. The History of the American Aircraft Industry. 1968. 32.50x (ISBN 0-262-19045-1). MIT Pr.
Stinton, Darrol. Anatomy of the Aeroplane. (Illus.). 350p. 1985. pap. text ed. 35.00x (ISBN 0-00-383178-7, Pub. by Collins England). Sheridan.
Taylor, John W., ed. Aircraft Annual. 1959. 10.00 (ISBN 0-8022-1701-X). Philos Lib.
--Jane's All the World's Aircraft 1985-86. 76th ed. (Jane's Yearbook). (Illus.). 900p. 1985. 125.00x (ISBN 0-7106-0821-7). Jane's Pub Inc.
World Market for General Aviation Aircraft, Avionics & Engines. 368p. 1985. 1900.00 (ISBN 0-86621-673-1). Frost & Sullivan.

AIRCRAFT INSTRUMENTS

see Aeronautical Instruments

AIRCRAFT MECHANICS (PERSONS)

see Aviation Mechanics (Persons)

AIRCRAFT NOISE

see Airplanes–Noise

AIRCRAFT PRODUCTION

see Aerospace Industries

AIRCRAFT RECOGNITION

see Airplanes–Recognition

AIRCRAFT SAFETY MEASURES

see Aeronautics–Safety Measures

AIRCRAFT STRESS ANALYSIS

see Airframes

AIRCRAFT STRUCTURES

see Airframes

AIRDROMES

see Airports

AIREDALE TERRIERS

see Dogs–Breeds–Airedale Terriers

AIRFOILS

see also Aerofoils

Aviation Publications. Comprehensive Reference Guide to Airfoil Sections for Light Aircraft. (Illus.). 168p. 1982. pap. 19.95 (ISBN 0-87994-038-7). Aviat Pub.

AIRFRAMES

see also Airplanes–Wings

Airframe & Systems Fitting. 1982. 50.00x (ISBN 0-85083-158-X, Pub. by Engineering Ind). State Mutual Bk.
American Society for Testing & Materials. Symposium on Materials for Aircraft, Missiles, & Space Vehicles. LC 63-20730. (American Society for Testing & Materials. Special Technical Publication Ser.: 345). pap. 37.30 (ISBN 0-317-09214-6, 2000136). Bks Demand UMI.
Argyris, J. H. & Kelsey, S. Energy Theorems & Structural Analysis. 85p. 1960. 22.50x (ISBN 0-306-30664-6, Plenum Pr). Plenum Pub.
Aviation Maintenance Publishers. Aircraft Logbook. 74p. 1975. pap. 4.95 (ISBN 0-89100-190-5, EA-AFL-1). Aviation Maintenance.
Aviation Maintenance Publishers & & Crane, Dale. Aircraft Bonded Structure. (Aviation Technician Training Ser.). (Illus.). 45p. 1977. pap. 3.95 (ISBN 0-89100-065-8, EA-NMR). Aviation Maint.
Aviation Mechanic Airframe Question Book Including Answers, Explanations & References. 196p. (Orig.). 1984. pap. text ed. 6.95 (ISBN 0-89100-275-8, EA-FAA-T-8080-12-C). Aviation Maintenance.
Conference on Aircraft Structures & Materials Application: Meeting Held September 9-11, 1969, Seattle, Washington. (The National SAMPE Technical Conference Ser.: Vol. 1). 563p. 1983. 10.00 (ISBN 0-938994-00-X). Soc Adv Material.
Crane, Dale. ITP Airframe Textbook. 679p. (Orig.). 1982. pap. 19.95 (ISBN 0-89100-248-0, ITP-AB); wkbk. 8.95 (ISBN 0-89100-249-9, ITP-AW-B); study guide 6.95 (ISBN 0-89100-244-8, ITP-ASG-B). Aviation Maintenance.
Damage Tolerance in Aircraft Structures, STP 486. 254p. 1971. 19.50 (ISBN 0-8031-0031-0, 04-486000-30). ASTM.
Federal Aviation Administration. Airframe & Powerplant Mechanics Airframe Writen Test Guide. rev. ed. 109p. 1981. pap. text ed. 5.50 (ISBN 0-939158-20-5). Flightshops.
--Airframe & Powerplant Mechanics General Written Test Guide. rev. ed. 95p. 1981. pap. text ed. 5.50 (ISBN 0-939158-19-1). Flightshops.
--Airframe & Powerplant Mechanic's Powerplant Written Test Guide. rev. ed. 90p. 1981. pap. text ed. 5.50 (ISBN 0-939158-21-3). Flightshops.
Green, C. J., et al, eds. Airframe & Systems Fitting. 2nd ed. (Engineering Craftsmen: No. H9). (Illus.). 1973. spiral bdg. 39.95x (ISBN 0-85083-218-7). Trans-Atlantic.
Ground Training for the Private Pilot Licence, No. 3: Principles of Flight, Airframes & Aero Engines, Aircraft Airworthiness & Aircraft Instruments. 264p. 1981. pap. 18.00x (ISBN 0-246-11700-1, Pub. by Granada England). Sheridan.
Handbook of Airfoil Sections for Light Aircraft. (Illus.). 143p. 1974. pap. 8.95 (ISBN 0-87994-015-8). Aviat Pub.
Heywood, J. E. Light Aircraft Maintenance: A Textbook for Airframe Maintenance. (Illus.). 225p. 1983. pap. 26.50x (ISBN 0-246-11909-8, Pub. by Granada England). Sheridan.
Kermode, Alfred C. The Aeroplane Structure. LC 41-8677. pap. 47.50 (ISBN 0-317-10238-9, 2013678). Bks Demand UMI.
Megson, T. Aircraft Structures for Engineering Students. 494p. 1972. pap. 25.50x (ISBN 0-8448-0592-0). Crane-Russak Co.
Rivello, Robert M. Theory & Analysis of Flight Structures. LC 68-25662. 1968. text ed. 48.00 (ISBN 0-07-052985-X). McGraw.
Rudman, Jack. Airframe or Powerplant Mechanics. (Occupational Competency Examination Ser.: OCE-2). (Cloth bdg. avail. on request). pap. 13.95 (ISBN 0-8373-5702-0). Natl Learning.
Spencer, Ruth & Spencer, Warren. Aircraft Dope & Frabic. 2nd ed. (Illus.). 160p. 1982. pap. 9.25 (ISBN 0-8306-2313-2, 2313). TAB Bks.
Testa, R. B., ed. Aerostructures, Selected Papers of Nicholas J. Hoff. LC 77-164024. 1974. 37.00 (ISBN 0-08-016834-5). Pergamon.
Venancio Filho, Fernando. Introduction to Matrix Structural Theory in Its Application to Civil & Aircraft Construction. LC 67-14507. 11.50 (ISBN 0-8044-4965-1). Ungar.

AIRLINERS

see Transport Planes

AIRPLANE ACCIDENTS

see Aeronautics–Accidents

AIRPLANE BOMBS

see Bombs

AIRPLANE CARRIERS

see Aircraft Carriers

AIRPLANE FUELS

see Airplanes–Fuel

AIRPLANE INDUSTRY

see Aircraft Industry

AIRPLANE RECOGNITION

see Airplanes–Recognition

AIRPLANES

see also Air-Ships; Aircraft Industry; Amphibian Planes; Autogiros; Bombers; Fighter Planes; Flying-Machines; Gliders (Aeronautics); Guided Missiles; Helicopters; Jet Planes; Jet Transports; Rocket Planes; Seaplanes; Short Take-Off and Landing Aircraft; Supersonic Planes; Vertically Rising Aircraft

also specific makes of airplanes, e.g. Boeing bombers; Lockheed airplanes; and headings beginning with the word Airplane

Adkins, Hal. The Directory of Homebuilt Ultra Light Aircraft. (Illus.). 106p. (Orig.). 1982. pap. 10.00 (ISBN 0-910907-00-5). Haljan Pubns.
Angelucci, Enzo. Encyclopedie Des Avions. (Fr.). 28p. 1976. 65.00 (ISBN 0-686-56894-X, M-6004). French & Eur.
Barnes, C. W. Handley Page Aircraft since 1907. (Putnam Aeronautical Books). (Illus.). 666p. 1979. 31.95 (ISBN 0-370-00030-7, Pub. by the Bodley Head). Merrimack Pub Cir.
Berger, Alain Y. & Burr, Norman. Berger-Burr's Ultralight & Microlight AirCraft of the World. 2nd ed. (Illus.). 320p. 1986. 17.95 (ISBN 0-85429-481-3, Pub. by G T Foulis Ltd). Interbook.

Aviation Maintenance Foundation. Aircraft Ignition & Electrical Systems. Crane, Dale, ed. LC 76-47110. (Aviation Technician Training Ser.). (Illus.). 76p. 1977. pap. 5.95 (ISBN 0-89100-063-1, EA-IGS). Aviation Maint.

Bent, Ralph D. & McKinley, James L. Aircraft Electricity & Electronics. 3rd, rev. ed. (Aviation Technology Ser.). (Illus.). 432p. 1981. pap. text ed. 30.20 (ISBN 0-07-004793-6). McGraw.

Pallett, E. H. Aircraft Electrical Systems. 2nd ed. (Aerospace Engineering Ser.). 169p. 1979. text ed. 31.50 (ISBN 0-273-08445-3). Pitman Pub MA.

AIRPLANES–ELECTRONIC EQUIPMENT

Bent, Ralph D. & McKinley, James L. Aircraft Electricity & Electronics. 3rd, rev. ed. (Aviation Technology Ser.). (Illus.). 432p. 1981. pap. text ed. 30.20 (ISBN 0-07-004793-6). McGraw.

Crane, Dale, ed. Basic Electronics & Radio Installation. (Aviation Technician Training Ser.). 77p. 1977. pap. 5.95 (ISBN 0-89100-064-X, EA-BEM). Aviation Maint.

Delp, Frank. Aircraft Governors. (Aviation Technician Training Course Ser.). 50p. (Orig.). 1982. pap. text ed. 4.95 (ISBN 0-89100-156-5, EA-AGV). Aviation Maintenance.

Ferrara, John M. Every Pilot's Guide to Aviation Electronics. 1976. pap. 12.75 (ISBN 0-911720-24-3). Aviation.

Harris, Frank. Electronic Circuit Devices. (Avionics Technician Training Course Ser.). 261p. (Orig.). 1983. pap. 7.95 (ISBN 0-89100-192-1, EA-192-1). Aviation Maintenance.

AIRPLANES–FLIGHT TESTING

Bramson, Alan. The Book of Flight Tests. LC 83-25751. (Illus.). 240p. 1984. 21.95 (ISBN 0-668-06152-9, 6152-9). Arco.

Crossfield, A. Scott & Blair, Clay, Jr. Always Another Dawn: The Story of a Rocket Test Pilot. LC 73-169413. (Literature & History of Aviation Ser). 1972. Repr. of 1960 ed. 31.00 (ISBN 0-405-03758-9). Ayer Co Pubs.

Smith, Hubert. Performance Flight Testing. (Illus.). 144p. 1982. pap. 9.95 (ISBN 0-8306-2340-X, 2340). TAB Bks.

AIRPLANES–FREIGHT

see Aeronautics, Commercial

AIRPLANES–FUEL

see also Jet Planes–Fuel

Aircraft Fuel Servicing. (Four Hundred Ser). 76p. 1974. pap. 3.50 (ISBN 0-685-44139-3, 407). Natl Fire Prot.

Goodger, Eric & Vere, Ray. Aviation Fuels Technology. (Illus.). 350p. 1985. text ed. 65.00x (ISBN 0-333-35787-6, Pub. by Macmillan Londan). Sheridan.

AIRPLANES–HISTORY

see also Aeronautics–Flights

Angelucci, Enzo. World Encyclopedia of Civil Aircraft, from Leonardo da Vinci to the Present. LC 82-4642. (Illus.). 414p. 1982. 24.95 (ISBN 0-517-54724-4). Crown.

Angelucci, Enzo & Matricardi, Paolo. World Aircraft: Commercial, 1935-1960. LC 79-51520. (Illus.). 1979. pap. 7.95 (ISBN 0-528-88206-6). Rand.

Antique Airplane Association. Classic Airplanes of the Thirties - Aircraft of the Roaring Twenties. Gilbert, James, ed. LC 79-7238. (Flight: Its First Seventy-Five Years Ser.). (Illus.). 1979. Repr. of 1965 ed. lib. bdg. 17.00x (ISBN 0-405-12153-9). Ayer Co Pubs.

Barnes, C. W. Handley Page Aircraft since 1907. (Putnam Aeronautical Books). (Illus.). 666p. 1979. 31.95 (ISBN 0-370-00030-7, Pub. by the Bodley Head). Merrimack Pub Cir.

Borge, Jacques & Viasnoff, Nicolas. The Dakota: The DC3 Story. 192p. 1982. 60.00x (ISBN 0-7232-2963-5, Pub. by F Warne England). State Mutual Bk.

Bullock, William B. Antiques & the Classics, Bk. 1. LC 79-53073. (Illus.). 1979. spiral 14.95 (ISBN 0-911721-59-2). Aviation.

Caproni, Gianni. Gli Aeroplane Caproni: Studi-Progetti-Realizzazioni dal 1908 al 1935. Gilbert, James, ed. LC 79-7234. (Flight: Its First Seventy-Five Years Ser.). Tr. of Caproni Airplanes: Studies, Plans, Fulfillments from 1908 to 1935. (Illus.). 1979. Repr. of 1936 ed. lib. bdg. 62.00x (ISBN 0-405-12150-4). Ayer Co Pubs.

Chanute, Octave. Progress in Flying Machines. 12.50 (ISBN 0-916494-00-4, Pub. by Lorenz & Herwig). Aviation.

Christy, Joe. The Complete Guide to Single-Engine Beechcrafts. 2nd ed. (Illus.). 1979. 7.95 (ISBN 0-8306-9791-8); pap. 4.95 o.p (ISBN 0-8306-2258-6, 2258). TAB Bks.

Close-up Fifteen: Japanese Cockpit Interiors, Pt. 2. LC 76-6214. 6.95 (ISBN 0-914144-15-4). Monogram Aviation.

Close-up One: Junkers Two Eighty-Seven. LC 74-26215. 6.95 (ISBN 0-914144-01-4). Monogram Aviation.

Close-up Seven: Gustav, Pt. 2. LC 75-22942. 6.95 (ISBN 0-914144-07-3). Monogram Aviation.

Close-up Thirteen: Aichi M6a1 Seiran. LC 75-22943. 6.95 (ISBN 0-914144-13-8). Monogram Aviation.

Close-up Three: Junkers Two Ninety. LC 74-26215. 6.95 (ISBN 0-914144-03-0). Monogram Aviation.

Close-up Two: Junkers Two Eighty-Eight. LC 74-26215. 6.95 (ISBN 0-914144-02-2). Monogram Aviation.

Crouch, Tom D. Bleriot XI: The Story of a Classic Airplane. LC 81-607931. (Famous Aircraft of the National Air & Space Museum Ser.). (Illus.). 144p. (Orig.). 1982. pap. 8.95 (ISBN 0-87474-345-1). Smithsonian.

Cynk, Jerzy B. Polish Aircraft: 1893-1939. (Putnam Aeronautical Bks.). (Illus.). 782p. 1979. 27.95 (ISBN 0-370-00085-4, Pub. by the Bodley Head). Merrimack Pub Cir.

De Vries, John A. Eaglerock: The History of the Alexander Aircraft Company. Feitz, Leland, ed. (Illus.). 120p. 1984. 24.95 (ISBN 0-937080-17-9); pap. 19.95 (ISBN 0-937080-18-7). Century One.

Francillon, Rene. Japanese Aircraft of the Pacific War. 2nd ed. (Illus.). 548p. 1980. 31.95 (ISBN 0-370-30251-6, Pub. by the Bodley Head). Merrimack Pub Cir.

Francillon, Rene J. McDonnell Douglas Aircraft Since Nineteen Twenty. LC 79-314590. (Putnam Aeronautical Bks.). (Illus.). 696p. 1979. 40.00 (ISBN 0-370-00050-1, Pub. by the Bodley Head). Merrimack Pub Cir.

Gilbert, James, ed. The Books of Miles, Westland & Bristol Aircraft: An Original Anthology, 3 vols. in 1. LC 79-7281. (Flight: Its First Seventy-Five Years Ser.). (Illus.). 1979. lib. bdg. 58.00x (ISBN 0-405-12190-3). Ayer Co Pubs.

Goodman, W. L. British Planemakers from Seventeen Hundred. 2nd ed. 50.00 (ISBN 0-904638-07-3). State Mutual Bk.

Green, William & Pollinger, Gerald. The Aircraft of the World. Gilbert, James, ed. LC 79-7262. (Flight: Its First Seventy-Five Years Ser.). (Illus.). 1979. Repr. of 1956 ed. lib. bdg. 30.00x (ISBN 0-405-12172-5). Ayer Co Pubs.

James, Derek N. Schneider Trophy Aircraft Nineteen Thirteen to Nineteen Thirty-One. (Putnam Aeronautical). (Illus.). 200p. 1981. 38.00 (ISBN 0-370-30328-8, Pub. by the Bodley Head). Merrimack Pub Cir.

Jane, Fred T., ed. Jane's All the World's Airships, 1909. LC 69-14964. 17.50 (ISBN 0-668-01956-5). Arco.

King, H. F. Armament of British Aircraft Nineteen Hundred Nine to Nineteen Thirty-Nine. (Putnam Aeronautical Ser.). (Illus.). 470p. 1980. 17.95 (ISBN 0-370-00057-9, Pub. by the Bodley Head). Merrimack Pub Cir.

Lewis, Peter. British Bomber Since Nineteen Fourteen. rev., 3rd ed. (Putnam Aeronautical Bks.). (Illus.). 432p. 1980. 21.95 (ISBN 0-370-30265-6, Pub. by the Bodley Head). Merrimack Pub Cir.

--British Fighter Since Nineteen Twelve. 4th ed. (Putnam Aeronautical Bks.). (Illus.). 416p. 1980. 21.95 (ISBN 0-370-30250-8, Pub. by the Bodley Head). Merrimack Pub Cir.

Miller, Jay. The X Planes: From the X-1 to the X-29. (Illus.). 192p. 1983. 29.95 (ISBN 0-933424-35-3). Specialty Pr.

Roberts, Kenneth D. Wooden Planes in Nineteenth Century America. 2nd ed. (Illus.). 324p. Repr. of 1978 ed. 30.00x (ISBN 0-913602-53-1). K Roberts.

Seo, Hiroshi. Civil Aircraft of the World. (Illus.). 96p. 1982. 12.95 (ISBN 0-86720-558-X). Jane's Pub Inc.

Smith, J. R. & Kay, Antony. German Aircraft of the Second World War. (Putnam Aeronautical Bks.). (Illus.). 760p. 1979. 32.95 (ISBN 0-370-00024-2, Pub. by the Bodley Head). Merrimack Pub Cir.

Spenser, Jay P. Aeronca C-2: The Story of the Flying Bathtub. LC 78-606098. (Famous Aircraft of the National Air & Space Museum Ser.: No. 2). (Illus.). 72p. 1978. pap. 6.95 (ISBN 0-87474-879-8). Smithsonian.

Stroud, John. Soviet Transport Aircraft Since 1945. (Putnam Aeronautical Bks.). (Illus.). 318p. 1979. 19.95 (ISBN 0-370-00126-5, Pub. by the Bodley Head). Merrimack Pub Cir.

Sutton, Clarence W. Notable Aircraft of the 1930's & How They Were Built, 10 vols. Incl. Vol. I. lib. bdg. 45.00 (ISBN 0-940300-01-X); Vol. II. lib. bdg. 45.00 (ISBN 0-940300-02-8); Vol. III. lib. bdg. 45.00 (ISBN 0-940300-03-6); Vol. IV. lib. bdg. 45.00 (ISBN 0-940300-04-4); Vol. V. lib. bdg. 45.00 (ISBN 0-940300-05-2); Vol. VI. lib. bdg. 45.00 (ISBN 0-940300-06-0); Vol. VII. lib. bdg. 45.00 (ISBN 0-940300-07-9); Vol. VIII. lib. bdg. 45.00 (ISBN 0-940300-08-7); Vol. IX. lib. bdg. 45.00; Vol. X. lib. bdg. 45.00. LC 81-90009. (Illus.). 140p. 1982. lib. bdg. 450.00 (ISBN 0-940300-00-1). Sutton Avn Pr.

Tapper, Oliver. Armstrong Whitworth Aircraft since 1913. (Putnam Aeronautical Books). (Illus.). 398p. 1979. 27.95 (ISBN 0-370-10004-2, Pub. by the Bodley Head). Merrimack Pub Cir.

Underwood, John W. Lightplane Since Nineteen Hundred & Nine. 3rd ed. (Illus.). 1981. pap. 10.95 (ISBN 0-911834-07-9). Aviation.

--Stinsons: Air Pioneers & Aircraft. LC 69-17708. (Illus.). 1976. pap. 9.95 (ISBN 0-911834-06-0, Pub. by Collingwood). Aviation.

--Vintage & Veteran Aircraft Guide. rev. ed. (Illus.). 64p. 1974. pap. 6.95 (ISBN 0-911834-02-8, Pub. by Collinwood). Aviation.

Wagner, William. Ryan Broughams & Their Builders. LC 74-79324. (Illus.). 98p. 1974. pap. 7.50 (ISBN 0-911852-76-X). Hist Aviation.

White, Gay B. The World's First Airline: The St. Peterburg-Tampa Airboat Line, 1914. 2nd ed. 1982. pap. 6.95 (ISBN 0-912522-74-7). Aero-Medical.

AIRPLANES–INSTRUMENTS

see Aeronautical Instruments

AIRPLANES–JET PROPULSION

see also Airplanes–Turbojet Engines

Aviation Mechanic Powerplant Question Book Including Answers, Explanations & References. (Pilot Training Ser.). 202p. 1984. pap. text ed. 6.95 (ISBN 0-89100-273-1, EA-FAA-T-8080-11-C). Aviation Maintenance.

Casamassa, J. V. & Bent, R. D. Jet Aircraft Power Systems. 3rd ed. 1965. text ed. 28.20 (ISBN 0-07-010199-X). McGraw.

Eames, James P. Turbine & Jet-Propelled Aircraft Powerplants. (Illus.). 1954. 5.25 (ISBN 0-910354-06-5). Chartwell.

Hill, Ian & Smith, Terry. Jet '85. (Illus.). 119p. 1985. pap. 7.95 (ISBN 0-941024-11-3, Pub. by AvCom Intl). Aviation.

Hill, Philip G. & Peterson, C. R. Mechanics & Thermodynamics of Propulsion. 1965. 41.95 (ISBN 0-201-02838-7). Addison-Wesley.

AIRPLANES–MAINTENANCE AND REPAIR

see also Flight Engineering

Aircraft Cabin Cleaning & Refurbishing Operations. (Four Hundred Ser.). 1970. pap. 2.00 (ISBN 0-685-58232-9, 410F). Natl Fire Prot.

Aircraft Cleaning, Painting & Paint Removal. (Four Hundred Ser.: No. 230). 1971. pap. 2.00 (ISBN 0-685-58230-2, 401D). Natl Fire Prot.

Aircraft Fuel System Maintenance. (Four Hundred Ser.). 1972. pap. 2.00 (ISBN 0-685-58229-9, 410C). Natl Fire Prot.

Aircraft Oxygen System Maintenance Operations. (Four Hundred Ser.). 1971. pap. 2.00 (ISBN 0-685-58228-0, 410B). Natl Fire Prot.

Aircraft Welding Operations. (Four Hundred Ser). 1970. pap. 2.00 (ISBN 0-685-58231-0, 410E). Natl Fire Prot.

Aviation Maintenance Publishers. Radio Logbook. 64p. 1974. pap. 3.95 (ISBN 0-89100-186-7, EA-ARL-1). Aviation Maintenance.

--Radio Logbook. 64p. 1974. text ed. 4.95 (ISBN 0-89100-195-6, EA-ARL-2). Aviation Maintenance.

Bent, Ralph D. & McKinley, James L. Aircraft Maintenance & Repair. 4th ed. (Aviation Technology Ser.). 1979. pap. text ed. 30.20 (ISBN 0-07-004794-4). McGraw.

Biehler, Fred. Aviation Maintenance Law. 172p. 1976. text ed. 18.95x (ISBN 0-89100-067-4, EA-AML-2). pap. 16.95x (ISBN 0-89100-061-5, EA-AML-1). Aviation Maintenance.

Brink, Randall. Restoring & Flying a Sport Plane on a Budget. (Illus.). 192p. 1982. pap. 8.95 (ISBN 0-8306-2319-1, 2319). TAB Bks.

Christy, Joe. How to Install & Finish Synthetic Aircraft Fabrics. (Modern Aviation Ser.). (Illus.). 1979. 8.95 (ISBN 0-8306-9828-0); pap. 4.95 (ISBN 0-8306-2252-7, 2252). TAB Bks.

--Lightplane Owner's Maintenance Guide. (Modern Aircraft Ser.). 1978. pap. 4.95 (ISBN 0-8306-2244-6, 2244). TAB Bks.

--Refinishing Metal Aircraft. (Modern Aircraft Ser.). (Illus.). 128p. (Orig.). 1980. pap. 4.95 (ISBN 0-8306-2291-8, 2291). TAB Bks.

Crane, Dale. Aircraft Fuel Metering Systems. (Aviation Maintenance Training Course Ser.). (Illus.). 69p. 1975. pap. 5.95 (ISBN 0-89100-057-7, EA-FMS). Aviation Maintenance.

--Aircraft Tires & Tubes. 2nd. ed. (Aviation Technician Training Ser.). (Illus.). 46p. 1980. pap. text ed. 4.95 (ISBN 0-89100-178-6, EA-ATT-2). Aviation Maintenance.

--Aircraft Wheels, Brakes & Antiskid Systems. (Aviation Technician Training Ser.). (Illus.). 61p. 1979. pap. text ed. 5.95 (ISBN 0-89100-099-2, EA-AWB). Aviation Maintenance.

Crane, Dale, et al. Aircraft Technical Dictionary. 2nd ed. (Aviation Maintenance Training Course Ser.). 262p. 1980. pap. 5.95 (ISBN 0-89100-124-7, EA-ATD-2). Aviation Maintenance.

Dzik, Stanley J. Aircraft Hardware Standards Manual & Engineering Reference. (Illus.). 142p. 1971. pap. 12.95 (ISBN 0-87994-012-3). Aviation.

Federal Aviation Administration. A&P Mechanics Airframe Question Book. (Aviation Maintenance Training Course Ser.). (Illus.). 84p. 1984. pap. 2.75 (ISBN 0-89100-274-X, EA-FFA-T-8080-12). Aviation Maintenance.

--A&P Mechanic's Certification Guide. 4th ed. (Aviation Maintenance Training Course Ser.). 64p. 1976. pap. 4.00 (ISBN 0-89100-082-8, EA-AC65-2D). Aviation Maintenance.

--Aviation Mechanics General Question Book. (Aviation Maintenance Training Course Ser.). 60p. 1984. pap. 2.75 (ISBN 0-89100-268-5, EA-FAA-T-8080-10). Aviation Maintenance.

--Federal Aviation Regulations for Aircraft Mechanics. 9th. ed. (Aviation Maintenance Training Course Ser.). 750p. 1985. pap. 14.95 (ISBN 0-89100-278-2, EA-FAR-1J). Aviation Maintenance.

Ford Motor Company, Airplane Division. Ford Tri-Motor Monoplane Instruction Book. Post, Dan R., ed. LC 76-57054. (Illus.). 1977. 12.95 (ISBN 0-911160-71-X). Post-Era.

Heywood, J. E. Light Aircraft Maintenance: A Textbook for Airframe Maintenance. (Illus.). 225p. 1983. pap. 26.50x (ISBN 0-246-11909-8, Pub. by Granada England). Sheridan.

Jones, David & Crane, Dale, eds. Aviation Maintenance Handbook & Standard Hardware Digest. 2nd. ed. 63p. 1975. pap. write for info. (ISBN 0-89100-151-4, EA-AHS-1). Aviation Maintenance.

Mann, J. Y. & Milligan, I. S., eds. Aircraft Fatigue: Design, Operational & Economic Aspects. LC 71-125094. 570p. 1975. 115.00 (ISBN 0-08-017526-0). Pergamon.

Merrill, Samuel W., compiled by. Regulations for Aircraft Maintenance. rev. ed. 1981. pap. 10.50x (ISBN 0-685-69727-4). Intermtn Air.

Reithmaier, Larry. Aircraft Mechanic's Shop Manual. new ed. LC 78-25800. (Illus.). 1979. pap. 11.95 (ISBN 0-932882-00-5). Palomar Bks.

Reithmaier, Larry, ed. Aircraft Mechanics Digest. LC 81-22593. (Illus.). 1982. pap. 6.95 (ISBN 0-932882-03-X). Palomar Bks.

Reithmaier, Larry, compiled by. Aircraft Repair Manual. 320p. 1981. pap. 10.95 (ISBN 0-932882-02-1). Palomar Bks.

Schutz, Noel W., Jr. & Derwing, Bruce L. Essentials of Aviation Technology: Aviation Mechanics. LC 80-51692. (The ALA ESP Ser.). (Illus.). xii, 180p. (Orig.). 1980. pap. text ed. 10.00x (ISBN 0-934270-10-4). Am Lang Acad.

Silitch, Nicholas E. Make Your Airplane Last Forever. (Illus.). 160p. 1982. pap. 10.95 (ISBN 0-8306-2328-0, 2328). TAB Bks.

Standard on Aircraft Maintenance. 84p. 3.75 (ISBN 0-686-68288-2). Natl Fire Prot.

Thomas, Kas. Light Plane Maintenance Aircraft Engine Operating Guide. Date not set. pap. 24.95 (ISBN 0-9615196-0-6). Belvoir Pubns.

--Personal Aircraft Maintenance. (Aviation Ser.). (Illus.). 256p. 1980. 26.50 (ISBN 0-07-064241-9). McGraw.

AIRPLANES–MATERIALS

see also Light Metals

Application of Composite Materials - STP 524. 191p. 1973. 30.75 (ISBN 0-8031-0115-5, 04-524000-33). ASTM.

Otte, H. M. & Locke, S. R., eds. Materials Science Research Series, Vol. 2. LC 63-17645. 319p. 1965. 39.50x (ISBN 0-306-38502-3, Plenum Pr). Plenum Pub.

AIRPLANES–MODELS

Beckman, Bob. Building & Flying Giant Scale Radio Control Aircraft. Angle, Burr, ed. (Illus.). 88p. (Orig.). 1983. pap. 9.95 (ISBN 0-89024-049-3). Kalmbach.

Bingelis, Tony. The Sportplane Builder. rev. ed. Rivers, David A., ed. (Illus.). 320p. 1980. pap. 17.95x (ISBN 0-911721-84-3, Pub. by Bingelis). Aviation.

Boddington, David. Building & Flying Radio-Controlled Model Aircraft. (Illus.). 227p. 1985. pap. 11.95 (ISBN 0-85242-790-5, Pub. by Argus). Aztex.

--Scale Model Aircraft Radio Control. (Illus.). 300p. (Orig.). 1984. pap. 19.95 (ISBN 0-85242-810-3, Pub. by ARGUS). Aztex.

Fisher, O. Collector's Guide to Model Aero Engines. (Illus.). 132p. 1985. pap. 7.95 (ISBN 0-85242-492-2, Pub. by Argus). Aztex.

Hampton, C. W. & Clifford, E. Planecraft. LC 79-57129. (Illus.). 1982. pap. 6.95 (ISBN 0-918036-00-3). Woodcraft Supply.

Harlem, Peter W. The UH-1C Huey. LC 85-70918. (Crewchief Ser.: No. 1). (Illus.). 56p. (Orig.). 1985. pap. 6.50 (ISBN 0-933907-00-1, CE-1). Cobra Co.

Hartill, William R., ed. World Free Flight Review. LC 78-64742. (Illus.). 1978. 30.00 (ISBN 0-933066-01-5). World Free Flight.

Lopshire, Robert. Radio Control Miniature Aircraft. LC 73-7355. (Illus.). 192p. 1974. pap. 9.95 (ISBN 0-02-080550-0, Collier). Macmillan.

Markham, Hugh. Scale Model Aircraft from Vac-Form Kits. 1980. 10.00x (ISBN 0-905418-34-4, Pub. by Gresham England). State Mutual Bk.
Musciano, Walter A. Building Flying Scale Model Aircraft. LC 73-77841. (Illus.). 256p. 1973. pap. 4.95 (ISBN 0-668-02994-3). Arco.
Poling, Mitch. Building & Flying Electric-Powered Model Aircraft. Angle, Burr, ed. (Illus.). 76p. (Orig.). 1984. pap. 9.95 (ISBN 0-89024-050-7). Kalmbach.
Sarpolus, Dick. Building & Flying Control-Line Model Aircraft. Angle, Burr, ed. (Illus.). 64p. (Orig.). 1984. pap. 7.95 (ISBN 0-89024-051-5). Kalmbach.
Schleicher, Robert. Building & Displaying Model Aircraft. LC 80-70385. 176p. 1981. pap. 10.95 (ISBN 0-8019-6949-2). Chilton.
Schleicher, Robert & Barr, James R. Building & Flying Model Aircraft. LC 79-8312. (Illus.). 192p. 1980. 14.95 (ISBN 0-8019-6903-4); pap. 10.95 (ISBN 0-8019-6904-2). Chilton.
Schroeder, Arthur F., Jr., ed. Giant Steps: A Book of Giant Radio Control Aircraft. (Illus.). 144p. (Orig.). 1982. pap. text ed. 12.95 (ISBN 0-911295-00-3). Air Age.
Staszak, E. R. Building & Improving Vacuum-Formed Model Aircraft. Angle, Burr, ed. (Illus.). 52p. (Orig.). 1984. pap. 6.95 (ISBN 0-89024-047-7). Kalmbach.
Woodason, V. J. Scale Model Aircraft in Wood. 64p. 1980. 10.00x (ISBN 0-905418-27-1, Pub. by Gresham England). State Mutual Bk.

AIRPLANES–MOTORS

see also Airplanes–Jet Propulsion; Flight Engineering

Aviation Maintenance Publishers. Engine Logbook. 74p. 1975. pap. 4.95 (ISBN 0-89100-187-5, EA-EFL-1). Aviation Maintenance.
Aviation Mechanic Powerplant Question Book Including Answers, Explanations & References. (Pilot Training Ser.). 202p. 1984. pap. text ed. 6.95 (ISBN 0-89100-273-1, EA-FAA-T-8080-11-C). Aviation Maintenance.
Bent, R. & McKinley, J. Aircraft Powerplants. 5th ed. 608p. 1985. 28.95 (ISBN 0-07-004797-9). McGraw.
Bent, Ralph D. & McKinley, James L. Aircraft Powerplants. 4th ed. Orig. Title: Powerplants for Aerospace Vehicles. (Illus.). 1978. 30.20 (ISBN 0-07-004792-8). McGraw.
Christy, Joe. Engines for Homebuilt Aircraft & Ultralights. (Illus.). 112p. 1984. pap. 8.95 (ISBN 0-8306-2347-7, 2347). TAB Bks.
--Maintenance-Overhaul Guide to Lycoming Aircraft Engines. (Modern Aviation Ser.). (Illus.). 128p. 1980. 9.95 (ISBN 0-8306-9733-0, 2277). TAB Bks.
Crane, Dale. Aircraft Reciprocating Engines. (Illus.). 113p. 1979. pap. 5.95 (ISBN 0-89100-075-5, EA-ARE). Aviation Maint.
Gentry, Everett. All about Stalls & Spins. (Illus.). 144p. (Orig.). 1983. pap. 9.95 (ISBN 0-8306-2349-3, 2349). TAB Bks.
Ground Training for the Private Pilot Licence, No. 3: Principles of Flight, Airframes & Aero Engines, Aircraft Airworthiness & Aircraft Instruments. 264p. 1981. pap. 18.00x (ISBN 0-246-11700-1, Pub. by Granada England). Sheridan.
Guide to Pre Nineteen Thirty Aircraft Engines. (Illus.). 60p. 1973. pap. 4.50 (ISBN 0-87994-016-6). Aviat Pub.
Merrill, Samuel W. Fluid Power for Aircraft: Modern Hydraulic Technology. 3rd ed. 1974. pap. 11.75x (ISBN 0-914680-01-3). Intermtn Air.
Nelson, John L. Lightplane Engines. 2nd ed. (Illus.). 144p. 1982. pap. 5.95 (ISBN 0-8306-2323-X, 2323). TAB Bks.
Rice, Michael S. Guide to Pre-Nineteen Thirty Aircraft Engines. 60p. 1972. pap. 4.50 (ISBN 0-87994-016-6, Pub. by AvPubns). Aviation.
Smith, Herschel. Aircraft Piston Engines: From the Manly Baltzer to the Continental Tiara. (Aviation Ser.). (Illus.). 264p. 1981. 28.95 (ISBN 0-07-058472-9). McGraw.
Thomas, Kas. Light Plane Maintenance Aircraft Engine Operating Guide. Date not set. pap. 24.95 (ISBN 0-9615196-0-6). Belvoir Pubns.
The Ultralight Engine Log. 1981. leatherette 3.95 (ISBN 0-317-01151-0, E-1). Ultralight Pubns.
Wilkinson, Paul H. Aircraft Engines of the World: 1970. LC 41-13397. 1970. 27.50x (ISBN 0-911710-24-8). Wilkinson.
Wilkinson, Paul H., ed. Aircraft Engines of the World: 1964-65. LC 41-13397. 1964-65. 25.00x (ISBN 0-685-44095-8). Wilkinson.
--Aircraft Engines of the World: 1966-67. LC 41-13397. 1966-67. 25.00x (ISBN 0-685-44094-X). Wilkinson.

AIRPLANES–NOISE

Civil Aviation Authority, ed. Aircraft Noise & Sleep Disturbance: A Description of the Noise Measurement & Analysis Programme for the Main Phase of the Study. 1980. 35.00x (ISBN 0-686-79160-6, Pub. by Civil Aviation England). State Mutual Bk.

AIRPLANES–PILOTING

see also Flight Simulators; Flight Training; Instrument Flying

Advanced Pilot Manual. 1st ed. (Pilot Training Ser.). (Illus.). 480p. 1981. text ed. 24.49 (ISBN 0-88487-068-5, JS314298). Jeppesen Sanderson.
Airline Transport Rating Course. (Pilot Training Ser.). (Illus.). 310p. 1981. 3-ring binder 64.95 (ISBN 0-88487-073-1, JS304127). Jeppesen Sanderson.
At Last We Can Fly. (Illus.). 1974. pap. 3.95 (ISBN 0-87994-014-X). Aviat Pub.
Baxter, Gordon. How to Fly. (Illus.). 224p. 1981. 12.95 (ISBN 0-671-44801-3). Summit Bks.
Bellomo, Chas & Lynch, John. Crash, Fire & Rescue Handbook. (Pilot Training Ser.). 94p. (Orig.). 1984. pap. text ed. 8.95 (ISBN 0-89100-250-2, EA-250-2). Aviation Maintenance.
Bergman, Jules. Anyone Can Fly. rev. ed. LC 73-9141. 1977. 19.95 (ISBN 0-385-02830-X). Doubleday.
Birch, N. H. & Bramson, A. E. The Pilot's Guide to Flight Emergency Procedures. LC 77-91556. (Illus.). 1978. 7.95 (ISBN 0-385-13544-0). Doubleday.
Borotto, A. V. Basic Flight Operations & Air Traffic Procedures for Pilots. LC 78-64346. 209p. 1978. pap. 9.95 (ISBN 0-87762-258-2). Technomic.
Bramson, Alan. Be a Better Pilot. LC 80-13401. (Illus.). 256p. 1980. 11.95 (ISBN 0-668-04901-4, 4901-4). Arco.
Breise, Frederic H. Fifty Years of Aviation Knowledge. 108p. 1981. 12.00 (ISBN 0-938576-00-3). F H Breise.
Brown, Harold N. Pilot's Aeromedical Guide. (Modern Aviation Ser.). (Illus.). 64p. (Orig.). 1980. pap. 3.95 (ISBN 0-8306-2287-X, 2287). TAB Bks.
Cambell, Ron & Jones, John. Microlight Flying Manual. 240p. 1982. pap. 19.50x (ISBN 0-246-11914-4, Pub. by Granada England). Sheridan.
Campbell, Ron & Hall, Joss. PPL Revision: Twelve Hundred Questions & Answers for the Private Pilot. 200p. 1982. pap. cancelled (ISBN 0-246-11882-2, Pub. by Granada England). Sheridan.
Canadian Private Pilot Manual. (Pilot Training Ser.). (Illus.). 428p. 1981. pap. text ed. 19.95 (ISBN 0-88487-074-X, JS314131). Jeppesen Sanderson.
Cessna Aircraft Co. Cessna, 1977 Model, 150 "Commuter" Pilot's Operating Handbook. (Illus.). 1977. pap. 15.00x (ISBN 0-911720-50-2, Cessna). Aviation.
--Cessna 1977 Model, 172 "Skyhawk" Pilot's Operating Handbook. pap. 15.00x (ISBN 0-911720-44-8, Cessna). Aviation.
Cole, Duane. Happy Flying, Safely. LC 77-79892. (Illus.). 1977. pap. 6.95x (ISBN 0-911721-19-3, Pub. by Cole). Aviation.
Coleman, John E. Flight Instructor: Questions, Answers, Explanations. rev. ed. (Illus.). 220p. 1985. pap. text ed. 12.95 (ISBN 0-941272-23-0). Astro Pubs.
Conway, Carle. The Joy of Soaring: A Training Manual. LC 73-98038. (Illus.). 134p. 1969. 17.00 (ISBN 0-911720-54-5, Pub. by Soaring). Aviation.
Delp, Frank. Commercial Pilot Question Book Including Answers, Explanations, & References. rev. ed. (Pilot Training Ser.). 475p. 1985. pap. text ed. 12.95 (ISBN 0-89100-261-8, EA-FAA-T-8080-2C). Aviation Maintenance.
Doberstein, Dick. Navigation Made Easy for Pilots. (Illus.). 98p. 1976. pap. text ed. 5.95x (ISBN 0-685-55701-4, Pub. by Simplified). Aviation.
Dole, Charles E. Flight Theory for Pilots. (Illus.). 244p. 1984. pap. 9.95 (ISBN 0-9614216-0-6). Aviation.
Dwyer, James. The Private Pilot's Blue Book. 1979. Repr. of 1977 ed. 9.95 (ISBN 0-8128-2146-7). Stein & Day.
Ethell, Jeffrey L. Moving Up to Twin-Engine Airplanes. (Illus.). 1979. 8.95 (ISBN 0-8306-9790-X); pap. 4.95 (ISBN 0-8306-2270-5, 2270). TAB Bks.
Federal Aviation Administration. Aviation Instructor's Handbook (AC-60-14) 1977. pap. text ed. 6.00 (ISBN 0-86677-017-8, Pub. by Cooper Aviation). Aviation.
--Commercial Pilot Question Book. (Pilot Training Ser.). (Illus.). 228p. 1984. pap. 6.50 (ISBN 0-89100-260-X, EA-FAA-T-8080-2). Aviation Maintenance.
--Flight Instructor Practical Test Guide (AC 61-58A) 1979. pap. 1.75 (ISBN 0-86677-011-9, Pub. by Cooper Aviation). Aviation.
--Flight Instructor Question Book. (Pilot Training Ser.). (Illus.). 150p. 1984. pap. 5.50 (ISBN 0-89100-262-6, EA-FAA-T-8080-3). Aviation Maintenance.
--Flight Test Guide, Instrument, Airplane AC 61-56A) 1976. pap. text ed. 1.75 (ISBN 0-86677-009-7, Pub. by Cooper Aviation). Aviation.
--Flight Training Handbook. LC 80-70552. (Illus.). 352p. 1981. 15.95 (ISBN 0-385-17599-X). Doubleday.
--Private Pilot Question Book. (Pilot Training Ser.). (Illus.). 138p. 1984. pap. 5.00 (ISBN 0-89100-258-8, EA-FAA-T-8080-1). Aviation Maintenance.
--Private Pilot Question Book & References. (Pilot Training Ser.). (Illus.). 234p. 1984. pap. 9.95 (ISBN 0-89100-259-6, EA-FAA-T-8080-1C). Aviation Maintenance.
--Student Pilot Guide (AC 61-12J) 1979. pap. text ed. 3.95 (ISBN 0-939158-05-1, Pub. by Natl Flightshops). Aviation.
--VFR Pilot Exam-O-Grams. Aviation Book Company Staff, ed. (Illus.). 120p. 1982. pap. 3.50 (ISBN 0-911721-78-9). Aviation.
Federal Aviation Administration & Aviation Book Company Editors. IFR Pilot Exam-O-Grams. (Illus.). 96p. 1984. pap. 3.25 (ISBN 0-911721-79-7). Aviation.
Federal Aviation Administration, Department of Transportation. Commercial Pilot Question Book. (Illus.). 236p. (Orig.). 1985. pap. text ed. 6.50 (ISBN 0-317-31554-4). Astro Pubs.
Federal Aviation Administration, Dept. of Transportation. Private Pilot-Airplane: Practical Test Standards for Airplane, Single-Engine, Land. 118p. (Orig.). 1984. pap. text ed. 4.95 (ISBN 0-941272-25-7). Astro Pubs.
Federal Aviation Administration of the U.S. Dept of Transportation. Instrument Flying Handbook (AC 61-27c) (Illus.). 272p. 1983. pap. 8.50 (ISBN 0-911721-96-7). Aviation.
Federal Aviation Administration Staff. Federal Aviation Regulations for Pilots, 1985. 9th ed. Winner, Walter P., ed. 216p. 1985. pap. 4.95 (ISBN 0-911721-99-1). Aviation.
--Private Pilot: Practical Test Standards for Airplane, Single-Engine, Land. 112p. 1984. pap. 3.95 (ISBN 0-916413-01-2). Aviation.
Flight Instructor Manual. 1st ed. (Pilot Training Ser.). (Illus.). 240p. 1981. pap. text ed. 14.95 (ISBN 0-88487-066-9, JS314126). Jeppesen Sanderson.
Flight Instructor Practical Test Guide. (Federal Aviation Administration Ser.). 17p. 1975. pap. text ed. 3.50 (ISBN 0-89100-175-1, EA-AC61-58A). Aviation Maintenance.
Foster, Timothy R. How to Become an Airline Pilot. (Illus.). 192p. 1982. pap. 10.95 (ISBN 0-8306-2308-6, 2308). TAB Bks.
Fowler, Ron. Making Perfect Landings in Light Airplanes. (Illus.). 128p. 1984. 12.95 (ISBN 0-8138-1081-7). Iowa St U Pr.
Frazier, David A. How to Master Precision Flight. (Illus.). 60p. (Orig.). 1984. pap. 9.95 (ISBN 0-8306-2354-X, 2354). TAB Bks.
Fundamentals of Instructing & Ground Instructor Basic-Advanced Question Book. (Pilot Training Ser.). 108p. 1984. pap. text ed. 4.25 (ISBN 0-89100-264-2, EA-FAA-T-8080-4). Aviation Maintenance.
Gallagher, Thomas B. Private Pilot Written Exam Course. LC 80-70132. (Illus.). 68p. (Orig.). 1981. pap. 19.95 (ISBN 0-938706-00-4). Fed Aviation.
Garrison, Paul. Night-Flying in Single-Engine Airplanes. (Illus.). 1979. 8.95 (ISBN 0-8306-9789-6); pap. 5.95 (ISBN 0-8306-2266-7, 2266). TAB Bks.
Garrison, Peter. Flying Airplanes: The First Hundred Hours. Parke, Robert B., ed. LC 80-7476. (Illus.). 240p. 1980. 11.95 (ISBN 0-385-14594-2). Doubleday.
Glaeser, et al. Invitation to Fly. 2nd ed. 640p. 1985. write for info. (ISBN 0-534-04800-5). Wadsworth Pub.
Goldstein, Avram. IFR Principles & Practice. (Illus.). 1978. pap. 6.50 (ISBN 0-911720-93-6). Aviation.
Griffin, Jeff W. Passing Your Instrument Pilot's Written Exam. (Modern Aviation Ser.). (Illus.). 1979. 7.95 (ISBN 0-8306-9818-3); pap. 4.95 (ISBN 0-8306-2255-1). TAB Bks.
Ground Studies for Pilots, Vol. 2: Plotting & Flight Planning. 3rd ed. 144p. 1979. 19.95x (ISBN 0-246-11176-3, Pub. by Granada England). Sheridan.
Ground Training for the Private Pilot Licence, No. 1: Air Legislation, Aviation Law, Flight Rules & Procedure. 182p. 1985. pap. 20.00x (ISBN 0-00-383112-4, Pub. by collins England). Sheridan.
Hoyt, John R. As the Pro Flies. (Illus.). 1959. 14.95 (ISBN 0-07-030610-9). McGraw.
Imeson, Sparky. Mountain Flying. (Illus.). 246p. 1982. pap. 7.50 (ISBN 0-911721-22-3, Pub. by Airguide). Aviation.
Instrument-Pilot-Airplane Flight Test Guide. (Pilot Training Ser.). 23p. 1976. pap. text ed. 3.75 (ISBN 0-89100-173-5, EA-AC61-56A). Aviation Maintenance.
Langewiesche, Wolfgang. Stick & Rudder. (Illus.). 1944. 16.95 (ISBN 0-07-036240-8). McGraw.
Larson, George C. Fly on Instruments. LC 79-7602. (Illus.). 240p. 1980. 12.95 (ISBN 0-385-14619-1). Doubleday.
Middlekauf, Dana & Horowitz, Milton. Instrument Rating Question Book Including Answers, Explanations, & References. rev. ed. (Pilot Training Ser.). 450p. 1984. pap. text ed. 12.95 (ISBN 0-89100-267-7, EA-FAA-T-8080-7C). Aviation Maintenance.
Multi-Engine Pilot Manual. 1st ed. (Pilot Training Ser.). (Illus.). 128p. 1981. pap. text ed. 16.95 (ISBN 0-88487-070-7, JS314127). Jeppesen Sanderson.
Newton, Dennis W. Severe Weather Flying. (McGraw-Hill Aviation Ser.). (Illus.). 160p. 1983. 26.50 (ISBN 0-07-046402-2). McGraw.
Ogilvy, David. Flying Light Aircraft. 2nd ed. (Illus.). 224p. 1979. 20.00 (ISBN 0-7136-1854-X). Transatlantic.
Private & Commercial Pilot Helicopter Flight Test Guide. (Pilot Training Ser.). 37p. 1977. 4.50 (ISBN 0-89100-176-X, EA-AC61-59A). Aviation Maintenance.
Private Pilot Course. (Pilot Training Ser.). (Illus.). 408p. 1983. 3-ring binder 39.95 (ISBN 0-88487-071-5, JS304197). Jeppesen Sanderson.
Private Pilot Manual. (Pilot Training Ser.). (Illus.). 400p. 1983. text ed. 20.95 (ISBN 0-88487-081-2, JS314301). Jeppesen Sanderson.
Private Pilot Manuevers Manual. (Pilot Training Ser.). (Illus.). 210p. 1982. pap. text ed. 9.95 (ISBN 0-88487-082-0, JS314302). Jeppesen Sanderson.
Professional Instrument Courses, Inc. & Dogan, Peter. Instrument Flight Training Manual. (Illus.). 208p. 1985. pap. 16.95t (ISBN 0-916413-02-0). Aviation.
Quirk, Ronald E. Night Flying for Private Pilots. LC 65-24311. (Illus.). 1965. pap. 2.00 (ISBN 0-911720-61-8, Pub. by Greater NY). Aviation.
Rice, Michael C., ed. Pilot's Manual for the Bell P-63 King Cobra. (Illus.). 1976. pap. 7.95 (ISBN 0-87994-036-0). Aviation.
Rice, Michael S. Pilot's Manual for deHavilland Mosquito. (Illus.). 56p. 1974. pap. 3.95 (ISBN 0-87994-027-1, Pub. by AvPubns). Aviation.
Smith, Robert T. How to Fly Lightplanes. (Illus.). 1979. 8.95 (ISBN 0-8306-9780-2); pap. 4.95 (ISBN 0-8306-2260-8, 2260). TAB Bks.
--Passing Your Flight Instructor Flight Test. (Modern Aircraft Ser.). (Illus.). 1978. 8.95 (ISBN 0-8306-9903-1); pap. 5.95 (ISBN 0-8306-2245-4, 2245). TAB Bks.
Stewart, Stanley. Flying the Big Jets. (Illus.). 288p. 1985. 16.95 (ISBN 0-668-06346-7). Arco.
Tannehill, Victor C. Martin Marauder Pilot's Flight Operating Instructions B-26. LC 81-67414. (Illus.). 72p. 1981. 7.95 (ISBN 0-9605900-1-3). Boomerang.
Taylor & Parmar. Ground Studies for Pilots, Vol. 1: Radio Aids. 3rd ed. 208p. 1979. 22.50x (ISBN 0-246-11169-0, Pub. by Granada England). Sheridan.
Type Rating Airplane Flight Test Guide. (Pilot Training Ser.). 29p. 1975. 4.25 (ISBN 0-89100-174-3, EA-AC61-57A). Aviation Maintenance.
The Ultralight Aircraft Log. 1981. leatherette 3.95 (ISBN 0-317-01150-2, A-1). Ultralight Pubns.
The Ultralight Pilot Flight Log. 1981. leatherette 3.95 (ISBN 0-317-01149-9, P-1). Ultralight Pubns.
Webb, Jim. Fly the Wing. 1971. pap. 15.50 (ISBN 0-8138-0545-7). Iowa St U Pr.

AIRPLANES–PILOTS

see Air Pilots

AIRPLANES–PROPELLERS

see Propellers, Aerial

AIRPLANES–RECOGNITION

Munson, Kenneth. American Aircraft of World War Two in Color. (Illus.). 160p. 1982. 19.95 (ISBN 0-7137-0944-8, Pub. by Blandford Pr England). Sterling.
Rice, Michael S. World War Two International Aircraft Recognition Guide. (Illus.). pap. 6.95 (ISBN 0-87994-017-4, Pub. by AvPubns). Aviation.
Thorpe, Donald W. Japanese Army Air Force Camouflage & Markings, World War II. Oishi, Yasuo, tr. LC 68-54880. (Illus.). 1968. pap. 11.95 (ISBN 0-8168-6579-5). Aero.
Wood, Derek. Jane's World Aircraft Recognition Handbook. (Illus.). 512p. 1982. 12.95 (ISBN 0-86720-636-5). Jane's Pub Inc.

AIRPLANES–SAFETY MEASURES

see Aeronautics–Safety Measures

AIRPLANES–STABILITY

see Stability of Airplanes

AIRPLANES–STRESSES

see Airframes

AIRPLANES–STRUCTURES

see Airframes

AIRPLANES–TURBOJET ENGINES

Adams, Harry & Simpson, R. W. Propjet '85. (Illus.). 148p. 1985. pap. 7.95 (ISBN 0-941024-10-5, Pub. by AvCom Intl). Aviation.

Aviation Mechanic Powerplant Question Book Including Answers, Explanations & References. (Pilot Training Ser.). 202p. 1984. pap. text ed. 6.95 (ISBN 0-89100-273-1, EA-FAA-T-8080-11-C). Aviation Maintenance.
Constant, Edward W., II. The Origins of the Turbojet Revolution. LC 80-11802. (JH Studies in the History of Technology). 328p. 1981. 29.50x (ISBN 0-8018-2222-X). Johns Hopkins.
Garrison, Paul. Aircraft Turbocharging. (Illus.). 144p. 1982. pap. 5.95 (ISBN 0-8306-2306-X, 2306). TAB Bks.
Hawthorne, William R. & Olson, W. T., eds. Design & Performance of Gas Turbine Power Plants. (High Speed Aerodynamics & Jet Propulsion, Vol. 11). 1960. 60.00 (ISBN 0-691-07942-0). Princeton U Pr.
Otis, Charles E. Aircraft Gas Turbine Powerplants. (Aviation Technician Training Course Ser.). (Illus.). 202p. 1979. pap. text ed. 8.95 (ISBN 0-89100-095-X, EA-TEP-1); wkbk. 7.95 (ISBN 0-89100-105-0, EA-ATE-1). Aviation Maintenance.
Treager, Irwin. Aircraft Gas Turbine Engine Technology. 2nd ed. (Illus.). 1978. pap. text ed. 34.55 (ISBN 0-07-065158-2). McGraw.
Whittle, Frank. Gas Turbine Aero-Thermodynamics: With Special Reference to Aircraft Propulsion. LC 80-41372. 240p. 1981. 35.00 (ISBN 0-08-026719-X); pap. 19.75 (ISBN 0-08-026718-1). Pergamon.

AIRPLANES–VIBRATION
see Vibration (Aeronautics)

AIRPLANES–WINGS
Abbott, Ira H. & Von Doenhoff, Albert E. Theory of Wing Sections: Including a Summary of Airfoil Data. (Illus.). 1949. pap. 9.95 (ISBN 0-486-60586-8). Dover.
Belotserkovskii, Sergei M. Theory of Thin Wings in Subsonic Flow. LC 67-17189. 250p. 1967. 30.00x (ISBN 0-306-30291-8, Plenum Pr). Plenum Pub.
Carafoli, E. Wing Theory in Supersonic Flow. 1969. 105.00 (ISBN 0-08-012330-9). Pergamon.
Cohen, Doris & Jones, Robert T. High Speed Wing Theory. (Aeronautical Paperbacks Ser.: Vol. 6). (Orig.). 1960. pap. 20.00 (ISBN 0-691-07975-7). Princeton U Pr.
Rice, M. S. Handbook of Airfoil Sections for Light Aircraft. LC 71-182597. (Illus.). 144p. 1972. pap. 8.95 spiral bdg. (ISBN 0-87994-015-8). Aviation.
Robinson, Abraham & Laurmann, J. A. Wing Theory. LC 57-601. (Cambridge Aeronautical Ser.: No. 2). pap. 144.80 (ISBN 0-317-10805-0, 2051692). Bks Demand UMI.

AIRPLANES, COMPANY
Corporate Aviation Safety Seminar. Safety in the Terminal Environment: Proceedings, 23rd Annual Meeting, April 9-12, 1978, Arlington Va. pap. 33.50 (ISBN 0-317-10145-5, 2010339). Bks Demand UMI.
Hansen, Paul E. Business Flying: The Profitable Use of Personal Aircraft. (Illus.). 288p. 1982. 22.50 (ISBN 0-07-026071-0). McGraw.
Taylor, John W. & Swanborough, Gordon. Civil Aircraft of the World. 3rd. ed. LC 77-74718. (Illus.). 1978. Encore ed. 9.95 (ISBN 0-684-15224-X, ScribT). Scribner.

AIRPLANES, JET PROPELLED
see Airplanes–Jet Propulsion; Jet Planes

AIRPLANES, MILITARY
see also Bombers; Fighter Planes; Jet Planes, Military
Angelucci, Enzo & Matricardi, Paolo. World Aircraft: Military, 1945-1960. (Illus.). 1980. pap. 7.95 (ISBN 0-528-88205-8). Rand.
The B-24 Liberator. (Illus.). 16p. 1977. pap. 10.95 (ISBN 0-87994-000-X). Aviat Pub.
Beaman, John. Messerschmitt BF 109 in Action, Part 2. (Illus.). 58p. 1983. 4.95. Squad Sig Pubns.
Bell P-39 Airacobra. (Illus.). 48p. 1974. pap. 6.95 (ISBN 0-87994-024-7). Aviat Pub.
The Bell P-63 Kingcobra. (Illus.). 52p. 1974. pap. 7.95 (ISBN 0-87994-036-0). Aviat Pub.
The Boeing B-17 Flying Fortress. (Illus.). 108p. 1974. pap. 8.95 (ISBN 0-87994-037-9). Aviat Pub.
Bowyer, Chaz. Surviving World War Two Aircraft. (Illus.). 64p. 1981. pap. 5.50 (ISBN 0-7134-2363-3, Pub. by Batsford England). David & Charles.
Boyne, Walter J. The Messerschmitt ME 262: Arrow to the Future. LC 80-607090. (Illus.). 192p. (Orig.). 1980. 19.95 (ISBN 0-87474-276-5); pap. 10.95 (ISBN 0-87474-275-7). Smithsonian.
Chance Vought F4U Corsair. (Illus.). 67p. 1973. pap. 7.95 (ISBN 0-87994-026-3). Aviat Pub.
Close-up Five Taifun. LC 75-22941. 6.95 (ISBN 0-914144-05-7). Monogram Aviation.
Close-up Four Buzz Bomb. LC 75-22940. 6.95 (ISBN 0-914144-04-9). Monogram Aviation.
Close-up Fourteen-Japanese Cockpit Interiors Part 1. LC 76-6214. 6.95 (ISBN 0-914144-14-6). Monogram Aviation.
Close-up Nineteen-NIKKA. LC 79-89872. 1978. 6.95 (ISBN 0-914144-19-7). Monogram Aviation.
Close-up Six-Gustav Part 1. LC 75-22942. 6.95 (ISBN 0-914144-06-5). Monogram Aviation.
Close-up Sixteen-ME One Hundred & Nine K. LC 79-89871. 6.95 (ISBN 0-914144-16-2). Monogram Aviation.
Curtiss OX-5 Aeronautical Engine. (Illus.). 20p. 1973. pap. 3.00 (ISBN 0-87994-039-5). Aviat Pub.
Curtiss P-40 Warhawk. (Illus.). 36p. 1974. pap. 6.95 (ISBN 0-87994-018-2). Aviat Pub.
The Curtiss Standard JN4-D-Jenny. (Illus.). 76p. 1973. pap. 6.95 (ISBN 0-87994-013-1). Aviat Pub.
DeHavilland Mosquito. (Illus.). 46p. 1974. pap. 3.95 (ISBN 0-87994-027-1). Aviat Pub.
Doll, Thomas E. Flying Leathernecks in World War Two. LC 79-123469. (Aero Pictorial Ser.: Vol. 4). (Illus., Orig.). 1971. pap. 4.95 (ISBN 0-8168-0312-9). Aero.
Drendel, Lou. Aircraft of the Vietnam War. LC 79-113405. (Famous Aircraft Ser.). (Illus.). 64p. 1980. pap. 6.95 (ISBN 0-8168-5651-6). Aero.
--HUEY. (Modern Military Aircraft Ser.: No. 5001). (Illus.). 64p. 1983. saddlestitch 6.95 (ISBN 0-89747-145-8). Squad Sig Pubns.
--SR-71 Blackbird in Action. (Illus.). 50p. 1982. 4.95 (ISBN 0-89747-136-9, 1055). Squad Sig Pubns.
Ellis, Paul. Aircraft of the Royal Navy. (Illus.). 192p. 1982. 17.95 (ISBN 0-86720-556-3). Jane's Pub Inc.
The F-82 Twin Mustang. (Illus.). 66p. 1973. pap. 7.95 (ISBN 0-87994-035-2). Aviat Pub.
Feuchtwanger, E. J. & Mason, R. A. Air Power in the Next Generation. 1979. text ed. 26.50x (ISBN 0-333-23609-2). Humanities.
The Flying Wings of Northrop. (Illus.). 100p. 1975. pap. 7.95 (ISBN 0-87994-031-X). Aviat Pub.
The Ford Trimotor. (Illus.). 120p. 1974. pap. 6.95 (ISBN 0-87994-023-9). Aviat Pub.
Freeman, Christopher J. Encyclopedia of World Air Power. (Illus.). 1980. 19.95 (ISBN 0-517-53754-0, Pub. by Crescent). Outlet Bk Co.
Ginter, Steve & Picciani, Ron. North American FJ-1 Fury. (Naval Fighter Ser.: No. 7). (Illus.). 1983. pap. 5.50 (ISBN 0-942612-07-8). Aviation.
Green, William & Swanborough, Gordon. The Observer's Directory of Military Aircraft. LC 82-71835. (Illus.). 256p. 1983. 16.95 (ISBN 0-668-05649-5, 5649). Arco.
The Grumman F6F "Hellcat". (Illus.). 60p. 1973. pap. 7.95 (ISBN 0-87994-033-6). Aviat Pub.
The Grumman Wildcat. (Illus.). 63p. 1978. pap. 10.95 (ISBN 0-87994-099-9). Aviat Pub.
Guide to Antogyros. 1984. write for info. Aviation.
Gunston, Bill. An Illustrated Guide to Spyplanes & Electronic Warfare Aircraft. LC 83-2809. (Illustrated Military Guides Ser.). (Illus.). 160p. 1983. 9.95 (ISBN 0-668-05825-0). Arco.
The Hawker Hurricane. (Illus.). 40p. 1974. pap. 3.95 (ISBN 0-87994-030-1). Aviat Pub.
Higham, Robin & Williams, Carol, eds. Flying Combat Aircraft of the USAAF-USAF, Vol. 2. (Illus.). 1978. 13.95 (ISBN 0-8138-0375-6). Iowa St U Pr.
Jane's Pocket Books. Jane's Pocket Book of Light Aircraft. Taylor, John, ed. (Jane's Pocket Books: Vol.6). (Illus.). 264p. 1975. pap. 5.95 (ISBN 0-02-080390-7, Collier). Macmillan.
Jet Planes of the Third Reich. LC 81-84360. 1982. 49.95 (ISBN 0-914144-27-8). Monogram Aviation.
Kilduff, Peter. Douglas A-4 Skyhawk. (Illus.). 200p. 1983. 19.95 (ISBN 0-85045-529-4, Pub. by Osprey England). Motorbooks Intl.
King, H. F. Sopwith Aircraft Nineteen Twelve to Nineteen Twenty. (Illus.). 320p. 1981. 36.00 (ISBN 0-370-30050-5, Pub. by the Bodley Head). Merrimack Pub Cir.
Linn, Don. Harrier in Action. (Illus.). 50p. 1982. 4.95 (ISBN 0-89747-139-3). Squad Sig Pubns.
--U. S. Naval & Marine Aircraft Today. (Warbirds Illustrated Ser.). (Illus.). 72p. (Orig.). 1985. pap. 5.95 (ISBN 0-85368-730-7, Pub. by Arms & Armour). Sterling.
Lockheed F-80 Shooting Star. (Illus.). 53p. 1974. pap. 7.95 (ISBN 0-87994-032-8). Aviat Pub.
Lockheed P-38 Lighting. (Illus.). 78p. 1974. pap. 6.95 (ISBN 0-87994-019-0). Aviat Pub.
The Luftwaffe in Sweden Nineteen Thirty-Nine to Nineteen Forty-Five. LC 82-63018. 1983. 24.95 (ISBN 0-914144-28-6). Monogram Aviation.
Maloney, Edward T. Grumman F8F Bearcat. LC 75-96071. (Aero Ser.: Vol. 20). (Illus.). 1969. pap. 3.95 (ISBN 0-8168-0576-8). Aero.
Messerschmitt ME-262 Sturmvogel. (Illus.). 66p. 1974. pap. 7.95 (ISBN 0-87994-020-4). Aviat Pub.
Messerschmitt O-Nine Gallery. LC 73-86748. 1985. write for info. (ISBN 0-914144-00-6). Monogram Aviation.
Monograph: Natural & Laboratory Testing. 60p. 1985. 20.00 (ISBN 0-915414-81-3). Inst Environ Sci.
Morgan, Len. The AT-6 Harvard. Gentle, Ernest J., ed. LC 65-26763. (The Famous Aircraft Ser.). (Illus.). 64p. 1985. pap. 7.95 (ISBN 0-8168-5661-3). Aero.
Munson, Kenneth. American Aircraft of World War Two in Color. (Illus.). 160p. 1982. 19.95 (ISBN 0-7137-0944-8, Pub. by Blandford Pr England). Sterling.
NATO Fighters & Attack Aircraft. (Illus.). 9.95 (ISBN 0-668-05823-4). Arco.
North American B-25 Mitchell Bomber. (Illus.). 84p. pap. 10.95 (ISBN 0-686-47072-9). Aviat Pub.
P-61 Black Widow. (Illus.). 72p. 1974. pap. 7.95 (ISBN 0-87994-025-5). Aviat Pub.
Polmar, Norman & Kennedy, Floyd. Military Helicopters of the World: Military Rotary-Wing Aircraft Since 1917. LC 80-84060. 1981. 31.95 (ISBN 0-87021-383-0). Naval Inst Pr.
Potgieter, Herman & Steenkamp, Willem. Aircraft of the South African Air Force. (Illus.). 180p. 1984. 19.95 (ISBN 0-7106-0117-4). Jane's Pub Inc.
Presentation Aircraft of the Two World Wars: A Pictorial Survey. 96p. 1981. 25.00x (ISBN 0-85153-233-0, Pub. by D B Bradford England). State Mutual Bk.
Republic P-47 Thunderbolt. (Illus.). 50p. 1974. pap. 6.95 (ISBN 0-87994-022-0). Aviat Pub.
Scarborough, William. PBY Catalina in Action. (In Action Ser.: No. 1062). (Illus.). 50p. 1983. pap. 4.95 (ISBN 0-89747-149-0). Squad Sig Pubns.
Seo, Hiroshi. Military Aircraft of the World. (Illus.). 96p. 1982. 12.95 (ISBN 0-86720-559-8). Jane's Pub Inc.
Singh, Pushpindar. Aircraft of the Indian Air Force, 1933-73. LC 74-903552. (Illus.). 186p. cancelled (ISBN 0-8002-0433-6). Intl Pubns Serv.
Spyplanes & Electronic Warfare Aircraft. (Illus.). 9.95 (ISBN 0-668-05612-6). Arco.
The Story of the Texan AT-6. (Illus.). 60p. 1974. pap. 6.95 (ISBN 0-87994-034-4). Aviat Pub.
Streetly, Martin. World Electronic Warfare Aircraft. 1983. 17.95 (ISBN 0-86720-665-9). Jane's Pub Inc.
The Supermarine Spitfire. (Illus.). 32p. 1974. pap. 3.95 (ISBN 0-87994-028-X). Aviat Pub.
Sweetman, Bill. Soviet Military Aircraft. (Concise Guide Ser.). (Illus.). 208p. 1981. 9.95 (ISBN 0-89141-135-6, Pub. by Hamlyn Pub England). Presidio Pr.
Taylor, Michael J. Warplanes of the World, Nineteen Eighteen to Nineteen Thirty-Nine. 1981. encore ed. 5.95 (ISBN 0-684-16984-3, ScribT). Scribner.
U. S. Pursuit Aircraft: A Pictorial Survey. 96p. 1981. 25.00x (ISBN 0-85153-185-7, Pub. by D B Barton England). State Mutual Bk.
Wagner, Ray. American Combat Planes. 3rd & enl. ed. LC 77-16952. (Illus.). 608p. 1982. 29.95 (ISBN 0-385-13120-8). Doubleday.
Wagner, William. Lightning Bugs & Other Reconnaissance Drones. LC 81-71064. 220p. 1982. 18.95 (ISBN 0-8168-6654-6). Aero.
Waters, Andrew W. All the U. S. Air Force's Airplanes 1907-1980. (Illus.). 1985. pap. 14.95 (ISBN 0-87052-031-8). Hippocrene Bks.
Wheeler, Barry C. Modern Fighters & Attack Aircraft. (Illus.). 9.95 (ISBN 0-668-04964-2). Arco.
World War II Airplanes, Vol. 1. LC 77-88441. (Illus.). 1978. pap. 9.95 (ISBN 0-528-88170-1). Rand.
World War II Airplanes, Vol. 2. LC 77-88441. (Illus.). 1978. pap. 9.95 (ISBN 0-528-88171-X). Rand.
World War II International Aircraft Recognition Manual. (Illus.). 160p. 1973. pap. 6.95 (ISBN 0-87994-017-4). Aviat Pub.

AIRPLANES, MILITARY–RECOGNITION
see Airplanes–Recognition

AIRPLANES, PERSONAL
see Airplanes, Private

AIRPLANES, PILOTLESS
see Guided Missiles

AIRPLANES, PRIVATE
see also Beechcraft 17 (Airplanes)
Bergman, Jules. Anyone Can Fly. rev. ed. LC 73-9141. 1977. 19.95 (ISBN 0-385-02830-X). Doubleday.
Canadian Private Pilot Manual. (Pilot Training Ser.). (Illus.). 428p. 1981. pap. text ed. 19.95 (ISBN 0-88487-074-X, JS314131). Jeppesen Sanderson.
Christy, Joe. Low-Cost Private Flying. (Modern Aviation Ser.). (Illus.). 160p. (Orig.). 1980. 9.95 (ISBN 0-8306-9930-9); pap. 4.95 (ISBN 0-8306-2298-5, 2298). TAB Bks.
Coleman, John E. Private Pilot Airplane: Questions-Answers-Explanations. (Illus.). 208p. 1984. pap. text ed. 10.95 (ISBN 0-317-18180-7, QAE 8080-1). Astro Pubs.
Ethell, Jeffrey L. Moving Up to Twin-Engine Airplanes. (Illus.). 1979. 8.95 (ISBN 0-8306-9790-X); pap. 4.95 (ISBN 0-8306-2270-5, 2270). TAB Bks.
FAA Dept. of Transportation. Private Pilot Question Book (with Answers) (Illus.). 160p. 1984. pap. text ed. 5.00 (ISBN 0-317-18182-3). Astro Pubs.
Quirk, Ronald E. Night Flying for Private Pilots. LC 65-24311. (Illus.). 1965. pap. 2.00 (ISBN 0-911720-61-8, Pub. by Greater NY). Aviation.
Rice, M. S. Handbook of Airfoil Sections for Light Aircraft. LC 71-182597. (Illus.). 144p. 1972. pap. 8.95 spiral bdg. (ISBN 0-87994-015-8). Aviation.
Taylor, John W. & Swanborough, Gordon. Civil Aircraft of the World. 3rd. ed. LC 77-74718. (Illus.). 1978. Encore ed. 9.95 (ISBN 0-684-15224-X, ScribT). Scribner.
Thurston, David B. Home Built Aircraft. (Illus.). 224p. 1981. 29.95 (ISBN 0-07-064552-3, P&RB). McGraw.

AIRPLANES, ROCKET PROPELLED
see Rocket Planes

AIRPLANES, VERTICALLY RISING
see Vertically Rising Aircraft

AIRPLANES IN AGRICULTURE
see Aeronautics in Agriculture

AIRPLANES IN FORESTRY
see Aeronautics in Forestry

AIRPORTS
see also Heliports
Aircraft Hangars. (Four Hundred Ser.). 68p. 1973. pap. 2.00 (ISBN 0-685-44140-7, 409). Natl Fire Prot.
Airport Terminal Buildings. (Four Hundred Ser). 1973. pap. 2.00 (ISBN 0-685-58235-3, 416). Natl Fire Prot.
Airports Conference, Atlanta, 1971. Airports: Key to the Air Transportation System. LC 73-171782. pap. 74.30 (ISBN 0-317-10158-7, 2010118). Bks Demand UMI.
American Society of Civil Engineers. Airports: Challenges of the Future. LC 76-371620. pap. 54.80 (ISBN 0-317-10152-8, 2010119). Bks Demand UMI.
Ashford, Norman & Wright, Paul H. Airport Engineering. 2nd ed. LC 83-23494. 433p. 1984. 38.95 (ISBN 0-471-86568-0, Pub. by Wiley-Interscience). Wiley.
Balachandran, Sarojini. Airport Planning: Nineteen Sixty-Five to Nineteen Seventy-Five, No. 1140. 1976. 5.00 (ISBN 0-686-20412-3). CPL Biblios.
Campbell, George E. Airport Management & Operations. 1972. 15.00x (ISBN 0-87511-015-0). Claitors.
Cedergren, Harry R. Drainage of Highway & Airfield Pavements. LC 74-13400. (Illus.). 285p. 1974. 47.95 (ISBN 0-471-14181-X, Pub. by Wiley-Interscience). Wiley.
Conway, McKinley. The Airport City: Development Concepts for the Twenty-First Century. rev. ed. LC 80-65254. (Illus.). 227p. 1980. 9.95 (ISBN 0-910436-14-2). Conway Data.
Crampton Associates, ed. Airport Transit Guide. (Illus.). 64p. Date not set. pap. price not set. Crampton Assoc.
Feldman, Elliot J. & Milch, Jerome. Technocracy vs. Democracy: The Comparative Politics of International Airports. (Illus.). 299p. 1981. 24.95 (ISBN 0-86569-063-4). Auburn Hse.
Fouquet, R. Pilot's Guide to California Airports. (Illus.). 24.95 (ISBN 0-911721-24-X, Pub. by Optima). Aviation.
Greif, Martin. The Airport Book: From Landing Field to Modern Terminal. (Illus.). 1979. 12.95 (ISBN 0-8317-0150-1, Mayflower Bks). Smith Pubs.
Horonjeff, R. & McKelvey, F. X. Planning & Design of Airports. 3rd ed. 640p. 1983. 48.95 (ISBN 0-07-030367-3). McGraw.
Institution of Civil Engineers Staff, compiled by. Airports for the Community. 132p. 1980. 47.00x (ISBN 0-7277-0087-1). Am Soc Civil Eng.
Institution of Civil Engineers Staff, ed. Airports for the Eighties. 221p. 1973. 55.50x (ISBN 0-901948-72-1). Am Soc Civil Eng.
Institution of Civil Engineers Staff, compiled by. Airports for the Future. 140p. 1967. 29.00x (ISBN 0-901948-36-5). Am Soc Civil Eng.
--Airports: The Challenging Future. 255p. 1976. 60.75x (ISBN 0-7277-0017-0). Am Soc Civil Eng.
International Air Safety Seminar Staff. Safety Needs in the Terminal Environment: Proceedings of the 30th Annual International Air Safety Seminar, Ottawa, 1977. pap. 58.00 (ISBN 0-317-10944-8, 2006140). Bks Demand UMI.
Kirchherr, Eugene C., ed. Studies of the Location, Planning, Zoning & Development of Civil Airports in the U. S. A Selected Bibliography of Sources for the Period 1920-1974, No. 830. 1975. 5.00 (ISBN 0-686-20360-7). CPL Biblios.

Louie De Irizarry, Florita Z. Airport Architecture: A Bibliography of Periodical Articles. (Architecture Ser.: Bibliography A-651). 52p. 1982. pap. 7.50 (ISBN 0-88066-132-1). Vance Biblios.
Miller, Jeffrey. Stapleton International Airport: The First Fifty Years. LC 82-22975. (Illus.). 1983. 24.95 (ISBN 0-87108-614-X). Pruett.
Moore, Kenneth C. Airport, Aircraft & Airline Security. LC 76-45104. (Illus.). 1976. 29.95 (ISBN 0-913708-26-7). Butterworth.
Reese, Richard G. Pilot's Guide to Southwestern Airports. (Illus.). 1983. 3 ring binder 28.95b (ISBN 0-686-43374-2, Pub. by RGR Pubns.). Aviation.
Richardson, J. D. Essentials of Aviation Management. LC 76-44189. (Illus.). 1977. pap. text ed. 18.95 (ISBN 0-8403-2430-8, 40243002). Kendall-Hunt.
Seay, Earl. Small Airports Managers Handbook. (Aviation Management Ser.). 78p. 1980. 8.95 (ISBN 0-89100-140-9, EA-140-9). Aviation Maintenance.
Senterfitt, Arnold D. Airports of Mexico & Central America. (Illus.). 1980. pap. 24.95 (ISBN 0-937260-00-2, Pub. by Senterfitt). Aviation.
Senter Fitt, Arnold D. Airports of Mexico & Central America. 16th ed. (Illus.). 656p. 1982. pap. 24.95 (ISBN 0-937260-01-0). Pathfinders.
Smith, Don & Shea, William. Airport Planning & Management. (Continuing Education Ser.). 300p. 1983. text ed. write for info (ISBN 0-534-02877-2). Wadsworth Pub.
Stroud, John. Airports of the World. (Putnam Aeronautical Bks.). (Illus.). 576p. 1981. 55.00 (ISBN 0-370-30037-8, Pub. by the Bodley Head). Merrimack Pub Cir.
Taylor, John. British Airports. pap. 5.00x (ISBN 0-392-07261-0, SpS). Sportshelf.

AIRSHIPS
see Air-Ships

AKITA (DOG)
see Dogs–Breeds–Akita

ALASKAN MALAMUTE (DOG)
see Dogs–Breeds–Alaskan Malamute

ALBATROSS D-3 (FIGHTER PLANE)
Mikesh, Robert C. Albatros D. Va: German World War I Fighter. LC 80-36711. (Famous Aircraft of the National Air & Space Museum Ser.: No. 4). (Illus.). 115p. (Orig.). 1980. pap. 7.95 (ISBN 0-87474-633-7). Smithsonian.

ALBATROSSES
Bailey, Alfred M. Laysan & Black Footed Albatrosses. (Museum Pictorial: No. 6). 1952. pap. 1.10 (ISBN 0-916278-35-2). Denver Mus Natl Hist.

ALCALOIDS
see Alkaloids

ALCES
Reynolds, S. H. Pleistocene Alces, Supplement. pap. 5.00 (ISBN 0-384-50390-X). Johnson Repr.
Wilder, Thornton. The Alcestiad or a Life in the Sun. 1979. pap. 2.25 (ISBN 0-380-41855-X, 41855-X, Bard). Avon.

ALCHEMY
Albertus, Frater. Alchemist's Handbook. LC 74-21127. 124p. 1974. cloth 12.50 (ISBN 0-87728-181-5). Weiser.
Alchemical Society. Journal, Vols. 1-3 In 1. LC 79-8591. Repr. of 1915 ed. 29.50 (ISBN 0-404-18445-6). AMS Pr.
Alpha Pyramis Research Division. Alchemy: A Bibliography. 50p. 1984. pap. 3.75 (ISBN 0-913597-40-6, Pub. by Alpha Pyramis). Prosperity & Profits.
Ashmole, Elias. Theatrum Chemicum Britannicum. 33.00 (ISBN 0-384-02185-9). Johnson Repr.
Atwood, Mary A. Hermetic Philosophy & Alchemy. LC 79-8592. Repr. of 1960 ed. 57.50 (ISBN 0-404-18446-4). AMS Pr.
Burland, Cottie A. The Arts of the Alchemists. LC 79-8598. Repr. of 1968 ed. 42.50 (ISBN 0-404-18451-0). AMS Pr.
Chikashige, M. Oriental Alchemy. LC 74-77742. 1974. pap. 1.95 (ISBN 0-87728-260-9). Weiser.
Chikashige, Masumi. Alchemy & Other Chemical Achievements of the Ancient Orient. LC 79-8602. Repr. of 1936 ed. 27.50 (ISBN 0-404-18456-1). AMS Pr.
Clymer, Reuben S. Alchemy & the Alchemists, 3 vols. LC 79-8603. Repr. of 1907 ed. Set. 105.00 (ISBN 0-404-18457-X). AMS Pr.
Dales, Richard C. Marius on the Elements. 200p. 1977. 24.00x (ISBN 0-520-02856-2). U of Cal Pr.
De Rola, Klossowski. Alchemy: The Secret of Art. (Art & the Cosmos Ser.). (Illus.). 128p. 1973. pap. 4.95 (ISBN 0-380-01012-7, 16907). Avon.
The Diary of an Alchemist. 1982. 40.00x (ISBN 0-906006-04-X, Pub. by Baker Pubns England). State Mutual Bk.
DiBernard, Barbara. Alchemy & Finnegans Wake. LC 79-22809. 1980. 49.50x (ISBN 0-87395-388-6); pap. 14.95x (ISBN 0-87395-429-7). State U NY Pr.
Dobbs, Betty J. The Foundation of Newton's Alchemy; or, "The Hunting of the Greene Lyon". LC 74-31795. (Illus.). 320p. 1976. 49.50 (ISBN 0-521-20786-X). Cambridge U Pr.
Doberer, Kurt K. The Goldmakers: Ten Thousand Years of Alchemy. Dickes, E. W., tr. LC 72-597. (Illus.). 301p. 1972. Repr. of 1948 ed. lib. bdg. 19.75x (ISBN 0-8371-6355-2, DOGM). Greenwood.
Eliadc, Mircea. Thc Forgc & the Crucible: The Origins & Structures of Alchemy. 2nd ed. Corrin, Stephen, tr. LC 78-55040. 1979. pap. 6.95 (ISBN 0-226-20390-5, P780, Phoen). U of Chicago Pr.
Ferguson, John. Bibliotheca Chemica: A Catalogue of the Alchemical, Chemical & Pharmaceutical Books in the Collection of the Late James Young of Kelly & Furris, 2 vols. LC 79-8610. Repr. of 1906 ed. 98.50 set (ISBN 0-404-18472-3). AMS Pr.
Fulcanelli. Fulcanelli: Master Alchemist, le Mystere Des Cathedrales. 2nd ed. Sworder, Mary, tr. (Illus.). 1977. Repr. of 1971 ed. cancelled (ISBN 0-914732-06-4). Bro Life Inc.
Geber. Of the Investigation, or Search of Perfection: Or, Search of Perfection. Russell, Richard, tr. 1983. pap. 2.95 (ISBN 0-916411-08-7, Pub. by Alchemical Pr). Holmes Pub.
Germain, Saint. Intermediate Studies in Alchemy. new ed. LC 74-82295. (Alchemy Ser.). (Illus.). 158p. 1975. pap. 3.95 (ISBN 0-916766-01-2). Summit Univ.
Gettings, Fred. Dictionary of Occult, Hermetic & Alchemical Sigils. 1981. 40.00 (ISBN 0-7100-0095-2). Routledge & Kegan.
Grossinger, Richard, ed. The Alchemical Tradition in the Late Twentieth Century. 2nd & rev ed. (Illus.). 320p. 1983. pap. 12.95 (ISBN 0-938190-11-3). North Atlantic.
Halka, Chester S. Melquiades, Alchemy & Narrative Theory: The Quest for Gold in 'Cien Anos de Soledad. 1981. 12.00x (ISBN 0-936968-01-X). Intl Bk Ctr.
Hall, Manly P. Orders of the Great Work - Alchemy. 5.95 (ISBN 0-89314-534-3). Philos Res.
Hanson, Dirk. The New Alchemists: Silicon Valley & the Microelectronics Revolution. 1982. 17.45i (ISBN 0-316-34342-0). Little.
Hitchcock, Ethan A. Alchemy & the Alchemists. 15.00 (ISBN 0-89314-400-2). Philos Res.
Ho Peng-Yoke. On the Dating of Taoist Alchemical Texts. (Griffith Asian Papers: No. 1). 79p. (Orig.). 1980. pap. text ed. 4.00 (ISBN 0-86857-075-3, 0583, Pub. by ANUP Australia). Australia N U P.
Hopkins, Arthur J. Alchemy Child of Greek Philosophy. LC 71-181908. Repr. of 1934 ed. 14.50 (ISBN 0-404-03338-5). AMS Pr.
Jabir, Ibn H. The Works of Geber. LC 79-8615. Repr. of 1928 ed. 32.50 (ISBN 0-404-18479-0). AMS Pr.
Jaffe, Bernard. Crucibles: The Story of Chemistry from Ancient Alchemy to Nuclear Fission. 4th rev. ed. 15.25 (ISBN 0-8446-5486-8). Peter Smith.
Johnson, Obed S. A Study of Chinese Alchemy. LC 74-352. (Gold Ser.: Vol. 12). 156p. 1974. Repr. of 1928 ed. 18.00x (ISBN 0-405-05914-0). Ayer Co Pubs.
Jung, C. G. Alchemical Studies. Adler, Gerhard, et al, eds. Hull, R. F., tr. (The Collected Works of C. G. Jung: No. 13). 1968. 35.00 (ISBN 0-691-09760-7); pap. 13.50x (ISBN 0-691-01849-9). Princeton U Pr.
Junius, Manfred M. Practical Handbook of Plant Alchemy: How to Prepare Medicinal Essences, Tinctures & Elixers. 272p. (Orig.). 1985. pap. 12.95 (ISBN 0-89281-060-2). Inner Tradit.
Kaushik, R. P. Organic Alchemy. 2nd ed. LC 77-94471. (Orig.). 1978. pap. 3.95 (ISBN 0-918038-07-3). Journey Pubns.
Kibre, Pearl. Studies in Medieval Science: Alchemy, Astrology, Mathematics & Medicine. 355p. 1983. 40.00 (ISBN 0-907628-21-4). Hambledon Press.
Lindsay, Jack. Ancient Egyptian Alchemy. O'Quinn, John, ed. 44p. 1981. pap. text ed. 6.95 (ISBN 0-9609802-4-5). Life Science.
Maier, Michael. The Secrets of Alchemy. 1984. pap. 3.95 (ISBN 0-916411-17-6, Pub. by Alchemical Pr). Holmes Pub.
Mercer, John E. Alchemy, Its Science & Romance. LC 79-8617. (Illus.). Repr. of 1921 ed. 27.50 (ISBN 0-404-18481-2). AMS Pr.
Morienus. A Testament of Alchemy: Being the Revelations of Morienus, Ancient Adept & Hermit of Jerusalem, to Khalid ibn Yazid ibn Mu'awiyya, King of the Arabs, of the Divine Secrets of the Magisterium & Accomplishment of the Alchemical Art. Stavenhagen, Lee, ed. & tr. from Lat. LC 73-91752. (Illus.). 86p. 1974. 10.00x (ISBN 0-87451-095-3). U Pr of New Eng.
Muhammad Ibn Zakariya. Practical Chemistry in the Twelfth Century. Steele, Robert R., ed. Gerard Of Cremona, tr. LC 79-8590. Repr. of 1929 ed. 19.50 (ISBN 0-404-18444-8). AMS Pr.
Muir, Matthew M. The Story of Alchemy & the Beginnings of Chemistry. LC 79-8618. Repr. of 1903 ed. 27.50 (ISBN 0-404-18482-0). AMS Pr.
Norton, Thomas. Ordinal of Alchemy. Reidy, John, ed. (Early English Text Society). (Illus.). 1975. 19.50x (ISBN 0-19-722274-9). Oxford U Pr.
Paracelsus. Werke, 5 vols. (Ger.). Repr. of 1591 ed. 209.00x set (ISBN 3-7965-0471-X). Adlers Foreign Bks.
Philalethes, Eirenaeus. Preparations of the Sophic Mercury. (Alchemical Treatise Ser.: No. 1). 1983. pap. 1.95 (ISBN 0-916411-05-2, Pub. by Alchemical Pr). Holmes Pub.
Ponce, Charles. Papers Toward Radical Metaphysics: Alchemy. 160p. (Orig.). 1984. 20.00 (ISBN 0-938190-02-4); pap. 8.95 (ISBN 0-938190-01-6). North Atlantic.
Porphyry. Life of Plotinus or Porphyry's Life of Plotinus. 1983. pap. 3.95 (ISBN 0-916411-12-5, Pub. by Alexandrian Pr). Holmes Pub.
Pritchard, Alan. Alchemy: A Bibliography of English Language Writings. 400p. 1980. 75.00x (ISBN 0-7100-0472-9). Routledge & Kegan.
Read, John. Prelude to Chemistry: An Outline of Alchemy, Its Literature & Relationships. LC 79-8622. (Illus.). Repr. of 1937 ed. 48.00 (ISBN 0-404-18488-X). AMS Pr.
--Through Alchemy to Chemistry: A Procession of Ideas & Personalities. LC 79-8623. (Illus.). 240p. Repr. of 1957 ed. 29.00 (ISBN 0-404-18489-8). AMS Pr.
Redgrove, H. Stanley. Alchemy, Ancient & Modern. (Illus.). 141p. 1980. 20.00 (ISBN 0-89005-344-8). Ares.
--Bygone Beliefs. (An Excursion into the Occult and Alchemical Nature of Man). 287p. 1981. pap. 10.00 (ISBN 0-89540-078-2, SB-078). Sun Pub.
Redgrove, Herbert S. Bygone Beliefs: Being a Series of Excursions in the Byways of Thought. (Folklore & Society Ser). (Illus.). 1969. Repr. of 1920 ed. 28.00 (ISBN 0-384-50050-1). Johnson Repr.
Ripley, George. The Compound of Alchymy. LC 77-7423. (English Experience Ser.: No. 887). 1977. Repr. of 1591 ed. lib. bdg. 10.50 (ISBN 90-221-0887-2). Walter J Johnson.
St. Germain. Studies in Alchemy. LC 77-75411. (Alchemy Ser.). (Illus.). 92p. 1974. pap. 3.95 (ISBN 0-916766-00-4). Summit Univ.
Saint Germain. Estudios Sobre La Alquimia. Prophet, Elizabeth C., ed. LC 80-52980. (Span.). 165p. 1981. pap. 4.95 (ISBN 0-916766-40-3). Summit Univ.
Sandbach, John. Astrology, Alchemy, & the Tarot. Robertson, Arlene, ed. 80p. (Orig.). 1981. pap. 4.95 (ISBN 0-930706-08-0). Seek-It Pubns.
Schueler, Gerald J. Enochian Magick: A Manual for Beginners. Buckland, Raymond, ed. LC 84-48087. (High Magick Ser.). (Illus.). 288p. (Orig.). 1985. pap. 12.95 (ISBN 0-87542-710-3, L-710). Llewellyn Pubns.
Silberer, Herbert. The Hidden Symbolism of Alchemy & the Occult Arts. Jelliffe, Smith E., tr. Orig. Title: Problems of Mysticism & Its Symbolism. 1971. pap. 6.95 (ISBN 0-486-20972-5). Dover.
Sivin, Nathan. Chinese Alchemy: Preliminary Studies. LC 67-27093. (Monographs in the History of Science Ser). 1968. 22.50x (ISBN 0-674-12150-3). Harvard U Pr.
Taylor, F. Sherwood. The Alchemist: Founders of Modern Chemistry, Vol. 1. LC 74-361. (Gold Ser.). (Illus.). 246p. 1974. Repr. of 1949 ed. 19.00x (ISBN 0-405-05922-1). Ayer Co Pubs.
--The Alchemists. (Illus.). 1977. pap. 4.95x (ISBN 0-8464-0124-X). Beekman Pubs.
Taylor, Frank S. A Survey of Greek Alchemy. LC 79-8627. Repr. of 1930 ed. 21.50 (ISBN 0-404-18493-6). AMS Pr.
Therapus, Janus L. A Form & Method of Perfecting Base Metals. Waite, A. E., ed. 1983. pap. 3.95 (ISBN 0-916411-04-4, Pub. by Alchemical Pr). Holmes Pub.
Thomas Aquinas, Saint. Aurora Consurgens, a Document Attributed to Thomas Aquinas on the Problem of Opposites in Alchemy. Von Franz, Marie-Louise, ed. Hull, R. F., tr. LC 65-10405. pap. 142.80 (ISBN 0-317-09046-1, 2051598). Bks Demand UMI.
Todd, Nancy J., ed. The Journal of the New Alchemists: Ecological Research Ser. LC 77-6479. (No. 7). (Illus.). 384p. 1981. pap. 12.95 (ISBN 0-8289-0406-5). Greene.
Vaughan, Thomas. A Notebook. Waite, A. E., ed. (Alchemical Treatise Ser.: No. 3). 1983. pap. 1.95 (ISBN 0-916411-11-7, Pub. by Alchemical Pr). Holmes Pub.
Von Hohenheim, Theophrastus P. Paracelsus Alchemical Catechism. Waite, A. E., tr. from Latin. 1983. pap. 3.95 (ISBN 0-916411-03-6, Pub. by Alchemical Pr). Holmes Pub.
Waite, A. E. A Compendium of Alchemical Processes. 176p. 1981. 17.50 (ISBN 0-87728-540-3). Weiser.
Waite, Arthur E. Alchemists Through the Ages, Vol. 25. LC 76-130814. (Steinerbooks Spiritual Science Library). (Illus.). 320p. 1985. Repr. of 1970 ed. lib. bdg. 17.00 (ISBN 0-89345-035-9). Garber Comm.
Ware, James R., ed. Alchemy, Medicine & Religion in the China of A.D. Three Hundred & Twenty: The Nei P'ien of Ko Hung. 13.25 (ISBN 0-8446-5918-5). Peter Smith.
Ware, James R., tr. from Chinese. Alchemy, Medicine, & Religion in the China of A. D. 320: The Nei P'ien of Ko Hung (Pao-p'u tzu) 416p. 1981. pap. 7.50 (ISBN 0-486-24088-6). Dover.
Webster, John. Metallograph: History of Metals, Wherein Is Declared the Signs of Ores & Minerals Both Before & After Digging. LC 77-6544. (History of Geology Ser.). Repr. of 1671 ed. lib. bdg. 34.50x (ISBN 0-405-10462-6). Ayer Co Pubs.
Westcott, William W. The Science of Alchymy. 1983. pap. 2.95 (ISBN 0-916411-02-8, Pub. by Alchemical Pr). Holmes Pub.
Westcott, William W., ed. The Hermetic Art: A Short Enquiry. pap. 3.95 (ISBN 0-916411-06-0, Pub. by Alchemical Pr). Holmes Pub.

ALCOHOL
see also Distillation; Liquors
also names of alcoholic liquors
Abel, Ernest L., compiled by. Alcohol & Reproduction: A Bibliography. LC 82-6202. ix, 219p. 1982. lib. bdg. 29.95 (ISBN 0-313-23474-4, AAR/). Greenwood.
CAN Task Force, National Research Council. Feeding Value of Ethanol Production by-Products. 79p. 1981. pap. text ed. 6.50 (ISBN 0-309-03136-2). Natl Acad Pr.
Fazey, C. The Aetiology of Psychoactive Substance Use: A Report & Critically Annotated Bibliography on Research into the Aetiology of Alcohol, Nicotine, Opiate & Other Psychoactive Substance Use. 226p. (With the Financial Support of the United Nations Fund for Drug Abruse Control). 1977. pap. 18.00 (ISBN 92-3-101508-7, U776, UNESCO). Unipub.
Goldstein, Dora B. Pharmacology of Alcohol. (Illus.). 1983. text ed. 24.95x (ISBN 0-19-503111-3); pap. text ed. 16.95x (ISBN 0-19-503112-1). Oxford U Pr.
International Conference Held in Helsinki, June 4-8, 1979, et al. Animal Models in Alcohol Research: Proceedings. Eriksson, K., ed. LC 80-40103. 1980. 55.00 (ISBN 0-12-240650-8). Acad Pr.
Jones, Kenneth L., et al. Drugs & Alcohol. 3rd ed. 1978. pap. text ed. 10.95 scp (ISBN 0-06-043436-8, HarpC). Har-Row.
Kricka, L. J. & Clark, P. M. Biochemistry of Alcohol & Alcoholism. LC 79-40252. (Chemical Science Ser.). 285p. 1979. 79.95x (ISBN 0-470-26712-7). Halsted Pr.
Ladewig, D., ed. Drogen & Alkohol. (Illus.). xii, 220p. 1980. pap. 14.25 (ISBN 3-8055-1624-X). S Karger.
--Drogen und Alkohol 2. viii, 172p. 1982. pap. 16.75 (ISBN 3-8055-3599-6). S Karger.
Lindros, K. O. & Eriksson, C. J., eds. The Role of Acetaldehyde in the Actions of Ethanol: Satellite Symposium to the Sixth International Congress of Pharmacology. (The Finnish Foundation for Alcohol Studies: Vol. 23). (Illus.). 1975. pap. 8.00 (ISBN 951-9191-23-2). Rutgers Ctr Alcohol.
Majchrowicz, Edward, ed. Biochemical Pharmacology of Ethanol. LC 75-8369. (Advances in Experimental Medicine & Biology Ser.: Vol. 56). 382p. 1975. 49.50x (ISBN 0-306-39056-6, Plenum Pr). Plenum Pub.
Majchrowicz, Edward & Noble, Ernest P., eds. Biochemistry & Pharmacology of Ethanol. LC 79-292. (Illus.). 1979. Vol. 1, 734p. 65.00x (ISBN 0-306-40125-8, Plenum Pr); Vol. 2, 600p. 55.00x (ISBN 0-306-40130-4). Plenum Pub.
Nash, Harvey. Alcohol & Caffeine: A Study of Their Psychological Effects. (Illus.). 184p. 1962. 19.50x (ISBN 0-398-04375-2). C C Thomas.
Pan, Lynn. Alcohol in Colonial Africa. (The Finnish Foundation for Alcohol Studies: Vol. 22). 1975. 6.50x (ISBN 951-9191-20-8). Rutgers Ctr Alcohol.
Solomon, Joel & Keeley, Kim. Perspective in Alcohol & Drug Abuse: Similarities & Differences. 270p. 1982. 26.00 (ISBN 0-88416-306-7). PSG Pub Co.
Thurman, Ronald, ed. Alcohol & Aldehyde Metabolizing Systems, IV. LC 80-18745. (Advances in Experimental Medicine & Biology Ser.: Vol. 132). 850p. 1980. 95.00x (ISBN 0-306-40476-1, Plenum Pr). Plenum Pub.

Thurman, Ronald G., et al, eds. Alcohol & Aldehyde Metabolizing Systems, 3 vols. (Johnson Foundation Colloquia Ser.). 1978. Vol. 1. 70.00 (ISBN 0-12-691450-8); Vol. 2. 70.00 (ISBN 0-12-691402-8); Vol. 3, 1977. 70.00 (ISBN 0-12-691403-6); Set. 170.00 (ISBN 0-686-77325-X). Acad Pr.

Wimer, William W., et al. Alcohols Toxicology. LC 83-2403. (Illus.). 277p. 1983. 36.00 (ISBN 0-8155-0948-0). Noyes.

ALCOHOL AS FUEL

The Alcohol Economy: What's Ahead. 1981. 950.00 (ISBN 0-89336-263-8, C-030). BCC.

Alcohol Production from Biomass in the Developing Countries. 69p. 1980. 5.00 (ISBN 0-686-36155-5, EN-8002). World Bank.

Barzelay, Michael. The Politicized Market Economy: Alcohol in the Brazilian Energy Strategy. 1986. 28.50x (ISBN 0-520-05382-6). U of Cal Pr.

Bereny, Justin A., ed. Alcohol Fuels Information Series: Vol. 1, U. S. Government Overviews. LC 80-51918. 1980. 54.95x (ISBN 0-89934-031-8, B941-SS); pap. 39.95x (ISBN 0-89934-032-6, B041-SS). Solar Energy Info.

Bernton, Hal, et al. The Forbidden Fuel: Power Alcohol in the Twentieth Century. LC 81-85112. (Illus.). 312p. 1982. 19.95 (ISBN 0-941726-00-2). Boyd Griffin.

Bolet, Adela M., et al. Ethanol: National Security Implications. LC 83-23919. (Significant Issues Ser.: Vol. 5, No. 7). 64p. 1983. 6.95 (ISBN 0-89206-050-6). CSI Studies.

Bossong, Ken, et al. Pioneers of Alcohol Fuels, 2 vols. 125p. (Orig.). 1981. 7.50 (ISBN 0-89988-067-3). Citizens Energy.

Carley, Larry W. How to Make Your Own Alcohol Fuels. 2nd ed. (Modern Automotive Ser.). (Illus.). 182p. 1983. 13.95o.p (ISBN 0-8306-0047-7); pap. 7.95 (ISBN 0-8306-2084-2, 2084). TAB Bks.

Davy McKee Corp. Fuel Alcohol: Report & Analysis of Plant Conversion Potential to Fuel Alcohol Production. 125p. 1981. pap. 29.50x (ISBN 0-89934-095-4, B016). Solar Energy Info.

Drane, Keat B. Convert Your Car to Alcohol. LC 80-81750. (Illus.). 64p. (Orig.). 1980. lib. bdg. 12.95 (ISBN 0-915216-61-2); pap. 4.95 (ISBN 0-915216-54-X). Marathon Intl Pub Co.

Hale, William J. Prosperity Beckons: Dawn of the Alcohol Era. (Illus.). 160p. pap. 6.95 (ISBN 0-936222-01-8). Rutan Pub.

Houghton-Alico, Doann. Alcohol Fuels: Policies, Production, & Potential. (Special Studies in Natural Resources & Energy Management). 275p. 1982. hardcover 26.00x (ISBN 0-86531-245-1). Westview.

Kerley, Michael R. & Mother Earth News Staff, eds. The Mother Earth News Alcohol Fuel Handbook. 120p. (Orig.). 1980. pap. 12.95 (ISBN 0-938432-00-1). Mother Earth.

Lucke, Charles E. & Woodward, S. M. The Use of Alcohol & Gasoline in Farm Engines. (Illus.). 100p. 1980. pap. 4.95 (ISBN 0-936222-04-2). Rutan Pub.

Mathewson, Stephen. Manual for Production of Alcohol Fuel. 208p. 7.95 (ISBN 0-686-35945-3). Rutan Pub.

Mathewson, Stephen W. The Manual for the Home & Farm Production of Alcohol Fuel. LC 80-51216. 224p. 1980. 12.95 (ISBN 0-89815-030-2); pap. 7.95 (ISBN 0-89815-029-9). Ten Speed Pr.

Nellis, Micki. Makin' It on the Farm: Alcohol Fuel is the Road to Independence. 88p. pap. 4.00 (ISBN 0-686-35950-X). Rutan Pub.

Paul, J. K., ed. Ethyl Alcohol Production & Use As a Motor Fuel. LC 79-22900. (Energy Tech Review No. 51, Chemical Tech Review: No. 144). (Illus.). 354p. 1980. 48.00 (ISBN 0-8155-0780-1). Noyes.

--Large & Small Scale Ethyl Alcohol Manufacturing Processes from Agricultural Raw Materials. LC 80-20219. (Chemical Tech. Rev. 169, Energy Tech. Rev. 58). (Illus.). 576p. 1981. 48.00 (ISBN 0-8155-0815-8). Noyes.

Pefley, Richard K., ed. Proceedings of Third International Symposium on Alcohol Fuel Technology. 838p. 1980. 84.95x (ISBN 0-89934-019-9, B-938); pap. 64.95x (ISBN 0-89934-020-2, B-038). Solar Energy Info.

Raphael Katzen Associates. Grain Motor Fuel Alcohol Technical & Economic Assessment Study. 344p. 1981. Repr. of 1978 ed. 59.50x (ISBN 0-89934-063-6, B.050). Solar Energy Info.

Raphael Katzen Associates International, Inc. Farm & Cooperative Alcohol Plant Study: Technical & Economic Assessment As a Commercial Venture. 230p. 1981. pap. 39.50x (ISBN 0-89934-117-9, B.018). Solar Energy Info.

Ross, James. Fuel Alcohol: How to Make It, How to Use It. 160p. 1981. St Martin.

Rothman, Harry, et al. Energy from Alcohol: The Brazilian Experience. LC 82-21956. 200p. 1983. 20.00x (ISBN 0-8131-1479-9). U Pr of Ky.

Rutan, Al. Alcohol Vaporizing Car Conversions. rev. ed. (Illus.). 100p. 1981. pap. 5.00 (ISBN 0-936222-03-4). Rutan Pub.

Schnittker Ssocs. for National Alcohol Fuels Commission. Ethanol: Farm & Fuel Issues. 137p. 1981. pap. 24.50x (ISBN 0-89934-096-2, B014). Solar Energy Info.

Seratt, Roger & Seratt, Virginia. The Alcohol Fuel Book. 1981. pap. 17.50 (ISBN 0-686-92646-3). Rutan Pub.

Shay, Griff & Panel on Alcohol Fuels, Board on Science & Technology for International Developement, National Research Council. Alcohol Fuels: Options for Developing Countries. 109p. 1983. pap. text ed. 8.95 (ISBN 0-309-03386-1). Natl Acad Pr.

Smith, Dennis E. Solar Fuel: How to Make Automotive Fuel Using Your Own Alcohol Solar Still. LC 80-80971. (Illus.). 96p. (Orig.). 1980. pap. 4.95 (ISBN 0-915216-53-1). Marathon Intl Pub Co.

Society of Automotive Engineers. Alcohols as Motor Fuels. LC 80-52454. 368p. 1980. Twenty papers. 45.00 (ISBN 0-89883-107-5, PT 19). Soc Auto Engineers.

Solar Energy Research Institute. Fuel from Farms: A Guide to Small-Scale Ethanol Production. 161p. 1980. 34.95x (ISBN 0-89934-050-4, B947-PP); pap. 19.95x (ISBN 0-89934-051-2, B047-PP). Solar Energy Info.

Solar Energy Research Institute (SERI) Guide to Commercial-Scale Ethanol Production & Financing. 305p. 1981. Repr. of 1980 ed. 49.50x (ISBN 0-89934-118-7, B.919). Solar Energy Info.

Tallgrass Research Center Editors, ed. Alcohol Fuel Handbook. 120p. 1980. looseleaf 25.00 (ISBN 0-686-92643-9). Rutan Pub.

TRW - Energy Systems Planning Division. Energy Balances in the Production & End-Use of Alcohols Derived from Biomass. 125p. 1981. pap. 24.50x (ISBN 0-89934-116-0, B.017). Solar Energy Info.

U. S. Department of Energy. Alcohol Fuels Program Plan. 60p. 1979. pap. 15.00x (ISBN 0-930978-96-X, B-034). Solar Energy Info.

--Proceedings of International Symposium on Alcohol Fuel Technology: Methanol & Ethanol U. S. Department of Energy. 498p. 1979. 59.95x (ISBN 0-930978-86-2, B-935); pap. 44.95x (ISBN 0-89934-000-8, B-035). Solar Energy Info.

--The Report of the Alcohol Fuels Policy Review. 119p. 1979. pap. 19.95x (ISBN 0-89934-024-5, B-040). Solar Energy Info.

U. S. Dept. of Agriculture. Small-Scale Fuel Alcohol Production. 242p. 1980. 49.95x (ISBN 0-89934-047-4, B946); pap. 34.95x (ISBN 0-89934-046-6, B046). Solar Energy Info.

U. S. National Alcohol Fuels Commission. Fuel Alcohol: An Energy Alternative for the 1980's. 146p. 1981. pap. 19.50x (ISBN 0-89934-126-8, B024, B024). Solar Energy Info.

U. S. National Alcohols Fuels Commission. Fuel Alcohol on the Farm: A Primer on Production & Use. 50p. 1981. pap. 8.50x (ISBN 0-89934-097-0, B015). Solar Energy Info.

University of California, Davis, ed. Biomass Alcohol for California: a Potential for the 1980's: Proceedings. 52p. 1980. pap. 14.95x (ISBN 0-89934-059-8, B002). Solar Energy Info.

Washington Gasohol Commission Staff. The American Artichoke, Vol. 1. (The Weed That Whips OPEC Ser.). 1306p. 1981. pap. 15.00 (ISBN 0-939864-00-2). Wash Gasohol.

Washington Gasohol Commission Staff, ed. The Washington Gasohol Seminars, 1980. 45p. 1980. pap. 6.00 (ISBN 0-939864-01-0). Wash Gasohol.

World Bank. Alcohol Production from Biomass in the Developing Countries. 71p. 1982. pap. 14.95x (ISBN 0-89934-151-9, B-027). Solar Energy Info.

Wortham, Jim & Whitener, Barbara. Forget the Gas Pumps-Make Your Own Fuel. LC 79-90459. (Illus., Orig.). 1979. lib. bdg. 12.95 (ISBN 0-915216-72-8); pap. 3.95 (ISBN 0-915216-43-4). Marathon Intl Pub Co.

ALCOHOLS

see also Alcohol; Cyclitols; Glycerin

Gmehling, J. & Onken, U. Vapor-Liquid Equilibrium Data Collection Tables & Diagrams of Data for Binary & Multicomponent Mixtures up to Moderate Pressures; Constants of Correlation Equations for Computer Use: Part 2a: Organic Hydroxy Compounds: Alcohols, No. 1. LC 79-670289. (Dechema Chemistry Data Ser.). 1978. text ed. 110.00x (ISBN 3-921567-09-2). Scholium Intl.

--Vapor-Liquid Equilibrium Data Collection: Volume I, Part 2C-Organic Hydroxy Compounds: Alcohols (Supplement 1) (Dechema Chemistry Data Ser.). (Illus.). 698p. 1982. lib. bdg. 105.00x (ISBN 3-921-56729-7). Scholium Intl.

Kertes, A. S. Alcohols with Water. Barton, A. F., ed. (Solubility Data Ser.: Vol. 15). 465p. 1984. 100.00 (ISBN 0-08-025276-1). Pergamon.

Preston, Seaton T., Jr. & Pandratz, Ronald. A Guide to the Analysis of Alcohols by Gas Chromatography. 3rd ed. 190p. 1984. pap. 35.00 (ISBN 0-913106-25-9). Polyscience.

Preston, Seaton T., Jr. & Pankratz, Ronald. A Guide to the Analysis of Alcohols by Gas Chromatography. 2nd ed. 1976. 25.00 (ISBN 0-913106-06-2). PolyScience.

Rodd, E. H. Rodd's Chemistry of Carbon Compounds, Vols. 1-3 in 20 pts. 2nd. ed. Coffey, S., ed. Incl. Vol. 1, Pt. A. Hydrocarbon-Halogen Derivatives. Coffey, S. 569p. 1964. 127.75 (ISBN 0-444-40131-8); Vol. 1, Pt. B. Monohydric Alcohols, Their Ethers & Esters. Coffey, S. 373p. 1965. 95.75 (ISBN 0-444-40132-6); Vol. 1, Pt. C. Monocarbonyl Derivatives of Aliphatic Hydrocarbons, Analogues & Derivatives. Coffey, S. 432p. 1965. 106.50 (ISBN 0-444-40133-4); Vol. 1, Pt. D. Dihydric Alcohols, Their Oxidation Products & Derivatives. Coffey, S. 418p. 1965. 106.50 (ISBN 0-444-40134-2); Vol. 1, Pt. E. Tri & Tetra-hydric Alcohols, Their Oxidation Products & Derivatives. Coffey, S. 488p. 1976. 117.00 (ISBN 0-444-40680-8); Vol. 1, Pt. F. Carbohydrate Chemistry. Coffey, S. 780p. 1968. 170.25 (ISBN 0-444-40135-0); Vol. 1, Pt. G. Enzymes, Macromolecules: Cumulative Index to Vol. 1. Coffey, S. 344p. 1976. 106.50 (ISBN 0-444-41447-9); Vol. 2, Pt. A. Monocarbocyclic Compounds to & Including Five Ring Atoms. Coffey, S. 228p. 1968. 95.75 (ISBN 0-444-40136-9); Vol. 2, Pt. B. Six & Higher-Membered Monocarbocyclic Compounds. Coffey, S. 463p. 1968. 106.50 (ISBN 0-444-40137-7); Vol. 2, Pt. C. Polycyclic Compounds Excluding Steroids. Coffey, S. 521p. 1969. 127.75 (ISBN 0-444-40681-6); Vol. 2, Pt. D. Steroids. Coffey, S. 500p. 1970. 127.75 (ISBN 0-444-40774-X); Vol. 2, Pt. E. Steroids. Coffey, S. 289p. 1971. 95.75 (ISBN 0-444-40775-8); Vol. 3, Pt. A. Mononucleic Hydrocarbons & Their Halogen Derivatives. 559p. 1971. 140.50 (ISBN 0-444-40878-9); Vol. 3, Pt. B. Benzoquinones & Related Compounds. Coffey, S. 559p. 1974. 140.50 (ISBN 0-444-40971-8); Vol. 3, Pt. C. Nuclear Sub-Benzene Hydrocarbons. Coffey, S. 334p. 1973. 102.25 (ISBN 0-444-41092-9); Vol. 3, Pt. D. Aralkyl Compounds: Their Derivatives & Oxidation Products. Coffey, S. 322p. 102.25 (ISBN 0-444-41209-3); Vol. 3, Pt. E. Monobenzine Hydrocarbons Derivatives with Functional Groups. 314p. 102.25 (ISBN 0-444-41210-7); Vol. 3, Pt. F. Polybenzine Hydrocarbons & their Derivatives. Coffey, S. 416p. 117.00 (ISBN 0-444-41211-5); Vol. 3, Pts. G & H. Aromatic Compounds with Fused Carbocyclic Ring Systems, 2 Pts. Coffey, S., ed. 1979. Pt. G. 102.25 (ISBN 0-444-41573-4); Pt. H. 159.75 (ISBN 0-444-41645-5). Elsevier.

Wickson, Edward J., ed. Monohydric Alcohols: Manufacture, Applications, & Chemistry. LC 81-5950. (ACS Symposium Ser.: No. 159). 1981. for info. 33.95rite (ISBN 0-8412-0637-6). Am Chemical.

ALDEHYDES

Collins, Michael A. Aldehyde Adducts in Alcoholism. (PCBR Ser.). 248p. 1985. 46.00 (ISBN 0-8451-5033-2). A R Liss.

Sawicki, Eugene & Sawicki, Carole R. Aldehydes-Photometric Analysis, 5 vols. (Analysis of Organic Materials Ser.). 1975. Vol. 1. 55.00 (ISBN 0-12-620501-9); Vol. 2. 59.00 (ISBN 0-12-620502-7); Vol. 3, 1976. 58.00 (ISBN 0-12-620503-5); Vol. 4. 1977. 55.00 (ISBN 0-12-620504-3); Vol. 5. 85.00 (ISBN 0-12-620505-1). Acad Pr.

Thurman, Ronald, ed. Alcohol & Aldehyde Metabolizing Systems, IV. LC 80-18745. (Advances in Experimental Medicine & Biology Ser.: Vol. 132). 850p. 1980. 95.00x (ISBN 0-306-40476-1, Plenum Pr). Plenum Pub.

Thurman, Ronald G., et al, eds. Alcohol & Aldehyde Metabolizing Systems, 3 vols. (Johnson Foundation Colloquia Ser.). 1978. Vol. 1. 70.00 (ISBN 0-12-691450-8); Vol. 2. 70.00 (ISBN 0-12-691402-8); Vol. 3, 1977. 70.00 (ISBN 0-12-691403-6); Set. 170.00 (ISBN 0-686-77325-X). Acad Pr.

ALDOSTERONE

Mueller, J. Regulation of Aldosterone Biosynthesis. LC 73-137143. (Monographs on Endocrinology: Vol. 5). (Illus.). 1971. 26.00 (ISBN 0-387-05213-5). Springer-Verlag.

Ross, E. J. Aldosterone & Aldosteronism. 502p. 1975. 40.00x (ISBN 0-686-79484-2, Pub. by Lloyd-Luke England). State Mutual Bk.

ALE

see also Beer; Malt

Marchant, W. In Praise of Ale. 59.95 (ISBN 0-8490-0391-1). Gordon Pr.

ALECTORIDES

Bent, Arthur C. Life Histories of North American Marsh Birds. (Illus.). 1927. pap. 7.50 (ISBN 0-486-21082-0). Dover.

--Life Histories of North American Marsh Birds. (Illus.). 15.00 (ISBN 0-8446-1639-7). Peter Smith.

ALFALFA

Flint, Mary L., ed. Integrated Pest Management for Alfalfa Hay. LC 81-65780. (Illus.). 96p. (Orig.). 1981. pap. 15.00x (ISBN 0-931876-46-X, 4104). Ag & Nat Res.

Hanson, C. H., ed. Alfalfa Science & Technology. (Illus.). 1972. 12.50 (ISBN 0-89118-016-8). Am Soc Agron.

Willis, Harold L. How to Grow Great Alfalfa...& Other Forages. (Illus.). 44p. (Orig.). 1983. pap. 4.50 (ISBN 0-912311-01-0). H L Willis.

ALFA-ROMEO (AUTOMOBILE)

see Automobiles, Foreign–Types–Alfa-Romeo

ALGAE

see also Agar; Chrysophyceae; Kelp; Marine Algae; Pyrrhophyta;

also names of families of algae, e.g. Zygnemaceae

Acleto, Cesar O., et al, eds. Phycologia Latino-Americana, Vol. 1. (Span., Illus.). 186p. 1981. text ed. 21.00x (ISBN 3-7682-1297-1). Lubrecht & Cramer.

Agardh, C. A. Species Algarum Rite Cognitae Cum Symonymus, Differentis Specificis et Descriptionibus Succinctis, 2 vols. 1970. Repr. of 1828 ed. 39.10 (ISBN 90-6123-001-2). Lubrecht & Cramer.

Alexopoulos, Constantine J. & Bold, Harold C. Algae & Fungi. 1967. pap. 12.95x (ISBN 0-02-301700-7, 30170). Macmillan.

Algae of the Indian Subcontinent: A Collection of Papers. (Bibliotheca Phycologica Ser.: Vol. 66). (Illus.). 446p. 1984. lib. bdg. 52.50x (ISBN 3-7682-1398-6). Lubrecht & Cramer.

Archibald, R. E. M. The Diatoms of the Sundays & Great Fish Rivers in the Eastern Cape Province of South Africa. (Bibliotheca Diatomologica: Vol.1). 432p. 1983. text ed. 42.00 (ISBN 3-7682-1365-X). Lubrecht & Cramer.

Aufermann, B. Zur Chemotaxonomie Mariner Rhodophyceen am Beispiel einer Leucin-Decarboxylase. (Bibliotheca Phycologica Ser.: No. 43). (Illus.). 1978. pap. text ed. 14.00x (ISBN 3-7682-1206-8). Lubrecht & Cramer.

Bold, Harold C. & Wynne, Michael. Introduction to the Algae. 2nd ed. (Illus.). 848p. 1985. text ed. 44.95 (ISBN 0-13-477746-8). P-H.

Bold, Harold C. & Wynne, Michael J. Introduction to the Algae: Structure & Reproduction. (P-H Biology Ser.). (Illus.). 1978. ref. ed. o.p. 36.95 (ISBN 0-13-477786-7). P-H.

Bornet, E. & Thuret, G. Notes Algologiques: Recueil D'observation Sur les Algues, 2 parts in 1 vol. (Bibl. Phyco.: Vol. 9). (Illus.). 1969. 70.00 (ISBN 3-7682-0601-7). Lubrecht & Cramer.

Brody, Marcia, et al. Bioenergetics & Metabolism of Green Algae, 2 vols. LC 74-515. 1974. Vol. 1. text ed. 21.50x (ISBN 0-8422-7200-3); Vol. 2. text ed. 21.50x (ISBN 0-8422-7201-1). Irvington.

Burlew, John S., ed. Algal Culture: From Laboratory to Pilot Plant. (Illus.). 366p. 1953. 16.00 (ISBN 0-87279-611-6, 600). Carnegie Inst.

Cardinal, Andre. Etude Sur les Ectocarpacees de la Manche. (Illus.). 1965. pap. 21.00 (ISBN 3-7682-5415-1). Lubrecht & Cramer.

Chapman, V. J. & Chapman, D. J. The Algae. 2nd ed. 500p. 1975. 29.95 (ISBN 0-312-01715-4). St Martin.

Collins, F. S. The Green Algae of North America & Supplements 1-2. 1970. 52.50 (ISBN 3-7682-0680-7). Lubrecht & Cramer.

Darley, W. Marshall. Algal Biology: A Physiological Approach. (Illus.). 176p. 1982. pap. text ed. 15.60x (ISBN 0-632-00608-0). Blackwell Pubns.

Drouet, F. Revision of the Stigonematacaea: With a Summary of the Classification of Blue-Green Algae. (Nova Hedwigia Beiheft: No. 66). (Illus.). 300p. 1981. lib. bdg. 42.00x (ISBN 3-7682-5466-6). Lubrecht & Cramer.

Drouet, Francais. Summary of the Classification of Blue-Green Algae. (Illus.). 1981. pap. text ed. 7.00x (ISBN 3-7682-1293-9). Lubrecht & Cramer.

Ettl, H. Die Gattungen Carteria und Provasoliella. (Nova Hedwigia: Suppl. 60). 1979. lib. bdg. 35.00x (ISBN 3-7682-5460-7). Lubrecht & Cramer.

Falkenberg, P. Die Rhodomelaceen Des Golfes Von Neapel und der Angrenzenden Meenesabschnitte. (Fauna & Flor d. Golfes v. Neapel). (Ger., Illus.). 1979. Repr. of 1901 ed. lib. bdg. 113.75x (ISBN 3-87429-143-X). Lubrecht & Cramer.

Feldmann-Mazoyer, Genevieve. Recherches sur les Ceramiaceae de la Mediterranee. 1977. pap. text ed. 61.60x (ISBN 3-87429-120-0). Lubrecht & Cramer.

Flugel, E., ed. Fossil Algae: Recent Results & Developments. LC 76-46461. (Illus.). 1977. 54.00 (ISBN 0-387-07974-2). Springer-Verlag.

--Intermediate Algebra. 2nd ed. (Illus.). 1980. text ed. 27.95 (ISBN 0-07-003750-7). McGraw.

Barros-Neto, Jose. Algebra & Trigonometry for College Students. (Illus.). 550p. 1985. text ed. 28.95 (ISBN 0-314-85218-2). West Pub.

--College Algebra with Applications. (Illus.). 450p. 1985. text ed. 27.95 (ISBN 0-314-85217-4). West Pub.

Basilevsky, A. Applied Matrix Algebra in the Statistical Sciences. 390p. 1983. 39.50 (ISBN 0-444-00756-3). Elsevier.

Bass, Hyman, et al, eds. Contributions to Algebra: A Collection of Papers Dedicated to Ellis Kolchin. LC 76-45980. 1977. 75.00 (ISBN 0-12-080550-2). Acad Pr.

Bazilevic, I. E., et al. Thirteen Papers on Algebra, Topology, Complex Variables, & Linear Programming. LC 51-5559. (Translations Ser.: No. 2, Vol. 71). 1968. 32.00 (ISBN 0-8218-1771-X, TRANS 2-71). Am Math.

Bear, H. S. Algebra & Elementary Functions. 2nd ed. LC 76-184869. (Page-Ficklin Math Ser). 1976. pap. text ed. 15.95x (ISBN 0-8087-2855-5). Burgess.

--College Algebra. 2nd ed. LC 79-83675. (Page-Ficklin Math Ser.). 1979. text ed. 14.95x (ISBN 0-8087-2892-X). Burgess.

Beckenbach, et al. College Algebra. 6th ed. 1984. write for info (ISBN 0-534-03653-8). Wadsworth Pub.

--Modern College Algebra & Trigonometry. 5th ed. 1985. text ed. write for info. Wadsworth Pub.

Bello, Ignacio. Contemporary Introductory Algebra. 589p. 1985. pap. text ed. 23.95 scp (ISBN 0-06-040617-8, HarpC). Har-Row.

Bello, Ignacio & Britton, Jack. Beginning Algebra. LC 75-12485. 450p. 1976. text ed. 25.95 (ISBN 0-7216-1688-7); instr's manual 1.95 (ISBN 0-03-057209-6). HR&W.

Benice, Daniel. Arithmetic & Algebra. 3rd ed. (Illus.). 464p. 1985. pap. text ed. 26.95 (ISBN 0-13-046111-3). P-H.

Bennett, Michael E., et al. Elementary Algebra. LC 80-21563. 400p. 1981. text ed. write for info. (ISBN 0-87150-303-4, 2391, Prindle). PWS Pubs.

Berlekamp, Elwyn R. Algebraic Coding Theory. rev. ed. 1984. pap. text ed. 38.80 (ISBN 0-89412-063-8). Aegean Park Pr.

Biedenharn, L. C. & Louck, J. D. Encyclopedia of Mathematics & Its Applications: The Racah-Wigner Algebra in Quantum Theory, Vol. 9. 1984. 59.50 (ISBN 0-521-30229-3). Cambridge U Pr.

Biedenharn, L. C., et al. Algebra of Representations of Some Finite Groups. (Rice University Studies: Vol. 54, No. 2). 68p. 1968. pap. 10.00x (ISBN 0-89263-196-1). Rice Univ.

Birjukov, A. P., et al. Sixteen Papers on Number Theory & Algebra. LC 51-5559. (Translations Ser.: No. 2, Vol. 82). 1969. 35.00 (ISBN 0-8218-1782-5, TRANS 2-82). Am Math.

Birkhoff, Garrett & MacLane, Saunders. Survey of Modern Algebra. 4th ed. 1977. text ed. write for info. (ISBN 0-02-310070-2, 31007). Macmillan.

Bloomfield, Derek. From Arithmetic to Algebra. 2nd ed. (Illus.). 1976. pap. 19.95 (ISBN 0-8359-2110-7); instrs'. manual avail. (ISBN 0-8359-2111-5). Reston.

--Intermediate Algebra. 1984. text ed. 24.95 (ISBN 0-8359-3132-3). Reston.

Bolker, Ethan D. Using Algebra. 1983. text ed. 25.95 (ISBN 0-316-10114-1). Little.

Bonsall, F. F. & Duncan, J. Complete Normed Algebras. Hilton, P. J., ed. (Ergenbnisse der Mathematik und Ihrer Grenzgebiete: Vol. 80). 208p. 1973. 45.00 (ISBN 0-387-06386-2). Springer Verlag.

--Numerical Ranges of Operators on Normed Spaces & of Elements of Normed Algebras. LC 71-128498. (London Mathematical Society Lecture Note Ser.: No. 2). 1971. 17.95x (ISBN 0-521-07988-8). Cambridge U Pr.

Boruvka, O. Foundations of the Theory of Groupoids & Groups. 216p. 1975. 39.95x (ISBN 0-8176-0780-3). Birkhauser.

Bosch, S., et al. Non-Archimedean Analysis. (Grundlehren der Mathematischen Wissenschaften Ser.: Vol. 261). 450p. 1984. 59.00 (ISBN 0-387-12546-9). Springer-Verlag.

Bosch, William. College Algebra. LC 83-18953. (Mathematics Ser.). 450p. 1983. text ed. 21.50 pub net (ISBN 0-534-02866-7). Brooks-Cole.

Bourdon, L. P. Elements of Algebra. 59.95 (ISBN 0-8490-0101-3). Gordon Pr.

Bozeck, H., et al. Fifteen Papers on Algebra. LC 51-5559. (Translations Ser.: No. 2, Vol. 45). 1965. 24.00 (ISBN 0-8218-1745-0, TRANS 2-45). Am Math.

Bradley, Gerald L. A Primer of Linear Algebra. (Illus.). 448p. 1975. text ed. 28.95 (ISBN 0-13-700328-5). P-H.

Brase, Charles H. & Brase, Corrine P. College Algebra. 544p. 1982. text ed. 22.95 (ISBN 0-669-02432-5); instr's guide 1.95 (ISBN 0-669-02433-3). Heath.

Brase, Corrinne P. & Brase, Charles H. Basic Algebra for College Students. LC 75-26093. (Illus.). 480p. 1976. text ed. 24.95 (ISBN 0-395-20656-1); instructional options guide & solutions manual 1.90 (ISBN 0-395-20655-3). HM.

Bremmer. Tables of Dominant Weight Multiplicites of Simple Lie Algebras of Rank Less Than or Equal to 8. (Pure & Applied Mathematics: Monographs & Textbooks). 232p. 1985. 65.00 (ISBN 0-8247-7270-9). Dekker.

Brett, William & Sentlowitz, Michael. Elementary Algebra by Example. LC 76-11979. (Illus.). 1977. pap. text ed. 24.95 (ISBN 0-395-24425-0); instr's. manual 1.90. HM.

Brink, Raymond W. College Life Algebra. 2nd ed. (Century Mathematics Ser.). 1951. text ed. 12.95x (ISBN 0-89197-084-3). Irvington.

Britton, Jack R. & Bello, Ignacio. Contemporary College Algebra & Trigonometry. 581p. 1982. text ed. 23.50 scp (ISBN 0-06-040989-4, HarpC); instr. manual avail. (ISBN 0-06-360922-3); chapter test avail. (ISBN 0-06-360923-1). Har-Row.

Bronstein, I. U., et al. Eleven Papers on Logic, Algebra, Analysis & Topology. LC 51-5559. (Translations, Ser.: No. 2, Vol. 97). 1970. 33.00 (ISBN 0-8218-1797-3, TRANS 2-97). Am Math.

Brook, Donald E. Elementary Algebra for Today. rev. ed. (Illus.). 352p. 1985. text ed. 25.95 (ISBN 0-13-252842-8). P-H.

Brudno, A. L., et al. Eighteen Papers on Algebra. LC 51-5559. (Translations, Ser.: No. 2, Vol. 27). 1963. 25.00 (ISBN 0-8218-1727-2, TRANS 2-27). Am Math.

Bryant, Steve J., et al. College Algebra. LC 73-81071. 1980. 25.55x (ISBN 0-673-16228-1). Scott F.

Buchberger, B., et al, eds. Computer Algebra. (Illus.). 283p. 1983. pap. 26.50 (ISBN 0-387-81776-X). Springer Verlag.

Bucur, Ionel. Selected Topics in Algebra. LC 83-24609. 1984. lib. bdg. 79.00 (ISBN 90-277-1671-4, Pub. by Reidel Holland). Kluwer Academic.

Cable, John, et al. Algebra & Trigonometry. 1984. text ed. 32.14 (ISBN 0-205-08208-4, 568208); study guide avail. (568210). Allyn.

Calenko, M. S., et al. Twenty-Two Papers on Algebra, Number Theory, & Differential Geometry. LC 51-5559. (Translations Ser.: No. 2, Vol. 37). 1964. 34.00 (ISBN 0-8218-1737-X, TRANS 2-37). Am Math.

--Twelve Papers on Algebra, Number Theory & Topology. LC 80-20715. (Translations Ser.: No. 2, Vol. 58). 1966. 34.00 (ISBN 0-8218-1758-2, TRANS 2-58). Am Math.

Calmet, J., ed. Computer Algebra: EUROCAM 82, Marseille, France 1982. (Lecture Notes in Computer Science: Vol. 144). 301p. 1982. pap. 16.00 (ISBN 0-387-11607-9). Springer-Verlag.

Campbell, Howard E. Concepts of Algebra & Trigonometry. 656p. 1982. text ed. write for info. (ISBN 0-87150-332-8, 2651, Prindle). PWS Pubs.

--Concepts of College Algebra. 480p. 1982. text ed. write for info. (ISBN 0-87150-325-5, 33L 2591, Prindle). PWS Pubs.

Cao, Z., et al. Incline Algebra & Its Applications. (Mathematics & Its Applications Ser.). 165p. 1984. 36.95 (ISBN 0-470-20116-9). Halsted Pr.

Caradus, S. R. Calkin Algebras & Algebras of Banach Spaces. (Pure & Applied Math Ser.: Vol. 9). 1974. 35.00 (ISBN 0-8247-6246-0). Dekker.

Carico, Charles C. College Algebra & Trigonometry. LC 82-11055. 500p. 1983. text ed. 29.50x (ISBN 0-471-07700-3); student ed. 13.45 (ISBN 0-471-09269-X). Wiley.

Carin, V. S., et al. Nine Papers on Foundations, Algebra, Topology, Functions of a Complex Variable. (Translations Ser.: No. 2, Vol. 15). 1960. 29.00 (ISBN 0-8218-1715-9, TRANS 2-15). Am Math.

Carman, R. A. & Carman, M. J. Basic Algebra: A Guided Approach. 2nd ed. 575p. 1982. pap. text ed. 27.45 (ISBN 0-471-04174-2); solutions manual 12.00 (ISBN 0-471-08688-6); tapes 209.45 (ISBN 0-471-08686-X). Wiley.

Carman, Robert A. & Carman, Marilyn J. Intermediate Algebra: A Guided Approach. 575p. 1980. text ed. 27.45x (ISBN 0-471-02104-0); student ed. 13.45 (ISBN 0-471-07912-X). Wiley.

Carnevale, Thomas & Shloming, Robert. Encounters with Algebra. 480p. 1981. pap. text ed. 21.95 (ISBN 0-15-522593-6, HC); instr's. manual avail. (ISBN 0-15-522594-4). HarBraceJ.

Ceitin, G. S., et al. Fourteen Papers on Logic, Geometry, Topology, & Algebra. LC 72-2350. (Translations Ser.: No. 2, Vol. 100). 1972. 48.00 (ISBN 0-8218-3050-3, TRANS 2-100). Am Math.

Centre De Mathematique Sociale Ecole Des Hautes Etudes En Sciences Sociales. Combinatorics Graphs & Algebra. (Methods & Models in the Social Sciences: No. 5). (Illus., Orig.). 1976. text ed. 16.80x (ISBN 90-2797-511-6). Mouton.

Cernikov, S. N., et al. Algebra. (Translations Ser.: No. 1, Vol. 1). 1968. 24.00 (ISBN 0-8218-1601-2, TRANS 1-1). Am Math.

--Seven Papers on Algebra. LC 51-5559. (Translations Ser.: No. 2, Vol. 69). 1968. 34.00 (ISBN 0-8218-1769-8, TRANS 2-69). Am Math.

--Twelve Papers on Algebra, Algebraic Geometry & Topology. LC 51-5559. (Translations Ser.: No. 2, Vol. 84). 1969. 36.00 (ISBN 0-8218-1784-1, TRANS 2-84). Am Math.

--Twelve Papers on Algebra & Real Functions. LC 51-5559. (Translations Ser.: No. 2, Vol. 17). 1961. 30.00 (ISBN 0-8218-1717-5, TRANS 2-17). Am Math.

Cherlin, G. Model Theoretic Algebra Selected Topics. LC 76-15388. (Lecture Notes in Mathematics: Vol. 521). 1976. pap. 16.00 (ISBN 0-387-07696-4). Springer-Verlag.

Chevalley, Claude. Fundamental Concepts of Algebra. (Pure and Applied Mathematics Ser.: Vol. 7). 1957. 49.50 (ISBN 0-12-172050-0). Acad Pr.

Childs, L. N. A Concrete Introduction to Higher Algebra. LC 78-21870. (Undergraduate Texts in Mathematics). (Illus.). 340p. 1979. 24.00 (ISBN 0-387-90333-X). Springer-Verlag.

CISM (International Center for Mechanical Sciences) A Survey of Algebraic Coding Theory. Berlekamp, E. R., ed. (CISM Pubns. Ser.: No. 28). (Illus.). 75p. 1973. pap. 12.40 (ISBN 0-387-81088-9). Springer-Verlag.

Cohen & Cameron. Intermediate Algebra. 1985. 30.31 (ISBN 0-205-07172-4, 567172). Allyn.

Cohen, Donald & Cameron, Roy. Elementary Algebra. 480p. 1982. pap. text ed. 29.29 (ISBN 0-205-07308-5, 567308); tchr's manual 7.86 (ISBN 0-205-07309-3, 567309). Allyn.

Cohn, P. M. Algebra, 2 vols. LC 73-2780. 1977. (Pub. by Wiley-Interscience); Vol. 2, 1977, 483. 39.95 (ISBN 0-471-01823-6); Vol. 1. pap. 23.95 (ISBN 0-471-16431-3, Pub. by Wiley-Interscience). Wiley.

--Algebra, Vol. 1. 2nd ed. 410p. 1982. pap. 34.95x (ISBN 0-471-10169-9, Pub. by Wiley-Interscience). Wiley.

Conference on Commutative Algebra. Proceedings. Brewer, J. W. & Rutter, E. A., eds. LC 72-96859. (Lecture Notes in Mathematics: Vol. 311). 251p. 1973. pap. 14.00 (ISBN 0-387-06140-1). Springer-Verlag.

Conte, A., ed. Algebraic Threefolds, Varenna, Italy 1981, Second Session: Proceedings. (Lecture Notes in Mathematics: Vol. 947). 315p. 1982. pap. 19.50 (ISBN 0-387-11587-0). Springer-Verlag.

Damarin, Suzanne K. & Leitzel, Joan R. Algebra: A Book for Adults. LC 83-7023. 334p. 1984. text ed. 26.95 (ISBN 0-471-86274-6); write for info. tchr's manual (ISBN 0-471-88838-9). Wiley.

Day, Mary S. Scheubel As an Algebraist. LC 78-176708. (Columbia University. Teachers College. Contributions to Education: No. 219). Repr. of 1926 ed. 22.50 (ISBN 0-404-55219-6). AMS Pr.

Demetropoulos, Andrew & Wolff, Kenneth. Elementary Algebra. 448p. 1984. text ed. write for info. (ISBN 0-02-328580-X). Macmillan.

Demetropoulos, Andrew & Wolff, Kenneth C. Elementary Algebra. 176p. 1984. write for info. supplement (ISBN 0-02-328650-4). Macmillan.

Demetropoulos, Andrew & Wolff, Kenneth. Intermediate Algebra. 560p. 1985. text ed. price not set (ISBN 0-02-328530-3); write for info. solutions manual (ISBN 0-02-328640-7). Macmillan.

Detmer, Richard C. & Smullen, Clinton W. Algebra Drill & Practice. 2nd ed. (A Software Microcomputer Program Ser.). 1982. user's guide 9.50scp (ISBN 0-06-041636-X, HarpC); complete package 125.00scp (ISBN 0-06-041635-1). Har-Row.

Dixmier, J. Enveloping Algebras. (North Holland Mathematical Library: Vol. 14). 376p. 1977. 55.50 (ISBN 0-7204-0430-4, North-Holland). Elsevier.

Dolciani, Mary P., et al. Intermediate Algebra for College Students. LC 71-146721. 1971. text ed. 24.95 (ISBN 0-395-12072-1); tchrs. ed. & key 8.50 (ISBN 0-395-12074-8). HM.

Dold, A. & Eckmann, B., eds. Cylindric Set Algebras. (Lecture Notes in Mathematics, Ser.: Vol. 883). 323p. 1981. pap. 20.00 (ISBN 0-387-10881-5). Springer-Verlag.

Donaghey, Robert & Ruddel, JoAnna. Fundamentals of Algebra: An Integrated Text-Workbook. (Illus.). 559p. 1978. pap. text ed. 19.95 (ISBN 0-15-529420-2, HC); instructor's manual with test resources avail. (ISBN 0-15-529421-0). HarBraceJ.

Dornhoff, Larry L. & Hohn, Franz E. Applied Modern Algebra. (Illus.). 1978. write for info. (ISBN 0-02-329980-0). Macmillan.

Dorsett, Joseph L. Integrated Algebra & Trigonometry. 2nd ed. 1977. pap. text ed. 16.95 (ISBN 0-8403-1699-2). Kendall-Hunt.

Downing. Algebra the Easy Way. (Easy Way Ser.). 1983. 7.95 (ISBN 0-8120-2716-7). Barron.

Draper. Analytic Methods in Communicative Algebra. (Lecture Notes in Pure & Applied Mathematics Ser.: Vol. 68). 1982. 45.00 (ISBN 0-8247-1282-X). Dekker.

Dressler, Isidore & Dressler, Robert. Introductory Algebra for College Students. (Orig.). 1976. pap. text ed. 9.47 (ISBN 0-87720-975-8). AMSCO Sch.

Dressler, Isidore, et al. Intermediate Algebra for College Students. 1977. pap. text ed. 9.47 (ISBN 0-87720-977-4). AMSCO Sch.

Drooyan & Wooton. Intermediate Algebra. 6th ed. 488p. write for info. (ISBN 0-534-01433-X); write for info study guide 263p. Wadsworth Pub.

Drooyan, I. & Hadel, W. Elementary Algebra: Structure & Skills. 5th ed. 351p. 1981. 28.45 (ISBN 0-471-08286-4); student ed. 14.00 (ISBN 0-471-08503-0). Wiley.

Drooyan, Irving & Wooton, William. Beginning Algebra: A Modular Approach, 8 Vols. LC 75-29776. Vol. 1. pap. 20.00 (ISBN 0-317-11109-4, 2012437); Vol. 2. pap. 26.00 (ISBN 0-317-11110-8); Vol. 3. pap. 24.30 (ISBN 0-317-11111-6); Vol. 4. pap. 20.30 (ISBN 0-317-11112-4); Vol. 5. pap. 35.80 (ISBN 0-317-11113-2); Vol. 6. pap. 35.80 (ISBN 0-317-11114-0); Vol. 7. pap. 20.50 (ISBN 0-317-11115-9); Vol. 8. pap. 26.50 (ISBN 0-317-11116-7). Bks Demand UMI.

--Beginning Algebra: An Individualized Approach. LC 78-625. 420p. 1978. 29.00x (ISBN 0-471-03877-6). Wiley.

--Elementary Algebra for College Students. 6th ed. LC 83-3556. 432p. 1984. text ed. 28.50 (ISBN 0-471-87387-X); student solution manual 10.50x (ISBN 0-471-88573-8); test avail. (ISBN 0-471-88595-9). Wiley.

--Elementary Algebra with Geometry. 2nd ed. 467p. 1984. text ed. 26.95 (ISBN 0-471-09825-6, Pub by Wiley); write for info. solutions manual (ISBN 0-471-88070-1). Wiley.

Drooyan, Irving, et al. Introductory Algebra: A Guided Worktext. LC 81-99. 410p. 1982. text ed. 30.95 (ISBN 0-471-06318-5); text suppl. avail. (ISBN 0-471-86591-5). Wiley.

Dubisch, Roy & Hood, Vernon. Elementary Algebra. LC 76-3846. 1977. text ed. 27.95 (ISBN 0-8053-2338-4); instr's guide o.p. 4.95 (ISBN 0-8053-2339-2). Benjamin-Cummings.

Durbin, J. R. College Algebra. 2nd ed. 528p. 1985. 25.95 (ISBN 0-471-81714-7). Wiley.

--Modern Algebra: An Introduction. 2nd ed. 346p. 1985. 29.95 (ISBN 0-471-88487-1). Wiley.

Durbin, John. College Algebra & Trigonometry. LC 83-16829. (Recreational Computing Ser.: 1-704). 688p. 1984. text ed. 27.95 (ISBN 0-471-03367-7); solutions manual avail. (ISBN 0-471-88351-4); test manual avail. (ISBN 0-471-81066-5). Wiley.

Durbin, John R. College Algebra. LC 81-11379. 506p. 1982. text ed. 25.95x (ISBN 0-471-03368-5); student solutions manual 8.00 (ISBN 0-471-86456-0). Wiley.

Dyckman, Thomas & Thomas, L. Joseph. Algebra & Calculus for Business. (Illus.). 464p. 1974. text ed. 29.95 (ISBN 0-13-021758-1). P-H.

Dynkin, E. B., et al. Five Papers on Algebra & Group Theory. LC 51-5559. (Translations Ser.: No. 2, Vol. 6). 1957. 55.00 (ISBN 0-8218-1706-X, TRANS 2-6). Am Math.

Easton, Richard J. & Graham, George P. Intermediate Algebra. LC 72-4744. (Illus.). 305p. 1973. text ed. 29.50x (ISBN 0-471-22939-3); wkbk. o.p. 13.95x (ISBN 0-471-22943-1). Wiley.

Effros, Edward G. Dimensions & C-Algebras. LC 81-1582. (CBMS Regional Conference Series in Mathematics: Vol. 46). 74p. 1981. pap. 9.00 (ISBN 0-8218-1697-7). Am Math.

Ehrig, H. & Mahr, B. Fundamentals of Algebraic Specification I. (EATCS Monographs on Theoretical Computer Science: Vol. 6). 336p. 1985. 29.50 (ISBN 0-387-13718-1). Springer-Verlag.

Eichler, Martin. Projective Varieties & Modular Forms. LC 78-166998. (Lecture Notes in Mathematics: Vol. 210). 1973. pap. 11.00 (ISBN 0-387-05519-3). Springer-Verlag.

Eisenschitz, R. K. Matrix Algebra for Physicists. LC 66-18972. 124p. 1966. 17.50x (ISBN 0-306-30214-4, Plenum Pr). Plenum Pub.

Elgot, C. C. Selected Papers. (Illus.). 456p. 1982. 39.00 (ISBN 0-387-90698-3). Springer-Verlag.

Elich, Joseph & Elich, Carletta J. College Algebra with Calculus. (Math-Mallion Ser.). (Illus.). 480p. 1981. text ed. 25.95x (ISBN 0-201-13340-7); instr's. manual 2.50 (ISBN 0-201-13341-5); answer bk. 2.50 (ISBN 0-201-13342-3); student guide 6.95 (ISBN 0-201-13343-1). Addison-Wesley.

Ellis, A. J. Basic Algebra & Geometry for Scientists & Engineers. 187p. 1982. 28.95x (ISBN 0-471-10174-5). Wiley.

Ellis, Robert & Gulick, Denny. College Algebra. 514p. 1981. text ed. 24.95 (ISBN 0-15-507905-0, HC); answer manual avail. (ISBN 0-15-507906-9). HarBraceJ.

--Fundamentals of College Algebra & Trigonometry. 448p. 1984. text ed. 24.95 (ISBN 0-15-529350-8, HC). HarBraceJ.

Endler, O. Valuation Theory. LC 72-92285. (Universitext). xii, 243p. 1972. pap. 18.50 (ISBN 0-387-06070-7). Springer-Verlag.

Engelsohn, Harold S. & Feit, Joseph. Basic Mathematics: Arithmetic & Algebra. LC 79-21287. 532p. 1980. pap. 34.00 (ISBN 0-471-24145-8). Wiley.

Estructuras Algebraicas. rev. ed. (Serie de Matematica: No. 3). (Span.). 1977. pap. 3.50 (ISBN 0-8270-6220-6). OAS.

Estructuras Algebraicas II (Algebra Lineal) (Serie de Matematica: No. 12). (Span.). 160p. 1971. pap. 3.50 (ISBN 0-8270-6285-0). OAS.

Eulenberg, Milton D., et al. Intermediate Algebra: A College Approach. LC 74-180243. Repr. of 1972 ed. 97.00 (ISBN 0-8357-9913-1, 2055123). Bks Demand UMI.

--Introductory Algebra. 3rd ed. LC 74-24338. 374p. lib. bdg. 28.95 (ISBN 0-471-24686-7). Krieger.

Eulenburg, Milton D., et al. Introductory Algebra. 3rd ed. LC 74-24338. 360p. 1975. text ed. 31.45x (ISBN 0-471-24686-7); avail. answers (ISBN 0-471-24687-5). Wiley.

Euler, L. Elements of Algebra. ix, 596p. 1984. Repr. of 1840 ed. 28.00 (ISBN 0-387-96014-7). Springer-Verlag.

Faddeev, D. K., et al. Five Papers on Logic, Algebra, & Number Theory. LC 51-5559. (Translations Ser.: No. 2, Vol. 3). 1956. 24.00 (ISBN 0-8218-1703-5, TRANS 2-3). Am Math.

Feinstein, Irwin K. & Murphy, Kenneth H. College Algebra: With Problems & Solutions (Pre-Calculus Algebra) 2nd. ed. (Quality Paperback Ser.: No. 39). 486p. (Orig.). 1981. pap. text ed. 6.95 (ISBN 0-8226-0039-0). Littlefield.

Feintuch, Abraham & Saeks, R. System Theory: A Hilbert Space Approach. LC 82-1816. (Pure & Applied Mathematics Ser.). 1982. 49.50 (ISBN 0-12-251750-4). Acad Pr.

Feldman, N. I., et al. Twelve Papers on Logic & Algebra. LC 51-5559. (Translations Ser.: No. 2, Vol. 59). 1966. 36.00 (ISBN 0-8218-1759-0, TRANS 2-59). Am Math.

Fiedorowicz, Z. & Priddy, S. Homology of Classical Groups Over Finite Fields & Their Associated Infinite Loop Spaces. LC 78-12091. (Lecture Notes in Mathematics: Vol. 674). 1978. pap. 27.00 (ISBN 0-387-08932-2). Springer-Verlag.

Filippov, N. D., et al. Ten Papers on Algebra & Functional Analysis. LC 51-5559. (Translations Ser.: No. 2, Vol. 96). 1970. 32.00 (ISBN 0-8218-1796-5, TRANS 2-96). Am Math.

Fisher, James L. Application-Oriented Algebra: An Introduction to Discrete Mathematics. 1977. text ed. 28.95 scp (ISBN 0-7002-2504-8, HarpC). Har-Row.

Fisher, Robert C. & Ziebur, Allen D. Integrated Algebra, Trigonometry & Analytic Geometry. 4th ed. (Illus.). 560p. 1982. 29.95 (ISBN 0-13-468967-4). P-H.

Flanders, Harley & Price, Justin J. Algebra. 2nd ed. 1981. text ed. 27.95 (ISBN 0-03-057801-9, CBS C); instr's manual 11.95 (ISBN 0-03-058633-X); study guide 11.95 (ISBN 0-03-058634-8). SCP.

--Algebra & Trigonometry. 2nd ed. 1981. text ed. 29.95 (ISBN 0-03-057779-9, CBS C); instr's manual 12.95 (ISBN 0-03-058249-0); study guide 11.95 (ISBN 0-03-058252-0). SCP.

Fleming, Walter & Varberg, Dale. Algebra & Trigonometry. 2nd ed. (Illus.). 576p. 1984. text ed. 29.95 (ISBN 0-13-021535-X). P-H.

--College Algebra. 2nd ed. (Illus.). 496p. 1984. text ed. 28.95 (ISBN 0-13-141630-8). P-H.

Frankenstein, Marilyn. Basic Algebra. (Illus.). 1979. pap. text ed. 27.95 (ISBN 0-13-056788-4). P-H.

Freese, R. S. & Garcia, O. C., eds. Universal Algebra & Lattice Theory. (Lecture Notes in Mathematics Ser.: Vol. 1004). 308p. 1983. pap. 17.00 (ISBN 0-387-12329-6). Springer-Verlag.

Freilich, Gerald & Greenleaf, Frederick P. Algebraic Methods: In Business, Economics, & the Social Sciences - a Short Course. (Mathematics Ser.). (Illus.). 311p. 1977. pap. text ed. 8.50 (ISBN 0-7167-0470-6). W H Freeman.

Frey, Alexander H., Jr. & Singmaster, David. Handbook of Cubik Math. LC 81-12525. (Illus.). 204p. 1982. text ed. 17.95x (ISBN 0-89490-060-9). Enslow Pubs.

Frieder, David. Algebra Simplified & Self-Taught. LC 83-2843. 144p. (Orig.). 1983. pap. 5.95 (ISBN 0-668-05797-1, 5797). Arco.

Fuller, Gordon. Algebra & Trigonometry. 1971. text ed. 28.95 (ISBN 0-07-022605-9). McGraw.

Gallo, Michael & Kiehl, Charles. Introductory Algebra. LC 83-21825. 450p. 1984. pap. text ed. 27.95 (ISBN 0-314-78001-7); test bank avail. (ISBN 0-314-78002-5). West Pub.

Gamelin, T. W. Uniform Algebras & Jensen Measures. LC 78-16213. (London Mathematical Society Lecture Note Ser.: No. 32). 1979. pap. 24.95 (ISBN 0-521-22280-X). Cambridge U Pr.

Gamelin, Theodore W. Uniform Algebras. x2nd ed. LC 83-72339. 270p. text ed. 17.95 (ISBN 0-8284-0311-2). Chelsea Pub.

--Uniform Algebras & Jensen Measures. LC 78-16213. (London Mathematical Society Lecture Note Ser.: 32). pap. 42.50 (ISBN 0-317-20600-1, 2024488). Bks Demand UMI.

Gaughan, Edward D. & Hall, Carl E. College Algebra & Trigonometry. LC 83-15470. (Mathematics Ser.). 550p. 1983. text ed. 22.75 pub net (ISBN 0-534-02777-6). Brooks-Cole.

Gilbert & Gilbert. Algebra & Trigonometry. 1986. text ed. write for info (ISBN 0-534-06120-6). Wadsworth Pub.

Gilbert, et al. College Algebra. 2nd ed. 1985. text ed. write for info (ISBN 0-534-05298-3). Wadsworth Pub.

Gilbert, Jimmie, et al. College Algebra. (Illus.). 496p. 1981. text ed. 29.95 (ISBN 0-13-141804-1). P-H.

Gilbert, Linda & Gilbert, Jimmie. Elements of Modern Algebra. 352p. 1983. pap. text ed. write for info (ISBN 0-87150-458-8, 2830, Prindle). PWS Pubs.

--Intermediate Algebra. (Illus.). 512p. 1983. text ed. 26.95 (ISBN 0-13-469536-4). P-H.

Gilligan, Lawrence & Nenno, Robert. Intermediate Algebra for College Students. 2nd ed. 567p. 1984. pap. text ed. 20.95 (ISBN 0-669-05696-0). Heath.

Gilligan, Lawrence & Nenno, Robert B. Basic Algebra: A Semi-Programmed Approach. LC 76-12810. (Illus.). 1977. pap. text ed. 21.70x (ISBN 0-673-16221-4). student solution manual 8.25 (ISBN 0-673-16222-2). Scott F.

--College Algebra. 1981. text ed. 25.55x (ISBN 0-673-16229-X). Scott F.

--College Algebra & Trigonometry: Precalculus Math. 1981. text ed. 25.55 (ISBN 0-673-16230-3). Scott F.

Gobran, Alfonse. Beginning Algebra. 3rd ed. 400p. 1982. text ed. write for info. (ISBN 0-87150-349-2, 2741, Prindle). PWS Pubs.

--Intermediate Algebra. 2nd ed. 1979. text ed. write for info. (ISBN 0-87150-230-5, PWS 1841, Prindle). PWS Pubs.

--Intermediate Algebra. 3rd ed. 528p. 1983. text ed. write for info (ISBN 0-87150-363-8, 2791, Prindle). PWS Pubs.

Goldhaber, Jacob K. & Ehrlich, Gertrude. Algebra. LC 78-9889. 430p. 1980. Repr. of 1970 ed. lib. bdg. 23.50 (ISBN 0-88275-765-2). Krieger.

Golinskii, B. L., et al. Thirteen Papers on Algebra & Analysis. LC 51-5559. (Translations Ser.: No. 2, Vol. 76). 1968. 35.00 (ISBN 0-8218-1776-0, TRANS 2-76). Am Math.

Gondin, William R. & Sohmer, Bernard. Advanced Algebra & Calculus Made Simple. (Made Simple Ser.). pap. 4.95 (ISBN 0-385-00438-9). Doubleday.

--Intermediate Algebra & Analytic Geometry Made Simple. (Made Simple Ser.). pap. 4.95 (ISBN 0-385-00437-0). Doubleday.

Goodearl, K. R. & Boyle, Ann K. Dimension Theory for Nonsingular Injective Modules. LC 76-26498. (Memoirs of the American Mathematical Society: 177). 112p. 1976. pap. 13.00 (ISBN 0-8218-2177-6, MEMO 177). Am Math.

Goodearl, K. R., et al. Affine Representations of Grothendieck Groups & Applications to Rickart C-Algebras & Aleph O-Continuous Regular Rings. LC 80-17018. (Memoirs: No. 234). 163p. 1980. pap. 9.00 (ISBN 0-8218-2234-9). Am Math.

Goodman, A. W., et al. The Mainstream of Algebra & Trigonometry. 2nd ed. LC 79-90059. (Illus.). 1980. text ed. 29.50 (ISBN 0-395-26765-X); solutions manual 7.50 (ISBN 0-395-26761-7). HM.

Goodman, Arthur & Hirsch, Lewis. Understanding Elementary Algebra. (Illus.). 460p. 1986. text ed. 22.36 (ISBN 0-314-93532-0). West Pub.

Goodson, C. E. & Miertschin, S. L. Technical Algebra with Applications. 592p. 1985. 26.95 (ISBN 0-471-08241-4). Wiley.

Gray, Al. Algebra; Beginning: Syllabus. 2nd ed. 1976. pap. text ed. 7.25 (ISBN 0-89420-033-X, 367015); cassette recordings 164.35 (ISBN 0-89420-125-5, 367007). Natl Book.

Green, Tom & Wooton, William. Intermediate Algebra. 608p. 1980. pap. text ed. write for info. (ISBN 0-534-00788-0). Wadsworth Pub.

Greenburg, Herbert J. & Murphy, Charlotte W. Intermediate Algebra. 512p. 1982. text ed. write for info. (ISBN 0-87150-324-7, 33L 2581, Prindle). PWS Pubs.

Greenleaf, F. & Gulick, D., eds. Banach Algebras & Several Complex Variables Conference: Proceedings. LC 84-18443. (Contemporary Mathematics Ser.: Vol. 32). 28.00 (ISBN 0-8218-5034-2). Am Math.

Gross, H. & Waerden, B. Studien zur Theorie der Quadratischen Formen. (Mathemische Reihe Ser.: No. 34). (Ger., Illus.). 254p. 1968. 41.95x (ISBN 0-8176-0401-4). Birkhauser.

Gross, Herbert F. Algebra by Example: An Elementary Course. 1978. 19.95 (ISBN 0-669-00473-1); instr's manual 1.95 (ISBN 0-669-00474-X); solutions manual 9.95x (ISBN 0-669-01014-6); cassettes 150.00 (ISBN 0-669-01154-1); tapescript 1.95 (ISBN 0-669-01018-9); demo tape 1.95 (ISBN 0-669-01633-0). Heath.

Groza, Vivian S. College Algebra. 1980. text ed. 27.95 (ISBN 0-03-040376-6, CBS C). SCP.

--Elementary Algebra. 3rd ed. LC 80-53936. (Illus.). 660p. 1981. pap. text ed. 28.95x (ISBN 0-03-057719-5). HR&W.

--Elementary Algebra. 4th ed. 1986. pap. text ed. 26.95 (ISBN 0-03-006079-6, CBS C); instr's manual 9.95 (ISBN 0-03-006069-9). SCP.

Groza, Vivian S. & Sellers, Gene. Algebra & Trigonometry. 1982. pap. 29.95 (ISBN 0-03-060107-X, CBS C). SCP.

--Intermediate Algebra. 2nd ed. 1981. pap. text ed. 27.95 (ISBN 0-03-057722-5, CBS C); pap. 9.95 instr's manual (ISBN 0-03-058256-3). SCP.

Gulati, Bodh R. College Algebra. 480p. 1982. text ed. 30.50 (ISBN 0-205-07683-1, 5676835); tchr's ed. free (ISBN 0-205-07684-X, 5676843); 8.93 (ISBN 0-205-07685-8, 5676851). Allyn.

Gulati, Bodh R. & Bass, Helen. Algebra & Trigonometry: Precalculus Mathematics. 676p. 1982. text ed. 33.39 scp (ISBN 0-205-07686-6, 567688); tchr's ed. free (ISBN 0-205-07687-4, 567688); scp avail. study guide 10.14 (ISBN 0-205-07688-2). Allyn.

Gustafson, R. D. & Frisk, Peter D. College Algebra. 2nd ed. LC 82-4389. (Mathematics Ser.). 475p. 1982. text ed. 21.50 pub net (ISBN 0-534-01202-7); single copy 29.25. Brooks-Cole.

--College Algebra & Trigonometry. LC 82-4388. (Mathematics Ser.). 600p. 1982. text ed. 22.75 pub net (ISBN 0-534-01203-5). Brooks-Cole.

Gustafson, R. David & Frisk, Peter D. Algebra for College Students. LC 84-23055. (Mathematics Ser.). 565p. 1985. text ed. 22.25 pub net (ISBN 0-534-05028-X). Brooks-Cole.

--Beginning Algebra. LC 84-23764. (Mathematics Ser.). 400p. 1985. text ed. 21.50 pub net (ISBN 0-534-04077-2). Brooks-Cole.

--Intermediate Algebra. LC 83-7585. (Mathematics Ser.). 512p. 1983. text ed. 20.75 pub net (ISBN 0-534-02906-X). Brooks-Cole.

Hackworth, Robert D. & Howland, Joseph W. College Algebra & Trigonometry As Socrates Might Have Taught Them. rev. ed. (Illus.). 295p. 1981. pap. text ed. 14.95x (ISBN 0-943202-01-9). H & H Pub.

Hackworth, Robert D. & Howland, Joseph. Introductory College Mathematics: Algebra One. LC 75-23621. 65p. 1976. pap. text ed. 9.95 (ISBN 0-7216-4414-7). HR&W.

--Introductory College Mathematics: Algebra Two. LC 75-23622. 66p. 1976. pap. text ed. 9.95 (ISBN 0-7216-4415-5). HR&W.

Hackworth, Robert D. & Howland, Joseph W. Programmed College Algebra. (Programmed Arithmetic Ser.). (Illus.). 535p. 1985. pap. text ed. 21.95x (ISBN 0-943202-11-6). H & H Pub.

Hall, James W. & Bennett, Richard D. College Algebra with Applications. 1985. text ed. write for info. (ISBN 0-87150-848-6, 33L2890, Prindle). PWS Pubs.

Harshbarger, Ronald J. Intermediate Algebra. 407p. 1976. text ed. 24.00 scp (ISBN 0-06-042683-7, HarpC); instr's. manual avail. (ISBN 0-06-362660-8). Har-Row.

--Introductory Algebra. 294p. 1976. text ed. 23.50 scp (ISBN 0-06-042682-9, HarpC); scp study guide o.p. 9.95 (ISBN 0-06-042673-X); instructor's manual avail. (ISBN 0-06-362662-4). Har-Row.

Hart, William L. & Waits, Bert K. College Algebra. 6th ed. 1978. text ed. 21.95 (ISBN 0-669-01025-1); instr's manual 1.95 (ISBN 0-669-01026-X). Heath.

--College Algebra & Trigonometry. 2nd ed. 1978. text ed. 21.95 (ISBN 0-669-01460-5); instr's. manual 1.95 (ISBN 0-669-01462-1). Heath.

Hartley, B. & Hawkes, T. Rings, Modules & Linear Algebra. (Mathematics Ser.). 1970. pap. 13.95x (ISBN 0-412-09810-5, NO. 6144, Pub. by Chapman & Hall). Methuen Inc.

Hejhal, D. A. The Selberg Trace Formula for PSL(2,R) (Lecture Notes in Mathematics: Vol. 548). 1976. soft cover 24.00 (ISBN 0-387-07988-2). Springer-Verlag.

Hermann, Robert. General Algebraic Ideas. (Interdisciplinary Mathematics Ser.: No. 1). 205p. 1973. 13.00 (ISBN 0-915692-00-7, 99160027 4). Math Sci Pr.

--Spinors, Clifford, & Cayley Algebras. (Interdisciplinary Mathematics Ser: Vol. 7). 276p. 1974. 25.00 (ISBN 0-915692-06-6, 991600215). Math Sci Pr.

Herstein, I. N. Topics in Algebra. 2nd ed. LC 74-82577. 432p. 1975. text ed. 40.95 (ISBN 0-471-01090-1). Wiley.

Hestenes, David & Sobczyk, Garrett. Clifford Algebra to Geometric Calculus. 1984. lib. bdg. 58.00 (ISBN 90-277-1673-0, Pub. by Reidel Holland). Kluwer Academic.

Hestenes, Marshall & Hill, Richard. Algebra & Trigonometry. 2nd ed. (Illus.). 656p. 1986. text ed. 28.95 (ISBN 0-13-021866-9). P H.

--College Algebra with Calculators. (Illus.). 416p. 1982. 28.95 (ISBN 0-13-140806-2). P-H.

Hestenes, Marshall D. & Hill, Richard O. College Algebra. 2nd ed. (Illus.). 448p. 1986. text ed. 24.94 (ISBN 0-13-140856-9). P-H.

Heywood. Elementary Algebra: Lecture-Lab. 480p. 1985. pap. text ed. 24.95 (ISBN 0-8403-3542-3). Kendall-Hunt.

Hoffman, P. T-Rings & Wreath Product Representations. (Lecture Notes in Mathematics: Vol. 746). 1979. pap. 14.00 (ISBN 0-387-09551-9). Springer-Verlag.

Holcombe, William M. Algebraic Automata Theory. LC 81-18169. (Cambridge Studies in Advanced Mathematics 1). 250p. 1982. 32.50 (ISBN 0-521-23196-5). Cambridge U Pr.

Holder. College Algebra & Trigonometry. 3rd ed. 582p. write for info. (ISBN 0-534-02917-5). Watts.

Holder, Leonard I. College Algebra. 3rd ed. 439p. write for info. (ISBN 0-534-02695-8). Watts.

Holloway, Ronald W. & Strozak, Victor S. Introductory Algebra: A Dual Approach. 1979. text ed. 23.50 scp (ISBN 0-06-383635-1, HarpC); instr. manual avail. (ISBN 0-06-373008-1). Har-Row.

Hotta, R., ed. Algebraic Groups & Related Topics: Proceedings of Symposium Held in Kyoto, Japan 5-7 Sept. 1983 & Nagoya, Japan 11-14 Oct 1983. (Advanced Studies in Pure Mathematics: Vol. 6). 544p. 1985. 115.00 (ISBN 0-444-87711-8, North-Holland). Elsevier.

Howson, A. G. A Handbook of Terms Used in Algebra & Analysis. LC 71-178281. (Illus.). 260p. 1972. 39.50 (ISBN 0-521-08434-2); pap. 16.95 (ISBN 0-521-09695-2). Cambridge U Pr.

Hughes-Hallett, Deborah. The Math Workshop: Algebra. (Illus.). 1980. text ed. 22.95x (ISBN 0-393-09030-2); tchrs'. manual avail. (ISBN 0-393-09024-8). Norton.

Hungerford, T. W. Algebra. (Graduate Texts in Mathematics: Vol. 73). 502p. 1980. 29.80 (ISBN 0-387-90518-9). Springer-Verlag.

Hungerford, Thomas W. & Mercer, Richard. Algebra & Trigonometry. 1982. text ed. 29.95 (ISBN 0-03-059519-3); instr's manual 10.95 (ISBN 0-03-059518-5). HR&W.

--College Algebra. 1982. text ed. 29.95 (ISBN 0-03-059521-5, CBS C). SCP.

Hutton, Lucreda A., et al. Success with Algebra. (Illus.). 512p. 1985. pap. text ed. 26.95 (ISBN 0-13-859372-8). P-H.

Iitaka, S., ed. Algebraic Varieties & Analytic Varieties: Proceedings of a Symposim Held in Tokyo, 13-24 July, 1981. (Advanced Studies in Pure Mathematics: No. 1). 384p. 1983. 74.50 (ISBN 0-444-86612-4, I-169-83, North Holland). Elsevier.

International Conference, Ottawa, 1974. Representations of Algebras: Proceedings. Dlab, V. & Gabriel, P., eds. (Lecture Notes in Mathematics: Vol. 488). xii, 378p. 1975. pap. 20.00 (ISBN 0-387-07406-6). Springer-Verlag.

Iversen, B. Generic Local Structure of the Morphisms in Commutative Algebra. LC 72-96863. (Lecture Notes in Mathematics: Vol. 310). 108p. 1973. pap. 11.00 (ISBN 0-387-06137-1). Springer-Verlag.

Iverson, K. E. Algebra: An Algorithmic Treatment. (Illus., Orig.). 1977. pap. text ed. 10.75 (ISBN 0-917326-09-1). APL Pr.

Jackiw, R., et al. Current Algebra & Anomalies. 550p. 1985. 63.00x (ISBN 0-317-27169-5, Pub by World Sci Singapore); pap. 30.00x (ISBN 0-317-27170-9). Taylor & Francis.

Jacobs, Harold R. Elementary Algebra. LC 78-10744. (Illus.). 876p. 1979. text ed. 17.95 (ISBN 0-7167-1047-1); tchrs. guide 8.95 (ISBN 0-7167-1075-7); test masters 8.00 (ISBN 0-7167-1077-3); transparency masters 50.00x (ISBN 0-7167-1076-5). W H Freeman.

Jacobson, N. PI-Algebras: An Introduction. LC 75-6644. (Lecture Notes in Mathematics Ser: Vol. 441). v, 115p. 1975. pap. 13.00 (ISBN 0-387-07143-1). Springer-Verlag.

Jacobson, Nathan. Basic Algebra I. 2nd ed. LC 84-25836. (Illus.). 499p. 1985. text ed. 35.95 (ISBN 0-7167-1480-9). W H Freeman.

--Basic Algebra Two. LC 73-22316. (Illus.). 666p. 1980. 38.95 (ISBN 0-7167-1079-X); answer bk. avail. W H Freeman.

Jacquet, H. & Langlands, R. P. Automorphic Forms on GL 2. LC 76-108338. (Lecture Notes in Mathematics Ser.: Vol. 114). (Orig.). 1970. pap. 21.90 (ISBN 0-387-04903-7). Springer-Verlag.

Janowitz, M. Intermediate Algebra. 1976. 23.95 (ISBN 0-13-469528-3). P-H.

Johnson, L. Murphy & Steffensen, Arnold R. Elementary Algebra. 1985. text ed. 22.95x (ISBN 0-673-15940-X). Scott F.

--Intermediate Algebra. 1985. text ed. 24.95x (ISBN 0-673-15632-X). Scott F.

Johnson, R. E., et al. Elementary Algebra. 1981. 27.95 (ISBN 0-8053-5052-7); instr.'s guide 4.95 (ISBN 0-8053-5053-5); study guide 10.95 (ISBN 0-8053-5055-1). Benjamin-Cummings.

Johnson, Richard E., et al. Elementary Algebra. 1981. 27.95 (ISBN 0-8053-5052-7); study guide by Lucille Groenke 10.95 (ISBN 0-8053-5055-1); instr's. guide 4.95 (ISBN 0-8053-5053-5). Benjamin-Cummings.

Johnston, et al. Essential Algebra. 4th ed. 608p. 1985. write for info. (ISBN 0-534-05022-0). Wadsworth Pub.

Johnston, Carol L. & Willis, Alden T. Developmental Mathematics. 544p. 1982. pap. text ed. write for info. (ISBN 0-534-01098-9). Wadsworth Pub.

--Intermediate Algebra. 3rd ed. 688p. 1982. pap. write for info. (ISBN 0-534-01425-9). Wadsworth Pub.

Jonah, David W. Cohomology of Coalgebras. LC 52-42839. (Memoirs Ser.: No. 82). 73p. 1968. pap. 9.00 (ISBN 0-8218-1282-3, MEMO-82). Am Math.

Kadison, R. V., ed. C-Algebras & Applications to Physics: Proceedings Second Japan-USA Seminar, Los Angeles, April 18 - 22, 1977. (Lecture Notes in Mathematics: Vol. 650). 1978. pap. 14.00 (ISBN 0-387-08762-1). Springer-Verlag.

Kadison, Richard V. & Ringrose, John R., eds. Fundamentals of the Theory of Operator Algebras, Vol. 1. LC 82-13768. 1983. 29.50 (ISBN 0-12-393301-3). Acad Pr.

Kahan, Steven. Intermediate Algebra. 588p. 1981. text ed. 20.95 (ISBN 0-15-541530-1, HC); instr's manual avail. (ISBN 0-15-541531-X); trigonometry supplement avail. (ISBN 0-15-541532-8). HarBraceJ.

Kaplan, rev. by. Barron's Regents Exams & Answers 9th Year Mathematics: Elementary Algebra. rev. ed. LC 58-33441. 1982. pap. 4.50 (ISBN 0-8120-3201-2). Barron.

Karpilovsky. Commutative Group Algebras. (Lecture Notes in Pure & Applied Mathematics). 328p. 1983. 39.75 (ISBN 0-8247-1918-2). Dekker.

Kaufmann. Elementary Algebra for College Students. 2nd ed. 1985. text ed. write for info. (ISBN 0-87150-934-2, 33L4000, Prindle). PWS Pubs.

--Intermediate Algebra for College Students. 2nd ed. 1986. text ed. write for info. (ISBN 0-87150-960-1, 33L4020, Prindle). PWS Pubs.

Kaufmann, Jerome. Algebra for College Students. 600p. 1984. text ed. write for info (ISBN 0-87150-464-2, 2850, Prindle). PWS Pubs.

Kaufmann, Jerome E. Elementary Algebra. 480p. 1982. text ed. write for info. (ISBN 0-87150-337-9, 2701, Prindle). PWS Pubs.

--Intermediate Algebra. 550p. 1982. text ed. write for info. (ISBN 0-87150-340-9, 2721, Prindle). PWS Pubs.

Keedy, Mervin & Bittinger, Marvin. Decimals & Percent. rev. ed. (Algebra, a Modern Introduction Ser.). 1981. pap. text ed. 4.32 (ISBN 0-201-03980-X). Addison-Wesley.

--Measures, Ratio & Averages. rev. ed. (Algebra, a Modern Introduction Ser.). 1981. pap. text ed. 4.32 (ISBN 0-201-03981-8, Sch Div). Addison-Wesley.

--The Numbers of Ordinary Arithmetic & Algebra. rev. ed. (Algebra, a Modern Introduction Ser.). 1981. pap. text ed. 4.08 (ISBN 0-201-03982-6). Addison-Wesley.

--Operations of the Numbers of Arithmetic. rev. ed. (Algebra, a Modern Introduction Ser.). 1981. pap. text ed. 4.32 (ISBN 0-201-03979-6). Addison-Wesley.

Keedy, Mervin L. Introductory Algebra. 4th ed. LC 82-13771. (Illus.). 566p. pap. text ed. 25.95 (ISBN 0-201-14785-8). Addison-Wesley.

Keedy, Mervin L. & Bittinger, Marvin L. Algebra & Trigonometry: A Functions Approach. 3rd ed. 1982. pap. 28.95 (ISBN 0-201-13404-7); Stu-Sol 5.95 (ISBN 0-201-13405-5); test 4.00 (ISBN 0-201-13406-3); ans 2.00 (ISBN 0-201-13407-1). Addison-Wesley.

--Fundamental Algebra & Trigonometry. 2nd ed. (Mathematics-Remedial & Precalculus Ser.). (Illus.). 576p. 1981. text ed. 28.95 (ISBN 0-201-03839-0); test bk 4.00 (ISBN 0-201-03844-7); answer bk 2.00 (ISBN 0-201-03843-9); student suppl. 5.95 (ISBN 0-201-03744-0). Addison-Wesley.

--Fundamental College Algebra. 2nd ed. (Mathematics-Remedial & Precalculus Ser.). 480p. 1981. text ed. 25.95 (ISBN 0-201-03847-1); student sol. manual 5.95 (ISBN 0-201-03848-X); answer bk 2.00 (ISBN 0-201-03849-8); test bk 4.00 (ISBN 0-201-03855-2). Addison-Wesley.

--A Problem-Solving Approach to Introductory Algebra. 2nd ed. text ed. write for info. (ISBN 0-201-12968-X). Addison-Wesley.

Keedy, Mervin L. & Bittinger, Marvin L. A Problem-Solving Approach to Intermediate Algebra. 2nd ed. 1985. text ed. write for info. (ISBN 0-201-12974-4). Addison-Wesley.

Keedy, Mervin L., et al. Algebra for College Students. LC 84-20447. 1985. text ed. 26.95 (ISBN 0-201-14835-8). Addison-Wesley.

Keller, Marion W. Intermediate Algebra: A Text Workbook. LC 74-171526. pap. text ed. 24.50 (ISBN 0-395-12643-6); test ans. & problems 3.20 (ISBN 0-395-12644-4). HM.

Kendig, K. Elementary Algebraic Theory. (Graduate Texts in Mathematics Ser: Vol. 44). 1977. 36.00 (ISBN 0-387-90199-X). Springer-Verlag.

Kertesz, A. Einfuehrung in die Transfinite Algebra. (Elemente der Math. Vom Hoeheren Standpunkt Aus: Vol. 7). (Ger.). 74p. 1974. pap. 18.95x (ISBN 0-8176-0735-8). Birkhauser.

Kim, Ki H. & Roush, Fred W. Applied Abstract Algebra. (Mathematics & Its Applications Ser.: I-176). 265p. 1983. pap. 24.95x (ISBN 0-470-27441-7). Halsted Pr.

King, K. Introductory Algebra & Related Topics for Technicians. 1979. pap. 23.95 (ISBN 0-13-501585-5). P-H.

Klentos, Gus & Newmyer, Joseph, Jr. Elementary Functions: Algebra & Analytic Geometry. 448p. 1975. pap. text ed. 23.95 (ISBN 0-675-08827-5); media: audiocassettes 160.00 (ISBN 0-675-08774-0). Additional supplements may be obtained from publisher. Merrill.

Kogbetliantz, E. G. Fundamentals of Mathematics from an Advanced Viewpoint, 4 vols. in 2. Incl. Vols. 1 & 2. Algebra & Analysis: Evolution of the Number Concept & Determinants-Equations-Logarithms-Limits. 596p. 1968. 112.25 (ISBN 0-677-02000-7); Vols. 3 & 4. Geometry & Geometric Analysis & Solid Geometry & Spherical Trigonometry. 602p. 1969. 112.25 (ISBN 0-677-02010-4). 1198p. 1969. Set. 191.50 (ISBN 0-677-00470-2); Set. pap. 131.95 (ISBN 0-677-00475-3). Gordon.

Kolman, Bernard. Elementary Linear Algebra. 3rd ed. 368p. 1982. text ed. write for info. (ISBN 0-02-365990-4). Macmillan.

Kolman, Bernard & Shapiro, Arnold. Algebra for College Students. 2nd ed. Date not set. text ed. price not set (ISBN 0-12-417900-2); instr's manual 2.50 (ISBN 0-12-417901-0). Acad Pr.

--College Algebra. 1981. 20.00i (ISBN 0-12-417884-7); instrs' manual 2.50i (ISBN 0-12-417886-3); study guide 6.50i (ISBN 0-12-417887-1). Acad Pr.

--College Algebra. 2nd ed. 1984. text ed. 21.00i (ISBN 0-12-417897-9). Acad Pr.

--College Algebra & Trigonometry. 1981. 21.00i (ISBN 0-12-417840-5); instr's. manual 2.50i (ISBN 0-12-417845-6); study guide 6.50i (ISBN 0-12-417841-3); test bank 2.50i (ISBN 0-12-417846-4). Acad Pr.

Kolman, Bernard & Shapiro, Arnold, eds. Test Bank for College Algebra. 1982. 2.50 (ISBN 0-12-417888-X); Test Bank for College Alegebra & Trigonometry. 2.50 (ISBN 0-12-417846-4). Acad Pr.

Komkov, Vadim. Algebra & Pre-Calculus Mathematics. 304p. 1982. pap. text ed. 12.95 (ISBN 0-8403-2754-4). Kendall-Hunt.

Kompaniec, V. P., et al. Fourteen Papers on Algebra, Topology, Algebraic & Differential Geometry. LC 51-5559. (Translations Ser.: No. 2, Vol. 73). 1968. 35.00 (ISBN 0-8218-1773-6, TRANS 2-73). Am Math.

Korobov, N. M., et al. Eight Papers on Algebra & Number Theory. LC 51-5559. (Translations, Ser.: No. 2, Vol. 4). 1956. 23.00 (ISBN 0-8128-1704-4, TRANS 2-4). Am Math.

Koshy, T. College Algebra & Trigonometry with Applications. 688p. 1986. 31.95 (ISBN 0-07-035471-5). McGraw.

Kostrikin, A. I. Introduction to Algebra. (Universitext Ser.). 575p. 1982. 33.00 (ISBN 0-387-90711-4). Springer-Verlag.

Krause, G. R. & Lenagan, T. H. Growth of Algebras & Gelfand-Kirillov Dimension. (Research Notes in Mathematics Ser.: No. 116). 192p. pap. text ed. 16.95 (ISBN 0-273-08662-6). Pitman Pub Ma.

Krishnan, N. S. University Algebra. 284p. 1981. 30.00x (ISBN 0-86125-295-0, Pub. by Orient Longman India). State Mutual Bk.

Kung, Joseph P., ed. Young Tableaux in Combinatorics, Invariant Theory, & Algebra: An Anthology of Recent Work. LC 82-11330. 347p. 1982. 32.00 (ISBN 0-12-428780-8). Acad Pr.

Kunz, Ernst. Commutative Algebra. 350p. 1985. text ed. 29.95 (ISBN 0-8176-3065-1). Birkhauser.

Kupper, et al, eds. Numerical Methods for Bifurcation Problems. (ISNM Ser.: No. 70). 1984. text ed. 51.95x (ISBN 3-764316-27-6). Birkhauser.

Kurosch, A. G. Curso de Algebra Superior. (Span.). 442p. 1977. 7.95 (ISBN 0-8285-1683-9, Pub. by Mir Pubs USSR). Imported Pubns.

Kurosh, A. Algebraic Equations of Arbitrary Degrees. 1977. pap. 1.95 (ISBN 0-8285-0701-5, Pub. by Mir Pubs USSR). Imported Pubns.

--Higher Algebra. 428p. 1975. 9.95 (ISBN 0-8285-0724-4, Pub. by Mir Pubs USSR). Imported Pubns.

Lang, S. Cyclotonic Fields: Two. (Graduate Texts in Mathematics Ser.: Vol. 69). 288p. 1980. 26.00 (ISBN 0-387-90447-6). Springer-Verlag.

Lang, Serge. Algebra. 2nd ed. 1984. 39.95 (ISBN 0-201-05487-6). Benjamin-Cummings.

Larson, Loren C. Algebra & Trigonometry Refresher for Calculus Students. LC 79-20633. (Mathematical Sciences Ser.). (Illus.). 192p. 1979. pap. 10.95 (ISBN 0-7167-1110-9). W H Freeman.

LeBarz, P. & Hervier, Y., eds. Enumerative Geometry & Classical Algebra. (Progress in Mathematics Ser.: Vol. 24). 246p. 1982. text ed. 20.00 (ISBN 0-8176-3106-2). Birkhauser.

Lee, Virginia. Basic Algebra. 1976. pap. text ed. 20.95 scp (ISBN 0-06-384821-X, HarpC); inst. manual avail. (ISBN 0-06-373850-3). Har-Row.

Lehmann, Charles H. College Algebra. LC 62-8778. pap. 108.00 (ISBN 0-317-09369-X, 2055102). Bks Demand UMI.

Leifman, Lev J., ed. Twelve Papers in Algebra. LC 82-24434. (Translations Ser. II: Vol. 119). 33.00 (ISBN 0-8218-3074-0). Am Math.

Leithold, Louis. College Algebra. 2nd ed. (Illus.). 1980. text ed. write for info. (ISBN 0-02-369580-3). Macmillan.

--Intermediate Algebra for College Students. 2nd ed. 1979. text ed. write for info/ (ISBN 0-02-369640-0). Macmillan.

Lentin, Andre. Equations dans les Monoides Libres. (Mathematiques et Sciences De L'homme: No. 16). 1972. pap. 7.60x (ISBN 0-686-21805-1). Mouton.

Lewis, Larry & Smyth, Vera G. Basic Algebra. (Illus.). 512p. 1982. 26.95 (ISBN 0-13-056762-0). P-H.

Lial, Margaret L. & Miller, Charles D. Algebra & Trigonometry. 3rd ed. 1983. text ed. 27.90x (ISBN 0-673-15794-6). Scott F.

--Algebra & Trigonometry. alt. ed. 1986. 27.95x (ISBN 0-673-18298-3). Scott F.

--Beginning Algebra. 4th ed. 1984. text ed. 25.80x (ISBN 0-673-15890-X). Scott F.

--College Algebra. 3rd ed. 1981. text ed. 24.95x (ISBN 0-673-15407-6); study guide 9.95x (ISBN 0-673-15477-7). Scott F.

--College Algebra. 4th ed. 1985. text ed. 25.95x (ISBN 0-673-18024-7); 6.95x (ISBN 0-673-18123-5); study guide 9.95x (ISBN 0-673-18025-5). Scott F.

--Intermediate Algebra. 4th ed. 1984. text ed. 25.80x (ISBN 0-673-15891-8). Scott F.

Lipson, John D. Elements of Algebra & Algebraic Computing. 1985. softcover 29.95 (ISBN 0-201-04480-3, 04480). Addison-Wesley.

Locher, Ernst. Arithmetik und Algebra. 4th ed. (Ger.). 72p. 1975. pap. 4.95x (ISBN 0-8176-0774-9). Birkhauser.

Longo, G., ed. Algebraic Coding Theory & Application. (CISM Courses & Lectures Ser.: Vol. 258). (Illus.). 529p. 1979. pap. 58.00 (ISBN 0-387-81544-9). Springer-Verlag.

Lovaglia, Florence. Algebra. (Span.). 1974. pap. 9.30 (ISBN 0-06-315513-3, IntlDept). Har-Row.

Lux, J. Richard & Pieters, Richard S. Basic Exercises in Algebra & Trigonometry. (Illus.). 365p. (Orig.). 1979. pap. text ed. 7.95x (ISBN 0-88334-122-0). Ind Sch Pr.

McHale, T. J. & Witzke, P. T. Advanced Algebra. (Milwaukee Area Technical College Mathematics Ser.). 1972. pap. 18.95 (ISBN 0-201-04633-4); bklt. o. p. 4.00 (ISBN 0-201-04634-2). Addison-Wesley.

McHale, Thomas J. & Witzke, Paul T. Applied Algebra II. 1980. pap. text ed. 21.95 (ISBN 0-201-04775-6); test booklet 3.50 (ISBN 0-201-04776-4). Addison-Wesley.

McHale, Thomas J., et al. Introductory Algebra: Programmed. 544p. 1977. text ed. 21.95 (ISBN 0-201-04747-0). Addison-Wesley.

McKeague, Charles P. Beginning Algebra. 1980. pap. 17.00i (ISBN 0-12-484765-X); instrs' manual 2.50i (ISBN 0-12-484766-8). Acad Pr.

--Beginning Algebra. 2nd ed. 1986. text ed. 18.50 (ISBN 0-12-484790-0); price not set instrs' resource manual (ISBN 0-12-484791-9). Acad Pr.

--Elementary Algebra. 2nd ed. 1981. 19.25i (ISBN 0-12-484755-2); instr's manual 2.50i (ISBN 0-12-484754-4); study guide 5.75i (ISBN 0-12-484764-1). Acad Pr.

--Intermediate Algebra. 1985. text ed. 19.00i (ISBN 0-12-484787-0). Acad Pr.

McKeague, Charles P., ed. Intermediate Algebra with Trigonometry. 1983. text ed. 21.00i (ISBN 0-12-484780-3); instrs' manual 10.00i. Acad Pr.

McKeaugue, Charles P. Intermediate Algebra. 494p. 1979. instr's. manual o.p. 3.50 (ISBN 0-12-484762-5); Pub. 1981. wkbk. 17.75 (ISBN 0-12-484763-3); Pub. 1981. student guide 5.75 (ISBN 0-12-484764-1). Acad Pr.

MacLachlan, Barbara. Algebra Essentials. 128p. 1985. pap. text ed. 25.00 (ISBN 0-933195-05-2). Cal College Pr.

MacLane, Saunders. Selected Papers: Saunders MacLane. Kaplansky, I., ed. LC 79-10105. 1979. 39.50 (ISBN 0-387-90394-1). Springer-Verlag.

MacLane, Saunders & Birkhoff, Garrett. Algebra. 2nd ed. 1979. write for info. (ISBN 0-02-374310-7). Macmillan.

Magnus, Wilhelm & Winkler, Stanley. Hill's Equation. LC 78-74114. 1979. pap. text ed. 3.95 (ISBN 0-486-63738-7). Dover.

Malliavin, M. P., ed. Seminaire D'Algebre Paul Dubreil: Proceedings, Paris 1976-1977. (Lecture Notes in Mathematics: Vol. 641). 1978. pap. 23.10 (ISBN 0-387-08665-X). Springer-Verlag.

Manes, E. G. Algebraic Theories. LC 75-11991. (Graduate Texts in Mathematics: Vol. 26). 374p. 1976. text ed. 36.00 (ISBN 0-387-90140-X). Springer-Verlag.

Mangan, Frances S. Elementary Algebra: A Self-Study Course. 1979. pap. text ed. 17.95 (ISBN 0-8403-1978-9, 40197803). Kendall-Hunt.

--Intermediate Algebra: A Self-Study Course. 2nd ed. 504p. 1983. pap. text ed. 24.95 (ISBN 0-8403-3124-X). Kendall-Hunt.

Manin, Ju. I., et al. Seven Papers on Algebra, Algebraic Geometry & Algebraic Topology. LC 51-5559. (Translations Ser.: No. 2, Vol. 63). 1967. 36.00 (ISBN 0-8218-1763-9, TRANS 2-63). Am Math.

Manocha & Srivastava. Algebra & Its Applications. 432p. 1984. 59.50 (ISBN 0-8247-7165-6). Dekker.

Manougian, M. N. Basic Algebra. 1981. text ed. 25.95 (ISBN 0-03-019711-2, CBS C). SCP.

Manougian, M. N. & Zerla, Fredric. Intermediate Algebra. LC 80-26579. (Illus.). 500p. 1981. text ed. 22.50 (ISBN 0-936166-04-5). Mariner Pub.

Marcus, Marvin. Finite Dimensional Multilinear Algebra, Pt. 2. (Pure & Applied Mathematics Ser.: Vol. 23). 600p. 1975. 95.00 (ISBN 0-8247-6203-7). Dekker.

Marcus, Marvin, ed. Introduction to Modern Algebra. (Monographs & Textbooks in Pure & Applied Math: Vol. 47). 1978. 45.00 (ISBN 0-8247-6479-X). Dekker.

Math Review. pocket ed. 150p. pap. text ed. cancelled (ISBN 0-8120-2198-3). Barron.

Matlis, Eben. Torsion-Free Modules. (Chicago Lectures in Mathematics Ser.). 1973. 9.00x (ISBN 0-226-51073-5); pap. text ed. 7.00x (ISBN 0-226-51074-3). U of Chicago Pr.

Matsumura, Hideyuki. Commutative Algebra. 2nd ed. (Math Lecture Notes Ser.: No. 38). 1970. pap. text ed. 30.95 (ISBN 0-8053-7026-9). Benjamin-Cummings.

Meadowcroft, James, II. Beginning Algebra for Mature Students. 1971. pap. text ed. 25.95 (ISBN 0-13-073726-7). P-H.

Mendelson, E. Boolean Algebra & Switching Circuits. (Schaum's Outline Ser). 1970. pap. 8.95 (ISBN 0-07-041460-2). McGraw.

Meserve, Bruce E. Fundamental Concepts of Algebra. (Mathematics Ser.). 320p. 1982. pap. 6.00 (ISBN 0-486-61470-0). Dover.

Meuller, Francis J. Elements of Algebra. 3rd ed. (Illus.). 496p. 1981. text ed. 25.95 (ISBN 0-13-262469-9). P-H.

Michael, Payne. Intermediate Algebra. (Illus.). 544p. 1985. 20.94 (ISBN 0-314-85285-9). West Pub.

Michaels, J. G. & Bloch, N. J. Intermediate Algebra. 480p. 1982. 28.95x (ISBN 0-07-041820-9). McGraw.

Michel, A. & Herget, C. Mathematical Foundations in Engineering & Science: Algebra & Analysis. 1981. 36.95 (ISBN 0-13-561035-4). P-H.

Miller, Charles D. & Lial, Margaret L. Fundamentals of College Algebra. 1982. text ed. 25.80 (ISBN 0-673-15613-3). Scott F.

Miller, Charles D. & Lial, Margeret L. Fundamentals of College Algebra. 2nd ed. 1986. text ed. 25.95x (ISBN 0-673-18242-8). Scott F.

Smith, Patrick & Boyle, Karl. Intermediate Algebra for College Students. 3rd ed. LC 84-21398. (Mathematics Ser.). 512p. 1984. text ed. 21.75 pub net (ISBN 0-534-03987-1). Brooks-Cole.

Sobel, Max A. & Lerner, Norbert. Algebra & Trigonometry: A Pre-Calculus Approach. 2nd ed. (Illus.). 608p. 1983. text ed. 29.95 (ISBN 0-13-021634-8). P-H.

--Algebra for College Students: An Intermediate Approach. 3rd ed. (Illus.). 540p. 1986. text ed. 27.95 (ISBN 0-13-021668-2). P-H.

--College Algebra. (Illus.). 576p. 1983. text ed. 26.95 (ISBN 0-13-141796-7). P-H.

Sobol, Max A. & Lerner, Norbert. Algebra for College Students: An Intermediate Approach. 2nd ed. 1980. text ed. 28.95 (ISBN 0-13-021584-8). P-H.

Solel, Baruch. Irreducible Triangular Algebras. LC 83-22524. (Memoirs Ser.: No. 290). 88p. 1984. pap. 9.00 (ISBN 0-8218-2290-X). Am Math.

Sperry, Bryan. Programmed Algebra. 352p. 1981. pap. text ed. 16.95 (ISBN 0-8403-2516-9). Kendall-Hunt.

Spiegel, Murray R. College Algebra. (Orig.). 1956. pap. 8.95 (ISBN 0-07-060226-3). McGraw.

Spitzbart, Abraham. College Algebra. 3rd ed. LC 77-81200. (Illus.). 1978. text ed. 21.95 (ISBN 0-201-07482-6). Addison-Wesley.

Springer, Melvin D. The Algebra of Random Variables. LC 78-9315. (Probability & Mathematical Statistics Series: Applied Probability & Statistics Section). 470p. 1979. 55.50 (ISBN 0-471-01406-0, Pub. by Wiley-Interscience). Wiley.

Stasheff, J. H-Spaces from a Homotopy Point of View. LC 71-134651. (Lecture Notes in Mathematics: Vol. 161). 1970. pap. 12.00 (ISBN 0-387-04940-1). Springer-Verlag.

Steffensen, Arnold J. & Johnson, L. M. Algebra & Trigonometry. 1981. pap. text ed. 22.70x (ISBN 0-673-15371-1). Scott F.

Steffensen, Arnold R. & Johnson, L. Murphy. College Algebra. 1981. pap. text ed. 22.70x (ISBN 0-673-15370-3). Scott F.

--Introductory Algebra. 2nd ed. 1984. pap. text ed. 22.70x (ISBN 0-673-15889-6). Scott F.

Stein, Edwin I. Introductory Algebra. 650p. 1981. text ed. 28.57 (ISBN 0-205-07710-2, 5677106). Allyn.

Stein, M. R., ed. Algebraic K-Theory. (Lecture Notes in Mathematics Ser.: Vol. 551). 1976. soft cover 23.00 (ISBN 0-387-07996-3). Springer-Verlag.

Stein, Sherman K. & Crabill, Calvin D. Elementary Algebra: A Guided Inquiry. rev. ed. 632p. 1984. text ed. 16.50 (ISBN 0-916327-00-0); tchr's. ed. 18.50 (ISBN 0-916327-01-9); solutions key, 107 pgs. 6.00 (ISBN 0-916327-02-7). Davis Math Pr.

Stein, Sherman K., et al. Algebra II-Trigonometry: A Guided Inquiry. rev. ed. 600p. 1985. text ed. 17.00 (ISBN 0-916327-20-5); solutions key, 160 pg. 9.00 (ISBN 0-916327-21-3). Davis Math Pr.

Steinberg, R. Conjugacy Classes in Algebraic Groups. (Lecture Notes in Mathematics: Vol. 366). vi, 159p. 1974. pap. 12.00 (ISBN 0-387-06657-8). Springer-Verlag.

Steinitz, Ernst. Algebraische Theorie der Koerper. LC 51-10623. 1976. text ed. 14.95 (ISBN 0-8284-0077-6). Chelsea Pub.

Steinlage, Ralph. College Algebra & Trigonometry. 1981. text ed. 26.65x (ISBN 0-673-16231-1). Scott F.

Steinlage, Ralph C. College Algebra. (Illus.). 450p. 1984. text ed. 27.95 (ISBN 0-314-77816-0); solutions avail. (ISBN 0-314-77820-9); instrs.' manual, test bank avail. (ISBN 0-314-80348-3); transparency masters avail. (ISBN 0-314-80577-X). West Pub.

--College Algebra & Trigonometry. (Illus.). 550p. 1984. text ed. 28.95 (ISBN 0-314-77821-7); instrs.' manual & test bank avail. (ISBN 0-314-80349-1); solutions manual avail. (ISBN 0-314-77824-1). West Pub.

Stenstroem, B. Rings & Modules of Quotients. (Lecture Notes in Mathematics: Vol. 237). 136p. 1971. pap. 9.00 (ISBN 0-387-05690-4). Springer-Verlag.

Stephens, Robert. Worktext in Intermediate Algebra. (Illus.). 1977. pap. text ed. 16.95 (ISBN 0-8299-0105-1). West Pub.

Stockton, Doris S. Essential Algebra & Trigonometry. LC 77-76337. (Illus.). 1978. text ed. 28.95 (ISBN 0-395-25413-2); instr's. manual 1.00 (ISBN 0-395-25414-0). HM.

--Essential College Algebra. LC 78-69526. (Illus.). 1979. text ed. 25.95 (ISBN 0-395-26544-4); instr's. manual 1.00 (ISBN 0-395-26538-X). HM.

Summer Research Inst. of the Australian Mathematical Society, 14th, Australia, Jan. 6, 1974. Algebra & Logic: Proceedings. Crossley, J. N., ed. LC 75-9903. (Lecture Notes in Mathematics Ser.: Vol. 450). viii, 307p. 1975. pap. 19.00 (ISBN 0-387-07152-0). Springer-Verlag.

Sweet, M. V. Algebra, Geometry & Trigonometry in Science Engineering & Mathematics. 617p. 1984. 45.00 (ISBN 0-470-20102-9). Halsted Pr.

Swokowski, Earl W. Algebra & Trigonometry with Analytic Geometry. 5th ed. LC 80-29056. 544p. 1981. text ed. write for info. (ISBN 0-87150-310-7, 33L 2471, Prindle). PWS Pubs.

--Algebra & Trigonometry with Analytic Geometry. 5th ed. write for info. (ISBN 0-87150-310-7, Prindle). PWS Pubs.

--Fundamentals of Algebra & Trigonometry. 5th ed. LC 80-26359. (The Swokowski Ser.). 523p. 1981. text ed. write for info. (ISBN 0-87150-307-7, 2451, Prindle); write for info program guide (ISBN 0-87150-317-4, 2455). PWS Pubs.

--Fundamentals of Algebra & Trigonometry. 6th ed. 1986. text ed. write for info. (ISBN 0-87150-877-X, 33L2980, Prindle). PWS Pubs.

--Fundamentals of Algebra & Trigonometry with Analytic Geometry. 6th ed. 1986. text ed. write for info. (33L2990, Prindle). PWS Pubs.

--Fundamentals of College Algebra. 5th ed. LC 80-27298. (The Swokowski Ser.). 385p. 1981. text ed. write for info. (ISBN 0-87150-308-5, 2461, Prindle); write for info. program guide (ISBN 0-87150-318-2). PWS Pubs.

--Fundamentals of College Algebra. 01/1986 ed. text ed. price not set (ISBN 0-87150-879-6, 33L3010, Prindle). PWS Pubs.

Symposium in Pure Mathematics - New York - 1968. Applications of Categorical Algebra: Proceedings. Heller, A., ed. LC 72-89866. (Proceedings of Symposia in Pure Mathematics: Vol. 17). 1970. 33.00 (ISBN 0-8218-1417-6, PSPUM-17). Am Math.

Takesaki, M. Theory of Operator Algebras One. LC 79-13655. 1979. 54.00 (ISBN 0-387-90391-7). Springer-Verlag.

Thompson, J. E. Algebra for the Practical Worker. 288p. 1982. pap. 7.95 (ISBN 0-442-28273-7). Van Nos Reinhold.

Thweatt, Evan W. Intermediate Algebra. (Illus.). 500p. 1984. text ed. 25.95 (ISBN 0-314-77832-2); instrs.' manual avail. (ISBN 0-314-77834-9); student study guide avail. West Pub.

Tomber, M. L. & Smith, C. L., eds. A Bibliography on Nonassociative Algebras, Vol III. 180p. pap. 50.00x (ISBN 0-911767-19-3). Hadronic Pr Inc.

Topping, D. M. Jordan Algebras of Self-Adjoint Operators. LC 52-42839. (Memoirs: No. 53). 48p. 1979. pap. 10.00 (ISBN 0-8218-1253-X, MEMO-53). Am Math.

Treiman, Sam B. & Jackiw, Roman. Lectures on Current Algebra & Its Applications. LC 70-181519. (Princeton Series in Physics). 280p. 1972. 23.00 (ISBN 0-691-08118-2). Princeton U Pr.

Upmeier, H. Symmetric Banach Manifolds & Jordan C-Algebras. (Mathematics Studies: Vol. 104). 444p. 1985. 55.75 (ISBN 0-444-87651-0, North-Holland). Elsevier.

Usiskin, Zalman. Algebra Through Applications with Probability & Statistics, 2 pts. LC 78-23568. (Illus.). 752p. 1979. Set. pap. 9.50 (ISBN 0-87353-134-5). Pt. 1 (ISBN 0-87353-135-3). Pt. 2 (ISBN 0-87353-136-1). NCTM.

Vancil, Chris. Algebra & Trigonometry. 544p. 1983. text ed. write for info. (ISBN 0-02-422400-6). Macmillan.

--College Algebra & College Algebra Trigonometry. 550p. 1983. text ed. write for info. (ISBN 0-02-422420-0). Macmillan.

Van der Waerden, B. L. Algebra, 2 vols. Incl. Vol. 1. Blum, Fred & Schulenberger, John R., trs. 16.50 (ISBN 0-8044-4950-3); Vol. 2. Schulenberger, John R., tr. 16.50 (ISBN 0-8044-4951-1). LC 71-10730. Set. (ISBN 0-8044-4948-1). Ungar.

--A History of Algebra. (Illus.). 290p. 1985. 34.50 (ISBN 0-387-13610-X). Springer-Verlag.

Van Hulzen, J. A., ed. Computer Algebra. (Lecture Notes in Computer Science: Vol. 162). 305p. 1983. pap. 17.00 (ISBN 0-387-12868-9). Springer Verlag.

Van Oystaeyen, F. Prime Spectra in Non-Communicative Algebra. LC 75-4877. (Lecture Notes in Mathematics Ser.: Vol. 444). v, 128p. 1975. pap. 13.00 (ISBN 0-387-07146-6). Springer-Verlag.

Veno, K. Classification Theory of Algebraic Varieties & Compact Complex Spaces. LC 75-1211. (Lecture Notes in Mathematics Ser.: Vol. 439). xix, 278p. 1975. pap. 19.00 (ISBN 0-387-07138-5). Springer-Verlag.

Verdier, Jean-Louis & Le Poitier, Joseph, eds. Module des Fibres Stables sur les Courbes Algebriques: Notes de l'Ecole Normale Superieure, Printemps 1983. (Progress in Mathematics Ser.: Vol. 54). (Fr. & Eng.). 1985. text ed. write for info. (ISBN 0-8176-3286-7). Birkhauser.

Viglino, Giovanni. Intermediate Algebra. 1981. text ed. write for info. (ISBN 0-02-423000-6). Macmillan.

Villamayor, Orlando E. Algebra Lineal. 4th ed. (Serie de matematica Monografia: No. 5). 129p. 1981. pap. text ed. 3.50 (ISBN 0-8270-1413-9). OAS.

Watkins, John H. Arithmetic & Algebra. 1977. pap. text ed. 21.95 scp (ISBN 0-06-046958-7, HarpC); test bklt. avail. (ISBN 0-06-367022-4). Har-Row.

Webber, Robert P. College Algebra & Trigonometry. LC 84-28585. (Mathematics Ser.). 540p. 1985. text ed. 23.75 pub net (ISBN 0-534-04209-0). Brooks-Cole.

Weber, Heinrich. Lehrbuch der Algebra, Vols. 1, 2, & 3. 3rd ed. LC 61-6890. 1979. Repr. of 1962 ed. Set. text ed. 95.00 (ISBN 0-8284-0144-6). Chelsea Pub.

Wefelscheid, H. & Arnold, H. J., eds. Beitrage Zur Geometrischen Algebra: Proceedings. (Mathematische Reihe Ser.: No. 21). (Ger.). 384p. 1977. 99.95x (ISBN 0-8176-0908-3). Birkhauser.

Willerding, Margaret F. Algebra: A First Course for College Students. 4th ed. write for info. (ISBN 0-87150-285-2, Prindle). PWS Pubs.

--College Algebra & Trigonometry. 2nd ed. LC 74-22391. 613p. 1975. text ed. 34.00x (ISBN 0-471-94671-0). Wiley.

--Modern Intermediate Algebra. 2nd ed. LC 82-15274. 426p. 1982. Repr. of 1975 ed. 24.50 (ISBN 0-89874-507-1). Krieger.

Williams, Gareth. A Course in Linear Algebra. 216p. 1972. 46.25x (ISBN 0-677-03570-5). Gordon.

Williams, Richard W. Basic Mathematics: Arithmetic & Algebra. 1984. pap. text ed. 20.65x (ISBN 0-673-15482-3). Scott F.

Willis, Alden T. & Johnston, Carol L. Elementary Algebra. 400p. 1982. text ed. write for info. (ISBN 0-534-01035-0). Wadsworth Pub.

Wise, Alan. Beginning Algebra & Problem Solving. 626p. 1985. pap. text ed. 25.95 (ISBN 0-15-505350-7, HC); study guide avail. (ISBN 0-15-505351-5); instr's manual avail. (ISBN 0-15-505352-3); answer key avail. (ISBN 0-15-505353-1). HarBraceJ.

Wise, Alan, et al. Intermediate Algebra & Problem Solving. 606p. 1985. pap. text ed. 25.95 (ISBN 0-15-541505-0, HC); instr's manual avail. (ISBN 0-15-541507-7); study guide 6.95 (ISBN 0-15-541506-9); answer key avail. (ISBN 0-15-541508-5). HarBraceJ.

Wood, et al. Developmental Mathematics. 3rd ed. 1985. pap. text ed. write for info. (ISBN 0-87150-853-2, 33L2920, Prindle). PWS Pubs.

Wood, June P. Introductory & Intermediate Algebra. 4th ed. 1983. text ed. 24.95 (ISBN 0-675-20001-6); Add. suppl. may be obtained from Publisher. student guide 9.95 (ISBN 0-675-20039-3). Merrill.

Wood, Martha M., et al. Intermediate Algebra. 528p. 1982. pap. text ed. write for info. (ISBN 0-87150-326-3, 2602, Prindle). PWS Pubs.

--Introductory Algebra. 528p. 1982. pap. text ed. write for info. (ISBN 0-87150-330-1, 2632, Prindle). PWS Pubs.

Word Problems in Algebra: Level Three Texts. rev. ed. (Math Components Ser.). 32p. 1983. 2.00 (ISBN 0-88336-832-3). New Readers.

Wright & New. Introductory Algebra. 298p. 1981. text ed. 29.64 (ISBN 0-205-07310-7, 5673100); tchr's ed. 6.02 (ISBN 0-205-07311-5, 567311); student guide 11.43 (ISBN 0-205-07312-3, 567312). Allyn.

Wright, D. Franklin & New, Bill D. Intermediate Algebra. 450p. 1981. text ed. 30.72 (ISBN 0-205-07185-6, 567185-X); tchr's ed. 7.86 (ISBN 0-205-07186-4, 567186); student guide 11.43 (567187). Allyn.

Yaglom, I. Unusual Algebra. 72p. 1978. pap. 1.95 (ISBN 0-8285-0749-X, Pub. by Mir Pubs USSR). Imported Pubns.

Yaglom, I. M. Algebra Extraordinaria. (Span.). 82p. 1977. pap. 1.95 (ISBN 0-8285-1682-0, Pub. by Mir Pubs USSR). Imported Pubns.

Zariski, O. & Samuel, P. Commutative Algebra One. LC 75-17751. (Graduate Texts in Mathematics: Vol. 28). 340p. 1975. Repr. of 1958 ed. 29.50 (ISBN 0-387-90089-6). Springer-Verlag.

--Commutative Algebra, Vol. 2. LC 75-17751. (Graduate Texts in Mathematics Ser.: Vol. 29). 1976. 29.50 (ISBN 0-387-90171-X). Springer-Verlag.

Zassenhaus, Hans. Number Theory & Algebra: Collected Papers Dedicated to Henry B. Mann, Arnold E. Ross & Olga Taussky-Todd. 1977. 77.00 (ISBN 0-12-776350-3). Acad Pr.

Zhevlakov, K. A., et al. Rings That are Nearly Associative. (Pure and Applied Mathematics Ser.). 1982. 59.50 (ISBN 0-12-779850-1). Acad Pr.

Zuckerman, M. M. Intermediate Algebra: A Straightforward Approach for College Students. alternate ed. LC 79-23469. 398p. 1981. text ed. 32.50 (ISBN 0-471-09385-8); wkbk. 13.45 (ISBN 0-471-09384-X); solutions manual 13.00 (ISBN 0-471-89691-8). Wiley.

--Intermediate Algebra: A Straightforward Approach. 2nd ed. LC 81-11610. 427p. 1983. 29.00 (ISBN 0-471-09731-4); sampler 6.50 (ISBN 0-471-87676-3); solutions manual 13.00 (ISBN 0-471-87686-0); wkbk. 15.45 (ISBN 0-471-86801-9). Wiley.

Zuckerman, Martin. Algebra & Trigonometry: A Straight Forward Approach. 2nd ed. LC 83-23589. 688p. 1985. 27.95x (ISBN 0-471-09789-6); write for info. tchr's ed. (ISBN 0-471-87977-0); pap. write for info. wkbk. (ISBN 0-471-87973-8); write for info. solutions manual (ISBN 0-471-87974-6). Wiley.

Zuckerman, Martin M. Algebra & Trigonometry: A Straightforward Approach. LC 79-22909. 595p. 1981. 31.45 (ISBN 0-471-09392-0); wkbk. 350 pgs. 14.45x (ISBN 0-471-09389-0). Wiley.

--Aritmetica Con una Introduccion al Algebra. Molinero, Leticia, tr. from Eng. (Span., Illus.). 300p. 1984. pap. text ed. 23.95 (ISBN 0-912675-01-2); manual avail. (ISBN 0-912675-03-9). Ardsley.

--College Algebra: A Straightforward Approach. LC 83-23548. 544p. 1985. 25.95x (ISBN 0-471-09619-9); write for info. tchr's. ed. (ISBN 0-471-87922-3); pap. write for info. solutions manual (ISBN 0-471-87975-4); pap. wkbk avail. (ISBN 0-471-09630-X). Wiley.

--Elementary Algebra: A Straightforward Approach. 2nd ed. 400p. 1982. 30.36 (ISBN 0-205-07624-6, 567624X); tchr's ed. 0.00 (ISBN 0-205-07625-4, 5676258); study guide 10.00 (ISBN 0-205-07626-2, 567626). Allyn.

ALGEBRA–BIBLIOGRAPHY

Kung, Joseph P., ed. Young Tableaux in Combinatorics, Invariant Theory, & Algebra: An Anthology of Recent Work. LC 82-11330. 347p. 1982. 32.00 (ISBN 0-12-428780-8). Acad Pr.

Lidl, R., ed. Papers in Algebra, Analysis & Statistics. LC 82-1826. (Contemporary Mathematics Ser.: Vol. 9). 400p. 1982. pap. 24.00 (ISBN 0-8218-5009-1, CONM-9). Am Math.

Rider, Robin E., compiled by. A Bibliography of Early Modern Algebra, Fifteen Hundred to Eighteen Hundred. LC 81-51030. (Berkeley Papers in History of Science: No. 7). 150p. (Orig.). 1982. pap. 8.00x (ISBN 0-918102-08-1). U Cal Hist Sci Tech.

Tomber, M. L., et al, eds. A Bibliography on Nonassociative Algebras, 3 vols, Vol. 1, 2 & 3. 545p. 1984. pap. 75.00 (ISBN 0-911767-17-7). Hadronic Pr Inc.

ALGEBRA–EARLY WORKS TO 1800

Hughes, Barnabas E., ed. Jordanus De Nemore, De Numeris Datis: A Critical Edition & Translation. (Publications of the Center for Medieval & Renaissance Studies, UCLA). 200p. 1981. 40.00x (ISBN 0-520-04283-2). U of Cal Pr.

Khayyam, Omar. The Algebra of Omar Khayyam. Kasir, Daoud S., ed. LC 70-177135. (Columbia University. Teachers College. Contributions to Education: No. 385). Repr. of 1931 ed. 22.50 (ISBN 0-404-55385-0). AMS Pr.

Record, Robert. The Whetstone of Witte, Whiche Is the Second Parte of Arithmetike. LC 76-26206. (English Experience Ser.: No. 142). 320p. 1969. Repr. of 1557 ed. 39.00 (ISBN 90-221-0142-8). Walter J Johnson.

Shuja Ibn Aslam, Abukamil. The Algebra of Abu Kamil, in a Commentary by Mordecai Finzi. Levey, Martin, tr. (Publications in Medieval Science No. 10). 240p. 1966. 37.50x (ISBN 0-299-03800-9). U of Wis Pr.

ALGEBRA–EXAMINATIONS, QUESTIONS, ETC.

Rudman, Jack. College Algebra. (College Level Examination Ser.: CLEP-6). (Cloth bdg. avail. on request). pap. 9.95 (ISBN 0-8373-5306-8). Natl Learning.

--College Algebra-Trigonometry. (College Level Examination Ser.: CLEP-7). (Cloth bdg. avail. on request). pap. 9.95 (ISBN 0-8373-5311-4). Natl Learning.

ALGEBRA–GRAPHICAL METHODS

see also Equations–Numerical Solutions; Geometry, Analytic

Algebraic Graphs: Level Three Texts. rev. ed. (Math Components Ser.). 32p. 1983. 1.75 (ISBN 0-88336-834-X). New Readers.

Hodges, W. Building Models by Games. (London Mathematical Society Student Text Ser.: No. 2). 311p. 1985. 42.50 (ISBN 0-521-26897-4); pap. 16.95 (ISBN 0-521-31716-9). Cambridge U Pr.

ALGEBRA–PROBLEMS, EXERCISES, ETC.

Barnett, R. A. College Algebra, Trigonometry & Analytic Geometry. 608p. 1984. 31.95 (ISBN 0-07-003881-3). McGraw.

Cohen, David. Precalculus. (Illus.). 625p. 1984. text ed. 26.95 (ISBN 0-314-77871-3); instrs.' manual avail. (ISBN 0-314-79135-3). West Pub.

Faddeev, D. K. & Sominskii, I. S. Problems in Higher Algebra. Brenner, Joel L., tr. LC 65-18946. 498p. 1965. pap. 10.95 (ISBN 0-7167-0426-9). W H Freeman.

Fogiel, M., pref. by. The Algebra & Trigonometry Problem Solver. rev. ed. LC 76-334. (Illus.). 928p. 1984. pap. text ed. 19.85 (ISBN 0-87891-508-7). Res & Educ.

Folland, G. B. & Kohn, J. J. The Neumann Problem for the Cauchy-Riemann Complex. LC 72-1984. (Annals of Mathematics Studies: No. 75). 180p. 1972. lib. bdg. 22.00 (ISBN 0-691-08120-4). Princeton U Pr.
Johnson, Mildred. How to Solve Word Problems in Algebra: A Solved Problem Approach. (Orig.). 1976. pap. 4.95 (ISBN 0-07-032620-7). McGraw.
Keedy, Mervin & Bittinger, Marvin. Rational Numbers, Algebra & Solving Equations. rev. ed. (Algebra, a Modern Introduction Ser.). 1981. pap. text ed. 4.32 (ISBN 0-201-03983-4). Addison-Wesley.
--Roots, Radicals & Quadratic Equations. rev. ed. (Algebra, a Modern Introduction Ser.). 1981. pap. text ed. 4.32 (ISBN 0-201-03988-5). Addison-Wesley.
--Whole Numbers, Addition & Subtraction. rev. ed. (Algebra, a Modern Introduction Ser.). 1981. pap. text ed. 4.32 (ISBN 0-201-03977-X, Sch Div). Addison-Wesley.
--Whole Numbers, Multiplication & Division. rev. ed. (Algebra, a Modern Introduction Ser.). 1981. pap. text ed. 4.32 (ISBN 0-201-03978-8, Sch Div). Addison-Wesley.
New York Times Staff, et al. Fundamentals of Algebra. Date not set. price not set. McGraw.
Olson-Olson. Developing Algebra Skills: Test Booklet. 80p. 1983. pap. 11.95 (ISBN 0-8403-3139-8). Kendall-Hunt.
Peterson, Thurman S. & Hobby, Charles R. Intermediate Algebra for College Students. 6th ed. 418p. 1984. text ed. 23.50scp (ISBN 0-06-045185-8, HarpC); Ans. Key avail. (ISBN 0-06-365154-8). Har-Row.
Powell, Jesse J. A Study of Problem Material in High School Algebra. LC 71-177162. (Columbia University. Teachers College. Contributions to Education: No. 405). Repr. of 1929 ed. 22.50 (ISBN 0-404-55405-9). AMS Pr.
Sanford, Vera. The History & Significance of Certain Standard Problems in Algebra. LC 79-177227. (Columbia University. Teachers College. Contributions to Education Ser.: No. 251). Repr. of 1927 ed. 22.50 (ISBN 0-404-55251-X). AMS Pr.
Selby, Peter H. Quick Algebra Review. LC 82-21966. (Self Teaching Guide Ser.). 231p. 1983. pap. 8.95 (ISBN 0-471-86471-4, Pub. by Wiley Pr). Wiley.
Soracco, Lionel J., Jr. Solving Word Problems in Algebra: A Systematic Method. Leschensky, William, ed. (Illus.). 71p. 1981. manual & cassettes 284.50 (ISBN 0-917792-07-6). Math Hse.
Stein, Edwin I. Algebra in Easy Steps. 1982. 19.44 (ISBN 0-205-06956-8, 566956); tchr's guide 7.52 (ISBN 0-205-06957-6, 566957X). Allyn.

ALGEBRA-PROGRAMMED INSTRUCTION

Alwin, Robert, et al. Algebra Programmed, Pt. 3. 2nd ed. 1980. pap. text ed. 23.95 (ISBN 0-13-021931-2). P-H.
Alwin, Robert H. & Hackworth, Robert D. Algebra Programmed, Pt. 1. 2nd ed. (Illus.). 1978. pap. text ed. 18.95 (ISBN 0-13-022038-8). P-H.
Beck, William C. & Trier, James R. Programmed Course in Basic Algebra. (Mathematics Ser). 1971. pap. 17.95 (ISBN 0-201-00445-3). Addison-Wesley.
Benz, C. William. Passion: Program for Algebraic Sequences Specifically of Input-Output Nature. LC 72-126524. (Illus.). 92p. 1971. pap. text ed. 10.95 (ISBN 0-7167-0441-2). W H Freeman.
Bila, Dennis, et al. Intermediate Algebra. LC 74-84642. (Illus.). xvii, 625p. (Prog. Bk.). 1975. text ed. 22.95x (ISBN 0-87901-038-X). Worth.
--Introductory Algebra. LC 74-84641. (Illus.). xviii, 610p. (Prog. Bk.). 1975. text ed. 22.95x (ISBN 0-87901-037-1). Worth.
Pettofrezzo, Anthony J. & Armstrong, Lee H. Elementary Algebra: A Programmed Approach. 1980. pap. text ed. 20.60x (ISBN 0-673-15293-6). Scott F.
--Intermediate Algebra: A Programmed Approach. 1981. pap. text ed. 20.60x (ISBN 0-673-15315-0). Scott F.
Saxon, John H., Jr. Algebra I: An Incremental Development. 462p. 1982. tchr's. ed 22.00 (ISBN 0-939798-02-6). Grassdale.
--Algebra One-Half: An Incremental Development. 1983. text ed. 21.00 (ISBN 0-939798-05-0); 21.00 (ISBN 0-939798-06-9). Grassdale.

ALGEBRA-STUDY AND TEACHING

Albert, A. A., ed. Studies in Modern Algebra. LC 63-12777. (MAA Studies: No. 2). 190p. 1963. 16.50 (ISBN 0-88385-102-4). Math Assn.
Alexander, Thomas L. Modular Study Guide-Lab Manual for Intermediate Algebra (Pre-Calculus) 408p. 1982. pap. text ed. 21.95 (ISBN 0-8403-3300-5, 40317001). Kendall-Hunt.
Angel, Allen R. Intermediate Algebra: A Practical Approach. (Illus.). 448p. 1986. pap. text ed. 26.95 (ISBN 0-13-469859-2). P-H.
Booth, Leseley R. Children's Strategies & Errors: Algebra. 156p. 1984. pap. 18.00X (ISBN 0-7005-0636-5, Pub. by NFER Nelson UK). Taylor & Francis.
Booth, Lesley R. Algebra: Children's Strategies & Errors. 156p. 1984. 20.00 (ISBN 0-7005-0636-5). Taylor & Francis.
Everett, John P. Fundamental Skills of Algebra. LC 78-176759. (Columbia University. Teachers College. Contributions to Education: No. 324). Repr. of 1928 ed. 22.50 (ISBN 0-404-55324-9). AMS Pr.
Fuller, Gordon, et al. College Algebra. 5th ed. LC 81-21779. (Mathematics Ser.). 500p. 1982. text ed. 21.50 (ISBN 0-534-01138-1). Brooks-Cole.
Goodman, Terry A., et al. A Guidebook for Teaching Algebra. (Guidebook for Teaching Ser.). 332p. 1985. pap. 32.95x (ISBN 0-205-08117-7, 238117, Pub. by Longwood Div). Allyn.
Haeussler, Ernest & Paul, Richard. Algebra for College Students. 3rd ed. 1985. text ed. 27.95 (ISBN 0-8359-9179-2). Reston.
Hart, William L. Basic College Algebra. 1972. text ed. 18.95 (ISBN 0-669-73999-5). Heath.
Hilton, Peter & Wu, Yel-Chiang. A Course in Modern Algebra. LC 73-18043. (Pure & Applied Mathematics Ser.). 249p. 1974. 43.50x (ISBN 0-471-39967-1, Pub. by Wiley-Interscience). Wiley.
Hotz, Henry G. First-Year Algebra Scales. LC 79-176881. (Columbia University. Teachers College. Contributions to Education: No. 90). Repr. of 1918 ed. 22.50 (ISBN 0-404-55090-8). AMS Pr.
Jacobson, Nathan. Basic Algebra One. LC 73-22316. (Illus.). 472p. 1974. text ed. 29.95 (ISBN 0-7167-0453-6); solutions manual avail. (ISBN 0-7167-1030-7). W H Freeman.
Keedy, Mervin L. & Bittinger, Marvin L. College Algebra: A Functions Approach. 3rd ed. 1982. pap. 26.95 (ISBN 0-201-13400-4); student sol. 5.95 (ISBN 0-201-13401-2); test booklet 3.50 (ISBN 0-201-13402-0); 2.00 (ISBN 0-201-13403-9). Addison-Wesley.
McHale, T. J. & Witzke, P. T. Basic Algebra. (Milwaukee Area Technical College Mathematics Ser.). 1971. pap. 21.95 (ISBN 0-201-04625-3); test bklt. 3.95 (ISBN 0-201-04591-5). Addison-Wesley.
McKim, Margaret G. The Reading of Verbal Material in Ninth Grade Algebra. LC 71-177032. (Columbia University. Teachers College. Contributions to Education Ser.: No. 850). Repr. of 1941 ed. 22.50 (ISBN 0-404-55850-X). AMS Pr.
Miller, Charles D. & Lial, Margaret L. Introductory Algebra: A Text-Workbook. 2nd ed. 1983. pap. text ed. 22.70 (ISBN 0-673-15796-2). Scott F.
Nanney & Cable. College Algebra: A Skills Approach, Lecture Version. 320p. 1980. text ed. 29.29 (ISBN 0-205-06914-2, 5669146); study guide o.p. 7.95 (ISBN 0-205-06916-9, 456691562). Allyn.
Northcott, Douglas G. A First Course of Homological Algebra. LC 72-97873. 250p. 1973. 34.50 (ISBN 0-521-20196-9). Cambridge U Pr.
Powell, Jesse J. A Study of Problem Material in High School Algebra. LC 71-177162. (Columbia University. Teachers College. Contributions to Education: No. 405). Repr. of 1929 ed. 22.50 (ISBN 0-404-55405-9). AMS Pr.
Price, E. A. Introduction to Algebra. LC 65-18480. (Illus.). 288p. 1965. pap. 2.95 (ISBN 0-668-01282-X). Arco.
Rasmussen, Peter. Key to Algebra Series. rev ed. 160p. 1975. Bk. 1. pap. text ed. 1.30 (ISBN 0-913684-01-5); Bk. 2. pap. text ed. 1.30 (ISBN 0-913684-02-3); Bk. 3. pap. text ed. 1.30 (ISBN 0-913684-03-1); Bk. 4. pap. text ed. 1.30 (ISBN 0-913684-04-X). tchrs' notes 0.50 (ISBN 0-913684-19-8); ans. bk. 1.75 (ISBN 0-913684-18-X). Key Curr Proj.
Rees, Paul K. & Sparks, Fred W. Algebra, Trigonometry & Analytic Geometry. 2nd ed. (Illus.). 512p. 1975. text ed. 34.95 (ISBN 0-07-051720-7). McGraw.
Reigh, Mildred, et al. Brief Algebra Review Manual: A Program for Self-Instruction. 1966. text ed. 25.95 (ISBN 0-07-051811-4). McGraw.
Rich, Barnett. Modern Elementary Algebra. (Schaum Outline Ser). 1973. pap. 7.95 (ISBN 0-07-052247-2). McGraw.
Symonds, Percival M. Special Disability in Algebra. LC 73-177728. (Columbia University. Teachers College. Contributions to Education: No. 132). Repr. of 1923 ed. 22.50 (ISBN 0-404-55132-7). AMS Pr.
Tronaas, Edward M. Introductory Algebra for College Students. 352p. 1980. pap. text ed. 19.95 (ISBN 0-8403-2314-X). Kendall-Hunt.

ALGEBRA, ABSTRACT

see also Algebra, Boolean; Algebra, Homological; Algebra, Universal; Fields, Algebraic; Groups, Theory Of; Jordan Algebras; Lattice Theory; Lie Algebras; Logic, Symbolic and Mathematical; Matrices; Nonassociative Algebras

Barbey, K. & Konig, H. Abstract Analytic Function Theory & Hardy Algebras. (Lecture Notes in Mathematics Ser.: Vol. 593). 1977. pap. 18.00 (ISBN 0-387-08252-2). Springer-Verlag.
Bruck, R. H. Survey of Binary Systems. 3rd ed. LC 79-143906. (Ergebnisse der Mathematik und Ihrer Grenzebiete: Vol. 20). 1971. 22.00 (ISBN 0-387-03497-8). Springer-Verlag.
Cartan, H. & Eilenberg, S. Homological Algebra. (Mathematical Ser.: Vol. 19). 1956. 46.00 (ISBN 0-691-07977-3). Princeton U Pr.
Chow, Y. Modern Abstract Algebra, 2 vols. 782p. 1976. Set. 113.50 (ISBN 0-677-03880-1). Gordon.
Clark, Allan. Elements of Abstract Algebra. 205p. 1984. pap. 6.00 (ISBN 0-486-64725-0). Dover.
Crown, et al. Abstract Algebra. (Pure & Applied Mathematics Ser.). 488p. 1986. price not set (ISBN 0-8247-7456-6). Dekker.
Curtis, Charles W. & Reiner, Irving. Representation Theory of Finite Groups & Associative Algebras. LC 62-16994. (Pure & Applied Mathematics Ser.). 685p. 1962. 69.50 (ISBN 0-470-18975-4, Pub. by Wiley-Interscience). Wiley.
Durbin, John R. Modern Algebra: An Introduction. LC 78-15778. 329p. 1979. text ed. 32.45 (ISBN 0-471-02158-X); tchrs. manual 6.00 (ISBN 0-471-03753-2). Wiley.
Fraleigh, J. B. A First Course in Abstract Algebra. 3rd ed. LC 81-14938. 1982. text ed. 31.95 (ISBN 0-201-10405-9). Addison-Wesley.
Gilbert, William J. Modern Algebra with Applications. LC 76-22756. 348p. 1976. 38.50x (ISBN 0-471-29891-3, Pub by Wiley-Interscience). Wiley.
Gill, Arthur. Applied Algebra for the Computer Sciences. (Illus.). 416p. 1976. 37.95 (ISBN 0-13-039222-7). P-H.
Golan, Jonathan S. Localization of Noncommutative Rings. (Pure & Applied Mathematics Ser.: Vol. 30). 352p. 1975. 55.00 (ISBN 0-8247-6198-7). Dekker.
Goldstein, Larry J. Abstract Algebra: A First Course. LC 72-12790. (Illus.). 1973. 33.95x (ISBN 0-13-000851-6). P-H.
Grove, Larry C. Algebra. (Pure & Applied Mathematics Ser.). 1983. 35.00 (ISBN 0-12-304620-3). Acad Pr.
Hall, F. M. Introduction to Abstract Algebra, Vol. 1. 2nd ed. (Illus.). 314p. 1980. pap. 16.95 (ISBN 0-521-29861-X). Cambridge U Pr.
--Introduction to Abstract Algebra, Vol. 2. (Illus.). 400p. 1980. pap. 22.95 (ISBN 0-521-29862-8). Cambridge U Pr.
Herstein, Israel N. Abstract Algebra. 355p. 1986. text ed. price not set (ISBN 0-02-353820-1). Macmillan.
Jacobson, N. Lectures in Abstract Algebra, Vol. 2. (Graduate Texts in Mathematics Ser.: Vol. 31). 290p. 1975. Repr. 29.50 (ISBN 0-387-90123-X). Springer-Verlag.
--Lectures in Abstract Algebra: Basic Concepts, Vol. 1. (Graduate Texts in Mathematics Ser.: Vol. 30). 1976. Repr. 29.50 (ISBN 0-387-90181-7). Springer-Verlag.
--Lectures in Abstract Algebra: Theory of Fields & Galois Theory, Vol. 3. (Graduate Texts in Mathematics Ser.: Vol. 32). 323p. 1964. 36.00 (ISBN 0-387-90168-X). Springer-Verlag.
Kuczkowski, Joseph E. & Gersting, Judith L. Abstract Algebra: A First Look. (Monographs & Textbooks in Pure & Applied Math: Vol. 38). 1977. 35.00 (ISBN 0-8247-6482-X). Dekker.
Lakshmikantham, V., ed. Nonlinear Equations in Abstract Spaces. 1978. 55.00 (ISBN 0-12-434160-8). Acad Pr.
Lidl, R. & Pilz, G. Applied Abstract Algebra. (Undergraduate Texts in Mathematics). (Illus.). 450p. 1984. 39.00 (ISBN 0-387-96035-X). Springer-Verlag.
McCoy, Neal. Introduction to Modern Algebra. 3rd ed. 296p. 1975. text ed. 34.29 (ISBN 0-205-04545-6, 564545X). Allyn.
Mackiw, George. Applications of Abstract Algebra. 184p. 1985. pap. text ed. 11.95 (ISBN 0-471-81078-9). Wiley.
Mal'cev, A. I. Algebraic Systems. Seckler, B. D. & Doohovskoy, A. P., trs. from Russian. (Die Grundlehren der Mathematischen Wissenschaften: Vol. 192). 320p. 1973. 59.00 (ISBN 0-387-05792-7). Springer-Verlag.
Miller, Kenneth S. Elements of Modern Abstract Algebra. LC 74-6497. 198p. 1975. Repr. of 1958 ed. 12.50 (ISBN 0-88275-178-6). Krieger.
Moore, J. T. Introduction to Abstract Algebra. 1975. text ed. 23.25i (ISBN 0-12-505750-4); ans. bklt. 2.50i (ISBN 0-12-505752-0). Acad Pr.
Pierce, Richard S. Introduction to the Theory of Abstract Algebras. LC 68-16477. 1968. 37.50x (ISBN 0-03-056010-1). Irvington.
Pinter, C. C. A Book of Abstract Algebra. 1982. 33.95x (ISBN 0-07-050130-0). McGraw.
Rosenfeld, Azriel. An Introduction to Algebraic Structures. LC 68-13895. 1968. 32.50x (ISBN 0-8162-7304-9). Holden-Day.
Saracino, Dan. Abstract Algebra: A First Course. LC 79-18692. (Illus.). 1980. text ed. 25.95 (ISBN 0-201-07391-9). Addison-Wesley.
Sawyer, W. W. A Concrete Approach to Abstract Algebra. 1978. pap. text ed. 5.95 (ISBN 0-486-63647-X). Dover.
Sims, Charles C. Abstract Algebra: A Computational Approach. 491p. 1984. text ed. 37.50 (ISBN 0-471-09846-9); tchr's manual avail. (ISBN 0-471-87233-4); user's manual 10.95 (ISBN 0-471-09844-2). Wiley.
Zaidman, S. Almost-Periodic Functions in Abstract Spaces. (Research Notes in Mathematics Ser.). 144p. 1985. pap. text ed. 14.95 (ISBN 0-273-08661-8). Pitman Pub MA.

ALGEBRA, BOOLEAN

see also Caratheodory Measure; Lattice Theory

Borger, E., et al, eds. Logic & Machines-Decision Problems & Complexity: Proceedings of the Symposium "Rekursive Kompinatorik" Held from May 23-28, 1983 at the Institut fur Mathematische Logik und Grundlagenfroschung der Universitat Munster-Westfalen. (Lecture Notes in Computer Science Ser.: Vol. 171). vi, 456p. 1984. pap. 20.40. Springer-Verlag.
Buchberger, B., et al, eds. Computer Algebra. (Illus.). 283p. 1983. pap. 26.50 (ISBN 0-387-81776-X). Springer Verlag.
Bukstein, Edward J. Practice Problems in Number Systems, Logic, & Boolean Algebra. 2nd ed. LC 77-72632. (Illus.). 144p. 1977. pap. 11.95 (ISBN 0-672-21451-2, 21451). Sams.
Burris, Stanley & McKenzie, Ralph. Decidability & Boolean Representations. LC 81-7902. (Memoirs of the American Mathematical Society Ser.: No. 246). 108p. 1981. pap. 9.00 (ISBN 0-8218-2246-2). Am Math.
Colloquium on Mathematics & Cybernetics in the Economy, Berlin, 1964. Pseudo-Boolean Programming & Applications. Ivanescu, P. L., ed. (Lecture Notes in Mathematics: Vol. 9). 1965. pap. 10.70 (ISBN 0-387-03352-1). Springer-Verlag.
European Meeting of the Institute of Management Sciences & of the Econometric Institute, Warsaw, 1966. Pseudo-Boolean Methods for Bivalent Programming. Ivanescu, P. L. & Rudeanu, S., eds. (Lecture Notes in Mathematics: Vol. 23). 1966. pap. 10.70 (ISBN 0-387-03606-7). Springer-Verlag.
Flament, C. L'analyse Booleenne de Questionnaire. 1977. 46.00x (ISBN 90-279-7733-X). Mouton.
Hailperin, T. Boole's Logic & Probability Theory. (Studies in Logic & the Foundations of Mathematics: Vol. 85). 246p. 1976. 55.50 (ISBN 0-7204-0374-X, North-Holland). Elsevier.
Helzer, Garry. Applied Linear Algebra with APL. 608p. 1982. text ed. 37.00 (ISBN 0-316-35526-7); tcher's manual avail. (ISBN 0-316-35527-5). Little.
Johnstone, Peter. Stone Spaces. LC 82-4506. (Cambridge Studies in Advanced Mathematics: No. 3). 300p. 1983. 62.50 (ISBN 0-521-23893-5). Cambridge U Pr.
Kulisch, Ulrich W. & Miranker, Willard L. Computer Arithmetic in Theory & Practice. LC 80-765. (Computer Science & Applied Mathematics Ser.). 1981. 42.50 (ISBN 0-12-428650-X). Acad Pr.
Levitz, Hilbert & Levitz, Kathleen. Logic & Boolean Algebra. LC 75-1006. 1979. pap. 8.95 (ISBN 0-8120-0537-6). Barron.
Levy, Leon S. Discrete Structures of Computer Science. LC 79-11218. 310p. 1980. text ed. 33.95x (ISBN 0-471-03208-5). Wiley.
Lipson, John D. Elements of Algebra & Algebraic Computing. 420p. 1980. text ed. 39.95 o. p. (ISBN 0-201-04115-4); pap. 29.95 (ISBN 0-201-04480-3). Addison-Wesley.
Nash, J. C. Compact Numerical Methods for Computers: Linear Algebra & Functional Minimization. LC 78-10144. 227p. 1979. 37.95x (ISBN 0-470-26559-0). Halsted Pr.
Pierce, R. S. Compact Zero-Dimensional Metric Spaces of Finite Type. LC 72-11822. (Memoirs: No. 130). 64p. 1972. pap. 9.00 (ISBN 0-8218-1830-9, MEMO-130). Am Math.
Rosser, Barkley J. Simplified Independence Proofs: Boolean Valued Models of Set Theory. (Pure & Applied Mathematics Ser: Vol. 31). 1969. 49.50 (ISBN 0-12-598050-7). Acad Pr.
Rueff, Marcel & Jeger, Max. Sets & Boolean Algebra. Howson, A. G., ed. LC 72-189267. (Mathematical Studies: A Series for Teachers & Students: No. 4). pap. 48.00 (ISBN 0-317-20064-X, 2023329). Bks Demand UMI.

Sain, Michael K. Introduction to Algebraic System Theory. LC 80-522. (Mathematics in Science & Engineering Ser.). 1981. 44.50 (ISBN 0-12-614850-3). Acad Pr.
Sikorski, R. Boolean Algebras. 3rd ed. LC 68-59302. (Ergebnisse der Mathematik und Ihrer Grenzgebiete: Vol. 25). 1969. 29.00 (ISBN 0-387-04469-8). Springer-Verlag.
Thayse, A. Boolean Calculus of Differences. (Lecture Notes in Computer Science Ser.: Vol. 101). 144p. 1981. pap. 12.00 (ISBN 0-387-10286-8). Springer-Verlag.
--P-Functions & Boolean Matrix Factorization: A Unified Approach for Wired, Programmed & Microprogrammed Implementations of Discrete Algorithms. (Lecture Notes in Computer Science Ser.: Vol. 175). xii, 248p. 1984. pap. 16.00 (ISBN 0-387-13358-5). Springer-Verlag.
Van Hulzen, J. A., ed. Computer Algebra. (Lecture Notes in Computer Science: Vol. 162). 305p. 1983. pap. 17.00 (ISBN 0-387-12868-9). Springer Verlag.
Williams, Gareth. Computational Linear Algebra with Models. 2nd ed. 1978. text ed. 32.74 (ISBN 0-205-05998-8, 565998); instr's man 32.74 (ISBN 0-205-05999-6). Allyn.

ALGEBRA, BOOLEAN–PROGRAMMED INSTRUCTION
Hestenes, Marshall & Hill, Richard. Algebra & Trigonometry with Calculators. (Illus.). 512p. 1981. text ed. 29.95 (ISBN 0-13-021857-X). P-H.
Hoernes, G. & Heilweil, M. Introduction to Boolean Algebra & Logic Design: A Program for Self-Instruction. 1964. pap. text ed. 27.95 (ISBN 0-07-029183-7). McGraw.

ALGEBRA, DIFFERENCE
Cohn, Richard M. Difference Algebra. LC 77-28532. 372p. 1980. Repr. of 1965 ed. lib. bdg. 24.50 (ISBN 0-88275-651-6). Krieger.

ALGEBRA, DIFFERENTIAL
see also Algebra, Difference
American Society of Mechanical Engineers. Differential Games: Theory & Applications. LC 74-128583. pap. 36.80 (ISBN 0-317-08724-X, 2013312). Bks Demand UMI.
Bronson, Richard. Modern Introductory Differential Equations. (Schaum Outline Ser.). 1973. pap. text ed. 8.95 (ISBN 0-07-008009-7). McGraw.
Kappel, F. & Schappacher, W. Abstract Cauchy Problems & Functional Differential Equations. LC 80-22557. (Research Notes in Mathematics Ser.: No. 48). 240p. (Orig.). 1981. pap. text ed. 28.95 (ISBN 0-273-08494-1). Pitman Pub MA.
Kolchin, E. R. Differential Algebra & Algebraic Groups. (Pure & Applied Mathematics Ser.: Vol. 55). 1973. 79.50 (ISBN 0-12-417650-X). Acad Pr.
--Differential Algebraic Groups. (Pure & Applied Mathematics Ser.). 1985. 60.00 (ISBN 0-12-417640-2). Acad Pr.

ALGEBRA, HOMOLOGICAL
see also Categories (Mathematics); Functor Theory
Bousfield, A. K. Homological Localization Towers for Groups & Pi-Modules. LC 77-3716. (Memoirs: No. 186). 68p. 1977. pap. 13.00 (ISBN 0-8218-2186-5, MEMO-186). Am Math.
Douglas, Ronald G. C-Algebra Extensions & K-Homology. LC 80-424. (Annals of Mathematics Studies: No. 95). (Illus.). 87p. 1980. 16.50x (ISBN 0-691-08265-0); pap. 7.95x (ISBN 0-691-08266-9). Princeton U Pr.
Gugenheim, V. K. & May, J. Peter. On the Theory & Applications of Differential Torsion Products. Gugenheim, A. M., tr. LC 74-2164. (Memoirs: No. 142). 73p. 1974. pap. 10.00 (ISBN 0-8218-1842-2, MEMO-142). Am Math.
Hilton, P. Lectures in Homological Algebra. LC 70-152504. (Conference Board of the Math Sciences Ser.: No. 8). 74p. 1980. pap. 10.00 (ISBN 0-8218-1657-8, CBMS-8). Am Math.
Hilton, P. J. & Stammbach, U. Course in Homological Algebra. LC 72-162401. (Graduate Texts in Mathematics: Vol. 4). 1972. 40.00 (ISBN 0-387-90032-2). Springer-Verlag.
Hodgkin, L. H. Topics in K-Theory: Two Independent Contributions. LC 75-41435. (Lecture Notes in Mathematics: Vol. 496). 1975. pap. 19.00 (ISBN 0-387-07536-4). Springer-Verlag.
MacLane, S. Homology. (Die Grundlehren der Mathematischen Wissenschaften: Vol. 114). (Illus.). x, 422p. 1965. 39.00 (ISBN 0-387-03823-X). Springer-Verlag.
Northcott, Douglas G. Finite Free Resolutions. LC 75-31397. (Tracts in Mathematics Ser.: No. 71). 250p. 1976. 57.50 (ISBN 0-521-21155-7). Cambridge U Pr.
--A First Course of Homological Algebra. LC 72-87873. 217p. 1980. pap. 15.95x (ISBN 0-521-29976-4). Cambridge U Pr.
Rotman, Joseph J. An Introduction to Homological Algebra. (Pure & Applied Mathematics Ser.). 1979. 31.00 (ISBN 0-12-599250-5). Acad Pr.
Strooker, J. R. Introduction to Categories, Homological Algebra & Sheaf Cohomology. LC 77-80849. 1978. 57.50 (ISBN 0-521-21699-0). Cambridge U Pr.
Wall, C. T., ed. Homological Groups Theory. LC 78-74013. (London Mathematical Society Lecture Note: No. 36). 1980. pap. 49.50 (ISBN 0-521-22729-1). Cambridge U Pr.

ALGEBRA, MULTIPLE
see Algebra, Universal

ALGEBRA, UNIVERSAL
see also Algebra, Abstract; Algebras, Linear; Ausdehnungslehre; Calculus of Operations; Categories (Mathematics); Matrices; Numbers, Complex; Quaternions; Vector Analysis
Albert, Abraham A. Modern Higher Algebra. LC 38-2937. (University of Chicago Science Ser.). pap. 82.80 (ISBN 0-317-09455-6, 2016998). Bks Demand UMI.
Atiyah, Michael F. & Macdonald, I. G. Introduction to Commutative Algebra. 1969. text ed. 24.95 (ISBN 0-201-00361-9). Addison-Wesley.
Burris, S. & Sankappanavar, H. P. A Course in Universal Algebra. (Graduate Texts in Mathematics Ser.: Vol. 78). (Illus.). 320p. 1981. 36.00 (ISBN 0-387-90578-2). Springer-Verlag.
Cohn, Paul M. Universal Algebra. rev. ed. 380p. 1982. 44.50 (ISBN 90-277-1240-9, Pub. by Reidel Holland). Kluwer Academic.
Csakany, B. & Schmidt, J. Contributions to Universal Algebra. (Colloquia Mathematica Ser.: Vol. 17). 608p. 1978. 119.25 (ISBN 0-7204-0725-7, North-Holland). Elsevier.
Graetzer, G. Universal Algebra. 2nd ed. LC 68-55539. xvi, 368p. 1979. 39.50 (ISBN 0-387-90355-0). Springer-Verlag.
Grumm, H. Peter. Geometrical Methods in Congruence Modular Algebras. LC 83-11810. (Memoirs: No. 286). 80p. 1983. pap. 8.00 (ISBN 0-8218-2286-1, MEMO 286). Am Math.
Johnstone, P. T., et al. Indexed Categories & Their Application. (Lecture Notes in Mathematics: Vol. 661). (Illus.). 1978. pap. 17.00 (ISBN 0-387-08914-4). Springer-Verlag.
Jonsson, Bjarni & Tarski, Alfred. Direct Decompositions of Finite Algebraic Systems. (Mathematical Lectures Ser.: No. 5). (Orig.). 1947. pap. 1.75x (ISBN 0-268-00081-6). U of Notre Dame Pr.
Neumann, H. Varieties of Groups. (Ergebnisse der Mathematik und Ihrer Grenzgebiete: Vol. 37). 1967. 33.00 (ISBN 0-387-03779-9). Springer-Verlag.
Seligman, G. B. On Lie Algebras of Prime Characteristics. LC 52-42839. (Memoirs: No. 19). 85p. 1970. pap. 10.00 (ISBN 0-8218-1219-X, MEMO-19). Am Math.

ALGEBRA OF CURRENTS
International Summer School for Theoretical Physics, University of Karlsruhe, 1968. Current Algebra & Phenomenological Lagrange Functions: Invited Papers. Hoehler, G., ed. (Springer Tracts in Modern Physics: Vol. 50). (Illus.). v, 156p. 1969. 34.30 (ISBN 0-387-04713-1). Springer-Verlag.
Lee, B. Chiral Dynamics. (Documents on Modern Physics Ser.). 130p. 1972. pap. 45.25x (ISBN 0-677-01385-X). Gordon.
Sakurai, J. J. Currents & Mesons. LC 69-15230. (Chicago Lectures in Physics Ser). 1969. pap. 7.00x (ISBN 0-226-73383-1). U of Chicago Pr.

ALGEBRA OF LOGIC
see Logic, Symbolic and Mathematical

ALGEBRAIC CONFIGURATIONS IN HYPERSPACE
see Hyperspace

ALGEBRAIC CURVES
see Curves, Algebraic

ALGEBRAIC FIELDS
see Fields, Algebraic

ALGEBRAIC FUNCTIONS
see Functions, Algebraic

ALGEBRAIC GEOMETRY
see Geometry, Algebraic

ALGEBRAIC NUMBER THEORY
Berrick, A. J. An Approach to Algebraic K-Theory. (Research Notes in Mathematics Ser.: No. 56). 120p. 1982. text ed. 17.95 (ISBN 0-273-08529-8). Pitman Pub MA.
Edwards, Harold M. Femat's Last Theorem: A Genetic Introduction to Algebraic Number Theory. LC 77-8222. (Graduate Texts in Mathematics Ser.: Vol. 50). 1977. 32.00 (ISBN 0-387-90230-9). Springer-Verlag.
Froehlich, A. Galois Module Structure of Algebraic Integers. (Ergebnisse der Mathematik und Ihrer Grenzgebiete 3. Folge.: Vol. 1). 262p. 1983. 34.00 (ISBN 0-387-11920-5). Springer-Verlag.
Godement, R. & Jacquet, H. Zeta-Functions of Simple Algebras. LC 72-76391. (Lecture Notes in Mathematics: Vol. 260). 197p. 1972. pap. 10.00 (ISBN 0-387-05797-8). Springer-Verlag.
Ishida, M. The Genus Fields of Algebraic Number Fields. (Lecture Notes in Mathematics: Vol. 555). 1976. soft cover 13.00 (ISBN 0-387-08000-7). Springer-Verlag.
Iwasawa, Kenkichi. Lectures on P-Adic L-Functions. LC 78-39058. (Annals of Mathematics Studies: No. 74). 114p. 1972. lib. bdg. 14.95 (ISBN 0-691-08112-3). Princeton U Pr.
Janusz, Gerald J. Algebraic Number Fields. (Pure & Applied Mathematics Ser.). 1973. 59.00 (ISBN 0-12-380250-4). Acad Pr.
Koblitz, N. P-Adic Analysis. (London Mathematical Society Lecture Note Ser.: No. 46). 150p. 1980. pap. 17.95 (ISBN 0-521-28060-5). Cambridge U Pr.
Landau, Edmund. Algebraische Zahlen. 2nd ed. (Ger). 9.95 (ISBN 0-8284-0062-8). Chelsea Pub.
Long, Robert. Algebraic Number Theory. (Monographs in Pure and Applied Mathamatics: Vol. 41). 1977. 39.75 (ISBN 0-8247-6540-0). Dekker.
Marcus, D. A. Number Fields (Universitext) LC 77-21467. 1977. text ed. 23.00 (ISBN 0-387-90279-1). Springer-Verlag.
Pollard, Harry & Diamond, H. G. The Theory of Algebraic Numbers. 2nd ed. LC 75-27003. (Carus Mathematical Monographs: No. 9). xii, 162p. 1975. 16.50 (ISBN 0-88385-018-4). Math Assn.
Reid, Legh W. The Elements of the Theory of Algebraic Numbers. LC 10-23524. pap. 118.50 (ISBN 0-317-08884-X, 2020743). Bks Demand UMI.
Ribenboim, Paulo. Algebraic Numbers. LC 74-37174. (Pure & Applied Mathematics Ser.). 300p. 1972. 49.95 (ISBN 0-471-71804-1, Pub. by Wiley-Interscience). Wiley.
Schmidt, W. M. Diophantine Approximation. (Lecture Notes in Mathematics: Vol. 785). 299p. 1980. pap. 23.00 (ISBN 0-387-09762-7). Springer-Verlag.
Serre, J. P. & Zagier, D. B., eds. Modular Functions of One Variable 5: Proceedings. LC 77-22148. (Lecture Notes in Mathematics: Vol. 601). 1977. pap. text ed. 18.00 (ISBN 0-387-08348-0). Springer-Verlag.
Shatz, Stephen S. Profinite Groups, Arithmetic, & Geometry. LC 77-126832. (Annals of Mathematics Studies: No. 67). 1972. 26.50 (ISBN 0-691-08017-8). Princeton U Pr.
Steklov Institute of Mathematics, Academy of Science, U. S. S. R., No. 80. Algebraic Number Theory & Representations: Proceedings. Faddeev, D. K., ed. (Proceedings of the Steklov Institute of Mathematics). 1968. 49.00 (ISBN 0-8218-1880-5, STEKLO-80). Am Math.
Stewart, I. N. & Tall, D. O. Algebraic Number Theory. LC 78-31625. 200p. 1979. pap. 16.95x (ISBN 0-412-16000-5, NO.6273, Pub. by Chapman & Hall). Methuen Inc.
Symposium in Pure Mathematics, Stony Brook, N.Y. 1969. Number Theory Institute, Nineteen Sixty-Nine: Proceedings. Lewis, Donald J., ed. LC 76-125938. (Proceeding of Symposia in Pure Mathematics: Vol. 20). 1971. 44.00 (ISBN 0-8218-1420-6, PSPUM-20). Am Math.
Warshauer, M. L. The Witt Group of Degree k Maps & Asymmetric Inner Product Spaces. (Lecture Notes in Mathematics: Vol. 914). 269p. 1982. pap. 19.00 (ISBN 0-387-11201-4). Springer-Verlag.
Weil, A. Number Theory for Beginners. 1979. pap. 9.50 (ISBN 0-387-90381-X). Springer-Verlag.
Weiss, Edwin. Algebraic Number Theory. 2nd ed. LC 76-5803. xii, 275p. 1976. 14.95 (ISBN 0-8284-0293-0). Chelsea Pub.
Weyl, Hermann. Algebraic Theory of Numbers. rev. ed. (Annals of Mathematics Studies: No. 1). (Orig.). 1954. pap. 26.50x (ISBN 0-691-07908-0). Princeton U Pr.
Zimmer, H. G. Computational Problems, Methods, & Results in Algebraic Number Theory. LC 72-78191. (Lecture Notes in Mathematics: Vol. 262). 108p. 1972. pap. 9.00 (ISBN 0-387-05822-2). Springer-Verlag.

ALGEBRAIC NUMBERS
see Fields, Algebraic

ALGEBRAIC RINGS
see Rings (Algebra)

ALGEBRAIC SPACES
Adams, R. A. Sobolev Spaces. (Pure & Applied Mathematics Ser.). 1975. 47.50 (ISBN 0-12-044150-0). Acad Pr.
Bourgain, J. New Classes of LP-Spaces. (Lecture Notes in Mathematics Ser.: Vol. 889). 143p. 1981. pap. 12.00 (ISBN 0-387-11156-5). Springer-Verlag.
Dubinsky, E. The Structure of Nuclear Frechet Spaces. (Lecture Notes in Mathematics: Vol. 720). 1979. pap. 14.00 (ISBN 0-387-09504-7). Springer-Verlag.
Johnstone, Peter. Stone Spaces. LC 82-4506. (Cambridge Studies in Advanced Mathematics: No. 3). 300p. 1983. 62.50 (ISBN 0-521-23893-5). Cambridge U Pr.
Knutson, D. Algebraic Spaces. (Lecture Notes in Mathematics: Vol. 203). 1971. pap. 12.00 (ISBN 0-387-05496-0). Springer-Verlag.
Koosis, P. J. Introduction to Hp Spaces. LC 80-65175. (London Mathematical Society Lecture Note Ser.: No. 40). (Illus.). 380p. (Orig.). 1980. pap. 29.95 (ISBN 0-521-23159-0). Cambridge U Pr.
McKennon, Kelly & Robertson, Jack M. Locally Convex Spaces. (Lecture Notes in Pure & Applied Mathematics Ser.: Vol. 15). 1976. 29.75 (ISBN 0-8247-6426-9). Dekker.
Szpiro, L. Lectures on Equations Defining Space Curves. (Tata Institute Lectures on Mathematics). (Illus.). 81p. 1979. pap. 11.00 (ISBN 0-387-09544-6). Springer-Verlag.
Wong, Y. C. Schwartz Spaces, Nuclear Spaces & Tensor Products. (Lecture Notes in Mathematics: Vol. 726). 1979. pap. 24.00 (ISBN 0-387-09513-6). Springer-Verlag.

ALGEBRAIC SURFACES
see Surfaces, Algebraic

ALGEBRAIC TOPOLOGY
see also Homology Theory; Hopf Algebras; K-Theory; Measure Theory; Sheaves, Theory Of
Adams, John F. Algebraic Topology: A Student's Guide. LC 75-163178. (London Mathematical Lecture Note Ser.: No. 4). (Illus.). 1972. 29.95 (ISBN 0-521-08076-2). Cambridge U Pr.
Agoston, Max K. Algebraic Topology: A First Course. (Pure & Applied Mathematics Ser.: Vol.32). 376p. 1976. 34.75 (ISBN 0-8247-6351-3). Dekker.
Andrianov, A. N., et al. Thirteen Papers on Group Theory, Algebraic Geometry & Algebraic Topology. LC 51-5559. (Translations Ser.: No. 2, Vol. 66). 1968. 35.00 (ISBN 0-8218-1766-3, TRANS 2-66). Am Math.
Barbasin, E. A., et al. Twelve Papers on Analysis, Applied Mathematics & Algebraic Topology. LC 51-5559. (Translations Ser.: No. 2, Vol. 25). 1963. 27.00 (ISBN 0-8218-1725-6, TRANS 2-25). Am Math.
Baues, H. J. Commutator Calculus & Groups of Homotopy Classes. (London Mathematical Society Lecture Note Ser.: No. 50). (Illus.). 220p. 1981. pap. 27.95 (ISBN 0-521-28424-4). Cambridge U Pr.
Boltyanskii, V. G., et al. Topology & Topological Algebra. (Translations Ser.: No. 1, Vol. 8). 1962. 24.00 (ISBN 0-8218-1608-X, TRANS 1-8). Am Math.
Bott, R. & Tu, L. W. Differential Forms in Algebraic Topology. (Graduate Texts in Mathematics Ser.: Vol. 82). (Illus.). 288p. 1982. 33.00 (ISBN 0-387-90613-4). Springer-Verlag.
Canadian Mathematical Society, NSERC & the University of Waterloo, June 1978, et al. Algebraic Topology: Proceedings. Hoffman, P., ed. (Lecture Notes in Mathmatics: Vol. 741). 1979. pap. 37.00 (ISBN 0-387-09545-4). Springer-Verlag.
Conference Held at Manheim, 21-25 July, 1975. Categorical Topology: Proceedings. Binz, E., ed. (Lecture Notes in Mathematics: Vol. 540). 1976. soft cover 33.00 (ISBN 0-387-07859-2). Springer-Verlag.
Conference on Set-Valued Mappings, SUNY, Buffalo, 1969. Set-Valued Mappings, Selections & Topological Properties of 2x: Proceedings. Fleischman, W. M., ed. (Lecture Notes in Mathematics: Vol. 171). 1970. pap. 11.00 (ISBN 0-387-05293-3). Springer-Verlag.
Conference on Topological Methods in Algebraic Topology, SUNY, Binghamton, Oct. 1973. Algebraic & Geometrical Methods in Topology: Proceedings. McAuley, L. F., ed. (Lecture Notes in Mathematics Ser.: Vol. 428). xi, 280p. 1974. pap. 18.00 (ISBN 0-387-07019-2). Springer-Verlag.
Conner, Pierre E. Lectures on the Action of a Finite Group. LC 68-57940. (Lecture Notes in Mathematics: Vol. 73). 1968. pap. 10.70 (ISBN 0-387-04243-1). Springer-Verlag.
Crabb, M. C. ZZ-Two-Homotopy Theory. (London Mathematical Lecture Note Ser.: No. 44). 100p. (Orig.). 1980. pap. 17.95 (ISBN 0-521-28051-6). Cambridge U Pr.
Dold, A. Lectures on Algebraic Topology. LC 79-79062. (Grundlehren der Mathematischen Wissenschaften Ser.: Vol. 200). (Illus.). 377p. 1980. 42.00 (ISBN 0-387-10369-4). Springer-Verlag.
Dupont, J. L. & Madsen, J. H., eds. Algebraic Topology: Aarhus Nineteen Seventy-Eight. (Lecture Notes in Mathematics: Vol. 763). 695p. 1979. pap. 38.00 (ISBN 0-387-09721-X). Springer-Verlag.

Eells, James J. Singularities of Smooth Maps. (Notes on Mathematics & Its Applications Ser.). 114p. (Orig.). 1967. 28.95 (ISBN 0-677-01330-2). Gordon.

Eilenberg, Samuel & Steenrod, Norman. Foundations of Algebraic Topology. LC 52-5841. (Princeton Mathematical Ser.: Vol. 15). pap. 86.00 (ISBN 0-317-09123-9, 2014638). Bks Demand UMI.

Giblin, P. J. Graphs, Surfaces & Homology: An Introduction to Algebraic Topology. 2nd ed. 1981. pap. 16.95 (ISBN 0-412-23900-0, NO. 6610, Pub. by Chapman & Hall). Methuen Inc.

Gitter, Samuel, ed. Algebraic Topology, Symposium in Honor of Jose Adem: Proceedings. LC 82-13812. (Contemporary Mathematics Ser.: Vol. 12). 372p. 1982. pap. 24.00 (ISBN 0-8218-5010-5, CONM-12). Am Math.

Glezerman, M., et al. Algebraic Topology. (Translations, Ser.: No. 1, Vol. 7). 1962. 24.00 (ISBN 0-8218-1607-1, TRANS 1-7). Am Math.

Greenberg, M. J. & Harper, J. R. Algebraic Topology: A First Course. 1981. 47.95 (ISBN 0-8053-3558-7); pap. 29.95 (ISBN 0-8053-3557-9). Benjamin-Cummings.

Greenberg, Marvin J. Lectures on Algebraic Topology. (Math Lecture Notes Ser.: No. 9). 1973. 27.95 (ISBN 0-8053-3557-9). Benjamin-Cummings.

Grunbaum, B. Arrangements & Spreads. LC 71-38926. (CBMS Regional Conference Series in Mathematics: No. 10). 114p. 1980. pap. 11.00 (ISBN 0-8218-1659-4, CBMS-10). Am Math.

Guichardet, A. Lecons Sur Certaines Algebres Topologiques. (Cours & Documents de Mathematiques & de Physique Ser.). (Fr.). 194p. 1967. 57.75x (ISBN 0-677-50010-6). Gordon.

--Special Topics in Topological Algebras. (Notes on Mathematics & Its Applications Ser.). 202p. (Orig.). 1968. 65.95 (ISBN 0-677-30010-7). Gordon.

Halpern, Edward. Twisted Polynomial Hyperalgebras. LC 52-42839. (Memoirs: No. 29). 61p. 1972. pap. 12.00 (ISBN 0-8218-1229-7, MEMO-29). Am Math.

Hermann, Robert. Algebraic & Geometric Structures in Current Algebra Theory. LC 77-133441. 120p. 1970. 22.00 (ISBN 0-403-04504-5). Scholarly.

Hewitt, E. & Ross, K. A. Abstract Harmonic Analysis: Vol. 2, Structure & Analysis for Compact Groups, Analysis on Locally Compact Abelian Groups. LC 63-12898. (Grundlehren der Mathematischen Wissenschaften: Vol. 152). 1970. 79.00 (ISBN 0-387-04832-4). Springer-Verlag.

Hoffman, P., et al, eds. Algebraic Topology: Proceedings, University of British Columbia, Vancouver, August 1977. LC 78-13254. (Lecture Notes in Mathematics: Vol. 673). 1978. pap. 20.00 (ISBN 0-387-08930-6). Springer-Verlag.

Husseini, S. Y. The Topology of Classical Groups & Related Topics. (Notes on Mathematics & Its Applications Ser.). 136p. 1968. 28.95x (ISBN 0-677-02160-7). Gordon.

Kaneyuki, S. Homogeneous Bounded Domains & Siegel Domains. LC 71-183988. (Lecture Notes in Mathematics: Vol. 241). v, 89p. 1971. pap. 9.00 (ISBN 0-387-05702-1). Springer-Verlag.

Kosniowski, Czes, ed. A First Course in Algebraic Topology. LC 79-41682. 280p. 1980. 54.50 (ISBN 0-521-23195-7); pap. 24.95 (ISBN 0-521-29864-4). Cambridge U Pr.

Laudal, O. A. Formal Moduli of Algebraic Structures. (Lecture Notes in Mathematics: Vol. 754). 1979. pap. 16.00 (ISBN 0-387-09702-3). Springer-Verlag.

Lefschetz, S. Applications of Algebraictopology, Graphs & Networks: The Picard-Lefschetz Theory & Feynman Integrals. LC 75-6924. (Applied Mathematical Sciences Ser.: Vol. 16). (Illus.). 200p. 1975. pap. 19.50 (ISBN 0-387-90137-X). Springer-Verlag.

Lefschetz, Solomon. Algebraic Topology. LC 41-6147. (Colloquium Publications Ser.: Vol. 27). 389p. 1980. pap. 41.00 (ISBN 0-8218-1027-8, COLL-27). Am Math.

Manin, Ju. I., et al. Seven Papers on Algebra, Algebraic Geometry & Algebraic Topology. LC 51-5559. (Translations Ser.: No. 2, Vol. 63). 1967. 36.00 (ISBN 0-8218-1763-9, TRANS 2-63). Am Math.

Massey, W. S. Algebraic Topology: An Introduction. LC 77-22206. (Graduate Texts in Mathematics: Vol. 56). (Illus.). 1977. 29.50 (ISBN 0-387-90271-6). Springer-Verlag.

Maunder, C. R. Algebraic Topology. LC 79-41610. (Illus.). 1980. 62.50 (ISBN 0-521-23161-2); pap. 27.95 (ISBN 0-521-29840-7). Cambridge U Pr.

May, J. Peter. Simplicial Objects in Algebraic Topology. LC 82-51078. vi, 162p. 1983. pap. text ed. 9.00x (ISBN 0-226-51180-4). U of Chicago Pr.

Michael, E. A. Locally Multiplicatively-Convex Topological Algebras. LC 52-42839. (Memoirs: No. 11). 82p. 1971. pap. 10.00 (ISBN 0-8218-1211-4, MEMO-11). Am Math.

Milgram, R. J., ed. Algebraic & Geometric Topology, 2 pts. LC 78-14304. (Proceedings of Symposia in Pure Mathematics: Vol. 32). 1980. Set. pap. 44.00 (ISBN 0-8218-1432-X, PSPUM 32.1); 25.00 (ISBN 0-686-77332-2, 32.2); 25.00 (ISBN 0-8218-1433-8). Am Math.

Millett, K. C., ed. Algebraic & Geometric Topology: Proceedings of a Symposium Held at Santa Barbara in Honor of Raymond L. Wilder, July 25-29, 1977. LC 78-15091. (Lecture Notes in Mathematics: Vol. 664). 1978. pap. 16.00 (ISBN 0-387-08920-9). Springer-Verlag.

Murasugi, Kunio. On Closed Three Braids. LC 74-17176. (Memoirs: No. 151). 1974. pap. 11.00 (ISBN 0-8218-1851-1, MEMO-151). Am Math.

Novak, J., ed. General Topology & Its Relation to Modern Analysis & Albegra IV: Proceedings of the Fourth Prague Topological Symposium, 1976 Part A. Invited Papers. (Lecture Notes in Mathematics: Vol. 609). 1977. pap. text ed. 18.00 (ISBN 0-387-08437-1). Springer-Verlag.

Oliver, I. Madsin, ed. Algebraic Topology, Aarhus 1982: Proceedings of a Conference Held in Aarhus, August 1-7, 1982. (Lecture Notes in Mathematics: Vol. 1051). (Fr. & Ger.). x, 665p. 1984. pap. 28.00 (ISBN 0-387-12902-2). Springer-Verlag.

Olum, Paul. Invariants for Effective Homotopy Classification & Extension of Mappings. LC 52-42839. (Memoirs: No. 37). 1978. pap. 14.00 (ISBN 0-8218-1237-8, MEMO-37). Am Math.

Palais, Richard S. Real Algebraic Differential Topology: Part One. LC 81-81990. (Mathematics Lecture Ser.: No. 10). v, 192p. 1981. text ed. 18.00 (ISBN 0-914098-19-5). Publish or Perish.

Ranicki, A., et al, eds. Algebraic & Geometric Topology. (Lecture Notes in Mathematics: Vol. 1126). v, 423p. 1985. pap. 25.80 (ISBN 0-387-15235-0). Springer Verlag.

Reiter, H. L-Prime Algebras & Segal Algebras. LC 76-178758. (Lecture Notes in Mathematics: Vol. 231). 113p. 1971. pap. 11.00 (ISBN 0-387-05651-3). Springer-Verlag.

Selick, Paul, et al, eds. Current Trends in Algebraic Topology: Proceedings. LC 82-13789. (Canadian Mathematical Society Conference Proceedings Ser.: Vol.2). 1000p. 1982. Pt.1. pap. 30.00 (ISBN 0-8218-6001-1, CMS2.1); Pt.2. pap. 28.00 (ISBN 0-8218-6002-X, CMS2.2); Set (Vols. 1 & 2) pap. 48.00 (ISBN 0-8218-6003-8). Am Math.

Sigrist, F., ed. H-Spaces. (Lecture Notes in Mathematics Ser.: Vol. 196). 1971. pap. 11.00 (ISBN 0-387-05461-8). Springer-Verlag.

Singer, I. M. & Thorpe, J. A. Lecture Notes on Elementary Topology & Geometry. LC 76-26137. (Undergraduate Texts in Mathematics). 1976. 26.50 (ISBN 0-387-90202-3). Springer-Verlag.

Spanier, E. H. Algebraic Topology. 528p. 1981. 34.00 (ISBN 0-387-90646-0). Springer-Verlag.

Switzer, R. M. Algebraic Topology-Homotopy & Homology. (Die Grundlehren der Mathematischen Wissenschaften Ser.: Vol. 212). 526p. 1975. 74.00 (ISBN 0-387-06758-2). Springer-Verlag.

Symposium on Algebraic Topology. Proceedings. Hilton, P. J., ed. LC 79-185401. (Lecture Notes in Mathematics: Vol. 249). 111p. 1971. pap. 9.00 (ISBN 0-387-05715-3). Springer-Verlag.

Warshauer, M. L. The Witt Group of Degree k Maps & Asymmetric Inner Product Spaces. (Lecture Notes in Mathematics: Vol. 914). 269p. 1982. pap. 19.00 (ISBN 0-387-11201-4). Springer-Verlag.

ALGEBRAS, BANACH

see Banach Algebras

ALGEBRAS, HILBERT

see Hilbert Algebras

ALGEBRAS, JORDAN

see Jordan Algebras

ALGEBRAS, LIE

see Lie Algebras

ALGEBRAS, LINEAR

see also Calculus of Operations; Complexes; Jordan Algebras; Lie Algebras; Line Geometry; Nonassociative Algebras; Topology; Vector Spaces

Agnew, Jeanne & Knapp, Robert C. Linear Algebra with Applications. 2nd ed. LC 82-20752. (Mathematics Ser.). 400p. text ed. 23.75 pub net (ISBN 0-534-01364-3). Brooks-Cole.

Akivis, M. A. & Goldberg, V. V. An Introduction to Linear Algebra & Tensors. rev. ed. Silverman, Richard A., ed. LC 77-78589. 1977. pap. 4.00 (ISBN 0-486-63545-7). Dover.

Aldrich, John H. & Nelson, Forrest D. Linear Probability, Logit, & Probit Models. LC 84-51766. 95p. 1984. pap. 5.00 (ISBN 0-8039-2133-0). Sage.

Algebra Lineal e Geometria Euclidiana. (Serie De Matematica: No. 6). (Port.). 1969. pap. 3.50 (ISBN 0-8270-6245-1). OAS.

Anton, H. Elementary Linear Algebra. 2nd ed. (Arabic.). 386p. 1982. pap. 16.50 (ISBN 0-471-06389-4). Wiley.

Anton, Howard. Elementary Linear Algebra. 4th ed. LC 83-27382. 464p. 1984. 27.45 (ISBN 0-471-09890-6); student solutions manual 8.95x (ISBN 0-471-87976-2). Wiley.

Anton, Howard & Rorres, Chris. Applications of Linear Algebra. 3rd ed. 364p. 1985. pap. text ed. 16.95x (ISBN 0-471-86800-0). Wiley.

Apostol, T. M. Calculus: One-Variable Calculus with an Introduction to Linear Algebra, Vol. 1. 2nd ed. LC 73-20899. 666p. 1967. text ed. 44.00x (ISBN 0-471-00005-1); 15.95 (ISBN 0-471-86902-3); calculus companion 16.95 (ISBN 0-471-09230-4). Wiley.

Balinski, M. L. & Cottle, R. W., eds. Complementary & Fixed Point Problems. (Mathematical Programming Studies: Vol. 7). 184p. 1978. pap. 30.00 (ISBN 0-444-85123-2, North-Holland). Elsevier.

Bhattacharya, P. B., et al. First Course in Linear Algebra. 190p. 1983. pap. 21.95x cloth (ISBN 0-470-27442-5). Halsted Pr.

Bloch, Norman J. & Michaels, John G. Linear Algebra. (Illus.). 1976. text ed. 33.00 (ISBN 0-07-005906-3). McGraw.

Bloom, D. M. Linear Algebra & Geometry. LC 77-26666. 1979. 41.50 (ISBN 0-521-21959-0); pap. 29.95 (ISBN 0-521-29324-3). Cambridge U Pr.

Blyth, T. S. Module Theory: An Approach to Linear Algebra. (Illus.). 1977. 49.00x (ISBN 0-19-853162-1). Oxford U Pr.

Bratteli, O. & Robinson, D. W., eds. Operators Algebra & Quantum Statistical Mechanics, Vol. II: Equilibrium States; Models. (Texts & Monographs in Physics Ser.). 496p. 1979. 51.00 (ISBN 0-387-09187-4). Springer-Verlag.

Brodskii, M. S. Triangular & Jordan Representations of Linear Operators. LC 74-162998. (Translations of Mathematical Monographs: Vol. 32). 1972. 34.00 (ISBN 0-8218-1582-2, MMONO-32). Am Math.

Bugrov, Y. S. & Nikolsky, S. M. Fundamentals of Linear Algebra & Analytical Geometry. Levant, Leonid, tr. 189p. 1982. pap. 3.45 (ISBN 0-8285-2445-9, Pub. by Mir Pubs USSR). Imported Pubns.

Campbell, Hugh. Linear Algebra with Applications. 2nd ed. (Illus.). 1980. text ed. 28.95 (ISBN 0-13-536979-7). P-H.

Cohen, Kesarwani. Linear Algebra. 256p. 1984. pap. text ed. 11.95 (ISBN 0-8403-3494-X). Kendall Hunt.

Cohn, P. M. Linear Equations. (Library of Mathematics). 1971. pap. 5.00x (ISBN 0-7100-6181-1). Routledge & Kegan.

Cullen, Charles G. Linear Algebra & Differential Equations. 1979. write for info. (ISBN 0-87150-262-3, PWS 2131, Prindle). PWS Pubs.

Cunninghame-Green, R. A. Minimax Algebra. LC 79-1314. (Lecture Notes in Economics & Mathematical Systems: Vol. 166). 1979. pap. 19.00 (ISBN 0-387-09113-0). Springer-Verlag.

Curtis, C. W. Linear Algebra: An Introductory Approach. (Undergraduate Texts in Mathematics Ser.). (Illus.). 340p. 1984. 24.00 (ISBN 0-387-90992-3). Springer-Verlag.

Daniels, James W. Elementary Linear Algebra & Its Applications. (Illus.). 368p. 1981. text ed. 28.95 (ISBN 0-13-258293-7). P-H.

Dickson, L. E. Linear Algebras. (Cambridge Tracts in Mathematics & Mathematical Physics Ser.: No. 16). 1969. Repr. of 1914 ed. 7.95x (ISBN 0-02-843920-1). Hafner.

Dubbelman, C. Disturbances in the Linear Model: Estimation & Hypothesis Testing. 1978. pap. 16.00 (ISBN 90-207-0772-8, Pub. by Martininus Nijhoff Netherlands). Kluwer Academic.

Dunford, Nelson & Schwartz, Jacob T. Linear Operators, 3 pts. Incl. Pt. 1. General Theory. 872p. 1958. 77.95x (ISBN 0-470-22605-6); Pt. 2. Spectral Theory, Self Adjoint Operators in Hilbert Space. 1072p. 1963. 101.95 (ISBN 0-470-22638-2); Pt. 3. Spectral Operators. 667p. 1971. 85.95x (ISBN 0-471-22639-4). LC 57-10545. (Pure & Applied Mathematics Ser). Set. 225.00 (ISBN 0-471-86913-9, Pub. by Wiley-Interscience). Wiley.

Edelen, D. G. & Kydoniefs, A. D. An Introduction to Linear Algebra for Science & Engineering. 2nd ed. (Illus.). 270p. 1976. 25.00 (ISBN 0-444-00195-6). Elsevier.

El-Baz, Edgard & Castel, Boris. Graphical Methods of Spin Algebras in Atomic, Nuclear, & Particle Physics. LC 74-179382. (Theoretical Physics Ser.: Vol. 2). pap. 110.00 (ISBN 0-317-08347-3, 2017694). Bks Demand UMI.

Faddeeva, V. N. Computational Methods of Linear Algebra. 1959. pap. 7.50 (ISBN 0-486-60424-1). Dover.

Farkas, I. Introduction to Linear Algebra. 1975. 23.75 (ISBN 0-9960018-3-2, Pub by. A Hilger England). Heyden.

Fekete. Real Linear Algebra. (Pure & Applied Mathematics Ser.). 448p. 1985. 39.50 (ISBN 0-8247-7238-5). Dekker.

Finkbeiner, Daniel T., 2nd. Introduction to Matrices & Linear Transformations. 3rd ed. LC 78-18257. (Mathematical Sciences Ser.). (Illus.). 462p. 1978. text ed. 29.95 (ISBN 0-7167-0084-0). W H Freeman.

Florey, Francis G. Elementary Linear Algebra with Applications. LC 78-9412. (Illus.). 1979. ref. ed. 28.95 (ISBN 0-13-258251-1). P-H.

Fox, Leslie. Introduction to Numerical Linear Algebra. (Monographs on Numerical Analysis Ser.). 1965. 19.95x (ISBN 0-19-500325-X). Oxford U Pr.

Friedberg, Stephen & Insel, Arnold. Introduction to Linear Algebra with Applications. (Illus.). 480p. 1986. text ed. 30.95 (ISBN 0-13-485988-X). P-H.

Friedberg, Stephen, et al. Linear Algebra. (Illus.). 1979. ref. ed. 32.95 (ISBN 0-13-537019-1). P-H.

Gastinel, Noel. Linear Numerical Analysis. LC 70-108619. 1971. 68.00 (ISBN 0-12-277150-8). Acad Pr.

Goldsmith, C. C., ed. Linear Algebra & Geometry (Draft Edition) LC 71-142241. (School Mathematics Project Ser., Further Mathematics). 1971. text ed. 9.95 (ISBN 0-521-08030-4). Cambridge U Pr.

Goult, R. J. Applied Linear Algebra. LC 78-40608. (Mathematics & Its Applications Ser.). 196p. 1979. pap. text ed. 25.95x (ISBN 0-470-26864-6). Halsted Pr.

Greub, W. Linear Algebra, Vol. 23. rev., 4th ed. (Graduate Texts in Mathematics Ser.: Vol. 23). (Illus.). 451p. 1975. 42.00 (ISBN 0-387-90110-8). Springer Verlag.

--Multilinear Algebra. 1978. pap. 29.50 (ISBN 0-387-90284-8). Springer-Verlag.

Grossman. Brief Introduction to Linear Algebra. 1984. lib. bdg. write for info (ISBN 0-534-03495-0). Wadsworth Pub.

Grossman, Stanley I. Elementary Linear Algebra. 2nd ed. 426p. write for info. (ISBN 0-534-02738-5). Wadsworth Pub.

Gruenberg, K. W. Linear Geometry. 2nd ed. LC 76-27693. (Graduate Texts in Mathematics Ser.). (Illus.). 1977. 25.00 (ISBN 0-387-90227-9). Springer-Verlag.

Henstock, R. Linear Analysis. LC 67-30197. 1968. 42.50x (ISBN 0-306-30620-4, Plenum Pr). Plenum Pub.

Hermann, Robert. Linear & Tensor Algebra. (Interdisciplinary Mathematics Ser.: No. 2). 183p. 1973. 13.00 (ISBN 0-915692-01-5, 991600266). Math Sci Pr.

Hill, Richard O. Elementary Linear Algebra. Date not set. text ed. price not set (ISBN 0-12-348460-X). Acad Pr.

Hoffman, Kenneth & Kunze, Ray. Linear Algebra. 2nd ed. LC 75-142120. (Illus.). 1971. ref. ed. o.p. 33.95 (ISBN 0-13-536797-2). P-H.

Ikramov, H. D. Linear Algebra: Problems Book. 327p. 1983. 9.95 (ISBN 0-8285-2772-5, Pub. by Mir Pubs USSR). Imported Pubns.

Institute of Mathematics, Oxford Conference, April 1970. Large Spare Sets of Linear Equations. Reid, R., ed. 1971. 39.50 (ISBN 0-12-586150-8). Acad Pr.

Isaak, Samuel & Manougian, Manoug. Basic Concepts of Linear Algebra. 416p. 1976. text ed. 21.95x (ISBN 0-393-09199-6). Norton.

Jacobson, D. H. Extensions of Linear-Quadratic Control, Optimization & Matrix Theory. 1977. 46.50 (ISBN 0-12-378750-5). Acad Pr.

Jamshidi, M. & Malek-Zavarei, M. Introduction to Linear Systems: Computer Aided Approach. 450p. 1984. 65.00 (ISBN 0-08-028701-8); pap. 20.00 (ISBN 0-08-028702-6). Pergamon.

Jeger, M. & Eckmann, M. Einfuehrung in die Vektorielle Geometrie und Lineare Algebra fur Ingenieure und Naturwissenschafter. (Ger.). 252p. 1967. 38.95x (ISBN 0-8176-0198-8). Birkhauser.

Johnson, Lee W. & Riess, R. Dean. Introduction to Linear Algebra. LC 80-19984. (Mathematics Ser.). (Illus.). 352p. 1981. text ed. 29.95 (ISBN 0-201-03392-5). Addison-Wesley.

Jones, Burton W. Linear Algebra. LC 72-83244. 1973. text ed. 21.95x (ISBN 0-8162-4544-4). Holden-Day.

Kaplansky, Irving. Linear Algebra & Geometry: A Second Course. LC 74-2393. xiv, 143p. 1974. Repr. of 1969 ed. text ed. 9.50 (ISBN 0-8284-0279-5). Chelsea Pub.

Knoke, David & Burke, Peter J. Log-Linear Models. LC 80-17031. (Quantitative Applications in the Social Sciences Ser.: No. 20). (Illus.). 80p. 1980. pap. 5.00 (ISBN 0-8039-1492-X). Sage.

Kolman, Bernard. Elementary Linear Algebra. 4th ed. 505p. 1986. text ed. write for info. (ISBN 0-02-366080-5). Macmillan.

--Essential Linear Algebra. 544p. 1984. text ed. cancelled (ISBN 0-02-366010-4). Macmillan.

--Introductory Linear Algebra with Applications. 2nd ed. (Illus.). 1980. text ed. write for info. (ISBN 0-02-365970-X). Macmillan.

--Introductory Linear Algebra with Applications. 3rd ed. (Illus.). 600p. 1984. text ed. write for info. (ISBN 0-02-366020-1). Macmillan.
Konvisser, Marc. Elementary Linear Algebra with Applications. 350p. 1981. write for info. (ISBN 0-87150-295-X, 2331, Prindle). PWS Pubs.
Kumpel, P. G. & Thorpe, J. A. Linear Algebra, with Differential Equations. LC 82-60630. 353p. 1983. text ed. 32.95x (ISBN 0-03-060556-3, CBS C). SCP.
Lang, Serge A. Introduction to Linear Algebra. LC 77-100872. (Mathematics Ser). 1970. pap. 12.95 (ISBN 0-201-04206-1). Addison-Wesley.
Larrieu, V. Principles of Linear Algebra. 282p. 1972. 74.25 (ISBN 0-677-01610-7). Gordon.
Leon, Steven J. Linear Algebra with Applications. (Illus.). 1980. text ed. write for info. (ISBN 0-02-369870-5). Macmillan.
--Linear Algebra with Applications. 2nd ed. 318p. 1986. text ed. price not set (ISBN 0-02-369810-1). Macmillan.
Lightstone, A. H. Linear Algebra. LC 74-93018. (Century Mathematics Ser.). (Illus.). 1969. 39.00x (ISBN 0-89197-275-7); pap. text ed. 19.50x (ISBN 0-89197-824-0). Irvington.
Lipschutz, Seymour. Linear Algebra. (Schaum's Outline Ser). (Orig.). 1968. pap. 8.95 (ISBN 0-07-037989-0). McGraw.
Lyons, Richard A. The Basic Essentials of Passive Linear Devices. 64p. 1983. pap. text ed. 7.50 (ISBN 0-8403-3112-6). Kendall-Hunt.
McCann, Roger C. Introduction to Linear Algebra. 419p. 1984. text ed. 27.95 (ISBN 0-15-543001-7, HC); answer manual avail. (ISBN 0-15-543002-5). HarBraceJ.
McDonald. Linear Algebra over Communtative Rings. (Pure & Applied Mathematics Ser.). 776p. 1984. 69.75 (ISBN 0-8247-7122-2). Dekker.
McIntosh, Allen A. Fitting Linear Models: An Application of Conjugate Gradient Algorithms. (Lecture Notes in Statistics Ser.: Vol. 10). (Illus.). 200p. 1982. pap. 14.00 (ISBN 0-387-90746-7). Springer-Verlag.
Magid, A. R. Applied Matrix Models: A Second Course in Linear Algebra with Computer Applications. 240p. 1985. 32.95 (ISBN 0-471-88865-6). Wiley.
Mansfield, Larry E. Linear Algebra with Geometric Applications. (Pure & Applied Mathematics Ser.: Vol. 34). 1976. 35.00 (ISBN 0-8247-6321-1). Dekker.
Marcus, Marvin. Finite Dimensional Multilinear Algebra, Pt. 1. (Pure & Applied Mathematics Ser: Vol. 23). 304p. 1973. 49.75 (ISBN 0-8247-6077-8). Dekker.
Mirsky, L. An Introduction to Linear Algebra. (Mathematics Ser.). 433p. 1982. Dover.
Morris, A. Linear Algebra: An Introduction. 2nd ed. 1979. pap. 16.95 (ISBN 0-442-30541-9). Van Nos Reinhold.
Munkres, James R. Elementary Linear Algebra. 1964. pap. text ed. 7.95 (ISBN 0-201-04895-7). Addison-Wesley.
Nef, W. Lehrbuch der Linearen Algebra. 2nd rev. ed. (Mathematische Reihe Ser.: No.31). (Ger.). 276p. 1977. 37.95x (ISBN 0-8176-0960-1). Birkhauser.
Nering, Evar D. Linear Algebra & Matrix Theory. 2nd ed. LC 76-91646. 352p. 1970. 37.50 (ISBN 0-471-63178-7). Wiley.
Nicholson. Linear Algebra with Applications. 1985. text ed. write for info. (ISBN 0-87150-902-4, 33L3050, Prindle). PWS Pubs.
Noble, Ben & Daniel, James W. Applied Linear Algebra. 2nd ed. (Illus.). 1977. ref. ed. 32.95 (ISBN 0-13-041343-7). P-H.
Nomizu, Katsumi. Fundamentals of Linear Algebra. LC 77-7468. 1979. text ed. 17.95 (ISBN 0-8284-0276-0). Chelsea Pub.
O'Meara, O. T. Lectures on Linear Groups. LC 74-8773. (CBMS Regional Conference Series in Mathematics: No. 22). 87p. 1977. pap. 12.00 (ISBN 0-8218-1672-1, CBMS-22). Am Math.
O'Nan, Michael. Linear Algebra. 2nd ed. LC 76-27597. (Illus.). 335p. 1977. text ed. 26.95 (ISBN 0-15-518560-8, HC); solutions manual avail. (ISBN 0-15-518561-6). HarBraceJ.
Paige, Lowell J. & Swift, J. Dean. Elements of Linear Algebra. LC 83-14891. 298p. 1983. Repr. of 1974 ed. lib. bdg. 25.50 (ISBN 0-89874-668-X). Krieger.
Paige, Lowell J., et al. Elements of Linear Algebra. 2nd ed. LC 73-82137. 1974. arabic translation avail. Wiley.
Palamodov, V. P. Linear Differential Operators with Constant Coefficients. Brown, A. A., tr. LC 79-104712. (Die Grundlehren der Mathematischen Wissenschaften: Vol. 168). 1970. 81.00 (ISBN 0-387-04838-3). Springer-Verlag.
Pedoe, Daniel. A Geometric Introduction to Linear Algebra. 2nd ed. LC 72-78369. xi, 224p. 1976. text ed. 9.95 (ISBN 0-8284-0286-8). Chelsea Pub.
Polya, G. & Szego, G. Problems & Theorems in Analysis II: Theory of Functions, Zeros, Polynomials, Determinants, Number Theory, Geometry. Billigheimer, C. E., tr. (Illus.). 1977. pap. text ed. 24.00 (ISBN 0-387-90291-0). Springer-Verlag.
Reiner, Irving. Introduction to Matrix Theory & Linear Algebra. LC 79-151082. 1971. pap. text ed. 18.95 (ISBN 0-03-085410-5, HoltC). HR&W.
Research & Education Association Staff. The Linear Algebra Problem Solver. rev. ed. LC 79-92402. (Illus.). 1024p. 1984. pap. text ed. 23.85 (ISBN 0-87891-518-4). Res & Educ.
Roberts, A. W. Elementary Linear Algebra. 1982. text ed. 27.95 (ISBN 0-8053-8302-6); instr's guide 4.95 (ISBN 0-8053-8303-4); student solution manual 7.95 (ISBN 0-8053-8304-2). Benjamin-Cummings.
Roberts, A. Wayne. Elementary Linear Algebra. 2nd ed. 1985. text ed. 26.95 (ISBN 0-8053-8305-0); instr's manual 5.95 (ISBN 0-8053-8306-9). Benjamin-Cummings.
Robinson, Enders A. Least Squares Regression Analysis in Terms of Linear Algebra. LC 81-82322. (Illus.). 520p. 1981. 25.00 (ISBN 0-910835-01-2). Goose Pond Pr.
Rothenberg, Ronald I. Linear Algebra with Computer Applications. LC 82-24806. (Self-Teaching Guides Ser.). 387p. 1983. pap. 12.95 (ISBN 0-471-09652-0, Pub. by Wiley Pr). Wiley.
Samelson, Hans. Introduction to Linear Algebra. LC 74-17001. (Pure & Applied Mathematics Ser.). 265p. 1974. 39.95x (ISBN 0-471-75170-7, Pub. by Wiley-Interscience). Wiley.
Satake, I. Linear Algebra. (Pure & Applied Mathematics Ser: Vol. 29). 392p. 1975. 45.00 (ISBN 0-8247-1596-9). Dekker.
Sawyer, W. W. Engineering Approach to Linear Algebra. LC 70-184143. (Illus.). 350p. 1972. text ed. 37.50x (ISBN 0-521-08476-8). Cambridge U Pr.
Schmidt, Garfield C. Basic Linear Algebra with Applications. LC 79-16225. (Applied Mathematics Ser.). 536p. 1980. text ed. 17.50 (ISBN 0-89874-000-2). Krieger.
Schneider, Dennis, et al. Linear Algebra: A Concrete Introduction. 2nd ed. 787p. 1986. text ed. price not set (ISBN 0-02-406910-8). Macmillan.
Schneider, Dennis M., et al. Linear Algebra: A Concrete Approach. 1982. write for info. (ISBN 0-02-476810-3). Macmillan.
Seminar on Periodic Maps. Proceedings. (Lecture Notes in Mathematics: Vol. 46). 1967. pap. 10.70 (ISBN 0-387-03917-1). Springer-Verlag.
Shaw, Ronald. Linear Algebra & Group Representations: Linear Algebra & Introduction to Group Representations, Vol. 1. 1983. 38.00 (ISBN 0-12-639201-3). Acad Pr.
--Linear Algebra & Group Representations: Multilinear Algebra & Group Representations, Vol. 11. 1983. 41.00 (ISBN 0-12-639202-1). Acad Pr.
Shields, Paul C. Elementary Linear Algebra. 3rd rev. ed. (Illus.). 1980. text ed. 26.95x (ISBN 0-87901-121-1). Worth.
Shilov, Georgi E. Linear Algebra. Silverman, Richard, tr. from Rus. LC 77-75267. 1977. pap. text ed. 6.95 (ISBN 0-486-63518-X). Dover.
Slodowy, P. Simple Singularities & Simple Algebraic Groups. (Lecture Notes in Mathematics: Vol. 815). 175p. 1980. pap. 15.00 (ISBN 0-387-10026-1). Springer-Verlag.
Smith, L. Linear Algebra. 2nd ed. (Undergraduate Texts in Mathematics Ser.). (Illus.). 415p. 1984. 29.95 (ISBN 0-387-96015-5). Springer-Verlag.
Steinberg, Robert. Endomorphisms of Linear Algebraic Groups. LC 52-42839. (Memoirs: No. 80). 1968. pap. 9.00 (ISBN 0-8218-1280-7, MEMO-80). Am Math.
Strang, W. Gilbert. Linear Algebra & Its Applications. 2nd ed. 1980. instr's. manual 2.50i (ISBN 0-12-673662-6). Acad Pr.
--Linear Algebra & Its Applications. 2nd ed. LC 79-53993. 1980. 22.50i (ISBN 0-12-673660-X). Acad Pr.
Tetra, B. C. Introduccion Al Algebra Lineal. (Span.). 1976. pap. text ed. 7.00 (ISBN 0-06-317000-0, IntlDept). Har-Row.
Thorpe, J. A. & Kumpel, P. G. Elementary Linear Algebra. LC 83-14442. 433p. 1984. text ed. 30.95x (ISBN 0-03-061249-7). SCP.
Toutenburg, Helge. Prior Information in Linear Models. LC 91-14653. (Series in Probabiliy & Mathematical Statistics-Tracts on Probability & Statistics Section). 192p. 1982. 44.95x (ISBN 0-471-09974-0, Pub. by Wiley-Interscience). Wiley.
Venit, Stewart & Bishop, Wayne. Elementary Linear Algebra. LC 80-18251. 364p. 1981. text ed. write for info. (ISBN 0-87150-300-X, 2361, Prindle). PWS Pubs.
--Elementary Linear Algebra. 2nd ed. 1985. text ed. write for info. (ISBN 0-87150-867-2, 33L2970, Prindle). PWS Pubs.
Voyevodin, V. V. Linear Algebra. 392p. 1983. 10.95 (ISBN 0-8285-2614-1, Pub. by Mir Pubs USSR). Imported Pubns.
Wehrfritz, B. A. Infinite Linear Groups: An Account of the Group-Theoretic Properties of Infinite Groups of Matrices. (Ergebnisse der Mathematik und Ihrer Grenzgebiete: Vol. 76). xiv, 229p. 1973. 40.00 (ISBN 0-387-06132-0). Springer-Verlag.
Weil, A. Adeles & Algebraic Groups. (Progress in Mathematics Ser.: Vol. 23). 126p. 1982. text ed. 12.50x (ISBN 0-8176-3092-9). Birkhauser.
Wilkinson, J. H. & Reinsch, C. Handbook for Automatic Computation, Vol. 2: Linear Algebra. Bauer, F. L., et al, eds. LC 75-154801. (Grundlehren der Mathematischen Wissenschaften: Vol. 186). (Illus.). 1971. 44.00 (ISBN 0-387-05414-6). Springer-Verlag.
Wilkinson, James H. Algebraic Eigenvalue Problem. (Monographs on Numerical Analysis). 1965. 77.00x (ISBN 0-19-853403-5). Oxford U Pr.
Williams. Elementary Linear Algebra with Applications. 1985. 32.74 (ISBN 0-317-30833-5, 685010). Allyn.
Williams, Gareth. A Course in Linear Algebra. 216p. 1972. 46.25x (ISBN 0-677-03570-5). Gordon.
--Linear Algebra with Applications. 1984. text ed. 32.74 for info. (ISBN 0-205-08010-3, 568010); write for info. instr's manual free (ISBN 0-205-08013-8, 568013). Allyn.
Wolf, J. A. Unitary Representations of Maximal Parabolic Subgroups of the Classical Groups. LC 76-44397. (Memoirs: No. 180). 193p. 1976. pap. 15.00 (ISBN 0-8218-2180-6, MEMO-180). Am Math.
Younger, Mary S. A Handbook for Linear Regression. 569p. 1979. text ed. write for info. (ISBN 0-87872-187-8, 4920, Pub. by Duxbury Pr). PWS Pubs.
Zelinsky, Daniel. First Course in Linear Algebra. 2nd ed. 1973. text ed. 21.75i (ISBN 0-12-779060-8). Acad Pr.
Zimmermann, U. Linear & Combinatorial Optimization in Ordered Algebraic Structures. (Annals of Discreet Mathematics Ser.: Vol. 10). 380p. 1981. 78.75 (ISBN 0-444-86153-X, North-Holland). Elsevier.
Zlatev, Z., et al. Y Twelve M: Solution of Large & Sparse Systems of Linear Algebraic Equations. (Lecture Notes in Computer Science Ser.: Vol. 121). 128p. 1981. pap. 12.00 (ISBN 0-387-10874-2). Springer-Verlag.

ALGEBRAS, NONASSOCIATIVE
see Nonassociative Algebras

ALGEBRAS, OPERATOR
see Operator Algebras

ALGEBRAS, TOPOLOGICAL
see Topological Algebras

ALGEBRAS, VON NEUMANN
see Von Neumann Algebras

ALGEBRAS, W
see C Algebras; Von Neumann Algebras

ALGOL (COMPUTER PROGRAM LANGUAGE)

Bajpai, Avi C. FORTRAN & Algol: A Programmed Course for Students of Science & Technology. LC 73-5712. pap. 51.90 (ISBN 0-317-08899-8, 2013981). Bks Demand UMI.
Brailsford, D. F. & Walker, A. N. Introductory ALGOL Sixty-Eight Programming. LC 79-40241. (Computers & Their Applications Ser.). 281p. 1979. 58.95x (ISBN 0-470-26746-1). Halsted Pr.
Branquart, P., et al. An Optimized Translation Process & Its Application to ALGOL 68. LC 75-45092. (Lecture Notes in Computer Science: Vol. 38). 1976. pap. 20.00 (ISBN 0-387-07545-3). Springer-Verlag.
Brundritt, Alan. Elementary ALGOL. (Illus.). 80p. 1976. pap. text ed. 16.50x (ISBN 0-7121-0549-2, Pub. by Macdonald & Evans Engalnd). Trans-Atlantic.
De Bakker, J. W. & Van Vliet, J., eds. Algorithmic Languages: Proceedings of the IFIP TC-2 International Symposium, October 1981. 432p. 1982. 45.00 (ISBN 0-444-86285-4, North-Holland). Elsevier.
Dijkstra, E. W. A Primer of ALGOL 60 Programming: Together with Report on the Algorithmic Language ALGOL 60. 1962. 29.50 (ISBN 0-12-216250-1). Acad Pr.
Ershov, A. & Koster, C. H., eds. Methods of Algorithmic Language Implementation. (Lecture Notes in Computer Science: Vol. 47). 1977. pap. 21.00 (ISBN 0-387-08065-1). Springer-Verlag.
Grau, A. A., et al. Handbook for Automatic Computation: Vol. 1. Part B Translation of ALGOL 60. Bauer, F. L., et al, eds. (Grundlehren der Mathematischen Wissenschaften: Vol. 137). 1967. 52.60 (ISBN 0-387-03828-0). Springer-Verlag.
Lindsey, C. H. & Vander Meulen, S. V. Informal Introduction to Algol 68. 2nd ed. 362p. 1977. text ed. 47.00 (ISBN 0-7204-0504-1, North-Holland); pap. text ed. 25.00 (ISBN 0-7204-0726-5). Elsevier.
McCracken, Daniel D. Guide to Algol Programming. LC 62-17464. 106p. 1962. pap. 19.95x (ISBN 0-471-58234-4, Pub. by Wiley-Interscience). Wiley.
McGettrick, Andrew D. ALGOL Sixty-Eight. LC 77-1104. (Computer Science Texts Ser.: No. 8). (Illus.). 1978. 54.50 (ISBN 0-521-21412-2); pap. 21.95x (ISBN 0-521-29143-7). Cambridge U Pr.
Madison, Alan W. Characteristics of Program Localities. Stone, Harold, ed. LC 82-4847. (Computer Science: Systems Programming Ser.: No. 5). 138p. 1982. 34.95 (ISBN 0-8357-1328-8). UMI Res Pr.
Meek, B. FORTRAN, PL-I & the ALGOLS. 385p. 1979. 29.50 (ISBN 0-444-19464-9, North Holland). Elsevier.
Pagan, F. G. A Practical Guide to Algol 68. LC 75-6925. (Computing Ser.). 1976. (Pub. by Wiley-Interscience); pap. 26.95x (ISBN 0-471-65747-6, Pub. by Wiley-Interscience). Wiley.
Peck, J. E., ed. Algol Sixty-Eight Implementation. (Proceedings). 1971. 29.50 (ISBN 0-7204-2045-8, North Holland). Elsevier.
Van Wijngaarden, A., et al. Report on the Algorithmic Language ALGOL 68. rev. ed. 1976. pap. 17.00 (ISBN 0-387-07592-5). Springer-Verlag.
Watson, F. R. An Introduction to Algol. 121p. 1976. 7.50 (ISBN 0-7135-1877-4). Transatlantic.
Wichmann, B. ALGOL Sixty Compilation & Assessment. (Automatic Programming Information Centre Studies in Data Processing). 1974. 63.50 (ISBN 0-12-748250-4). Acad Pr.
Woodward, P. M. Guide to Algol 68. 160p. 1983. pap. text ed. 24.50 (ISBN 0-7131-3490-9). E Arnold.

ALGORITHMIC LANGUAGE
see ALGOL (Computer Program Language)

ALGORITHMS
see also Machine Theory; Machine Translating; Numerical Analysis; Programming (Electronic Computers); Programming (Mathematics); Programming Languages (Electronic Computers); Recursive Functions; Transformations (Mathematics)

Adjan, S. I., ed. Mathematical Logic, the Theory of Algorithms & the Theory of Sets: Dedicated to Academician Petr Sergeevic Novikov. LC 77-3359. (Proceedings of the Steklov Institute of Mathematics Ser.: No. 133). 1977. 66.00 (ISBN 0-8218-3033-3, STEKLO 133). Am Math.
Aho, A. V., et al. Data Structures & Algorithms. 1982. 33.95 (ISBN 0-201-00023-7). Addison-Wesley.
Aho, Alfred & Hopcroft, John. The Design & Analysis of Computer Algorithms. 480p. 1974. text ed. 34.95 (ISBN 0-201-00029-6). Addison-Wesley.
Aiserman, Mark A., et al. Logic, Automata & Algorithms. (Mathematics in Science & Engineering Ser). (Rus). 1971. 80.50 (ISBN 0-12-046350-4). Acad Pr.
Akl, Selim G. Parallel Sorting Algorithms. Date not set. pap. 24.95 (ISBN 0-12-047681-9). Acad Pr.
--Parallel Sorting Alogorithms. Date not set. 49.00 (ISBN 0-12-047680-0). Acad Pr.
Apostolico, A. & Galil, Z., eds. Combinatorial Algorithms on Words. (NATO ASI Ser.: Series F, Vol. 12). viii, 361p. 1985. 48.50 (ISBN 0-387-15227-X). Springer-Verlag.
Ausiello, G. & Lucertini, M., eds. Analysis & Design of Algorithms for Combinational Problems. (Mathematical Studies: Vol. 109). 1985. 48.25 (ISBN 0-444-87699-5, North-Holland). Elsevier.
--Analysis & Design of Algorithms in Combinatorial Optimization. (CISM International Centre for Mechanical Sciences Ser.: Vol. 266). 209p. 1981. pap. 26.00 (ISBN 0-387-81626-7). Springer-Verlag.
Ausiello, G., et al, eds. Algorithm Design for Computer System Design. (CISM International Centre for Mechanical Sciences Courses & Lectures: No. 284). (Illus.). vii, 236p. 1984. pap. 18.30 (ISBN 0-387-81816-2). Springer-Verlag.
Baase, Sara. Computer Algorithms: Introduction to Design & Analysis. LC 77-81197. 1978. text ed. 31.95 (ISBN 0-201-00327-9). Addison-Wesley.
Bach, Eric. Analytic Methods in the Analysis & Design of Number Theoretic Algorithms. (ACM Distinguished Dissontation Award Ser.). 50p. 1985. text ed. 15.00x (ISBN 0-262-02219-2). MIT Pr.
Ball, John A. Algorithms for RPN Calculators. LC 77-14977. 330p. 1977. 35.50 (ISBN 0-471-03070-8, Pub. by Wiley-Interscience). Wiley.
Barr, R. S., et al. A New Alternating Basis Algorithm for Semi-Assignment Networks. 1977. 2.50 (ISBN 0-686-64190-6). U CO Busn Res Div.
--The Alternating Basis Algorithm for Assignment Problems. 1977. 2.50 (ISBN 0-686-64191-4). U CO Busn Res Div.

Bazaraa, Mokhtar S. & Shetty, C. M. Nonlinear Programming: Theory & Algorithms. LC 78-986. 560p. 1979. text ed. 47.00 (ISBN 0-471-78610-1). Wiley.

Beckett, Royce & Hurt, James. Numerical Calculations & Algorithms. LC 81-20894. 1983. 19.50 (ISBN 0-89874-415-6). Krieger.

Bellman, Richard E., et al. Algorithms, Graphs & Computers. (Mathematics in Science & Engineering Ser.: Vol. 62). 1970. 35.00 (ISBN 0-12-084840-6). Acad Pr.

Bernstein, L. Jacobi-Perron Algorithm: Its Theory & Application. LC 70-169956. (Lecture Notes in Mathematics: Vol. 207). 1971. pap. text ed. 11.00 (ISBN 0-387-05497-9). Springer-Verlag.

Bezdek, James C. Pattern Recognition with Fuzzy Objective Function Algorithms. LC 81-4354. (Advanced Applications in Pattern Recognition Ser.). 272p. 1981. 39.50 (ISBN 0-306-40671-3, Plenum Pr). Plenum Pub.

Birta-Probert. Algorithm Design I. 148p. 1983. shrink wrapped 11.95 (ISBN 0-8403-3138-X). Kendall-Hunt.

Blahut, Richard E. Fast Algorithms for Digital Signal Processing. 1985. 41.95 (ISBN 0-201-10155-6). Addison-Wesley.

Booth, Taylor L. & Chien, Yi-Tzuu. Computing: Fundamentals & Applications. LC 73-20157. 497p. 1974. 40.95x (ISBN 0-471-08847-1). Wiley.

Bruell, S. C. & Balbo, G., eds. Computational Algorithms for Closed Queuing Networks. (Operating & Programming Systems Ser.: Vol. 7). 190p. 1980. 29.95 (ISBN 0-444-00421-1, North-Holland). Elsevier.

Buckley, A. G. & Goffin, J. L. Algorithms for Constrained Minimumization of Smooth Nonlinear Functions. (Mathematical Programming Studies: Vol. 16). 190p. 1982. Repr. 25.75 (ISBN 0-444-86390-7, North-Holland). Elsevier.

Burns, C. S. & Parks, T. W. DFT-FFT & Convolution Alogrithms. (Illus.). 232p. 1985. pap. 22.50 (ISBN 0-317-27322-1, LCB8481). Tex Instr Inc.

Burrus, C. S. & Parks, T. W. DFT-FFT & Convolution Algorithms & Implementation. 232p. 1985. 22.50 (ISBN 0-471-81932-8). Wiley.

Carnahan, Brice, et al. Applied Numerical Methods. LC 67-27555. 604p. 1969. 45.50 (ISBN 0-471-13507-0). Wiley.

Cash, J. R. Stable Recursions: With Applications to the Numerical Solution of Stiff Systems. LC 79-50521. (Computational Mathematics & Application Ser.). 1980. 55.00 (ISBN 0-12-163050-1). Acad Pr.

Chachra, V., et al. Applications of Graph Theory Algorithms. 422p. 1979. 35.75 (ISBN 0-444-00268-5, North-Holland). Elsevier.

Christoffersen, Ralph E., ed. Algorithms for Chemical Computations. LC 77-5030. (ACS Symposium Ser.: No. 46). 1977. 24.95 (ISBN 0-8412-0371-7). Am Chemical.

Chua, L. & Lin, P. Computer-Aided Analysis of Electronic Circuits: Algorithms & Computational Techniques. 1975. 41.95 (ISBN 0-13-165415-2). P-H.

Coffman, Edward G., Jr. & Denning, Peter J. Operating Systems Theory. LC 73-491. 400p. 1973. ref. ed. 34.95 (ISBN 0-13-637868-4). P-H.

Colbourn, C. J. & Colbourn, M. J., eds. Algorithms in Combinatorial Design Theory. (Mathematics Studies: Vol. 114). 334p. 1985. 45.00 (ISBN 0-444-87802-5, North-Holland). Elsevier.

Conte, S. D. & De Boor, C. Elementary Numerical Analysis: An Algorithmic Approach. 3rd ed. 1980. 37.95 (ISBN 0-07-012447-7). McGraw.

Cook, Charles C., illus. Spatial Algorithms for Processing Land Data with a Microcomputer: Lincoln Institute Monograph. (84-2). 278p. 1984. pap. text ed. 9.00 (ISBN 0-318-03877-3). Lincoln Inst Land.

Cullum, Jane K. & Willoughby, Ralph A. Lanczos Algorithms for Large Symmetric Eigenvalue Computations (Vol. 1, Theory) (Progress in Scientific Computing: Vol. 3). 287p. 1985. text ed. 29.95x (ISBN 0-8176-3058-9). Birkhauser.

--Lanczos Algorithms for Large Symmetric Eigenvalue Computations (Vol. 2, Programs) (Progress in Scientific Computing Ser.: Vol. 4). 1985. text ed. 49.95x (ISBN 0-8176-3295-6). Birkhauser.

Davio, M., et al. Digital Systems with Algorithm Implementation. 654p. 1983. 58.95 (ISBN 0-471-10413-2); pap. 34.95 (ISBN 0-471-10414-0). Wiley.

De Mori, Renato. Computer Models of Speech Using Fuzzy Algorithms. (Advanced Applications in Pattern Recognition Ser.). 508p. 1983. 59.50x (ISBN 0-306-41381-7, Plenum Pr). Plenum Pub.

Durnin, John. Toward Educational Engineering. LC 81-40101. (Illus.). 134p. (Orig.). 1982. PLB 21.75 (ISBN 0-8191-2435-4); pap. text ed. 9.50 (ISBN 0-8191-2436-2). U Pr of Amer.

Ershov, A. P. & Knuth, D. E., eds. Algorithms in Modern Mathematics & Computer Science: Proceedings. (Lecture Notes in Computer Science Ser.: Vol. 122). 487p. 1981. pap. 26.50 (ISBN 0-387-11157-3). Springer-Verlag.

Even, Shimon. Graph Algorithms. LC 79-17150. 249p. 1979. 34.95 (ISBN 0-914894-21-8). Computer Sci.

Fishburn, John P. Analysis of Speedup in Distributed Algorithms. Stone, Harold, ed. LC 83-18307. (Computer Science Ser.: Distributed Database Systems: No. 14). 128p. 1984. 39.95 (ISBN 0-8357-1527-2). UMI Res Pr.

Fudge, Don. Getting Graphic II: More Complex Algorithms. 275p. 1985. pap. 14.95 (ISBN 0-13-354952-6). P-H.

Gaidukov, N & Elenkin, A. A. Algological Bibliography of the USSR from Beginning to 1960. (Collectanea Bibliographia Ser.: No. 3). 1976. Repr. lib. bdg. 84.00 (ISBN 3-87429-105-7). Lubrecht & Cramer.

Garcia-Molina, Hector. Performance of Update Algorithms for Replicated Data. Stone, Harold S., ed. LC 81-10454. (Computer Science Ser.: Distributed Database Systems: No. 5). 338p. 1981. 49.95 (ISBN 0-8357-1219-2). UMI Res Pr.

Gavrilov, M. A. & Zakrevsky, A. D., eds. LYAPAS: A Programming Language for Logic & Coding Algorithms. (ACM Monograph Ser). 1969. 90.00 (ISBN 0-12-277850-2). Acad Pr.

Gibbons, Alan. Algorithmic Graph Theory. 250p. 1985. 47.50 (ISBN 0-521-24659-8); pap. 17.95 (ISBN 0-521-28881-9). Cambridge U Pr.

Giloi, Wolfgang K. Interactive Computer Graphics: Data Structures, Algorithms, Languages. (Illus.). 1978. ref. ed. 34.95 (ISBN 0-13-469189-X). P-H.

Golender, V. E. & Rozenblit, A. B. Logical & Combinatorial Algorithms for Drug Design. 289p. 1983. 68.95x (ISBN 0-471-90266-7, Pub by Res Stud Pr). Wiley.

Goodman, S. E. & Hedetniemi, S. T. Introduction to the Design & Analysis of Algorithms. (Computer Science Ser.). (Illus.). 1977. text ed. 41.95 (ISBN 0-07-023753-0). McGraw.

Greene, D. & Knuth, D. Mathematics for the Analysis of Algorithms. 144p. 1981. text ed. 10.00x (ISBN 3-7643-3046-5). Birkhauser.

Greene, D. & Knuth, D., eds. Mathematics for the Analysis of Algorithms. 2nd ed. (Progress in Computer Science: Vol. 1). 144p. text ed. 12.95x (ISBN 0-8176-3102-X). Birkhauser.

Griffiths, P. & Hill, I. D. Applied Statistics Algorithms. (Mathematics & Its Applications Ser.). 1985. 51.95 (ISBN 0-470-20184-3). Halsted Pr.

Grishman, Ralph. Assembly Language Programming for Control Data 6000 & Cyber Ser. (Illus.). 248p. 1981. 15.00x (ISBN 0-917448-04-9). Algorithmics.

Hamilton, J. David & Trenary, Robert G. Macro-86: Programming Algorithms. Hubbard, John D., ed. LC 84-12805. (Macro-86 Software Design Ser.). (Illus.). 498p. 1984. 3 ring-binder 59.95 (ISBN 0-87119-089-3, EC-1202). HeathKit-Zenith Ed.

Hartigan, J. A. Clustering Algorithms. LC 74-14573. (Wiley Series in Probability & Mathematical Statistics). 368p. 1975. 38.50 (ISBN 0-471-35645-X, Pub. by Wiley-Interscience). Wiley.

Hartigan, John A. Clustering Algorithms. LC 74-14573. (Wiley Series in Probability & Mathematical Statistics). pap. 69.40 (ISBN 0-317-09401-7, 2019502). Bks Demand UMI.

Hecht, Matthew S. Flow Analysis of Computer Programs. (Programming Languages Ser.: Vol. 5). 232p. 1977. 30.75 (ISBN 0-444-00210-3, North Holland). Elsevier.

Heesterman, A. R. Matrices & Simplex Algorithms. 1982. lib. bdg. 96.00 (ISBN 90-277-1514-9, Pub. by Reidel Holland). Kluwer Academic.

Hennie, Fred. Introduction to Computability. LC 76-12796. (Illus.). 1977. text ed. 38.95 (ISBN 0-201-02848-4). Addison-Wesley.

Hockney, R. W. & Jesshope, C. R. Parallel Computers: Architecture, Programming & Algorithms. 1981. 49.00 (ISBN 0-9960022-8-6, Pub. by A Hilger England); pap. 18.00 (ISBN 0-9960025-5-3). Heyden.

Horabin, Ivan & Lewis, Brian. Algorithms. Langdon, Danny G., ed. LC 78-2307. (Instructional Design Library). (Illus.). 80p. 1978. 19.95 (ISBN 0-87778-106-0). Educ Tech Pubns.

Hu, T. C., et al. Combinatorial Algorithms. LC 81-15024. (Computer Science Ser.). 500p. 1981. text ed. 28.95 (ISBN 0-201-03859-5); program manual 15.00 (ISBN 0-201-11469-0). Addison-Wesley.

Iverson, K. E. Algebra: An Algorithmic Treatment. (Illus., Orig.). 1977. pap. text ed. 10.75 (ISBN 0-917326-09-1). APL Pr.

Katzan, Harry, Jr. The Standard Data Encryption Algorithm. LC 77-13582. (Illus.). 1977. text ed. 14.00 (ISBN 0-89433-016-0). Petrocelli.

Kaufmann, A. Introduction to the Theory of Fuzzy Subsets, Vol. 1: Fundamental Theoretical Elements. 1975. 67.50 (ISBN 0-12-402301-0). Acad Pr.

Kennington, Jeff L. & Helgason, Richard V. Algorithms for Network Programming. LC 80-258. 291p. 1980. 40.95x (ISBN 0-471-06016-X, Pub. by Wiley Interscience). Wiley.

Knuth, Donald E. Art of Computer Programming: Semi-Numerical Algorithms, Vol. 2. 2nd ed. 1981. text ed. 36.95 (ISBN 0-201-03822-6). Addison-Wesley.

Kotov, V. E. & Miklosko, J., eds. Algorithms, Software & Hardware of Parallel Computers. (Illus.). 380p. 1984. 32.00 (ISBN 0-387-13657-6). Springer-Verlag.

Kronsjo, L. Algorithms: Their Complexity & Efficiency. 361p. 1979. 67.95x (ISBN 0-471-99752-8). Wiley.

Kuck, David J., et al, eds. High Speed Computer & Algorithm Organization. 1977. 49.50 (ISBN 0-12-427750-0). Acad Pr.

Lakshmivarahan, S. Learning Algorithms Theory & Applications. 279p. 1981. pap. 25.00 (ISBN 0-387-90640-1). Springer-Verlag.

Landa, L. N. Algorithmization in Learning & Instruction. Kopstein, Felix F., ed. Bennett, Virginia, tr. from Rus. LC 73-11044. 752p. 1974. Repr. of 1966 ed. 37.95 (ISBN 0-87778-063-3). Educ Tech Pubns.

Lee, John A. Computer Semantics: Studies of Algorithms Processors & Languages. LC 77-7263. 416p. 1978. Repr. of 1972 ed. 24.00 (ISBN 0-88275-546-3). Krieger.

Lehman, Richard S., ed. Programming for the Social Sciences: Algorithms & FORTRAN 77 Coding. 1985. text ed. write for info. (ISBN 0-89859-588-6). L Erlbaum Assocs.

Louchard, G. & Latouche, G., eds. Probability Theory & Computer Science. (International Lecture Series in Computer Science). 1983. 29.50 (ISBN 0-12-455820-8). Acad Pr.

Lucantoni, D. M. Algorithmic Analysis of a Communication Model with Retransmission of Fluid Messages. (Research Notes in Mathematics Ser. No. 81). 154p. 1983. pap. text ed. 20.95 (ISBN 0-273-08571-9). Pitman Pub MA.

MacCormack, Dave & Michael, Toni. Algorithms for Personal Computing. (Essential Algorithms Ser.). (Illus.). 250p. (Orig.). 1985. pap. 14.95 (ISBN 0-931145-07-4). Microcomscribe.

Machtey, M. & Young, P. An Introduction to the General Theory of Algorithms. 2nd ed. (Theory of Computation Ser.: Vol. 2). 264p. 1978. 31.50 (ISBN 0-444-00226-X, North Holland); pap. text ed. 16.95 (ISBN 0-444-00227-8). Elsevier.

McIntosh, Allen A. Fitting Linear Models: An Application of Conjugate Gradient Algorithms. (Lecture Notes in Statistics Ser.: Vol. 10). (Illus.). 200p. 1982. pap. 14.00 (ISBN 0-387-90746-7). Springer-Verlag.

Maly, Kurt & Hanson, Allen R. Fundamentals of the Computing Sciences. (Illus.). 1978. ref. ed. 32.95 (ISBN 0-13-335240-4); supplementary vol. 14.95 (ISBN 0-13-335257-9). P-H.

Mardia, K. & Zemroch. Tables of the F-E Related Distribution Algorithms. 1979. 47.50 (ISBN 0-12-471140-5). Acad Pr.

Matney, Roy M., 2nd & Roth, C. H., Jr. Parallel Computing Structures & Algorithms for Logic Design Problems. LC 72-133318. 124p. 1969. 19.00 (ISBN 0-403-04518-5). Scholarly.

Mehlhorn, K. Data Structures & Algorithms Three: Multi-Dimensional Searching & Computational Geometry. (EATCS Monographs on Theoretical Computer Science). (Illus.). xii, 284p. 1984. 17.50 (ISBN 0-387-13642-8). Springer-Verlag.

--Data Structures & Algorithms Two: Graph Algorithms & NP-Completeness. (EATCS Monographs on Theoretical Computer Science Ser.). (Illus.). xii, 260p. 1984. 17.50 (ISBN 0-387-13641-X). Springer-Verlag.

--Data Structures & Alogrithms One: Sorting & Searching. (EATCS Monographs on Theoretical Computer Science). (Illus.). xiv, 336p. 1984. 17.50 (ISBN 0-387-13302-X). Springer-Verlag.

Miller, Webb & Wrathall, Celia. Software for Roundoff Analysis of Matrix Algorithms. LC 80-12662. (Computer Science & Applied Mathematics Ser.). 1980. 28.50 (ISBN 0-12-497250-0). Acad Pr.

Minieka, Edward. Optimization Algorithms for Networks & Graphs. LC 77-29166. (Industrial Engineering--a Ser. of Reference Books & Textbooks: Vol. 1). 1978. 39.75 (ISBN 0-8247-6642-3). Dekker.

Mitchell, William. Prelude to Programming: Problem Solving & Algorithms. 1984. text ed. 22.95 (ISBN 0-8359-5614-8); pap. text ed. 16.95 (ISBN 0-8359-5627-X). Reston.

Moffat, David V. Common Algorithms in Pascal with Programs for Reading. (Software Ser.). 192p. 1983. pap. 12.95 (ISBN 0-13-152637-5). P-H.

Newman, Morris. Algorithmic Matrix Theory. 1984. text ed. write for info. (ISBN 0-914894-47-1). Computer Sci.

Nijenhuis, Albert & Will, Herbert S. Combinatorial Algorithms: For Computers & Hard Calculators. 2nd ed. (Computer Science & Applied Math. Ser.). 1978. 22.50 (ISBN 0-12-519260-6). Acad Pr.

Paige, Robert A. Formal Differentiation-A Program Synthesis Technique. Stone, Harold, ed. LC 81-7632. (Computer Science Ser.: Artificial Intelligence: No. 6). 290p. 1981. 49.95 (ISBN 0-8357-1213-3). UMI Res Pr.

Pavlidis, Theo. Algorithms for Graphics & Image Processing. LC 81-9832. (Illus.). 416p. 1982. text ed. 37.95 (ISBN 0-914894-65-X). Computer Sci.

Reingold, et al. Combinatorial Algorithms: Theory & Practice. 1977. text ed. 36.95 (ISBN 0-13-152447-X). P-H.

Rustin, Randall, ed. Courant Computer Science Symposium 9: Combinatorial Algorithms. (Illus.). 126p. 1973. 20.00x (ISBN 0-917448-03-0). Algorithmics.

Saito, N. & Nishizeki, T., eds. Graph Theory & Algorithms: Proceedings. (Lecture Notes in Computer Sciences: Vol. 108). 216p. 1981. pap. 16.00 (ISBN 0-387-10704-5). Springer-Verlag.

Schweiger, F. Metrical Theory of Jacobi-Perron Algorithm. LC 73-9201. (Lecture Notes in Mathematics: Vol. 334). v, 111p. 1973. pap. 13.00 (ISBN 0-387-06388-9). Springer-Verlag.

Sedgewick, Robert. Algorithms. (Computer Science Ser.). (Illus.). 560p. 1983. 34.95 (ISBN 0-201-06672-6). Addison-Wesley.

Sellers, Peter H. Combinatorial Complexes. (Mathematics & Its Applications: No. 2). 1979. lib. bdg. 19.00 (ISBN 90-277-1000-7, Pub. by Reidel Holland). Kluwer Academic.

Shore, John. The Sachertorte Algorithm & Other Antidotes to Computer Anxiety. LC 84-48843. 256p. 1985. 16.95 (ISBN 0-670-80541-6). Viking.

Smith, David K. Network Optimization Practice: A Computational Guide. LC 82-3028. (Ellis Horwood Series in Mathematics Its Applications). 237p. 1982. 64.95X (ISBN 0-470-27347-X). Halsted Pr.

Solow, Daniel. Linear Programming: An Introduction to Finite Improvement Algorithms. 1984. 37.00 (ISBN 0-444-00912-4). Elsevier.

Sorenson, D. & Wets, R. J. Algorithms & Theory in Filtering & Control. (Mathematical Programming Studies: Vol. 18). 160p. 1982. 30.00 (ISBN 0-444-86399-0, I-125-82, North-Holland). Elsevier.

Spaeth, Helmut. Cluster Analysis Algorithms: For Data Reduction & Classification of Objects. (Computers & Their Applications). 226p. 1980. 74.95x (ISBN 0-470-26946-4). Halsted Pr.

Stiny, George & Gips, James. Algorithmic Aesthetics: Computer Models for Criticism & Design in the Arts. 1979. 28.50x (ISBN 0-520-03467-8). U of Cal Pr.

Swamy, M. N. & Thulasiraman, K. Graphs, Networks & Algorithms. LC 80-17782. 592p. 1981. 53.50 (ISBN 0-471-03503-3, Pub. by Wiley-Interscience). Wiley.

Symposium on Semantics of Algorithmic Languages. Proceedings. Engeler, E., ed. LC 78-151406. (Lecture Notes in Mathematics: Vol. 188). (Illus.). 1971. pap. 18.00 (ISBN 0-387-05377-8). Springer-Verlag.

Syslo, Maciej, et al. Discrete Optimization Algorithms with Pascal Programs. (Illus.). 544p. 1983. text ed. 45.00 (ISBN 0-13-215509-5). P-H.

Tarjan, Robert E. Data Structures & Network Algorithms. LC 83-61374. (CBMS-NSF Regional Conference Ser.: No. 44). vii, 131p. 1983. pap. text ed. 14.50 (ISBN 0-89871-187-8). Soc Indus-Appl Math.

Teo, K. L. & Wu, Z. S. Computational Methods for Optimal Distributed Parameter Systems of Parabolic Type. (Research Notes in Mathematics Ser.). 320p. pap. text ed. cancelled (ISBN 0-273-08611-1). Pitman Pub MA.

Tremblay, Jean-Paul & Bunt, Richard B. Introduction to Computer Science: An Algorithmic Approach. (Illus.). 1979. text ed. 37.95 (ISBN 0-07-065163-9). McGraw.

Werther, Manfred H. Recursive Algorithm for the Best Approximate Solution of Linear Equations with Applications to System Identification & State Estimation. LC 70-132895. 143p. 1969. 19.00 (ISBN 0-403-04547-9). Scholarly.

Wirth, Niklaus. Algorithms & Data Structures. (Illus.). 288p. 1986. text ed. 32.95 (ISBN 0-13-022005-1). P-H.

Wirth, Niklavs. Algorithms Plus Data Structures Equals Programs. (Illus.). 400p. 1976. 34.95 (ISBN 0-13-022418-9). P-H.

Wong, C. K. Algorithmic Studies in Mass Storage Systems. LC 82-22207. (Illus.). 411p. 1983. text ed. 35.95 (ISBN 0-914894-91-9). Computer Sci.

Zadeh & Fu, King-Sun, eds. Fuzzy Sets & Their Applications to Cognitive & Decision Processes. 1975. 60.00 (ISBN 0-12-775260-9). Acad Pr.

Zimmer, J. A. Abstraction for Programmers. 288p. 1985. 17.95 (ISBN 0-07-072832-1). McGraw.

ALICYCLIC COMPOUNDS

Hart, Harold & Karabatsos, Gerasimos J., eds. Advances in Alicyclic Chemistry, 3 vols. Incl. Vol. 1. 1966. 80.00 (ISBN 0-12-001301-0); Vol. 2. 1968. 80.00 (ISBN 0-12-001302-9); Vol. 3. 1971. 80.00 (ISBN 0-12-001303-7); Suppl. 1. Carbocyclic Ring Expansion Reactions. Gutsche, C. David & Redmore, Derek. 1968. 63.00 (ISBN 0-12-001351-7). Acad Pr.

McQuillin, F. J. & Baird, M. S. Alicyclic Chemistry. 2nd ed. LC 82-12835. (Texts in Chemistry & Biochemistry Ser.). 250p. 1983. 42.50 (ISBN 0-521-23987-7); pap. 17.95 (ISBN 0-521-28391-4). Cambridge U Pr.

Parker, W., ed. Alicyclic Chemistry, Vols. 2-6. Incl. Vols. 2 & 3. 1972 Literature. LC 72-82047. Vol. 2, 1974. 47.00 (ISBN 0-85186-522-4, Royal Soc Chem London); Vol. 3, 1973 Literature. 61.00 (ISBN 0-85186-552-6); Vol. 4. 1974 Literature. LC 72-82047. 1976. 70.00 (ISBN 0-85186-582-8, Royal Soc Chem London); Vol. 5. 1975 Literature. 1977. 72.00 (ISBN 0-85186-612-3, Royal Soc Chem London); Vol. 6. 1976 Literature. 1978. 73.00 (ISBN 0-85186-632-8, Royal Soc Chem London). LC 72-82047. Am Chemical.

ALIEN ANIMALS

see Animal Introduction

ALIGNMENT CHARTS

see Nomography (Mathematics)

ALIMENTARY CANAL

see also Digestive Organs

Bertaccini, G., ed. Meditators & Drugs in Gastrointestinal Motility I: Morphological Basis & Neurophysiological Control. (Handbook of Experimental Pharmacology Ser.: Vol. 59, I). (Illus.). 468p. 1982. 160.00 (ISBN 0-387-11296-0). Springer-Verlag.

Dobrilla, G., et al, eds. Current Therapy of Gastrointestinal Disorders. 250p. 1983. text ed. 67.00. Raven.

Gitnick, Gary. Gastroenterology. (Medical Outline Ser.). 1984. pap. text ed. write for info (ISBN 0-87488-172-2). Med Exam.

Grundy, D. Gastroinestal Motility. 1985. lib. bdg. 38.75 (ISBN 0-85200-894-5, Pub. by MTP Pr England). Kluwer Academic.

Koldovsky, Otakar & Walker, W. A. Development of Gastrointestinal Functions in Mammals & Man. 250p. 86. 40.00x (ISBN 0-03-061992-0). Praeger.

Kurtz, Robert C., ed. Nutrition In Gastrointestinal Disease. (Contemporary Issues in Clinical Nutrition: Vol. 1). (Illus.). 1981. text ed. 20.00 (ISBN 0-443-08128-X). Churchill.

Nolan, Daniel J. Radiological Atlas of Gastrointestinal Disease. 313p. 1983. 75.00 (ISBN 0-471-25917-9, Pub. by Wiley Med). Wiley.

Taylor, Kenneth J. W., ed. Diagnostic Ultrasound in Gastrointestinal Disease. (Clinics in Diagnostic Ultrasound: Vol. 1). (Illus.). 1979. text ed. 24.00 (ISBN 0-443-08046-1). Churchill.

Young, David B., ed. Gastrointestinal Physiology IV. (International Review of Physiology Ser.). (Illus.). 208p. 1983. text ed. 37.00 (ISBN 0-8391-1725-6, 14192). Univ Park.

ALIPHATIC COMPOUNDS

see also Polyamines

Aliphatic Solvents. 193p. 1983. 1400.00 (ISBN 0-86621-098-9, A1148). Frost & Sullivan.

Georgiev, V. St. Aliphatic Derivatives. (Survey of Drug Research in Immunologic Disease: Vol. 1). (Illus.). x, 542p. 1982. 208.75 (ISBN 3-8055-3503-1). S Karger.

McKillop, A. Aliphatic Chemistry, Vols. 2-5. Vol. 2 1972 Literature. 1974 41.00 (ISBN 0-85186-512-7, Royal Soc Chem London); Vol. 3 1973 Literature. 1975 43.00 (ISBN 0-85186-542-9); Vol. 4 1974 Literature. 1976 45.00 (ISBN 0-85186-572-0); Vol. 5 1975 Literature. 1977 61.00 (ISBN 0-85186-602-6). Am Chemical.

Parker, W., ed. Aliphatic, Alicyclic, & Saturated Heterocyclic Chemistry: 1970-1971 Literature, 3 pts, Vol. 1. LC 72-83454. 1973. Pt. 1. 29.00 (ISBN 0-85186-502-X, Royal Soc Chem London); Pt. 2. 43.00 (ISBN 0-685-55721-9); Pt. 3. 41.00 (ISBN 0-685-55722-7). Am Chemical.

ALIPHATIC-CYCLIC COMPOUNDS

see Alicyclic Compounds

ALKALI HALIDES

Davidovits, P. & McFadden, D. L., eds. Alkali Halide Vapors: Structure, Spectra, & Reaction Dynamics. LC 78-4812. 1979. 85.50 (ISBN 0-12-204250-6). Acad Pr.

Fowler, W. Beall. Physics of Color Centers. LC 68-18667. (Illus.). 1968. 83.00 (ISBN 0-12-262950-7). Acad Pr.

Jackson, C., ed. Modern Chlor-Alkali Technology, Vol. 2. LC 81-131882. 389p. 1983. 95.00 (ISBN 0-470-27471-9). Halsted Pr.

Markham, Jordon J. F-Centers in Alkali Halides. (Solid State Physics Ser.: Suppl. 8). 1966. 77.50 (ISBN 0-12-607768-1). Acad Pr.

ALKALI INDUSTRY AND TRADE

Coulter, M. O. Modern Chlor-Alkali Technology. LC 80-41236. 289p. 1980. 122.95 (ISBN 0-470-27005-5). Halsted Pr.

Warren, Kenneth. Chemical Foundations: The Alkali Industry in Britain to Nineteen Twenty-Six. (Oxford Research Studies in Geography). (Illus.). 1980. text ed. 54.00x (ISBN 0-19-823231-4). Oxford U Pr.

ALKALI METALS

British Nuclear Energy Society, ed. Liquid Alkali Metals. 315p. 1973. 70.00x (ISBN 0-901948-77-2, Pub. by Brit Nuclear England). State Mutual Bk.

Cohen-Adad. Alkali-Metal Chlorides (Binary Systems) Solubilities of Solids. (IUPAC Solubility Data Ser.). 1986. 100.00 (ISBN 0-08-023918-8). Pergamon.

Dunitz, J. D., et al, eds. Alkali Metal Complexes with Organic Ligands. LC 67-11280. (Structure & Bonding Ser.: Vol. 16). (Illus.). iii, 189p. 1973. pap. 40.00 (ISBN 0-387-06423-0). Springer-Verlag.

Mausteller, J. W. Alkali Metal Handling & Systems Operating Techniques. LC 67-26578. 241p. 1967. 10.50 (ISBN 0-685-58266-3, 450007). Am Nuclear Soc.

Miyamoto, A. S. Alkali Metal & Ammonium Halates. 100.01 (ISBN 0-08-029210-0). Pergamon.

Morton, Avery A. Solid Organoalkali Metal Reagents. 256p. 1964. 69.50x (ISBN 0-677-00560-1). Gordon.

Ohse, R. W. Thermodynamic & Transport Properties of Alkali Metals, 2 vols. Date not set. Set. 350.00 (ISBN 0-08-026176-0). Pergamon.

Scrosati & Vincent, Colin A., eds. Alkali Metal, Alkaline-Earth Metal & Ammonium Halides in Amide Solvents. (IUPAC Solubility Data Ser.: Vol. 11). 374p. 1980. 100.00 (ISBN 0-08-023917-X). Pergamon.

ALKALIES

see also Ammonia; Potassium; Sodium

Black, R. & Boden, P., eds. Alkaline Ring Complexes in Africa: Proceedings of the International Conference Held in Zaria, Nigeria, Dec. 6-10, 1983. 286p. 1985. pap. 46.75 (ISBN 0-08-032613-7, Pub by PPL). Pergamon.

ALKALINE EARTH METALS

Bauman. Alkali- & Alkaline-Earth Metal Oxides & Hydroxides in Water: Solubilities of Solids. (Solubility Data Ser.). 1986. 100.01 (ISBN 0-08-023920-X). Pergamon.

Henderson, B., et al. Defects in the Alkaline Earth Oxides. 276p. 1977. cancelled (ISBN 0-686-44435-3). Taylor & Francis.

International Commission on Radiological Protection. Alkaline Earth Metabolism in Adult Man. (ICRP Publication Ser: No. 20). 1973. pap. 15.25 (ISBN 0-08-017191-5). Pergamon.

Lorimer. Alkaline-Earth Sulfates in All Solvents: Solubilities of Solids. (IUPAC Solubility Data Ser.). 1986. 100.00 (ISBN 0-08-023916-1). Pergamon.

Scrosati & Vincent, Colin A., eds. Alkali Metal, Alkaline-Earth Metal & Ammonium Halides in Amide Solvents. (IUPAC Solubility Data Ser.: Vol. 11). 374p. 1980. 100.00 (ISBN 0-08-023917-X). Pergamon.

Vol'nov, I. I. Peroxides, Superoxides & Ozonides of Alkali & Alkaline Earth Metals. LC 66-22125. (Monographs in Inorganic Chemistry Ser.). 146p. 1966. 35.00x (ISBN 0-306-30259-4, Plenum Pr). Plenum Pub.

ALKALOIDS

see also names of Alkaloids

Agnoli, A., et al, eds. Aging Brain & Ergot Alkaloids. (Aging Ser.: Vol. 23). 464p. 1983. text ed. 59.00 (ISBN 0-89004-853-3). Raven.

Brossi. The Alkaloids, Vol. 23. 1984. 85.00 (ISBN 0-12-469523-X). Acad Pr.

Brossi, Arnold. The Alkaloids, Vol. 27. Edited Treatise ed. (Serial Publication). 1986. price not set (ISBN 0-12-469527-2). Acad Pr.

Brossi, Arnold, ed. The Alkaloids: Chemistry & Pharmacology, Vol. 24. 1985. 85.00 (ISBN 0-12-469524-8). Acad Pr.

Coffey, S. Rodd's Chemistry of Carbon Compounds, Vol. 4, Pt. A: Three, Four & Five Membered Heterocyclic Compounds. 1973. 159.50 (ISBN 0-444-41093-7). Elsevier.

Cordell, Goeffrey A. Introduction to Alkaloids: A Biogenetic Approach. LC 80-39651. 1056p. 1981. cloth 171.50 (ISBN 0-471-03478-9, Pub. by Wiley-Interscience). Wiley.

Dalton. The Alkaloids. (Studies in Organic Chemistry: Vol. 7). 1979. 110.00 (ISBN 0-8247-6788-8). Dekker.

Glasby, J. Encyclopedia of the Alkaloids, Vol. 4. 408p. 1983. 75.00x (ISBN 0-306-41217-9, Plenum Pr). Plenum Pub.

Glasby, J. S. Encyclopedia of the Alkaloids, 2 Vols. LC 75-17753. 1423p. 1975. Set. 145.00x (ISBN 0-306-30845-2, Plenum Pr). Plenum Pub.

--Encyclopedia of the Alkaloids, Vol. 3. LC 75-17753. 527p. 1977. 85.00x (ISBN 0-306-31026-0, Plenum Pr). Plenum Pub.

Grundon, M. F., ed. The Alkaloids, Vols. 1-8. Incl. Vol. 1. 1969-70 Literature. 1971. 43.00 (ISBN 0-85186-257-8, Royal Soc Chem London); Vol. 2. 1970-71 Literature. 1972. 36.00 (ISBN 0-85186-267-5); Vol. 3. 1971-72 Literature. 1973. 37.00 (ISBN 0-85186-277-2); Vol. 4. 1972-73 Literature. 1974. 43.00 (ISBN 0-85186-287-X); Vol. 5. 1973-74 Literature. 1975. 47.00 (ISBN 0-85186-297-7); Vol. 6. 1974-75 Literature. 1976. 50.00 (ISBN 0-85186-307-8); Vol. 7. 1975-76 Literature. 1977. 65.00 (ISBN 0-85186-317-5); Vol. 8. 1976-77 Literature. 1978. 61.00 (ISBN 0-85186-327-2). LC 70-616637. Am Chemical.

Hesse, Manfred. Alkaloid Chemistry. LC 80-22828. 231p. 1981. 36.95 (ISBN 0-471-07973-1, Pub. by Wiley-Interscience). Wiley.

Horikoshi, K. & Akiba, T. Alkalophilic Microorganisms: A New Microbial World. 270p. 1982. 42.00 (ISBN 0-387-10924-2). Springer-Verlag.

Iizuka, H. & Naito, A. Microbial Conversion of Steroids & Alkaloids. 396p. 1981. 53.00 (ISBN 0-387-10794-0). Springer-Verlag.

Knoll. Symposium on Pharmacology of Vinca Alkaloids, Vol. 5. 1979. 7.00 (ISBN 0-9960007-8-X, Pub. by Akademiai Kaido Hungary). Heyden.

Manske, R. & Rodrigo, R., eds. The Alkaloids: Chemistry & Pharmacology, Vol. 20. 1982. 69.50 (ISBN 0-12-469520-5). Acad Pr.

Manske, R. F. & Holmes, H. L., eds. The Alkaloids: Chemistry & Pharmacology, Vol. 21. 1983. 55.00 (ISBN 0-12-469521-3). Acad Pr.

Manske, R. G., ed. The Alkaloids: Vol. 19, Chemistry & Physiology. 1981. 55.00 (ISBN 0-12-469519-1). Acad Pr.

Manske, R. H., ed. The Alkaloids: Chemistry & Pharmacology, Vol 22. 1983. 55.00 (ISBN 0-12-469522-1). Acad Pr.

Manske, R. H. & Rodrigo, R. G., eds. The Alkaloids: Vol. 18, Chemistry & Physiology. LC 50-5522. 1981. 71.50 (ISBN 0-12-469518-3). Acad Pr.

Manske, R. H., et al, eds. The Alkaloids: Chemistry & Physiology. Incl. Vol. 1. 1965. 91.50 (ISBN 0-12-469501-9); Vol. 2. 1952. 91.50 (ISBN 0-12-469502-7); Vol. 3. 1965. 82.00 (ISBN 0-12-469503-5); Vol. 4. 1965. 78.00 (ISBN 0-12-469504-3); Vol. 5. Pharmacology. 1965. 78.00 (ISBN 0-12-469505-1); Vol. 6. Supplement to Volumes 1 & 2. 1965. 78.00 (ISBN 0-12-469506-X); Vol. 7. Supplement to Volumes 2, 3, 4 & 5. 1960. 87.00 (ISBN 0-12-469507-8); Vol. 8. The Indole Alkaloids. 1965. 107.00 (ISBN 0-12-469508-6); Vol. 9. 1967. 94.50 (ISBN 0-12-469509-4); Vol. 10. 1968. 94.50 (ISBN 0-12-469510-8); Vol. 11. 1968. 94.50 (ISBN 0-12-469511-6); Vol. 12. 1970. 94.50 (ISBN 0-12-469512-4); Vol. 13. 1971. 80.50 (ISBN 0-12-469513-2); Vol. 14. 1973. 100.00 (ISBN 0-12-469514-0); Vol. 15. 1975. 80.50 (ISBN 0-12-469515-9); Vol. 16. 1977. 100.50 (ISBN 0-12-469516-7); Vol. 17. 1979. 73.50 (ISBN 0-12-469517-5). Acad Pr.

Mothes, K., et al, eds. Biochemistry of Alkaloids. (Illus.). 490p. 1985. lib. bdg. 86.50 (ISBN 0-89573-072-3). VCH Pubs.

Pelletier, S. W. Alkaloids: Chemical & Biological Perspectives, Vol. 1. LC 82-11071. (Alkaloids: Chemical Biological Perspectives Ser.). 398p. 1983. 59.95x (ISBN 0-471-08811-0, Pub by Wiley-Interscience). Wiley.

Pelletier, S. W., ed. Alkaloids: Chemical & Biological Perspectives, Vol. 2. 490p. 1984. 59.95 (ISBN 0-471-89299-8, Pub by Wiley-Interscience). Wiley.

Phillipson, J. D., et al, eds. The Chemistry & Biology of Isoquinoline Alkaloids. (Proceedings in Life Sciences Ser.). (Illus.). 300p. 1985. 39.00 (ISBN 0-387-13980-X). Springer-Verlag.

Raffauf, Robert F. A Handbook of Alkaloids & Alkaloid-containing Plants. LC 73-113713. pap. 160.00 (ISBN 0-317-28188-7, 2020190). Bks Demand UMI.

Robinson, T. The Biochemistry of Alkaloids. 2nd ed. (Molecular Biology, Biochemistry & Biophysics Ser.: Vol. 3). (Illus.). 225p. 1981. 38.00 (ISBN 0-387-10795-9). Springer-Verlag.

Saxton, J. Edwin. Monoterpenoid Indole Alkaloids, Part 4. LC 82-21958. (Chemistry of Heterocyclic Compounds Monographs: Vol. 25). 995p. 1983. 214.50 (ISBN 0-471-89748-5, 1-079, Pub. by Wiley-Interscience). Wiley.

Shamma, Maurice. The Isoquinoline Alkaloids: Chemistry & Pharmacology. 1972. 43.50 (ISBN 0-12-638250-6). Acad Pr.

Shamma, Maurice & Moniot, Jerome L., eds. Isoquinoline Alkaloids Research: 1972-1977. LC 77-26929. (Illus.). 443p. 1978. 65.00x (ISBN 0-306-31059-7, Plenum Pr). Plenum Pub.

Taylor, W. I. & Farnsworth, N. R. Catharanthus Alkaloids: Botany, Chemistry, Pharmacology & Clinical Use. 336p. 1975. 85.00 (ISBN 0-8247-6276-2). Dekker.

Verpoorte, R. & Baerheim, S. Chromatography of Alkaloids, Part B: Gas-Liquid Chromatography & High-Performance Liquid Chromatography. (Journal of Chromatography Library: Vol. 23B). 1984. 90.75 (ISBN 0-444-42265-X). Elsevier.

Waller, G. R. & Nowacki, E. K. Alkaloid Biology & Metabolism in Plants. LC 76-30903. (Illus.). 312p. 1978. 27.50 (ISBN 0-306-30981-5, Plenum Pr). Plenum Pub.

ALKANES

see Paraffins

ALKYLATION

Albright, Lyle F. & Goldsby, Arthur R., eds. Industrial & Laboratory Alkylations. LC 77-23973. (ACS Symposium Ser.: No. 55). 1977. 39.95 (ISBN 0-8412-0385-7). Am Chemical.

Loveless, Anthony. Genetic & Allied Effects of Alkylating Agents. LC 66-24944. (Illus.). 1966. 36.00x (ISBN 0-271-00047-3). Pa St U Pr.

National Research Council Assembly of Life Sciences. The Alkyl Benzenes. 384p. 1981. pap. 11.00 (ISBN 0-309-03180-X). Natl Acad Pr.

Parker, W., ed. Aliphatic, Alicyclic, & Saturated Heterocyclic Chemistry: 1970-1971 Literature, 3 pts, Vol. 1. LC 72-83454. 1973. Pt. 1. 29.00 (ISBN 0-85186-502-X, Royal Soc Chem London); Pt. 2. 43.00 (ISBN 0-685-55721-9); Pt. 3. 41.00 (ISBN 0-685-55722-7). Am Chemical.

ALL TERRAIN VEHICLES

see also Tracklaying Vehicles

Robson, Graham. The Range Rover - Land Rover. (Illus.). 192p. 1982. 19.95 (ISBN 0-7153-7707-8). David & Charles.

Waar, Bob. Off-Road Handbook. LC 74-83546. (Illus.). 160p. 1974. pap. 9.95 (ISBN 0-912656-15-8). H P Bks.

Woodall's RV Owner's Handbook, Vol. 1. pap. 6.95 (ISBN 0-671-24614-3). Woodall.

Woodall's RV Owner's Handbook, Vol. 2. pap. 4.95 (ISBN 0-671-25163-5). Woodall.

ALLEN RADIATION BELTS

see Van Allen Radiation Belts

ALLEYS

see Streets

ALLIGATOR PEAR

see Avocado

ALLIGATORS

Here are entered works on the American species of crocodiles. General works are entered under the heading Crocodiles.

Bothwell, Dick. Alligators. LC 62-52731. (Orig.). pap. 3.95 (ISBN 0-8200-0302-6). Great Outdoors.

Crocodiles: Proceedings of the First Working Meeting of Crocodile Specialists. (Illus.). 191p. 1971. pap. 12.50 (ISBN 2-88032-008-9, IUCN5, IUCN). Unipub.

Hirschhorn, Howard H. Complete Guide to Alligators & Crocodilians of Florida & the Caribbean. 60p. 1984. pap. write for info. (ISBN 0-940810-04-2). Phoenix FL.

Toops, Connie M. The Alligator-Monarch of the Everglades. LC 79-51891. 64p. 1979. pap. 3.95 (ISBN 0-686-84286-3). Banyan Bks.

ALLIUM

Kraehenbuehl, W. Phyllom Morphogenese bei Allium und Juncus unter besonderer Beruecksichtigung der Morphogenese. (Dissertationes Botanicae: No. 67). (Ger., Illus.). 320p. 1983. pap. text ed. 35.00X (ISBN 3-7682-1358-7). Lubrecht & Cramer.

ALLOYS

see also Heat Resistant Alloys; Metallic Glasses; Metallurgy

also aluminum Alloys, Steel Alloys and similar headings

Achievement of High Fatigue Resistance in Metals & Alloys - STP 467. 298p. 1970. 28.75 (ISBN 0-8031-0030-2, 04-467000-30). ASTM.

Allen, Peter, ed. Superalloys. 295p. 1984. pap. 985.00 (ISBN 0-931634-37-7). FIND-SVP.

American Society for Metals. Source Book on Industrial Alloy & Engineering Data: A Comprehensive Collection of Alloy & Engineering Data in Tabular & Graphical Form. LC 77-28985. pap. 120.80 (ISBN 0-317-26761-2, 2024347). Bks Demand UMI.

American Society for Testing & Materials. Compilation & Index of Trade Names, Specifications, & Producers of Stainless Alloys & Superalloys. LC 72-91409. (ASTM Data Ser.: DS45A). pap. 20.00 (ISBN 0-317-08287-6, 2019652). Bks Demand UMI.

Costin, Alec B., et al. Kosciusko Alpine Flora. (Illus.). 408p. 1979. 35.00x (ISBN 0-643-02473-5, Pub. by Brit Mus Nat Hist England). Sabbot-Natural Hist Bks.
Elliot, Roy. Alpine Gardening. (Illus.). 1978. Repr. 15.00 (ISBN 0-913728-13-6). Theophrastus.
Farrer, Reginald. Alpines & Bog Plants. LC 75-42433. 1976. Repr. of 1908 ed. 12.50 (ISBN 0-913728-10-1). Theophrastus.
Gabrielson, Ira N. Western American Alpines. LC 71-174546. (Illus.). 1972. Repr. of 1932 ed. 10.00 (ISBN 0-685-61146-9). Theophrastus.
High Mountain Plants in China. Date not set. price not set (ISBN 0-442-20076-5). Sci Pr.
Hills, Lawrence D. The Propagation of Alpines. (Illus.). 1976. Repr. of 1959 ed. write for info (ISBN 0-913728-11-X). Theophrastus.
Ingwersen, Will. Alpine & Rock Plants. 304p. 1980. 40.00x (ISBN 0-460-04386-2, Pub. by J M Dent England). State Mutual Bk.
--Ingwersen's Manual of Alpine Plants. 1978. 22.00x (ISBN 0-686-26159-3, Pub by W Ingwersen & Dunnsprint England). HHH Horticult.
Miller, Millie. Kinnikinnick: The Mountain Flower Book. 1980. pap. 3.95 (ISBN 0-933472-09-9). Johnson Bks.
Spring, Ira & Manning, Harvey. Mountain Flowers. LC 79-9284. (Illus.). 1979. pap. 4.95 (ISBN 0-916890-92-9). Mountaineers.
Tranquillini, W. Physiological Ecology of the Alpine Timberline. (Ecological Studies: Vol. 31). (Illus.). 1979. 37.00 (ISBN 0-387-09065-7). Springer-Verlag.
Zwinger, Ann H. & Willard, Beatrice E. Land Above the Trees: A Guide to American Alpine Tundra. LC 72-79702. (Illus.). 448p. 1972. 19.18i (ISBN 0-06-014823-3, HarpT). Har-Row.

ALPINE GARDENS

Bloom, Alan. Alpines for Your Garden. 128p. 1981. 14.95 (ISBN 0-938804-01-4, Pub. by Floraprint). Intl Spec Bk.
Elliot, Roy. Alpine Gardening. (Illus.). 1978. Repr. 15.00 (ISBN 0-913728-13-6). Theophrastus.
Farrer, Reginald. Alpines & Bog Plants. LC 75-42433. 1976. Repr. of 1908 ed. 12.50 (ISBN 0-913728-10-1). Theophrastus.
Foster, Raymond. Rock Garden & Alpine Plants. LC 81-67009. (Illus.). 272p. 1981. 31.50 (ISBN 0-7153-8203-9). David & Charles.
Heath, Royton. Collectors Alpines. (Illus.). 543p. 1982. 39.95 (ISBN 0-917304-47-0). Timber.
Ingwersen, Will. Alpine & Rock Plants. (Illus.). 220p. 1983. 22.50x (ISBN 0-460-04386-2, Pub. by J M Dent England). Biblio Dist.
--Alpine Garden Plants. (Illus.). 153p. 1981. pap. 6.95 (ISBN 0-7137-1143-4, Pub. by Blandford Pr England). Sterling.

ALPOVA

Zeller, Sanford M. Developmental Morphology of Alpova. (Studies in Botany Ser: No. 2). (Illus.). 20p. 1939. pap. 3.95x (ISBN 0-87071-012-5). Oreg St U Pr.

ALSATIAN WOLF DOGS

see Dogs–Breeds–German Shepherd Dogs

ALTERNATING CURRENT MACHINERY

see Electric Machinery–Alternating Current

ALTERNATING CURRENTS

see Electric Currents, Alternating

ALTERNATING GENERATIONS

see Generations, Alternating

ALTIMETER

Gracey, William. Measurement of Aircraft Speed & Altitude. LC 80-23503. 262p. 1981. 54.50x (ISBN 0-471-08511-1). Wiley.

ALTITUDE, INFLUENCE OF

see also Anoxemia; Man–Influence of Environment

Baker, P. T., ed. The Biology of High-Altitude Peoples. LC 76-50311. (International Biological Programme Ser.: No. 14). (Illus.). 1978. 79.50 (ISBN 0-521-21523-4). Cambridge U Pr.
Heath, Donald & Williams, David R. Man at High Altitude: The Pathophysiology of Acclimatization & Adaptation. 2nd ed. (Illus.). 1981. text ed. 65.00 (ISBN 0-443-02081-7). Churchill.
Houston, Charles S. High Altitude Physiology Study. (Illus., Orig.). 1982. 12.00 (ISBN 0-686-37171-2). Houston C.
McClung, Jean. Effects of High Altitude on Human Birth: Observations on Mothers, Placentas, & the Newborn in Two Peruvian Populations. LC 72-91629. 1969. 11.00 (ISBN 0-674-24065-0). Harvard U Pr.
Monge, M. Carlos & Monge, C. Carlos. High-Altitude Diseases: Mechanism & Management. (Illus.). 112p. 1966. 12.50x (ISBN 0-398-01329-2). C C Thomas.
West, John B., ed. High Altitude Physiology. (Benchmark Papers in Human Physiology: Vol. 15). 480p. 1981. 55.00 (ISBN 0-87933-388-X). Van Nos Reinhold.

ALUCONIDAE

see Owls

ALUMINUM

see also Silicates

Achar, D. G. & Ruge, J. Joining of Aluminium to Steel with Particular Reference to Welding. (Monograph). 1981. 30.00 (ISBN 0-9960034-7-9, Pub. by Aluminium W Germany). Heyden.
Altenpohl, D. Aluminium Viewed from Within. 1982. 42.00 (ISBN 0-9960034-3-6, Pub. by Aluminium W Germany). Heyden.
Aluminium-Zentrade, ed. European Aluminium Statistics, 1982. 1983. 24.00 (ISBN 0-9911000-4-2, Pub. by Aluminium W Germany). Heyden.
Aluminium-Zentrale, ed. Aluminium & the Automobile. 1981. 81.00 (ISBN 0-9960034-4-4, Pub. by Aluminium W Germany). Heyden.
Aluminium-Zentrale Editors. European Aluminium Statistics. 1980. 18.00 (ISBN 0-9960034-5-2, Pub. by Aluminium W Germany). Heyden.
Ammen, C. W. Casting Aluminum. (Illus.). 252p. (Orig.). 1985. 18.95 (ISBN 0-8306-0910-5, 1910); pap. 11.95 (ISBN 0-8306-1910-0). TAB Bks.
Banks, Ferdinand E. Bauxite & Aluminum: An Introduction to the Economics of Non-Fuel Minerals. LC 78-24632. 208p. 1979. 26.00x (ISBN 0-669-02771-5). Lexington Bks.
Bauer, C. O. Screw Joints in Aluminium Components. 1983. 30.00 (ISBN 0-9911000-3-4, Pub. by Aluminium W Germany). Heyden.
Billehaug, K. & Oye, H. A. Invert Cathodes & Anodes for Aluminium Electrolysis. (Monograph). 1981. 24.00 (ISBN 0-9960034-8-7, Pub. by Aluminium W Germany). Heyden.
Boron Reinforced Aluminum Systems, Part 2. (Materials Technology Ser.: Vol. II). 137p. 1982. pap. 35.00 (ISBN 0-87762-312-0). Technomic.
Corey, A. Raymond. The Development of Markets for New Materials: A Study of Building New End-Product Markets for Aluminum, Fibrous Glass, & the Plastics. LC 56-9764. pap. 69.80 (ISBN 0-317-29992-1, 2051840). Bks Demand UMI.
Dichtl, et al. Air-Cooled Aluminium Cylinder Heads. 1983. 30.00 (ISBN 0-9911000-2-6, Pub. by Aluminium W Germany). Heyden.
Dorre, E., et al. Alumina: Processing, Properties & Applications. (Materials Research & Engineering Ser.). (Illus.). 330p. 1984. 36.00 (ISBN 0-387-13576-6). Springer-Verlag.
Gaylord, Edwin H. & Gaylord, Charles N. Design of Steel Structures. 2nd ed. (Civil Engineering Ser.). (Illus.). 640p. 1972. text ed. 46.00 (ISBN 0-07-023110-9). McGraw.
Gerard, Gary, ed. Extractive Metallurgy of Aluminum: Proceedings. LC 63-13591. Vol. 2, Aluminum. pap. 147.30 (ISBN 0-317-10300-8, 2000688). Bks Demand UMI.
Gitzen, Walter, ed. Alumina as a Ceramic Material. 16.00 (ISBN 0-916094-46-4). Am Ceramic.
Grjotheim. Aluminum Electrolysis: Chemistry of Hall-Heroult Process. 2nd ed. 1982. 69.00 (ISBN 0-9960035-4-1). Heyden.
Grjotheim, K. & Krohn, C. Aluminium Electrolysis: Fundamentals of the Hall-Heroult Process. 2nd ed. 1982. 69.00 (ISBN 0-9960035-4-1, Pub. by Aluminium W Germany). Heyden.
Grjotheim, K. & Welch, B. J. Aluminium Smelter Technology-A Pure & Applied Approach. 1980. 34.00 (ISBN 0-9960033-9-8, Pub. by Aluminium W Germany). Heyden.
Hatch, John E, ed. Aluminum: Properties & Physical Metallurgy. 1984. 70.00 (ISBN 0-87170-176-6). Am Soc Pub Admin.
Henley, V. F. Anodic Oxidation of Aluminum & Its Alloys. (Materials Engineering Practice Ser.). (Illus.). 150p. 1982. 28.00 (ISBN 0-08-026726-2, A145, A115); pap. 13.25 (ISBN 0-08-026725-4). Pergamon.
Herrmann, E. & Hoffmann, D. Handbook on Continuous Casting. 1980. 480.00 (ISBN 0-9960033-7-1, Pub. by Aluminium W Germany); leather 616.00 (ISBN 0-9960033-8-X). Heyden.
Hufnagel, W. Key to Aluminium Alloys. 1982. 28.00 (ISBN 0-9960035-2-5, Pub. by Aluminium W Germany). Heyden.
Hutchinson, G. Evelyn & Wollack, Anne. Biological Accumulators of Aluminum. 1943. pap. 29.50x (ISBN 0-686-50040-7). Elliots Bks.
Johne, P. Machining of Aluminium. (Monograph). 1981. 30.00 (ISBN 0-9960034-9-5, Pub. by Aluminium W Germany). Heyden.
Kehler, W. F. Surface Treatment of Aluminium: Dictionary of Technical Terms. (Eng., Fr. & Ger.). 1975. 12.00 (ISBN 0-9960034-1-X, Pub. by Aluminium W Germany). Heyden.
Kutner, F. Aluminium Conductor Materials: Monography. 1981. 30.00 (ISBN 0-9960034-6-0, Pub. by Aluminium W Germany). Heyden.
Lee, Royal & Lee Foundation Staff. The Effect of Aluminum Compounds in Foods. 1983. pap. 4.95x (ISBN 0-911238-94-8, Regent House). B of A.
Processing & Finishing of Aluminum. (Sixty Ser). 1973. pap. 2.00 (ISBN 0-685-58074-1, 65). Natl Fire Prot.
Rao, S. & Dawson, P. R. A State of the Art Report on Secondary Aluminum Production Processes with Particular Emphasis Fluxes & Emission Control, 1980. 1981. 90.00x (ISBN 0-686-97165-5, Pub. by W Spring England). State Mutual Bk.
Recycling Consort Division Staff. Aluminum Recycling: A Correspondence Course Workbook. 20p. 1984. pap. text ed. 11.95 (ISBN 0-318-01195-6, Pub. by Consortium). Prosperity & Profits.
Sinia, R. J. Aluminium in Packaging. (Illus.). 1973. pap. 30.00 (ISBN 90-6156-504-9). Heinman.
Specification for Aluminum & Aluminum Alloy Covered Arc Welding Electrodes: A5.3. 10p. 1980. 10.00 (ISBN 0-87171-204-0); member 7.50. Am Welding.
Specifications for Aluminum & Aluminum-Alloy Bare Welding Rods & Bare Electrodes: A5.10-80. 10.00 (ISBN 0-87171-203-2). Am Welding.
Standard for the Manufacture of Aluminum or Magnesium Powder. (Sixty Ser.). 1974. pap. 2.00 (ISBN 0-685-58073-3, 651). Natl Fire Prot.
Starke, E. A., Jr. & Sanders, T. H., Jr., eds. Aluminum-Lithium Alloys II: Proceedings, Monterey, California, 1983. (Illus.). 692p. 1984. 62.00; members 32.00; student members 17.00. Metal Soc.
TMS-AIME 113th Annual Meeting, Los Angeles, Feb. 26 - March 1, 1984. High Conductivity Copper & Aluminum Alloys. Taubenblat, P. W. & Ling, E., eds. (Proceedings). 190p. 55.00 (ISBN 0-89520-479-7, 249); members 34.00 (ISBN 0-317-37163-0); student members 18.00 (ISBN 0-317-37164-9). Metal Soc.
Wernick, S., et al. The Surface Treatment & Finishing of Aluminium & Its Alloys. 4th ed. 1274p. 1973. 175.00x (ISBN 0-85218-041-1, Pub. by Portcullio Pr). State Mutual Bk.

ALUMINUM, STRUCTURAL

Goodman, J. W., ed. Advanced Aluminum & Titanium Structures (AD-02) 52p. 1981. 14.00 (ISBN 0-686-34473-1, H00193). ASME.
Mazzolani, F. M. Aluminum Alloy Structures. (Surveys in Structural Engineering & Structural Mechanics Ser.). 1985. text ed. 49.95 (ISBN 0-273-08653-7). Pitman Pub MA.

ALUMINUM ALLOYS

Falkenstein, H. P. Formability of Aluminium Sheet Alloys. 1984. 33.00 (ISBN 0-9911000-5-0, Pub. by Aluminium W Germany). Heyden.
Henley, V. F. Anodic Oxidation of Aluminum & Its Alloys. (Materials Engineering Practice Ser.). (Illus.). 150p. 1982. 28.00 (ISBN 0-08-026726-2, A145, A115); pap. 13.25 (ISBN 0-08-026725-4). Pergamon.
International Aluminum-Lithium Conference. Aluminum-Lithium Alloys: Proceedings of the First International Aluminum-Lithium Conference. Sanders, T. H. & Starke, E. A., Jr., eds. LC 81-80989. pap. 97.30 (ISBN 0-317-28255-7, 2025447). Bks Demand UMI.
Kehler, W. Handbook of International Alloy Compositions & Designations, Vol. 3. 859p. 1981. pap. text ed. 224.00 (ISBN 0-9911001-6-6, Pub. by Aluminium W Germany). Heyden.
Ling, E. & Taubenblat, P. W., eds. High Conductivity Cooper & Aluminum Alloys. LC 84-61484. (Illus.). 189p. 1984. 55.00 (ISBN 0-89520-479-7). Metal Soc.
--High Conductivity Copper & Aluminum Alloys. 190p. 1984. 55.00 (ISBN 0-317-37221-1); members 34.00 (ISBN 0-317-37222-X). Metal Soc.
Mazzolani, F. M. Aluminum Alloy Structures. (Surveys in Structural Engineering & Structural Mechanics Ser.). 1985. text ed. 49.95 (ISBN 0-273-08653-7). Pitman Pub MA.
Morris, James G., ed. Thermo-mechanical Processing of Aluminum Alloys. 233p. 1978. 28.00 (ISBN 0-89520-354-5); members 18.00 (ISBN 0-317-37223-8). Metal Soc.
Thrall & Shannon. Adhesive Bonding of Aluminum Alloys. 1985. 79.95 (ISBN 0-8247-7405-1). Dekker.

ALUMINUM CONSTRUCTION

Aluminum for Engine Applications. 68p. 1983. 22.00 (ISBN 0-89883-305-1, SP534). Soc Auto Engineers.
First International Aluminum Welding Conference. 162p. 1981. pap. text ed. 56.00 (ISBN 0-9911001-9-0, Pub. by Akademiai Kaido Hungary). Heyden.
Vance, Mary. Aluminum Construction. (Architecture Ser.: Bibliography A 1354). 1985. pap. 2.00 (ISBN 0-89028-324-9). Vance Biblios.

ALUMINUM INDUSTRY AND TRADE

Aluminium Association. Aluminium Industry Energy Conservation Workshop, 7: Proceedings. 357p. 1983. 102.00 (ISBN 0-9911000-8-5, Pub. by Aluminium W Germany). Heyden.
Aluminium Industry Energy Conservation Workshop: Proceedings, No. VI. 260p. 1981. 96.00 (ISBN 0-9911002-4-7, Pub. by Aluminium W Germany). Heyden.
Aluminium Weldments: Second International Conference, Proceedings. 1982. 99.00 (ISBN 0-9960035-6-8, Pub. by Aluminium W Germany). Heyden.
Barron, Terry. The Aluminum Industry of Texas. (Mineral Resource Circular Ser.: No. 67). (Illus.). 16p. 1981. 1.50 (ISBN 0-686-36996-3). Bur Econ Geology.
Environmental Aspects of Aluminum Smelting: A Technical Review. (Industry Technical Review Ser.: Vol. 3). 167p. 1981. pap. 25.00 (ISBN 92-807-1014-1, UNEP050, UNEP). Unipub.
Environmental Aspects of the Aluminum Industry. (Industry Overviews: Vol. 2). 32p. 1977. pap. 6.75 (ISBN 0-686-93504-7, UNEP027, UNEP). Unipub.
Environmental Aspects of the Aluminum Industry. (Industry Technical Review Ser.: Vol. 4). pap. 5.00 (UNEP016, UNEP). Unipub.
Nutting, Jack, ed. Aluminium & Its Future Patterns of Use in Great Britain. 40p. (Orig.). 1982. pap. text ed. 16.00x (ISBN 0-904357-46-5, Metals Soc). Brookfield Pub Co.
The Processing & Marketing of Bauxite, Alumina, Aluminium: Areas for International Co-operation. (Studies in the Processing, Marketing & Distribution of Commodities). 89p. 11.00 (ISBN 0-317-18697-3, E.84.II.D.18). UN.
Seventh International Light Metals Congress, Vienna, Austria, 1981. 114.00 (ISBN 0-9960035-5-X, Pub. by Aluminium W Germany). Heyden.
UNCTAD Secretariat. Studies in the Processing, Marketing & Distribution of Commodities: The Processing & Marketing of Bauxite, Alumina, Aluminum: Areas for International Cooperation. 89p. 1985. pap. 11.00 (UN84/2D15 5071, UN). Unipub.
Wallace, Donald H. Market Control in the Alumininum Industry. Wilkins, Mira, ed. LC 76-29774. (European Business Ser.). (Illus.). 1977. Repr. of 1937 ed. lib. bdg. 36.00x (ISBN 0-405-09786-7). Ayer Co Pubs.
Woods, Douglas & Burrows, James C. The World Aluminum-Bauxite Market: Policy Implications for the United States. LC 78-19455. 254p. 1980. 39.95 (ISBN 0-03-044356-3). Praeger.

AMATEUR MOVING-PICTURES

Brodsky, Bob & Treadway, Toni. Super Eight in the Video Age. 2nd ed. (Illus.). 124p. (Orig.). 1983. pap. text ed. 14.95 (ISBN 0-9610914-2-8). B&T.
Cheshire, David. The Book of Movie Photography. LC 79-2128. (Illus.). 1979. 22.50 (ISBN 0-394-50787-8). Knopf.

AMATEUR RADIO STATIONS

Ameco Publishing. Radio Amateur Log Book. 1965. spiral bdg. 1.50 (ISBN 0-912146-09-5). AMECO.
Anderson, Philip N. Computers & the Radio Amateur. (Illus.). 224p. 1982. 25.95 (ISBN 0-13-166306-2). P-H.
Helfrick, Albert D. Amateur Radio Equipment Fundamentals. (Illus.). 336p. 1982. 27.95 (ISBN 0-13-023655-1). P-H.
Schumacher, Alice C. Hiram Percy Maxim, Father of Amateur Radio. LC 76-57438. (Illus.). 1977. pap. 4.50 (ISBN 0-918232-04-X, HR-HPM). Comm Tech.
Schwartz, Martin. Novice Class Radio Amateur License Guide. LC 81-67778. 1983. pap. 1.50 (ISBN 0-912146-19-2). AMECO.
Schwartz, Martin & Kenneally, John. Advanced Class Radio Amateur License Guide. LC 81-67620. 1983. pap. 1.95 (ISBN 0-912146-21-4). AMECO.
Tech-General License Manual. 1985. 5.00 (ISBN 0-87259-014-3). Am Radio.
Tune in the World with Ham Radio. LC 76-13248. (Illus.). 8.50 (ISBN 0-87259-455-6). Am Radio.

AMBER

Laufer, Berthold. Historical Jottings on Amber in Asia. LC 8-11467. (Amer Anthro Assn Memoirs). 1906. pap. 15.00 (ISBN 0-527-00502-9). Kraus Repr.
Rice, Patty C. Amber: The Golden Gem of the Ages. 1980. 28.50 (ISBN 0-442-26138-1). Van Nos Reinhold.

AMBLYSTOMA

Campos, Emilio C., ed. Sensory Evaluation of Strabismus & Amblyopia in a Natural Environment. (Documenta Ophthalmologica Proceedings Ser.). 1984. lib. bdg. 34.50 (ISBN 90-6193-508-3, Pub. by Junks Pubs Netherlands). Kluwer Academic.

Matunas, Edward. American Ammunition & Ballistics. LC 79-10921. (Illus.). 1979. 18.95 (ISBN 0-8329-2900-X, Pub. by Winchester Pr). New Century.

Nonte, George C., Jr. Handloading for Handgunners. LC 78-64340. (Illus.). 288p. 1978. pap. 11.95 (ISBN 0-695-81199-1). DBI.

Parkerson, Codman. A Brief History of Bullet Moulds. 1.75 (ISBN 0-913150-26-6). Pioneer Pr.

Sears & Roebuck C1910 Ammunition Catalog: Chicago, Ill. (Illus.). soft bdg 2.00 (ISBN 0-686-20760-2). Sand Pond.

Steindler, R. A. Reloader's Guide. 3rd ed. (Illus.). 224p. pap. 8.95 (ISBN 0-88317-021-3). Stoeger Pub Co.

AMOEBA CHROMATOSA

Jeon, Kwang W., ed. The Biology of Amoeba. (Cell Biology: A Series of Monographs). 1973. 85.00 (ISBN 0-12-384850-4). Acad Pr.

AMPHIBIAN PLANES

Andrews, C. F. & Morgan, E. B. Supermarine Aircraft since Nineteen Fourteen. (Illus.). 352p. 1981. 29.95 (ISBN 0-370-10018-2, Pub. by the Bodley Head). Merrimack Pub Cir.

Knott, Richard C. The American Flying Boat. LC 79-84247. 262p. 1979. 31.95 (ISBN 0-87021-070-X). Naval Inst Pr.

Wigton, Don C. Those Fabulous Amphibians. LC 72-94377. (Illus.). 192p. 1973. 14.95 (ISBN 0-8187-0012-2). Harlo Pr.

AMPHIBIANS

see also Anura; Frogs; Salamanders; Toads

Amphibian Development: New Research, 2 vols. Incl. Vol. 1. Dumont, James N., et al, eds.; Vol. 2. Grippo, P., et al, eds. (ISBN 0-8422-7250-X). 1977. text ed. 29.00x ea. Irvington.

Arnold & Burton. A Field Guide to Reptiles & Amphibians of Britain & Europe. 29.95 (ISBN 0-00-219318-3, Collins Pub England). Greene.

Ashton, Ray E., Jr. & Ashton, Patricia S. Handbook of Reptiles & Amphibians of Florida: Lizards, Turtles & Crocodilians, Part 2. LC 81-51066. (Illus.). 192p. 1985. pap. 16.95 (ISBN 0-89317-036-4). Windward Pub.

Audubon Society & King, F. Wayne. The Audubon Society Field Guide to North American Reptiles & Amphibians. LC 79-2217. (Illus.). 1979. flexible bdg. 13.50 (ISBN 0-394-50824-6). Knopf.

Ballinger, Royce E. & Lynch, John D. How to Know the Amphibians & Reptiles. (Pictured Key Nature Ser.). 240p. 1983. write for info. wire coil (ISBN 0-697-04786-5). Wm C Brown.

Basey, Harold E. Discovering Sierra Reptiles & Amphibians. (Discovering Sierra Ser.). (Illus.). 50p. (Orig.). 1976. pap. 2.50 (ISBN 0-939666-03-0). Yosemite Natl Hist.

Benirschke, K. & Hsu, T. C., eds. Chromosome Atlas: Fish, Amphibians, Reptiles & Birds, Vol. 1. LC 73-166079. (Illus.). 225p. 1972. loose leaf 25.00 (ISBN 0-387-05507-X). Springer-Verlag.

Boulenger, G. A. Catalogue of the Batrachia Salienta S. Ecaudata: Collection of the British Museum. (Illus.). 1966. 47.60 (ISBN 3-7682-0291-7). Lubrecht & Cramer.

Boulenger, George A. The Tailless Batrachians of Europe, 2 parts in one. Sterling, Keir B., ed. LC 77-81096. (Biologists & Their World Ser.). (Illus.). 1978. Repr. of 1898 ed. lib. bdg. 38.50x (ISBN 0-405-10679-3). Ayer Co Pubs.

Breckenridge, Walter J. Reptiles & Amphibians of Minnesota. (Illus.). 1944. 7.50x (ISBN 0-8166-0573-4). U of Minn Pr.

Breen, John F. Encyclopedia of Reptiles & Amphibians. (Illus.). 576p. 1974. text ed. 24.95 (ISBN 0-87666-220-3, H-935). TFH Pubns.

Breukelman, John & Smith, Hobart M. Selected Records of Reptiles & Amphibians from Kansas. (Museum Ser.: Vol. 1, No. 5). 12p. 1946. 1.25 (ISBN 0-317-04837-6). U of KS Mus Nat Hist.

Brown, Vinson. Reptiles & Amphibians of the West. LC 74-3204. (Illus.). 80p. 1974. text ed. 11.95 (ISBN 0-87961-029-8); pap. text ed. 5.95 (ISBN 0-87961-028-X). Naturegraph.

Chambers, Kenneth. The Country Lover's Guide to Wildlife: Mammals, Amphibians, & Reptiles of the Northeastern United States. LC 79-4338. (Illus.). 248p. 1979. 18.50 (ISBN 0-8018-2207-6). Johns Hopkins.

Cogger, Harold G. Reptiles & Amphibians of Australia. 3rd ed. (Illus.). 660p. 1983. 59.50 (ISBN 0-88359-012-3). R Curtis Bks.

Coldiron, Ronn W. Possible Functions of Ornament in Labryinthodont Amphibians. (Occasional Papers: No. 33). 19p. 1974. pap. 1.25 (ISBN 0-686-79813-9). U of KS Mus Nat Hist.

Collins, Joseph T., ed. Amphibians & Reptiles in Kansas. (University of Kansas, Museum of Natural History Public Education Ser. No. 8). (Illus.). 356p. (Orig.). 1982. 17.00 (ISBN 0-89338-013-X); pap. 12.00 (ISBN 0-89338-012-1). U of KS Mus Nat Hist.

Conant, Roger. A Field Guide to Reptiles & Amphibians of Eastern & Central North America. 2nd ed. LC 74-13425. (Peterson Field Guide Ser.). 448p. 1975. 16.95 (ISBN 0-395-19979-4); pap. 11.95 (ISBN 0-395-19977-8). HM.

Cook, Francis R. Introduction to Canadian Amphibians & Reptiles. (National Museum of Science Ser.). 200p. 1984. pap. text ed. 12.95x (ISBN 0-317-03314-X, 56396-0, Pub. by Natl Mus Canada). U of Chicago Pr.

Cope, E. D. Batrachia of North America. (Illus.). 1963. 10.00 (ISBN 0-910914-01-X). J Johnson.

Duellman, W. E. Biology of Amphibians. (Illus.). 623p. 1985. 40.00 (ISBN 0-07-017977-8). McGraw.

Duellman, William E. A Distributional Study of the Amphibians of the Isthmus of Tehuantepec, Mexico. (Museum Ser.: Vol. 13, No.2). 54p. 1960. pap. 3.00 (ISBN 0-686-79840-6). U of KS Mus Nat Hist.

Duellman, William E., et al, eds. The South American Herpetofauna: Its Origin, Evolution & Dispersal. (U of KS Museum of Nat. Hist. Monograph: No. 7). (Illus.). 485p. 1979. 30.00 (ISBN 0-89338-009-1); pap. 15.00 (ISBN 0-89338-008-3). U of KS Mus Nat Hist.

Eaton, Theodore H. A Pennsylvanian Dissorophid Amphibian from Kansas. (Occasional Papers: No. 14). 8p. 1973. 1.25 (ISBN 0-317-04787-6). U of KS Mus Nat Hist.

Eaton, Theodore H., Jr. & Stewart, Peggy Lou. A New Order of Fishlike Amphibia from the Pennsylvanian of Kansas. (Museum Ser.: Vol. 12, No. 4). 24p. 1960. pap. 1.50 (ISBN 0-686-79814-7). U of KS Mus Nat Hist.

Epple, Anne O. Amphibians of New England. LC 82-73602. (Illus.). 1983. pap. 7.95 (ISBN 0-89272-159-6). Down East.

Fite, Katherine V., ed. The Amphibian Visual System: A Multidisciplinary Approach. 1976. 67.00 (ISBN 0-12-257450-8). Acad Pr.

Foreman, Brian & Schultze, Peter. A New Gymnarthrid Microsaur from the Lower Permian of Kansas with a Review of the Tuditanomorph Microsaurs (Amphibia) (Occasional Papers: No. 91). 25p. 1981. 1.50 (ISBN 0-317-04814-7). U of KS Mus Nat Hist.

Fox, Harold. Amphibian Morphogenesis. LC 83-26526. (Bioscience Ser.). 320p. 1984. 54.50 (ISBN 0-89603-043-1). Humana.

Frazer, J. F. Amphibians. (The Wykeham Science Ser.: No. 25). 128p. 1972. pap. cancelled (ISBN 0-85109-330-2). Taylor & Francis.

Frazer, J. F. & Frazer, O. H. Amphibians. (Wykeham Science Ser.: No. 25). 128p. 1972. 9.95x (ISBN 0-8448-1152-1). Crane Russak Co.

Frost, Darrel R., ed. Amphibian Species of the World: A Taxonomic & Geographic Reference. 750p. 1985. 85.00 (ISBN 0-942924-11-8). Assn Syst Coll.

Gibbons, Whit. Their Blood Runs Cold: Adventures with Reptiles & Amphibians. LC 82-17395. (Illus.). 158p. (Orig.). 1983. pap. 9.95 (ISBN 0-8173-0133-X). U of Ala Pr.

Gilbert, Stephen G. Pictorial Anatomy of the Necturus. LC 78-152332. (Illus.). 54p. (Orig.). 1973. pap. text ed. 7.95x (ISBN 0-295-95149-4). U of Wash Pr.

Harding, K. A. Catalogue of New World Amphibians. 420p. 1983. 80.00 (ISBN 0-08-028899-5, 02). Pergamon.

Higgins, George M. Nasal Organ in Amphibia. (Illinois Biographical Monographs Ser.: Vol. 6, No. 1). 1921. pap. 8.00 (ISBN 0-384-23080-6). Johnson Repr.

Huheey, James E. & Stupka, Arthur. Amphibians & Reptiles of Great Smoky Mountains National Park. LC 67-21108. (Illus.). 1967. pap. 4.95 (ISBN 0-87049-077-X). U of Tenn Pr.

Johnson, Tom R. Amphibians of Missouri. (Public Education Ser.: No. 6). 142p. 1977. pap. 5.00 (ISBN 0-89338-005-9). U of KS Mus Nat Hist.

Karns, Daryl, Jr., et al. Illustrated Guide to Amphibians & Reptiles in Kansas. (Public Education Ser.: No. 2). 26p. 1974. pap. 1.00 (ISBN 0-686-80364-7). U of KS Mus Nat Hist.

Kilgore, Ullmann. Hydrodynamic Aspects of Tracked Amphibians. (University of Michigan, Dept. of Naval Architecture & Marine Engineering, Report: No. 20). pap. 20.00 (ISBN 0-317-27205-5, 2023867). Bks Demand UMI.

Lofts, Brian, ed. Physiology of the Amphibia. 1974. Vol. 2. 90.00 (ISBN 0-12-455402-4); Vol. 3, 1976. 95.00 (ISBN 0-12-455403-2). Acad Pr.

Martof, Bernard S., et al. Amphibians & Reptiles of the Carolinas & Virginia. LC 79-11790. (Illus.). 264p. 1980. 14.95 (ISBN 0-8078-1389-3). U of NC Pr.

Mattison, Christopher. Care of Reptiles & Amphibians in Captivity. (Illus.). 256p. 1982. 17.95 (ISBN 0-7137-1158-2, Pub. by Blandford Pr England). Sterling.

Mizell, M., ed. Biology of Amphibian Tumors. LC 72-101624. (Recent Results in Cancer Research Special Supplement). (Illus.). 1969. 72.00 (ISBN 0-387-04430-2). Springer-Verlag.

Mount, Robert H. The Reptiles & Amphibians of Alabama. (Illus.). 347p. 1975. pap. 9.95 (ISBN 0-8173-0054-6, Pub. by Ag Experiment). U of Ala Pr.

Nussbaum, Ronald A. & Brodie, Edmund D., Jr. Amphibians & Reptiles of the Pacific Northwest. LC 82-60055. (Illus.). 332p. 1983. 19.95 (ISBN 0-89301-086-3). U Pr of Idaho.

Palmer, Jean. Reptiles & Amphibians. (Blandford Pet Handbooks Ser.). 96p. 1983. 6.95 (ISBN 0-7137-1201-5, Pub. by Blandford Pr England). Sterling.

Parmalee, Paul W. Amphibians of Illinois. (Story of Illinois Ser.: No. 10). (Illus.). 38p. 1954. pap. 1.00 (ISBN 0-89792-011-2). Ill St Museum.

Pickwell, Gayle. Amphibians & Reptiles of the Pacific States. (Illus.). 14.00 (ISBN 0-8446-4597-4). Peter Smith.

Red Data Book: Amphibia & Reptilia, Vol. 3. 1980. pap. 22.50 (IUCN109, IUCN). Unipub.

Rivero, Juan A. Los Anfibios y Reptiles De Puerto Rico. LC 76-11798. (Bilingue., Illus.). 448p. (Orig.). 1976. pap. 20.00 (ISBN 0-8477-2317-8). U of PR Pr.

Sicard, Raymond, ed. Regulation of Vertebrate Limb Regeneration. (Illus.). 256p. 1985. 39.95 (ISBN 0-19-503604-2). Oxford U Pr.

Smith, Hobart M. The Systematic Status of Eumeces Pluvialis Cope, & Noteworthy Records of Other Amphibians & Reptiles from Kansas & Oklahoma. (Museum Ser.: Vol. 1, No. 2). 1946. pap. 1.25 (ISBN 0-686-80378-7). U of KS Mus Nat Hist.

Smith, Malcolm A. Reptilia & Amphibia: Loricata, Te Studines, Vol. 1. 2nd ed. Shipley, A. B., ed. (Fauna of British India Ser.). (Illus.). xxviii, 185p. 1981. Repr. of 1933 ed. 20.00 (ISBN 0-88065-216-0, Pub. by Messers Today & Tomorrows Printers & Publishers India). Scholarly Pubns.

--Reptillia & Amphibia: Sauria, Vol. 2. 2nd ed. Shipley, A. B., ed. (Fauna of British India Ser.). (Illus.). ix, 440p. 1981. Repr. of 1935 ed. 35.00 (ISBN 0-88065-217-9, Pub. by Messers Today & Tomorrows Printers & Publsihers India). Scholarly Pubns.

Stebbins, Robert. A Field Guide to Western Reptiles & Amphibians. 2nd ed. 1985. 17.95 (ISBN 0-395-38254-8); pap. 12.95 (ISBN 0-395-38253-X). HM.

Stebbins, Robert C. Amphibians & Reptiles of California. LC 72-165229. (California Natural History Guides: No. 31). (Illus.). 112p. 1972. pap. 6.95 (ISBN 0-520-02090-1). U of Cal Pr.

--A Field Guide to Western Reptiles & Amphibians. LC 66-16381. (Peterson Field Guide Ser.). 279p. 1966. 16.95 (ISBN 0-395-08211-0); pap. 10.95 (ISBN 0-395-19421-0). HM.

Stewart, Margaret M. Amphibians of Malawi. LC 67-63247. (Illus.). 1967. 42.50x (ISBN 0-87395-027-5). State U NY Pr.

Swinton, W. E. Fossil Amphibians & Reptiles. 5th ed. (Illus.). 133p. 1973. pap. 3.25x (ISBN 0-565-00543-X, Pub. by Brit Mus Nat Hist England). Sabbot-Natural Hist Bks.

Tanara, Milli U. The World of Amphibians & Reptiles. Pleasance, Simon, tr. LC 79-1441. (Abbeville Press Encyclopedia of Natural Science). (Illus.). 256p. 1979. 13.95 (ISBN 0-89659-037-2). Abbeville Pr.

Tata, J. R. Metamorphosis. Head, J. J., ed. LC 78-52662. (Carolina Biology Readers Ser.). (Illus.). 16p. 1983. pap. 1.60 (ISBN 0-89278-246-3, 45-9646). Carolina Biological.

Taylor, D. H. & Guttman, S. I., eds. The Reproductive Biology of Amphibians. LC 77-11004. 485p. 1977. 59.50x (ISBN 0-306-31103-8, Plenum Pr). Plenum Pub.

Vogt, Richard C. Natural History of Amphibians & Reptiles of Wisconsin. Hine, Ruth, ed. LC 80-84961. (Illus.). 208p. 1981. 25.95 (ISBN 0-89326-060-6). Milwaukee Pub Mus.

Walkers, Charles F. The Amphibians of Ohio: Frogs & Toads. 109p. pap. 3.40. Ohio Hist Soc.

Wauer, Roland H. Reptiles & Amphibians of Zion National Park. (Illus.). 55p. 1964. 0.75 (ISBN 0-685-83465-4). Zion.

Wilson, Larry D. & Porras, Louis. The Ecological Impact of Man on the South Florida Herpetofauna. Collins, Joseph T., ed. (Special Publications Ser.: No. 9). 89p. (Orig.). 1983. pap. 7.00 (ISBN 0-89338-018-0). U of KS Mus Nat Hist.

AMPHIBIANS–BIBLIOGRAPHY

Henderson, Robert W. & Schwartz, Albert. A Guide to the Identification of the Amphibians & Reptiles of Hispaniola. 70p. 1984. 6.95 (ISBN 0-89326-103-3). Milwaukee Pub Mus.

Hughes, G. M., ed. Respiration of Amphibious Vertebrates. 1976. 63.50 (ISBN 0-12-360750-7). Acad Pr.

AMPHIBIANS–EMBRYOLOGY

see Embryology–Amphibians

AMPHIMIXIS

see Fertilization (Biology); Reproduction

AMPHIPODA

Bousfield, E. L. Shallow-Water Gammaridean Amphipoda of New England. 17.50 (ISBN 0-8014-0726-5). Brown Bk.

Lincoln, R. J. British Marine Amphipoda: Gammaridea. (Illus.). 658p. 1979. 108.00x (ISBN 0-565-00818-8, Pub. by Brit Mus Nat Hist England). Sabbot-Natural Hist Bks.

AMPHIUMA TRIDACTYLA

Shockman, Gerald & Wicken, Anthony, eds. Chemistry & Biological Activities of Bacterial Surface Amphiphiles. LC 81-15023. 1981. 44.00 (ISBN 0-12-640380-5). Acad Pr.

AMPLIFIERS (ELECTRONICS)

Angelo, E. James, Jr. Electronics: BJT's, FET's & Microcircuits. LC 78-6803. 646p. 1979. Repr. of 1969 ed. lib. bdg. 38.50 (ISBN 0-88275-678-8). Krieger.

Carr, Joseph J. The Complete Handbook of Amplifiers, Oscillators & Multivibrators. (Illus.). 364p. 1981. pap. 11.50 (ISBN 0-8306-1230-0, 1230). TAB Bks.

CES Industries, Inc. Ed-Lab Six Hundred & Fifty Experiment Manual: Operational Amplifiers, Bk. IV. (Illus.). 148p. 1979. 9.50 (ISBN 0-86711-016-3). CES Industries.

Davidson, C. W. Wideband Voltage Amplifiers. 1974. pap. text ed. 18.95x (ISBN 0-7002-0235-8). Intl Ideas.

Dostal, J. Operational Amplifiers. (Studies in Electrical & Electronic Engineering Ser.: Vol. 4). 488p. 1981. 83.00 (ISBN 0-444-99760-1). Elsevier.

Doyle, Michael. The Sound of Rock: The History of Marshall Valve (Tube) Amplifiers. Clinton, George, ed. (Illus.). 67p. 1983. 12.95 (ISBN 0-86175-330-5, Pub. by Mus New Serv Ltd England). Bold Strummer Ltd.

Evans, Charles H. Electronic Amplifiers: Theory, Design, & Use. LC 76-3950. 1979. pap. text ed. 26.00 (ISBN 0-8273-1626-7); instr's. manual 6.15 (ISBN 0-8273-1627-5). Delmar.

Fox, Harry W., Jr. Master OP Amp Applications Handbook. (Illus.). 1977. pap. 13.95 (ISBN 0-8306-6856-X, 856). TAB Bks.

Fukui, Hatsuaki, ed. Low-Noise Microwave Transistors & Amplifiers. LC 81-6994. 1981. 38.45 (ISBN 0-87942-151-7, PC01487). Inst Electrical.

Graeme, Jerald G. Application of Operational Amplifiers: Third Generation Techniques. (Illus.). 1973. 43.00 (ISBN 0-07-023890-1). McGraw.

Herpy, Miklos. Analog Integrated Circuits: Operational Amplifiers & Analog Multipliers. LC 77-21008. 479p. 1980. 82.95 (ISBN 0-471-99604-1, Pub. by Wiley-Interscience). Wiley.

Irvine, Robert G. Operational Amplifier Characteristics & Applications. (Illus.). 416p. 1981. text ed. 36.95 (ISBN 0-13-637751-3). P-H.

Johnson, David E. & Jayakumar, V. Operational Amplifier Circuits Design & Applications. (Illus.). 272p. 1982. 36.95 (ISBN 0-13-637447-6). P-H.

MacDonald, Lorne. Practical Analysis of Amplifier Circuits Through Experimentation. 3rd ed. 432p. 1981. pap. 16.50x (ISBN 0-911908-14-5). Tech Ed Pr.

MacLean, D. J. Broadband Feedback Amplifiers. LC 82-2066. (Electronic Circuits & Systems Ser.). 323p. 1982. 44.95 (ISBN 0-471-10214-8, Pub. by Res Stud Pr). Wiley.

Mirtes, B. D C Amplifiers. (Illus.). 520p. 1971. 16.75 (ISBN 0-8088-2824-X). Davey.

Roberge, James K. Operational Amplifiers: Theory & Practice. LC 75-2309. 659p. 1975. 47.50x (ISBN 0-471-72585-4). Wiley.

Seippel, Robert. Operational Amplifiers. 1983. text ed. 24.95 (ISBN 0-8359-5242-8). Reston.

Tobey, G. E., et al. Operational Amplifiers: Design & Application. 51.50 (ISBN 0-07-064917-0). McGraw.

Vendelin, George D. Design of Amplifiers & Oscillators by the S-Parameter Method. LC 81-13005. 190p. 1982. 31.95x (ISBN 0-471-09226-6, Pub. by Wiley-Interscience). Wiley.

Wojslaw, C. F. & Moustakas, E. A. Operational Amplifiers: The Devices & their Applications. 416p. 1985. 31.95 (ISBN 0-471-80646-3). Wiley.

AMPLIFIERS, FLUID

see Fluid Amplifiers

AMPLIFIERS, MAGNETIC

see Magnetic Amplifiers

AMPLIFIERS, PARAMETRIC

see Parametric Amplifiers

AMPLIFIERS, TRANSISTOR

see Transistor Amplifiers

Cohn, Sidney A. & Gottlieb, Marvin. Anatomy Review. 6th ed. LC 61-668476. (Basic Science Review Bks.). 1980. pap. 12.75 (ISBN 0-87488-201-X). Med Exam.
Cook, Margaret J. The Anatomy of the Laboratory Mouse. 1976. 34.00 (ISBN 0-12-186956-3). Acad Pr.
Corner, George W. Anatomist at Large. facs. ed. LC 76-86743. (Essay Index Reprint Ser). 1958. 18.00 (ISBN 0-8369-1176-8). Ayer Co Pubs.
Crowley, Leonard V. Introductory Concepts in Anatomy & Physiology. LC 76-2249. (Illus.). Repr. of 1976 ed. 115.50 (ISBN 0-8357-9612-4, 2015077). Bks Demand UMI.
Cunningham. Cunningham's Textbook of Anatomy. 12th ed. Romanes, G. J., ed. (Illus.). 1981. text ed. 43.50x (ISBN 0-19-263134-9). Oxford U Pr.
Dean, W. B. & Farrar, G. E., Jr. Basic Concepts of Anatomy & Physiology. 2nd ed. (Illus.). 400p. 1982. pap. text ed. 15.50 (ISBN 0-397-54378-6, 64-03208, Lippincott Medical). Lippincott.
European Anatomical Congress, 4th. Abstracts. (Acta Anatomica: Vol. 99, No. 3). 1977. 38.75 (ISBN 3-8055-2776-4). S Karger.
Gold, B. Brown. The Organization of Afferents from the Brain Stem Nuclei to the Cerebellar Cortex in the Cat. (Advances in Anatomy, Embryology & Cell Biology: Vol. 62). (Illus.). 100p. 1980. pap. 32.00 (ISBN 0-387-09960-3). Springer-Verlag.
Goldberg, Stephen. Clinical Anatomy Made Ridiculously Simple. (Illus.). 175p. 1984. pap. text ed. 14.95 (ISBN 0-940780-02-X). Medmaster.
Gray. Gray's Anatomy: The Unabridged Running Press Color Edition of the American Classic 1901. LC 74-19510. (Illus.). 800p. 1973. lib. bdg. 19.80 (ISBN 0-914294-49-0); pap. 8.95 (ISBN 0-914294-08-3). Running Pr.
Gray's Pocket Anatomy. 1984. pap. 5.95 (ISBN 0-517-55452-6, Pub. by Bounty). Outlet Bk Co.
Harrison, R. J. & Holmes, R. L., eds. Progress in Anatomy, Vol. 1. (Illus.). 250p. 1981. 77.50 (ISBN 0-521-23603-7). Cambridge U Pr.
Haupt, R., et al. Introductory Physiology & Anatomy: A Laboratory Guide. 4th ed. 1977. pap. text ed. write for info. (ISBN 0-02-351710-7). Macmillan.
Henrich, M. H. Klinische Anatomie der Pylorica Region. (Bibliotheca Anatomica: No. 26). (Illus.). x, 142p. 1985. 41.75 (ISBN 3-8055-4050-7). S Karger.
Hilscher, W. Problems of the Keimbahn. (Bibliotheca Anatomica: No. 24). (Illus.). viii, 128p. 1983. pap. 41.75 (ISBN 3-8055-3614-3). S Karger.
Holtzmeier, Dawn K. Applied Anatomy & Physiology: A Laboratory Manual & Workbook for Health Careers. 304p. 1983. pap. text ed. 21.95 (ISBN 0-8403-2915-6). Kendall-Hunt.
Lassau, J. P., et al. Atlas of Neonatal Anatomy. (Illus.). 136p. 1982. 58.00x (ISBN 0-89352-139-6). Masson Pub.
Last, R. J. Anatomy: Regional & Applied. 7th ed. (Illus.). 1984. pap. text ed. 33.00 (ISBN 0-443-02989-X). Churchill.
Leyshon, Glynn A. Programmed Functional Anatomy. (Illus.). 1984. pap. text ed. 9.80X (ISBN 0-87563-249-1). Stipes.
Lopez-Antunez, Luis. Atlas of Human Anatomy. LC 69-17808. pap. 99.50 (ISBN 0-317-26109-6, 2124996). Bks Demand UMI.
Lyons, Richard T. & Reed, Ray. An Instructional Manual for Anatomy & Physiology. 1984. pap. text ed. 19.95 (ISBN 0-89917-434-5). Tichenor Pub.
McGrath, Philomena & Mills, P. Atlas of Sectional Anatomy. (Illus.). viii, 238p. 1984. 35.00 (ISBN 3-8055-3624-0). S Karger.
MacGregor, Roderick. Structure of the Meat Animals: A Guide to Their Anatomy & Physiology. 2nd ed. (Illus.). 1965. pap. 22.50x (ISBN 0-291-39536-8). Intl Ideas.
Montgomery, Royce L. Basic Anatomy for the Allied Health Professions. LC 79-19131. (Illus.). 463p. 1980. text ed. 22.75 (ISBN 0-8067-1231-7). Urban & S.
Morley, Patricia, et al, eds. Ultrasonic Sectional Anatomy. LC 81-71720. (Illus.). 238p. 1983. text ed. 69.00 (ISBN 0-443-01690-9). Churchill.
Navaratnam, V. & Harrison, R. J. Progress in Anatomy Three. 350p. 1984. 74.50 (ISBN 0-521-24953-8). Cambridge U Pr.
Pernkopf, Eduard. Anatomy. Terner, Helmut, ed. 100p. 1980. 15.00 (ISBN 0-7216-7197-7). Saunders.
Platzer, W., ed. Seventh European Anatomical Congress, Innsbruck, September 1984: Abstracts. (Journal: Acta Anatomica: Vol. 120, No. 1-2). 92p. 1984. pap. 16.25 (ISBN 3-8055-3955-X). S Karger.
PreTest Service Inc. & April, Ernest W. Anatomy: PreTest Self-Assessment & Review. 3rd ed. (Basic Science Ser.). 260p. 1983. 12.95 (ISBN 0-07-051931-5). McGraw.
Reutter, K. Taste Organ in the Bullhead (Teleostei) (Advances in Anatomy, Embryology & Cell Biology: Vol. 55, Pt. 1). (Illus.). 1978. pap. 32.00 (ISBN 0-387-08880-6). Springer-Verlag.
Riddle, Janet T. Anatomy & Physiology Applied to Nursing. 6th ed. (Livingstone Nursing Text Ser.). (Illus.). 1984. pap. text ed. 6.95 (ISBN 0-443-03030-8). Churchill.
Riegler, Hubert F. & Peppard, Alan P. Surface Anatomy for Coaches & Athletic Trainers. (Illus.). 80p. 1979. photocopy ed. 13.75x (ISBN 0-398-03856-2). C C Thomas.
Rudman, Jack. Anatomy & Physiology. (ACT Proficiency Examination Program: PEP-4). 22.95 (ISBN 0-8373-5554-0); pap. 13.95 (ISBN 0-8373-5504-4). Natl Learning.
--Anatomy & Physiology. (College Proficiency Examination Ser.: CLEP-37). (Cloth bdg. avail. on request). pap. 9.95 (ISBN 0-8373-5437-4). Natl Learning.
--Anatomy, Physiology & Microbiology. (College Level Examination Ser.: CLEP-38). (Cloth bdg. avail. on request). 1977. pap. 11.95 (ISBN 0-8373-5388-2). Natl Learning.
--Introduction to Anatomy & Physiology. (College Proficiency Examination Ser.: CPEP-28). 1977. 17.95 (ISBN 0-8373-5478-1); pap. 9.95 (ISBN 0-8373-5428-5). Natl Learning.
Schneider, L. K. Anatomical Case Histories. (Illus.). 1976. pap. 22.50 (ISBN 0-8151-7561-2). Year Bk Med.
Singer, Charles. Short History of Anatomy & Physiology: From the Greeks to Harvey. Orig. Title: Evolution of Anatomy. (Illus.). 1957. pap. text ed. 4.95 (ISBN 0-486-20389-1). Dover.
Smith, Alastair G. Irving's Anatomy Mnemonics. 4th ed. 1972. Repr. 1.75 (ISBN 0-443-00253-3). Churchill.
Steen, Edwin B. & Ashley Montagu. Anatomy & Physiology, 2 vols. Incl. Cells, Tissues, Integument, Skeletal, Muscular & Digestive Systems, Blood, Lymph, Circulatory System. rev. ed. 1984. Vol. I. 6.68 (ISBN 0-06-460190-0, 98); Urinary, Respiratory & Nervous Systems, Sensations & Sense Organs, Endocrine & Reproductive Systems. 1971. Vol. II. 5.95 (ISBN 0-06-460099-8, CO 99). COS). Har-Row.
Stevenson, Lloyd. G. & Multhauf, Robert P., eds. Medicine, Science, & Culture: Historical Essays in Honor of Owsei Temkin. LC 68-15445. (Illus.). 312p. 1968. 22.00x (ISBN 0-8018-0615-1). Johns Hopkins.
Sucheston, Martha E. & Cannon, M. Samuel. Congenital Malformations: Case Studies in Developmental Anatomy. (Illus.). 271p. 1973. pap. text ed. 11.00x (ISBN 0-8036-8210-7). Davis Co.
Swindler, Daris R. & Wood, Charles D. Atlas of Primate Gross Anatomy. LC 81-19350. 384p. 1982. Repr. of 1973 ed. lib. bdg. 39.50 (ISBN 0-89874-321-4). Krieger.
Tortora. Principios de Anatomia y Fisiolologia. 3rd ed. 1983. pap. text ed. write for info. (ISBN 0-06-317153-8, Pub. by HarLA Mexico). Har-Row.
Tortora, Gerald J. & Anagnostakos, Nicholas. Laboratory Exercises in Anatomy & Physiology. 2nd, rev. ed. (Illus.). 512p. 1986. pap. price not set lab manual (ISBN 0-8087-3665-5). Burgess.
Tortora, Gerard J. & Anagnostakos, Nicholas P. Principles of Anatomy & Physiology. 4th ed. 864p. 1984. text ed. 33.50 scp (ISBN 0-06-046656-1, HarpC); inst. manual avail. (ISBN 0-06-366641-3); scp learning guide 12.50 (ISBN 0-06-045302-8); transparencies avail. (ISBN 0-06-366639-1); test bank avail. (ISBN 0-06-366640-5). Har-Row.
Verralls, Sylvia. Anatomy & Physiology Applied to Obstetrics. (Illus.). 1977. pap. text ed. 30.00x (ISBN 0-685-82798-4). State Mutual Bk.
Wagner, Marvin & Lawson, Thomas L. Segmental Anatomy. (Illus.). 650p. 1982. write for info. (ISBN 0-02-423700-0). Macmillan.
Waldeyer, Anton. Anatomie des Menschen fuer Studierende und Aerzte: Dargestellt nach systematischen, topographischen und praktischen Gesichtspunkten. Contd. by Von A. Mayet, 2 vols. 14th ed. Incl. Vol. 1. Allgemeine Anatomie: Ruecken, Bauch, Becken, Bein. (Illus.). 32.00x (ISBN 3-11-005733-6); Vol. 2. Kopf und Hals, Auge, Ohr, Gehirn, Arm, Brust. (Illus.). 32.00x (ISBN 3-11-005734-4). (Ger.). 1979. De Gruyter.
Woodburne, Russell T. A Guide to Dissection in Gross Anatomy. 4th ed. (Illus.). 1980. pap. text ed. 9.95x spiral bdg. (ISBN 0-19-502670-5). Oxford U Pr.

ANATOMY–BIBLIOGRAPHY

European Conference on Microcirculation, 7th, Aberdeen, Aug.-Sept. 1972, Part I. Methodology in Microcirculation: Proceedings. Lewis, D. H. & Ditzel, J., eds. (Bibliotheca Anatomica: No. 11). 1973. 121.75 (ISBN 3-8055-1571-5). S Karger.

ANATOMY–DICTIONARIES

Diderot, Denis. Anatomie-Chirurgie Encyclopedie Ou Dictionnaire Raissonne des Sciences. 2nd ed. (Fr.). 1977. 46.00 (ISBN 3-88210-002-8, M-7053). French & Eur.
Lovasy, Ernst. Dictionnaire des Termes d'Anatomie, d'Embryologie et d'Histologie. (Fr.). 624p. 1954. 17.50 (ISBN 0-686-57022-7, M-6380). French & Eur.
Nomina Anatomica. 5th ed. 196p. 1983. text ed. 31.00 (ISBN 0-683-06550-5). Williams & Wilkins.
Squires, Bruce. Basic Terms in Anatomy & Physiology. (Illus.). 165p. 1981. pap. 10.95 (ISBN 0-7216-8537-4). Saunders.

ANATOMY–EARLY WORKS TO 1800

Adelmann, Howard B., ed. & tr. from Lat. The Embryological Treatises of Hieronymus Fabricius of Aquapendente, 2 vols. Incl. Vol. 1. The Formation of the Egg & of the Chick. Tr. of De Formatione Ovi et Pulli; Vol. 2. The Formed Fetus. Tr. of De Formato Foetu. (History of Science Ser.). (Illus.). xxiv, 907p. (A facsimile reprint of the latin text). 1967. 69.50x (ISBN 0-8014-0122-4). Cornell U Pr.
Banister, John. The Historie of Man. LC 74-26164. (English Experience Ser.: No. 122). (Illus.). 250p. 1969. Repr. of 1578 ed. 42.00 (ISBN 90-221-0122-3). Walter J Johnson.
Da Vinci, Leonardo. The Corpus of the Anatomical Studies in the Collection of Her Majesty Queen Elzabeth II at the Royal Library, Windsor Castle. facsimile ed. 1978. 8000.00. Johnson Repr.
De Mondeville, Henri. Chirurgie De Maitre Henri De Mondeville, 2 Vols. Bos, A., ed. 1965. Set. 77.00 (ISBN 0-384-05155-3); Set. pap. 65.00 (ISBN 0-384-05156-1). Johnson Repr.
O'Malley, Charles D. & Saunders, J. B. de, eds. Leonardo da Vinci on the Human Body: The Anatomical, Physiological & Embryological Drawings of Leonardo da Vinci. (Illus.). 512p. 1983. 12.98 (ISBN 0-517-38105-2, Greenwich Hse). Outlet Bk Co.
Saunders, J. B. de & O'Malley, C. D., trs. The Anatomical Drawings of Andreas Vesalius. (Illus.). 256p. 1982. 7.98 (ISBN 0-517-35638-4, Bonanza). Outlet Bk Co.
Vesalius, Andreas. The Illustrations from the Works of Andreas Vesalius of Brussels. 256p. 1950. pap. 8.50 (ISBN 0-486-20968-7). Dover.
Vicary, Thomas. Profitable Treatise of the Anatomy of Man's Body. LC 73-6166. (English Experience Ser.: No. 629). 116p. 1973. Repr. of 1577 ed. 8.00 (ISBN 90-221-0629-2). Walter J Johnson.

ANATOMY–LABORATORY MANUALS

Alexander, Herman D. Laboratory Manual for Anatomy. 1978. wire coil bdg. 7.95 (ISBN 0-88252-080-6). Paladin Hse.
Anthony, Catherine P. & Thibodeau, Gary A. Anatomy & Physiology Laboratory Manual. 10th ed. LC 78-11927. (Illus.). 1979. pap. text ed. 11.95 (ISBN 0-8016-0270-X). Mosby.
Benson, Harold J., et al. Anatomy & Physiology Laboratory Textbook. 3rd ed. 448p. 1983. write for info. wire coil short version (ISBN 0-697-04739-3); instr's. manual avail. (ISBN 0-697-04740-7); complete version, 592p. 1983 (ISBN 0-697-04737-7); instr's. manual avail. (ISBN 0-697-04738-5). Wm C Brown.
Costa, Philip J. & Cotty, Richard G. Laboratory Textbook in Anatomy & Physiology. 4th ed. 1981. wire coil bdg. 9.95 (ISBN 0-8403-2014-0). Kendall-Hunt.
Dixon, Adrian K. Body C. T. (Illus.). 176p. (Orig.). 1983. pap. text ed. 24.00 (ISBN 0-443-02956-3). Churchill.
Donnelly, Patricia J. Manual & Dissection Guide for Mammalian Anatomy. (Illus.). 116p. 1972 pap. text ed. 10.95x (ISBN 0-8036-2680-0); instructor's guide, 20 slides 15.00 set incl. (ISBN 0-8036-2681-9). Davis Co.
Donnelly, Patricia J. & Wistreich, George A. Laboratory Manual for Anatomy & Physiology: With Cat Dissection. 636p. 1982. pap. text ed. 20.50 scp (ISBN 0-06-046644-8, HarpC); instr's manual avail. (ISBN 0-06-361701-3). Har-Row.
Drakontides, Anna B., et al. Anatomy & Physiology: Workbook & Laboratory Manual. (Illus.). 1977. pap. text ed. write for info. (ISBN 0-02-330050-7, 33005). Macmillan.
Erskine, Irene. Laboratory Guide for Anatomy & Physiology. 176p. 1980. pap. text ed. 9.95 (ISBN 0-8403-2350-6). Kendall-Hunt.
Furgeson, Michael D. & Bohr, Paula. Living Anatomy Laboratory Manual. LC 83-43292. (Illus.). 200p. (Orig.). 1984. 12.95x (ISBN 0-940122-12-X). Multi Media Co.
Klingener, David. Laboratory Anatomy of the Mink. 2nd ed. (Laboratory Anatomy Ser.). 64p. 1979. write for info. wire coil (ISBN 0-697-04629-X). Wm C Brown.
McLaughlin, Charles A. & Chiasson, Robert B. Laboratory Anatomy of the Rabbit. 2nd ed. (Laboratory Anatomy Ser.). 80p. 1979. write for info. wire coil (ISBN 0-697-04628-1). Wm C Brown.
Neff, Robert & Plaisted, Elinor. Laboratory Manual in Anatomy & Physiology. (Illus.). 106p. 1970. pap. text ed. 6.95x (ISBN 0-8422-0100-9). Irvington.
Steen, Edwin B. Laboratory Manual & Study Guide for Anatomy & Physiology. 3rd ed. 188p. 1976. write for info. wire coil (ISBN 0-697-04635-4). Wm C Brown.
Tortora, Gerald J., et al. Laboratory Exercises in Anatomy & Physiology with Cat Dissections. 2nd ed. (Illus.). 416p. 1984. pap. text ed. write for info. (ISBN 0-8087-3658-2). Burgess.
Tortora, Gerard & Anagnostakos, Nicholas P. Laboratory Exercises in Anatomy & Physiology: Brief Edition. 328p. 1982. pap. text ed. 18.95x (ISBN 0-8087-3621-3). Burgess.

ANATOMY, COMPARATIVE

see also Man–Origin; Morphology;
also names of organs and regions of the body;
also subdivision Anatomy under names of animals, e.g. Cats–Anatomy

Andrew, Warren. Anatomy of Aging in Man & Animals. LC 73-92018. (Illus.). 259p. 1971. 71.50 (ISBN 0-8089-0640-2, 790101). Grune.
Ariens, C. U., et al. The Comparative Anatomy of the Nervous System of Vertebrates Including Man, 3 vols. 2nd ed. (Illus.). 1845p. 1936. Set. 97.50x (ISBN 0-02-840400-9). Hafner.
Beaver, Bonnie. Comparative Anatomy of Domestic Animals: A Guide. (Illus.). 210p. 1980. pap. 11.95x (ISBN 0-8138-1545-2). Iowa St U Pr.
Beklemishev, V. N. Principles of Comparative Anatomy of Invertebrates, 2 Vols. Kabata, Z., ed. McLennan, J. M., tr. LC 70-97749. 1970. Set. 60.00x (ISBN 0-226-04175-1). U of Chicago Pr.
Belt, Elmer. Leonardo the Anatomist. LC 69-13818. (Illus.). 76p. Repr. of 1955 ed. lib. bdg. 18.75 (ISBN 0-8371-0304-5, BELA). Greenwood.
Black, Davidson. On an Adolescent Skull of Sinanthropus Pekinensis: In Comparison with an Adult Skull of the Same Species & with Other Hominid Skulls, Recent & Fossil. LC 77-86442. (China. Geological Survey. Palaeontologia Sinica. Ser. D.: Vol. 7, Fasc. 2). Repr. of 1930 ed. 23.00 (ISBN 0-404-16685-7). AMS Pr.
Cole, F. J. A History of Comparative Anatomy: From Aristotle to the Eighteenth Century. LC 75-12173. (Illus.). 544p. 1975. pap. 8.50 (ISBN 0-486-60224-9). Dover.
--A History of Comparative Anatomy, from Aristotle to the 18th Century. (Illus.). 13.25 (ISBN 0-8446-5172-9). Peter Smith.
Fox, Richard C. Chorda Tympani Branch of the Facial Nerve in the Middle Ear of the Tetrapods. (Museum Ser.: Vol. 17, No. 2). 7p. 1965. 1.25 (ISBN 0-317-04773-6). U of KS Mus Nat Hist.
Gerrick, David J. Anatomy of the Sheep Kidney: Clinical Implications. (Illus.). 1978. 20.00 (ISBN 0-916750-04-3). Dayton Labs.
Griffin, Donald R. & Novick, A. Animal Structure & Function. 2nd ed. LC 70-77810. (Modern Biology Ser). 1970. pap. text ed. 16.95 (ISBN 0-03-077505-1, HoltC). HR&W.
Holmes, Bruce E. Manual of Comparative Anatomy: A Laboratory Guide & Brief Text. 416p. 1980. pap. text ed. 14.50 (ISBN 0-8403-2254-2). Kendall-Hunt.
Jarvik, E. Basic Structure & Evolution of Vertebrates, Vol. 1. 1981. 98.50 (ISBN 0-12-380801-4). Acad Pr.
--Basic Structure & Evolution of Vertebrates, Vol. 2. LC 80-40244. 1981. 65.00 (ISBN 0-12-380802-2). Acad Pr.
Kent, George C. Comparative Anatomy of the Vertebrates. 5th ed. LC 82-2078. (Illus.). 604p. 1983. pap. text ed. 27.95 (ISBN 0-8016-2651-X). Mosby.
Kohncke, M. The Chondrocranium of Cryptoprocta Ferox: Bennet, 1833. (Advances in Anatomy, Embryology & Cell Biology Ser.: Vol. 95). (Illus.). 110p. 1985. pap. 21.00 (ISBN 0-387-15337-3). Springer Verlag.
Marsh, Reginald. Anatomy for Artists. LC 75-129078. (Illus.). 1970. pap. 6.00 (ISBN 0-486-22613-1). Dover.
Mossman, Harland W. & Duke, Kenneth L. Comparative Morphology of the Mammalian Ovary. LC 72-143765. (Illus.). 492p. 1973. 35.00x (ISBN 0-299-05930-8, 593); pap. 15.00x (ISBN 0-299-05934-0). U of Wis Pr.
Price, C. J. & Reed, J. E. Histology: Notes for Students of Animal Husbandry. (Illus.). 109p. (Orig.). 1972. pap. 4.50 (ISBN 92-5-101579-1, F226, FAO). Unipub.

Singer, Charles. Short History of Anatomy & Physiology: From the Greeks to Harvey. Orig. Title: Evolution of Anatomy. (Illus.). 1957. pap. text ed. 4.95 (ISBN 0-486-20389-1). Dover.

Snell, Richard S. Clinical Anatomy for Medical Students. 2nd ed. 1981. text ed. 37.50x (ISBN 0-316-80215-8). Little.

Solomon, Eldra P. & Davis, P. William. Human Anatomy & Physiology. 1983. text ed. 39.95 (ISBN 0-03-059992-X, CBS C); instr's manual 20.00 (ISBN 0-03-059993-8); study guide 13.95 (ISBN 0-03-059994-6). SCP.

Spence, A. Basic Human Anatomy. 1982. text ed. 34.95 (ISBN 0-8053-6994-5); instr' guide 6.95 (ISBN 0-8053-6998-8). Benjamin-Cummings.

Spence, A. P. & Mason, E. B. Human Anatomy & Physiology. 2nd ed. 1983. 38.95 (ISBN 0-8053-6985-6, 36985); instr's guide o.p. 5.95; instr's resource manual o.p. 150.00 (ISBN 0-8053-6982-1). Benjamin-Cummings.

Tatarinov, V. G. Anatomia y Fisiologia Humanas. (Span.). 364p. 1980. 10.00 (ISBN 0-8285-1660-X, Pub. by Mir Pubs USSR). Imported Pubns.

Thompson, James S. Core Textbook of Anatomy. LC 76-49549. 1977. pap. text ed. 25.50 (ISBN 0-397-52078-6, 65-04765, Lippincott Medical). Lippincott.

Tortora, Gerald & Anagnostakos, Nicholos. Anatomia y Fisiologica. (Span.). 1978. pap. text ed. 18.70 (ISBN 0-06-317150-3, IntlDept). Har-Row.

Tortora, Gerard J. Principles of Human Anatomy. 3rd ed. 725p. 1983. text ed. 31.95 scp (ISBN 0-06-046634-0, HarpC); instr's. manual avail. (ISBN 0-06-366638-3); scp learning guide 10.95 (ISBN 0-06-045291-9). Har-Row.

Van De Graaff, Kent M. Human Anatomy. 744p. 1984. text ed. write for info (ISBN 0-697-04743-1); instr's manual avail. (ISBN 0-697-04744-X); lab manual avail. (ISBN 0-697-04789-X); transparencies avail. (ISBN 0-697-00255-1). Wm C Brown.

Van De Graaff, Kent M. & Fox, Stuart I. Concept's of Human Anatomy & Physiology. 896p. 1986. text ed. price not set (ISBN 0-697-04791-1); price not set instr's. manual (ISBN 0-697-00064-8); price not set student guide (ISBN 0-697-00584-4); price not set lab manual (ISBN 0-697-00585-2); price not set transparencies (ISBN 0-697-00889-4); price not set instr's. manual for lab manual (ISBN 0-697-00867-3). Wm C Brown.

Von Arb, Sondra. Body Structure & Function: An Individualized Course Guide & Work Book for Nursing & Health Related Occupations. LC 79-83909. 1983. pap. text ed. 10.95 (ISBN 0-933474-06-7). Minn Scholarly.

Von Haller, Albrecht. First Lines of Physiology, 2 Vols. in 1. 1966. Repr. of 1786 ed. 37.00 (ISBN 0-384-21060-0). Johnson Repr.

Watt, Sandra F. & Bean, Dale. Introduction to Human Anatomy & Physiology. (Illus.). 226p. 1985. pap. text ed. 35.00 (ISBN 0-933195-04-4). Cal College Pr.

Wicke, Lothar. Atlas of Radiologic Anatomy. 3rd ed. (Illus.). 248p. 1982. text ed. 19.50 (ISBN 0-8067-2113-8). Urban & S.

Williams, Peter & Warwick, Roger. Gray's Anatomy. 36th ed. (Illus.). 1578p. 1980. 79.00 (ISBN 0-7216-9128-5). Saunders.

Wilson, Doris B. & Wilson, Wilfred J. Human Anatomy. 2nd ed. (Illus.). 1982. 26.95x (ISBN 0-19-503108-3). Oxford U Pr.

Wittrup, Robert C. Human Anatomy & Physiology: Laboratory Manual with Cat Dissections. (Orig.). 1981. pap. text ed. 18.95x (ISBN 0-8087-2384-7). Burgess.

Woodburne, Russell T. Essentials of Human Anatomy. 7th ed. (Illus.). 1983. text ed. 35.95x (ISBN 0-19-503171-7). Oxford U Pr.

Zuidema, George D., ed. The Johns Hopkins Atlas of Human Functional Anatomy. rev., 2nd ed. LC 79-25191. 128p. 1980. pap. text ed. 10.95 (ISBN 0-8018-2364-1); of 40 color slides 60.00 set (ISBN 0-8018-2002-2). Johns Hopkins.

ANATOMY, HUMAN–ATLASES

Ansell, I. D. Atlas of Male Reproductive System Pathological. (Current Histopathology Ser.). 1985. lib. bdg. 77.00 (ISBN 0-85200-327-7, Pub. by MTP Pr England). Kluwer Academic.

Atlas of Human Anatomy, No. 1446. (Illus.). 1981. pap. 1.75 (ISBN 0-8416-1446-6); pap. span. lang. ed. avail. Am Map.

Beck, Ernest W. & Monsen, Harry. Mosby's Atlas of Functional Human Anatomy. LC 81-14110. (Illus.). 310p. 1982. pap. 16.95 (ISBN 0-8016-0554-7). Mosby.

Berry, Charles N. & Hovde, Christian A. Human Anatomy Atlas. (Illus.). 36p. (Orig.). 1960. pap. 2.95x (ISBN 0-8437-9083-0). Hammond Inc.

Bo, Walter J., et al. Basic Atlas of Cross-Sectional Anatomy: A Clinical Approach. (Illus.). 357p. 1980. 44.00 (ISBN 0-7216-1767-0). Saunders.

Boyle, A. C. Color Atlas of Rheumatology. 2nd ed. (Year Book Color Atlas Ser.). 1980. 49.95 (ISBN 0-8151-1126-6). Year Bk Med.

Cahill, Donald R. & Orland, Matthew J. Atlas of Human Cross-Sectional Anatomy. LC 83-13613. (Illus.). 139p. 1984. text ed. 29.50 (ISBN 0-8121-0890-6). Lea & Febiger.

Crouch, James E. Essential Human Anatomy: A Text-Atlas. LC 80-20699. (Illus.). 562p. 1982. text ed. 23.50 (ISBN 0-8121-0755-1). Lea & Febiger.

Dickinson, Robert L. Atlas of Human Sex Anatomy. LC 50-5564. (Illus.). 382p. 1970. Repr. of 1949 ed. 37.50 (ISBN 0-88275-014-3). Krieger.

Elias, Hans. Basic Human Anatomy As Seen in the Fetus. LC 68-20944. (Illus.). 176p. 1971. 22.50 (ISBN 0-87527-031-X). Green.

Evans, F. Gaynor. Atlas of Human Anatomy. 204p. 1957. 7.50x (ISBN 0-87471-222-X). Rowman.

--Atlas of Human Anatomy Simplified. (Quality Paperback Ser.: No. 60). 204p. (Orig.). 1975. pap. 1.95 (ISBN 0-8226-0060-9). Littlefield.

Feneis, Heinz & Kaiser, Hans E. Pocket Atlas of Human Anatomy. (Illus.). 480p. 1985. pap. text ed. 15.00 (ISBN 0-86577-167-7). Thieme Stratton.

Frohse, Franz, et al. Atlas of Human Anatomy. 7th ed. pap. 6.95 (ISBN 0-06-460206-0, CO 206, COS). B&N NY.

Gray's Anatomy: The Unabridged Running Press Edition of the American Classic. pap. 8.95 (ISBN 0-914294-08-3); 19.80 (ISBN 0-914294-49-0). Running Pr.

Hausman, Louis. Illustrations of the Nervous System: Atlas Three. (Illus.). 208p. 1971. 18.75x (ISBN 0-398-00800-0). C C Thomas.

Kieffer, Stephen A. & Heitzman, E. Robert. Atlas of Cross-Sectional Anatomy: Computed Tomography, Ultrasound, Radiography, Gross Anatomy. (Illus.). 1979. text ed. 70.00x (ISBN 0-06-141152-3, 14-11529, Harper Medical). Lippincott.

Lee, Bok Y. Atlas of Surgical & Sectional Anatomy. (Illus.). 353p. 1983. 39.00 (ISBN 0-8385-0458-2). ACC.

McGrath, Philomena & Mills, P. Atlas of Sectional Anatomy. 2nd ed. (Illus.). viii, 238p. cancelled (ISBN 3-8055-4060-4). S Karger.

McMinn, R. M. Color Atlas of Head & Neck Anatomy. 1981. 47.50 (ISBN 0-8151-5826-2). Year Bk Med.

--Color Atlas of Human Anatomy. (Illus.). 1977. 39.95 (ISBN 0-8151-5823-8). Year Bk Med.

McMinn, R. M. & Hutchings, R. T. Colour Atlas of Human Anatomy. (Illus.). 1977. 75.00 (ISBN 0-684-15362-9, ScribT). Scribner.

O'Connor, Barbara H. A Color Atlas & Instruction Manual of Peripheral Blood Morphology. (Illus.). 340p. 1984. pap. text ed. 24.95 (ISBN 0-683-06624-2). Williams & Wilkins.

Pauchet, Victor & Dupret, S. Pocket Atlas of Anatomy. 3rd ed. (Illus.). 1937. pap. 14.95x (ISBN 0-19-263131-4). Oxford U Pr.

Pavlov, Helene, et al. Atlas of Knee Menisci: An Arthrographic-Pathologic Correlation. (Illus.). 174p. (Orig.). 1983. 57.50 (ISBN 0-317-19909-9). ACC.

Pernkopf, Eduard. Atlas of Topograhical & Applied Human Anatomy, Vol. 3: Index. 2nd ed. Ferner, Helmut, ed. LC 79-25264. 100p. 1980. text ed. 12.00 (ISBN 0-8067-1572-3). Urban & S.

--Atlas of Topographical & Applied Human Anatomy, Vol. 1: Head & Neck. 2nd ed. Ferner, Helmut, ed. Monsen, Harry, tr. from Ger. LC 79-25264. Tr. of Atlas der Topographischen und Angewnadten Anatomie Des Menschen. (Illus.). 312p. 1980. text ed. 98.00 (ISBN 0-8067-1552-9). Urban & S.

--Atlas of Topographical & Applied Human Anatomy, Vol. 2: Thorax, Abdomen & Extremities. 2nd ed. Ferner, Helmut, ed. Monsen, Harry, tr. from Ger. LC 79-25264. (Illus.). 417p. 1980. text ed. 98.00 (ISBN 0-8067-1562-6). Urban & S.

Rowett, H. G. Basic Anatomy & Physiology. (Illus.). 1973. text ed. 13.25 (ISBN 0-7195-2872-0). Transatlantic.

Royce, Joseph. Surface Anatomy. (Illus.). 270p. 1973. pap. text ed. 15.00x (ISBN 0-8036-7641-7). Davis Co.

Salamon, G. & Huang, Y. P. Computed Tomography of the Brain Atlas of Normal Anatomy. (Illus.). 160p. 1980. 129.00 (ISBN 0-387-08825-3). Springer-Verlag.

Schade, J. P. Introduction to Functional Human Anatomy: An Atlas. LC 73-76188. (Illus.). 190p. 1974. text ed. 10.00 (ISBN 0-7216-7945-5). Saunders.

Schider, Fritz. Atlas of Anatomy for Artists. 3rd ed. Wolf, Bernard, tr. (Illus.). 6.50 (ISBN 0-486-20241-0). Dover.

Schnitzlein, H. Norman & Murtagh, F. Reed. Imaging Anatomy of the Head & Spine: A Photographic Color Atlas of MRI, CT, & Microscopic Anatomy in Axial, Coronal, & Sagittal Planes. (Illus.). 324p. 1985. 149.50 (ISBN 0-8067-1881-1). Urban & S.

Shandong Medical College. Anatomical Atlas of Chinese Acupuncture Points. (Illus.). 265p. 1982. 50.00 (ISBN 0-8351-0954-2). China Bks.

Shrewsbury, Marvin M. & Chin, Edwin, Jr. Coloring Atlas of Human Anatomy. 196p. 1982. pap. text ed. 14.95 (ISBN 0-15-511800-5, HC). HarBraceJ.

Snell, Richard S. Atlas of Clinical Anatomy. 1978. text ed. 37.50 (ISBN 0-316-80209-3). Little.

Yokochi, C. Photographic Anatomy of the Human Body. 2nd ed. (Illus.). 110p. 1978. text ed. 26.50 (ISBN 0-8391-1104-5). Univ Park.

Zuckerman, et al. A New System of Anatomy: Being a Dissector's Guide & Atlas. 2nd ed. (Illus.). 1981. 65.00x (ISBN 0-19-263137-3); pap. 37.50x (ISBN 0-19-263136-5). Oxford U Pr.

ANATOMY, HUMAN–CHARTS, DIAGRAMS, ETC.

Doherty, Terence. The Anatomical Works of George Stubbs. LC 74-15259. (Illus.). 356p. 1975. 125.00 (ISBN 0-87923-117-3). Godine.

Jaynes, Thomas L. The Organ: A Guide for Student & Teacher. 27p. 1979. pap. 9.00 (ISBN 0-935514-00-7). T L Jaynes.

Schlossberg, Leon. Scale Model of Human Surface Anatomy & Musculature. 1979. 39.50 (ISBN 0-8018-2165-7). Johns Hopkins.

ANATOMY, MICROSCOPIC

see Histology

ANATOMY, VEGETABLE

see Botany–Anatomy

ANATOMY, VETERINARY

see Veterinary Anatomy

ANATOMY OF PLANTS

see Botany–Anatomy

ANDRENA

Timberlake, P. H. Supplementary Studies on the Systematics of the Genus Perdita (Hymenoptera, Andrenidae, Part II. (U. C. Publications in Entomology Ser.: Vol. 85). 1980. pap. 15.00x (ISBN 0-520-09605-3). U of Cal Pr.

ANDROIDS

Conference on Remotely Manned Systems, 2nd, June 1975. Robots & Manipulator Systems: Papers, 2 pts. Heer, E., ed. LC 77-73105. 336p. 1977. pap. text ed. 32.00 ea. Pt. 1 (ISBN 0-08-021727-3). Pt. 2 (ISBN 0-08-022681-7). Pergamon.

Dodd, G. G. & Rossol, L., eds. Computer Vision & Sensor-Based Robots. LC 79-18698. (General Motors Symposia Ser.). 363p. 1979. 55.00x (ISBN 0-306-40305-6, Plenum Pr). Plenum Pub.

Dorf, Richard C. Robotics & Automated Manufacturing. 208p. 1983. text ed. 27.95 (ISBN 0-8359-6686-0). Reston.

Dubreuil, Hyacinth. Robots or Men: French Workman's Experience in American Industry. Stein, Leon, ed. LC 77-70491. (Work Ser.). 1977. Repr. of 1930 ed. lib. bdg. 24.50x (ISBN 0-405-10163-5). Ayer Co Pubs.

Hoekstra. Introduction to Industrial Robots. 320p. Date not set. 13.00 (ISBN 0-317-05372-8, IE66). SW Pub.

International Conference, 1st, Birmingham, UK, April 1982. Robots in the Automotive Industry: Proceedings. 218p. 1982. text ed. 62.00x (ISBN 0-903608-22-7, Pub. by IFSPUBS). Scholium Intl.

International Conference, 1st Stratford-upon-Avon, UK April 1-3, 1981. Robot Vision & Sensory Controls: Proceedings. 348p. 1981. pap. text ed. 88.00x (ISBN 0-903608-15-4, IFSPUBS). Scholium Intl.

Mason, Matthew T. & Salisbury, J. Kenneth. Robot Hands: Design & Use. (Artificial Intelligence Ser.). (Illus.). 275p. 1985. text ed. 30.00x (ISBN 0-262-13205-2). MIT Pr.

A Survey of Industrial Robots. 2nd ed. 143.00 (ISBN 0-686-31442-5). C I M Systems.

Susnjara, Ken. A Manager's Guide to Industrial Robots. LC 81-86624. (Illus.). 186p. 1982. 8.95 (ISBN 0-86551-018-0). Corinthian.

Weinstein, Martin. Android Design. (Illus.). 248p. (Orig.). 1981. pap. 13.95 (ISBN 0-8104-5192-1). Hayden.

Young, Kay. Robotics, Nineteen Seventy to Nineteen Eighty-Three. (Public Administration Ser.: P-1444). 93p. 1984. 14.25 (ISBN 0-88066-964-0). Vance Biblios.

ANELASTICITY

see Internal Friction

ANESTHESIOLOGY

Benumof, A. & Jonathan, L. Clinical Frontiers in Anesthesiology: Anesthesia Update. 1983. 32.00 (ISBN 0-8089-1580-0, 790548). Grune.

Catron, Donald G. The Anesthesiologist's Handbook. 3rd ed. LC 83-6489. (Illus.). 288p. 1983. pap. text ed. 15.00 (ISBN 0-8391-1822-8, 19879). Univ Park.

Chung, David C. & Lamb, Arthur M. Essentials of Anesthesiology. (A Volume in the Saunders Blue Book Ser.). (Illus.). 256p. 1983. pap. 15.95 spiral bound (ISBN 0-7216-1042-0). Saunders.

Churchill-Davidson, H. C., ed. Wylie & Churchill-Davidson: A Practice of Anesthesia. 4th ed. (Illus.). 1542p. 1978. 25.00 (ISBN 0-7216-2577-0). Saunders.

DeKornfeld, Thomas J. Anesthesiology: Continuing Education Review. 2nd ed. 1983. pap. text ed. 26.00 (ISBN 0-87488-353-9). Med Exam.

Eckenhoff, James E. Controversies in Anesthesiology. (Illus.). 312p. 1979. 33.95 (ISBN 0-7216-3322-6). Saunders.

Knapp, Richard B. The Gift of Surgery to Mankind: A History of Modern Anesthesiology. (Illus.). 138p. 1983. 21.75x (ISBN 0-398-04817-7). C C Thomas.

Pichlmayr, I., et al. The Electroencephalogram in Anesthesiology: Fundamentals, Practical Applications, Examples. Bonatz, E. & Masyk-Iverson, T., trs. from German. (Illus.). 225p. 1984. 38.50 (ISBN 0-387-13159-0). Springer-Verlag.

Stark, Robert, et al. Practical Points in Anesthesiology. 3rd ed. Pederson, Hilda, ed. 1985. pap. text ed. write for info. (ISBN 0-87488-480-2). Med Exam.

Trickey, David L. Self-Assessment of Current Knowledge in Anesthesiology. 3rd ed. 1984. pap. write for info. (ISBN 0-87488-047-5). Med Exam.

Vickers, M. D. & Crul, J., eds. Mass Spectrometry in Anaesthesiology. (European Academy of Anaesthesiology Ser.: Vol. 1). (Illus.). 158p. 1981. pap. 27.00 (ISBN 0-387-11012-7). Springer-Verlag.

Vickers, M. D. & Lunn, J. N., eds. Mortality in Anaesthesia. (European Academy of Anaesthesiology: Vol. 3). (Illus.). 350p. 1983. pap. 48.20 (ISBN 0-387-12824-7). Springer-Verlag.

Vincent, J. L., ed. Intensive Care & Emergency Medicine: Proceedings of the Fourth International Symposium. (Anaesthesiologie & Intensivemedizin. Anaesthesiology & Intensive Care Medicine: Band 167). (Illus.). xiii, 190p. 1984. pap. 20.40 (ISBN 0-387-13412-3). Springer Verlag.

World Congress of Anaesthesiology, 3rd, Sao Paulo, 1964. Proceedings. Frey, R., et al, eds. (Anaesthesiology & Resuscitation Ser.: Vol. 8). 1966. pap. 23.10 (ISBN 0-387-03450-1). Springer-Verlag.

ANGIOSPERMS

see also Dicotyledons; Monocotyledons

Adams, C. D. Flowering Plants of Jamaica. 848p. 1972. 40.00x (ISBN 0-565-00841-2, Pub. by Brit Mus Nat Hist England). Sabbot-Natural Hist Bks.

--Flowering Plants of Jamaica. 848p. 1972. 78.50 (ISBN 0-686-78655-6, Pub. by Brit Mus Pubns England). State Mutual Bk.

Aitken, Yvonne. Flowering Time, Climate & Growth. (Illus.). 193p. 1975. 36.00x (ISBN 0-522-84071-X, Pub. by Melbourne U Pr Australia). Intl Spec Bk.

Arber, Agnes. Water Plants: Study of Aquatic Angiosperms. (Illus.). 1963. Repr. of 1920 ed. 28.00 (ISBN 3-7682-0157-0). Lubrecht & Cramer.

Beck, Charles B., ed. Origin & Early Evolution of Angiosperms. LC 75-15939. (Illus.). 341p. 1976. 45.00x (ISBN 0-231-03857-7). Columbia U Pr.

Bhojwani, S. S. & Bhatnagar, S. P. The Embryology of Angiosperms. 1978. 17.50x (ISBN 0-7069-0335-8, Pub. by Vikas India). Advent NY.

--Embryology of Angiosperms. (Illus.). 1976. 10.50 (ISBN 0-7069-0335-8). Intl Bk Dist.

Bouman, F. Development of Ovule & Seed Coat Structure in Angiosperms. (International Bioscience Monographs: No. 6). 80p. 1978. 7.50 (ISBN 0-88065-067-2, Pub. by Messers Today & Tomorrows Printers & Publishers India). Scholarly Pubns.

Cox, Donald D. Common Flowering Plants of the Northeast. 430p. 1985. lib. bdg. 29.50x (ISBN 0-87395-889-6); pap. text ed. 9.95x (ISBN 0-87395-890-X). State U NY Pr.

Cronquist, Arthur. An Integrated System of Classification of Flowering Plants. LC 80-39556. (Illus.). 1152p. 1981. 132.00x (ISBN 0-231-03880-1). Columbia U Pr.

Davis, P. H. & Cullen, J. The Identification of Flowering Plant Families. LC 78-8125. (Illus.). 1979. 29.95 (ISBN 0-521-22111-0); pap. 8.95x (ISBN 0-521-29359-6). Cambridge U Pr.

Davis, P. H. & Heywood, V. H. Principles of Angiosperm Taxonomy. 578p. 1973. Repr. of 1963 ed. 32.50 (ISBN 0-88275-129-8). Krieger.

Eames, A. J. Morphology of the Angiosperms. LC 76-57780. 532p. 1977. Repr. of 1961 ed. 32.50 (ISBN 0-88275-527-7). Krieger.

Fedorov, A., ed. Chromosome Numbers of Flowering Plants. 926p. 1969. Repr. of 1974 ed. lib. bdg. 77.00x (ISBN 3-87429-067-0). Lubrecht & Cramer.

Solounias, N. The Turolian Fauna from the Island of Samos, Greece. (Contributions to Vertebrate Evolution: Vol. 6). (Illus.). xvi, 232p. 1981. pap. 21.00 (ISBN 3-8055-2692-X). S Karger.
Stonehouse, Bernard, ed. Evolutionary Ecology. (Biology & Environment). (Illus.). 318p. 1979. text ed. 27.00 (ISBN 0-8391-0885-0). Univ Park.
Swingland, Ian R. & Greenwood, Paul J., eds. The Ecology of Animal Movement. (Illus.). 1983. 54.00x (ISBN 0-19-857575-0). Oxford U Pr.
Tinbergen, Niko. The Animal in Its World, Explorations of an Ethologist, 1932-1972, Vol. 2: Laboratory Experiments & General Papers. LC 72-94876. 296p. 1973. text ed. 16.00x (ISBN 0-674-03727-8); pap. 6.95x (ISBN 0-674-03728-6). Harvard U Pr.
Twesten, Gary. Wildlife Ecology: A Guide to the Ecological Approach of Studying the Wildlife of the Central United States. 3rd ed. Baum, Urban, ed. LC 73-174002. (Illus.). 710p. 1979. 20.00 (ISBN 0-9602428-2-1). G Twesten.
Woodbury, Angus, et al. Ecological Studies of the Flora & Fauna of Navajo Reservoir Basin, Colorado & New Mexico. (Upper Colorado Ser: No. 5). Repr. of 1961 ed. 34.50 (ISBN 0-404-60655-5). AMS Pr.
Woodbury, Angus M., et al. Ecological Studies of Flora & Fauna in Glen Canyon. (Glen Canyon Ser: No. 7). Repr. of 1959 ed. 42.00 (ISBN 0-404-60640-7). AMS Pr.
--Ecological Studies of the Flora & Fauna of the Curecanti Reservoir Basins, Western Colorado. (Upper Colorado Ser.: No. 8). Repr. of 1962 ed. 42.50 (ISBN 0-404-60659-8). AMS Pr.

ANIMAL ELECTRICITY
see Electrophysiology

ANIMAL FLUIDS AND HUMORS
see Body Fluids

ANIMAL FOOD

Altschul, Aaron M. & Wilcke, Harold L., eds. New Protein Foods Vol. 3, Animal Protein Supplies, Part A. (Food Science & Technology Ser.). 1978. 75.00 (ISBN 0-12-054803-8). Acad Pr.
Animal Feed Industry. (UNIDO Guides to Information Sources: No. 13). pap. 4.00 (ISBN 0-686-93205-6, UN131, UN). Unipub.
Beitz, Donald & Hansen, R. G. Animal Products in Human Nutrition. (Nutrition Foundation Monograph). 1982. 69.50 (ISBN 0-12-086380-4). Acad Pr.
Bickel, Hans, ed. Palatability & Flavor Use in Animal Feeds. (Advances in Animal Physiology & Animal Nutrition: Vol. 11). (Illus.). 148p. (Orig.). 1980. pap. text ed. 34.10 (ISBN 3-490-41115-3). Parey Sci Pubs.
Bullard, Roger W., ed. Flavor Chemistry of Animal Foods. LC 77-27295. (ACS Symposium Ser.: No. 67). 1978. 19.95 (ISBN 0-8412-0404-7). Am Chemical.
Committee on Scholarly Communication with the People's Republic of China, National Research Council. Animal Agriculture in China. 197p. 1980. pap. text ed. 13.25 (ISBN 0-309-03092-7). Natl Acad Pr.
Liener, Irvin E., ed. Toxic Constituents of Animal Foodstuffs. (Food Science & Technology Ser.). 1974. 49.50 (ISBN 0-12-449940-6). Acad Pr.
Lister, D., ed. In Vivo Measurement of Body Composition in Meat Animals: Proceedings of a Workshop Held at the Agricultural & Food Research Council's Meat Research Institute, Langford, Bristol, UK, 30 November-1 December 1983. 252p. 1984. 42.00 (ISBN 0-85334-319-5, Pub. by Elsevier Applied Sci England). Elsevier.
Lister, D., et al, eds. Meat Animals: Growth & Productivity. LC 76-985. (NATO ASI Series A, Life Sciences: Vol. 8). 553p. 1976. 65.00x (ISBN 0-306-35608-2, Plenum Pr). Plenum Pub.
Muller, Z. O. Feed from Animal Wastes: Feeding Manual. (Animal Production & Health Papers: No. 28). 224p. 1982. pap. 16.00 (ISBN 92-5-101188-5, F2278, FAO). Unipub.
Tongren, Sally. What's for Lunch: Animal Feeding at the Zoo. LC 81-80981. (Illus.). 128p. (Orig.). 1981. 12.95 (ISBN 0-939456-00-1); pap. 8.95 (ISBN 0-939456-01-X). GMG Pub.

ANIMAL HEAT
see also Body Temperature

Girardier, Lucien & Stock, Michael J., eds. Mammalian Thermogenesis. LC 83-1929. (Illus.). 359p. 1983. 80.00 (ISBN 0-412-23550-1, NO. 6822, Pub. by Chapman & Hall). Methuen Inc.
Mendelsohn, Everett I. Heat & Life: The Development of the Theory of Animal Heat. LC 64-16067. 1964. 14.00x (ISBN 0-674-38650-7). Harvard U Pr.
Webb, Paul. Human Calorimeters. 176p. 1985. 34.95 (ISBN 0-03-003008-0). Praeger.
Wieser, E., ed. Effects of Temperature on Ectothermic Organisms: Ecological Implications & Mechanisms of Compensation. LC 73-10671. (Illus.). 298p. 1974. 59.00 (ISBN 0-387-06420-6). Springer-Verlag.

ANIMAL HOMES
see Animals, Habitations Of

ANIMAL INDUSTRY
see also Cattle Trade; Dairying; Domestic Animals; Livestock; Poultry Industry

Acker, Duane. Animal Science & Industry. x ed. (Illus.). 720p. 1983. 33.95 (ISBN 0-13-037416-4). P-H.
Animal Genetic Resources Conservation by Management, Data Banks & Training. (Animal Production & Health Papers: No. 44-1). 186p. 1985. pap. 13.75 (ISBN 92-5-102110-4, F2656, FAO). Unipub.
Australian Society. Animal Production: Proceedings of the Australian Society of Animal Production 13th Biennial Conference, Perth, August 1980. (Illus.). 544p. 1980. 79.00 (ISBN 0-08-024812-8). Pergamon.
Battaglia, R. A. & Mayrose, V. Handbook of Livestock Management Techniques. 1981. text ed. 25.95x (ISBN 0-8087-2957-8). Burgess.
Calabrese, E. J. Principles of Animal Extrapolation. (Environmental Science & Technology Ser.). 603p. 1982. 74.95 (ISBN 0-471-08762-9). Wiley.
Casady, R. B. & Jawin, P. B. Commerical Rabbit Raising. (Shorey Lost Arts Ser.). (Illus.). 69p. pap. 3.95 (ISBN 0-8466-6054-7, U54). Shorey.
Cole, H. H., ed. Introduction to Livestock Production: Including Dairy & Poultry. 2nd ed. LC 66-16377. (Illus.). 827p. 1966. 35.95 (ISBN 0-7167-0812-4). W H Freeman.
Folsch, D. W., ed. The Ethology & Ethics of Farm Animal Production. (Animal Management Ser.: No. 6). (Ger. & Eng.). 144p. 1978. pap. 22.95x (ISBN 0-8176-1004-9). Birkhauser.
Gordon, I. Controlled Breeding in Farm Animals. 200p. 1983. 60.00 (ISBN 0-08-024410-6); pap. 30.00 (ISBN 0-08-024409-2). Pergamon.
Kiflewahid, Berhane & Potts, Gordon R., eds. By-Product Utilization for Animal Production: Proceedings of a Workshop on Applied Research Held in Nairobi, Kenya, 26-30 September 1982. 158p. 1983. pap. text ed. 13.00 (ISBN 0-88936-365-X, IDRC206, IDRC). Unipub.
Marketing Livestock & Meat. 2nd ed. (Animal Production & Health Papers: No. 1). 198p. 1977. pap. 15.50 (ISBN 92-5-100168-5, F1529, FAO). Unipub.
Pond, Wilson G., et al, eds. Animal Agriculture: Human Needs in the 21st Century. 600p. 1980. 29.50x (ISBN 0-86531-032-7). Westview.
Report of the FAO-WHO Symposium on the Use of Anabolic Agents in Animal Production & Its Public Health Aspects. 24p. 1975. pap. 7.50 (ISBN 0-685-61023-3, F1092, FAO). Unipub.
Yousef, Mohamed, ed. Animal Production in the Tropics. LC 82-5372. 394p. 1982. 49.95x (ISBN 0-03-060482-6). Praeger.

ANIMAL INDUSTRY–INDIA

Pathak, N. N. & Jakhmola, R. C. Forages & Livestock Production. viii, 274p. 1983. text ed. 27.50x (ISBN 0-7069-2323-5, Pub. by Vikas India). Advent NY.

ANIMAL INSTINCT
see Instinct

ANIMAL INTELLIGENCE
see also Animals, Habits and Behavior of; Instinct

Bitterman, M. E., et al, eds. Animal Learning: Survey & Analysis. LC 78-9894. (NATO ASI Series A, Life Sciences: Vol. 19). 522p. 1979. 55.00x (ISBN 0-306-40061-8, Plenum Pr). Plenum Pub.
Broadhurst, P. L. Science of Animal Behaviour. 1963. lib. bdg. 13.50x (ISBN 0-88307-035-9). Gannon.
Burroughs, John. Ways of Nature. facsimile ed. LC 77-157963. (Essay Index Reprint Ser). Repr. of 1905 ed. 19.00 (ISBN 0-8369-2217-4). Ayer Co Pubs.
Corning, W. C. & Ratner, S. C., eds. Chemistry of Learning: Invertebrate Research. LC 67-25103. 468p. 1967. 42.50x (ISBN 0-306-30305-1, Plenum Pr). Plenum Pub.
Davey, Graham. Animal Learning & Conditioning. (Illus.). 512p. 1981. 21.00 (ISBN 0-8391-4149-1). Univ Park.
Fink, Harold K. Mind & Performance: A Comparative Study of Learning in Mammals, Birds, & Reptiles. LC 70-138229. (Illus.). 113p. 1972. Repr. of 1954 ed. lib. bdg. 22.50x (ISBN 0-8371-5586-X, FIMI). Greenwood.
Flaherty, Charles. Animal Cognition. 450p. 1985. text ed. 26.00 (ISBN 0-394-33042-0, KnopfC). Knopf.
Graven, Jacques. Non-Human Thought. LC 67-10324. 224p. 1974. pap. 1.95 (ISBN 0-8128-1751-6). Stein & Day.
Griffin, Donald. The Question of Animal Awareness. 2nd ed. LC 81-51221. (Illus.). 221p. pap. 9.95 (ISBN 0-86576-002-0). W Kaufmann.
Griffin, Donald R. Animal Thinking. 256p. 1985. pap. 7.95 (ISBN 0-674-03713-8). Harvard U Pr.
--Question of Animal Awareness: Evolutionary Continuity of Mental Experience. rev. ed. LC 81-51221. 224p. 1981. 13.95x (ISBN 0-87470-035-3). Rockefeller.
Honig, Werner K. & James, Henry, eds. Animal Memory. 1971. 45.00 (ISBN 0-12-355050-5). Acad Pr.
Jarrard, Leonard E., ed. Cognitive Processes of Nonhuman Primates. 1971. 42.00 (ISBN 0-12-380850-2). Acad Pr.
Kendrick, Donald F., et al, eds. Animal Cognition: Theories of Animal Memory. 350p. Date not set. text ed. 17.95 (ISBN 0-89859-697-1). L Erlbaum Assocs.
Knowledge Unlimited Staff, ed. Are They Really Dumb? Intelligence & Language among the Animals. (Illus.). 29p. tchr's. guide & color filmstrip 13.00 (ISBN 0-915291-42-8). Know Unltd.
Lindsay, William L. Mind in the Lower Animal in Health & Disease. (Contributions to the History of Psychology Ser.: Vols. 6 & 7, Pt. D, Comparative Psychology). 1983. Repr. of 1879 ed. 30.00 ea. (ISBN 0-89093-323-5). U Pubns Amer.
McIntyre, Joan. Mind in the Waters: A Book to Celebrate the Consciousness of Whales & Dolphins. LC 74-13000. (Illus.). 224p. 1984. pap. 16.95 (ISBN 0-684-14443-3, ScribT). Scribner.
Mackintosh, N. J. Psychology of Animal Learning. 1974. 41.00 (ISBN 0-12-464650-6). Acad Pr.
MacPhail, Euan. Brain & Intelligence in Vertebrates. (Illus.). 1982. 32.50x (ISBN 0-19-854550-9); pap. 15.95x (ISBN 0-19-854551-7). Oxford U Pr.
Mayer, et al. Perspectives on the Educational Use of Animals. (Illus.). 77p. 1980. pap. 3.00 (ISBN 0-913098-38-8). Myrin Institute.
Morgan, C. Lloyd. Animal Behavior. LC 3-12891. (Psychology Ser). 1970. Repr. of 1900 ed. 27.00 (ISBN 0-384-40134-1). Johnson Repr.
Patterson, Francine & Linden, Eugene. The Education of Koko. LC 81-1325. (Illus.). 240p. 1981. 15.95 (ISBN 0-03-046101-4); pap. 7.95 (ISBN 0-03-063551-9). HR&W.
Romanes, George J. Animal Intelligence. (Contributions to the History of Psychology Ser.: Vol. 7, Pt. A: Orientations). 1978. 30.00 (ISBN 0-89093-156-9). U Pubns Amer.
Sebeok, Thomas A. How Animals Communicate. LC 76-48862. pap. 160.00 (ISBN 0-317-27862-2, 2056058). Bks Demand UMI.
Smythe, R. H. Animal Psychology: A Book of Comparative Psychology Which Discusses the Behavior of Animals & Man. (Illus.). 268p. 1961. 25.75x (ISBN 0-398-01800-6). C C Thomas.
Smythe, Reginald H. Mind of the Horse. LC 65-22225. 1965. 9.95 (ISBN 0-8289-0042-6). Greene.
Spear, Norman E. & Miller, Ralph R., eds. Information Processing in Animals: Memory Mechanisms. 432p. 1981. text ed. 39.95x (ISBN 0-89859-157-0). L Erlbaum Assocs.
Sutherland, N. S. & MacKintosh, N. J. Mechanisms of Animal Discrimination & Learning. LC 79-127705. 1971. 73.50 (ISBN 0-12-677750-0). Acad Pr.
Tarpy, Roger M. Principles of Animal Learning & Motivation. 1982. pap. text ed. 23.80x (ISBN 0-673-15383-5). Scott F.
Taylor, Thomas. Vindication of the Rights of Brutes. LC 66-10010. 1966. Repr. of 1792 ed. 30.00x (ISBN 0-8201-1045-0). Schol Facsimiles.
Terian, Abraham. Philonis Alexandrini De Animalibus. Hilgert, Earle, ed. LC 81-836. (Supplements to Studia Philonica). 1981. 16.50 (ISBN 0-89130-472-X, 18-00-01). Scholars Pr GA.
Tolman, Edward C. Purposive Behavior in Animals & Men. LC 67-20666. (Century Psychology Ser.). (Illus.). 1967. text ed. 39.50x (ISBN 0-89197-544-6). Irvington.
Walker, Stephen. Animal Thought. (International Library of Psychology). 452p. 1985. pap. 15.95 (ISBN 0-7102-0707-7). Routledge & Kegan.
Weir, James. The Dawn of Reason or Mental Traits in the Lower Animals. Repr. of 1899 ed. 15.00 (ISBN 0-89987-088-0). Darby Bks.
Weiskrantz, L., ed. Animal Intelligence. (Oxford Psychology Ser.: No. 7). (Illus.). 298p. 1985. 47.50 (ISBN 0-19-852124-3). Oxford U Pr.

ANIMAL INTRODUCTION

Baker, H. G. & Stebbins, G. L., eds. The Genetics of Colonizing Species. 1965. 74.50 (ISBN 0-12-075150-X). Acad Pr.
Milne, Lorus J. & Milne, Margery. Ecology Out of Joint: New Environments & Why They Happen. LC 76-48933. (Illus.). 1977. 8.95 (ISBN 0-684-14846-3, ScribT). Scribner.

ANIMAL KINGDOM
see Zoology

ANIMAL LANGUAGE
see Animal Communication; Animal Sounds; Sound Production by Animals

ANIMAL LOCOMOTION

Alexander, R. McNeill. Locomotion of Animals. (Tertiary Level Biology Ser.). 192p. 1982. 35.00x (ISBN 0-412-00001-6, NO.5001, Pub. by Chapman & Hall); pap. 18.95x (ISBN 0-412-00011-3, NO. 5002). Methuen Inc.
Aristotle. Parts of Animals. Bd. with Movement of Animals; Progression of Animals. (Loeb Classical Library: No. 323). (Gr. & Eng.). 12.50x (ISBN 0-674-99357-8). Harvard U Pr.
Bush, B. M. & Clarac, F., eds. Co-ordination of Motor Behaviour. (Society for Experimental Biology Seminar Ser.: No. 24). 324p. 1985. 37.50 (ISBN 0-521-26425-1). Cambridge U Pr.
Clark, Robert B. Dynamics in Metazoan Evolution: The Origin of the Coelom & Segments. 1964. 45.00x (ISBN 0-19-854353-0). Oxford U Pr.
Elder, H. Y. & Trueman, E. R., eds. Aspects of Animal Movement. LC 79-8520. (Society for Experimental Biology Seminar Ser.: No. 5). (Illus.). 250p. 1980. 54.50 (ISBN 0-521-23086-1); pap. 18.95 (ISBN 0-521-29795-8). Cambridge U Pr.
Herman, Robert H., et al, eds. Neural Control of Locomotion. LC 76-18949. (Advances in Behavioral Biology: Vol. 18). 822p. 1976. 85.00x (ISBN 0-306-37918-X, Plenum Pr). Plenum Pub.
Howell, Alfred B. Speed in Animals, Their Specialization for Running & Leaping. (Illus.). 1965. Repr. of 1944 ed. 17.95x (ISBN 0-02-846110-X). Hafner.
Muybridge, Eadweard. Animals in Motion. Brown, Lewis S., ed. (Illus.). 1957. 19.95 (ISBN 0-486-20203-8). Dover.
--Human Figure in Motion. (Illus.). 1955. 18.95 (ISBN 0-486-20204-6). Dover.
--Muybridge's Complete Human & Animal Locomotion: All 781 Plates from the 1887 Animal Locomotion, 3 vols. Incl. Vol. 1. 33.34 (ISBN 0-486-23792-3); Vol. 2. 33.33 (ISBN 0-486-23793-1); Vol. 3. 33.33 (ISBN 0-486-23794-X). (Illus.). 1979. Repr. of 1887 ed. Set. 100.00. Dover.
Stein, R. B., et al, eds. Control of Posture & Locomotion. LC 73-19634. (Advances in Behavioral Biology Ser.: Vol. 7). 648p. 1974. 55.00x (ISBN 0-306-37907-4, Plenum Pr). Plenum Pub.
Steindler, Arthur. Kinesiology: Of the Human Body Under Normal & Pathological Conditions. (Illus.). 736p. 1977. photocopy 84.75x (ISBN 0-398-01846-4). C C Thomas.
University of Pennsylvania. Animal Locomotion: The Muybridge Work at the University of Pennsylvania. LC 72-9239. (The Literature of Photography). 1973. Repr. of 1888 ed. 16.00 (ISBN 0-405-04944-7). Ayer Co Pubs.
Wu, Theodore Y., et al, eds. Swimming & Flying in Nature. LC 75-33753. 1975. Vol. 1, 442p. 55.00 (ISBN 0-306-37088-3, Plenum Pr); Vol. 2, 597p. 65.00 (ISBN 0-306-37089-1). Plenum Pub.

ANIMAL LUMINESCENCE
see Bioluminescence

ANIMAL MAGNETISM
see also Hypnotism

Davis, Albert R. & Rawls, Walter C., Jr. The Magnetic Blueprint of Life. 1979. 10.95 (ISBN 0-682-49215-9). Exposition Pr FL.
Deleuze, Jean P. Practical Instruction in Animal Magnetism. Hartshorn, Thomas, tr. from Fr. (Hypnosis & Altered States of Consciousness Ser.). 1982. Repr. of 1843 ed. lib. bdg. 45.00 (ISBN 0-306-76074-6). Da Capo.
Dupotet de Sennevoy, Jean. An Introduction to the Study of Animal Magnetism. LC 75-36837. (Occult Ser.). 1976. Repr. of 1838 ed. 30.00x (ISBN 0-405-07950-8). Ayer Co Pubs.
Durant, Charles. Exposition: A New Theory of Animal Magnetism. (Hypnosis & Altered States of Consciousness Ser.). 225p. 1982. Repr. of 1837 ed. lib. bdg. 27.50 (ISBN 0-306-76075-4). Da Capo.
Gregory, William. Animal Magnetism: or Mesmerism & Its Phenomena. 5th ed. LC 75-7384. (Perspectives in Psychical Research Ser.). 1975. Repr. of 1909 ed. 20.00x (ISBN 0-405-07032-2). Ayer Co Pubs.
Poyen, Charles. Progress of Animal Magnetism. (Hypnosis & Altered States of Consciousness Ser.). 1982. Repr. of 1837 ed. lib. bdg. 25.00 (ISBN 0-306-76163-7). Da Capo.
Shaftesbury, Edmund. Universal Magnetism, Vol. 2. 14.95x (ISBN 0-685-22150-4). Wehman.

ANIMAL MECHANICS
see also Animal Locomotion

Royce, Joseph. Surface Anatomy. (Illus.). 270p. 1973. pap. text ed. 15.00x (ISBN 0-8036-7641-7). Davis Co.

ANIMAL MIGRATION
see also Birds–Migration

Aidley, D. J., ed. Animal Migration. LC 81-3905. (Society for Experimental Biology Seminar Ser.: No. 13). 1981. 44.50 (ISBN 0-521-23274-0); pap. 22.95 (ISBN 0-521-29888-1). Cambridge U Pr.

Akimushkin, I. Animal Travelers. 375p. 1973. pap. 3.45 (ISBN 0-8285-0814-3, Pub. by Mir Pubs USSR). Imported Pubns.

Baker, R. Robin. The Evolutionary Ecology of Animal Migration. LC 78-34. (Illus.). 1024p. 1978. text ed. 135.00x (ISBN 0-8419-0368-9). Holmes & Meier.

Gathreaux, S. A., Jr., ed. Animal Migration, Orientation & Navigation. 1981. 55.00 (ISBN 0-12-277750-6). Acad Pr.

Jarman, Cathy. Atlas of Animal Migration. LC 72-1748. (John Day Bk.). (Illus.). 128p. 1974. 14.37i (ISBN 0-381-98129-0, A06030). T Y Crowell.

Por, F. D. Lessepsian Migration: The Influx of Red Sea Biota into the Mediterranaen by Way of the Suez Canal. LC 77-24546. (Ecological Studies: Vol. 23). (Illus.). 1978. 41.00 (ISBN 0-387-08381-2). Springer-Verlag.

Schmidt-Koenig, K. Migration & Homing in Animals. (Zoo Physiology & Ecology Ser.: Vol. 6). (Illus.). 150p. 1975. 29.00 (ISBN 0-387-07433-3). Springer-Verlag.

Schmidt-Koenig, K. & Keeton, W. T., eds. Animal Migration, Navigation, & Homing: Symposium Held at the University of Tuebingen, August 17 - 20, 1977. LC 78-8656. (Proceedings in Life Sciences). (Illus.). 1978. 41.00 (ISBN 0-387-08777-X). Springer-Verlag.

Street, Philip. Animal Migration & Navigation. LC 75-30276. (Illus.). 1976. 9.95 (ISBN 0-684-14516-2, ScribT). Scribner.

Swingland, Ian R. & Greenwood, Paul J., eds. The Ecology of Animal Movement. (Illus.). 1983. 54.00x (ISBN 0-19-857575-0). Oxford U Pr.

ANIMAL NAVIGATION

see also Animal Migration; Bird Navigation

Purves, P. E. & Pilleri, G., eds. Echolocation in Whales & Dolphins. 1983. 47.00 (ISBN 0-12-567960-2). Acad Pr.

Schmidt-Koenig, K. & Keeton, W. T., eds. Animal Migration, Navigation, & Homing: Symposium Held at the University of Tuebingen, August 17 - 20, 1977. LC 78-8656. (Proceedings in Life Sciences). (Illus.). 1978. 41.00 (ISBN 0-387-08777-X). Springer-Verlag.

Street, Philip. Animal Migration & Navigation. LC 75-30276. (Illus.). 1976. 9.95 (ISBN 0-684-14516-2, ScribT). Scribner.

ANIMAL NUTRITION

see also Feeds;

also subdivision Feeding and Feeds under names of animals and groups of animals, e.g. Poultry–Feeding and Feeds

Ad Hoc Consultation on the Value of Non-Protein Nitrogen for Ruminants: Report. 1971. pap. 15.00 (F1086, FAO). Unipub.

Agriculture & Renewable Resources Board, National Research Council. Urea & Other Nonprotein Nitrogen Compounds in Animal Nutrition. LC 76-8240. 1976. pap. 6.95 (ISBN 0-309-02444-7). Natl Acad Pr.

Aitken, F. C. Sodium & Potassium in Nutrition of Mammals. 296p. 1976. cloth 50.00x (ISBN 0-85198-370-7, Pub. by CAB Bks England). State Mutual Bk.

Aitken, F. c. & Hankin, R. G. Vitamins in Feeds for Livestock. 230p. 1970. cloth 40.00x (ISBN 0-686-45671-8, Pub. by CAB Bks England). State Mutual Bk.

Anderson, R. S., ed. Nutrition & Behavior in Dogs & Cats: Proceedings of the First Nordic Symposium on Small Animal Veterinary Medicine, Oslo, Norway, September 15-18, 1982. LC 83-17281. 246p. 1983. 30.00 (ISBN 0-08-029778-1). Pergamon.

--Nutrition of the Dog & Cat: Proceedings of an International Symposium 26 June 1978, Hanover. LC 80-40449. (Illus.). 212p. 1980. 37.00 (ISBN 0-08-025526-4). Pergamon.

Banerjee, G. C. Animal Nutrition. 576p. 1981. 45.00x (ISBN 0-686-72939-0, Pub. by Oxford & IBH India). State Mutual Bk.

Board on Agriculture, National Research Council. Nutrient Requirements of Mink & Foxes. 2nd rev. ed. 72p. 1982. pap. text ed. 9.50 (ISBN 0-309-03325-X). Natl Acad Pr.

Bourne, G. H., ed. Human & Veterinary Nutrition. (World Review of Nutrition & Dietetics: Vol. 26). (Illus.). 1977. 70.75 (ISBN 3-8055-2392-0). S Karger.

Bourne, Geoffrey H., ed. Some Aspects of Human & Veterinary Nutrition. (World Review of Nutrition & Dietetics: Vol. 28). 1978. 68.75 (ISBN 3-8055-2672-5). S Karger.

Butler, G. W. & Bailey, R. W., eds. Chemistry & Biochemistry of Herbage, 3 vols. Incl. Vol. 1. 1973. 90.00 (ISBN 0-12-148101-8); Vol. 2. 1974; Vol. 3. 1974. 55.00 (ISBN 0-12-148103-4). Acad Pr.

Cassard, Daniel W., et al. Approved Practices in Feeds & Feeding. 5th ed. LC 76-62743. (Illus.). 444p. 1977. 18.60 (ISBN 0-8134-1901-8, 1901); text ed. 13.95x. Interstate.

Cole, D. J. & Haresign, W., eds. Recent Developments in Pig Nutrition. 336p. 1985. pap. text ed. 25.95 (ISBN 0-407-00339-8). Butterworth.

Committee On Animal Nutrition. Nutrient Requirements of Dairy Cattle, 1978. 5th ed. (Nutrient Requirements of Domestic Animals Ser). 76p. 1978. pap. text ed. 6.50 (ISBN 0-309-02749-7). Natl Acad Pr.

Committee on Animal Nutrition Board on Agriculture & Renewable Resources, National Research Council. Nutrient Requirements of Beef Cattle. 5th, rev. ed. LC 75-43977. (Nutrient Requirements of Domestic Animals Ser.). 56p. 1976. pap. 8.95 (ISBN 0-309-02419-6). Natl Acad Pr.

Committee on Animal Nutrition, Board of Agriculture, National Research Council. Selenium in Nutrition. rev. ed. 1983. pap. text ed. 14.50 (ISBN 0-309-03375-6). Natl Acad Pr.

Committee on Animal Nutrition, National Research Council. Nutrient Requirements of Cats. LC 78-5976. (Nutrient Requirements of Domestic Animals Ser.). 49p. 1978. pap. text ed. 6.95 (ISBN 0-309-02743-8). Natl Acad Pr.

--Nutritional Energetics of Domestic Animals & Glossary of Energy Terms. 54p. (Orig.). 1981. pap. text ed. 5.25 (ISBN 0-309-03127-3). Natl Acad Pr.

Conrad, Joseph H., et al. Mineraux pour les Ruminants de Paturage des Regions Tropicales. LC 84-72137. Tr. of Minerals for Grazing Ruminants in Tropical Regions. (Fr., Illus., Orig.). 1984. write for info. extension billetin (ISBN 0-916287-02-5, Pub. by Ctr Tropical Agri). Univ Fla Food.

--Minerais Para Ruminantes em Pastejo em Regioes Tropicais. Euclides, Valeria P., tr. from Eng. LC 84-72136. Tr. of Minerals for Grazing Ruminants in Tropical Regions. (Portuguese., Illus., Orig.). 1984. write for info. extension bulletin (ISBN 0-916287-03-3, Pub. by Ctr Tropical Agri). Univ Fla Food.

Crampton, E. W. & Harris, L. E. Applied Animal Nutrition: The Use of Feedstuffs in the Formulation of Livestock Rations. 2nd ed. LC 68-10996. (Animal Science Ser.). (Illus.). 753p. 1969. text ed. 35.95 (ISBN 0-7167-0814-0). W H Freeman.

Culpin, Claude. Farm Machinery. 10th ed. (Illus.). 464p. 1981. pap. text ed. 24.50x (ISBN 0-246-11539-4, Pub. by Granada England). Brookfield Pub Co.

Decontamination of Animal Feeds by Irridation. (Panel Proceedings Ser.). (Illus.). 153p. 1979. pap. 22.75 (ISBN 92-0-111079-0, ISP508, IAEA). Unipub.

Digestibility for Veal Calves of Fish Protein Concentrates. (Agricultural Research Reports: No. 819). 1974. pap. 5.00 (ISBN 90-220-0515-1, PDC194, PUDOC). Unipub.

Edney, A. T., ed. Dog & Cat Nutrition: A Handbook for Students, Veterinarians, Breeders & Owners. (Illus.). 124p. 1982. 26.00 (ISBN 0-08-028891-X); pap. 12.00 (ISBN 0-08-028890-1). Pergamon.

Festing, Michael F., ed. Animal Models of Obesity. 1979. 38.50x (ISBN 0-19-520171-X). Oxford U Pr.

Hacker, J. B., ed. Nutritional Limits to Animal Production from Pastures: Proceedings of an International Symposium Held at St. Lucia, Queensland, Australia August 24th-28 1981. 548p. 1982. 99.00x (ISBN 0-85198-492-4, Pub. by CAB Bks England). State Mutual Bk.

Hardman, A. Leighton. Equine Nutrition. (Illus.). 128p. 1981. 12.95 (ISBN 0-7207-1244-0, Pub. by Michael Joseph). Merrimack Pub Cir.

Haresign & Lewis, D., eds. Recent Advances in Animal Nutrition 1979. (Studies in the Agricultural & Food Sciences Ser.). 1980. text ed. 59.95 (ISBN 0-408-71012-8). Butterworth.

Haresign, W. Recent Advances in Animal Nutrition 1983. 256p. 1983. text ed. 75.00 (ISBN 0-408-71016-0). Butterworth.

Haresign, W., ed. Recent Advances in Animal Nutrition - 1980. LC 80-41606. (Studies in the Agricultural & Food Sciences). (Illus.). 256p. 1981. text ed. 59.95 (ISBN 0-408-71013-6). Butterworth.

Haresign, W. & Cole, D. J., eds. Recent Advances in Animal Nutrition, 1984. (Studies in Agricultural & Food Sciences). 288p. 1984. text ed. 110.00 (ISBN 0-407-01160-9). Butterworth.

Harris, Robert S., ed. Feeding & Nutrition of Nonhuman Primates. 1970. 55.00 (ISBN 0-12-327360-9). Acad Pr.

Hintz, Harold F. Horse Nutrition: A Practical Guide. LC 82-16294. (Illus.). 240p. 1983. 15.95 (ISBN 0-668-05416-6). Arco.

Hume, I. D. Digestive Physiology & Nutrition of Marsupials. LC 81-17032. (Monographs on Marsupial Biology). (Illus.). 220p. 1982. 49.50 (ISBN 0-521-23892-7). Cambridge U Pr.

Jensen, Rue & Mackey, Donald R. Diseases of Feedlot Cattle. 3rd ed. LC 78-18729. (Illus.). 300p. 1979. text ed. 22.50 (ISBN 0-8121-0646-6). Lea & Febiger.

Jurgens, Marshall H. Animal Feeding & Nutrition. 4th ed. 1978. wire coil bdg. 22.95 (ISBN 0-8403-2669-6, 40266902). Kendall Hunt.

Kamstra, Leslie D. Livestock Nutrition. (Illus.). 223p. 1982. pap. text ed. 9.95x (ISBN 0-89641-081-1). American Pr.

Lane, Ronald J. & Cross, Tim L. Microcomputer Applications for Agricultural Financial Management. 1986. 29.95 (ISBN 0-8359-4410-7); pap. text ed. 19.95 (ISBN 0-8359-4409-3). Reston.

Lassiter, J. W. & Edwards, Hardy M. Animal Nutrition. 1982. text ed. 23.95 (ISBN 0-8359-0222-6); instr's. manual free (ISBN 0-8359-0223-4). Reston.

Lewis, Lon D. Feeding & Care of the Horse. LC 81-8137. (Illus.). 248p. 1982. text ed. 16.00 (ISBN 0-8121-0803-5). Lea & Febiger.

Loosli, J. K. & McDonald, I. Nonprotein Nitrogen in the Nutrition of Ruminants. (Agricultural Planning Studies: No. 75). 94p. (2nd Printing 1976). 1968. pap. 13.25 (ISBN 92-5-101563-5, F299, FAO). Unipub.

McCullough, Marshall E. Optimum Feeding of Dairy Animals for Meat & Milk. rev. ed. LC 74-90556. 194p. 1973. pap. 9.00x (ISBN 0-8203-0239-2). U of Ga Pr.

McDonald, P. & Edwards, R. A. Animal Nutrition. 3rd ed. LC 80-41375. (Illus.). 475p. 1982. pap. text ed. 26.00x (ISBN 0-582-44399-7). Longman.

McDowell, Lee R., et al, eds. Minerals for Grazing Ruminants in Tropical Regions. LC 84-70238. (Illus.). 80p. (Orig.). 1984. write for info. (ISBN 0-916287-00-9, Pub. by Ctr Tropical Agri). Univ Fla Food.

--Minerales para Rumiantes en Pastoreo en Regiones Tropicales. LC 84-71582. Tr. of Minerals for Grazing Ruminants in Tropical Regions. (Span., Illus.). 106p. (Orig.). 1984. write for info. extension bulletin (ISBN 0-916287-01-7, Pub. by Ctr Tropical Agri). Univ Fla Food.

Maynard, L. A., et al. Animal Nutrition. 7th ed. (Illus.). 1979. text ed. 42.95 (ISBN 0-07-041049-6). McGraw.

Mitchell, Harold H. Comparative Nutrition of Man & Domestic Animals, Vol. 2. 1964. 63.50 (ISBN 0-12-499602-7). Acad Pr.

Muller, Z. O. Feed from Animal Wastes: State of Knowledge. (Animal Production & Health Papers: No. 18). 201p. 1980. pap. 13.00 (ISBN 92-5-100946-5, F2100, FAO). Unipub.

National Academy of Sciences. Effect of Genetic Variance on Nutritional Requirements of Animals. 1975. 8.25 (ISBN 0-309-02342-4). Natl Acad Pr.

Nelson, R. H. An Introduction to Feeding Farm Livestock. 2nd ed. 1979. pap. text ed. 9.75 (ISBN 0-08-023756-8). Pergamon.

Nuclear Techniques in Animal Production & Health. (Proceedings Ser.). (Illus.). 607p. (Orig.). 1976. pap. 63.75 (ISBN 92-0-010276-X, ISP431, IAEA). Unipub.

The Nutrient Requirement of Pigs: Technical Review by an Agricultural Research Council Working Party. 307p. 1981. cloth 135.00x (ISBN 0-85198-483-5, Pub. by CAB Bks England). State Mutual Bk.

The Nutrient Requirements of Ruminant Livestock: Technical Review by an Agricultural Research Council Working Party. 352p. 1980. cloth 135.00x (ISBN 0-85198-459-2, Pub. by CAB Bks England). State Mutual Bk.

OECD Staff. Animal Feeding & Production: New Technical & Economic Development. (Agricultural Products & Markets Ser.). 214p. (Orig.). 1981. pap. 12.50x (ISBN 92-64-12167-6). OECD.

Owen, Jennifer. Feeding Strategy. LC 82-2569. (Phoenix Ser.). (Illus.). 160p. 1982. pap. 12.50 (ISBN 0-226-64186-4). U of Chicago Pr.

Parks, J. R. A Theory of Feeding & Growth of Animals. (Advanced Series in Agriculture: Vol. 11). (Illus.). 322p. 1982. 57.00 (ISBN 0-387-11122-0). Springer-Verlag.

Perry, T. W. Animal Life Cycle Feeding & Nutrition. (Animal Feeding & Nutrition Ser.). 1984. 24.50 (ISBN 0-12-552060-3). Acad Pr.

Pond, Wilson G. & Maner, Jerome H. Swine Production & Nutrition. (Illus.). 733p. 1984. 59.00 (ISBN 0-87055-450-6). AVI.

Price, D. Porter. Cattle Nutrition Primer. 1986. price not set (ISBN 0-9606246-4-3). SW Sci Pub.

Ranjhan, S. K. Animal Nutrition & Feeding Practices in India. (Illus.). 339p. 1977. 11.00x (ISBN 0-7069-0509-1, Pub. by Vikas India). Advent NY.

--Animal Nutrition in Tropics. 2nd. ed. xiv, 480p. 1981. text ed. 30.00x (ISBN 0-7069-1374-4, Pub. by Vikas India). Advent NY.

--Animal Nutrition in Tropics. 2nd ed. 480p. 1982. 50.00x (ISBN 0-7069-1374-4, Pub. by Garlandfold England); pap. 40.00x (ISBN 0-7069-1375-2). State Mutual Bk.

Rechcigl, M., ed. Handbook of Nutritive Value of Processed Food: Animal Foodstuffs, Vol. II. 520p. 1982. 73.00 (ISBN 0-8493-3953-7). CRC Pr.

Rechcigl, M., Jr., ed. Carbohydrates, Lipids & Accessory Growth Factors. (Comparative Animal Nutrition: Vol. 1). (Illus.). 1976. 41.75 (ISBN 3-8055-2268-1). S Karger.

Robbins, Charles T. Wildlife Feeding & Nutrition. LC 82-13720. 1983. 31.50 (ISBN 0-12-589380-9). Acad Pr.

Sodano, C. S. Animal Feeds & Pet Foods: Recent Developments. LC 78-70746. (Food Technology Review Ser.: No. 50). 1979. 36.00 (ISBN 0-8155-0737-2). Noyes.

Underwood, E. J. The Mineral Nutrition of Livestock. 180p. 1981. 85.00x (ISBN 0-85198-466-5, Pub. by CAB Bks England). State Mutual Bk.

Wilkinson, J. M. Milk & Meat from Grass. (Illus.). 224p. 1984. pap. 20.00x (ISBN 0-246-12290-0, Pub. by Granada England). Sheridan.

Wilson, P. N. Improved Feeding of Cattle & Sheep: Practical Guide to Modern Concepts of Ruminant Nutrition. 256p. 1982. pap. 19.95x (ISBN 0-246-11210-7, Pub. by Granada England). Sheridan.

ANIMAL OILS

see Oils and Fats

ANIMAL PARASITES

see Parasites

ANIMAL POISONS

see Venom

ANIMAL POPULATIONS

see also Bird Populations; Fish Populations; Population Genetics

Andrewartha, H. G. & Birch, L. C. Selections from the Distribution & Abundance of Animals. LC 82-6948. (Illus.). 288p. 1982. lib. bdg. 25.00x (ISBN 0-226-02031-2); pap. 9.00x (ISBN 0-226-02032-0). U of Chicago Pr.

Andrewartha, Herbert G. Introduction to the Study of Animal Populations. 2nd. ed. LC 73-135741. (Illus.). xvii, 281p. 1971. 12.00x (ISBN 0-226-02029-0, P519, Phoen). U of Chicago Pr.

Bacon, Philip J., ed. Population Dynamics of Rabies in Wildlife. Date not set. price not set (ISBN 0-12-071350-0). Acad Pr.

Baker, H. G. & Stebbins, G. L., eds. The Genetics of Colonizing Species. 1965. 74.50 (ISBN 0-12-075150-X). Acad Pr.

Barnard, C. J., ed. Producers & Scroungers Strategics of Exploitation & Parasitism. 267p. 1984. 39.95 (ISBN 0-412-00541-7, NO. 9017, Pub. by Chapman & Hall England). Methuen Inc.

Begon, Michael. Investigating Animal Abundance. (Illus.). 104p. 1979. pap. text ed. 15.00 (ISBN 0-8391-1387-0). Univ Park.

Begon, Michael & Mortimer, Martin. Population Ecology: A Unified Study of Animal & Plants. LC 81-5641. (Illus.). 256p. 1981. pap. text ed. 18.95x (ISBN 0-87893-067-1). Sinauer Assoc.

Blair, W. Frank. The Rusty Lizard: A Population Study. LC 59-8122. pap. 47.80 (ISBN 0-317-29262-5, 2055521). Bks Demand UMI.

Blake, Irving H. A Comparison of the Animal Communities of Coniferous & Deciduous Forests. Repr. of 1927 ed. 15.00 (ISBN 0-384-04665-7). Johnson Repr.

Blower, J. G., et al. Estimating the Size of Animal Populations. 96p. (Orig.). 1981. text ed. 22.50x (ISBN 0-04-591017-0); pap. text ed. 9.95x (ISBN 0-04-591018-9). Allen Unwin.

Caughley, Graeme. Analysis of Vertebrate Populations. LC 76-913. 1977. 53.95 (ISBN 0-471-01705-1, Pub. by Wiley-Interscience). Wiley.

Colbert, Edwin H. Wandering Lands & Animals: The Story of Continental Drift & Animal Populations. 352p. 1985. pap. 7.95 (ISBN 0-486-24918-2). Dover.

Cold Spring Harbor Symposia on Quantitative Biology: Population Studies, Vol. 22. LC 34-8174. (Illus.). 451p. 1958. 38.00x (ISBN 0-87969-021-6). Cold Spring Harbor.

Collins, Henry H., Jr. & Ransom, Jay E., eds. Harper & Row's Complete Field Guide to North American Wildlife: Eastern Edition. LC 80-8198. (Illus.). 810p. 1981. 17.50i (ISBN 0-690-01977-7, HarpT); flexible vinyl cover 12.95i (ISBN 0-690-01969-6); western edition 17.50i (ISBN 0-690-01979-3). Har-Row.

Craighead, John J. & Craighead, Frank C., Jr. Hawks, Owls & Wildlife. LC 74-81670. 1969. pap. 7.95 (ISBN 0-486-22123-7). Dover.

Errington, Paul L. Of Predation & Life. facsimile ed. (Illus.). 1967. pap. 12.75x (ISBN 0-8138-2325-0). Iowa St U Pr.

Goel, N. S., et al. On the Volterra & Other Nonlinear Models of Interacting Populations. (Reviews of Modern Physics Monographs). 1971. 39.00 (ISBN 0-12-287450-1). Acad Pr.

Golley, Frank B., ed. Ecological Succession. LC 76-52930. (Benchmark Papers in Ecology Ser.: Vol. 5). 1977. 46.50 (ISBN 0-87933-256-5). Van Nos Reinhold.

Krishnan, T. N. General Animal Ecology. 1976. 11.00x (ISBN 0-8364-0405-X); pap. 8.00x (ISBN 0-8364-0406-8). South Asia Bks.

Kunz, Thomas H. Population Studies of the Cave Bat (Myotis Velifer) Reproduction, Growth, & Development. (Occasional Papers: No. 15). 43p. 1973. pap. 2.50 (ISBN 0-317-04873-2). U of KS Mus Nat Hist.

Levins, Richard. Evolution in Changing Environments: Some Theoretical Explorations. LC 68-20871. (Monographs in Population Biology: No. 2). (Illus.). 1968. pap. 9.95 (ISBN 0-691-08062-3). Princeton U Pr.

Martin, Edwin P. A Population Study of the Prairie Vole (Microtus Ochrogaster) Northeastern Kansas. (Museum Ser.: Vol. 8, No. 6). 56p. 1956. pap. 3.00 (ISBN 0-317-04886-4). U of KS Mus Nat Hist.

May, Robert M. Stability & Complexity in Model Ecosystems. (Population Biology Monographs: No. 6). 150p. 1973. 26.00x (ISBN 0-691-08125-5); pap. 9.95x (ISBN 0-691-08130-1). Princeton U Pr.

Morisita, T., ed. Studies on Methods of Estimating Population Density, Biomass & Productivity in Terrestrial Animals, Vol. 17. (Japan International Biological Program Synthesis Ser.). 237p. 1977. 26.00x (ISBN 0-86008-227-X, Pub. by U of Tokyo Japan). Columbia U Pr.

Moss, R., et al. Animal Population Dynamics. LC 82-9531. 1982. 7.50 (ISBN 0-412-22240-X, NO. 2297, Pub. by Chapman & Hall). Methuen Inc.

National Research Council Institute of Laboratory Animal Resources. Primate Population Ecology. 1981. pap. text ed. 14.50 (ISBN 0-309-03179-6). Natl Acad Pr.

Pefaur, Jaime E. & Hoffmann, Robert S. Studies of Small Mammal Populations at Three Sites on the Northern Great Plains. (Occasional Papers: No. 37). 27p. 1975. pap. 1.75 (ISBN 0-317-04897-X). U of KS Mus Nat Hist.

Seber, George A. Estimation of Animal Abundance. 2nd ed. (Illus.). 600p. 1982. 55.00 (ISBN 0-02-852010-6). Macmillan.

--The Estimation of Animal Abundance & Related Parameters. 672p. 1982. 90.00x (ISBN 0-85264-262-8, Pub. by Griffin England). State Mutual Bk.

Slobodkin, Lawrence B. Growth & Regulation of Animal Populations. (Illus.). 1980. pap. 7.95 (ISBN 0-486-63958-4). Dover.

Tanner, James T. Guide to the Study of Animal Populations. LC 77-13630. 1978. 14.95x (ISBN 0-87049-235-7). U of Tenn Pr.

Tuttle, Merlin D. Population Ecology of the Gray Bat (Myotis Grisescens) Factors Influencing Early Growth & Development. (Occasional Papers: No. 36). 24p. 1975. pap. 1.50 (ISBN 0-317-04951-8). U of KS Mus Nat Hist.

--Population Ecology of the Gray Bat (Myotis Grisescens) Philopatry, Timing & Patterns of Movement, Weight Loss During Migration, & Seasonal Adaptive Strategies. (Occasional Papers: No. 54). 38p. 1976. pap. 2.25 (ISBN 0-317-04955-0). U of KS Mus Nat Hist.

ANIMAL PRODUCTS

see also Dairy Products; Meat; Raw Materials; also names of particular products, e.g. Ivory, Wool, etc.

Agricultural & Renewable Resources Board & Food & Nutrition Board, Natural Research Council. Fat Content & Composition of Animal Products. LC 76-6496. 254p. 1976. pap. 10.75 (ISBN 0-309-02440-4). Natl Acad Pr.

Beitz, Donald & Hansen, R. G. Animal Products in Human Nutrition. (Nutrition Foundation Monograph). 1982. 69.50 (ISBN 0-12-086380-4). Acad Pr.

CRC Handbook of Agricultural Productivity, Vol. II: Animal Productivity. 416p. 1981. 72.00 (ISBN 0-8493-3963-4). CRC Pr.

Divakaran, S. Animal Blood Processing & Utilization: Processing & Utilization. (Agricultural Services Bulletins: No. 32). (Eng. & Span.). 107p. 1982. pap. 7.75 (ISBN 92-5-100491-9, F2315, FAO). Unipub.

Kiflewahid, Berhane & Potts, Gordon R., eds. By-Product Utilization for Animal Production: Proceedings of a Workshop on Applied Research Held in Nairobi, Kenya, 26-30 September 1982. 158p. 1983. pap. text ed. 13.00 (ISBN 0-88936-365-X, IDRC206, IDRC). Unipub.

Mann, I. Animal By-Products Processing & Utilization. (Agricultural Development Papers: No. 75). 246p. 1978. pap. 7.50 (ISBN 92-5-100455-2, F1456, FAO). Unipub.

Nestel, B. L. Development of Animal Production Systems. (World Animal Science Ser.: Vol. 2A). 350p. 1983. 98.00 (ISBN 0-444-42050-9, I-474-83). Elsevier.

OECD Staff. Animal Feeding & Production: New Technical & Economic Development. (Agricultural Products & Markets Ser.). 214p. (Orig.). 1981. pap. 12.50x (ISBN 92-64-12167-6). OECD.

Riis, P. M. Dynamic Biochemistry of Animal Production. (World Animal Science Ser.: Vol. 3A). 502p. 1983. 109.25 (ISBN 0-444-42052-5, I-311-83). Elsevier.

Yagil, R. Camels & Camel Milk. (Animal Production & Health Papers: No. 26). 72p. 1982. pap. 7.50 (ISBN 92-5-101169-9, F2310, FAO). Unipub.

ANIMAL RUNNING

see Animal Locomotion

ANIMAL SOCIETIES

Here are entered works on groups of animals which are characterized by specific social patterns due to their proximity, interrelationships and-or similarities.

see also Insect Societies

Allee, Warder C. Animal Aggregations, A Study in General Sociology. LC 75-41007. Repr. of 1931 ed. 28.00 (ISBN 0-404-14501-9). AMS Pr.

Espinas, Alfred V. Des Societies Animals: Animal Societies. Egerton, Frank N., 3rd, ed. LC 77-74219. (History of Ecology Ser.). 1978. Repr. of 1878 ed. lib. bdg. 34.00 (ISBN 0-405-10390-5). Ayer Co Pubs.

ANIMAL SOUNDS

see also Bird-Song

Bright, Michael. Animal Language. (Illus.). 247p. (Orig.). 1985. text ed. 24.95x (ISBN 0-8014-1837-2); pap. 12.95 (ISBN 0-8014-9340-4). Cornell U Pr.

Lanyon, W. E. & Tavolga, W. N. Animal Sound & Communications. 1960. 5.00 (ISBN 0-934454-07-8). Lubrecht & Cramer.

ANIMAL TAXONOMY

see Zoology–Classification

ANIMAL TRACKS

DeLorme Publishing Company Staff. Wildlife Signatures: A Guide to the Identification of Tracks & Scat. Abridged ed. (Maine Geographic Ser.). (Illus.). 48p. 1983. pap. 2.95 (ISBN 0-89933-064-9). DeLorme Pub.

Headstrom, Richard. Identifying Animal Tracks: Mammals, Birds & Other Animals of the Eastern United States. (Illus.). 128p. 1983. pap. 3.50 (ISBN 0-486-24442-3). Dover.

Olaus, Murie J. A Field Guide to Animal Tracks. 2nd ed. LC 74-6294. (Peterson Field Guide Ser.). 1975. 15.95 (ISBN 0-395-19978-6); pap. 9.95 (ISBN 0-395-18323-5). HM.

Pandell, Karen & Stall, Chris. Animal Tracks of the Pacific Northwest. LC 81-2041. (Illus.). 120p. (Orig.). 1981. pap. 3.95 (ISBN 0-89886-012-1). Mountaineers.

ANIMAL TRAINING

see Animals, Training Of

ANIMAL WALKING

see Animal Locomotion

ANIMAL WEAPONS

see also Animal Defenses

Street, Philip. Animal Weapons. LC 74-153075. (Illus.). 1971. 7.95 (ISBN 0-8008-0265-9). Taplinger.

ANIMALS

see also Animals and Civilization; Aquatic Animals; Color of Animals; Invertebrates; Mammals; Vertebrates; Zoo Animals; Zoology; also names of kinds of animals, e.g. Bears, cats, deer, etc.

Adams, Charles C., 3rd. Guide to the Study of Animal Ecology. Edgerton, Frank N., ed. LC 77-74201. (History of Ecology Ser.). (Illus.). 1978. Repr. of 1913 ed. lib. bdg. 16.00x (ISBN 0-405-10371-9). Ayer Co Pubs.

Akimushkin, I. Adonde? y Como? (Span.). 375p. 1973. 5.95 (ISBN 0-8285-1462-3, Pub. by Mir Pubs USSR). Imported Pubns.

Alcala, Angel C. Philippine Land Vertebrates: Field Biology. 1976. wrps. 6.50x (ISBN 0-686-09425-5). Cellar.

Alexander, R. McNeill. Optima for Animals. 120p. 1982. pap. text ed. 13.95 (ISBN 0-7131-2843-7). E Arnold.

Allen, Thomas B., et al. Earth's Amazing Animals. Parker, Ceilia I., ed. LC 83-17324. (Illus.). 208p. 1983. 18.95 (ISBN 0-912186-48-8). Natl Wildlife.

Audubon Society. Encyclopedia of Animal Life. Farrand, John, Jr., ed. (Illus.). 1982. 45.00 (ISBN 0-517-54657-4, C N Potter Bks). Crown.

Bernard, Claude. Lectures on the Phenomena of Life Common to Animals & Plants, Vol. 1. Hoff, Hebbel E., et al, trs. (Illus.). 336p. 1974. 34.75x (ISBN 0-398-02857-5). C C Thomas.

Brant, George. Introductory Animal Science. 1980. perfect binding 9.95 (ISBN 0-88252-112-8). Paladin Hse.

Burton, Maurice. True Book About Animals. 13.75x (ISBN 0-392-08507-0, SpS). Sportshelf.

Burton, Maurice & Burton, Jane. The Colorful World of Animals. (Illus.). 1979. 10.95 (ISBN 0-8317-1507-3, Mayflower Bks). Smith Pubs.

Chambers, Kenneth. The Country Lover's Guide to Wildlife: Mammals, Amphibians, & Reptiles of the Northeastern United States. LC 79-4338. (Illus.). 248p. 1979. 18.50 (ISBN 0-8018-2207-6). Johns Hopkins.

Chambers, Kenneth A. A Country Lover's Guide to Wildlife. (Illus.). 1980. pap. 8.95 (ISBN 0-452-25239-3, Plume). NAL.

Chapman, Royal N. Animal Ecology: Special Reference to Insects. Egerton, Frank N., 3rd, ed. LC 77-74208. (History of Ecology Ser.). 1978. Repr. of 1932 ed. lib. bdg. 36.50x (ISBN 0-405-10379-4). Ayer Co Pubs.

Chinery, Michael, ed. Dictionary of Animals. LC 84-716. (Illus.). 380p. 1984. 17.95 (ISBN 0-668-06155-3, 6155-3). Arco.

Convention on International Trade in Endangered Species of Wild Fauna & Flora. Guidelines for the Transport & Preparation of Shipment of Live Wild Animals & Plants. 109p. 1981. pap. 13.00 (ISBN 0-686-93565-9, UPB100, UNEP); pap. 13.00 Fr. ed. (ISBN 0-686-99140-0, UPB102); pap. 13.00 Span. ed. (ISBN 0-686-99141-9, UPB101). Unipub.

Cornett, Jim. Wildlife of the Western Mountains. (Illus.). 244p. (Orig.). 1982. pap. 7.95 (ISBN 0-937794-03-1). Nature Trails.

Davenport, Richard. Outline of Animal Development. LC 78-62548. (Life Sciences Ser.). (Illus.). 1979. text ed. 24.95 (ISBN 0-201-01814-4). Addison-Wesley.

Dillon, Lawrence S. Animal Variety: An Evolutionary Account. 4th ed. 325p. 1980. pap. text ed. write for info. (ISBN 0-697-04590-0). Wm C Brown.

Druett, Joan. Exotic Intruders: The Introduction of Plants & Animals into New Zealand. (Illus.). 291p. 1984. 24.95x (ISBN 0-86863-397-6, Pub. by Heinemann Pub New Zealand). Intl Spec Bk.

Durrell, Gerald. Birds, Beasts, & Relatives. 1977. pap. 3.95 (ISBN 0-14-004385-3). Penguin.

--Birds, Beasts & Relatives. 1983. 12.75 (ISBN 0-8446-6071-X). Peter Smith.

Eberhard, William G. Sexual Selection & Animal Genitalia. (Illus.). 288p. 1985. text ed. 25.00x (ISBN 0-674-80283-7). Harvard U Pr.

Enciclopedia De los Animales. (Espn.). 400p. 1976. 50.00 (ISBN 84-278-0457-1, S-50536). French & Eur.

Encyclopedie Illustree Du Monde Animal. (Fr.). 600p. 14.95 (ISBN 0-686-57159-2, M-6218). French & Eur.

Farrand, John, Jr., ed. The Audubon Society Encyclopedia of Animal Life. LC 82-81466. (Illus.). 600p. 1982. 19.95 (ISBN 0-517-54657-4, Pub. by Potter). Crown.

Fowler, Murray E. Restraint & Handling of Wild & Domestic Animals. (Illus.). 332p. 1978. text ed. 28.95x (ISBN 0-8138-1890-7). Iowa St U Pr.

Foy, Sally & Oxford Scientific Films. The Grand Design: Form & Color in Animals. (Illus.). 238p. 1983. 24.95 (ISBN 0-13-362574-5). P-H.

Freshney, Ian R., ed. Culture of Animal Cells: A Manual of Basic Technique. LC 82-24960. 310p. 1983. 49.50 (ISBN 0-8451-0223-0). A R Liss.

Friedhoff, Herman, ed. Encyclopedia of the Animal World. (Illus.). 2000p. 1980. lib. bdg. 169.95x (ISBN 0-85835-427-6). M Cavendish Corp.

Gack & Jahn. Herder - Lexikon Tiere. (Ger.). 342p. 1976. pap. 15.95 (ISBN 3-451-17371-9, M-7459, Pub. by Herder). French & Eur.

Gentry, Christine. When Dogs Run Wild: The Sociology of Feral Dogs & Wildlife. LC 82-17223. (Illus.). 208p. 1983. lib. bdg. 16.95X (ISBN 0-89950-062-5). McFarland & Co.

Goto, H. E. Animal Toxonomy. (Studies in Biology Ser.: No. 143). 64p. 1982. pap. text ed. 8.95 (ISBN 0-7131-2847-X). E Arnold.

Gozmany, L., et al, eds. Septemlingual Dictionary of the Names of European Animals, 2 vols. (Eng., Rus., Span., Ger., Hungarian, Fr., & Lat.). 2232p. 1979. Set. 230.00 (ISBN 963-05-1381-1, Pub. by Akademiai Kaido Hungary). Heyden.

Gozmany, Laslo. Septemligual Dictionary of the Names of European Animals, 2 vols. 2188p. 1980. 500.00x (ISBN 0-569-08577-2, Pub. by Collet's). State Mutual Bk.

Graham, C. F. & Wareing, P. F. Developmental Control in Animals & Plants. 2nd ed. (Illus.). 424p. 1984. pap. text ed. 32.50x (ISBN 0-632-00758-3, Pub. by Blackwell Sci UK). Blackwell Pubns.

Hall, Rebecca. Animals Are Equal: An Exploration of Animal Consciousness. 256p. 1983. pap. 7.50 (ISBN 0-7045-0438-3, Pub. by Salem Hse Ltd). Merrimack Pub Cir.

Headstrom, Richard. Weird & the Beautiful. LC 81-67780. (Illus.). 240p. 1984. 14.95 (ISBN 0-8453-4727-6). Cornwall Bks.

Hickin, N. E. Animal Life of the Galapagos. 1980. 39.00x (ISBN 0-317-07025-8, Pub. by EW Classey UK). State Mutual Bk.

International Association of Fish & Wildlife Agencies, 70th Convention: Proceedings. 1981. 13.00 (ISBN 0-932108-05-9). IAFWA.

Johnson, F. B. Basenji: Dog from the Past. 65p. 1972. pap. 5.00 (ISBN 0-9600510-1-5). F B Johnson.

Johnson, Martin. Safari: A Saga of the African Blue. LC 72-170251. (Tower Bks). (Illus.). x, 294p. 1972. Repr. of 1928 ed. 40.00x (ISBN 0-8103-3934-X). Gale.

Jonch, Cuspinera & Antonio y Bas Peired, Carlos. La Vida Maravillosa De los Animales, 2 vols. 6th ed. (Espn.). 960p. 1977. Set. leather 110.00 (ISBN 84-85009-32-0, S-50487). French & Eur.

Jordan, David S., et al. Animal Studies. 1907. 20.00 (ISBN 0-8482-4653-5). Norwood Edns.

Kerrich, G. J., et al, eds. Key Words to the Fauna & Flora of the British Isles & Northwestern Europe. (Systematic Association Special Ser.). 1978. 40.00 (ISBN 0-12-405550-8). Acad Pr.

Kershaw, Diana R. Animal Diversity. (Illus.). 442p. (Orig.). 1983. pap. text ed. 26.50x (ISBN 0-7231-0847-1, Pub. by U Tutor Pr England). Sheridan.

L. H. An Atlas of the Biologic Resources of the Hudson Estuary. (Illus.). 104p. (Orig.). 1977. pap. 5.50 (ISBN 0-89062-096-2, Pub. by Boyce Thompson Inst Plant Res). Pub Ctr Cult Res.

Lawrence, R. D. The Zoo That Never Was. LC 80-18956. (Illus.). 304p. 1981. 13.95 (ISBN 0-03-056811-0). HR&W.

Lehmann, Val W. Forgotten Legions: Sheep in the Rio Grande Plain of Texas. LC 76-102787. 1969. 10.00 (ISBN 0-87404-022-1). Tex Western.

Levy, Charles K. A Field Guide to Dangerous Animals of North America. LC 83-1440. (Illus.). 192p. 1983. 16.95 (ISBN 0-8289-0524-X); pap. 9.95 (ISBN 0-8289-0503-7). Greene.

Lewin, Ralph. Biology of Women & Other Animals. (Orig.). 1983. pap. 5.95 (ISBN 0-910286-91-4). Boxwood.

Lockwood, A. P. & Lee, A. G. The Membranes of Animal Cells. 3rd ed. (Studies in Biology: No. 27). 88p. 1984. pap. text ed. 8.95 (ISBN 0-7131-2886-0). E Arnold.

Maciejowski, J. & Zieba, J. Genetic & Animal Breeding, 2 pts. (Developments in Animal & Veterinary Science Ser.: Vol. 10). 1983. Pt. A, Biological & Genetic Foundation of Animal Breeding. 57.50 (ISBN 0-444-99696-6); Pt. B, Stock Improvement Methods. 57.50 (ISBN 0-444-99732-6, I-528-82); 115.00 set (ISBN 0-444-99676-1). Elsevier.

Mech, L. David. Handbook of Animal Radio-Tracking. (Illus.). 128p. 1983. 25.00x (ISBN 0-8166-1222-6); pap. 9.95x (ISBN 0-8166-1221-8). U of Minn Pr.

Mertens, Thomas R. & Geary, Michael. Animal Development. 2nd ed. (Programed Biology Studies). 1977. 6.95 (ISBN 0-88462-039-5, Ed Methods). Longman USA.

Moberg, Gary P. Animal Stress. 332p. 1985. 42.50 (ISBN 0-683-06101-1). Waverly Pr.

Morrison, Susan. Arkansas Wildlife. LC 80-52076. 64p. 1980. 14.95 (ISBN 0-914546-32-5). Rose Pub.

Ray, G. Carleton & McCormick-Ray, M. G. Wildlife of the Polar Regions. (Wildlife Habitat Ser.). (Illus.). 232p. 1981. 19.95 (ISBN 0-8109-1768-8). Abrams.

Reader's Digest Editors. Our Magnificent Wildlife: How to Enjoy & Preserve It. LC 74-30861. (Illus.). 352p. 1975. 19.98 (ISBN 0-89577-022-9). RD Assn.

Roderman & Booth. Animals. (Science in Action Ser.). (Illus.). 48p. 1984. pap. text ed. 2.85 (ISBN 0-88102-022-2). Janus Bks.

Rousselet-Blanc, Pierre. Larousse Des Animaux Familiers Insolites. (Fr.). 1976. 15.95 (ISBN 0-686-56994-6, M-6334). French & Eur.

Seton, Ernest T. Wild Animals I Have Known. 1898. 40.00 (ISBN 0-8482-6460-6). Norwood Edns.

Seton, Ernst T. Animal Heroes: Being the Histories of a Cat, a Dog, a Pigeon, a Lynx, Two Wolves & a Reindeer, & Elucidation of the Same. 40.00 (ISBN 0-8482-6307-3). Norwood Edns.

Shelford, Victor E. Animal Communities in Temperate America: Illustrated in the Chicago Region, Study in Animal Ecology. Egerton, Frank N., 3rd, ed. LC 77-74252. (History of Ecology Ser.). (Illus.). 1978. Repr. of 1937 ed. lib. bdg. 32.00x (ISBN 0-405-10421-9). Ayer Co Pubs.

Sims, R. W. Animal Identification: A Reference Guide, 2 vols. Incl. Vol. 1. Marine & Brackish Water Animals. (Animal Identification Ser.). 111p. 1980 (ISBN 0-471-27765-7); Vol. 2. Land & Freshwater Animals. 120p. 37.95 (ISBN 0-471-27766-5). 391p. 1980. 34.95x ea.; 128.95x set (ISBN 0-471-27768-1). Wiley.

Stanbury, Peter & Phipps, Graeme. Australia's Animals Discovered. (Illus.). 120p. 1980. 28.00 (ISBN 0-08-024796-2). Pergamon.

Taylor, C. Richard, et al, eds. A Companion to Animal Physiology. LC 81-17055. 304p. 1982. 39.50 (ISBN 0-521-24437-4); pap. 15.95 (ISBN 0-521-28685-9). Cambridge U Pr.

Telford, Lawrence S. Wild Life in Alaska. 1980. 7.50 (ISBN 0-682-49581-6). Exposition Pr FL.

Thorndike Press, ed. Maine Animals. LC 78-9725. (Maine Nature Ser.). (Illus.). pap. 3.95 (ISBN 0-89621-012-X). Thorndike Pr.

Thornton, John W. Animal Biology Laboratory Exercises. 120p. 1984. pap. 8.95 (ISBN 0-8403-3442-7). Kendall Hunt.

Tinbergen, Niko. The Animal in Its World, Explorations of an Ethologist, 1932-1972, Vol. 2: Laboratory Experiments & General Papers. LC 72-94876. 296p. 1973. text ed. 16.00x (ISBN 0-674-03727-8); pap. 6.95x (ISBN 0-674-03728-6). Harvard U Pr.

Todt, Dietmar. Vox--Enciclopedia Cultural, Tomo 9: Los Animales. (Espn.). 210p. 1977. leatherette 29.95 (ISBN 84-7153-496-7, S-50500). French & Eur.

Wagner, Frederic H. Wildlife of the Deserts. (Wildlife Habitat Ser.). (Illus.). 232p. 1980. 19.95 (ISBN 0-8109-1764-5, 1764-5). Abrams.

Whittaker, Neville, et al. Animals by Air: The Extraordinary Adventures of a Modern-Day Noah. (Illus.). 208p. 1984. 11.95 (ISBN 0-283-98839-8, Pub. by Sidgwick & Jackson). Merrimack Pub Cir.

Wilburn, Jack. Wild Animals of California & the West: Mountains & Desert, Vol. 1. LC 76-29497. (Nature's Wild Ser.). (Illus.). 1980. pap. 7.95 (ISBN 0-917982-12-6). Cougar Bks.

Wood, Dennis. Principles of Animal Physiology. 350p. 1982. pap. text ed. 19.95 (ISBN 0-7131-2861-5). E Arnold.

Zahradnik, Jiri & Cihar, Jiri. A Field Guide in Color to Animals. LC 79-13565. (Field Guides in Color Ser.). (Illus.). 1979. 7.95 (ISBN 0-7064-1081-5, Mayflower Bks). Smith Pubs.

ANIMALS, ABNORMALITIES OF

see Abnormalities (Animals)

ANIMALS, AQUATIC

see Fresh-Water Biology; Marine Fauna

ANIMALS, COLOR OF

see Color of Animals

ANIMALS, CRUELTY TO

see Animals, Treatment Of

ANIMALS, DOMESTIC

see Domestic Animals

ANIMALS, EXPERIMENTAL

see Laboratory Animals

ANIMALS, EXTINCT

see Extinct Animals

ANIMALS, FOOD HABITS OF

see also Food Chains (Ecology); also subdivisions Feeding and Feeds and Food under kinds of animals, e.g. Poultry–Feeding and Feeds; Dogs–Food

Bourne, G. H., ed. Human Nutrition & Animal Feeding. (World Review of Nutrition & Dietetics: Vol. 37). (Illus.). xii, 292p. 1981. 105.25 (ISBN 3-8055-2143-X). S Karger.

Crop Residues & Agro-Industrial By-Products in Animal Feeding: Proceedings of the FAO/ILCA Workshop Dakar, Senegal, September 1982. (Animal Production & Health Papers: No. 32). (Eng. & Fr.). 152p. 1984. pap. 11.00 (ISBN 92-5-001227-6, F2483, FAO). Unipub.

Egerton, Frank N., ed. Ecological Investigations of Stephen Alfred Forbes: An Original Anthology. LC 77-74217. (History of Ecology Ser.). 1978. lib. bdg. 53.00x (ISBN 0-405-10387-5). Ayer Co Pubs.

Fiennes, R. N., ed. Biology of Nutrition, Pts. 1-2. Incl. Pt. 1. The Evolution & Nature of Living Systems; Pt. 2. The Organizations & Nutritional Methods of Life Forms. 688p. 1972. Set. text ed. 150.00 (ISBN 0-08-016470-6). Pergamon.

Hoebel, B. G. & Novin, D., eds. The Neural Basis of Feeding & Reward. (Illus.). 575p. (Orig.). 1982. pap. text ed. 39.95 (ISBN 0-940090-02-3). Haer Inst.

Kamil, Alan C. & Sargent, Theodore D. Foraging Behavior: Ecological, Ethological, & Psychological Approaches. LC 79-24143. 448p. 1980. lib. bdg. 57.50 (ISBN 0-8240-7068-2). Garland Pub.

Picconi, Marcello. Dictionnaire des Aliments pour les Animaux. (Fr.). 620p. 1965. 42.50 (ISBN 0-686-57077-4, M-6452). French & Eur.

Robbins, Charles T. Wildlife Feeding & Nutrition. LC 82-13720. 1983. 31.50 (ISBN 0-12-589380-9). Acad Pr.

Subcommittee on Toxicity in Animals, Board on Agricultural & Renewable Resources. Mineral Tolerance of Domestic Animals. 577p. 1980. pap. text ed. 15.95 (ISBN 0-309-03022-6). Natl Acad Pr.

ANIMALS, FOSSIL

see Paleontology

ANIMALS, GEOGRAPHICAL DISTRIBUTION OF

see Zoogeography

ANIMALS, HABITATIONS OF

Boardman, Richard S., et al. Animal Colonies: Development & Function Through Time. LC 73-14960. 603p. 1973. 63.50 (ISBN 0-87933-035-X). Van Nos Reinhold.

Elton, C. S. The Pattern of Animal Communities. 1966. pap. 19.95 (ISBN 0-412-21880-1, NO. 6579, Pub. by Chapman & Hall). Methuen Inc.

Grasse, P. P., ed. La Vie des Animaux, 4 vols. (Fr., Illus.). 1969. Vols. 1-3. 57.25x ea.; Vol. 4. 49.95x (ISBN 0-685-92813-6). Larousse.

Haviland, Maud D. Forest, Steppe & Tundra: Studies in the Animal Environment. LC 76-44734. Repr. of 1926 ed. 24.00 (ISBN 0-404-15933-8). AMS Pr.

Sweton, Ernest T. Wild Animals at Home. 126p. 1982. Repr. of 1913 ed. lib. bdg. 30.00 (ISBN 0-89760-852-6). Telegraph Bks.

ANIMALS, HABITS AND BEHAVIOR OF

see also Animal Defenses; Animal Intelligence; Animal Migration; Animals, Food Habits of; Animals, Infancy of; Behavior Genetics; Birds–Behavior; Hibernation; Insect Societies; Instinct; Mimicry (Biology); Nature Study; Nocturnal Animals; Primates–Behavior also names of particular animals

Adler, Norman T., ed. Neuroendocrinology of Reproduction: Physiology & Behavior. LC 80-28245. 576p. 1981. 42.00x (ISBN 0-306-40600-4, Plenum Pr); pap. 18.95x (ISBN 0-306-40611-X). Plenum Pub.

Albone, Eric S. Mammalian Semiochemistry: The Investigation of Chemical Signals Between Mammals. LC 83-10231. 360p. 1984. 57.00x (ISBN 0-471-10253-9, Pub. by Wiley-Interscience). Wiley.

Alcock, John. Animal Behavior: An Evolutionary Approach. 3rd, rev. ed. LC 83-14420. (Illus.). 380p. 1983. text ed. 27.50 (ISBN 0-87893-021-3). Sinauer Assoc.

Allen, Thomas B. Vanishing Wildlife of North America. LC 73-833. (Special Publications Ser.). 1974. avail. only from Natl. Geog. 6.95 (ISBN 0-87044-129-9). Natl Geog.

Alverdes, F. Social Life in the Animal World. LC 27-17110. Repr. of 1927 ed. 17.00 (ISBN 0-527-01700-0). Kraus Repr.

American Psychological Association. Natural Behavior in Humans & Animals. (Human Behavior Curriculum Project Ser.). 55p. (Orig.). 1981. pap. text ed. 3.95x (ISBN 0-8077-2613-3); tchrs. manual & duplication masters 9.95x (ISBN 0-8077-2614-1). Tchrs Coll.

Amos, William H. Wildlife of the Rivers. LC 80-21928. (Wildlife Habitat Ser.). (Illus.). 232p. 1981. 19.95 (ISBN 0-8109-1767-X). Abrams.

Aoki, K., et al, eds. Animal Behavior. 274p. 1984. 42.00 (ISBN 0-387-13046-2). Springer Verlag.

Ardrey, Robert. The Social Contract: A Personal Inquiry into the Evolutionary Source of Order & Disorder. LC 73-124967. (Illus.). 1970. 10.00 (ISBN 0-689-10347-6). Atheneum.

--The Territorial Imperative: A Personal Inquiry into the Animal Origins of Property & Nations. LC 66-23572. (Illus.). 1966. 10.95 (ISBN 0-689-10015-9). Atheneum.

Aronson, Lester R., et al, eds. Development & Evolution of Behavior, Essays in Memory of T. C. Schneirla. LC 76-84600. (Illus.). 656p. 1970. text ed. 41.95 (ISBN 0-7167-0921-X). W H Freeman.

Aspey, Wayne P. & Lustick, Sheldon I., eds. Behavioral Energetics: The Cost of Survival in Vertebrates. LC 82-12512. (Ohio State Univ. Biosciences Colloquia: No. 7). 312p. 1983. 27.50x (ISBN 0-8142-0332-9). Ohio St U Pr.

Bailey, Vernon. Animal Life of Yellowstone National Park. (Illus.). 232p. 1930. 19.75x (ISBN 0-398-04198-9). C C Thomas.

Baker, Samuel W. Wild Beasts & Their Ways. 45.00 (ISBN 0-686-19867-0). Ridgeway Bks.

Banks, Edwin M. & Heisey, John A. Animal Behavior. (Programmed Biology Ser.). (Illus.). 1977. pap. text ed. 6.95 (ISBN 0-88462-026-3, Ed Methods). Longman USA.

Barnard, C. J. Animal Behaviour: Ecology & Evolution. 339p. 1983. 21.50 (ISBN 0-471-88929-6, Pub. by Wiley-Interscience). Wiley.

Barnett, S. A. Modern Ethology: The Science of Animal Behavior. (Illus.). 1981. text ed. 25.95x (ISBN 0-19-502780-9). Oxford U Pr.

Barnett, S. A., ed. Lessons from Animal Behaviour for the Clinician. (Clinics in Developmental Medicine Ser. No. 7). 50p. 1962. 4.00i (ISBN 0-685-24713-9). Har-Row.

Bartholini, G., et al, eds. Gaba & Mood Disorders: Animal & Clinical Studies. (L. E. R. S. Monograph: Vol. 4). 1985. text ed. price not set (ISBN 0-88167-129-0). Raven.

Bateson, P. P. & Hinde, R. A., eds. Growing Points in Ethology. LC 76-8291. (Illus.). 500p. 1976. 72.50 (ISBN 0-521-21287-1); pap. 21.95x (ISBN 0-521-29086-4). Cambridge U Pr.

Biology Colloquium, 32nd, Oregon State University, 1971. The Biology of Behavior: Proceedings. Kiger, John A., Jr., ed. LC 52-19235. (Illus.). 1972. 9.95x (ISBN 0-87071-171-7). Oreg St U Pr.

Bliss, Eugene L., ed. Roots of Behavior: Genetics, Instinct, & Socialization in Animal Behavior. (Illus.). 1969. Repr. of 1962 ed. 22.95x (ISBN 0-02-841540-X). Hafner.

Bonner, John T. Cells & Societies. 1955. 25.00x (ISBN 0-691-07919-6). Princeton U Pr.

Boone, J. Allen. Kinship with All Life. LC 54-6901. 160p. 1976. pap. 6.68 (ISBN 0-06-060912-5, RD128, HarpR). Har-Row.

Borchelt, Peter, et al, eds. Animal Behavior & Thanatology. (Current Thanatology Ser.). 100p. 1986. pap. 13.95 (ISBN 0-930194-37-3). Ctr Thanatology.

Box, Hilary O. Organization in Animal Communities: Experimental & Naturalistic Studies of the Social Behavior of Animals. 251p. 1973. pap. 19.95x (ISBN 0-8448-0655-2). Crane-Russak Co.

Breland, Osmond P. Animal Life & Lore. rev. ed. (Illus.). 448p. 1972. 12.50i (ISBN 0-06-010464-3, HarpT). Har-Row.

Brinker, W. O., et al, eds. Manual of Internal Fixation in Small Animals. (Illus.). 304p. 1984. 159.00 (ISBN 0-387-10629-4); slides 143.80 (ISBN 0-387-92118-4). Springer-Verlag.

Broadhurst, P. L. Science of Animal Behaviour. 1963. lib. bdg. 13.50x (ISBN 0-88307-035-9). Gannon.

Brown, Jerram. The Evolution of Behavior. 900p. 1975. text ed. 22.95x (ISBN 0-393-09295-X). Norton.

Burroughs, John. Ways of Nature. facsimile ed. LC 77-157963. (Essay Index Reprint Ser). Repr. of 1905 ed. 19.00 (ISBN 0-8369-2217-4). Ayer Co Pubs.

Burton, Maurice & Burton, Robert. Enciclopedia de la Vida Animal, 6 vols. 2nd ed. (Espn.). 2770p. 1978. Set. leather 264.00 (ISBN 84-02-03435-7, S-50508). French & Eur.

Burtt, E. T. The Sense of Animals. (The Wykeham Science Ser.: No. 26). 128p. 1974. pap. cancelled (ISBN 0-85109-370-1). Taylor & Francis.

Busnel, R. G. & Fish, J. F., eds. Animal Sonar Systems. LC 79-23074. (NATO ASI Series A, Life Sciences: Vol. 28). 1159p. 1980. 95.00x (ISBN 0-306-40327-7, Plenum Pr). Plenum Pub.

Bustad, Leo K. Animals, Aging, & the Aged. (Wesley W. Spink Lectures in Comparative Medicine Ser.). (Illus.). 224p. 1981. 19.50x (ISBN 0-8166-0997-7). U of Minn Pr.

Camhi, Jeffrey M. Neuroethology: Nerve Cells & the Natural Behavior of Animals. LC 83-14957. (Illus.). 360p. 1983. text ed. 32.50x (ISBN 0-87893-075-2). Sinauer Assoc.

Campbell, Bernard, ed. Sexual Selection & the Descent of Man. LC 70-169510. 388p. 1972. 39.95x (ISBN 0-202-02005-3). Aldine Pub.

Clutton-Brock, T. H. & Guinness, F. E. Red Deer: Behavior & Ecology of Two Sexes. LC 81-22025. (Wildlife Behavior & Ecology (WBE)). (Illus.). 1982. lib. bdg. 40.00x (ISBN 0-226-11056-7); pap. 14.00x (ISBN 0-226-11057-5). U of Chicago Pr.

Collias, Nicholas E. & Collias, Elsie C., eds. External Construction by Animals. LC 75-34185. (Benchmark Papers in Animal Behavior: Vol. 4). 1976. 63.00 (ISBN 0-12-786250-1). Acad Pr.

Cowles, Raymond B. Zulu Journal: Field Notes of a Naturalist in South Africa. LC 59-8760. 1959. pap. 1.95 (ISBN 0-520-00276-8, CAL73). U of Cal Pr.

Cramond, Mike. Killer Bears. (Illus.). 224p. 1981. 7.95 (ISBN 0-684-17285-2, ScribT). Scribner.

Dethier, Vincent G. & Stellar, Eliot. Animal Behavior. 3rd ed. LC 78-110092. 1970. pap. 17.95 ref ed. (ISBN 0-13-037440-7). P-H.

Dewsbury, Donald, ed. Leaders in the Study of Animal Behavior. LC 83-46153. (Illus.). 512p. 1985. 59.50 (ISBN 0-317-18333-8). Bucknell U Pr.

Dewsbury, Donald A. Comparative Animal Behavior. (Illus.). 1978. text ed. 38.95 (ISBN 0-07-016673-0). McGraw.

Dickinson, Anthony. Contemporary Animal Learning Theory. (Problems in the Behavioral Sciences Ser.). (Illus.). 180p. 1981. 34.50 (ISBN 0-521-23469-7); pap. 11.95 (ISBN 0-521-29962-4). Cambridge U Pr.

Ditmars, Raymond L. Confessions of a Scientist. facs. ed. LC 75-121463. (Essay Index Reprint Ser). 1934. 20.00 (ISBN 0-8369-1800-2). Ayer Co Pubs.

Drickamer, Lee & Vessey, Steve. Animal Behavior: Concepts, Processes & Methods. 528p. 1982. text ed. write for info. (ISBN 0-87150-751-X, 4371, Pub. by Willard Grant Pr). PWS Pubs.

Durrell, Gerald. The Whispering Land. (Illus.). 224p. 1975. pap. 3.95 (ISBN 0-14-002083-7). Penguin.

Eisenberg, John F. The Mammalian Radiations: An Analysis of Trends in Evolution, Adaption & Behavior. LC 80-27940. (Illus.). 640p. 1983. pap. 22.00x (ISBN 0-226-19538-4). U of Chicago Pr.

Eleftheriou, Basil E. The Neurobiology of the Amygdala. LC 77-188921. (Advances in Behavioral Biology Ser.: Vol. 2). 843p. 1972. 75.00x (ISBN 0-306-37902-3, Plenum Pr). Plenum Pub.

Elementary Science Study. Animals in the Classroom: A Book for Teachers. 1970. 12.32 (ISBN 0-07-017706-6). McGraw.

Elwood, R. W., ed. Parental Behaviour of Rodents. LC 82-8625. 296p. 1983. text ed. 53.95x (ISBN 0-471-10252-0, Pub. by Wiley-Interscience). Wiley.

Embery, Joan & Lucaire, Ed. Joan Embery's Collection of Amazing Animal Facts. 1984. pap. 3.50 (ISBN 0-440-14232-6). Dell.

Esmay, Merle L. Principles of Animal Environment. 1978. text ed. 24.50 (ISBN 0-87055-263-5). AVI.

Etkin, William. Social Behavior from Fish to Man. abr. ed. LC 67-28654. 1967. pap. 2.45x (ISBN 0-226-22037-0, P533, Phoen). U of Chicago Pr.

Etkin, William, ed. Social Behavior & Organization Among Vertebrates. LC 64-13974. (Illus.). 1964. 15.00x (ISBN 0-226-22036-2). U of Chicago Pr.

Fassnacht, C. Theory & Practice of Observing Behavior. (Behavioural Development Monographs). 1982. 36.00 (ISBN 0-12-249780-5). Acad Pr.

Ferry, Georgina, ed. The Understanding of Animals. (New Scientist Guides Ser.). (Illus.). 336p. 1984. 24.95x (ISBN 0-85520-729-9); pap. 8.95 (ISBN 0-85520-728-0). Basil Blackwell.

Fox, M. W. Concepts in Ethology: Animal & Human Behavior. LC 73-93834. (Wesley W. Spink Lectures on Comparative Medicine Ser: Vol. 2). (Illus.). 160p. 1974. 8.50x (ISBN 0-8166-0723-0). U of Minn Pr.

Fraser. Ethology of Farm Animals. Date not set. price not set (ISBN 0-444-42359-1). Elsevier.

Fraser, A. F., ed. Reproductive & Developmental Behavior in Sheep: An Anthology from "Applied Animal Ethology". (Developments in Animal & Veterinary Sciences Ser.: Vol. 18). 478p. 1985. 59.25 (ISBN 0-444-42444-X). Elsevier.

Glaessner, Martin. The Dawn of Animal Life: A Biohistorical Study. LC 83-5188. (Cambridge Earth Science Ser.). 256p. 1985. 49.50 (ISBN 0-521-23507-3); pap. 19.95 (ISBN 0-521-31216-7). Cambridge U Pr.

Glass, David C., ed. Neurophysiology & Emotion. LC 67-31389. (Illus.). 256p. 1967. 13.00x (ISBN 0-87470-006-X). Rockefeller.

Granda, A. M. & Hayes, W. N., eds. Neural Mechanisms in Animal Behavior. (Illus.). 1972. 19.25 (ISBN 3-8055-1558-8). S Karger.

Grier, James W. Biology of Animal Behavior. 704p. 1983. pap. text ed. 27.95 (ISBN 0-8016-1971-8). Mosby.

Griffin, Donald R. Animal Thinking. 256p. 1984. text ed. 17.50x (ISBN 0-674-03712-X). Harvard U Pr.

Halliday, T. R. & Slater, P. J. Animal Behavior: Communication, Vol. II. LC 83-5497. (Illus.). 228p. 1983. text ed. 30.95 (ISBN 0-7167-1580-5); pap. text ed. 16.95 (ISBN 0-7167-1581-3). W H Freeman.

--Animal Behavior: Genes, Development & Learning, Vol. III. LC 83-5497. (Illus.). 246p. 1983. text ed. 30.95 (ISBN 0-7167-1582-1); pap. text ed. 16.95 (ISBN 0-7167-1583-X). W H Freeman.

--Animal Behaviour: Causes & Effects, Vol. I. LC 83-5497. (Illus.). 228p. 1983. text ed. 30.95 (ISBN 0-7167-1578-3); pap. text ed. 16.95 (ISBN 0-7167-1579-1). W H Freeman.

Hammond, A. E. How Animals Solve Their Problems. 1981. 5.95 (ISBN 0-8062-1810-X). Carlton.

Hansell, Michael H. & Aitken, John J. Experimental Animal Behavior: A Selection of Laboratory Exercises. (Illus.). 1977. 39.95x (ISBN 0-216-90325-4). Intl Ideas.

Hart, Benjamin L. The Behavior of Domestic Animals. LC 84-25893. (Illus.). 390p. 1985. text ed. 29.95 (ISBN 0-7167-1595-3). W H Freeman.

Hediger, H. Psychology & Behavior of Animals in Zoos & Circuses. Sircom, Geoffrey, tr. LC 68-55533. 1969. pap. text ed. 4.00 (ISBN 0-486-62218-5). Dover.

--The Psychology & Behavior of Animals in Zoos & Circuses. 1983. 13.00 (ISBN 0-8446-2230-3). Peter Smith.

--Wild Animals in Captivity. Sircom, tr. (Illus.). 1964. 12.50 (ISBN 0-8446-2231-1). Peter Smith.

--Wild Animals in Captivity: An Outline of the Biology of Zoological Gardens. Sircom, Geoffrey, tr. Orig. Title: Wildtiere -in Gefaengschaft: ein Grundriss -Des Tiergartenbiologie. 1950. pap. text ed. 4.95 (ISBN 0-486-21260-2). Dover.

Hicks, Bernice E. All the World Is Kin. LC 82-2086. (Illus.). 224p. 1982. 11.95 (ISBN 0-87961-116-2); pap. 6.95 (ISBN 0-87961-117-0). Naturegraph.

Hopkins, Brian. Forest & Savannah. 1974. pap. text ed. 9.95x (ISBN 0-435-93421-X). Heinemann Ed.

Hornaday, William T. The Minds & Manners of Wild Animals. 328p. 1979. Repr. of 1922 ed. lib. bdg. 35.00 (ISBN 0-8495-2267-6). Arden Lib.

Houpt, Katherine A. & Wolski, Thomas R. Domestic Animal Behavior for Veterinarians & Animal Scientists. (Illus.). 356p. 1982. text ed. 29.95x (ISBN 0-8138-1060-4). Iowa St U Pr.

Hudson, William H. A Hind in Richmond Park. Repr. of 1923 ed. 35.00 (ISBN 0-404-03413-6). AMS Pr.

--Naturalist in La Plata. Repr. of 1923 ed. 35.00 (ISBN 0-404-03393-8). AMS Pr.

Huntingford, F. A. The Study of Animal Behavior. (Illus.). 411p. 1984. 49.95x (ISBN 0-412-22320-1, NO. 6884); pap. 22.00x (ISBN 0-412-22330-9, NO. 6885). Methuen Inc.

Jaeger, Edmund C. Desert Wildlife. (Illus.). 1961. 11.95 (ISBN 0-8047-0123-7); pap. 6.95 (ISBN 0-8047-0124-5, SP68). Stanford U Pr.

Jennison, George. Noah's Cargo: Some Curious Chapters of Natural History. LC 70-174390. (Illus.). Repr. of 1928 ed. 22.00 (ISBN 0-405-08670-9, Blom Pubns). Ayer Co Pubs.

Johnson, H. D. Progress in Animal Biometeorology: The Effects of Weather & Climate on Animals; Vol 1 Period 1963-1973, 2 pts. Incl. Pt. 1. Effects of Temperature on Animals: Including Effects of Humidity, Radiation & Wind. 624p. 1976. text ed. 115.00 (ISBN 90-265-0196-X); Effect of Light, High Actitude, Noise, Electric, Magnetic & Electro-Magnetic Fields, Ionization, Gravity & Air Pollutions on Animals. 322p. 1976. text ed. 57.00 (ISBN 90-265-0235-4). (Progress in Biometeorology Ser.). 1976 (Pub. by Swets Pub Serv Holland). Swets North Am.

Jolly, Alison. Lemur Behavior: A Madagascar Field Study. LC 66-23690. pap. 53.30 (ISBN 0-317-26513-X, 2024050). Bks Demand UMI.

Kellogg, Winthrop N. Porpoises & Sonar. LC 61-11294. (Illus.). xiv, 178p. 1963. pap. 2.25x (ISBN 0-226-43005-7, P518, Phoen). U of Chicago Pr.

Krebs, John R. & Davies, Nicholas B. An Introduction to Behavioural Ecology. LC 80-25843. (Illus.). 300p. 1981. pap. text ed. 18.50x (ISBN 0-87893-432-4). Sinauer Assoc.

Krushinskii, L. V. Animal Behavior: Its Normal & Abnormal Development. LC 61-15172. 619p. 1962. 25.00x (ISBN 0-306-10506-3, Consultants). Plenum Pub.

Kruuk, Hans. The Spotted Hyena: A Study of Predation & Social Behavior. LC 70-175304. (Wildlife Behavior & Ecology Ser.). 1979. pap. 8.95x (ISBN 0-226-45508-4, P854, Phoen). U of Chicago Pr.

Lehrman, D. S., et al, eds. Advances in the Study of Behavior, Vols. 1-9. Incl. Vol. 1. 1965. 50.00 (ISBN 0-12-004501-X); Vol. 2. 1969. 50.00 (ISBN 0-12-004502-8); Vol. 3. 1971. 50.00 (ISBN 0-12-004503-6); Vol. 4. 1972. 50.00 (ISBN 0-12-004504-4); Vol. 5. 1974. 50.00 (ISBN 0-12-004505-2); Vol. 6. 1976. 50.00 (ISBN 0-12-004506-0); Vol. 7. 1976. 60.00 (ISBN 0-12-004507-9); Vol. 8. 1978. 45.00 (ISBN 0-12-004508-7); Vol. 9. 1979. 45.00 (ISBN 0-12-004509-5). Acad Pr.

Leister, Mary. Wildlings. LC 76-2063. (Illus.). 192p. 1976. 8.95 (ISBN 0-916144-06-2). Stemmer Hse.

Loeb, Jacques. Forced Movements, Tropisms & Animal Conduct. (Illus.). 224p. 1973. pap. text ed. 5.50 (ISBN 0-486-60989-8). Dover.

--Forced Movements, Tropisms, & Animal Conduct. (Illus.). 9.00 (ISBN 0-8446-4776-4). Peter Smith.

Lorenz, Konrad. Studies in Animal & Human Behaviour, 2 vols. LC 75-11087. 390p. Vol. 2. 1971. 22.50x (ISBN 0-674-84631-1). Harvard U Pr.

Lorenz, Konrad Z. King Solomon's Ring. LC 52-7373. (Illus.). 1979. pap. 5.95xi (ISBN 0-06-131976-7, TB 1976, Torch). Har-Row.

McFarland, D. & Houston, A. Quantitative Ethology. 224p. 1981. text ed. 28.50 (ISBN 0-273-08417-8). Pitman Pub MA.

McFarland, David, ed. The Oxford Companion to Animal Behavior. (Illus.). 1982. 35.00 (ISBN 0-19-866120-7). Oxford U Pr.

Manning, Aubrey. Introduction to Animal Behavior. (Life Sciences Ser.). 1979. pap. text ed. 15.95 (ISBN 0-201-04446-3). Addison-Wesley.

Markowitz, Hal & Stevens, Victor, eds. Behavior of Captive Wild Animals. LC 77-18156. (Illus.). 320p. 1978. text ed. 24.95x (ISBN 0-88229-385-0). Nelson-Hall.

Marler, Peter R., et al. The Marvels of Animal Behavior. Allen, Tom, ed. LC 72-76734. (Natural Science Library). (Illus.). 422p. 1972. 11.95, avail. only from Natl Geog (ISBN 0-87044-105-1). Natl Geog.

Martin, Alexander C., et al. American Wildlife & Plants: A Guide to Wildlife Food Habits. 15.75 (ISBN 0-8446-2536-1). Peter Smith.

Mellgren, R. L., ed. Animal Cognition & Behavior. (Advances in Psychology Ser.: Vol. 13). 514p. 1983. 59.75 (ISBN 0-444-86627-2, I-122-83, North Holland). Elsevier.

Morgan, C. Lloyd. Animal Behavior. LC 3-12891. (Psychology Ser). 1970. Repr. of 1900 ed. 27.00 (ISBN 0-384-40134-1). Johnson Repr.

Morse, Douglass H. Behavioral Mechanisms in Ecology. LC 80-12130. 1982. text ed. 27.50x (ISBN 0-674-06460-7); pap. 9.95x (ISBN 0-674-06461-5). Harvard U Pr.

Muller-Schwarze, D. & Silverstein, R. M., eds. Chemical Signals in Vertebrates 2: Vertebrates & Aquatic Invertebrates. LC 80-184. 455p. 1980. 55.00x (ISBN 0-306-40339-0, Plenum Pr). Plenum Pub.

Muller-Schwarze, Dietland. The Behavior of Penguins: Adapted to Ice & Tropics. (Animal Behavior Ser.). (Illus.). 160p. 1984. 29.50x (ISBN 0-87395-866-7); pap. 10.95x (ISBN 0-87395-867-5). State U NY Pr.

Nussbaum, Martha C. Aristotle's De Motu Animalium. LC 77-72132. 1978. 45.00x (ISBN 0-691-07224-8). Princeton U Pr.

Pommery, Jean. How Human the Animals. LC 78-24613. 224p. 1981. pap. 6.95 (ISBN 0-8128-6086-1). Stein & Day.

Price, Edward O. & Stokes, Allen W. Animal Behavior in Laboratory & Field. 2nd ed. (Illus.). 130p. 1975. pap. text ed. 12.95x (ISBN 0-7167-0762-4); tchr's manual avail. W H Freeman.

Reese, Ernst S. & Lighter, Frederick J. Contrasts in Behavior: Adaptations in the Aquatic & Terrestrial Environments. LC 78-8284. 406p. 1978. 50.95 (ISBN 0-471-71390-2, Pub. by Wiley-Interscience). Wiley.

Richelle, M. & Lejeune, H. Time in Animal Behaviour. (Illus.). 1980. 61.00 (ISBN 0-08-023754-1); pap. 23.00 (ISBN 0-08-025489-6). Pergamon.

Riesen, Austin H. & Kinder, E. F. Postural Development of Infant Chimpanzees. 1952. 59.50x (ISBN 0-685-69858-0). Elliots Bks.

Robinson, David F. Living Wild: The Secrets of Animal Survival. MacConomy, Alma D., ed. LC 80-80702. (Illus.). 208p. 1980. 11.95 (ISBN 0-912186-37-2). Natl Wildlife.

--A Wildlife Family Album. MacConomy, Alma D. & Peters, Barbara, eds. LC 81-81904. (Illus.). 208p. 1981. 16.95 (ISBN 0-912186-41-0). Natl Wildlife.

Roots, Clive. Animal Invaders. LC 76-5088. (Illus.). 208p. 1976. 12.50x (ISBN 0-87663-226-6). Universe.

Ruwet, Jean-Claude. Introduction to Ethology: The Biology of Behavior. LC 72-186505. 208p. 1973. text ed. 20.00 (ISBN 0-8236-2730-6). Intl Univs Pr.

Schanenberg, Paul. Enciclopedia De la Vida Animal, 2 vols. (Espn.). 840p. 1978. Set. pap. 110.00 (ISBN 84-330-0391-7, S-50531). French & Eur.

Schmidt, H. D. & Tembrock, G., eds. Evolution & Determination of Animal & Human Behavior. 134p. 1983. 34.00 (ISBN 0-444-86346-X, I-123-82, North-Holland). Elsevier.

Scott, John P. Animal Behavior. rev. 2nd ed. LC 76-188823. 328p. 1972. pap. 6.95X (ISBN 0-226-74337-3, P480, Phoen). U of Chicago Pr.

Sebeok, Thomas A. How Animals Communicate. LC 76-48862. pap. 160.00 (ISBN 0-317-27862-2, 2056058). Bks Demand UMI.

Seton, Ernest T. Wild Animals at Home. 226p. 1981. Repr. of 1913 ed. lib. bdg. 30.00 (ISBN 0-89984-417-0). Century Bookbindery.

Shye, Samuel, ed. Theory Construction & Data Analysis in the Behavioral Sciences. LC 78-62554. (Social & Behavioral Science Ser.). (Illus.). 1978. text ed. 39.95x (ISBN 0-87589-379-1). Jossey-Bass.

Silverman, Paul. Animal Behavior in the Laboratory. LC 77-8842. (Illus.). 1978. text ed. 35.00x (ISBN 0-87663-727-6, Pica Pr). Universe.

Smith, Donald F. Lithium & Animal Behavior. Horrobin, D. F., ed. (Lithium Research Review Ser.: Vol. I). 66p. 1980. Repr. of 1977 ed. 12.95 (ISBN 0-87705-961-6). Human Sci Pr.

Smith, Donald F. & Horrobin, D. F. Lithium & Animal Behavior. LC 81-13321. (Lithium Research Review Ser.: Vol. II). 134p. 1982. 16.95 (ISBN 0-89885-075-4). Human Sci Pr.

Smith, Stevenson & Guthrie, Edwin R. General Psychology in Terms of Behavior. LC 22-444. (Psychology Ser). 1970. Repr. of 1921 ed. 18.00 (ISBN 0-384-56175-6). Johnson Repr.

Smythe, R. H. Animal Habits: The Things Animals Do. (Illus.). 192p. 1962. 18.75x (ISBN 0-398-01799-9). C C Thomas.

Snedigar, Robert. Our Small Native Animals: Their Habits & Care. (Illus.). 1963. pap. 5.95 (ISBN 0-486-21022-7). Dover.

--Our Small Native Animals: Their Habits & Care. rev. ed. (Illus.). 14.75 (ISBN 0-8446-2961-8). Peter Smith.

Sorensen, A. M., Jr. Repro Lab: A Laboratory Manual for Animal Reproduction. 4th ed. (Illus.). 151p. 1979. pap. text ed. 7.95x (ISBN 0-89641-011-0). American Pr.

Stebbins, William C. The Acoustic Sense of Animals. (Illus.). 192p. 1983. text ed. 16.50x (ISBN 0-674-00326-8). Harvard U Pr.

Sterman, M. B., et al. Brain Development & Behavior. 1971. 77.50 (ISBN 0-12-666350-5). Acad Pr.

Stokes, Allen W., ed. Territory. LC 73-18327. (Benchmark Papers in Animal Behavior Ser.). 416p. 1974. 52.95 (ISBN 0-87933-113-5). Van Nos Reinhold.

Sweton, Ernest T. Wild Animals at Home. 126p. 1982. Repr. of 1913 ed. lib. bdg. 30.00 (ISBN 0-89760-852-6). Telegraph Bks.

Tarpy, Roger M. Principles of Animal Learning & Motivation. 1982. pap. text ed. 23.80x (ISBN 0-673-15383-5). Scott F.

Thompson, Edward P. Passions of Animals. (Contributions to the History of Psychology Ser.: Comparative Psychology). 1980. Repr. of 1851 ed. 30.00 (ISBN 0-89093-322-7). U Pubns Amer.

Tinbergen, N. Social Behavior in Animals. 1965. pap. 8.95x (ISBN 0-412-20000-7, NO. 6135, Pub. by Chapman & Hall England). Methuen Inc.

Tinbergen, Niko. The Animal in Its World, Explorations of an Ethologist 1932-1972, Vol. 1: Field Studies. LC 72-94876. 1973. 17.50x (ISBN 0-674-03725-1); pap. 6.95x (ISBN 0-674-03724-3). Harvard U Pr.

Toates, Frederick M. Animal Behaviour: A Systems Approach. LC 79-41485. 299p. 1980. 64.95 (ISBN 0-471-27724-X); pap. 26.95x (ISBN 0-471-27723-1). Wiley.

Tomikel, John. The Nature of Things: Animals & Habitats. LC 82-70061. (Illus.). 180p. 1983. pap. 4.95 (ISBN 0-910042-44-6). Allegheny.

Topoff, Howard, intro. by. Animal Societies & Evolution: Readings from Scientific American. LC 81-7830. (Illus.). 106p. 1981. 17.95x (ISBN 0-7167-1333-0); pap. 9.95x (ISBN 0-7167-1334-9). W H Freeman.

Van Soest, Peter J. Nutritional Ecology of the Ruminant. LC 81-83655. 375p. 1982. 32.00x (ISBN 0-9601586-0-X). O & B Bks.

La Vie des animaux. (Illus.). 1978. 59.95x (ISBN 0-685-89361-8). Larousse.

Wallace, Robert A. Animal Behavior: Development, Ecology, Evolution. LC 78-11616. 1979. text ed. 28.45x (ISBN 0-673-16243-5). Scott F.

--Ecology & Evolution of Animal Behavior. 2nd ed. 1979. pap. text ed. 17.95x (ISBN 0-673-16246-X). Scott F.

Walther, Fritz R. Communication & Expression in Hoofed Mammals. LC 82-49011. (Animal Communication Ser.). (Illus.). 448p. 1983. 35.00x (ISBN 0-253-31380-5). Ind U Pr.

Whitfield, Philip. The Animal Family: The Fascinating Variety of Parenthood, from the Courtship Displays to the Day the Children Leave Home. (Illus.). 1980. 21.95 (ISBN 0-393-01304-9). Norton.

Williams, Leonard. Samba. LC 80-40597. (Illus.). 224p. 1980. 12.95 (ISBN 0-8052-8055-3, Pub. by Allison & Busby England); pap. 6.95 (ISBN 0-8052-8054-5). Schocken.

Wittenberger. Animal Social Behavior. (Illus.). 736p. 1981. text ed. write for info. (ISBN 0-87872-295-5, Pub. by Willard Grant Pr). PWS Pubs.

Wood-Gush, D. G. Elements of Ethology: A Textbook of Agricultural & Veterinary Students. LC 82-243446. (Illus.). 225p. 1983. 34.00 (ISBN 0-412-23160-3, NO. 6793, Pub. by Chapman & Hall); pap. 15.95 (ISBN 0-412-23170-0, NO. 6792). Methuen Inc.

Young, Paul T. Motivation of Behaviour: The Fundamental Determinants of Human & Animal Activity. 562p. 1984. Repr. of 1936 ed. lib. bdg. 65.00 (ISBN 0-89987-904-7). Darby Books.

Zuckerman, S. The Social Life of Monkey & Apes. 356p. 1981. Repr. of 1932 ed. lib. bdg. 40.00 (ISBN 0-89984-547-9). Century Bookbindery.

ANIMALS, INFANCY OF

see also Parental Behavior in Animals

Altmann, Jeanne. Baboon Mothers & Infants. LC 79-21568. (Illus.). 1980. text ed. 18.50x (ISBN 0-674-05856-9); pap. text ed. 8.95x (ISBN 0-674-05857-7). Harvard U Pr.

Bell, Robert W. & Smotherman, William F., eds. Maternal Influences & Early Behavior. LC 78-17074. (Illus.). 465p. 1980. text ed. 60.00 (ISBN 0-89335-059-1). SP Med & Sci Bks.

Plooij, Frans X. The Behavioral Development of Free-Living Chimpanzee Babies & Infants. Lipsitt, Lewis P., ed. LC 83-25804. (Monographs on Infancy: Vol. 4). (Illus.). 208p. (Orig.). 1984. text ed. 27.50 (ISBN 0-89391-114-3). Ablex Pub.

ANIMALS, INJURIOUS AND BENEFICIAL

see Zoology, Economic

ANIMALS, MIGRATION OF

see Animal Migration

ANIMALS, MOVEMENTS OF

see Animal Locomotion; Animal Mechanics

ANIMALS, NOCTURNAL

see Nocturnal Animals

ANIMALS, ORIENTATION OF

see Orientation

ANIMALS, PHOTOGRAPHY OF

see Photography of Animals

ANIMALS, POISONOUS

see Poisonous Animals

ANIMALS, PREDATORY

see Predatory Animals

ANIMALS, PREHISTORIC

see Extinct Animals; Paleontology

ANIMALS, PROTECTION OF

see Animals, Treatment Of; Wildlife Conservation

ANIMALS, RARE

see Rare Animals

ANIMALS, RESPIRATION OF

see Respiration

ANIMALS, SEA

see Marine Fauna

ANIMALS, SOUND PRODUCTION BY

see Sound Production by Animals

ANIMALS, TRAINING OF

see also Dogs–Training

Helfer, Toni R. The Gentle Jungle. LC 80-10275. (Illus.). 336p. 1980. 9.95 (ISBN 0-8425-1790-1). Brigham.

O'Hara, Maggie. Wild Animals & Gentle People. LC 82-71077. (Illus.). 108p. 1982. pap. 5.95 (ISBN 0-939116-08-1). Creative Comm.

Woodhouse, Barbara. Talking to Animals. 208p. 1985. pap. 3.50 (ISBN 0-425-08470-1). Berkley Pub.

ANIMALS, TREATMENT OF

American Association of Laboratory Animal Science, New Jersey, 1970. Environmental Variables in Animal Experimentation: Symposium. Magalhaes, Hulda, ed. LC 72-3526. (Illus.). 146p. 1974. 15.00 (ISBN 0-8387-1231-2). Bucknell U Pr.

Animal Welfare Encyclopedia, 6 vols. Incl. Vol. 1. Legislation-Litigation of Interest to Dog Owners. Ford, Lee E. 1971 (ISBN 0-88017-061-1); Vol. 2. Study of the Fur Seals International Treaty. 1973 (ISBN 0-88017-062-X); Vol. 3. Model Laws for Dog Welfare. 1973 (ISBN 0-88017-063-8). pap. 10.00 ea. Ford Assocs.

Animal Welfare Encyclopedia: Legislation-Litigation of Interest to Dog Owners, 1976, Vol. 19. (Orig.). 1977. pap. 10.00 (ISBN 0-88017-112-X). Ford Assocs.

Bryant, Alan. Second Chance: The Story of the New Quay Hospital. (Illus.). 208p. 1982. 11.95 (ISBN 0-312-70828-9). St Martin.

Carlson, Delbert G. & Giffin, James M. Cat Owner's Home Veterinary Handbook. LC 82-23383. (Illus.). 392p. 1985. 18.95 (ISBN 0-87605-814-4). Howell Bk.

Chesney, W. Inhuman Medical Experiments on Humans & Pets. 1966. 1.25x (ISBN 0-686-32627-X). Cancer Control Soc.

Dodds, W. Jean & Orlans, F. Barbara, eds. Scientific Perspectives in Animal Welfare: Symposium. LC 82-24375. 1983. 19.00 (ISBN 0-12-219140-4). Acad Pr.

Everiss, S. F. Animal Management, 3 Vols. 1982. 125.00x set (ISBN 0-86082-195-1, Pub. by Natl Ext England). State Mutual Bk.

Ford, Lee E. Animal Welfare Encyclopedia, Vol. 17: Legislation-Litigation of Interest to Dog Owners. 100p. 1976. pap. 10.00 (ISBN 0-88017-067-0). Ford Assocs.

Ford, Lee E., ed. Indiana Directory of Humane Societies. 100p. 1980. pap. 10.00 (ISBN 0-88017-099-9). Ford Assocs.

Fox, Michael W. Returning to Eden: Animal Rights & Human Responsibility. LC 79-56281. 300p. 1980. 13.95 (ISBN 0-670-12722-1). Viking.

Frey, R. G. Interests & Rights: The Case Against Animals. (Clarendon Library of Logic & Philosophy Ser.). 1980. 27.95x (ISBN 0-19-824421-5). Oxford U Pr.

How Animals Protect Themselves. (Wonders of Learning Kits Ser.). 1980. incl. cassette & tchrs. guide 24.95 (ISBN 0-686-74405-5, 04969). Natl Geog.

Lodrick, Deryck O. Sacred Cows, Sacred Places: Origins & Survivals of Animal Homes in India. (Illus.). 350p. 1981. 32.50x (ISBN 0-520-04109-7). U of Cal Pr.

Magel, Charles R. A Bibliography on Animal Rights & Related Matters. LC 80-5636. 622p. 1981. lib. bdg. 34.50 (ISBN 0-8191-1488-X). U Pr of Amer.

Miller, Harlan B. & Williams, William H., eds. Ethics & Animals. (Contemporary Issues in Biomedicine, Ethics, & Society Ser.). 416p. 1983. 39.50 (ISBN 0-89603-036-9). Humana.

Rowan, Andrew N. Of Mice, Models, & Men: A Critical Evaluation of Animal Research. LC 83-4986. 323p. 1984. 39.50x (ISBN 0-87395-776-8); pap. 14.95x (ISBN 0-87395-777-6). State U NY Pr.

Ryder, Richard D. Victims of Science. 1983. 32.00x (ISBN 0-905225-05-8, Pub. by Centaur Pr England). State Mutual Bk.

Salt, Henry S. Animals' Rights: Considered in Relation to Social Progress. rev. ed. LC 80-50160. 1980. 9.95 (ISBN 0-9602632-0-9); members 4.95. Soc Animal Rights.

Shultz, William J. Humane Movement in the United States, 1910-1922. LC 68-57581. (Columbia University. Studies in the Social Sciences: No. 252). Repr. of 1924 ed. 18.50 (ISBN 0-404-51252-6). AMS Pr.

ANIMALS, USEFUL AND HARMFUL

see Zoology, Economic

ANIMALS AND CIVILIZATION

see also Zoology, Economic

Baky, John S., ed. Humans & Animals. (Reference Shelf Ser.). 1980. 8.00 (ISBN 0-8242-0647-9). Wilson.
Garrison, Webb B. Codfish, Cats & Civilization. LC 77-120898. (Essay & General Literature Index Reprint Ser). 1971. Repr. of 1959 ed. 22.50x (ISBN 0-8046-1407-5, Pub. by Kennikat). Assoc Faculty Pr.
Magel, Charles R. A Bibliography on Animal Rights & Related Matters. LC 80-5636. 622p. 1981. lib. bdg. 34.50 (ISBN 0-8191-1488-X). U Pr of Amer.
O'Connor, T. & Wilkinson, M. Animal Bones from Flaxengate: Lincoln C. 870-1500. (Archaeology of Lincoln: Vol. XVIII-1). (Illus.). 52p. 1982. pap. text ed. 19.00x (ISBN 0-906780-13-6, Pub. by Coun Brit Archaeology England). Humanities.

ANIMALS AS CARRIERS OF DISEASE

see also Insects As Carriers of Disease

Levine, Norman D., ed. Natural Nidality of Diseases & Questions of Parasitology. Plous, Frederick K., Jr., tr. LC 68-11027. (Illus.). Repr. of 1968 ed. 94.10 (ISBN 0-8357-9691-4, 2019031). Bks Demand UMI.
Thrash, Agatha M. & Thrash, Calvin L., Jr. The Animal Connection: Link Between Cancer & Other Diseases from Animals & Foods of Animal Origin. 262p. (Orig.). 1983. pap. 4.95 (ISBN 0-942658-04-3). Thrash Pubns.

ANIMATION (CINEMATOGRAPHY)

Artwick, Bruce A. Microcomputer Displays, Graphics, & Animation. LC 84-61429. (Illus.). 384p. 1985. pap. text ed. 18.95 (ISBN 0-13-580226-1). P-H.
Brasch, Walter M. Cartoon Monikers: An Insight into the Animation Industry. LC 83-72011. (Illus.). 150p. 1983. 21.95 (ISBN 0-87972-243-6); pap. 9.95 (ISBN 0-87972-244-4). Bowling Green Univ.
Film Animation: A Simplified Approach. (Monographs on Communication Technology & Utilization: No. 2). (Illus.). 92p. (2nd Printing 1979). 1976. pap. 5.50 (ISBN 92-3-101367-X, U238, UNESCO). Unipub.
Fox, David & Waite, Mitch. Computer Animation Primer. (Illus.). 208p. 1984. pap. 22.95 (ISBN 0-07-021742-4, BYTE Bks). McGraw.
Gilliam, Terry & Cowel, Lucinda. Animations of Mortality. LC 78-60982. (Illus.). 1978. pap. 9.95 (ISBN 0-413-39380-1, NO.0066). Methuen Inc.
Hoffer, Thomas W. Animation: A Reference Guide. LC 81-67. (American Popular Culture Ser.). (Illus.). 448p. 1981. lib. bdg. 35.00 (ISBN 0-313-21095-0, HAG). Greenwood.
Macek, Carl. The Art of Heavy Metal: Animation for the Eighties. LC 81-82982. (Illus.). 128p. (Orig.). 1981. pap. 9.95 (ISBN 0-918432-38-3). NY Zoetrope.
Madsen, Roy. Animated Film, Concepts, Methods, Uses. LC 69-16776. 234p. 1969. lib. bdg. 14.75 (ISBN 0-87989-029-0). Interland Pub.
Salt, Brian G. Basic Animation Stand Techniques. LC 76-40298. 1977. text ed. 31.00 (ISBN 0-08-021368-5). Pergamon.
--Movements in Animation, 2 vols. LC 76-276. 1976. Set. text ed. 225.00 (ISBN 0-08-020904-1). Pergamon.
Stark, Ron & Solomon, Charles. The Complete Kodak Animation Book (H-6) Eastman Kodak Company Staff, ed. (Illus.). 192p. (Orig.). pap. 17.95 (ISBN 0-87985-330-1). Eastman Kodak.
Thomas, Frank & Johnston, Ollie. Disney Animation: The Illusion of Life. LC 81-12699. (Illus.). 576p. 1981. text ed. 75.00 (ISBN 0-89659-232-4); collector's edition 125.00 (ISBN 0-89659-233-2). Abbeville Pr.
Whitaker, Harold & Halas, John. Timing for Animation. LC 80-41303. (Illus.). 144p. 1981. 34.95 (ISBN 0-240-50871-8). Focal Pr.

ANIONS

Brodsky, William A., ed. Anion & Proton Transport, Vol. 341. LC 80-15917. (Annals of the New York Academy of Sciences). 570p. 1980. 109.00x (ISBN 0-89766-070-6); pap. 107.00x (ISBN 0-89766-071-4). NY Acad Sci.
Gloxhuber, C. Anionic Surfactants, Vol. 10: Biochemistry, Toxicology, Dermatology. (Surfactant Ser.: Vol. 10). 472p. 75.00 (ISBN 0-8247-6946-5). Dekker.
Morton, Maurice, ed. Anionic Polymerization. LC 82-11627. 268p. 1983. 44.00 (ISBN 0-12-508080-8). Acad Pr.
Prelec, Krsto, ed. Production & Neutralization of Negative Ions & Beams: International Symposium, Brookhaven, 1983. 3rd ed. LC 84-70379. (AIP Conference Proceedings Ser.: No. 111). 778p. 1984. lib. bdg. 53.75 (ISBN 0-88318-310-2). Am Inst Physics.
Smirnov, B. M. Negative Ions. 1982. 70.95 (ISBN 0-07-058447-8). McGraw.
Williams, W. J. Handbook of Anion Determination. 768p. 1979. 149.95 (ISBN 0-408-71306-2). Butterworth.

ANISOTROPY

Atroshenko, V. S., et al. Calculation of the Brightness of Light in the Case of Anisotropic Scattering, Pt. 2. LC 60-8720. (Institute of Physics of the Atmosphere Ser.: No. 2). 226p. 1963. 27.50x (ISBN 0-306-17002-7, Consultants). Plenum Pub.
Boehler, J. P., ed. Mechanical Behavior of Anisotropic Solids. 1983. lib. bdg. 120.00 (ISBN 90-2472-813-4, Pub. by Martinus Nijhoff Netherlands). Kluwer Academic.
Klemen, M. Points, Lines & Walls: In Liquid Crystals, Magnetic Systems & Various Ordered Media. LC 81-21976. 322p. 1982. 64.95 (ISBN 0-471-10194-X, Pub. by Wiley-Interscience). Wiley.
Lekhnitskii, S. G. Theory of Elasticity of an Anisotropic Body. 1981. 8.00 (ISBN 0-8285-1902-1, Pub. by Mir Pubs USSR). Imported Pubns.
Vahldiek, F. W. & Mersol, S. A., eds. Anisotropy in Single-Crystal Refractory Compounds, 2 Vols. LC 68-20273. 898p. 1968. Vol. 1, 405p. 45.00x (ISBN 0-306-37038-7, Plenum Pr); Vol. 2, 493p. 45.00x (ISBN 0-306-37039-5). Plenum Pub.
Weber, Harald W., ed. Anisotropy Effects in Superconductors. LC 76-56737. 316p. 1977. 49.50x (ISBN 0-306-31006-6, Plenum Pr). Plenum Pub.

ANNELIDA

see also Earthworms; Leeches; Oligochaeta; Polychaeta

Mill, P. J., ed. Physiology of Annelids. 1978. 95.00 (ISBN 0-12-496550-4). Acad Pr.
Wu, B., et al. The Nereidae Polychaetous Annelids of the Chinese Coast. (Illus.). 320p. 1985. 79.50 (ISBN 0-387-13953-2). Springer-Verlag.

ANNIHILATION, POSITRON

see Positron Annihilation

ANNUALS (PLANTS)

Sinnes, Cort & McKinley, Mike. All about Annuals. ORTHO Books Editorial Staff, ed. LC 80-85224. (Illus.). 96p. (Orig.). 1982. pap. 5.95 (ISBN 0-917102-91-6). Ortho.
Thomas, Graham S. Perennial Garden Plants or the Modern Florilegium. 410p. 1981. 40.00x (ISBN 0-460-03993-8, Pub. by J M Dent England). State Mutual Bk.

ANOXEMIA

see also Oxygen in the Body

Bogolepov, N. N. Ultrastructure of the Brain in Hypoxia. Burov, Michael, tr. 208p. 1983. 8.95 (ISBN 0-8285-2573-0, Pub. by Mir Pubs USSR). Imported Pubns.
Bouverot, P. Adaptation to Altitude-Hypoxia in Vertebrates. (Zoophysiology Ser.: Vol. 16). (Illus.). 195p. 1985. 35.00 (ISBN 0-387-13602-9). Springer-Verlag.
Breccia, A., et al, eds. Advanced Topics on Radiosensitizers of Hypoxic Cells. LC 82-427. (NATO ASI Series A, Life Sciences: Vol. 43). 296p. 1982. 45.00 (ISBN 0-306-40915-1, Plenum Pr). Plenum Pub.
McClung, Jean. Effects of High Altitude on Human Birth: Observations on Mothers, Placentas, & the Newborn in Two Peruvian Populations. LC 72-91629. 1969. 11.00 (ISBN 0-674-24065-0). Harvard U Pr.
Sutton, John R. & Houston, Charles S., eds. Hypoxia: Man at Altitude. LC 81-84773. (Illus.). 213p. (Orig.). 1982. pap. text ed. 24.95 (ISBN 0-86577-048-4). Thieme-Stratton.

ANT

see Ants

ANTAGONISTS ENZYME

see Enzyme Inhibitors

ANTARCTIC FLORA

see Botany--Antarctic Regions

ANTARCTIC REGIONS

see also Polar Regions; Scientific Expeditions also names of exploring expeditions, and names of explorers

Adams, Richard & Lockley, Ronald. Voyage Through the Antarctic. LC 82-48484. (Illus.). 160p. 1982. 13.95 (ISBN 0-394-52858-1). Knopf.
Adie, Raymond, ed. Antarctic Geology & Geophysics. (Illus.). 876p. 1973. 50.00x (ISBN 8-200-02253-6, Dist. by Columbia U Pr). Universitet.
Antarctic Annual Report. 10.00 (ISBN 0-318-18100-2). NSF.
Bailey, Alfred M. & Sorenson, J. H. Subantarctic Campbell Island. (Proceedings: No. 10). 1962. 4.00 (ISBN 0-916278-62-X); pap. 2.00 (ISBN 0-916278-63-8). Denver Mus Natl Hist.
Barnes, James N. Let's Save Antarctica! (Illus.). 112p. 1983. pap. 6.95 (ISBN 0-87663-408-0). Universe.
Bonner, W. N. & Berry, R. J., eds. Ecology in the Antarctic. (Linnean Society of London). 1981. 30.00 (ISBN 0-12-114950-1). Acad Pr.
Brewster, Barney. Antarctica: Wilderness at Risk. LC 82-70159. (Illus.). 125p. 1982. pap. 14.95 (ISBN 0-913890-51-0). Brick Hse Pub.
Charcot, Jean. The Voyage of the Pourquoi Pas? in the Antarctic: The Journal of the Second French South Polar Expedition, 1908-1910. (Illus.). vi, 315p. 1978. Repr. of 1911 ed. 30.00 (ISBN 0-208-01644-9, Archon). Shoe String.
Charney, Jonathan I., ed. The New Nationalism & the Use of Common Spaces: Issues in Marine Pollution & the Exploitation of Antarctica. LC 81-65006. (Illus.). 358p. 1982. text ed. 39.50x (ISBN 0-86598-012-8). Allanheld.
Craddock, Campbell, ed. Antarctic Geoscience: Proceedings of 1977 Symposium. (International Union of Geological Sciences Ser. B: No. 4). (Illus.). 1204p. 1982. 50.00x (ISBN 0-299-08410-8). U of Wis Pr.
Dalrymple, Paul, et al. A Year of Snow Accumulation at Plateau Station; Thermal Properties & Heat Transfer Processes of Low-Temperature Snow; Radiative Heat Transfer; Process in Snow & Ice; Papers 1, 2, 3 & 4: Meteorological Studies at Plateau Station, Antarctica. Businger, Joost A., ed. (Antarctic Research Ser.: Vol. 25). (Illus.). 1977. pap. 13.50 (ISBN 0-87590-125-5). Am Geophysical.
Foster, M. W., ed. Recent Antarctic & Subantarctic Brachiopods. LC 74-9234. (Antarctic Research Ser.: Vol. 21). (Illus.). 1974. 39.00 (ISBN 0-87590-121-2). Am Geophysical.
Furse, Chris. Elephant Island: An Antarctic Expedition. (Illus.). 1979. 27.50 (ISBN 0-904614-02-6, Pub. by Anthony Nelson Ltd, England). Buteo.
--Elephant Island: An Antarctic Expedition. 264p. 1981. 35.00x (ISBN 0-904614-02-6, Pub. by Nelson Ltd). State Mutual Bk.
Gjelsvik, Tore. Results from Norwegian Antarctic Research, 1974-1977. (Norsk Polarinstitutt Skrifter: Vol. 169). (Illus.). 117p. 1980. pap. 9.00x (ISBN 8-2903-0703-9). Universitet.
Gunderson, E. K., ed. Human Adaptability to Antarctic Conditions. LC 74-18498. (Antarctic Research Ser.: Vol. 22). (Illus.). 131p. 1974. 17.00 (ISBN 0-87590-122-0). Am Geophysical.
Harrington, Richard. Richard Harrington's Antarctic. LC 75-43581. (Illus.). 1976. Album Style. pap. 8.95 (ISBN 0-88240-054-1). Alaska Northwest.
Jones, A. G. Antarctica Observed. 130p. 1982. 39.00x (ISBN 0-686-44560-0, Pub. by Caedmon of Whitby). State Mutual Bk.
Kott, P., ed. Antarctic Ascidiacea. LC 77-601086. (Antarctic Research Ser.: Vol. 13). (Illus.). 239p. 1969. 18.00 (ISBN 0-87590-113-1). Am Geophysical.
Lamb, I. Mackenzie & Zimmerman, Martin H. Benthic Marine Algae of the Antarctic Peninsula: Paper 4 in Biology of the Antarctic Seas V. Pawson, David L., ed. (Antarctic Research Ser.: Vol. 23). 104p. 1977. pap. 39.95 (ISBN 0-87590-128-X). Am Geophysical.
Laws, Richard M., ed. Antarctic Ecology. 1984. Vol. 1. 55.00 (ISBN 0-12-439501-5); Vol. 2. 75.00 (ISBN 0-12-439502-3). Acad Pr.
Llano, George, ed. Adaptions Within Antarctic Ecosystems: Proceedings of the Third SCAR Symposium on Antarctic Biology. LC 76-21500. 1296p. 1977. 19.95x (ISBN 0-87201-000-7). Gulf Pub.
Marvin, Ursula B. Field & Laboratory Investigations of Meteorites from Victoria Land, Antarctica. Marvin, Ursula B. & Mason, Brian, eds. LC 83-20087. (Smithsonian Contributions to the Earth Sciences: No. 26). pap. 34.50 (ISBN 0-317-20102-6, 2023163). Bks Demand UMI.
Mawson, Douglas. Home of the Blizzard, Being the Story of the Australian Antarctic Expedition, 1911-1914, 2 Vols. LC 68-55202. (Illus.). 1968. Repr. of 1915 ed. Set. lib. bdg. 71.75x (ISBN 0-8371-3849-3, MAHB). Greenwood.
Neider, Charles. Beyond Cape Horn: Travels in the Antarctic. LC 80-13220. (Illus.). 400p. 1980. 16.95 (ISBN 0-87156-233-2). Sierra.
Nordenskjold, Otto. Antarctica: Or Two Years Amongst the Ice of the South Pole. (Illus.). xviii, 608p. 1977. Repr. of 1905 ed. 35.00 (ISBN 0-208-01642-2, Archon). Shoe String.
Oliver, R. L., ed. Antarctic Earth Science: Fourth International Symposium, Adelaide, South Australia, 1982. LC 83-7872. 750p. 1984. 79.50 (ISBN 0-521-25836-7). Cambridge U Pr.
Parker, Bruce C., ed. Conservation Problems in Antarctica. LC 72-85836. (Illus.). 356p. 1972. 25.00x (ISBN 0-8139-0840-X). U Pr of Va.
--Environmental Impact in Antarctica. (Illus.). 390p. 1978. 14.95x (ISBN 0-8139-0847-7). U Pr of Va.
Peacock, Donald. People, Peregrines, & Arctic Pipelines: The Critical Battle to Build Canada's Northern Gas Pipelines. LC 77-375197. (Illus.). 224p. 1977. pap. 5.95x (ISBN 0-295-95722-0). U of Wash Pr.
Rabassa, Jorge, ed. Quaternary of South America & Antartic Peninsula. (Illus.). 168p. 1983. lib. bdg. 20.00 (ISBN 90-6191-513-9, Pub. by Balkema RSA). IPS.
Reid, Joseph L., ed. Antarctic Oceanology One. LC 78-151300. (Antarctic Research Ser.: Vol. 15). (Illus.). 343p. 1971. 28.50 (ISBN 0-87590-115-8). Am Geophysical.
Ross, James C. Voyage of Discovery & Research in the Southern & Antarctic Regions 1839-43, 2 Vols. LC 69-10852. (Illus.). Repr. of 1847 ed. 75.00x (ISBN 0-678-05624-2). Kelley.
Ross, M. J. Ross in the Antarctic: The Voyages of James Clark Ross, 1839-1843, in H.M. Ships Erebus & Terror. 300p. 1982. 60.00x (ISBN 0-686-44556-2, Pub. by Caedmon of Whitby). State Mutual Bk.
Schwerdtfeger, W. Weather & Climate of the Antarctic. (Developments in Atmospheric Science Ser.: Vol. 15). 1984. 46.25 (ISBN 0-444-42293-5, I-092-84). Elsevier.
Scott, Robert F. Voyage of the Discovery, 2 Vols. LC 68-55218. (Illus.). 1969. Repr. of 1905 ed. Set. lib. bdg. 57.00x (ISBN 0-8371-1334-2, SCDI). Greenwood.
Scott, Robert S. Voyage of the 'Discovery' (Illus.). 1951. 18.00 (ISBN 0-685-20649-1). Transatlantic.
Shackleton, Ernest H. Heart of the Antarctic, Being the Story of the British Antarctic Expedition, 1907-1909, 2 Vols. LC 68-55219. 1968. Repr. of 1909 ed. Set. lib. bdg. 74.50x (ISBN 0-8371-3865-5, SHAN). Greenwood.
Siegfried, W. R., et al, eds. Antarctic Nutrient Cycles & Food Webs. (Illus.). 700p. 1985. 59.00 (ISBN 0-387-13417-4). Springer-Verlag.

ANTEDILUVIAN ANIMALS

see Paleontology

ANTELOPES

see also Pronghorn Antelope

The Indian Blackbuck Antelope: A Texas View. (Kleberg Studies in Natural Resources). (Illus.). 184p. 1978. pap. 8.95 (ISBN 0-89096-197-2). Tex A&M Univ Pr.
Jarman, Martha V. Impala Social Behavior: Territory, Hierarchy, Mating, & the Use of Space. (Advances in Ethology Ser.: Vol. 21). (Illus.). 96p. (Orig.). 1979. pap. text ed. 33.00 (ISBN 3-489-60936-0). Parey Sci Pubs.
Sheffield, William J., et al. The Nilgai Antelope in Texas. (Kleberg Studies in Natural Resources). (Illus.). 100p. 1984. pap. 10.95x (ISBN 0-89096-199-9). Tex A&M Univ Pr.
Spinage, C. A. A Territorial Antelope: The Ugnad Waterbuck. 1982. 55.00 (ISBN 0-12-657720-X). Acad Pr.

ANTENNAS (ELECTRONICS)

see also Radio--Antennas; Radio Telescope

Antenna Theory & Design. (Illus.). 608p. 1981. 47.95 (ISBN 0-13-038356-2). P-H.
Bahl, I. J. & Bhartia, P. Microstrip Antennas. (Illus.). 355p. 1980. 64.00 (ISBN 0-89006-098-3). Artech Hse.
Balanis, Constantine A. Antenna Theory: Analysis & Design. 790p. 1982. text ed. 38.45 scp (ISBN 0-06-040458-2, HarpC); sol. manual avail. (ISBN 0-06-360410-8). Har-Row.
Bevensee, Robert M. Handbook of Conical Antennas & Scatterers. LC 71-172793. (Illus.). 182p. 1973. 67.25 (ISBN 0-677-00480-X). Gordon.
Blake, Lamont V. Antennas. 425p. 1984. text ed. 55.00 (ISBN 0-89006-154-8). Artech Hse.
Brown, R. G., et al. Lines, Waves & Antennas: The Transmission of Electric Energy. 2nd ed. (Illus.). 471p. 1973. text ed. 41.50 (ISBN 0-471-06677-X). Wiley.
Burrows, M. L. E. L. F. Communication Antennas. (IEE Electromagnetic Waves Ser.: No. 5). (Illus.). 343p. 1978. casebound 46.00 (ISBN 0-906048-00-1, EW005, Pub. by Peregrinus England). Inst Elect Eng.
Carr, Joseph J. Antenna Data Reference Manual-Including Dimension Tables. (Illus.). 1979. 15.95 (ISBN 0-8306-9738-1); pap. 7.95o.p (ISBN 0-8306-1152-5, 1152). TAB Bks.
Clarke, R. H. & Brown, John. Diffraction Theory & Antennas. LC 80-40388. (Ser. in Electrical & Electronic Engineering). 292p. 1980. 101.95x (ISBN 0-470-27003-9). Halsted Pr.
Collin, R. E. Antennas & Radiowave Propagation. 528p. 1985. 45.95 (ISBN 0-07-011808-6). McGraw.
Damiamayan, Dikran. Analysis of Aperture Antennas in Inhomogeneous Media. LC 77-141023. 93p. 1969. 17.50 (ISBN 0-403-04493-6). Mgmt Info Serv.
Dubost, G. Flat Radiating Dipoles & Applications to Arrays. (Electronic & Electrical Engineering Research Studies: Research Studies on Antennas Ser.). 103p. 1981. 38.95x (ISBN 0-471-10050-1, Pub. by Res Stud Pr). Wiley.
Enemark, Donald C. Feasibility Study & Design of an Antenna Pointing System with an in-Loop, Time Shared Digital Computer. LC 76-135076. 241p. 1970. 19.00 (ISBN 0-403-04499-5). Scholarly.

Grantham, Donald J. Antennas, Transmission Lines, & Microwaves. LC 77-25369. (The Grantham Electronics-with-Mathematics Ser.: Vol. 6). (Illus.). 1977. pap. text ed. 18.95x (ISBN 0-915668-06-8). G S E Pubns.

Harmuth, H. F. Advances in Electronics & Electron Physics: Antennas & Waveguides for Nonsinusoidal Waves. Marton, L., ed. (Serial Publication Ser.: Supplement 15). 1984. 60.00 (ISBN 0-12-014577-4). Acad Pr.

Institute of Electrical & Electronics Engineers, Inc. IEEE Standard Test Procedures for Antennas. LC 79-92425. 143p. 1980. 15.95x (ISBN 0-471-08032-2, Pub. by Wiley Interscience). Wiley.

Jasik, Henry & Johnson, Richard C. Antenna Engineering Handbook. 2nd ed. 1408p. 1984. 95.00 (ISBN 0-07-032291-0). McGraw.

Jull, E. V. Aperture Antennas & Diffraction Theory. (IEE Electromagnetic Waves Ser.: No. 10). 192p. 1981. 76.00 (ISBN 0-906048-52-4, EW010, Pub. by Peregrinus England). Inst Elect Eng.

King, R. W., et al. Arrays of Cylindrical Dipoles. LC 67-26069. (Illus.). 1968. 85.00 (ISBN 0-521-05887-2). Cambridge U Pr.

King, Ronald W. Tables of Antenna Characteristics. LC 74-157425. 400p. 1971. 85.00x (ISBN 0-306-65154-8, IFI Plenum). Plenum Pub.

King, Ronold W., et al. Antennas in Matter: Fundamentals, Theory & Applications. 784p. 1980. 85.00x (ISBN 0-262-11074-1). MIT Pr.

Kraus, John D. Antennas. (Electrical & Electronic Engineering Ser.). 1950. text ed. 48.00 (ISBN 0-07-035410-3). McGraw.

Kuecken, John A. Exploring Antennas & Transmission Lines by Personal Computer. (Illus.). 384p. 1985. 39.95 (ISBN 0-442-24714-1). Van Nos Reinhold.

Kuzmin, A. D. & Salomonovich, A. E. Radioastronomical Methods of Antenna Measurements. (Electrical Science Monographs). 1967. 49.50 (ISBN 0-12-431150-4). Acad Pr.

Lee, Kai Fong. Principles of Antenna Theory. LC 83-7042. 324p. 1984. 29.95X (ISBN 0-471-90167-9, Pub. by Wiley-Interscience). Wiley.

Love, A. W. Reflector Antennas. LC 77-94519. 427p. 1978. 47.95x (ISBN 0-471-04605-1); pap. 31.50x (ISBN 0-471-04606-X). Wiley.

Love, A. W., ed. Electromagnetic Horn Antennas. LC 75-44649. 1976. 20.75 (ISBN 0-87942-076-6, PP00752). Inst Electrical.

--Reflector Antennas. LC 77-94519. 1978. 49.85 (ISBN 0-87942-103-7, PC01008). Inst Electrical.

Ma, M. T. Theory & Application of Antenna Arrays. LC 73-15615. pap. 107.30 (ISBN 0-317-09841-1, 2022491). Bks Demand UMI.

Milligan, T. Modern Antenna Design. 448p. 1984. write for info. (ISBN 0-07-042318-0). McGraw.

Mittra, R., et al, eds. Satellite Communication Antenna Technology. 600p. 1984. 76.75 (ISBN 0-444-86733-3, North-Holland). Elsevier.

Moore, J. & Pizer, R. Moment Methods in Electromagnetics: Techniques & Applications. LC 84-2133. (Antenna Ser.: Nos. 1-641). 398p. 1984. 74.95x (ISBN 0-471-90414-7, Pub. by Wiley). Wiley.

Popovic, B. D. & Dragovic, M B. Analysis & Synthesis of Wire Antennas. 304p. 1983. 63.95 (ISBN 0-471-90008-7, Pub. by Res Stud Pr). Wiley.

Pozar, David M. Antenna Design Using Personal Computers. 1985. pap. text ed. 40.00 (ISBN 0-89006-175-0). Artech Hse.

Rusch, W. V. & Potter, P. D. Analysis of Reflector Antennas. (Electrical Science Ser). 1970. 60.00 (ISBN 0-12-603450-8). Acad Pr.

Sams Editorial Staff. Handbook of Antenna Theory & Design. 1985. 79.95 (ISBN 0-317-29695-7, 22054). Sams.

Shifrin, A. S. Statistical Antenna Theory. Beckmann, Petr, tr. from Rus. LC 73-158655. (Electromagnetics Ser.: Vol. 7). (Illus.). 1971. 25.00x (ISBN 0-911762-11-6). Golem.

Stutzman, Warren L. & Thiele, Gary A. Antenna Theory & Design. LC 80-23498. 598p. 1981. text ed. 45.50 (ISBN 0-471-04458-X); sol. manual 25.00 (ISBN 0-471-09441-2). Wiley.

Westcott, Brian S. Shaped Reflector Antenna Design. 200p. 1983. 48.95 (ISBN 0-471-90152-0, Res Stud Pr). Wiley.

Zakharyev, L. N., et al. Radiation from Apertures in Convex Bodies: Flush-Mounted Antennas. Beckmann, Petr, tr. from Rus. LC 76-114987. (Electromagnetics Ser.: Vol. 4). 1970. 25.00x (ISBN 0-911762-06-X). Golem.

ANTHELMINTICS

Bard, J. H. Anthelmintic Index. 71p. 1972. 40.00x (ISBN 0-85198-257-3, Pub. by CAB Bks England). State Mutual Bk.

ANTHOZOA

see also Corals; Sea-Anemones

Verrill, Addison E. Hawaiian Shallow Water Anthozoa. (BMB). pap. 8.00 (ISBN 0-527-02155-5). Kraus Repr.

ANTHRACITE COAL

see Coal

ANTHROPOLOGISTS

Cesara, Manda. No Hiding Place: Reflections of a Woman Anthropologists. (Studies in Anthropology Ser.). 1982. 27.50 (ISBN 0-12-164880-X). Acad Pr.

Cimino, Louis & Chatelain, Agnes, eds. Directory of Practicing Anthropologists. 1981. pap. 6.00 (ISBN 0-686-36594-1). Am Anthro Assn.

Freeman, S. T. & Walters, L. R. Europeanist Social Anthropologists in North America: A Directory. 1975. pap. 1.50 (ISBN 0-686-36564-X). Am Anthro Assn.

Hare, Peter H. A Woman's Quest for Science: A Portrait of Anthropologist Elsie Clews Parsons. LC 84-43055. (Illus.). 192p. 1985. 22.95 (ISBN 0-87975-274-2). Prometheus Bks.

Linton, Adelin & Wagley, Charles. Ralph Linton. LC 76-174708. (Leaders of Modern Anthropology Ser). 196p. 1971. 29.00x (ISBN 0-231-03355-9); pap. 13.00x (ISBN 0-231-03398-2). Columbia U Pr.

Mark, Joan T. Four Anthropologists. LC 80-25414. 1980. 20.00 (ISBN 0-88202-190-7). Watson Pub Intl.

Mead, Margaret. Letters from the Field: Nineteen Twenty-Five to Nineteen Seventy-Five. Anshen, Ruth N., ed. LC 73-4110. (World Perspectives Ser.). (Illus.). 1978. 14.37i (ISBN 0-06-012961-1, HarpT). Har-Row.

Tax, Sol, intro. by. Fifth International Directory of Anthropologists: Cosponsored by the Wenner-Gren Foundation for Anthropological Research. LC 74-11615. x, 496p. 1975. text ed. 29.95x (ISBN 0-226-79077-0). U of Chicago Pr.

Turner, Victor R. On the Edge of the Bush: Anthropology as Experience. Turner, Edith L., ed. (Anthroplology of Form & Meaning Ser.). 1985. 29.95 (ISBN 0-8165-0949-2). U of Ariz Pr.

ANTHROPOLOGY

see also Aerial Photography in Anthropology; Anthropometry; Archaeology; Craniology; Man; Physical Anthropology

also names of races, tribes etc., and subdivision Race Question under names of countries, e.g. United States–Race Question

Ames, Michael M. Museums, the Public & Anthropology: A Study in the Anthropology of Anthropology. 140p. 1985. 12.50 (ISBN 0-7748-0213-8). U BC Pr.

Anderson, E. N. The Floating World of Castle Peak Bay. (American Anthropological Association-Anthropological Studies: No. 4). pap. 69.80 (ISBN 0-317-10012-2, 2000776). Bks Demand UMI.

Barrett, Stanley R. The Rebirth of Anthropological Theory. 288p. 1984. 25.00 (ISBN 0-8020-5638-5). U of Toronto Pr.

Bascom, William. Ponape: A Pacific Economy in Transition. LC 65-64597. (University of California, Anthropological Records: Vol. 22). pap. 41.50 (ISBN 0-317-29120-3, 2021322). Bks Demand UMI.

Benjamin, Elsie. The Stanzas of Dzyan: Notes for Study on Cosmogenesis & Anthropogenesis. (Study Ser.: No. 5). 45p. 1981. pap. 3.00 (ISBN 0-913004-40-5). Point Loma Pub.

Blackwood, Evelyn. Anthropology & Homosexuality. (Journal of Homosexuality: Vol. 11, No. 3-4). 256p. 1985. 29.95 (ISBN 0-86656-328-8); pap. text ed. 19.95 (ISBN 0-86656-420-9). Haworth Pr.

Bodley, John H. Anthropology & Contempory Human Problems. 2nd ed. 258p. 1985. pap. text ed. 10.95 (ISBN 0-87484-671-4). Mayfield Pub.

Buettner-Janusch, John. Origins of Man: Physical Anthropology. LC 66-14128. pap. 120.00 (ISBN 0-317-28455-X, 2055138). Bks Demand UMI.

Burrill, Richard. The Human Almanac: People Through Time. (Illus.). 432p. (Orig.). 1983. pap. 14.50 (ISBN 0-943238-00-5). Sierra Pr.

Canfield, Robert, intro. by. The Encyclopedia of Mankind. (Illus.). 2712p. 1984. lib. bdg. 324.95x (ISBN 0-86307-231-3). M Cavendish Corp.

Cantwell, Anne M., et al, eds. The Research Potential of Anthropological Museum Collections. (Annals of The New York Academy of Science Ser.: Vol. 376). 585p. 1981. lib. bdg. 115.00x (ISBN 0-89766-141-9); pap. 115.00x (ISBN 0-89766-142-7). NY Acad Sci.

Charlsey, Simon. Culture & Sericulture: Social Anthropology & Development in a South Indian Livestock Industry. (Studies in Anthropology). 1982. 35.00 (ISBN 0-12-169380-5). Acad Pr.

Clammer, John. Anthropology & Political Economy: Theoretical & Asian Perspectives. 224p. 1985. 27.50 (ISBN 0-312-04345-7). St Martin.

DeWalt, Billie R. & Pelto, Pertti J., eds. Micro & Macro Levels of Analysis in Anthropology: Issues in Theory & Research. (WVSS Ser.). 210p. 1985. pap. text ed. 20.00x (ISBN 0-8133-0251-X). Westview.

Epstein, A. L. The Experience of Shame in Melanesia: An Essay in the Anthropology of Affect. (Occasional Papers Ser.: No. 40). 58p. 1984. pap. text ed. 8.25x (Pub. by Royal Anthro Inst England). Humanities.

Fitzgerald, Thomas K., ed. Nutrition & Anthropology in Action. (Studies of Developing Countries: No. 21). (Orig.). 1976. pap. text ed. 16.50x (ISBN 90-232-1447-1). Humanities.

Fowler, Don D. & Matley, John F. Material Culture of the Numa: The John Wesley Powell Collection, 1867-1880. LC 78-22066. (Smithsonian Contributions to Anthropology Ser.: No. 26). pap. 46.80 (ISBN 0-317-28871-7, 2020307). Bks Demand UMI.

Gans, Eric. The End of Culture: Toward a Generative Anthropology. LC 84-16180. 1985. 35.00x (ISBN 0-520-05181-5). U of Cal Pr.

Haddon, Alfred. The Study of Man. (Classics of Anthropology Ser.). 74.00 (ISBN 0-8240-9647-9). Garland Pub.

Haviland, William A. Anthropology. 3rd ed. 1982. pap. text ed. 26.95 (ISBN 0-03-059279-8); instr's. manual 25.00 (ISBN 0-03-059281-X). HR&W.

Holy, Ladislav & Stuchlik, Milan. Actions, Norms & Representations: Foundations of Anthropological Inquiry. LC 83-1851. (Cambridge Studies in Social Anthropology Ser.: No. 45). 200p. 1984. 37.50 (ISBN 0-521-25492-2); pap. 10.95 (ISBN 0-521-27493-1). Cambridge U Pr.

Howell, Signe. Society & Cosmos: Chewong of Peninsular Malaysia. (Illus.). 294p. 1984. 47.50x (ISBN 0-19-582543-8). Oxford U Pr.

Hsu, Francis L. Exorcising the Trouble Makers: Magic, Science, & Culture. LC 83-5522. (Contributions to the Study of Religion Ser.: No. 11). (Illus.). xvi, 164p. 1983. lib. bdg. 27.95 (ISBN 0-313-23780-8, HET/). Greenwood.

Hutterer, Karl L. & MacDonald, William K., eds. Houses Built on Scattered Poles: Prehistory & Ecology in Negros Oriental, Philippines. (San Carlos Publications, Humanities Ser.: No. 12). (Illus.). 372p. 1982. pap. 12.50x (ISBN 0-686-39296-5). Cellar.

International Committee for Social Sciences Information & Documentation. Anthropology XXVII: International Bibliography of the Social Sciences. 560p. 1985. lib. bdg. 80.00 (ISBN 0-422-80960-8, 4054, Pub. by Tavistock England). Methuen Inc.

International Congress of Anthropology & Prehistoric Archaeology, 1st: Neuchatel, 1866, (Proces-Verbal) Repr. 20.00 (ISBN 0-317-15383-8). Kraus Repr.

International Congress of Anthropology & Prehistoric Archaeology, 10th: Paris, 1889, (Compte-Rendu) Repr. 65.00 (ISBN 0-317-15399-4). Kraus Repr.

International Congress of Anthropology & Prehistoric Archaeology, 11th: Moscow, 1892, (Compte-Rendu, 4 vols. in 2. Repr. Set. 140.00 (ISBN 0-317-15402-8). Kraus Repr.

International Congress of Anthropology & Prehistoric Archaeology, 12th: Paris, 1900, (Compte-Rendu) Repr. 60.00 (ISBN 0-317-15403-6). Kraus Repr.

International Congress of Anthropology & Prehistoric Archaeology, 13th: Monaco, 1906, (Compte-Rendu, 2 vols. Repr. Set. 100.00 (ISBN 0-317-15405-2). Kraus Repr.

International Congress of Anthropology & Prehistoric Archaeology, 14th: Geneva, 1912, (Compte-Rendu, 2 vols. Repr. Set. 120.00 (ISBN 0-317-15406-0). Kraus Repr.

International Congress of Anthropology & Prehistoric Archaeology, 15th: Coimbra, 1930; Paris, 1931, (Actes, 2 vols. Repr. Set. 165.00 (ISBN 0-317-15407-9). Kraus Intl.

International Congress of Anthropology & Prehistoric Archaeology, 16th: Brussels, 1935, (Rapport, 2 vols. Repr. Set. 140.00 (ISBN 0-317-15408-7). Kraus Repr.

International Congress of Anthropology & Prehistoric Archaeology, 2nd: Paris, 1867, (Compte-Rendu) Repr. 60.00 (ISBN 0-317-15386-2). Kraus Repr.

International Congress of Anthropology & Prehistoric Archaeology, 3rd: London, 1868, (Transactions) Repr. 60.00 (ISBN 0-317-15387-0). Kraus Repr.

International Congress of Anthropology & Prehistoric Archaeology, 4th: Copenhagen, 1869, (Compte-Rendu) Repr. 60.00 (ISBN 0-317-15388-9). Kraus Repr.

International Congress of Anthropology & Prehistoric Archaeology, 5th: Bologna, 1871, (Compte-Rendu) Repr. 62.00 (ISBN 0-317-15390-0). Kraus Repr.

International Congress of Anthropology & Prehistoric Archaeology, 6th: Brussels, 1872, (Compte-Rendu) Repr. 80.00 (ISBN 0-317-15391-9). Kraus Repr.

International Congress of Anthropology & Prehistoric Archaeology, 7th: Stockholm, 1874, (Compte-Rendu, 2 vols. Repr. Set. 100.00 (ISBN 0-317-15394-3). Kraus Repr.

International Congress of Anthropology & Prehistoric Archaeology, 8th: Budapest, 1876, (Compte-Rendu, 2 vols. Repr. Set. 150.00 (ISBN 0-317-15396-X). Kraus Repr.

International Congress of Anthropology & Prehistoric Archaeology, 9th: Lisbon, 1880, (Compte-Rendu) Repr. 100.00. Kraus Repr.

Kerewsky-Halpern, Barbara. Anthropology: Study of People. (Literacy Volunteers of America Readers Ser.). 48p. (Orig.). 1983. pap. 2.46 (ISBN 0-8428-9613-9). Cambridge Bk.

Kidder, Alfred V. The Artifacts of Pecos. (Classics of Anthropology Ser.). 1985. 53.00 (ISBN 0-8240-9630-4). Garland Pub.

Lawrence, Edward. Spiritualism among Civilised & Savage Races: A Study in Anthropology. 17.00 (ISBN 0-8369-5848-9, 6912). Ayer Co Pubs.

Macha, Karel. Ein Hundert Thesen zu Einer Integralen Anthropologie. (Ger.). 84p. 1983. 12.65 (ISBN 3-8204-7759-4). P Lang Pubs.

Maday, Bela C., ed. Anthropology & Society. (Anthropological Society of Washington Ser.). (Illus.). 116p. 1984. text ed. 12.50 (ISBN 0-87474-658-2); pap. 6.95 (ISBN 0-87474-659-0). Smithsonian.

Mavalwala, J. Learning about Ourselves: Readings in Anthropology. 232p. 1984. pap. text ed. 15.50 (ISBN 0-8403-3473-7). Kendall Hunt.

--Ultimate Roots: Readings in Physical Anthropology. 232p. 1984. pap. text ed. 16.50 (ISBN 0-8403-3474-5). Kendall-Hunt.

Mielke, James H. & Crawford, Michael H., eds. Current Developments in Anthropological Genetics, Vol. 1: Theory & Methods. LC 79-24900. 450p. 1980. 59.50x (ISBN 0-306-40390-0, Plenum Pr). Plenum Pub.

Montessori, Maria. Pedagogical Anthropology, 3 vols. (Illus.). 517p. 1984. 37.15 (ISBN 0-89901-160-8). Found Class Reprints.

Morris, Desmond. The Naked Ape. 1984. pap. 3.50 (ISBN 0-440-36266-0, LE). Dell.

Mourant, A. E. Blood Relations: Blood Groups & Anthropology. (Illus.). 1983. 29.50x (ISBN 0-19-857580-7). Oxford U Pr.

Pandian, Jacob. Anthropology & the Western Traditon: Toward An Authentic Anthropology. 135p. (Orig.). 1985. pap. text ed. 7.95x (ISBN 0-88133-127-9). Waveland Pr.

Partridge, William L., ed. Training Manual in Development Anthropology. (American Anthropological Association Special Publication Ser.: No. 17). 122p. 1984. pap. text ed. 9.00 (ISBN 0-913167-02-9). Am Anthro Assn.

Rappaport, Roy A. Ecology, Meaning, & Religion. 2nd ed. 1979. 20.00 (ISBN 0-938190-28-8); pap. 9.95 (ISBN 0-938190-27-X). North Atlantic.

Richards, Audrey I. & Kuper, Adam, eds. Councils in Action. LC 76-160101. (Cambridge Papers in Social Anthropology: No. 6). pap. 55.50 (ISBN 0-317-27985-8, 2025594). Bks Demand UMI.

Rock, J. F. A Monographic Study of the Hawaiian Species of the Tribe Lobelioideae, Family Campanulaceae. (BMB). (Orig.). 1919. 116.00 (ISBN 0-527-01651-9). Kraus Repr.

Steward, Julian. Evolution & Ecology: Essays on Social Transformation. Steward, Jane C. & Murphy, Robert F., eds. LC 76-46341. 410p. 1977. 29.50x (ISBN 0-252-00612-7); pap. 9.95x (ISBN 0-252-00709-3). U of Ill Pr.

Stoddard, Robert H., et al. Geography of Humans & Their Cultures. (Illus.). 544p. 1986. text ed. 35.95 (ISBN 0-13-351578-8). P-H.

Swanson, Richard A. Gourmantche Ethnoanthropology: A Theory of Human Being. (Illus.). 488p. (Orig.). 1984. lib. bdg. 21.50 (ISBN 0-8191-4176-3); pap. text ed. 18.25 (ISBN 0-8191-4177-1). U Pr of Amer.

Tanaka, Jiro. The San, Hunter-Gatherers of the Kalahari: A Study in Ecological Anthropology. 199p. 1980. 20.00x (ISBN 0-86008-276-8, Pub. by U of Tokyo Japan). Columbia U Pr.

Van Willegen, John. Applied Anthropology: An Inrtoduction. 288p. 1986. 34.95 (ISBN 0-89789-096-5); pap. 17.95 (ISBN 0-89789-097-3). Bergin & Garvey.

Wallace, Edwin R., IV. Freud & Anthropology: A History & Reappraisal. LC 83-193. (Psychological Issues Monograph: No. 55). xi, 306p. 27.50 (ISBN 0-8236-2012-3). Intl Univs Pr.

Werner, Dennis. Anthropology: Study Guide & Workbook. 4th ed. 192p. 1985. pap. text ed. 11.95 (ISBN 0-13-037086-X). P-H.

Rudbach, B. & Baker, R., eds. Immunology of Bacterial Polysaccharides. LC 78-31961. (Developments in Immunology Ser.: Vol. 2). 158p. 1979. 45.50 (ISBN 0-444-00315-0, Biomedical Pr). Elsevier.

Schlessinger, David, ed. Microbiology 1977. LC 74-33538. 1977. 28.00 (ISBN 0-914826-13-1). Am Soc Microbio.

Sela, Michael. The Antigens, Vol. 6. LC 73-799. 1982. 65.00 (ISBN 0-12-635506-1). Acad Pr.

Snell, George D. & Hildemann, W. H. Cell Surface Antigens: Studies in Mammals Other Than Man. LC 72-13690. (Illus.). 220p. 1973. text ed. 23.00x (ISBN 0-8422-7100-7). Irvington.

Wachtel, Stephen, ed. H-Y Antigen & the Biology of Sex Determination. 304p. 1982. 51.50 (ISBN 0-8089-1514-2, 794715). Grune.

ANTIMETABOLITES

Langen, J. Antimetabolites of Nucleic Acid Metabolism. 286p. 1975. 62.50x (ISBN 0-677-30760-8). Gordon.

Odell, William D. & Frauchimont, Paul. Principles of Competitive Protein-Binding Assays. 2nd ed. LC 82-10941. 311p. 1982. 45.00 (ISBN 0-471-08924-9, Pub. by Wiley Med). Wiley.

Roy-Burman, P. Analogues of Nucleic Acid Components: Mechanisms of Action. LC 75-96737. (Recent Results in Cancer Research: Vol. 25). 1970. 21.00 (ISBN 0-387-04990-8). Springer-Verlag.

Skoda, J. & Langen, P., eds. Antimetabolites in Biochemistry, Biology & Medicine: Proceedings, Prague, 1978. (Federation of European Biochemical Societies Symposium: Vol. 57). (Illus.). 1979. text ed. 72.00 (ISBN 0-08-024384-3). Pergamon.

ANTIMONY

Doak, George D. & Freedman, Leon D. Organometallic Compounds of Arsenic, Antimony, & Bismuth. LC 75-120703. 509p. 1970. 42.50 (ISBN 0-471-21650-X, Pub. by Wiley). Krieger.

Dub, M., ed. Organometallic Compounds: Methods of Synthesis, Physical Constants & Chemical Reactions, 3 vols. Incl. Vol. 1. Compounds of Transition Metals. 2nd ed. xviii, 828p. 1966. 83.00 (ISBN 0-387-03632-6); Vol. 2. Compounds of Germanium, Tin & Lead, Including Biological Activity & Commercial Application. 2nd ed. Weiss, R. W., ed. xx, 627p. 1967. 83.00 (ISBN 0-387-03948-1); 91.00 (ISBN 0-387-06304-8); Vol. 3. Compounds of Arsenic, Antimony & Bismuth. 2nd ed. xx, 925p. 1968. 83.00 (ISBN 0-387-04296-2); Formula Index to Volumes 1-3. 2nd ed. vii, 343p. 1970. 57.00 (ISBN 0-387-04985-1). LC 66-28249. Springer-Verlag.

Purdy, C. Phillips, Jr. Antimony Occurrences of Washington. (Bulletin Ser.: No. 39). 186p. 1951. 1.00 (ISBN 0-686-34696-3). Geologic Pubns.

ANTINEOPLASTIC AGENTS

see also Antimetabolites

Bardos, T. J. & Kalman, T. I., eds. New Approaches to the Design of Antineoplastic Agents. 344p. 1983. 78.00 (ISBN 0-444-00724-5, Biomedical Pr). Elsevier.

Clark, William R. & Golstein, Pierre, eds. Mechanisms of Cell-Mediated Cytotoxicity. LC 82-5312. (Advances in Experimental Medicine & Biology: Vol. 146). 610p. 1982. 79.50x (ISBN 0-306-41012-5, Plenum Pr). Plenum Pub.

Colowick, Sidney P. & Kaplan, Nathan O., eds. Methods in Enzymology: Immunochemical Techniques, Conventional Antibodies, FC Receptors & Cytotoxicity, Vol. 93, Pt. F. 393p. 1983. 55.00 (ISBN 0-12-181993-0). Acad Pr.

Cortes Funes, H. & Rozencweig, M., eds. New Approaches in Cancer Therapy. (European Organization for Research on Treatment of Cancer (EORTC) Monograph: Vol. 11). 204p. 1982. text ed. 59.00 (ISBN 0-89004-781-2). Raven.

Emanuel, N. M. Kinetics of Experimental Tumour Processes. (Illus.). 350p. 1982. 77.00 (ISBN 0-08-024909-4). Pergamon.

Endo, H., et al, eds. Chemistry & Biological Actions of 4-Nitroquinoline 1-Oxide. LC 6-129622. (Recent Results in Cancer Research: Vol. 34). (Illus.). 1971. 26.00 (ISBN 0-387-05230-5). Springer-Verlag.

Lohrmann, H. P. & Schreml, W., eds. Cytotoxic Drugs & the Granulopoietic System. (Recent Results in Cancer Research Ser.: Vol. 81). (Illus.). 235p. 1982. 48.00 (ISBN 0-387-10962-5). Springer-Verlag.

Meek, E. S. Antitumour & Antiviral Substances of Natural Origin. LC 74-108340. (Recent Results in Cancer Research: Vol. 28). 1970. 14.00 (ISBN 0-387-04993-2). Springer-Verlag.

Pettit, George R. Biosynthetic Products for Cancer Chemotherapy, Vol. 1. LC 76-54146. (Illus.). 227p. 1977. 35.00x (ISBN 0-306-37687-3, Plenum Pr). Plenum Pub.

Remers, William A. Antineoplastic Agents. LC 83-12411. (Chemistry & Pharmacology of Drugs a Series of Monographs: 1-406). 269p. 1984. 59.50 (ISBN 0-471-08080-2, Pub. by Wiley-Interscience). Wiley.

Roy-Burman, P. Analogues of Nucleic Acid Components: Mechanisms of Action. LC 75-96737. (Recent Results in Cancer Research: Vol. 25). 1970. 21.00 (ISBN 0-387-04990-8). Springer-Verlag.

Sartorelli, A. C. & Johns, D. G., eds. Antineoplastic & Immunosuppressive Agents, Pt. 1. LC 73-10507. (Handbook of Experimental Pharmacology: Vol. 38). (Illus.). 720p. 1974. 154.20 (ISBN 0-387-06402-8). Springer-Verlag.

ANTIOXIDANTS

Business Communications Staff. Antioxidants: Markets, Materials, Trends. 1985. 1750.00 (ISBN 0-89336-367-7, C-020B). BCC.

Critser, James R., Jr. Antioxidants & Stabilizers for Polymers. Incl. Indexes & Abstracts 1967-1971. 315.00 (ISBN 0-914428-06-3). (Ser. 3-6771B). 1972. Lexington Data Inc.

--Antioxidants & Stabilizers for Polymers. (Ser. 3-76). 1977. 125.00 (ISBN 0-914428-50-0). Lexington Data.

Ranney, M. W. Antioxidants-Recent Developments. LC 79-84425. (Chemical Technology Review Ser.: No. 127). (Illus.). 372p. 1979. 42.00 (ISBN 0-8155-0747-X). Noyes.

Scott, G. Atmospheric Oxidation & Antioxidants. 528p. 1966. 106.50 (ISBN 0-444-40519-4). Elsevier.

ANTIPOISONOUS AGENTS

see Antidotes

ANTISTATIC COMPOUNDS

see Petroleum Products

ANTITANK GUNS

Hoffschmidt, E. J. Know Your Antitank Rifles. LC 77-70570. (Know Your Gun Ser.). (Illus.). 80p. (Orig.). 1977. pap. 5.95 (ISBN 0-941540-04-9). Blacksmith Corp.

Hoffschmidt, Edward J. & Tantum, William H. German Tank & Antitank. 260p. 1968. 12.50 (ISBN 0-87364-151-5). Paladin Pr.

ANTITHROMBOTIC AGENTS

see Fibrinolytic Agents

ANTITOXINS

see Toxins and Antitoxins

ANTLIATA

see Diptera

ANTS

see also Army Ants

Ball, George E., ed. Taxonomy, Phylogeny & Zoogeography of Beetles & Ants. (Entomologica Ser.). 1985. lib. bdg. 105.00 (ISBN 90-6193-511-3, Pub. by Junk Pubs Netherlands). Kluwer Academic.

Beattie, Andrew J. The Evolutionary Ecology of Ant-Plant Mutualisms. (Illus.). 176p. Date not set. price not set (ISBN 0-521-25281-4); pap. price not set (ISBN 0-521-27272-6). Cambridge U Pr.

Brian, M. V., ed. Production Ecology of Ants & Termites. LC 76-54061. (International Biological Programme Ser.: No. 13). (Illus.). 1977. 95.00 (ISBN 0-521-21519-6). Cambridge U Pr.

Buckley, R. Ant-Plant Interactions in Australia. 1982. text ed. 54.50 (ISBN 90-6193-684-5, Pub. by Junk Pubs Netherlands). Kluwer Academic.

De Reaumur, Rene A. F. The Natural History of Ants from an Unpublished Manuscript in the Archives of the Academy of Sciences of Paris. Egerton, Frank N., 3rd, ed. Wheeler, Morton, tr. LC 77-74211. (History of Ecology Ser.). 1978. Repr. of 1926 ed. lib. bdg. 23.50x (ISBN 0-405-10382-4). Ayer Co Pubs.

Dumpert, Klaus. The Social Biology of Ants. Johnson, K. C., tr. LC 79-25013. (Pitman International Series in Bio Science). 298p. 1981. text ed. 59.95 (ISBN 0-273-08479-8). Pitman Pub MA.

Gregg, Robert E. The Ants of Colorado: Their Ecology, Taxonomy & Geographic Distribution. LC 62-63446. (Illus.). 1963. 23.50x (ISBN 0-87081-027-8). Colo Assoc.

Huxley, Julian. Ants. 1978. Repr. of 1930 ed. lib. bdg. 10.00 (ISBN 0-8495-2245-5). Arden Lib.

Huxley, Julian S. Ants. LC 71-98627. Repr. of 1930 ed. 11.50 (ISBN 0-404-03467-5). AMS Pr.

Larson, Peggy P. & Larson, Mervin W. All about Ants. (Apollo Eds.). (Illus.). 1976. pap. 4.95i (ISBN 0-8152-0417-5). T Y Crowell.

Lofgren, Clifford S. & Vander-Meer, Robert K. Fire Ants & Leaf-Cutting Ants: Research for Improving Pest Management Strategies. (Studies in Insect Biology). 400p. 1985. pap. text ed. 45.00x (ISBN 0-8133-7071-X). Westview.

Maeterlinck, Maurice. La Vie des Fourmis. 260p. 1969. 10.95 (ISBN 0-686-56294-1). French & Eur.

Moody, J. V. & Francke, O. F. The Ants (Hymenoptera, Formicidae) of Western Texas: Part I - Subfamily Myrmicinae. (Graduate Studies Ser.: No. 27). 80p. (Orig.). 1982. pap. 12.00 (ISBN 0-89672-107-8). Tex Tech Pr.

Sudd, John H. Introduction to the Behavior of Ants. (Illus.). 1967. 20.00 (ISBN 0-312-42560-0). St Martin.

Weber, Neal A. Gardening Ants, the Attines. LC 76-184169. (Memoirs Ser.: Vol. 92). (Illus.). 1972. 10.00 (ISBN 0-87169-092-6). Am Philos.

Wheeler, William M. Ants: Their Structure, Development, & Behavior. rev. ed. LC 10-8253. (Columbia Biological Ser.: No. 9). (Illus.). 1960. 65.00x (ISBN 0-231-00121-5). Columbia U Pr.

--Fungus-Growing Ants of North America. (Illus.). 146p. 1974. pap. 3.95 (ISBN 0-486-21164-9). Dover.

--The Fungus-Growing Ants of North America. (Illus.). 6.75 (ISBN 0-8446-5097-8). Peter Smith.

ANURA

see also Toads

Caldwell, Jan. A Re-Evaluation of the Hyla Bistincta Species Group, with Descriptions of Three New Species (Anura: Hylidae) (Occasional Papers: No. 28). 37p. 1974. pap. 3.00 color plate (ISBN 0-686-79835-X). U of KS Mus Nat Hist.

Cannatella, David C. A Review of the Phyllomedusa Buckleyi Group: (Anura: Hylidae) (Occasional Papers: Vol. 87). 40p. 1980. 2.25 (ISBN 0-317-04840-6). U of KS Mus Nat Hist.

Variation, Systematics, & Zoogeography of Eleutherodactylus Guentheri & Closely Related Species: Amphibia: Anura: Leptodactylidae. LC 84-600184. (Smithsonian Contributions to Zoology: No. 402). pap. 20.00 (ISBN 0-317-26747-7, 2024353). Bks Demand UMI.

A-ONE SKYRAIDER

see Skyraider (Fighter Planes)

APARTMENT HOUSES

Apartment Building Exterior Inspection Form. 1.50 (ISBN 0-686-46399-4, 981). Inst Real Estate.

Apartment Unit Interior Inspection Form. 1.50 (ISBN 0-686-46400-1, 982). Inst Real Estate.

Holt, Mary M. Guide to Apartment House Management. LC 70-159493. 1971. 6.00 (ISBN 0-682-47269-7, Banner). Exposition Pr FL.

APES

see also Chimpanzees; Gibbons; Gorillas; Orangutans

Berger, Gotthard. Monkeys & Apes. LC 84-2846. (Illus.). 240p. 1984. 24.95 (ISBN 0-668-06204-5, 6204). Arco.

Bromley, Lynn. Monkeys, Apes & Other Primates. (Illus.). 64p. 1981. pap. 3.95 (ISBN 0-686-80426-0). Bellerophon Bks.

Graham, Charles E. & Bowen, James A. Clinical Management of Infant Great Apes. LC 84-25019. 228p. 1985. 48.00 (ISBN 0-8451-3404-3). A R Liss.

Graham, Charles E., ed. Reproductive Biology of the Great Apes: Comparative & Biomedical Perspectives. LC 80-89417. 1981. 60.00 (ISBN 0-12-295020-8). Acad Pr.

The Great Apes of Africa. 174p. 1980. 79.00x (Pub. by Biochemical England). State Mutual Bk.

Hamburg, David A. & McGown, Elizabeth R. The Great Apes. 1979. text ed. 35.95x (ISBN 0-8053-3669-9). Benjamin-Cummings.

Kavanagh, Michael. A Complete Guide to Monkeys, Apes & Other Primates. (Illus.). 224p. 1984. 19.95 (ISBN 0-670-43543-0). Viking.

Napier, J. R. & Napier, P. H., eds. Old World Monkeys: Evolution, Systematics & Behavior. 1970. 76.50 (ISBN 0-12-513860-1). Acad Pr.

Premack, David & Premack, Ann J. The Mind of an Ape. (Illus.). 1983. 14.95 (ISBN 0-393-01581-5). Norton.

Preuschoft, Holger & Chivers, David, eds. The Lesser Apes: Evolutionary & Behavioral Ecology. (Illus.). 1984. 70.00x (Pub. by Edinburgh U Pr Scotland). Columbia U Pr.

Rumbaught, Duane M., ed. Gibbon & Siamang: A Series of Volumes on the Lesser Apes, 4 vols. Incl. Vol. 1. Evolution, Ecology, Behavior & Captive Maintenance. 1972. 57.50 (ISBN 3-8055-1362-3); Vol. 2. Anatomy, Dentition, Taxonomy & Molecular Evolution & Behavior. 1973. 57.50 (ISBN 3-8055-1341-0); Vol. 3. Natural History, Social Behavior, Reproduction, Vocalizations, Prehension. 1974. 55.50 (ISBN 3-8055-1602-9); Vol. 4. Suspensory Behavior, Locomotion, & Other Behaviors of Captive Gibbons; Cognition. 1976. 100.00 (ISBN 3-8055-1658-4). (Illus.). Set. 270.25 (ISBN 3-8055-2308-4). S Karger.

Yerkes, Robert M. The Great Apes, a Study of Anthropoid Life. LC 75-139379. Repr. of 1929 ed. 60.00 (ISBN 0-384-70150-7). Johnson Repr.

Zuckerman, S. The Social Life of Monkeys & Apes. 2nd ed. (Illus.). 496p. 1981. 39.95x (ISBN 0-7100-0691-8). Routledge & Kegan.

APICULTURE

see Bee Culture

APL (COMPUTER PROGRAM LANGUAGE)

Anscombe, F. Computing in Statistical Science Through APL. (Springer Series in Statistics). 416p. 1981. 29.50 (ISBN 0-387-90549-9). Springer-Verlag.

Berry, et al. APL & Insight. (Orig.). 1978. pap. 5.25 (ISBN 0-917326-08-3). APL Pr.

Blaauw, Gerritt A. Digital System Implementation. (Illus.). 1976. 36.95 (ISBN 0-13-212241-3). P-H.

Bryson, Susan M. Understanding APL. LC 82-18462. (An Alfred Handy Guide Ser.). 45p. 1982. pap. 3.50 (ISBN 0-88284-220-X). Alfred Pub.

Franksen, Ole I. Mr. Babage's Secret: The Tale of a Cipher-& APL. (Illus.). 320p. 1985. text ed. 32.00 (ISBN 0-13-604729-7). P-H.

Gilman, Leonard & Rose, Allen J. APL: An Interactive Approach. 3rd ed. LC 83-14716. 366p. 1983. pap. 26.45x (ISBN 0-471-09304-1). Wiley.

Grey, Louis D. Course in APL with Applications. 2nd ed. LC 76-5079. 300p. 1976. pap. text ed. 23.95 (ISBN 0-201-02563-9). Addison-Wesley.

Harms, Edward & Zabinski, Michael P. Introduction to APL & Computer Programming. LC 76-20587. 1977. pap. text ed. 29.45 (ISBN 0-471-35201-2); write for info tchr's manual (ISBN 0-471-01940-2). Wiley.

Hellerman, Herbert & Smith, I. APL Three-Sixty Programming & Applications. 1977. 29.95 (ISBN 0-07-027950-0). McGraw.

Helzer, Garry. Applied Linear Algebra with APL. 608p. 1982. text ed. 37.00 (ISBN 0-316-35526-7); tcher's manual avail. (ISBN 0-316-35527-5). Little.

Ijiri, Yuji. Accounting Structured in APL, Vol. 6. LC 83-73175. (Studies in Accounting Education). 164p. 1984. 8.00 (ISBN 0-86539-047-9); members 6.00 (ISBN 0-318-00401-1). Am Accounting.

Iverson, K. E. APL in Exposition. (Orig.). 1976. pap. text ed. 1.15 (ISBN 0-917326-02-4). APL Pr.

Legrand, B. APL Management Problems & Answers with "Kit of Tools". Matthews, Julian G., tr. 166p. 1984. 18.95 (ISBN 0-471-90334-5, Wiley-Interscience). Wiley.

Legrand, Bernard. Learning & Applying APL. LC 83-10620. 400p. 1984. 24.95x (ISBN 0-471-90243-8, Pub. by Wiley-Interscience). Wiley.

LePage, Wilbur R. Applied APL Programming. LC 78-6619. (Illus.). 1978. pap. 21.95 ref. (ISBN 0-13-040063-7). P-H.

McDonnell, Eugene E., ed. A Source Book in APL: Papers by Adin D. Falkoff & Kenneth E. Iverson. 144p. (Orig.). 1981. pap. 10.35 (ISBN 0-917326-10-5). APL Pr.

Mason, James A. Learning APL: An Array Processing Language. 288p. 1985. pap. text ed. write for info. (ISBN 0-06-046426-7, HarpC). Har-Row.

Murray, William H. & Pappas, Chris H. An Introduction to APL for the IBM PC & Xt. (Illus.). 224p. 1985. 29.95 (ISBN 0-89303-567-X). Brady Comm.

Pakin, Sandra. APL-360 Reference Manual. 2nd ed. 192p. 1972. pap. text ed. 11.95 (ISBN 0-574-16135-X, 13-0005). SRA.

Pakin, Sandra & Computer Innovations Staff. APL: A Short Course. (Illus.). 176p. 1973. pap. 16.95x ref. ed. (ISBN 0-13-038877-7). P-H.

Peelle, Howard. APL: An Introduction. 1978. pap. text ed. 11.50 (ISBN 0-8104-5122-0). Hayden.

Polivka, Raymond P. & Pakin, Sandra. APL: The Language & Its Usage. (Illus.). 496p. 1975. 31.95 (ISBN 0-13-038885-8); solutions manual 6.95 (ISBN 0-13-039008-9). P-H.

Pommier, S. An Introduction to APL. LC 83-7374. (Cambridge Computer Science Texts Ser.: No. 17). 120p. 1984. 29.95 (ISBN 0-521-24977-5); pap. 11.95 (ISBN 0-521-27109-6). Cambridge U Pr.

Ramsey, James B. & Musgrave, Gerald L. APL-STAT: A Do-It-Yourself Guide to Computation Statistics Using APL. LC 80-15016. 340p. 1981. pap. 18.95 (ISBN 0-534-97985-8). Lifetime Learn.

--APL-STAT: A Do-it-Yourself Guide to Computational Statistics Using APL. 340p. 1981. pap. 8.95 (ISBN 0-534-97985-8). Van Nos Reinhold.

Rose, Allen J. & Schick, Barbara A. APL in Practice: What You Need to Know to Install & Use Successful APL Systems & Major Applications. LC 80-5351. 374p. 1980. 37.95 (ISBN 0-471-08275-9, Pub. by Wiley-Interscienc). Wiley.

Smith, Adrian. APL: A Design Handbook for Commercial Systems. (Wiley Information Processing Ser.). 180p. 1982. 30.95x (ISBN 0-471-10092-7, Pub. by Wiley-Interscience). Wiley.

Van der Linden, G. A., ed. APL Eighty: Proceedings of the International APL Congress, Leiden, June 1980. 320p. 1980. 51.00 (ISBN 0-444-86015-0, North-Holland). Elsevier.

Zaks, Rodnay. A Microprogrammed APL Implementation. LC 78-58355. (Illus.). 347p. 1978. pap. 45.00 (ISBN 0-89588-005-9, Z-10). SYBEX.

APOLLO PROJECT

see Project Apollo

APPALOOSA HORSE

Richardson, Bill & Richardson, Dana. Appaloosa Horse. pap. 5.00 (ISBN 0-87980-182-4). Wilshire.

Richardson, Bill & Richardson, Dona. The Appaloosa. LC 68-27225. (Illus.). 1969. 10.00 (ISBN 0-668-02744-4). Arco.

APPARATUS, CHEMICAL

see Chemical Apparatus

APPARATUS, ELECTRICAL

see Electric Apparatus and Appliances

APPARATUS, SCIENTIFIC

see Scientific Apparatus and Instruments

APPLE

Bultitude, John. Apples: A Guide to the Identification of International Varieties. (Illus.). 332p. 1984. 50.00x (ISBN 0-295-96041-8). U of Wash Pr.

Carlson, R. F., et al. North American Apples: Varieties, Rootstocks, Outlook. (Illus.). 197p. 1971. text ed. 8.50x (ISBN 0-87013-157-5). Mich St U Pr.

Cookbook Consortium. Apples: Uses for the Whole Apple Recipes & Suggestions. 14p. 1984. pap. text ed. 1.95 (Pub. by Cookbk Consort). Prosperity & Profits.

APPLE COMPUTERS

see also Apple Ii (Computer); Apple Ii Plus (Computer); Apple Iic (Computer); Apple Iie (Computer); Apple Iii (Computer); Lisa (Computer); Macintosh (Computer)

Abelson, Hal. Apple LOGO. (Illus.). 256p. 1982. pap. 18.95 (ISBN 0-07-000425-0, BYTE Bks). McGraw.

Adams, Steve. The Quick & Easy Guide to Word Processing on the Apple. 128p. 1984. 4.95 (ISBN 0-912003-29-4). Bk Co.

Allen, Brandt R. VisiCalc: Apple. 1984. pap. text ed. 10.95 (ISBN 0-8359-8410-9). Reston.

Alves, Jeff & Curtin, Dennis. Planning & Budgeting for Higher Profits: An Apple Business User's Guide. 144p. 1983. pap. 14.95 (ISBN 0-930764-62-5). Van Nos Reinhold.

Anbarlian, Harry. An Introduction to VisiCalc Matrixing for Apple & IBM. (Personal Computing Ser.). 260p. 1982. pap. 26.95 (ISBN 0-07-001605-4, BYTE Bks). McGraw.

Anstis, Stuart. Write Your Own Apple Games. (Illus.). 174p. 1983. 12.95 (ISBN 0-916688-49-6, 2W). Creative Comp.

Apple Computer BPI Descriptive Brochure. Date not set. 4.95 (ISBN 0-317-04442-7, D2L0001). Apple Comp.

Apple Computer Pascal Manual Set. (Lisa Reference Manuals). Date not set. 95.00 set (ISBN 0-317-04436-2, A6L0111). Apple Comp.

Apple Computer Personal Computers in Business Guide. Date not set. 2.95 (ISBN 0-317-04434-6, A2G0034). Apple Comp.

Apple Computer Personal Guide to Personal Computers. Date not set. 2.50 (ISBN 0-317-04449-4, A2G0035). Apple Comp.

Apple PILOT Editor's Manual. (Apple II Plus & IIe Reference Manuals Ser.). Date not set. 15.00 (ISBN 0-317-04463-X, A2L0042). Apple Comp.

Apple PILOT Language Manual. (Apple II Plus & IIe Reference Manuals Ser.). Date not set. 20.00 (ISBN 0-317-04464-8, A2L0041). Apple Comp.

Apple User's Manual. 20.00 (ISBN 0-318-01351-7). Mountain View Pr.

Applied Research Staff & Shaffer. BASIC Booster Library: Apple. 250p. 1985. pap. 29.95 incl. disk (ISBN 0-912677-26-0). Apple IIc-IIe (ISBN 0-912677-51-1). Ashton-Tate Bks.

Arnow, Murray. The Apple CP-M Book. LC 85-2393. 164p. 1985. pap. 12.95 (ISBN 0-673-18068-9). Scott F.

Avante-Garde Publishing Corporation Staff, et al. Getting Graphic on the Apple. 204p. 1985. pap. 14.95 (ISBN 0-13-354044-8). P-H.

Avery, Rachel R. LOGO & the Apple. (Illus.). 224p. 1985. pap. 16.95 (ISBN 0-13-539933-5). P-H.

Babbie. Procedures Disk for Apple LOGO for Teachers. 1984. write for info. (ISBN 0-317-14709-9). Wadsworth Pub.

Bailey, Harold & Kerlin, Edward. Apple Graphics: Activities Handbook for the Beginner. LC 83-21406. 432p. 1984. 16.95 (ISBN 0-89303-308-1); bk. & diskette 36.95 (ISBN 0-89303-309-X); diskette 20.00 (ISBN 0-89303-310-3). Brady Comm.

Bateson, Robert & Raygor, Robin. BASIC Programming for the Apple Computer. (Illus.). 250p. 1985. pap. text ed. 14.95 (ISBN 0-314-85290-5). West Pub.

Beekman, George & Corliss, Dennis. Apple Home Companion. (The Companion Ser.). (Illus.). 355p. (Orig.). 1984. pap. 19.95 (ISBN 0-88190-318-3, BO318). Datamost.

Bell, Frederick. Apple Programming for Learning & Teaching. (Illus.). 1984. text ed. 21.95 (ISBN 0-8359-0098-3); pap. 16.95 (ISBN 0-8359-0097-5). Reston.

Bennett, Melba. First Nibbles of the Apple Computer. (Illus.). 288p. 1984. pap. 17.95 (ISBN 0-89303-456-8). Brady Comm.

Bent, Robert J. & Sethares, George C. BASIC: An Introduction to Computer Programming with the Apple. 1983. pub net 19.00 (ISBN 0-534-01370-8, 82-20572). Brooks-Cole.

--BASIC: An Introduction to Computer Programming with the Apple. 250p. 1983. pap. write for info. Wadsworth Pub.

Berentes, Drew. Apple LOGO: A Complete, Illustrated Handbook. (Illus.). 406p. (Orig.). 1984. pap. 13.95 (ISBN 0-8306-1751-5, 1751). TAB Bks.

Birnes. The Apple Megabook. Date not set. pap. 12.95 (ISBN 0-671-54386-5). S&S.

Bishop, Bob, et al. Apple Visions. 256p. (Orig.). 1985. pap. 39.95 315 bk. disk package (ISBN 0-201-15324-6). Addison-Wesley.

Bitter, Gary & Watson, Nancy. The Apple LOGO Primer. 1983. pap. 16.95 (ISBN 0-8359-0314-1). Reston.

Blackwood, Brian D. & Blackwood, George H. Apple FORTRAN. LC 81-86556. 240p. 1982. pap. 14.95 (ISBN 0-672-21911-5, 21911). Sams.

--Applesoft Language. 2nd ed. LC 83-60172. 288p. 1983. 14.95 (ISBN 0-672-22073-3, 22073). Sams.

--Intimate Instructions in Integer BASIC. LC 81-51551. 160p. 1982. pap. 8.95 (ISBN 0-672-21812-7, 21812). Sams.

Blankenship, John. The Apple House. LC 83-16052. (Illus.). 160p. 1984. text ed. 22.95 (ISBN 0-13-038729-0); pap. text ed. 14.95 (ISBN 0-13-038711-8). P-H.

The Blue Book for the Apple Computer. 3rd. ed. 1983. pap. 24.95 (ISBN 0-684-17927-X). Scribner.

The Blue Book for the Apple Computer. 4th ed. 24.95 (ISBN 0-927853-01-9). WIDL Video.

The Book of Apple Software 1983. 491p. 1983. 19.95 (ISBN 0-317-05196-2). Bk Co.

Brady, Stephen W. & Farmer, Gale E. The Function Plotter: A Calculus Primer, Apple II Version. 1984. pap. text ed. 23.95 (ISBN 0-471-80189-5). Wiley.

Brain Bank. The BASIC Conversions Handbook for Apple, Commodore, TRS-80, & Atari Users. write for info. Hayden.

Brain, David, et al. The BASIC Conversions Handbook for Apple, TRS-80 & PET Users. 80p. (Orig.). 1982. pap. 9.95 (ISBN 0-8104-5534-X). Hayden.

Brannon, Charles & Martin, Kevin. SpeedScript: The Word Processor for Apple Personal Computers. Compute Editors, ed. (Orig.). 1985. pap. 9.95 (ISBN 0-87455-000-9). Compute Pubns.

Carmony, Lowell A., et al. Problem Solving in Apple Pascal: Teacher's Guide & Solution Manual. 1984. 15.00 (ISBN 0-88175-021-2). Computer Sci.

Cavallari, Ford, ed. Micro on the Apple Series, 3 vols. with disk 24.95 ea. (ISBN 0-938222-05-8). Vol. 1 (ISBN 0-938222-06-6). Vol. 2 (ISBN 0-938222-08-2). Vol. 3. Set. 59.95 (ISBN 0-686-46817-1). Computerist.

Chance, David. Thirty-Three Challenging Computer Games for the TRS-80, Apple & PET. (Illus.). 252p. 15.95 (ISBN 0-8306-9703-9, 1275); pap. 9.25 (ISBN 0-8306-1275-0). TAB Bks.

Chaya, Ruth K. & Miller, Joan M. More BASIC Programming for the Classroom & Home Teacher (IBM PC, IBM PCjr, Commodore, Apple, Macintosh) 262p. (Orig.). 1985. pap. text ed. 17.95X (ISBN 0-8077-2780-6). Tchrs Coll.

Clark, Roger E. Executive VisiCalc for the Apple Computer. LC 82-11663. (Microcomputer Bks.-Executive). 192p. 1982. pap. 14.95 (ISBN 0-201-10242-0). Addison-Wesley.

Clarke, Frank H. & Henkel, James G., eds. Molecular Graphics on the Apple Microcomputer. 1985. 129.50 (ISBN 0-12-175780-3). Acad Pr.

Close, Kenneth. AppleWorks with Advanced Applications: Calc, File, Write & GRAPH. (Micropower Ser.). 208p. 1985. deluxe ed. 24.95 incl. diskette (ISBN 0-697-00805-3); pap. 13.95 (ISBN 0-697-00804-5). Wm C Brown.

Coan, James S. Basic Apple BASIC. 1983. pap. 14.95 (ISBN 0-8104-5626-5, 5626). Hayden.

Coffron, James W. The Apple Connection. LC 82-50620. (Illus.). 263p. 1982. pap. 14.95 (ISBN 0-89588-085-7, C405). SYBEX.

Cohen, Phil. The Three-D Animated Apple. 1984. 21.50 (ISBN 0-13-920224-2). P-H.

Coletta, Paul. Apple Graphics Games. LC 82-23161. 1983. 16.95 (ISBN 0-8359-0325-7); disk 15.00 (ISBN 0-8359-0313-3); bk. & disk o.p. 34.95 (ISBN 0-8359-0326-5). Reston.

Compute Editors. Compute's First Book of Apple. (Orig.). 1984. pap. 12.95 (ISBN 0-942386-69-8). Compute Pubns.

--Compute's Second Book of Apple. (Orig.). 1985. pap. 12.95 (ISBN 0-87455-008-4). Compute Pubns.

Consumer Digest Editors, ed. How to Win at Apple Computer Games. 64p. 1984. spiral bound 8.95 (ISBN 0-671-49559-3). S&S.

Consumer Guide Editors. The User's Guide to APPLE 1000, 2000. (Orig.). 1983. pap. 3.95 (ISBN 0-671-49502-X). PB.

Consumer Guide Editors & Adams, Roe R., III. Apple Software: Rating the Best. LC 83-73275. 154p. 1984. pap. 4.98 spiral bdg. (ISBN 0-517-42475-4). Outlet Bk Co.

Continental Software. The Home Accountant - Apple. (Orig.). 1985. pap. 9.95 manual (ISBN 0-538-01010-X, AO11). SW Pub.

Culp, George H. & Nickles, Herbert L. An Apple for the Teacher: Fundamentals of Instructional Computing. 2nd ed. 275p. 1986. pap. text ed. 15.00 (ISBN 0-534-05832-9). Brooks-Cole.

Curtin, Dennis & Alves, Jeff. Controlling Financial Performance for Higher Profits: An Apple Business User's Guide. 160p. 1983. pap. 14.95 (ISBN 0-930764-58-7). Van Nos Reinhold.

Curtin, Dennis & Alves, Jefffey. Controlling Financial Performance: Apple Business Users Guide. (Illus.). 224p. (Orig.). 1983. pap. 15.50. Curtin & London.

Darnall, William H. The Epson Connection: Apple. (Illus.). 1984. pap. text ed. 16.95 (ISBN 0-8359-1750-9). Reston.

Datapro-McGraw-Hill. Datapro-McGraw-Hill Guide to Apple Software. 2nd ed. 1985. 22.95 (ISBN 0-07-015406-6). McGraw.

Datapro Research Corporation. Datapro-McGraw-Hill Guide to Apple Software. 2nd ed. LC 84-20022. 350p. 1984. pap. 22.95 (ISBN 0-07-015406-6). Datapro Res.

Dennis, Terry L. Apple Pascal: A Problem-Solving Approach. (Illus.). 400p. 1985. pap. text ed. 16.95 (ISBN 0-314-85228-X). West Pub.

DeWitt, Stephen. Apple LOGO Activities. 1984. pap. text ed. 16.95x (ISBN 0-8359-0088-6). Reston.

DiElsi, John, et al. Programming Apple BASIC. 1984. 19.95 (ISBN 0-03-063733-3). HR&W.

Directories from InfoSource Inc. Staff. Business Software for the Apple II: An Applications Directory. LC 83-45382. 176p. (Orig.). 1984. pap. 12.95 (ISBN 0-8019-7431-3). Chilton.

Dunn, Seamus & Morgan, Valerie. The Apple Personal Computer for Beginners. 1983. 17.95 (ISBN 0-13-039131-X). P-H.

Englesher, Charles J. Interfacing & Digital Experiments with Your APPLE. (Illus.). 320p. (Orig.). 1984. 21.95 (ISBN 0-8306-0717-X, 1717); pap. 15.50 (ISBN 0-8306-1717-5). TAB Bks.

Erickson, Jonathan & Cramer, William D. The Apple Graphics & Sound Book. 256p. (Orig.). 1985. pap. cancelled (ISBN 0-88134-167-3, 167-3). Osborne McGraw.

Faulk, Ed, ed. How to Write an Apple Program. (How to Write Ser.). (Illus.). 224p. 1982. pap. 14.95 (ISBN 0-88190-027-3, BO027). Datamost.

Filler, Aaron. Apple Thesaurus. 896p. (Orig.). 1984. pap. 29.95 (ISBN 0-88190-346-9, BO346). Datamost.

Finkel, LeRoy & Brown, Jerald R. Apple BASIC: Data File Programming. LC 81-13100. 303p. 1982. pap. 14.95 (ISBN 0-471-09157-X, Pub. by Wiley Pr); software diskette 24.95 (ISBN 0-471-86836-1); pap. 34.90 bk. & disk set (ISBN 0-471-89843-0). Wiley.

Floegel, Ekkehard. The Apple in Your Hand. 220p. 12.95 (ISBN 3-88963-178-9). Blue Cat.

Flynn, Brian. Compute's Easy BASIC Programs for the Apple. Compute Editors, ed. 400p. (Orig.). 1985. pap. 14.95 (ISBN 0-942386-88-4). Compute Pubns.

Foster, Dennis L. & D. L. Foster Book Company Editors. The Addison-Wesley Book of Apple Software 1985. 416p. 1985. pap. 19.95 (ISBN 0-201-12018-6). Addison-Wesley.

Franklin, Howard M., et al. Golden Delicious Games for the Apple Computer. LC 81-23074. (Self Teaching Guides Ser.: No. 1-704). 150p. 1982. pap. 12.95 (ISBN 0-471-09083-2); Avail. software disk set 47.90 (ISBN 0-471-89842-2); disk 34.95 (ISBN 0-471-86837-X). Wiley.

Friedman, Steve. Kids Love the Apple. (Illus.). 1985. pap. 12.95 (ISBN 0-452-25645-3, Plume). NAL.

Gader, Bertram & Nodar, Manuel V. Apple Software for Pennies. (Orig.). 1985. pap. 10.95 (ISBN 0-446-38206-X). Warner Bks.

Geenen, Donald J. Learning Apple FORTRAN. LC 84-19936. 160p. Date not set. pap. 17.95 (ISBN 0-88175-024-7). Computer Sci.

Gilder, Jules H. Apple IIc & IIe Assembly Language. 220p. 1985. pap. 18.95 (ISBN 0-412-01121-2, 9667). Methuen Inc.

Glau, Gregory R. Business Power for Your Apple. 288p. 1984. 32.50 (ISBN 0-442-22779-5). Van Nos Reinhold.

Goez, Eric & Sanders, William. Apple Almanac. (Illus.). 1984. pap. 19.95 (ISBN 0-8359-0096-7). Reston.

Goez, Eric & Sanders, William B. Apple Almanac. 240p. 1983. pap. 19.95 (ISBN 0-88190-109-1, BO109). Datamost.

Goldberg, Harry & Culbertson, Ron. A Slice of the Apple. 1983. 12.95 (ISBN 0-317-04728-0). Hayden.

Grauer, Robert T., et al. BASIC Is Child's Play: Apple Edition. (Illus.). 112p. 1984. pap. text ed. 18.95 (ISBN 0-13-058785-0). P-H.

--More BASIC Is Child's Play, Apple Edition. (Illus.). 192p. 1985. pap. 16.95 (ISBN 0-13-601022-9). P-H.

Gray, John. Pocket Guide: Programming for the Apple. (Pitman Programming Pocket Guides Ser.). 64p. (Orig.). 1984. pap. 6.95 (ISBN 0-273-01991-0). Pitman Pub MA.

Haigh, Roger W. & Radford, Loren E. BASIC for Microcomputers: Apple, TRS-80, PET. 337p. 1983. 21.95 (ISBN 0-442-27843-8). Van Nos Reinhold.

--LOGO for Apple Computers. (Wiley Self Teaching Guides Ser.: 1-581). 272p. 1984. pap. 14.95 (ISBN 0-471-88023-X, Pub. by Wiley Pr). Wiley.

Halpern, Richard. Microcomputer Graphics Using Pascal: Apple Version. 250p. 1985. pap. text ed. 22.50 scp (ISBN 0-06-042583-0, HarpC). Har-Row.

Heller, Dave & Heller, Dorothy. Free Software for Your Apple. (Free Software Ser.). (Illus.). 224p. 1984. pap. 8.95 (ISBN 0-86582-123-2, EN79213). Enrich.

Hergert, Douglas & Kalash, Joseph T. Apple Pascal Games. LC 81-16577. (Illus.). 371p. 1981. pap. 15.95 (ISBN 0-89588-074-1, P360). SYBEX.

Hite, Eugene & Close, Kenneth S. Spreadsheets: Principles & Applications Using VisiCalc Apple. 1985. pap. text ed. 14.95 wkbk. & template diskette (ISBN 0-538-10200-4, J20). SW Pub.

Hoffberg, Alan M. Apple Computers Supplement to FORTRAN IV. 2nd ed. (Wiley Self Teaching Guides: No. 1-581). 30p. 1981. pap. 4.50x (ISBN 0-471-09813-2, Pub. by Wiley Pr). Wiley.

Honig, Herbert M. Polishing Your Apple, Vol. 2. LC 82-61967. 108p. 1983. pap. text ed. 4.95 (ISBN 0-672-22160-8, 22160). Sams.

Howell, Richard D. & Scott, Patrick B. Selected Microcomputer Applications for Teachers: A Hands-on Approach with the Apple. 112p. (Orig.). 1985. pap. 17.95 (ISBN 0-89787-411-0). Gorsuch Scarisbrick.

Hume, J. N. & Holt, B. C. Better BASIC for the Apple. 1983. pap. 16.95 (ISBN 0-8359-0466-0). Reston.

Humphries, Robert. The Illustrated Apple LOGO Book. (Illustrated Ser.). (Illus.). 200p. (Orig.). 1985. pap. 16.95 (ISBN 0-915381-72-9). Wordware Pub.

Hyde, Randy. P-Source. 464p. (Orig.). 1983. pap. text ed. 24.95 (ISBN 0-88190-004-4, BO342). Datamost.

Hyler, Linda, et al. A Byte of the Apple: A Beginner's Guide. (Illus.). 250p. 17.95x (ISBN 0-8359-0543-8); incl. disk 21.95 (ISBN 0-8359-0546-2). Reston.

InfoWorld Editors & Hogan, Thom. InfoWorld's Essential Guide to the Apple. (InfoWorld's Essential Guides Ser.). (Orig.). 1984. pap. 16.95 (ISBN 0-06-669001-3). Har Row.

Inman, Don & Inman, Kurt. Apple Machine Language. 224p. 1980. text ed. 21.95 (ISBN 0-8359-0231-5); pap. text ed. 16.95 (ISBN 0-8359-0230-7). Reston.

Irwin, Paul. Apple Programmer's Handbook. LC 84-50062. 22.95 (ISBN 0-672-22175-6). Sams.

Jensen, Paul A. Microsolve-Operations Research. 186p. 1985. IBM Version. 65.00 (ISBN 0-8162-4503-7). Apple Version (ISBN 0-8162-4502-9). Holden-Day.

Johansson, Anders B. Data Entry on Vedic Master Astrology Software for Apple Computers. Johansson, Lilian M., ed. (Illus.). 170p. 1984. 23.45 (ISBN 0-914725-09-2); pap. 19.75 (ISBN 0-914725-07-6). Astro Dynasty Pub Hse.

Jones, Aubrey B., Jr. I Speak BASIC to My Apple. (I Speak BASIC Ser.). 224p. 1982. pap. text ed. 9.75 (ISBN 0-8104-6175-7); tchr's manual 18.75 (ISBN 0-8104-6165-X); exam set 15.00 (ISBN 0-686-81490-8); classroom set (tchr's manual, 20 student texts & exam set) 200.00 (ISBN 0-686-81491-6). Hayden.

Jones, Warren, et al. Computer Literacy: Programming, Problem-Solving, Projects on the Apple. 1983. pap. text ed. 21.95 (ISBN 0-8359-0861-5); pap. 16.95 (ISBN 0-8359-0860-7). Reston.

Kamins, S. & Waite, M. Apple Backpack: Humanized Programming in BASIC. 224p. 1982. pap. 16.95 (ISBN 0-07-033356-4, BYTE Bks). McGraw.

Kelly, Brian W. & Grimes, Dennis J. Apple Computer Directory: Hardware, Software & Peripherals. (Kelly-Grimes Buyers Guide Ser.: 1-702). 469p. 1984. pap. 26.95 (ISBN 0-471-87818-9, Pub. by Wiley Pr). Wiley.

Kidd, Clark & Kidd, Kathy. Compute's Apple Games for Kids. Compute Editors, ed. 320p. (Orig.). 1985. pap. 12.95 (ISBN 0-942386-91-4). Compute Pubns.

Kreutner, Donald C. Apple Favorite Programs Explained. LC 84-61400. (Favorite Program Ser.). 200p. (Orig.). 1984. pap. 12.95 (ISBN 0-88022-130-5, 160). Que Corp.

Lamoitier, J. P. BASIC Exercises for the Apple. LC 82-80721. (Illus.). 251p. 1982. pap. 14.95 (ISBN 0-89588-084-9, B500). SYBEX.

Lampton, Christopher. Assembly Language Programming 6502 for the Apple, Commodore 64, & Atari Computers. (Computer Literacy Skills Ser.). 128p. 1985. PLB 10.90 (ISBN 0-531-04923-X). Watts.

Lancaster, Don. Enhancing Your Apple, Vol. I. 2nd ed. LC 83-51704. 15.95 (ISBN 0-672-21822-4). Sams.

Lewis, C. & Lewis, P. Marketing Peanut Butter: A Microcomputer Simulation. 1984. Apple. 199.00 (ISBN 0-07-079587-8). IBM-PC (ISBN 0-07-079588-6). TRS-80 (ISBN 0-07-079586-X). McGraw.

Lewis, Theodore G. Pascal Programming for the Apple. 224p. 1981. O.P. 20.95 (ISBN 0-8359-5455-2); pap. 14.95 (ISBN 0-8359-5454-4). Reston.

Little, Gary B. Apple ProDOS: Advanced Features for Programmers. (Illus.). 352p. 1985. pap. 17.95 (ISBN 0-89303-441-X). Brady Comm.

Lord, Kenniston, Jr. Using Apple Business Computer. 1983. 19.95 (ISBN 0-442-26016-4); pap. 13.95 (ISBN 0-442-25933-6). Van Nos Reinhold.

Lord, Kenniston W., Jr. Using the Apple Business Computers. 286p. 1983. 19.95 (ISBN 0-442-26016-4); pap. 13.95 (ISBN 0-442-25933-6). Van Nos Reinhold.

Luebbert, William F. What's Where in the Apple: The Complete Guide to the Apple. rev. ed. (Illus.). 280p. 1985. pap. 19.95 (ISBN 0-938222-18-X). Computerist.

Luehrmann, Arthur & Peckham, Herbert. Apple Pascal: A Hands-on Approach. (Programming Language Ser.). (Illus.). 384p. 1982. pap. 23.95 spiral bdg. (ISBN 0-07-049171-2). McGraw.

McAffee, Michael, ed. Apple Access: Users' Guide to Apple Computer-Related Periodical Literature (Jan.-June 1984) (Apple Access of Semi-Annual Ser.: Vol. 1). (Illus.). 256p. (Orig.). 1985. pap. 19.95 (ISBN 0-931293-00-6). Stony Point Pubns.

--Apple Access-Users' Guide to Apple Computer-Related Periodical Literature, July - Dec. 1984. (Apple Access Of Semi-Annual Ser.: Vol. 2). (Orig.). Date not set. pap. price not set (ISBN 0-931293-02-2). Stony Point Pubns.

MacCallum, Iain. Pascal for the Apple. 1983. incl. disk 35.00 (ISBN 0-13-652909-7). P-H.

McMullen, Barbara E. & McMullen, John F. The Apple Companion. (General Trade Books). 288p. 1985. pap. 14.95 (ISBN 0-471-87334-9). Wiley.

Mansfield, Richard. Apple Machine Language for Beginners. Compute Editors, ed. (Orig.). 1985. pap. 14.95 (ISBN 0-87455-002-5). Compute Pubns.

Martin & Martin, Donald. Apple LOGO Programming Primer. LC 84-50735. 454p. 1984. pap. 19.95 (ISBN 0-672-22342-2). Sams.

Martin, Don & Martin, Jennifer. Eighty-Eight Apple LOGO Programs. LC 84-50181. 19.95 (ISBN 0-672-22343-0). Sams.

Masalski, William J. Programming Animation & Graphics Task Cards for the Apple. Fanning, Tom, ed. 1982. 9.95 (ISBN 0-88049-063-2, 7889). Milton Bradley Co.

Matthews, Carole B. AppleWorks Made Easy. 224p. (Orig.). 1985. pap. 17.95 (ISBN 0-07-881163-5, 163-5). Osborne-McGraw.

Maurer, W. Douglas. Apple Assembly Language. LC 82-18190. 403p. 1984. 21.95 (ISBN 0-914894-82-X); diskette 15.00 (ISBN 0-914894-85-4). Computer Sci.

Mears, Peter. Introduction to Apple Keyboarding. 1984. 39.95 (ISBN 0-03-064131-4); with diskette 40.45 (ISBN 0-03-064129-2). HR&W.

--Introduction to Apple Keyboarding. 1984. pap. 40.45 incl. disk (ISBN 0-03-064138-1). HR&W.

--Teach Yourself Apple BASIC. 12.95 (ISBN 0-201-05217-2); incl. disk 34.95 (ISBN 0-201-05218-0). Addison-Wesley.

Mears, Peter & Raho, Louis. Basic Business Basic: Using the Apple. 2nd ed. (Computer Science Ser.). 312p. 1986. pap. 218.00 (ISBN 0-534-05622-9). Brooks-Cole.

Mellin, Michael. The Quick & Easy Guide to Database Management on the Apple. 200p. Date not set. pap. cancelled (ISBN 0-912003-26-X). Bk Co.

Mellin, Michael, et al, eds. The Book of Apple Software. 700p. (Orig.). pap. 24.95 (ISBN 0-912003-51-0). Bk Co.

--The Book of Apple Software 1985. 726p. 1984. pap. 24.95 (ISBN 0-912003-39-1). Bk Co.

Miller, David. Apple ProDOS Data Files: A Basic Tutorial. (Illus.). 232p. 18.95 (ISBN 0-8359-0134-3). Reston.

Minter, Greg & Ruffner, John. Designing Apple Games with Pizazz! (Illus.). 328p. (Orig.). 1984. pap. 14.95 (ISBN 0-88190-387-6, BO387). Datamost.

Moritz, Michael. The Little Kingdom: The Private Story of Apple Computer. LC 84-60845. 320p. 1984. 16.95 (ISBN 0-688-03973-1). Morrow.

Morrison, James. Expanding & Maintaining Your Apple Personal Computer. 1630p. 1984. pap. 16.95 (ISBN 0-201-05157-5). Addison-Wesley.

MVP-FORTH Assembly Source Code: For CP-M, IBM-PC & Apple. (MVP-FORTH Books: Vol. 2). 20.00 (ISBN 0-318-01342-8). Mountain View Pr.

Noonan, Larry. Basic BASIC-English Dictionary for the Apple, PET & TRS-80. (Illus.). 154p. 1983. 17.95 (ISBN 0-8306-1521-0, 1521). TAB Bks.

Oleksy, Jerome. Apple Instrumentation & Control: Circuits & Software. 1985. pap. text ed. 18.95 (ISBN 0-8359-9222-5). Reston.

Osgood, William & Molloy, James, Jr. Business Decision Making: An Apple Business User's Guide. 1983. Set. pap. 14.95 (ISBN 0-930764-66-8); incl. disk 39.95 (ISBN 0-930764-95-1). Van Nos Reinhold.

Osgood, William R. & Molloy, James F., Jr. Business Decision Making: An Apple Business User's Guide. (Illus.). 160p. (Orig.). 1983. pap. 15.50 (ISBN 0-930764-66-8). Curtin & London.

Parker, Alan & Stewart, John. The Executive Guide to the Apple Computer, BASIC: Programming & VisiCalc. 1984. incl. disk 59.95 (ISBN 0-8359-1808-4). Reston.

Parker, Alan J. & Stewart, John. Executive's Guide to the Apple Computer: BASIC Programming & VisiCalc. 1984. software package 59.95 (ISBN 0-8359-1808-4). Reston.

Parker, Bill. The Intermediate Apple. (Orig.). 1984. pap. 14.95 (ISBN 0-88190-241-1, BO241). Datamost.

Pawluk, Michael F. Creating Audiology & Speech-Language Pathology: Programs on Your Apple Computer. (Illus.). 224p. 1985. pap. text ed. 25.00 (ISBN 0-8391-2063-X, 21768). Univ Park.

PC Telemart-VanLoves Apple Software Directory. 956p. 1984. pap. 24.95 (ISBN 0-88674-001-0). Bowker.

Peddicord, Richard G. Understanding Apple BASIC. (Handy Guide Ser.). 64p. (Orig.). 1984. pap. 3.50 (ISBN 0-88284-246-3). Alfred Pub.

Pelczarski, Mark & Tate, Joe, eds. The Creative Apple. (The Creative Ser.). (Illus.). 448p. 1983. 16.95 (ISBN 0-916688-25-9, 18R). Creative Comp.

Personal Computer Software Directory for Apple 1985. 1000p. 1985. 24.95 (ISBN 0-912603-20-8). Micro Info.

Pirisino, Jim. Minute Manual for Appleworks. 150p. 1985. 12.95 (ISBN 0-913131-07-5). Minuteware.

Pitter, K. Using Microcomputers: An Apple Lab Manual. 237p. 1984. pap. text ed. 14.95x (ISBN 0-938188-21-6). Mitchell Pub.

Poirot, James L. Microcomputer Systems & Apple BASIC. (Illus.). 150p. (Orig.). 1980. pap. 8.95 (ISBN 0-88408-136-2). Sterling Swift.

Polen-Jannazo. A KASE for Microcomputers: A First Course in Apple BASIC. 240p. 1983. pap. text ed. 21.95 (ISBN 0-8403-3171-1). Kendall-Hunt.

Polin, Glenn, ed. Will Someone Please Tell Me What an Apple Can Do. (Orig.). 1983. pap. text ed. 12.95 (ISBN 0-88408-152-4). Sterling Swift.

Presley & Corica. Guide to Programming in Apple Pascal. 1986. 19.95 (ISBN 0-931717-21-3); 19.95 (ISBN 0-931717-27-2). Lawrenceville Pr.

Presley & Deckel. Beginner's Guide to the Apple. 288p. 1985. pap. 16.95 (ISBN 0-931717-02-7); drilled for a 3 ring binder tchr's guide 19.95 (ISBN 0-931717-05-1). Lawrenceville Pr.

Rabkin, Richard. Biting Deeper into the Apple's Core. 352p. 1985. pap. 14.95 spiral bdg. (ISBN 0-671-50129-1, Pub. by Computer Bks). S&S.

Renko, Hal & Sandra, Emerson. Astounding Games for Your Apple Computer. pap. 5.95 (ISBN 0-201-16482-5). Addison-Wesley.

Rose, Richard. Appleworks User's Handbook. 200p. 1985. pap. 15.95 (ISBN 0-938862-09-X). Weber Systems.

Rosen, Robert. Apple Machine Language. 256p. pap. 20.45 (ISBN 0-03-063336-2). HR&W.

Rubin, Charles. Appleworks: Boosting your Business with Integrated Software. (Illus.). 288p. (Orig.). 1985. pap. 16.95 (ISBN 0-914845-47-0). Microsoft.

Rugg, Tom & Feldman, Phil. Thirty-Two BASIC Programs for the Apple Computer. LC 80-68533. (Illus.). 280p. 1983. pap. 19.95 (ISBN 0-918398-34-7); incl. disk 39.95 (ISBN 0-88056-151-3). Dilithium Pr.

Russell, Clyde B. Introduction to Computer Programming with BASIC & the Apple. 458p. 1984. pap. 22.95x (ISBN 0-89787-404-8). Gorsuch Scarisbrick.

Sagan, Hans. Calculus Accompanied by the Apple. 1984. pap. 16.95 (ISBN 0-8359-0633-7). Reston.

Sanders, William B. The Elementary Apple. (Elementary Ser.). (Illus.). 214p. (Orig.). 1982. pap. text ed. 14.95 (ISBN 0-88190-010-9, BO010). Datamost.

Santoro, Rocco M., et al. Sunbrite Laundry Company: A Computerized Practice Set for a Service Establishment - Apple & IBM Edition. (Career Accounting Ser.). 25p. 1984. pap. 8.95 (ISBN 0-471-80857-1). Wiley.

Sawusch, Mark R. & Summers, Tan A. One Thousand One Things to Do with Your Apple. (Illus.). 256p. (Orig.). 1984. 15.95 (ISBN 0-8306-0816-8, 1816); pap. 9.95 (ISBN 0-8306-1816-3). TAB Bks.

Sayre, Clifford L. Design & Graphics Using the APPLE Computer: An Engineers Guide. 1985. pap. text ed. 24.95 (ISBN 0-8359-1328-7). Reston.

Schwartz, Roberta & Callery, Michael. Apple Graphics: Tools & Techniques. (Illus.). 288p. 1986. pap. 17.95 (ISBN 0-13-039512-9). P-H.

Simon, Sheridan. Unprintable Physics: Introductory Physics for the Apple Computer. 80p. 1984. pap. text ed. 34.95 (ISBN 0-13-938366-2). P-H.

Simondi, Tom. The Quick & Easy Guide to Spreadsheets on the Apple. 128p. 1984. pap. 4.95 (ISBN 0-912003-28-6). Bk Co.

Skarbet Software Directory. 14.95 (ISBN 0-318-01612-5). Vogeler Pub.

Smith, Gary D. & Smith, Scott N. Agricultural Software Directory for the Apple Computer. 197p. 1983. pap. 19.95 (ISBN 0-912859-00-8). Agriware Pubns.

--Commodity Software Directory for the Apple Computer. 142p. 1983. pap. 19.95 (ISBN 0-912859-01-6). Agriware Pubns.

Software Arts Inc. TK! Solver: Apple Version. 300p. 1984. 299.00 (ISBN 0-07-059564-X). McGraw.

Spangenburg, Ray & Moser, Dian. The Survival Kit for Apple Computer Games. LC 82-17912. (Illus.). 162p. 1983. pap. write for info. (ISBN 0-534-01432-1). Wadsworth Pub.

Speitel, Tom, et al. Science Computer Programs for Kids... & Other People: Apple Version. (Illus.). 1984. pap. 12.95 (ISBN 0-8359-6901-0). Reston.

Stanton, Jeffrey. Apple Graphics & Arcade Game Design. 288p. 1982. pap. 19.95 (ISBN 0-912003-01-4). Bk Co.

Steck, Richard. Apple to IBM PC Conversion Guide. 1985. pap. 11.95 (ISBN 0-673-18047-6). Scott F.

Stewart, George. The Apple Program Factory. 150p. (Orig.). 1984. 12.95 (ISBN 0-07-881132-5, 132-5). Osborne-McGraw.

Taffee, Stephen & Keogh, Andrew. The Quick & Easy Guide to Education on the Apple: Elementary & Early Childhood. Hays, Nancy, pref. by. 300p. Date not set. pap. cancelled (ISBN 0-912003-27-8). Bk Co.

--The Quick & Easy Guide to Education on the Apple: Secondary & Adult. Hays, Nancy, ed. 300p. Date not set. pap. cancelled (ISBN 0-912003-42-1). Bk Co.

The Tax Advantage - Apple. (Orig.). pap. text ed. cancelled (ISBN 0-538-01336-2, A452-5). SW Pub.

Thornburg, David D. Discovering Apple LOGO: An Introduction to the Art & Pattern of Nature. LC 82-20704. 176p. 1983. pap. 14.95 (ISBN 0-201-07769-8). Addison-Wesley.

Tucker, Allen B., Jr. Apple Pascal: A Programming Guide. LC 82-912. 247p. 1982. pap. text ed. 19.95 (ISBN 0-03-059547-9). HR&W.

Tymes, Elna. Mastering AppleWorks. 201p. 1984. pap. 15.95 (ISBN 0-89588-240-X). SYBEX.

Van Loves Apple Software Directory, 1985. 965p. Date not set. pap. text ed. 29.95 (ISBN 0-8352-1971-2). Bowker.

Watt, Daniel. Learning with Apple LOGO. (Illus.). 322p. 1984. pap. 19.95 spiral bound (ISBN 0-07-068571-1, BYTE Bks). McGraw.

Webb, et al. Explorer's Guide to Apple LOGO, LCSI Version. 1984. student text 12.50 (ISBN 0-317-05873-8, 6227). Hayden.

Weber Systems, Inc. Staff. Apple Lisa User's Handbook. (WSI's User's Handbook to Personal Computers Ser.). 350p. (Orig.). pap. cancelled (ISBN 0-938862-23-5). Weber Systems.

Wells, Robert P. The Quick & Easy Guide to Educational Software on the Apple. 128p. pap. 4.95 (ISBN 0-912003-27-8). Bk Co.

White, Fred. Apple Computer Program Writing Workbook. 96p. 1983. 4.95 (ISBN 0-86668-813-7). ARCsoft.

--Apple Computer Programs for Beginners. 96p. 1984. 8.95 (ISBN 0-86668-035-7). ARCsoft.

--Easy Apple Computer Programs. 96p. 1984. 8.95 (ISBN 0-86668-047-0). ARCsoft.

--One Hundred One Apple Computer Programming Tips & Tricks. 128p. (Orig.). 1982. pap. 8.95 (ISBN 0-86668-015-2). ARCsoft.

--Thirty-Three New Apple Computer Programs for Home, School & Office. (Illus.). 96p. (Orig.). 1982. pap. 8.95 (ISBN 0-86668-016-0). ARCsoft.

Wilcox, Clifford M. Apple Fun & Games. 194p. (Orig.). 1985. pap. 13.95 (ISBN 0-07-881168-6, 168-6). Osborne McGraw.

Williams, Gene B. How to Repair & Maintain Your Apple Computer. LC 84-45353. 224p. (Orig.). 1985. spiral bdg. incl. disk 49.95 (ISBN 0-8019-7623-5); pap. 12.95 (ISBN 0-8019-7549-2). Chilton.

Williams, Robert. The Power of Apple Works. 19.95 (ISBN 0-13-688045-2). P-H.

Williams, Robert E. The Power of Apple Works. (Illus.). 240p. 1984. 19.95 (ISBN 0-943518-16-4); 34.95, incl. diskette. Mgmt Info Inc.

Wolfe, Philip & Koelling, C. Patrick. BASIC Engineering Science & Business Programs for the Apple II & IIe. 352p. 1984. pap. 19.95 (ISBN 0-89303-284-0); bk. & diskette 44.95 (ISBN 0-89303-290-5); diskette 25.00 (ISBN 0-89303-288-3). Brady Comm.

Worth, Don & Lechner, Pieter. Beneath Apple DOS. 1981. 19.95 (ISBN 0-912985-00-3, 6493). Quality Soft.

Worth, Don D. & Lechner, Pieter M. Beneath Apple ProDos. LC 84-61383. (Illus.). 288p. 1984. pap. 19.95 (ISBN 0-912985-05-4, 5054). Quality Soft.

Wyatt, Allen. Apple Games. LC 84-51166. 8.95 (ISBN 0-672-22394-5). Sams.

Wyatt, Allen L. BASIC Tricks for the Apple. LC 83-50830. 144p. 1983. pap. 8.95 (ISBN 0-672-22208-6, 22208). Sams.

Zimmerman, S. Scott & Zimmerman, Beverly B. Action Games for the Apple: How to Design Computer Games. 1985. pap. 12.95 (ISBN 0-673-18091-3). Scott F.

APPLE II (COMPUTER)

Abelson, Hal. LOGO for the Apple II. 1982. 18.95 (ISBN 0-07-000426-9, BYTE Bks). McGraw.

Antonovich, Michael P. User's Guide to the Apple II Computer. LC 80-70465. (WSI's How to Use Your Personal Computer Ser.). 350p. 1985. pap. 13.95 (ISBN 0-938862-03-0). Weber Systems.

Atwater, Dorothea. First Aid for Your Apple II-IIe. 144p. (Orig.). 1985. pap. 6.95 (ISBN 0-345-31942-7). Ballantine.

Banse, Timothy P. Home Applications & Games for the Apple II, II Plus & IIe Computers. (Microcomputer Bookshelf Ser.). 170p. (Orig.). 1984. pap. 14.50 (ISBN 0-316-08045-4). Little.

Berenbon, Howard. Mostly BASIC: Applications for Your Apple II, Bk. 1. LC 80-53273. 160p. 1980. pap. 13.95 (ISBN 0-672-21789-9, 21864). Sams.

--Mostly BASIC: Applications for Your Apple II, Bk. 2. LC 80-53273. 224p. 1982. pap. 12.95 (ISBN 0-672-21864-X). Sams.

Berlin, Howard M. Circuit Design Programs for the Apple II. LC 81-85516. 132p. 1982. pap. 15.95 (ISBN 0-672-21863-1, 21863). Sams.

Bitter, Gary G. & Gore, Kay. The Best of Educational Software for Apple II Computers. 375p. 1984. pap. 12.95 (ISBN 0-89588-206-X). SYBEX.

Blackwood, Brian D. & Blackwood, George H. Disks, Files, & Printers for the Apple II. LC 83-61068. 264p. 1983. pap. text ed. 15.95 (ISBN 0-672-22163-2, 22163). Sams.

Blankenship, John. Apple II-IIe Robotic Arm Projects. (Illus.). 192p. 1985. text ed. 21.95 (ISBN 0-13-038324-4); pap. text ed. 16.95 (ISBN 0-13-038316-3). P-H.

--The Gradebook System: Apple II-IIe. (Illus.). 80p. 1984. pap. 14.95 (ISBN 0-13-362526-5); incl. disk 29.95 (ISBN 0-13-362542-7); disk 15.95 (ISBN 0-13-362534-6). P-H.

Bonynge, David B. MicroMansion: Using Your Apple II-IIe Computer to Have a Safer, More Convenient Home. (Illus.). 176p. (Orig.). 1985. pap. 11.95 (ISBN 0-8306-1916-X, 1916). TAB Bks.

Brener, Robert. Apple II, IIe Troubleshooting & Ripais Manual. LC 84-71058. 19.95 (ISBN 0-672-22353-8). Sams.

Brown, Jerald R., et al. BASIC for the Apple II. LC 82-10962. (Self-Teaching Guide Ser.: No. 1-581). 410p. 1982. pap. 12.95 (ISBN 0-471-86596-6, Pub. by Wiley Pr); pap. tchr's guide avail. Wiley.

Bruno, James E. Designing Education Information Systems Using 2BaseII & the Apple II: A Systems Guide to the Apple & dBase II. 250p. 1985. pap. text ed. 29.95 (ISBN 0-86542-314-8). Blackwell Pubns.

Bryan, Paul. Programming Your Apple II Computer. (Illus.). 294p. 1982. 15.95o.p (ISBN 0-8306-0081-7); pap. 10.25 (ISBN 0-8306-1394-3, 1394). TAB Bks.

Burdick, John & Weiser, Peter B. ProDOS Quick & Simple: For the Apple II Family. 288p. 1985. pap. 19.95 (ISBN 0-673-18077-8). Scott F.

Burke, Ronald & Kramer, Arthur. Microcomputer Courseware for Technical Mathematics (Apple II & TRS-80) User's Manual. 1983. 11.70 (ISBN 0-07-009050-5). McGraw.

Burns, Robert V. & Johnson, Rees C. Sixty Forms for the Entrepreneur: Forms Generator - Apple II, II Plus, IIc & IIe. 192p. 1985. pap. cancelled (ISBN 0-88056-256-0). Dilithium Pr.

--Sixty Forms for the Landlord: Forms Generator - Apple II, II Plus, IIc & IIe. 192p. 1985. pap. cancelled (ISBN 0-88056-253-6). Dilithium Pr.

--Sixty Forms for Your Household: Forms Generator for Your Apple II, Apple II Plus, & Apple IIc & IIe. 192p. 1985. pap. 29.95 incl. disk (ISBN 0-88056-250-1). Dilithium Pr.

Busch, David D. Keyboard Challenge with Apple II, IIe & III. (Illus.). 192p. pap. cancelled (ISBN 0-89303-600-5). Brady Comm.

California State University. Constructing the Paragraph: The Ramblestones on the Road for Use with Apple II. 1984. 39.95 (ISBN 0-07-831012-1). McGraw.

--Contestination: Developing Successful Estimating Abilities for Use with Apple II. 1984. 49.950 (ISBN 0-07-831020-2). McGraw.

--Introduction to Language for Use with Apple II. 1984. 49.95 (ISBN 0-07-831034-2). McGraw.

--Miranda: Understanding Poetry-Alliteration & Assonance; Images; Metaphors; Similies & Symbols for Use with Apple II, Pt. 2. 1984. write for info. (ISBN 0-07-831002-4). McGraw.

--Miranda: Understanding Poetry-Meter, Rhythm, Rhyme for Use with Apple II, Pt. 1. 1984. write for info. (ISBN 0-07-831010-5). McGraw.

--Ten Common Inferences: Oscar-The Big Escape for Use with Apple II. 1984. write for info. (ISBN 0-07-831014-8). McGraw.

Campbell, John. Programming Tips & Techniques for the Apple II & IIe. LC 83-22363. (Illus.). 416p. 1984. pap. 19.95 (ISBN 0-89303-273-5); diskette 30.00 (ISBN 0-89303-782-6); bk. & diskette 49.95 (ISBN 0-89303-776-1). Brady Comm.

Campbell, John L. & Zimmerman, Lance. Programming the Apple II & IIe: A Structured Approach. rev. & enl. ed. LC 83-21441. (Illus.). 464p. 1984. pap. 19.95 (ISBN 0-89303-779-6); diskette 30.00 (ISBN 0-89303-780-X); bk. & diskette 49.95 (ISBN 0-89303-777-X). Brady Comm.

Carr, Joseph J. Sixty-Eight Scientific & Engineering Programs for the Apple II & IIe. 1984. 19.95 (ISBN 0-8359-6920-7). Reston.

Chance, David W. Thirty-Three Adult Computer Games in BASIC for the IBM PC, Apple II, IIe & TRS-80. (Illus.). 378p. 1983. 18.95 (ISBN 0-8306-0627-0, 1627); pap. 13.50 (ISBN 0-8306-1627-6). TAB Bks.

Chase, Cochran, et al. Solving Marketing Problems with VisiCalc on Apple II, IIe Computers. 300p. (Orig.). 1984. pap. 29.95 incl. disc (ISBN 0-8019-7422-4). Chilton.

Christensen, Conway B., ed. Programmer's Handbook to the Apple II. rev. ed. (Illus.). 108p. 1983. pap. 12.95 (ISBN 0-913249-01-7); looseleaf bdr. ed. o.p. 29.95 (ISBN 0-913249-00-9). Comp Stations.

Consumer Guide Editors. The User's Guide to Apple II, II Plus & IIe Computers, Software & Peripherals. 1983. spiral bdg. 2.98 (ISBN 0-517-41678-6). Outlet Bk Co.

Cooke. Applied Finite Element Analysis: An Apple II Implementation. 1984. pap. write for info. (ISBN 0-471-82337-6); supplementary material avail. Wiley.

Craver, John. VisiCalc for Apple II, II Plus, & IIe. (Illus.). 192p. 1983. 14.95 (ISBN 0-89586-274-3). H P Bks.

Creative Programming Inc., Staff. Creative Programming: Apple II, IIe, Vol. III. rev. ed. 77p. 1983. spiral wkbk. 9.95 (ISBN 0-912079-05-3, 203). Creat Prog Inc.

--Creative Programming: Apple II, IIe, Vol. IV. rev. ed. 80p. 1983. spiral wkbk. 9.95 (ISBN 0-912079-11-8, 204). Creat Prog Inc.

--Creative Programming: Apple II, IIe, Vol. I. (Illus.). 74p. 1983. spiral wkbk 9.95 (ISBN 0-912079-02-9). Creat Prog Inc.

--Creative Programming: Apple II, IIe, Vol. II. 66p. 1983. spiral wkbk. 9.95 (ISBN 0-912079-21-5, 202). Creat Prog Inc.

--Creative Programming: Teacher Resource Book, Apple II, IIe. 130p. (Orig.). 1983. 19.95 (ISBN 0-912079-09-6, 299). Creat Prog Inc.

Cronenberger, J. Helen, et al. The Apple II in the Clinical Laboratory. 225p. 1984. spiral bdg. 22.50 (ISBN 0-316-15748-1). Little.

De Jong, Marvin L. Apple II Assembly Language. LC 82-50015. 336p. 1982. pap. 15.95 (ISBN 0-672-21894-1, 21894). Sams.

Desautels, Edouard J. VisiCalc for the Apple II Plus & IIe Computers. (Microcomputer Power Ser.). 164p. 1982. plastic comb 16.95 (ISBN 0-697-00345-0); deluxe ed. bk. & Diskette 27.95 (ISBN 0-697-00329-9). Wm C Brown.

Des Jardins, Paul R., et al. Apple II & II Plus Microcomputer, BASIC & 6502. rev. ed. (Nanos Reference Cards Ser.). 16p. 1982. 4.95 (ISBN 0-915069-10-5). Nanos Sys.

--The Apple II & II Plus Microcomputer, BASIC. rev. ed. (Nanos Reference Cards Ser.). (Illus.). 14p. 1982. 3.95 (ISBN 0-915069-11-3). Nanos Sys.

De Witt, William H. Art & Graphics on the Apple II-IIe. (Professional Software Ser.). 1984. No. 1-598. incl. disk 39.90 (ISBN 0-471-80253-0, Wiley Professional Software); disk 24.95 (ISBN 0-471-80252-2). Wiley.

Fabbri, Tony. Animation, Games, & Sound for the Apple II-IIe. (P-H Personal Computing Ser.). (Illus.). 144p. 1984. pap. text ed. 17.95 incl. cassette (ISBN 0-13-037284-6); incl. disk 31.95 (ISBN 0-13-037276-5). P-H.

Fiske, Thomas S. Low Cost Costing: Product Costing with Your Microcomputer. (Illus.). 94p. (Orig.). 1984. pap. 24.95 spiral bound (ISBN 0-88006-084-0); Apple II, II Plus, IIe. spiral bound incl. disk 24.95 (ISBN 0-88006-067-0, CC7399); IBM-PC. spiral bound incl. disk 24.95 (ISBN 0-88006-071-9, CC7402); TRS-80 Model I, Model III. spiral bound incl. disk 24.95 (ISBN 0-88006-072-7, CC7403); spiral bound incl. disk 24.95 (ISBN 0-88006-092-1, CC7421). Green Pub Inc.

Garrison, Paul. Fun, Games & Graphics for the Apple II, IIe & IIc. (Illus.). 320p. (Orig.). 1984. 18.95 (ISBN 0-8306-0752-8, 1752); pap. 13.95 (ISBN 0-8306-1752-3). TAB Bks.

Gayler, Winston D. The Apple II Circuit Description. LC 82-61966. 240p. 1983. pap. 22.95 (ISBN 0-672-21959-X, 21959). Sams.

Good, Phillip I. A Critic's Guide to Apple II Computers. LC 83-72438. (Illus.). 254p. 1983. pap. 12.95 (ISBN 0-8019-7412-7). Chilton.

Goodfellow, David C. Apple II BASIC. (Illus.). 240p. (Orig.). 1983. o.p 19.95 (ISBN 0-8306-0113-9); pap. 13.50 (ISBN 0-8306-1513-X, 1513). TAB Bks.

Graff, Lois & Goldstein, Larry. Applesoft BASIC for the Apple II & IIe. LC 83-15527. 336p. 1983. 16.95 (ISBN 0-89303-320-0). Brady Comm.

Gruenberger, Fred. Computing with the Apple. 208p. 1984. pap. text ed. 14.95 (ISBN 0-8359-0866-5). Reston.

Grushcow, Jack. VisiCalc Extensions for the Apple II & IIe. (Illus.). 1984. pap. 16.95 (ISBN 0-8359-8403-6); text ed. 21.95 (ISBN 0-8359-8404-4). Reston.

Hallgren, Richard. Interface Projects for the Apple II. (Illus.). 192p. 1982. 18.95 (ISBN 0-13-469395-7); pap. 12.95 (ISBN 0-13-469387-6). P-H.

Hanson, R. N. & Rigby, S. D. Gregg Personal Keyboarding: Apple Version. 96p. 1982. 36.95 (ISBN 0-07-079994-6). McGraw.

Haskell, Richard E. Apple II: 6502 Assembly Language Tutor. (Illus.). 240p. 1983. incl. disk 34.95 (ISBN 0-13-039230-8, Spec). P-H.

Haviland, Robert P. Computer Companion for the Apple II-Apple IIe. 128p. 1983. pap. 10.25 (ISBN 0-8306-1603-9, 1603). TAB Bks.

Heilborn, John, ed. Science & Engineering Programs: Apple II Edition. 223p. 1981. pap. 15.99 (ISBN 0-07-931063-X, 63-X). Osborne-McGraw.

Heiserman, David L. Intermediate Level Apple II Handbook. LC 82-61963. 328p. 1983. pap. 16.95 (ISBN 0-672-21889-5, 21889). Sams.

--Intermediate-Level Apple II Handbook. 1983. write for info. Bobbs.

--Programming Surprises & Tricks for Your Apple II, IIe Computers. 208p. (Orig.). 1984. pap. 11.50 (ISBN 0-8306-1721-3, 1721). TAB Bks.

Held, Gilbert. Apple II BASIC: A Quick Reference Guide. 1982. pap. 2.95 (ISBN 0-471-87039-0, Pub. by Wiley Pr); pap. 29.50 set of ten (ISBN 0-471-87043-9). Wiley.

Henderson, Joe. Running Your Best Race Computerized Edition: Apple II, II Plus & IIe Version. 224p. 1984. plastic comb 18.95 (ISBN 0-697-00459-7). Wm C Brown.

Hergert, Douglas. The Apple II BASIC Handbook. LC 83-61381. (Illus.). 250p. 1983. pap. 14.95 (ISBN 0-89588-115-2). SYBEX.

Honig, Herbert M. Polishing Your Apple: Vol. 1. LC 82-61967. 80p. 1982. pap. 4.95 (ISBN 0-672-22026-1, 22026). Sams.

Hurley, Richard B. Decision Tables in Software Engineering. (VNR Data Processing Ser.). 184p. 1982. text ed. 22.95 (ISBN 0-442-23599-2); disks for Apple II & IBM-PC 59.50 ea. (ISBN 0-442-23666-2). Van Nos Reinhold.

Ingram, R. The Kaufman Method of WISC-R Hypothesis Generation for the Apple II-IIe. 1985. incl. disk 161.95 (ISBN 0-471-82458-5). Wiley.

Irby, Thomas C. & Ward, D. L. Hypergraphics User's Guide: Apple II Version. 1983. 19.95 (ISBN 0-07-068143-0). McGraw.

Jong, Marvin L. De. Apple II Applications. LC 83-61064. 240p. 1983. pap. text ed. 13.95 (ISBN 0-672-22035-0, 22035). Sams.

Kantaris, Noel. The Apple's BASIC Core. LC 83-16811. 222p. 1984. pap. text ed. 14.95 (ISBN 0-471-80233-6, Pub by Wiley). Wiley.

Kascmer, Joseph. The Easy Guide to Your Apple II. LC 83-60949. (Illus.). 147p. 1983. pap. 9.95 (ISBN 0-89588-122-5). SYBEX.

Keeler, Graham. Apple Prodos Disk-File Handling. 300p. 1985. pap. 14.95 (ISBN 0-13-038829-7). P-H.

--Machine Level Programming on the Apple II-IIe. 1984. 15.95 (ISBN 0-13-541897-6); incl. disk 29.95 (ISBN 0-13-541913-1). P-H.

Kelley. An Accounting Experience with the Apple II Microcomputer: A Service Firm. 1983. pap. 16.95t (ISBN 0-256-02955-5). Business Pubns.

Kirkpatrick, Michael. Essential Programs for Small Business for the Apple II-IIe. LC 84-2303. 1984. 16.95 (Pub. by Wiley Pr); bk. & software set 46.90 (ISBN 0-471-80602-1, Wiley Professional Software); disk 29.95 (ISBN 0-471-80547-5). Wiley.

Lancaster, Don. Enhancing Your Apple II & IIe, Vol. 2. 17.95 (ISBN 0-672-22425-9). Sams.

Lavine, Ronald M. Introduction to Apple II BASIC. 1984. pap. text ed. 9.48 (ISBN 0-395-35600-8); tchr's resource material 64.00 (ISBN 0-395-35601-6). HM.

Levin, Burgess A. The Apple User's Guide to Beating the Stock Market. (Illus.). 192p. 1984. pap. 14.95 (ISBN 0-8359-0137-8). Reston.

Lewis, Ted. Microbook: Database Management for the Apple II Computer. (Illus.). 322p. (Orig.). 1982. pap. 19.95 (ISBN 0-88056-072-X); incl. disk 39.95 (ISBN 0-88056-156-4). Dilithium Pr.

Lippman, Gary. Your Second Apple II Program. LC 84-51238. (Illus.). 240p. 1984. pap. 13.95 (ISBN 0-89588-208-6). SYBEX.

Luehrmann, A. & Peckham, H. Computer Literacy: A Hands-On Approach. 1983. Apple II. 23.96 (ISBN 0-07-049186-0); TRS-80. 23.96 (ISBN 0-07-049199-2); Apple II. wkbk. & diskette 6.68 (ISBN 0-07-049187-9); TRS-80. wkbk. 6.68; Apple II. guide & diskette 31.96; TRS-80. guide & diskette 31.96 (ISBN 0-07-049200-X). McGraw.

--Computer Literacy Survival Kit: For the Apple II, IIe Family of Computers. 384p. 1984. pap. 29.95 (ISBN 0-07-049206-9, BYTE Bks). McGraw.

McDougall, Anne, et al. Learning LOGO on the Apple II. (Illus.). 1984. pap. 14.95 (ISBN 0-13-527747-7). P-H.

Mandell, Steven L. Introduction to Computers Using the Apple II. (Illus.). 450p. 1985. text ed. 26.95 (ISBN 0-314-85265-4). West Pub.

Marcus, Jeffrey & Marcus, Marvin. Computing Without Mathematics: BASIC & Pascal Applications (School Edition) LC 85-4144. 300p. (Orig.). 1985. pap. 32.95 (ISBN 0-88175-110-3); pap. text ed. 21.95 (ISBN 0-88175-105-7); wkbk. 10.00 (ISBN 0-88175-115-4); diskette 15.00 (ISBN 0-88175-106-5). Computer Sci.

Mears, Peter. Teach Yourself Apple BASIC. 192p. 1983. write for info., spiral bound incl. disk. Addison-Wesley.

Meck, H. R. Numerical Analysis with the T1 99-4A, Apple II, IIe & TRS 80 Model I-III. 256p. 1984. 19.95 (ISBN 0-13-626649-5); pap. 14.95 (ISBN 0-13-626631-2). P-H.

Mottola, Robert. Assembly Language Programming for the Apple II. 143p. (Orig.). 1982. pap. 16.95 (ISBN 0-07-931051-6, 51-6). Osborne-McGraw.

Myers, Roy & Schneider, David. Handbook of Applesoft BASIC for the Apple II & IIe. (Illus.). 352p. 1984. pap. 16.95 (ISBN 0-89303-504-1). Brady Comm.

Naumer, Janet N. Media Center Management with an Apple II. 125p. 1984. lib. bdg. 19.50 (ISBN 0-87287-392-7). Libs Unl.

Parker, Alan. Apple BASIC for Business for the Apple II. 2nd ed. 1984. pap. text ed. 17.95 (ISBN 0-8359-0101-7); instr's manual avail. (ISBN 0-8359-0102-5). Reston.

Parker, Alan & Stewart, John. Accountant's BASIC Programming for the Apple II. 1983. 16.95 (ISBN 0-8359-0047-9). Reston.

Peddicord, Richard G. Understanding Apple Graphics. (Handy Guide Ser.). 64p. (Orig.). 1983. pap. 3.50 (ISBN 0-88284-250-1). Alfred Pub.

Phillips, Gary. Apple II Free Software. 250p. pap. cancelled (ISBN 0-89588-200-0). SYBEX.

--Apple II-IIe-IIc Expansion Guide. (Illus.). 320p. (Orig.). 1985. 22.95 (ISBN 0-8306-0901-6, 1901); pap. 16.95 (ISBN 0-8306-1901-1). TAB Bks.

Phillips, Gary, et al. The Apple User's Encyclopedia: Apple II, II Plus, IIe & III. Mellin, Michael F. & Ritz, Roberta, eds. 350p. 1983. pap. 19.95 (ISBN 0-912003-14-6). Bk Co.

Poirot, James & Retzlaff, Don. Microcomputer Workbook: Apple II, II Plus, & IIe edition. 137p. (Orig.). 1983. pap. text ed. 6.95 (ISBN 0-88408-287-3); teacher's manual 6.95. Sterling Swift.

Poole, Lon. Apple II User's Guide. 3rd ed. 512p. (Orig.). 1985. pap. 18.95 (ISBN 0-07-881176-7, 176-7). Osborne-McGraw.

Porter, Alan & Rezmer, Martin. BASIC Business Subroutines for the Apple II & Apple IIe. 160p. 1983. pap. 12.95 (ISBN 0-201-05663-1). Addison-Wesley.

Porter, Alan G. & Rezmer, Martin G. BASIC Subroutines for the Apple II & IIe. 240p. 12.95 (ISBN 0-201-05663-1); incl. disk 29.95 (ISBN 0-201-05692-5); IBM 29.95 (ISBN 0-201-05658-5). Addison-Wesley.

Porter, Kent. Porter's Programs for the Apple II Family: For the Apple II, II Plus, IIe & IIc. 167p. 1985. pap. 6.95 (ISBN 0-451-82107-6, Sig). NAL.

Price, Robert V. & Willis, Jerry. How to Use the Apple II & IIe. 100p. 1984. pap. 5.95 (ISBN 0-88056-139-4). Dilithium Pr.

Renko, Hal, et al. The Antagonists: A Complete Microworld Adventure for the Apple II. 128p. 1985. pap. 8.95 (ISBN 0-201-16490-6). Addison-Wesley.

Rice, Jean & Henke, James. Friendly BASIC: For the Apple II, Apple IIplus, Apple IIe & Apple IIc. 15.95 (ISBN 0-8359-2103-4). Reston.

Rob, Peter. AppleStat: Regression-Correlation Programs for the Apple II-IIe, Vol. 1. LC 84-115048. (Illus.). 96p. 1984. 49.95 (ISBN 0-13-038951-X). P-H.

Ross, Peter. Introducing LOGO for the Texas Instruments 99-4A, Tandy Color Computer, & Apple II Computer. 160p. 1983. pap. 12.95 (ISBN 0-201-14652-5). Addison-Wesley.

Rubin, Charles. The Endless Apple: How to Maintain State-of-the-Art Performance on Your Apple II & IIe. (Illus.). 288p. 1984. pap. 15.95 (ISBN 0-914845-27-6). Microsoft.

Sandler, Corey. Desktop Graphics for the Apple II: Printers, Plotters, Charts & Graphs. (Illus., Orig.). pap. cancelled (ISBN 0-916688-91-7, 91-7). Creative Comp.

Sather, Jim. Understanding the Apple II. LC 84-111632. 1983. 22.95 (ISBN 0-912985-01-1, 5011). Quality Soft.

Scanlon, Leo. Apple II-IIe Assembly Language Exercises. LC 82-2822. 204p. 1982. pap. 12.95x (ISBN 0-471-86598-2, Pub. by Wiley Pr). Wiley.

Shane, June G. Programming for Microcomputers: Apple II BASIC. LC 83-8163. 432p. 1984. pap. text ed. 16.95 (ISBN 0-395-35206-1); Grid sheet bklt. 3.95 (ISBN 0-395-35207-X). HM.

Shneiderman, Ben. Let's Learn BASIC: A Kid's Introduction to Basic Programming on the Apple II Series. 175p. 1984. 8.95 (ISBN 0-316-78721-3). Little.

Simpson, Henry. Serious Programming for Your Apple II, IIe, IIc. (Illus.). 192p. (Orig.). 1985. 18.95 (ISBN 0-8306-0960-1, 1960); pap. 12.95 (ISBN 0-8306-1960-7). Tab Bks.

Stephenson, J. W., et al. Brain Games for Kids & Adults Using the Apple II, IIe, & IIc. (Illus.). 256p. 1984. pap. 13.95 (ISBN 0-89303-362-6); diskett 20.00 (ISBN 0-89303-366-9). Brady Comm.

Swift's Educational Software Directory for Corvus Networks 1984: Apple II Edition. 16.95 (ISBN 0-317-03120-1). Sterling Swift.

Swift's 1984-1985 Educational Software Directory: Apple II Edition. 480p. soft spiral bdg. 24.95 (ISBN 0-88408-270-9). Sterling Swift.

Targ, Joan & Levinsky, Jeff. Ready, Run, Fun: Apple II Edition, Vol. II. (Illus.). 150p. 1984. pap. 14.95 (ISBN 0-13-762212-0). P-H.

--Ready, Run, Fun: Apple II-IIe Edition, Vol. I. (Illus.). 150p. 1984. pap. 14.95 (ISBN 0-13-762204-X). P-H.

Tebbe, Paul. Programming the Apple II in BASIC. LC 83-10895. (Illus.). 176p. 1983. text ed. 21.95 (ISBN 0-13-729591-X); pap. text ed. 17.95 (ISBN 0-13-729749-1). P-H.

Thomas, Rick. Discover BASIC: Problem Solving with the Apple II Computer. 1983. wkbk. for students 5.95 (ISBN 0-686-47364-7); tchr's guide & disks 74.95 (ISBN 0-686-47365-5); disks each 9.95. Sterling Swift.

Thompson, Andrew V. Micro-Cap Analog Circuit Design Software: Package Apple II Version. 1983. 475.00 (ISBN 0-07-060016-3). Mcgraw.

Tice, Robert L. & Stevens, Dorothy J. Hi-Res Graphics for the Apple II-IIe-IIc. LC 84-23954. (Illus.). 1985. 21.95 (ISBN 0-8306-0849-4, 1849); pap. 14.95 (ISBN 0-8306-1849-X). TAB Bks.

Titus, Jonathan S., et al. Apple II Interfacing. LC 81-84282. 208p. 1981. pap. 11.95 (ISBN 0-672-21862-3, 21862). Sams.

Trester, Kenneth R., et al. Complete Business BASIC for the Apple II, II Plus, IIe, & IIc: A Self-Instructional Approach. LC 84-12439. 368p. 1985. pap. 21.95 (ISBN 0-201-16281-4); write for info. tchrs. manual (ISBN 0-201-16282-2). Addison-Wesley.

Trost, Stanley R. Apple II BASIC Programs in Minutes. LC 83-61385. (Illus.). 176p. 1983. pap. 12.95 (ISBN 0-89588-121-7). SYBEX.

Tucker, Allan B., Jr. BASIC Apple II. 3rd ed. 304p. 1983. pap. 17.95 (ISBN 0-03-061769-3). HR&W.

Vile, Richard. Apple II Programmer's Handbook. (Illus.). 276p. 1982. 24.95 (ISBN 0-13-039206-5); pap. 16.95 (ISBN 0-13-039198-0). P-H.

Wadsworth, Nat. The Graphics Cookbook for the Apple. 72p. 1983. pap. 10.95 (ISBN 0-317-00363-1). Hayden.

Washington Apple Pi, Ltd. Staff. Perfect Pascal Programs. Platt, Robert, ed. LC 84-24017. (Illus.). 288p. (Orig.). 1985. 22.95 (ISBN 0-8306-0894-X, 1894); pap. 16.95 (ISBN 0-8306-1894-5). TAB Bks.

Wattenberg, Frank. Your Apple II Needs You: Thirty Programming Projects for the Apple II. (Illus.). 352p. 1984. pap. text ed. 15.95 (ISBN 0-13-977975-2). P-H.

Williams, K. & Kernaghan, B. Apple II & IIe Computer Graphics. LC 83-3871. (Illus.). 192p. 1983. pap. 19.95 (ISBN 0-89303-315-4); diskette 12.50 (ISBN 0-89303-318-9). Brady Comm.

Wolfe, Philip & Koelling, C. Patrick. BASIC Engineering Science & Business Programs for the Apple II & IIe. 352p. 1984. pap. 19.95 (ISBN 0-89303-284-0); bk. & diskette 44.95 (ISBN 0-89303-290-5); diskette 25.00 (ISBN 0-89303-288-3). Brady Comm.

Zabinski & Mazzola. Apple II for Kids from Eight to Eighty. LC 83-51232. 176p. 1984. pap. 10.95 (ISBN 0-672-22297-3). Sams.

Zaks, Rodnay. Your First Apple II Program. LC 83-50717. (Illus.). 182p. 1983. pap. 12.95 (ISBN 0-89588-136-5). SYBEX.

Zimmerman, Steven, et al. Business Applications for the Apple II & IIe under CP-M. 270p. 1984. 15.95 (ISBN 0-89303-354-5). Brady Comm.

APPLE II PLUS (COMPUTER)

Algebra Arcade. 1983. Apple II Plus or Apple IIe. write for info; IBM-PC. write for info (ISBN 0-534-02973-6); Atari 800. write for info; Commodore 64. write for info (ISBN 0-686-46802-3). Wadsworth Pub.

Apple PILOT Editor's Manual. (Apple II Plus & IIe Reference Manuals Ser.). Date not set. 15.00 (ISBN 0-317-04463-X, A2L0042). Apple Comp.

Apple PILOT Language Manual. (Apple II Plus & IIe Reference Manuals Ser.). Date not set. 20.00 (ISBN 0-317-04464-8, A2L0041). Apple Comp.

Aylsworth, Sandra. Apple LOGO for Apple II Plus, Apple IIe & IIc. (Computer Fun Ser.). (Illus.). 1984. pap. 3.95 (ISBN 0-86582-166-6, EN79252). Enrich.

Banse, Timothy P. Home Applications & Games for the Apple II, II Plus & IIe Computers. (Microcomputer Bookshelf Ser.). 170p. (Orig.). 1984. pap. 14.50 (ISBN 0-316-08045-4). Little.

Barnett, Michael P. & Barnett, Graham K. Personal Graphics for Profit & Pleasure on the Apple II Plus and IIe Personal Computers. (Microcomputer Bookshelf Ser.). 208p. 1982. pap. text ed. 14.50 (ISBN 0-316-08164-7). Little.

Barron's Computer SAT Study Program. 1983. entire pkg. 89.95 (ISBN 0-8120-7160-3). Apple IIe-48K, Apple II-48K & Apple II Plus. IBM-PC (ISBN 0-8120-7189-1). Commodore 64 (ISBN 0-8120-7192-1). mathematics wkbk., verbal wkbk., user's manual avail. Barron.

Budin, Howard. Speed Walker: Fun to Program Your Apple II Plus or IIe. 96p. (Orig.). 1984. pap. 2.95 (ISBN 0-523-42243-1). Pinnacle Bks.

Burns, Robert V. & Johnson, Rees C. Sixty Forms for the Entrepreneur: Forms Generator - Apple II, II Plus, IIc & IIe. 192p. 1985. pap. cancelled (ISBN 0-88056-256-0). Dilithium Pr.

--Sixty Forms for the Landlord: Forms Generator - Apple II, II Plus, IIc & IIe. 192p. 1985. pap. cancelled (ISBN 0-88056-253-6). Dilithium Pr.

--Sixty Forms for Your Household: Forms Generator for Your Apple II, Apple II Plus, & Apple IIc & IIe. 192p. 1985. pap. 29.95 incl. disk (ISBN 0-88056-250-1). Dilithium Pr.

Busch, David D. Apple Soft Subroutine Cookbook. (Illus.). 208p. 1985. pap. 12.95 (ISBN 0-89303-322-7). Brady Comm.

Carmony, Lowell A., et al. Apple Pascal: A Self-Study Guide for the Apple II Plus, IIe, & IIc. LC 84-19950. (Illus.). 233p. 1985. pap. text ed. 18.95 (ISBN 0-88175-076-X); diskette 15.00 (ISBN 0-88175-095-6). Computer Sci.

Cathcart, Glee. Apple Music for Apple II Plus, IIe & IIc. (Computer Fun Ser.). (Illus.). 48p. 1984. pap. 3.95 (ISBN 0-86582-167-4, EN79253). Enrich.

Consumer Guide Editors. The User's Guide to Apple II, II Plus & IIe Computers, Software & Peripherals. 1983. spiral bdg. 2.98 (ISBN 0-517-41678-6). Outlet Bk Co.

Craver, John. VisiCalc for Apple II, II Plus, & IIe. (Illus.). 192p. 1983. 14.95 (ISBN 0-89586-274-3). H P Bks.

Des Jardins, Paul R., et al. Apple II & II Plus Microcomputer, BASIC & 6502. rev. ed. (Nanos Reference Cards Ser.). 16p. 1982. 4.95 (ISBN 0-915069-10-5). Nanos Sys.

--The Apple II & II Plus Microcomputer, BASIC. rev. ed. (Nanos Reference Cards Ser.). (Illus.). 14p. 1982. 3.95 (ISBN 0-915069-11-3). Nanos Sys.

DeWitt, William H. Art & Graphics on the Apple II Plus. (Recreational Computing Ser.). 128p. 1984. pap. text ed. 14.95 (ISBN 0-471-88728-5, Pub. by Wiley Pr); software disk (Apple II) 24.95; book & disk set 39.90. Wiley.

Evaluation Consultants Inc. Realval: Apple II Plus Version. 1984. 250.00 ea. (ISBN 0-07-021110-8). Apple II plus. TRS-80 Model III (ISBN 0-07-021112-4). McGraw.

Haigh, Roger & Radford, Loren. UCSD Pascal: Featuring the Apple IIe & II Plus. 461p. 1983. text ed. write for info (ISBN 0-87150-457-X, 8090). PWS Pubs.

Haugaard, Jim & Powers, Judy. Apple Fun for Apple II Plus, IIe, & IIc. (Computer Fun Ser.). (Illus.). 1984. 3.95 (ISBN 0-86582-164-X, EN79250). Enrich.

Henderson, Joe. Running Your Best Race Computerized Edition: Apple II, II Plus & IIe Version. 224p. 1984. plastic comb 18.95 (ISBN 0-697-00459-7). Wm C Brown.

Hofemann, Bob. Apple Graphics for Apple II Plus, Apple IIe & IIc. (Illus.). 48p. 1984. pap. 3.95 (ISBN 0-86582-165-8, EN79251). Enrich.

Jones, Jo Lynne & Greenfield, Howard. Applesoft BASIC Primer for the Apple II Plus, IIe, & IIc. LC 84-19937. 1985. pap. 9.95 (ISBN 0-88175-047-6); diskette 17.00 (ISBN 0-88175-048-4). Computer Sci.

Laric, Michael V. & Stiff, M. R. Multiplan for the Apple II Plus & IIe. (Microcomputer Power Ser.). 150p. 1984. pap. 16.95 (ISBN 0-697-00259-4); incl. disk 27.95 (ISBN 0-697-00331-0). Wm C Brown.

Lewis, P. Enterprise Sandwich Shops: A Market Simulation Apple II Plus (on Apple with Applesoft) Version. 1983. 199.00 (ISBN 0-07-037536-4). McGraw.

Lewis, P. C. Enterprise Sandwich Shops: A Market Simulation, Apple IIe & Apple II Plus Version. 1983. 199.00 (ISBN 0-07-079636-X). McGraw.

Muscat, E. & Lorton, P. Microcomputer Applications for the Data Processing Work Kit TRS-80 Diskette. (Microcomputer Software Ser.). 1982. 99.00 (ISBN 0-07-044107-3); Apple II Plus Version. 99.00 (ISBN 0-07-044108-1); user's guide 4.80 (ISBN 0-07-044109-X). McGraw.

Music Made Easy: Apple IIe-II Plus. 1984. incl. disk 29.95 (ISBN 0-88284-290-0). Alfred Pub.

Parallel Interface Card Manual. (Apple II Plus & IIe Reference Manuals Ser.). Date not set. 2.00 (ISBN 0-317-04466-4, A2L0004). Apple Comp.

Pascal Language Reference Manual. (Apple II Plus & IIe Reference Manuals Ser.). Date not set. 20.00 (ISBN 0-317-04468-0, A2L0027). Apple Comp.

Pascal Operating System Manual. (Apple II Plus & IIe Reference Manuals). Date not set. 25.00 (ISBN 0-317-04469-9, A2L0028). Apple Comp.

Peckham, H. Hands-on BASIC: For the Apple II Plus Computer. (Personal Programming Ser.). 1982. pap. 23.95 (ISBN 0-07-049179-8, BYTE Bks). McGraw.

Phillips, Gary, et al. The Apple User's Encyclopedia: Apple II, II Plus, IIe & III. Mellin, Michael F. & Ritz, Roberta, eds. 350p. 1983. pap. 19.95 (ISBN 0-912003-14-6). Bk Co.

Pirisino, Jim. Primer for the Apple II Plus & IIe. 120p. 1984. pap. cancelled. Brady Comm.

Poirot, James & Retzlaff, Don. Microcomputer Workbook: Apple II, II Plus, & IIe edition. 137p. (Orig.). 1983. pap. text ed. 6.95 (ISBN 0-88408-287-3); teacher's manual 6.95. Sterling Swift.

Poole, Lon, et al. Apple II User's Guide for Apple II Plus & Apple IIe. 2nd ed. (Illus.). 448p. (Orig.). 1983. pap. 17.95 (ISBN 0-07-047855-4, 855-4). Osborne-McGraw.

Porter, Kent. Porter's Programs for the Apple II Family: For the Apple II, II Plus, IIe & IIc. 167p. 1985. pap. 6.95 (ISBN 0-451-82107-6, Sig). NAL.

ProDOS Technical Reference Manual. (Apple II Plus & IIe Reference Manuals Ser.). Date not set. 25.00 (ISBN 0-317-04470-2, A2W0010). Apple Comp.

Rice, Jean & Henke, James. Friendly BASIC: For the Apple II, Apple IIplus, Apple IIe & Apple IIc. 15.95 (ISBN 0-8359-2103-4). Reston.

Rosenberg, R. C. Software Toolkit: Apple II Plus Version. 1984. write for info. (ISBN 0-07-053912-X); IBM-PC software toolkit 1100.00 (ISBN 0-07-053914-6). McGraw.

Shaffer & Shaffer Applied Research & Development, Inc. VisiCalc Programming: No Experience Necessary: A Self Instructional Disk & Book for Use with the Apple II Plus Computer. 256p. 1983. disk & manual in slipcase 59.95 (ISBN 0-316-78239-4). Little.

Shneiderman, Ben. Let's Learn BASIC: A Kid's Introduction to Basic Programming on the Apple II Series. 175p. 1984. 8.95 (ISBN 0-316-78721-3). Little.

Trester, Kenneth R., et al. Complete Business BASIC for the Apple II, II Plus, IIe, & IIc: A Self-Instructional Approach. LC 84-12439. 368p. 1985. pap. 21.95 (ISBN 0-201-16281-4); write for info. tchrs. manual (ISBN 0-201-16282-2). Addison-Wesley.

Uffenbeck, John. Hardware Interfacing with the Apple II Plus. LC 83-3186. (Illus.). 240p. 1983. 24.95 (ISBN 0-13-383851-X); pap. 14.95 (ISBN 0-13-383844-7). P-H.

Wadsworth, Nat. Data Base Management for the Apple. 128p. pap. 12.95 (ISBN 0-8104-6282-6, 6282). Hayden.

APPLE IIC (COMPUTER)

Aylsworth, Sandra. Apple LOGO for Apple II Plus, Apple IIe & IIc. (Computer Fun Ser.). (Illus.). 1984. pap. 3.95 (ISBN 0-86582-166-6, EN79252). Enrich.

Blackadar, Thomas. The Apple IIC: A Practical Guide. 197p. 1984. pap. 8.95 (ISBN 0-89588-241-8). SYBEX.

Burns, Robert V. & Johnson, Rees C. Sixty Forms for the Entrepreneur: Forms Generator - Apple II, II Plus, IIc & IIe. 192p. 1985. pap. cancelled (ISBN 0-88056-256-0). Dilithium Pr.

--Sixty Forms for the Landlord: Forms Generator - Apple II, II Plus, IIc & IIe. 192p. 1985. pap. cancelled (ISBN 0-88056-253-6). Dilithium Pr.

--Sixty Forms for Your Household: Forms Generator for Your Apple II, Apple II Plus, & Apple IIc & IIe. 192p. 1985. pap. 29.95 incl. disk (ISBN 0-88056-250-1). Dilithium Pr.

Carmony, Lowell A., et al. Apple Pascal: A Self-Study Guide for the Apple II Plus, IIe, & IIc. LC 84-19950. (Illus.). 233p. 1985. pap. text ed. 18.95 (ISBN 0-88175-076-X); diskette 15.00 (ISBN 0-88175-095-6). Computer Sci.

Chien. Using BASIC for Business: Apple IIe. (Illus.). 250p. 1985. pap. text ed. write for info. (ISBN 0-8087-6402-0). Burgess.

Coleman, Horace. The Apple IIc BASIC Programming Book. 1986. pap. 19.95 (ISBN 0-673-18278-9). Scott F.

Enright, Thomas E., et al. Compute's Guide to Telecomputing on the Apple. Compute Editors, ed. (Orig.). 1985. pap. 9.95 (ISBN 0-942386-98-1). Compute Pubns.

Fabbri, Tony. Using & Programming the Apple IIc: Including Ready-to-Run Programs. (Illus.). 256p. 1985. 19.95 (ISBN 0-8306-0981-4, 1981); pap. 14.95 (ISBN 0-8306-1981-X). TAB Bks.

Freiberger, Paul & McNeill, Dan. The Apple IIc: Your First Computer. Compute Editors, ed. (Orig.). 1985. pap. 9.95 (ISBN 0-87455-001-7). Compute Pubns.

Garrison, Paul. Fun, Games & Graphics for the Apple II, IIe & IIc. (Illus.). 320p. (Orig.). 1984. 18.95 (ISBN 0-8306-0752-8, 1752); pap. 13.95 (ISBN 0-8306-1752-3). TAB Bks.

Goodman, Danny. Going Places with the New Apple IIc: All You'll Ever Need to Know to Get There. 256p. 1984. pap. 3.95 (ISBN 0-671-53188-3). PB.

Graff, Lois & Goldstein, Larry J. Apple IIc: An Introduction to Applesoft BASIC. (Illus.). 384p. 1984. pap. 16.95 (ISBN 0-89303-291-3). Brady Comm.

Grillo, John P. & Robertson, J. D. Apple Sampler: A Guide to Good BASIC Subroutines for the IIe-IIc. 1985. pap. 14.95 (ISBN 0-471-81729-5). Wiley.

Hicks, Bruce & Baron, Sylvia. Apple IIc BASIC Paint. (General Trade Books). 224p. 1985. pap. 16.95 (ISBN 0-471-80503-3). Wiley.

Jones, Jo Lynne & Greenfield, Howard. Applesoft BASIC Primer for the Apple II Plus, IIe, & IIc. LC 84-19937. 1985. pap. 9.95 (ISBN 0-88175-047-6); diskette 17.00 (ISBN 0-88175-048-4). Computer Sci.

Lieberman, Philip. Introducing the Apple IIc. LC 84-50864. 400p. 1984. pap. 17.95 (ISBN 0-672-22393-7, 22393). Sams.

Linzmayer, Owen & Kennedy, Don. Insider's Guide to the Apple IIc: Tips, Shortcuts & Helpful Hints from the Professionals. (Illus.). 240p. (Orig.). pap. cancelled (ISBN 0-916688-92-5, 92-5). Creative Comp.

Little, Gary B. Inside the Apple IIc. (Illus.). 256p. 1985. pap. 19.95 (ISBN 0-89303-564-5); diskette 30.00 (ISBN 0-89303-565-3). Brady Comm.

Mullish, H. & Kruger, D. Programming the Apple IIc. 384p. 1985. 16.95 (ISBN 0-07-044042-5, Byte Bks). McGraw.

O'Brien, Bill. The Apple IIc Book: Your Complete Guide to Mastering Apple's Newest Computer. 288p. (Orig.). 1984. pap. 12.95 (ISBN 0-553-34149-9). Bantam.

Parker, Alan & Stewart, John. BASIC Business Application Programming for the Apple IIc. 1984. pap. text ed. 16.95 (ISBN 0-8359-0386-9). Reston.

Person, Ron. Animation Magic with Your Apple IIe & IIc. 224p. (Orig.). 1985. pap. 15.95 (ISBN 0-07-881161-9, 161-9). Osborne McGraw.

Phillips, Gary. Apple II-IIe-IIc Expansion Guide. (Illus.). 320p. (Orig.). 1985. 22.95 (ISBN 0-8306-0901-6, 1901); pap. 16.95 (ISBN 0-8306-1901-1). TAB Bks.

Phillips, Gary & Scellato, Donald. Apple IIc User Guide. (Illus.). 384p. 1984. pap. 14.95 (ISBN 0-89303-307-3); 34.95 (ISBN 0-89303-292-1); 20.00 (ISBN 0-89303-293-X). Brady Comm.

Phillips, Gary, et al. Apple IIe & IIc Software Encyclopedia. 320p. Date not set. pap. cancelled (ISBN 0-89303-213-1). Brady Comm.

Poole, Lon. Apple IIc User's Guide. 480p. (Orig.). 1984. pap. 18.95 (ISBN 0-07-881156-2, 156-2). Osborne-McGraw.

Porter, Kent. Porter's Programs for the Apple II Family: For the Apple II, II Plus, IIe & IIc. 167p. 1985. pap. 6.95 (ISBN 0-451-82107-6, Sig). NAL.

Rice, Jean & Henke, James. Friendly BASIC: For the Apple II, Apple IIplus, Apple IIe & Apple IIc. 15.95 (ISBN 0-8359-2103-4). Reston.

Rubin, Charles. The Endless Apple: How to Maintain State-of-the-Art Performance on Your Apple II & IIe. (Illus.). 288p. 1984. pap. 15.95 (ISBN 0-914845-27-6). Microsoft.

Searle, Bill & Jones, Donna. BASIC for the Apple IIe & IIc. (Illus.). 352p. 1985. pap. 16.95 (ISBN 0-89303-337-5). Brady Comm.

Shaffer & Shaffer Applied Research & Development. Apple IIc-IIe Advanced Graphics. 270p. Date not set. pap. 16.95 (ISBN 0-912003-50-2). Bk Co.

--Apple IIc-IIe Beginning Graphics. Ritz, Roberta, ed. 270p. (Orig.). 1985. pap. 16.95 (ISBN 0-912003-49-9). Bk Co.

Simpson, Henry. Serious Programming for Your Apple II, IIe, IIc. (Illus.). 192p. (Orig.). 1985. 18.95 (ISBN 0-8306-0960-1, 1960); pap. 12.95 (ISBN 0-8306-1960-7). Tab Bks.

Stephenson, J. W., et al. Brain Games for Kids & Adults Using the Apple II, IIe, & IIc. (Illus.). 256p. 1984. pap. 13.95 (ISBN 0-89303-362-6); diskett 20.00 (ISBN 0-89303-366-9). Brady Comm.

Tice, Robert L. & Stevens, Dorothy J. Hi-Res Graphics for the Apple II-IIe-IIc. LC 84-23954. (Illus.). 1985. 21.95 (ISBN 0-8306-0849-4, 1849); pap. 14.95 (ISBN 0-8306-1849-X). TAB Bks.

APPLE IIE (COMPUTER)

Algebra Arcade. 1983. Apple II Plus or Apple IIe. write for info; IBM-PC. write for info (ISBN 0-534-02973-6); Atari 800. write for info; Commodore 64. write for info (ISBN 0-686-46802-3). Wadsworth Pub.

Apple Computer, Inc. Staff. Apple IIe Technical Reference Manual. 1985. write for info. (ISBN 0-201-17720-X). Addison-Wesley.

Apple IIe Guide to the New Features. Date not set. 2.00 (ISBN 0-317-04448-6, A2F2114). Apple Comp.

Apple IIe Owner's Manual. Date not set. 20.00 (ISBN 0-317-04455-9, A2L2001); card supplement 15.00 (A2L2007). Apple Comp.

Apple IIe Reference Manual. Date not set. 30.00 (ISBN 0-317-04456-7, A2L2005). Apple Comp.

Apple IIe 80-Column Text Card Manual. Date not set. 20.00 (ISBN 0-317-04453-2, A2L2006). Apple Comp.

Apple PILOT Editor's Manual. (Apple II Plus & IIe Reference Manuals Ser.). Date not set. 15.00 (ISBN 0-317-04463-X, A2L0042). Apple Comp.

Apple PILOT Language Manual. (Apple II Plus & IIe Reference Manuals Ser.). Date not set. 20.00 (ISBN 0-317-04464-8, A2L0041). Apple Comp.

Applesoft Manual Set for IIe. (Apple II Plus & IIe Reference Manuals Ser.). Date not set. 50.00 (ISBN 0-317-04450-8, A2P2001). Apple Comp.

APPLE IIE PLUS (COMPUTER)

Schwieder, Pete H. How to Repair & Maintain Your Own Apple IIe plus. (Illus.). 154p. 1985. pap. 19.95 (ISBN 0-915097-06-0). Personal Sys Pubns.

Simpson, Henry. Serious Programming for Your Apple II, IIe, IIc. (Illus.). 192p. (Orig.). 1985. 18.95 (ISBN 0-8306-0960-1, 1960); pap. 12.95 (ISBN 0-8306-1960-7). Tab Bks.

APPLE III (COMPUTER)

Adamis, Eddie. BASIC Key Words for the Apple III. LC 83-12327. 143p. 1984. pap. text ed. 14.95 (ISBN 0-471-88389-1, Pub. by Wiley Pr). Wiley.

--Business BASIC for the Apple III: A Self Teaching Guide. LC 83-12328. 245p. 1984. pap. 16.95 (ISBN 0-471-88388-3, Pub. by Wiley Pr). Wiley.

Burdick, John & Weiser, Peter B. ProDOS Quick & Simple: For the Apple II Family. 288p. 1985. pap. 19.95 (ISBN 0-673-18077-8). Scott F.

Busch, David D. Keyboard Challenge with Apple II, IIe & III. (Illus.). 192p. pap. cancelled (ISBN 0-89303-600-5). Brady Comm.

Miastkowski, Stanley. The Osborne-McGraw-Hill Guide to Your Apple III. 352p. 1983. 17.95 (ISBN 0-07-881101-5, 101-5). Osborne-McGraw.

Pascal Program Preparation Tools Manual. (Apple III Reference Manuals). Date not set. 20.00 (ISBN 0-317-04437-0, A3L0005). Apple Comp.

Pascal Programmer's Manual, 2 vols. (Apple III Reference Manuals). Date not set. 30.00 (ISBN 0-317-04438-9, A3L0003). Apple Comp.

Pascal Technical Reference Manual. (Apple III Reference Manuals). Date not set. 50.00 (ISBN 0-317-04439-7, A3L0006). Apple Comp.

Phillips, Gary, et al. The Apple User's Encyclopedia: Apple II, II Plus, IIe & III. Mellin, Michael F. & Ritz, Roberta, eds. 350p. 1983. pap. 19.95 (ISBN 0-912003-14-6). Bk Co.

APPLE SCAB

Influence of Weather Conditions on the Occurrence of Apple Scab. (Technical Note Ser.: No. 55). 55p. 1963. pap. 5.00 (ISBN 0-685-22309-4, W26, WMO). Unipub.

APPLE WRITER (COMPUTER PROGRAM)

Finkel, LeRoy. Learning Word Processing Concepts Using AppleWriter. (Illus.). 80p. 1983. pap. text ed. 8.48 (ISBN 0-07-020986-3). McGraw.

Gittleson, Stephen & Pirisino, Jim. Filing System for Apple Writer: Minute Manual for WPL. 200p. 1985. bk. & software disk 99.95 (ISBN 0-913131-11-3). Minuteware.

Lehman, Carol, et al. The AppleWriter Word Processing Book: Applications for the Apple II & IIe. 1985. text ed. 21.95 (ISBN 0-8359-9228-4); instr's. manual free (ISBN 0-8359-9229-2). Reston.

Pirisino, Jim. Minute Manual for AppleWriter. 150p. 1985. pap. 9.95 (ISBN 0-913131-08-3). Minuteware.

Segal. Business Writing Using Word Processing: Apple Writer. 1985. pap. write for info. (ISBN 0-471-81720-1). Wiley.

APPLE WRITER II (COMPUTER PROGRAM)

Freiwald, Leah. AppleWriter II Made Easy. 210p. (Orig.). 1985. pap. 16.95 (ISBN 0-07-881166-X, 166-X). Osborne McGraw.

Leshowitz, Barry. Apple Writer Tutor: A Step-by-Step Tutorial on Apple Writer IIe-II-III. 288p. 1985. pap. 15.95 (ISBN 0-673-18012-3). Scott F.

Robbins, Jane E. & Johnson, Kate L. Contemporary Business Letters with AppleWriter II or IIe. 240p. 1984. pap. 18.95 (ISBN 0-930764-80-3). Van Nos Reinhold.

Thro, Ellen. Making Friends with AppleWriter II. (Illus.). 160p. 1984. pap. text ed. 16.95 (ISBN 0-13-547183-4). P-H.

APPLE WRITER IIE (COMPUTER PROGRAM)

Layman, Katie & Renner, Adrienne G. Learn Apple Writer IIe the Easy Way. (Illus.). 176p. 1985. pap. 17.95 (ISBN 0-13-527060-X). P-H.

Leshowitz, Barry. Apple Writer Tutor: A Step-by-Step Tutorial on Apple Writer IIe-II-III. 288p. 1985. pap. 15.95 (ISBN 0-673-18012-3). Scott F.

Robbins, Jane E. & Johnson, Kate L. Contemporary Business Letters with AppleWriter II or IIe. 240p. 1984. pap. 18.95 (ISBN 0-930764-80-3). Van Nos Reinhold.

APPLE WRITER III (COMPUTER PROGRAM)

Adamis, Eddie. BASIC Key Words for the Apple III. LC 83-12327. 143p. 1984. pap. text ed. 14.95 (ISBN 0-471-88389-1, Pub. by Wiley Pr). Wiley.

Leshowitz, Barry. Apple Writer Tutor: A Step-by-Step Tutorial on Apple Writer IIe-II-III. 288p. 1985. pap. 15.95 (ISBN 0-673-18012-3). Scott F.

APPLESOFT (COMPUTER PROGRAM)

Applesoft Manual Set for IIe. (Apple II Plus & IIe Reference Manuals Ser.). Date not set. 50.00 (ISBN 0-317-04450-8, A2P2001). Apple Comp.

Applesoft Reference Manual for IIe, Vols. 1 & 2. (Apple Plus & IIe Reference Manuals). Date not set. 25.00 (ISBN 0-317-04451-6, A2L2004). Apple Comp.

Applesoft Tutorial for IIe. (Apple II Plus & IIe Reference Manuals Ser.). Date not set. 30.00 (ISBN 0-317-04452-4, A2L2003). Apple Comp.

Blackwood, Brian D. & Blackwood, George H. Applesoft Language. 2nd ed. LC 83-60172. 288p. 1983. 14.95 (ISBN 0-672-22073-3, 22073). Sams.

Blackwood, George & Blackwood, Brian. Applesoft for the Apple IIe. LC 83-50833. 304p. 1983. 19.95 (ISBN 0-672-22259-0, 22259). Sams.

Busch, David D. Apple Soft Subroutine Cookbook. (Illus.). 208p. 1985. pap. 12.95 (ISBN 0-89303-322-7). Brady Comm.

Coan, James S. Basic Apple BASIC. 1983. pap. 14.95 (ISBN 0-8104-5626-5, 5626). Hayden.

Cuellar, Gabriel. Fancy Programming in Applesoft. 1983. 16.95 (ISBN 0-8359-1856-4); incl. disk 30.00 (ISBN 0-8359-1858-0). Reston.

Dwyer, Thomas A. & Critchfield, Margot. A Bit of Applesoft BASIC. (Illus.). 240p. 1985. pap. 12.95 (ISBN 0-201-11161-6). Addison-Wesley.

Finley, Clarence W., Jr. & Myers, Roy E. Assembly Language for the Applesoft Programmer. 1630p. 1984. pap. 16.95 (ISBN 0-201-05209-1). Addison-Wesley.

Gabriele, Peter & Gabriele, Rosemarie. Game Techniques in Applesoft BASIC. (Illus.). 148p. 1985. pap. cancelled (ISBN 0-8159-5617-7). Devin.

Gehman, Walt & Sumner, Lee E., Jr. Advanced Sound & Graphics in Applesoft. (Illus.). 176p. (Orig.). 1985. 12.95 (ISBN 0-8306-0892-3); pap. 12.45 (ISBN 0-8306-1892-9). TAB Bks.

Graff, Lois & Goldstein, Larry. Applesoft BASIC for the Apple II & IIe. LC 83-15527. 336p. 1983. 16.95 (ISBN 0-89303-320-0). Brady Comm.

Graff, Lois & Goldstein, Larry J. Apple IIc: An Introduction to Applesoft BASIC. (Illus.). 384p. 1984. pap. 16.95 (ISBN 0-89303-291-3). Brady Comm.

Heller, David & Johnson, John. Dr. C. Wacko Presents Applesoft BASIC & the Whiz-Bang Miracle Machine. 1245p. 1985. pap. 12.95 (ISBN 0-201-11507-7). Addison-Wesley.

Jones, Jo Lynne & Greenfield, Howard. Applesoft BASIC Primer for the Apple II Plus, IIe, & IIc. LC 84-19937. 1985. pap. 9.95 (ISBN 0-88175-047-6); diskette 17.00 (ISBN 0-88175-048-4). Computer Sci.

Lewis, P. Enterprise Sandwich Shops: A Market Simulation Apple II Plus (on Apple with Applesoft) Version. 1983. 199.00 (ISBN 0-07-037536-4). McGraw.

McShane, Roger. Exploring Applesoft. 170p. 1983. pap. 17.50 (ISBN 0-13-295916-X). P-H.

Morrill, Harriet H. Mini & Micro BASIC: Introducing Applesoft, Microsoft & BASIC Plus. (Microcomputer Bookshelf Ser.). 224p. 1983. pap. text ed. 14.50i (ISBN 0-316-58400-2); tchr's manual (ISBN 0-316-58401-0). Little.

Mullish, H. & Kruger, D. Applesoft BASIC: From the Ground Up. (Illus.). 240p. 1983. pap. 10.95 (ISBN 0-07-044034-4, BYTE Bks). McGraw.

Myers, Roy & Schneider, David. Handbook of Applesoft BASIC for the Apple II & IIe. (Illus.). 352p. 1984. pap. 16.95 (ISBN 0-89303-504-1). Brady Comm.

Parker, Alan J. & Stewart, John F. Applesoft BASIC for the Business Executive. 1984. pap. 15.95 (ISBN 0-8359-0075-4). Reston.

Presley, Bruce. Guide to Programming in Applesoft. 2nd ed. 292p. 1984. 16.50 (ISBN 0-931717-07-8); 3 ring binder tchr's guide 19.95 (ISBN 0-931717-08-6). Little.

Spurlock, Loy. Applesoft Encyclopedia. (Illus.). 864p. (Orig.). Date not set. 29.95 (ISBN 0-88190-078-8, BO078). Datamost.

Strausbaugh, William G. & Higgins, William R. The Techniques of Applesoft Programming. 232p. 1985. pap. text ed. 16.95 (ISBN 0-89787-408-0). Gorsuch Scarisbrick.

APPLIANCES, ELECTRIC

see Electric Apparatus and Appliances

APPLIED MECHANICS

see Mechanics, Applied

APPLIED SCIENCE

see Technology

APPROXIMATE COMPUTATION

see also Differential Equations, Partial–Numerical Solutions; Perturbation (Mathematics)

Korovkin, P. P. Linear Operators & Approximation Theory. (Russian Monographs & Texts on the Physical Sciences). 234p. 1961. 61.50 (ISBN 0-677-20170-2). Gordon.

Sazanov, V. V. Normal Approximation: Some Recent Advances. (Lecture Notes in Mathematics Ser.: Vol. 879). 105p. 1981. pap. 12.00 (ISBN 0-387-10863-7). Springer-Verlag.

Singer, Ivan. The Theory of Best Approximation & Functional Analysis. (CBMS-NSF Regional Conference Ser.: No. 13). vii, 95p. (Orig.). 1974. pap. text ed. 13.00 (ISBN 0-89871-010-3). Soc Indus-Appl Math.

Vichnevetsky, R. & Bowles, J. B. Fourier Analysis of Numerical Approximations of Hyperbolic Equations. LC 81-85699. (SIAM Studies in Applied Mathematics: No. 5). xii, 140p. 1982. text ed. 23.50 (ISBN 0-89871-181-9). Soc Indus Appl Math.

APPROXIMATION THEORY

see also Chebyshev Approximation; Numerical Analysis; Perturbation (Mathematics); Spline Theory

Akhiezer, N. I. Theory of Approximation. Hyman, Charles J., tr. LC 56-11950. 1956. 16.50 (ISBN 0-8044-4019-0). Ungar.

Alexits. Approximation Theory. 1984. 34.00 (ISBN 0-9910001-0-2, Pub. by Akademiai Kaido Hungary). Heyden.

Aupetit, Bernard. Complex Approximation, Proceedings, Quebec, Canada. (Progress in Mathematics Ser.: No. 4). 128p. 1980. pap. 12.50x (ISBN 0-8176-3004-X). Birkhauser.

Babenko, K. I., et al. Twelve Papers on Approximations & Integrals. LC 51-5559. (Translations Ser.: No. 2, Vol. 44). 1966. Repr. of 1965 ed. 24.00 (ISBN 0-8218-1744-2, TRANS 2-44). Am Math.

Baker, George A., Jr. Essentials of Pade Approximants in Theoretical Physics. 1975. 60.00 (ISBN 0-12-074855-X). Acad Pr.

Baker, George A., Jr. & Gammel, John L., eds. Pade Approximant in Theoretical Physics. (Mathematics in Science & Engineering Ser.: Vol. 71). 1970. 80.00 (ISBN 0-12-074850-9). Acad Pr.

Balasov, L. A., et al. Fourteen Papers on Series & Approximation. LC 51-5559. (Translations Ser.: No. 2, Vol. 77). 1968. 35.00 (ISBN 0-8218-1777-9, TRANS 2-77). Am Math.

Barbu, V. & Da Prato, G. Hamilton-Jacobi Equations in Hilbert Space. (Research Notes in Mathematics Ser.: No. 86). 240p. 1983. pap. text ed. 18.95 (ISBN 0-273-08597-2). Pitman Pub MA.

Bari, N. K., et al. Series & Approximation, Vol. 3. (Translations Ser.: No. 1). 1962. 24.00 (ISBN 0-8218-1603-9, TRANS 1-3). Am Math.

Barroso, J. A., ed. Functional Analysis, Holomorphy & Approximation Theory: Proceedings of the Seminario de Analise Funcional, Holomorfia e Teoria da Approximacao, Universidade Federal do Rio de Janeiro, Aug. 4-8, 1980. (Mathematics Studies: Vol. 71). 486p. 1983. 64.00 (ISBN 0-444-86527-6, I-421-82, North Holland). Elsevier.

Bhattacharya, R. N. & Rao, R. R. Normal Approximation & Asymptotic Expansions. LC 83-19559. 288p. 1985. Repr. of 1976 ed. lib. bdg. write for info (ISBN 0-89874-690-6). Krieger.

Blatter, Joerg. Grothendieck Spaces in Approximation Theory. LC 52-42839. (Memoirs: No. 120). 121p. 1972. pap. 9.00 (ISBN 0-8218-1820-1, MEMO-120). Am Math.

Block, I. E., et al, eds. Studies in Approximation & Analysis. vi, 195p. 1966. text ed. 15.50 (ISBN 0-89871-156-8). Soc Indus-Appl Math.

Brink, D. M. Semi-Classical Methods for Nucleus-Nucleus Scattering. (Cambridge Monographs on Mathematical Physics). 300p. Date not set. price not set. (ISBN 0-521-23940-0). Cambridge U Pr.

Brosowski, Bruno & Martensen, Erich, eds. Approximation & Optimization in Mathematical Physics. 205p. 1983. pap. 25.80 (ISBN 3-8204-7631-8). P Lang Pubs.

Burstein, Joseph. Approximation by Exponentials. LC 83-73529. (Illus.). 85p. (Orig.). 1984. pap. 18.00 (ISBN 0-9607126-1-5). Metrics Pr.

Butzer, et al, eds. Approximation Theory & Functional Analysis: Anniversary Volume. (International Series of Numerical Math: Vol. 65). 632p. 1984. text ed. 48.95x (ISBN 3-76431-574-1). Birkhauser.

Butzer, P. L. & Berens, H. Semi-Groups of Operators & Approximation. LC 68-11980. (Grundlehren der Mathematischen Wissenschaften: Vol. 145). 1967. 39.00 (ISBN 0-387-03832-9). Springer-Verlag.

Butzer, P. L. & Korevaar, J. On Approximation Theory. 2nd ed. (International Series of Numerical Mathematics: No. 5). (Illus.). 262p. 1972. 39.95x (ISBN 0-8176-0189-9). Birkhauser.

Cheney, E. W., ed. Approximation Theory III. LC 80-19723. 1980. 74.50 (ISBN 0-12-171050-5). Acad Pr.

Cheney, Ward. Introduction to Approximation Theory. 2nd ed. LC 81-6208. x, 260p. 1980. text ed. 14.95 (ISBN 0-8284-0317-1). Chelsea Pub.

Christensen, R. General Description of Entropy Minimax. (Entropy Minimax Sourcebook Ser.: Vol. I). 692p. 1981. text ed. 39.50 (ISBN 0-938876-06-6). Entropy Ltd.

Chui, C. K., et al, eds. Approximation Theory IV: Symposium. 1984. 55.00 (ISBN 0-12-174580-5). Acad Pr.

Ciesielski, Z. Approximation & Function Spaces: Proceedings of the International Conference in Gdansk, Aug. 1979. 898p. 1982. 117.00 (ISBN 0-444-86143-2, North-Holland). Elsevier.

Collatz, L., et al, eds. Numerical Methods of Approximation Theory, Vol. 7. (International Series of Numerical Mathematics: Vol. 67). (Eng. & Ger.). 148p. 1984. 24.95 (ISBN 3-7643-1580-6). Birkhauser.

Collatz, Lothar, et al, eds. Numerical Methods of Approximation, Vol. 5. (International Ser. of Numerical Mathematics: No. 52). 337p. 1980. pap. 33.95x (ISBN 0-8176-1103-7). Birkhauser.

Cuyt, A. Pade Approximants for Operators: Theory & Applications. (Lecture Notes in Mathematics Ser.: Vol. 1065). ix, 138p. 1984. pap. 10.50 (ISBN 0-387-13342-9). Springer-Verlag.

Cwikel, M. & Peetre, J. Interpolation Spaces & Allied Topics in Analysis: Proceedings of the Conference Held in Lund, Sweden, August 29 - September 1, 1983. (Lecture Notes in Mathematics Ser.: Vol. 1070). iii, 239p. 1984. pap. 13.50 (ISBN 0-387-13363-1). Springer-Verlag.

Davis, Philip J. Interpolation & Approximation. LC 75-2568. (Illus.). 416p. 1975. pap. text ed. 7.00 (ISBN 0-486-62495-1). Dover.

De Bruin, M. G. & Van Rossum, H., eds. Pade Approximation & Its Applications, Amsterdam 1980: Proceedings. (Lecture Notes in Mathematics Ser.: Vol. 888). 383p. 1981. pap. 22.00 (ISBN 0-387-11154-9). Springer-Verlag.

De Vore, R. A. The Approximation of Continuous Functions by Positive Linear Operators. LC 72-91891. (Lecture Notes in Mathematics: Vol. 293). viii, 289p. 1972. pap. 13.00 (ISBN 0-387-06038-3). Springer-Verlag.

DeVore, R. A. & Scherer, K., eds. Quantitative Approximation. LC 80-17554. 1980. 35.00 (ISBN 0-12-213650-0). Acad Pr.

Epstein, Richard L. Minimal Degrees of Unsolvability & the Full Approximation Construction. LC 75-20308. (Memoirs: No. 162). 136p. 1975. pap. 13.00 (ISBN 0-8218-1862-7, MEMO-162). Am Math.

Finlayson, Bruce A. The Method of Weighted Residuals & Variational Principles. (Mathematics in Science & Engineering Ser.). 1972. 85.00 (ISBN 0-12-257050-2). Acad Pr.

Fisher, S. W. & Jerome, J. W. Minimum Norm Extremals in Function Spaces: With Applications to Classical & Modern Analysis. (Lecture Notes in Mathematics: Vol. 479). viii, 209p. (Orig.). 1975. pap. 16.00 (ISBN 0-387-07394-9). Springer-Verlag.

Furman, T. T. Approximate Methods in Engineering Design. LC 80-40891. (Mathematics in Science & Engineering Ser.). 408p. 1981. 65.00 (ISBN 0-12-269960-2). Acad Pr.

Gaier. Lectures in Complex Approximation. 1985. text ed. 24.95 (ISBN 0-8176-3147-X). Birkhauser.

Gaier, Dieter. Vovlesungen Veber Approximation Im Komplexen. (Ger.). 150p. 1980. pap. 19.95x (ISBN 0-8176-1161-4). Birkhauser.

Glashoff, K. & Gustafson, S. A. Linear Optimization & Approximation: An Introduction to the Theoretical Analysis & Numerical Treatment of Semi-Infinite Programs. (Applied Mathematical Science Ser.: Vol. 45). (Illus.). 197p. 1983. pap. 21.50 (ISBN 0-387-90857-9). Springer-Verlag.

Graves-Morris, P. R. Pade Approximants & Their Applications. 1973. 56.50 (ISBN 0-12-295950-7). Acad Pr.

Graves-Morris, P. R., ed. Pade Approximants. (Illus.). 1973. pap. 24.75 (ISBN 0-9960018-4-0, Pub. by A Hilger England). Heyden.

Graves-Morris, P. R., et al, eds. Rational Approximation & Interpolation, Vol. 1105. (Lecture Notes in Mathematics Ser.). xii, 528p. 1984. pap. 28.00 (ISBN 0-387-13899-4). Springer-Verlag.

Groetsch, C. W. Generalized Inverses of Linear Operators: Representation & Approximation. (Pure & Applied Math Ser.: Vol. 37). 1977. 39.75 (ISBN 0-8247-6615-6). Dekker.

Handscomb, D. C., ed. Multivariate Approximation. 1979. 50.00 (ISBN 0-12-323350-X). Acad Pr.

Hastings, Cecil. Approximations for Digital Computers. (Rand Corporation Research Studies). 1955. 30.00x (ISBN 0-691-07914-5). Princeton U Pr.

Ivanov, V. V. The Theory of Approximate Methods & Their Application to the Numerical Solution of Singular Integral Equations, No. 2. (Mechanics Analysis Ser.). 348p. 1976. 40.00x (ISBN 90-286-0036-1). Sijthoff & Noordhoff.

Jackson, Dunham. Theory of Approximation. LC 30-32147. (Colloquium Pbns. Ser.: Vol. 11). 178p. 1982. Repr. of 1930 ed. 27.00 (ISBN 0-8218-1011-1, COLL-11). Am Math.

Krabs, W. Optimization & Approximation. LC 78-10448. 220p. 1979. 54.95x (ISBN 0-471-99741-2, Pub. by Wiley-Interscience). Wiley.

Kushner, H. Probability Methods for Approximations in Stochastic Control & for Elliptic Equations. (Math in Science & Engineering Ser.). 1977. 55.00 (ISBN 0-12-430140-1). Acad Pr.

Kushner, Harold. Approximization & Weak Convergence Methods for Random Processes with Application to Stochastic Systems Theory. (Signal Processing, Optimization & Control Ser.). (Illus.). 361p. 1984. text ed. 40.00x (ISBN 0-262-11090-3). MIT Pr.

Langer, Rudolph E., ed. On Numerical Approximation: Proceedings of a Symposium Conducted by the Mathematics Research Center, United States Army, at the University of Wisconsin, Madison, April 21-23 1958. LC 59-9018. (Army. Mathematics Research Center Ser.: No. 1). pap. 118.50 (ISBN 0-317-09181-6, 2021136). Bks Demand UMI.

Law, Alan G. & Sahney, Badri N., eds. Theory of Approximation: With Applications. 1976. 55.00 (ISBN 0-12-438950-3). Acad Pr.

Lorentz, G. G., ed. Approximation Theory. 1973. 65.00 (ISBN 0-12-455750-3). Acad Pr.

Lorentz, George G. Approximation of Functions. 2nd ed. ix, 184p. 1985. text ed. 14.95 (ISBN 0-8284-0322-8, 322). Chelsea Pub.

Luke, Yudell L. Special Functions & Their Approximations, 2 Vols. LC 68-23498. (Mathematics in Science & Engineering Ser.,: Vol. 53). 1969. Vol. 1. 70.00 (ISBN 0-12-459901-X); Vol. 2. 80.00 (ISBN 0-12-459902-8). Acad Pr.

Machade, S., ed. Functional Analysis, Holomorphy, & Approximation Theory: Proceedings. (Lecture Notes in Mathematics Ser.: Vol. 843). 636p. 1981. pap. 38.00 (ISBN 0-387-10560-3). Springer-Verlag.

Mathematical Institute of the Polish Academy of Sciences & Institute of Mathematics of the Adam Mickiewicz University, Poznan, Aug. 22-26, 1972. Approximation Theory: Proceedings. Ciesielski, Z. & Musielak, J., eds. LC 74-80524. 289p. 1975. 47.50 (ISBN 90-277-0483-X, Pub. by Reidel Holland). Kluwer Academic.

Meinardus, Guenter. Approximation of Functions: Theory & Numerical Methods. Schumaker, L. L., tr. LC 67-21464. (Springer Tracts in Natural Philosophy: Vol. 13). (Illus.). 1967. 41.30 (ISBN 0-387-03985-6). Springer-Verlag.

Michelli, Charles A. & Rivlin, Theodore J., eds. Optimal Estimation in Approximation Theory. LC 77-4329. (IBM Research Symposia Ser.). (Illus.). 300p. 1977. 49.50x (ISBN 0-306-31049-X, Plenum Pr). Plenum Pub.

Migdal, Arkadii B. & Krainov, Vladimir P. Approximation Methods of Quantum Mechanics. Schensted, Irene V., tr. 150p. 1968. 6.00 (ISBN 0-911014-06-3). Neo Pr.

Mikhlin, S. G. Approximation on a Rectangular Grid: With Application to Finite Element Methods & Other Problems, No. 4. (Mechanics Analysis Ser.). 235p. 1979. 35.00x (ISBN 90-286-0008-6). Sijthoff & Noordhoff.

Mitrinovic, D. S. & Vasic, P. M. Analytic Inequalities. LC 76-116492. (Grundlehren der Mathematischen Wissenschaften: Vol. 165). (Illus.). 1970. 47.00 (ISBN 0-387-04837-5). Springer-Verlag.

Mordell, L. J. Diophantine Equations. (Pure & Applied Mathematics Ser: Vol. 30). 1969. 59.50 (ISBN 0-12-506250-8). Acad Pr.

Murray, J. D. Asymptotic Analysis. (Applied Mathematical Sciences Ser.: Vol. 48). (Illus.). 160p. 1984. 22.00 (ISBN 0-387-90937-0). Springer-Verlag.

Nachbin, Leopoldo. Elements of Approximation Theory. LC 76-48. 132p. 1976. Repr. of 1967 ed. 11.50 (ISBN 0-88275-388-6). Krieger.

Newman, D. J. Approximation with Rational Functions. LC 79-14971. (CBMS Regional Conference Ser. in Mathematics: Vol. 41). 1982. pap. 12.00 (ISBN 0-8218-1691-8). Am Math.

Nonweiler, Terence R. Computational Mathematics: An Introduction to Numerical Approximation. LC 83-12224. (Mathematics & It's Applications, Ellis Horwood Ser.: I-176). 470p. 1984. 59.95x (ISBN 0-470-27472-7). Halsted Pr.

Oden, J. T. & Reddy, J. N. An Introduction to the Mathematical Theory of Finite Elements. LC 76-6953. (Pure & Applied Mathematics Ser.). 429p. 1976. 50.95x (ISBN 0-471-65261-X, Pub. by Wiley-Interscience). Wiley.

Pinkus, A. N-Widths in Approximation Theory. (Ergebnisse der Mathematik und ihrer Grenzgebiete, 3 Folge, A Series of Modern Surveys in Mathematics: Vol. 7). 300p. 1985. 39.00 (ISBN 0-387-13638-X). Springer-Verlag.

Powell, M. J. Approximation Theory & Methods. (Illus.). 300p. 1981. 70.00 (ISBN 0-521-22472-1); pap. 27.95 (ISBN 0-521-29514-9). Cambridge U Pr.

Prolla, J. B. Approximation Theory & Functional Analysis. (Mathematical Studies: Vol. 35). 450p. (Proceedings). 1979. 70.25 (ISBN 0-444-85264-6, North-Holland). Elsevier.

Saff, E. B. & Varga, R. S., eds. Pade & Rational Approximation: Theory & Applications. 1977. 47.50 (ISBN 0-12-614150-9). Acad Pr.

Sahney, Badri N., ed. Polynomial & Spline Approximation. (NATO Advanced Study Institutes Ser.: No. C-49). 1979. lib. bdg. 37.00 (ISBN 90-277-0984-X, Pub. by Reidel Holland). Kluwer Academic.

Sard, Arthur. Linear Approximation. LC 63-11988. (Mathematical Surveys Ser.: No. 9). 544p. 1982. pap. 50.00 (ISBN 0-8218-1509-1, SURV-9). Am Math.

Schaback, R., et al, eds. Approximation Theory, Bonn 1976: Proceedings of an International Colloquium Held at Bonn, Germany, June 8-11, 1976. (Lecture Notes in Mathematics Ser.: Vol. 556). (Eng., Ger. & Fr.). 1976. pap. 23.00 (ISBN 0-387-08001-5). Springer-Verlag.

Schempp, W. & Zeller, K., eds. Multivariate Approximation Theory. (Internationale Schriftenreihe zur Numerischen Mathematik: No. 51). (Illus.). 455p. 1979. pap. text ed. 43.95x (ISBN 0-8176-1102-9). Birkhauser.

Schmidt, W. M. Diophantine Approximation. (Lecture Notes in Mathematics: Vol. 785). 299p. 1980. pap. 23.00 (ISBN 0-387-09762-7). Springer-Verlag.

Schoenberg, I. J., ed. Approximations with Special Emphasis on Spline Functions: Proceedings. 1969. 24.00 (ISBN 0-12-628850-X). Acad Pr.

Sewell, Walter E. Degree of Approximation by Polynomials in the Complex Domain. (Annals of Mathematic Studies: No. 9). 1942. 18.00 (ISBN 0-527-02725-1). Kraus Repr.

Shapiro, H. S. Topics in Approximation Theory. LC 73-151323. (Lecture Notes in Mathematics: Vol. 187). 1971. pap. 14.00 (ISBN 0-387-05376-X). Springer-Verlag.

Singer, I. Best Approximation in Normed Linear Spaces by Elements of Linear Subspaces. LC 73-110407. (Grundlehren der Mathematischen Wissenschaften: Vol. 171). 1970. 46.00 (ISBN 0-387-05116-3). Springer-Verlag.

Steckin, S. B. Approximation of Functions by Polynomials & Splines. LC 81-2805. (Proceedings of the Steklor Institute of Mathematics: No. 145). 270p. 1981. pap. 92.00 (ISBN 0-8218-3049-X). Am Math.

Steckin, S. B., ed. Approximations of Functions & Operators. LC 77-8940. (Steklov Institute of Mathematics, Proceedings: No. 138). 1977. 48.00 (ISBN 0-8218-3038-4, STEKLO 138). Am Math.

Steklov Institute of Mathematics. Approximation of Periodic Functions: Proceedings. Steckin, S. B., ed. LC 74-11473. (Proceedings of the Steklov Institute of Mathematics: No. 109). 1974. 42.00 (ISBN 0-8218-3009-0, STEKLO-109). Am Math.

--Selected Problems of Weighted Approximation & Spectral Analysis: Proceedings. Nikolskii, N. K., ed. LC 76-46375. (Proceeding of the Steklov Institute of Mathematics: No. 120). 1976. 67.00 (ISBN 0-8218-3020-1, STEKLO-120). Am Math.

Steklov Institute of Mathematics, Academy of Sciences, U S S R, No. 88. Approximation of Functions in the Mean: Proceedings. Steckin, S. B., ed. (Proceedings of the Steklor Institute of Mathematics: No. 88). 1969. 42.00 (ISBN 0-8218-1888-0, STEKLO-88). Am Math.

Traub, J. F., et al. Information, Uncertainty, Complexity. 220p. 1983. text ed. 37.95x (ISBN 0-201-07890-2). Addison-Wesley.

Trebels, W. Multipliers for (C, Alpha) - Bounded Fourier Expansions in Banach Spaces & Approximation Theory. (Lecture Notes in Mathematics: Vol. 329). vii, 103p. 1973. pap. 13.00 (ISBN 0-387-06357-9). Springer-Verlag.

Vilenkin, N. A. Method of Successive Approximations. 110p. 1979. pap. 2.95 (ISBN 0-8285-1532-8, Pub. by Mir Pubs USSR). Imported Pubns.

Watson, G. A. Approximation Theory & Numerical Methods. LC 79-42725. 229p. 1980. 34.95 (ISBN 0-471-27706-1, Pub. by Wiley-Interscience). Wiley.

Werner, H. & Buenger, H. J., eds. Pade Approximations & Its Applications: Bad Honnef 1983. (Lecture Notes in Mathematics: Vol. 1071). (Fr. & Eng.). vi, 264p. 1984. pap. 16.00 (ISBN 0-387-13364-X). Springer-Verlag.

Zalcman, L. Analytic Capacity & Rational Approximation. LC 68-19414. (Lecture Notes in Mathematics: Vol. 50). (Orig.). 1968. pap. 10.70 (ISBN 0-387-04220-2). Springer-Verlag.

Zienkiewicz, O. C. Finite Elements & Approximations. LC 82-16051. 328p. 1983. 39.95x (ISBN 0-471-98240-7, Pub. by Wiley-Interscience). Wiley.

APT (COMPUTER PROGRAM LANGUAGE)

Childs, James J. Numerical Control Part Programming. LC 73-9766. (Illus.). 340p. 1973. 24.95 (ISBN 0-8311-1099-6). Indus Pr.

AQUACULTURE

see also Fish-Culture

Allen, P. G., et al. Bioeconomics of Aquaculture. (Developments in Aquaculture & Fisheries Science Ser.: Vol. 13). 1984. 75.00 (ISBN 0-444-42301-X, I-102-84). Elsevier.

Aquaculture Economics Research in Asia: Proceedings of a Workshop Held in Singapore, 2-5 June 1981. 152p. 1982. pap. 15.00 (ISBN 0-88936-330-7, IDRC193, IDRC). Unipub.

Aquaculture in Alaska: A Resource Potential. write for info. (ISBN 0-914500-03-1). U of AK Inst Marine.

Aquaculture in Canada: The Practice & the Promise. (Fisheries Research Board of Canada Reports: No. 188). 1978. pap. 8.00 (ISBN 0-685-87429-X, SSC84, SSC). Unipub.

Assessment of the Effects of Pollution on Fisheries & Aquaculture in Japan. (Fisheries Technical Papers: No. 163). 114p. 1976. pap. 8.00 (F895, FAO). Unipub.

Board on Renewable Resources. Aquaculture in the United States: Constraints & Opportunities. 123p. 1978. pap. 8.95 (ISBN 0-309-02740-3). Natl Acad Pr.

Busch, Lawerence & Lacy, William B. Science, Agriculture, & Government: The Politics of Research. LC 82-15923. (WVSS in Agriculture Aquaculture Science & Policy Ser.). (Illus.). 325p. (Orig.). 1982. lib. bdg. 32.00x (ISBN 0-86531-225-7); pap. text ed. 13.50x (ISBN 0-86531-230-3). Westview.

Chaston, Ian. Business Management in Fisheries & Aquaculture. (Illus.). 128p. 1985. pap. 18.00 (ISBN 0-85238-132-8, FN109, FNB). Unipub.

Chen, T. P. Aquaculture Practices in Taiwan. (Illus.). 176p. 21.50 (ISBN 0-85238-080-1, FN2, FNB). Unipub.

Chonchuenchob, Pradit, et al. Hanging Culture of the Green Mussel in Thailand (Mytilus Smaragdinus Chemnitz) (Illus.). 1983. pap. 2.00 (ISBN 0-89955-383-4, Pub. by ICLARM Philippines). Intl Spec Bk.

Coche, Andre, ed. Aquaculture in Marine Waters: A List of Reference Books, 1962-1982. (Fisheries Circulars: No. 723, Rev. 1). 18p. 1982. pap. 7.50 (F2358, FAO). Unipub.

Coche, Andre G., ed. Coastal Aquaculture: Development Perspectives in Africa & Case Studies from Other Regions. (Commission for Inland Fisheries of Africa (CIFA): Technical Papers: No. 9). (Eng. & Fr.). 264p. 1983. pap. text ed. 19.00 (ISBN 92-5-001300-0, F2422, FAO). Unipub.

--A List of FAO Publications Related to Aquaculture: 1966-1982. (Fisheries Circulars: No. 744). 21p. 1982. pap. 7.50 (F2359, FAO). Unipub.

Colwell, Rita R. & Pariser, E. Ray, eds. Biotechnology in the Marine Sciences: Proceedings of the First Annual MIT Sea Grant Lecture & Seminar. 1984. text ed. 37.50 (ISBN 0-471-88276-3, Pub. by Wiley-Interscience). Wiley.

Edwards, P. Food Potential of Aquatic Macrophytes. (Illus.). 51p. 1983. pap. text ed. 7.00 (ISBN 0-89955-382-6, Pub. by ICLARM Philippines). Intl Spec Bk.

Falkowski, Paul G., ed. Primary Productivity in the Sea. LC 80-24664. (Environmental Science Research Ser.: Vol. 19). 542p. 1980. 67.50 (ISBN 0-306-40623-3, Plenum Pr). Plenum Pub.

FAO. Advances in Aquaculture. 1978. 150.00 (ISBN 0-685-63391-8). State Mutual Bk.

Fishelson, Lev. Tilapia in Aquaculture. (Illus.). 600p. pap. 69.00 (ISBN 0-86689-018-1). Balaban Intl Sci Serv.

Freshwater Aquaculture Development in China: Report of the FAO/UNDP Study Tour Organized for French-speaking African Countries April-May 1980. (Fisheries Technical Papers: No. 215). (Eng. & Fr.). 137p. 1983. pap. 5.50 (ISBN 92-5-101113-3, FAO). Unipub.

Hambly, Barbara. The Walls of Air. 320p. (Orig.). 1983. pap. 2.95 (ISBN 0-345-29670-2, Del Rey). Ballantine.

Huner, Jay V. & Brown, E. Evan. Crustacean & Mollusk Aquaculture in the United States. (Illus.). 1985. text ed. 59.00 (ISBN 0-87055-468-9). AVI.

Limburg, Peter R. Farming the Waters. LC 80-23362. (Illus.). 256p. 1981. 10.95 (ISBN 0-8253-0009-6). Beaufort Bks NY.

Marine Aquaculture Association & Northeast Regional Coastal Information Center. Directory of Aquaculturists in the Northeast. 56p. 1980. pap. 1.00 (ISBN 0-938412-22-1, P856). URI MAS.

Morse, D. E., et al, eds. Recent Innovations in Cultivation of Pacific Molluscs: Proceedings of an International Symposium of the California Sea Grant College Program & the Pacific Sea Grant College Programs in Alaska, Hawaii, Oregon & Washington, at La Jolla, CA, 1-3 Dec., 1982. (Developments in Aquaculture & Fisheries Science Ser.: Vol. 14). 420p. 1984. 85.25 (ISBN 0-444-42350-8). Elsevier.

Muir, James F. & Roberts, Ronald J., eds. Recent Advances in Aquaculture. 320p. 1980. 50.00x (ISBN 0-686-69936-X, Pub. by Croom Helm England). State Mutual Bk.

--Recent Advances in Aquaculture. 450p. 1982. lib. bdg. 52.50x (ISBN 0-86531-464-0). Westview.

--Recent Advances in Aquaculture, Vol. 2. LC 82-50692. 288p. 1985. 42.50 (ISBN 0-8133-0221-8). Westview.

Nash, Colin E. & Shahadeh, Ziad H., eds. Review of Breeding & Propagation Techniques for Grey Mullet Mugil Cephalus L. (Illus.). 87p. 1983. pap. text ed. 11.50x (ISBN 0-89955-392-3, Pub. by ICLARM Philippines). Intl Spec Bk.

Outline Research Programmes for the Regional Aquaculture Lead Centres in Asia: ADCP-REP, Pts. 1 & 2. 47p. 1980. pap. 7.50 (ISBN 92-5-101020-X, F2141, FAO). Unipub.

Pillay, T. & Dill, W. A., eds. Advances in Aquaculture. (Illus.). 672p. 1979. 175.00 (ISBN 0-85238-092-5, FN080, FNB). Unipub.

Pillay, T. V. Planning of Aquaculture Development. 1978. 40.00 (ISBN 0-685-63447-7). State Mutual Bk.

--Planning of Aquaculture Development: An Introductory Guide. (Illus.). 72p. 1979. pap. 17.50 (ISBN 0-85238-089-5, FN66, FNB). Unipub.

Pond, Wilson G. & Mumpton, Frederick A., eds. Zeo-Agriculture: The Use of Natural Zeolites in Agriculture & Aquaculture. 450p. 1983. lib. bdg. 52.50x (ISBN 0-86531-602-3). Westview.

Pullin, Roger S. & Shehadeh, Ziad H., eds. Integrated Agriculture-Aquaculture Farming Systems. (Illus.). 208p. 1983. pap. text ed. 25.00 (ISBN 0-89955-385-0, Pub. by ICLARM Philippines). Intl Spec Bk.

Report of the Ad Hoc Consultation of Aquaculture Research. (Fisheries Reports: No. 238). 26p. 1980. pap. 7.50 (ISBN 92-5-100949-X, F2038, FAO). Unipub.

Report of the Fifth Session of the Indo-Pacific Fishery Commission Working Party on Aquaculture & Environment. (Fisheries Technical Papers). 16p. 1981. pap. 11.50 (ISBN 92-5-100962-7, FAO). Unipub.

Report of the Indo-Pacific Fishery Commission, Working Party on Aquaculture & Environment: 5th Session, Jakarta, Indonesia, 1980. (Fisheries Reports: No. 241). 12p. 1980. pap. 7.50 (ISBN 92-5-100962-7, F2081, FAO). Unipub.

Report of the Second Session of the Working Party on Aquaculture: Advisory Committee on Marine Resources Research (ACMRR), Rome, March 1983. (Fisheries Reports: No. 287). (Eng., Fr. & Span.). 19p. 1983. pap. text ed. 7.50 (ISBN 92-5-101363-2, F2454, FAO). Unipub.

Report of the Symposium on Aquaculture in Africa: Review & Experience Papers, Accra, Ghana, 30 Sept. - 2 Oct. 1975. (Commission for Inland Fisheries of Africa (CIFA): Technical Papers: No. 4 & Suppl. 1). (Eng. & Fr.). No. 4, 41p. pap. 7.50 (ISBN 92-5-101918-5, F738, FAO); Suppl. 1, 794p. pap. 29.50 (ISBN 92-5-000241-6, F739). Unipub.

Report on the Fourth Session of the Cooperative Programme of Research on Aquaculture of the General Fisheries Council for the Mediterranean. (Fisheries Reports: No. 232). (Eng. & Fr.). 32p. 1981. pap. 7.50 (ISBN 92-5-100927-9, F2068, FAO). Unipub.

Shang, Yung C. Aquaculture Economics: Basic Concepts & Methods of Analysis. (Westview Special Studies in Agricultural Sciences). 140p. 1981. softcover 26.00x (ISBN 0-86531-047-5). Westview.

Sleeter, Thomas D., ed. Assessment of the Potential for Aquaculture in Bermuda. (Special Publication Ser.: No. 27). (Illus.). 189p. (Orig.). 1984. pap. 10.00 (ISBN 0-917642-27-9). Bermuda Bio.

Smith, Leah J. & Peterson, Susan, eds. Aquaculture Development in Less Developed Countries: Social, Economic, & Political Problems. (Special Studies in Agricultural-Aquaculture Sci.). 175p. 1981. 26.00x (ISBN 0-86531-235-4). Westview.

Utilization of Heated Effluents & Recirculation Systems for Intensive Aquaculture. (European Inland Fisheries Advisory Commission (EIFAC): Technical Papers: No. 39). (Eng. & Fr.). 37p. 1981. pap. 7.50 (ISBN 92-5-101059-5, F2184, FAO). Unipub.

Watson, A. Shaw. Aquaculture & Algae Culture-Processes & Products. LC 79-17067. (Food Technology Review: No. 53). (Illus.). 310p. 1980. 32.00 (ISBN 0-8155-0779-8). Noyes.

Wheaton, Frederick W. Aquacultural Engineering. LC 84-21820. 728p. 1985. Repr. of 1977 ed. lib. bdg. 59.50 (ISBN 0-89874-788-0). Krieger.

Wilkins, N. P. & Gosling, E. M., eds. Genetics in Aquaculture. (Developments in Aquaculture & Fisheries Science Ser.: Vol. 12). 436p. 1983. 91.50 (ISBN 0-444-42209-9). Elsevier.

AQUARIUM PLANTS

Brunner, Gerhard. Aquarium Plants. Vevers, Gwynne, tr. from Ger. 1973. 19.95 (ISBN 0-87666-455-9, H-966). TFH Pubns.

De Thabrew. Popular Tropical Aquarium Plants. 1981. 30.00x (ISBN 0-686-98215-0, Pub. by Thornhill Pr England). State Mutual Bk.

Jacobsen, Niels. Aquarium Plants in Color. 1979. 9.95 (ISBN 0-7137-0865-4, Pub. by Blandford Pr England). Sterling.

Schoitz & Dahlstrom. Collins Guide to Aquarium Fishes & Plants. 29.95 (ISBN 0-00-219165-2, Collins Pub England). Greene.

AQUARIUMS

see also Fish-Culture; Goldfish; Marine Aquariums; Tropical Fish

Alderton, David. Caring for Aquarium Fish. LC 83-62525. (Illus.). 112p. 1984. pap. 8.95 (ISBN 0-399-51017-6, G&D). Putnam Pub Group.

Axelrod, Herbert R. Breeding Aquarium Fishes, Bk.6. (Illus.). 288p. 1980. 16.95 (ISBN 0-87666-536-9, H-995). TFH Pubns.

Axelrod, Herbert R. & Vorderwinkler, W. Encyclopedia of Tropical Fish. new ed. 1975. 14.95 (ISBN 0-87666-158-4, H-905). TFH Pubns.

Axelrod, Herbert R., et al. Exotic Tropical Fishes. 19.95 (ISBN 0-87666-051-0, H-907); looseleaf 29.95 (ISBN 0-87666-052-9, H-907L). TFH Pubns.

--Dr. Axelrod's Atlas of Freshwater Aquarium Fishes. (Illus.). 780p. 1985. text ed. 49.95 (ISBN 0-86622-052-6, H-1077). TFH Pubns.

Bardach, John E., et al. Aquaculture: The Farming & Husbandry of Freshwater & Marine Organisms. LC 72-2516. 868p. 1972. pap. 34.95x (ISBN 0-471-04826-7, Pub. by Wiley-Interscience). Wiley.

Boardman, Edward T. Guide to Higher Aquarium Animals. (Bulletin Ser.: No. 21). (Illus.). 107p. 1944. 2.00x (ISBN 0-87737-006-0). Cranbrook.

Dawes, John. The Freshwater Aquarium Questions & Answers. 128p. 1984. 29.00x (ISBN 0-947728-00-7, Pub. by R Royce UK). State Mutual Bk.

Deans, Nora L. Aquatic Life in the John G. Shedd Aquarium: A Guide to Exhibit Animals. (Illus.). 272p. (Orig.). 1983. pap. 6.95 guidebook (ISBN 0-9611074-0-5). Shedd Aquarium.

Friese, U. Erich. Aquarium Fish. (Illus.). 96p. 1980. 4.95 (ISBN 0-87666-512-1, KW-026). TFH Pubns.

Gos, Michael W. Brackish Aquariums. (Illus.). 1979. 4.95 (ISBN 0-87666-519-9, KW-046). TFH Pubns.

Hawkins, A. D., ed. Aquarium Systems. LC 81-66388. 1981. 67.00 (ISBN 0-12-333380-6). Acad Pr.

Innes, William T. Innes Exotic Aquarium Fish. 6.95 (ISBN 0-87666-090-1, PS642). TFH Pubns.

Institute of Laboratory Animal Resources. Research in Zoos & Aquariums. 1975. pap. 11.50 (ISBN 0-309-02319-X). Natl Acad Pr.

Kubler, Rolf. Light in the Aquarium. Ahrens, Christa, tr. from Ger. 1973. pap. 4.95 (ISBN 0-87666-096-0, PS-301). TFH Pubns.

Lewis, William M. Maintaining Fishes for Experimental & Instructional Purposes. LC 62-15001. 109p. 1963. 5.95x (ISBN 0-8093-0077-X); pap. 3.95 (ISBN 0-8093-0078-8). S Ill U Pr.

Mann, Lucile Q. Tropical Fish. rev. ed. LC 74-32560. (Illus.). 132p. (Orig.). 1974. pap. 2.25 (ISBN 0-668-03257-X). Arco.

Mayland, Hans J. The Complete Home Aquarium. LC 76-20307. (Illus.). 1981. pap. 10.95 (ISBN 0-399-50971-2, G&D). Putnam Pub Group.

Mills, Dick. Aquarium Fishes. LC 80-80742. (Arco Fact Guides in Color Ser.). (Illus.). 128p. 1980. 7.95 (ISBN 0-668-04944-8, 4944-8). Arco.

Neugebauer, Wilbert. Marine Aquarium Fish Identifier. LC 74-82341. (Illus.). 256p. 1982. pap. 6.95 (ISBN 0-8069-7614-4). Sterling.

Paysan, Klaus. Larousse Guide to Aquarium Fishes. LC 81-81045. (Larousse Nature Guide Ser.). (Illus.). 240p. (Orig.). 1981. pap. text ed. 10.95 (ISBN 0-88332-257-9, 8186). Larousse.

Schmitz, Siegfried. Aquarium Fishes. LC 78-32633. (Nature Guides Ser.). (Illus.). 144p. 1979. pap. 4.95 (ISBN 0-7011-2356-7, Pub. by Chatto & Windus). Merrimack Pub Cir.

Schneider, Earl. All about Aquariums. (Illus., Orig.). 6.95 (ISBN 0-87666-768-X, PS-601). TFH Pubns.

Spotte, Stephen. Seawater Aquariums: The Captive Environment. LC 79-11038. 413p. 1979. 37.50 (ISBN 0-471-05665-0, Pub. by Wiley-Interscience). Wiley.

Sterba, Gunther & Mills, Dick. The Aquarium Encyclopedia: Freshwater & Saltwater Fish & Plants. (Illus.). 608p. 1983. 37.50 (ISBN 0-262-19207-1). MIT Pr.

Thomas, George L., Jr. Goldfish Pools, Water Lilies & Tropical Fish. (Illus.). 1965. 19.95 (ISBN 0-87666-080-4, H-919). TFH Pubns.

Torney, John A., Jr. & Clayton, Robert D. Aquatic Organization & Management. 190p. 1981. pap. text ed. 10.95x (ISBN 0-8087-3624-8). Burgess.

Vevers, Gwynne. The Pocket Guide to Aquarium Fishes. 1980. 6.95 (ISBN 0-671-25451-0). S&S.

Videla, E., illus. Your First Aquarium. (Illus.). 32p. 1982. 3.95 (ISBN 0-87666-548-2, ST-001). TFH Pubns.

Weigel, Wilfried. Aquarium Decorating & Planning. Vevers, Gwynne, tr. from Ger. Orig. Title: Das Schmuck-und Schauaquarium. (Illus.). 128p. (Orig.). 1973. 7.95 (ISBN 0-87666-794-9, PS-691). TFH Pubns.

Zoos & Aquariums in the Americas: 1980-81 Directory. 50.00 (ISBN 0-686-16897-6). Am Assoc Z Pk.

AQUATIC ANIMALS

see also Aquatic Mammals; Fishes; Fresh-Water Biology; Fresh-Water Fauna; Marine Fauna

Agricultural Board. Aquatic Animal Health. LC 73-15707. 46p. 1973. pap. 4.50 (ISBN 0-309-02142-1). Natl Acad Pr.

Deans, Nora L. Aquatic Life in the John G. Shedd Aquarium: A Guide to Exhibit Animals. (Illus.). 272p. (Orig.). 1983. pap. 6.95 guidebook (ISBN 0-9611074-0-5). Shedd Aquarium.

Halstead, Bruce W. Atlas of Dangerous Aquatic Animals of the World. LC 84-70417. (Illus.). 400p. 1986. 75.00 (ISBN 0-87850-045-6). Darwin Pr.

--Poisonous & Venomous Marine Animals of the World. 2nd, rev. ed. LC 84-70414. (Illus.). 1500p. 1986. 200.00 (ISBN 0-87850-050-2). Darwin Pr.

Kraybill, H. F., et al, eds. Aquatic Pollutants & Biologic Effects with Emphasis on Neoplasia, Vol. 298. (Annals of the New York Academy of Sciences). 604p. 1977. 54.00x (ISBN 0-89072-044-4). NY Acad Sci.

Malins, Donald C., ed. Effects of Petroleum on Arctic & Subarctic Marine Environments & Organisms: Biological Effects, Vols. 1 &2. 1977. Vol. 1. 39.00 (ISBN 0-12-466901-8); Vol. 2. 37.50 (ISBN 0-12-466902-6). Acad Pr.

Mantai, Kenneth E. A Field Guide to the Aquatic Life of Chautauqua County. (Marhginal Media Bioguide Ser.: No.5). (Illus.). 48p. 1983. pap. 3.00 (ISBN 0-942788-10-9). Marginal Med.

Ostrow, Marshall. Bettas. (Illus.). 96p. 1980. 4.95 (ISBN 0-87666-522-9, KW-052). TFH Pubns.

Pott, Eckart. Rivers & Lakes. (Illus.). 150p. 1981. pap. 5.95 (ISBN 0-7011-2544-6, Pub. by Chatto & Windus). Merrimack Pub Cir.

Preparation of Synopses on the Biology of Species of Living Aquatic Organisms. (Fisheries Synopses: No. 1, Rev. 1). 83p. 1965. pap. 7.50 (ISBN 0-686-92884-9, F1753, FAO). Unipub.

Rhoads, Donald C. & Lutz, Richard A., eds. Skeletal Growth of Aquatic Organisms: Biological Records of Environmental Change. LC 79-25825. (Topics in Geobiology Ser.: Vol. I). (Illus.). 761p. 1980. 75.00x (ISBN 0-306-40259-9, Plenum Pr). Plenum Pub.

U. S. Department of the Interior, Federal Water Pollution Control Administration, Committee on Water Quality Criteria, 1968. Facsimile of Section Three: Fish, Other Aquatic Life, & Wildlife - Report. (Fisheries Technical Papers: No. 94). 113p. 1969. pap. 7.50 (ISBN 0-686-92755-9, F1744, FAO). Unipub.

World List of Aquatic Sciences & Fisheries Serial Titles. (Fisheries Technical Papers: No. 147, Suppl. 3). 158p. 1978. pap. 11.50 (ISBN 92-5-100617-2, F1490, FAO). Unipub.

AQUATIC BIOLOGY

see also Aquatic Ecology

Angel, Heather & Wolseley, Pat. The Water Naturalist. 192p. 1982. 19.95 (ISBN 0-87196-642-5). Facts on File.

Droop, M. R. & Jannasch, H. W., eds. Advances in Aquatic Microbiology, Vol. 3. (Serial Publication). Date not set. price not set (ISBN 0-12-003003-9). Acad Pr.

Eckblad, James W. Laboratory Manual of Aquatic Biology. 210p. 1978. write for info. wire coil (ISBN 0-697-04627-3). Wm C Brown.

Ecological Analysts. The Sources, Chemistry, Fate & Effects of Chromium in Aquatic Environments. LC 82-71261. (Orig.). 1982. pap. 8.10 (ISBN 0-89364-046-8, 847-89600). Am Petroleum.

Fisheries & Aquatic Sciences in Canada: An Overview. (Fisheries Research Board of Canada Reports). 53p. 1979. pap. 4.75 (ISBN 0-660-01195-6, SSC134, SSC). Unipub.

Rheinheimer, G. Aquatic Microbiology. 3rd ed. 29.95 (ISBN 0-471-90657-3). Wiley.

Seki, H., ed. Organic Materials in Aquatic Ecosystems. 208p. 1982. 64.00 (ISBN 0-8493-6446-9). CRC Pr.

World List of Aquatic Sciences & Fisheries Serial Titles. (Fisheries Technical Papers: No. 147, Suppl. 1). 173p. 1976. pap. 12.50 (ISBN 92-5-100124-3, F879, FAO). Unipub.

AQUATIC BIRDS

see Water-Birds

AQUATIC CHEMISTRY

see Water Chemistry

AQUATIC ECOLOGY

see also Fresh-Water Ecology; Marine Ecology

Agrochemical Residue-Biota Interactions in Soil & Aquatic Ecosystems. (Panel Proceedings Ser.). (Illus.). 305p. 1981. pap. 38.50 (ISBN 92-0-111280-7, ISP548, IAEA). Unipub.

Aquatic Environmental Quality: Problems & Proposals. (Fisheries Research Board of Canada Reports). (Illus.). 37p. 1978. pap. 5.50 (ISBN 0-660-00878-5, SSC89, SSC). Unipub.

Aquatic Environmental Quality: Toxicology. (Fisheries Research Board of Canada Reports). 18p. 1978. pap. 5.75 (ISBN 0-660-00879-3, SSC87, SSC). Unipub.

ASTM Committee D-19 on Water. Ecological Assessment of Macrophyton: Collection, Use, & Meaning of Data. Dennis, W. M. & Isom, W. G., eds. LC 83-73513. (Special Technical Publications Ser.: No. 843). (Illus.). 120p. 1984. pap. text ed. 20.00 (ISBN 0-8031-0204-6, 04-843000-16). ASTM.

Barnes, R. S. & Mann, K. H., eds. Fundamentals of Aquatic Ecosystems. (Illus.). 240p. 1980. 16.00x (ISBN 0-632-00014-7). Blackwell Pubns.

Beyer, Jan E. Aquatic Ecosystems: An Operational Research Approach. LC 79-57217. (Illus.). 328p. 1981. 22.50x (ISBN 0-295-95719-0). U of Wash Pr.

Buikema, Arthur L., Jr. & Hendricks, Albert C. Benzene, Xylene, & Toluene in Aquatic Systems: A Review. LC 80-67170. (Illus.). 69p. (Orig.). pap. 3.75 (ISBN 0-89364-038-7, API 847-86250). Am Petroleum.

Emerson & Imbode. Aquatic Dynamics. (Environmental Science & Technology Ser.). 1986. price not set (ISBN 0-471-81272-2). Wiley.

Foerstner, U. & Wittmann, G. T. Metal Pollution in the Aquatic Environment. rev., 2nd ed. (Illus.). 486p. 1981. 56.00 (ISBN 0-387-10724-X). Springer-Verlag.

Hasler, A. D., ed. Coupling of Land & Water Systems. LC 74-8931. (Ecological Studies: Vol. 10). (Illus.). xviii, 336p. 1975. 43.00 (ISBN 0-387-06707-8). Springer-Verlag.

Herdendorf, Charles E., et al. Lake Erie Bibliography in Environmental Sciences. 1974. 4.00 (ISBN 0-86727-068-3). Ohio Bio Survey.

Hickling, C. F. Water As a Productive Environment. LC 75-4394. 200p. 1975. 25.00 (ISBN 0-312-85680-6). St Martin.

Hopkins, Kevin D. The ICLARM-CLSU Integrated Animal-Fish Farming Project: Final Report. Cruz, Emmanuel M., ed. (ICLARM Technical Reports Ser.: No. 5). (Illus.). 96p. (Orig.). 1983. pap. 14.85x (ISBN 0-89955-384-2, Pub. by ICLARM Philippines). Intl Spec Bk.

Husmann, Siegfried, ed. Proceedings of the International Symposium on Groundwater Ecology, 1st, Schlitz, September 1975. 232p. 1976. pap. text ed. 29.95 (ISBN 90-265-0240-0, Pub. by Swets Pub Serv Holland). Swets North Am.

Hynes. The Ecology of Running Waters. 580p. 1982. 60.00x (ISBN 0-85323-100-1, Pub. by Liverpool Univ England). State Mutual Bk.

Jenkins, S. H. Aeration in Aquatic Systems. 1979. 50.00x (ISBN 0-08-023989-7). Pergamon.

Judd, John B. & Taub, Stephen H. The Effects of Ecological Changes on Buckeye Lake, Ohio, with Emphasis on Largemouth Bass & Aquatic Vascular Plants. 1973. 2.00 (ISBN 0-86727-065-9). Ohio Bio Survey.

Khan, Mohammad A., ed. Pesticides in Aquatic Environments. LC 77-5380. (Environmental Science Research Ser.: Vol. 10). 271p. 1977. 37.50x (ISBN 0-306-36310-0, Plenum Pr). Plenum Pub.

Langford, T. E. Electricity Generation & the Ecology of Natural Waters. 376p. 1982. 90.00x (ISBN 0-85323-334-9, Pub. by Liverpool Univ England). State Mutual Bk.

Lockwood, A. P., ed. Effects of Pollutants on Aquatic Organisms. LC 75-32448. (Society for Experimental Biology Seminar Ser.: No. 2). 180p. 1976. pap. 17.95x (ISBN 0-521-29044-9). Cambridge U Pr.

Meyers, Dewey G. & Strickler, Rudi J., eds. Trophic Interactions within Aquatic Ecosystems. (AAAS Selected Symposium Ser.: No. 85). 500p. 1984. lib. bdg. 43.50x (ISBN 0-8133-0015-0). Westview.

Native Aquatic Bacteria: Enumeration, Activity & Ecology, STP 695. 219p. 1979. 25.00x (ISBN 0-8031-0526-6, 4-695000-16). ASTM.

Panayotou, Theodore, et al. The Economics of Catfish Farming in Central Thailand. (ICLARM Technical Reports: No. 4). (Illus.). 60p. (Orig.). 1983. pap. 10.00x (ISBN 0-89955-379-6, Pub. by ICLARM Philippines). Intl Spec Bk.

Pauly, Daniel & Wade-Pauly, Sandra. An Annotated Bibliography of Slipmouths: Pisces: Leiognathidae. (ICLARM Bibliographies: No. 2). 62p. (Orig.). 1983. pap. 7.00x (ISBN 0-89955-374-5, Pub. by ICLARM Philipines). Intl Spec Bk.

Pullin, R. S. & Lowe-McConnell, R. H., eds. The Biology & Culture of Tilapias. (ICLARM Conference Proceedings: No. 7). 432p. 1982. 29.50x (ISBN 971-04-0003-7, Pub. by ICLARM Philippines); pap. 25.00x (ISBN 971-04-0004-5, Pub. by ICLARM Philippines). Intl Spec Bk.

Report of the FAO Technical Conference on Aquaculture: Kyoto, Japan, 26 May - 2 June 1976. (Fisheries Reports: No. 188). (Eng., Fr. & Span.). 96p. 1976. pap. 7.50 (ISBN 92-5-100244-4, F836, FAO). Unipub.

Report of the Indo-Pacific Fishery Commission, Working Party on Aquaculture & Environment: 5th Session, Jakarta, Indonesia, 1980. (Fisheries Reports: No. 241). 12p. 1980. pap. 7.50 (ISBN 92-5-100962-7, F2081, FAO). Unipub.

Schoenen, Peter. Bibliography of Important Tilapiasas for Aquaculture: (Pisces: Cichlidae) (ICLARM Bibliographies Ser.: No. 3). 336p. (Orig.). 1983. pap. 25.00x (ISBN 0-89955-376-1, Pub. by ICLARM Philippines). Intl Spec Bk.

Seki, H., ed. Organic Materials in Aquatic Ecosystems. 208p. 1982. 64.00 (ISBN 0-8493-6446-9). CRC Pr.

Symoens, J. J. & Burgis, Mary. The Ecology & Utilization of African Inland Waters. (Reports & Proceedings Ser.: Vol. 1). 191p. 1982. pap. 20.00 (ISBN 92-807-1039-7, UNEP055, UNEP). Unipub.

Symposium on Aquaculture in Latin America: Proceedings, 1972. (Fisheries Reports: No. 159, Annex F, Revision 1). 44p. 1977. pap. 7.50 (ISBN 92-5-100214-2, F802, FAO). Unipub.

Wilber, Charles G. Turbidity in the Aquatic Environment: An Environmental Factor in Fresh & Oceanic Waters. (Illus.). 144p. 1983. 18.75x (ISBN 0-398-04726-X). C C Thomas.

AQUATIC FAUNA

see Aquatic Animals

AQUATIC FLORA

see Aquatic Plants

AQUATIC INSECTS

see Insects, Aquatic

AQUATIC MAMMALS

Howell, A. Brazier. Aquatic Mammals: Their Adaptations to Life in the Water. (Illus.). 332p. 1930. 32.50x (ISBN 0-398-04290-X). C C Thomas.

AQUATIC PLANTS

see also Fresh-Water Flora; Marine Flora

Anderson, J. R. Sprig of Sea Lavender. 1980. pap. 2.25 (ISBN 0-440-18321-9). Dell.

Aquatic Vegetation & Its Use & Control. 135p. 1982. pap. 10.00 (ISBN 92-3-101082-4, U1212, UNESCO). Unipub.

ASTM Committee D-19 on Water. Ecological Assessment of Macrophyton: Collection, Use, & Meaning of Data. Dennis, W. M. & Isom, W. G., eds. LC 83-73513. (Special Technical Publications Ser.: No. 843). (Illus.). 120p. 1984. pap. text ed. 20.00 (ISBN 0-8031-0204-6, 04-843000-16). ASTM.

Business Communications Staff. Aquaculture: Food from the Sea & Waterways. rev. ed. 192p. 1982. 975.00 (ISBN 0-89336-130-5, GA-014). BCC.

Cook, C. D. Water Plants of the World. (Illus.). 1974. 125.00 (ISBN 9-0619-3024-3). Heinman.

Correll, Donovan S. & Correll, Helen B. Aquatic & Wetland Plants of Southwestern United States, 2 vols. LC 74-82776. (Illus.). 1808p. 1972. Set. 95.00x (ISBN 0-8047-0866-5). Stanford U Pr.

Drake Del Castillo, E. Illustrationes Florae Insularum Maris Pacifici. 1977. Repr. of 1892 ed. 87.50 (ISBN 3-7682-1130-4). Lubrecht & Cramer.

Ecology of Water Weeds in the Neotropics. LC 72-87508. (Technical Papers in Hydrology: No. 12). 50p. (Orig.). 1972. pap. 5.00 (ISBN 92-3-100961-3, U176, UNESCO). Unipub.

Gangstad, Edward O. Weed Control Methods for Public Health Applications. 320p. 1980. 84.50 (ISBN 0-8493-5326-2). CRC Pr.

Gareth Jones, E. B. Recent Advances in Aquatic Mycology. LC 74-27179. 748p. 1976. 99.95x (ISBN 0-470-29176-1). Halsted Pr.

Gehu, M. J., ed. Colloques Phytosociologiques: Les Vegetations Aquatiques et Amphibiens, Lille, 1981, Vol. X. (Fr., Illus.). 1983. lib. bdg. 52.50x (ISBN 3-7682-1383-8). Lubrecht & Cramer.

Godfrey, Robert K. & Wooten, Jean W. Aquatic & Wetland Plants of Southeastern United States: Dicotyledons. LC 80-16452. (Illus.). 944p. 1981. lib. bdg. 45.00x (ISBN 0-8203-0532-4). U of Ga Pr.

--Aquatic & Wetland Plants of Southeastern United States: Monocotyledons. LC 76-28924. 736p. 1979. 40.00x (ISBN 0-8203-0420-4). U of Ga Pr.

Gupta, O. P. Aquatic Weeds: Their Menace & Control. (Illus.). 272p. 1979. 20.00 (ISBN 0-88065-096-6, Pub. by Messers Today & Tomorrows Printers & Publishers India). Scholarly Pubns.

Imahori, Kozo. Ecology, Phytogeography & Taxonomy of the Japanese Charophyta. (Illus.). 1977. pap. text ed. 38.50x (ISBN 3-87429-126-X). Lubrecht & Cramer.

Kirk, John. Light & Photosynthesis in Aquatic Ecosystems. LC 83-5189. 300p. 1984. 77.50 (ISBN 0-521-24450-1). Cambridge U Pr.

Little, E. C. Handbook of Utilization of Aquatic Plants: A Review of World Literature. (Fisheries Technical Papers: No. 187). 181p. 1979. pap. 13.00 (ISBN 92-5-100825-6, F1863, FAO). Unipub.

Lumpkin, Thomas A. & Plucknett, Donald L. Azolla As An Aquatic Green Manure: Use & Management in Crop Production. (Tropical Agriculture Ser.: No. 15). 1982. softcover 23.50x (ISBN 0-89158-451-X). Westview.

Meriaux, J. Etude Analytique et Comparative de la Vegetation Aquatique D'Etangs et Marais du Nord de la France. (Valle de la Sensee et Bassin Houillier du Nord-Pas-de-Calais) (Offprint from Documents Phytosociolgique Ser.). (Fr.). 1979. pap. 17.50x (ISBN 3-7682-1238-6). Lubrecht & Cramer.

Mitchell, D. S., ed. Aquatic Vegetation & Its Control. (Illus.). 135p. (Orig.). 1974. pap. 7.50 (ISBN 0-686-83001-6, U36, UNESCO). Unipub.

Muhlberg, Helmut. The Complete Guide to Water Plants. Lindsay, Ilse, tr. (Illus.). 392p. 1982. 14.95 (ISBN 0-7158-0789-7, Pub. by EP Publishing England). Sterling.

Pospisilova, J. & Solarova, J., eds. Water in Plants Bibliography, Vol. 9: 1983. 1985. pap. text ed. 46.50 (ISBN 90-6193-520-2, Pub. by Junk Pub Netherlands). Kluwer-Academic.

Pott, Eckart. Rivers & Lakes. (Illus.). 150p. 1981. pap. 5.95 (ISBN 0-7011-2544-6, Pub. by Chatto & Windus). Merrimack Pub Cir.

Prescott, G. W. How to Know the Aquatic Plants. 2nd ed. (Picture Key Nature Ser.). 180p. 1980. write for info. wire coil (ISBN 0-697-04775-X). Wm C Brown.

Raven, John A. Energetics & Transport in Aquatic Plants. LC 84-12525. (MBL Lectures in Biology Ser.: Vol. 4). 576p. 1984. 83.00 (ISBN 0-8451-2203-7). A R Liss.

Swindells, Philip. Waterlilies. (Illus.). 159p. 1983. 17.95 (ISBN 0-917304-52-7). Timber.

Symoens, J. J. & Hooper, S. S. Studies on Aquatic Vascular Plants: Proceedings of the International Colloquium on Aquatic Vascular Plants, Brussels. (Illus.). 424p. 1982. pap. text ed. 35.00x (ISBN 3-87429-202-9). Lubrecht & Cramer.

Winterringer, Glen S. & Lopinot, Alvin C. Aquatic Plants of Illinois. rev. ed. (Popular Science Ser.: Vol. VI). (Illus.). 142p. 1977. pap. 4.00 (ISBN 0-89792-068-6). Ill St Museum.

AQUATIC RESOURCES

see also Algae; Fisheries; Fishery Products; Marine Resources

Adams, V. Dean, ed. Aquatic Resources Management of the Colorado River Ecosystem. Lamarra, Vincent A. LC 82-72349. 400p. 1983. 34.95 (ISBN 0-250-40594-6). Butterworth.

Godfriaux, Bruce L., ed. Power Plant Waste Heat Utilization in Aquaculture. LC 78-73590. 288p. 1979. text ed. 38.00 (ISBN 0-916672-24-7). Allanheld.

Hills, Christopher & Nakamura, Hiroshi. Food from Sunlight. new ed. LC 78-9582. (Illus.). 384p. (Orig.). 1978. pap. 14.95 (ISBN 0-916438-13-9). Univ of Trees.

Lippson, Alice J., ed. & illus. The Chesapeake Bay in Maryland: An Atlas of Natural Resources. LC 72-12352. (Illus.). 64p. 1973. 20.00 (ISBN 0-8018-1467-7); pap. 9.95 (ISBN 0-8018-1468-5). Johns Hopkins.

Stickney, Robert R. Principles of Warmwater Aquaculture. LC 78-25642. 375p. 1979. 37.50x (ISBN 0-471-03388-X, Pub. by Wiley-Interscience). Wiley.

Thorp, James H. & Gibbons, J. Whitfield, eds. Energy & Environmental Stress in Aquatic Systems: Proceedings. LC 78-27913. (DOE Symposium Ser.). 876p. 1978. pap. 30.00 (ISBN 0-87079-115-X, CONF-771114); microfiche 4.50 (ISBN 0-87079-191-5, CONF-771114). DOE.

Toward a Relevant Science: Fisheries & Aquatic Scientific Resource Needs in Canada. (Fisheries Research Board of Canada Reports: No. 14). 29p. 1978. pap. 5.50 (ISBN 0-685-60676-7, SSC103, SSC). Unipub.

Wheaton, Frederick & Lawson, Thomas B. Processing Aquatic Food Products. 528p. 1985. 70.00 (ISBN 0-471-09736-5). Wiley.

World List of Aquatic Sciences & Fisheries Serial Titles. (Fisheries Technical Papers: No. 147, Suppl. 5). 96p. 1981. pap. 7.75 (ISBN 92-5-101129-X, F2263, FAO). Unipub.

AQUEDUCTS

see also names of particular aqueducts

Earth & Traffic Loads on Conduits. 52p. 1967. pap. 3.00 (ISBN 0-89312-064-2, EB063W). Portland Cement.

Jacobsen, Thorkild & Lloyd, Seton. Sennacherib's Aqueduct at Jerwan. LC 66-20583. (Oriental Institute Pubns. Ser.: No. 24). (Illus.). 1935. 20.00x (ISBN 0-226-62120-0, OIP24). U of Chicago Pr.

AQUICULTURE

see Aquaculture

ARAB SCIENCE

see Science, Arab

ARABIAN HORSE

Borden. Arab Horse. 9.50 (ISBN 0-87505-112-X). Borden.

Forbis, Judith. The Classic Arabian Horse. (Illus.). 416p. 1976. 27.50(f) (ISBN 0-87140-612-8). Liveright.

Mulder. Imported Foundation Stock of North American Arabian Horses, Vol. 2. 15.00 (ISBN 0-87505-111-1). Borden.

Reese, Herbert H. Arabian Horse Breeding. 9.50 (ISBN 0-87505-110-3). Borden.

--Kellogg Arabians: Their Background & Influence. 1958. 14.95 (ISBN 0-87505-114-6). Borden.

Summerhays, Reginald S. Arabian Horse. pap. 5.00 (ISBN 0-87980-183-2). Wilshire.

Tweedie, W. The Arabian Horse: His Country & People. (Arab Background Ser.). 1972. 30.00x (ISBN 0-86685-170-4). Intl Bk Ctr.

ARABIC MATHEMATICS

see Mathematics, Arabic

ARACEAE

Knecht, Marianne. Contribution a l'Etude Biosystematique des Representants d'Aracees de la Cote d'Ivoire. (Illus.). 314p. 1983. lib. bdg. 35.00x (ISBN 3-7682-1372-2). Lubrecht & Cramer.

ARACHNIDA

see also Mites; Spiders

Barth, F. G., ed. Neurobiology of Arachnids. (Illus.). 400p. 1985. 69.50 (ISBN 0-387-15303-9). Springer-Verlag.

Gertsch, Willis J. American Spiders. 2nd ed. 320p. 1979. 36.50 (ISBN 0-442-22649-7). Van Nos Reinhold.

The Insects & Arachnids of Canada. Incl. Pt. 1. Collecting, Preparing & Preserving Insects, Mites & Spiders. 182p. 1979. pap. 6.50 (ISBN 0-660-01650-8, SSC118); Pt. 2. Bark Beetles of Canada & Alaska. 241p. 1977. pap. 22.95 (ISBN 0-685-79716-3, SSC52); Pt. 3. The Aradidae of Canada, Hemiptera: Aradidae. (Illus.). 116p. 1979. pap. 7.50 (ISBN 0-660-01428-9, SSC120); Pt. 4. The Anthocoridae of Canada & Alaska. 101p. 1977. pap. 7.50 (ISBN 0-686-93215-3, SSC165); Pt. 5. The Crab Spiders of Canada & Alaska, Araneae: Philodromidae & Thomisidae. 254p. 1980. pap. 14.00 (ISBN 0-660-10104-1, SSC142); Pt. 6. The Mosquitoes of Canada, Diptera: Cilicidae. 390p. 1980; Pt. 8. The Plant Bugs of the Prairie Provinces of Canada, Heteroptera: Miridae. 407p. 1981. pap. 18.50 (ISBN 0-660-10613-2, SSC154); Pt. 10. 1983. pap. 14.75 (SSC174). (Illus., SSC). Unipub.

Nutting, William B., ed. Mammalian Diseases & Arachnids, Vol. I. 288p. 1984. 80.00 (ISBN 0-8493-6562-7). CRC Pr.

--Mammalian Diseases & Arachnids, Vol. II. 304p. 1984. 83.50 (ISBN 0-8493-6563-5). CRC Pr.

Pittard, Kay & Mitchell, Robert W. Comparative Morphology of the Life Stages of Cryptocellus Pelaezi (Arachnida, Ricinulie) (Graduate Studies: No. 1). (Illus.). 77p. (Orig.). 1972. pap. 4.00 (ISBN 0-89672-008-X). Tex Tech Pr.

Savory, Theodore. Evolution in the Arachnida. 48p. 1971. 39.00x (ISBN 0-900541-04-0, Pub. by Meadowfield Pr England). State Mutual Bk.

--Introduction to Arachnology. (Illus.). 111p. 1975. 11.50x (ISBN 0-8448-0407-X). Crane-Russak Co.

Snow, Keith R. Arachnids. LC 70-109151. 1970. 21.00x (ISBN 0-231-03419-9). Columbia U Pr.

Walker, Mary E. A Revision of the Order Phalangida of Ohio. 1928. 1.00 (ISBN 0-86727-018-7). Ohio Bio Survey.

ARANEIDA

see Spiders

ARBORICULTURE

see Forests and Forestry; Fruit-Culture; Nurseries (Horticulture); Tree Breeding; Trees

ARC, ELECTRIC

see Electric Arc

ARC WELDING

see Electric Welding

ARCH

see Arches

ARCHAEAN PERIOD

see Geology, Stratigraphic–Archaean

ARCHAEOLOGISTS

Phillips, P., ed. The Archaeologist & the Laboratory. (CBA Research Reports: No. 58). (Illus.). 78p. 1985. pap. text ed. 31.00x (ISBN 0-906780-45-4, Pub. by Coun Brit Archaeology). Humanities.

ARCHAEOLOGY

see also Excavations (Archaeology); Iron Age; Pottery; Stone Implements; Underwater Archaeology

also subdivision Antiquities under names of countries, regions, cities, etc., e.g. Crete–Antiquities

Addyman, Peter & Morris, Richard, eds. The Archaeological Study of Churches. LC 77-365546. (Council for British Archaeology Research Report Ser.: No. 13). (Illus.). pap. 24.00 (ISBN 0-317-09531-5, 2014021). Bks Demand UMI.

Astrom, P., et al. Hala Sultan Tekke: Excavations 1971-79. (Studies in Mediterranean Archaeology: Vol. 8). 253p. 1983. pap. text ed. 69.50x (ISBN 91-86098-04-7, Pub. by Paul Astroms Sweden). Humanities.

Baez-Camargo, Gonzalo. Archaeological Commentary on the Bible: From Genesis to Revelation. LC 82-45473. (Illus.). 336p. 1984. 17.95 (ISBN 0-385-17968-5). Doubleday.

Bareis, Charles J. & Porter, James W., eds. American Bottom Archaeology: A Summary of the FAI-270 Project Contribution to the Culture History of the Mississippi River Valley. LC 83-15366. (Illus.). 304p. 1984. 22.50x (ISBN 0-252-01111-2). U of Ill Pr.

Bearden, Susan E. A Study of Basketmaker II Settlement on Northern Black Mesa, Arizona: Excavations 1973-1979. LC 84-72847. (Center for Archaeological Investigations Research Paper: No. 44). (Illus.). xv, 198p. 1984. pap. 8.00 (ISBN 0-88104-021-5). Center Archaeo.

Bender, Marilyn & Webb, Paul. Archaeological Investigations at the Roos Site, St. Clair County Illinois. new ed. Jeffries, Richard W., ed. (Research Paper Ser.: No. 43). (Illus.). 59p. 1984. pap. 1.25 (ISBN 0-88104-015-0). Center Archaeo.

Broderick, M. & Morton, A. A. Concise Dictionary of Egyptian Archaeology. 1985. pap. 7.50 (ISBN 0-89005-303-0). Ares.

Brown, Ian W. Natchez Indian Archaeology: Culture Change & Stability in the Lower Mississippi Valley. (Mississippi Department of Archives & History Archaeological Report Ser.: No. 15). (Illus.). xiv, 304p. (Orig.). 1984. pap. write for info (ISBN 0-938896-42-3). Mississippi De.

Buccellati, G. & Rouault, O. Tergra Preliminary Report, No. 12: Digital Plotting of Archaeological Floor Plans. (Computer Aided Research in Near Eastern Studies: Vol. 1, Issue 1). 40p. 1983. pap. text ed. 6.50x (ISBN 0-89003-146-0). Undena Pubns.

Burleigh, R. Carbon-Fourteen Dating. LC 74-183462. (International Monographs on Science in Archaeology). Date not set. price not set (ISBN 0-12-785082-1). Acad Pr.

Carter, Giles F., ed. Archaeological Chemistry, Vol. II. LC 78-26128. (Advances in Chemistry Ser.: No. 171). 1978. 54.95 (ISBN 0-8412-0397-0). Am Chemical.

Charles-Picard, Gilbert, ed. Larousse Encyclopedia of Archaeology. Ward, Anne, tr. LC 83-80485. (Illus.). 432p. 1983. 24.95 (ISBN 0-88332-316-8, 8052). Larousse.

Coles, John. Archaeology of the Wetlands. 120p. 1984. pap. 10.00x (ISBN 0-85224-448-7, Pub. by Edinburgh U Pr Scotland). Columbia U Pr.

Connaway, John M. The Wilsford Site 22-Co-516, Coahoma County Mississippi. LC 84-620008. (Mississippi Department of Archives & History Archaeological Reports Ser.: No. 14). 222p. (Orig.). pap. 15.00. Mississippi De.

Coutts, Peter J. An Archaeological Perspective of Panay Island, Philippines. (San Carlos Humanities Ser.: No. 13). (Illus.). 342p. (Orig.). 1983. pap. 13.50x (ISBN 971-100-043-1, Pub. by San Carlos Phillipines). Cellar.

Cunliffe, Barry. Danebury: Anatomy of an Iron Age Hillfort. 192p. 1985. 24.00 (ISBN 0-7134-0998-3, NO. 9351). Methuen Inc.

David, Nicholas & Bricker, Harvey, eds. Excavation of the Abri Pataud, les Eyzies (Dordogne) The Noaillian, Level 4. (American School of Prehistoric Research Bulletin: No. 37). (Illus.). 400p. 1985. pap. 35.00x (ISBN 0-87365-540-0). Peabody Harvard.

Dickens, Roy S., Jr. & Ward, H. Trawick, eds. Structrue & Process in Southeastern Archaelology. LC 84-23. (Illus.). 336p. 1985. 35.00 (ISBN 0-8173-0216-6). U of Ala Pr.

Dornemann, Rudolph H. The Archaeology of the Transjordan in the Bronze & Iron Ages, No. 10. LC 83-61718. (Publications in Anthropology & History: No. 4). (Illus.). 288p. 1983. pap. text ed. 50.00 (ISBN 0-89326-053-3). Milwaukee Pub Mus.

Dyer, James. Teaching Archaeology in Schools. (Shire Archaeology Ser.: No. 29). (Illus.). 64p. 1983. pap. 5.95 (ISBN 0-85263-622-9, Pub. by Shire Pubns England). Seven Hills Bks.

Emerson, Thomas E. & Jackson, Douglas K. The BBB Motor Site. LC 83-18196. (American Bottom Archaeology: Selected Fai-270 Site Reports Ser.: Vol. 6). (Illus.). 454p. 1984. pap. 13.95 (ISBN 0-252-01068-X). U of Ill Pr.

Eogan, George. Excavations at Knowth. (Royal Irish Academy Monograph in Archeology). (Illus.). 358p. 1985. 42.00 (ISBN 0-901714-34-8, Pub. by Salem Acad). Merrimack Pub Cir.

Fagan, Brian M. In the Beginning: An Introduction to Archaeology. 5th ed. LC 84-7887. 1984. text ed. 23.95 (ISBN 0-316-25988-8). Little.

Fitzhugh, William W. Environmental Archaeology & Cultural Systems in Hamilton Inlet, Labrador: A Survey of the Central Labrador Coast from 3000 B.C. to the Present. LC 79-171589. (Smithsonian Contributions to Anthropology Ser.: No. 16). pap. 68.00 (ISBN 0-317-28679-X, 2051626). Bks Demand UMI.

Fix, William R. Pyramid Odyssey. LC 78-14540. (Illus.). 291p. 1984. pap. 9.95 (ISBN 0-932487-00-9). Mercury Media.

Fleming, S. J. Thermoluminescence Techniques in Archaeology. (Illus.). 1979. 52.00x (ISBN 0-19-859929-3). Oxford U Pr.

Foster, Michael S. & Weigand, Phil C., eds. The Archaelogy of West & Northwest America. (A Westview Special Study). 325p. 1985. softcover 30.00x (ISBN 0-8133-0201-3). Westview.

Frurip, David J., et al. Colonial Nails from Michilamackinac: Differentiation by Chemical & Statistical Analysis. (Archaeological Completion Report Ser.: No. 7). (Illus.). 83p. (Orig.). 1983. pap. 8.50 (ISBN 0-911872-47-7). MacKinac Island.

Galinsky, Gotthard K. Aeneas, Sicily & Rome. LC 69-18059. (Princeton Monographs in Art & Archaeology: 40). pap. write for info. (2055272). Bks Demand UMI.

Gibbon, Guy. Anthropological Archaeology. LC 84-4321. 432p. 1984. 29.50 (ISBN 0-317-05136-9). Columbia U Pr.

Gibbon, Guy & Spencer, Robert F., eds. Prairie Archaeology: Papers in Honor of David A. Baerreis. (University of Minnesota, Publications in Anthropology: No. 3). 170p. 1983. pap. 9.50 (ISBN 0-911599-02-9). Dept Anthro U Minn.

Gowlett, John. Ascent to Civilization: The Archaeology of Early Man. LC 83-48713. (Illus.). 208p. 1984. pap. 14.95 (ISBN 0-394-72266-3); pap. text ed. 9.95 (ISBN 0-394-34294-1). Knopf.

Grayson, Donald K. Quantitative Zooarchaeology: Topics in the Analysis of Archaeological Faunas. Dimbleby, G. W., ed. (Studies in Archaeological Science). 1984. 34.50 (ISBN 0-12-297280-5). Acad Pr.

Gumerman, George J. A View from Black Mesa: The Changing Face of Archaeology. LC 84-8581. (Illus.). 184p. 1984. 18.95x (ISBN 0-8165-0848-8). U of Ariz Pr.

Hargrave, Michael L., et al. The Bridges Site: A Late Prehistoric Settlement in the Central Kaskaskia Valley. LC 83-72530. (Research Paper Ser.: No. 38). (Illus.). 395p. (Orig.). 1983. pap. 10.00 (ISBN 0-88104-014-2). Center Archaeo.

Harrington, J. C. Archaeology & the Enigma of Fort Raleigh. (Illus.). xi, 36p. (Orig.). 1984. pap. 3.00 (ISBN 0-86526-203-9). NC Archives.

Helms, S. W. Jawa: Lost City of the Black Desert. LC 80-69820. (Illus.). 182p. 1981. 37.50x (ISBN 0-8014-1364-8). Cornell U Pr.

Higgins, Michael J., et al. Archaeology of White Walnut Creek. (Illus.). 220p. (Orig.). 1983. pap. 9.95 (ISBN 0-913415-00-6). Am Resources.

Hodder, Ian & Orton, C. Spatial Analysis in Archaeology. LC 75-44582. (New Studies in Archaeology). (Illus.). 260p. 1980. pap. 17.95 (ISBN 0-521-29738-9). Cambridge U Pr.

International Conference of the Association of South Asian Archaeologists in Western Europe, 6th. South Asian Archaeology 1981: Proceedings. Allchin, Bridget, et al, eds. LC 83-14377. (University of Cambridge Oriental Publications Ser.: No. 34). (Illus.). 300p. 1984. 69.50 (ISBN 0-521-25599-6). Cambridge U Pr.

International Congress of Anthropology & Prehistoric Archaeology, 1st: Neuchatel, 1866, (Proces-Verbal) Repr. 20.00 (ISBN 0-317-15383-8). Kraus Repr.

International Congress of Anthropology & Prehistoric Archaeology, 10th: Paris, 1889, (Compte-Rendu) Repr. 65.00 (ISBN 0-317-15399-4). Kraus Repr.

International Congress of Anthropology & Prehistoric Archaeology, 11th: Moscow, 1892, (Compte-Rendu, 4 vols. in 2. Repr. Set. 140.00 (ISBN 0-317-15402-8). Kraus Repr.

International Congress of Anthropology & Prehistoric Archaeology, 12th: Paris, 1900, (Compte-Rendu) Repr. 60.00 (ISBN 0-317-15403-6). Kraus Repr.

International Congress of Anthropology & Prehistoric Archaeology, 13th: Monaco, 1906, (Compte-Rendu, 2 vols. Repr. Set. 100.00 (ISBN 0-317-15405-2). Kraus Repr.

International Congress of Anthropology & Prehistoric Archaeology, 14th: Geneva, 1912, (Compte-Rendu, 2 vols. Repr. Set. 120.00 (ISBN 0-317-15406-0). Kraus Repr.

International Congress of Anthropology & Prehistoric Archaeology, 15th: Coimbra, 1930; Paris, 1931, (Actes, 2 vols. Repr. Set. 165.00 (ISBN 0-317-15407-9). Kraus Intl.

International Congress of Anthropology & Prehistoric Archaeology, 16th: Brussels, 1935, (Rapport, 2 vols. Repr. Set. 140.00 (ISBN 0-317-15408-7). Kraus Repr.

International Congress of Anthropology & Prehistoric Archaeology, 2nd: Paris, 1867, (Compte-Rendu) Repr. 60.00 (ISBN 0-317-15386-2). Kraus Repr.

International Congress of Anthropology & Prehistoric Archaeology, 3rd: London, 1868, (Transactions) Repr. 60.00 (ISBN 0-317-15387-0). Kraus Repr.

International Congress of Anthropology & Prehistoric Archaeology, 4th: Copenhagen, 1869, (Compte-Rendu) Repr. 60.00 (ISBN 0-317-15388-9). Kraus Repr.

International Congress of Anthropology & Prehistoric Archaeology, 5th: Bologna, 1871, (Compte-Rendu) Repr. 62.00 (ISBN 0-317-15390-0). Kraus Repr.

International Congress of Anthropology & Prehistoric Archaeology, 6th: Brussels, 1872, (Compte-Rendu) Repr. 80.00 (ISBN 0-317-15391-9). Kraus Repr.

International Congress of Anthropology & Prehistoric Archaeology, 7th: Stockholm, 1874, (Compte-Rendu, 2 vols. Repr. Set. 100.00 (ISBN 0-317-15394-3). Kraus Repr.

International Congress of Anthropology & Prehistoric Archaeology, 8th: Budapest, 1876, (Compte-Rendu, 2 vols. Repr. Set. 150.00 (ISBN 0-317-15396-X). Kraus Repr.

International Congress of Anthropology & Prehistoric Archaeology, 9th: Lisbon, 1880, (Compte-Rendu) Repr. 100.00. Kraus Repr.

Jolly, Clifford & Plog, Fred. Physical Anthropology & Archeology. 3rd ed. 1982. pap. text ed. 20.00 (ISBN 0-394-32672-5, KnopfC). Knopf.

Jurmain, et al. Understanding Physical Anthropology & Archaeology. (Illus.). 1981. pap. text ed. 21.95 (ISBN 0-8299-0388-7). West Pub.

Jurmain, Robert & Nelson, Harry. Understanding Physical Anthropology & Archeology. 2nd ed. (Illus.). 525p. 1983. pap. text ed. 25.95 (ISBN 0-314-77989-2); write for info. instr's. manual (ISBN 0-314-77993-0). West Pub.

Kennedy, K. & Possehl, G., eds. Studies in the Archaeology & Palaeoanthropology of South Asia. 144p. 1984. text ed. 22.00x (ISBN 0-391-03049-3). Humanities.

Kenyon, Kathleen M. Archaeology in the Holy Land. 368p. 1985. pap. 12.95 (ISBN 0-8407-7521-0). Nelson.

Kerr, Mary & Kerr, Nigel. Anglo-Saxon Architecture. (Shire Archaeology Ser.: No. 18). (Illus.). 1983. pap. 5.95 (ISBN 0-85263-570-2, Pub. by Shire Pubns England). Seven Hills Bks.

Kidder, Alfred V. The Artifacts of Pecos. (Classics of Anthropology Ser.). 1985. 53.00 (ISBN 0-8240-9630-4). Garland Pub.

King, Thomas F. & Parker, Patricia L. Pisekin Noomw Noon Tonaachaw: Archeology in the Tonaachaw Historic Distric, Moen Island. LC 84-71523. (Center for Archaeological Investigations Occasional: No. 3). (Illus.). xxxii, 541p. 1984. pap. 20.00 (ISBN 0-88104-018-5). Center Archaeo.

Knudson, S. J. Culture in Retrospect: An Introduction to Archaeology. (Illus.). 555p. 1985. pap. text ed. 18.95x (ISBN 0-88133-168-6). Waveland Pr.

Krupp, E. C., ed. Archaeoastronomy & the Roots of Science. (AAAS Selected Symposium Ser.: No. 71). 400p. 1984. softcover 42.50x (ISBN 0-86531-406-3). Westview.

Lambrick, George. Archaeology & Agriculture. 46p. 1977. pap. text ed. 7.45x (ISBN 0-900312-44-0, Pub. by Coun Brit Archaeology). Humanities.

Lankester, Edwin R. Secrets of Earth & Sea. LC 76-93352. (Essay Index Reprint Ser). 1920. 19.00 (ISBN 0-8369-1301-9). Ayer Co Pubs.

Lutyk, Carol, ed. The Adventure of Archeology. (Illus.). 368p. 1985. price not set (ISBN 0-87044-603-7); deluxe ed. price not set (ISBN 0-87044-604-5). Natl Geog.

McGrail, Sean. Ancient Boats. (Shire Archaeology Ser.: No. 31). (Illus.). 64p. 1983. pap. 5.95 (ISBN 0-85263-626-1, Pub. by Shire Pubns England). Seven Hills Bks.

Maxwell. Prehistory of the Eastern Arctic. (New World Archaeological Record Ser.). 1985. 49.00 (ISBN 0-12-481270-8). Acad Pr.

Maxwell, Gordon. The Impact of Aerial Reconnaissance on Archaeology. (CBA Research Reports Ser.: No. 49). 140p. 1983. pap. text ed. 37.25x (ISBN 0-906780-24-1, Pub. by Coun Brit Archaeology England). Humanities.

Mazar, Benjamin & Shanks, Hershel, eds. Recent Archaeology in the Land of Israel. Finkelstein, Aryeh, tr. from Hebrew. LC 83-73556. (Illus.). 191p. 1984. write for info. (ISBN 0-9613089-0-7). Biblical Arch Soc.

Merrill, William L. An Investigation of Ethnographic & Archaeological Specimens of Mescalbeans (Sophora secundiflora) in American Museums. (Technical Reports: No. 6). (Illus., Contribution 1 in Research Reports in Ethnobotany). 1977. pap. 5.00x (ISBN 0-932206-15-8). U Mich Mus Anthro.

Meyers, Thomas & Denies, Mark. Longterm & Peakscan: Neutron Activation Analysis Computer Programs. (Technical Reports Ser.: No. 2). (Illus., Contribution 2 in computer applications to archaeology). 1972. pap. 1.00x (ISBN 0-932206-11-5). U Mich Mus Anthro.

Michael, Henry N., ed. The Archaeology & Geomorphology of Northern Asia: Selected Works. LC 65-1456. (Arctic Institute of North America-Anthropology of the North; Translation from Russian Sources Ser.: No. 5). pap. 132.00 (ISBN 0-317-10857-3, 2019174). Bks Demand UMI.

Milner, George R. The Turner & DeMange Sites, Vol. 4. (American Bottom Archaeology: Selected FAI-270 Site Reports Ser.). (Illus.). 256p. 1984. 10.95 (ISBN 0-252-01066-3). U of Ill Pr.

Plog, Stephen & Powell, Shirley, eds. Papers on the Archaeology of Black Mesa, Arizona, Vol. II. LC 75-32340. (Papers in Archaeology Ser.). (Illus.). 224p. 1984. 25.00x (ISBN 0-8093-1149-6). S Ill U Pr.

Prahl, Earl J. & Branster, Mark. Archaeological Investigations on Mackinac Island 1983: The Watermain & Sewer Project. (Archaeological Completion Report Ser.: No. 8). (Illus.). 125p. (Orig.). 1984. pap. 12.00 (ISBN 0-911872-50-7). Mackinac Island.

Rahtz, Philip. Invitation to Archaeology. (Invitation Ser.). 192p. 1985. 24.95x (ISBN 0-631-14106-5); pap. 7.95x (ISBN 0-631-14107-3). Basil Blackwell.

Rapp, George & Gifford, John A., eds. Archaeological Geology. LC 84-40201. (Illus.). 448p. 1985. text ed. 35.00 (ISBN 0-300-03142-4). Yale U Pr.

Rice, Prudence M., ed. Pots & Potters: Current Approaches in Ceramic Archaeology. (Monographs: No. XXIV). (Illus.). 255p. 1984. pap. 22.50 (ISBN 0-917956-44-3). UCLA Arch.

Roe, F. & May, J., eds. Guide to Undergraduate Courses in Archaeology. 2nd ed. 60p. 1983. pap. text ed. 3.25x (ISBN 0-906780-35-7, Pub. by Coun Brit Archaeology). Humanities.

Salmon, Merrilee H. Philosophy & Archaeology. (Studies in Archaeology Ser.). 1982. 21.00 (ISBN 0-12-615650-6). Acad Pr.

Satterthwaite, L., Jr. Sweathouses. (Piedras Negras Archaeology: Architecture: Pt. 5). (Illus.). 93p. 1952. pap. 6.00 (ISBN 0-318-01004-6). Univ Mus of U PA.

Satterthwaite, Linton, Jr. Unclassified Buildings & Substructures, Nos. 3-12. (Piedras Negras Archaeology Architecture: Pt. 6). (Illus.). 92p. 1954. pap. 5.00 (ISBN 0-318-01016-X). Univ Mus of U PA.

Seeman, Mark. The Locust Site 33Mu160: The 1983 Test Excavation of a Multicomponent Workshop in East Central Ohio. (Kent State Research Papers in Archaeology: No. 7). 90p. 1985. pap. text ed. 7.00x (ISBN 0-87338-318-4). Kent St U Pr.

Shackley, Myra. Environmental Archaeology. (Illus.). 256p. 1981. text ed. 40.00x (ISBN 0-04-913020-X); pap. text ed. 19.95x (ISBN 0-04-913021-8). Allen Unwin.

Shaw, John. Water Power in Scotland: Fifteen Fifty to Eighteen Seventy. 600p. 1984. text ed. 48.00x (ISBN 0-85976-072-3, Pub. by John Donald Scotland). Humanities.

Shearer, Tony. Beneath the Moon & under the Sun. (Illus.). 164p. 1975. 8.50 (ISBN 0-89540-042-1, SB-042). Sun Pub.

Smiley, F. E., et al, eds. Excavations on Black Mesa, 1981: A Descriptive Report. LC 82-72189. (Southern Illinois University at Carbondale Center for Archaeological Investigations Research Paper: No. 36). (Illus.). 538p. 1983. 18.00 (ISBN 0-88104-007-X). Center Archaeo.

Spoerl, Patricia M. & Gumerman, George J., eds. Prehistoric Cultural Development in Central Arizona: Archaeology of the Upper New River Region. LC 84-72846. (Center for Archaeological Investigations Occasional: No. 5). (Illus.). xix, 379p. 1984. pap. 20.00 (ISBN 0-88104-050-9). Center Archaeo.

Taylor, R. E., ed. Advances in Obsidian Glass Studies: Archaeological & Geochemical Perspectives. LC 76-43192. (Illus.). 36p. 1977. 32.00 (ISBN 0-8155-5050-2, NP). Noyes.

Vardaman, E. Jerry & Garrett, James L., Jr., eds. The Teacher's Yoke: Studies in Memory of Henry Trantham. 320p. 1964. 4.95 (ISBN 0-918954-02-9). Baylor Univ Pr.

Wendorf, Fred & Close, Angela E. Advances in World Archaeology, Vol. 3. (Serial Publication). 1984. 65.50 (ISBN 0-12-039903-2). Acad Pr.

Wendorf, Fred & Close, Angela, eds. Advances in World Archaeology, Vol. 2. (Serial Publication). 1983. 45.00 (ISBN 0-12-039902-4). Acad Pr.

Wendorf, Fred & Close, Angela E., eds. Advances in World Archaeolgy, Vol. 4. (Serial Publication Ser.). Date not set. 80.00 (ISBN 0-12-039904-0). Acad Pr.

Willey, Gordon R. Archaeology of the Florida Gulf Coast. 1982. Repr. of 1949 ed. 45.00 (ISBN 0-317-27694-8). Kallman.

Willey, Gordon R., ed. Archaeological Researches in Retrospect. LC 81-43603. (Illus.). 316p. 1982. pap. text ed. 15.00 (ISBN 0-8191-2239-4). U Pr of Amer.

Wood, John E. Sun, Moon, & Standing Stones. (Illus.). 1978. 22.50x (ISBN 0-19-211443-3). Oxford U Pr.

Xinglian, Zhang. A Glossary of Chinese Archaeology. Shuhan, Zhao, ed. (Chinese & Eng.). 199p. (Orig.). 1983. 4.95 (ISBN 0-8351-1210-1); pap. 3.95 (ISBN 0-8351-1082-6). China Bks.

Yegul, Fikret K. The Bath-Gymnasium Complex at Sardis. (The Archaeological Exploration of Sardis Report: No. 3). (Illus.). 232p. 1985. text ed. 45.00x (ISBN 0-674-06345-7). Harvard U Pr.

Zeuner, Frederic E. Dating the Past: An Introduction to Geochronology. 4th ed. (Illus.). 1970. Repr. of 1946 ed. 28.95x (ISBN 0-02-855790-5). Hafner.

ARCHAEOLOGY–DATA PROCESSING

Gaines, Sylvia W. Data Bank Applications in Archaeology. LC 81-901. 142p. 1981. pap. 14.95x (ISBN 0-8165-0686-8). U of Ariz Pr.

Gross, Jonathan L. & Rayner, Steve. Measuring Culture: A Paradigm for the Analysis of Social Organization. 144p. 1985. 32.50 (ISBN 0-231-06032-7). Columbia U Pr.

Richards, Julian & Ryan, Nick. Data Processing in Archaeology. (Manuals in Archaeology Ser.). (Illus.). 200p. 1985. 24.95 (ISBN 0-521-25769-7). Cambridge U Pr.

Stickel, E. Gary, ed. New Uses of Systems Theory in Archaeology. LC 82-13811. (Ballen Press Anthropological Papers: No. 24). (Illus.). 104p. (Orig.). 1982. pap. 9.95 (ISBN 0-87919-096-5). Ballena Pr.

ARCHAEOLOGY–DICTIONARIES

Apelt, M. German-English Dictionary: Art History-Archaeology. 1982. 25.00 (ISBN 3-503-01619-8). Heinman.

Champion, Sara. A Dictionary of Terms & Techniques in Archaeology. LC 80-66774. pap. 36.00 (ISBN 0-317-20683-4, 2025147). Bks Demand UMI.

Phillips, Steven J. An Architectural Lexicon for the Historical Archaeologist. (Illus.). 484p. (Orig.). pap. cancelled (ISBN 0-89301-098-7). U Pr of Idaho.

Whitehouse, Ruth D., ed. The Facts on File Dictionary of Archaeology. (Illus.). 608p. 1984. 24.95 (ISBN 0-87196-048-6). Facts on File.

ARCHAEOLOGY–METHODOLOGY

see also Radiocarbon Dating

Addington, Lucile R. Lithic Illustration: Drawing Flaked Stone Artifacts for Publication. LC 85-8121. (Prehistoric Archeology & Ecology Ser.). (Illus.). 160p. 1985. lib. bdg. 29.99x (ISBN 0-226-00634-4); pap. 10.00x (ISBN 0-226-00635-2). U of Chicago Pr.

Barker, Philip. Techniques of Archaeological Excavation. 2nd, rev., & extended ed. LC 82-23792. (Illus.). 288p. 1983. text ed. 25.00x (ISBN 0-87663-399-8); pap. text ed. 12.50x (ISBN 0-87663-587-7). Universe.

Beck, Curt W., ed. Archeological Chemistry. LC 74-22372. (Advances in Chemistry Ser: No. 138). 1974. 39.95 (ISBN 0-8412-0211-7). Am Chemical.

Berger, Rainer, ed. Scientific Methods in Medieval Archaeology. LC 75-99771. (UCLA Center for Medieval & Renaissance Studies: No. 4). (Illus.). 1971. 58.50x (ISBN 0-520-01626-2). U of Cal Pr.

Bird, J. R., et al. Ion Beam Techniques in Archaeology & the Arts. 172p. 1984. 26.00 (ISBN 3-7186-0188-5). Harwood Academic.

Blakely, Jeffry A. & Toombs, Lawrence E. The Tell el-Hesi Field Manual: Joint Archaeological Expedition to Tell el-Hesi: Vol. 1. LC 80-21724. (Excavation Reports Ser.: No. 3). 134p. 1981. text ed. 15.00x (ISBN 0-89757-205-X, Am Sch Orient Res); pap. text ed. 12.00x (ISBN 0-89757-203-3). Eisenbrauns.

Carr, Christopher, ed. The Analysis of Archaeological Data Structures. (Studies in Archaeology). Date not set. price not set (ISBN 0-12-160520-5). Acad Pr.

Connah, Graham. Australian Field Archaeology: A Guide to Techniques. 182p. 1983. pap. text ed. 19.75x (ISBN 0-85575-136-3, Pub. by Australian Inst. Australia). Humanities.

Dillon, Brian D., ed. Practical Archaeology: Field & Laboratory Techniques & Archaeological Logistics. (Archaeological Research Tools: Vol. 2). 100p. 1982. pap. 8.50 (ISBN 0-917956-38-9). UCLA Arch.

--The Student's Guide to Archaeological Illustrating. rev. ed. (Archaeological Research Tools Ser.: Vol. 1). (Illus.). 154p. Date not set. pap. 8.50x (ISBN 0-917956-38-9). UCLA Arch.

Doran, James E. & Hodson, Frank R. Mathematics & Computers in Archaeology. (Illus.). 371p. 1975. text ed. 22.50x (ISBN 0-674-55455-8). Harvard U Pr.

Fischer, P. Applications of Technical Devices in Archaeology. (Studies in Mediterranean Archaeology: Vol. LXIII). 64p. 1981. pap. text ed. 30.50x (ISBN 91-85058-33-5, Pub. by Paul Astroms Sweden). Humanities.

Hesse, Brian & Wapnish, Paula. Animal Bone Archeology: From Objectives to Analysis. LC 83-51521. (Manuals on Archeology Ser.: No. 5). (Illus.). xii, 132p. 1985. 18.00x (ISBN 0-9602822-3-8). Taraxacum.

Hietala, Harold J., ed. Intrasite Spatial Analysis in Archaeology. (New Directions in Archaeology). (Illus.). 292p. 1985. 49.50 (ISBN 0-521-25071-4). Cambridge U Pr.

Hodder, Ian, ed. Symbolic & Structural Archaeology. LC 81-17992. (New Directions in Archaeology Ser.). (Illus.). 250p. 1982. 44.50 (ISBN 0-521-24406-4). Cambridge U Pr.

Hodges, Henry. Artifacts: An Introduction to Early Materials & Technology. rev. ed. (Illus., Orig.). 1981. pap. text ed. 16.50x (ISBN 0-391-02246-6). Humanities.

Klein, Richard G. & Cruz-Uribe, Kathryn. The Analysis of Animal Bones from Archeological Sites. (Prehistoric Archeology & Ecology Ser.). (Illus.). 1984. lib. bdg. 20.00x (ISBN 0-226-43957-7); pap. text ed. 9.00x (ISBN 0-226-43958-5). U of Chicago Pr.

Lambert, Joseph B., ed. Archaeological Chemistry, Vol. III. LC 83-15736. (Advances in Chemistry Ser.: No. 205). 487p. 1984. lib. bdg. 89.95x (ISBN 0-8412-0767-4). Am Chemical.

Leach, Peter, ed. Archaeology in Kent to AD 1500. (CBA Research Report: No. 48). 144p. 1982. pap. text ed. 30.50x (ISBN 0-906780-18-7, 50019, Pub. by Coun Brit Archaeology England). Humanities.

Major-Poetzl, Pamela. Michel Foucault's Archaeology of Western Culture: Toward a New Science of History. LC 81-19689. 280p. 1982. 24.00x (ISBN 0-8078-1517-9). U of NC Pr.

Moeller, Roger W. Practicing Environmental Archaeology: Methods & Interpretations. LC 82-73087. (Occasional Papers No. 3). (Illus.). 112p. 1982. pap. text ed. 10.00 (ISBN 0-936322-00-4). Am Indian Arch.

Moore, James A. & Keene, Arthur S., eds. Archaeological Hammers & Theories. LC 82-11669. 1983. 34.50 (ISBN 0-12-505980-9). Acad Pr.

Orton, Clive. Mathematics in Archaeology. LC 81-21608. (Illus.). 248p. 1982. pap. 11.95 (ISBN 0-521-28922-X). Cambridge U Pr.

Peltenburg, E. J. Vrysi: A Subterranean Settlement in Cyprus - Excavations of Ayios Epiktitos, 1969-1973. (Illus.). 132p. 1982. pap. text ed. 42.50x (ISBN 0-85668-217-9, Pub. by Aris & Phillips England). Humanities.

Redman, Charles L., ed. Research & Theory in Current Archeology. LC 73-6717. 390p. 1973. pap. text ed. 31.95 (ISBN 0-471-71291-4, Pub. by Wiley-Interscience). Wiley.

Riley, D. N. Aerial Archaeology in Britain. LC 83-131437. (Shire Archaeology Ser.: No. 22). (Illus.). 64p. 1982. pap. 5.95 (ISBN 0-85263-592-3, Pub. by Shire Pubns England). Seven Hills Bks.

Sabloff, Jeremy A., ed. Simulations in Archaeology. LC 80-54508. (School of American Research Advanced Seminar Ser.). (Illus.). 440p. 1981. 32.50x (ISBN 0-8263-0576-8). U of NM Pr.

Schiffer, Michael, ed. Advances in Archaeological Methods & Theory, Vol. 5. (Serial Publication Ser.). 1982. pap. 42.00 (ISBN 0-12-003105-1). Acad Pr.

Kemper, Alfred M. Presentation Drawings by American Architects. LC 76-40891. 380p. 1977. 59.50x (ISBN 0-471-01369-2, Pub. by Wiley-Interscience). Wiley.

Kliment, Stephen. Architectural Sketching & Rendering. (Illus.). 200p. 1984. pap. 16.95 (ISBN 0-8230-7053-0, Whitnet Lib). Watson-Guptill.

Konig, Felix. Perspectives in Architectural Drawings. LC 83-10238. (Illus.). 96p. 1984. pap. 14.95 (ISBN 0-442-24747-8). Van Nos Reinhold.

Kuckein, H. Eberhard. Architectural Illustration & Presentation. 1984. text ed. 24.95 (ISBN 0-8359-0323-0). Reston.

Levinson, E. D. Architectural Rendering. LC 82-17151. 256p. 1983. 21.60 (ISBN 0-07-037413-9). McGraw.

Lewis, J. Architectural Draftsman's Reference Handbook. 1982. 33.95 (ISBN 0-13-044164-3). P-H.

Liebing, Ralph W. & Paul, Mimi F. Architectural Working Drawings. 2nd ed. LC 82-21911. 394p. 1983. 32.50x (ISBN 0-471-86649-0, Pub. by Wiley-Interscience). Wiley.

Lockard, William K. Drawing As a Means to Architecture. 1977. 29.95 (ISBN 0-442-26009-1). Van Nos Reinhold.

Mitooka, Eiji. Airbrushing in Rendering. LC 84-13098. (Illus.). 144p. 1984. pap. 35.00 (ISBN 0-442-26082-2). Van Nos Reinhold.

Muller, Edward J. Architectural Drawing & Light Construction. 3rd ed. (Illus.). 560p. 1985. text ed. 34.95 (ISBN 0-13-044561-4). P-H.

Nelson, John. Drafting for Trades & Industry - Architectural. LC 77-91450. (Drafting Ser.). 138p. 1979. pap. text ed. 10.80 (ISBN 0-8273-1839-1); instructor's guide 5.25 (ISBN 0-8273-1641-0). Delmar.

Palmes, J. C. Architectural Drawing in the R. I. B. A. pap. 5.00 (ISBN 0-685-20562-2). Transatlantic.

Patten, Lawton M. & Rogness, Milton. Architectural Drawing. 3rd ed. (Illus.). 1977. pap. text ed. 12.50 (ISBN 0-8403-1809-X). Kendall-Hunt.

Powell, Helen & Leatherbarrow, David, eds. Masterpieces of Architectural Drawing. LC 82-22643. (Illus.). 192p. 1983. 49.95 (ISBN 0-89659-326-6). Abbeville Pr.

Ratensky, Alexander. Drawing & Modelmaking: A Primer for Students of Architecture & Design. (Illus.). 160p. 1983. 19.50 (ISBN 0-8230-7369-6, Whitney Lib). Watson-Guptill.

Reekie, Fraser. Draughtsmanship: Architectural & Building Graphics. 3rd ed. (Illus.). 248p. 1976. pap. 18.50x (ISBN 0-7131-3368-6). Intl Ideas.

Russell, James E. Graphics for Architects & Planners. 1985. text ed. 27.95 (ISBN 0-8359-2565-X). Reston.

Spence, W. Construction: Architectural Drawing. 1976. pap. 8.34 (ISBN 0-13-169425-1). P-H.

Spence, William P. Architecture: Design-Engineering-Drawing. rev. ed. 1979. text ed. 21.97 (ISBN 0-87345-099-X); quizzes & problems 6.00 (ISBN 0-87345-098-1); ans. key avail. (ISBN 0-685-14523-9). McKnight.

Wakita, O. A. & Linde, R. M. The Professional Handbook of Architectural Working Drawings. 530p. 1984. 49.95 (ISBN 0-471-88575-4); study guide 13.95 (ISBN 0-471-89131-2); drawings 150.00 (ISBN 0-471-80203-4). Wiley.

White, Anthony G. Architectural Drawings-Collections: A Selected Bibliography. (Architecture Ser.: Bibliography A 1348). 1985. pap. 2.00 (ISBN 0-89028-318-4). Vance Biblios.

Wright, Frank L. Drawings & Plans of Frank Lloyd Wright: The Early Period (1893-1909) 2nd ed. Orig. Title: Ausgefuhrte Bauten Und Entwurfe Von Frank Lloyd Wright. (Illus.). 112p. 1983. pap. 7.95 (ISBN 0-486-24457-1). Dover.

Wyatt, William E. General Architectural Drafting. 1976. student guide 6.64 (ISBN 0-02-664130-5); drafting masters 20.00 (ISBN 0-02-664150-X). Bennett IL.

Zukowsky, John. Walter Burley Griffin, Marion Mahoney Griffin: Architectural Drawings in the Burnham Library of Architecture. (Illus.). 16p. (Orig.). 1981. pap. 4.00 (ISBN 0-86559-047-8). Art Inst Chi.

ARCHITECTURAL ENGINEERING

see Building; Building, Iron and Steel; Strains and Stresses; Strength of Materials; Structures, Theory Of

ARCHITECTURAL IRONWORK

see also Building Fittings

Badger, Carl B. Badger's Illustrated Catalogue of Cast-Iron Architecture. 1982. pap. 9.95 (ISBN 0-486-24223-4). Dover.

D'Allemagne, Henry R. Decorative Antique Ironwork: A Pictorial Treasury. Ostoia, Vera K., tr. LC 67-20193. (Illus.). 1968. pap. 11.95 (ISBN 0-486-22082-6). Dover.

Southworth, Susan & Southworth, Michael. Ornamental Ironwork: An Illustrated Guide to Its Design, History & Use in American Architecture. LC 77-94111. (Illus.). 208p. 1978. 32.50x (ISBN 0-87923-233-1); pap. 12.50 (ISBN 0-87923-234-X). Godine.

Steiner, Frances H. French Iron Architecture. Foster, Stephen, ed. LC 84-133. (Architecture & Urban Design Ser.: No. 3). 254p. 1984. 39.95 (ISBN 0-8357-1544-2). UMI Res Pr.

ARCHITECTURAL MODELS

see also Structural Frames–Models

Pattinson, Graham D. A Guide to Professional Architectural & Industrial Scale Model Building. (Illus.). 400p. 1982. 40.95 (ISBN 0-13-370601-X). P-H.

Ratensky, Alexander. Drawing & Modelmaking: A Primer for Students of Architecture & Design. (Illus.). 160p. 1983. 19.50 (ISBN 0-8230-7369-6, Whitney Lib). Watson-Guptill.

ARCHITECTURE

see also Arches; Building; Building Materials; Buildings; Columns; Concrete Construction; Environmental Engineering (Buildings); Factories; Farm Buildings; Hospitals–Design and Construction; Lighting; Lighting, Architectural and Decorative; Military Architecture; Naval Architecture; Skyscrapers; Space Frame Structures; Strains and Stresses; Strength of Materials; Structural Engineering; Theaters–Construction

also headings beginning with the word Architectural

Attoe, Wayne. Skylines: Understanding & Molding Urban Silhouettes. LC 80-41684. 128p. 1981. 48.95x (ISBN 0-471-27940-4, Pub. by Wiley-Interscience). Wiley.

Badger, D. D. & Bogardus, James. Origins of Cast Iron Architecture in America. LC 68-25760. (Architecture & Decorative Art Ser.: Vol. 13). (Illus.). 1970. Repr. of 1856 ed. lib. bdg. 55.00 (ISBN 0-306-71039-0). Da Capo.

Bibiena, Ferdinando G. Da. Architettura Civile. LC 68-57184. (Illus., It). 1969. 50.00 (ISBN 0-405-08268-1, Blom Pubns). Ayer Co Pubs.

Blaser, Werner, ed. Architecture & Nature. (Eng., Fr. & Ger.). 160p. 1983. text ed. 29.95 (ISBN 3-7643-1524-5). Birkhauser.

Cowan, H. J. Models in Architecture. 1968. 29.75 (ISBN 0-85334-624-0, Pub. by Elsevier Applied Sci England). Elsevier.

Coxe, Weld. Marketing Architectural & Engineering Services. 2nd ed. 1982. 26.95 (ISBN 0-442-22011-1). Van Nos Reinhold.

Creighton, Thomas H., ed. Building for Modern Man. facs. ed. LC 74-80385. (Essay Index Reprint Ser). 1949. 17.50 (ISBN 0-8369-1029-X). Ayer Co Pubs.

Dagostino, Frank. Mechanical & Electrical Systems in Construction & Architecture. (Illus.). 1978. ref. ed. 29.95 (ISBN 0-87909-511-3); solutions manual avail. (ISBN 0-87909-510-5). Reston.

Exemplary Design Research Nineteen Eighty-Three Results of the Design Research Recognition Program. (Illus.). 56p. 1984. pap. 2.50x (ISBN 0-89062-198-5, Pub. by Natl Endow Arts). Pub Ctr Cult Res.

Giedion, Sigfried. Architecture & the Phenomena of Transition: The Three Space Conceptions in Architecture. LC 71-95921. (Illus.). pap. 79.50 (ISBN 0-317-10591-4, 2021592). Bks Demand UMI.

Hafemeister, David & Buffa, A. Physics for Modern Architecture. 1983. perfect bdg. 12.95 (ISBN 0-317-11346-1). Paladin Hse.

Heath, Tom. Method in Architecture. 241p. 1984. 34.95x (ISBN 0-471-90409-0). Wiley.

Hejduk, John. Mask of Medusa. Shkapich, Kim, ed. LC 84-42769. (Illus.). 480p. 1984. pap. 35.00 (ISBN 0-8478-0567-0). Rizzoli Intl.

Heschong, Lisa. Thermal Delight in Architecture. 1979. pap. 5.95 (ISBN 0-262-58039-X). MIT Pr.

Hitchcock, Henry-Russell & Johnson, Philip. International Style. (Illus.). 1966. pap. 6.95 (ISBN 0-393-00311-6, Norton Lib). Norton.

Hough, Michael. City Form & Natural Process: Towards a New Urban Vernacular. (Illus.). 176p. 1984. 29.95 (ISBN 0-442-26400-3). Van Nos Reinhold.

Leibbrand, Kurt. Stadt und Verkehr: Theorie und Praxis der Stadtischen Verkehrsplanung. (Ger.). 404p. 1980. 75.95x (ISBN 0-8176-1072-3). Birkhauser.

Lever, Jill & Richardson, Margaret. The Architect As Artist. (Illus.). 144p. 1985. 25.00 (ISBN 0-8478-0568-9). Rizzoli Intl.

Mumford, Lewis. From the Ground Up: Observations on Contemporary Architecture, Housing, Highway Building, & Civic Design. LC 56-13736. (Orig.). 1956. pap. 3.50 (ISBN 0-15-634019-4, Harv). HarBraceJ.

Nervi, Pier L. Aesthetics & Technology in Building. Einaudi, R., tr. LC 65-16686. (Charles Eliot Norton Lectures Ser: 1961-1962). (Illus.). 1965. 15.00x (ISBN 0-674-00701-8). Harvard U Pr.

Perez-Gomez, Alberto. Architecture & the Crisis of Modern Science. LC 82-18010. (Illus.). 400p. 1983. 32.50x (ISBN 0-262-16091-9). MIT Pr.

Perez Gomez, Alberto. Architecture & the Crisis of Modern Science. (Illus.). 416p. 1985. pap. 10.95 (ISBN 0-262-66055-5). MIT Pr.

Pougatchenkova, G., et al. Tachkent: A Deux Mille Ans. (Fr.). 99p. 1983. pap. text ed. 33.75 (ISBN 92-3-202146-3, U1323, UNESCO). Unipub.

Ragette, Friedrich, ed. Engineering & Architecture & the Future Environment of Man. 1968. pap. 14.95x (ISBN 0-8156-6013-8, Am U Beirut). Syracuse U Pr.

Rasmussen, Steen E. Towns & Buildings. 1969. pap. 10.95s (ISBN 0-262-68011-4). MIT Pr.

Riseboro, Bill. The Story of Western Architecture. (Illus.). 269p. 1985. pap. 9.95x (ISBN 0-262-68047-5). MIT Pr.

Salvadori, Mario G. & Heller, Robert. Structure in Architecture: Building of Buildings. 2nd ed. (Illus.). 336p. 1975. 30.95 (ISBN 0-13-854109-4). P-H.

Satterthwaite, Linton, Jr. Unclassified Buildings & Substructures, Nos. 3-12. (Piedras Negras Archaeology Architecture: Pt. 6). (Illus.). 92p. 1954. pap. 5.00 (ISBN 0-318-01016-X). Univ Mus of U PA.

Tyng, Alexandra. Beginnings: Louis I. Kahn's Philosophy of Architecture. LC 83-6799. 192p. 1984. 29.95x (ISBN 0-471-86586-9, Pub. by Wiley-Interscience). Wiley.

Vance Bibliographies. Subject Index to Architecture Series: Bibliography No. A 1 to A 1000(June 1978-July1983) (Architecture Ser.: Bibliography: No. A-998). 111p. 1983. pap. 15.50 (ISBN 0-88066-568-8). Vance Biblios.

Willis, Arthur J. & Willis, Christopher J. Specification Writing for Architects & Surveyors. 8th ed. 98p. 1983. pap. text ed. 24.50x (ISBN 0-246-12228-5, Pub. by Granada England). Brookfield Pub Co.

Wilson, Grace, et al. Geometry for Architects. 2nd ed. (Illus.). 1975. spiral bdg. 9.80x (ISBN 0-87563-092-8). Stipes.

Yannas, S., ed. Passive & Low Energy Architecture: Proceedings of the International Conference, 28 June - 3 July 1983, Crete, Greece. 835p. 1983. 160.00 (ISBN 0-08-030581-4). Pergamon.

Zeidler, Eberhard H. Multi-Use Architecture. 192p. 1982. 110.00x (ISBN 0-686-45583-5, Pub. by L Brooks England). State Mutual Bk.

Zucker, Paul, ed. New Architecture & City Planning. facs. ed. LC 76-128337. (Essay Index Reprint Ser). 1944. 42.00 (ISBN 0-8369-2035-X). Ayer Co Pubs.

ARCHITECTURE–BIBLIOGRAPHY

Bibliographic Guide to Art & Architecture, 1984. (Bibliographic Guides Ser.). 1984. lib. bdg. 195.00 (ISBN 0-8161-7001-0). G K Hall.

Cable, Carole. The Architecture of Houston, Texas: A Bibliography of Articles, 1978 to 1983, An Update to Architecture Ser: Bibliography A-2. (Architecture Ser.: Bibliogrpy A 1325). 1985. pap. 2.00 (ISBN 0-89028-275-7). Vance Biblios.

--A Bibliography of Writings by & about Sir Reginald Theodore Bloomfield, 1856 to 1942. (Architecture Ser.: Bibliography A 1342). 1985. pap. 2.00 (ISBN 0-89028-312-5). Vance Biblios.

--Periodical Scholarship on Islamic Architecture Published 1973-1983: A Bibliography. (Architecture Ser. Bibliography A-1307). 7p. 1985. pap. 2.00 (ISBN 0-89028-237-4). Vance Biblios.

--The Publications of William Pain, 1730 to 1790: Architect & Carpenter. (Architecture Ser.: Bibliography A 1338). 1985. pap. 2.00 (ISBN 0-89028-308-7). Vance Biblios.

Coppa & Avery Consultants. An Architectural Guide to Wood Construction, Preservation, Conservation, Restoration & Framing. (Architecture Series: Bibliography: A-1312). 11p. 1985. pap. 2.00 (ISBN 0-89028-242-0). Vance Biblios.

--Bus Terminals: An Architectural Overview. (Architecture Ser.: Bibliography A-1308). 1985. pap. 2.00 (ISBN 0-89028-238-2). Vance Biblios.

De Malave, Florita Z. Charles W. Moore, North American Architect. (Architecture Ser.: Bibliography A 1344). 1985. pap. 2.00 (ISBN 0-89028-314-1). Vance Biblios.

Doumato, Lamia. Aldo Van Eyck. (Architecture Ser.: Bibliography A-1303). 1985. pap. 2.00 (ISBN 0-89028-233-1). Vance Biblios.

--John Merven Carrere: Eighteen Fifty-Eight to Nineteen Eleven. (Architecture Ser.: Bibliography A 1340). 1985. pap. 2.25 (ISBN 0-89028-310-9). Vance Biblios.

--Russell Sturgis: Eighteen Thirty-Six to Nineteen Nine. (Architecture Ser.: Bibliography A 1339). 1985. pap. 2.00 (ISBN 0-89028-309-5). Vance Biblios.

Dyal, Donald H. Addison Mizner: The Palm Beach Architect. (Architecture Ser.: Bibliography A 1341). 1985. pap. 2.00 (ISBN 0-89028-311-7). Vance Biblios.

Godel, Jules B. Sources of Construction Information: An Annotated Guide to Reports, Books, Periodicals, Standards, and Codes. LC 77-4671. 673p. 1977. 40.00 (ISBN 0-8108-1030-1). Scarecrow.

Gwin, William & Gwin, Mary M. Semiology, Symbolism & Architecture: A Selected & Partially Annotated Bibliography. (Architecture Ser.: Bibliography A 1346). 1985. pap. 3.00 (ISBN 0-89028-316-8). Vance Biblios.

Harvard University - Graduate School Of Design. Catalogue of the Library of the Graduate School of Design, 44 Vols. 1968. Set. 3725.00 (ISBN 0-8161-0812-9, Hall Library). G K Hall.

Index to Architecture Series: Bibliography, No. A 877-A 1116 (January 1983-December 1983) (A-1117). 72p. 1984. pap. 10.50 (ISBN 0-88066-807-5). Vance Biblios.

Louie De Irizarry, Florita Z. Airport Architecture: A Bibliography of Periodical Articles. (Architecture Ser.: Bibliography A-651). 52p. 1982. pap. 7.50 (ISBN 0-88066-132-1). Vance Biblios.

Louis de Malave, Florita Z. Harald Deilmann, Architect. (Architecture Ser.: Bibliography A-1304). 6p. 1985. pap. 2.00 (ISBN 0-89028-234-X). Vance Biblios.

Roos, Frank J., Jr. Bibliography of Early American Architecture: Writings on Architecture Constructed Before 1860 in Eastern & Central U.S. LC 68-24624. (Illus.). Repr. of 1968 ed. 75.90 (ISBN 0-8357-9665-5, 2014984). Bks Demand UMI.

Tatman, Sandra L. & Moss, Roger W. Biographical Dictionary of Philadelphia Architects & Master Builders: 1760-1930. 1984. lib. bdg. 99.50 (ISBN 0-8161-0437-9, Hall Reference). G K Hall.

Teague, Edward H. Architecture Librarianship: A Selective Bibliography. (Architecture Ser.: Bibliography A 1349). 1985. pap. 2.00 (ISBN 0-89028-319-2). Vance Biblios.

--John Lautner: Bibliography & Building List. (Architecture Ser.: Bibliography A 1345). 1985. pap. 2.00 (ISBN 0-89028-315-X). Vance Biblios.

Vance Bibliographies. Author Index to Architecture Series: Bibliography No. A 1 to A 1000 (June 1978-July 1983) (Architecture Ser.: Bibliography: A-999). 58p. 1983. pap. 9.00 (ISBN 0-88066-569-6). Vance Biblios.

--Title Index to Architecture Series: Bibliography No. A 1 to A 1000 (June 1978-July 1983) (Architecture Ser.: Bibliography: No. A-997). 58p. 1983. pap. 9.00 (ISBN 0-88066-567-X). Vance Biblios.

Vance Bibliographies Staff. Index to Architecture Series: Bibliography No. A-877- to A-1296 (January 1983-December 1984) (Architecture Ser.: Bibliography A-1297). 130p. 1985. pap. 16.50 (ISBN 0-89028-227-7). Vance Biblios.

Vance, Mary. Aesthetics: Monographs, 2 vols. (Architecture Series Bibliography: A-1246). 258p. 1984. Set. pap. 20.00 (ISBN 0-89028-096-7). Vance Biblios.

--Aggregates-Building Materials: Monographs. (Architecture Ser.: Bibliography A 1329). 1985. pap. 3.75 (ISBN 0-89028-279-X). Vance Biblios.

--Aluminum Construction. (Architecture Ser.: Bibliography A 1354). 1985. pap. 2.00 (ISBN 0-89028-324-9). Vance Biblios.

--Architect-Client Relationship. (Architecture Ser.: Bibliography A-1301). 1985. pap. 2.00 (ISBN 0-89028-231-5). Vance Biblios.

--Architects' Contracts: A Bibliography. (Architecture Ser.: Bibliography A 1352). 1985. pap. 2.00 (ISBN 0-89028-322-2). Vance Biblios.

--Architectural Design: Monographs. (Architecture Ser.: Bibliography A-1299). 21p. 1985. pap. 3.00 (ISBN 0-89028-229-3). Vance Biblios.

--Art Nouveau: Monographs. (Architecture Series Bibliography: A-1288). 77p. 1984. pap. 11.25 (ISBN 0-89028-198-X). Vance Biblios.

--Automation in Buildings. (Architecture Ser.: Bibliograpphy A 1332). 1985. pap. 2.00 (ISBN 0-89028-282-X). Vance Biblios.

--Bibliographical Exhibitions: Monographs. (Architecture Ser.: Bibliography A 1350). 1985. pap. 3.00 (ISBN 0-89028-320-6). Vance Biblios.

--Building Laws: A Bibliography. (Architecture Ser.: Bibliography A-1316). 96p. 1985. pap. 14.25 (ISBN 0-89028-246-3). Vance Biblios.

--Modern Architecture of the Twentieth Century: Monographs. (Architecture Ser.: Bibliography: No. A-1100). 157p. 1983. pap. 18.00 (ISBN 0-88066-770-2). Vance Biblios.

--New Publications for Architecture Libraries (February 1985) (Architecture Ser.: Bibliography A 1317). 1985. pap. 10.50 (ISBN 0-89028-267-6). Vance Biblios.

--New Publications for Architecture Libraries (March 1985) (Architecture Ser.: Bibliography A 1337). 1985. pap. 12.75 (ISBN 0-89028-307-9). Vance Biblios.

--Rapid Construction: A Bibliography. (Architecture Ser.: Bibliography A 1330). 1985. pap. 2.00 (ISBN 0-89028-280-3). Vance Biblios.

White, Anthony G. Architectural Drawings-Collections: A Selected Bibliography. (Architecture Ser.: Bibliography A 1348). 1985. pap. 2.00 (ISBN 0-89028-318-4). Vance Biblios.

ARCHITECTURE–CONSERVATION AND RESTORATION

see also Buildings–Repair and Reconstruction

Architectural Record Magazine. New Life for Old Buildings. 200p. 1982. 38.50 (ISBN 0-07-002364-6). McGraw.

Bullock, Orin M., Jr. The Restoration Manual. LC 66-15647. 196p. 1966. 12.95 (ISBN 0-87231-009-4). Silvermine.

--The Restoration Manual: An Illustrated Guide to the Preservation & Restoration of Old Buildings. 192p. 1983. pap. 12.95 (ISBN 0-442-21433-2). Van Nos Reinhold.

Cantacuzino, Sherban, ed. Architectural Conservation in Europe. (Illus.). 144p. 1975. 20.00 (ISBN 0-8230-7044-1, Whitney Lib). Watson-Guptill.

Flavin, Christopher. Energy & Architecture: The Solar & Conservation Potential. LC 80-54002. (Worldwatch Papers). 1980. pap. 2.00 (ISBN 0-916468-39-9). Worldwatch Inst.

Hosmer, Charles B., Jr. Preservation Comes of Age: From Williamsburg to the National Trust, 1926-1949, 2 vols. LC 80-26067. (Illus.). 1291p. 1981. Set. 37.50x (ISBN 0-8139-0712-8). U Pr of Va.

Hutchins, Nigel. Restoring Houses of Brick & Stone. 192p. 1983. 29.95 (ISBN 0-7706-0029-8). Van Nos Reinhold.

Landry, Arthur W. Restoring Old Houses: A Guide for the Self-Builder & Building Professional. LC 83-6635. (Illus.). 160p. (Orig.). 1983. pap. 8.95 (ISBN 0-8069-7722-1). Sterling.

Markowitz, Arnold L., ed. Historic Preservation: A Guide to Information Sources. LC 80-14313. (Art & Architecture Information Guide Ser.: Vol. 13). 220p. 1980. 60.00x (ISBN 0-8103-1460-6). Gale.

National Trust for Historic Preservation. New Energy from Old Buildings. LC 81-8516. (Illus.). 208p. (Orig.). 1981. pap. 9.95 (ISBN 0-89133-095-X). Preservation Pr.

The Old House. LC 79-18936. (Home Repair & Improvement Ser.). (Illus.). 1979. lib. bdg. 13.27 kivar bdg (ISBN 0-8094-2422-3, Pub. by Time-Life). Silver.

Smith, John F., compiled by. A Critical Bibliography of Building Conservation: Historic Towns, Buildings, Their Furnishings & Fittings. 234p. 1978. lib. bdg. 43.00x (ISBN 0-7201-0707-5). Mansell.

Stoddard, Robert. A Grand Strategy: The Scenario for Saving the Grand Opera House, Wilmington, Delaware. LC 78-61052. (Case Studies in Preservation Ser.). (Illus.). 44p. 1978. 4.50 (ISBN 0-89133-057-7). Preservation Pr.

Vance, Mary. Conservation & Restoration of Historic Sites: Monographs. (Architecture Ser.: Bibliography A-1061). 59p. 1983. pap. 9.00 (ISBN 0-88066-691-9). Vance Biblios.

Will, Margaret T. Recycled Buildings: A Bibliography of Adaptive Use Literature Since Nineteen Seventy. (Architecture Ser.: Bibliography A-154). 71p. 1979. pap. 7.50 (ISBN 0-88066-041-4). Vance Biblios.

ARCHITECTURE–DATA PROCESSING

American Institute of Architects. The Architect's Guide to Facility Programming. 304p. 1981. 39.95 (ISBN 0-07-001490-6). McGraw.

Bernitsas, Michael M. & Guha-Thakurta, S. Program HYDCYL: A Database for Calculation of Hydrodynamic Loading of Circular Cylinders. (University of Michigan, Dept. of Naval Architecture & Marine Engineering, Report: No. 267). pap. 20.00 (ISBN 0-317-27134-2, 2024682). Bks Demand UMI.

Cadd Roundtable. 1984. 12.00 (ISBN 0-317-06680-3). Am Inst Arch.

Evans, Nigel. The Architect & the Computer, a Guide Through the Jungle. (Illus.). 40p. 1982. pap. 6.00 (ISBN 0-900630-77-9, Pub. by RIBA). Intl Spec Bk.

Gero, John S., ed. Computer Applications in Architecture. (Illus.). 1977. 77.75 (ISBN 0-85334-737-9, Pub. by Elsevier Applied Sci England). Elsevier.

Imron, A. & Bernitsas, M. M. Program STARI-3D: A Program for Static Risers, 3-Dimensional Analysis. (University of Michigan, Dept. of Naval Architecture & Marine Engineering, Report: No. 280). pap. 20.00 (ISBN 0-317-27124-5, 2024684). Bks Demand UMI.

Kemper, Alfred M. Pioneers of CADD in Architecture. (Illus.). 654p. 1985. 78.00 (ISBN 0-9614667-0-7); pap. 68.00 (ISBN 0-9614667-1-5). Hurland-Swenson.

Lee, Kaiman. Computer Aided Architectural Design: 16 ARK-2 Articles. LC 74-160961. 1973. 30.00x (ISBN 0-915250-04-7). Environ Design.

--Computer Aided Space Planning. LC 76-366704. 1976. 30.00x (ISBN 0-915250-20-9). Environ Design.

--The Computer as an Architectural Design Tool: An Exploration into Certain Multi-Story Building Plan Layouts. 190p. 1979. 25.00x (ISBN 0-915250-00-4). Environ Design.

--Interactive Computer Graphics in Architecture. LC 76-366950. 100p. 1976. 30.00x (ISBN 0-915250-21-7). Environ Design.

Leighton, Natalie L. Computers in the Architectural Office. 208p. 1984. 26.50 (ISBN 0-442-25967-0). Van Nos Reinhold.

Levy, Henry M. & Eckhouse, Richard H. Computer Programming & Architecture: The VAX-11. (Illus.). 407p. 1980. 28.00 (ISBN 0-932376-07-X, EY-AX008-DP). Digital Pr.

MacDougall, E. B., ed. Microcomputers in Landscape Architecture. 268p. 1983. pap. 34.50 (ISBN 0-444-00771-7). Elsevier.

Negroponte, Nicholas. The Architecture Machine. (Illus.). 164p. 1970. pap. 4.95x (ISBN 0-262-64010-4). MIT Pr.

Obermeyer, T. Architectural CAD Workbook. 192p. 1985. price not set (ISBN 0-07-047509-1). McGraw.

Person, R. Animation Magic Toolkit, IBM PC. 1985. write for info. (ISBN 0-07-881173-2). McGraw.

Reynolds, R. A. Computer Methods for Architects. (Illus.). 160p. 1980. text ed. 59.95 (ISBN 0-408-00476-2). Butterworth.

Ryan. Computer-Aided Architectural Graphics, Pt. I. 416p. 1983. 49.75 (ISBN 0-8247-1901-8). Dekker.

Stewart, Clifford D., et al, eds. Comprogram: Hospital Space Allocation, 2 vols. LC 73-158290. 1973. 58.00x (ISBN 0-915250-02-0). Environ Design.

Yassinsky, George. Fifty-Two Programs for Engineers & Architects, Vol. 1. (Illus.). 352p. 1984. 18.95 (ISBN 0-931379-00-8). Polymus Pub.

ARCHITECTURE–DESIGNS AND PLANS

see also Architecture, Domestic–Designs and Plans; Hospitals–Design and Construction; Theaters–Construction

Abbott, Derek & Pollit, Kimball. Hill Housing: A Guide to Design & Construction. 304p. 1981. 34.50 (ISBN 0-8230-7259-2, Whitney Lib). Watson-Guptill.

Aiello, J. R. & Baum, A., eds. Residential Crowding & Design. LC 79-357. (Illus.). 270p. 1979. 25.00x (ISBN 0-306-40205-X, Plenum Pr). Plenum Pub.

Aloi, R. Museums: Architecture, Technics. (Illus.). 1962. 50.00 (ISBN 0-685-12032-5). Heinman.

Ambrose, James. Building Structures Primer. 2nd ed. LC 81-4336. 136p. 1981. 30.95 (ISBN 0-471-08678-9, Pub. by Wiley-Interscience). Wiley.

Ambrose, James & Vergun, Dimitry. Simplified Building Design for Wind & Earthquake Forces. LC 79-26660. 142p. 1980. 37.50x (ISBN 0-471-05013-X, Pub. by Wiley-Interscience). Wiley.

American Institute of Architects. Materials Components & Design: An Integrated Approach Handbook. Rush, Richard D., ed. 500p. 1985. 84.95x. Wiley.

Andreasen, M. Myrup, et al. Design for Assembly. (Eng.). 189p. 1983. 41.50 (ISBN 0-387-12544-2). Springer-Verlag.

Antoniades, Anthony C. Architecture & Allied Design: An Environmental Design Perspective. (Illus.). 384p. (Orig.). 1980. pap. text ed. 19.50 (ISBN 0-8403-2154-6). Kendall-Hunt.

Art Institute of Chicago & Rizzoli International Publications & Rubin, Rebecca. Chicago Architects Design. LC 82-60339. (Illus.). 174p. 1982. pap. 25.00 (ISBN 0-8478-0466-6). Art Inst Chi.

Baker, Geoffrey H. Le Corbusier: An Analysis of Form. 288p. 1984. pap. 14.95 (ISBN 0-442-30557-5). Van Nos Reinhold.

Ball, John E. Architectural Drafting Fundamentals. (Illus.). 336p. 1980. text ed. 20.95 (ISBN 0-8359-0254-4). Reston.

Benton, Tim & Benton, Charlotte, eds. Form & Function: A Source Book for the History of Architecture & Design 1890-1939. 276p. 1975. pap. 17.50x (ISBN 0-246-11278-6, Pub by Granada England). Sheridan.

Blackwell, William. Geometry in Architecture. LC 83-10281. 185p. 1984. 37.50x (ISBN 0-471-09683-0, Pub. by Wiley-Interscience). Wiley.

Broadbent, Geoffrey. Design in Architecture & the Human Sciences. LC 71-39233. 504p. 1973. pap. 32.95x (ISBN 0-471-99527-4). Wiley.

Brown, G. Z. Sun, Wind & Light: Architectural Design Strategies. 192p. 1985. 32.95 (ISBN 0-471-89506-7); pap. text ed. 15.95 (ISBN 0-471-82063-6). Wiley.

Callender, J. Time-Saver Standards for Architectural Design Data. 6th ed. 1982. 75.00 (ISBN 0-07-009663-5). McGraw.

Clayton, George T. The Site Plan for Architectural Working Drawings. (Illus.). 42p. 1973. pap. text ed. 3.00X (ISBN 0-87563-252-1). Stipes.

Cohen, Aaron & Cohen, Elaine. Designing & Space Planning for Libraries: A Behavioral Guide. LC 79-12478. (Illus.). 1979. 32.50 (ISBN 0-8352-1150-9). Bowker.

Crowe & Laseau. Visual Notes for Architects & Designers. 1984. 24.95 (ISBN 0-442-29335-6). Van Nos Reinhold.

Crump, Ralph W., ed. The Design Connection: Energy & Technology in Architecture. Harms, Martin J. (Preston Thomas Memorial Series in Architecture). 144p. 1981. 23.95 (ISBN 0-442-23125-3). Van Nos Reinhold.

Design of Buildings for Fire Safety, STP 685. 290p. 1979. 28.00x (ISBN 0-8031-0320-4, 04-685000-31). ASTM.

De Vido, Alfredo. Designing Your Client's House: The Architect's Guide for Meeting Design Goals & Budgets. (Illus.). 208p. 1983. 27.50 (ISBN 0-8230-7142-1, Whitney Lib). Watson-Guptill.

Dibner, D. R. & Dibner-Dunlap, A. Building Additions Design. 256p. 1985. 39.95 (ISBN 0-07-016761-3). McGraw.

Dike, R. Architectural Common Sense Site, Vol. 1. 1983. 22.95 (ISBN 0-442-21364-6); pap. 14.95 (ISBN 0-442-21805-2). Van Nos Reinhold.

Doblin, Jay. Perspective: A New System for Designers. (Illus.). 68p. 1956. 14.95 (ISBN 0-8230-7419-6, Whitney Lib). Watson-Guptill.

Duffy, Francis, et al. Planning Office Space. (Illus.). 1976. 98.50 (ISBN 0-85139-505-8, Pub. by Architectural Pr). Nichols Pub.

Evans, Benjamin. Daylight in Architecture. LC 80-26066. (Illus.). 204p. 1982. 42.50x (ISBN 0-07-019768-7). McGraw.

Fabrick, Martin N. & O'Rourke, Joseph J. Environmental Planning for Design & Construction. LC 81-23070. (Construction Management & Engineering Ser.). 304p. 1982. 48.50x (ISBN 0-471-05848-3, Pub. by Wiley-Interscience). Wiley.

Forseth, Kevin. Graphics for Architecture. (Illus.). 288p. 1979. pap. 12.95 (ISBN 0-442-26390-2). Van Nos Reinhold.

Gheorghiu, A. & Dragomir, V. Geometry of Structural Forms. (Illus.). 319p. 1978. 44.50 (ISBN 0-85334-683-6, Pub. by Elsevier Applied Sci England). Elsevier.

Gibbs, James. Book of Architecture. LC 68-17153. (Illus.). 1968. Repr. of 1728 ed. 66.00 (ISBN 0-405-08560-5, Blom Pubns). Ayer Co Pubs.

Grant, Donald P. Design by Objectives: Multiple Objective Design Analysis & Evaluation in Architectural, Environmental & Product Design. LC 82-73290. 50p. (Orig.). 1982. pap. text ed. 6.00x (ISBN 0-910821-00-3). Design Meth.

Greater London Council Department of Architecture & Civic Design. Good Practice Details. (Illus.). 148p. 1980. 24.95 (ISBN 0-85139-241-5); pap. 17.50 (ISBN 0-85139-242-3). Nichols Pub.

Greenbeg, Alan & George, Michael, eds. Monograph of the Work of McKim, Mead & White 1879-1915. (Illus.). 160p. 1981. pap. 10.95 student ed. (ISBN 0-8038-6775-1). Architectural.

Greif, Martin. The Airport Book: From Landing Field to Modern Terminal. (Illus.). 1979. 12.95 (ISBN 0-8317-0150-1, Mayflower Bks). Smith Pubs.

Handler, A. Benjamin. Systems Approach to Architecture. LC 79-100397. (Elsevier Architectural Science Ser.). pap. 48.00 (ISBN 0-317-10850-6, 2007768). Bks Demand UMI.

Haneman, John T. Pictorial Encyclopedia of Historic Architectural Plans, Details & Elements. (Architecture, Interior Design, Period Style Ser.). 140p. 1984. pap. 6.95 (ISBN 0-486-24605-1). Dover.

Harkness, Sarah & Groom, James N. Building Without Barriers for the Disabled. (Illus.). 80p. (Orig.). 1976. 14.95 (ISBN 0-8230-7082-4, Whitney Lib). Watson-Guptill.

Haviland, David. Managing Architectural Projects: The Process. (Illus.). 112p. 1981. pap. 22.50x (ISBN 0-913962-31-7); pap. 18.00x. Am Inst Arch.

Hill, David A. Design Procedures: Level II. cancelled (ISBN 0-442-30484-6); pap. cancelled (ISBN 0-442-30485-4). Van Nos Reinhold.

Hilleborg, Arno. Strip Method of Design. 2nd ed. (C & CA Viewpoint Publication Ser.). (Illus.). 1976. pap. text ed. 26.50x (ISBN 0-7210-1012-1). Scholium Intl.

Hitchcock, Henry-Russell & Johnson, Philip. International Style. (Illus.). 1966. pap. 6.95 (ISBN 0-393-00311-6, Norton Lib). Norton.

Home Planners, Inc. Four-Hundred, One-&-a-Half & Two-Story Homes. (Design Category Ser.: Vol. 1). (Illus.). 320p. 1982. pap. 5.95 (ISBN 0-918894-26-3). Home Planners.

Home Planners, Inc., Staff. One Hundred Two Home Plans. 96p. 1980. 2.75 (ISBN 0-918894-41-7). Home Planners.

--Two Hundred Ten Home Plans: One Story Designs over 2,000 Sq. Ft. (Illus.). 192p. 1982. pap. 3.95 (ISBN 0-918894-27-1). Home Planners.

Hopf, Peter. Designer's Guide to OSHA: A Practical Design Guide to the Occupational Safety & Health Act for Architects, Engineers, & Builders. 2nd ed. (Illus.). 1982. 42.50 (ISBN 0-07-030317-7). McGraw.

Itoh, Teiji. Kura: Design & Tradition of the Japanese Storehouse. abr. ed. Terry, Charles S., tr. from Japanese. LC 80-21087. (Illus.). 192p. 1980. pap. 17.50 (ISBN 0-914842-53-6). Madrona Pubs.

Jacoby, Helmut, compiled by. New Techniques of Architectural Rendering. 2nd ed. 1981. pap. 16.95 (ISBN 0-442-21211-9). Van Nos Reinhold.

Jencks, Charles, ed. Abstract Representation: An Architectural Design Profile. (Academy Architecture Series). (Illus.). 112p. 1983. pap. 14.95 (ISBN 0-312-00197-5). St Martin.

Jensen, Robert & Conway, Patricia. Ornamentalism: The New Decorativeness in Architecture & Design. (Illus.). 312p. 1982. 40.00 (ISBN 0-517-54383-4, C N Potter Bks). Crown.

John, Geraint & Heard, Helen, eds. The Handbook of Sports & Recreational Building Design, Vols. 1-4. (Illus.). 728p. 1981. 265.00x set (ISBN 0-85139-600-3). Nichols Pub.

--The Handbook of Sports & Recreational Building Design, Vol. 1: Ice Rinks & Swimming Pools. (Illus.). 168p. 1981. 75.00x (ISBN 0-85139-586-4). Nichols Pub.

--The Handbook of Sports & Recreational Building Design, Vol. 2: Indoor Sports. (Illus.). 224p. 1981. 90.00x (ISBN 0-85139-587-2). Nichols Pub.

--The Handbook of Sports & Recreational Building Design, Vol. 3: Outdoor Sports. (Illus.). 192p. 1981. 78.50x (ISBN 0-85139-598-8). Nichols Pub.

Johnson, Philip & Burgee, John. Philip Johnson & John Burgee: Architecture. LC 79-4786. 1979. 35.00 (ISBN 0-394-50744-4). Random.

Jones, J. Christopher. Design Methods: Seeds of Human Futures 1980 Edition a Review of New Topics. LC 80-41757. 448p. 1981. 29.95x (ISBN 0-471-27958-7, Pub. by Wiley Interscience). Wiley.

Kemper, Alfred M. Presentation Drawings by American Architects. LC 76-40891. 380p. 1977. 59.50x (ISBN 0-471-01369-2, Pub. by Wiley-Interscience). Wiley.

King, Jean C. & Esposito, Tony, eds. The Designer's Guide to Text Type. 320p. 1980. pap. 26.50 (ISBN 0-442-25425-3). Van Nos Reinhold.

Krier, Rob. Elements of Architecture: An Architectural Design Profile. 96p. 1984. pap. 14.95 (ISBN 0-312-24127-5). St Martin.

Kulterman, Udo. Architecture in the Seventies. (ABPC Ser.). (Illus.). 160p. 1980. 29.95 (ISBN 0-8038-0019-3). Architectural.

Lee, Kaiman. Computer Aided Space Planning. LC 76-366704. 1976. 30.00x (ISBN 0-915250-20-9). Environ Design.

--Interactive Computer Aided Architectural Design: Four Applications. 1976. pap. 12.00x (ISBN 0-915250-26-8). Environ Design.

Lifchez, Raymond & Winslow, Barbara. Design for Independent Living: The Environment & Physically Disabled People. (Illus.). 208p. 1981. pap. 9.95 (ISBN 0-520-04434-7, CAL 512). U of Cal Pr.

Lin, Mike W. Architectural Rendering Techniques. LC 84-25812. (Illus.). 256p. 1985. 40.00 (ISBN 0-442-25953-0). Van Nos Reinhold.

Llewellyn, Robert, photos by. The Academical Village: Thomas Jefferson University. (Illus.). 80p. 1982. 25.00 (ISBN 0-934738-03-3). Thomasson-Grant.

Martin, Leslie. Buildings & Ideas, Nineteen Thirty-Four to Nineteen Eighty-Three: From the Studio of Leslie Martin & His Associates. LC 82-4359. (Illus.). 233p. 1984. 89.50 (ISBN 0-521-23107-8). Cambridge U Pr.

Mejetta, Mirko & Spada, Simonetta. Creating Interiors in Limited Spaces. (Illus.). 128p. 1984. 32.50 (ISBN 0-8230-7131-6, Whitney Lib). Watson-Guptill.

Melaragno, Michele G. Wind in Architectural & Environmental Design. 512p. 1981. 38.50 (ISBN 0-442-25130-0). Van Nos Reinhold.

Meyer, William T. Energy Economics & Building Design. 352p. 1983. 29.95 (ISBN 0-07-041751-2). McGraw.

Mitchell, William. Computer-Aided Architectural Design. 1977. pap. 21.50 (ISBN 0-442-26248-5). Van Nos Reinhold.

Monograph on Tall Buildings. 1981. 250.00x (ISBN 0-87262-289-4). Am Soc Civil Eng.

Muller, E. Reading Architectural Working Drawings. 2nd ed. 1981. 32.95 (ISBN 0-13-753939-8). P-H.

Mun, David. Shops: A Manual of Planning & Design. (Illus.). 192p. 1982. 87.50 (ISBN 0-89397-112-X). Nichols Pub.

Natural Disasters & Educational Building Design. (Illus.). 33p. 1977. pap. 6.00 (ISBN 0-685-76009-X, UB39, UB). Unipub.

Nelson, John A. Handbook of Architectural & Civil Drafting. 296p. 1983. 32.95 (ISBN 0-442-26865-3); pap. 16.95 (ISBN 0-442-26864-5). Van Nos Reinhold.

Nichols, Frederick D., ed. Thomas Jefferson's Architectural Drawings. 2nd ed. LC 76-163982. (Illus.). 48p. (Orig.). 1961. pap. 3.95 (ISBN 0-8139-0328-9). U Pr of Va.

Oles, Paul S. Architectural Illustration: The Value Delineation Process. 1982. Van Nos Reinhold.

Passini, Romedi. Wayfinding in Architecture. 234p. 1984. 29.50 (ISBN 0-442-27590-0). Van Nos Reinhold.

Plan Reading & Nonstructural Plan Review. 69.00 (ISBN 0-318-00070-9, BIT-101). Intl Conf Bldg Off.

Plan Review Manual, 1980. 15.90 (ISBN 0-318-00052-0). Intl Conf Bldg Off.

Porter, Tom & Goodman, Sue. Manual of Graphic Techniques 4: For Architects, Graphic Designers, & Artists. (Illus.). 128p. 1985. pap. 10.95 (ISBN 0-684-18216-5, ScribT). Scribner.

Prenzel, Rudolph. Working & Design Drawings. 136p. 1982. 100.00x (ISBN 0-686-45592-4, Pub. by L Brooks England). State Mutual Bk.

Prudon, Theodore. Architectural Preservation & Conservation Handbook: A Color Reference. 1986. cancelled (ISBN 0-442-26641-3). Van Nos Reinhold.

Quinn, A. D. Design & Construction of Ports & Marine Structures. 2nd ed. 1971. 49.95 (ISBN 0-07-051064-4). McGraw.

Radford, William A. Old House Measured & Scaled Drawings for Builders & Carpenters: An Early 20th Century Pictorial Sourcebook, with 183 Detailed Plates. 2nd ed. (Illus.). 200p. 1983. pap. 8.95 (ISBN 0-486-24438-5). Dover.

Rich, Stephen. Rendering Standards in Architecture & Design. 1984. pap. 17.95 (ISBN 0-442-22671-3). Van Nos Reinhold.

Risebero, Bill. Modern Architecture & Design. 256p. 1982. 40.00x (ISBN 0-906969-18-2, Pub. by Benn Pubns). State Mutual Bk.

--Modern Architecture & Design: An Alternative History. (Illus.). 256p. 1985. pap. 9.95 (ISBN 0-262-68046-7). MIT Pr.

Robertson, J. C. The Basic Principles of Architectural Design. (Illus.). 127p. 1983. 67.25 (ISBN 0-86650-058-8). Gloucester Art.

Rosen, H. J. Construction Materials for Architecture. (Practical Construction Guides Ser.). 248p. 1985. 42.95 (ISBN 0-471-86421-8). Wiley.

Rubens, Peter P. Palazzi Di Genova, 2 vols in 1. LC 68-21226. (Illus.). 1968. Repr. of 1622 ed. 60.00 (ISBN 0-405-08901-5). Ayer Co Pubs.

Russell, Beverly. Designers' Workplaces: Thirty-Three Offices by Designers for Designers. (Illus.). 144p. 1983. 27.50 (ISBN 0-8230-7492-7, Whitney Lib). Watson-Guptill.

Safdie, Moshe. Form & Purpose: Is The Emperor Naked. (Illus.). 144p. 1982. 19.95 (ISBN 0-395-31663-4); pap. 9.95 (ISBN 0-395-31664-2). HM.

Salvadori, Mario. Why Buildings Stand Up: The Stength of Architecture. (Illus.). 1982. pap. 6.95 (ISBN 0-07-054482-4). Mcgraw.

Schild, Erich, et al. Environmental Physics in Construction: Its Application in Architectural Design. 211p. 1982. text ed. 65.00 (ISBN 0-246-11224-7, Pub. by Granada England). Brookfield Pub Co.

Scully, Vincent. Shingle Style & the Stick Style: Architectural Theory & Design from Richardson to the Origins of Wright. rev. ed. (Publications in the History of Art Ser.: No. 20). (Illus.). 1971. pap. 14.95x (ISBN 0-300-01519-4). Yale U Pr.

Sherratt, A. F., ed. Integrated Environment in Building Design. LC 74-22250. 281p. 1975. 58.95x (ISBN 0-470-78575-6). Halsted Pr.

Sleeper, Harold R. Building Planning & Design Standards for Architects, Engineers, Designers, Consultants, Building Committees, Draftsmen & Students. 331p. 1955. 53.50x (ISBN 0-471-79761-8, Pub. by Wiley-Interscience). Wiley.

Sloan, Samuel. Sloan's Victorian Buildings: Illustrations & Floor Plans for 60 Residences & Other Structures, 2 vols. in 1. (Illus.). 400p. 1981. pap. 13.95 (ISBN 0-486-24009-6). Dover.

Spring, Elizabeth & Sherman, Harvey, eds. A New American House, Architectural Design Competition 1984: A Catalouge of Winning & Selected Entries. (Illus.). 31p. (Orig.). 1984. pap. 6.00 (ISBN 0-9611672-0-3). Minneapolis Coll Art.

Steadman, Philip. Architectural Morphology: An Introduction to the Geometry of Building Plans. (Illus.). 280p. 1983. 27.00 (ISBN 0-85086-086-5, NO. 5052, Pub. by Pion). Methuen Inc.

Stonis, Richard E. & Pulgram, William L. Designing the Automated Office: A Guide for Architects & Interior Designers. (Illus.). 224p. 1984. 34.50 (ISBN 0-8230-7136-7, Whitney Lib). Watson Guptill.

Suckle, Abby, ed. By Their Own Design. (Illus.). 160p. 1980. 19.95 (ISBN 0-8230-7097-2, Whitney Lib). Watson-Guptill.

Swinburne, Herbert. Design Cost Analysis for Architects & Engineers. (Illus.). 1980. 35.95 (ISBN 0-07-062635-9). McGraw.

Taylor, Anne. Stars under the Blanket: Ornamentation & Design in the Architecture of John Gaw Meem. LC 85-2785. (Illus.). 96p. 1985. pap. 14.95 (ISBN 0-86534-069-2). Sunstone Pr.

Two Hundred Five Home Plans: Multi-Level Designs. (Design Category Ser.: Vol. 4). 192p. 1982. pap. 3.95 (ISBN 0-918894-29-8). Home Planners.

Ungers, O. M. Architecture As Theme. LC 82-60199. (Illus.). 128p. 1982. pap. 25.00 (ISBN 0-8478-5363-2). Rizzoli Intl.

Unwin, Raymond. Legacy of Raymond Unwin: A Human Pattern for Planning. Creese, Raymond, ed. 1967. 32.50x (ISBN 0-262-03022-5). MIT Pr.

Vogt, Lloyd J. & Eskew, R. Allen. Modern Architectural Forms: A Project Sourcebook. 250p. 1974. 16.50x (ISBN 0-913690-05-8). Aloray.

Wakita, Osamu A. & Linde, Richard M. The Professional Practice of Architectural Working Drawings. LC 83-21838. 561p. 1984. text ed. 29.95 (ISBN 0-471-05636-7). Wiley.

Wallach, Paul I. Basic Architectural Drafting. LC 81-85599. (Illus.). 272p. 1982. text ed. 12.50 (ISBN 0-538-33300-6); write for info. tchr's. manual & key (ISBN 0-538-33301-4); write for info. wkbk. (ISBN 0-538-33302-2, IE30). SW Pub.

--Interior Design: A Space Planning Kit. (Illus.). 1983. text ed. 11.50 (ISBN 0-538-32020-6, HE02). SW Pub.

Wang, T. Space for Architecture. 1986. pap. price not set (ISBN 0-442-29304-6). Van Nos Reinhold.

Wang, Thomas C. Plan & Section Drawing. (Illus.). 100p. 1979. pap. 9.95 (ISBN 0-442-29178-7). Van Nos Reinhold.

Weidhaas, Ernest R. Reading Architectural Plans for Residential & Commercial Construction. 2nd ed. 336p. 1980. text ed. 35.46 (ISBN 0-205-07155-4, 3271552); tchr's guide free (ISBN 0-205-07167-8). Allyn.

Wheater, Delma J. Environmental Design: An Analysis of the Field, Its Implication for Libraries & a Guide to the Literature, Nos. 747-748. 1975. 8.50 (ISBN 0-686-20341-0). CPL Biblios.

Winning Low Energy Building Designs. 651p. 1980. 37.00 (ISBN 0-660-50675-0, SSC156, SSC). Unipub.

ARCHITECTURE–DETAILS

see also Domes; Doors and Doorways; Fireplaces; Floors; Foundations; Roofs; Windows; Woodwork

Ambrose, James. Simplified Design of Building Structures. LC 79-413. 268p. 1979. 34.95 (ISBN 0-471-04721-X, Pub. by Wiley-Interscience). Wiley.

Ashihara, Yoshinobu. The Aesthetic Townscape. Riggs, Lynne E., tr. from Japanese. (Illus.). 196p. 1983. 24.75 (ISBN 0-262-01069-0); pap. 9.95 (ISBN 0-262-51031-6). MIT Pr.

Austin, Richard L. Site Graphics. (Illus.). 128p. 1984. text ed. 19.95 (ISBN 0-442-21077-9). Van Nos Reinhold.

Boyne, Colin & Wright, Lance. Best of Architect's Working Details, Vol. 2: Internal. 200p. 1982. 36.50 (ISBN 0-89397-143-X). Nichols Pub.

Buildings for Industry. LC 72-142926. (An Architectural Record Book). (Illus.). ix, 309p. Repr. of 1957 ed. lib. bdg. 31.75x (ISBN 0-8371-5928-8, ARBI). Greenwood.

Clark, Roger. Precedents in Architecture. 1984. pap. 19.95 (ISBN 0-442-21668-8). Van Nos Reinhold.

Hornbostel, Caleb. Architectural Detailing Simplified. (Illus.). 160p. 1985. 22.95 (ISBN 0-13-044173-2). P-H.

Larsen, Jack. Interface: Plating & Related Structures. cancelled (ISBN 0-442-24508-4); pap. cancelled (ISBN 0-442-24509-2). Van Nos Reinhold.

Orr, Frank. Scale in Architecture. (Illus., Orig.). 1984. cancelled; pap. write for info. (ISBN 0-442-27245-6). Van Nos Reinhold.

Porter, Tom. Architectural Color. (Illus.). 128p. 1982. 29.95 (ISBN 0-8230-7407-2, Whitney Lib). Watson-Guptill.

Pracht, Klaus. Modern Oriels on Roofs & Facades. (Illus.). 160p. 1984. 35.00 (ISBN 0-442-27286-3). Van Nos Reinhold.

Robertson, J. C. The Basic Principles of Architectural Design. (Illus.). 127p. 1983. 67.25 (ISBN 0-86650-058-8). Gloucester Art.

Vance, Mary. Monographs on Architectural Details. LC 84-188560. (Architecture Series Bibliography: A-1168). 68p. 1984. 10.50 (ISBN 0-88066-938-1). Vance Biblios.

ARCHITECTURE–DICTIONARIES

Abd-El-Gawad, Tawfik. Technical Dictionary: Archtiecture & Building. (Eng., Fr., Ger. & Arabic.). 1319p. 1976. 35.00x (ISBN 0-686-44745-X, Pub. by Collets). State Mutual Bk.

Barry, W. R., ed. Architectural, Construction, Manufacturing & Engineering Glossary of Terms. 519p. 1979. pap. 40.00 (ISBN 0-930284-05-4). Am Assn Cost Engineers.

Binstead, Harry E. The Fully Illustrated Book of Decorative Details from Major Architectural Styles. (Illus.). 157p. Repr. of 1894 ed. 89.45 (ISBN 0-89901-057-1). Found Class Reprints.

Bucksch, Herbert. Dictionary of Architecture, Building Construction & Materials, Vol. II. (Eng. & Ger.). 1137p. 1976. 175.00 (ISBN 3-7625-0714-7, M-7130). French & Eur.

--Dictionary of Architecture, Building Construction & Materials, Vol. I. (Eng. & Ger.). 942p. 1974. 175.00 (ISBN 3-7625-0357-5, M-7131). French & Eur.

--Dictionary of Architecture, Building Construction & Materials, 2 vols. 1974-76. plastic bdg.cancelled 120.00x ea. Vol. 1, Ger.-Eng (ISBN 3-7625-0357-5). Vol. 2, Eng.-Ger (ISBN 3-7625-0714-7). Intl Pubns Serv.

Bucksch, Herbert, ed. Dictionary of Architecture, Building Constrution & Materials-Worterbuch Fur Architektur, Hochbau Und Baustoffe, 2 vols. 2nd ed. Incl. Vol. 1. 942p. 1980. English-German. plastic cover 180.00x (ISBN 3-7625-1399-6); Vol. 2. 1137p. 1983. English-German. plastic cover 180.00x (ISBN 3-7625-2075-5). Intl Pubns Serv.

Calsat, Jean-Henri & Sydler, Jean P. Vocabulaire International des Termes d'Urbanisme et d'Architecture. (Fr., Ger. & Eng.). 350p. 1970. 95.00 (ISBN 0-686-56935-0, M-6057). French & Eur.

Cowan, Henry J. A Dictionary of Architectural Science. LC 73-15839. (Illus.). 354p. 1973. pap. 19.95x (ISBN 0-470-18070-6). Halsted Pr.

Dictionnaire Pour l'Architecture, le Batiment et les Materiaux de Construction, 2 vols. (Ger. & Fr.). 820p. 1977. band I 236.00 (ISBN 3-7625-0786-4, M-7095). French & Eur.

Dictionnaire Pour l'Architecture, le Batiment et les Materiaux de Construction, 2 vols. (Ger. & Fr.). 688p. 1979. band II 236.00 (ISBN 3-7625-0787-2, M-7096). French & Eur.

English-Chinese Architectural Engineering Dictionary. (Eng. & Chinese.). 441p. 1973. 14.95 (ISBN 0-686-92620-X, M-9254). French & Eur.

Fairholt, F. W. The Art, Architecture, Heraldry & Archeology Dictionary Profusely Illustrated, 3 vols. (Illus.). 430p. 1985. Repr. Set. 385.85 (ISBN 0-89901-214-0). Found Class Reprints.

Gaward, Abd El. Architecture & Building Dictionary: English-French-German-Arabic. (Eng., Fr., Ger. & Arabic.). 465p. 1976. Leatherette 45.00 (ISBN 0-686-92255-7, M-9753). French & Eur.

Harris, Cyril M. Dictionary of Architecture & Construction. 1975. 49.50 (ISBN 0-07-026756-1). McGraw.

Lampugnani, Vittorio M., ed. Encyclopedia of Twentieth Century Architecture. rev. ed. (Illus.). 384p. 1985. text ed. 24.95 (ISBN 0-8109-0860-3). Abrams.

Neve, Richard. City & Country Purchaser & Builder's Dictionary. LC 69-16762. Repr. of 1726 ed. 29.50x (ISBN 0-678-05616-1). Kelley.

Phillips, Steven J. An Architectural Lexicon for the Historical Archaeologist. (Illus.). 484p. (Orig.). pap. cancelled (ISBN 0-89301-098-7). U Pr of Idaho.

Putnam, R. & Carlson, G. E. Architectural & Building Trades Dictionary. 3rd ed. (Illus.). 1974. 15.50 (ISBN 0-8269-0402-5). Am Technical.

Putnam, R. E. & Carlson, G. E. Architectural & Building Trades Dictionary. 3rd ed. 512p. 1983. 17.95 (ISBN 0-442-27461-0). Van Nos Reinhold.

Reference International Publishers. Encyclopedia of Architectural Technology. (Illus.). 1979. 38.00 (ISBN 0-07-051740-1). McGraw.

Stierlin, Henri. Encyclopedia of World Architecture. 416p. 1982. pap. 18.95 (ISBN 0-442-27957-4). Van Nos Reinhold.

Tatman, Sandra L. & Moss, Roger W. Biographical Dictionary of Philadelphia Architects & Master Builders: 1760-1930. 1984. lib. bdg. 99.50 (ISBN 0-8161-0437-9, Hall Reference). G K Hall.

Ware, Dora. Diccionario Manual Ilustrado De Arquitectura, Con los Terminos Mas Comunes Empleados En la Construccion. 6th ed. 224p. 1977. pap. 11.50 (ISBN 84-252-0021-0, S-50275). French & Eur.

Wilt, J. Encyclopedia of Architecture. Papworth, W., ed. (Illus.). 1392p. 1982. 12.98 (ISBN 0-517-37985-6, Bonanza). Outlet Bk Co.

ARCHITECTURE–HANDBOOKS, MANUALS, ETC.

Benjamin, Asher. The Practical House Carpenter. 119p. Repr. of 1830 ed. 39.00 (ISBN 0-318-04471-4). Am Repr Serv.

Briggs, Martin S. Everyman's Concise Encyclopaedia of Architecture. (Everyman's References Library). 372p. 1974. Repr. of 1959 ed. 17.95x (ISBN 0-460-03002-7, Pub by J M Dent England). Biblio Dist.

Cooper, N. The Opulent Eye. (Illus.). 264p. 1980. pap. text ed. 18.80x (ISBN 0-85139-506-6, Pub. by Architectural Pr England). Humanities.

Crump, Ralph W., ed. The Design Connection: Energy & Technology in Architecture. Harms, Martin J. (Preston Thomas Memorial Series in Architecture). 144p. 1981. 23.95 (ISBN 0-442-23125-3). Van Nos Reinhold.

Green, Ronald. The Architect's Guide to Running a Job. 3rd ed. 140p. 1980. 14.50 (ISBN 0-85139-011-0). Nichols Pub.

Kemper, Alfred A. Architectural Handbook: Environmental Analysis, Architectural Programming, Design & Technology, & Construction. 591p. 1979. 74.95x (ISBN 0-471-02697-2). Wiley.

Kidder, Frank E. & Parker, Harry. Architects' & Builders' Handbook. 18th ed. 2315p. 1931. 117.95 (ISBN 0-471-47421-5, Pub. by Wiley-Interscience). Wiley.

Noble, John. Activities & Spaces: Dimensional Data for Housing Design. (Illus.). 32p. 1983. pap. 8.95 (ISBN 0-85139-745-X). Nichols Pub.

Proulx, E. Annie. Plan & Make Your Own Fences & Gates, Walkways, Walls & Drives. Halpin, Anne, ed. (Illus.). 224p. 1983. pap. 11.95 (ISBN 0-87857-453-0, 14-048-1). Rodale Pr Inc.

Rosengarten, A. Handbook of Architectural Styles. Smith, Roger T., ed. Collet-Sandars, W., tr. from Ger. 532p. 1984. pap. 12.50 cancelled (ISBN 0-89341-489-1). Longwood Pub Group.

Spence, William P. Architecture: Design-Engineering-Drawing. rev. ed. 1979. text ed. 21.97 (ISBN 0-87345-099-X); quizzes & problems 6.00 (ISBN 0-87345-098-1); ans. key avail. (ISBN 0-685-14523-9). McKnight.

Stitt, F. Designing Buildings That Work: The Architect's Problem Prevention Sourcebook. LC 84-23398. 192p. 1985. 32.50 (ISBN 0-07-047952-6). McGraw.

Sturgis, Russell, compiled by. Architecture Sourcebook. LC 84-7275. (Illus.). 416p. 1984. pap. 19.95 (ISBN 0-442-28031-9). Van Nos Reinhold.

Willis, Arthur J. & Willis, Christopher J. Practice & Procedure for the Quantity Surveyor. 8th ed. 239p. 1980. text ed. 30.75x (ISBN 0-246-11172-0, Pub. by Granada England); pap. text ed. 19.25x (ISBN 0-246-11242-5, Pub. by Granada England). Brookfield Pub Co.

ARCHITECTURE–RESTORATION

see Architecture–Conservation and Restoration

ARCHITECTURE–STUDY AND TEACHING

Gropius, Walter. New Architecture & the Bauhaus. (Illus.). 1965. pap. 5.95 (ISBN 0-262-57006-8). MIT Pr.

Ready, Barbara C. & McCommons, Richard E., eds. Architecture Schools in North America. 3rd ed. LC 82-9116. 285p. (Orig.). 1982. pap. 11.95 (ISBN 0-87866-177-8). Petersons Guides.

Weidhaas, Ernest R. A Guide for Teaching Architectural Drafting & Design. (Illus.). 208p. 1982. pap. 28.95x (ISBN 0-205-07808-7, Pub. by Longwood Div). Allyn.

ARCHITECTURE–JAPAN

Frampton, Kenneth, ed. Tadao Ando. 144p. 1984. pap. 19.95 (ISBN 0-8478-0547-6). Rizzoli Intl.

Itoh, Teiji. Kura: Design & Tradition of the Japanese Storehouse. abr. ed. Terry, Charles S., tr. from Japanese. LC 80-21087. (Illus.). 192p. 1980. pap. 17.50 (ISBN 0-914842-53-6). Madrona Pubs.

ARCHITECTURE–UNITED STATES

Arnell, Peter & Bickford, Ted, eds. Frank O. Gehry: Buildings & Projects 1954-1984. LC 84-42646. (Illus.). 304p. 1985. 45.00 (ISBN 0-8478-0542-5); pap. 29.95 (ISBN 0-8478-0543-3). Rizzoli Intl.

Art Institute of Chicago & Rizzoli International Publications & Rubin, Rebecca. Chicago Architects Design. LC 82-60339. (Illus.). 174p. 1982. pap. 25.00 (ISBN 0-8478-0466-6). Art Inst Chi.

Wallace, Hugh N. The Navy, the Company, & Richard King: British Exploration in the Canadian Arctic, 1829-1860. (Illus.). 265p. 1980. 25.00x (ISBN 0-7735-0338-2). McGill-Queens U Pr.

Weller, Gunter & Bowling, Sue A. Climate of the Arctic: Twenty-Fourth Alaska Science Conference, 1973. LC 53-481. 436p. 1975. 10.00 (ISBN 0-915360-01-2). Geophysical Inst.

Westermeyer, W. E. & Shusterich, K. M., eds. United States Arctic Interests: The 1980's & 1990's. (Illus.). 304p. 1984. 35.00 (ISBN 0-387-96009-0). Springer-Verlag.

ARDEIDAE

see Herodiones

AREA MEASUREMENT

see also Planimeter

Breed, C. B. Surveying. 3rd ed. 495p. 1971. 43.45x (ISBN 0-471-10070-6). Wiley.

AREA SEPTALIS

see Septum (Brain)

AREOMETER

see Hydrometer

ARGON

Clever. Argon: Gas Solubilities. (IUPAC Solubility Data Ser.: Vol. 4). (Illus.). 348p. 1980. 100.00 (ISBN 0-08-022353-2). Pergamon.

Mendeleev, D. I. Principles of Chemistry, 4 pts. in 2 vols. 3rd ed. Pope, Thomas H., ed. Kamensky, G., tr. 1905. Set. 70.00 (ISBN 0-527-63100-0). Kraus Repr.

ARGON-POTASSIUM DATING

see Potassium-Argon Dating

ARID REGIONS

see also Deserts

Amiran, David H. K. & Wilson, Andrew H., eds. Coastal Deserts: Their Natural & Human Environments. LC 73-76305. 207p. 1973. 22.50x (ISBN 0-8165-0312-5). U of Ariz Pr.

Arid-Zone Hydrology: Investigations with Isotope Techniques. (Panel Proceedings Ser.). (Illus.). 265p. 1981. pap. 29.50 (ISBN 92-0-141180-4, ISP547, IAEA). Unipub.

Bishay, A. & McGinnies, W. G., eds. Applications of Science & Technology for Desert Development. (Advances in Desert & Arid Land Technology & Development: Vol. 1). 630p. 1979. lib. bdg. 102.95 (ISBN 3-7186-0002-1). Harwood Academic.

Campos-Lopez, Enrique & Anderson, Robert J., eds. Natural Resources & Development in Arid & Semi-Arid Regions. 350p. 1982. lib. bdg. 29.00x (ISBN 0-86531-418-7). Westview.

Conservation in Arid & Semi-Arid Zones. (Conservation Guides: No. 3). (Eng. & Fr., Illus.). 134p. (3rd Printing, 1983). 1976. pap. 9.75 (ISBN 92-5-100130-8, F743, FAO). Unipub.

Environmental Physiology & Psychology in Arid Conditions: Review of Research. (Arid Zone Research Ser.: No. 22). 345p. 1963. 26.00 (ISBN 92-3-100531-6, U221, UNESCO); pap. write for info (ISBN 92-3-100532-4). Unipub.

Golany, Gideon, ed. Urban Planning for Arid Zones: American Experiences & Directions. LC 77-10472. pap. 66.80 (ISBN 0-317-28052-X, 2055775). Bks Demand UMI.

Goodall, D. W. & Perry, R. A., eds. Arid Land Ecosystems, Vol. 1. LC 77-84810. (International Biological Programme Ser.: No. 16). (Illus.). 1979. 140.00 (ISBN 0-521-21842-X). Cambridge U Pr.

--Arid-Land Ecosystems: Structure, Functioning & Management, Vol. 2. LC 77-84810. (International Biological Programme Ser.: No. 17). 550p. 1981. 130.00 (ISBN 0-521-22988-X). Cambridge U Pr.

Goodin, J. R. & Northington, David K., eds. Plant Resources of Arid & Semiarid Lands: A Global Perspective. Edited Treatise ed. Date not set. price not set (ISBN 0-12-289745-5). Acad Pr.

Goudie, A. & Wilkinson, J. The Warm Desert Environment. LC 76-9731. (Topics in Geography Ser). (Illus.). 1977. 16.95 (ISBN 0-521-21330-4); pap. 8.95 o. p. (ISBN 0-521-29105-4); slides 27.95x (ISBN 0-521-21912-4). Cambridge U Pr.

Graetz, R. D. & Howes, K. M. Studies of the Australian Arid Zone: Chenopod Shrublands, Pt. 4. 202p. 1981. 40.00x (ISBN 0-643-00347-9, Pub. by CSIRo Australia). State Mutual Bk.

Gupta, S. K., ed. Current Trends in Arid Zone Hydrology: Proceedings of Symposium Held at Physical Research Laboratory, Ahmedabad, April 5-8, 1978. 540p. 1979. 40.00 (ISBN 0-88065-097-4, Pub. by Messers Today & Tomorrows Printers & Publishers India). Scholarly Pubns.

Hagin, Josef & Tucker, Billy. Fertilization of Dryland & Irrigated Soils. (Advanced Series in Agricultural Sciences: Vol. 12). (Illus.). 210p. 1982. 42.00 (ISBN 0-387-11121-2). Springer-Verlag.

Hopkins, Stephen T. & Jones, Douglas E., eds. Research Guide to Arid Lands of the World. LC 83-42500. 400p. 1983. 85.00x (ISBN 0-89774-066-1). Oryx Pr.

Howes, K. M. Studies of the Australian Arid Zone: Water in Rangelands, Pt. 3. 256p. 1981. 40.00x (ISBN 0-643-00289-8, Pub. by CSIRO Australia). State Mutual Bk.

Johl, S. S. & De Clerq, C. Irrigation & Agricultural Development. LC 80-40435. (Illus.). 386p. 1980. 68.00 (ISBN 0-08-025675-9). Pergamon.

Jones, K. & Berney, O. Arid Zone Hydrology for Agricultural Development. (Irrigation & Drainage Papers: No. 37). 383p. 1981. pap. 27.50 (ISBN 92-5-101079-X, F2204, FAO). Unipub.

Mabbutt, J. A. Research & Training for Management of Arid Lands. 48p. 1981. pap. 10.00 (ISBN 92-808-0198-8, TUNU129, UNU). Unipub.

Mabbutt, J. A., ed. Strategies for Improved Management of Latin American Drylands. Schneider, H. J., et al. 29p. 1981. pap. 5.00 (ISBN 92-808-0227-5, TUNU127, UNU). Unipub.

McGinnies, William G., et al, eds. Food, Fiber, & the Arid Lands. LC 75-152038. 437p. 1971. 30.00x (ISBN 0-8165-0299-4). U of Ariz Pr.

Manassah, Jamal & Briskey, Ernest J., eds. Advances in Food Producing Systems for Arid & Semi-Arid Lands, 2 pts. 1981. Pt. A. 69.50 (ISBN 0-12-467301-5); Pt. B. 69.50 (ISBN 0-12-467302-3). Acad Pr.

Mann, H. S. Arid Zone Research & Development. 586p. 1980. 90.00x (ISBN 0-686-45798-6, Pub. by United Bk Traders India). State Mutual Bk.

Map of the World Distribution of Arid Regions. 54p. 1979. pap. 18.75 map sheet & book (ISBN 92-3-101484-6, U933, UNESCO). Unipub.

Paylore, Patricia, ed. Arid-Lands Research Institutions: A World Directory, 1977. LC 67-20092. 317p. 1977. pap. 12.50x (ISBN 0-8165-0631-0). U of Ariz Pr.

Powell, John W. Report on the Lands of the Arid Region of the U. S. 224p. 1983. pap. 9.95 (ISBN 0-916782-28-X). Harvard Common Pr.

Pronzini, Bill, et al, eds. The Arbor House Treasury of Horror & the Supernatural. LC 80-70220. 512p. (Orig.). 1981. 19.95 (ISBN 0-87795-309-0); pap. 8.95 (ISBN 0-87795-319-8). Arbor Hse.

Report of the Workshop on Arid Lands Management. 22p. 1980. pap. 7.50 (ISBN 0-686-61621-9, TUNU043, UNU). Unipub.

Russell, J. S. & Greacen, E. L. Soil Factors in Crop Production in a Semi-Arid Environment. 1978. text ed. 30.25x (ISBN 0-7022-1303-9). U of Queensland Pr.

Shuval, Hillel I., ed. Developments in Arid Zone Ecology & Environmental Quality, Vol. 1. xiv, 418p. 1982. 35.00 (ISBN 0-86689-005-X, 992200164). Balaban Intl Sci Serv.

Singh, Alam. Current Practices in Dryland Resources & Technology. (International Overviews-Geo Environ Academia Ser.). (Illus.). 260p. 1985. text ed. 55.00x (ISBN 0-317-18528-4, Pub. by Geo Environ Academia Jodhpur India). Apt Bks.

Skogerboe, G. V. Water & Energy Development in an Arid Environment: The Colorado River Basin. flexi-cover 57.00 (ISBN 0-08-028752-2). Pergamon.

Smythe, William E. Conquest of Arid America. LC 76-8950. (Americana Library Ser.: No. 14). (Illus.). 1969. 15.00x (ISBN 0-295-95029-3); pap. 6.95x (ISBN 0-295-95100-1, ALP14). U of Wash Pr.

Timmerhaus, Klaus D., ed. Energy Resource Recovery in Arid Lands. (Illus.). 200p. 1981. 15.95 (ISBN 0-8263-0583-0); pap. 8.95 (ISBN 0-8263-0582-2). U of NM Pr.

Walker, B. J., ed. Management of Semi-Arid Ecosystems. (Developments in Agricultural & Managed-Forest Ecology Ser.: Vol. 7). 398p. 1980. 85.00 (ISBN 0-444-41759-1). Elsevier.

White, Gilbert F. Science & the Future of Arid Lands. LC 76-4551. (Illus.). 95p. 1976. Repr. of 1960 ed. lib. bdg. 15.00 (ISBN 0-8371-8786-9, WHSF). Greenwood.

Wickens, G. E., et al. Plants For Arid Lands. (Illus.). 500p. 1985. text ed. 50.00x (ISBN 0-04-581019-2). Allen Unwin.

Young, M. D. Differences Between States in Arid Land Administration. 84p. 1981. 15.00x (ISBN 0-643-00336-3, Pub. by CSIRO Australia). State Mutual Bk.

ARISTARCHUS OF SAMOTHRACE

Romer, Adolf. Homerexegese Aristarchs in Ihren Grundzugen. Repr. of 1924 ed. 22.00 (ISBN 0-384-51650-5). Johnson Repr.

ARITHMETIC

see also Addition; Decimal System; Division; Fractions; Metric System; Multiplication; Numbers, Real; Numeration; Percentage; Ratio and Proportion; Subtraction

Apostol, Tom M. Introduction to Analytic Number Theory. (Undergraduate Texts in Mathematics Ser.). (Illus.). 370p. 1976. text ed. 29.80 (ISBN 0-387-90163-9). Springer-Verlag.

The Arithmetic Classroom: Addition, 3 pts. (Courses by Computers Ser.). Apple. 49.95 (ISBN 0-88408-196-6); IBM-PC, PCjr. 49.95 (ISBN 0-88408-284-9); Acom. 49.95 (ISBN 0-88408-340-3). Sterling Swift.

The Arithmetic Classroom: Decimals. (Courses by Computers Ser.). Apple. 49.95 (ISBN 0-88408-203-2); IBM-PC, PCjr. 49.95 (ISBN 0-88408-291-1); 49.95 (ISBN 0-88408-348-9). Sterling Swift.

The Arithmetic Classroom: Division, 3 pts. (Courses by Computers Ser.). Apple. 49.95 (ISBN 0-88408-199-0); IBM-PC, PCjr. 49.95; Acom. 49.95 (ISBN 0-88408-344-6). Sterling Swift.

The Arithmetic Classroom: Fraction - Addition & Subtraction. (Courses by Computers Ser.). Apple. 49.95 (ISBN 0-88408-201-6); IBM-PC, PCjr. 49.95; Acom. 49.95 (ISBN 0-88408-346-2). Sterling Swift.

The Arithmetic Classroom: Fraction - Multiplication & Division, 3 pts. (Courses by Computers Ser.). Apple. 49.95 (ISBN 0-88408-202-4); IBM-PC, PCjr. 49.95 (ISBN 0-88408-290-3); Acom. 49.95 (ISBN 0-88408-347-0). Sterling Swift.

The Arithmetic Classroom: Fractions - Basic Concepts, 3 pts. (Courses by Computers Ser.). Apple. 49.95 (ISBN 0-88408-200-8); IBM-PC, PCjr. 49.95 (ISBN 0-88408-293-8); Acom. 49.95 (ISBN 0-88408-345-4). Sterling Swift.

The Arithmetic Classroom: Games, 3 pts. (Courses by Computers Ser.). Apple. 29.95 (ISBN 0-88408-204-0); IBM-PC, PCjr. 29.95 (ISBN 0-88408-294-6); Acom. 29.95 (ISBN 0-88408-349-7). Sterling Swift.

The Arithmetic Classroom: Multiplication, 3 pts. (Courses by Computers Ser.). Apple. 49.95 (ISBN 0-88408-198-2); IBM-PC, PCjr. 49.95 (ISBN 0-88408-286-5); Acom. 49.95 (ISBN 0-88408-343-8). Sterling Swift.

The Arithmetic Classroom: Subtraction, 3 pts. (Courses by Computers Ser.). Apple. 49.95 (ISBN 0-88408-197-4); Acom. 49.95 (ISBN 0-88408-341-1); IBM-PC, PCjr. 49.95 (ISBN 0-88408-285-7). Sterling Swift.

Artin, M. & Tate, John, eds. Arithmetic, Vol. 1. (Progress in Mathematics Ser.). 350p. 1983. 29.95 (ISBN 0-8176-3132-1). Birkhauser.

Austin, Jacqueline & Isern, Margarita. Arithmetic. 432p. 1984. pap. text ed. write for info. (ISBN 0-02-304720-8). Macmillan.

Benice, Daniel. Arithmetic & Algebra. 3rd ed. (Illus.). 464p. 1985. pap. text ed. 26.95 (ISBN 0-13-046111-3). P-H.

Beron, Alberto, et al. Guia de Studios Essential Arithmetic: Spanish Study Guide for Essential Arithmetic. 174p. write for info. Watts.

Bila, Dennis, et al. Arithmetic. LC 76-19446. 1976. 9.95x (ISBN 0-87901-058-4). Worth.

Bloomfield, Derek. From Arithmetic to Algebra. 2nd ed. (Illus.). 1976. pap. 19.95 (ISBN 0-8359-2110-7); instrs'. manual avail. (ISBN 0-8359-2111-5). Reston.

Bond, Elias A. Short Method Arithmetic. pap. 1.00 (ISBN 0-685-19500-7). Powner.

Bostock, David. Logic & Arithmetic, Vol. I: Natural Numbers. 1974. 45.00x (ISBN 0-19-824366-9). Oxford U Pr.

Bowden, Aberdeen O. Consumers Uses of Arithmetic: An Investigation to Determine the Actual Uses Made of Arithmetic in Adult Social Life. LC 71-176583. (Columbia University. Teachers College. Contributions to Education: No. 340). Repr. of 1929 ed. 22.50 (ISBN 0-404-55340-0). AMS Pr.

Brownell, William A. Arithmetical Abstractions: The Movement Toward Conceptual Maturity under Differing Systems of Instructions. LC 67-65751. (University of California Publications in Education Ser.: Vol. 17). pap. 58.00 (ISBN 0-317-11014-4, 2021359). Bks Demand UMI.

Burke, Michael & Rundberg, William. Arithmetic. 500p. 1984. 23.95 (ISBN 0-02-317320-3). Dellen Pub.

Carnevale, Thomas & Shloming, Robert. Encounters with Arithmetic. 449p. 1979. pap. text ed. 21.95 (ISBN 0-15-522596-0, HC); instructor's manual avail. (ISBN 0-15-522597-9). HarBraceJ.

Cleary, Joseph & Gleason, Joseph. Arithmetic: A Problem Solving Approach. (Illus.). 550p. 1985. pap. text ed. 23.95 (ISBN 0-314-78011-4). West Pub.

Cooke, Nelson M. & Adams, Herbert F. Arithmetic Review for Electronics. 1968. 23.85 (ISBN 0-07-012516-3). McGraw.

Drooyan, Irving & Rosen, William. Elementary Arithmetic: A Problem Solving Approach. 480p. 1985. text ed. 20.95x (ISBN 0-471-80814-8). Wiley.

Eliopoulos, Nicholas C. Golden Arithmetization. 403p. (Orig.). 1980. pap. text ed. 30.00x (ISBN 0-9605396-0-3). Eliopoulos.

Engelsohn, Harold S. & Feit, Joseph. Basic Mathematics: Arithmetic & Algebra. LC 79-21287. 532p. 1980. pap. 34.00 (ISBN 0-471-24145-8). Wiley.

Erdsneker, Barbara & Haller, Margaret. Civil Service Arithmetic & Vocabulary. LC 81-7988. 256p. 1981. pap. 8.00 (ISBN 0-668-04872-7). Arco.

Gallo, Michael & Kiehl, Charles. Basic Arithmetic. 1981. pap. text ed. 21.70x (ISBN 0-673-16223-0). Scott F.

Gauss, Karl F. Disquisitiones Arithmetcae. Clarke, Arthur A., tr. LC 65-22318. pap. 124.00 (ISBN 0-317-08644-8, 2005389). Bks Demand UMI.

Gioia, A. A. & Goldsmith, D. L., eds. The Theory of Arithmetic Functions. (Lecture Notes in Mathematics: Vol. 251). 287p. 1972. pap. 13.00 (ISBN 0-387-05723-4). Springer-Verlag.

Godfrey, Charles & Price, E. A. Arithmetic. pap. 121.30 (ISBN 0-317-08560-3, 2051353). Bks Demand UMI.

H, Francis & Wise, Joyce M. Dr. Wise Arithmetic Series, Vol. II. (Illus.). 105p. 1980. pap. text ed. 7.50 (ISBN 0-915766-56-6). Wise Pub.

Holcomb, Eldon. Arithmetic for Rig Personnel. 59p. (Orig.). 1982. pap. text ed. 2.00 (ISBN 0-88698-106-9, 1.61010). Petex.

Hollister, Herbert. Fundamentals of Mathematics: Arithmetic. 1984. pap. text ed. 23.95 (ISBN 0-8359-2144-1); solutions manual avail. (ISBN 0-8359-2145-X). Reston.

Humphreys, J. E. Arithmetics Groups. (Lecture Notes in Mathematics: Vol. 789). 158p. 1980. pap. 15.00 (ISBN 0-387-09972-7). Springer-Verlag.

Hyatt, Herman R., et al. Arithmetic with Pushbutton Accuracy. LC 76-4558. 304p. 1977. 32.50 (ISBN 0-471-22308-5); tchrs. manual avail. (ISBN 0-471-02395-7). Wiley.

Johnston, C. L., et al. Essential Arithmetic. 534p. 1984. pap. text ed. write for info. (ISBN 0-534-03240-0). Wadsworth Pub.

Kaufmann, Arnold & Gupta, Madan. Introduction to Fuzzy Arithmetic. (Electrical-Computer Science & Engineering Ser.). (Illus.). 384p. 1985. 44.95 (ISBN 0-442-23007-9). Van Nos Reinhold.

Kluge, Eike-Henner, tr. from Ger. Gottlob Frege on the Foundations of Geometry & Formal Theories of Arithmetic. LC 74-140533. Repr. of 1971 ed. 39.00 (ISBN 0-8357-9190-4, 2016768). Bks Demand UMI.

Layton, William I. College Arithmetic. 2nd ed. LC 73-155121. pap. 61.00 (ISBN 0-317-08545-X, 2055108). Bks Demand UMI.

LeBlanc, John F., et al. Mathematics-Methods Program: Addition & Subtraction. (Mathematics Ser.). 176p. 1976. pap. text ed. 6.95 (ISBN 0-201-14608-8). Addison-Wesley.

McHale, T. J. & Witzke, P. T. Arithmetic Module Series: One Volume Non-Programmed Edition. 400p. 1976. pap. text ed. 18.95 (ISBN 0-201-04757-8); tests 4.95 (ISBN 0-201-04758-6). Addison-Wesley.

Mangan, Frances S. Arithmetic for Self-Study. 2nd ed. 1975. text ed. write for info (ISBN 0-534-00380-X). Wadsworth Pub.

Miller, Charles D. & Salzman, Stanley A. Arithmetic: A Text-Workbook. 1981. pap. text ed. 22.70 (ISBN 0-673-15274-X). Scott F.

Mira, Julio A. Arithmetic Clear & Simple. (Orig.). 1965. pap. 3.80i (ISBN 0-06-463270-9, EH 270, EH). B&N NY.

Nanney, J. Louis & Shaffer, Richard D. Arithmetic: A Review. LC 75-93297. pap. 79.00 (ISBN 0-317-19820-3, 2023213). Bks Demand UMI.

Nelkon, M. Basic Mathematics for Science. 1978. pap. text ed. 7.50x (ISBN 0-435-50610-2). Heinemann Ed.

Nielsen, Kaj L. Mathematics for Practical Use. (Orig.). 1962. pap. 5.72i (ISBN 0-06-463212-1, EH 212, EH). B&N NY.

Pacholski, L., et al, eds. Model Theory of Algebra & Arithmetics: Procedings. (Lecture Notes in Mathematics Ser.: Vol. 834). 410p. 1980. pap. 28.00 (ISBN 0-387-10269-8). Springer-Verlag.

Pascoe, L. C. Arithmetic: Decimalized & Metricated. (Teach Yourself Ser.). 1972. pap. 5.95 (ISBN 0-679-10452-6). McKay.

Peck, Lyman C. Secret Codes, Remainder Arithmetic, & Matrices. LC 61-12376. 54p. 1961. pap. 2.90 (ISBN 0-87353-090-X). NCTM.

Pettofrezzo, Anthony J. & Armstrong, Lee H. Arithmetic: A Programmed Approach. 1982. pap. text ed. 21.70x (ISBN 0-673-15314-2). Scott F.

Proga. Arithmetic & Algebra. 1986. pap. write for info. (ISBN 0-87150-907-5, 33L3060, Prindle). PWS Pubs.

Shapiro, Heschel. Fundamentals of Arithmetic. 1982. sppiral bdg. 10.95 (ISBN 0-88252-067-9). Paladin Hse.

Smithsi, T. Basic Mathematical Skills. 1974. pap. 24.95 (ISBN 0-13-063420-4). P-H.

Sperling, A. P. Arithmetic Made Simple. pap. 4.95 (ISBN 0-385-00983-6, Made). Doubleday.

Steffensen, Arnold R. & Johnson, L. Murphy. Fundamentals of Arithmetic. 1982. pap. text ed. 21.70x (ISBN 0-673-15481-5). Scott F.

Stehman, Mary E. Pre-Nursing Reviews in Arithmetic. 2nd ed. 33p. 1961. pap. 3.00x (ISBN 0-8036-8140-2). Davis Co.

Stephens, Alan A. Sum. LC 70-179819. (New Poetry Ser). Repr. of 1958 ed. 16.00 (ISBN 0-404-56019-9). AMS Pr.

Thompson, J. E. Arithmetic for the Practical Worker. 4th ed. 272p. 1982. pap. 7.95 (ISBN 0-442-28275-3). Van Nos Reinhold.

Thorndike, Edward L. The Psychology of Arithmetic. 314p. 1980. Repr. of 1922 ed. lib. bdg. 30.00 (ISBN 0-89760-890-9). Telegraph Bks.

Trivieri, Lawrence. Basic Arithmetic with Applications. 400p. 1981. pap. text ed. write for info. (ISBN 0-87150-322-0, 33L 2562, Prindle). PWS Pubs.

Waser, Shlomo & Flynn, Michael J. Introduction to Arithmetic for Digital System Designers. LC 82-12163. 308p. 1983. text ed. 39.95 (ISBN 0-03-060571-7). HR&W.

Williams, Richard W. Basic Mathematics: Arithmetic & Algebra. 1984. pap. text ed. 20.65x (ISBN 0-673-15482-3). Scott F.

Wilson, Guy M. A Survey of the Social & Business Usage of Arithmetic. LC 74-177633. (Columbia University. Teachers College. Contributions to Education: No. 100). Repr. of 1919 ed. 17.50 (ISBN 0-404-55100-9). AMS Pr.

Wise, Francis H. & Wise, Joyce M. Arithmetic Series, 10 bks. Incl. Bk. I. Countable Numbers. (Illus.). 21p. 1979. pap. 1.50 (ISBN 0-915766-45-0); Vol. 2. Add. (Illus.). 21p. 1980. pap. 1.50 (ISBN 0-915766-46-9); Bk. 4. Subtraction. 1980; Bk. 5. Column. 1980 (ISBN 0-915766-48-5); Bk. 6. Multiply. 1980 (ISBN 0-915766-49-3); Bk. 7. Division. 1980 (ISBN 0-915766-50-7); Bk. 8. Fractions. 1980 (ISBN 0-915766-52-3); Bk. 9. Carry. 1980 (ISBN 0-915766-53-1); Bk. 10. Borrow. 1980 (ISBN 0-915766-54-X). (Illus.). 21p. pap. 1.50 ea. Wise Pub.

--Dr. Wise Arithmetic Series, Vol. I. (Illus.). 105p. 1980. pap. text ed. 7.50 (ISBN 0-915766-55-8). Wise Pub.

Zuckerman, Martin M. Aritmetica Con una Introduccion al Algebra. Molinero, Leticia, tr. from Eng. (Span., Illus.). 300p. 1984. pap. text ed. 23.95 (ISBN 0-912675-01-2); manual avail. (ISBN 0-912675-03-9). Ardsley.

ARITHMETIC–BEFORE 1846

Blundeville, Thomas. M. Blundeville, His Exercises Containing Sixe Treatises. LC 78-171736. (English Experience Ser.: No. 361). (Illus.). 718p. 1971. Repr. of 1594 ed. 64.00 (ISBN 90-221-0361-7). Walter J Johnson.

Levey, Martin & Petruck, Marvin, eds. Kushyar ibn Labban: "Principles of Hindu Reckoning". (Medieval Science Pubns., No. 8). 128p. 1965. 30.00x (ISBN 0-299-03610-3). U of Wis Pr.

Napier, John. De Arte Logistica Joannis Naperi Merchistonii, Baronis Libri Qui Supersunt. LC 76-173010. (Maitland Club, Glasgow. Publications: No. 47). Repr. of 1839 ed. 27.50 (ISBN 0-404-52773-6). AMS Pr.

Nicomachus, Gerasenus. Introduction to Arithmetic. D'Ooge, Martin L., tr. Repr. of 1926 ed. 37.00 (ISBN 0-384-38816-7). Johnson Repr.

Record, Robert. The Grounde of Artes, Teachying the Worke & Practise of Arithmetike. LC 77-26032. (English Experience Ser.: No. 174). (Illus.). 1969. Repr. of 1542 ed. 16.00 (ISBN 90-221-0174-6). Walter J Johnson.

--The Whetstone of Witte, Whiche Is the Second Parte of Arithmetike. LC 76-26206. (English Experience Ser.: No. 142). 320p. 1969. Repr. of 1557 ed. 39.00 (ISBN 90-221-0142-8). Walter J Johnson.

Salignacus, Bernard. The Principles of Arithmeticke. Bedwell, W., tr. LC 70-26250. (English Experience Ser.: No. 130). 134p. 1969. Repr. of 1616 ed. 16.00 (ISBN 90-221-0130-4). Walter J Johnson.

Smith, David E. & De Morgan, Augustus. Rara Arithmetica & Arithmetical Books, 2 vols. in 1. 4th ed. LC 74-113148. (Eng., Illus.). 1970. text ed. 35.00 (ISBN 0-8284-0192-6). Chelsea Pub.

Taran, Leonardo. Asclepius of Tralles: Commentary to Nicomachus' Introduction to Arithmetic. LC 69-18747. (Transactions Ser.: Vol. 59, Pt. 4). 1969. pap. 2.00 (ISBN 0-87169-594-4). Am Philos.

ARITHMETIC–EXAMINATIONS, QUESTIONS, ETC.

McCully, Ron. Testing Program: Up with Math. Jacobs, Helen J., ed. 120p. (Orig.). 1979. pap. 2.25 (ISBN 0-918272-05-X); tchrs. manual 1.75 (ISBN 0-918272-06-8). Jacobs.

Rudman, Jack. Civil Service Arithmetic. (Career Examination Ser.: CS-6). (Cloth bdg. avail. on request). pap. 8.00 (ISBN 0-8373-3706-2). Natl Learning.

Wilbur. Skill Tester: Computer-Analyzed Arithmetic Test. 1985. write for info. (ISBN 0-205-08537-7, 568537); write for info. (568538). Allyn.

ARITHMETIC–FOUNDATIONS

see also Algorithms; Goedel's Theorem; Recursive Functions

Coutourat, Louis. De l'Infini Mathematique. LC 68-56776. (Research & Source Works Ser.: No. 262). (Fr). 1969. Repr. of 1896 ed. 35.50 (ISBN 0-8337-0706-X). B Franklin.

Davenport, H. The Higher Arithmetic. 5th ed. LC 81-21786. 180p. 1982. 27.95 (ISBN 0-521-24422-6); pap. 10.95 (ISBN 0-521-28678-6). Cambridge U Pr.

Frege, Gottlob. Foundations of Arithmetic: A Logico-Mathematical Enquiry into the Concept of Numbers. Austin, J. L., tr. LC 68-8996. (Eng. & Ger.). 1968. 17.95 (ISBN 0-8101-0023-1); pap. 9.95 (ISBN 0-8101-0605-1). Northwestern U Pr.

Halmos, P. R. Naive Set Theory. LC 74-10687. (Undergraduate Texts in Mathematics Ser.). 110p. 1974. pap. 19.00 (ISBN 0-387-90092-6). Springer-Verlag.

Kaluzhnim, L. Fundamental Theorem of Arithmetic. 50p. 1979. pap. 1.95 (ISBN 0-8285-0721-X, Pub. by Mir Pubs USSR). Imported Pubns.

Wright, C. Frege's Conception of Numbers As Objects. (Scots Philosophical Monographs: No. 2). 224p. 1983. 22.50 (ISBN 0-08-030352-8); pap. 15.50 (ISBN 0-08-025726-7). Pergamon.

ARITHMETIC–HISTORY

Dantzig, Tobias. Number: The Language of Science. 4th rev. ed. (Illus.). 340p. 1967. pap. text ed. 10.95x (ISBN 0-02-906990-4). Free Pr.

Jackson, Lambert L. Educational Significance of Sixteenth-Century Arithmetic from the Point of View of the Present Time. LC 75-176900. (Columbia University. Teachers College. Contributions to Educaton: No. 8). Repr. of 1906 ed. 22.50 (ISBN 0-404-55008-8). AMS Pr.

ARITHMETIC–PROBLEMS, EXERCISES, ETC.

see also Arithmetic–Examinations, Questions, etc.

Brown, Sam E. One, Two, Buckle My Shoe: Math Activities for Young Children. (Illus., Orig.). 1982. pap. 6.95 (ISBN 0-87659-103-9). Gryphon Hse.

Edward, W. Visually & Transfer Skill Mastery, 2 levels. Incl. Level 2. Subtraction & Division (ISBN 0-89039-850-X). pap. 8.50 ea. Ann Arbor FL.

Gossage, Loyce C. Basic Mathematical Skills: A Text Workbook. 2nd ed. (Illus.). 320p. 1975. pap. text ed. 25.95 wkbk (ISBN 0-07-023852-9). McGraw.

Klaf, A. Albert. Arithmetic Refresher for Practical Men. (Orig.). 1964. pap. 5.95 (ISBN 0-486-21241-6). Dover.

Koch, Marianna & Barbata, Jean. Figures That Count: Mathematics for Nurses. (Quality Paperback Ser.: No. 301). 127p. (Orig.). 1974. pap. 3.50 (ISBN 0-8226-0301-2). Littlefield.

Neulen, Leon N. Problem Solving in Arithmetic. LC 70-177116. (Columbia University. Teachers College. Contributions to Education: No. 483). Repr. of 1931 ed. 22.50 (ISBN 0-404-55483-0). AMS Pr.

Snyder, Llewellyn R. Computational Arithmetic. LC 67-26174. 1968. text ed. 28.95 (ISBN 0-07-059552-6). McGraw.

Sutherland, Mary E. One-Step Problem Patterns & Their Relation to Problem Solving in Arithmetic. LC 76-177734. (Columbia University. Teachers College. Contributions to Education: No. 925). Repr. of 1947 ed. 22.50 (ISBN 0-404-55925-5). AMS Pr.

Wheat, Harry G. The Relative Merits of Conventional & Imaginative Types of Problems in Arithmetic. LC 71-177643. (Columbia University. Teachers College. Contributions to Education: No. 359). Repr. of 1929 ed. 17.50 (ISBN 0-404-55359-1). AMS Pr.

ARITHMETIC–PROGRAMMED INSTRUCTION

Baley, John D. Semi-Programmed Arithmetic for College Students. 144p. 1975. pap. text ed. 8.95x (ISBN 0-669-90886-X). Heath.

Baley, John D., et al. Basic Mathematics: A Program for Semi-Independent Study. 1978. pap. text ed. 19.95x (ISBN 0-669-01019-7); inst. resource bk. 1.95 (ISBN 0-669-01020-0); Set. cassette 150.00 (ISBN 0-669-01165-7); free tapescript (ISBN 0-669-01022-7). Heath.

Carman, Robert A. & Carman, Marilyn J. Quick Arithmetic: A Self-Teaching Guide. 2nd ed. LC 83-3531. 286p. 1984. pap. 7.95 (ISBN 0-471-88966-0, 1-581, Pub. by Wiley Press). Wiley.

George, F. H. Computer Arithmetic. 1966. pap. 8.50 (ISBN 0-08-011463-6). Pergamon.

Hackworth, Robert D. & Howland, Joseph W. Programmed Arithmetic. 2nd ed. (Illus.). 410p. (Orig.). 1983. pap. text ed. 15.95x (ISBN 0-943202-08-6). H & H Pub.

Heywood, Arthur H. Arithmetic: A Programmed Worktext. 4th ed. LC 81-10231. (Mathematics Ser.). 405p. 1982. pap. text ed. 20.50 pub net (ISBN 0-8185-0490-0). Brooks-Cole.

Learning Achievement Corporation. Number Systems, Addition & Personal Communication; Subtraction & Recreation. (MATCH Bks.: Bk. 1). (Illus.). 128p. 1981. 7.48 (ISBN 0-07-037111-3). McGraw.

McHale, T. J. & Witzke, P. T. Arithmetic Modules. 125p. 1975. module 1, whole nos. 7.95 (ISBN 0-201-04751-9); module 2 fractions 7.95 (ISBN 0-201-04752-7); module 3 decimal nos. 7.95 (ISBN 0-201-04753-5); module 4 perfect ratio 7.95 (ISBN 0-201-04754-3); module 5 6.95 (ISBN 0-201-04756-X); test bklt 4.95 (ISBN 0-201-04758-6). Addison-Wesley.

Preis, Sandra & Cocks, George. Arithmetic. 2nd ed. (Illus.). 416p. 1980. pap. text ed. 25.95 (ISBN 0-13-046201-2). P-H.

Whimbey, Arthur & Lochhead, Jack. Developing Mathematical Skills. (Illus.). 480p. 1981. pap. text ed. 26.95 (ISBN 0-07-069517-2). McGraw.

ARITHMETIC–STUDY AND TEACHING

Bond, Elias A. The Professional Treatment of the Subject Matter of Arithmetic for Teacher-Training Institutions. LC 75-176576. (Columbia University. Teachers College. Contributions to Education: No. 525). Repr. of 1934 ed. 22.50 (ISBN 0-404-55525-X). AMS Pr.

Bowden, Aberdeen O. Consumers Uses of Arithmetic: An Investigation to Determine the Actual Uses Made of Arithmetic in Adult Social Life. LC 71-176583. (Columbia University. Teachers College. Contributions to Education: No. 340). Repr. of 1929 ed. 22.50 (ISBN 0-404-55340-0). AMS Pr.

Buswell, Guy T. Teaching of Arithmetic. LC 51-9871. (National Society for the Study of Education Yearbooks Ser: No. 50, Pt. 2). 1951. 6.50x (ISBN 0-226-60015-7); pap. 4.50x (ISBN 0-226-60016-5). U of Chicago Pr.

Fuller, Kenneth G. An Experimental Study of Two Methods of Long Division. LC 78-176791. (Columbia University. Teachers College. Contributions to Education: No. 951). Repr. of 1949 ed. 22.50 (ISBN 0-404-55951-4). AMS Pr.

Ginsburg, Herbert. Children's Arithmetic: How They Learn It & How You Teach It. LC 76-47212. (Illus.). 208p. 1983. pap. text ed. 16.00 (ISBN 0-936104-29-5, 0377). Pro Ed.

Hershey, Robert L. How to Think with Numbers. LC 81-17181. (Illus.). 140p. (Orig.). 1982. pap. 7.95 (ISBN 0-86576-014-4). W Kaufmann.

Husserl, E. Studien zur Arithmetik und Geometrie. 1983. 91.50 (ISBN 90-247-2497-X, Pub. by Martinus Nijhoff Netherlands). Kluwer Academic.

Jackson, Lambert L. Educational Significance of Sixteenth-Century Arithmetic from the Point of View of the Present Time. LC 75-176900. (Columbia University. Teachers College. Contributions to Educaton: No. 8). Repr. of 1906 ed. 22.50 (ISBN 0-404-55008-8). AMS Pr.

National Council of Teachers of Mathematics. Instruction in Arithmetic, 25th Yearbk. LC 60-7488. 366p. 1960. 14.00 (ISBN 0-87353-003-9). NCTM.

Neulen, Leon N. Problem Solving in Arithmetic. LC 70-177116. (Columbia University. Teachers College. Contributions to Education: No. 483). Repr. of 1931 ed. 22.50 (ISBN 0-404-55483-0). AMS Pr.

Robinson, Arthur E. The Professional Education of Elementary Teachers in the Field of Arithmetic. LC 78-177196. (Columbia University. Teachers College. Contributions to Education: No. 672). Repr. of 1936 ed. 22.50 (ISBN 0-404-55672-8). AMS Pr.

Rubado, Clarence A. Problems of the City School Superintendent in the Field of Arithmetic. LC 71-177217. (Columbia University. Teachers College. Contributions to Education: No. 406). Repr. of 1930 ed. 22.50 (ISBN 0-404-55406-7). AMS Pr.

Seeley, Levi. Grube's Methods of Teaching Arthmetic. (Educational Ser.). 1888. Repr. 10.00 (ISBN 0-8482-6406-1). Norwood Edns.

Simmons, Vickie & Williams, Irene. Pre-Math: The Success Training Program of Increasingly Complex Number Skills. (Steps up to Number Skills for the Learning Impaired Ser.). 96p. 1982. pap. text ed. 11.95 (ISBN 0-88450-820-X, 2068-B). Communication Skill.

Steele, Robert, ed. The Earliest Arithmetics in English. (EETS, ES Ser.: No. 118). Repr. of 1916 ed. 12.00 (ISBN 0-527-00321-2). Kraus Repr.

Sutherland, Mary E. One-Step Problem Patterns & Their Relation to Problem Solving in Arithmetic. LC 76-177734. (Columbia University. Teachers College. Contributions to Education: No. 925). Repr. of 1947 ed. 22.50 (ISBN 0-404-55925-5). AMS Pr.

Wheat, Harry G. The Psychology & Teaching of Arithmetic. 591p. 1984. Repr. of 1937 ed. lib. bdg. 50.00 (ISBN 0-918377-15-3). Russell Pr.

Woody, Clifford. Measurements of Some Achievements in Arithmetic. LC 73-177622. (Columbia University. Teachers College. Contributions to Education: No. 80). Repr. of 1920 ed. 17.50 (ISBN 0-404-55080-0). AMS Pr.

ARITHMETIC–1961-

Bakst, Aaron. Arithmetic for the Modern Age. LC 60-53374. pap. 87.30 (ISBN 0-317-08507-7, 2007243). Bks Demand UMI.

Brown, Ross F. Basic Arithmetic. 2nd ed. 1985. pap. text ed. 18.95x (ISBN 0-673-18017-4). Scott F.

Chinn, William G., et al. Arithmetic & Calculators: How to Deal with Arithmetic in the Calculator Age. LC 77-11111. (Illus.). 488p. 1978. pap. text ed. 17.95 (ISBN 0-7167-0015-8). W H Freeman.

Dubisch, Roy. Basic Mathematics with Hand-Held Calculator. LC 78-57267. 1979. text ed. 29.95 (ISBN 0-8053-2341-4); instr's guide 4.95 (ISBN 0-8053-2344-9). Benjamin-Cummings.

Gossage, Loyce C. Basic Mathematical Skills: A Text Workbook. 2nd ed. (Illus.). 320p. 1975. pap. text ed. 25.95 wkbk (ISBN 0-07-023852-9). McGraw.

Hirschfeld, J. & Wheeler, W. H. Forcing, Arithmetic, Division Rings. (Lecture Notes in Mathematics Ser.: Vol. 454). vii, 266p. 1975. pap. 17.00 (ISBN 0-387-07157-1). Springer-Verlag.

Johnson, C. Practical Arithmetic: The Third "R". (Illus.). 1977. 23.95 (ISBN 0-13-689273-6). P-H.

Keedy, Mervin L. Arithmetic. 4th ed. LC 82-18492. (Illus.). 560p. 1983. pap. text ed. 25.95 (ISBN 0-201-14780-7); tests 3.00 (ISBN 0-201-14781-5); answer bk. 1.50 (ISBN 0-201-14783-1). Addison-Wesley.

Lieberthal, Edwin M. The Complete Book of Fingermath. (Illus.). 1979. 25.60 (ISBN 0-07-037680-8). McGraw.

McKeague, Pat. Introductory Mathematics. 384p. 1981. text ed. write for info. (ISBN 0-534-00865-8). Wadsworth Pub.

Moon, Robert. Basic Arithmetic. 2nd ed. (Mathematics Ser.). 1977. pap. text ed. 21.95 (ISBN 0-675-08627-2); cassettes 95.00 (ISBN 0-675-08515-2). Additional supplements may be obtained from publisher. Merrill.

Preis, Sandra & Cocks, George. Arithmetic. 2nd ed. (Illus.). 416p. 1980. pap. text ed. 25.95 (ISBN 0-13-046201-2). P-H.

Steinhoff, Richard. Arithmetic. (Illus.). 1977. pap. text ed. 27.95 (ISBN 0-07-061127-0). McGraw.

Watkins, John H. Arithmetic & Algebra. 1977. pap. text ed. 21.95 scp (ISBN 0-06-046958-7, HarpC); test bklt. avail. (ISBN 0-06-367022-4). Har-Row.

Willerding, Margaret F. A First Course in College Mathematics. 4th ed. 408p. 1980. write for info. (ISBN 0-87150-285-2, PWS 2241, Prindle). PWS Pubs.

Wood, et al. Developmental Mathematics. 3rd ed. 1985. pap. text ed. write for info. (ISBN 0-87150-853-2, 33L2920, Prindle). PWS Pubs.

ARITHMETIC, MECHANICAL

see Calculating-Machines

ARITHMETIC, MENTAL

Sticker, Henry. How to Calculate Quickly. 1955. pap. 2.95 (ISBN 0-486-20295-X). Dover.

ARMADILLOS

Jobson, Tracy, illus. Armadillos Incognito. LC 83-4319. 1983. pap. 4.95 (ISBN 0-86663-988-8). Ide Hse.

ARMAMENTS

see also Aeronautics, Military; Ammunition; Firearms Industry and Trade; Munitions also Armies and navies of individual countries, e.g. United States–Army; Defenses under names of countries

Abbey, Staton. Book of Vauxhall Viva & Bedford Beagle. (Illus.). pap. 6.00x (ISBN 0-392-02366-0, SpS). Sportshelf.

Abbiatico, Mario. Grandi Incisioni su Armi d'Oggi. (Illus.). Repr. of 1976 ed. 30.00 (ISBN 0-686-70832-6). Arma Pr.

Durie, Sheila & Edwards, Rob. Fueling the Nuclear Arms Race: The Links between Nuclear Power & Nuclear Weapons. 129p. (Orig.). 1982. pap. 5.95 (ISBN 0-86104-372-3, Pub by Pluto Pr). Longwood Pub Group.

Hodges, Peter. The Big Gun: Battleship Main Armament, 1860-1945. LC 80-84051. (Illus.). 160p. 1981. 22.95 (ISBN 0-87021-917-0). Naval Inst Pr.

Jane's Infantry Weapons, 1977. 79.50 (ISBN 0-531-03263-9). Key Bk Serv.

McGuire, Martin C. Secrecy & the Arms Race: A Theory of the Accumulation of Strategic Weapons & How Secrecy Affects It. LC 65-22062. (Economic Studies: No. 125). (Illus.). 1965. 15.00x (ISBN 0-674-79665-9). Harvard U Pr.

Noel-Baker, Philip. The Private Manufacture of Armaments. 11.50 (ISBN 0-8446-4593-1). Peter Smith.

Reitzel, Robert. Des Armen Teufel: Gesammelte Schriften, 3 vols. 1975. Set. lib. bdg. 150.95 (ISBN 0-685-57118-1). Revisionist Pr.
Royal United Services Institute. Rusi & Brassey's Defence Yearbook 1982. 92nd ed. 365p. 1981. 40.00 (ISBN 0-08-027039-5); pap. 25.00 (ISBN 0-08-027040-9). Pergamon.
SIPRI. SIPRI Yearbook, 1982: World Armaments & Disarmament. 516p. 1982. 55.00x (ISBN 0-85066-230-3). Taylor & Francis.
Stockholm International Peace Research Institute (SIPRI) Incendiary Weapons. 175p. 1975. text ed. 35.00x (ISBN 0-262-19139-3). MIT Pr.
Stockholm International Peace Research Institute. S I P R I Yearbook of World Armaments & Disarmaments 1968-69. 1970. text ed. 19.50x (ISBN 0-391-00012-8). Humanities.
Thee, Marek, ed. Armaments, Arms Control & Disarmament: A UNESCO Reader for Disarmament. (Illus.). 446p. 1981. pap. 37.25 (ISBN 92-3-101920-1, U1203, UNESCO). Unipub.

ARMATURES

Heller, Samuel. Three-Phase Motor Winding Data from Simple Measurements. 3rd ed. (Illus., Orig.). 1961. pap. 32.00 (ISBN 0-911740-00-7). Datarule.

ARMIES–SUPPLIES
see Military Supplies

ARMOR
see Arms and Armor

ARMORED CARS (TANKS)
see Tanks (Military Science)

ARMORED VEHICLES, MILITARY
see also Tanks (Military Science)

Ayliffe-Jones, Noel. World Tanks & Reconnaissance Vehicles since 1945. (Illus.). 144p. 1984. 19.95 (ISBN 0-88254-978-2). Hippocrene Bks.
Foss, Christopher. Armoured Fighting Vehicles of the World. 192p. 1981. 35.00x (ISBN 0-7110-0778-0, Pub. by Ian Allan). State Mutual Bk.
--Jane's World Armoured Fighting Vehicles. LC 76-57887. 1977. 25.00 (ISBN 0-312-44047-2). St Martin.
Foss, Christopher F. The Illustrated Guide to Modern Tanks & Fighting Vehicles. LC 80-65165. (Illustrated Military Guides Ser.). (Illus.). 160p. 1980. 9.95 (ISBN 0-668-04965-0, 4965-0). Arco.
Fuller, John F. Armored Warfare. LC 83-45766. Repr. of 1943 ed. 23.50 (ISBN 0-404-20102-4, UG446). AMS Pr.
Hoffschmidt, Edward J. & Tantum, William H. German Tank & Antitank. 260p. 1968. 12.50 (ISBN 0-87364-151-5). Paladin Pr.
Paine, Sheperd. Modeling Tanks & Military Vehicles. Angle, Burr, ed. (Illus.). 76p. (Orig.). 1982. pap. 8.95 (ISBN 0-89024-045-0). Kalmbach.
White, B. T. Tanks & Other Armoured Fighting Vehicles, 1942-1945. (Illus.). 172p. 1983. 9.95 (ISBN 0-7137-0705-4, Pub. by Blandford Pr England). Sterling.
--Wheeled Armoured Fighting Vehicles in Service. (Illus.). 144p. 1983. 16.95 (ISBN 0-7137-1022-5, Pub. by Blandford Pr England). Sterling.

ARMORED VESSELS
see Warships

ARMS AND ARMOR
see also Bayonets; Firearms; Pistols; Rifles; Swords

American Machines & Foundry Co. Silencers, Patterns, & Principles, Vol. II. (Illus.). 78p. 1969. pap. 12.95 (ISBN 0-87364-018-7). Paladin Pr.
Ancient Armour & Weapons of Japan & Their Ten Complements, 10 Vols. 2800p. 1983. pap. 175.00 Set (ISBN 0-87556-476-3). Saifer.
Ancient Japanese Weapons: Bow & Arrow Designs. (Illus.). 1983. pap. 12.50 (ISBN 0-87556-561-1). Saifer.
Anti-Submarine Warfare Market. 1075p. 1983. 1700.00 (ISBN 0-86621-113-6, A1164). Frost & Sullivan.
Ashdown, Charles H. Armour & Weapons in the Middle Ages. (Illus.). 22.00 (ISBN 0-87556-603-0). Saifer.
Balent, Matthew. The Palladium Book of Exotic Weapons. Marciniszyn, Alex, ed. (Weapons Ser.: No. 6). (Illus.). 48p. (Orig.). 1984. pap. 5.95 (ISBN 0-916211-06-1). Palladium Bks.
Beckett, Brian. Weapons of Tomorrow. 160p. 1983. (full discount avail.) 14.95 (ISBN 0-306-41383-3, Plenum Pr). Plenum Pub.
Bidwell, Shelford & Graham, Dominick. Fire Power: British Army Weapons & Theories (1904-1945) (Illus.). 366p. 1985. pap. text ed. 14.95x (ISBN 0-04-942190-5). Allen Unwin.
Birla Institute of Scientific Research, Economic Research Division & Agarwal, R. J. Defence Production & Development. (Birla Institute of Scientific Research Ser.). 1978. text ed. 10.00x (ISBN 0-8426-1081-2). Verry.
Bivens, John. Art of the Fire-Lock, Twentieth Century: Being a Discourse Upon the Present & Past Practices of Stocking & Mounting the Sporting Fire-Lock Rifle-Gun, 3 vols. (The Longrifle Ser.). 1986. 40.00 (ISBN 0-686-75398-4). Shumway.
Boccia & Coehlo. Armi Bianche Italiane. (Illus.). 462p. 1976. 135.00 (ISBN 0-686-14972-6). Arma Pr.
Collier, Basil. Arms & the Men: The Arms Trade & Governments. (Illus.). 320p. 1980. 26.50 (ISBN 0-241-10308-8, Pub. by Hamish Hamilton England). David & Charles.
Constant, James N. Fundamentals of Strategic Weapons. 940p. 1981. 140.00 (ISBN 90-286-0129-5). Sijthoff & Noordhoff.
Cowper, H. S. The Art of Attack: Being a Study in the Development of Weapons & Appliances of Offence, from the Earliest Times to the Age of Gunpowder. (Illus.). 312p. 1977. Repr. of 1906 ed. 21.50x (ISBN 0-8476-6061-3). Rowman.
Curtis, Tony, ed. Lyle Official Arms & Armour Review, 1982. (Illus.). 1980. 24.95 (ISBN 0-8256-9687-9). Apollo.
Diagram Group. Weapons. (Illus.). 320p. 1980. 27.50 (ISBN 0-312-85946-5). St Martin.
Dunnigan, James F. How to Make War: A Comprehensive Guide to Modern Warfare. (Illus.). 416p. 1982. 14.50 (ISBN 0-688-00780-5). Morrow.
--How to Make War: A Comprehensive Guide to Modern Warfare. rev., upd. ed. LC 82-23065. (Illus.). 444p. 1983. pap. 8.95 (ISBN 0-688-01975-7, Quill NY). Morrow.
Dupuy, Trevor N. The Evolution of Weapons & Warfare. (Illus.). 360p. 1984. Repr. of 1980 ed. text ed. 19.95 (ISBN 0-915979-05-5). Hero Books.
Ezell, Edward C. Small Arms Today: Latest Reports on the World's Weapons & Ammunition. 256p. (Orig.). 1984. pap. 16.95 (ISBN 0-8117-2197-3). Stackpole.
Fadala, Sam. Black Powder Handgun. LC 81-65102. 288p. (Orig.). 1981. pap. 11.95 (ISBN 0-910676-22-4, 9266). DBI.
Featherstone, Donald. Weapons & Equipment of the Victorian Soldier. (Illus.). 1978. 19.95 (ISBN 0-7137-0847-6, Pub. by Blandford Pr England). Sterling.
Ffoulkes, Charles J. Armourer & His Craft. LC 67-13328. (Illus.). 1967. Repr. of 1912 ed. 24.50 (ISBN 0-405-08501-X). Ayer Co Pubs.
Flax, Brian D., ed. Best of the Hammer, Vol. I. (Illus.). vi, 200p. (Orig.). 1985. pap. 6.00 (ISBN 0-943228-04-2). Raymonds Quiet Pr.
Frost, H. Gordon. Blades & Barrels: Six Centuries of Combination Weapons. 16.95 (ISBN 0-686-11627-5); deluxe ed. 25.00 (ISBN 0-686-11628-3); presentation ed. 50.00 (ISBN 0-686-11629-1). Walloon Pr.
Funcken, Lilane & Funcken, Fred. Arms & Uniforms: The Second World War, Vol. I. (Illus.). 128p. 1984. 17.95 (ISBN 0-13-046343-4); pap. 8.95 (ISBN 0-13-046269-1). P-H.
Funcken, Liliane & Funcken, Fred. Arms & Uniforms: The Napoleonic Wars, Vol. I. (Illus.). 160p. (Orig.). 1984. 17.95 (ISBN 0-13-046236-5); pap. 9.95 (ISBN 0-13-046228-4). P-H.
--Arms & Uniforms: The Napoleonic Wars, Vol. II. (Illus.). 160p. 17.95 (ISBN 0-13-046251-9); pap. 9.95 (ISBN 0-13-046244-6). P-H.
--Arms & Uniforms: The Second World War, Vol. III. (Illus.). 120p. 1984. 17.95 (ISBN 0-13-046384-1); pap. 8.95 (ISBN 0-13-046376-0). P-H.
--Arms & Uniforms: The Second World War, Vol. IV. (Illus.). 120p. 1984. 17.95 (ISBN 0-13-046400-7); pap. 8.95 (ISBN 0-13-046392-2). P-H.
Gaibi, Agostino. Armi Da Fuoco Italiane. (Illus.). 532p. (Eng. captions). 1976. 95.00 (ISBN 0-686-14973-4). Arma Pr.
Gambordella, Ted. Weapons of the Street. (Illus.). 80p. (Orig.). 1984. pap. 8.00 (ISBN 0-87364-281-3). Paladin Pr.
Gordon, Don E. Electronic Warfare: Element of Strategy & Multiplier of Combat Power. (Pergamon Policy Studies on Security Affairs). (Illus.). 200p. 1982. 17.50 (ISBN 0-08-027189-8). Pergamon.
Gudgin, Peter. British Army Equipment. 80p. 1982. 8.95 (ISBN 0-85368-377-8). Stackpole.
Guthman, William, ed. Guns & Other Arms. (Illus.). 160p. 1980. pap. 7.95 (ISBN 0-8317-4182-1, Mayflower Bks). Smith Pubs.
Hart, Harold H. Weapons & Armor: A Pictorial Archive of Woodcuts & Engravings. 1983. 14.50 (ISBN 0-8446-5937-1). Peter Smith.
Hawley, W. M. Introduction to Japanese Swords. 1973. pap. 3.00 (ISBN 0-685-31544-4, 910704-53). Hawley.
Hogg, Ian V. Modern Small Arms. (Illus.). 224p. 1983. 20.00 (ISBN 0-89141-184-4). Presidio Pr.
Holmes, Bill. Home Workshop Guns for Defense & Resistance: The Handgun, Vol. II. (Illus.). 144p. (Orig.). 1979. pap. 10.00 (ISBN 0-87364-154-X). Paladin Pr.
International Institute for Strategic Studies. Military Balance, 1980 to 1981. 119p. 1980. 17.95x (ISBN 0-87196-446-5). Facts on File.
Joly, H. L. Naunton Collection of Japanese Sword Fitting. 1973. Repr. of 1912 ed. 50.00 (ISBN 0-685-31543-6, 910704-55). Hawley.
Journal of the Arms & Armour Society, Vol. 1. LC 77-114230. (Illus.). 240p. 1970. casebound 12.00 (ISBN 0-87387-029-8). Shumway.
Kemp, Anthony & Haythornthwaite, Philip. Weapons & Equipment Series, 3 vols. (Illus.). 525p. 1982. boxed set 50.00 (ISBN 0-7137-1296-1, Pub. by Blandford Pr England). Sterling.
Kozan, S. Manufacture of Armour & Helmets in Sixteenth Century Japan. 35.00 (ISBN 0-87556-547-6). Saifer.
Laking, Guy F. A Record of European Armour & Arms Through Seven Centuries, 5 vols. LC 79-8365. (Illus.). Repr. 295.00 set (ISBN 0-404-18344-1). AMS Pr.
Lightweight Armor, 1964-May 1982. 281p. 1982. 78.00 (ISBN 0-686-48336-7, LS132). T-C Pubns CA.
McAulay, John D. Carbines of the Civil War, 1861-1865. 1981. 7.95 (ISBN 0-913150-45-2). Pioneer Pr.
Mallory, Franklin B. Serial Numbers of U. S. Martial Arms. LC 82-63083. 112p. 1983. 10.00 (ISBN 0-9603306-1-5). Springfield Res Serv.
Marchant-Smith, D. J. & Haslem, P. R. Small Arms & Cannons. (Brassey's Battlefield Weapons System & Technology: Vol. 5). 160p. 1982. 26.00 (ISBN 0-08-028330-6); pap. 13.00 (ISBN 0-08-028331-4). Pergamon.
Masterpieces of Tula Gunsmiths (Shedevry Tul'skikh Oruzheynikov) 144p. 1981. 60.00x (ISBN 0-317-14254-2, Pub. by Collet's). State Mutual Bk.
Mesko, Jim. U. S. Infantry: Vietnam. (Weapons in Action Ser.: No. 3006). (Illus.). 50p. 1983. pap. 4.95 (ISBN 0-89747-151-2). Squad Sig Pubns.
Military Display Market. 305p. 1985. 1675.00 (ISBN 0-86621-197-7, A1261). Frost & Sullivan.
Ming, Yang J. Introduction to Ancient Chinese Weapons. (Illus.). 180p. pap. 8.95 (ISBN 0-86568-052-3, 107). Unique Pubns.
Mowbray, E. Andrew, ed. Arms - Armor: From the Atelier of Ernst Schmidt, Munich. LC 67-31469. (Illus.). 1967. 15.00 (ISBN 0-917218-00-0). Mowbray.
Moyer, Frank A. Special Forces Foreign Weapons Handbook. LC 70-93554. (Illus.). 330p. 1970. 19.95 (ISBN 0-87364-009-8). Paladin Pr.
Ng, Yiu. Pak Mei Tiger Fork. 1984. 20.00x (ISBN 0-901764-38-8, Pub. by P H Crompton Ltd UK). State Mutual Bk.
O. S. S. Weapons. (Illus.). 54p. pap. 10.95x (ISBN 0-86695-018-4). Interserv Pub.
Owen, J. I., ed. Brassey's Infantry Weapons of the World. 2nd ed. 488p. 1979. 61.00 (ISBN 0-08-027013-1). Pergamon.
--Infantry Weapons of the Armies of Africa, the Orient & Latin America. 196p. 1980. pap. 24.00 (ISBN 0-08-027017-4). Pergamon.
--Infantry Weapons of the NATO Armies. 2nd ed. 192p. 1979. pap. 24.00 (ISBN 0-08-027015-8). Pergamon.
--Infantry Weapons of the Warsaw Pact Armies. 2nd ed. 160p. 1979. pap. 24.00 (ISBN 0-08-027016-6). Pergamon.
Perrett, Bryan. Weapons of the Falklands Conflict. (Illus.). 1983. 9.95 (ISBN 0-7137-1315-1, Pub. by Blandford Pr England). Sterling.
Peterson, Harold L. The American Sword, Seventeen Seventy-Five to Nineteen Forty-Five. LC 65-25409. (Illus.). 1983. 35.00 (ISBN 0-9603094-1-1). Ray Riling.
Pierre, Andrew J. The Global Politics of Arms Sales. 353p. 1981. 27.00 (ISBN 0-691-07635-9); pap. 8.95 (ISBN 0-691-02207-0). Princeton U Pr.
Royal United Services Institute for Defence Studies, ed. International Weapon Developments: A Survey of Current Developments in Weapon Systems. 4th ed. (Illus.). 203p. 1980. pap. 14.25 (ISBN 0-08-027028-X). Pergamon.
Schuyler-Hartley-Graham Military Furnishers. Illustrated Catalog Arms & Military Goods. facsimile ed. (Illus.). 1864. 9.50 (ISBN 0-910598-00-2). Flayderman.
Seaton, Lionel. The International Arms Review, Vol. I. (Illus.). 1977. 6.95 (ISBN 0-89149-008-6). Jolex.
Seaton, Lionel, tr. The International Arms Review, Vol. II. (Illus.). 1979. 6.95 (ISBN 0-89149-029-9). Jolex.
Shepperd, G. A. A History of War & Weapons, 1660-1918. (Illus.). 224p. 1972. 12.45i (ISBN 0-690-39367-9). T Y Crowell.
Smith, W. H. Small Arms of the World: A Basic Manual of Small Arms. 12th ed. 896p. 1983. 49.95 (ISBN 0-8117-1687-2). Stackpole.
Snodgrass, A. M. Arms & Armour of the Greeks. (Aspects of Greek & Roman Life). (Illus.). 150p. 1967. 29.95x (ISBN 0-8014-0399-5). Cornell U Pr.
Suenaga, M. Pictorial History of Ancient Japanese Weapons, Armour, & Artifacts. (Illus.). 100p. 1983. pap. 12.50 (ISBN 0-87556-582-4). Saifer.
Traister, John. Learn Gunsmithing: The Troubleshooting Method. LC 80-17763. (Illus.). 208p. 1980. 16.95 (ISBN 0-8329-3176-4, Pub. by Winchester Pr). New Century.
Truby, J. David. Quiet Killers, Vol. 1. (Illus.). 80p. 1972. pap. 8.00 (ISBN 0-87364-014-4). Paladin Pr.
--Quiet Killers II: Silencer Update. (Illus.). 90p. (Orig.). 1979. pap. 8.00 (ISBN 0-87364-163-9). Paladin Pr.
Von Mellenthin, F. W. Panzer Battles: A Study of the Employment of Armor in the Second World War. Turner, L. C., ed. Betzler, H., tr. (Illus.). 1971. pap. write for info. U of Okla Pr.
Warry, John. Warfare in the Classical World: An Illustrated Encyclopedia of Weapons, Warriors & Warfare in the Ancient Civilizations of Greece & Rome. LC 80-54639. (Illus.). 224p. 1981. 24.95 (ISBN 0-312-85614-8). St Martin.
Wintringham, Thomas H. Story of Weapons & Tactics. facs. ed. LC 79-128335. (Essay Index Reprint Ser). 1943. 18.00 (ISBN 0-8369-2093-7). Ayer Co Pubs.

ARMS AND ARMOR, PRIMITIVE
see also Boomerangs; Bow and Arrow

Wong, James I. Chinese Weapon: The Double-End Spear. LC 82-83050. 59p. (Orig.). 1982. pap. 6.95 (ISBN 0-86635-209-0). Koinonia Prods.

ARMY ANTS

Schneirla, T. C. Army Ants: A Study in Social Organization. Topoff, Howard R., ed. LC 70-149408. (Illus.). 349p. 1971. text ed. 23.95x (ISBN 0-7167-0933-3). W H Freeman.
Watkins, Julian F., II. The Identification & Distribution of New World Army Ants: Dorylinae: Formicidae. LC 76-17690. (Illus.). 102p. 1976. pap. 5.00x (ISBN 0-918954-18-5). Baylor Univ Pr.

ARMY SUPPLIES
see Military Supplies

ARMY WAGONS
see Vehicles, Military

AROMATIC COMPOUNDS

Akhrem, A. A., et al. Birch Reduction of Aromatic Compounds. LC 70-183103. 132p. 1972. 45.00x (ISBN 0-306-65158-0, Plenum Pr). Plenum Pub.
Bergmann, E. D. & Pullman, B., eds. Aromaticity, Pseudoaromaticity, Antiaromaticity. LC 79-134838. 1971. 76.00 (ISBN 0-12-091040-3). Acad Pr.
Berlman, I. Energy Transfer Parameters of Aromatic Compounds. 1973. 66.00 (ISBN 0-12-092640-7). Acad Pr.
Berlman, Isadore B. Handbook of Fluorescence Spectra of Aromatic Molecules. 2nd ed. 1971. 76.00 (ISBN 0-12-092656-3). Acad Pr.
Bird, C. W. & Cheeseman, G. W., eds. Aromatic & Heteroaromatic Chemistry, Vols. 1-6. Incl. Vol. 1. 1971-72 Literature. 1973. 42.00 (ISBN 0-85186-753-7); Vol. 2. 1972-73 Literature. 1974. 47.00 (ISBN 0-85186-763-4); Vol. 3. 1973-74 Literature. 1975. 53.00 (ISBN 0-85186-773-1); Vol. 4. 1974-75 Literature. 1976. 70.00 (ISBN 0-85186-783-9); Vol. 5. 1975-76 Literature. 1977. 87.00 (ISBN 0-85186-793-6); Vol. 6. 1976-77 Literature. 1978. 70.00 (ISBN 0-85186-803-7). LC 72-95095 (Pub. by Royal Soc Chem London). Am Chemical.
Ciba Foundation. Aromatic Amino Acids in the Brain. LC 73-91643. (Ciba Foundation Symposium: New Ser.: No. 22). pap. 101.50 (ISBN 0-317-29189-0, 2022152). Bks Demand UMI.
Clar, E. Polycyclic Hydrocarbons, 2 Vols. 1964. Vol. 1. 79.50 (ISBN 0-12-174701-8); Vol. 2. 79.50 (ISBN 0-12-174702-6). Acad Pr.
Cooke, Marcus & Dennis, Anthony J. Polynuclear Aromatic Hydrocarbons: Formation, Metabolism & Measurement. (International Poynuclear Aromatic Symposium on Hydrocarbons). 1301p. 1983. 65.00 (ISBN 0-935470-16-6). Battelle.
Dorland, Wayne E. & Rogers, James A. The Fragrance & Flavor Industry. (Illus.). 1977. 30.00 (ISBN 0-9603250-1-8). Dorland Pub Co.
Georgiev, V. St. Noncondensed Aromatic Derivatives, Part III. (Survey of Drug Research in Immunologic Disease Series: Vol. 4). x, 334p. 1984. 123.50 (ISBN 3-8055-3799-9). S Karger.
Gmehling, J., et al. Aromatic Hydrocarbons: Vol. I, Pt. 7, Vapor-Liquid Equilibrium Data Collection. Behrens, D. & Eckermann, R., eds. (Dechema Chemistry Data Ser.). 564p. 1980. text ed. 110.00x (ISBN 3-9215-6723-8, Pub. by Dechema Germany). Scholium Intl.

Goodwin, B. L. Handbook of Intermediate Metabolism of Aromatic Compounds. 1976. 49.95x (ISBN 0-412-12920-5, NO. 6130, Pub. by Chapman & Hall). Methuen Inc.

Hancock, E. G., ed. Toluene, the Xylenes & Their Industrial Derivatives. (Chemical Engineering Monographs: Vol. 15). 552p. 1982. 125.75 (ISBN 0-444-42058-4). Elsevier.

High-Modulus Wholly Aromatic Fibers. Black, W. Bruce & Preston, Jack, eds. (Fiber Science Ser.: No. 5). 388p. 1973. 75.00 (ISBN 0-8247-6069-7). Dekker.

Karcher, W., et al, eds. Spectral Atlas of Polcyclic Aromatic Compounds: Including Data on Occurence & Biological Activity. 1985. lib. bdg. 94.00 (ISBN 90-277-1652-8, Pub. by Reidel Holland). KLuwer Academic.

Lewis, David & Peters, David. Facts & Theories of Aromaticity. 109p. 1975. 19.50x (ISBN 0-8448-0663-3). Crane-Russak Co.

Maarse, H. & Belz, R. Isolation, Separation & Identification of Volatile Compounds in Aroma Research. 1982. lib. bdg. 54.50x (ISBN 90-277-1432-0, Pub. by Reidel Holland). Kluwer Academic.

Matsumura, F., ed. Differential Toxicities of Insecticides & Halogenated Aromatics. (International Encyclopedia of Pharmacology & Therapeutics Ser.). (Illus.). 560p. 1983. 140.00 (ISBN 0-08-029826-5). Pergamon.

Memory, J. D. & Wilson, Nancy K. NMR of Aromatic Compounds. LC 82-8588. 252p. 1982. 45.95 (ISBN 0-471-08899-4, Pub. by Wiley-Interscience). Wiley.

Nicholson, William J. & Moore, John A., eds. Health Effects of Halogenated Aromatic Hydrocarbons. LC 79-12253. (Annals of the New York Academy of Sciences: Vol. 320). 730p. 1979. 117.00x (ISBN 0-89766-008-0). NY Acad Sci.

Rossi, Roberto A. & De Rossi, Rita H., eds. Aromatic Substitution by the SRN1 Mechanism. LC 82-22829. (ACS Monographs: No. 178). 300p. 1983. lib. bdg. 49.95x (ISBN 0-8412-0648-1). Am Chemical.

St. Georgiev, V. Noncondensed Aromatic Derivatives, Pt. I. (Survey of Drug Research in Immunological Disease: Vol. 2). xii, 656p. 1983. 208.75 (ISBN 3-8055-3566-X). S Karger.

Saunders, K. H. & Allen, R. L. Aromatic Diazo Compounds. 3rd ed. 850p. 1985. 175.00 (ISBN 0-7131-3499-2). E Arnold.

Smith, B. H. Bridged Aromatic Compounds. (Organic Chemistry: Vol. 2). 1965. 81.00 (ISBN 0-12-650350-8). Acad Pr.

Snyder, James P., ed. Nonbenzenoid Aromatics, Vols. 1-2. (Organic Chemistry Ser: Vol. 16). 1971. Vol. 2. 77.00. Acad Pr.

Symposium on Aroma Research, May 1975, Zeist, Netherlands. Aroma Research: Proceedings. 250p. 1975. pap. 44.00 (ISBN 90-220-0573-9, PDC2, Pub. by PUDOC). Unipub.

Tisserand, R. B. The Art of Aromatherapy. 320p. 1977. 18.00x (ISBN 0-8464-0993-3). Beekman Pubs.

Weiss, Ulrich & Edwards, John. Biosynthesis of Aromatic Compounds. LC 78-1496. 728p. 1980. 65.50x (ISBN 0-471-92690-6, Pub by Wiley-Interscience). Wiley.

AROMATIC PLANT PRODUCTS

see Essences and Essential Oils

ARROW (FIGHTER PLANES)

see Pfeil (Fighter Planes)

ARROWS

see Bow and Arrow

ARSENIC

Doak, George D. & Freedman, Leon D. Organometallic Compounds of Arsenic, Antimony, & Bismuth. LC 75-120703. 509p. 1970. 42.50 (ISBN 0-471-21650-X, Pub. by Wiley). Krieger.

Dub, M., ed. Organometallic Compounds: Methods of Synthesis, Physical Constants & Chemical Reactions, 3 vols. Incl. Vol. 1. Compounds of Transition Metals. 2nd ed. xviii, 828p. 1966. 83.00 (ISBN 0-387-03632-6); Vol. 2. Compounds of Germanium, Tin & Lead, Including Biological Activity & Commercial Application. 2nd ed. Weiss, R. W., ed. xx, 627p. 1967. 83.00 (ISBN 0-387-03948-1); 91.00 (ISBN 0-387-06304-8); Vol. 3. Compounds of Arsenic, Antimony & Bismuth. 2nd ed. xx, 925p. 1968. 83.00 (ISBN 0-387-04296-2); Formula Index to Volumes 1-3. 2nd ed. vii, 343p. 1970. 57.00 (ISBN 0-387-04985-1). LC 66-28249. Springer-Verlag.

Krannich, Larry K., ed. Compounds Containing AS-N Bonds. LC 76-11783. (Benchmark Papers in Inorganic Chemistry: Vol. 5). 1976. 75.00 (ISBN 0-12-786869-0). Acad Pr.

Lederer, William H. & Fensterheim, Robert J., eds. Arsenic: Industrial, Biomedical, Enviornmental Perspectives. 464p. 1982. 48.50 (ISBN 0-442-21496-0). Van Nos Reinhold.

Woolson, E. A., ed. Arsenical Pesticides. LC 74-31378. (ACS Symposium Ser.: No. 7). 1975. 18.95 (ISBN 0-8412-0243-5). Am Chemical.

ART AND SCIENCE

see also Scientific Illustration

Brisson, David W. Hypergraphics: Visualizing Complex Relationships in Art, Science & Technology. (Illus.). 1979. 28.50x (ISBN 0-89158-292-4). Westview.

Dutton, D. & Krausz, M., eds. The Concept of Creativity in Science & Art. (Martinus Nijhoff Philosophy Library: No. 6). 262p. 1981. 31.00 (ISBN 90-247-2418-X, Pub. by Martinus Nijhoff Netherlands). Kluwer Academic.

Fourth International Exhibition of Twentieth Century Botanical Art & Illustration. Catalogue. Secrist, S. & Howard, N., eds. (Illus.). 1977. 12.00x (ISBN 0-913196-19-3). Hunt Inst Botanical.

Holden, Alan. Orderly Tangles: Cloverleafs, Gordian Knots, & Regular Polylinks. (Illus.). 96p. 1983. 20.00x (ISBN 0-231-05544-7). Columbia U Pr.

Johnson, Martin. Art & Scientific Thought. LC 70-118944. 192p. Repr. of 1949 ed. 16.50 (ISBN 0-404-00593-4). AMS Pr.

Korach, K., ed. Catalogue: Third International Exhibition of Twentieth Century Botanical Art & Illustration. (Illus.). 1972. 10.00x (ISBN 0-913196-14-2). Hunt Inst Botanical.

Research Laboratory Museum Of Fine Arts - Seminar - Boston - 1958. Applications of Science in Examination of Works of Art: Proceedings. LC 78-99280. 1960. 15.00 (ISBN 0-405-00070-7). Ayer Co Pubs.

Rhodes, Lynette I. Science Within Art. LC 79-93193. (Illus.). pap. 20.00 (ISBN 0-317-10007-6, 2022660). Bks Demand UMI.

Richardson, John A. Modern Art & Scientific Thought. LC 74-122914. (Illus.). pap. 40.10 (ISBN 0-317-10480-2, 2014895). Bks Demand UMI.

Schillinger, Joseph. Mathematical Basis of the Arts. LC 76-8189. (Music Reprint Ser.). 696p. 1976. Repr. of 1948 ed. 55.00 (ISBN 0-306-70781-0). Da Capo.

Second International Exhibition of Twentieth Century Botanical Art & Illustration. Catalogue. Lawrence, G., compiled by. (Illus.). 1968. 7.00x (ISBN 0-913196-11-8). Hunt Inst Botanical.

Smith, Cyril S. From Art to Science: Seventy-Two Objects Illustrating the Nature of Discovery. (Illus.). 118p. 1980. 27.50x (ISBN 0-262-19181-4). MIT Pr.

--A Search for Structure: Selected Essays on Science, Art & History. (Illus.). 410p. 1981. 42.50x (ISBN 0-262-19191-1); pap. 15.00x (ISBN 0-262-69082-9). MIT Pr.

ARTHRODESIS

Liechti, R. Hip Arthrodesis & Its Problems. Casey, P. A., tr. from Ger. (Illus.). 1978. 89.00 (ISBN 0-387-08614-5). Springer-Verlag.

ARTHROPLASTY

Charnley, J. Low Friction Arthroplasty of the Hip: Theory & Practice. (Illus.). 1978. 59.00 (ISBN 0-387-08893-8). Springer-Verlag.

Eftekhar, Nas S. Principles of Total Hip Arthroplasty. LC 78-18471. (Illus.). 656p. 1978. text ed. 74.50 (ISBN 0-8016-1496-1). Mosby.

ARTHROPODA

see also Arachnida; Crustacea; Insects; Myriapoda; Nervous System–Arthropoda

Alexander, J. O'Donel. Arthropods & Human Skin. (Illus.). 430p. 1984. 90.00 (ISBN 0-387-13235-X). Springer-Verlag.

Bettini, S., ed. Arthropod Venoms. (Handbook of Experimental Pharmacology: Vol. 48). (Illus.). 1977. 265.00 (ISBN 0-387-08228-X). Springer-Verlag.

Blum, Murray S., ed. Chemical Defenses of Arthopods. LC 81-7925. 1981. 66.00 (ISBN 0-12-108380-2). Acad Pr.

Boudreaux, H. Bruce. Anthropod Phylogeny. LC 84-3960. 328p. 1985. Repr. of 1979 ed. lib. bdg. write for info. (ISBN 0-89874-746-5). Krieger.

Brown, A. W. & Pal, R. Insecticide Resistance in Arthropods. 2nd ed. (Monograph Ser: No. 38). (Illus.). 491p. 1971. pap. 16.40 (ISBN 92-4-140038-2, 943). World Health.

Cloudsley-Thompson, J. L. Evolutionary Trends in the Mating of Arthropoda. 92p. 1976. 39.00x (ISBN 0-900541-82-2, Pub. by Meadowfield Pr England). State Mutual Bk.

Edney, E. B. Water Balance in Land Arthropods. (Zoophysiology & Ecology Ser.: Vol. 9). 1977. 49.00 (ISBN 0-387-08084-8). Springer-Verlag.

Frazier, Claude A. Insect Allergy: Allergic & Toxic Reactions to Insects & Other Arthropods. 2nd ed. (Illus.). 480p. 1985. 42.50 (ISBN 0-87527-324-6). Green.

Gupta, Ayodhya P. Anthropod Phylogeny. 768p. 1979. 42.50 (ISBN 0-442-22973-9). Van Nos Reinhold.

Herreid, Clyde F., II & Fourtner, Charles R., eds. Locomotion & Energetics in Anthropods. LC 81-13779. 554p. 1981. text ed. 69.50 (ISBN 0-306-40830-9, Plenum Pr). Plenum Pub.

Jenkins, D. W. Pathogens, Parasites & Predators of Medically Important Arthropods. (WHO Bulletin Supplement: Vol. 30). 1964. pap. 3.60 (ISBN 92-4-168301 5). World Health.

Manton, S. M. The Arthropoda: Habits, Functional Morphology & Evolution. (Illus.). 1977. 79.00x (ISBN 0-19-857391-X). Oxford U Pr.

Mattson, W. J., ed. The Role of Arthropods in Forest Ecosystems: Proceedings in Life Sciences. (Illus.). 1977. 26.50 (ISBN 0-387-08296-4). Springer-Verlag.

Miller, T. A. Cuticle Techniques in Arthropods. (Springer Series in Experimental Entomology). (Illus.). 410p. 1980. 69.00 (ISBN 0-387-90475-1). Springer-Verlag.

Moore, Raymond C., ed. Treatise on Invertebrate Paleontology, Pt. O: Arthropoda 1. LC 53-12913. (Illus.). 1959. 23.50 (ISBN 0-8137-3015-5). Geol Soc.

--Treatise on Invertebrate Paleontology, Pt. P: Arthropoda 2. LC 53-12913. (Illus.). 1955. 14.00 (ISBN 0-8137-3016-3). Geol Soc.

--Treatise on Invertebrate Paleontology, Pt. Q: Arthropoda 3. LC 53-12913. (Illus.). 1961. 22.75 (ISBN 0-8137-3017-1). Geol Soc.

--Treatise on Invertebrate Paleontology, Pt. R. Arthropoda 4, Vols. 1-2. LC 53-12913. (Illus.). 1969. 26.00 (ISBN 0-8137-3018-X). Geol Soc.

Muzzarelli, Riccardo A. Chitin. LC 76-52421. 365p. 1977. text ed. 67.00 (ISBN 0-08-020367-1). Pergamon.

Neville, A. C. Biology of the Anthropod Cuticle, 2 vols. in 1, Vols. 4-5. LC 74-30175. (Zoophysiology & Ecology Ser). (Illus.). 500p. 1975. 87.00 (ISBN 0-387-07081-8). Springer-Verlag.

Neville, Charles. The Biology of the Arthropod Cuticle. Head, J. J., ed. LC 78-51261. (Carolina Biology Readers Ser.). (Illus.). 16p. 1978. pap. 1.60 (ISBN 0-89278-303-6, 45-9703). Carolina Biological.

Pal, R. & Wharton, R. H., eds. Control of Arthropods: Medical & Veterinary Importance. LC 74-4172. 143p. 1974. 32.50x (ISBN 0-306-30790-1, Plenum Pr). Plenum Pub.

Procedures to Investigate Arthropod-Borne & Rodent Borne Illness. 93p. 2.00 (ISBN 0-318-17809-5); bulk rates avail. Intl Assn Milk.

ARTHROPODA–PARASITES

see Parasites–Arthropoda

ARTIFICIAL DELAY LINES

see Delay Lines

ARTIFICIAL FIBERS

see Textile Fibers, Synthetic

ARTIFICIAL FUELS

see Synthetic Fuels

ARTIFICIAL INSEMINATION

Buffalo Reproduction & Artificial Insemination: Proceedings of the Seminar Sponsored by SIDA-Govt. of India, held at the National Dairy Research Institute, Karnal, India, Dec. 4-15, 1978. (Animal Production & Health Papers: No. 13). 370p. 1979. pap. 26.50 (ISBN 92-5-100743-8, F2086, FAO). Unipub.

Herman, H. A. & Madden, F. A. Artificial Insemination of Dairy & Beef Cattle. 6th ed. 1980. 14.95x (ISBN 0-87543-109-7). Lucas.

Woynarovich, E. & Horvath, L. The Artificial Propagation of Warm-Water Finfishes: A Manual for Extension. (Fisheries Technical Papers: No. 201). (Eng., Fr., & Span.). 192p. (2nd Printing 1980). 1980. pap. 14.00 (ISBN 92-5-100999-6, F2125, FAO). Unipub.

ARTIFICIAL INTELLIGENCE

see also Adaptive Control Systems; Error-Correcting Codes (Information Theory); Machine Translating; Perceptrons

AAAI Artificial Intelligence Conference, 1983. Proceedings. pap. 45.00 (ISBN 0-86576-065-9). W Kaufmann.

AAAI Artificial Intelligence Conference, 1980. Proceedings. pap. 40.00 (ISBN 0-86576-052-7). W Kaufmann.

Abelson, Harold & DiSessa, Andrea. Turtle Geometry: The Computer As a Medium for Exploring Mathematics. (Artificial Intelligence Ser.). (Illus.). 477p. 1981. text ed. 27.00x (ISBN 0-262-01063-1). MIT Pr.

Allen, Peter, ed. Artificial Intelligence: A Market Assessment. 200p. 1984. pap. 1250.00 (ISBN 0-931634-44-X). FIND-SVP.

American Association for Artifical Intelligence. Artificial Intelligence: Proceedings of the National Conference, 4th, 1984. 500p. 1984. pap. 45.00 (ISBN 0-86576-080-2). W Kaufmann.

American Association for Artifical Intelligence, National Conference on Artificial Intelligence, AAAI 82, Pittsburgh, Pa., Aug. 1982. Proceedings. 437p. (Orig.). 1982. pap. text ed. 45.00x (ISBN 0-86576-043-8). W Kaufmann.

American Association for Artificial Intelligence National Conference, 1982. Artificial Intelligence: Proceedings. 1982. 45.00 (ISBN 0-86576-043-8). W Kaufmann.

American Association for Artificial Intelligence. Artificial Intelligence: Proceedings of the First Annual National Conference, 1980. (Illus.). 350p. 1980. 40.00 (ISBN 0-86576-052-7). W Kaufmann.

--Artificial Intelligence: Proceedings of the National Conference, 1983. (Illus.). 368p. (Orig.). 1983. 45.00 (ISBN 0-86576-065-9). W Kaufmann.

American Association for Artificial Intelligence Staff. Artificial Intelligence: Proceedings of the National Conference, 1984. (Illus.). 500p. 1984. ref. ed. 45.00 (ISBN 0-86576-080-2). Amer Artificial.

Anderson, Alan R., ed. Minds & Machines. (Orig.). 1964. pap. 12.95 ref. ed. (ISBN 0-13-583393-0). P-H.

Andrew, A. M. Artificial Intelligence. 1983. 26.00 (ISBN 0-85626-165-3, Pub. by Abacus England). Heyden.

Andriole, Stephen J., ed. Applications in Artificial Intelligence. 1985. 49.95 (ISBN 0-89433-219-8). Petrocelli.

Arbib, Michael. The Metaphorical Brain: An Introduction to Cybernetics As Artificial Intelligence & Brains Theory. LC 72-2490. (Illus.). 243p. 1972. 36.95x (ISBN 0-471-03249-2, Pub. by Wiley-Interscience). Wiley.

Arnold, William R. & Bowie, John S. Artificial Intelligence: A Personal Commonsense Journey. (Illus.). 224p. 1986. text ed. 24.95 (ISBN 0-13-048877-1). P-H.

Artificial Intelligence. 167p. 1983. 1650.00. Intl Res Dev.

Artificial Intelligence. 1985. write for info. (ISBN 0-86621-394-5, A1469). Frost & Sullivan.

Baba, N. New Topics in Learning Automata Theory & Applications. (Lecture Notes in Control & Information Sciences: Vol. 71). 150p. 1985. pap. 10.00 (ISBN 0-387-15613-5). Springer-Verlag.

Banerji, R. B. Artificial Intelligence: A Theoretical Approach. 254p. 1980. 33.50 (ISBN 0-444-00334-7). Elsevier.

Barr, Avron, et al, eds. The Handbook of Artificial Intelligence, 3 vols. LC 80-28621. 1982. Set. 120.00x (ISBN 0-86576-004-7). Vol. 1. 39.50x (ISBN 0-86576-005-5); Vol. 2. 42.50x (ISBN 0-86576-006-3); Vol. 3. 59.50x (ISBN 0-86576-007-1). W Kaufmann.

--The Handbook of Artificial Intelligence, 3 vols. 1985. Set. pap. 79.95 (ISBN 0-86576-088-8); Vol. 1. pap. 27.95 (ISBN 0-86576-089-6); Vol. 2. pap. 28.95 (ISBN 0-86576-090-X); Vol. 3. pap. 32.95 (ISBN 0-86576-091-8). W Kaufmann.

Bellman, Richard. Artificial Intelligence: Can Computers Think? LC 78-9474. (Chinese & Japanese.). 147p. 1978. text ed. 20.00x (ISBN 0-87835-066-7); pap. text ed. 9.95x (ISBN 0-87835-149-3). Boyd & Fraser.

--An Introduction to Artificial Intelligence: Can Computers Think? LC 78-9474. 160p. 1978. text ed. 20.00x (ISBN 0-87835-066-7). Boyd & Fraser.

Benson, Ian, ed. Intelligent Machinery: Theory & Practice. 250p. Date not set. price not set (ISBN 0-521-30836-4). Cambridge U Pr.

Bernold, T. & Albers, G., eds. Artificial Intelligence: Towards Practical Application. (Proceedings of the Joint Technology Assessment Conference of the Gottlieb Duttweiler Institute & the European Coordinating Committee for Artificial Intelligence). 334p. 1985. 44.50 (ISBN 0-444-87719-3, North-Holland). Elsevier.

Bernstein, Jeremy. Science Observed: Essays Out of My Mind. 1982. 16.95 (ISBN 0-465-07340-9). Basic.

Berwick, Robert. The Acquisition of Syntactic Knowledge. (Series in Artificial Intelligence). (Illus.). 350p. 1985. text ed. 27.50x (ISBN 0-262-02226-5). MIT Pr.

Bibel, W. & Kowalski, R., eds. Fifth Conference on Automated Deduction: Les Arcs Proceedings. (Lecture Notes in Computer Science: Vol. 87). (Illus.). 385p. 1980. pap. 26.00 (ISBN 0-387-10009-1). Springer-Verlag.

Bible, W. & Petkoff, B., eds. Artifical Intelligence: Methodology, Systems, Applications: Proceedings of the International Conference on Artificial Intelligence Varna, Bulgaria, 17-20 Sept., 1984. 248p. 1985. 44.50 (ISBN 0-444-87743-6, North Holland). Elsevier.

Boden, Margaret. Artificial Intelligence & Natural Man. LC 76-8117. (Illus.). 537p. 1981. pap. 15.95x (ISBN 0-465-00453-9, TB-5063). Basic.

Bolc, L., ed. Natural Language Communication with Pictorial Information Systems. (Symbolic Computation: Artificial Intelligence Ser.). (Illus.). 340p. 1984. 31.00 (ISBN 0-387-13478-6). Springer-Verlag.

Bonnet, Alain. Artificial Intelligence. (Illus.). 272p. 1986. pap. text ed. 19.95 (ISBN 0-13-048869-0). P-H.

Brady, M., et al, eds. Robotics & Artificial Intelligence. (NATO ASI Ser.: Series F: No. 11). xviii, 694p. 1984. 62.50 (ISBN 0-387-12888-3). Springer-Verlag.

Brady, Michael, ed. Computer Vision. (Journal of Artificial Intelligence Ser.: Vol. 17). vi, 508p. 1982. 64.00 (ISBN 0-444-86343-5, North-Holland). Elsevier.

Bramer, M. A. Computer Game-Playing: Theory & Practice. LC 83-10678. (Artificial Intelligence Ser.). 306p. 1983. 61.95x (ISBN 0-470-27466-2). Halsted Pr.

Brooks, Rodney A. Model-Based Computer Vision. Stone, Harold, ed. LC 84-2416. (Computer Science Series: Artificial Intelligence: No. 14). 162p. 1984. 39.95 (ISBN 0-8357-1526-4). UMI Res Pr.

Browston, Lee, et al. Programming Expert Systems in OPS5: An Introduction to Rule-Based Programming. (Artificial Intellegence Ser.). 1985. text ed. 35.95 (ISBN 0-201-10647-7). Addison-Wesley.

Bundy, A., ed. Artificial Intelligence: An Introductory Course. 386p. 1979. 32.50 (ISBN 0-444-19463-0, North Holland). Elsevier.

--Catalogue of Artificial Intelligence Tools. (Symbolic Computation, Artificial Intelligence Ser.). (Illus.). xxv, 150p. 1984. pap. 17.00 (ISBN 0-387-13938-9). Springer-Verlag.

Business Communications Staff. Artificial Intelligence. 1984. 1750.00 (ISBN 0-89336-392-8, G-086). BCC.

Carbonell, Jaime G. Subjective Understanding: Computer Models of Belief Systems. Stone, Harold S., ed. LC 81-11528. (Computer Science Ser.: Artificial Intelligence: No. 5). 304p. 1981. 49.95 (ISBN 0-8357-1212-5). UMI Res Pr.

Chacko, George K. Robotics-Artificial Intelligence-Productivity. (Illus.). 360p. 1985. text ed. 39.95 (ISBN 0-89433-228-7). Petrocelli.

--Robotics-Artificial Intelligence-Productivity: Japan & the USA. (Illus.). 340p. 1985. 39.95 (ISBN 0-317-31197-2). Van Nos Reinhold.

Chang, Chin-Liang. Introduction to Artificial Intelligence Techniques. LC 85-60670. 182p. (Orig.). 1985. pap. 18.00 (ISBN 0-9614742-0-3). JMA Pr.

Charniak, Eugene & McDermott, Drew. Introduction to Artificial Intelligence. 1985. text ed. 33.95 (ISBN 0-201-11945-5). Addison-Wesley.

Charniak, Eugene, et al, eds. Artificial Intelligence Programming. LC 79-22120. (Illus.). 336p. 1980. text ed. 24.95x (ISBN 0-89859-004-3). L Erlbaum Assocs.

Chase, Leslie R. & Landers, Robert, eds. Artificial Intelligence: Reality or Fantasy? 1984. 59.95 (ISBN 0-942774-19-1). Info Indus.

Chen, C. H., ed. Pattern Recognition & Artificial Intelligence: Proceedings of a Joint Workshop held at Hyannis, Mass., June 1976. 1976. 68.50 (ISBN 0-12-170950-7). Acad Pr.

Ciampi, C. Artificial Intelligence & Legal Information Systems. 476p. 1982. 57.50 (ISBN 0-444-86414-8, I-187-82, North-Holland). Elsevier.

Ciampi, C. & Martino, A. A. Artificial Intelligence & Legal Information. 1984. 108.50 (ISBN 0-444-86413-X). Elsevier.

Cohen, Donald N. Knowledge-Based Theorem Proving & Learning. Stone, Harold, ed. LC 81-7494. (Computer Science Ser.: Artificial Intelligence: No. 4). 212p. 1981. 44.95 (ISBN 0-8357-1202-8). UMI Res Pr.

Cohen, Paul R. Heuristic Reasoning about Uncertainty: An Artificial Intelligence Approach. (Research Notes in Artificial Intelligence Ser.). 1985. pap. text ed. 19.50 (ISBN 0-273-08667-7). Pitman Pub MA.

Comtex Staff. Artificial Intelligence Reports from Bolt, Beranek & Newman. 1984. write for info. (ISBN 0-471-82286-8). Wiley.

--Artificial Intelligence Reports from Carnegie Mellon University. 1984. write for info. (ISBN 0-471-82289-2). Wiley.

--Artificial Intelligence Reports from Carnegie Mellon University, Pt. 1. 1984. write for info. (ISBN 0-471-82288-4). Wiley.

--Artificial Intelligence Reports from Carnegie Mellon University, Pt. 2. 1984. write for info. (ISBN 0-471-82287-6). Wiley.

--Artificial Intelligence Reports from the University of Illinois. 1985. write for info. (ISBN 0-471-82284-1). Wiley.

--Artificial Intelligence Reports from the University of Pennsylvania. 1984. write for info. (ISBN 0-471-82283-3). Wiley.

--Artificial Intelligence Reports from Yale University. 1985. write for info. (ISBN 0-471-82285-X). Wiley.

Conference on Computer Simulation Staff. UKSC '84: Proceedings. Murray-Smith, D. J., ed. (Illus.). 560p. 1984. text ed. 89.00 (ISBN 0-408-01504-7). Butterworth.

Crosson, Frederick J., ed. Human & Artificial Intelligence. LC 78-131431. (Orig.). 1970. pap. text ed. 7.95x (ISBN 0-89197-220-X). Irvington.

Davis, Randall & Lenat, Douglas. Knowledge-Based Systems in Artificial Intelligence: Two Case Studies. (Artificial Intelligence Ser.). (Illus.). 416p. 1982. text ed. 51.95 (ISBN 0-07-015557-7). McGraw.

Dietschmann, Hans J., ed. Representation & Exchange of Knowledge As a Basis of Information Processes: Proceedings of the 5th International Research Forum in Information Science (IRFIS 5) Heidelberg, 5-7 Sept., 1983. 434p. 1984. 55.75 (ISBN 0-444-87563-8, I-302-84, North Holland). Elsevier.

Dreyfus, Hubert L. What Computers Can't Do: A Critique of Artificial Reason. 1979. pap. 7.64i (ISBN 0-06-090613-8, CN 613, CN). Har-Row.

Dyer, Michael G. In-Depth Understanding: A Computer Model of Integrated Processing for Narrative Comprehension. (Artificial Intelligence Ser.). (Illus.). 458p. 1983. text ed. 37.50x (ISBN 0-262-04073-5). MIT Pr.

Eisenstadt, Mark & O'Shea, Tim. Artificial Intelligence: Tools, Techniques, & Applications. LC 84-502. 576p. 1984. pap. text ed. 23.95 scp (ISBN 0-06-041894-X, HarpC). Har-Row.

Elcock, E. W. & Michie, D., eds. Machine Intelligence: Machine Representations of Knowledge. (Machine Intelligence Ser.: Vol. 8). 680p. 1977. 114.95x (ISBN 0-470-99059-7). Halsted Pr.

El-Hadidy, B. & Horne, E. E., eds. The Infrastructure of an Information Society: Proceedings of the 1st International Conference in Cairo, Egypt, 13-15 Dec. 1982. 644p. 1984. 69.00 (ISBN 0-444-87549-2, I-303-84, North Holland). Elsevier.

Elithorn, A. & Banerji, R., eds. Artificial & Human Intelligence. 350p. 1984. 40.00 (ISBN 0-444-86545-4, North-Holland). Elsevier.

Ennals, R. Artificial Intelligence: Applications to Logical Reasoning & Historical Research. (Cognitive Sciences Ser.). 1985. 29.95 (ISBN 0-470-20181-9). Halsted Pr.

Fahlman, Scott E. NETL: A System for Representing & Using Real-World Knowledge. (Artificial Intelligence Ser.). (Illus.). 278p. 1979. text ed. 27.50x (ISBN 0-262-06069-8). MIT Pr.

Feigenbaum, Edward A. Computers & Thought. LC 80-29508. 550p. 1981. Repr. of 1963 ed. lib. bdg. 31.50 (ISBN 0-89874-199-8). Krieger.

Feigenbaum, Edward A. & McCorduck, Pamela. The Fifth Generation: Artificial Intelligence & Japan's Computer Challenge to the World. LC 83-3765. 288p. 1983. 15.95 (ISBN 0-201-11519-0). Addison-Wesley.

Felsen, Jerry. Decision Making Under Uncertainty: An Artificial Intelligence Approach. LC 75-32712. (Illus.). 150p. 1976. pap. 20.00 (ISBN 0-916376-00-1). CDS Pub.

Findler, Nicholas V., ed. Associative Networks: The Representation & Use of Knowledge by Computers. LC 78-31318. 1979. 61.50 (ISBN 0-12-256380-8). Acad Pr.

Firschein, Oscar, ed. Artificial Intelligence, Vol. VI. (Information Technology Ser.). (Illus.). 250p. 1984. 23.00 (ISBN 0-88283-044-9). AFIPS Pr.

Forsyth, Richard & Naylor, Chris. The Hitch-Hiker's Guide to Artificial Intelligence. 184p. 1985. pap. 15.95 (ISBN 0-412-27090-0, Pub. by Chapman & Hall England). Methuen Inc.

Frude, Neil. The Intimate Machine: Close Encounters with Computers & Robots. LC 83-8344. 256p. 1983. 14.95 (ISBN 0-453-00450-4). NAL.

Fu, K. S. & Tou, Julius T., eds. Learning Systems & Intelligent Robots. LC 74-11212. 452p. 1974. 65.00x (ISBN 0-306-30801-0, Plenum Pr). Plenum Pub.

Gardner, Howard. Mind's New Science: The Cognitive Revolution in the Computer Age. LC 85-47555. 512p. 1985. 24.95 (ISBN 0-465-04634-7). Basic.

George, F. H. Artificial Intelligence: Its Philosophy & Neural Context. (Studies in Cybernetics: Vol. 9). 222p. 1985. text ed. 39.00 (ISBN 0-317-26990-9). Gordon.

German Workshop on Artificial Intelligence, Bad Honnef, BRD, Jan. 1981. GWAI-Eighty-One. Siekmann, Joerg H., ed. (Informatik-Fachberichte: 47). 317p. 1981. pap. 17.10 (ISBN 3-540-10859-9). Springer-Verlag.

Gevarter, William B. Artificial Intelligence, An Overview: Combined Compilation of Volumes 5A, 5B, 5C of Robotics. LC 83-73202. (Artificial Intelligence Applications Ser.). 244p. 1984. lib. bdg. 49.00x (ISBN 0-89934-225-6, BT916). Business Technology Bks.

--Artificial Intelligence, An Overview, Pt. A. The Core Ingredients. LC 83-73201. (Robotics & Artificial Intelligence Applications Ser.: Vol. 5A). 76p. 1984. pap. 19.50x (ISBN 0-89934-194-2, BT013). Business Technology Bks.

--Artificial Intelligence, An Overview, Part B. Fundamental Application Areas. LC 83-73201. (Robotics & Artificial Intelligence Applications Ser.: Vol. 5B). 110p. pap. 24.50x (ISBN 0-89934-196-9, BT014, Pub. by Business-Technology Bks). Business Technology Bks.

--Artificial Intelligence, An Overview, Part C: Basic Topics. LC 83-73201. (Robotics & Artificial Intelligence Applications Ser.: Vol. 5C). 56p. pap. 19.50x (ISBN 0-89934-198-5, BT015, Pub. by Business-Technology Bks). Business Technology Bks.

--Artificial Intelligence & Robotics: Five Overviews (Robotics, Expert Systems, Computer Vision, Computer-Based Natural Language Processing & Artificial Inteligence) LC 84-70998. (Robotics & Artificial Intelligence Applications Ser.: Vols. 1-5C). 696p. 1984. lib. bdg. 99.50x (ISBN 0-89934-227-2, BT918). Business Technology Bks.

--Artificial Intelligence, Expert Systems, Computer Vision, & Natural Language Processing. LC 84-6014. (Illus.). 226p. 1984. 36.00 (ISBN 0-8155-0994-4). Noyes.

--Computer-Based Natural Language Processing: An Overview. LC 83-70570. (Robotics & Artificial Intelligence Applications Ser.: Vol. 4). 75p. 1984. pap. 19.50x (ISBN 0-89934-182-9, BT-004). Business Technology Bks.

--Computer Vision: An Overview. LC 83-70569. (Robotics & Artificial Intelligence Applications Ser.: Vol. 3). 175p. 1984. pap. 34.50x (ISBN 0-89934-180-2, BT-003). Business Technology Bks.

--Expert Systems: An Overview. LC 83-70568. (Robotics & Artificial Intelligence Applications Ser.: Vol. 2). 80p. 1984. pap. 19.50x (ISBN 0-89934-178-0, BT-002). Business Technology Bks.

--Intelligent Machines: An Introductory Perspective of Artificial Intelligence & Robotics. LC 84-22326. (Illus.). 240p. 1985. text ed. 33.95 (ISBN 0-13-468810-4). P-H.

Gevarter, William B., ed. Robotics & Artificial Intelligence: Four Overviews, Vols. 1-4 in 1 combined ed. Incl. Robotics: An Overview; Expert Systems: An Overview; Computer Vision: An Overview; Computer-Based Natural Language Processing: An Overview. LC 83-70571. (Robotics & Artificial Intelligence Applications Ser.). 1984. lib. bdg. 85.00x (ISBN 0-89934-184-5, BT905). Business Technology Bks.

Gilbert, G. Nigel & Heath, Christian. Social Actions & Artificial Intelligence. 206p. 1985. text ed. 27.00x (ISBN 0-566-00768-1). Gower Pub Co.

Gomersall, Alan. Machine Intelligence: An International Bibliography with Abstracts of Sensors in Automated Manufacturing. 240p. 1984. 50.50 (ISBN 0-387-13191-4). Springer Verlag.

Graham, Neill. Artificial Intelligence. LC 78-26512. (Illus.). 1979. pap. 10.25 (ISBN 0-8306-1076-6, 1076). TAB Bks.

Hand, D. J. Artificial Intelligence & Psychiatry. (Scientific Basis of Psychiatry: No. 1). 266p. 1985. 39.50 (ISBN 0-521-25871-5). Cambridge U Pr.

Harmon, Paul & King, David. Expert Systems: Artificial Intelligence in Business. 256p. 1985. 24.95 (ISBN 0-471-81554-3, Pub. by Wiley Pr); pap. 16.95 (ISBN 0-471-80824-5). Wiley.

Hartnell, Tim. Exploring Artificial Intelligence: Basic Programs That Reason & Learn. (Illus.). 240p. (Orig.). pap. cancelled (ISBN 0-916688-94-1). Creative Comp.

Haugeland, John. Artificial Intelligence: The Very Idea. (Illus.). 224p. 1985. 15.00 (ISBN 0-262-08153-9, Pub. by Bradford). MIT Pr.

Hayes, J. Intelligent Systems: The Unprecedented Opportunity. (Ellis Horwood Series in Artificial Intelligence). 1984. pap. 19.95 (ISBN 0-470-20139-8). Wiley.

Hayes, J. E. & Michie, Donald. Intelligent Systems: The Unprecedented Opportunity. 206p. 1983. 39.95x (ISBN 0-470-27501-4). Halsted Pr.

Hayes, Jean E., et al. Machine Intelligence: Intelligent Systems Practice & Perspective. (Business Data Processing; A Wiley Ser.: Vol. 10). 576p. 1982. 114.95x (ISBN 0-470-27323-2). Halsted Pr.

Heiserman, David L. Projects in Machine Intelligence for Your Home Computer. LC 81-18233. (Illus.). 103p. 1982. pap. 10.95 (ISBN 0-8306-1391-9, 1391). TAB Bks.

--Robot Intelligence... with Experiments. LC 80-21440. (Illus.). 322p. 1981. 16.95 (ISBN 0-8306-9685-7, 1191); pap. 10.95 (ISBN 0-8306-1191-6). TAB Bks.

Hilts, Philip J. Scientific Temperaments: Three Lives in Contemporary Science. 1984. pap. 7.95 (ISBN 0-671-50590-4, Touchstone Bks). S&S.

Hobbs, Jerry & Moore, Robert C. Formal Theories of the Commonsense World. (Ablex Series in Artificial Intelligence). 480p. 1985. text ed. 59.50 inst. ed. (ISBN 0-89391-213-1); text ed. 37.50 pers. ed. Ablex Pub.

Holland, John H. Adaptation in Natural & Artificial Systems: An Introductory Analysis with Applications to Biology, Control & Artificial Intelligence. LC 74-78988. (Illus.). 1975. 14.95x (ISBN 0-472-08460-7). U of Mich Pr.

Hunt, Earl B. Artificial Intelligence. (Cognition & Perception Ser.). 1975. 40.00 (ISBN 0-12-362340-5). Acad Pr.

Intelligent Terminanls Market. 184p. 1983. 1275.00 (ISBN 0-86621-114-4). Frost & Sullivan.

International Joint Conference on Artificial Intelligence, 1975. Advance Papers, 2 vols. in 1. pap. 65.00 (ISBN 0-86576-056-X). W Kaufmann.

International Joint Conference on Artificial Intelligence, 1973. Advance Papers. pap. 65.00 (ISBN 0-86576-055-1). W Kaufmann.

International Joint Conference on Artificial Intelligence, 1971. Advance Papers. pap. 80.00 (ISBN 0-86576-054-3). W Kaufmann.

International Joint Conference on Artificial Intelligence, 4th, 1975. Artificial Intelligence: Advance Papers of the Fourth International Joint Conference, 1975. (Illus.). 960p. 1983. 65.00 (ISBN 0-86576-056-X). W Kaufmann.

International Joint Conference on Artificial Intelligence, 7th, Vancouver, BC, Aug. 1981. Artificial Intelligence: Proceedings, 2 Vols. Drinan, Ann, ed. (Illus.). 1120p. 1981. Set. 40.00 (ISBN 0-86576-059-4). W Kaufmann.

International Joint Conference on Artificial Intelligence, 8th, 1983. Artificial Intelligence: Proceedings of the Eighth International Joint Conference, 1983, 2 Vols. Bundy, Alan, ed. (Illus.). 1983. Set. 50.00 (ISBN 0-86576-064-0). W Kaufmann.

International Joint Conference on Artificial Intelligence, 5th. Artificial Intelligence: Proceedings of the Fifth International Joint Conference, 2 Vols. (Illus.). 1977. Set. 40.00 (ISBN 0-86576-057-8). W Kaufmann.

International Joint Conference on Artificial Intelligence, 1st, 1969. Artificial Intelligence: Proceedings of the International Joint Conference, 1969. Walker, Donald E. & Nortan, Lewis M., eds. (Illus.). 726p. 1983. 80.00 (ISBN 0-86576-053-5). W Kaufmann.

International Joint Conference on Artificial Intelligence, 6th, 1979. Artificial Intelligence: Proceedings of the Sixth International Joint Conference, 1979, 2 Vols. (Illus.). 1979. Set. 40.00 (ISBN 0-86576-058-6). W Kaufmann.

International Joint Conference on Artificial Intelligence, 2nd, 1971. Artificial Intelligence: Proceedings of the Second International Joint Conference, 1971. (Illus.). 1983. 80.00 (ISBN 0-86576-054-3). W Kaufmann.

International Joint Conference on Artificial Intelligence, 3rd, 1973. Artificial Intelligence: Proceedings of the Third Joint Conference, 1973. Nilsson, Nils, ed. (Illus.). 1983. 65.00 (ISBN 0-86576-055-1). W Kaufmann.

International Joint Conference on Artificial Intelligence, 1983. Proceedings, 2 Vols. Set. pap. 50.00 (ISBN 0-86576-064-0). W Kaufmann.

International Joint Conference on Artificial Intelligence, 1981. Proceedings, 2 Vols. Set. pap. 40.00 (ISBN 0-86576-059-4). W Kaufmann.

International Joint Conference on Artificial Intelligence, 1979. Proceedings, 2 Vols. Set. pap. 40.00 (ISBN 0-86576-058-6). W Kaufmann.

International Joint Conference on Artificial Intelligence, 1977. Proceedings, 2 Vols. Set. pap. 40.00 (ISBN 0-86576-057-8). W Kaufmann.

International Joint Conference on Artificial Intelligence, 1969. Proceedings. pap. 80.00 (ISBN 0-317-07141-6). W Kaufmann.

International Resource Development Inc., Staff. Artificial Intelligence. 167p. Date not set. 1650.00x (ISBN 0-88694-552-6). Intl Res Dev.

Jackson, Philip C., Jr. Introduction to Artificial Intelligence. 2nd, enl. ed. (Popular Science Ser.). 512p. 1985. pap. 8.95 (ISBN 0-486-24864-X). Dover.

Jaki, Stanley L. Brain, Mind & Computers. LC 72-76283. 1978. pap. 5.95 (ISBN 0-89526-907-4). Regnery-Gateway.

Johnson. The Theory of Knowledge & Artificial Intelligence. (Information Tecnology Ser.). 1984. write for info (ISBN 0-9901003-4-0, Pub. by Abacus England). Heyden.

Johnson-Laird, P. N. & Wason, P. C., eds. Thinking: Readings in Cognitive Science. LC 77-78887. (Illus.). 1978. 59.50 (ISBN 0-521-21756-3); pap. 17.95x (ISBN 0-521-29267-0). Cambridge U Pr.

Kanal, L. N. & Rosenfeld, A., eds. Progress in Pattern Recognition 2, Vol. 1. (Machine Intelligence & Pattern Recognition Ser.). 402p. 1985. 55.00 (ISBN 0-444-87723-1, North-Holland). Elsevier.

Kender, John R. Shape from Texture. (Research Notes in Artificial Intelligence Ser.). 1985. pap. text ed. 19.50 (ISBN 0-273-08666-9). Pitman Pub MA.

Kent, Ernest W. The Brains of Men & Machines. 272p. 1980. 21.95 (ISBN 0-07-034123-0, BYTE Bks). McGraw.

Freeman, J. W., ed. Solar Power Satellites: Proceedings of the International Symposium, Toulouse, France, June 1980. 200p. 1981. pap. 39.00 (ISBN 0-08-027592-3). Pergamon.

Future Systems, Inc. Satellite Systems of the U. S. Domestic Communications Carriers. rev. ed. (Illus.). 313p. 1983. pap. 475.00x (ISBN 0-940520-46-X, F118). Monegon Ltd.

Goldberg, Joel. Satellite Television Reception: A Personal User's Guide. (Illus.). 128p. 1984. 24.95 (ISBN 0-13-791269-2); pap. 19.95 (ISBN 0-13-791251-X). P-H.

Home Satellite Terminal. 1985. write for info. (ISBN 0-86621-265-5). Frost & Sullivan.

Kopal, Zdenek. Figures of Equilibrium of Celestial Bodies: With Emphasis on Problems of Motion of Artificial Satellites. (Mathematics Research Center Pubns., No. 3). (Illus.). 142p. 1960. 17.50x (ISBN 0-299-02010-X). U of Wis Pr.

Kurnosova, L. V., ed. Artificial Earth Satellities, 6 vols. LC 49-14596. (Illus.). Vol. 1-2. pap. 58.30 (ISBN 0-317-10841-7, 2019400); Vol. 3-5. pap. 146.00 (ISBN 0-317-10842-5); Vol. 6. pap. 44.00 (ISBN 0-317-10843-3). Bks Demand UMI.

Mezerik, Avrahm G., ed. Arms Race: Satellites-Nuclear. 1957. pap. 15.00 (ISBN 0-685-13187-4, 38). Intl Review.

Morando, Bruno. Movement d'un Satellite Artificiel de la Terre. new ed. (Cours & Documents de Mathematiques & de Physique Ser.). 270p. 1974. 62.50x (ISBN 0-677-50750-X). Gordon.

Nacozy, Paul E. & Ferraz-Mello, Sylvio, eds. Natural & Artificial Satellite Motion. (Illus.). 450p. 1979. text ed. 27.50x (ISBN 0-292-75514-7). U of Tex Pr.

Napolitano, L. G. Using Space, Today & Tomorrow, Vol. 2: Communications Satellite Symposium. 53.00 (ISBN 0-08-023232-9). Pergamon.

Petrov, V. Artificial Satellites of the Earth. (Illus.). 288p. 1960. 74.25x (ISBN 0-677-20540-6). Gordon.

Porter, Richard W. The Versatile Satellite. (Illus.). 1977. text ed. 16.95x (ISBN 0-19-885104-9). Oxford U Pr.

Queeney, K. M. Direct Broadcast Satellites & the United Nations. 344p. 1978. 41.00x (ISBN 90-286-0069-8). Sijthoff & Noordhoff.

Soviet Writings on Earth Satellites & Space Travel. LC 78-117846. (Essay Index Reprint Ser). 1958. 14.50 (ISBN 0-8369-1719-7). Ayer Co Pubs.

Symposium On Scientific Satellites. Scientific Satellites. Jeter, I. E., ed. (Advances in the Astronautical Sciences Ser.: Vol. 12). 1962. 25.00x (ISBN 0-87703-013-8, Pub. by Am Astronaut). Univelt Inc.

ARTIFICIAL SATELLITES–ATTITUDE CONTROL SYSTEMS

IFAC-ESA Symposium, Noorwjkerhout, The Netherlands, July 1982 & Van Woerkom, L. M. Automatic Control in Space 1982: Proceedings. (IFAC Proceedings Ser.). 580p. 1983. 145.00 (ISBN 0-08-029328-X). Pergamon.

Singer, S. Fred, ed. Torques & Attitude Sensing in Earth Satellites. (Applied Mathematics & Mechanics Ser.: Vol. 7). 1964. 65.00 (ISBN 0-12-646850-8). Acad Pr.

ARTIFICIAL SATELLITES–ORBITS

Nacozy, Paul E. & Ferraz-Mello, Sylvio, eds. Natural & Artificial Satellite Motion. (Illus.). 450p. 1979. text ed. 27.50x (ISBN 0-292-75514-7). U of Tex Pr.

Sagirow, P. Stochastic Methods in the Dynamics of Satellites. (CISM - International Centre for Mechanical Sciences, Courses & Lectures: Vol. 57). 132p. 1975. pap. 17.20 (ISBN 0-387-81092-7). Springer-Verlag.

Szebehely, Victor G., ed. Celestial Mechanics & Astrodynamics. (Progress in Astronautics & Aeronautics: Vol. 14). 1964. 51.50 (ISBN 0-12-680650-0). Acad Pr.

ARTIFICIAL SATELLITES–SCIENTIFIC APPLICATIONS

see Scientific Satellites

ARTIFICIAL SATELLITES–TRACKING

Hayes, E. Nelson, ed. Trackers of the Skies. LC 68-28835. (Illus.). 1968. pap. 3.00x (ISBN 0-87299-003-6). Howard Doyle.

ARTIFICIAL SATELLITES IN GEOGRAPHICAL RESEARCH

Bullard, R. K. & Dixon-Gough, R. W. Britain from Space: An Atlas of Landsat Images. 120p. 1984. 23.00 (ISBN 0-85066-277-X, Pub. by Falmer Pr). Taylor & Francis.

Conference on the Use of Orbiting Spacecraft in Geographic Research - Houston - Tex 1965. Spacecraft in Geographic Research. 1966. pap. 4.00 (ISBN 0-309-01353-4). Natl Acad Pr.

Gower, J. F., ed. Oceanography from Space. LC 81-12060. (Marine Science Ser.: Vol. 13). 998p. 1981. 125.00x (ISBN 0-306-40808-2, Plenum Pr). Plenum Pub.

Laboratory for Computer Graphics & Spatial Analysis, Harvard University Graduate School of Design. Computer Mapping in Natural Resources & Environment: Including Applications of Satellite-Derived Data, Vol. 4. (The Harvard Library of Computer Graphics, Mapping Collection). (Illus.). 138p. 1979. pap. 12.50 (ISBN 0-8122-1184-7). U of Pa Pr.

--Computer Mapping of Natural Resources & the Environment: Including Applications of Satellite-Derived Data, Vol. 10. (The Harvard Library of Computer Graphics, Mapping Collection). (Illus.). 131p. 1980. pap. 12.50 (ISBN 0-8122-1190-1). U of Pa Pr.

--Computer Mapping of Natural Resources & the Environment: Plus Satellite-Derived Data Applications, Vol. 15. (The Harvard Library of Computer Graphics, Mapping Collection). (Illus.). 180p. 1981. pap. 12.50 (ISBN 0-8122-1195-2). U of Pa Pr.

ARTIFICIAL SATELLITES IN TELECOMMUNICATION

see also Radiotelephone; Television

An Advanced Domestic Satellite Communications System. 45.00 (ISBN 0-686-33000-5). Info Gatekeepers.

An Advanced Domestic Satellite Communications System. (Orig.). 1980. pap. 45.00x (ISBN 0-940520-16-8, Pub. by Future Syst Inc). Monegon Ltd.

AIAA Tenth Communications Satellite Systems Conference. 743p. 1984. 95.00 (ISBN 0-317-36844-3, CP842); members 85.00 (ISBN 0-317-36845-1). AIAA.

Andriole, Stephen J. & Paschall, Lee M., eds. Air & Satellite Communications. LC 84-72110. (AFCEA C31 Ser.: Vol. II). (Illus.). 373p. 1985. 29.95 (ISBN 0-916159-03-5). AFCEA Intl Pr.

ARINC Research Corporation. Thirty Twenty GHz Communications Satellite Trunking Network Study. 1981. 100.00 (ISBN 0-686-37982-9). Info Gatekeepers.

Bhargava, V. K. & Haccoun, D. Digital Communications by Satellite: Modulation, Multiple Access & Coding. 569p. 1981. 45.00 (ISBN 0-686-98094-8). Telecom Lib.

Bhargava, Vijay K., et al. Digital Communications by Satellite: Modulaton, Multiple Access & Coding. LC 81-10276. 569p. 1981. 58.95x (ISBN 0-471-08316-X, Pub. by Wiley-Interscience). Wiley.

Botein, M., et al. Development & Regulation of New Communication Technologies: Cable Television, Subscription Television, Multipoint Distribution Service & Direct Broadcast Satellites. 140p. 1980. pap. 50.00 (ISBN 0-941888-03-7). Comm Media.

Brown, Martin B. Compendium & Communication & Broadcast Satellites 1958-1981. LC 81-81858. 375p. 1981. 38.95x (ISBN 0-471-86198-7, Pub. by Wiley Interscience). Wiley.

Brown, Martin P. Jr., ed. Compendium of Communication & Broadcast Satellites. LC 81-81858. 1981. 40.50 (ISBN 0-87942-153-3, PC01461). Inst Electrical.

Buckland, R. A. Broadcasting by Satellite. 220p. 1985. pap. text ed. 400.00x (ISBN 0-86353-028-1, Pub. by Online). Brookfield Pub Co.

Cable '84: Proceedings of the Second European Conference on Satellite & Cable TV, London, July 1984. 373p. 1984. pap. text ed. 150.00x (ISBN 0-86353-011-7, Pub. by Online). Brookfield Pub Co.

The Case Against Satellites. 1974. 2.00, institutions 5.00 (ISBN 0-686-09555-3). Network Project.

Chander, Romesh & Karnik, Kiran. Planning for Satellite Broadcasting: The Indian Instructional Television Experiment. (Reports & Papers on Mass Communication: No. 78). 71p. 1976. pap. 5.00 (ISBN 92-3-101392-0, U453, UNESCO). Unipub.

Chu, Alfian, ed. Satellite Television in Indonesia. Chu, Godwin C. vi, 211p. (Orig.). 1981. pap. 6.00 (ISBN 0-86638-002-7). E W Center HI.

Communication in the Space Age: The Use of Satellites by the Mass Media. 200p. 1968. pap. 7.50 (ISBN 92-3-100719-X, U78, UNESCO). Unipub.

Communications Satellites Calendar, Nineteen Fifty-Eight to Nineteen Eighty-Two. 75.00 (ISBN 0-686-32991-0). Info Gatekeepers.

Concepts for Eighteen-Thirty GHZ Satellite Communications System Study. Exec. Summary. 20.00 (ISBN 0-686-33009-9); Final Report. 100.00 (ISBN 0-686-33010-2). Info Gatekeepers.

Convention Relating to the Distribution of Programme-Carrying Signals Transmitted by Satellite. 1974. pap. 7.50 (ISBN 0-686-53126-4, WIPO28, WIPO). Unipub.

Crowe, Steve. Satellite Television & Your Backyard Dish. Krieger, Robin, ed. LC 81-90593. (Illus.). 200p. (Orig.). 1982. 20.00 (ISBN 0-910419-00-0); pap. 15.00 (ISBN 0-910419-01-9); trade special 15.00 (ISBN 0-910419-02-7). Satellite.

Direct Broadcast Satellite Systems. (Reports Ser.: No. 514). 187p. 1982. 985.00x (ISBN 0-88694-514-3). Intl Res Dev.

Easton, Anthony T. Satellite TV Handbook. LC 83-60155. 440p. 1983. pap. 16.95 (ISBN 0-672-22055-5). Sams.

Eighteen & Thirty GHz Fixed Service Communications Satellite System Study. Exec. Study. 20.00 (ISBN 0-686-33005-6); Final Report. 100.00 (ISBN 0-686-33006-4). Info Gatekeepers.

Feher, K., ed. Satellite Communications: Proceedings of the Canadian Domestic & International Conference, 1st, June 15-17, Ottawa, Canada. 670p. 1983. 85.00 (ISBN 0-444-86690-6, North-Holland). Elsevier.

Feher, Kamilo. Digital Communications: Satellite-Earth Station Engineering. (Illus.). 496p. 1983. 41.95 (ISBN 0-13-212068-2). P-H.

Gagliardi, Robert M. Satellite Communications-An Introduction. (Engineering Ser.). (Illus.). 475p. 1984. 39.00 (ISBN 0-534-02976-0). Lifetime Learn.

Goddard Memorial Symposium, 14th. Satellite Communications in the Next Decade: Proceedings. Jaffe, Leonard, ed. (Science & Technology: Vol. 44). (Illus.). 1977. 20.00x (ISBN 0-87703-088-X, Pub. by Am Astronaut). Univelt Inc.

Gould, R. G. & Lum, L. F., eds. Communication Satellite Systems: An Overview of the Technology. LC 75-39327. 1976. 24.90 (ISBN 0-87942-065-0, PC00703). Inst Electrical.

Grange, J. L., ed. Satellite & Computer Communications. 380p. 1984. 51.00 (ISBN 0-444-86730-9, North Holland). Elsevier.

Heller, Gerhard B., ed. Thermophysics of Spacecraft & Planetary Bodies. LC 67-30649. (Illus.). 975p. 1967. 24.50 (ISBN 0-317-36816-8); members 49.00 (ISBN 0-317-36817-6). AIAA.

INTELSAT-IEE International Conference on Digital Satellite Communication (1969: London) INTELSAT-IEE International Conference on Digital Satellite Communication, 25-27 November 1969, London. LC 72-561801. (Institution of Electrical Engineers Conference Publications Ser.: No. 59). pap. 143.00 (ISBN 0-317-10127-7, 2007386). Bks Demand UMI.

International Resource Development Inc. Satellite Communications Services & Equipment Markets. 322p. 1983. write for info. (ISBN 0-88694-581-X). Intl Res Dev.

Jones, Erin B. Earth Satellite Telecommunications Systems & International Law. LC 68-66976. 1970. 7.50 (ISBN 0-87959-059-9). U of Tex H Ransom Ctr.

Katzman, Morris. Laser-Satellite Communications. 1985. text ed. 39.95 (ISBN 0-8359-3946-4). Reston.

Legal & Political Aspects of Satellite Telecommunications: An Annotated Bibliography. 126p. 1971. pap. 7.50x (ISBN 0-299-97034-5). U of Wis Pr.

Legal Aspects of Satellite Teleconferencing. 213p. 1971. pap. 7.50x (ISBN 0-299-97039-6). U of Wis Pr.

Leibert, A. The Benefit of Environmental Satellites to Offshore Industries. 116p. (Orig.). 1980. pap. text ed. 80.95x (ISBN 0-903796-67-8, Pub. by Online Conferences England). Brookfield Pub Co.

Manual on the Global Observing System, 2 Vols. in 1. (Eng., Fr., Rus. & Span.). 50p. 1981. pap. 18.00 (ISBN 92-63-12544-9, W512, WMO); Vol. 1: Global Aspects. Vol. 2: Regional Aspects. Unipub.

Maral, G. & Bousquet, M. Satellite Communications Systems. Date not set. price not set (ISBN 0-471-90220-9). Wiley.

Martin, James. Communications Satellite Systems. 398p. 1978. 39.50 (ISBN 0-686-98090-5). Telecom Lib.

Military Satellite Communications Market. 296p. 1982. 1250.00 (ISBN 0-86621-030-X, A1062). Frost & Sullivan.

Military Satellite Communications Market. 305p. 1984. 1475.00 (ISBN 0-86621-219-1, A1287). Frost & Sullivan.

Mittra, R., et al, eds. Satellite Communication Antenna Technology. 600p. 1984. 76.75 (ISBN 0-444-86733-3, North-Holland). Elsevier.

Murray, Bruce C. & Burgess, Eric. Flight to Mercury. LC 76-25017. (Illus.). 162p. 1976. 26.00x (ISBN 0-231-03996-4). Columbia U Pr.

Ninth Communication Satelite Systems. 110.00 (ISBN 0-317-06663-3). AIAA.

North American Satellite Communications Market. 388p. 1984. 1575.00 (ISBN 0-86621-233-7). Frost & Sullivan.

Platte, Mary K. The Beginning of Satellite Communication Airborne ITV, MPATI, & the Ohio Story. 104p. 1982. pap. text ed. 6.95 (ISBN 0-8403-2794-3). Kendall-Hunt.

Powell, Jon T. International Broadcasting by Satellite: Issues of Regulations, Barriers to Communications. LC 85-6342. 304p. 1985. lib. bdg. 39.95 (ISBN 0-89930-067-7, Pub. by Quorum Bks). Greenwood.

Prentiss, Stan. Satellite Communications. (Illus.). 288p. 1983. 16.95 (ISBN 0-8306-0632-7); pap. 11.95 (ISBN 0-8306-1632-2, 1632). TAB Bks.

Pritchard, Wilbur L. & Sciulli, Joseph A. Communications Satellite Systems Engineering. (Illus.). 352p. 1986. text ed. 42.95 (ISBN 0-13-153388-6). P-H.

Rosner, Roy D. Distributed Telecommunications Networks via Satellites & Packet Switching. (Engineering Ser.). 235p. 1982. 31.50 (ISBN 0-534-97933-5). Lifetime Learn.

Satellite Communications. 4.75 (ISBN 0-87259-302-9). Am Radio.

Satellite Communications. (Online Conference, London 1980). 134p. (Orig.). 1980. pap. text ed. 98.00x (ISBN 0-903796-61-9, Pub. by Online Conferences England). Brookfield Pub Co.

Satellite Communications: Developments, Applications & Future Prospects. 217p. 1984. pap. text ed. 90.00x (ISBN 0-86353-007-9, Pub. by Online). Brookfield Pub Co.

Satellite Communications: Developments. 64.00x (Pub. by Online). Taylor & Francis.

Satellite Home Subscription Television Service, 5 vols. & executive summary. Executive Summary. 15.00 (ISBN 0-686-32993-7); Vol. 1. 75.00 (ISBN 0-686-32994-5); Vol. 2. 100.00 (ISBN 0-686-32995-3); Vol. 3. 75.00 (ISBN 0-686-32996-1); Vol. 4. 100.00 (ISBN 0-686-32997-X); Vol. 5. 125.00 (ISBN 0-686-32998-8). Info Gatekeepers.

Satellite Systems of the U. S. Domestic Communications Carriers. 275.00 (ISBN 0-686-32999-6). Info Gatekeepers.

Satellite Systems of the U. S. Domestic Communications Carriers. rev. ed. 1982. pap. 375.00 (ISBN 0-940520-19-2, Pub. by Future Syste Inc). Monegon Ltd.

Satellite Teleconferencing: An Annotated Bibliography. 130p. 1972. pap. 7.50x (ISBN 0-299-97048-5). U of Wis Pr.

Satellite: Terrestrial Cost Tradeoff Study. 200.00 (ISBN 0-686-32992-9). Info Gatekeepers.

Schmidt, William G. & LaVean, Gilbert E., eds. Communications Satellite Developments: Technology. LC 75-45243. (Illus.). 419p. 1976. 45.00 (ISBN 0-915928-06-X, PAAS42); members 25.00 (ISBN 0-317-32135-8). AIAA.

Smith, D. D. Communication Via Satellite: A Vision in Respect, No. 1. (Policy Issues in Satellite Applications Ser.). 356p. 1976. 35.00x (ISBN 90-286-0296-8). Sijthoff & Noordhoff.

Spilker, J., Jr. Digital Communication by Satellite. 1976. 49.95 (ISBN 0-13-214155-8). P-H.

Spilker, James J., Jr., ed. Digital Communications by Satellite. 670p. 1977. 41.00 (ISBN 0-686-98091-3). Telecom Lib.

Sprague, Michael. New Communications Technologies & Public Broadcasting: Impacts & Opportunities. 30p. 1981. pap. 25.00 (ISBN 0-941888-07-X). Comm Media.

Tenth Communication Satellite Systems. 95.00 (ISBN 0-317-06650-1). AIAA.

A Traffic Forecast for U. S. Domestic Satellite Commnunications. 275.00 (ISBN 0-686-33001-3). Info Gatekeepers.

A Traffic Forecast for U. S. Domestic Satellite Communications 1980-1995. (Illus.). 145p. (Orig.). 1979. pap. 275.00x (ISBN 0-940520-24-9, F106, Pub. by Future Syst Inc). Monegon Ltd.

Transmission Cost Comparison for Satellite, Fiber Optics & Microwave Radio Communications. 1982. pap. 495.00 (ISBN 0-940520-18-4, Pub. by Future Syst Inc). Monegon Ltd.

Twentieth Century Fund. Task Force on International Satellite Communications. Communicating by Satellite. Laskin, P. L., ed. LC 70-117923. 1969. pap. 15.00 (ISBN 0-527-02810-X). Kraus Repr.

--The Future of Satellite Communications: Resources Management & the Needs of Nations. 1970. pap. 10.00 (ISBN 0-527-02844-4). Kraus Repr.

Unger, J. H. Literature Survey of Communications Satellite Systems & Technology. 420p. 1976. 27.00 (ISBN 0-317-05143-1, PC00729). Inst Electrical.

Unger, J. H., ed. Lit Survey of Communications Satellite System & Technology. LC 75-39326. 1976. 27.00 (ISBN 0-87942-067-7). Inst Electrical.

The Use of INTELSAT Transponders for Domestic Satellite Communications. 95.00 (ISBN 0-686-33003-X). Info Gatekeepers.

Van Trees, H. L., ed. Satellite Communications. LC 78-65704. 1979. 59.25 (ISBN 0-87942-121-5, PC01222). Inst Electrical.

Van Trees, Harry L., ed. Satellite Communications. LC 78-65704. (A Volume in the IEEE Press Selected Reprint Ser). 1980. 56.95x (ISBN 0-471-06101-8, Pub. by Wiley-Interscience); pap. 37.00x (ISBN 0-471-06100-X, Pub. by Wiley-Interscience). Wiley.

Feingold, Carl. Introduction to Assembler Language Programming. 427p. 1978. pap. text ed. write for info. (ISBN 0-697-08124-9); instrs.' manual avail. (ISBN 0-697-08158-3). Wm C Brown.

Fernandez, Judi & Ashley, Ruth. Introduction to 8080-8085 Assembly Language Programming. LC 80-39650. (Wiley Self Teaching Guide Ser.: No. 1-581). 303p. 1981. pap. text ed. 12.95 (ISBN 0-471-08009-8, Pub. by Wiley Pr). Wiley.

Fernandez, Judi N., et al. Assembly Language Programming: 6502. (Wiley Self-Teaching Guides Ser.). 277p. 1983. pap. 14.95 (ISBN 0-471-86120-0, Pub. by Wiley Pr). Wiley.

Finley, Clarence W., Jr. & Myers, Roy E. Assembly Language for the Applesoft Programmer. 1630p. 1984. pap. 16.95 (ISBN 0-201-05209-1). Addison-Wesley.

Franklin, Mark. Programming the IBM Personal Computer: Organization & Assembly Language Programming. 1984. 19.95 (ISBN 0-03-062862-8). HR&W.

Gill, Arthur. Machine & Assembly Language Programming of the PDP-11. 2nd ed. (Illus.). 224p. 1983. text ed. 28.95 (ISBN 0-13-541888-7). P-H.

Gorin, Ralph E. Introduction to DECsystem 20: Assembly Language Programming. 545p. 1981. pap. 39.00 (ISBN 0-932376-12-6, EY-AX017-DP). Digital Pr.

Grishman, Ralph. Assembly Language Programming for Control Data 6000 & Cyber Ser. (Illus.). 248p. 1981. 15.00x (ISBN 0-917448-04-9). Algorithmics.

--Assembly Language Programming for the Control Data 6000 Series & the Cyber Series. Date not set. pap. 15.00 (ISBN 0-686-46118-5). Algorithmics.

Gust, Philip. Introduction to Machine & Assembly Language Programming. (Illus.). 528p. 1985. text ed. 32.95 (ISBN 0-13-486416-6). P-H.

Hamilton, J. David & Trenary, Robert G. Macro-86: Programming Algorithms. Hubbard, John D., ed. LC 84-12805. (Macro-86 Software Design Ser.). (Illus.). 498p. 1984. 3 ring-binder 59.95 (ISBN 0-87119-089-3, EC-1202). HeathKit-Zenith Ed.

Haskell, Richard. IBM PC Assembly Language Tutor. 240p. 1985. pap. cancelled (ISBN 0-13-448662-5). P-H.

Haskell, Richard E. Apple II: 6502 Assembly Language Tutor. (Illus.). 240p. 1983. incl. disk 34.95 (ISBN 0-13-039230-8, Spec). P-H.

Heath Company Staff. Programming in Assembly Language. (Illus.). 1979. 49.95 (ISBN 0-87119-085-0, EC-1108). Heathkit-Zenith Ed.

Heginbotham, W., ed. Programmable Assembly. (International Trends in Manufacturing Technology Ser.). (Illus.). 349p. 1984. 43.00 (ISBN 0-387-13479-4). Springer-Verlag.

Holt, Charles A. Microcomputer Systems: Hardware, Assembly Langauge, & Pascal. 547p. 1986. text ed. price not set write for info. (ISBN 0-02-356370-2). Macmillan.

Howe, Hubert S., Jr. TRS-80 Assembly Language. (Illus.). 192p. 1981. text ed. 15.95 (ISBN 0-13-931139-4, Spec); pap. text ed. 9.95 (ISBN 0-13-931121-1, Spec). P-H.

Hyde, Randy. Assembly Language. 19.95 (ISBN 0-88190-003-6). Datamost.

--Using 6502 Assembly Language. (Illus.). 301p. 1981. 19.95 (ISBN 0-88190-003-6, B0003). Datamost.

--Using 6502 Assembly Language, Vol. II. (Using 6502 Assembly Language Ser.). 608p. (Orig.). Date not set. pap. 19.95 (ISBN 0-88190-437-6, BO437). Datamost.

Inman, Don. Assembly Language Graphics for the TRS-80 Color Computer. 1984. 14.95 (ISBN 0-317-06050-3). Micro Works.

Intel Staff. ASM286 Assembly Language Reference Manual. rev. ed. 406p. 1983. pap. 42.00 (ISBN 0-917017-06-4, 121924-002). Intel Corp.

--ASM86 Language Reference Manual. rev. ed. 400p. 1983. pap. 42.00 (ISBN 0-917017-05-6, 121703-003). Intel Corp.

--ASM86 Macro Assembler Operating Instructions for 8086-Based Systems Manual. rev. ed. 100p. 1983. pap. 13.00 (ISBN 0-917017-28-5, 121628-003). Intel Corp.

--ASM86 Macro Assembler Pocket Reference. rev. ed. 86p. 1982. pap. 5.00 (ISBN 0-917017-03-X, 121674-002). Intel Corp.

--Assembly Language Programming 8080-8085. 224p. (Orig.). 1980. pap. 13.00 (ISBN 0-917017-26-9, 980940-001). Intel Corp.

Jernigan, Barney G. Assist Simulator. 80p. 1984. pap. text ed. 7.95 (ISBN 0-8403-3441-9). Kendall-Hunt.

Kapps & Stafford. Vax Assembly Language & Architecture. 1985. text ed. write for info. (ISBN 0-87150-837-0, 37L8500). PWS Pubs.

Kapps, Charles S. & Stafford, Robert L. Assembly Language for the PDP-11. LC 80-39985. 353p. 1981. text ed. write for info. (ISBN 0-87150-304-2, 37L 8000, Prindle). PWS Pubs.

Kapur, Gopal K. IBM 360 Assembler Language Programming. LC 76-12572. 560p. 1971. 40.50 (ISBN 0-471-45840-6). Wiley.

Knuth, Donald E. MIX. LC 79-139160. (Computer Science Ser). 1971. pap. text ed. 6.95 (ISBN 0-201-03808-0). Addison-Wesley.

Krute, Stan. Introduction to Assembly Language for the Commodore 64. cancelled 17.95 (ISBN 0-89303-572-6). Brady Comm.

Kudlick, Michael D. Assembly Language Programming for the IBM Systems 360 & 370 for OS-DOS. 2nd ed. 624p. 1983. write for info. (ISBN 0-697-08166-4); instr's. manual avail. (ISBN 0-697-08184-2). Wm C Brown.

Kuo, Shan S. Assembler Language for FORTRAN, COBOL & PL-1 Programmers. LC 73-2138. 1974. text ed. 29.95 (ISBN 0-201-03954-0). Addison-Wesley.

Lampton, Christopher. Assembly Language Programming 6502 for the Apple, Commodore 64, & Atari Computers. (Computer Literacy Skills Ser.). 128p. 1985. PLB 10.90 (ISBN 0-531-04923-X). Watts.

--Z80 Assembly Language Programming: For the Radio Shack, Adam, Timex Sinclair, & CP M Computers. (Computer Literacy Skills Ser.). 128p. 1985. PLB 10.90 (ISBN 0-531-04924-8). Watts.

Lancaster, Don. Assembly Cookbook for the Apple II-IIe. LC 82-50247. 408p. 1984. 21.95 (ISBN 0-672-22331-7). Sams.

--Hexadecimal Chronicles. LC 81-50563. 304p. 1981. pap. 17.95 (ISBN 0-672-21802-X, 21802). Sams.

Larsen, Lawrence P. Macro 86 Assembly Language Programming. LC 84-19295. (Marcro 86 Software Designer Ser.). (Illus.). 900p. 1984. 3 ring-binder 59.95 (ISBN 0-87119-100-8, EC-1201). HeathKIt-Zenith Ed.

Lavery, Robert G. Programming with System 370 Assembler Language. 528p. 1981. pap. text ed. 24.95 (ISBN 0-8403-2583-5). Kendall-Hunt.

Lemone. Assembly Language & Systems for the IBM PC. 1985. 16.45i (ISBN 0-316-52069-1). Little.

Lemone, Karen A. & Kaliski, Martin E. Assembly Language Programming for the VAX-11. 1983. pap. text ed. 24.95 (ISBN 0-316-52072-1). Little.

Levanthal, Lance A., et al. Assembly Language Programming: Z-80. 640p. (Orig.). 1979. pap. text ed. 18.95 (ISBN 0-07-931021-4, 21-4). Osborne-McGraw.

Leventhal, Lance, et al. Assembly Language Programming: 6502. 640p. (Orig.). 1979. pap. text ed. 18.95 (ISBN 0-07-931027-3, 27-3). Osborne-McGraw.

--Assembly Language Programming: 6800. 624p. 1981. pap. 18.95 (ISBN 0-07-931062-1, 62-1). Osborne-McGraw.

Leventhal, Lance A. Assembly Language Programming: 8080A-8085. 448p. (Orig.). 1978. pap. text ed. 18.95 (ISBN 0-07-931010-9, 10-9). Osborne-McGraw.

Leventhal, Lance A. & Saville, Winthrop. Sixty-Five Zero Two Assembly Language Subroutines. 546p. (Orig.). 1979. pap. 17.95 (ISBN 0-07-931059-1, 59-1). Osborne-McGraw.

--Z80 Assembly Language Subroutines. 550p. (Orig.). 1983. pap. 17.95 (ISBN 0-07-931091-5, 91-5). Osborne-McGraw.

Leventhal, Lance A., et al. Assembly Language Programming: Z8000. 928p. (Orig.). 1980. pap. text ed. 19.99 (ISBN 0-07-931036-2, 36-2). Osborne-McGraw.

--Assembly Language Programming: 6800. 480p. (Orig.). 1978. pap. text ed. 18.95 (ISBN 0-07-931012-5, 12-5). Osborne-McGraw.

--Assembly Language Programming: 6809. 576p. (Orig.). 1981. pap. text ed. 18.95 (ISBN 0-07-931035-4, 35-4). Osborne-McGraw.

Lin, Wen C. Computer Organization & Assembly Language Programming: PDP 11 & VAX 11. 384p. 1985. text ed. 28.50 scp (ISBN 0-06-044061-9, HarpC). Har-Row.

Lindley, Craig A. TRS-80 Z80 Assembly Language Library. (Illus.). 355p. (Orig.). 1983. looseleaf binder 34.97 (ISBN 0-88006-060-3, BK7395). Green Pub Inc.

Lindsay, John. CP-M-86 Assembly Language. 19.95 (ISBN 0-89303-390-1). Brady Comm.

Lindsay, Jon. CP-M 86 Assembly Language. 352p. 1985. pap. 21.95 (ISBN 0-89303-390-1). Brady Comm.

--Introduction to CP-M Assembly Language: Functions & Applications. 2nd ed. 174p. 1983. pap. text ed. 15.95 (ISBN 0-943892-00-7). Exec Computer.

Lloyd, Don. Computer Architecture & Assembly Language. LC 83-43296. 192p. (Orig.). pap. cancelled (ISBN 0-8019-7446-1). Chilton.

Longo, Stephen A. Introduction to DECsystem 20 Assembly Programming. LC 83-7414. (Computer Science Ser.). 224p. 1983. pap. text ed. 14.50 pub net (ISBN 0-534-02942-6). Brooks-Cole.

--Introduction to DECsystem 20 Assembly Programming. 200p. 1984. pap. write for info. Wadsworth Pub.

Lottrup, Peter. Compute's Beginner's Guide to Assembly Language on the TI-99-4A. (Orig.). 1985. pap. 14.95 (ISBN 0-942386-74-4). Compute Pubns.

McBeth. IBM Assembler: An Intuitive Approach. 1986. price not set (ISBN 0-471-82424-0). Wiley.

McCaul, Earles. TRS-80 Assembly Language Made Simple. LC 81-84281. 192p. 1981. pap. 12.95 (ISBN 0-672-21851-8, 21851). Sams.

McComic, Ira. Learning TI 99-4A Home Computer Assembly Language Programming. (Illus.). 224p. 1984. cancelled (ISBN 0-13-527870-8); pap. 16.95 (ISBN 0-13-527862-7). P-H.

--Learning TI-99-4A Home Computer Assembly Language Programming. Stultz, Russell A., ed. LC 83-23386. (Illus.). 240p. 1984. pap. 16.95 (ISBN 0-915381-56-7). WordWare Pub.

McQuillen, Kevin. System 360-370 Assembler Language (DOS) LC 74-29645. (Illus.). 450p. (Orig.). 1975. pap. 22.50 (ISBN 0-911625-02-X). M Murach & Assoc.

--System 360-370 Assembler Language (DOS) LC 74-76436. (Illus.). 407p. (Orig.). 1974. pap. 22.50 (ISBN 0-911625-01-1). M Murach & Assoc.

Massie, Paul. Programming IBM Assembly Language. (Illus.). 500p. 1985. pap. text ed. write for info. (ISBN 0-8087-6405-5). Burgess.

Mathews, Keith. Assembly Language Primer for the Macintosh. (Illus.). 1985. pap. 24.95 (ISBN 0-452-25642-9, Plume). NAL.

Maurer, W. Douglas. Apple Assembly Language. LC 82-18190. 403p. 1984. 21.95 (ISBN 0-914894-82-X); diskette 15.00 (ISBN 0-914894-85-4). Computer Sci.

--Commodore Vic-20 Assembly Language. (Illus.). 400p. 1985. pap. text ed. 19.95 (ISBN 0-88175-003-4). Computer Sci.

--Commodore 64 Assembly Language. LC 84-16981. 420p. 1985. pap. 19.95 (ISBN 0-88175-040-9); diskette 15.00 (ISBN 0-88175-041-7). Computer Sci.

Miller, Alan R. Eighty-Eighty & 280 Assembly Language: Techniques for Improved Programming. LC 80-21492. 318p. 1981. pap. text ed. 12.95 (ISBN 0-471-08124-8). Wiley.

Molesworth, Ralph. Introduction to Assembly Language for the TI Home Computer. Davis, Steve, ed. LC 83-90770. (Illus.). 144p. (Orig.). 1983. pap. 16.95 (ISBN 0-911061-01-0). S Davis Pub.

More TRS-80 Assembly Language Programming. 430p. 5.95 (ISBN 0-317-05258-6, 62-2075). Radio Shack.

Morgan, Christopher L. Bluebook of Assembly Routines for the IBM PCjr & XT. (Plume-Waite Computer Ser.). (Illus.). 1984. pap. 19.95 (ISBN 0-452-25498-1, Plume). NAL.

Morley, M. S. Fundamentals of TI 99-4A Assembly Language. (Illus.). 322p. (Orig.). 1984. 16.95 (ISBN 0-8306-0722-6, 1722); pap. 11.95 (ISBN 0-8306-1722-1). TAB Bks.

Morris, Norl. Pocket Guide: Assembly Language for the 8085. (Pitman Programming Pocket Guides Ser.). 64p. (Orig.). 1984. pap. 6.95 (ISBN 0-273-02123-0). Pitman Pub MA.

Mottola, Robert. Assembly Language Programming for the Apple II. 143p. (Orig.). 1982. pap. 16.95 (ISBN 0-07-931051-6, 51-6). Osborne-McGraw.

Overbeek, Ross A. & Singletary, Wilson E. Assembler Language with ASSIST. LC 75-31713. (Illus.). 416p. 1983. text ed. 31.95 (ISBN 0-574-21435-6, 13-4435); instr. guide avail. (ISBN 0-574-21436-4, 13-4436). SRA.

Peterson, James, ed. Computer Organization & Assembly Language Programming. (Computer Science & Applied Mathematics Ser.). 1978. 24.00i (ISBN 0-12-552250-9); instrs' manual 2.50i (ISBN 0-12-552252-5). Acad Pr.

Rudd, Walter G. Assembly Language Programming & the IBM 360 & 370 Computers. 1976. 28.95 (ISBN 0-13-049536-0); wkbk. 12.95 (ISBN 0-13-049510-7). P-H.

Sanders, William B. Assembly Language for Kids: Commodore 64. (Illus.). 337p. (Orig.). 1984. pap. 14.95 (ISBN 0-931145-00-7). Microcomscribe.

Scanlon, L. J. Eighty Eighty-Six, Eighty Eighty-Eight Assembly Language Programming. (Illus.). 224p. 1984. pap. 15.95 (ISBN 0-89303-424-X). Brady Comm.

Scanlon, Leo. Apple II-IIe Assembly Language Exercises. LC 82-2822. 204p. 1982. pap. 12.95x (ISBN 0-471-86598-2, Pub. by Wiley Pr). Wiley.

--IBM PC & XT Assembly Language: A Guide for Programmers. LC 83-3848. (Illus.). 384p. 1983. pap. 19.95 (ISBN 0-89303-241-7); bk. & diskette 54.95 (ISBN 0-89303-535-1); disk 35.00 (ISBN 0-89303-536-X). Brady Comm.

Scanlon, Leo J. IBM PC & XT Assembly Language: A Guide for Programmers. rev. & expanded ed. (Illus.). 352p. 1985. pap. 21.95 (ISBN 0-89303-575-0). Brady Comm.

Schneider, Al. Fundamentals of IBM PC Assembly Language. (Illus.). 320p. (Orig.). 1984. 19.95 (ISBN 0-8306-0710-2); pap. 15.50 (ISBN 0-8306-1710-8, 1710); IBM-PC Disk. 24.95 (ISBN 0-8306-6609-5, 6609); IBM-PC. incl. disk 35.50 (ISBN 0-8306-5057-1). TAB Bks.

Schneider, Michael G. The Principles of Computer Organization with Assembly Language Programming with the PDP-11. 544p. 1985. text ed. 29.95 (ISBN 0-471-88552-5). Wiley.

Sebesta. Structured Assembly Language Programming for the Vax II. 1983. 29.95 (ISBN 0-8053-7001-3); instr's. guide 5.95 (ISBN 0-8053-7004-8). Benjamin-Cummings.

Sebesta, Robert W. PDP-11 Structured Assembly Language Programming. 352p. 1985. text ed. 29.95 (ISBN 0-8053-7005-6); instr's. guide 5.95 (ISBN 0-8053-7006-4). Benjamin Cummings.

Shapiro, Harvey. Assembly Language Programming for the PDP-11. 349p. 1984. text ed. 27.95 (ISBN 0-87484-704-4). Mayfield Pub.

Singer, M. Introduction to the DEC System Ten Assembler Language Programming. LC 78-8586. 147p. 1978. 22.95 (ISBN 0-471-03458-4). Wiley.

Singer, Michael. PDP-11 Assembler Language Programming & Machine Organization. 178p. 1980. 22.95 (ISBN 0-471-04905-0). Wiley.

Skier, K. The Sixty-Eight Hundred Nine Primer: Assembly Language & Subroutines for the TRS-80 Color Computer. 280p. 1983. pap. 16.95 (ISBN 0-07-057862-1, BYTE Bks). McGraw.

--Top-Down Assembly Language Programming for Your VIC-20 & Commodore-64. 434p. 1983. pap. 19.95 (ISBN 0-07-057863-X, BYTE Bks). McGraw.

--Top-Down Assembly Language Programming for Your 6502 Personal Computer. 434p. 1983. pap. 16.95 (CC 07-057863-X). SYBEX.

Skinner, Thomas P. An Introduction to Assembly Language Programming for the 8086 Family: A Self-Teaching Guide. 1985. pap. 17.95 (ISBN 0-471-80825-3). Wiley.

Smith, Bruce. Commodore 64 Assembly Language. 200p. 1985. pap. 17.95 (ISBN 0-412-00851-3, NO. 9407, Pub. by Chapman & Hall England). Methuen Inc.

Smith, Dean L. Assembly Language Programming. (Illus.). 294p. (Orig.). 1984. pap. text ed. 30.00x (ISBN 0-918699-05-3). D L Smith.

Smith, Mike. Sixty-Five Hundred Two Machine & Assembly Language Programming. (Illus.). 322p. (Orig.). 1985. 19.95 (ISBN 0-8306-0750-1, 1750); pap. 12.95 (ISBN 0-8306-1750-7). TAB Bks.

Socha, John. Assembly Language Programming Techniques for the IBM PCjr. (Illus.). 320p. Date not set. pap. 16.95 (ISBN 0-89303-462-2). Brady Comm.

--Assembly Language Safari on the IBM PC: First Explorations. (Illus.). 384p. 1984. pap. 16.95 (ISBN 0-89303-321-9); bk. & diskette 56.95 (ISBN 0-89303-294-8); diskette 40.00 (ISBN 0-89303-295-6). Brady Comm.

Sowell, Edward F. Programming in Assembly Language: Macro-11. LC 83-3774. (Computer Science Ser.). (Illus.). 512p. 1984. 31.95 (ISBN 0-201-07788-4). Addison-Wesley.

Stabley, Don H. Assembler Language for Application Programming. (Illus.). 700p. 1982. 35.00 (ISBN 0-89433-176-0). Petrocelli.

--System 360 Assembler Language. LC 67-30037. 129p. 1967. pap. 25.50x (ISBN 0-471-81950-6, Pub. by Wiley-Interscience). Wiley.

Stern. Study Guide to Accompany 370-360 Assembler Language Programming. 2nd ed. 1986. pap. price not set (ISBN 0-471-82570-0). Wiley.

Stern, Nancy, et al. Three Seventy Three Sixty Assembler Language Programming. LC 78-10504. 516p. 1979. pap. text ed. 34.50 (ISBN 0-471-03429-0); write for info. tchrs. manual (ISBN 0-471-05393-7). Wiley.

Struble, George W. Assembler Language Programming: The IBM System 360. 2nd ed. 496p. 1975. text ed. 27.95 (ISBN 0-201-07322-6). Addison-Wesley.

Sutton, James. Power Programming the Commodore 64: Assembly Language, Graphics & Sound Power Programming the Commodore 64. (Illus.). 304p. 1985. pap. 19.95 (ISBN 0-13-687849-0). P-H.

Tabler. IBM PC Assembly Language. 1985. pap. 18.95 (ISBN 0-471-82497-6). Wiley.

Tabler, Donna & Ashley, Ruth. IBM OS Assembler Language: Language Basics. (Data Processing Training Ser.: 1-615). 250p. 1985. pap. text ed. 49.95x (ISBN 0-471-80134-8). Wiley.

Tabler, Donna N., et al. IBM OS Assembler Language: Advanced Techniques, Bk. 5. (Data Processing Training Ser.: No. 1-615). 256p. 1984. text ed. 49.95x (ISBN 0-471-80718-4). Wiley.

Templeton, Harley & Berliner, Thomas H. From BASIC to 8086-8088 Assembly Language. LC 84-19644. (Illus.). 240p. 1984. pap. 19.95 (ISBN 0-915381-51-6). WordWare Pub.
Templeton, Harley & Wordware, Inc. From BASIC to 8086-8088 Assembly Language. 175p. 1985. pap. 19.95 (ISBN 0-13-331364-6). P H.
Tepolt, Laurence A. Assembly Language Programming for the TRS-80 Color Computer. (Illus.). 256p. (Orig.). 1985. 21.95 (ISBN 0-8306-0785-4, 1785); pap. 14.95 (ISBN 0-8306-1785-X). TAB Bks.
Triebel, Walter A. & Singh, Avtar. IBM PC 8088 Assembly Language Programming. (Illus.). 256p. 1984. pap. text ed. 14.95 (ISBN 0-13-448358-8); pap. text ed. 39.95 (bk. & diskette) (ISBN 0-13-448309-X); disk 24.95 (ISBN 0-13-448317-0). P-H.
TRS-80 Z80 Assembly Language Library. incl. disks 29.97 (ISBN 0-317-06047-3). Green Pub Inc.
Tuggle, Sharon. Assembler Language Programming: Systems-360 & 370. LC 74-84276. 400p. 1975. pap. text ed. 22.95 (ISBN 0-574-19160-7, 13-4015); instr's guide avail. (ISBN 0-574-19161-5, 13-4016). SRA.
Ullman, Julian. Pocket Guide: Assembly Language for the Z80. (Pitman Programming Pocket Guides Ser.). 64p. (Orig.). 1984. pap. 6.95 (ISBN 0-273-01987-2). Pitman Pub MA.
Weller, Walter J. Assembly Level Programming for Small Computers. LC 75-13436. (Illus.). 304p. 1975. 25.00x (ISBN 0-669-00049-3). Lexington Bks.
Willen, David C. IBM PCjr Assembler Language. LC 84-71060. 286p. 1984. pap. 15.95 (ISBN 0-672-22360-0, 22360). Sams.
Willent, David C. & Krantz, Jeffrey. Eighty Eighty-Eight Assembler Language Programming: The IBM-PC. 2nd ed. LC 84-51720. 272p. 1984. pap. 15.95 (ISBN 0-672-22400-3). Sams.
Yeung, B. C. Eighty-Eighty Six - Eighty-Eighty Eight Assembly Language Programming. 265p. 1984. pap. 19.95 (ISBN 0-471-90463-5). Wiley.

ASSEMBLING (ELECTRONIC COMPUTERS)
see also Compiling (Electronic Computers); Electronic Data Processing; Electronic Digital Computers–Programming
Berry, R. E. Programming Language Translation. (Computers & Their Applications Ser.). 175p. 1983. pap. 28.95x (ISBN 0-470-27468-9). Halsted Pr.
Calingaert, Peter. Assemblers, Compilers, & Program Translation. LC 78-21905. 270p. 1979. 28.95 (ISBN 0-914894-23-4). Computer Sci.
Fohl, Mark E. An Assembly Course. (Illus.). 216p. 1982. 17.50 (ISBN 0-89433-149-3). Petrocelli.
Gust, Philip. Introduction to Machine & Assembly Language Programming. (Illus.). 528p. 1985. text ed. 32.95 (ISBN 0-13-486416-6). P-H.

ASSEMBLY LANGUAGE (COMPUTER PROGRAM LANGUAGE)
see Assembler Language (Computer Program Language)

ASSEMBLY-LINE METHODS
see also Automation
Assembly Automation: Proceedings of the 4th International Conference, Tokyo, Japan, Oct. 1983. (Illus.). 1983. 84.00 (ISBN 0-903608-48-0, Pub. by IFSPUBS). Scholium Intl.
Assembly Automation: Proceedings of the 6th International Conference. 1985. 80.00x (ISBN 0-903608-88-X, Pub. by IFS Pubns UK). Air Sci Co.
Duarte, Salvador R. & Duarte, R. L. Electronics Assembly & Fabrication Methods. 2nd ed. LC 72-6495. 1973. text ed. 18.25 (ISBN 0-07-017880-1). McGraw.
Heginbotham, W. B., ed. Assembly Automation 1985: Proceedings of the Sixth International Conference Birmingham, U. K. 14-17, May 1985. 450p. 1985. 83.50 (ISBN 0-444-87767-3, North-Holland). Elsevier.
Hollier, R. H., ed. Automated Materials Handling 1985: Proceedings of the Second International Conference, Birmingham, UK, 14-17 May 1985. 350p. 1985. 83.50 (ISBN 0-444-87770-3, North-Holland). Elsevier.
Hundy, B. B., ed. Automated Manufacturing 1985: Proceedings of the Third European Conference, Birmingham, U. K. 14-17 May 1985. 400p. 1985. 83.50 (ISBN 0-444-87772-X, North-Holland). Elsevier.
International Conference on Assembly Automation, 3rd, Stuttgart, BRD, May 1982. Assembly Automation: Proceedings. (Illus.). 626p. 1982. pap. text ed. 95.00x softbound (ISBN 0-903608-25-1, Pub. by IFSPUBS). Scholium Intl.
International Conference on Assembly Automation, 2nd, Brighton, UK, 1981. Assembly Automation: Proceedings. 300p. 1981. softbound 80.00 (ISBN 0-903608-07-3, Pub. by IFSPUBS). Scholium Intl.
Krautter, J., ed. Assembly Automation: Proceedings of the 5th International Conference, Paris, France, 22-24 May, 1984. 380p. 1984. 72.25 (ISBN 0-444-87552-2, Pub. by North Holland). Elsevier.
Linhart, Robert. The Assembly Line. Crosland, Margaret, tr. from Fr. LC 81-1703. Orig. Title: L'Etabli. 160p. (Orig.). 1981. pap. text ed. 7.95x (ISBN 0-87023-322-X). U of Mass Pr.
Makino, H. Assembly Automation: Proceedings of the 4th International Conference, Tokyo, Japan, 11-13 Oct., 1983. 408p. 1984. 71.25 (ISBN 0-444-86768-6). Elsevier.
Miller, Richard K. Robots in Industry: Applications for Assembly. 2nd ed. (Illus.). 210p. 1984. pap. text ed. 125.00 (ISBN 0-89671-054-8). SEAI Tech Pubns.
Owen, A. E. Flexible Assembly Systems: Assembly by Robots & Computerized Integrated Systems. 230p. 1984. 42.50x (ISBN 0-306-41527-5). Plenum Pub.
Rathmill, K., ed. Robotic Assembly. (International Trends in Manufacturing Technology Ser.). 350p. 1985. 39.50 (ISBN 0-387-15483-3). Springer-Verlag.
Technical Insights Inc. Robots in Industry: Applications for Assembly. LC 82-9926. 212p. 1984. 125.00 (ISBN 0-89671-039-4). Tech Insights.
Treer, Kenneth R. Automated Assembly. LC 78-75097. pap. 114.80 (ISBN 0-317-28123-2, 2055739). Bks Demand UMI.

ASSOCIATIONS, INSTITUTIONS, ETC.–DIRECTORIES
Gibaldi, Joseph & Achtert, Walter S. A Guide to Professional Organizations for Teachers of Language & Literature. vii, 62p. 1978. pap. 5.00x (ISBN 0-87352-125-0, W325). Modern Lang.
Kruzas, Anthony T. & Gill, Kay, eds. International Research Centers. 2nd ed. 600p. 1984. 295.00x (ISBN 0-8103-0467-8). Gale.
Washington Representatives. 264p. 1983. 40.00 (ISBN 0-686-62452-1). B Klein Pubns.
Yacyshyi, R. J., ed. Directory of Engineering Societies & Related Organizations. 11th ed. 1984. 100.00 (ISBN 0-87615-003-2). AAES.

ASSOCIATIVE RINGS
Amitsur, S. A & Saltman, D. J., eds. Algebraists' Homage: Papers in Ring Theory & Related Topics. LC 82-18934. (Contemporary Mathematics Ser.: vol. 13). 412p. 1982. pap. 32.00 (ISBN 0-8218-5013-X, CONM/13). Am Math.
Bass, H., ed. Algebraic K-Theory 3: Hermitian K-Theory & Geometric Applications. LC 73-13421. (Lecture Notes in Mathematics: Vol. 343). xv, 572p. 1973. pap. 27.00 (ISBN 0-387-06436-2). Springer-Verlag.
Conference in Orders, Group Rings & Related Topics. Proceedings. Hsia, J. S., et al, eds. (Lecture Notes in Mathematics: Vol. 353). 224p. 1973. pap. 16.00 (ISBN 0-387-06518-0). Springer-Verlag.
Dicks, W. Groups, Trees & Projective Modules. (Lecture Notes in Mathematics: Vol. 790). 127p. 1980. pap. 13.00 (ISBN 0-387-09974-3). Springer-Verlag.
Faith, C. & Wiegand, S., eds. Module Theory: Proceedings, Seattle, August 15-18, 1977. LC 79-4636. (Lecture Notes in Mathematics: Vol. 700). 1979. pap. 17.00 (ISBN 0-387-09107-6). Springer-Verlag.
Faith, Carl & Page, Stanley. FPF Ring Theory: Faithful Modules & Generators of Mod-R. LC 83-24067. (London Mathematical Society Lecture Note Ser.: No. 88). 176p. 1984. pap. text ed. 19.95 (ISBN 0-521-27738-8). Cambridge U Pr.
Fossum, R. M., et al. Trivial Extensions of Abelian Categories: Homological Algebra of Trivial Extensions of Abelian Categories with Applications to Ring Theory. (Lecture Notes in Mathematics Ser.: Vol. 456). xi, 122p. (Orig.). 1975. pap. 13.00 (ISBN 0-387-07159-8). Springer-Verlag.
Goodearl, K. R. & Boyle, Ann K. Dimension Theory for Nonsingular Injective Modules. LC 76-26498. (Memoirs of the American Mathematical Society: 177). 112p. 1976. pap. 13.00 (ISBN 0-8218-2177-6, MEMO 177). Am Math.
Gordon, Robert & Robson, J. C. Krull Dimension. LC 73-6825. (Memoirs: No. 133). 78p. 1978. pap. 12.00 (ISBN 0-8218-1833-3, MEMO-133). Am Math.
McDonald, Bernard R. Finite Rings with Identity. (Pure & Applied Mathematics Ser.: Vol. 28). 448p. 1974. 75.00 (ISBN 0-8247-6161-8). Dekker.
Ringel, C. M. Tame Algebras & Integral Quadratic Forms. (Lecture Notes in Mathematics Ser.: Vol. 1099). xiii, 376p. 1984. pap. 18.00 (ISBN 0-387-13905-2). Springer-Verlag.

ASTEROIDEA
see Starfishes

ASTEROIDS
see Planets, Minor

ASTRAGALUS
Barneby, Rupert C. Atlas of North American Astragalus, 2 vols. (Memoirs of the New York Botanical Garden Ser.: Vol. 13). 1964. Set. 40.00x (ISBN 0-89327-225-6); Set. pap. 35.00x (ISBN 0-89327-224-8). Vol. 1 (ISBN 0-89327-226-4). Vol. 2 (ISBN 0-89327-227-2). NY Botanical.
Becht, R. Revision der Sektion Alopecuroideae DC. der Gattung Astragalus L. (Phanerogamarum Monographiae Ser: No. 10). (Illus.). 1979. lib. bdg. 21.00 (ISBN 3-7682-1188-6). Lubrecht & Cramer.
Ott, E. Revision der Sektion Chronopus Bge. der Gattung Astragalus. L. (Phanerogamarum Monographiae Ser.: No. 9). (Illus.). 1979. lib. bdg. 17.50 (ISBN 3-7682-1187-8). Lubrecht & Cramer.

ASTRIONICS
see also Astronautics–Communication Systems; Ground Support Systems (Astronautics); Space Vehicles–Guidance Systems
Space Electronics Symposium - Los Angeles - 1965. Space Electronics Symposium: Proceedings. Wong, C. M., ed. (Science & Technology Ser.: Vol. 6). 1965. 30.00x (ISBN 0-87703-034-0, Pub. by Am Astronaut). Univelt Inc.

ASTROBIOLOGY
see Life on Other Planets; Space Biology

ASTRODYNAMICS
see also Artificial Satellites–Orbits; Astronautics; Navigation (Astronautics); Space Flight; Space Trajectories
American Mathematical Society. Space Mathematics, 3 vols. Rosser, J. B., ed. Incl. Pt.1. LC 66-20435. (Vol. 5). 1979. paper 41.00 (ISBN 0-8218-1105-3, LAM-5); Pt. 2. LC 66-20437. (Vol. 6). 1974. Repr. of 1966 ed. 33.00 (ISBN 0-8218-1106-1, LAM-6); Pt. 3. LC 66-20435. (Vol. 5-7). 1966. 35.00 (ISBN 0-8218-1107-X, LAM-7). LC 66-20435. (Lectures in Applied Mathematics Ser). Am Math.
Anthony, M. L., ed. Space Flight Mechanics Symposium. (Science & Technology Ser.: Vol. 11). 1966. 45.00 (ISBN 0-87703-039-1, Pub. by Am Astronaut). Univelt Inc.
Bate, R. R., et al. Fundamentals of Astrodynamics. (Illus.). 16.00 (ISBN 0-8446-0025-3). Peter Smith.
Bate, Roger R., et al. Fundamentals of Astrodynamics. 1971. pap. 6.95 (ISBN 0-486-60061-0). Dover.
COSPAR-IAU-IAG-IUGG-IUTAM - May 20-24, 1969. Dynamics of Satellites: Proceedings. Morando, B., ed. (Eng. & Fr., Illus.). vii, 312p. 1970. 82.10 (ISBN 0-387-04792-1). Springer-Verlag.
COSPAR-IAU-IUTAM Symposium, Paris, 1965. Trajectories of Artificial Celestial Bodies As Determined from Observations: Proceedings. Kovalevsky, J., ed. (Illus.). 1966. 52.00 (ISBN 0-387-03681-4). Springer-Verlag.
Friedlander, Alan L. & Cefola, Paul J., eds. Astrodynamics 1981. LC 57-43769. (Advances in the Astronautical Sciences Ser.: Vol. 46). (Illus.). 1124p. (Orig.). 1982. Pt. 1. lib. bdg. 55.00x (ISBN 0-87703-159-2, Pub. by Am Astronaut); Pt. 2. lib. bdg. 55.00x (ISBN 0-87703-161-4); Pt. 1. pap. text ed. 45.00x (ISBN 0-87703-160-6); Pt. 2. pap. text ed. 45.00x (ISBN 0-87703-162-2); Microfiche Supplement 40.00x (ISBN 0-87703-163-0). Univelt Inc.
Leimanis, E. General Problem of the Motion of Coupled Rigid Bodies About a Fixed Point. (Springer Tracts in Natural Philosophy: Vol. 7). (Illus.). 1965. 36.00 (ISBN 0-387-03408-0). Springer-Verlag.
Penzo, P. A., ed. Astrodynamics, 1979, Vol. 40. LC 57-43769. (Advances in the Astronautical Science Ser.). (Illus.). 1980. Part 1, 494pp. 325part 2, 502pp. 45.00x (ISBN 0-87703-107-X, Pub. by Am Astronaut); Part 2,502pp. 45.00x (ISBN 0-87703-109-6); microfiche suppl. 20.00x (ISBN 0-87703-139-8); pap. 35.00x (ISBN 0-87703-108-8); pap. 35.00x (ISBN 0-87703-110-X). Univelt Inc.
Powers, William F. & Rauch, Herbert E., eds. Astrodynamics, 1975. new ed. LC 57-43769. (Advances in the Astronautical Science Ser: Vol. 33). (Illus.). 1976. lib. bdg. 35.00x (ISBN 0-87703-079-0, Pub. by Am Astronaut); microfiche supplement 40.00x (ISBN 0-87703-142-8). Univelt Inc.
Richards, P. B., ed. Recent Developments in Space Flight Mechanics. (Science & Technology Ser.: Vol. 9). 1966. 25.00x (ISBN 0-87703-037-5). Univelt Inc.
Tseng, G. T., et al, eds. Astrodynamics, 1983. LC 57-43769. (Advances in the Astronautical Sciences Ser.: Vol. 54, Pts. I & II). (Illus.). 1984. lib. bdg. 120.00x (ISBN 0-87703-190-8, Pub. by Am Astro Soc); pap. text ed. 90.00x (ISBN 0-87703-191-6); fiche suppl. 40.00x (ISBN 0-87703-192-4). Univelt Inc.

ASTROGATION
see Navigation (Astronautics)

ASTROLABES
Blagrave, John. Astrolabium Vranicum Generale: Nova Orbis Terrarum Descripto (A Map to Accompany the Astrolabium) LC 78-38156. (English Experience Ser.: No. 435). (Illus.). 69p. 1972. Repr. of 1596 ed. 9.50 (ISBN 90-221-0435-4). Walter J Johnson.
--The Mathematicall Iewell. LC 74-171735. (English Experience Ser.: No. 294). 1971. Repr. of 1585 ed. 20.00 (ISBN 90-221-0294-7). Walter J Johnson.
Bringas, Ernie. The Malignant Majority. Horwege, Richard A., ed. LC 82-9758. 164p. (Orig.). 1984. pap. 6.95 cancelled (ISBN 0-89865-143-3). Donning Co.
Gunther, Robert T. Astrolabes of the World, 2 vols. in one. (Illus.). 100.00 (ISBN 0-87556-604-9). Saifer.
National Museum of American History Ser. & Gibbs, Sharon. Planispheric Astorlabes from the National Museum of American History. LC 83-600270. (Smithsonian Studies in History & Technology: 45). pap. 59.80 (ISBN 0-317-20136-0, 2023165). Bks Demand UMI.
Skeat, W. W., ed. Chaucer's Treatise on the Astrolabe. (EETS ES Ser.: Vol. 16). Repr. of 1872 ed. 17.00 (ISBN 0-317-15544-X). Kraus Repr.
Skeat, Walter W. A Treatise on the Astrolabe. 45.00 (ISBN 0-8274-3646-7). R West.
Turner, Anthony. Time Museum Catalogue of the Collection; Volume I: Time Measuring Instruments, Part 1: Astrolabes & Related Devices. Chandler, Bruce, ed. (Illus.). 220p. 1985. 95.00 (ISBN 0-912947-02-0). Time Museum.

ASTROLOGY–DATA PROCESSING
Cratch, Stephen C. & Johansson, Anders B. The Hindu Vedic Master Operations Guide: Astrological Software for the IBM PC. Johansson, Lilian M., ed. (Illus.). 200p. (Orig.). 1985. 30.00 (ISBN 0-914725-12-2); pap. 18.00 (ISBN 0-914725-10-6); spiral 24.00 (ISBN 0-914725-11-4). Astro Dynasty Pub Hse.
Friedman, Hank. Astrology on Your Personal Computer. 256p. 1984. pap. 8.95 (ISBN 0-89588-226-4). SYBEX.
Johansson, Anders B. Instruction Book for the Hindu Vedic Astrology Computer Program. LC 83-7001. (Illus.). 295p. 1984. 26.95 (ISBN 0-914725-05-X); pap. 20.95 (ISBN 0-914725-00-9); spiral 19.95 (ISBN 0-914725-02-5). Astro Dynasty Pub Hse.
Juliann. The Calculator Key to Astrology: Or Calculations for Dummies Like Me. new ed. (Illus., Orig.). 1977. pap. 4.00 (ISBN 0-933646-02-X). Aries Pr.

ASTROMETRY
Boehme, S., ed. Astronomy & Astrophysics Abstracts, Vol. 29: Literature 1981, Pt. 1. 853p. 1981. 65.00 (ISBN 0-387-11264-2). Springer-Verlag.
I.A.U Symposium No. 61, Perth, Western Australia, 13-17 August, 1973. New Problems in Astronomy: Proceedings. Gliese, W., et al, eds. LC 73-94453. (Symposium of International Astronomical Union Ser.: No. 61). 280p. 1974. lib. bdg. 53.00 (ISBN 90-277-0444-9, Pub. by Reidel Holland); pap. 39.50 (ISBN 90-277-0445-7). Kluwer Academic.
Podobed, Vladimir V. Fundamental Astrometry: Determination of Stellar Coordinates. Vyssotsky, A. N., ed. LC 64-15810. pap. 62.00 (ISBN 0-317-08497-6, 2020145). Bks Demand UMI.
Robbins, A. R., et al. Satellite Doppler Tracking & Its Geodetic Applications. (Royal Society Ser.). (Illus.). 196p. 1980. Repr. of 1980 ed. text ed. 54.00x (ISBN 0-85403-128-6, Pub. by Royal Society London). Scholium Intl.
Van De Kamp, Peter. Principles of Astrometry: With Special Emphasis on Long-Focus Photographic Astrometry. LC 66-22077. (Illus.). 227p. 1967. 27.95x (ISBN 0-7167-0318-1). W H Freeman.
--Stellar Paths: Photographic Astrometry with Long-Focus Instruments. xix, 149p. 1981. 34.95 (ISBN 90-277-1256-5, Pub. by Reidel Holland). Kluwer Academic.

ASTRONAUTICAL ACCIDENTS
see Astronautics–Accidents

ASTRONAUTICAL INSTRUMENTS
see also Artificial Satellites–Attitude Control Systems; Astrionics; Astronautics–Communication Systems; Spectrograph;
also headings for special astronautical vehicles with subdivisions for instruments or instrument systems, e.g. Space vehicles–Guidance systems
Angelo, Joseph A., Jr. Dictionary of Space Technology. LC 81-3144. (Illus.). 392p. 1982. 19.95x (ISBN 0-87196-583-6). Facts on File.
Culp, Robert D., et al, eds. Guidance & Control 1985: Feb. 2-6, 1985, Keystone, CO. LC 57-43769. (Advances in the Asronautical Sciences Ser.: Vol. 57). (Illus.). 618p. (Orig.). 1985. lib. bdg. 65.00 (ISBN 0-87703-211-4, Pub By Am Astro Soc); pap. text ed. 50.00 (ISBN 0-87703 212 2). Univelt Inc.

International Instrumentation Symposium, 25th, Anaheim, California, 1979. Fundamentals of Aerospace Instrumentation, Vol.11 & Fundamentals of Test Measurement, Vol. 6: Tutorial Proceedings. Bd. with Vol.6. Fundamentals of Test Measurement. LC 68-59468. 97p. 1979. pap. text ed. 15.00x (ISBN 0-87664-435-3). Instru Soc.

International Instrumentation Symposium 26th, Seattle, Washington, 1980. Fundamentals of Aerospace Instrumentation, Vol. 12 & Fundamentals of Test Measurement, Vol. 7: Tutorial Proceedings. Bd. with Vol.7. Fundamentals of Test Measurement. LC 68-59468. 128p. 1980. pap. text ed. 18.00x (ISBN 0-87664-474-4). Instru Soc.

International Instrumentation Symposium. Instrumentation in the Aerospace Industry & Advances in Test Measurement: Proceedings of the 26th International Instrumentation Symposium, 2 Pts, Vol. 26 & Vol. 17. Bd. with Vol.17. Advances in Test Measurement. 404p. LC 69-59467. 440p. 1980. Set. pap. text ed. 96.00x (ISBN 0-87664-649-6); pap. text ed. 54.00x ea. Pt. 1, 440 Pp (ISBN 0-87664-473-6). Pt. 2, 404 Pp (ISBN 0-87664-654-2). Instru Soc.

Shapley, Harlow. Inner Metagalaxy. 1957. 49.50x (ISBN 0-686-83589-1). Elliots Bks.

ASTRONAUTICAL RESEARCH

Aerospace Testing Seminar Proceedings, 3rd, September 1976. LC 62-38584. (Illus.). 122p. 1977. pap. text ed. 20.00 (ISBN 0-915414-50-3). Inst Environ Sci.

Bauman, Edward J., ed. Guidance & Control, 1981. LC 57-43769. (Advances in the Astronautical Sciences Ser.: Vol. 45). (Illus.). 506p. 1981. lib. bdg. 60.00x (ISBN 0-87703-150-9, Pub. by Am Astronaut); pap. text ed. 50.00x (ISBN 0-87703-151-7); fiche suppl. 10.00x (ISBN 0-87703-156-8). Univelt Inc.

E S L A B-E S R I N Symposium, 5th, Noordwijk, The Netherlands, 1971. Infrared Detection Techniques for Space Research: Proceedings. Manno, V. & Ring, J., eds. LC 70-179894. (Astrophysics & Space Library: No. 30). 344p. 1972. lib. bdg. 50.00 (ISBN 90-277-0226-8, Pub. by Reidel Holland). Kluwer Academic.

Flinn, E., ed. Scientific Results of Viking Project. (Illus.). 725p. 1977. 15.00 (ISBN 0-87590-207-3). Am Geophysical.

Goldman, Nathan C. Space Commerce: Free Enterprise on the High Frontier. LC 84-16761. 208p. 1985. 25.00 ea. (ISBN 0-88730-003-0). Ballinger Pub.

Grandal, Bjorn, ed. Artificial Particles Beams in Space Plasma Studies. LC 82-470. (NATO ASI Series B, Physics: Vol. 79). 722p. 1982. 95.00 (ISBN 0-306-40985-2, Plenum Pr). Plenum Pub.

International Astronautical Federation, 23rd, 1972. Astronautical Research 1972: Proceedings. Napolitano, L. G., et al, eds. LC 72-97959. 300p. 1973. lib. bdg. 63.00 (ISBN 90-277-0333-7, Pub. by Reidel Holland). Kluwer Academic.

Kuchemann, D., ed. Progress in Aerospace Sciences (Incorporating Progress in Astronautical Sciences, Vols. 7-8, 10-16. Incl. Vol. 7. 1966. 125.00 (ISBN 0-08-011560-8); Vol. 8. 1967. write for info.; Vol. 10. 1970. 125.00 (ISBN 0-08-013117-4); Vol. 11. 1970. 125.00 (ISBN 0-08-015616-9); Vol. 12. 1972. 125.00 (ISBN 0-08-016656-3); Vol. 13. 1973. 125.00 (ISBN 0-08-017012-9); Vol. 14. 1973. 125.00 (ISBN 0-08-017138-9); Vol. 15. 1974. 125.00 (ISBN 0-08-017838-3); Vol. 16. 1975-76. Pt. 1. pap. text ed. 15.50 (ISBN 0-08-019606-3); Pt. 2. pap. text ed. 21.00 (ISBN 0-08-019607-1); Pt. 3. pap. text ed. 22.00 (ISBN 0-08-019608-X); Pt. 4. pap. text ed. 18.50 (ISBN 0-08-019609-8); Vol. 16, Complete (cloth) 82.50 (ISBN 0-08-018178-3). LC 74-618347. Pergamon.

Napolitano, L. G., ed. Applications of Space Developments: Space & Energy Earth-Oriented Applications, Low-Gravity Environment: Selected Proceedings of the XXXI International Astronautical Congress, Tokyo, Japan, 21-28 September 1980. 360p. 1981. 79.00 (ISBN 0-08-026729-7). Pergamon.

Rycroft, M. J. Space Research, Vol. 20: Proceedings of the Open Meetings of the Working Groups on Physical Sciences of the Twenty-Second Plenary Meeting of the Committee on Space Research, Bangalore, India, 29 May- 9 June 1979. LC 79-41359. (Illus.). 294p. 1980. 64.00 (ISBN 0-08-024437-8). Pergamon.

Steinhoff, Ernst, ed. Aerospace Research & Development. (Science & Technology Ser.: Vol. 24). (Illus.). 1970. lib. bdg. 40.00x (ISBN 0-87703-052-9, Pub. by Am Astronaut). Univelt Inc.

Symposium, Advanced Study Institute and ESRO, Cortina, Italy, 1971. Earth's Magnetospheric Processes: Proceedings. McCormac, B. M., ed. LC 70-188007. (Astrophysics & Space Science Library: No. 32). 417p. 1972. 60.50 (ISBN 90-277-0231-4, Pub. by Reidel Holland). Kluwer Academic.

Thompson, G. V., ed. Space Research & Technology. 224p. 1962. 60.25x (ISBN 0-677-11910-0). Gordon.

Tiffany, O. L. & Zaitzeff, E., eds. Advanced Space Experiments. LC 57-43769. (Advances in the Astronautical Sciences Ser.: Vol. 25). (Illus.). 1969. 40.00x (ISBN 0-87703-028-6, Pub. by Am Astronaut). Univelt Inc.

Willmore, A. P. & Willmore, S. R., eds. Aerospace Research Index: A Guide to the World Research in Aeronautics, Meteorology, Astronomy & Space Science. LC 82-139202. pap. 151.80 (ISBN 0-317-27833-9). Bks Demand UMI.

Wukelic, G. E., ed. Handbook of Soviet Space Science Research. 526p. 1968. 100.75 (ISBN 0-677-11770-1). Gordon.

ASTRONAUTICS

see also Aerothermodynamics; Artificial Satellites; Astrodynamics; Astronauts; Manned Space Flight; Navigation (Astronautics); Outer Space; Outer Space–Exploration; Rocketry; Space Flight; Space Flight to Mars; Space Flight to the Moon; Space Sciences; Space Ships; Space Simulators; Space Stations; Space Vehicles; Space Vehicles–Atmospheric Entry; X-Fifteen (Rocket Aircraft)

AAS - AAAS Symposium - Montreal - 1964. Towards Deeper Space Penetration. Van Driest, Edard R., ed. (Science & Technology Ser.: Vol. 2). 1964. 20.00x (ISBN 0-87703-030-8, Pub. by Am Astronaut). Univelt Inc.

Advanced Aerospace Materials. 1984. 25.00 (ISBN 0-89883-818-5, SP597). Soc Auto Engineers.

Aerospace Testing Seminar Proceedings. LC 62-38584. 165p. 1982. pap. text ed. 25.00 (ISBN 0-915414-71-6). Inst Environ Sci.

American Assembly. Outer Space: Prospects for Man & Society. rev. ed. Bloomfield, Lincoln P., ed. LC 72-3391. (Essay Index Reprint Ser.). Repr. of 1968 ed. 17.00 (ISBN 0-8369-2886-5). Ayer Co Pubs.

American Astronautical Society. Advances in the Astronautical Sciences. Incl. Vol. 6. Sixth Annual Meeting, New York, 1960. Jacobs, H. & Burgess, E., eds. 45.00x (ISBN 0-87703-007-3); Vol. 9. Fourth Western Regional Meeting, San Francisco, 1961. Jacobs, H. & Burgess, E., eds. 45.00x (ISBN 0-87703-010-3); Vol. 11. Eighth Annual Meeting, Washington, 1962. 45.00x (ISBN 0-87703-012-X); Vol. 13. Ninth Annual Meeting, Interplanetary Missions, Los Angeles, 1963. Burgess, E., ed. 45.00x (ISBN 0-87703-014-6). Am Astronaut). Univelt Inc.

American Astronautical Society Annual Meeting, San Francisco, Oct. 1977. The Industrialization of Space: Proceedings. Van Patten, R. A., et al, eds. LC 57-43769. (Advances in the Astronautical Sciences: Vol. 36). (Illus.). 1978. Pt. I. lib. bdg. 55.00x (ISBN 0-87703-094-4, Pub. by Am Astronaut); Pt. II. lib. bdg. 45.00x (ISBN 0-87703-095-2); microfiche suppl. 15.00x (ISBN 0-87703-121-5). Univelt Inc.

Bent, Ralph D. & McKinley, James L. Aircraft Electricity & Electronics. 3rd, rev. ed. (Aviation Technology Ser.). (Illus.). 432p. 1981. pap. text ed. 30.20 (ISBN 0-07-004793-6). McGraw.

Bicentennial Space Symposium. New Themes for Space - Mankind's Future Needs & Aspirations: Proceedings. Schneider, William C., ed. & intro. by. LC 57-43769. (Advances in the Astronautical Sciences Ser.: Vol. 35). (Illus.). 1977. lib. bdg. 25.00x (ISBN 0-87703-090-1, Pub. by Am Astronaut). Univelt Inc.

Bolger, Philip H., ed. Space Rescue & Safety, 1975. New ed. (Science & Technology Ser: Vol. 41). (Illus.). 1976. lib. bdg. 25.00x (ISBN 0-87703-077-4, Pub. by Am Astronaut). Univelt Inc.

Burke, James D. & Whitt, April S., eds. Space Manufacturing 1983. (Advances in the Astronautical Sciences Ser.: Vol. 53). (Illus.). 496p. 1983. lib. bdg. 60.00x (ISBN 0-87703-188-6, Pub. by Am Astronaut); 50.00x (ISBN 0-87703-189-4). Univelt Inc.

Calder, Nigel. Spaceships of the Mind. 1979. pap. 6.95 (ISBN 0-14-005231-3). Penguin.

Carter, L. J. & Bainum, Peter M., eds. Space: A Developing Role for Europe, 18th European Space Symposium. (Science & Technology Ser.: Vol. 56). (Illus.). 278p. 1984. lib. bdg. 45.00x (ISBN 0-87703-193-2, Pub. by Am Astro Soc); pap. text ed. 35.00 (ISBN 0-87703-194-0); fiche suppl. 20.00 (ISBN 0-87703-195-9). Univelt Inc.

Collins. Takeoffs & Landings. 1983. write for info. Macmillan.

Colloquium on the Law of Outer Space-International Institute of Space Law of the International Astronautical Federation, 14th, 1971. Proceedings. Schwartz, Mortimer D., ed. iv, 298p. 1972. pap. text ed. 27.50x (ISBN 0-8377-0409-X). Rothman.

Compton, David W. & Benson, Charles D. Living & Working in Space: A History of Skylab. (NASA SP 4208, NASA History Ser.). 462p. 20.00 (ISBN 0-318-11796-7). Gov Printing Office.

Congress of the International Astronautical Federation, 22nd, Brussels, Sept. 1971. Astronautical Research 1971: Proceedings. Napolitano, L. G., ed. LC 72-92536. (Illus.). 586p. 1973. lib. bdg. 76.00 (ISBN 90-277-0306-X, Pub. by Reidel Holland). Kluwer Academic.

Davies, Geoff, ed. Nineteen Seventy-Nine Astronautics Convention: Proceedings, 2 pts. 314p. (Orig.). 1981. pap. text ed. 40.00 (ISBN 0-9596726-5-6, Pub. by Astronautical Soc W Australia). Univelt Inc.

Durant, Frederick C., III, ed. Between Sputnik & the Shuttle: New Perspectives on American Astronautics, 1957-1980. (American Astronautical Society History Ser.: Vol. 3). (Illus.). 350p. 1981. text ed. 40.00x (ISBN 0-87703-145-2, Pub. by Am Astronaut); pap. text ed. 30.00x (ISBN 0-87703-149-5). Univelt Inc.

Emme, Eugene M., ed. Two Hundred Years of Flight in America. 2nd ed. (AAS History Ser.: Vol. 1). (Illus.). 1977. lib. bdg. 35.00x (ISBN 0-87703-091-X); soft cover 25.00x (ISBN 0-87703-101-0). Univelt Inc.

Estes, John E. & Senger, Leslie W. Remote Sensing: Techniques for Environmental Analysis. LC 73-8601. 340p. 1975. 33.45x (ISBN 0-471-24595-X). Wiley.

Ferdman, S., ed. The Second Fifteen Years in Space. (Science & Technology Ser.: Vol. 31). 1973. lib. bdg. 25.00x (ISBN 0-87703-064-2, Pub. by Am Astronaut). Univelt Inc.

Fourth Aerospace Testing Seminar: Proceedings. LC 62-38584. (Illus.). 1978. pap. text ed. 20.00 (ISBN 0-915414-55-4). Inst Environ Sci.

French, Bevan M. Meeting with the Universe: Science Discoveries from the Space Program. (NASA Ep 177 Ser.). 231p. 1981. pap. 14.00 (ISBN 0-318-11803-3). Gov Printing Office.

Goddard Memorial Symposium, Twelfth. Skylab & Pioneer Report. Bolger, Philip H. & Richards, Paul B., eds. (Science & Technology Ser: Vol. 36). (Illus.). 160p. 1975. lib. bdg. 20.00x (ISBN 0-87703-071-5, Pub. by Am Astronaut). Univelt Inc.

Goddard Memorial Symposium - Washington D.C. - 1961. Space Age in Fiscal Year 2001. Konecci, E., et al, eds. (Science & Technology Ser.: Vol. 10). 1967. 35.00x (ISBN 0-87703-038-3, Pub. by Am Astronaut). Univelt Inc.

International Astronautical Congress, Tokyo, Japan, September 22-27, 1980 & Napolitano, L. G. Applications of Space Developments II: Selected Papers. 310p. 1981. pap. 70.00 (ISBN 0-08-028676-3). Pergamon.

International Astronautical Congress, 29th, Dubrovnik, 1-8 October 1978. Astronautics for Peace & Human Progress: Proceedings. Napolitano, L. G., ed. LC 79-40049. (Illus.). 1979. 97.00 (ISBN 0-08-024732-6). Pergamon.

Jacobs, H., ed. AAS Index: Numerical-Chronological-Author. 1979. lib. bdg. 40.00x (ISBN 0-87703-102-9, Pub. by Am Astronaut); pap. 30.00x (ISBN 0-87703-103-7). Univelt Inc.

Johnson, F. S., ed. International Congress of Space Benefits. (Advances in the Astronautical Sciences Ser.: Vol. 30). 1974. 40.00x (ISBN 0-87703-065-0, Pub. by Am Astronaut). Univelt Inc.

Johnson, W. L., ed. Management of Aerospace Programs. (Science & Technology Ser.: Vol. 12). 1967. 30.00x (ISBN 0-87703-040-5, Pub. by Am Astronaut). Univelt Inc.

Johnston, Richard S., et al, eds. Future U. S. Space Programs, 2 pts. (Advances in the Astronautical Sciences: Vol. 38). (Illus.). 1979. lib. bdg. 85.00x (ISBN 0-87703-119-3, Pub. by Am Astronaut); Pt. I. 45.00x (ISBN 0-87703-098-7); Pt. II. 40.00x (ISBN 0-87703-099-5); microfiche suppl. 10.00x (ISBN 0-87703-129-0). Univelt Inc.

Kavanau, L. L., ed. Practical Space Applications. (Advances in the Astronautical Sciences Ser.: Vol. 21). 1967. 40.00x (ISBN 0-87703-024-3, Pub. by Am Astronaut). Univelt Inc.

Levy, Lillian, ed. Space: Its Impact on Man & Society. LC 72-13181. (Essay Index Reprint Ser.). Repr. of 1965 ed. 16.75 (ISBN 0-8369-8164-2). Ayer Co Pubs.

Lunc, M., ed. International Astronautical Congress: Proceedings, 20th, Argentina, 1969. 155.00x (ISBN 0-08-016841-8). Pergamon.

McElroy, John H. & Heacock, Larry E., eds. Space Applications of the Crossroads. (Science & Technology Ser.: Vol. 55). (Illus.). 308p. 1983. lib. bdg. 45.00x (ISBN 0-87703-186-X, Pub. by Am Astronaut); 35.00x (ISBN 0-87703-187-8). Univelt Inc.

McLucas, John L. & Sheffield, Charles, eds. Commercial Operations in Space Nineteen Eighty to Two Thousand. (Science & Technology Ser.: Vol. 51). (Illus.). 214p. 1981. lib. bdg. 30.00x (ISBN 0-87703-140-1, Pub. by Am Astronaut); pap. text ed. 20.00x (ISBN 0-87703-141-X); Microfiche Supple. 5.00x (ISBN 0-87703-165-7). Univelt Inc.

Marsden, B. G. & Cameron, A. G. The Earth-Moon System. LC 65-26632. 288p. 1966. 35.00x (ISBN 0-306-30223-3, Plenum Pr). Plenum Pub.

Moore, Patrick. The Next Fifty Years in Space. LC 75-26326. (Illus.). 1978. pap. 7.50 (ISBN 0-8008-5529-9). Taplinger.

Morgenthaler, G. W., ed. Space Shuttle Payloads. (Science & Technology Ser.: Vol. 30). 530p. 1973. lib. bdg. 40.00x (ISBN 0-87703-063-4, Pub. by Am Astronaut). Univelt Inc.

Morgenthaler, G. W. & Morra, R. G., eds. Unmanned Exploration of the Solar System. (Advances in the Astronautical Sciences Ser.: Vol. 19). 1965. 45.00x (ISBN 0-87703-021-9, Pub. by Am Astronaut). Univelt Inc.

Morgenthaler, George W., ed. Future Space Program & Impact on Range & Network Development. (Science & Technology Ser.: Vol. 15). 1967. 40.00x (ISBN 0-87703-043-X, Pub. by Am Astronaut). Univelt Inc.

Morgenthaler, George W. & Morra, Robert, eds. Planning Challenges of the Seventies in Space. LC 57-43769. (Advances in the Astronautical Sciences Ser.: Vol. 26). (Illus.). 1970. lib. bdg. 35.00x (ISBN 0-87703-053-7, Pub. by Am Astronaut); microfiche suppl. 15.00x (ISBN 0-87703-130-4). Univelt Inc.

Morine, L. A., ed. Guidance & Control, 1980. (Advances in the Astronautical Sciences Ser.: Vol. 42). (Illus.). 738p. 1980. lib. bdg. 60.00x (ISBN 0-87703-137-1, Pub. by Am Astronaut); pap. text ed. 45.00x (ISBN 0-87703-138-X). Univelt Inc.

Napolitano, L., ed. Space Two Thousand-Activities to be Performed for the Next Decade: Selected Papers from the 33rd IAF Congress, Paris, France, 27 September - 2 October 1982. 150p. 1983. pap. 82.50 (ISBN 0-08-031106-7). Pergamon.

Napolitano, L. G., ed. Space Developments for the Future of Mankind-II: Proceedings of the Thirtieth International Astronautical Congress, Munich, FRG. September 16-23 1979. 228p. 1980. pap. 53.00 (ISBN 0-08-026159-0). Pergamon.

Napolitano, Luigi G. Space Two Thousand. LC 83-8795. 709p. 65.00 (ISBN 0-915928-73-6). AIAA.

Napolitano, Luigi G. & International Astronautical Congress, 27th, Anaheim, Ca., Oct. 1976. Proceedings. 1978. text ed. 70.00 (ISBN 0-08-021732-X). Pergamon.

Naumann, Albert & Alexander, Grover, eds. Developing the Space Frontier. LC 57-43769. (Advances in the Astronautical Sciences Ser.: Vol. 52). (Illus.). 436p. 1983. lib. bdg. 55.00x (ISBN 0-87703-184-3, Pub. by Am Astronaut); 45.00x (ISBN 0-87703-185-1). Univelt Inc.

OIL Symposia, 3rd & 4th, 1970 & 1971. Orbital International Laboratory: Proceedings. Steinhoff, Ernst A., ed. (Science & Technology Ser.: Vol. 33). 322p. 1974. lib. bdg. 30.00x (ISBN 0-87703-068-5, Pub. by Am Astronaut). Univelt Inc.

Ordway, Frederick I., 3rd, ed. Advances in Space Science & Technology, Vols. 1-11. Incl. Vols. 1-7. 1959-65. 85.00 ea. Vol. 1 (ISBN 0-12-037301-7). Vol. 3. Vol. 4. Vol. 6. Vol. 7; Vol. 8. 1966. 85.00 (ISBN 0-12-037308-4); Vol. 9. 1967. 85.00 (ISBN 0-12-037309-2); Vol. 10. 1970. 85.00 (ISBN 0-12-037310-6); Vol. 11. 1972. 95.00 (ISBN 0-12-037311-4); Suppl. 1. Space Carrier Vehicles: Design, Development & Testing of Launching Rockets. Lange, O. H. & Stein, R. J. 1963. 75.00 (ISBN 0-12-037361-0); Suppl. 2. Lunar & Planetary Surface Conditions. Weil, N. A. 1965. 75.00 (ISBN 0-12-037362-9). Acad Pr.

Pal, Yash, ed. Space & Development: Proceedings of Vikram Sarabhi Symposium of the Twenty-Second Plenary Meeting of the Committee on Space Research, Bangalore, India, 29 May -9 June 1979. LC 79-41358. (Illus.). 100p. 1980. 23.00 (ISBN 0-08-024441-6). Pergamon.

Pardoe, Geoffrey K. The Future for Space Technology. LC 84-4307. (The Future for Science & Technology Ser.). 206p. 1984. 18.75 (ISBN 0-86187-462-5, Pub. by Frances Pinter). Longwood Pub Group.

Philip, Alan T., ed. Australian Astronautics Convention Proceedings 1975. (Illus.). 1977. pap. text ed. 18.00x (ISBN 0-9596726-1-3). Univelt Inc.

Philip, A. Davis & Hayes, D. S., eds. Astronomical Parameters for Globular Clusters: IAU Colloquium, No. 68. 614p. (Orig.). 1982. 37.00 (ISBN 0-9607902-2-5); pap. 27.00 (ISBN 0-9607902-1-7). Davis Pr.

ASTRONOMICAL MODELS

see also Planetaria

King, Henry C. & Millburn, John R. Geared to the Stars: The Evolution of Planetariums, Orreries & Astronomical Clocks. LC 78-18262. 1978. 80.00 (ISBN 0-8020-2312-6). U of Toronto Pr.

ASTRONOMICAL OBSERVATORIES

see also individual observatories

Donnelly, Marian. A Short History of Observatories. LC 73-175209. 1973. 7.50 (ISBN 0-87114-058-6). U of Oreg Bks.

Kloeppel, James E. Realm of the Long Eyes: A Brief History of Kitt Peak National Observatory. (Illus.). 148p. (Orig.). 1983. pap. 15.00x (ISBN 0-912183-01-2). Univelt Inc.

Williams, Roger C. McDonald Observatory. 1970. pap. 2.00 (ISBN 0-914208-04-7). Longhorn Pr.

ASTRONOMICAL PHOTOGRAPHY

see also Spectrograph

Covington, Michael. Basic Astrophotography. (Illus.). 224p. Date not set. price not set (ISBN 0-521-25391-8). Cambridge U Pr.

Gordon, Barry. Astrophotography. 2nd ed. (Illus.). 224p. 1985. pap. text ed. 18.95 (ISBN 0-943396-07-7). Willmann-Bell.

Mayall, R. N. & Mayall, M. W. Skyshooting: Photography for Amateur Astronomers. (Illus.). 13.25 (ISBN 0-8446-2553-1). Peter Smith.

Mayall, Robert N. & Mayall, Margaret W. Skyshooting: Photography for Amateur Astronomers. rev. ed. pap. 4.00 (ISBN 0-486-21854-6). Dover.

ASTRONOMICAL PHOTOMETRY

see Photometry, Astronomical

ASTRONOMICAL PHYSICS

see Astrophysics

ASTRONOMICAL RESEARCH

An Account of a Geographical & Astronomical Expedition to the Northern Par ts of Russia. 420p. 1984. Repr. of 1802 ed. 42.00x (ISBN 0-85546-172-1, Pub. by Richmond Pub England). State Mutual Bk.

Bauman, Edward J. & Emsley, Zubin W., eds. Guidance & Control: 1983. LC 57-43769. (Advances in the Astronautical Sciences Ser.: Vol. 51). (Illus.). 494p. 1983. lib. bdg. 60.00x (ISBN 0-87703-182-7, Pub. by Am Astronaut); pap. text ed. 50.00x (ISBN 0-87703-183-5); fiche suppl. 6.00x. Univelt Inc.

Davidson, M. The Stars & the Mind: A Study of the Impact of Astronomical Development on Human Thought. 59.95 (ISBN 0-8490-1121-3). Gordon Pr.

Stephenson, F. Richard & Clark, David H. Applications of Early Astronomical Records. LC 78-10121. (Monographs on Astronomical Subjects). (Illus.). 1978. 19.95x (ISBN 0-19-520122-1). Oxford U Pr.

ASTRONOMICAL SPECTROSCOPY

Buscombe, William. MK Spectral Classifications-Fifth General Catalogue. LC 81-9555. 250p. (Orig.). 1981. pap. text ed. 10.00x (ISBN 0-939160-03-X). NWU Astro.

Gisler, Galen R. & Friel, Eileen D. Index of Galaxy Spectra. (Astronomy & Astrophysics Ser.: Vol. 10). 200p. 1979. 38.00x (ISBN 0-912918-19-5, 0919). Pachart Pub Hse.

Hunt, G. E. & Ballard, J., eds. Atmospheric Spectroscopy: Proceedings of the International Workshop SERC Rutherford Appleton Laboratory, Chilton, Didcot, Oxon, UK, 19-21 July 1983. (Illus.). 120p. 1985. 75.00 (ISBN 0-08-030278-5). Pergamon.

I.A.U. Symposium, No. 37, Rome, Italy, May 8-18, 1969. Non-Solar X-Gamma-Ray Astronomy: Proceedings. Gratton, L., ed. LC 73-83561. (I.A.U. Symposia). 425p. 1970. lib. bdg. 45.00 (ISBN 90-277-0160-1, Puub. by Reidel Holland). Kluwer Academic.

Meaburn, J. Detection & Spectrometry of Faint Light. (Astrophysics & Space Science Library: No. 56). 1976. PLB 47.50 (ISBN 90-277-0678-6, Pub. by Reidel Holland); pap. 14.95 (ISBN 90-277-1198-4, Pub. by Reidel Holland). Kluwer Academic.

ASTRONOMY

see also Almanacs; Astrometry; Astronautics in Astronomy; Astrophysics; Calendar; Chronology; Comets; Constellations; Cosmogony; Earth; Eclipses; Ephemerides; Geodesy; Infra-Red Astronomy; Life on Other Planets; Mechanics, Celestial; Meteorites; Meteors; Milky Way; Moon; Nautical Almanacs; Nautical Astronomy; Nebulae; Nutation; Orbits; Outer Space; Planets; Quasars; Radio Astronomy; Satellites; Seasons; Solar System; Space Environment; Space Sciences; Spectrum Analysis; Stars; Statistical Astronomy; Sun; Tides; Transits

Abell, George. Drama of the Universe. 1978. pap. text ed. 32.95 (ISBN 0-03-022401-2, CBS C); instr's manual 8.95 (ISBN 0-03-039231-4). SCP.

--Exploration of the Universe. 4th ed. 1982. text ed. 36.95 (ISBN 0-03-058502-3, CBS C); instr's manual 20.00 (ISBN 0-03-058503-1). SCP.

--Realm of the Universe. 3rd ed. 1984. pap. text ed. 28.95 (ISBN 0-03-058504-X, CBS C); instr's manual 10.95 (ISBN 0-03-058506-6). SCP.

Adams. Cosmic X-Ray Astronomy. 1980. 37.50 (ISBN 0-9960019-2-1, Pub. by A Hilger England). Heyden.

Alksne, Z. K. & Ikaunieks, Ya Y. Carbon Stars. rev. ed. Baumert, J. H., ed. (Astronomy & Astrophysics Ser.: Vol. 11). Orig. Title: Uglerodnye Zvezdy. (Illus.). 192p. pap. 24.00 (ISBN 0-912918-16-0, 0016). Pachart Pub Hse.

Andrew, Bryan H., ed. Interstellar Molecules. (International Astronomical Union Symposia: No. 87). 500p. 1980. PLB 76.50 (ISBN 90-277-1160-7, Pub. by Reidel Holland); pap. 34.00 (ISBN 90-277-1161-5, Pub. by Reidel Holland). Kluwer Academic.

Applications of Digital Image Processing to Astronomy: Proceedings. (SPIE Seminar Proceedings: Vol. 264). 314p. 35.00 (ISBN 0-89252-293-3); members 27.00 (ISBN 0-317-34594-X). SPIE.

Armstong, Ray. X-Ray Astronomy, Including a Catalogue & Bibliography of Galactic X-Ray Sources: Proceedings of the 21st Plenary Meeting, Innsbruck, Austria, 1978. Baity, W. A. & Peterson, L. E., eds. (Illus.). 1979. text ed. 69.00 (ISBN 0-08-023418-6). Pergamon.

Asimov, Isaac. The Collapsing Universe: The Story of Black Holes. LC 76-53639. (Illus.). 256p. 1977. 14.95 (ISBN 0-8027-0486-7). Walker & Co.

--Quasar, Quasar, Burning Bright. 1979. pap. 2.25 (ISBN 0-380-44610-3, 44610-3, Discus). Avon.

--The Universe: From Flat Earth to Quasar. 1976. pap. 3.95 (ISBN 0-380-01596-X, 62208-4, Discus). Avon.

Astronomy & Astrophysics for the 1980's: Reports of the Astronomy Survey Committee, 2 vols. 1983. Vol. I,1982 189pgs. 15.95 (ISBN 0-309-03249-0); Vol. II,1983 442pgs. pap. text ed. 25.00 (ISBN 0-309-03334-9). Natl Acad Pr.

Astronomy Survey Committee, National Research Council. Challenges to Astronomy & Astrophysics: Working Documents of the Astronomy Survey Committee. 296p. 1983. pap. text ed. 14.50 (ISBN 0-309-03335-7). Natl Acad Pr.

Athanassoula, E. Internal Kinematics & Dynamics of Galaxies. 1983. lib. bdg. 49.50 (ISBN 90-277-1546-7, Pub. by Reidel Holland). Kluwer Academic.

Atreya, S. K. & Caldwell, J. J., eds. Planetary Aeronomy & Astronomy. (Advances in Space Research Ser.: Vol. 1, No.9). (Illus.). 216p. 1981. pap. 31.00 (ISBN 0-08-028385-3). Pergamon.

Audouze, J., et al, eds. Diffuse Matter in Galaxies. 1983. lib. bdg. 39.50 (ISBN 90-277-1626-9, Pub. by Reidel Holland). Kluwer Academic.

Avensand, Anthony F., ed. Ethnoastronomy & Archaeoastronomy in the American Tropics, Vol. 385. 365p. 1982. 77.00x (ISBN 0-89766-160-5); pap. 77.00x (ISBN 0-89766-161-3). NY Acad Sci.

Baker, Bevan B. & Copson, E. T. The Mathematical Theory of Huygens Principle. 2nd ed. LC 50-8926. pap. 50.00 (ISBN 0-317-08620-0, 2051166). Bks Demand UMI.

Barlow, B. V. The Astronomical Telescope. (Wykeham Science Ser.: No. 31). 220p. 1975. pap. cancelled (ISBN 0-85109-440-6). Taylor & Francis.

Bartky, Walter. Highlights of Astronomy. (Illus.). 1961. pap. 2.95x (ISBN 0-226-03840-8, P509, Phoen). U of Chicago Pr.

Bash, Frank N. Astronomy. (Illus.). 1977. pap. text ed. 22.85 scp (ISBN 0-06-043853-3, HarpC). Har-Row.

Basov, N. G., ed. Techniques & Methods of Radio-Astronomic Reception. LC 78-26720. (P. N. Lebedev Physics Institutes Ser.: Vol. 93). (Illus.). 156p. 1979. 59.50x (ISBN 0-306-10955-7, Consultants). Plenum Pub.

Bath, Geoffrey, ed. The State of the Universe. (Illus.). 1980. 27.50x (ISBN 0-19-857549-1). Oxford U Pr.

Beckman, J. E. & Phillips, J. P. Submillimetre Wave Astronomy. LC 82-4487. (Illus.). 370p. 1982. 52.50 (ISBN 0-521-24733-0). Cambridge U Pr.

Beer, P. & Beer, A. Vistas in Astronomy, Vol. 23 Complete. 1980. 125.00 (ISBN 0-08-026046-2). Pergamon.

Beer, P., ed. Vistas in Astronomy, Vol. 26. (Illus.). 426p. 1985. 162.00 (ISBN 0-08-032314-6). Pergamon.

Beer, P. & Pounds, K., eds. Vistas in Astronomy, Vol. 25. (Illus.). 436p. 1983. 144.00 (ISBN 0-08-031042-7). Pergamon.

Berendzen. Man Discovers the Galaxies. 1976. 15.95 (ISBN 0-07-004845-2). McGraw.

Berg, Rebecca M. & Frederick, Lawrence W. Descriptive Astronomy. LC 77-89365. 336p. (Orig.). pap. 19.95 (ISBN 0-442-25472-5). Krieger.

Berman, Louis & Evans, John C. Exploring the Cosmos. 4th. ed. 1983. 28.95 (ISBN 0-316-09184-7); teacher's manual avail. (ISBN 0-316-09187-1). Little.

Best, Elsdon. The Astronomical Knowledge of the Maori, Genuine & Empirical. Bd. with The Maori Division of Time. LC 75-35226. Repr. of 1922 ed. 12.50 (ISBN 0-404-14405-5). AMS Pr.

Boehme, S., ed. Astronomy & Astrophysics Abstracts: Literature, Vol. 32; 1982, Pt. 2. 848p. 1983. 72.00 (ISBN 0-387-12516-7). Springer-Verlag.

--Astronomy & Astrophysics Abstracts, Vol. 29: Literature 1981, Pt. 1. 853p. 1981. 65.00 (ISBN 0-387-11264-2). Springer-Verlag.

--Astronomy & Astrophysics Abstracts, Vol. 3: Literature 1970, Pt. 1. x, 490p. 1970. 50.20 (ISBN 0-387-05314-X). Springer-Verlag.

--Astronomy & Astrophysics Abstracts, Vol. 4: Literature 1970, Pt. 2. x, 562p. 1971. 50.20 (ISBN 0-387-05514-2). Springer-Verlag.

--Astronomy & Astrophysics Abstracts, Vol. 5: Literature 1971, Pt. 1. x, 505p. 1971. 50.20 (ISBN 0-387-05701-3). Springer-Verlag.

--Astronomy & Astrophysics Abstracts, Vol. 6: Literature 1971, Pt. 2. x, 560p. 1972. 50.20 (ISBN 0-387-05888-5). Springer-Verlag.

Boehme, S., et al, eds. Astronmomy & Astrophysics Abstracts, Vol. 25: Literature 1979, Pt. 1. x, 871p. 1979. 82.00 (ISBN 0-387-09831-3). Springer-Verlag.

--Astronomy & Abstrophysics Abstracts, Vol. 9: Literature 1973, Pt. 1. vii, 610p. 1973. 50.20 (ISBN 0-387-06560-1). Springer-Verlag.

--Astronomy & Astrophysics Abstacts, Vol. 1: Literature 1969, Part 1. vii, 435p. 1969. 50.20 (ISBN 0-387-04421-3). Springer-Verlag.

--Astronomy & Astrophysics Abstracts: Vol. 23-24. 1127p. 1979. 77.00 (ISBN 0-387-09830-5). Springer-Verlag.

--Astronomy & Astrophysics Abstracts: Literature 1979, Pt. 2, Vol. 26. 794p. 1980. 80.00 (ISBN 0-387-10134-9). Springer-Verlag.

--Astronomy & Astrophysics Abstracts, Vol. 10: Literature 1973, Pt. 2. viii, 661p. 1974. 50.80 (ISBN 0-387-06795-7). Springer-Verlag.

--Astronomy & Astrophysics Abstracts, Vol. 11: Literature 1974, Pt. 1. viii, 579p. 1975. 54.00 (ISBN 0-387-07003-6). Springer-Verlag.

--Astronomy & Astrophysics Abstracts, Vol. 12: Literature 1974. Pt. 2. viii, 699p. 1975. 58.00 (ISBN 0-387-07339-6). Springer-Verlag.

--Astronomy & Astrophysics Abstracts, Vol. 13: Literature 1975, Pt. 1. viii, 632p. 1975. 51.00 (ISBN 0-387-07492-9). Springer-Verlag.

--Astronomy & Astrophysics Abstracts, Vol. 14: Literature 1975, Pt. 2. viii, 747p. 1976. 58.00 (ISBN 0-387-07784-7). Springer-Verlag.

--Astronomy & Astrophysics Abstracts, Vol. 18: Literature 1976, Pt. 2. x, 859p. 1977. 58.00 (ISBN 0-387-08319-7). Springer-Verlag.

--Astronomy & Astrophysics Abstracts, Vol. 19: Literature 1977, Pt. 1. viii, 732p. 1977. 66.00 (ISBN 0-387-08555-6). Springer-Verlag.

--Astronomy & Astrophysics Abstracts, Vol. 15-16: Author & Subject Indexes to Volumes 1-10, Literature 1969-1973. v, 655p. 1976. 58.00 (ISBN 0-387-07905-X). Springer-Verlag.

Boehme, S, et al, eds. Astronomy & Astrophysics Abstracts, Vol. 27: Literature 1980, Pt. 1. 939p. 1980. 80.00 (ISBN 0-387-10479-8). Springer-Verlag.

Boehme, S., et al, eds. Astronomy & Astrophysics Abstracts, Vol. 2: Literature 1969, Pt. 2. x, 516p. 1970. 50.20 (ISBN 0-387-04773-5). Springer-Verlag.

--Astronomy & Astrophysics Abstracts, Vol. 21: Literature 1978, Pt. 1. viii, 834p. 1978. 65.00 (ISBN 0-387-09067-3). Springer-Verlag.

--Astronomy & Astrophysics Abstracts, Vol. 22: Literature 1978, Pt. 2. viii, 849p. 1979. 60.00 (ISBN 0-387-09464-4). Springer-Verlag.

--Astronomy & Astrophysics Abstracts, Vol. 28: Literature 1980, Pt. 2. 841p. 1981. 70.00 (ISBN 0-387-10799-1). Springer-Verlag.

--Astronomy & Astrophysics Abstracts, Vol. 30: Literature, 1981. 792p. 1982. 72.00 (ISBN 0-387-11721-0). Springer-Verlag.

--Astronomy & Astrophysics Abstracts, Vol. 7: Literature 1972, Pt. 1. E. x, 526p. 1972. 50.20 (ISBN 0-387-06072-3). Springer-Verlag.

--Astronomy & Astrophysics Abstracts, Vol. 8: Literature 1972, Pt. 2. x, 594p. 1973. 50.20 (ISBN 0-387-06352-8). Springer-Verlag.

--Literature Nineteen Seventy Eight, Part 1. (Astronomy & Astrophysics Abstracts Ser.: Vol. 21). 1978. 65.00 (ISBN 0-387-09067-3). Springer-Verlag.

Bohme, S., et al, eds. Astronomy & Astrophysics Abstracts, Vol. 37. Schmadel, L. D., tr. (Literature 1984: Pt. 1). 920p. 1984. 68.50 (ISBN 0-387-13937-0). Springer-Verlag.

Bok, Bart J. & Bok, Priscilla F. The Milky Way. 5th ed. LC 80-22544. (Harvard Books on Astronomy Ser.). (Illus.). 384p. 1981. text ed. 25.00 (ISBN 0-674-57503-2). Harvard U Pr.

Bonneau, B. Lee & Smith, Billy A. Astronomy Illustrated. 3rd ed. 1980. wire coil bdg. 15.95 (ISBN 0-8403-2168-6). Kendall Hunt.

Boslough, John. Stephen Hawking's Universe. LC 84-4673. (Illus.). 160p. 1984. 12.95 (ISBN 0-688-03530-2). Morrow.

Brandt, John C. & Maran, Stephen P. New Horizons in Astronomy. 2nd ed. LC 78-11717. (Illus.). 614p. 1979. text ed. 25.95 (ISBN 0-7167-1043-9). W H Freeman.

Branley, F., et al. Astronomy. 1975. text ed. 21.95 scp (ISBN 0-690-00760-4, HarpC). Har-Row.

A Brief Introduction to Astronomy. rev. ed. 20p. Set. 2.00 (ISBN 0-318-17838-9). Astron Soc Pacific.

British Astronomical Association. Guide to Observing the Moon. LC 83-1610. (Illus.). 128p. 1985. pap. text ed. 11.95x (ISBN 0-89490-085-4). Enslow Pubs.

Brown, Hanbury. Man & the Stars. (Illus.). 1978. 22.50x (ISBN 0-19-851001-2). Oxford U Pr.

Bruck, H. A. The Story of Astronomy in Education: From Its Beginnings until 1975. 151p. 1984. 18.50 (ISBN 0-85224-480-0, Pub. by Edinburgh Pr Scotland). Columbia U Pr.

Bullinger, Ethelbert W. Witness of the Stars. LC 68-16762. 1972. 12.95 (ISBN 0-8254-2209-4). Kregel.

Burnham, Robert, Jr. Burnham's Celestial Handbook: An Observer's Guide to the Universe Beyond the Solar System, Vols. 1 & 2. LC 77-82888. (Illus.). 1978. pap. 9.95. Vol. 1 (ISBN 0-486-23567-X). Vol. 2. pap. 10.95 (ISBN 0-486-23568-8). Dover.

Buscombe, William. MK Spectral Classifications: Sixth General Catalogue. LC 81-9555. 310p. (Orig.). 1984. pap. 20.00x (ISBN 0-939160-04-8). NWU Astro.

Calder, Nigel. Violent Universe: An Eyewitness Account of the New Astronomy. LC 73-83246. (Illus.). 1970. 14.95 (ISBN 0-670-74720-3). Viking.

Campbell-Jones, Simon, ed. At the Edge of the Universe. LC 83-6680. (Illus.). 172p. 1983. 9.95x (ISBN 0-87663-433-1). Universe.

Capt, E. Raymond. The Glory of the Stars. LC 79-116390. (Illus.). 144p. (Orig.). 1976. pap. 5.00 (ISBN 0-934666-02-4). Artisan Sales.

Chapman, Clark R. & Cruikshank, Dale P., eds. Observing the Moon, Planets, & Comets, 2 vols. LC 83-11556. (Orig.). 1985. Set. pap. text ed. 46.00 (ISBN 0-89490-098-6). Enslow Pubs.

Chapman, Robert D. Discovering Astronomy. LC 77-16024. (Illus.). 518p. 1978. text ed. 34.95 (ISBN 0-7167-0034-4); pap. text ed. 20.95 (ISBN 0-7167-0033-6); instructors' guide avail. W H Freeman.

Cherrington, Ernest H. Exploring the Moon Through Binoculars & Small Telescopes. (Illus.). 224p. 1983. pap. 10.95 (ISBN 0-486-24491-1). Dover.

Chriss, Michael & Brooks, Judith K. Astronomy One Hundred: A Handbook. LC 79-92143. 250p. (Orig.). 1980. pap. text ed. 11.20 (ISBN 0-936064-00-5). Perspicilli Pr.

Christiansen, Wayne & Kaitchuck, Ron. Investigations in Observational Astronomy. 1978. coil bdg. 9.95 (ISBN 0-88252-054-7). Paladin Hse.

Christianson, Gale E. This Wild Abyss: The Story of the Men Who Made Modern Astronomy. LC 77-81428. (Illus.). 1979. pap. text ed. 9.95 (ISBN 0-02-905660-8). Free Pr.

--This Wild Abyss: The Story of the Men Who Made Modern Astronomy. LC 77-81428. (Illus.). 1978. 14.95 (ISBN 0-02-905380-3). Free Pr.

Clark, Cumberland. Astronomy in the Poets. LC 72-191653. lib. bdg. 17.50 (ISBN 0-8414-3038-1). Folcroft.

Clark, David. The Quest for SS433. 224p. 1985. 15.95 (ISBN 0-670-80388-X). Viking.

Cooke, Donald A. Life & Death of Stars. LC 84-4266. 228p. 1985. 29.95 (ISBN 0-517-55268-X). Crown.

Cornell, James & Carr, John, eds. Infinite Vistas: How the Space Telescope & Other Advances Are Revolutionizing Our Knowledge of the Universe. 256p. 1985. 18.95 (ISBN 0-684-18287-4, ScribT). Scribner.

Cornell, James & Gorenstein, Paul, eds. Astronomy from Space: Sputnik to Space Telescope. 264p. 1985. pap. 8.95 (ISBN 0-262-53061-9). MIT Pr.

Cornell, James & Lightman, Alan P., eds. Revealing the Universe: Prediction & Proof in Astronomy. (Illus.). 264p. 1981. pap. text ed. 8.95 (ISBN 0-262-53043-0). MIT Pr.

Culver, Roger B. Astronomy. (Illus.). 1979. pap. 4.95 (ISBN 0-06-460158-7, CO 158, COS). B&N NY.

Lombardo, Stanley, tr. Sky Signs: Aratus' Phaenomena. 100p. 1983. 20.00 (ISBN 0-938190-15-6); pap. 7.95 (ISBN 0-938190-16-4). North Atlantic.

Long, Charles E. Discovering the Universe. 1980. pap. text ed. 21.50 scp (ISBN 0-06-044034-1, HarpC); instr's. manual avail. (ISBN 0-06-364038-4). Har-Row.

Longo, Guiseppe & De Vaucouleurs, Antoinette. A General Catalogue of Photoelectric Magnitudes & Colors in the UBV System of 3,578 Galaxies Brighter than the 16th V-Magnitude 1936-1982. LC 83-50257. (Monographs in Astronomy Ser.). 214p. (Orig.). 1983. pap. 12.00 (ISBN 0-9603796-2-2). U of Tex Dept Astron.

Loomis, Elias. The Recent Progress of Astronomy: Especially in the United States. Cohen, I. Bernard, ed. LC 79-7972. (Three Centuries of Science in America Ser.). 1980. Repr. of 1851 ed. lib. bdg. 21.00x (ISBN 0-405-12554-2). Ayer Co Pubs.

Lovell, B. Astronomy, 2 vols. (Royal Institution Library of Science). (Illus.). 813p. 1970. 70.50 (ISBN 0-444-20102-5, Pub. by Elsevier Applied Sci England). Elsevier.

McElroy, John H., et al, eds. Space Science & Applications. 275p. 1985. write for info. (ISBN 0-87942-195-9). Inst Electrical.

McGraw-Hill Editors. Encyclopedia of Astronomy. 464p. 1983. 54.50 (ISBN 0-07-045251-2). McGraw.

MacMillan, W. D., et al. The World Mechanism. 1979. Repr. of 1929 ed. lib. bdg. 20.00 (ISBN 0-8482-1738-1). Norwood Edns.

Maffei, Paolo. Beyond the Moon. 1980. pap. 7.95 (ISBN 0-380-48744-6, 48744-6). Avon.

--Monsters in the Sky. 352p. 1981. pap. 8.95 (ISBN 0-380-55517-4, 55517-4). Avon.

--Monsters in the Sky. (Illus.). 1980. 27.50x (ISBN 0-262-13153-6). MIT Pr.

Mallas, John H. & Kreimer, E. The Messier Album. LC 79-16714. (Illus.). 1979. 16.95 (ISBN 0-521-23015-2). Cambridge U Pr.

Manilius. Astronomica. (Loeb Classical Library: No. 469). 1980. text ed. 12.00x (ISBN 0-674-99516-3). Harvard U Pr.

Mariolopoulos, E. Compendium in Astronomy. 1982. 49.50 (ISBN 90-277-1373-1, Pub. by Reidel Holland). Kluwer Academic.

Massey, H. S., et al, eds. Gamma-Ray Astronomy. (Royal Society of London Ser.). (Illus.). 211p. 1981. 62.00x (ISBN 0-85403-170-7, Pub. by Royal Soc London). Scholium Intl.

Mehlin, Theodore G. & Schweighauser, Charles A. Astronomy & the Origin of the Earth. 3rd ed. 150p. 1979. pap. text ed. write for info. (ISBN 0-697-05018-1). Wm C Brown.

Messel, H. & Butler, S. T. Focus on the Stars. 287p. 1978. 19.50x (ISBN 0-8448-1299-4). Crane-Russak Co.

Mihalas, Dimitri M. & Binney, James J. Galactic Astronomy: Structure & Kinematics. 2nd ed. LC 81-1612. (Illus.). 597p. 1981. text ed. 38.95x (ISBN 0-7167-1280-6). W H Freeman.

Milton, Simon. Cambridge Encyclopedia of Astronomy. 1977. 35.00 (ISBN 0-13-112722-5). P-H.

MIT Students' System Project. Project Icarus. rev. ed. Li, Yao T. & Sandorf, Paul, eds. 1979. pap. 4.95x (ISBN 0-262-63068-0). MIT Pr.

Mitchel, Ormsby M. The Planetary & Stellar Worlds: A Popular Exposition of the Great Discoveries & Theories of Modern Astronomy. Cohen, I. Bernard, ed. LC 79-7976. (Three Centuries of Science in America Ser.). (Illus.). 1980. Repr. of 1848 ed. lib. bdg. 23.00x (ISBN 0-405-12559-3). Ayer Co Pubs.

Mitra, A. P. Ionospheric Effects of Solar Flares. LC 74-76480. (Astrophysics & Space Science Library: No. 46). 200p. 1974. lib. bdg. 50.00 (ISBN 90-277-0467-8, Pub. by Reidel Holland). Kluwer Academic.

Mitton, J. & Mitton, S. Concise Book of Astronomy. 1979. 12.95x (ISBN 0-13-166967-2). P-H.

Moche, Dinah L. Astronomy: A Self-Teaching Guide. 2nd ed. LC 81-10470. (Self-Teaching Guide Ser.). 284p. 1981. pap. text ed. 9.95 (ISBN 0-471-09713-6, Pub. by wiley Pr). Wiley.

Moore, Patrick. Amateur Astronomy. rev. ed. Orig. Title: Amateur Astronomer. (Illus.). 1968. 12.95 (ISBN 0-393-06362-3). Norton.

--The Moon. Hunt, Garry, ed. (Rand McNally Library of Astronomical Atlases for Amateur & Professional Photographers). (Illus.). 96p. 1981. 16.95 (ISBN 0-528-81541-5). Rand.

--Patrick Moore's Armchair Astronomy. (Illus.). 1986. 16.95 (ISBN 0-393-02253-6). Norton.

--Pocket Guide to Astronomy. 1980. pap. 7.95 (ISBN 0-671-25309-3, 25309). S&S.

--Suns, Myths & Men. rev. ed. LC 68-27145. (Illus.). 1969. 7.95 (ISBN 0-393-06364-X). Norton.

Moore, Patrick, ed. Modern Astronomy. (Illus.). 1977. 11.95 (ISBN 0-393-06417-4). Norton.

--Yearbook of Astronomy 1970. rev. ed. 1970. 4.95 (ISBN 0-393-06375-5). Norton.

--Yearbook of Astronomy 1975. (Illus.). 1975. 8.95 (ISBN 0-393-06401-8). Norton.

--Yearbook of Astronomy 1977. (Illus.). 1977. 9.95 (ISBN 0-393-06412-3). Norton.

--Yearbook of Astronomy, 1980. (Illus.). 1980. 12.95 (ISBN 0-393-01318-9). Norton.

--Yearbook of Astronomy, 1981. (Illus.). 1981. 14.95 (ISBN 0-393-01415-0). Norton.

--Yearbook of Astronomy, 1982. (Illus.). 1982. 15.95 (ISBN 0-393-01492-4). Norton.

Morfill, G. E. & Buccheri, R., eds. Galactic Astrophysics & Gamma Ray Astronomy. 1983. lib. bdg. 60.00 (ISBN 90-277-1645-5, Pub. by Reidel Holland). Kluwer Academic.

Morgenthaler, George W. & Greyber, Howard D., eds. Astronomy from a Space Platform. (Science & Technology Ser.: Vol. 28). 1972. lib. bdg. 35.00x (ISBN 0-87703-061-8, Am Astronaut). Univelt Inc.

Motz, Lloyd. This Is Astronomy. LC 56-12016. (Illus.). 279p. (Orig.). 1958. pap. 12.00x (ISBN 0-231-08549-4). Columbia U Pr.

Motz, Lloyd & Duveen, Anneta. Essentials of Astronomy. 2nd ed. LC 76-19068. 763p. 1977. 29.00x (ISBN 0-231-04009-1). Columbia U Pr.

Muirden, James. The Amateur Astronomer's Handbook. 3rd ed. LC 81-48044. (Illus.). 480p. 1982. 19.18 (ISBN 0-06-181622-1, HarpT). Har-Row.

--Astronomy with a Small Telescope. 1985. 16.95 (ISBN 0-13-049941-2). P-H.

--Astronomy with Binoculars. LC 83-7099. (Illus.). 192p. 1983. pap. 7.95 (ISBN 0-668-05832-3, 5832-3). Arco.

Mulfinger, George, ed. Design & Origins in Astronomy. (Creation Research Society Monograph: No. 2). (Illus.). 152p. (Orig.). 1984. pap. 7.95 (ISBN 0-940384-03-5). Creation Res.

Muller, Edith A., ed. Highlights of Astronomy, 2 pts, Vol. 4. 1977. Pt. 1. lib. bdg. 45.00 (ISBN 90-277-0849-5, Pub. by Reidel Holland); Pt. 2. lib. bdg. 50.00 (ISBN 90-277-0850-9); Pt. 1. pap. 29.00 (ISBN 90-277-0830-4); Pt. 2. pap. 33.00 (ISBN 90-277-0832-0). Kluwer Academic.

--Reports on Astronomy, 3 pts. (Transactions of the International Astronomical Union Ser.: Vol. XVII A). 1979. lib. bdg. 29.50 ea. (Pub. by Reidel Holland); Pt. 1. (ISBN 90-277-1005-8). Pt. 2. (ISBN 90-277-1006-6); Pt. 3. (ISBN 90-277-1007-4). Kluwer Academic.

Murdin, Paul & Murdin, Lesley. The New Astronomy. LC 77-5788. (Illus.). 1978. 12.95i (ISBN 0-690-01474-0). T Y Crowell.

Murray, C. A. Vectorial Astrometry. 1983. 49.00 (ISBN 0-9960025-3-7, Pub. by A Hilger England). Heyden.

Narlikar, Jayant V. The Structure of the Universe. (Illus.). 1977. pap. 9.95x (ISBN 0-19-289082-4, OPUS 77). Oxford U Pr.

NATO Advanced Study Institute in Dynamical Astronomy, Cortina d'ampezzo, Aug., 1972. Recent Advances in Dynamical Astronomy: Proceedings. Tapley, B. D. & Szebehely, V., eds. LC 73-83571. (Astrophysics & Space Science Library: No. 39). 490p. 1973. lib. bdg. 71.00 (ISBN 90-277-0348-5, Pub. by Reidel Holland). Kluwer Academic.

Norman, Ernest L. Tempus Interludium, Vol. 2. Norman, Ruth E., ed. 251p. 1982. 8.95 (ISBN 0-932642-48-9). Unarius.

Norman, Ruth E. Return to Atlantis, Vol. 3, Pt. 2. (Illus.). 300p. (Orig.). 1982. pap. text ed. 6.95 (ISBN 0-932642-74-8). Unarius.

Nowell, Eppler. Sky Scanner. 2nd ed. (Illus.). 17p. (Orig.). 1980. pap. text ed. 4.95x (ISBN 0-9611454-0-4). E Nowell.

Oster, Ludwig. Modern Astronomy. LC 72-83247. 500p. 1973. text ed. 22.50x (ISBN 0-8162-6523-2). Holden-Day.

Ottewell, Guy. Astronomical Calender, 1985. 1984. pap. 10.00 huge atla-size bk. (ISBN 0-934546-13-4). Astron Cal.

--Astronomical Companion. (Illus.). 1979. pap. 12.00 (ISBN 0-934546-01-0). Astron Cal.

Pananides, Nicholas A. & Arny, Thomas. Introductory Astronomy. 2nd ed. LC 78-55825. (Physics Ser.). (Illus.). 1979. text ed. 31.95 (ISBN 0-201-05674-7). Addison-Wesley.

Panorama de la Astronomia Moderna. rev. ed. (Serie de Fisica: No. 2). (Span.). 1976. pap. 3.50 (ISBN 0-8270-6150-1). OAS.

Papon, Donald. The Lure of the Heavens: A History of Astrology. (Illus.). 320p. 1980. pap. 7.95 (ISBN 0-87728-502-0). Weiser.

Parker, Barry. Concepts of the Cosmos: An Introduction to Astronomy. 516p. 1984. text ed. 30.95 (ISBN 0-15-512850-7, HC); study guide 8.95 (ISBN 0-15-512851-5); instr's manual avail. (ISBN 0-15-512852-3). HarBraceJ.

Parnov, E. I. At the Crossroads of Infinities. Talmy, Vladimir, tr. from Rus. 397p. 1971. 14.95x (ISBN 0-8464-0159-2). Beekman Pubs.

Pasachoff, Jay M. Astronomy: From the Earth to the Universe. 2nd ed. 1983. pap. text ed. 28.95 (ISBN 0-03-058419-1, CBS C). SCP.

--Astronomy Now. 1978. pap. text ed. 32.95 (ISBN 0-7216-7100-4, CBS C); instr's manual 7.95 (ISBN 0-03-057251-7). SCP.

Payne, George. Naked Eye Astronomy. 1980. lab manual 5.50 (ISBN 0-88252-102-0). Paladin Hse.

--Solar System Astronomy. 1980. text ed. 9.95 wire coil bdg. (ISBN 0-88252-103-9). Paladin Hse.

Philip, A. Davis, ed. The HR Diagram: The 100th. (Symposium of the International Astronomical Union: No. 80). 1978. lib. bdg. 58.00 (ISBN 90-277-0905-X, Pub. by Reidel Holland); pap. 37.00 (ISBN 90-277-0906-8). Kluwer Academic.

Pierce, David. Learning Exercises in Astronomy. (Illus.). 1978. pap. text ed. 10.95 (ISBN 0-03-044351-2, HoltC). HR&W.

Polish Academy of Science. Poetic Potentials in Information of Astronomy. 1976. pap. 1.95 (ISBN 0-934982-05-8). Primary Pr.

Price, Derek J. The Equatorie of the Planets. 214p. 1984. Repr. of 1955 ed. lib. bdg. 85.00 (ISBN 0-89987-696-X). Darby Bks.

Protheroe, et al. Exploring the Universe. 544p. 1984. Additional supplements may be obtained from publisher. text ed. 29.95 (ISBN 0-675-20145-4). Merrill.

Raine. Isotropic Universe. 1981. 49.00 (ISBN 0-9960020-8-1, Pub. by Inst Physics England). Heyden.

Raymo, Chet. The Soul of the Night: An Astronomical Pilgrimage. (Illus.). 223p. 1985. 15.95 (ISBN 0-13-822883-3). P-H.

Rees, M. & Stoneham, R. Supernovae: A Survey of Current Research. 1982. 69.00 (ISBN 90-277-1442-8, Pub. by Reidel Holland). Kluwer Academic.

Reports on Astronomy. Transactions of the International Astronomical Union, Vol. 13a. Perek, L., ed. 1047p. 1968. lib. bdg. 66.00 (ISBN 90-277-0138-5, Pub. by Reidel Holland). Kluwer Academic.

Riban, David M. Introduction to Physical Science. (Illus.). 656p. 1981. text ed. 32.95 (ISBN 0-07-052140-9). McGraw.

Robbins, R. Robert & Hemenway, Mary K. Modern Astronomy: An Activities Approach. (Illus.). 290p. 1982. pap. text ed. 20.00 (ISBN 0-292-75064-1). U of Tex Pr.

Roberts, Morton S., ed. Astronomy & Astrophysics. 1985. text ed. price not set (ISBN 0-87168-311-3); pap. text ed. write for info. (ISBN 0-87168-275-3). AAAS.

Robinson, J. Hedley & Muirden, James. Astronomy Data Book. 2nd ed. LC 78-21698. 272p. 1979. 34.95x (ISBN 0-470-26594-9). Halsted Pr.

Rogers, Eric M. Astronomy for the Inquiring Mind: The Growth & Use of Theory in Science. rev. ed. LC 81-47286. (Illus.). 1981. pap. 8.95x (ISBN 0-691-02370-0). Princeton U Pr.

Ronan, Colin. Deep Space: A Guide to the Cosmos. LC 82-9966. 208p. 1982. 25.95 (ISBN 0-02-604510-9). Macmillan.

--The Practical Astronomer. (Illus.). 153p. 1981. 20.00 (ISBN 0-02-604500-1). Macmillan.

Ronan, Colin & Dunlop, Storm. The Golden Book of Astronomy. (Illus.). 256p. 1984. 19.95 (ISBN 0-307-46649-3, Golden Pr). Western Pub.

Rossano, G. S. & Craine, E. R. Near Infrared Photographic Sky Survey: A Field Index. (Astronomy & Astrophysics Ser.: Vol. 8). (Illus.). 208p. 1980. 38.00x (ISBN 0-912918-11-X, 0911). Pachart Pub Hse.

Roth, G. D., ed. Astronomy: A Handbook. Beer, A., tr. from Ger. LC 74-11408. (Illus.). 1975. 33.00 (ISBN 0-387-06503-2). Springer-Verlag.

Roy, A. E. & Clarke, D. Astronomy: Principles & Practice. LC 76-51875. 248p. 1977. 34.50x (ISBN 0-8448-1071-1). Crane-Russak Co.

--Astronomy: Principles & Practice. 2nd ed. 1982. 44.00 (ISBN 0-9960024-6-4, Pub. by A Hilger England); pap. 19.50 (ISBN 0-9960024-7-2). Heyden.

--Astronomy: Structure of the Universe. 2nd ed. 1982. 44.00 (ISBN 0-9960024-8-0, Pub. by A Hilger England); pap. 19.50 (ISBN 0-9960024-9-9). Heyden.

Roy, Archie E. & Clarke, David. Astronomy: The Structure of the Universe. LC 76-51877. 342p. 1977. pap. 25.50x (ISBN 0-8448-1074-6). Crane-Russak Co.

Russell, C. T., ed. Auroral Process: Advances in Earth & Planetary Science, No. 4. 1979. 32.50x (ISBN 0-89955-128-9, Pub. by Japan Sci Soc Japan). Intl Spec Bk.

Sanford, Peter W., et al, eds. Geolactoc X-Ray Sources. LC 82-2031. 245p. 1982. 52.95x (ISBN 0-471-27963-3, Pub. by Wiley-Interscience). Wiley.

Schaaf, Fred. Wonders of the Sky. 1984. 16.00 (ISBN 0-8446-6099-X). Peter Smith.

Schaifers, K. & Voigt, H. H., eds. Astronomy & Astrophysics: Interstellar Matter, Galaxy, Universe. (Landolt-Boernstein, New Series. Group VI: Vol. 2, Subvol. C). (Illus.). 490p. 1982. 310.90 (ISBN 0-387-10977-3). Springer-Verlag.

Schatzman, Evry. Astronomie. (Methodique Ser.). 1860p. write for info. French & Eur.

Schiaparelli, G. V. Le Opere Publicate per Cura Della Reale Specola Di Brera, Vols. 1-11. (Sources of Science Ser). (It). Repr. of 1930 ed. Set. 440.00 (ISBN 0-384-53780-4). Johnson Repr.

Searls, Robert & Martin, Kaye. Visible Universe: A Student Course. 160p. 1981. pap. text ed. 8.95 (ISBN 0-8403-2464-2). Kendall-Hunt.

Seeds, Michael. Foundations of Astronomy. 608p. 1984. text ed. write for info. (ISBN 0-534-02953-1). Wadsworth Pub.

Seeds, Michael, ed. Astronomy: Selected Readings. 1980. pap. 18.95 (ISBN 0-8053-8531-2). Benjamin-Cummings.

Sersic, J. L. Extragalactic Astronomy: Lecture Notes from Cordoba. viii, 241p. 1982. 49.50 (ISBN 90-277-1321-9, Pub. by Reidel Holland). Kluwer Academic.

Shapiro, Maurice M., ed. Composition & Origin of Cosmic Rays. 1983. lib. bdg. 58.50 (ISBN 90-2771-609-9, Pub. by Reidel Holland). Kluwer Academic.

Shipman, Harry L. The Restless Universe: An Introduction to Astronomy. LC 77-78584. (Illus.). 1978. text ed. 32.50 (ISBN 0-395-25392-6); instr's. manual 0.50 (ISBN 0-395-25393-4). HM.

Shuter, W. L. Kinematics, Dynamics & Structure of the Milky Way. 1983. lib. bdg. 54.50 (ISBN 90-277-1540-8, Pub. by Reidel Holland). Kluwer Academic.

Sidgwick, J. B. Amateur Astronomer's Handbook. (Illus.). 576p. 1981. pap. 7.95 (ISBN 0-486-24034-7). Dover.

--Observational Astronomy for Amateurs. 4th ed. LC 82-1499. (Illus.). 358p. 1982. text ed. 19.95x (ISBN 0-89490-067-6); pap. 7.95 (ISBN 0-89490-068-4). Enslow Pubs.

Silk, Joseph. The Big Bang: The Creation & Evolution of the Universe. LC 79-19340. (Illus.). 394p. 1980. pap. text ed. 11.95x (ISBN 0-7167-1085-4). W H Freeman.

Skobel'tsyn, D. V., ed. Stellarators. LC 74-31314. (P. N. Lebedev Physics Institute Ser.: Vol. 65). (Illus.). 132p. 1974. 55.00 (ISBN 0-306-10908-5, Consultants). Plenum Pub.

Smart, William M. Foundations of Astronomy. LC 42-3618. pap. 69.00 (ISBN 0-317-07807-0, 2003655). Bks Demand UMI.

Smith, A. Smith's Illustrated Astronomy. (Illus.). 79p. 1984. pap. text ed. 25.00 (ISBN 0-87556-396-1). Saifer.

Smith, Elske P. & Jacobs, Kenneth C. Introductory Astronomy & Astrophysics. LC 72-88853. (Illus.). 480p. 1973. text ed. 36.95 (ISBN 0-7216-8387-8). HR&W.

Snow, Theodore P., Jr. The Dynamic Universe: An Introduction to Astronomy. 2nd ed. (Illus.). 550p. 1985. text ed. 32.95 (ISBN 0-314-88512-9). West Pub.

--The Essentials of the Dynamic Universe: An Introduction. (Illus.). 490p. 1984. pap. text ed. 27.95 (ISBN 0-314-77798-9); write for info. transparencies (ISBN 0-314-80350-5); instrs.' manual & test bank avail. (ISBN 0-314-77799-7); study guide 9.95 (ISBN 0-314-77800-4). West Pub.

Snyder, George S. Maps of the Heavens. LC 84-6478. (Illus.). 148p. 1984. 45.00 (ISBN 0-89659-456-4). Abbeville Pr.

Starbird, William & Oriti, Ronald. Introduction to Astronomy. 1977. text ed. write for info. (ISBN 0-02-478560-1). Macmillan.

Sulentic, Jack W. & Tifft, William G. The Revised New General Catalogue of Nonstellar Astronomical Objects. LC 73-83378. 384p. 1973. 35.00x (ISBN 0-8165-0421-0). U of Ariz Pr.

Sullivan & Sullivan. Programmed Astronomy: The Night Sky. 1972. pap. text ed. 9.00 (ISBN 0-8449-0504-6); tchrs' manual 4.00; test 3.00. Learning Line.

--Programmed Astronomy: The Solar System. 1972. pap. text ed. 9.00 (ISBN 0-8449-0500-3); tchrs' manual 4.00; test 3.00. Learning Line.

Suter, Heinrich. Die Mathematiker und Astronomen der Araber und Ihre Werke: Einschliesslich Nachtrage und Berichtungen. Repr. of 1900 ed. 30.00 (ISBN 0-384-58855-7). Johnson Repr.

Swihart, Thomas L. Basic Physics of Stellar Atmospheres. (Astronomy & Astrophysics Ser.: Vol. 1). 86p. 1971. 9.95 (ISBN 0-912918-04-7). Pachart Pub Hse.

--Journey Through the Universe: An Introduction to Astronomy. LC 77-76343. (Illus.). 1978. text ed. 32.50 (ISBN 0-395-25518-X); instr's. manual 0.50 (ISBN 0-395-25519-8). HM.

--Physics of Stellar Interiors. (Astronomy & Astrophysics Ser.: Vol. 2). 1972. 9.95 (ISBN 0-912918-05-5). Pachart Pub Hse.

Symposium No. 49 of the International Astronomical Union, Buenos Aires, Argentina. Aug. 1971. Wolf-Rayet & High Temperature Stars: Proceedings. Bappu, M. K. & Sahade, J, eds. LC 72-87470. 263p. 1973. lib. bdg. 45.00 (ISBN 90-277-0246-2, Pub. by Reidel Holland); pap. text ed. 31.50 (ISBN 90-277-0361-2). Kluwer Academic.

Symposium of the International Astronomical Union, No. 72. Abundance Effects in Classification: Proceedings. Hauck, B. & Keenan, P. C., eds. 1976. PLB 45.00 (ISBN 90-277-0674-3, Pub. by Reidel Holland); pap. 31.50 (ISBN 90-277-0675-1, Pub. by Reidel Holland). Kluwer Academic.

Taff, L. G. Celestial Mechanics: A Computational Guide for the Practitioner. 528p. 1985. 52.95 (ISBN 0-471-89316-1). Wiley.

Tatsch, J. H. The Moon: Its Past Development & Present Behavior. LC 73-88554. (Illus.). 338p. 1974. 20.00 (ISBN 0-912890-05-3). Tatsch.

Tattersfield, D. Projects & Demonstrations in Astronomy. LC 79-84264. 1979. 39.95x (ISBN 0-470-26715-1). Halsted Pr.

Tengstrom, Erik & Teleki, George, eds. Refractional Influences in Astrometry & Geodesy. (International Astronomical Union Symposium: No. 89). 1979. lib. bdg. 50.00 (ISBN 90-277-1037-6); pap. 26.50 (ISBN 90-277-1038-4, Pub. by Reidel Holland). Kluwer Academic.

Thacker, Jerrold. The Deceptive Universe. LC 82-71785. (Illus.). 224p. 1983. 15.95 (ISBN 0-9608568-0-3). Astro Pr Tx.

Tirion, Wil. Sky Atlas 2000.0: Twenty-Six Star Charts Covering Both Hemispheres. LC 81-52999. (Illus.). 26p. 1981. 39.50 (ISBN 0-521-24467-6). Cambridge U Pr.

Traister, Robert J. & Harris, Susan E. Astronomy & Telescopes: A Beginner's Handbook. (Illus.). 192p. 1983. o.p 19.95 (ISBN 0-8306-0419-7, 1419); pap. 14.95 (ISBN 0-8306-1419-2). TAB Bks.

Turner, H. H. Astronomical Discovery. (Illus.). 12.00 (ISBN 0-8446-3096-9). Peter Smith.

Verschuur, G. L. & Kellerman, K. I., eds. Galactic & Extra-Galactic Radio-Astronomy. LC 72-97680. (Illus.). 440p. 1974. 69.00 (ISBN 0-387-06504-0). Springer-Verlag.

Vincentius, Bellovacensis. Hier Begynneth the Table of the Rubrices of This Presente Volume Namde the Myrrour of the Worlde or Thymage of the Same. Caxton, William, tr. from Fr. LC 79-84143. (English Experience Ser.: No. 960). (Eng.). 204p. 1979. Repr. of 1481 ed. lib. bdg. 30.00 (ISBN 90-221-0960-7). Walter J Johnson.

Von Baravalle, Hermann. Astronomy: An Introduction. 1974. pap. 3.50 (ISBN 0-916786-08-0, Pub by Waldorf School Monographs). St George Bk Serv.

Ward, Charlotte R. This Blue Planet: Introduction to Physical Science. 417p. 1972. text ed. 24.95 (ISBN 0-316-92230-7); instuctor's Manual avail. (ISBN 0-316-92222-6). Little.

Warren, Henry W. Recreations in Astronomy. 1978. Repr. of 1879 ed. lib. bdg. 30.00 (ISBN 0-8492-2899-9). R West.

Waters, John C. Maintaining a Sense of Place: A Citizen's Guide to Community Preservation. LC 83-12810. 110p. (Orig.). 1983. pap. 6.50 (ISBN 0-911847-00-6). Inst Community.

Waxman, Gerald D. Introductory Astronomy. 1980. 25.95 (ISBN 0-88252-078-4). Paladin Hse.

Wayman, P. Reports on Astronomy. 1982. 67.50 (ISBN 90-277-1423-1, Pub. by Reidel Holland). Kluwer Academic.

Wayman, Patrick A., ed. Transactions of the International Astronomical Union, Vol. 17b. 536p. 1980. PLB 68.50 (ISBN 90-277-1159-3, Pub. by Reidel Holland). Kluwer Academic.

Whitcomb, John C. The Bible & Astronomy. 1984. pap. 2.25 (ISBN 0-88469-156-X). BMH Bks.

Wilhelm, Friedrich G. Etudes D'Astronomie Stellaire. Cohen, I. Bernard, ed. LC 80-2147. (Development of Science Ser.). (Illus.). 1981. Repr. of 1847 ed. lib. bdg. 15.00 (ISBN 0-405-13954-3). Ayer Co Pubs.

Worvill, Roy. Stars & Telescopes for the Beginner. LC 79-14034. (Illus.). 1980. 7.95 (ISBN 0-8008-4464-5). Taplinger.

Wyatt, Stanley P. Principles of Astronomy. 3rd ed. 1977. text ed. 31.52 (ISBN 0-205-05679-2, 7356794); answer bk. avail. (ISBN 0-205-05680-6). Allyn.

Zeilik, Michael. Astronomy: The Evolving Universe. 3rd ed. 623p. 1982. text ed. 16.95 scp (ISBN 0-06-047376-2, HarpC); scp study guide 4.50 (ISBN 0-06-047375-4); instr. manual avail. (ISBN 0-06-367372-X). Har-Row.

--Astronomy: The Evolving Universe. 4th ed. 494p. 1985. text ed. 33.50 scp (ISBN 0-06-047374-6, HarpC). Har-Row.

Zeilik, Michael & Gaustad, John E. Astronomy: The Cosmic Perspective. 954p. 1983. text ed. 34.50 scp (ISBN 0-06-047387-8, HarpC). Har-Row.

Zharkov, V. N. & Triubitsyn, V. P. Physics of Planetary Interiors. (Astronomy & Astrophysics Ser.: Vol. 6). 38.00 (ISBN 0-686-87510-9). Pachart Pub Hse.

Zombeck, Martin V. Handbook of Space Astronomy & Astrophysics. LC 82-12944. (Illus.). 341p. 1983. 27.95 (ISBN 0-521-24194-4). Cambridge U Pr.

ASTRONOMY–ADDRESSES, ESSAYS, LECTURES

American Association for the Advancement of Science Staff. Astronomical Photoelectric Photometry. Wood, Frank B., ed. LC 53-12745. pap. 37.30 (ISBN 0-317-07843-7, 2000204). Bks Demand UMI.

Asimov, Isaac. Asimov on Astronomy. LC 73-80946. (Illus.). 288p. 1975. pap. 5.50 (ISBN 0-385-06881-6, Anch). Doubleday.

--Counting the Eons. 224p. 1984. pap. 3.95 (ISBN 0-380-67090-9, 67090, Discus). Avon.

Boehme, S., et al. Astronomy & Astrophysics Abstracts, Vol. 31: Literature 1982, Pt. 1. x, 776p. 1982. 72.00 (ISBN 0-387-12072-6). Springer-Verlag.

Bohme, S., et al, eds. Literature, 1984, Pt. 2. Heinrich, I. & Hofmann, W. Zech, G., tr. (Astronomy & Astrophysics Abstracts Ser.: Vol. 38). 920p. 1985. 69.50 (ISBN 0-387-15562-7). Springer-Verlag.

Brandt, John C. & Maran, Stephen P., eds. The New Astronomy & Space Science Reader. LC 76-54316. (Illus.). 371p. 1977. text ed. 23.95 (ISBN 0-7167-0350-5); pap. text ed. 12.95 (ISBN 0-7167-0349-1). W H Freeman.

Contopoulos, G., ed. Reports on Astronomy, 3 pts. (Transactions of the International Astronomical Union: Vol. XVIA). 1976. Pt. 1. lib. bdg. 47.50 (ISBN 90-277-0739-1, Pub. by Reidel Holland); Pt. 2. lib. bdg. 47.50 (ISBN 90-277-0740-5); Pt. 3. lib. bdg. 47.50 (ISBN 90-277-0741-3); Set. lib. bdg. 126.00 (ISBN 90-277-0703-0). Kluwer Academic.

Cook, Alan H. The Astronomer As Natural Philosopher: An Inaugural Lecture. LC 73-89007. (Illus.). pap. 20.00 (ISBN 0-317-07952-2, 2051372). Bks Demand UMI.

Cornell, James & Gorenstein, Paul, eds. Astronomy from Space: Sputnik to Space Telescope. (Illus.). 264p. 1983. 20.00x (ISBN 0-262-03097-7). MIT Pr.

Fazio, G. G., et al, eds. Astronomy from Space: Proceedings of the Topical Meeting of the COSPAR Interdisciplinary Scientific Commission E (Meetings E3, E4, & E5) of the COSPAR 25th Plenary Meeting held in Graz, Austria, 25 June - 7 July 1984. (Illus.). 220p. 1985. pap. 49.50 (ISBN 0-08-033192-0, PUb by PPL). Pergamon.

General Assembly 14th,Brighton,1970. Transactions of the International Astronomical Union: Proceedings, Vol. 14b. De Jager, C. & Jappels, A., eds. LC 30-10103. 378p. 1971. lib. bdg. 42.00 (ISBN 90-277-0190-3, Pub. by Reidel Holland). Kluwer Academic.

General Assembly 15th,Sydney,1973 & Extraordinary General Assembly,Poland,1973. Transactions of the International Astronomical Union: Proceedings, Vol. 15b. Contopoulos, G. & Jappel, A., eds. LC 73-81827. 334p. 1974. lib. bdg. 63.00 (ISBN 90-277-0451-1, Pub. by Reidel Holland). Kluwer Academic.

Highlights of Astronomy, Vol. 5. (International Astronomical Union Highlights Ser.: No. 5). 868p. 1980. 84.00 (ISBN 90-277-1146-1, Pub. by Reidel Holland); pap. 39.50 (ISBN 90-277-1147-X). Kluwer Academic.

Hunt, Garry, ed. Uranus & the Outer Planets: Proceedings of the IAU-RAS Colloquium, No. 60. LC 81-17047. (Illus.). 350p. 1982. 39.50 (ISBN 0-521-24573-7). Cambridge U Pr.

I.A.U. General Assembly, 14th. Highlights of Astronomy, Vol. 3. Contopoulos, G. & Contopoulos, G., eds. ix, 574p. 1974. lib. bdg. 95.00 (ISBN 90-277-0452-X, Pub. by Reidel Holland). Kluwer Academic.

Lang, Kenneth R. & Gingerich, Owen, eds. A Source Book in Astronomy & Astrophysics, 1900-1975. LC 78-9463. (Source Bks. in the History of the Sciences). 1979. 60.00x (ISBN 0-674-82200-5). Harvard U Pr.

Moore, Patrick, ed. Yearbook of Astronomy, 1985. (Illus.). 1984. pap. 9.95 (ISBN 0-393-30203-2). Norton.

Morris, Mark & Zuckerson, Ben, eds. Mass Loss from Red Giants. 1985. lib. bdg. 49.00 (ISBN 90-277-2075-4, Pub. by Reidel Holland). Kluwer Academic.

Saslaw, William C., et al, eds. The Emerging Universe: Essays on Contemporary Astronomy. LC 72-188526. (Illus.). pap. 51.30 (ISBN 0-317-07948-4, 2016966). Bks Demand UMI.

Simon, P. A., ed. Solar Maximum Analysis: Proceedings of Symposium 2 of the COSPAR 25th Plenary Meeting, Graz, Austria, 25 June-7 1984. (Illus.). 412p. 1985. pap. 49.50 (ISBN 0-08-032735-4, Pub. by PPL). Pergamon.

West, Richard M., ed. Reports on Astronomy: Transactions of the International Astronomical Union Volume XIXA. 1985. lib. bdg. 69.00 (ISBN 90-277-2039-8, Pub. by Reidel Netherlands). Kluwer Academic.

ASTRONOMY–ATLASES

see Stars–Atlases

ASTRONOMY–BIBLIOGRAPHY

Houzeau, J. C. & Lancaster, A. Bibliographie Generale De L'astronomie, 3 Vols. rev ed. Dewhirst, D., ed. 150.00 (ISBN 0-87556-127-6). Saifer.

Pingree, David. Sanskrit Astronomical Tables in the United States. LC 68-19148. (Transactions Ser.: Vol. 58, Pt. 3). 1968. pap. 1.50 (ISBN 0-87169-583-9). Am Philos.

Seal, Robert A. & Martin, Sarah S. A Bibliography of Astronomy 1970 to 1979. LC 81-20877. 408p. 1982. text ed. 37.50x (ISBN 0-87287-280-7). Libs Unl.

ASTRONOMY–CHARTS, DIAGRAMS, ETC.

see also Moon–Photographs, Maps, Etc.; Stars–Atlases

Athanassoula, E. International Kinematics & Dynamics of Galaxies. 1983. 49.50 (ISBN 90-2771-546-7, Pub. by Reidel Holland); pap. 26.00 (ISBN 90-2771-547-5). Kluwer Academic.

Brown, Peter L. Star & Planet Spotting: A Field Guide to the Night Sky. rev. ed. (Illus.). 176p. 1981. 9.95 (ISBN 0-7137-0655-4, Pub. by Blandford Pr England); pap. 6.95 (ISBN 0-7137-1265-1). Sterling.

Buscombe, William. MK Spectral Classifications: Sixth General Catalogue. LC 81-9555. 310p. (Orig.). 1984. pap. 20.00x (ISBN 0-939160-04-8). NWU Astro.

Gingerich, Owen & Welther, Barbara L. Planetary, Lunar & Solar Positions, 1650-1805. LC 83-1805. (Memoirs: Vol. 59S). 1983. 20.00 (ISBN 0-87169-590-1). Am Philos.

Moore, Patrick, ed. Yearbook of Astronomy, 1985. (Illus.). 1984. pap. 9.95 (ISBN 0-393-30203-2). Norton.

Pasachoff, Jay M. A Field Guide to the Stars & Planets. LC 63-7017. (Peterson Field Guide Ser.). 1983. 17.95 (ISBN 0-395-34641-X); pap. 12.95 (ISBN 0-395-34835-8). HM.

ASTRONOMY–CURIOSA AND MISCELLANEA

Corliss, William R. Mysterious Universe: A Handbook of Astronomical Anomalies. LC 78-65616. (Illus.). 1979. 16.95 (ISBN 0-915554-05-4). Sourcebook.

Corliss, William R., ed. The Moon & the Planets. LC 85-61380. (Catalog of Astronomical Anomalies Ser.). (Illus.). 380p. 1985. 18.95 (ISBN 0-915554-19-4). Sourcebook.

Klinger, Jurgen, et al, eds. Ices in the Solar System. 1985. lib. bdg. 99.00 (ISBN 90-277-2062-2, Pub. by Reidel Holland). Kluwer Academic.

Moore, Patrick. Guinness Book of Astronomy Facts & Feats. 2nd ed. (Illus.). 304p. 1983. 14.95 (ISBN 0-85112-258-2, Pub. by Guinness Superlatives England); pap. 9.95 (ISBN 0-85112-291-4, Pub. by Guinness Superlatives England). Sterling.

West, Richard M., ed. Highlights of Astronomy, Vol. 6. 1983. lib. bdg. 93.50 (ISBN 90-277-1564-5, Pub. by Reidel Holland); pap. 43.50 (ISBN 90-277-1565-3). Kluwer Academic.

--Transactions of the International Astronomical Union, Vol. 18b. 1983. lib. bdg. 69.50 (ISBN 90-277-1563-7, Pub. by Reidel Holland). Kluwer Academic.

ASTRONOMY–DATA PROCESSING

Burgess, Eric. Celestial BASIC: Astronomy On Your Computer. LC 82-60187. (Illus.). 300p. 1982. pap. 16.95 (ISBN 0-89588-087-3). SYBEX.

Burgess, Eric & Burgess, Howard J. More Uses for Your Timex-Sinclair 1000: Astronomy on Your Computer. LC 83-61386. (Illus.). 153p. 1983. pap. 8.95 (ISBN 0-89588-112-8). SYBEX.

Duffett-Smith, Peter. Astronomy on Your Personal Computer. (Illus.). 240p. Date not set. price not set (ISBN 0-521-26620-3); pap. price not set (ISBN 0-521-31976-5). Cambridge U Pr.

--Practical Astronomy with Your Calculator. 2nd ed. LC 81-6191. 200p. 1981. 37.50 (ISBN 0-521-24059-X); pap. 10.95 (ISBN 0-521-28411-2). Cambridge U Pr.

Genet, Russell M., ed. Microcomputers in Astronomy. LC 82-84769. 253p. (Orig.). 1983. pap. 23.95 (ISBN 0-911351-03-5). Fairborn Observ.

Genet, Russell M. & Genet, Karen A., eds. Microcomputers in Astronomy, II. 200p. (Orig.). 1984. pap. 23.95 (ISBN 0-911351-06-X). Fairborn Observ.

Klein, Fred. Pocket Computer Programs for Astronomers. 100p. (Orig.). 1983. pap. 12.95 (ISBN 0-913051-01-2). F Klein Pubns.

Marshall, Kim A. & Romesburg, H. Charles. Users Manual for Clustar-Clustid: Computer Programs for Hierarchical Cluster Analysis. 1984. 8.95 (ISBN 0-534-03420-9). Lifetime Learn.

Matsumoto, H. & Sato, T. Computer Simulation of Space Plasmas. 1985. lib. bdg. 67.00 (ISBN 0-318-04239-8, Pub. by Reidel Holland). Kluwer Academic.

Simon, Sheridan A. The Astronomy Disk. 48p. 1984. pap. text ed. 34.95 incl. disk (ISBN 0-13-049834-3). P-H.

ASTRONOMY–DICTIONARIES

Dictionary of Astronomy. (Eng. & Chinese.). 103p. 1974. pap. 3.95 (ISBN 0-686-92284-0, M-9574). French & Eur.

Fairbridge, R., ed. Encyclopedia of Atmospheric Sciences & Astrogeology. (Encyclopedia of Earth Sciences Ser: Vol. II). 1967. 91.50 (ISBN 0-12-786458-X). Acad Pr.

Hopkins, Jeanne, ed. Glossary of Astronomy & Astrophysics. 2nd, rev. & enl. ed. LC 80-5226. (Phoenix Ser.). x, 196p. 1982. pap. 10.00x (ISBN 0-226-35169-6). U of Chicago Pr.

--Glossary of Astronomy & Astrophysics. rev. ed. LC 80-5226. 224p. 1980. lib. bdg. 19.00x (ISBN 0-226-35171-8). U of Chicago Pr.

Illingworth, Valerie. The Anchor Dictionary of Astronomy. LC 79-6538. (Illus.). 448p. (Orig.). 1980. pap. 7.50 (ISBN 0-385-15936-6, Anch). Doubleday.

Illingworth, Valerie, ed. Facts on File: Dictionary of Astronomy. (Illus.). 1979. 17.50 (ISBN 0-87196-326-4). Facts on File.

Jehan, L. F. Dictionnaire d'Astronomie de Physique et de Meteorologie. Migne, J. P., ed. (Encyclopedie Theologique Ser.: Vol. 42). (Fr.). 780p. Repr. of 1850 ed. lib. bdg. 99.00x (ISBN 0-89241-247-X). Caratzas.

Kleczek, Josip. Astronomical Dictionary: In Six Languages. (Eng., Fr., Ger., Ital., Rus. & Czech.). 1962. 95.00 (ISBN 0-12-411950-6). Acad Pr.

Mateu Sancho, Pedro. Diccionario de la Astronomica y Astronautica. (Span.). 350p. 1962. 37.50 (ISBN 84-233-0114-1, S-12334). French & Eur.

Meinikov, O. English-Russian Astronomical Dictionary. (Eng. & Rus.). 504p. 1980. 15.00x (ISBN 0-569-06519-4, Pub. by Collet's). State Mutual Bk.

Mitton, Jacqueline. Key Definitions in Astronomy. LC 82-183. (Quality Paperback: No. 375). 174p. (Orig.). 1982. pap. text ed. 4.95 (ISBN 0-8226-0375-6). Littlefield.

Nicolson, Iain, ed. Dictionary of Astronomy. (Illus.). 250p. 1980. pap. 4.95 (ISBN 0-06-463524-4, EH 524). B&N NY.

Ridpath, Ian, ed. The Illustrated Encyclopedia of Astronomy & Space. rev. ed. LC 76-3577. (Illus.). 1980. 19.18i (ISBN 0-690-01838-X). T Y Crowell.

Schnitzler, Ilse. Lexikon Fuer Planetenbilder. (Ger.). 1975. 25.00 (ISBN 3-920807-07-3, M-7196). French & Eur.

Vega, Vincente. Diccionario Ilustrado de Efemerides, 2 vols. (Span.). 1901p. 1968. Set. leatherette 47.95 (ISBN 84-252-0600-6, S-12366); pap. 38.95 (ISBN 84-252-0600-6, S-50279). French & Eur.

Vocabulaire d'Astronomie. (Fr., Eng. & Ger.). 1978. pap. 39.95 (ISBN 0-686-57249-1, M-6555). French & Eur.

Weigert & Zimmerman. ABC Astronomie. (Ger.). 480p. 1974. 15.95 (ISBN 0-686-56592-4, M-7289, Pub. by W. Dausien). French & Eur.

Weigert, A. & Zimmerman, H. Concise Encyclopedia of Astronomy. 2nd ed. 540p. 1976. 29.50x (ISBN 0-8448-1002-9). Crane-Russak Co.

ASTRONOMY–DIRECTORIES

Gall, James. Astronomical Directory. 1979. pap. 8.00 (ISBN 0-88904-082-6). Gall Pubns.

Moore, Patrick, ed. Yearbook of Astronomy, 1984. (Illus.). 1984. pap. 9.95 (ISBN 0-393-30147-8). Norton.

Shea, Dion, ed. Directory of Physics & Astronomy Staff Members, 1984-85. 412p. 1984. pap. 30.00 (ISBN 0-88318-458-3). Am Inst Physics.

--Graduate Programs in Physics, Astronomy & Related Fields, 1984-85. 912p. 1984. pap. 17.50 (ISBN 0-88318-459-1). Am Inst Physics.

ASTRONOMY–EARLY WORKS TO 1800

Aristotle. On the Heavens. (Loeb Classical Library: No. 338). 12.50x (ISBN 0-674-99372-1). Harvard U Pr.

Astronomical Cuneiform Texts, 3 vols. (Sources in the History of Mathematics & Physical Sciences Ser.: Vol. 5). (Illus.). 799p. 1983. 92.00 (ISBN 0-387-90812-9). Springer-Verlag.

Bernoulli, Jakob. Die Gesammelten Werke Vol. 3: Wahrscheinlichkeitsrechnung. (Ger., Illus.). 594p. 1975. 85.80x (ISBN 3-7643-0713-7). Birkhauser.

Blundeville, Thomas. M. Blundeville, His Exercises Containing Sixe Treatises. LC 78-171736. (English Experience Ser.: No. 361). (Illus.). 718p. 1971. Repr. of 1594 ed. 64.00 (ISBN 90-221-0361-7). Walter J Johnson.

Borde, Andrew. The Pryncyples of Astronamye in Maner a Pronosticacyon to Worldes End. LC 73-6101. (English Experience Ser.: No. 570). 61p. 1973. Repr. of 1542 ed. 6.00 (ISBN 90-221-0570-9). Walter J Johnson.

Brahe, Tycho. Learned Tico Brahe His Astronomical Conjecture of the New & Much Admired Star Which Appeared in the Year 1572. LC 74-6157. (English Experience Ser.: No. 86). 28p. 1969. Repr. of 1632 ed. 14.00 (ISBN 90-221-0086-3). Walter J Johnson.

Copernicus, Nicholas. De Revolutionibus Orbium Coelestium. 1965. Repr. of 1543 ed. Facsimile Ed. 50.00 (ISBN 0-384-09806-1). Johnson Repr.

--On the Revolutions: Manuscript. facsimile ed. (Illus.). 1972. Repr. 85.00 (ISBN 0-384-09805-3). Johnson Repr.

Cuningham, William. The Cosmographical Glasse, Conteinyng the Principles of Cosmographie, Etc. LC 68-54632. (English Experience Ser.: No. 44). 1968. Repr. of 1559 ed. 49.00 (ISBN 90-221-0044-8). Walter J Johnson.

De Lalande, Joseph. Astronomie, 3 Vols. 1965. Repr. of 1792 ed. Set. 145.00 (ISBN 0-384-31065-6). Johnson Repr.

Goldstein, Bernard R., ed. Ibn al-Muthannea's Commentary on the Astronomical Tables of al-Khwearizmei: Two Hebrew Versions. LC 67-13434. (Yale Studies in the History of Science & Medicine Ser.: No. 2). (Illus.). pap. 105.00 (ISBN 0-317-09378-9, 2016770). Bks Demand UMI.

Gregory, David. The Elements of Physical & Geometrical Astronomy, 2 vols. 1972. Repr. of 1726 ed. Set. 70.00 (ISBN 0-384-19920-8). Johnson Repr.

Heath, Thomas L. Greek Astronomy. Barker, Earnest, ed. LC 77-89685. (Library of Greek Thought: No. 6). 1969. Repr. of 1932 ed. 15.00 (ISBN 0-404-03232-X). AMS Pr.

Henisch, Georg. The Principles of Geometrie Gathered Out of G. Henischius by F. Cooke. LC 71-25788. (English Experience Ser.: No. 321). 88p. 1971. Repr. of 1591 ed. 8.00 (ISBN 90-221-0321-8). Walter J Johnson.

Hevelius, Johannes. Machina Coelestis, 2 pts. in 3 vols. (Lat). 1969. Repr. of 1673 ed. Set. 295.00 (ISBN 0-384-22800-3). Johnson Repr.

Jackob Bernoulli: Astronomia-Philosophia Naturalist. (Ger., Illus.). 541p. 1969. 83.95x (ISBN 0-8176-0028-0). Birkhauser.

Kepler, Johann. Somnium: The Dream, or Posthumous Work on Lunar Astronomy. Rosen, Edward, tr. LC 65-20639. pap. 72.30 (ISBN 0-317-07803-8, 2004977). Bks Demand UMI.

Marek Marzi Kronlandu, Jan. Thaumantias, Liber de Arcu Coelesti Deque Colorum Apparentium Natura Ortu et Causis. (Lat). Repr. of 1648 ed. slip case 26.00 (ISBN 0-384-35320-7). Johnson Repr.

Medina, Pedro De. A Navigator's Universe: The Libro De Cosmographia of 1538. Lamb, Ursula, ed. & tr. LC 70-128870. (Studies in the History of Discoveries Ser). 328p. 1972. U of Chicago Pr.

Moxon, Joseph. Tutor to Astronomy & Geography. 3rd rev., enl. ed. LC 68-56778. (Research & Source Works Ser.: No. 264). (Illus.). 1968. Repr. of 1674 ed. 24.50 (ISBN 0-8337-2478-9). B Franklin.

North, J. D., ed. Richard of Wallingford: An Edition of His Writings with Introduction, English Translation & Commentary, 3 vols. (Illus.). 1976. 275.00x (ISBN 0-19-858139-4). Oxford U Pr.

Shumaker, Wayne & Heilbron, J. L. John Dee on Astronomy: Propaedeumata Aphoristica (1558 & 1568) LC 76-50254. 1978. 37.50x (ISBN 0-520-03376-0). U of Cal Pr.

Whiston, William. Astronomical Lectures. 2nd ed. Repr. of 1728 ed. 37.00 (ISBN 0-384-67975-7). Johnson Repr.

Wright, Edward. The Description & Use of the Sphere. LC 71-25883. (English Experience Ser.: No. 136). 104p. 1969. Repr. of 1613 ed. 14.00 (ISBN 90-221-0136-3). Walter J Johnson.

ASTRONOMY–EPHEMERIDES

see Nautical Almanacs

ASTRONOMY–EXAMINATIONS, QUESTIONS, ETC.

Lacy, Claud H. Astronomy Laboratory Exercises. (Illus.). 72p. 1981. pap. text ed. 8.95 (ISBN 0-8403-2564-9). Kendall-Hunt.

Rudman, Jack. Astronomer. (Career Examination Ser.: C-54). (Cloth bdg. avail. on request). pap. 14.00 (ISBN 0-8373-0054-1). Natl Learning.

ASTRONOMY–HISTORY

Anton, John P., ed. Science & the Sciences in Plato. LC 78-13418. 1980. 25.00x (ISBN 0-88206-301-4). Caravan Bks.

Asbrook, Joseph. Astronomical Scrapbook-One. (Illus.). text ed. 19.95 (ISBN 0-933346-24-7). Sky Pub.

Ashbrook, Joseph. The Astronomical Scrapbook: Skywatchers, Pioneers & Seekers in Astronomy. (Illus.). 384p. 1985. 19.95 (ISBN 0-521-30045-2). Cambridge U Pr.

Aveni, A. F., ed. Archaeoastronomy in the New World: American Primitive Astronomy. LC 82-1344. 230p. 1982. 34.50 (ISBN 0-521-24731-4). Cambridge U Pr.

Berendzen, Richard. Man Discovers the Galaxies. 1984. 30.00x; pap. 12.00. Columbia U Pr.

Berry, Arthur. Short History of Astronomy: From Earliest Times Through the 19th Century. (Illus.). 1961. pap. 8.95 (ISBN 0-486-20210-0). Dover.

Bond, William C. History & Description of the Astronomical Observatory & Results of Astronomical Observations Made at the Observatory of Harvard College, Vol. 1. Cohen, D. Bernard, ed. LC 79-7967. (Three Centuries of Science in America Ser.). (Illus.). 1980. Repr. of 1856 ed. lib. bdg. 51.50x (ISBN 0-405-12548-8). Ayer Co Pubs.

Brecher, Kenneth & Feirtag, Michael, eds. Astronomy of the Ancients. (Illus.). 1979. pap. 8.95 (ISBN 0-262-52070-2). MIT Pr.

Christianson, Gale E. This Wild Abyss: The Story of the Men Who Made Modern Astronomy. 1979. pap. 9.95x (ISBN 0-317-30517-4). Free Pr.

Clerke, Agnes M. A Popular History of Astronomy in the Nineteenth Century. LC 70-166614. 1908. Repr. 39.00 (ISBN 0-403-01492-1). Scholarly.

Cohen, I. Bernard, ed. Aspects of Astronomy in America in the Nineteenth Century: An Original Anthology. LC 79-7948. (Three Centuries of Science in America Ser.). (Illus.). 1980. lib. bdg. 44.00x (ISBN 0-405-12529-1). Ayer Co Pubs.

Delambre, Jean B. Histoire De l'Astronomie Ancienne, 2 Vols. facsimile ed. 1817. Set. 105.00 (ISBN 0-384-11203-X). Johnson Repr.

--Histoire de L'astronomie du Moyen Age. 1965. Repr. of 1819 ed. 55.00 (ISBN 0-384-11265-X). Johnson Repr.

--Histoire De L'astronomie Moderne, 2 Vols. (Sources of Science, House Ser.: No. 25). (Fr). 1969. Repr. of 1821 ed. Set. 140.00 (ISBN 0-384-11300-1). Johnson Repr.

DeVorkin, David H. The History of Modern Astronomy & Astrophysics. LC 81-43349. 462p. 1985. lib. bdg. 79.00 (ISBN 0-8240-9283-X). Garland Pub.

Dicks, D. R. Early Greek Astronomy to Aristotle. LC 76-109335. (Aspects of Greek & Roman Life Ser.). (Illus.). 272p. (Orig.). 1985. pap. text ed. 9.95x (ISBN 0-8014-9310-2). Cornell U Pr.

Dreyer, John L. History of Astronomy from Thales to Kepler. pap. 8.50 (ISBN 0-486-60079-3). Dover.

--History of Astronomy from Thales to Kepler. 15.50 (ISBN 0-8446-1997-3). Peter Smith.

Durham, Frank & Purrington, Robert D. Frame of the Universe. 284p. 1985. pap. 12.50x (ISBN 0-231-05393-2). Columbia U Pr.

Eliot, James & Kerr, Richard. Rings: Discoveries from Galileo to Voyager. (Illus.). 224p. 1985. 17.50 (ISBN 0-262-05031-5). MIT Pr.

Ettisch, Ernst. The Hebrew Vowels & Consonants as Symbols of Ancient Astronomic Concepts. Zohn, Harry, tr. from Ger. (Illus.). 1986. 19.50 (ISBN 0-8283-1883-2). Branden Pub Co.

Gillis, James M. Collected Writings. 600.00 (ISBN 0-87968-905-6). Gordon Pr.

Gingerich, Owen, ed. Astrophysics & Twentieth Century Astronomy to 1950, Vol. 4, Pt. A. LC 83-10164. (General History of Astronomy Ser.). 206p. 1984. 29.95 (ISBN 0-521-24256-8). Cambridge U Pr.

Goldstein, B. R. The Astronomy of Levi Ben Gerson, 1288-1344. (Studies in the History of Mathematics & Physical Science: Vol. 11). (Illus.). 300p. 1985. 68.00 (ISBN 0-387-96132-1). Springer-Verlag.

Grant, Robert. History of Physical Astronomy. 1966. Repr. of 1852 ed. 35.00 (ISBN 0-384-19670-5). Johnson Repr.

Hadingham, Evan. Early Man & the Cosmos. LC 84-40697. (Illus.). 288p. (Orig.). 1985. pap. 11.95 (ISBN 0-8061-1919-5). U of Okla Pr.

Hanson, N. R. & Humphreys, W. C., Jr. Constellations & Conjectures. LC 70-159654. (Synthese Library: No. 48). (Illus.). 282p. 1973. lib. bdg. 39.50 (ISBN 90-277-0192-X, Pub. by Reidel Holland). Kluwer Academic.

Hellman, Doris. The Comet of Fifteen Seventy-Seven: Its Place in the History of Astronomy. LC 72-110569. (Columbia University. Studies in the Social Sciences: No. 510). Repr. of 1944 ed. 18.50 (ISBN 0-404-51510-X). AMS Pr.

Heninger, S. K., Jr. The Cosmographical Glass: Renaissance Diagrams of the Universe. LC 76-62637. (Illus.). 209p. 1977. 20.00 (ISBN 0-87328-070-9). Huntington Lib.

Herrmann, D. B. The History of Astronomy from Herschel to Hertzsprung. Krisciunas, Kevin, ed. (Illus.). 300p. 1984. 24.95 (ISBN 0-521-25733-6). Cambridge U Pr.

Hodson, F. R., ed. The Place of Astronomy in the Ancient World: A Joint Symposium of the Royal Society & the British Academy. (Illus.). 1974. 69.00x (ISBN 0-19-725944-8). Oxford U Pr.

Mallas, John H. & Kreimer, Evered. The Messier Album. LC 78-63243. (Illus.). 1978. 13.95 (ISBN 0-933346-04-2). Sky Pub.

Martin, Thomas H. Memoire sur les Hypotheses Astronomiques des Plus Anciens Philosophes de la Grece. Vlastos, Gregory, ed. (History of Ideas in Ancient Times Ser). 1976. Repr. 35.50x (ISBN 0-405-07320-8). Ayer Co Pubs.

Moore, Patrick. Patrick Moore's History of Astronomy. Rev. ed. (Illus.). 328p. 1984. 19.95 (ISBN 0-356-08607-0, Pub. by Salem Hse Ltd). Merrimack Pub Cir.

Nakayama, Shigeru. History of Japanese Astronomy: Chinese Background & Western Impact. LC 68-21980. (Harvard-Yenching Institute Monograph: No. 18). (Illus.). 1969. 20.00x (ISBN 0-674-39725-8). Harvard U Pr.

Neugebauer, O. Astronomy & History: Selected Essays. (Illus.). 538p. 1983. pap. 22.00 (ISBN 0-387-90844-7). Springer-Verlag.

--The Exact Sciences in Antiquity. 2nd ed. LC 57-12342. (Illus.). 256p. 1957. 22.50x (ISBN 0-87057-044-7). U Pr of New Eng.

Neugebauer, O. & Parker, R. A. Egyptian Astronomical Texts: Decans, Planets, Constellations & Zodiacs, Vol. 3. LC 60-15723. (Brown Egyptological Studies: No. 6). (Illus.). Repr. of 1969 ed. 28.20 (ISBN 0-8357-9045-2, 2012292); plates 53.00. Bks Demand UMI.

Newton, Robert R. The Crime of Claudius Ptolemy. LC 77-4211. 1977. text ed. 32.50x (ISBN 0-8018-1990-3). Johns Hopkins.

Orchard, Thomas N. Astronomy of Milton's Paradise Lost. LC 68-4178. (Studies in Milton, No. 22). (Illus.). 1969. Repr. of 1896 ed. lib. bdg. 75.00x (ISBN 0-8383-0672-1). Haskell.

Rothenberg, Marc. The History of Science & Technology in the United States: A Critical, Selective Bibliography. LC 81-43355. (Bibliographies on the History or Science & Technology Ser.). 262p. 1982. lib. bdg. 48.00 (ISBN 0-8240-9278-3). Garland Pub.

Tauber, Gerald. Man's View of the Universe. (Illus.). 1979. 19.95 (ISBN 0-517-52674-3). Crown.

Van Der Waerden, Bartel. Science Awakening 2: The Birth of Astronomy. (Illus.). 1974. 45.00x (ISBN 0-19-519753-4). Oxford U Pr.

Van Helden, Albert. Measuring the Universe: Cosmic Dimensions from Aristarchus to Halley. LC 84-16397. (Illus.). 260p. 1985. lib. bdg. 30.00x (ISBN 0-226-84881-7). U of Chicago Pr.

Wilkins, John. The Discovery of a World in the Moone: 1638. LC 73-14920. 1973. lib. bdg. 35.00x (ISBN 0-8201-1123-6). Schol Facsimiles.

Williamson, Ray A., ed. Archaeoastronomy in the Americas. LC 81-19147. (Anthropological Papers: No. 22). (Illus.). 405p. (Orig.). 1981. pap. 19.95 (ISBN 0-87919-094-9). Ballena Pr.

Wolf, Rudolf. Geschichte der Astronomie. 50.00 (ISBN 0-384-69050-5). Johnson Repr.

ASTRONOMY–LABORATORY MANUALS

Kafatos, Minas. Astronomy Laboratory Manual. 88p. 1984. pap. 11.95 (ISBN 0-8403-3405-2). Kendall-Hunt.

ASTRONOMY–MISCELLANEA

Craine, Eric R. A Handbook of Quasistellar & BL Lacertae Objects. (Astronomy & Astrophysics Ser.: Vol. 4). 292p. 1977. 19.00x (ISBN 0-912918-23-3, 0923). Pachart Pub Hse.

Klein, Fred. Pocket Computer Programs for Astronomers. 100p. (Orig.). 1983. pap. 12.95 (ISBN 0-913051-01-2). F Klein Pubns.

Severin, Gregory. The Paris Codex: Decoding an Astronomical Ephemeris. LC 80-68488. (Transactions Ser.: Vol. 71, Pt. 5). 1981. 10.00 (ISBN 0-87169-715-7). Am Philos.

ASTRONOMY–OBSERVATIONS

see also Astronomical Observatories; Errors, Theory Of; Least Squares

Hall, Douglas S. & Genet, Russell M. Photoelectric Photometry of Variable Stars: A Practical Guide for the Smaller Observatory. (Illus.). 282p. (Orig.). 1982. pap. 17.95 (ISBN 0-911351-00-0). Fairborn Observ.

Madore, B. F. Cepheids: Theory & Observation, Proceedings of the IAU Colloquium 82. 300p. 1985. 39.50 (ISBN 0-521-30091-6). Cambridge U Pr.

Mallas, John H. & Kreimer, Evered. The Messier Album. LC 78-63243. (Illus.). 1978. 13.95 (ISBN 0-933346-04-2). Sky Pub.

Norton, Arthur P. Norton's Star Atlas. (Illus.). 1978. Repr. of 1910 ed. 24.95x (ISBN 0-85248-900-5). Sky Pub.

Sherrod, P. Clay & Koed, Thomas L. A Complete Manual of Amateur Astronomy: Tools & Techniques for Astronomical Observations. (Illus.). 319p. 1981. 24.95 (ISBN 0-13-162115-7); pap. 10.95 (ISBN 0-13-162107-6). P-H.

Stephenson, F. Richard & Clark, David H. Applications of Early Astronomical Records. LC 78-10121. (Monographs on Astronomical Subjects). (Illus.). 1978. 19.95x (ISBN 0-19-520122-1). Oxford U Pr.

ASTRONOMY–OBSERVATORIES

see Astronomical Observatories

ASTRONOMY–OBSERVERS' MANUALS

Argyle, R. W. & Webb Society. Webb Society Deep-Sky Observer's Handbook, Volume 1: Double Stars. rev. ed. Jones, Kenneth G., ed. (Illus.). 192p. 1985. pap. 12.95x (ISBN 0-89490-122-2). Enslow Pubs.

Barker, Edmund S. Webb Society Deep-Sky Observer's Handbook: Vol. 4, Galaxies. Glyn-Jones, Kenneth, ed. 250p. 1982. 40.00x (ISBN 0-7188-2527-6, Pub. by Lutterworth Pr England). State Mutual Bk.

Bullock, J. Benbow. Stars for Lincoln, Doctors & Dogs. LC 80-66936. (Illus.). 100p. (Orig.). 1981. pap. 4.95 (ISBN 0-937024-00-7). Gourmet Guides.

Burnham, Robert. The Star Book. LC 83-15603. (Illus.). 20p. 1983. pap. 6.95 (ISBN 0-913135-00-3). AstroMedia Corp.

Burnham, Robert, Jr. Burnham's Celestial Handbook: An Observer's Guide to the Universe Beyond the Solar System, Vol. 3. (Illus.). 1979. pap. 12.95 (ISBN 0-486-23673-0). Dover.

Culver, Roger B. Introduction to Experimental Astronomy. 2nd ed. (Illus.). 208p. 1983. pap. text ed. 9.95x (ISBN 0-7167-1495-7). W H Freeman.

Hartung, E. J. Astronomical Objects for Southern Telescopes with an Addendum for Northern Observatories: A Handbook for Amateur Observers. (Illus.). 264p. 1985. 17.95 (ISBN 0-521-31887-4). Cambridge U Pr.

Howard, Neale E. The Telescope Handbook & Star Atlas. rev. ed. LC 75-6601. (Illus.). 226p. 1975. 21.10i (ISBN 0-690-00686-1). T Y Crowell.

Kals, W. S. The Stargazer's Bible. LC 77-25598. (Outdoor Bible Ser.). (Illus.). 1980. pap. 5.95 (ISBN 0-385-13057-0). Doubleday.

Morales, Ronald J. Eyepiece Impressions of Five Hundred Deep-Sky Objects: Astronomy for the Serious Amateur. (Illus.). 128p. 1985. pap. 9.95 (ISBN 0-89404-076-6). Aztex.

Muirden, James. Astronomy Handbook. LC 82-1780. (Illus.). 192p. 1982. 8.95 (ISBN 0-668-05586-3, 5586). Arco.

--Astronomy Handbook. LC 82-1780. (Illus.). 192p. 1984. 8.95 (ISBN 0-668-05586-3, 6235-5); pap. 6.95 (ISBN 0-668-06235-5). Arco.

--Astronomy with Binoculars. LC 77-11568. (Illus.). 1979. 13.41i (ISBN 0-690-01723-5). T Y Crowell.

Norton, Arthur P. Norton's Star Atlas. (Illus.). 1978. Repr. of 1910 ed. 24.95x (ISBN 0-85248-900-5). Sky Pub.

Sidgwick, J. B. Amateur Astronomer's Handbook. 4th, rev. ed. LC 80-20596. (Illus.). 568p. 1982. text ed. 24.95x (ISBN 0-89490-049-8); pap. 9.95 (ISBN 0-89490-076-5). Enslow Pubs.

--Observational Astronomy for Amateurs. (Illus.). 384p. 1981. pap. 5.95 (ISBN 0-486-24033-9). Dover.

Webb Society. Webb Society Deep-Sky Observer's Handbook: Open & Globular Clusters, Vol. III. Jones, Kenneth G., ed. LC 78-31260. (Illus.). 224p. 1980. pap. 14.95x (ISBN 0-89490-034-X). Enslow Pubs.

Webb Society & Jones, Kenneth G., eds. Webb Society Deep-Sky Observer's Handbook: Galaxies, Vol. IV. LC 77-359099. 256p. 1981. pap. 16.95x (ISBN 0-89490-050-1). Enslow Pubs.

--Webb Society Deep-Sky Observer's Handbook: Double Stars, Vol. I. LC 78-31260. 120p. 1979. pap. 8.95x (ISBN 0-89490-027-7). Enslow Pubs.

--Webb Society Deep-Sky Observer's Handbook: Planetary & Gaseous Nebulae, Vol. II. LC 78-31260. 160p. 1979. pap. 10.95x (ISBN 0-89490-028-5). Enslow Pubs.

Webb, Thomas W. Celestial Objects for Common Telescopes, 2 Vol. Mayall, Margaret W., ed. (Illus.). 1962. pap. 5.00 ea.; Vol. 1. pap. (ISBN 0-486-20917-2); Vol. 2. pap. (ISBN 0-486-20918-0); Two vol. Set, 645 pgs. pap. 10.00. Dover.

ASTRONOMY–PICTORIAL WORKS

Alter, Dinsmore, et al. Pictorial Astronomy. 5th ed. LC 81-47878. (Illus.). 384p. 1983. 19.18i (ISBN 0-06-181019-3, HarpT). Har-Row.

Brown, Peter L. Astronomy in Color. (Illus.). 264p. 1982. 9.95 (ISBN 0-7137-0729-1, Pub. by Blandford Pr England). Sterling.

Ferris, Timothy. Galaxien. Ehlers, Anita, tr. from Eng. (Ger.). 184p. 1981. 94.00 (ISBN 0-8176-1250-5). Birkhauser.

Friedman, Herbert. The Amazing Universe. National Geographic Society, ed. LC 74-28806. (Special Publications Ser.). (Illus.). 200p. 1975. 6.95 (ISBN 0-87044-179-5); lib. bdg. 8.50 (ISBN 0-87044-184-1). Natl Geog.

Newton, Jack & Teece, Philip. The Cambridge Deep Sky Album. LC 83-14301. (Illus.). 128p. 1983. 22.95 (ISBN 0-521-25668-2). Cambridge U Pr.

Olsen, Roberta J. Fire & Ice: A History of Comets in Art. LC 85-7295. (Illus.). 134p. 1985. 24.95 (ISBN 0-8027-0855-2); pap. 14.95 (ISBN 0-8027-7283-8). Walker & Co.

Tauber, Gerald. Man's View of the Universe. (Illus.). 1979. 19.95 (ISBN 0-517-52674-3). Crown.

ASTRONOMY–POPULAR WORKS

Calder, Nigel. The Violent Universe: An Eyewitness Account of the New Astronomy. LC 76-30435. (Illus.). 1977. pap. 8.95 (ISBN 0-14-004485-X). Penguin.

--Violent Universe: An Eyewitness Account of the New Astronomy. LC 73-83246. (Illus.). 1970. 14.95 (ISBN 0-670-74720-3). Viking.

Dexter, W. A. Field Guide to Astronomy Without a Telescope. (Earth Science Curriculum Project Pamphlet Ser.). 1971. pap. text ed. 4.08 (ISBN 0-395-02623-7). HM.

Engelbrekston, Sune. Stars, Planets & Galaxies. (Knowledge Through Color Ser.: No. 54). 160p. 1975. pap. 3.95 (ISBN 0-553-23528-1). Bantam.

Friedman, Herbert. The Amazing Universe. National Geographic Society, ed. LC 74-28806. (Special Publications Ser.). (Illus.). 200p. 1975. 6.95 (ISBN 0-87044-179-5); lib. bdg. 8.50 (ISBN 0-87044-184-1). Natl Geog.

Gibilisco, Stan. Black Holes, Quasars & Other Mysteries of the Universe. (Illus.). 208p. 1984. pap. 13.50 (ISBN 0-8306-1525-3, 1525). TAB Bks.

Goldsmith, Donald & Levy, Donald. From the Black Hole to the Infinite Universe. LC 73-86412. (Illus.). 300p. 1974. pap. text ed. 17.00x (ISBN 0-8162-3323-3). Holden-Day.

Henbest, Nigel & Mots, Lloyd. The Night Sky. LC 79-605. (Spotter's Guides). (Illus.). 1979. 3.95 (ISBN 0-8317-6375-2, Mayflower Bks); pap. 1.95 (ISBN 0-8317-6376-0). Smith Pubs.

Hodge, Paul W., ed. Universe of Galaxies. (Readings from Scientific American Ser.). (Illus.). 113p. 1984. 20.95 (ISBN 0-7167-1675-5); pap. 10.95 (ISBN 0-7167-1676-3). W H Freeman.

Jastrow, Robert. Red Giants & White Dwarfs. (Illus.). 1979. 14.95 (ISBN 0-393-85002-1). Norton.

Moore, Patrick. The New Atlas of the Universe. 2nd, rev. ed. (Illus.). 1984. 40.00 (ISBN 0-517-55500-X). Crown.

--The Unfolding Universe. (Illus.). 256p. 1982. 17.95 (ISBN 0-517-54836-4). Crown.

Moore, Patrick, ed. Yearbook of Astronomy, 1976. (Yearbook of Astronomy Ser.). (Illus.). 215p. 1976. 9.95 (ISBN 0-393-06404-2). Norton.

--Yearbook of Astronomy, 1978. (Yearbook of Astronomy Ser.). (Illus.). 1978. 10.95 (ISBN 0-393-06430-1). Norton.

Sagan, Carl. Cosmos. 400p. 1985. pap. 4.50 (ISBN 0-345-33135-4). Ballantine.

Schatzman, E. L. Structure of the Universe. (Illus., Orig.). 1968. pap. 3.95 (ISBN 0-07-055172-3). McGraw.

Shapley, Harlow. Of Stars & Men: Human Response to an Expanding Universe. LC 83-22528. vi, 157p. 1984. Repr. of 1958 ed. lib. bdg. 24.75x (ISBN 0-313-24302-6, SHST). Greenwood.

Snow, Theodore P. The Cosmic Cycle. LC 83-15086. (Illus.). 109p. 1984. 19.95 (ISBN 0-87850-041-3). Darwin Pr.

Toulmin, Stephen & Goodfield, June. Fabric of the Heavens: The Development of Astronomy & Dynamics. (Illus.). pap. 7.95xi (ISBN 0-06-130579-0, TB579, Torch). Har-Row.

Von Ditfurth, Hoimar. Children of the Universe. LC 73-91629. 1976. pap. 4.95 (ISBN 0-689-70529-8, 217). Atheneum.

Ziguel, F. Los Tesoros Del Firmamento. (Span.). 280p. 1973. pap. 4.95 (ISBN 0-8285-1471-2, Pub. by Mir Pubs USSR). Imported Pubns.

ASTRONOMY–PROBLEMS, EXERCISES, ETC.

Atanasijevi'c, I. Selected Exercises in Galactic Astronomy. (Astrophysics & Space Science Library: No.26). 144p. 1971. lib. bdg. 21.00 (ISBN 90-277-0198-9, Pub. by Reidel Holland). Kluwer Academic.

Meeus, Jean. Astronomical Formulae for Calculators. LC 82-8495. 1982. pap. text ed. 14.95 (ISBN 0-943396-01-8). Willmann-Bell.

Minnaert, M. J. Practical Work in Elementary Astronomy. 247p. 1969. lib. bdg. 29.00 (ISBN 90-277-0133-4, Pub. by Reidel Holland). Kluwer Academic.

ASTRONOMY–RESEARCH

see Astronomical Research

ASTRONOMY–STUDY AND TEACHING

Levitt, I. M. & Marshall, Roy. Star Maps for Beginners. pap. 8.95 (ISBN 0-671-68810-3, Fireside). S&S.

ASTRONOMY–TABLES, ETC.

Davies, Thomas D. Sight Reduction Tables for Sun, Moon, & Planets: Assumed Altitude Method of Celestial Navigation. LC 81-9725. 247p. 1982. spiral text ed. 27.50x (ISBN 0-87033-276-7). Cornell Maritime.

Goldstein, Bernard R., ed. Ibn al-Muthannea's Commentary on the Astronomical Tables of al-Khwarizmei: Two Hebrew Versions. LC 67-13434. (Yale Studies in the History of Science & Medicine Ser.: No. 2). (Illus.). pap. 105.00 (ISBN 0-317-09378-9, 2016770). Bks Demand UMI.

Meeus, Jean. Astronomical Tables of the Sun, Moon, & Planets. LC 83-5762. 400p. (Orig.). 1983. pap. text ed. 19.95x (ISBN 0-943396-02-6). Willmann-Bell.

Michelsen, Neil. Uranian Transneptune Ephemeris Eighteen Fifty to Two Thousand. 1978. 8.95 (ISBN 0-89159-001-3). Uranian Pubns.

Moore, Patrick, ed. Yearbook of Astronomy, 1983. (Illus.). 1983. 15.95 (ISBN 0-393-01700-1). Norton.

Pingree, David. Sanskrit Astronomical Tables in the United States. LC 68-19148. (Transactions Ser.: Vol. 58, Pt. 3). 1968. pap. 1.50 (ISBN 0-87169-583-9). Am Philos.

Stahlman, William D., et al. Solar & Planetary Longitudes for Years Minus 2500 to Plus 2000 by 10-day Intervals. LC 63-10534. pap. 149.00 (ISBN 0-317-07758-9, 2051912). Bks Demand UMI.

Voigt, H. H., ed. Landolt-Boernstein Numerical Data & Functional Relationships in Science & Technology, Group 6, Vol. 1: Astronomy & Astrophysics. xl, 711p. 1965. 216.30 (ISBN 0-387-03347-5). Springer-Verlag.

ASTRONOMY–VOCATIONAL GUIDANCE

see Astronomy As a Profession

ASTRONOMY, ANCIENT

see also Astronomy–Early Works to 1800

Astronomical Cuneiform Texts, 3 vols. (Sources in the History of Mathematics & Physical Sciences Ser.: Vol. 5). (Illus.). 799p. 1983. 92.00 (ISBN 0-387-90812-9). Springer-Verlag.

Astronomy Before the Telescope: The Earth-Moon System. LC 81-86234. (History of Astronomy Ser.: Vol. 1). 163p. 1984. 38.00 (ISBN 0-88126-201-3). Pachart Pub Hse.

Burl, Aubrey. Prehistoric Astronomy & Ritual. (Shire Archaeology Ser.: No. 32). (Illus.). 56p. 1983. pap. 5.95 (ISBN 0-85263-621-0, Pub. by Shire Pubns England). Seven Hills Bks.

Cornell, James. The First Stargazers: An Introduction to the Origins of Astronomy. 1981. 15.95 (ISBN 0-684-16799-9, ScribT). Scribner.

Delambre, Jean B. Histoire De l'Astronomie Ancienne, 2 Vols. facsimile ed. 1817. Set. 105.00 (ISBN 0-384-11203-X). Johnson Repr.

Hashimi, Ali Ibn Sulayman al. The Book of the Reasons Behind Astronomical Tables (Kitab Fi 'ilal Al-Zijat) Kennedy, E. S. & Pingree, David, eds. Haddad, Fuad I., tr. from Arabic. LC 77-14160. 408p. 1981. 60.00x (ISBN 0-8201-1298-4). Schol Facsimiles.

Heath, Thomas L. Greek Astronomy. Barker, Earnest, ed. LC 77-89685. (Library of Greek Thought: No. 6). 1969. Repr. of 1932 ed. 15.00 (ISBN 0-404-03232-X). AMS Pr.

Krupp, E. C., ed. In Search of Ancient Astronomies: Stonehenge to von Daniken: Archaeoastronomy Discovers Our Sophisticated Ancestors. (Illus.). 1979. pap. 6.95 (ISBN 0-07-035556-8). McGraw.

Neugebauer, O. A History of Ancient Mathematical Astronomy, 3 pts. LC 75-8778. (Studies in the History of Mathematics & Physical Sciences: Vol. 1). (Illus.). 1500p. 1975. text ed. 180.00 (ISBN 0-387-06995-X). Springer-Verlag.

Neugebauer, Otto. The Exact Sciences in Antiquity. 2nd ed. LC 69-20421. (Illus.). 1969. pap. 5.00 (ISBN 0-486-22332-9). Dover.

Newton, Robert R. Ancient Astronomical Observations & the Accelerations of the Earth & Moon. LC 70-122011. (Illus.). Repr. of 1970 ed. 62.60 (ISBN 0-8357-9264-1, 2013730). Bks Demand UMI.

Orr, Mary A. Dante & the Early Astronomers. LC 71-101029. 1969. Repr. of 1956 ed. 26.50x (ISBN 0-8046-0696-X, Pub. by Kennikat). Assoc Faculty Pr.

Pinches, Theophilus G., et al. Late Babylonian Astronomical & Related Texts Copied by J. Schaumberger. Sachs, A. J. & Schaumberger, J., eds. LC 56-1209. (Brown University Studies: No. 18). pap. 81.50 (ISBN 0-317-09132-8, 2004668). Bks Demand UMI.

Pomerance, Leon. The Phaistos Disc: An Interpretation of Astronomical Symbols. (Studies in Mediterranean Archaeology Pocket Bk.: No. 6). (Illus.). 1976. pap. text ed. 9.50x (ISBN 91-85058-67-X). Humanities.

Ptolemy, Claudius. Cosmography. prepub 6000.00 (ISBN 0-384-48140-X); 7500.00. Johnson Repr.

Tannery, Paul. Recherches sur L'Histoire de L'Astronomie Ancienne. facsimile ed. LC 75-13297. (History of Ideas in Ancient Greece Ser.). (Fr.). 1976. Repr. of 1893 ed. 23.50x (ISBN 0-405-07341-0). Ayer Co Pubs.

Theon Of Smyrna. Theon of Smyrna: Mathematics Useful for Understanding Plato or, Pythagorean Arithmetic, Music, Astronomy, Spiritual Disciplines. Lawlor, Robert, tr. from Greek. LC 77-73716. (Secret Doctrine Reference Ser.). (Illus.). 200p. 1978. 12.00 (ISBN 0-913510-24-6). Wizards.

Wood, John E. Sun, Moon, & Standing Stones. (Illus.). 1978. 22.50x (ISBN 0-19-211443-3). Oxford U Pr.

ASTRONOMY, CHINESE

Bernard, Henri. Matteo Ricci's Scientific Contribution to China. Werner, Edward C., tr. LC 73-863. (China Studies Ser). (Illus.). 108p. 1973. Repr. of 1935 ed. 13.75 (ISBN 0-88355-059-8). Hyperion Conn.

Commission on International Relations. Astronomy in China. 109p. 1979. pap. 7.75 (ISBN 0-309-02867-1). Natl Acad Pr.

Current Topics in Chinese Science: Section E: Astronomy. 220p. 1984. pap. text ed. 24.00 (ISBN 0-677-06260-5). Gordon.

Schafer, Edward H. Pacing the Void: T'ang Approaches to the Stars. LC 76-48362. 1978. 49.50x (ISBN 0-520-03344-2). U of Cal Pr.

Staal, Julius D. Stars of Jade. LC 84-50263. (Chinese Astronomy Ser.). (Illus.). 225p. (Orig.). 1984. pap. text ed. 19.95 (ISBN 0-317-01265-7). Writ Pr.

ASTRONOMY, EGYPTIAN

Fix, William R. Star Maps. (Octopus Bk.). (Illus.). 1979. 14.95 (ISBN 0-7064-1066-1, Mayflower Bks); pap. 8.95 (ISBN 0-7064-1085-8). Smith Pubs.

King, David A. Mathematical Astronomy in Medieval Yemen: A Biobibliographical Survey. LC 81-71733. (American Research Center in Egypt, Catalogs Ser.: Vol. 4). (Illus.). xiv, 108p. (Orig.). 1983. 27.00x (ISBN 0-89003-099-5); pap. 17.00x (ISBN 0-89003-098-7). Undena Pubns.

Neugebauer, O. & Parker, R. A. Egyptian Astronomical Texts: Decans, Planets, Constellations & Zodiacs, Vol. 3. LC 60-15723. (Brown Egyptological Studies: No. 6). (Illus.). Repr. of 1969 ed. 28.20 (ISBN 0-8357-9045-2, 2012292); plates 53.00. Bks Demand UMI.

ASTRONOMY, INFRA-RED

see Infra-Red Astronomy

ASTRONOMY, JAPANESE

Nakayama, Shigeru. History of Japanese Astronomy: Chinese Background & Western Impact. LC 68-21980. (Harvard-Yenching Institute Monograph: No. 18). (Illus.). 1969. 20.00x (ISBN 0-674-39725-8). Harvard U Pr.

ASTRONOMY, MAYA

Willson, R. W. Astronomical Notes on the Maya Codices. (Harvard University Peabody Museum of Archaeology & Ethnology Papers Ser). Repr. of 1924 ed. 11.00 (ISBN 0-527-01208-4). Kraus Repr.

ASTRONOMY, MEDIEVAL

Delambre, Jean B. Histoire de L'astronomie du Moyen Age. 1965. Repr. of 1819 ed. 55.00 (ISBN 0-384-11265-X). Johnson Repr.

Grimm, Florence M. Astronomical Lore in Chaucer. LC 73-168207. (University of Nebraska Studies in Language, Literature & Criticism). 1970. Repr. of 1919 ed. 12.00 (ISBN 0-404-02919-1). AMS Pr.

King, David A. Mathematical Astronomy in Medieval Yemen: A Biobibliographical Survey. LC 81-71733. (American Research Center in Egypt, Catalogs Ser.: Vol. 4). (Illus.). xiv, 108p. (Orig.). 1983. 27.00x (ISBN 0-89003-099-5); pap. 17.00x (ISBN 0-89003-098-7). Undena Pubns.

Newton, Robert R. Medieval Chronicles & the Rotation of the Earth. LC 78-39780. pap. 120.00 (ISBN 0-317-07955-7, 2012291). Bks Demand UMI.

Orr, Mary A. Dante & the Early Astronomers. LC 71-101029. 1969. Repr. of 1956 ed. 26.50x (ISBN 0-8046-0696-X, Pub. by Kennikat). Assoc Faculty Pr.

ASTRONOMY, NAUTICAL

see Nautical Astronomy

ASTRONOMY, SPHERICAL AND PRACTICAL

see also Eclipses; Longitude; Nautical Astronomy; Navigation; Nutation; Time

Green, Robin. Spherical Astronomy. 480p. Date not set. price not set. (ISBN 0-521-23988-5); pap. price not set. (ISBN 0-521-31779-7). Cambridge U Pr.

Hill, Thomas. The Schoole of Skil, Containing Two Bookes: The First, of the Sphere of Heaven, Etc., the Second, of the Sphericall Elements. LC 73-7083. (English Experience Ser.: No. 607). 267p. 1973. Repr. of 1599 ed. 26.50 (ISBN 90-221-0607-1). Walter J Johnson.

Mills, H. R. Positional Astronomy & Astro-Navigation Made Easy: A New Approach Using the Pocket Calculator. LC 77-13142. 267p. 1978. 42.95x (ISBN 0-470-99324-3). Halsted Pr.

Mueller, Ivan I. Spherical & Practical Astronomy As Applied to Geodesy. LC 68-31453. (Illus.). 1969. 40.00 (ISBN 0-8044-4667-9). Ungar.

Record, Robert. The Castle of Knowledge. LC 74-28882. (English Experience Ser.: No. 760). 1975. Repr. of 1556 ed. 44.00 (ISBN 90-221-0760-4). Walter J Johnson.

Smart, W. M. Textbook on Spherical Astronomy. 6th ed. LC 76-50643. (Illus.). 1977. 64.50 (ISBN 0-521-21516-1); pap. 23.95x (ISBN 0-521-29180-1). Cambridge U Pr.

Taff, Laurence G. Computational Spherical Astronomy. LC 80-18834. 233p. 1981. 39.95 (ISBN 0-471-06257-X, Pub. by Wiley-Interscience). Wiley.

ASTRONOMY, STATISTICAL

see Statistical Astronomy

ASTRONOMY AS A PROFESSION

Peltier, Leslie C. Starlight Nights. LC 65-20992. (Illus.). 236p. 1980. pap. 8.95 (ISBN 0-933346-02-6, 6026). Sky Pub.

ASTROPHYSICS

see also Astronomical Spectroscopy; Cosmic Electrodynamics; Interstellar Matter; Magnetic Fields (Cosmic Physics); Mechanics, Celestial; Nuclear Astrophysics; Radiative Transfer; Spectrum Analysis; Stars–Atmospheres

Abt, H. A., ed. Astrophysical Journal Supplement. 100.00 (ISBN 0-318-18120-7); members 40.00 (ISBN 0-318-18121-5). Am Astro Soc.

Alksne, Z. K. & Ikaunieks, Ya Y. Carbon Stars. rev. ed. Baumert, J. H., ed. (Astronomy & Astrophysics Ser.: Vol. 11). Orig. Title: Uglerodnye Zvezdy. (Illus.). 192p. pap. 24.00 (ISBN 0-912918-16-0, 0016). Pachart Pub Hse.

Allen, C. W. Astrophysical Quantities. 310p. 1976. text ed. 65.00 (ISBN 0-485-11150-0, Pub. by Athlone Pr Ltd). Longwood Pub Group.

American Meteorological Society - Boston. Cumulated Bibliography & Index to Meteorological & Geoastrophysical Abstracts: 1950-1969. 1972. Author Sequence, 9 Vols. 1395.00 (ISBN 0-8161-0942-7, Hall Library); Dec. Class, 4 Vols. 835.00 (ISBN 0-8161-0183-3). G K Hall.

Arnott, Struther, et al, eds. Molecular Biophysics of the Extracellular Matrix. LC 84-6640. (Molecular Biology & Biophysics Ser.). 224p. 1984. 39.50 (ISBN 0-89603-051-2). Humana.

Astrofisica. (Monografia: No. 10). (Span.). 108p. 1982. pap. 3.50 (ISBN 0-8270-1902-5). OAS.

Astronomy & Astrophysics for the 1980's: Reports of the Astronomy Survey Committee, 2 vols. 1983. Vol. I,1982 189pgs. 15.95 (ISBN 0-309-03249-0); Vol. II,1983 442pgs. pap. text ed. 25.00 (ISBN 0-309-03334-9). Natl Acad Pr.

Astronomy Survey Committee, National Research Council. Challenges to Astronomy & Astrophysics: Working Documents of the Astronomy Survey Committee. 296p. 1983. pap. text ed. 14.50 (ISBN 0-309-03335-7). Natl Acad Pr.

Athay, R. G. Radiation Transport in Spectral Lines. LC 72-188002. (Geophysics & Astrophysics Monographs: No. 1). 266p. 1972. lib. bdg. 39.50 (ISBN 90-277-0228-4, Pub. by Reidel Holland); pap. 21.50 (ISBN 90-277-0241-1, Pub. by Reidel Holland). Kluwer Academic.

Audouze, Jean, ed. CNO Isotopes in Astrophysics. (Astrophysics & Space Science Lib. Ser.: No. 67). 1977. lib. bdg. 29.00 (ISBN 90-277-0807-X, Pub. by Reidel Holland). Kluwer Academic.

Avrett, Eugene, ed. Frontiers of Astrophysics. (Illus.). 1976. 32.50x (ISBN 0-674-32559-1); pap. text ed. 12.95x (ISBN 0-674-32660-1). Harvard U Pr.

Baliunas, S. L. & Hartmann, L., eds. Cool Stars, Stellar Systems, & the Sun: Proceedings of the Third Cambridge Workshop on Cool Stars, Stellar Systems, & the Sun, Held in Cambridge MA, October 5-7. (Lecture Notes in Physics Ser.: Vol. 193). vii, 364p. 1984. pap. 22.00 (ISBN 0-387-12907-3). Springer-Verlag.

Bancel, Daniel & Signore, Monique, eds. Problems of Collapse & Numerical Relativity. 1984. lib. bdg. 59.00 (ISBN 90-277-1816-4, Pub. by Reidel Holland). Kluwer Academic.

Barnes, Charles A., et al, eds. Essays in Nuclear Astrophysics. LC 81-9992. 555p. 1982. 85.00 (ISBN 0-521-24410-2); pap. 34.50 (ISBN 0-521-28876-2). Cambridge U Pr.

Bernacca, Pier L., ed. Astrophysics from Spacelab. Ruffini, Remo. (Astrophysics & Space Science Library: No. 81). 720p. 1980. lib. bdg. 47.50 (ISBN 90-277-1064-3, Pub. by Reidel Holland). Kluwer Academic.
Boehme, S., ed. Astronomy & Astrophysics Abstracts: Literature, Vol. 32; 1982, Pt. 2. 848p. 1983. 72.00 (ISBN 0-387-12516-7). Springer-Verlag.
--Astronomy & Astrophysics Abstracts, Vol. 29: Literature 1981, Pt. 1. 853p. 1981. 65.00 (ISBN 0-387-11264-2). Springer-Verlag.
--Astronomy & Astrophysics Abstracts, Vol. 3: Literature 1970, Pt. 1. x, 490p. 1970. 50.20 (ISBN 0-387-05314-X). Springer-Verlag.
--Astronomy & Astrophysics Abstracts, Vol. 4: Literature 1970, Pt. 2. x, 562p. 1971. 50.20 (ISBN 0-387-05514-2). Springer-Verlag.
--Astronomy & Astrophysics Abstracts, Vol. 5: Literature 1971, Pt. 1. x, 505p. 1971. 50.20 (ISBN 0-387-05701-3). Springer-Verlag.
--Astronomy & Astrophysics Abstracts, Vol. 6: Literature 1971, Pt. 2. x, 560p. 1972. 50.20 (ISBN 0-387-05888-5). Springer-Verlag.
Boehme, S., et al. Astronomy & Astrophysics Abstracts, Vol. 31: Literature 1982, Pt. 1. x, 776p. 1982. 72.00 (ISBN 0-387-12072-6). Springer-Verlag.
Boehme, S., et al, eds. Astronmomy & Astrophysics Abstracts, Vol. 25: Literature 1979, Pt. 1. x, 871p. 1979. 82.00 (ISBN 0-387-09831-3). Springer-Verlag.
--Astronomy & Abstrophysics Abstracts, Vol. 9: Literature 1973, Pt. 1. vii, 610p. 1973. 50.20 (ISBN 0-387-06560-1). Springer-Verlag.
--Astronomy & Astrophysics Abstacts, Vol. 1: Literature 1969, Part 1. vii, 435p. 1969. 50.20 (ISBN 0-387-04421-3). Springer-Verlag.
--Astronomy & Astrophysics Abstracts: Vol. 23-24. 1127p. 1979. 77.00 (ISBN 0-387-09830-5). Springer-Verlag.
--Astronomy & Astrophysics Abstracts: Literature 1979, Pt. 2, Vol. 26. 794p. 1980. 80.00 (ISBN 0-387-10134-9). Springer-Verlag.
--Astronomy & Astrophysics Abstracts, Vol. 10: Literature 1973, Pt. 2. viii, 661p. 1974. 50.80 (ISBN 0-387-06795-7). Springer-Verlag.
--Astronomy & Astrophysics Abstracts, Vol. 11: Literature 1974, Pt. 1. viii, 579p. 1975. 54.00 (ISBN 0-387-07003-6). Springer-Verlag.
--Astronomy & Astrophysics Abstracts, Vol. 12: Literature 1974. Pt. 2. viii, 699p. 1975. 58.00 (ISBN 0-387-07339-6). Springer-Verlag.
--Astronomy & Astrophysics Abstracts, Vol. 13: Literature 1975, Pt. 1. viii, 632p. 1975. 51.00 (ISBN 0-387-07492-9). Springer-Verlag.
--Astronomy & Astrophysics Abstracts, Vol. 14: Literature 1975, Pt. 2. viii, 747p. 1976. 58.00 (ISBN 0-387-07784-7). Springer-Verlag.
--Astronomy & Astrophysics Abstracts, Vol. 18: Literature 1976, Pt. 2. x, 859p. 1977. 58.00 (ISBN 0-387-08319-7). Springer-Verlag.
--Astronomy & Astrophysics Abstracts, Vol. 19: Literature 1977, Pt. 1. viii, 732p. 1977. 66.00 (ISBN 0-387-08555-6). Springer-Verlag.
--Astronomy & Astrophysics Abstracts, Vol. 15-16: Author & Subject Indexes to Volumes 1-10, Literature 1969-1973. v, 655p. 1976. 58.00 (ISBN 0-387-07905-X). Springer-Verlag.
Boehme, S, et al, eds. Astronomy & Astrophysics Abstracts, Vol. 27: Literature 1980, Pt. 1. 939p. 1980. 80.00 (ISBN 0-387-10479-8). Springer-Verlag.
Boehme, S., et al, eds. Astronomy & Astrophysics Abstracts, Vol. 2: Literature 1969, Pt. 2. x, 516p. 1970. 50.20 (ISBN 0-387-04773-5). Springer-Verlag.
--Astronomy & Astrophysics Abstracts, Vol. 21: Literature 1978, Pt. 1. viii, 834p. 1978. 65.00 (ISBN 0-387-09067-3). Springer-Verlag.
--Astronomy & Astrophysics Abstracts, Vol. 22: Literature 1978, Pt. 2. viii, 849p. 1979. 60.00 (ISBN 0-387-09464-4). Springer-Verlag.
--Astronomy & Astrophysics Abstracts, Vol. 28: Literature 1980, Pt. 2. 841p. 1981. 70.00 (ISBN 0-387-10799-1). Springer-Verlag.
--Astronomy & Astrophysics Abstracts, Vol. 30: Literature, 1981. 792p. 1982. 72.00 (ISBN 0-387-11721-0). Springer-Verlag.
--Astronomy & Astrophysics Abstracts, Vol. 7: Literature 1972, Pt. 1. x, 526p. 1972. 50.20 (ISBN 0-387-06072-3). Springer-Verlag.
--Astronomy & Astrophysics Abstracts, Vol. 8: Literature 1972, Pt. 2. x, 594p. 1973. 50.20 (ISBN 0-387-06352-8). Springer-Verlag.
--Literature Nineteen Seventy Eight, Part 1. (Astronomy & Astrophysics Abstracts Ser.: Vol. 21). 1978. 65.00 (ISBN 0-387-09067-3). Springer-Verlag.
Bogoyavlensky, O. I. Methods in the Qualitative Theory of Dynamical Systems in Astrophysics & Gas Dynamics. Gokhman, D., tr. from Russ. (Soviet Mathematics Ser.). (Illus.). 320p. 1985. 49.00 (ISBN 0-387-13614-2). Springer-Verlag.
Bohme, S., et al, eds. Astronomy & Astrophysics Abstracts, Vol. 37. Schmadel, L. D., tr. (Literature 1984: Pt. 1). 920p. 1984. 68.50 (ISBN 0-387-13937-0). Springer-Verlag.
--Literature Nineteen Eighty-Three, Pt. 2. (Astronomy & Astrophysics Abstracts Ser.: Vol. 34). 960p. 1984. 68.50 (ISBN 0-387-13485-9). Springer-Verlag.
--Literature, 1984, Pt. 2. Heinrich, I. & Hofmann, W. Zech, G., tr. (Astronomy & Astrophysics Abstracts Ser.: Vol. 38). 920p. 1985. 69.50 (ISBN 0-387-15562-7). Springer-Verlag.
Bowers, Richard & Deeming, Terry. Astrophysics. (Illus.). 1984. Vol. 1, Stars 343pps. text ed. write for info. (ISBN 0-86720-018-9); Vol. 2, Interstellar Matter & Galaxies, 300pps. text ed. write for info. (ISBN 0-86720-047-2). Jones & Bartlett.
Bravais, A. On the Systems Formed by Points Regularly Distributed on a Plane or in Space. (American Crystallographic Association Monograph: Vol. 4). 113p. 1969. pap. 3.00 (ISBN 0-686-60370-2). Polycrystal Bk Serv.
Brecher, Kenneth & Setti, Ginancarlo, eds. High Energy Astrophysics & Its Relation to Elementary Particle Physics. LC 74-19794. 1974. 45.00x. MIT Pr.
Burger, Jan J., et al, eds. Atmospheric Physics from Spacelab. (Astrophysics & Space Science Library: No. 61). 1976. lib. bdg. 55.00 (ISBN 90-277-0768-5, Pub. by Reidel Holland). Kluwer Academic.
Burke, P. G. & Eissner, W. B., eds. Atoms in Astrophysics. (Physics of Atoms & Molecules Ser.). 345p. 1983. 52.50x (ISBN 0-306-41097-4, Plenum Pr). Plenum Pub.
Burns, M. L. & Harding, A. K., eds. Positron-Electron Pairs in Astrophysics: AIP Conference Proceeding Center, Goddard Space Flight Center, 1983, No. 101. LC 83-71926. 447p. 1983. lib. bdg. 38.50 (ISBN 0-88318-200-9). Am Inst Physics.
Calder, Nigel. The Key to the Universe. (Large Format Ser.). 1978. pap. 8.95 (ISBN 0-14-005065-5). Penguin.
Cameron, A. G., ed. Astrophysics Today. LC 84-70879. (Readings from Physics Today Ser.). (Illus.). 348p. 1984. pap. 25.00 (ISBN 0-88318-446-X). Am Inst Physics.
Carlton, N., ed. Astrophysics, Pt. A: Optical & Infrared Astronomy. (Methods of Experimental Physics Ser.: Vol. 12). 1974. 80.00 (ISBN 0-12-475912-2). Acad Pr.
Carovillano, R. L. & Forbes, J. M., eds. Solar-Terrestial Physics: Principles & Theoretical Foundations. 1983. lib. bdg. 115.00 (ISBN 90-277-1632-3, Pub. by Reidel Holland). Kluwer Academic.
Centrella, Joan, et al, eds. Numerical Astrophysics. 548p. 1985. text ed. write for info (ISBN 0-86720-048-0). Jones & Bartlett.
Chandrasekhar, S. The Mathematical Theory of Black Holes. (International Series of Monographs on Physics). (Illus.). 1982. 110.00x (ISBN 0-19-851291-0). Oxford U Pr.
Chandrasekhar, Subrahmanyan. An Introduction to the Study of Stellar Structure. 1939. pap. 8.95 (ISBN 0-486-60413-6). Dover.
--Radiative Transfer. (Illus.). 1960. pap. 7.95 (ISBN 0-486-60590-6). Dover.
Chupp, E. L. Gamma-Ray Astronomy: Nuclear Transition Region. LC 76-21711. (Geophysics & Astrophysics Monographs: No. 14). 1976. lib. bdg. 55.00 (ISBN 90-277-0695-6, Pub. by Reidel Holland); pap. 26.00 (ISBN 90-277-0696-4, Pub. by Reidel Holland). Kluwer Academic.
CNRS Staff. Fundamental Physics & Astrophysics. 176p. Date not set. 55.00 (ISBN 0-677-30860-4). Gordon.
Cole, G. H. The Physics of Planetary Interiors. 224p. 1984. 39.00 (ISBN 0-9903000-4-8, Pub. by A Hilger Techo Hse UK); pap. 17.00 (ISBN 0-9903000-8-0, Pub. by A Hilger Techo Hse UK). Heyden.
Collins, George W. The Virial Theorem in Stellar Astrophysics. (Astronomy & Astrophysics Ser: Vol. 7). 143p. 1978. pap. text ed. 19.00 (ISBN 0-912918-13-6, 0013). Pachart Pub Hse.
Conference of the Summer School, Banff Centre, Banff, Alberta, Canada, August 14-26, 1972. Relativity, Astrophysics & Cosmology: Proceedings. Israel, Werner, ed. LC 72-97957. (Astrophysics & Space Science Library: Vol. 38). 340p. 1973. lib. bdg. 52.65 (ISBN 90-277-0369-8, Pub. by Reidel Holland). Kluwer Academic.
Conference on Physics of the Magnetosphere, Boston College, 1967. Physics of the Magnetosphere: Proceedings. Carovillano, R. L. & McClay, J. F., eds. (Astrophysics & Space Science Library: No.10). 686p. 1968. lib. bdg. 68.50 (ISBN 90-277-0111-3, Pub. by Reidel Holland). Kluwer Academic.
Conti, Peter S. & De Loore, C. W., eds. Mass Loss & Evolution of O-Type Stars. (International Astronomical Union Symposium Ser.: No. 83). 1979. lib. bdg. 63.00 (ISBN 90-277-0988-2, Pub. by Reidel Holland); pap. 31.50 (ISBN 90-277-0989-0, Pub. by Reidel Holland). Kluwer Academic.
Coulomb, J. & Caputo, M., eds. Mantle & Core in Planetary Physics. (Italian Physical Society: Course 50). 1972. 75.00 (ISBN 0-12-368850-7). Acad Pr.
Demianski, M. Relativistic Astrophysics. (International Studies of Natural Philosophy: Vol. 110). (Illus.). 300p. 1985. 45.00 (ISBN 0-08-025042-4). Pergamon.
DeVorkin, David H. The History of Modern Astronomy & Astrophysics. LC 81-43349. 462p. 1985. lib. bdg. 79.00 (ISBN 0-8240-9283-X). Garland Pub.
DeWitt, C., et al, eds. Les Houches Lectures: 1966, High Energy Astrophyspics, 3 vols. Incl. Vol. 1. Radiosources & their Interpretations. 264p. 69.50 (ISBN 0-677-11130-4); Vol. 2. Elementary Processes & Acceleration Mechanisms. 344p. 93.75 (ISBN 0-677-11140-1); Vol. 3. General Relativity & High Density Astrophysics. 462p. 113.50 (ISBN 0-677-11150-9). LC 74-80848. 1070p. 1967-68. Set. 244.95 (ISBN 0-677-11160-6). Gordon.
Dyson, J. E. & Williams, D. A. Physics of the Interstellar Medium. LC 80-13713. 194p. 1980. 28.95x (ISBN 0-470-26983-9). Halsted Pr.
Ehlers, J., ed. Relativity Theory & Astrophysics: Stellar Structure. LC 62-21481. (Lectures in Applied Mathematics Ser.: Vol. 10). 136p. 1967. 23.00 (ISBN 0-8218-1110-X, LAM-10). Am Math.
Ehlers, Jurgen, et al, eds. Texas Symposium on Relativistic Astrophysics, 9th. LC 80-11614. (Annals of the New York Academy of Sciences: Vol. 336). 599p. 1980. 107.00x (ISBN 0-89766-045-5). NY Acad Sci.
ESLAB Symposium, 7th, Saulgau, Germany, May 22-25, 1973. Correlated Interplanetary & Magnetospheric Observations: Proceedings. Page, D. E., ed. LC 73-91433. (Astrophysics & Space Science Library: No. 42). 676p. 1974. lib. bdg. 103.00 (ISBN 90-277-0429-5, Pub. by Reidel Holland). Kluwer Academic.
ESRIN-ESLAB Symposium, 4th, Frascati, Italy, July 6-10, 1970. Mesospheric Models & Related Experiments: Proceedings. Fiocco, G., ed. LC 70-154737. (Astrophysics & Space Science Library: No.25). 298p. 1971. lib. bdg. 42.00 (ISBN 90-277-0200-4, Pub. by Reidel Holland). Kluwer Academic.
European Astronomical Meeting, 1st, Athens, 1972. Stars & the Milky Way System: Proceedings, Vol. 2. Mavridis, L. N., ed. LC 73-9108. (Illus.). 300p. 1974. 85.00 (ISBN 0-387-06383-8). Springer-Verlag.
Evans, David S., intro. by. Eleventh Texas Symposium on Relativistic Astrophysics. (Annals of the New York Academy of Sciences: Vol. 422). 396p. 79.00x (ISBN 0-89766-234-2); pap. 79.00x (ISBN 0-89766-235-0). NY Acad Sci.
Fang, L. Z. & Ruffini, R. Cosmology of the Early Universe. (Advanced Series in Astrophysics: Vol. 1). 350p. 37.00x (ISBN 9971-950-92-8, Pub. by World Sci Singapore); pap. 21.00x (ISBN 9971-950-93-6, Pub. by World Sci Singapore). Taylor & Francis.
Fang, L. Z. & Ruffini, J., eds. Basic Concepts in Relativistic Astrophysics. 1983. 33.00x (ISBN 9971-950-66-9, Pub. by World Sci Singapore). Taylor & Francis.
Fazio, G. G., ed. Infrared & Submillimeter Astronomy. (Astrophysics & Space Science Library: No. 63). 1977. lib. bdg. 34.00 (ISBN 90-277-0791-X, Pub. by Reidel Holland). Kluwer Academic.
Ferrara, Sergio, et al, eds. Unification of the Fundamental Particle Interactions. LC 80-24447. (Ettore Majorana International Science Series-Physical Sciences: Vol. 7). 740p. 1981. 115.00x (ISBN 0-306-40575-X, Plenum Pr). Plenum Pub.
Field, George B. & Chaisson, Eric J. The Invisible Universe: Probing The Frontiers of Astrophysics. 200p. 1985. 19.95. Birkhauser.
Fiorini, Ettore, ed. Neutrino Physics & Astrophysics. LC 81-11999. (Ettore Majorana International Science Series, Physical Sciences: Vol. 12). 432p. 1982. 62.50x (ISBN 0-306-40746-9, Plenum Pr). Plenum Pub.
Fowler, William A. Nuclear Astrophysics. LC 67-18204. (Memoirs Ser.: Vol. 67). (Illus.). 1967. 5.00 (ISBN 0-87169-067-5). Am Philos.
Frank, J., et al, eds. Accretion Power in Astrophysics. 273p. 1985. 59.50 (ISBN 0-521-24530-3). Cambridge U Pr.
Fustero, X. & Verdaguer, E. Relativistic Astrophysics & Cosmology: Proceedings of the XIV Gift International Seminar Sant Feliu de Guixols, Spain, June 27-July 1, 1983. 320p. 1984. 37.00x (ISBN 9971-966-60-3, Pub. by World Sci Singapore). Taylor & Francis.
Gingerich, Owen, ed. Astrophysics & Twentieth Century Astronomy to 1950, Vol. 4, Pt. A. LC 83-10164. (General History of Astronomy Ser.). 206p. 1984. 29.95 (ISBN 0-521-24256-8). Cambridge U Pr.
Ginzberg, V. L. Theoretical Physics & Astrophysics. Haar, D. Ter, tr. (International Series in Natural Philosophy: Vol. 99). (Illus.). 1979. pap. 37.00 (ISBN 0-08-023066-0). Pergamon.
Ginzburg, V. Key Problems of Physics & Astrophysics. 167p. 1978. 4.45 (ISBN 0-8285-0789-9, Pub. by Mir Pubs USSR). Imported Pubns.
Ginzburg, Vitalii L. The Astrophysics of Cosmic Rays. 2nd., Rev. & Supplemented ed. Hardin, Ron, ed. LC 73-606893. (U. S. National Aeronautics & Space Administration. NASA Technical Translation Ser.: TT F-561). pap. 20.00 (ISBN 0-317-09306-1, 2003731). Bks Demand UMI.
Ginzburg, Vitaly L. Elementary Processes for Cosmic Ray Astrophysics. (Topics in Astrophysics & Space Physics Ser.). 140p. 1969. 45.25 (ISBN 0-677-01980-7). Gordon.
Gordon, C. W. & Canuto, V. The Earth One: The Upper Atmosphere, Ionisphere & Magnetosphere. (Handbook of Astronomy, Astrophysics & Geophysics Ser.: Vol. I). 420p. 1978. 103.95 (ISBN 0-677-16100-X). Gordon.
--Handbook of Astronomy, Astrophysics & Geophysics Vol. 1. (The Earth 1: The Upper Atmosphere, Ionosphere & Magnetosphre). 420p. 1978. 103.95. Gordon.
Gough. Problems of Solar & Stellar Oscillations. 1983. lib. bdg. 84.50 (ISBN 90-277-1554-8, Pub. by Reidel Holland). Kluwer Academic.
Gratton, L. High Energy Astrophysics. (Italian Physical Society: Course 35). 1967. 75.00 (ISBN 0-12-368835-3). Acad Pr.
Greisen, Kenneth. The Physics of Cosmic X-Ray, Gamma-Ray & Particle Sources. 2nd ed. Cameron, A. G. W. & Field, G. B., eds. LC 78-135063. (Topics in Astrophysics & Space Physics Ser.). (Illus.). 124p. 1971. 28.95 (ISBN 0-677-03380-X). Gordon.
Gursky, H. & Ruffini, R., eds. Neutron Stars, Black Holes & Binary X-Ray Sources. LC 75-15716. (Astrophysics & Space Science Library: No. 48). 441p. (Orig.). 1975. lib. bdg. 71.00 (ISBN 90-277-0541-0, Pub. by Reidel Holland); pap. 34.00 (ISBN 90-277-0542-9). Kluwer Academic.
Hack, M. Modern Astrophysics: A Memorial to Otto Struve. 364p. 1967. 80.95 (ISBN 0-677-12690-5). Gordon.
Harrison, B. Kent, et al. Gravitation Theory & Gravitational Collapse. LC 65-17293. 1965. 11.00x (ISBN 0-226-31802-8). U of Chicago Pr.
Harwit, Martin. Astrophysical Concepts. 1984. Repr. of 1973 ed. 25.00 (ISBN 0-910533-01-6). Concepts.
Heinrich, I. & Schmadel, L. D., eds. Astronomy & Astrophysics Abstracts: Vols. 35-36, Author & Subject Indexes to Vols. 25-34, Literature 1979-1983. (Astronomy & Astrophysics Abstracts Ser.). 915p. 1984. 68.50 (ISBN 0-387-13651-7). Springer-Verlag.
Hellwege, K. H., ed. Astronomy & Astrophysics: Methods-Constants-Solar System. (Landolt Boernstein Ser.: Vol. 2). (Illus.). 320p. 1981. 237.50 (ISBN 0-387-10054-7). Springer-Verlag.
Hopkins, Jeanne, ed. Glossary of Astronomy & Astrophysics. 2nd, rev. & enl. ed. LC 80-5226. (Phoenix Ser.). x, 196p. 1982. pap. 10.00x (ISBN 0-226-35169-6). U of Chicago Pr.
--Glossary of Astronomy & Astrophysics. rev. ed. LC 80-5226. 224p. 1980. lib. bdg. 19.00x (ISBN 0-226-35171-8). U of Chicago Pr.
Hoyle, Fred & Narlikar, Jayant V. The Physics-Astronomy Frontier. LC 80-11708. (Illus.). 438p. 1980. text ed. 27.95 (ISBN 0-7167-1160-5). W H Freeman.
Hu Ning, ed. General Relativity: Proceedings of the Third Marcel Grossman Meeting, 30 Aug-3 Sept. 1982, Shanghai, China, 2 vols. 1524p. 1985. Set. 150.00 (ISBN 0-444-86746-5, North Holland). Elsevier.
IAU Symposium, No. 36, Lunteren, Netherlands, June 1969. Ultraviolet Stellar Spectra & Related Ground-Based Observations: Proceedings. Houziaux, K. & Butler, H. E., eds. 361p. 1970. lib. bdg. 37.00 (ISBN 90-277-0152-0, Pub by Reidel Holland). Kluwer Academic.
International Astronomical Union Symposium, 55, Madrid, May 11-13, 1972. X- & Gamma-Ray Astronomy: Proceedings. Bradt, H. & Giaconni, R., eds. LC 72-92526. (Illus.). 323p. 1973. lib. bdg. 50.00 (ISBN 90-277-0303-5, Pub. by Reidel Holland); pap. 26.00 (ISBN 90-277-0337-X). Kluwer Academic.
International Astronomical Union, 10th Colliquium, Cambridge University, 1970. Gravitational N-Body Problem: Proceedings. Lecar, M., ed. LC 72-154740. (Astrophysics & Space Science Library: No. 31). 441p. 1972. lib. bdg. 60.50 (ISBN 90-277-0203-9, Pub. by Reidel Holland). Kluwer Academic.

Ibragimov, I. A. & Has'Minskii, R. Z. Statistical Estimation: Asymtotic Theory. (Applications of Mathematics Ser.: Vol. 16). 420p. 1981. 48.50 (ISBN 0-387-90523-5). Springer-Verlag.
Mandl, P. & Huskova, M., eds. Asymptotic Statistics 2: Proceedings of the Prague Symposium on Asymptotic Physics, 3rd, Aug. 29-Sept. 2, 1983. 462p. 1984. 55.75 (ISBN 0-444-87525-5). Elsevier.
Olver, F. W. Introduction to Asymptotics & Special Functions. 1974. 25.00 (ISBN 0-12-525856-9). Acad Pr.
Verhulst, F., ed. Asymptotic Analysis II: Surveys & New Trends. (Lecture Notes in Mathematics: Vol. 985). 497p. 1983. pap. 29.00 (ISBN 0-387-12286-9). Springer-Verlag.

ASYMPTOTIC EXPANSIONS

Akahira, M. & Takeuchi, K. Asymptotic Efficiency of Statistical Estimators: Concepts & Higher Order Asymptotic Efficiency. (Lecture Notes in Statistics Ser.: Vol. 7). 256p. 1981. pap. 18.00 (ISBN 0-387-90576-6). Springer-Verlag.
Axelsson, O., et al, eds. Analytical & Numerical Approaches to Asymptotic Problems in Analysis. (Mathematical Studies: Vol. 47). 382p. 1981. 64.00 (ISBN 0-444-86131-9). Elsevier.
Barenblatt, G. I., ed. Similarity, Self-Similarity & Intermediate Asymptotics. LC 79-14621. (Illus.). 236p. 1980. 55.00 (ISBN 0-306-10956-5, Consultants). Plenum Pub.
Basawa, I. V. & Scott, D. J. Asymptotic Optimal Inference for Non-Ergodic Models. (Lecture Notes in Statistics Ser.: Vol. 17). 170p. 1983. pap. 16.00 (ISBN 0-387-90810-2). Springer-Verlag.
Bensoussan, A., et al. Asymptotic Analysis for Periodic Structures. (Studies in Mathematics & Its Applications Ser.: Vol. 5). 700p. 1978. 70.25 (ISBN 0-444-85172-0, North-Holland). Elsevier.
Borovkov, A. A. Asymptotic Methods in Queuing Theory. LC 83-12557. (Probability & Mathematical Statistics-Probability & Mathematical Statistics: 1-345). 276p. 1984. 47.95x (ISBN 0-471-90286-1, Pub. by Wiley-Interscience). Wiley.
Copson, Edward T. Asymptotic Expansions. (Cambridge Tracts in Mathematics & Mathematical Physics). 1965. 29.95 (ISBN 0-521-04721-8). Cambridge U Pr.
De Bruijn, N. G. Asymptotic Methods in Analysis. viii, 200p. 1982. pap. 4.50 (ISBN 0-486-64221-6). Dover.
Eckhaus, Wiktor. Matched Asymptotic Expansions & Singular Perturbations. LC 72-96145. (Mathematics Studies: Vol. 6). 146p. 1973. pap. text ed. 36.25 (ISBN 0-7204-2606-5, North-Holland). Elsevier.
Erdelyi, A. Asymptotic Expansions. 1961. pap. 3.50 (ISBN 0-486-60318-0). Dover.
Ford, Walter B. Studies in Divergent Series & Summability, & the Asymptotic Development of Functions. LC 60-16836. 371p. 1985. text ed. 19.50 (ISBN 0-8284-0143-8). Chelsea Pub.
Guillemin, Victor & Sternberg, Shlomo. Geometric Asymptotics. LC 77-8210. (Mathematical Surveys Ser.: No. 14). 474p. 1977. 58.00 (ISBN 0-8218-1514-8, SURV-14). Am Math.
Immink, G. K. Asymptotics of Analytic Difference Equations. (Lecture Notes in Mathematics Ser.: Vol. 1085). v, 134p. 1984. pap. 10.00 (ISBN 0-387-13867-6). Springer-Verlag.
Kromer, Ralph E. Asymptotic Properties of the Autoregressive Spectral Estimator. LC 73-131403. 196p. 1969. 22.00 (ISBN 0-403-04512-6). Scholarly.
Majima, H. Asymptotic Analysis for Integrable Connections with Irregular Singular Points. (Lecture Notes in Mathematics Ser.: Vol. 1075). ix, 159p. 1984. pap. 12.00 (ISBN 0-387-13375-5). Springer-Verlag.
Nayfeh, Ali-Hasan. Perturbation Methods. LC 72-8068. (Pure & Applied Mathematics Ser.). 425p. 1973. 42.95x (ISBN 0-471-63059-4, Pub. by Wiley-Interscience). Wiley.
Olver, F. W. J. Asymptotics & Special Functions. (Computer Science & Applied Mathematics Ser.). 1974. 70.00 (ISBN 0-12-525850-X). Acad Pr.
O'Malley, Robert E., ed. Asymptotic Methods & Singular Perturbations: Proceedings of a Symposium, New York, April 1976. LC 76-27872. (SIAM-AMS Proceedings: Vol. 10). 1976. 30.00 (ISBN 0-8218-1330-7, SIAMS10). Am Math.
Rockland, C. Hypoellipticity & Eigenvalue Asymptotics. (Lecture Notes in Mathematics Ser.: Vol. 464). 171p. 1975. pap. 14.00 (ISBN 0-387-07175-X). Springer-Verlag.
Roseau, M. Asymptotic Wave Theory. LC 74-26167. (Applied Mathematics & Mechanics Ser.: Vol. 20). 349p. 1976. 74.50 (ISBN 0-444-10798-3, North-Holland). Elsevier.
Sibuya, Yasataka. Uniform Simplification in a Full Neighborhood of a Transition Point. LC 74-11246. (Memoirs: No. 149). 106p. 1974. pap. 10.00 (ISBN 0-8218-1849-X, MEMO-149). Am Math.
Sirovich, Lawrence. Techniques of Asymptotic Analysis. LC 70-149141. (Applied Mathematical Sciences Ser.: Vol. 2). (Illus.). 1971. pap. 21.95 (ISBN 0-387-90022-5). Springer-Verlag.
Strodt, Walter. Contributions to the Asymptotic Theory of Ordinary Differential Equations in the Complex Domain. LC 52-42839. (Memoirs: No. 13). 81p. pap. 9.00 (ISBN 0-8218-1213-0, MEMO-13). Am Math.
Verhulst, F., ed. Asymptotic Analysis II: Surveys & New Trends. (Lecture Notes in Mathematics: Vol. 985). 497p. 1983. pap. 29.00 (ISBN 0-387-12286-9). Springer-Verlag.

ASYNCHRONOUS ELECTRIC MOTORS

see Electric Motors, Induction

AT AND T 3B2 (COMPUTER)

AT&T Information Systems Inc. Staff. AT&T Computer Software Guide 3B2. 1985. pap. 19.95 (ISBN 0-8359-9279-9). Reston.

AT AND T 3B5–3B20 (COMPUTER)

AT&T Information Systems Inc. Staff. AT&T Computer Software Guide 3B5-3B20. 1985. pap. 19.95 (ISBN 0-8359-9277-2). Reston.

AT AND T PC6300 (COMPUTER)

AT&T Information Systems Inc. Staff. AT&T Computer Software Guide PC 6300. 1985. pap. 19.95 (ISBN 0-8359-9279-9). Reston.
Traister, Robert J. A Guide to the AT&T PC 6300. (Illus.). 1985. pap. 17.95 (ISBN 0-13-368796-1). P-H.

ATARI XL COMPUTERS

see also Atari 600xl (Computer); Atari 800xl (Computer)

Albrecht, Bob, et al. Atari BASIC. XL ed. (General Trade Books). 388p. 1985. pap. 14.95 (ISBN 0-471-80726-5). Wiley.
Albrecht, Bob L., et al. Atari BASIC. LC 79-12513. (Self-Teaching Guides). 333p. 1981. pap. text ed. 12.95 (ISBN 0-471-06496-3, Pub. by Wiley Pr). Wiley.
Andrews, Mark. Atari Roots: Atari Assembly Language. (Orig.). 1984. pap. 14.95 (ISBN 0-88190-171-7, BO171). Datamost.
Banse, Timothy P. Home Applications & Games for Atari Home Computers. (Microcomputer Bookshelf Ser.). 134p. 1983. pap. text ed. 14.50 (ISBN 0-316-08044-6). Little.
Bearden, Donna. Atari LOGO in the Classroom. 1984. pap. text ed. 14.95 (ISBN 0-8359-0121-1). Reston.
Berenbon, Howard. Mostly BASIC: Applications for Your Atari, 2 vols. LC 83-61071. 184p. 1983. Bk. 1, 184 pp. 12.95 (ISBN 0-672-22075-X, 22075); Bk. 2, 224 pp. 15.95 (ISBN 0-672-22092-X, 22092). Sams.
The Blue Book for the Atari Computer. 17.95 (ISBN 0-684-17921-0). WIDL Video.
Boom, Michael. Everything You Can Do with Your Atari Computer. (Everything You Can Do with Your... Ser.). 1984. pap. cancelled (ISBN 0-88284-277-3). Alfred Pub.
--How to Use Atari Computers. (An Alfred Handy Guide Ser.). 64p. 1983. 3.50 (ISBN 0-88284-235-8). Alfred Pub.
--How to Use Atari Computers. 1984. pap. 2.95 cancelled (ISBN 0-317-13948-7). Alfred Pub.
Brain Bank. The BASIC Conversions Handbook for Apple, Commodore, TRS-80, & Atari Users. write for info. Hayden.
Brannon, Charles. SpeedScript: The Word Processor for the Atari. Compute Editors, ed. (Orig.). 1985. pap. 9.95 (ISBN 0-87455-003-3). Compute Pubns.
Chadwick, Ian. Mapping the Atari. 194p. 1983. 14.95 (ISBN 0-942386-09-4). Compute Pubns.
--Mapping the Atari. rev. ed. Compute Editors, ed. (Orig.). 1985. pap. 16.95 (ISBN 0-87455-004-1). Compute Pubns.
Chamberlain, Judy & Chamberlain, Tom. Atari (400, 800, & XL Series) for the Beginning Beginner. (Illus.). 128p. 1983. Atari 400, 800 & XL Models. pap. 8.95 (ISBN 0-86582-119-4, EN79222). Enrich.
Chasin, Mark. Assembly Language: Programming for the Atari Computer. (A BYTE Book). 1984. pap. 15.95 (ISBN 0-07-010679-7). Mcgraw.
Coan, James S. & Kushner, Richard. Basic Atari BASIC. 256p. pap. 14.95 (6526). Hayden.
Cohen, Scott. Zap! The Rise & Fall of Atari. 192p. 1984. 14.95 (ISBN 0-07-011543-5). McGraw.
Collins, Joseph W. Atari Color Graphics: A Beginner's Workbook. pap. 12.95 (ISBN 0-912003-19-7). Bk Co.
Compute Magazine Staff. Compute's First Book of Atari. (Illus.). 184p. (Orig.). 1981. pap. 12.95 (ISBN 0-942386-00-0). Compute Pubns.
Compute! Magazine Staff. Compute's First Book of Atari Games. 232p. (Orig.). 1983. pap. 12.95 (ISBN 0-942386-14-0). Compute Pubns.
Compute Magazine Staff. Compute's Second Book of Atari. (Illus.). 250p. (Orig.). 1983. pap. 12.95 (ISBN 0-942386-06-X). Compute Pubns.
Compute! Magazine Staff. Compute's Second Book of Atari Graphics. 220p. (Orig.). 1983. pap. 12.95 (ISBN 0-942386-28-0). Compute Pubns.
--Compute's Third Book of Atari. 308p. (Orig.). 1984. pap. 12.95 (ISBN 0-942386-18-3). Compute Pubns.
Compute Magazine Staff, ed. Compute's First Book of Atari Graphics. 248p. (Orig.). 1983. pap. 12.95 (ISBN 0-942386-08-6). Compute Pubns.
Compute's Atari Collection, Vol. I. 1985. pap. 12.95 (ISBN 0-942386-79-5). Compute Pubns.
Consumer Guide Editors. Atari Software: Rating the Best. LC 83-737274. 154p. 1984. spiral bd. 1.98 (ISBN 0-517-42474-6). Outlet Bk Co.
--How to Win at Atari Computer Games. (Illus.). 64p. 1983. pap. 8.95 spiral bound cancelled (ISBN 0-671-49558-5, Fireside). S&S.
--The User's Guide to Atari, 400, 800, 1200XL. (Orig.). 1983. pap. 3.95 (ISBN 0-671-49503-8). PB.
DeWitt, Steve. Atari LOGO Activities. 1984. pap. 12.95 (ISBN 0-8359-0115-7). Reston.
Ellis, Mark & Ellis, Robert. Atari User's Guide: BASIC & Graphics for the Atari 400, 800, 1200. 288p. 1984. pap. 14.95 (ISBN 0-89303-323-5). Brady Comm.
Engel Enterprises & Engel, C. W. Stimulating Simulations. 2nd ed. 112p. 1979. pap. 7.50 ea. (ISBN 0-8104-5170-0). Atari Version (ISBN 0-8104-5197-2, 5197). Microsoft Version (5170). VIC Version (5173). Apple Version (6317). Commodore 64 Version (5201). TI-99-4A Version (6404). Hayden.
Englisch, Lothar & Walkowiak, Jorg. Presenting the Atari ST. 1985. write for info. Abacus Soft.
Evans, Carl M. Atari BASIC: Faster & Better. 300p. 19.95 (ISBN 0-936200-29-4). Blue Cat.
Floegel, Ekkehard. FORTH on the Atari: Learning by Using. 118p. 7.95 (ISBN 0-936200-38-3). Blue Cat.
FORTH on the Atari: Learning by Using. 116p. 7.95 (ISBN 0-317-07022-3). Elcomp.
Foster, Dennis L. & D. L. Foster Book Company Editors. The Addison-Wesley Book of Atari Software 1985. 416p. 1985. pap. 19.95 (ISBN 0-201-12019-4). Addison-Wesley.
Garb, Forrest A. Waterflood Manual for Hewlett Packard Calculators. LC 81-20274. (Illus.). 94p. (Orig.). 1982. 21.95x (ISBN 0-87201-895-4). Gulf Pub.
Glicksman, Hal & Simon, Kent. Games Ataris Play. (Illus.). 224p. 1983. pap. text ed. 14.95 (ISBN 0-88190-118-0, BO118). Datamost.
Goodman, Danny. The Simon & Schuster's Guide to Atari's "My First Computer". 128p. 1984. pap. 5.95 (ISBN 0-671-49255-1, Pub. by Computer Bks). S&S.
Haskell, Richard E. Atari BASIC. (Illus.). 175p. 1983. 19.95 (ISBN 0-13-049809-2, Spec); pap. 13.95 (ISBN 0-13-049791-6). P-H.
Heiserman, David. One Hundred One Programming Surprises & Tricks for Your Atari Computer. (Illus.). 208p. (Orig.). 1984. pap. 11.50 (ISBN 0-8306-1731-0, 1731). TAB Bks.
Heller, Dave & Heller, Dorothy. Free Software for Your Atari. (Free Software Ser.). (Illus.). 208p. 1983. pap. 8.95 (ISBN 0-86582-117-8, EN79211). Enrich.
Heller, David & Johnson, John. Dr. C. Wacko Presents Atari BASIC & the Whiz-Bang Miracle Machine. 1245p. 1984. pap. 12.95 (ISBN 0-201-11491-7). Addison-Wesley.
Heller, David, et al. Dr. C. Wacko's Miracle Guide to Designing & Programming Your Own Atari Computer Arcade Games. 1983. pap. 12.95 (ISBN 0-201-11488-7); book & software 24.95 (ISBN 0-201-11490-9). Addison-Wesley.
Hunter, James & Rondot, Troy. Atari Trivia Data Base. LC 84-51541. 8.95 (ISBN 0-672-22397-X). Sams.
James, Mike, et al. The Atari Book of Games. 156p. 1984. pap. 12.95 (ISBN 0-07-881159-7, 159-7). Osborne-McGraw.
Jones, Warren, et al. Programming, Problem Solving & Projects for Atari Computers. 14.95 (ISBN 0-8359-5685-7). Reston.
Kepner, Terry, et al. Atari XE Program Book. 180p. (Orig.). 1985. pap. 12.95 (ISBN 0-938862-05-7). Weber Systems.
Lamoitier, J. P. BASIC Exercises for the Atari. LC 82-63019. (Illus.). 251p. 1983. pap. 14.95 (ISBN 0-89588-101-2). SYBEX.
Lamothe, Adrien Z. The Atari Experience. (Illus.). 200p. 1983. pap. text ed. 14.95 (ISBN 0-88190-239-X, BO239). Datamost.
Mace, Scott & InfoWorld Editors. InfoWorld's Essential Guide to Atari Computers. (InfoWorld's Essential Guides Ser.). 250p. (Orig.). 1984. pap. 16.95 (ISBN 0-06-669006-4). Har Row.
Mently, David. ABC's of the Atari Computer. (Orig.). 1984. pap. text ed. 14.95 (ISBN 0-88190-367-1, BO367). Datamost.
Moore, Herb. Shapes & Sounds for the Atari. (Professional Software Ser.). 1984. incl. disks 45.00 (ISBN 0-471-88547-9). Wiley.
North, Alan. Atari Computer Program Writing Workbook. 96p. 1983. 4.95 (ISBN 0-86668-814-5). ARCsoft.
--One Hundred One Atari Computer Programming Tips & Tricks. 128p. (Orig.). 1982. pap. 8.95 (ISBN 0-86668-022-5). ARCsoft.
--Thirty-One New Atari Computer Programs for Home, School & Office. (Illus.). 96p. (Orig.). 1982. pap. 8.95 (ISBN 0-86668-018-7). ARCsoft.
Orwig, Gary W. & Hodges, William S. The Computer Tutor for the Atari: Learning Activities for Homes & Schools for the Atari 400, 800 & 1200 XL Home Computers. (Microcomputing Bookshelf Ser.). 350p. (Orig.). 1983. pap. 15.95 (ISBN 0-316-66502-9). Little.
Parker, Bill. The Intermediate Atari. (Intermediate Ser.). cancelled (ISBN 0-317-07089-4). Datamost.
Parker, Charlie. Music Major: Atari. (Illus.). 48p. 1984. pap. 24.95 canceled (ISBN 0-88056-208-0). Dilithium Pr.
Phillips, Gary & White, Jerry. The Atari User's Encyclopedia. Mellin, Michael F. & McCroskey, Mia, eds. 272p. (Orig.). 1983. pap. 19.95 (ISBN 0-912003-17-0). Bk Co.
Reisinger, John M. A-Plus Programming in Atari BASIC. 1984. pap. 15.95 (ISBN 0-8359-0004-5). Reston.
Renko, Hal & Edwards, Sam. Awesome Games for Your Atari Computer. pap. 5.95 (ISBN 0-201-16477-9). Addison-Wesley.
Roberts, Sam. Games for the Atari. 1982. pap. 7.95 (ISBN 0-936200-36-7). Blue Cat.
Roberts, Sam D. Games for the Atari Computer. 115p. 7.95 (ISBN 0-936200-36-7, 162). Elcomp.
--How to Program Your Atari in 6502 Machine Language. 106p. 1982. 9.95 (ISBN 0-936200-37-5). Blue Cat.
Rowley, Thomas E. Atari BASIC: Learning by Using. 73p. 7.95 (ISBN 0-936200-35-9). Blue Cat.
Rugg, Tom & Feldman, Phil. Thirty-Two BASIC Programs for the Atari Computer. (Illus.). 288p. 1983. pap. 19.95 (ISBN 0-88056-084-3); incl. disk 39.95 (ISBN 0-88056-172-6). Dilithium Pr.
Sanders, William B. The Elementary Atari. (Illus.). 288p. (Orig.). 1983. pap. text ed. 14.95 (ISBN 0-88190-117-2, BO117). Datamost.
Shneiderman, Ben. Let's Learn BASIC: A Kid's Introduction to BASIC Programming on the Atari Home Computers. (Orig.). 1984. pap. 8.95 (ISBN 0-316-78722-1). Little.
Small, David, et al, eds. The Creative Atari. LC 82-71997. (The Creative Ser.). (Illus.). 244p. 1983. pap. 15.95 (ISBN 0-916688-34-8, 18B). Creative Comp.
Stanton, Jeffrey & Pinal, Dan. Atari Graphics & Arcade Game Design. 1983. pap. 16.95 (ISBN 0-912003-05-7). Bk Co.
Stanton, Jeffrey, et al, eds. The Book of Atari Software 1983. 19.95. Bk Co.
--Book of Atari Software 1985. (Software Reference Guides Ser.). 468p. 1984. pap. 19.95 (ISBN 0-912003-04-9). Bk Co.
Thompson, Mark. Programming Your Atari Computer. (Illus.). 280p. (Orig.). 1983. 16.95 (ISBN 0-8306-0453-7); pap. 11.50 (ISBN 0-8306-1453-2, 1453). TAB Bks.
Trost, Stanley R. Atari BASIC Programs in Minutes. LC 83-51097. (Illus.). 171p. (Orig.). 1984. pap. 12.95 (ISBN 0-89588-143-8). SYBEX.
Verheiden, Eric. Secrets of Atari I-O. Evans, Carl M. & Trapp, Charles, eds. (ATARI Information Ser.: Vol. 2). (Illus.). 288p. 1984. 15.95 (ISBN 0-936200-33-2). Blue Cat.
Wagner, H. C. Hackerbook for Your Atari Computer. 116p. 9.95 (ISBN 3-88963-172-X). Blue Cat.
Watt, D. Learning with Atari LOGO. (Illus.). 320p. 1983. pap. 16.95 (ISBN 0-07-068579-7, BYTE Bks). McGraw.
Weber Systems Inc. Staff. Atari ST Business Software in BASIC. 330p. (Orig.). 1986. pap. 17.95 (ISBN 0-317-19095-4). Weber Systems.
--Atari ST User's Handbook. 300p. (Orig.). 1985. pap. 15.95 (ISBN 0-938862-40-5). Weber Systems.
--Atari XE User's Handbook. 300p. (Orig.). 1985. pap. 15.95 (ISBN 0-938862-41-3). Weber Systems.
Weber Systems, Inc. Staff. Atari XL User's Handbook. LC 84-50834. (User's Handbooks to Personal Computers Ser.). 350p. 1984. pap. 15.95 (ISBN 0-938862-08-1). Weber Systems.
Wilkinson, Bill. Inside Atari DOS. Compute! Magazine, ed. 108p. (Orig.). 1983. pap. 19.95 (ISBN 0-942386-02-7). Compute Pubns.

Henderson-Sellers, A., ed. The Origin & Evolution of Planetary Atmospheres. 1983. 34.00 (ISBN 0-9960027-0-7, Pub. by A Hilger England). Heyden.
Hidy, G. H., ed. Aerosols & Atmospheric Chemistry. 1972. 50.50 (ISBN 0-12-347250-4). Acad Pr.
Hinkley, ed. Laser Monitoring of the Atmosphere. (Topics in Applied Physics Ser.: Vol. 14). (Illus.). 1976. 60.00 (ISBN 0-387-07743-X). Springer-Verlag.
Holton, J. R, ed. Dynamics of the Middle Atmosphere. Matsuno, T. LC 84-8291. 550p. 1984. lib. bdg. 89.50 (ISBN 90-277-1758-3, Pub. by Reidel Holland). Kluwer Academic.
Hoskins, Brian & Pearce, Robert, eds. Large-Scale Dynamical Processes in the Atmosphere. 1983. 54.50 (ISBN 0-12-356680-0). Acad Pr.
Houghton, J. T. The Physics of Atmospheres. LC 76-26373. (Illus.). 1977. 39.50 (ISBN 0-521-21443-2). Cambridge U Pr.
Hunt, G. E. & Ballard, J., eds. Atmospheric Spectroscopy: Proceedings of the International Workshop SERC Rutherford Appleton Laboratory, Chilton, Didcot, Oxon, UK, 19-21 July 1983. (Illus.). 120p. 1985. 75.00 (ISBN 0-08-030278-5). Pergamon.
Interlaboratory Cooperative Study of the Precision & Accuracy of the Measurement of Nitrogen Dioxide Content in the Atmosphere Using ASTM D 1607, DS 55. 81p. 1974. pap. 5.00 (ISBN 0-8031-0381-6, 05-055000-17). ASTM.
Interlaboratory Cooperative Study of the Precision & Accuracy of the Measurement of Sulfur Dioxide Content in the Atmosphere Using ASTM D 2914, DS 55-S1. 82p. 1974. pap. 5.00 (ISBN 0-8031-0382-4, 05-055010-17). ASTM.
Interlaboratory Cooperative Study of the Precision & Accuracy of the Measurement of Particulate Matter in the Atmosphere Using ASTM D 1704, DS 55-S3. 65p. 1974. pap. 5.00 (ISBN 0-8031-0384-0, 05-055030-17). ASTM.
Iribarne, J. V. & Cho, H. R. Atmospheric Physics. xii, 208p. 1980. lib. bdg. 15.95 (ISBN 90-277-1033-3, Pub. by Reidel Holland). Kluwer Academic.
Iribarne, J. V. & Godson, W. L. Atmospheric Thermodynamics. LC 73-88591. (Geophysics & Astrophysics Monographs: No. 6). 1973. lib. bdg. 34.00 (ISBN 9-02-770370-1, Pub. by Reidel Holland); pap. text ed. 15.80 (ISBN 9-02-770371-X). Kluwer Academic.
Junge, C. E. Air Chemistry & Radioactivity. (International Geophysics Ser.: Vol. 4). 1963. 65.00 (ISBN 0-12-392150-3). Acad Pr.
Kammermeyer, Karl, ed. Atmosphere in Space Cabins & Closed Environments. LC 66-22190. 271p. 1966. 25.00x (ISBN 0-306-50038-8, Plenum Pr). Plenum Pub.
Kato, S. & Roper, R. G. Electric Current & Atmospheric Motion. (Advances in Earth & Planetary Sciences Ser.: No. 7). 294p. 1980. 24.50x (ISBN 0-89955-314-1, Pub. by Japan Sci Soc Japan). Intl Spec Bk.
Kondratyav, K. Ya. Radiation in the Atmosphere. (International Geophysics Ser.: Vol. 12). 1969. 99.00 (ISBN 0-12-419050-2). Acad Pr.
Lanzerotti, L. J. & Park, C., eds. Upper Atmosphere Research in Antarctica. (Illus.). 264p. 1977. 50.00 (ISBN 0-87590-141-7). Am Geophysical.
Longhetto, A. Atmospheric Planetary Boundary Layer Physics: Proceedings of the International Course Held in Erice, Sicily, February, 1978. (Developments in Atmospheric Science Ser.: Vol. 11). 424p. 1980. 74.50 (ISBN 0-444-41885-7). Elsevier.
Lutgens, Frederick K. & Tarbuck, Edward J. The Atmosphere: An Introduction to Meteorology. (Illus.). 496p. 1982. text ed. 31.95 (ISBN 0-13-050120-4). P-H.
--The Atmosphere: An Introduction to Meteorology. 3rd ed. (Illus.). 576p. 1986. 30.95 (ISBN 0-13-049917-X). P H.
McCormac, B. M., ed. Atmospheres of Earth & the Planets. LC 75-4954. (Astrophysics & Space Science Library: No. 51). 430p. 1975. lib. bdg. 87.00 (ISBN 90-277-0575-5, Pub. by Reidel Holland). Kluwer Academic.
Mead, Margaret & Kellogg, William W., eds. The Atmosphere: Endangered & Endangering. 154p. 1980. pap. text ed. 13.00 (ISBN 0-7194-0057-0, Pub. by Castle Hse England). J K Burgess.
Measurement of Lead in the Atmosphere; Sampling Stacks for Particulates; & Determination of Oxides of Nitrogen in Combustion Products- DS 55-S5, S6, S8. 343p. 1975. pap. 18.00 (ISBN 0-8031-0387-5, 05-0550990-17). ASTM.
Measurement to Lead in the Atmosphere: Sampling Stacks for Particulates; & Determination of Oxides of Nitrogen in Combustion Products, DS 55. 343p. (Supplements S5, S6, S8 are also available). 1975. pap. 18.00 (ISBN 0-8031-0387-5, 05-055099-17). ASTM.
Meszaros, E. Atmospheric Chemistry: Fundamental Aspects. (Studies in Environmental Science: Vol. 11). 202p. 1981. 42.75 (ISBN 0-444-99753-9). Elsevier.
Murcray, David G., ed. Handbook of High Resolution Infrared Laboratory Spectra of Gases of Atmospheric Interest. 288p. 1981. 56.00 (ISBN 0-8493-2950-7). CRC Pr.
National Center for Atmospheric Research. National Hail Research Experiment: Final Report, 2 vols. 24.50x ea. Vol. 1, March 1982 (ISBN 0-87081-096-0). Vol. II, December 1982 (ISBN 0-87081-097-9). Colo Assoc.
National Research Council Commission on Natural Resources. Atmosphere-Biosphere Interactions: Toward a Better Understanding of the Ecological Consequences of Fossil Fuel Combustion. 280p. 1981. pap. text ed. 13.00 (ISBN 0-309-03196-6). Natl Acad Pr.
Neiburger, Morris & Edinger, James G. Understanding Our Atmospheric Environment. 2nd ed. LC 81-15160. (Illus.). 453p. 1982. text ed. 25.95x (ISBN 0-7167-1348-9). W H Freeman.
Nemenyi, R. Controlled Atmospheres for Heat Treatment. (Illus.). 225p. 1983. text ed. 44.00 (ISBN 0-08-019883-X); pap. 17.00 (ISBN 0-08-029997-0). Pergamon.
Numerical Modeling of the Tropical Atmosphere. (Garp Publications Ser.: No. 20). xvi, 79p. 1978. pap. 15.00 (ISBN 0-685-90699-X, W412, WMO). Unipub.
Oppenheim, A. K. Impact of Aerospace Technology on Studies of the Earth's Atmosphere. LC 74-5410. 1974. text ed. 28.00 (ISBN 0-08-018131-7). Pergamon.
Palmen, Eric H. & Newton, Chester W. Atmospheric Circulation Systems: Their Structure & Physical Interpretation. (International Geophysics Ser.: Vol. 13). 1969. 68.50 (ISBN 0-12-544550-4). Acad Pr.
Panel on Atmospheric Chemistry, Committee on Impacts of Stratospheric Change, National Research Council. Halocarbons: Effects on Stratospheric Ozone. 352p. 1976. pap. 11.75 (ISBN 0-309-02532-X). Natl Acad Pr.
Rasool, S. I. Chemistry of the Lower Atmosphere. LC 72-90336. 335p. 1973. 45.00x (ISBN 0-306-30591-7, Plenum Pr). Plenum Pub.
Reiter, Elmar R. Atmospheric Transport Processes, Pt. 2: Chemical Tracers. LC 76-603262. (DOE Critical Review Ser.). 382p. 1971. pap. 17.50 (ISBN 0-87079-140-0, TID-25314); microfiche 4.50 (ISBN 0-87079-141-9, TID-25314). DOE.
--Atmospheric Transport Processes, Pt. 3: Hydrodynamic Tracers. LC 76-603262. (DOE Critical Review Ser.). 212p. 1972. pap. 13.25 (ISBN 0-87079-142-7, TID-25731); microfiche 4.50 (ISBN 0-87079-143-5, TID-25731). DOE.
--Atmospheric Transport Processes, Pt. 4: Radioactive Tracers. LC 76-603262. (DOE Critical Review Ser.). 620p. 1978. 23.50 (ISBN 0-87079-114-1, TID-27114); microfiche 4.50 (ISBN 0-87079-145-1, TID-27114). DOE.
Report of the Thirteenth Session of the Joint Organizing Committee for GARP: Stockholm, 14-20 April 1977. (Illus.). 1977. pap. 25.00 (ISBN 0-685-86036-1, W330, WMO). Unipub.
Richardson, D. G. & Meheriuk, M. Third National Controlled Atmosphere Research Conference. LC 82-723. 385p. 1982. 39.95x (ISBN 0-917304-26-8). Timber.
Rowe, J. N. An Investigation of the Effects of Solar Flares & Stratospheric Warmings on the Lower Ionosphere. LC 72-135091. 90p. 1970. 15.00 (ISBN 0-403-04533-9). Scholarly.
Royal Society, et al. The Middle Atmosphere As Observed from Baloons, Rockets & Satellites. (Royal Society Ser.). (Illus.). 268p. 1980. lib. bdg. 71.00x (ISBN 0-85403-137-5, Pub. by Royal Soc London). Scholium Intl.
Schaefer, Vincent J. & Day, John A. A Field Guide to the Atmosphere. LC 80-25473. (Peterson Field Guide: No. 26). (Illus.). 359p. 1983. 13.95 (ISBN 0-395-24080-8); pap. 10.95 (ISBN 0-395-33033-5). HM.
Schmidtke, G. & Champion, K. S. W. The Mesosphere & Thermosphere. flexi-cover 33.00x (ISBN 0-08-028393-4). Pergamon.
Schwerdtfeger, P. Physical Principles of Micro-Meteorological Measurements. (Developments in Atmospheric Science Ser.: Vol. 6). 1976. 57.50 (ISBN 0-444-41489-4). Elsevier.
Sladd, Robin. The Earth's Atmosphere: Syllabus. 1978. pap. text ed. 5.85 (ISBN 0-89420-045-3, 235011); cassette recordings 41.25 (ISBN 0-89420-141-7, 235000). Natl Book.
Stewart, R. Atmospheric Boundary Layer. 44p. (3rd IMO Lecture). 1979. pap. 20.00 (ISBN 92-63-10523-5, W433, WMO). Unipub.
Strohbehn, J. W., ed. Laser Beam Propagation in the Atmosphere. (Topics in Applied Physics: Vol. 25). (Illus.). 1978. 67.00 (ISBN 0-387-08812-1). Springer-Verlag.
Studies of the Atmosphere Using Aerospace Probings. Incl. Annual Report-1969. 243p. 1970. pap. 7.50x (ISBN 0-299-97032-9). pap. U of Wis Pr.
The Study of Radiation in a Tropical Atmosphere: Final Report. 100p. 1970. pap. 5.00x (ISBN 0-299-97028-0). U of Wis Pr.
Summer Advanced Study Institute, Queen's University, Kingston, Ontario, August 3-14, 1970. The Radiating Atmosphere: Proceeding. Mc Cormac, B. M., ed. LC 70-154742. (Astrophysics & Space Science Library: No.24). 455p. 1971. lib. bdg. 58.00 (ISBN 90-277-0184-9, Pub. by Reidel Holland). Kluwer Academic.
Torrance, K. E. Environmental Effects of Atmospheric Heat-Moisture Releases: Cooling Towers, Cooling Ponds & Area Sources, No. H00110. Watts, R. G., ed. 1978. pap. 18.00 (ISBN 0-685-99207-1). ASME.
Turber, Walter A., et al. The Atmosphere. (Exploring Earth Science Program Ser.). 1976. pap. text ed. 7.04 (ISBN 0-205-04744-0, 6947441). Allyn.
Twomey, S. Atmospheric Aerosols. (Developments in Atmospheric Science Ser.: Vol. 7). 302p. 1977. 81.00 (ISBN 0-444-41527-0). Elsevier.
Vinnichenko, N. K., et al. Turbulence in the Free Atmosphere. 2nd ed. LC 80-23743. (Illus.). 325p. 1980. 55.00x (ISBN 0-306-10959-X, Consultants). Plenum Pub.
Vinnichenko, N. K., et al, eds. Turbulence in the Free Atmosphere. LC 72-157935. (Illus.). 260p. 1973. 42.50 (ISBN 0-306-10857-7, Consultants). Plenum Pub.
Volland, Hans, ed. Handbook of Atmospherics, Vol. I. 392p. 1982. 94.00 (ISBN 0-8493-3226-5). CRC Pr.
--Handbook of Atmospherics, Vol. II. 336p. 1982. 94.00 (ISBN 0-8493-3227-3). CRC Pr.
Walker, James C. Evolution of the Atmosphere. LC 77-23796. (Illus.). 1978. 21.95x. Hafner.
--Evolution of the Atmosphere. 1978. 16.95 (ISBN 0-02-854390-4). Macmillan.
Walker, Jearl, intro. by. Light from the Sky: Readings from Scientific American. LC 79-28222. (Illus.). 78p. 1980. text ed. 14.95x (ISBN 0-7167-1221-0); pap. 9.95x (ISBN 0-7167-1222-9). W H Freeman.
Wallace, John M. & Hobbs, Peter. Atmospheric Sciences: An Introductory Survey. 467p. 1977. 22.50i (ISBN 0-12-732950-1). Acad Pr.
Wayne, Richard P. Chemistry of Atmospheres: An Introduction to the Chemistry of the Atmospheres of Earth, the Planets, & Their Satellites. (Illus.). 1985. 39.95x (ISBN 0-19-855176-2); pap. 19.95x (ISBN 0-19-855175-4). Oxford U Pr.
Zuev, V. E. & Naats, I. E. Inverse Problems of Lidar Sensing of the Atmosphere. (Springer Ser. in Optical Sciences: Vol. 29). (Illus.). 260p. 1983. 44.00 (ISBN 0-387-10913-7). Springer-Verlag.

ATMOSPHERE-OCEAN INTERACTION
see Ocean-Atmosphere Interaction

ATMOSPHERE, UPPER
see also Jet Stream; Stratosphere

Advanced Summer Institute, Sheffield, England, 13-12 August, 1973. Magnetospheric Physics: Proceedings. McCormac, B. M., ed. LC 74-76472. (Astrophysics & Space Science Library: No. 44). 370p. 1974. lib. bdg. 66.00 (ISBN 90-277-0454-6, Pub. by Reidel Holland). Kluwer Academic.
Akasofu, S. I., ed. Dynamics of the Magnetosphere. (Astrophysics & Space Science Library: No. 78). 1980. lib. bdg. 79.00 (ISBN 90-277-1052-X, Pub. by Reidel Holland). Kluwer Academic.
Bolle, H. J., ed. Radiation in the Atmosphere: Proceedings. LC 77-5205. (Illus.). 1977. lib. bdg. 62.00 (ISBN 0-89500-002-4). Sci Pr.
Burke, P. G. & Moiseiwitsch, B. L., eds. Atomic Processes & Applications. 1976. 76.75 (ISBN 0-7204-0444-4, North-Holland). Elsevier.
Craig, Richard A. Upper Atmosphere: Meteorology & Physics. (International Geophysics Ser.: Vol. 8). 1965. 49.50 (ISBN 0-12-194850-1). Acad Pr.
Geophysics Study Committee. Upper Atmosphere & Magnetosphere. 1977. pap. 11.50 (ISBN 0-309-02633-4). Natl Acad Pr.
Georgii, H. W. & Jaeschke, W., eds. Chemistry of the Unpolluted & Polluted Troposphere. 1982. 63.00 (ISBN 90-277-1487-8, Pub. by Reidel Holland). Kluwer Academic.
Haurwitz, B. Tidal Phenomena in the Upper Atmosphere. (Technical Note Ser.: No. 58). 28p. 1964. pap. 6.00 (ISBN 0-685-22345-0, W27, WMO). Unipub.
Hines, C. O., et al, eds. Upper Atmosphere in Motion. LC 74-28234. (Geophysical Monograph Ser.: Vol. 18). (Illus.). 1027p. 1974. 29.00 (ISBN 0-87590-018-6). Am Geophysical.
Johnson, Francis S., ed. Satellite Environment Handbook. rev. ed. (Illus.). 1965. 15.00x (ISBN 0-8047-0090-7). Stanford U Pr.
Kato, Susumo, ed. Dynamics of the Upper Atmosphere. (Developments in Earth & Planetary Sciences Ser.: No. 1). 233p. 1980. PLB 30.00 (ISBN 90-277-1132-1, Pub. by Reidel Holland). Kluwer Academic.
Kellogg, W. W. Meteorological Soundings in the Upper Atmosphere. (Technical Note Ser.: No. 60). 48p. 1964. pap. 8.00 (ISBN 0-685-22322-1, W28, WMO). Unipub.
Lanzerotti, L. J. & Park, C., eds. Upper Atmosphere Research in Antarctica. (Illus.). 264p. 1977. 50.00 (ISBN 0-87590-141-7). Am Geophysical.
McCormac, Billy M. & Seliga, Thomas A., eds. Solar-Terrestrial Influences on Weather & Climate. 1979. lib. bdg. 24.00 (ISBN 90-277-0978-5, Pub. by Reidel Holland). Kluwer Academic.
Massey, H. S. & Boyd, R. F. Upper Atmosphere. 17.50 (ISBN 0-685-28383-6). Philos Lib.
Michigan University Greenland Expeditions 1926-1933. Reports of the Greenland Expeditions of the University of Michigan, 2 vols. LC 68-55203. (Illus.). 1968. Repr. of 1941 ed. Set. lib. bdg. 55.00x (ISBN 0-8371-3850-7, MUGE). Greenwood.
Neil Brice Memorial Symposium, Frascati, Italy, May 28-June 1 1974. The Magnetospheres of the Earth & Jupiter: Proceedings. Formisano, V., ed. LC 75-4587. (Astrophysics & Space Science Library: No. 52). 481p. 1975. lib. bdg. 87.00 (ISBN 90-277-0564-X, Pub. by Reidel Holland). Kluwer Academic.
Olson, W. P., ed. Quantitative Modeling of Magnetospheric Processes. (Geophysical Monograph Ser.: Vol. 21). (Illus.). 655p. 1979. 30.00 (ISBN 0-87590-021-6, GM2100). Am Geophysical.
Rex, D. F., ed. Climate of the Free Atmosphere. (World Survey of Climatology Ser.: Vol. 4). 450p. 1969. 127.75 (ISBN 0-444-40703-0). Elsevier.
Summer Advanced Study Institute Symposium, University of Orleans, France, July 31-Aug. 11, 1972. Physics & Chemistry at Upper Atmospheres: Proceedings. McCormac, B. M., ed. LC 72-92533. (Astrophysics & Space Science Library: No. 35). 385p. 1973. lib. bdg. 60.50 (ISBN 90-277-0283-7, Pub. by Reidel Holland). Kluwer Academic.
Summer Advanced Study Institute, University of California, Santa Barbara, California, August 4-15, 1969. Particles & Fields in the Magnetosphere: Proceedings. Mc Cormac, B. M., ed. LC 78-115884. (Astrophysics & Space Science Library: No. 17). 453p. 1970. lib. bdg. 53.00 (ISBN 90-277-0131-8, Pub. by Reidel Holland). Kluwer Academic.
Thomas, L. & Rishbeth, H., eds. Photochemical & Transport Processes in the Upper Atmosphere. LC 76-26741. 1977. pap. text ed. 30.00 (ISBN 0-08-021312-X). Pergamon.
Verniani, F. Structure & Dynamics of the Upper Atmosphere. (Developments in Atmospheric Sciences Ser.: Vol. 1). 535p. 1974. 121.50 (ISBN 0-444-41105-4). Elsevier.
Webb, Willis L. Structure of the Stratosphere & Mesosphere. (International Geophysics Ser.: Vol. 9). 1966. 63.00 (ISBN 0-12-739850-3). Acad Pr.

ATMOSPHERE, UPPER–ROCKET OBSERVATIONS
see also Ionospheric Research

Sixth Sounding Rocket. 1982. 50.00 (ISBN 0-317-06667-6). AIAA.

ATMOSPHERIC ABSORPTION OF SOLAR RADIATION
see Solar Radiation

ATMOSPHERIC CHEMISTRY

Global Tropospheric Chemistry Panel, National Research Council. Global Tropospheric Chemistry: A Plan for Action. 208p. 1984. pap. 20.95 (ISBN 0-309-03481-7). Natl Acad Pr.

ATMOSPHERIC ELECTRICITY
see also Auroras; Ionization of Gases; Lightning

Coroniti, Samuel C. & Hughes, J., eds. Planetary Electrodynamics, 2 Vols. (Illus.). 1132p. 1969. Set. 216.25 (ISBN 0-677-13600-5). Gordon.
Dolezalek, H. The Application of Atmospheric Electricity Concepts & Methods to Other Parts of Meteorology. (Technical Note Ser.: No. 162). 130p. 1978. pap. 20.00 (ISBN 92-63-10507-3, W414, WMO). Unipub.
Ruhnke, Lothar H. & Latham, John, eds. Proceedings in Atmospheric Electricity. LC 83-10096. (Illus.). 1983. 45.00 (ISBN 0-937194-04-2). A Deepak Pub.
Volland, H. Atmospheric Electrodynamics. (Physics & Chemistry in Space Ser.: Vol. 11). (Illus.). 210p. 1984. 35.50 (ISBN 0-387-13510-3). Springer-Verlag.
Weinberg, Michael A. Atmospheric Humidity in Electrical Cost-of-Service: An Outline Bibliography. 1982. 1.77 (ISBN 0-9601014-7-0). Weinberg.

ATMOSPHERIC ENTRY PROBLEMS
see Space Vehicles–Atmospheric Entry

ATMOSPHERIC HUMIDITY
see Humidity

ATMOSPHERIC NUCLEATION
see also Condensation (Meteorology); Ionization of Gases

ATOMISM

Charleton, Walter. Physiologia Epicuro-Gassendo-Charltoniana; or, a Fabrick of Science Natural Upon the Hypothesis of Atoms. 1967. Repr. of 1654 ed. 50.00 (ISBN 0-384-08535-0). Johnson Repr.

Latanision, R. M. & Pickens, J. R., eds. Atomistics of Fracture. (NATO Conference Series IV, Materials Science: Vol. 5). 1090p. 1982. 135.00x (ISBN 0-306-41029-X, Plenum Pr). Plenum Pub.

Mudry, Joseph. Philosophy of Atomic Physics. 1958. 6.00 (ISBN 0-8022-1163-1). Philos Lib.

ATOMIZATION

see also Aerosols; Spraying

Beddow, J. K. The Production of Metal Powders by Atomizaton. (Powder Advisory Centre Publication Ser. (POWTECH)). 106p. 1978. 59.95 (ISBN 0-471-25601-3, Wiley Heyden). Wiley.

ATOMS

see also Atomic Mass; Cyclotron; Electrons; Magnetic Resonance; Matter; Neutrons; Nuclear Models; Nuclear Physics; Nuclear Shell Theory; Particle Accelerators; Protons; Transmutation (Chemistry)

Aller, Lawrence H. Atoms, Stars, & Nebulae. Rev. ed. LC 76-134951. (The Harvard Books on Astronomy). (Illus.). pap. 90.80 (ISBN 0-317-09183-2, 2019508). Bks Demand UMI.

Bates, D. R. & Esterman, L., eds. Advances in Atomic & Molecular Physics, Vol. 20. (Serial Publication Ser.). 1985. 95.00 (ISBN 0-12-003820-X). Acad Pr.

Blum, Karl. Density Matrix Theory & Applications. LC 81-268. (Physics of Atoms & Molecules Ser.). 230p. 1981. 37.50x (ISBN 0-306-40684-5, Plenum Pr). Plenum Pub.

Burke, P. G. & Eissner, W. B., eds. Atoms in Astrophysics. (Physics of Atoms & Molecules Ser.). 345p. 1983. 52.50x (ISBN 0-306-41097-4, Plenum Pr). Plenum Pub.

Chernogorova, V. Enigmas Del Micromundo. (Span.). 317p. 1977. pap. 3.45 (ISBN 0-8285-1694-4, Pub. by Mir Pubs USSR). Imported Pubns.

Chin, S. L. & Lambropoulos, Peter. Multiphoton Ionization of Atoms: Quantum Electronics; Principles & Applications. LC 83-98663. 1984. 59.50 (ISBN 0-12-172780-7). Acad Pr.

Crowe, Kenneth, et al, eds. Exotic Atoms, 1979: Fundamental Interactions & Structure of Matter. LC 79-23072. (Ettore Majorana International Science Ser., Physical Science: Vol. 4). 410p. 1980. 65.00x (ISBN 0-306-40322-6, Plenum Pr). Plenum Pub.

Datz, Sheldon, et al. Atomic Collisions in Solids, 2 vols. Incl. Vol. 1. 502p. 75.00x (ISBN 0-306-38211-3); Vol. 2. 477p. 75.00x (ISBN 0-306-38212-1). LC 74-26825. 1975. price 135.00 set (Plenum Pr). Plenum Pub.

Del Re, G., et al. Electronic States of Molecules & Atom Clusters. (Lecture Notes in Chemistry: Vol. 13). (Illus.). 180p. 1980. pap. 21.00 (ISBN 0-387-09738-4). Springer-Verlag.

Elsasser, Walt er M. Atom & Organism: A New Approach to Theoretical Biology. LC 66-21832. pap. 38.30 (ISBN 0-317-27619-0, 2014639). Bks Demand UMI.

Fabian, Derek J., et al, eds. Inner-Shell & X-Ray Physics of Atoms & Solids. LC 81-11945. (Physics of Atoms & Molecules Ser.). 976p. 1981. 125.00x (ISBN 0-306-40819-8, Plenum Pr). Plenum Pub.

Fano, U. & Fano, L. Physics of Atoms & Molecules: An Introduction to the Structure of Matter. LC 76-184808. 456p. 1973. text ed. 35.00x (ISBN 0-226-23782-6). U of Chicago Pr.

Fischer, C. F. The Hartree Fock Method for Atoms: A Numerical Approach. LC 76-50015. 308p. 1977. 44.95 (ISBN 0-471-25990-X). Krieger.

Fraga, S. & Muszynska, J. Atoms in External Fields. (Physical Sciences Data Ser.: Vol. 8). 558p. 1981. 106.50 (ISBN 0-444-41936-5). Elsevier.

Fraga, S., et al. Handbook of Atomic Data. (Physical Sciences Data Ser.: Vol. 5). 552p. 1976. 106.50 (ISBN 0-444-41461-4). Elsevier.

Gladkov, K. The Atom from A to Z. Zimmerman, Michael, tr. from Russian. 263p. 1971. 9.95x (ISBN 0-8464-0160-6). Beekman Pubs.

Goldring, Gvirol & Kalish, Rafael. Hyperfine Interactions of Excited Nuclei, 4 vols. LC 78-127883. (Illus.). 1378p. 1971. Set. 377.75 (ISBN 0-677-14600-0); 106.50 ea. Vol. 1, 386p (ISBN 0-677-15120-9). Vol. 2, 400p (ISBN 0-677-15130-6). Vol. 3, 280p (ISBN 0-677-15140-3). Vol. 4, 396p (ISBN 0-677-15150-0). Gordon.

Herzberg, Gerhard. Atomic Spectra & Atomic Structure. 2nd ed. Spinks, J. W., tr. (Illus.). 1944. pap. text ed. 4.50 (ISBN 0-486-60115-3). Dover.

Hoffmann, Banesh. Strange Story of the Quantum. 1959. pap. text ed. 4.95 (ISBN 0-486-20518-5). Dover.

Holden, Alan. Bonds Between Atoms. (Illus.). 1971. pap. text ed. 4.95x (ISBN 0-19-501498-7). Oxford U Pr.

--Nature of Atoms. (Illus.). 104p. 1971. pap. text ed. 4.95x (ISBN 0-19-501499-5). Oxford U Pr.

Horvath, D. & Lambrech, T. Exotic Atoms: A Bibliography, 1939-1982. (Physical Sciences Data Ser.: Vol. 19). 1984. 132.75 (ISBN 0-444-42319-2, I-096-84). Elsevier.

Huber, K. P. & Herzberg, G. Molecular Spectra & Molecular Structure, Vol. 4. 1979. 32.50 (ISBN 0-442-23394-9). Van Nos Reinhold.

Kaganov, M. & Lifshits, I. Quasiparticles. 96p. 1979. pap. 2.95 (ISBN 0-8285-1531-X, Pub. by Mir Pubs USSR). Imported Pubns.

Kitaigorodsky, A. I. Order & Disorder in the World of Atoms. 165p. 1980. pap. 5.95 (ISBN 0-8285-1724-X, Pub. by Mir Pubs USSR). Imported Pubns.

Klabunde, Kenneth J. Chemistry of Free Atoms & Particles. 1980. 35.00 (ISBN 0-12-410750-8). Acad Pr.

Klabunde, Kenneth J., ed. Thin Films from Free Atoms & Particles. Date not set. price not set (ISBN 0-12-410755-9). Acad Pr.

Kleinpoppen, H. & MacDowell, M. R., eds. Electron & Photon Interactions with Atoms. LC 75-37555. (Illus.). 682p. 1976. 79.50x (ISBN 0-306-30846-0, Plenum Pr). Plenum Pub.

Lectures, International Winter College, Trieste, 1973. Atoms, Molecules & Lasers. (Illus.). 710p. 1975. pap. 69.25 (ISBN 92-0-130374-2, ISP356, IAEA). Unipub.

Mittleman, Marvin H. Introduction to the Theory of Laser-Atom Interactions. LC 82-12321. (Physics of Atoms & Molecules Ser.). 210p. 1982. 35.00x (ISBN 0-306-41049-4, Plenum Pr). Plenum Pub.

Neel, L., ed. Nonlinear Behaviour of Molecules, Atoms & Ions in Electric, Magnetic or Electromagnetic Fields. 516p. 1979. 100.00 (ISBN 0-444-41790-7). Elsevier.

Nye, Mary J., ed. The Question of the Atom: From the Karlsruhe Congress to the First Solvay Conference, 1860-1911. (History of Modern Physics 1800-1950 Ser.: Vol. 4). (Illus.). 1984. 48.00x (ISBN 0-938228-07-2). Tomash Pubs.

Palmer, D., et al. Atomic Collision Phenomena in Solids. 1970. 68.00 (ISBN 0-444-10021-0). Elsevier.

Perez, A. & Coussement, R., eds. Site Characterization & Aggregation of Implanted Atoms in Materials. LC 79-19008. (NATO ASI Series B, Physics: Vol. 47). 530p. 1980. 75.00x (ISBN 0-306-40299-8, Plenum Pr). Plenum Pub.

Robin. Higher Excited States of Polyatomic Molecules. Vol. 1. 1974. 72.00 (ISBN 0-12-589901-7); Vol. 2. 1975. 76.00 (ISBN 0-12-589902-5). Acad Pr.

Sellin, A., ed. Structure & Collisions of Ions & Atoms. (Topics in Current Physics: Vol 5). (Illus.). 1978. 48.00 (ISBN 0-387-08576-9). Springer-Verlag.

Smith, Kenneth. The Calculation of Atomic Collision Processes. LC 78-168645. 230p. 1971. 23.50 (ISBN 0-471-80000-7). Krieger.

Szasz. Pseudopotential Theory of Atoms & Molecules. 400p. 1985. 42.50 (ISBN 0-471-82417-8). Wiley.

Torrens, Ian M. Interatomic Potentials. 1972. 58.50 (ISBN 0-12-695850-5). Acad Pr.

Vainshtein, L. A. Research on Spectroscopy & Luminescence, Part 1: Calculation of Wave Functions & Oscillator Strengths of Complex Atoms. LC 62-12860. (P. N. Lebedev Physics Institute Ser.: Vol. 15). 50p. 1962. 17.50x (ISBN 0-306-17041-8, Consultants). Plenum Pub.

Valyi, L. Atom & Ion Sources. LC 76-44880. 429p. 1978. 122.95x (ISBN 0-471-99463-4, Pub. by Wiley-Interscience). Wiley.

Very, Frank W. Luminiferous Ether. (Orig.). 1919. pap. 25.00 (ISBN 0-8283-1189-7). Branden Pub Co.

Weissbluth, Mitchel. Atoms & Molecules: Student Edition. 1980. 27.00 (ISBN 0-12-744452-1). Acad Pr.

Weissmantel, Cristian. Kleine Enzyklopaedie Atom. 2nd ed. (Ger.). 1973. pap. 28.50 (ISBN 3-527-25066-2, M-7088). French & Eur.

Weltner, W. Magnetic Atoms & Molecules. 1983. 42.50 (ISBN 0-442-29206-6). Van Nos Reinhold.

Woodward, R. B. & Hoffmann, R. The Conservation of Orbital Symmetry. LC 79-103636. (Illus.). 178p. 1970. pap. 14.95x (ISBN 0-89573-109-6). VCH Pubs.

ATOMS–MODELS

March, Norman H. Self-Consistent Fields in Atoms. 1975. pap. text ed. 16.00 (ISBN 0-08-017820-0). Pergamon.

ATOMS–SPACE ARRANGEMENT

see Stereochemistry

ATOMS–SPECTRA

see Atomic Spectra

ATOMS, NUCLEI OF

see Nuclear Physics

ATTACK AND DEFENSE (MILITARY SCIENCE)

Bellany, Ian & Blacker, Coit D., eds. Antiballistic Missile Defense in the 1980s. 100p. 1983. text ed. 27.50x (ISBN 0-7146-3207-4, F Cass Co). Biblio Dist.

Boyes, Jon L. & Andriole, Stephen J., eds. Issues in C3I Program Management: Requirements, Systems & Operations. (AFCEA-Signal Magazine C3I Ser.: Vol. I). (Illus.). 420p. 1984. 29.95 (ISBN 0-916159-02-7); Set. write for info. (ISBN 0-916159-01-9). AFCEA Intl Pr.

Bray, Frank T. & Moodie, Michael. Defense Technology & the Atlantic Alliance: Competition or Collaboration? LC 77-80297. (Foreign Policy Report Ser.). 42p. 1977. 5.00 (ISBN 0-89549-000-5). Inst Foreign Policy Anal.

Eccles, Henry E. Logistics in the National Defense. LC 81-4920. (Illus.). xviii, 347p. 1981. Repr. lib. bdg. 42.50 (ISBN 0-313-22716-0, ECLO). Greenwood.

Edmonds, Martin, ed. Central Organizations of Defense. (Special Study Ser.). 230p. 1985. 32.50x (ISBN 0-86531-684-8). Westview.

Friedman, Richard S., et al. Advanced Technology Warfare. (Illus.). 1985. 22.95 (ISBN 0-517-55850-5, Harmony); pap. 12.95 (ISBN 0-517-55851-3, Harmony). Crown.

Fusion Energy Foundations Staff, ed. Beam Defense: An Alternative to Nuclear Destruction. (Illus.). 176p. 1983. pap. 7.95 (ISBN 0-8168-4138-1). Aero.

Goure, Leon, et al. The Emerging Strategic Environment: Implications for Ballistic Missile Defense. LC 79-53108. 75p. 1979. 6.50 (ISBN 0-89549-008-0). Inst Foreign Policy Anal.

Gunston, Bill. An Illustrated Guide to NATO Fighters & Attack Aircraft. LC 82-74479. (Illustrated Military Guides Ser.). (Illus.). 160p. 1983. 9.95 (ISBN 0-668-05823-4, 5823). Arco.

Jones, Rodney W., ed. Small Nuclear Forces & U. S. Security Policy: Threats & Potential Conflicts in the Middle East & South Asia. LC 83-47790. 304p. 1984. 25.50x (ISBN 0-669-06736-9). Lexington Bks.

Record, Jeffrey. Force Reductions in Europe: Starting Over. LC 80-83753. (Special Report Ser.). 92p. 1980. 6.50 (ISBN 0-89549-027-7). Inst Foreign Policy Anal.

Roherty, James M., ed. & intro. by. Defense Policy Formation: Towards Comparative Analysis. LC 79-54443. (Illus.). 315p. 1980. lib. bdg. 22.75 (ISBN 0-89089-152-4). Carolina Acad Pr.

Wong-Fraser, Agatha S. Symmetry & Selectivity in the U. S. Defense Policy: A Grand Design or a Major Mistake? LC 80-5610. 172p. 1980. lib. bdg. 23.25 (ISBN 0-8191-1182-1); pap. text ed. 11.00 (ISBN 0-8191-1183-X). U Pr of Amer.

Yanarella, Ernest J. The Missile Defense Controversy: Strategy, Technology, & Politics, 1955-1972. LC 76-46034. 248p. 1977. 22.00x (ISBN 0-8131-1355-5). U Pr of Ky.

ATTAPULGITE

see Fullers Earth

ATTITUDE CONTROL SYSTEMS (ASTRONAUTICS)

see Artificial Satellites–Attitude Control Systems

AUDI (AUTOMOBILE)

see Automobiles, Foreign–Types–Audi

AUDIO EQUIPMENT

see Sound–Apparatus

AUDIO-VISUAL EQUIPMENT

Here are entered general works on projects, screens, sound equipment, pointers, tables, exhibit boards, etc.

see also names of particular equipment, e.g. Moving picture projectors; Record changers

Baur, W. & Schilling, G. Audiovisuelle Medien im Sport - Schriftenreihe der ETS. (STSM Ser.: No. 27). (Ger.). 424p. 1980. pap. 38.95x (ISBN 0-8176-1157-6). Birkhauser.

Business Communications Staff. New Burgeoning Video Industries. 1983. 1250.00 (G-060). BCC.

Dorsett, Loyd G. Audio-Visual Teaching Machines. LC 71-125871. (Illus.). 128p. 1971. pap. 11.95 (ISBN 0-87778-009-9). Educ Tech Pubns.

Eboch, Sidney C. Operating Audio-Visual Equipment. 2nd ed. (Illus., Orig.). 1968. pap. text ed. 12.50 scp (ISBN 0-8102-0093-7, HarpC). Har-Row.

Ingram, Dave. Video Electronics Technology. (Illus.). 256p. (Orig.). 1983. 16.95 (ISBN 0-8306-2474-0); pap. 11.50 (ISBN 0-8306-1474-5, 1474). TAB Bks.

Mannino, Philip. ABC's of Audio-Visual Equipment & the School Projectionist Manual. 2nd ed. pap. 4.00 (ISBN 0-911328-01-7). Sch Proj Club.

Mattingly, E. Grayson. Expert Techniques for Home Video Production. (Illus.). 176p. 1983. 15.95 (ISBN 0-8306-0102-3); pap. 10.95 (ISBN 0-8306-0602-5, 1602). TAB Bks.

Nakajima, H., et al. Digital Audio Technology. (Illus.). 320p. 1983. pap. 11.95 (ISBN 0-8306-1451-6, 1451). TAB Bks.

Oates, Stanton C. Audiovisual Equipment: Self Instruction Manual. 4th ed. 336p. 1979. write for info. wire coil (ISBN 0-697-06047-0). Wm C Brown.

Roberts, R. S. Dictionary of Audio, Radio & Video. 256p. 1981. 39.95 (ISBN 0-408-00339-1). Butterworth.

Rosenberg, Kenyon C. & Doskey, John S. Media Equipment: A Guide & Dictionary. LC 76-25554. (Illus.). 190p. 1976. lib. bdg. 18.50 (ISBN 0-87287-155-X). Libs Unl.

Rosenberg, Kenyon C. & Feinstein, Paul T. Dictionary of Library & Educational Technology. 2nd, rev., & enl. ed. 197p. 1983. lib. bdg. 24.50 (ISBN 0-87287-396-X). Libs Unl.

Schroeder, Don & Lare, Gary. Audiovisual Equipment & Materials: A Basic Repair & Maintenance Manual. LC 79-384. 172p. 1979. pap. text ed. 15.00 (ISBN 0-8108-1206-1). Scarecrow.

Stevens, Mary, ed. The Equipment Directory of Audio-Visual Computer & Video Products, 1985-1986. 31st ed. LC 53-35264. (Illus.). 564p. 1985. 25.00 (ISBN 0-939718-04-9). Internatl Comms.

Traister, Robert J. Make Your Own Professional Home Video Recordings. (Illus.). 304p. 1982. 18.95 (ISBN 0-8306-2433-3); pap. 12.95 (ISBN 0-8306-1433-8, 1433). TAB Bks.

Wadsworth, Raymond. Basic of Audio & Visual Systems Design. LC 82-61968. 128p. 1983. pap. 15.95 (ISBN 0-672-22038-5). Sams.

Wyman, Raymond. Mediaware: Selection, Operation & Maintenance. 2nd ed. 240p. 1976. pap. text ed. write for info. (ISBN 0-697-06045-4). Wm C Brown.

AUDIOLOGY

Engelberg, Marvin W. Audiological Evaluation for Exaggerated Hearing Level. (Illus.). 132p. 1970. 14.50x (ISBN 0-398-00513-3). C C Thomas.

Guide to Professional Services in Speech-Language Pathology & Audiology 1983-84. 208p. 1983. pap. text ed. write for info. (ISBN 0-910329-11-7). Am Speech Lang Hearing.

Jerger, Susan & Jerger, James. Audiologic Tests of Central Auditory Function. Date not set. pap. text ed. 16.00 (ISBN 0-8391-1801-5, 15644). Univ Park.

Keidel, W. D. & Finkenzeller, P., eds. Artificial Auditory Stimulation Theories. (Advances in Audiology: Vol. 1). (Illus.). viii, 152p. 1984. 53.25 (ISBN 3-8055-3720-4). S Karger.

Martin, Frederick N. Introduction to Audiology. 3rd ed. (Illus.). 480p. 1986. text ed. 30.95 (ISBN 0-13-478173-2). P-H.

Michelsen, A., ed. Time Resolution in Auditory Systems. (Proceedings in Life Sciences Ser.). (Illus.). 255p. 1985. 25.00 (ISBN 0-387-15637-2). Springer-Verlag.

Newby, Hayes A. Audiology. 4th ed. LC 78-14797. (Illus.). 1979. ref. 32.95 (ISBN 0-13-050856-X). P-H.

Pawluk, Michael F. Creating Audiology & Speech-Language Pathology: Programs on Your Apple Computer. (Illus.). 224p. 1985. pap. text ed. 25.00 (ISBN 0-8391-2063-X, 21768). Univ Park.

Readings in Audiology. 1984. 16.00 (ISBN 0-89568-429-2). Spec Learn Corp.

Ventry, I. & Schiavetti, N. Evaluating Research in Speech Pathology & Audiology. 2nd ed. 384p. 1985. 27.95 (ISBN 0-471-88210-0). Wiley.

Ventry, M. & Shiavetti, N. Evaluating Research in Speech Pathology & Audiology: A Guide to Clinicians & Students. 371p. 1980. 30.00 (ISBN 0-471-87918-5). Wiley.

AUDIOMETER

see Audiometry

AUDIOMETRY

Aten, James. The Denver Auditory Phoneme Sequencing Test. LC 79-651. (Illus.). 310p. 1979. clinical test 65.00 (ISBN 0-933014-51-1). College-Hill.

Beagley, H. A. & Barnard, S. A. Manual of Audiometric Techniques. (Illus.). 1982. pap. 18.95x (ISBN 0-19-261372-3). Oxford U Pr.

Boller, Francois & Dennis, Maureen, eds. Auditory Comprehension: Clinical & Experimental Studies with the Token Test. LC 79-22510. 1979. 32.00 (ISBN 0-12-111650-6). Acad Pr.

Bradford, Larry J., ed. Physiological Measures of the Audiovestibular System. 1975. 63.00 (ISBN 0-12-123650-1). Acad Pr.

Chaiklin, J. B., et al. Hearing Measurement: A Book of Readings. 2nd ed. 466p. 1982. 29.95 (ISBN 0-471-87864-2). Wiley.

Emerick, Lon L. A Workbook in Clinical Audiometry. (Illus.). 152p. 1971. spiral 14.50x (ISBN 0-398-02159-7). C C Thomas.

Engelberg, Marvin W. Audiological Evaluation for Exaggerated Hearing Level. (Illus.). 132p. 1970. 14.50x (ISBN 0-398-00513-3). C C Thomas.

Fudala, Jan. Auditory Point Test. 1972. pap. 22.00x complete test package (ISBN 0-87879-081-0). Acad Therapy.

Fudala, Janet B. Tree-Bee Test of Auditory Discrimination. 1978. pap. 7.50x manual (ISBN 0-87879-196-5); flip-book 15.00x (ISBN 0-87879-197-3); form A 7.50x (ISBN 0-87879-198-1); Set Of 10. form B 7.50 (ISBN 0-87879-199-X); Set Of 10. recording forms 1 & 2 1.50x ea. Acad Therapy.

Fulton, Robert T. & Lloyd, Lyle L., eds. Auditory Assessment of the Difficult-to-Test. LC 71-93742. 297p. 1975. 19.95 (ISBN 0-686-74200-1). Krieger.

Gerber, Sanford E. Audiometry in Infancy. 368p. 1977. 37.00 (ISBN 0-8089-1038-8, 791545). Grune.

Glorig, Aram, ed. Audiometry: Principles & Practices. LC 77-10869. 286p. 1977. lib. bdg. 18.00 (ISBN 0-88275-604-4). Krieger.

Jacobson, John T., ed. The Auditory Brainstem Response. (Illus.). 482p. 1984. 49.50 (ISBN 0-933014-15-5). College-Hill.

Jerger, Susan & Jerger, James. Audiologic Tests of Central Auditory Function. Date not set. pap. text ed. 16.00 (ISBN 0-8391-1801-5, 15644). Univ Park.

Kimmell, Geraldine M. & Wahl, Jack. Screening Test for Auditory Perception Form. rev. 2nd ed. 2p. 1981. Fifty per pkg. pap. 7.00 (ISBN 0-87879-255-4). Acad Therapy.

--Screening Test for Auditory Perception Manual. rev. ed. 48p. 1981. pap. 7.50 (ISBN 0-87879-254-6). Acad Therapy.

Konkle, Dan. F., ed. Principles of Speech Audiometry. (Perspectives in Audiology Ser.). (Illus.). 432p. 1982. text ed. 32.00 (ISBN 0-8391-1767-1). Univ Park.

Lloyd, Lyle L. & Kaplan, Harriet. Audiometric Interpretation: A Manual of Basic Audiometry. (Illus.). 236p. 1978. pap. text ed. 26.50 (ISBN 0-8391-0759-5). Univ Park.

Meyerson, Lee. Hearing for Speech in Children: A Verbal Audiometric Test. pap. 12.00 (ISBN 0-384-38470-6). Johnson Repr.

Miller, Maurice H. & Polisar, Ira A. Audiological Evaluation of the Pediatric Patient. (Illus.). 132p. 1971. 13.75x (ISBN 0-398-02160-0). C C Thomas.

Roberts, Jean & Ahuja, Elizabeth M. Hearing Sensitivity & Related Medical Findings among Youths Twelve to Seventeen Years: U.S. Stevenson, Taloria, ed. LC 75-619079. (Data from the Health Examination Survey Series 11: No. 154). 51p. 1975. pap. text ed. 1.50 (ISBN 0-8406-0043-7). Natl Ctr Health Stats.

Rowland, Michael. Basic Hearing Level Findings of Adults Twenty-Five to Seventy-Four Years: United States 1971-1975. Cox, Klaudia, ed. (Series 11: No. 215). 1979. pap. text ed. 1.75 (ISBN 0-8406-0165-4). Natl Ctr Health Stats.

Rudman, Jack. Audiologist. (Career Examination Ser.: C-1124). (Cloth bdg. avail. on request). pap. 12.00 (ISBN 0-8373-1124-1). Natl Learning.

--Consultant in Audiology. (Career Examination Ser.: C-1213). (Cloth bdg. avail on request). pap. 12.00 (ISBN 0-8373-1213-2). Natl Learning.

--Hearing Examiner. (Career Examination Ser.: C-351). (Cloth bdg. avail. on request). pap. 10.00 (ISBN 0-8373-0351-6). Natl Learning.

AUDITING–DATA PROCESSING

Arkin, H. & Arkin, R. Statistical Sampling Software for Auditing & Accounting. 160p. 1985. 275.00 (ISBN 0-07-079119-8). McGraw.

Audit & Control Considerations in an On-Line Environment. (Computer Services Guidelines Ser.). 32p. 1983. pap. 8.50 (ISBN 0-317-02602-X). Am Inst CPA.

Dawley, Donald L. What Auditors Should Know about Data Processing. Farmer, Richard N., ed. LC 83-17879. (Research for Business Decisions Ser.: No. 63). 250p. 1983. 39.95 (ISBN 0-8357-1483-7). UMI Res Pr.

Eason, Tom S., et al, eds. Systems Auditability & Control Study, 3 Vols. Russell, Susan H. & Ruder, Brian. Incl. Data Processing Audit Practices Report. pap. text ed. 15.00 (ISBN 0-89413-052-8); Data Processing Control Practices Report. pap. text ed. 15.00 (ISBN 0-89413-051-X); Executive Report. pap. text ed. 15.00 (ISBN 0-89413-050-1). (Illus.). 1977. Set. pap. text ed. 37.50 (ISBN 0-686-86121-3). Inst Inter Aud.

Lott, Richard W. Auditing the Data Processing Function. LC 79-54841. pap. 55.50 (ISBN 0-317-26945-3, 2023588). Bks Demand UMI.

AUDITORY NERVE

see Acoustic Nerve

AUDUBON, JOHN JAMES, 1785-1851

Audubon, John J. Audubon & His Journals, 2 vols. Audubon, Maria R., ed. LC 75-38340. (Select Bibliographies Reprint Ser.). 1897. Set. 56.50 (ISBN 0-8369-6660-0). Ayer Co Pubs.

--The Eighteen Twenty-Six Journal of John James Audubon. Ford, Alice, ed. (Illus.). 1967. 22.95x (ISBN 0-8061-0731-6). U of Okla Pr.

Durant, Mary & Harwood, Michael. On the Road with John James Audubon. LC 79-22734. (Illus.). 576p. 1980. 19.95 (ISBN 0-396-07740-4). Dodd.

Proby, Kathryn H. Audubon in Florida: With Selections from the Writings of John James Audubon. LC 72-85114. (Illus.). 384p. 1974. pap. 15.95 (ISBN 0-87024-301-2). U of Miami Pr.

Warren, Robert Penn. Audobon: A Vision. 1969. 9.95 (ISBN 0-394-40301-0). Random.

AUGER EFFECT

Hawkins, Donald T. Auger Electron Spectroscopy: A Bibliography, 1925-1975. LC 76-55815. 312p. 1977. 95.00x (ISBN 0-306-65168-8, Plenum Pr). Plenum Pub.

Temkin, Aaron, ed. Autoionization: Recent Developments & Applications. (Physics of Atoms & Molecules Ser.). 275p. 1985. 45.00x (ISBN 0-306-41854-1, Plenum Pr). Plenum Pub.

AURORAS

see also Atmospheric Electricity; Magnetic Storms; Magnetism, Terrestrial

Alaska Geographic Staff, ed. Aurora Borealis. LC 72-92087. (Alaska Geographic Ser.: Vol. 6, No. 2). (Illus.). 1979. pap. 7.95 album style (ISBN 0-88240-124-6). Alaska Northwest.

Brekke, A. & Egeland, A. The Northern Light: From Mythology to Space Research. (Illus.). 190p. 1983. 45.00 (ISBN 0-387-12429-2). Springer-Verlag.

Corliss, William R. Lightning, Auroras, Nocturnal Lights & Related Luminous Phenomena. LC 82-99902. (A Catalog of Geophysical Anomalies Ser.). (Illus.). 248p. 1982. 11.95 (ISBN 0-915554-09-7). Sourcebook.

Eather, Robert. Majestic Lights. (Illus.). 324p. 1980. 49.00 (ISBN 0-87590-215-4). Am Geophysical.

Jones, A. V. Aurora. LC 74-26994. (Geophysics & Astrophysics Monographs: No.9). 301p. 1974. lib. bdg. 45.00 (ISBN 90-277-0272-1, Pub. by Reidel Holland); pap. 34.00 (ISBN 90-277-0273-X). Kluwer Academic.

Kremser, G., et al. X-Ray Measurements in the Auroral Zone from July to October 1964. (Illus.). 1965. pap. 10.70 (ISBN 0-387-03365-3). Springer-Verlag.

Lockheed Research Symposium on Space Science (1st: 1964 Palo Alto CAlif.) Auroral Phenomena: Experiments & Theory. Walt, Martin, ed. LC 78-17993. pap. 45.00 (ISBN 0-317-27760-X, 2015528). Bks Demand UMI.

Omholt, A. Optical Aurora. LC 79-163747. (Physics & Chemistry in Space: Vol. 4). (Illus.). 1971. 38.00 (ISBN 0-387-05486-3). Springer-Verlag.

AUSDEHNUNGSLEHRE

Forder, Henry G. Calculus of Extension. LC 59-1178. 25.00 (ISBN 0-8284-0135-7). Chelsea Pub.

Stoll, Wilhelm. Invariant Forms on Grassman Manifolds. LC 77-85946. (Annals of Mathematics Studies Ser.: No. 89). 128p. 1978. 20.00 (ISBN 0-691-08198-0); pap. 10.50 (ISBN 0-691-08199-9). Princeton U Pr.

AUSTENITE

see also Steel, Heat Resistant

Properties of Austenitic Stainless Steels & Their Weld Metals: Influence of Slight Chemistry Variations - STP 679. 153p. 1979. pap. 13.50x (ISBN 0-8031-0537-1, 04-679000-02). ASTM.

Retained Austenite & Its Measurement by X-Ray Diffraction. 64p. 1980. pap. 15.00 (ISBN 0-89883-224-1, SP453). Soc Auto Engineers.

AUSTIN (AUTOMOBILE)

see Automobiles, Foreign–Types–Austin

AUSTIN-HEALEY (AUTOMOBILE)

see Automobiles, Foreign–Types–Healey

AUSTIN MINI AUTOMOBILE

see Automobiles, Foreign–Types–Morris Mini Minor

AUSTRALASIAN ANTARCTIC EXPEDITION, 1911-1914

Mawson, Douglas. Home of the Blizzard, Being the Story of the Australian Antarctic Expedition, 1911-1914, 2 Vols. LC 68-55202. (Illus.). 1968. Repr. of 1915 ed. Set. lib. bdg. 71.75x (ISBN 0-8371-3849-3, MAHB). Greenwood.

AUSTRALIAN LOVEBIRD

see Budgerigars

AUSTRALOPITHECINES

Brain, C. K. The Hunters or the Hunted? An Introduction to African Cave Taphonomy. LC 79-28104. 1981. lib. bdg. 40.00x (ISBN 0-226-07089-1); pap. 17.50x (ISBN 0-226-07090-5). U of Chicago Pr.

Oxnard, Charles. Uniqueness & Diversity in Human Evolution: Morphometric Studies of Australopithecines. LC 74-16689. viii, 134p. 1975. text ed. 17.50x (ISBN 0-226-64253-4). U of Chicago Pr.

Rak, Yoel. The Australopithecine Face: (Monograph) LC 83-2591. 169p. 1983. 45.00 (ISBN 0-12-576280-1). Acad Pr.

Reichs, Kathleen J., ed. Hominid Origins: Inquiries Past & Present. LC 82-20161. (Illus.). 278p. (Orig.). 1983. lib. bdg. 25.50 (ISBN 0-8191-2864-3); pap. text ed. 13.25 (ISBN 0-8191-2865-1). U Pr of Amer.

Robinson, John T. Early Hominid Posture & Locomotion. LC 72-77306. 384p. 1973. 31.00x (ISBN 0-226-72230-9). U of Chicago Pr.

AUTHORSHIP–DATA PROCESSING

Burke, Anna M. Microcomputers for Writers. 124p. 1985. 9.95 (ISBN 0-912603-22-4). Micro Info.

Daiute. Computers & Writing. 200p. (Orig.). 1983. pap. 16.95 (ISBN 0-201-10368-0). Addison-Wesley.

Gonzales, Laurence. Computers for Writers: User Friendly Guides. 144p. 1984. 6.95 (ISBN 0-345-31476-X). Ballantine.

--User Friendly Guides: Computers for Writers. 144p. (Orig.). 1984. pap. 6.95 (ISBN 0-345-31476-X). Ballantine.

Hinckley, Dan. Writing with a Computer: Using Your Word Processor for a New Freedom & Creativity in Writing. 256p. 1985. pap. 12.95 (ISBN 0-671-49197-0, Pub. by Computer Bks). S&S.

Stultz, Russell A. Writing & Publishing on Your Microcomputer. Berliner, Thomas H., ed. LC 84-15178. (Illus.). 240p. 1984. pap. 13.95 (ISBN 0-915381-59-1). WordWare Pub.

Williams, Frederick. Framework for Writers. 1985. pap. 15.95 (ISBN 0-912677-54-6). Ashton-Tate Bks.

AUTO MECHANICS

see Automobile Mechanics

AUTOCODES

see Programming Languages (Electronic Computers)

AUTOGENOUS WELDING

see Welding

AUTOGIROS

Crowe, Alfred. A Guide to Autogyros. (Illus.). 64p. pap. cancelled (ISBN 0-933078-08-0). Aviation.

AUTO-IONIZATION

see Auger Effect

AUTOMATA

see Machine Theory

AUTOMATED BATTLEFIELD

see Electronics in Military Engineering

AUTOMATED INFORMATION NETWORKS

see Information Networks

AUTOMATED MAINTENANCE

see Automatic Checkout Equipment

AUTOMATED TYPESETTING

see Computerized Type-Setting

AUTOMATIC CHECKOUT EQUIPMENT

see also Error-Correcting Codes (Information Theory)

Kneen, John. Logic Analyzers for Microprocessors. 128p. pap. 11.95 (0953). Hayden.

Luetzow, Robert H. Interfacing Test Circuits with Single-Board Computers. (Illus.). 256p. (Orig.). 1983. 19.95 (ISBN 0-8306-0183-X); pap. 13.50 (ISBN 0-8306-0583-5, 1583). TAB Bks.

Saeks, Richard & Liberty, Stanley, eds. Rational Fault Analysis. (Electrical Engineering & Electronics Ser.: Vol. 1). 1977. 55.00 (ISBN 0-8247-6541-9). Dekker.

Stover, Allan C. ATE: Automatic Test Equipment. LC 83-14917. (Illus.). 239p. 1984. 34.50 (ISBN 0-07-061792-9). McGraw.

AUTOMATIC CONTROL

see also Automatic Timers; Automation; Carrier Control Systems; Cybernetics; Delay Lines; Electric Controllers; Error-Correcting Codes (Information Theory); Feedback Control Systems; Guidance Systems (Flight); Hydraulic Control; Machine Tools–Numerical Control; Pneumatic Control; Process Control; Servomechanisms; Switching Theory

Aerospace Fluid Power & Control Systems, 8 papers. 112p. 1983. pap. 22.00 (ISBN 0-89883-325-6, SP554). Soc Auto Engineers.

Akashi. Control Science & Technology for the Progress of Society: Proceedings, 7 Vols. LC 81-23491. (IFAC Proceedings). 3800p. 1982. Set. 825.00 (ISBN 0-08-027580-X); Vol. 1. 180.00 (ISBN 0-08-028713-1); Vol. 2. 180.00 (ISBN 0-08-028714-X); Vol. 3. 99.00 (ISBN 0-08-028715-8); Vol. 4. 125.00 (ISBN 0-08-028716-6); Vol. 5. 110.00 (ISBN 0-08-028717-4); Vol. 6. 99.00 (ISBN 0-08-028718-2); Vol. 7. 110.00 (ISBN 0-08-028719-0). Pergamon.

Al Fateh-IFAC Workshop, 1st, Tripoli, Libya, May 1980 & El Hares, H. Automatic Control in Desalination & the Oil Industry: Appropriate Applications: Proceedings. Dali, T., ed. LC 81-23412. (Illus.). 209p. 1982. 50.00 (ISBN 0-08-028698-4, A115, A135). Pergamon.

American Automatic Control Conference: Proceedings, Joint Automatic Control, 1979. LC 79-52918. 923p. 1979. text ed. 120.00 (ISBN 0-8169-0051-5, P-23). Am Inst Chem Eng.

American Automatic Control Conference: Proceedings, Joint Automatic Control, 1980, Vols. 1 & 2. LC 80-67739. 850p. 1980. text ed. 50.00 ea. (ISBN 0-8169-0192-9, P-27). Am Inst Chem Eng.

American Society of Mechnical Engineers. Singular Perturbations: Order Reduction in Control System Design. LC 72-87029. pap. 20.00 (ISBN 0-317-08441-0, 2012304). Bks Demand UMI.

Anand, D. K. Introduction to Control Systems. 2nd ed. LC 83-6320. (International Series on Systems & Control: Vol. 8). (Illus.). 448p. 1983. 55.00 (ISBN 0-08-030002-2); pap. 25.00 (ISBN 0-08-030001-4). Pergamon.

Andrew, William G. & Williams, H. B. Applied Instrumentation in the Process Industries, Vol. 1: A Survey. 2nd ed. LC 79-9418. 407p. 1979. 45.95x (ISBN 0-87201-382-0). Gulf Pub.

Application of Digital Control of Power Plant Systems. 70p. 1982. 95.00x (ISBN 0-85298-497-9, Pub. by Mechanical Eng Pubns). State Mutual Bk.

Astrom, Karl J. & Wittenmark, Bjorn. Computer Controlled Systems: Theory & Design. (Illus.). 432p. 1984. text ed. 38.95 (ISBN 0-13-164319-3). P-H.

Athans, Michael & Falb, P. Optimal Controls. 1966. 58.00 (ISBN 0-07-002413-8). McGraw.

Automated Education Center. Simulation of a Production Control System. LC 71-118564. 259p. 1969. 29.00 (ISBN 0-403-04478-2). Scholarly.

Automated Guided Vehicle Systems: Proceedings of the 2nd International Conference, Stuttgart, GFR, June 1983. (Illus.). 1983. 75.00 (ISBN 0-903608-45-6, Pub. by IFSPUBS). Scholium Intl.

Automated Inspection & Product Control: Proceedings of the 7th International Conference. 1985. 77.00x (ISBN 0-903608-86-3, Pub. by IFS Pubns UK). Air Sci Co.

Barney, George C. Intelligent Instrumentation: Microprocessor Applications in Measurement & Control. (Illus.). 528p. 1986. text ed. 39.95 (ISBN 0-13-468943-7). P-H.

Bennett, S. A History of Control Engineering, 1800-1930. (IEE Control Engineering Ser.: No. 8). (Illus.). 224p. 1979. 66.00 (ISBN 0-906048-07-9, CE008). Inst Elect Eng.

Bretschi, Jurgen. Automated Inspection Systems for Industry: Scope for Intelligent Measuring. (Eng., Illus.). 190p. 1982. Repr. of 1979 ed. text ed. 52.00x softbound (ISBN 0-903608-20-0, IFSPUBS). Scholium Intl.

Brill, Alan E. Building Controls into Structured Systems. LC 82-70209. (Illus.). 168p. (Orig.). 1983. 29.00 (ISBN 0-917072-38-3); pap. 22.00 (ISBN 0-917072-27-8). Yourdon.

Bryson, A. E. & Ho, Y. C. Applied Optimal Control: Optimization, Estimation, & Control. rev. ed. LC 75-16114. (Illus.). 481p. 1981. pap. text ed. 27.95 (ISBN 0-89116-228-3). Hemisphere Pub.

Burger, J. & Jarny, Y., eds. Simulation in Engineering Sciences: Applications to the Automatic Control of Mechanical & Energy Systems. 438p. 1984. 52.00 (ISBN 0-444-86795-3, North Holland). Elsevier.

Case, S. G., et al. Electronic Measurement & Control Applications, 3 vols. (Illus.). 1981. Set. 154.00x (ISBN 0-87683-015-7); Vol. 1; 370p. looseleaf 60.00x (ISBN 0-87683-016-5); Vol. 2; lab. manual; 175p. looseleaf 47.00x (ISBN 0-87683-017-3); Vol. 3; solutions maual; 175p. looseleaf 47.00x (ISBN 0-87683-018-1); looseleaf & lesson plans 1250.00x (ISBN 0-317-11867-6). G P Courseware.

Chesmond, C. J. Control Systems Technology. 480p. 1984. pap. text ed. 29.95 (ISBN 0-7131-3508-5). E Arnold.

Chironis, Nicholas P. Mechanisms, Linkages, & Mechanical Controls. 1965. 57.75 (ISBN 0-07-010775-0). McGraw.

Coiffet, Philippe. Robot Technology, Vol. 1: Modelling & Control. (Illus.). 160p. 1983. 41.95 (ISBN 0-13-782094-1). P-H.

Computer Control of Transport. 61p. (Orig.). 1981. pap. text ed. 24.00x (ISBN 0-85825-149-3, Pub. by Inst Engineering Australia). Brookfield Pub Co.

Control Valve Capacity Test Procedure: ISA Standard S75.02. LC 81-174761. 20p. 1981. pap. text ed. 16.00x (ISBN 0-87664-510-4). Instru Soc.

Control Valve Sizing Equations: An ANSI Approved Standard ISA-S75.01. 12p. 1977. pap. text ed. 10.00 (ISBN 0-87664-400-0). Instru Soc.

Diebold, John. Automation. 224p. 1983. 14.95 (ISBN 0-8144-5756-8). AMACOM.

Dorf, Richard C. Modern Control Systems. 2nd ed. LC 73-7664. 1974. 38.95 (ISBN 0-201-01258-8); ans. bk avail. (ISBN 0-201-01259-6). Addison-Wesley.

Driskell, Leslie R. Control Valve Selection & Sizing: An Independent Learning Module of the Instrument Society of America. LC 82-48157. 520p. 1983. text ed. 59.95x (ISBN 0-87664-628-3). Instru Soc.

Elonka, Stephen M. & Parsons, Alonzo R. Standard Instrumentation Questions & Answers for Production-Processes Control, 2 vols. in 1. Incl. Vol. 1. Measuring Systems; Vol. 2. Control Systems. LC 79-1385. 1979. Repr. of 1962 ed. lib. bdg. 32.50 (ISBN 0-88275-896-9). Krieger.
Enemark, Donald C. Feasibility Study & Design of an Antenna Pointing System with an in-Loop, Time Shared Digital Computer. LC 76-135076. 241p. 1970. 19.00 (ISBN 0-403-04499-5). Scholarly.
Faurre, Pierre & Depeyrot, Michel. Elements of System Theory. LC 76-3056. 1976. 47.00 (ISBN 0-7204-0440-1, North-Holland). Elsevier.
Fleming, W. H. & Gorostiza, L. G., eds. Advances in Filtering & Optimal Stochastic Control: Proceedings; Cocoyoc, Mexico 1982. (Lecture Notes in Control & Information Science: Vol. 42). 392p. 1982. pap. 19.50 (ISBN 0-387-11936-1). Springer-Verlag.
Fluegge-Lotz, Irmgard. Discontinuous Automatic Control. LC 52-13156. (Illus.). pap. 44.00 (ISBN 0-317-10759-3, 2000032). Bks Demand UMI.
Fortmann, Thomas E. & Hitz, Konrad L. Introduction to Linear Control Systems. (Control & Systems Theory: Vol. 5). 1977. 37.75 (ISBN 0-8247-6512-5). Dekker.
Frederick, Dean K. & Carlson, A. Bruce. Linear Systems in Communication & Control. LC 71-155118. 575p. 1971. 46.50x (ISBN 0-471-27721-5). Wiley.
Friedland, B. Control System Design: An Introduction to State-Space Methods. (Electrical Engineering Ser.). 512p. 1985. text ed. price not set (ISBN 0-07-022441-2). McGraw.
Garner, K. C. Introduction to Control Systems Performance Measurements. 1968. 28.00 (ISBN 0-08-012499-2); pap. 11.25 (ISBN 0-08-012498-4). Pergamon.
Gopal, M. Modern Control System Theory. 644p. 1984. 27.95 (ISBN 0-470-27424-7). Halsted Pr.
Gupta, Someshwar C. & Hasdorff, Lawrence. Fundamentals of Automatic Control. LC 82-20338. 602p. 1983. Repr. of 1970 ed. lib. bdg. 39.50 (ISBN 0-89874-578-0). Krieger.
Haines, Roger W. Control Systems for Heating, Ventilating & Air Conditioning. 3rd ed. (Van Nostrand Reinhold Engineering Ser.). 320p. 1983. text ed. 28.50 (ISBN 0-442-23649-2). Van Nos Reinhold.
Hale, Francis J. Introduction to Control System Analysis & Design. (Illus.). 400p. 1973. ref. ed. 35.95 (ISBN 0-13-479824-4). P-H.
Halmos, F. & Somogyi, J. Optimization of Design & Computation of Control Networks. 1981. 129.00x (ISBN 0-569-08552-7, Pub. by Collet's). State Mutual Bk.
Harrison, Howard L. & Bollinger, John G. Introduction to Automatic Controls. 2nd ed. 460p. 1969. text ed. 33.50 scp (ISBN 0-7002-2241-3, HarpC); scp solution manual 11.50 (ISBN 0-352-00650-1). Har-Row.
Hatvany, J., ed. Computer Languages for Numerical Control. 152p. (Proceedings). 1973. 41.00 (ISBN 0-444-10572-7, Biomedical Pr). Elsevier.
Heller, Samuel. Automatic Control Basics: Designing & Repairing Controllers Using Schematic Diagrams. LC 66-30564. (Illus., Orig.). 1966. 19.50 (ISBN 0-911740-04-X). Datarule.
Hunt, J. A. An Outline of Features of Microprocessor-Based Controllers, 1979. 1981. 69.00x (ISBN 0-686-97138-8, Pub. by W Spring England). State Mutual Bk.
Hunter, Ronald P. Automated Process Control Systems: Concepts & Hardware. (Illus.). 1978. ref. ed. 27.95 (ISBN 0-13-054502-3). P-H.
IFAC Conference, Cairo, Egypt, Nov. 1977. Systems Approach for Development: Proceedings. Ghonaimy, M. A., ed. (IFAC Proceedings). 658p. 1979. text ed. 150.00 (ISBN 0-08-022017-7). Pergamon.
IFAC Congress, 9th, Budapest, Hungary, July 1984. World Congress, 1984: Proceedings. 400p. 1985. write for info. Pergamon.
IFAC-ESA Symposium, Noorwjkerhout, The Netherlands, July 1982 & Van Woerkom, L. M. Automatic Control in Space 1982: Proceedings. (IFAC Proceedings Ser.). 580p. 1983. 145.00 (ISBN 0-08-029328-X). Pergamon.
IFAC-IFIP Symposium on Software for Computer Control, 2nd, Prague, Czechoslovakia, 11-15, June 1979. Software for Computer Control: Proceedings. Novak, M., ed. (IFAC Proceedings). (Illus.). 420p. 1979. 99.00 (ISBN 0-08-024448-3). Pergamon.
IFAC-IFIP Symposium, 3rd, Madrid, Spain, Oct. 1982. Software for Computer Control: Proceedings. Ferrate, G., ed. Puente, E. A. (IFAC Proceedings Ser.). 586p. 1983. 145.00 (ISBN 0-08-029352-2). Pergamon.
IFAC International Symposium, 4th, Fredericton, NB, Canada, July 1977. Multivariable Technological Systems: Proceedings. Atherton, D. P., ed. 666p. 1978. text ed. 140.00 (ISBN 0-08-022010-X). Pergamon.
IFAC Symposium, Paris, France, Dec. 1982. Components & Instruments for Distributed Computer Control Systems: Proceedings. Binder, Z. & Perret, R., eds. LC 83-11448. (IFAC Proceedings). 178p. 1983. 60.00 (ISBN 0-08-029991-1). Pergamon.
IFAC Symposium, Warsaw, Poland, May 1980. Pneumatic & Hydraulic Components & Instruments in Automatic Control: Proceedings. Leskiewicz, H. J. & Zaremba, M., eds. LC 80-41658. (IFAC Proceedings Ser.). (Illus.). 308p. 1981. 83.00 (ISBN 0-08-027317-3). Pergamon.
IFAC Symposium, Zurich, Switzerland, 29-31 Aug. 1979. Computer Aided Design of Control Systems: Proceedings. Cuenod, M. A., ed. LC 79-42655. (IFAC Proceedings Ser.). (Illus.). 702p. 1980. 170.00 (ISBN 0-08-024488-2). Pergamon.
IFAC Symposium, 2nd, Coventry, UK, June 1977. Control of Distributed Parameter Systems: Proceedings. Banks, S. P. & Pritchard, A. J., eds. 541p. 1978. 140.00 (ISBN 0-08-022018-5). Pergamon.
IFAC Symposium, 3rd, Toulouse, France, June-July 1982 & Babary, J. P. Control of Distributed Parameter Systems: Proceedings. Le Letty, L., ed. (IFAC Proceedings Ser.). 660p. 1983. 145.00 (ISBN 0-08-029361-1). Pergamon.
IFAC Symposium, 8th, Oxford, UK, 2-6 July 1979. Automatic Control in Space: Proceedings. Munday, C. W., ed. (IFAC Proceedings Ser.). 362p. 1980. 125.00 (ISBN 0-08-024449-1). Pergamon.
IFAC Workshop, Beijing, China, Aug. 1981 & Miller, W. E. Distributed Computer Control Systems 1981: Proceedings. (IFAC Proceedings Ser.). (Illus.). 176p. 1982. 55.00 (ISBN 0-08-028672-0). Pergamon.
IFAC Workshop, Karlsruhe, BRD, Nov. 1983. Design of Work in Automated Manufacturing Systems: Proceedings. Martin, T., ed. 1984. write for info. Pergamon.
IFAC Workshop, Stuttgart, BRD, May 1979. Safety of Computer Control Systems: Proceedings. Lauber, R., ed. (Illus.). 230p. 1980. 62.00 (ISBN 0-08-024453-X). Pergamon.
IFAC Workshop, Tampa, Fla., Oct. 1979. Distributed Computer Control Systems: Proceedings. Harrison, T. J., ed. (IFAC Proceedings). (Illus.). 240p. 1980. 76.00 (ISBN 0-08-024490-4). Pergamon.
IFAC Workshop, 4th, DCCS-82, Tallin, USSR, May 1982 & Gellie, R. W. Distributed Computer Control Systems 1982: Proceedings. Tavast, R. R., ed. (IFAC Proceedings Ser.). 215p. 1983. 60.00 (ISBN 0-08-028675-5). Pergamon.
IFAC Workshop, 4th, San Francisco, Calif., June 1983 & Rauch, H. E. Applications of Nonlinear Programming to Optimization & Control: Proceedings. LC 83-21936. (IFAC Proceedings). 230p. 1983. 45.00 (ISBN 0-08-030574-1). Pergamon.
IFAC Workshop, 5th, Johannesburg, South Africa, May 1983 & Rodd, M. Distributed Computer Control Systems, 1983: Proceedings. (IFAC Proceedings Ser.). 160p. 1983. 56.00 (ISBN 0-08-030546-6). Pergamon.
International Conference on Automated Inspection & Product Control, 6th, Brighton, UK, April 1982. Automated Inspection & Product Control: Proceedings. 324p. 1982. pap. text ed. 95.00x (ISBN 0-903608-23-5, Pub. by IFSPUBS). Scholium Intl.
International Conference on Distributed Computer Control Systems (1977: University of Aston) International Conference on Distributed Computer Control Systems, 26-28 September, 1977. LC 79-306653. (Institution of Electrical Engineers Conference Publication Ser.: Vol. 153). (Illus.). pap. 49.00 (ISBN 0-317-09909-4, 2051590). Bks Demand UMI.
International Conference on Information Sciences & Systems, 1st, Patras, Greece, Aug. 1976. Applications & Research in Information Systems & Sciences: Proceedings, 3 vols. new ed. Lainiotis, Demetrios G. & Tzannes, Nicolaos, eds. LC 77-15000. (Illus.). 920p. 1977. Set. pap. text ed. 169.00 (ISBN 0-89116-078-7). Hemisphere Pub.
International Conference, 1st Stratford-upon-Avon, UK April 1-3, 1981. Robot Vision & Sensory Controls: Proceedings. 348p. 1981. pap. text ed. 88.00x (ISBN 0-903608-15-4, IFSPUBS). Scholium Intl.
International Federation of Automatic Control, Triennial World Congress, 7th, Helsinki, Finland, June 1978. A Link Between Science & Applications of Automatic Control: Proceedings, 4 vols. Niemi, A., et al, eds. Incl. Vol. 1. 800p. 225.00 (ISBN 0-08-022436-9); Vol. 2. 812p. 225.00 (ISBN 0-08-022437-7); Vol. 3. 712p. 205.00 (ISBN 0-08-022438-5); Vol. 4. 340p. 88.00 (ISBN 0-08-022439-3). (International Federation of Automatic Control Ser.). 2667p. 1979. Set. 805.00 (ISBN 0-08-022414-8). Pergamon.
International Federation of Automatic Control. Proceedings of the IFAC Sixth World Congress, Boston-CAmbridge, Massachusetts, U. S. A., August 24-30, 1975, Part 4. LC 62-121. pap. 160.00 (ISBN 0-317-26301-3, 2052149). Bks Demand UMI.
Joint Automatic Control Conference (1974: University of Texas at Austin) Identification of Parameters in Distributed Systems. Goodson, R. E. & Polis, M., eds. LC 74-80956. pap. 25.80 (ISBN 0-317-12989-9, 2016914). Bks Demand UMI.
Jury, Eliahu I. Sampled-Data Control Systems. LC 76-57949. 476p. 1977. Repr. of 1958 ed. 27.50 (ISBN 0-88275-529-3). Krieger.
King, P. J. & Hunt, J. A. The Application of Microprocessors for Control in the Food Industry, 1980. 1981. 30.00x (ISBN 0-686-97026-8, Pub. by W Spring England). State Mutual Bk.
Klaasen, K. B. Reliability of Analogue Electronic Systems. (Studies in Electrical & Electronic Engineering: Vol. 13). 278p. 1984. 61.00 (ISBN 0-444-42388-5). Elsevier.
Kompass, Edward J. & Williams, Theodore J., eds. Industrial Computing Control after 25 Years: Micros to Hierarchies (Proceedings of the 10th Annual Advanced Control Conference) 276p. 1984. Conference papers 37.50 (ISBN 0-914331-09-4). Control Eng.
--Learning Systems & Pattern Recognition in Industrial Control: Proceedings of the 9th Annual Advenced Control Conference. 91p. 1983. conference papers 30.00 (ISBN 0-914331-08-6). Control Eng.
--On-Line Process Simulation Techniques in Industrial Control: Proceedings of the Eleventh Annual Advanced Control Conference. 200p. 1985. 45.00 (ISBN 0-914331-11-6). Control Eng.
Kuo, B. C., ed. Proceedings: Symposium on Incremental Motion Control Systems & Devices, 10th Annual. (Illus.). 362p. 1981. 45.00x (ISBN 0-931538-03-3). Incremental Motion.
Kuo, Benjamin C. Automatic Control System. 4th ed. (Illus.). 720p. 1982. 40.95 (ISBN 0-13-054817-0). P-H.
Kwakernaak, Huibert & Sivan, Raphael. Linear Optimal Control Systems. LC 72-3576. 575p. 1972. 59.95x (ISBN 0-471-51110-2, Pub. by Wiley-Interscience). Wiley.
Laning, J. Halcombe, Jr. & Battin, Richard H. Random Processes in Automatic Control. LC 76-30384. (Illus.). 444p. 1977. Repr. of 1956 ed. lib. bdg. 25.50 (ISBN 0-88275-501-3). Krieger.
Ledgerwood, Byron K., ed. Control Engineering Conference: Proceedings of the First Annual Control Engineering Conference. 239p. 1982. 77.50 (ISBN 0-914331-50-7). Control Eng.
--Control Engineering Conference: Proceedings of the Second Annual Control Engineering Conference. 347p. 1983. 77.50 (ISBN 0-914331-51-5). Control Eng.
--Control Engineering Conference: Proceedings of the Third Annual Control Engineering Conference. 486p. 1984. 87.50 (ISBN 0-914331-52-3). Control Eng.
--Proceedings of the Fourth Annual Control Engineering Conference. 500p. 1985. 87.50 (ISBN 0-914331-54-X). Control Eng.
Lefcourt, Herbert, ed. Research with the Locus of Control Construct: Assessment Methods, Vol. I. LC 81-7876. 1981. 39.50 (ISBN 0-12-443201-8). Acad Pr.
Lenk, John D. Handbook of Controls & Instrumentation. (Illus.). 1980. text ed. 27.95 (ISBN 0-13-377069-9). P-H.
Leondes, C. T. Control and Dynamic Systems: Advances in Theory & Applications, Vol. 21. (Serial Publication Ser.). 1984. 49.00 (ISBN 0-12-012721-0). Acad Pr.
Leondes, C. T., ed. Advances in Control Systems, Vols. 1-8. Incl. Vol. 1. 1964 (ISBN 0-12-012701-6); Vol. 2. 1965 (ISBN 0-12-012702-4); Vol. 3. 1966 (ISBN 0-12-012703-2); Vol. 4. 1966 (ISBN 0-12-012704-0); Vol. 5. 1967 (ISBN 0-12-012705-9); Vol. 6. 1968 (ISBN 0-12-012706-7); Vol. 7. 1969 (ISBN 0-12-012707-5); Vol. 8. 1971 (ISBN 0-12-012708-3). 70.00 ea. Acad Pr.
--Control of Dynamic Systems: Advances in Theory & Application, Vols. 9, 10, 13 & 15. Incl. Vol. 9. 1973. 65.00 (ISBN 0-12-012709-1); Vol. 10. 1973. 65.00 (ISBN 0-12-012710-5); Vol. 13. 1977. 65.00 (ISBN 0-12-012713-X); Vol. 15. 1979. 44.00 (ISBN 0-12-012715-6). 1973. Acad Pr.
Leone, William C. Production Automation & Numerical Control. LC 67-21679. (Illus.). pap. 46.60 (ISBN 0-317-11119-1, 2012419). Bks Demand UMI.
Letherman, K. M. Automatic Controls for Heating & Air Conditioning: Principles & Applications. LC 80-42155. (International Ser. on Heating, Ventilation & Refrigeration: Vol. 15). (Illus.). 235p. 1981. 33.00 (ISBN 0-08-023222-1). Pergamon.
Letov, A. M. Stability in Nonlinear Control Systems. 35.00x (ISBN 0-691-08040-2). Princeton U Pr.
Loskutov, V. Mathematical Control Machines: The Application of Computers in Production Control. MIR Publishers, tr. from Rus. (Illus.). 414p. 1975. text ed. 18.00x (ISBN 0-8464-0619-5). Beekman Pubs.
Luggen, William W. Fundamentals of Numerical Control. LC 83-71970. (Illus.). 256p. 1984. text ed. 26.00 (ISBN 0-8273-2162-7); instrs' guide 3.00 (ISBN 0-8273-2163-5). Delmar.
Mayr, Otto. Origins of Feedback Control. 1970. pap. 4.95x (ISBN 0-262-63056-7). MIT Pr.
Melsa, James L. & Schultz, Donald. Linear Control Systems. LC 68-8664. (Electronic Systems Ser.). (Illus.). 1969. text ed. 48.00 (ISBN 0-07-041481-5). McGraw.
Merriam, C. W. Automated Design of Control Systems. LC 73-86001. 356p. 1975. 14.25x (ISBN 0-677-04440-2). Gordon.
Miller, Richard K., ed. Automated Guided Vehicle Systems: A Technical Report for Engineers & Managers. (Illus.). 110p. 1984. 85.00 (ISBN 0-89671-047-5). SEAI Tech Pubns.
Mohler, Ronald R. Bilinear Control Processes: With Applications to Engineering, Ecology & Medicine. (Mathematics in Science & Engineering Ser.). 1973. 60.00 (ISBN 0-12-504140-3). Acad Pr.
Moore, Ralph L. The Dynamic Analysis of Automatic Process Control. 276p. 1985. pap. 10.00 instr. guide (ISBN 0-87664-817-0); pap. 34.95 student guide (ISBN 0-87664-818-9). Instru Soc.
Moorhead, Jack, ed. Numerical Control Applications. LC 80-52613. (Manufacturing Update Ser.). (Illus.). 260p. 1980. 32.00 (ISBN 0-87263-058-7). SME.
Moroney, Paul. Issues in the Implementation of Digital Feedback Compensators. (Signal Processing, Optimization & Control Ser.). (Illus.). 224p. 1983. 35.00x (ISBN 0-262-13185-4). MIT Pr.
Morris, N. M. Control Engineering. 3rd ed. 256p. 1983. write for info. (ISBN 0-07-084666-9). McGraw.
Mueller, Thomas. Automated Guided Vehicle Systems. (Eng.). 290p. 1983. 34.50 (ISBN 0-387-12629-5). Springer-Verlag.
Nagrath, I. J. & Gopal, M. Control Systems Engineering. 2nd ed. LC 81-17470. 525p. 1982. 26.95x (ISBN 0-470-27148-5). Halsted Pr.
Natars. 160p. 1982. pap. text ed. 12.50 (ISBN 0-935920-05-6). Natl Pub Black Hills.
Netushil, A., ed. Theory of Automatic Control. 806p. 1978. 15.00 (ISBN 0-8285-0698-1, Pub. by Mir Pubs USSR). Imported Pubns.
Network Editors. Design Development & Applications of ATE. 1982. 60.00x (ISBN 0-904999-73-4, Pub. by Network). State Mutual Bk.
--Design of Telecontrol & Telemetry Systems. 1982. 60.00x (ISBN 0-904999-28-9, Pub. by Network). State Mutual Bk.
Network Editors, ed. Advanced Techniques & Future Developments. 1982. 49.00x (ISBN 0-904999-22-X, Pub. by Network). State Mutual Bk.
--Application of Telecontrol Systems. 1982. 60.00x (ISBN 0-904999-33-5, Pub. by Network). State Mutual Bk.
--Applications of ATE. 1982. 95.00x (ISBN 0-904999-37-8, Pub. by Network). State Mutual Bk.
--Component Testing. 1982. 69.00x (ISBN 0-904999-40-8, Pub. by Network). State Mutual Bk.
--Control Systems. 1982. 59.00x (ISBN 0-904999-49-1, Pub. by Network). State Mutual bk.
--Economic & Manpower Aspects of Using ATE. 69.00x (ISBN 0-904999-39-4, Pub. by Network). State Mutual Bk.
--Economics, Planning, & Standards. 1982. 60.00x (ISBN 0-904999-31-9, Pub. by Network). State Mutual Bk.
--Field Maintenance of Complex Systems. 1982. 49.00x (ISBN 0-904999-20-3, Pub. by Network). State Mutual Bk.

--Future Trends & Software. 1982. 65.00x (ISBN 0-904999-80-7, Pub. by Network). State Mutual Bk.

--Maintenance Testing of Telecom Systems & Military Applications. 1982. 65.00x (ISBN 0-904999-79-3, Pub. by Network). State Mutual Bk.

--Monitoring Systems. 1982. 50.00x (ISBN 0-904999-50-5, Pub. by Network). State Mutual Bk.

--Navigational Aids. 1982. 50.00x (ISBN 0-904999-48-3, Pub. by Network). State Mutual Bk.

--New Techniques in Telecontrol Using Microprocessors, Computer Based Communication Networks. 1982. 60.00x (ISBN 0-904999-32-7, Pub. by Network). State Mutual Bk.

--Production Quality Assurance & Diagnostic Testing. 1982. 49.00x (ISBN 0-904999-19-X, Pub. by Network). State Mutual Bk.

--Production Testing & Testing of PCBs & Components. 1980. 90.00x (ISBN 0-904999-78-5, Pub. by Network). State Mutual Bk.

--Software. 1982. 69.00x (ISBN 0-904999-41-6, Pub. by Network). State Mutual Bk.

--Software & Future Developments. 1982. 95.00x (ISBN 0-904999-38-6, Pub. by Network). State Mutual Bk.

--Specification, Management & Ownership of ATE. 1982. 60.00x (ISBN 0-904999-72-6, Pub. by Network). State Mutual Bk.

--Test of Components & Microprocessors. 1982. 79.00x (ISBN 0-904999-36-X, Pub. by Network). State Mutual Bk.

--Test System Concepts: Test Systems Applications. 1981. 110.00x (ISBN 0-686-87120-0, Pub. by Network). State Mutual Bk.

--Testing & Maintenance of Complex Systems. 1982. 69.00x (ISBN 0-904999-43-2, Pub. by Network). State Mutual Bk.

--Tutorial & User Experience. 1982. 49.00x (ISBN 0-904999-17-3, Pub. by Network). State Mutual Bk.

--User Requirements & Staff Training. 1982. 49.00x (ISBN 0-904999-18-1, Pub. by Network). State Mutual Bk.

Numerical Control. (Productivity Equipment Ser.). 411p. 1983. pap. 36.00 (730). SME.

Ogata, Katsuhiko. Modern Control Engineering. LC 72-84843. (Electrical Engineering Ser). 1970. ref. ed. 40.95 (ISBN 0-13-590232-0). P-H.

Oldenbourg, Rudolf C. & Sartorius, Hans. The Dynamics of Automatic Controls. Mason, H. L., ed. LC 49-2386. pap. 69.00 (ISBN 0-317-08004-0, 2051945). Bks Demand UMI.

Palm, William J. Modeling, Analysis & Control of Dynamic Systems. LC 82-8530. 740p. 1983. text ed. 46.50 (ISBN 0-471-05800-9); solutions manual avail. (ISBN 0-471-88581-9). Wiley.

Papageorgiou, M. Applications of Automatic Control Concepts to Traffic Flow Modeling & Control. (Lecture Notes in Control & Information Sciences: Vol. 50). (Illus.). 186p. 1983. pap. 12.00 (ISBN 0-387-12237-0). Springer-Verlag.

Perlmutter, Daniel D. Introduction to Chemical Process Control. LC 75-11904. 218p. 1975. Repr. of 1965 ed. 13.50 (ISBN 0-88275-300-2). Krieger.

Pervozvanskii, A. A. Random Processes in Nonlinear Control Systems. (Mathematics in Science & Engineering Ser.: Vol. 15). 1965. 77.00 (ISBN 0-12-551650-9). Acad Pr.

Phelan, Richard M. Automatic Control Systems. LC 76-28020. 288p. 1977. 29.95x (ISBN 0-8014-1033-9). Cornell U Pr.

Popov, V. M. Hyperstability of Control Systems. Georgescu, R., tr. from Romanian. LC 73-83000. (Die Grundlehren der Mathematischen Wissenschaften: Vol. 204). 400p. 1973. 51.00 (ISBN 0-387-06373-0). Springer-Verlag.

Power, Henry M. & Simpson, Robert J. Introduction to Dynamics & Control. (Illus.). 1978. pap. text ed. 39.00 (ISBN 0-07-084081-4). McGraw.

Prather, Ronald E. Discrete Mathematical Structures for Computer Science. LC 75-25014. (Illus.). 680p. 1976. text ed. 34.50 (ISBN 0-395-20622-7); solutions manual 3.50 (ISBN 0-395-20623-5). HM.

Principles of Automatic Process Control. rev. ed. (Illus.). 48p. pap. text ed. 6.00x (ISBN 0-87664-108-7). Instru Soc.

Rademaker, O., et al. Dynamics & Control of Continuous Distillation Units. LC 74-83315. 726p. 1975. 127.75 (ISBN 0-444-41234-4). Elsevier.

Raven, Francis. Automatic Control Engineering. 3rd ed. (Illus.). 1978. text ed. 44.00 (ISBN 0-07-051228-0). McGraw.

Rizvi, S. F. Multivariate Control System Design in the Presence of Interaction, 1978. 1981. 50.00x (ISBN 0-686-97119-1, Pub. by W Spring England). State Mutual Bk.

Roberts, Sanford M. Dynamic Programming in Chemical Engineering & Process Control. (Mathematics in Science & Engineering Ser.: Vol. 12). 1964. 70.00 (ISBN 0-12-589450-3). Acad Pr.

Sage, A. P., ed. Control Frontiers in Knowledge Based & Man-Machine Systems. 180p. 1983. pap. 34.75 (ISBN 0-08-031153-9). Pergamon.

Sante, Daniel P. Automatic Control System Technology. (Illus.). 1980. text ed. 27.95 (ISBN 0-13-054627-5). P-H.

Schmitt, Neil M. & Farwell, Robert F. Understanding Electronic Control of Automation Systems. Luecke, G. & Battle, C., eds. LC 81-85603. (Understanding Ser.). (Illus.). 280p. 1983. pap. 6.95 (ISBN 0-89512-052-6, LCB6641). Tex Instr Inc.

Schneider, Raymond K. HVAC Control Systems. LC 80-23588. 358p. 1981. text ed. 30.95 (ISBN 0-471-05180-2); avail. tchr's manual (ISBN 0-471-09274-6). Wiley.

Shinners, Stanley M. Modern Control, System Theory & Application. 2nd ed. LC 78-52497. (Electrical Engineering Ser.). 1978. text ed. 34.95 (ISBN 0-201-07494-X); instr's man. 3.00 (ISBN 0-201-07495-8). Addison-Wesley.

Smeaton, R. W. Switchgear & Control Handbook. 1976. 57.50 (ISBN 0-07-058439-7). McGraw.

Smith, Donald N., ed. Numerical Control for Tomorrow. Peelle, David M. (Illus.). 181p. 1969. 12.00 (ISBN 0-938654-04-7, NC TOM). Indus Dev Inst Sci.

Software & Advanced Automatic Test Techniques. 1982. 90.00x (ISBN 0-904999-74-2, Pub. by Network). State Mutual Bk.

Sorenson, D. & Wets, R. J. Algorithms & Theory in Filtering & Control. (Mathematical Programming Studies: Vol. 18). 160p. 1982. 30.00 (ISBN 0-444-86399-0, I-125-82, North-Holland). Elsevier.

Stamper, Eugene & Koral, Richard L., eds. Handbook of Air Conditioning, Heating & Ventilating. 3rd ed. LC 78-71559. (Illus.). 1420p. 1979. 70.00 (ISBN 0-8311-1124-0). Indus Pr.

Steckhahn, A. D. & Otter, J. Den. Industrial Applications for Microprocessors. 1982. text ed. 28.95 (ISBN 0-8359-3067-X). Reston.

Tabak, Daniel & Kuo, Benjamin C. Optimal Control by Mathematical Programming. LC 75-137985. 1971. 24.00x (ISBN 0-13-638106-5). SRL Pub Co.

Takahashi, Y., et al. Control & Dynamic Systems. 1970. 39.95 (ISBN 0-201-07440-0). Addison-Wesley.

Taylor & Billis. Control Engineering for Marine Engineers. (Illus.). 320p. 1985. text ed. 49.95 (ISBN 0-408-01313-3). Butterworth.

Testing of Complex Systems. 1982. 60.00x (ISBN 0-904999-62-9, Pub. by Network). State Mutual Bk.

Texas Instruments Engineering Staff. The Linear Control Circuits Data Book. 2nd, rev. ed. LC 79-92000. 416p. 1980. pap. 3.90 (ISBN 0-89512-104-2, LCC4781). Tex Instr Inc.

Tzafestas, S. G., ed. Distributed Parameter Control Systems: Theory & Application. (International Series on Systems & Control: Vol. 6). 525p. 1982. 66.00 (ISBN 0-08-027624-5). Pergamon.

Voronov, A. A. Basic Principles of Automatic Control Theory: Special Linear & Nonlinear Systems. 319p. 1984. 9.95 (ISBN 0-8285-2985-X, Pub. by Mir Pubs USSR). Imported Pubns.

Vukobratovic, M. & Potkonjak, V. Scientific Fundamentals of Robotics 6. (Communications & Control Engineering Ser.). (Illus.). xiii, 305p. 1985. 42.00 (ISBN 0-387-13074-8). Springer-Verlag.

Westerlund, T., ed. Automation in Mining, Mineral & Metal Processing, 1983: Proceedings of the 4th IFAC Symposium, Helsinki, Finland, 22-25 August 1983. (IFAC Proceedings Ser.). 776p. 1984. 185.00 (ISBN 0-08-030569-5). Pergamon.

Weyrick, Robert C. Fundamentals of Automatic Control. (Illus.). 480p. 1975. text ed. 30.95 (ISBN 0-07-069493-1). McGraw.

Wierzbicki, A. Models & Sensitivity of Control Systems. (Studies in Automation & Control: Vol. 5). 1985. 83.50 (ISBN 0-444-99620-6). Elsevier.

Yang Wen-Jei & Masabuchi, M. Dynamics for Process & System Control. 456p. 1970. 87.95x (ISBN 0-677-01830-4). Gordon.

AUTOMATIC CONTROL–BIBLIOGRAPHY

Broida, V., ed. Automatic Control. 1058p. 1964. 243.95 (ISBN 0-677-00090-1). Gordon.

Witt, Howard. Navigation with a Micro-Computer. 1983. pap. text ed. 14.95 (ISBN 0-87567-082-2). Entelek.

AUTOMATIC CONTROL–DICTIONARIES

Broadbent, D. T. & Masubuchi, M., eds. Multilingual Glossary of Automatic Control Technology: English, French, German, Russian, Italian, Spanish, Russian, Japanese. (Polyglot.). 250p. 1981. 50.00 (ISBN 0-08-027607-5). Pergamon.

Meetham, A. R. Encyclopedia of Linguistics, Information & Control. 1969. 140.00 (ISBN 0-08-012337-6). Pergamon.

Sykora, Jiri, ed. Dictionary of Automatical Technique. (Eng., Ger., Fr., Rus., Span., Pol., Madasko & Sloven.). 1023p. 1975. 150.00 (ISBN 0-686-92413-4, M-9892). French & Eur.

Terminological Dictionary of Automatic Control. 641p. 1977. Leatherette 19.95 (ISBN 0-686-92164-X, M-9059). French & Eur.

AUTOMATIC COUNTING DEVICES

see Digital Counters

AUTOMATIC DATA COLLECTION SYSTEMS

Cline, Ben E. An Introduction to Automated Data Acquisition. (Illus.). 294p. 1984. 29.95 (ISBN 0-89433-192-2). Van Nos Reinhold.

Strock, O. J. Telemetry Computer Systems: An Introduction. LC 82-49001. 380p. 1983. text ed. 44.95x (ISBN 0-87664-711-5). Instru Soc.

AUTOMATIC DATA PROCESSING

see Electronic Data Processing

AUTOMATIC DATA PROCESSORS

see Computers

AUTOMATIC DATA STORAGE

see Information Storage and Retrieval Systems

AUTOMATIC DIGITAL COMPUTERS

see Electronic Digital Computers

AUTOMATIC DRAFTING

see Computer Graphics

AUTOMATIC FACTORIES

see Automation

AUTOMATIC INDEXING

Feinberg, Hilda. Title Derivative Indexing Techniques: A Comparative Study. LC 73-2671. 307p. 1973. 27.50 (ISBN 0-8108-0602-9). Scarecrow.

Richmond, Phyllis A. Introduction to PRECIS for North American Usage. LC 80-25977. 321p. 1981. lib. bdg. 30.00 (ISBN 0-87287-240-8). Libs Unl.

Salton, Gerard. A Theory of Indexing. (CBMS-NSF Regional Conference Ser.: No. 18). v, 56p. (Orig.). 1975. pap. text ed. 9.00 (ISBN 0-89871-015-4). Soc Indus-Appl Math.

AUTOMATIC MACHINE-TOOLS

see Machine-Tools

AUTOMATIC PILOT (SHIPS)

Garrison, Paul. Autopilots, Flight Directors & Flight-Control Systems. (Illus.). 160p. (Orig.). 1985. pap. 12.95 (ISBN 0-8306-2356-6). TAB Bks.

AUTOMATIC PRODUCTION

see Automation

AUTOMATIC PROGRAMMING LANGUAGES

see Programming Languages (Electronic Computers)

AUTOMATIC SPEECH RECOGNITION

Business Communications Staff. Speech Synthesis & Recognition Equipment: G-056. 1982. 975.00 (ISBN 0-89336-299-9). BCC.

Cater, John P. Electronically Hearing Computer Speech Recognition. LC 84-50051. 13.95 (ISBN 0-672-22173-X). Sams.

Dixon, N. Rex & Martin, Thomas B., eds. Automatic Speech & Speaker Recognition. LC 78-65703. 1979. 41.55 (ISBN 0-87942-117-7, PC01149). Inst Electrical.

--Automatic Speech & Speaker Recognition. LC 78-65703. 433p. 1979. 39.95 (ISBN 0-471-05833-5); pap. 25.95x (ISBN 0-471-05834-3, Pub. by Wiley-Interscience). Wiley.

Flanagan, J. L. & Rabiner, L. R., eds. Speech Synthesis. LC 73-9728. (Benchmark Papers in Acoustics: Vol. 3). 511p. 1973. 57.95 (ISBN 0-87933-044-9). Van Nos Reinhold.

Fu, K. S., ed. Digital Pattern Recognition. 2nd ed. (Communication & Cybernetics: Vol. 10). (Illus.). 234p. 1980. pap. 36.00 (ISBN 0-387-10207-8). Springer-Verlag.

Haton, Jean-Paul, ed. Automatic Speech Analysis & Recognition. 1982. lib. bdg. 48.00 (ISBN 90-277-1443-6, Pub. by Reidel Holland). Kluwer Academic.

Hess, W. Pitch Determination of Speech Signals: Algorithms & Devices. (Springer Series in Information Sciences: Vol. 3). (Illus.). 698p. 1983. 40.00 (ISBN 0-387-11933-7). Springer-Verlag.

Lea, W. Trends in Speech Recognition. 1980. text ed. 43.95 (ISBN 0-13-930768-0). P-H.

Longe, G., ed. Multi-User Communication Systems. (CISM International Centre for Mechanical Sciences Ser.: Vol. 265). (Illus.). 259p. 1981. pap. 22.50 (ISBN 0-387-81612-7). Springer-Verlag.

Rigsby, Mike. Verbal Control with Microcomputers. (Illus.). 312p. (Orig.). 1982. pap. 11.95 (ISBN 0-8306-1468-0, 1468). TAB Bks.

Schafer, R. W. & Markel, J. D., eds. Speech Analysis. LC 78-65706. (IEEE Press Selected Reprint Ser.). 469p. 1979. 44.95x (ISBN 0-471-05830-0); pap. 29.50x (ISBN 0-471-05832-7, Pub. by Wiley-Interscience). Wiley.

Wayne, Lea A. Computer Recognition of Speech. (Speech Technology Ser.). (Illus.). 450p. 1982. 79.00 (ISBN 0-686-37642-0); student ed. 54.00 (ISBN 0-686-37643-9). Speech Science.

AUTOMATIC TIMERS

see also Delay Lines

Gilder, Jules. One Hundred & Ten IC Timer Projects. 1979. pap. 6.95 (ISBN 0-8104-5688-5). Hayden.

AUTOMATIC TRANSLATING

see Machine Translating

AUTOMATIC TRANSMISSIONS, AUTOMOBILE

see Automobiles–Transmission Devices

AUTOMATICALLY PROGRAMMED TOOLS (COMPUTER PROGRAM LANGUAGE)

see APT (Computer Program Language)

AUTOMATION

see also Assembly-Line Methods; Automatic Checkout Equipment; Automatic Control; Electronic Control; Feedback Control Systems; Man-Machine Systems; Robotics; Servomechanisms; Systems Engineering

Airline Plating & Metal Finishing 18th Annual Forum: Proceedings. 68p. (Automation of the Thermal Spray Process). 1982. pap. 30.00 (ISBN 0-89883-073-7, P108). Soc Auto Engineers.

American Society for Materials & Testing. Computer Automation of Materials Testing, STP 710. (710). 235p. 1980. 21.75x (ISBN 0-8031-0267-4, 04-710000-32). ASTM.

Arden, Bruce W., ed. What Can Be Automated? Computer Science & Engineering Research Study. 933p. 1980. 47.50x (ISBN 0-262-01060-7); pap. 17.50x (ISBN 0-262-51026-X). MIT Pr.

Assembly Automation: Proceedings of the 4th International Conference, Tokyo, Japan, Oct. 1983. (Illus.). 1983. 84.00 (ISBN 0-903608-48-0, Pub. by IFSPUBS). Scholium Intl.

Assembly Automation: Proceedings of the 6th International Conference. 1985. 80.00x (ISBN 0-903608-88-X, Pub. by IFS Pubns UK). Air Sci Co.

AUTOFACT Five Conference on Computer Integrated Manufacturing & the Automated Factory, Detroit, Mich., Nov. 1983. Autofact Five: Proceedings. xvi, 1048p. 1983. pap. 60.00 (ISBN 0-87263-127-3). SME.

Autofact Five Conference on Computer-Integrated Manufacturing & the Automated Factory, Detroit, Mich., Nov. 1983. Autofact Five: Proceedings. xvi, 1048p. 1983. 60.00 (ISBN 0-444-86820-8). Elsevier.

Autofact Four Conference on Computer-Integrated Manufacturing & the Automated Factory, Philadelphia, Pa., Nov.-Dec. 1982. Autofact Four: Proceedings. 688p. 1983. 60.00 (ISBN 0-87263-093-5). Elsevier.

Automated Materials Handling: Proceedings of the 2nd International Conference. 1985. 80.00x (ISBN 0-903608-90-1, Pub. by IFS Pubns UK). Air Sci Co.

Automated Systems, NEMA. Automation User Survey. 15.00 (ISBN 0-318-18039-1). Natl Elec Mfrs.

--Strategic Justification of Flexible Automation. 10.00 (ISBN 0-318-18040-5). Natl Elec Mfrs.

Automation & Instrumentation: M2. (AWWA Manuals Ser.). (Illus.). 160p. 1977. pap. text ed. 19.20 (ISBN 0-89867-060-8). Am Water Wks Assn.

The Automation Hysteria. 6.00 (ISBN 0-686-11609-7); members 4.00 (ISBN 0-686-11610-0). M & A Products.

Automation in Warehousing: Proceedings of the Fifth International Conference, Atlanta, GA, U. S. A., December 1983. 80.00 (ISBN 0-903608-52-9, IFSPUBS). Scholium Intl.

Automation in Warehousing: Proceedings of the Third International Conference, Chicago, 1979 & Stratford-upon-Avon, 1980, 2 Vols. 456p. 1980. Set. pap. 76.00 set (ISBN 0-317-05233-0, Pub. by IFSPUBS). Scholium Intl.

Automation Systems for Highway Organizations. (Special Report). 128p. 1972. 3.80 (ISBN 0-309-01997-4). Transport Res Bd.

Automation Technology Symposium, 3rd, Monterey, Calif., Sept. 1981. Automation Technology for Management & Productivity Advancements Through CAD-CAM & Engineering Data Handling: Proceedings. Wang, Peter C., ed. (Illus.). 336p. 1983. text ed. 36.95 (ISBN 0-13-054593-7). P-H.

Barcomb, David. Office Automation: A Survey of Tools & Technology. 241p. 1981. pap. 21.00 (ISBN 0-932376-15-0, EY-00004-DP). Digital Pr.

--Office Automation: A Survey of Tools & Technology. 256p. 1981. 15.00 (ISBN 0-686-98086-7). Telecom Lib.

Barzan, A. Automation in Electrical Power Systems. 430p. 1977. 9.45 (ISBN 0-8285-0670-1, Pub. by Mir Pubs USSR). Imported Pubns.

Behavioral Objectives in Aviation Automated Systems Symposium. 378p. 1982. pap. 45.00 (ISBN 0-89883-079-6, P114). Soc Auto Engineers.

Bernardo, F. P., Jr. Design & Implementation of Low Cost Automation. LC 72-86487. 116p. 1972. 7.75 (ISBN 92-833-1020-9, APO17, APO). Unipub.

Bolz, Roger W. Manufacturing Automation Management: A Productivity Handbook. 220p. 1985. 27.50 (ISBN 0-412-00731-2, NO. 9094, Pub. by Chapman & Hall England). Methuen Inc.

Boothroyd. Automatic Assembly. (Mechanical Engineering Ser.: Vol. 6). 352p. 1982. 45.00 (ISBN 0-8247-1531-4). Dekker.

Bretschi, Jurgen. Automated Inspection Systems for Industry: Scope for Intelligent Measuring. (Eng., Illus.). 190p. 1982. Repr. of 1979 ed. text ed. 52.00x softbound (ISBN 0-903608-20-0, IFSPUBS). Scholium Intl.

Brown, John A. Computers & Automation. rev. ed. LC 73-76928. (Illus.). 248p. 1974. 7.50 (ISBN 0-668-01623-X); pap. 5.95 (ISBN 0-668-01745-7). Arco.

Bubnicki, Z. Identification of Control Plants. (Studies in Automation & Control: Vol. 3). 312p. 1980. 64.00 (ISBN 0-444-99767-9). Elsevier.

Butera, F. & Thurman, J. E., eds. Automation & Work Design: A Study Prepared by International Labour Office. LC 84-8169. 758p. 1984. 74.00 (ISBN 0-444-87538-7, I-318-84, Pub. by North Holland). Elsevier.

Carmody, Edmond, et al. Automation in the Marriage Tribunal: A Report from a Special Committee of the Canon Law Society of America. viii, 90p. (Orig.). pap. 9.95 (ISBN 0-943616-27-1). Canon Law Soc.

Casale, James F., et al, eds. Papers & Proceedings of Syntopican XII: Anthology. (Illus., Orig.). 1984. pap. 30.00 (ISBN 0-935220-11-9). Assn Info Sys.

Cecil, Paula B. Office Automation: Concepts & Application. 3rd ed. 1984. 23.95 (ISBN 0-8053-1763-5); instr's guide 7.95 (ISBN 0-8053-1764-3); study guide 6.95 (ISBN 0-8053-1765-1). Benjamin-Cummings.

Chin, F. Automation & Robots: A Selected Bibliography of Books. (Public Administration Ser.: Bibliography P-969). 19p. 1982. 3.00 (P-969). Vance Biblios.

Chorafas, D. N. Management Workstations for Greater Productivity. 256p. 1986. 24.95 (ISBN 0-07-010859-5). McGraw.

Cohen, Aaron & Cohen, Elaine. Planning the Electronic Office. (Illus.). 256p. 1983. 37.50 (ISBN 0-07-011583-4). McGraw.

Control Engineering, 1982 Conference: Merging of Technology & Theory to Solve Industrial Automation Problems. 236p. (Orig.). 1982. pap. text ed. 42.00x (ISBN 0-85825-168-X, Pub. by Inst Engineering Australia). Brookfield Pub Co.

Cunningham, John E. & Horn, Delton T. Handbook of Remote Control & Automation Techniques. 2nd ed. (Illus.). 350p. 1984. 21.95 (ISBN 0-8306-0777-3); pap. 13.95 (ISBN 0-8306-1777-9, 1777). TAB Bks.

Curran, Susan & Mitchell, Horace. Office Automation: An Essential Management Strategy. 225p. 1982. pap. 16.00x (ISBN 0-8448-1487-3). Crane-Russak Co.

Designing Your Product for Robotics. 52p. 1982. pap. 15.00 (ISBN 0-89883-288-8, SP517). Soc Auto Engineers.

The Development of Flexible Automation Systems. (IEE Conference Publications Ser.: No. 237). 123p. 1984. pap. 50.00 (ISBN 0-85296-294-0). Inst Elect Eng.

Digital-Computer-Controlled Traffic Signal System for a Small City. (National Cooperative Highway Research Program Report). 82p. 1966. 4.00 (ISBN 0-317-36075-2, 1474). Transport Res Bd.

Displays, Electronics, & Sensor Technology. 215p. 1984. pap. 50.00 (ISBN 0-89883-336-1, SP565). Soc Auto Engineers.

Dornfield, D. A., ed. Automation in Manfacturing: Systems, Processes, & Aids. (PED Ser.: Vol. 4). 176p. 1981. 30.00 (ISBN 0-686-34504-5, H00211). ASME.

Draper Lab Inc., ed. Flexible Manufacturing Systems Handbook. LC 84-4097. (Illus.). 392p. 1984. 48.00 (ISBN 0-8155-0983-9). Noyes.

Electronic Displays & Information Systems. 128p. 1981. pap. 38.00 (ISBN 0-89883-060-5, P92). Soc Auto Engineers.

Electronic Displays, Information Systems, & On-Board Electronics. 164p. 1982. pap. 38.00 (ISBN 0-89883-068-0, P103). Soc Auto Engineers.

European Automated Manufacturing Conference, 2nd, Birmingham, UK, May 1983. Automated Manufacturing, 1983: Proceedings. Rooks, B., ed. iv, 452p. 1983. 81.00 (ISBN 0-444-86687-6, I-277-83, North-Holland). Elsevier.

European Automated Manufacturing: Proceedings of the 3rd International Conference. 1985. 75.00x (ISBN 0-903608-91-X, Pub. by IFS Pubns UK). Air Sci Co.

Factory Automation Markets. 129p. 1983. 985.00x. Intl Res Dev.

Fawcett, J. R. Pneumatic Circuits & Low Cost Automation. 150p. 1969. 25.00x (ISBN 0-85461-029-4, Pub. by Trade & Tech England). Brookfield Pub Co.

--Pneumatic Circuits & Low Cost Automation. 150p. 1982. 70.00x (Trade & Tech). State Mutual Bk.

Field, R. M. A Glossary of Office Automation Terms. 32p. 1982. pap. text ed. 15.00x (ISBN 0-914548-42-5). Univelt Inc.

Finn, Nancy B. The Electronic Office. (Illus.). 160p. 1983. pap. 15.95 (ISBN 0-13-251819-8). P-H.

Fitch, Donald. Increasing Productivity in the Microcomputer Age. 386p. 1981. 16.95 (ISBN 0-201-04072-7). Addison-Wesley.

Fitzgerald, Jerry. Business Data Communications: Basic Concepts, Security & Design. LC 83-14798. (Wiley Series in Computers & Information Processing Systems for Business: 1-661). 502p. 1984. 33.45x (ISBN 0-471-89549-0); tchr's. ed. avail. (ISBN 0-471-88327-1). Wiley.

Fraade, David J., ed. Automation of Pharmaceutical Operations. 360p. 1983. 57.50 (ISBN 0-943330-02-5). Aster Pub Corp.

--Automation of Pharmaceutical Operations: Supplement. (Illus.). 150p. (Orig.). 1985. pap. 27.00x (ISBN 0-943330-06-8). Aster Pub Corp.

Galitz, Wilbert O. Humanizing Office Automation: The Impact of Ergonomics on Productivity. LC 83-83115. 250p. 1984. pap. 34.50 (ISBN 0-89435-107-9). QED Info Sci.

Gardner, Leonard B., ed. Automated Manufacturing-STP 862. LC 85-1243. (Illus.). 255p. 1985. text ed. 38.00 (ISBN 0-8031-0422-7, 04-862000-32). ASTM.

Godwin, Nadine. Complete Guide to Travel Agency Automation. LC 81-83505. (Travel Management Library). (Illus.). 160p. 1982. 12.95 (ISBN 0-916032-13-2). Merton Hse.

Greenwood, Frank & Greenwood, Mary. Office Automation: The Challenge of Technology. 1984. text ed. 22.50 (ISBN 0-8359-5165-0). Reston.

Gregory, Judith & Marshall, Daniel, eds. Office Automation: Jekyll or Hyde. LC 83-60764. 240p. (Orig.). 1983. pap. 12.95 (ISBN 0-912663-00-6). Work Women Educ.

Groover, Mikell P. Automation, Production Systems & Computer-Aided Manufacturing. 1980. text ed. 34.95 (ISBN 0-13-054668-2). P-H.

Hartley, J. Flexible Automation in Japan. (Illus.). 250p. 1984. 38.00 (ISBN 0-387-13499-9). Springer-Verlag.

Hawk, Gerald L. & Strimaitis, Janet R., eds. Advances in Laboratory Automation-Robotics, 1984. (Illus.). 360p. 1984. 45.00 (ISBN 0-931565-00-6). Zymark Corp.

--Advances in Laboratory Automation: Robotics, 1985. (Illus.). 540p. 1986. 55.00 (ISBN 0-931565-01-4). Zymark Corp.

Holland, J. R., ed. Flexible Manufacturing Systems. 250p. 1984. 39.00 (ISBN 0-317-07082-7, 817). SME.

Hollier, R. H., ed. Automated Materials Handling: Proceedings of the First International Conference, London, UK, April 1983. iv, 284p. 1983. 72.50 (ISBN 0-444-86666-3, I-279-83, North-Holland). Elsevier.

Hollingum, J. Machine Vision. (Illus.). 100p. 1984. pap. 19.50 (ISBN 0-387-13837-4). Springer-Verlag.

Hunter, Ronald P. Automated Process Control Systems: Concepts & Hardware. (Illus.). 1978. ref. ed. 27.95 (ISBN 0-13-054502-3). P-H.

IFAC Conference, 4th, Ghent, Belgium, June 1980. Instrumentation & Automation in the Paper, Rubber, Plastics & Polymerisation Industries: Proceedings. Van Cauwenberghe, A., ed. LC 80-41889. (IFAC Proceedings Ser.). (Illus.). 550p. 1981. 130.00 (ISBN 0-08-024487-4). Pergamon.

IFAC-IFIP Symposium, Leiden, The Netherlands, June 1983 & Rijnsdorp. Training for Tomorrow, Educational Aspects of Computerized Automation: Proceedings. Immink, L., ed. (IFAC Proceedings Ser.). 600p. 1984. 69.00 (ISBN 0-08-031111-3). Pergamon.

IFAC Workshop, Karlsruhe, BRD, Nov. 1983. Design of Work in Automated Manufacturing Systems: Proceedings. Martin, T., ed. 1984. write for info. Pergamon.

Institute of Production Engineers. Automated Assembling, 20 Vols. Set. 720.00 (ISBN 0-317-07073-8, 698). SME.

International Conference on Assembly Automation, 3rd, Stuttgart, BRD, May 1982. Assembly Automation: Proceedings. (Illus.). 626p. 1982. pap. text ed. 95.00x softbound (ISBN 0-903608-25-1, Pub. by IFSPUBS). Scholium Intl.

International Conference on Assembly Automation, 2nd, Brighton, UK, 1981. Assembly Automation: Proceedings. 300p. 1981. softbound 80.00 (ISBN 0-903608-07-3, Pub. by IFSPUBS). Scholium Intl.

International Conference on Automated Inspection & Product Control, 6th, Brighton, UK, April 1982. Automated Inspection & Product Control: Proceedings. 324p. 1982. pap. text ed. 95.00x (ISBN 0-903608-23-5, Pub. by IFSPUBS). Scholium Intl.

International Conference on Automation in Warehousing, 1st, Univ. of Nottingham, Eng., April 1975. Proceedings. 380p. 1977. pap. 39.00x (ISBN 0-685-89048-1). Scholium Intl.

International Conference on Automation in Warehousing, 2nd, Keele, Eng., Mar. 1977. Proceedings. 300p. 1977. softbound 70.00x (ISBN 0-685-89050-3). Scholium Intl.

International Conference on Distributed Computer Control Systems (1977: University of Aston) International Conference on Distributed Computer Control Systems, 26-28 September, 1977. LC 79-306653. (Institution of Electrical Engineers Conference Publication Ser.: Vol. 153). (Illus.). pap. 49.00 (ISBN 0-317-09909-4, 2051590). Bks Demand UMI.

International Conference on Flexible Manufacturing Systems, Brighton, UK, Oct. 1982. Flexible Manufacturing Systems 1: Proceedings. iv, 520p. 1983. 85.00 (ISBN 0-444-86591-8, I-152-83, North Holland). Elsevier.

International Congress on Transportation & Electronics, Convergence '82: Proceedings. 265p. 1982. pap. 38.00 (ISBN 0-89883-076-1, P111). Soc Auto Engineers.

International Labour Office Staff. Automation, Work Organisation & Occupational Stress. viii, 188p. 1984. 12.85 (ISBN 92-2-103866-1). Intl Labour Office.

The Japanese Automobile Industry: Model & Challenge for the Future? 147p. 1981. pap. 15.00 (ISBN 0-939512-08-4, P95). Soc Auto Engineers.

Kaplinsky, Raphael. Automation. (Illus.). 224p. 1984. pap. text ed. 18.95 (ISBN 0-582-90203-7). Longman.

Kato, Ichiro. Mechanical Hands Illustrated. rev. ed. LC 84-27906. (Illus.). 240p. Date not set. 39.95 (ISBN 0-89116-374-3). Hemisphere Pub.

Katzan, Harry, Jr. Office Automation: A Manager's Guide. 224p. 1982. 32.50 (ISBN 0-8144-5752-5). AMACOM.

Kompass, Edward J. & Williams, Theodore J., eds. Learning Systems & Pattern Recognition in Industrial Control: Proceedings of the 9th Annual Advenced Control Conference. 91p. 1983. conference papers 30.00 (ISBN 0-914331-08-6). Control Eng.

Krautter, J., ed. Assembly Automation: Proceedings of the 5th International Conference, Paris, France, 22-24 May, 1984. 380p. 1984. 72.25 (ISBN 0-444-87552-2, Pub. by North Holland). Elsevier.

Kurman, K. J. Feedback Control: Theory & Design. (Studies in Automation & Control: Vol. 4). 1984. 90.75 (ISBN 0-444-99640-0, I-122-84). Elsevier.

Langstrom, Carla T. Methods & Instrumentation for Medical Automation. LC 84-45004. 150p. 1984. 29.95 (ISBN 0-88164-182-0); pap. 21.95 (ISBN 0-88164-183-9). ABBE Pubs Assn.

Larcombe. Factory Automation, 2 vols. (Infotech Computer State of the Art Reports). 600p. 1980. Set. 310.00x (ISBN 0-08-028526-0). Pergamon.

Leone, William C. Production Automation & Numerical Control. LC 67-21679. (Illus.). pap. 46.60 (ISBN 0-317-11119-1, 2012419). Bks Demand UMI.

Lieberman, Mark A., et al. Office Automation: A Manager's Guide for Improved Productivity. LC 81-23114. 331p. 1982. 34.95x (ISBN 0-471-07983-9, Pub. by Wiley-Interscience). Wiley.

Luke, Hugh D. Automation for Productivity. LC 72-5441. 298p. 1972. 18.00 (ISBN 0-471-55400-6, Pub. by Wiley). Krieger.

Makino, H. Assembly Automation: Proceedings of the 4th International Conference, Tokyo, Japan, 11-13 Oct., 1983. 408p. 1984. 71.25 (ISBN 0-444-86768-6). Elsevier.

Mann, Floyd C. & Hoffman, L. Richard. Automation & the Worker: A Study of Social Change in Power Plants. LC 83-12978. (Illus.). xiv, 272p. 1983. Repr. of 1960 ed. lib. bdg. 35.00x (ISBN 0-313-24222-4, MAUW). Greenwood.

Martin, T., ed. Design of Work in Automated Manufacturing Systems: Proceedings of the IFAC Workshop, Karlsruhe, FRG, 7-9 November 1983. (IFAC Proceedings Ser.). 188p. 1984. 46.00 (ISBN 0-08-031118-0). Pergamon.

Miller, Richard S. Planning & Designing the Totally Automated Manufacturing Plant. (Illus.). 240p. 1984. pap. text ed. cancelled (ISBN 0-89671-059-9). SEAI Tech Pubns.

Morgan-Grampian Book, ed. The Directory of Instruments, Electronics, Automation, 1984. 320p. 1985. 150.00x (ISBN 0-686-75507-3, Pub. by Morgan-Grampian Bk). State Mutual Bk.

Mullins, Carolyn & West, Thomas. The Office Automation Primer: Harnessing Information Technologies for Greater Productivity. 158p. 1982. 18.95 (ISBN 0-13-631085-0); pap. 9.95 (ISBN 0-13-631077-X). P-H.

Naffah, N. Office Information Systems. 656p. 1982. 76.75 (ISBN 0-444-86398-2, North-Holland). Elsevier.

Needler, Marvin & Baker, Don. Digital & Analog Controls. 1985. text ed. 31.95 (ISBN 0-8359-1314-7). Reston.

Nelson, Raymond A. Computerizing Warehouse Operations. 250p. 1985. 29.95 (ISBN 0-13-163924-2, Busn). P-H.

Office Automation: Current Perspectives. (Special Interest Packages Ser.). pap. 23.00 (PO20); pap. 18.00 member. Assn Inform & Image Mgmt.

Office Automation Markets. (Reports Ser.: No. 182). 170p. 1981. 985.00x (ISBN 0-88694-182-2). Intl Res Dev.

Ouellette, Robert P. & Thomas, Lydia W. Automation Impacts on Industry. LC 82-48646. (Illus.). 200p. 1983. 39.95 (ISBN 0-250-40609-8). Butterworth.

Peltu, Malcolm. A Guide to the Electronic Office. 200p. 1981. 34.95x (ISBN 0-470-27308-9). Halsted Pr.

Perlin, Neil. Business Technology for Managers: An Office Automation Handbook. LC 85-223. (Information & Communications Management Guides Ser.). 216p. 1985. 32.95 (ISBN 0-86729-124-9, 714-BW); pap. text ed. 24.95 (ISBN 0-86729-123-0). Knowledge Indus.

Pilla, Lou, ed. Automating Your Office: Pathways to Management Succcess. (Illus.). 158p. (Orig.). 1984. 19.95 (ISBN 0-916323-03-X); pap. 13.95 (ISBN 0-916323-02-1). Admin Mgmt.

Planning for the Factory of the Future. 1984. write for info. C I M Systems.

Practical Experience with Shipboard Automation: A Joint Conference Held on March 6, 1974. (Illus.). 58p. 1975. pap. 15.00x (ISBN 0-900976-40-3, Pub. by Inst Marine Eng). Intl Spec Bk.

Prokes, J. Hydraulic Mechanisms in Automation. 334p. 1977. 64.00 (ISBN 0-444-99829-2). Elsevier.

Pyke, Magnus. Automation: Its Purpose. 10.00 (ISBN 0-685-28341-0). Philos Lib.

Race. Computer Based Systems. (Teach Yourself Ser). pap. 5.95 (ISBN 0-679-10513-1). McKay.

Riley, Frank J. Assembly Automation: A Management Handbook. (Illus.). 352p. 1983. text ed. 39.95 (ISBN 0-8311-1153-4). Indus Pr.

Roessner, J. David, et al. The Impact of Office Automation on Clerical Employment, 1985-2000: Forcasting & Plausible Futures Futures in Banking & Insurance. LC 85-6523. (Illus.). 336p. 1985. lib. bdg. 49.95 (ISBN 0-89930-119-3, ROU/, Quorum Bks.). Greenwood.

Rogers, D. F., ed. Computer Applications in the Automation of Shipyard Operation & Ship Design, Vol. 4. (Computer Applications in Shipping & Shipbuilding: Vol. 9). 356p. 1982. 53.25 (ISBN 0-444-86408-3, I-300-82, North-Holland). Elsevier.

Roodyn, D. B. Automated Enzyme Assays, Vol. 2, Pt. 1. (Laboratory Techniques in Biochemistry & Molecular Biology). 1970. pap. 18.50 (ISBN 0-444-10056-3, North-Holland). Elsevier.

Rudman, Jack. Maintenance Mechanic (Automated Mail Processing Equipment) (A.M.P.E) (U.S.P.S.) (Career Examination Ser.: C-1606). (Cloth bdg. avail. on request). 1984. pap. 12.00 (ISBN 0-8373-1606-5). Natl Learning.

Ruprecht, Mary M. & Wagoner, Kathleen P. Managing Office Automation. LC 83-17046. 680p. 1984. 29.95 (ISBN 0-471-88731-5). Wiley.

Saffady, William. The Automated Office: An Introduction to the Technology. Plunka, Gene A., ed. (Reference Ser.). 241p. 1981. 17.75 (ISBN 0-89258-072-0, R017); member 13.25. Assn Inform & Image Mgmt.

Saridis, George N., ed. Advances in Automation & Robotics: Theory & Application, Vol. 1. 1984. 45.00 (ISBN 0-89232-399-X). Jai Pr.

Schmitt, Neil M. & Farwell, Robert F. Understanding Automation Systems. 2nd ed. LC 84-51472. (Understanding Ser.). 280p. 1984. pap. 14.95 (ISBN 0-89512-164-6, LCB8472). Tex Instr Inc.

--Understanding Electronic Control of Automation Systems. Luecke, G. & Battle, C., eds. LC 81-85603. (Understanding Ser.). (Illus.). 280p. 1983. pap. 6.95 (ISBN 0-89512-052-6, LCB6641). Tex Instr Inc.

Scientific American. The Mechanization of Work. LC 82-17509. (Illus.). 128p. 1982. text ed. 21.95 (ISBN 0-7167-1438-8); pap. text ed. 10.95x (ISBN 0-7167-1439-6). W H Freeman.

Shaiken, Harley. Work Transformed: Automation & Labor in the Computer Age. 288p. 1985. 17.95 (ISBN 0-03-042681-2). HR&W.

BOOKS - SUBJECT INDEX AUTOMOBILE ENGINEERING

Sharma, Vinay K., et al. Aster Guide to Tablet Coating Automation. (Monograph: No. 2). (Illus.). 100p. (Orig.). 1984. pap. 20.00x (ISBN 0-943330-08-4). Aster Pub Corp.
Society of Manufacturing Engineers. Applying Automated Inspection. 1985. 35.00 (ISBN 0-87263-194-X). SME.
--Autofact Europe: Proceedings. 1985. write for info. (ISBN 0-87263-197-4). SME.
--Automach Australia 1985: Proceedings. 1985. 55.00 (ISBN 0-87263-191-5). SME.
Stout, Ken. Quality Control in Automation. (Illus.). 224p. 1985. text ed. 29.95 (ISBN 0-13-745159-8). P-H.
Theobald, R., et al. Perspective on Automation: Three Talks to Educators. 1974. 2.50 (ISBN 0-8156-7023-0, NES 43). Syracuse U Cont Ed.
Thrift Institution Automation Survey. 300p. 1982. 200.00 (ISBN 0-318-14107-8); members 50.00 (ISBN 0-318-14108-6). Finan Mgrs Soc.
Thurber, Kenneth A. Office Automation Systems. (Tutorial Texts Ser.). 201p. 1980. 20.00 (ISBN 0-8186-0339-9, Q339). IEEE Comp Soc.
Thursland, Arthur L. Administrative Support: Economic Justification for Office Automation. 152p. 1984. 45.00 (ISBN 0-935220-10-0). Assn Info Sys.
Tou, J. T., ed. Computer-Based Automation. 609p. 1985. 85.00x (ISBN 0-306-41903-3, PLenum Pr). Plenum Pub.
Uhlig, Ronald P. & Farber, David J. The Office of the Future. 378p. 1979. 35.00 (ISBN 0-686-98082-4). Telecom Lib.
Van Cauwenberghe, A., ed. Instrumentation & Automation in the Paper, Rubber, Plastics & Polymerisation Industries: Proceedings of the IFAC-IMEKO Symposium, 5th, Antwerp, Belgium, Oct. 3-5, 1983. 600p. 110.00 (ISBN 0-08-031112-1). Pergamon.
Van Cauwenbergue, A. R., ed. Instrumentation & Automation in the Paper, Rubber, Plastics & Polymerization Industries: Proceedings of the Fifth International IFAC-IMEKO Symposium, Antwerp, Belgium, 11-13 October 1983. (IFAC Proceedings Ser.). 528p. 1984. 120.00 (ISBN 0-08-031112-1). Pergamon.
Vance, Mary. Automation in Buildings. (Architecture Ser.: Bibliographby A 1332). 1985. pap. 2.00 (ISBN 0-89028-282-X). Vance Biblios.
Wagoner, Kathleen P. & Ruprecht, Mary M. Office Automation: A Management Approach. LC 83-16702. 680p. 1984. text ed. 26.95 (ISBN 0-471-09061-1). Wiley.
Walker, Charles R. Toward the Automatic Factory: A Case Study of Men & Machines. LC 76-45083. (Illus.). 1977. Repr. of 1957 ed. lib. bdg. 22.50x (ISBN 0-8371-9301-X, WATA). Greenwood.
Warnecke, H. J., ed. Automated Guided Vehicle Systems: Proceedings of the 2nd International Conference on AGVS & 16th IPA Conference, Stuttgart, F. R. G. June 7-9, 1983. iv, 346p. 1984. 75.00 (ISBN 0-444-86686-8, I-507-83). Elsevier.
Water Plant Instrumentation & Automation. (AWWA Handbooks-Proceedings Ser.). (Illus.). 304p. 1976. pap. text ed. 14.40 (ISBN 0-89867-049-7). Am Water Wks Assn.
Waterhouse, Shirley A. Office Automation & Word Processing Fundamentals. 356p. 1983. pap. text ed. 14.50 scp (ISBN 0-06-046955-2, HarpC); instr's. manual avail. (ISBN 0-06-367007-0). Har-Row.
Webster, Tony. Office Automation & Word Processing Buyer's Guide. LC 83-18694. (Illus.). 328p. 1983. pap. 19.95 (ISBN 0-07-068962-8, BYTE Bks). Mcgraw.
Weeks, Robert P., ed. Machines & the Man: A Sourcebook on Automation. LC 61-6338. (Illus., Orig.). 1961. pap. text ed. 5.95x (ISBN 0-89197-282-X). Irvington.
White, J. A., ed. Automation in Warehousing: Proceedings of the 5th International Conference, Atlanta, GA, Dec. 4-7, 1983. 280p. 1984. 67.50 (ISBN 0-444-86886-0, I-130-84). Elsevier.
Wierzbicki, A. Models & Sensitivity of Control Systems. (Studies in Automation & Control: Vol. 5). 1985. 83.50 (ISBN 0-444-99620-6). Elsevier.
Wilson, T. D. Office Automation & Information Services: Final Report on a Study of Current Development. (LIR Report 31). (Orig.). 1985. pap. 16.50 (ISBN 0-7123-3045-3, Pub. by British Lib). Longwood Pub Group.

AUTOMATION–BIBLIOGRAPHY

Forest & Tracey, eds. Automation & Informatics Technology: Effects on Labour & Employment. (OECD Library Special Annotated Bibliography: 51, 1981). (Eng. & Fr.). 99p. 1981. pap. write for info. OECD.
Solomon, Martin B., Jr. & Lovan, Nora G. Annotated Bibliography of Films in Automation, Data Processing, & Computer Science. LC 67-23778. 44p. 1967. pap. 5.00x (ISBN 0-8131-1145-5). U Pr of Ky.

AUTOMATION–DICTIONARIES

Carlson, Don, ed. Automation in Housing & Systems Building News: Dictionary of Industrialized Manufactured Housing. (Illus.). 1981. 15.00 (ISBN 0-9607408-0-5). Automation in Housing Mag.
Edwards, Nancy M. & Shaw, Carmine, eds. Office Automation: A Glossary & Guide. LC 82-4714. (Information & Communications Management Guides Ser.). 275p. 1982. 59.50 (ISBN 0-86729-012-9, 703-BW). Knowledge Indus.
Fach Lexikon ABC Automatisierung. (Ger.). 739p. 1976. 22.50 (ISBN 3-87144-243-7, M-7377, Pub. by Verlag Harri Deutsch). French & Eur.
Rosenthal, Steven. Rosenthal's Dictionary of the Automated Office. 350p. 1984. 19.95 (ISBN 0-13-783218-4); pap. 12.95 cancelled (ISBN 0-13-783200-1). P-H.
Sykora, Jiri. Dictionary of Automation Techniques. 1024p. 1980. 80.00x (Pub. by Collet's). State Mutual Bk.
--Dictionary of Automation Techniques. 1024p. 1975. 95.00x (ISBN 0-569-08528-4, Pub. by Collets). State Mutual Bk.

AUTOMATION–SOCIAL ASPECTS

Automation, Work Organisation & Occupational Stress. 188p. 1985. pap. 12.85 (ISBN 92-2-103866-1, ILO355, ILO). Unipub.
Buckingham, Walter S. Automation: Its Impact on Business & People. LC 81-20228. ix, 196p. 1982. Repr. of 1961 ed. lib. bdg. 19.75x (ISBN 0-313-23339-X, BUAU). Greenwood.
Chorafas, Dimitris N. Office Automation: The Productivity Challenge. (Illus.). 304p. 1982. text ed. 36.95 (ISBN 0-13-631028-1). P-H.
Cohen, B. G. F., ed. Human Aspects in Office Automation. (Elsevier Series in Office Automation: no. 1). 340p. 1984. 50.00 (ISBN 0-444-42327-3, I-133-84). Elsevier.
Faunce, William. Problems of an Industrial Society. 2nd ed. Munson, Eric M., ed. 256p. 1981. pap. text ed. 18.95 (ISBN 0-07-020105-6). McGraw.
Forest & Tracey, eds. Automation & Informatics Technology: Effects on Labour & Employment. (OECD Library Special Annotated Bibliography: 51, 1981). (Eng. & Fr.). 99p. 1981. pap. write for info. OECD.
Forslin, Jan, et al, eds. Automation & Industrial Workers: A Fifteen Nation Study, 2 pts, Vol. 1. (Publications of the Vienna Centre). (Illus.). 721p. 1979-81. Vol. 1, Pt. 1. 73.00 (ISBN 0-08-023339-2); Vol. 1, Pt. 2. 62.00 (ISBN 0-08-024310-X). Pergamon.
Fossum, Eystein. Computerisation of Working Life. (Computers & Their Applications Ser.). 148p. 1983. 42.95x (ISBN 0-470-27409-3). Halsted Pr.
Martin, James T. & Norman, Adrian R. Computerized Society. (Automatic Computation Ser). 1970. ref. ed. 24.95 (ISBN 0-13-165977-4). P-H.
Shepard, Jon M. Automation & Alienation: A Study of Office & Factory Workers. 1971. 25.00x (ISBN 0-262-19075-3). MIT Pr.
Soule, George. What Automation Does to Human Beings. Stein, Leon, ed. LC 77-70534. (Work Ser.). 1977. Repr. of 1956 ed. lib. bdg. 20.00x (ISBN 0-405-10202-X). Ayer Co Pubs.
Terborgh, George. Automation Hysteria. 1966. pap. 1.45x (ISBN 0-393-00376-0, Norton Lib). Norton.

AUTOMATONS

see Robots

AUTOMOBILE ACCESSORIES

see Automobiles–Equipment and Supplies

AUTOMOBILE BRAKES

see Automobiles–Brakes

AUTOMOBILE BODIES

see Automobiles–Bodies

AUTOMOBILE DRIVER EDUCATION

Aaron, James E. & Strasser, Marland K. Driving Task Instruction: Dual Control, Simulation, & Multiple-Car. 1974. pap. write for info. (ISBN 0-02-300040-6, 30004). Macmillan.
Driver Education & Training Project. LC 76-133319. 268p. 1968. 25.00 (ISBN 0-403-04495-2). Scholarly.
Driver Instruction. (Road Research Ser.). 1976. 5.50x (ISBN 92-64-11514-5). OECD.
Glassman, J. Driver Education & Traffic Safety. 2nd ed. 1976. pap. text ed. 10.64 (ISBN 0-13-220582-3); student guide 9.12 (ISBN 0-13-220566-1). P-H.
Lybrand, William A., et al. A Study on Evaluation of Driver Education. LC 75-121262. 225p. 1968. 19.00 (ISBN 0-403-04515-0). Scholarly.
Marek, Julius & Sten, Terje. Traffic Environment & the Driver: Driver Behavior & Training in International Perspective. (Illus.). 284p. 1977. pap. 29.50x (ISBN 0-398-03509-1). C C Thomas.
Neff, Donald E. You're Driving Me Crazy. 1982. 6.95 (ISBN 0-533-04899-0). Vantage.

AUTOMOBILE DRIVERS

see also Automobile Driving

Heimstra, Norman W. Injury Control in Traffic Safety. 256p. 1970. 27.50x (ISBN 0-398-00823-X). C C Thomas.
Less, Menaham & Colverd, Edward C. Hand Controls & Assistive Devices For The Physically Disabled Driver. (Illus.). 60p. 1977. 5.00 (ISBN 0-686-38804-6). Human Res Ctr.
Shinar, David. Psychology on the Road: The Human Factor in Traffic Safety. LC 78-18219. 212p. 1978. 40.00 (ISBN 0-471-03997-7). Wiley.

AUTOMOBILE DRIVING

see also Automobile Driver Education

Fales, E. D., Jr. The Book of Expert Driving. LC 79-83943. (Illus.). 1979. pap. 5.95 (ISBN 0-8015-0808-8, Hawthorn). Dutton.
Felsen, Henry G. Handbook for Teen-Age Drivers. pap. 1.25 (ISBN 0-87502-044-5). Benjamin Co.
Grebel, Rosemary & Pogrund, Phyllis. Becoming a Driver. 2nd ed. Katz, Elaine, ed. (Survival Guides Ser.). (Illus.). 64p. 1981. pap. text ed. 3.95 (ISBN 0-915510-57-X). Janus Bks.
Lauer, A. R. The Psychology of Driving: Factors of Traffic Enforcement. (Illus.). 352p. 1972. 39.50x (ISBN 0-398-02337-9). C C Thomas.
Prothero, Jon C. Driving & Surviving. LC 80-82627. (Illus.). 73p. (Orig.). 1980. pap. 5.00 (ISBN 0-938026-01-1). Instruct Res.
Puhn, Fred. How to Make Your Car Handle. LC 80-85270. 1976. pap. 9.95 (ISBN 0-912656-46-8). H P Bks.
Robinson, W. Heath. How to Be a Motorist. (Illus.). 130p. 1975. 10.95 (ISBN 0-7156-1180-1, Pub. by Duckworth England). Biblio Dist.
Rudman, Jack. Garageman-Driver (U.S.P.S.) (Career Examination Ser.: C-1757). (Cloth bdg. avail. on request). 1976. pap. 10.00 (ISBN 0-8373-1757-6). Natl Learning.
Vehicle Noise & Vibration. 1984. 56.00 (MEP198). Soc Auto Engineers.

AUTOMOBILE DRIVING–SAFETY MEASURES

see Traffic Safety

AUTOMOBILE ENGINEERING

Annual Index of SAE Technical Papers: 1984. 40.00 (ISBN 0-317-37147-9) (ISBN 0-89883-605-0). Soc Auto Engineers.
Applications of Electronics to Off-Highway Equipment, 7 papers. (Illus.). 80p. 1981. pap. 22.00 (ISBN 0-89883-267-5, SP 496). Soc Auto Engineers.
Automobile Aerodynamics: Wakes, Wind Effect, Vehicle Development. 136p. 1984. 18.00 (ISBN 0-89883-340-X, SP569). Soc Auto Engineers.
Automotive Consultants Directory. 1984. 16.00 (ISBN 0-89883-750-2). Soc Auto Engineers.
Automotive Electronics. (Reports Ser.: No. 159). 189p. 1980. 985.00x (ISBN 0-88694-159-8). Intl Res Dev.
Automotive Electronics & Electronic Vehicles, Convergence '80: Proceedings, International Conference, 1980, 100 papers. 600p. 1980. pap. 45.00 (ISBN 0-89883-058-3, P90). Soc Auto Engineers.
Automotive Manufacturing Update. 375p. 1978. casebound 70.00 (ISBN 0-85298-382-4, MEP 148). Soc Auto Engineers.
Bailey, Frank A. Basic Mathematics for Automotive Technology. 1977. pap. 9.75x (ISBN 0-673-15065-8). Scott F.
Cassell, Douglas. Microcomputer & Modern Control Engineering. 1983. text ed. 31.95 (ISBN 0-8359-4365-8). Reston.
Combustion of Heterogeneous Mixtures. 140p. 1983. 28.00 (ISBN 0-89883-328-0, SP557). Soc Auto Engineers.
Coombes, B., et al, eds. Vehicle Body Building: Pt. 1. (Engineering Craftsmen: Pt. 2). (Illus.). 1968. 49.95x (ISBN 0-89563-035-4). Intl Ideas.
Designing Your Product for Robotics. 52p. 1982. pap. 15.00 (ISBN 0-89883-288-8, SP517). Soc Auto Engineers.
Desk Top Computing for Engineers. 58p. 1982. pap. 19.00 (ISBN 0-85298-503-7, MEP157). Soc Auto Engineers.
Displays, Electronics, & Sensor Technology. 215p. 1984. pap. 50.00 (ISBN 0-89883-336-1, SP565). Soc Auto Engineers.
Drives-Motors-Controls '84. 280p. 1984. pap. 65.00 (ISBN 0-86341-030-8, PC 023). Inst Elect Eng.
Efficiency in the Design Office. 85p. 1983. pap. 14.50 (ISBN 0-85298-528-2, MEP188). Soc Auto Engineers.
Electrohydraulics Applications. 68p. 1984. 15.00 (ISBN 0-89883-801-0, SP580). Soc Auto Engineers.
Electronic Automotive Reliability. 52p. 1984. 18.00 (ISBN 0-89883-344-2, SP573). Soc Auto Engineers.
Electronic Control & Monitoring of Off-Highway Equipment, 6 papers. 84p. 1982. pap. 18.00 (ISBN 0-89883-291-8, SP520). Soc Auto Engineers.
Electronic Displays & Information Systems. 128p. 1981. pap. 38.00 (ISBN 0-89883-060-5, P92). Soc Auto Engineers.
Electronic Displays, Information Systems, & On-Board Electronics. 164p. 1982. pap. 38.00 (ISBN 0-89883-068-0, P103). Soc Auto Engineers.
Electronic Engine-Drivetrain Control, 12 papers. 132p. 1983. pap. 30.00 (ISBN 0-89883-311-6, SP540). Soc Auto Engineers.
Electronic Engine Management & Driveline Controls. 184p. 1982. pap. 38.00 (ISBN 0-89883-069-9, P104). Soc Auto Engineers.
Electronics Technologies & Systems for Commercial Vehicles of the 80's, 6 papers. 61p. 1981. pap. 15.00 (ISBN 0-89883-276-4, SP505). Soc Auto Engineers.
Engineering & Clinical Aspects of Endoprosthetic Fixation. 160p. 1984. write for info. (ISBN 0-85298-538-X, MEP199). Soc Auto Engineers.
Fourth International Conference on Vehicle Structural Mechanics, 27 papers. 286p. 1981. pap. 45.00 (ISBN 0-89883-065-6, P99). Soc Auto Engineers.
Garrett Lecture (History & Future) 1985. 5.00 (ISBN 0-89883-823-1, SP602). Soc Auto Engineers.
Government Automotive Research: Recent Developments. 1984. 25.00 (ISBN 0-89883-804-5, SP 583). Soc Auto Engineers.
Hedrick, J. Karl, ed. The Dynamics of Vehicles on Roads & On Tracks: Proceedings of 8th IAVSD Symposium held at Massachusetts Institute of Technology, Cambridge, MA, August 15-19, 1983. x, 704p. 1984. pap. text ed. 45.00x (ISBN 90-265-0461-6, Pub. by Swets Pub Serv Holland). Swets North Am.
Instruments & Computers for Cost Effective Fluid Power Testing. 95p. 1979. pap. 37.00 (ISBN 0-85298-436-7, MEP105). Soc Auto Engineers.
International Conference on Automotive Electronics, 3rd: Proceedings. 354p. 1981. pap. 50.00 (ISBN 0-85298-477-4, P102). Soc Auto Engineers.
International Conference, 1st, Birmingham, UK, April 1982. Robots in the Automotive Industry: Proceedings. 218p. 1982. text ed. 62.00x (ISBN 0-903608-22-7, Pub. by IFSPUBS). Scholium Intl.
International Congress on Transportation & Electronics, Convergence '82: Proceedings. 265p. 1982. pap. 38.00 (ISBN 0-89883-076-1, P111). Soc Auto Engineers.
The Japanese Automobile Industry: Model & Challenge for the Future? 147p. 1981. pap. 15.00 (ISBN 0-939512-08-4, P95). Soc Auto Engineers.
Just in Time. 1985. 25.00 (ISBN 0-89883-838-X, SP617). Soc Auto Engineers.
Littlewood Lecture. 1984. 5.00 (ISBN 0-89883-822-3, SP601). Soc Auto Engineers.
Managing Computer Aided Design, 7 papers. 56p. 1980. pap. 30.00 (ISBN 0-85298-470-7, MEP133). Soc Auto Engineers.
Mathematical Simulation of Occupant & Vehicle Kinematics. 1984. 40.00 (ISBN 0-89883-702-2, P146). Soc Auto Engineers.
Mattavi, James N. & Amann, Charles A., eds. Combustion Modeling in Reciprocating Engines. LC 80-10451. (General Motors Research Symposia Ser.). 714p. 89.50x (ISBN 0-306-40431-1, Plenum Pr). Plenum Pub.
Microprocessor Controller Developments: Proceedings. 72p. 1978. pap. 22.00 (ISBN 0-89883-198-9, SP-426). Soc Auto Engineers.
Miller, Kenneth S. & Leskin, Donald M. An Introduction to Kalman Filtering with Applications. LC 85-12606. 1986. lib. bdg. price not set (ISBN 0-89874-824-0). Krieger.
Moffat, E. A. & Moffat, C. A., eds. Highway Collision Reconstruction. 124p. 1980. pap. text ed. 18.00 (ISBN 0-317-02624-0, G00190). ASME.
Peters, George A. & Peters, Barbara J., eds. Automotive Engineering & Litigation, Vol. 1. LC 83-16542. 897p. 1984. 96.00 (ISBN 0-8240-6100-4). Garland Pub.
Presidential Papers: 1984. 1985. 8.00 (ISBN 0-89883-824-X, SP604). Soc Auto Engineers.
Quality Assurance in Design, 7 papers. 54p. 1982. pap. 31.00 (ISBN 0-85298-502-9, MEP156). Soc Auto Engineers.
Remling, John. Steering & Suspension. 2nd ed. (Automotive Ser.). 422p. 1983. 26.95x (ISBN 0-471-87614-3). Wiley.
SAE Cumulative Index 1965-83. 7th ed. 1984. 75.00 (ISBN 0-89883-589-5). Soc Auto Engineers.
Schweitzer, Gerald. Basics of Fractional Horsepower Motors & Repair. (Illus.). 1960. pap. 8.25 (ISBN 0-8104-0418-4). Hayden.
Sensors & Actuators. 128p. 1982. pap. 32.00 (ISBN 0-89883-282-9, SP511). Soc Auto Engineers.
Stock Drive Products Staff Engineers, et al. Handbook of Synchronous Drive Components. 356p. 1974. pap. 3.95 (ISBN 0-686-05807-0). Stock Drive.
Tenth Conference on Production Research & Technology: Proceedings, 32 papers. 240p. 1983. pap. 38.00 (ISBN 0-89883-087-7, P128). Soc Auto Engineers.

Transactions, Vol. 92. 1984. lib. bdg. 495.00 (ISBN 0-89883-591-7). Soc Auto Engineers.
An Update on Automotive Electronic Displays & Information Systems. 276p. 1983. pap. 45.00 (ISBN 0-89883-084-2, P123). Soc Auto Engineers.
Venk, Ernest A. & Billiet, Walter E. Automotive Fundamentals. 3rd ed. LC 74-112971. pap. 143.80 (ISBN 0-317-10997-9, 2004579). Bks Demand UMI.
Vollnhals, Otto. Woerterbuch des Kraftfahrzeugwesens. (Ger. & Ital.). 1975. 92.00 (ISBN 3-7736-5120-1, M-6936). French & Eur.
Wickens, A. H., ed. The Dynamics of Vehicles on Roads & On Tracks: Proceedings of the 7th IAVSD Symposium held at the University of Cambridge, UK, September 1981. x, 568p. 1982. pap. text ed. 40.00 (ISBN 90-265-0392-X, Pub. by Swets Pub Serv Holland). Swets North Am.

AUTOMOBILE ENGINEERING–DICTIONARIES

Bosch, R., ed. Technical Dictionary for Automotive Engineering, 2 vols. (Eng. & Ger.). 1976. 68.00 (ISBN 0-9961072-5-8, Pub. by VDI W Germany). Heyden.
De Coster, Jean. Dictionary for Automotive Engineering: English-French-German. 298p. 1982. lib. bdg. 28.00 (ISBN 3-598-10430-8). K G Saur.
Kondo, K. Elsevier's Dictionary of Automobile Engineering. (Eng., Ger., Fr., Ital. & Span.). 640p. 1977. 138.50 (ISBN 0-444-41590-4). Elsevier.

AUTOMOBILE EXHAUST GAS

see Automobiles–Motors–Exhaust Gas

AUTOMOBILE FILLING STATIONS

see Automobiles–Service Stations

AUTOMOBILE FUEL SYSTEMS

see Automobiles–Fuel Systems

AUTOMOBILE INDUSTRY AND TRADE

see also Automobiles–Service Stations

Aftermarket for Imported Cars, & Light Trucks. 232p. 1984. 1400.00 (ISBN 0-86621-174-8). Frost & Sullivan.
Automobile Club of Italy, ed. World Cars 1978. LC 74-643381. (Illus.). 1978. 50.00 (ISBN 0-910714-10-X). Herald Bks.
Bhaskar, Krish. Future of the World Motor Industry. 300p. 1980. 50.00x (ISBN 0-89397-083-2). Nichols Pub.
Chandler, Alfred D., Jr. & Bruchley, Stuart, eds. Giant Enterprise: Ford, General Motors, & the Automobile Industry. LC 80-18483. (Multinational Corporations Ser.). 1980. Repr. of 1964 ed. lib. bdg. 28.50x (ISBN 0-405-13349-9). Ayer Co Pubs.
Cole, David E., et al, eds. Strategic & Product Planning for the Automotive Industry. 1981. 12.00 (ISBN 0-938654-30-6). Indus Dev Inst Sci.
Computer Strategies. The Auto Dealer's Computer Handbook. 150p. 1983. looseleaf 45.00x (ISBN 0-913505-02-1). Computer Strat.
Conde, John A. The Cars That Hudson Built. LC 80-53376. (Illus.). 224p. 1980. 19.95 (ISBN 0-9605048-0-X). Arnold-Porter Pub.
Construction Automobile: Anglais Technique. (Fr. & Eng.). 216p. (Automobile Construction: Technical English). 1976. pap. 25.00 (ISBN 0-686-56755-2, M-6086). French & Eur.
Current & Future Directions of Supercomputer Applications in the Automotive Industry. Date not set. 13.00 (ISBN 0-89883-845-2, SP624). Soc Auto Engineers.
Epstein, Ralph C. The Automobile Industry: Its Economic & Commercial Development. LC 72-5045. (Technology & Society Ser.). (Illus.). 429p. 1972. Repr. of 1928 ed. 26.50 (ISBN 0-405-04697-9). Ayer Co Pubs.
Fine, Sidney. Automobile Under the Blue Eagle: Labor, Management, & the Automobile Manufacturing Code. LC 63-14016. 1963. 19.95 (ISBN 0-472-32947-2). U of Mich Pr.
Forbes, Bertie C. & Foster, Orline D. Automotive Giants of America: Men Who Are Making Our Motor Industry. LC 72-5603. (Essay Index Reprint Ser.). 1972. Repr. of 1926 ed. 19.00 (ISBN 0-8369-2989-6). Ayer Co Pubs.
The Future of the Automobile in an Oil-Short World. (Worldwatch Institute Papers: No. 32). 64p. 1979. pap. 2.95 (ISBN 0-916468-31-3, WW32, WW). Unipub.
Heasley, Jerry. The Production Figure Book for U. S. Cars. LC 77-4149. 1977. pap. 7.95 (ISBN 0-87938-042-X). Motorbooks Intl.
Hu, Y. S. Impact of U. S. Investment in Europe: A Case Study of the Automotive & Computer Industries. LC 73-5163. (Special Studies in International Economics & Development). 1973. 39.50x (ISBN 0-275-28746-7); pap. text ed. 19.95x (ISBN 0-89197-792-9). Irvington.
Hunker, Jeffrey A., ed. Structural Change in the U. S. Automobile Industry. LC 82-48529. 288p. 1983. 32.00x (ISBN 0-669-06267-7). Lexington Bks.
Husband, T., ed. Robots in the Automotive Industry 1985: Proceedings of the Second International Conference, Birmingham, U. K. 14-17 May, 1985. 300p. 1985. 74.00 (ISBN 0-444-87769-X, North-Holland). Elsevier.
International Transfer of Automotive Technology to Developing Countries. pap. 4.00 (UN75/15/RR8, UN). Unipub.
Jamerson, F. E., ed. Physics in the Automotive Industry: APS-AAPT Topical Conference. LC 80-70987. (AIP Conference Proceedings: No. 66). 174p. 1981. lib. bdg. 26.50 (ISBN 0-88318-165-7). Am Inst Physics.
Kennedy, Edward D. Automobile Industry. LC 68-56238. Repr. of 1941 ed. 27.50x (ISBN 0-678-00906-6). Kelley.
Kimes, Beverly R., ed. Automobile Quarterly's Complete Handbook of Automobile Hobbies. (Hobby Bks.). (Illus.). 400p. 1981. 24.95 (ISBN 0-915038-28-5). Auto Quarterly.
Laux, James M. The Automobile Revolution: The Impact of an Industry. Fridenson, Bardon, et al, eds. LC 81-11571. xvi, 335p. 1982. 20.00x (ISBN 0-8078-1496-2). U of NC Pr.
Longstreet, Stephen. A Century on Wheels, the Story of Studebaker: A History, 1852-1952. LC 70-100238. (Illus.). 121p. Repr. of 1952 ed. lib. bdg. 15.00x (ISBN 0-8371-3978-3, LOCW). Greenwood.
Maxcy, George. The Multinational Automobile Industry. 1981. 35.00x (ISBN 0-312-55251-3). St Martin.
Monden, Yasuhiro. Toyota Production System. 1983. pap. text ed. 31.00 (ISBN 0-89806-034-6). Inst Indus Eng.
Moore, Russell M. Multinational Corporations & the Regionalization of the Latin American Automotive Industry. Bruchey, Stuart, ed. LC 80-584. (Multinational Corporations Ser.). 1980. lib. bdg. 33.50x (ISBN 0-405-13376-6). Ayer Co Pubs.
Mortimer, G., et al, eds. Coach (Automoblie) Trimming: Part One, 2 vols. (Engineering Craftsmen: No. E3). (Illus.). 1969. Set. spiral bdg. 62.50x set (ISBN 0-85083-041-9). Trans-Atlantic.
--Coach (Automoblie) Trimming: Part Two. (Engineering Craftsmen: No. E23). (Illus.). 1970. spiral bdg. 45.00x (ISBN 0-85083-124-5). Trans-Atlantic.
OECD Staff. Long Term Outlook for the World Automobile Industry. 120p. 1984. pap. 15.00 (ISBN 92-64-12523-X). OECD.
Okochi, Akio & Shimokawa, Koichi, eds. The Development of Marketing in the Automobile Industry. (The International Conference on Business History Ser.: No. 7). 303p. 1981. 29.50x (ISBN 0-86008-288-1, Pub. by U of Tokyo Japan). Columbia U Pr.
Peters, George A. & Peters, Barbara J., eds. Automotive Engineering & Litigation, Vol. 1. LC 83-16542. 897p. 1984. 96.00 (ISBN 0-8240-6100-4). Garland Pub.
Peterson, John C. & DeKryger, William J. Math for the Automotive Trade. (Illus.). 1983. pap. text ed. 4.65 wkbk. (ISBN 0-538-33020-1, IE02). SW Pub.
Phillips, Richard, et al. Auto Industries of Europe, United States & Japan. (Economist Intelligence Ser.). 352p. 1982. 29.95x (ISBN 0-89011-584-2). Ballinger Pub.
Rader, James. Penetrating the U.S. Auto Market: German & Japanese Strategies, 1965-1976. Dufey, Gunter, ed. LC 80-15530. (Research for Business Decisions: No. 22). 210p. 1980. 39.95 (ISBN 0-8357-1106-4). UMI Res Pr.
Rae, John B. American Automobile: A Brief History. LC 65-24981. (Chicago History of American Civilization Ser). (Illus.). 1965. 13.00x (ISBN 0-226-70263-4); pap. 9.00X (ISBN 0-226-70264-2, CHAC23). U of Chicago Pr.
Robots in Automobile Industy: Proceedings of the 2nd International Conference. 1985. 67.00x (ISBN 0-317-19986-2, Pub by IFS Pubns UK). Air Sci Co.
Rudman, Jack. Senior Automotive Facilities Inspector. (Career Examination Ser.: C-2214). (Cloth bdg. avail. on request). pap. 12.00 (ISBN 0-8373-2214-6). Natl Learning.
--Supervising Automotive Facilities Inspector. (Career Examination Ser.: C-2215). (Cloth bdg. avail. on request). pap. 10.00 (ISBN 0-8373-2215-4). Natl Learning.
Sakiya, Tetsuo. Honda Motor: The Men, the Management & the Machines. LC 82-80983. (Illus.). 230p. 1982. 13.95 (ISBN 0-87011-522-7). Kodansha.
Schnapp, John B., et al. Corporate Strategies of the Automotive Manufacturers. LC 79-2788. 224p. 1979. 28.00x (ISBN 0-669-03243-3). Lexington Bks.
Smith, Albert C., Jr. Wake Up Detroit! The EVs Are Coming. Smith, Albert, 3rd, ed. LC 81-68726. (Illus., Orig.). 1982. pap. 3.95 (ISBN 0-933086-03-2). Cromwell-Smith.
Strobel, Lee P. Reckless Homicide: Ford's Pinto Trial. LC 80-123374. (Illus.). 285p. 1980. 8.95 (ISBN 0-89708-022-X). And Bks.
Techno-Economic Aspects of the International Division of Labour in the Automotive Industry. 246p. (Orig.). pap. 23.00 (UN83/2E14, UN). Unipub.
Wright, Roy V., ed. Box, Stock & Flat Cars from the 1943 Car Builder's Cyclopedia. (Train Shed Cyclopedia Ser., No. 17). (Illus.). 1974. pap. 3.95 (ISBN 0-912318-46-5). N K Gregg.

AUTOMOBILE INDUSTRY AND TRADE–VOCATIONAL GUIDANCE

Rudman, Jack. Automotive Parts Supervisor. (Career Examination Ser.: C-2841). (Cloth bdg. avail. on request). 1980. pap. 12.00 (ISBN 0-8373-2841-1). Natl Learning.

AUTOMOBILE MAINTENANCE

see Automobiles–Maintenance and Repair

AUTOMOBILE MECHANICS

Calvert, Rodger & Smith, Mike. Drive It! The Complete Book of Long-Circuit Karting. (Drive It Ser.). (Illus.). 128p. 1985. 9.95 (ISBN 0-85429-416-3, Pub. by G T Foulis Ltd). Interbook.
Carroll, Bill. Auto Mechanics Basic Engineering Guide. LC 70-102903. (Performance Engineering Handbooks Ser.). (Illus.). 228p. 1974. pap. 9.95 (ISBN 0-910390-19-3). Auto Bk.
Chek-Chart Engineers. Auto Mechanics Refresher Course. wkbk. 42.00 (ISBN 0-88098-078-8). H M Gousha.
Crouse, W. H. & Anglin, D. L. Automotive Mechanics. 9th ed. 672p. 1984. 26.70 (ISBN 0-07-014860-0); 11.95 (ISBN 0-07-014871-6). McGraw.
Crouse, William H. Automotive Mechanics. 8th ed. LC 79-12845. (Illus.). 1980. text ed. 26.70 (ISBN 0-07-014820-1). McGraw.
DeKryger, et al. Auto Mechanics: Theory & Servicing. 1986. text ed. 17.50 (IE09). SW Pub.
DeKryger, William J., et al. Auto Mechanics: Theory & Service. Sprague & Sturzenberger, eds. (Automotive Ser.). (Illus.). 800p. 1985. text ed. 23.48x (ISBN 0-538-33090-2); write for info. (ISBN 0-538-33091-0); instr's. manual avail. (ISBN 0-538-33092-9). SW Pub.
Duffy, James E. Modern Automotive Mechanics. 1985. text ed. 24.00 (ISBN 0-87006-479-7); tchr's. ed. 18.00. Goodheart.
Hammer, Hy, ed. Auto Mechanic-Auto Serviceman. 6th ed. LC 81-17606. (Illus.). 208p. 1982. pap. 8.00 (ISBN 0-668-05397-6, 5397). Arco.
Hendrix, T. G. & LaFevor, C. S. Mathematics for Auto Mechanics. LC 77-72431. 1978. pap. text ed. 14.80 (ISBN 0-8273-1630-5). Delmar.
Hughes. Guide to the Automobile Certification Examination. rev. ed. 1983. pap. 13.95 (ISBN 0-8359-2616-8). Reston.
Martin, Philip R. Auto Mechanics for the Complete Dummy. 2nd ed. LC 82-62322. (Illus.). 192p. 1983. pap. 4.95 (ISBN 0-930968-02-6). Motormatics.
Pearce, Charles. Essentials of Auto Mechanics. (Auto Mechanics Motivational Program). 1973. pap. text ed. 7.95 (ISBN 0-89036-816-3); tchrs' guide 1.50 (ISBN 0-89036-821-X); vocabulary 2.95 (ISBN 0-89036-818-X); unit tests 3.50 (ISBN 0-89036-817-1); study guide pap. 7.50 (ISBN 0-89036-820-1); guide bk. 2.95 (ISBN 0-89036-815-5). Hawkes Pub Inc.
Rudman, Jack. Auto Mechanics. (Occupational Competency Examination Ser.: OCE-7). (Cloth bdg. avail. on request). 13.95 (ISBN 0-8373-5707-1). Natl Learning.
--Automotive Mechanic. (Career Examination Ser.: C-1131). (Cloth bdg. avail. on request). pap. 12.00 (ISBN 0-8373-1131-4). Natl Learning.
--Certified General Automobile Mechanic: CGAM. (Career Examination Ser.: C-1664). (Cloth bdg. avail. on request). 1977. pap. 14.00 (ISBN 0-8373-1664-2). Natl Learning.
--Foreman Auto Mechanic. (Career Examination Ser.: C-263). (Cloth bdg. avail. on request). pap. 10.00 (ISBN 0-8373-0263-3). Natl Learning.
--Garageman. (Career Examination Ser.: C-1292). (Cloth bdg. avail. on request). pap. 10.00 (ISBN 0-8373-1292-2). Natl Learning.
--Substitute Garageman (U.S.P.S.) (Career Examination Ser.: C-1497). (Cloth bdg. avail. on request). pap. 8.00 (ISBN 0-8373-1497-6). Natl Learning.
Sachs, H. K., ed. Proceedings of the First International Conference on Vehicle Mechanics, Detroit, 16-18 July, 1968. 735p. 1969. text ed. 80.00 (ISBN 90-265-0101-3, Pub. by Swets Pub Serv Holland). Swets North Am.
--Proceedings of the Third International Conference on Vehicle System Dynamics, Blacksburg, VA, 12-15 August, 1974. 324p. 1975. text ed. 54.00 (ISBN 90-265-0197-8, Pub. by Swets Pub Serv Holland). Swets North Am.
Sachs, H. K. & Rapin, P., eds. Proceedings of the Second International Conference on Vehicle Mechanics, Paris, 6-10 September, 1971. 500p. 1973. text ed. 54.00 (ISBN 90-265-0166-8, Pub. by Swets Pub Serv Holland). Swets North Am.
Vehicle Structural Mechanics, 3rd International Conference Proceedings. LC 79-90695. 310p. 1979. Twenty-Five papers. pap. 40.00 (ISBN 0-89883-053-2, P83). Soc Auto Engineers.
Webster, Jay. Auto Mechanics. LC 79-2488. 576p. 1980. text ed. 17.40 (ISBN 0-02-829770-9); instrs'. manual 9.60 (ISBN 0-02-829780-6); auto shop act. guide 5.40 (ISBN 0-02-829790-3). Glencoe.

AUTOMOBILE OPERATION

see Automobile Driving

AUTOMOBILE RADIOS

see Automobiles–Radio Equipment

AUTOMOBILE REPAIR

see Automobiles–Maintenance and Repair

AUTOMOBILE TIRES

see Automobiles–Tires

AUTOMOBILE TRANSMISSION

see Automobiles–Transmission Devices

AUTOMOBILE TRUCKS

see Motor-Trucks

AUTOMOBILE WORKERS

see Automobile Mechanics

AUTOMOBILES

see also Motor Buses; Motorcycles; Motor-Trucks; Sports Cars;
also names of automobiles under Automobiles–Types; Automobiles, Foreign–Types, e.g. Automobiles–Types–Ford; Automobiles, Foreign–Types–Volkswagen; also headings beginning with the word automobile

Aluminium-Zentrale, ed. Aluminium & the Automobile. 1981. 81.00 (ISBN 0-9960034-4-4, Pub. by Aluminium W Germany). Heyden.
Automobile Almanac-Annual. 1981. 6.95 (ISBN 0-686-51337-1); pap. 2.95 (ISBN 0-686-51338-X). Am Sports Sales.
Automobile Club of Italy. World Cars, 1972. Orig. Title: World Car Catalogue. (Illus.). 440p. 1972. 85.00 (ISBN 0-910714-04-5). Herald Bks.
--World Cars 1982. LC 74-643381. (Illus.). 440p. 1982. 45.00 (ISBN 0-910714-14-2). Herald Bks.
Automobile Club of Italy, ed. World Cars 1978. LC 74-643381. (Illus.). 1978. 50.00 (ISBN 0-910714-10-X). Herald Bks.
Brigham, Grace R. The Serial Number Book for U. S. Cars: 1900-1975. LC 78-27640. 1979. pap. 12.95 (ISBN 0-87938-056-X). Motorbooks Intl.
Brown, Lester, et al. Running on Empty: The Future of the Automobile in An Oil-Short World. 1979. 9.95 (ISBN 0-393-01334-0). Norton.
Brown, Lester R., et al. The Future of the Automobile in an Oil-Short World. LC 79-67316. (Worldwatch Papers). 1979. pap. 2.00 (ISBN 0-916468-31-3). Worldwatch Inst.
Burness, Tad. American Car Spotter's Guide 1940-1965. rev. ed. LC 78-14879. (Illus.). 1978. pap. 13.95 (ISBN 0-87938-057-8). Motorbooks Intl.
--American Car Spotter's Guide: 1966-1980. LC 80-26337. (Illus.). 432p. (Orig.). 1981. pap. 18.95 (ISBN 0-87938-102-7). Motorbooks Intl.
Carm-Chilton's Automotive Repair Manual: 1972-79. 1154p. 1980. 22.95 (ISBN 0-8019-6914-X). Chilton.
Chilton's Automotive Editorial Staff. AMC, Nineteen Seventy to Nineteen Eighty-Two. 1982. pap. 11.95 (ISBN 0-8019-7199-3). Chilton.
Chilton's Diesel Guide. LC 78-22145. (New Automotive Bks.). 224p. 1980. 11.95 (ISBN 0-8019-6753-8); pap. 11.95 (ISBN 0-8019-6754-6). Chilton.
Chilton's More Miles per Gallon. (New Automotive Bks.). 176p. 1980. 12.95 (ISBN 0-8019-6907-7); pap. 11.95 (ISBN 0-8019-6908-5). Chilton.
Fisher, Bill & Waar, Bob. How to Hotrod Big-Block Chevys. LC 72-159282. (Illus.). 1971. pap. 9.95 (ISBN 0-912656-04-2). H P Bks.
Harding, Anthony, ed. Motorist's Miscellany. 17.50x (ISBN 0-392-05932-0, SpS). Sportshelf.
Hollander Publishing Company, Inc. Domestic Car Inventory Index, 1972-1982. 910p. 1982. 189.00 (ISBN 0-943032-25-3). Hollander Co.
Kallir, Rudolf F. Autographensammler - Lebenslaenglich. (Illus.). 1977. 18.70x (ISBN 3-7611-0518-5). M S Rosenberg.
Kamal, Mounir M. & Wolf, Joseph A., Jr. Modern Automotive Structural Analysis. 480p. 1982. 39.50 (ISBN 0-442-24839-3). Van Nos Reinhold.
The Motor Vehicle. 10th ed. 742p. 1984. 20.00 (ISBN 0-317-37146-0, #BMV-1) (ISBN 0-408-01157-2). Soc Auto Engineers.
Motor Vehicle Manufacturers Association of the United States. Automobiles of America: Milestones, Pioneers, Roll Call, Highlights. 4th ed. (Illus.). 301p. 1974. pap. 5.95 (ISBN 0-8143-1515-1). Wayne St U Pr.

Neely, William. Five Hundred Five Automobile Questions Your Friends Can't Answer. LC 83-40408. 1984. pap. 3.95 (ISBN 0-8027-7212-9). Walker & Co.

Niles Cars Catalog. 44p. 1982. pap. 9.95 (ISBN 0-87004-292-0). Caxton.

Shilton, Neale. A Million Miles Ago. (Illus.). 300p. 1982. 19.95 (ISBN 0-85429-313-2, F313). Haynes Pubns.

Vauxhall Motors. Motor Car: The Inside Story. (Illus.). pap. 4.00x (ISBN 0-392-04019-0, SpS). Sportshelf.

Wagner, Richard & Wagner, Birdella. Curved-Side Cars. 120p. 1965. vinyl bdg. 10.00 (ISBN 0-914196-02-2). Trolley Talk.

Webb, Charles. The Investor's Guide to American Convertible & Special-Interest Automobiles, 1946-1976. LC 77-84592. (Illus.). 1980. 25.00 (ISBN 0-498-02183-1). A S Barnes.

Woody, Bob. The Car Crisis: How to Cope with the ABC's of Auto Emergencies. LC 77-91261. 1977. pap. 4.95 (ISBN 0-930938-01-1). Vista Pubns.

Wright, Roy V., ed. Tank Cars, 1922-1943. (Train Shed Cyclopedia Ser., No. 12). (Illus.). 1973. pap. 4.50 (ISBN 0-912318-41-4). N K Gregg.

AUTOMOBILES–ACCESSORIES

see Automobiles–Equipment and Supplies

AUTOMOBILES–AIR-CONDITIONING

Crouse, W. H. & Anglin, D. L. Automotive Air Conditioning. 2nd ed. LC 82-4682. 304p. 1983. text ed. 21.10x (ISBN 0-07-014857-0). McGraw.

Doolin, James H. Auto Air Conditioning. 48p. 1982. pap. 15.00 (ISBN 0-914626-03-5). Doolco Inc.

Dwiggins, Boyce. Automotive Air Conditioning. 5th ed. LC 82-46007. 480p. 1983. pap. text ed. 18.00 (ISBN 0-8273-1940-1); tchr's. guide 5.70 (ISBN 0-8273-1942-8). Delmar.

Kirkpatrick, James M. & Weaver, Michael K. Automotive Air Conditioning & Climate Control. LC 78-994. 1978. pap. 21.72 scp (ISBN 0-672-97098-8); scp wkbk. 7.20 (ISBN 0-672-97099-6); scp tchr's manual 3.67 (ISBN 0-672-97100-3). Bobbs.

Langley, Billy C. Principles & Service of Automotive Air Conditioning. 1984. 26.95 (ISBN 0-8359-5638-5); pap. 19.95 (ISBN 0-8359-5615-6). Reston.

Samuels, Clifford L. Automotive Air Conditioning. (Illus.). 288p. 1981. text ed. 24.95 (ISBN 0-13-054213-X); pap. text ed. 21.95 (ISBN 0-13-054205-9). P-H.

Traister, John E. Automotive Air Conditioning Handbook: Installation, Service & Repair. (Illus.). 1978. pap. 10.95 (ISBN 0-8306-1020-0, 1020). TAB Bks.

Weissler, Paul. Automotive Air Conditioning. (Illus.). 1981. text ed. 24.95 (ISBN 0-8359-0261-7); pap. 18.95 (ISBN 0-8359-0260-9). Reston.

AUTOMOBILES–BODIES

Alderwyck, A. How to Restore Wooden Body Framing. (Osprey Restoration Guide Ser.). (Illus.). 128p. 1984. text ed. 14.95 (ISBN 0-85045-590-1, Pub. by Osprey England). Motorbooks Intl.

Beattie, Ian. The Complete Book of Automobile Body Design. 12.95 (ISBN 0-85429-217-9, 217). Haynes Pubns.

Butler, Herbert J., ed. Antique Auto Body Leather Work for the Restorer. LC 82-62713. (Vintage Craft Ser.: No. 3). (Illus.). 1969. pap. 6.95 (ISBN 0-911160-03-5). Post-Era.

--Antique Auto Body Top Work for the Restorer. LC 76-18437. (Vintage Craft Ser.: No. 4). (Illus.). 1970. pap. 6.95 (ISBN 0-911160-04-3). Post-Era.

Caldwell, Brice & Caldwell, Craig, eds. Basic Bodywork & Painting. 5th ed. LC 73-79967. (Illus.). 192p. (Orig.). 1981. pap. 6.95 (ISBN 0-8227-5057-0, Dist. by Kampmann). Petersen Pub.

Chilton's Automotive Editorial Staff. GM X-Body, 1980 to 1981. (Illus.). 1981. pap. 11.95 (ISBN 0-8019-7049-0). Chilton.

Chilton'sAutomotive Editorial Staff, ed. Chilton's Mechanics' Handbook: Automobile Sheet Metal Repair, Vol. III. (Illus.). 300p. 1981. pap. 16.95 (ISBN 0-8019-7034-2). Chilton.

Coombes, B., ed. Vehicle Body Building, Pt. 2, 2 vols. (Engineering Craftsmen: No. E22). (Illus.). 1969. Set. spiral bdg. 82.50x (ISBN 0-85083-063-X). Intl Ideas.

Crouse, William H. & Anglin, Donald L. Automotive Chassis & Body. 5th ed. (Automotive Technology Ser.). (Illus.). 416p. 1975. soft cover 21.60 (ISBN 0-07-014653-5). McGraw.

Deroche, Andre & Huldebrand, Nicholas. The Principles of Autobody Repairing & Repainting. 3rd ed. (Illus.). 672p. 1981. text ed. 29.95 (ISBN 0-13-705665-6). P-H.

Duenk, Lester G., et al. Autobody Repair. 1977. student guide 5.00 (ISBN 0-02-662320-X). Bennett IL.

Exterior Body Panel Developments. 1985. 30.00 (ISBN 0-89883-841-X, SP620). Soc Auto Engineers.

Fournier, Ron. Metal Fabricator's Handbook: Race & Custom Car. 176p. 1982. pap. 12.95 (ISBN 0-89586-171-2). H P Bks.

Greenspan, Rick. Fixing Cars. LC 75-302457. 1974. pap. 5.00 (ISBN 0-9603356-0-9). Rose Pub Co CA.

Institute of Mechanical Engineers. Vehicle Structures. 1984. 63.00 (MEP200). Soc Auto Engineers.

Jaderquist, Eugene. New How to Build Hot Rods. LC 62-16909. (Illus.). 1957. lib. bdg. 4.95 (ISBN 0-668-00553-X). Arco.

Lewerenz, Alfred S. Antique Auto Body Brass Work for the Restorer. (Vintage Craft Ser.: No. 5). (Illus.). 1970. pap. 6.95 (ISBN 0-911160-05-1). Post-Era.

Lewerenz, Alfred S., ed. Antique Auto Body Accessories for the Restorer. (Vintage Craft Ser.: No. 7). (Illus.). 1970. pap. 6.95 (ISBN 0-911160-07-8). Post-Era.

MacPherson, R. C. Collision Repair Guide. 1971. 23.85 (ISBN 0-07-044690-3). McGraw.

Neubecker, William, ed. Antique Auto Body Metal Work for the Restorer. LC 82-62579. (Vintage Craft Ser.: No. 1). (Illus.). 1969. pap. 6.95 (ISBN 0-911160-01-9). Post-Era.

Rhone, L. C. & Yates, H. David. Total Auto Body Repair. 2nd ed. 464p. 1982. text ed. 28.99 scp (ISBN 0-672-97967-5); scp instr's. guide 3.67 (ISBN 0-672-97969-1); scp kbk. 8.40 (ISBN 0-672-97968-3). Bobbs.

Rudman, Jack. Auto Body Repair. (Occupational Competency Examination Ser.: OCE-5). (Cloth bdg. avail. on request). 13.95 (ISBN 0-8373-5705-5). Natl Learning.

Schmidt, Robert P. Autobody Repair & Refinishing. 350p. 1981. text ed. 26.95 (ISBN 0-8359-0247-1); instr's. manual free (ISBN 0-8359-0248-X). Reston.

Schriber, Fritz, ed. Antique Auto Body Decoration for the Restorer. LC 82-62673. (Vintage Craft Ser.: No. 6). (Illus.). 1970. pap. 6.95 (ISBN 0-911160-06-X). Post-Era.

Smith, B. How to Restore Sheet Metal Bodywork. (Osprey Restoration Ser.). (Illus.). 128p. 1984. text ed. 14.95 (ISBN 0-85045-591-X, Pub. by Osprey England). Motorbooks Intl.

Terry, C. W. Antique Auto Body Wood Work for the Restorer. LC 77-74129. (Vintage Craft Ser.: No. 2). (Illus.). 1969. pap. 6.95 (ISBN 0-911160-02-7). Post-Era.

Toboldt, Bill. Auto Body Repairing & Repainting. rev. ed. LC 82-14320. (Illus.). 264p. 1983. text ed. 14.00 (ISBN 0-87006-423-1). Goodheart.

Vehicle Body Building One. 75.00x (ISBN 0-85083-023-0, Pub. by Engineering Ind). State Mutual Bk.

Vehicle Body Building Two, 2 vols. Set. 75.00x (ISBN 0-85083-063-X, Pub. by Engineering Ind). State Mutual Bk.

Wills, John A. Glass Fiber Auto Body Construction Simplified. rev. ed. LC 76-24573. (Illus.). 1965. pap. 7.95 (ISBN 0-911160-52-3). Post-Era.

AUTOMOBILES–BRAKES

Abbott, Sheldon. Automotive Brakes: Text-Lab Manual. 1st ed. 1977. pap. 17.00 (ISBN 0-02-810150-2); tchrs manual 3.20 (ISBN 0-02-810160-X). Glencoe.

Abbott, Sheldon L. Automotive Brakes: A Text-Lab Manual. (Illus.). 1977. pap. 13.95x (ISBN 0-02-810150-2). Macmillan.

Billiet, Walter E. & Alley, Walter. Automotive Suspensions, Steering, Alignment & Brakes. 5th ed. (Illus.). 1974. 15.95 (ISBN 0-8269-0122-0). Am Technical.

Braking: Recent Developments. 80p. 1984. 18.00 (ISBN 0-89883-341-8, SP570). Soc Auto Engineers.

Chilton's Automotive Editorial Staff. Mechanics' Handbook, Vol. 5: Brakes-Steering-Suspension. 1983. pap. 16.95 (ISBN 0-8019-7205-1). Chilton.

Coghlan, David A. Automotive Brake System. 1980. pap. text ed. write for info. (ISBN 0-534-00822-4, Breton Pubs). Wadsworth Pub.

--Automotive Chassis Systems: Steering, Suspension, Alignment, & Brakes. 2nd ed. (Illus.). 440p. 1985. pap. text ed. 19.00 (ISBN 0-534-04848-X, 77F6066). Breton Pubs.

Crouse, William H. & Anglin, Donald L. Automotive Brakes, Suspension & Steering. 6th ed. LC 82-17187. (Automotive Technology Ser.). 1983. 21.60 (ISBN 0-07-014828-7). McGraw.

Ellinger, Herbert E. & Hathaway, Richard B. Automotive Suspension, Steering & Brakes. (Transportation & Technology Ser.). (Illus.). 1980. text ed. 24.95 (ISBN 0-13-054288-1). P-H.

Frazee, Irving A. & Billiet, Walter. Automotive Brakes & Power Transmission Systems. LC 56-7199. (Automotive Ser.). (Illus.). pap. 69.30 (ISBN 0-317-11020-9, 2004568). Bks Demand UMI.

Heller, Carl T. Automotive Braking System. 1985. text ed. 26.95 (ISBN 0-8359-9357-4); pap. text ed. 19.95 (ISBN 0-8359-9355-8). Reston.

Newcomb, T. P. & Spurr, R. T. Automobiles Brakes & Braking Systems. LC 71-93994. (Motor Manuals Ser.: Vol. 8). text ed. 10.95x (ISBN 0-8376-0076-6). Bentley.

Remling, John. Brakes. 2nd ed. LC 82-2798. (Automotive Mechanics Ser.). 328p. 1983. pap. 25.95x (ISBN 0-471-09583-4); write for info. tchrs. manual (ISBN 0-471-03764-8). Wiley.

Theissen, Frank & Dales, Dave. Automotive Steering, Suspension, & Braking Systems: Principles & Service. 1982. text ed. 28.95 (ISBN 0-8359-0291-9); pap. text ed. 21.95 (ISBN 0-8359-0290-0); instrs.' manual free (ISBN 0-8359-0292-7). Reston.

AUTOMOBILES–CONSTRUCTION

see Automobiles–Design and Construction

AUTOMOBILES–DESIGN AND CONSTRUCTION

see also Automobiles–Bodies

Airline Plating & Metal Finishing 18th Annual Forum: Proceedings. 68p. (Automation of the Thermal Spray Process). 1982. pap. 30.00 (ISBN 0-89883-073-7, P108). Soc Auto Engineers.

Automotive Manufacturing Update. 375p. 1978. casebound 70.00 (ISBN 0-85298-382-4, MEP 148). Soc Auto Engineers.

Aylen, R., et al, eds. Vehicle Fitting. (Engineering Craftsmen: No. H8). (Illus.). 1978. spiral bdg. 39.95x (ISBN 0-89563-036-2). Intl Ideas.

Blelloch, A., ed. Measurements of the Impacts of Materials Substitution: A Case Study in the Automobile Industry. 1978. 8.00 (ISBN 0-685-66804-5, H00131). ASME.

Bosch. Fachwoerterbuch Kraftfahrtechnik, 2 vols, Vol. 1. (Ger. & Eng.). 354p. (Technical Dictionary for Automotive Engineering). 1976. 85.00 (ISBN 3-18-419044-7, M-7638, Pub. by VDI Verlag GMBH). French & Eur.

--Fachwoerterbuch Kraftfahrtechnik, 2 vols, Vol. 2. (Ger. & Eng.). 369p. (Technical dictionary of automotive engineering). 1977. 59.95 (ISBN 3-18-419046-3, M-7639, Pub. by VDI Verlag GMBH). French & Eur.

Burnham, Colin. Customizing Cars. LC 79-24124. (Illus.). 1980. 12.95 (ISBN 0-668-04888-3); pap. 8.95 (ISBN 0-668-04892-1). Arco.

Caldwell, Bruce & Caldwell, Craig, eds. Best of Hot Rod. (Illus.). 192p. (Orig.). 1981. pap. 9.95 (ISBN 0-8227-5060-0, Dist. by Kampmann). Green Hill.

Campbell, Colin. New Directions in Suspension Design: Making the Fast Car Faster. LC 80-24348. (Illus.). 224p. 1981. 14.95 (ISBN 0-8376-0150-9). Bentley.

--The Sports Car: Its Design & Performance. 4th ed. LC 77-94089. (Illus.). 306p. 1979. 14.95 (ISBN 0-8376-0158-4). Bentley.

Current & Future Directions of Supercomputer Applications in the Automotive Industry. Date not set. 13.00 (ISBN 0-89883-845-2, SP624). Soc Auto Engineers.

Designing Your Product for Robotics. 52p. 1982. pap. 15.00 (ISBN 0-89883-288-8, SP517). Soc Auto Engineers.

Displays, Electronics, & Sensor Technology. 215p. 1984. pap. 50.00 (ISBN 0-89883-336-1, SP565). Soc Auto Engineers.

Efficiency in the Design Office. 85p. 1983. pap. 14.50 (ISBN 0-85298-528-2, MEP188). Soc Auto Engineers.

Electronic Automotive Reliability. 52p. 1984. 18.00 (ISBN 0-89883-344-2, SP573). Soc Auto Engineers.

Electronic Displays & Information Systems. 128p. 1981. pap. 38.00 (ISBN 0-89883-060-5, P92). Soc Auto Engineers.

Electronic Displays, Information Systems, & On-Board Electronics. 164p. 1982. pap. 38.00 (ISBN 0-89883-068-0, P103). Soc Auto Engineers.

Electronics Technologies & Systems for Commercial Vehicles of the 80's, 6 papers. 61p. 1981. pap. 15.00 (ISBN 0-89883-276-4, SP505). Soc Auto Engineers.

Fourth International Conference on Vehicle Structural Mechanics, 27 papers. 286p. 1981. pap. 45.00 (ISBN 0-89883-065-6, P99). Soc Auto Engineers.

Gear Design & Performance. 1984. 25.00 (ISBN 0-89883-805-3, SP584). Soc Auto Engineers.

Government Automotive Research: Recent Developments. 1984. 25.00 (ISBN 0-89883-804-5, SP 583). Soc Auto Engineers.

Gurr, Robert H. Automobile Design, the Complete Styling Book. (Illus.). 1955. pap. 10.00 (ISBN 0-911160-55-8). Post-Era.

Institute of Mechanical Engineers. Vehicle Structures. 1984. 63.00 (MEP200). Soc Auto Engineers.

International Conference on Automotive Electronics, 3rd: Proceedings. 354p. 1981. pap. 50.00 (ISBN 0-85298-477-4, P102). Soc Auto Engineers.

International Congress on Transportation & Electronics, Convergence '82: Proceedings. 265p. 1982. pap. 38.00 (ISBN 0-89883-076-1, P111). Soc Auto Engineers.

The Japanese Automobile Industry: Model & Challenge for the Future? 147p. 1981. pap. 15.00 (ISBN 0-939512-08-4, P95). Soc Auto Engineers.

Jones, N., ed. Impact Crashworthiness: First International Symposium on Structural Crashworthiness, University of Liverpool, September 14-16, 1983. 120p. 1983. pap. 16.50 (ISBN 0-08-031121-0, 11/1, 11). Pergamon.

Jute, Andre. Designing & Building Special Cars. (Illus.). 168p. 1985. 28.00 (ISBN 0-7134-0778-6, Pub. by Batsford England). David & Charles.

Korff, Walter H. Designing Tomorrow's Cars: From Concept-Step-by-Step-to Detail Design. LC 80-80522. (Illus.). 271p. 1980. 19.95 (ISBN 0-9603850-0-2). M-C Pubns.

Kulkarni, S. V., et al. Composite Materials in the Automobile Industry. 216p. 1978. 30.00 (ISBN 0-685-66793-6). ASME.

Light Vehicle Fitting. 1982. 50.00x (ISBN 0-85083-487-2, Pub. by Engineering Ind). State Mutual Bk.

Limpert, Rudolf. Vehicle System Components: Design & Safety. LC 81-23061. 144p. 1982. 42.95x (ISBN 0-471-08133-7, Pub. by Wiley-Interscience). Wiley.

McComb, F. Wilson. MG by McComb. (Illus.). 1979. 22.95 (ISBN 0-85045-310-0, Pub. by Osprey Pub. Ltd. England). Motorbooks Intl.

Managing Computer Aided Design, 7 papers. 56p. 1980. pap. 30.00 (ISBN 0-85298-470-7, MEP133). Soc Auto Engineers.

Materials Availability for Automotive Applications. 52p. 1980. Eight papers. pap. 15.00 (ISBN 0-89883-233-0, SP462). Soc Auto Engineers.

Mobile Equipment Design. 1983. 25.00 (ISBN 0-89883-322-1, SP551). Soc Auto Engineers.

Murray, Spence, ed. Creative Customizing. LC 78-50827. (Illus.). 176p. (Orig.). 1978. pap. 6.95 (ISBN 0-8227-5026-0). Petersen Pub.

Naul, G. Marshall. The Specification Book for U. S. Cars: 1930-1969. LC 80-11999. 399p. (Orig.). 1980. pap. 12.95 (ISBN 0-87938-068-3). Motorbooks Intl.

New Developments & Requirements for Automotive Fabrics. 99p. 1983. 50.00 (ISBN 0-318-01531-5, 16024). Indus Fabrics.

New Developments in Electronic Engine Management. (Illus.). 1984. pap. 35.00 (ISBN 0-89883-343-4, SP572). Soc Auto Engineers.

Norbye, Jan P. Car Design: Structure & Architecture. (Illus.). 384p. 1984. pap. 20.50 (ISBN 0-8306-2104-0, 2104). TAB Bks.

Past, Present & Future of Automotive Elastomer Applications. 48p. 1980. Seven papers. 15.00 (ISBN 0-89883-235-7, SP464). Soc Auto Engineers.

Plastics & Passenger Cars. 1984. 30.00 (ISBN 0-89883-337-X, SP566). Soc Auto Engineers.

Quality Assurance in Design, 7 papers. 54p. 1982. pap. 31.00 (ISBN 0-85298-502-9, MEP156). Soc Auto Engineers.

Scott, Curt. Kit Car Catalog, 1985. Scott, Judy, ed. (Illus.). 184p. 1985. pap. 8.95 (ISBN 0-9614882-0-4, Dist. by Motorbooks Intl). Homebuilt Pubns.

Seiffert, Ulrich & Walzer, Peter. The Future for Automotive Technology. LC 84-42620. (The Future for Science & Technology Ser.). 197p. 1984. 22.50 (ISBN 0-86187-460-9). F Pinter Pubs.

Sensors & Actuators. 128p. 1982. pap. 32.00 (ISBN 0-89883-282-9, SP511). Soc Auto Engineers.

Shepard, Margaret E. Studies Relating Automobile Design & Vehicle Safety: An Annotated Bibliography. (CPL Bibliographies Ser.: No. 93). 93p. 1982. 15.00 (ISBN 0-86602-093-4). Coun Plan Librarians.

Smith, Philip H. The Design & Tuning of Competition Engines. 6th rev. ed. Wenner, David N., ed. LC 77-78834. (Illus.). 1977. 19.95 (ISBN 0-8376-0140-1). Bentley.

Smith, Philip H. & Morrison, John C. Scientific Design of Exhaust & Intake Systems. 3rd rev. ed. LC 72-86569. (Illus.). 294p. 1972. 16.95 (ISBN 0-8376-0309-9). Bentley.

Society of Automotive Engineers. Automotive Aerodynamics. LC 78-57059. 282p. 1978. Eighteen papers. 38.00 (ISBN 0-89883-104-0, PT 16). Soc Auto Engineers.

--Cumulative Index of SAE Technical Papers, 1965-1983. 7th ed. 1984. 75.00 (ISBN 0-89883-589-5). Soc Auto Engineers.

--Current Trends in Truck Suspensions. LC 80-53531. 92p. 1980. Six papers. 18.00 (ISBN 0-89883-246-2, SP475). Soc Auto Engineers.

Society of Manufacturing Engineers. AUTOFACT Europe '84: Proceedings. 1984. 45.00 (ISBN 0-87263-123-0). SME.

--AUTOFACT Six: Proceedings. 1984. 68.00 (ISBN 0-87263-161-3). SME.

Statistical Process Control, 11 papers. 88p. 1983. pap. 30.00 (ISBN 0-89883-318-3, SP547). Soc Auto Engineers.

Tenth Conference on Production Research & Technology: Proceedings, 32 papers. 240p. 1983. pap. 38.00 (ISBN 0-89883-087-7, P128). Soc Auto Engineers.

Terry, Len & Baker, Alan. Racing Car Design & Development. LC 73-85159. 1973. 14.95 (ISBN 0-8376-0080-4). Bentley.

Universal Joint & Driveshaft Design Manual. LC 79-63005. 440p. 1979. Forty-one papers. 45.00 (ISBN 0-89883-007-9, AE7). Soc Auto Engineers.

Vehicle Fitting One. 50.00x (ISBN 0-85083-402-3, Pub. by Engineering Ind). State Mutual Bk.

Vehicular Structural Mechanics: Proceedings of the Fifth International Conference. 260p. 1984. 38.00 (ISBN 0-89883-700-6, P 144). Soc Auto Engineers.

AUTOMOBILES–DICTIONARIES

Baudoin, Anne-Marie. Vocabulaire Francais-Anglais De L'automobile: Le Moteur. (Eng. & Fr.). 174p. 1973. pap. 9.95 (ISBN 0-686-56909-1, M-6025). French & Eur.

Blok, C. & Jezewski, W. Dictionnaire Illustre de l'Automobile "Kluwer," en 6 Langues. (Fr., Eng., Ger., Ital., Rus. & Dutch.). 504p. 1979. 145.00 (ISBN 0-686-56923-7, M-6039). French & Eur.

Blok, Czeslaw & Jezewski, Wieslaw. Illustrated Automobile Dictionary. (Illus.). 1978. lib. bdg. 89.00 (ISBN 9-0201-1070-5, Pub. by Kluwer Tech Netherlands). Kluwer Academic.

Bosch. Fachwoerterbuch Kraftfahrtechnik, 2 vols, Vol. 1. (Ger. & Eng.). 354p. (Technical Dictionary for Automotive Engineering). 1976. 85.00 (ISBN 3-18-419044-7, M-7638, Pub. by VDI Verlag GMBH). French & Eur.

--Fachwoerterbuch Kraftfahrtechnik, 2 vols, Vol. 2. (Ger. & Eng.). 369p. (Technical dictionary of automotive engineering). 1977. 59.95 (ISBN 3-18-419046-3, M-7639, Pub. by VDI Verlag GMBH). French & Eur.

Burger, E., ed. Technical Dictionary of Automatization & Programming: English, French, German, Russian, Slovene. (Eng., Fr., Ger., Rus. & Slovene.). 479p. 1976. 95.00 (ISBN 0-686-92330-8, M-9889). French & Eur.

Drackett, Phil, ed. Encyclopedia of the Motor Car. (Illus.). 1979. 12.98 (ISBN 0-517-53833-4). Crown.

Enciclopedia Salvat Del Automovil, 10 vols. (Espn.). 3280p. 1974. Set. 320.00 (ISBN 84-7137-415-3, S-50545). French & Eur.

Equipo Reactor de Ceac. Manual del Automovil en 5 Idiomas: Diccionario Idiomatico del Automovil. (Span., Fr., Eng., It. & Ger.). 240p. 1974. 8.50 (ISBN 84-329-1403-7, S-50224). French & Eur.

Equipo Reactor de CEAC, ed. Diccionario del Automovil. (Span.). 916p. 1978. 37.50 (ISBN 84-329-1010-4, S-14232). French & Eur.

Guerber, Roger. Diccionario del Automovil. 4th ed. (Span., Eng., Fr & Ger.). 237p. 1972. pap. 16.75 (ISBN 84-252-0065-2, S-14249). French & Eur.

Lima, Robert F., ed. Arco Motor Vehicle Dictionary: English & Spanish. LC 76-77605. (Eng. & Span.). 368p. 1980. pap. 7.95 (ISBN 0-668-04982-0, 4982-0). Arco.

Schuurmans, G., ed. Elseviers Automobile Dictionary. (Eng., Fr., Span., Port., Ger., Rus., Ital. & Japanese.). 946p. 1960. 159.75 (ISBN 0-444-40517-8). Elsevier.

Sikora, G. Technical Automotive Dictionary: Russian-English-German-French-Bulgarian. (Rus., Eng., Ger., Fr. & Bulgarian.). 624p. 1977. leatherette 95.00 (ISBN 0-686-92472-X, M-9828). French & Eur.

Toboldt, William K. & Johnson, Larry. Automotive Encyclopedia. Rev ed. (Illus.). 840p. 1983. text ed. 20.00 (ISBN 0-87006-436-3). Goodheart.

Tver, David F. & Bolz, Roger W. Encyclopedic Dictionary of Industrial Technology Materials, Processes & Equipment: A New York Publication. (Illus.). 400p. 1984. 34.50 (ISBN 0-412-00501-8, 9005, Pub. by Chapman & Hall). Methuen Inc.

Zlatovski, George. Dictionnaire Technique de L'Automobile. Russek, P. R., ed. (Fr., Eng. & Ger.). 184p. 1973. pap. 22.50 (ISBN 0-686-57262-9, M-6575). French & Eur.

Zurita Ruiz, Jose. Diccionario Basico de la Construccion. 16th ed. (Span.). 248p. 1976. pap. 8.95 (ISBN 84-329-2905-0, S-50223). French & Eur.

AUTOMOBILES–DIESEL MOTORS

see Automobiles–Motors

AUTOMOBILES–DRIVING

see Automobile Driving

AUTOMOBILES–DYNAMICS

Automobile Aerodynamics: Wakes, Wind Effect, Vehicle Development. 136p. 1984. 18.00 (ISBN 0-89883-340-X, SP569). Soc Auto Engineers.

Huntington, Roger. American Supercar. LC 82-84044. (Illus.). 176p. 1983. pap. 9.95 (ISBN 0-89586-221-2). H P Bks.

AUTOMOBILES–ELECTRIC EQUIPMENT

Ayres, Robert U. & McKenna, Richard P. Alternatives to the Internal Combustion Engine: Impacts on Environmental Quality. LC 74-181555. (Resources for the Future Ser). 340p. 1972. 27.50x (ISBN 0-8018-1369-7). Johns Hopkins.

Billiet, W. E. & Goings, L. F. Automotive Electrical Systems. 3rd ed. (Illus.). 1970. 15.95 (ISBN 0-8269-0040-2). Am Technical.

Blanchard, Harold F. & Ritchen, Ralph. Motor Auto Engines & Electrical Systems. 7th ed. LC 77-88821. (Illus.). 1977. 14.95 (ISBN 0-910992-73-8). Hearst Bks.

Brejcha, M. F. & Samuels, C. L. Automotive Chassis & Accessory Circuits. LC 76-14835. (Illus.). 1977. 24.95 (ISBN 0-13-055475-8). P-H.

Canfield-ChekChart. Automotive Electrical Systems, 2 vols. 294p. 1978. pap. text ed. 21.50 (ISBN 0-06-454000-6, HarpC); instructors manual avail. (ISBN 0-06-454004-9). Har-Row.

Chilton Staff. Chilton's Wiring Diagram Manual 1984-86 Import Cars: 1984-86 IMport Cars, Motor-Age Professional Mechanics Edition. LC 85-47955. 1088p. 1986. pap. 59.00 (ISBN 0-8019-7642-1). Chilton.

Crouse, William H. Automotive Electronics & Electrical Equipment. 9th ed. LC 79-24438. (Illus.). 1980. pap. text ed. 22.85 (ISBN 0-07-014831-7). McGraw.

Dwiggins, Boyce H. Automotive Electricity. (Illus.). 352p. 1981. text ed. 25.95 (ISBN 0-8359-0268-4); pap. text ed. 19.95 (ISBN 0-8359-0267-6). Reston.

Ellinger, Herbert. Automotive Electrical Systems 21E. 224p. 1985. pap. text ed. 21.95 (ISBN 0-13-054271-7). P-H.

Ellinger, Herbert E. Automotive Electrical Systems. 1975. 21.95 (ISBN 0-13-054262-8); pap. write for info. P-H.

Gonzales, Ronald F. Automotive Electrical & Electronic Systems Lab Manual. 1985. pap. text ed. 16.95 (ISBN 0-8359-0019-3). Reston.

--Automotive Electricity & Electronics. LC 84-3450. 1984. text ed. 29.95 (ISBN 0-8359-0343-5); pap. text ed. 21.95 (ISBN 0-8359-0342-7). Reston.

Jay, Jon C., ed. Basic Ignition & Electrical Systems. 5th rev. ed. LC 73-79968. (Basic Repair & Maintenance Ser.). (Illus.). 1977. pap. 6.95 (ISBN 0-8227-5014-7). Petersen Pub.

Judge, Arthur W. Modern Electrical Equipment for Automobiles. LC 68-31549. (Motor Manuals Ser.: Vol. 6). 10.95x (ISBN 0-8376-0002-2). Bentley.

Motor Auto Engines & Electrical Systems. 8th ed. (Illus.). 656p. 1984. 28.50 (ISBN 0-87851-577-1, Hearst Motor Bk). Morrow.

Motor Introduction to Auto Electrical Systems. (Illus.). 326p. 1984. 15.50 (ISBN 0-87851-558-5, Hearst Motor Bk); study guide 7.25 (ISBN 0-87851-589-5). Morrow.

Petersen's Basic Ignition & Electrical Systems. 6th ed. 256p. 1984. pap. 9.95 (ISBN 0-89803-141-9, Dist. by Kampmann). Green Hill.

Peterson Pub. Co. Basic Ignition & Electrical Systems. 192p. 1984. pap. 9.95 (ISBN 0-317-02891-X). Green Hill.

Thiessen, Frank & Dales, Davis. Automotive Electronics & Engine Performance. 1983. text ed. 27.95 (ISBN 0-8359-0311-7); pap. text ed. 21.95 (ISBN 0-8359-0310-9); solutions manual avail. (ISBN 0-8359-0312-5). Reston.

Weathers, Thomas & Hunter, Claud. Fundamentals of Electricity & Automotive Electrical Systems. (Illus.). 256p. 1981. pap. 24.95 (ISBN 0-13-337030-5). P-H.

Webster, Jay. Auto Electrical & Electronic Systems. 1985. 14.95 (ISBN 0-538-33070-8, IE07). SW Pub.

AUTOMOBILES–ELECTRONIC EQUIPMENT

see also Automobiles–Radio Equipment

Applications of Electronics to Off-Highway Equipment, 7 papers. (Illus.). 80p. 1981. pap. 22.00 (ISBN 0-89883-267-5, SP 496). Soc Auto Engineers.

Automotive Electronic Displays & Information Systems. 1985. 42.00 (ISBN 0-89883-829-0, SP608). Soc Auto Engineers.

Automotive Electronic Instrumentation: Displays & Sensors, 19 papers. LC 80-65214. 116p. 1980. pap. 38.00 (ISBN 0-89883-228-4, SP457). Soc Auto Engineers.

Automotive Electronic Systems, 14 papers. LC 79-63390. 92p. 1979. pap. 33.00 (ISBN 0-89883-212-8, SP440). Soc Auto Engineers.

Automotive Electronics & Electronic Vehicles, Convergence '80: Proceedings, International Conference, 1980, 100 papers. 600p. 1980. pap. 45.00 (ISBN 0-89883-058-3, P90). Soc Auto Engineers.

Automotive Sensors, 8 papers. LC 79-83913. 68p. 1979. pap. 22.00 (ISBN 0-89883-213-6, SP441). Soc Auto Engineers.

Brady, Robert. Electric & Electronic Systems for Automobiles & Trucks. 1983. text ed. 30.95 (ISBN 0-8359-1610-3); solutions manual free (ISBN 0-8359-1611-1). Reston.

Chilton's Automotive Editorial Staff. Chilton's Guide to Auto Electronic Accessories: Sound, Safety & Security. LC 82-72906. 224p. 1983. pap. 11.95 (ISBN 0-8019-7322-8). Chilton.

--Chilton's Professional Wiring Diagrams Manual: American Cars 1979 to 1981. (Illus.). 1981. pap. 34.00 (ISBN 0-8019-7020-2). Chilton.

--Mechanics Handbook: New Electronic Engine Control, Vol. 8. LC 84-45481. 816p. (Orig.). 1985. pap. 16.95 (ISBN 0-8019-7535-2). Chilton.

Crouse, William H. Automotive Electronics & Electrical Equipment. 9th ed. LC 79-24438. (Illus.). 1980. pap. text ed. 22.85 (ISBN 0-07-014831-7). McGraw.

Developments in Electronic Engine Management & Driveline Controls. 1985. 22.00 (ISBN 0-89883-830-4, SP609). Soc Auto Engineers.

Electronic Automotive Reliability. 52p. 1984. 18.00 (ISBN 0-89883-344-2, SP573). Soc Auto Engineers.

Electronic Control & Monitoring of Off-Highway Equipment, 6 papers. 84p. 1982. pap. 18.00 (ISBN 0-89883-291-8, SP520). Soc Auto Engineers.

Electronic Engine-Drivetrain Control, 12 papers. 132p. 1983. pap. 30.00 (ISBN 0-89883-311-6, SP540). Soc Auto Engineers.

Electronic Engine Management & Driveline Controls. 184p. 1982. pap. 38.00 (ISBN 0-89883-069-9, P104). Soc Auto Engineers.

Electronics Technologies & Systems for Commercial Vehicles of the 80's, 6 papers. 61p. 1981. pap. 15.00 (ISBN 0-89883-276-4, SP505). Soc Auto Engineers.

Gonzales, Ronald F. Automotive Electricity & Electronics. LC 84-3450. 1984. text ed. 29.95 (ISBN 0-8359-0343-5); pap. text ed. 21.95 (ISBN 0-8359-0342-7). Reston.

Judge, Arthur W. Modern Electrical Equipment for Automobiles. LC 68-31549. (Motor Manuals Ser.: Vol. 6). 10.95x (ISBN 0-8376-0002-2). Bentley.

Microprocessor Controller Developments: Proceedings. 72p. 1978. pap. 22.00 (ISBN 0-89883-198-9, SP-426). Soc Auto Engineers.

Ribbens, William B. & Mansour, Norman P. Understanding Automotive Electronics. 2nd ed. Luecke, Gerald, et al, eds. LC 84-51470. (Understanding Ser.). (Illus.). 288p. 1984. pap. 14.95 (ISBN 0-89512-167-0, LCB8475). Tex Instr Inc.

Rudman, Jack. Electrician (Automobile) (Career Examination Ser.: C-1268). (Cloth bdg. avail. on request). pap. 12.00 (ISBN 0-8373-1268-X). Natl Learning.

Sensors & Actuators: New Approaches. 1984. pap. 35.00 (ISBN 0-89883-338-8, SP567). Soc Auto Engineers.

Sensors & Actuators, 1983, 10 papers. 92p. 1983. pap. 25.00 (ISBN 0-89883-307-8, SP536). Soc Auto Engineers.

Sensors & Actuators (1985) 1985. 38.00 (ISBN 0-89883-839-8, SP618). Soc Auto Engineers.

Sensors for Automotive Systems, 14 papers. LC 80-50094. 120p. 1980. pap. 35.00 (ISBN 0-89883-229-2, SP458). Soc Auto Engineers.

An Update on Automotive Electronic Displays & Information Systems. 276p. 1983. pap. 45.00 (ISBN 0-89883-084-2, P123). Soc Auto Engineers.

Webster, Jay. Auto Electrical & Electronic Systems. 1985. 14.95 (ISBN 0-538-33070-8, IE07). SW Pub.

AUTOMOBILES–ENGINES

see Automobiles–Motors

AUTOMOBILES–EQUIPMENT AND SUPPLIES

Auto-Truck Interchange Manual: Wheel Covers. 47th ed. 88p. 1982. 15.95 (ISBN 0-943032-20-2). Hollander Co.

Friedman, S. H. International Drive Belt Interchange Guide, 1984. 3rd ed. LC 82-83334. 672p. 1984. 75.00 (ISBN 0-916966-11-9). Interchange.

--International Seal Interchange Guide, 1984. 5th ed. LC 82-83333. 704p. 1984. 75.00 (ISBN 0-916966-12-7). Interchange.

Hollander Publishing Company Inc. Auto-Truck Interchange Manual. 16th ed. 504p. 1979. Repr. of 1949 ed. 28.50 (ISBN 0-943032-12-1). Hollander Co.

--Auto-Truck Interchange Manual. 23rd ed. 528p. 1979. Repr. of 1957 ed. 34.50 (ISBN 0-943032-13-X). Hollander Co.

--Auto-Truck Interchange Manual. 32nd ed. 1184p. 1982. Repr. of 1966 ed. 48.50 (ISBN 0-943032-08-3). Hollander Co.

--Auto-Truck Interchange Manual, 2 vols. 40th ed. 1664p. 1982. Repr. of 1974 ed. Set. 69.50 (ISBN 0-943032-09-1). Hollander Co.

--Auto-Truck Interchange Manual, Vol. II. 40th ed. 560p. 1982. Repr. of 1974 ed. 28.50 (ISBN 0-943032-11-3). Hollander Co.

--Auto-Truck Interchange Manual. 45th ed. 1784p. 64.50 (ISBN 0-943032-16-4). Hollander Co.

--Auto-Truck Interchange Manual, 2 vols. 46th ed. 1938p. 1980. Set. 74.50 (ISBN 0-943032-15-6). Hollander Co.

--Auto-Truck Interchange Manual, Vol. 1. 40th ed. 1104p. 1982. Repr. of 1974 ed. 48.50 (ISBN 0-943032-10-5). Hollander Co.

--Auto-Truck Interchange Manual: Group 9B. 34th ed. 234p. 1968. 12.50 (ISBN 0-943032-14-8). Hollander Co.

--Auto-Truck Interchange Manual: Wheel Covers. 46th ed. 86p. 1980. 8.00 (ISBN 0-943032-18-0). Hollander Co.

--Auto-Truck Interchange Manual: Wheels. 47th ed. 12p. 1981. 5.95 (ISBN 0-943032-21-0). Hollander Co.

--Clark, New Process, Warner Edition. (Truck Interchange Ser.). 244p. 1972. 35.00 (ISBN 0-943032-07-5). Hollander Co.

--Eaton Edition. (Truck Interchange Ser.). 322p. 1974. 39.50 (ISBN 0-943032-04-0). Hollander Co.

--Foreign Interchange Manual. 5th ed. 982p. 1981. 64.50 (ISBN 0-943032-00-8). Hollander Co.

--Foreign Interchange Manual. 6th ed. 1058p. 1982. 76.50 (ISBN 0-943032-01-6). Hollander Co.

--Fuller Edition. (Truck Interchange Ser.). 326p. 1979. 49.50 (ISBN 0-943032-03-2). Hollander Co.

--Rockwell Edition. (Truck Interchange Ser.). 588p. 1977. 49.50 (ISBN 0-943032-06-7). Hollander Co.

--Spicer Edition. (Truck Interchange Ser.). 420p. 1975. 39.50 (ISBN 0-943032-05-9). Hollander Co.

--Truck Parts Edition. (Truck Interchange Ser.). 510p. 1972. 43.75 (ISBN 0-943032-02-4). Hollander Co.

Lahue, Kalton C., ed. Basic Tune-up & Test Equipment. 2nd rev. ed. LC 74-78228. (Basic Repair & Maintenance Manuals Ser.). (Illus.). 1978. pap. 6.95 (ISBN 0-8227-5018-X). Petersen Pub.

Rudman, Jack. Motor Equipment Partsman. (Career Examination Ser.: C-1790). (Cloth bdg. avail. on request). pap. 10.00 (ISBN 0-8373-1790-8). Natl Learning.

Sumpter, Thomas. Automobile Part Management. 1985. text ed. 24.95 (ISBN 0-8359-0330-3). Reston.

Williams, William C. Motoring Mascots of the World. LC 79-4529. (Illus.). 1979. 34.95 (ISBN 0-87938-036-5). Motorbooks Intl.

AUTOMOBILES–EXHAUST GAS

see Automobiles–Motors–Exhaust Gas

AUTOMOBILES–FUEL SYSTEMS

see also Carburetors

Alternate Fuels for S.I. & Diesel Engines. 128p. 1983. 25.00 (ISBN 0-89883-313-2, SP542). Soc Auto Engineers.

Alternate Fuels for S.I. Engines. 112p. 1983. 28.00 (ISBN 0-89883-330-2, SP559). Soc Auto Engineers.

Automobile Fuel Consumption in Actual Traffic Conditions. 118p. 1982. pap. 8.50 (ISBN 92-64-12304-0). OECD.

Automotive Fuel Economy. 9.50 (ISBN 0-686-15357-X). Autotronic Conversions.

Automotive Fuel Economy: Part 2. LC 76-25691. 325p. 1979. Seventeen papers. 45.00 (ISBN 0-89883-106-7, PT 18). Soc Auto Engineers.

Brady, Robert N. Automotive & Small Truck Fuel Injection Systems: Gas & Diesel. 1985. text ed. 32.95 (ISBN 0-8359-0315-X). Reston.

Chilton Automotive Editorial Staff. Chilton's Guide to Fuel Injection & Carburetors. LC 83-45323. 256p. 1985. pap. 16.95 (ISBN 0-8019-7488-7). Chilton.

Crouse, William H. & Anglin, Donald L. Automotive Fuel, Lubricating & Cooling Systems. 6th ed. Gilmore, D. E., ed. (Illus.). 352p. 1980. pap. text ed. 21.10 (ISBN 0-07-014862-7). McGraw.

Frazee, Irving A. & Landon, William. Automotive Fuel & Ignition Systems. LC 53-1714. (Automotive Ser.). (Illus.). pap. 128.00 (ISBN 0-317-11015-2, 2004569). Bks Demand UMI.

Fuel Alternatives for S. I. & Diesel Engines. 108p. 1983. 25.00 (ISBN 0-89883-319-1, SP548). Soc Auto Engineers.

Gonzales, Ron. Automotive Fuel & Emission Systems. 1985. text ed. 24.95 (ISBN 0-8359-0117-3); pap. text ed. 19.95 (ISBN 0-8359-0116-5). Reston.

Hilliard, J. C. & Springer, George S., eds. Fuel Economy: In Road Vehicles Powered by Spark Ignition Engines. 468p. 1984. 59.50x (ISBN 0-306-41438-4, Plenum Pr). Plenum Pub.

Husselbee, William L. Automotive Fuel, Cooling, Lubrication & Exhaust Systems. 1984. text ed. 29.95 (ISBN 0-8359-0300-1); pap. text ed. 22.95 (ISBN 0-8359-0299-4). Reston.

Ireland, Glen E. Automotive Fuel, Ignition, & Emission Control Systems. 1980. pap. write for info. (ISBN 0-534-00866-6, Breton Pubs). Wadsworth Pub.

--Volkswagen Rabbit-Scirocco Service Manual, Gasoline Models, 1975, 1976, 1977, 1978, 1979. rev. ed. LC 79-57170. (Illus.). 628p. (Orig.). 1980. pap. 26.50 (ISBN 0-8376-0098-7). Bentley.

Robert Bentley Inc. Volkswagen Rabbit: Scirocco 1980-1981. (Illus.). pap. 19.95 (ISBN 0-8376-0099-5). Bentley.

Russell, John. Involuntary Repossession or in the Steal of the Night. (Illus.). 64p. 1980. pap. 10.95 (ISBN 0-87364-233-3). Paladin Pr.

Shoemark, Pete. Ducati V-Twins '75 - '77: V. Twins '71 Thru '77. (Owners Workshop Manuals Ser.: No. 259). 1979. 10.50 (ISBN 0-85696-259-7, Pub. by J H Haynes England). Haynes Pubns.

Strasman, Peter. Nissan Sentra. (Haynes Automotive Manuals). 12.95 (ISBN 0-85696-982-6, 982). Haynes Pubns.

Strasman, Peter G. Nissan Stanza 'Eighty-Two to Eighty-Three' (Haynes Automotive Manuals). 12.95 (ISBN 0-85696-981-8, 981). Haynes Pubns.

Volkswagen of America Inc. Volkswagen Beetle & Karmann Ghia Official Service Manual Type 1, 1966, 1967, 1968, 1969. LC 70-189047. (Illus.). 512p. (Orig.). 1972. pap. 24.95 (ISBN 0-8376-0416-8). Bentley.

Volkswagen of America, Inc. Volkswagen Fastback & Squareback Official Service Manual, Type 3, 1968-1973. LC 73-85200. (Illus.). 422p. 1974. pap. 34.95 (ISBN 0-8376-0057-X). Bentley.

Volkswagen of America Inc. Volkswagen Official Service Manual Type 1. Beetle, Super Beetle, & Karmann Ghia, 1970-1979. LC 78-75039. (Illus.). 448p. 1979. pap. 29.95 (ISBN 0-8376-0096-0). Bentley.

--Volkswagen Official Service Manual Type 2, Station Wagon-Bus, 1968-1979. 4th rev. ed. LC 78-75038. (Illus.). 464p. 1979. pap. 34.95 (ISBN 0-8376-0094-4). Bentley.

Volkswagen of America, Inc. Volkswagen Vanagon Official Factory Repair Manual, 1980-1983: Diesel & Aircooled Gasoline Engines. rev. ed. LC 83-70840. (Illus.). 512p. (Orig.). 1983. pap. 34.95 (ISBN 0-8376-0353-6). Bentley.

Ward, Ian, ed. Anatomy of the Motor Car. (Illus.). 1977. 12.95 (ISBN 0-312-03465-2). St Martin.

Wolfe, J. & Phelps. The Mechanics Vest Pocket Reference Book. 1982. pap. 6.95 (ISBN 0-13-571505-9). P-H.

Woods Dual Power: Manual on Woods Automobile. (Illus.). 24p. pap. 2.95 (ISBN 0-8466-6019-9, U19). Shorey.

Wright, Roy V., ed. Caboose Cars Eighteen Seventy-Nine to Nineteen Forty-Three. (Train Shed Cyclopedia Ser., No. 11). (Illus.). 1973. pap. 3.95 (ISBN 0-912318-40-6). N K Gregg.

AUTOMOBILES–HISTORY

Association of Licensed Automobile Manufacturers. Handbook of Gasoline Automobiles, 1904 to 1906. (Illus.). 9.00 (ISBN 0-8446-4705-5). Peter Smith.

Bail, Eli. From Railway to Freeway: Pacific Electric & the Motorbus. Sebree, Mac, ed. (Interurbans Special Ser.: No. 90). (Illus.). 200p. 1984. 29.95 (ISBN 0-916374-61-0). Interurban.

Barrett, Paul. The Automobile & Urban Transit: The Formation of Public Policy in Chicago, 1900-1930. 360p. 1983. 34.95 (ISBN 0-87722-294-0). Temple U Pr.

Bowden, Robert C. Boss Wheels: End of the Supercar Era. (Modern Automotive Ser.). (Illus.). 1979. 9.95 (ISBN 0-8306-9838-8); pap. 7.95 (ISBN 0-8306-2050-8, 2050). TAB Bks.

Butler, Don. The History of Hudson. Dammann, George H., ed. LC 81-121. (Automotive Ser.). (Illus.). 336p. 1982. 29.95 (ISBN 0-912612-19-3). Crestline.

Butler, F. Donald. The Plymouth & De Soto Story. Dammann, George H., ed. LC 77-93182. (Automotive Ser.). (Illus.). 1979. 29.95 (ISBN 0-912612-14-2). Crestline.

Cain, Mike. Autos of Interest. 1977. pap. 4.50 (ISBN 0-9601458-1-8). M Cain.

Caunter, C. F. The Light Car: A Technical History of Cars with Engines of Less Than 1600cc. 14.95 (ISBN 0-8376-0053-7). Bentley.

Clarke, R. M. American Motors Muscle Cars 1966-1970. (Illus.). 100p. 1982. pap. 11.95 (ISBN 0-907073-58-1, Pub. by Brooklands Bks England). Motorbooks Intl.

Cox, Harold E. Early Electric Cars of Philadelphia 1885-1911. (Illus.). 136p. (Orig.). 1969. pap. 8.00 (ISBN 0-911940-09-X). Cox.

Curtis, Tony, ed. Veteran & Vintage Cars. (Illus.). 1978. 2.00 (ISBN 0-902921-53-3). Apollo.

De Angelis, George & Francis, Edward P. The Ford Model "A"-As Henry Built It. 3rd ed. (Illus.). 244p. 1983. 17.95 (ISBN 0-911383-02-6). Motor Cities.

Demaus, A. B. Motoring in the Twenties & Thirties. 1979. 18.95 (ISBN 0-7134-1538-X, Pub. by Batsford England). David & Charles.

Drackett, Phil. All Color World of Cars. (Illus.). 1979. 5.98 (ISBN 0-7064-1007-6, Mayflower Bks). Smith Pubs.

Evans, Arthur N. The Motor Car. LC 82-9713. (Cambridge Introduction to the History of Mankind Topic Bk.). (Illus.). 48p. 1983. pap. 4.50 (ISBN 0-521-28416-3). Cambridge U pr.

Flower, Raymond & Jones, Michael W. One Hundred Years of Motoring: An RAC Social History of the Car. 224p. 1981. 50.00x (ISBN 0-86211-018-1, Pub. by Biblios Pubs). State Mutual Bk.

Georgano, G. N., ed. The New Complete Encyclopedia of Motorcars: Eighteen Eighty-Five to the Present. (Illus.). 704p. 1982. 45.00 (ISBN 0-525-93254-2). Dutton.

Gunnel, John, ed. The Standard Catalog of American Cars, 1946-1975. LC 82-84065. (Illus.). 704p. 1982. pap. 19.95 (ISBN 0-87341-027-0). Krause Pubns.

Gunnell, John G. Convertibles: The Complete Story. (Illus.). 224p. 20.50 (ISBN 0-8306-2110-5, 2110). TAB Bks.

Hildebrand, George, ed. The Golden Age of the Luxury Car: An Anthology of Articles & Photographs from "Autobody" Nineteen Twenty-Seven to Nineteen Thirty-One. 16.50 (ISBN 0-8446-5773-5). Peter Smith.

Hirsch, Jay. Great American Dream Machines: Classic Cars of the 50's & 60's. (Illus.). 224p. 1985. 29.95 (ISBN 0-02-551830-5). MacMillan.

Martinez, Alberto & Nory, J. L. American Automobiles of the 50's & 60's. LC 81-72090. (Illus.). 192p. 1982. 29.95 (ISBN 0-86710-018-4). Edns Vilo.

Mayborn, Mitch, ed. The Last Years of Studebaker 1952-1966. new ed. (Highland Ser. 3: Bk. 1). (Illus.). 52p. 1973. pap. 2.98 (ISBN 0-913490-08-3). Highland Ent.

Miller, Ray & McCalley, Bruce. From Here to Obscurity: An Illustrated History of the Model T Ford. LC 75-27314. (The Ford Road Ser: Vol. 1). (Illus.). 303p. 1971. 35.00 (ISBN 0-913056-01-4). Evergreen Pr.

Moloney, James. Encyclopedia of American Cars, 1930-1942. Dammann, George H., ed. LC 77-89427. (Automotive Ser.). (Illus.). 384p. 1977. 29.95 (ISBN 0-912612-12-6). Crestline.

Nassau, Kurt. Gems Made by Man. LC 78-14645. (Illus.). 384p. 1980. 32.00. Chilton.

Naul, G. Marshall. The Specification Book for U. S. Cars: 1930-1969. LC 80-11999. 399p. (Orig.). 1980. pap. 12.95 (ISBN 0-87938-068-3). Motorbooks Intl.

Nicholson, T. R. The Birth of the British Motor Car, 1769-1897, Vol. 1: A New Machine, 1769-1842. 224p. 1982. text ed. 40.50x (ISBN 0-333-23764-1, Pub. by Macmillan England). Humanities.

--The Birth of the British Motor Car, 1769-1897, Vol. 2: Revival & Defeat, 1842-1893. 224p. 1982. text ed. 40.50x (ISBN 0-333-28561-1, Pub. by Macmillan England). Humanities.

--The Birth of the British Motor Car, 1769-1897, Vol. 3: The Last Battle, 1894-1897. 224p. 1981. text ed. 40.50x (ISBN 0-333-28563-8, Pub. by Macmillan England). Humanities.

OECD Staff. The Future of the Use of the Car. (ECMT Round Tables Ser.). 232p. (Orig.). 1982. pap. 15.50x (ISBN 92-821-1075-3). OECD.

Oliver, George. Cars & Coachbuilding: One Hundred Years of Road Vehicle Development. (Illus.). 256p. 1981. 47.50 (ISBN 0-85667-105-3, Pub. by Sotheby Pubns England). Biblio Dist.

Pitrone, Jean M. & Elwart, Joan P. The Dodges: The Auto Family Fortune & Misfortune. (Illus.). 352p. 1981. 18.95 (ISBN 0-89651-150-2). Icarus.

Rasmussen, Henry. American Classic Cars. LC 77-71617. 1977. 29.95 (ISBN 0-918506-02-6). Picturama.

--European Classic Cars. LC 75-37385. 1975. 29.95 (ISBN 0-918506-01-8). Picturama.

Sedgwick, Michael. The Motor Car, Nineteen Forty-Six to Fifty-Six. (Illus.). 272p. 1980. 38.00 (ISBN 0-7134-1271-2, Pub. by Batsford England). David & Charles.

Shank, W. H. History of York-Pullman Auto, 1903-1917. 1970. 2.50 (ISBN 0-933788-24-X). Am Canal & Transport.

Vanderveen, Bart H. American Cars of the Nineteen Fifties. (Olyslager Auto Library). (Illus.). 80p. 1973. 10.95 (ISBN 0-7232-1707-6, Pub. by Warne Pubs England). Motorbooks Intl.

--American Cars of the Nineteen Forties. (Olyslager Auto Library). (Illus.). 70p. 1972. 10.95 (ISBN 0-7232-1465-4, Pub. by Warne Pubs England). Motorbooks Intl.

--American Cars of the Nineteen Sixties. (Olyslager Auto Library). (Illus.). 80p. 1977. 10.95 (ISBN 0-7232-2061-1, Pub. by Warne Pubs England). Motorbooks Intl.

--American Cars of the Nineteen Thirties. (Olyslager Auto Library). (Illus.). 80p. 1971. 10.95 (ISBN 0-7232-1266-X, Pub. by Warne Pubs England). Motorbooks Intl.

--American Trucks of the Early Thirties. (Olyslager Auto Library). (Illus.). 63p. 1974. 10.95 (ISBN 0-7232-1803-X, Pub. by Warne Pubs England). Motorbooks Intl.

--British Cars of the Late Forties, 1947-1949. (Olyslager Auto Library). (Illus.). 64p. 1974. 11.95 (ISBN 0-7232-1756-4, Pub. by Warne Pubs England). Motorbooks Intl.

--Cross-Country Cars from Nineteen Forty-Five. (Olyslager Auto Library). (Illus.). 72p. 1975. 11.95 (ISBN 0-7232-1823-4, Pub. by Warne Pubs England). Motorbooks Intl.

--Fire & Crash Vehicles from Nineteen Fifty. (Olyslager Auto Library). (Illus.). 72p. 1976. 10.95 (ISBN 0-7232-1845-5, Pub. by Warne Pubs England). Motorbooks Intl.

--Fire-Fighting Vechicles, Eighteen Forty to Nineteen Fifty. (Olyslager Auto Library). (Illus.). 80p. 1972. 10.95 (ISBN 0-7232-1464-6, Pub. by Warne Pubs England). Motorbooks Intl.

Voller, David J. British Cars of the Early Sixties, 1960-1964. (Olyslager Auto Library). (Illus.). 64p. 1981. 11.95 (ISBN 0-7232-2764-0, Pub. by Warne Pubs England). Motorbooks Intl.

Watkins, M. AC. (Mini Marque History Ser.). 7.95 (ISBN 0-85429-204-7, F204). Haynes Pubns.

AUTOMOBILES–IGNITION

Blanchard, Harold F. & Ritchen, Ralph. Motor Auto Engines & Electrical Systems. 7th ed. LC 77-88821. (Illus.). 1977. 14.95 (ISBN 0-910992-73-8). Hearst Bks.

Derato, F. C. Automotive Ignition Systems: Diagnosis & Repair. LC 81-8285. 320p. 1982. 20.50x (ISBN 0-07-016501-7). McGraw.

Frazee, Irving A. & Landon, William. Automotive Fuel & Ignition Systems. LC 53-1714. (Automotive Ser.). (Illus.). pap. 128.00 (ISBN 0-317-11015-2, 2004569). Bks Demand UMI.

Ireland, Glen E. Automotive Fuel, Ignition, & Emission Control Systems. 1980. pap. write for info. (ISBN 0-534-00866-6, Breton Pubs). Wadsworth Pub.

Leigh, Bob, et al. Tune-Up Ignition & Fuel Induction Systems. rev. ed. Fennema, Roger L. & Wiseman, Leslie A., eds. (Automobile Mechanics Refresher Course Ser.: Book 1). (Illus.). 104p. 1981. pap. 9.95x wkbk. (ISBN 0-88098-062-1); cassette tape 13.90 (ISBN 0-88098-068-0). H M Gousha.

Russell, John. Involuntary Repossession or in the Steal of the Night. (Illus.). 64p. 1980. pap. 10.95 (ISBN 0-87364-233-3). Paladin Pr.

Starting Systems Technology. 1984. 32.00 (ISBN 0-89883-819-3, SP598). Soc Auto Engineers.

AUTOMOBILES–LUBRICATION

American Society for Testing & Materials. Symposium on Lubricants for Automotive Equipment. LC 63-15729. (American Society for Testing & Materials. Special Technical Publication Ser.: No. 334). pap. 64.80 (ISBN 0-317-09152-2, 2000122). Bks Demand UMI.

Chek-Chart Staff. Master Lubrication Handbook, 1985. (Illus.). 1000p. wkbk. 90.00 (ISBN 0-88098-059-1); Supplement 85.45 (ISBN 0-88098-075-3). H M Gousha.

Chilton's Automotive Editorial Staff. Import Automotive Service Manual 1977-1985. LC 82-72910. (Professional Mechanics Ser.). 1848p. 1985. 36.00 (ISBN 0-8019-7595-6). Chilton.

Committee D-2 on Petroleum Products & Lubricants. Multi-Cylinder Test Sequences for Evaluating Automotive Engine Oils, Pt. 3, Sequence V-D- STP 315H. LC 83-68369. 146p. pap. 24.00 (ISBN 0-8031-0238-0, 04-315100-12); 20.00 (ISBN 0-8031-0525-8). ASTM.

Crouse, William H. & Anglin, Donald L. Automotive Fuel, Lubricating & Cooling Systems. 6th ed. Gilmore, D. E., ed. (Illus.). 352p. 1980. pap. text ed. 21.10 (ISBN 0-07-014862-7). McGraw.

Doornbos, Daniel, ed. Farm Tractor 1985: Self Propelled Implement Lubrication Guide. rev. ed. (Illus.). 384p. 1984. pap. 37.85 wkbk. (ISBN 0-88098-060-5). H M Gousha.

Ellinger, H. Automotive Systems Fuel Lubrication & Cooling. 1975. pap. 24.95 (ISBN 0-13-055269-0). P-H.

Husselbee, William L. Automotive Fuel, Cooling, Lubrication & Exhaust Systems. 1984. text ed. 29.95 (ISBN 0-8359-0300-1); pap. text ed. 22.95 (ISBN 0-8359-0299-4). Reston.

Knowles, Don. Automotive Fuel, Lubrication & Cooling Systems. 1984. text ed. 29.95 (ISBN 0-8359-0320-6); pap. text ed. 22.95 (ISBN 0-8359-0319-2). Reston.

Leigh, Bob, et al. Engines, Lubricating & Coding Systems. rev. ed. Fennema, Roger L. & Wiseman, Leslie A., eds. (Automobile Mechanics Refresher Course Ser.: Book 2). (Illus.). 80p. 1981. pap. 9.95x wkbk. (ISBN 0-88098-063-X); cassette tape 13.90 (ISBN 0-88098-069-9). H M Gousha.

Multicylinder Test Sequences for Evaluating Autumotive Engine Oils, Part 1: Sequence IID- STP 315H. 111p. 1980. looseleaf 16.00 (ISBN 0-8031-0521-5, 04-315081-12); pap. 13.00 (ISBN 0-8031-0520-7, 04-315080-12). ASTM.

Multigrade Oils for Diesel Engines. LC 80-53469. 60p. 1980. Five papers. pap. 15.00 (ISBN 0-89883-243-8, SP472). Soc Auto Engineers.

Relationship Between Engine Oil Viscosity & Engine Performance, Pts. V & VI. LC 77-150198. 204p. 1980. 35.00 (ISBN 0-89883-231-4, SP460). Soc Auto Engineers.

Society of Automotive Engineers. Engines, Fuels & Lubricants: Perspective on the Future. LC 80-53468. 112p. 1980. Eight papers. pap. 18.00 (ISBN 0-89883-242-X). SAE.

AUTOMOBILES–MAINTENANCE AND REPAIR

Ahlstrand, Alan. Datsun 200 SX 1980-1982. Jorgensen, Eric, ed. (Illus.). pap. text ed. 12.95 (ISBN 0-89287-339-6, A206). Clymer Pubns.

--Datsun 4-Wheel Drive Pickups: 1980-1983 Shop Manual. Wauson, Sydnie A., ed. (Illus., Orig.). 1981. pap. 12.95 (ISBN 0-89287-344-2, A207). Clymer Pubns.

--MGA-MGB All Models: 1956-1980 Service, Repair Handbook. Robinson, Jeff, ed. (Illus.). pap. 12.95 (ISBN 0-89287-279-9, A165). Clymer Pubns.

--Nissan Sentra Nineteen Eighty-Two to Nineteen Eighty-Three Gas & Diesel Shop Manual. Wauson, Sydnie & Hamlin, Steve, eds. (Illus.). 287p. (Orig.). 1984. pap. 13.95 (ISBN 0-89287-386-8, A208). Clymer Pubns.

--Toyota Tercel 1980-1982: Shop Manual. Wauson, Sidnie A., ed. (Illus., Orig.). pap. text ed. 12.95 (ISBN 0-89287-342-6, A295). Clymer Pubns.

Alderwyck, A. How to Restore Wooden Body Framing. (Osprey Restoration Guide Ser.). (Illus.). 128p. 1984. text ed. 14.95 (ISBN 0-85045-590-1, Pub. by Osprey England). Motorbooks Intl.

Alexandrowicz, Harry. Six Hundred Ninety-Nine Ways to Improve the Performance of Your Car. LC 79-93251. (Illus.). 192p. 1980. lib. bdg. 17.79 (ISBN 0-8069-5551-1). Sterling.

Alland, Guy & Hemingway, Patricia D. The Auto Repair Primer. LC 77-18808. 1978. pap. 8.95 (ISBN 0-316-35528-3). Little.

Allen, William R. Modern Autobody Repair. 1985. text ed. 24.95 (ISBN 0-8359-4525-1); wkbk avail. (ISBN 0-8359-4526-X). Reston.

American Bantam Car Company. Bantam Model BRC Jeep, 1941 Prototype: TM-10-1205. Post, Dan R., ed. LC 75-185932. (Illus.). 128p. 1971. pap. 12.95 (ISBN 0-911160-44-2). Post-Era.

Artzberger, William, Jr. Corvair: A History & Restoration Guide. (Illus.). 240p. 1984. pap. 19.95 (ISBN 0-89404-079-0). Aztex.

ATA Vehicle Maintenance Reporting Standards Handbook. 1983. text ed. 60.00 (ISBN 0-88711-024-X). Am Trucking Assns.

Ballweber, Duane. Practical Applications in Basic Auto Body Repair. (Illus.). 288p. 1983. text ed. 24.95 (ISBN 0-13-689216-7). P-H.

Barbarossa, Fred. The Car Care Book. 1983. pap. text ed. 8.35 (ISBN 0-538-33030-9, IE03). SW Pub.

Basic Car Care Illustrated. 3rd ed. (Illus.). 500p. 1984. pap. 16.95 (ISBN 0-87851-594-1, Hearst Motor Bk). Morrow.

Bear, W. Forrest. Electric Motors, Principles, Controls, Service & Maintenance. Hoerner, Harry J. & Hoerner, Thomas A., eds. (Illus.). 202p. 1983. pap. text ed. 10.00x (ISBN 0-913163-15-5, 183); tchr's. ed. 2.50x (ISBN 0-913163-16-3, 283). Hobar Pubns.

Beck, John H. Understanding the Automobile. 88p. pap. 6.60 (ISBN 0-8428-2288-7). Cambridge Bk.

Becker, C. J. The Joy of Automobile Repair. 1979. pap. 5.95 (ISBN 0-89581-025-5). Asian Human Pr.

Billiet, W. E. Automotive Engines - Maintenance & Repair. 4th ed. (Illus.). 1973. 15.95 (ISBN 0-8269-0062-3). Am Technical.

Billiet, Walter E. Do-It-Yourself Automotive Maintenance & Repair. LC 78-15055. (Illus.). 1979. 17.95 (ISBN 0-13-217190-2, Spec); pap. 7.95 (ISBN 0-13-217182-1). P-H.

Bishop, Ron. Troubleshooting Old Cars. (Illus.). 182p. 1982. 13.95o.p (ISBN 0-8306-3075-9); pap. 9.25 (ISBN 0-8306-2075-3, 2075). TAB Bks.

Blower, W. E. The MG Workshop Manual: From "M" Type to "T.F. 1500". LC 75-33494. (Illus.). 608p. 1975. pap. 40.00 (ISBN 0-8376-0117-7). Bentley.

Bodywork & Painting Illustrated. LC 79-66360. (Illus.). 1979. 19.95 (ISBN 0-87851-515-1); pap. 8.95 (ISBN 0-87851-514-3). Hearst Bks.

Boyce, Terry. Car Interior Restoration. 3rd ed. LC 81-9175. (Illus.). 144p. 1983. pap. 7.95 (ISBN 0-8306-2102-4, 2102). TAB Bks.

British Leyland Motors. Complete Official Austin-Healey 100-Six & 3000, 1956-1968. LC 77-72588. (Illus.). 416p. 1977. pap. 25.00 (ISBN 0-8376-0133-9). Bentley.

--The Complete Official Jaguar 'E' Comprising the Official Driver's Handbook, Workshop Manual, Special Tuning Manual. 2nd, rev. ed. LC 73-94377. (Orig.). 1974. pap. 40.00 (ISBN 0-8376-0136-3). Bentley.

--The Complete Official MG Midget 1500, Model Years 1975-1979, Comprising the Official Driver's Handbook & Workshop Manual. LC 79-53185. (Illus.). 1980. pap. 35.00 (ISBN 0-8376-0131-2). Bentley.

--The Complete Official MGB Model Years 1962-1974: Comprising the Official Driver's Handbook, Workshop Manual, Special Tuning Manual. 4th rev. ed. LC 75-7766. (Illus.). 480p. 1975. pap. 25.00 (ISBN 0-8376-0115-0). Bentley.

--Complete Official MGB, Model Years 1975-1980: Comprising the Official Driver's Handbook & Workshop Manual. LC 80-65229. (Illus.). 304p. 1980. pap. 29.95 (ISBN 0-8376-0112-6). Bentley.

--Complete Official Sprite-Midget 948cc & 1098cc: Comprising the Official Driver's Handbook, Workshop Manual, Special Tuning Manual. LC 67-28432. (Illus.). 384p. (Orig.). 1968. pap. 25.00 (ISBN 0-8376-0023-5). Bentley.

--Complete Official Triumph GT6, GT6 Plus & GT6 MD III 1967-1973: Official Driver's Handbook & Official Workshop Manual. LC 74-21353. (Illus.). 480p. 1975. pap. 25.00 (ISBN 0-8376-0120-7). Bentley.

--The Complete Official Triumph Spitfire MK III, MK IV & 1500, Model Years 1968-1974: Comprising the Official Driver's Handbook & Workshop Manual. LC 74-20004. (Illus.). 480p. 1975. pap. 35.00 (ISBN 0-8376-0123-1). Bentley.

--The Complete Official Triumph Spitfire 1500, Model Years 1975-1980: Comprising the Official Driver's Handbook & Workshop Manual. LC 79-53184. (Illus.). 1980. pap. 25.00 (ISBN 0-8376-0122-3). Bentley.

--The Complete Official Triumph TR2 & TR3: Comprising the Official Driver's Instruction Book & Service Instruction Manual, Model Years 1953-1961. LC 75-42893. (Illus.). 464p. (Orig.). 1976. pap. 40.00 (ISBN 0-8376-0125-8). Bentley.

--Complete Official Triumph TR4 & TR4A 1961-1968: Official Driver's Handbook, Workshop Manual, Competition Preparation Manual. LC 74-21354. (Illus.). 400p. 1975. pap. 35.00 (ISBN 0-8376-0121-5). Bentley.

--The Complete Official Triumph TR6 & TR250, 1967-1976: Comprising the Official Driver's Handbook & Workshop Manual. LC 77-91592. (Illus.). 608p. 1978. pap. 35.00 (ISBN 0-8376-0108-8). Bentley.

--Complete Official Triumph TR7, 1975-1981: Comprising the Official Driver's Handbook & Repair Operation Manual. LC 78-73515. (Illus.). 464p. 1979. pap. 35.00 (ISBN 0-8376-0116-9). Bentley.

--The Complete Official 1275 cc Sprite-Midget 1967-1974: Comprising the Official Driver's Handbook, Workshop Manual, Emission Control Supplement. LC 75-37232. (Illus.). 400p. 1975. pap. 35.00 (ISBN 0-8376-0127-4). Bentley.

Caiati, Carl. Basic Body Repair & Refinishing for the Weekend Mechanic. (Illus.). 192p. 1984. pap. 13.50 (ISBN 0-8306-2122-9, 2122). TAB Bks.

Caldwell, Brice & Caldwell, Craig, eds. Basic Bodywork & Painting. 5th ed. LC 73-79967. (Illus.). 192p. (Orig.). 1981. pap. 6.95 (ISBN 0-8227-5057-0, Dist. by Kampmann). Petersen Pub.

Calkins, Michael. Tune-Up Service Manual. rev. ed. Phelps, Jo L. & Fennema, Roger, eds. (Apprentice Mechanics Ser.). (Illus.). 192p. 1985. pap. 8.75 wkbk. (ISBN 0-88098-002-8); quiz 3.45x (ISBN 0-88098-003-6). H M Gousha.

Carlson, Margaret B. & Shafer, Ronald G. How to Get Your Car Repaired Without Getting Gypped. LC 72-11811. (Illus.). 288p. 1973. 11.49i (ISBN 0-06-010612-3, HarpT). Har-Row.

Carroll, Bill. Honda Civic Guide. LC 74-75225. (Performance Engineering Handbooks Ser.). (Illus.). 214p. 1975. pap. 9.95 (ISBN 0-910390-21-5). Auto Bk.

Carroll, William. Automotive Troubleshooting: Glossary. 144p. (Orig.). 1973. pap. 5.95 (ISBN 0-910390-18-5, 118). Auto Bk.

Cavert, C. Edward, et al. Keep It Running: A Study Guide. (Illus.). 1978. pap. text ed. 16.95 (ISBN 0-07-009880-8). McGraw.

Chek-Chart. Car & Light Truck Diesel Engine Service Manual. (Automotive Service Ser.). 128p. 1983. pap. text ed. 9.95x (ISBN 0-88098-016-8); 3.50x (ISBN 0-88098-046-X). H M Gousha.

--Complete Automotive Service Library. (Automotive Service Ser.). (Illus.). 665p. 1983. pap. text ed. 52.55 (ISBN 0-88098-053-2). H M Gousha.

Chek Chart Staff. Car Care Guide, 1985. Fennema, Roger L., ed. (Illus.). 432p. 1985. pap. 39.75x wkbk. (ISBN 0-88098-058-3). H M Gousha.

--Car Service Manual. rev. ed. Fennema, Roger & Phelps, Jennifer, eds. (Apprentice Mechanics Ser.). (Illus.). 144p. 1984. pap. 9.15x wkbk. (ISBN 0-88098-051-6); quiz 3.45x (ISBN 0-317-18170-X). H M Gousha.

Chilton. Chilton's Easy Car Care. 3rd ed. LC 78-7152. 1985. text ed. 14.95 (ISBN 0-8019-7554-9); pap. 12.95 (ISBN 0-8019-7553-0). Chilton.

--Chilton's Repair & Tune-Up Guide: Ford Bronco, 1983, Vol. II. LC 83-70993. 224p. (Orig.). 1984. pap. 11.95 (ISBN 0-8019-7408-9). Chilton.

--Chilton's Repair & Tune-up Guide for Ford-Mercury FWD 1982-1985. 240p. 1985. pap. 11.95 (ISBN 0-8019-7544-1). Chilton.

--Chilton's Repair & Tune Up Guide: Mustang & Cougar, 1965-83. LC 83-70992. 252p. (Orig.). 1983. pap. 11.95 (ISBN 0-8019-7405-4). Chilton.

Chilton Automotive Editorial Staff. Chilton's Auto Repair Manual 1985. LC 76-648878. 1344p. 1984. 22.95 (ISBN 0-8019-7470-4); 21.75 (ISBN 0-8019-7471-2); pap. cancelled. Chilton.

--Chilton's Spanish Auto Repair Manual 1979-83. LC 76-648878. (Span.). 1296p. 1984. 22.95 (ISBN 0-8019-7476-3). Chilton.

Chilton Automotive Editors. Chilton's Import Auto Repair Manual 1986. 1985. price not set. Chilton.

Chilton Staff. Chilton's Auto Repair Manual (CARM) 1980-87. LC 76-648878. 1416p. 1986. 21.95 (ISBN 0-8019-7670-7); slipcase 22.70 (ISBN 0-8019-7671-5). Chilton.

--Chilton's Auto Service Manual: 1983-87. LC 82-72944. 1824p. 1986. pap. 46.00 (ISBN 0-8019-7690-1). Chilton.

--Chilton's Emission Control Manual 1986-87 Domestic Cars: 1986-87 Domestic Cars, Motor-Age Professional Mechanics Edition (Supplement) LC 85-47954. 336p. 1986. pap. 30.00 (ISBN 0-8019-7693-6). Chilton.

--Chilton's Emission Control Manual 1986-87 Import Cars: 1986-87 Import Cars, Motor-Age Professional Mechanics Edition (Supplement) LC 85-47953. 336p. 1986. pap. 30.00 (ISBN 0-8019-7694-4). Chilton.

--Chilton's Import Car Repair Manual: 1980-87. LC 80-68280. 1488p. 1986. 21.95 (ISBN 0-8019-7672-3); slipcase 22.70 (ISBN 0-8019-7673-1). Chilton.

--Chilton's Import Car Repair Manual 1979-86: 1979-86 Motor-Age Professional Mechanics Edition. LC 82-72910. 1848p. 1986. 46.00 (ISBN 0-8019-7638-3). Chilton.

--Chilton's Parts & Labor Guide: 1983-87, Motor-Age Professional Mechanic's Edition. LC 82-72943. 1688p. 1986. 48.00 (ISBN 0-8019-7691-X). Chilton.

--Chilton's Repair & Tune-up Guide: Cadillac 1967-86. LC 85-47984. 314p. (Orig.). 1986. pap. 12.50 (ISBN 0-8019-7684-7). Chilton.

--Chilton's Repair & Tune-up Guide: Chevrolet Mid-Size 1964-86. LC 85-47968. 336p. (Orig.). 1986. pap. 12.50 (ISBN 0-8019-7677-4). Chilton.

--Chilton's Repair & Tune-up Guide: Chevrolet Nova 1985. LC 85-47959. 188p. (Orig.). 1986. pap. 12.50 (ISBN 0-8019-7658-8). Chilton.

--Chilton's Repair & Tune-up Guide: Chevette-Pontiac T1000 1976-86. LC 85-47967. 256p. (Orig.). 1986. pap. 12.50 (ISBN 0-8019-7666-9). Chilton.

--Chilton's Repair & Tune-up Guide: Datsun-Nissan F-10, 310 & Stanza 1970-85. LC 85-47961. 256p. (Orig.). 1986. pap. 12.50 (ISBN 0-8019-7660-X). Chilton.

--Chilton's Repair & Tune-up Guide: Datsun-Nissan Z & ZX 1970-86. LC 85-47965. 256p. (Orig.). 1986. pap. 12.50 (ISBN 0-8019-7664-2). Chilton.

--Chilton's Repair & Tune-up Guide: Datsun-Nissan 200SX, 510, 610, 710, 810 Maxima 1973-1986. LC 85-47980. 336p. (Orig.). 1986. pap. 12.50 (ISBN 0-8019-7680-4). Chilton.

--Chilton's Repair & Tune-up Guide: GM N-Body 1985-86 Buick, Somerset, Olds Calais & Pontiac Grand Am. LC 85-47958. 224p. (Orig.). 1986. pap. 12.50 (ISBN 0-8019-7657-X). Chilton.

--Chilton's Repair & Tune-up Guide: Honda 1973-86. LC 85-47978. 304p. (Orig.). 1986. pap. 12.50 (ISBN 0-8019-7676-6). Chilton.

--Chilton's Repair & Tune-up Guide: Jeep CJ 1945-85. LC 85-47977. 388p. (Orig.). 1986. pap. 12.50 (ISBN 0-8019-7675-8). Chilton.

--Chilton's Repair & Tune-up Guide: Mazda Pickup 1971-86. LC 85-47960. 312p. (Orig.). 1986. pap. 12.50 (ISBN 0-8019-7659-6). Chilton.

--Chilton's Repair & Tune-up Guide: Omni, Horizon, Rampage 1978-86. LC 85-47985. 256p. (Orig.). 1986. pap. 12.50 (ISBN 0-8019-7685-5). Chilton.

--Chilton's Repair & Tune-up Guide: Subaru 1970-86. LC 85-47979. 304p. (Orig.). 1986. pap. 12.50 (ISBN 0-8019-7678-2). Chilton.

--Chilton's Repair & Tune-up Manual: Corvette 1963-83. LC 85-47981. 264p. (Orig.). 1986. pap. 12.50 (ISBN 0-8019-7681-2). Chilton.

--Chilton's Service Bay Handbook: 1980-87. LC 85-47989. 148p. 1986. pap. 5.00 (ISBN 0-8019-7692-8). Chilton.

--Chilton's Wiring Diagram Manual 1984-86 Import Cars: 1984-86 IMport Cars, Motor-Age Professional Mechanics Edition. LC 85-47955. 1088p. 1986. pap. 59.00 (ISBN 0-8019-7642-1). Chilton.

--Chilton's Wiring Diagram Manual: 1985-86 Domestic Cars, Motor-Age Professional Mechanics Edition. 1512p. 1986. pap. 47.00 (ISBN 0-8019-7641-3). Chilton.

--Corvette: 1984-86. LC 85-47982. 224p. (Orig.). 1986. pap. 12.50 (ISBN 0-8019-7682-0). Chilton.

--Guide to Auto Body Repair & Painting. LC 85-47970. 304p. (Orig.). 1986. pap. 16.95 (ISBN 0-8019-7667-7). Chilton.

--Guide to Diagnosis & Repair of GM Cars & Trucks 1970-85. (Orig.). 1986. pap. 16.95 (ISBN 0-8019-7668-5). Chilton.

--Toyota Corona, Cressida, Crown, Mark II, Camry, Van: 1970-86. LC 85-47976. 312p. (Orig.). 1986. pap. 12.50 (ISBN 0-8019-7674-X). Chilton.

Chilton's Auto Repair Manual: 1986. LC 80-68280. (Illus.). 1344p. 1985. 21.95 (ISBN 0-8019-7575-1). Chilton.

Chilton's Automotive Editorial Staff. Chilton's Motor Age Professional Transmission Manual. 1980. 65.00x (ISBN 0-8019-6927-1). Chilton.

--Cadillac Nineteen Sixty-Seven to Nineteen Eighty Four: RTUG. LC 83-45304. 288p. 1984. pap. 11.95 (ISBN 0-8019-7462-3). Chilton.

--Chevette T-1000 1976-84. LC 83-45300. 212p. 1984. pap. 11.95 (ISBN 0-8019-7457-7). Chilton.

--Chevrolet-GMC Pick-Ups 1970-82: RTUG. LC 83-45311. 352p. 1984. pap. 11.95 (ISBN 0-8019-7468-2). Chilton.

--Chevrolet GMC Pick-Ups 1970-84: RTUG - Includes Suburban. LC 83-45306. 312p. 1984. pap. 11.95 (ISBN 0-8019-7464-X). Chilton.

--Chevrolet-GMC Vans 1967-84: RTUG. LC 83-45322. 248p. 1985. pap. 11.95 (ISBN 0-8019-7487-9). Chilton.

--Chevrolet Mid-Size 1964-84. LC 83-45299. 304p. 1984. pap. 11.95 (ISBN 0-8019-7456-9). Chilton.

--Chevrolet, Nineteen Sixty-Eight to Nineteen Seventy-Nine. LC 78-20251. (Chilton's Repair & Tune-Up Guides). (Illus.). 1979. pap. text ed. 11.95 (ISBN 0-8019-6839-9, 6839). Chilton.

--Chevy Two & Nova, Nineteen Sixty-Two to Nineteen Seventy-Nine. LC 78-20253. (Chilton's Repair & Tune-up Guides). (Illus.). 1979. pap. 11.95 (ISBN 0-8019-6841-0, 6841). Chilton.

--Chilton's Auto Repair Manual, 1940-1953 Ed. LC 54-17274. (Illus.). 1971. Repr. of 1953 ed. 22.95 (ISBN 0-8019-5631-5). Chilton.

--Chilton's Auto Repair Manual, 1954-1963 Ed. LC 54-17274. (Illus.). 1971. 22.95 (ISBN 0-8019-5652-8). Chilton.

--Chilton's Auto Repair Manual, 1964-1971. LC 54-17274. (Illus.). 1536p. 1974. 22.95 (ISBN 0-8019-5974-8). Chilton.

--Chilton's Auto Repair Manual 1979-86. LC 76-648878. 1344p. 1985. shrink 21.95 (ISBN 0-8019-7575-1); hollow 22.75 (ISBN 0-8019-7574-3). Chilton.

--Chilton's Auto Repair Manual, 1980. LC 76-648878. (Chilton's Do-It Yourself Repair Manuals). (Illus.). 1979. 15.95. Chilton.

--Chilton's Auto Service Manual 1979-84. LC 82-72944. (Motor-Age Professional Mechanics Edition Ser.). 1824p. 1983. 33.00 (ISBN 0-8019-7348-1). Chilton.

--Chilton's Auto Service Manual 1979-85. LC 83-45331. (Motor Age Professional Mechanics Edition Ser.). 1632p. 1985. text ed. 36.00 (ISBN 0-8019-7495-X). Chilton.

--Chilton's Automatic Transmission Service Manual: 1980-84. LC 83-45327. 1536p. 1984. pap. 54.00 (ISBN 0-8019-7390-2). Chilton.

--Chilton's B.E.S.T. Service Manual: Brakes, Exhaust, Suspension & Steering Tune Up. LC 83-70521. (Motor Age Professional Mechanics Edition Ser.). 480p. 1983. pap. 17.00 (ISBN 0-8019-7398-8). Chilton.

--Chilton's Diesel Engine Service Manual 1978-84. LC 83-45326. (Motor Age Professional Mechanics Edition). 1216p. 1984. text ed. 37.50 (ISBN 0-8019-7444-5). Chilton.

--Chilton's Easy Car Care Study Guide. LC 83-70015. 64p. 1984. pap. 6.60 (ISBN 0-8019-7380-5). Chilton.

--Chilton's Emission Diagnostic Manual: Import Cars 1983-84. LC 83-45334. (Motor Age Professional Mechanics Edition Ser.). 480p. 1984. pap. 20.00 (ISBN 0-8019-7491-7). Chilton.

--Chilton's Emission Diagnostic Manual 1983-84. LC 83-45333. (Motor Age Professional Mechanics Edition Ser.). 480p. 1984. pap. 20.00 (ISBN 0-8019-7497-6). Chilton.

--Chilton's GM Diagnosis & Repair Manual. LC 83-70014. 624p. 1983. pap. 17.95 (ISBN 0-8019-7374-0). Chilton.

--Chilton's Guide to Auto Body Repair & Painting. LC 83-70543. 197p. 1983. pap. 11.95 (ISBN 0-8019-7378-3). Chilton.

--Chilton's Guide to Auto Tune-Up & Troubleshooting. LC 83-70544. 220p. 1983. pap. 11.95 (ISBN 0-8019-7376-7). Chilton.

--Chilton's Guide to Diesel Cars & Trucks. LC 82-72915. 216p. 1983. pap. 11.95 (ISBN 0-8019-7377-5). Chilton.

--Chilton's Guide to Small Engine Repair 6-20HP. LC 82-72908. 304p. 1983. 12.95 (ISBN 0-8019-7333-3); pap. 11.95 (ISBN 0-8019-7334-1). Chilton.

--Chilton's Guide to Small Engine Repair: Up to Six Horse Power. LC 82-72907. 350p. 1983. 12.95 (ISBN 0-8019-7319-8); pap. 11.95 (ISBN 0-8019-7320-1). Chilton.

--Chilton's Guide to Small Engine Repair: Up to Twenty Horse Power. LC 83-70013. 250p. 1983. pap. 11.95 (ISBN 0-8019-7379-1). Chilton.

--Chilton's Illustrated Diagnostic Manual. LC 83-70019. (Motor-Age Professional Mechanics Edition Ser.). 624p. 1983. pap. 20.00 (ISBN 0-8019-7375-9). Chilton.

--Chilton's Import Auto Parts & Labor Guide 1976-83. LC 82-72911. (Motor-Age Professional Mechanics Edition Ser.). 1488p. 1983. 34.00 (ISBN 0-8019-7351-1). Chilton.

--Chilton's Import Auto Repair Manual 1977-84. LC 78-20243. 1488p. 1983. 20.95 (ISBN 0-8019-7328-7). Chilton.

--Chilton's Import Auto Service Manual 1976-83. LC 82-72910. (Motor-Age Professional Mechanics Edition Ser.). 1920p. 1983. 33.00 (ISBN 0-8019-7350-3). Chilton.

Chilton's Automotive Editorial Staff, ed. Chilton's Import Car Repair Manual, 1975-81. LC 78-20243. (Illus.). 1536p. 1981. 19.95 (ISBN 0-8019-7029-6). Chilton.

Chilton's Automotive Editorial Staff. Chilton's Import Car Repair Manual 1979-86. LC 78-20243. 1464p. 1985. shrink 21.95 (ISBN 0-8019-7577-8); hollow 22.75 (ISBN 0-8019-7578-6). Chilton.

--Chilton's Import Car Repair Manual 1985. LC 78-20243. 1468p. 1984. 20.95 (ISBN 0-8019-7473-9); 21.75 (ISBN 0-8019-7474-7); pap. cancelled. Chilton.

--Chilton's Import Car Wiring Diagram Manual 1978-84. LC 83-70545. (Motor-Age Professional Mechanics Edition Ser.). 1000p. 1983. pap. 49.00 (ISBN 0-8019-7389-9). Chilton.

--Chilton's Mechanics Handbook, 2 vols. Incl. Vol. 1. Emission Diagnosis, Tune-Up, Allignment; Vol. 2. Engine Rebuilding, Engine Repair, Engine Theory (ISBN 0-8019-7006-7). (Illus.). 1980. 16.95 ea.; pap. 16.95 ea. Chilton.

--Chilton's Mechanics Handbook: Emission, Tune-Up & Vacuum Diagrams, Vol. 7. LC 82-72909. 544p. 1983. pap. 16.95 (ISBN 0-8019-7324-4). Chilton.

--Chilton's Mechanics's Handbook, Vol. 4: Automatic Transmission Repair. (Illus.). 1981. pap. 14.95 (ISBN 0-8019-7060-1). Chilton.

--Chilton's Mercedes-Benz: 1974-1979, Repair & Tune-up Guide. LC 78-22141. (Repair & Tune-up Guides Ser.). (Illus.). 1979. pap. 11.95 (ISBN 0-8019-6809-7). Chilton.

--Chilton's Motor Professional Automotive Service Manual 1981. LC 54-17274. (Illus.). 1980. 26.00 (ISBN 0-8019-6976-X). Chilton.

--Chilton's Motor Professional Labor Guide & Parts Manual 1981. LC 78-66360. (Illus.). 1980. 29.00 (ISBN 0-8019-7005-9). Chilton.

--Chilton's Mustang II: 1974-1978, Repair & Tune-up Guide. LC 78-22143. (Repair & Tune-up Guides Ser.). (Illus.). 1979. pap. 11.95 (ISBN 0-8019-6812-7). Chilton.

--Chilton's Parts & Labor Guide 1978-84. LC 82-72943. (Motor-Age Professional Mechanics Edition Ser.). 1568p. 1984. 34.00 (ISBN 0-8019-7347-3). Chilton.

--Chilton's Professional Import Labor Guide & Parts Manual, 1981. (Illus.). 1981. 29.00 (ISBN 0-8019-6998-0). Chilton.

--Chilton's Professional Labor Guide & Parts Manual, 1981. (Illus.). 1981. 29.00 (ISBN 0-8019-7005-9). Chilton.

--Chilton's Professional Mechanics Reference Guide. LC 82-72913. 128p. 1983. pap. 5.00 (ISBN 0-8019-7349-X). Chilton.

--Chilton's Repair & Tune-Up Guide: Blazer-Jimmy 1983. LC 83-70018. 224p. 1983. pap. 11.95 (ISBN 0-8019-7383-X). Chilton.

--Chilton's Repair & Tune-Up Guide: BMW 1970-82. LC 82-72937. 272p. 1983. pap. 11.95 (ISBN 0-8019-7315-5). Chilton.
--Chilton's Repair & Tune-Up Guide: Buick Century-Regal 1975-83. LC 82-72929. 224p. 1983. pap. 11.95 (ISBN 0-8019-7307-4). Chilton.
--Chilton's Repair & Tune-Up Guide: Buick-Olds-Pontiac Full Size 1975-83. LC 82-72930. 308p. 1983. pap. 11.95 (ISBN 0-8019-7308-2). Chilton.
--Chilton's Repair & Tune-Up Guide: Camaro 1982-83. LC 82-72939. 217p. 1983. pap. 11.95 (ISBN 0-8019-7317-1). Chilton.
--Chilton's Repair & Tune-Up Guide: Chevrolet-GMC S-10, S-15 1982-83. LC 82-72932. 224p. 1983. pap. 11.95 (ISBN 0-8019-7310-4). Chilton.
--Chilton's Repair & Tune-Up Guide: Chevrolet 1968-83. LC 82-72935. 288p. 1983. pap. 11.95 (ISBN 0-8019-7313-9). Chilton.
--Chilton's Repair & Tune-Up Guide: Colt-Challenger 1971-83. LC 82-72925. 224p. 1983. pap. 11.95 (ISBN 0-8019-7343-0). Chilton.
--Chilton's Repair & Tune-Up Guide: Corvette 1963-84. LC 83-45315. 288p. 1984. pap. 11.95 (ISBN 0-8019-7480-1). Chilton.
--Chilton's Repair & Tune-up Guide for Barracuda & Challenger: 1965-1972. LC 72-7036. (Illus.). 128p. 1972. pap. 11.95 (ISBN 0-8019-5807-5). Chilton.
--Chilton's Repair & Tune-up Guide: Ford Bronco 1966-83. LC 82-72919. 288p. 1983. pap. 11.95 (ISBN 0-8019-7337-6). Chilton.
--Chilton's Repair & Tune-up Guide for Chevrolet 1968-1977. LC 76-57317. (Chilton's Repair & Tune-up Guides). (Illus., Orig.). 1977. pap. 11.95 (ISBN 0-8019-6615-9, 6615). Chilton.
Chilton's Automotive Editorial Staff, ed. Chilton's Repair & Tune-up Guide for Colt, 1971-1976. (Illus.). 1976. pap. 11.95 (ISBN 0-8019-6475-X). Chilton.
Chilton's Automotive Editorial Staff. Chilton's Repair & Tune-Up Guide: Ford Courier 1972-82. LC 82-72923. 232p. 1983. pap. 11.95 (ISBN 0-8019-7341-4). Chilton.
--Chilton's Repair & Tune-up Guide for Cutlass-442, 1970-1977. LC 77-89117. (Chilton's Repair & Tune-up Guides). (Illus., Orig.). 1978. pap. 11.95 (ISBN 0-8019-6597-7, 6597). Chilton.
--Chilton's Repair & Tune-up Guide for Dodge 1968-1977. LC 77-71635. (Chilton's Repair & Tune-up Guides Ser.). (Illus.). 1977. pap. 11.95 (ISBN 0-8019-6554-3). Chilton.
--Chilton's Repair & Tune-up Guide for Datsun 240-260-280z, 1970-1977. LC 77-85345. (Chilton's Repair & Tune-up Guides). (Illus., Orig.). 1977. pap. 11.95 (ISBN 0-8019-6638-8, 6638). Chilton.
--Chilton's Repair & Tune-up Guide for Ford Courier 1972-78. (Repair & Tune-up Guides Ser.). (Illus.). pap. 11.95 (ISBN 0-8019-6723-6). Chilton.
--Chilton's Repair & Tune-up Guide for Ford Vans 1966-1977. LC 76-57320. (Chilton's Repair & Tune-up Guides). (Illus., Orig.). 1977. pap. 11.95 (ISBN 0-8019-6585-3, 6585). Chilton.
--Chilton's Repair & Tune-up Guide for Maverick & Comet 1970-1977. LC 77-75991. (Chilton's Repair & Tune-up Guides). (Illus., Orig.). 1977. pap. 11.95 (ISBN 0-8019-6634-5, 6634). Chilton.
--Chilton's Repair & Tune-up Guide for Mercedes Benz 2, 1968-1973. (Illus.). 224p. 1974. pap. 11.95 (ISBN 0-8019-5907-1). Chilton.
--Chilton's Repair & Tune-up Guide for Mazda 1971-78. (Repair & Tune-up Guides Ser.). (Illus.). 1978. pap. 11.95 (ISBN 0-8019-6746-5). Chilton.
--Chilton's Repair & Tune-Up Guide: Ford-Mercury 1968-83. LC 82-72940. 288p. 1983. pap. 11.95 (ISBN 0-8019-7318-X). Chilton.
--Chilton's Repair & Tune-up Guide for Rabbit-Scirocco 1975-1978. (Repair & Tune-up Guides Ser.). (Illus.). 1978. pap. 11.95 (ISBN 0-8019-6736-8). Chilton.
--Chilton's Repair & Tune-up Guide: Ford Ranger 1983. LC 82-72920. 240p. 1983. pap. 11.95 (ISBN 0-8019-7338-4). Chilton.
--Chilton's Repair & Tune-up Guide for Tempest, GTO & Le Mans, 1968-1973. LC 73-10219. (Illus.). 190p. 1973. pap. 11.95 (ISBN 0-8019-5905-5). Chilton.
--Chilton's Repair & Tune-up Guide for Triumph 2, 1969-1973. LC 73-18387. (Illus.). 224p. 1974. pap. 11.95 (ISBN 0-8019-5910-1). Chilton.
--Chilton's Repair & Tune-Up Guide: GM A-Body (Front Wheel Drive) 1982-83. LC 82-72931. 177p. 1983. pap. 11.95 (ISBN 0-8019-7309-0). Chilton.
--Chilton's Repair & Tune-up Guide: GM X-Body 1980-83. LC 82-72917. 256p. 1983. pap. 11.95 (ISBN 0-8019-7335-X). Chilton.
--Chilton's Repair & Tune-Up Guide: Granada-Monarch 1975-83. LC 82-72933. 260p. 1983. pap. 11.95 (ISBN 0-8019-7311-2). Chilton.
--Chilton's Repair & Tune-up Guide: Pontiac Mid-Size 1974-83. LC 82-72928. 288p. 1983. pap. 11.95 (ISBN 0-8019-7346-5). Chilton.
--Chilton's Repair & Tune-up Guide: Toyota Corona, Crown, Cressida, Mark II, Camry 1970-84. LC 88-70268. 288p. 1984. pap. 11.95 (ISBN 0-8019-7342-2). Chilton.
--Chilton's Repair & Tune-Up Guide: Toyota Corolla, Carina Tercel, Starlet 1970-83. LC 82-72938. 240p. 1983. pap. 11.95 (ISBN 0-8019-7316-3). Chilton.
--Chilton's Repair & Tune-Up Guide: Toyota Celica-Supra 1971-83. LC 82-72936. 328p. 1983. pap. 11.95 (ISBN 0-8019-7314-7). Chilton.
--Chilton's Repair & Tune-up Guide: Toyota Truck 1970-83. LC 82-72918. 288p. 1983. pap. 11.95 (ISBN 0-8019-7336-8). Chilton.
--Chilton's Repair & Tune-Up Guide: Volvo 1970-83. LC 82-72922. 304p. 1983. pap. 11.95 (ISBN 0-8019-7340-6). Chilton.
--Chilton's Repair & Tune up Guide: VW Front Wheel Drive 1974-83. LC 82-72921. 288p. 1982. pap. 11.95 (ISBN 0-8019-7339-2). Chilton.
--Chilton's Service Bay Handbook 1977-84. LC 83-45330. (Motor Age Professional Mechanics Edition Ser.). 148p. 1984. pap. 5.00 (ISBN 0-8019-7494-1). Chilton.
--Chilton's Small Engine Repair Activity Guide. LC 83-70016. 64p. 1985. pap. 6.60 (ISBN 0-8019-7381-3). Chilton.
--Chilton's Spanish Language Edition of Chilton's Easy Car Care. 2nd ed. (Illus.). 1983. 14.95 (ISBN 0-8019-7085-7). Chilton.
--Chilton's Spanish Language Edition of Chevrolet 1968 to 1979 Repair & Tune-up Guide. (Illus.). 1981. 11.95 (ISBN 0-8019-7082-2). Chilton.
--Chilton's Spanish Language Edition of Datsun 1973 to 1980 Repair & Tune-up Guide. (Illus.). 1981. 11.95 (ISBN 0-8019-7083-0). Chilton.
--Chilton's Spanish Language Edition of Ford 1968 to 1979 Repair & Tune-up Guide. (Illus.). 304p. 1981. 11.95 (ISBN 0-8019-7084-9). Chilton.
--Chilton's Spanish Language Edition of Volkswagen 1970 to 1979 Repair Tune-up Guide. (Illus.). 1981. 11.95 (ISBN 0-8019-7081-4). Chilton.
--Chilton's Wiring Diagram Manual: Domestic Cars 1982-84. LC 83-45329. (Motor Age Professional Mechanics Edition). 1200p. 1984. text ed. 37.00 (ISBN 0-8019-7493-3). Chilton.
--Datsun Z & ZX 1970-84: RTUG. LC 83-45308. 224p. 1984. pap. 11.95 (ISBN 0-8019-7466-6). Chilton.
--Datsun 1200, 210 & Nissan Sentra 1973-84: RTUG. LC 83-45325. 112p. 1984. pap. 11.95 (ISBN 0-8019-7490-9). Chilton.
--Datsun 200 SX, 510, 610, 710, 810, 1973-84: RTUG. LC 83-45313. 212p. 1984. pap. 11.95 (ISBN 0-8019-7478-X). Chilton.
--Dodge - Plymouth Vans 1967-84: RTUG. LC 83-45307. 264p. 1984. pap. 11.95 (ISBN 0-8019-7465-8). Chilton.
--Dodge Caravan 1984: RTUG (New Dodge FWD Van) LC 83-45317. 192p. 1984. pap. 11.95 (ISBN 0-8019-7482-8). Chilton.
--Dodge Trucks Nineteen Sixty-Seven through Eighty-Four: RTUG - Includes Pick-Ups, Ramcharger, Trailduster. LC 83-45302. 288p. 1984. pap. 11.95 (ISBN 0-8019-7459-3). Chilton.
--Firebird 1982-85. LC 84-45474. 208p. (Orig.). 1985. pap. 12.50 (ISBN 0-8019-7582-4). Chilton.
--Ford Fiesta, 1978 to 1980. LC 78-20258. (Chilton's Repair & Tune-up Guides). (Illus.). 1979. pap. 11.95 (ISBN 0-8019-6846-1, 6846). Chilton.
--Ford Mercury Mid-Size: 1971-1985. LC 84-45484. 392p. (Orig.). 1985. pap. 11.95 (ISBN 0-8019-7566-2). Chilton.
--Ford Pick-Ups: 1965-1982 RTUG. Span. ed. LC 83-45312. 362p. 1984. pap. 11.95 (ISBN 0-8019-7469-0). Chilton.
--Ford Pick-Ups 1965-84: RTUG. LC 83-45303. 312p. 1984. pap. 11.95 (ISBN 0-8019-7461-5). Chilton.
--Ford Vans 1961-84. LC 83-45301. 308p. 1984. pap. 11.95 (ISBN 0-8019-7458-5). Chilton.
--Honda 1973-84: RTUG. LC 83-45324. 224p. 1984. pap. 11.95 (ISBN 0-8019-7489-5). Chilton.
--Jeep CJ 1945-1984: RTUG. LC 83-45320. 312p. 1984. pap. 11.95 (ISBN 0-8019-7484-4). Chilton.
--Mazda, 1971-84: RTUG. LC 83-45321. 248p. 1985. pap. 11.95 (ISBN 0-8019-7486-0). Chilton.
--Mechanics' Handbook, Vol. 5: Brakes-Steering-Suspension. 1983. pap. 16.95 (ISBN 0-8019-7205-1). Chilton.
--Mercedes Benz Nineteen Seventy-Four to Nineteen Eighty-Four: RTUG. LC 83-45305. 224p. 1984. pap. 11.95 (ISBN 0-8019-7463-1). Chilton.
--Motor Age Service Bay Handbook for Mechanics. LC 84-45461. 144p. 1985. pap. 5.00 (ISBN 0-8019-7599-9). Chilton.
--Omni & Horizon, Nineteen Seventy-Eight to Nineteen Eighty. LC 78-20257. (Chilton's Repair & Tune-Up Guides Ser.). (Illus.). 1979. pap. 11.95 (ISBN 0-8019-6845-3, 6845). Chilton.
--Volkswagen, 1970-81. LC 78-20249. (Chilton's Repair & Tune-up Guides Ser.). (Illus.). 1979. pap. 11.95 (ISBN 0-8019-6837-2). Chilton.
Chilton's Mechanics Handbook: Diagnosis for Repair GM Cars, Vol. 6. (RTUG). 300p. 1983. pap. 17.95 (ISBN 0-8019-7291-4). Chilton.
Chilton's Repair & Tune-up Guide: Cutlass, 1970-1980. pap. 11.95 (ISBN 0-8019-6933-6). Chilton.
Chilton's Repair & Tune-up Guide for Capri 1970-1978. LC 77-90926. (Illus.). 1978. pap. 11.95 (ISBN 0-8019-6695-7). Chilton.
Chilton's Repair & Tune-up Guide for Corvair, 1960-1969. LC 70-161623. (Illus.). 1978. pap. 11.95 (ISBN 0-8019-6691-4). Chilton.
Chilton's Repair & Tune-up Guide for Datsun, 1973-1978. LC 77-90862. (Illus.). 1978. pap. 11.95 (ISBN 0-8019-6694-9). Chilton.
Chilton's Repair & Tune-up Guide for Subaru, 1970-78. (Illus.). 1978. pap. 11.95 (ISBN 0-8019-6693-0). Chilton.
Chilton's Repair & Tune-up Guide: GM Sub-Compacts, 1971-1980. (New Automotive Ser.). 256p. 1980. pap. 11.95 (ISBN 0-8019-6935-2). Chilton.
Chilton'sAutomotive Editorial Staff, ed. Chilton's Mechanics' Handbook: Automobile Sheet Metal Repair, Vol. III. (Illus.). 300p. 1981. pap. 16.95 (ISBN 0-8019-7034-2). Chilton.
Christ, Steve. How to Rebuild Your Big-Block Ford. (Illus.). 160p. 1983. pap. 9.95 (ISBN 0-89586-070-8). H P BKs.
Chrysler, Dodge, Plymouth: 1972-1984 Rear Wheel Drive Tune-up Maintenance. (Illus.). 196p. (Orig.). 1984. pap. 13.95 (ISBN 0-89287-383-3). Clymer Pubns.
Corvette Stingray, 1963 to 1979. LC 78-20255. (Chilton's Repair & Tune-up Guides). (Illus.). 1979. pap. 11.95 (ISBN 0-8019-6843-7, 6843). Chilton.
Crouse, W. H. & Anglin, D. L. Automotive Body Repair & Refinishing. 2nd ed. 400p. 1985. 28.95 (ISBN 0-07-014867-8); wkbk. 12.00 (ISBN 0-07-014868-6). McGraw.
--Automotive Tune-Up. 2nd ed. LC 82-7320. (Automotive Technology Ser.). 1983. text ed. 21.60 (ISBN 0-07-014836-8). McGraw.
Crouse, William H. Car Troubles: Causes & Cures. (Illus.). 144p. pap. 5.95 (ISBN 0-911709-00-2). W Kaufmann.
Crouse, William H. & Anglin, Don L. Auto Shop Workbook. 256p. 1984. 12.15 (ISBN 0-07-014572-5). McGraw.
Crouse, William H. & Anglin, Donald L. The Auto Book. 2nd ed. (Illus.). 1978. text ed. 28.20 (ISBN 0-07-014560-1). McGraw.
--Automotive Body Repair & Refinishing. (Illus.). 1980. text ed. 29.95 (ISBN 0-07-014791-4). McGraw.
Curfman, F. L. Automotive Radiator Construction & Restoration for Antique & Classic. LC 76-6299. Orig. Title: Manual of Automotive Radiator Construction & Repair. (Illus.). 1976. Repr. of 1921 ed. 15.00 (ISBN 0-911160-00-0). Post-Era.
Cutlass: Nineteen Sixty-Seven to Eighty Repair & Tune-up Guide. (New Automotive Bks.). 224p. 1980. 11.95 (ISBN 0-8019-6933-6). Chilton.
DeKryger, et al. Auto Mechanics: Theory & Servicing. 1986. text ed. 17.50 (IE09). SW Pub.
DeKryger, William J., et al. Auto Mechanics: Theory & Service. Sprague & Sturzenberger, eds. (Automotive Ser.). (Illus.). 800p. 1985. text ed. 23.48x (ISBN 0-538-33090-2); write for info. (ISBN 0-538-33091-0); instr's. manual avail. (ISBN 0-538-33092-9). SW Pub.
Doyle, John. Auto Repair. 381p. 1983. write for info. (ISBN 0-89434-031-X). Ferguson.
Duenk, et al. Auto Body Repair. 1984. text ed. 21.28 (ISBN 0-02-662340-4). Bennett Il.
Duenk, Lester G., et al. Autobody Repair. 1977. student guide 5.00 (ISBN 0-02-662320-X). Bennett IL.
Edmonds, I. G. & Gonzales, Ronald. Understanding Your Car. 320p. 1975. pap. text ed. 19.95 scp (ISBN 0-06-453806-0, HarpC). Har-Row.
Ellinger, Herb. Automechanics. 3rd ed. (Illus.). 592p. 1983. text ed. 29.95 (ISBN 0-13-054767-0); wkbk. 10.95 (ISBN 0-13-054775-1). P-H.
English, W. E. & Lien, David A. Complete Guide for Easy Car Care. (Illus.). 384p. 1975. 22.95 (ISBN 0-13-160226-8). P-H.
Eves, Edward. Land-Rover Restoration & Maintenance Manual. (Illus.). 208p. 1986. 18.95 (ISBN 0-7153-8429-5). David & Charles.
Fendell, Bob. How to Make Your Car Last a Lifetime. LC 80-19759. (Illus.). 216p. 1981. 14.95 (ISBN 0-03-053661-8); pap. 7.95 (ISBN 0-03-053656-1). HR&W.
Flammang, James M. How to Make Your Old Car Run Like New. (Illus., Orig.). 1980. pap. 7.95 (ISBN 0-8306-2062-1, 2062). TAB Bks.
Fodor, Ronald V. Complete Do-It-Yourself Handbook for Auto Maintenance: With the Repair-O-Matic Guide. 228p. cancelled 12.95 (ISBN 0-686-92143-7, Parker). P-H.
Ford Four-Wheel Drive Tune-up: 1969-1982. (Illus.). pap. 9.95 (ISBN 0-89287-173-3, A232). Clymer Pubns.
Ford Motor Company. Ford Model GP Prototype Jeep: TM-10-1101. Post, Dan R., ed. LC 72-185934. (Illus.). 128p. 1971. pap. 12.95 (ISBN 0-911160-46-9). Post-Era.
--Ford Passenger Car Shop Manual: 1949-1951. (Illus.). 320p. 1977. 21.95 (ISBN 0-911160-36-1). Post-Era.
--Ford V-8 Service Bulletins: 1941-1948, Complete. Post, Dan R., ed. LC 76-26325. (Illus.). 1977. 21.95 (ISBN 0-911160-34-5). Post-Era.
Ford Service-Repair Handbook: Courier Pickups, 1972-1982. (Illus.). pap. 12.95 (ISBN 0-89287-198-9, A172). Clymer Pubns.
Fremon, George & Fremon, Suzanne. Why Trade It in? LC 81-82363. 256p. 1982. pap. 3.50 (ISBN 0-87216-983-9). Jove Pubns.
--Why Trade It In? How to Keep Your Car Running Almost Indefinitely. 2nd ed. LC 76-42603. (Illus.). 176p. 1982. pap. 5.95 (ISBN 0-89709-039-X). Liberty Pub.
Garrett, Thomas B., ed. Vintage Station Wagon Shop Service. LC 76-57074. (Illus.). 160p. 1977. pap. 18.95 (ISBN 0-911160-85-X). Post-Era.
General Motors Buick, Chevrolet, Oldsmobile, Pontiac 1972-1984 Tune-up Maintenance. (Illus.). 1985. 9.95 (ISBN 0-89287-375-2, A275). Clymer Pubns.
General Motors X Cars Tune-up & Repair. 156p. (Orig.). 1981. pap. 6.95 (ISBN 0-8227-5058-9). Petersen Pub.
Glenn, Harold. Automechanics. rev. ed. 1976. text ed. 21.28 (ISBN 0-02-662380-3); wkbk & ans. sheets 6.64 (ISBN 0-02-662390-0); tchr's. guide free. Bennett IL.
Glenn, Harold T. Glenn's Firebird Tune-up & Repair Guide. new ed. LC 73-20678. (Glenn's Automotive Ser.). (Illus.). 336p. 1974. 7.75 (ISBN 0-8092-8437-5). Contemp Bks.
GM Subcompact, Nineteen Seventy One to Eighty Repair & Tune-up Guide. (New Autommotive Bks.). 256p. 1980. 11.95 (ISBN 0-8019-6935-2). Chilton.
GM X-Body Nineteen Eighty Repair & Tune-up Guide: Covers 1980 Models Only: Chevrolet Citation, Oldsmobile Omega, Pontiac Phoenix, Buick Skylark. (New Automotive Bks.). 192p. 1980. 11.95 (ISBN 0-8019-6909-3). Chilton.
Granada-Monarch: Nineteen Seventy-Five to Eighty Repair & Tune-up Guide. (New Automotive Bks.). 240p. 1980. 11.95 (ISBN 0-8019-6937-9). Chilton.
Grant, H. Vehicle Rescue. (Illus.). 1975. pap. 21.95 (ISBN 0-87618-137-X); instr's guide 7.95 (ISBN 0-87618-611-8); systems chart o.p. 7.95 (ISBN 0-87618-610-X). Brady Comm.
Greifinger, David, et al. Glove Compartment Book. Jenny, Brian P., ed. 181p. (Orig.). 1984. pap. 5.95 (ISBN 0-915765-04-7). Natl Pr Inc.
Grieco, Joseph. The One Hundred Seventy-Five Thousand-Mile-Car. Myers, Marye, ed. (Illus.). 40p. (Orig.). 1984. pap. 7.95 (ISBN 0-931843-00-6). Grieco.
Hammond, Keith. Automobile Refinishing. 243p. 1972. 40.00x (ISBN 0-85218-040-3, Pub. by Portcullio Pr). State Mutual Bk.
Harman, Robert D. Chilton's Minor Auto Body Repair. LC 76-915. (Illus.). 1979. pap. 11.95 (ISBN 0-8019-6869-0). Chilton.
Harmon, Robert D. Chilton's Minor Auto Body Repair. 2nd ed. (New Automotive Bks.). 208p. 1980. pap. 11.95 (ISBN 0-8019-6940-9). Chilton.
Haynes, J. H. & Chalmers-Hunt, B. L. Toyota Carina '71 - '74. (Owners Workshop Manual Ser.: No. 150). 1975. 12.95 (ISBN 0-85696-150-7, Pub. by J H Haynes England). Haynes Pubns.
--Toyota Corolla '67 - '74. (Owners Workshop Manual Ser.: No. 201). 1975. 12.95 (ISBN 0-85696-201-5, Pub. by J H Haynes England). Haynes Pubns.
Hill, Harry G. Automotive Service & Repair Tools. LC 73-907400. 343p. 1975. pap. 16.00 (ISBN 0-8273-1035-8). Delmar.
Hollander, Rene & Percy, Bernard. Everyone's Guide to Saving Gas. (Illus., Orig.). 1979. pap. 2.95 (ISBN 0-9603194-0-9). Old Oaktree.
Honda V45 & V65: 1982-1983 Service Repair Performance. (Illus.). 309p. (Orig.). 1984. pap. 13.95 (ISBN 0-89287-384-1). Clymer Pubns.
Hossain, Tony. The Nineteen Sixties Supercars: A Repair & Restoration Guide. LC 82-19389. (Illus.). 214p. 1983. pap. 13.50 (ISBN 0-8306-2077-X, 2077). TAB Bks.

--Automotive Maintenance Supervisor. (Career Examination Ser.: C-2096). (Cloth bdg. avail. on request). 1977. pap. 12.00 (ISBN 0-8373-2096-8). Natl Learning.

--Automotive Serviceman. (Career Examination Ser.: C-65). (Cloth bdg. avail. on request). pap. 12.00 (ISBN 0-8373-0065-7). Natl Learning.

--Car Cleaner. (Career Examination Ser.: C-181). (Cloth bdg. avail. on request). pap. 8.00 (ISBN 0-8373-0181-5). Natl Learning.

--Foreman (Buses & Shops) (Career Examination Ser.: C-264). (Cloth bdg. avail. on request). pap. 10.00 (ISBN 0-8373-0264-1). Natl Learning.

--Foreman (Cars & Shops) (Career Examination Ser.: C-265). (Cloth bdg. avail. on request). pap. 10.00 (ISBN 0-8373-0265-X). Natl Learning.

--Foreman of Mechanics (Motor Vehicles) (Career Examination Ser.: C-272). (Cloth bdg. avail. on request). pap. 10.00 (ISBN 0-8373-0272-2). Natl Learning.

--Senior Automotive Serviceman. (Career Examination Ser.: C-1879). (Cloth bdg. avail. on request). pap. 12.00 (ISBN 0-8373-1879-3). Natl Learning.

--Supervising Automotive Mechanic. (Career Examination Ser.: C-2575). (Cloth bdg. avail. on request). pap. 10.00 (ISBN 0-8373-2575-7). Natl Learning.

--Supervisor (Buses & Shops) (Career Examination Ser.: C-1504). (Cloth bdg. avail. on request). pap. 10.00 (ISBN 0-8373-1504-2). Natl Learning.

--Supervisor of Motor Repair. (Career Examination Ser.: C-1875). (Cloth bdg. avail. on request). pap. 10.00 (ISBN 0-8373-1875-0). Natl Learning.

Schmidt, Robert P. Autobody Repair & Refinishing. 350p. 1981. text ed. 26.95 (ISBN 0-8359-0247-1); instr's. manual free (ISBN 0-8359-0248-X). Reston.

Scott, Ed. Honda ATC25OR Singles, 1981-1982. Wauson, Sydnie A., ed. (Service Repair Performance Ser.). pap. 13.95 (ISBN 0-89287-371-X). Clymer Pubns.

--Honda CB650 Fours: 1979-1982 (Includes Custom Service, Repair, Performance) Wauson, Sydnie A., ed. (Illus., Orig.). 1981. pap. 13.95 (ISBN 0-89287-343-4, M336). Clymer Pubns.

--Honda CB900, 1000 & 1100 Fours: 1980-1983 Service Repair Performance. Wauson, Sydnie A., ed. (Illus., Orig.). 1981. pap. 13.95 (ISBN 0-89287-352-3, M325). Clymer Pubns.

Self, Charles. Do-It-Yourselfer's Guide to Auto Body Repair & Painting. (Illus.). 1978. pap. 9.95 (ISBN 0-8306-6949-3, 949). TAB Bks.

Sikorsky, R. Drive It Forever: Your Key to Long Automobile Life. 144p. 1983. 12.95 (ISBN 0-07-057294-1); pap. 6.95 (ISBN 0-07-057293-3). McGraw.

Smith, B. How to Restore Sheet Metal Bodywork. (Osprey Restoration Ser.). (Illus.). 128p. 1984. text ed. 14.95 (ISBN 0-85045-591-X, Pub. by Osprey England). Motorbooks Intl.

Smith, LeRoi. How to Fix Up Old Cars. rev. ed. LC 80-10614. (Illus.). 260p. 1980. 9.95 (ISBN 0-396-07830-3); pap. 3.95 (ISBN 0-396-07831-1). Dodd.

Spearl, Alexander. Living with a Car. 14.50x (ISBN 0-392-05915-0, SpS). Sportshelf.

Spicer, Edward D. Automotive Collision Work. 4th ed. (Illus.). 1972. 15.95 (ISBN 0-8269-0022-4). Am Technical.

Standards for Vocational Automotive Service Instruction. 118p. 1979. write for info. (ISBN 0-943350-07-7). Motor Veh Man.

Standards for Vocational Truck-Tractor-Trailer Service Instruction. 84p. 1982. write for info. (ISBN 0-943350-06-9). Motor Veh Man.

Stephenson, James. A Doctor's Auto Checkup. 1979. softbound 9.00 (ISBN 0-931210-00-3). Medicanto.

Thiessen, Frank & Dales, Davis. Diesel Fundamentals: Principles & Service. 2nd. ed. 1985. text ed. 28.95 (ISBN 0-8359-1286-8); tchr's. manual avail (ISBN 0-8359-1287-6). Reston.

Toboldt, William K. Automotrix Three: Manual de Reparaciones Automotrices. rev. ed. (Span., Illus.). 1983. 50.00 (ISBN 0-916628-04-3). Lineal Cleworth.

--Manual de Reparaciones Automotrices. (Span., Illus.). 243p. 1980. 19.95 (ISBN 0-916628-03-5). Lineal Cleworth.

Toyota Celica 1971-1981: Shop Manual. (Illus., Orig.). pap. 12.95 (ISBN 0-89287-332-9, A196). Clymer Pubns.

Toyota Corona, 1970-1982: Shop Manual. (Illus., Orig.). pap. 12.95 (ISBN 0-89287-333-7, A195). Clymer Pubns.

Troise, Joe. Drive It Till It Drops: Keep Your Car Running Forever. LC 80-123393. (Illus.). 120p. 1980. pap. 4.95 (ISBN 0-89708-024-6). And Bks.

Tuneup & Troubleshooting. 2nd, rev. ed. (Illus.). 300p. 1984. pap. 14.95 (ISBN 0-87851-595-X, Hearst Motor Bk). Morrow.

Tuneup & Troubleshooting Illustrated. LC 79-66361. (Illus.). 320p. 1979. 19.95 (ISBN 0-87851-513-5); pap. 8.95 (ISBN 0-87851-512-7). Hearst Bks.

United States War Department & Post, Dan R., eds. The Military Jeep Complete, for Willys Model MB & Ford Model GPW, Service Manuals: TM-9-1803, TM-9-1803a, TM-9-1803b. LC 76-185935. (Illus.). 512p. 1971. 24.95 (ISBN 0-911160-47-7). Post-Era.

Urich, Mike. Fifty-Two Hundred Holley Carburetor Handbook. LC 81-82587. (Orig.). 1982. pap. 4.95 (ISBN 0-89586-050-3). H P Bks.

Vann, William F. Automotive Tune-Up & Emission. LC 84-50059. 13.95 (ISBN 0-672-21712-0). Sams.

Vizard, David. How to Rebuild Your 1.3, 1.6 & 2.0 OHC Ford. (Orig.). 1980. pap. 7.95 (ISBN 0-912656-68-9). H P Bks.

Volkswagen of America Inc. Volkswagen Beetle & Karmann Ghia Official Service Manual Type 1, 1966, 1967, 1968, 1969. LC 70-189047. (Illus.). 512p. (Orig.). 1972. pap. 24.95 (ISBN 0-8376-0416-8). Bentley.

Volkswagen of America, Inc. Volkswagen Fastback & Squareback Official Service Manual, Type 3, 1968-1973. LC 73-85200. (Illus.). 422p. 1974. pap. 34.95 (ISBN 0-8376-0057-X). Bentley.

Volkswagen of America Inc. Volkswagen Official Service Manual Type 1. Beetle, Super Beetle, & Karmann Ghia, 1970-1979. LC 78-75039. (Illus.). 448p. 1979. pap. 29.95 (ISBN 0-8376-0096-0). Bentley.

--Volkswagen Official Service Manual Type 2, Station Wagon-Bus, 1968-1979. 4th rev. ed. LC 78-75038. (Illus.). 464p. 1979. pap. 34.95 (ISBN 0-8376-0094-4). Bentley.

Volkswagen of America, Inc. Volkswagen Vanagon Official Factory Repair Manual, 1980-1983: Diesel & Aircooled Gasoline Engines. rev. ed. LC 83-70840. (Illus.). 512p. (Orig.). 1983. pap. 34.95 (ISBN 0-8376-0353-6). Bentley.

Wallace, Angelo, tr. from Ital. Ferrari 365 GTC-4 Repair Instructions. 65.00 (ISBN 0-9606804-6-2). Wallace Pub.

Weissler, Paul. Basic Car Repairs & Maintenance. LC 77-6560. (Popular Science Skill Bk). 1978. pap. 3.95i (ISBN 0-06-014577-3, TD-294, HarpT). Har-Row.

Wetzel, Guy F. Automotive Diagnosis & Tune-up. 1974. text ed. 19.96 (ISBN 0-87345-100-7). McKnight.

Wheatley, Richard C. & Morgan, Brian. Antique & Classic Cars: Their Maintenance & Operation. LC 75-37230. (Illus.). 1976. 12.50 (ISBN 0-8376-0203-3). Bentley.

--Restoration of Antique & Classic Cars. LC 74-25850. (Illus.). 1975. 14.95 (ISBN 0-8376-0135-5). Bentley.

Willys-Overland Motors, Inc. Willys Model MA Prototype Jeep: TM-10-1103. Post, Dan R., ed. LC 79-185933. (Illus.). 128p. 1971. pap. 12.95 (ISBN 0-911160-45-0). Post-Era.

Wolfe, J. & Phelps. The Mechanics Vest Pocket Reference Book. 1982. pap. 6.95 (ISBN 0-13-571505-9). P-H.

Wood, Jonathan. Restoration & Preservation of Vintage & Classic Cars. 2nd ed. 279p. 19.95 (ISBN 0-85429-391-4, 391). Haynes Pubns.

Woody, Bob. The Car Crisis: How to Cope with the ABC's of Auto Emergencies. LC 77-91261. 1977. pap. 4.95 (ISBN 0-930938-01-1). Vista Pubns.

Wyatt, Barb. The Greasy Thumb Automechanics Manual for Women. (Illus.). 1976. pap. 8.00 (ISBN 0-918040-00-0). Aunt Lute Bk Co.

Young, Paul. Datsun Tune-up for Everybody. LC 80-5102. (Illus.). 120p. 1980. pap. 7.95 (ISBN 0-89815-026-4). Ten Speed Pr.

--Honda Tune-up for Everybody. LC 81-50156. (Illus.). 144p. (Orig.). 1981. pap. 7.95 (ISBN 0-89815-031-0). Ten Speed Pr.

Young, Paul B. Toyota Tune-up for Everybody. LC 79-63720. (Illus.). 149p. 1979. pap. 7.95 (ISBN 0-913668-89-3). Ten Speed Pr.

AUTOMOBILES–MAINTENANCE AND REPAIR–RATES

Chilton's Automotive Editorial Staff. Chilton's Labor Guide & Parts Manual 1979-85. LC 83-45332. (Motor Age Professional Mechanics Edition Ser.). 1632p. 1985. text ed. 38.00 (ISBN 0-8019-7496-8). Chilton.

--Import Automotive Parts & Labor Guide 1975-85. LC 82-72911. (Motor Age Professional Mechanics Ser.). 1428p. 1985. 38.00 (ISBN 0-8019-7596-4). Chilton.

--Labor Guide & Parts Manual 1980-86. LC 83-45332. (Motor Age Professional Mechanics Ser.). 1632p. 1985. 41.00 (ISBN 0-8019-7598-0). Chilton.

Chilton's Guide to Consumers' Auto Repairs & Prices. (New Automotive Bks.). 176p. 1980. 10.95 (ISBN 0-8019-6941-7); pap. 11.95 (ISBN 0-8019-6942-5). Chilton.

Conroy, Larry & O'Connell, Paul. The Consumer Cost Guide to Car Repair. (Illus.). 144p. 1983. text ed. 13.95 (ISBN 0-13-168872-3); pap. 6.95 (ISBN 0-13-168864-2). P-H.

Inglis, Alan G. Service Equals Sales: A Guide to Automotive Retail Service Management. 1977. pap. 25.45 (ISBN 0-915260-04-2). Atcom.

Mettersheimer, John H. How to Save Money on Automobile Repairs. 1982. 6.95 (ISBN 0-533-05017-0). Vantage.

Pendergrass, Donald H. Collision Repair Estimating. 160p. (Orig.). 1985. pap. text ed. 21.28 scp (ISBN 0-672-98386-9); instr's. guide 3.67scp (ISBN 0-672-98387-7). Bobbs.

AUTOMOBILES–MODELS

Burkinshaw, Bill. Manual of Electric Radio Control Cars. (Illus.). 96p. 1983. pap. 9.95 (ISBN 0-85242-821-9, Pub. by Argus). Aztex.

Collecting & Constructing Model Buses. 96p. 1984. 20.00x (ISBN 0-905418-44-1, Pub. by Gresham England). State Mutual Bk.

Hood, Philip B. & Kutner, Richard M. The Complete Buyer's Guide to Kit Cars. Marketello, Joel, ed. 164p. (Orig.). 1984. pap. 9.95 (ISBN 0-915845-01-6). Auto Logic Pubns.

Laidlaw-Dickson, D. J. Radio Controlled Model Racing Cars. (Illus.). 160p. 1985. pap. 11.50 (ISBN 0-85242-675-5, Pub. by Argus). Aztex.

Rose, Alan. Nineteen Eighty-Four Paper Corvette. (Illus.). 72p. 1984. pap. 10.95 (ISBN 0-385-27768-7, Dolp). Doubleday.

Santos, Saul. Scratchbuilding Model Cars. (Illus.). 224p. (Orig.). 1983. 15.95 (ISBN 0-8306-3085-6, 2085); pap. 10.95 (ISBN 0-8306-2085-0). TAB Bks.

Thompson, Graham. British Diecasts: A Collector's Guide to 'Toy' Cars, Vans & Trucks. 160p. 19.95 (ISBN 0-85429-264-0, F264). Haynes Pubns.

Williams, Guy R. The World of Modern Cars. (Illus.). 256p. 1976. 19.95 (Pub. by A Deutsch England). David & Charles.

Wingrove, G. A. The Model Cars of Gerald Wingrove. (Illus.). 1979. 49.95 (ISBN 0-904568-12-1, Pub. by Eyre Methuen England). Motorbooks Intl.

AUTOMOBILES–MOTORS

see also Automobiles, Racing–Motors; Automotive Gas Turbines

Abd-El-Wahed. Automotive Engineering Dictionary: English-French-German-Arabic. (Eng., Fr., Ger. & Arabic.). 436p. 1978. 45.00 (ISBN 0-686-92337-5). French & Eur.

Adiabatic Engines: Worldwide Review. 115p. 1984. 30.00 (ISBN 0-89883-342-6, SP571). Soc Auto Engineers.

Advances in Adiabatic Engines. 1985. 28.00 (ISBN 0-89883-831-2, SP610). Soc Auto Engineers.

Advances in Elastometric Applications. 8p. 1984. 18.00 (ISBN 0-89883-346-9, SP575). Soc Auto Engineers.

Alternate Fuels for S.I. Engines. 112p. 1983. 28.00 (ISBN 0-89883-330-2, SP559). Soc Auto Engineers.

Aluminum for Engine Applications. 68p. 1983. 22.00 (ISBN 0-89883-305-1, SP534). Soc Auto Engineers.

Baudoin, Anne-Marie. Vocabulaire Francais-Anglais De L'automobile: Le Moteur. (Eng. & Fr.). 174p. 1973. pap. 9.95 (ISBN 0-686-56909-1, M-6025). French & Eur.

Bear, W. Forrest. Electric Motors, Principles, Controls, Service & Maintenance. Hoerner, Harry J. & Hoerner, Thomas A., eds. (Illus.). 202p. 1983. pap. text ed. 10.00x (ISBN 0-913163-15-5, 183); tchr's. ed. 2.50x (ISBN 0-913163-16-3, 283). Hobar Pubns.

Bishop, Ron. Rebuilding the Famous Ford Flathead. (Illus.). 140p. (Orig.). 1981. 9.95 (ISBN 0-8306-9965-1); pap. 7.25 (ISBN 0-8306-2066-4, 2066). TAB Bks.

Blanchard, Harold F. & Ritchen, Ralph. Motor Auto Engines & Electrical Systems. 7th ed. LC 77-88821. (Illus.). 1977. 14.95 (ISBN 0-910992-73-8). Hearst Bks.

Brady, Robert N. Automotive & Small Truck Fuel Injection Systems: Gas & Diesel. 1985. text ed. 32.95 (ISBN 0-8359-0315-X). Reston.

Building the 'James Coombes' Table Engine. (Illus.). 32p. 1978. pap. 3.50 (ISBN 0-85242-537-6). Aztex.

Building the Stuart No. 9 Engine. (Illus.). 48p. 1979. pap. 4.75 (ISBN 0-905180-07-0). Aztex.

Canfield Press-Chek-Chart. Engine Performance Diagnosis & Tune-up, 2 vols. 1978. pap. text ed. 21.50 scp (ISBN 0-06-454003-0, HarpC); instructors manual avail. (ISBN 0-06-454006-5). Har-Row.

Canfield Presschek-Chart Engine Repair & Rebuilding, 2 Vols. 1982. pap. text ed. 21.50 scp (ISBN 0-06-454008-1, HarpC); instr's. manual avail. (ISBN 0-06-454009-X). Har-Row.

Chilton's Automotive Editorial Staff. Chilton's Diesel Engine Service Manual 1978-84. LC 83-45326. (Motor Age Professional Mechanics Edition). 1216p. 1984. text ed. 37.50 (ISBN 0-8019-7444-5). Chilton.

--Chilton's Guide to Turbocharged Cars & Trucks. LC 83-45309. 248p. 1984. pap. 11.95 (ISBN 0-8019-7397-X). Chilton.

Collie, M. J. Stirling Engine Design & Feasibility for Automotive Use. LC 79-13444. (Energy Technology Review Ser.: No. 47). (Illus.). 470p. 1979. 36.00 (ISBN 0-8155-0763-1). Noyes.

Crouse, William H. & Anglin, D. L. Automotive Engine Design. 1970. text ed. 21.60 (ISBN 0-07-014671-3). McGraw.

Crouse, William H. & Anglin, Donald L. Automotive Engines. 5th ed. (Automotive Technology Ser.). 1975. 22.60 (ISBN 0-07-014602-0). McGraw.

Day, Richard. Automotive Engine Tuning. 1981. pap. text ed. 16.95 (ISBN 0-8359-0270-6). Reston.

Dempsy, Paul. How to Convert Your Car, Van or Pickup to Diesel. (Illus.). 1978. pap. 7.95 (ISBN 0-8306-7968-5, 968). TAB Bks.

Diesel Engine Thermal Loading. LC 79-66979. 1979. 25.00 (ISBN 0-89883-220-9, SP449). Soc Auto Engineers.

Diesel Engines for Passenger Cars & Light Duty Vehicles. 1982. 200 pp 110.00x, (ISBN 0-85298-496-0, Pub. by Mechanical Eng Pubns). State Mutual Bk.

Diesel Engines Noise Conference: Proceedings. LC 79-83912. 370p. 1979. Thirty papers. 45.00 (ISBN 0-89883-050-8, P80). Soc Auto Engineers.

Eickman, J. L. The Ford Y-Block. (Illus.). 120p. 1984. pap. 12.95 (ISBN 0-87938-185-X). Motorbooks Intl.

Electronic Engine-Drivetrain Control, 12 papers. 132p. 1983. pap. 30.00 (ISBN 0-89883-311-6, SP540). Soc Auto Engineers.

Electronic Engine Management & Driveline Controls. 184p. 1982. pap. 38.00 (ISBN 0-89883-069-9, P104). Soc Auto Engineers.

Ellinger, Herbert E. Automotive Engines: Theory & Servicing. 432p. 1981. text ed. 24.95 (ISBN 0-13-054999-1); 10.95 (ISBN 0-13-054890-1). P-H.

Engine Power Boosting. 136p. 1984. 30.00 (ISBN 0-89883-335-3, SP564). Soc Auto Engineers.

Engine Testing. 148p. 1984. 22.00 (ISBN 0-89883-803-7, SP582). Soc Auto Engineers.

Ergonomic Aspects of Electronic Instrumentation: A Guide for Designers. 1984. 12.00 (ISBN 0-89883-347-7, SP576). Soc Auto Engineers.

Evans, Martin. Evening Star. 222p. 1978. pap. 11.95 (ISBN 0-85242-634-8). Aztex.

Fuel Alternatives for S. I. & Diesel Engines. 108p. 1983. 25.00 (ISBN 0-89883-319-1, SP548). Soc Auto Engineers.

Haining, John. Introducing Model Traction Engine Construction. (Illus.). 112p. 1983. pap. 9.95 (ISBN 0-85242-805-7). Aztex.

Hinerman, Ivan D. Automotive Engine Repair. LC 77-81911. 512p. 1979. pap. text ed. 19.16 (ISBN 0-02-818600-1); instrs'. manual 3.20 (ISBN 0-686-61256-6). Glencoe.

Huges, James G. Automotive Engine Diagnosis & Tune-Up. 1985. text ed. 29.95 (ISBN 0-8359-0285-4). Reston.

Hughes, W. J. Building the Allchin. (Illus.). 256p. 1979. pap. 13.95 (ISBN 0-85242-635-6). Aztex.

Laidlaw-Dickson, D. J. The Book of the Unimat. (Illus.). 128p. 1979. pap. 7.95 (ISBN 0-85242-591-0). Aztex.

Lauda, Niki. The New Formula One: A Turbo Age, Serial Excerpt: Road & Track Autoweek Magazine. 1984. 21.95 (ISBN 0-87938-179-5). Motorbooks Intl.

Liptak, Bela, ed. The Instrument Engineers' Handbook: Process Measurement. 75.00. Chilton.

McCue, C. F., et al, eds. Performance Testing of Lubricants for Automotive Engines & Transmissions. (Illus.). 811p. 1974. 48.00 (ISBN 0-85334-468-X, Pub. by Elsevier Applied Sci England). Elsevier.

Mackerle, J. Air-Cooled Automotive Engines. 518p. 1972. 59.00x (ISBN 0-85264-205-9, Pub. by Griffin England). State Mutual Bk.

Motor Auto Engines & Electrical Systems. 8th ed. (Illus.). 656p. 1984. 28.50 (ISBN 0-87851-577-1, Hearst Motor Bk). Morrow.

Motor Auto Repair Manual: Early Model Edition 1969-1976. 7th ed. 1520p. 1981. 19.95 (ISBN 0-87851-541-0). Hearst Bks.

Motor Auto Repair Manual: Vintage Model Edition 1935-1953. 861p. 1981. 30.00 (ISBN 0-87851-545-3). Hearst Bks.

Motor Auto Repair Manual 1982. 45th ed. 1075p. 1981. 18.95 (ISBN 0-87851-539-9). Hearst Bks.

Motor Imported Car Repair Manual. 4th ed. 1000p. 1981. 22.95 (ISBN 0-87851-543-7). Hearst Bks.

Motor Introduction to Auto Engines. (Illus.). 456p. 1984. pap. 15.50 (ISBN 0-87851-557-7, Hearst Motor Bk); study guide 7.50 (ISBN 0-87851-587-9). Morrow.

Multicylinder Test Sequences for Evaluating Autumotive Engine Oils, Part 1: Sequence IID- STP 315H. 111p. 1980. looseleaf 16.00 (ISBN 0-8031-0521-5, 04-315081-12); pap. 13.00 (ISBN 0-8031-0520-7, 04-315080-12). ASTM.

New Developments in Electronic Engine Management. (Illus.). 1984. pap. 35.00 (ISBN 0-89883-343-4, SP572). Soc Auto Engineers.

Norbye, Jan P. The Complete Handbook of Automotive Power Trains. (Illus.). 364p. (Orig.). 1980. pap. 9.95 (ISBN 0-8306-2069-9, 2069). TAB Bks.

Piston Engine: Meeting the Challenge of the 1980's. 1980. Four papers. pap. 12.00 (ISBN 0-89883-238-1, SP467). Soc Auto Engineers.

Power Boosting. 1985. 17.00 (ISBN 0-89883-837-1, SP616). Soc Auto Engineers.

Practical Treatise on Engine Crankshaft Torsional Vibration Control. 44p. 1979. pap. 10.00 (ISBN 0-89883-216-0, SP445). Soc Auto Engineers.

Ralbovsky, Edward. Automotive Diesels. LC 84-19956. 288p. 1985. pap. text ed. 16.80 (ISBN 0-8273-2217-8); instr's guide 3.00 (ISBN 0-8273-2218-6). Delmar.

The Relationship Between Engine Oil Viscosity & Engine Performance, STP 621. 116p. 1977. pap. 15.00 (ISBN 0-8031-0549-5, 04-621000-12); Suppl. No. 1. pap. 12.00 (ISBN 0-8031-0550-9, 04-621010-12); Suppl. No. 2. pap. 15.00 (ISBN 0-8031-0551-7, 04-621030-12); Suppl. No. 3. pap. 15.00 (ISBN 0-8031-0552-5, 04 621030 12); Suppl. 4. pap. 18.00 (ISBN 0-8031-0553-3). ASTM.

Rudman, Jack. Auto Engineman. (Career Examination Ser.: C-61). (Cloth bdg. avail. on request). pap. 12.00 (ISBN 0-8373-0061-4). Natl Learning.

Sakiya, Tetsuo. Honda Motor. LC 82-80983. (Illus.). 242p. Date not set. pap. 5.95 (ISBN 0-87011-697-5). Kodansha.

Schorr, Martyn L. Mopar Performance Years, Vol. II. 200p. 1984. 8.95 (ISBN 0-940346-17-6). Motorbooks Intl.

Smith, Philip H. & Morrison, John C. Scientific Design of Exhaust & Intake Systems. 3rd rev. ed. LC 72-86569. (Illus.). 294p. 1972. 16.95 (ISBN 0-8376-0309-9). Bentley.

Society of Automotive Engineers. Engines, Fuels & Lubricants: Perspective on the Future. LC 80-53468. 112p. 1980. Eight papers. pap. 18.00 (ISBN 0-89883-242-X). SAE.

State of the Art on Design & Performance of Power Cylinder Components. 130p. 1983. 25.00 (ISBN 0-89883-323-X, SP552). Soc Auto Engineers.

Taylor, Dan & Hofer, Larry. How to Rebuild Small-Block Mopar. LC 81-84588. (Orig.). 1982. pap. 9.95 (ISBN 0-89586-128-3). H P Bks.

Thiessen, Frank & Dales, D. N. Automotive Engines & Related Systems: Principles & Service. (Illus.). 1981. text ed. 27.95 (ISBN 0-8359-0280-3); pap. 21.95 (ISBN 0-8359-0279-X); instr's manual free (ISBN 0-8359-0281-1). Reston.

Thiessen, Frank & Dales, Davis. Automotive Electronics & Engine Performance. 1983. text ed. 27.95 (ISBN 0-8359-0311-7); pap. text ed. 21.95 (ISBN 0-8359-0310-9); solutions manual avail. (ISBN 0-8359-0312-5). Reston.

Tingey, Rex. Making the Most of the Unimat. rev. ed. (Illus.). 128p. 1984. pap. 7.95 (ISBN 0-85242-676-3, Pub. by Argus). Aztex.

Transmissions-Off Highway Equipment. 1983. 15.00 (ISBN 0-89883-320-5, SP549). Soc Auto Engineers.

Turbocharged High Performance Engines. 1984. 12.00 (ISBN 0-89883-339-6, SP568). Soc Auto Engineers.

Turbochargers & Turbocharged Engines. LC 79-50459. 158p. 1979. Twelve papers. 30.00 (ISBN 0-89883-214-4, SP442). Soc Auto Engineers.

VDI, ed. Fisita: Combustion Engines 1980 VDI 370. 1980. 98.00 (ISBN 0-9961073-0-4, Pub. by VDI W Germany). Heyden.

--Fisita Nineteen Eighty: Transport Systems VDI 367. 1980. pap. 86.00 (ISBN 0-9961072-7-4, Pub. by VDI W Germany). Heyden.

--Fisita: Passenger Cars 1980 VDI 368. 1980. 90.00 (ISBN 0-9961072-8-2, Pub. by VDI W Germany). Heyden.

--Fisita: Vehicle 1980 Components VDI 369. 1980. 42.00 (ISBN 0-9961072-9-0, Pub. by VDI W Germany). Heyden.

Walshaw, T. D. Building the Beam Engine Mary. (Illus.). 82p. 1979. pap. 4.95 (ISBN 0-85242-754-9). Aztex.

--Building the Overcrank Engine Georgina. (Illus.). 64p. 1978. pap. 4.95 (ISBN 0-317-00056-X). Aztex.

--Building the Williamson Engine. (Illus.). 82p. 1978. pap. 4.95 (ISBN 0-85242-719-0). Aztex.

Whited, N. W. Automotive Oscilloscope. LC 76-3937. (Illus.). 99p. 1977. pap. 8.40 (ISBN 0-8273-1033-1). Delmar.

Whittington, Herschel & Whittington, Ray. Step-by-Step Guide: Carburetor Tuneup & Overhaul. (Illus.). 224p. 1982. pap. 10.95 (ISBN 0-8306-4814-3, 814). TAB Bks.

AUTOMOBILES–MOTORS–CONTROL SYSTEMS

Automatic Slack Adjusters. 36p. 1984. 12.00 (ISBN 0-89883-345-0, SP574). Soc Auto Engineers.

Chilton's Automotive Editorial Staff. Mechanics Handbook: New Electronic Engine Control, Vol. 8. LC 84-45481. 816p. (Orig.). 1985. pap. 16.95 (ISBN 0-8019-7535-2). Chilton.

Stern, Marc. Automotive Computers. 200p. 1984. 19.95 (ISBN 0-13-054651-8); pap. 12.95 (ISBN 0-13-054644-5). P-H.

Weathers, Tom & Hunter, Claud. Automotive Computers & Control Systems. (Illus.). 256p. 1984. text ed. 24.95 (ISBN 0-13-054693-3). P-H.

AUTOMOBILES–MOTORS–EXHAUST GAS

see also Motor Vehicles–Pollution Control Devices

Canfield-ChekChart. Fuel Systems & Emission Controls, 2 vols. 248p. 1978. pap. text ed. 21.50 scp (ISBN 0-06-454002-2, HarpC); instructors manual avail. (ISBN 0-06-454005-7). Har-Row.

Chilton Staff. Chilton's Emission Control Manual 1986-87 Domestic Cars: 1986-87 Domestic Cars, Motor-Age Professional Mechanics Edition (Supplement) LC 85-47954. 336p. 1986. pap. 30.00 (ISBN 0-8019-7693-6). Chilton.

--Chilton's Emission Control Manual 1986-87 Import Cars: 1986-87 Import Cars, Motor-Age Professional Mechanics Edition (Supplement) LC 85-47953. 336p. 1986. pap. 30.00 (ISBN 0-8019-7694-4). Chilton.

The Cost & Effectiveness of Automotive Exhaust Emission Control Regulations. (Document Ser.). 94p. 1979. 6.50x (ISBN 92-64-11913-2). OECD.

Diesel Engine Combustion & Emissions. 1984. 28.00 (ISBN 0-89883-802-9, SP581). Soc Auto Engineers.

Diesel Exhaust Emissions: Particulate Studies & Transient Cycle Testing. 188p. 1984. 30.00 (ISBN 0-89883-349-3, SP 578). Soc Auto Engineers.

Diesel Particulate Traps. 1984. 38.00 (ISBN 0-89883-096-6, P140). Soc Auto Engineers.

Effect of Automotive Emission Requirements on Gasoline Characteristics, STP 487. 165p. 1971. pap. 9.50 (ISBN 0-8031-0004-3, 04-487000-12). ASTM.

Engine Combustion Analysis: New Approaches. 1985. 22.00 (ISBN 0-89883-717-0, P156). Soc Auto Engineers.

Environmental Guidelines for the Motor Vehicle & Its Use. (Industry & Environment Guidelines: Vol. 2). 31p. 1981. pap. 10.00 (ISBN 92-807-1040-0, UNEP051, UNEP). Unipub.

Husselbee, William. Automotive Emission Control. 1984. text ed. 25.95 (ISBN 0-8359-0173-4). Reston.

Husselbee, William L. Automotive Fuel, Cooling, Lubrication & Exhaust Systems. 1984. text ed. 29.95 (ISBN 0-8359-0300-1); pap. text ed. 22.95 (ISBN 0-8359-0299-4). Reston.

Knowles, Don. Automotive Emission Controls & Computer Systems. 1984. text ed. 29.95 (ISBN 0-8359-0150-5); pap. text ed. 22.95 (ISBN 0-8359-0135-1). Reston.

Krier, James E. & Ursin, Edmund. Pollution & Policy: A Case Essay on California & Federal Experience with Motor Vehicle Air Pollution, 1940-1975. LC 76-3881. 1978. 24.50x (ISBN 0-520-03204-7). U of Cal Pr.

McEvoy, James E., ed. Catalysts for the Control of Automotive Pollutants. LC 75-20298. (Advances in Chemistry Ser: No. 143). 1975. 24.95 (ISBN 0-8412-0219-2). Am Chemical.

Measurement & Control of Diesel Particulate Emissions. LC 79-67589. 388p. 1979. 45.00 (ISBN 0-89883-105-9, PT17). Soc Auto Engineers.

National Research Council Diesel Impacts Study Committee. Health Effects of Exposure to Diesel Exhaust. 1981. pap. 9.75 (ISBN 0-309-03130-3). Natl Acad Pr.

R. H. Chandler Ltd., ed. Automotive Emission Control, Vol. VII: Oxygen-Sensors for Exhaust Gas Emissions 1975-79. 51p. 1981. 325.00x (ISBN 0-686-78864-8, Pub. by Chandler England). State Mutual Bk.

Smith, Philip H. & Morrison, John C. Scientific Design of Exhaust & Intake Systems. 3rd rev. ed. LC 72-86569. (Illus.). 294p. 1972. 16.95 (ISBN 0-8376-0309-9). Bentley.

Society of Automotive Engineers. Diesel Combustion & Emissions, Pt. I. LC 80-50154. 308p. 1980. Twenty-three papers. 45.00 (ISBN 0-89883-055-9, P86). Soc Auto Engineers.

--New Diesel Engines, Combustion & Emissions Research in Japan. LC 80-52981. 248p. 1980. Fourteen papers. 38.00 (ISBN 0-89883-239-X, SP 468). Soc Auto Engineers.

Springer, G. S. & Patterson, D. J., eds. Engine Emissions: Pollutant Formation & Measurement. LC 71-188716. 371p. 1973. 55.00x (ISBN 0-306-30585-2, Plenum Pr). Plenum Pub.

Springer, Lyton L. Automobile Exhaust in Health & Disease: Medical Analysis Index with Reference Bibliography. LC 85-47572. 150p. 1985. 29.95 (ISBN 0-88164-318-1); pap. 21.95 (ISBN 0-88164-319-X). ABBE Pubs Assn.

Taylor, K. C. Automobile Catalytic Converters. (Illus.). 70p. 1984. pap. 12.00 (ISBN 0-387-13064-0). Springer-Verlag.

White, Lawrence J. Regulation of Air Pollutant Emissions from Motor Vehicles. 1982. 13.95 (ISBN 0-8447-3492-6); pap. 4.95 (ISBN 0-8447-3487-X). Am Enterprise.

AUTOMOBILES–PAINTING

Brown, F., et al, eds. Vehicle Painting, Pt. 1. (Engineering Craftsmen: No. E1). (Illus.). 1968. spiral bdg. 45.00x (ISBN 0-85083-032-X). Intl Ideas.

--Vehicle Painting, Pt. 2. (Engineering Craftsmen: No. E21). 1970. spiral bdg. 45.00x (ISBN 0-85083-116-4). Intl Ideas.

Caldwell, Brice & Caldwell, Craig, eds. Basic Bodywork & Painting. 5th ed. LC 73-79967. (Illus.). 192p. (Orig.). 1981. pap. 6.95 (ISBN 0-8227-5057-0, Dist. by Kampmann). Petersen Pub.

Chilton Staff. Guide to Auto Body Repair & Painting. LC 85-47970. 304p. (Orig.). 1986. pap. 16.95 (ISBN 0-8019-7667-7). Chilton.

Chudy, Harry T. The Complete Guide to Automotive Refinishing. (Illus.). 464p. 1982. reference 24.95 (ISBN 0-13-160440-6). P-H.

Deroche, Andre & Huldebrand, Nicholas. The Principles of Autobody Repairing & Repainting. 3rd ed. (Illus.). 672p. 1981. text ed. 29.95 (ISBN 0-13-705665-6). P-H.

Hammond, Keith. Automobile Refinishing. 243p. 1972. 40.00x (ISBN 0-85218-040-3, Pub. by Portcullio Pr). State Mutual Bk.

Schreib, Larry & Atherton, Larry. Custom Painting: A Do-It-Yourself Guide. 144p. 10.95 (ISBN 0-931472-10-5). Motorbooks Intl.

Self, Charles. Do-It-Yourselfer's Guide to Auto Body Repair & Painting. (Illus.). 1978. pap. 9.95 (ISBN 0-8306-6949-3, 949). TAB Bks.

Vehicle Painting One. 75.00x (ISBN 0-85083-032-X, Pub. by Engineering Ind). State Mutual Bk.

Vehicle Painting Two. 75.00x (ISBN 0-85083-116-4, Pub. by Engineering Ind). State Mutual Bk.

AUTOMOBILES–RADIO EQUIPMENT

Automobile Audio Systems: Worldwide Developments. 1985. 40.00 (ISBN 0-89883-718-9, P157). Soc Auto Engineers.

Automotive Audio Systems. 243p. 1984. 43.00 (ISBN 0-89883-098-2, P142). Soc Auto Engineers.

Clifford, Martin. Complete Guide to Car Audio. LC 80-50560. 256p. 1981. pap. 9.95 (ISBN 0-672-21820-8). Sams.

Gonzales, Ronald F. Automotive Electrical & Electronic Systems Lab Manual. 1985. pap. text ed. 16.95 (ISBN 0-8359-0019-3). Reston.

Green, Michael L., ed. CB, Carsound & Communication Equipment. 1978. pap. 1.95 (ISBN 0-89552-016-8). DMR Pubns.

Minutti, D. Panasonic Car Sound Fact Book & Shopper's Guide. 1978. pap. 1.95 (ISBN 0-89552-025-7). DMR Pubns.

Mobile Radio Systems & Techniques. (IEE Conference Publications Ser.: No. 238). 229p. 1984. pap. 70.00 (ISBN 0-85296-297-5). Inst Elect Eng.

Salm, Walter G. Auto Audio: How to Select & Install Stereo Equipment. 144p. 1980. pap. 7.70 (ISBN 0-8104-0759-0). Hayden.

AUTOMOBILES–REPAIRING

see Automobiles–Maintenance and Repair

AUTOMOBILES–SAFETY MEASURES

Advances in Seat Belt Restraints: Design, Performance & Usage. 1984. 60.00 (ISBN 0-89883-097-4, P141). Soc Auto Engineers.

Eastman, Joel W. Styling vs. Safety: The American Automobile Industry & the Development of Automobile Safety, 1900-1966. 296p. (Orig.). 1984. lib. bdg. 25.00 (ISBN 0-8191-3685-9); pap. text ed. 13.75 (ISBN 0-8191-3686-7). U Pr of Amer.

Manne, Henry G. & Miller, Roger L., eds. Auto Safety Regulation: The Cure or the Problem? LC 76-1676. 1976. 15.95 (ISBN 0-913878-09-X). T Horton & Dghts.

Peltzman, Sam. Regulation of Automobile Safety. LC 75-39779. 1975. pap. 4.25 (ISBN 0-8447-3194-3). Am Enterprise.

AUTOMOBILES–SERVICE STATIONS

Crouse, William H. Automotive Service Business: Operation & Management. LC 72-666. 1972. pap. text ed. 21.60 (ISBN 0-07-014605-5). McGraw.

AUTOMOBILES–SERVICING

see Automobiles–Maintenance and Repair

AUTOMOBILES–SPRINGS AND SUSPENSION

Campbell, Colin. New Directions in Suspension Design: Making the Fast Car Faster. LC 80-24348. (Illus.). 224p. 1981. 14.95 (ISBN 0-8376-0150-9). Bentley.

Coghlan, David A. Automotive Chassis Systems: Steering, Suspension, Alignment, & Brakes. 2nd ed. (Illus.). 440p. 1985. pap. text ed. 19.00 (ISBN 0-534-04848-X, 77F6066). Breton Pubs.

Crouse, William H. & Anglin, Donald L. Automotive Brakes, Suspension & Steering. 6th ed. LC 82-17187. (Automotive Technology Ser.). 1983. 21.60 (ISBN 0-07-014828-7). McGraw.

Ellinger, Herbert E. & Hathaway, Richard B. Automotive Suspension, Steering & Brakes. (Transportation & Technology Ser.). (Illus.). 1980. text ed. 24.95 (ISBN 0-13-054288-1). P-H.

Theissen, Frank & Dales, Dave. Automotive Steering, Suspension, & Braking Systems: Principles & Service. 1982. text ed. 28.95 (ISBN 0-8359-0291-9); pap. text ed. 21.95 (ISBN 0-8359-0290-0); instrs.' manual free (ISBN 0-8359-0292-7). Reston.

AUTOMOBILES–STEERING GEAR

Abbott, Sheldon L. & Hinerman, Ivan D. Automotive Suspension & Steering. LC 74-25602. 377p. 1982. pap. text ed. 18.08 (ISBN 0-02-810350-5); instrs'. manual 3.20 (ISBN 0-02-810360-2). Glencoe.

Billiet, Walter E. & Alley, Walter. Automotive Suspensions, Steering, Alignment & Brakes. 5th ed. (Illus.). 1974. 15.95 (ISBN 0-8269-0122-0). Am Technical.

Chilton's Automotive Editorial Staff. Mechanics' Handbook, Vol. 5: Brakes-Steering-Suspension. 1983. pap. 16.95 (ISBN 0-8019-7205-1). Chilton.

Coghlan, David A. Automotive Chassis Systems: Steering, Suspension, Alignment, & Brakes. 2nd ed. (Illus.). 440p. 1985. pap. text ed. 19.00 (ISBN 0-534-04848-X, 77F6066). Breton Pubs.

Crouse, William H. & Anglin, Donald L. Automotive Brakes, Suspension & Steering. 6th ed. LC 82-17187. (Automotive Technology Ser.). 1983. 21.60 (ISBN 0-07-014828-7). McGraw.

Ellinger, Herbert E. & Hathaway, Richard B. Automotive Suspension, Steering & Brakes. (Transportation & Technology Ser.). (Illus.). 1980. text ed. 24.95 (ISBN 0-13-054288-1). P-H.

Gear Design & Performance. 1984. 25.00 (ISBN 0-89883-805-3, SP584). Soc Auto Engineers.

AUTOMOBILES–TESTING

Engine Testing. 148p. 1984. 22.00 (ISBN 0-89883-803-7, SP582). Soc Auto Engineers.

Instruments & Computers for Cost Effective Fluid Power Testing. 95p. 1979. pap. 37.00 (ISBN 0-85298-436-7, MEP105). Soc Auto Engineers.

Lahue, Kalton C., ed. Basic Tune-up & Test Equipment. 2nd rev. ed. LC 74-78228. (Basic Repair & Maintenance Manuals Ser.). (Illus.). 1978. pap. 6.95 (ISBN 0-8227-5018-X). Petersen Pub.

Society of Automotive Engineers. Fatigue Resistance: Forecasting & Testing. LC 79-66724. 88p. 1979. Five papers. pap. 15.00 (ISBN 0-89883-219-5, SP448). Soc Auto Engineers.

Whited, N. W. Automotive Oscilloscope. LC 76-3937. (Illus.). 99p. 1977. pap. 8.40 (ISBN 0-8273-1033-1). Delmar.

AUTOMOBILES–TIRES

ASTM Committees E-17 on Skid Resistance & F-9 on Tires, ed. Frictional Interaction of Tire & Pavement. LC 82-72886. (Special Technical Publications Ser.: No. 793). 330p. 1983. text ed. 30.00 (ISBN 0-8031-0231-3, 04-793000-37). ASTM.

Surface Texture Versus Skidding - STP 583. 154p. 1975. 12.00 (ISBN 0-8031-0786-2, 04-583000-37). ASTM.

AUTOMOBILES–TRAILERS

see also Campers and Coaches, Truck; Mobile Homes

Brejcha, Mathias F. Automotive Transmissions--Automotive. LC 72-186233. pap. 87.00 (ISBN 0-317-10791-7, 2014472). Bks Demand UMI.

Thompson, John & Trailer Life Editors. Trailer Life's RV Repair & Maintenance Manual: The Most Comprehensive & Authoritative Technical Guide Ever Published Specifically for Rvers. LC 79-66970. (Illus.). 1980. 12.98 (ISBN 0-934798-00-1). TL Enterprises.

AUTOMOBILES–TRANSMISSION DEVICES

Abbott, Sheldon L. Automotive Transmissions. 320p. 1980. pap. text ed. 17.00 (ISBN 0-02-810170-7); instr. manual 3.20 (ISBN 0-02-810180-4). Glencoe.

Brycha, M. Automatic Transmissions. 2nd ed. 1982. 26.95 (ISBN 0-13-054577-5). P-H.

Chilton's Automotive Editorial Staff. Chilton's Motor Age Professional Transmission Manual. 1980. 65.00x (ISBN 0-8019-6927-1). Chilton.

--Chilton's Mechanics's Handbook, Vol. 4: Automatic Transmission Repair. (Illus.). 1981. pap. 14.95 (ISBN 0-8019-7060-1). Chilton.

Crouse, William H. & Anglin, Donald L. Automotive Automatic Transmissions. 6th ed. LC 81-14262. (Illus.). 304p. 1983. pap. 20.05 (ISBN 0-07-014771-X). McGraw.

--Automotive Manual Transmissions & Power Trains. 6th ed. LC 81-17206. (Illus.). 352p. 1983. pap. text ed. 20.05 (ISBN 0-07-014776-0). McGraw.

Crow, James T. & Warren, Cameron A. Four Wheel Drive Handbook. (Illus.). 96p. 1976. Repr. 3.95. Norton.

Frazee, Irving A. & Billiet, Walter. Automotive Brakes & Power Transmission Systems. LC 56-7199. (Automotive Ser.). (Illus.). pap. 69.30 (ISBN 0-317-11020-9, 2004568). Bks Demand UMI.

Gear Design & Performance. 1984. 25.00 (ISBN 0-89883-805-3, SP584). Soc Auto Engineers.

Husselbee, William. Automatic Transmission Service: A Text-Workbook. (Orig.). 1981. pap. 15.95 (ISBN 0-8359-0266-8). Reston.

Husselbee, William K. Automatic Transmission Fundamentals. (Illus.). 1980. text ed. 22.95 (ISBN 0-8359-0257-9). Reston.

Judge, Arthur W. Modern Transmission Systems. 2nd ed. LC 69-18141. (Motor Manuals Ser.: Vol. 5). text ed. 10.95x (ISBN 0-8376-0074-X). Bentley.

Kovacik, Robert T. & Creager, Clifford. Manual Transmissions & Drivetrains. (Illus.). 502p. 1983. pap. text ed. 14.95 (ISBN 0-538-33050-3, IE05). SW Pub.

Long. Transmission: Communication Skills for Technicians. (Illus.). 1980. pap. text ed. 15.95 (ISBN 0-8359-7816-8); write for info. instr's manual (ISBN 0-8359-7818-4). Reston.

McCue, C. F., et al, eds. Performance Testing of Lubricants for Automotive Engines & Transmissions. (Illus.). 811p. 1974. 48.00 (ISBN 0-85334-468-X, Pub. by Elsevier Applied Sci England). Elsevier.

North, Paul. Hurst. (Source Bks.). (Illus.). 144p. 1986. pap. 12.95 (ISBN 0-934780-78-1). Bookman Dan.

Passenger Car Transmissions. 1985. 17.00 (ISBN 0-89883-840-1, SP619). Soc Auto Engineers.

Power Transmissions. 1985. 17.00 (ISBN 0-89883-840-1, SP619). Soc Auto Engineers.

Stock Drive Products Staff Engineers. Handbook of Stock Gears. 1975. pap. 2.95 (ISBN 0-686-11503-1). Stock Drive.

Thiessen, Frank & Dales, David. Automatic Transmissions: Principles & Service. 1984. text ed. 29.95 (ISBN 0-8359-0328-1); pap. text ed. 22.95 (ISBN 0-8359-0327-3); instr's manual avail. (ISBN 0-8359-0329-X). Reston.

Transmissions-Off Highway Equipment. 1983. 15.00 (ISBN 0-89883-320-5, SP549). Soc Auto Engineers.

Tucker, Howard. Automatic Transmissions Workbook on Service & Repair. LC 80-67593. (Automotive Technology Ser.). (Illus.). 64p. (Orig.). 1982. pap. text ed. 7.20 (ISBN 0-8273-1894-4). Delmar.

Tucker, Howard F. Automatic Transmissions. LC 78-62623. 1980. pap. text ed. 17.00 (ISBN 0-8273-1648-8); instructor's guide 3.00 (ISBN 0-8273-1649-6); filmstrips 125.00 (ISBN 0-8273-1919-3). Delmar.

Webster, Jay. Principles of Automatic Transmissions. rev. & enl. ed. LC 79-51618. (Illus.). 1980. pap. 6.95x (ISBN 0-911168-43-5). Prakken.

AUTOMOBILES–TYPES–AMC EAGLE

Lahue, Kalton C. AMC Eagle SX-4 Kammback: 1980-1983 Shop Manual. Wauson, Sydnie A. & Hamlin, Steve, eds. (Illus.). 280p. (Orig.). 1984. pap. 13.95 (ISBN 0-89287-392-2, A127). Clymer Pubns.

AUTOMOBILES–TYPES–BARRACUDA

Chilton's Automotive Editorial Staff. Chilton's Repair & Tune-up Guide for Barracuda & Challenger: 1965-1972. LC 72-7036. (Illus.). 128p. 1972. pap. 11.95 (ISBN 0-8019-5807-5). Chilton.

North, Paul. Barracuda-Challenger, Vol. II. (Source Bks.). (Illus.). 144p. 1985. pap. 12.95 (ISBN 0-934780-54-4). Bookman Dan.

Shields, Samuel A., Jr. Barracuda: A Source Book. (Illus.). 144p. (Orig.). 1983. pap. 12.95 (ISBN 0-934780-19-6). Bookman Dan.

Zavitz, R. Perry. Barracuda-Challenger Databook & Price Guide, 1964-1974. (Data Bks.). (Illus.). 128p. 1985. pap. 9.95 (ISBN 0-934780-76-5). Bookman Dan.

AUTOMOBILES–TYPES–BUICK

Bonsall, Thomas. Muscle Buicks. (Muscle Car Ser.). (Illus.). 96p. 1985. pap. 8.95 (ISBN 0-934780-65-X). Bookman Dan.

Chilton Staff. Chilton's Repair & Tune-up Guide: GM N-Body 1985-86 Buick, Somerset, Olds Calais & Pontiac Grand Am. LC 85-47958. 224p. (Orig.). 1986. pap. 12.50 (ISBN 0-8019-7657-X). Chilton.

Chilton's Automotive Editorial Staff. Buick Century-Regal 1975-85. LC 84-45479. 256p. (Orig.). 1985. pap. 11.95 (ISBN 0-8019-7570-0). Chilton.

--Chilton's Repair & Tune-Up Guide: Buick Century-Regal 1975-83. LC 82-72929. 224p. 1983. pap. 11.95 (ISBN 0-8019-7307-4). Chilton.

--Chilton's Repair & Tune-Up Guide: Buick-Olds-Pontiac Full Size 1975-83. LC 82-72930. 308p. 1983. pap. 11.95 (ISBN 0-8019-7308-2). Chilton.

Clarke, R. M., ed. Buick Muscle 1965-1970. 100p. 1984. pap. 11.95 (ISBN 0-946489-41-6, Pub. by Brookland Bks England). Motorbooks intl.

Haynes, J. H. & Du Pre, Peter D. Buick Mid-size Models 1974 thru 1984. (Haynes Automotive Manuals). 12.95 (ISBN 1-85010-069-1, 627). Haynes Pubns.

Haynes, J. H. & Paul, Rik. Buick Skylark. (Haynes Automotive Manuals). 12.95 (ISBN 0-85696-552-9, 552). Haynes Pubns.

Hoy, Ray. Opel Service Repair Handbook: All Models, 1966-1975. (Illus.). pap. 12.95 (ISBN 0-89287-171-7, A175). Clymer Pubns.

Norbye, Jan P. & Dunne, Jim. Buick: The Postwar Years. LC 77-25850. (Marques of America Ser.). (Illus.). 1978. 19.95 (ISBN 0-87938-044-6). Motorbooks Intl.

Warson, Sydnie A., ed. GMC J Cars: Buick Skylark, Cadillac Cimarron, Chevrolet Cavalier, Oldsmobile Firenza, Pontiac J-2000 Shop Manual, 1982-1983. 384p. (Orig.). 1983. pap. 12.95 (ISBN 0-89287-362-0). Clymer Pubns.

Zavitz, R. P. Big Buicks Nineteen Fifty-Nine to Nineteen Seventy-Three: A Source Book. (Source Bks.). (Illus.). 144p. 1984. pap. 12.95 (ISBN 0-934780-45-5). Bookman Dan.

Zavitz, R. Perry. Riviera. (Classic Source Bks.). (Illus.). 144p. 1984. pap. 12.95 (ISBN 0-934780-46-3). Bookman Dan.

AUTOMOBILES–TYPES–CADILLAC

Bonsall, Thomas. Eldorado. (Classic Source Bks.). (Illus.). 144p. 1984. pap. 12.95 (ISBN 0-934780-40-4). Bookman Dan.

Chilton Staff. Chilton's Repair & Tune-up Guide: Cadillac 1967-86. LC 85-47984. 314p. (Orig.). 1986. pap. 12.50 (ISBN 0-8019-7684-7). Chilton.

Chilton's Automotive Editorial Staff. Cadillac Nineteen Sixty-Seven to Nineteen Eighty Four: RTUG. LC 83-45304. 288p. 1984. pap. 11.95 (ISBN 0-8019-7462-3). Chilton.

--Cavalier: Cimarron, J-2000, 1982. (Illus.). 1981. pap. 11.95 (ISBN 0-8019-7059-8). Chilton.

Clarke, R. M. Cadillac in the Sixties Collection, No. 1. (Brooklands Bks.). (Illus.). 70p. 1982. pap. 8.95 (ISBN 0-907073-53-0, Pub. by Brooklands Bks England). Motorbooks Intl.

Edwards, Owen. Cadillac. LC 85-42867. (Illus.). 144p. 1985. 50.00 (ISBN 0-8478-0608-1). Rizzoli Intl.

Hendry, Maurice D. Cadillac, Standard of the World: The Complete History. 3rd ed. LC 72-85846. 1979. 29.95 (ISBN 0-915038-10-2). Auto Quarterly.

Lehwald, Edward A. Cadillac Nineteen Forty to Nineteen Eighty-Four. (ID Guide Ser.). (Illus.). 96p. 1984. pap. 8.95 (ISBN 0-934780-47-1). Bookman Dan.

McCall, Walter M. Eighty Years of Cadillac-LaSalle. Dammann, George H., ed. LC 79-50804. (Automotive Ser.). (Illus.). 448p. 1982. 34.95 (ISBN 0-912612-17-7). Crestline.

Warson, Sydnie A., ed. GMC J Cars: Buick Skylark, Cadillac Cimarron, Chevrolet Cavalier, Oldsmobile Firenza, Pontiac J-2000 Shop Manual, 1982-1983. 384p. (Orig.). 1983. pap. 12.95 (ISBN 0-89287-362-0). Clymer Pubns.

Zavitz, R. Perry. Cadillac Databook & Price Guide, Nineteen Sixty to Nineteen Sixty-Nine. (Data Bks.). (Illus.). 128p. 1985. pap. 9.95 (ISBN 0-934780-74-9). Bookman Dan.

AUTOMOBILES–TYPES–CAMARO

Antonick, Mike. Illustrated Camaro Buyer's Guide. (Buyer's Guide Ser.). (Illus.). 156p. 1985. pap. 13.95 (ISBN 0-87938-187-6). Motorbooks Intl.

Chilton's Automotive Editorial Staff. Camaro, 1967-1981. (Illus.). 1981. pap. 11.95 (ISBN 0-8019-7045-8). Chilton.

--Camaro, 1982-1985. LC 84-45480. 208p. (Orig.). 1985. pap. 11.95 (ISBN 0-8019-7569-7). Chilton.

Clarke, R. M. Camaro Muscle Cars, 1966-1972. (Illus.). 100p. 1982. pap. 11.95 (ISBN 0-907073-65-4, Pub. by Brooklands Bks England). Motorbooks Intl.

--Camaro, 1966-1970. (Brooklands Bks.). (Illus.). 100p. (Orig.). 1980. pap. 11.95 (ISBN 0-906589-82-7, Pub. by Brooklands Bks England). Motorbooks Intl.

Collins, Joe. Z-28. (Source Bks.). (Illus.). 144p. 1984. pap. 12.95 (ISBN 0-934780-36-6). Bookman Dan.

Haynes, J. H. & Raffa, John B. Chevrolet Camaro '82 thru '84. (Haynes Automotive Manuals). 12.95 (ISBN 0-85696-866-8, 866). Haynes Pubns.

Jorgensen, Eric, ed. Camaro Service-Repair Handbook: 1967-1981. (Illus.). pap. 12.95 (ISBN 0-89287-226-8, A136). Clymer Pubns.

Lahue, Kalton C. Camaro & Firebird Shop Manual, 1982-1985. Wauson, Sydnie, ed. (Illus.). 342p. 1984. pap. 12.95 (ISBN 0-89287-377-9, A257). Clymer Pubns.

Lamm, Michael. The Camaro Book. (Illus.). 144p. 1985. 17.95 (ISBN 0-932128-00-9). Lamm-Morada.

--Camaro, the Third Generation. (Illus.). 96p. 1983. 15.95 (ISBN 0-932128-02-5). Lamm Morada.

Langworth, Richard. Camaro 1966-1984: A Collector's Guide. 1985. lib. bdg. 18.95 (ISBN 0-900549-94-7, Pub. by Motor Racing England). Motorbooks Intl.

Miller, Ray. Camaro! Chevy's Classy Chassis. (The Chevy Chase Ser.: Vol. 4). (Illus.). 320p. 1981. 35.00 (ISBN 0-913056-10-3). Evergreen Pr.

Witzenburg, Gary L. Camaro! From Challenger to Champion: The Complete History. (Marque History Bks). (Illus.). 216p. 1982. 29.95 (ISBN 0-915038-33-1); leather bdg. 62.50 (ISBN 0-915038-34-X). Auto Quarterly.

AUTOMOBILES–TYPES–CAPRI

Chilton's Repair & Tune-up Guide for Capri 1970-1978. LC 77-90926. (Illus.). 1978. pap. 11.95 (ISBN 0-8019-6695-7). Chilton.

Glenn, Harold T. Glenn's Capri. 1975. pap. 7.75 (ISBN 0-8092-8165-1). Contemp Bks.

Haynes, J. H. & Chalmers, B. L. Capri Owners Workshop Manual: MK-I Twenty-Six Hundred, Twenty-Eight Hundred 1971 thru 1975. (Haynes Owners Workshop Manuals: No. 205). 1976. 12.95 (ISBN 0-85696-205-8, Pub by J H Haynes England). Haynes Pubns.

Haynes, J. H. & Hunt-Chalmers, B. L. Capri 2600 & 2800 V6 1971 thru 1975. (Haynes Automotive Manuals). 12.95 (ISBN 0-317-31364-9, 205). Haynes Pubns.

Haynes, J. H. & Strasman, P. G. Capri 2000 1971 thru 1975. (Haynes Automotive Manuals). 12.95 (ISBN 0-85696-296-1, 296). Haynes Pubns.

Haynes, J. H., et al. Capri Owner's Workshop Manual: MK-I Two Thousand 1971 thru '75. (Haynes Owners Workshop Manual: No. 296). 1976. 12.95 (ISBN 0-85696-296-1, Pub. by J H Haynes England). Haynes Pubns.

--Ford Mustang & Mercury Capri (V6 & V8) (Haynes Automotive Manuals). 12.95 (ISBN 1-85010-000-4, 558). Haynes Pubns.

Walton, Jeremy. Capri. (Illus.). 285p. 1982. 19.95 (ISBN 0-85429-279-9, F328). Haynes Pubns.

--Capri: The Development & Competition History of Ford's European GT Car. 205p. 19.95 (ISBN 0-85429-328-0, F328). Haynes Pubns.

Wright, Ron. Ford Mustang & Mercury Capri 1979-1983: Includes Turbo Shop Manual. Wauson, Sydnie A., ed. (Illus.). 384p. 1983. 12.95 (ISBN 0-89287-378-7, A255). Clymer Pubns.

AUTOMOBILES–TYPES–CHALLENGER

Chilton's Automotive Editorial Staff. Chilton's Repair & Tune-Up Guide: Colt-Challenger 1971-83. LC 82-72925. 224p. 1983. pap. 11.95 (ISBN 0-8019-7343-0). Chilton.

--Chilton's Repair & Tune-Up Guide: Firebird 1982-83. LC 82-72927. 217p. 1983. pap. 11.95 (ISBN 0-8019-7345-7). Chilton.

--Chilton's Repair & Tune-up Guide for Barracuda & Challenger: 1965-1972. LC 72-7036. (Illus.). 128p. 1972. pap. 11.95 (ISBN 0-8019-5807-5). Chilton.

--Colt-Challenger-Vista, 1971-85. LC 84-45471. 256p. (Orig.). 1985. pap. 11.95 (ISBN 0-8019-7584-0). Chilton.

--Dodge Colt & Challenger Nineteen Seventy-one to Nineteen Eighty-One. LC 80-70346. (Illus.). 242p. 1980. pap. 11.95 (ISBN 0-8019-7037-7). Chilton.

North, Paul. Barracuda-Challenger, Vol. II. (Source Bks.). (Illus.). 144p. 1985. pap. 12.95 (ISBN 0-934780-54-4). Bookman Dan.

Zavitz, R. Perry. Barracuda-Challenger Databook & Price Guide, 1964-1974. (Data Bks.). (Illus.). 128p. 1985. pap. 9.95 (ISBN 0-934780-76-5). Bookman Dan.

AUTOMOBILES–TYPES–CHEVELLE

Collins, Joe. Chevelle vs. the Pack. (Pack Ser.). (Illus.). 128p. 1985. pap. 10.95 (ISBN 0-934780-70-6). Bookman Dan.

Lehwald, Edward A. Chevelle SS, Vol. II. (Source Bks.). (Illus.). 144p. 1985. pap. 12.95 (ISBN 0-934780-53-6). Bookman Dan.

--Chevelle SS: A Source Book. (Illus.). 144p. (Orig.). 1982. pap. 12.95 (ISBN 0-934780-11-0). Bookman Dan.

AUTOMOBILES–TYPES–CHEVROLET

see also Automobiles–Types–Chevelle; Automobiles–Types–Chevy II; Automobiles–Types–Corvette; Automobiles–Types–Nova; Automobiles–Types–Vega

Bell, Doug. Early Chevrolet History: 1912-1945. Clymer Publications, ed. (Illus.). pap. 5.00 (ISBN 0-89287-269-1, H544). Clymer Pubns.

Bonsall, Thomas. Muscle Chevys. (Muscle Car Ser.). (Illus.). 96p. 1985. pap. 8.95 (ISBN 0-934780-53-6). Bookman Dan.

Bonsall, Thomas E. Trans-Am: A Source Book. (Illus.). 144p. (Orig.). 1983. pap. 12.95 (ISBN 0-934780-23-4). Bookman Dan.

Boyce, Terry V. Chevy Super Sports: 1961-1976. (Illus.). 1981. pap. 14.95 (ISBN 0-87938-096-9). Motorbooks Intl.

Burness, Tad. Chevy Spotter's Guide: 1920-1980. 9.95 (ISBN 0-87938-151-5). Motorbooks Intl.

Chappell, Pat. The Hot One: Chevrolet, Nineteen Fifty-Five to Nineteen Fifty-Seven. 3rd ed. LC 77-21298. (Illus.). 228p. 1981. 23.95 (ISBN 0-9606148-0-X). Dragonwyck Pub.

Chevrolet Luv: Nineteen Seventy-Two to Nineteen Eighty-One. (Illus.). 1981. pap. 11.95 (ISBN 0-8019-7051-2). Chilton.

Chevrolet Luv Owners Workshop Manual: 72 thru '82. (Owners Workshop Manuals Ser.: No. 319). 1978. 12.95 (ISBN 0-85696-515-4, Pub. by J H Haynes England). Haynes Pubns.

Chevrolet Motor Co. Chevrolet Passenger Car Shop Manual: 1949-54. Post, Dan R., ed. LC 78-68380. 512p. 1978. 28.95 (ISBN 0-911160-24-8); pap. 21.95 (ISBN 0-911160-25-6). Post-Era.

Chevrolet S-10 & GMC S-15 Pick-up. (Haynes Automotive Manuals). write for info. (ISBN 0-85696-831-5, 831). Haynes Pubns.

Chevrolet S-10 & GMC S-15 Pickups. (Haynes Automotive Manuals). 12.95 (ISBN 0-317-31365-7, 831). Haynes Pubns.

Chevy. LC 80-80770. (Popular Mechanic Motor Car Care Guides). (Illus.). 176p. 12.95 (ISBN 0-87851-933-5); pap. 6.95 (ISBN 0-87851-925-4). Hearst Bks.

Chilton Staff. Chilton's Repair & Tune-up Guide: Chevrolet Mid-Size 1964-86. LC 85-47968. 336p. (Orig.). 1986. pap. 12.50 (ISBN 0-8019-7677-4). Chilton.

--Chilton's Repair & Tune-up Guide: Chevette-Pontiac T1000 1976-86. LC 85-47967. 256p. (Orig.). 1986. pap. 12.50 (ISBN 0-8019-7666-9). Chilton.

Chilton's Automotive Editorial Staff. Chevette-T-1000, 1976-1982. 1982. pap. 11.95 (ISBN 0-8019-7162-4). Chilton.

--Chevette T-1000 1976-84. LC 83-45300. 212p. 1984. pap. 11.95 (ISBN 0-8019-7457-7). Chilton.

--Chevrolet-GMC Pick-Ups 1970-82: RTUG. LC 83-45311. 352p. 1984. pap. 11.95 (ISBN 0-8019-7468-2). Chilton.

--Chevrolet GMC Pick-Ups 1970-84: RTUG - Includes Suburban. LC 83-45306. 312p. 1984. pap. 11.95 (ISBN 0-8019-7464-X). Chilton.

--Chevrolet-GMC Vans, 1967-1982. 1982. pap. 11.95 (ISBN 0-8019-7169-1). Chilton.

--Chevrolet-GMC Vans 1967-84: RTUG. LC 83-45322. 248p. 1985. pap. 11.95 (ISBN 0-8019-7487-9). Chilton.

--Chevrolet Mid-Size 1964-84. LC 83-45299. 304p. 1984. pap. 11.95 (ISBN 0-8019-7456-9). Chilton.

--Chevrolet: Nineteen Sixty-Eight to Nineteen Eighty-One. (Illus.). 1981. pap. 11.95 (ISBN 0-8019-7135-7). Chilton.

--Chevrolet, Nineteen Sixty-Eight to Nineteen Seventy-Nine. LC 78-20251. (Chilton's Repair & Tune-Up Guides). (Illus.). 1979. pap. text ed. 11.95 (ISBN 0-8019-6839-9, 6839). Chilton.

--Chevrolet 1968-85. LC 84-45467. 272p. (Orig.). 1985. pap. 11.95 (ISBN 0-8019-7588-3). Chilton.

--Chilton's Repair & Tune-Up Guide: Chevrolet-GMC S-10, S-15 1982-83. LC 82-72932. 224p. 1983. pap. 11.95 (ISBN 0-8019-7310-4). Chilton.

--Chilton's Repair & Tune-Up Guide: Chevrolet 1968-83. LC 82-72935. 288p. 1983. pap. 11.95 (ISBN 0-8019-7313-9). Chilton.

--Chilton's Repair & Tune-up Guide for Chevrolet 1968-1977. LC 76-57317. (Chilton's Repair & Tune-up Guides). (Illus., Orig.). 1977. pap. 11.95 (ISBN 0-8019-6615-9, 6615). Chilton.

--Chilton's Spanish Language Edition of Chevrolet 1968 to 1979 Repair & Tune-up Guide. (Illus.). 1981. 11.95 (ISBN 0-8019-7082-2). Chilton.

--Dodge Colt & Challenger Nineteen Seventy-one to Nineteen Eighty-One. LC 80-70346. (Illus.). 242p. 1980. pap. 11.95 (ISBN 0-8019-7037-7). Chilton.

Clarke, R. M. Chevrolet Muscle Cars, 1966-1971. (Illus.). 100p. 1982. pap. 11.95 (ISBN 0-907073-61-1, Pub. by Brooklands Bks England). Motorbooks Intl.

Dammann, George H. Sixty Years of Chevrolet. 3rd ed. LC 79-186267. (Automotive Ser.). (Illus.). 320p. 1973. 24.95 (ISBN 0-912612-03-7). Crestline.

Chilton's Repair & Tune-up Guide for Bronco, 1966-77. (Illus.). 1978. pap. 11.95 (ISBN 0-8019-6701-5). Chilton.

Christ, Steve. How to Rebuild Your Big-Block Ford. (Illus.). 160p. 1983. pap. 9.95 (ISBN 0-89586-070-8). H P BKs.

Clarke, R. M. Ford GT40 1964-1978. (Brooklands Bks.). (Illus.). 70p. (Orig.). 1981. pap. 8.95 (ISBN 0-907073-14-X, Pub. by Brooklands Bks England). Motorbooks Intl.

Clymer Publications. Ford Fairmont and Mercury Zephyr, 1978-1983: Shop Manual. Jorgensen, Eric, ed. (Illus., Orig.). 12.95 (ISBN 0-89287-307-8, A174). Clymer Pubns.

--Jeep Service, Repair Handbook: Covers Willy-Overland Model MB & Ford Model GPW. (Illus.). pap. 7.95 (ISBN 0-89287-250-0, A162). Clymer Pubns.

--Mustang II Service Repair Handbook All Models, 1974-1978. (Illus., Orig.). pap. text ed. 12.95 (ISBN 0-89287-119-9, A169). Clymer Pubns.

Dammann, George H. Illustrated History of Ford, 1903-1970. 3rd ed. LC 73-101694. (Automotive Ser.). (Illus.). 320p. 1974. 24.95 (ISBN 0-912612-02-9). Crestline.

Fahnestock, Murray. Know Your Model A Ford: The Gem from the River Rouge. LC 75-41921. (Illus.). 1958. 11.95 (ISBN 0-911160-30-2). Post-Era.

--Model T Ford Owner. LC 83-61109. (Illus.). 528p. 1983. 21.95 (ISBN 0-911160-23-X). Post-Era.

Fahnestock, Murray, ed. The Model T Speed Secrets, Fast Ford Handbook. (Illus.). 192p. 1968. pap. 10.00 (ISBN 0-911160-17-5). Post-Era.

--Those Wonderful Unauthorized Accessories for Model A Ford. LC 73-164930. (Illus.). 256p. 1971. pap. 12.95 (ISBN 0-911160-27-2). Post-Era.

Fairmont-Zephyr 1978-1983. LC 82-72934. (Illus.). 240p. 1983. pap. 11.95 (ISBN 0-8019-7312-0). Chilton.

Ford & Mercury (Full - Size) Passenger Cars. (Haynes Automotive Manuals). 12.95 (ISBN 0-317-31378-9, 754). Haynes Pubns.

Ford & Mercury (Full-Size) (Haynes Automotive Manuals). write for info. (754). Haynes Pubns.

Ford & Mercury (Mid-Size) (Haynes Automotive Manuals). write for info. (ISBN 0-85696-773-4, 773). Haynes Pubns.

Ford & Mercury Mid-Size Passenger Cars. (Haynes Automotive Manuals). 12.95 (ISBN 0-317-31380-0, 773). Haynes Pubns.

Ford Cortina MK III 1600 & 2000 ohc '70 thru '75. (Haynes Owners Workshop Manuals Ser.: No. 295). 1976. 12.95 (ISBN 0-85696-295-3, Pub by J H Haynes England). Haynes Pubns.

Ford Cortina 1600E. (Super Profile CAR Ser.). 9.95 (ISBN 0-85429-310-8, F310). Haynes Pubns.

Ford Escort-EXP & Mercury Lynx-LN7, 1981 t0 1982: Shop Manual. 320p. 1983. 12.95 (ISBN 0-89287-361-2, A287). Clymer Pubns.

Ford Four-Wheel Drive Tune-up: 1969-1982. (Illus.). pap. 9.95 (ISBN 0-89287-173-3, A232). Clymer Pubns.

Ford, Lincoln, Mercury 1972-1984: Tune-up Maintenance. (Illus.). 176p. 1983. 9.95 (ISBN 0-89287-374-4, A254). Clymer Pubns.

Ford-Mercury Mid-Size. LC 81-70239. (Illus.). 288p. 1982. pap. 11.95 (ISBN 0-8019-7194-2). Chilton.

Ford Motor Co. Ford Passenger Car Shop Manual: 1952-1954. (Illus.). 560p. 1977. 28.95 (ISBN 0-911160-37-X). Post-Era.

Ford Motor Company. Ford Passenger Car Shop Manual: 1949-1951. (Illus.). 320p. 1977. 21.95 (ISBN 0-911160-36-1). Post-Era.

--Ford V-8 Service Bulletins 1932-1937 Complete. Post, Dan R., ed. LC 76-8817. (Illus.). 544p. 1968. 21.95 (ISBN 0-911160-32-9). Post-Era.

--Ford V-8 Service Bulletins 1938-1940 Complete. Post, Dan R., ed. (Illus.). 576p. 1970. Post-Era.

--Ford V-8 Service Bulletins: 1941-1948, Complete. Post, Dan R., ed. LC 76-26325. (Illus.). 1977. 21.95 (ISBN 0-911160-34-5). Post-Era.

--Matchless Model A, a Tour Through the Factory. Post, Dan R., ed. (Illus.). 1961. pap. 3.00 (ISBN 0-911160-29-9). Post-Era.

--Model A Ford Service Bulletins Complete. Post, Dan R., ed. LC 72-90821. (Illus.). 320p. 1957. 13.95 (ISBN 0-911160-28-0). Post-Era.

--Model T Ford Service Bulletin Essentials. Post, Dan R., ed. LC 73-89603. (Illus.). 520p. 1966. 21.95 (ISBN 0-911160-19-1). Post-Era.

Ford Ranger & Bronco II. (Haynes Automotive Manuals). write for info. (ISBN 1-85010-026-8, 1026). Haynes Pubns.

Ford Ranger-Bronco II. (Haynes Automotive Manuals). 12.95 (ISBN 0-317-31377-0, 1026). Haynes Pubns.

Ford Service-Repair Handbook: Courier Pickups, 1972-1982. (Illus.). pap. 12.95 (ISBN 0-89287-198-9, A172). Clymer Pubns.

Ford Spotter's Guide: 1920-1980. 9.95 (ISBN 0-87938-150-7). Motorbooks Intl.

Gill, Barrie & Frostick, Michael. Ford Competition Cars. 19.95 (ISBN 0-85429-440-6, F440). Haynes Pubns.

Hall, Phil. Fearsome Fords, 1959-1973. (Illus.). 184p. 1982. pap. 14.95 (ISBN 0-87938-138-8). Motorbooks Intl.

Haynes, J. H. Ford Cortina MK II '66 thru '70. (Haynes Owners Workshop Manuals Ser.: No. 014). 1974. 12.95 (ISBN 0-900550-14-7, Pub. by J H Haynes England). Haynes Pubns.

Haynes, J. H. & Daniels, M. S. Ford V-Eight Econoline Vans Owners Workshop Manual: '69 Thru 1977. (Haynes Owners Workshop Manuals Ser.: No. 344). 1978. 12.95 (ISBN 0-85696-344-5, Pub by J H Haynes England). Haynes Pubns.

Haynes, J. H. & Page, S. F. Ford 105E & 123E '59 Thru '68. (Haynes Automotive Manuals). 12.95 (ISBN 0-900550-01-5, 001). Haynes Pubns.

Haynes, J. H. & Ward, P. Ford Courier Pick-up '72 thru '82. (Haynes Owners Workshop Manuals Ser.: No. 268). 12.95 (ISBN 0-85696-853-6, Pub by J H Haynes England). Haynes Pubns.

Hoy, Ray. Ford Pickups: 1969-1984 Shop Manual. (F Ser.). (Illus.). pap. text ed. 12.95 (ISBN 0-89287-303-5, A248). Clymer Pubns.

--Ford Vans: 1969-1983 Shop Manual. (Illus.). pap. text ed. 12.95 (ISBN 0-89287-302-7, A249). Clymer Pubns.

Kimes, Beverly R. The Cars That Henry Ford Built. LC 78-51029. 1978. 19.95 (ISBN 0-915038-08-0). Auto Quarterly.

Lahue, Kalton C. Ford Ranger & Bronco II 1983-1984: Includes Diesel & 4-wheel Drive Shop Manual. Wauson, Sydnie A., ed. (Illus.). 320p. 1983. pap. 12.95 (ISBN 0-89287-376-0, A253). Clymer Pubns.

Langworth, Richard M. The Thunderbird Story: Personal Luxury. LC 80-20358. 1980. 29.95 (ISBN 0-87938-093-4). Motorbooks Intl.

Lewis, David L. The Book of Ford Books. (Illus.). 200p. 1981. cancelled (ISBN 0-934780-04-8); pap. write for info. (ISBN 0-934780-05-6). Bookman Dan.

Mayborn, Mitch, ed. Thunderbird 1955-1976. new ed. LC 73-89319. (Highland Ser. 3: Bk. 2). (Illus.). 1975. pap. 2.98 (ISBN 0-913490-09-1). Highland Ent.

Miller, Ray. Falcon! The New Size Ford. LC 82-90194. (Ford Road Ser.: Vol. 7). (Illus.). 320p. 1982. 35.00 (ISBN 0-913056-11-1). Evergreen Pr.

Miller, Ray & Embree, Glenn. Henry's Lady: An Illustrated History of the Model A Ford. LC 72-77244. (The Ford Road Ser.: Vol. 2). (Illus.). 300p. 1972. 35.00 (ISBN 0-913056-03-0). Evergreen Pr.

--Thunderbird! An Illustrated History of the Ford T-Bird. LC 73-75630. (The Ford Road Ser: Vol. 4). (Illus.). 1973. 35.00 (ISBN 0-913056-04-9). Evergreen Pr.

--The V-Eight Affair: An Illustrated History of the Pre-War Ford V-8. LC 70-174898. (The Ford Road Ser: Vol. 3). (Illus.). 303p. 1972. 35.00 (ISBN 0-913056-02-2). Evergreen Pr.

Monroe, Tom. How to Rebuild Your Ford V-8. LC 80-80171. (Orig.). 1980. pap. 9.95 (ISBN 0-89586-036-8). H P Bks.

--How to Rebuild Your Small-Block Ford. LC 78-74545. (Illus.). 1979. pap. 9.95 (ISBN 0-912656-89-1). H P Bks.

Murray, Spence, ed. Ford Pickup Repair. LC 78-65688. (Pickups & Vans Ser.). (Illus.). 1979. pap. text ed. 4.95 (ISBN 0-8227-5042-2). Petersen Pub.

North, Paul. Shelby, Vol. II. (Source Bks.). (Illus.). 144p. 1985. pap. 12.95 (ISBN 0-934780-62-5). Bookman Dan.

Page, Victor W. Model A Ford: Construction, Operation, Repair for the Restorer. LC 73-83509. (Illus.). 576p. 1961. 14.95 (ISBN 0-911160-31-0). Post-Era.

Pepperdine, George, ed. Model T Ford Owner's Supply Book. (Illus.). 1959. pap. 6.95 (ISBN 0-911160-20-5). Post-Era.

Pulfer, Harry, ed. Model T Ford in Speed & Sport. LC 74-26384. (Illus.). 224p. 1956. pap. 12.95 (ISBN 0-911160-15-9). Post-Era.

Pushkariov, V. Treasures of the Russian Museum. 266p. 1975. 39.00x (ISBN 0-317-14324-7, Pub. by Collet's). State Mutual Bk.

Robinson, Jeff, ed. Mustang Service-Repair Handbook: All Models, 1964-1973. (Illus.). pap. text ed. 12.95 (ISBN 0-89287-088-5, A167). Clymer Pubns.

Robson, Graham. Ford Escort RS. (Auto History Ser.). (Illus.). 128p. 1981. 14.95 (ISBN 0-85045-401-8, Pub. by Osprey England). Motorbooks Intl.

--Sporting Fords: Cortinas. (Collector's Guide Ser.). (Illus.). 130p. 1982. 18.95 (ISBN 0-900549-68-8, Pub. by Motor Racing England). Motorbooks Intl.

--The Sporting Fords: Escorts. (Collector's Guide Ser.). (Illus.). 130p. 1982. 27.50 (ISBN 0-900549-71-8, 65-06422, Pub. by Motor Racing England). Motorbooks Intl.

Sheilds, Samuel. Big Fords & Mercurys. (Source Bks.). 144p. 1984. pap. 12.95 (ISBN 0-934780-38-2). Bookman Dan.

Siuru & Holder. Ford Ranchero Nineteen Fifty-Seven to Nineteen Seventy-Nine Photofacts. (Photofacts Ser.). (Illus.). 80p. 1985. pap. 9.95 (ISBN 0-87938-183-3). Motorbooks Intl.

Sorensen, Lorin. The Classy Ford V8. (Illus.). 240p. 1983. 35.00 (ISBN 0-942636-00-7, F705). Motorbooks Intl.

--The Ford Shows. (Fordiana Ser.). (Illus.). 245p. 1976. 49.50 (ISBN 0-87938-080-2). Silverado.

Toboldt, Bill. Fix Your Ford. rev. ed. (Illus.). 416p. 1983. 8.00 (ISBN 0-87006-446-0). Goodheart.

Vizard, David. How to Rebuild Your 1.3, 1.6 & 2.0 OHC Ford. (Orig.). 1980. pap. 7.95 (ISBN 0-912656-68-9). H P Bks.

Witzenburg, Gary L. Firebird! America's Premier Performance Car: The Complete History. LC 82-71935. (Marque History Book Ser.). (Illus.). 240p. 1982. 29.95 (ISBN 0-915038-36-6); leather binding 62.50 (ISBN 0-915038-37-4). Auto Quarterly.

AUTOMOBILES–TYPES–GREMLIN

Hayden, D. & Strasman, P. G. AMC Owners Workshop Manual: Gremlin Spirit, Hornet & Concord Six Cylinder 1973 Thru 1983. (Haynes Owners Workshop Manuals Ser.: No. 694). 1984. 12.95 (ISBN 0-85696-694-0, Pub. by J H Haynes England). Haynes Pubns.

AUTOMOBILES–TYPES–JEEP

Blazer-Jimmy Nineteen Sixty-Nine to Nineteen Eighty-Two. LC 81-70234. (Illus.). 288p. 1982. pap. 11.95 (ISBN 0-8019-7203-5). Chilton.

Chilton Staff. Chilton's Repair & Tune-up Guide: Jeep CJ 1945-85. LC 85-47977. 388p. (Orig.). 1986. pap. 12.50 (ISBN 0-8019-7675-8). Chilton.

Chilton's Automotive Editorial Staff. Jeep CJ 1945-1984: RTUG. LC 83-45320. 312p. 1984. pap. 11.95 (ISBN 0-8019-7484-4). Chilton.

Clarke, R. M. Jeep Collection, No. 1. (Illus.). 70p. (Orig.). 1982. pap. 8.95 (ISBN 0-907073-54-9, Pub. by Brooklands Bks. England). Motorbooks Intl.

Clayton, Michael. Jeep. (Illus.). 128p. 1982. 21.00 (ISBN 0-7153-8066-4). David & Charles.

Gurney, G. Jeep Book. 1986. cancelled (ISBN 0-442-21912-1). Van Nos Reinhold.

Haynes, J. H. & Warren, Larry. Jeep CJ. (Haynes Automotive Manuals). 12.95 (ISBN 0-85696-412-3, 412). Haynes Pubns.

Jeudy, J. G. & Tararine, Marc. The Jeep. LC 81-66413. (Illus.). 272p. 1981. 24.95 (ISBN 0-86710-008-7). Edns Vilo.

Richards, T. Military Jeeps, Nineteen Forty-One to Nineteen Forty-Five. 100p. 1985. pap. 11.95 (ISBN 0-946489-27-0). Portrayal.

--Off Road Jeeps: Civilian & Military, 1944-1971. 100p. 1985. pap. 11.95 (ISBN 0-946489-83-1). Portrayal.

Vanderveen, Bart H. The Jeep. (Olyslager Auto Library). (Illus.). 64p. 1981. 11.95 (ISBN 0-7232-2778-0, Pub. by Warne Pubs England). Motorbooks Intl.

Wauson, Sydnie A., ed. AMC Jeep CJ-5, CJ-6, CJ-7: 1968-1984. Lahue, Kalton C. (Illus.). 392p. (Orig.). pap. 12.95 (ISBN 0-89287-364-7). Clymer Pubns.

Willinger, Kurt & Gurney, Gene. The American Jeep. 1983. 17.95 (ISBN 0-517-54734-1); pap. 8.95 (ISBN 0-517-54735-X). Crown.

AUTOMOBILES–TYPES–LINCOLN

Bonsall, Thomas E. The Lincoln Motorcar: Sixty Years of Excellence. (Illus.). 325p. 1981. 32.95 (ISBN 0-934780-05-6). Bookman Dan.

Mayborn, Mitch, ed. Lincoln-Classic Legend of Excellence. new ed. (Highland Ser. 1: Bk. 3). (Illus.). 52p. 1972. pap. 2.98 (ISBN 0-913490-02-4). Highland Ent.

Wagner, William. Continental: Its Motors & Its People. (Illus.). 256p. 1983. 19.95 (ISBN 0-8168-4506-9). Aero.

Woudenberg, Paul. Lincoln & Continental: The Postwar Years. LC 80-12242. (Marques of America Ser.). (Illus.). 152p. 1980. 19.95 (ISBN 0-87938-063-2). Motorbooks Intl.

AUTOMOBILES–TYPES–MAVERICK

Chilton's Automotive Editorial Staff. Chilton's Repair & Tune-up Guide for Maverick & Comet 1970-1977. LC 77-75991. (Chilton's Repair & Tune-up Guides). (Illus., Orig.). 1977. pap. 11.95 (ISBN 0-8019-6634-5, 6634). Chilton.

AUTOMOBILES–TYPES–MERCURY

Bonsall, Thomas. Muscle Mercurys. (Muscle Car Ser.). (Illus.). 96p. 1984. pap. 8.95 (ISBN 0-934780-48-X). Bookman Dan.

Bonsall, Thomas E. Mercury & Edsel Identification Guide, 1939-1969. (Identification Guide Ser.). (Illus.). 96p. 1982. pap. 8.95 (ISBN 0-934780-15-3). Bookman Dan.

Carley, Larry W. Ford Escort-Mercury Lynx Cars, Nineteen Eighty-One to Nineteen Eighty-Four: Do-it-Yourself Car Care. (Illus.). 352p. (Orig.). 1984. pap. 11.95 (ISBN 0-8306-2133-4, 2133). TAB Bks.

Chilton. Chilton's Repair & Tune-up Guide for Ford-Mercury FWD 1982-1985. 240p. 1985. pap. 11.95 (ISBN 0-8019-7544-1). Chilton.

Chilton's Automotive Editorial Staff. Chilton's Repair & Tune-up Guide for Maverick & Comet 1970-1977. LC 77-75991. (Chilton's Repair & Tune-up Guides). (Illus., Orig.). 1977. pap. 11.95 (ISBN 0-8019-6634-5, 6634). Chilton.

--Chilton's Repair & Tune-Up Guide: Ford-Mercury 1968-83. LC 82-72940. 288p. 1983. pap. 11.95 (ISBN 0-8019-7318-X). Chilton.

--Escort & Lynx, 1981 to 1982. (Illus.). 1981. pap. 11.95 (ISBN 0-8019-7055-5). Chilton.

--Ford Mercury Mid-Size: 1971-1985. LC 84-45484. 392p. (Orig.). 1985. pap. 11.95 (ISBN 0-8019-7566-2). Chilton.

--Ford Mercury: 1968-1985. LC 84-45476. 288p. (Orig.). 1985. pap. 11.95 (ISBN 0-8019-7573-5). Chilton.

Ford & Mercury (Full - Size) Passenger Cars. (Haynes Automotive Manuals). 12.95 (ISBN 0-317-31378-9, 754). Haynes Pubns.

Ford & Mercury (Full-Size) (Haynes Automotive Manuals). write for info. (754). Haynes Pubns.

Ford & Mercury (Mid-Size) (Haynes Automotive Manuals). write for info. (ISBN 0-85696-773-4, 773). Haynes Pubns.

Ford & Mercury Mid-Size Passenger Cars. (Haynes Automotive Manuals). 12.95 (ISBN 0-317-31380-0, 773). Haynes Pubns.

Ford Escort-EXP & Mercury Lynx-LN7, 1981 t0 1982: Shop Manual. 320p. 1983. 12.95 (ISBN 0-89287-361-2, A287). Clymer Pubns.

Ford-Mercury Mid-Size. LC 81-70239. (Illus.). 288p. 1982. pap. 11.95 (ISBN 0-8019-7194-2). Chilton.

Halla, Chris. Mercury Cougar Nineteen Sixty-Seven to Nineteen Seventy-Three Photofacts. (Photofacts Ser.). (Illus.). 80p. 1985. pap. 9.95 (ISBN 0-87938-176-0). Motorbooks Intl.

Jorgenson, Eric, ed. Ford Pinto & Mercury Bobcat: 1971-1980. pap. 12.95 (ISBN 0-89287-211-X). Clymer Pubns.

Pinto & Bobcat Ninteen Seventy-One to Eighty. LC 80-70340. (Illus.). 280p. 1980. pap. 11.95 (ISBN 0-8019-7027-X). Chilton.

Sheilds, Samuel. Big Fords & Mercurys. (Source Bks.). 144p. 1984. pap. 12.95 (ISBN 0-934780-38-2). Bookman Dan.

AUTOMOBILES–TYPES–MUSTANG

Ackerson, Robert C. Mustangs. (Source Bks.). (Illus.). 144p. 1984. pap. 12.95 (ISBN 0-934780-41-2). Bookman Dan.

Chilton. Chilton's Repair & Tune Up Guide: Mustang & Cougar, 1965-83. LC 83-70992. 252p. (Orig.). 1983. pap. 11.95 (ISBN 0-8019-7405-4). Chilton.

Chilton's Automotive Editorial Staff. Chilton's Mustang II: 1974-1978, Repair & Tune-up Guide. LC 78-22143. (Repair & Tune-up Guides Ser.). (Illus.). 1979. pap. 11.95 (ISBN 0-8019-6812-7). Chilton.

--Mustang Capri, Nineteen Seventy-Nine to Nineteen Eighty-Five. LC 84-45470. 272p. (Orig.). 1985. pap. 11.95 (ISBN 0-8019-7585-9). Chilton.

Clarke, R. M. Ford Mustang: Nineteen Sixty-Four to Nineteen Sixty-Seven. (Brooklands Bks.). (Illus.). 100p. (Orig.). 1979. pap. 11.95 (ISBN 0-906589-70-3, Pub. by Brooklands Bks England). Motorbooks Intl.

--Ford Mustang Nineteen Sixty-Seven to Nineteen Seventy-Three. (Brooklands Bks.). (Illus.). 100p. (Orig.). 1981. pap. 2.95 (ISBN 0-907073-29-8, Pub. by Brooklands Bks England). Motorbooks Intl.

Dobbs, Larry & Farr, Donald. How to Restore Your Mustang. 1980. 14.95 (ISBN 0-941596-01-X). Mustang Pubns.

Farr, Donald. Mustang Boss 302. 1983. 12.95 (ISBN 0-941596-03-6). Mustang Pubns.

--Mustang How To. 1983. pap. 6.95 (ISBN 0-941596-04-4). Mustang Pubns.

Haynes, J. H. & Daniels, M. S. Ford Mustang II Owners Workshop Manual: 74 Thru 78. (Haynes Owners Workshop Manuals Ser.: No. 231). 1977. 12.95 (ISBN 0-85696-629-0, Pub. by J H Haynes England). Haynes Pubns.

Haynes, J. H. & Gilmour, M. B. Ford Mustang I Owners Workshop Manual V-Eight: '65 Thru '73. (Haynes Owners Workshop Manuals Ser.: No. 357). 1978. 12.95 (ISBN 0-85696-357-7, Pub by J H Haynes England). Haynes Pubns.

--Ford Mustang V8. (Haynes Automotive Manuals). 12.95 (ISBN 0-85696-357-7, 357). Haynes Pubns.

Haynes, J. H., et al. Ford Mustang & Mercury Capri (V6 & V8) (Haynes Automotive Manuals). 12.95 (ISBN 1-85010-000-4, 558). Haynes Pubns.

Heasley, Jerry. The Ford Mustang Nineteen Sixty Four to Nineteen Seventy Three. (Illus.). 1979. pap. 8.25 (ISBN 0-8306-2048-6, 2048). TAB Bks.

--How to Paint Your Mustang. 1982. pap. 7.95 (ISBN 0-941596-02-8). Mustang Pubns.
Mayborn, Mitch, ed. Mustang 1964-1977. (Highland Ser. 3: Bk. 4). (Illus.). 1977. pap. 2.98 (ISBN 0-913490-10-5). Highland Ent.
Miller, Ray. Mustang Does It. LC 77-78278. (The Ford Road Ser.: Vol. 6). 1978. lib. bdg. 35.00 (ISBN 0-913056-09-X). Evergreen Pr.
Mustang Monthly Staff. Mustang Monthly Parts & Services Directory. 1984. pap. 4.95 (ISBN 0-941596-05-2). Mustang Pubns.
P51 Mustang. (Super Profile AC Ser.). 9.95 (ISBN 0-85429-423-6, F423). Haynes Pubns.
Strange, Stephen B. Boss 429 Performance Mustang Style. LC 84-73250. (Illus.). 100p. 1985. pap. 16.95 (ISBN 0-931417-02-3). Boss Perform.
Witzenburg, Gary. Mustang. (Automobile Quarterly Marque History Ser.). 1979. 27.95 (ISBN 0-525-16175-9). Dutton.
Wright, Ron. Ford Mustang & Mercury Capri 1979-1983: Includes Turbo Shop Manual. Wauson, Sydnie A., ed. (Illus.). 384p. 1983. 12.95 (ISBN 0-89287-378-7, A255). Clymer Pubns.

AUTOMOBILES–TYPES–NOVA

Chilton Staff. Chilton's Repair & Tune-up Guide: Chevrolet Nova 1985. LC 85-47959. 188p. (Orig.). 1986. pap. 12.50 (ISBN 0-8019-7658-8). Chilton.
Chilton's Automotive Editorial Staff. Chevy Two & Nova, Nineteen Sixty-Two to Nineteen Seventy-Nine. LC 78-20253. (Chilton's Repair & Tune-up Guides). (Illus.). 1979. pap. 11.95 (ISBN 0-8019-6841-0, 6841). Chilton.
Haynes, J. H. & Ward, P. Chevrolet Nova Owners Workshop Manual: V-Eight 1969 thru 1975. (Haynes Owners Workshop Manuals: No. 241). 1976. 12.95 (ISBN 0-85696-693-2, Pub by J H Haynes England). Haynes Pubns.
--Chevrolet Nova Owners Workshop Manual: V8 '69 Thru '79. (Owners Workshop Manuals: No. 241). 1980. 12.95 (ISBN 0-85696-693-2, Pub. by J H Haynes England). Haynes Pubns.
Jorgensen, Eric, ed. Chevy Nova 1971-1979: Shop Manual. (Illus.). pap. text ed. 12.95 (ISBN 0-89287-317-5, A133). Clymer Pubns.
Lehwald, Edward A. Nova SS, Vol. II. (Source Bks.). (Illus.). 144p. 1985. pap. 12.95 (ISBN 0-934780-58-7). Bookman Dan.
--Nova SS: A Source Book. (Illus.). 144p. (Orig.). 1983. pap. 12.95 (ISBN 0-934780-18-8). Bookman Dan.

AUTOMOBILES–TYPES–OLDSMOBILE

Bonsall, Thomas. Muscle Oldsmobiles. (Muscle Car Ser.). (Illus.). 96p. 1985. pap. 8.95 (ISBN 0-934780-59-5). Bookman Dan.
Casteele, Dennis. The Cars of Oldsmobile. Dammann, George H., ed. LC 76-5767. (Automotive Ser.). (Illus.). 416p. 1981. 29.95 (ISBN 0-912612-11-8). Crestline.
--Four-Four-Two: A Source Book. (Illus.). 144p. 1982. pap. 12.95 (ISBN 0-934780-12-9). Bookman Dan.
Chilton Staff. Chilton's Repair & Tune-up Guide: GM N-Body 1985-86 Buick, Somerset, Olds Calais & Pontiac Grand Am. LC 85-47958. 224p. (Orig.). 1986. pap. 12.50 (ISBN 0-8019-7657-X). Chilton.
Chilton's Automotive Editorial Staff. Chilton's Repair & Tune-Up Guide: Buick-Olds-Pontiac Full Size 1975-83. LC 82-72930. 308p. 1983. pap. 11.95 (ISBN 0-8019-7308-2). Chilton.
--Chilton's Repair & Tune-up Guide for Cutlass-442, 1970-1977. LC 77-89117. (Chilton's Repair & Tune-up Guides). (Illus., Orig.). 1978. pap. 11.95 (ISBN 0-8019-6597-7, 6597). Chilton.
--Cutlass 1970-85. LC 84-45464. 296p. (Orig.). 1985. pap. 11.95 (ISBN 0-8019-7591-3). Chilton.
Chilton's Repair & Tune-up Guide: Cutlass, 1970-1980. pap. 11.95 (ISBN 0-8019-6933-6). Chilton.
Collins, Joe. Four-Four-Two vs. the Pack. (Pack Ser.). (Illus.). 128p. 1985. pap. 10.95 (ISBN 0-934780-69-2). Bookman Dan.
Cutlass Nineteen Seventy to Nineteen Eighty-Two. LC 81-70246. (Illus.). 288p. 1982. pap. 11.95 (ISBN 0-8019-7190-X). Chilton.
Cutlass: Nineteen Sixty-Seven to Eighty Repair & Tune-up Guide. (New Automotive Bks.). 224p. 1980. 11.95 (ISBN 0-8019-6933-6). Chilton.
Haynes, J. H. & Mauck, Scott. Oldsmobile Cutlass: 1974 Thru 1980. (Owners Workshop Manuals: 658). 331p. 1984. pap. 12.95 (ISBN 1-85010-071-3). Haynes Pubns.
Norbye, Jan & Dunne, Jim. Oldsmobile: The Postwar Years. LC 81-1251. (Illus.). 152p. 1981. 19.95 (ISBN 0-87938-122-1). Motorbooks Intl.
North, Paul. Four-Four-Two, Vol. II. (Source Bks.). (Illus.). 144p. 1985. pap. 12.95 (ISBN 0-934780-57-9). Bookman Dan.
Warson, Sydnie A., ed. GMC J Cars: Buick Skylark, Cadillac Cimarron, Chevrolet Cavalier, Oldsmobile Firenza, Pontiac J-2000 Shop Manual, 1982-1983. 384p. (Orig.). 1983. pap. 12.95 (ISBN 0-89287-362-0). Clymer Pubns.
Zavitz, R. Perry. Four-Four-Two Databook & Price Guide, 1964-1985. (Data Bks.). (Illus.). 128p. 1985. pap. 9.95 (ISBN 0-934780-75-7). Bookman Dan.

AUTOMOBILES–TYPES–PACKARD

Schroeder, Otto A., compiled by. Packard, Ask the Man Who Owned One. new ed. LC 73-83510. (Illus.). 384p. 1975. 16.95 (ISBN 0-911160-63-9). Post-Era.

AUTOMOBILES–TYPES–PIERCE ARROW

Ralston, Mark A. Pierce Arrow. LC 80-15214. (Illus.). 366p. 1980. 25.00 (ISBN 0-498-02451-2). A S Barnes.

AUTOMOBILES–TYPES–PINTO

Hall, Al, ed. Pinto Tune-up & Repair. LC 79-64837. (Tune-up & Repair Ser.). (Illus.). 198p. (Orig.). 1979. pap. 4.95 (ISBN 0-8227-5047-3). Petersen Pub.
Haynes, J. H. & Chalmers-Hunt, B. L. Ford Pinto '70 thru '74. (Haynes Owners Workshop Manuals Ser.: No. 204). 1975. 12.95 (ISBN 0-85696-628-2, Pub by J H Haynes England). Haynes Pubns.
Jorgensen, Eric, ed. Ford Pinto & Mercury Bobcat Service Repair Handbook: All Models 1971-1980. (Illus.). pap. 13.95 (ISBN 0-89287-211-X, A171). Clymer Pubns.
Jorgenson, Eric, ed. Ford Pinto & Mercury Bobcat: 1971-1980. pap. 12.95 (ISBN 0-89287-211-X). Clymer Pubns.
Pinto & Bobcat Nineteen Seventy-One to Eighty. LC 80-70340. (Illus.). 280p. 1980. pap. 11.95 (ISBN 0-8019-7027-X). Chilton.

AUTOMOBILES–TYPES–PLYMOUTH

see also Automobiles–Types–Barracuda; Automobiles–Types–Valiant

Arrow & Dodge D-Fifty Pick-Ups 1979-81. LC 80-70343. (Illus.). 192p. pap. 11.95 (ISBN 0-8019-7032-6). Chilton.
Aspen-Volare Nineteen Seventy-Six to Nineteen Eighty. LC 81-70240. (Illus.). 224p. 1982. pap. 11.95 for info. (ISBN 0-8019-7193-4). Chilton.
Bonsall, Thomas. Muscle Plymouths. (Muscle Car Ser.). (Illus.). 96p. 1984. pap. 8.95 (ISBN 0-934780-49-8). Bookman Dan.
Bonsall, Thomas E. Muscle Plymouths: The Story of a Supercar. (Muscle Bks.). (Illus.). 96p. 1985. pap. 8.95 (ISBN 0-934780-71-4). Bookman Dan.
Butler, F. Donald. The Plymouth & De Soto Story. Dammann, George H., ed. LC 77-93182. (Automotive Ser.). (Illus.). 1979. 29.95 (ISBN 0-912612-14-2). Crestline.
Chilton. Plymouth Car: How to Fix. 1954. 3.95x (ISBN 0-685-21976-3). Wehman.
Chilton Staff. Chilton's Repair & Tune-up Guide: Dodge-Plymouth Trucks 1967-86. LC 85-47983. 288p. (Orig.). 1986. pap. 12.50 (ISBN 0-8019-7683-9). Chilton.
Chilton's Automotive Editorial Staff. Chilton's Repair & Tune-up Guide for Road Runner, Satellite, Belvedere, GTX, 1968-1973. LC 73-4347. (Illus.). 224p. 1973. pap. 11.95 (ISBN 0-8019-5821-0). Chilton.
--Dodge - Plymouth Vans 1967-84: RTUG. LC 83-45307. 264p. 1984. pap. 11.95 (ISBN 0-8019-7465-8). Chilton.
--Dodge-Plymouth Vans, Nineteen Sixty-Seven to Nineteen Eighty-Two. 1982. pap. 11.95 (ISBN 0-8019-7168-3). Chilton.
--Omni & Horizon, Nineteen Seventy-Eight to Nineteen Eighty. LC 78-20257. (Chilton's Repair & Tune-Up Guides Ser.). (Illus.). 1979. pap. 11.95 (ISBN 0-8019-6845-3, 6845). Chilton.
--Omni-Horizon 1978-84: RTUG. LC 83-45319. 224p. 1984. pap. 11.95 (ISBN 0-8019-7485-2). Chilton.
--Plymouth Champ-Arrow-& Sapporo, 1977 to 1981. LC 80-70347. (Illus.). 208p. 1981. pap. 11.95 (ISBN 0-8019-7041-5). Chilton.
Chrysler, Dodge, Plymouth: 1972-1984 Rear Wheel Drive Tune-up Maintenance. (Illus.). 196p. (Orig.). 1984. pap. 13.95 (ISBN 0-89287-383-3). Clymer Pubns.
Haynes, J. H. & Gilmour, M. B. Dodge Omni & Plymouth Horizon '78 -'84. (Haynes Automotive Manuals). 12.95 (ISBN 0-317-31367-3, 545). Haynes Pubns.
Haynes, J. H. & Strasman, P. G. Plymouth Valiant & Barracuda '67 - '76. (Owners Workshop Manuals: No. 233). 1977. 12.95 (ISBN 0-85696-233-3, Pub. by J H Haynes England). Haynes Pubns.
Jorgensen, Eric, ed. Plymouth Arrow: 1976-1980 Shop Manual. (Illus.). pap. 12.95 (ISBN 0-89287-275-6, A178). Clymer Pubns.
North, Paul. Kit Cars. (Source Bks.). (Illus.). 144p. 1986. pap. 12.95 (ISBN 0-934780-76-5). Bookman Dan.
Shields, Samuel A., Jr. Road Runner: A Source Book. (Illus.). 144p. (Orig.). 1983. pap. 12.95 (ISBN 0-934780-20-X). Bookman Dan.
Warson, Sydnie A., ed. Chrysler, Dodge, Plymouth: LeBaron, Aries, 400, Reliant 1981-1985. (Orig.). pap. 13.95. Clymer Pubns.

AUTOMOBILES–TYPES–PONTIAC

Bonsall, Thomas. GTO, Vol. II. (Source Bks.). (Illus.). 144p. 1985. pap. 12.95 (ISBN 0-934780-50-1). Bookman Dan.
--Muscle Pontiacs. (Muscle Car Ser.). (Illus.). 96p. 1984. pap. 8.95 (ISBN 0-934780-44-7). Bookman Dan.
Bonsall, Thomas E. Pontiac Identification Guide, 1926-1966. (Identification Guide Ser.). (Illus.). 96p. (Orig.). 1982. pap. 8.95 (ISBN 0-934780-14-5). Bookman Dan.
--Pontiac: The Complete History, 1926-1986. Date not set. price not set. Bookman Dan.
--Pontiac: The Complete History, 1926-79. LC 79-56550. (Illus.). 352p. 1985. 29.95 (ISBN 0-934780-02-1). Bookman Dan.
Bonsall, Thomas E., ed. GTO: A Source Book. (Illus.). 142p. (Orig.). 1980. pap. 12.95 (ISBN 0-934780-03-X). Bookman Dan.
--Muscle Pontiacs: The Years of Excitement. (Muscle Bks). (Illus.). 96p. 1985. pap. 8.95 (ISBN 0-934780-68-4). Bookman Dan.
Chilton Staff. Chilton's Repair & Tune-up Guide: Chevette-Pontiac T1000 1976-86. LC 85-47967. 256p. (Orig.). 1986. pap. 12.50 (ISBN 0-8019-7666-9). Chilton.
--Chilton's Repair & Tune-up Guide: GM N-Body 1985-86 Buick, Somerset, Olds Calais & Pontiac Grand Am. LC 85-47958. 224p. (Orig.). 1986. pap. 12.50 (ISBN 0-8019-7657-X). Chilton.
Chilton's Automotive Editorial Staff. Chilton's Repair & Tune-Up Guide: Buick-Olds-Pontiac Full Size 1975-83. LC 82-72930. 308p. 1983. pap. 11.95 (ISBN 0-8019-7308-2). Chilton.
--Chilton's Repair & Tune-Up Guide: Firebird 1982-83. LC 82-72927. 217p. 1983. pap. 11.95 (ISBN 0-8019-7345-7). Chilton.
--Chilton's Repair & Tune-up Guide: Pontiac Mid-Size 1974-83. LC 82-72928. 288p. 1983. pap. 11.95 (ISBN 0-8019-7346-5). Chilton.
--Firebird, Nineteen Sixty-Seven to Nineteen Eighty-One. (Illus.). 1981. pap. 11.95 (ISBN 0-8019-7046-6). Chilton.
--Pontiac Fiero: 1984-85. LC 84-45478. 224p. (Orig.). 1985. pap. 11.95 (ISBN 0-8019-7571-9). Chilton.
Clarke, R. M. Pontiac Firebird, 1967 to 1973. (Brooklands Bks.). (Illus.). 100p. (Orig.). 1981. pap. 11.95 (ISBN 0-907073-30-1, Pub. by Brooklands Bks England). Motorbooks Intl.
Haynes, J. H. & Raffa, J. B. Pontiac Firebird '82-'84. (Haynes Automotive Manuals). 12.95 (ISBN 0-85696-867-6, 867). Haynes Pubns.
Jorgensen, Eric, ed. Pontiac Firebird 1970-1981 Shop Manual. (Illus., Orig.). pap. text ed. 12.95 (ISBN 0-89287-306-X, A235). Clymer Pubns.
Lahue, Kalton C. Camaro & Firebird Shop Manual, 1982-1985. Wauson, Sydnie, ed. (Illus.). 342p. 1984. pap. 12.95 (ISBN 0-89287-377-9, A257). Clymer Pubns.
Lamm, Michael. The Fabulous Firebird. (Illus.). 160p. 1979. 19.95 (ISBN 0-932128-01-7). Lamm-Morada.
Norbye, Jan P. & Dunne, Jim. Pontiac: The Postwar Years. LC 79-17430. (Illus.). 205p. 1980. 19.95 (ISBN 0-87938-060-8). Motorbooks Intl.
Oldham, Joe. Supertuning Your Firebird Trans-Am. (Illus.). 288p. 1982. pap. 9.95 (ISBN 0-8306-2088-5, 2088). TAB Bks.
Sass, Dale. Grand Prix. (Classic Source Bks.). (Illus.). 144p. 1985. pap. 12.95 (ISBN 0-934780-67-6). Bookman Dan.
Warson, Sydnie A., ed. GMC J Cars: Buick Skylark, Cadillac Cimarron, Chevrolet Cavalier, Oldsmobile Firenza, Pontiac J-2000 Shop Manual, 1982-1983. 384p. (Orig.). 1983. pap. 12.95 (ISBN 0-89287-362-0). Clymer Pubns.
Zavitz, R. Perry. GTO Databook & Price Guide, 1964-1974. (Data Bks.). (Illus.). 128p. 1985. pap. 9.95 (ISBN 0-934780-73-0). Bookman Dan.

AUTOMOBILES–TYPES–ROADRUNNER

North, Paul. Road Runner, Vol. II. (Source Bks.). (Illus.). 144p. 1985. pap. 12.95 (ISBN 0-934780-55-2). Bookman Dan.

AUTOMOBILES–TYPES–VALIANT

Chilton's Automotive Editorial Staff. Chilton's Repair & Tune-up Guide for Valiant & Duster, 1968-1976. (Illus.). 190p. 1975. pap. 10.95 (ISBN 0-8019-6326-5). Chilton.

AUTOMOBILES–TYPES–STUDEBAKER

Mayborn, Mitch, ed. The Last Years of Studebaker 1952-1966. new ed. (Highland Ser. 3: Bk. 1). (Illus.). 52p. 1973. pap. 2.98 (ISBN 0-913490-08-3). Highland Ent.

AUTOMOBILES–TYPES–VEGA

Combs, Jim & Robinson, Jeff. Vega Service, Repair Handbook 1971-1977 Models. 3rd ed. (Illus.). pap. 13.95 (ISBN 0-89287-130-X, A135). Clymer Pubns.
Haynes, J. H. & Strasman, P. G. Chevrolet Vega Owners Workshop Manual: '70 Thru '77. (Owners Workshop Manuals: No. 208). 1978. 12.95 (ISBN 0-85696-630-4, Pub. by J H Haynes England). Haynes Pubns.

AUTOMOBILES–TYPES–WILLYS-KNIGHT

Clymer Publications. Jeep Service, Repair Handbook: Covers Willy-Overland Model MB & Ford Model GPW. (Illus.). pap. 7.95 (ISBN 0-89287-250-0, A162). Clymer Pubns.

AUTOMOBILES–WHEELS

Thiessen, Frank J. Automotive Wheel Alignment: Principles & Service. 1985. text ed. 29.95 (ISBN 0-8359-0008-8); pap. text ed. 21.95 (ISBN 0-8359-0007-X). Reston.

AUTOMOBILES, DIESEL

see Automobiles–Motors

AUTOMOBILES, ELECTRIC

Christian, Jeffrey M. & Reibsamen, Gary G. World Guide to Battery Powered Road Transportation. (Illus.). 352p. 1980. 59.50 (ISBN 0-07-010790-4). McGraw.
The Electric Vehicle E-016R: Inevitable? 1980. 800.00 (ISBN 0-89336-189-5). BCC.
Traister. All about Electric & Hybrid Cars. (Illus.). 308p. 1982. 16.95 (ISBN 0-8306-0098-1, 2097); pap. 9.95 (ISBN 0-8306-2097-4). TAB Bks.
Unnewehr, L. E. & Nasar, S. A. Electric Vehicle Technology. LC 81-21909. 256p. 1982. 54.95x (ISBN 0-471-08378-X, Pub. by Wiley-Interscience). Wiley.
Whitener, Barbara. The Electric Car Book. LC 80-80973. (Illus.). 88p. (Orig.). 1980. pap. 6.95 (ISBN 0-915216-58-2). Marathon Intl Pub Co.

AUTOMOBILES, FOREIGN

Aftermarket for Imported Cars, & Light Trucks. 232p. 1984. 1400.00 (ISBN 0-86621-174-8). Frost & Sullivan.
Anselmi, Angelo T. Isotta Fraschini. (Illus.). 1978. 49.95 (ISBN 0-87938-052-7, Pub. by Milani Italy). Motorbooks Intl.
Bockelmann, W. D. Auge, Brille, Auto. (Illus.). xii, 496p. 1982. pap. 46.75 (ISBN 3-8055-3445-0). S Karger.
Bolster, John. Lotus Elan & Europa: A Collector's Guide. (Collector's Guide Ser.). (Illus.). 138p. 1980. 18.95 (ISBN 0-900549-48-3, Pub. by Motor Racing England). Motorbooks Intl.
Browning, Peter. The Works Minis. (Illus.). 206p. pap. 6.95 (ISBN 0-85429-278-0, F278). Haynes Pubns.
Burness, Tad. Imported Car Spotter's Guide. LC 79-24498. (Illus.). 351p. 1980. pap. 15.95 (ISBN 0-87938-067-5). Motorbooks Intl.
Chilton's Automotive Editorial Staff. Import Automotive Service Manual 1977-1985. LC 82-72910. (Professional Mechanics Ser.). 1848p. 1985. 36.00 (ISBN 0-8019-7595-6). Chilton.
--Zephyr 1978-1980. (Illus.). 1980. pap. 11.95 (ISBN 0-8019-6965-4). Chilton.
Clarke, R. M. Jensen-Healey 1972-1976. (Brooklands Bks). (Illus.). 100p. (Orig.). 1981. pap. 11.95 (ISBN 0-906589-89-4, Pub. by Brooklands Bks England). Motorbooks Intl.
--Jensen Interceptor 1966-1976. (Brooklands Bks.). (Illus.). 100p. (Orig.). 1981. pap. 11.95 (ISBN 0-686-30670-8, Pub. by Brooklands Bks England). Motorbooks Intl.
--TVR: Nineteen Sixty to Nineteen Eighty. (Illus.). 100p. 1981. 11.95 (ISBN 0-907073-20-4, Pub. by Brooklands Bks England). Motorbooks Intl.
Daniels, Jeff. Citroen SM. (Osprey Auto History Ser.). (Illus.). 136p. 1981. 14.95 (ISBN 0-85045-381-X, Pub. by Osprey England). Motorbooks Intl.
Edmund's Foreign Car Prices. (Orig.). 1984. pap. 2.95 (ISBN 0-440-02385-8). Dell.
Hudson, Bruce. British Light Cars 1930-1939. (Illus.). 334p. 22.95 (ISBN 0-85429-167-9, F167). Haynes Pubns.
--Post-War British Thoroughbreds: Their Purchase & Restoration. LC 71-187270. (Illus.). 1976. 13.50 (ISBN 0-85429-136-9, Pub. by J. H. Haynes & Co. England). Motorbooks Intl.
Marshall, D. & Fraser, I. British Leyland Minis: Maintenance, Tuning & Modification. 266p. 12.95 (ISBN 0-85429-156-3, F156). Haynes Pubns.
Rasmussen, Henry. European Classic Cars. LC 75-37385. 1975. 29.95 (ISBN 0-918506-01-8). Picturama.
--European Sports Cars of the Fifties. LC 78-56942. 1978. 29.95 (ISBN 0-918506-03-4). Picturama.
Robson, Graham. An Encyclopedia of European Sports & GT Cars from 1945 to 1960. 328p. 34.95 (ISBN 0-85429-281-0, F281). Haynes Pubns.
--An Encyclopedia of European Sports & GT Cars from 1961. 471p. 34.95 (ISBN 0-85429-256-X, F256). Haynes Pubns.
Smith, Larry, Jr. The Import Book, Vol. 1. Thmpson day Graphics, tr. (Illus.). 106p. (Orig.). 1984. pap. 19.95 (ISBN 0-931741-00-9). L Smith Assoc.
Steinwedel, Louis W. & Newport, J. Herbert. The Duesenberg. (Automobile Ser.). (Illus.). 1983. 15.95 (ISBN 0-393-01589-0). Norton.
Vann, Peter & Asaria, Gerald. Extraordinary Automobiles. LC 83-80553. (Illus.). 224p. 1983. 39.95 (ISBN 0-86710-059-1). Edns Vilo.
Voller, David J. British Cars of the Late Sixties: 1965-1969. 1982. 35.00x (ISBN 0-7232-2897-3, Pub. by F Warne England). State Mutual Bk.

Whyte, A. Aston Martin & Lagonda: Six-Cylinder DB Models, Vol. 1. (Collector Guide Ser.). (Illus.). 144p. 1984. text ed. 18.95 (ISBN 0-900549-83-1, Pub. by Motor Racing England). Motorbooks Intl.

Wilson, M. H. British Cars. pap. 3.00x (ISBN 0-392-10192-0, SpS). Sportshelf.

Wyss, Wallace A. De Tomaso Automobiles. (Illus.). 208p. 1981. 32.50 (ISBN 0-85045-440-9, Pub. by Osprey England). Motorbooks Intl.

AUTOMOBILES, FOREIGN–MAINTENANCE AND REPAIR

see Automobiles–Maintenance and Repair

AUTOMOBILES, FOREIGN–TYPES–ALFA-ROMEO

Clarke, R. M. Alfa Romeo Spider 1966-1981. (Illus.). 100p. 1982. pap. 11.95 (ISBN 0-907073-56-5, Pub. by Brooklands Bks England). Motorbooks Intl.

Green, Evan. Alfa Romeo. (Illus.). 1977. 13.50 (ISBN 0-9596637-0-3, Pub. by Evan Green Pty. Ltd. England). Motorbooks Intl.

Hull, P. Alfa Romeo. (Mini Marque History Ser.). 7.95 (ISBN 0-85429-198-9, F198). Haynes Pubns.

Owen, David. Alfa Romeo Spiders. (AutoHistory Ser.). (Illus.). 136p. 1982. 14.95 (ISBN 0-85045-462-X, Pub. by Osprey England). Motorbooks Intl.

--Viva! Alfa Romeo. 160p. 19.95 (ISBN 0-85429-207-1, F207). Haynes Pubns.

AUTOMOBILES, FOREIGN–TYPES–ANGLIA

Haynes, J. H. & Page, S. F. Ford Anglia Owners Workshop Manual: '59 Thru '68. (Owners Workshop Manuals Ser.: No. 001). 1979. 12.95 (ISBN 0-900550-01-5, Pub. by J H Haynes England). Haynes Pubns.

AUTOMOBILES, FOREIGN–TYPES–ASTON MARTIN

Bowler, Michael. Aston Martin V-8. (High Performance Ser.). (Illus.). 176p. 1985. 16.95 (ISBN 0-668-06428-5). Arco.

Frostick, Michael. Aston Martin & Lagonda. 196p. 1981. 50.00x (ISBN 0-686-97069-1, Pub. by D Watson England). State Mutual Bk.

Hunter, Inman. Aston Martin 1914 to 1940: A Pictorial Review. (Illus.). 1977. 5.95 (ISBN 0-85184-020-5, Pub. by Transport Bookman England). Motorbooks Intl.

McComb, F. Wilson. Aston Martin V8s. (Osprey AutoHistory Ser.). (Illus.). 136p. 1981. 14.95 (ISBN 0-85045-399-2, Pub. by Osprey England). Motorbooks Intl.

Whyte, A. Aston Martin & Lagonda: Six-Cylinder DB Models, Vol. 1. (Collector Guide Ser.). (Illus.). 144p. 1984. text ed. 18.95 (ISBN 0-900549-83-1, Pub. by Motor Racing England). Motorbooks Intl.

AUTOMOBILES, FOREIGN–TYPES–AUDI

Audi Four Thousand-Five Thousand 1978-81. LC 80-70341. (Illus.). 208p. 1980. pap. 11.95 (ISBN 0-8019-7028-8). Chilton.

Haynes, J. H. & Kinchin, K. F. Audi Fox 1973 thru 1979. (Haynes Automotive Manuals). 12.95 (ISBN 0-85696-207-4, 207). Haynes Pubns.

--Audi Owners Workshop Manual: Fox 1973 Thru 1979. (Haynes Owners Workshop Manuals Ser.: No. 207). 1976. 12.95 (ISBN 0-85696-207-4, Pub by J H Haynes England). Haynes Pubns.

Haynes, J. H. & Ward, L. P. Audi 100 Owners Workshop Manual: 1969 Thru 1977. (Haynes Owners Workshop Manuals Ser.: No. 162). 1978. 12.95 (ISBN 0-85696-500-6, Pub. by J H Haynes England). Haynes Pubns.

Haynes, J. H. & Ward, P. Audi 100 1969 thru 1977. (Haynes Automotive Manuals). 12.95 (ISBN 0-85696-500-6, 162). Haynes Pubns.

Henry, Alan. Audi Quattro. LC 83-73408. (High Performance Ser.). (Illus.). 176p. 1984. 16.95 (ISBN 0-668-06144-8, 6144-8). Arco.

Robert Bentley, Inc. Audi Fox Service Manual, 1973, 1974, 1975, 1976, 1977, 1978, 1979. LC 79-53187. (Illus.). 1979. pap. 24.95 (ISBN 0-8376-0097-9). Bentley.

--Audi Fox 1973-1977. (Illus.). pap. 14.95 (ISBN 0-8376-0090-1). Bentley.

--Audi Fox 1973-1978. (Illus.). pap. 14.95 (ISBN 0-8376-0091-X). Bentley.

Volkswagen of America, Inc. Audi Five Thousand Official Factory Service Manual, 1977-1983, Standard & Turbocharged, Gasoline & Diesel. LC 83-71486. (Illus.). 960p. (Orig.). 1983. pap. 44.95 (ISBN 0-8376-0352-8). Bentley.

--Audi Four Thousand Coupe Service Manual 1980 to 1983. LC 83-70221. (Illus.). 920p. (Orig.). 1983. pap. 44.95 (ISBN 0-8376-0349-8). Bentley.

Walton, Jeremy. Audi Quattro: The Development & Competition History. 29.95 (ISBN 0-85429-410-4, F410). Haynes Pubns.

AUTOMOBILES, FOREIGN–TYPES–AUSTIN

see also Automobiles, Foreign–Types–Morris Mini Minor

British Leyland Motors. Complete Official Austin-Healey 100-Six & 3000, 1956-1968. LC 77-72588. (Illus.). 416p. 1977. pap. 25.00 (ISBN 0-8376-0133-9). Bentley.

Clarke, R. M. Austin Healey One Hundred & Three Thousand Collection, No. 1. (Brooklands Bks.). (Illus.). 70p. (Orig.). 1982. pap. 8.95 (ISBN 0-907073-51-4, Pub. by Brooklands Bks England). Motorbooks Intl.

--Austin-Healy 3000 1959-1967. (Brookland Bks.). (Illus.). 100p. 1979. pap. text ed. 11.95 (ISBN 0-906589-64-9, Pub. by Brooklands Bks England). Motorbooks Intl.

Haynes, J. H. & Chalmers-Hunt, B. L. Austin-Healey 100-6 & 3000 1959 thru 1968. (Haynes Automotive Manuals). 12.95 (ISBN 0-900550-49-X, 049). Haynes Pubns.

--Austin Marina 1971 thru 1978. (Haynes Automotive Manuals). 12.95 (ISBN 0-900550-74-0, 074). Haynes Pubns.

--Austin Owners Workshop Manual: Healey 100-6 Three Thousand 1956 Thru 1968. (Haynes Owners Workshop Manuals Ser.: No. 049). 1974. 12.95 (ISBN 0-900550-49-X, Pub by J H Haynes England). Haynes Pubns.

--B.L.M.C. Austin America Owner's Workshop Manual: 1962 thru 1974. (Haynes Owners Workshop Manuals: No. 260). 1975. 12.95 (ISBN 0-85696-260-0, Pub. by J H Haynes England). Haynes Pubns.

Haynes, J. H. & Chalmers-Hunt, R. L. Austin Owners Workshop Manual: Marina 1971 Thru 1975. (Haynes Owners Workshop Manuals Ser.: No. 074). 1974. 12.95 (ISBN 0-900550-74-0, Pub. by J H Haynes England). Haynes Pubns.

Page, S. F. Cassell Book of Austin A40 Farina. 10.00x (ISBN 0-392-05820-0, SpS). Sportshelf.

Porter, Lindsay. Super Profile: Austin-Healey 'Frogeye' Sprite. (Illus.). 56p. 1983. 9.95 (ISBN 0-85429-343-4, F343). Haynes Pubns.

Williams, L. M. Austin Seven Specials. (Illus.). 160p. 9.95 (ISBN 0-85429-115-6, F115). Haynes Pubns.

Wyatt, R. J. The Austin. LC 80-68896. (Illus.). 256p. 1981. 32.00 (ISBN 0-7153-7948-8). David & Charles.

--The Austin Seven, Nineteen Twenty-Two to Nineteen Thirty-Nine. (Illus.). 216p. 1982. 22.50 (ISBN 0-7153-8394-9). David & Charles.

AUTOMOBILES, FOREIGN–TYPES–BENTLEY

Bastow, Donald. W.O. Bentley: Engineer. 39.95 (ISBN 0-85429-215-2, F215). Haynes Pubns.

Bird, Anthony & Hallows, Ian. The Rolls-Royce Motor Car: And the Bentley since 1931. 5th, rev. ed. (Illus.). 328p. 1985. 39.95 (ISBN 0-312-68957-8). St Martin.

Green, Johnnie. Bentley Fifty Years of the Marque. 296p. 1981. 75.00x (ISBN 0-686-97071-3, Pub. by D Watson England). State Mutual Bk.

AUTOMOBILES, FOREIGN–TYPES–BMW

BMW R-69 & R-69s. (Super Profile MC Ser.). 9.95 (ISBN 0-85429-387-6, F387). Haynes Pubns.

Busenkell, Richard L. BMW. (Modern Automobile Ser.). (Illus.). 1981. 12.95 (ISBN 0-393-01342-1). Norton.

Clarke, R. M. BMW 1600 Collection. (Brooklands Bks: No. 1). (Illus.). 70p. (Orig.). 1981. pap. 8.95 (ISBN 0-907073-27-1, Pub. by Brooklands Bks England). Motorbooks Intl.

--BMW 2002 Collection. (Brooklands Bks: No. 1). (Illus.). 70p. (Orig.). 1981. pap. 8.95 (ISBN 0-907073-28-X, Pub. by Brooklands Bks England). Motorbooks Intl.

Frostick, Michael. BMW the Bavarian Motor Works. 207p. 1981. 50.00x (ISBN 0-686-97072-1, Pub. by D Watson England). State Mutual Bk.

Gross, Ken. Illustrated BMW Buyer's Guide. (Buyer's Guide Ser.). (Illus.). 176p. 1985. pap. 13.95 (ISBN 0-87938-165-5). Motorbooks Intl.

Haynes, J. H. & Barge, C. D. BMW 2500, 2800, 3.o & Bavaria. (Haynes Automotive Manuals). 12.95 (ISBN 0-85696-348-8, 348). Haynes Pubns.

Haynes, J. H. & Strasman, P. G. BMW Owners Workshop Manual: Fifteen Hundred to Two Thousand Two, 59 thru '77. (Haynes Owners Workshop Manuals: No. 240). 1978. 12.95 (ISBN 0-85696-240-6, Pub by J H Haynes England). Haynes Pubns.

--BMW 1500, 1602 & 2002 1959 thru 1977. (Haynes Automotive Manuals). 12.95 (ISBN 0-85696-240-6, 240). Haynes Pubns.

Jorgensen, Eric, ed. BMW Service, Repair, Performance: 500-1000cc Twins, 1970-1982. (Illus.). pap. 13.95 (ISBN 0-89287-225-X, M309). Clymer Pubns.

Oswald, Werner & Walton, Jeremy. BMW-The Complete Story from 1928. (Illus.). 191p. 1983. 29.95 (ISBN 0-85429-315-9, F315). Haynes Pubns.

Walton, Jeremy. BMW Six Series. LC 84-70869. (High Performance Ser.). (Illus.). 176p. 1984. 16.95 (ISBN 0-668-06147-2, 6147-2). Arco.

AUTOMOBILES, FOREIGN–TYPES–BUGATTI

Conway, H. G. Bugatti "le pur - sang des automobiles". 3rd ed. LC 74-80931. (Illus.). 463p. 1974. 24.95 (ISBN 0-85429-158-X, G. T. Foulis England). Motorbooks Intl.

--Grand Prix! Bugatti. (Illus.). 272p. 39.95 (ISBN 0-85429-293-4, F293). Haynes Pubns.

AUTOMOBILES, FOREIGN–TYPES–DASHER

Haynes, J. H. & Kinchin, K. F. VW Dasher '74-'81. (Haynes Owners Workshop Manuals: No. 238). 1976. 12.95 (ISBN 0-85696-962-1, Pub by J H Haynes England). Haynes Pubns.

Robert Bentley, Inc. Volkswagen Dasher, Including Diesel: 1974-1980. (Illus.). pap. 19.95 (ISBN 0-8376-0084-7). Bentley.

--Volkswagen Dasher Service Manual, 1974-1981, Including Diesel. rev. ed. LC 81-66944. (Illus.). 692p. (Orig.). 1981. pap. 24.95 (ISBN 0-8376-0083-9). Bentley.

--Volkswagen Dasher: 1974-1977. (Illus.). pap. 12.95 (ISBN 0-8376-0063-4). Bentley.

--Volkswagen Dasher: 1974-1979. (Illus.). pap. 18.50 (ISBN 0-8376-0086-3). Bentley.

AUTOMOBILES, FOREIGN–TYPES–DATSUN

Ahlstrand, Alan. Datsun 200 SX 1980-1982. Jorgensen, Eric, ed. (Illus.). pap. text ed. 12.95 (ISBN 0-89287-339-6, A206). Clymer Pubns.

--Datsun 4-Wheel Drive Pickups: 1980-1983 Shop Manual. Wauson, Sydnie A., ed. (Illus., Orig.). 1981. pap. 12.95 (ISBN 0-89287-344-2, A207). Clymer Pubns.

Ahlstrand, Alan & Wauson, Sydnie A. Datsun 280ZX 1979-1983 Includes Turbo Shop Manual. (Illus.). pap. 12.95 (ISBN 0-89287-346-9). Clymer Pubns.

Chilton Staff. Chilton's Repair & Tune-up Guide: Datsun-Nissan F-10, 310 & Stanza 1970-85. LC 85-47961. 256p. (Orig.). 1986. pap. 12.50 (ISBN 0-8019-7660-X). Chilton.

--Chilton's Repair & Tune-up Guide: Datsun-Nissan Z & ZX 1970-86. LC 85-47965. 256p. (Orig.). 1986. pap. 12.50 (ISBN 0-8019-7664-2). Chilton.

--Chilton's Repair & Tune-up Guide: Datsun-Nissan 200SX, 510, 610, 710, 810 Maxima 1973-1986. LC 85-47980. 336p. (Orig.). 1986. pap. 12.50 (ISBN 0-8019-7680-4). Chilton.

Chilton's Automotive Editorial Staff. Chilton's Repair & Tune-up Guide for Datson Pick-Ups, 1970-1975. LC 75-22134. (Illus.). 180p. 1975. pap. 11.95 (ISBN 0-8019-6333-8). Chilton.

--Chilton's Repair & Tune-up Guide for Datsun: 1961-1972. LC 72-188664. (Illus.). 1972. pap. 11.95 (ISBN 0-8019-5790-7). Chilton.

--Chilton's Repair & Tune-up Guide for Datsun 240-260-280z, 1970-1977. LC 77-85345. (Chilton's Repair & Tune-up Guides). (Illus., Orig.). 1977. pap. 11.95 (ISBN 0-8019-6638-8, 6638). Chilton.

--Chilton's Spanish Language Edition of Datsun 1973 to 1980 Repair & Tune-up Guide. (Illus.). 1981. 11.95 (ISBN 0-8019-7083-0). Chilton.

--Datsun F-Ten, Three Ten, & Nissan Stanza, Nineteen Seventy-Seven to Nineteen Eighty-Two. 1982. pap. 11.95 (ISBN 0-8019-7196-9). Chilton.

--Datsun Pick-Ups, 1970 to 1981. (Illus.). 1981. pap. 11.95 (ISBN 0-8019-7050-4). Chilton.

--Datsun Two Ten & Twelve Hundred, Nineteen Seventy-Three to Nineteen Eighty-Two. 1982. pap. 11.95 (ISBN 0-8019-7197-7). Chilton.

--Datsun Z & ZX, Nineteen Seventy to Nineteen Eighty-Two. 1982. pap. 11.95 (ISBN 0-8019-7172-1). Chilton.

--Datsun Z & ZX 1970-84: RTUG. LC 83-45308. 224p. 1984. pap. 11.95 (ISBN 0-8019-7466-6). Chilton.

--Datsun 1200, 210 & Nissan Sentra 1973-84: RTUG. LC 83-45325. 112p. 1984. pap. 11.95 (ISBN 0-8019-7490-9). Chilton.

--Datsun 200 SX, 510, 610, 710, 810, 1973-84: RTUG. LC 83-45313. 212p. 1984. pap. 11.95 (ISBN 0-8019-7478-X). Chilton.

Chilton's Repair & Tune-up Guide for Datsun, 1973-1978. LC 77-90862. (Illus.). 1978. pap. 11.95 (ISBN 0-8019-6694-9). Chilton.

Haynes, J. H. & Chalmers-Hunt, B. L. Datsun 510 & PL521 Pick-up '68 - '73al. (Haynes Owners Workshop Manual: No. 123). 1974. 12.95 (ISBN 0-85696-123-X, Pub. by J H Haynes England). Haynes Pubns.

Haynes, J. H. & Gilmour, M. B. Datsun Six-Ten Owners Workshop Manual: '72 Thru '76. (Haynes Owners Workshop Manuals: No. 372). 1977. 12.95 (ISBN 0-85696-372-0, Pub by J H Haynes England). Haynes Pubns.

Haynes, J. H. & Paul, Rik. Datsun 200SX '80 - '81. (Haynes Automotive Manuals). 12.95 (ISBN 0-85696-647-9, 647). Haynes Pubns.

Haynes, J. H. & Strasman, P. G. Datsun B Two-Ten Owners Workshop Manual: '73 Thru Aug. '78. (Haynes Owners Workshop Manuals: No. 228). 1975. 12.95 (ISBN 0-85696-228-7, Pub by J H Haynes England). Haynes Pubns.

--Datsun Seven-Ten Owners Workshop Manual: 1973 Thru 1977. (Haynes Owners Workshop Manuals: No. 235). 1978. 12.95 (ISBN 0-85696-235-X, Pub by J H Haynes England). Haynes Pubns.

--Datsun Twelve Hundred Owners Workshop Manual: '70 Thru '73. (Haynes Owners Workshop Manuals: No. 124). 1973. 12.95 (ISBN 0-85696-124-8, Pub by J H Haynes England). Haynes Pubns.

--Datsun 240Z, 260Z, & 280Z Owners Workshop Manual: 1970-1978. (Haynes Owners Workshop Manuals Ser.: No. 206). 1979. 12.95 (ISBN 0-85696-206-6, Pub by J H Haynes England). Haynes Pubns.

Haynes, J. H. & Ward, P. Datsun Six-Twenty Owners Pick-up Workshop Manual: 73 Thru 79. (Haynes Owners Workshop Manuals: No. 277). 1978. 12.95 (ISBN 0-85696-663-6, Pub by J H Haynes England). Haynes Pubns.

--Datsun 810-Maxima '77 -'84. 12.95 (376). Haynes Pubns.

Hutton, Ray. The Z-Series Datsun. (Collector's Guide Ser.). (Illus.). 1982. 18.95 (ISBN 0-900549-61-0, Pub. by Motor Racing England). Motorbooks Intl.

Jorgensen, Eric, ed. Datsun 200 SX 1977-1979 Shop Manual. (Illus.). pap. text ed. 12.95 (ISBN 0-89287-294-2, A200). Clymer Pubns.

--Datsun 240, 260 & 280-Z: 1970-78 Service-Repair Handbook. (Illus.). pap. 12.95 (ISBN 0-89287-290-X, A152). Clymer Pubns.

--Datsun 510 1978-1979 Shop Manual. (Illus.). pap. text ed. 12.95 (ISBN 0-89287-244-6, A201). Clymer Pubns.

Morris, James. Datsun 240Z-260Z-280Z: Super Profile. (Illus.). 56p. 1986. 9.95 (ISBN 0-85429-488-0, Pub. by G T Foulis Ltd). Interbook.

Rae, John B. Nissan-Datsun: A History of Nissan Motor Corporation in the U. S. A. 1960-1980. (Illus.). 1982. 27.50 (ISBN 0-07-051112-8). McGraw.

Robinson, Jeff, ed. Datsun Service-Repair Handbook 2W Pickups, 1970-1983. (Illus.). pap. 12.95 (ISBN 0-89287-151-2, A-148). Clymer Pubns.

--Datsun Service Repair Handbook 510, 610, & 710, 1968-1977. (Illus.). pap. text ed. 12.95 (ISBN 0-89287-281-0, A149). Clymer Pubns.

--Datsun 1200 & B210: 1971-78 Service-Repair Handbook. (Illus.). pap. 12.95 (ISBN 0-89287-284-5, A151). Clymer Pubns.

Young, Paul. Datsun Tune-up for Everybody. LC 80-5102. (Illus.). 120p. 1980. pap. 7.95 (ISBN 0-89815-026-4). Ten Speed Pr.

AUTOMOBILES, FOREIGN–TYPES–FERRARI

Ackerson, Robert C. Ferraris of the Seventies. (Source Bks.). (Illus.). 144p. 1984. pap. 12.95 (ISBN 0-934780-35-8). Bookman Dan.

Batchelor, D. Ferrari: The Early Spyders & Competition Roadsters. (Illus.). 128p. (Orig.). 1975. pap. 10.95 (ISBN 0-914792-01-6, Pub. by DB Pubns). Motorbooks Intl.

--Ferrari: The Gran Turismo & Competition Berlinettas. (Illus.). 94p. (Orig.). 1977. pap. 10.95 (ISBN 0-914792-02-4, Pub. by DB Pubns). Motorbooks Intl.

Batchelor, Dean. Illustrated Ferrari Buyer's Guide. (Illus.). 176p. 1981. pap. 13.95 (ISBN 0-87938-118-3). Motorbooks Intl.

Clarke, R. M. Ferrari Cars: 1962-1966. (Brooklands Bks.). (Illus.). 100p. 1979. pap. 11.95 (ISBN 0-906589-57-6, Pub. by Brooklands Bks England). Motorbooks Intl.

--Ferrari Cars, 1966 to 1969. (Brooklands Bks.). (Illus., Orig.). 1979. pap. 11.95 (ISBN 0-906589-59-2, Pub. by Enthusiast Pubns. England). Motorbooks Intl.

--Ferrari Cars: 1977-1981. (Brooklands Bks.). (Illus.). 100p. (Orig.). 1981. pap. 11.95 (ISBN 0-686-75135-3, Pub. by Brooklands Bks England). Motorbooks Intl.

--Ferrari: Collection No. 1. (Illus.). 70p. (Orig.). 1980. pap. 8.95 (ISBN 0-907073-10-7, Brooklands Bks). Motorbooks Intl.

Ferrari: The Early Berlinettas & Competition Coupes. (Illus.). 80p. (Orig.). 1974. pap. 10.95 (ISBN 0-914792-00-8, Pub. by DB Pubns). Motorbooks Intl.

Ferrari 250 GTO. (Super Profile CAR Ser.). 9.95 (ISBN 0-85429-308-6, F308). Haynes Pubns.

Fitzgerald, W. W., et al. Ferrari: The Sports & Gran Tursimo Cars. 4th enlarged ed. (Illus.). 1979. 39.95 (ISBN 0-393-01276-X). Norton.

Grayson, Stan, ed. Ferrari: The Man, the Machines. (Marque History Bks.). (Illus.). 348p. 1982. 29.95 (ISBN 0-915038-05-6). Auto Quarterly.

Nichols, Mel. Ferrari Berlinetta Boxer. (Autohistory Ser.). (Illus.). 1979. 14.95 (ISBN 0-85045-326-7, Pub. by Osprey Pubns. England). Motorbooks Intl.

Nye, Doug. Dino: The Little Ferrari. (Illus.). 328p. 1979. 35.00 (ISBN 0-914822-24-1). Barnes Pub.

Clarke, R. M. MG MGA 1955-1962. (Brooklands Bks.). (Illus.). 100p. (Orig.). 1981. pap. 11.95 (ISBN 0-906589-97-5, Pub. by Brooklands Bks England). Motorbooks Intl.
--MG MGB 1970-1980. (Brooklands Bks.). (Illus.). 100p. (Orig.). 1981. pap. 11.95 (ISBN 0-906589-90-8, Pub. by Brooklands Bks England). Motorbooks Intl.
Fletcher, A. F. MG: Past & Present. 2nd ed. (Illus.). 280p. 1986. 17.95 (ISBN 0-85429-425-2, Pub. by G T Foulis Ltd). Interbook.
Fletcher, Rivers. MG: Past & Present. (Illus.). 256p. Date not set. 25.95 (ISBN 0-85614-074-0, Pub. by Wilton Hse England). Motorbooks Intl.
Fowler, John. MGB '62 - '80. (Haynes Owners Workshop Manuals: No. 111). 1982. 12.95 (ISBN 0-85696-623-1, Pub by J H Haynes England). Haynes Pubns.
Garnier. MG Sports Cars. Autocar Editors, ed. LC 78-65889. 1979. 14.95 (ISBN 0-312-50156-0). St Martin.
Harvey, Chris. MG: The A, B & C. (Illus.). 1980. 36.50 (ISBN 0-902280-69-4, Pub. by Oxford Ill England). Motorbooks Intl.
Hawes, R. G. MG Midget, AH Sprite '58 - '80. (Haynes Owners Workshop Manuals: No. 265). 1974. 12.95 (ISBN 0-85696-588-X, Pub by J H Haynes England). Haynes Pubns.
McComb, F. Wilson. MGB: MGB Roadster & GT, MGC, MGB V8. (AutoHistory Ser.). (Illus.). 136p. 1982. 14.95 (ISBN 0-85045-455-7, Pub. by Osprey England). Motorbooks Intl.
McLellan, John. MG: The Art of Abingdon. 1983. 37.50 (ISBN 0-900549-45-9, Pub. by Motor Racing Pubns. Ltd. England). Motorbooks Intl.
MG 1961-1981. 1982. 11.95 (ISBN 0-8019-7173-X). Chilton.
MGB. (Super Profile CAR Ser.). 9.95 (ISBN 0-317-30550-6, F305). Haynes Pubns.
MIG-21. (Super Profile MC Ser.). 9.95 (ISBN 0-85429-439-2, F439). Haynes Pubns.
Robson, Graham. The MGA, MGB & MGC: A Collector's Guide. 1979. 18.95 (ISBN 0-900549-43-2, Pub. by Motor Racing Pubns. Ltd. England). Motorbooks Intl.
--The Mighty MG's: The Twin-Cam. MGC & MGB GT V8 Stories. (Illus.). 224p. 1982. 27.50 (ISBN 0-7153-8226-8, Pub by Gollancz England). David & Charles.
--The T Series MG: A Collector's Guide. (Collector's Guide Ser.). (Illus.). 128p. 1980. 18.95 (ISBN 0-900549-51-3, Pub. by Motor Racing England). Motorbooks Intl.
Vitrikas, Robert P. MGA: A History, & Restoration Guide. LC 80-54250. (Illus.). 208p. 1980. pap. 19.95 (ISBN 0-89404-031-6). Aztex.
Wherry, Joseph H. MG: Sports Car Supreme. LC 81-3633. (Illus.). 240p. 1982. 25.00 (ISBN 0-498-02565-9). A S Barnes.

AUTOMOBILES, FOREIGN–TYPES–MASERATI

Clarke, R. M. Maserati 1965-1970. (Brooklands Bks.). (Illus.). 100p. (Orig.). 1981. pap. 11.95 (ISBN 0-906589-98-3, Pub. by Brooklands Bks England). Motorbooks Intl.
--Maserati 1970-1975. (Brooklands Bks.). (Illus.). 100p. (Orig.). 1981. pap. 11.95 (ISBN 0-906589-99-1, Pub. by Brooklands Bks England). Motorbooks Intl.
Crump, Richard. Maserati Road Cars 1946-1979. (Illus.). 229p. 1979. 35.00 (ISBN 0-914822-26-8). Barnes Pub.
Crump, Richard & Box, Rob de la. Maserati: Sports Racing & GT Cars from 1926. (Illus.). 28.95 (ISBN 0-85429-302-7, F302). Haynes Pubns.
Norbye, Jan P. Maserati Bora & Merak. (AutoHistory Ser.). (Illus.). 136p. 1982. 14.95 (ISBN 0-85045-471-9, Pub. by Osprey England). Motorbooks Intl.

AUTOMOBILES, FOREIGN–TYPES–MAZDA

Chilton Staff. Chilton's Repair & Tune-up Guide: Mazda Pickup 1971-86. LC 85-47960. 312p. (Orig.). 1986. pap. 12.50 (ISBN 0-8019-7659-6). Chilton.
Chilton's Automotive Editorial Staff. Chilton's Repair & Tune-up Guide for Mazda 1971-78. (Repair & Tune-up Guides Ser.). (Illus.). 1978. pap. 11.95 (ISBN 0-8019-6746-5). Chilton.
--Mazda, 1971-84: RTUG. LC 83-45321. 248p. 1985. pap. 11.95 (ISBN 0-8019-7486-0). Chilton.
Haynes, J. H. & Larminie, J. C. Mazda RX2 Rotary '71 - '75. (Haynes Owners Workshop Manuals: No. 109). 1974. 12.95 (ISBN 0-85696-109-4, Pub by J H Haynes England). Haynes Pubns.
--Mazda RX3 Rotary '72 -'76. (Haynes Owners Workshop Manuals Ser.: No. 096). 1977. 12.95 (ISBN 0-900550-96-1, 096, Pub by J H Haynes England). Haynes Pubns.
Haynes, J. H. & Ward, P. Mazda Sports Truck Owners Workshop Manual: Four Cylinder, Thru '72-'78. (Haynes Owners Workshop Manuals Ser.: No. 267). 1976. 12.95 (ISBN 0-85696-510-3, Pub by J H Haynes England). Haynes Pubns.
Mazda GLC 1981-1982 Front Wheel Drive Shop Manual. (Illus.). 312p. 1983. 12.95 (ISBN 0-89287-373-6, A274). Clymer Pubns.
Mazda Nineteen Seventy to Nineteen Eighty-Two. LC 81-70236. (Illus.). 256p. 1982. 11.95 (ISBN 0-8019-7198-5). Chilton.
Mazda RX-7 Nineteen Seventy-Eight to Eighty-One. LC 80-70342. (Illus.). 208p. 1980. pap. 11.95 (ISBN 0-8019-7031-8). Chilton.
Wright, Ron. Mazda RX-7: 1979-1984 Shop Manual. Wauson, Sydnie, ed. (Illus., Orig.). 1982. text ed. 12.95 (ISBN 0-89287-357-4). Clymer Pubns.
--Mazda 626, 1979-1980. Wauson, Sydnie A., ed. (Illus., Orig.). 1982. 12.95 (ISBN 0-89287-358-2, A269). Clymer Pubns.

AUTOMOBILES, FOREIGN–TYPES–MERCEDES

Chilton's Automotive Editorial Staff. Chilton's Mercedes-Benz: 1974-1979, Repair & Tune-up Guide. LC 78-22141. (Repair & Tune-up Guides Ser.). (Illus.). 1979. pap. 11.95 (ISBN 0-8019-6809-7). Chilton.
--Chilton's Repair & Tune-up Guide for Mercedes-Benz: 1961-1970. LC 70-131236. (Illus.). 1970. pap. 11.95 (ISBN 0-8019-6065-7). Chilton.
--Chilton's Repair & Tune-up Guide for Mercedes Benz 2, 1968-1973. (Illus.). 224p. 1974. pap. 11.95 (ISBN 0-8019-5907-1). Chilton.
--Mercedes Benz Nineteen Seventy-Four to Nineteen Eighty-Four: RTUG. LC 83-45305. 224p. 1984. pap. 11.95 (ISBN 0-8019-7463-1). Chilton.
Clarke, R. M. Mercedes-Benz Cars, Nineteen Forty-Nine to Nineteen Sixty-One. (Brooklands Bks). (Illus.). 1979. pap. 11.95 (ISBN 0-906589-27-4, Pub. by Enthusiast Pubns. England). Motorbooks Intl.
Haynes, J. H. & Legg, A. K. Mercedes-Benz 280. (One Hundred Twenty-Three Ser.). 12.95 (ISBN 0-85696-983-4, 983). Haynes Pubns.
Haynes, J. H. & Strasman, P. G. Mercedes Benz 230, 250 & 280 '68 - '72. (Haynes Owners Workshop Manuals: No. 346). 1978. 12.95 (ISBN 0-85696-346-1, Pub by J H Haynes England). Haynes Pubns.
Howard, Geoffrey. Mercedes Benz S Class. LC 84-70871. (High Performance Ser.). (Illus.). 176p. 1984. 16.95 (ISBN 0-668-06145-6, 6145-6). Arco.
Mercedes-Benz Cars Nineteen Fifty-Seven to Nineteen Sixty-One. (Brooklands Bks). (Illus.). 100p. (Orig.). 1979. pap. 11.95 (ISBN 0-906589-71-1, Pub. by Brooklands Bks England). Motorbooks Intl.
Nitske, W. Robert. Mercedes-Benz: A History. LC 78-9044. (Illus.). 1978. 19.95 (ISBN 0-87938-055-1). Motorbooks Intl.
--Mercedes-Benz Production Models Nineteen Forty-Six to Nineteen Seventy-Five. LC 77-8354. (Illus.). 1977. 18.95 (ISBN 0-87938-047-0). Motorbooks Intl.
--Mercedes-Benz Three Hundred SL. LC 74-22377. (Illus.). 164p. 1974. 19.95 (ISBN 0-87938-021-7). Motorbooks Intl.
Pascal, Dominique. Mercedes-Benz Pocket History. (Pocket History Ser.). (Illus.). 66p. (Orig.). 1982. pap. 5.95 (ISBN 0-686-94763-0, Pub. by Automobilia Italy). Motorbooks Intl.
Setright, Leonard. Mercedes-Benz Roadsters. (Auto History Ser.). (Illus.). 1979. 14.95 (ISBN 0-85045-325-9, Pub. by Osprey England). Motorbooks Intl.

AUTOMOBILES, FOREIGN–TYPES–MIDGET

British Leyland Motors. Complete Official Sprite-Midget 948cc & 1098cc: Comprising the Official Driver's Handbook, Workshop Manual, Special Tuning Manual. LC 67-28432. (Illus.). 384p. (Orig.). 1968. pap. 25.00 (ISBN 0-8376-0023-5). Bentley.
--The Complete Official 1275 cc Sprite-Midget 1967-1974: Comprising the Official Driver's Handbook, Workshop Manual, Emission Control Supplement. LC 75-37232. (Illus.). 400p. 1975. pap. 35.00 (ISBN 0-8376-0127-4). Bentley.
Dymock, Eric. The Sprites & Midgets: Collector's Guide. (Illus.). 136p. 1981. 18.95 (ISBN 0-900549-53-X, Pub. by Motor Racing Pubns England). Motorbooks Intl.

AUTOMOBILES, FOREIGN–TYPES–MORGAN

Blakemore, John & Rasmussen, Henry. Postwar MG & Morgan. (Illus.). 1979. 29.95 (ISBN 0-918506-04-2). Picturama.
Hill, Ken. The Four-Wheeled Morgan, Vol. 2. 1980. 18.95 (ISBN 0-900549-54-8, Pub. by Motor Racing Pubns. Ltd. England). Motorbooks Intl.

AUTOMOBILES, FOREIGN–TYPES–MORRIS

Jarman, Lytton P. & Barraclough, Robin I. The Bullnose & Flatnose Morris. LC 75-42598. (Illus.). 264p. 1976. 21.00 (ISBN 0-7153-6665-3). David & Charles.
Porter, Lindsay. Mini: Guide to Purchase & DIY Restoration. (Illus.). 19.95 (ISBN 0-85429-379-5, F379). Haynes Pubns.

AUTOMOBILES, FOREIGN–TYPES–MORRIS MINI MINOR

Skilleter, Paul. Morris Minor: The World's Supreme Small Car. (Illus.). 224p. 1981. 22.95 (ISBN 0-85045-344-5, Pub. by Osprey England). Motorbooks Intl.

AUTOMOBILES, FOREIGN–TYPES–MORRIS MINOR

Clarke, R. M. Morris Minor 1948-1970. (Brooklands Bks.). (Illus.). 100p. (Orig.). 1981. pap. 11.95 (ISBN 0-906589-83-5, Pub. by Brooklands Bks England). Motorbooks Intl.
Haynes, J. H. Morris Minor 1000 Owners Workshop Manual: 1956 Thru 1971. (Haynes Owners Workshop Manuals: No. 024). 1971. 12.95 (ISBN 0-900550-24-4, Pub by J H Haynes England). Haynes Pubns.
Morris Minor. (Super Profile CAR Ser.). 9.95 (ISBN 0-85429-412-0, F412). Haynes Pubns.
Porter, Lindsay. Morris Minor: Guide to Purchase & D. I. Y. Restoration. (Guide to Purchase & D. I. Y. Restoration Ser.: No. 4). (Illus.). 224p. 1986. 13.95 (ISBN 0-85429-442-2, Pub. by G T Foulis Ltd). Interbook.

AUTOMOBILES, FOREIGN–TYPES–NISSAN SENTRA

Ahlstrand, Alan. Nissan Sentra Nineteen Eighty-Two to Nineteen Eighty-Three Gas & Diesel Shop Manual. Wauson, Sydnie & Hamlin, Steve, eds. (Illus.). 287p. (Orig.). 1984. pap. 13.95 (ISBN 0-89287-386-8, A208). Clymer Pubns.
Chilton Staff. Chilton's Repair & Tune-up Guide: Datsun-Nissan F-10, 310 & Stanza 1970-85. LC 85-47961. 256p. (Orig.). 1986. pap. 12.50 (ISBN 0-8019-7660-X). Chilton.

AUTOMOBILES, FOREIGN–TYPES–OPEL

Clarke, R. M. Opel GT 1968-1973. (Illus.). 100p. 1982. pap. 11.95 (ISBN 0-907073-63-8, Pub. by Brooklands Bks England). Motorbooks Intl.
Haynes, J. H. & Sharp, A. Opel Manta Coupe (Buick) '70 - '74. (Haynes Owners Workshop Manuals: No. 157). 1975. 12.95 (ISBN 0-85696-157-4, Pub by J H Haynes England). Haynes Pubns.
Opel Nineteen Seventy-One to Nineteen Seventy-Five. LC 76-28578. (Illus.). 200p. 1976. 11.95 (ISBN 0-8019-6575-6). Chilton.

AUTOMOBILES, FOREIGN–TYPES–PANTERA

Clarke, R. M. Pantera, Nineteen Seventy to Nineteen Seventy-Three. (Brooklands Bks.). (Illus., Orig.). 1979. pap. 8.95 (ISBN 0-906589-75-4, Pub. by Brooklands Bks England). Motorbooks Intl.
Clarke, R. M., ed. Pantera & Mangusta, Ninieteen Sixty-Nine to Nineteen Seventy-Four. (Illus.). 70p. (Orig.). 1980. pap. 8.95 (ISBN 0-907073-00-X). Motorbooks Intl.

AUTOMOBILES, FOREIGN–TYPES–PEUGEOT

Haynes, J. H. & Chalmers-Hunt, B. L. Peugeot 504 (gasoline) '68 - '79. (Haynes Owners Workshop Manuals: No. 161). 1975. 12.95 (ISBN 0-85696-501-4, Pub by J H Haynes England). Haynes Pubns.
Peugeot Nineteen Seventy to Nineteen Seventy-Four. (Illus.). 214p. 1975. 11.95 (ISBN 0-8019-5982-9). Chilton.

AUTOMOBILES, FOREIGN–TYPES–POPULAR

Clarke, R. M. Porsche 911 Collection, No. 2. (Brooklands Bks.). (Illus.). 70p. (Orig.). 1982. pap. 8.95 (ISBN 0-907073-44-1, Pub. by Brooklands Bks England). Motorbooks Intl.
--Porsche 924: 1975 to 1981. (Brooklands Bks.). (Illus.). 100p. (Orig.). 1982. pap. 11.95 (ISBN 0-907073-43-3, Pub. by Brooklands Bks England). Motorbooks Intl.

AUTOMOBILES, FOREIGN–TYPES–PORSCHE

Barth, Jurgen. Porsche Pocket History. (Pocket History Ser.). (Illus.). 66p. (Orig.). 1982. pap. 5.95 (ISBN 88-85058-16-7, Pub. by Automobilia Italy). Motorbooks Intl.
Boschen, Lothar & Barth, Jurgen. The Porsche Book: A Definitive Illustrated History. Frere, Paul, tr. LC 78-695. (Illus.). 1978. 29.95 (ISBN 0-668-04576-0, 4576). Arco.
Chilton's Automotive Editorial Staff. Porsche Nine Twenty-Four & Nine Twenty-Eight, 1977-1981. (Illus.). 1981. pap. 11.95 (ISBN 0-8019-7048-2). Chilton.
Clarke, R. M. Porsche Cars 1960-1964. (Brooklands Bks.). (Illus.). 100p. (Orig.). pap. 11.95 (ISBN 0-906589-45-2, Pub. by Brooklands Bks England). Motorbooks Intl.
--Porsche Turbo: Collection No. 1. (Illus.). 70p. (Orig.). 1980. pap. 8.95 (ISBN 0-907073-09-3, Brooklands Bks). Motorbooks Intl.
--Porsche 911: Collection No. 1. (Illus.). 70p. (Orig.). 1980. pap. 8.95 (ISBN 0-907073-12-3, Pub. by Brooklands Bks England). Motorbooks Intl.
--Porsche 914: 1969-1975. (Brooklands Bks.). (Illus.). 100p. (Orig.). 1980. 11.95 (ISBN 0-906589-84-3). Motorbooks Intl.
Clausager, Anders D. Porsche. 224p. 1983. 29.95 (ISBN 0-312-63170-7). St Martin.
Clymer Publications. Porsche Owners Handbook & Service Manual: Covers All Porsche Models up to 356c. (Illus.). pap. 7.95 (ISBN 0-89287-251-9, A181). Clymer Pubns.
Cotton, Michael. Porsche 911: Collector's Guide. (Illus.). 128p. 1980. 18.95 (ISBN 0-900549-52-1, Pub. by Motor Racing Pubns. England). Motorbooks Intl.
--Porsche 911 Turbo. (Auto History Ser.). (Illus.). 128p. 1981. 14.95 (ISBN 0-85045-400-X, Pub. by Osprey England). Motorbooks Intl.
Frere, Paul. Porsche 911 Story. 3rd ed. 216p. 19.95 (ISBN 0-668-06158-8). Arco.
Harvey, Chris. Porsche: The Complete Story. (Mini Marque History Ser.). 7.95 (ISBN 0-85429-322-1, F322). Haynes Pubns.
--The Porsche 911. (Illus.). 225p. 1982. 29.95 (ISBN 0-902280-78-3, P978). Haynes Pubns.
--Super Profile: Porsche 911 Carrera. 56p. 9.95 (ISBN 0-85429-311-6, F311). Haynes Pubns.
Haynes, J. H. & Ward, P. Porsche Nine-Eleven (Not Turbo) Owners Workshop Manual: '65 Thru '81. (Haynes Owners Workshop Manuals: No. 264). 1977. 12.95 (ISBN 0-85696-264-3, Pub by J H Haynes England). Haynes Pubns.
--Porsche 911 '65 - '81. (No. 264). 1982. 12.95 (ISBN 0-85696-691-6, Pub by J H Haynes England). Haynes Pubns.
--Porsche 914 (4-cyl.) '73 - '76. (Haynes Owners Workshop Manuals: No. 239). 1976. 12.95 (ISBN 0-85696-239-2, Pub by J H Haynes England). Haynes Pubns.
Ludvigsen, Karl, ed. Porsche: Excellence Was Expected. LC 77-83507. 1977. text ed. 64.95 (ISBN 0-915038-09-9). Auto Quarterly.
MacNamara, Julian. Porsche 944. LC 84-70870. (High Performance Ser.). (Illus.). 176p. 1984. 16.95 (ISBN 0-668-06146-4, 6146-4). Arco.
Miller, Susann. Porsche 911, 1974-1984. (Source Bks.). (Illus.). 144p. 1985. pap. 12.95 (ISBN 0-934780-51-X). Bookman Dan.
Miller, Susann, ed. Porsche Year 1982. (Illus.). 96p. (Orig.). 1982. 29.95x (ISBN 0-910597-01-4); pap. 17.95 (ISBN 0-910597-00-6). M M Pub Inc.
Miller, Susann C. & Merritt, Richard F. Porsche Brochures & Sales Literature: A Sourcebook 1948-1965. rev. ed. 312p. 1985. Repr. of 1978 ed. 49.95 (ISBN 0-915927-02-0). M M Pub Inc.
Pellow, Harry C. The ABC's & Nine Twelve's of Porsche Engines: Porsche Engines & the Future of the Human Race. rev. ed. (Illus.). 700p. 1981. perfect bound 29.95 (ISBN 0-941210-04-9). HCP Res.
--Secrets of the Inner Circle. 2nd ed. 388p. 1983. perfect bd. 29.95 (ISBN 0-941210-06-5). HCP Res.
Porsche Racing Cars of the 70's. 19.95 (ISBN 0-668-05113-2). Arco.
Porsches for the Road. LC 81-11314. (Survivor's Ser.). (Illus.). 128p. 1981. 12.98 (ISBN 0-87938-152-3). Motorbooks Intl.
Post, Dan W. Porsche Owner's Companion: A Manual of Preservation & Theft Protection. LC 80-82464. (Illus.). 192p. 1981. 14.95 (ISBN 0-911160-64-7). Post-Era.
Robisnson, Jeff, ed. Porsche Service-Repair Handbook: 911 Series, 1965-1982. (Illus.). pap. text ed. 12.95 (ISBN 0-89287-060-5, A183). Clymer Pubns.
Rusz, Joe. Porsche Sport 72. LC 72-97717. (Illus.). 1973. 4.95 (ISBN 0-393-60016-5). Norton.
--Porsche Sport 73. LC 73-89096. 1974. 5.95 (ISBN 0-393-60017-3). Norton.
Sessler, Peter. Illustrated High Performance Mustang Buyer's Guide. (Buyer's Guide Ser.). (Illus.). 152p. 1983. pap. 13.95 (ISBN 0-87938-171-X). Motorbooks Intl.
Sloniger, Jerry. Porsche: The Four-Cylinder, Four-Cam Sports & Racing Cars. (Illus.). 120p. (Orig.). 1977. pap. 5.95 (ISBN 0-914792-03-2, Pub. by DB Pubns). Motorbooks Intl.
--Porsche 924, 928, 944: The New Generation. 1981. 27.95 (ISBN 0-85045-415-8, Pub. by Osprey England). Motorbooks Intl.
Von Frankenberg, Richard. Porsche, the Man & His Cars. LC 70-77459. (Illus.). 1969. 10.95 (ISBN 0-8376-0329-3). Bentley.
Von Frankenburg, Richard & Cotton, Michael. Porsche Double World Champions Nineteen-Hundred to Nineteen Seventy-Seven. (Illus.). 276p. 19.95 (ISBN 0-317-30497-6, F171). Haynes Pubns.

AUTOMOBILES, FOREIGN–TYPES–RABBIT

Cheeke, Peter R., et al. Rabbit Production. 5th ed. 250p. 1982. 12.50 (ISBN 0-8134-2222-1). Interstate.
Chilton's Automotive Editorial Staff. Rabbit Scirocio, 1974-1980. (Illus.). 1980. pap. 11.95 (ISBN 0-8019-6962-X). Chilton.
Legg, A. K. VW Rabbit, Jetta, Scirocco & Pick-up '74-'81. (Haynes Owners Workshop Manuals Ser.: No. 884). 1982. 12.95 (ISBN 0-85696-884-6, Pub by J H Haynes England). Haynes Pubns.

--Chilton's Repair & Tune up Guide: VW Front Wheel Drive 1974-83. LC 82-72921. 288p. 1982. pap. 11.95 (ISBN 0-8019-7339-2). Chilton.

--Chilton's Spanish Language Edition of Volkswagen 1970 to 1979 Repair Tune-up Guide. (Illus.). 1981. 11.95 (ISBN 0-8019-7081-4). Chilton.

--Rabbit Scirocio, 1974-1980. (Illus.). 1980. pap. 11.95 (ISBN 0-8019-6962-X). Chilton.

--Volkswagen, 1970-81. LC 78-20249. (Chilton's Repair & Tune-up Guides Ser.). (Illus.). 1979. pap. 11.95 (ISBN 0-8019-6837-2). Chilton.

--VW Front Wheel Drive 1974-85. LC 84-45463. 256p. (Orig.). 1985. pap. 11.95 (ISBN 0-8019-7593-X). Chilton.

Clarke, R. M. VW Karmann-Ghia Collection, No. 1. (Brooklands Bks.). (Illus.). 70p. 1981. pap. 8.95 (ISBN 0-907073-35-2). Motorbooks Intl.

Fisher, Bill. How to Hotrod Volkswagen Engines. LC 72-28084. (Illus.). 1970. pap. 9.95 (ISBN 0-912656-03-4). H P Bks.

Haynes, J. H. & Kinchin, K. F. VW Beetle (Bug) 1600 '72-'74. (Haynes Owners Workshop Manuals: No. 159). 1974. 12.95 (ISBN 0-85696-159-0, Pub by J H Haynes England). Haynes Pubns.

--VW Dasher '74-'81. (Haynes Owners Workshop Manuals: No. 238). 1976. 12.95 (ISBN 0-85696-962-1, Pub by J H Haynes England). Haynes Pubns.

Haynes, J. H & Kinchin, K. F. VW 411 & 412: '72 Thru '73. (Owners Workshop Manuals Ser.: No. 091). 1974. 12.95 (ISBN 0-900550-91-0, Pub. by J H Haynes England). Haynes Pubns.

Haynes, J. H & Knichin, K. F. VW Transporter 1700, 1800 & 2000 '75-'79. (Owners Workshop Manuals Ser.: No. 226). 1980. 12.95 (ISBN 0-85696-614-2, Pub. by J H Haynes England). Haynes Pubns.

Haynes, J. H. & Stead, D. H. VW Super Beetle (Bug) '70-'72. (Haynes Owners Workshop Manuals: No. 110). 1974. 12.95 (ISBN 0-85696-110-8, Pub by J H Haynes England). Haynes Pubns.

Haynes, J. H & Stead, D. H. VW Transporter 1600 '68-'79. (Owners Workshop Manuals Ser.: No. 082). 1980. 12.95 (ISBN 0-85696-660-6, Pub. by J H Haynes England). Haynes Pubns.

--VW Type 3 1500 & 1600 '63 - '73. (Owners Workshop Manuals Ser.: No. 084). 1974. 12.95 (ISBN 0-900550-84-8, Pub. by J H Haynes England). Haynes Pubns.

Haynes, J. H. & Stead, D. M. VW Beetle (Bug) 1200 '54-'66. (Haynes Owners Workshop Manuals: No. 036). 1974. 12.95 (ISBN 0-85696-524-3, Pub by J H Haynes England). Haynes Pubns.

--VW Beetle (Bug) 1300 & 1500: '66-'70. (Haynes 0wners Workshop Manuals: no. 039). 1974. 12.95 (ISBN 0-85696-494-8, Pub by J H Haynes England). Haynes Pubns.

Hibbard, Jeff. Baja Bugs & Buggies. 106p. 1982. pap. 9.95 (ISBN 0-89586-186-0). H P Bks.

Legg, A. K. VW Rabbit, Jetta, Scirocco & Pick-up '74-'81. (Haynes Owners Workshop Manuals Ser.: No. 884). 1982. 12.95 (ISBN 0-85696-884-6, Pub by J H Haynes England). Haynes Pubns.

Marcantonio, Alfredo, intro. by. Is the Bug Dead? LC 82-19202. (Illus.). 144p. 1983. pap. 9.95 (ISBN 0-941434-24-9). Stewart Tabori & Chang.

Mead, John S. VW Vanagon (air-cooled) 12.95 (ISBN 0-317-31432-7, 1029). Haynes Pubns.

Muir, John. Como Mantener Tu Volkswagen Vivo. rev. ed. Holt, Virginia, tr. from Eng. LC 75-21414. (Illus., Orig.). 1980. pap. 10.00 (ISBN 0-912528-21-4). John Muir.

--Es Lebe Mein Volkswagen. Shamai, Ruth & Jeschke, Herbert, trs. (Illus.). 308p. 1978. pap. 10.00 (ISBN 3-980018-90-3). John Muir.

Muir, John & Gregg, Tosh. How to Keep Your Volkswagen Alive: A Manual of Step by Step Procedures for the Compleat Idiot. 30th, rev. ed. LC 79-63486. (Illus.). 368p. 1983. pap. 14.00 (ISBN 0-912528-16-8). John Muir.

Post, Dan R. Volkswagen: Nine Lives Later. 2nd ed. LC 82-173212. (Illus.). 320p. 1982. pap. 19.95 (ISBN 0-911160-42-6). Post-Era.

Robert Bentley, Inc. Volkswagen Dasher, Including Diesel: 1974-1980. (Illus.). pap. 19.95 (ISBN 0-8376-0084-7). Bentley.

--Volkswagen Dasher: 1974-1979. (Illus.). pap. 18.50 (ISBN 0-8376-0086-3). Bentley.

--Volkswagen GTI, Golf, Jetta Official Factory Repair Manual: 1985 Including, GLI, Gasoline, Diesel & Turbo Diesel Models. (Illus.). 1985. pap. 39.95 (ISBN 0-8376-0185-1). Bentley.

--Volkswagen Quantum Official Factory Service Manual: 1982-1985. (Illus.). 1985. pap. 39.95 (ISBN 0-8376-0355-2). Bentley.

--Volkswagen Rabbit-Jetta Diesel Service Manual 1978-1982, Including Pickup Truck. rev. ed. LC 82-70738. (Illus.). 520p. (Orig.). 1982. pap. 21.95 (ISBN 0-8376-0105-3). Bentley.

--Volkswagen Rabbit-Jetta Diesel Service Manual: 1977-84 Including Pickup Truck & Turbo-Diesel. 4th, rev. ed. LC 84-70138. (Illus.). 600p. (Orig.). 1984. pap. 26.50 (ISBN 0-8376-0184-3). Bentley.

--Volkswagen Rabbit-Scirocco Service Manual, Gasoline Models, 1975, 1976, 1977, 1978, 1979. rev. ed. LC 79-57170. (Illus.). 628p. (Orig.). 1980. pap. 26.50 (ISBN 0-8376-0098-7). Bentley.

Robert Bentley Inc. Volkswagen Rabbit: Scirocco 1980. (Illus.). pap. 18.50 (ISBN 0-8376-0102-9). Bentley.

--Volkswagen Rabbit: Scirocco 1980-1981. (Illus.). pap. 19.95 (ISBN 0-8376-0099-5). Bentley.

Robert Bentley, Inc. Volkswagen Vanagon Official Factory Repair Manual: 1980-1982 Including Diesel & Camper. (Illus.). 34.95 (ISBN 0-8376-0351-X). Bentley.

Robinson, Jeff, ed. Volkswagen Service Repair Handbook: Beetle, Super Beetle, Karmann Ghia, 1961-1979. (Illus.). pap. 12.95 (ISBN 0-89287-144-X, A104). Clymer Pubns.

--Volkswagen Transporter: 1961-1979, Service, Repair Handbook. (Illus.). pap. 12.95 (ISBN 0-89287-277-2, A110). Clymer Pubns.

Steinwedel, Louis W. The Beetle Book. (Illus.). 140p. 1981. 19.95 (ISBN 0-13-071316-3); pap. 10.95 (ISBN 0-13-071308-2). P-H.

U. S. War Department. Volkswagen for the Wehrmacht. Post, Dan R., ed. LC 72-84803. 160p. 1972. pap. 14.95 (ISBN 0-911160-43-4). Post-Era.

Vintage Volkswagens. (Illus.). 120p. 1985. pap. 8.95 (ISBN 0-87701-357-8). Chronicle Bks.

Volkswagen of America Inc. Volkswagen Beetle & Karmann Ghia Official Service Manual Type 1, 1966, 1967, 1968, 1969. LC 70-189047. (Illus.). 512p. (Orig.). 1972. pap. 24.95 (ISBN 0-8376-0416-8). Bentley.

--Volkswagen Official Service Manual Type 1. Beetle, Super Beetle, & Karmann Ghia, 1970-1979. LC 78-75039. (Illus.). 448p. 1979. pap. 29.95 (ISBN 0-8376-0096-0). Bentley.

--Volkswagen Official Service Manual Type 2, Station Wagon-Bus, 1968-1979. 4th rev. ed. LC 78-75038. (Illus.). 464p. 1979. pap. 34.95 (ISBN 0-8376-0094-4). Bentley.

Volkswagen of America, Inc. Volkswagen Vanagon Official Factory Repair Manual, 1980-1983: Diesel & Aircooled Gasoline Engines. rev. ed. LC 83-70840. (Illus.). 512p. (Orig.). 1983. pap. 34.95 (ISBN 0-8376-0353-6). Bentley.

AUTOMOBILES, FOREIGN–TYPES–VOLVO

Chilton's Automotive Editorial Staff. Chilton's Repair & Tune-Up Guide: Volvo 1970-83. LC 82-72922. 304p. 1983. pap. 11.95 (ISBN 0-8019-7340-6). Chilton.

Clarke, R. M. Volvo Eighteen Hundred: Nineteen Sixty to Nineteen Seventy-Three. (Illus.). 100p. 1981. 11.95 (ISBN 0-907073-15-8, Pub. by Brooklands Bks England). Motorbooks Intl.

Haynes, J. H & Chalmers-Hunt, B. L. Volvo 120 & 130 Series & 1800 Sports '61 - '73: '61 thru '73. (Owners Workshop Manuals: No. 203). 1976. 12.95 (ISBN 0-85696-203-1, Pub. by J H Haynes England). Haynes Pubns.

Haynes, J. H. & Gilmour, M. B. Volvo 240 Series '74-'84. (Owners Workshop Manuals Ser.: No. 270). 1981. 12.95 (ISBN 0-85696-964-8, Pub. by J H Haynes England). Haynes Pubns.

Haynes, J. H & Shirland, S. Volvo 140 Series '66-'74. (Owners Workshop Manuals Ser.: No. 129). 1974. 12.95 (ISBN 0-85696-129-9, Pub. by J H Haynes England). Haynes Pubns.

Haynes, J. H. & Strasman, P. G. Volvo 164: '68 Thru '75. (Owners Workshop Manuals Ser.: No. 244). 1976. 12.95 (ISBN 0-85696-244-9, Pub. by J H Haynes England). Haynes Pubns.

Hoy, Ray. Volvo: 240 Series 1975-1983--Service, Repair Handbook. (Illus.). pap. 12.95 (ISBN 0-89287-278-0, A223). Clymer Pubns.

Volvo Nineteen Fifty-Six to Nineteen Sixty-Nine. LC 74-146881. (Illus.). 136p. 11.95 (ISBN 0-8019-6529-2). Chilton.

Volvo Nineteen Seventy to Nineteen Eighty-one. LC 80-66512. (Illus.). 288p. 1981. 11.95 (ISBN 0-8019-7040-7). Chilton.

AUTOMOBILES, FOREIGN–TYPES–ZEPHYR

Chilton's Automotive Editorial Staff. Zephyr 1978-1980. (Illus.). 1980. pap. 11.95 (ISBN 0-8019-6965-4). Chilton.

AUTOMOBILES, GAS-TURBINE

Odgers, J. & Kretschmer, D. Gas Turbine Fuels & Their Influence on Combustion. (Energy & Engineering Science Ser.). 1984. 40.00 (ISBN 0-9901004-7-2, Pub. by Abacus England). Heyden.

AUTOMOBILES, GAS-TURBINE–MOTORS

see Automotive Gas Turbines

AUTOMOBILES, RACING

see also Sports Cars; also names of specific racing automobiles listed under Automobiles–Types, or Automobiles, Foreign–Types e.g. Automobiles, Foreign–Types–Healey

Borgeson, Griffith. Golden Age of the Italian Racing Car. write for info. (ISBN 0-393-08583-X). Norton.

Fisher, Bill & Waar, Bob. How to Hotrod Small-Block Chevys. rev. ed. LC 73-173702. (Illus.). 192p. 1976. pap. 7.95 (ISBN 0-912656-06-9). H P Bks.

Hochman, Louis. Hot Rod Handbook. (Illus.). 144p. 1974. lib. bdg. 3.95 (ISBN 0-668-00602-1). Arco.

Huntington, Roger. Design & Development of the Indy Car. LC 81-80683. (Illus.). 176p. 1981. 9.95 (ISBN 0-89586-103-8). H P Bks.

Incandela, Sal. The Anatomy & Development of the Formula One Racing Car from 1975. 2nd ed. 29.95 (ISBN 0-85429-441-4, F441). Haynes Pubns.

Maiden, R. L. British Racing Cars. pap. 3.00x (ISBN 0-392-07213-0, SpS). Sportshelf.

Pulfer, Harry, ed. Model T Ford in Speed & Sport. LC 74-26384. (Illus.). 224p. 1956. pap. 12.95 (ISBN 0-911160-15-9). Post-Era.

Terry, Len & Baker, Alan. Racing Car Design & Development. LC 73-85159. 1973. 14.95 (ISBN 0-8376-0080-4). Bentley.

Yates, Brock. Sunday Driver. (Illus.). 258p. 1972. 7.95 (ISBN 0-374-27183-6). FS&G.

AUTOMOBILES, RACING–MOTORS

Fisher, Bill. How to Hotrod Corvair Engines. LC 76-28085. (Illus.). 1969. pap. 9.95 (ISBN 0-912656-00-X). H P Bks.

--How to Hotrod Volkswagen Engines. LC 72-28084. (Illus.). 1970. pap. 9.95 (ISBN 0-912656-03-4). H P Bks.

Fisher, Bill & Waar, Bob. How to Hotrod Big-Block Chevys. LC 72-159282. (Illus.). 1971. pap. 9.95 (ISBN 0-912656-04-2). H P Bks.

Jaderquist, Eugene. New How to Build Hot Rods. LC 62-16909. (Illus.). 1957. lib. bdg. 4.95 (ISBN 0-668-00553-X). Arco.

Smith, Philip H. The Design & Tuning of Competition Engines. 6th rev. ed. Wenner, David N., ed. LC 77-78834. (Illus.). 1977. 19.95 (ISBN 0-8376-0140-1). Bentley.

AUTOMOBILES, TURBINE POWERED

see Automobiles, Gas-Turbine

AUTOMORPHIC FORMS

Bump, D. Automorphic Forms on GL (3r R) (Lecture Notes in Mathematics Ser.: Vol. 1083). xi, 184p. 1984. pap. 12.00 (ISBN 0-387-13864-1). Springer-Verlag.

Cohn, Leslie. Dimension of Spaces of Automorphic Forms on a Certain Two-Dimensional Complex Domain. (Memoirs: No. 158). 97p. 1975. pap. 11.00 (ISBN 0-8218-1858-9, MEMO-158). Am Math.

Fourier Coefficients of Automorphic Forms. (Lecture Notes in Mathematics: Vol. 865). 201p. 1981. pap. 16.00 (ISBN 0-387-10839-4). Springer-Verlag.

Gelbart, Stephen S. Automorphic Forms & Adele Groups. (Annals of Mathematics Studies: No. 83). 280p. 1975. 26.50x (ISBN 0-691-08156-5). Princeton U Pr.

Gerritzen, L. & Van Der Put, M. Schottky Groups & Mumford Curves. (Lecture Notes in Mathematics: Vol. 817). 317p. 1980. pap. 23.00 (ISBN 0-387-10229-9). Springer-Verlag.

Satake, Ichiro, et al, eds. Automorphic Forms of Several Variables: Taniguchi Symposium, Katata, Vol. 46. (Progress in Mathematics Ser.). 398p. 1984. 29.95 (ISBN 0-8176-3172-0). Birkhauser.

Stiller, P. F. Automorphic Forms & the Picard Number of an Elliptic Surface, Vol. 5. (Aspects of Mathematics Ser.). Date not set. pap. 15.00 (ISBN 0-9904001-1-5, Pub. by Vieweg & Sohn Germany). Heyden.

Tata Institute Studies in Mathematics Bombay 1979. Automorphic Forms, Respresentation Theory & Arithmetics: Proceedings. Gelbart, S., et al, eds. 355p. 1981. pap. 10.00 (ISBN 0-387-10697-9). Springer-Verlag.

AUTOMORPHIC FUNCTIONS

see Functions, Automorphic

AUTOMOTIVE FUEL SYSTEMS

see Automobiles–Fuel Systems

AUTOMOTIVE FUELS

see Motor Fuels

AUTOMOTIVE GAS-TURBINE ENGINES

see Automotive Gas Turbines

AUTOMOTIVE GAS TURBINES

O'Brien, John P., ed. Gas Turbines for Automotive Use. LC 79-24891. (Energy Technology Review Ser.: No. 54). (Illus.). 342p. 1980. 42.00 (ISBN 0-8155-0786-0). Noyes.

Society of Automotive Engineers. Advanced Gas Turbine Systems for Automobiles. LC 80-80308. 96p. 1980. Seven papers. 22.00 (ISBN 0-89883-236-5, SP465). Soc Auto Engineers.

Turbochargers & Turbocharged Engines. LC 79-50459. 158p. 1979. Twelve papers. 30.00 (ISBN 0-89883-214-4, SP442). Soc Auto Engineers.

AUTOMOTIVE TRANSPORTATION

see Transportation, Automotive

AUTOMOTIVE VEHICLES

see Motor Vehicles

AUTORADIOGRAPHY

Fischer, Helmut A. & Werner, Gottfried. Autoradiography. Ashworth, M. R., tr. from Ger. LC 70-164842. (Working Methods in Modern Science Ser.). 1971. 31.60x (ISBN 3-1100-3523-5). De Gruyter.

Gahan, P. B., ed. Autoradiography for Biologists. 1972. 25.00 (ISBN 0-12-273250-2). Acad Pr.

International Society for Cell Biology. Use of Radioautography in Investigating Protein Synthesis, Proceedings. Leblond, C. P. & Warren, K. B., eds. (Vol. 4). 1966. 67.50 (ISBN 0-12-611904-X). Acad Pr.

Luettge, U., ed. Microautoradiography & Electron Probe Analysis: Their Application to Plant Physiology. LC 72-97599. (Illus.). 280p. 1972. pap. 29.00 (ISBN 0-387-05950-4). Springer-Verlag.

Phelps, Michael E., et al, eds. Principles of Pet & Autoradiography in the Study of Cerebral & Myocardial Function. (Illus.). 450p. 1985. text ed. 74.00 (ISBN 0-88167-118-5). Raven.

Rogers, A. W. Techniques of Autoradiography. 3rd, rev. & enl. ed. LC 78-16861. 430p. 1979. 87.25 (ISBN 0-444-80063-8, Biomedical Pr). Elsevier.

Roth, Lloyd J. & Stumpf, Walter, eds. Autoradiography of Diffusible Substances. 1969. 72.00 (ISBN 0-12-598550-9). Acad Pr.

AUTOSYN

see Synchros

AVALANCHES

see also Landslides; Railroads–Snow Protection and Removal

Diltz-Siler, Barbara. Understanding Avalanches: A Handbook for Snow Travelers in the Sierra & Cascades. (Illus.). 32p. 1977. pap. 2.95 (ISBN 0-913140-24-4). Signpost Bk Pub.

Tufty, Barbara. One Thousand & One Questions Answered about Earthquakes, Avalanches, Floods, & Other Natural Disasters. LC 78-51736. 1978. lib. bdg. 12.50x (ISBN 0-88307-612-8). Gannon.

--One Thousand & One Questions Answered about Earthquakes, Avalanches, Floods & Other Natural Disasters. 14.25 (ISBN 0-8446-5826-X). Peter Smith.

Voight, B. Rockslides & Avalanches, Pt. 1: Natural Phenomena. (Development in Geotechnical Engineering Ser.: Vol. 14A). 834p. 1978. 119.25 (ISBN 0-444-41507-6). Elsevier.

--Rockslides & Avalanches, Pt. 2: Engineering Sites. (Developments in Geotechnical Engineering Ser.: Vol. 14B). 850p. 1980. 119.25 (ISBN 0-444-41508-4). Elsevier.

AVIATION

see Aeronautics

AVIATION ACCIDENTS

see Aeronautics–Accidents

AVIATION FUELS

see Airplanes–Fuel

AVIATION GASOLINE

see Airplanes–Fuel

AVIATION MECHANICS (PERSONS)

Aviation Mechanic Airframe Question Book Including Answers, Explanations & References. 196p. (Orig.). 1984. pap. text ed. 6.95 (ISBN 0-89100-275-8, EA-FAA-T-8080-12-C). Aviation Maintenance.

Aviation Mechanic Powerplant Question Book Including Answers, Explanations & References. (Pilot Training Ser.). 202p. 1984. pap. text ed. 6.95 (ISBN 0-89100-273-1, EA-FAA-T-8080-11-C). Aviation Maintenance.

Aviation Mechanics General Question Book Including Answers, Explanations & References. 116p. 1984. pap. text ed. 6.95 (ISBN 0-89100-271-5, EA-FAA-T-8080-10C). Aviation Maintenance.

International Air Safety Seminar. Human Factors in Managing Aviation Safety: Proceedings of the 37th Annual Meeting. pap. 70.00 (ISBN 0-317-26167-3, 2025190). Bks Demand UMI.

Reithmaier, Larry, ed. Aviation Mechanics Certification Guide. LC 80-11630. (Illus.). 1980. 6.95 (ISBN 0-932882-01-3). Palomar Bks.

AVIATORS

see Air Pilots

AVIGATION

see Navigation (Aeronautics)

AVIONICS

see Electronics in Aeronautics

AVOCADO

Alexander, D. M. Some Avocado Varieties for Australia. (Illus.). 36p. 1978. pap. 6.00 (ISBN 0-643-02276-7, C010, CSIRO). Unipub.

Doeser, Linda & Richardson, Rosamond. The Little Green Avocado Book. (Illus.). 64p. 1983. 5.95 (ISBN 0-312-48862-9). St Martin.

Koch, Frank D. Avocado Grower's Handbook. Thomson, Paul H., ed. LC 83-70334. 286p. 1983. pap. 17.50 (ISBN 0-9602066-2-0). Bonsall Pub.

Spain, Hensley. The Avocado Cookbook. (Illus.). 150p. pap. 5.50 (ISBN 0-916870-24-3). Creative Arts Bk.

AXES

Brown, Rodney H. American Polearms, Fifteen Twenty-Six to Eighteen Sixty-Five. LC 67-19981. (Illus.). 1968. 14.50 (ISBN 0-910598-08-8). Flayderman.

Knutsen, Ronald. Japanese Polearms. 35.00x (ISBN 0-87556-138-1). Saifer.

Leakey, L. S. & Tobias, P. V., eds. Olduvai Gorge, Vol. 1 & 2: Nineteen Fifty-One To Nineteen Sixty-One. 1965. Vol. 1. 80.00 (ISBN 0-521-05527-X); Vol. 2. 110.00 (ISBN 0-521-06901-7). Cambridge U Pr.

Leakey, M. D., ed. Olduvai Gorge, Vol. 3: Nineteen Sixty - Nineteen Sixty-Three. 1972. 135.00 (ISBN 0-521-07723-0). Cambridge U Pr.

AXIAL FLOW COMPRESSORS

see Compressors

AXIOMATIC SET THEORY

Carnes, John. Axiomatics & Dogmatics. (Theology & Scientific Culture Ser.). 1982. 14.95x (ISBN 0-19-520377-1). Oxford U Pr.

Dodd, A. J. The Core Model. LC 81-17989. (London Mathematical Society Lecture Note Series 61). 272p. 1982. 27.95 (ISBN 0-521-28530-5). Cambridge U Pr.

Fremlin, D. H. Consequences of Martin's Axiom. (Cambridge Tracts in Mathematics Ser.: 84). 352p. 1984. 54.50 (ISBN 0-521-25091-9). Cambridge U Pr.

Hervey, Sandor G. Axiomatic Semantics: A Linguistic Theory. 320p. 1980. 20.00x (ISBN 0-7073-0222-6, Pub. by Scottish Academic Pr). Columbia U Pr.

Krivine, J. L. Introduction to Axiomatic Set Theory. Miller, D. W., tr. LC 71-146965. (Synthese Library: No. 34). 1974. lib. bdg. 15.00 (ISBN 90-277-0169-5, Pub. by Reidel Holland); pap. text ed. 8.00 (ISBN 90-277-0411-2, Pub. by Reidel Holland). Kluwer Academic.

Quine, Willard V. Set Theory & Its Logic. rev. ed. LC 68-14271. 1969. 8.95 (ISBN 0-674-80207-1, Belknap Pr). Harvard U Pr.

Stoll, Robert R. Sets, Logic, & Axiomatic Theories. 2nd ed. LC 74-8932. pap. 61.00 (ISBN 0-317-08628-6, 2055554). Bks Demand UMI.

Suppes, Patrick. Axiomatic Set Theory. 275p. 1972. pap. text ed. 5.00 (ISBN 0-486-61630-4). Dover.

AXIOMS

Fremlin, D. H. Consequences of Martin's Axiom. (Cambridge Tracts in Mathematics Ser.: 84). 352p. 1984. 54.50 (ISBN 0-521-25091-9). Cambridge U Pr.

Hamilton, A. G. Numbers, Sets & Axioms: The Apparatus of Mathematics. LC 82-4206. 250p. 1983. 44.50 (ISBN 0-521-24509-5); pap. 18.95 (ISBN 0-521-28761-8). Cambridge U Pr.

Heyting, A. Axiomatic Projective Geometry. 2nd, rev. ed. 150p. 1980. 42.75 (ISBN 0-444-85431-2, North-Holland). Elsevier.

Ludwig, G. An Axiomatic Basis for Quantum Mechanics, Vol. 1. (Illus.). 240p. 1985. 41.50 (ISBN 0-387-13773-4). Springer-Verlag.

AZALEA

Clarke, J. Harold. Getting Started with Rhododendrons & Azaleas. LC 82-16995. (Illus.). 268p. 1982. pap. 14.95 (ISBN 0-917304-30-6). Timber.

Galle, Fred & Fell, Derek. All about Azaleas, Camellias & Rhododendrons. Beley, Jim, ed. LC 85-70879. (Illus.). 96p. (Orig.). 1985. pap. 5.95 (ISBN 0-89721-064-6). Ortho.

Lee, F. Azalea Book. 1986. cancelled (ISBN 0-442-25842-9). Van Nos Reinhold.

Sunset Editors. Azaleas, Rhododendrons, Camellias. LC 81-82866. (Illus.). 96p. 1982. pap. 4.95 (ISBN 0-376-03020-8, Sunset Bks). Sunset-Lane.

West, Franklin H., et al. Hybrids & Hybridizers: Rhododendrons & Azaleas for Eastern North America. Livingston, Philip A., ed. LC 77-16822. (Illus.). 1978. 30.00 (ISBN 0-915180-04-9). Harrowood Bks.

Wilson, Ernest & Rehder, Alfred. A Monograph of Azaleas. LC 77-23265. (Illus.). 1977. Repr. of 1921 ed. 12.50 (ISBN 0-913728-22-5). Theophrastus.

AZIDES

Fair, H. D. & Walker, R. F. Energetic Materials. Incl. Vol. 1. Physics & Chemistry of the Inorganic Azides. 503p. 69.50x (ISBN 0-306-37076-X); Vol. 2. Technology of the Inorganic Azides. 296p. 65.00x (ISBN 0-306-37077-8). LC 76-30808. (Illus.). 1977 (Plenum Pr). Plenum Pub.

Patai, S. The Chemistry of Halides, Pseudohalides & Azides: Supplement D. (Chemistry of Functional Groups Ser.). 1983. Pt. 1, 931p. 288.95 (ISBN 0-471-10087-0); Part 2, 936p. 288.95 (ISBN 0-471-10088-9); Set. 577.95 (ISBN 0-471-10089-7). Wiley.

Scriven. Azides & Nitrenes. 1984. 99.50 (ISBN 0-12-633480-3). Acad Pr.

AZIRIDINE

Dermer, O. C. & Ham, G. E. Ethylenimine & Other Aziridines: Chemistry - Applications. 1969. 95.50 (ISBN 0-12-209650-9). Acad Pr.

AZO COMPOUNDS

Patai, Saul, ed. Chemistry of Hydrazo, Azo & Azoxy Groups, 2 pts. LC 75-2194. 1975. Pt. 1. 134.95 (ISBN 0-471-66926-1); (Pub. by Wiley-Interscience). Wiley.

AZOLE

see Pyrrol

AZTEC CALENDAR

see Calendar, Mexican

B

B-FIFTY-TWO BOMBER

B-52 Two in Action. (Aircraft in Action Ser.). (Illus.). 1984. pap. 4.95 (ISBN 0-89747-022-2, 1023). Squad Sig Pubns.

Boyne, Walter. Boeing B-52: A Documentary History. (Illus.). 158p. 1982. 22.50 (ISBN 0-87474-246-3, Pub. by Janes England). Smithsonian.

--Boeing B-52: A Documentary History. (Illus.). 160p. 1982. 19.95 (ISBN 0-86720-550-4). Jane's Pub Inc.

Keaveney, K. Boeing B-52G-4: Minigraph 6. write for info. (ISBN 0-942548-11-6). Aerofax.

B-SEVENTEEN BOMBER

Birdsall, Steve. The B-17 Flying Fortress. LC 65-16862. (Famous Aircraft Ser.). (Illus.). 1979. pap. 6.95 (ISBN 0-8168-5646-X). Aero.

Davis, Larry. B-17 in Action. (In Action Ser.: No. 1063). (Illus.). 58p. 1984. pap. 4.95 (ISBN 0-89747-152-0). Squad Sig Pubns.

Jablonski, Edward. Flying Fortress. LC 65-19886. (Illus.). 1965. 22.95 (ISBN 0-385-03855-0). Doubleday.

Lloyd, Alwyn T. B-17 Flying Fortress: Part 2. LC 81-67592. (Detail & Scale Ser.: Vol. 11). (Illus.). 72p. 1983. pap. 7.95 (ISBN 0-8168-5021-6). Aero.

Lloyd, Alwyn T. & Moore, Terry D. B-17 Flying Fortress in Detail & Scale: Part 1 (Production Version) LC 81-67592. (Detail & Scale Ser.: Vol. 2). (Illus.). 72p. (Orig.). 1981. pap. 7.95 (ISBN 0-8168-5012-7). Aero.

Rice, Michael S. Pilot's Manual for the Boeing B-17 Flying Fortress. (Illus.). 1976. pap. 8.95 (ISBN 0-87994-037-9, Pub. by AvPubns). Aviation.

Willmott, H. P. B-17 Flying Fortress. (Illus.). 64p. 1983. pap. 4.95 (ISBN 0-13-056713-2). P-H.

B-TWENTY-FOUR BOMBER

Birdsall, Steve. B-24 in Action. (Aircraft in Action Ser.). (Illus.). 50p. 1984. pap. 4.95 (ISBN 0-89747-020-6, 1021). Squad Sig Pubns.

--The B-24 Liberator. Gentle, Ernest J., ed. LC 67-14200. (The Famous Aircraft Ser.). (Illus.). 64p. 1985. pap. 7.95 (ISBN 0-8168-5657-5). Aero.

O'Dwyer, Eamonn, ed. Flight Manual for the B-24 Liberator. 1977. pap. 10.95 (ISBN 0-87994-000-X). Aviation.

B-TWENTY-NINE BOMBER

Anderton, David. B-29 Super Fortress at War. (Illus.). 1978. 19.95 (ISBN 0-684-15884-1, ScribT). Scribner.

B-29 Superfortress in Action. (Aircraft in Action Ser.). (Illus.). 1984. pap. 4.95 (ISBN 0-89747-030-3, 1031). Squad Sig Pubns.

Lloyd, Alwyn T. B-29 Superfortress: Part 1. LC 83-2789. (Detail & Scale Ser.: Vol. 10). (Illus.). 72p. (Orig.). 1982. pap. 7.95 (ISBN 0-8168-5019-4). Aero.

Pimlott, John. B-29 Superfortress. 64p. 1983. pap. 4.95 (ISBN 0-13-056721-3). P-H.

U. S. Air Force. B-29 Superfortress Manual. (Illus.). 92p. 1984. pap. 10.95 (ISBN 0-317-14795-1). Boomerang.

BABOONS

Abegglen, Jean-Jacques. On Socialization in Hamadryas Baboons. LC 80-70316. (Illus.). 208p. 1984. 35.00 (ISBN 0-8387-5017-6). Bucknell U Pr.

Altmann, Jeanne. Baboon Mothers & Infants. LC 79-21568. (Illus.). 1980. text ed. 18.50x (ISBN 0-674-05856-9); pap. text ed. 8.95x (ISBN 0-674-05857-7). Harvard U Pr.

Dunbar, R. & Dunbar, Patsy. Social Dynamics of Gelada Baboons. (Contributions to Primatology: Vol. 6). (Illus.). 176p. 1975. 38.00 (ISBN 3-8055-2137-5). S Karger.

Hausfater, G. Dominance & Reproduction in Baboons (Papio Cynocephalus) A Quantitative Analysis. Kuhn, H., et al, eds. (Contributions to Primatology: Vol. 7). (Illus.). viii, 149p. 1975. pap. 29.25 (ISBN 3-8055-2139-1). S Karger.

Kalter, S. S. The Baboon: Microbiology, Clinical Chemistry & Some Hematological Aspects. (Primates in Medicine: Vol. 8). (Illus.). 1973. 30.75 (ISBN 3-8055-1442-5). S Karger.

Kawai, M., ed. Ecological & Sociological Studies of Gelada Baboons. (Contributions to Primatology: Vol. 16). (Illus.). 1978. 63.00 (ISBN 3-8055-2873-6). S Karger.

Kummer, Hans. Social Organization of Hamadryas Baboons: A Field Study. LC 67-25082. 1968. 16.00x (ISBN 0-226-46171-8). U of Chicago Pr.

Ransom, Timothy W. The Beach Troop of the Gombe. LC 77-92573. 1979. 35.00 (ISBN 0-8387-1704-7). Bucknell U Pr.

Smuts, Barbara B. Sex & Friendship in Baboons. (Biological Foundations of Human Behavior Ser.). (Illus.). 300p. 1985. lib. bdg. 24.95x (ISBN 0-202-02027-4). Aldine Pub.

BABY ANIMALS

see Animals, Infancy of

BACON, ROGER, 1214-1294

Bacon, Roger. Roger Bacon Essays: Contributed by Various Writers on the Occasion of the Commemoration of the Seventh Centenary of His Birth. Little, A. G., ed. LC 71-173549. 425p. 1972. Repr. of 1914 ed. 18.00x (ISBN 0-8462-1656-6). Russell.

Bridges, John H. The Life & Work of Roger Bacon. Jones, H. Gordon, ed. LC 79-8597. Repr. of 1914 ed. 21.50 (ISBN 0-404-18450-2). AMS Pr.

--The Life & Work of Roger Bacon: An Introduction to the Opus Majus. Jones, H. Gordon, ed. LC 76-1120. 1977. Repr. of 1914 ed. lib. bdg. 15.00x (ISBN 0-915172-14-3). Richwood Pub.

Easton, Stewart C. Roger Bacon & His Search for a Universal Science. LC 70-100159. Repr. of 1952 ed. lib. bdg. 15.00x (ISBN 0-8371-3399-8, EARB). Greenwood.

Newbold, William R. & Kent, Roland G. The Cipher of Roger Bacon. 224p. 1983. lib. bdg. 85.00 (ISBN 0-89984-822-2). Century Bookbindery.

Westacott, Evelyn. Roger Bacon in Life & Legend. LC 74-14623. 1974. Repr. of 1953 ed. lib. bdg. 17.50 (ISBN 0-8414-9547-5). Folcroft.

BACTERIA

see also Bacterial Cell Walls; Bacterial Genetics; Endotoxin; Fermentation; Flagella (Microbiology); Spores (Bacteria); Viruses;

also names of specific bacteria, e.g. staphyloccoccus

Aly, Raza & Shinefield, Henry R. Bacterial Interference. 192p. 1982. 62.00 (ISBN 0-8493-6285-7). CRC Pr.

Anderson, Laurens & Unger, Frank M., eds. Bacterial Lipopolysacharides: Structure, Synthesis, & Biological Activities. LC 83-158282. (ACS Symposium Ser.: No. 231). 325p. 1983. lib. bdg. 44.95x (ISBN 0-8412-0800-X). Am Chemical.

Andrew, Malcolm H. & Russell, A. Denver. The Revival of Injured Microbes. (Society for Applied Bacteria Symposium Ser.). 1984. 44.00 (ISBN 0-12-058520-0). Acad Pr.

Balows, Albert & Sonnenwirth, Alex C. Bacteremia: Laboratory & Clinical Aspects. (Illus.). 142p. 1983. 22.50x (ISBN 0-398-04807-X). C C Thomas.

Bousfield, I. J. & Callely, A. G., eds. Coryneform Bacteria. (Special Publication of the Society for General Microbiology). 1979. 37.50 (ISBN 0-12-119650-X). Acad Pr.

Clayton, R. K. & Sistrom, W. R., eds. The Photosynthetic Bacteria. LC 78-2835. (Illus.). 968p. 1978. 115.00x (ISBN 0-306-31133-X, Plenum Pr). Plenum Pub.

Committee on Germplasm Resources. Conservation of Germplasm Resource: An Imperative. 1978. pap. 7.95 (ISBN 0-309-02744-6). Natl Acad Pr.

Conn, H. W. The Story of Germ Life. 1904. 10.00 (ISBN 0-8274-4192-4). R West.

Doelle, H. W. Bacterial Metabolism. 2d ed. 1975. 77.50 (ISBN 0-12-219352-0). Acad Pr.

Dworkin, Martin. Procaryotic Development. 272p. 1985. text ed. 29.95x (ISBN 0-8053-2460-7). Benjamin-Cummings.

Ewing, W. H. Identification of Enterobacteriacea. Date not set. write for info. (ISBN 0-444-00841-1). Elsevier.

Fenchel, T. & Blackburn, T. H. Bacteria & Mineral Cycling. 1979. 44.00 (ISBN 0-12-252750-X). Acad Pr.

Fletcher, Madilyn M. & Floodgate, George D., eds. Bacteria in Their Natural Environments. (Society for General Microbiology Special Publications: Vol. 16). Date not set. price not set (ISBN 0-12-260560-8). Acad Pr.

Gel'man, N. S., et al. Respiration & Phosphorylation of Bacteria. LC 66-26220. 238p. 1967. 32.50x (ISBN 0-306-30296-9, Plenum Pr). Plenum Pub.

Gilardi, Gerald L. Glucose Nonfermenting Gramnegative Bacteria in Clinical Microbiology. 256p. 1978. 76.00 (ISBN 0-8493-5331-9). CRC Pr.

Gottschalk, G. Bacterial Metabolism. LC 78-7880. (Springer Ser. in Microbiology). (Illus.). 1979. 27.50 (ISBN 0-387-90308-9). Springer-Verlag.

Gould, G. W. & Corry, Janet E. Microbial Growth & Survival in Extremes of Environment. LC 79-41561. (Society for Applied Bacteriology Technical Ser.: No. 15). 1980. 42.50 (ISBN 0-12-293680-9). Acad Pr.

Gunsalus, I. C., ed. The Bacteria; a Treatise on Structure & Function, Vol. 8: Archaebacteria. 1985. 85.00 (ISBN 0-12-307208-5). Acad Pr.

Gunsalus, I. C., et al, eds. Bacteria: A Treatise on Structure & Function, 7 vols. Incl. Vol. 1. Structure. 1960. 72.00 (ISBN 0-12-307201-8); Vol. 2. Metabolism. 1961. 72.00 (ISBN 0-12-307202-6); Vol. 3. Biosynthesis. 1962. 81.00 (ISBN 0-12-307203-4); Vol. 4. Physiology of Growth. 1963. 67.50 (ISBN 0-12-307204-2); Vol. 5. Heredity. 1964. 72.00 (ISBN 0-12-307205-0); Vol. 6. Bacterial Diversity. 1978. 68.50 (ISBN 0-12-307206-9); Vol. 7. Mechanism of Adaption. 1979. 60.50 (ISBN 0-12-307207-7). LC 59-13831. Acad Pr.

Hayflick, Leonard, ed. The Mycoplasmatales & the L-Phase of Bacteria. LC 68-54562. pap. 160.00 (ISBN 0-317-26220-3, 2055686). Bks Demand UMI.

Helinski, Donald R., et al, eds. Plasmids in Bacteria. (Basic Life Sciences Ser.: Vol. 30). 1005p. 1985. 110.00x (ISBN 0-306-41901-7, Plenum Pr). Plenum Pub.

Henrici, Arthur T. Morphologic Variation & Rate of Growth of Bacteria. (Illus.). 194p. 1928. 18.50x (ISBN 0-398-04277-2). C C Thomas.

Inouye. Bacterial Outer Membranes As Model Systems. 1985. write for info. (ISBN 0-471-82500-X). Wiley.

Jeljackzewicz, Janusz, et al, eds. Bacteria & Cancer. 1983. 39.50 (ISBN 0-12-383820-7). Acad Pr.

Knowles, Christopher J. Diversity of Bacterial Respiratory Systems, 2 vols. 1980. Vol. 1, 272p. 79.50 (ISBN 0-8493-5399-8); Vol. 2, 256p. 72.00 (ISBN 0-8493-5400-5). CRC Pr.

Koser, Stewart A. Vitamin Requirements of Bacteria & Yeasts. (Illus.). 672p. 1968. 59.75x (ISBN 0-398-01041-2). C C Thomas.

Lapage, S. P., et al, eds. International Code of Nomenclature of Bacteria. LC 75-20730. 152p. 1975. 7.50 (ISBN 0-914826-04-2). Am Soc Microbio.

Leadbetter, Edward R. & Poindexter, Jeanne S., eds. Bacteria in Nature, Vol. 1: Bacterial Activities in Perspective. 255p. 1985. 39.50x (ISBN 0-306-41944-0, Plenum Pr). Plenum Pub.

Leifson, Einar. Atlas of Bacterial Flagellation. (Illus.). 1959. 38.00 (ISBN 0-12-441650-0). Acad Pr.

Lin, Edmund C., et al. Bacteria, Plasmids, & Phages: An Introduction to Molecular Biology. (Illus.). 352p. 1984. text ed. 35.00x (ISBN 0-674-58165-2); pap. text ed. 18.50x (ISBN 0-674-58166-0). Harvard U Pr.

McLaren, Anne. Germ Cells & Soma: A New Look at Old Problem. LC 81-2971. (Silliman Lectures: No. 5). (Illus.). 128p. 1981. text ed. 18.50x (ISBN 0-300-02694-3). Yale U Pr.

Mitruka, Brij M. Methods of Detection & Identification of Bacteria. (Uniscience Ser.). 250p. 1977. 66.00 (ISBN 0-8493-5116-2). CRC Pr.

Mitscherlich, E. & Marth, E. H. Microbial Survival in the Environment: Bacteria & Rickettsiae Important in Human & Animal Health. (Illus.). 820p. 1984. 142.00 (ISBN 0-387-13726-2). Springer-Verlag.

Mitsuhashi, S. Drug Resistance in Bacteria. 380p. 35.00 (ISBN 0-86577-085-9). Thieme-Stratton.

Native Aquatic Bacteria: Enumeration, Activity & Ecology, STP 695. 219p. 1979. 25.00x (ISBN 0-8031-0526-6, 4-695000-16). ASTM.

OAS. Bacteriofagos. 2nd rev. ed. OAS General Secretariat Department of Technological & Scientific Affairs, ed. (Biologia Ser.: No. 12). (Span., Illus.). 102p. 1980. pap. 2.00 (ISBN 0-8270-1301-9). OAS.

Ormerod, J. G., ed. The Phototrophic Bacteria. LC 83-47855. (Studies in Microbiology: Vol. 3). (Illus.). 320p. 1983. text ed. 40.00x (ISBN 0-520-05092-4). U of Cal Pr.

Palmieri, F., et al, eds. Vectoral Reactions in Electron & Ion Transport in Michondria & Bacteria. (Developments in Bioenergetics & Biomembranes Ser.: Vol. 5). 430p. 1981. 73.75 (ISBN 0-444-80372-6, Biomedical Pr). Elsevier.

Parry, Jennifer M., et al. A Colour Atlas of Bacillus Species. (Illus.). 269p. 1983. text ed. 65.00x (ISBN 0-7234-0777-0, Pub. by Wolfe Medical England). Sheridan.

Pascher, A. Suesswasserflora von Mittelieropa, Vol. 20: Schyzomyceten-Bakterien, von J. Haeisler. Ettl, H. & Gerloff, J., eds. (Ger., Illus.). 588p. 1982. lib. bdg. 63.65 (ISBN 3-437-30344-9). Lubrecht & Cramer.

Rosen, Barry P. Bacterial Transport. (Microbiology Ser.: Vol. 4). 1978. 99.75 (ISBN 0-8247-6670-9). Dekker.

Saeir, Milton H., Jr. Mechanisms & Regulation of Carbohydrate Transfer in Bacteria. 1985. 39.00 (ISBN 0-12-614780-9). Acad Pr.

Schlessinger, David, ed. Microbiology 1976. LC 74-33538. 1976. 28.00 (ISBN 0-914826-11-5). Am Soc Microbio.

Seeley, Harry W., Jr. & VanDemark, Paul J. Microbes in Action: A Laboratory Manual of Microbiology. 3rd ed. (Illus.). 385p. 1981. pap. text ed. 14.95x (ISBN 0-7167-1259-8); instrs'. manual avail. W H Freeman.

--Selected Exercises from Microbes in Action: A Laboratory Manual of Microbiology. 3rd ed. (Illus.). 286p. 1981. 13.95x (ISBN 0-7167-1260-1); instr's manual avail. W H Freeman.

Singleton, Paul & Sainsbury, Diana. Introduction to Bacteria: For Students in the Biological Sciences. LC 81-210885. 166p. 1981. 34.95x (ISBN 0-471-10034-X, Pub. by Wiley-Interscience); pap. 14.95x (ISBN 0-471-10035-8, Pub. by Wiley-Interscience). Wiley.

Sinha, U. & Srivastava, S. An Introduction to Bacteria. (Illus.). 180p. 1983. pap. text ed. 8.95x (ISBN 0-7069-2134-8, Pub. by Vikas India). Advent NY.

Sokatch, John R. Bacterial Physiology. 1969. 69.50 (ISBN 0-12-654250-3). Acad Pr.

Starr, M. P., ed. Phytopathogenic Bacteria: Selections from the "The Prokaryotes-A Handbook on Habitats, Isolation, & Identification of Bacteria". (Illus.). 168p. 1983. pap. 29.95 (ISBN 0-387-90880-3). Springer-Verlag.

Starr, M. P., et al, eds. Prokaryotes. A Handbook on Habitats. Isolation, & Identification of Bacteria, 2 pts. (Illus.). 2624p. 1981. Set. 435.00 (ISBN 0-387-08871-7). Springer-Verlag.

Sulfur Bacteria. 129p. 1979. pap. 15.00x (ISBN 0-8031-0582-7, 04-650000-16). ASTM.

Thompson, J. P. & Skerman, V. D. Azotobacteraceae. LC 79-41053. 1980. 88.50 (ISBN 0-12-689050-1). Acad Pr.

Urbaschek, B. & Urbaschek, R., eds. Gram-Negative Bacterial Infections & Mode of Endotoxin Actions - Pathophysiologic, Immunologic, & Clinical Aspects. LC 74-34099. (Illus.). 550p. 1975. 45.00 (ISBN 0-387-81292-X). Springer-Verlag.

Van Iterson, Woutera. Inner Structures of Bacteria. 1984. 57.50 (ISBN 0-442-28830-1). Van Nos Reinhold.

Von Graevenitz, Alexander & Rubin, Sally Jo. The Genus Serratia. 224p. 1980. 66.00 (ISBN 0-8493-5533-8). CRC Pr.

Woolcock, J. B. Bacterial Infection & Immunity in Domestic Animals. (Developments in Animal & Veterinary Science Ser.: Vol. 3). 254p. 1979. 70.25 (ISBN 0-444-41767-2). Elsevier.

Zehr, Eldon I., ed. Methods for Evaluating Plant Fungicides, Nematicides, & Bactericides. LC 78-63414. 141p. 1978. lib. bdg. 18.00 (ISBN 0-89054-025-X). Am Phytopathol Soc.

BACTERIA–CULTURES AND CULTURE MEDIA

see Microbiology–Cultures and Culture Media

BACTERIA–GENETICS

see Bacterial Genetics

BACTERIA, AEROBIC

Berkeley, Roger & Goodfellow, Michael, eds. The Aerobic Endosphere-Forming Bacteria: Classification & Identification. (Society for General Microbiology Special Publication: No. 4). 1981. 45.00 (ISBN 0-12-091250-3). Acad Pr.

BACTERIA, ANAEROBIC

Balows, Albert, et al. Anaerobic Bacteria: Role in Disease. (Illus.). 656p. 1975. photocopy ed. 76.75x (ISBN 0-398-03074-X). C C Thomas.

Hill, M. J., ed. Models of Anaerobic Infection. (New Perspectives in Clinical Microbiology Ser.). 1984. lib. bdg. 46.00 (ISBN 0-89838-688-8, Pub. by Martinus Nijhoff Netherlands). Kluwer Academic.

Hughes, D. E., et al, eds. Anaerobic Digestion, 1981. 430p. 1982. 73.25 (ISBN 0-444-80406-4, Biomedical Pr). Elsevier.

Lambe, Dwight W., et al, eds. Anaerobic Bacteria: Selected Topics. LC 80-18505. 324p. 1980. 45.00x (ISBN 0-306-40546-6, Plenum Pr). Plenum Pub.

McClung. The Anaerobic Bacteria. 1982. Set. 999.00; Pt. 1, Vol. 1. (ISBN 0-8247-1202-1); Pt. 1, Vol. 2. (ISBN 0-8247-1203-X); Pt. 1, Vol. 3. (ISBN 0-8247-1204-8); Pt. 1, Vol. 4. (ISBN 0-8247-1205-6); Pt. 2, Vol. 1. (ISBN 0-8247-1207-2). Pt. 2, Vol. 2 (ISBN 0-8247-1208-0). Dekker.

Pohland, Frederick G., ed. Anaerobic Biological Treatment Processes. LC 74-176092. (Advances in Chemistry Ser: No. 105). 196p. 1971. 21.95 (ISBN 0-8412-0131-5). Am Chemical.

Shapton, D. A. & Board, R. G., eds. Isolation of Anaerobes. (Society for Applied Bacteriology Technical Ser.: No. 5). 270p. 1971. 41.00 (ISBN 0-12-638840-7). Acad Pr.

Silver, Sylvia. Anaerobic Bacteriology for the Clinical Laboratory. LC 79-23329. 118p. 1980. pap. 12.50 (ISBN 0-8016-4625-1). Mosby.

Smith, Louis D., et al. The Pathogenic Anaerobic Bacteria. 3rd ed. 348p. 1984. 39.75x (ISBN 0-398-05001-5). C C Thomas.

Suzuki, Shoichiro & Ueno, Kazue. Anaerobic Bacteria, Vol 1. Kosakai, Nozomu, ed. LC 81-83039. (Illustrated Laboratory Techniques Ser.). (Illus.). 82p. 1981. 11.00 (ISBN 0-89640-062-X). Igaku-Shoin.

Willis, Allen T., et al. Management of Anaerobic Infections: Prevention & Treatment. LC 80-42345. (Antimicrobial Chemotherapy Research Studies). 97p. 1981. 32.95 (ISBN 0-471-28037-2, Pub. by Res Stud Pr). Wiley.

BACTERIA, PATHOGENIC

see also Bacteria, Phytopathogenic; Bacterial Diseases; Biological Warfare;

also names of specific bacteria e.g. Streptococcus and headings beginning with the word Bacillus, e.g. Bacillus Tuberculosis

Colwell, Rita R., ed. Vibrios in the Environment. LC 83-21720. (Enviromental Science & Technology Ser.: 1-121). 634p. 1983. 45.00x (ISBN 0-471-87343-8, Pub. by Wiley-Interscience). Wiley.

Cowan, S. T. Cowan & Steel's Manual for the Identification of Medical Bacteria. (Illus.). 240p. 1974. 44.50 (ISBN 0-521-20399-6). Cambridge U Pr.

Holder, I. A., ed. Bacterial Enzymes & Virulence. 206p. 1985. 70.00 (ISBN 0-8493-5296-7). CRC Pr.

International Conference on Plant Pathogenic Bacteria, Third: Proceedings. 1972. pap. 45.00 (PDC67, PUDOC). Unipub.

Jackson, G. G. & Thomas, H., eds. The Pathogenesis of Bacterial Infections. (Bayer Symposium: 8). (Illus.). 430p. 1985. 49.50 (ISBN 0-387-15304-7). Springer-Verlag.

Schlessinger, David, ed. Microbiology 1975. LC 74-33538. 1975. 28.00 (ISBN 0-914826-05-0). Am Soc Microbio.

Schoolnik, Gary K., et al, eds. The Pathogenic Neisseriae: Proceedings of the Fourth International Symposium. 600p. 1985. 47.00 (ISBN 0-914826-76-X). Am Soc Microbio.

Smith, Harry & Arbuthnott, J. P., eds. The Determinants of Bacterial & Viral Pathogenicity. (Philosophical Transactions of the Royal Society: Series B, Vol. 303). (Illus.). 163p. 1984. Repr. text ed. 56.00x (ISBN 0-85403-216-9, Pub. by Royal Soc London). Scholium Intl.

Smith, Louis D., et al. The Pathogenic Anaerobic Bacteria. 3rd ed. 348p. 1984. 39.75x (ISBN 0-398-05001-5). C C Thomas.

Taylor, Frank S. Conquest of Bacteria, from Salvarsan to Sulphapyridine. facsimile ed. LC 78-142705. (Essay Index Reprint Ser). Repr. of 1942 ed. 17.00 (ISBN 0-8369-2375-8). Ayer Co Pubs.

BACTERIA, PHYTOPATHOGENIC

see also Plant Diseases

Mount, M. S. & Lacy, George, eds. Phytopathogenic Prolaryotes, Vol. I. LC 82-13954. 488p. 1982. 59.50 (ISBN 0-12-509001-3); 51.00. Acad Pr.

Mount, Mark S. & Lacy, George. Phytopathogenic Prokaryotes, Vol. II. 448p. 1982. 57.00 (ISBN 0-12-509002-1). Acad Pr.

BACTERIAL CELL WALLS

Auvil, D. L. Calculus with Applications. LC 81-14914. 1982. text ed. 32.95 (ISBN 0-201-10063-0); student supplement 9.95 (ISBN 0-201-10064-9). Addison-Wesley.

Hammond, Stephen M., et al. The Bacterial Cell Surface. (Illus.). 226p. 1984. text ed. 36.00 (ISBN 0-916845-02-8). Kapitan Szabo.

Inouye, Masayori. Bacterial Outer Membranes: Biogenesis & Functions. LC 79-13999. 534p. 1980. 101.50 (ISBN 0-471-04676-0, Pub. by Wiley-Interscience). Wiley.

Jeljaszewitz, J. & Wadstrom, T., eds. Bacterial Toxins & Cell Membranes. 1978. 71.00 (ISBN 0-12-383850-9). Acad Pr.

Leive, Loretta, ed. Bacterial Membranes & Walls (Microbiology Ser.: Vol. 1). 520p. 1973. 95.00 (ISBN 0-8247-6085-9). Dekker.

Prebble, J. N. Mitochondria, Chloroplasts & Bacterial Membranes. (Illus.). 1981. text ed. 26.00x (ISBN 0-582-44133-1). Longman.

Schlessinger, David, ed. Microbiology 1977. LC 74-33538. 1977. 28.00 (ISBN 0-914826-13-1). Am Soc Microbio.

Stewart-Tull, D. E. Immunology of the Bacterial Cell Envelope. Davies, M., ed. LC 84-20993. 1985. price not set (ISBN 0-471-90552-6). Wiley.

BACTERIAL CULTURES

see Microbiology–Cultures and Culture Media

BACTERIAL DISEASES

see also Bacteria, Pathogenic;

also names of specific bacterial diseases, e.g. Anthrax, Botulism

Brook, Itzhak. A Medical Update on Lincomycin: The Management of Infectious Disease. (Illus.). 70p. (Orig.). 1983. pap. 13.95 (ISBN 0-88678-000-4). Omega Comms.

Evans, Alfred S. & Feldman, Harry A., eds. Bacterial Infections in Humans: Epidemiology & Control. 744p. 1984. pap. 27.50x (ISBN 0-306-41705-7, Plenum Med Bk). Plenum Pub.

Grange, J. M. Mycobacterial Diseases. (Current Topics in Infection Ser.: Vol. 1). 1981. 37.50 (ISBN 0-444-00625-7, Biomedical Pr). Elsevier.

Keusch, G. & Wadstrom, T., eds. Experimental Bacterial & Parasitic Infections. 500p. 1983. 90.00 (ISBN 0-444-00794-6, Biomedical Pr). Elsevier.

Levy, Stuart B., et al, eds. Molecular Biology, Pathogenicity, & Ecology of Bacterial Plasmids. LC 81-8692. 720p. 1981. 72.50 (ISBN 0-306-40753-1, Plenum Pr). Plenum Pub.

Liu & Dutka. Toxicity Screening Procedures Using Bacterial Systems. (Toxicity Ser.). 448p. 1984. 79.75 (ISBN 0-8247-7171-0). Dekker.

Sharp, John T. The Role of Mycoplasmas & Forms of Bacteria in Disease. (Illus.). 400p. 1970. photocopy ed. 39.50x (ISBN 0-398-01733-6). C C Thomas.

Urbaschek, B. & Urbaschek, R., eds. Gram-Negative Bacterial Infections & Mode of Endotoxin Actions - Pathophysiologic, Immunologic, & Clinical Aspects. LC 74-34099. (Illus.). 550p. 1975. 45.00 (ISBN 0-387-81292-X). Springer-Verlag.

BACTERIAL GENETICS

see also Episomes

Birge, E. A. Bacterial & Bacteriophage Genetics: An Introduction. (Springer Ser. in Microbiology). (Illus.). 359p. (Corrected 2nd printing). 1981. 29.50 (ISBN 0-387-90504-9). Springer-Verlag.

Bridges, B. A. Bacterial Reaction to Radiation. 78p. 1976. 39.00x (ISBN 0-904095-21-5, Pub. by Meadowfield Pr England). State Mutual Bk.

Davis, R., et al, eds. Advanced Bacterial Genetics. LC 80-25695. 254p. (Orig.). 1980. lab manual 38.00x (ISBN 0-87969-130-1). Cold Spring Harbor.

Finnegan, David J. Bacterial Conjugation. 48p. 1976. 39.00x (ISBN 0-686-96975-8, Pub. by Meadowfield Pr England). State Mutual Bk.

Ganesan, A. T., et al. Molecular Cloning & Gene Regulation in Bacilli. 392p. 1982. 35.00 (ISBN 0-12-274150-1). Acad Pr.

Genetic, Morphological & Physiological Relationships Among Coryneform Bacteria. (Agricultural Research Reports: No. 824). 1974. pap. 7.00 (ISBN 90-220-0528-3, PDC195, PUDOC). Unipub.

Jacob, Francois & Wollman, E. Sexuality & the Genetics of Bacteria. rev. ed. 1961. 64.50 (ISBN 0-12-379450-1). Acad Pr.

Pettigrew, G. W. Bacterial Cytochrome. 1979. 39.00x (ISBN 0-904095-30-4, Pub. by Meadowfield Pr England). State Mutual Bk.

Primrose, S. B. Bacterial Transduction. 56p. 1977. 39.00x (ISBN 0-904095-23-1, Pub. by Meadowfield Pr England). State Mutual Bk.

Puhler, A., ed. Molecular Genetics of the Bacteria Plant Interaction. (Proceedings in Life Sciences). (Illus.). 385p. 1983. 47.00 (ISBN 0-387-12798-4). Springer-Verlag.

Streips, Uldis N., et al, eds. Genetic Exchange: A Celebration & a New Generation. (Genetic & Cellular Technology Ser.: Vol. 1). (Illus.). 392p. 1982. 69.50 (ISBN 0-8247-1418-0). Dekker.

Winkler, U., et al. Bacterial, Phage & Molecular Genetics. 250p. 1976. pap. 18.00 (ISBN 0-387-07602-6). Springer-Verlag.

BACTERIAL MEMBRANES

see Bacterial Cell Walls

BACTERIAL SPORES

see Spores (Bacteria)

BACTERIAL SYNTHESIS

see Microbiological Synthesis

BACTERIAL WARFARE

see Biological Warfare

BACTERIOLOGICAL WARFARE

see Biological Warfare

BACTERIOLOGY

see also Bacteria; Bacterial Genetics; Bacteriology, Agricultural; Biological Products; Disinfection and Disinfectants; Fermentation; Sanitary Microbiology; Sewage–Purification; Sewage Disposal

also subdivision Bacteriology under particular subjects, e.g. Milk–Bacteriology

Archer. Bacterial Transformation. 1973. 65.00 (ISBN 0-12-059450-1). Acad Pr.

Baldry, P. E. The Battle Against Bacteria: A Fresh Look. LC 76-639. (Illus.). 140p. 1976. 29.95 (ISBN 0-521-21268-5). Cambridge U Pr.

Brown, F. Topley & Wilson's Principles of Bacteriology, Virology & Immunity, Vol. 4. 7th ed. 704p. 1984. 90.00 (ISBN 0-683-09067-4). Williams & Wilkins.

Browning, Carl H. Bacteriology. 1920. 10.00 (ISBN 0-8274-4188-6). R West.

Bryan, Arthur H., et al. Bacteriology: Principles & Practice. 6th rev ed. (Orig.). 1962. pap. 5.95 (ISBN 0-06-460003-3, CO 3, COS). B&N NY.

Collins, D. H. & Grange, J. M., eds. Isolation & Identification of Microorganisms of Medical & Veterinary Importance. (Society for Applied Bacteriology Technical Ser.: Vol. 21). 1985. 55.00 (ISBN 0-12-181460-2). Acad Pr.

Dobson, R. L., et al, eds. Bactroban. (Current Clinical Practice Ser.: Vol. 16). 1985. 83.50 (ISBN 0-444-90407-7). Elsevier.

Fletcher, Madilyn M. & Floodgate, George D., eds. Bacteria in Their Natural Environments. (Society for General Microbiology Special Publications: Vol. 16). Date not set. price not set (ISBN 0-12-260560-8). Acad Pr.

Ford, William W. Bacteriology. LC 75-23671. (Clio Medica Ser.: No. 22). (Illus.). Repr. of 1939 ed. 18.00 (ISBN 0-404-58922-7). AMS Pr.

Fuller, R., ed. Microbial Ultrastructure. 1977. 65.00 (ISBN 0-12-269450-3). Acad Pr.

Genetic, Morphological & Physiological Relationships Among Coryneform Bacteria. (Agricultural Research Reports: No. 824). 1974. pap. 7.00 (ISBN 90-220-0528-3, PDC195, PUDOC). Unipub.

Gilbert, R. J. & Lovelock, D. W., eds. Microbial Aspects of the Deterioration of Materials. (Society of Applied Bacteriology Technical Ser.). 1975. 39.00 (ISBN 0-12-282950-6). Acad Pr.

Gillies, R. R. Gillies & Dodds Bacteriology Illustrated. 5th ed. LC 82-23595. (Illus.). 224p. (Orig.). 1984. pap. text ed. 28.00 (ISBN 0-443-02809-5). Churchill.

Glagolev, A. N. Motility & Taxis in Prokaryotes. (Physicochemical Biology Reviews Supplement Ser.: Soviet Scientific Reviews, Sect. B, Vol. 4). 310p. 1984. text ed. 126.00 (ISBN 3-7186-0160-5). Harwood Academic.

Goodfellow, M., et al, eds. Computer-Assisted Bacterial Systematics. (Society for General Microbiology Special Publications Ser.: No. 15). 1985. 75.00 (ISBN 0-12-289665-3). Acad Pr.

Goodfellow, Michael & Minnikin, David E., eds. Chemical Methods in Bacterial Systematics. (Society for Applied Bacteriology Technical Ser.). 1985. 69.50 (ISBN 0-12-289675-0). Acad Pr.

Gunsalus, I. C., et al, eds. Bacteria: A Treatise on Structure & Function, 7 vols. Incl. Vol. 1. Structure. 1960. 72.00 (ISBN 0-12-307201-8); Vol. 2. Metabolism. 1961. 72.00 (ISBN 0-12-307202-6); Vol. 3. Biosynthesis. 1962. 81.00 (ISBN 0-12-307203-4); Vol. 4. Physiology of Growth. 1963. 67.50 (ISBN 0-12-307204-2); Vol. 5. Heredity. 1964. 72.00 (ISBN 0-12-307205-0); Vol. 6. Bacterial Diversity. 1978. 68.50 (ISBN 0-12-307206-9); Vol. 7. Mechanism of Adaption. 1979. 60.50 (ISBN 0-12-307207-7). LC 59-13831. Acad Pr.

Hahn, F. E., ed. Mechanism of Action of Antibacterial Agents. (Antibiotics Ser.: Vol. 5, Pt. I). (Illus.). 1979. 120.00 (ISBN 0-387-09342-7). Springer-Verlag.

Holt, John G. & Krieg, Noel R., eds. Bergey's Manual of Systematic Bacteriology, Vol 1. (Illus.). 992p. 1984. lib. bdg. 80.00 (ISBN 0-683-04108-8). Williams & Wilkins.

Ingraham, John L. & Maaloe, Ole. Growth of the Bacterial Cell. LC 83-496. (Illus.). 375p. 1983. text ed. 28.75x (ISBN 0-87893-352-2). Sinauer Assoc.

Lichstein, Herman C., ed. Bacterial Nutrition. LC 82-11720. (Benchmark Papers in Microbiology: Vol. 19). 377p. 1983. 49.95 (ISBN 0-87933-439-8). Van Nos Reinhold.

Lovelock, D. W., ed. Plant Pathogens. (Society of Applied Bacteriology Technical Ser.). 1979. 29.00 (ISBN 0-12-457050-X). Acad Pr.

Lovelock, D. W. & Davies, R., eds. Techniques for the Study of Mixed Populations. (Society for Applied Bacteriology Technical Ser.). 1979. 39.50 (ISBN 0-12-456650-2). Acad Pr.

Madoff, Sarabelle. Mycoplasma & the L Forms of Bacteria. (Illus.). 116p. 1971. 31.75x (ISBN 0-677-14790-2). Gordon.

Mandelstam, Joel, et al. Biochemistry of Bacterial Growth. 3rd ed. LC 81-6895. 449p. 1982. pap. 39.95x (ISBN 0-470-27249-X). Halsted Pr.

Oberhofer, T. R. Manual of Non-Fermenting Gram-Negative Bacteria. 154p. 1985. spiral 22.95 (ISBN 0-471-80544-0). Wiley.

Parker, M. T. Topley & Wilson's Principles of Bacteriology, Virology & Immunity, Vol. 2. 7th ed. 576p. 1983. lib. bdg. 90.00 (ISBN 0-683-09065-8). Williams & Wilkins.

Peppler, Henry J., ed. Microbial Technology. LC 67-26866. pap. 116.00 (ISBN 0-317-10486-1, 2005811). Bks Demand UMI.

Postgate, J. R. The Sulfate-Reducing Bacteria. 2nd ed. LC 83-15307. 250p. 1984. 39.50 (ISBN 0-521-25791-3). Cambridge U Pr.

Reeves, P. The Bacteriocins. LC 77-188625. (Molecular Biology, Biochemistry & Biophysics Ser.: Vol. 11). (Illus.). 164p. 1972. 36.00 (ISBN 0-387-05735-8). Springer-Verlag.

Rhodes-Roberts, Muriel, ed. Bacteria & Plants. (Society for Applied Bacteriology Symposium Ser.: No. 10). 1982. 33.00 (ISBN 0-12-587080-9). Acad Pr.

Rose, A. H. & Wilkinson, J. F., eds. Advances in Microbial Physiology, 2 vols. 1979. Vol. 18. 55.00 (ISBN 0-12-027718-2); Vol. 19. 60.00 (ISBN 0-12-027719-0). Acad Pr.

Riedler, W., ed. Scientific Ballooning: Proceedings of a Symposium of the 21st Plenary Meeting of the Committee on Space Research, Innsbruck, Austria, May 29-June 10 1978. LC 78-41182. (Illus.). 226p. 1979. 69.00 (ISBN 0-08-023420-8). Pergamon.

Riedler, W. & Friedrich, M., eds. Scientific Ballooning -II. (Advances in Space Research: Vol. 1, No. 11). (Illus.). 274p. 1981. pap. 38.00 (ISBN 0-08-028390-X). Pergamon.

Time-Life Books Editors & Botting, Douglas. The Giant Airships. (The Epic of Flight). (Illus.). 176p. 1981. 14.95 (ISBN 0-8094-3270-6). Time-Life.

Wise, John. Through the Air: A Narrative of Forty Years' Experience As an Aeronaut. LC 79-169444. (Literature & History of Aviation Ser). 1971. Repr. of 1873 ed. 40.00 (ISBN 0-405-03787-2). Ayer Co Pubs.

BALLOONS, DIRIGIBLE

see Air-Ships

BALSAM FIR

Photosynthesis & Respiration in White Spruce & Balsam Fir, No. 85. 1961. 0.65 (ISBN 0-686-20697-5). SUNY Environ.

BALTIMORE AND OHIO RAILROAD COMPANY

Adams, Herbert B. Maryland's Influence Upon Land Cessions to the United States. LC 4-8520. 1885. 5.00x (ISBN 0-403-00136-6). Scholarly.

Barr, Howard N. Fifty Best of Baltimore & Ohio Railroad, Bk. 1. (Illus.). 1977. 12.00 (ISBN 0-934118-16-7). Barnard Robert.

Barr, Howard N. & Barringer, W. A. Q-Baltimore & Ohio Railroad Q-Class Mikado Locomotives. LC 78-52708. (Illus.). 1978. 30.00 (ISBN 0-934118-15-9). Barnard Robert.

Harwood, Herbert H., Jr. Impossible Challenge: The Baltimore & Ohio Railroad in Maryland. LC 79-54967. (Illus.). 1979. 40.00 (ISBN 0-934118-17-5). Barnard Roberts.

Kelly, John C. Fifty Best of Baltimore & Ohio Railroad, Bk. 3. (Illus.). 1977. 12.00 (ISBN 0-934118-02-7). Barnard Robert.

Lorenz, Bob. Fifty Best of Baltimore & Ohio Railroad, Bk. 5. (Illus.). 1979. 12.00 (ISBN 0-934118-04-3). Barnard Robert.

BAMBOO

Austin, Robert & Ueda, Koichiro. Bamboo. LC 70-96051. (Illus.). 216p. 1970. 27.50 (ISBN 0-8348-0048-9). Weatherhill.

Gamble, James S. The Bambusae of British India. (Illus.). Repr. of 1896 ed. 32.00 (ISBN 0-384-17605-4). Johnson Repr.

Munro, William. Monograph of the Bambusaceae, Including Descriptions of All the Species. (Illus.). 23.00 (ISBN 0-384-40570-3). Johnson Repr.

Production & Cost of Logging & Transport of Bamboo. (No. 157). (Illus.). 72p. 1975. pap. 7.50 (ISBN 0-685-57606-X, F1144, FAO). Unipub.

Takama, Shinji. The World of Bamboo. Ooka, D. T., tr. from Japanese. (Illus.). 237p. (Orig.). 1983. 75.00 (ISBN 0-89346-203-9). Heian Intl.

BANACH ALGEBRAS

see also C Algebras; Function Algebras; Harmonic Analysis; Von Neumann Algebras

Bacher, J. M., et al, eds. Radical Banach Algebras & Automatic Continuity: Long Beach, California, 1981, Proceedings. (Lecture Notes in Mathematics: Vol. 975). 470p. 1983. pap. 26.00 (ISBN 0-387-11985-X). Springer-Verlag.

Bade, W. G., et al. Multipliers of Radical Banach Algebras of Power Series, No. 303. LC 84-3070. (Memoirs: No. 303). 86p. 1984. pap. 10.00 (ISBN 0-8218-2304-3). Am Math.

Barbu, V. & Precupanu, T. Convexity & Optimization in Banach Spaces. (Mathematics & its Applications: East European Ser.). 1985. lib. bdg. 64.00 (ISBN 90-277-1761-3, Pub. by Reidel Holland). Kluwer-Academic.

Barnes, B. A. & Murphy, G. J. Riesz & Fredholm Theory in Banach Algebras. (Research Notes in Mathematics Ser.: No. 67). 300p. 1982. pap. text ed. 19.95 (ISBN 0-273-08563-8). Pitman Pub MA.

Behrends, E. M-Structured & the Banach-Stone Theorem. (Lecture Notes in Mathematics: Vol. 736). 1979. pap. 17.00 (ISBN 0-387-09533-0). Springer-Verlag.

Burckel, R. B. Characterization of C(X) Among Its Subalgebras. (Lecture Notes in Pure & Applied Mathematics Ser: Vol. 6). 176p. 1972. 35.00 (ISBN 0-8247-6038-7). Dekker.

De la Harpe, P. Classical Banach-Lie Algebras & Banach-Lie Groups of Operators in Hilbert Space. LC 72-88729. (Lecture Notes in Mathematics: Vol. 285). 160p. 1972. pap. 9.00 (ISBN 0-387-05984-9). Springer-Verlag.

Doran, R. S. & Wichmann, J. Approximate Identities & Factorization in Banach Modules. (Lecture Notes in Mathematics: Vol. 768). 305p. 1979. pap. 23.00 (ISBN 0-387-09725-2). Springer-Verlag.

Douglas, R. G. Banach Algebra Techniques in the Theory of Toeplitz Operators. LC 73-1021. (CBMS Regional Conference Ser. in Mathematics: No. 15). 53p. 1980. pap. 15.00 (ISBN 0-8218-1665-9, CBMS-15). Am Math.

Douglas, Ronald G. Banach Algebra Techniques in Operator Theory. (Pure & Applied Mathematics Ser). 1972. 44.00 (ISBN 0-12-221350-5). Acad Pr.

Fell, J. M. Extension of Mackey's Method to Banach-Algebraic Bundles. LC 52-42839. (Memoirs: No. 90). 168p. 1969. pap. 10.00 (ISBN 0-8218-1290-4, MEMO-90). Am Math.

Grabiner, Sandy. Derivations & Automorphisms of Banach Algebras of Power Series. LC 74-7124. (Memoirs: No. 146). 124p. 1974. pap. 11.00 (ISBN 0-8218-1846-5, MEMO-146). Am Math.

Jarosz, K. Perturbations of Banach Algebras. (Lecture Notes in Mathematics Ser.: Vol. 1120). v, 118p. 1985. pap. 9.80 (ISBN 0-387-15218-0). Springer-Verlag.

Johnson, B. E. Cohomology in Banach Algebras. LC 72-4561. (Memoirs Ser.: No. 127). 96p. 1972. pap. 10.00 (ISBN 0-8218-1827-9, MEMO-127). Am Math.

Mosak, Richard D. Banach Algebras. LC 75-25957. (Chicago Lectures in Mathematics Ser.). 180p. 1975. pap. text ed. 7.00x (ISBN 0-226-54204-1). U of Chicago Pr.

Owen, T. C. Characterization of Organic Compounds by Chemical Methods: An Introductory Laboratory Textbook. 256p. 1969. 22.75 (ISBN 0-8247-1510-1). Dekker.

Pelczynski, Aleksander. Banach Spaces of Analytic Functions & Absolutely Summing Operators. LC 77-9884. (Conference Board of the Mathematical Sciences Ser.: No. 30). 1980. pap. 10.00 (ISBN 0-8218-1680-2, CBMS30). Am Math.

Sinclair, Allan M. Continuous Semigroups in Banach Algebras. LC 81-21627. (London Mathematical Society Lecture Note: No. 63). 180p. 1982. pap. 21.95 (ISBN 0-521-28598-4). Cambridge U Pr.

Taylor, Joseph L. Measure Algebras. LC 73-5930. (CBMS Regional Conference Series in Mathematics: No. 16). 108p. 1979. pap. 11.00 (ISBN 0-8218-1666-7, CBMS-16). Am Math.

Wagon, Stan. Encyclopedia of Mathematics & Its Applications: The Banach-Tarski Paradox, Vol. 24. (Illus.). 272p. 1985. 37.50 (ISBN 0-521-30244-7). Cambridge U Pr.

Wang, H. C. Homogeneous Banach Algebras. (Lecture Note Ser.: Vol. 29). 216p. 1977. 45.00 (ISBN 0-8247-6588-5). Dekker.

Wermer, J. Banach Algebras & Several Complex Variables. (Graduate Texts in Mathematics Ser.: Vol. 35). 185p. 1976. 27.50 (ISBN 0-387-90160-4). Springer-Verlag.

Zelazko, W. Banach Algebras. 182p. 1973. 57.50 (ISBN 0-444-40991-2). Elsevier.

BANACH RINGS

see Banach Algebras

BANACH SPACES

see also Banach Algebras; Hilbert Space; Normed Linear Spaces

Baker, J. & Cleaver, C., eds. Banach Spaces of Analytic Functions, Kent 1976: Proceedings of a Conference Held at Kent State University July 12-16, 1976. LC 77-11202. (Lecture Notes in Mathematics: Vol. 604). 1977. pap. text ed. 14.00 (ISBN 0-387-08356-1). Springer-Verlag.

Banas & Goebel. Measures of Noncompactness in Banach Spaces. (Lecture Notes in Pure & Applied Mathematics Ser.: Vol. 60). 112p. 1980. 29.75 (ISBN 0-8247-1248-X). Dekker.

Beck, A., ed. Probability in Banach Spaces Two. (Lecture Notes in Mathematics Ser.: Vol. 709). 1979. pap. 17.00 (ISBN 0-387-09242-0). Springer-Verlag.

Beck, A. & Jacobs, K., eds. Probability in Banach Spaces IV. (Lecture Notes in Mathematics Ser.: Vol. 990). 234p. 1983. pap. 13.00 (ISBN 0-387-12295-8). Springer-Verlag.

Behrends, E., et al. L-P Structure in Real Banach Spaces. (Lecture Notes in Mathematics: Vol. 613). 1977. pap. text ed. 14.00 (ISBN 0-387-08441-X). Springer-Verlag.

Beuzamy, Bernard. Introduction to Banach Spaces & Their Geometry. (North Holland Mathematical Studies: Vol. 68). 308p. 1982. 38.50 (ISBN 0-444-86416-4, North-Hooand). Elsevier.

Blei, R. C. & Sidney, S. J., eds. Lectures in Banach Spaces Harmonic Analysis & Probability Theory. (Lecture Notes in Mathematics: Vol. 995). 173p. 1983. pap. 12.00 (ISBN 0-387-12314-8). Springer-Verlag.

Butzer, P. L. & Berens, H. Semi-Groups of Operators & Approximation. LC 68-11980. (Grundlehren der Mathematischen Wissenschaften: Vol. 145). 1967. 39.00 (ISBN 0-387-03832-9). Springer-Verlag.

Chao, J. A. & Woyczynski, W. A., eds. Martingale Theory in Harmonic Analysis & Banach Spaces, Cleveland, Ohio 1981: Proceedings. (Lecture Notes in Mathematics: Vol. 939). 225p. 1982. pap. 14.00 (ISBN 0-387-11569-2). Springer-Verlag.

Cigler, et al. Banach Modules & Functors on Categories of Banach Spaces. (Lecture Notes in Pure & Applied Mathematics Ser.: Vol. 46). 1979. 55.00 (ISBN 0-8247-6867-1). Dekker.

Daleckii, Ju. L. & Krein, M. G. Stability of Solutions of Differential Equations in Banach Space. LC 74-8403. (Translations of Mathematical Monographs: Vol. 43). 1974. 72.00 (ISBN 0-8218-1593-8, MMONO-43). Am Math.

Da Prato, G. Institutiones Mathematicae: Applications Croissantes & Equations d'revolutions dans les Espaces de Banach. 1977. 35.00 (ISBN 0-12-363602-7). Acad Pr.

Diestel, J. Sequences & Series in Banach Spaces. (Graduate Texts in Mathematics Ser.: Vol. 92). 280p. 1984. 38.00 (ISBN 0-387-90859-5). Springer-Verlag.

Diestel, J. & Uhl, J. J. Vector Measures. LC 77-9625. (Mathematical Surveys Ser.: No. 15). 322p. 1979. pap. 36.00 (ISBN 0-8218-1515-6, SURV15). Am Math.

Erdelyi, I. & Lange, R. Spectral Decompositions on Banach Spaces. LC 77-26174. (Lecture Notes in Mathematics: Vol. 623). 1977. pap. 14.00 (ISBN 0-387-08525-4). Springer-Verlag.

Erdelyi, Ivan N. & Shengwang, Wang. A Local Spectral Theory for Closed Operators. (London Mathematical Society Lecture Note Ser.: No. 105). 200p. 1985. pap. 22.95 (ISBN 0-521-31314-7). Cambridge U Pr.

Golovkin, K. K. Parametric-Normed Spaces & Normed Massives. (Proceedings of the Steklov Institute of Mathematics: No. 106). 1971. 39.00 (ISBN 0-8218-3006-6, STEKLO-106). Am Math.

Gretsky, Neil E. Representation Theorems on Banach Function Spaces. LC 52-42839. (Memoirs: No. 84). 56p. 1968. pap. 9.00 (ISBN 0-8218-1284-X, MEMO-84). Am Math.

International Conference on Probability in Banach Spaces, First, Oberwolfach, July 20-26, 1975. Probability in Banach Spaces: Proceedings. Beck, A., ed. (Lecture Notes in Mathematics Ser.: Vol. 526). 1976. soft cover 19.00 (ISBN 0-387-07793-6). Springer-Verlag.

Johnson, W. B. Symmetric Structures in Banach Spaces. LC 79-10225. (Memoirs: No. 217). 298p. 1979. paper 14.00 (ISBN 0-8218-2217-9). Am Math.

Kantorovitz, S. Spectral Theory of Banach Space Operators. (Lecture Notes in Mathematics: Vol. 1012). 179p. 1983. pap. 12.00 (ISBN 0-387-12673-2). Springer Verlag.

Krein, S. G. Linear Differential Equations in Banach Space. LC 71-37141. (Translations of Mathematical Monographs Ser.: Vol. 29). 1972. 50.00 (ISBN 0-8218-1579-2, MMONO-29). Am Math.

--Linear Equations in Banach Spaces. 128p. 1982. text ed. 14.95 (ISBN 3-7643-3101-1). Birkhauser.

Kuelbs. Probability on Banach Space. (Advances in Probability & Related Topics Ser.: Vol. 4). 1978. 75.00 (ISBN 0-8247-6799-3). Dekker.

Kuo, H. H. Gaussian Measures in Banauch Spaces. (Lecture Notes in Mathematics Ser.: Vol. 463). vi, 224p. 1975. pap. 16.00 (ISBN 0-387-07173-3). Springer-Verlag.

Lacey, H. E. The Isometric Theory of Classical Banach Spaces. LC 74-394. (Die Grundlehren der Mathematischen Wissenchaften: Vol. 208). 270p. 1974. 51.00 (ISBN 0-387-06562-8). Springer-Verlag.

Lacey, H. Elton, ed. Notes in Banach Spaces. 447p. 1980. text ed. 30.00x (ISBN 0-292-75520-1). U of Tex Pr.

Larsen, Ronald. Multiplier Problem. LC 74-97959. (Lecture Notes in Mathematics: Vol. 105). 1969. pap. 14.70 (ISBN 0-387-04624-0). Springer-Verlag.

Lindenstrauss, J. & Tzafriri, L. Classical Banach Spaces II: Function Spaces. (Ergebnisse der Mathematik und Ihrer Granzgebiete: Vol. 97). 1979. 46.00 (ISBN 0-387-08888-1). Springer-Verlag.

Liudenstrauss, J. & Tzafriri, L. Classical Banach Spaces I: Sequence Spaces. (Ergebnisse der Mathematik und Ihrer Grenzgebiete: Vol. 92). 1977. 35.00 (ISBN 0-387-08072-4). Springer-Verlag.

Marti, J. T. Introduction to the Theory of Bases. LC 73-83680. (Springer Tracts in Natural Philosophy: Vol. 18). 1969. 25.00 (ISBN 0-387-04716-6). Springer-Verlag.

Martin, Robert H. Nonlinear Operations & Differential Equations in Banach Spaces. 456p. (Orig.). 1985. Repr. of 1976 ed. write for info. (ISBN 0-89874-803-8). Krieger.

Michor, P. W. Functors & Categories of Banach Spaces: Tensor Products, Operator Ideals & Functors on Categories of Banach Spaces. (Lecture Notes in Mathematics: Vol. 651). 1978. pap. 12.00 (ISBN 0-387-08764-8). Springer-Verlag.

Nachbin, Leopoldo. Introduction to Functional Analysis: Banach Spaces & Different Calculus. (Pure & Applied Mathematics: Monographs & Textbooks: Vol. 60). (Illus.). 184p. 1981. 35.00 (ISBN 0-8247-6984-8). Dekker.

Pelczynski, Aleksander. Banach Spaces of Analytic Functions & Absolutely Summing Operators. LC 77-9884. (Conference Board of the Mathematical Sciences Ser.: No. 30). 1980. pap. 10.00 (ISBN 0-8218-1680-2, CBMS30). Am Math.

Pietsch, A. & Popa, N., eds. Banach Space Theory & Its Applications. (Lecture Notes in Mathematics: Vol. 991). 302p. 1983. pap. 18.00 (ISBN 0-387-12298-2). Springer-Verlag.

Schochetman, I. E. Kernels & Integral Operators for Continuous Sums of Banach Spaces. LC 78-4580. (Memoirs Ser.: No. 202). 120p. pap. 13.00 (ISBN 0-8218-2202-0, MEMO 202). Am Math.

Schwartz, L. Geometry & Probability in Banach Spaces. (Lecture Notes in Mathematics Ser.: Vol. 852). 101p. 1981. pap. 12.00 (ISBN 0-387-10691-X). Springer-Verlag.

Singer, I. Bases in Banach Spaces I. LC 75-99014. (Grundlehren der Mathematischen Wissenschaften: Vol. 154). 1970. 78.00 (ISBN 0-387-04833-2). Springer-Verlag.

--Bases in Banach Spaces II. 880p. 1981. 79.50 (ISBN 0-387-10394-5). Springer-Verlag.

Sundaresan, K. & Swaminathan, S. Geometry & Nonlinear Analysis in Banach Spaces. (Lecture Notes in Mathematics: Vol. 1131). iii, 116p. 1985. pap. 9.80 (ISBN 0-387-15237-7). Springer-Verlag.

BANANA

Bananas. (Economic & Social Development Papers: No. 18). 27p. 1977. pap. 7.50 (ISBN 92-5-100149-9, F76, FAO). Unipub.

MacDaniels, L. H. Study of the Fe'i Banana & Its Distribution with Reference to Polynesian Migrations. (BMB Ser.). 1947. 11.00 (ISBN 0-527-02298-5). Kraus Repr.

Report of the Seventh Session of the Intergovernmental Group on Bananas to the Committee on Commodity Problems: Rome, April-May 1980. 17p. 1981. pap. 8.00 (ISBN 92-5-100950-3, F2091, FAO). Unipub.

Reynolds, P. K. The Banana: Its History & Cultivation. 1977. lib. bdg. 69.95 (ISBN 0-8490-1474-3). Gordon Pr.

Simmonds, N. W. Bananas. 2nd ed. LC 82-116. (Tropical Agriculture Ser.). (Illus.). 568p. 1982. pap. text ed. 29.95x (ISBN 0-582-46355-6). Longman.

Stover, R. H. Banana, Plantain & Abaca Diseases. 316p. 1972. 70.00x (ISBN 0-686-45707-2, Pub. by CAB Bks England). State Mutual Bk.

Wardlaw, Claude W. Banana Diseases: Including Plantains & Abaca. 2nd ed. LC 73-161513. (Illus.). pap. 160.00 (ISBN 0-317-07891-7, 2016311). Bks Demand UMI.

BAND SAWS

Scharff, Robert. Getting the Most of Your Band Saw. 1981. 9.95 (ISBN 0-8359-2449-1). Reston.

BAND THEORY OF SOLIDS

see Energy-Band Theory of Solids

BANKS, JOSEPH, SIR, BART., 1743-1820

Carter, H. B. Sir Joseph Banks & the Plant Collection from Kew Sent to the Empress Catherine II of Russia 1795. (Bulletin of the British Museum Natural History, Historical Ser.: Vol. 4, No. 5). (Illus.). 1975. text ed. 20.00x (ISBN 0-565-00768-8, Pub. by Brit Mus Nat Hist); pap. text ed. 22.00x (ISBN 0-8277-4351-3). Sabbot-Natural Hist Bks.

Dawson, Warren R., ed. The Banks Letters: A Calendar of the Manuscript Correspondence of Sir Joseph Banks Preserved in the British Museum, the British Museum (Natural History) & Other Collections in Great Britain. 965p. 1958. 94.00x (ISBN 0-565-00085-3, Pub. by Brit Mus Nat Hist England). Sabbot-Natural Hist Bks.

Hermannsson, Halldor. Sir Joseph Banks & Iceland. LC 28-11080. (Islandica Ser.: Vol. 18). 1928. 18.00 (ISBN 0-527-00348-4). Kraus Repr.

Smith, Edward. The Life of Sir Joseph Banks. LC 74-26292. (History, Philosophy & Sociology of Science Ser). (Illus.). 1975. Repr. 30.00x (ISBN 0-405-06618-X). Ayer Co Pubs.

BANKS AND BANKING–AUTOMATION

ATM Cost Model: How to Determine & Analyze Transactional Costs. 64p. 1983. 60.00 (ISBN 0-317-36447-2, 653B); members 40.00 (ISBN 0-317-36448-0). Bank Admin Inst.

ATM Security. 196p. 1983. 65.00 (ISBN 0-318-03367-4, 304). Bank Admin Inst.

ATMs for Community Banks. 140p. 1982. 60.00 (ISBN 0-317-36449-9, 691); members 40.00 (ISBN 0-317-36450-2). Bank Admin Inst.

Automated Teller Machines: A Cost-Effectiveness Review. 84p. 16.00 (ISBN 0-317-33717-3, 606); members 8.00 (ISBN 0-317-33718-1). Bank Admin Inst.

Automation Alternatives & Costs. (Community Bank Series on Operations & Automation: No. 6). 113p. 15.00 (ISBN 0-317-33719-X, 605); members 7.50 (ISBN 0-317-33720-3). Bank Admin Inst.

Automation Alternatives for Community Banks: Selecting & Implementing Data Processing Services. 104p. 24.00 (ISBN 0-317-33721-1, 633); members 12.00 (ISBN 0-317-33722-X). Bank Admin Inst.

Bank Administration Institute. Acquisitions Guidelines for Small Computer Systems. 288p. 1982. 60.00 (264). Bank Admin Inst.

--EDP Facility Accounting, 2 Vols. 1975. Vol. 1: Implementation; 205 pp. 50.00 (630); Vol. 2: Technical Foundations; 191 pp. 40.00 (631). Bank Admin Inst.

Bender, Mark. EFTS: Electronic Funds Transfer Systems - Elements & Impact. 112p. 1975. 19.50x (ISBN 0-8046-9119-3, Pub. by Kennikat). Assoc Faculty Pr.

Bosworth, Seymour. Handbook of Banking & Automation. 1986. cancelled (ISBN 0-87094-565-3). Dow Jones-Irwin.

Check Truncation. 148p. 1980. 30.00 (639); member 15.00. Bank Admin Inst.

Colton, Kent W. & Kramer, Kenneth L., eds. Computers & Banking. LC 79-9307. (Applications of Modern Technology in Business Ser.). (Illus.). 325p. 1979. 39.50x (ISBN 0-306-40255-6, Plenum Pr). Plenum Pub.

Community Bank Series on Operations & Automation, 6 Vols. Incl. No. 1. Outline. 25p. 1975. 5.00 (600); No. 2. Demand Deposit Accounting. 70p. 1975. 15.00 (601); No. 3. Savings & Time Deposit Accounting. 82p. 1975. 15.00 (602); No. 4. General Ledger & Automated Financial Reporting. 33p. 1976. 15.00 (603); No. 5. The Customer Information File. 76p. 1976. 15.00 (604); No. 6. Automation Alternatives & Costs. 113p. 1977. 15.00 (605). (599). Bank Admin Inst.

Consumer Electronic Banking. (Reports Ser.: No. 520). 167p. 1982. 985.00x (ISBN 0-88694-520-8). Intl Res Dev.

Demand Deposit Accounting. (Community Bank Series on Operations & Automation: No. 2). 70p. 15.00 (ISBN 0-317-33756-4, 601); members 7.50 (ISBN 0-317-33757-2). Bank Admin Inst.

Gottlieb Duttweiler Institut. Elektronisches Geld. (Ger. & Fr.). 88p. 1983. pap. 30.00 (ISBN 0-89192-367-5). Interbk Inc.

Greguras, Fred M. & Wright, Ann. The Consumer-Financial Instituiton Relationship in Electronic Funds Transfer Legislation. LC 79-55491. (Computer Law Monograph Ser). 160p. (Orig.). 1979. 20.00 (ISBN 0-935200-00-2). Ctr Comp Law.

Institute of Bankers, ed. The Banks & Technology in the 1980s. 1982. 20.00x (ISBN 0-317-20361-4, Pub. by Inst Bankers UK). State Mutual Bk.

Notes from ATM-6. 219p. 1984. 40.00 (ISBN 0-318-03425-5, 688). Bank Admin Inst.

OECD Staff. Banking & Electronic Fund Transfer. 190p. (Orig.). 1983. pap. 22.00x (ISBN 92-64-12505-1). OECD.

Security, Audit, & Control Considerations in the Design of Electronic Funds Transfer Systems. 52p. 1977. 14.00 (ISBN 0-317-33816-1, 206); members 7.00 (ISBN 0-317-33817-X). Bank Admin Inst.

Security, Audit & Control of Small Computer Systems. 264p. 1981. 60.00 (ISBN 0-317-36408-1, 214); members 40.00 (ISBN 0-317-36409-X). Bank Admin Inst.

Security, Audit & Control of Small Computer Systems. 264p. 1981. 60.00 (214). Bank Admin Inst.

Survey of the Electronic Funds Transfer Transaction System. Set; incl. 1979. 1980 & 1981. 28.00 (721). Bank Admin Inst.

Yavitz, B. Automation in Commercial Banking. LC 67-12521. 1967. 9.95 (ISBN 0-02-935690-3). Free Pr.

BANKS AND BANKING–DATA PROCESSING

Assessing Data Processing Needs & Capabilities for Savings Associations. 63p. 1980. 50.00 (ISBN 0-318-16792-1, 13466). US League Savi Inst.

Auditing Bank EDP Systems. 123p. 1968. 16.00 (ISBN 0-317-33711-4, 210); members 8.00 (ISBN 0-317-33712-2). Bank Admin Inst.

Automated Retail Branch Banking in Europe. 270p. 1984. 1775.00 (ISBN 0-86621-575-1). Frost & Sullivan.

Bank Administration Institute. EDP Facility Accounting, 2 Vols. 1975. Vol. 1: Implementation; 205 pp. 50.00 (630); Vol. 2: Technical Foundations; 191 pp. 40.00 (631). Bank Admin Inst.

Banking & Financial Institution Software Guide. 327p. 1984. 19.95 (ISBN 0-912603-26-7); IBM Volume. 16.95 (ISBN 0-912603-02-X). Micro Info.

Bechhoefer, Ina S., ed. Guide to Real Estate & Mortgage Banking Software, 2 vols. 1200p. 1985. Set. 115.00 (ISBN 0-917935-02-0). Real Est Sol.

Bender, Mark. EFTS: Electronic Funds Transfer Systems - Elements & Impact. 112p. 1975. 19.50x (ISBN 0-8046-9119-3, Pub. by Kennikat). Assoc Faculty Pr.

Colton, Kent W. & Kramer, Kenneth L., eds. Computers & Banking. LC 79-9307. (Applications of Modern Technology in Business Ser.). (Illus.). 325p. 1979. 39.50x (ISBN 0-306-40255-6, Plenum Pr). Plenum Pub.

Computer Control & Audit. 1978. 29.50 (ISBN 0-89982-005-0, 061300); non-members 37.50. Am Bankers.

Computer Security Guide for Financial Institutions. 1978. 15.00 (ISBN 0-89982-004-2, 212400); non-members 18.75. Am Bankers.

Glass, G. Bank: EDV von A-Z. (Ger. & Eng.). 96p. (Bank - Data Processing A-Z). 1977. 9.95 (ISBN 3-7819-1090-3, M-7303, Pub. by Knapp). French & Eur.

Greguras, Fred M. & Wright, Ann. The Consumer-Financial Instituiton Relationship in Electronic Funds Transfer Legislation. LC 79-55491. (Computer Law Monograph Ser). 160p. (Orig.). 1979. 20.00 (ISBN 0-935200-00-2). Ctr Comp Law.

Halligan, Joseph. Banking & Finance-SOFTWHERE. Winther, Richard, ed. (SOFTWHERE Software Directories Ser.: Vol. 1). (Orig.). 1984. pap. 39.95 (ISBN 0-918451-20-5). Moore Data.

Information Processing Services Market in Banking. 302p. 1984. 1600.00 (ISBN 0-86621-100-4, A1150). Frost & Sullivan.

International Computer Programs Inc. ICP Software Directory, Vol. 4: Banking Insurance & Finance Systems. Hamilton, Dennis L., ed. 1984. pap. 95.00 (ISBN 0-88094-028-X). Intl Computer.

International Computer Programs Staff. ICP Software Directory, Vol. 4: Banking, Insurance & Finance Systems. Hamilton, Dennis, ed. 1985. pap. 95.00 (ISBN 0-88094-045-X). Intl Computer.

Iserson, Andrew R. A Data Processing Primer for Banking Professionals. Iserson, Rochelle M., ed. (Illus.). 96p. 1983. pap. text ed. 12.95 (ISBN 0-9610734-0-3). Compu-Sul.

Lipis, A. H., et al. Electronic Banking. (Professional Banking & Finance Ser.). 220p. 1985. 34.95 (ISBN 0-471-88224-0). Wiley.

Microcomputers in Banking. 64p. 1984. 36.00 (ISBN 0-318-03417-4, 263); members 24.00 (ISBN 0-318-03418-2). Bank Admin Inst.

Micros in Banking. 1984. 75.00 (ISBN 0-318-01747-4). CBSI.

Miller, James C. Microcomputer Support of Commercial Lending: A Management Perspective. (Illus.). 80p. (Orig.). 1985. pap. text ed. write for info (ISBN 0-936742-25-9). Robt Morris Assocs.

National Operations-Automation Survey, 1981. members 200.00 (ISBN 0-686-95675-3, 064800); non-members 125.00 ea. (ISBN 0-686-99567-8); bulk orders 140.00 (ISBN 0-686-99568-6); members bulk orders 60.00 (ISBN 0-686-99569-4); results of 1978 60.00 (ISBN 0-686-99570-8); members results of 1978 20.00 (ISBN 0-686-99571-6). Am Bankers.

OECD Staff. Banking & Electronic Fund Transfer. 190p. (Orig.). 1983. pap. 22.00x (ISBN 92-64-12505-1). OECD.

Office Automation Market in Banking. 1985. write for info. (ISBN 0-86621-193-4, A1255). Frost & Sullivan.

On-Line Systems in Branch Banking. 312p. 1983. 1275.00 (ISBN 0-86621-058-X). Frost & Sullivan.

Richardson, Dennis W. Electric Money: Evolution of an Electronic Funds-Transfer System. 1970. pap. 6.95x (ISBN 0-262-68025-4). MIT Pr.

Security, Audit & Control of Small Computer Systems. 264p. 1981. 60.00 (214). Bank Admin Inst.

Self Service Banking in the 80's: Critical Trends & Developments. 1982. 1250.00 (ISBN 0-686-46218-1, G-069). BCC.

Svigals, Terome. Planning for Future Market Events Using Data Processing Support: A Five Step Growth Plan. LC 82-48765. 1983. 27.95x (ISBN 0-02-949740-X). Macmillan.

Trust Software Directory. 1982. 50.000 (ISBN 0-89982-058-1, 366900); members 7.50. Am Bankers.

Veith, Richard H. Multinational Computer Nets: The Case of International Banking. LC 80-8386. 160p. 1981. 24.50x (ISBN 0-669-04092-4). Lexington Bks.

Yavitz, B. Automation in Commercial Banking. LC 67-12521. 1967. 9.95 (ISBN 0-02-935690-3). Free Pr.

BANNEKER, BENJAMIN, 1731-1806

Allen, Will W., ed. Banneker: The Afro-American Astronomer. facsimile ed. LC 77-168504. (Black Heritage Library Collection). Repr. of 1921 ed. 10.00 (ISBN 0-8369-8858-2). Ayer Co Pubs.

Allen, William G. Wheatley, Banneker & Horton. facs. ed. LC 77-133145. (Black Heritage Library Collection Ser). 1849. Repr. of 1849 ed. 7.00 (ISBN 0-8369-8657-1). Ayer Co Pubs.

BARBED WIRE

Clifton, Robert T. Barbs, Prongs, Points, Prickers, & Stickers: Complete & Illustrated Catalogue of Antique Barbed Wire. LC 78-88140. (Illus.). 1970. pap. 12.95 (ISBN 0-8061-0876-2). U of Okla Pr.

McCallum, Henry D. & McCallum, Frances T. Wire That Fenced the West. (Illus.). 1979. Repr. of 1965 ed. 9.95 (ISBN 0-8061-0651-4). U of Okla Pr.

BARGES

Smith, Peter L. Canal Barges & Narrow Boats. (Album Ser.: No. 8). (Illus.). 32p. 1983. pap. 2.95 (ISBN 0-85263-651-2, Pub. by Shire Pubns England). Seven Hills Bks.

BARIUM TITANATE

Anan'eva, A. A., et al. Ceramic Acoustic Detectors. LC 65-11334. 122p. 1965. 35.00x (ISBN 0-306-10702-3, Consultants). Plenum Pub.

BARK

see also Wood

Nanko, Heroki & Cote, Wilfred A. Bark Structure: Hardwoods Grown on Southern Pine Sites. 1980. pap. 12.00x (ISBN 0-8156-2234-1). Syracuse U Pr.

BARLEY

Competition & Its Consequences for Selection in Barley Breeding. (Agricultural Research Reports: No. 893). 268p. 1980. pap. 36.00 (ISBN 90-220-0712-X, PDC152, PUDOC). Unipub.

Fitzsimmons, R. W. & Wrigley, C. W. Australian Barley. 62p. 1980. 20.00x (ISBN 0-643-00344-4, Pub. by CSIRO Australia). State Mutual Bk.

--Australian Barleys. 86p. 1980. 9.95x (ISBN 0-643-00344-4, Pub. by CSIRO Australia). Intl Spec Bk.

--Australian Barleys: Identifications of Varieties, Grain Defects & Foreign Seeds. 62p. 1979. pap. 13.50 (ISBN 0-643-00344-4, C002, CSIRO). Unipub.

Mathre, D. E., ed. Compendium of Barley Diseases. LC 82-72159. 78p. 1982. pap. 17.00 (ISBN 0-89054-047-0). Am Phytopathol Soc.

Report of the First FAO-SIDA Seminar on Improvement of Nutritional Quality in Barley & Spring Wheat. 1978. pap. 7.50 (ISBN 92-5-100283-5, F1267, FAO). Unipub.

BARNACLES

Nilsson-Cantell, Carl A. Cirripedia Thoracica & Acrothoracica. (Illus.). 1978. pap. 16.50 (ISBN 82-00-01670-6, Dist. by Columbia U Pr). Universitet.

BARNS

see also Stables

Burch, Monte. Building Small Barns, Sheds & Shelters. Stetson, Fred, ed. LC 82-15439. (Illus.). 236p. 1982. pap. 12.95 (ISBN 0-88266-245-7). Garden Way Pub.

Fitchen, John. New World Dutch Barn: A Study of Its Characteristics, Its Structural System & Its Probable Erectional Procedures. LC 68-20485. (New York State Studies). (Illus.). 1968. 15.00x (ISBN 0-8156-2126-4). Syracuse U Pr.

Pelley, Lee. In One Barn: Efficient Livestock Housing & Management Under One Roof. (Illus.). 166p. (Orig.). 1984. pap. 11.95 (ISBN 0-88150-006-2). Countryman.

Rawson, Richard. Old Barn Plans. (Old House Bk). (Illus., Orig.). 1979. pap. 6.95 (ISBN 0-8317-6587-9, Mayflower Bks). Smith Pubs.

Sloane, Eric. Americana, 3 vols. Incl. Vol. 1. American Barns & Covered Bridges. LC 54-12510. 112p; Vol. 2. American Yesterday. LC 56-10710. 123p. 10.95i (ISBN 0-308-70042-2); Vol. 3. Our Vanishing Landscape. LC 55-12078. 107p. 10.95i (ISBN 0-308-70047-3). (Funk & W Bk.). (Illus.). T Y Crowell.

BAROMETER

see also Atmospheric Pressure

Goodison, Nicholas. English Barometers 1680-1860. 2nd ed. (Illus.). 388p. 1977. Repr. of 1968 ed. 49.50 (ISBN 0-902028-52-9). Antique Collect.

Middleton, William E. The History of the Barometer. LC 64-10942. pap. 127.80 (ISBN 0-317-08446-1, 2003887). Bks Demand UMI.

BARRACUDAS

De Sylva, Donald P. Systematics & Life History of the Great Barracuda, Sphyraena Barracuda (Walbaum) (Studies in Tropical Oceanography Ser: No. 1). 1970. 7.95x (ISBN 0-87024-082-X). U Miami Marine.

BARREL-SHELL ROOFS

see Roofs, Shell

BARS (ENGINEERING)

see also Girders; Springs (Mechanism)

Brann, Donald R. How to Build Bars. LC 67-15263. 1979. pap. 6.95 (ISBN 0-87733-690-3). Easi-Bild.

Society of Manufacturing Engineers. Bar Coding. 1985. 35.00 (ISBN 0-87263-180-X). SME.

Symposium on Heat Transfer in Rod Bundles, New York, 1968. Heat Transfer in Rod Bundles: Papers Presented at the Winter Annual Meeting of the American Society of Mechanical Engineers, New York, December 3, 1968. LC 68-58742. pap. 44.00 (ISBN 0-317-12986-4, 2011326). Bks Demand UMI.

BARTRAM, JOHN, 1699-1777

Berkeley, Edmund & Berkeley, Dorothy S. The Life & Travels of John Bartram: From Lake Ontario to the River St. John. LC 81-4083. (Illus.). xv, 376p. 1982. 25.00 (ISBN 0-8130-0700-3). U Presses Fla.

BARYONS

see also Hyperons; Neutrons; Protons

Bransden, B. H. & Moorhouse, R. Gordon. The Pion-Nucleon System. (Illus.). 552p. 1973. 52.00x (ISBN 0-691-08115-8); pap. 15.50x (ISBN 0-691-08129-8). Princeton U Pr.

Lichtenberg, D. B. Meson & Baryon Spectroscopy. rev. ed. (Illus.). 1975. pap. 11.00 (ISBN 0-387-90000-4). Springer-Verlag.

BASALT

Augustithis, S. S. Atlas of the Textural Patterns of Basalts & Their Genetic Significance. 324p. 1978. 102.25 (ISBN 0-444-41566-1). Elsevier.

Hawkesworth, C. J. & Norry, M. J., eds. Continental Basalts & Mantle Xenoliths. 300p. 1983. text ed. 39.95 (Pub. by Shiva Pub Ltd.); (Pub. by Shiva Pub Ltd.). Birkhauser.

Helms, S. W. Jawa: Lost City of the Black Desert. LC 80-69820. (Illus.). 182p. 1981. 37.50x (ISBN 0-8014-1364-8). Cornell U Pr.

Morse, S. A. Basalts & Phase Diagrams: An Introduction to the Quantitative Use of Phase Diagrams in Igneous Petrology. (Illus.). 400p. 1980. 33.00 (ISBN 0-387-90477-8). Springer-Verlag.

Ragland, Paul & Rogers, John, eds. Basalts. (Benchmark Papers in Geology). 448p. 1984. 55.00 (ISBN 0-442-27769-5). Van Nos Reinhold.

Yoder, H. S., Jr. Generation of Basaltic Magma. LC 76-29672. 1976. pap. text ed. 9.50 (ISBN 0-309-02504-4). Natl Acad Pr.

BASE-EXCHANGE

see Ion Exchange

BASE-PLATES

see Plates, Iron and Steel

BASEMENTS

Bubel, Mike & Bubel, Nancy. Root Cellaring the Simple no-Processing Way to Store Fruits & Vegetables. (Illus.). 320p. 1979. 12.95 (ISBN 0-87857-277-5). Rodale Pr Inc.

BASENJI DOGS

see Dogs–Breeds–Basenji

BASES, CHEMISTRY

Imelik, B. Catalysis by Acids & Bases. (Studies in Surface Science & Catalysis: Vol. 20). 1985. 94.50 (ISBN 0-444-42449-0). Elsevier.

Jensen, William B. The Lewis Acid-Base Concepts: An Overview. LC 79-15561. 364p. 1980. 53.50x (ISBN 0-471-03902-0, Pub. by Wiley-Interscience). Wiley.

Pearson, R. G., ed. Hard & Soft Acids & Bases. LC 72-93262. (Benchmark Paprs in Inorganic Chemistry Ser). 496p. 1973. 55.00 (ISBN 0-87933-021-X). Van Nos Reinhold.

Tanabe, Kozo. Solid Acids & Bases: Their Catalytic Properties. 1971. 47.00 (ISBN 0-12-683250-1). Acad Pr.

BASIC (COMPUTER PROGRAM LANGUAGE)

Abrahams, Douglas. An Introduction to BASIC Programming for Microcomputers. 2nd ed. 96p. 1984. 6.94x (ISBN 0-7715-0691-0); tchr's manual 6.94x (ISBN 0-7715-0791-7). Forkner.

Academic Computing Services, University of Kansas. Learning Z-BASIC on the Heath-Zenith Z-100. (Illus.). 304p. 1985. pap. 17.95 (ISBN 0-89303-621-8). Brady Comm.

Adamis, Eddie. BASIC Key Words: A User's Reference. LC 82-21759. 292p. 1983. pap. 14.95 (ISBN 0-471-86542-7, Pub. by Wiley Pr). Wiley.

--BASIC Key Words for the Apple III. LC 83-12327. 143p. 1984. pap. text ed. 14.95 (ISBN 0-471-88389-1, Pub. by Wiley Pr). Wiley.

--BASIC Keywords for the IBM PC. (IBM Personal Computer Ser.). 150p. 1984. pap. 14.95 (ISBN 0-471-88402-2, Pub. by Wiley Pr). Wiley.

--BASIC Subroutines for Commodore Computers. LC 82-21874. 312p. 1983. pap. text ed. 12.95 (ISBN 0-471-86541-9, Pub. by Wiley Pr). Wiley.

--Business BASIC for the IBM PC. (IBM PC Ser.: No. 1-646). 200p. 1984. pap. 14.95 (ISBN 0-471-88401-4, Pub. by Wiley Pr). Wiley.

Adams, David & Leigh, William E. Programming Business Systems with BASIC. 1984. text ed. 16.95 wkbk. (ISBN 0-538-10980-7, J98). SW Pub.

Adler, Howard. VIC-20 & Commodore 64 Computer Program Writing Workbook. 96p. 1983. 4.95 (ISBN 0-86668-811-0). ARCsoft.

Ageloff & Mojena. Applied Structured BASIC. LC 84-25835. 568p. 1985. write for info (ISBN 0-534-04740-8). Wadsworth Pub.

Ageloff, Roy & Mojena, Richard. Applied BASIC Programming. 464p. 1980. pap. text ed. write for info (ISBN 0-534-00808-9). Wadsworth Pub.

Ahl, David H. The Microsoft BASIC Ideabook. (Ideabook Ser.: No. 4). (Illus.). 144p. (Orig.). 1984. pap. 8.95 (ISBN 0-916688-67-4, 67-4). Creative Comp.

Ahl, David H. & North, Steve. More BASIC Computer Games. LC 78-74958. (Illus.). 186p. 1979. pap. 7.95 (ISBN 0-916688-09-7, 6C2). Creative Comp.

Ahl, David H., ed. BASIC Computer Games: Microcomputer Edition. LC 78-50028. (Illus.). 180p. 1978. pap. 7.95 (ISBN 0-916688-07-0, 6C). Creative Comp.

--BASIC Computer Games: Microcomputer Edition. LC 78-17624. (Illus.). 188p. 1978. pap. 7.95 (ISBN 0-89480-052-3, 215). Workman Pub.

--More BASIC Computer Games. LC 80-57619. (Illus.). 188p. 1980. pap. 8.95 (ISBN 0-89480-137-6, 438). Workman Pub.

Aker, Sharon Z. Microsoft BASIC Programming for the Mac. 1985. pap. 17.95 (ISBN 0-673-18167-7). Scott F.

Albrecht, Bob, et al. Atari BASIC. XL ed. (General Trade Books). 388p. 1985. pap. 14.95 (ISBN 0-471-80726-5). Wiley.

--TRS-80 BASIC: A Self Teaching Guide. LC 80-10268. (Self Teaching Guides Ser.: No. 1581). 351p. 1980. pap. 12.95 (ISBN 0-471-06466-1, Pub. by Wiley Pr). Wiley.

Albrecht, Bob L., et al. Atari BASIC. LC 79-12513. (Self-Teaching Guides). 333p. 1981. pap. text ed. 12.95 (ISBN 0-471-06496-3, Pub. by Wiley Pr). Wiley.

Albrecht, R. L., et al. BASIC for Home Computers. LC 78-9010. (Self-Teaching Guides). 336p. 1978. pap. 10.95x (ISBN 0-471-03204-2, Pub. by Wiley Pr). Wiley.

Albrecht, Robert L., et al. BASIC. 2nd ed. LC 77-14998. (Self-Teaching Guide Ser.). 325p. 1978. pap. text ed. 12.95 (ISBN 0-471-03500-9, Pub. by Wiley Pr). Wiley.

Alcock, Donald. Illustrating BASIC: A Simple Programming Language. (Illus.). 120p. 1977. 27.95 (ISBN 0-521-21703-2); pap. 10.95 (ISBN 0-521-21704-0). Cambridge U Pr.

Al-Sarraf, Hassan S. Programming with BASIC. (Arabic.). 200p. 1985. pap. 13.00 (ISBN 0-471-80970-5). Wiley.

Amsbury, Wayne. Structured BASIC & Beyond. LC 80-18382. 310p. 1980. pap. 19.95 (ISBN 0-914894-16-1). Computer Sci.

Anderson, Ronald W. From BASIC to Pascal. (Illus.). 324p. 18.95 (ISBN 0-8306-2466-X, 1466); pap. 11.50 (ISBN 0-8306-1466-4, 1466). TAB Bks.

Andree, Richard V. & Andree, Josephine P. Explore Computing with the TRS-80 & with Programming in BASIC. (Illus.). 256p. 1982. pap. text ed. 12.95 (ISBN 0-13-296137-7). P-H.

Andren, John, Jr., et al. IBM PC to Apple II BASIC Program Translation. 100p. 1984. 15.00. Med Software.

Andrews. BASIC Theory of Structures. (Illus.). 160p. 1985. pap. text ed. 15.95 (ISBN 0-408-01357-5). Butterworth.

Applied Research Staff & Shaffer. BASIC Booster Library: Apple. 250p. 1985. pap. 29.95 incl. disk (ISBN 0-912677-26-0). Apple IIc-IIe (ISBN 0-912677-51-1). Ashton-Tate Bks.

Arnold, William. The Compaq Portable Computer: Use, Applications & BASIC. LC 84-19219. 1985. pap. text ed. 18.45 (ISBN 0-03-064119-5). HR&W.

Asquith, George. Log Analysis by Microcomputer. 104p. 1980. 39.95x (ISBN 0-87814-118-9). Pennwell Bks.

Atherton, Roy. Structured BASIC for Acorn Computers. 207p. (Orig.). 1983. pap. 15.95 (ISBN 0-471-80600-5, Pub. by Wiley Pr). Wiley.

Athey, Thomas H. & Zmud, Robert W. Introduction to Computers & Information Systems with BASIC. 1986. text ed. 26.95x (ISBN 0-673-18185-5). Scott F.

Austrian, Geoffrey D. Herman Hollerith: Forgotten Giant of Information Processing. 418p. 1982. 25.00 (ISBN 0-231-05146-8, EY-00020-DP). Digital Pr.

Baker, Allen & Hamrick, Kathy. Conceptual Programming Using BASIC. (Illus.). 224p. 1984. pap. text ed. 18.95 (ISBN 0-13-166678-9). P-H.

Bangley, Bernard K. Bible BASIC: Bible Games for Personal Computers. LC 83-48461. 128p. (Orig.). 1983. pap. 9.57 (ISBN 0-06-250042-2, CN 4092, HarpR). Har-Row.

Barber, Sandra & Mihankhah, Kianpour. Learning by Doing BASIC. 101p. (Orig.). 1983. pap. text ed. 8.50x (ISBN 0-89917-393-4). Tichenor Pub.

Barnard, David T., et al. Microcomputer Programming with Microsoft BASIC. (Illus.). 1983. text ed. 22.95 (ISBN 0-8359-4357-7); pap. 17.95 (ISBN 0-8359-4356-9). Reston.

Barnett, Coleman. An Introduction to Structured Programming Using BASIC. 520p. 1984. pap. text ed. 23.95x (ISBN 0-89787-402-1). Gorsuch Scarisbrick.

Bartee, Thomas C. BASIC Computer Programming. 2nd ed. 368p. 1985. pap. text ed. 20.50 scp (ISBN 0-06-040519-8, HarpC). Har-Row.

--Learning BASIC on the IBM PCjr. 372p. 1984. pap. text ed. 18.70 scp (ISBN 0-06-040521-X, HarpC). Har-Row.

Bartorillo, Andrew. PCjr BASIC Programs for the Home: Programs That Make the PCjr a Useful Member of the Family. 272p. 1984. pap. 14.95 (ISBN 0-88693-069-3). Banbury Bks.

BASIC. (Alfred's Language Bks.). 1981. pap. 3.50 (ISBN 0-317-04674-8). Alfred Pub.

BASIC Computer Language. 232p. 5.95 (ISBN 0-317-05250-0, 62-2016). Radio Shack.

BASIC Conversions Handbook for TRS-80, Apple & PET Users. 96p. 5.95 (ISBN 0-317-05253-5, 62-2088). Radio Shack.

BASIC Faster & Better & Other Mysteries. 288p. 29.95 (ISBN 0-317-05268-3, 62-1002). Radio Shack.

BASIC for Beginners. (DECbooks). 166p. 1982. spiral bdg. 10.00 (ISBN 0-932376-46-0, AA-L333A-DP). Digital Pr.

BASIC for Microcomputers. 1979. write for info. tchr's. manual (ISBN 0-89525-271-6); 5 filmstrips & audiocassetts 115.00. Ed Activities.

Bateson, Robert & Raygor, Robin. BASIC Programming for the Apple Computer. (Illus.). 250p. 1985. pap. text ed. 14.95 (ISBN 0-314-85290-5). West Pub.

Beech, Graham. Successful Software for Small Computers: Structured Programming in BASIC. LC 82-10881. 182p. 1982. pap. text ed. 14.95 (ISBN 0-471-87458-2). Wiley.

Beers, Robert E. Best Book on BASIC. 448p. 1985. pap. 24.95 (ISBN 0-471-88844-3). Wiley.

Belkin, G. S. Twelve-Hour Basic for the IBM PC Compatibles. 240p. 1985. price not set (ISBN 0-07-004374-4). McGraw.

Bell, Frederick. Apple Programming for Learning & Teaching. (Illus.). 1984. text ed. 21.95 (ISBN 0-8359-0098-3); pap. 16.95 (ISBN 0-8359-0097-5). Reston.

Belluardo, Connie, et al. BASIC Programming 1. LC 84-71291. (Illus.). 103p. (Orig.). 1985. pap. text ed. 9.95 (ISBN 0-917531-04-3); pap. text ed. 16.95 tchr's. guide (ISBN 0-917531-14-0). Compu Tech Pub.

--BASIC Programming 2. LC 84-71291. (Illus.). 112p. (Orig.). 1985. pap. text ed. 9.95 (ISBN 0-917531-05-1); pap. text ed. 16.95 tchr's. guide (ISBN 0-917531-15-9). Compu Tech Pub.

--BASIC Programming 3. LC 84-71291. (Illus.). 120p. (Orig.). 1985. pap. text ed. 9.95 (ISBN 0-917531-06-X); pap. text ed. 16.95 tchr's. guide (ISBN 0-917531-16-7). Compu Tech Pub.

--BASIC Programming 4. LC 84-71291. (Illus., Orig.). 1985. pap. text ed. 9.95 (ISBN 0-917531-07-8); pap. text ed. 16.95 tchr's. guide (ISBN 0-917531-17-5). Compu Tech Pub.

--Discovering BASIC 1. LC 84-71290. (Illus.). 90p. (Orig.). 1985. pap. text ed. 8.95 (ISBN 0-917531-00-0); pap. text ed. 16.95 tchr's guide (ISBN 0-917531-10-8). Compu Tech Pub.

--Discovering BASIC 2. LC 84-71290. (Illus., Orig.). 1985. pap. text ed. 8.95 (ISBN 0-917531-01-9); pap. text ed. 16.95 tchr's guide (ISBN 0-917531-11-6). Compu Tech Pub.

--Discovering BASIC 3. LC 84-71290. (Illus.). 90p. (Orig.). 1985. pap. text ed. 8.95 (ISBN 0-917531-02-7); pap. text ed. 16.95 tchr's guide (ISBN 0-917531-12-4). Compu Tech Pub.

--Discovering BASIC 4. LC 84-71290. (Illus.). 96p. (Orig.). 1985. pap. text ed. 8.95 (ISBN 0-917531-03-5); pap. text ed. 16.95 tchr's guide (ISBN 0-917531-13-2). Compu Tech Pub.

Bent, Robert J. & Sethares, George C. BASIC: An Introduction to Computer Programming. 2nd ed. LC 81-17033. (Computer Science Ser.). 408p. 1982. pap. text ed. 19.00 pub net (ISBN 0-534-01101-2). Brooks-Cole.

--BASIC: An Introduction to Computer Programming. 2nd ed. 349p. 1982. pap. write for info. Wadsworth Pub.

--BASIC: An Introduction to Computer Programming with the Apple. 1983. pub net 19.00 (ISBN 0-534-01370-8, 82-20572). Brooks-Cole.

--BASIC: An Introduction to Computer Programming with the Apple. 250p. 1983. pap. write for info. Wadsworth Pub.

--Business BASIC. 2nd ed. LC 83-19024. (Computer Science Ser.). 240p. 1984. pap. text ed. 18.25 pub net (ISBN 0-534-03179-X). Brooks-Cole.

--Business BASIC. 2nd ed. 200p. 1984. write for info. Wadsworth Pub.

Benton, Stan & Weekes, Len. Program It Right: Structured Methods in BASIC. (Orig.). 1985. pap. text ed. write for info. Yourdon.

Berenbon, Howard. Mostly BASIC: Application for the Commodore 64. LC 84-50183. Bk. 1. 12.95 (ISBN 0-672-22355-4); Bk. 2. 14.95 (ISBN 0-672-22356-2). Sams.

--Mostly BASIC: Applications for Your Apple II, Bk. 1. LC 80-53273. 160p. 1980. pap. 13.95 (ISBN 0-672-21789-9, 21864). Sams.

--Mostly BASIC: Applications for Your Apple II, Bk. 2. LC 80-53273. 224p. 1982. pap. 12.95 (ISBN 0-672-21864-X). Sams.

--Mostly BASIC: Applications for Your Atari, 2 vols. LC 83-61071. 184p. 1983. Bk. 1, 184 pp. 12.95 (ISBN 0-672-22075-X, 22075); Bk. 2, 224 pp. 15.95 (ISBN 0-672-22092-X, 22092). Sams.

--Mostly BASIC: Applications for Your IBM-PC, 2 Vols. 1983. Bk. 1. 12.95 (ISBN 0-672-22076-8, 22093); Bk. 2. 14.95 (ISBN 0-672-22093-8). Bobbs.

--Mostly BASIC: Applications for Your IBM-PC, 2 vols. LC 83-61072. 1983. Bk. 1, 192 pp. 12.95 (ISBN 0-672-22076-8, 22076); Bk. 2, 248 pp. 14.95 (ISBN 0-672-22093-8, 22093). Sams.

--Mostly BASIC: Applications for Your PET. LC 80-53274. 160p. 1980. Book 1. pap. 13.95 (ISBN 0-672-21790-2, 21790). Sams.

--Mostly BASIC: Applications for Your PET, Bk. 2. LC 80-53274. 224p. 1983. pap. 13.95 (ISBN 0-672-22001-6, 22001). Sams.

--Mostly BASIC: Applications for Your TRS-80, Bk. 1. LC 80-53269. 168p. 1980. pap. 12.95 (ISBN 0-672-21788-0, 21788). Sams.

--Mostly BASIC Applications for Your TRS-80, Bk.2. 224p. 1981. pap. 12.95 (ISBN 0-672-21865-8, 21865). Sams.

Berman, Lee & Leonard, Ken. The BASIC Explorer for the Commodore 64. (Illus.). 200p. 1984. pap. 11.95 (ISBN 0-07-881139-2, 139-2). Osborne-McGraw.

Besag, Frank P. & Levine, Leonard P. BASIC for Teachers. 1984. pap. 14.95 (ISBN 0-8039-2329-5). Sage.

Bird, Stuart L. Converting to Timex-Sinclair BASIC. 206p. 1983. spiral binding 14.95 (ISBN 0-88006-063-8, BK7396). Green Pub Inc.

Bitter, Gary G. & Cook, Paul M. IBM BASIC for Business. (Illus.). 192p. 1986. pap. text ed. 19.95 (ISBN 0-13-448093-7). P-H.

Bitter, Gary G. & Gateley, Wilson Y. BASIC for Beginners. 2nd ed. (Illus.). 1978. pap. text ed. 22.95 (ISBN 0-07-005492-4). McGraw.

Blackwood, Brian D. & Blackwood, George H. Intimate Instructions in Integer BASIC. LC 81-51551. 160p. 1982. pap. 8.95 (ISBN 0-672-21812-7, 21812). Sams.

Blechman, Fred. Programs for Beginners on the TRS-80. (Illus.). 150p. 1981. pap. 10.95 (ISBN 0-8104-5182-4). Hayden.

Bocchino, William A. Simplified Guide to Microcomputers with Practical Programs & Applications. LC 82-3671. 256p. 1982. 19.95 (ISBN 0-13-810085-3, Busn). P-H.

Bogart, Theodore F., Jr. Applied BASIC for Technology. 320p. 1984. pap. text ed. 21.95 (ISBN 0-574-21585-9, 13-4585); instr's guide avail. (ISBN 0-574-21586-7, 13-4586). SRA.

--BASIC Programs for Electrical Circuits Analysis. 1985. pap. 22.95 (ISBN 0-8359-0406-7). Reston.

--Experiments for Electrical Circuit Analysis with BASIC Programming. 288p. 1982. pap. text ed. 18.95 (ISBN 0-574-21565-4, 13-4565); solutions manual avail. (ISBN 0-574-21569-7, 13-4569). SRA.

Boggs, Roy A. Advanced BASIC. 1983. text ed. 24.95 (ISBN 0-8359-0163-7); pap. 17.95 (ISBN 0-8359-0161-0). Reston.

--Advanced BASIC for the IBM PC. 1985. pap. 16.95 (ISBN 0-8359-9142-3). Reston.

--Applied BASIC for Microcomputers. (Illus.). 225p. 1984. 16.95 (ISBN 0-8359-0042-8). Reston.

Bohl, Marilyn, ed. Information Processing with BASIC. 4th ed. 688p. 1984. 25.95 (ISBN 0-574-21465-8, 13-4465); study guide o.p. 9.95 (ISBN 0-574-21448-8, 13-4448); study guide 9.95 (ISBN 0-574-21447-X); telecourse study guide avail. (ISBN 0-574-21448-8, 13-4448); transparencies avail. (ISBN 0-574-21449-6, 13-4449); test bank avail. (ISBN 0-574-21466-6, 13-4466); instr's guide avail. (ISBN 0-574-21446-1, 13-4446). SRA.

Boillot, Michel. Understanding BASIC in Business. 1978. pap. text ed. 22.95 (ISBN 0-8299-0206-6). West Pub.

Boillot, Michel & Boillot, Mona. BASIC: Concepts & Structured Problem Solving. (Illus.). 500p. 1984. pap. text ed. 21.95 (ISBN 0-314-77843-8); intr's. manual avail. (ISBN 0-314-77844-6). West Pub.

Boillot, Michel & Horn, L. Wayne. BASIC. 3rd ed. (Illus.). 375p. 1983. pap. text ed. 20.95 (ISBN 0-314-69636-9). West Pub.

Bomze, Howard. Programming Digital's Personal Computer: BASIC. 1986. text ed. 17.75 (ISBN 0-03-063729-5). HR&W.

Borgerson, M. J. Advanced BASIC Programming Set. (General Trade Books). 1985. incl. disk 22.90 (ISBN 0-471-89547-4). Wiley.

Borgerson, Mark J. A BASIC Programmer's Guide to Pascal. LC 81-16281. 118p. 1982. pap. text ed. 11.95 (ISBN 0-471-09293-2, Pub. by Wiley Pr). Wiley.

Bosworth, Bruce. Business Programming Projects with BASIC. 256p. 1984. pap. text ed. 17.95 (ISBN 0-574-21480-1, 13-4480); tchr's ed. (ISBN 0-574-21481-X, 13-4481). SRA.

--Programs in BASIC, a Lecture Notebook. 2nd ed. 1978. pap. text ed. 6.50 (ISBN 0-8403-1210-5). Kendall-Hunt.

Brady & Richardson. BASIC Programming Language. rev. ed. (Plaid Ser.). 1981. 9.95 (ISBN 0-256-02124-4). Dow Jones-Irwin.

Brain Bank. The BASIC Conversions Handbook for Apple, Commodore, TRS-80, & Atari Users. write for info. Hayden.

Brain, David, et al. The BASIC Conversions Handbook for Apple, TRS-80 & PET Users. 80p. (Orig.). 1982. pap. 9.95 (ISBN 0-8104-5534-X). Hayden.

Bramer, Max A. Adding Structure to BASIC with Comal 80. 288p. 1983. write for info (ISBN 0-201-14632-0). Addison-Wesley.

Brenan, Kathleen M. & Mandell, Steven L. Introduction to Computers & BASIC Programming. (Illus.). 409p. 1983. text ed. 20.95 (ISBN 0-314-78551-5); tchrs.' manual avail. (ISBN 0-314-81042-0). West Pub.

Brickner, Dave, et al. Annotated BASIC: A New Technique for Neophytes, Vol. 2. McCarthy, Nan & Crocker, Chris, eds. (Illus.). 125p. 1982. pap. 10.95 (ISBN 0-88006-037-9, BK 7385). Green Pub Inc.

Bridges, George. Forty IBM PCjr Programs for Home, School & Office. 96p. 1984. 7.95 (ISBN 0-86668-037-3). ARCsoft.

--IBM Personal Computer Program Writing Workbook. 96p. 1983. 4.95 (ISBN 0-86668-818-8). ARCsoft.

Brooner, E. G. BASIC Business Software. LC 80-52232. 144p. 1981. pap. 11.95 (ISBN 0-672-21751-1, 21751). Sams.

Brown, Charles & Kreta, Eleanor. Introduction to Data Entry Devices with a Subset of BASIC. 1979. pap. text ed. 6.95 (ISBN 0-8403-1952-5, 40195201). Kendall-Hunt.

Brown, Jerald R. Instant BASIC: Third Edition. (Illus.). 224p. 1984. pap. 12.95 (ISBN 0-88056-344-3). Dilithium Pr.

Brown, Jerald R., et al. BASIC for the Apple II. LC 82-10962. (Self-Teaching Guide Ser.: No. 1-581). 410p. 1982. pap. 12.95 (ISBN 0-471-86596-6, Pub. by Wiley Pr); pap. tchr's guide avail. Wiley.

Brown, Peter. Pascal from BASIC. 1982. pap. 12.95 (ISBN 0-201-10158-0). Addison-Wesley.

Bruey, Alfred J. From BASIC to FORTRAN. (Illus.). 144p. (Orig.). 1984. 17.95 (ISBN 0-8306-0753-6); pap. 9.95 (ISBN 0-8306-1753-1, 1753). TAB Bks.

Bui, X. T. Executive Planning with BASIC. LC 81-85954. (Illus.). 196p. 1982. pap. 15.95 (ISBN 0-89588-083-0, B380). SYBEX.

Bunday, B. D. BASIC Linear Programming. 192p. 1984. pap. 14.95 (ISBN 0-7131-3509-3). E Arnold.

Buscaino, Dale & Daniel, Scott. IBM BASIC Decoded & Other Mysteries. 29.95 (ISBN 0-317-06580-7). Blue Cat.

Busch, David. BASIC Games for Your Commodore 64. cancelled 14.95 (ISBN 0-89303-909-8). Brady Comm.

--BASIC Games for Your IBM Peanut. cancelled 9.95 (ISBN 0-89303-908-X). Brady Comm.

--BASIC Games for Your VIC-20 Computer. 9.95 (ISBN 0-89303-910-1). Brady Comm.

Carmony, Lowell A. & Holliday, Robert L. Macintosh BASIC. LC 84-23051. (Illus.). Date not set. pap. 19.95 (ISBN 0-88175-082-4). Computer Sci.

Carris, Bill & Wolfe, Bob. Inside Commodore 64 BASIC. 12.95 (ISBN 0-8359-3087-4). Reston.

Carter, L. R. & Huzan, E. Teach Yourself Computer Programming in BASIC. (Teach Yourself Ser.). 174p. 1981. pap. 5.95 (ISBN 0-679-10535-2). McKay.

Carver, D. K. Computers & Data Processing: Introduction with BASIC. 3rd ed. LC 78-19131. 366p. 1983. text ed. 24.95 (ISBN 0-471-09834-5). wkbk. 11.95 (ISBN 0-471-86252-5). Wiley.

Carver, D. Keith. Beginning BASIC. LC 79-20457. 1980. pap. text ed. 17.50 pub net (ISBN 0-8185-0368-8). Brooks-Cole.

Ettlin, Walter A. & Solberg, Gregory. The Microsoft BASIC Book! Macintosh Edition. 464p. (Orig.). 1985. pap. 18.95 (ISBN 0-07-881169-4, 169-4). Osborne McGraw.

Evans, Carl M. Atari BASIC: Faster & Better. 300p. 19.95 (ISBN 0-936200-29-4). Blue Cat.

Farina, Mario V. Flowcharting. 1970. pap. 14.95 ref. ed. (ISBN 0-13-322750-2). P-H.

--Programming in BASIC: The Time-Sharing Language. (Orig.). 1968. pap. 18.95 ref. ed. (ISBN 0-13-730424-2). P-H.

Farley, Patrick, et al. Mastering BASIC: A Beginner's Guide. 1979. pap. text ed. 6.50 (ISBN 0-89669-039-3). Collegium Bk Pubs.

Farvour, James. Microsoft BASIC Decoded & Other Mysteries. (TRS-80 Information Ser.: Vol. II). (Illus.). 312p. (Orig.). 1981. pap. 29.95 (ISBN 0-936200-01-4). Blue Cat.

Fassnacht, Philip R., et al. The TRS-80 & TDP-100 Color BASIC & Extended System. rev. ed. (Nanos Reference Cards Ser.). (Illus.). 16p. 1982. 4.95 (ISBN 0-915069-08-3). Nanos Sys.

Faulk, Ed. How to Write a TRS-80 Program. (How to Write Ser.). (Illus.). 224p. 1982. pap. 14.95 (ISBN 0-88190-033-8, BO033). Datamost.

Finkel, LeRoy & Brown, Jerald R. Apple BASIC: Data File Programming. LC 81-13100. 303p. 1982. pap. 14.95 (ISBN 0-471-09157-X, Pub. by Wiley Pr); software diskette 24.95 (ISBN 0-471-86836-1); pap. 34.90 bk. & disk set (ISBN 0-471-89843-0). Wiley.

--Data File Programming in BASIC. LC 80-39790. (Self-Teaching Guide Ser.). 338p. 1981. pap. text ed. 14.95 (ISBN 0-471-08333-X, Pub. by Wiley Pr). Wiley.

--TRS-80 Data File Programming. (Self-Teaching Guides: No. 1-581). 320p. 1983. pap. text ed. 14.95 (ISBN 0-471-88486-3, Pub. by Wiley Press). Wiley.

Flanders, Dennis. BASIC Programming for the IBM PC. 1985. cancelled (ISBN 0-89303-240-9). Brady Comm.

Floegel, Ekkehard. ZX-81 Timex: Programming in BASIC & Machine Language. 139p. 9.95 (ISBN 0-317-05097-4). Elcomp.

--ZX-81 Timex: Programming in BASIC & Machine Language. 139p. 9.95 (ISBN 3-921682-98-3). Blue Cat.

Flynn, Brian. Compute's Easy BASIC Programs for the Apple. Compute Editors, ed. 400p. (Orig.). 1985. pap. 14.95 (ISBN 0-942386-88-4). Compute Pubns.

Flynn, Christopher. Compute's Guide to Extended BASIC Home Applications on the TI 99-4A. 172p. 1984. pap. 12.95 (ISBN 0-942386-41-8). Compute Pubns.

--Home Applications in BASIC for the IBM PC & PCjr. Compute Editors, ed. (Illus., Orig.). 1985. pap. 12.95 (ISBN 0-942386-60-4). Compute Pubns.

Forkner, Irvine F. BASIC Programming for Business. (Illus.). 288p. 1978. pap. text ed. 21.95x (ISBN 0-13-066423-5). P-H.

Forsyth, Richard. The BASIC Idea: An Introduction to Computer Programming. 1978. pap. 8.95 (ISBN 0-412-21470-9, NO.6111, Pub. by Chapman & Hall). Methuen Inc.

Fox, Annie & Fox, David. Armchair BASIC: An Absolute Beginner's Guide to Programming in BASIC. 264p. (Orig.). 1982. pap. 12.95 (ISBN 0-07-047858-9, 858-9). Osborne-McGraw.

Frates, Jeffrey. Programming in BASIC: Communicating with Computers. (Illus.). 304p. 1985. pap. text ed. 19.95 (ISBN 0-13-729369-0). P-H.

Friedman, Paul. Computer Programs in BASIC. 1981. pap. 10.95 (ISBN 0-13-165225-7). P-H.

Froehlich, John P. TRS-80 More than BASIC. LC 81-52158. 224p. 1981. pap. 10.95 (ISBN 0-672-21813-5, 21813). Sams.

Fry, Larry. BASIC Programming for Business: A Structured Approach. LC 84-14268. 352p. 1985. pap. text ed. 20.00 (ISBN 0-8273-2245-3); instr's. guide 4.10 (ISBN 0-8273-2246-1). Delmar.

Gabriele, Peter & Gabriele, Rosemarie. Game Techniques in Applesoft BASIC. (Illus.). 148p. 1985. pap. cancelled (ISBN 0-8159-5617-7). Devin.

Gaby, E. & Gaby, S. GoSubs: A Hundred Program-Building Subroutines in Timex-Sinclair BASIC. 176p. 1983. pap. 9.95 (ISBN 0-07-022677-6, BYTE Bks). McGraw.

Gallo, Michael A. & Nenno, Robert B. Computers in Society with BASIC & Pascal. 1985. pap. text ed. write for info. (ISBN 0-87150-852-4, 37L8700). PWS Pubs.

Gardner, David A. & Gardner, Marianne L. Apple BASIC Made Easy. (Illus.). 224p. 1984. text ed. 21.95 (ISBN 0-13-038928-5); pap. 15.95 (ISBN 0-13-038910-2). P-H.

--VIC-20 BASIC Made Easy. (Illus.). 256p. 1984. text ed. 19.95 (ISBN 0-13-941980-2); pap. text ed. 14.95 (ISBN 0-13-941972-1). P-H.

Garrison, Paul. Turbo Pascal for BASIC Programmers. 250p. 1985. pap. 14.95 (ISBN 0 88022 167 4, 184). Que Corp.

Gee, S. M. Programming the Timex-Sinclair 2000. 144p. 1983. 17.95 (ISBN 0-13-729582-0); pap. 10.95 (ISBN 0-13-729574-X). P-H.

Genzlinger, R. Barry, et al. Straight Forward BASIC. 163p. 1984. pap. 12.95 (ISBN 0-9612704-0-3). Champlain Coll Pr.

Gerlach, Vernon S. An Interactive Approach to BASIC. 326p. 1983. pap. text ed. write for info. (ISBN 0-02-341500-2). Macmillan.

Getting Started with Color BASIC. 300p. 5.95 (ISBN 0-317-05261-6, 26-3191). Radio Shack.

Getting Started with TRS-80 BASIC. 6.95 (ISBN 0-317-05267-5, 26-2107). Radio Shack.

Ghedini, Silvano. Software for Photometric Astronomy. LC 82-8574. (Illus.). 224p. 1982. pap. text ed. 26.95 (ISBN 0-943396-00-X). Willmann-Bell.

Giarratano, Joseph C. BASIC: Advanced Concepts, 4 vols. LC 82-50018. 214p. 1982. pap. 22.95 (ISBN 0-672-21942-5, 21942); Vols. 3 & 4. 39.95 (21943-3); Vols. 1-4. 69.95 (22045-8). Sams.

--BASIC: Fundamental Concepts. LC 82-50017. 198p. 1982. pap. 22.95 (ISBN 0-672-21941-7, 21941). Sams.

--Commodore 64 BASIC Guide. Starnes, C., ed. 200p. 1984. pap. 14.95 (ISBN 0-913847-01-1). Computext Inc.

Glau, Gregory R., et al. Annotated BASIC: A New Technique for Neophytes, Vol. 1. McCarthy, Nan & Crocker, Chris, eds. 160p. (Orig.). 1981. pap. 10.95 (ISBN 0-88006-028-X, BK 7384). Green Pub Inc.

Glentop & Honeytold. Commodore 64 BASIC Programming. 1984. incl. disk 29.95 (ISBN 0-317-06577-7, 7630). Hayden.

Going Ahead with Extended Color BASIC. 210p. 5.95 (ISBN 0-317-05262-4, 26-3192). Radio Shack.

Goldsmith, W. B., Jr. BASIC Programs for Home Financial Management. 314p. 1981. 18.95 (ISBN 0-13-066522-3); pap. 12.95 (ISBN 0-13-066514-2). P-H.

Goldstein, Larry J. The Adam Home Computer: An Introduction to SmartBASIC & Applications. (Illus.). 240p. 1985. pap. 7.95 (ISBN 0-89303-296-4). Brady Comm.

--Advanced BASIC & Beyond for the IBM PC. LC 83-15725. (Illus.). 384p. 1983. pap. text ed. 19.95 (ISBN 0-89303-324-3); bk. & diskette 49.95 (ISBN 0-89303-325-1); diskette 30.00 (ISBN 0-89303-326-X). Brady Comm.

--IBM PCjr: Introduction to BASIC Programming & Applications. (Illus.). 384p. 1984. pap. 14.95 (ISBN 0-89303-539-4); diskette 20.00 (ISBN 0-89303-537-8); cancelled 34.95 (ISBN 0-89303-545-9). Brady Comm.

Goldstein, Larry J. & Goldstein, Martin. IBM Personal Computer: An Introduction to Operating System, BASIC Programming & Applications. rev. ed. LC 83-11780. (Illus.). 400p. 1983. 18.95 (ISBN 0-89303-530-0); diskette 25.00 (ISBN 0-89303-526-2); bk. & diskette 43.95 (ISBN 0-89303-527-0). Brady Comm.

Goldstein, Larry J. & Mosher, F. Commodore 64 BASIC Programming & Applications. LC 83-25705. (Illus.). 320p. 1984. 15.95 (ISBN 0-89303-381-2). Brady Comm.

Goldstein, Larry J. & Schneider, David. Microsoft BASIC for the Macintosh. (Illus.). 576p. 1984. pap. 21.95 (ISBN 0-89303-662-5). Brady Comm.

Gomez, Alfredo. The Basics of BASIC. 1983. pap. text ed. 19.95 (ISBN 0-03-063069-X). HR&W.

Goodfellow, David C. Apple II BASIC. (Illus.). 240p. (Orig.). 1983. o.p 19.95 (ISBN 0-8306-0113-9); pap. 13.50 (ISBN 0-8306-1513-X, 1513). TAB Bks.

Goodman, Paul. The Commodore 64 Guide to Data Files & Advanced BASIC. (Illus.). 176p. 1984. pap. 12.95 (ISBN 0-89303-375-8); diskett 20.00 (ISBN 0-89303-370-7). Brady Comm.

Gottfried, B. S. Schaum's Outline of Programming with BASIC. 2nd ed. (Schaum's Outline Ser.). 1982. pap. 9.95 (ISBN 0-07-023855-3). McGraw.

Graff, Lois & Goldstein, Larry. Applesoft BASIC for the Apple II & IIe. LC 83-15527. 336p. 1983. 16.95 (ISBN 0-89303-320-0). Brady Comm.

Graham, Neill. Computing & Computers: An Introduction Through BASIC. (Illus.). 525p. 1982. text ed. 21.95 (ISBN 0-8299-0382-8). West Pub.

--Programming the IBM Personal Computer: Fundamentals of BASIC. 1984. 17.95 (ISBN 0-03-059561-4). HR&W.

--Programming the IBM Personal Computer: BASIC. LC 82-11706. 256p. 1983. 17.50 (ISBN 0-03-063667-1). HR&W.

Grame, Carl A. & O'Donnell, Daniel J. Learning BASIC Programming Essentials. 320p. 1984. pap. text ed. 17.95 (ISBN 0-574-21370-8, 13-4370); TRS 80 6.95 (ISBN 0-574-21372-4, 13-4372); Apple II 6.95 (ISBN 0-574-21374-0, 13-4374); IBM-PC 6.95 (ISBN 0-574-21377-5, 13-4377); instr's guide avail. (ISBN 0-574-21376-7, 13-4376); avail. audio tapes 62.50 (ISBN 0-574-21375-9, 13-4375). SRA.

Grant, John & Grant, Catherine. The ZX Programmer's Companion. LC 83-23967. 256p. 1984. pap. 11.95 (ISBN 0-521-27044-8). Cambridge U Pr.

Gratzer, G. A. & Gratzer, T. G. Fast BASIC: Beyond TRS-80 BASIC. 278p. 1982. pap. 14.95 (ISBN 0-471-09849-3). Wiley.

Gratzer, George A. Fast BASIC: Model 1. (Wiley Professional Software Ser.). 320p. 1982. pap. 34.90 incl. disk (ISBN 0-471-89844-9); pap. 34.90 (ISBN 0-471-89845-7). Wiley.

Grauer, Robert T., et al. BASIC Is Child's Play: Commodore 64 Edition. (Illus.). 160p. 1984. pap. text ed. 18.95 (ISBN 0-13-058819-9). P-H.

--BASIC Is Child's Play: IBM-PC Edition. (Illus.). 112p. 1984. pap. text ed. 18.95 (ISBN 0-13-058793-1). P-H.

--BASIC Is Child's Play: TRS-80 Edition. (Illus.). 112p. 1984. pap. text ed. 18.95 (ISBN 0-13-058801-6). P-H.

--BASIC Is Child's Play: Apple Edition. (Illus.). 112p. 1984. pap. text ed. 18.95 (ISBN 0-13-058785-0). P-H.

--BASIC Is Child's Play: IBM-PCjr Edition. (Illus.). 192p. 1984. pap. text ed. 18.95 (ISBN 0-13-058827-X). P-H.

--More BASIC Is Child's Play: IBM Edition. (Illus.). 256p. 1985. pap. 21.95 (ISBN 0-13-601097-0). P-H.

Greene, Greg. Database Manager in Microsoft BASIC. (Illus.). 176p. 1983. 18.95 (ISBN 0-8306-0167-8, 1567); pap. 12.50 (ISBN 0-8306-0567-3). TAB Bks.

Greenwood, Richard & Brodzinski, Ignatius. Enjoying BASIC: A Comprehensive Guide to Programming. 368p. 1984. 19.50 (ISBN 0-06-042504-0, HarpC); write for info. instr's manual (ISBN 0-06-362461-3). Har-Row.

Griffin, Marvin A., et al. Computer Science Using BASIC. 1978. 13.95 (ISBN 0-8403-1965-7, 40196502). Kendall-Hunt.

Grillo, John P. & Robertson, J. D. Apple Sampler: A Guide to Good BASIC Subroutines for the IIe-IIc. 1985. pap. 14.95 (ISBN 0-471-81729-5). Wiley.

--More Subroutine Sandwich. LC 82-13506. 260p. 1983. pap. text ed. 12.95 (ISBN 0-471-86921-X). Wiley.

--Subroutine Sandwich. LC 82-13516. 251p. 1983. pap. text ed. 12.95 (ISBN 0-471-86920-1). Wiley.

--Subroutine Sandwiches Set. 224p. 1983. pap. 25.90 (ISBN 0-471-88923-7). Wiley.

Grout, Jarrell C. Programming with BASIC: A Structured Approach. 376p. 1985. pap. text ed. write for info. (ISBN 0-697-00077-X); instr's. manual avail. (ISBN 0-697-00505-4). Wm C Brown.

Gruenberger, Fred. Computing with the Apple. 208p. 1984. pap. text ed. 14.95 (ISBN 0-8359-0866-6). Reston.

Guay, E. Joseph & Bryant College Staff. Programming in Vax-BASIC. LC 84-14602. 288p. 1985. pap. text ed. 23.95 (ISBN 0-201-11566-2, 160A16); write for info. instrs' manual (ISBN 0-201-11567-0); write for info. tape of sample programs (ISBN 0-201-11568-9). Addison Wesley.

Guido, Raymond. Calculating with BASIC. (Da Capo Quality Paperbacks Ser.). (Illus.). 80p. 1981. pap. text ed. 8.95 (ISBN 0-306-80144-2). Da Capo.

Gulledge, Earl N. BASIC for Technicians. LC 84-7659. 352p. 1985. pap. text ed. 19.80 (ISBN 0-8273-2310-7); instr's. guide 4.00 (ISBN 0-8273-2311-5). Delmar.

Gustavson, Frances & Sackson, Marian. Problem Solving & BASIC: A Modular Approach. LC 78-21904. 335p. 1979. pap. text ed. 17.95 (ISBN 0-574-21240-X, 13-4240); instr's guide avail. (ISBN 0-574-21241-8, 13-4241). SRA.

Haigh, Roger & Radford, Loren. BASIC for Microcomputers: Apple, TRS-80, PET. 300p. 1982. pap. text ed. write for info. (ISBN 0-87150-334-4, 8050). PWS Pubs.

Haigh, Roger W. & Radford, Loren E. BASIC for Microcomputers: Apple, TRS-80, PET. 337p. 1983. 21.95 (ISBN 0-442-27843-8). Van Nos Reinhold.

Hampshire, Nick. Library of PET Subroutines. 140p. (Orig.). 1982. pap. 17.95 (ISBN 0-8104-1050-8); 1 PET disk & documentation 25.00. Hayden.

Hare, Robert R. Personal Computing: BASIC Programming on the TRS-80. LC 83-7502. (Computer Science Ser.). 500p. 1983. pap. text ed. 18.00 pub net (ISBN 0-534-02768-7). Brooks-Cole.

Hare, Van Court, Jr. BASIC Programming. 2nd ed. 407p. 1982. pap. text ed. 19.95 (ISBN 0-15-505002-8, HC, HC). HarBraceJ.

Harris, J. Mel & Scofield, Michael L. IBM PC Conversion Handbook of BASIC. LC 83-13977. 176p. 1983. pap. text ed. 15.95 (ISBN 0-13-448481-9). P-H.

Hartnell, Tim. Getting Acquainted with Your ZX-81. 3rd ed. 120p. 1981. pap. 9.95 (ISBN 0-916688-33-X, 15Y). Creative Comp.

Haskell, Richard. PET-CBM BASIC. (Illus.). 154p. 1982. 18.95 (ISBN 0-13-661769-7); pap. 12.95 (ISBN 0-13-661751-4). P-H.

--TRS-80 Extended Color BASIC. (Illus.). 170p. 1983. 19.95 (ISBN 0-13-931253-6); pap. 12.95 (ISBN 0-13-931246-3). P-H.

Haskell, Richard & Haskell, Jeff. TI BASIC. (Illus.). 208p. 1984. pap. 14.95 (ISBN 0-13-921107-1). P-H.

Haskell, Richard & Jackson, Glenn. IBM PCjr BASIC. 1985. 13.95 (ISBN 0-13-448705-2). P-H.

Haskell, Richard & Jackson, Glenn A. IBM PC BASIC Programming. (Illus.). 184p. 1984. 19.95 (ISBN 0-13-448432-0); pap. 13.95 (ISBN 0-13-448424-X). P-H.

Haskell, Richard & Windeknecht, Thomas. Commodore 64 & VIC-20 BASIC. (Illus.). 200p. 1984. pap. 14.95 (ISBN 0-13-152281-7). P-H.

Haskell, Richard E. Apple BASIC. (Illus.). 183p. 1982. 19.95 (ISBN 0-13-039107-7); pap. 12.95 (ISBN 0-13-039099-2). P-H.

--Atari BASIC. (Illus.). 175p. 1983. 19.95 (ISBN 0-13-049809-2, Spec); pap. 13.95 (ISBN 0-13-049791-6). P-H.

--Coleco Adam BASIC. 230p. 1985. pap. 10.95 (ISBN 0-13-140450-4). P-H.

Hastings, Nicholas & Willis, Robert. VAX BASIC for Business. 210p. 1985. pap. text ed. 18.95 (ISBN 0-13-940941-6). P-H.

Hawkins, Harry M. & Bisbee, Kolan K. Commodore 64 Programming: A Hands-on Approach to BASIC. (Illus.). 192p. (Orig.). 1984. 15.95 (ISBN 0-8306-0831-1); pap. 9.95 (ISBN 0-8306-1831-7, 1831). TAB Bks.

Hearn, D. Donald & Baker, M. Pauline. Computer Graphics for the IBM Personal Computer. (Illus.). 320p. 1983. text ed. 24.95 (ISBN 0-13-164335-5); pap. text ed. 19.95 (ISBN 0-13-164327-4). P-H.

Heath Company Staff. BASIC Programming. (Illus.). 564p. 1977. looseleaf with experiments 44.95 (ISBN 0-87119-083-4, EC-1100). Heathkit-Zenith Ed.

--How to Program Your Microcomputer in BASIC. (Illus.). 244p. 1980. pap. text ed. 19.95 (ISBN 0-87119-074-5, EB-6100); tchr's. ed 9.95 (ISBN 0-87119-076-1). Heathkit-Zenith Ed.

--Programming in Microsoft BASIC. (Illus.). 920p. 1981. looseleaf with 3 audiocassetes 99.95 (ISBN 0-87119-086-9, EC-1110). Heathkit-Zenith Ed.

Heid, James. Programming in Macintosh BASIC. 1985. pap. 24.95 (ISBN 0-912677-48-1). Ashton-Tate Bks.

Heilborn, John. Beginner's Guide to BASIC on the IBM PCjr. (Orig.). 1984. pap. cancelled (ISBN 0-942386-59-0). Compute Pubns.

Heilborn, John & Talbott, Ran. VIC-20 User Guide. 388p. (Orig.). 1983. pap. 15.95 (ISBN 0-07-047854-6, 54-6). Osborne-McGraw.

Heiserman, D. Programming in BASIC for Personal Computers. 1981. 22.95 (ISBN 0-13-730747-0); pap. 12.95 (ISBN 0-13-730739-X). P-H.

Heiserman, David L. Programming in BASIC for the IBM PC. (Illus.). 416p. 1984. text ed. 25.95 (ISBN 0-13-729450-6); pap. text ed. 16.95 (ISBN 0-13-729443-3). P-H.

Held, Gilbert. Apple II BASIC: A Quick Reference Guide. 1982. pap. 2.95 (ISBN 0-471-87039-0, Pub. by Wiley Pr); pap. 29.50 set of ten (ISBN 0-471-87043-9). Wiley.

--Atari BASIC: A Quick Reference Guide. 1982. pap. 29.50 shrink-wrapped set (ISBN 0-471-87044-7, Pub. by Wiley Pr); pap. 29.50 ten unit set. Wiley.

--Commodore 64 BASIC: A Quick Reference Guide. 1983. pap. 2.95 (ISBN 0-471-88240-2, Pub. by Wiley Pr); pap. 29.50 prepack of 10 (ISBN 0-471-88250-X). Wiley.

--IBM PC BASIC: A Quick Reference Guide. (Illus.). 80p. 1982. Set of 10. 29.50 (ISBN 0-471-87045-5). Wiley.

--VIC-20 BASIC: Quick Reference Guide. 1983. pap. 2.95 (ISBN 0-471-88238-0); pap. 29.50 prepack of 10 (ISBN 0-471-88248-8). Wiley.

Heller, David & Johnson, John. Dr. C. Wacko Presents Applesoft BASIC & the Whiz-Bang Miracle Machine. 1245p. 1985. pap. 12.95 (ISBN 0-201-11507-7). Addison-Wesley.

--Dr. C. Wacko Presents Atari BASIC & the Whiz-Bang Miracle Machine. 1245p. 1984. pap. 12.95 (ISBN 0-201-11491-7). Addison-Wesley.

--Computer Programming for the Compleat Idiot: Microsoft BASIC Edition. 2nd ed. (Illus.). 224p. 1984. 18.95 (ISBN 0-932538-11-8); pap. 10.95 (ISBN 0-932538-12-6). Design Ent SF.

--Computer Programming for the Complete Idiot. LC 79-53299. 128p. (Orig.). 1979. pap. 6.95 (ISBN 0-932538-04-5). Design Ent SF.

McDermott, Vern & Fisher, Diana. Advanced BASIC Step by Step. LC 83-24014. 1984. pap. 29.96 (ISBN 0-88175-011-5). Computer Sci.

--Advanced BASIC Step by Step Solution Manual. LC 84-17020. 1984. 15.00 (ISBN 0-88175-034-4). Computer Sci.

--Learning BASIC: Step by Step. LC 82-5046. 139p. 1982. text ed. 19.95 (ISBN 0-914894-49-8); tchr's guide 23.95 (ISBN 0-914894-33-1); examination package 30.00 (ISBN 0-914894-89-7). Computer Sci.

Mcghee, Fred H. Introduction to Programming in BASIC. (NAVEDTRA 10079-1. Rate Training Manual & Officer-Enlisted Correspondence Course Ser.). (Illus.). 184p. (Orig.). 1984. pap. 4.50 (ISBN 0-318-11737-1). Gov Printing Office.

McNichols, Charles. IBM PC Statistics: BASIC Programs & Applications. pap. text ed. 16.95 (ISBN 0-8359-3014-9). Reston.

McNichols, Charles W. IBM PC Statistics: Basic Programs & Applications. 1984. write for info. P-H.

McRitchie, Margaret. Programming in BASIC. 1982. pap. text ed. 23.95 (ISBN 0-03-061376-0). HR&W.

Mandell, Steven J. Complete BASIC Programming. (Illus.). 300p. 1984. pap. text ed. 21.95 (ISBN 0-314-77921-3); instrs.' manual & test bank avail. (ISBN 0-314-77922-1). West Pub.

Mandell, Steven L. Beginning BASIC for the Commodore 64. (Illus.). 150p. (Orig.). 1985. pap. text ed. 13.95 (ISBN 0-314-85264-6). West Pub.

--Computers & Data Processing: Concepts & Applications, with BASIC. 2nd ed. (Illus.). 600p. 1982. text ed. 25.95 (ISBN 0-314-63263-8); instr's. manual avail. (ISBN 0-314-63264-6); study guide avail. (ISBN 0-314-63265-4). West Pub.

--Computers & Data Processing Today with BASIC. (Illus.). 510p. pap. text ed. 24.95 (ISBN 0-314-70646-1). West Pub.

--Computers & Data Processing Today with BASIC. 2nd ed. (Illus.). 600p. 1985. pap. text ed. 27.95 (ISBN 0-314-96079-1). West Pub.

--Introduction to BASIC Programming. New ed. (Illus.). 160p. 1982. pap. 10.95 (ISBN 0-314-68082-9). West Pub.

--Introduction to BASIC Programming. 2nd ed. LC 84-17393. (Illus.). 176p. 1984. pap. text ed. 11.95 (ISBN 0-314-85263-8). West Pub.

Mansour, A. Fundamentals of Programming with BASIC. (Arabic.). 1986. pap. price not set (ISBN 0-471-82973-0). Wiley.

Marateck, Samuel. BASIC. 2nd ed. 1982. 17.00i (ISBN 0-12-470455-7); instr's manual 10.00i (ISBN 0-12-470456-5). Acad Pr.

Marateck, Samuel L. BASIC. 3rd ed. Date not set. text ed. price not set (ISBN 0-12-470465-4). Acad Pr.

Marcus, Jeffrey & Marcus, Marvin. Computing Without Mathematics: BASIC & Pascal Applications (School Edition) LC 85-4144. 300p. (Orig.). 1985. pap. 32.95 (ISBN 0-88175-110-3); pap. text ed. 21.95 (ISBN 0-88175-105-7); wkbk. 10.00 (ISBN 0-88175-115-4); diskette 15.00 (ISBN 0-88175-106-5). Computer Sci.

Marcus, Marvin. Discrete Mathematics: A Computational Approach Using BASIC. LC 82-14376. 329p. 1983. pap. 21.95 (ISBN 0-914894-38-2); Apple diskette 17.00 (ISBN 0-88175-001-8); IBM diskette 17.00 (ISBN 0-88175-091-3). Computer Sci.

--Solution Manual Discrete Mathematics: A Computational Approach Using BASIC. 92p. 1983. 15.00 (ISBN 0-88175-005-0). Computer Sci.

Masalski, William J. Beginning with BASIC Task Cards. Fanning, Tom, ed. (Computer Literacy Ser.). 1982. 9.95 (ISBN 0-88049-064-0, 7887). Milton Bradley Co.

Mason, J. BASIC Numerical Mathematics. (BASIC Ser.). (Illus.). 160p. (Orig.). 1983. pap. text ed. 19.95 (ISBN 0-408-01137-8). Butterworth.

Mason, John C. BASIC Matrix Methods. (BASIC Ser.). (Illus.). 160p. 1984. pap. 15.95 (ISBN 0-408-01390-7). Butterworth.

Mateosian, Richard. Inside BASIC Games. LC 80-53281. (Illus.). 347p. 1981. pap. 14.95 (ISBN 0-89588-055-5, B245). SYBEX.

Mau, Ernest E. Secrets of Better BASIC. 1984. 16.95 (ISBN 0-317-02386-1, 6254). Hayden.

Mears, Peter. Introduction to Apple Keyboarding. 1984. 39.95 (ISBN 0-03-064131-4); with diskette 40.45 (ISBN 0-03-064129-2). HR&W.

--Teach Yourself Apple BASIC. 12.95 (ISBN 0-201-05217-2); incl. disk 34.95 (ISBN 0-201-05218-0). Addison-Wesley.

--Teach Yourself Apple BASIC. 192p. 1983. write for info., spiral bound incl. disk. Addison-Wesley.

Mears, Peter & Raho, Louis. Basic Business BASIC: Using Microcomputers. LC 82-17881. (Computer Science Ser.). 300p. 1983. pap. text ed. 18.00 pub net (ISBN 0-534-01352-X). Brooks-Cole.

--Basic Business Basic: Using the Apple. 2nd ed. (Computer Science Ser.). 312p. 1986. pap. 218.00 (ISBN 0-534-05622-9). Brooks-Cole.

Mears, Peter M. & Raho, Louis E. Basic Business BASIC: Using Microcomputers. 304p. 1983. pap. write for info. Wadsworth Pub.

Miller, Alan R. BASIC Programs for Scientists & Engineers. LC 81-84003. (Scientists & Engineers Ser.: No. 2). (Illus.). 318p. 1981. pap. 16.95 (ISBN 0-89588-073-3, B240). SYBEX.

Miller, Deborah. Teach Yourself BASIC with the Commodore 64: A Beginner's Guide to Writing Programs. (Illus.). 192p. pap. cancelled (ISBN 0-89303-876-8). Brady Comm.

Miller, George L. Primarily Basic. 216p. (Orig.). pap. text ed. 12.95 (ISBN 0-8403-2620-3, 40262003). Kendall-Hunt.

Miller, Joan M. & Chaya, Ruth K. BASIC Programming for the Classroom & Home Teacher. 262p. 1982. pap. text ed. 17.95x (ISBN 0-8077-2728-8). Tchrs Coll.

Miller, Merl & Knecht, Ken. Microsoft BASIC 2.0 for the Apple Macintosh. LC 85-60684. (Illus.). 336p. (Orig.). 1985. pap. 16.95x (ISBN 0-933557-00-0). Merl Miller Assoc.

Mittleman, Don. BASIC Computing. 430p. 1982. pap. text ed. 19.95 (ISBN 0-15-504910-0, HC). HarBraceJ.

Mole. Basic Investment Appraisal. (Illus.). 160p. 1986. pap. 17.95. Butterworth.

Monro, Donald M. Basic BASIC: An Introduction to Programming. 98p. (Orig.). 1979. pap. text ed. 10.95 (ISBN 0-316-57840-1). Little.

--Interactive Computing with BASIC. 160p. 1974. pap. text ed. 16.95 (ISBN 0-7131-2488-1). E Arnold.

More BASIC for Beginners. (DECbooks). 166p. 1982. spiral bdg. 12.00 (ISBN 0-932376-51-7, AA-M587A-DP). Digital Pr.

Moriber, Harry A. Structured BASIC Programming. 512p. 1984. Additional supplements may be obtained from publisher. pap. text ed. 20.95 (ISBN 0-675-20106-3). Merrill.

Morrill, Harriet. BASIC Programming for the IBM Personal Computer. (Microcomputer Bookshelf Ser.). 175p. (Orig.). 1983. pap. 14.50 (ISBN 0-316-58402-9); tchr's. manual avail. (ISBN 0-316-58403-7). Little.

Morrill, Harriet H. Mini & Micro BASIC: Introducing Applesoft, Microsoft & BASIC Plus. (Microcomputer Bookshelf Ser.). 224p. 1983. pap. text ed. 14.50i (ISBN 0-316-58400-2); tchr's manual (ISBN 0-316-58401-0). Little.

Morton, Jeffrey B. Introduction to BASIC. (Illus.). 206p. 1977. pap. 14.95 (ISBN 0-916460-22-3). Matrix Pub.

Mosher, Frederick E. & Schneider, David I. Handbook of BASIC for the Commodore 64. LC 83-26618. 354p. 1984. pap. 14.95 (ISBN 0-89303-505-X). Brady Comm.

Moulton, Peter. Foundation of Programming Through BASIC. LC 78-21569. 1979. 26.45 (ISBN 0-471-03311-1); tchrs. manual avail. (ISBN 0-471-05414-3). Wiley.

Moursund, David. BASIC Programming for Computer Literacy. 1978. text ed. 24.95 (ISBN 0-07-043565-0). McGraw.

Mulcahy, Michael. Conversational BASIC: A Dialogue Approach to Programming. 304p. 1984. pap. 14.95 (ISBN 0-8436-1600-8). Van Nos Reinhold.

Mulcahy, Michael E. Experiencing BASIC. Fanning, Tom, ed. (Computer Literacy Ser.). 1981. task cards 10.95 (ISBN 0-88049-060-8, 7396); duplicating masters 6.95. Milton Bradley Co.

Mullen, Brian & Rosenthal, Robert. BASIC Meta-Analysis: Procedures & Programs. 128p. 1985. text ed. write for info. (ISBN 0-89859-619-X). L Erlbaum Assocs.

Mullish, H. & Kruger, D. Applesoft BASIC: From the Ground Up. (Illus.). 240p. 1983. pap. 10.95 (ISBN 0-07-044034-4, BYTE Bks). McGraw.

Mullish, Henry. A Basic Approach to Structured BASIC. 2nd ed. LC 82-11073. 375p. 1982. pap. 22.95 (ISBN 0-471-06071-2); pap. 17.95. Wiley.

Mullish, Henry & Kruger, Dov. At Home with BASIC: The Simon & Schuster Guide to Programming the Commodore 64. 192p. 1984. pap. 12.95 spiral bdg. (ISBN 0-671-49861-4, Pub. by Computer Bks). S&S.

Myers, Roy & Schneider, David. Handbook of Applesoft BASIC for the Apple II & IIe. (Illus.). 352p. 1984. pap. 16.95 (ISBN 0-89303-504-1). Brady Comm.

Nashelsky, Louis & Boylestad, Robert. BASIC for Electronic & Computer Technology. (Illus.). 480p. 1986. text ed. 26.95 (ISBN 0-13-060195-0). P-H.

--IBM PC XT: BASIC Programming & Applications. (Illus.). 304p. 1984. pap. 14.95 (ISBN 0-13-448325-1); incl. disk 39.95 (ISBN 0-13-448341-3). P-H.

--IBM PCjr BASIC Programming & Application & Including LOGO. (Illus.). 352p. 1985. 14.95 (ISBN 0-13-448234-4); write for info. incl. disk (ISBN 0-13-448226-3); disk. 24.95 (ISBN 0-13-448242-5). P-H.

National Computer Centre Staff & Milan, Michael. A Young Persons Guide to BBC BASIC. 110p. 1983. pap. 7.75x (ISBN 0-471-87935-5). Wiley.

National Computing Centre Ltd. Elements of BASIC. (Computers & the Professional Ser.). 100p. 1979. pap. 25.00x (ISBN 0-85012-118-3). Intl Pubns Serv.

Necessary, James R. The Necessary Steps to BASIC: A Modular Approach. 168p. 1982. pap. text ed. 6.95x (ISBN 0-917974-90-5). Waveland Pr.

Nevison, John M. Little Book of BASIC Style: How to Write a Program You Can Read. LC 77-88882. (Illus.). 160p. 1978. pap. text ed. 7.95 (ISBN 0-201-05247-4). Addison-Wesley.

Nickerson, Robert C. Fundamentals of Programming in BASIC. 400p. (Orig.). 1981. pap. text ed. 23.95 (ISBN 0-316-60646-4); tchr's ed. avail. (ISBN 0-316-60647-2). Little.

Nicks, J E. BASIC Programming Solutions for Manufacturing. (Illus.). 298p. 1982. 32.00 (ISBN 0-87263-076-5). SME.

Noonan, Larry. The Basic BASIC-English Dictionary: For the Apple, IBM-PC, Commodore 64, VIC-20, Atari, TRS-80, TRS-80 Color Computer, TI 99-4A, PET & Timex-Sinclair. (Illus.). 288p. 1985. pap. 19.95 (ISBN 0-88056-354-0). Dilithium Pr.

--Basic BASIC-English Dictionary for the Apple, PET & TRS-80. (Illus.). 154p. 1983. 17.95 (ISBN 0-8306-1521-0, 1521). TAB Bks.

Norling, Richard. Using Macintosh BASIC. 496p. (Orig.). 1985. pap. 17.95 (ISBN 0-07-881157-0, 157-0). Osborne-McGraw.

Norman, Robin. Timex-Sinclair 1000 ZX-81 BASIC Book. LC 82-50022. 192p. 1983. pap. 12.95 (ISBN 0-672-21957-3, 21957). Sams.

North, Alan. Atari Computer Program Writing Workbook. 96p. 1983. 4.95 (ISBN 0-86668-814-5). ARCsoft.

Oatey, M. J. & Payne, C. BASIC: A Short Self-Instructional Course. 64p. 1984. pap. 7.95 (ISBN 0-273-01940-6). Pitman Pub MA.

O'Malley, Timothy J. Twenty-Five Graphics Programs in Microsoft BASIC. (Illus.). 160p. 1983. 17.95 (ISBN 0-8306-0133-3, 1533); pap. 11.95 (ISBN 0-8306-0533-9). TAB Bks.

One Hundred One BASIC Computer Games. (DECbooks). 249p. 1975. pap. 10.00 (ISBN 0-932376-24-X, EB-04873-DP). Digital Pr.

Orilia, L. Structured BASIC. 384p. 1984. 22.95 (ISBN 0-07-047839-2). McGraw.

Osborne, Adam, et al. CBASIC User Guide. 212p. 1981. pap. 17.95 (ISBN 0-07-931061-3, 61-3). Osborne-McGraw.

Page, Edward. Timex-Sinclair Computer Games Programs. 96p. 1983. 7.95 (ISBN 0-86668-026-8). ARCsoft.

--Timex-Sinclair Computer Program Writing Workbook. 96p. 1983. 4.95 (ISBN 0-86668-810-2). ARCsoft.

Pantumsinchai, Pricha & Hassan, M. Zia. BASIC Programs for Production & Operations Management. (Illus.). 448p. 1983. pap. 18.95 (ISBN 0-686-38834-8). P H.

Parker, A. J. VS BASIC for Business: For the IBM 360-370. 1982. pap. text ed. 12.95 (ISBN 0-8359-8439-7). Reston.

Parker, Alan. Apple BASIC for Business for the Apple II. 2nd ed. 1984. pap. text ed. 17.95 (ISBN 0-8359-0101-7); instr's manual avail. (ISBN 0-8359-0102-5). Reston.

Parker, Alan & Stewart, John. Accountant's BASIC Programming for the Apple II. 1983. 16.95 (ISBN 0-8359-0047-9). Reston.

--The Executive Guide to the Apple Computer, BASIC: Programming & VisiCalc. 1984. incl. disk 59.95 (ISBN 0-8359-1808-4). Reston.

Parker, Alan J. BASIC for Business for the IBM Personal Computer. 1983. text ed. 21.95 (ISBN 0-8359-0356-7); pap. text ed. 17.95 (ISBN 0-8359-0355-9). Reston.

--BASIC for Business for the VAX & PDP-11. 2nd ed. 1983. text ed. 22.95 (ISBN 0-8359-0358-3); pap. text ed. 18.95 (ISBN 0-8359-0357-5); instr's Manual avail. (ISBN 0-8359-0360-5). Reston.

Parker, Alan J. & Stewart, John F. Applesoft BASIC for the Business Executive. 1984. pap. 15.95 (ISBN 0-8359-0075-4). Reston.

Parker, Charles S. Understanding Computers & Data Processing: Today & Tomorrow with BASIC. LC 83-22724. 630p. 1984. 26.95x (ISBN 0-03-063427-X). HR&W.

Parry, John. Getting Started with BASIC. 144p. 1984. pap. 12.95 (ISBN 0-946576-15-7, Pub. by Phoenix Pub). David & Charles.

Passman, Marjorie. First Steps with BASIC: A Gentle Introduction to Programming. 1984. pap. 16.95 (ISBN 0-8359-2056-9). Reston.

Payne, Donald T. IBM BASIC. 234p. 1983. 22.95 (ISBN 0-13-448696-X, Spec); pap. 15.95 (ISBN 0-13-448688-9). P-H.

Peapell, P. N. & Belk, J. A. Basic Materials Studies. 160p. 1985. pap. text ed. 15.95 (ISBN 0-408-01374-5). Butterworth.

Pearson, O. R. Programming with BASIC: A Practical Approach. 496p. 1986. price not set (ISBN 0-07-049071-6). McGraw.

Peckham, H. Hands-on BASIC: For the Apple II Plus Computer. (Personal Programming Ser.). 1982. pap. 23.95 (ISBN 0-07-049179-8, BYTE Bks). McGraw.

--Structured BASIC for the IBM PC. (Personal Programming Ser.). 320p. 1985. 22.00 (ISBN 0-07-049162-3). McGraw.

Peckham, H. D. Hands-on BASIC for the Commodore 64. 344p. 1984. 23.95 (ISBN 0-07-049154-2). McGraw.

--Hands-on BASIC for the TI 99-4A. 352p. 1984. 22.00 (ISBN 0-07-049155-0). McGraw.

Peckham, Herbert. Hands-on BASIC for the Atari 400, 800 & 1200XL Computers. (Personal Programming Ser.). 352p. 1983. 23.95 (ISBN 0-07-049194-1, BYTE Bks). McGraw.

--Hands-on BASIC for the DEC Professional Computer. 312p. 1984. pap. 22.00 (ISBN 0-932376-66-5, EY-00033-DP). Digital Pr.

Peckham, Herbert D. BASIC: A Hands-on Method. 2nd ed. (Illus.). 320p. 1981. pap. text ed. 23.95 (ISBN 0-07-049160-7, BYTE Bks). McGraw.

--Hands-on BASIC: For the IBM Personal Computer. LC 82-81497. 352p. 1982. pap. text ed. 23.95 (ISBN 0-07-049178-X, BYTE Bks). McGraw.

--Hands-on BASIC with a PET. (Illus.). 1982. pap. 23.95 (ISBN 0-07-049157-7, BYTE Bks). McGraw.

--Programming in BASIC with the TI Home Computer. 1979. pap. text ed. 23.95 (ISBN 0-07-049156-9, BYTE Bks). McGraw.

Peddicord, Richard G. Beginning BASIC on the Commodore 64. 187p. 1984. 19.95 (ISBN 0-88284-306-0). Alfred Pub.

--Understanding Apple BASIC. (Handy Guide Ser.). 64p. (Orig.). 1984. pap. 3.50 (ISBN 0-88284-246-3). Alfred Pub.

--Understanding BASIC. rev. ed. (An Alfred Handy Guide Ser.). 1982. 3.50 (ISBN 0-88284-146-7). Alfred Pub.

--Understanding Commodore 64 BASIC. (Handy Guide Ser.). 64p. (Orig.). 1984. pap. 3.50. Alfred Pub.

Peluso, Anthony P., et al. Basic BASIC Programming: Self-Instructional Manual & Text. (Computer Science Ser.). 1971. pap. 21.95 (ISBN 0-201-05845-6). Addison-Wesley.

Peters, James F. & Sallam, Hamed. Business Computing: A Structured Approach to BASIC on the PDP-11 & VAX-11. 1984. pap. 21.95 (ISBN 0-8359-0549-7). Reston.

Petras, Shirley J. Business Programming Using Vax-11 BASIC. 180p. (Orig.). 1983. pap. text ed. 7.90x (ISBN 0-9606666-4-8). Greenfield Pubns.

Poirot, James, et al. Computer Science with Structured BASIC. 338p. 1984. pap. 18.95 (ISBN 0-88408-279-2). Sterling Swift.

Poirot, James L. Microcomputer Systems & Apple BASIC. (Illus.). 150p. (Orig.). 1980. pap. 8.95 (ISBN 0-88408-136-2). Sterling Swift.

Poirot, James L. & Adams, R. Clark. Forty Easy Steps to Programming in BASIC & LOGO. 64p. 1984. pap. 5.95 (ISBN 0-88408-275-X); tchr's guide 4.95 (ISBN 0-88408-276-8). Sterling Swift.

Poirot, James L. & Retzlaff, Don. How to Program in BASIC: Apple II Edition. 1979. pap. 69.00 disks (ISBN 0-317-05325-6). Sterling Swift.

--How to Program in BASIC: PET Commodore Edition. 1979. pap. 69.00 disks (ISBN 0-317-05323-X). Sterling Swift.

--How to Program in BASIC: TRS-80 Edition. 1979. pap. 69.00 disks (ISBN 0-317-05324-8). Sterling Swift.

Polen-Jannazo. A KASE for Microcomputers: A First Course in Apple BASIC. 240p. 1983. pap. text ed. 21.95 (ISBN 0-8403-3171-1). Kendall-Hunt.

--A KASE for Microcomputers: A First Course in IBM BASIC. 336p. 1984. pap. text ed. 21.95 (ISBN 0-8403-3334-X). Kendall-Hunt.

Porter, Alan G. & Rezmer, Martin G. BASIC Subroutines for the Apple II & IIe. 240p. 12.95 (ISBN 0-201-05663-1); incl. disk 29.95 (ISBN 0-201-05692-5); IBM 29.95 (ISBN 0-201-05658-5). Addison-Wesley.

Porter, Kent. Beginning with BASIC: An Introduction to Computer Programming. (Computer Language Library). 300p. 1984. 10.95 (ISBN 0-452-25491-4, Plume). NAL.

Price, Jonathan. The Instant Expert's Guide to IBM BASIC. Dvorak, John C., ed. (Dvorak's Instant Expert Ser.). 192p. (Orig.). 1984. 7.95 (ISBN 0-440-53940-4). Dell.

Price, Wilson T. Fundamentals of Computers & Data Processing with BASIC. 430p. 1983. pap. text ed. 23.95 (ISBN 0-03-063231-5). HR&W.

--Programming the IBM Personal Computer: Business BASIC. 318p. 1984. pap. text ed. 17.95 (ISBN 0-03-063746-5). HR&W.

--Using Business BASIC. 267p. 1983. pap. text ed. 21.95 (ISBN 0-03-063176-9). HR&W.

Programming Techniques for Level II BASIC. 142p. 4.95 (ISBN 0-317-05252-7, 62-2062). Radio Shack.

Purdum, Jack J. BASIC-80 & CP-M: Digital Research BASIC-80-Microsoft. 288p. 1983. pap. text ed. write for info. (ISBN 0-02-397020-0). Macmillan.

Quasney, James S. & Maniotes, John. BASIC Fundamentals & Style. (Programming Language Ser.). (Illus.). 1984. pap. text ed. 23.75 (ISBN 0-87835-138-8); instr's manual 7.95 (ISBN 0-87835-141-8). Boyd & Fraser.

--Complete BASIC: For the Short Course. (Illus.). 196p. 1985. pap. text ed. 10.00 (ISBN 0-87835-151-5); tchr's. ed. avail. (ISBN 0-87835-158-2). Boyd & Fraser.

--Standard BASIC Programming: For Business & Management Applications. LC 80-65168. (Illus.). 428p. 1980. pap. text ed. 18.75x (ISBN 0-87835-081-0). Boyd & Fraser.

Regena, C. Compute's BASIC Programs for Small Computers: Things to Do in 4k or Less. 267p. (Orig.). 1984. pap. 12.95 (ISBN 0-942386-38-8). Compute Pubns.

Reh, Jane G. Commodore's Handbook of Simons' BASIC. (Illus.). 224p. 1985. pap. 12.95 (ISBN 0-89303-419-3). Brady Comm.

Reisinger, John M. A-Plus Programming in Atari BASIC. 1984. pap. 15.95 (ISBN 0-8359-0004-5). Reston.

Rensin, Joseph K. & Goldstein, Larry J. BASICally Kaypro: Programming the 2, 4 & 10. (Illus.). 288p. 1984. 16.95 (ISBN 0-89303-360-X). Brady Comm.

Rice, Jean & Henke, James. Friendly BASIC: Commodore 64 Version. 1984. cancelled. Reston.

--Friendly BASIC: For the Apple II, Apple IIplus, Apple IIe & Apple IIc. 15.95 (ISBN 0-8359-2103-4). Reston.

Rice, John R. Introduction to Computing with BASIC. LC 73-2438. 1973. text ed. 17.95 (ISBN 0-03-086300-7, HoltC). HR&W.

Richter, Michael. Advanced BASIC Programming for the Commodore 64 & Other Commodore Computers. LC 83-15604. 134p. 1983. pap. 12.95 (ISBN 0-89303-302-2); diskette 25.00 (ISBN 0-89303-299-9). Brady Comm.

Rienhardt, Mona. Programmer's Desk Reference for Commodore 64 BASIC. (Illus.). 176p. 1985. pap. 15.95 (ISBN 0-89303-770-2). Brady Comm.

Rob. Big Blue BASIC: Programming the IBM-PC & Compatibles. write for info (ISBN 0-534-04578-2). Wadsworth Pub.

Roberts, Don. Two Hundred Twenty-two BASIC Computer Programs for Home, School & Office. 256p. 1984. 9.95 (ISBN 0-86668-039-X). ARCsoft.

--Universal BASIC Computer Program Writing Workbook. 96p. 1983. 4.95 (ISBN 0-86668-819-6). ARCsoft.

Rogers, Donald W. BASIC Microcomputing & Biostatistics. LC 81-85465. (Contemporary Instrumentation & Analysis Ser.). 304p. 1983. 39.50 (ISBN 0-89603-015-6). Humana.

Rosenfelder, Lewis. BASIC Disk I-O Faster & Better & Other Mysteries. 432p. 1984. 29.95 (ISBN 0-936200-09-X). Blue Cat.

--BASIC Faster & Better & Other Mysteries. (TRS-80 Information Ser.: Vol. 4). (Illus.). 290p. (Orig.). 1981. pap. text ed. 29.95 (ISBN 0-936200-03-0). Blue Cat.

--IBM BASIC Faster & Better. Evans, Carl M. & Trapp, Charles, eds. (IBM PC Information Ser.: Vol. 1). (Illus.). 392p. 1984. pap. text ed. 19.95 (ISBN 0-936200-52-9). Blue Cat.

Ross, Steven M. BASIC Programming for Educators. (Illus.). 400p. 1986. pap. text ed. 21.95 (ISBN 0-13-066127-9). P H.

Rowley, Thomas C. Atari BASIC: Learning by Using. 73p. 7.95 (ISBN 0-936200-35-9, 164). Elcomp.

Rowley, Thomas E. Atari BASIC: Learning by Using. 73p. 7.95 (ISBN 0-936200-35-9). Blue Cat.

Ruckdeschel, Fred. BASIC Scientific Subroutines, 2 vols. 1981. Vol. 1. 27.95 (ISBN 0-07-054201-5); Vol. 2. 27.95 (ISBN 0-07-054202-3). McGraw.

Ruder. Business Program Development with IBM PC BASIC. 1986. write for info. (ISBN 0-471-82636-7). Wiley.

Rugg, Tom & Feldman, Phil. More Than Thirty-Two BASIC Programs for the Commodore 64. (Illus.). 350p. 1983. pap. 19.95 (ISBN 0-88056-112-2); incl. disk 39.95 (ISBN 0-88056-180-7); incl. cassette 39.95 (ISBN 0-88056-183-1). Dilithium Pr.

--More Than Thirty-two BASIC Programs for the IBM Personal Computer. (Illus.). 350p. 1983. pap. 19.95 (ISBN 0-88056-078-9); incl. disk 39.95 (ISBN 0-88056-171-8). Dilithium Pr.

--Thirty-Two BASIC Programs for the Apple Computer. LC 80-68533. (Illus.). 280p. 1983. pap. 19.95 (ISBN 0-918398-34-7); incl. disk 39.95 (ISBN 0-88056-151-3). Dilithium Pr.

--Thirty-Two BASIC Programs for the Atari Computer. (Illus.). 288p. 1983. pap. 19.95 (ISBN 0-88056-084-3); incl. disk 39.95 (ISBN 0-88056-172-6). Dilithium Pr.

--Thirty-Two BASIC Programs for the Coleco Adam. 288p. 1984. pap. 19.95 (ISBN 0-88056-141-6); incl. disk 39.95 (ISBN 0-88056-201-3). Dilithium Pr.

--Thirty-Two BASIC Programs for the TI 99-4A. (Illus.). 288p. 1983. pap. 19.95 (ISBN 0-88056-136-X); incl. cassette 39.95 (ISBN 0-88056-188-2); incl. disk 39.95 (ISBN 0-88056-203-X). Dilithium Pr.

--Thirty-Two BASIC Programs for the TRS-80 (Level II) Computer. LC 79-56399. 270p. 1983. pap. 19.95 (ISBN 0-918398-27-4); incl. disk 39.95; incl. cassette 39.95. Dilithium Pr.

Rugg, Tom, et al. More Than Thirty-Two BASIC Programs for the VIC-20 Computer. LC 83-5198. (Illus.). 270p. 1983. pap. 19.95 (ISBN 0-88056-181-5); incl. cassette 39.95 (ISBN 0-88056-059-2). Dilithium Pr.

Rushton, Jeremy. Pascal with Your BASIC Micro. 136p. 1983. pap. 9.95 (ISBN 0-672-22036-9, 22036). Sams.

Russell, Clyde B. Introduction to Computer Programming with BASIC & the Apple. 458p. 1984. pap. 22.95x (ISBN 0-89787-404-8). Gorsuch Scarisbrick.

Sack, John & Gabriel, Judy M. Entering BASIC. 2nd ed. 160p. 1980. pap. text ed. 14.95 (ISBN 0-574-21270-1, 13-4270). SRA.

Sagan, Hans & Meyer, Carl D., Jr. Ten Easy Pieces: Creative Programming for Fun & Profit. 192p. 1980. pap. 10.50 (ISBN 0-8104-5160-3, 5160). Hayden.

Sage, Edwin R. Fun & Games with the Computer. 351p. 1975. pap. text ed. 14.95 (ISBN 0-87567-075-X). Entelek.

Sanders, D. More About BASIC: Supplement. 352p. 1983. pap. 7.95 (ISBN 0-07-054664-9). McGraw.

Sanders, William B. The Computer of the Century: Radio Shack Model 100. (Orig.). 1984. pap. 19.95 (ISBN 0-88190-343-4, BO343). Datamost.

--The Elementary Timex-Sinclair. (Elementary Ser.). (Illus.). 192p. (Orig.). 1983. pap. text ed. 14.95 (ISBN 0-88190-058-3, B0058). Datamost.

Sass, C. Joseph. BASIC Programming & Applications. 368p. 1976. pap. text ed. 27.43 scp (ISBN 0-205-05422-6, 2054221); scp answer bk. 5.04 (ISBN 0-205-05423-4, 205423X). Allyn.

--A Structured Approach to BASIC Programming. 1980. pap. text ed. 27.43 (ISBN 0-205-06726-3, 2067269); solutions manual free (ISBN 0-205-06727-1). Allyn.

Savage, Earl R. BASIC Programmer's Notebook. LC 81-84279. 112p. 1981. pap. 14.95 (ISBN 0-672-21841-0, 21841). Sams.

Savic, Dusko. BASIC Interactive Graphics. (Illus.). 176p. 1985. pap. text ed. 15.95 (ISBN 0-408-01522-5). Butterworth.

Sawatzky, Jasper J. & Chen, Shu-Jen. Programming in BASIC -Plus. LC 80-27869. 273p. 1981. pap. 23.00 (ISBN 0-471-07729-1); sol. man. avail. (ISBN 0-471-86867-1). Wiley.

--Programming in BASIC-PLUS: VAX-11 BASIC Compatible. 2nd ed. 452p. 1985. pap. 19.95 (ISBN 0-471-88655-6). Wiley.

Schat, Stan. Business & Home Applications for the Macintosh Using Microsoft BASIC. 224p. 1984. pap. 14.95 (ISBN 0-89303-403-7). Brady Comm.

Schechter, Gil. Learn BASIC Programming in Fourteen Days on Your Commodore 64. LC 84-50052. 12.95 (ISBN 0-672-22279-5). Sams.

Schneider, David I. Handbook of BASIC for the IBM PC. LC 83-15508. 512p. 1983. pap. 19.95 (ISBN 0-89303-506-8); bk. & diskette 44.95 (ISBN 0-89303-508-4); diskette 25.00 (ISBN 0-89303-507-6). Brady Comm.

--Handbook of BASIC for the IBM PC. rev. & enl. ed. (Illus.). 592p. 1985. pap. 24.95 (ISBN 0-89303-510-6). Brady Comm.

Schneiderman, Ben. Let's Learn BASIC: A Kid's Introduction to BASIC Programming on the IBM Personal Computers. (Let's Learn BASIC Ser.). 1984. pap. 8.95 (ISBN 0-316-78726-4). Little.

Schoman, Kenneth E., Jr. The BASIC Workbook: Creative Techniques for Beginning Programmers. 1977. pap. text ed. 9.95 (ISBN 0-8104-5104-2). Hayden.

Schreiber, Linda M. Atari Programming... with Fifty-five Programs. (Illus.). 256p. (Orig.). 1982. 21.95 (ISBN 0-8306-1385-4); pap. 14.50 (ISBN 0-8306-1485-0, 1485). TAB Bks.

Schwartz, Arleen G. & Jabarin, Dorothy. The Book of BASIC. (Orig.). 1984. pap. 12.95 (ISBN 0-942386-61-2). Compute Pubns.

Schwartz, Ron & Basso, David. Statistical Programs in BASIC. 1984. cancelled (ISBN 0-8359-7107-4); pap. text ed. 16.95 (ISBN 0-8359-7106-6). Reston.

Searle, Bill. Introduction to BASIC with the TI 99-4A. cancelled 9.95 (ISBN 0-89303-571-8). Brady Comm.

Searle, Bill & Jones, Donna. BASIC for the Apple IIe & IIc. (Illus.). 352p. 1985. pap. 16.95 (ISBN 0-89303-337-5). Brady Comm.

Searle, W. & Jones, D. Smart BASIC for the Adam. (Illus.). 384p. 1984. pap. 12.95 (ISBN 0-89303-846-6). Brady Comm.

Sebesta, Robert W. & Kraushaar, James M. Computer Concepts, Structured Programming & Interactive BASIC. LC 82-81084. (Illus.). 280p. 1982. pap. text ed. 16.95x (ISBN 0-938188-04-6). Mitchell Pub.

Seeborg, Irmtraud & Ma, Cynthia. BASIC for the DEC-10. LC 82-13957. 204p. 1982. pap. 12.95x (ISBN 0-910554-37-4). Engineering.

Seiden, Eric A. & Parisse, David A. LBASIC Reference Manual. Dar Systems International Staff, ed. 65p. (Orig.). 1984. spiral bd. 24.95 (ISBN 0-916163-51-2); incl. Software for Apple Computer 99.95 (ISBN 0-916163-46-6). Dar Syst.

Seiter, Charles & Weiss, Robert. Pascal for BASIC Programmers. (Microbooks Popular Ser.). 224p. 1982. pap. 10.95 (ISBN 0-201-06577-0). Addison-Wesley.

Shaffer & Shaffer, Applied Research & Development, Inc. BASIC Booster Library: IBM-PC. (BASIC Booster Ser.). 1985. pap. 29.95 incl. disk (ISBN 0-912677-26-0). Ashton-Tate Bks.

Shane, June G. Programming for Microcomputers: Apple II BASIC. LC 83-8163. 432p. 1984. pap. text ed. 16.95 (ISBN 0-395-35206-1); Grid sheet bklt. 3.95 (ISBN 0-395-35207-X). HM.

Sharpe, William F. & Jacob, Nancy L. BASIC: An Introduction to Computer Programming Using the BASIC Language. 3rd ed. LC 78-72148. (Illus.). 1979. 17.00 (ISBN 0-02-928380-9); pap. text ed. 7.95 (ISBN 0-02-928390-6). Free Pr.

Shelly, Gary B. & Cashman, Thomas J. Introduction to BASIC Programming. 424p. 1982. pap. text ed. 23.95 (ISBN 0-88236-118-X). Anaheim Pub Co.

--Introduction to BASIC Programming. (Illus.). 320p. 1983. pap. text ed. 10.95x wkbk. & study guide (ISBN 0-88236-119-8). Anaheim Pub Co.

Shelly, Gary B., et al. Apple Supplement to Accompany Introduction to BASIC Programming. 64p. 1985. pap. text ed. 6.95 (ISBN 0-88236-132-5). Anaheim Pub Co.

Shipman, Carl. How to Program Your Commodore 64: BASIC for Beginners. 336p. 1984. pap. 12.95 (ISBN 0-89586-310-3). H P Bks.

--How to Program Your IBM PC: Advanced BASIC Programming. 192p. 1984. ringbinder 14.95 (ISBN 0-89586-264-6). H P Bks.

--How to Program Your IBM PC: BASIC for Beginners. 192p. 1983. 14.95 (ISBN 0-89586-263-8). H P Bks.

Shneiderman, Ben. Let's Learn BASIC: A Kid's Introduction to BASIC Programming on the Atari Home Computers. (Orig.). 1984. pap. 8.95 (ISBN 0-316-78722-1). Little.

--Let's Learn BASIC: An Introduction to Programming the Commodore 64. (Microcomputer Bookself Ser.). 175p. (Orig.). 1984. pap. 8.95 (ISBN 0-316-78725-6). Little.

Shoemaker, Tom. Information Management with BASIC for the IBM PC. 1984. 16.95 (ISBN 0-8359-3076-9); incl. disk 34.95 (ISBN 0-317-06173-9). Reston.

Sickler, Albert N. Using & Programming the ZX-81 & TS-1000, Including Ready-to-Run Programs. (Illus.). 168p. 1983. 14.95 (ISBN 0-8306-0117-1); pap. 8.95 (ISBN 0-8306-0617-3, 1617). TAB Bks.

Silver, Gerald A. & Silver, Myrna. Simplified BASIC Programming for Microcomputers. 288p. 1984. text ed. 15.34i (ISBN 0-06-046162-4, HarpC). Har-Row.

Simon, David. BASIC from the Ground Up. (Computer Programming Ser.). 1978. pap. 13.95 (ISBN 0-8104-5760-1); pap. text ed. 12.95 (ISBN 0-8104-5117-4). Hayden.

Simon, David E. BASIC from the Ground Up. Hayden. 1983. 13.95 (ISBN 0-317-04690-X). Hayden.

--IBM BASIC from the Ground Up. 1984. 15.95 (ISBN 0-317-02352-7, 6350). Hayden.

Simpson, Henry. Serious Programming for Your Apple II, IIe, IIc. (Illus.). 192p. (Orig.). 1985. 18.95 (ISBN 0-8306-0960-1, 1960); pap. 12.95 (ISBN 0-8306-1960-7). Tab Bks.

--True BASIC: A Complete Manual. (Illus.). 208p. 1985. 22.95 (ISBN 0-8306-0970-9, 1970); pap. 14.95 (ISBN 0-8306-1970-4). TAB Bks.

Sinclair, Ian. Working with MSX BASIC. (Illus.). 160p. 1984. pap. 17.95 (ISBN 0-00-383103-5, Pub. by Collins England). Sheridan.

Singer, Bernard M. Programming in BASIC, with Applications. 1973. text ed. 26.90 (ISBN 0-07-057480-4). McGraw.

Siragusa, Chris. Introduction to BASIC: A Structured Approach. 250p. 1980. write for info. (ISBN 0-87150-289-5, 2282, Prindle). PWS Pubs.

Siragusa, Chris R. Introduction to Programming BASIC: A Structured Approach. 2nd ed. 340p. 1983. pap. text ed. write for info. (ISBN 0-87150-386-7, 8020). PWS Pubs.

Smith, Brian R. Introduction to Computer Programming: BASIC for Beginners. 1982. write for info. Ed Devel Corp.

Society of Manufacturing Engineers. BASIC Programming Solutions for Manufacturing. 300p. 1982. 45.95 (ISBN 0-13-066332-8). P-H.

Softsync & West, Gary. Joy of BASIC for the Adam. (Illus.). 352p. pap. cancelled (ISBN 0-89303-589-0). Brady Comm.

Sondak, Norman & Hatch, Richard. Using BASIC on the CYBER. 272p. 1982. pap. text ed. 20.95 (ISBN 0-574-21395-3, 13-4395); instr. guide avail. (ISBN 0-574-21396-1, 13-4396). SRA.

Sordillo, Donald A. The Personal Computer BASIC(s) Reference Manual. (Illus.). 320p. 1983. pap. text ed. 18.95 (ISBN 0-13-658047-5). P-H.

--The Personal Computer BASIC(S) Reference Manual, Bk. II. LC 83-9463. (Illus.). 300p. 1985. pap. text ed. 18.95 (ISBN 0-13-658428-4). P-H.

Spear, Bob. BASIC for Baseball Buffs. 1985. pap. write for info. (ISBN 0-912083-14-X). Diamond Communications.

Speelhoffer, Thomas J. BASICally Speaking: A Beginner's Workbook. 1982. 5.25 (ISBN 0-318-01169-7). J W Walch.

Spencer, Donald. Sixty Challenging Problems with BASIC Solutions. LC 79-50793. 1979. pap. 9.95 (ISBN 0-8104-5180-8). Hayden.

Spencer, Donald D. BASIC: A Unit for Secondary Schools. 2nd ed. 1980. pap. 4.50x (ISBN 0-89218-039-0); tchr's. Manual 9.95x (ISBN 0-89218-041-2). Camelot Pub.

--BASIC Programming. LC 82-17689. 1983. 14.95 (ISBN 0-89218-062-5). Camelot Pub.

--BASIC Programming. LC 82-17689. (Illus.). 224p. 1983. pap. 8.95 (ISBN 0-684-18039-1, ScribT). Scribner.

--BASIC Quiz Book. 1983. 5.95x (ISBN 0-89218-076-5). Camelot Pub.

--BASIC Workbook for Microcomputers. 1983. 7.95x (ISBN 0-89218-040-4). Camelot Pub.

--Data Processing: An Introduction with BASIC. 2nd ed. 576p. 1982. pap. text ed. 23.95 (ISBN 0-675-09854-8); study guide 9.95 (ISBN 0-675-09803-3). Additional supplements can be obtained from publisher. Merrill.

--Game Playing with BASIC. 1977. pap. 12.50 (ISBN 0-8104-5109-3). Hayden.

--Guide to BASIC Programming. 2nd ed. 1975. text ed. 22.95 (ISBN 0-201-07106-1). Addison-Wesley.

--Problem Solving with BASIC. LC 82-17875. (Illus.). 160p. 1984. pap. 7.95 (ISBN 0-684-18036-7, ScribT). Scribner.

--Problem Solving with BASIC. 1983. pap. 5.95x (ISBN 0-317-04725-6). Camelot Pub.

--Programming the TRS-80 Pocket Computer. (Illus.). 176p. 1982. pap. text ed. 8.95 (ISBN 0-13-730531-1). P-H.

--Visual Masters for BASIC Programming. 2nd ed. 1982. 9.95x (ISBN 0-89218-049-8). Camelot Pub.

Stair, Ralph, Jr. & Janaro, Ralph. Essentials of BASIC Programming. 1981. pap. 8.95x (ISBN 0-256-02993-8); study guide 9.95x (ISBN 0-256-02485-5). Irwin.

Stair, Ralph M., Jr. Programming in BASIC. rev. ed. 1982. pap. 17.95x (ISBN 0-256-02611-4). Irwin.

--Programming in BASIC: Structured Programming, Cases, Applications & Modules. 3rd ed. Fetter, Robert B. & McMillan, Claude, eds. LC 84-81735. (Irwin Series in Information & Decision Sciences). (Illus.). 454p. 1985. pap. 22.95x (ISBN 0-256-03213-0). Irwin.

Stat, Robert W. Macintosh BASIC: A Beginner's Guide to Structured Programming. 280p. 1985. pap. 14.95 (ISBN 0-88693-164-9). Banbury Bks.

Stauffer, Marge & Grove, Maria. The Basis of BASIC. 1982. 4.50 (ISBN 0-317-04627-6). Educ Insights.

Stedman, Robert & Cosgrove, Ron. Kids BASIC for the TI 99-4A. cancelled 9.95 (ISBN 0-89303-603-X). Brady Comm.

Steiner, John P. The Standard BASIC Dictionary for Programming. LC 84-11436. 256p. 1983. 23.95 (ISBN 0-13-841560-9, Busn); pap. 19.95 (ISBN 0-13-841552-8). P-H.

Stern, Robert A. & Stern, Nancy. Concepts of Information Processing with BASIC. LC 82-17630. 216p. 1983. pap. text ed. 18.45x (ISBN 0-471-87617-8). Wiley.

Sternberg, Charles D. BASIC Computer Programs for the Home. 336p. 1984. 13.95 (7100); incl. 2 apple disks 39.95 (ISBN 0-8104-5154-9). Hayden.

Stevens, William F. & Lind, Mary R. Programming with IBM PC BASIC with Business Applications. 1984. 23.95 (ISBN 0-8359-5674-1). Reston.

Struble, George. Business Information Processing with BASIC. LC 79-1423. 1980. text ed. 21.95 (ISBN 0-201-07640-3); wkbk. 7.95 (ISBN 0-201-07642-X); instr's. manual 2.95 (ISBN 0-201-07641-1); transparency avail. (ISBN 0-201-07643-8). Addison-Wesley.

Sutherland, Robert F. This Is BASIC: An Introduction to Computer Programming. (Illus.). 384p. 1984. pap. text ed. write for info. (ISBN 0-02-418370-9). Macmillan.

Swadley, Richard & Wikert, Joseph. Using Your Apple Macintosh: Beginning BASIC & Applications. 300p. 1985. pap. 13.95 (ISBN 0-13-937350-0); incl. disk 24.95 (ISBN 0-13-938556-8). P-H.

--Using Your Coleco Adam: Beginning BASIC & Applications. 300p. 1985. pap. 11.95 (ISBN 0-13-937368-3); incl. tape 24.95 (ISBN 0-13-939018-9). P-H.

--Using Your PCjr: Beginning BASIC & Applications. 300p. 1985. pap. 11.95 (ISBN 0-13-937376-4); 24.95 (ISBN 0-13-939372-2). P-H.

Taylor, R. P. Programming Primer: A Graphic Introduction to Computer Programming with BASIC & Pascal. LC 81-2209. 1982. 21.95 (ISBN 0-201-07400-1). Addison-Wesley.

Tebbe, Paul. Programming the Apple II in BASIC. LC 83-10895. (Illus.). 176p. 1983. text ed. 21.95 (ISBN 0-13-729591-X); pap. text ed. 17.95 (ISBN 0-13-729749-1). P-H.

Teglovic, Steve & Douglas, Kenneth D. Structured BASIC: A Modular Approach for the PDP-11 & VAX-11. 1983. pap. 19.50x (ISBN 0-256-02930-X). Irwin.

Templeton, Harley & Wordware, Inc. From BASIC to 8086-8088 Assembly Language. 175p. 1985. pap. 19.95 (ISBN 0-13-331364-6). P H.

Thomas, D. Portable BASIC: Programming the TRS-80 Model 100 & NEC PC-8201A Computers. 352p. 1985. 9.95 (ISBN 0-07-064260-5). McGraw.

Thomas, Rick. Discover BASIC: A Student's Guide to Problem Solving in BASIC. 1983. 5.95. Sterling Swift.

--Discover BASIC: Problem Solving with the Apple II Computer. 1983. wkbk. for students 5.95 (ISBN 0-686-47364-7); tchr's guide & disks 74.95 (ISBN 0-686-47365-5); disks each 9.95. Sterling Swift.

Thompson, Robert G. BASIC: A First Course. (Data Processing Ser.). (Illus.). 352p. 1981. text ed. 18.95 (ISBN 0-675-08057-6). Additional supplements may be obtained from publisher. Merrill.

--BASIC: A Modular Approach. 2nd ed. 385p. 1985. pap. text ed. 19.95 (ISBN 0-675-20280-9). Additional supplements may be obtained from publisher. Merrill.

Thrall, Susan E. & Springer, Fred A. Teachers' Guide to the Commodore Computer. 135p. 1984. pap. 9.95 (ISBN 0-8039-2311-2). Sage.

Titus, Jonathan S., et al. Apple II Interfacing. LC 81-84282. 208p. 1981. pap. 11.95 (ISBN 0-672-21862-3, 21862). Sams.

Ton & Ton. Entertainment Games in TI BASIC & Extended BASIC Programs. LC 83-50493. 176p. pap. 8.95 (ISBN 0-672-22204-3, 22204). book & tape 15.95 (ISBN 0-672-26169-3, 26169). Sams.

Tortorelli, Martens. BASIC Programming with Applications in Business. 176p. 1984. pap. text ed. 9.95 (ISBN 0-8403-3523-7). Kendall-Hunt.

Tracton, Ken. Fifty-Seven Practical Programs & Games in BASIC. (Illus.). 210p. 1978. 13.95 (ISBN 0-8306-9987-2); pap. 8.25 (ISBN 0-8306-1000-6, 1000). TAB Bks.

--The Most Popular Subroutines in BASIC. (Illus.). 1979. 13.95 (ISBN 0-8306-9740-3); pap. 7.95 (ISBN 0-8306-1050-2, 1050). TAB Bks.

--Twenty-Four Tested Ready-to-Run Game Programs in BASIC. (Illus.). 1978. pap. 10.25 (ISBN 0-8306-1085-5, 1085). TAB Bks.

Tracton, Ken & Wells, Thomas A. The BASIC Cookbook. 2nd ed. 168p. 1985. 12.95 (ISBN 0-8306-0855-9, 1855); pap. 7.95 (ISBN 0-8306-1855-4). TAB Bks.

Traister, Robert J. C from BASIC. 64p. 1985. pap. text ed. 49.95 incl. disk (ISBN 0-13-110081-5). P-H.

--Going from BASIC to C. (Illus.). 176p. 1985. pap. 17.95 (ISBN 0-13-357799-6). P-H.

Trester, Kenneth R., et al. Complete Business BASIC for the Apple II, II Plus, IIe, & IIc: A Self-Instructional Approach. LC 84-12439. 368p. 1985. pap. 21.95 (ISBN 0-201-16281-4); write for info. tchrs. manual (ISBN 0-201-16282-2). Addison-Wesley.

Trivette, Donald B. A BASIC Primer for the IBM Personal Computer: Programming Business Applications. 208p. 1984. pap. 18.95 (ISBN 0-673-15997-3). Scott F.

Trost, Stanley R. Atari BASIC Programs in Minutes. LC 83-51097. (Illus.). 171p. (Orig.). 1984. pap. 12.95 (ISBN 0-89588-143-8). SYBEX.

--Commodore 64 BASIC Programs in Minutes. LC 83-51192. (Illus.). 173p. (Orig.). 1984. pap. 12.95 (ISBN 0-89588-154-3). SYBEX.

--IBM PCjr BASIC Programs in Minutes. 160p. 1984. pap. 14.95 (ISBN 0-89588-205-1). SYBEX.

--Timex-Sinclair 1000 BASIC Programs in Minutes. LC 83-61015. (Illus.). 145p. 1983. pap. 7.95 (ISBN 0-89588-119-5). SYBEX.

--Useful BASIC Programs for the IBM PC. LC 83-60487. (Illus.). 174p. 1983. pap. 12.95 (ISBN 0-89588-111-X). SYBEX.

Tucker, Allan B., Jr. BASIC Apple II. 3rd ed. 304p. 1983. pap. 17.95 (ISBN 0-03-061769-3). HR&W.

--Basic Apple IIe. 304p. pap. 18.45 (ISBN 0-03-063747-3). HR&W.

Turner, Lawrence E. & Howson, Rosemary J. Basic BASIC for Basic Beginners. x, 293p. 1982. pap. text ed. 9.95 (ISBN 0-943872-82-0). Andrews Univ Pr.

Turner, Len. Texas Instruments Computer Program Writing Workbook. 96p. 1983. 4.95 (ISBN 0-86668-812-9). ARCsoft.

Understanding PC-BASIC. 1984. pap. 14.95 (ISBN 0-911699-27-9). Calabrese Pubns.

Vernon, Peter. Making the Most of Your TRS-80 Color Computer. LC 83-10976. (Illus.). vii, 189p. 1984. pap. 16.95 (ISBN 0-13-547647-X). P-H.

Very BASIC. (Computer Literacy Ser.). pap. 9.95 (ISBN 0-318-04030-1). Sperry Comp Syst.

Vickers, Ralph. Beyond Beginning BASIC. 220p. 1983. pap. 14.95 (ISBN 0-88056-126-2). Dilithium Pr.

--IBM PC BASIC: A Guide to Programming Your IBM PC, XT, PCjr & PC Compatible Computer. (Hands On! Computer Bks.). 300p. 1984. pap. 16.95 (ISBN 0-06-669013-7). Har-Row.

Vitalari, Nicholas P. Structured BASIC for Business. (Illus.). 288p. 1985. pap. text ed. 21.95 (ISBN 0-13-854407-7). P-H.

Vonk, John A. & Erickson, Fritz J. Student Guide for Learning BASIC, for Classroom or Independent Study, Vol. I: Applesoft. LC 83-82120. 125p. 1983. pap. text ed. 9.95 (ISBN 0-918452-53-8). Learning Pubns.

--Teaching BASIC: Thirty Lesson Plans, Activities, & Quizzes, Applesoft, 2 Vols. LC 83-80815. 152p. (Orig.). 1983. Vol. 1, Applesoft. pap. 19.95 (ISBN 0-918452-45-7); Vol. 2, TRS-80. pap. 19.95 (ISBN 0-918452-48-1). Learning Pubns.

Waite Group. BASIC Primer for the IBM PC & XT. (Plume-Waite Computer Ser.). (Illus.). 1984. pap. 16.95 (ISBN 0-452-25495-7, Plume). NAL.

Waite Group & Waite, Mitchell. Microsoft Macinations: An Introduction to Microsoft BASIC for the Apple Macintosh. (Illus.). 480p. 1985. pap. 19.95 (ISBN 0-914845-34-9). Microsoft.

Waite Group, et al. Macintosh Midnight Madness: Games Utilities & Other Diversions in Microsoft Basic for the Apple Macintosh. 400p. 1985. pap. 18.95 (ISBN 0-914845-30-6). Microsoft.

Waite, Mitchell & Pardee, Michael. BASIC Programming Primer. 2nd ed. LC 82-51042. 368p. 1982. pap. 17.95 (ISBN 0-672-22014-8, 22014). Sams.

Walker, Henry M. Problems for Computer Solution Using BASIC. 189p. (Orig.). 1980. pap. text ed. 16.95 (ISBN 0-316-91834-2). Little.

Walsh, Brian C. Proper BASIC. 384p. 1983. 29.95 (ISBN 0-471-90081-8, Pub. by Wiley-Interscience). Wiley.

Warme, Paul. My Micro Speaks BASEX. 164p. (Orig.). 1981. pap. 9.95 (ISBN 0-8104-5187-5). Hayden.

Watson. Sixty-Seven Ready-to-Run Programs in BASIC: Graphics, Home & Business, Education, Games. 182p. 1981. pap. 9.25 (ISBN 0-8306-1195-9, 1195). TAB Bks.

Watson, Nancy R. Taking off with BASIC on the IBM PCjr. (Illus.). 224p. 1985. pap. 14.95 (ISBN 0-89303-869-5). Brady Comm.

Watson, W. Scott. Fifty-Five Advanced Computer Programs in BASIC. (Illus.). 252p. 16.95 (ISBN 0-8306-0012-4); pap. 10.25 (ISBN 0-8306-1295-5, 1295). TAB Bks.

Watson, Wayne T. An Introduction to Structured BASIC for the Cromemco C-10. 256p. 1984. pap. text ed. write for info. (ISBN 0-02-424580-1). Macmillan.

Wattenberg, Frank. Programming Projects for Your Timex-Sinclair 1000. (Illus.). 96p. 1983. pap. text ed. 8.95 (ISBN 0-13-729673-8). P-H.

Weber, Jeffrey R. CBASIC Simplified. LC 82-70598. (WSI's How to Use Your Personal Computer). 1982. pap. 13.95 (ISBN 0-938862-10-3). Weber Systems.

--Users Handbook to IBM BASIC. LC 82-51012. (WSI's How to Use Your Personal Computer). 300p. 1982. pap. text ed. cancelled (ISBN 0-938862-14-6). Weber Systems.

--User's Handbook to IBM BASIC Version 2.0. (How to Use Your Personal Computer Ser.). 330p. 1983. pap. cancelled (ISBN 0-938862-46-4). Weber Systems.

Weber Systems Inc. Staff. Atari ST Business Software in BASIC. 330p. (Orig.). 1986. pap. 17.95 (ISBN 0-317-19095-4). Weber Systems.

Weber Systems, Inc. Staff. BASIC Accounting System for TRS-80 Computers. cancelled (ISBN 0-317-05716-2). Weber Systems.

--IBM BASIC User's Handbook. 360p. 1984. pap. 9.95 (ISBN 0-345-31593-6). Ballantine.

--IBM PCjr Business Software in BASIC. (Applications Software Ser.). 300p. (Orig.). pap. cancelled; diskette 49.95. Weber Systems.

Weber Systems Inc. Staff. Kaypro Business Software in BASIC. (Applications Software Ser.). 330p. 1985. pap. 17.95 (ISBN 0-938862-51-0); diskette & bk 20.00 (ISBN 0-938862-52-9). Weber Systems.

--Sanyo Basic User's Handbook. LC 85-5346. (WSI User's Handbooks to Personal Computers Ser.). 350p. (Orig.). 1985. pap. 17.95 (ISBN 0-938862-02-2). Weber Systems.

--Sanyo MBC Business Software in BASIC. LC 85-5386. (Application Software Ser.). 330p. (Orig.). 1985. pap. 17.95 (ISBN 0-938862-37-5); incl. diskette 20.00 (ISBN 0-938862-38-3). Weber Systems.

Weber Systems Staff. Apple Macintosh Business Software in BASIC. 300p. 1985. pap. 17.95 (ISBN 0-938862-20-0); incl. disk 20.00 (ISBN 0-938862-21-9). Weber Systems.

--BASIC Business Package for TRS-80 Computers. LC 82-70599. (Applications Software Ser.). 210p. (Orig.). 1984. pap. 14.95 (ISBN 0-938862-27-8). Weber Systems.

--IBM PC Business Software in BASIC. LC 84-51354. (Applications Software Ser.). 300p. 1985. pap. 17.95 (ISBN 0-938862-35-9); incl. disk 20.00 (ISBN 0-938862-36-7). Weber Systems.

Weinman, David & Kursham, Barbara. VAX BASIC. 1982. text ed. 22.95 (ISBN 0-8359-8239-4); pap. text ed. 17.95 (ISBN 0-8359-8238-6). Reston.

Wells, Timothy. A Structured Approach to Building Programs: BASIC, Vol. 1. (Orig.). 1985. pap. text ed. write for info. (ISBN 0-917072-45-6). Yourdon.

Wen, David Y. A Guide to BASIC Programming. 144p. 1983. pap. text ed. 8.50 (ISBN 0-8403-2948-2). Kendall-Hunt.

West, Gary. Joy of BASIC for IBM PCjr. cancelled 14.95 (ISBN 0-89303-590-4). Brady Comm.

White, Fred. Apple Computer Program Writing Workbook. 96p. 1983. 4.95 (ISBN 0-86668-813-7). ARCsoft.

Whitsitt, Robert E., II. TI Extended BASIC. Quiram, Jacquelyn F., ed. LC 80-54899. 224p. (Orig.). 1981. pap. text ed. 12.95 (ISBN 0-89512-045-3). Tex Instr Inc.

Wilkinson, Bill, et al. The Atari BASIC Sourcebook. 296p. (Orig.). 1983. pap. 12.95 (ISBN 0-942386-15-9). Compute Pubns.

Willen, David C. BASIC Programming with the IBM PCjr. LC 84-50284. 200p. 1984. pap. 12.95 (ISBN 0-672-22359-7, 22359). Sams.

Wnorowski, Thomas. One-Hour BASIC. LC 84-9449. (Illus.). 220p. (Orig.). 1984. pap. text ed. 19.95 (ISBN 0-931543-00-2). IM-Pr.

Wohl, Gerald & Murach, Mike. BASIC: A Direct Approach. LC 77-2851. 1977. pap. text ed. 9.95 (ISBN 0-574-21125-X, 13-4125). SRA.

Wolfe, Carvel. Linear Programming with BASIC & FORTRAN. LC 84-24758. 1985. pap. text ed. 19.95 (ISBN 0-8359-4082-9); instr's manual avail. (ISBN 0-8359-4083-7). Reston.

Wolfe, Philip & Koelling, C. Patrick. Basic Engineering & Scientific Programs for the IBM PC. LC 83-7100. (Illus.). 356p. 1983. pap. text ed. 21.95 (ISBN 0-89303-330-8); bk. & diskette 46.95 (ISBN 0-89303-331-6); 25.00 (ISBN 0-89303-333-2). Brady Comm.

--BASIC Engineering Science & Business Programs for the Apple II & IIe. 352p. 1984. pap. 19.95 (ISBN 0-89303-284-0); bk. & diskette 44.95 (ISBN 0-89303-290-5); diskette 25.00 (ISBN 0-89303-288-3). Brady Comm.

Woram, John. BASIC Programming on the IBM PCjr. 224p. (Orig.). pap. cancelled (ISBN 0-916688-73-9, 73-9). Creative Comp.

Worland, Peter B. Introduction to BASIC Programming. 2nd ed. LC 83-80944. 300p. pap. text ed. 20.95 (ISBN 0-395-32750-4); instr's resource manual 2.00 (ISBN 0-395-32751-2). HM.

Worth, Thomas. BASIC for Everyone. (Illus.). 368p. 1976. 19.95 (ISBN 0-13-061481-5); pap. write for info. P-H.

Wu, Nesa L. BASIC: The Time-Sharing Language. 2nd ed. 340p. 1980. pap. text ed. write for info. (ISBN 0-697-08138-9); solutions manual avail. (ISBN 0-697-08139-7). Wm C Brown.

Wyatt, Allen. BASIC Tricks for the TI-99 4A. LC 84-50802. 9.95 (ISBN 0-672-22384-8). Sams.

Wyatt, Allen L. BASIC Tricks for the IBM. LC 83-51185. 136p. 1984. pap. 7.95 (ISBN 0-672-22250-7, 22250). Sams.

Zabinski, Michael P. Introduction to TRS-80 Level II BASIC. 1980. 9.95 (ISBN 0-318-01180-8). Radio Shack.

Zabinski, P. Introduction to TRS-80 Level II BASIC & Computer Programming. (Illus.). 256p. 1980. text ed. 17.95 (ISBN 0-13-499970-3); pap. text ed. 12.95 (ISBN 0-13-499962-2). P-H.

Zaks, Rodnay. Your First BASIC Program. LC 83-60488. (Illus.). 182p. 1983. pap. 12.95 (ISBN 0-89588-092-X). SYBEX.

BASIC-PLUS (COMPUTER PROGRAM LANGUAGE)

Hwang, C. Jinshing & Ho, Thomas. Structured Programming in BASIC-PLUS & BASIC PLUS-2: Including VAX-11 BASIC Compatability. LC 83-10259. 492p. 1984. pap. text ed. 28.45 (ISBN 0-471-06338-X). Wiley.

Morrill, Harriet H. Mini & Micro BASIC: Introducing Applesoft, Microsoft & BASIC Plus. (Microcomputer Bookshelf Ser.). 224p. 1983. pap. text ed. 14.50i (ISBN 0-316-58400-2); tchr's manual (ISBN 0-316-58401-0). Little.

Presley, Bruce. A Guide to Programming in BASIC-PLUS. 324p. 1983. 16.50 (ISBN 0-442-27363-0). Lawrenceville Pr.

Price, Wilson T. BASIC-PLUS for Business. 350p. 1983. pap. text ed. 19.95 (ISBN 0-03-061768-5). HR&W.

--Elements of BASIC Plus Programming. 1982. pap. text ed. 21.95 (ISBN 0-03-060148-7). HR&W.

Sawatzky, Jasper J. & Chen, Shu-Jen. Programming in BASIC -Plus. LC 80-27869. 273p. 1981. pap. 23.00 (ISBN 0-471-07729-1); sol. man. avail. (ISBN 0-471-86867-1). Wiley.

BASIDIOMYCETES

see also Gasteromycetes; Hymenomycetes; Mushrooms; Rusts (Fungi)

Donk, M. A. Revision der Niederlaendishen Heterobasidiomycetae und Homobasidiomycetae-Aphyllophoraceae, 2 parts in 1 vol. (Illus.). 1969. Repr. of 1933 ed. 28.00 (ISBN 3-7682-0621-1). Lubrecht & Cramer.

Juelich, Walter. Higher Taxa of Basidiomycetes. (Bibliotheca Mycologica Ser.: No. 85). (Illus.). 486p. 1981. lib. bdg. 60.00x (ISBN 3-7682-1324-2). Lubrecht & Cramer.

Kubitzki, Klaus & Renner, Susanne. Lauraceae I (Aniba & Aiouea) (Flora Neotropica Ser.: No. 31). (Illus.). 1982. pap. 22.50x (ISBN 0-89327-244-2). NY Botanical.

Lindsey, J. P. & Gilbertson, R. L. Basidiomycetes That Decay Aspen in North America. (Bibliotheca Mycologica Ser.: No. 63). 1978. lib. bdg. 42.00 (ISBN 3-7682-1193-2). Lubrecht & Cramer.

Petersen, Ronald H., ed. Evolution in the Higher Basidiomycetes: An International Symposium. LC 73-100410. pap. 148.00 (ISBN 0-317-29306-0, 2022221). Bks Demand UMI.

Rea, C. British Basidomysetaceae: A Handbook to the Larger British Fungi. 1968. pap. 40.00 (ISBN 3-7682-0561-4). Lubrecht & Cramer.

Schwalb, Marvin N. & Miles, Philip G., eds. Genetics & Morphogenesis in the Basidiomycetes. 1978. 32.50 (ISBN 0-12-632050-0). Acad Pr.

Singer, R. The Genera Marasmiellus, Crepidotus & Simocybe in the Neotropics. 1973. 70.00 (ISBN 3-7682-5444-5). Lubrecht & Cramer.

Singer, Rolf. Hydropus (Basidiomycetes-Tricholomataceae-Myceneae) (Flora Neotropica Ser.: No. 32). (Illus.). 1982. pap. 25.00x (ISBN 0-89327-242-6). NY Botanical.

Von Netzer, U. Induktion der Primordienbildung bei dem Basidiomyceten Pleurotus ostreatus. (Bibliotheca Mycologica Ser.: No. 62). (Illus.). 1978. pap. text ed. 8.75 (ISBN 3-7682-1185-1). Lubrecht & Cramer.

Wells, K. & Wells, E. K., eds. Basidium & Basidiocarp: Evolution, Cytology, Function & Development. (Springer Series in Microbiology). (Illus.). 187p. 1982. 43.00 (ISBN 0-387-90631-2). Springer-Verlag.

BASSET HOUNDS

see Dogs–Breeds–Basset Hounds

BAT

see Bats

Bishop, Owen & Bishop, Audrey. BBC Micro Wargaming. (Illus.). 170p. (Orig.). 1985. pap. 15.95 (ISBN 0-00-383000-4, Pub. by Collins England). Sheridan.

--Practical Programs for the BBC Micro. (Illus.). 120p. (Orig.). 1983. pap. 13.95 (ISBN 0-246-12405-9, Pub. by Granada England). Sheridan.

Cockerell, P. J. Using BBC BASIC. 380p. 1983. pap. 16.95 (ISBN 0-471-90242-X). Wiley.

Cryer, Neil. Graphics on the BBC Microcomputer. 16.95 (ISBN 0-13-363283-0); disk 12.95 (ISBN 0-13-363242-3). P-H.

Cryer, Neil & Cryer, Pat. BASIC Programming on the BBC Microcomputer. xii, 195p. 1983. 16.95 (ISBN 0-13-066407-3); pap. 11.95. P-H.

--Pocket Guide: Programming for the BBC Micro. (Pitman Programming Pocket Guide Ser.). 64p. (Orig.). 1984. pap. 6.95 (ISBN 0-273-01979-1). Pitman Pub MA.

Curran, Susan & Norman, Margaret. Business Applications on the BBC Micro. (Illus.). 218p. (Orig.). 1984. pap. 15.95 (ISBN 0-246-12530-6, Pub. by Granada England). Sheridan.

Dane, P. M. Learning to Use the BBC Microcomputer: A Gower Read-Out Publication. (Learning to Use Computer Ser.). 96p. (Orig.). 1982. pap. text ed. 12.00x (ISBN 0-566-03452-2). Gower Pub Co.

Dunn, Seamus & Morgan, Valerie. BBC Microcomputer for Beginners. 1984. pap. 15.95 (ISBN 0-13-069328-6). P-H.

Ellis, Miles & Ellis, David. Adventure into BBC BASIC. LC 83-16998. 315p. 1984. pap. text ed. 14.95x (ISBN 0-471-90171-7, Pub. by Wiley Pr). Wiley.

Ewban, Kay, et al. BBC Micro Gamemaster. (Illus.). 159p. (Orig.). 1984. pap. 11.95 (ISBN 0-246-12581-0, Pub. by Granada England). Sheridan.

Gardner, Philip, et al. The BBC Micro Add-On Guide. (Illus.). 160p. (Orig.). 1985. pap. 13.95 (ISBN 0-00-383009-8, Pub. by Collins England). Sheridan.

Gordon, John. One Hundred Programs for the BBC Microcomputer. (Illus.). 1984. pap. 11.95 (ISBN 0-13-634741-X); cassette 9.95 (ISBN 0-13-634733-9). P-H.

Jackson, Peter. Business Programming on Your BBC Micro. (Illus.). 192p. 1984. pap. 14.95 (ISBN 0-946576-20-3, Pub. by Phoenix Pub). David & Charles.

James, Mike. The Acorn-BBC Micro: An Expert Guide. 1984. pap. 14.95 (ISBN 0-13-003161-5). P-H.

Ludinski, G. Brainteasers for the BBC & Electron Computers. 144p. 1984. pap. 12.95 (ISBN 0-946576-03-3, Pub. by Phoenix Pub). David & Charles.

Money, Steve. BBC Micro Graphics & Sound. (Illus.). 170p. 1983. pap. 13.95 (ISBN 0-246-12156-4, Pub. by Granada England). Sheridan.

National Computer Centre Staff & Milan, Michael. A Young Persons Guide to BBC BASIC. 110p. 1983. pap. 7.75x (ISBN 0-471-87935-5). Wiley.

Opie, C. Interfacing the BBC Microcomputer. 208p. 1984. write for info. (ISBN 0-07-084724-X). McGraw.

Sinclair, Ian. Disk Systems for the BBC Micro. (Illus.). 115p. (Orig.). 1984. pap. 13.95 (ISBN 0-246-12325-7, Pub. by Granada England). Sheridan.

--Introducing the Acorn-BBC Micro. 1984. pap. 12.95 (ISBN 0-13-477266-0). P-H.

Smith, Bruce. The BBC Micro Machine Code Portfolio. (Illus.). 212p. (Orig.). 1985. pap. 15.95 (ISBN 0-246-12643-4, Pub. by Granada England). Sheridan.

Stephenson, A P. Discovering BBC Micro Machine: How to Get More Speed & Power. (Illus.). 160p. (Orig.). 1983. pap. 13.95 (ISBN 0-246-12160-2, Pub. by Granada England). Sheridan.

Stephenson, A. P. & Stephenson, D. J. Advanced Machine Code Techniques for the BBC Micro. (Illus.). 260p. (Orig.). 1984. pap. 15.95 (ISBN 0-246-12227-7, Pub. by Granada England). Sheridan.

--Filing Systems & Database for the BBC Micro. (Illus.). 219p. (Orig.). 1984. pap. 15.95 (ISBN 0-246-12423-7, Pub. by Granada England). Sheridan.

Wood, Michael. Word Processing on the BBC Micro: Wordwise & Epson. 100p. 1982. pap. text ed. 9.05 (ISBN 0-471-81046-0). Wiley.

BEACH BIRDS

see Shore Birds

BEACH EROSION

see also Coast Changes; Shore Protection

Fisher, John S. & Dolan, Robert, eds. Beach Processes & Coastal Hydrodynamics. (Benchmark Papers in Geology Ser.: Vol. 39). 1977. 63.00 (ISBN 0-12-786471-7). Acad Pr.

BEACHES

see also Beach Erosion; Sand Dunes; Seashore

Bascom, Willard. Waves & Beaches: The Dynamics of the Ocean Surface. rev. updated ed. LC 79-7038. (Illus.). 1980. pap. 8.95 (ISBN 0-385-14844-5, Anchor Pr). Doubleday.

Kaufman, Wallace & Pilkey, Orrin. The Beaches are Moving: The Drowning of America's Shoreline. (Living with the Shore Ser.). (Illus.). 326p. 1983. pap. 9.75 (ISBN 0-8223-0574-7). Duke.

Rudman, Jack. Bay Constable II. (Career Examination Ser.: C-885). (Cloth bdg. avail. on request). pap. 12.00 (ISBN 0-8373-0885-2). Natl Learning.

--Beach Supervisor. (Career Examination Ser.: C-836). (Cloth bdg. avail. on request). pap. 12.00 (ISBN 0-8373-0836-4). Natl Learning.

Schwartz, M. L., ed. The Encyclopedia of Beaches & Coastal Environments. (Encyclopedia of Earth Sciences Ser.: Vol. XV). 940p. 1982. 95.00 (ISBN 0-87933-213-1). Van Nos Reinhold.

Wilman, Elizabeth A. External Costs of Coastal Beach Pollution: An Hedonic Approach. LC 84-42690. 208p. (Orig.). 1984. pap. text ed. 15.00 (ISBN 0-915707-08-X). Resources Future.

BEAGLE EXPEDITION, 1831-1836

Darwin, Charles. Journal of Researches into the Natural History & Geology of the Countries Visited During the Voyage of H. M. S. "Beagle" Round the World, under the Command of Capt. Fitz Roy, R. A. 1977. Repr. of 1892 ed. lib. bdg. 30.00 (ISBN 0-8482-0544-8). Norwood Edns.

--Voyage of the "Beagle". 1979. 10.95x (ISBN 0-460-00104-3, Evman); pap. 6.95x (ISBN 0-460-01104-9, Evman). Biblio Dist.

--Voyage of the Beagle. LC 62-2990. 1962. 6.95 (ISBN 0-385-02767-2, Anchor). Natural Hist.

Fitz-Roy, Robert, et al. Narrative of the Surveying Voyages of His Majesty's Ships Adventure & Beagle, 3 Vols. in 4 Pts. Repr. of 1839 ed. Set. 295.00 (ISBN 0-404-09900-9). Vol. 1 (ISBN 0-404-09901-7). Vol. 2 Pt. 1 (ISBN 0-404-09902-5). Vol. 2 Pt. 2 (ISBN 0-404-09903-3). Vol. 3 (ISBN 0-404-09904-1). AMS Pr.

Keynes, Darwin R., ed. The Beagle Record. LC 77-82500. (Illus.). 1979. 95.00 (ISBN 0-521-21822-5). Cambridge U Pr.

Moorehead, Alan. Darwin & the Beagle. LC 69-17879. (Illus.). 1972. (HarpT); pap. 8.95i (ISBN 0-06-013017-2, TD-120, HarpT). Har-Row.

--Darwin & the Beagle. rev. ed. 224p. 1979. pap. 10.95 (ISBN 0-14-003327-0). Penguin.

BEAGLES (DOGS)

see Dogs–Breeds–Beagles

BEAMS

see Girders

BEAMS, CONCRETE

see Concrete Beams

BEAMS, PARTICLE

see Particle Beams

BEAR (SHIP)

Ransom, M. A. & Engle, Eloise K. Sea of the Bear. LC 79-6122. (Navies & Men Ser.). (Illus.). 1980. Repr. of 1964 ed. lib. bdg. 22.00x (ISBN 0-405-13076-7). Ayer Co Pubs.

BEARINGS (MACHINERY)

Here are entered all works relating to the supports used in engineering, more particularly in machinery, especially for the moving parts.

see also Ball-Bearings; Fluid Film Bearings; Friction; Lubrication and Lubricants; Roller Bearings

ASME-ASLE Lubrication Conference, Washington, DC, Oct. 1982. Advances in Computer-Aided Bearing Design. Chang, C. M. & Kennedy, F. E., eds. 156p. 1982. 30.00 (G00220). ASME.

Barwell, F. T. Bearing Systems: Principles & Practice. (Illus.). 1979. 78.00x (ISBN 0-19-856319-1). Oxford U Pr.

Bradley, Ian. Bearing Design & Fitting. (Illus.). 80p. 1979. pap. 4.50 (ISBN 0-85242-463-9). Aztex.

Broersma, G. Couplings & Bearings. 122p. 1968. 50.00x (ISBN 0-85950-050-0, Pub. by Stam Pr England). State Mutual Bk.

Burton, Ralph A., ed. Bearing & Seal Design in Nuclear Power Machinery: Proceedings of the Symposium on Lubrication in Nuclear Applications, Miami Beach, Florida, June 5-7, 1967. LC 67-27785. pap. 134.80 (ISBN 0-317-10009-2, 2016809). Bks Demand UMI.

Constantinescu, V. N., et al. Sliding Bearings. xx, 543p. 1984. 80.00x (ISBN 0-89864-011-3). Allerton Pr.

Eschmann, et al. Ball & Roller Bearings. LC 84-13120. (BRO Handbook Methods in the Neuroscience Ser.). 488p. 1985. 34.95x (ISBN 0-471-26283-8). Wiley.

Harris, Tedric A. Rolling Bearing Analysis. 2nd ed. LC 83-23481. 565p. 1984. 74.95x (ISBN 0-471-79979-3, Pub. by Wiley-Interscience). Wiley.

Rieger, N. F. Unbalance Response & Balancing of Flexible Rotors in Bearings. LC 72-92595. (Flexible Rotor-Bearing System Dynamics Ser.: Vol. 2). (Illus.). pap. 20.00 (ISBN 0-317-11118-3, 2012305). Bks Demand UMI.

Watson, Stewart C., ed. Joint Sealing & Bearing Systems for Concrete Structures. (SP-70: Vol. 1 & 2). (Orig.). 1981. pap. 99.00 (ISBN 0-686-95239-1). ACI.

BEARINGS, GAS-LUBRICATED

see Gas-Lubricated Bearings

BEARS

see also Black Bear; Grizzly Bear; Polar Bear

Bear Cub Scout Action Book. 64p. 1981. pap. 1.00 (ISBN 0-8395-3903-7, SL3903). BSA.

Bears: Their Biology & Management. (Illus.). 371p. 1972. pap. 25.00 (IUCN1, IUCN). Unipub.

Cramond, Mike. Killer Bears. (Illus.). 224p. 1981. 7.95 (ISBN 0-684-17285-2, ScribT). Scribner.

DeHart, Don. All about Bears. 96p. 1971. pap. 2.95 (ISBN 0-933472-41-2). Johnson Bks.

Dobie, J. Frank. Ben Lilly Legend. (Illus.). 1950. 14.45 (ISBN 0-316-18792-5). Little.

Kurten, Bjorn. The Cave Bear Story. Life & Death of a Vanished Animal. LC 76-3723. (Illus.). 163p. 1976. 21.50x (ISBN 0-231-04017-2). Columbia U Pr.

McNamee, Thomas. The Grizzly Bear. LC 84-47640. (Illus.). 281p. 1984. 18.45 (ISBN 0-394-52998-7). Knopf.

Moore, Marsha E. The Teddy Bear Book. Toth, Cecelia K. & Murphy, Margaret D., eds. 160p. 1984. 18.95 (ISBN 0-668-06256-8, 6256-8). Arco.

Schullery, Paul, ed. American Bears: Selections from the Writings of Theodore Roosevelt. LC 82-71701. (Illus.). 1983. pap. 6.95 (ISBN 0-87081-136-3). Colo Assoc.

Shea, George. Bears. LC 80-20367. (Creatures Wild & Free Ser.). 1981. 6.95 (ISBN 0-88436-772-X, 35454). EMC.

Wexo, John B., ed. Bears. (Zoobooks). (Illus.). 20p. (Orig.). 1982. pap. 1.95 (ISBN 0-937934-07-0). Wildlife Educ.

Wilson, Derek. Bear Rampant. 320p. 1982. 40.00x (ISBN 0-241-10147-6, Pub. by Hamish Hamilton England). State Mutual Bk.

BEASTS

see Domestic Animals; Zoology

BEAVERS

Allred, Morrell. Beaver Behavior: Architect of Fame & Bane! (Illus.). 80p. 10.95 (ISBN 0-87961-154-5); pap. 4.95 (ISBN 0-87961-155-3). Naturegraph.

Animals That Build Their Homes: Beavers. (Learning Shelf Kits Ser.). 1977. incl. cassette & tchrs. guide 14.95 (ISBN 0-686-74393-8, 04991). Natl Geog.

Durrant, Stephen D. & Crane, Harold S. Three New Beavers from Utah. (Museum Ser.: Vol. 1, No. 20). 11p. 1948. pap. 1.25 (ISBN 0-317-05005-2). U of KS Mus Nat Hist.

Morgan, Lewis H. The American Beaver: A Classic of Natural History & Ecology. 384p. 1986. pap. 8.95 (ISBN 0-486-24995-6). Dover.

--American Beaver & His Works. LC 78-114828. (Research & Source Ser.: No. 509). (Illus.). 1970. Repr. of 1868 ed. 24.50 (ISBN 0-8337-2461-4). B Franklin.

BEE

see Bees

BEE CULTURE

see also Bees

Adams, John F. Beekeeping. 1980. pap. 2.25 (ISBN 0-380-01043-7, 48124-3). Avon.

Adjare, Stephen. The Golden Insect: A Handbook on Beekeeping for Beginners. (Illus.). 104p. (Orig.). 1984. pap. 10.75x (ISBN 0-946688-60-5, Pub. by Intermediate Tech England). Intermediate Tech.

Aebi, Harry & Aebi, Ormund. The Art & Adventure of Beekeeping. (Illus.). 186p. 1983. pap. 7.95 (ISBN 0-87857-483-2). Rodale Pr Inc.

Ambrose, John T. & Shimanuki, H. The Beekeeper's Manual. (Illus.). 400p. 86. 39.95x (ISBN 0-03-058689-5). Praeger.

Bee Pollen, the Miracle Food, Source of Youth, Vitality & Longevity. 36th ed. 1.50 (ISBN 0-317-16704-9). F Murat.

Campion, Alan. Bees at the Bottom of the Garden. (Illus.). 112p. 1985. pap. 6.95 (ISBN 0-7136-2433-7, Pub. by A & C Black UK). Sterling.

Cannon, Hal, compiled by. The Grand Beehive. (Illus.). 88p. (Orig.). 1980. pap. 8.95 (ISBN 0-87480-190-7). U of Utah Pr.

Carrier, Franklin H. Begin to Keep Bees. (Illus.). 234p. 1981. text ed. 14.95 (ISBN 0-9607550-0-4). Carrier's Bees.

--Keeping Bees: A Handbook for the Hobbyist Beekeeper. (Illus.). 1983. 15.95 (ISBN 0-9607550-1-2). Carriers Bees.

Crane, Eva. The Archaeology of Beekeeping. LC 82-74021. (Illus.). 320p. 1983. 39.50x (ISBN 0-8014-1609-4). Cornell U Pr.

Dadant & Sons, ed. The Hive & the Honey Bee. rev. ed. LC 63-15838. (Illus.). 3740p. 1976. 19.95 (ISBN 0-684-14790-4, ScribT). Scribner.

Dadant & Sons Inc. Beekeeping Questions & Answers. LC 77-80061. (Illus.). 1978. 9.50 (ISBN 0-915698-04-8). Dadant & Sons.

Dadant & Sons, Inc. First Lessons in Beekeeping. (Illus.). 128p. 1982. pap. 4.95 (ISBN 0-684-17423-5, ScribT). Scribner.

Dadant, C. P. First Lessons in Beekeeping. rev. ed. (Illus.). 128p. 1980. 7.95 (ISBN 0-684-16747-6, ScribT). Scribner.

Dadant, C. P., ed. First Lessons in Beekeeping. LC 75-38347. (Illus.). 128p. 1976. 1.92 (ISBN 0-915698-02-1). Dadant & Sons.

Deans, Alexander S. The Bee Keepers Encyclopedia. LC 75-23248. (Illus.). 1979. Repr. of 1949 ed. 65.00x (ISBN 0-8103-4176-X). Gale.

Eckert, John E. & Shaw, Frank R. Beekeeping. (Illus.). 1960. 19.95 (ISBN 0-02-534910-4). Macmillan.

Gleanings Staff. Five Hundred Answers. 1975. pap. text ed. 1.50 (ISBN 0-686-20933-8). A I Root.

--Honey Plants Manual. 1977. pap. text ed. 2.50 (ISBN 0-686-20934-6). A I Root.

--Starting Right with Bees. (Illus.). 1976. pap. text ed. 1.50 (ISBN 0-686-20935-4). A I Root.

Gojmerac, Walter L. Bees, Beekeeping, Honey & Pollination. (Illus.). 1980. lib. bdg. 19.50 (ISBN 0-87055-342-9). AVI.

Griffith, Roger & Tompkins, Enoch. Practical Beekeeping. LC 76-51401. (Illus.). 224p. 1977. o. p. 9.95 (ISBN 0-88266-092-6); pap. 8.95 (ISBN 0-88266-091-8). Garden Way Pub.

Hopper, Ted. Guide to Bees & Honey. (Illus.). 1981. 12.95 (ISBN 0-7137-1382-8, Pub. by Blandford Pr England). Sterling.

Kimsey, Lynn S. Systematics of Bees of the Genus Eufriesea (Hymenoptera, Apidae) LC 81-7400. (University of California Publications in Entomology: Vol. 95). 136p. 1982. 14.50x (ISBN 0-520-09643-6). U of Cal Pr.

Laidlaw, Harry H. Contemporary Queen Rearing. LC 79-50568. (Illus.). 1979. 10.95 (ISBN 0-915698-05-6). Dadant & Sons.

--Instrumental Insemination of Honey Bee Queens: Pictorial Instructional Manual. new ed. (Illus.). 1977. 11.40 (ISBN 0-915698-03-X). Dadant & Sons.

Laidlaw, Harry H., Jr. & Eckert, J. E. Queen Rearing. 2nd ed. LC 62-19242. (Illus.). 1962. 11.50 (ISBN 0-520-00687-9). U of Cal Pr.

Langstroth, Lorenzo L. Langstroth on the Hive & the Honey-Bee. (Illus.). 1977. Repr. of 1914 ed. text ed. 10.95 (ISBN 0-686-23279-8). A I Root.

Levett, John. The Ordering of Bees. LC 70-171773. (English Experience Ser.: No. 398). 96p. 1971. Repr. of 1634 ed. 14.00 (ISBN 90-221-0398-6). Walter J Johnson.

Loring, Murray. Bees & the Law. LC 80-66362. 128p. 1981. 8.84 (ISBN 0-915698-07-2). Dadant & Sons.

Meyer, Owen. The Beekeeper's Handbook: A Practical Manual of Bee Management. LC 83-5048. (Illus.). 253p. (Orig.). 1983. pap. 8.95 (ISBN 0-8069-7794-9). Sterling.

Miller, C. C. Fifty Years among the Bees. (Illus.). 328p. 1980. pap. 8.95x (ISBN 0-931308-05-4). Molly Yes.

Moffett, Joseph O. Some Beekeepers & Associates, Pt. I. (Illus.). 140p. lib. bdg. 19.90 (ISBN 0-686-31814-5); pap. 9.90 (ISBN 0-686-28741-X). Moffett.

Morse, Roger. A Year in the Beeyard. (Illus.). 192p. 1983. 14.95 (ISBN 0-684-17876-1, ScribT). Scribner.

Morse, Roger A. Bees & Beekeeping. LC 74-14082. (Illus.). 320p. 1975. 29.95x (ISBN 0-8014-0884-9). Comstock.

Phillips, E. F. Beekeeping As a Hobby. facs. ed. (Shorey Lost Arts Ser.). 40p. pap. 1.95 (ISBN 0-8466-6039-3, U39). Shorey.

Root, A. I. ABC & XYZ of Bee Culture. 38th ed. (Illus.). 738p. 1982. 24.95 (ISBN 0-684-17479-0, ScribT). Scribner.

--ABC & XYZ of Bee Culture. 39th ed. (Illus.). 738p. 1983. 24.95 (ISBN 0-684-18024-3, ScribT). Scribner.

--Eighteen Ninety ABC of Bee Culture. (Illus.). 403p. 1981. 17.95x (ISBN 0-931308-08-9); pap. 11.50x (ISBN 0-931308-09-7). Molly Yes.

Root, A. I., et al. ABC & XYZ of Bee Culture. 1978. text ed. 13.80 (ISBN 0-686-20932-X). A I Root.

Sammataro, Diana & Avitabile, Alphonse. The Beekeeper's Handbook. 131p. (Orig.). 1981. pap. 10.95 (ISBN 0-684-17331-X, ScribT). Scribner.

Stelley, Diane G. Beekeeping: An Illustrated Handbook. (Illus.). 256p. 1983. 15.95 (ISBN 0-8306-0124-4, 1524); pap. 12.95 (ISBN 0-8306-1524-5). TAB Bks.

Taylor, Richard. Beekeeping for Gardeners. LC 81-85711. (Illus.). 1982. pap. 2.95 (ISBN 0-9603288-7-4). Linden Bks.

--The How-To-Do-It Book of Beekeeping. LC 77-72235. (Illus.). 1977. 9.95 (ISBN 0-686-18972-8); pap. 8.95 (ISBN 0-9603288-2-3). Linden Bks.

--The New Comb Honey Book. LC 81-85431. (Illus.). xii, 112p. 1982. 8.95 (ISBN 0-9603288-5-8); pap. 6.95. Linden Bks.

--A Monograph of the Immature Stages of the African Timber Beetles (Cerambycidae) Supplement. 186p. 1980. 89.00x (ISBN 0-85198-473-8, Pub. by CAB Bks England). State Mutual Bk.

Erwin, T. L., et al, eds. Carabid Beetles. 1979. lib. bdg. 118.50 (ISBN 90-6193-596-2, Pub. by Junk Pubs Netherlands). Kluwer Academic.

Evans, M. E. The Life of Beetles. LC 74-18499. (Illus.). 1975. 22.95x (ISBN 0-02-844330-6). Hafner.

Fall, Henry C. List of the Coleoptera of Southern California, 2 vols. in 1. Bd. with A Handbook of the Trees of California. Eastwood, Alice. 86p. Repr. of 1905 ed. 282p. Repr. of 1901 ed. 46.00 (ISBN 0-384-15128-0). Johnson Repr.

Foster, David E. Revision of North American Trichodes (Herbst) (Coleoptera: Cleridae) (Special Publications: No. 11). (Illus.). 86p. 1976. pap. 4.00 (ISBN 0-89672-037-3). Tex Tech Pr.

Gressitt, J. L. The Coconut Rhinoceros Beetle with Particular Reference to the Palau Islands. (BMB). Repr. of 1953 ed. 19.00 (ISBN 0-527-02320-5). Kraus Repr.

Hatch, Melville H., et al. Beetles of the Pacific Northwest, 5 pts. Incl. Pt. 1. Introduction & Adephaga. 348p. 1953; Pt. 2. Staphyliniformia. 384p. 1957; Pt. 3. Pselaphidae & Diversicornia 1. 503p. 1962. 30.00x (ISBN 0-295-73717-4); Pt. 4. Macrodactyles, Palpicornes, & Heteromera. 268p. 1965; Pt. 5. Rhipiceroidea, Sternoxi, Phytophaga, Rhynchophora, & Lamellicornia. 650p. 1971. 30.00x (ISBN 0-295-73719-0). LC 53-9444. (Publications in Biology Ser.: No. 16). (Illus.). U of Wash Pr.

Joy, N. H. A Practical Handbook of British Beetles. 622p. 1932. 65.00x (ISBN 0-317-07170-X, Pub. by FW Classey Uk). State Mutual Bk.

Knull, Josef N. The Checkered Beetles of Ohio (Coleoptera: Cleridae) 1972. Repr. of 1951 ed. 3.00 (ISBN 0-86727-041-1). Ohio Bio Survey.

--The Long-Horned Beetles of Ohio. 1946. 4.00 (ISBN 0-86727-038-1). Ohio Bio Survey.

LeConte, John L. & Horn, George H. Classification of the Coleoptera of North America: Smithsonian Miscellaneous Collections, No. 507. Sterling, Keir B., ed. LC 77-81103. (Biologists & Their World Ser.). 1978. Repr. of 1883 ed. lib. bdg. 46.50x (ISBN 0-405-10689-0). Ayer Co Pubs.

Linsley, E. Gorton. The Cerambycidae of North America. Incl. Pt. I. Introduction. (U. C. Publ. in Entomology: Vol. 18). 1961; Pt. II. Taxonomy & Classification of the Parandrinae, Prioninae, Spondylinae, & Aseminae. (U. C. Publ. in Entomology: Vol. 19). 1962; Pt. III. Taxonomy & Classification of the Subfamily Cerambycinae, Tribes Opsimini Through Megaderini. (U. C. Publ. in Entomology: Vol. 20). 1962. pap. 14.00x (ISBN 0-520-09081-0); Pt. IV. Taxonomy & Classification of the Subfamily Cerambycinae, Tribes Elaphidionini Through Rhinotragini. (U. C. Publ. in Entomology: Vol. 21). 1963; Pt. V. Taxonomy & Classification of the Subfamily Cerambycinae, Tribes Callichromini Through Ancylocerini. (U. C. Publ. in Entomology: Vol. 22). 1964. pap. 14.00x (ISBN 0-520-09083-7). pap. U of Cal Pr.

Linsley, E. Gorton & Sterling, Keir B., eds. Beetles from the Early Russian Explorations of the West Coast of North America: 1815-1857. original anthology ed. (Biologists & Their World Ser.). (Fr. Ger. & Latin., Illus.). 1978. lib. bdg. 53.00x (ISBN 0-405-10691-2). Ayer Co Pubs.

Mitton, Jeffry B. & Sturgeon, Kareen B., eds. Bark Beetles in North American Conifers: A System for the Study of Evolutionary Biology. (Corrie Herring Hooks Ser.: No. 6). (Illus.). 539p. 1982. text ed. 30.00x (ISBN 0-292-70735-5); pap. 17.50x (ISBN 0-292-70744-4). U of Tex Pr.

Moore, Ian & Legner, E. F. An Illustrated Guide to the Genera of the Staphylinidae of America North of Mexico. LC 78-75027. (Illus.). 1979. pap. 10.00x (ISBN 0-931876-31-1, 4093). Ag & Nat Res.

O'Brien, Charles & Widner, Guillermo. Annotated Checklist of the Weevils of North America, Central America, & the West Indies: Circulionoidea Memoir Thirty-Four. (Memoir Ser.: No. 34). 382p. 1982. 26.00 (ISBN 0-686-40427-0). Am Entom Inst.

Pinto, J. D. Behavior & Taxonomy of the Epicauta Maculata Group (Coleoptera: Meloidae) (U. C. Publications in Entomology Ser.: Vol. 89). 1980. pap. 19.50x (ISBN 0-520-09616-9). U of Cal Pr.

Sharp, D. & Muir, F. A. The Comparative Anatomy of the Male Genital Tube in Coleoptera. 1969. Repr. of 1912 ed. 40.00x (ISBN 0-317-07061-4, Pub. by EW Classey UK). State Mutual Bk.

Shelford, Victor E. Color & Color-Pattern Mechanism of Tiger Beetles. Repr. of 1917 ed. 12.00 (ISBN 0-384-55090-8). Johnson Repr.

Stickney, Fenner S. The Head-Capsule of Coleoptera. Repr. of 1923 ed. 12.00 (ISBN 0-384-58200-1). Johnson Repr.

Taxonomy & Classification of the Subfamily Lamiinae: Tribes Parmenini Through Acanthoderini, Part vii, No.1. 1985. 21.00x (ISBN 0-317-27272-1). U of Cal Pr.

Udayagiri, Susjaya & Wadhi, Sukhdev R. Catalog of the Coleoptera of the World: 130 Bruchidae. Arnett, R. H., Jr., ed. (Coleopterorum Catalagus (New Series)). 110p. 1985. pap. 30.00 (ISBN 0-916846-35-0). Flora & Fauna.

White, Richard E. The Anobiidae of Ohio. 1962. 2.50 (ISBN 0-86727-046-2). Ohio Bio Survey.

--A Field Guide to the Beetles of North America. 1983. 15.95 (ISBN 0-395-31808-4); pap. 10.95 (ISBN 0-395-33953-7). HM.

Wilcox, John A. Host Plants of Chrysomelidae, Leaf Beetles, of Northeastern United States & Eastern Canada. 1978. pap. text ed. 4.95 (ISBN 0-916846-09-1). World Natural Hist.

--Leaf Beetle Host Plants in Northeastern North America: Coleoptera: Chrysomelidae. 32p. 1979. pap. 4.95x (ISBN 0-916846-09-1). Flora & Fauna.

--Leaf Beetles of Ohio. 1954. 3.00 (ISBN 0-86727-042-X). Ohio Bio Survey.

Wilcox, John A. & Arnett, Ross H., Jr. Checklist of the Beetles of North & Central America & the West Indies: The Leaf Beetles & the Bean Weevils, Vol. 8. 178p. 1983. 20.00x (ISBN 0-916846-20-2). Flora & Fauna.

Zimmerman, E. C. Cryptorhynchinae of Rapa. (BMB). Repr. of 1938 ed. 14.00 (ISBN 0-527-02259-4). Kraus Repr.

BEETS AND BEET SUGAR

Arrington, Leonard J. Beet Sugar in the West: A History of the Utah-Idaho Sugar Company, 1891-1966. LC 66-28453. (Illus.). 248p. 1966. 20.00x (ISBN 0-295-74037-X). U of Wash Pr.

Cits. Technological Value of the Sugar Beet. 1968. 32.00 (ISBN 0-444-40112-1). Elsevier.

Effect of Nitrogen Dressings on Growth & Development of Sugar-Beet. (Agricultural Research Reports: 791). 1973. pap. 10.00 (ISBN 90-220-0434-1, PDC31, PUDOC). Unipub.

Hills, F. J., et al. Sugarbeet Pest Management: Aphid-Borne Viruses. (Illus.). 12p. (Orig.). 1982. pap. 2.00 (ISBN 0-931876-60-5, 3277). Ag & Nat Res.

--Sugarbeet Pest Management: Leaf Diseases. (Illus.). 12p. (Orig.). 1982. pap. 2.00 (ISBN 0-931876-59-1, 3278). Ag & Nat Res.

The Ionic Balance of the Sugar-Beet Plant. (Agricultural Research Reports: No. 832). 1975. pap. 12.25 (ISBN 90-220-0548-8, PDC196, PUDOC). Unipub.

Lof, George O. G. & Kneese, Allen V. The Economics of Water Utilization in the Beet Sugar Industry. LC 68-16166. (Resources for the Future Ser). (Illus.). Repr. of 1968 ed. 25.70 (ISBN 0-8357-9268-4, 2015741). Bks Demand UMI.

Molybdenum Uptake by Beets in Dutch Soils. (Agricultural Research Reports: No. 775). 1972. pap. 8.25 (ISBN 90-220-0393-0, PDC189, PUDOC). Unipub.

Roberts, Philip S. & Thomason, Ivan J. Sugarbeet Pest Management: Nematodes. (Illus.). 36p. 1981. pap. text ed. 3.00 (ISBN 0-931876-52-4, 3272). Ag & Nat Res.

Ulrich, Albert & Hills, F. Jackson. Sugar Beet Nutrient Deficiency Symptoms: A Color Atlas & Chemical Guide. 1969. pap. 3.00 (ISBN 0-931876-18-4, 4051). Ag & Nat Res.

Vukov, Konstantin. Physics & Chemistry of Sugar-Beet in Sugar Manufacture. LC 76-7400. 596p. 1977. 106.50 (ISBN 0-444-99836-5). Elsevier.

BEGONIAS

Catterall, E. Growing Begonias. (Illus.). 132p. 1984. 17.95 (ISBN 0-917304-88-8). Timber.

Haegeman, J. Tuberous Begonias: Origin & Development. 1979. lib. bdg. 28.00x (ISBN 3-7682-1219-X). Lubrecht & Cramer.

Thompson, Mildred L. & Thompson, Edward J. Begonias: A Complete Reference Book. LC 78-65078. (Illus.). 1981. 37.50 (ISBN 0-8129-0824-4). Times Bks.

BEHAVIOR GENETICS

Baerends, Gerard, et al, eds. Function & Evolution in Behaviour. (Illus.). 1975. 69.00x (ISBN 0-19-857382-0). Oxford U Pr.

Colligan, Michael J., et al, eds. Mass Psychogenic Illness: A Social Psychological Analysis. 272p. 1982. 29.95x (ISBN 0-89859-160-0). L Erlbaum Assocs.

Commons, Michael L., et al, eds. Acquisition. (The Quantitative Analyses of Behavior Ser.: Vol. III). 496p. 1984. prof ref 55.00x (ISBN 0-88410-740-X). Ballinger Pub.

--Matching & Maximizing Accounts, Vol II. LC 81-2654. (The Quantitative Analyses of Behavior Ser.). 624p. 1982. prof ref 55.00x (ISBN 0-88410-739-6). Ballinger Pub.

Davis, David E. Behavior as an Ecological Factor. LC 79-3006. (Benchmark Papers in Ecology Ser.: Vol. 2). 390p. 1974. 51.95 (ISBN 0-87933-132-1). Van Nos Reinhold.

Ehrman, Lee & Parsons, Peter. Behavior Genetics & Evolution. (Illus.). 448p. 1981. text ed. 36.95 (ISBN 0-07-019276-6). McGraw.

Ehrmann, Lee & Omenn, Gilbert S., eds. Genetics, Environment & Behavior: Implications for Educational Policy. 1972. 59.50 (ISBN 0-12-233450-7). Acad Pr.

Fuller, J. L. & Simmel, E. C., eds. Behavior Genetics: Principles & Applications. 512p. 1983. text ed. 39.95x (ISBN 0-89859-211-9). L Erlbaum Assocs.

Glass, David C., ed. Genetics. LC 68-24635. (Illus.). 270p. 1968. 13.00x (ISBN 0-87470-008-6). Rockefeller.

Hirsch, J. & McGuire, T. R., eds. Behavior-Genetic Analysis. LC 81-13323. (Benchmark Papers in Behavior: Vol. 16). 393p. 1982. 49.95 (ISBN 0-87933-419-3). Van Nos Reinhold.

Kaplan, Arnold R. Human Behavior Genetics. (Illus.). 496p. 1976. 98.50 (ISBN 0-398-03378-1). C C Thomas.

Lindzey, Gardner & Thiessen, Delbert D., eds. Contributions to Behavior - Genetic Analysis. LC 73-92661. (Century Psychology Ser). 1970. 29.50x (ISBN 0-89197-109-2); pap. text ed. 10.95x (ISBN 0-89197-110-6). Irvington.

McClearn, G. E. & DeFries, J. C. Introduction to Behavioral Genetics. LC 73-8862. (Psychology Ser.). (Illus.). 347p. 1973. text ed. 25.95x (ISBN 0-7167-0835-3). W H Freeman.

Mazur, Allan & Robertson, Leon S. Biology & Social Behavior. LC 72-169236. 1972. 14.95 (ISBN 0-02-920450-X); pap. text ed. 3.00 (ISBN 0-02-920410-0). Free Pr.

Plomin, Robert, et al. Behavioral Genetics: A Primer. LC 79-24456. (Psychology Ser.). (Illus.). 417p. 1980. text ed. 33.95x (ISBN 0-7167-1127-3); pap. 19.95 (ISBN 0-7167-1128-1). W H Freeman.

Research & Education Association Staff, ed. Behavioral Genetics. LC 82-80748. (Illus.). 224p. 1982. text ed. 13.30x (ISBN 0-87891-537-0). Res & Educ.

Robinson, Daniel N., ed. Heredity & Achievement: A Book of Readings. (Orig.). 1970. pap. text ed. 7.95x (ISBN 0-19-501036-1). Oxford U Pr.

Roe, Anne & Simpson, George G. Behavior & Evolution. LC 58-11260. pap. 141.80 (ISBN 0-317-10613-9, 2003070). Bks Demand UMI.

Rosenblatt, J. S. & Komisaruk, B. R., eds. Reproductive Behavior & Evolution. LC 77-10855. (Evolution, Development, & Organization of Behavior Ser.: Vol. 1). (Illus.). 181p. 1977. 29.50x (ISBN 0-306-34481-5, Plenum Pr). Plenum Pub.

Royce, J. R. & Mos, L. P., eds. Theoretical Advances in Behavior Genetics, No. 2. (NATO Advanced Study Institute Ser.). 722p. 1980. 75.00x (ISBN 90-286-0569-X). Sijthoff & Noordhoff.

Simmons, H. Psychogenic Biochemical Aspects: Cancer. 9.95x (ISBN 0-87312-010-8). Cancer Control Soc.

Thoday, J. M. & Parkes, A. S., eds. Genetic & Environmental Influences on Behavior. LC 68-54003. (Eugenics Society Symposia Ser.: Vol. 4). 210p. 1969. 29.50x (ISBN 0-306-38704-2, Plenum Pr). Plenum Pub.

BELL, ALEXANDER GRAHAM, 1847-1922

Eber, Dorothy H. Genius at Work: Images of Alexander Graham Bell. (Illus.). 192p. 1982. 16.95 (ISBN 0-670-27389-9, Studio). Viking.

MacKenzie, Catherine. Alexander Graham Bell: the Man Who Contracted Space. facsimile ed. LC 77-150193. (Select Bibliographies Reprint Ser). Repr. of 1928 ed. 30.00 (ISBN 0-8369-5706-7). Ayer Co Pubs.

Rhodes, Frederick L. Beginnings of Telephony. LC 7-4694. (Telecommunications Ser). (Illus.). 286p. 1974. Repr. of 1929 ed. 25.50x (ISBN 0-405-06057-2). Ayer Co Pubs.

BELLS

Anthony, Dorothy M. World of Bells, No. 2. (Illus.). 50p. 1980. Repr. of 1974 ed. mechanical bdg. 8.95 (ISBN 0-9607944-2-5). Anthony D M.

Coleman, Satis N. Bells, Their History, Legends, Making, & Uses. LC 70-109722. (Illus.). ix, 462p. Repr. of 1928 ed. lib. bdg. 24.75x (ISBN 0-8371-4212-1, COBE). Greenwood.

Rossing, Thomas D., ed. Acoustics of Bells. 416p. 1984. 67.50 (ISBN 0-442-27817-9). Van Nos Reinhold.

Williams, Edwards V. The Bells of Russia: History & Technology. (Illus.). 304p. 1985. text ed. 57.50x (ISBN 0-691-09131-5). Princeton U Pr.

BELT CONVEYORS

see Conveying Machinery

BENTHOS

Holme, N. A. & McIntyre, A. D. Methods for the Study of Marine Benthos. 2nd ed. (Illus.). 394p. 1983. pap. text ed. 44.00x (ISBN 0-632-00894-6). Blackwell Pubns.

Lowry, James K. Soft Bottom Macrobenthic Community of Arthur Harbor, Antarctica: Paper 1 in Biology of the Antarctic Seas V. Pawson, David L., ed. LC 75-22056. (Antarctic Research Ser: Vol. 23). (Illus.). 20p. 1975. pap. 5.20 (ISBN 0-87590-123-9). Am Geophysical.

BENTLEY AUTOMOBILE

see Automobiles, Foreign–Types–Bentley

BENTONITE

Folk, R. L. Field Excursion, Central Texas: Tertiary Bentonites of Central Texas. 53p. 1978. Repr. of 1961 ed. 1.25 (ISBN 0-686-29312-6, GB 3). Uranium-Bearing Clays & Tuffs of South-Central Texas, by D. H. Eargle & A. D. Weeks. Vermiculite Deposits Near Liano, by V. E. Barnes & S. E. Clabaugh. Bur Econ Geology.

Hasruddin Siddiqui, M. K. Bleaching Earths. 1968. text ed. 23.00 (ISBN 0-08-012738-X). Pergamon.

BENZENE

Benfey, O. Theodor, ed. Kekule Centennial. LC 66-30726. (Advances in Chemistry Ser: No. 61). 1966. 19.95 (ISBN 0-8412-0062-9). Am Chemical.

Bryce-Smith, D. & Gilbert, A. The Organic Photochemistry of Benzene-I. 18p. 1976. pap. text ed. 14.00 (ISBN 0-08-020464-3). Pergamon.

Buikema, Arthur L., Jr. & Hendricks, Albert C. Benzene, Xylene, & Toluene in Aquatic Systems: A Review. LC 80-67170. (Illus.). 69p. (Orig.). pap. 3.75 (ISBN 0-89364-038-7, API 847-86250). Am Petroleum.

Cherimisinoff & Moresi. Benzene: Basic & Hazardous Properties. (Pollution Engineering & Technology Ser.: Vol. 9). 1979. 49.75 (ISBN 0-8247-6860-4). Dekker.

Gilchrist, T. L. & Rees, C. W. Carbenes, Nitrenes, & Arynes. 131p. 1969. pap. 12.50x (ISBN 0-306-50026-4, Plenum Pr). Plenum Pub.

Horuath. Halogenated Benzenes: Mutual Solubility of Liquids. (Solubility Data Ser.). 1985. 100.00 (ISBN 0-08-023926-9). Pergamon.

Laskin, Sidney & Goldstein, Bernard D., eds. Benzene Toxicity: A Critical Evaluation. LC 77-17128. pap. 38.00 (ISBN 0-317-28660-9, 2055329). Bks Demand UMI.

Mehlman, Myron A. Benzene: Scientific Update. LC 85-5217. 140p. 1985. 24.00 (ISBN 0-8451-0245-1). A R Liss.

Mustafa, Ahmed. Benzofurans, Vol. 29. LC 73-4780. (Heterocyclic Compounds Ser.). 513p. 1974. 62.50 (ISBN 0-471-38207-8). Krieger.

National Research Council Assembly of Life Sciences. The Alkyl Benzenes. 384p. 1981. pap. 11.00 (ISBN 0-309-03180-X). Natl Acad Pr.

Wyckoff, Ralph W. Crystal Structures: The Structure of Benzene Derivatives, Vol. 6, Pt. 1. 2nd ed. LC 63-22897. 455p. 1969. 46.00 (ISBN 0-471-96869-2, Pub. by Wiley). Krieger.

BERING LAND BRIDGE

Hadleigh-West, Frederick. The Archaeology of Beringia. (Illus.). 320p. 1981. 36.00x (ISBN 0-231-05172-7). Columbia U Pr.

Hopkins, David M., ed. The Bering Land Bridge. (Illus.). 1967. 42.50x (ISBN 0-8047-0272-1). Stanford U Pr.

BERING SEA

Butler, B. F. & Marquis Of Lorne. Bering Sea Controversy. facs. ed. (Shorey Historical Ser.). 24p. pap. 2.50 (ISBN 0-8466-0035-8, S35). Shorey.

Coachman, Lawrence K., et al. Bering Strait: The Regional Physical Oceanography. LC 75-40881. (Illus.). 186p. 1976. 35.00x (ISBN 0-295-95442-6). U of Wash Pr.

Hood, Donald W. & Calder, John A., eds. The Eastern Bering Sea Shelf: Oceanography & Resources, 2 Vols. LC 81-60035. (Illus.). 1339p. 1982. Vol. I. 65.00x (ISBN 0-295-95884-7, Pub. by US Dept Natl Oceanic & Atmos Admin); Vol. II. 65.00x (ISBN 0-295-95885-5). U of Wash Pr.

Sayles, Myron A., et al. Oceanographic Atlas of the Bering Sea Basin. LC 76-49165. (Illus.). 170p. 1980. 35.00x (ISBN 0-295-95545-7). U of Wash Pr.

BERNOULLI, JACQUES, 1654-1705

Bernoulli, Jakob. Die Gesammelten Werke Vol. 3: Wahrscheinlichkeitsrechnung. (Ger., Illus.). 594p. 1975. 85.80x (ISBN 3-7643-0713-7). Birkhauser.

Jackob Bernoulli: Astronomia-Philosophia Naturalist. (Ger., Illus.). 541p. 1969. 83.95x (ISBN 0-8176-0028-0). Birkhauser.

BERNSTEIN POLYNOMIALS

Lorentz, G. G. Bernstein Polynomials. LC 55-527. (Mathematical Expositions Ser.: No. 8). pap. 35.00 (ISBN 0-317-08664-2, 2051966). Bks Demand UMI.

Lorentz, George G. Bernstein Polynomials. x, 132p. 1985. text ed. 12.95 (ISBN 0-8284-0323-6, 323). Chelsea Pub.

Whitt, Frank R. & Wilson, David G. Bicycling Science: Ergonomics & Mechanics. 2nd ed. (Illus.). 320p. 1982. 25.00x (ISBN 0-262-23111-5); pap. 9.95 (ISBN 0-262-73060-X). MIT Pr.

Wiley, J. The Bicycle Builder's Bible. 1982. 40.00 (ISBN 0-686-45834-6, Pub. by Selpress Bks England). State Mutual Bk.

XYZYX Information Corporation. How to Maintain & Repair Your Five, Ten & Fifteen-speed Bicycle. 1983. 14.50 (ISBN 0-8446-6064-7). Peter Smith.

BIGHORN SHEEP

Geist, Valerius. Mountain Sheep: A Study in Behavior & Evolution. LC 77-149596. (Wildlife Behavior & Ecology Ser.). (Illus.). xvi, 384p. 1976. pap. 12.00x (ISBN 0-226-28573-1, P666, Phoen). U of Chicago Pr.

BILE

see also Biliary Tract

Barbara, Luigi, et al, eds. Recent Advances in Bile Acid Research. 1985. text ed. price not set (ISBN 0-88167-146-0). Raven.

Gilhuus-Moe, Carl. Proceedings of the First International Symposium on Bile Acids in Hepatobiliary & Gastrointestinal Diseases. (Illus.). 201p. (Orig.). 1984. pap. 30.00 (ISBN 0-904147-70-3). IRL Pr.

BILE ACIDS

Paumgartner, G. & Gerok, W., eds. Bile Acids & Cholesterol in Health & Disease. 350p. 1983. text ed. write for info. (ISBN 0-85200-729-9, Pub. by MTP Pr England). Kluwer Academic.

BILE-DUCTS

White, Thomas T., et al. Liver, Bile Ducts & Pancreas. 448p. 1977. 79.00 (ISBN 0-8089-1002-7, 794827). Grune.

BILIARY TRACT

see also Bile; Liver

Classen, M., et al, eds. Nonsurgical Biliary Drainage. (Illus.). 150p. 1984. 25.00 (ISBN 0-387-11786-5). Springer-Verlag.

Daum. Extrahepatic Biliary Atresia. (Gastroenterology Ser.). 336p. 1983. 45.00 (ISBN 0-8247-7017-X). Dekker.

Dowdy, Gerald S., Jr. The Biliary Tract. LC 73-78536. (Illus.). Repr. of 1969 ed. 82.50 (ISBN 0-8357-9396-6, 2014541). Bks Demand UMI.

BILTMORE FOREST

Pinchot, Gifford. Biltmore Forest. LC 70-125757. (American Environmental Studies). 1970. Repr. of 1893 ed. 13.00 (ISBN 0-405-02683-8). Ayer Co Pubs.

Schenck, Carl A. Birth of Forestry in America: Biltmore Forest School 1898-1913. Butler, Ovid, ed. LC 74-84457. (Illus.). xvi, 224p. 1974. 10.95; pap. 4.50. Forest Hist Soc.

BINARY FORMS

see Forms, Binary

BINARY-QUATERNARY SYSTEM

see Binary System (Mathematics)

BINARY STARS

see Stars, Double

BINARY SYSTEM (MATHEMATICS)

see also Error-Correcting Codes (Information Theory)

Bruck, R. H. Survey of Binary Systems. 3rd ed. LC 79-143906. (Ergebnisse der Mathematik und Ihrer Grenzebiete: Vol. 20). 1971. 22.00 (ISBN 0-387-03497-8). Springer-Verlag.

Carling, E. B. & Kopal, Z., eds. Photometric & Spectroscopic Binary Systems. xii, 546p. 1982. 69.50 (ISBN 90-277-1281-6, Pub. by Reidel Holland). Kluwer Academic.

Cox, D. R. Analysis of Binary Data. 1970. 15.95 (ISBN 0-412-15340-8, NO.6065, Pub. by Chapman & Hall). Methuen Inc.

Eggleton, P. P. & Pringle, J. E., eds. Interacting Binaries. 1985. lib. bdg. 59.00 (ISBN 90-277-1966-7, Pub. by Reidel Holland). Kluwer Academic.

Hoffman, Martin. Hoffman on Pairs Play. (Illus.). 184p. 1982. 15.95 (ISBN 0-571-11750-3). Faber & Faber.

Kubaschwewski, Ortrud. Iron-Binary Phase Diagrams. (Illus.). 188p. 1982. 59.20 (ISBN 0-387-11711-3). Springer-Verlag.

Loos, O. G. Jordan Pairs. LC 75-9851. (Lecture Notes in Mathematics Ser.: Vol. 460). xvi, 218p. 1975. pap. 16.00 (ISBN 0-387-07166-0). Springer-Verlag.

Mittelmann, Hans D. & Weber, H., eds. Bifurcation Problems & Their Numerical Solution. (Internationale Schriftenreihe zur Numerischen Mathematik, Ser.: No. 54). 252p. 1980. pap. text ed. 28.95 (ISBN 0-8176-1204-1). Birkhauser.

Rodgers, Richard C. Quality Control & Data Analysis of Binder-Ligand Assays: Radioimmunoassay, Enzymeimmunoassay, Fluoroimmunoassay & Other Immunoassay Methods: A Programmed Text, Volume II, Statistical Considerations. (Illus.). 1981. text ed. 38.50 (ISBN 0-930914-08-2). Sci Newsletters.

BINDING OF BOOKS

see Bookbinding

BINOCULAR VISION

Hering, Ewald. The Theory of Binocular Vision. LC 76-30836. (Illus.). 218p. 1977. 39.50x (ISBN 0-306-31016-3, Plenum Pr). Plenum Pub.

Pickwell, David. Binocular Vision Anomalies: Investigation & Treatment. 160p. 1984. text ed. 39.95 (ISBN 0-407-00268-5). Butterworth.

Reading, R. W. Binocular Vision: Foundations & Applications. 366p. 1983. text ed. 39.95 (ISBN 0-409-95033-5). Butterworth.

BIOACOUSTICS

see also Animal Sounds; Hearing; Sound Production by Animals

Lewis, B., ed. Bioacoustics: A Comparative Approach. (Illus.). 1983. 55.00 (ISBN 0-12-446550-1). Acad Pr.

BIOASSAY

see Biological Assay

BIOCHEMICAL ENGINEERING

see also Fermentation; Microbiological Synthesis

Agrawal, A., ed. Bioprocess Parameter Control. (Advances in Biochemical Engineering-Biochemistry Ser.: Vol. 30). (Illus.). 210p. 1984. 39.50 (ISBN 0-387-13539-1). Springer-Verlag.

Bailey, J. & Ollis, D. Biochemical Engineering Fundamentals. 2nd ed. (Chemical Engineering Ser.). 928p. 1986. price not set (ISBN 0-07-003212-2). McGraw.

Biochemical Engineering Conference, 2nd, Henniker, New Hampshire, July 13-18, 1980. Biochemical Engineering II. Constantinides, A., et al, eds. (Annals of the New York Academy of Sciences Ser.: Vol. 369). 384p. 1981. 75.00x (ISBN 0-89766-127-3); pap. 75.00x (ISBN 0-89766-128-1). NY Acad Sci.

Bittiger, H. & Schnebli, H. P., eds. Concanavalin A as a Tool. LC 75-37841. (Wiley-Interscience Publication Ser.). pap. 160.00 (ISBN 0-317-26200-9, 2052066). Bks Demand UMI.

Chose, T. K., et al, eds. Downstream Processing. (Advances in Biochemical Engineering-Biotechnology: Vol. 26). (Illus.). 209p. 1983. 37.50 (ISBN 0-387-12096-3). Springer-Verlag.

Di Chiara, G. & Gessa, G. L., eds. GABA & the Basal Ganglia. (Advances in Biochemical Psychopharmacology Ser.: Vol. 30). 252p. 1981. text ed. 41.00 (ISBN 0-89004-752-9). Raven.

Fiechter, A. Space & Terrestrial Biotechnology. (Advances in Biochemical Engineering Ser.: Vol. 22). (Illus.). 230p. 1982. 41.00 (ISBN 0-387-11464-5). Springer-Verlag.

Fiechter, A., ed. Advances in Biochemical Engineering, Vol. 27. (Illus.). 186p. 1983. 39.00 (ISBN 0-387-12182-X). Springer-Verlag.

--Chromatography. (Advances in Biochemical Engineering Ser.: Vol. 25). (Illus.). 145p. 1982. 27.00 (ISBN 0-387-11829-2). Springer-Verlag.

--Microbes & Engineering Aspects. (Advances in Biochemical Engineering Ser.: Vol. 21). (Illus.). 240p. 1982. 41.00 (ISBN 0-387-11019-4). Springer-Verlag.

--Reaction Engineering. LC 65-6745. (Advances in Biochemical Engineering Ser.: Vol. 24). (Illus.). 150p. 1982. 38.00 (ISBN 0-387-11699-0). Springer-Verlag.

Ghose, T. K., et al, eds. Advances in Biochemical Engineering, Vol. 3. LC 73-152360. (Illus.). 250p. 1974. 49.00 (ISBN 0-387-06546-6). Springer-Verlag.

--Advances in Biochemical Engineering, Vol. 5. LC 72-152360. 1977. 35.00 (ISBN 0-387-08074-0). Springer-Verlag.

Glick, D. Methods of Biochemical Analysis, Vol. 31. 480p. 1985. 64.95 (ISBN 0-471-82177-2). Wiley.

Gogotov, L. N., et al. Microbial Activities. (Advances in Biochemical Engineering-Biotechnology Ser.: Vol. 28). (Illus.). 200p. 1983. 35.50 (ISBN 0-387-12791-7). Springer-Verlag.

Plant Cell Culture. (Advances in Biochemical Engineering - Biotechnology Ser.: Vol. 31). (Illus.). 140p. 1985. 29.50 (ISBN 0-387-15489-2). Springer-Verlag.

Products from Various Feedstocks. (Advances in Biochemical Engineering: Vol. 17). (Illus.). 170p. 1980. 50.00 (ISBN 0-387-09955-7). Springer-Verlag.

Rehm, H. J. & Reed, G. Fundamentals of Biochemical Engineering: Biotechnology, 8 vols, Vol. 2. Brauer, H., ed. & intro. by. (A Comprehensive Treatise Ser.). 807p. 1985. 298.00 (ISBN 0-89573-042-1). VCH Pubs.

Trudinger, P. A., ed. Biogeochemistry of Ancient & Modern Environments. 723p. 1980. 55.00 (ISBN 0-387-10303-1). Springer-Verlag.

Venkatasubramanian, K., et al, eds. Biochemical Engineering, No. 3, Vol. 413. 112.00 (ISBN 0-89766-220-2); pap. 112.00 (ISBN 0-89766-221-0). NY Acad Sci.

Vieth, W. R., et al, eds. Biochemical Engineering. (Annals of the New York Academy of Sciences: Vol. 326). (Orig.). 1979. pap. 57.00x (ISBN 0-89766-019-6). NY Acad Sci.

Vogel, Henry C., ed. Fermentation & Biochemical Engineering Handbook: Principles, Process Design, & Equipment. LC 83-12164. (Illus.). 440p. 1984. 64.00 (ISBN 0-8155-0950-2). Noyes.

Weetall, Howard H. & Royer, Garfield P., eds. Enzyme Engineering, Vol. 5. LC 74-13768. 503p. 1979. 65.00 (ISBN 0-306-40471-0, Plenum Pr). Plenum Pub.

Wu, Yeun C. & Smith, Ed D., eds. Fixed-Film Biological Processes for Wastewater Treatment. LC 83-13126. (Pollution Technology Review No. 104). (Illus.). 493p. 1984. 48.00 (ISBN 0-8155-0963-4). Noyes.

BIOCHEMICAL EVOLUTION

see Chemical Evolution

BIOCHEMICAL GENETICS

Ananthakrishnan, R., et al. Human Biochemical Genetics. LC 73-645. 147p. 1973. text ed. 22.50x (ISBN 0-8422-7095-7). Irvington.

Brock, D. J. & Mayo, O., eds. The Biochemical Genetics of Man. 2nd ed. 1979. 87.50 (ISBN 0-12-134760-5). Acad Pr.

De Serres, Frederick J., ed. Genetic Consequences of Nucleotide Pool Imbalance. (Basic Life Sciences Ser.: Vol. 31). 504p. 1985. 69.50x (ISBN 0-306-41902-5, Plenum Pr). Plenum Pub.

Harris, H., ed. Principles of Human Biochemical Genetics. 3rd ed. LC 75-108280. (Frontiers of Biology Ser.: Vol. 19). 477p. 1981. 71.00 (ISBN 0-444-80264-9, Biomedical Pr); pap. 25.00 (ISBN 0-444-80256-8). Elsevier.

Hecht, Max K., et al, eds. Evolutionary Biology, Vol. 9. (Illus.). 474p. 1976. 42.50x (ISBN 0-306-35409-8, Plenum Pr). Plenum Pub.

Koch, Gerhard & Richter, Dietmar. Biochemical & Clinical Aspects of Neuropeptides: Synthesis, Processing, & Gene Structure. LC 83-22381. 1983. 35.00 (ISBN 0-12-417320-9). Acad Pr.

Mani, G. S., ed. Evolutionary Dynamics of Genetic Diversity: Proceedings of a Symposium Held in Manchester, England, March 29-30, 1983. (Lecture Notes in Biomathematics: Vol. 53). vii, 312p. 1984. pap. 19.00 (ISBN 0-387-12903-0). Springer-Verlag.

Manwell, Clyde & Baker, C. M. Molecular Biology & the Origin of Species: Heterosis, Protein Polymorphism, & Animal Breeding. LC 70-103299. (Biology Ser). (Illus.). 446p. 1970. 20.00x (ISBN 0-295-95065-X). U of Wash Pr.

Porter, R. R., et al, eds. Biochemistry & Genetics of Complement: Proceedings of a Royal Society Discussion Meeting Held January 25-26, 1984. (Illus.). 152p. 1985. lib. bdg. 47.00x (ISBN 0-85403-234-7). Scholium Intl.

Schlessinger, David, ed. Microbiology 1976. LC 74-33538. 1976. 28.00 (ISBN 0-914826-11-5). Am Soc Microbio.

Vogel, H. J., ed. Nucleic Acid-Protein Recognition. 1977. 75.00 (ISBN 0-12-722560-9). Acad Pr.

Webb, Sydney J. Nutrition, Time & Motion in Metabolism & Genetics. (Illus.). 426p. 1976. 39.75x (ISBN 0-398-03158-4). C C Thomas.

BIOCHEMISTRY

see Biological Chemistry

BIOCHEMISTRY, QUANTUM

see Quantum Biochemistry

BIOCHEMISTS

Baum, H. The Biochemist's Songbook. (Illus.). 64p. 1982. pap. 5.50 (ISBN 0-08-027370-X). Pergamon.

Biochemists in Industry. 58p. 1973. 25.00x (ISBN 0-686-45133-3, Pub. by Biochemist England). State Mutual Bk.

Krebs, Hans. Otto Warburg: Biochemist & Eccentric. (Illus.). 1981. 26.95x (ISBN 0-19-858171-8). Oxford U Pr.

BIOCLIMATOLOGY

see also Crops and Climate

Eighth International Biometeorological Congress 9-15 September 1979. Biometeorology Seven: Proceedings, Supplement to Volume 24 of the International Journal of Biometeorology, Pt. 2. Zemel, Z. & Hyslop, N., eds. 1981. pap. text ed. 44.75 (ISBN 90-265-0350-4). Swets North Am.

Hadlow, Leonard. Climate, Vegetation & Man. Repr. of 1952 ed. lib. bdg. 24.75x (ISBN 0-8371-2127-2, HACV). Greenwood.

--Climate, Vegetation & Man. 6.00 (ISBN 0-685-28346-1). Philos Lib.

Hatfield, Jerry L. & Thomason, Ivan J., eds. Biometerology in Integrated Pest Management. LC 81-22780. 1982. 49.50 (ISBN 0-12-332850-0). Acad Pr.

International Biometeorological Congress, 7th, College Park, MD 1975. Biometeorology: Proceedings, Vol. 6. Landsberg, H. E., ed. 380p. (Supplements to vol. 19 & 20 of the international journal of biometeorology). 1976. pap. text ed. 77.50 (ISBN 90-265-0241-9, Pub. by Swets Pub Serv Holland). Swets North Am.

International Biometeorological Congress, Eighth, 9-15 September 1979. Biometeorology Seven: Proceedings, Supplement to Volume 24, of the International Journal of Biometeorology, Pts. 1 & 2. Zemel, Z. & Hyslop, N., eds. 1981. pap. text ed. 78.95 (ISBN 90-265-0354-7). Swets North Am.

Johnson, H. D. Progress in Animal Biometeorology: The Effects of Weather & Climate on Animals; Vol 1 Period 1963-1973, 2 pts. Incl. Pt. 1. Effects of Temperature on Animals: Including Effects of Humidity, Radiation & Wind. 624p. 1976. text ed. 115.00 (ISBN 90-265-0196-X); Effect of Light, High Actitude, Noise, Electric, Magnetic & Electro-Magnetic Fields, Ionization, Gravity & Air Pollutions on Animals. 322p. 1976. text ed. 57.00 (ISBN 90-265-0235-4). (Progress in Biometeorology Ser.). 1976 (Pub. by Swets Pub Serv Holland). Swets North Am.

Lieth, H., et al, eds. Interactions between Climate & Biosphere: Transactions of the C.E.C. Symposium in Osnabruck. (Progress in Biometeorology Ser.: Vol. 3). xviii, 394p. 1984. text ed. 82.00 (ISBN 90-265-0527-2, Pub. by Swets Pub Serv Holland). Swets North Am.

Monteith, J. L., ed. Vegetation & the Atmosphere, Vol. 1. 1976. 55.00 (ISBN 0-12-505101-8). Acad Pr.

--Vegetation & the Atmosphere, Vol. 2. 1976. 72.00 (ISBN 0-12-505102-6). Acad Pr.

Munn, R. E. Biometeorological Methods. LC 71-97488. (Environmental Science Ser). 1970. 31.50 (ISBN 0-12-510250-X); pap. 15.00 (ISBN 0-12-510256-9). Acad Pr.

Norwine, Jim. Climate & Human Ecology. LC 78-52975. (Illus.). 1978. pap. 9.95 (ISBN 0-918464-19-6). D Armstrong.

Overdieck, D., et al, eds. Biometeorology: Ninth International Biometeorological Congress held in Osnabruck & Stuttgart-Hohenheim 1981, Vol. 8, Pts. 1 & 2. 540p. 1983. pap. text ed. 55.00 (ISBN 90-265-0384-9, Pub. by Swets Pub Serv Holland). Swets North Am.

Robertson, N. G. Meteoro-Pathological Forecasting - Diseases of Livestock: Facial Eczema - An Account of Research Into the Causes & Its Relation to Weather Factors. (Eng. & Fr.). 23p. 1969. pap. 4.00 (ISBN 0-686-93891-7, W344, WMO). Unipub.

Schnitzler, H. & Lieth, H., eds. The Twenty-Five Years International Journal of Biometeorology Index. viii, 144p. pap. text ed. 16.00 (ISBN 90-265-0508-6, Pub. by Swets Pub Serv Holland). Swets North Am.

Smith, L. P., ed. Progress in Plant Biometeorology: The Effect of Weather & Climate on Plants, 1963-1974, Vol. 1. (Progress in Biometeorology Ser.). 490p. 1975. pap. text ed. 88.00 (ISBN 90-265-0183-8, Pub. by Pub Serv Holland). Swets North Am.

Sulman, Felix G. The Effect of Air Ionization, Electric Fields, Atmospherics & Other Electric Phenomena on Man & Animal. (Illus.). 424p. 1980. photocopy ed. spiral 40.50x (ISBN 0-398-03930-5). C C Thomas.

Tromp, S. W. Biometeorology. Thomas, L. C., ed. (Heyden International Topics in Science Ser.). 224p. 1979. 49.95x (ISBN 0-471-26062-2, Pub. by Wiley Heyden). Wiley.

Tromp, S. W. & Bouma, J. J., eds. Biometeorological Survey, Vol. 1. LC 81-156652. 437p. 1979. 126.95x (ISBN 0-471-26066-5, Pub. by Wiley Heyden). Wiley.

--Biometeorological Survey: Human Biometeorology, 1973-1978, 2 vols, Vol. 1. (Biometeorology Survey Ser.: Pt. A). 257p. 1979. 87.95x (ISBN 0-471-26063-0, Pub. by Wiley Heyden). Wiley.

Tromp, Solco W. Progress in Human Biometeorology: The Effect of Weather & Climate on Man & His Living Environment, Period 1963 to 1970-75, Vol. 1. Incl. Pt. 1. The Micro & Macroenvironments in the Atmosphere & Their Effects on Basic Physiological Mechanisms of Man. 726p. 1974. pap. text ed. 144.00 (ISBN 90-265-0167-6); Pt. 2. Pathological Biometeorology. 444p. 1977. pap. text ed. 86.50 (ISBN 90-265-0245-1); Pt. 3. Biometeorological Aspects of Plants, Trees & Animals in Human Life. 158p. 1972. pap. text ed. 31.50 (ISBN 90-265-0156-0). (Progress in Biometeorology Ser.). pap. (Pub. by Swets Pub Serv Holland). Swets North Am.

Zemel, Z. & Hyslop, N. St. G., eds. Biometeorology Seven: Proceedings of the Eighth International Biometeorological Congress 9-15 September 1979, Supplement to Volume 24 of the International Journal of Biometeorology, No.7, Pt.1. vi, 150p. 1980. pap. text ed. 44.75 (ISBN 90-265-0349-0). Swets North Am.

BIOCOMPATIBLE MATERIALS

see Biomedical Materials

BIOCOMPUTERS

see Conscious Automata

Sasse, Ludwig. Biogas Plants: Design & Details of Simple Biogas Plants. 85p. 1984. pap. 8.00 (ISBN 0-9904002-5-5, Pub. by Vieweg & Sohn Germany). Heyden.
Schneck, D. J., ed. Biofluid Mechanics, Vol. 2. LC 80-10092. 530p. 1980. 69.50x (ISBN 0-306-40426-5, Plenum Pr). Plenum Pub.
Thibault, L., ed. Advances in Bioengineering: 1982. 180p. 1982. 40.00 (H00247). ASME.
Thompson, Richard F. & Patterson, Michael, eds. Bioelectric Recording Techniques, 3 pts. Incl. Pt. A. Cellular Processes & Brain Potentials. 1973. 75.00 (ISBN 0-12-689401-9); Pt. B. 1974. 60.00 (ISBN 0-12-689402-7); Pt. C. Receptor & Effector Processes. 1974. 60.00 (ISBN 0-12-689403-5). 160.00 set (ISBN 0-686-66929-0). Acad Pr.
Todd, Nancy J. & Todd, John. Bioshelters, Ocean Arks, City Farming: Ecology as the Basis of Design. LC 83-51436. (Illus.). 256p. 1984. 25.00 (ISBN 0-87156-348-7); pap. 10.95 (ISBN 0-87156-814-4). Sierra.
Uhlmann, Dietrich. Hydrobiology: A Text for Engineers & Scientists. LC 77-24258. 313p. 1979. 71.95x (ISBN 0-471-99557-6, Pub. by Wiley-Interscience). Wiley.
Viano, D. C., ed. Nineteen Eighty-One Advances in Bioengineering. 232p. 1981. 40.00 (ISBN 0-686-34502-9, H00199). ASME.
Walters, LeRoy, ed. Bibliography of Bioethics, Vol. 8. 1982. 60.00 (ISBN 0-02-933780-1). Macmillan.
Welkowitz, Walter, ed. Bioengineering: Proceedings of the Ninth Northeast Conference, March, 1981, Rutgers University, Piscataway, New Jersey. (Illus.). 432p. 1981. 66.00 (ISBN 0-08-027207-X). Pergamon.
Wingard, L., et al, eds. Applied Biochemistry & Bioengineering: Vol. 3: Analytical Applications of Immobilized Enzymes & Cells. (Serial Publication). 1981. 55.00 (ISBN 0-12-041103-2); lib. ed. o.p. 59.50 (ISBN 0-12-041174-1). Acad Pr.
Wod, S. & Mates, R. E., eds. Biomechanics Symposium, 1983, Vol. 1. 7th ed. (AMD Ser.: Vol. 56). 246p. 1983. pap. text ed. 40.00 (ISBN 0-317-02553-8, G00228). ASME.

BIOFEEDBACK TRAINING

Abildness, Abby J. Biofeedback Strategies. (Illus.). 160p. (Orig.). 1982. pap. text ed. 24.00 (ISBN 0-910317-09-7). Am Occup Therapy.
American Psychiatric Association. Biofeedback: Task Force Report Nineteen. LC 80-66989. (Monographs). 128p. 1981. 11.00x (ISBN 0-89042-219-2, 42-219-2). Am Psychiatric.
Basmajian, John V. Biofeedback: Principles & Practice for Clinicians. 2nd ed. (Illus.). 390p. 1983. lib. bdg. 39.95 (ISBN 0-683-00356-9). Williams & Wilkins.
Beatty, Jackson & Legewie, Heiner, eds. Biofeedback & Behavior. LC 77-830. (NATO Conference Series III, Human Factors: Vol. 2). 541p. 1977. 49.50x (ISBN 0-306-32882-8, Plenum Pr). Plenum Pub.
Birbaumer, N. & Kimmel, H. D., eds. Biofeedback & Self-Regulation. 496p. 1976. 49.95x (ISBN 0-89859-428-6). L Erlbaum Assocs.
Blanchard, Edward B. & Epstein, Leonard H. Biofeedback Primer. LC 76-74321. (Illus.). 218p. 1978. pap. text ed. 11.95 (ISBN 0-394-34759-5, RanC). Random.
Brown, Barbara. Stress & the Art of Biofeedback. LC 76-5115. (Illus.). 1977. 14.37i (ISBN 0-06-010544-5, HarpT). Har-Row.
Brown, Barbara B. The Biofeedback Syllabus: A Handbook for the Psychophysiologic Study of Biofeedback. 516p. 1975. 45.50x (ISBN 0-398-03268-8). C C Thomas.
--Infinite Well-Being. 400p. 1985. 16.95 (ISBN 0-8290-1158-7). Irvington.
--New Mind, New Body: Bio-Feedback; New Directions for the Mind. LC 73-14249. (Illus.). 416p. 1974. 16.50i (ISBN 0-06-010549-6, HarpT). Har-Row.
Butler, Francine. Biofeedback: A Survey of the Literature. LC 78-6159. 352p. 1978. 59.50x (ISBN 0-306-65173-4, IFI Plenum). Plenum Pub.
Carroll, Douglas. Biofeedback in Practice. LC 83-9399. (Applied Psychology Ser.). 160p. (Orig.). 1984. pap. text ed. 9.95 (ISBN 0-582-29616-1). Longman.
Danskin, David G. & Crow, Mark A. Biofeedback: An Introduction & Guide. LC 80-84020. 116p. (Orig.). 1981. pap. text ed. 7.95 (ISBN 0-87484-530-0). Mayfield Pub.
Eglash, Albert. The Mind-Body-Machine Connection: A Psychologist Discusses Biofeedback with Electronic Engineers. 75p. 1981. pap. 15.00 (ISBN 0-935320-23-7). San Luis Quest.
Electromyographic Biofeedback: An Anthology. 1984. pap. 7.00 (ISBN 0-912452-44-7). Am Phys Therapy Assn.
Fischer-Williams, Mariella, et al. A Textbook of Biological Feedback. LC 80-15235. 576p. 1981. 39.95 (ISBN 0-89885-014-2). Human Sci Pr.
Fuller, George D. Biofeedback: Methods & Procedures in Clinical Practice. (Orig.). 1977. pap. 18.00 (ISBN 0-686-25138-5). Biofeed Pr.
--Projects in Biofeedback. (Orig.). 1980. pap. 16.95 (ISBN 0-686-27974-3). Biofeed Pr.
Gaarder, Kenneth R. & Montgomery, Penelope S. Clinical Biofeedback: A Procedural Manual for Behavioral Medicine. 2nd ed. (Illus.). 288p. 1981. pap. 26.95 (ISBN 0-683-03401-4). Williams & Wilkins.
Hume, Wilfred & Horroblin, David F. Biofeedback. LC 80-15617. (Biofeedback Research Review Ser.: Vol. III). 83p. 1981. 14.95 (ISBN 0-87705-969-1). Human Sci Pr.
Hume, Wilfred I. Biofeedback, Vol. II. Horrobin, D. F., ed. (Biofeedback Research Review Ser.). 126p. 1980. Repr. of 1976 ed. 14.95 (ISBN 0-87705-965-9). Human Sci Pr.
--Biofeedback. Horrobin, D. F., ed. (Biofeedback Research Review Ser.: Vol. I). 126p. 1977. Repr. of 1976 ed. 14.95 (ISBN 0-87705-966-7). Human Sci Pr.
Miller, Neal E. Fact & Fancy About Biofeedback & Its Clinical Implications. (Master Lectures on Physiological Psychology: Manuscript No. 1329). 9.50x (ISBN 0-912704-23-3). Am Psychol.
Olton, D. & Noonberg, A. Biofeedback: Clinical Applications in Behavioral Medicine. 1980. 34.95 (ISBN 0-13-076315-2). P-H.
Peper, Erik & Williams, Elizabeth A. From the Inside Out: A Self-Teaching & Laboratory Manual for Biofeedback. LC 80-20551. 446p. 1981. spiral bound 27.50x (ISBN 0-306-40535-0, Plenum Pr). Plenum Pub.
Peper, Erik, et al, eds. Mind-Body Integration: Essential Readings in Biofeedback. LC 78-27224. (Illus.). 606p. 1978. 34.50x (ISBN 0-306-40102-9, Plenum Pr). Plenum Pub.
Richter-Heinrich, E. & Miller, N. E. Biofeedback: Basic Problems in Clinical Applications. 141p. 1982. 34.00 (ISBN 0-444-86345-1, I-122-82, North-Holland). Elsevier.
Shapiro, David, et al, eds. Biofeedback & Behavioral Medicine: Therapeutic Applications & Experimental Foundations, 1979-1980. LC 80-71045. 1981. lib. bdg. 59.95x (ISBN 0-202-25129-2). Aldine Pub.
Stern, Robert M. & Ray, William J. Biofeedfack: Potential & Limits. LC 79-18700. (Illus.). viii, 197p. 1980. pap. 3.95 (ISBN 0-8032-9114-0, BB 721, Bison). U of Nebr Pr.
Taylor, Lyn P. & Tom, Gary F. Electromyometric Biofeedback Therapy. (Illus.). 1981. text ed. 28.00x (ISBN 0-686-36334-5). BATI.
Weiss, Anne E. Biofeedback: Fact or Fad. LC 84-5808. 85p. 1984. 9.90 (ISBN 0-531-04851-9). Watts.
Wentworth-Rohr, Ivan. Symptom Reduction Through Clinical Biofeedback. 256p. 1983. text ed. 34.95x (ISBN 0-89885-135-1). Human Sci Pr.
White, Leonard & Tursky, Bernard, eds. Clinical Biofeedback: Efficacy & Mechanisms. LC 81-1048. 468p. 1982. 39.50 (ISBN 0-89862-619-6). Guilford Pr.
Yates, Aubrey J. Biofeedback & the Modification of Behavior. LC 79-400. (Illus.). 524p. 1980. 29.50x (ISBN 0-306-40226-2, Plenum Pr). Plenum Pub.

BIOGENESIS

see Life–Origin

BIOGEOCHEMISTRY

Caldwell, Douglas E. & Brierley, Corale L., eds. Planetary Ecology. (Illus.). 544p. 1985. 54.50 (ISBN 0-442-24007-4). Van Nos Reinhold.

BIOGEOGRAPHY

see Geographical Distribution of Animals and Plants

BIOLOGICAL ANTHROPOLOGY

see Physical Anthropology

BIOLOGICAL APPARATUS AND SUPPLIES

Elemental Analysis of Biological Materials: Current Problems & Techniques with Special Reference to Trace Elements. (Technical Reports Ser.: No. 197). 371p. 1980. pap. 53.75 (ISBN 92-0-115080-6, IDC197, IAEA). Unipub.
Saffady, William, ed. International File of Micrographics Equipment & Accessories Nineteen Seventy-Nine to Nineteen Eighty. 2nd ed. 1979. binder 250.00 (ISBN 0-913672-33-5). Microform Rev.
Stacy, Ralph W. Biological & Medical Electronics. LC 59-14465. pap. 77.00 (ISBN 0-317-28676-5, 2055293). Bks Demand UMI.
Tolansky, S. Interference Microscopy for the Biologist. (Illus.). 180p. 1968. photocopy ed. 19.75x (ISBN 0-398-01930-4). C C Thomas.

BIOLOGICAL ASSAY

Ashton, W. D. The Logit Transformation. 1972. pap. 9.75 (ISBN 0-02-840570-6). Hafner.
Bourliere, F. Assessment of Biological Age in Man. (Public Health Papers Ser: No. 37). 67p. 1970. pap. 2.80 (ISBN 92-4-130037-X, 60). World Health.
Chayen & Chayen, Bitensky. Cytochemical Bioassays: Techniques & Applications. (Basic & Clinical Endocrinology Ser.). 424p. 1983. 65.00 (ISBN 0-8247-7001-3). Dekker.
Chayen, J. The Cytochemical Bioassay of Polypeptide Hormones. (Monographs on Endocrinology: Vol. 17). (Illus.). 230p. 1980. 51.00 (ISBN 0-387-10040-7). Springer-Verlag.
Finney, David J. Statistical Method in Biological Assay. 3rd ed. LC 78-64339. 60.00x (ISBN 0-02-844640-2). Hafner.
Hubert, John J. Bioassay. 1980. pap. text ed. 13.95 (ISBN 0-8403-2126-0). Kendall-Hunt.
Kavanagh, Frederick, ed. Analytical Microbiology. Vol.1. 1963. 91.50 (ISBN 0-12-403550-7); Vol. 2. 1972. 91.50 (ISBN 0-12-403502-7). Acad Pr.
Waters, M. D., et al, eds. Applications of Short-Term Bioassays in the Fractionation & Analysis of Complex Environmental Mixtures. LC 79-22240. (Environmental Science Research Ser.: Vol. 15). 602p. 1979. 65.00x (ISBN 0-306-40319-6, Plenum Pr). Plenum Pub.
--Short-Term Bioassays in the Analysis of Complex Environmental Mixtures, III. (Environmental Science Reseach: Vol. 27). 606p. 1983. 69.50x (ISBN 0-306-41191-1, Plenum Pr). Plenum Pub.

BIOLOGICAL CHEMISTRY

see also Acid Base Equilibrium; Biochemical Engineering; Biochemical Genetics; Biodegradation; Bioenergetics; Biosynthesis; Blood–Analysis and Chemistry; Chemical Embryology; Chemical Genetics; Chromatographic Analysis; Enzymes; Histochemistry; Immunochemistry; Metabolism; Microbial Metabolites; Molecular Biology; Photosynthesis; Physiological Chemistry; Quantum Biochemistry

Adams, A. & Schots, C., eds. Biochemical & Biological Applications of Isotachophoresis: Proceedings of the 1st International Symposium, Baconfoy, May 1979. (Analytical Chemistry Symposia Ser.: Vol. 5). vii, 278p. 1980. 70.25 (ISBN 0-444-41891-1). Elsevier.
Adrain, R. H., et al, eds. Reviews of Physiology, Biochemistry & Pharmacology, Vol. 90. (Illus.). 300p. 1981. 52.00 (ISBN 0-387-10657-X). Springer-Verlag.
Adrian, J., ed. Dictionary of Food, Nutrition & Biochemsitry. (Illus.). 240p. 1985. 29.00 (ISBN 0-89573-404-4, Pub. by Ellis Horwood Ltd UK). VCH Pubs.
Adrian, R. H. Reviews of Physiology, Biochemistry, & Pharmacology, Vol. 88. (Illus.). 264p. 1981. 54.00 (ISBN 0-387-10408-9). Springer-Verlag.
Adrian, R. H., ed. Reviews of Physiology, Biochemistry & Pharmacology, Vol. 73. LC 74-3674. (Illus.). 190p. 1975. 57.00 (ISBN 0-387-07357-4). Springer-Verlag.
--Reviews of Physiology, Biochemistry & Pharmacology, Vol. 79. LC 74-3674. 1977. 64.00 (ISBN 0-387-08326-X). Springer-Verlag.
--Reviews of Physiology, Biochemistry & Pharmacology, Vol. 89. (Illus.). 260p. 1981. 56.00 (ISBN 0-387-10495-X). Springer-Verlag.
--Reviews of Physiology, Biochemistry, & Pharmacology, Vol. 95. (Illus.). 235p. 1983. 45.50 (ISBN 0-387-11736-9). Springer-Verlag.
Adrian, R. H., et al, eds. Reviews of Physiology, Biochemistry & Pharmacology, Vol. 70. (Illus.). 260p. 1974. 52.00 (ISBN 0-387-06716-7). Springer-Verlag.
--Reviews of Physiology, Biochemistry & Pharmacology, Vol. 76. LC 74-3674. (Illus.). 1976. 71.00 (ISBN 0-387-07757-X). Springer-Verlag.
--Reviews of Physiology, Biochemistry & Pharmacology, Vol. 77. LC 74-3674. (Illus.). 1977. 74.00 (ISBN 0-387-07963-7). Springer-Verlag.
--Reviews of Physiology, Biochemistry & Pharmacology, Vol. 78. LC 74-3674. 1977. 61.00 (ISBN 0-387-07975-0). Springer-Verlag.
--Reviews of Physiology, Biochemistry & Pharmacology, Vol. 80. LC 74-3674. (Illus.). 1977. 56.00 (ISBN 0-387-08466-5). Springer-Verlag.
--Reviews of Physiology, Biochemistry & Pharmacology, Vol. 81. LC 74-3674. (Illus.). 1978. 56.00 (ISBN 0-387-08554-8). Springer-Verlag.
--Reviews of Physiology, Biochemistry & Pharmacology, Vol. 82. (Illus.). 1978. 52.00 (ISBN 0-387-08748-6). Springer-Verlag.
--Reviews of Physiology, Biochemistry & Pharmacology, Vol. 85. (Illus.). 1979. 51.00 (ISBN 0-387-09225-0). Springer-Verlag.
--Reviews of Physiology, Biochemistry & Pharmacology, Vol. 91. (Illus.). 240p. 1981. 42.00 (ISBN 0-387-10961-7). Springer-Verlag.
--Reviews of Physiology, Biochemistry, & Pharmacology, Vol. 92. (Illus.). 220p. 1982. 42.50 (ISBN 0-387-11105-0). Springer-Verlag.
--Reviews of Physiology, Biochemistry & Pharmacology, Vol. 94. (Illus.). 225p. 1982. 46.00 (ISBN 0-387-11701-6). Springer-Verlag.
--Reviews of Physiology, Biochemistry & Pharmacology, Vol. 96. (Illus.). 194p. 1983. 41.00 (ISBN 0-387-11849-7). Springer-Verlag.
--Reviews of Physiology, Biochemistry, & Pharmacology, Vol. 97. (Illus.). 176p. 1983. 37.50 (ISBN 0-387-12135-8). Springer-Verlag.
Aebi, H., et al, eds. Einfuehrung in die Praktische Biochemie. 3rd ed. xii, 462p. 1982. pap. 32.00 (ISBN 3-8055-3448-5). S Karger.
Agrawal, A., ed. Bioprocess Parameter Control. (Advances in Biochemical Engineering-Biochemistry Ser.: Vol. 30). (Illus.). 210p. 1984. 39.50 (ISBN 0-387-13539-1). Springer-Verlag.
Ahmad, Fazal, et al, eds. Miami Winter Symposium: Vol. 19: From Gene to Protein: Translation into Biotechnology (Symposium) (Serial Publication). 1982. 45.00 (ISBN 0-12-045560-9). Acad Pr.
Alaeddinoglue, Gurdal N., et al, eds. Industrial Aspects of Biochemistry & Genetics, Volume 87. (NATO ASI Series A, Life Sciences). 227p. 1985. 45.00x (ISBN 0-306-41934-3, Plenum Pr). Plenum Pub.
Allen, Mary B., ed. Comparative Biochemistry of Photoreactive Systems. 1960. 71.50 (ISBN 0-12-051750-7). Acad Pr.
Anfinsen, C. B., et al. Current Topics in Biochemistry: National Institute of Health Lectures in Biomedical Sciences. 1972. pap. 45.00 (ISBN 0-12-058750-5). Acad Pr.
Angieski, S. Biochemical Aspects of Renal Function. Dubach, C., ed. 242p. 1975. 75.00 (ISBN 3-456-80208-0, Pub. by Holdan Bk Ltd UK). State Mutual Bk.
Armstrong, Frank B. Biochemistry. 2nd ed. (Illus.). 1983. 34.95x (ISBN 0-19-503109-1). Oxford U Pr.
Arnold, P., et al, eds. Marker Proteins in Inflammation: Proceedings of the Second Symposium, Lyon, France, June 27-30, 1983, Vol. 2. LC 84-9462. (Illus.). xix, 687p. 1984. 98.00x (ISBN 3-11-009872-5). De Gruyter.
Aston, S. R. Silicon Geochemistry & Biogeochemistry. 1983. 44.50 (ISBN 0-12-065620-5). Acad Pr.
Atkinson, B. & Mavituna, F. Biochemical Engineering & Biotechnology Handbook. 1982. 105.00x (ISBN 0-943818-02-8, Nature Pr). Groves Dict Music.
Avery, J., ed. Membrane Structure & Mechanisms of Biolological Energy Transduction. LC 72-95064. 608p. 1974. 57.50x (ISBN 0-306-30718-9, Plenum Pr). Plenum Pub.
Bachelard, H. S. Brain Biochemistry. 2nd ed. 1981. pap. 7.50 (ISBN 0-412-23470-X, NO.6490, Pub. by Chapman & Hall). Methuen Inc.
Baker, Richard, ed. Controlled Release of Bioactive Materials. LC 80-198721. 1980. 55.00 (ISBN 0-12-074450-3). Acad Pr.
Balaban, A. T., et al, eds. Steric Fit in Quantitative Structure-Activity Relations. (Lecture Notes in Chemistry: Vol. 15). (Illus.). 178p. 1980. pap. 21.00 (ISBN 0-387-09755-4). Springer-Verlag.
Banks, P., et al. The Biochemistry of the Tissues. 2nd ed. LC 75-26739. 493p. 1976. (Pub. by Wiley-Interscience); pap. 35.95 (ISBN 0-471-01923-2, Pub. by Wiley-Interscience). Wiley.
Barnes, John E. & Waring, Alan J. Pocket Programmable Calculators in Biochemistry. LC 79-2547. 363p. 1980. 47.50x (ISBN 0-471-06434-3, Pub. by Wiley-Interscience); pap. 29.95 (ISBN 0-471-04713-9). Wiley.
Barrett, Graham C., ed. Chemistry & Biochemistry of the Amino Acids. 720p. 1985. 99.00 (ISBN 0-412-23410-6, NO. 6835, Pub. by Chapman & Hall). Methuen Inc.
Barrett, John. Biochemistry of Parasitic Helminths. (Illus.). 320p. 1981. pap. text ed. 21.00 (ISBN 0-8391-4141-6). Univ Park.
Baum, H. & Gergely, J., eds. Molecular Aspects of Medicine, Vol. 2. LC 80-40473. (Illus.). 453p. 1980. 77.00 (ISBN 0-08-026355-0). Pergamon.
Baum, H., et al, eds. Molecular Aspects of Medicine, Vol. 6. (Illus.). 584p. 1984. 162.00 (ISBN 0-08-031724-3). Pergamon.
Baum, Stuart, et al. Exercises in Organic & Biological Chemistry. 2nd ed. 1981. write for info. (ISBN 0-02-306540-0). Macmillan.
Baum, Stuart J. Introduction to Organic & Biological Chemistry. 3rd ed. 1981. write for info. (ISBN 0-02-306640-7); pap. write for info. (ISBN 0-02-306580-X). Macmillan.
Beermann, W., ed. Biochemical Differentiation in Insect Glands. LC 77-23423. (Results & Problems in Cell Differentiation: Vol. 8). (Illus.). 1977. 51.00 (ISBN 0-387-08286-7). Springer-Verlag.
Berk, Z. Braverman's Introduction to the Biochemistry of Foods. 2nd, rev. ed. 316p. 1976. 41.50 (ISBN 0-444-41450-9, Biomedical Pr). Elsevier.
Berlow, Peter. Introduction to Chemistry of Life. 1982. text ed. 32.95 (ISBN 0-03-058516-3, CBS C); instr's manual 4.95 (ISBN 0-03-058517-1); lab manual 18.95 (ISBN 0-03-058519-8); overheads 400.00 (ISBN 0-03-060583-0). SCP.

Eleventh IUPAC International Symposium on Chemistry: Bulgarian Academy of Sciences, 4 vols. Incl. Vol. 1. Bio-Organic Chemistry. pap. 39.50 (ISBN 0-686-28576-X); Vol. 2. Structural Elucidation & Chemical Transformation of Natural Products & Physical Methods for Investigation of Natural Products. pap. 45.00 (ISBN 0-686-28577-8); Vol. 3. Synthesis of Natural Products. pap. 29.00 (ISBN 0-686-28578-6); Vol. 4. Half-Hour Plenary Lectures in Two Parts. pap. 58.00 (ISBN 0-686-28579-4). 1979. Set. pap. 155.00 (ISBN 0-686-28575-1). Kluwer Academic.

Engelman, Donald M., ed. Annual Review of Biophysics & Biophysical Chemistry, Vol. 14. LC 79-188446. (Illus.). 478p. 1985. text ed. 47.00 (ISBN 0-8243-1814-5). Annual Reviews.

Eskin, N. A., et al. Biochemistry of Foods. 1971. 45.00 (ISBN 0-12-242350-X). Acad Pr.

Facchetti, S., ed. Analytical Techniques for Heavy Metals in Biological Fluids: Lectures of a Course Held at the Joint Research Centre, Ispar, Italy, 22-26 June, 1981. 287p. 1983. 83.00 (ISBN 0-444-42212-9, I-183-83). Elsevier.

Fasman, Gerald D., ed. Handbook of Biochemistry & Molecular Biology, CRC: Lipids, Carbohydrates, & Steroids Section, Vol. 1. 3rd ed. LC 75-29514. (Handbook Ser.). 570p. 1976. 76.50 (ISBN 0-87819-508-4). CRC Pr.

--Handbook of Biochemistry & Molecular Biology, CRC: Physical & Chemical Data Section, 2 vols. 3rd ed. Incl. Pt. 1. Physical & Chemical Data. LC 75-29514. (Handbook Ser.). 1976. Vol. 1, 576 Pgs. 76.50 (ISBN 0-87819-509-2); Vol. 2, 456 Pgs. 66.00 (ISBN 0-8493-0516-0). CRC Pr.

Favez, Gerard, et al, eds. The Cells of the Alveolar Unit. (Current Problems in Clinical Biochemistry Ser.: Vol. 13). (Illus.). 225p. 1983. pap. text ed. 28.00 (ISBN 3-456-81304-X, Pub. by Hans Huber Switzerland). J K Burgess.

Feigl, Dorothy M. & Hill, John W. General, Organic, & Biological Chemistry: Foundations of Life. 2nd, rev. ed. (Illus.). 544p. 1985. text ed. price not set (ISBN 0-8087-3026-6); price not set student guide (ISBN 0-8087-3027-4). Burgess.

Fiechter, A., ed. Biotechnology. (Advances in Biochemical Engineering: Vol. 7). (Illus.). 1977. 39.00 (ISBN 0-387-08397-9). Springer-Verlag.

--Mass Transfer in Biotechnology. LC 72-152360. (Advances in Biochemical Engineering: Vol. 8). (Illus.). 1978. 38.00 (ISBN 0-387-08557-2). Springer-Verlag.

Fiechter, A., et al, eds. Advances in Biochemical Engineering, Vol. 2. LC 72-152360. (Illus.). 220p. 1972. 32.50 (ISBN 0-387-06017-0). Springer-Verlag.

Finean, J. B. & Engstrom, Arne. Biological Ultrastructure. 2nd ed. 1967. 69.00 (ISBN 0-12-256550-9). Acad Pr.

Finland, Maxwell & Kass, Edward H., eds. Trimethoprim-Sulfamethoxazole. LC 73-92601. viii, 392p. 1974. 17.95x (ISBN 0-226-24916-6). U of Chicago Pr.

Fisher, Richard B. A Dictionary of Body Chemistry. (Illus.). 208p. pap. 6.95 (ISBN 0-586-08382-0, Pub. by Granada England). Academy Chi Pubs.

Fishman, William H., ed. Metabolic Conjugation & Metabolic Hydrolysis, 3 vols. LC 79-107556. Vol. 1, 1970. 90.00 (ISBN 0-12-257601-2); Vol. 2, 1971. 95.00 (ISBN 0-12-257602-0); Vol. 3, 1973. 90.00 (ISBN 0-12-257603-9). Acad Pr.

Florkin, M. & Neuberger, A., eds. Comprehensive Biochemistry, Vol. 19B, Pt. 1: Part 1: Protein Metabolism, Vol.19B. 528p. 1980. 101.50 (ISBN 0-444-80171-5, Biomedical Pr). Elsevier.

Florkin, M. & Stotz, eds. Comprehensive Biochemistry, Vol. 33A: Unravelling of Biosynthetic Pathways. 434p. 1979. 96.50 (ISBN 0-444-80067-0, Biomedical Pr). Elsevier.

Florkin, M. & Stotz, E., eds. Comprehensive Biochemistry: Amino Acids Metabolism & Sulphur Metabolism, Vol. 19A. 482p. 1981. 103.50 (ISBN 0-444-80257-6, Biomedical Pr). Elsevier.

--Comprehensive Biochemistry: Unraveling of Biosynthetic Pathways, Vol. 33B. 320p. 1979. 78.50 (ISBN 0-444-80068-9, Biomedical Pr). Elsevier.

--Comprehensive Biochemistry, Vol. 34A: The Recognition of Molecular Correlate of Biological Concepts. 1984. write for info. (ISBN 0-444-41544-0, Biomedical Pr). Elsevier.

--Comprehensive Biochemistry, Vol. 34B: From Ordered Polymers to Molecular Complementarities. 200p. 1984. write for info. (Biomedical Pr). Elsevier.

Florkin, M. & Stotz, E. E., eds. Comprehensive Biochemistry, Vol. 34: From Biological Biochemistry to Molecular Biology. Date not set. write for info. Elsevier.

Florkin, M. & Stotz, E. H., eds. Comprehensive Biochemistry, Section 3: Biochemical Reaction Mechanics, Vols. 12-16. Incl. Vol. 12. Enzymes - General Considerations. 3rd ed. 1964. o. p. 71.00 (ISBN 0-444-40225-X); Vol. 13. Nomenclature of Enzymes & Coenzymes. 1973. o. p. 104.75 (ISBN 0-444-41140-2); Vol. 14. Biological Oxidations. 1966. 121.75 (ISBN 0-444-40229-2); Vol. 15. Group-Transfer Reactions. 1964. o. p. 59.75 (ISBN 0-444-40230-6); Vol. 16. Hydrolytic Reactions, Cobamide & Biotin Coenzymes. 1965. o. p. 64.25 (ISBN 0-444-40231-4). North Holland). Elsevier.

--Comprehensive Biochemistry, Section 5: Chemical Biology, Vols. 22-29. Incl. Vol. 22. Bioenergetics. 1967. 53.00 (ISBN 0-444-40233-0); Vol. 23. Cytochemistry. 1969. o. p. 41.50 (ISBN 0-444-40687-5); Vol. 25. Regulatory Functions - Mechanisms of Hormone Action. 1975. 39.25 (ISBN 0-444-41281-6); Vol. 26. Extracellular & Supporting Structures, 3 pts. 1968-71. Pt. A. 71.00 (ISBN 0-444-40234-9); Pt. B. 71.00 (ISBN 0-444-40235-7); Pt. C. o. p. 73.75 (ISBN 0-444-40870-3); Vol. 27. Photobiology, Ionizing Radiation. 1967. o. p. 93.00 (ISBN 0-444-40236-5); Vol. 28. Morphogenesis, Differentiation & Development. o. p. 69.00 (ISBN 0-444-40237-3); Vol. 29. Comparative Biochemistry, Molecular, 2 pts. 1980. Pt. A. o. p. 87.25 (ISBN 0-444-41192-5); Pt. B. 69.00 (ISBN 0-444-41282-4); Vol. 24. Biological Information Transfer. 1977. 74.50 (ISBN 0-444-41583-1). 1967-71 (North Holland). Elsevier.

Florkin, M., et al, eds. Comprehensive Biochemistry, Vol. 19B, Pt. 2: Protein Metabolism. 514p. 1982. 74.50 (ISBN 0-444-80346-7, Biomedical Pr). Elsevier.

Florkin, Marcel & Mason, Howard S., eds. Comparative Biochemistry: A Comprehensive Treatise, 7 vols. Incl. Vol. 1. Sources of Free Energy. 1960. 76.50 (ISBN 0-12-261001-6); Vol. 2. Free Energy & Biological Function. 1960. 78.00 (ISBN 0-12-261002-4); Vol. 3. Constituents of Life. 1962. 95.00 (ISBN 0-12-261003-2); Vol. 4. Constituents of Life. 1962. 97.50 (ISBN 0-12-261004-0); Vol. 5. Constituents of Life. 1963. 78.00 (ISBN 0-12-261005-9); Vol. 6. Cells & Organisms. 1963. 78.00 (ISBN 0-12-261006-7); Vol. 7. Supplementary Volume. 1964. 76.50 (ISBN 0-12-261007-5). LC 67-23158. Acad Pr.

Forsen, S., et al. Chlorine, Bromine & Iodine NMR Physico-Chemicall & Biological Applications. Diehl, P., et al, eds. (Basic Principles & Progress: Vol. 12). (Illus.). 1976. 59.00 (ISBN 0-387-07725-1). Springer-Verlag.

Fotherby, K. & Pal, S. B., eds. The Role of Drugs & Electrolytes in Hormonogenesis. LC 84-7611. (Illus.). xii, 360p. 1984. 72.00x (ISBN 3-11-008463-5). De Gruyter.

Frederick. Origins & Evolution of Eukaryotic Intracellular Organalles, Vol. 361. 1981. 101.00x (ISBN 0-89766-111-7); pap. 101.00x (ISBN 0-89766-112-5). NY Acad Sci.

Fredericq. Electric Dichroism & Electric Birefringence. (Monographs in Physical Biochemistry). (Illus.). 1973. 47.50x (ISBN 0-19-854616-5). Oxford U Pr.

Frieden, Earl, ed. Biochemistry of the Essential Ultratrace Elements. (Biochemistry of the Elements Ser.: Vol. 3). 444p. 1984. 59.50x (ISBN 0-306-41682-4, Plenum Pr). Plenum Pub.

Friedman, Paul J. Biochemistry: A Review with Questions. 2nd ed. 1982. 15.95 (ISBN 0-316-29352-0). Little.

Friend, J. & Threlfall, D. R., eds. Biochemical Aspects of Plant Parasite Relationship. (Phytochemical Society Ser.). 1977. 60.00 (ISBN 0-12-267950-4). Acad Pr.

Frigerio, A. & Castagnoli, N., Jr., eds. Mass Spectrometry in Biochemistry & Medicine. LC 73-91164. (Monographs of the Mario Negri Institute for Pharmacological Research). 379p. 1974. 69.50 (ISBN 0-911216-53-7). Raven.

Frisell, Wilhelm R. Human Biochemistry. (Illus.). 845p. 1982. text ed. write for info. (ISBN 0-02-339820-5). Macmillan.

Gaede, K. & Gaede, K., eds. Molecular Basis of Biological Activity, Vol. 1. 1972. 65.00 (ISBN 0-12-272850-5). Acad Pr.

Gandour, R. D. & Schowen, R. L., eds. Transition States of Biochemical Processes. LC 78-6659. (Illus.). 636p. 1978. 75.00x (ISBN 0-306-31092-9, Plenum Pr). Plenum Pub.

Garland, P. B. & Crumpton, M. J., eds. The Lymphocyte Cell Surface. (Symposia Ser.: No. 45). 124p. 1981. 60.00x (ISBN 0-904498-10-7, Pub. by Biochemical England). State Mutual Bk.

Garland, P. B. & Hales, C. N., eds. Substrate Mobilization & Energy Provision in Man. (Symposia Ser.: No. 43). 228p. 1981. 32.00x (ISBN 0-904498-07-7, Pub. by Biochemical England). State Mutual Bk.

Garland, P. B. & Mathias, A. P., eds. Biochemistry of the Cell Nucleus. (Symposia Ser.: No. 42). 244p. 1981. 30.00x (ISBN 0-904498-03-4, Pub. by Biochemical England). State Mutual Bk.

Garland, P. B. & Williamson, R., eds. Biochemistry of Genetic Engineering. (Symposia Ser.: No. 44). 145p. 1981. 27.50x (ISBN 0-904498-08-5, Pub. by Biochemical England). State Mutual Bk.

Gesellschaft Fuer Biologische Chemie, 24th, Mossbach-Baden, 1973. Regulation of Transcription & Translation in Eukaryotes: Proceedings. Bautz, E., ed. (Illus.). 300p. 1973. 52.00 (ISBN 0-387-06472-9). Springer-Verlag.

Gilleland, Martha J. Introduction to General, Organic & Biological Chemistry. (Illus.). 832p. 1982. text ed. 31.95 (ISBN 0-314-63173-9). West Pub.

Gillette, J. R. & Mitchell, J. R., eds. Concepts in Biochemical Pharmacology, Part 3: Pharmacokinetics. (Handbook of Experimental Pharmacology Ser.: Vol. 28). (Illus.). xxxiii, 480p. 1975. 147.00 (ISBN 0-387-07001-X). Springer-Verlag.

Gilmour, D. Biochemistry of Insects. 1961. 56.50 (ISBN 0-12-284050-X). Acad Pr.

Glick, David. Methods of Biochemical Analysis, Vol. 28. LC 54-7232. 430p. 1982. 58.50 (ISBN 0-471-08370-4, Pub. by Wiley-Interscience). Wiley.

--Methods of Biochemical Analysis, Vol. 30. (Methods of Biochemical Analysis Ser.: No. 2180). 377p. 1984. 49.50 (ISBN 0-471-80276-X, Pub. by Wiley-Interscience). Wiley.

Glick, David, ed. Methods of Biochemical Analysis, Vol. 4. LC 54-7232. 372p. 1957. 31.50 (ISBN -470-30525-8). Krieger.

--Methods of Biochemical Analysis, Vol. 6. LC 54-7232. 368p. 1958. 33.00 (ISBN -470-30591-6). Krieger.

--Methods of Biochemical Analysis, Vol. 8. LC 54-7232. 410p. 1960. 33.50 (ISBN -470-30657-2). Krieger.

--Methods of Biochemical Analysis, Vol. 11. 442p. (Orig.). 1963. 35.00 (ISBN 0-470-30738-2). Krieger.

--Methods of Biochemical Analysis, Vol. 12. 499p. (Orig.). 1964. 35.00 (ISBN 0-470-30742-0). Krieger.

--Methods of Biochemical Analysis, Vol. 16. 446p. (Orig.). 1968. 35.00 (ISBN 0-470-30750-1). Krieger.

--Methods of Biochemical Analysis, Vols. 14, 15, 17-19. Vol. 14, 1966, 562p. 35.00 (ISBN 0-470-30747-1); Vol. 15, 1967, 531p. 35.00 (ISBN 0-470-30749-8); Vol. 17, 1969, 428p. 35.00 (ISBN 0-470-30752-8); Vol. 18, 1969, 416p. 35.00 (ISBN 0-471-30753-X); Vol. 19, 1971, 632p. 35.00 (ISBN 0-471-30754-8, Pub. by Wiley). Krieger.

--Methods of Biochemical Analysis, Vol. 20. 572p. (Orig.). 1973. 35.00 (ISBN 0-471-30755-6). Krieger.

--Methods of Biochemical Analysis, Vol. 23. LC 54-7232. 356p. 1976. 35.00 (ISBN 0-471-01413-3). Krieger.

--Methods of Biochemical Analysis: Analysis of Biogenic Amines & Their Related Enzymes. LC 54-7232. 358p. (Orig.). 1971. Supplemental Ed. 35.00 (ISBN 0-471-30420-4). Krieger.

--Methods of Biochemical Analysis: Analysis of Biochemical Amines & Their Related Enzymes, Vol. 24. LC 54-7232. 512p. 1977. 35.00 (ISBN -471-02764-2). Krieger.

Glick, David M. Biochemistry Review. 7th ed. LC 80-19927. (Basic Science Review Bks.). 1980. pap. 12.75. Med Exam.

Glick, David M., ed. Biochemistry Review. 6th ed. (Basic Science Review Bks.). 1975. spiral bdg. 12.75 (ISBN 0-87488-202-8). Med Exam.

Gogotov, L. N., et al. Microbial Activities. (Advances in Biochemical Engineering-Biotechnology Ser.: Vol. 28). (Illus.). 200p. 1983. 35.50 (ISBN 0-387-12791-7). Springer-Verlag.

Goldberg, David M. Clinical Biochemistry Reviews, Vol. 3. (Clinical Biochemistry Reviews Ser.). 477p. 1982. 48.00x (ISBN 0-471-09868-X, Pub. by Wiley Med). Wiley.

Goldberg, David M., ed. Annual Review of Clinical Biochemistry, Vol. 1. LC 80-15463. 379p. 1980. 44.00x (ISBN 0-471-04036-3, Pub. by Wiley Med); Vol. 2. 48.00x (ISBN 0-471-08297-X). Wiley.

Goodman, Murray & Morehouse, Frank. Organic Molecules in Action. LC 72-85025. (Illus.). 368p. 1973. 24.50x (ISBN 0-677-01810-X). Gordon.

Green, A. Richard & Costain, David W. Pharmacology & Biochemistry of Psychiatric Disorders. 217p. 1981. 39.95x (ISBN 0-471-09998-8); pap. 19.95 (ISBN 0-471-10000-5). Wiley.

Greengard, Paul, et al, eds. Advances in Cyclic Nucleotide & Protein Phosphorylation Research, Vol. 18. 298p. 1984. text ed. 54.50 (ISBN 0-88167-020-0). Raven.

Gregory, R. P. Biochemistry of Photosynthesis. 2nd ed. 221p. 1977. 44.95 (ISBN 0-471-32676-3). Wiley.

Grenell, Robert. From Nerve to Mind. 244p. 1972. 67.25 (ISBN 0-677-12310-8). Gordon.

Gresser, Ion. Interferon: 1979. LC 79-41412. (Essays in Biochemistry Ser.). 1980. 27.50 (ISBN 0-12-302250-9). Acad Pr.

Grierson, Donald & Covey, Simon. Plant Molecular Biology. (Tertiary Level Biology Ser.). 184p. (Orig.). 1985. 39.95 (ISBN 0-317-17304-9, NO. 9028, Pub. by Chapman & Hall England); pap. 17.95 (ISBN 0-412-00661-8, NO. 9029, Pub. by Chapman & Hall England). Methuen Inc.

Grisolia, Santiago, et al. The Urea Cycle. LC 76-7382. (A Wiley-Interscience Publication Ser.). pap. 150.30 (ISBN 0-317-26102-9, 2025174). Bks Demand UMI.

Guder, W. & Schmidt, U. Biochemical Nephrology. 484p. 1978. 95.00 (ISBN 3-456-80627-2, Pub. by Holdan Bk Ltd UK). State Mutual Bk.

Gurd, Frank R., ed. Chemical Specificity in Biological Interactions. 1954. 41.50 (ISBN 0-12-307950-0). Acad Pr.

Hames, B. D. & Higgins, S. J., eds. Transcription & Translation: A Practical Approach. (Practical Approach Ser.). (Illus.). 346p. (Orig.). 1984. pap. 24.00 (ISBN 0-904147-52-5). IRL Pr.

Hancock & Sparrow. Handbook of HPLC of Biological Compounds. 464p. 1983. 39.75 (ISBN 0-8247-7140-0). Dekker.

Handbook of Biochemistry & Molecular Biology, CRC: Cumulative Index. 295p. 1977. 56.00 (ISBN 0-8493-0511-X). CRC Pr.

Hanson, R. W. Essentials of Bio-Organic Chemistry. 224p. 1984. pap. text ed. 14.95 (ISBN 0-7131-3500-X). E Arnold.

Hanzlik, Robert P., ed. Inorganic Aspects of Biological & Organic Chemistry. 1976. 52.50 (ISBN 0-12-324050-6). Acad Pr.

Harborne, J. B. Introduction to Ecological Biochemistry. 2nd ed. 1982. 38.50 (ISBN 0-12-324680-6); pap. 17.50 (ISBN 0-12-324682-2). Acad Pr.

Hardy, R. W. F., et al. A Treatise on Dinitrogen Fixation Sections I & II: Inorganic & Physical Chemistry & Biochemistry. LC 76-15278. 1979. 85.95x (ISBN 0-471-35134-2, Pub. by Wiley-Interscience); Sect. IV. 69.95x (ISBN 0-471-02343-4); Sect III. 82.95 (ISBN 0-471-35138-5). Wiley.

Harrison, P. M. & Hoare, R. J. Metals in Biochemistry. LC 79-41813. 80p. 1980. pap. 7.50x (ISBN 0-412-13160-9, NO. 6361, Pub. by Chapman & Hall England). Methuen Inc.

Hassall, H. & Turner, A. J. Multiple Choice Questions in Biochemistry. 256p. (Orig.). 1985. pap. 11.50 (ISBN 0-272-79758-8, Pitman Med UK). Urban & S.

Havemann, K. & Janoff, A., eds. Neutral Proteases of Human Polymorphonuclear Leukocytes: Biochemistry, Physiology & Clinical Significance. LC 78-7037. (Illus.). 480p. 1978. text ed. 44.50 (ISBN 0-8067-0801-8). Urban & S.

Hay, R. W. An Introduction to Bio-Inorganic Chemistry. (Series in Chemical Science: 1-449). 210p. 1984. pap. text ed. 24.95x (ISBN 0-470-20066-9, Wiley-Interscience). Wiley.

Hayaischi, O., et al, eds. Biochemical & Medical Aspects of Tryptophan Metabolism. (Development in Biochemistry Ser.: Vol. 16). 1981. 67.25 (ISBN 0-444-80297-5). Elsevier.

Hein, Morris, et al. College Chemistry: An Introduction to Inorganic, Organic & Biochemistry. 3rd ed. LC 83-25284. (Chemistry Ser.). 775p. 1985. text ed. 27.25 pub net (ISBN 0-534-02863-2); pap. text ed. 16.50 pub net lab. bk. 400pps. (ISBN 0-534-03091-2). Brooks-Cole.

Heinz, Erich. Electrified Potentials in Biological Membrane Transport. (Molecular Biology, Biochemistry, & Biophysics Ser.: Vol. 33). (Illus.). 100p. 1981. 35.00 (ISBN 0-387-10928-5). Springer-Verlag.

Helene. Structure, Dynamics, Interactions & Evolution of Biological Macromolecules. 1983. lib. bdg. 65.00 (ISBN 90-277-1531-9, Pub. by Reidel Holland). Kluwer Academic.

Hill, Donald L. The Biochemistry & Physiology of Tetrahymena. (Cell Biology Ser). 1972. 49.50 (ISBN 0-12-348350-6). Acad Pr.

Hill, T. L. Cooperativity Theory in Biochemistry. (Springer Series in Molecular Biology). (Illus.). 650p. 1985. 120.00 (ISBN 0-387-96103-8). Springer-Verlag.

Hindley, et al. DNA Sequencing: Laboratory Techniques in Biochemistry & Molecular Biology, Vol. 10. 384p. 1983. 83.00 (ISBN 0-444-80497-8, Biomedical Pr); pap. 27.95 (ISBN 0-444-80385-8). Elsevier.

Ho. Biological Monitoring of Exposure to Chemicals: Organic Compounds, Vol. 1. 1985. write for info (ISBN 0-471-82275-2). Wiley.

Hochachka, P. W., ed. Biochemistry at Depth. 203p. 1976. text ed. 44.00 (ISBN 0-08-019960-7). Pergamon.

Hodgson, E. & Bend, J. R., eds. Reviews in Biochemical Toxicology, Vol. 2. 300p. 1980. 52.25 (ISBN 0-444-00386-X, Biomedical Pr). Elsevier.

Hodgson, E., et al, eds. Reviews in Biochemical Toxicology, Vol. 3. 1981. 65.25 (ISBN 0-444-00436-X, Biomedcial Pr). Elsevier.

Hofmann, E. Reviews of Physiology, Biochemistry & Pharmacology, Vol. 75. LC 74-3674. 1976. 71.00 (ISBN 0-387-07639-5). Springer-Verlag.

Holloway, C. J., ed. Analytical & Preparative Isotachophoresis: Proceedings of the International Symposium on Isotachophoresis Goslar, 3rd, Germany, June 1-4, 1982. LC 84-12056. (Illus.). xiii, 404p. 1984. 68.00x (ISBN 3-11-010178-5). De Gruyter.

Holme, David J. & Peck, Hazel. Analytical Biochemistry. LC 82-8937. (Illus.). 480p. 1983. text ed. 57.00 (ISBN 0-582-45082-9). Longman.

Holum, J. R. Elements of General & Biological Chemistry. 6th ed. LC 82-11046. 523p. 1983. 31.95 (ISBN 0-471-09935-X); pap. 18.50 (ISBN 0-471-08236-8); tchr's. manual 10.95 (ISBN 0-471-87194-X); pap. 13.50 study guide (ISBN 0-471-89033-2). Wiley.

--Fundamentals of General, Organic, & Biological Chemistry. 2nd ed. LC 81-14716. 717p. 1982. 34.50 (ISBN 0-471-06314-2); S.G. 13.95 (ISBN 0-471-86354-8); write for info. tests (ISBN 0-471-87473-6); tchr's manual 11.25 (ISBN 0-471-86362-9); trans. 15.00 (ISBN 0-471-86361-0). Wiley.

Holum, John R. Organic & Biological Chemistry. LC 78-634. 494p. 1978. text ed. 31.50 (ISBN 0-471-40872-7). Wiley.

--Principles of Physical, Organic, & Biological Chemistry: An Introduction to the Molecular Basis of Life. LC 68-9249. (Illus.). pap. 120.00 (ISBN 0-317-09458-0, 2055142). Bks Demand UMI.

Hou, Ching T. Methylotrophs: Microbiology, Biochemistry & Genetics. 192p. 1984. 65.00 (ISBN 0-8493-5992-9). CRC Pr.

Hughes, M. N. The Inorganic Chemistry of Biological Processes. 2nd ed. LC 80-40499. 338p. 1981. pap. 37.95x (ISBN 0-471-27815-7, Pub. by Wiley-Interscience). Wiley.

Hulliger, M., et al. Reviews of Physiology, Biochemistry & Pharmacology, Vol. 101. (Illus.). 255p. 1984. 35.50 (ISBN 0-387-13679-7). Springer-Verlag.

Hutson, D. H. & Roberts, T. R. Progress in Pesticide Biochemistry, Vol. 3. 449p. 1983. 199.95 (ISBN 0-471-90053-2, Pub. by Wiley Interscience). Wiley.

Hutzinger, O., ed. Anthropogenic Compounds, Pt. B. (Handbook of Experimental Chemistry Ser.: Vol. 3). (Illus.). 230p. 1982. 54.00 (ISBN 0-387-11108-5). Springer-Verlag.

--The Natural Environment & the Biogeochemical Cycles. (The Handbook of Environmental Chemistry Ser.: Vol. 1, Pt. D). (Illus.). 260p. 1985. 59.00 (ISBN 0-387-15000-5). Springer-Verlag.

--Reactions & Processes. (The Handbook of Environmental Chemistry Ser.: Vol. 2, Pt. C). 180p. 1985. 38.00 (ISBN 0-387-13819-6). Springer-Verlag.

Jacobs, A. & Worwood, M., eds. Iron in Biochemistry & Medicine. 1974. 95.00 (ISBN 0-12-379150-2). Acad Pr.

Jakubke, H. D. Lexikon Biochemie. (Ger.). 1976. 25.00 (ISBN 3-527-25662-8, M-7285). French & Eur.

James, M. Lynn & Schreck, James O. General, Organic & Biological Chemistry: A Brief Introduction. 560p. 1982. text ed. 27.95 (ISBN 0-669-03862-8); lab guide 11.95 (ISBN 0-669-03864-4); student guide 9.95 (ISBN 0-669-03865-2); instr's guide 1.95 (ISBN 0-669-03866-0). Heath.

James, M. Lynn, et al. General, Organic & Biological Chemistry: Chemistry for the Living System. 1980. text ed. 29.95 (ISBN 0-669-01329-3); lab guide 12.95 (ISBN 0-669-01332-3); study guide 9.95 (ISBN 0-669-01331-5); instrs'. guide 1.95 (ISBN 0-669-01330-7). Heath.

James, Thomas L. Nuclear Magnetic Resonance in Biochemistry: Principles & Applications. 1975. 65.50 (ISBN 0-12-380950-9). Acad Pr.

Jamieson, A. M. & Rippon, W. B. Instrumental Methods for Characterization of Biological Macromolecules. write for info. (ISBN 0-685-84733-0). Elsevier.

Jamieson, Graham A. Interaction of Platelets & Tumor Cells. LC 82-6530. (Progress in Clinical & Biological Research Ser.: Vol. 89). 526p. 1982. 48.00 (ISBN 0-8451-0089-0). A R Liss.

Jeanloz, Roger W. & Balazs, Endre A., eds. The Amino Sugars: The Chemistry & Biology of Compounds Containing Amino Sugars, 2 vols. Incl. Vol. 1, Pt. A. 1969. 71.50 (ISBN 0-12-381801-X); Vol. 2, Pt. A. 1965. subscription 83.50 (ISBN 0-12-381802-8); Vol. 2, Pt. B. 1966. 81.00 (ISBN 0-12-381842-7). Acad Pr.

Johnson, C. D. The Hammet Equation. LC 79-42670. (Cambridge Texts in Chemistry & Biochemistry). (Illus.). 196p. 1980. pap. 16.95 (ISBN 0-521-29970-5). Cambridge U Pr.

Kahl, Guenter. Biochemistry of Wounded Plant Tissues. 1978. 72.00x (ISBN 3-11-006801-X). De Gruyter.

Kaneko, J. J. & Cornelius, C. E., eds. Clinical Biochemistry of Domestic Animals, Vols. 1 & 2. 2nd ed. 1970. Vol. 1. 60.00 (ISBN 0-12-396301-X); Vol. 2, 1971. 58.00 (ISBN 0-12-396302-8). Acad Pr.

Kaplan, Nathan O. & Kennedy, Eugene P., eds. Current Aspects of Biochemical Energetics. 1967. 71.50 (ISBN 0-12-397350-3). Acad Pr.

Kerkut, G. A., ed. Comprehensive Insect Physiology, Biochemistry & Pharmacology, 13 vols. (Illus.). 8536p. 1985. Set. 2750.00 (ISBN 0-08-026850-1). Pergamon.

Kervran, C. L. Biological Transmutations. (Illus.). 180p. 1980. text ed. 14.95 (ISBN 0-8464-1069-9). Beekman Pubs.

Keverling Buisman, K. A., ed. Biological Activity & Chemical Structure. (Pharmaco-Chemistry Library: Vol. 2). 314p. 1978. 66.00 (ISBN 0-444-41659-5). Elsevier.

Keyzer, Hendrik & Gutmann, Felix, eds. Bioelectrochemistry. LC 80-14838. 440p. 1980. 65.00x (ISBN 0-306-40453-2, Plenum Pr). Plenum Pub.

Kinne, R. K., ed. Renal Biochemistry: Cells, Membranes, Molecules. 476p. 1985. 125.75 (ISBN 0-444-80627-X). Elsevier.

Knuttgen, Howard G., et al, eds. Biochemistry of Exercise. LC 82-84696. (International Series on Sport Sciences: Vol. 13). 958p. 1983. text ed. 45.00x (ISBN 0-931250-41-2, BKNU0041). Human Kinetics.

Kohler, Robert E. From Medical Chemistry to Biochemistry: The Making of a Biomedical Discipline. LC 81-10189. (Cambridge Monographs on the History of Medicine). (Illus.). 380p. 1982. 39.50 (ISBN 0-521-24312-2). Cambridge U Pr.

Kohn, L. D. Hormone Receptors. (Horizons in Biochemistry & Biophysics Ser.: Vol. 6). 392p. 1982. 74.95x (ISBN 0-471-10049-8, Pub. by Wiley-Interscience). Wiley.

Kornberg, A., et al. Reflections on Biochemistry. 1976. text ed. 53.00 (ISBN 0-08-021011-2); pap. text ed. 16.50 (ISBN 0-08-021010-4). Pergamon.

Koshland, Daniel E., Jr. Bacterial Chemotaxis As a Model Behavioral System. (Distinguished Lecture Series of the Society of General Physiologists: Vol. 2). 210p. 1980. text ed. 28.50 (ISBN 0-89004-468-6). Raven.

Krishnamurthy, Subramanya & Tolbert, Margeret E. Stereochemical Insights into Biochemistry. (Illus.). 1981. 6.95 (ISBN 0-8062-1812-6). Carlton.

Kulaev, I. S. The Biochemistry of Inorganic Polyphosphates. LC 78-31627. 255p. 1980. 86.95x (ISBN 0-471-27574-3, Pub. by Wiley-Interscience). Wiley.

Kustin, K., et al. Inorganic Biochemistry II. LC 76-2616. (Topics in Current Chemistry: Vol. 69). 1977. 55.00 (ISBN 3-540-08157-7). Springer-Verlag.

Laskin, Allen I. Enzymes & Immobilized Cells in Biotechnology. 1985. 41.95 (ISBN 0-8053-6360-2). Benjamin-Cummings.

Latner, Albert L. Cantarow & Trumper Clinical Biochemistry. 7th ed. LC 73-89933. 770p. 1975. text ed. 34.00 (ISBN 0-7216-5637-4). Saunders.

Lazzari, Eugene P., ed. CRC Handbook of Experimental Aspects of Oral Biochemistry. 384p. 1983. 98.00 (ISBN 0-8493-3162-5). CRC Pr.

Lee, Jessie C. & Bettelheim, Frederick A. Introduction to General, Organic & Biochemistry: Laboratory Manual. 384p. 1984. pap. 18.95x (ISBN 0-03-063307-9). SCP.

Lehninger, Albert L. Biochemistry: The Molecular Bases of All Structure & Function. 2nd ed. LC 75-11082. 1975. text ed. 39.95x (ISBN 0-87901-047-9). Worth.

--Principles of Biochemistry. (Illus.). 1011p. 1982. text ed. 38.95x (ISBN 0-87901-136-X); By Paul van Eikeren- 544pp, 1984. study guide & solutions manual 18.95x (ISBN 0-87901-178-5). Worth.

--A Short Course in Biochemistry. LC 72-93199. (Illus.). 400p. 1973. text ed. 31.95x (ISBN 0-87901-024-X). Worth.

Leicester, Henry M. Development of Biochemical Concepts from Ancient to Modern Times. LC 73-83965. (Monographs in the History of Science Ser). 296p. 1974. text ed. 17.50x (ISBN 0-674-20018-7). Harvard U Pr.

Levandowsky, M. & Hunter, S. H., eds. Biochemistry & Physiology of Protozoa, Vol. 4. 2nd ed. 1983. 69.50 (ISBN 0-12-444604-3). Acad Pr.

Levitzki, A. Quantitative Aspects of Allosteric Mechanisms. (Molecular Biology, Biochemistry & Biophysics Ser.: Vol. 28). (Illus.). 1978. 27.00 (ISBN 0-387-08696-X). Springer-Verlag.

Liebig, Justus. Animal Chemistry. 1964. Repr. of 1842 ed. 40.00 (ISBN 0-384-32640-4). Johnson Repr.

Likens, G. E., et al. Biogeochemistry of a Forested Ecosystem. LC 76-50113. 1977. pap. 15.50 (ISBN 0-387-90225-2). Springer-Verlag.

Linder, Maria C., ed. Nutritional Biochemistry & Metabolism, with Clinical Applications. 1985. 55.00 (ISBN 0-444-00910-8). Elsevier.

Lipmann, Fritz. Wanderings of a Biochemist. LC 75-138915. 229p. 1971. 16.00 (ISBN 0-471-54080-3). Krieger.

Liu, T. Y., et al, eds. Frontiers in Protein Chemistry. Yasunobu. (Developments in Biochemistry Ser.: Vol. 10). 570p. 1980. 89.75 (ISBN 0-444-00414-9, Biomedical Pr). Elsevier.

--Frontiers in Biochemical & Biophysical Studies of Proteins & Membranes: Proceedings of the International Conference on Frontiers in Biochemical & Biophysical Studies of Macromolecules, University of Hawaii, Honolulu, Aug. 6-8, 1982. 1983. 100.00 (ISBN 0-444-00822-5, Biomedical Pr). Elsevier.

Longworth, J. W., et al, eds. Photobiology 1984. LC 85-604. 1985. write for info. (ISBN 0-03-000848-4). Praeger.

Lowenstein, O., ed. Advances in Comparative Physiology & Biochemistry, Vol. 7. 1978. 80.00 (ISBN 0-12-011506-9). Acad Pr.

Lowman, Robert G., et al. Experimental Introductory Chemistry: Organic & Biochemistry. (Illus.). 84p. 1983. pap. text ed. 4.95x (ISBN 0-89641-125-7). American Pr.

Luckner, M. Secondary Metabolism in Microorganisms, Plants & Animals. 2nd, rev. ed. (Illus.). 570p. 1984. 48.50 (ISBN 0-387-12771-2). Springer-Verlag.

Luckner, Martin. The Secondary Metabolism of Plants & Animals. 1972. 75.00 (ISBN 0-12-459050-0). Acad Pr.

Luisi, P. L. & Straub, B. E., eds. Reverse Micelles: Biological & Technological Relevance of Amphiphilic Structures in Apolar Media. 364p. 1984. 55.00x (ISBN 0-306-41620-4, Plenum Pr). Plenum Pub.

McGilvery, Robert W. Biochemistry: A Functional Approach. 3rd ed. (Illus.). 912p. 1983. 39.95 (ISBN 0-7216-5913-6). Saunders.

McMurray, W. C. Essentials of Human Metabolism: The Relationship of Biochemistry to Human Physiology & Disease. 2nd ed. (Illus.). 331p. 1983. pap. text ed. 21.00 (ISBN 0-06-141643-6, 14-16437, Harper Medical). Lippincott.

--Synopsis of Human Biochemistry: With Medical Applications. (Illus.). 336p. 1982. pap. text ed. 17.75 (Harper Medical). Lippincott.

Magill, Jane M. & Moore, John B., Jr. Experiments in Biochemistry. (Illus.). 100p. (Orig.). 1978. pap. text ed. 5.95x plastic comb. bdg. (ISBN 0-89641-007-2). American Pr.

Maier, Mary & Rodriguez, Nelson. Elements of General, Organic & Biochemistry. 600p. 1984. text ed. write for info (ISBN 0-87150-782-X, 4551). Brooks-Cole.

Makin, H. L., ed. Biochemistry of Steroid Hormones. 2nd ed ed. (Illus.). 640p. 1984. text ed. 125.00x (ISBN 0-632-00986-1). Blackwell Pubns.

Mandelstam, Joel, et al. Biochemistry of Bacterial Growth. 3rd ed. LC 81-6895. 449p. 1982. pap. 39.95x (ISBN 0-470-27249-X). Halsted Pr.

Mann, Kenneth G. & Taylor, Fletcher B. Regulation of Coagulation. (Developments in Biochemistry: Vol. 8). 640p. 1980. 73.25 (ISBN 0-444-00371-1, Biomedical Pr). Elsevier.

Mann, Roger, ed. Exotic Species in Mariculture. (Illus.). 1979. text ed. 30.00x (ISBN 0-262-13155-2). MIT Pr.

Massry, Shaul G., et al, eds. Phosphate & Minerals in Health & Disease. LC 80-14464. (Advances in Experimental Medicine & Biology: Vol. 128). 690p. 1980. 79.50x (ISBN 0-306-40451-6, Plenum Pr). Plenum Pub.

Messing, Ralph A., ed. Immobilized Enzymes for Industrial Reactors. 1975. 37.50 (ISBN 0-12-492350-X). Acad Pr.

Metzler, David. Biochemistry: The Chemical Reactions of Living Cells. 1129p. 1977. 32.00i (ISBN 0-12-492550-2); instr's. manual 10.00i (ISBN 0-12-492552-9). Acad Pr.

Meynell, G. G. Drug-Resistance Factors & Other Bacterial Plasmids. 1973. 27.50x (ISBN 0-262-13085-8). MIT Pr.

Meyrath, J. & Bu'Lock, J. D., eds. Biotechnology & Fungal Differentiation. (Federation of European Microbiological Societies Ser.). 1978. 41.00 (ISBN 0-12-493550-8). Acad Pr.

Miami Winter Symposium. The Molecular Basis of Electron Transport. Schultz, Julius & Cameron, Bruce F., eds. 1972. 49.50 (ISBN 0-12-632650-9). Acad Pr.

Mildvan, A. S., et al. Biochemistry. LC 67-11280. (Structure & Bonding Ser.: Vol. 20). 180p. 1974. 43.00 (ISBN 0-387-07053-2). Springer-Verlag.

Miller, H. & Harrison, D. C. Biomedical Electrode Technology. 1974. 65.00 (ISBN 0-12-496850-3). Acad Pr.

Miller, J. H. & Reznikoff, W. S., eds. The Operon. 2nd ed. LC 80-15490. (Monograph Ser.: No. 7). (Illus.). 469p. (Orig.). 1980. pap. text ed. 25.00x (ISBN 0-87969-133-6). Cold Spring Harbor.

Montgomery, Rex, et al. Biochemistry: A Case Oriented Approach. 3rd ed. LC 80-11370. (Illus.). 712p. 1980. pap. text ed. 24.95 (ISBN 0-8016-3470-9). Mosby.

Moore, Lorna G., et al. The Biocultural Basis of Health: Expanding Views of Medical Anthropology. LC 80-11554. (Illus.). 294p. 1980. pap. text ed. 14.95 (ISBN 0-8016-3481-4). Mosby.

Moulder, James W. Biochemistry of Intracellular Parasitism. LC 62-12636. (Illus.). 1962. 12.50x (ISBN 0-226-54248-3). U of Chicago Pr.

Murray, R. D. H., et al. The Natural Coumarins: Occurance, Chemistry & Biochemistry. LC 81-14776. 702p. 1983. 187.95 (ISBN 0-471-28057-7, Pub. by Wiley-Interscience). Wiley.

Muzzarelli, Riccardo A. Chitin. LC 76-52421. 365p. 1977. text ed. 67.00 (ISBN 0-08-020367-1). Pergamon.

Nath, R. L. Practice of Biochemistry in Clinical Medicine. 262p. 1981. 30.00x (ISBN 0-686-72963-3, Pub. by Oxford & IBH India). State Mutual Bk.

The Natural Environment & the Biogeochemical Cycles. (The Handbook of Environmental Chemistry Ser.: Vol. 1, Pt. A). (Illus.). 270p. 1980. 64.00 (ISBN 0-387-09688-4). Springer-Verlag.

Needham, Joseph. Biochemistry & Morphogenesis. 1942. 125.00 (ISBN 0-521-05797-3). Cambridge U Pr.

--Chemistry of Life: Eight Lectures on the History of Biochemistry. LC 78-85733. (Illus.). 1970. 39.50 (ISBN 0-521-07379-0). Cambridge U Pr.

Neilands. Siderophores, Vol. 1. 1985. price not set (ISBN 0-471-82501-8). Wiley.

--Siderophores, Vol. 2. 1985. price not set (ISBN 0-471-82502-6). Wiley.

New York Academy of Sciences, March 10-12, 1980. Modulation of Cellular Interactions by Vitamin A & Derivatives: Retinoids, Vol. 359. De Luca, Luigi M. & Shapiro, Stanley S., eds. 431p. 1981. 85.00x (ISBN 0-89766-107-9). NY Acad Sci.

Newcombe, David S. Inherited Biochemical Disorders & Uric Acid Metabolism. pap. 74.50 (ISBN 0-317-26192-4, 2052074). Bks Demand UMI.

Neyra, Carlos A. Biochemical Basis Plant Breeding: Carbon Metabolism, Vol. 1. 192p. 1985. 60.00 (ISBN 0-8493-5741-1). CRC Pr.

Nicolau, C. Experimental Methods in Biophysical Chemistry. LC 72-5720. Repr. of 1973 ed. 160.00 (ISBN 0-8357-9888-7, 2016155). Bks Demand UMI.

Nicolis, G. & Prigogine, I. Self-Organization in Non-Equilibrium Systems: From Dissipative Structures to Order Through Fluctuations. LC 76-49019. 491p. 1977. 70.00 (ISBN 0-471-02401-5, Pub. by Wiley-Interscience). Wiley.

Nitecki, Matthew H., ed. Biochemical Aspects of Evolutionary Biology. LC 82-70746. (Chicago Originals Ser.). 334p. 1982. lib. bdg. 17.00x (ISBN 0-226-58684-7). U of Chicago Pr.

Nriagu, J. O., ed. The Biogeochemistry of Lead in the Environment, 2 pts. (Topics in Environmental Health Ser.: Vol. 1). 1978. Pt. A, Ecological Cycles. 105.75 (ISBN 0-444-41599-8, Biomedical Pr); Pt. B, Biological Effects. 101.50 (ISBN 0-444-80050-6); 125.75. Elsevier.

O'Connor, R. F. Chemical Principles & Their Biological Implications. LC 74-3367. 413p. 1974. 31.95 (ISBN 0-471-65246-6); lab. manual 15.50 (ISBN 0-471-65247-4); tchrs.' manual avail. (ISBN 0-471-65250-4). Wiley.

Oparin, Alexander I. The Chemical Origin of Life. (Illus.). 152p. 1964. photocopy ed. 14.75x (ISBN 0-398-01426-4). C C Thomas.

Orten, James M. & Neuhaus, Otto W. Human Biochemistry. 10th ed. LC 81-14089. (Illus.). 984p. 1982. text ed. 32.95 (ISBN 0-8016-3730-9). Mosby.

Ory, Robert L. & Rittig, Falk R. Bioregulators: Chemistry & Uses. LC 84-10987. (ACS Symposium Ser.: No. 257). 283p. 1984. 44.95x (ISBN 0-8412-0853-0). Am Chemical.

Ottaway, J. H. & Apps, D. K. Biochemistry. 4th ed. (Illus.). 310p. 1984. write for info. (ISBN 0-7216-0946-5, Pub. by Bailliere-Tindall). Saunders.

Ouellette, Robert J. Introduction to General, Organic, & Biological Chemistry. (Illus.). 720p. 1984. text ed. write for info. (ISBN 0-02-389880-1); write for info. test bank (ISBN 0-02-390220-5). Macmillan.

Ovchinnikov, Yu, ed. Frontiers in Bio-Organic Chemistry & Molecular Biology. (ICSU Press Symposium Ser.: No. 4). 1984. write for info. (ISBN 0-444-80643-1). ICSU Pr.

Page, David S. Principles of Biological Chemistry. 2nd ed. LC 80-39968. 454p. 1981. text ed. 22.00 pub net (ISBN 0-87150-740-4, 31N4311); pub net study guide 7.00 (ISBN 0-87150-746-3, 31N4316). Brooks-Cole.

Paparella, Michael M. Biochemical Mechanisms in Hearing & Deafness. (Illus.). 416p. 1970. photocopy ed. 44.50x (ISBN 0-398-01445-0). C C Thomas.

Parker, Frank S. Applications of Infrared, Raman, & Resonance Raman Spectroscopy in Biochemistry. 515p. 1983. 65.00x (ISBN 0-306-41206-3, Plenum Pr). Plenum Pub.

Parpart, Arthur K., ed. Chemistry & Physiology of Growth. LC 79-159099. 1971. Repr. of 1949 ed. 24.50x (ISBN 0-8046-1642-6, Pub. by Kennikat). Assoc Faculty Pr.

Pasternak, C. A. An Introduction to Human Biochemistry. (Illus.). 1979. pap. text ed. 19.95x (ISBN 0-19-261127-5). Oxford U Pr.

Pasternak, Charles A., ed. Radioimmunoassay in Clinical Biochemistry. LC 76-675546. pap. 79.30 (ISBN 0-317-29335-4, 2024025). Bks Demand UMI.

Paterson, C. R. Essentials of Human Biochemistry. 284p. (Orig.). 1983. pap. 19.50 (ISBN 0-272-79713-8, Pub. by Pitman Bks Ltd UK). Urban & S.

Paul, Armine D. Programmed Topics in Organic & Biochemistry. 1981. coil bdg. 7.50 (ISBN 0-88252-060-1). Paladin Hse.

Peacocke, A. R. An Introduction to the Physical Chemistry of Biological Organization. (Illus.). 1983. 65.00x (ISBN 0-19-855359-5). Oxford U Pr.

Piez, K. A. & Reddi, A. H., eds. Extracellular Matrix Biochemistry. 528p. 1984. 60.00 (ISBN 0-444-00799-7). Elsevier.

Pigman, Ward & Horton, Derek, eds. Advances in Carbohydrate Chemistry & Biochemistry, Vol. 33. 1976. 90.00 (ISBN 0-12-007233-5). Acad Pr.

--Advances in Carbohydrate Chemistry & Biochemistry, Vol. 34. 1977. 90.00 (ISBN 0-12-007234-3). Acad Pr.

Plummer, David. Introduction to Practical Biochemistry: The Greatest Adventure in Modern Archaeology. 2nd ed. 1978. pap. text ed. 39.95x (ISBN 0-07-084074-1). McGraw.

Poland, D. Cooperative Equilibria in Physical Biochemistry. (Monographs on Physical Biochemistry). (Illus.). 1978. text ed. 55.00x (ISBN 0-19-854622-X). Oxford U Pr.

Poland, D. & Scheraga, H. A. Theory of Helix Coil Transitions in Biopolymers. (Molecular Biology). 1970. 75.00 (ISBN 0-12-559550-6). Acad Pr.

Pollak, J. K. & Lee, J. W., eds. The Biochemistry of Gene Expression in Higher Organisms: Proceedings. LC 72-97960. 656p. 1973. lib. bdg. 71.00 (ISBN 90-277-0289-6, Pub. by Reidel Holland). Kluwer Academic.

Pomeroy, Lawrence R., ed. Cycles of Essential Elements. LC 74-4252. (Benchmark Papers in Ecology Ser: Vol. 1). 384p. 1974. 52.95 (ISBN 0-87933-129-1). Van Nos Reinhold.

Poortmans, Jacques, ed. Biochemistry of Exercise IV-IIB, No. IV-b. (International Series on Sports Science: Vol. IIB). 334p. 1981. text ed. 42.00 (ISBN 0-8391-1620-9). Univ Park.

Poortmans, Jacques & Niset, Georges, eds. Biochemistry of Exercise IV-IIA. (International Series on Sports Sciences: Vol. IIA). 320p. 1981. text ed. 42.00 (ISBN 0-8391-1619-5). Univ Park.

Porter, John W. & Spurgeon, Sandra L. Biosynthesis of Isoprenoid Compounds, Vol. I. LC 80-28511. 576p. 1981. 85.50 (ISBN 0-471-04807-0, Pub. by Wiley-Interscience). Wiley.

Powell, Eric F. Biochemistry up to Date. 66p. 1963. pap. 5.50x (ISBN 0-8464-0995-X). Beekman Pubs.

--Biochemistry up-to-Date. 1963. pap. 3.50 (ISBN 0-85032-098-4, Pub. by Formur Intl). Formur Intl.

--Biochemistry up to Date. 1980. 25.00 (ISBN 0-85032-175-1, Pub. by Daniel Co England). State Mutual Bk.

PreTest Service Inc. Biochemistry: PreTest Self-Assessment & Review. 4th ed. (Illus.). 200p. 1985. pap. 13.95 (ISBN 0-07-051942-0). McGraw-Pretest.

Priest, Nicholas D., ed. Metals in Bone. 1985. lib. bdg. 54.75 (ISBN 0-85200-909-7, Pub. by MTP Pr Netherlands). Kluwer Academic.

Pullman, Bernard, ed. Electronic Aspects of Biochemistry: Proceedings. 1964. 81.00 (ISBN 0-12-566950-X). Acad Pr.

--Specificity in Biological Interactions. 1984. lib. bdg. 86.00 (ISBN 90-277-1813-X, Pub. by Reidel Holland). Kluwer Academic.

Pullman, Bernard & Goldblum, Nathan, eds. Excited States in Organic Chemistry & Biochemistry. (The Jerusalem Symposia on Quantum Chemistry & Biochemistry Ser.: No. 10). 1977. lib. bdg. 53.00 (ISBN 90-277-0853-3, Pub. by Reidel Holland). Kluwer Academic.

Ragan, Mark A. & Chapman, David J., eds. Biochemical Phylogeny of the Protists. 1978. 55.50 (ISBN 0-12-575550-3). Acad Pr.

Rajagopal, G. & Ramakrishnan, S. Practical Biochemistry for Medical Students. (Illus.). 80p. (Orig.). 1983. pap. text ed. 8.95x (ISBN 0-86131-415-8, Pub by Orient Longman Ltd India). Apt Bks.

Ramachandran, G. N. & Reddi, A. H., eds. Biochemistry of Collagen. LC 76-7075. (Illus.). 536p. 1976. 69.50x (ISBN 0-306-30855-X, Plenum Pr). Plenum Pub.

Rawn, J. David. Biochemistry. 1139p. 1983. text ed. 37.00 scp (ISBN 0-06-045335-4, HarpC); scp study guide 11.50 (ISBN 0-06-045334-6). Har-Row.

Reactions & Processes. (The Handbook of Environmental Chemistry: Vol. 2, Pt. A). (Illus.). 320p. 1980. 78.00 (ISBN 0-387-09689-2). Springer-Verlag.

Reavis, Marshall W. Illinois Insurance Law: A License Preparation Manual for Life & Health, Property & Casualty. LC 83-5437. 174p. 1983. pap. text ed. 15.95 (ISBN 0-88462-628-8, 4101-03, Longman Fin Serv Pub); text ed. 15.95. Longman USA.

Reid, Eric, et al, eds. Investigation of Membrane-Located Receptors. (Methodological Surveys in Biochemistry & Analysis Ser.: Vol. 13). 542p. 1984. 75.00x (ISBN 0-306-41499-6, Plenum Pr). Plenum Pub.

Reid, Robert A. & Leech, Rachel M. Biochemistry & Structure of Cell Organelles. (Tertiary Level Biology Ser.). 176p. 1980. pap. text ed. 23.95x (ISBN 0-470-26981-2). Halsted Pr.

Rensing, L. & Jaeger, N. I., eds. Temporal Order. (Springer Series in Synergetics: Vol. 29). (Illus.). ix, 325p. 1985. 36.00 (ISBN 0-387-15274-1). Springer-Verlag.

Reviews of Physiology, Biochemistry & Pharmacology, Vol. 100. (Illus.). 250p. 1984. 36.50 (ISBN 0-387-13327-5). Springer-Verlag.

Reviews of Physiology, Biochemistry & Pharmacology, Vol. 74. LC 74-3674. (Illus.). 270p. 1975. 59.00 (ISBN 0-387-07483-X). Springer-Verlag.

Reviews of Physiology, Biochemistry & Pharmacology, Vol. 84. (Illus.). 1978. 51.00 (ISBN 0-387-08984-5). Springer-Verlag.

Reviews of Physiology, Biochemistry & Pharmacology, Vol. 86. (Illus.). 1979. 57.00 (ISBN 0-387-09488-1). Springer-Verlag.

Reviews of Physiology Biochemistry & Pharmacology, Vol. 87. (Illus.). 250p. 1980. 58.00 (ISBN 0-387-09944-1). Springer-Verlag.

Reviews of Physiology, Biochemistry & Pharmacology, Vol. 99. (Illus.). 240p. 1984. 40.00 (ISBN 0-387-12989-8). Springer-Verlag.

Ricard, J. & Cornish-Bowden, A., eds. Dynamics of Biochemical Systems. (NATO ASI Series A, Life Sciences: Vol. 81). 316p. 1984. 49.50x (ISBN 0-306-41830-4, Plenum Pr). Plenum Pub.

Rickwood, D., ed. Centrifugation: A Practical Approach. 2nd ed. (The Practical Approach Ser.). (Illus.). 364p. 1984. 24.00 (ISBN 0-904147-55-X). IRL Pr.

Roberts, Anita B. & Sporn, Michael B. The Retinoids, Vol. 1. 1984. 49.50 (ISBN 0-12-658101-0). Acad Pr.

--The Retinoids, Vol. 2. 1984. 50.00 (ISBN 0-12-658102-9). Acad Pr.

Robison, G. Alan. Cyclic AMP. 528p. 1971. 71.50 (ISBN 0-12-590450-9). Acad Pr.

Romanoff, Alexis L. & Romanoff, A. J. Biochemistry of the Avian Embryo. LC 67-13961. Repr. of 1967 ed. 104.00 (ISBN 0-8357-9846-1, 2013077). Bks Demand UMI.

Roodyn, Donald B., ed. Subcellular Biochemistry, Vol. 6. LC 73-643479. 544p. 1979. 69.50x (ISBN 0-306-40113-4, Plenum Pr). Plenum Pub.

--Subcellular Biochemistry, Vol. 9. 442p. 1983. 59.50x (ISBN 0-306-41091-5, Plenum Pr). Plenum Pub.

--Subcellular Biochemistry, Vol. 10. 568p. 1984. 72.50x (ISBN 0-306-41528-3, Plenum Pr). Plenum Pub.

Rothstein, Morton. Biochemical Approaches to Aging. 1982. 44.50 (ISBN 0-12-598780-3). Acad Pr.

Routh, Joseph I. Introduction to Biochemistry. 2nd ed. LC 76-28945. (Illus.). 1978. pap. text ed. 20.95 (ISBN 0-7216-7759-2). HR&W.

Routh, Joseph I., et al. Introduction to Biochemistry. 2nd ed. 1978. pap. text ed. 20.95 (ISBN 0-7216-7759-2, CBS C). SCP.

Ruegamer, W. R. Elementary Biochemistry. 1985. 15.00 (ISBN 0-8151-7457-8). Year Bk Med.

Russell, N. J. & Powell, G. M. Blood Biochemistry. (Biology in Medicine Ser.). (Illus.). 186p. 1982. text ed. 27.25x (ISBN 0-7099-0003-1). Sheridan.

Samuelsson, Bengt & Paoletti, Rodolfo, eds. Leukotrienes & Other Lipoxygenase Products. (Advances in Prostaglandin, Thromboxane, & Leukotriene Research Ser.: Vol. 9). 384p. 1982. text ed. 63.50 (ISBN 0-89004-741-3). Raven.

San Pietro, Anthony G., ed. Biochemical & Photosynthetic Aspects of Energy Production. 1980. 28.50 (ISBN 0-12-618980-3). Acad Pr.

Sarkar, Bibudhendra, ed. Biological Aspects of Metals & Metal-Related Diseases. 330p. 1983. text ed. 68.50 (ISBN 0-89004-807-X). Raven.

Sarma, Ramaswamy H. Nucleic Acid Geometry & Dynamics. LC 80-10620. (Illus.). 424p. 1980. 65.00 (ISBN 0-08-024631-1); pap. 29.00 (ISBN 0-08-024630-3). Pergamon.

Sawtell, Vanda. Astrology & Biochemistry. 1980. lib. bdg. 15.95 (ISBN 0-85032-174-3, Pub. by Daniel Co England). State Mutual Bk.

Sawyer, Donald T., ed. Electrochemical Studies of Biological Systems. LC 76-30831. (ACS Symposium Ser.: No. 38). 1977. 24.95 (ISBN 0-8412-0361-X). Am Chemical.

Schachman, Howard K. Ultracentrifugation in Biochemistry. 1959. 60.00 (ISBN 0-12-621050-0). Acad Pr.

Schambye, Per, ed. Proceedings: FEBS Meeting, 11th, 9 vols. (Illus.). 1978. Set. text ed. 345.00 (ISBN 0-08-021527-0). Pergamon.

Scheinmann, Feodor & Ackroyd, John. Leukotriene Syntheses: A New Class of Biologically Active Compounds Including SRS-A. (Illus.). 110p. 1984. text ed. 29.50 (ISBN 0-89004-897-5). Raven.

Scheuer, Paul J. Chemistry of Marine Natural Products. 1973. 44.00 (ISBN 0-12-624050-7). Acad Pr.

Scheve, Larry G. Elements of Biochemistry. 500p. 1984. scp 37.86 (ISBN 0-205-07909-1, 687909); instrs' manual avail. Allyn.

Schlessinger, Bernard S., ed. Biochemistry Collections. LC 81-13408. (Special Collections Ser.: Vol. 1, No. 2). 147p. 1982. 29.95 (ISBN 0-917724-48-8, B48). Haworth Pr.

Schoffeniels, E., ed. Biochemical Evolution & the Origin of Life. 1971. 30.75 (ISBN 0-444-10081-4). Elsevier.

Schreiber, William E. Medical Aspects of Biochemistry. 304p. 1984. pap. text ed. 19.95 (ISBN 0-316-77473-1). Little.

Schwarz, Victor. A Clinical Companion to Biochemical Studies. LC 77-17132. (Illus.). 114p. 1978. text ed. 23.95x (ISBN 0-7167-0078-6); pap. text ed. 12.95x (ISBN 0-7167-0077-8). W H Freeman.

--A Clinical Companion to Biochemical Studies. 2nd ed. (Illus.). 192p. 1984. pap. text ed. 14.95 (ISBN 0-7167-1601-1). W H Freeman.

Scott, Ronald M. Introduction to Organic & Biochemistry. 1980. text ed. 23.95 scp (ISBN 0-06-388450-X, HarpC); scp study guide 8.95 (ISBN 0-06-385760-X); instr's. manual avail. (ISBN 0-06-376250-1). Har-Row.

Scott, Thomas & Brewer, Mary, eds. Concise Encyclopedia of Biochemistry. LC 82-22148. Tr. of Brockhaus ABC biochemie. (Illus.). vi, 519p. 1983. 29.95 (ISBN 3-11-007860-0). De Gruyter.

Scouten, William H. Solid Phase Biochemistry: Analytical & Synthetic Aspects. LC 82-21886. (Chemical Analysis: Monographs on Analytical Chemistry & its Application). 779p. 1983. 80.50x (ISBN 0-471-08585-5, Pub. by Wiley-Interscience). Wiley.

Semenza, G., ed. Selected Topics in the History of Biochemistry. (Comprehensive Biochemistry Ser.: Vol. 35). 400p. 1984. 81.00 (ISBN 0-444-80507-9). Elsevier.

Shapot, V. S. Biochemical Aspects of Tumour Growth. 334p. 1980. 11.00 (ISBN 0-8285-0006-1, Pub. by Mir Pubs USSR). Imported Pubns.

Shapovalou, I. A., et al. Reviews of Physiology, Biochemistry & Pharmacology, Vol. 72. LC 74-3674. (Illus.). 200p. 1975. 68.00 (ISBN 0-387-07077-X). Springer-Verlag.

Shephard, Roy J. Biochemistry of Physical Activity. (Illus.). 400p. 1984. 44.75x (ISBN 0-398-04854-1). C C Thomas.

--Physiology & Biochemistry of Exercise. LC 81-1833. 682p. 1985. 35.00 (ISBN 0-03-003674-7). Praeger.

Sicuteri, F., et al, eds. Bradykinin & Related Kinins: Cardiovascular, Biochemical & Neural Actions. LC 78-119055. (Advances in Experimental Medicine & Biology Ser.: Vol. 8). 676p. 1970. 79.50x (ISBN 0-306-39008-6, Plenum Pr). Plenum Pub.

Sigel, Helmut, ed. Metal Ions in Biological Systems: Reactivity of Coordination Compounds, Vol. 5. 416p. 1976. 75.00 (ISBN 0-8247-6032-8). Dekker.

Silverman, Morris. Biochemistry Review. LC 81-10828. (Medical Review Ser.). (Illus.). 336p. (Orig.). 1982. pap. 13.95 (ISBN 0-668-04359-8). ACC.

Simic, Michael G. & Karel, Marcus, eds. Autoxidation in Food & Biological Systems. LC 80-23849. 672p. 1980. 79.50x (ISBN 0-306-40561-X, Plenum Pr). Plenum Pub.

Simon, Z. Quantum Biochemistry & Specific Interactions. 1976. 33.00 (ISBN 0-9961002-8-8, Pub. by Abacus England). Heyden.

Sinclair, Walton B. The Biochemistry & Physiology of the Lemon & Other Citrus Fruits. LC 83-72137. (Illus.). 1000p. (Orig.). 1983. 55.00x (ISBN 0-931876-64-8, 3306). Ag & Nat Res.

Sinex, F. Marott. Biochemistry of Aging. Date not set. price not set (ISBN 0-89004-172-5). Raven.

Smellie, R. M. & Pennock, J. F., eds. Symposia No. Forty One: Biochemical Adaptation to Environmental Change. 240p. 1981. 29.00x (ISBN 0-904498-01-8, Pub. by Biochemical England). State Mutual Bk.

Smith, Emil L. & Hill, Robert L. Principles of Biochemistry. 7th ed. Incl. General Aspects. 960p. text ed. 36.00 (ISBN 0-07-069762-0); Mammalian Biochemistry. 672p. text ed. 42.00 (ISBN 0-07-069763-9). (Illus.). 1983. McGraw.

Smith, J. E. & Berry, D. R. An Introduction to the Biochemistry of Fungal Development. 1975. 55.00 (ISBN 0-12-650950-6). Acad Pr.

Snyder, Robert, et al. Biological Reactive Intermediates II: Chemical Mechanisms & Biological Effects. LC 81-12003. (Advances in Experimental Medicine & Biology Ser.: Vol. 136). 1500p. 1981. 145.00 (ISBN 0-306-40802-3, Plenum Pr). Plenum Pub.

Snyder, Solomon H., ed. Biochemistry & Behavior. 100p. 1976. pap. text ed. 8.95x (ISBN 0-262-69051-9). MIT Pr.

Societe de Chimie Physique, 23rd. Dynamic Aspects of Conformation Changes in Biological Macromolecules: Proceedings. Sadron, C., ed. LC 72-97962. 400p. 1973. lib. bdg. 79.00 (ISBN 90-277-0334-5, Pub. by Reidel Holland). Kluwer Academic.

Society for Industrial & Applied Mathematical - American Mathematical Society Symposia - New York - April, 1974. Mathematical Aspects of Chemical & Biochemical Problems & Quantum Chemistry: Proceedings. Cohen, Donald S, ed. LC 74-26990. (SIAM-AMS Proceedings Ser.: Vol. 8). 1974. 33.00 (ISBN 0-8218-1328-5, SIAMS-8). Am Math.

Spiegel, Herbert, ed. Clinical Biochemistry: Contemporary Theories & Techniques, Vol. 1. LC 81-14933. 1981. 39.50 (ISBN 0-12-657101-5). Acad Pr.

--Clinical Biochemistry: Contemporary Theories & Techniques, Vol. 2. LC 81-14933. 1982. 45.00 (ISBN 0-12-657102-3). Acad Pr.

Srinivasan, P. R., et al, eds. The Origins of Modern Biochemistry: A Retrospect on Proteins. (Annals of the New York Academy of Sciences: Vol. 325). 373p. (Orig.). 1979. pap. 67.00x (ISBN 0-89766-018-8). NY Acad Sci.

Srinivasan, R. Biomolecular Structure, Conformation, Function & Evolution, 2 vols. Incl. Vol. 1. Diffraction & Related Studies; Vol. 2. Physico-Chemical & Theoretical Studies. 1981. Set. 320.00 (ISBN 0-08-023187-X). Pergamon.

Stec, W. J. Phosphorous Chemistry Directed Towards Biology: International Symposium on Phosphorus Chemistry Directed Towards Biology, Burzenin, Poland, 25-28 September 1979. (IUPAC Symposium Ser.). 240p. 1980. 81.00 (ISBN 0-08-023969-2). Pergamon.

Stenesh, Jochanan. Dictionary of Biochemistry. LC 75-23037. 344p. 1975. 45.50 (ISBN 0-471-82105-5, Pub. by Wiley-Interscience). Wiley.

Stephens, Newman L. Biochemistry of Smooth Muscle, Vol. I. 208p. 1983. 69.00 (ISBN 0-8493-6575-9). CRC Pr.

Stephens, Newman L., ed. Biochemistry of Smooth Muscle, 2 Vols. 1983. Vol. II, 304p. 86.00 (ISBN 0-8493-6576-7); Vol. III, 208p. 63.00 (ISBN 0-8493-6577-5). CRC Pr.

Stoker, H. Stephen & Slabaugh, Michael R. General, Organic & Biochemistry: A Brief Introduction. 1981. text ed. 26.65x (ISBN 0-673-15091-7); study guide 8.95x (ISBN 0-673-15501-3). Scott F.

Stryer, Lubert. Biochemistry. 2nd ed. LC 80-24699. (Illus.). 949p. 1981. text ed. 38.95x (ISBN 0-7167-1226-1). W H Freeman.

Suckling, Colin J. & Suckling, Keith E. Biological Chemistry. LC 79-51830. (Cambridge Texts in Chemistry & Biochemistry Ser.). (Illus.). 350p. 1980. 69.50 (ISBN 0-521-22852-2); pap. 22.95 (ISBN 0-521-29678-1). Cambridge U Pr.

Szantay, C., et al, eds. Chemistry & Biotechnology of Biologically Active Natural Products: Proceedings of the International Conference, 2nd, Budapest, 15-19 Aug., 1983. (Studies in Organic Chemistry: No. 17). 378p. 1984. 74.00 (ISBN 0-444-99608-7, I-232-84). Elsevier.

Srivastava, Satish K. Red Blood Cell & Lens Metabolism. (Developments in Biochemistry: Vol. 9). 508p. 1980. 85.25 (ISBN 0-444-00388-6, Biomedical Pr). Elsevier.

Wrigglesworth, J. M. Biochemical Research Techniques: A Practical Introduction. LC 82-21963. 239p. 1983. 44.95x (ISBN 0-471-10323-3, Pub. by Wiley-Interscience). Wiley.

BIOLOGICAL CHEMISTRY–STUDY AND TEACHING

Baldwin, Ernest. An Introduction to Comparative Biochemistry. 4th ed. LC 64-21524. pap. 49.80 (ISBN 0-317-26096-0, 2024418). Bks Demand UMI.

BIOLOGICAL CHEMISTRY–TECHNIQUE

Alexander, Renee R. Basic Biochemical Methods. LC 84-13215. 1984. 24.95 (ISBN 0-471-88027-2, Pub. by Wiley-Interscience). Wiley.

Cantor, Charles R. & Schimmel, Paul R. Biophysical Chemistry, Part II: Techniques for the Study of Biological Structure & Function. LC 79-24854. (Illus.). 554p. 1980. text ed. 46.95 (ISBN 0-7167-1189-3); pap. text ed. 26.95 (ISBN 0-7167-1190-7). W H Freeman.

Catsimpoolas, Nicholas, ed. Isoelectric Focusing. 1976. 55.00 (ISBN 0-12-163950-9). Acad Pr.

Cooper. The Tools of Biochemistry. 2nd ed. 1985. price not set (ISBN 0-471-82358-9). Wiley.

Cooper, Terrance C. The Tools of Biochemistry. LC 76-30910. 423p. 1977. 34.95x (ISBN 0-471-17116-6, Pub. by Wiley-Interscience). Wiley.

Dunlap, R. Bruce, ed. Immobilized Biochemicals & Affinity Chromatography. LC 74-7471. (Advances in Experimental Medicine & Biology Ser.: Vol. 42). 388p. 1974. 59.50x (ISBN 0-306-39042-6, Plenum Pr). Plenum Pub.

Franks, Felix. Biophysics & Biochemistry at Low Temperatures. (Illus.). 224p. 1985. 44.50 (ISBN 0-521-26320-4). Cambridge U Pr.

Glick, David. Methods of Biochemical Analysis, Vol. 27. (Methods of Biochemical Analysis Ser.). 537p. 1981. 62.50 (ISBN 0-471-06503-X, Pub. by Wiley-Interscience). Wiley.

--Methods of Biochemical Analysis, Vol. 29. 507p. 1983. text ed. 64.50 (ISBN 0-471-86283-5, 2-180, Pub. by Wiley-Interscience). Wiley.

Glick, David, ed. Methods of Biochemical Analysis. LC 54-7273. 435p. (Pub. by Wiley Interscience); Vol. 26, 1980. 59.50 (ISBN 0-471-04798-8). Wiley.

Haschemeyer, Rudolph & Haschemeyer, Audrey H. Proteins: A Guide to Study by Physical & Chemical Methods. LC 72-13134. 445p. 1973. 47.50x (ISBN 0-471-35850-9, Pub. by Wiley-Interscience). Wiley.

Hillman, Harold H. Certainty & Uncertainty in Biochemical Techniques. 1972. 39.95x (ISBN 0-903384-00-0). Intl Ideas.

International Symposium on Quantitative Mass Spectrometry in Life Sciences, 1st, State University of Ghent Belgium June 16-18 1976. Quantitative Mass Spectrometry in Life Sciences: Proceedings. DeLeenheer, A. P. & Roncucci, Romeo R, eds. LC 77-3404. 254p. 1977. 64.00 (ISBN 0-444-41557-2). Elsevier.

Turner, Ralph B., ed. Analytical Biochemistry of Insects. LC 76-54362. 316p. 1977. 64.00 (ISBN 0-444-41539-4). Elsevier.

BIOLOGICAL CLOCKS

see Biological Rhythms

BIOLOGICAL CLOCKS, DAILY

see Circadian Rhythms

BIOLOGICAL CONTROL OF INSECTS

see Insect Control–Biological Control

BIOLOGICAL CONTROL SYSTEMS

see also Biofeedback Training; Homeostasis

Abou-Sabe, Morad, ed. Microbial Genetics. LC 73-13002. (Benchmark Papers in Microbiology: Vol. 3). 451p. 1977. 57.95 (ISBN 0-87933-046-5). Van Nos Reinhold.

Advances in Control & Dynamic Systems, Vol. 18. (Serial Publication Ser.). 448p. 1982. 48.50 (ISBN 0-12-012718-0). Acad Pr.

Banks, H. T. Modelling & Control in the Biomedical Sciences. LC 75-25771. (Lecture Notes in Biomathematics: Vol. 6). v, 114p. 1975. pap. 13.00 (ISBN 0-387-07395-7). Springer-Verlag.

Chandebois, Rosine & Faber, J., eds. Automation in Animal Development. (Monographs in Developmental Biology: Vol. 16). (Illus.). xii, 204p. 1983. 70.25 (ISBN 3-8055-3666-6). S Karger.

Cruz, Jose B., Jr., ed. Advances in Control Systems: Theory & Application. 1983. 45.00 (ISBN 0-89232-411-2). Jai Pr.

Delucchi, Vittorio L., ed. Studies in Biological Control. LC 75-16867. (International Biological Programme Ser.: No. 9). pap. 80.00 (ISBN 0-317-29377-X, 2024479). Bks Demand UMI.

Gangstad, Edward O. Weed Control Methods for Public Health Applications. 320p. 1980. 84.50 (ISBN 0-8493-5326-2). CRC Pr.

Grodins, Fred S. Control Theory & Biological Systems. LC 63-10521. 205p. 1963. 32.00x (ISBN 0-231-02517-3). Columbia U Pr.

Groves, R. H. & Burdon, J. J., eds. The Ecology of Biological Invasions. (Illus.). 225p. Date not set. price not set (ISBN 0-521-30355-9). Cambridge U Pr.

Huijing, F. & Lee, E. Y., eds. Protein Phosphorylation in Control Mechanisms. (Miami Winter Symposia: No. 5). 1973. 49.50 (ISBN 0-12-360950-X). Acad Pr.

IFAC Workshop, 1st, Helsinki, Finland, Aug. 1982 & Halme, A. Modelling & Control of Biotechnical Processes: Proceedings. (IFAC Proceedings Ser.). 296p. 1983. 75.00 (ISBN 0-08-029978-4). Pergamon.

Leondes, C. T., ed. Control of Dynamic Systems: Advances in Theory & Application, Vols. 9, 10, 13 & 15. Incl. Vol. 9. 1973. 65.00 (ISBN 0-12-012709-1); Vol. 10. 1973. 65.00 (ISBN 0-12-012710-5); Vol. 13. 1977. 65.00 (ISBN 0-12-012713-X); Vol. 15. 1979. 44.00 (ISBN 0-12-012715-6). 1973. Acad Pr.

MacDonald, N. Trees & Networks in Biological Models. 216p. 1984. 39.95x (ISBN 0-471-10508-2, Pub. by Wiley-Interscience). Wiley.

Meints, Russel H. & Davies, Eric, eds. Control Mechanisms in Development: Activation, Differentiation, & Modulation in Biological Systems. LC 75-28152. (Advances in Experimental Medicine & Biology Ser.: Vol. 62). 239p. 1975. 37.50x (ISBN 0-306-39062-0, Plenum Pr). Plenum Pub.

Mohler, Ronald R. Bilinear Control Processes: With Applications to Engineering, Ecology & Medicine. (Mathematics in Science & Engineering Ser.). 1973. 60.00 (ISBN 0-12-504140-3). Acad Pr.

Pattee, Howard H., ed. Hierarchy Theory: The Challenge of Complex Systems. LC 72-93477. 1973. 7.95 (ISBN 0-8076-0674-X). Braziller.

Pavlidis, Theodosios. Biological Oscillators: Their Mathematical Analysis. 1973. 56.00 (ISBN 0-12-547350-8). Acad Pr.

Paxton, Mary. The Female Body in Control: How the Control Mechanisms in a Woman's Physiology Make Her Special. (Illus.). 290p. 1981. 17.95 (ISBN 0-13-314104-7); pap. 8.95 (ISBN 0-13-314096-2). P-H.

Rankin, J. C., et al. Control Processes in Fish Physiology. 298p. 1983. 39.95x (ISBN 0-471-88404-9, Pub. by Wiley-Interscience). Wiley.

San Pietro, Anthony, et al, eds. Regulatory Mechanisms for Protein Synthesis in Mammalian Cells. 1968. 65.00 (ISBN 0-12-618960-9). Acad Pr.

Savory, T. H. Zoological Systematics. 1979. 39.00x (ISBN 0-904095-31-2, Pub. by Meadowfield Pr England). State Mutual Bk.

Savory, Theodore. The Principles of Mechanistic Biology. 43p. 1971. 39.00x (ISBN 0-900541-46-6, Pub. by Meadowfield Pr England). State Mutual Bk.

Shirley, Hunter B. Inside the Human Control System. LC 81-81614. Date not set. 8.95 (ISBN 0-87212-153-4). Libra.

Simpson, T. L. & Yolcani, B. E., eds. Silicon & Siliceous Structures in Biological Systems. (Illus.). 587p. 1981. 120.00 (ISBN 0-387-90592-8). Springer-Verlag.

Systems Symposium, 3rd, Case Western Reserve University, Institute of Technology. Systems Theory & Biology: Proceedings. Mesavoric, M. D., ed. (Illus.). 1968. 53.00 (ISBN 0-387-04356-X). Springer-Verlag.

Toates, F. M. Control Theory in Biology & Experimental Psychology. 1980. text ed. 21.50x (ISBN 0-09-119660-4, Hutchinson U Lib). Humanities.

Troch, I., ed. Simulation of Control Systems With Special Emphasis on Modelling & Redundancy. 312p. (Proceedings). 1978. 64.00 (ISBN 0-444-85199-2, North-Holland). Elsevier.

Van Den Bosch, Robert, et al. An Introduction to Biological Control. LC 81-21125. 261p. 1981. 18.95x (ISBN 0-306-40706-X, Plenum Pr). Plenum Pub.

Varela, F. J. Principles of Biological Autonomy. (North Holland Ser. in General Systems Research: Vol. 2). 336p. 1979. 52.25 (ISBN 0-444-00321-5, North Holland). Elsevier.

Vassileva-Popova, Julia G., ed. Physical & Chemical Bases of Biological Information Transfer. LC 75-30849. 475p. 1975. 59.50x (ISBN 0-306-30862-2, Plenum Pr). Plenum Pub.

Walcher, Dwain N. & Peters, Donald L., eds. Early Childhood: The Development of Self-Regulatory Mechanisms. 1971. 47.50 (ISBN 0-12-731750-3). Acad Pr.

Yasumatsu, K. & Mori, H., eds. Approaches to Biological Control, Vol. 7. (Japan International Biological Program Synthesis Ser.). 141p. 1975. 17.00x (ISBN 0-86008-217-2, Pub. by U of Tokyo Japan). Columbia U Pr.

Zeleny, M., ed. Autopoiesis: A Theory of Living Organization. (Series in General Systems Research: Vol. 3). 314p. 1981. 77.00 (ISBN 0-444-86178-5, North-Holland). Elsevier.

BIOLOGICAL DEGRADATION

see Biodegradation

BIOLOGICAL ELECTRONICS

see Electronics in Biology

BIOLOGICAL ENGINEERING

see Bioengineering

BIOLOGICAL ILLUSTRATION

Downey, John C. & Kelly, James L. Biological Illustration: Techniques & Exercises. (Illus.). 126p. 1982. pap. text ed. 11.75x (ISBN 0-8138-0201-6). Iowa St U Pr.

Farr, Gerald G. Biology Illustrated. (Illus.). 117p. 1979. pap. text ed. 5.95x (ISBN 0-89641-054-4). American Pr.

West, Keith. How to Draw Plants: The Art of Botanical Illustrations. (Illus.). 152p. 1983. 22.50 (ISBN 0-8230-2355-9). Watson-Guptill.

Zweifel, Frances W. Handbook of Biological Illustration. LC 61-19734. (Orig.). 1961. pap. 6.00x (ISBN 0-226-99699-9, P510, Phoen). U of Chicago Pr.

BIOLOGICAL LABORATORIES

Benton, Allen H. & Cudia, S. J. Experiences & Problems in the Biology Laboratory. 3rd ed. 96p. 1980. 9.00 (ISBN 0-942788-04-4). Marginal Med.

Campbell, June M. & Campbell, Joe B. Laboratory Mathematics: Medical & Biological Applications. 3rd ed. LC 83-8203. (Illus.). 320p. 1984. text ed. 15.95 (ISBN 0-8016-0800-7). Mosby.

Directory of Cell Research Laboratories. 516p. 1969. 27.50 (ISBN 92-3-000773-0, U160, UNESCO). Unipub.

Eberhard, Carolyn. Biology Laboratory. 328p. 1982. pap. text ed. 17.95x (ISBN 0-03-059963-6). SCP.

Emmel, Victor E. & Cowdry, E. V. Laboratory Technique in Biology & Medicine. 4th ed. LC 64-13546. 1970. Repr. of 1964 ed. 24.00 (ISBN 0-88275-016-X). Krieger.

Friedman, Richard, et al. Effects of Disease on Clinical Laboratory Tests, Vol. 26, No. 4. LC 81-65486. 476p. 1980. 30.00 (ISBN 0-915274-16-7). Am Assn Clinical Chem.

Fry, Virginia. Exploring Biology in the Laboratory. 2nd ed. 250p. 1984. pap. 16.95x (ISBN 0-03-063373-7). SCP.

Glase, Jon C. Tested Studies for Laboratory Teaching: Proceedings of the Second Workshop-Conference of the Association of Biology-Laboratory Education (ABLE) LC 81-81747. 288p. 1981. text ed. 19.95 (ISBN 0-8403-2471-5). Kendall-Hunt.

Glase, Jon C., ed. Tested Studies for Laboratory Teaching: Proceedings of the First Workshop of the Association for Biology Laboratory Education. LC 80-82832. 288p. 1980. text ed. 19.95 (ISBN 0-8403-2271-2). Kendall-Hunt.

Hickman, Frances M. & Hickman, Cleveland P. Laboratory Studies in Integrated Zoology. 6th ed. (Illus.). 480p. 1983. text ed. 13.95 (ISBN 0-8016-2178-X). Mosby.

Keeton, William T., et al. Biology in the Laboratory. 1970. pap. 9.95x (ISBN 0-393-09943-1). Norton.

Stetler, David A. & Via, Jerry W. Biology Laboratory. rev. ed. (Illus.). 240p. 1983. lab manual 10.95 (ISBN 0-89459-208-4). Hunter Textbks.

WHO Expert Group, Geneva, 1965. Requirements for Biological Substances: Manufacturing Establishments & Control Laboratories, a Report. (Technical Report Ser: No. 323). (Eng, Fr, Rus, & Span.). 71p. 1966. pap. 2.00 (ISBN 92-4-120323-4). World Health.

Young, Donald, et al. Effects of Drugs on Clinical Laboratory Tests, Vol. 21, No. 5. LC 81-65486. 432p. 1975. 25.00 (ISBN 0-915274-00-0); members 20.00. Am Assn Clinical Chem.

BIOLOGICAL LITERATURE

Davis. Using the Biological Literature. (Books in Library & Information Science: Vol. 35). 272p. 1981. 45.00 (ISBN 0-8247-7209-1). Dekker.

Wyatt, H. V. A Directory of Information Resources in Biology in the UK. 1980. 40.00x (ISBN 0-905984-65-X, Pub. by Brit Lib England). State Mutual Bk.

BIOLOGICAL MODELS

see also Biology–Mathematical Models; Stereology

Banks, H. T. Modelling & Control in the Biomedical Sciences. LC 75-25771. (Lecture Notes in Biomathematics: Vol. 6). v, 114p. 1975. pap. 13.00 (ISBN 0-387-07395-7). Springer-Verlag.

Hall, Charles A. & Day, John W., Jr., eds. Ecosystem Modeling in Theory & Practice: An Introduction with Case Histories. LC 76-57204. 684p. 1977. 71.00 (ISBN 0-471-34165-7, Pub. by Wiley-Interscience). Wiley.

Innis, G. S., ed. Grassland Simulation Model. LC 77-23016. (Ecological Studies: Vol. 26). (Illus.). 1978. 39.00 (ISBN 0-387-90269-4). Springer-Verlag.

Systems Symposium, 3rd, Case Western Reserve University, Institute of Technology. Systems Theory & Biology: Proceedings. Mesavoric, M. D., ed. (Illus.). 1968. 53.00 (ISBN 0-387-04356-X). Springer-Verlag.

Vansteenkiste, G. C. & Young, P. C., eds. Modelling & Data Analysis in Biotechnology & Medical Engineering. 376p. 1983. 51.00 (ISBN 0-444-86596-9, I-179-83, North Holland). Elsevier.

Whipp, B. J. & Wiberg, D. M., eds. Modelling & Control of Breathing. 392p. 1983. 72.00 (ISBN 0-444-00783-0, Biomedical Pr). Elsevier.

BIOLOGICAL OXIDATION

see Oxidation, Physiological

BIOLOGICAL PEST CONTROL

see Pest Control–Biological Control

BIOLOGICAL PHYSICS

see also Absorption (Physiology); Biological Control Systems; Biomechanics; Biomedical Engineering; Bionics; Cells; Electronics in Biology; Homeostasis; Medical Electronics; Molecular Biology; Radiobiology; Rheology (Biology)

Abdel-Malek, Anouar & Pandeya, A. N., eds. Intellectual Creativity in Endogenous Culture. 632p. 1981. 36.25 (ISBN 92-808-0265-8, TUNU184, UNU). Unipub.

Arnott, Struther, et al, eds. Molecular Biophysics of the Extracellular Matrix. LC 84-6640. (Molecular Biology & Biophysics Ser.). 224p. 1984. 39.50 (ISBN 0-89603-051-2). Humana.

Asimov, Isaac. Life & Energy. 384p. 1972. pap. 4.50 (ISBN 0-380-00942-0, 60007-2, Discus). Avon.

Bajzer, Z., et al, eds. Applications of Physics to Medicine & Biology: Proceedings of the 2nd International Conference on the Applications of Physics to Medicine & Biology, Italy, November 1983. 664p. 1985. 60.00x (ISBN 9971-966-81-6, Pub. by World Sci Singapore). Taylor & Francis.

--Proceedings of the Second International Conference On Applications of Physics to Medicine & Biology. 664p. 1984. 86.00 (ISBN 9971-966-81-6). Taylor & Francis.

Bauldree, John, et al. Biophysical Lab Manual. 1976. spiral bdg. 21.95 (ISBN 0-88252-057-1). Paladin Hse.

Benedek, G. B. & Villars, F. M. Physics with Illustrative Examples from Medicine & Biology, Vol. 3. 1979. pap. text ed. 25.95 (ISBN 0-201-00559-X). Addison-Wesley.

Berliner, L. J. & Reuben, J., eds. Biological Magnetic Resonance, Vol. 2. LC 78-16035. (Illus.). 352p. 1980. 52.50x (ISBN 0-306-40264-5, Plenum Pr). Plenum Pub.

Blumenfeld, L. A. Problems of Biological Physics. (Series in Synergetics: Vol. 7). (Illus.). 300p. 1981. 39.00 (ISBN 0-387-10401-1). Springer-Verlag.

Borsellino, Antonio, et al, eds. Developments in Biophysical Research. LC 80-25985. 378p. 1981. 55.00x (ISBN 0-306-40627-6, Plenum Pr). Plenum Pub.

Brill, A. S. Transition Metals in Biochemistry. (Molecular Biology, Biochemistry & Biophysics: Vol. 26). 1977. 34.00 (ISBN 0-387-08291-3). Springer-Verlag.

Butler, J. A. & Noble, D., eds. Progress in Biophysics & Molecular Biology, Vols. 5-11, & 13-30. Incl. Vol. 5. 1955. Vol. 10. 62.50 (ISBN 0-08-009293-4); Vol. 6. 1956. write for info.; Vol. 7. 1957. write for info.; Vol. 8. 1958. write for info.; Vol. 9. 1959. write for info.; Vol. 10. 1960. write for info.; Vol. 11. 1961. write for info.; Vol. 13. 1963. 60.00 (ISBN 0-08-010028-7); Vol. 14. 1964. 60.00 (ISBN 0-08-010612-9); Vol. 15. 1965; Vol. 16. 1966. 10.50 (ISBN 0-08-011581-0); Vol. 17. 1967. 60.00 (ISBN 0-08-012046-6); Vol. 18. 1968. 60.00 (ISBN 0-08-012753-3); Vol. 19, Pt. 1. 1969. 31.00 (ISBN 0-08-013034-8); Vol. 19, Pt. 2. 1969. 31.00 (ISBN 0-08-006522-8); Vol. 19, Complete. 62.50 (ISBN 0-08-006523-6); Vol. 20. 1970. 62.50 (ISBN 0-08-006627-5); Vol. 21. 1970. 60.00 (ISBN 0-08-015696-7); Vol. 22. 1971. 60.00 (ISBN 0-08-016348-3); Vol. 23. 1971. 60.00 (ISBN 0-08-016740-3); Vol. 24. 1972. 60.00 (ISBN 0-08-016868-X); Vol. 25. 1972. 60.00 (ISBN 0-08-016935-X); Vol. 26. 1973. 62.50 (ISBN 0-08-017048-X); Vol. 27. 1973. 60.00 (ISBN 0-08-017142-7); Vol. 28. 1974. 60.00 (ISBN 0-08-018005-1); Vol. 29. 1975-76. Pt. 1. 60.00 (ISBN 0-08-019719-1); Vol. 29, Pt. 2, 1975. pap. 18.50 (ISBN 0-08-019784-1); Vol. 29, Pt. 3, 1975. pap. 18.50 (ISBN 0-08-019890-2); Vol. 29, Complete, 1976. 55.00 (ISBN 0-08-020201-2); Vol. 30. 1976. Pt. 1. 60.00 (ISBN 0-08-019972-0); Pts. 2-3. 55.00 (ISBN 0-08-020207-1); Vol. 30, Complete. pap. 22.00 (ISBN 0-686-66314-4). Pergamon.

--Progress in Biophysics & Molecular Biology, Vols. 31-33. Incl. Vol. 31. 1976-1977. Pt. 1. 60.00 (ISBN 0-08-021065-1); Vol, 31, Pt. 2. pap. 13.00 (ISBN 0-08-021415-0); Vol. 31, Pt. 3. pap. 14.00 (ISBN 0-08-021522-X); Vol. 31. Complete. 55.00 (ISBN 0-08-020293-4); Vol. 32, Pt. 1. 60.00 (ISBN 0-08-021547-5); Pt. 2. pap. 15.00 (ISBN 0-08-021554-8); Pt. 3, 1978. pap. 15.00 (ISBN 0-08-022656-6); Vol. 32 Complete 1978. 55.00 (ISBN 0-08-020295-0); Vol. 33. Date not set. Pt. 1. pap. 15.00 (ISBN 0-08-022675-2); Pt. 2. pap. 15.00 (ISBN 0-08-023166-7); Pt. 3. pap. 15.00 (ISBN 0-08-023184-5). Pergamon.

Campbell, G. S. An Introduction to Environmental Biophysics. LC 76-43346. (Heidelberg Science Library). 1977. pap. 17.00 (ISBN 0-387-90228-7). Springer-Verlag.

Cantor, Charles R. & Schimmel, Paul R. Biophysical Chemistry, Part I: The Conformation of Biological Macromolecules. LC 79-22043. (Illus.). 365p. 1980. 40.95 (ISBN 0-7167-1042-0); pap. text ed. 23.95 (ISBN 0-7167-1188-5). W H Freeman.

Cerdonio, M. & Noble, R. W. Introductory Biophysics. 220p. 1984. 26.00 (ISBN 9971-966-33-6). Taylor & Francis.

Chan, H. W., ed. Biophysical Methods in Food Research. (Illus.). 176p. 1984. pap. text ed. 39.00x (ISBN 0-632-01212-9, Pub. by Blackwell Sci UK). Blackwell Pubns.

Chance, Britton, et al, eds. Biological & Biochemical Oscillators. 1973. 70.00 (ISBN 0-12-167872-5). Acad Pr.

Conway, B. E. Ionic Hydration in Chemistry & Biophysics. (Studies in Physical & Theoretical Chemistry: Vol. 12). 774p. 1981. 132.00 (ISBN 0-444-41947-0). Elsevier.

Curry, Guy L. & Feldman, Richard M. Mathematical Foundations of Population Dynamics. LC 85-40054. (TEES Monograph Ser.: No. 3). 284p. 1985. lib. bdg. 46.50 (ISBN 0-89096-256-1). Tex A&M Univ Pr.

Dallos, Peter. The Auditory Periphery: Biophysics & Physiology. 1973. 78.00 (ISBN 0-12-200750-6). Acad Pr.

Deutsche Gesellschaft Fur Biophysik, Annual Meeting, Konstanz, October 1979. Abstracts of Presentations: Proceedings. Adam, G. & Stark, G., eds. 1979. soft cover 17.20 (ISBN 0-387-09684-1). Springer-Verlag.

Devons, Samuel, ed. Biology & the Physical Sciences. LC 78-80272. 379p. 1969. 36.50x (ISBN 0-231-03134-3). Columbia U Pr.

DeWitt, C. & Matricon, J. Les Houches Lectures: 1969 Physical Problems in Biological Systems. 450p. 1970. 85.75 (ISBN 0-677-14020-7). Gordon.

Diercksen, G. H. & Wilson, S., eds. Methods in Computational Molecular Physics. 1983. lib. bdg. 48.00 (ISBN 90-2771-638-2, Pub. by Reidel Holland). Kluwer Academic.

Dinno, Mumtaz A., et al. Membrane Biophysics: Vol. II: Physical Methods in the Study of Epithelia. LC 83-9862. (Progress in Clinical & Biological Research Ser.: Vol. 126). 392p. 1983. 48.00 (ISBN 0-8451-0126-9). A R Liss.

Dora, J. Della, et al, eds. Numerical Methods in the Study of Critical Phenomena: Proceedings. (Springer Series in Synergetics: Vol. 9). (Illus.). 269p. 1981. 31.00 (ISBN 0-387-11009-7). Springer Verlag.

Edsall, John T. & Wyman, Jeffries. Biophysical Chemistry, Vol. 1: Thermodynamics, Electrostatics & the Biological Significance of the Properties of Matter. 1958. 72.00 (ISBN 0-12-232201-0). Acad Pr.

Engelman, Donald M., ed. Annual Review of Biophysics & Biophysical Chemistry, Vol. 14. LC 79-188446. (Illus.). 478p. 1985. text ed. 47.00 (ISBN 0-8243-1814-5). Annual Reviews.

Fokkens, O., et al, eds. Medinfo Seminars, 1983: Proceedings of the MEDINFO '83 Seminars, Amsterdam, Aug. 22-26, 1983. 370p. 1983. 57.50 (ISBN 0-444-86749-X, I-412-83, North Holland). Elsevier.

Franks, Felix. Biophysics & Biochemistry at Low Temperatures. (Illus.). 224p. 1985. 44.50 (ISBN 0-521-26320-4). Cambridge U Pr.

Furchtgott, Ernest. Pharmacological & Biophysical Agents & Behavior. 1971. 73.50 (ISBN 0-12-269950-5). Acad Pr.

Gabler, Raymond. Molecular Biophysics: An Introduction to Electrical Interactions. (Molecular Biology Ser.). 1978. 38.50 (ISBN 0-12-271350-8). Acad Pr.

Gates, D. M. & Schmere, R. B., eds. Perspectives of Biophysical Ecology. LC 74-17493. (Illus.). 1975. 55.00 (ISBN 0-387-06743-4). Springer-Verlag.

Ghosh, Bijan K., ed. Organization of Prokaryotic Cell Membrane, Vols. I & II. 1981. Vol. I, 272p. 86.00 (ISBN 0-8493-5653-9); Vol. II, 224p. 86.00 (ISBN 0-8493-5654-7). CRC Pr.

Guelph. Biophysics Handbook II. 208p. 1982. pap. text ed. 7.95 (ISBN 0-8403-2816-8). Kendall-Hunt.

Hallett, F. R., et al. Introductory Biophysics. LC 76-21809. 243p. 1977. pap. text ed. 24.95x (ISBN 0-470-15195-1). Halsted Pr.

Hamaguchi, Koza, ed. Aspects of Cellular & Molecular Physiology. 1973. 25.00x (ISBN 0-86008-078-1, Pub. by Japan Sci Soc Japan). Intl Spec Bk.

Hoppe, W., et al, eds. Biophysics. (Illus.). 980p. 1983. 59.00 (ISBN 0-387-12083-1). Springer-Verlag.

Hughes, William. Aspects of Biophysics. LC 78-8992. 362p. 1979. text ed. 42.50 (ISBN 0-471-01990-9). Wiley.

Hussey, M. Basic Physics & Technology of Medical Diagnostic Ultrasound. 240p. 1985. pap. 24.00 (ISBN 0-444-00945-0). Elsevier.

International Conference, 3rd, Versailles, 1971. From Theoretical Physics to Biology: Proceedings. Marois, M., ed. 1973. 50.25 (ISBN 3-8055-1578-2). S Karger.

Joseph, N. R. Comparative Physical Biology. (Illus.). 260p. 1973. 37.25 (ISBN 3-8055-1485-9). S Karger.

Kathren, Ronald L., et al, eds. Computer Applications in Health Physics. (Illus.). 822p. 1984. 35.00 (ISBN 0-9613108-0-4). Health Phys Soc.

Katz, Arnold M. Physiology of the Heart. LC 75-14580. 464p. 1977. o. p. 31.00 (ISBN 0-89004-053-2); pap. 23.00 (ISBN 0-686-67627-0). Raven.

Kerner, Edward H. Gibbs Ensemble: Biological Ensemble, Vol. 12. LC 73-185038. (International Science Review Ser.). 180p. 1970. 64.95 (ISBN 0-677-14180-7). Gordon.

Kohn, L. D. Hormone Receptors. (Horizons in Biochemistry & Biophysics Ser.: Vol. 6). 392p. 1982. 74.95x (ISBN 0-471-10049-8, Pub. by Wiley-Interscience). Wiley.

Latin School of Physics, 14th Caracas, Venezuela July 10-28, 1972. Selected Topics in Physics: Astrophysic & Biophysics, Proceedings. Abecassis De Laredo, E. & Jurisic, N. K., eds. LC 73-83563. 420p. 1973. lib. bdg. 71.00 (ISBN 90-277-0367-1, Pub. by Reidel Holland). Kluwer Academic.

Lawrence, John H. & Hamilton, J. G., eds. Advances in Biological & Medical Physics, 17 vols. Incl. Vol. 1. 1948 (ISBN 0-12-005201-6); Vol. 2. 1951 (ISBN 0-12-005202-4); Vol. 3. Lawrence, John H. & Tobias, Cornelius, eds. 1953 (ISBN 0-12-005203-2); Vol. 4. 1956 (ISBN 0-12-005204-0); Vol. 5. 1957 (ISBN 0-12-005205-9); Vol. 6. Tobias, Cornelius A. & Lawrence, John H., eds. 1958 (ISBN 0-12-005206-7); Vol. 7. 1960 (ISBN 0-12-005207-5); Vol. 8. 1963 (ISBN 0-12-005208-3); Vol. 9. Lawrence, John H. & Gofman, John W., eds. 1964 (ISBN 0-12-005209-1); Vol. 10. 1965 (ISBN 0-12-005210-5); Vol. 11. 1967. (ISBN 0-12-005211-3); Vol. 12. 1968 (ISBN 0-12-005212-1); Vol. 13. 1971 (ISBN 0-12-005213-X); Vol. 14. 1973 (ISBN 0-12-005214-8); Vol. 15. 1974 (ISBN 0-12-005215-6); Vol. 16. 1978. 85.00 (ISBN 0-12-005216-4); Vol. 17. 1980. 80.00 (ISBN 0-12-005217-2). Vols. 1-16. 85.00 ea. Acad Pr.

Liu, T. Y., et al, eds. Frontiers in Biochemical & Biophysical Studies of Proteins & Membranes: Proceedings of the International Conference on Frontiers in Biochemical & Biophysical Studies of Macromolecules, University of Hawaii, Honolulu, Aug. 6-8, 1982. 1983. 100.00 (ISBN 0-444-00822-5, Biomedical Pr). Elsevier.

Luettge, U. & Higinbotham, N. Transport in Plants. (Illus.). 1979. 37.00 (ISBN 0-387-90383-6). Springer-Verlag.

Marshall, Alan G. Biophysical Chemistry: Principles, Techniques & Applications. LC 77-19136. 812p. 1978. text ed. 49.95 (ISBN 0-471-02718-9); students manual 9.50 (ISBN 0-471-03674-9). Wiley.

Marton, Clare & Lecar, Harold, eds. Methods of Experimental Physics: Biophysics, Vol. 20. 568p. 1982. 74.50 (ISBN 0-12-475962-9). Acad Pr.

Metcalf, H. Topics in Classical Biophysics. 1980. pap. 19.95 (ISBN 0-13-925255-X). P-H.

Molecular Structure. (Structure & Bonding Ser.: Vol. 41). (Illus.). 146p. 1980. 41.00 (ISBN 0-387-09958-1). Springer-Verlag.

Monteith, John L. Principles of Environmental Physics. (Contemporary Biology Ser.). 254p. 1973. pap. text ed. 20.00 (ISBN 0-7131-2375-3). Univ Park.

--Principles of Environmental Physics. (Contemporary Biology Ser.). 256p. 1973. pap. text ed. 19.95 (ISBN 0-7131-2375-3). E Arnold.

Morales, M. F., et al, eds. Annual Review of Biophysics & Bioengineering, Vol. 1. Incl. Vol. 1. Morales, M. F., et al, eds. LC 79-188446. (Illus.). 1972. text ed. 20.00 (ISBN 0-8243-1801-3); Vol. 2. Mullims, L. J., et al, eds. LC 79-18846. (Illus.). 1973. text ed. 20.00 (ISBN 0-8243-1802-1). LC 79-188446. (Illus.). 1972. text ed. 20.00 (ISBN 0-8243-1801-3). Annual Reviews.

Noble, D. & Blundell, T. L. Progress in Biophysics & Molecular Biology, Vol. 36, Nos. 1-3 Complete. (Illus.). 130p. 1981. 75.00 (ISBN 0-08-028394-2). Pergamon.

Noble, D. & Blundell, T. L., eds. Progress in Biophysics & Molecular Biology, Vol. 35. (Illus.). 206p. 1981. 69.00 (ISBN 0-08-027122-7). Pergamon.

--Progress in Biophysics & Molecular Biology, Vol. 37. (Illus.). 229p. 1982. 86.00 (ISBN 0-08-029120-1). Pergamon.

--Progress in Biophysics & Molecular Biology, Vol. 38. (Illus.). 210p. 1982. 85.00 (ISBN 0-08-029683-1). Pergamon.

--Progress in Biophysics & Molecular Biology, Vol. 39. (Illus.). 230p. 1983. 78.00 (ISBN 0-08-030015-4). Pergamon.

--Progress in Biophysics & Molecular Biology, Vol. 42. LC 50-11295. (Illus.). 202p. 1984. 90.00 (ISBN 0-08-031691-3). Pergamon.

--Progress in Biophysics & Molecular Biology, Vol. 43. (Illus.). 268p. 1985. 102.00 (ISBN 0-08-032324-3). Pergamon.

Pain, R. H. & Smith, B. J., eds. New Techniques in Biophysics & Cell Biology, Vol. 1. LC 72-8611. pap. 64.80 (ISBN 0-317-29873-9, 2016156). Bks Demand UMI.

Quastler, H. & Morowitz, H., eds. Proceedings of the First National Biophysics Conference, Columbus, Ohio, March 4-6th 1957: Proceedings. 1959. 85.00x (ISBN 0-686-83712-6). Elliots Bks.

Rensing, L. & Jaeger, N. I., eds. Temporal Order. (Springer Series in Synergetics: Vol. 29). (Illus.). ix, 325p. 1985. 36.00 (ISBN 0-387-15274-1). Springer-Verlag.

Richards, E. G. & Dover, S. D. An Introduction to the Physical Properties of Large Molecules in Solution. LC 79-41583. (IUPAB Biophysics Ser.: No. 3). (Illus.). 200p. 1980. 39.50 (ISBN 0-521-23110-8); pap. 14.95 (ISBN 0-521-29817-2). Cambridge U Pr.

Ruch, Theodore C. & Patton, Harry D., eds. Physiology & Biophysics. 2nd ed. Incl. Vol. 1. The Brain & Neural Function. text ed. 38.00 (ISBN 0-7216-7821-1); Vol. 2. Circulation, Respiration & Fluid Balance. 495p. text ed. 30.00 (ISBN 0-7216-7818-1); Vol. 3. Digestion, Metabolism, Endocrine Function & Reproduction. text ed. 30.00 (ISBN 0-7216-7819-X); Vol. 4. Excitable Tissues & Reflex Control of Muscle. 39.50 (ISBN 0-7216-7817-3). LC 73-180188. (Illus.). 1973-82. Saunders.

Scott, Alwyn C. Neurophysics. LC 77-2762. Repr. of 1977 ed. 88.00 (2055136). Bks Demand UMI.

Spencer, Michael. Fundamentals of Light Microscopy. LC 82-1163. (International Union of Pure & Applied Biophysics: No. 6). (Illus.). 170p. 1982. 22.95 (ISBN 0-521-24794-2); pap. 8.95 (ISBN 0-521-28967-X). Cambridge U Pr.

Stanford, A. L. Exercises & Solutions Manual for Foundations in Biophysics. 1977. 7.00 (ISBN 0-12-663352-5). Acad Pr.

Stanford, A. L., Jr. Foundations of Biophysics. 1975. text ed. 29.50 (ISBN 0-12-663350-9). Acad Pr.

Stanley, H. Eugene, ed. Biomedical Physics & Biomaterials Science. LC 72-8855. 1972. pap. 16.50x (ISBN 0-262-69038-1). MIT Pr.

Trieste. Proceedings of the International Conference on Applications of Physics to Medicine & Biology. Alberi, et al, eds. 688p. 1982. 67.00. Taylor & Francis.

Trincher, K. S. Biology & Information: Elements of Biological Thermodynamics. LC 65-17784. 93p. 1965. 27.50x (ISBN 0-306-10719-8, Consultants). Plenum Pub.

University of Guelph. Biophysics Handbook I: Lab Manual. 208p. 1982. pap. text ed. 8.95 (ISBN 0-8403-2815-X). Kendall-Hunt.

Van Holde, K. E. Physical Biochemistry. 2nd ed. (Illus.). 320p. 1985. pap. text ed. 20.95 (ISBN 0-13-666272-2). P-H.

Vasilescu, V. & Margineanu, D. G. An Introduction to Neurobiophysics. 1981. 32.00 (ISBN 0-9961004-5-8, Pub. by Abacus England). Heyden.

Velo, G. & Wightman, A. S., eds. Rigorous Atomic & Molecular Physics. LC 81-12059. (NATO ASI Series B, Physics: Vol. 74). 504p. 1981. text ed. 75.00x (ISBN 0-306-40829-5, Plenum Pr). Plenum Pub.

Volkenshtein, M. V. Biophysics. 640p. 1983. 12.95 (ISBN 0-8285-2405-X, Pub. by Mir Pubs USSR). Imported Pubns.

Volkenstein, V., ed. General Biophysics, Vol. 1. LC 82-8853. 1963. 49.00 (ISBN 0-12-723001-7). Acad Pr.

--General Biophysics, Vol. 2. LC 82-8848. 1983. 0.49.00 (ISBN 0-12-723002-5). Acad Pr.

Ward-Smith, A. J. Biophysical Aerodynamics & the Natural Environment. 172p. 1984. 38.95 (ISBN 0-471-90436-8). Wiley.

Zotin, A. I. & Lamprecht, I., eds. Thermodynamics of Biological Processes. 1978. 76.00x (ISBN 3-11-007312-9). De Gruyter.

BIOLOGICAL PRODUCTIVITY

see also Food Chains (Ecology); Primary Productivity (Biology)

Russell-Hunter, W. D. Aquatic Productivity: An Introduction to Some Basic Aspects of Biological Oceanography & Limnology. (Illus.). 1970. text ed. 12.95x (ISBN 0-685-04258-8). Macmillan.

BIOLOGICAL PRODUCTS

Biological Substances: International Standards & Reference Preparations. (Also avail. in French & Spanish). 1975. pap. 2.80 (ISBN 92-4-154049-4). World Health.

International Symposium on Freezedrying of Biological Products. Proceedings. International Association of Biological Standardization & Regamey, R. H., eds. (Developments in Biological Standardizations: Vol. 36). (Illus.). 1977. 18.00 (ISBN 3-8055-2783-7). S Karger.

Stark, L. & Agarwal, G. C., eds. Biomaterials. LC 72-80083. 284p. 1969. 37.50x (ISBN 0-306-30405-8, Plenum Pr). Plenum Pub.

Vincent, J. F. & Currey, J. D., eds. The Mechanical Properties of Biological Materials. LC 80-40111. (Society of Experimental Biology Symposia Ser.: No. 34). (Illus.). 400p. 1981. 85.00 (ISBN 0-521-23478-6). Cambridge U Pr.

WHO Expert Committee. Geneva, 1971, 24th. WHO Expert Committee on Biological Standardization: Report. (Technical Report Ser.: No. 486). (Also avail. in French, Russian & Spanish). 1972. pap. 2.00 (ISBN 92-4-120486-9). World Health.

WHO Expert Committee. Geneva, 1973, 25th. WHO Expert Committee on Biological Standardization: Report. (Technical Report Ser.: No. 530). (Also avail. in French & Spanish). 1973. pap. 2.00 (ISBN 92-4-120530-X). World Health.

WHO Expert Committee. Geneva, 1974, 26th. WHO Expert Committee on Biological Standardization: Report. (Technical Report Ser.: No. 565). (Also avail. in French & Spanish). 1975. pap. 2.80 (ISBN 92-4-120565-2). World Health.

BIOLOGICAL RESEARCH

see also Bioclimatology; Biology, Experimental; Biotelemetry; Germfree Life; Radiobiology–Research

Ambrose, Harrison W. & Ambrose, Katherine P. A Handbook of Biological Investigation. 3rd ed. 170p. (Orig.). 1981. pap. text ed. 8.95 (ISBN 0-89459-148-7). Hunter Textbks.

Asberg, M. & Stern, W. T., eds. Linnaeus's Oland & Gotland Journey, 1741: Casebound Edition of Biological Journal of the Linnean Society, Vol. 5, No's 1 & 2. 1974. 41.50 (ISBN 0-12-064750-8). Acad Pr.

Battistin, Leontino, et al, eds. Neurochemistry & Clinical Neurology. LC 80-7475. (Progress in Clinical & Biological Research Ser.: Vol. 39). 512p. 1980. 51.00 (ISBN 0-8451-0039-4). A R Liss.

Biological Sciences Curriculum Study. Research Problems in Biology. 2nd ed. (Investigations for Students Ser.: No. 1-2-3). 1976. pap. text ed. 8.95x; Ser. 1. pap. text ed. (ISBN 0-19-502063-4); Ser. 2. pap. text ed. (ISBN 0-19-502064-2); Ser. 3. pap. text ed. (ISBN 0-19-502065-0). Oxford U Pr.

Blanchard, J. Richard & Farrell, Lois. Guide to Sources for Agricultural & Biological Research. 672p. 1981. 48.50x (ISBN 0-520-03226-8). U of Cal Pr.

Bures, J., et al. Electrophysiological Methods in Biological Research. 3rd ed. 1967. 95.00 (ISBN 0-12-142956-3). Acad Pr.

Committee on an Assessment of Quality-Related Characteristics of Research-Doctorate Programs in the U. S., National Research Council. An Assessment of Research-Doctorate Programs in the U. S. Biological Sciences. 264p. 1982. pap. text ed. 11.50 (ISBN 0-309-03340-3). Natl Acad Pr.

Dethier, Vincent G. To Know a Fly. LC 62-21838. (Illus.). 1963. pap. 7.95x (ISBN 0-8162-2240-1). Holden-Day.

Elsasser, Walt er M. Atom & Organism: A New Approach to Theoretical Biology. LC 66-21832. pap. 38.30 (ISBN 0-317-27619-0, 2014639). Bks Demand UMI.

Escherich, Peter C. & McManus, Roger E., eds. Sources of Federal Funding for Biological Research. 1983. pap. 15.00 (ISBN 0-942924-04-5). Assn Syst Coll.

Gabbiani, Giulio, et al. Reflections on Biologic Research. LC 67-26012. (Illus.). 256p. 1967. 10.50 (ISBN 0-87527-035-2). Green.

Gridgeman, N. T. Biological Sciences at the National Research Council of Canada: The Early Years to 1952. 153p. 1979. text ed. 15.50x (ISBN 0-88920-082-3, Pub. by Wilfrid Laurier U Pr Canada). Humanities.

Haine, Duane E. & Stevens, James L. An Atlas & Sourcebook of the Lesser Bushbaby, Galago Senegalensis. 320p. 1982. 89.50 (ISBN 0-8493-6320-9). CRC Pr.

Holman, H. H. Biological Research Method: Practical Statistics for Non-Mathematicians. (Illus.). 1969. 18.95x (ISBN 0-02-846050-2). Hafner.

ICN-UCLA Symposium, Keystone, Colo., February 1979. Biological Recognition & Assembly: Proceedings. Lake, J. & Fox, C. Fred, eds. LC 80-7797. (Progress in Clinical & Biological Research Ser.: Vol. 40). 362p. 1980. 68.00x (ISBN 0-8451-0040-8). A R Liss.

International Symposium on the Brattleboro Rat, Sept. 4-7, 1981. The Brattleboro Rat: Proceedings, Vol. 394. Sokol, Hilda W. & Valtin, Heinz, eds. 828p. 1982. 150.00x (ISBN 0-89766-178-8). NY Acad Sci.

Konner, Melvin. The Tangled Wing: Biological Constraints on the Human Spirit. LC 83-47566. 564p. 1983. pap. 8.61i (ISBN 0-06-091070-4, CN1070, CN). Har-Row.

Kopp, Friedrich. Electron Microscopy. Head, J. J., ed. LC 78-58243. (Carolina Biology Reader Ser.). (Illus.). 32p. 1981. pap. 2.00 (ISBN 0-89278-305-2, 45-9705). Carolina Biological.

Krushchov, N. Problems of Developmental Biology. 207p. 1981. pap. 6.95 (ISBN 0-8285-2444-0, Pub. by Mir Pubs USSR). Imported Pubns.

Mills, Harlow B., et al. A Century of Biological Research. Egerton, Frank N., 3rd, ed. LC 77-74240. (History of Ecology Ser.). (Illus.). 1978. Repr. of 1958 ed. lib. bdg. 14.00x (ISBN 0-405-10409-X). Ayer Co Pubs.

Oster, Gerald, et al, eds. Physical Techniques in Biological Research. Incl. Vol. 1A. Optical Techniques. 2nd ed. Oster, Gerald, ed. 1971. 74.50 (ISBN 0-12-529601-0); Vols. 2A-2B. Physical Chemical Techniques. 2nd ed. Moore, Dan H., ed. 1968-69. Vol. 2A. 74.50 (ISBN 0-12-505552-8); Vol. 2B. 74.50 (ISBN 0-12-505554-4); Vol. 3. Cells & Tissues, 3 Pts. 2nd ed. Pollister, Arthur W., ed. 1966-69. Pt. A. 74.50 (ISBN 0-12-560903-5); Pt. B. 74.50 (ISBN 0-12-560943-4); Pt. C. 74.50 (ISBN 0-12-560953-1); Vol. 4. Special Methods. Nastuk, William L., ed. 1962; Vol. 5. Electrophysiological Methods, Pt. A. Nastuk, William L., ed. 1964. 74.50 (ISBN 0-12-514105-X); Vol. 6. Electrophysiological Methods, Pt. B. 1963. 74.50 (ISBN 0-12-514106-8). Acad Pr.

Pankhurst, R. J., ed. Biological Identification with Computers. (Systematics Association Ser.). 1975. 59.50 (ISBN 0-12-544850-3). Acad Pr.

Regamey, R. H., ed. European Society of Animal Cell Technology, General Meeting. (Developments in Biological Standardization: Vol. 42). (Illus.). 1979. pap. 25.75 (ISBN 3-8055-2989-9). S Karger.

Research in British Universities, Polytechnics & Colleges: Biological Sciences, Vol. 2. 1982. 60.00x (ISBN 0-904654-24-9, Pub. by Brit Lib England). State Mutual Bk.

Rogers, Michael. Biohazard. 1979. pap. 2.25 (ISBN 0-380-41731-6, 41731). Avon.

Rosen, Robert, ed. Progress in Theoretical Biology, Vol. 6. 1981. 47.50 (ISBN 0-12-543106-6). Acad Pr.

Selye, Hans. In Vivo: The Case for Supramolecular Biology. 1967. 5.95x (ISBN 0-87140-849-X). Liveright.

Sharma & Sharma. Chromosome Techniques. 3rd ed. LC 79-41279. 1980. 165.00 (ISBN 0-408-70942-1). Butterworth.

Siler, William & Lindberg, Donald A., eds. Computers in Life Science Research. LC 75-34075. (Illus.). 272p. 1975. 45.00x (ISBN 0-306-34502-1, Plenum Pr). Plenum Pub.

Tice, Raymond R. & Hollaender, Alexander, eds. Sister Chromatid Exchanges: Twenty-Five Years of Experimental Research, 2 vols, Pts. A & B. Incl. Pt. A. The Nature of the SCEs. 560p. 75.00x (ISBN 0-306-41881-9, Plenum Pr); Pt. B. Genetic Toxicology & Human Studies. 560p. 75.00x (ISBN 0-306-41882-7, Plenum Pr). (Basic Life Sciences Ser.: Vols. 29A & 29B). 1120p. 1984. Set. 135.00 (ISBN 0-317-17199-2, Plenum Pr). Plenum Pub.

BIOLOGICAL RHEOLOGY

see Rheology (Biology)

BIOLOGICAL RHYTHMS

see also Circadian Rhythms; Photoperiodism

Aschoff, Jurgen, ed. Handbook of Behavioral Neurobiology, Vol. 4: Biological Rhythms. 582p. 1981. 55.00x (ISBN 0-306-40585-7, Plenum Pr). Plenum Pub.

Assenmacherm, I. & Farner, D. S., eds. Environmental Endocrinology: Proceedings of an International Symposium Held in Montpellier (France), July 11-15, 1977. (Proceedings in Life Sciences). (Illus.). 1978. 45.00 (ISBN 0-387-08809-1). Springer-Verlag.

Ayensu, Edward S. Rhythms of Life. (Illus.). 208p. 1982. 35.00 (ISBN 0-517-54523-3). Crown.

Baum, Harold & Shade, Peter. Biorhythms 1: Human Biology. 86p. 1984. 17.95 (ISBN 0-85066-291-5). Taylor & Francis.

--Biorhythms 2: General Biology. 86p. 1984. 17.95 (ISBN 0-85066-292-3). Taylor & Francis.

Beloussov, V. V. Continental Endogenous Regimes. 295p. 1981. 10.00 (ISBN 0-8285-2281-2, Pub. by Mir Pubs USSR). Imported Pubns.

Bennett, Miriam F. Living Clocks in the Animal World. (Illus.). 236p. 1974. 24.75x (ISBN 0-398-02872-9). C C Thomas.

Biology & Agriculture Division. Biochronometry. LC 79-610527. (Illus.). 662p. 1971. text ed. 18.25 (ISBN 0-309-01866-8). Natl Acad Pr.

Brady, J., ed. Biological Timekeeping. LC 81-15506. (Society for Experimental Biology Seminar: No. 14). 220p. 1982. 44.50 (ISBN 0-521-23307-0); pap. 19.95 (ISBN 0-521-29899-7). Cambridge U Pr.

Cold Spring Harbor Symposia on Quantitative Biology: Biological Clocks, Vol. 25. LC 34-8174. (Illus.). 537p. 1961. 38.00x (ISBN 0-87969-024-0). Cold Spring Harbor.

Colquhoun, W. P., ed. Biological Rhythms & Human Performance. 1971. 49.50 (ISBN 0-12-182050-5). Acad Pr.

Cosnard, M., et al, eds. Rhythms in Biology & Other Fields of Application: Deterministic & Stochastic Approaches. (Lecture Notes in Biomathematics: Vol. 49). 400p. 1983. pap. 24.00 (ISBN 0-387-12302-4). Springer-Verlag.

Dale, Arbie. Biorhythm. (Orig.). 1976. pap. 1.75 (ISBN 0-671-80779-X). PB.

Duster, Troy & Garrett, Karen. Cultural Perspectives on Biological Knowledge. LC 83-27174. (Modern Sociology Ser.). 208p. 1984. text ed. 29.50 (ISBN 0-89391-059-7). Ablex Pub.

Eurich, Alvin C., ed. Major Transitions in the Human Life Cycle. LC 81-47067. 544p. 1981. 28.50x (ISBN 0-669-04559-4). Lexington Bks.

Finerty, James P. The Population Ecology of Cycles in Small Mammals: Mathematical Theory & Biological Fact. LC 79-23774. (Illus.). 1981. text ed. 24.50x (ISBN 0-300-02382-0). Yale U Pr.

Gedda, Luigi & Brenci, Gianni. Chronogenetics: The Inheritance of Biological Time. (Illus.). 232p. 1978. 32.75x (ISBN 0-398-03641-1). C C Thomas.

Gittelson, Bernard. Biorhythm: A Personal Science. rev. ed. 1984. pap. 3.95 (ISBN 0-446-32276-8). Warner Bks.

Handyside, Joann. Bio Rhythms in Man. (Illus.). 1978. wkbk. 20.00 (ISBN 0-916750-09-4). Dayton Labs.

Hedlund, Laurence W., et al. Biological Rhythms & Endocrine Function. LC 74-23448. (Advances in Experimental Medicine & Biology Ser.: Vol. 54). 204p. 1975. 35.00x (ISBN 0-306-39054-X, Plenum Pr). Plenum Pub.

International Congress Of Anatomy - 8th - Wiesbaden - 1965. Cellular Aspects of Biorhythms: Proceedings. Von Mayersbach, H., ed. (Illus.). 1967. 36.00 (ISBN 0-387-03744-6). Springer-Verlag.

Luce, Gay G. Biological Rhythms in Human & Animal Physiology. Orig. Title: Biological Rhythms in Psychiatry & Medicine. 1971. pap. text ed. 6.00 (ISBN 0-486-22586-0). Dover.

Mendlewicz, J. & Van Pragg, H. M. Biological Rhythms & Behavior. (Advances in Biological Psychiatry: Vol. 11). (Illus.). iv, 150p. 1983. pap. 42.25 (ISBN 3-8055-3672-0). S Karger.

Palmer, John D. An Introduction to Biological Rhythms. 1976. 44.00 (ISBN 0-12-544450-8). Acad Pr.

Pavlidis, Theodosios. Biological Oscillators: Their Mathematical Analysis. 1973. 56.00 (ISBN 0-12-547350-8). Acad Pr.

Pengelley, Eric T. Circannual Clocks: Annual Biological Rhythms. 1974. 59.50 (ISBN 0-12-550150-1). Acad Pr.

Reinberg, A. & Smolensky, M. H., eds. Biological Rhythms & Medicine: Cellular, Metabolic, Physiopathologic, Pharmacologic Aspects. (Topics in Environmental Physiology & Medicine Ser.). (Illus.). 304p. 1983. 72.00 (ISBN 0-387-90791-2). Springer-Verlag.

Richter, Curt P. Biological Clocks in Medicine & Psychiatry. (Illus.). 120p. 1979. photocopy ed. 15.50x (ISBN 0-398-01586-4). C C Thomas.

Saunders, D. S. Insect Clocks. 2nd ed. LC 81-13815. (Illus.). 420p. 1982. 99.00 (ISBN 0-08-028848-0); pap. 48.00 (ISBN 0-08-028847-2). Pergamon.

Saunders, David C. An Introduction to Biological Rhythms. LC 76-48623. (Tertiary Level Biology Ser.). 170p. 1978. text ed. 26.95x (ISBN 0-470-99019-8). Halsted Pr.

Scheving, Lawrence E. & Halberg, Franz. Chronobiology: Principles & Applications to Shifts in Schedules. (NATO Advanced Study Institute: Behavioral Social Sciences, No. 3). 597p. 1981. 65.00x (ISBN 90-286-0940-7). Sijthoff & Noordhoff.

Spencer, Carol M. The Complete BioCycle Kit. (Illus.). 1974. 6.95 (ISBN 0-918882-01-X). PSI Rhythms.

Sweeney, B. M. Rhythmic Phenomena in Plants. (Experimental Botany Monographs, Vol. 3). 1969. 33.50 (ISBN 0-12-679050-7). Acad Pr.

Thommen, George. Is This Your Day? How Biorhythm Helps You Determine Your Life Cycles. rev. ed. (Illus.). 160p. 1973. 6.95 (ISBN 0-517-50599-1). Crown.

Thomson, Howard M. Biorhythm for Life. LC 76-29578. (Illus.). 84p. (Orig.). 1976. pap. 5.95 (ISBN 0-9601070-1-0). Evergreen Pubs.

Urquhart, J. & Yates, F. E., eds. Temporal Aspects of Therapeutics. LC 73-13685. 223p. 1973. 37.50x (ISBN 0-306-36202-3, Plenum Pr). Plenum Pub.

Valliere, James T., et al. Valliere's Natural Cycles Almanac 1986. (Illus.). 43p. (Orig.). 1985. pap. 8.95 (ISBN 0-87199-038-5). Astrolabe SW.

Webb, W. B. Biological Rhythms, Sleep & Performance. (Studies in Human Performance). 248p. 1982. 39.95x (ISBN 0-471-10047-1, Pub. by Wiley-Interscience). Wiley.

Wernli, Hans J. Biorhythm. 1976. pap. 2.95 (ISBN 0-346-12234-1). Cornerstone.

BIOLOGICAL SPECIMENS–COLLECTION AND PRESERVATION

Glauert, A. Fixation, Dehydration & Embedding of Biological Specimens. (Practical Methods in Electron Microscopy Ser.: Vol. 3, No. 1). 1975. pap. 18.00 (ISBN 0-444-10666-9, Biomedical Pr). Elsevier.

Hower, Rolland O. Freeze-Drying Biological Specimens: A Laboratory Manual. LC 78-10750. (Illus.). 196p. 1979. 27.50x (ISBN 0-87474-532-2). Smithsonian.

Knudsen, Jens W. Collecting & Preserving Plants & Animals. abr. ed. 1972. pap. text ed. 16.95 scp (ISBN 0-06-043744-8, HarpC). Har-Row.

Lee, Welton L. & Bell, Bruce M., eds. Guidelines for Acquisition & Management of Biological Specimens. 44p. 1982. pap. 5.00 (ISBN 0-942924-02-9). Assn Syst Coll.

Roomans, Godfried M., ed. Preparation of Biological Specimens for Scanning Electron Microscopy. Murphy, Judith A. (Illus.). 352p. (Orig.). 1984. pap. text ed. 32.00 (ISBN 0-931288-33-9). Scanning Electron.

Simpkins, John. Techniques of Biological Preparation. (Illus.). 1974. 21.00x (ISBN 0-216-89767-X). Intl Ideas.

BIOLOGICAL TELEMETRY

see Biotelemetry

BIOLOGICAL TRANSPORT

see also Plant Translocation; Secretion

Andreoli, Thomas E., et al, eds. Membrane Physiology. 482p. 1980. pap. text ed. 19.95x (ISBN 0-306-40432-X, Plenum Pr). Plenum Pub.

Antolini, Renzo, et al, eds. Transport in Biomembranes: Model Systems & Reconstitution. 288p. 1982. text ed. 42.00 (ISBN 0-89004-868-1). Raven.

Berridge, Michael J. & Oschman, James L. Transporting Epithelia. (Monographs in the Ultrastructure of Cells & Organisms Ser.). 1972. 27.50 (ISBN 0-12-454135-6). Acad Pr.

Blank, M., ed. Surface Chemistry of Biological Systems. LC 70-110799. (Advances in Experimental Medicine & Biology Ser.: Vol. 7). 352p. 1970. 49.50x (ISBN 0-306-39007-8, Plenum Pr). Plenum Pub.

Blaustein, Mordecai P. & Lieberman, Melvyn, eds. Electrogenic Transport: Fundamental Principles & Physiological Implications. (Society of General Physiologists Ser.: Vol. 38). (Illus.). 416p. 1984. text ed. 71.50 (ISBN 0-89004-959-9). Raven.

Bronner, Felix & Kleinzeller, Annost, eds. Current Topics in Membranes & Transport, Vols. 1-9, 11. Incl. Vol. 1. 1970. 47.50 (ISBN 0-12-153301-8); Vol. 2. 1971. 47.50 (ISBN 0-12-153302-6); Vol. 3. 1972. 69.00 (ISBN 0-12-153303-4); Vol. 4. 1974. 69.00 (ISBN 0-12-153304-2); Vol. 5. 1974. 69.00 (ISBN 0-12-153305-0); Vol. 6. 1975. 65.00 (ISBN 0-12-153306-9); Vol. 7. 1975. 65.00 (ISBN 0-12-153307-7); Vol. 8. 1976. 65.00 (ISBN 0-12-153308-5); Vol. 9. 1977. 69.50 (ISBN 0-12-153309-3); Vol. 11. 1978. 70.00 (ISBN 0-12-153311-5). Acad Pr.

Bronner, Felix & Kleinzeller, Arnost, eds. Current Topics in Membranes & Transport, Vol. 21. 1984. 79.00 (ISBN 0-12-153321-2). Acad Pr.

Bronner, Felix & Razin, Shmuel, eds. Current Topics in Membranes & Transport: Vol. 17: Membrane Lipids of Prokaryotes. (Serial Publication). 1982. 55.00 (ISBN 0-12-153317-4). Acad Pr.

Case, Maynard, et al, eds. Electrolyte & Water Transport Across Gastrointestinal Epithelia. 335p. 1982. text ed. 53.50 (ISBN 0-89004-765-0). Raven.

Civan, Mortimer M. Epithelial Ions & Transport: Application of Biophysical Techniques. (Membrane Transport in Life Sciencies Ser.). 204p. 1983. 64.50 (ISBN 0-471-04869-0, Pub. by Wiley-Interscience). Wiley.

Duncan, C. J. & Hopkins, C. R., eds. Secretory Mechanisms. LC 79-10003. (Society for Experimental Biology Symposium: No. 33). (Illus.). 1980. 82.50 (ISBN 0-521-22684-8). Cambridge U Pr.

Heinz, E. Mechanics & Energetics of Biological Transport. (Molecular Biology, Biochemistry & Biophysics: Vol. 29). (Illus.). 1978. 36.00 (ISBN 0-387-08905-5). Springer-Verlag.

International Society For Cell Biology. Intracellular Transport. Warren, Katherine B., ed. (Proceedings: Vol. 5). 1967. 67.50 (ISBN 0-12-611905-8). Acad Pr.

International Symposium, Prilly-Lausanne, July 6-7, 1978. Transport Mechanisms of Tryptophan in Blood Cells, Nerve Cells, & at the Blood-Brain Barrier: Proceedings. Baumann, P., ed. (Journal of Neural Transmission: Suppl. 15). (Illus.). 1979. 64.40 (ISBN 0-387-81519-8). Springer-Verlag.

Lakshminarayanaiah, N. Transport Phenomena in Membranes. 1969. 82.00 (ISBN 0-12-434250-7). Acad Pr.

Lih, M. Transport Phenomena in Medicine & Biology. LC 74-6059. 531p. 1975. 35.00 (ISBN 0-471-53532-X, Pub. by Wiley). Krieger.

Mackey, M. C. Ion Transport Through Biological Membranes: An Integrated Theoretical Approach. (Lecture Notes in Biomathematics Ser.: Vol. 7). 256p. 1975. pap. 17.00 (ISBN 0-387-07532-1). Springer-Verlag.

Martonosi, Anthony N., ed. Membranes & Transport, Vol. 1. LC 82-3690. 722p. 1982. 85.00x (ISBN 0-306-40853-8, Plenum Pr); Set price with Vol. 2. 145.00. Plenum Pub.

Mayr, Ernst. Evolution & the Diversity of Life: Selected Essays. 592p. 1976. 35.00x (ISBN 0-674-27104-1). Harvard U Pr.

Miami Winter Symposium. Molecular Basis of Biological Transport. Woessner, J. F., Jr. & Huijing, F., eds. 1972. 49.50 (ISBN 0-12-761250-5). Acad Pr.

Moorby, J. Transport Systems in Plants. (Integrated Themes in Biology Ser.). (Illus.). 176p. (Orig.). 1981. pap. text ed. 14.95x (ISBN 0-582-44379-2). Longman.

Mujumdar, Arun S. & Mashelkar, R. A. Advances in Transport Processes, Vol. 3. (Advances in Transport Processes Ser.: I-489). 432p. 1983. 44.95x (ISBN 0-470-27394-1). Halsted Pr.

Rothman, S. S. & Ho, J. J. Nonvesicular Transport. LC 84-11869. 394p. 1985. 74.95 (ISBN 0-471-86570-2). Wiley.

Schmidt-Nielsen, Knut, et al, eds. Comparative Physiology: Water, Ions & Fluid Mechanics. LC 77-7320. (Illus.). 1978. 64.50 (ISBN 0-521-21696-6). Cambridge U Pr.

Schultz, Stanley G. Principles of Membrane Transport. LC 79-54015. (IUPAB Biophysics Ser.: No. 2). (Illus.). 1980. 34.50 (ISBN 0-521-22992-8); pap. 12.95x (ISBN 0-521-29762-1). Cambridge U Pr.

Snell, F. M. & Noell, W. K., eds. Transcellular Membrane Potentials & Ionic Fluxes. (Life Sciences Ser). 140p. 1964. 41.75x (ISBN 0-677-10520-7). Gordon.

Solomon, Arthur K. & Karnovsky, Manfred, eds. Molecular Specialization & Symmetry in Membrane Function. LC 77-134. 1978. 27.50x (ISBN 0-674-58179-2). Harvard U Pr.

Stein, W. D., ed. Movement of Molecules Across Cell Membranes. (Theoretical & Experimental Biology: Vol. 6). 1967. 65.00 (ISBN 0-12-664650-3). Acad Pr.

Tosteson, D. C., ed. Transport Across Single Biological Membranes. LC 78-17668. (Membrane Transport in Biology: Vol. 2). (Illus.). 1979. 99.00 (ISBN 0-387-08780-X). Springer-Verlag.

Weiss, D. G. & Gorio, A., eds. Axioplasmic Transport in Physiology & Pathology. (Proceedings in Life Science). (Illus.). 220p. 1982. 34.00 (ISBN 0-387-11663-X). Springer-Verlag.

Weiss, Dieter G., ed. Axioplasmic Transport. (Proceedings in Life Sciences Ser.). (Illus.). 477p. 1982. 64.00 (ISBN 0-387-11662-1). Springer-Verlag.

West, I. C. The Biochemistry of Membrane Transport. (Outline Studies in Biology). 96p. 1983. pap. 7.50 (ISBN 0-412-24190-0, NO. 6063). Methuen Inc.

Ziegler, Thomas W. Transport in High Resistance Epithelia, Vol. 1. Horrobin, D., ed. 1978. 21.60 (ISBN 0-88831-012-9). Eden Pr.

BIOLOGICAL WARFARE

Alexander, A., et al. Control of Chemical & Biological Weapons. LC 73-151279. 1971. pap. 1.50 (ISBN 0-87003-016-7). Carnegie Endow.

Cookson, John & Nottingham, Judith. Survey of Chemical & Biological Warfare. LC 79-128595. 432p. pap. 3.95 (ISBN 0-85345-223-7). Monthly Rev.

Fabrics for Clinical-Biological Warfare. 110p. 1982. 50.00 (ISBN 0-318-01476-9, 10030). Indus Fabrics.

Health Aspects of Chemical & Biological Weapons: Report of a WHO Group of Consultants. 132p. 1970. pap. 5.60 (ISBN 92-4-156034-7, 188). World Health.

Livingstone, Neil C. & Douglass, Joseph D. CBW: The Poor Man's Atomic Bomb. LC 84-47502. (National Security Papers: No. 1). 36p. 1984. pap. 5.00 (ISBN 0-89549-057-9, IFPA35, IFPA). Unipub.

Depew, David J. & Weber, Bruce H., eds. Evolution at a Crossroads: The New Biology & the New Philosophy of Science. 288p. 1985. text ed. 25.00x (ISBN 0-262-04079-4). MIT Pr.

Dobzhansky, T., et al. Evolutionary Biology, 6 vols. Incl. Vol. 1. 455p. 1967 (ISBN 0-306-50011-6); Vol. 2. 463p. 1968 (ISBN 0-306-50012-4); Vol. 3. 317p. 1969 (ISBN 0-306-50013-2); Vol. 4. 321p. 1970 (ISBN 0-306-50014-0); Vol. 5. 326p. 1972 (ISBN 0-306-50015-9); Vol. 6. 458p. 1972 (ISBN 0-306-50016-7). LC 67-11961. 35.00x ea. (Plenum Pr). Plenum Pub.

Dobzhansky, T., et al, eds. Evolutionary Biology, Vol. 7. LC 67-11961. (Illus.). 324p. 1974. 35.00x (ISBN 0-306-35407-1, Plenum Pr). Plenum Pub.

--Evolutionary Biology, Vol. 8. (Illus.). 405p. 1975. 39.50x (ISBN 0-306-35408-X, Plenum Pr). Plenum Pub.

Duffy, Thomas & Waller, Robert, eds. Designing Usable Texts. (Educational Technology Ser.). 1985. 48.00 (ISBN 0-12-223260-7). Acad Pr.

Dwek, R. A., et al, eds. NMR in Biology. 1977. 56.50 (ISBN 0-12-225850-9). Acad Pr.

Earnshaw, J. C. & Steer, M. W., eds. The Application of Laser Light Scattering to the Study of Biological Motion. (NATO ASI Series A, Life Sciences: Vol. 59). 675p. 1983. 95.00x (ISBN 0-306-41268-3, Plenum Pr). Plenum Pub.

Easton, Tom & Rishcer, Carl. Bioscope. 2nd ed. (Illus.). 640p. 1984. pap. text ed. 19.95 (ISBN 0-675-20137-3); Additional supplements may be obtained from publisher. study guide 9.95 (ISBN 0-675-20233-7). Merrill.

Enger, Eldon D., et al. Concepts in Biology. 3rd ed. 512p. 1982. pap. text ed. write for info. (ISBN 0-697-04712-1); instrs.' manual avail. (ISBN 0-697-04715-6); lab manual o.p. avail. (ISBN 0-697-04714-8). Wm C Brown.

--Concepts in Biology. 4th ed. 560p. 1985. pap. text ed. write for info. (ISBN 0-697-05023-8); lab manual avail. (ISBN 0-697-04799-7); instr's. manual avail. (ISBN 0-697-05101-3); transparencies avail. (ISBN 0-697-05102-1). Wm C Brown.

Erwin, Joe & Dukelow, Richard W. Comparative Primate Biology, Vol. 3: Reproduction & Development. 430p. 1985. write for info. (ISBN 0-8451-4003-5). A R Liss.

Erwin, Joe & Swindler, Daris R. Comparative Primate Biology, Vol. 1: Systematics, Evolution & Anatomy. 754p. 1985. write for info. (ISBN 0-8451-4000-0). A R Liss.

Evolutionary Biology Staff. Evolutionary Biology, Vol. 6, 1972. Vol. 1. pap. 113.80 (ISBN 0-317-26223-8); Vol. 6. pap. 81.50. Bks Demand UMI.

Farish, Donald. Introduction to Biology: A Human Perspective. 550p. 1984. text ed. write for info (ISBN 0-87150-787-0, 4561, Pub. by Willard Grant Pr). PWS Pubs.

Farner, Donald S., et al, eds. Avian Biology, Vol. 8. 1985. 49.50 (ISBN 0-12-249408-3). Acad Pr.

Fay, Peter. The Blue-Greens. (Studies in Biology: No. 160). 80p. 1984. pap. text ed. 8.95 (ISBN 0-7131-2878-X). E Arnold.

Fennel, William E. A Pig Watcher's Guide to Biology. 88p. 1982. pap. text ed. 8.95 (ISBN 0-8403-2797-8). Kendall-Hunt.

Ferri, E., et al. Biology Learning Guide. 1984. Paladin Hse.

Fingerman, Milton. Animal Diversity. 3rd ed. 1981. pap. text ed. 16.95 (ISBN 0-03-049611-X, CBS C). SCP.

Fisher, Kenneth & Nixon, Ann, eds. The Science of Life: Contributions of Biology to Human Welfare. LC 75-5777. 382p. 1975. 37.50x (ISBN 0-306-34501-3, Plenum Pr). Plenum Pub.

Fishman, William H., ed. On Codevelopmental Markers: Biologic Diagnostic & Monitoring Aspects, Vol. 1. 1983. 70.00 (ISBN 0-12-257701-9). Acad Pr.

Fontijn, A. & Clyne, M. A., eds. Reactions of Small Transient Species, Kinetics & Energetics. 1984. 89.00 (ISBN 0-12-262040-2). Acad Pr.

Friedman, I. The Human Ear. Head, J. J., ed. LC 78-571217. (Carolina Biology Readers Ser.). (Illus.). 16p. 1979. pap. 1.60 (ISBN 0-89278-273-0, 45-9673). Carolina Biological.

Frohlich, H. & Kremer, F., eds. Coherent Excitations in Biological Systems. (Proceedings in Life Sciences). (Illus.). 224p. 1983. 27.50 (ISBN 0-387-12540-X). Springer-Verlag.

Fry, Virginia. Exploring Biology in the Laboratory. 2nd ed. 250p. 1984. pap. 16.95x (ISBN 0-03-063373-7). SCP.

Galbraith, D & Wilson, D. Biological Science: Principles & Patterns of Life. 3rd ed. 1978. text ed. 13.00 (ISBN 0-03-922202-0, Pub. by HR&W Canada). HR&W.

Garnsey, Wayne & Licata, Guy. A General Biology Review. (Illus.). 160p. 1981. pap. text ed. 3.00 (ISBN 0-9606036-3-8). N & N Pub.

Gaunt, P. N. Three Dimensional Reconstruction in Biology. 184p. 1978. 40.00 (ISBN 0-272-79394-9, Pub by P Man Bks England). State Mutual Bk.

Goin, Coleman J. & Goin, Olive B. Man & the Natural World: An Introduction to Life Science. 2nd ed. (Illus.). 672p. 1975. text ed. write for info. (ISBN 0-02-344240-9, 34424). Macmillan.

Goto, H. E. Animal Toxonomy. (Studies in Biology Ser.: No. 143). 64p. 1982. pap. text ed. 8.95 (ISBN 0-7131-2847-X). E Arnold.

Graham, Julia B. & Wiedeman, Varley E. Biology of Populations. 136p. 1982. pap. text ed. 8.95 (ISBN 0-8403-2784-6). Kendall-Hunt.

Graham, Tom M. Biology: The Essential Principles. LC 81-53071. 736p. 1982. text ed. 33.95x (ISBN 0-03-057838-8). SCP.

Gray, Robert C. Biology Concepts: Illustrated Lecture Outline. (Illus.). 154p. (Orig.). 1982. pap. text ed. 5.75x (ISBN 0-9606666-1-3). Greenfield Pubns.

Gray, W. & Rizzo, N. D., eds. Unity Through Diversity: Festschrift in Honor of Ludwig, 2 vols. (Current Topics of Contemporary Thought Ser.). 1168p. 1973. Set. 123.75 (ISBN 0-677-14860-7); 69.50x ea. Vol. 1, 596p (ISBN 0-677-14840-2). Vol. 2, 572p (ISBN 0-677-14850-X). Gordon.

Greenstein, Julius S., ed. Contemporary Readings in Biology. 1972. 34.00x (ISBN 0-8422-5013-1). Irvington.

Greulach, Victor A. & Chiapetta, Vincent J. Biology. 1977. text ed. 26.65x (ISBN 0-673-15301-0); study guide 9.25x (ISBN 0-673-15302-9). Scott F.

Grobstein, Clifford. The Strategy of Life. 2nd ed. LC 73-18061. (Biology Ser.). (Illus.). 174p. 1974. text ed. 20.95 (ISBN 0-7167-0591-5). W H Freeman.

Gruver, W. A. Simulation & Identification in Biological Science. 160p. 1985. Repr. lib. bdg. 19.95x (ISBN 0-89370-892-5). Borgo Pr.

Gulland, J. A. Manual of Sampling & Statistical Methods for Fisheries Biology, Pt. 1. (Manuals in Fisheries Science: No. 3). (Orig.). 1972. pap. 5.25, 4 fascicules (ISBN 92-5-101605-4, F268, FAO). Unipub.

Gunstream, Stanley E. & Babel, John S. Explorations in Basic Biology. 4th, rev. ed. (Illus.). 368p. 1986. pap. price not set (ISBN 0-8087-4161-6). Burgess.

Guttman, Burton S. & Hopkins, Johns W., III. Understanding Biology. 978p. 1983. text ed. 31.95 (ISBN 0-15-592701-9, HC); pap. text ed. test file avail. (ISBN 0-15-592704-3); study guide 11.95 (ISBN 0-15-592702-7); pap. text ed. instr's manual avail. (ISBN 0-15-592703-5). HarBraceJ.

Haglund, H., et al, eds. Electrofocus '78. (Developments in Biochemistry Ser.: Vol. 7). 200p. 1980. 49.50 (ISBN 0-444-00375-4, Biomedical Pr). Elsevier.

Halcane, John S. Mechanism, Life & Personality. LC 72-7966. 152p. 1973. Repr. of 1923 ed. lib. bdg. 15.00x (ISBN 0-8371-6557-1, HAML). Greenwood.

Hall, D. O., et al. Biomass for Energy in the Developing Countries: Current Role-Potential-Problems-Prospects. (Illus.). 200p. 1982. 20.00 (ISBN 0-08-028689-5). Pergamon.

Hall, J. R. Biology. (Teach Yourself Ser.). 1974. pap. 6.95 (ISBN 0-679-10388-0). McKay.

Hall, Mark A. & Lesser, Milton S. Review Text in Biology. (Illus., Orig.). 1966. pap. text ed. 7.42 (ISBN 0-87720-051-3). AMSCO Sch.

Halvorson, Harlyn O. & Van Holde, Kensal E., eds. The Origins of Life & Evolution. LC 80-21901. (MBL Lectures in Biology: Vol. 1). 140p. 1981. 16.00 (ISBN 0-8451-2200-2). A R Liss.

Ham, Richard G. & Veomett, Marilyn J. Mechanisms of Development. LC 79-9236. (Illus.). 830p. 1979. text ed. 29.95 (ISBN 0-8016-2022-8). Mosby.

Hanauer, Ethel R. Biology Made Simple. LC 72-76229. (Made Simple Ser.). pap. 4.95 (ISBN 0-385-01972-6). Doubleday.

Hardin, Garrett & Bajema, Carl. Biology: Its Principles & Implications. 3rd ed. LC 77-28507. (Illus.). 790p. 1978. text ed. 24.95 (ISBN 0-7167-0028-X); instrs.' manual avail. W H Freeman.

Haskel, Sebastian & Sygoda, David. Fundamental Concepts of Modern Biology. (Orig.). 1972. text ed. 13.33 (ISBN 0-87720-055-6); pap. text ed. 10.00 (ISBN 0-87720-054-8). AMSCO Sch.

Hecht, Max K., et al, eds. Evolutionary Biology, Vol. 10. (Illus.). 500p. 1977. 45.00x (ISBN 0-306-35410-1, Plenum Pr). Plenum Pub.

--Evolutionary Biology, Vol. 14. 458p. 1982. text ed. 49.50 (ISBN 0-306-40775-2, Plenum Pr). Plenum Pub.

--Evolutionary Biology, Vol. 16. 514p. 1983. 49.50x (ISBN 0-306-41408-2, Plenum Pr). Plenum Pub.

--Evolutionary Biology, Vol. 17. 338p. 1984. 42.50x (ISBN 0-306-41651-4, Plenum Pr). Plenum Pub.

--Evolutionary Biology, Vol. 18. 280p. 1984. 37.50x (ISBN 0-306-41760-X, Plenum Pr). Plenum Pub.

Hems, D. A. Biologically Active Substances: Exploration & Exploitation. 309p. 1978. 74.95x (ISBN 0-471-99489-8, Pub. by Wiley-Interscience). Wiley.

Hendrickson, Herbert T. Essential Biology. LC 80-24656. (Illus.). 329p. 1981. text ed. 20.95 scp (ISBN 0-06-042792-2, HarpC); instr. manual avail. (ISBN 0-06-362698-5). Har-Row.

Hennessen, W., ed. Fifth General Meeting of European Society of Animal Cell Technology (ESACT) (Developments in Biological Standardization: Vol. 55). (Illus.). xii, 292p. 1984. pap. 36.25 (ISBN 3-8055-3849-9). S Karger.

--Immunization of Adult Birds with Inactive Oil Adjuvant Vaccines. (Developments in Biological Standardization: Vol. 51). (Illus.). 400p. 1982. pap. 36.25 (ISBN 3-8055-3473-6). S Karger.

Herreid, Clyde F. Biology. (Illus.). 1978. write for info. (ISBN 0-02-353780-9). Macmillan.

Holland, et al. Laboratory Explorations in General Biology. 4th ed. 1983. 15.95 (ISBN 0-8403-2961-X, 40296101). Kendall-Hunt.

Hughes, Arthur F. The American Biologist Through Four Centuries. 432p. 1982. pap. 32.50x (ISBN 0-398-04598-4). C C Thomas.

Huxley, Thomas H. Discourses Biological & Geological. 1896. 12.00 (ISBN 0-8274-4221-1). R West.

Inui, Naomichi, ed. Mutation, Promotion & Transformation in Vitro. 260p. 1982. text ed. 40.00x (ISBN 0-89955-402-4, Pub. by Japan Sci Soc Japan). Intl Spec Bk.

Jackson, J. A., et al. Discovering Biology. 2nd. ed. (Illus.). 1979. lab manual 6.95 (ISBN 0-89459-035-9). Hunter Textbks.

Jacquez, John A. Compartmental Analysis in Biology & Medicine. 2nd ed. LC 85-51250. (Illus.). 576p. 1985. text ed. 39.95x (ISBN 0-472-10063-7). U of Mich Pr.

Jaeger, Edmund C. Denizens of the Mountains. (Illus.). 168p. 1929. photocopy ed. 16.75x (ISBN 0-398-04293-4). C C Thomas.

Jaeger, W., ed. Biological Growth & Spread: Proceedings. (Lecture Notes in Biomathematics: Vol. 38). 511p. 1980. pap. 39.00 (ISBN 0-387-10257-4). Springer-Verlag.

Jennings, Herbert S. Universe & Life. 1933. 12.50x (ISBN 0-686-83841-6). Elliots Bks.

Jensen, William A., et al. Biology. 1979. text ed. write for info (ISBN 0-534-00621-3); write for info study guide (ISBN 0-534-00721-X). Wadsworth Pub.

Jepson, Maud. Illustrated Biology, 2 pts. Incl. Pt. 1. Plants (ISBN 0-7195-0735-9); Pt. 2. Animals (ISBN 0-7195-0734-0). (Illus.). 6.95x ea. Transatlantic.

Johnson, K., et al. Biology: An Introduction. 1984. 31.95 (ISBN 0-8053-7887-1); study guide 10.95 (ISBN 0-8053-7888-X); instr's guide 6.95 (ISBN 0-8053-7889-8); write for info. transparencies (ISBN 0-8053-7891-X). Benjamin-Cummings.

Johnson, Leland G. Biology. 1983. text ed. write for info. (ISBN 0-697-04706-7); instr's. manual avail. (ISBN 0-697-04732-6); study guide avail. (ISBN 0-697-04733-4); lab manual (complete version) avail. (ISBN 0-697-04721-0); lab manual (short version) avail. (ISBN 0-697-04736-9); transparencies avail. (ISBN 0-697-04908-6); slides avail. (ISBN 0-697-04909-4); test item file avail. (ISBN 0-697-04921-3). Wm C Brown.

Johnson, Leland G. & Johnson, Rebecca L. Essentials of Biology. 752p. 1985. text ed. price not set (ISBN 0-697-00149-0); price not set instr's. manual (ISBN 0-697-00760-X); price not set student study guide (ISBN 0-697-00550-X); price not set avail. transparencies (ISBN 0-697-00786-3); price not set avail. lab manual (ISBN 0-697-00066-4). WM C Brown.

Jones, C. W. Biological Energy Conservation. 2nd ed. (Outline Studies in Biology). 1981. pap. 7.50 (ISBN 0-412-13970-7, NO. 6489, Pub. by Chapman & Hall). Methuen Inc.

Jungers, William L., ed. Size & Scaling in Primate Biology. (Advances in Primatology Ser.). 508p. 1984. 69.50x (ISBN 0-306-41560-7, Plenum Pr). Plenum Pub.

Kaplan, Eugene H. Problem Solving in Biology. 3rd ed. 448p. 1983. pap. text ed. write for info. (ISBN 0-02-362050-1). Macmillan.

Karpoff, Arnold J. Biology One Hundred Two: An Introduction to the Biological Sciences. 152p. 1982. pap. text ed. 11.95 (ISBN 0-8403-2931-8). Kendall-Hunt.

Karreman, George, ed. Cooperative Phenomena in Biology. LC 78-16572. 1980. 53.00 (ISBN 0-08-023186-1). Pergamon.

Katyal, K. K. & Ali, M. New Secondary Biology. 272p. 1981. 30.00x (ISBN 0-86125-664-6, Pub. by Orient Longman India). State Mutual Bk.

Keeton, William T. Biological Science. 2nd ed. (Illus.). 1972. text ed. 17.95x (ISBN 0-393-09387-5). Norton.

--Biological Science. 3rd ed. (Illus.). 1980. text ed. 31.95x (ISBN 0-393-95021-2); pap. 2.95x tchr's manual (ISBN 0-393-95031-X); study guide 9.95x (ISBN 0-393-95028-X). Norton.

--Elements of Biological Science. 2nd ed. (Illus.). 1973. text ed. 20.95x (ISBN 0-393-09346-8). Norton.

Keeton, William T. & McFadden, Carol H. Elements of Biological Science. 3rd ed. (Illus.). 1983. 28.95x (ISBN 0-393-95255-X); study guide 8.95x (ISBN 0-393-95259-2); tchr's. manual avail. (ISBN 0-393-95262-2); test bank avail. (ISBN 0-393-95373-4). Norton.

Keleti, Georg & Lederer, William H. Handbook of Micromethods for the Biological Sciences. LC 73-12027. pap. 45.50 (ISBN 0-317-29999-9, 2051849). Bks Demand UMI.

Kelly, James L. & Orr, Alan R. Self-Pacing Biology Experiences. (Illus.). 1980. lib. bdg. 13.75x (ISBN 0-8138-1725-0); tchr's resource manual 8.50x (ISBN 0-8138-1770-6). Iowa St U Pr.

Kimball, John. Biology. 4th ed. LC 77-74322. (Life Sciences Ser.). 1978. text ed. 30.20 (ISBN 0-201-03761-0); lab manual 10.95 (ISBN 0-201-03692-4); study guide 8.95 (ISBN 0-201-03764-5). Addison-Wesley.

Kimball, John W. Biology. 5th ed. LC 82-11636. (Biology Ser.). (Illus.). 1040p. 1983. text ed. 36.95 (ISBN 0-201-10245-5); instructor's manual 1.50 (ISBN 0-201-10247-1); student guide 10.95 (ISBN 0-201-10246-3). test bank 3.95 (ISBN 0-201-10265-X). Addison-Wesley.

Kirk, David L. Biology Today. 3rd ed. 1036p. 1980. (RanC); wkbk. 6.95 (ISBN 0-394-32452-8). Random.

Kirk, Thomas G., Jr. Library Research Guide to Biology: Illustrated Search Strategy & Sources. LC 78-61710. (Library Research Guides Ser.: No. 2). 1978. 19.50 (ISBN 0-87650-098-X); pap. 12.50 (ISBN 0-87650-099-8). Pierian.

Krommenhoek, W. Biological Structure. 144p. 1979. text ed. 21.00 (ISBN 0-8391-1402-8). Univ Park.

Lamprecht, I. & Zotin, A. I., eds. Thermodynamics & Regulation of Biological Processes. LC 84-23302. (Illus.). xiv, 573p. 1984. 123.00x (ISBN 3-11-009789-3). De Gruyter.

Larwood, G. & Rosen, B., eds. Biology & Systematics of Colonial Organisms: Proceedings. (A Volume in the Systematic Association Special Volume Ser.). 1979. 95.00 (ISBN 0-12-436960-X). Acad Pr.

Latta, Virginia G., et al, eds. Principles of Biology: Laboratory Investigations. 4th ed. 1984. 9.95 (ISBN 0-88725-019-X). Hunter Textbks.

Law, Elmo A. A Workbook for the Life Sciences. 1980. pap. text ed. 8.95 (ISBN 0-8403-2122-8). Kendall-Hunt.

Lenneberg, Eric H. Biological Foundations of Language. LC 83-19988. 512p. 1984. Repr. of 1967 ed. 39.95 (ISBN 0-89874-700-7). Krieger.

Lenzen, Victor F. Causality in Natural Science. 128p. 1954. spiral 10.75x (ISBN 0-398-04334-5). C C Thomas.

Levy, Charles K. Elements of Biology. 3rd ed. LC 81-17556. (Biology Ser.). (Illus.). 620p. 1983. text ed. 31.95 (ISBN 0-201-04564-8). Addison-Wesley.

Lewin, Ralph. Biology of Women & Other Animals. (Orig.). 1983. pap. 5.95 (ISBN 0-910286-91-4). Boxwood.

Li Kung Shaw. Purposive Biology. LC 81-90747. (Illus.). 359p. 1982. text ed. 20.00 (ISBN 0-9607806-0-2); pap. text ed. 15.00 (ISBN 0-9607806-1-0). Li Kung Shaw.

Loomis, William F. Developmental Biology. 495p. 1986. text ed. price not set (ISBN 0-02-371790-4). Macmillan.

Luria, Salvador E. Thirty Six Lectures in Biology. LC 74-19136. (Illus.). 439p. 1975. pap. text ed. 16.50x (ISBN 0-262-62029-4). MIT Pr.

Luria, Salvador E., et al. A View of Life. 1981. 37.95 (ISBN 0-8053-6648-2); instr's. guide 6.95 (ISBN 0-8053-6649-0). Benjamin-Cummings.

Macedo, Jorge. The Theoretical Basis of the Living System. LC 75-17399. (Illus.). 84p. 1979. 10.50 (ISBN 0-87527-158-8). Fireside Bks.

MacMillan, W. D., et al. The World Mechanism. 1979. Repr. of 1929 ed. lib. bdg. 20.00 (ISBN 0-8482-1738-1). Norwood Edns.

MacQueen, Jean & Hanes, Ted. The Living World: Exploring Modern Biology. LC 78-2601. (Illus.). 1978. 17.95 (ISBN 0-13-538975-5, Spec). P-H.

White, J. M. & Barnes, R. P. Manual for Hands On Biology: An Audio Tutorial Approach. 349p. 1974. pap. text ed. 28.50x (ISBN 0-471-94016-X). Wiley.

Wolfe, Stephen L. Biology: The Foundations. 2nd ed. 608p. 1982. pap. text ed. write for info (ISBN 0-534-01169-1). Wadsworth Pub.

Wong & Bernstein. Ideas & Investigations in Science: Life Science. 2nd ed. 1977. 21.84 (ISBN 0-13-449991-3). lab data bk. o.p. 4.72 (ISBN 0-685-78778-8). P-H.

Wunderli, J. Die Biologie des Menschen. 4th ed. (Illus.). xiv, 194p. 1982. pap. 10.25 (ISBN 3-8055-2613-X). S Karger.

Wyatt, H. V. A Directory for Informantion Resources in Biology in the U. K. (R&D Report: No. 5606). 89p. (Orig.). 1981. pap. 12.00 (ISBN 0-905984-65-X, Pub. by British Lib). Longwood Pub Group.

Wynn, Tommy E. Biology in the Modern World. 2nd ed. 178p. 1979. pap. 9.95x lab manual (ISBN 0-89459-052-9). Hunter Textbks.

--Biology in the Modern World. 3rd ed. 178p. 1984. pap. 12.95 (ISBN 0-317-17647-1). Hunter Textbks.

Young, R. T. Biology in America. 1978. Repr. of 1922 ed. lib. bdg. 50.00 (ISBN 0-8492-3113-2). R West.

BIOLOGY–ADDRESSES, ESSAYS, LECTURES

Atlan, Henri, et al. Laying Down a Path in Walking: Essays for a New Philosophy of Biology. LC 83-82697. 96p. (Orig.). pap. 7.50postponed (ISBN 0-940262-05-3). Lindisfarne Pr.

Barnett, Samuel, ed. Century of Darwin. facs. ed. LC 71-76891. (Essay Index Reprint Ser). 1958. 21.25 (ISBN 0-8369-1019-2). Ayer Co Pubs.

Baumel, Howard B. & Berger, J. Joel. Biology - Its People & Its Papers. 1973. pap. 5.00 (ISBN 0-87355-002-1). Natl Sci Tchrs.

Biology Colloquium, 29th, Oregon State University 1968. Biochemical Coevolution: Proceedings. Chambers, Kenton L., ed. LC 52-19235. (Illus.). 128p. 1970. 9.95x (ISBN 0-87071-168-7). Oreg St U Pr.

Cedar Bog Symposium, Urbana College, Nov. 3, 1973. Proceedings. King, Charles C. & Frederick, Clara M., eds. 1974. 3.00 (ISBN 0-686-86536-7). Ohio Bio Survey.

Cold Spring Harbor, N. Y., Biological Laboratory. Cold Spring Harbor Symposia on Quantitative Biology, 11 vols, Vols. 1-8 & 10-12. Repr. of 1933 ed. Set. 295.00 (ISBN 0-384-09523-2); 27.00 ea. Johnson Repr.

Cold Spring Harbor Symposia on Quantitative Biology: The Synapse, Vol. 40. LC 34-8174. (Illus.). 694p. 1976. 88.50x (ISBN 0-87969-039-9). Cold Spring Harbor.

Desowitz, Robert S. New Guinea Tapeworms & Jewish Grandmothers: Tales of Ecology, Parasites, & Progress. 1981. 12.95 (ISBN 0-393-01474-6). Norton.

East, Edward M., ed. Biology in Human Affairs. LC 72-313. (Essay Index Reprint Ser.). Repr. of 1931 ed. 23.50 (ISBN 0-8369-2790-7). Ayer Co Pubs.

Feher, G., ed. Electron Paramagnetic Resonance with Applications to Selected Problems in Biology. (Documents in Biology Ser.: Vol. 3). 152p. 1970. 45.25 (ISBN 0-677-02670-6). Gordon.

Fokkens, O., et al, eds. Medinfo Seminars, 1983: Proceedings of the MEDINFO '83 Seminars, Amsterdam, Aug. 22-26, 1983. 370p. 1983. 57.50 (ISBN 0-444-86749-X, I-412-83, North Holland). Elsevier.

Ginzberg, Lev R. & Golenberg, Edward. Lectures in Theoretical Population Biology. (Illus.). 352p. 1985. pap. text ed. 18.95 (ISBN 0-13-528043-5). P-H.

Glass, Bentley. Progress or Catastrophe: The Nature of Biological Science & Its Impact on Human Society. Anshen, Ruth N., ed. 160p. 1985. 29.95 (ISBN 0-03-001747-5); pap. 9.95 (ISBN 0-03-001748-3). Praeger.

Haken, H. Evolution of Order & Chaos in Physics, Chemistry, & Biology: Schloss Elmau, FRG, 1982 Proceedings. (Springer Series in Synergetics: Vol. 17). (Illus.). 287p. 1982. 35.00 (ISBN 0-387-11904-3). Springer-Verlag.

Halvorson, Harlyn O. & Van Holde, Kensal E., eds. The Origins of Life & Evolution. LC 80-21901. (MBL Lectures in Biology: Vol. 1). 140p. 1981. 16.00 (ISBN 0-8451-2200-2). A R Liss.

Horowitz, Norman H. & Hutchings, Edward, Jr., eds. Genes, Cells, & Behavior: A View of Biology Fifty Years Later. LC 80-18744. (Biology Ser.). (Illus.). 169p. 1980. text ed. 18.95 (ISBN 0-7167-1217-2). W H Freeman.

Hutchinson, George E. The Enchanted Voyage, & Other Studies. LC 77-26010. (Illus.). 1978. Repr. of 1962 ed. lib. bdg. 19.75x (ISBN 0-313-20098-X, HUEV). Greenwood.

Huxley, Julian. Essays of a Biologist. 304p. 1980. Repr. of 1929 ed. lib. bdg. 25.00 (ISBN 0-8495-2274-9). Arden Lib.

Huxley, Julian S. Essays of a Biologist. facsimile ed. LC 72-111838. (Essay Index Reprint Ser.). 1923. 19.00 (ISBN 0-8369-1613-1). Ayer Co Pubs.

--Man Stands Alone. LC 72-128265. (Essay Index Reprint Ser.). 1941. 22.00 (ISBN 0-8369-1961-0). Ayer Co Pubs.

Kennedy, Donald, intro. by. From Cell to Organism: Readings from Scientific American. LC 66-30156. (Illus.). 256p. 1967. text ed. 19.95 (ISBN 0-7167-0963-5); pap. text ed. 11.95 (ISBN 0-7167-0962-7). W H Freeman.

Loeb, Jacques. Mechanistic Conception of Life. Fleming, Donald, ed. LC 64-13426. (The John Harvard Library). (Illus.). 1964. 15.00x (ISBN 0-674-55950-9). Harvard U Pr.

Lowdin, P. O. Proceedings of the Tenth International Symposium on Quantum Biology & Quantum Pharmacology, Palm Coast, Florida, March 4-6, 1982. 416p. 1982. pap. 74.95 (ISBN 0-471-88168-6). Wiley.

Nobel Foundation. Nobel Lectures in Physiology-Medicine, 1901-1970, 4 vols. Incl. Vol. 1. 1901-1921. 1967. 68.00 (ISBN 0-444-40419-8); Vol. 2. 1922-1941. 1965. 68.00 (ISBN 0-444-40420-1); Vol. 3. 1942-1962. 1964. 44.00 (ISBN 0-444-40421-X); Vol. 4. 1963-1970. 1973. 68.00 (ISBN 0-444-40994-7). Elsevier.

Research Symposium on Complexes of Biologically Active Substances with Nucleic Acids & Their Modes of Action. Proceedings. Hahn, F. E., et al, eds. (Progress in Molecular & Subcellular Biology: Vol. 2). (Illus.). 1971. 45.00 (ISBN 0-387-05321-2). Springer-Verlag.

Rose, Steven, ed. Against Biological Determinism: The Dialectics of Biology Group. (Allison & Busby Motive Ser.). 192p. 1982. 14.95 (ISBN 0-8052-8111-8, Pub. by Allison & Busby England); pap. 8.95 (ISBN 0-8052-8112-6, Pub. by Allison & Busby England). Schocken.

--Towards a Liberatory Biology: The Dialectics of Biology Group. (Allison & Busby Motive Ser.). 170p. 1982. 14.95 (ISBN 0-8052-8113-4, Pub. by Allison & Busby England); pap. 8.95 (ISBN 0-8052-8114-2). Schocken.

Schechter, Alan N. & Dean, Ann. The Impact of Protein Chemistry on the Biomedical Sciences. 1984. 55.00 (ISBN 0-12-622780-2). Acad Pr.

Scientific American Editors. The Biosphere: A Scientific American Book. LC 78-140849. (Illus.). 134p. 1970. pap. text ed. 10.95x (ISBN 0-7167-0945-7). W H Freeman.

Scott, Walter N. & Strand, Fleur L., eds. First Colloquium in Biological Sciences. (Annals of The New York Academy of Sciences Ser.: Vol. 435). 621p. 1984. lib. bdg. 140.00x (ISBN 0-89766-264-4); text ed. 140.00x (ISBN 0-89766-265-2). NY Acad Sci.

Skulachev, V. P., ed. Biology Reviews, Vol. 3. (Soviet Scientific Reviews Ser.: Section D). 452p. 1982. 170.00 (ISBN 3-7186-0111-7). Harwood Academic.

--Physicochemical Biology Reviews, Vol. 4. (Soviet Scientific Reviews: Section D). 270p. 1984. text ed. 170.00 (ISBN 3-7186-0140-0). Harwood Academic.

Snell, Frank M., ed. Progress in Theoretical Biology, 4 vols. Vol. 1. 1967. 46.50 (ISBN 0-12-543101-5); Vol. 2 1972. 69.50 (ISBN 0-12-543102-3); Vol. 3. 1974. 69.50 (ISBN 0-12-543103-1); Vol. 4. 1976. 69.50 (ISBN 0-12-543104-X). Acad Pr.

Stevenson, Lloyd. G. & Multhauf, Robert P., eds. Medicine, Science, & Culture: Historical Essays in Honor of Owsei Temkin. LC 68-15445. (Illus.). 312p. 1968. 22.00x (ISBN 0-8018-0615-1). Johns Hopkins.

Swain, Roger B. Earthly Pleasures: Tales from a Biologist's Garden. (Penguin Nonfiction Ser.). 256p. 1985. pap. 6.95 (ISBN 0-14-007683-2). Penguin.

Takashima, Shiro & Fishman, Harvey M., eds. Electrical Properties of Biological Polymers, Water, & Membranes Conference Jan, 26-28, 1977: Proceeding, Vol. 303. 1977. 47.00x (ISBN 0-686-44468-X). NY Acad Sci.

Thomas, Lewis. The Medusa & the Snail: More Notes of a Biology Watcher. 1979. 10.95 (ISBN 0-670-46568-2). Viking.

Wilson, Samuel & Roe, Richard, eds. Biology Anthology: Readings in the Life Sciences. LC 74-2810. 320p. 1974. pap. text ed. 13.50 (ISBN 0-8299-0019-5). West Pub.

BIOLOGY–APPARATUS AND SUPPLIES

see Biological Apparatus and Supplies

BIOLOGY–BIBLIOGRAPHY

see also Biological Literature

Blanchard, J. Richard & Farrell, Lois. Guide to Sources for Agricultural & Biological Research. 672p. 1981. 48.50x (ISBN 0-520-03226-8). U of Cal Pr.

Krumphanzl, V., et al, eds. Overproduction of Microbial Products. 1982. 75.00 (ISBN 0-12-426920-6). Acad Pr.

Prescott, Gerald W. Bibliographia Desmidiacearum Universalis: A Contribution to a Bibliography of Desmid Systematics, Biology & Ecology from 1744 to 1982. 600p. 1985. lib. bdg. 70.00 (ISBN 3-87429-215-0). Lubrecht & Cramer.

Reich, Warren T., ed. Encyclopedia of Bioethics, 2 vols. LC 78-8821. 1982. Set. lib. bdg. 145.00X (ISBN 0-02-925910-X). Macmillan.

Walters, LeRoy, ed. Bibliography of Bioethics, Vol. 8. 1982. 60.00 (ISBN 0-02-933780-1). Macmillan.

BIOLOGY–CLASSIFICATION

see also Species

Cole, A. J., ed. Numerical Taxonomy. 1969. 55.00 (ISBN 0-12-179650-7). Acad Pr.

During, Ingemar. Aristotle's De Partibus Animalium: Critical & Literary Commentaries. LC 78-66548. (Ancient Philosophy Ser.). 223p. 1980. lib. bdg. 26.00 (ISBN 0-8240-9602-9). Garland Pub.

Jones, Susan, et al. Classification. (Illus.). 32p. (Orig.). 1983. pap. 2.50x (ISBN 0-565-00876-5, Pub. by Brit Mus Nat Hist England). Sabbot-Natural Hist Bks.

McGraw-Hill Editors. Synopsis & Classification of Living Organism, 2 vols. 1982. Set. 185.00 (ISBN 0-07-079031-0). McGraw.

Mertens, Thomas R. & Lines, Judy L. Principles of Biosystematics. 2nd ed. (Programed Biology Studies). (Illus.). 1978. pap. text ed. 6.95 (ISBN 0-88462-038-7, Ed Methods). Longman USA.

Winsor, Mary P. Starfish, Jellyfish & the Order of Life: Issues of Nineteenth-Century Science. LC 74-29739. (Studies in the History of Science & Medicine Ser.: No. 10). (Illus.). 256p. 1976. 33.00x (ISBN 0-300-01635-2). Yale U Pr.

BIOLOGY–COLLECTED WORKS

Avery, G. S., Jr., ed. Survey of Biological Progress, Vols. 2-4. Incl. Vol. 2. 1952. 49.50 (ISBN 0-12-609802-6); Vol. 3. Glass, Bentley, ed. 1957. 48.00 (ISBN 0-12-609803-4); Vol. 4. 1962. 57.50 (ISBN 0-12-609804-2). Acad Pr.

Benedek, G. B. & Villars, F. M. Physics with Illustrative Examples from Medicine & Biology, 2 vols. 1974. 25.95 ea.; Vol. 1. 23.95 (ISBN 0-201-00551-4). Vol. 2 (ISBN 0-201-00558-1). Addison-Wesley.

Knobloch, Irving W., ed. Readings in Biological Science. 3rd ed. LC 72-93743. 1973. pap. text ed. 4.95x (ISBN 0-89197-371-0). Irvington.

Szilard, Leo. Collected Works of Leo Szilard: Scientific Papers. Feld, Bernard T. & Szilard, Gertrud W., eds. 1972. 47.50x (ISBN 0-262-06039-6). MIT Pr.

WHO Expert Committee on Biological Standardization, 17th, Geneva, 1964. Report. (Technical Report Ser: No. 293). (Eng, Fr, Rus, & Span.). 86p. 1964. pap. 2.00 (ISBN 92-4-120293-9). World Health.

WHO Expert Committee on Biological Standardization, 19th, Geneva, 1966. Report. (Technical Report Ser: No. 361). (Eng, Fr, & Span.). 120p. 1967. pap. 2.80 (ISBN 92-4-120361-7). World Health.

BIOLOGY–DATA PROCESSING

Calow, P. Biological Machines: A Cybernetic Approach to Life. LC 76-27603. 133p. 1976. pap. 14.95x (ISBN 0-8448-1005-3). Crane-Russak Co.

Clarke, Frank H. Calculator Programming for Chemistry & the Life Sciences. LC 81-15046. 1981. 33.00 (ISBN 0-12-175320-4). Acad Pr.

Computer Models & Application of the Sterile-Male Technique. (Panel Proceedings Ser.). (Illus.). 195p. (Orig.). 1973. pap. 18.00 (ISBN 92-0-111573-3, ISP340, IAEA). Unipub.

Cutbill, J. L. Data Processing in Biology & Geology. (Systematics Association Ser.: Special Vol. 3). 1971. 59.50 (ISBN 0-12-199750-2). Acad Pr.

Davies, R. G. Computer Programming in Quantitative Biology. 1972. 77.50 (ISBN 0-12-206250-7). Acad Pr.

Enslein, K., ed. Data Acquisition & Processing in Biology & Medicine: Proceedings. Incl. Vol. 3. Rochester Conference, 1963 (ISBN 0-08-010904-7); Vol. 4. Rochester Conference, 1964; Vol. 5. Rochester Conference, 1966 (ISBN 0-08-012671-5). Vols. 3 & 5. 40.00 ea. Pergamon.

Fielding, Alan. Computing for Biologists: An Introduction to BASIC Programming with Applications in the Life Sciences. 1985. pap. 19.95 (ISBN 0-8053-2515-8). Benjamin Cummings.

Geisow, Michael J. & Barrett, Anthony N., eds. Computing in Biological Sciences. 456p. 1983. 65.00 (ISBN 0-444-80435-8, North-Holland). Elsevier.

Heinmets, Ferdinand. Analysis of Normal & Abnormal Cell Growth: Model-System Formulations & Analog Computer Studies. LC 66-11882. 288p. 1966. 39.50x (ISBN 0-306-30225-X, Plenum Pr). Plenum Pub.

Ireland, C. R. & Long, S. P., eds. Microcomputers in Biology: A Practical Approach. (The Practical Approach Ser.). (Illus.). 338p. (Orig.). 1984. pap. 27.00 (ISBN 0-904147-57-6). IRL Pr.

Iyengar, S. Sitharama, ed. Computer Modeling of Complex Biological Systems. 152p. 1984. 59.00 (ISBN 0-8493-5208-8). CRC Pr.

Karanja, Linda, ed. Computers in Clinical & Biomedical Engineering. (Illus.). 120p. 1983. pap. 12.00x (ISBN 0-930844-10-6). Quest Pub.

Klopfenstein, Charles E. & Wilkins, Charles L., eds. Computers in Chemical & Biochemical Research, Vol. 1. 1972. 65.00 (ISBN 0-12-151301-7). Acad Pr.

Lewis, R., ed. Computers in the Life Sciences: Applications in Research & Education. 123p. 1979. 25.00x (ISBN 0-85664-863-9, Pub. by Croom Helm Ltd). Longwood Pub Group.

Mize, R. R., ed. Microcomputer in Cell & Neurobiology Research. 448p. 1985. 49.50 (ISBN 0-444-00842-X). Elsevier.

Nelder, J. A. Computers in Biology. (The Wykeham Science Ser.: No. 32). 168p. 1974. pap. cancelled (ISBN 0-85109-450-3). Taylor & Francis.

Nelder, J. A. & Kime, R. D. Computers in Biology. (Wykeham Science Ser.: No. 32). 168p. 1974. 9.95x (ISBN 0-8448-1159-9). Crane Russak Co.

Pankhurst, R. J., ed. Biological Identification with Computers. (Systematics Association Ser.). 1975. 59.50 (ISBN 0-12-544850-3). Acad Pr.

Spain, James D. Basic Microcomputer Models in Biology. 368p. 1982. text ed. 31.95x (ISBN 0-201-10678-7). Benjamin Cummings.

Stacy, Ralph W. & Waxman, Bruce. Computers in Biomedical Research, 4 vols. 1965-1964. Vol. 1. 80.50 (ISBN 0-12-662301-5); Vol. 2. 73.50 (ISBN 0-12-662302-3); Vol. 3. 73.50 (ISBN 0-12-662303-1); Vol. 4. 1974. 68.50 (ISBN 0-12-662304-X). Acad Pr.

Stuper, Andrew J., et al. Computer Assisted Studies of Chemical Structure & Biological Function. LC 78-12337. 220p. 1979. 56.95 (ISBN 0-471-03896-2, Pub. by Wiley-Interscience). Wiley.

BIOLOGY–DICTIONARIES

Abercrombie, M., et al. Diccionario de Biologia. (Span.). 242p. 1978. pap. 16.75 (ISBN 0-686-57336-6, S-50068). French & Eur.

--Dictionary of Biology. 6th ed. (Reference Ser.). (Orig.). 1951. pap. 5.95 (ISBN 0-14-051003-6). Penguin.

--The Penguin Dictionary of Biology. 1978. 12.95 (ISBN 0-670-27222-1). Viking.

Aguayo, Carlos A. & Biaggi, Virgilio. Diccionario De Biologia Animal. LC 76-41882. (Span.). 1977. 15.00 (ISBN 0-8477-2318-6). U of PR Pr.

Bergfeld, R. Herder-Lexikon Biologie. (Ger.). 238p. 1975. pap. 24.95 (ISBN 3-451-16453-1, M-7453, Pub. by Herder). French & Eur.

Bergfeld, Rainer. Diccionario Rioduero: Biologia. 2nd ed. (Span.). 244p. 1977. 9.95 (ISBN 84-220-0683-9, S-50169). French & Eur.

Bleifeld. Encyclopedia of Biology Terms. 320p. Date not set. 6.95 (ISBN 0-8120-2511-3). Barron.

Carpovich, Eugene A. Russian-English Biological & Medical Dictionary. 2nd ed. LC 58-7915. (Rus. & Eng.). 1960. 25.00 (ISBN 0-911484-01-9). Tech Dict.

Chibisova, O. I. & Kozar, L. A., eds. English-Russian Biological Dictionary. 3rd ed. LC 78-40145. 1980. text ed. 145.00 (ISBN 0-08-023163-2). Pergamon.

Cihui, Y. Dongwuxue. English-Chinese Biology Dictionary. (Eng. & Chinese.). 477p. 1975. 25.00 (ISBN 0-686-92343-X, M-9277). French & Eur.

Dictionnaire de la Biologie--B.L.V. (Eng., Ger., Fr. & Span.). 496p. 1976. 95.00 (ISBN 0-686-57097-9, M-6121). French & Eur.

Fachlexikon ABC Biologie. 2nd ed. (Ger.). 1972. leatherette 49.95 (ISBN 3-87144-001-9, M-7378, Pub. by Harri Deutsch). French & Eur.

Geissler, E. Kleine Enzyklopaedie Biologie. (Ger.). 896p. 1976. 28.50 (ISBN 3-87144-281-X, M-7089). French & Eur.

Gray, Peter. The Dictionary of the Biological Sciences. LC 81-19369. 622p. 1982. Repr. of 1967 ed. lib. bdg. 42.50 (ISBN 0-89874-441-5). Krieger.

--Encyclopedia of the Biological Sciences. LC 80-28590. 1056p. 1981. Repr. of 1970 ed. lib. bdg. 55.00 (ISBN 0-89874-326-5). Krieger.

Gutheridge, Anne. Barnes & Noble Thesaurus of Biology. (Illus.). 256p. 1984. pap. 6.68i (EH 581). B&N NY.

Haensch, G. & Haberkamp De Anton, G. Dictionary of Biology. 2nd, rev. & enl. ed. (Eng., Fr., Ger. & Span.). 680p. 1981. 117.00 (ISBN 0-444-41968-3). Elsevier.

Haensch, Guenther. Dictionary of Biology. (Eng., Ger., Fr & Span.). 1976. pap. 78.00 (ISBN 3-405-10950-7, M-7128). French & Eur.

--Woerterbuch der Biologie. (Eng., Ger., Fr. & Span., Dictionary of Biology). 1976. pap. 78.00 (ISBN 3-405-10933-7, M-7040). French & Eur.

Holmes, Sandra. Henderson's Dictionary of Biological Terms. 9th ed. 521p. 42.50 (ISBN 0-442-24865-2). Van Nos Reinhold.

Jacobs, Werner. Woerterbuch der Biologie. (Ger.). 1976. pap. 15.00 (ISBN 3-437-30195-0, M-7039). French & Eur.

Jugendhandbuch Naturwissen: Wirbellose Tiere, Vol. 2. (Ger.). 128p. 1976. pap. 5.95 (ISBN 3-499-16204-0, M-7487, Pub. by Rowohlt). French & Eur.
Landau, Sidney C. International Dictionary of Medicine & Biology, 3 vols. 3168p. Set. 395.00 (ISBN 0-471-01849-X). Wiley.
Lepine, Pierre. Dictionnaire Francais-Anglais et Anglais-Francais des Termes Medicaux et Biologiques. 2nd ed. (Fr. & Eng.). 896p. 1974. 65.00 (ISBN 0-686-57292-0, M-4665). French & Eur.
McGraw-Hill Editors. Dictionary of Biology. 400p. 1985. write for info. (ISBN 0-07-045419-1). McGraw.
Manuila, A & Nicole, M. Dictionnaire Francais de Medicine el de Biologie, Vol. 2. (Fr.). 1971. 175.00 (ISBN 0-686-57033-2, M-6393). French & Eur.
Manuila, A. & Nicole, M. Dictionnaire Francais de Medicine et de Biologie, Vol. 1. (Fr.). 866p. 1970. 175.00 (ISBN 0-686-57032-4, M-6392). French & Eur.
Manuila, A., et al. Dictionnaire Francais de Medicine el de Biologie, Vol. 4. (Fr.). 580p. 1975. 130.00 (ISBN 0-686-57035-9, M-6395). French & Eur.
Mauila, A., et al. Dictionnaire Francais de Medicine el de Biologie, Vol. 3. (Fr.). 1200p. 1972. 195.00 (ISBN 0-686-57034-0, M-6394). French & Eur.
Medawar, P. B. & Medawar, J. S. Aristotle to Zoos: A Philosophical Dictionary of Biology. (Illus.). 352p. 1983. 18.50 (ISBN 0-674-04535-1). Harvard U Pr.
--Aristotle to Zoos: A Philosophical Dictionary of Biology. 320p. 1985. pap. 7.95 (ISBN 0-674-04537-8). Harvard U Pr.
Parker, Sybil P. McGraw-Hill Dictionary of Biology. pap. 15.95. McGraw.
Roe, Keith E. & Frederick, Richard G. Dictionary of Theoretical Concepts in Biology. LC 80-19889. 380p. 1981. 21.00 (ISBN 0-8108-1353-X). Scarecrow.
Steen. Dictionary of Biology. 1983. pap. text ed. 15.50 (ISBN 0-06-318241-6, Pub. by Har-Row Ltd England). Har-Row.
Steen, Edwin B. Dictionary of Biology. LC 70-156104. (EH); pap. 6.25i (ISBN 0-06-463321-7). B&N NY.
--Dictionary of Biology. LC 70-156104. 630p. 1971. text ed. 21.50x (ISBN 0-686-83546-8). B&N Imports.
Tootill, Elizabeth, ed. The Facts on File Dictionary of Biology. 288p. 1981. 14.95 (ISBN 0-87196-510-0). Facts on File.

BIOLOGY–ECOLOGY
see Ecology

BIOLOGY–EXAMINATIONS, QUESTIONS, ETC.

Bancheri, Louis, et al. Biology. LC 82-20671. (Arco's Regents Review Ser.). 304p. (Orig.). 1983. pap. 3.95 (ISBN 0-668-05697-5, 5697). Arco.
Bleifeld, Maurice. How to Prepare for the College Board Achievement Test - Biology. 7th ed. LC 81-3892. 352p. 1981. 9.50 (ISBN 0-8120-5416-4); pap. 7.95 (ISBN 0-8120-2345-5). Barron.
Edwards, Gabrielle & Cimmino, Marion. Barron's How to Prepare for the Advanced Placement Examination - Biology. 2nd ed. Bleifeld, Maurice, ed. 1982. pap. text ed. 7.95 (ISBN 0-8120-2328-5). Barron.
Edwards, Gabrielle I., ed. Barron's Regents Exams & Answers Biology. rev. ed. LC 58-19074. 300p. 1982. pap. text ed. 4.50 (ISBN 0-8120-3197-0). Barron.
Fogiel, Max, intro. by. The Biology Problem Solver. rev. ed. LC 78-63610. (Illus.). 1984. pap. text ed. 19.85 (ISBN 0-87891-514-1). Res & Educ.
Garnsey, Wayne & Licota, Guy. A Regents Biology Review. (Illus.). 250p. (Orig.). 1985. pap. text ed. 2.50 (ISBN 0-9606036-6-2). N & N Pub.
Miller, Arnold I. & Solomon, Lawrence. Biology: Advanced Test for the G.R.E. 5th ed. 1983. pap. 7.95 (ISBN 0-668-05863-3). Arco.
Practicing to Take the GRE Biology Test. (Orig.). 1983. pap. 6.95 (ISBN 0-88685-001-0). Educ Testing Serv.
Rodgers, Leland. Barron's How to Prepare for the Graduate Record Examination - Advanced Biology. LC 74-10918. 1975. pap. 6.95 (ISBN 0-8120-2072-3). Barron.
Rudman, Jack. Biological Aide. (Career Examination Ser.: C-86). (Cloth bdg. avail. on request). pap. 12.00 (ISBN 0-8373-0086-X). Natl Learning.
--Biological Sciences. (Graduate Record Area Examination Ser.: GRE-41). (Cloth bdg. avail. on request). pap. 13.95 (ISBN 0-8373-5241-X). Natl Learning.
--Biology. (College Level Examination Ser.: CLEP-5). (Cloth bdg. avail. on request). pap. 9.95 (ISBN 0-8373-5305-X). Natl Learning.
--Biology. (College Proficiency Examination Ser.: CPEP-5). (Cloth bdg. avail. on request). pap. 9.95 (ISBN 0-8373-5405-6). Natl Learning.
--Biology. (Graduate Record Examination Ser.: GRE-1). (Cloth bdg. avail. on request). pap. 13.95 (ISBN 0-8373-5201-0). Natl Learning.
--Biology & General Science. (National Teachers Examination Ser.: NT-3). (Cloth bdg. avail. on request). pap. 11.95 (ISBN 0-8373-8413-3). Natl Learning.
--Biology & General Science - Sr. H.S. (Teachers License Examination Ser.: T-4). (Cloth bdg. avail. on request). pap. 13.95 (ISBN 0-8373-8004-9). Natl Learning.
--Laboratory Specialist (Biology) Sr. H.S. (Teachers License Examination Ser.: T-34). (Cloth bdg. avail. on request). pap. 13.95 (ISBN 0-8373-8034-0). Natl Learning.
Solomon, Lawrence. College Board Achievement Test in Biology. 3rd ed. LC 83-11799. 395p. (Orig.). 1984. pap. 7.95 (ISBN 0-668-05861-7, 5861). Arco.
--Graduate Record Examination in Biology. 5th ed. LC 83-22482. 256p. 1983. pap. 7.95 (ISBN 0-668-05863-3, 5863). Arco.

BIOLOGY–EXPERIMENTS
see also Biology, Experimental

Gill, John L. Design & Analysis of Experiments in the Animal & Medical Sciences, Vol. 1. (Illus.). 1978. text ed. 18.50x (ISBN 0-8138-0020-X). Iowa St U Pr.
--Design & Analysis of Experiments in the Animal & Medical Sciences, Vol. 2. (Illus.). 1978. text ed. 16.95x (ISBN 0-8138-0060-9). Iowa St U Pr.
Leonard, William H. Laboratory Investigations in Biology. 192p. 1982. spiral bdg.. 14.95x (ISBN 0-8087-3848-8). Burgess.
Linder, A. Planen und Auswerten von Versuchen. 3rd ed. (Reihe der Experimentellen Biologie Ser.: No. 13). (Ger., Illus.). 344p. 1969. 52.95x (ISBN 0-8176-0248-8). Birkhauser.
Platnick, Norman I. & Funk, Vicki A., eds. Advances in Cladistics: Proceedings of the Second Meeting of the Willi Hennig Society, Vol. 2. 288p. 1983. 37.00x (ISBN 0-231-05646-X). Columbia U Pr.

BIOLOGY–FIELD WORK
see also Nature Study

Bennett, Donald P. & Humphries, David A. Introduction to Field Biology. 2nd ed. 1974. pap. text ed. 18.95x (ISBN 0-7131-2458-X). Intl Ideas.
Benton, Allen H. & Werner, William, Jr. Manual of Field Biology & Ecology. 6th ed. 174p. 1983. 14.95x (ISBN 0-8087-4086-5). Burgess.
Lederer, Roger J. Ecology & Field Biology. 1984. 26.95 (ISBN 0-8053-5718-1, 35718). Benjamin-Cummings.

BIOLOGY–HISTORY

Asimov, Isaac. A Short History of Biology. LC 80-15464. (American Museum Science Bks.). (Illus.). ix, 189p. 1980. Repr. of 1964 ed. lib. bdg. 32.50x (ISBN 0-313-22583-4, ASSB). Greenwood.
Baumel, Howard B. Biology: Its Historical Development. LC 77-87937. (Illus.). 1978. 6.00 (ISBN 0-8022-2217-X). Philos Lib.
Boylan, Michael. Method & Practice in Aristotle's Biology. LC 82-23708. (Illus.). 300p. (Orig.). 1983. lib. bdg. 25.50 (ISBN 0-8191-2952-6); pap. text ed. 13.25 (ISBN 0-8191-2953-4). U Pr of Amer.
Cameron, Jenks. The Bureau of Biological Survey: Its History, Activities, & Organization. LC 73-17805. (Natural Sciences in America Ser.). 354p. 1974. Repr. 24.50x (ISBN 0-405-05722-9). Ayer Co Pubs.
Coleman, W. Biology in the Nineteenth Century. LC 77-83989. (Cambridge History of Science Ser.). (Illus.). 1978. pap. 11.95 (ISBN 0-521-29293-X). Cambridge U Pr.
Coleman, William & Limoges, Camille. Studies in the History of Biology, Vol. 2. LC 76-47139. (Historical Studies in the Life Sciences). (Illus.). 1978. text ed. 23.00x (ISBN 0-8018-2034-0). Johns Hopkins.
--Studies in the History of Biology, Vol. 4. LC 76-47139. 1979. text ed. 20.00x (ISBN 0-8018-2362-5). Johns Hopkins.
Coleman, William & Limoges, Camille, eds. Studies in History of Biology, Vol. 3. 304p. 1979. 25.00x (ISBN 0-8018-2215-7). Johns Hopkins.
--Studies in History of Biology, Vol. 5. LC 78-647138. 224p. 1981. text ed. 22.00x (ISBN 0-8018-2566-0). Johns Hopkins.
--Studies in History of Biology, Vol. 6. LC 76-47139. 240p. 1983. text ed. 25.00x (ISBN 0-8018-2856-2). Johns Hopkins.
--Studies in History of Biology, Vol. 7. LC 78-647138. 160p. 1984. text ed. 20.00x (ISBN 0-8018-2995-X). Johns Hopkins.
--Studies in History of Biology, Vol. 1. LC 76-47139. (Historical Studies in the Life Sciences). 232p. 1977. 23.00x (ISBN 0-8018-1862-1). Johns Hopkins.
Gardner, Eldon. History of Biology. 3rd ed. LC 75-188575. 1972. text ed. 18.95x (ISBN 0-8087-0702-7). Burgess.
Hendrix, Roger W., et al, eds. Lambda II. LC 81-70528. (Monagraph: Vol. 13). 694p. 1984. pap. 38.00 (ISBN 0-87969-177-8). Cold Spring Harbor.
Judson, H F. The Eighth Day of Creation: The Makers of the Revolution in Biology. 686p. 1980. 40.00 (ISBN 0-317-14262-3, Pub. by Holdan Bk Ltd UK). State Mutual Bk.
Marder, William. The History & Technique of a New Diffusion Process. 1980. pap. 10.00 (ISBN 0-9607480-5-9). Pine Ridge.
Mayr, Ernst. The Growth of Biological Thought: Diversity, Evolution, & Inheritance. 1982. 30.00 (ISBN 0-674-36445-7). Harvard U Pr.
Nordenskiod, Erik. The History of Biology: A Survey. 1935. Repr. 75.00x (ISBN 0-403-01788-2). Scholarly.
Ospovat, Dov. The Development of Darwin's Theory: Natural History, Natural Theology, & Natural Selection, 1838-1859. LC 81-4077. (Illus.). 228p. 1981. 47.50 (ISBN 0-521-23818-8). Cambridge U Pr.
Overmier, Judith. The History of Biology: An Annotated Bibliography. LC 82-49290. 350p. 1985. lib. bdg. 45.00 (ISBN 0-8240-9118-3). Garland Pub.
Radl, Emanuel. The History of Biological Theories. LC 30-28974. 498p. 1930. Repr. 69.00x (ISBN 0-403-01791-2). Scholarly.
Ritterbush, Philip. Overtures to Biology: Speculations of Eighteenth Century Naturalists. 1964. 59.50x (ISBN 0-685-69859-9). Elliots Bks.
Russett, Cynthia E. Darwin in America: The Intellectual Response, 1865-1912. LC 75-40476. (Illus.). 228p. 1976. pap. text ed. 8.95x (ISBN 0-7167-0563-X). W H Freeman.
Simpson, George G. Why & How: Some Problems & Methods in Historical Biology. LC 79-42774. (Illus.). 270p. 1980. 52.00 (ISBN 0-08-025785-2); pap. 24.00 (ISBN 0-08-025784-4). Pergamon.
Singer, Charles J. Greek Biology & Greek Medicine. LC 75-23760. Repr. of 1922 ed. 14.50 (ISBN 0-404-13366-5). AMS Pr.
Taylor, Henry O. Greek Biology & Greek Medicine. LC 63-10282. (Our Debt to Greece & Rome Ser). Repr. of 1930 ed. 18.50 (ISBN 0-8154-0235-X). Cooper Sq.
Thompson, John A. Great Biologists. facs. ed. LC 67-23272. (Essay Index Reprint Ser). 1932. 18.00 (ISBN 0-8369-0935-6). Ayer Co Pubs.
Weinstock, John. Contemporary Perspectives on Linnaeus. LC 85-7397. (Illus.). 204p. (Orig.). 1985. lib. bdg. 24.00 (ISBN 0-8191-4697-8); pap. 12.00 (ISBN 0-8191-4698-6). U Pr of Amer.
Winsor, Mary P. Starfish, Jellyfish & the Order of Life: Issues of Nineteenth-Century Science. LC 74-29739. (Studies in the History of Science & Medicine Ser.: No. 10). (Illus.). 256p. 1976. 33.00x (ISBN 0-300-01635-2). Yale U Pr.

BIOLOGY–LABORATORIES
see Biological Laboratories

BIOLOGY–LABORATORY MANUALS

Abramoff, Peter & Thomson, Robert G. Laboratory Outlines in Biology III. (Illus.). 479p. 1982. pap. text ed. 15.95x (ISBN 0-7167-1323-3). W H Freeman.
Adams, Caroline, et al. Laboratory Manual for Principles of Biology. 3rd ed. 94p. 1984. pap. 8.95 (ISBN 0-88725-026-2). Hunter Textbks.
--Laboratory Manual for Principles of Biology. 2nd ed. (Illus.). 94p. 1979. pap. 7.95x lab manual (ISBN 0-89459-147-9). Hunter Textbks.
Anderson. Adventures in the Biology Laboratory. 1978. 9.00 (ISBN 0-942788-03-6). Marginal Med.
Armitage, Kenneth B. Investigations in General Biology. 1970. text ed. 15.00i (ISBN 0-12-062460-5). Acad Pr.
Auleb, Leigh & Auleb, Ann W. Laboratory Exercises for Human Biology. (Illus.). 104p. 1983. lab manual 6.95x (ISBN 0-917962-81-8). Peek Pubns.
Behringer, Marjorie P. Techniques & Materials in Biology. LC 80-12458. 608p. 1981. Repr. of 1973 ed. lib. bdg. 30.50 (ISBN 0-89874-175-0). Krieger.
Bowen, William. Biology: A Laboratory Experience. 176p. 1984. pap. text ed. 5.95 (ISBN 0-8403-3492-3). Kendall-Hunt.
Brett, William. Biological Explorations I: Laboratory Manual. 1978. pap. text ed. 10.95 (ISBN 0-8403-1925-8). Kendall-Hunt.
Brett, William J. Biological Explorations II: Laboratory Manual. 1979. 12.95 (ISBN 0-8403-1938-X, 40193801). Kendall-Hunt.
Brown, Robert H. & Wishard, Roy H. Biology Lab Text. 2nd ed. 1978. pap. text ed. 13.95 (ISBN 0-8403-0366-1). Kendall-Hunt.
Browne, Louis & Romero, Adrian. Manual de Investigaciones Biologicas. (Span.). 1979. pap. text ed. 6.95 (ISBN 0-8403-1949-5, 40194901). Kendall-Hunt.
Cibula, Adam B. Biological Science Laboratory Guide, Vol. 1. 1976. pap. text ed. 7.95 (ISBN 0-8403-1049-8). Kendall-Hunt.
--Biological Science Laboratory Guide: Preliminary Edition, Vol. 2. 1977. pap. text ed. 7.95 (ISBN 0-8403-1844-8). Kendall-Hunt.
--Biological Sciences Laboratory Guide, Volume 3. 1977. pap. text ed. 5.95 (ISBN 0-8403-1732-8). Kendall-Hunt.
Connell, Mary U. Biology Laboratory Manual, Pt. I. 146p. (Orig.). 1983. lab manual 8.95x (ISBN 0-89459-216-5). Hunter Textbks.
--Biology Laboratory Manual, Pt. II. 166p. 1983. lab manual 8.95x (ISBN 0-89459-217-3). Hunter Textbks.
Dalrymple, Mason. Human Biology Laboratory Manual. 80p. 1985. pap. text ed. 9.95 (ISBN 0-8403-3530-X). Kendall-Hunt.
Devine, Edward & Staudinger, Lennette. Biological Investigations: Lab Exercises for Introductory Biology. 3rd ed. 128p. 1983. pap. text ed. 8.95 (ISBN 0-8403-3060-X). Kendall-Hunt.
Elgart, Robert. The BioLab Book: Laboratory Studies in Life. (Illus.). 138p. 1985. 14.95 (ISBN 0-9609098-3-4). Biomat Pub Co.
Evert, Ray, et al. Laboratory Topics in Biology. 1979. text ed. 13.95x (ISBN 0-87901-103-3). Worth.
Fritchie, G. Edward & Ooi, Wan H. Biology: A Laboratory Experience. 2nd ed. (Illus.). 236p. 1982. pap. text ed. 14.95x (ISBN 0-89641-082-X). American Pr.
Gerrath, Jean, et al. A Plant Biology Lab Manual for a One Semester Course: Form & Function. 152p. 1982. pap. text ed. 7.95 (ISBN 0-8403-2814-1). Kendall-Hunt.
Graham, Tom M. Biology Laboratory Manual for the Nonscience Major I. 2nd ed. 1978. pap. text ed. 10.95 (ISBN 0-8403-1137-0). Kendall-Hunt.
Gray, Robert C. Biology Laboratory Experiences. (Illus.). 160p. (Orig.). 1983. 6.90x (ISBN 0-9606666-2-1). Greenfield Pubns.
Grey, Robert D., et al. A Laboratory Text for Developmental Biology. 160p. 1982. pap. text ed. 12.95 (ISBN 0-8403-2801-X). Kendall-Hunt.
Gunstream, Stanley E. & Babel, John S. Explorations in Basic Biology. 3rd ed. 1982. pap. text ed. 14.95x (ISBN 0-8087-4122-5). Burgess.
Harmet, Kenneth H. Laboratory Exercises & Experiments in Biology. 1980. coil bdg. 6.95 (ISBN 0-88252-003-2). Paladin Hse.
Hartman, Margaret & Russell, Mercer P. Laboratory Manual for Biology of Animals. 1980. coil binding 9.95. Paladin Hse.
Howard, Lauren D. Principles of Biology Laboratory Manual. (Illus.). 1980. pap. 12.50 (ISBN 0-87055-354-2). AVI.
Indiana University & Charnego, Michael. General Biology Laboratory Manual. 3rd ed. 1981. 8.95 (ISBN 0-8403-3054-5, 40305403). Kendall-Hunt.
Jope, Charlene A. Cellular & Molecular Laboratory Manual. 64p. 1981. pap. text ed. 5.95 (ISBN 0-8403-2353-0). Kendall-Hunt.
Kaplan, E. H. Problem Solving in Biology: A Laboratory Workbook. 2nd ed. 1976. pap. write for info. (ISBN 0-02-361760-8). Macmillan.
Kaplan, Eugene H. Experiences in Life Science: A Laboratory Guide. 2nd ed. (Illus.). 256p. 1976. pap. text ed. write for info. (ISBN 0-02-361770-5). Macmillan.
Keeton, William T., et al. Laboratory Guide for Biological Science. (Orig.). 1968. pap. text ed. 12.95x (ISBN 0-393-09823-0, NortonC). Norton.
--Biology in the Laboratory. 1970. pap. 9.95x (ISBN 0-393-09943-1). Norton.
--Biological Investigations in the Laboratory: A Manual to Accompany Biological Science & Elements of Biological Science. (Illus.). 1986. pap. write for info. (ISBN 0-393-95260-6); write for info. instr's. manual (ISBN 0-393-95367-X). Norton.
Kirkwood, Robert T. Laboratory Exercises in Biology. 2nd ed. 1981. pap. text ed. 8.95 (ISBN 0-8403-3005-7, 40300501). Kendall-Hunt.
Knox, Carol & Rowsey, Katheryn. Problems in Biology. (Illus.). 90p. (Orig.). 1980. lab manual 4.95x (ISBN 0-88334-132-8). Ind Sch Pr.
Latta, Virginia G., et al. Principles of Biology: Laboratory Investigations. 3rd ed. (Illus.). 1982. lab manual 8.95x (ISBN 0-89459-177-0). Hunter Textbks.
Legg, Larry. Biological Science: Lab Lecture Guide Biology 116. 502p. (Orig.). 1982. pap. text ed. 22.95x (ISBN 0-88136-008-2). Jostens.
--Biological Science: Lab-Lecture Guide Biology, No. 115. (Illus.). 384p. 19.95x (ISBN 0-88136-000-7). Jostens.
Mason, William H. & Lawrence, Faye B. Laboratory Manual & Study Guide in Animal Biology. 176p. 1982. pap. text ed. 13.95 (ISBN 0-8403-2740-4). Kendall-Hunt.
Mason, William H. & Marshall, Norton L. General Biology Laboratory Manual. 2nd ed. 144p. 1984. pap. text ed. 11.95 (ISBN 0-8403-3353-6, 40335301). Kendall-Hunt.

Northern Virginia Community College Staff. Biology 101 Lab Manual. 128p. 1983. pap. text ed. 7.95 (ISBN 0-8403-3074-X). Kendall-Hunt.

--Biology 102 Lab Manual. 120p. 1983. pap. text ed. 7.95 (ISBN 0-8403-3075-8). Kendall-Hunt.

Oswald, Vernon H. Laboratory Manual for General Biology. 3rd ed. (Orig.). 1980. pap. text ed. 8.95 (ISBN 0-8403-0313-0). Kendall-Hunt.

Salter, Charlie J. Biology Laboratory Manual. (Illus.). 142p. 1979. lab manual 6.95x (ISBN 0-89459-046-4). Hunter Textbks.

--Biology Laboratory Manual. 2nd ed. 142p. 1984. pap. 8.95 (ISBN 0-88725-027-0). Hunter Textbks.

Scheel, Carl A., et al. Exploring Laboratory Biology. new ed. LC 74-28778. (Illus.). 132p. (Orig.). 1976. 6.25 (ISBN 0-87812-147-1). Pendell Pub.

Schultz, Janet L. Biology & Man Laboratory Guide. 80p. 1981. pap. text ed. 7.95 (ISBN 0-8403-2351-4). Kendall-Hunt.

Scott, Leroy & Weih, Starr. Biology Laboratory Manual. 1980. coil binding 9.95 (ISBN 0-88252-106-3). Paladin Hse.

Sharp, Marjorie. Biology Laboratory Manual. 3rd ed. 212p. 1984. lab manual 10.95x (ISBN 0-88725-009-2). Hunter Textbks.

Southern University, Department of Biological Sciences Staff. General Biology 104 Manual. 160p. 1983. pap. text ed. 11.95 (ISBN 0-8403-3010-3). Kendall-Hunt.

Stiles, George, et al. Laboratory Guide for Freshman Biology. 2nd ed. 1980. pap. text ed. 12.95 (ISBN 0-8403-2227-5). Kendall-Hunt.

Thornton, et al. Principles of Biology Laboratory Investigations & Lecture Supplements. 144p. 1984. pap. text ed. 8.95 (ISBN 0-8403-3452-4). Kendall-Hunt.

Trelease, Richard N., et al. Biology One Hundred One Laboratory Manual. 1982. pap. text ed. 6.50 (ISBN 0-8403-2745-5). Kendall-Hunt.

--Biology One Hundred Two Laboratory Manual. 1982. pap. text ed. 9.95 (ISBN 0-8403-2763-3). Kendall-Hunt.

Unbehaun, Laraine, et al. Principles of Biology Laboratory Manual. 222p. (Orig.). 1980. pap. text ed. 13.95x (ISBN 0-8087-2115-1). Burgess.

Urban, Emil K., et al. Laboratory Manual for Introductory Biology. 2nd ed. (Illus.). 196p. 1982. lab manual 16.95x (ISBN 0-88725-017-3). Hunter Textbks.

Wachtmeister, et al. Encounters with Life: Laboratory Manual. (Illus.). 368p. 1982. text ed. 14.95x (ISBN 0-89582-067-6). Morton Pub.

Walker, Warren F., Jr. Dissection of the Frog: Laboratory Studies in Biology, 770-776, 7 studies. 1981. loose-leaf 0.95 ea.; tchr's guide avail. W H Freeman.

--Dissection of the Rat: Laboratory studies in Biology, 840-845, 6 studies. 1981. loose-leaf 0.75 ea.; tchr's guide avail. W H Freeman.

Walsh, Eileen, et al. Laboratory Studies in General Biology. 2nd ed. 1978. pap. text ed. 12.95 (ISBN 0-8403-2440-5). Kendall-Hunt.

White, J. M. & Barnes, R. P. Manual for Hands On Biology: An Audio Tutorial Approach. 349p. 1974. pap. text ed. 28.50x (ISBN 0-471-94016-X). Wiley.

Widdows, Richard E. General Biology Laboratory Manual. 2nd ed. 1978. pap. text ed. 14.95 (ISBN 0-8403-1803-0). Kendall-Hunt.

Winchester, A. M. Biology Laboratory Manual. 6th ed. 344p. 1979. write for info. wire coil (ISBN 0-697-04548-X). Wm C Brown.

Wochok, Zachary S., et al. Laboratory Manual: Plant Biology. 6th ed. 1981. pap. text ed. 13.95 (ISBN 0-8403-2530-4). Kendall-Hunt.

Wodsedalek, J. E., et al. General Biology Laboratory Guide. 4th ed. 288p. 1980. write for info. wire coil (ISBN 0-697-04589-7). Wm C Brown.

Zimmerman & Beitinger. Laboratory Manual in Human Biology. 160p. 1984. pap. text ed. 10.95 (ISBN 0-8403-3200-9). Kendall-Hunt.

BIOLOGY–MATHEMATICAL MODELS

Barigozzi, Claudio, ed. Vito Volterra Symposium on Mathematical Models in Biology: Proceedings. (LN in Biomathematics Ser.: Vol. 39). (Illus.). 417p. 1980. pap. 32.00 (ISBN 0-387-10279-5). Springer-Verlag.

Burton. Modeling & Differential Equations in Biology. (Lecture Notes in Pure & Applied Mathematics Ser.: Vol. 58). 296p. 1980. 49.50 (ISBN 0-8247-1075-4). Dekker.

Burton, T. A., ed. Mathematical Biology-a Conference on Theoretical Aspects of Molecular Science: Proceedings of a Conference Held at Southern Illinois University at Carbondale, May 27-28, 1980. (Illus.). 241p. 1981. 33.00 (ISBN 0-08-026348-8). Pergamon.

Cullen, Charles G. Math for Biosciences. 800p. 1983. text ed. write for info. (ISBN 0-87150-352-2, 2761, Prindle). PWS Pubs.

Fife, P. C. Mathematical Aspects of Reacting & Diffusing Systems. LC 79-10216. (Lecture Notes in Biomathematics Ser.: Vol. 28). 1979. pap. text ed. 14.00 (ISBN 0-387-09117-3). Springer-Verlag.

Finkelstein, L. & Carson, E. R. Mathematical Modelling of Dynamic Biological Systems. 2nd ed. (Medical Computing Ser.). 59.95 (ISBN 0-471-90688-3). Wiley.

Finkelstein, Ludwick & Carson, Ewart R. Mathematical Modeling of Dynamic Biological Systems, Vol. 3. (Medical Computing Ser.). 329p. 1979. 48.95x (ISBN 0-471-27890-4, Research Studies Pr). Wiley.

Getz, W. M., ed. Mathematical Modelling in Biology & Ecology: Proceedings of a Symposium Held at the CSIR, Pretoria, July 1979. (Lecture Notes in Biomathematics Ser.: Vol. 33). viii, 355p. 1980. pap. 28.00 (ISBN 3-540-09735-X). Springer-Verlag.

Goel, Narendra & Richter-Dyn, Nira. Stochastic Models in Biology. 1974. 47.50 (ISBN 0-12-287460-9). Acad Pr.

Gold, Harvey J. Mathematical Modeling of Biological Systems: An Introductory Guidebook. LC 77-8193. 357p. 1977. 43.50x (ISBN 0-471-02092-3, Pub. by Wiley-Interscience). Wiley.

Gurland, John. Stochastic Models in Medicine & Biology: Proceedings of a Symposium Conducted by the Mathematics Research Center, 1963. LC 64-14509. (U. S. Army Mathematics Research Center Ser.: No. 10). pap. 102.50 (ISBN 0-317-12991-0, 2021134). Bks Demand UMI.

Hethcote, H. W. & Yorke, J. A. Gonorrhea Transmission Dynamics & Control. (Lecture Notes in Biomathematics Ser.: Vol. 56). ix, 105p. 1984. pap. 11.00 (ISBN 0-387-13870-6). Springer-Verlag.

Hummel, K. & Gerchow, J., eds. Biomathematical Evidence of Paternity: Festschrift for Erik Essen-Moeller. (Illus.). 235p. 1982. pap. 43.60 (ISBN 0-387-11133-6). Springer-Verlag.

Iosifescu, M. & Tautu, P. Stochastic Processes & Application in Biology & Medicine, Pt. 1: Theory. LC 73-77733. (Biomathematics, Ser.: Vol. 3). 331p. 1973. 42.00 (ISBN 0-387-06270-X). Springer-Verlag.

Jager, W. & Murry, J., eds. Modelling of Patterns in Space & Time. (Lecture Notes in Biomathematics: Vol. 55). viii, 405p. 1984. pap. 25.00 (ISBN 0-387-13892-7). Springer-Verlag.

Kerner, Edward H. Gibbs Ensemble: Biological Ensemble, Vol. 12. LC 73-185038. (International Science Review Ser.). 180p. 1970. 64.95 (ISBN 0-677-14180-7). Gordon.

Lambrecht, R. M. & Rescigno, A., eds. Tracer Kinetics & Physiologic Modeling - Theory & Practice: Proceedings, St. Louix, Missouri, 1983. (Lecture Notes in Biomathematics: Vol. 48). 509p. 1983. pap. 30.00 (ISBN 0-387-12300-8). Springer-Verlag.

MacDonald, N. Time Lags in Biological Models. (Lecture Notes in Biomathematics: Vol. 27). (Illus.). 1978. pap. 14.00 (ISBN 0-387-09092-4). Springer-Verlag.

Rashevsky, Nicolas. Mathematical Principles in Biology & Their Applications. (Illus.). 144p. 1961. 14.50x (ISBN 0-398-01552-X). C C Thomas.

--Some Medical Aspects of Mathematical Biology. (Illus.). 342p. 1964. 33.75x (ISBN 0-398-01553-8). C C Thomas.

Ricciardi, L. & Scott, A., eds. Biomathematics in Nineteen Eighty. (Mathematics Studies: Vol. 58). 298p. 1982. 51.00 (ISBN 0-444-86355-9, North-Holland). Elsevier.

Roberts, Fred S. Discrete Mathematical Models with Applications to Social Biological & Environmental Problems. (Illus.). 560p. 1976. Ref. Ed. 39.95 (ISBN 0-13-214171-X). P-H.

Rothe, F. Global Solutions of Reaction-Diffusion Systems. (Lecture Notes in Mathematics Ser.: Vol. 1072). v, 216p. 1984. pap. 13.50 (ISBN 0-387-13365-8). Springer-Verlag.

Rubinow, Sol I. Mathematical Problems in the Biological Sciences. (CBMS-NSF Regional Conference Ser.: No. 10). vii, 90p. (Orig.). 1973. pap. text ed. 10.00 (ISBN 0-89871-008-1). Soc Indus-Appl Math.

Waltman, Paul. Competition Models in Population Biology. LC 83-50665. (CBMS-NSF Regional Conference Ser.: No. 45). v, 77p. 1983. pap. text ed. 12.50 (ISBN 0-89871-188-6). Soc Indus-Appl Math.

BIOLOGY–METHODOLOGY

Bailey, Norman T. Elements of Stochastic Processes with Applications to the Natural Sciences: Applied Probability & Statistics Section. LC 63-23220. (Probability & Mathematical Statistics Ser.). 249p. 1964. 45.95x (ISBN 0-471-04165-3, Pub. by Wiley-Interscience). Wiley.

Day, Stacey B., ed. Some Systems of Biological Communication. (Biosciences Communications: Vol. 3, No. 5-6). (Illus.). 1977. 24.25 (ISBN 3-8055-2817-5). S Karger.

Griffith, Jack D., ed. Electron Microscopy in Biology, Vol. 2. (Electron Microscopy in Biology Ser.). 349p. 1982. text ed. 97.50x (ISBN 0-471-05526-3). Wiley.

Nuclear Activation Techniques in the Life Sciences. Incl. 1966. (Proceedings Ser.). 709p. 1967. pap. 46.50 (ISBN 92-0-010267-0, ISP155, IAEA); 1972. (Proceedings Ser.). (Illus.). 664p. (Orig.). 1973. pap. 56.50 (ISBN 92-0-010272-7, ISP310, IAEA); 1978. (Proceedings Ser.). 1979. pap. 112.75 (ISBN 92-0-010079-1, ISP42, IAEA). (Proceedings Ser.). 709p. 1967. pap. 46.50 (ISBN 92-0-010267-0, ISP155, IAEA). Unipub.

Yoshida, Z. I, ed. New Synthetic Methodology & Biologically Active Substances. (Studies in Organic Chemistry Ser.: Vol. 6). 282p. 1981. 74.50 (ISBN 0-444-99742-3). Elsevier.

BIOLOGY–NOMENCLATURE

see Botany–Nomenclature; Zoology–Nomenclature

BIOLOGY–OUTLINES, SYLLABI, ETC.

Alexander, Gordon & Alexander, Douglas G. Biology. 9th ed. LC 77-118098. (Illus.). 1970. pap. 6.95 (ISBN 0-06-460004-1, CO 4, COS). B&N NY.

Morholt, Evelyn, et al. Sourcebook for the Biological Sciences. 2nd ed. (Teaching Science Ser.). 795p. 1966. text ed. 25.95 (ISBN 0-15-582850-9, HC). HarBraceJ.

Winokur, Morris. General Biology. (Quality Paperback: No. 9). (Orig.). 1970. pap. 1.95 (ISBN 0-8226-0009-9). Littlefield.

BIOLOGY–PERIODICITY

see Biological Rhythms

BIOLOGY–PHILOSOPHY

Atlan, Henri, et al. Laying Down a Path in Walking: Essays for a New Philosophy of Biology. LC 83-82697. 96p. (Orig.). pap. 7.50postponed (ISBN 0-940262-05-3). Lindisfarne Pr.

Ayala, Francisco & Dobzhansky, Theodosius, eds. Studies in the Philosophy of Biology: Reduction & Related Problems. LC 73-90656. 1974. 38.50x (ISBN 0-520-02649-7). U of Cal Pr.

Boughton, Donald C. Reality Embraced. 132p. 1983. 14.95 (ISBN 0-87975-225-4). Prometheus Bks.

Breck, A. D. & Yourgrau, W., eds. Biology, History, & Natural Philosophy. LC 70-186262. 370p. 1972. 45.00x (ISBN 0-306-30573-9, Plenum Pr). Plenum Pub.

Breck, Allan D. & Yourgrau, Wolfgang, eds. Biology, History & Natural Philosophy. LC 74-774. 370p. 1974. pap. 6.95x (ISBN 0-306-20009-0, Rosetta). Plenum Pub.

Chasis, Herbert & Goldring, William, eds. Homer William Smith, Sc. D. His Scientific & Literary Achievements. LC 65-10765. pap. 58.60 (ISBN 0-8357-9478-4, 2010289). Bks Demand UMI.

Crick, Francis. Of Molecules & Men. LC 66-26994. (Jesse & John Danz Lecture Ser.). 118p. 1967. pap. 5.95x (ISBN 0-295-97869-4, WP-26). U of Wash Pr.

Grene, M. Boston Studies in the Philosophy of Science, Vol. 23: The Understanding of Nature. Essays in the Philosophy of Biology. LC 74-76477. (Synthese Library: No. 66). 366p. 1974. 44.00 (ISBN 90-277-0462-7, Pub. by Reidel Holland); pap. 24.00 (ISBN 90-277-0463-5). Kluwer Academic.

Grene, M. & Mendelsohn, E., eds. Boston Studies in the Philosophy of Science, Vol. 27: Topics in the Philosophy of Biology. LC 75-12875. (Synthese Library: No. 84). 425p. 1975. 58.00 (ISBN 90-277-0595-X, Pub. by Reidel Holland); pap. 29.00 (ISBN 90-277-0596-8). Kluwer Academic.

Haldane, J. B. The Philosophical Basis of Biology. 1931. 25.00 (ISBN 0-8274-4213-0). R West.

--The Philosophy of a Biologist. 1955. 25.00 (ISBN 0-8274-4211-4). R West.

Hans, Jonas. The Phenomenon of Life: Toward a Philosophical Biology. LC 78-31180. 1979. Repr. of 1966 ed. lib. bdg. 21.00x (ISBN 0-313-20961-8, JOPO). Greenwood.

Haraway, Donna J. Crystals, Fabrics, & Fields: Metaphors of Organicism in the Twentieth-Century Developmental Biology. LC 75-18174. 240p. 1976. 27.00x (ISBN 0-300-01864-9). Yale U Pr.

Hull, David L. Philosophy of Biological Science. LC 73-12981. (Foundations of Philosophy Ser.). (Illus.). 192p. 1974. pap. text ed. 13.95 (ISBN 0-13-663609-8). P-H.

Iberall, A. S. On Nature, Life, Mind & Society. LC 76-43594. (Technical Monographs). 1976. pap. 6.00 (ISBN 0-914780-04-2). Gen Tech Serv.

Jennings, Herbert S. The Universe & Life. facsimile ed. (Select Bibliographies Reprint Ser). Repr. of 1933 ed. 14.00 (ISBN 0-8369-6695-3). Ayer Co Pubs.

Judson, Herrick C. Fatalism or Freedom: A Biologist's Answer. 1979. Repr. of 1926 ed. lib. bdg. 15.00 (ISBN 0-8492-5334-9). R West.

Loeb, Jacques. Mechanistic Conception of Life. Fleming, Donald, ed. LC 64-13426. (The John Harvard Library). (Illus.). 1964. 15.00x (ISBN 0-674-55950-9). Harvard U Pr.

Mayr, Ernst. The Growth of Biological Thought: Diversity, Evolution, & Inheritance. 1982. 30.00 (ISBN 0-674-36445-7). Harvard U Pr.

Medawar, P. B. & Medawar, J. S. Aristotle to Zoos: A Philosophical Dictionary of Biology. 320p. 1985. pap. 7.95 (ISBN 0-674-04537-8). Harvard U Pr.

Mishra, R. K., ed. The Living State, No. II. 500p. 1985. 75.00 (ISBN 0-317-30931-5). Taylor & Francis.

Needham, Joseph. Order & Life. 1968. pap. 6.95x (ISBN 0-262-64001-5). MIT Pr.

Paradis, James G. T. H. Huxley: Man's Place in Nature. LC 78-5492. xiv, 226p. 1978. 18.95x (ISBN 0-8032-0917-7). U of Nebr Pr.

Rensch, Bernhard. Biophilosophy. Sym, Cecilia, tr. from Ger. LC 72-132692. 1971. 36.00x (ISBN 0-231-03299-4). Columbia U Pr.

Roberts, Catherine. Science, Animals & Evolution: Reflections on Some Unrealized Potentials of Biology & Medicine. LC 79-52322. (Contributions in Philosophy Ser.: No. 14). 1980. lib. bdg. 27.50x (ISBN 0-313-21479-4, RSA/). Greenwood.

Rosenberg, Alexander. The Structure of Biological Science. (Illus.). 352p. 1985. 37.50 (ISBN 0-521-25566-X); pap. 12.95 (ISBN 0-521-27561-X). Cambridge U Pr.

Sahlins, Marshall D. The Use & Abuse of Biology: An Anthropological Critique of Sociobiology. 1976. pap. 5.00 (ISBN 0-472-76600-7). U of Mich Pr.

Schoffeniels, E. Anti-Chance. 1976. pap. text ed. 11.75 (ISBN 0-08-021008-2). Pergamon.

Schrodinger, Erwin. What Is Life? Bd. with Mind & Matter. pap. 11.95x (ISBN 0-521-09397-X). Cambridge U Pr.

Sinnott, Edmund W. Matter, Mind & Man: The Biology of Human Nature. LC 56-13282. 1962. pap. text ed. 2.75x (ISBN 0-689-70182-9, 9). Atheneum.

Stent, Gunther S., ed. Morality As a Biological Phenomenon: The Presuppositions of Sociobiological Research. 1980. 23.00x (ISBN 0-520-04028-7); pap. 5.95 (ISBN 0-520-04029-5, CAL 482). U of Cal Pr.

Thomas, Lewis. The Lives of a Cell: Notes of a Biology Watcher. 192p. 1975. pap. 3.95 (ISBN 0-553-24562-7). Bantam.

--The Lives of a Cell: Notes of a Biology Watcher. 1978. pap. 3.95 (ISBN 0-14-004743-3). Penguin.

--Lives of a Cell: Notes of a Biology Watcher. 1974. 10.95 (ISBN 0-670-43442-6). Viking.

Thorpe, William H. Science, Man, & Morals. LC 76-14962. (Illus.). 1976. Repr. of 1965 ed. lib. bdg. 16.00x (ISBN 0-8371-8143-7, THSMM). Greenwood.

Varela, F. J. Principles of Biological Autonomy. (North Holland Ser. in General Systems Research: Vol. 2). 336p. 1979. 52.25 (ISBN 0-444-00321-5, North Holland). Elsevier.

BIOLOGY–PROGRAMMED INSTRUCTION

Pentz, Lundy. The Bio Lab Book. LC 82-49066. 144p. 1983. pap. text ed. 9.95x (ISBN 0-8018-2512-1). Johns Hopkins.

BIOLOGY–RESEARCH

see Biological Research

BIOLOGY–SOCIAL ASPECTS

Academy Forum. Research with Recombinant DNA. 1977. pap. text ed. 9.95 (ISBN 0-309-02641-5). Natl Acad Pr.

Bandman, Elsie L. & Bandman, Bertram. Bioethics & Human Rights. 1978. pap. text ed. 14.95 (ISBN 0-316-07998-7). Little.

Darrough, Masako N. & Blank, Robert H., eds. Biological Differences & Social Equality: Implications for Social Policy. (Illus.). 272p. 1983. lib. bdg. 29.95 (ISBN 0-313-23022-6, DAS/). Greenwood.

Galperine, Charles, ed. Biology & the Future of Man. (Illus.). 1976. pap. 27.50x (ISBN 2-7042-0093-9, Pub. by U of Paris). Intl Spec Bk.

Kelly, P. J. & Schaefer, G., eds. Biological Education for Community Development. 200p. 1980. 21.00x (ISBN 0-85066-214-1). Taylor & Francis.

Volpe, E. Peter. Biology & Human Concerns. 3rd ed. 704p. 1983. text ed. write for info. (ISBN 0-697-04734-2); instr's. manual avail. (ISBN 0-697-04748-2); study guide avail. (ISBN 0-697-04747-4); lab manual avail. (ISBN 0-697-04746-6). Wm C Brown.

Weissmann, Gerald, ed. The Biological Revolution: Applications of Cell Biology to Public Welfare. LC 79-12369. (Illus.). 154p. 1979. 19.95 (ISBN 0-306-40241-6, Plenum Pr). Plenum Pub.

Wiegele, Thomas C., ed. Biology & the Social Sciences: An Emerging Revolution. LC 81-14808. 383p. (Orig.). 1981. 36.00x (ISBN 0-86531-201-X). Westview.

BIOLOGY–STATISTICAL MODELS

see Biometry

BIOLOGY–STUDY AND TEACHING

Ali, Masur & Pitre, B. G. Secondary Biology Workshop. 218p. 1981. 40.00 (ISBN 0-86131-054-3, Pub. by Orient Longman India). State Mutual Bk.

Association for Biology Laboratory Education Staff. Tested Studies for Laboratory Teaching: Proceedings of the Third Workshop-Conference of Association for Biology Laboratory Education. 240p. 1984. text ed. 19.95 (ISBN 0-8403-3178-9). Kendall-Hunt.

Baird, Don O. A Study of Biology Notebook Work in New York State. LC 71-176532. (Columbia University. Teachers College. Contributions to Education: No. 400). Repr. of 1929 ed. 22.50 (ISBN 0-404-55400-8). AMS Pr.

Bhattacharya, S. S. & Antia, K. K. Biology Practicals for the Higher Secondary Std.X1. 138p. 1981. 29.00x (ISBN 0-86125-108-3, Pub. by Orient Longman India). State Mutual Bk.

Biological Sciences Curriculum Study. Biology Teacher's Handbook. 3rd ed. LC 77-27548. 585p. 1978. text ed. 40.95x (ISBN 0-471-01945-3). Wiley.

Biology Education in Asia: Report of a Regional Workshop. (APEID Ser.). 169p. 1981. pap. 14.00 (ISBN 0-686-72899-8, UB91, UB). Unipub.

Bybee, Rodger W. Human Ecology: A Perspective for Biology Education. LC 84-29595. (Monograph Ser. II). 63p. 1984. pap. write for info. (ISBN 0-941212-04-1). Natl Assn Bio Tchrs.

Developing Materials for Biology Teaching: Report of a Sub-regional Workshop, Bangkok, August 3-12, 1981. (APEID Ser.). 32p. 1983. pap. 5.00 (ISBN 0-686-44001-3, UB117, UB). Unipub.

Edwards. Biology. (Easy Way Ser.). 1983. pap. 7.95 (ISBN 0-8120-2625-X). Barron.

Egan, Robert S., ed. Topics Aids: Biology: A Catalog in Instructional Media for College Biology. LC 77-13587. 296p. 1978. pap. 5.00x (ISBN 0-89096-042-9). Tex A&M Univ Pr.

Falk, Doris. Biology Teaching Methods. LC 79-19132. 302p. (Prog. Bk.). 1980. Repr. of 1971 ed. lib. bdg. 18.50 (ISBN 0-89874-038-X). Krieger.

Ferri, E., et al. Biology Learning Guide. 1984. Paladin Hse.

Finley, Charles W. Biology in Secondary Schools & the Training of Biology Teachers. LC 77-176772. (Columbia University. Teachers College. Contributions to Education: No. 199). Repr. of 1926 ed. 22.50 (ISBN 0-404-55199-8). AMS Pr.

Goldstein, Amy J. & Ready, Barbara C., eds. Graduate Programs in the Biological, Agricultural, & Health Sciences 1986. 20th ed. (Annual Guides to Graduate Study Ser.). 2050p. (Orig.). 1985. pap. 28.95 (ISBN 0-87866-344-4). Petersons Guides.

Harding, Delma E., et al. Creative Biology Teaching. (Illus.). 1969. 11.50x (ISBN 0-8138-0359-4). Iowa St U Pr.

Harley, John P. Biology: Study Guide. 1986. pap. text ed. 12.95 (ISBN 0-13-076605-4). P-H.

Haskel, Sebastian & Sygoda, David. Biology Investigations. 1973. lab manual 9.00 (ISBN 0-87720-056-4). AMSCO Sch.

Heller, R. New Trends in Biology Teaching, 4 vols. (Teaching of Basic Sciences Ser.). (Illus., Orig.). (UNESCO); Vol. 2, 1969. pap. 9.25 (ISBN 92-3-000755-2, U411); Vol. 3. pap. 10.50 (ISBN 0-685-23604-8, U412); Vol. 4, 1977. pap. 18.75 (ISBN 92-3-101402-1, U793). Unipub.

Hickman, Faith M. & Kahle, Jane B., eds. New Directions in Biology Teaching. LC 81-16788. (Illus.). 144p. (Orig.). 1982. pap. text ed. 12.00 (ISBN 0-941212-01-7). Natl Assn Bio Tchrs.

Hollenbeck, E. I. & Stevenson, Elmo N. Selected Procedures in Teaching Biology. (Studies in Education & Guidance Ser: No. 3). 58p. 1970. pap. 4.95x (ISBN 0-87071-043-5). Oreg St U Pr.

McKenna, Harold J. & Hand, Marge. A Guidebook for Teaching Biology. (Guidebook for Teaching Ser.). 279p. 1985. pap. 29.95x (ISBN 0-205-08302-1, 238302, Pub. by Longwood Div). Allyn.

Mertens, Thomas R. & Cooper, Sandra F. Probability & Chi Square. 2nd ed. LC 77-79901. (Programed Biology Ser.). 1974. pap. text ed. 6.95 (ISBN 0-88462-024-7, 3304-21, Ed Methods). Longman USA.

Morholt, Evelyn, et al. Sourcebook for the Biological Sciences. 2nd ed. (Teaching Science Ser.). 795p. 1966. text ed. 25.95 (ISBN 0-15-582850-9, HC). HarBraceJ.

Nelson, George E. The Introductory Biological Sciences in the Traditional Liberal Arts College. LC 74-177101. (Columbia University. Teachers College. Contributions to Education: No. 501). Repr. of 1932 ed. 22.50 (ISBN 0-404-55501-2). AMS Pr.

Principios Basicos Para la Ensenanza De la Biologia. rev. ed. (Serie De Biologia: No. 4). (Span.). 1976. pap. 1.25 (ISBN 0-8270-1385-X). OAS.

Rodgers, Leland. Barron's How to Prepare for the Graduate Record Examination - Advanced Biology. LC 74-10918. 1975. pap. 6.95 (ISBN 0-8120-2072-3). Barron.

Ruesink, Albert & Slovin, Malcolm. Biological Science for Elementary Teachers: Laboratory Manual. 1979. pap. text ed. 8.95x (ISBN 0-89917-318-7). TIS Inc.

Selmes, Cyril. New Movements in the Study & Teaching of Biology. 350p. 1982. 26.00x (ISBN 0-85117-145-1, Pub. by M Temple Smith). State Mutual Bk.

BIOLOGY–TERMINOLOGY

see also Botany–Terminology

Ayers, Donald M. Bioscientific Terminology. LC 74-163010. 325p. 1972. pap. 6.95x (ISBN 0-8165-0305-2). U of Ariz Pr.

Borror, Donald J. Dictionary of Word Roots & Combining Forms. LC 60-15564. 134p. 1960. pap. 5.95 (ISBN 0-87484-053-8). Mayfield Pub.

Holmes, Sandra. Henderson's Dictionary of Biological Terms. 9th ed. 521p. 42.50 (ISBN 0-442-24865-2). Van Nos Reinhold.

Jaeger, Edmund. The Biologists Handbook of Pronunciations. (Illus.). 336p. 1960. 30.75x (ISBN 0-398-00915-5). C C Thomas.

Jaeger, Edmund C. A Source-Book of Biological Names & Terms. 3rd ed. (Illus.). 360p. 1978. 35.50x (ISBN 0-398-00916-3). C C Thomas.

Jeffrey, Charles. Biological Nomenclature. 2nd ed. LC 77-90821. 72p. 1978. 13.00x (ISBN 0-8448-1264-1). Crane-Russak Co.

Savory, Theodore. Latin & Greek for Biologists. (Lat. & Gr.). 42p. 1971. 39.00x (ISBN 0-900541-47-4, Pub. by Meadowfield Pr England). State Mutual Bk.

Schmidt, J. E. Analyzer of Medical-Biological Words: A Clarifying Dissection of Medical Terminology, Showing How It Works, for Medics, Paramedics, Students, & Visitors from Foreign Countries. 224p. 1973. 10.75x (ISBN 0-398-02682-3). C C Thomas.

Sebeok, Thomas A. The Play of Musement. LC 80-8846. (Advances in Semiotics Ser.). (Illus.). 320p. 1981. 35.00x (ISBN 0-253-39994-7). Ind U Pr.

BIOLOGY–VOCATIONAL GUIDANCE

see Biology As a Profession

BIOLOGY, ELECTRONICS IN

see Electronics in Biology

BIOLOGY, EXPERIMENTAL

see also Biology–Experiments; Ovum Implantation

Abramoff, Peter & Thomson, Robert G. An Experimental Approach to Biology. 2nd ed. (Illus.). 305p. 1976. lab manual 13.95x (ISBN 0-7167-0578-8); individual experiments 0.95 (ISBN 0-685-55248-9); instr's hndbk. avail. (ISBN 0-685-55249-7). W H Freeman.

Clarke, Geoffrey M. Statistics & Experimental Design. 2nd ed. 200p. 1980. pap. text ed. 19.95 (ISBN 0-7131-2797-X). E Arnold.

Mead, R. & Curnow, R. N. Statistical Methods in Agriculture & Experimental Biology. 300p. 1983. 49.95 (ISBN 0-412-24230-3, NO. 6767); pap. 25.00 (ISBN 0-412-24240-0, NO. 6768). Methuen Inc.

Society for Experimental Biology Staff. Dormancy & Survival. LC 77-97957. (Symposia of the Society for Experimental Biology Ser.: No. 23). pap. 155.50 (ISBN 0-317-27897-5, 2014672). Bks Demand UMI.

Wardlaw, A. C. Practical Statistics for Experimental Biologists. Date not set. price not set (ISBN 0-471-90737-5); pap. price not set (ISBN 0-471-90738-3). Wiley.

BIOLOGY, MOLECULAR

see Molecular Biology

BIOLOGY AS A PROFESSION

Conley, Diane & Ready, Barbara C., eds. Graduate Programs in the Biological, Agricultural, & Health Sciences 1985. 19th ed. (Annual Guides-Graduate Study Ser.). 2038p. (Orig.). 1984. pap. 25.95 (ISBN 0-87866-236-7). Petersons Guides.

Eastom, Thomas A. Working for Life: Careers in Biology. (Illus.). 118p. 1984. 12.95x (ISBN 0-937548-06-5). Plexus Pub.

Winter, Charles A. Opportunities in Biological Science. (VGM Career Bks.). (Illus.). 160p. 1983. 7.95 (ISBN 0-8442-6254-4, 6254-4, Passport Bks.); pap. 5.95 (ISBN 0-8442-6255-2, 6255-2). Natl Textbk.

BIOLUMINESCENCE

see also Fireflies

Burr. Chemi-& Bioluminescence. (Clinical & Biochemical Analysis Ser.). 658p. 1985. 85.00 (ISBN 0-8247-7277-6). Dekker.

Cormier, M. J., et al, eds. Chemiluminescence & Bioluminescence. LC 73-76169. 515p. 1973. 55.00x (ISBN 0-306-30733-2, Plenum Pr). Plenum Pub.

Deluca, Marlene & McElroy, William, eds. Bioluminescence & Chemiluminescence: Basic Chemistry & Analytical Applications. 1981. 59.50 (ISBN 0-12-208820-4). Acad Pr.

Dyke, Knox V., ed. Bioluminesence & Chemiluminescence Instruments & Applications, Vols. I & II. 1985. Vol. I, 288 pgs. 83.00 (ISBN 0-8493-5863-9); Vol. II, 320 pgs. 93.00 (ISBN 0-8493-5864-7). CRC Pr.

Herring, Peter, ed. Bioluminescence in Action. 1979. 79.50 (ISBN 0-12-342750-9). Acad Pr.

Johnson, F. H. & Haneda, Y., eds. Bioluminescence in Progress. 1966. 65.00x (ISBN 0-691-07917-X). Princeton U Pr.

Kricka. Analytical Applications of Bioluminescence & Chemiluminescence. 1984. 49.00 (ISBN 0-12-426290-2). Acad Pr.

Serio, M. & Pazzagli, M., eds. Luminescent Assays: Perspectives in Endocrinology & Clinical Chemistry. (Serono Symposia Publications from Raven Press Ser.: Vol. I). 304p. 1982. text ed. 51.00 (ISBN 0-89004-740-5). Raven.

BIOMASS ENERGY

see also Refuse As Fuel

Alcohol Production from Biomass in the Developing Countries. 69p. 1980. 5.00 (ISBN 0-686-36155-5, EN-8002). World Bank.

Battelle Columbus Laboratories. Preliminary Environmental Assessment of Biomass Conversion to Synthetic Fuels. 346p. 1980. pap. 49.95x (ISBN 0-89934-049-0, B049-PP). Solar Energy Info.

Battelle Pacific Northwest Labs Staff. Biomass Thermochemical Conversion Program Annual Report, 1983. 51p. Date not set. pap. 9.95 (ISBN 0-914287-34-6, B-052). Solar Energy Info.

Benemann, John R. Biofuels: A Survey. 106p. 1980. pap. 19.95x (ISBN 0-89934-006-7, B045). Solar Energy Info.

Bente, Paul F., Jr., ed. The Increasing Use of Biomass for Energy & Chemicals: Proceedings. 21p. (Orig.). 1983. pap. 15.00 (ISBN 0-940222-05-1). Bio Energy.

Biogas: What It Is, How It Is Made, How To Use It. (Better Farming Ser.: No. 31). (Illus.). 52p. 1985. pap. 5.50 (ISBN 92-5-101290-3, F2627, FAO). Unipub.

Boyles, David T. Bio-Energy: Technology, Thermodynamics & Costs. LC 84-4647. (Energy & Fuel Science Ser.: 1-624). 225p. 1984. text ed. 49.95 (ISBN 0-470-20085-5). Halsted Pr.

Braunstein, Helen, ed. Biomass Energy Systems & the Environment. (Illus.). 189p. 1981. 16.50 (ISBN 0-08-027194-4). Pergamon.

California State Legislature. California Synthetic Fuels Program: Final Report. 176p. 1980. pap. 19.95x (ISBN 0-89934-058-X, B001). Solar Energy Info.

Campbell, Ian. Biomass, Catalysts, & Liquid Fuels. 169p. 1983. 36.00 (ISBN 0-87762-331-7). Technomic.

Chartier, P. & Palz, W., eds. Energy from Biomass. x, 220p. 1981. 28.00 (ISBN 90-277-1348-0, Pub. by Reidel Holland). Kluwer Academic.

Dawes, E. A. Microbial Energetics. (Illus.). 192p. 1985. 39.95 (ISBN 0-412-01041-0, 9444); pap. 19.95 (ISBN 0-412-01051-8, 9445). Methuen Inc.

Energy from Biomass & Wastes Symposium, 7th. 1417p. 1983. 100.00 (ISBN 0-910091-02-1). Inst Gas Tech.

Energy from Biomass: Technology & Global Prospects. (Illus.). 195p. (Orig.). 1980. pap. 225.00x (ISBN 0-940520-05-2, M106, Pub. by Future Syst Inc). Monegon Ltd.

Fry, L. John. Practical Building of Methane Power Plants for Rural Energy Independence. Knox, D. Anthony, ed. LC 76-16224. (Illus.). 1974. pap. text ed. 12.00 (ISBN 0-9600984-1-0). L J Fry.

Grassi, G. & Palz, W., eds. Energy from Biomass. 1982. 39.50 (ISBN 90-277-1482-7, Pub. by Reidel Holland). Kluwer Academic.

Guidebook on Biogas Development. (Energy Resources Development Ser.: No. 21). pap. 11.00 (UN80 2F10, UN). Unipub.

Hall, Carl. Biomass As an Alternative Fuel. (Illus.). 281p. 1981. 38.00 (ISBN 0-86587-087-X). Gov Insts.

Hiler, Edward A., ed. Biomass Energy: A Monograph. LC 84-40559. (Tees Monograph: No. 2). (Illus.). 272p. 1985. text ed. 32.50x (ISBN 0-89096-231-6). Tex A&M Univ Pr.

Institute of Gas Technology. Energy from Biomass & Wastes Symposium, 8th. xii, 1529p. 1984. 100.00 (ISBN 0-910091-50-1). Inst Gas Tech.

International Conference on Biomass 1st, Brighton, England, November, 1980. Energy from Biomass: 1st E. C. Conference Proceedings. Palz, W., et al, eds. (Illus.). 982p. 1981. 85.00 (ISBN 0-85334-970-3, Pub. by Elsevier Applied Sci England). Elsevier.

Kaupp, A. Rice Hull Gasification: Theory & Praxis. (Illus.). 303p. (Orig.). 1984. 40.00 (ISBN 0-942914-05-8); lib. bdg. 40.00 (ISBN 0-942914-06-6); pap. 20.00 (ISBN 0-942914-04-X). Tipi Wkshp Bks.

Marten, Gerald G. & Babor, Daryl. Environmental Considerations for Biomass Energy Development: Hawaii Case Study. LC 81-22046. (East-West Environment & Policy Institute Research Report: No. 9). vi, 58p. (Orig.). 1981. pap. text ed. 3.00 (ISBN 0-86638-031-0). E W Center HI.

Nathan, R. A., ed. Fuels from Sugar Crops. 137p. 1980. pap. 19.95x (ISBN 0-930978-91-9, B.036). Solar Energy Info.

National Academy of Sciences. Potential of Lignocellulosic Materials for the Production of Chemicals, Fuels, & Energy. 91p. 1979. pap. 19.95x (ISBN 0-930978-92-7, B-037). Solar Energy Info.

National Research Council. Diffusion of Biomass Energy Technologies in Developing Countries. 120p. 1984. pap. 9.25 (ISBN 0-309-03442-6). Natl Acad Pr.

OAO Corp. for U. S. Department of Energy. Biomass Energy Systems Program Summary 1980. 220p. 1981. pap. 29.50x (ISBN 0-89934-103-9, B.022). Solar Energy Info.

Office of Technology Assessment, U.S. Congress. Energy from Biological Processes. 200p. 1981. lib. bdg. 28.50x (ISBN 0-86531-171-4). Westview.

Organization for Economic Cooperation & Development. Biomass for Energy: Economic & Policy Issues. 136p. (Orig.). 1984. pap. 15.00X (ISBN 92-64-12632-5). OECD.

Overend, R. P., et al, eds. Fundamentals of Thermochemical Biomass Conversion: Based on the Edited & Refereed Papers from the International Conference Held in Estes Park, Colorado, 18-22 October 1982. (Illus.). 1056p. 1985. 165.00 (ISBN 0-85334-306-3, Pub. by Elsevier Applied Sci England). Elsevier.

Palz, W. & Pirrwitz, D. Energy from Biomass. 1984. lib. bdg. 54.50 (ISBN 90-277-1700-1, Pub. by Reidel Holland). Kluwer Academic.

Palz, W. & Grassi, G., eds. Energy from Biomass. 1982. lib. bdg. 26.00 (ISBN 90-277-1370-7, Pub. by Reidel Holland). Kluwer Academic.

The Potential for Production of "Hydrocarbon" Fuels from Crops in Australia. 86p. 1983. pap. 7.25 (ISBN 0-643-02931-1, CO67, CSIRO). Unipub.

Ramsay, William. Bioenergy & Economic Development: Planning for Biomass Energy Programs in the Third World. (CSIS Energy Research Ser.). 300p. 1985. soft cover 25.00x (ISBN 0-8133-7037-X). Westview.

Sarkanen, Kyosti V. & Tillman, David A., eds. Progress in Biomass Conversion, Vol. 3. (Serial Publication). 304p. 1982. 27.50 (ISBN 0-12-535903-9). Acad Pr.

Schiffman, Yale M. & D'Alessio, Gregory J. Limits to Solar & Biomass Energy Growth. LC 81-48071. 320p. 1983. 32.00 (ISBN 0-669-05253-1). Lexington Bks.

Smil, Vaclav. Biomass Energies: Resources, Links, Constraints. (Modern Perspectives in Energy Ser.). 476p. 1983. 55.00x (ISBN 0-306-41312-4, Plenum Pr). Plenum Pub.

Smith, W. Ramsay, ed. Energy from Forest Biomass. LC 82-20745. (Symposium). 1983. 33.50 (ISBN 0-12-652780-6). Acad Pr.

Sofer, Samir S. & Zaborsky, Oskar R., eds. Biomass Conversion Processes for Energy & Fuels. LC 81-15721. 435p. 1981. text ed. 59.50x (ISBN 0-306-40663-2, Plenum Pr). Plenum Pub.

Stout, B. Biomass Energy Profiles. (Agricultural Services Bulletins: No. 54). 144p. 1983. pap. text ed. 10.50 (ISBN 92-5-101302-0, F2448, FAO). Unipub.

Technical Insights. Energy from Biomass: A Process Manual for Ninety Conversion Routes. LC 83-51107. (Illus.). 311p. 1983. 540.00 (ISBN 0-914993-00-3). Tech Insights.

Technical Insights Inc. Biomass Process Handbook. rev. & upd. ed. 385p. 1983. 540.00 (ISBN 0-317-07305-2). Tech Insights.

Tillman, David A. & Jahn, Edwin C. Progress in Biomass Conversion, Vol. 4. (Serial Publication Ser.). 1983. 35.00 (ISBN 0-12-535904-7). Acad Pr.

Tillman, David A. & Jahn, Edwin C., eds. Progress in Biomass Conversion, Vol. 5. (Serial Publications). 1984. 49.00 (ISBN 0-12-535905-5). Acad Pr.

U. S. Dept. of Energy. Anaerobic Fermentation of Agricultural Residue: Potential for Improvement & Implementation. 430p. 1981. pap. 59.50x (ISBN 0-89934-099-7, B.021). Solar Energy Info.

Updated Guidebook on Biogas Development. 2nd ed. (Energy Resources Development Ser.: No. 27). (Illus.). 178p. 1985. pap. 17.50 (UN84/2F14, UN). Unipub.

White, L. P. & Plaskett, L. G. Biomass As Fuel. LC 81-66689. 211p. 1983. 29.50 (ISBN 0-12-746750-5). Acad Pr.

Wise, Donald L. Liquid Fuel Developments. 224p. 1983. 71.00 (ISBN 0-8493-6094-3). CRC Pr.

Wise, Donald L., ed. Fuel Gas Production from Biomass, 2 vols. 1981. Vol. I, 280 Pgs. 83.00 (ISBN 0-8493-5990-2); Vol. II, 296 Pgs. 91.50 (ISBN 0-8493-5991-0). CRC Pr.

--Fuel Gas Systems. 272p. 1983. 79.00 (ISBN 0-8493-6091-9). CRC Pr.

--Liquid Fuel Systems. 224p. 1983. 70.00 (ISBN 0-8493-6093-5). CRC Pr.

World Bank. Alcohol Production from Biomass in the Developing Countries. 71p. 1982. pap. 14.95x (ISBN 0-89934-151-9, B-027). Solar Energy Info.

BIOMATERIALS

see Biomedical Materials

BIOMATHEMATICS

see also Biology–Mathematical Models; Biometry; Genetics–Mathematical Models; Information Theory in Biology

Amari, S. & Arbib, M. A., eds. Competition & Cooperation in Neural Nets, Kyoto, Japan, 1982: Proceedings. (Lecture Notes in Biomathematics: Vol. 45). 441p. 1982. pap. 28.00 (ISBN 0-387-11574-9). Springer-Verlag.

Arya, J. C. & Lardner, R. W. Mathematics for the Biological Sciences. (Illus.). 1979. 34.95 (ISBN 0-13-562439-8). P-H.

Bailey, N. T. J. The Biomathematics of Diseases: The Biomathematics of Malaria. (No. 1). 224p. 1982. 88.00x (ISBN 0-85264-266-0, Pub. by Griffin England). State Mutual Bk.

Batschelet, E. Introduction to Mathematics for Life Scientists. 2nd ed. LC 75-11755. (Biomathematics Ser.: Vol. 2). (Illus.). 643p. 1979. 45.00 (ISBN 0-387-09662-0). Springer-Verlag.

--Introduction to Mathematics for Life Scientists. 3rd ed. (Springer Study Edition). (Illus.). 1979. pap. 24.00 (ISBN 0-387-09648-5). Springer-Verlag.

Capasso, V., et al, eds. Mathematics in Biology & Medicine. (Lecture Notes in Biomathematics Ser.: Vol. 57). xviii, 524p. pap. 36.00 (ISBN 0-387-15200-8). Springer-Verlag.

Centro Internationale Mathematico Estivo. Bifurcation Theory & Applications: Lectures Given at the Second Session of the Centro Internationale Mathematico Estivo held at Montecatini, Italy, June 24-July 2, 1983. Salvadori, L., ed. (Lecture Notes in Mathematics Ser.: Vol. 1057). vii, 223p. 1984. pap. 12.50 (ISBN 0-387-12931-6). Springer-Verlag.

Christiansen, F. B. & Fenchel, T. M., eds. Measuring Selection in Natural Populations. LC 77-11040. (Lecture Notes in Biomathematics: Vol. 19). 1977. pap. text ed. 28.00 (ISBN 0-387-08435-5). Springer-Verlag.

Cosnard, M., et al, eds. Rhythms in Biology & Other Fields of Application: Deterministic & Stochastic Approaches. (Lecture Notes in Biomathematics: Vol. 49). 400p. 1983. pap. 24.00 (ISBN 0-387-12302-4). Springer-Verlag.

Crowe, A. & Crowe, A. Mathematics for Biologists. 1969. 27.50 (ISBN 0-12-198250-5). Acad Pr.

Cushing, C. M. Integrodifferential Equations & Delay Models in Population Dynamics. LC 77-17425. (Lecture Notes in Biomathematics: Vol. 20). 1977. pap. text ed. 14.00 (ISBN 0-387-08449-5). Springer-Verlag.

Dobryshin, R. L., et al, eds. Locally Interacting Systems & Their Application in Biology: Proceedings of the School - Seminar on Markov Interaction Processes in Biology, Held in Pushchino, Moscow Region, March, 1976. (Lecture Notes in Mathematics Ser.: Vol. 653). 1978. pap. 16.00 (ISBN 0-387-08450-9). Springer-Verlag.

Eason, G., et al. Mathematics & Statistics for the Bio-Sciences. LC 79-41815. (Mathematics & Its Applications Ser.). 578p. 1980. pap. 37.95x (ISBN 0-470-27400-X). Halsted Pr.

Ewens, W. J. Mathematical Population Genetics. LC 79-18938. (Biomathematics Ser.: Vol. 9). (Illus.). 1979. 38.00 (ISBN 0-387-09577-2). Springer-Verlag.

Fife, P. C. Mathematical Aspects of Reacting & Diffusing Systems. LC 79-10216. (Lecture Notes in Biomathematics Ser.: Vol. 28). 1979. pap. text ed. 14.00 (ISBN 0-387-09117-3). Springer-Verlag.

Finney, D. J. Probit Analysis. 3rd ed. LC 78-134618. (Illus.). 1971. 70.00 (ISBN 0-521-08041-X). Cambridge U Pr.

Freedman, H. I. & Strobeck, C., eds. Population Biology. (Lecture Notes in Biomathematics Ser.: Vol. 52). 440p. pap. 26.00 (ISBN 0-387-12677-5). Springer-Verlag.

Frehland, E. Stochastic Transport Processes in Discrete Biological Systems. (Lecture Notes in Biomathematics Ser.: Vol. 47). 169p. 1982. pap. 13.00 (ISBN 0-387-11964-7). Springer-Verlag.

Frehland, E., ed. Synergetics: From Microscopic to Macroscopic Order. (Springer Series in Synergetics: Vol. 22). (Illus.). 280p. 1984. 36.00 (ISBN 0-387-13131-0). Springer-Verlag.

Gause, G. F. Struggle for Existence. (Illus.). 1969. Repr. of 1934 ed. 11.95x (ISBN 0-02-845200-3). Hafner.

Getz, W. M., ed. Mathematical Modelling in Biology & Ecology: Proceedings of a Symposium Held at the CSIR, Pretoria, July 1979. (Lecture Notes in Biomathematics Ser.: Vol. 33). viii, 355p. 1980. pap. 28.00 (ISBN 3-540-09735-X). Springer-Verlag.

Gittins, R. Canonical Analysis. (Biomathematics Ser.: Vol. 12). (Illus.). 320p. 1984. 45.00 (ISBN 0-387-13617-7). Springer-Verlag.

Heim, R. & Palm, G., eds. Theoretical Approaches to Complex Systems: Proceedings, Tuebingen, Germany, June 11-12, 1977. (Lecture Notes in Biomathematics: Vol. 21). 1978. pap. 16.00 (ISBN 0-387-08757-5). Springer-Verlag.

Hodgson, J. P., ed. Oscillations in Mathematical Biology. (Lecture Notes in Biomathematics: Vol. 51). 196p. 1983. pap. 15.00 (ISBN 0-387-12670-8). Springer-Verlag.

Holman, H. H. Biological Research Method: Practical Statistics for Non-Mathematicians. (Illus.). 1969. 18.95x (ISBN 0-02-846050-2). Hafner.

Jones, D. S. & Sleeman, B. D. Differential Equations & Mathematical Biology. 320p. 1982. text ed. 35.00x (ISBN 0-04-515001-X). Allen Unwin.

Kajiya, F. & Kodama, S., eds. Compartmental Analysis. x, 190p. 1985. 56.25 (ISBN 3-8055-3696-8). S Karger.

Katz, Murray A. Calculus for the Life Sciences: An Introduction. (Biology Textbooks: Vol. 1). 1976. 29.75 (ISBN 0-8247-6465-X). Dekker.

Koch, G. & Hazewinkel, M., eds. Mathematics of Biology. 1985. lib. bdg. 24.50 (ISBN 90-277-2069-X, Pub. by Reidel Holland). Kluwer Academic.

Lambrecht, R. M. & Rescigno, A., eds. Tracer Kinetics & Physiologic Modeling - Theory & Practice: Proceedings, St. Louix, Missouri, 1983. (Lecture Notes in Biomathematics: Vol. 48). 509p. 1983. pap. 30.00 (ISBN 0-387-12300-8). Springer-Verlag.

Lewis, E. R. Network Models in Population Biology. LC 77-5873. (Biomathematics Ser.: Vol 7). 1977. 41.00 (ISBN 0-387-08214-X). Springer-Verlag.

Liggett, T. M. Interacting Particle Systems. (Grundlehren der Mathematischen Wissenschaften Ser.: Vol. 276). (Illus.). 500p. 1985. 54.00 (ISBN 0-387-96069-4). Springer-Verlag.

Lotka, Alfred J. Elements of Mathematical Biology. Orig. Title: Elements of Physical Biology. 1957. pap. text ed. 8.50 (ISBN 0-486-60346-6). Dover.

Magar, Magar E. Data Analysis in Biochemistry & Biophysics. 1972. 71.50 (ISBN 0-12-465650-1). Acad Pr.

Marchuk, G. I. & Nisevich, N. I., eds. Mathematical Methods in Clinical Practice. (Illus.). 150p. 1980. 72.00 (ISBN 0-08-025493-4). Pergamon.

Nagylaki, T. Selection in One-&-Two-Locus Systems. (Lecture Notes in Biomathematics: Vol. 15). 1977. 18.00 (ISBN 0-387-08247-6). Springer-Verlag.

Nahikian, Howard M. Modern Algebra for Biologists. LC 64-13948. Repr. of 1964 ed. 47.20 (ISBN 0-8357-9650-7, 2015760). Bks Demand UMI.

Newmark, Joseph. The Usefulness of Calculus: For the Behavioral, Life & Managerial Sciences. 1978. scp 26.50 (ISBN 0-06-385750-2, HarpC); solutions manual avail. (ISBN 0-06-375775-3). Har-Row.

Ohta, T. Evolution & Variation of Multigene Families. (Lecture Notes in Biomathematics: Vol. 37). 131p. 1980. pap. 13.00 (ISBN 0-387-09998-0). Springer-Verlag.

Okubo, A. Diffusion & Ecological Problems: Mathematical Models. Krickeberg, K. & Levin, S. A., eds. (Biomathematics: Vol. 10). (Illus.). 1980. 48.00 (ISBN 0-387-09620-5). Springer-Verlag.

Pollard, J. H. A Handbook of Numerical & Statistical Techniques. LC 76-27908. (Illus.). 1977. 59.50 (ISBN 0-521-21440-8); pap. 22.95 (ISBN 0-521-29750-8). Cambridge U Pr.

Ricciardi, L. & Scott, A., eds. Biomathematics in Nineteen Eighty. (Mathematics Studies: Vol. 58). 298p. 1982. 51.00 (ISBN 0-444-86355-9, North-Holland). Elsevier.

Rosen, Robert, ed. Foundations of Mathematical Biology, 3 vols. Incl. Vol. 1. Subcellular Systems. 1972. 57.50 (ISBN 0-12-597201-6); Vol. 2. Cellular Systems. 1972. 65.00 (ISBN 0-12-597202-4); Vol. 3. 1973. 74.50 (ISBN 0-12-597203-2). Set. 156.00. Acad Pr.

Rotenberg, M., ed. Biomathematics & Cell Kinetics. (Developments in Cell Biology Ser.: Vol. 8). 424p. 1981. 70.25 (ISBN 0-444-80371-8, Biomedical Pr). Elsevier.

Rubinow, S. I. Introduction to Mathematical Biology. LC 75-12520. 386p. 1975. 54.95 (ISBN 0-471-74446-8, Pub. by Wiley-Interscience). Wiley.

Smith, D. P. & Keyfitz, N. Mathematical Demography: Selected Readings. (Biomathematics: Vol. 6). 1977. 46.00 (ISBN 0-387-07899-1). Springer-Verlag.

Smith, J. Maynard. Mathematical Ideas in Biology. LC 68-25088. (Illus.). 1968. 24.95 (ISBN 0-521-07335-9); pap. 11.95 (ISBN 0-521-09550-6). Cambridge U Pr.

Srinivasan, S. K. & Sampath, G. Stochastic Models for Spike Trains of Single Neurons. (Lecture Notes in Biomathematics: Vol. 16). 1977. 14.00 (ISBN 0-387-08257-3). Springer-Verlag.

Symposium in Applied Mathematics - New York - 1961. Mathematical Problems in the Biological Sciences: Proceedings. Bellman, R., ed. LC 50-1183. (Proceedings of Symposia in Applied Mathematics: Vol. 14). 1962. 23.00 (ISBN 0-8218-1314-5, PSAPM-14). Am Math.

Walter, C. F. & Solomon, D. L., eds. Mathematical Model in Biological Discoveries. (Lecture Notes in Biomathematics: Vol. 13). 1977. pap. 18.00 (ISBN 0-387-08134-8). Springer-Verlag.

Walter, E. Identifiability of State Space Models: With Applications to Transformation Systems. (Lecture Notes in Biomathematics: Vol. 46). 202p. 1982. pap. 16.00 (ISBN 0-387-11590-0). Springer-Verlag.

Winfree, A. T. The Geometry of Biological Time. LC 79-12375. (Biomathematics: Vol. 8). (Illus.). 1980. 36.00 (ISBN 0-387-09373-7). Springer-Verlag.

Woerz-Busekros, A. Algebras in Genetics. (Lecture Notes in Biomathematics: Vol. 36). 237p. 1980. pap. 19.00 (ISBN 0-387-09978-6). Springer-Verlag.

BIOMECHANICS

see also Animal Mechanics; Human Engineering

Akkas, N. Progress on Biomechanics. (NATO Advaned Study Institute Ser.). 395p. 1979. 37.50x (ISBN 90-286-0479-0). Sijthoff & Noordhoff.

Asmussen, E. Biomechanics. (Illus.). 1978. VI-A, 592p. text ed. 48.00 (ISBN 0-8391-1242-4); VI-B, 390p. text ed. 48.00 (ISBN 0-8391-1243-2). Univ Park.

Biomechanical & Human Factors Conference (2nd: 1967: Washington, D.C.) Biomechanical & Human Factors Symposium: 1967. Gage, Howard, ed. LC 67-21480. (Illus.). pap. 46.00 (ISBN 0-317-08409-7, 2016814). Bks Demand UMI.

Black, Jonathan & Dumbleton, John. Clinical Biomechanics: A Case History Approach. (Illus.). 416p. 1980. text ed. 50.00 (ISBN 0-443-08022-4). Churchill.

Cooper, John M., ed. Biomechanics. LC 78-159585. 1971. pap. 5.00 (ISBN 0-87670-852-1). Athletic Inst.

Demes, B. Biomechanics of the Primate Skull Base. (Advances in Anatomy, Embryology & Cell Biology Ser.: Vol. 94). (Illus.). 70p. 1985. pap. 22.00 (ISBN 0-387-15290-3). Springer-Verlag.

Ducheyne, P. G., et al, eds. Biomaterials & Biomechanics, 1983: Proceedings of the 4th European Conference on Biomaterials, Leuven, Belgium, Aug. 31-Sept. 2, 1983. (Advances in Biomaterials Ser.: No. 5). 500p. 1984. 96.50 (ISBN 0-444-42352-4). Elsevier.

Easterby, Ronald, et al, eds. Anthropometry & Biomechanics: Theory & Applications. LC 81-11982. (NATO Conference Series III - Human Factors: Vol. 16). 334p. 1982. 49.50x (ISBN 0-306-40745-0, Plenum Pr). Plenum Pub.

Engle, Eloise & Lott, Arnold. Man in Flight: Biomedical Achievements in Aerospace. LC 79-63780. (A Supplement to the American Astronautical Society History Ser.). (Illus.). 414p. 1979. 20.00x (ISBN 0-915268-24-8). Univelt Inc.

Frost, Harold M. An Introduction to Biomechanics. (Illus.). 160p. 1971. photocopy ed. 15.75x (ISBN 0-398-00622-9). C C Thomas.

--Orthopaedic Biomechanics: Orthopaedic Lectures, Vol. 5. (Illus.). 664p. 1973. 49.50x (ISBN 0-398-02824-9). C C Thomas.

Fung, Y. C. Biomechanics: Mechanical Properties of Living Tissues. (Illus.). 400p. 1981. 34.50 (ISBN 0-387-90472-7). Springer-Verlag.

Gallagher, R. H., et al. Finite Elements in Biomechanics. LC 81-13084. (Wiley Series in Numerical Methods in Engineering). 404p. 1982. 54.95x (ISBN 0-471-09996-1, Pub. by Wiley-Interscience). Wiley.

Gans, Carl. Biomechanics: An Approach to Vertebrate Biology. LC 80-18705. 272p. 1980. pap. text ed. 6.50x (ISBN 0-472-08016-4). U of Mich Pr.

Ghista, D. Biomechanics of Medical Devices. LC 80-15480. (Biomedical Engineering & Instrumentation Ser.: Vol. 7). 1981. 99.75 (ISBN 0-8247-6848-5). Dekker.

Huiskes, R. Biomechanics: Principles & Applications. 1982. 65.00 (ISBN 90-247-3047-3, Pub. by Martinus Nijhoff Netherlands). Kluwer Academic.

International Seminar on Biomechanics, 3rd, Rome, 1971. Biomechanics 3: Proceedings. Cerquiglini, S., et al, eds. (Medicine & Sport: Vol 8). 512p. 1973. 68.25 (ISBN 3-8055-1406-9). S Karger.

Kirby, Ronald E. Introducing Biomechanics. (Illus.). 500p. 1985. pap. write for info. (ISBN 0-932392-22-9). Mouvement Pubns.

Kreigbaum, Ellen & Barthels, Katherine. Biomechanics: A Qualitative Approach for Studying Human Movement. 2nd ed. (Illus.). 576p. 1985. text ed. write for info. (ISBN 0-8087-4922-6). Burgess.

Maquet, P. G. Biomechanics of the Hip. (Illus.). 320p. 1985. 95.00 (ISBN 0-387-13257-0). Springer-Verlag.

Morecki, A., ed. Biomechanics of Motion. (CISM-Courses & Lectures: Vol. 263). (Illus.). 217p. 1980. pap. 31.00 (ISBN 0-387-81611-9). Springer-Verlag.

Morecki, Adam. Biomechanics VII-A. (International Series on Biomechanics: Vol. 3A). (Illus.). 300p. 1982. text ed. 37.00 (ISBN 0-8391-1383-8). Univ Park.

--Biomechanics VII-B. (International Series on Biomechanics: Vol. 3B). (Illus.). 300p. 1982. text ed. 37.00 (ISBN 0-8391-1384-6). Univ Park.

Nahum, Alan M. & Melvin, John, eds. Biomechanics of Trauma. 496p. 1984. 65.00 (ISBN 0-8385-0660-7). ACC.

Northrip, John W., et al. Analysis of Sport Motion: Anatomic & Biomechanic Perspectives. 3rd ed. 448p. 1983. pap. text ed. write for info. (ISBN 0-697-07206-1). Wm C Brown.

Phillips, Chandler A. & Petrofsky, Jerrold S. Mechanics of Skeletal & Cardiac Muscle. (Illus.). 324p. 1983. 24.75x (ISBN 0-398-04721-9). C C Thomas.

Roach, G. F., ed. Mathematics in Medicine & Biomechanics. 236p. 1984. 29.95 (ISBN 0-906812-41-0); pap. 15.95 (ISBN 0-906812-40-2). Birkhauser.

Simonian, Charles. Fundamentals of Sports Biomechanics. (Illus.). 224p. 1981. text ed. 21.95 (ISBN 0-13-344499-6). P-H.

Skalak, R. & Schultz, A. B., eds. Biomechanics Symposium 1977, AMD, Vol. 23. 1977. pap. text ed. 30.00 (ISBN 0-685-81973-6, I00111). ASME.

--Biomechanics Symposium, 1977: Proceedings, Vol. 23. 1977. pap. text ed. 30.00 (ISBN 0-685-81928-0, I00111). ASME.

Stockholm, Alan J. Biomechanics Manual for Coaches & Physical Educators. LC 85-1269. 150p. 1985. pap. 12.00 (ISBN 0-935496-04-1). AC Pubns.

Van Buskirk, W. C., ed. Biomechanics Symposium, 1979. LC 73-83552. (Applied Mechanics Division Ser.: Vol. 32). 240p. 1980. 30.00 (ISBN 0-686-62961-2, G00142). ASME.

--Nineteen Eighty-One Biomechanics Symposium. (AMD Ser.: vol. 43). 310p. 1981. 40.00 (ISBN 0-686-34475-8, G00201). ASME.

Webb, Paul W. & Weihs, Daniel, eds. Fish Biomechanics. 414p. 1983. 46.95x (ISBN 0-03-059461-8). Praeger.

Wiktorin Christina, von Heigne & Nordin, Margareta. Introduction to Problem Solving in Biomechanics. LC 84-26076. (Illus.). 245p. 1985. pap. price not set (ISBN 0-8121-0941-4). Lea & Febiger.

Winter, David A. Biomechanics of Human Movement. LC 79-12660. (Biomedical Engineering & Health Systems Ser.). 202p. 1979. 36.95x (ISBN 0-471-03476-2, Pub. by Wiley-Interscience). Wiley.

Winter, David A., et al, eds. Biomechanics IX, 2 vols. LC 82-84703. (International Series on Biomechanics). 1985. Set. text ed. 80.00x (ISBN 0-931250-52-8, BWIN0052). Human Kinetics.

--Biomechanics IX-A. LC 82-84703. (International Series on Biomechanics). 1985. text ed. 45.00x (ISBN 0-931250-53-6, BWIN0053). Human Kinetics.

--Biomechanics IX-B. LC 82-84703. (International Series on Biomechanics). 1985. text ed. 45.00x (ISBN 0-931250-54-4, BWIN0054). Human Kinetics.

BIOMEDICAL ENGINEERING

see also Biomedical Materials; Electronics in Biology; Medical Electronics; Medical Instruments and Apparatus

Altman, Barry J. Biomedical Equipment Database. 203p. 1984. 196.00x (ISBN 0-930844-12-2). Quest Pub.

Automated Education Center. An Annotated Bibliography of Biomedical Computer Applications. LC 79-120081. 19.00 (ISBN 0-403-04451-0). Scholarly.

Bartone, John C. Politics & Biomedicine: Subject Analysis & Research Index with Bibliography. LC 83-48714. 155p. 1984. 29.95 (ISBN 0-88164-078-6); pap. 21.95 (ISBN 0-88164-079-4). ABBE Pubs Assn.

Bayless, William C. & Pacela, Allan F., eds. Guide to Biomedical Standards 1984-1985. 11th ed. (Orig.). 1984. pap. 12.00x (ISBN 0-930844-13-0). Quest Pub.

Bement, A. L., Jr., ed. Biomaterials: Bioengineering Applied to Materials for Hard & Soft Tissue Replacement. LC 71-152333. (Illus.). 361p. 1971. text ed. 25.00x (ISBN 0-295-95160-5). U of Wash Pr.

Bio-Organization: Diagnosis & Therapy. (Medical Ser.). (Illus.). 184p. 1983. pap. text ed. 12.95 (ISBN 0-935920-13-7). Natl Pub Black Hills.

Blesser, William B. A Systems Approach to Biomedicine. LC 80-11717. 632p. 1981. Repr. of 1969 ed. lib. bdg. 36.50 (ISBN 0-89874-146-7). Krieger.

Boeynaems, J. J. & Dumont, J. E., eds. Outlines of Receptor Theory. 1980. 67.00 (ISBN 0-444-80131-6). Elsevier.

Brock, D. Heyward, ed. The Culture of Biomedicine. LC 82-40438. (Studies in Science & Culture: Vol. 1). 200p. 1983. 24.50 (ISBN 0-87413-229-0). U Delaware Pr.

Brown, J. H. Advances in Biomedical Engineering, Vol. 5. (Serial Publication Ser.). 1975. 85.00 (ISBN 0-12-004905-8). Acad Pr.

Brown, J. H., ed. Advances in Biomedical Engineering, Vol. 4. (Serial Publication Ser.). 1974. 85.00 (ISBN 0-12-004904-X). Acad Pr.

Brown, J. H. & Dickson, James F., eds. Advances in Biomedical Engineering, Vol. 6. 1976. 85.00 (ISBN 0-12-004906-6). Acad Pr.

Brown, J. H. U. & Gann, Donald, eds. Engineering Principles in Physiology, 2 vols. Vol. 1, 1973. 65.00 (ISBN 0-12-136201-9); Vol. 2, 1973. 76.50 (ISBN 0-12-136202-7). Acad Pr.

Bulla, L. & Cheng, T., eds. Comparative Pathobiology: Treatise. Incl. Vol. 1. Biology of the Microsporidia. 387p. 1976. 55.00x (ISBN 0-306-38121-4); Vol. 2. Systematics of the Microsporidia. 521p. 1977. 59.50x (ISBN 0-306-38122-2); Vol. 3. Invertebrate Immune Responses. 206p. 1977. 32.50x (ISBN 0-306-38123-0); Vol. 4. Invertebrate Models for Biomedical Research. 179p. 1978. 29.50x (ISBN 0-306-40055-3). LC 76-46633 (Plenum Pr). Plenum Pub.

Caceres, Cesar A. Management & Clinical Engineering. 470p. 1980. 25.00 (ISBN 0-89006-094-0). Artech Hse.

Capasso, V., et al, eds. Mathematics in Biology & Medicine. (Lecture Notes in Biomathematics Ser.: Vol. 57). xviii, 524p. pap. 36.00 (ISBN 0-387-15200-8). Springer-Verlag.

Carson, E. R., et al. The Mathematical Modeling of Metabolic & Endocrine Systems: Model Formulation, Identification & Validation. (Biomedical Engineering & Health Systems Ser.). 394p. 1983. 57.50 (ISBN 0-471-08660-6). Wiley.

Chang, T. M., ed. Biomedical Applications of Immobilized Enzymes & Proteins, 2 vols. Incl. Vol. 1. 448p. 1977. 49.50x (ISBN 0-306-34311-8); Vol. 2. LC 76-56231. 379p. 1977. 49.50x (ISBN 0-306-34312-6). (Illus., Plenum Pr). Plenum Pub.

Cobbold, Richard S. Transducers for Biomedical Measurements: Principles & Applications. LC 74-2480. (Biomedical Engineering & Health Systems Ser.). 486p. 1974. 50.95x (ISBN 0-471-16145-4, Pub. by Wiley-Interscience). Wiley.

Cohen, A. Biomedical Scanning Electron Micro Handbook. 1986. cancelled (ISBN 0-442-25160-2). Van Nos Reinhold.

Cook, Albert M. & Webster, John G., eds. Clinical Engineering: Principles & Practices. (Illus.). 1979. text ed. 43.95 (ISBN 0-13-137737-X). P-H.

Cooney, David, ed. Biomedical Engineering Principles: An Introduction to Fluid, Heat and Mass Transport Processes. (Biomedical Engineering & Instrumentation Ser.: Vol. 2). 464p. 1976. 49.50 (ISBN 0-8247-6347-5); text ed. 26.50. Dekker.

Cromwell, Leslie, et al. Biomedical Instrumentation & Measurements. 2nd ed. (Illus.). 1980. text ed. 31.95 (ISBN 0-13-076448-5). P-H.

Dendy, Philip P., ed. Technical Advances in Biomedical Physics. 1984. lib. bdg. 57.00 (ISBN 90-247-2934-3, Pub. by Martinus Nijhoff Netherlands). Kluwer Academic.

Dickson, J. F., 3rd & Brown, J. H., eds. Future Goals of Engineering in Biology & Medicine: Proceedings. 1969. 73.50 (ISBN 0-12-215250-6). Acad Pr.

Driscoll. Instrumental Evaluation in Biomedical Science. (Clinical & Biochemical Analysis Ser.). 312p. 1984. 59.75 (ISBN 0-8247-7184-2). Dekker.

DuBovy, Joseph L. Introduction to Biomedical Electronics. (Illus.). 1978. text ed. 25.15 (ISBN 0-07-017895-X). McGraw.

Eisenfeld, J. & Delisi, C., eds. Mathematics & Computers in Biomedical Applications. 390p. 1985. 40.00 (ISBN 0-444-87678-2). Elsevier.

Feinberg, Barry. Applied Clinical Engineering. (Illus.). 544p. 1986. text ed. 42.95 (ISBN 0-13-039488-2). P-H.

Fleming, David & Ko, Wen H., eds. Indwelling & Implantable Pressure Transducers. LC 76-48168. (Uniscience Ser.). 224p. 1977. 66.00 (ISBN 0-8493-5195-2). CRC Pr.

Fleming, David G. & Feinberg, Barry N. Handbook of Engineering in Medicine & Biology, CRC: Section B-Instruments & Measurements, Vol. 2. (Engineering in Medicine & Biology Ser.). 446p. 1978. 66.00 (ISBN 0-8493-0242-0). CRC Pr.

Fleming, David G. & Feinberg, Barry N., eds. Handbook of Engineering in Medicine & Biology, CRC. LC 75-44222. (Handbook Ser.). 1976. General Date, Vol. 1, 432 Pgs. 64.00 (ISBN 0-87819-285-9). CRC Pr.

Folkers, K. & Yamamura, Y., eds. Biomedical & Clinical Aspects of Coenzyme Q: Proceedings of the International Symposium on Coenzyme Q, 4th, Held in Martinsried, Munich, West Germany, 6-9 November, 1983, Vol. 4. 432p. 1984. 83.00 (ISBN 0-444-80380-7, I-480-84, Biomedical Pr). Elsevier.

Foster, Henry, et al, eds. The Mouse in Biomedical Research: Vol. 2, Diseases. LC 80-70669. (American College of Laboratory Animal Medicine Ser.). 1982. 80.00 (ISBN 0-12-262502-1). Acad Pr.

Francoeur, Robert T. Biomedical Ethics: A Guide to Decision Making. LC 83-6812. 341p. 1983. pap. 17.50 (ISBN 0-471-09827-2, Pub. by Wiley Med). Wiley.

Francois, D. Advances in Fracture Research: Proceedings of the 5th International Conference on Fracture, 1981, Cannes, France, 6 vols. LC 80-41879. (International Series on the Strength & Fracture of Materials & Structures). 3000p. 1981. Set. text ed. 495.00 (ISBN 0-08-025428-4). Pergamon.

Frankel, Victor H. & Burstein, Albert H. Orthopaedic Biomechanics: The Application of Engineering to the Musculoskeletal System. LC 77-78537. pap. 49.00 (ISBN 0-317-30000-8, 2051852). Bks Demand UMI.

Friedman, et al. Fundamentals of Clinical Trials. 2nd ed. 1985. 27.50 (ISBN 0-88416-499-3). PSG Pub Co.

Fu, K. S. & Pavlidis, T., eds. Biomedical Pattern Recognition & Image Processing. (Dahlem Workshop Reports-Life Sciences Reseach Report Ser.: No. 15). 443p. 1979. 33.80x (ISBN 0-89573-097-9). VCH Pubs.

Fudenberg, H. Hugh, ed. Biomedical Institutions, Biomedical Funding, & Public Policy. 209p. 1983. 29.50x (ISBN 0-306-41231-4, Plenum Pr). Plenum Pub.

Ghista, D. N. & Yang, W. J., eds. Cardiovascular Engineering. (Advances in Cardiovascular Physics: Pt. I-IV). (Illus.). xxxxviii, 960p. 1983. 184.75 (ISBN 3-8055-3613-5). S Karger.

--Cardiovascular Engineering, Part I: Modelling. (Advances in Cardiovascular Physics: Vol. 5). (Illus.). xiv, 230p. 1983. 61.00 (ISBN 3-8055-3609-7). S Karger.

--Cardiovascular Engineering, Part II: Monitoring. (Advances in Cardiovascular Physics: Vol. 5). (Illus.). viii, 280p. 1983. 61.00 (ISBN 3-8055-3610-0). S Karger.

--Cardiovascular Engineering: Protheses, Assist & Artificial Organs, Pt. IV. (Advances in Cardiovascular Physics: Vol. 5). (Illus.). viii, 292p. 1983. 61.00 (ISBN 3-8055-3612-7). S Karger.

Glantz, Stanton A. Mathematics for Biomedical Applications. LC 77-20320. 1979. 24.50x (ISBN 0-520-03599-2). U of Cal Pr.

Gross, Alan J. & Clark, Virginia A. Survival Distributions: Reliability Applications in the Biomedical Sciences. 350p. 1985. Repr. of 1975 ed. write for info. (ISBN 0-89874-817-8). Krieger.

--Survival Distributions: Reliability Applications in the Biomedical Sciences. LC 75-6808. (Wiley Series in Probability & Mathematical Statistics). pap. 86.50 (ISBN 0-317-28063-5, 2055770). Bks Demand UMI.

Hall, C. William, ed. Biomedical Engineering II: Recent Developments: Second Southern Biomedical Engineering Conference, Proceedings, September 26-27, 1983, San Antonio, Texas, U. S. A. 448p. 1983. pap. 75.00 (ISBN 0-08-030145-2, 11/3). Pergamon.

Hershey, Daniel, ed. Chemical Engineering in Medicine & Biology. LC 67-17376. 658p. 1967. 57.50x (ISBN 0-306-30288-8, Plenum Pr). Plenum Pub.

Holt, Katie L. Questionnaires in Biomedicine: Research Subject Reference Dictionary with Bibliography. Bartone, John C., ed. 115p. 1983. 29.95 (ISBN 0-88164-040-9); pap. 21.95 (ISBN 0-88164-041-7). ABBE Pubs Assn.

Instrument Society of America Staff. Biomedical Sciences Instrumentation: Proceedings of the Fourteenth Annual Rocky Mountain Bioengineering Symposium & the Fourteenth International ISA Biomedical Sciences Instrumentation Symposium, Vol. 13. LC 63-21220. pap. 40.50 (ISBN 0-317-29817-8, 2051997). Bks Demand UMI.

--Biomedical Sciences Instrumentation: Proceedings of the Fifteenth Annual Rocky Mountain Bioengineering Symposium & the Fifteenth International ISA Biomedical Sciences Instrumentation Symposium, Vol. 14. Carlson, David, ed. LC 63-21220. pap. 42.80 (ISBN 0-317-29815-1, 2051998). Bks Demand UMI.

Jacobson, Bertil & Webster, John G. Medicine & Clinical Engineering. LC 76-13842. (Illus.). 1977. text ed. 42.95 (ISBN 0-13-572966-1). P-H.

Kenedi, R. M., ed. Advances in Biomedical Engineering. Incl. Vol. 1. 1971. 55.00 (ISBN 0-12-004901-5); Vol. 2. Brown, J. H. & Dickson, James F., 3rd, eds. 1972. 85.00 (ISBN 0-12-004902-3); Vol. 3. 1973. 85.00 (ISBN 0-12-004903-1). Acad Pr.

Kline, Jacob. Biological Foundations of Biomedical Engineering. LC 74-20221. 1976. text ed. 52.50 (ISBN 0-316-49857-2). Little.

Lamble, J. W. & Cuthbert, eds. More about Receptors. (Current Reviews in Biomedicine Ser.: Vol. 2). 180p. 1982. 25.00 (ISBN 0-444-80428-5, Biomedical Pr). Elsevier.

Lynch, Henry T. & Anton-Guirgis, Hoda. Biomarkers, Genetics & Cancer. (Illus.). 192p. 1985. 47.50 (ISBN 0-442-24958-6). Van Nos Reinhold.

Marks, Ronald G. The Basics of Biomedical Research Methodology, 2 vols. (Illus.). 193p. 1982. Vol. 1: Designing A Research Project. 25.00 (ISBN 0-534-97940-8); Vol. 2: Analyzing Research Data. 25.00 (ISBN 0-534-97939-4). Lifetime Learn.

Martonosi, Anthony, ed. The Enzymes of Biological Membranes, Vols. 1-4. Incl. Vol. 1. Physical & Chemical Techniques. 270p. 1976. 35.00x (ISBN 0-306-35031-9); Vol. 2. Biosynthesis of Cell Components. 671p. 1976. 65.00x (ISBN 0-306-35032-7); Vol. 3. Membrane Transport. 474p. 1976. 55.00x (ISBN 0-306-35033-5); Vol. 4. Electron Transport Systems & Receptors. 446p. 1976. 55.00x (ISBN 0-306-35034-3). (Illus., Plenum Pr). Plenum Pub.

Matsui, Hideji & Kobayashi, Kando, eds. Biomechanics VIII, 2 vols. LC 82-84703. (International Series on Biomechanics). 1983. text ed. 75.00x (ISBN 0-931250-42-0, BMAT0042). Human Kinetics.

--Biomechanics VIII, Vol. A. LC 82-84703. (International Series on Biomechanics). 640p. 1983. text ed. 39.95x (ISBN 0-931250-43-9, BMAT0043). Human Kinetics.

--Biomechanics VIII, Vol. B. LC 82-84703. (International Series on Biomechanics). 664p. 1983. text ed. 39.95x (ISBN 0-931250-44-7, BMAT0044). Human Kinetics.

Metherell, A. F., ed. Acoustical Imaging, Vol. 8. LC 69-12533. 801p. 1980. 110.00x (ISBN 0-306-40171-1, Plenum Pr). Plenum Pub.

Miura, Y., et al. Advances in Biomedical Engineering, Vol. 4. (Illus.). 1976. 38.00 (ISBN 0-387-07747-2). Springer-Verlag.

Nair, Sreedhar, ed. Computers in Critical Care & Pulmonary Medicine, Vol. 1. LC 80-14503. 437p. 1980. 55.00x (ISBN 0-306-40449-4, Plenum Pr). Plenum Pub.

National Committee for Clinical Laboratory Standards. Design of Clinical Laboratory Instruments Relative to Powerline Disturbances: Proposed Guideline. 1984. 15.00 (ISBN 0-318-03278-3, I13-P). Natl Comm Clin Lab Stds.

--Determining Performance of Volumetric Equipment: Proposed Guideline. 1984. 15.00 (ISBN 0-318-03275-9, I8-P). Natl Comm Clin Lab Stds.

--Development of User-Oriented Instrument Support Manuals: Proposed Guideline. 1984. 15.00 (ISBN 0-318-03279-1, I15-P). Natl Comm Clin Lab Stds.

--Directory & Handbook, 1983. 1984. write for info. Natl Comm Clin Lab Stds.

--Establishing Performance Claims for Clinical Chemical Methods, Comparison of Methods Experiment: Tentative Guideline for Manufacturers. 1984. 15.00 (ISBN 0-318-03269-4, EP4-T). Natl Comm Clin Lab Stds.

--Inventory Control Systems for Laboratory Supplies: Proposed Guidelines. 1984. 15.00 (ISBN 0-318-03272-4, GP6-P). Natl Comm Clin Lab Stds.

National Research Council. Models for Biomedical Research: A New Perspective. 180p. 1985. pap. text ed. 18.50 (ISBN 0-309-03538-4). Natl Acad Pr.

Nicolini, C., ed. Modeling & Analysis in Biomedicine: Proceedings of the 4th Course of the International School of Pure & Applied Biostructure, Erice, Italy, Oct. 18-27,1982. 460p. 1984. 67.00x (ISBN 9971-950-81-2, Pub. by World Sci Singapore). Taylor & Francis.

Norton, Harry N. Biomedical Sensors: Fundamentals & Applications. LC 81-19022. (Illus.). 130p. 1982. 20.00 (ISBN 0-8155-0890-5). Noyes.

Pacela, Allan F., ed. How to Build Seven Basic C. E. Test Devices. 1980. pap. 8.00x (ISBN 0-930844-08-4). Quest Pub.

Park, J. B. Biomaterials: An Introduction. LC 78-12542. (Illus.). 262p. 1979. 25.00x (ISBN 0-306-40103-7, Plenum Pr). Plenum Pub.

Planck, H., et al. Polyurethanes in Biomedical Engineering. (Progress in Biomedical Engineering Ser.: Vol. 1). 1984. 87.00 (ISBN 0-444-42399-0). Elsevier.

Preston, K. & Onoe, M., eds. Digital Processing of Biomedical Images. LC 76-25538. 457p. 1976. 69.50x (ISBN 0-306-30967-X, Plenum Pr). Plenum Pub.

Regier, Mary H., et al. Biomedical Statistics with Computing. LC 82-2839. (Medical Computing Ser.). 112p. 1982. 41.95 (ISBN 0-471-10449-3, Pub. by Res Stud Pr). Wiley.

Roberts, Edward, et al, eds. Biomedical Innovation. (Illus.). 368p. 1982. 37.50x (ISBN 0-262-18103-7). MIT Pr.

Rushmer, Robert F. Medical Engineering: Projections for Health Care Delivery. 1972. 76.00 (ISBN 0-12-603650-0). Acad Pr.

Rutstein, David D. & Eden, Murray. Engineering & Living Systems. 1970. 22.50x (ISBN 0-262-18048-0). MIT Pr.

Sauer, B. W., ed. Biomedical Engineering IV: Recent Developments: Proceedings of the Fourth Southern Biomedical Engineering Conference, Jackson, MS, U. S. A. October 11-12, 1985. (Illus.). 300p. 1985. pap. 70.00 (ISBN 0-08-033137-8, Pub. by PPI). Pergamon.

Schepartz, B. Dimensional Analysis in the Biomedical Sciences. (Illus.). 184p. 1980. 19.75x (ISBN 0-398-03991-7). C C Thomas.

Schneck, D. J., ed. Biofluid Mechanics, Vol. 2. LC 80-10092. 530p. 1980. 69.50x (ISBN 0-306-40426-5, Plenum Pr). Plenum Pub.

Selvey, Nancy & White, Philip L. Nutrition in the Nineteen Eighties: Constraints on Our Knowledge. LC 81-8454. (Progress in Clinical & Biological Research Ser.: Vol. 67). 620p. 1981. 80.00 (ISBN 0-8451-0067-X). A R Liss.

Society of Photo-Optical Instrumentation Engineers, Seminar. Quantitative Imagery in the Bio-Medical Sciences, 2: Proceedings, Vol. 40. Herron, R. E., ed. 28.00 (ISBN 0-89252-052-3). Photo-Optical.

Spiegel, Herbert, ed. Clinical Biochemistry: Contemporary Theories & Techniques, Vol. 1. LC 81-14933. 1981. 39.50 (ISBN 0-12-657101-5). Acad Pr.

Stark, L. & Agarwal, G. C., eds. Biomaterials. LC 72-80083. 284p. 1969. 37.50x (ISBN 0-306-30405-8, Plenum Pr). Plenum Pub.

Stroeve, Pieter, et al, eds. Biomedical Engineering. LC 83-9253. (AIChE Symposium: Vol. 79). 174p. 1983. pap. 40.00 (ISBN 0-8169-0252-6, S227); pap. 20.00 members (ISBN 0-317-03744-7). Am Inst Chem Eng.

Subrata Saha, Louisiana State University Medical Center, Shreveport, Louisiana, USA, ed. Biomedical Engineering I: Recent Developments. Proceedings of the First Southern Biomedical Engineering Conference, June 7-8, 1982, Shreveport, Louisiana, U. S. A. (Illus.). 432p. 1982. 61.00 (ISBN 0-08-028826-X, H220). Pergamon.

Symposium on Science Policy & Biomedical Research: Proceedings. (Science Policy Studies & Documents: No. 16). pap. 3.50 (U487, UNESCO). Unipub.

Symposium, Woods Hole, Mass., October, 1978. Biomedical Applications of the Horseshoe Crab (Limulidae) Cohen, Elias, ed. LC 79-1748. (Progress in Clinical & Biological Research Ser.: Vol. 29). 720p. 1979. 68.00x (ISBN 0-8451-0029-7). A R Liss.

Takashima, Shiro & Postow, Elliot. Interaction of Acoustical & Electromagnetic Fields with Biological Systems. LC 82-7206. (Progress in Clinical & Biological Research Ser.: Vol. 86). 196p. 1982. 28.00 (ISBN 0-8451-0086-6). A R Liss.

Technomic Research Staff. Biomedical Electronics: Marketing Guide & Company Directory for Patient Care Systems & Laboratory Equipment. LC 72-77087. (Illus.). 200p. 1972. pap. 9.95 (ISBN 0-87762-082-2). Technomic.

Tischler, Morris. Experiments in General & Biomedical Instrumentation. Haas, Mark, ed. (Illus.). 176p. 1980. pap. text ed. 18.55x (ISBN 0-07-064781-X). McGraw.

User Evaluation of Precision Performance of Clinical Chemistry Devices: Tentative Guideline. 1984. 15.00 (ISBN 0-318-03271-6, EP5-T). Natl Comm Clin Lab Stds.

Welkowitz, Walter & Deutsch, Sid. Biomedical Instrument: Theory & Design. 1976. 36.00 (ISBN 0-12-744150-6). Acad Pr.

West, John B., ed. Bioengineering Aspects of the Lung. (Lung Biology & Health Ser.: Vol. 3). 1977. 89.75 (ISBN 0-8247-6378-5). Dekker.

Zimmerman, Roy R. Disability Evaluation in Biomedicine: Subject Analysis & Research Index with Bibliography. LC 83-48720. 159p. 1984. 29.95 (ISBN 0-88164-080-8); pap. 21.95 (ISBN 0-88164-081-6). ABBE Pubs Assn.

BIOMEDICAL MATERIALS

Bayless, William C. & Pacela, Allan F. Guide to Biomedical Standards. 10th ed. LC 7-640292. 1984. Quest Pub.

Biomedical Sciences Instrumentation: Proceedings of the 21st Annual Rocky Mountain Bioengineering Symposium & the 21st Annual International ISA Biomedical Sciences Instrumentation Symposium, 1984, Vol. 20. LC 66-21220. 172p. 1984. pap. text ed. 35.00x (ISBN 0-87664-805-7). Instru Soc.

Black, Jonathan. Biological Performance of Materials: Fundamentals of Biocompatibility. (Biomedical Engineering & Instrumentation Ser.: Vol. 8). (Illus.). 264p. 1981. 45.00 (ISBN 0-8247-1267-6). Dekker.

Bruck, Stephen D. Properties of Biomaterials in the Physiological Environment. 160p. 1980. 62.00 (ISBN 0-8493-5685-7). CRC Pr.

Carr, Joseph J. & Brown, John M. Introduction to Biomedical Equipment Technology. LC 80-6218. (Electronic Technology Ser.). 430p. 1981. 32.95x (ISBN 0-471-04143-2); tchr's manual avail. (ISBN 0-471-04144-0). Wiley.

Cooper, Stuart L. & Peppas, Nicholas A., eds. Biomaterials: Interfacial Phenomena & Applications. LC 82-6763. (ACS Advances in Chemistry Ser.: No. 199). 539p. 1982. lib. bdg. 69.95x (ISBN 0-8412-0631-7). Am Chemical.

Ducheyne, P. G., et al, eds. Biomaterials & Biomechanics, 1983: Proceedings of the 4th European Conference on Biomaterials, Leuven, Belgium, Aug. 31-Sept. 2, 1983. (Advances in Biomaterials Ser.: No. 5). 500p. 1984. 96.50 (ISBN 0-444-42352-4). Elsevier.

Ducheyne, Paul & Hastings, Garth W., eds. Metal & Ceramic Biomaterials: Structure, Vol. I. 160p. 1984. 50.00 (ISBN 0-8493-6261-X). CRC Pr.

Gebelein, Charles G. & Koblitz, Frank K., eds. Biomedical & Dental Applications of Polymers. LC 80-29429. (Polymer Science & Technology Ser.: Vol. 14). 504p. 1981. 75.00x (ISBN 0-306-40632-2, Plenum Pr). Plenum Pub.

Goldberg, E. P. & Nakajima, A. Biomedical Polymers: Polymeric Materials & Pharmaceuticals for Biomedical Use. LC 80-17691. 1980. 43.50 (ISBN 0-12-287580-X). Acad Pr.

Gregor, Harry P., ed. Biomedical Applications of Polymers. LC 75-6846. (Polymer Science & Technology Ser.: Vol. 7). 239p. 1975. 42.50x (ISBN 0-306-36407-7, Plenum Pr). Plenum Pub.

Hastings, G. W. & Williams, D. F., eds. Mechanical Properties of Biomaterials: Proceedings Held at Keele University, September 1978. LC 79-41776. (Advances in Biomaterials Ser.: Vol. 2). pap. 147.50 (ISBN 0-317-08540-9, 2022102). Bks Demand UMI.

Hastings, Garth W. & Ducheyne, Paul, eds. Macromolecular Biomaterials. 320p. 1984. 89.00 (ISBN 0-8493-6263-6). CRC Pr.

Hench, L. L. & Ethridge, E. C. Biomaterials: An Interfacial Approach. (Biophysics & Bioengineering Ser.). 335p. 1982. 42.00 (ISBN 0-12-340280-8). Acad Pr.

Lee, A. J. & Albrektsson, T. Clinical Applications of Biomaterials. (Advances in Biomaterials Ser.: Vol. 4). 356p. 1982. 74.95X (ISBN 0-471-10403-5, Pub. by Wiley-Interscience). Wiley.

Park, Joon B. Biomaterials Science & Engineering. 478p. 1984. 35.00x (ISBN 0-306-41689-1, Plenum Pr). Plenum Pub.

Szycher, Michael & Robinson, William J., eds. Synthetic Biomedical Polymers: Concepts & Applications. LC 80-52137. (Illus.). 235p. 1980. 39.00 (ISBN 0-87762-290-6). Technomic.

Vincent, Julian F. Structural Biomaterials. LC 81-6797. 224p. 1982. 26.95x (ISBN 0-470-27174-4). Halsted Pr.

Williams, D. F. Biocompatibility of Clinical Implant Materials, 2 vols, Vols. I & II. 1981. Vol. I, 288 Pgs. 84.50 (ISBN 0-8493-6625-9); Vol. II, 288 Pgs. 84.50 (ISBN 0-8493-6626-7). CRC Pr.

--Fundamental Aspects of Biocompatibility, 2 vols. (Biocompatability Ser.: Vol. 1). 1981. vol. 1, 240 pgs. 76.50 (ISBN 0-8493-6611-9); vol. 2, 328 pgs. 96.00 (ISBN 0-8493-6612-7). CRC Pr.

Williams, David F., ed. Biocompatibility of Orthopedic Implants, Vol. II. 264p. 1982. 84.50 (ISBN 0-8493-6614-3). CRC Pr.

Winter, George D., ed. Evaluation of Biomaterials. LC 79-42730. (Advances in Biomaterials Ser.). 553p. 1980. 174.95x (ISBN 0-471-27658-8, Pub. by Wiley-Interscience). Wiley.

Winter, George D., et al, eds. Biomaterials, Nineteen Eighty, Vol. 3. LC 81-15923. (Advances in Biomaterials Ser.). 221p. 1982. 81.95x (ISBN 0-471-10126-5, Pub. by Wiley-Interscience). Wiley.

BIOMETEROLOGY

see Bioclimatology

BIOMETRY

see also Biomathematics; Entomology–Statistical Methods; Mathematical Statistics; Sampling (Statistics)

Bailey, Norman T. J., ed. Statistical Methods in Biology. 2nd ed. LC 80-15774. (Biological Science Text Ser.). 216p. 1981. pap. 12.95x (ISBN 0-470-27006-3). Halsted Pr.

Balaam, L. N. Fundamentals of Biometry. 259p. 1972. 32.95 (ISBN 0-470-04571-X). Halsted Pr.

Batschelet, Edward. Circular Statistics in Biology. LC 81-66364. (Mathematics in Biology Ser.). 1981. 69.50 (ISBN 0-12-081050-6). Acad Pr.

Brown, Byron W., Jr. & Hollander, Myles. Statistics: A Biomedical Introduction. LC 77-396. (Probability & Mathematical Statistics Ser). 456p. 1977. 34.95 (ISBN 0-471-11240-2, Pub. by Wiley-Interscience). Wiley.

Bulpitt, Christopher J. Randomised Controlled Clinical Trials. 1983. lib. bdg. 52.50 (ISBN 90-247-2749-9, Pub. by Martinus Nijhoff Netherlands). Kluwer Academic.

Campbell, R. C. Statistics for Biologists. 2nd ed. (Illus.). 300p. 1974. 59.50 (ISBN 0-521-20381-3); pap. 15.95 (ISBN 0-521-09836-X). Cambridge U Pr.

Causton, David & Venus, Jill. Biometry of Plant Growth. 320p. 1981. text ed. 59.50 (ISBN 0-7131-2812-7). E Arnold.

Causton, David R. & Venus, Jill C. The Biometry of Plant Growth. 272p. 1981. 90.00x (ISBN 0-7131-2812-7, Pub. by E Arnold England). State Mutual Bk.

Choi, Sung C. Introductory Applied Statistics in Science. (Illus.). 1978. ref. ed. 26.95 (ISBN 0-13-501619-3). P-H.

Daniel, Wayne W. Biostatistics: A Foundation for Analysis in the Health Sciences. 3rd ed. LC 77-28253. (Probability & Mathematical Statistics Ser.). 534p. 1983. text ed. 38.45 (ISBN 0-471-09753-5). Wiley.

Delaunois, A. L., ed. Biostatistics in Pharmacology. new ed. LC 78-40220. (International Encyclopedia of Pharmacology & Therapeutics: Section 7, Vol. 3). (Illus.). 1979. text ed. 89.00 (ISBN 0-08-021514-9). Pergamon.

--Biostatistics in Pharmacology, Vol. 1-2. 1128p. 1973. Set. text ed. 150.00 (ISBN 0-08-016556-7). Pergamon.

Duncan, Robert C. & Knapp, Rebecca G. Introductory Biostatistics for the Health Sciences. 2nd ed. LC 82-23822. 249p. 1983. pap. 18.50 (ISBN 0-471-07869-7, Wiley Med). Wiley.

Elandt-Johnson, Regina C. Probability Models & Statistical Methods in Genetics. LC 75-140177. (A Wiley Publication in Applied Statistics). pap. 153.00 (ISBN 0-317-28077-5, 2055764). Bks Demand UMI.

Fisher, Ronald A. Statistical Methods for Research Workers. 14th ed. (Illus.). 1973. 19.95x (ISBN 0-02-844730-1). Hafner.

Hallaway. Biological Indicators. Date not set. price not set. Elsevier.

Heshmat, M. Y. & Herson, J., eds. Introduction to Epidemiology & Biometrics. LC 74-11495. 184p. 1974. pap. text ed. 6.00x (ISBN 0-8422-0394-X). Irvington.

Hubert & Hykle. A Study Guide to Biostatistics. 184p. 1984. pap. text ed. 9.50 (ISBN 0-8403-3448-6). Kendall-Hunt.

Hubert, J. J. & Carter. Biostatistics: 1064 Answers. 64p. 1980. pap. text ed. 5.50 saddle stitched (ISBN 0-8403-2288-7). Kendall-Hunt.

--Biostatistics: 1064 Questions. LC 80-82899. 160p. 1980. pap. text ed. 7.95 (ISBN 0-8403-2287-9). Kendall-Hunt.

Ingelfinger, Joseph A., et al. Biostatistics in Clinical Medicine. (Illus.). 316p. 1983. pap. write for info. (ISBN 0-02-360010-1). Macmillan.

Iyengar, S. Sitharama, ed. Computer Modeling of Complex Biological Systems. 152p. 1984. 59.00 (ISBN 0-8493-5208-8). CRC Pr.

Leaverton, Paul E. A Review of Biostatistics: A Program for Self-Instruction. 2nd ed. 1978. spiral bdg. 9.95 (ISBN 0-316-51852-2, Little Med Div). Little.

Lewis. Biostatics. 2nd ed. 1984. 24.95 (ISBN 0-442-25954-9). Van Nos Reinhold.

Miller, Rupert G., et al. Biostatistics Casebook. (Applied Probability & Statistics Ser.). 256p. 1980. pap. 21.50x (ISBN 0-471-06258-8, Pub. by Wiley-Interscience). Wiley.

Milton, J. Susan & Tsokos, Janice O. Statistical Methods in the Biological & Health Sciences. (Illus.). 512p. 1983. 36.95 (ISBN 0-07-042359-8). McGraw.

Morton, Richard F. & Hebel, J. Richard. Study Guide to Epidemiology & Biostatistics. 2nd ed. LC 83-23286. (Illus.). 160p. 1984. pap. text ed. 14.00 (ISBN 0-8391-1974-7, 20737). Univ Park.

Murphy, Edmond A. Biostatistics in Medicine. LC 81-48191. (Illus.). 560p. 1982. text ed. 37.50x (ISBN 0-8018-2727-2). Johns Hopkins.

Powell, F. C. Statistical Tables for the Social, Biological & Physical Sciences. LC 80-42241. (Illus.). 96p. 1982. 17.95 (ISBN 0-521-24141-3); pap. 6.95 (ISBN 0-521-28473-2). Cambridge U Pr.

Proschan, Frank & Serfling, R. J., eds. Reliability & Biometry: Statistical Analysis of Lifelength. LC 74-78907. x, 815p. 1974. text ed. 40.00 (ISBN 0-89871-159-2). Soc Indus-Appl Math.

Remington, Richard & Schork, M. Anthony. Statistics with Applications to the Biological & Health Sciences. 2nd ed. (Illus.). 432p. 1985. text ed. 33.95 (ISBN 0-13-846171-6). P-H.

Rosner, Bernard. Fundamentals of Biostatistics. 560p. 1982. text ed. write for info. (ISBN 0-87872-254-8, 2100, Duxbury Pr). PWS Pubs.

Rudman, Jack. Associate Biostatistician. (Career Examination Ser.: C-2292). (Cloth bdg. avail. on request). 1977. pap. 14.00 (ISBN 0-8373-2292-8). Natl Learning.

--Biostatistician. (Career Examination Ser.: C-1135). (Cloth bdg. avail. on request). pap. 12.00 (ISBN 0-8373-1135-7). Natl Learning.

Schefler, William C. Statistics for the Biological Sciences. 2nd ed. LC 78-55830. (Illus.). 1979. text ed. 22.95 (ISBN 0-201-07500-8). Addison-Wesley.

Shammas, H. John. Atlas of Ophthalmic Ultrasonography & Biometry. (Illus.). 342p. 1983. text ed. 49.95 (ISBN 0-8016-4546-8). Mosby.

Singh, B. K. & Chaudhury, B. D. Biometrical Techniques in Breeding & Genetics. 350p. 1977. 10.00 (ISBN 0-88065-193-8, Pub. by Messers Today & Tomorrows Printers & Publishers India). Scholarly Pubns.

Sokal, Robert R. & Rohlf, F. James. Biometry: The Principles & Practice of Statistics in Biological Research. 2nd ed. LC 81-4. (Illus.). 859p. 1981. text ed. 35.95x (ISBN 0-7167-1254-7). W H Freeman.

--Introduction to Biostatistics. LC 71-178257. (Illus.). 368p. 1973. text ed. 30.95x (ISBN 0-7167-0693-8). W H Freeman.

Von Fraunhofer, J. A. & Murray, J. J. Statistics in Medical, Dental & Biological Studies. 120p. 1981. 30.00x (ISBN 0-905402-00-6, Pub. by Tri-Med England). State Mutual Bk.

Wardlaw, A. C. Practical Statistics for Experimental Biologists. Date not set. price not set (ISBN 0-471-90737-5); pap. price not set (ISBN 0-471-90738-3). Wiley.

Zar, Jerrold H. Biostatistical Analysis. 2nd ed. (Illus.). 736p. 1984. text ed. 37.95 (ISBN 0-13-077925-3). P-H.

BIOMETRY–TABLES, ETC.

Pearson, E. S. & Hartley, H. O., eds. Biometrika Tables for Statisticians, Vol. 1. 270p. 1976. 40.00x (ISBN 0-85264-700-X, Pub. by Griffin England). State Mutual Bk.

--Biometrika Tables for Statisticians, Vol. 2. 1976. 50.00x (ISBN 0-85264-701-8, Pub. by Griffin England). State Mutual Bk.

Rimm, Alfred A., et al. Basic Biostatistics in Medicine & Epidemiology. (Illus.). 353p. 1980. pap. 19.95 (ISBN 0-8385-0528-7). ACC.

BIONICS

see also Artificial Intelligence; Optical Data Processing

Abelson, Philip H., ed. Biotechnology & Biological Frontiers. LC 84-21655. 516p. 1984. 29.95 (ISBN 0-87168-308-3); pap. 14.95 (ISBN 0-87168-266-4). AAAS.

Atkinson, B. & Mavituna, F. Biochemical Engineering & Biotechnology Handbook. 1982. 105.00x (ISBN 0-943818-02-8, Nature Pr). Groves Dict Music.

Biotechnology Equipment & Supplies. (Reports Ser.: No. 513). 179p. 1982. 985.00x (ISBN 0-88694-513-5). Intl Res Dev.

Biotechnology in Energy Product Symposium, 5th & Scott, Charles. Biotechnology & Bioengineering: Proceedings, Vol. 13. 672p. 1983. pap. 89.95x (ISBN 0-471-88173-2, Pub. by Wiley-Interscience). Wiley.

British Library Staff. European Biotechnology Information Project (EBIP) Biotechnology Information Seminar Course Book. 1984. 30.00 (Pub. by British Lib). Longwood Pub Group.

--European Biotechnology Information Project (EBIP) Business Information Sources in Biotechnology. 1984. 15.00 (ISBN 0-317-26872-4, Pub. by British Lib). Longwood Pub Group.

--European Biotechnology Information Project (EBIP) Culture Collections. 1984. 7.50 (ISBN 0-317-26875-9, Pub. by British Lib). Longwood Pub Group.

--European Biotechnology Information Project (EBIP) Forthcoming Conferences. 1984. 7.50 (ISBN 0-317-26881-3, Pub. by British Lib). Longwood Pub Group.

--European Biotechnology Information Project (EBIP) Market Research Reports. 2nd ed. 1984. 7.50 (ISBN 0-317-26879-1, Pub. by British Lib). Longwood Pub Group.

Business Communications Staff. Scaleup in Biotechnology. 1985. pap. 1750.00 (ISBN 0-89336-421-5, C-061). BCC.

Cauwels, Janice M. The Body Shop: Bionic Revolutions in Medicine. 1985. 12.95 (ISBN 0-8016-0944-5). Mosby.

Colwell, Rita R. & Pariser, E. Ray, eds. Biotechnology in the Marine Sciences: Proceedings of the First Annual MIT Sea Grant Lecture & Seminar. 1984. text ed. 37.50 (ISBN 0-471-88276-3, Pub. by Wiley-Interscience). Wiley.

Coombs, Jim. The Biotechnology Directory 1985. 464p. 1985. pap. 130.00x (ISBN 0-943818-06-0). Stockton Pr.

--The International Biotechnology Directory 1984: Products, Companies, Research & Organizations. LC 83-12138. 426p. 1983. 100.00 (ISBN 0-943818-03-6, Nature Pr). Groves Dict Music.

Cooper, Iver P. Biotechnology & the Law. LC 82-12957. 1982. 86.50 (ISBN 0-87632-311-5). Boardman.

Crafts-Lighty, A. Information Sources in Biotechnology. LC 83-17479. 306p. 1983. 80.00 (ISBN 0-943818-04-4, Nature Pr). Groves Dict Music.

Critser, James R., Jr. Biotechnical Engineering: Equipment & Processes. (Ser. 14-81). 1982. 210.00 (ISBN 0-914428-92-6). Lexington Data.

--Biotechnical Engineering: Equipment & Processes. (Ser. 14-83). 318p. 1984. 210.00 (ISBN 0-88178-012-X). Lexington Data.

Crueger, Wulf & Crueger, Anneliese. Biotechnology: A Textbook of Industrial Microbiology. Science Tech Inc., tr. from Ger. LC 84-1340. Tr. of Lehrbuch der Angewandten Mikrobiologie. (Illus.). 350p. 1984. text ed. 30.00x (ISBN 0-87893-126-0). Sinauer Assoc.

Daly, Peter. The Biotechnology Business: A Strategic Analysis. 150p. 1985. 25.00x (ISBN 0-8476-7460-6). Rowman.

Dechema, ed. Third European Congress on Biotechnology, 3 vols. 2014p. 1984. Set. pap. 275.30x (ISBN 0-89573-414-1). VCH Pubs.

DECHEMA, Deutsche Gesellschaft Fuer Chemisches Apparatewesen E. V., ed. Biotechnology: Proceedings of the First European Congress on Biotechnology. (Dechema Monographs: Vol. 82). 304p. 1979. pap. 37.50x (ISBN 3-527-10765-7). VCH Pubs.

Fogarty, William M., ed. Microbial Enzymes & Biotechnology. (Illus.). 382p. 1983. 63.00 (ISBN 0-85334-185-0, Pub. by Elsevier Applied Sci England). Elsevier.

Gogotov, L. N., et al. Microbial Activities. (Advances in Biochemical Engineering-Biotechnology Ser.: Vol. 28). (Illus.). 200p. 1983. 35.50 (ISBN 0-387-12791-7). Springer-Verlag.

Gruver, W. A. Simulation & Identification in Biological Science. 160p. 1985. Repr. lib. bdg. 19.95x (ISBN 0-89370-892-5). Borgo Pr.

Higgins, I. J., et al, eds. Biotechnology: Principles & Applications. (Illus.). 300p. 1985. text ed. 50.00x (ISBN 0-632-01029-0); pap. text ed. 27.00x (ISBN 0-632-01034-7). Blackwell Sci.

Houwink, E. H. & Van Der Meer, R. R., eds. Innovations in Biotechnology: Proceedings of a Poster Symposium, Delft, the Netherlands, Nov. 22, 1983. (Progress in Industrial Microbiology Ser.: No. 20). 530p. 1984. 90.75 (ISBN 0-444-42275-7, I-309-84). Elsevier.

Joglekar, Rajani & Clerman, Robert J. Biotechnology in Industry: Selected Applications & Unit Operations. LC 82-48642. (Illus.). 200p. 1983. 39.95 (ISBN 0-250-40605-5). Butterworth.

Mizrahi, Avshalom & Van Wezel, Antonius L. Advances in Biotechnological Processes, Vol. 4. 372p. 1985. 34.00 (ISBN 0-8451-3203-2). A R Liss.

Mizrahi, Avshalom & Wezel, Antonius L. van. Advances in Biotechnological Processes, Vol. 3. 380p. 1984. 68.00 (ISBN 0-8451-3202-4). A R Liss.

Mizrahi, Avshalom & Van Wezel, Antonius L., eds. Advances in Biotechnological Processes, Vol. 1. 360p. 1983. 58.00 (ISBN 0-8451-3200-8). A R Liss.

Kendeigh, S. Charles. Bird Populations in East Central Illinois: Fluctuations, Variations, & Developments over a Half-Century. LC 81-16073. (Illinois Biological Monographs: No. 52). (Illus.). 152p. 1982. pap. 14.50 (ISBN 0-252-00955-X). U of Ill Pr.

Lack, David. Ecological Isolation in Birds. LC 70-151286. 1971. 27.50x (ISBN 0-674-22442-6). Harvard U Pr.

BIRD-SONG

Borror, Donald & Glitz, Maurice L. Florida Bird Songs. 1980. pap. 4.95 record & booklet (ISBN 0-486-23956-X). Dover.

Borror, Donald J. Bird Song & Bird Behavior. 1971. pap. 5.95 booklet with record (ISBN 0-486-22779-0). Dover.

--Common Bird Songs. (Orig.). 1968. pap. 5.95 booklet with record (ISBN 0-486-21829-5). Dover.

--Songs of Eastern Birds. pap. 5.95 booklet with record (ISBN 0-486-22378-7). Dover.

--Songs of Western Birds. 1970. pap. 4.95 booklet with record (ISBN 0-486-22765-0). Dover.

Jellis, Rosemary. Bird Sounds & Their Meaning. (Illus.). 1977. text ed. 18.00x (ISBN 0-563-12126-2). Humanities.

Schuyler, Mathews F. Field Book of Wild Birds & Their Music: Description of Character & Music of Birds, Intended to Assist in Identification of Species Common in the U.S. East of the Rocky Mountains. 1978. Repr. of 1904 ed. lib. bdg. 35.00 (ISBN 0-8495-3755-X). Arden Lib.

Stokes, Donald W. A Guide to the Behavior of Common Birds. LC 79-17864. (Illus.). 1979. 14.45i (ISBN 0-316-81722-8). Little.

Thielcke, Gerhard. Bird Sounds. Drury, John, tr. from Ger. (Ann Arbor Science Library). Tr. of Vogelstimmen. (Illus.). 1976. pap. 4.95 (ISBN 0-472-05021-4, AA). U of Mich Pr.

BIRD WATCHING

see also Birds–Study and Teaching

Berruti, A. & Sinclair, J. C. Where to Watch Birds in Southern Africa. (Illus.). 302p. 1985. 24.95 (ISBN 0-88072-066-2). Tanager Bks.

Clarke, Hockley. Bird Watching for Everyone. 128p. 1980. 29.00x (ISBN 0-905418-30-1, Pub. by Gresham England). State Mutual Bk.

Eriksson, Paul S. The Bird Finder's Three Year Notebook, 1985. rev. ed. LC 75-19198. (Illus.). 384p. 1984. plastic comb 12.95 (ISBN 0-8397-1029-1). Eriksson.

Farrand, John, ed. The Audubon Society Master Guide to Birding, 3 Vols. (Illus.). 1984. Boxed set. 42.00 (ISBN 0-394-54121-9). Knopf.

Ferguson-Lees, James & Hockliffe, Quentin. A Guide to Bird-Watching in Europe. (Illus.). 335p. 9.95 (ISBN 0-684-14475-1). Brown Bk.

Ferguson-Lees, James, et al, eds. A Guide to Bird-Watching in Europe. LC 75-329356. 336p. 1979. 14.95 (ISBN 0-370-10476-5, Pub. by the Bodley Head); pap. 6.95 (ISBN 0-370-10477-3). Merrimack Pub Cir.

Fisher, James & Flegg, James. Watching Birds. rev. ed. (Illus.). 1974. 10.00 (ISBN 0-85661-005-4, Pub. by T & A D Poyser). Buteo.

Fisk, Erma J. The Peacocks of Baboquivari: A Journal. (Illus.). 1983. 14.95 (ISBN 0-393-01758-3). Norton.

Fitter. Collins Pocket Guide to Bird Watching. 29.95 (ISBN 0-00-219171-7, Collins Pub England). Greene.

Frandsen, Joy. Birds of the South Western Cape. (Illus.). 236p. 1985. 24.95 (ISBN 0-88072-067-0, Pub. by Tanager). Longwood Pub Group.

Geffen, Alice. A Birdwatcher's Guide to Eastern United States. LC 77-21436. 1978. 15.95 (ISBN 0-8120-5301-X). Barron.

Gooders, John. Bird Seeker's Guide. (Illus.). 208p. 1985. pap. 6.95 (ISBN 0-233-97380-X, Pub. by A Deutsch England). David & Charles.

--Where to Watch Birds in Europe. LC 77-84451. (Illus.). 1978. 10.95 (ISBN 0-8008-8246-6). Taplinger.

Harding, John J. & Harding, Justin J. Birding the Delaware Valley Region: A Comprehensive Guide to Birdwatching in Southeastern Pennsylvania, Central & Southern New Jersey, & Northcentral Delaware. 233p. 1980. 15.95x (ISBN 0-87722-179-0); pap. 9.95 (ISBN 0-87722-182-0). Temple U Pr.

Harrison, George H. Backyard Bird Watcher. 1979. 16.95 (ISBN 0-671-22664-9). S&S.

Heintelman, Donald S. Guide to Owl Watching in North America. LC 84-13067. (Illus.). 144p. (Orig.). 1984. pap. 8.95 (ISBN 0-8329-0361-2, Pub. by Winchester Pr). New Century.

Heintzelman, Donald S. A Manual for Bird Watching in the Americas. LC 78-66169. (Illus.). 264p. 1980. 17.95x (ISBN 0-87663-336-X); pap. 9.95 (ISBN 0-87663-967-8). Universe.

Hickey, Joseph J. A Guide to Bird Watching. LC 74-18718. (Illus.). xxii, 252p. 1975. Repr. of 1943 ed. 4.95 (ISBN 0-486-21596-2). Dover.

--A Guide to Bird Watching. (Illus.). 11.25 (ISBN 0-8446-5200-8). Peter Smith.

Holmgren, Virginia. SCANS: Key to Bird Watching. LC 82-25597. (Illus.). 176p. (Orig.). 1983. pap. 12.95 (ISBN 0-917304-48-9). Timber.

Hume, Rob. Birdwatcher's Miscellany. (Illus.). 192p. 1985. 16.95 (ISBN 0-7137-1385-2, Pub. by Blandford Pr England). Sterling.

Hunn, Eugene S. Birding in Seattle & King County. LC 82-61828. (Trailside Ser.). (Illus.). 1982. pap. 7.50 (ISBN 0-914516-05-1). Seattle Audubon Soc.

Laycock, George. Bird Watcher's Bible. LC 74-2532. (Outdoor Bible Ser.). (Illus.). 192p. 1976. softbound 4.95 (ISBN 0-385-09611-9). Doubleday.

--The Birdwatcher's Bible. LC 74-2532. 192p. 1976. pap. 4.95 (ISBN 0-385-09611-9). Doubleday.

Lederer, Roger J. Pacific Coast Bird Finder: A Manual for Identifying 61 Common Birds of Pacific Coast. 1977. pap. 1.50 (ISBN 0-912550-04-X). Nature Study.

Lentz, Joan E. & Young, Judith. Birdwatching: A Guide for Beginners. LC 84-23676. (Illus.). 178p. (Orig.). 1985. pap. 8.95 (ISBN 0-88496-231-8). Capra Pr.

Mallett, Sandy. A Year with New England's Birds: A Guide to Twenty-Five Field Trips. LC 77-26352. (Illus.). 120p. 1978. pap. 5.95 (ISBN 0-912274-87-5). Backcountry Pubns.

Mitchell, W. R. Birdwatch Around Scotland. (Illus.). 175p. 1984. 15.95 (ISBN 0-88072-062-X, Pub. by Tanager). Longwood Pub Group.

Ogilvie, Malcolm. Bird Watching on Inland Freshwaters. 16p. 1982. 45.00x (ISBN 0-7278-2004-4, Pub. by Severn Hse). State Mutual Bk.

Pierson, Elizabeth C. & Pierson, Jan Erik. A Birder's Guide to the Coast of Maine. LC 81-67953. (Illus.). 224p. 1981. pap. 8.95 (ISBN 0-89272-118-9, PIC471). Down East.

Pistorius, Alan. The Country Journal Book of Birding & Bird Attraction. (Illus.). 1981. 15.95 (ISBN 0-393-01493-2). Norton.

Richards, Alan J. The Birdwatcher's A-Z. (Illus.). 328p. 1981. 37.50 (ISBN 0-7153-8016-8). David & Charles.

Rivera Cianchini, Osvaldo & Mojica Sandoz, Luis. Pajaros Notables De Puerto Rico: Guia Para Observadores De Aves. (Illus.). v, 101p. 1981. 7.50 (ISBN 0-8477-2324-0); pap. 9.00 (ISBN 0-8477-2325-9). U of PR Pr.

Scofield, Michael. The Complete Outfitting & Resource Book for Bird Watching. (Illus.). 1978. pap. 6.95 (ISBN 0-03-045615-0). HR&W.

Sequoia Audubon Society. San Francisco Peninsula Birdwatching. Scanlan-Rohrer, Anne, ed. (Illus., Orig.). 1985. pap. 8.95 (ISBN 0-9614301-0-9). Sequoia Aud Soc.

Sinclair, Ian. Field Guide to the Birds of Southern Africa. (Illus.). 368p. 1985. pap. 19.95 (ISBN 0-88072-064-6, Pub. by Tanager). Longwood Pub Group.

Skutch, Alexander F. A Bird Watcher's Adventures in Tropical America. LC 77-3478. (Corrie Herring Hooks Ser.: No. 3). (Illus.). 343p. 1977. 22.50 (ISBN 0-292-70722-3). U of Tex Pr.

Soper, Tony. Birdwatch. 1982. 19.95 (ISBN 0-03-061469-4). Webb & Bower.

Starling, Alfred. Enjoying Indiana Birds. LC 78-3247. (Illus.). 384p. 1978. 17.50x (ISBN 0-253-31956-0). Ind U Pr.

Stokes, Donald W. & Stokes, Lillian Q. A Guide to Bird Behavior: In the Wild & at Your Feeder, Vol. II. (Illus.). 352p. 1983. 16.45i (ISBN 0-316-81726-0); pap. 9.70i (ISBN 0-316-81729-5). Little.

Vardaman, James M. Call Collect, Ask for Birdman: The Record-Breaking Attempt to Sight 700 Species of North American Birds Within One Year. (McGraw-Hill Paperback Ser.). 256p. 1980. pap. 5.95 (ISBN 0-07-067151-6). McGraw.

Whitlock, Ralph. Birdwatch in an English Village. 1982. 37.00x (ISBN 0-905868-09-9, Pub. by Gavin Pr). State Mutual Bk.

Wilds, Claudia. Finding Birds in the National Capital Area. LC 82-600348. (Illus.). 216p. 1983. pap. 10.95 (ISBN 0-87474-959-X). Smithsonian.

Wood, Richard H. Wood Notes: A Companion & Guide for Birdwatchers. (Illus.). 192p. 1984. 15.95 (ISBN 0-13-962580-1); pap. 6.95 (ISBN 0-13-962572-0). P-H.

BIRDS

see also Cage-Birds; Game and Game-Birds; Ornithology; Water-Birds

also names of particular birds, e.g. Robins

Acworth, Bernard. Bird & Butterfly Mysteries. 1956. 10.00 (ISBN 0-8022-0004-4). Philos Lib.

Af Enehjelm, Curt. Cages & Aviaries. Friese, U. Erich, tr. from Ger. Orig. Title: Kafige und Volieren. (Illus.). 160p. 1981. 9.95 (ISBN 0-87666-840-6, H-1039). TFH Pubns.

Agenjo Cecilia, Cesar. Enciclopedia de la Avicultura. 2nd ed. (Espn.). 990p. 1964. 59.95 (ISBN 84-239-6004-8, S-14560). French & Eur.

Allaire, Pierre. Bird Species on Mined Lands. (Illus.). 72p. (Orig.). 1982. pap. text ed. 10.00 (ISBN 0-86607-010-9). Ky Ctr Energy Res.

Altum, Bernard. Der Vogel und Sein Leben. Sterling, Keir B., ed. LC 77-81082. (Biologists & Their World Ser.). (Ger.). 1978. Repr. of 1868 ed. lib. bdg. 17.00x (ISBN 0-405-10652-1). Ayer Co Pubs.

Arndt, Thomas. Encyclopedia of Conures: The Aratingas. (Illus.). 176p. 1982. 29.95 (ISBN 0-87666-873-2, H-1042). TFH Pubns.

Audubon, John J. Audubon & His Journals, 2 Vols. Audubon, Maria, ed. (Illus.). Set. 32.00 (ISBN 0-8446-1566-8). Peter Smith.

Austin, Oliver L., Jr. Families of Birds: Golden Field Guides Ser. rev. ed. (Illus.). 200p. 1985. pap. 7.95 (ISBN 0-307-13669-8, 13669, Golden Pr). Western Pub.

Belding, Lyman. Land Birds of the Pacific District. Repr. of 1890 ed. 37.00 (ISBN 0-384-03792-5). Johnson Repr.

Benirschke, K. & Hsu, T. C., eds. Chromosome Atlas: Fish, Amphibians, Reptiles & Birds, Vol. 1. LC 73-166079. (Illus.). 225p. 1972. loose leaf 25.00 (ISBN 0-387-05507-X). Springer-Verlag.

Berger, Andrew J. Bird Study. LC 72-143678. (Illus.). 1971. pap. 7.95 (ISBN 0-486-22699-9). Dover.

Bernstein, Chuck. The Joy of Birding: A Guide to Better Bird Watching. LC 84-7778. (Illus.). 201p. (Orig.). 1984. pap. 8.95 (ISBN 0-88496-220-2). Capra Pr.

Bohlen, H. David. Annotated Checklist of the Birds of Illinois. (Popular Science Ser.: Vol. IX). 154p. 1978. pap. 3.00 (ISBN 0-89792-071-6). Ill St Museum.

Bologna, Gianfranco. The World of Birds. Pleasance, Simon, tr. LC 79-1190. (Abbeville Press Encyclopedia of Natural Science). (Illus.). 256p. 1979. 13.95 (ISBN 0-89659-034-8). Abbeville Pr.

Bond, James. Birds of the West Indies. (Illus.). 1971. 14.95 (ISBN 0-395-07431-2). HM.

Bond, Mary W. Far Afield in the Caribbean. LC 75-140150. (Illus.). 1971. 4.95 (ISBN 0-915180-13-8). Harrowood Bks.

Bougerol, Christian. Larousse des oiseaux de cage et de voliere. (Larousse des animaux familiers). (Illus.). 120p. 1975. 26.00x (ISBN 2-03-014853-9). Larousse.

British Museum. Dinosaurs & Their Living Relatives. LC 79-14504. (Natural History Ser.). 1980. 24.95 (ISBN 0-521-22887-5); pap. 8.95 (ISBN 0-521-29698-6). Cambridge U Pr.

Brown, Vinson, et al. Handbook of California Birds. 3rd rev. ed. LC 73-6826. (Illus.). 223p. 1979. 14.95 (ISBN 0-911010-17-3); pap. 8.95 (ISBN 0-911010-16-5). Naturegraph.

Brush, Alan H. & Clark, George A., Jr., eds. Perspectives in Ornithology: Essays Presented for the Centennial of the American Ornithologists' Union. LC 83-3931. 544p. 1983. 32.50 (ISBN 0-521-24857-4). Cambridge U Pr.

Buchan, J. Foreign Birds: Exhibition & Management. 1981. 15.75 (ISBN 0-86230-039-8). Saiga.

Bull, John. S&S Guide to Birds of the World. 1981. (Fireside); pap. 9.95 (ISBN 0-671-42235-9). S&S.

Campbell, Bruce & Campbell, Margaret, eds. The Countryman Bird Book. (Countryman Books). (Illus.). 200p. 1974. 5.95 (ISBN 0-7153-6418-9). David & Charles.

Chimery, Michael. Garden Birds. (Illus.). 112p. 1983. 19.95 (ISBN 0-396-08170-3). Dodd.

Collins, Henry H., Jr. What Bird Is This? Orig. Title: Birdwatcher's Quiz Book. (Illus.). 1961. pap. 2.95 (ISBN 0-486-21490-7). Dover.

Cooper, J. E. & Eley, J. T. First Aid & Care of Wild Birds. 1979. 24.95 (ISBN 0-7153-7664-0). David & Charles.

Cooper, Jo. Handfeeding Baby Birds. (Illus.). 1979. 4.95 (ISBN 0-87666-992-5, KW-017). TFH Pubns.

Coues, Elliott. Audubon & His Journals, 2 vols. 250.00 (ISBN 0-87968-677-4). Gordon Pr.

Cruickshank, Allan D. & Cruickshank, Helen G. One-Thousand One Questions Answered About Birds. 14.50 (ISBN 0-8446-5483-3). Peter Smith.

Cuisin, Michel. Dictionnaire oiseaux. (Fr., Illus.). pap. 8.50 (ISBN 0-685-13879-8, 3729). Larousse.

Curtis, Jane & Curtis, Will. Welcome the Birds to Your Home. LC 79-20819. (Illus.). 1980. pap. 5.95 (ISBN 0-8289-0354-9). Greene.

Davis, John & Baldridge, Alan. The Bird Year: A Book for Birders with Special Reference to the Monterey Bay Area. 1980. pap. 5.95 (ISBN 0-910286-62-0). Boxwood.

Dormon, Caroline. Bird Talk. 1969. 4.95 (ISBN 0-87511-024-X). Claitors.

Dorst, Jean. The Life of Birds, 2 vols. (Illus.). 717p. 1974. 85.00x (ISBN 0-231-03909-3). Columbia U Pr.

Doughty, Robin W. Feather Fashions & Bird Preservation: A Study in Nature Protection. LC 72-619678. 1975. 26.50x (ISBN 0-520-02588-1). U of Cal Pr.

Dupuy, William A. Our Bird Friends & Foes. (Illus.). 10.75 (ISBN 0-8446-0601-4). Peter Smith.

Durrell, Gerald. Birds, Beasts, & Relatives. 1977. pap. 3.95 (ISBN 0-14-004385-3). Penguin.

Edwards, Ernest P. A Coded Workbook of Birds of the World: Vol. 1 Non-Passerines. 2nd ed. LC 82-82891. (Illus.). xxi, 134p. 1982. pap. 12.00 plastic comb bdg. (ISBN 0-911882-07-3). E P Edwards.

--Finding Birds in Mexico. 2nd ed. LC 68-58738. (Incl. 1985 Supplement to Finding Birds in Mexico). 1968. 20.00 set (ISBN 0-911882-01-4). E P Edwards.

Eifert, Virginia S. Birds in Your Backyard. rev. ed. (Popular Science Ser.: Vol. II). (Illus.). 224p. 1967. Ill St Museum.

Elliot, Daniel G. Birds of Paradise. 1977. leather bd. 995.00 (ISBN 0-686-86227-9); portfolio ed 650.00. Johnson Repr.

Endangered Birds of the World: The ICBP Bird Red Data Book. 600p. 1979. pap. 9.95 (ISBN 0-686-93121-1, IUCN101, IUCN); 20.95 (IUCN112). Unipub.

Epple, August & Stetson, Milton. Avian Endocrinology. 1980. 55.00 (ISBN 0-12-240250-2). Acad Pr.

Etchecopar, R. D. Titmice of the World. 1981. 750.00x (ISBN 0-686-78892-3, Pub. by Wheldon & Wesley England). State Mutual Bk.

Farner, Donald, et al, eds. Avian Biology, Vol. 6. LC 79-178216. 1982. 65.00 (ISBN 0-12-249406-7). Acad Pr.

Farner, Donald S., et al, eds. Avian Biology, Vol. 7. 1983. 69.50 (ISBN 0-12-249407-5). Acad Pr.

--Avian Biology, Vol. 8. 1985. 49.50 (ISBN 0-12-249408-3). Acad Pr.

Feduccia, Alan. The Age of Birds. LC 80-11926. (Illus.). 208p. 1980. 20.00 (ISBN 0-674-00975-4). Harvard U Pr.

Fisher, James. Thorburn's Birds. (Illus.). 190p. 1985. pap. 12.95 (ISBN 0-7181-2183-X, Pub. by Michael Joseph). Merrimack Pub Cir.

Flegg, Jim. Garden Birds. (Picture-Perfect Miniatures Ser.). (Illus.). 48p. 1983. 4.95 (ISBN 0-8253-0172-6). Beaufort Bks NY.

Foy, Charles. Pigeons for Pleasure & Profit. (Illus.). 1972. pap. 4.00 (ISBN 0-911466-19-3). Swanson.

Frasure, David W. Bluebirds. 1978. pap. 4.95 (ISBN 0-932298-08-7). Copple Hse.

Freethy, Ron. How Birds Work: A Guide to Bird Biology. (Illus.). 182p. 1982. 15.95 (ISBN 0-7137-1156-6, Pub. by Blandford Pr England). Sterling.

French, Richard. A Guide to the Birds of Trinidad & Tobago. rev. ed. LC 76-25609. (Illus.). 1976. Repr. of 1973 ed. 25.00 (ISBN 0-915180-03-0). Harrowood Bks.

Friedman, Herbert. The Cowbirds. (Illus.). 421p. 1929. photocopy ed. 36.50x (ISBN 0-398-04259-4). C C Thomas.

Fry, C. H. The Bee-eaters. LC 84-70385. (Illus.). 320p. 1984. write for info (ISBN 0-931130-11-5). Buteo.

Gooders, John. Birds That Came Back. 180p. 1983. 25.00 (ISBN 0-88072-050-6). Tanager Bks.

--Birds That Came Back. (Illus.). 180p. 1984. 24.95 (ISBN 0-233-97445-8, Pub. by A Deutsch England). David & Charles.

Goodwin, Derek. Birds of Man's World. LC 77-74922. (Illus.). 190p. 1978. 17.50x (ISBN 0-8014-1167-X). Comstock.

Groebbels, F. Der Vogel Atmungs-und Nahrungswelt, Gesehlecht und Fortoflanzung. 1969. 77.00 (ISBN 3-7682-0241-0). Lubrecht & Cramer.

Hall, Frances W. Birds of Florida. (Illus.). 1979. pap. 2.95 (ISBN 0-8200-0906-7). Great Outdoors.

Harrison, Colin. An Atlas of the Birds of the Western Palaearctic. LC 82-800069. (Illus.). 322p. 1982. 27.50 (ISBN 0-691-08307-X). Princeton U Pr.

Hartert, E. Die Voegel der Palaearkischen Fauna. 1970. 210.00 (ISBN 3-7682-0604-1). Lubrecht & Cramer.

Hatton, Austin L. A Calendar of Birds. (Illus.). 14.50x (ISBN 0-392-02450-0, SpS). Sportshelf.

Hudson, William H. Adventures Among Birds. Repr. of 1923 ed. 35.00 (ISBN 0-404-03407-1). AMS Pr.

--Adventures Among Birds. 1973. lib. bdg. 25.00 (ISBN 0-8414-5184-2). Folcroft.

--Birds & Man. Repr. of 1923 ed. 35.00 (ISBN 0-404-03399-7). AMS Pr.

--Birds in Town & Village. Repr. of 1923 ed. 35.00 (ISBN 0-404-03409-8). AMS Pr.

Hurlbutt, Catherine. Adventures with Talking Birds. (Illus.). 288p. 1981. 14.95 (ISBN 0-87666-895-3, H-1029). TFH Pubns.

Jennings, Michael C. Birds of the Arabian Gulf. (The Natural History of the Arabian Gulf Ser.). (Illus.). 176p. 1981. text ed. 25.00x (ISBN 0-04-598009-8). Allen Unwin.

Long, John L. Introduced Birds of the World. LC 81-50625. (Illus.). 528p. 1981. text ed. 50.00x (ISBN 0-87663-318-1). Universe.

McElroy, Thomas P., Jr. The Habitat Guide to Birding. 1974. 11.95 (ISBN 0-394-47492-9). Knopf.

Martin, Richard M. How to Keep Softbilled Birds in Cage or Aviary. (Illus.). 96p. 1980. pap. 3.95 (ISBN 0-7028-8010-8). Avian Pubns.

Menaboni, Sarah. Menaboni's Birds. (Illus.). 176p. 1984. 24.95 (ISBN 0-517-55130-6, C N Potter Bks). Crown.

Michelet, Jules. The Bird. 350p. 1983. pap. 9.95 (ISBN 0-7045-0444-8, Pub. by Salem Hse Ltd). Merrimack Pub Cir.

Mikami, S., et al, eds. Avian Endocrinology: Environmental & Ecological Perspectives. 380p. 1983. 55.00 (ISBN 0-387-11871-3). Springer-Verlag.

Montier, David. Atlas of Breeding Birds: London. 1977. 60.00 (ISBN 0-7134-0876-6, Pub. by Batsford England). David & Charles.

Moon, Geoff. The Birds Around Us: New Zealand Birds; Their Habits & Habitats. (Illus.). 207p. 1983. 25.95 (ISBN 0-908592-03-5, Pub. by Heinemann Pub New Zealand). Intl Spec Bk.

Morrow, Skip. For the Birds. LC 81-21284. (Illus.). 96p. (Orig.). 1982. pap. 3.95 (ISBN 0-394-17646-4). Seaver Bks.

Murphy, Robert C., et al. Canton Island. (Museum Pictorial Ser.: No. 10). 1954. pap. 1.10 (ISBN 0-916278-39-5). Denver Mus Natl Hist.

Nehls, Harry J. Familiar Birds of the Northwest. 2nd ed. 1983. 7.95 (ISBN 0-931686-05-9). Audubon Soc Portland.

Nethersole-Thompson, Desmond. Pine Crossbills. (Illus.). 1975. 20.00 (ISBN 0-85661-011-9, Pub by T & A D Poyser). Buteo.

Nicolai, Jurgen. Breeding Birds at Home. Friese, U. Erich, tr. from Ger. Tr. of Kafig-und Volieren-Vogel. (Illus.). 160p. 1981. 19.95 (ISBN 0-87666-841-4, H-1038). TFH Pubns.

O'Connor, Raymond. The Growth & Development of Birds. 315p. 1984. 39.95 (ISBN 0-471-90345-0). Wiley.

Palmer, Ralph S. Handbook of North American Birds: Vol. 1, Loons Through Flamingos. LC 62-8259. (Illus.). 1962. 52.00x (ISBN 0-300-00814-7). Yale U Pr.

Penny. The Birds of the Seychelles & Outlying Islands. 19.95 (ISBN 0-00-219618-2, Collins Pub England). Greene.

Peterson, Roger T. Field Guide to Western Birds PA. (Peterson Field Guide Ser.). 1972. 16.95 (ISBN 0-395-08085-1); pap. 11.95 (ISBN 0-395-13692-X); Set. 3 records 27.50 (ISBN 0-395-08089-4); Set. 3 cassettes 29.95 (ISBN 0-395-19430-X). HM.

--How to Know the Birds. 1982. pap. 4.50 (ISBN 0-451-12939-3, E2939, Sig). NAL.

Poole, Robert M., ed. The Wonder of Birds. (Illus.). 280p. 1983. deluxe ed. 39.95 (ISBN 0-87044-471-9); Includes Field Guide to the Birds of North America & 4 record album of bird sounds. 29.95 (ISBN 0-87044-470-0). Natl Geog.

Radtke, Georg A. The T.F.H. Book of Lovebirds. Lambrich, Annemarie, tr. from Ger. (Illus.). 80p. 6.95 (ISBN 0-87666-846-5, HP-001). TFH Pubns.

Ray, John. Synopsis Methodica Avium & Piscium. Derham, William & Sterling, Keir B., eds. LC 77-81111. (Biologists & Their World Ser.). (Latin., Illus.). 1978. Repr. of 1713 ed. lib. bdg. 35.50x (ISBN 0-405-10695-5). Ayer Co Pubs.

Richards, Alan J. The Birdwatcher's A-Z. (Illus.). 328p. 1981. 37.50 (ISBN 0-7153-8016-8). David & Charles.

Ripley, S. Dillon. Rails of the World. LC 75-619273. (Illus.). 432p. 1977. 125.00 (ISBN 0-87923-198-X); ltd. ed. 400.00 (ISBN 0-87923-199-8). Godine.

Robiller, Franz. Birds Throughout the World. 262p. 1980. 49.00x (ISBN 0-905418-39-5, Pub. by Gresham England). State Mutual Bk.

Rogers, Cyril. How to Keep Seedeating Birds in Cage & Aviary. (Illus.). 96p. 1974. pap. 3.95 (ISBN 0-7028-1068-1). Avian Pubns.

Rowley, Ian. Bird Life. (Illus.). 284p. 1983. pap. 12.50 (ISBN 0-00-216436-1, Pub. by W Collins Australia). Intl Spec Bk.

Rutgers, A. The Handbook of Foreign Birds, Volumes 1 & 2. Incl. Vol. 1. The Small Seed-& Insect-Eating Birds. rev. ed. 1977. Repr. of 1964 ed (ISBN 0-7137-0815-8); Vol. 2. Larger Birds, Including Parrots & Parakeets. rev. ed. 1969. Repr. of 1965 ed (ISBN 0-7137-0769-0). (Color Ser.). 9.95 ea. (Pub. by Blandford Pr England). Sterling.

Rutgers, A. & Norris, K. A. Encyclopedia of Aviculture, 3 vols. (Illus.). 900p. 1982. boxed set 125.00 (ISBN 0-7137-1295-3, Pub. by Blandford Pr England). Sterling.

Rutgers, A. & Norris, K. A., eds. The Encyclopedia of Aviculture, 3 vols. Incl. Vol. 1. 1970 (ISBN 0-7137-0800-X); Vol. 2. 1973 (ISBN 0-7137-0801-8); Vol. 3. 1977 (ISBN 0-7137-0802-6). (Illus.). 45.00 ea. (Pub. by Blandford Pr England). Sterling.

Scollard, Clinton & Rittenhouse, Jessie B.compiled by. The Bird-Lovers Anthology. LC 72-11919. (Granger Index Reprint Ser.). 1973. Repr. of 1930 ed. 21.00 (ISBN 0-8369-6407-1). Ayer Co Pubs.

Sharp, Dallas L. Sanctuary! Sanctuary! facs. ed. LC 73-128312. (Essay Index Reprint Ser). 1926. 12.00 (ISBN 0-8369-2134-8). Ayer Co Pubs.

Sheaffer, Billie C. A Manual for the Care of Wild Birds. (Illus.). 64p. 1980. 5.00 (ISBN 0-682-49617-0). Exposition Pr FL.

Silva, Tony & Kotlar, Barbara. Breeding Lovebirds. (Illus.). 96p. 1981. 4.95 (ISBN 0-87666-831-7, KW-125). TFH Pubns.

Simms, Eric. The Natural History of Birds. 1982. 49.00x (ISBN 0-460-04469-9, Pub. by Dent Australia). State Mutual Bk.

Skutch, Alexander F. Birds of Tropical America. LC 82-8597. (Corrie Herring Hooks Ser.: No. 5). (Illus.). 317p. 1983. 29.95 (ISBN 0-292-74634-2). U of Tex Pr.

Soderberg, P. M. All about Lovebirds. new ed. Orig. Title: Foreign Birds for Cage & Aviary; Lovebirds, Cardinals & Buntings. (Illus.). 1977. pap. 5.95 (ISBN 0-87666-957-7, PS-742). TFH Pubns.

Stanford, J. K. Awl-Birds. (Illus.). 1949. Devin.

Stewart. Welcome the Birds. 11.50 (ISBN 0-392-07518-0, LTB). Sportshelf.

Sturkie, P. D., ed. Avian Physiology. 3rd ed. LC 75-9954. (Springer Series in Life Sciences). (Illus.). 1976. text ed. 36.50 (ISBN 0-387-07305-1). Springer-Verlag.

Swanson, Leslie C. Pigeons, Racing Homer Facts & Secrets. 1958. pap. 2.50 (ISBN 0-911466-17-7). Swanson.

--Pigeons, Racing Homer Topics. 1955. pap. 2.50 (ISBN 0-911466-18-5). Swanson.

Teitler, Risa. Lovebirds, Taming & Training. (Illus.). 1979. 4.95 (ISBN 0-87666-988-7, KW-038). TFH Pubns.

Terres, John K. Songbirds in Your Garden. 3rd ed. Conrad, Jeff, ed. (Illus.). 228p. 1980. pap. 5.95 (ISBN 0-8015-6945-1, Hawthorn). Dutton.

Van Vleck, Sarita. Growing Wings: Perennial Cycle of Bird Life. LC 76-16585. 1977. pap. 4.95 (ISBN 0-87233-039-7). Bauhan.

Voitkevich, A. A. The Feathers & Plumage of Birds. Scripta-Technica, tr. from Rus. (Biology Monograph). 335p. 1966. text ed. 14.95x (ISBN 0-8464-1175-X). Beekman Pubs.

Voitkevick, A. A. Feather & Plumage of Birds. 1966. 10.50 (ISBN 0-8079-0050-8). October.

Vriends, Matthew M. The Complete Cockatiel. LC 83-4351. (Illus.). 176p. 1984. 13.95 (ISBN 0-87605-817-9). Howell Bk.

Walters, Michael. Birds of the World. (Illus.). 704p. 1980. 60.00 (ISBN 0-87666-894-5, H-1022). TFH Pubns.

--The Complete Birds of the World. LC 79-56434. 256p. 1980. 38.00 (ISBN 0-7153-7666-7). David & Charles.

Warren, Rachel L. Type-Specimens of Birds in the British Museum (Natural History) Vol. 1, Non-Passerines. ix, 320p. 1966. pap. 30.00x (ISBN 0-565-00651-7, Pub. by Brit Mus Nat Hist). Sabbot-Natural Hist Bks.

Warren, Rachel L. & Harrison, C. J. Type-Specimens of Birds in the British Museum (Natural History) Vol. 3, Systematic Index. xi, 76p. 1973. pap. 12.50x (ISBN 0-565-00716-5, Pub. by Brit Mus Nat Hist). Sabbot-Natural Hist Bks.

Warren, Rachel M. & Harrison, C. J. Type Specimens of Birds in the British Museum (Natural History) Vol. 2, Passerines. vi, 628p. 1971. pap. 56.00x (ISBN 0-565-00691-6, Pub. by Brit Mus Nat Hist). Sabbot-Natural Hist Bks.

Watson, Donald. The Hen Harrier. (Illus.). 1977. 27.50 (ISBN 0-85661-015-1, Pub by T & A D Poyser). Buteo.

Welker, Robert H. Birds & Men: American Birds in Science, Art, Literature & Conversation. 1984. 13.50 (ISBN 0-8446-6083-3). Peter Smith.

Welty, Carl. The Life of Birds. 3rd ed. 1982. text ed. 39.95 (ISBN 0-03-057917-1, CBS C). SCP.

Wilson, Barry W., intro. by. Birds: Readings from Scientific American. LC 79-26134. (Illus.). 276p. 1980. text ed. 21.95x (ISBN 0-7167-1206-7); pap. 11.95x (ISBN 0-7167-1207-5). W H Freeman.

Wilson, Tom. This Book Is for the Birds. 1980. pap. 1.95 (ISBN 0-451-13294-7, AE3294, Sig). NAL.

Wright, E. N., et al, eds. Bird Problems in Agriculture. 210p. 1981. 28.00x (ISBN 0-901436-48-8, Pub. by B C P C England). Intl Spec Bk.

BIRDS–ANATOMY

Baker-Cohen, K. F. Comparative Enzyme Histochemical Observations on Submammalian Brains. Incl. Pt. 1: Striatal Structures in Reptiles & Birds; Pt. 2: Basal Structures of the Brainstem in Reptiles & Birds. (Advances in Anatomy: Vol. 40, Pt. 6). (Illus.). 70p. 1968. pap. 18.90 (ISBN 0-387-04090-0). Springer-Verlag.

Bang, Betsy G. Functional Anatomy of the Olfactory System in 23 Orders of Birds. (Acta Anatomica: Suppl. 58, Vol. 79). 1971. pap. 9.50 (ISBN 3-8055-1193-0). S Karger.

Baumel, Julian, et al, eds. Nomina Anatomica Avium. LC 78-67890. 1980. 79.00 (ISBN 0-12-083150-3). Acad Pr.

George, J. C. & Berger, Andrew J. Avian Myology. 1966. 74.50 (ISBN 0-12-280150-4). Acad Pr.

Gilbert, B. Miles & Martin, Larry D. Avian Osteology. LC 81-90059. (Illus.). 252p. (Orig.). 1981. pap. 20.00 (ISBN 0-9611174-1-9). Bone Bks.

Hargrave, Lyndon L. Mexican Macaws: Comparative Osteology. LC 72-125168. (Anthropological Papers: No. 20). 67p. 1970. pap. 4.95x (ISBN 0-8165-0212-9). U of Ariz Pr.

Holmes, E. Bruce. Variation in the Muscles & Nerves of the Leg in Two Genera of Grouse: Tympanuchus & Pedioecetes. (Museum Ser.: Vol. 12, No. 9). 112p. 1963. 5.75 (ISBN 0-317-04590-3). U of KS Mus Nat Hist.

Jenkinson, Marion A. Thoracic & Coracoid Arteries in Two Families of Birds, Columbidae & Hirundinidae. (Museum Ser.: Vol. 12, No. 13). 21p. 1964. pap. 1.25 (ISBN 0-317-04601-2). U of KS Mus Nat Hist.

King, A. S. & McLelland, J., eds. Form & Function in Birds, Vol. 1. LC 79-50523. 1980. 74.00 (ISBN 0-12-407501-0). Acad Pr.

--Forms & Function in Birds, Vol. 2. 1981. 80.00 (ISBN 0-12-407502-9). Acad Pr.

Merz, Robert L. Jaw Musculature of the Mourning & White-Winged Doves. (Museum Ser.: Vol. 12, No. 12). 31p. 1963. pap. 1.75 (ISBN 0-317-04619-5). U of KS Mus Nat Hist.

Nickel, R., et al. Anatomy of the Domestic Birds. 1977. 58.00 (ISBN 0-387-91134-0). Springer-Verlag.

Philips, J. G., et al. Physiological Strategies Avian Biology. 192p. 1985. 39.95 (ISBN 0-412-00921-8, 9432); pap. 19.95 (ISBN 0-412-00931-5, 9433). Methuen Inc.

Phillips, J. G., et al. Physiological Strategies in Avian Biology. (Tertiary Level Biology Ser.). 192p. 1985. text ed. 39.95 (ISBN 0-412-00921-8, 9432, Pub. by Chapman & Hall); pap. text ed. 19.95 (ISBN 0-412-00931-5, 9433, Pub. by Chapman & Hall). Methuen Inc.

Richards, Lawrence P. & Bock, Walter J. Functional Anatomy & Adaptive Evolution of the Feeding Apparatus in the Hawaiian Honeycreeper Genus Loxops (Drepanididae. 173p. 1973. 9.00. Am Ornithologists.

Stallcup, William B. Myology & Serology of the Avian Family Fringillidae: A Taxonomic Study. (Museum Ser.: Vol. 8, No. 2). 55p. 1954. pap. 3.00 (ISBN 0-317-04635-7). U of KS Mus Nat Hist.

Wood, D. Scott, et al. World Inventory Of Avian Skeletal Specimens, 1982. 224p. 1982. bound 25.00 (ISBN 0-943610-36-2). AM Ornithologists.

--World Inventory of Avian Spirit Specimens, 1982. 181p. 1982. bound 25.00 (ISBN 0-943610-37-0). AM Ornithologists.

Wood, Scott & Jenkinson, Marion A. World Inventory of Avian Anatomical Specimens, 1982: Geographic Analysis. 290p. 1984. bound 25.00 (ISBN 0-943610-42-7). Am Ornithologists.

Zusi, Richard L. A Functional & Evolutionary Analysis of Rhynchokinesis in Birds. LC 83-20230. (Smithsonisn Contribution to Zoology: No. 395). pap. 20.00 (ISBN 0-317-26040-5). Bks Demand UMI.

--Structural Adaptations of the Head & Neck in the Black Skimmer Rynchops Nigra Linnaeus. (Publications: No.3). (Illus.). 101p. 1962. 5.00 (ISBN 0-686-35789-2). Nuttall Ornith.

BIRDS–BEHAVIOR

see also Bird Populations; Birds–Eggs and Nests; Birds–Migration

Alison, Robert M. Breeding Biology & Behavior of the Oldsquaw (Clangula Hyemalis L.) 52p. 1975. 3.50 (ISBN 0-943610-18-4). Am Ornithologists.

Anderson, Anders H. & Anderson, Anne. The Cactus Wren. LC 72-77133. 226p. 1973. pap. 8.95 (ISBN 0-8165-0314-1). U of Ariz Pr.

Angell, Tony. Ravens, Crows, Magpies, & Jays. LC 77-15185. (Illus.). 112p. 1978. 25.00 (ISBN 0-295-95589-9). U of Wash Pr.

Armstrong, Edward. Discovering Bird Courtship. (Discovering Ser.: No. 236). (Illus., Orig.). 1978. pap. 3.50 (ISBN 0-85263-415-3, Pub. by Shire Pubns England). Seven Hills Bks.

Barnard, C. J. & Thompson, D. B. Gulls & Plovers: The Ecology of Mixed-Species Feeding Groups. 320p. 1985. 30.00x (ISBN 0-231-06262-1). COlumbia U Pr.

Bent, Arthur C. Life Histories of North American Birds of Prey, 2 Vols. (Illus.). 1958. Vol. 1. pap. 8.50 (ISBN 0-486-20931-8); Vol. 2. pap. 8.50 (ISBN 0-486-20932-6). Dover.

Borror, Donald J. Bird Song & Bird Behavior. 1971. pap. 5.95 booklet with record (ISBN 0-486-22779-0). Dover.

Buffon, Georges L. The History of Singing Birds Containing an Exact Description of Their Habits & Customs... Sterling, Keir B., ed. LC 77-81118. (Biologists & Their World Ser.). (Illus.). 1978. Repr. of 1791 ed. lib. bdg. 22.00x (ISBN 0-405-10709-9). Ayer Co Pubs.

Burger, Joanna. Pattern, Mechanism, & Adaptive Significance of Territoriality in Herring Gulls (Larus argentatus) 92p. 1984. 9.00 (ISBN 0-943610-41-9). Am Ornithologists.

Burger, Joanna & Olla, Bori L., eds. Shorebirds: Breeding Behavior & Populations. (Behavior of Marine Animals Ser.: Vol. 5). 421p. 1984. 59.50x (ISBN 0-306-41590-9, Plenum Pr). Plenum Pub.

Cody, Martin L. Competition & the Structure of Bird Communities. (Monographs in Population Biology: No. 7). (Illus.). 352p. 1974. 32.00x (ISBN 0-691-08134-4); pap. 13.50x (ISBN 0-691-08135-2). Princeton U Pr.

Cody, Martin L., ed. Habitat Selection in Birds. (Physiology Ecology Ser.). 1985. 69.50 (ISBN 0-12-178080-5). Acad Pr.

Dennis, John V. Beyond the Bird Feeder: The Habits & Behavior of Feeding Station Birds When They Are Not at Your Feeder. LC 81-47491. (Illus.). 224p. 1981. 14.95 (ISBN 0-394-50890-4). Knopf.

Dorst, Jean. The Life of Birds, 2 vols. (Illus.). 717p. 1974. 85.00x (ISBN 0-231-03909-3). Columbia U Pr.

Foelsch, D. & Vestergaard, K. Das Verhalten von Huehnern. (Animal Management Ser.: 12). 176p. 1981. 17.95x (ISBN 0-8176-1240-8). Birkhauser.

Goodman, Irving & Schein, Martin, eds. Birds: Brain & Behavior. 1974. 49.50 (ISBN 0-12-290350-1). Acad Pr.

Hamilton, Robert B. Comparative Behavior of the American Avocet & the Black-Necked Stilt (Recurvirostridae) 98p. 1975. 7.50 (ISBN 0-943610-17-6). Am Ornithologists.

Harrison, Hal H. Wood Warblers' World. (Illus.). 288p. 1984. 19.95 (ISBN 0-671-47798-6). S&S.

Howard, Eliot. Territory in Bird Life. LC 64-20247. 1964. pap. 1.75 (ISBN 0-689-70100-4, 62). Atheneum.

Howard, Henry E. Territory in Bird Life. Sterling, Keir B., ed. LC 77-84443. (Biologists & Their World Ser.). (Illus.). 1978. Repr. of 1920 ed. lib. bdg. 25.50x (ISBN 0-405-10696-3). Ayer Co Pubs.

Huxley, Julian. Courtship Habits of the Great Crested Grebe. LC 68-55824. (Cape Editions Ser). 1968. 6.95 (ISBN 0-670-24426-0, Grossman). Viking.

Johnston, Richard F. Replication of Habitat Profiles for Birds. (Occasional Papers: No. 82). 11p. 1979. pap. 1.25 (ISBN 0-317-04610-1). U of KS Mus Nat Hist.

Keast, Allen & Morton, Eugene S., eds. Migrant Birds in the Neotropics: Ecology, Behavior, Distribution & Conservation. LC 80-607031. (Symposia of the National Zoological Park: No. 5). 576p. (Orig.). 1980. pap. text ed. 22.50x (ISBN 0-87474-661-2). Smithsonian.

King, A. S. & McLelland, J., eds. Form & Function in Birds, Vol. 3. Date not set. 99.50 (ISBN 0-12-407503-7). Acad Pr.

Kress, Stephen W. Audubon Society Handbook for Birders. (Illus.). 320p. 1981. 17.95 (ISBN 0-684-16838-3, ScribT). Scribner.

Kroodsma, Donald, et al, eds. Acoustic Communication in Birds: Vol. 1: Sounds Production, Perception & Design Features of Sounds. (Communication & Behavior Ser.). 318p. 1983. 39.00 (ISBN 0-12-426801-3). Acad Pr.

--Acoustic Communication in Birds: Vol. 2: Song Learning & Its Consequences. (Communication & Behavior Ser.). 318p. 1983. 42.00 (ISBN 0-12-426802-1). Acad Pr.

Lorenz, Konrad Z. King Solomon's Ring. LC 52-7373. (Illus.). 1979. pap. 5.95xi (ISBN 0-06-131976-7, TB 1976, Torch). Har-Row.

Lyman, Charles, et al. Hibernation & Torpor in Mammals & Birds. (Physiological Ecology Ser.). 317p. 1982. 43.50 (ISBN 0-12-460420-X). Acad Pr.

MacRoberts, Michael H. & MacRoberts, Barbara R. Social Organization & Behavior of the Acorn Woodpecker in Central Coastal California. 115p. 1976. 7.50 (ISBN 0-943610-21-4). Am Ornithologists.

Moynihan, Martin. Geographic Variation in Social Behavior & in Adaptations to Competition Among Andean Birds. (Illus.). 162p. 1979. 17.50 (ISBN 0-686-35808-2, 18). Nuttall Ornith.

Murton, R. K. & Westwood, N. J. Avian Breeding Cycles. (Illus.). 1978. 84.00x (ISBN 0-19-857357-X). Oxford U Pr.

Nolan, Val, Jr. Ecology & Behavior of the Prairie Warbler Dendroica discolor. 595p. 1978. 29.50 (ISBN 0-943610-26-5). Am Ornithologists.

Patterson, I. J. The Shelduck: A Study in Behavioural Ecology. LC 81-21231. 250p. 1982. 54.50 (ISBN 0-521-24646-6). Cambridge U Pr.

Power, Harry W. Foraging Behavior of Mountain Bluebirds with Emphasis on Sexual Foraging Differences. 72p. 1980. 8.50 (ISBN 0-943610-28-1). Am Ornithologists.

Queeny, Edgar M. Prairie Wings. (Illus.). 256p. 1979. Repr. of 1946 ed. 50.00 (ISBN 0-916838-21-8). Schiffer.

Rysavy, B. & Ryzhikov, K. M., eds. Helminths of Fish Eating Birds of the Palaeartic Region: Volume 1, Nematoda. (Illus.). 1978. lib. bdg. 50.00 (ISBN 90-6193-551-2, Pub. by Junk Pubs Nethherlands). Kluwer Academic.

Schreiber, Ralph W. Maintenance Behavior & Communication in the Brown Pelican. 78p. 1977. 6.50 (ISBN 0-943610-22-2). Am Ornithologists.

Skutch, Alexander F. Parent Birds & Their Young. LC 75-2195. (Corrie Herring Hooks Ser.: No. 2). (Illus.). 521p. 1976. 45.00 (ISBN 0-292-76424-3). U of Tex Pr.

Smith, Susan T. Communication & Other Social Behavior in Parus Carolinensis. (Illus.). 125p. 1972. 7.75 (ISBN 0-686-35799-X, 11). Nuttall Ornith.

Smith, W. J. Communication & Relationships in the Genus Tyrannus. (Illus.). 250p. 1966. 8.00 (ISBN 0-686-35792-2, 6). Nuttall Ornith.

Sowls, Lyle K. Prairie Ducks: A Study of Their Behavior, Ecology & Management. LC 77-14153. (Illus.). xiv, 194p. 1978. pap. 3.50 (ISBN 0-8032-5895-X, BB 665, Bison). U of Nebr Pr.

Stiles, F. Gary & Wolf, Larry L. Ecology & Evolution of Lek Mating Behavior in the Long-tailed Hermit Hummingbird. 78p. 1979. 8.50 (ISBN 0-943610-27-3). Am Ornithologists.

Stokes, Donald W. A Guide to the Behavior of Common Birds. LC 79-17864. (Illus.). 1979. 14.45i (ISBN 0-316-81722-8). Little.

Tanabe, Y., et al, eds. Biological Rhythms in Birds: Neural & Endocrine Aspects. 373p. 1980. 55.00 (ISBN 0-387-10311-2). Springer-Verlag.

Van Tets, Gerard F. Comparative Study of Some Social Communication Patterns in the Pelecaniformes. American Ornithologists' Union, ed. 88p. 1965. 3.50 (ISBN 0-943610-02-8). Am Ornithologists.

Walter, Hartmut. Eleonora's Falcon: Adaptations to Prey & Habitat in a Social Raptor. LC 78-14933. (Wildlife Behavior & Ecology). (Illus.). 1979. 25.00x (ISBN 0-226-87229-7). U of Chicago Pr.

Willis, Edwin O. Behavior of Spotted Antbirds. 162p. 1972. 9.00 (ISBN 0-943610-10-9). Am Ornithologists.

Wolf, Larry L. Species Relationships in the Avian Genus Aimophila. 220p. 1977. 12.00 (ISBN 0-943610-23-0). Am Ornithologists.

BIRDS–BIBLIOGRAPHY

Zimmer, John T. Catalogue of the Edward E. Ayer Ornithological Library. LC 73-17850. (Natural Sciences in America Ser.). 726p. 1974. Repr. 43.00x (ISBN 0-405-05773-3). Ayer Co Pubs.

BIRDS–BREEDING

Burger, Joanna & Olla, Bori L., eds. Shorebirds: Breeding Behavior & Populations. (Behavior of Marine Animals Ser.: Vol. 5). 421p. 1984. 59.50x (ISBN 0-306-41590-9, Plenum Pr). Plenum Pub.

Klaas, Erwin E. Cowbird Parasitism & Nesting Success in the Eastern Phoebe. (Occasional Papers: Vol. 41). 18p. 1975. pap. 1.25 (ISBN 0-317-04614-4). U of KS Mus Nat Hist.

Martin, Richard M. The Encyclopedia of Aviculture: Keeping & Breeding Birds. LC 82-20716. (Illus.). 240p. 1983. 14.95 (ISBN 0-668-05782-3, 5782). Arco.

BIRDS–CARE AND HYGIENE

Axelson, R. Dean. Caring for Your Pet Bird. (Illus.). 168p. 1985. 12.95 (ISBN 0-7137-1438-7, Pub. by Blandford Pr England); pap. 6.95 (ISBN 0-7137-1538-3). Sterling.

Martin, Richard M. The Encyclopedia of Aviculture: Keeping & Breeding Birds. LC 82-20716. (Illus.). 240p. 1983. 14.95 (ISBN 0-668-05782-3, 5782). Arco.

Palmer, Joan. Cage Birds. (Blandford Pet Handbook Ser.). (Illus.). 96p. (Orig.). 1983. pap. 6.95 (ISBN 0-7137-1203-1, Pub. by Blandford Pr England). Sterling.

Schutz, Walter E. How to Attract, House & Feed the Birds. 1983. 14.75 (ISBN 0-8446-5965-7). Peter Smith.

Trollope, Jeffrey. The Care & Breeding of Seed-Eating Birds: Finches & Allied Species-Doves, Quail & Hempipodes. (Illus.). 352p. 1983. 17.95 (ISBN 0-7137-1160-4, Pub. by Blandford Pr England). Sterling.

Vriends, T. Cage Birds in Color: Choosing-Caring-Feeding. (Illus.). 144p. 1985. 14.95 (ISBN 0-668-06038-7); pap. 9.95 (ISBN 0-668-06042-5). Arco.

BIRDS–CLASSIFICATION

Burton, Philip. Birds of North America. LC 79-730. (Spotter's Guide Ser.). (Illus.). 1979. 3.95 (ISBN 0-8317-0875-1); pap. 1.95 (ISBN 0-8317-0876-X). Smith Pubs.

Campbell, Bruce & Lack, Elizabeth, eds. A Dictionary of Birds. LC 84-72101. (Illus.). 700p. 1985. 75.00 (ISBN 0-931130-12-3). Buteo.

Clements, James. Birds of the World: A Checklist. 600p. 1981. 24.95 (ISBN 0-87196-556-9). Facts on File.

Feduccia, Alan. The Age of Birds. LC 80-11926. (Illus.). 208p. 1980. 20.00 (ISBN 0-674-00975-4). Harvard U Pr.

Van Tyne, Josselyn & Berger, Andrew J. Fundamentals of Ornithology. 2nd. ed. LC 75-20430. 808p. 1976. 53.50x (ISBN 0-471-89965-8, Pub. by Wiley-Interscience). Wiley.

BIRDS–COLLECTION AND PRESERVATION

see also Zoological Specimens–Collection and Preservation

Christie, Irene. Birds: A Guide to a Mixed Collection. Denham, Ken, ed. (Illus.). 144p. 1985. 13.95 (ISBN 0-948075-00-7). Howell Bk.

Coues, Elliott. Key to North American Birds: Containing a Concise Account of Every Species of Living & Fossil Bird at Present Known from the Continent North of the Mexican and the United States Boundary, Inclusive of Greenland and Lower California, 2 vols. 5th ed. LC 73-17816. (Natural Sciences in America Ser.). (Illus.). 1189p. 1974. Repr. Set. 77.00x (ISBN 0-405-05732-6); 38.50x ea. Vol. 1 (ISBN 0-405-05774-1). Vol. 2 (ISBN 0-405-05775-X). Ayer Co Pubs.

Decoteau, A. E. Exhibiting Birds. (Illus.). 192p. 1983. 19.95 (ISBN 0-87666-830-9, H-1036). TFH Pubns.

Harrison, C. J. & Cowles, G. S. Birds: Instructions for Collectors, No. 2a. (Illus.). 48p. (Orig.). 1970. pap. 2.75x (ISBN 0-565-00561-8, Pub. by Brit Mus Nat Hist England). Sabbot-Natural Hist Bks.

Harrison, James M. Bird Taxidermy. LC 76-50731. (Illus.). 1977. 12.50 (ISBN 0-7153-7372-2). David & Charles.

Keast, Allen & Morton, Eugene S., eds. Migrant Birds in the Neotropics: Ecology, Behavior, Distribution & Conservation. LC 80-607031. (Symposia of the National Zoological Park: No. 5). 576p. (Orig.). 1980. pap. text ed. 22.50x (ISBN 0-87474-661-2). Smithsonian.

Keith & Gooders. Collins Bird Guide. pap. 17.95 (ISBN 0-00-219119-9, Collins Pub England). Greene.

Martin & Ellis. Cage & Aviary Birds. pap. 16.95 (ISBN 0-00-219238-1, Collins Pub England). Greene.

Nicolai, Jurgen. Bird Keeping. Bleher, Petra, tr. from Ger. (Illus.). 96p. 1980. 4.95 (ISBN 0-87666-997-6, KW-034). TFH Pubns.

Rotroff, Susan I. & Lamberton, Robert D. Birds of the Athenian Agora. (Excavations of the Athenian Agora Picture Bk.: No. 22). (Illus.). 32p. 1985. pap. 1.50 (ISBN 0-87661-627-9). Am Sch Athens.

Sauer, Gordon C. John Gould, the Bird Man: A Chronology & Bibliography. (Illus.). 416p. 1982. 65.00 (ISBN 0-7006-0230-5). U Pr of KS.

BIRDS–COLLISIONS WITH AIRPLANES

see Aeronautics–Accidents

BIRDS–CONTROL

see Bird Control

BIRDS–DISEASES

see also specific diseases of birds, e.g. Ornithosis

Arnall, L. & Keymer, I. F. Bird Diseases: 'An Introduction to the Study of Birds in Health & Disease' (Illus.). 1975. 34.95 (ISBN 0-87666-950-X, H-964). TFH Pubns.

Burr, Elisha W. Diseases of Parrots. (Illus.). 318p. 1982. 24.95 (ISBN 0-87666-843-0, H-1037). TFH Pubns.

Engholm, Eva. Bird Infirmary. LC 72-6617. (Illus.). 1973. 6.95 (ISBN 0-8008-0742-1). Taplinger.

Goodman, Leon. Aviculturalist's Handbook: Management & Treatment of Diseases, Disorders & Ailments. 200p. 1983. 13.50 (ISBN 0-86230-051-7). Triplegate.

Pavlovsky, Evgeny N. Natural Nidality of Transmissible Diseases: With Special Reference to the Landscape Epidemiology of Zooanthroponoses. Levine, Norman D., ed. LC 66-11023. pap. 68.80 (ISBN 0-317-28739-7, 2020244). Bks Demand UMI.

Raethel, Heinz-Sigurd. Bird Diseases. Ahrens, Christa, tr. from Ger. (Illus.). 96p. 1981. 4.95 (ISBN 0-87666-897-X, KW-122). TFH Pubns.

Steiner, Charles V., Jr. & Davis, Richard B. Caged Bird Medicine: Selected Topics. (Illus.). 176p. 1981. 20.50x (ISBN 0-8138-1715-3). Iowa St U Pr.

BIRDS–ECONOMIC ASPECTS

see Birds, Injurious and Beneficial

BIRDS–EGGS AND NESTS

see also Bird-Houses

Bendire, Charles E. Life Histories of North American Birds: Their Breeding Habits & Eggs, 2 vols. in one. LC 73-17802. (Natural Sciences in America Ser.). (Illus.). 1042p. 1974. Repr. 68.50x (ISBN 0-405-05720-2). Ayer Co Pubs.

Bonhote, J. Lewis. Birds of Britain & Their Eggs. Repr. of 1907 ed. 35.00 (ISBN 0-686-20650-9). Lib Serv Inc.

Brodie, H. J. The Bird's Nest Fungi. LC 75-18476. 1975. 25.00x (ISBN 0-8020-5307-6). U of Toronto Pr.

Grant, Gilbert S. Avian Incubation: Egg Temperature, Nest Humidity, & Behavioral Thermoregulation in a Hot Environment. 75p. 1982. 9.00 (ISBN 0-943610-30-3). Am Ornithologists.

Harrison. A Field Guide to Nests, Eggs, Nestlings of British & European Birds. 29.95 (ISBN 0-00-219249-7, Collins Pub England). Greene.

Harrison, Colin. A Field Guide to the Nests, Eggs & Nestlings of North American Birds. (Illus.). 416p. 1984. pap. 19.95 (ISBN 0-8289-0532-0, Collins Pub England). Greene.

Harrison, Hal. A Field Guide to Western Birds' Nests. (Peterson Field Guide Ser.). (Illus.). 1979. 11.95 (ISBN 0-395-27629-2). HM.

Harrison, Hal H. A Field Guide to Birds Nests Found East of the Mississippi River. LC 74-23804. (Peterson Field Guide Ser.). 304p. 1975. 15.95 (ISBN 0-395-20434-8). HM.

Johnsgard, Paul A. Birds of the Great Plains: Breeding Species & Their Distribution. LC 79-1419. (Illus.). xlviii, 539p. 1979. 27.50x (ISBN 0-8032-2550-4). U of Nebr Pr.

Kepler, Cameron B. Breeding Biology of the Blue-Faced Booby Sula Dactylatra Personata on Green Island, Kure Atoll. (Illus.). 97p. 1969. 6.50 (ISBN 0-686-35795-7). Nuttall Ornith.

Layton, R. B., illus. Thirty Birds That Will Build in Bird Houses. LC 77-81805. 1977. pap. 7.95x (ISBN 0-912542-05-5). Nature Bks Pubs.

Pavlovsky, Evgeny N. Natural Nidality of Transmissible Diseases: With Special Reference to the Landscape Epidemiology of Zooanthroponoses. Levine, Norman D., ed. LC 66-11023. pap. 68.80 (ISBN 0-317-28739-7, 2020244). Bks Demand UMI.

Steyn, Peter. Eagle Days: A Study of African Eagles at the Nest. 2nd ed. (Illus.). 163p. 1985. 24.95 (ISBN 0-88072-065-4, Pub. by Tanager). Longwood Pub Group.

Zi, Ju. Birds' Homes. (Illus.). 36p. (Orig.). 1982. 4.50 (ISBN 0-8351-1129-6); pap. 3.50 (ISBN 0-8351-1123-7). China Bks.

BIRDS–EMBRYOLOGY

see Embryology–Birds

BIRDS–FLIGHT

Da Vinci, Leonardo. Codex on the Flight of Birds. 295.00 (ISBN 0-384-32299-9). Johnson Repr.

Greenewalt, Crawford H. The Flight of Birds. LC 75-7170. (Transaction Ser: Vol. 65, Pt. 4). (Illus.). 1975. pap. 7.00 (ISBN 0-87169-654-1). Am Philos.

Porter, R. F., et al. Flight Identification of European Raptors. 3rd ed. (Illus.). 1976. 30.00 (ISBN 0-85661-012-7, Pub by T & A D Poyser). Buteo.

Queeny, Edgar M. Prairie Wings. (Illus.). 256p. 1979. Repr. of 1946 ed. 50.00 (ISBN 0-916838-21-8). Schiffer.

BIRDS–FOOD

Black, Robert. Nutrition of Finches & Other Cagebirds. 362p. 1981. 19.95 (ISBN 0-910631-01-8). Avian Pubns.

Cosgrove, Irene & Cosgrove, Ed. My Recipes Are for the Birds. LC 76-23757. 62p. 1976. pap. 4.95 (ISBN 0-385-12634-4). Doubleday.

Dennis, John V. A Complete Guide to Bird Feeding. 1975. 16.95 (ISBN 0-394-47937-8). Knopf.

Mahnken, Jan. Feeding the Birds. Griffith, Roger, ed. (Illus.). 160p. (Orig.). 1983. pap. 7.95 (ISBN 0-88266-361-5). Garden Way Pub.

Warren, B. H. Report of Birds of Pennsylvania with Special Reference to the Food Habits, Based on over 4,000 Stomach Examinations. 434p. 1984. Repr. of 1890 ed. lib. bdg. 150.00 (ISBN 0-89760-957-3). Telegraph Bks.

BIRDS–GEOGRAPHICAL DISTRIBUTION

see also Bird Populations

Chapman, Frank M. Essays in South American Ornithogeography: Original Anthology. Sterling, Keir B., ed. LC 77-81087. (Biologists & Their World Ser.). (Illus.). 1978. lib. bdg. 59.50x (ISBN 0-405-10663-7). Ayer Co Pubs.

Hicks, Lawrence E. Distribution of Breeding Birds of Ohio. 1935. 2.00 (ISBN 0-86727-031-4). Ohio Bio Survey.

Moreau, R. E. Bird Faunas of Africa & Its Islands. 1967. 67.50 (ISBN 0-12-506650-3). Acad Pr.

Robinson, Peter. Bird Detective. (Illus.). 224p. 1982. 19.95 (ISBN 0-241-10709-1, Pub. by Hamish Hamilton England). David & Charles.

BIRDS–MIGRATION

see also Orientation

Burger, Joanna & Olla, Bori L., eds. Shorebirds: Migration & Foraging Behavior. (Behavior of Marine Animals Ser.: Vol. 6). 323p. 1984. 49.50x (ISBN 0-306-41591-7, Plenum Pr). Plenum Pub.

Curry-Lindahl, Kai. Bird Migration in Africa, Vol. I. LC 80-40245. 1982. 99.50 (ISBN 0-12-200101-X). Acad Pr.

Elman, Robert. The Atlantic Flyway. LC 80-17133. (Illus.). 280p. 1980. 29.95 (ISBN 0-8329-3290-6, Pub. by Winchester Pr). New Century.

Griffin, Donald R. Bird Migration. LC 74-76321. (Illus.). 192p. 1974. pap. 4.95 (ISBN 0-486-20529-0). Dover.

Hochbaum, H. Albert. Travels & Traditions of Waterfowl. (Illus.). 1967. pap. 2.95 (ISBN 0-8166-0448-7, MP8). U of Minn Pr.

Klaas, Erwin E. Summer Birds from the Yucatan Peninsula, Mexico. (Museum Ser.: Vol. 17, No. 14). 33p. 1968. pap. 1.75 (ISBN 0-317-04613-6). U of KS Mus Nat Hist.

Lowrey, George H., Jr. A Quantitative Study of the Nocturnal Migration of Birds. (Museum Ser.: Vol. 3, No. 2). 112p. 1951. pap. 5.75 (ISBN 0-317-04617-9). U of KS Mus Nat Hist.

Matthews, G. V. Bird Navigation. 3rd ed. LC 68-23181. (Cambridge Monographs in Experimental Biology). (Illus.). 1968. pap. 12.95x (ISBN 0-521-09541-7). Cambridge U Pr.

Mead, Christopher. Bird Migration. LC 82-15385. (Illus.). 224p. 1983. 19.95 (ISBN 0-87196-694-8). Facts on File.

Moreau, R. E. The Palaeartic-African Bird Migration System. Monk, J. F., ed. 1972. 68.50 (ISBN 0-12-506660-0). Acad Pr.

Schmidt-Koenig, K. Avian Orientation & Navigation. 1979. 39.50 (ISBN 0-12-626550-X). Acad Pr.

Tordoff, Harrison B. & Mengel, Robert M. Studies of Birds Killed in Nocturnal Migration. (Museum Ser.: Vol. 10, No. 1). 44p. 1956. pap. 2.50 (ISBN 0-317-04637-3). U of KS Mus Nat Hist.

BIRDS–NAVIGATION

see Bird Navigation

BIRDS–NESTS

see Birds–Eggs and Nests

BIRDS–NOMENCLATURE

Choate, Ernest A. The Dictionary of American Bird Names. Rev. ed. 240p. 1985. 17.95 (ISBN 0-87645-121-0, Pub. by Gambit); pap. 9.95 (ISBN 0-87645-117-2). Harvard Common Pr.

Cross, Diana H. Some Birds Have Funny Names. LC 80-28168. (Illus.). 1981. lib. bdg. 7.95 (ISBN 0-517-54005-3). Crown.

Gotch, A. F. Birds: Their Latin Names Explained. (Illus.). 288p. 1981. 22.50 (ISBN 0-7137-1175-2, Pub. by Blandford Pr England). Sterling.

Greppin, John A. Classical & Middle Armenian Bird Names. LC 77-25361. 1978. 35.00x (ISBN 0-88206-017-1). Caravan Bks.

Swainson, Charles. The Folk-Lore & Provincial Names of British Birds. (Folk-Lore Society, London, Monographs: Vol. 17). pap. 24.00 (ISBN 0-317-15647-0). Kraus Repr.

Swann, Harry K. Dictionary of English & Folk-Names of British Birds. LC 68-30664. 1968. Repr. of 1913 ed. 35.00x (ISBN 0-8103-3340-6). Gale.

BIRDS–PARASITES

see Parasites–Birds

BIRDS–PICTORIAL WORKS

Anglesea, Martyn, notes by. Birds of Ireland. (Illus.). 120p. with slip case 460.00 (ISBN 0-85640-297-4, Pub. by Blackstaff Pr); limited ed. 750.00 (ISBN 0-317-02588-0). Longwood Pub Group.

Anker, Jean. Bird Books & Bird Art: An Outline of the Literary History & Iconography of Descriptive Ornithology, Based Principally on the Collection in the University Library at Copenhagen. LC 73-17795. (Natural Sciences in America Ser.). (Illus.). 326p. 1974. Repr. 23.50x (ISBN 0-405-05705-9). Ayer Co Pubs.

Audubon, John J. Birds of America, 7 vols. (Illus.). Repr. of 1840 ed. Set. 73.50 (ISBN 0-8446-1567-6); 10.50ea. Peter Smith.

Bannon, Lois & Clark, Taylor. Handbook of Audubon Prints. LC 79-1319. (Illus.). 122p. 1980. 12.50 (ISBN 0-88289-202-9). Pelican.

Bates, Henry & Busenbark, R. Finches & Softbilled Birds. 19.95 (ISBN 0-87666-421-4, H-908). TFH Pubns.

Heinzel & Fitter. The Birds of Britain & Europe with North Africa & the Middle East. pap. 11.95 (ISBN 0-00-219210-1, Collins Pub England). Greene.

Ogilvie, M. A. Wildfowl of Britain & Europe. 1982. 16.50x (ISBN 0-19-217723-0). Oxford U Pr.

Peterson & Mountfort. A Field Guide to the Birds of Britain & Europe. 22.95 (ISBN 0-00-219177-6, Collins Pub England). Greene.

Pforr, Manfred & Limbrunner, Alfred. Breeding Birds of Europe, Vols. 1 & 2. Robertson, Iain, ed. Stoneman, Richard, tr. from Ger. (Illus.). 728p. 1983. Set. 48.00 (ISBN 0-88072-024-7, Pub. by Tanager). Longwood Pub Group.

--Breeding Birds of Europe: Vol. 1-Divers to Auks. Robertson, Iain, ed. Stoneman, Richard, tr. from Ger. (Illus.). 334p. 1983. 24.00 (ISBN 0-88072-026-3, Pub. by Tanager). Longwood Pub Group.

--Breeding Birds of Europe: Vol. 2-Sandgrouse to Crows. Robertson, Iain, ed. Stoneman, Richard, tr. from Ger. (Illus.). 394p. 1983. 24.00 (ISBN 0-88072-027-1, Pub. by Tanager). Longwood Pub Group.

Porter, R. F., et al. Flight Identification of European Raptors. 3rd ed. (Illus.). 1976. 30.00 (ISBN 0-85661-012-7, Pub by T & A D Poyser). Buteo.

Wallace, Ian. Birds of Prey of Britain & Europe. (Illus.). 1983. 15.95x (ISBN 0-19-217729-X). Oxford U Pr.

Woodcock & Heinzel. The Birds of Britain & Europe. pap. 8.95 (ISBN 0-00-219445-7, Collins Pub England). Greene.

BIRDS–GREAT BRITAIN

Avon, Dennis & Tilford, Tony. Birds of Britain & Europe. (Illus.). 1975. 11.95 (ISBN 0-7137-0762-3, Pub by Blandford Pr England). Sterling.

Bannerman, D. A. History of the Birds of the Balearic Islands. 384p. 1982. 100.00x (ISBN 0-686-78891-5, Pub. by Wheldon & Wesley England). State Mutual Bk.

Barnes, John G. Titmice of the British Isles. LC 74-33156. (Illus.). 224p. 1975. 15.95 (ISBN 0-7153-6955-5). David & Charles.

Beames, Thomas. Rookeries of London. (Illus.). 312p. 1970. Repr. of 1850 ed. 25.00x (ISBN 0-7146-2415-2, F Cass Co). Biblio Dist.

Bonhote, J. Lewis. Birds of Britain & Their Eggs. Repr. of 1907 ed. 35.00 (ISBN 0-686-20650-9). Lib Serv Inc.

Fair, John. Dorset Birds. 1982. 37.00x (ISBN 0-905868-12-9, Pub. by Gavin Pr). State Mutual Bk.

Fitter & Richardson. Collins Pocket Guide to British Birds. 26.95 (ISBN 0-00-219174-1, Collins Pub England). Greene.

Fuller, R. J. Bird Habitats in Britain. (Illus.). 320p. 1982. 35.00 (ISBN 0-85661-031-3, Pub. by T & A D Poyser England). Buteo.

Gillham, E. H. & Hope, M. A. Birds of the North Kent Marshes. 1981. 26.00x (ISBN 0-905540-43-3, Pub. by Hollewell Pubns). State Mutual Bk.

Gooders, John. Collins British Birds. (Illus.). 384p. 1983. 39.95 (ISBN 0-00-219121-0, Collins Pub England). Greene.

Grimes, Brian. British Wild Birds. 1982. 45.00x (ISBN 0-340-27970-2, Pub. by Hodder & Stoughton England). State Mutual Bk.

Harrison. A Field Guide to Nests, Eggs, Nestlings of British & European Birds. 29.95 (ISBN 0-00-219249-7, Collins Pub England). Greene.

Heinzel & Fitter. The Birds of Britain & Europe with North Africa & the Middle East. pap. 11.95 (ISBN 0-00-219210-1, Collins Pub England). Greene.

Hudson, William H. Birds in London. Repr. of 1923 ed. 35.00 (ISBN 0-404-03397-0). AMS Pr.

--British Birds. Repr. of 1923 ed. 35.00 (ISBN 0-404-03396-2). AMS Pr.

Lander, Peter V., ed. British Birds in Aviculture. 236p. 1981. 15.75x (ISBN 0-86230-035-5). Saiga.

Martin, Brian P. Sporting Birds of the British Isles. (Illus.). 256p. 1984. 32.00 (ISBN 0-7153-8447-3). David & Charles.

Mitchell, W. R. Birdwatch Around Scotland. (Illus.). 175p. 1984. 15.95 (ISBN 0-88072-062-X, Pub. by Tanager). Longwood Pub Group.

Morris, F. O. British Birds. 240p. 50.00x (ISBN 0-906671-37-X, Pub. by Webb & Bower). State Mutual Bk.

--British Birds. (Illus.). 240p. 1981. 40.00 (ISBN 0-03-059838-9). Webb & Bower.

Nethersole-Thompson, Desmond & Nethersole-Thompson, Maimie. Greenshanks. LC 78-67031. (Illus.). 1979. 27.50 (ISBN 0-931130-02-6). Buteo.

Ogilvie, Malcolm. The Birdwatcher's Guide to the Wetlands of Britain. 1979. 18.75 (ISBN 0-7134-0847-2, Pub. by Batsford England). David & Charles.

Peterson & Mountfort. A Field Guide to the Birds of Britain & Europe. 22.95 (ISBN 0-00-219177-6, Collins Pub England). Greene.

Prater, A. J. Estuary Birds of Britain & Ireland. (Illus.). 1981. 37.50 (ISBN 0-85661-029-1, Pub. by T & A D Poyser England). Buteo.

Prendergast, E. D. & Boys, J. V. The Birds of Dorset. (Illus.). 304p. 1983. 32.00 (ISBN 0-7153-8380-9). David & Charles.

Prestt, Ian. British Birds: Lifestyles & Habitats. (Illus.). 136p. 1982. 18.95 (ISBN 0-7134-1864-8, Pub. by Batsford England). David & Charles.

Richards, Alan J. British Birds: A Field Guide. LC 79-52375. (Illus.). 1979. 14.95 (ISBN 0-7153-7834-1). David & Charles.

Sharrock, J. T., ed. Birds New to Britain & Ireland. (Illus.). 1983. 25.00 (ISBN 0-85661-033-X, Pub. by T & A D Poyser England). Buteo.

Sharrock, J. T. R., compiled by. The Atlas of Breeding Birds in Britain & Ireland. (Illus.). 1977. 45.00 (ISBN 0-85661-018-6, Pub by T & A D Poyser). Buteo.

Simms, Eric. A Natural History of British Birds. (Illus.). 382p. 1983. 24.95x (ISBN 0-460-04469-9, Pub. by J M Dent England). Biblio Dist.

Soper, Tony. Everyday Birds. LC 76-20134. 1976. 10.50 (ISBN 0-7153-7277-7). David & Charles.

Swaine, Christopher. Birds of Gloucestershire. 256p. 1982. text ed. 17.25x (ISBN 0-86299-012-2, Pub. by Sutton England). Humanities.

Swainson, Charles. The Folk-Lore & Provincial Names of British Birds. (Folk-Lore Society, London, Monographs: Vol. 17). pap. 24.00 (ISBN 0-317-15647-0). Kraus Repr.

--Provincial Names & Folk Lore of British Birds. (English Dialect Society Publications Ser.: No. 47). pap. 25.00 (ISBN 0-317-15930-5). Kraus Repr.

Wallace, Ian. Birds of Prey of Britain & Europe. (Illus.). 1983. 15.95x (ISBN 0-19-217729-X). Oxford U Pr.

Woodcock & Heinzel. The Birds of Britain & Europe. pap. 8.95 (ISBN 0-00-219445-7, Collins Pub England). Greene.

BIRDS–HAWAII

Berger, Andrew J. Hawaiian Birdlife. 2nd & rev. ed. LC 80-26332. (Illus.). 275p. 1981. 29.95 (ISBN 0-8248-0742-1). UH Pr.

Bryan, William A. Key to the Birds of the Hawaiian Group. (BMM). 1901. Repr. of 1901 ed. 24.00 (ISBN 0-527-01628-4). Kraus Repr.

Richardson, F. Breeding Cycles of Hawaiian Sea Birds. (BMB). pap. 10.00 (ISBN 0-527-02326-4). Kraus Repr.

Wilson, B. Scott & Evans, A. H. Aves Hawaiienses: The Birds of the Sandwich Islands. LC 73-17848. (Natural Sciences in America Ser.). (Illus.). 356p. 1974. Repr. 31.00x (ISBN 0-405-05771-7). Ayer Co Pubs.

BIRDS–INDIA

Ali, Salim & Ripley, Dillon. Compact Edition of the Handbook of the Birds of India & Pakistan, Together with Those of Bangladesh, Nepal, Bhutan & Sri Lanka. (Illus.). 1983. 98.00x (ISBN 0-19-561245-0). Oxford U Pr.

Ali, Salim & Ripley, S. D. Handbook of the Birds of India & Pakistan, Vol. II: Megapodes to Crab Plover. 2nd ed. (Illus.). 1980. 37.50x (ISBN 0-19-561201-9). Oxford U Pr.

Ali, Salim & Ripley, S. Dillon. Handbook of the Birds of India & Pakistan: Vol. 1, Divers to Hawks. 2nd ed. (Illus.). 1978. 37.50x (ISBN 0-19-561115-2). Oxford U Pr.

Woodcock. Birds of the Indian Sub-Continent. pap. 10.95 (ISBN 0-00-219788-X, Collins Pub England). Greene.

BIRDS–IRELAND

Anglesea, Martyn, notes by. Birds of Ireland. (Illus.). 120p. with slip case 460.00 (ISBN 0-85640-297-4, Pub. by Blackstaff Pr); limited ed. 750.00 (ISBN 0-317-02588-0). Longwood Pub Group.

Ruttledge, Robert F. Ireland's Birds. (Illus.). 224p. 1971. 14.95x (ISBN 0-8464-0531-8). Beekman Pubs.

Sharrock, J. T., ed. Birds New to Britain & Ireland. (Illus.). 1983. 25.00 (ISBN 0-85661-033-X, Pub. by T & A D Poyser England). Buteo.

BIRDS–ISLANDS OF THE ATLANTIC

Bannerman, D. A. History of the Birds of the Balearic Islands. 384p. 1982. 100.00x (ISBN 0-686-78891-5, Pub. by Wheldon & Wesley England). State Mutual Bk.

Brudenell-Bruce, P. G. Birds of the Bahamas. LC 74-7342. (Illus.). 160p. 1975. 10.95 (ISBN 0-8008-0780-4). Taplinger.

Emlen, John T. Land Bird Communities of Grand Bahama Island: The Structure & Dynamics of an Avifauna. 129p. 1977. 9.00 (ISBN 0-943610-24-9). Am Ornithologists.

Ffrench, Richard. A Guide to the Birds of Trinidad & Tobago. (Illus.). 516p. 1973. 27.50 (ISBN 0-915180-03-0). Livingston.

Harris, James. The Peregrine Falcon in Greenland: Observing an Endangered Species. LC 78-67404. (Illus.). 256p. (Orig.). 1981. 19.00x (ISBN 0-8262-0267-5); pap. 8.95 (ISBN 0-8262-0343-4). U of Mo Pr.

Paterson, Andrew. Birds of the Bahamas. 1972. 6.00 (ISBN 0-911764-08-9). Durrell.

BIRDS–ISLANDS OF THE PACIFIC

Ball, S. C. Jungle Fowls from Pacific Islands. (BMB). Repr. of 1933 ed. 21.00 (ISBN 0-527-02214-4). Kraus Repr.

Fleet, Robert R. Red-tailed Tropicbird on Kure Atoll. 64p. 1974. 5.50 (ISBN 0-943610-16-8). Am Ornithologists.

Gill, Frank B. Intra-Island Variation in the Mascarene White-eye Zosterops Borbonica. 66p. 1973. 3.50 (ISBN 0-943610-12-5). Am Ornithologists.

Mayr, Ernst. Birds of the Southwest Pacific. (Illus.). 1968. pap. 11.80 (ISBN 3-7682-0533-9). Lubrecht & Cramer.

--Birds of the Southwest Pacific: A Field Guide to the Birds of the Area Between Samoa, New Caledonia & Micronesia. LC 77-83043. 1978. pap. 5.75 (ISBN 0-8048-1250-0). C E Tuttle.

Muse, Corey & Muse, Shirley. The Birds & Birdlife of Samoa: O Manu ma Tala'aga o Manu o Samoa. LC 82-81085. (Illus.). 166p. (Orig.). 1983. pap. 15.00 (ISBN 0-295-95983-5, Pub. by Blue Mtn Audobon). U of Wash Pr.

Thompson, Max C. Birds from North Borneo. (Museum Ser.: Vol. 17, No. 8). 57p. 1966. pap. 3.00 (ISBN 0-317-04636-5). U of KS Mus Nat Hist.

Wan-Fu Chang, James. A Field Guide to the Birds of Taiwan. (Illus.). 324p. 1980. 39.95 (ISBN 0-917056-43-4, Pub. by Tunghai U Taiwan). Cheng & Tsui.

Watling, Dick. Birds of Fiji, Tonga & Samoa. (Illus.). 1983. 45.00 (ISBN 0-88072-028-X, Pub. by Tanager). Longwood Pub Group.

BIRDS–LATIN-AMERICA

Blake, Emmet R. Manual of Neotropical Birds: Spheniscidae (Penguins) to Laridae (Gulls & Allies, Vol. 1. LC 75-43229. (Illus.). 640p. 1977. lib. bdg. 100.00x (ISBN 0-226-05641-4). U of Chicago Pr.

Bond, Mary W. Far Afield in the Caribbean: Migratory Flights of a Naturalist's Wife. (Illus.). 1971. 4.95 (ISBN 0-915180-13-8). Livingston.

Chapman, Frank M. Essays in South American Ornithogeography: Original Anthology. Sterling, Keir B., ed. LC 77-81087. (Biologists & Their World Ser.). (Illus.). 1978. lib. bdg. 59.50x (ISBN 0-405-10663-7). Ayer Co Pubs.

Dunning, John S. South American Land Birds: A Photographic Aid to Identification. Ridgely, Robert S., ed. LC 82-9351. (Illus.). 400p. 1982. 37.50 (ISBN 0-915180-21-9); pap. 27.50 (ISBN 0-915180-22-7). Harrowood Bks.

Harris. A Field Guide to the Birds of the Galapagos. 19.95 (ISBN 0-00-219237-3, Collins Pub England). Greene.

Hilty, Steven L. & Brown, William L. A Guide to the Birds of Colombia. LC 84-18211. (Illus.). 750p. 1985. 95.00 (ISBN 0-691-08371-1); pap. 42.50 (ISBN 0-691-08372-X). Princeton U Pr.

Humphrey, Philip S. & Pefaur, Jaime E. Glaciation & Species Richness of Birds on Austral South American Islands. (Occasional Papers: No. 80). 9p. 1979. pap. 1.25 (ISBN 0-317-04595-4). U of KS Mus Nat Hist.

Humphrey, Philip S., et al. Birds of Isla Grande (Tierra del Fuego) 1970. 7.00 (ISBN 0-317-04594-6). U of KS Mus Nat Hist.

Jenkinson, Marion A. & Mengel, Robert M. Notes on an Important Nineteenth Century Collection of Central & North American Birds Made by N. S. Goss. (Occasional Papers: No. 81). 10p. 1979. pap. 1.25 (ISBN 0-317-04603-9). U of KS Mus Nat Hist.

Lill, A. Lek Behavior in the Golden-Headed Manakin, Pipra erythrocephala in Trinidad (West Indies) (Advances in Ethology Ser.: Vol. 18). (Illus.). 84p. (Orig.). 1976. pap. text ed. 34.00 (ISBN 3-489-72536-0). Parey Sci Pubs.

Meyer de Schauensee, Rodolphe. A Guide to the Birds of South America. 463p. 1982. pap. 25.00 (ISBN 0-317-04625-X). U of KS Mus Nat Hist.

Monroe, Burt L., Jr. Distributional Survey of the Birds of Honduras. 458p. 1968. 14.00 (ISBN 0-943610-07-9). Am Ornithologists.

Peterson, Roger T. & Chalif, Edward L. Field Guide to Mexican Birds. (Peterson Field Guide Ser). 1973. 15.95 (ISBN 0-395-17129-6). HM.

Skutch, Alexander F. A Bird Watcher's Adventures in Tropical America. LC 77-3478. (Corrie Herring Hooks Ser.: No. 3). (Illus.). 343p. 1977. 22.50 (ISBN 0-292-70722-3). U of Tex Pr.

--Birds of Tropical America. LC 82-8597. (Corrie Herring Hooks Ser.: No. 5). (Illus.). 317p. 1983. 29.95 (ISBN 0-292-74634-2). U of Tex Pr.

Snow, David. The Web of Adaptation: Bird Studies in the American Tropics. LC 85-7890. 192p. (Orig.). 1985. pap. text ed. 7.95x (ISBN 0-8014-9316-1). Cornell U Pr.

Sutton, George M. At a Bend in a Mexican River. LC 72-83709. (Illus.). 184p. 1972. 14.95 (ISBN 0-8397-0780-0). Eriksson.

Wetmore, Alexander. The Birds of the Republic of Panama, 3 pts. Incl. Part 1. Tinamidae (Tinamous) to Rynchopidae (Skimmers) LC 66-61601. (Illus.). 438p. 1965. 25.00x (ISBN 0-87474-063-0); Part 2. Columbidae (Pigeons) to Picidae (Woodpeckers) LC 66-61061. (Illus.). 605p. 25.00x (ISBN 0-87474-064-9); Part 3. Passeriformes: Dendrocolaptidae (Woodcreepers) to Oxyruncidae (Sharpbills) 631p. 1965. 25.00x (ISBN 0-87474-122-X). LC 66-61061. (Illus.). 1968. Smithsonian.

Woods, Robin W. Birds of the Falkland Islands. (Illus.). 1975. 27.50 (ISBN 0-904614-00-X, Pub. by Anthony Nelson Ltd, England). Buteo.

BIRDS–MEXICO

Edwards, Ernest P. Appendix for a Field Guide to the Birds of Mexico, 1978. LC 78-185930. 1978. pap. 8.00 (ISBN 0-911882-06-5). E P Edwards.

Klaas, Erwin E. Summer Birds from the Yucatan Peninsula, Mexico. (Museum Ser.: Vol. 17, No. 14). 33p. 1968. pap. 1.75 (ISBN 0-317-04613-6). U of KS Mus Nat Hist.

Lowrey, George H., Jr. & Dalquest, Walter W. Birds from the State of Veracruz, Mexico. (Museum Ser.: Vol. 3, No. 4). 119p. 1951. 6.25 (ISBN 0-317-04618-7). U of KS Mus Nat Hist.

Peterson, Roger T. & Chalif, Edward L. Field Guide to Mexican Birds. (Peterson Field Guide Ser). 1973. 15.95 (ISBN 0-395-17129-6). HM.

Sutton, George M. At a Bend in a Mexican River. LC 72-83709. (Illus.). 184p. 1972. 14.95 (ISBN 0-8397-0780-0). Eriksson.

--Portraits of Mexican Birds: Fifty Selected Paintings. LC 74-15911. (Illus.). 18p. 1980. pap. 17.95 (ISBN 0-8061-1685-4). U of Okla Pr.

Urban, Emil K. Birds from Coahuila, Mexico. (Museum Ser.: Vol. 11, No. 8). 74p. 1959. pap. 4.00 (ISBN 0-317-04638-1). U of KS Mus Nat Hist.

Wheeler, Margaret L. A Bird Watcher's Guide to Mexico. 1979. pap. 5.50 (ISBN 0-912434-07-4). Ocelot Pr.

BIRDS–NEPAL

Inskepp, Carol & Inskipp, Tim. A Guide to the Birds of Nepal. (Illus.). 392p. 1985. 35.00 (ISBN 0-317-30643-X, Pub. by Tanager). Longwood Pub Group.

BIRDS–NEW GUINEA

Beehler, Bruce, et al. Birds of New Guinea. LC 85-42673. (Illus.). 370p. 1985. 65.00 (ISBN 0-691-08385-1); pap. 37.50 (ISBN 0-691-02394-8). Princeton U Pr.

Diamond, Jared M. Avifauna of the Eastern Highlands of New Guinea. (Illus.). 438p. 1972. 15.00 (ISBN 0-686-35800-7). Nuttall Ornith.

Majnep, Ian S. & Bulmer, Ralph. Birds of My Kalam Country. (Illus.). 1977. 32.50x (ISBN 0-19-647953-3). Oxford U Pr.

Peckover, W. S. Birds of New Guinea & Tropical Australia. (Illus.). 1977. 25.50 (ISBN 0-589-07202-1, Dist. by C E Tuttle). Reed.

Turbott, E. G., ed. Buller's Birds of New Zealand. 206p. 1982. 150.00x (ISBN 0-7233-0022-4, Pub. by Whitcoulls New Zealand). State Mutual Bk.

BIRDS–NEW ZEALAND

Buller, Walter L. Buller's Birds of New Zealand: A History of the Birds of New Zealand. Turbott, E. G., ed. LC 67-20253. 1967. 35.00 (ISBN 0-8248-0064-8, Eastwest Ctr). UH Pr.

Falla & Sibson. A New Guide to the Birds of New Zealand. 39.95 (ISBN 0-00-219622-0, Collins Pub England). Greene.

Falla, R. A. & Sibson, R. B. The New Guide to the Birds of New Zealand. (Illus.). 247p. 1983. 17.95 (ISBN 0-00-216928-2, Pub. by W Collins New Zealand). Intl Spec Bk.

Harvey, Bruce. Portfolio of New Zealand Birds. LC 71-138066. (Illus.). 1971. 17.50 (ISBN 0-8048-0666-7). C E Tuttle.

Lockley, Ronald. New Zealand Birds. (Illus.). 179p. 1983. 45.00 (ISBN 0-86863-392-5, Pub. by Heinemann Pub New Zealand). Intl Spec Bk.

Power, Elaine. Small Birds of the New Zealand Bush. (Illus.). 27p. 1983. pap. 9.95 (ISBN 0-00-216984-3, Pub. by W Collins New Zealand). Intl Spec Bk.

Soper, M. F. New Zealand Birds. (Illus.). 288p. 1972. 22.50x (ISBN 0-7233-0249-9). Intl Pubns Serv.

--New Zealand Birds. (Illus.). 216p. 1975. 15.00 (ISBN 0-912728-18-3). Newbury Bks.

BIRDS–NORTH AMERICA

see also Birds–Alaska; Birds–Canada; Birds–United States

American Ornithological Bibliography. LC 73-17794. (Natural Sciences in America Ser.). 650p. 1974. Repr. 33.00x (ISBN 0-405-05704-0). Ayer Co Pubs.

Anderson, Ted R. Population Studies of European Sparrows in North America. (Occasional Papers: No. 70). 58p. 1978. pap. 3.25 (ISBN 0-317-04581-4). U of KS Mus Nat Hist.

Coues, Elliott. Birds of the Colorado Valley: A Repository of Scientific & Popular Information Concerning North American Ornithology, Vol. 11. LC 73-17814. (Natural Sciences in America Ser.). 820p. 1974. Repr. 54.00x (ISBN 0-405-05730-X). Ayer Co Pubs.
--Birds of the Northwest: A Handbook of the Ornithology of the Region Drained by the Missouri River & Its Tributaries. LC 73-17815. (Natural Sciences in America Ser.). 808p. 1974. Repr. 53.00x (ISBN 0-405-05731-8). Ayer Co Pubs.
Dean, Blanche E. Birds. (Southern Regional Nature Ser). (Illus.). pap. 5.00 (ISBN 0-87651-018-7). Southern U Pr.
Dickey, Florence V. Familiar Birds of the Pacific Southwest. (Illus.). 1935. 6.95 (ISBN 0-8047-0350-7). Stanford U Pr.
Dinsmore, James J., et al. Iowa Birds. (Illus.). 356p. 1984. 27.95 (ISBN 0-8138-0206-7). Iowa St U Pr.
Drennan, Susan R. Where to Find Birds in New York State: The Top 500 Sites. LC 81-16744. (York State Bks.). (Illus.). 532p. 1981. text ed. 38.00x (ISBN 0-8156-2250-3); pap. 18.95 (ISBN 0-8156-0173-5). Syracuse U Pr.
Eifert, Virginia S. Invitation to Birds. (Story of Illinois Ser.: No. 5). (Illus.). 64p. 1953. pap. 1.00 (ISBN 0-89792-006-6). Ill St Museum.
Fitch, Henry S. Observations on the Mississippi Kite in Southwestern Kansas. (Museum Ser.: Vol. 12, No. 11). 17p. 1963. pap. 1.25 (ISBN 0-317-04587-3). U of KS Mus Nat Hist.
Forbush, Edward H. Birds or Massachusetts & Other New England States, Pts. 1, 2 & 3. Sterling, Keir B., ed. LC 77-81083. (Biologists & Their World Ser.). (Illus.). 1978. Repr. of 1929 ed. lib. bdg. 156.00x (ISBN 0-405-10659-9). Ayer Co Pubs.
--Natural History of American Birds of Eastern & Central North America. May, John R., ed. (Illus.). 22.95 (ISBN 0-395-07699-4). HM.
Geffen, Alice. A Birdwatcher's Guide to Eastern United States. LC 77-21436. 1978. 15.95 (ISBN 0-8120-5301-X). Barron.
Gillespie, Mabel. Where the Birds Are. LC 76-55062. (Illus., Orig.). 1976. pap. 4.95 (ISBN 0-932384-03-X). Tashmoo.
Gillette, John. Coat Pocket Bird Book. McKee, Russell, ed. (Illus.). 160p. 1984. pap. 9.95 (ISBN 0-941912-05-1). TwoPeninsula Pr.
Godfrey, Michael A. Winter Birds of the Carolinas & Nearby States. LC 76-56988. (Illus.). 1977. 10.00 (ISBN 0-910244-94-4). Blair.
Green, Janet & Janssen, Robert B. Minnesota Birds: Where, When, & How Many. LC 74-16980. (Illus.). xvi, 248p. 1975. 10.95x (ISBN 0-8166-0738-9). U of Minn Pr.
Green, Janet C. & Janssen, Robert B. Minnesota Birds: Where, When, & How Many. LC 74-16980. (Illus.). 1980. pap. 6.95 (ISBN 0-8166-0958-6). U of Minn Pr.
Grinnell, Joseph. An Account of the Mammals & Birds of the Lower Colorado Valley, with Especial Reference to the Distributional Problems Presented. Sterling, Keir B., ed. LC 77-81116. (Biologists & Their World Ser.). (Illus.). 1978. Repr. of 1914 ed. lib. bdg. 22.00x (ISBN 0-405-10708-0). Ayer Co Pubs.
Gromme, Owen J. Birds of Wisconsin. (Illus.). 236p. 1963. 45.00 (ISBN 0-299-03001-6). U of Wis Pr.
Grzybowski, Joseph A. & Schnell, Gary D. Oklahoma Orinthology: An Annotated Bibliography. 192p. 19.95 (ISBN 0-317-12257-6). U of Okla Pr.
--Oklahoma Ornithology: An Annotated Bibliography. (Stovall Museum Publications Ser.: Vol. 5). 176p. 19.95 (ISBN 0-8061-1887-3). U of Okla Pr.
Hall, George A. West Virginia Birds: Distribution & Ecology. (Special Publication Ser.: No. 7, CMNH). (Illus.). 1983. 20.00 (ISBN 0-935868-05-4). Carnegie Board.
Harrison, Hal. A Field Guide to Western Birds' Nests. (Peterson Field Guide Ser.). (Illus.). 1979. 11.95 (ISBN 0-395-27629-2). HM.
Heintzelman, Donald S. A Manual for Bird Watching in the Americas. LC 78-66169. (Illus.). 264p. 1980. 17.95x (ISBN 0-87663-336-X); pap. 9.95 (ISBN 0-87663-967-8). Universe.
Hudson, William H. Birds of La Plata. Repr. of 1923 ed. 35.00 (ISBN 0-404-03411-X). AMS Pr.
Hunn, Eugene S. Birding in Seattle & King County. LC 82-61828. (Trailside Ser.). (Illus.). 1982. pap. 7.50 (ISBN 0-914516-05-1). Seattle Audubon Soc.
Imhof, Thomas A. Alabama Birds. 2nd ed. LC 76-4506. (Illus.). 530p. (4#530). 1976. 27.50 (ISBN 0-8173-1701-5). U of Ala Pr.
Jackson, Jerome A. The Mid-South Bird Notes of Ben B. Coffey, Jr. (Special Publications: No. 1). 127p. (Orig.). 1981. pap. 10.00 (ISBN 0-686-37622-6). Mississippi Orni.
Johnsgard, Paul A. Birds of the Great Plains: Breeding Species & Their Distribution. LC 79-1419. (Illus.). xlviii, 539p. 1979. 27.50x (ISBN 0-8032-2550-4). U of Nebr Pr.
Johnston, Richard F. The Breeding Birds of Kansas. (Museum Ser.: Vol. 12, No. 14). 81p. 1964. 4.25 (ISBN 0-317-04606-3). U of KS Mus Nat Hist.
--A Directory to the Birds of Kansas. (Miscellaneous Publications Ser.: No. 41). 67p. 1965. pap. 3.50 (ISBN 0-317-04611-X). U of KS Mus Nat Hist.
Judd, Sylvester D. Birds of a Maryland Farm: Local Study of Economic Ornithology. Egerton, Frank N., 3rd, ed. LC 77-74233. (History of Ecology Ser.). (Illus.). 1978. Repr. of 1902 ed. lib. bdg. 14.00x (ISBN 0-405-10402-2). Ayer Co Pubs.
Keller, Charles E., et al. Indiana Birds & Their Haunts: A Checklist & Finding Guide. LC 78-20406. (Midland Bks.: No. 233). (Illus.). 224p. 1979. 12.50x (ISBN 0-253-15437-5); pap. 6.95x (ISBN 0-253-20233-7). Ind U Pr.
Kelley, Alice H. Birds of Southeastern Michigan & Southwestern Ontario. LC 78-54302. (Bulletin Ser.: No. 57). 99p. 1978. pap. 3.50x (ISBN 0-87737-034-6). Cranbrook.
Kidwell, Al. Coastal Birds: A Guide to Birds of Maine's Beautiful Coastline. (Maine Geographic Ser.). (Illus.). 48p. 1983. pap. 2.95 (ISBN 0-89933-052-5). DeLorme Pub.
Laughlin, Sarah B. & Kibbe, Douglas P., eds. The Atlas of Breeding Birds of Vermont. LC 84-40589. (Illus.). 480p. 1985. 45.00x (ISBN 0-87451-326-X). U Pr of New Eng.
Leberman, Robert C. The Birds of Ligonier Valley. Janosik, H. Jon & Rudy, Carol H., trs. (Special Publication Ser.: No. 3, CMNH). (Illus.). 67p. 1976. pap. 5.00 (ISBN 0-911239-07-3). Carnegie Board.
Lowrey, George H., Jr. Additions to the List of the Birds of Louisiana. (Museum Ser.: Vol. 1, No. 9). 16p. 1947. pap. 1.25 (ISBN 0-317-04616-0). U of KS Mus Nat Hist.
Meanley, Brooke. Waterfowl of the Chesapeake Bay Country. LC 81-18361. (Illus.). 224p. 1982. 19.95 (ISBN 0-87033-281-3). Tidewater.
Miller, Olive T. Bird-Lover in the West. LC 76-125753. (American Environmental Studies). 1970. Repr. of 1900 ed. 17.00 (ISBN 0-405-02679-X). Ayer Co Pubs.
Mlodinow, Steven. Chicago Area Birds. 280p. 17.00 (ISBN 0-914091-55-7); pap. 9.95 (ISBN 0-914091-56-5). Chicago Review.
Monson, Gale & Phillips, Allan. Annotated Checklist of the Birds of Arizona. 2nd, rev. ed. LC 81-11687. 240p. 1981. pap. 5.95 (ISBN 0-8165-0753-8). U of Ariz Pr.
Murphy, Lawrence & Murphy, Bernadette. Field Guide to New Mexico Birds. Ratkevich, Ronald P., ed. (Illus.). 1979. pap. 3.95 (ISBN 0-932680-02-X). Dinograph SW.
Oberholser, Harry C. The Bird Life of Texas, 2 vols. Kincaid, Edgar B., Jr., et al, eds. LC 73-21216. (Corrie Herring Hooks Ser.: No. 1). (Illus.). 1108p. 1974. Set. 100.00 (ISBN 0-292-70711-8). U of Tex Pr.
Orr, Robert T. & Moffitt, James. Birds of the Lake Tahoe Region. (Illus.). 150p. 1971. 8.00 (ISBN 0-940228-08-4). Calif Acad Sci.
Pearson, T. Gilbert, et al. Bird of North Carolina. 1978. Repr. of 1919 ed. lib. bdg. 100.00 (ISBN 0-8495-4276-6). Arden Lib.
Peterson, Roger T. Birds over America. (Illus.). 358p. 1983. pap. 12.95 (ISBN 0-396-08269-6). Dodd.
--A Field Guide to the Birds of Texas & Adjacent States. (Peterson Field Guide Ser.). 1979. pap. 11.95 (ISBN 0-395-26252-6). HM.
Pettingill, Olin S., Jr. A Guide to Bird Finding East of the Mississippi. 2nd ed. 1980. pap. 7.95 (ISBN 0-395-29132-1). HM.
--A Guide to Bird Finding East of the Mississippi. 2nd ed. LC 76-9253. (Illus.). 1977. 25.00 (ISBN 0-19-502097-9). Oxford U Pr.
--A Guide to Bird Finding West of the Mississippi. 2nd ed. LC 80-18666. (Illus.). 1981. 25.00 (ISBN 0-19-502818-X). Oxford U Pr.
Phillips, Allan, et al. The Birds of Arizona. LC 64-17265. (Illus.). 220p. 1964. 40.00 (ISBN 0-8165-0012-6). U of Ariz Pr.
Pierson, Elizabeth C. & Pierson, Jan Erik. A Birder's Guide to the Coast of Maine. LC 81-67953. (Illus.). 224p. 1981. pap. 8.95 (ISBN 0-89272-118-9, PIC471). Down East.
Platt, Dwight. Food of the Crow, Corvus Brachyrynochos Brehm, in South-Central Kansas. (Museum Ser.: Vol. 8, No. 8). 22p. 1956. pap. 1.25 (ISBN 0-317-04631-4). U of KS Mus Nat Hist.
Potter, Eloise F., et al. Birds of the Carolinas. LC 79-14201. (Illus.). viii, 408p. 1980. 14.95 (ISBN 0-8078-1399-0). U of NC Pr.
Proby, Kathryn H. Audubon in Florida: With Selections from the Writings of John James Audubon. LC 72-85114. (Illus.). 384p. 1974. pap. 15.95 (ISBN 0-87024-301-2). U of Miami Pr.
Rappole, John H. & Blacklock, Gene W. Birds of the Texas Coastal Bend: Abundance & Distribution. LC 84-40567. (W. L. Moody, Jr. Natural History Ser.: No. 7). (Illus.). 184p. 1985. 19.50 (ISBN 0-89096-221-9). Tex A&M Univ Pr.
Rea, Amadeo M. Once a River: Bird Life & Habitat Changes on the Middle Gila. LC 82-23815. (Illus.). 285p. 1983. 24.50x (ISBN 0-8165-0799-6). U of Ariz Pr.
Reed, Chester A. Bird Guide: Land Birds East of the Rockies. 7.95 (ISBN 0-385-04809-2). Doubleday.
Richardson, John & Swainson, William. Fauna Boreali-Americana: Pt. II, the Birds. Sterling, Keir B., ed. LC 73-17837. (Natural Science in America Ser.). (Illus.). 1974. Repr. of 1831 ed. lib. bdg. 49.50x (ISBN 0-405-05760-1). Ayer Co Pubs.
Ridgway, Robert. Ornithology: United States Geological Exploration of the Fortieth Parallel. LC 73-17839. (Natural Sciences in America Ser.: Pt. 3). (Illus.). 370p. 1974. Repr. 25.50x (ISBN 0-405-05761-X). Ayer Co Pubs.
Roberts, Thomas S. Manual for the Identification of the Birds of Minnesota & Neighboring States. 4th ed. (Illus.). 1955. 9.95x (ISBN 0-8166-0117-8). U of Minn Pr.
Rue, Leonard L., 3rd. Pictorial Guide to the Birds of North America. LC 73-109905. 1970. 14.37i (ISBN 0-690-62158-2). T Y Crowell.
Ryser, Fred A., Jr. Birds of the Great Basin: A Natural History. LC 84-25763. (Max C. Fleischmann Series in Great Basin Natural History). (Illus.). 642p. (Orig.). 1985. 27.50 (ISBN 0-87417-079-6); pap. 15.00 (ISBN 0-87417-080-X). U of Nev Pr.
Schuyler, Mathews F. Field Book of Wild Birds & Their Music: Description of Character & Music of Birds, Intended to Assist in Identification of Species Common in the U.S. East of the Rocky Mountains. 1978. Repr. of 1904 ed. lib. bdg. 35.00 (ISBN 0-8495-3755-X). Arden Lib.
Sequoia Audubon Society. San Francisco Peninsula Birdwatching. Scanlan-Rohrer, Anne, ed. (Illus., Orig.). 1985. pap. 8.95 (ISBN 0-9614301-0-9). Sequoia Aud Soc.
Slater, Peter. Field Guide to American Birds: The Passerines, Vol. 2. LC 70-131130. (Illus.). 1972. 25.00 (ISBN 0-915180-15-4). Harrowood Bks.
Starling, Alfred. Enjoying Indiana Birds. LC 78-3247. (Illus.). 384p. 1978. 17.50x (ISBN 0-253-31956-0). Ind U Pr.
Stebbins, Cyril A. & Stebbins, Robert C. Birds of Yosemite. Rev. ed. (Illus.). 80p. 1974. pap. 2.50 (ISBN 0-939666-00-6). Yosemite Natl Hist.
Stone, Witmer. Bird Studies at Old Cape May: An Ornithology of Coastal New Jersey, 2 Vols. (Illus.). Set. 16.00 (ISBN 0-8446-3018-7). Peter Smith.
Stull, Jean, et al. Birds of Erie County Pennsylvania. LC 84-73239. (Illus.). 175p. 1985. pap. 7.95 (ISBN 0-910042-47-0). Allegheny.
Sutton, George M. Fifty Common Birds of Oklahoma & the Southern Great Plains. LC 77-24336. (Illus.). 113p. 1981. pap. 8.95 (ISBN 0-8061-1704-4). U of Okla Pr.
--Fifty Common Birds of Oklahoma & the Southern Great Plains. (Illus.). 1984. 14.95 (ISBN 0-8061-1439-8). U of Okla Pr.
Telfair, Ray C., II. The Cattle Egret: A Texas Focus & World View. (Kleberg Studies in Natural Resources). (Illus.). 144p. 1984. 16.95x (ISBN 0-89096-198-0); pap. 10.95x (ISBN 0-89096-200-6). Tex A&M Univ Pr.
Terres, John K. Songbirds in Your Garden. rev ed. LC 68-11071. (Illus.). 1968. 9.95i (ISBN 0-690-75151-6). T Y Crowell.
Thorndike Press, ed. Maine Birds. LC 78-9702. (Maine Nature Ser.). (Illus.). 1978. 8.50x (ISBN 0-89621-011-1); pap. 3.95x (ISBN 0-89621-010-3). Thorndike Pr.
Warren, B. H. Report on the Birds of Pennsylvania: With Special Reference to the Food-Habits, Based on Over Four Thousand Stomach Examinations. 1978. Repr. of 1890 ed. lib. bdg. 125.00 (ISBN 0-8495-5641-4). Arden Lib.
Wauer, Roland. A Field Guide to Birds of the Big Bend. (Field Guide Ser.). (Illus.). 224p. 1985. pap. 9.95 (ISBN 0-87719-010-0); text ed. 16.95 (ISBN 0-87719-027-5). Texas Month Pr.
Wauer, Roland H. & Carter, Dennis. Birds of Zion National Park & Vicinity. (Illus.). 92p. 1965. 0.75 (ISBN 0-685-83464-6). Zion.
Weathers, Wesley W. Birds of Southern California's Deep Canyon. LC 82-13382. (Illus.). 267p. 1983. 35.00 (ISBN 0-520-04754-0). U of Cal Pr.
Woolfendon, Glen E. & Fitzpatrick, John W. The Florida Scrub Jay: Demography of a Cooperative-Breeding Bird. LC 84-42545. (Monographs in Popular Biology). (Illus.). 432p. 1984. text ed. 45.00x (ISBN 0-691-08366-5); pap. 14.50x (ISBN 0-691-08367-3). Princeton U Pr.

BIRDS–VENEZUELA

De Schauensee, Raadolphe M. & Phelps, William H., Jr. A Guide to the Birds of Venezuela. LC 76-45903. (Illus.). 1977. 70.00x (ISBN 0-691-08188-3); pap. 27.50 (ISBN 0-691-08205-7). Princeton U Pr.

BIRDS–VIETNAM

Wildash, Philip. Birds of South Vietnam. LC 67-20953. (Illus.). 1968. 8.25 (ISBN 0-8048-0064-2). C E Tuttle.

BIRDS, AQUATIC

see Water-Birds

BIRDS, ATTRACTING OF

Arbib, Robert & Soper, Tony. Hungry Bird Book: How to Make Your Garden Their Haven on Earth. LC 75-122251. (Illus.). 1970. 8.95 (ISBN 0-8008-4020-8). Taplinger.
DeGraaf, Richard M. & Witman, Gretchin M. Trees, Shrubs, & Vines for Attracting Birds: A Manual for the Northeast. LC 78-19698. (Illus.). 160p. 1981. pap. 11.50 (ISBN 0-87023-202-9). U of Mass Pr.
Knight, Maxwell. Bird Gardening. 1977. 25.00 (ISBN 0-685-80017-2). State Mutual Bk.
Laycock, George. The Birdwatcher's Bible. LC 74-2532. 192p. 1976. pap. 4.95 (ISBN 0-385-09611-9). Doubleday.
Soper, Tony. The Bird Table Book in Colour. LC 77-89367. (Illus.). 1978. 11.95 (ISBN 0-7153-7404-4). David & Charles.

BIRDS, EXTINCT

see also Passenger Pigeons; Rare Birds; also names of extinct birds, e.g. Dodo

Greenway, James C., Jr. Extinct & Vanishing Birds of the World. 2nd ed. (Illus.). 1967. pap. 7.95 (ISBN 0-486-21869-4). Dover.
--Extinct & Vanishing Birds of the World. 2nd ed. (Illus.). 15.25 (ISBN 0-8446-2164-1). Peter Smith.
Mowat, Farley. Sea of Slaughter. LC 84-72722. (Illus.). 438p. 1985. 24.95 (ISBN 0-87113-013-0). Atlantic Monthly.
Rotroff, Susan I. & Lamberton, Robert D. Birds of the Athenian Agora. (Excavations of the Athenian Agora Picture Bk.: No. 22). (Illus.). 32p. 1985. pap. 1.50 (ISBN 0-87661-627-9). Am Sch Athens.

BIRDS, INJURIOUS AND BENEFICIAL

see also Birds of Prey

Clear, Val. Making Money with Birds. (Illus.). 192p. 1981. 12.95 (ISBN 0-87666-825-2, H-1031). TFH Pubns.
Dickson, James G., et al, eds. The Role of Insectivorous Birds in Forest Ecosystems. LC 79-12111. 1979. 55.00 (ISBN 0-12-215350-2). Acad Pr.
Judd, Sylvester D. Birds of a Maryland Farm: Local Study of Economic Ornithology. Egerton, Frank N., 3rd, ed. LC 77-74233. (History of Ecology Ser.). (Illus.). 1978. Repr. of 1902 ed. lib. bdg. 14.00x (ISBN 0-405-10402-2). Ayer Co Pubs.
Price, James H., et al. Consumer Health: Contemporary Issues & Choices. 576p. 1985. pap. write for info. (ISBN 0-697-00146-6); instr's. manual avail. (ISBN 0-697-00568-2). Wm C Brown.
Weber, Walter. Health Hazards from Pigeons, Starlings & English Sparrows. LC 79-55324. 1979. 13.00 (ISBN 0-913702-10-2). Thomson Pub Ca.

BIRDS, ORNAMENTAL

see also Cage-Birds; Ducks; Peafowl; Pheasants

Vriends, T. Cage Birds in Color: Choosing-Caring-Feeding. (Illus.). 144p. 1985. 14.95 (ISBN 0-668-06038-7); pap. 9.95 (ISBN 0-668-06042-5). Arco.

BIRDS, PHOTOGRAPHY OF

see Photography of Birds

BIRDS, PROTECTION OF

see also Birds, Attracting of; Game Protection

Gerstenfeld, Sheldon L. The Bird Care Book. (Illus.). 224p. 1981. o. p. 11.95 (ISBN 0-201-03908-7); pap. 7.95 (ISBN 0-201-03909-5). Addison-Wesley.
Terres, John K. Songbirds in Your Garden. rev ed. LC 68-11071. (Illus.). 1968. 9.95i (ISBN 0-690-75151-6). T Y Crowell.
Zeleny, Lawrence. The Bluebird: How You Can Help Its Fight for Survivial. 170p. 1978. pap. 7.95 (ISBN 0-253-20212-4). Nature Bks Pubs.

BIRDS, RARE

see Rare Birds

BIRDS' NESTS

see Birds–Eggs and Nests

BIRDS OF PREY

see also Owls

Bent, Arthur C. Life Histories of North American Birds of Prey, 2 Vols. (Illus.). 1958. Vol. 1. pap. 8.50 (ISBN 0-486-20931-8); Vol. 2. pap. 8.50 (ISBN 0-486-20932-6). Dover.
--Life Histories of North American Birds of Prey, 2 vols. (Illus.). Set. 32.50 (ISBN 0-8446-1630-3). Peter Smith.
Bouchner, Miroslav. Birds of Prey of Britain & Europe. (Concise Guide in Colour Ser.). (Illus.). 1978. 7.95 (ISBN 0-686-89165-1). Transatlantic.

Phillips, David R. & Shuman, Marc A., eds. Biochemistry of the Platelets. Date not set. price not set (ISBN 0-12-553240-7). Acad Pr.

Rotman, A., et al. Platelets, Cellular Response Mechanisms & Their Biological Significance: Proceedings. LC 80-4127. 327p. 1980. 69.95 (ISBN 0-471-27896-3, Pub. by Wiley-Interscience). Wiley.

Salmon, Charles, ed. Blood Groups & Other Red Cell Surface Markers in Health & Disease. LC 82-13096. (Illus.). 150p. 1982. 39.50 (ISBN 0-89352-193-0). Masson Pub.

Thakur, M. L., ed. Radiolabelled Cellular Blood Elements: Pathophysiology, Techniques, & Scintigraphic Techniques. (NATO ASI Series A, Life Sciences: Vol. 88). 438p. 1985. 69.50x (ISBN 0-306-41935-1, Plenum Pr). Plenum Pub.

Vroman, Leo & Leonard, Edward F., eds. The Behavior of Blood & Its Components at Interface, Vol. 283. (Annals of the New York Academy of Sciences). 1977. 43.00x (ISBN 0-89072-029-0). NY Acad Sci.

Wintrobe, Maxwell M. Blood, Pure & Eloquent. new ed. (Illus.). 1980. text ed. 50.00 (ISBN 0-07-071135-6). McGraw.

BLOOD–ANALYSIS AND CHEMISTRY

see also Anoxemia; Glycolysis

Aminoff, David, ed. Blood & Tissue Antigens: A Symposium Volume. 1970. 84.00 (ISBN 0-12-057050-5). Acad Pr.

Bessis, M. Blood Smears Reinterpreted. (Illus.). 1977. 57.00 (ISBN 0-387-07206-3). Springer-Verlag.

Critser, James R., Jr. Blood Technology. (Ser. 10BT-84). 1985. 100.00 (ISBN 0-88178-052-9). Lexington Data.

Fulwood, Robinson & Johnson, Clifford L. Hematological & Nutritional Biochemistries References Data of Persons 6 Months-74 Years of Age: United States, 1976-1980. Cox, Klaudia, tr. (Ser. 11: No. 232). 60p. 1982. pap. 1.95 (ISBN 0-8406-0267-7). Natl Ctr Health Stats.

Gray, C. H. & James, V. H. T., eds. Hormones in Blood, Vol. 1. 3rd ed. 1979. 90.00 (ISBN 0-12-296201-X). Acad Pr.

--Hormones in Blood, Vol. 2. 3rd ed. 1979. 80.00 (ISBN 0-12-296202-8). Acad Pr.

Hollenberg, N. K. The Haemodynamics of Nadolol. (Royal Society of Medicine International Congress & Symposium Ser.: No. 51). 1982. 7.50 (ISBN 0-8089-1535-5, 792048). Grune.

Kugelmass, I. Newton. Biochemistry of Blood in Health & Disease. (Illus.). 554p. 1959. 49.50x (ISBN 0-398-01061-7). C C Thomas.

Lasslo, A., ed. Blood Platelet Function & Medicinal Chemistry. 336p. 1984. 49.50 (ISBN 0-444-00790-3, Biomedical Pr). Elsevier.

Lowe, G. D., et al, eds. Clinical Aspects of Blood Viscosity & Cell Deformability. (Illus.). 264p. 1981. 44.00 (ISBN 0-387-10299-X). Springer-Verlag.

Russell, N. J. & Powell, G. M. Blood Biochemistry. (Biology in Medicine Ser.). (Illus.). 186p. 1982. text ed. 27.25x (ISBN 0-7099-0003-1). Sheridan.

Russell, N. J., et al. Blood Biochemistry. (Biology in Medicine). (Illus.). 178p. 1982. text ed. 30.00x (ISBN 0-7099-0003-1, Pub. by Croom Helm England); pap. text ed. 15.50x (ISBN 0-7099-0004-X). Sheridan.

Serneri, Gian G. N., et al, eds. Platelets, Prostaglandins & the Cardiovascular System. (Advances in Prostaglandin, Thromboxane, & Leukotriene Research Ser.: Vol. 13). (Illus.). 422p. 1985. text ed. 29.50 (ISBN 0-88167-062-6). Raven.

BLOOD–CIRCULATION

see also Blood-Vessels; Cardiovascular System; Heart; Microcirculation

Abramson, David I., ed. Blood Vessels & Lymphatics. 1962. 90.00 (ISBN 0-12-042550-5). Acad Pr.

Advanced Aerohemodynamics. 1984. 17.95 (ISBN 0-930835-04-2). Med Res Assocs.

Altura, B. M., ed. Ionic Regulation of the Microcirculation. (Advances in Microcirculation: Vol. 11). (Illus.). x, 174p. 1982. 63.50 (ISBN 3-8055-3429-9). S Karger.

Basar, E. & Weiss, C. Vasculature & Circulation: The Role of Myogenic Reactivity in the Regulation of Blood Flow. 272p. 1981. 90.00 (ISBN 0-444-80271-1). Elsevier.

Basic Aerohemodynamics. 1984. 17.95 (ISBN 0-930835-03-4). Med Res Assocs.

Becker, Anton E. & Anderson, Robert H. Cardiac Pathology: An Intergrated Text & Color Atlas. (Illus.). 280p. 1984. text ed. 97.00 (ISBN 0-89004-972-6). Raven.

Blunt, M. H. The Blood of Sheep: Composition & Function. (Illus.). 250p. 1975. 43.00 (ISBN 0-387-07234-9). Springer-Verlag.

Burton, A. C. Physiology & Biophysics of the Circulation. 1972. pap. 14.95 (ISBN 0-8151-1364-1). Year Bk Med.

Critser, James R., Jr. Blood Technology. (Ser. 10BT-80). 1981. 100.00 (ISBN 0-914428-84-5). Lexington Data.

DeLoach, et al, eds. Red Blood Cells As Carriers for Drugs. (Bibliotheca Haematologica: No. 51). (Illus.). viii, 162p. 1985. 44.25 (ISBN 3-8055-3940-1). S Karger.

De Sousa, Maria. Lymphocyte Circulation: Experimental & Clinical Aspects. LC 80-40848. 259p. 1981. 69.95x (ISBN 0-471-27854-8, Pub. by Wiley-Interscience). Wiley.

Donovan, Arthur & Prentiss, Joseph. James Hutton's Medical Dissertation. LC 80-65850. (Transaction Ser.: Vol. 70). 1980. 8.00 (ISBN 0-87169-706-8). Am Philos.

Folkow, Bjoern & Neil, Eric. Circulation. (Illus., Orig.). 1971. text ed. 39.95x (ISBN 0-19-501343-3). Oxford U Pr.

Gore, Joel M. & Alpert, Joseph S. Handbook of Hemodynamic Monitoring. 240p. 1984. pap. text ed. 13.95 (ISBN 0-316-32085-4). Little.

Harders, H., ed. Advances in Microcirculation, Vol. 4. (Illus.). 1972. 37.25 (ISBN 3-8055-1353-4). S Karger.

Harvey, William. Circulation of the Blood & Other Writings. Franklin, Kenneth J., ed. 1977. Repr. of 1963 ed. 12.95x (ISBN 0-460-00262-7, Evman). Biblio Dist.

--De Motu Cordis: Anatomical Studies on the Motion of the Heart & Blood. 5th ed. Leake, Chauncey D., tr. (Illus.). 186p. 1978. pap. 6.75x (ISBN 0-398-00793-4). C C Thomas.

--Works. Willis, Robert, tr. 1965. Repr. of 1847 ed. 45.00 (ISBN 0-384-21710-9). Johnson Repr.

Heuck, F. H., ed. Radiological Functional Analysis of the Vascular System: Contrast Media-Methods - Results. (Illus.). 296p. 1983. 50.00 (ISBN 0-387-12185-4). Springer-Verlag.

Hirsh, Jack, et al. Venous Thromboembolism. 1981. 39.50 (ISBN 0-8089-1408-1, 791992). Grune.

Hoffman, Brian F. Brief Reviews from Circulation Research, 1978. (AHA Monograph: No. 62). pap. cancelled (ISBN 0-686-59599-8, 73-048-A). Am Heart.

--Brief Reviews from Circulation Research, 1978. (AHA Monograph: No. 64). pap. 6.00 (ISBN 0-686-59600-5, 73-049A). Am Heart.

Hughes, Maysie J. & Barnes, Charles D., eds. Neural Control of Circulation. LC 79-6784. (Research Topics in Physiology Ser.). 1980. 37.50 (ISBN 0-12-360850-3). Acad Pr.

Iberall, A., et al. On Pulsatile & Steady Arterial Flow-the GTs Contribution. new ed. LC 72-96894. (Technical Monographs). (Illus.). 225p. (Orig.). 1973. pap. 6.00 (ISBN 0-914780-01-8). Gen Tech Serv.

Little. Physiology of the Heart & Circulation. 2nd ed. (Illus.). 352p. 1981. pap. 18.95 (ISBN 0-8151-5476-3). Year Bk Med.

McDonald, D. A. Blood Flow in the Arteries. 2nd ed. 512p. 1974. text ed. 57.50 (ISBN 0-7131-4213-8). E Arnold.

Machovich, Raymund, ed. The Thrombin. 176p. 1984. Vol. I. 58.00 (ISBN 0-8493-6186-9); Vol. II, 128pp. 43.00 (ISBN 0-8493-6187-7). CRC Pr.

Mates, R. E., et al, eds. Mechanics of the Coronary Circulation. 94p. 1983. pap. text ed. 24.00 (ISBN 0-317-02632-1, G00221). ASME.

Matsumoto, Teruo. Manual for Vascular Medicine & Surgery. (Illus.). 350p. 1982. pap. 26.95 (ISBN 0-8385-6132-2). ACC.

Messenger, Joseph. Lost Circulation. 112p. 1981. 39.95x (ISBN 0-87814-175-8). Pennwell Bks.

Minderhoud, J. M., ed. Cerebral Blood Flow. (The Jonxis Lectures: Vol. 7). 314p. 1982. 39.75 (ISBN 0-444-90207-4, Excerpta Medica). Elsevier.

Neil, Eric. The Human Circulation. Head, J. J., ed. LC 78-66621. (Carolina Biology Readers Ser.). (Illus.). 16p. 1979. pap. 1.60 (ISBN 0-89278-282-X, 45-9682). Carolina Biological.

Noordergraaf, Abraham. Circulatory System Dynamics. (Bioengineering Ser.). 1979. 41.00 (ISBN 0-12-520950-9). Acad Pr.

Patel, D. Basic Hemodynamics & Its Role in Disease Processes. 528p. 1980. 37.00 (ISBN 0-8391-1552-0). Univ Park.

Peripheral Circulation & Organ Blood Flow. (Handbook of Physiology: Section 2: The Cardiovascular System, Vol. III). 1100p. 1983. 245.00 (ISBN 0-683-07693-0). Am Physiological.

Rainer, Lick F. Atlas De Patogia Quirgica. 600p. 1981. pap. text ed. 90.00 (ISBN 0-06-315030-1, Pub. by HarLA Mexico). Har-Row.

Schmid-Schoenbein, H., et al, eds. Hemodilution & Flow Improvement: Bibliotheca Haematologica, No. 47. (Illus.). viii, 356p. 1982. pap. 80.50 (ISBN 3-8055-2899-X). S Karger.

Shepherd, A. P. & Granger, D. N., eds. Physiology of the Intestinal Circulation. LC 84-9858. (Illus.). 440p. 1984. text ed. 84.00 (ISBN 0-88167-025-1). Raven.

Tardos,., et al, eds. Pharmacological Control of Heart & Circulation: Proceedings of the Third Congress of the Hungarian Pharmacological Society, Budapest, 1979. LC 80-41281. (Advances in Pharmacological Research & Practice Ser.: Vol. I). 445p. 1981. 92.00 (ISBN 0-08-026386-0). Pergamon.

Tschopp, H. M. Microsurgical Neurovascular Anastomoses. LC 75-34226. 1975. pap. 36.00 (ISBN 0-387-07517-8). Springer-Verlag.

Walsh, S. Zoe, et al. The Human Fetal & Neonatal Circulation: Function & Structure. (Illus.). 368p. 1974. photocopy ed. 36.75x (ISBN 0-398-02662-9). C C Thomas.

Wolf, Stewart & Werthessen, Nicholas T., eds. Dynamics of Arterial Flow. LC 79-9770. (Advances in Experimental Medicine & Biology Ser.: Vol. 115). 480p. 1979. 65.00 (ISBN 0-306-40165-7, Plenum Pr). Plenum Pub.

Wolf, Stewart, et al, eds. Structure & Function of the Circulation, Vol. 1. 829p. 1980. 95.00x (ISBN 0-306-40278-5, Plenum Pr). Plenum Pub.

Yang, Sing S., et al. From Cardiac Catheterization Data to Hemodynamic Parameters. 2nd ed. LC 77-26630. (Illus.). 527p. 1978. text ed. 40.00x (ISBN 0-8036-9706-6). Davis Co.

BLOOD–COAGULATION

Abe, T. & Yamamaka, M., eds. Disseminated Intravascular Coagulation. (Bibliotheca Haematologica: No. 49). (Illus.). xiv, 356p. 1983. bound 84.00 (ISBN 3-8055-3726-3). S Karger.

Austen, D. E. & Rhymes, I. L. A Laboratory Manual of Blood Coagulation. (Illus.). 160p. 1976. 19.95 (ISBN 0-632-00781-8, B 0376-5, Blackwell). Mosby.

Bick, Roger L., ed. Disseminated Intravascular Coagulation & Related Syndromes. 144p. 1983. 57.00 (ISBN 0-8493-6636-4). CRC Pr.

Corrigan, James J., Jr. Hemorrhagic & Thrombotic Diseases in Childhood & Adolescence. (Illus.). 216p. 1985. text ed. 29.50 (ISBN 0-443-08425-4). Churchill.

Gaffney, P. J. Fibrinolysis: Current Fundamental & Clinical Concepts. Balkuv-Ulutin, S., ed. 1978. 47.00 (ISBN 0-12-273050-X). Acad Pr.

Hathaway, William E. & Bonnar, J. Perinatal Coagulation. (Monographs in Neonatology). 256p. 1978. 37.00 (ISBN 0-8089-1119-8, 791935). Grune.

Hemker, H. C. Prothrombin & Related Coagulation Factors. 1975. lib. bdg. 47.50 (ISBN 90-6021-236-3, Pub. by Leiden Univ Holland). Kluwer Academic.

Lijnen, H. R., et al, eds. Synthetic Substrates in Clinical Blood Coagulation Assays. (Developments in Hematology Ser.: No. 1). 142p. 1981. PLB 23.50 (ISBN 90-247-2409-0, Pub. Bymartinus Nijhoff). Kluwer Academic.

Morawitz, Paul. The Chemistry of Blood Coagulation. 192p. 1958. 19.75x (ISBN 0-398-01343-8). C C Thomas.

Ogston, D. & Bennett, R. Haemostasis: Biochemistry, Physiology & Pathology. LC 76-44231. 529p. 1977. 131.95x (ISBN 0-471-99459-6, Pub. by Wiley-Interscience). Wiley.

Parvez, Z. Immunoassays in Coagulation Testing. (Illus.). xvi, 173p. 1984. 37.50 (ISBN 0-387-90932-X). Springer-Verlag.

Protides of the Biological Fluids: Proceedings of the 28th Colloquium on Protides of the Biological Fluids, Brussels, 5-8 May 1980. LC 58-5908. (Illus.). 600p. 1980. 120.00 (ISBN 0-08-026370-4). Pergamon.

Prydz, H., ed. The Cell Biology of Triggers in Coagulation. (Journal: Haemostasis: Vol. 14 No. 5). (Illus.). 68p. 1985. pap. 24.00 (ISBN 3-8055-4046-9). S Karger.

Thomson, Jean, ed. Blood Coagulation & Haemostasis: A Practical Guide. 2nd ed. (Illus.). 1980. text ed. 46.25 (ISBN 0-443-01813-8). Churchill.

Triplett, Douglas A., ed. Laboratory Evaluation of Coagulation. LC 82-1654. (Illus.). 400p. 1982. text ed. 35.00 (ISBN 0-89189-073-4, 45-5-007-00). Am Soc Clinical.

Walz, Daniel A. & McCoy, Lowell E., eds. Contributions to Hemostasis, Vol. 370. 856p. 1981. 161.00x (ISBN 0-89766-129-X); pap. 161.00x (ISBN 0-89766-130-3). NY Acad Sci.

Witt, I., ed. New Methods for the Analysis of Coagulation Using Chromogenic Substrates. 275p. 1977. text ed. 33.60x (ISBN 3-11007-116-9). De Gruyter.

BLOOD–PARASITES

Weinman, David & Ristic, Miodrag. Infectious Blood Diseases of Man & Animals, 2 Vols. LC 68-18685. 1968. Vol. 1. 89.50 (ISBN 0-12-742501-2); Vol. 2. 95.00 (ISBN 0-12-742502-0). Acad Pr.

BLOOD BANKS–DATA PROCESSING

Wilson, Jan & Elliott, D. Mike, eds. Computers in the Blood Bank. (Illus.). 256p. 1984. pap. text ed. 30.00 (ISBN 0-914404-98-9). Am Assn Blood.

BLOOD-VESSELS

see also Blood–Circulation; Capillaries also names of organs and regions of the body, with or without the subdivision Blood Vessels

Abramson, David I., ed. Blood Vessels & Lymphatics. 1962. 90.00 (ISBN 0-12-042550-5). Acad Pr.

Back, N. & Sicuteri, F., eds. Vasopeptides: Chemistry, Pharmocology & Pathophysiology. LC 78-190395. (Advances in Experimental Medicine & Biology Ser.: Vol. 21). 519p. 1972. 65.00x (ISBN 0-306-39021-3, Plenum Pr). Plenum Pub.

Born, G. V. & Vane, J. R., eds. Interactions Between Platelets & Vessel Walls: Proceedings. (Royal Society of London Ser.). (Illus.). 196p. 1982. lib. bdg. 62.00x (ISBN 0-85403-164-2, Pub. by Royal Soc London). Scholium Intl.

Chazov, E. I. & Smirnov, V. N., eds. Vessel Wall in Athero & Thrombogenesis: Studies in the U. S. S. R. (Illus.). 224p. 1982. pap. 56.90 (ISBN 0-387-11384-3). Springer-Verlag.

Ciba Foundation. Blood Cells & Vessel Walls: Functional Interractions. (Ciba Symposium Ser.: No. 71). 1980. 47.00 (ISBN 0-444-90112-4). Elsevier.

Crock, H. V. & Yoshizaua, H. The Blood Supply of the Vertebral Column & Spinal Cord in Man. LC 76-40960. 1977. 63.00 (ISBN 0-387-81402-7). Springer-Verlag.

Effert, S. & Meyer-Erkelenz, J. D., eds. Blood Vessels: Eighth Scientific Conference of the Gesellschaft Deutscher Naturforscher & Artze, 20th-21st Oct., 1975 Rottach-Egern. (Illus.). 1976. soft cover 28.40 (ISBN 0-387-07909-2). Springer-Verlag.

Gross, D. R. & Hwang, N. H. The Rheology of Blood, Blood Vessels & Associated Tissues. (NATO Advanced Study, Applied Science Ser.: No. 41). 382p. 1981. 42.50 (ISBN 90-286-0950-4). Sijthoff & Noordhoff.

Hammersen, F., ed. Angiogenesis. (Mikrozirkulation in Forschung und Klinik; Progress in Applied Microcirculation: Vol. 4). (Illus.). vi, 90p. 1984. pap. 25.75 (ISBN 3-8055-3883-9). S Karger.

Heuck, F. H., ed. Radiological Functional Analysis of the Vascular System: Contrast Media-Methods - Results. (Illus.). 296p. 1983. 50.00 (ISBN 0-387-12185-4). Springer-Verlag.

Jang, G. D. Angioplasty. 752p. 1985. price not set (ISBN 0-07-032286-4). McGraw.

Keatinge, W. R. & Harman, M. Clare. Local Mechanisms Controlling Blood Vessels. (Monographs of the Physiological Society: No. 37). 1980. 36.00 (ISBN 0-12-402850-0). Acad Pr.

Kirk, John E. Enzymes of the Arterial Wall. 1969. 76.50 (ISBN 0-12-409650-6). Acad Pr.

Lasjaunias, Pierre. Craniofacial & Upper Cervical Arteries: Collateral Circulation & Angiographic Protocols. 300p. 1983. lib. bdg. 77.50 (ISBN 0-683-04898-8). Williams & Wilkins.

Oates, John A., et al. Interaction of Platelets with the Vessel Wall. 180p. 1985. 32.50 (ISBN 0-683-06622-6). Waverly Pr.

Pedley, T. J. The Fluid Mechanics of Large Blood Vessels. LC 78-73814. (Cambridge Monographs on Mechanics & Applied Mathematics). (Illus.). 1980. 99.50 (ISBN 0-521-22626-0). Cambridge U Pr.

Stehbens, William E. Hemodynamics & the Blood Vessel Wall. (Illus.). 664p. 1979. 75.25x (ISBN 0-398-03786-8). C C Thomas.

Symposia Angiologica Santoriana, 3rd Intl. Symposium, Fribourg, 1970. Physiology of Blood & Lymph Vessels: Proceedings, 2 pts. Comel, M. & Lastz, L., eds. Incl. Pt. 1. Angiologica, Vol. 8, Nos. 3-5; Pt. 2. Angiologica, Vol. 8, Additament. 1971. 1 vol. ed. reprint 33.00 (ISBN 3-8055-1263-5); Pt. 1. pap. text ed. 26.00 (ISBN 3-8055-2472-2); Pt. 2. pap. text ed. 17.50 (ISBN 3-8055-1289-9); Set. pap. text ed. 33.00 (ISBN 3-8055-1726-2). S Karger.

Symposium on the Mechanisms of Vasodilatation. Abstracts. Vanhoutte, P. M., ed. (Journal: Blood Vessels: Vol. 17, No. 3). 56p. 1980. soft cover 15.75 (ISBN 3-8055-1252-X). S Karger.

Symposium on the Transfer of Molecules & Ions Between Capillary Blood & Tissue - Alfred Benzon Symposium 2. Capillary Permeability: Proceedings. Crone, C. Z. & Lassen, N. A., eds. 1970. 70.00 (ISBN 0-12-197650-5). Acad Pr.

Woolf, Neville, ed. Pathology of the Vessel Wall: A Modern Appraisal. 360p. 1983. 48.50 (ISBN 0-03-064149-7). Praeger.

BLOODHOUNDS

see Dogs–Breeds–Bloodhounds

BLOWERS

see Compressors; Fans (Machinery)

BLOWING ENGINES

see Fans (Machinery)

BLOWOUTS, OILWELL

see Oil Well Blowouts

BLOWPIPE

see also Assaying; Chemistry, Analytic–Qualitative

Landauer, J. Blowpipe Analysis. 1984. pap. 8.95 (ISBN 0-917914-19-8). Lindsay Pubns.

BLUE-PRINTS

Bellis, Herbert F. & Schmidt, Walter A. Blueprint Reading for the Construction Trades. 2nd ed. (Illus.). 1978. pap. text ed. 26.90 (ISBN 0-07-004410-4). McGraw.

Bennett & Siy. Blueprint Reading for Welders. LC 76-29579. (Illus.). 180p. 1978. instructor's guide o.p. 5.00 (ISBN 0-8273-1060-9); charts 11.40wall (ISBN 0-8273-1063-3); transparencies 160.00 (ISBN 0-8273-1889-8). Delmar.

Bennett, A. E. & Sly, Louis J. Blueprint Reading for Welders. 3rd ed. 1983. 22.95 (ISBN 0-442-21358-1). Van Nos Reinhold.

Blueprint Reading for Machinists-Advanced. LC 75-138355. 86p. 1972. 12.80 (ISBN 0-8273-0087-5); instructor's guide o.p. 2.75 (ISBN 0-8273-0088-3). Delmar.

Brown, Walter C. Blueprint Reading for Construction. LC 79-23958. 336p. 1980. pap. text ed. 16.80 spiral bdg. (ISBN 0-87006-286-7). Goodheart.

--Blueprint Reading for Industry. Rev. ed. LC 82-20949. 345p. 1983. spiral bdg. 15.00 (ISBN 0-87006-429-0). Goodheart.

Gerbert, Kenneth L. National Electrical Code Blueprint Reading: Based on 1981. 8th ed. LC 80-67345. pap. 50.00 (ISBN 0-317-19779-7, 2023203). Bks Demand UMI.

Hardman, William E. How To Read Shop Prints & Drawings With Blueprints. 236p. 1982. pap. text ed. 19.95 (ISBN 0-910399-01-8). Natl Tool & Mach.

Helsel, Jay. Reading Engineering Drawings Through Conceptual Sketching. (Illus.). 1979. pap. text ed. 21.60 (ISBN 0-07-028031-2). McGraw.

Hoffman. Print Reading & Sketching Fundamentals. 1985. text ed. 11.25 (ISBN 0-538-33380-4, IE38). SW Pub.

--Print Reading for Industry. 1984. text ed. 12.95 (ISBN 0-538-33340-5, IE34). SW Pub.

Hoffman, Edward G. & Romero, Felix. Welding Blueprint Reading. 1983. pap. text ed. write for info. (ISBN 0-534-01431-3, Breton Pubs). Wadsworth Pub.

Huth, Mark W. Basic Construction Blueprint Reading. LC 79-50919. 1980. pap. text ed. 11.80 (ISBN 0-8273-1865-0); instructor's guide 3.60 (ISBN 0-8273-1866-9). Delmar.

--Basic Construction Blueprint Reading. 144p. 1980. 15.95 (ISBN 0-442-23874-6). Van Nos Reinhold.

Ihne, R. W. & Streeter, W. E. Machine Trades Blueprint Reading. 6th ed. 1972. pap. 12.50 spiral bound (ISBN 0-8269-1862-X). Am Technical.

Jensen, Cecil H. & Hines, Raymond D. Interpreting Engineering Drawings. LC 80-65469. (Blueprint Reading Ser.). 352p. 1984. pap. text ed. 14.80 (ISBN 0-8273-1936-3); instr's guide 5.10 (ISBN 0-8273-1937-1). Delmar.

Lightle, R. Paul. Blueprint Reading & Sketching. 1983. pap. 5.28 (ISBN 0-87345-067-1). McKnight.

Lockhart, Darrell C. Blueprint Reading for the Welding Trade. LC 83-14690. 206p. 1984. pap. text ed. 16.95 (ISBN 0-471-86844-2); write for info. tchr's manual (ISBN 0-471-86829-9). Wiley.

McCabe, Francis T., et al. Mechanical Drafting Essentials. 4th ed. text ed. 23.76 (ISBN 0-13-568931-7). P-H.

McDonnell, Leo & Ball, John. Blueprint Reading & Sketching for Carpenters: Residential. 3rd ed. LC 80-66027. (Blueprint Reading Ser.). (Illus.). 151p. 1981. pap. text ed. 12.40 (ISBN 0-8273-1354-3); instructor's guide 4.20 (ISBN 0-8273-1355-1). Delmar.

Mann, Peter A. Blueprint Reading for the Construction Trades. 1984. text ed. cancelled; pap. text ed. 22.95 (ISBN 0-8359-0517-9). Reston.

Nelson, John A. How to Read & Understand Blueprints. 304p. 1982. 22.95 (ISBN 0-442-26188-8). Van Nos Reinhold.

Olivo, C. Thomas & Payne, Albert V. Basic Blueprint Reading & Sketching. 4th ed. LC 82-71044. (Illus.). 176p. 1983. pap. text ed. 10.80 (ISBN 0-8273-2139-2); instr's guide 3.00 (ISBN 0-8273-2140-6). Delmar.

Olivo, Thomas, et al. Introduction to Blueprint Reading & Sketching. rev. ed. 1983. 21.50 (ISBN 0-442-27067-4). Van Nos Reinhold.

Olivo, Thomas P. & Olivo, C. Thomas. Blueprint Reading & Technical Sketching for Industry. LC 83-26174. 464p. 1985. pap. text ed. 16.00 (ISBN 0-8273-2205-4); instr's. guide 5.60 (ISBN 0-8273-2206-2). Delmar.

Palmquist, Roland. Answers on Blueprint Reading. 4th ed. LC 77-71585. 1985. 12.95 (ISBN 0-8161-1704-7). Audel.

Pouler, Wilfred. Print Reading for Machinist. 1984. text ed. 12.95 (ISBN 0-538-33350-2, IE35). SW Pub.

Putnam, Robert. Building Trades Blueprint Reading. 1985. pap. text ed. 24.95 (ISBN 0-8359-0507-1); tchr's. ed. avail. (ISBN 0-8359-0508-X). Reston.

--Construction Blueprint Reading. 1984. pap. text ed. 34.95 (ISBN 0-8359-0950-6); instrs' manual avail. (ISBN 0-8359-0951-4). Reston.

Putnam, Robert E. Basic Blueprint Reading: Residential. LC 80-80673. (Illus.). pap. 64.00 (ISBN 0-317-10898-0, 2017842). Bks Demand UMI.

Rayshich, Hale & McGuire. Blueprint Reading for Machine Technology. 1985. pap. text ed. 17.00 (ISBN 0-534-01383-X, 77F6040). Breton Pubs.

Resource Systems International. Blueprint Reading: Boilermaker. 1982. pap. text ed. 15.00 (ISBN 0-8359-0511-X). Reston.

--Blueprint Reading: Tanks & Vessels. 1982. pap. text ed. 15.00 (ISBN 0-8359-0512-8). Reston.

--Boiler: Installation. 1982. pap. text ed. 15.00 (ISBN 0-8359-0556-X). Reston.

--Construction Materials II. 1982. pap. text ed. 15.00 (ISBN 0-8359-0941-7). Reston.

Riggs, R. Print Reading for Machine Shop. (Illus.). 1982. 11.95 (ISBN 0-8269-1870-0). Am Technical.

Rohlmeier, Charles. Residential Construction: Blueprint Reading & Practices. 1983. pap. write for info. (ISBN 0-534-01387-2, Breton). Wadsworth Pub.

Rudman, Jack. Blueprint Machine Operator. (Career Examination Ser.: C-1136). (Cloth bdg. avail. on request). pap. 10.00 (ISBN 0-8373-1136-5). Natl Learning.

Schultz, Russel R. Blueprint Reading for the Machine Trades. (Illus.). 304p. 1981. text ed. 20.95 (ISBN 0-13-077727-7). P-H.

Shumaker, Terrence M. Process Piping Blueprint Reading. (Illus.). 176p. 1982. 19.95 (ISBN 0-13-723502-X). P-H.

Steinike, Otto A. Blueprint Reading, Checking & Testing, 2 Pts. 3rd ed. (Illus.). 1956. Pt. 1. pap. text ed. 5.00 (ISBN 0-87345-080-9); Pt. 2. text ed. 5.00 (ISBN 0-87345-082-5). McKnight.

Styles, Keith. Working Drawings Handbook. 128p. (Orig.). 1982. pap. 25.75 (ISBN 0-89397-118-9). Nichols Pub.

Sundberg, E. Building Trades Blueprint Reading, Pt. 3. rev. ed. (Illus.). 246p. 1981. spiral bdg. 15.95 (ISBN 0-8269-0453-X). Am Technical.

Sundberg, E. W. Building Trades Blueprint Reading, Pt. 2. 2nd ed. (Illus.). 240p. pap. 14.50 spiral (ISBN 0-8269-0447-5). Am Technical.

Sundberg, Elmer W. Building Trades Blueprint Reading. 5th ed. 1973. Pt. 1 (Fundamentals) pap. text ed. 11.50 (ISBN 0-8269-0435-1); Pt. 2 (Residential & Light Construction) pap. text ed. 13.75 (ISBN 0-8269-0447-5); Pt. 3 (General Construction, Specifications, & Heavy Construction, Rev.) pap. text ed. 15.50 (ISBN 0-8269-0453-X). Am Technical.

Taylor, David. Elementary Blueprint Reading for Machinists. LC 80-65572. (Blueprint Reading Ser.). 145p. 1981. pap. text ed. 8.80 (ISBN 0-8273-1895-2); instr's. guide 3.60 (ISBN 0-8273-1892-8). Delmar.

Taylor, David L. Blueprint Reading for Machinists. 4th, advanced ed. LC 85-6890. 224p. 1985. pap. text ed. 13.80 (ISBN 0-8273-1087-0); write for info. instr's. guide (ISBN 0-8273-1088-9). Delmar.

Traister. Blueprint Reading for the Building Trades. (Illus.). 1980. pap. 17.95 (ISBN 0-8359-0513-6). Reston.

Traister, John E. Basic Blueprint Reading for Practical Applications. (Illus.). 304p. 1983. price not set; pap. 13.95 (ISBN 0-8306-0146-5, 1546). TAB Bks.

Vanderloop, Thomas. Blueprint Reading for the Machine Trades. 1982. pap. text ed. 22.95 (ISBN 0-8359-0515-2); solutions manual free (ISBN 0-8359-0516-0). Reston.

Vogts, Raymond. Engineering Drawing & Blueprint Reading. LC 81-5047. (Illus.). 272p. 1981. pap. text ed. 8.00 (ISBN 0-668-05295-3, 5295). Arco.

Wallach, Paul I. & Hepler, Donald E. Reading Construction Drawings. (Illus.). 1979. pap. text ed. 19.55 (ISBN 0-07-067935-5). McGraw.

Weaver, Rip. Blueprint Reading Basics. LC 82-6104. 296p. (Orig.). 1982. 16.95x (ISBN 0-87201-075-9). Gulf Pub.

Willis, Charles D. Blueprint Reading for Commercial Construction. LC 77-87887. 1979. pap. 14.80 (ISBN 0-8273-1654-2); instructor's guide 4.80 (ISBN 0-8273-1655-0). Delmar.

Yearling, Robert A. Machine Trades Blueprint Reading. (Illus.). 320p. 1983. text ed. 21.95 (ISBN 0-13-542001-6). P-H.

Zinngrabe. Sheet Metal Blueprint Reading: For the Building Trades. LC 79-2748. 138p. 1980. 15.20 (ISBN 0-8273-1352-7); instr.'s guide 4.80 (ISBN 0-8273-1353-5). Delmar.

BLUEBERRIES

Eck, Paul & Childers, N. F., eds. Blueberry Culture. 1967. 27.50x (ISBN 0-8135-0535-6). Rutgers U Pr.

BLUEPRINTS

see Blue-Prints

BOAT-BUILDING

see also Fiberglass Boats; Ship-Building; Yacht-Building

Atkin, William & Atkin, John. The Book of Boats. LC 76-25311. (Illus.). 1976. Repr. of 1948 ed. 10.95 (ISBN 0-87742-081-5). Intl Marine.

Bingham, Bruce. The Sailor's Sketchbook. LC 83-531. (Illus.). 144p. 1983. pap. 9.95 (ISBN 0-915160-55-2). Seven Seas.

Birmingham, Richard. Boat Building Techniques Illustrated. LC 83-81366. (Illus.). 320p. 1984. 28.50 (ISBN 0-87742-176-5, B144). Intl Marine.

Brown, et al. Rip, Strip & Row: A Builder's Guide to the Cosine Wherry. LC 85-51141. 1985. pap. 19.95 (ISBN 0-917436-02-4). Tamal Vista.

Brown, Jim. The Case for the Cruising Trimaran. LC 78-64789. (Illus.). 1979. 15.95 (ISBN 0-87742-100-5). Intl Marine.

Chapelle, Howard I. American Small Sailing Craft. (Illus.). 1951. 26.95 (ISBN 0-393-03143-8). Norton.

--Boatbuilding. (Illus.). 1941. 25.95 (ISBN 0-393-03113-6). Norton.

Colvin, Thomas. Cruising Designs. (Illus.). 112p. 1977. pap. 5.95 (ISBN 0-915160-17-X). Seven Seas.

--Practical Steel Boatbuilding, Vol. 2. (Illus.). 224p. 1985. 25.00 (ISBN 0-87742-203-6). Intl Marine.

--Practical Steel Boatbuilding, Vol. 1. LC 84-48520. (Illus.). 288p. 1985. 30.00 (ISBN 0-87742-189-7). Intl Marine.

Desoutter, Denny. The Boat-Owner's Practical Dictionary. (Practical Handbooks for the Yachtsman Ser.). (Illus.). 1978. 14.95 (ISBN 0-370-30041-6). Transatlantic.

Estep, H. C. How Wooden Ships Are Built. (Illus.). 1983. 22.50 (ISBN 0-393-03288-4). Norton.

Gardner, John. Building Classic Small Craft. LC 76-8778. 1977. 27.50 (ISBN 0-87742-065-3). Intl Marine.

--Building Classic Small Craft, Vol. 2. LC 82-80401. (Illus.). 256p. 1984. 35.00 (ISBN 0-87742-157-9). Intl Marine.

Gibbs, Tony. The Coastal Cruiser. (Illus.). 1981. 24.95 (ISBN 0-393-03267-1). Norton.

Guzzwell, John. Modern Wooden Yacht Construction: Cold-Molding Joinery, Fitting Out. LC 78-64787. (Illus.). 1979. 27.50 (ISBN 0-87742-106-4). Intl Marine.

Hankinson, Ken. Fiberglass Boat Building for Amateurs. LC 82-80253. (Illus.). 1982. text ed. 22.95 (ISBN 0-686-37096-1). Glen-L Marine.

Henderson, Richard. Fifty-Three Boats You Can Build. LC 84-47853. (Illus.). 128p. 1984. pap. 12.95 (ISBN 0-87742-185-4). Intl Marine.

Herreshoff, L. Francis. Sensible Cruising Designs. LC 73-88019. 1973. 35.00 (ISBN 0-87742-035-1). Intl Marine.

How to Build Three Boats for Children. 1986. cancelled (ISBN 0-442-26330-9). Van Nos Reinhold.

Klingel, Gilbert & Colvin, Thomas. Boatbuilding with Steel (Including Boatbuilding with Aluminum) LC 72-97402. 260p. 1973. 20.00 (ISBN 0-87742-029-7). Intl Marine.

Lefebvre, R. Handbook of Artisanal Boatbuilding. (Commission for Inland Fisheries of Africa (CIFA): Technical Papers: No. 2). (Eng. & Fr., Illus.). 131p. 1975. pap. 9.50 (ISBN 0-685-57603-5, F734, FAO). Unipub.

Lipe, Bob & Lipe, Karen. Boat Canvas from Cover to Cover. LC 78-62679. 160p. 1978. 16.00 (ISBN 0-915160-27-7). Seven Seas.

Lipke, Paul. Plank on Frame: The Who, What & Where of 150 Boatbuilders. LC 80-80779. (Illus.). 320p. 1980. pap. 7.95 (ISBN 0-87742-121-8). Intl Marine.

Lowell, Royal. Boatbuilding Down East: How to Build the Maine Lobsterboat. LC 76-52309. (Illus.). 1977. 20.00 (ISBN 0-87742-088-2). Intl Marine.

McCormack, Carol. The Joy of Backyard Boat Building. LC 84-2320. (Illus.). 207p. 1984. pap. 8.95 (ISBN 0-918024-32-3). Ox Bow.

Mate, Ferenc. Best Boats To Build: From Bare Hull Up. (Illus.). 1982. 29.95 (ISBN 0-920256-06-6). Norton.

Nicolson, Ian. Build Your Own Boat. (Illus.). 1982. 22.95 (ISBN 0-393-03273-6). Norton.

--Cold-Moulded & Strip-Planked Wood Boatbuilding. (Illus.). 187p. 1983. 32.50 (ISBN 0-540-07147-1, Pub. by Stanford Maritime). Sheridan.

--Marinize Your Boat. 192p. 39.00x (ISBN 0-540-07139-0, Pub. by Stanford Maritime England). State Mutual Bk.

Patterson, H. W. Small Boat Building. (Shorey Lost Arts Ser.). (Illus.). 164p. pap. 9.95 (ISBN 0-8466-6052-0). Shorey.

Purdy, Donald, ed. Boatbuilder's International Directory. 7th ed. (Illus.). 116p. 1984. pap. 6.50 (ISBN 0-931339-00-6). Privateer Pub Co.

Rabl, S. S. Boatbuilding in Your Own Backyard. 2nd ed. LC 57-11361. 239p. 1958. 24.50 (ISBN 0-87033-009-8). Cornell Maritime.

Reinhart, Johanna M., ed. Small Boat Design. (Illus.). 79p. 1983. pap. text ed. 12.00 (ISBN 0-89955-393-1, Pub. by ICLARM Philippines). Intl Spec Bk.

Roberts, John. Fiber Glass Boats: Construction, Repair & Maintenance. (Illus.). 1984. 19.95 (ISBN 0-393-03291-4). Norton.

Roberts-Goodson, R. B. Illustrated Custom Boat Building. (Illus.). 192p. (Orig.). pap. 12.95 (ISBN 0-8227-8029-1). Petersen Pub.

Rose, Pat R. The Solar Boat Book. rev. ed. LC 83-70115. (Illus.). 266p. 1983. 14.95 (ISBN 0-89815-089-2); pap. 8.95 (ISBN 0-89815-086-8). Ten Speed Pr.

Setzer, Andrew R. Setzer's Cruising Designs-Power & Sail. (Illus.). 1979. pap. 4.00 (ISBN 0-915160-16-1). Seven Seas.

Simmons, Walter J. Lapstrake Boatbuilding, Vol. 2. LC 78-55779. (Illus.). 1980. 17.50 (ISBN 0-87742-127-7). Intl Marine.

--Lapstrake Boatbuilding: With Drawings by the Author. LC 78-55779. pap. 46.00 (ISBN 0-317-26552-0, 2023939). Bks Demand UMI.

Steward, Robert M. Boatbuilding Manual. 2nd ed. LC 79-90479. (Illus.). 228p. 1980. 25.00 (ISBN 0-87742-130-7). Intl Marine.

Sucher, Harry V. Simplified Boatbuilding: Flat Bottom. (Illus.). 1973. 24.95 (ISBN 0-393-03173-X). Norton.

--Simplified Boatbuilding: The V-Bottom Boat. LC 73-22340. (Illus.). 458p. 1974. 24.95 (ISBN 0-393-03180-2). Norton.

Taube, Allen. The Boatwrights Companion. (Illus.). 144p. 1985. pap. 15.95 (ISBN 0-87742-198-6). Intl Marine.

Taylor, Zack. Customizing Small Boats. LC 81-10474. 176p. 1981. pap. 10.95 (ISBN 0-8329-3320-1, Pub. by Winchester Pr). New Century.

Vaitses, Allan. Lofting. LC 78-75110. 1980. 17.50 (ISBN 0-87742-113-7). Intl Marine.

Vaitses, Allan H. Boatbuilding One-Off in Fiberglass. LC 82-48431. (Illus.). 288p. 1984. pap. 35.00 (ISBN 0-87742-156-0, B142). Intl Marine.

Verney, M. Complete Amateur Boat Building. pap. cancelled (ISBN 0-442-28834-4). Van Nos Reinhold.

Verney, Michael P. Complete Amateur Boat Building. 3rd ed. LC 78-68943. pap. 98.00 (ISBN 0-317-26555-5, 2023941). Bks Demand UMI.

West, Gordon & Pittman, Freeman. The Straightshooter's Guide to Marine Electronics. (Illus.). 112p. 1985. pap. 9.95 (ISBN 0-87742-202-8). Intl Marine.

White, Mark. Building the St. Pierre Dory. LC 78-55785. (Illus.). 1978. 7.95 (ISBN 0-87742-098-X). Intl Marine.

Whitener, Jack R. Ferro-Cement Boat Construction. LC 76-124468. (Illus.). 141p. 1971. 7.50 (ISBN 0-87033-140-X). Cornell Maritime.

Wiley, Jack. Boatbuilding from Fiberglass Hulls & Kits. LC 85-51060. (Illus.). 162p. 1985. pap. 26.95 (ISBN 0-913999-09-1). Solipaz Pub Co.

Witt, Glen L. & Hankinson, Ken. Boat Building with Plywood. 2nd ed. LC 78-58132. 1978. text ed. 15.95 (ISBN 0-686-08738-0). Glen-L Marine.

Wood, Charles E. Building Your Dream Boat. LC 81-5381. (Illus.). 522p. 1981. 26.00 (ISBN 0-87033-259-7). Cornell Maritime.

Wooden Shipbuilding & Small Craft Preservation. (Illus.). 104p. (Orig.). 1976. pap. 6.50 (ISBN 0-89133-045-3). Preservation Pr.

BOATS, CONCRETE

see Concrete Boats

BOATS, SUBMARINE

see Submarines

BOATS AND BOATING

see also Boat-Building; Canoes and Canoeing; Concrete Boats; Fiberglass Boats; Fishing Boats; Life-Boats; Motor-Boats; Sailboats; Ships; Steamboats and Steamboat Lines; Submarines; Yachts and Yachting

Abbey, Staten. Motorist Afloat. 14.50x (ISBN 0-392-01623-0, SpS). Sportshelf.

Ainsworth, Fay, ed. Better Boating: A Guide to Safety Afloat. LC 77-88516. (Illus.). 1982. Students Ed. 2.50 (ISBN 0-916682-31-5); Instr. Ed. 3.50 (ISBN 0-916682-30-7). Outdoor Empire.

Atkin, John. Practical Small Boat Designs. LC 82-48618. (Illus.). 192p. 1983. pap. 14.95 (ISBN 0-87742-160-9, P577). Intl Marine.

Averitt, Max W. Boatwatch. (Encore Edition). (Illus., Orig.). 1979. pap. 1.95 (ISBN 0-684-17689-0, SL854, ScribT). Scribner.

Beebe, Robert P. Voyaging under Power. LC 74-21847. (Illus.). 272p. 1975. 19.95 (ISBN 0-915160-18-8). Seven Seas.

Bingham, Fred P. Practical Yacht Joinery: Tools, Techniques, Tips. LC 81-81418. (Illus.). 320p. 1983. 32.50 (ISBN 0-87742-140-4). Intl Marine.

Blackburn, Graham. The Illustrated Encyclopedia of Ships, Boats & Vessels. LC 78-16565. (Illus.). 448p. 1978. 35.00 (ISBN 0-87951-082-X); pap. 14.95 (ISBN 0-87951-141-9). Overlook Pr.

Blandford, Percy. Illustrated History of Small Boats. (Illus.). 1974. 9.50 (ISBN 0-902875-51-5). Transatlantic.

Block, Richard A., ed. Understanding T-Boat Regulations. (Illus.). 143p. 1979. pap. text ed. 12.00 (ISBN 0-934114-22-6, BK-115). Marine Educ.

Bolger, Philip C. Thirty-Odd Boats. LC 82-80403. (Illus.). 224p. 1982. 22.50 (ISBN 0-87742-152-8). Intl Marine.

Bond, Bob & Sleight, Steve. Cruising Boat Sailing: The Basic Guide. LC 82-48882. (Illus.). 1983. 14.95 (ISBN 0-394-52447-0). Knopf.

Brewer, Edward S. & Betts, Jim. Understanding Boat Design. 3rd ed. LC 70-147872. (Illus.). 1980. pap. 9.95 (ISBN 0-87742-015-7). Intl Marine.

Brown, Robert, ed. Boater's Safety Handbook. (Illus.). 52p. (Orig.). 1982. pap. 2.95 (ISBN 0-89886-072-5). Mountaineers.

Brown, T. Nigel, ed. Brown's Nautical Almanac, 1983. 106th ed. LC 32-280. (Illus.). 946p. 1982. 47.00x (ISBN 0-8002-3066-3). Intl Pubns Serv.

Carstensen, Russell V. EMI Control in Boats & Ships. White, Donald R., ed. LC 80-51209. (Illus.). 280p. 1981. text ed. 37.00 (ISBN 0-932263-20-8). White Consult.

Chapman, Charles F. & Maloney, E. S. Chapman's Piloting, Seamanship & Small Boat Handling. 56th rev. ed. (Illus.). 624p. 1983. FPT 23.95 (ISBN 0-87851-814-2, Pub. by Hearst Bks); deluxe ed. 33.95 FPT (ISBN 0-87851-815-0). Morrow.

Colvin, Thomas. Cruising Wrinkles. 112p. 1975. pap. 5.95 (ISBN 0-915160-14-5). Seven Seas.

--Practical Steel Boatbuilding, Vol. 1. LC 84-48520. (Illus.). 288p. 1985. 30.00 (ISBN 0-87742-189-7). Intl Marine.

Colvin, Thomas E. Coastwise & Offshore Cruising Wrinkles. pap. 5.95 (ISBN 0-915160-14-5). Seven Seas.

--Cruising Designs from the Board of Thomas E. Colvin. (Illus.). 112p. 1977. 5.95 (ISBN 0-915160-17-X). Seven Seas.

Crowley, William, ed. Rushton's Rowboats & Canoes, 1903. LC 82-48169. (Illus.). 128p. 1983. pap. 8.95 (ISBN 0-87742-164-1). Intl Marine.

Damour, Jacques. One Hundred & One Tips & Hints for Your Boat. Howard-Williams, Jeremy, tr. from Fr. (Illus.). 1981. 13.95 (ISBN 0-393-03262-0). Norton.

Derrick, David. Boat Maintenance. (Illus.). 128p. 1984. 18.95 (ISBN 0-7153-8412-0). David & Charles.

Douglas, Gilean. The Protected Place. (Illus.). 190p. 1979. pap. 7.95 (ISBN 0-88826-080-6). Superior Pub.

Durant, Kenneth & Durant, Helen. The Adirondack Guide-Boat. (Illus.). xvii, 250p. 1980. 30.00 (ISBN 0-686-75279-1). Adirondack Mus.

Engineering Applications: Vol. 1: Installation & Maintainance of Engines in Small Fishing Vessels. (Fisheries Technical Papers: No. 196). (Eng., Fr. & Span., Illus.). 138p. (2nd Printing 1982). 1979. pap. 9.75 (ISBN 92-5-100862-0, F1948, FAO). Unipub.

Evinrude Johnson Outboards, 2-40 hp: 1973-1984. (Illus.). 300p. 1984. 22.95 (ISBN 0-89287-404-X). Western Marine Ent.

Evinrude Johnson Outboards, 50-235hp: 1973-1985. (Illus.). 320p. 1984. 22.95 (ISBN 0-89287-397-3). Western Marine Ent.

Fisher, Hank. The Floater's Guide to Montana. LC 79-52411. (Illus.). 160p. (Orig.). 1979. pap. 6.95 (ISBN 0-934318-00-X). Falcon Pr MT.

Fraser, Bruce. Weekend Navigator. 1981. 18.50 (ISBN 0-8286-0090-2). J De Graff.

French, John. Electrics & Electronics for Small Craft. new ed. (Illus.). 255p. 1986. write for info. (ISBN 0-229-11612-4, Pub. by Adlard Coles). Sheridan.

Gannaway, Dave. Buying a Secondhand Boat. 104p. 1980. 15.00x (ISBN 0-245-53446-6, Pub. by Nautical England). State Mutual Bk.

Gardner, John. Dory Book. LC 77-85409. 1978. 27.50 (ISBN 0-87742-090-4). Intl Marine.

Getchell, David R., et al, eds. Mariner's Catalog, Vol. 2. LC 73-88647. 1974. pap. 2.00 (ISBN 0-87742-046-7). Intl Marine.

Glasspool, John. Boats of the Longshoremen. 136p. 1980. 18.00x (ISBN 0-245-53111-4, Pub. by Nautical England). State Mutual Bk.

Gould, Jan. The Boathouse Question. 132p. 1978. pap. 6.95 (ISBN 0-686-74132-3). Superior Pub.

Grant, Sea. First Aid for Boaters & Divers. 128p. 1980. pap. 6.95 (ISBN 0-8329-1425-8). New Century.

Grayson, Stan. The Dinghy Book. LC 80-84743. (Illus.). 272p. 1981. 7.95 (ISBN 0-87742-135-8). Intl Marine.

Greenwood, John O. & Dills, Michael. Greenwood's & Dills' Lake Boats, 1983. 19th, rev. ed. 180p. 1983. 4.75 (ISBN 0-912514-04-3). Freshwater.

Gruss, Robert. Dictionnaire de Marine, Francais et Anglais. (Fr. & Eng.). 368p. 1978. 49.95 (ISBN 0-686-57319-6, M-6302). French & Eur.

Guthorn, Peter J. The Sea Bright Skiff & Other Shore Boats. rev. ed. LC 82-62951. (Illus.). 256p. 1983. pap. 13.95 (ISBN 0-916838-73-0). Schiffer.

Hedley, Eugene. Boating For the Handicapped: Guidelines for the Physically Handicapped. LC 79-91181. (Illus.). 124p. 1979. 5.65 (ISBN 0-686-38820-8). Human Res Ctr.

Henderson, Richard. The Racing-Cruiser. 2nd ed. LC 82-84658. (Illus.). 240p. 1983. 24.95 (ISBN 0-87742-169-2, R586). Intl Marine.

--Sea Sense. 2nd ed. LC 79-64104. 1979. 20.00 (ISBN 0-87742-124-2). Intl Marine.

Herreshoff, L. Francis. Compleat Cruiser: The Art, Practice & Enjoyment of Boating. LC 56-12511. (Illus.). 384p. 1983. Repr. of 1956 ed. 16.50 (ISBN 0-911378-05-7). Sheridan.

Hubbard, Don. The Complete Book of Inflatable Boats. LC 79-27460. (Illus.). 256p. (Orig.). 1980. pap. 7.95 (ISBN 0-930030-18-4). Western Marine Ent.

Imhoff, Fred & Pranger, Lex. Boat Tuning for Speed. 152p. 1981. 30.00x (ISBN 0-333-32044-1, Pub. by Nautical England). State Mutual Bk.

Jarman, Colin. Buying a Boat. LC 80-68904. (Illus.). 160p. 1981. 16.95 (ISBN 0-7153-7960-7). David & Charles.

Jones, Charles. Boat Maintenance: Ideas & Practice. 192p. 1980. 12.00x (ISBN 0-245-52347-2, Pub. by Nautical England). State Mutual Bk.

Lahue, Kalton C. OMC Stern Drive Shop Manual 1964-1985. Wauson, Sydnie A. & Hamlin, Steve, eds. (Illus.). 384p. (Orig.). 1984. pap. 22.95 (ISBN 0-89287-398-1, B730). Clymer Pubns.

Leather, John. Sail & Oar. LC 82-48098. (Illus.). 144p. 1982. 22.50 (ISBN 0-87742-161-7). Intl Marine.

Lipe, Bob & Lipe, Karen. Boat Canvas from Cover to Cover. (Illus.). 134p. 1982. pap. 16.00 (ISBN 0-915160-21-8, 53172-7). Seven Seas.

McGrail, Sean. Ancient Boats. (Shire Archaeology Ser.: No. 31). (Illus.). 64p. 1983. pap. 5.95 (ISBN 0-85263-626-1, Pub. by Shire Pubns England). Seven Hills Bks.

Mariner Outboards, Two - Forty Eight HP: 1976-1984. (Illus.). 334p. 1984. 22.95 (ISBN 0-89287-400-7). Western Marine Ent.

Markow, Herbert L. Small Boat Law: Nineteen Seventy-Nine to Nineteen Eighty Supplement. LC 77-154289. 174p. 1981. pap. 24.00x (ISBN 0-934108-02-1). H L Markow.

Martin, Fred W. Nineteen Hundred One Album of Designs for Boats, Launches & Yachts. rev. ed. LC 80-69290. (Illus.). 80p. 1980. pap. 5.00x (ISBN 0-9604976-0-9). Altair Pub Co.

Mate, Ferenc. The Finely Fitted Yacht, 2 vols. (Illus.). 1979. Vol. 1. Vol. 2. Comp. ed. 27.95 (ISBN 0-920256-05-8). Norton.

The Mechanization of Small Fishing Craft. pap. 7.00 (FN47, FNB). Unipub.

Mercury Outboards, Fifty to Two Hundred Twenty Five HP: 1972-1984. (Illus.). 344p. 1984. 22.95 (ISBN 0-89287-396-5). Western Marine Ent.

Mercury Outboards, Three Point Five to Forty HP: 1972-1984. (Illus.). 280p. 1984. 22.95 (ISBN 0-89287-395-7). Western Marine Pub.

Miller, Conrad & Maloney, E. S. Your Boat's Electrical System, 1981-1982. 1984. 17.45 (ISBN 0-87851-805-3, Hearst Marine Bk). Morrow.

Mosenthal, Basil & Hewitt, Dick. Ready for Sea: Check Your Boat. 1981. pap. 3.95 encore ed. (ISBN 0-684-17587-8, ScribT). Scribner.

National Fisherman Editors. Sixty Boat Designs for Power & Sail from National Fisherman. LC 81-82487. (Illus.). 64p. 1981. pap. 7.95 (ISBN 0-87742-146-3). Intl Marine.

Nicolson, Ian. Boat Data Book. 194p. 1982. 32.00x (ISBN 0-333-32042-5, Pub. by Nautical England). State Mutual Bk.

--Surveying Small Craft: Fault Finding in Boats. 2nd ed. (Illus.). 272p. 1984. 17.95 (ISBN 0-911378-47-2). Sheridan.

Nielson, Christian. Wooden Boat Designs: Classic Danish Boats. 152p. 1981. 35.00x (ISBN 0-540-07396-2, Pub. by Stanford Maritime England). State Mutual Bk.

Norgrove, Ross. Cruising Rigs & Rigging. LC 81-82489. (Illus.). 272p. 1982. 27.50 (ISBN 0-87742-145-5). Intl Marine.

Paasch, Henri. Dictionnaire Anglais-Francais et Francais-Anglais des Termes et Locutions Maritimes. 2nd ed. (Fr. & Eng.). 320p. 1974. pap. 23.50 (ISBN 0-686-57065-0, M-6437). French & Eur.

Painter, A. A. Consumer Protection for Boat Users. 104p. 1980. 12.00x (ISBN 0-245-53450-4, Pub. by Nautical England). State Mutual Bk.

Powerboat Maintenance. (Illus.). 288p. pap. 9.95 (ISBN 0-89287-069-9). Western Marine Ent.

Putz, George & Spectre, Peter, eds. Mariner's Catalog, Vol. 5. LC 73-88647. (Illus.). 1977. pap. 2.00 (ISBN 0-87742-093-9). Intl Marine.

--Mariner's Catalog, Vol. 6. LC 73-88647. (Illus.). 1978. pap. 2.00 (ISBN 0-87742-109-9). Intl Marine.

Richey, David. The Small Boat Handbook. LC 78-3315. (Illus.). 1979. 10.95i (ISBN 0-690-01697-2). T Y Crowell.

Robb, Frank. Handling Small Boats in Heavy Weather. (Illus.). 133p. 1977. 12.95x (ISBN 0-8464-1105-9). Beekman Pubs.

Rowboat Book. 1986. cancelled (ISBN 0-442-25866-6). Van Nos Reinhold.

Royce, Patrick M. Trailerboating Illustrated. 2nd rev. ed. LC 81-11398. (Planing Hulls, Trailers, Seamanship Ser.: No. 1). (Illus.). 192p. 1981. pap. 8.95 (ISBN 0-930030-19-2). Western Marine Ent.

Russell, P. J. Sea Signalling Simplified. rev. ed. 1977. 5.95 (ISBN 0-8286-0072-4). J De Graff.

Sandahl, Bertil. Middle English Sea Terms: Masts, Spars & Sails, Pt. 2. (Essays & Studies on English Language & Literature: Vol. 20). 1958. pap. 16.00 (ISBN 0-317-17948-9). Kraus Repr.

Saunders, A. E. Small Craft Piloting & Coastal Navigation. LC 81-71657. (Illus.). 287p. 1982. 19.95 (ISBN 0-442-29699-1). Van Nos Reinhold.

Scarlett, John. Wooden Boat Repair Manual. LC 81-80232. (Illus.). 272p. 1981. 22.50 (ISBN 0-87742-143-9). Intl Marine.

Schult, Joachim. Curious Boating Inventions. LC 74-1525. (Illus.). 150p. 1974. 14.95 (ISBN 0-8008-2103-3). Taplinger.

Sea Explorer Safe Boating Instructor's Guide. 3.75 (ISBN 0-8395-6662-X, SL6662). BSA.

Sleightholme, Des. Better Boat Handling. LC 82-19210. (Illus.). 178p. 1983. 15.95 (ISBN 0-915160-30-7). Seven Seas.

--Better Boat Handling. 1982. 39.00x (ISBN 0-540-07148-X, Pub. by Stanford Maritime England). State Mutual Bk.

Sleightholme, J. D. Fitting Out: Maintenance & Repair of Small Craft. (Illus.). 130p. 1977. 14.95x (ISBN 0-8464-1096-6). Beekman Pubs.

--The Trouble with Cruising: Hard Learned Lessons in Small Boats. (Illus.). 113p. 1982. 13.50 (ISBN 0-333-33009-9, Pub. by Macmillan London). Sheridan.

Small Steel Craft. 2nd ed. LC 82-84779. (Illus.). 220p. 1983. 22.50 (ISBN 0-87742-170-6, S690). Intl Marine.

Snyder, Paul & Snyder, Arthur. Handling Ropes & Lines Afloat. 112p. 1982. 25.00x (ISBN 0-333-32066-2, Pub. by Nautical England). State Mutual Bk.

Strahm, Virgil. Does Your Fiberglass Boat Need Repair? LC 81-90093. (Illus.). 46p. (Orig.). pap. 5.00 (ISBN 0-9606050-0-2). Strahm.

Taylor, Roger C. Still More Good Boats. LC 80-84847. (Illus.). 304p. 1981. 30.00 (ISBN 0-87742-136-6). Intl Marine.

Temple. The Complete Step-by-Step Boat Repair & Restoration Handbook. 416p. pap. 12.95 (ISBN 0-8306-1246-7, 1246). TAB Bks.

Thomson, David. Pair Trawling & Pair Seining: The Technology of Two-Boat Fishing. (Illus.). 168p. 1978. 35.00 (ISBN 0-85238-087-9, FN73, FNB). Unipub.

Toghill, Jeff. The Boat Owner's Fitting Out Manual. 224p. 1981. 50.00x (ISBN 0-540-07398-9, Pub. by Stanford Maritime England). State Mutual Bk.

Toghill, Jeff E. Boat Owner's Maintenance Manual. 1971. 15.00 (ISBN 0-8286-0043-0). J De Graff.

Toss, Brion. The Rigger's Apprentice. LC 84-47755. (Illus.). 208p. 1985. 27.50 (ISBN 0-87742-165-X). Intl Marine.

United States Coast Guard Auxiliary. Boating Skills & Seamanship. 9th ed. LC 74-164688. (Illus.). 252p. 1984. pap. text ed. 8.00 (ISBN 0-930028-00-7). US Coast Guard.

Vaitses, Alan. What Shape Is She In? A Guide to the Surveying of Boats. LC 84-48689. (Illus.). 176p. 1985. 14.95 (ISBN 0-87742-192-7). Intl Marine.

Verney, M. Boat Repairs & Conversions. 1986. pap. cancelled (ISBN 0-442-28835-2). Van Nos Reinhold.

Walliser, Blair. New Basic Seamanship & Safe Boat Handling. 1985. pap. 11.95 (ISBN 0-385-23074-5). Doubleday.

Watney, John. Boat Electrics. LC 80-68680. (Illus.). 160p. 1981. 18.95 (ISBN 0-7153-7957-7). David & Charles.

--Cruising in British & Irish Waters. (Illus.). 224p. 1983. 23.95 (ISBN 0-7153-8402-3). David & Charles.

Whiting, John & Bottomley, Tom. Chapman's Log & Owner's Manual. 192p. 1980. 14.95 (ISBN 0-87851-801-0); deluxe ed. o.p. 75.00 (ISBN 0-686-96737-2). Hearst Bks.

Willerton, P. F. Basic Shiphandling for Masters, Mates & Pilots. 152p. 1981. 25.00x (Pub. by Stanford England). State Mutual Bk.

Williams, H. G. Hints & Gadgets for Small Craft Owners. 169p. 1964. pap. 2.50x (ISBN 0-85174-183-5). Sheridan.

Winters, David D. The Boat Officer's Handbook. LC 81-607042. 112p. 1981. pap. 9.95x (ISBN 0-87021-102-1). Naval Inst Pr.

Witt, Glen L. How to Build Boat Trailers. (Illus.). pap. 6.50 (ISBN 0-686-05390-7). Glen-L Marine.

BOBCAT

Ryden, Hope. Bobcat Year. LC 81-65265. (Illus.). 224p. 1981. 15.95 (ISBN 0-670-17730-X). Viking.

Young, Stanley P. The Bobcat of North America: Its History, Life Habits, Economic Status & Control, with List of Currently Recognized Subspecies. LC 77-14021. (Illus.). xviii, 213p. 1978. pap. 5.95 (ISBN 0-8032-5894-1, BB 663, Bison). U of Nebr Pr.

BOBWHITES

see Quails

BODY FLUIDS

see also Bile; Biological Transport; Blood; Homeostasis; Osmosis; Perspiration

Brooks, Chandler M., et al. Humors, Hormones, & Neurosecretions: The Origins & Development of Man's Present Knowledge of the Humoral Control of Body Functions. LC 61-14336. 1962. 39.00x (ISBN 0-87395-006-2). State U NY Pr.

Burgess, Audrey. The Nurse's Guide to Fluid & Electrolyte Balance. 2nd ed. (Illus.). 1979. pap. text ed. 26.95 (ISBN 0-07-008955-8). McGraw.

Burke, Shirley R. The Composition & Function of Body Fluids. 3rd ed. LC 80-17952. (Illus.). 208p. 1980. pap. text ed. 12.95 (ISBN 0-8016-0903-8). Mosby.

Cort, Joseph. Electrolytes, Fluid Dynamics, & the Nervous System. 1966. 46.00 (ISBN 0-12-190150-5). Acad Pr.

Cywinski, Jozef. The Essentials in Pressure Monitoring: Blood & Other Body Fluids. (The Tardieu Ser.: No. 3). (Illus.). 120p. 1980. pap. 20.00 (ISBN 90-247-2385-X, Pub. by Martinus Nijhoff Netherlands). Kluwer Academic.

Gall, Lorraine S. & Curby, William A. Instrumented Systems for Microbiological Analysis of Body Fluids. 192p. 1980. 56.00 (ISBN 0-8493-5681-4). CRC Pr.

Groer, Maureen W. Physiology & Pathophysiology of the Body Fluids. LC 80-28583. (Illus.). 299p. 1981. pap. text ed. 16.95 (ISBN 0-8016-1989-0). Mosby.

Kidney & Body Fluids. (Advances in Physiological Sciences Ser.: Vol. 11). 70.00x (ISBN 0-08-026825-0). Pergamon.

Klahr, Saulo, ed. The Kidney & Body Fluids in Health & Disease. 616p. 1984. pap. 29.50x (ISBN 0-306-41660-3, Plenum Med Bk). Plenum Pub.

Lockwood, Antony P. Animal Body Fluids & Their Regulation. LC 64-9913. (Illus.). 1963. 12.00x (ISBN 0-674-03700-6). Harvard U Pr.

Peeters, H., ed. Protides of the Biological Fluids, Colloquium 32: Proceedings of the 32nd Colloquium on Protides of the Biological Fluids, Brussels, Belgium, May 1984. (Illus.). 1240p. 1984. 204.00 (ISBN 0-08-031739-1). Pergamon.

--Protides of the Biological Fluids: Proceedings, Colloquium on Protides of the Biological Fluids, 16th-23rd. Incl. 16th. 1969 (ISBN 0-08-013348-7); 17th. 1970 (ISBN 0-08-015566-9); 18th. 1971 (ISBN 0-08-016622-9); 19th. 1972 (ISBN 0-08-016876-0); 20th. 1973 (ISBN 0-08-017131-1); 21st. 1974 (ISBN 0-08-017822-7); 22nd. 1976 (ISBN 0-08-018233-X); 23rd. 1976 (ISBN 0-08-019929-1). LC 58-5908. 131.00 ea. (ISBN 0-08-029797-8). Pergamon.

Pitts, Robert F. Physiology of the Kidney & Body Fluids. 3rd ed. (Illus.). 307p. 1974. pap. 15.95 (ISBN 0-8151-6703-2). Year Bk Med.

Ragin, Douglas. Hearthrobs. 1984. 6.95 (ISBN 0-533-06052-4). Vantage.

Reddi, A. H. Extracellular Matrix: Structure & Function. (UCLA Ser.: Vol. 25). 230p. 1985. 96.00 (ISBN 0-8451-2624-5). A R Liss.

Ross, Doris & Neely, Ann E. Textbook of Urinalysis & Body Fluids. (Illus.). 348p. 1983. 27.95 (ISBN 0-8385-8913-8). ACC.

Schmidt-Nielsen, Knut, et al, eds. Comparative Physiology: Water, Ions & Fluid Mechanics. LC 77-7320. (Illus.). 1978. 64.50 (ISBN 0-521-21696-6). Cambridge U Pr.

Signeur, Austin V. Literature Guide to the GLC of Body Fluids. LC 82-490. (IFI Data Base Library). 396p. 1982. 95.00x (ISBN 0-306-65203-X, AACR2, Plenum Pr). Plenum Pub.

Stroot, Violet R., et al. Fluids & Electrolytes: A Practical Approach. 3rd ed. LC 84-1804. (Illus.). 358p. 1984. 12.95x (ISBN 0-8036-8207-7). Davis Co.

Vanatta, John C. & Fogelman, Morris J. Moyer's Fluid Balance: A Clinical Manual. 3rd ed. (Illus.). 1982. pap. 15.95 (ISBN 0-8151-8963-X). Year Bk Med.

Weldy, Norma J. Body Fluids & Electrolytes: A Programmed Presentation. 3rd ed. (Illus.). 132p. 1980. pap. 10.95 (ISBN 0-8016-5383-5). Mosby.

BOILING WATER REACTORS

Boiling Water Reactor Transient Response. (Illus.). 102p. 1979. Set. 2476.00x (ISBN 0-87683-063-7); text ed. 20.00x spiral bdg. (ISBN 0-87683-064-5); Videotape 1. 620.00x (ISBN 0-87683-065-3); Videotape 2. 620.00x (ISBN 0-87683-066-1); Videotape 3. 620.00x (ISBN 0-87683-067-X); Videotape 4. 620.00x (ISBN 0-87683-068-8). G P Courseware.

British Nuclear Energy Society, ed. Boiler Dynamics & Control in Nuclear Power Stations, No. 1. 215p. 1973. 90.00x (ISBN 0-901948-73-X, Pub. by Brit Nuclear England). State Mutual Bk.

--Boiler Dynamics & Control in Nuclear Power Stations, No. 2. 436p. 1980. 100.00x (ISBN 0-7277-0095-2, Pub. by Brit Nuclear England). State Mutual Bk.

Deutsch, R. W., et al. Introduction to Boiling Water Reactor Nuclear Power Plants. (Illus.). 240p. 1976. looseleaf 60.00x (ISBN 0-87683-298-2). G P Courseware.

Lahey, R. T. & Moody, Frederick J. The Thermal Hydraulics of a Boiling Water Nuclear Reactor. LC 76-45712. (Nuclear Science Technology Ser.). (Illus.). 1977. 41.95 (ISBN 0-89448-010-3, 300011). Am Nuclear Soc.

Pressurized Water Reactor Transient Response. (Illus.). 1978. Set. 2476.00x (ISBN 0-87683-069-6); spiral bdg. 20.00x (ISBN 0-87683-070-X); Videotape 1. 620.00x (ISBN 0-87683-071-8); Videotape 2. 620.00x (ISBN 0-87683-072-6); Videoatpe 3. 620.00x; Videotape 4. 620.00x (ISBN 0-87683-074-2). G P Courseware.

BOLETI

Coker, William C. & Beers, Alma H. The Boleti of North Carolina. (Illus.). 10.00 (ISBN 0-8446-5016-1). Peter Smith.

Dennis, R. W., et al. New Check List of British Agarics & Boleti. 1974. Repr. of 1960 ed. 14.00 (ISBN 3-7682-0935-0). Lubrecht & Cramer.

Moser, Meinhard. The Polypores, Boletes & Agarica. Kibby, G. & Rayner, R., trs. from Ger. (Illus.). 355p. 1983. text ed. 33.95x (ISBN 0-916422-43-7). Mad River.

Singer, Rolf. Boletes & Related Groups in South America. (Illus.). pap. 6.40 (ISBN 3-7682-0212-7). Lubrecht & Cramer.

Smith, Alexander H. & Thiers, Harry D. Boletes of Michigan. LC 77-107979. (Illus.). 1970. 20.00x (ISBN 0-472-85590-5). U of Mich Pr.

Snell, W. H. & Dick, E. A. The Boleti of Northeastern North America. (Illus.). 1970. 87.50 (ISBN 3-7682-0681-5). Lubrecht & Cramer.

Thiers, Harry. California Mushrooms: A Field Guide to the Boletes. LC 74-11002. (Illus.). 1974. text ed. 19.95x (ISBN 0-02-853410-7). Hafner.

BOMB RECONNAISSANCE

Here are entered works on the location, identification, and application of safety measures as protection against unexploded bombs which have been set to detonate.

Brodie, Thomas G. Bombs & Bombings: A Handbook to Detection, Disposal & Investigation for Police & Fire Departments. (Illus.). 200p. 1980. photycopy ed. 24.75x (ISBN 0-398-02245-3). C C Thomas.

Knowles, Graham. Bomb Security Guide. LC 76-41301. (Illus.). 1976. pap. 22.95 (ISBN 0-913708-25-9). Butterworth.

BOMBARDMENT, ION

see Ion Bombardment

BOMBARDMENTS WITH PARTICLES

see Collisions (Nuclear Physics)

BOMBERS

see also B-Seventeen Bomber; B-Twenty-Four Bomber; Boeing Bombers; Heinkel One Hundred Seventy-Seven (Bombers); Stuka (Bombers)

Aero Publishers Aeronautical Staff. Junkers JU87. LC 66-22651. (Aero Ser: Vol. 8). 1966. pap. 3.95 (ISBN 0-8168-0528-8). Aero.

B-26 Marauder in Action. (Illus.). 50p. 1984. pap. 4.95 (ISBN 0-89747-119-9, 1050). Squad Sig Pubns.

B-29 Superfortress in Action. (Aircraft in Action Ser.). (Illus.). 1984. pap. 4.95 (ISBN 0-89747-030-3, 1031). Squad Sig Pubns.

B-36 in Action. 1980. pap. 4.95 (ISBN 0-89747-101-6). Squad Sig Pubns.

B-52 Two in Action. (Aircraft in Action Ser.). (Illus.). 1984. pap. 4.95 (ISBN 0-89747-022-2, 1023). Squad Sig Pubns.

Birdsall, Steve. B-24 in Action. (Aircraft in Action Ser.). (Illus.). 50p. 1984. pap. 4.95 (ISBN 0-89747-020-6, 1021). Squad Sig Pubns.

Bombers of World War II. (Illus.). 9.95 (ISBN 0-668-05094-2). Arco.

Clark, Ronald W. Role of the Bomber. (Illus.). 160p. 14.95 (ISBN 0-690-01720-0). Presidio Pr.

Downey, Bob. V-Bombers. (Warbirds Illustrated Ser.). (Illus.). 72p. (Orig.). 1985. pap. 5.95 (ISBN 0-85368-740-4, Pub. by Arms & Armour). Sterling.

DuBuque, Jean H. & Gleckner, Robert F. The Development of the Heavy Bomber, 1918-1944. (USAF Historical Studies: No. 6). 188p. 1951. pap. text ed. 19.00x (ISBN 0-89126-030-7). MA-AH Pub.

Ethell, Jeff & Christy, Joe. B-52 Strato Fortress at War. 1981. encore ed. 5.50 (ISBN 0-684-16980-0, ScribT). Scribner.

Gunston, Bill. The Illustrated Guide to Modern Fighters & Attack Aircraft. LC 80-65164. (Illustrated Military Guides Ser.). (Illus.). 160p. 1980. 9.95 (ISBN 0-668-04964-2, 4964-2). Arco.

--An Illustrated Guide to the Bombers of World War II. LC 80-67628. (Illustrated Guide Ser.). 1981. 9.95 (ISBN 0-668-05094-2). Arco.

Holder, William G. Rockwell International, B-1B. Gentle, Ernest J., ed. (Aero Ser.: Vol. 32). (Illus.). 104p. 1985. pap. 9.95 (ISBN 0-8168-0613-6). Aero.

Jackson, B. R. & Doll, Thomas E. Douglas TBD-1 Devastator. LC 72-85151. (Aero Ser.: Vol. 23). (Illus.). 52p. 1973. pap. 3.95 (ISBN 0-8168-0586-5). Aero.

Jones, Lloyd S. U. S. Bombers, Pt. II. 4th ed. LC 83-70229. (Illus.). 280p. 1984. pap. 15.95 (ISBN 0-8168-9130-3). Aero.

McClendon, Dennis E. The Lady be Good: Mystery Bomber of World War II. (Illus.). 208p. 1982. pap. 10.95 (ISBN 0-8168-6624-4). Aero.

McDowell, Ernie & Greer, Don. B-25 Mitchell in Action. (Aircraft in Action Ser.). (Illus.). 1984. pap. 4.95 (ISBN 0-89747-033-8, 1034). Squad Sig Pubns.

Mendenhall, Charles A. Deadly Duo: The B25-B26 in World War Two. LC 80-52625. (Illus.). 160p. 1981. 19.95 (ISBN 0-933424-22-1). Specialty Pr.

O'Rourke, G. G. F-4 Phantom 2. LC 78-79407. (Famous Aircraft Ser.). (Illus.). 1979. pap. 6.95 (ISBN 0-8168-5645-1). Aero.

Pace, Steve. Valkyrie North American X-B 70 A. Gentle, Ernest J., ed. (Aero Ser.: Vol. 30). (Illus.). 104p. (Orig.). 1984. pap. 9.95 (ISBN 0-8168-0610-1). Aero.

Sanger, E. & Bredt, J. Rocket Drive for Long Range Bombers. Hamermesh, M., tr. 1944. pap. 3.95 (ISBN 0-910266-21-2). Bk Page.

Slow to Take Offense: Bombers, Cruise Missles & Prudent Deterrence. 2nd ed. 136p. 1980. pap. 15.00 (ISBN 0-89206-015-8, CSIS017, CSIS). Unipub.

Sweetman, Bill. Mosquito. (Combat Aircraft of World War II Ser.). (Illus.). 1982. 6.98 (ISBN 0-517-54854-2). Crown.

BOMBS

see also Atomic Bomb; Bomb Reconnaissance; Guided Missiles; Hydrogen Bomb

Brodie, Thomas G. Bombs & Bombings: A Handbook to Detection, Disposal & Investigation for Police & Fire Departments. (Illus.). 200p. 1980. photycopy ed. 24.75x (ISBN 0-398-02245-3). C C Thomas.

Lenz, Robert R. Explosives & Bomb Disposal Guide. (Illus.). 320p. 1976. photocopy ed. 34.50x (ISBN 0-398-01097-8). C C Thomas.

Pike, Earl A. Protection Against Bombs & Incendiaries: For Business, Industrial & Educational Institutions. (Illus.). 92p. 1973. 9.50x (ISBN 0-398-02517-7). C C Thomas.

Stoffel, Joseph. Explosives & Homemade Bombs. 2nd ed. (Illus.). 324p. 1977. photocopy ed. 33.50x (ISBN 0-398-02424-3). C C Thomas.

BOMBS, AERIAL

see Bombs

BOMBYLUDAE

Austen, E. E. Bombylidae of Palestine. (Illus.). 188p. 1937. 17.50x (ISBN 0-565-00108-6, Pub. by Brit Mus Nat Hist England). Sabbot-Natural Hist Bks.

BOND GRAPHS

Karnopp, Dean, et al. Bond Graph Techniques for Dynamic Systems in Engineering & Biology. 1979. pap. text ed. 31.00 (ISBN 0-08-025056-4). Pergamon.

Thoma, J. Bond Graphs: Introduction & Application. LC 75-9763. 192p. 1975. pap. text ed. 19.00 (ISBN 0-08-018881-8). Pergamon.

BONDING (TECHNOLOGY)

see Sealing (Technology)

BONDS, CHEMICAL

see Chemical Bonds

BONE

see also Bones; Calcification

Brighton, Carl T., et al. Electical Properties of Bone & Cartilage: Experimental Effects & Clinical Applications. 686p. 1979. 65.00 (ISBN 0-8089-1228-3, 790663). Grune.

Cohn, S. H., ed. Non-Invasive Measurements of Bone Mass & Their Clinical Application. 240p. 1981. 76.00 (ISBN 0-8493-5789-6). CRC Pr.

Cowin, S. C., ed. Mechanical Properties of Bone. (AMD Ser.: Vol. 45). 238p. 1981. 20.00 (ISBN 0-686-34477-4, G00203). ASME.

Dequeker, J. V. & Johnston, C. C., Jr., eds. Non-Invasive Bone Measurements: Methodological Problems Proceedings. 266p. 1982. pap. 33.00 (ISBN 0-904147-47-9). IRL Pr.

Ghista, D. N. Osteoarthromechanics. 1982. 58.00 (ISBN 0-07-023168-0). McGraw.

Glantz, P. O., et al, eds. Oral Interfacial Reactions of Bone, Soft Tissue & Saliva. (Illus.). 150p. 1985. pap. text ed. 40.00 (ISBN 0-947946-41-1). IRL Pr.

Halstead, L. B. & Hill, R. Vertebrate Hard Tissues. (Wykeham Science Ser.: No. 30). 192p. 1974. 9.95x (ISBN 0-8448-1157-2). Crane Russak Co.

Peck, W. Bone & Mineral Research Annual, Vol. 2. 1984. 73.00 (ISBN 0-444-90337-2, I-498-83). Elsevier.

Priest, Nicholas D., ed. Metals in Bone. 1985. lib. bdg. 54.75 (ISBN 0-85200-909-7, Pub. by MTP Pr Netherlands). Kluwer Academic.

Vaughan, Janet. The Physiology of Bone. 3rd ed. (Illus.). 1981. PLB 49.00x (ISBN 0-19-857584-X). Oxford U Pr.

BONEFISH

Sosin, Mark & Kreh, Lefty. Fishing the Flats. LC 82-20158. (Illus.). 160p. 1983. 16.95 (ISBN 0-8329-0278-0, Pub. by Winchester Pr); pap. 9.95 (ISBN 0-8329-0280-2, Pub. by Winshester Pr). New Century.

BONES

see also Anthropometry; Bone; Skeleton; Skull

Anderson, C. Manual for the Examination of Bone. 128p. 1982. 47.00 (ISBN 0-8493-0725-2). CRC Pr.

Cohn, D. V., et al. Endocrine Control of Bone & Calcium Metabolism, Vol. 8A. (International Congress Ser.: Vol. 619). 1984. 107.50 (ISBN 0-444-80589-3). Elsevier.

--Endocrine Control of Bone & Calcium Metabolism, Vol. 8B. (International Congress Ser.: Vol. 635). 1984. 102.00 (ISBN 0-444-80590-7). Elsevier.

Davies, Robertson. What's Bred in the Bone. 1985. 17.95 (ISBN 0-670-80916-0). Viking.

Diblos, Pablo E., et al. Atlas of Nuclear Medicine, Vol. 4, Bone. LC 74-81820. pap. 52.30 (ISBN 0-317-07791-0, 2016659). Bks Demand UMI.

Evans, Frances G., ed. Studies on the Anatomy & Function of Bone & Joints. (Illus.). 1966. 36.00 (ISBN 0-387-03677-6). Springer-Verlag.

Fazelas, Gy I & Kosa, F. Forensic Fetal Osteology. 1979. 41.50 (ISBN 0-9960011-9-0, Pub. by Akademiai Kaido Hungary). Heyden.

Frost, H. M. The Laws of Bone Structure. (Illus.). 184p. 1964. photocopy ed. 19.75x (ISBN 0-398-00623-7). C C Thomas.

Garattini, Silvio, ed. Bone Resorption, Metastasis, & Diphosphonates. (Monographs of the Mario Negri Institute for Pharmacological Research). 225p. 1985. text ed. 39.50 (ISBN 0-88167-137-1). Raven.

Hall, Michael C. The Architecture of Bone. (Illus.). 360p. 1966. photocopy ed. 36.75x (ISBN 0-398-00757-8). C C Thomas.

Johnston, Richard F. Estimating Variation in Bony Characters & a Comment on the Kluge-Kerfoot Effect. (Occasional Papers: No. 53). 8p. 1976. pap. 1.25 (ISBN 0-317-04608-X). U of KS Mus Nat Hist.

Murray, P. D. Bones. (Cambridge Science Classics Ser.). (Illus.). 252p. 1985. pap. 19.95 (ISBN 0-521-31549-2). Cambridge U Pr.

Pauwels, E. K. Bone Scintigraphy. 224p. 1981. 47.00 (ISBN 90-6021-476-5, Pub. by Martinus Nijhoff Netherlands). Kluwer Academic.

Recker, Robert R., ed. Bone Histomorphometry: Techniques & Interpretation. 312p. 1983. 89.50 (ISBN 0-8493-5373-4). CRC Pr.

Rittmann, W. W., et al. Cortical Bone Healing After Internal Fixation & Infection: Biochemechanics & Biology. (Illus.). 76p. 1974. 43.00 (ISBN 0-387-06944-5). Springer-Verlag.

BONKEI

Hirota, Jozan. Bonkei: Tray Landscapes. LC 79-117384. (Illus.). 128p. 1980. pap. 9.50 (ISBN 0-87011-495-6). Kodansha.

BONSAI

Adams, Peter. The Art of Bonsai. 176p. 1981. 35.00x (ISBN 0-7063-5860-0, Pub. by Ward Lock Ed England). State Mutual BK.

Black, Don. South African Bonsai Book. 93p. 1981. cloth 15.95x (ISBN 0-86978-136-7, Pub. by Timmins Africa). Intl Spec Bk.

Bonsai for Indoors. 2.25 (ISBN 0-686-21173-1). Bklyn Botanic.

Bonsai: Special Techniques. 2.25 (ISBN 0-686-21146-4). Bklyn Botanic.

Bonsai: The Dwarfed Potted Trees of Japan. 2.25 (ISBN 0-686-21122-7). Bklyn Botanic.

Dunton, Darlene. Complete Bonsai Handbook. 1978. pap. 12.95 (ISBN 0-8128-6008-X). Stein & Day.

Japan Bonsai Association Directors. Masters' Book of Bonsai. LC 67-12585. (Illus.). 1967. 15.95 (ISBN 0-87011-040-3). Kodansha.

Kawasumi, Masakuni & Murata, Kyuzo. Bonsai with American Trees. LC 75-10588. (Illus.). 131p. 1975. 15.95 (ISBN 0-87011-246-5). Kodansha.

Naka, John Y. Bonsai Techniques II. 2nd ed. LC 81-69341. (Illus.). 488p. 1984. pap. 30.00x (ISBN 0-930422-33-3). Dennis-Landman.

Nakamura, Zeko. Bonsai Miniatures. (Quick & Easy Ser.). (Illus.). 62p. 1980. pap. 3.95 (ISBN 4-07-973760-2, Pub. by Shufunmoto Co Ltd Japan). C E Tuttle.

Okita, Yoshihiro & Hollenberg, J. L. Miniature Palms of Japan: Its Care & Cultivation. (Illus.). 150p. 1981. 19.95 (ISBN 0-8348-0160-4, Pub. by John Weatherhill Inc Tokyo). C E Tuttle.

Perry, Lynn R. Bonsai: Trees & Shrubs. LC 64-20123. 234p. (Orig.). 1964. 11.50 (ISBN 0-471-06820-9). Krieger.

Pipe, Ann K. Bonsai: The Art of Dwarfing Trees. (Illus.). 1964. pap. 6.75 (ISBN 0-8015-0796-0, Hawthorn). Dutton.

Severn, Gillian E. Miniature Trees in the Japanese Style. (Illus.). 112p. 1967. 6.95 (ISBN 0-571-08624-1). Faber & Faber.

Shufunotomo Editors. The Essentials of Bonsai. (Illus.). 108p. 1982. 9.95 (ISBN 0-917304-27-6). Timber.

Stowell, Jerald P. The Beginner's Guide to American Bonsai. LC 77-15372. 1978. 15.50 (ISBN 0-87011-326-7). Kodansha.

Valavanis, William N. Bonsai Creation & Design Using Propagation Techniques. 1978. pap. 3.95 (Pub. by Symmes Syst). Intl Spec Bk.

--Japanese Five-Needle Pine: Nature-Gardens-Bonsai-Taxonomy. new ed. Symmes, Edwin C., Jr., tr. LC 76-5780. (The Encyclopedia of Classical Bonsai Art: Vol. 2). (Illus.). 68p. 1976. lib. bdg. 15.00 (ISBN 0-916352-05-6); pap. text ed. 9.95 (ISBN 0-916352-04-8). Symmes Syst.

Yoshimura, Yuji. Yoshimura School of Bonsai, Vol. 1: Commemorative Album, the Muriel R. Leeds Bonsai Collection. new ed. Symmes, Edwin C., Jr., ed. (Illus.). 1977. pap. text ed. 15.00x (ISBN 0-916352-08-0); limited edition 25.00 (ISBN 0-916352-09-9). Symmes Syst.

Yoshimura, Yuji & Halford, Giovanna M. Japanese Art of Miniature Trees & Landscapes. LC 57-8794. (Illus.). pap. 15.00 (ISBN 0-8048-0282-3). C E Tuttle.

BOOK DESIGN

see also Printing–Layout and Typography

Burbidge, P. G. Prelims & End-Pages. (Cambridge Authors & Printers' Guide Ser). 3.95 (ISBN 0-521-07508-4). Cambridge U Pr.

Godine, David R. The Well Made Book. (Illus.). 48p. Date not set. 6.95 (ISBN 0-87923-481-4). Godine.

Jackson, Holbrook. Printing of Books. LC 70-134100. (Essay Index Reprint Ser.). 1939. 24.50 (ISBN 0-8369-1931-9). Ayer Co Pubs.

Lennon, Tom, ed. The Thirteenth, Fourteenth, & Fifteenth Publication Design Annual. (Illus.). 700p. 1982. 39.95 (ISBN 0-937414-24-7). R Silver.

Levarie, Norma. The Art & History of Books. (Quality Paperbacks Ser.). (Illus.). 315p. 1982. pap. 18.95 (ISBN 0-306-80181-7). Da Capo.

McLean, Ruari. Modern Book Design: From William Morris to the Present Day. (Illus.). 1959. 3.40x (ISBN 0-19-519593-0). Oxford U Pr.

Williamson, Hugh. Methods of Book Design. 3rd ed. LC 83-3610. 416p. 1983. text ed. 42.00x (ISBN 0-300-02663-3); pap. 12.95x (ISBN 0-300-03035-5, Y-482). Yale U Pr.

Wilson, Adrian. The Design of Books. LC 67-14162. (Illus.). 160p. 1974. pap. 10.95 (ISBN 0-87905-019-5, Peregrine Smith). Gibbs M Smith.

BOOK INDUSTRIES AND TRADE–DATA PROCESSING

see also Computerized Type-Setting

Caird, Kenneth A. Cameraready. (Illus.). 400p. 1973. looseleaf 40.00x (ISBN 0-87703-066-9). Univelt Inc.

BOOK REPAIRING

see Books–Conservation and Restoration

BOOKBINDING

Arnett, John A. Bibliopegia; or, the Art of Bookbinding in All Its Branches. Bidwell, John, ed. LC 78-74390. (Nineteenth-Century Book Arts & Printing History Ser.: Vol. 5). (Illus.). 1980. lib. bdg. 33.00 (ISBN 0-8240-3879-7). Garland Pub.

Burdett, Eric. The Craft of Bookbinding: A Practical Guide. 1977. 32.00 (ISBN 0-7153-6656-4). David & Charles.

Callery, Bernadette G. & Mosimann, E. A., eds. The Tradition of Fine Bookbinding in the Twentieth Century. (Illus.). 120p. 1979. 25.00x (ISBN 0-913196-28-2); unbd. o.p. 22.00 (ISBN 0-686-65642-3). Hunt Inst Botanical.

Cockerell, Douglas. Bookbinding & the Care of Books. 1978. pap. 9.95 (ISBN 0-8008-0946-7, Pentalic). Taplinger.

Colonial Williamsburg Foundation Staff. Bookbinder in Eighteenth Century Williamsburg. (Williamsburg Craft Ser). (Illus.). 32p. (Orig.). pap. 1.25 (ISBN 0-910412-15-4). Williamsburg.

Cundall, Joseph. On Bookbindings, Ancient & Modern. LC 77-94568. 1979. Repr. of 1881 ed. lib. bdg. 20.00 (ISBN 0-89341-236-8). Longwood Pub Group.

Bailey, John A. & Mansfield, John W. Phytoalexins. LC 81-13192. 256p. 1982. 79.95x (ISBN 0-470-27291-0). Halsted Pr.

Board on Agriculture & Renewable Resources, National Research Council. Genetic Improvement of Seed Proteins. LC 76-17097. 1976. pap. 16.75 (ISBN 0-309-02421-8). Natl Acad Pr.

Bohlmann, F., et al. Naturally Occurring Acetylenes. 1973. 98.00 (ISBN 0-12-111150-4). Acad Pr.

Bonner, James & Varner, Joseph, eds. Plant Biochemistry. 3rd ed. 1976. text ed. 42.50 (ISBN 0-12-114860-2). Acad Pr.

Callow, J. A. Biochemical Plant Pathology. 484p. 1983. 69.95x (ISBN 0-471-90092-3, Pub. by Wiley-Interscience). Wiley.

Carboxylates & the Uptake of Ammonium by Excised Maize Roots. (Agricultural Research Reports: No. 837). 1975. pap. 13.00 (ISBN 90-220-0570-4, PDC198, PUDOC). Unipub.

Cation Selectivity & Cation-Anion Balance as Factors Governing Mineral Composition of Pasture Herbage. 1959. pap. 4.00 (ISBN 90-220-0027-3, PDC155, PUDOC). Unipub.

Cherry, Joe H. Molecular Biology of Plants: A Text Manual. (A Molecular Biology Ser.). 204p. 1973. 29.50x (ISBN 0-231-03642-6). Columbia U Pr.

An Experimental Study of Influence of Micro-Elements on Uptake of Macroelements by Plants. 1961. pap. 4.00 (ISBN 90-220-0202-0, PDC159, PUDOC). Unipub.

Geissman, T. A. & Crout, D. H. Organic Chemistry of Secondary Plant Metabolism. LC 71-81384. 1969. pap. 20.00 (ISBN 0-87735-201-1). Freeman Cooper.

Goldstein, Irwin J. & Etzler, Marilynn E. Chemical Taxonomy, Molecular Biology, & Function of Plant Lectins. LC 83-19937. (Progress in Clinical & Biological Research Ser.: Vol 138). 314p. 1983. 38.00 (ISBN 0-8451-0138-2). A R Liss.

Goodwin, T. W. Biochemical Functions of Terpenoids in Plants Royal Society. LC 79-670276. (Illus.). 1979. Repr. of 1978 ed. text ed. 38.00x (ISBN 0-85403-105-7). Scholium Intl.

Goodwin, T. W. & Mercer, E. I. Introduction to Plant Biochemistry. 2nd ed. 1972. 99.00 (ISBN 0-08-024922-1). Pergamon.

Goodwin, T. W., ed. Chemistry & Biochemistry of Plant Pigments, Vol. 1. 2nd ed. 1976. 90.00 (ISBN 0-12-289901-6). Acad Pr.

--Chemistry & Biochemistry of Plant Pigments, Vol. 2. 2nd ed. 1976. 70.00 (ISBN 0-12-289902-4). Acad Pr.

Harborne, Jeffrey B. & Turner, Billie L. Plant Chemosystematics. 1984. 95.00 (ISBN 0-12-324640-7). Acad Pr.

International Congress on Pharmacognosy & Phytochemistry, Munich, 1970. Proceedings. Wagner, H. & Hoerhammer, L., eds. LC 79-149122. (Illus.). 1971. pap. 46.10 (ISBN 0-387-05316-6). Springer-Verlag.

The Ionic Balance of the Sugar-Beet Plant. (Agricultural Research Reports: No. 832). 1975. pap. 12.25 (ISBN 90-220-0548-8, PDC196, PUDOC). Unipub.

Kahl, Guenter. Biochemistry of Wounded Plant Tissues. 1978. 72.00x (ISBN 3-11-006801-X). De Gruyter.

Lewin, Ralph A., ed. Physiology & Biochemistry of Algae. 1962. 99.00 (ISBN 0-12-446150-6). Acad Pr.

Loewus, Frank A. & Ryan, Clarence A., eds. The Phytochemistry of Cell Recognition & Cell Surface Interactions. LC 81-10558. (Recent Advances in Phytochemistry Ser.: Vol. 15). 288p. 1981. text ed. 42.50x (ISBN 0-306-40758-2, Plenum Pr). Plenum Pub.

Misaghi, I. J. Physiology & Biochemistry of Plant-Pathogen Interactions. 302p. 1982. 32.50x (ISBN 0-306-41059-1, Plenum Pr). Plenum Pub.

Phytochemical Society. Perspectives in Phytochemistry: Proceedings. Harborne, J. B. & Swain, T., eds. 1969. 39.50 (ISBN 0-12-324660-1). Acad Pr.

--Phytochemical Phylogeny: Proceedings. Harborne, J. B., ed. 1970. 61.50 (ISBN 0-12-324666-0). Acad Pr.

Phytochemical Society of North America. Recent Advances in Phytochemistry, Vol. 2: Proceedings of the 7th Annual Symposium of the Phytochemical Society of North America. Seikel, Margaret K., ed. pap. 45.80 (ISBN 0-317-26217-3, 2055689). Bks Demand UMI.

--Symposia, Vols. 5 & 6. Runeckles, V. C. & Tso, T. C., eds. Incl. Vol. 5. Structural & Functional Aspects of Phytochemistry. 1972. 67.00 (ISBN 0-12-612405-1); Vol. 6. Terpenoids: Structure, Biogenesis, Distribution. 1973. 51.00 (ISBN 0-12-612406-X). Acad Pr.

Reinhold, L. & Liwschitz, Y., eds. Progress in Phytochemistry, 2 vols, Vols. 1 & 2. LC 68-24347. Vol. 1. pap. 160.00 (ISBN 0-317-29865-8, 2016177); Vol. 2. pap. 130.80 (ISBN 0-317-29866-6). Bks Demand UMI.

Reinhold, L., et al. Progress in Phytochemistry, Vol. 7. LC 68-24347. (Illus.). 410p. 1981. 96.00 (ISBN 0-08-026362-3). Pergamon.

Reinhold, L., et al, eds. Progress in Phytochemistry, 2 vols, Vols. 4-5. LC 68-24347. 1977-78. Vol. 5. text ed. 96.00 (ISBN 0-08-022645-0). Pergamon.

Rodriguez, Eloy, et al, eds. Biology & Chemistry of Plant Trichomes. 244p. 1983. 39.50x (ISBN 0-306-41393-0, Plenum Pr). Plenum Pub.

Runeckles, V. C., ed. Phytochemistry in Disease & Medicine. LC 67-26242. (Recent Advances in Phytochemistry Ser.: Vol. 9). 318p. 1975. 42.50x (ISBN 0-306-34709-1, Plenum Pr). Plenum Pub.

Runeckles, V. C., et al, eds. Recent Advances in Phytochemistry, 4 vols. Incl. Vol. 1: 6th Symposium, Austin, Texas, 1966. Mabry, T. J. & Alson, R. E., eds. 437p. 1968. 42.50x (ISBN 0-306-50041-8); Vol. 2: 7th Symposium, Madison, Wis., 1967. Seikel, Margaret K., ed. 175p. 1969. 25.00x (ISBN 0-306-50042-6); Vol. 3: 8th Symposuim, Tuscon, Ariz., 1968. Steelink, Cornelius, ed. 268p. 1970. 29.50x (ISBN 0-306-50043-4); Vol. 4: 9th Symposuim, School of Fine Arts, Baniff, Alberta, 1969. Watkin, J. E., ed. 317p. 1972. 35.00x (ISBN 0-306-50044-2). LC 67-26242 (Plenum Pr). Plenum Pub.

Stumpf, P. K. & Conn, E. E., eds. The Biochemistry of Plants: A Comprehensive Treatise, Secondary Plant Products, Vol. 7. LC 80-13168. 1981. 85.00 (ISBN 0-12-675407-1). Acad Pr.

Stumpf, P. K., et al, eds. The Biochemistry of Plants: A Comprehensive Treatise, Vol. 6: Proteins & Nucleic Acids. 1981. 75.00 (ISBN 0-12-675406-3). Acad Pr.

Swain, Tony, ed. Topics in the Biochemistry of Natural Products. (Recent Advances in Phytochemistry Ser.: Vol. 13). 263p. 1979. 32.50x (ISBN 0-306-40188-6, Plenum Pr). Plenum Pub.

Swain, Tony & Kleiman, Robert, eds. The Resource Potential in Phytochemistry. (Recent Advances in Phytochemistry: Vol. 14). 228p. 1980. 35.00 (ISBN 0-306-40572-5). Plenum Pub.

Swain, Tony, et al, eds. Biochemistry of Plant Phenolics. LC 78-19010. (Recent Advances in Phytochemistry Ser.: Vol. 10). 661p. 1978. 69.50x (ISBN 0-306-40028-6, Plenum Pr). Plenum Pub.

Thompson, Alonzo C., ed. The Chemistry of Allelopathy: Biochemical Interactions Among Plants. LC 84-24626. (ACS Symposium Ser.: No. 268). 470p. 1984. lib. bdg. 79.95x (ISBN 0-8412-0886-7). Am Chemical.

Timmermann, Barbara N., et al, eds. Phytochemical Adaptations to Stress. (Recent Advances in Phytochemistry Ser.: Vol. 18). 334p. 1984. 49.50x (ISBN 0-306-41720-0, Plenum Pr). Plenum Pub.

Wallace, James, ed. Biochemical Interaction Between Plants & Insects. LC 67-26242. (Recent Advances in Phytochemistry Ser.: Vol. 10). 437p. 1976. 49.50 (ISBN 0-306-34710-5, Plenum Pr). Plenum Pub.

Waller, G. R. & Nowacki, E. K. Alkaloid Biology & Metabolism in Plants. LC 76-30903. (Illus.). 312p. 1978. 27.50 (ISBN 0-306-30981-5, Plenum Pr). Plenum Pub.

Young, David A. & Seigler, David S., eds. Phytochemistry & Angiosperm Phylogeny. LC 81-8603. 304p. 1981. 49.95 (ISBN 0-03-056079-9). Praeger.

BOTANICAL GARDENS

Brockway, Lucile H. Science & Colonial Expansion: The Role of the British Royal Botanic Gardens. LC 79-51669. (Studies in Social Discontinuity). 1979. 29.50 (ISBN 0-12-134150-X). Acad Pr.

Gerard, John. Catalogus Arborum, Fructicum Ac Plantarum Tam Indigenarum Quam Exoticarum in Horto Johannis Gerardi. LC 73-6132. (English Experience Ser.: No. 598). 22p. 1973. Repr. of 1599 ed. 6.00 (ISBN 0-685-72641-X). Walter J Johnson. •

Irwin, Howard S. & Barneby, Rupert C. Cassiinae. (Memoirs of the New York Botanical Garden Ser.: Vol. 35). 918p. 1982. pap. 100.00x (ISBN 0-89327-241-8). NY Botanical.

Prest, John. The Garden of Eden: The Botanic Garden & the Re-Creation of Paradise. LC 81-11365. (Illus.). 128p. 1982. 28.50x (ISBN 0-300-02726-5). Yale U Pr.

Ryan & Rycroft. Kirstenbosch. (Illus.). 137p. 1981. 47.50x (ISBN 0-86978-174-X, Pub. by Timmins Africa). Intl Spec Bk.

Simmons, J. B., et al, eds. Conservation of Threatened Plants. LC 76-20762. (NATO Conference Ser. I, Ecology: Vol. 1). 352p. 1976. 49.50x (ISBN 0-306-32801-1, Plenum Pr). Plenum Pub.

Stone, Doris M. The Great Public Gardens of the Eastern United States: A Guide to Their Beauty & Botany. (Illus.). 248p. 1982. 12.95 (ISBN 0-394-70664-1). Pantheon.

Thomas, W. W. The Systematics of Rhynchospora Section Dichromena. (Memoirs of the New York Botanical Garden Ser.: Vol. 37). 1984. 21.00x (ISBN 0-89327-251-5). NY Botanical.

BOTANICAL GEOGRAPHY

see Phytogeography

BOTANICAL NOMENCLATURE

see Botany–Nomenclature

BOTANICAL RESEARCH

Callow, J. A. & Woolhouse, H. W., eds. Advances in Botanical Research, Vol. 11. (Serial Publication Ser.). 1985. 55.00 (ISBN 0-12-005911-8). Acad Pr.

Douglass, A. E. Climatic Cycle & Tree Growth, 3 vols. in one. (Vols. 1 & 2, A Study of the Annual Rings of Trees in Relation to Climate & Solar Activity; Vol. 3, A Study of Cycles). 1971. 52.50 (ISBN 3-7682-0720-X). Lubrecht & Cramer.

Gunckel, J. E. Current Topics in Plant Science. 1969. 72.00 (ISBN 0-12-305750-7). Acad Pr.

Khoshoo, T. N. & Nair, P. K. Progress in Plant Research, 2 vols, Vols. 1 & 2. (Orig.). 1979. Set. 82.50 (ISBN 0-686-75230-9). Vol. 1 - Applied Morphology & Allied Subjects. Vol. 2 - Plant Improvement & Horticulture. Krieger.

Khoshoo, T. N. & Nair, P. K., eds. Progress in Plant Research: Applied Morphology & Allied Subjects, Vol. 1. 320p. 1979. 50.00 (ISBN 0-88065-145-8, Pub. by Messers Today & Tomorrows Printers & Publishers India). Scholarly Pubns.

--Progress in Plant Research: Plant Improvement & Horticulture, Vol. 2. 248p. 1979. 50.00 (ISBN 0-88065-146-6, Pub. by Messers Today & Tomorrows India Printers & Publishers India). Scholarly Pubns.

--Progress in Plant Research: Silver Jubilee Publication of NBRI, 2 vols. 1979. Set. 90.00 (ISBN 0-88065-144-X, Pub. by Messers Today & Tomorrows Printers & Publishers India). Scholarly Pubns.

Kiger, Robert W., et al, eds. International Register of Specialists & Current Research in Plant Systematics. viii, 346p. 1981. pap. 10.00 (ISBN 0-913196-39-8). Hunt Inst Botanical.

Nair, P. K. Glimpses in Plant Research. (Botanical Lectures & Essays Ser.: Vol. V.). 400p. 1980. text ed. 50.00x (ISBN 0-7069-0827-9, Pub. by Vikas India). Advent NY.

Nair, P. K., ed. Glimpses in Plant Research, Vol. 3. 1976. 19.50x (ISBN 0-7069-0432-X). Intl Bk Dist.

Orloci, Laszlo. Multivariate Analysis in Vegetation Research. 1978. lib. bdg. 53.00 (ISBN 90-6193-567-9, Pub. by Junk Pubs Netherlands). Kluwer Academic.

Preston, R. D., ed. Advances in Botanical Research. Incl. Vol. 1. 1963. 65.00 (ISBN 0-12-005901-0); Vol. 2. 1965. 65.00 (ISBN 0-12-005902-9); Vol. 3. 1970. 65.00 (ISBN 0-12-005903-7). Acad Pr.

--Advances in Botanical Research, Vol. 6. 1979. 70.00 (ISBN 0-12-005906-1). Acad Pr.

Raghavan, V. Experimental Embryognesis in Vascular Plants. (Experimental Botany Ser.). 1977. 95.00 (ISBN 0-12-575450-7). Acad Pr.

Rashap, Arthur W., et al, eds. The Ginseng Research Institute's Indexed Bibliography. LC 84-81467. 120p. 1984. pap. 65.00 (ISBN 0-9613800-0-4). Ginseng Res Inst.

Stump, David S. Research Summary: The Census of Horticultural Specialties. (Illus.). 76p. 1982. pap. text ed. 10.00 (ISBN 0-935336-01-X). Horticult Research.

Tibbitts, T. & Kozlowski, T. K., eds. Controlled Environment Guidelines for Plant Research. LC 79-23521. 1980. 37.50 (ISBN 0-12-690950-4). Acad Pr.

Woolhouse, H. W., ed. Advances in Botanical Research, 2 vols. (Serial Publication Ser.). 1981. Vol. 8. 70.00 (ISBN 0-12-005908-8); Vol. 9. 60.00 (ISBN 0-12-005909-6). Acad Pr.

--Advances in Botanical Research, Vol. 4. 1978. 80.00 (ISBN 0-12-005904-5). Acad Pr.

--Advances in Botanical Research, Vol. 7. LC 62-21144. (Serial Publication Ser.). 1980. 99.50 (ISBN 0-12-005907-X). Acad Pr.

Woolhouse, Harold W., ed. Advances in Botanical Research, Vol. 10. (Serial Publication Ser.). 320p. 1983. 70.00 (ISBN 0-12-005910-X). Acad Pr.

BOTANICAL SPECIMENS–COLLECTION AND PRESERVATION

see Plants–Collection and Preservation

BOTANISTS

see also Horticulturists

Budge, E. A. Wallis. Divine Origin of the Craft of the Herbalist. LC 78-174013. (Illus.). 1971. Repr. of 1928 ed. 40.00x (ISBN 0-8103-3794-0). Gale.

Cunningham, Isabel S. Frank N. Meyer: Plant Hunter in Asia. (Illus.). 318p. 1984. 29.95 (ISBN 0-8138-1148-1). Iowa St U Pr.

Dakin, Susanna. The Perennial Adventure: A Tribute to Alice Eastwood, 1859-1943. 48p. 1954. 2.50 (ISBN 0-940228-09-2). Calif Acad Sci.

Daniels, G., ed. A Linnaean Keepsake. (Eng. & Lat., Illus.). 1973. 13.00x (ISBN 0-913196-15-0). Hunt Inst Botanical.

Desmond, Ray. Dictionary of British & Irish Botanists & Horticulturists: Including Plant Collectors & Botanical Artists. 3rd ed. 747p. 1977. 99.50x (ISBN 0-8476-1392-5). Rowman.

Desmond, Ray, ed. Dictionary of British & Irish Botanists & Horticulturists. 3rd ed. 764p. 1977. cancelled (ISBN 0-85066-089-0). Taylor & Francis.

Eifert, Virginia L. Tall Trees & Far Horizons: Adventures & Discoveries of Early Botanists in America. LC 70-39100. (Essay Index Reprint Ser.). (Illus.). Repr. of 1965 ed. 27.50 (ISBN 0-8369-2686-2). Ayer Co Pubs.

Gunther, R. W., ed. Early British Botanists & Their Gardens. Repr. of 1922 ed. 29.00 (ISBN 0-527-36850-4). Kraus Repr.

Hall, Norman. Botanists of the Eucalypts. 1979. pap. 10.00x (ISBN 0-643-00271-5, Pub. by CSIRO). Intl Spec Bk.

Hawks, Ellison & Boulger, George S. Pioneers of Plant Study. facs. ed. LC 75-86759. (Essay Index Reprint Ser). 1928. 19.00 (ISBN 0-8369-1139-3). Ayer Co Pubs.

Huxley, Leonard. Life & Letters of Sir Joseph Dalton Hooker: Materials Collected & Arranged by Lady Hooker, 2 vols. Sterling, Keir B., ed. LC 77-81130. (Biologists & Their World Ser.). (Illus.). 1978. Repr. of 1918 ed. Set. lib. bdg. 93.00x (ISBN 0-405-10726-9); lib. bdg. 46.50x ea. Vol. 1 (ISBN 0-405-10727-7). Vol. 2 (ISBN 0-405-10728-5). Ayer Co Pubs.

Jackson, Benjamin D., illus. George Bentham. LC 78-170834. (English Men of Science: No. 5). (Illus.). Repr. of 1906 ed. 22.00 (ISBN 0-404-07895-8). AMS Pr.

Jacobs, M. Herman Johannes Lam (1892-1977) The Life & Work of a Dutch Botanist. 271p. 1984. pap. text ed. 21.50x (ISBN 90-6203-545-0, Pub. by Rodopi Holland). Humanities.

Kelly, Howard A. Some American Medical Botanists: Commemorated in Our Botanical Nomenclature. LC 77-3485. 1977. Repr. of 1913 ed. lib. bdg. 25.00 (ISBN 0-89341-145-0). Longwood Pub Group.

Kiger, Robert W., et al, eds. International Register of Specialists & Current Research in Plant Systematics. viii, 346p. 1981. pap. 10.00 (ISBN 0-913196-39-8). Hunt Inst Botanical.

New York Botanical Library. Biographical Notes Upon Botanists, 3 Vols. 1965. Set. 340.00 (ISBN 0-8161-0695-9, Hall Library). G K Hall.

Rosseau, G. S., ed. The Letters & Papers of Sir John Hill, Seventeen Fourteen to Seventeen Seventy-Five. LC 81-68993. (Studies in the Eighteenth Century: No. 6). (Illus.). 264p. 1982. 39.50 (ISBN 0-404-61472-8). AMS Pr.

Vance, Dwain & Rogers, John. General Botany. 2nd ed. 1984. pap. 8.95 (ISBN 0-88725-030-0). Hunter Textbks.

Ward, Frank K. Plant Hunting on the Edge of the World. (Illus.). 1976. Repr. 12.50 (ISBN 0-913728-21-7). Theophrastus.

BOTANY

see also Alpine Flora; Aquatic Plants; Botanical Research; Bulbs; Climbing Plants; Desert Flora; Ferns; Fertilization of Plants; Floriculture; Flowers; Forest Flora; Fresh-Water Biology; Fresh-Water Flora; Fruit; Grafting; Growth (Plants); Herbaria; Hybridization, Vegetable; Insectivorous Plants; Leaves; Marine Flora; Microscope and Microscopy; Mycology; Natural History; Paleobotany; Parasitic Plants; Phytogeography; Plants; Poisonous Plants; Pollen; Seeds; Shrubs; Trees; Tropical Plants; Variation (Biology); Vegetables; Vegetation and Climate; Weeds; Wild Flowers; Woody Plants

also divisions, classes, etc. of the vegetable kingdom, e.g. Cryptograms, Fungi; also headings beginning with the word plant; and names of plants

Ainsworth, G. C. & Bisby. Dictionary of the Fungi (Including the Lichens) 7th Ed. ed. (Illus.). 412p. 1983. lib. bdg. 27.50 (ISBN 0-85198-515-7). Lubrecht & Cramer.

Allen, Grant. The Story of the Plants. 1978. Repr. of 1904 ed. lib. bdg. 20.00 (ISBN 0-8495-0120-2). Arden Lib.

Antia, K. K. & Bhattacharya, S. S. Botany Practicals: Including General Biology. 120p. 1981. 29.00x (ISBN 0-86125-641-7, Pub. by Orient Longman India). State Mutual Bk.

Arroyo, Mary T. The Systematics of the Legume Genus Harpalyce: Leguminosae. Lotoideae. Incl. A Monographs of the Genus Hamelia: Rubiaceae. Elias, Thomas S. LC 66-6394. (Memoirs of the New York Botanical Garden: Vol. 26, No. 4). 1976. pap. 16.00x (ISBN 0-89327-001-6). NY Botanical.

Aufermann, B. Zur Chemotaxonomie Mariner Rhodophyceen am Beispiel einer Leucin-Decarboxylase. (Bibliotheca Phycologica Ser.: No. 43). (Illus.). 1978. pap. text ed. 14.00x (ISBN 3-7682-1206-8). Lubrecht & Cramer.

Baker, J. G. Handbook of the Amaryllideae: Including the Alstromeriae & Agaveae. (Plant Monograph: No.7). 1972. Repr. of 1888 ed. 14.00 (ISBN 3-7682-0677-7). Lubrecht & Cramer.

--Handbook of the Irideae. (Plant Monograph Ser.: No.9). 1972. Repr. of 1892 ed. 14.00 (ISBN 3-7682-0753-6). Lubrecht & Cramer.

Batra, Lekh R., ed. Insect Fungus Symbiosis: Nutrition, Mutualism & Commensalism. LC 78-20640. 288p. 1979. text ed. 27.50x (ISBN 0-470-26671-6). Allanheld.

Bazilevskaya, N. A. On the Races of the Opium Poppy Growing in Semirech'e & the Origin of Their Culture. 1981. 25.00x (ISBN 0-686-76652-0, Pub. by Oxford & IBH India). State Mutual Bk.

Beltman, H. A. Vegetative Strukturen der Parmeliaceae und Ihre Entwicklung. (Bibliotheca Lichenologica Ser.: No. 11). (Illus.). 1978. lib. bdg. 21.00x (ISBN 3-7682-1199-1). Lubrecht & Cramer.

Biegert, E., ed. A Topical Guide to "Folia Primatologica", Volumes 1-30 (1963-1978) 160p. 1980. pap. 16.75 (ISBN 3-8055-0781-X). S Karger.

Bigelow, Howard E. North American Species of Clitocybe. Part 2. (Nova Hedwigia, Beiheft: No. 81). 250p. 1985. text ed. 42.00x (ISBN 3-7682-5481-X). Lubrecht & Cramer.

Bilgrami, K. S., et al. Fundamentals of Botany. (Illus.). 1979. text ed. 25.00x (ISBN 0-7069-0775-2, Pub. by Vikas India). Advent NY.

Bir, S. S. Aspects of Plant Sciences, Vol. III. 170p. 1980. 15.00 (ISBN 0-88065-172-5, Pub. by Messers Today & Tomorrows Printers & Publishers India). Scholarly Pubns.

Bir, S. S., ed. Aspects of Plant Sciences, Vol. VI. (Illus.). 261p. 1983. 19.00x (ISBN 0-88065-235-7, Pub. by Messers Today & Tomorrow Printers & Publishers). Scholarly Pubns.

Blake, S. F. Geographical Guide to Floras of the World: Annotated List with Special Reference to Useful Plants & Common Plant Names, Pt. II. LC 78-51431. (Landmark Reprints in Plant Science). 1978. Repr. of 1961 ed. text ed. 40.00x (ISBN 0-86598-006-3). Allanheld.

Blake, S. F. & Atwood, A. C. Geographical Guide to the Floras of the World: Western Europe, Finland, Sweden etc, Pt. 2. 742p. 1974. Repr. of 1961 ed. text ed. 49.00X (ISBN 3-87429-060-3). Lubrecht & Cramer.

Blume, K. L. Catalogus van eenige der merkwaardigste zoo in- als uitheemsche Gewassen: te vinden in's land Plantentium te Buitenzorg. 1946. pap. 5.00 (ISBN 0-934454-20-5). Lubrecht & Cramer.

Bocquet, Gilbert. Revisio Physolychnidum: Silene Subg. Physolychnis. (Phanero Gamarum Monographiae: Vol. 1). (Illus.). 1969. 52.50 (ISBN 3-7682-0624-6). Lubrecht & Cramer.

Bold, Harold C. & Hundell, C. L. The Plant Kingdom. 4th ed. (Foundation of Modern Biology Ser.). (Illus.). 1977. pap. 19.95 (ISBN 0-13-680389-X). P-H.

Borg, John. Descriptive Flora of the Maltese Islands Including the Ferns & Flowering Plants. 846p. 1976. pap. text ed. 69.30 (ISBN 3-87429-104-9). Lubrecht & Cramer.

Bower, Frederick O. Botany of the Living Plant. 4th ed. LC 84-1800. (Illus.). 1969. Repr. of 1947 ed. 23.95x (ISBN 0-02-841800-X). Hafner.

Briggs, Winslow R., et al, eds. Annual Review of Plant Physiology, Vol. 24. LC 51-1660. (Illus.). 1973. text ed. 20.00 (ISBN 0-8243-0624-4). Annual Reviews.

British Museum (Natural History), ed. Conspectus Florae Angolensis, 6 vols. Set. 500.00x (ISBN 0-686-78653-X, Pub. by Brit Mus Pubns England). State Mutual Bk.

Burns, George W. Plant Kingdom. (Illus.). 640p. 1974. text ed. write for info. (ISBN 0-02-317200-2, 31720). Macmillan.

Cardot, J. Cryptogamic Botany. (Harriman Alaska Expedition: Vol. 5). Repr. of 1904 ed. 41.00 (ISBN 0-527-38165-9). Kraus Repr.

Carpenter, Steven E. Monograph of Crocicreas: Ascomycetes, Helotiales, Helotiaceae, Vol. 33. (Memoirs of the New York Botanical Garden Ser.). (Illus.). 1981. pap. 35.00x (ISBN 0-89327-230-2). NY Botanical.

Christensen, C. M. E. C. Stakman, Statesman of Science. LC 84-70114. (Illus.). 156p. 1984. text ed. 18.00 (ISBN 0-89054-056-X). Am Phytopathol Soc.

Christensen, Carl. Index Filicum. 1973. 92.75 (ISBN 3-87429-048-4). Lubrecht & Cramer.

--Index Filicum: Supplementum, Vols. 1, 2 & 3. 1973. 59.50 (ISBN 3-87429-049-2). Lubrecht & Cramer.

Clarkson, Quentin D. Handbook of Field Botany. LC 61-13273. (Illus.). 1961. pap. 2.00 (ISBN 0-8323-0350-X). Binford.

Commonwealth Scientific & Industrial Research Institute. A Curious & Diverse Flora. Commonwealth Scientific & Industrial Research Institute & Australian Academy of Science, eds. 1982. slides 35.00x (ISBN 0-89955-361-3, Pub. by CSIRO). Intl Spec Bk.

Corner, E. J. The Life of Plants. LC 81-11436. 1981. 10.95 (ISBN 0-226-11586-0, Phoen). U of Chicago Pr.

Coulter, Merle C. Story of the Plant Kingdom. 3rd ed. rev ed. LC 64-10093. (Illus.). 1964. text ed. 17.50x (ISBN 0-226-11621-2). U of Chicago Pr.

--The Story of the Plant Kingdom. rev. ed. Dittmer, Howard J., ed. LC 64-10093. 480p. 1973. pap. text ed. 4.95x (ISBN 0-226-11611-5, P494, Phoen). U of Chicago Pr.

Cronquist, Arthur. Basic Botany. 2nd ed. 662p. 1981. text ed. 28.95 scp (ISBN 0-06-041429-4, HarpC). Har-Row.

Daniels, G., ed. A Linnaean Keepsake. (Eng. & Lat., Illus.). 1973. 13.00x (ISBN 0-913196-15-0). Hunt Inst Botanical.

Darwin, Charles R. The Power of Movement in Plants. 2nd ed. LC 65-23402. 1966. Repr. of 1881 ed. lib. bdg. 55.00 (ISBN 0-306-70921-X). Da Capo.

De Candolle, A. P. Collection de Memoires pour servir a l'Histoire du Regne Vegetal et plus specialement pour servir de complement a quelques parties du Prodromus Regni Vegetabilis. (Illus.). 1972. 87.50 (ISBN 3-7682-0728-5). Lubrecht & Cramer.

De Candolle, Augustin P. & Sprengel, Kurt. Elements of the Philosophy of Plants: Containing the Principles of Scientific Botany. Sterling, Keir B., ed. LC 77-81123. (Biologists & Their World Ser.). (Illus.). 1978. Repr. of 1821 ed. lib. bdg. 40.00x (ISBN 0-405-10719-6). Ayer Co Pubs.

Dennis, LaRae. Know Your Poison. 1972. pap. text ed. 3.95x (ISBN 0-88246-026-9). Oreg St U Bkstrs.

Dieterlen, F. Zur Phaenologie des aequatorialen Regenwaldes im Ost-Zaire (Kivu) nebst Planzenliste und Klimadaten. (Dissertations Botanica: No. 47). (Illus.). 1979. pap. 10.00x (ISBN 3-7682-1215-7). Lubrecht & Cramer.

Dodd, John D. Course Book in General Botany. (Illus.). 1977. text ed. 16.95x (ISBN 0-8138-0690-9). Iowa St U Pr.

Dostal, Rudolf. On Integration in Plants. Thimann, Kenneth V., ed. Kiely, Jana M., tr. LC 67-27083. (Illus.). 1967. 16.50x (ISBN 0-674-63450-0). Harvard U Pr.

Dyer, A. F. & Duckett, J. G., eds. The Experimental Biology of Bryophytes. (Experimental Botany: An International Series Of Monographs). 1984. 68.50 (ISBN 0-12-226370-7). Acad Pr.

Edlin, Herbert L. & Huxley, Anthony. Atlas of Plant Life. LC 73-734361. (John Day Bk.). (Illus.). 128p. 1973. 14.37i (ISBN 0-381-98245-9). T Y Crowell.

Ellenberg, H., et al, eds. Progress in Botany, Vol. 39. LC 33-15850. (Illus.). 1977. 62.00 (ISBN 0-387-08501-7). Springer-Verlag.

Elliott, J. H. Botany. (Teach Yourself Ser.). 1973. pap. 4.95 (ISBN 0-679-10390-2). McKay.

Engler, A. Syllabus der Pflanzenfamilien, 2 vols. 12th ed. Incl. Vol. 1. Allgemeiner Teil: Bakterien Bis Gymnospermen. 1954. 30.34 (ISBN 3-4433-9015-3); Vol. 2. Angiospermen Vebersicht Ueber Die Florengebiete der Erde. 1964. 55.00 (ISBN 3-4433-9016-1). (Illus.). Lubrecht & Cramer.

Engler, A. & Drude, O., eds. Vegetation der Erde. Repr. of 1976 ed. of 13 vols. 700.00 set (ISBN 3-7682-0984-9). Lubrecht & Cramer.

Evert, Ray F. & Eichhorn, Susan E. Laboratory Topics in Botany. 3rd ed. (Illus.). vii, 196p. 1981. lab manual 13.95x (ISBN 0-87901-142-4). Worth.

Ewan, J. Introduction to the Reprint of Pursh's Flora Americae Septentrionalis. 118p. 1980. pap. text ed. 8.75 (ISBN 3-7682-1272-6). Lubrecht & Cramer.

A Facsimile Reprint of Systema Naturae by Carolus Linnaeus. 95.00 (ISBN 0-930466-89-6). Meckler Pub.

Fineran, J. M. A Taxonomic Revision of the Genus Entorrhiza C. Weber (Ustilaginales) (Nova Hedwigia Ser.). (Illus.). 1979. pap. text ed. 8.75 (ISBN 3-7682-1211-4). Lubrecht & Cramer.

Flammer, R. Differentialdiagnosen der Pilzvergiftungen, mit Bestimmungsschluesselein fuer Mediciner und Mykologen. (Ger., Illus.). 92p. 1980. text ed. 11.60 (ISBN 3-437-10636-8). Lubrecht & Cramer.

Fourth International Exhibition of Twentieth Century Botanical Art & Illustration. Catalogue. Secrist, S. & Howard, N., eds. (Illus.). 1977. 12.00x (ISBN 0-913196-19-3). Hunt Inst Botanical.

France, R. H. Germs of Mind in Plants. Simons, A. M., tr. from Ger. (Science for the Workers Ser.). (Illus.). 151p. 9.95 (ISBN 0-88286-083-6). C H Kerr.

Frodin, D. G. Guide to Standard Floras of the World. LC 82-4501. 580p. 1985. 175.00 (ISBN 0-521-23688-6). Cambridge U Pr.

Fulling, Edmund H., compiled by. Index to Botany As Recorded in the Botanical Review: Volumes 1-25, 1935-1959. Plant Names. (The Botanical Review). 1967. 12.50x (ISBN 0-89327-214-0). NY Botanical.

Gaillard, M. J. Etude Palynologique de L'Evolution Tardiet Postglaciare de la Vegetation du Moyen-Pays Romad: Suisse. (Dissertationes Botanicae Ser.: No. 77). (Illus.). 346p. 1985. lib. bdg. 42.00x (ISBN 3-7682-1396-X). Lubrecht & Cramer.

Gehu, J. M. Documents Phytosociologiques. (Nouv. Ser.: No. 3). 1978. lib. bdg. 35.00 (ISBN 3-7682-1202-5). Lubrecht & Cramer.

Gehu, J. M., ed. La Vegetation des Pelouses Seches a Therophytes. (Colloques Phytosociologiques Ser.: No. 6). 1979. lib. bdg. 42.00 (ISBN 3-7682-1207-6). Lubrecht & Cramer.

George, Alex. The Banksia Book. (Illus.). 1985. 24.95 (ISBN 0-88192-050-9, Dist. by Intl Spec Bk). Timber.

Gibbons, Bob. How Flowers Work: A Guide to Plant Biology. (Illus.). 160p. 1984. 15.95 (ISBN 0-7137-1278-3, Pub. by Blandford Pr England). Sterling.

Gill, G. B. & Willis, M. R. Pericyclic Reactions. 1974. pap. 15.50x (ISBN 0-412-12490-4, NO. 6125, Pub. by Chapman & Hall). Methuen Inc.

Gilmore, Melvin R. Uses of Plants by the Indians of the Missouri River Region. LC 77-89833. (Illus.). xviii, 149p. 1977. 13.95x (ISBN 0-8032-0935-5); pap. 5.95 (ISBN 0-8032-5872-0, BB 644, Bison). U of Nebr Pr.

Gleason, Henry A. & Cronquist, Arthur. Manual of Vascular Plants. 810p. 1963. text ed. write for info. (ISBN 0-87150-760-9, Pub. by Willard Grant Pr). PWS Pubs.

Glimn-Lacy, Janice & Kaufman, Peter B. Botany Illustrated. 1984. pap. 19.45 (ISBN 0-442-22969-0). Van Nos Reinhold.

Gottlieb, Otto R. Micromolecular Evolution, Systematics, & Ecology: An Essay into a Novel Botanical Discipline. (Illus.). 170p. 1982. 36.00 (ISBN 0-387-11655-9). Springer-Verlag.

Grant, Susan T. Beauty & the Beast: The Coevolution of Plants & Animals. 224p. 1984. 14.95 (ISBN 0-684-18186-X, ScribT). Scribner.

Gray, Asa. Elements of Botany. LC 73-125739. (American Environmental Studies). 1970. Repr. of 1887 ed. 23.50 (ISBN 0-405-02664-1). Ayer Co Pubs.

Groves, E. W. Vascular Plant Collections from the Tristan de Cunha Group of Islands. 72p. 50.00x (ISBN 0-686-78669-6, Pub. by Brit Mus Pubns England). State Mutual Bk.

Guerke, W. R. A Monograph of the Genus Jubula Dumortier. (Bryophytorum Bibliotheca Ser.: No. 17). (Illus.). 1979. pap. 14.00 (ISBN 3-7682-1213-0). Lubrecht & Cramer.

Guiry, M. D. A Consensus & Bibliography of Irish Seaweeds. (Bibliotheca Phycologica Ser.: No. 44). 1979. pap. text ed. 14.00x (ISBN 3-7682-1209-2). Lubrecht & Cramer.

Hafellner, J. Karschia: Revision einer Sammelgattung an der Grenze von lichenisierten und nicht lichenisierten Ascomyceten. (Beihefte Nova Hedwigia: No. 62). (Ger., Illus.). 1979. lib. bdg. 42.00 (ISBN 3-7682-5462-3). Lubrecht & Cramer.

Hall, Timothy C. & Davies, Jeffrey W. Nucleic Acids in Plants, 2 vols. 1979. Vol. 1, 272p. 76.00 (ISBN 0-8493-5291-6); Vol. 2, 256p. 71.00 (ISBN 0-8493-5292-4). CRC Pr.

Haney, Alan W. Plants & Life. (Illus.). 1978. text ed. write for info. (ISBN 0-02-349950-8). Macmillan.

Hanlin, R. T. Index to Genera & Authors in Grevillea. (Bibliotheca Mycologica Ser.: No. 64). 1978. pap. text ed. 14.00x (ISBN 3-7682-1205-X). Lubrecht & Cramer.

Hansen, Bertel. Balanophoraceae. LC 79-28385. (Flora Neotropica Monograph: No. 23). 1980. 10.50x (ISBN 0-89327-195-0). NY Botanical.

Hansgirg, A. Prodromus der Algenflora von Boehmen. (From: Archiv F. Naturw. Landesdurchf.. (Boehmens)). (Ger.). 1979. Repr. of 1892 ed. lib. bdg. 70.00x (ISBN 3-7682-0922-9). Lubrecht & Cramer.

Harley, J. L., ed. The Soil-Root Interface. 1979. 59.50 (ISBN 0-12-325550-3). Acad Pr.

Harrison, James, ed. Nature's Secret World. LC 84-9169. (Illus.). 192p. 1984. 19.95 (ISBN 0-668-06213-4, 6213). Arco.

Haslam, S. M. & Wolseley, P. A. River Vegetation: Its Identification, Assessment & Management; a Field Guide to the Macrophytic Vegetation of British Watercourses. 96p. 1981. text ed. 44.50 (ISBN 0-521-23186-8). Cambridge U Pr.

Hawkes, J. G., et al, eds. The Biology & Taxonomy of the Solanaceae. (Linnean Society Symposia Ser.). 1979. 98.00 (ISBN 0-12-333150-1). Acad Pr.

Heiser, Charles B., Jr. Of Plants & People. LC 84-40688. (Illus.). 272p. 1985. 24.95 (ISBN 0-8061-1931-4). U of Okla Pr.

Henfrey, Arthur, ed. Botanical & Physiological Memoirs. Repr. of 1853 ed. 55.00 (ISBN 0-384-22310-9). Johnson Repr.

--Reports & Papers on Botany. Repr. of 1849 ed. 37.00 (ISBN 0-384-22312-5). Johnson Repr.

Hill, John B., et al. Botany, a Textbook for Colleges. 4th ed. LC 76-57931. (Illus.). 644p. 1977. Repr. of 1967 ed. 28.00 (ISBN 0-88275-516-1). Krieger.

Hillman, Peter. How Does Your Garden Grow? Simple Garden Science. (Illus.). 160p. 1985. 10.00 (ISBN 0-7099-3711-3, Pub. by Croom Helm Ltd). Longwood Pub Group.

Hocker, Harold W., Jr. Introduction to Forest Biology. LC 78-26878. 467p. 1979. 43.95 (ISBN 0-471-01978-X). Wiley.

Hoffman, P. Genetische Grundlagen der Artbildung in der Gattung Polyporus. (Bibliotheca Mycologica Ser.: No. 65). (Illus.). 1978. pap. text ed. 11.20x (ISBN 3-7682-1210-6). Lubrecht & Cramer.

Hooker, W. J. Icones Plantarum, 4 vols, Vols. 1-20. (Ser. 1-3). 1966. 336.00 (ISBN 3-7682-0250-X). Lubrecht & Cramer.

Hooker, W. J. & Walker-Arnott, G. A. The Botany of Captain Beechey's Voyage. (Illus.). 1965. 42.50 (ISBN 3-7682-0263-1). Lubrecht & Cramer.

Huxley, Anthony. Plant & Planet. LC 75-2403. (Illus.). 432p. 1975. 16.95 (ISBN 0-670-55886-9). Viking.

Industries in Trouble. 178p. 1981. pap. 11.40 (ISBN 92-2-102679-5, ILO183, ILO). Unipub.

Jensen, William A. & Salisbury, Frank B. Botany. 2nd ed. 720p. 1984. text ed. write for info. (ISBN 0-534-02900-0); pap. write for info. study guide (ISBN 0-534-02901-9). Wadsworth Pub.

Jermy, T., ed. The Host-Plant in Relation to Insect Behavior & Reproduction. LC 75-37209. 322p. 1976. 42.50x (ISBN 0-306-30909-2, Plenum Pr.). Plenum Pub.

Johansen, Donald A. Plant Microtechnique. (Botanical Sciences Ser.). 1940. text ed. 66.95 (ISBN 0-07-032540-5). McGraw.

Joshi, G. V., et al. A Foundation Course in Botany. 342p. 1981. 32.00x (ISBN 0-86125-406-6, Pub. by Orient Longman India). State Mutual Bk.

Kachroo, P., ed. Recent Advances in Botany. 1978. 43.75x (ISBN 0-89955-302-8, Pub. by Intl Bk Dist). Intl Spec Bk.

Kaufman, Peter B. & La Croix, Don, eds. Plants, People, & Environment. 1979. text ed. write for info. (ISBN 0-02-362120-6). Macmillan.

Koedam, A. & Margaris, N. Aromatic Plants. 1982. text ed. 41.50 (ISBN 90-247-2720-0, Pub. by Martinus Nijhoff Netherlands). Kluwer Academic.

Komarkova, V. Alpine Vegetation of the Indian Peaks Area, Front Range, Colorado Rocky Mountains. (Flora et Vegetatio Mundi: No. 7). (Illus.). 1979. lib. bdg. 70.00x (ISBN 3-7682-1208-4). Lubrecht & Cramer.

Korach, K., ed. Catalogue: Third International Exhibition of Twentieth Century Botanical Art & Illustration. (Illus.). 1972. 10.00x (ISBN 0-913196-14-2). Hunt Inst Botanical.

Kramer, Jack. Picture Encyclopedia of Small Plants. LC 78-1089. 192p. 1981. pap. 11.95 (ISBN 0-8128-2497-0). Stein & Day.

Kranich, Ernst M. Planetary Influences Upon Plants: Cosmological Botany. 184p. (Orig.). 1984. pap. 12.50 (ISBN 0-938250-20-5). Anthroposophic.

Kuenne, Horst. Laubwaldgesellschaften der Frankenalb. (Illus.). 1969. 10.50 (ISBN 3-7682-0610-6). Lubrecht & Cramer.

Kurtz, Edwin B. & Allen, Chris. Adventures in Living Plants. pap. 30.00 (ISBN 0-317-28658-7, 2055330). Bks Demand UMI.

Laetsch, Watson M. Plants: Basic Concepts in Botany. 1979. text ed. 25.95 (ISBN 0-316-51186-2); tchrs' manual avail. (ISBN 0-316-51185-4). Little.

Langenheim, Jean H. & Thimann, Kenneth V. Botany: Plant Biology & Its Relation to Human Affairs. LC 81-7466. 624p. 1982. text ed. 37.50 (ISBN 0-471-85880-3). Wiley.

Largent, D. L. Leptonia & Related Genera of the West Coast. 1976. 28.00 (ISBN 3-7682-1114-2). Lubrecht & Cramer.

Lawrence, G., ed. A Catalogue of Redouteana Exhibited at the Hunt Botanical Library. (Illus.). 1963. pap. 15.00x (ISBN 0-913196-03-7). Hunt Inst Botanical.

Lawrence, G. H. The Hunt Botanical Library: A Decennial Report. (Illus.). 45p. 4.00 (ISBN 0-317-19695-2); pap. text ed. 3.00 (ISBN 0-317-19696-0). Hunt Inst Botanical.

Li, P. H. & Sakai, A., eds. Plant Cold Hardiness & Freezing Stress: Vol. 2: Mechanisms & Crop Implications. LC 78-7038. (Symposium). 1982. 43.50 (ISBN 0-12-447602-3). Acad Pr.

Lindley, John & Moore, Thomas, eds. The Encyclopedia or the Treasury of Botany: Pt. I (A-L), Pt II (M-Z, 2 Vols. 1352p. 1981. Set. text ed. 65.00x (ISBN 0-391-02436-1, Pub. by Concept India). Humanities.

Linnaeus, C. Mantissa Plantarum: 1767-71, 2 Vols. in 1. 1960. 42.00 (ISBN 3-7682-0037-X). Lubrecht & Cramer.

--Philosophia Botanica. (Illus.). 1966. Repr. of 1751 ed. 52.50 (ISBN 3-7682-0350-6). Lubrecht & Cramer.

Linnaeus, Carl. Carl Linnaeus, Species Plantarium: A Facsimile of the First Edition, 1753, Vols. I & II. Repr. of 1753 ed. Set. 80.00x (ISBN 0-686-33346-2, Pub. by Brit Mus Nat Hist England). Vol. I, 1957; Xiv, 772p., 0-903874-10-5. Vol. II, 1959; Xv, 823p., 0-903874-11-3. Sabbot-Natural Hist Bks.

Littlefield, Larry J. Biology of the Plant Rusts: An Introduction. (Illus.). 104p. 1981. text ed. 15.95x (ISBN 0-8138-1670-X). Iowa St U Pr.

Loveless, A. R. Principles of Plant Biology for the Tropics. LC 81-20876. (Illus.). 544p. 1983. 21.95x (ISBN 0-582-44757-7). Longman.

Luettge, U. & Higinbotham, N. Transport in Plants. (Illus.). 1979. 37.00 (ISBN 0-387-90383-6). Springer-Verlag.

Luig, Norbert H. A Survey of Virulence Genes in Wheat Stem Rust, Puccinia Graminis. (Advances in Plant Breeding Ser.: No. 11). (Illus.). 199p. 1983. pap. text ed. 25.20x (ISBN 3-489-74110-2). Parey Sci Pubs.

Lusigi, W. Planning Human Activities on Protected Natural Ecosystems. (Dissertationes Botanica Ser.: No. 48). (Illus.). 1979. pap. 14.00x (ISBN 3-7682-1214-9). Lubrecht & Cramer.

Mabberly, D. J., ed. Revolutionary Botany: "Thalassiophyta" & Other Essays of A. H. Church. (Illus.). 1981. 49.95x (ISBN 0-19-854548-7). Oxford U Pr.

MacFarlane, Ruth B. Collecting & Preserving Plants for Science & Pleasure. (Illus.). 192p. 1984. lib. bdg. 13.95 (ISBN 0-668-06009-3); pap. 8.95 (ISBN 0-668-06013-1). Arco.

Mangham, Sydney. An Introduction to Botany. 1979. Repr. of 1928 ed. lib. bdg. 12.50 (ISBN 0-8495-3775-4). Arden Lib.

--An Introduction to Botany. 1928. 15.00 (ISBN 0-8274-4237-8). R West.

Mantell, S. H., et al. Principles of Plant Biotechnology. (Illus.). 200p. 1985. text ed. 32.00x (ISBN 0-632-01214-5); pap. text ed. 17.00x (ISBN 0-632-01215-3). Blackwell Pubns.

Marvan, P. & Pribil, S. Algal Assays & Monitoring Eutrophication. (Illus.). 253p. 1979. 20.10 (ISBN 3-510-65091-3). Lubrecht & Cramer.

Mayrhofer, '. & Poelt, J. Die Saxicolen Arten der Flechtengattung Rinodina in Europa. (Bibliotheca Lichenologica: No. 12). (Ger., Illus.). 1979. lib. bdg. 21.00 (ISBN 3-7682-1237-8). Lubrecht & Cramer.

Meikle, R. D. Flora of Cyprus, Vol. 1. (Illus.). xii, 832p. 1977. 46.00x (ISBN 0-9504876-3-5, Pub. by Brit Mus Nat Hist England). Sabbot-Natural Hist Bks.

Merkel, J. Die Vegetation in Gebiet des Messtischblattes 6434 Hersbruck. (Dissertationes Botanica Ser.: No. 51). (Ger., Illus.). 176p. 1980. pap. text ed. 17.50 (ISBN 3-7682-1235-1). Lubrecht & Cramer.

Merrill, E. D. A Commentary on Loureiro's "Flora Cochinchinensis". 1935. pap. 10.00 (ISBN 0-934454-24-8). Lubrecht & Cramer.

Michael, E. Handbuch fuer Pilzfreunde: Volume 4: Blaetterilze-Dunkelblaettler. Kreisel, H, ed. (Illus.). 472p. text ed. 23.25 (ISBN 3-437-30349-X). Lubrecht & Cramer.

Miehe, Georg. Vegetationsgeographische Untersuchungen im Dhaulagiri-und Annapurna-Himalaya, 2 vols. (Dissertationes Botanica Ser.: No. 66). (Illus.). 500p. 1982. lib. bdg. 59.10 (ISBN 3-7682-1356-0). Lubrecht & Cramer.

Mills, Howard L. Laboratory Studies in Plant Biology. 1977. pap. text ed. 7.95 (ISBN 0-8403-0686-5). Kendall-Hunt.

Mirza, F. Taxonomic Investigations on the Ascomycetous Genus Cucurbitaria S. F. Gray. (Fronova Hedwigia Ser.: No. 16). (Illus.). 54p. 1968. pap. text ed. 5.60 (ISBN 3-7682-0614-9). Lubrecht & Cramer.

Mohlenbrock, Robert H. Flowering Plants: Basswoods to Spurges. LC 81-8585. (Illustrated Flora of Illinois). (Illus.). 256p. 1982. 22.95x (ISBN 0-8093-1025-2). S Ill U Pr.

Moreau, Fernand. Botanique. (Methodique Ser.). 1534p. 55.95 (ISBN 0-686-56433-2). French & Eur.

Mukherji, S. M. Pericyclic Reactions: A Mechanistic Study. 1980. 16.00x (ISBN 0-8364-0637-0, Pub. by Macmillan India). South Asia Bks.

Muller, Walter H. Botany: A Functional Approach. 4th ed. 1979. write for info. (ISBN 0-02-384700-X). Macmillan.

Nadakavukaren, Mathew J. & McCracken, Derek. Botany: An Introduction to Plant Biology. (Illus.). 520p. (Orig.). 1985. pap. text ed. 24.95 (ISBN 0-314-85279-4). West Pub.

Nair, P. K., ed. Aspects of Plant Sciences, Vol. I. 210p. 1976. 12.00 (ISBN 0-88065-170-9, Pub. by Messers Today & Tomorrows Printers & Publishers India). Scholarly Pubns.

--Aspects of Plant Sciences, Vol. II. 164p. 1979. 12.00 (ISBN 0-88065-171-7, Pub. by Messers Today & Tomorrows Printers & Publishers India). Scholarly Pubns.

Northen, Henry & Northen, Rebecca. Ingenious Kingdom: The Remarkable World of Plants. LC 76-110413. (Illus.). 1970. 8.95 (ISBN 0-13-464859-5). P-H.

Northington, David K. & Goodin, J. R. The Botanical World. (Illus.). 656p. 1984. text ed. 23.95 (ISBN 0-8016-1893-2). Mosby.

Pandey, S. N. & Trivedi, P. S. A Textbook of Botany, Vol. I. 6th rev. ed. 531p. 1983. (Pub. by Vikas India); 40.00x (ISBN 0-7069-1844-4). Advent NY.

Pandey, S. N., et al. Textbook of Botany: Vol. II. 9th ed. viii, 531p. 1981. text ed. 40.00x (ISBN 0-7069-2397-9, Pub. by Vikas India). Advent NY.

--Textbook of Botany: Vol II (Bryophyta, Pteridophyta, Gymnosperms & Paleobotany) (Illus.). 1974. 10.50 (ISBN 0-686-20315-1). Intl Bk Dist.

Parkinson, John. Paradisi in Sole, Paradisus Terrestris, or a Garden of All Sorts of Pleasant Flowers Which Our English Ayre Will Permit. LC 74-28880. (English Experience Ser.: No. 758). 1975. Repr. of 1629 ed. 110.00 (ISBN 90-221-0758-2). Walter J Johnson.

Pascher, A. Suesswasserflora von Suedeuropa, Vol. 24: Pteridophyta und Antophyta, Part 2-Saururaceae bis Asteraceae. Ettl, H., et al, eds. (Illus.). 540p. 1981. lib. bdg. 59.35 (ISBN 3-437-30341-4). Lubrecht & Cramer.

Peterson, Curt M. Plant Biology Laboratory Manual. 2nd ed. 1976. pap. text ed. 9.95 (ISBN 0-8403-1405-1). Kendall-Hunt.

Preston, R. D., ed. Advances in Botanical Research. Incl. Vol. 1. 1963. 65.00 (ISBN 0-12-005901-0); Vol. 2. 1965. 65.00 (ISBN 0-12-005902-9); Vol. 3. 1970. 65.00 (ISBN 0-12-005903-7). Acad Pr.

Pringsheim, E. G. Farblose Algen. Ein Beitrag zur Evolutionsforschung. (Ger., Illus.). 471p. 1963. lib. bdg. 44.00 (ISBN 0-318-00461-5). Lubrecht & Cramer.

Progress in Botany, Vol. 37. LC 33-15850. (Illus.). 460p. 1975. 75.00 (ISBN 0-387-07504-6). Springer-Verlag.

Progress in Botany, Vol. 45. (Illus.). 440p. 1984. 66.40 (ISBN 0-387-12997-9). Springer-Verlag.

Progress in Botany, Vol. 46. (Illus.). 410p. 1984. (tent). 90.30 (ISBN 0-387-13731-9). Springer-Verlag.

The Rachel McMasters Miller Hunt Botanical Library. (Illus.). viii, 35p. 1961. 5.00 (ISBN 0-317-19699-5). Hunt Inst Botanical.

Rafinesque, C. S. Flora Telluriana, 4pts. in 1. 1946. pap. 10.00 (ISBN 0-934454-33-7). Lubrecht & Cramer.

Rattan, S. S. & Khurana, I. P. S. The Clavaria of the Sikkim Himalayas. (Bibliotheca Mycologica Ser.: No. 66). (Illus.). 1978. pap. text ed. 8.75x (ISBN 3-7682-1212-2). Lubrecht & Cramer.

Raunkiaer, Christen. The Life Forms of Plants & Statistical Plants Geography. Egerton, Frank N., 3rd, ed. Gilbert-Carter, H. & Fausboll, A., trs LC 77-74249. (History of Ecology Ser.). (Illus.). 1978. Repr. of 1934 ed. lib. bdg. 51.00x (ISBN 0-405-10418-9). Ayer Co Pubs.

Raven, Peter H., et al. Biology of Plants. 3rd ed. 1981. text ed. 36.95 (ISBN 0-87901-132-7); lab manual 13.95x; prep guide avail. (ISBN 0-87901-143-2). Worth.

Ray, J. Methodus Plantarum Nova. (Illus.). 1962. Repr. of 1682 ed. 12.60 (ISBN 3-7682-0119-8). Lubrecht & Cramer.

Ray, Peter & Steeves, Taylor. Botany. 1983. text ed. 37.95 (ISBN 0-03-089942-7, CBS C). SCP.

Rayle, David L. & Wedburg, Hale L. Botany: A Human Concern. 1980. text ed. 32.95 (ISBN 0-03-056753-X, CBS C); instr's manual 6.95 (ISBN 0-03-056754-8). SCP.

Reid, G. Mcg. A Revision of African Species of Labeo: Pieces, Cyprinidae & a Redefinition of the Genus. (THeses Zoologicae Ser.: No. 6). (Illus.). 322p. 1985. lib. bdg. 56.00x (ISBN 3-7682-1413-3). Lubrecht & Cramer.

Riley, Ralph & Lewis, K. R., eds. Chromosome Manipulation & Plant Genetics: The Contributions to a Symposium Held During the Tenth International Botanical Congress, Edinburgh, 1964. LC 66-71193. pap. 33.50 (ISBN 0-317-28828-8, 2020701). Bks Demand UMI.

Rojo, J. P. Pterocarpus (Leguminosae-Papilionaceae) Revised for the World. 1971. 21.00 (ISBN 3-7682-0726-9). Lubrecht & Cramer.

Romagnesi, H. Les Fondements de la Taxonomie des Rhodophylles et Leur Classification. (Nova Hedwigia Beiheft Ser.: No. 59). (Illus.). 1979. pap. text ed. 8.70 (ISBN 3-7682-1191-6). Lubrecht & Cramer.

Romberger, J. A. Meristems, Growth & Development in Woody Plants: An Analytical Review of Anatomical, Physiological & Morphogenis Aspects. LC 78-51432. (Landmark Reprints in Plant Science Ser.). (Illus.). 224p. 1978. Repr. of 1963 ed. text ed. 15.00x (ISBN 0-86598-005-5). Allanheld.

Rost, Thomas L., et al. Botany: A Brief Introduction to Plant Biology. 2nd ed. LC 83-21809. 416p. 1984. text ed. 30.95 (ISBN 0-471-87454-X); tchrs.' manual avail. (ISBN 0-471-80570-X). Wiley.

Roth, Charles E. The Plant Observer's Guidebook: A Field Botany Manual for the Amateur Naturalist. (Illus.). 240p. 1984. 17.95 (ISBN 0-13-680752-6); pap. 9.95 (ISBN 0-13-680745-3). P-H.

Rubenstein, Irwin, et al, eds. Molecular Biology of Plants. LC 79-18510. 1979. 41.50 (ISBN 0-12-601950-9). Acad Pr.

Rutishauser, Rolf. Blattstellung und Sprossentwicklung bei Bluetenpflanzen unter Besonderer Beruecksichtigung der Nelkengewaechse. (Dissertationes Botanica: Vol. 62). (Ger., Illus.). 200p. pap. text ed. 14.00x (ISBN 3-7682-1304-8). Lubrecht & Cramer.

Saigo, Roy H. & Saigo, Barbara W. Botany: Principles & Applications. (Illus.). 560p. 1983. 31.95 (ISBN 0-13-080234-4). P-H.

Sapody, C & Toth, I., eds. A Colour Atlas of Flowering Trees & Shrubs. 312p. 1982. 51.00 (Pub. by Akademiai Kiado Hungary). Heyden.

Scagel, Robert F., et al. Plants: An Evolutionary Survey. 757p. 1984. write for info. (ISBN 0-534-00677-9); pap. write for info. (ISBN 0-534-02802-0). Wadsworth Pub.

Schleiden, M. J. Principles of Scientific Botany: Or Botany As an Inductive Science. Lankester, Edwin, tr. 1849. 38.00 (ISBN 0-527-80150-X). Kraus Repr.

Schleiden, Mathias J. Principles of Scientific Botany. Lankester, E., tr. (Sources of Science Ser.: No. 40). Repr. of 1849 ed. 48.00 (ISBN 0-384-53950-5). Johnson Repr.

Schloss, S. Pollenanalytische und Stratigraphische Untersuchungen im Sewensee. Ein Beitrag Zur Spaet- und Postglazealen Vegetations-Geschichte der Suedvogesen. (Dissertationes Botanica 52 Ser.). (Ger., Illus.). 1980. lib. bdg. 17.50x (ISBN 3-7682-1240-8). Lubrecht & Cramer.

Schnetter, R. Marine Algen der Karibischen Kuest E Von Kolumbien: Chlorophyceae, Vol. II. (Bibliotheca Phycologica Ser.: No. 42). (Illus.). 1978. lib. bdg. 21.00x (ISBN 3-7682-1204-1). Lubrecht & Cramer.

Schumann, Donna N. Living with Plants: A Guide to the Practical Application of Botany. (Illus.). 328p. (Orig.). 1980. pap. 13.95x (ISBN 0-916422-20-8). Mad River.

Schumann, K. M. & Lauterbach, C. A. Die Flora der Deutschen Schutzgebiete in der Suedsee: With Suppl. 1976. 105.00 (ISBN 3-7682-1078-2). Lubrecht & Cramer.

Schuster, H. Experimentelle Untersuchungen Zur Schwermetallresistenz Von Sumersen Makrophyten. (Dissertationes Botanica 50 Ser.). (Ger., Illus.). 1980. pap. text ed. 14.00x (ISBN 3-7682-1229-7). Lubrecht & Cramer.

Second International Exhibition of Twentieth Century Botanical Art & Illustration. Catalogue. Lawrence, G., compiled by. (Illus.). 1968. 7.00x (ISBN 0-913196-11-8). Hunt Inst Botanical.

Second International Symposium Bratislava, September, 1980. Structure & Function of Plant Roots: Proceedings. Brouwer, R., et al, eds. 1982. lib. bdg. 65.00 (ISBN 90-247-2510-0, Pub. by Martinus Nijhoff Netherlands). Kluwer Academic.

Sen, S. P., ed. Recent Developments in Plant Sciences: Prof. S. M. Sircar Memorial Volume. (Illus.). 395p. 1982. 39.00 (ISBN 0-88065-241-1, Pub. by Messers Today & Tomorrow Printers & Publishers). Scholarly Pubns.

Sharsmith, Helen K. Flora of the Mount Hamilton Range of California. LC 82-9600. (Special Publications Ser.: No. 6). (Illus.). 96p. (Orig.). 1982. pap. 8.95x (ISBN 0-943460-08-5). Calif Native.

Simon, E. W., et al. Lowson's Textbook of Botany. 14th ed 1981. 30.00x (ISBN 0-7231-0614-2, Pub. by Univ Tutorial England). State Mutual Bk.

Simpson, B. B. & Conner-Ogorzaly, M. Economic Botany: Plants in Our World. (Illus.). 753p. 1986. price not set (ISBN 0-07-057443-X). McGraw.

Singer, R. A Monograph of Favolastcha. 1974. 21.00 (ISBN 3-7682-5450-X). Lubrecht & Cramer.

Skellern, Claire & Rogers, Paul. Basic Botany. (Illus.). 208p. (Orig.). 1977. pap. text ed. 14.95x (ISBN 0-7121-0255-8, Pub. by Macdonald & Evans England). Trans-Atlantic.

Sleumer, H. O. Flacourtiaceae. LC 79-22365. (Flora Neotropica Monograph: No. 22). 1980. 47.50x (ISBN 0-89327-194-2). NY Botanical.

Smith, H. Regulation of Enzyme Synthesis & Activity in Higher Plants. 1978. 68.00 (ISBN 0-12-650850-X). Acad Pr.

Smith, H., ed. Commentaries in Plant Science, Vol. 2. LC 80-41007. (Illus.). 250p. 1981. 61.00 (ISBN 0-08-025898-0). Pergamon.

Smith, Harry, ed. Commentaries in Plant Science. LC 76-7531. 272p. 1976. text ed. 54.00 (ISBN 0-08-019759-0). Pergamon.

Smith, James P., Jr. Vascular Plant Families. (Illus.). 320p. 1977. pap. 10.95x (ISBN 0-916422-11-9). Mad River.

Specht, R. L., ed. Heathlands & Related Shrublands, 2 Vols. (Ecosystems of the World Ser.: Vols. 9A-B). 1980-81. Set. 144.75 (ISBN 0-444-41810-5); Vol. 1: Descriptive Studies, 498p. 85.00 (ISBN 0-444-41701-X); Vol. 2: Analytical Studies, 386p. 85.00 (ISBN 0-444-41809-1). Elsevier.

Spruce, Richard. Notes of a Botanist on the Amazon & Andes, 2 Vols. Wallace, A. R., ed. (Landmarks in Anthropology Ser.). Repr. of 1908 ed. Set. 73.00 (ISBN 0-384-57200-6). Johnson Repr.

Stace, Helen M. & Edye, Leslie Andrew, eds. The Biology & Agronomy of Stylosanthes. Date not set. 75.00 (ISBN 0-12-661680-9). Acad Pr.

Stapf, O. & Wordsell, W. C. Index Londinensis, 6 vols. & 2 suppl. 1979. Repr. of 1929 ed. 882.00 (ISBN 3-87429-151-0). Lubrecht & Cramer.

Stern, Kingsley. Introductory Plant Biology. 3rd ed. 656p. 1985. pap. text ed. write for info. (ISBN 0-697-05024-6); instr's. manual avail. (ISBN 0-697-05117-X); lab manual avail. (ISBN 0-697-04930-2); transparencies avail. (ISBN 0-697-04943-4). Wm C Brown.

Stone, Doris M. The Lives of Plants: Exploring the Wonders of Botany. (Illus.). 256p. 1983. 15.95 (ISBN 0-684-17907-5, ScribT). Scribner.

Swartley, John. Cultivated Hemlocks. Welch, Humphrey & Dudley, T. R., eds. (Illus.). 270p. 1984. 24.95 (ISBN 0-917304-74-8). Timber.

Taylor, William I. & Farnsworth, Norman, eds. The Vinca Alkaloids: Botany, Chemistry, & Pharmacology. LC 73-83859. pap. 94.30 (ISBN 0-317-28688-9, 2055284). Bks Demand UMI.

Terrien, Jean, et al. Light, Vegetation & Chlorophyll. 6.00 (ISBN 0-685-28370-4). Philos Lib.

Textbook of Botany: Algae, Fungi, Bacteria, Virus, Lichens, Mycoplasma & Elementary Plant Pathology, Vol. I. 1977. 12.00x (ISBN 0-7069-0516-4). Intl Bk Dist.

Thomas, E., et al. From Single Cells to Plants. (Wykeham Science Ser.: No. 38). 188p. 1975. 9.95x (ISBN 0-8448-1453-9). Crane Russak Co.

Tiemann, A. Untersuchungen zur Embryologie, Bluetenmorphologie und Systematik der Rapateaceen und der Xyridaceen-Gattung Abolboda: Monocotyledoneae. (Dissertatones Botanicae Ser.: No. 82). (Illus.). 202p. 1985. pap. text ed. 28.00x (ISBN 3-7682-1436-2). Lubrecht & Cramer.

Ting, Irwin P. Plant Physiology. LC 80-16448. (Illus.). 635p. 1981. text ed. 34.95 (ISBN 0-201-07406-0). Addison-Wesley.

Tippo, Oswald & Stern, William L. Humanistic Botany. (Illus.). 1977. text ed. 22.95x (ISBN 0-393-09126-0); tchr's manual 1.50x (ISBN 0-393-09130-9). Norton.

Tixier, P. Contribution a la Connaissance des Cololejeunnoideae. (Bryophytorum Bibliotheca Ser.: No. 27). (Illus.). 440p. 1985. lib. bdg. 52.50 (ISBN 3-7682-1418-4). Lubrecht & Cramer.

Traub, H., et al, eds. The Ceratophyllidae. 1984. 93.00 (ISBN 0-12-697680-5). Acad Pr.

Trelease, William. Winter Botany. 3rd ed. (Illus.). 14.50 (ISBN 0-8446-3086-1). Peter Smith.

Tuexen, R. & Schwabe-Braun, Angelika, eds. Internationale Vereinigung Fuer Vegetationskunde: Berichte der Internationalen Symposien: Vegetation Als Anthrop-Oekologischer Gegenstand (1971) Gefaehrdete Vegetation und Ihre Erhaltung (1972) (Ger., Illus.). 662p. 1981. lib. bdg. 70.00x (ISBN 3-7682-1311-0). Lubrecht & Cramer.

U. S. Department of Agriculture. Plant Science Catalog: Botany Subject Index, 15 vols. 1958. Set. lib. bdg. 1485.00 (ISBN 0-8161-0506-5, Hall Library) G K Hall.

Vance, B. Dwain. General Botany. 92p. (Orig.). 1981. pap. 7.95 lab manual (ISBN 0-89459-218-1). Hunter Textbks.

Varghese, T. M., ed. Vistas in Plant Sciences, Vol. 6. (Illus.). 117p. 1983. 14.00 (ISBN 0-88065-232-2, Pub. by Messers Today & Tomorrow Printers & Publishers). Scholarly Pubns.

Verghese, T. M., ed. Vistas in Plant Sciences: Special Volume in Genetics & Plant Breeding, Vol. III. 166p. 1978. 14.00 (ISBN 0-88065-203-9, Pub. by Messers Today & Tomorrow Printers & Publishers India). Scholarly Pubns.

Veselevskaya, M. A. The Poppy, Its Classification & Importance As an Oleiferous Crop. 1981. 40.00x (ISBN 0-686-76658-X, Pub by Oxford & IBH India). State Mutual Bk.

Vogel, Andreas. Klimabedingungen und Stickstoff-Versorgung von Wiesengesellschaften verschiedener Hoehenstufen des Westharzes. (Dissertationes Botanicae: Vol. 60). (Ger., Illus.). 168p. 1981. pap. text ed. 14.00x (ISBN 3-7682-1299-8). Lubrecht & Cramer.

Von Dalla Torre, K. W. & Harms, H. Register to "Genera Siphonogamarum". 1958. Repr. of 1907 ed. 24.00 (ISBN 3-7682-0072-8). Lubrecht & Cramer.

Von Wiesner, J. & Von Regel, C. Die Rohstoffe Des Pflanzenreichs, 7 pts. 5th ed. Incl. Pt. 1. Tanning Materials (Gerbstoffe) Endres, H., et al. (Eng. & Ger.). 1962. 28.00 (ISBN 3-7682-0111-2); Pt. 2. Antibiotiques (Antibiotica) Hagemann, G. (Fr.). 1964. 33.25 (ISBN 3-7682-0170-8); Pt. 3. Organic Acids. Whitting, G. C. 1964. 23.80 (ISBN 3-7682-0244-5); Pt. 4. Insecticides. Fuell, A. J. 1965. 28.00 (ISBN 3-7682-0259-3); Pt. 5. Glykoside. Zechner, L. 1966. 28.00 (ISBN 3-7682-0298-4); Pt. 6. Staerke. Samecl, E. & Bling, M. (Illus.). 1966. 28.00 (ISBN 3-7682-0186-4); Pt. 7. Aetherische Oele. Bournot, K. & Weber, M. (Illus.). 1968. 28.00 (ISBN 3-7682-0562-2). Lubrecht & Cramer.

Walter, T. Flora Caroliniana, Secundum Systema Vegetabilium per Illustris Linnaei Digesta: Characteres Essentiales, Naturalesve & Differentias Veras Exhibens, Etc. 1946. pap. 10.00 (ISBN 0-934454-32-9). Lubrecht & Cramer.

Wandtner, Reinhard. Indikatoreigenschaften der Vegetation von Hochmooren der BR Deutschland fuer Schwermetallimmissionen. (Dissertationes Botanicae: Vol. 59). (Ger., Illus.). 190p. 1981. pap. text ed. 14.00x (ISBN 3-7682-1295-5). Lubrecht & Cramer.

Watling, Roy. How to Identify Mushrooms to Genus V. Using Cultural & Developmental Features. 1981. pap. 8.95x (ISBN 0-916422-17-8). Mad River.

Watson, Hewett C. Cybele Britannica: British Plants, & Their Geographical Relations, Vols. 1 & 4. Egerton, Frank N., 3rd, ed. LC 77-74255. (History of Ecology Ser.). 1978. lib. bdg. 46.50x (ISBN 0-405-10424-3). Ayer Co Pubs.

Wehmeyer, L. E. A Revision of Melanconis, Pseudovalva, Prostecium & Titania. (Univ. of Michigan Studies: No. 14). (Illus.). 1941. Repr. 17.50 (ISBN 3-7682-0929-6). Lubrecht & Cramer.

Weier, Elliot T., et al. Botany: An Introduction to Plant Biology. 6th ed. LC 81-10304. 720p. 1982. text ed. 37.45 (ISBN 0-471-01561-X); study guide 13.95 (ISBN 0-471-08519-7). Wiley.

White, Richard A. & Dickison, William C., eds. Contemporary Problems in Plant Anatomy (Syposium) 1984. 49.00 (ISBN 0-12-746620-7). Acad Pr.

Willi Henning Society, 1st Meeting. Advances in Cladistics: Proceedings. Funk, V. A. & Brooks, D. R., eds. (Illus.). 1981. 29.50x (ISBN 0-89327-240-X). NY Botanical Garden.

Worsdell, W. C. The Principles of Plant-Teratology, 2 Vols. Repr. of 1916 ed. Set. 83.00 (ISBN 0-384-69263-X). Johnson Repr.

Young, Paul. The Botany Coloring Book. (Illus.). 224p. (Orig.). 1982. pap. 8.61i (ISBN 0-06-460302-4, CO 302, COS). B&N NY.

BOTANY–ADDRESSES, ESSAYS, LECTURES

Gehu, M. J., ed. Colloques Phytosociologiques: Les Vegetations Aquatiques et Amphibiens, Lille, 1981, Vol. X. (Fr., Illus.). 1983. lib. bdg. 52.50x (ISBN 3-7682-1383-8). Lubrecht & Cramer.

Mantell, S. H. & Smith, H., eds. Plant Biotechnology: Society for Experimental Biology Seminar 18. (Illus.). 334p. Date not set. pap. 19.95 (ISBN 0-521-28782-0). Cambridge U Pr.

Olsen-Gisel, H. Developments in Stamens of Viola Odorata. (Dissertationes Botanicae: Vol. 70). (Illus.). 192p. 1983. pap. text ed. 28.00x (ISBN 3-7682-1362-5). Lubrecht & Cramer.

Stieber, M. T. & Karg, A. L., eds. Guide to the Botanical Records & Papers in the Archives of the Hunt Institute, Part 1. (Illus.). 89p. 1982. pap. text ed. 10.00 (ISBN 0-317-19693-6). Hunt Inst Botanical.

Stone, Doris, ed. Pre-Columbian Plant Migration from Lowland South America to Mesoamerica. (Peabody Museum Papers: Vol. 76). (Illus.). 220p. (Orig.). 1984. pap. text ed. 30.00x (ISBN 0-87365-202-9). Harvard U Pr.

Trinci, A. P. & Ryley, J. F., eds. Mode of Action of Antifungal Agents. (British Mycological Society Symposium Ser.: No. 9). 390p. 1984. 79.50 (ISBN 0-521-26171-6). Cambridge U Pr.

BOTANY–ANATOMY

see also Botany–Morphology; Plant Cells and Tissues

Almeda, Frank, Jr. Systematics of the Genus Monochaetum (Melastomataceae) in Mexico & Central America. (U. C. Publications in Botany Ser.: Vol. 75). 1978. 18.50x (ISBN 0-520-09587-1). U of Cal Pr.

Bracegirdle, Brian & Miles, Patricia H. An Atlas of Plant Structure, 2 vols. 1971. Vol. 1. text ed. 15.50x (ISBN 0-435-60312-4); Vol. 2. text ed. 15.50x (ISBN 0-435-60314-0). Heinemann Ed.

Braun-Blanquet, J. Plant Sociology: The Study of Plant Communities. Fuller, George D. & Conard, Henry S., trs. (Illus.). 439p. 1983. Repr. of 1932 ed. lib. bdg. 33.60X (ISBN 3-87429-208-8). Lubrecht & Cramer.

Chandurkar, P. J. Plant Anatomy. 256p. 1974. 40.00x (ISBN 0-686-84462-9, Pub. by Oxford & I B H India). State Mutual Bk.

Cole, G. H. The Structure of Planets. (Wykeham Science Ser.: No. 45). 232p. 1977. write for info. (ISBN 0-85109-610-7); pap. cancelled (ISBN 0-85109-600-X). Taylor & Francis.

Cottenie, A. Soil & Plant Testing As a Basis of Fertilizer Recommendations. (Soils Bulletins: No. 38-2). 120p. 1980. pap. 9.00 (ISBN 92-5-100956-2, F2034, FAO). Unipub.

Eames, Arthur J. An Introduction to Plant Anatomy. 2nd ed. LC 76-30812. 446p. 1977. Repr. of 1947 ed. 26.50 (ISBN 0-88275-526-9). Krieger.

Esau, Katherine. Anatomy of Seed Plants. 2nd ed. LC 76-41191. 550p. 1977. text ed. 39.45 (ISBN 0-471-24520-8). Wiley.

Fahn, A. Plant Anatomy. 3rd ed. LC 81-13813. (Illus.). 528p. 1982. 66.00 (ISBN 0-08-028030-7); pap. 29.50 (ISBN 0-08-028029-3). Pergamon.

Fahn, Abraham. Plant Anatomy. 2nd ed. LC 73-5808. 616p. 1974. pap. text ed. 29.50 (ISBN 0-08-028029-3). Pergamon.

Grew, Nehemiah. The Anatomy of Plants, with an Idea of a Philosophical History of Plants & Several Other Lectures. 1965. Repr. of 1682 ed. Facsimile Ed. 60.00 (ISBN 0-384-19950-X). Johnson Repr.

Haberlandt, G. Physiological Plant Anatomy. 4th ed. Drummond, M., tr. from Ger. 398p. 1979. Repr. of 1928 ed. lib. bdg. 15.00 (ISBN 0-934454-89-2). Lubrecht & Cramer.

--Physiological Plant Anatomy. 777p. 1979. Repr. of 1965 ed. 20.00 (ISBN 0-88065-098-2, Pub. by Messers Today & Tomorrow Printers & PublishersIndia). Scholarly Pubns.

Hawker, Lilian E. Physiology of Fungi. (Illus.). 1968. Repr. of 1950 ed. 28.00 (ISBN 3-7682-0530-4). Lubrecht & Cramer.

Leaver, C. J., ed. Genome Organization & Expression in Plants. LC 79-28255. (NATO Advanced Study Institutes Ser., Series A, Life Sciences: Vol. 29). 618p. 1980. 75.00x (ISBN 0-306-40340-4, Plenum Pr). Plenum Pub.

Lloyd, C. W., ed. The Plant Cytoskeleton in Growth & Development. 1983. 60.00 (ISBN 0-12-453780-4). Acad Pr.

Loomis, William, ed. The Development of Dictyostelium Disoideum. 522p. 1982. 74.50 (ISBN 0-12-455620-5). Acad Pr.

Metcalfe, C. R., ed. Anatomy of the Monocotyledons, 4 vols. Incl. Vol. 3. Commelinales-Zingiberales. Tomlinson, P. B. 1969. 62.00x (ISBN 0-19-854365-4); Vol. 4. Juncales. Cutler, D. F. 1969. 55.00x (ISBN 0-19-854369-7); Vol. 5. Cyperaceae. Metcalfe, C. R. (Illus.). 1971. 76.00x (ISBN 0-19-854372-7); Vol. 6. Dioscoreales. Ayensu, E. S. (Illus.). 1972. 65.00x (ISBN 0-19-854376-X); Vol. 7. 1982. 98.00x (ISBN 0-19-854502-9). Oxford U Pr.

Moore, T. C. Research Experiences in Plant Physiology: A Laboratory Manual. 2nd ed. (Illus.). 348p. 1981. pap. 22.00 (ISBN 0-387-90606-1). Springer-Verlag.

Northcote, D. H. Differentiation in Higher Plants. Head, J. J., ed. LC 78-74134. (Carolina Biology Readers Ser.). (Illus.). 32p. 1980. pap. 2.00 (ISBN 0-89278-244-7, 45-9644). Carolina Biological.

Roland, J. C. & Roland, F. Atlas of Flowering Plant Structure. Baker, Denis, tr. from Fr. (Illus.). 112p. 1981. pap. text ed. 14.95x (ISBN 0-582-45589-8). Longman.

Shah, J. J., ed. Form Structures & Function in Plant, Pt. I. iv, 148p. 1975. 22.50 (ISBN 0-88065-191-1, Pub. by Messers Today & Tomorrows Printers & Publishers India). Scholarly Pubns.

Siegenthaler, P. A. & Eichenberger, W., eds. Structure, Function & Metabolism of Plant Lipids: Proceedings of the International Symposium, 6th, Held in Neuchatel, Switzerland, July 16-20, 1984. (Developments in Plant Biology Ser.: Vol. 9). 634p. 1984. 120.75 (ISBN 0-444-80626-1). Elsevier.

Soil & Plant Testing & Analysis: Report of an Expert Consultation, Held in Rome, 13-17 June 1977. (Soils Bulletins: No. 38-1). 251p. 1980. pap. 18.00 (ISBN 92-5-100961-9, F2033, FAO). Unipub.

Sprengel, Christian K. Das Entdeckte Geheimnis der Natur Im Bau & der Befruchtung der Blumen. 1973. Repr. of 1793 ed. 35.00 (ISBN 3-7682-0828-1). Lubrecht & Cramer.

Uphof, C. J. Plant Hairs. (Encycopedia of Plant Anatomy Ser.: Vol. 5). (Illus.). 292p. 1962. lib. bdg. 48.00X (ISBN 0-318-01340-1). Lubrecht & Cramer.

BOTANY–BIBLIOGRAPHY

Burbidge, Nancy T. Plant Taxonomic Literature in Australian Libraries. 1979. 28.00x (ISBN 0-643-00286-3, Pub. by CSIRO). Intl Spec Bk.

Harvard University. Catalog of the Farlow Reference Library of Cryptogamic Botany. 1979. lib. bdg. 690.00 (ISBN 0-8161-0279-1, Hall Library). G K Hall.

Jackson, Benjamin D. Guide to the Literature of Botany: Being a Classified Selection of Botanical Works, Including Nearly 600 Titles Not Given in Pritzel's Thesaurus. 626p. 1874. Repr. of 1881 ed. lib. bdg. 33.95x (ISBN 3-87429-069-7). Lubrecht & Cramer.

Korf, Richard P. & Gruff, Susan C. Mycotaxon Cumulative Index for Volumes I-XX (1974-1984) LC 75-640802. 232p. (Orig.). 1985. pap. text ed. 17.50 (ISBN 0-930845-00-5). Mycotaxon Ltd.

Lawrence, G. H., ed. Adanson: The Bicentennial of Michel Adanson's "Familles des plantes", 2 vols. (Illus.). 1963-1964. Vol. 1. 19.00x (ISBN 0-913196-23-1); Vol. 2. 15.00x (ISBN 0-913196-24-X); Vol. 1. softcover 17.00x (ISBN 0-913196-25-8); Vol. 2. softcover 13.00x (ISBN 0-913196-26-6). Hunt Inst Botanical.

Linnaeus, C. Bibliotheca Botanica. 1968. 10.00 (ISBN 0-934454-13-2). Lubrecht & Cramer.

Merrill, E. D. Polynesian Botanical Bibliography, 1773-1935. 1937. 24.00 (ISBN 0-527-02252-7). Kraus Repr.

Merrill, E. D. & Walker, E. H. A Bibliography of Eastern Asiatic Botany: Supplement 1. 1960. 18.50 (ISBN 0-934454-11-6). Lubrecht & Cramer.

Miller, Ethel M. Bibliography of Ohio Botany. 1932. 2.00 (ISBN 0-86727-026-8). Ohio Bio Survey.

Pritzel, G. A. Thesaurus Literature Botanicae. 2nd ed. 1972. 63.00 (ISBN 3-87429-035-2). Lubrecht & Cramer.

Rashap, Arthur W., et al, eds. The Ginseng Research Institute's Indexed Bibliography. LC 84-81467. 120p. 1984. pap. 65.00 (ISBN 0-9613800-0-4). Ginseng Res Inst.

Rehder, Alfred. Bibliography of Cultivated Trees & Shrubs Hardy in the Cooler Temperature Regions of the Northern Hemisphere. (Collectanea Bibliographica Ser.: No. 9). 1978. lib. bdg. 84.00x (ISBN 3-87429-128-6). Lubrecht & Cramer.

Royal Botanic Gardens Library, Kew, England. Author & Classified Catalogues of the Royal Botanic Gardens Library, 9 vols. 1974. lib. bdg. 495.00 author 5 vols. (ISBN 0-8161-1086-7, Hall Library); lib. bdg. 415.00 4 vols. (ISBN 0-8161-1087-5). G K Hall.

Stieber, M. T. & Karg, A. L., eds. Guide to the Botanical Records & Papers in the Archives of the Hunt Institute, Part 1. (Illus.). 89p. 1982. pap. text ed. 10.00 (ISBN 0-317-19693-6). Hunt Inst Botanical.

Swift, L. H. Botanical Bibliographies: Guide to Bibliographic Materials Applicable to Botany. 800p. 1974. Repr. of 1970 ed. lib. bdg. 77.00x (ISBN 3-87429-076-X). Lubrecht & Creamer.

Torrey Botanical Club, N.Y. Annual Index to Botanical Literature: 1979. 1980. lib. bdg. 135.00 (ISBN 0-8161-0369-0, Hall Library). G K Hall.

Van Landingham, S. L. Catalogue of the Fossil & Recent Genera & Species of Diatoms & Their Synonyms-Part 7: Rhoicosphenia Through Zygoceros. 1979. lib. bdg. 35.00x (ISBN 3-7682-0477-4). Lubrecht & Cramer.

Von Haller, A. Bibliotheca Botanica, 2 Vols. 1771-1772. 110.00 (ISBN 0-384-21050-3). Johnson Repr.

BOTANY–BIO-BIBLIOGRAPHY

see also Botanists

Daniels, G., ed. A Linnaean Keepsake. (Eng. & Lat., Illus.). 1973. 13.00x (ISBN 0-913196-15-0). Hunt Inst Botanical.

Desmond, Ray, ed. Dictionary of British & Irish Botanists & Horticulturists. 3rd ed. 764p. 1977. cancelled (ISBN 0-85066-089-0). Taylor & Francis.

Grumann, V. Biographisch-bibliographisches Handbuch der Lichenologie. Nach dem Tode des Verfassers ed. by O. Klement. 1979. lib. bdg. 87.50x (ISBN 3-7682-0907-5). Lubrecht & Cramer.

BOTANY–CLASSIFICATION

see also Plants–Identification

Abbott, Lois A., et al. Taxonomic Analysis in Biology: Computers, Models & Databases. 320p. 1985. 35.00x (ISBN 0-231-04926-9); pap. 15.00x (ISBN 0-231-04927-7). Columbia U Pr.

Adanson, M. Familles des Plantes, 2 vols. in 1. (Illus.). 1966. Repr. of 1763 ed. 70.00 (ISBN 3-7682-0345-X). Lubrecht & Cramer.

Affolter, James M. A Monograph of the Genus Lilaeopsis (Umbelliferae) Anderson, Christiane, ed. LC 85-1291. (Systematic Botany Monographs: Vol. 6). (Illus.). 140p. (Orig.). 1985. pap. 18.00 (ISBN 0-912861-06-1). Am Soc Plant.

Baranov, A. Basic Latin for Plant Taxonomists. 1971. pap. text ed. 16.00 (ISBN 3-7682-0727-7). Lubrecht & Cramer.

Barker, Reginald W. Taxonomic Notes on the Species. LC 62-6771. (Society of Economic Paleontologists & Mineralogists, Special Publication: No. 9). pap. 65.50 (ISBN 0-317-27163-6, 2024735). Bks Demand UMI.

Batson, Wade T. Genera of the Eastern Plants. (Illus.). 203p. 1984. pap. 8.95 (ISBN 0-87249-450-0). U of SC Pr.

--Genera of the Western Plants. (Illus.). 210p. 1984. pap. 8.95 (ISBN 0-87249-451-9). U of SC Pr.

Bendz, Gerd & Santesson, Johann, eds. Chemistry in Botanical Classification. 1974. 66.00 (ISBN 0-12-086650-1). Acad Pr.

Benson, Lyman. Plant Classification. 2nd ed. 1979. text ed. 31.95 (ISBN 0-669-01489-3). Heath.

Bentham, G. & Hooker, J. D. Genera Plantarum, 3 vols. 1966. 231.00 (ISBN 3-7682-0277-1). Lubrecht & Cramer.

--Supplemental Papers to Bentham & Hooker's Genera Plantarum. 1971. Repr. of 1881 ed. 77.00 (ISBN 3-7682-0706-4). Lubrecht & Cramer.

Bisby, F. A., et al, eds. Chemosystematics: Principles & Practice. LC 80-41428. (Systematic Association Ser.: No. 16). 1981. 85.00 (ISBN 0-12-101550-5). Acad Pr.

Bolton, B. A Revision of Six Minor Genera of Myrmicinae (Hymenoptera; Formicidae) in the Ethiopian Zoogeographical Region. 40.00x (ISBN 0-686-78662-9, Pub. by Brit Mus Pubns England). State Mutual Bk.

Buek, H. W. Genera, Species & Synonyma Candolleana Alphabetico Ordine Disposita: Seu Index Generalis & Specialis Ad A. P. De Candolle Prodromum Systematis Naturalis Regni Vegetabilis, 4 vols. in two. 1967. 97.65 (ISBN 90-6123-029-2). Lubrecht & Cramer.

Burbidge, Nancy T. Plant Taxonomic Literature in Australian Libraries. 520p. 1978. pap. 31.50 (ISBN 0-643-00286-3, C015, CSIRO). Unipub.

--Plant Taxonomic Literature in Australian Libraries. 1979. 28.00x (ISBN 0-643-00286-3, Pub. by CSIRO). Intl Spec Bk.

Burdsall, Harold H., Jr. A Contribution to the Taxonomy of the Genus Phanerochaete (Corticiaceae, Aphyllophorales) (Mycologia Memoir Ser.: No. 10). (Illus.). 170p. 1985. lib. bdg. 24.00 (ISBN 3-7682-1392-7). Lubrecht & Cramer.

Caballero, Arturo. Flora Analitica de Espana. (Floras of the World Ser.: Vol. 3). (Span., Illus.). 617p. 1984. pap. text ed. 128.00 (ISBN 3-87429-214-2). Lubrecht & Cramer.

Clifford, H. T. & Stephenson, W. An Introduction to Numerical Classification: Primarily for Biologists. 1975. 41.00 (ISBN 0-12-176750-7). Acad Pr.

De Menezes, Carlos A. Flora do Archipelago da Madeira. (Floras of the World Ser.: Vol. 4). (Port.). 282p. 1984. pap. text ed. 50.40 (ISBN 3-87429-214-2). Lubrecht & Cramer.

Dixon, P. S. & Price, J. H. The Genus Callithamnion Rhodophyta: Ceramiaceae in the British Isles. 59.00x (ISBN 0-686-78657-2, Pub. by Brit Mus Pubns England). State Mutual Bk.

Drouet, Francais. Summary of the Classification of Blue-Green Algae. (Illus.). 1981. pap. text ed. 7.00x (ISBN 3-7682-1293-9). Lubrecht & Cramer.

Dunn, G. & Everitt, B. S. An Introduction to Mathematical Taxonomy. LC 81-7658. (Cambridge Studies in Mathematical Biology: No. 5). 120p. 1982. 34.50 (ISBN 0-521-23979-6); pap. 13.95 (ISBN 0-521-28388-4). Cambridge U Pr.

Elisens, Wayne J. Monograph of the Maurandyinae (Scrophulariaceae-Antirrhineae) Anderson, Christiane, ed. LC 85-1266. (Systematic Botany Monographs: Vol. 5). (Illus.). 97p. (Orig.). 1985. pap. 12.00 (ISBN 0-912861-05-3). Am Soc Plant.

Emig, C. C. British & Other Phoronids: Keys & Notes for the Identification of the Species. (Synopses of the British Fauna Ser.). 1979. pap. 12.00 (ISBN 0-12-238750-3). Acad Pr.

Engler, A. Syllabus der Pflanzenfalien: Kapitael V, 2 - Bryophytina, Laubmoose. 13th Ed. ed. Gerloff, J., et al, eds. (Ger., Illus.). 109p. 1983. pap. 18.04x (ISBN 3-443-02001-1). Lubrecht & Cramer.

Estabrook, G. F., ed. Proceedings of the Eighth International Conference on Numerical Taxonomy. LC 75-31878. (Illus.). 429p. 1976. 38.95 (ISBN 0-7167-0555-9). W H Freeman.

Eyre, S. R., ed. World Vegetation Types. LC 78-147779. 264p. 1971. 39.00x (ISBN 0-231-03503-9). Columbia U Pr.

Fuchs, H. P. Nomenklatur, Taxonomie & Systematik der Gattung Isoetes Linnaeus in Geschichtlicher Entwicklung. (Illus.). 1962. pap. 14.00 (ISBN 3-7682-5403-8). Lubrecht & Cramer.
Furtado, Joao S. Taxonomy of Amauroderma (Basidiomycetes, Polyporaceae) (Memoirs of the New York Botanical Garden: Vol. 34). (Illus.). 1981. pap. 17.50x (ISBN 0-89327-234-5). NY Botanical.
Harvey, William H. & Sonder, Otto W. Flora Capensis, 7 vols. bd. in 11. 210.00 (ISBN 3-7682-0637-8). Lubrecht & Cramer.
Hawksworth, D. L. The Lichenicolous Coelomycetes. 60.00x (ISBN 0-686-78659-9, Pub. by Brit Mus Pubns England). State Mutual Bk.
Hegberg, Don. Systematics. 748p. (Orig.). 1977. pap. 10.00 (ISBN 0-686-32735-7). Systematic Dev.
Heywood, Vernon H. & Moore, D. M. Current Concepts in Plant Taxonomy. (Systematic Association Ser.: Vol. 25). 1984. 50.00 (ISBN 0-12-347060-9). Acad Pr.
Higgins, L. G. A Revision of Phyciodes Hubner & Related Genera, with a Review of the Classification of the Melitaeinae (Lepidoptera; Nymphalidae) 100.00x (ISBN 0-686-78661-0, Pub. by Brit Mus Pubns England). State Mutual Bk.
Holmes, Sandra. Outline of Plant Classification. (Illus.). 192p. 1983. 17.95 (ISBN 0-582-44648-1). Longman.
Hopkins, H. C. Parkia Leguminosae. (Flora Neotropica Monograph). Date not set. price not set (ISBN 0-317-11875-7). NY Botanical.
Ietswaart, J. H. Taxonomic Review of the Genus Origanum (Labiatae) (Leiden Botanical Ser.: No. 4). (Illus.). 1980. pap. 31.50 (ISBN 90-6021-463-3, Pub. by Leiden Univ. Holland). Kluwer Academic.
International Association of Briologists, Taxonomic Workshop, 1979. Bryophyte Taxonomy: Methods, Practices & Floristic Exploration: Proceedings. Geissler, P. & Greene, S. W., eds. (Beiheft zu Nova Hedwigia Ser.: No. 71). (Illus.). 600p. 1982. 70.00 (ISBN 3-7682-5471-2). Lubrecht & Cramer.
Jago, N. D. A Revision of the Genus Usambilla Sjosted (Orthoptera; Acridoidea) & Its Allies. 30.00x (ISBN 0-686-78664-5, Pub. by Brit Mus Pubns England). State Mutual Bk.
Jaques, Harry E. How to Know the Plant Families. 2nd ed. (Pictured Key Nature Ser.). 184p. 1948. write for info. wire coil (ISBN 0-697-04840-3). Wm C Brown.
Jeffrey, C. An Introduction to Plant Taxonomy. 2nd ed. LC 81-17090. 100p. 1982. pap. 13.95 (ISBN 0-521-28775-8). Cambridge U Pr.
Jermy, A. C., et al. The Phylogeny & Classification of the Ferns. (Illus.). 1984. Repr. of 1973 ed. lib. bdg. 52.50 (ISBN 3-87429-218-5). Lubrecht & Cramer.
Johnson, A. M. Taxonomy of the Flowering Plants. (Illus.). 1977. Repr. of 1931 ed. lib. bdg. 52.50x (ISBN 3-7682-1169-X). Lubrecht & Cramer.
Jones, Samuel & Luchsinger, Arlene E. Introduction to Plant Systematics. Vastyan, James E., ed. (Organismic Ser.). (Illus.). 1979. text ed. 36.95 (ISBN 0-07-032795-5). McGraw.
Jussieu, A. L. Genera Plantarum Secundum Ordines Naturales Disposita. 1964. Repr. of 1789 ed. 35.00 (ISBN 3-7682-7107-2). Lubrecht & Cramer.
Kapoor, V. C. Taxonomic Approach to Insects. 500p. 1980. 25.00x (ISBN 0-686-69938-6, Pub. by Croom Helm England). State Mutual Bk.
Kennedy, Helen. Systematics & Pollination of the "Closed Flowered" Species of Calathea (Mar Antaceae) (Publications in Botany: No. 71). 1978. pap. 15.50x (ISBN 0-520-09572-3). U of Cal Pr.
Kresanek, Jaroslav. Healing Plants. (Illus.). 224p. 1985. 8.95 (ISBN 0-668-06306-8). Arco.
Kubitzki, K., ed. Flowering Plants-Evolution & Classification of Higher Categories: Symposium, Hamburg, September 8-12, 1976. (Plant Systematics & Evolution Supplementum: Supplementum 1). (Illus.). 1977. pap. 116.90 (ISBN 0-387-81434-5). Springer-Verlag.
Kunth, C. S. Nova Genera & Species Plantarum Quas in Peregrinatione Orbis Collegerunt: 1815-25, 7 vols. in 3. 1963. 420.00 (ISBN 3-7682-0165-1). Lubrecht & Cramer.
Lawrence, G. H., ed. Adanson: The Bicentennial of Michel Adanson's "Familles des plantes", 2 vols. (Illus.). 1963-1964. Vol. 1. 10.00x (ISBN 0-913196-23-1); Vol. 2. 15.00x (ISBN 0-913196-24-X); Vol. 1. softcover 17.00x (ISBN 0-913196-25-8); Vol. 2. softcover 13.00x (ISBN 0-913196-26-6). Hunt Inst Botanical.
Lawrence, George H. Introduction to Plant Taxonomy. (Illus.). 1955. text ed. write for info. (ISBN 0-02-368120-9). Macmillan.
--Taxonomy of Vascular Plants. (Illus.). 1951. text ed. write for info. (ISBN 0-02-368190-X). Macmillan.
Lewranich, A. A Revision of the Old World Species of Sciropophaga (Lepidoptera; Pyralidae) 120p. 90.00x (ISBN 0-686-78666-1, Pub. by Brit Mus Pubns England). State Mutual Bk.
Linnaeus, C. Genera Plantarum. 1960. Repr. of 1754 ed. 52.50 (ISBN 3-7682-0014-0). Lubrecht & Cramer.
Love, A. & Love, D. Cytotaxonomical Atlas of the Arctic Flora. (Cytotaxonomical Atlases: Vol. 2). (Illus.). 598p. 1975. lib. bdg. 70.00x (ISBN 3-7682-0976-8). Lubrecht & Cramer.
--Cytotaxonomical Atlas of the Slovenian Flora. (Cytotaxonimcal Atlases: Vol. 1). (Illus.). 1242p. 1974. lib. bdg. 70.00x (ISBN 3-7682-0932-6). Lubrecht & Cramer.
Lovelady, Janet. SOAR: A Program for the Gifted Using Bloom's Taxonomy - Student's Workbook. (Illus.). 40p. (Orig.). 1982. pap. 4.95 (ISBN 0-935266-10-0, GI-227). B L Winch.
McVaugh, Rogers. Flora Novo-Galiciana: A Descriptive Account of the Vascular Plants of Western Mexico. Anderson, William R., ed. LC 82-13537. (Graminae Ser.: Vol. 14). (Illus.). 384p. 1983. text ed. 38.00x (ISBN 0-472-04814-7). U of Mich Pr.
Modern Methods in Plant Taxonomy. 1968. 59.50 (ISBN 0-12-346950-3). Acad Pr.
Muenscher, Walter C. & Petry, Loren C. Keys to Spring Plants. 6th ed. 34p. 1958. pap. 3.95x (ISBN 0-8014-9828-7). Comstock.
Oxford System of Decimal Classification for Forestry. 115p. 1976. Repr. of 1954 ed. 40.00x (ISBN 0-686-45588-6, Pub. by CAB Bks England). State Mutual Bk.
Patrick, R., et al. The Catherwood Foundation Peruvian-Amazon Expedition: Limnological & Systematic Studies. (Monograph: No. 14). (Illus.). 495p. (Orig.). 1966. pap. 23.00 (ISBN 0-910006-22-9). Acad Nat Sci Phila.
Peterken, G. F. Guide to the Check Sheet of International Biological Programme Areas. (International Biological Program Handbook No. 4). (Illus.). 1968. pap. 3.50 (ISBN 0-632-04670-8, B 3804-6, Blackwell). Mosby.
Porter, Cedric L. Taxonomy of Flowering Plants. 2nd ed. LC 66-19914. (Illus.). 472p. 1967. 30.95x (ISBN 0-7167-0709-8). W H Freeman.
Rafinesque, S. C. Precis de Descouvertes Somiologiques. 11.25 (ISBN 0-8446-1371-1). Peter Smith.
Reid, Charlotte & Reid, John D. SOAR: A Program for the Gifted Using Bloom's Taxonomy - Teacher's Guidebook. Lovelady, Janet, ed. (Illus.). 40p. (Orig.). 1982. pap. 4.95 (ISBN 0-935266-09-7, GI-226). B L Winch.
Rendle, Alfred B. Classification of Flowering Plants, 2 bks. Incl. Bk. 1. Gymnosperms & Monocotyledons; Bk. 2. Dicotyledons. 90.00 (ISBN 0-521-06057-5). Cambridge U Pr.
Richards, O. W. A Revision of the Genus Belongogaster (Hymenoptera; Vespidae) 60.00x (ISBN 0-686-78663-7, Pub. by Brit Mus Pubns England). State Mutual Bk.
Robinson, Harold. A Generic Review of the Tribe Liabeae (Asteraceae) LC 82-10807. (Smithsonian Contributions to Botany Ser.: No. 54). pap. 20.00 (ISBN 0-317-28805-9, 2020337). Bks Demand UMI.
Rogers, G. K. Gleasonia, Henriquezia & Platcarpum. (Flora Neotropica Ser.: No. 39). 1984. 26.00x (ISBN 0-89327-257-4). NY Botanical.
Scholz, H. & Scholz, U. Flore descriptive des Cyperacees et Graminees du Togo. (Pherogamarum Monographiae Ser.: Vol. 15.). (Fr., Illus.). 360p. 1983. lib. bdg. 52.50X (ISBN 3-7682-1364-1). Lubrecht & Cramer.
Sendulsky, Tatiana. Revision of the South American Genus Otachyrium. LC 84-600087. (Smithsonian Contributions to Botany Ser.: No. 57). pap. 20.00 (ISBN 0-317-20823-3, 2024794). Bks Demand UMI.
Shelley, A. J., et al. The Taxonomy, Biology & Medical Importance of Simulium Amazonicum Goeldi (Diptera; Simuliidae), with a Review of Related Species. 25.00x (ISBN 0-686-78668-8, Pub. by Brit Mus Pubns England). State Mutual Bk.
Shimwell, David W. Description & Classification of Vegetation. LC 75-180238. (Biology Ser). (Illus.). 336p. 1972. 14.95x (ISBN 0-295-95168-0). U of Wash Pr.
Shukla, Priti & Misra, Shital P. An Introduction to Taxonomy of Angiosperms. (Illus.). 1979. text ed. 27.50x (ISBN 0-7069-0764-7, Pub. by Vikas India). Advent NY.
Silberhorn, Gene M. Common Plants of the Mid-Alantic Coast: A Field Guide. 272p. 1982. text ed. 24.50x (ISBN 0-8018-2319-6); pap. 8.95 (ISBN 0-8018-2725-6). Johns Hopkins.
Smiles, R. L. The Taxonomy & Phylogeny of the Genus Polyura Billberg (Rhopalocera; Nymphalidae) 59.00 (ISBN 0-686-78667-X, Pub. by Brit Mus Pubns England). State Mutual Bk.
Stace, Clive A. Plant Taxonomy & Biosystematics. (Contemporary Biology Ser.). 288p. 1980. pap. text ed. 19.50 (ISBN 0-7131-2802-X). E Arnold.
Stafleu & Cowan, R. S. Taxonomic Literature: LH-O, Vol. 3. 1982. 135.00 (ISBN 90-313-0444-1, Pub. by Junk Pubs Netherlands). Kluwer Academic.
Stafleu, F. A. Introduction to Jussieu's Genera Plantarum. 7.00 (ISBN 3-7682-0000-0). Lubrecht & Cramer.
Stafleu, F. A. & Cowan, R. S., eds. Taxonomic Literature, Volume Four: P-Sack. (Regnum Vegetabile: No. 110). 1984. pap. text ed. 155.00 (ISBN 90-3130-549-9, Pub. by Junk Pubs Netherlands). Kluwer Academic.
Starnecker, Gerhard. Oekophysiologische Anpassungen im Gasstoffwechsel bei der Gattung Peperomia Ruiz y Pavon, Vol. 75. (Dissertationes Botanicae Ser.). (Ger., Illus.). 140p. 1984. pap. text ed. 17.50X (ISBN 3-7682-1390-0). Lubrecht & Cramer.
Steinaker, Norman & Bell, M. Robert. The Experiential Taxonomy: A New Approach to Teaching & Learning. LC 79-1141. (Educational Psychology Ser.). 1979. 29.00 (ISBN 0-12-665550-2). Acad Pr.
Steyskal, G. C., et al. Taxonomy of North American Flies of the Genus Limnia (Diptera: Sciomyzidae) (Publications in Entomology Ser.: No. 83). 1978. pap. 16.50x (ISBN 0-520-09577-4). U of Cal Pr.
Street, H. E., ed. Essays in Plant Taxonomy. 1978. 59.50 (ISBN 0-12-673360-0). Acad Pr.
Taxonomia y la Revolucion En las Ciencias Biologicas. rev. ed. (Serie De Biologia: No. 3). (Span.). 1980. pap. 3.50 (ISBN 0-8270-6050-5). OAS.
Vasil'chenko, I. T. Novitates Systematicae: Plantarum Vascularium Nineteen Seventy-Two, Vol. 9. 378p. 1978. 82.00 (ISBN 0-686-84461-0, Pub. by Oxford & I B H India). State Mutual Bk.
Vasil chenko, J. T. Novitates Systematicae: Plantarum Vascularium Nineteen Seventy-One, Vol. 8. 342p. 1978. 77.00x (ISBN 0-686-84460-2, Pub. by Oxford & I B H India). State Mutual Bk.
Voser-Huber, M. L. Studien an eingebuergerten Arten der Gattung Solidago L. (Dissertationes Botanicae: No. 68). (Ger., Illus.). 158p. 1983. pap. text ed. 17.50 (ISBN 3-7682-1359-5). Lubrecht & Cramer.
Walter, T. Flora Caroliniana, Secundum Systema Vegetabilium per Illustris Linnaei Digesta: Characteres Essentiales, Naturalesve & Differentias Veras Exhibens, Etc. 1946. pap. 10.00 (ISBN 0-934454-32-9). Lubrecht & Cramer.
Walters, Dirk R. Vascular Plant Taxonomy. 2nd ed. 1977. pap. text ed. 11.95 (ISBN 0-8403-1747-6). Kendall-Hunt.
Waterman, Peter G. & Grundon, Michael F., eds. Chemistry & Chemical Taxonomy of the Rutales. (Phytochemical Society of Europe Symposia Ser.). 1984. 75.00 (ISBN 0-12-737680-1). Acad Pr.
Webb, M. D. The Asian, Australasian & Pacific Paraboloponinae (Hempitera; Cicadellidae) A Taxonomic Revision with a Key to All the Known Genera of the Subfamily. 48p. 35.00x (ISBN 0-686-78652-1, Pub. by Brit Mus Pubns England). State Mutual Bk.
Wettstein, Richard. Handbuch der Systematischen Botanik. (Illus.). 1962. Repr. of 1935 ed. 42.50. Lubrecht & Cramer.
Whittaker, Robert H. Classification of Natural Communities. Egerton, Frank N., 3rd, ed. LC 77-74257. (History of Ecology Ser.). 1978. Repr. of 1962 ed. lib. bdg. 19.00x (ISBN 0-405-10426-X). Ayer Co Pubs.
Woelkering, Wm. J. Foslie & the Corallinaceae: An Analysis & Index. (Bibliotheca Phycologica: No. 69). 142p. 1984. pap. text ed. 17.50x (ISBN 3-7682-1394-3). Lubrecht & Cramer.

BOTANY–DATA PROCESSING

Abbott, Lois A., et al. Taxonomic Analysis in Biology: Computers, Models & Databases. 320p. 1985. 35.00x (ISBN 0-231-04926-9); pap. 15.00x (ISBN 0-231-04927-7). Columbia U Pr.

BOTANY–DICTIONARIES

Alcock, Randal H. Botanical Names for English Readers. LC 73-174935. xviii, 236p. 1971. Repr. of 1876 ed. 40.00x (ISBN 0-8103-3823-8). Gale.
Bastian, Hartmut. Ullstein Lexikon der Pflanzenwelt. (Ger.). 1973. 27.50 (ISBN 0-686-56471-5, M-7675, Pub. by Ullstein Verlag VA). French & Eur.
Cecchini, Tina. Enciclopedia Practica de Floricultura y Jardineria. 2nd ed. (Espn.). 588p. 1978. pap. 28.50 (ISBN 84-315-0972-4, S-14572). French & Eur.
Cook, J. Gordon. ABC of Plant Terms. 293p. 1968. 39.00x (ISBN 0-900541-56-3, Pub. by Meadowfield Pr England). State Mutual Bk.
Davidov, H. Botanical Dictionary: Russian-English-German-French-Latin. (Rus., Eng., Ger., Fr. & Lat.). 335p. 1981. Repr. of 1960 ed. lib. bdg. 28.00x (ISBN 3-87429-197-9). Lubrecht & Cramer.
Desmond, Ray, ed. Dictionary of British & Irish Botanists & Horticulturists. 3rd ed. 764p. 1977. cancelled (ISBN 0-85066-089-0). Taylor & Francis.
Diccionario De Botanica. (Span.). 256p. 1973. leatherette 11.50 (ISBN 84-307-8268-0, S-50258). French & Eur.
Erevan University Press. A Polyglot Dictionary of Plant Names. 180p. 1981. pap. 40.00x (ISBN 0-686-82330-3, Pub. by Collets). State Mutual Bk.
A Facsimile Reprint of Systema Naturae by Carolus Linnaeus. 95.00 (ISBN 0-930466-89-6). Meckler Pub.
Gatin, Charles Louis. Dictionnaire Aide Memoire de Botanique. (Fr.). 867p. 1924. 99.50 (ISBN 0-686-56785-4, M-6581, Pub. by Lechevalier). French & Eur.
Genaust, Helmut. Etymologisches Woertenbuch der Botanischen Pflanzennamen. (Ger.). 390p. 1976. 62.50 (ISBN 3-7643-0755-2, M-7368, Pub. by Birkhaeuser). French & Eur.
Gledhill, D. The Names of Plants. 150p. Date not set. price not set (ISBN 0-521-30549-7); pap. price not set (ISBN 0-521-31562-X). Cambridge U Pr.
Graf, Alfred B. Exotica IV: Pictorial Cyclopedia of Exotic Plants & Trees. (Illus.). 2580p. 1985. 187.00 (ISBN 0-684-17477-4). Scribner.
Grebenshchikov, O. S. Geobotanic Dictionary. (Rus., Eng., Ger. & Fr.). 1979. lib. bdg. 31.50x (ISBN 3-87429-164-2). Lubrecht & Cramer.
Har, R. & Synge, P. M. Diccionario Ilustrado en Color de Plantas de Jardin con Plantas de Interior y de Invernadero. (Span.). 364p. 1977. 60.00 (ISBN 84-252-0376-7, S-12330). French & Eur.
Heywood, V. H. & Chant, S. R., eds. Popular Encyclopedia of Plants. LC 81-21713. (Illus.). 1982. 34.50 (ISBN 0-521-24611-3). Cambridge U Pr.
Howes, F. N. Dictionary of Useful & Everyday Plants & Their Common Names. LC 73-91701. 300p. 1974. 39.50 (ISBN 0-521-08520-9). Cambridge U Pr.
Jehan, L. F. Dictionnaire de Botanique. Migne, J. P., ed. (Nouvelle Encyclopedie Theologique Ser.: Vol. 8). (Fr.). 758p. Repr. of 1860 ed. lib. bdg. 105.00x (ISBN 0-89241-258-5). Caratzas.
Lawrence Urdang Associates, Ltd., The Penguin Dictionary of Botany. Blackmore & Toothill, eds. (Reference Ser.). 288p. 1984. pap. 7.95 (ISBN 0-14-051126-1). Penguin.
Little, R. John & Jones, C. Eugene. A Dictionary of Botany. 400p. 1983. pap. text ed. 14.95 (ISBN 0-442-26019-9). Van Nos Reinhold.
Macura, P. Dictionary of Botany, Vol. 2: General Terms. (Eng., Fr., Ger. & Rus.). 744p. 1982. 117.00 (ISBN 0-444-41787-7). Elsevier.
--Elsevier's Dictionary of Botany, Vol. 1: Plant Names. LC 79-15558. 580p. 1979. 117.00 (ISBN 0-444-41787-7). Elsevier.
Macura, Paul. Russian-English Botanical Dictionary. (Rus. & Eng.). 678p. 1982. 49.95 (ISBN 0-89357-092-3). Slavica.
Marzell. Woerterbuch der Deutschen Pflanzennamen. (Ger.). fascs. 1-22 550.00 (ISBN 0-686-56642-4, M-7031). French & Eur.
Miller, P. The Gardener's Dictionary. 1969. Repr. of 1754 ed. 56.00 (ISBN 3-7682-0613-0). Lubrecht & Cramer.
Pont Quer, Pio. Diccionario De Botanica. (Span.). 1244p. 1977. 59.95 (ISBN 84-335-5804-8, S-50066). French & Eur.
Ricken, A. Vademekum fuer Pilzfreunde. (Ger.). 1969. 32.00 (ISBN 3-7682-0603-3, M-7137). French & Eur.
Rodriguez De La Fuente, Felix. Enciclopedia Salvat de la Fauna, 11 vols. (Espn.). 3300p. 1970. Set. 370.00 (ISBN 84-7137-260-6, S-12299). French & Eur.
--Enciclopedia Salvat de la Fauna Iberica y Europea, 8 vols. (Espn.). 2464p. 1975. Set. 255.00 (ISBN 84-345-3645-5, S-50539). French & Eur.
Tootill, Elizabeth & Blackmore, Stephen, eds. The Facts on File Dictionary of Botany. LC 83-25309. 400p. 1984. 21.95x (ISBN 0-87196-861-4). Facts on File.
Usher, George. A Dictionary of Botany. 408p. 1979. text ed. 24.50x (ISBN 0-8448-1387-7). Crane-Russak Co.
Willis, J. C. A Dictionary of the Flowering Plants & Ferns Vol. 1: Generic & Family Names. 8th ed. LC 72-83581. 1300p. 1973. 115.00 (ISBN 0-521-08699-X). Cambridge U Pr.

BOTANY–EARLY WORKS

see Botany–Pre-Linnean Works

BOTANY–ECOLOGY

see also Coastal Flora; Desert Flora; Forest Ecology; Halophytes; Insectivorous Plants; Island Flora and Fauna; Parasitic Plants; Phytogeography; Plant Communities; Plant Indicators; Symbiosis

Agarwal, V. P. & Sharma, V. K., eds. Progress of Plant Ecology in India, Vol. 4. 167p. 1980. 10.00 (ISBN 0-686-82969-7, Pub. by Messers Today & Tomorrows Printers & Publishers India). Scholarly Pubns.
Barbour, Michael G., et al. Terrestrial Plant Ecology. 1980. 31.95 (ISBN 0-8053-0540-8). Benjamin-Cummings.
Barry, John M. The Natural Vegetation of South Carolina. LC 79-19678. (Illus.). 214p. 1980. lib. bdg. 19.95 (ISBN 0-87249-384-9); pap. 6.95 (ISBN 0-87249-214-1). U of SC Pr.
Boehm, W. Methods of Studying Root Systems. LC 79-9706. (Ecological Studies: Vol. 33). (Illus.). 1979. 45.00 (ISBN 0-387-09329-X). Springer-Verlag.
Braun, E. Lucy. An Ecological Survey of the Vegetation of Fort Hill State Memorial. 1969. 6.50 (ISBN 0-86727-059-4). Ohio Bio Survey.
Buckley, R. Ant-Plant Interactions in Australia. 1982. text ed. 54.50 (ISBN 90-6193-684-5, Pub. by Junk Pubs Netherlands). Kluwer Academic.
Carlquist, Sherwin. Ecological Strategies of Xylem Evolution. LC 74-76382. (Illus.). 1975. 36.50x (ISBN 0-520-02730-2). U of Cal Pr.
Chabot, Brain F. & Mooney, Hal. A, eds. Physiological Ecology of North American Plant Communities. 400p. 1985. 39.95 (ISBN 0-412-23240-5, NO. 6536, Pub. by Chapman & Hall England). Methuen Inc.
Chattopadhyay, S. B. Principles & Procedures of Plant Protection. 480p. 1980. 69.00x (ISBN 0-686-84466-1, Oxford & I B H India). State Mutual Bk.
Clements, Frederic E. Research Methods in Ecology. Egerton, Frank, 3rd, ed. LC 77-74210. (History of Ecology Ser.). (Illus.). 1977. Repr. of 1905 ed. lib. bdg. 30.00x (ISBN 0-405-10381-6). Ayer Co Pubs.
Conard, Henry S. The Background of Plant Ecology: Translation from the German the Plant Life of the Danube Basin. Egerton, Frank N., 3rd, ed. LC 77-74234. (History of Ecology Ser.). 1978. Repr. of 1951 ed. lib. bdg. 19.00 (ISBN 0-405-10403-0). Ayer Co Pubs.
Daubenmire, Rexford. Plants & Environment: A Textbook of Plant Autecology. 3rd ed. LC 73-13826. 422p. 1974. 38.50 (ISBN 0-471-19636-3). Wiley.
Dirzo, Rodolfo & Sarukhan, Jose, eds. Perspectives on Plant Population Ecology. LC 83-20182. (Illus.). 450p. 1984. text ed. 47.50x (ISBN 0-87893-142-2); pap. text ed. 28.75x (ISBN 0-87893-143-0). Sinauer Assoc.
Downs, R. G. & Hellmers, H. Environment & the Experimental Control of Plant Growth. (Experimental Botany Ser.). 1975. 31.50 (ISBN 0-12-221450-1). Acad Pr.
Egerton, Frank N., ed. American Plant Ecology, Eighteen Ninety-Seven to Nineteen Seventeen: An Original Anthology. LC 77-74202. (History of Ecology Ser.). (Illus.). 1978. lib. bdg. 59.50x (ISBN 0-405-10372-7). Ayer Co Pubs.
--Ecological Phytogeography in the Nineteenth Century: An Original Anthology. LC 77-74218. (History of Ecology Ser.). 1978. lib. bdg. 51.00x (ISBN 0-405-10388-3). Ayer Co Pubs.
Etherington, John R. Environment & Plant Ecology. 2nd ed. LC 81-16167. 487p. 1982. 69.95x (ISBN 0-471-10136-2, Pub. by Wiley-Interscience); pap. 29.95x (ISBN 0-471-10146-X, Pub. by Wiley-Interscience). Wiley.
Flowers, Seville, et al. Ecological Studies of the Flora & Fauna of Flaming Gorge Reservoir Basin, Utah & Wyoming. (Upper Colorado Ser: No. 3). 42.00 (ISBN 0-404-60648-2). AMS Pr.
Frank, J. H., ed. Phytotelmata: Terrestrial Plants As Hosts of Aquatic Insect Communities. Lounibos, L. P. 304p. 1983. pap. text ed. 24.95 (ISBN 0-937548-05-7). Plexus Pub.
Gehu, J. M. Documents Phytosociologiques. (Nouv. Ser.: No. 3). 1978. lib. bdg. 35.00 (ISBN 3-7682-1202-5). Lubrecht & Cramer.
Gehu, J. M., ed. Documents Phytosociologiques, IV: Festschrift R. Tuexen", 2 vols. (Illus.). 1979. Set. lib. bdg. 70.00x (ISBN 3-7682-1233-5). Lubrecht & Cramer.
Godwin, Harry. Fenland: Its Ancient Past & Uncertain Future. LC 77-8824. (Illus.). 1978. 37.50 (ISBN 0-521-21768-7). Cambridge U Pr.
Good, Ronald. The Geography of Flowering Plants. 4th ed. LC 73-85684. (Illus.). 584p. 1974. text ed. 33.00x (ISBN 0-582-46611-3). Longman.
Gottlieb, Otto R. Micromolecular Evolution, Systematics, & Ecology: An Essay into a Novel Botanical Discipline. (Illus.). 170p. 1982. 36.00 (ISBN 0-387-11655-9). Springer-Verlag.
Greig-Smith, P. Quantitative Plant Ecology. 3rd ed. LC 83-1302. (Studies in Ecology: Vol. 9). 355p. 1983. text ed. 42.00x (ISBN 0-520-04989-6); pap. text ed. 22.00x (ISBN 0-520-05080-0). U of Cal Pr.
Grime, J. P. Plant Strategies & Vegetation Processes. LC 78-18523. 222p. 1979. 54.95x (ISBN 0-471-99695-5); pap. 23.95x (ISBN 0-471-99692-0). Wiley.
Hall, D. O., et al, eds. Economics of Ecosystem Management. (Talks for Vegetation Science). 1985. lib. bdg. 67.50 (ISBN 0-318-04529-X, Pub. by Junk Pubs Netherlands). Kluwer-Academic.
Hastings, James R. & Turner, Raymond. The Changing Mile. LC 65-25019. (Illus.). 317p. 1965. 25.00x (ISBN 0-8165-0014-2). U of Ariz Pr.
Heidt, Volber. Flechtenkartierung und Die Beziehung zur Immissionsbelastung des sudlichen Munsterlands. (Biogeographica Ser.: No. 12). 1978. lib. bdg. 21.00 (ISBN 90-6193-213-0, Pub. by Junk Pubs. Netherlands). Kluwer Academic.
Heydecker, W., ed. Seed Ecology. LC 73-1459. 488p. 1973. 34.50x (ISBN 0-271-01158-0). Pa St U Pr.
Holzner, W. & Werger, M. J. Man's Impact on Vegetation. 1983. 98.00 (ISBN 90-6193-685-3, Pub. by Junk Pubs Netherlands). Kluwer Academic.
Howell, John T. Marin Flora: Manual of the Flowering Plants & Ferns of Marin County, California. 2nd ed. LC 71-100608. (Supplement). 1970. 22.50 (ISBN 0-520-00578-3); pap. 12.95 (ISBN 0-520-05621-3, CAL 773). U of Cal Pr.
Hueck, Kurt. Urlandschaft, Raublandschaft und Kulturlandschaft in der Provinz Tucuman Im Nordwestlichen Argentinien. 1953. 20.00 (ISBN 0-384-24820-9). Johnson Repr.
Knapp, Ruediger. Gegenseitige Beeinflussung und Temperatur-Wirkung bei tropischen und subtropischen Pflanzen: Bericht ueber neue experimentelle Untersuchungen an Nutzpflanzen und Arten der spontanen Vegetation. (Illus.). 1967. pap. 6.00 (ISBN 3-7682-0576-2). Lubrecht & Cramer.
Koopowitz, Harold & Kaye, Hilary. Plant Extinction: A Global Crisis. LC 82-62894. (Illus.). 256p. 1983. 16.95 (ISBN 0-913276-44-8). Stone Wall Pr.
Lange, O. L., et al. Physiological Plant Ecology II: Water Relations & Carbon Assimilation. (Encyclopedia of Plant Physioilogy Ser.: Vol. 12 B). (Illus.). 153p. 1982. 133.00 (ISBN 0-387-10906-4). Springer-Verlag.
Lange, O. L., et al, eds. Physiological Plant Ecology I: Responses to the Physical Environment. (Encylopedia of Plant Physiology Ser.: Vol. 12 A). (Illus.). 625p. 1981. 120.00 (ISBN 0-387-10763-0). Springer-Verlag.
--Physiological Plant Ecology III: Responses to the Chemical & Biological Environment. (Encyclopedia of Plant Physiology Ser.: Vol. 12C). (Illus.). 850p. 1983. 125.00 (ISBN 0-387-10907-2). Springer-Verlag.
Larcher, W. Physiological Plant Ecology. rev. ed. Biederman-Thorson, M. A., tr. LC 79-26396. (Illus.). 304p. 1980. 28.00 (ISBN 3-540-09795-3). Springer-Verlag.
Levitt, J. Responses of Plants to Environmental Stresses. (Physiological Ecology Ser). 1972. 83.00 (ISBN 0-12-445560-3). Acad Pr.
--Responses of Plants to Environmental Stresses, Vol. 2: Water, Radiaton, Salt & Other Stresses. LC 79-51680. (Physiological Ecology Ser.). 1980. 55.00 (ISBN 0-12-445502-6). Acad Pr.
Line, Les & Hodge, Walter H. The Audubon Society Book of Wildflowers. (Audubon Society Bks.). (Illus.). 1978. 50.00 (ISBN 0-8109-0671-6). Abrams.
Mani, M. S. Ecology & Phytogeography of High Altitude Plants of the Northwest Himalayas. 1979. 41.95x (ISBN 0-412-15710-1, NO.6186, Pub. by Chapman & Hall). Methuen Inc.
Medina, E., et al, eds. Physiological Ecology of Plants of the Wet Tropics. (Tasks for Vegetation Science). 1984. lib. bdg. 60.00 (ISBN 90-6193-952-6, Pub. by Junk Pubs Netherlands). Kluwer Academic.
Mishra, R., et al, eds. Progress in Ecology: Vol. I: Progress of Plant Ecology in India. (Illus.). 162p. 1973. 12.00 (ISBN 0-88065-160-1, Pub. by Messers Today & Tomorrows Printers & Publishers India). Scholarly Pubns.
Misra, R. & Das, R. R. Proceedings of the School on Plant Ecology. 384p. 1971. 62.00x (ISBN 0-686-84467-X, Oxford & I B H India). State Mutual Bk.
Misra, R. C. Manual of Plant Ecology. 1980. 52.00x (ISBN 0-686-84459-9, Pub. by Oxford & I B H India). State Mutual Bk.
Morris, I., ed. The Physiological Ecology of Phytoplankton. (Studies in Ecology: Vol. 7). 1981. 78.50x (ISBN 0-520-04308-1). U of Cal Pr.
Nobel, Park S. Biophysical Plant Physiology & Ecology. LC 82-20974. (Illus.). 608p. 1983. text ed. 36.95 (ISBN 0-7167-1447-7). W H Freeman.
Osmond, C. B., et al. Physiological Processes in Plant Ecology: Towards a Synthesis with Atriplex. (Ecololgical Studies: Vol. 36). (Illus.). 500p. 1980. 57.00 (ISBN 0-387-10060-1). Springer-Verlag.
Poissonet, P., ed. Vegetation Dynamics in Grasslands, Heathlands & Mediterranean Ligneous Formations. 1982. lib. bdg. 85.00 (ISBN 0-686-36955-6, Pub. by Junk Pubs Netherlands). Kluwer Academic.
Prance, Ghillian T. & Elias, Thomas S., eds. Extinction Is Forever: Threatened & Endangered Species of Plants in the Americas & Their Significance in Ecosystems Today & in the Future. LC 77-302. 437p. 1977. 20.00x (ISBN 0-89327-196-9). NY Botanical.
Rauner, Yu. L. Heat Balance of the Plant Cover. 220p. 1977. 70.00x (ISBN 0-686-84456-4, Pub. by Oxford & I B H India). State Mutual Bk.
Raunkiaer, Christen. The Life Forms of Plants & Statistical Plants Geography. Egerton, Frank N., 3rd, ed. Gilbert-Carter, H. & Fausboll, A., trs. LC 77-74249. (History of Ecology Ser.). (Illus.). 1978. Repr. of 1934 ed. lib. bdg. 51.00x (ISBN 0-405-10418-9). Ayer Co Pubs.
Report of the Fourth Session of the Caribbean Plant Protection Commission. 1978. pap. 7.50 (ISBN 92-5-100369-6, F1239, FAO). Unipub.
Report of the Government Consultation on the International Plant Protection Convention. 50p. 1977. pap. 7.50 (ISBN 92-5-100355-6, F1983, FAO). Unipub.
Ross, Juhan. The Radiation Regime & Architecture of Plant Stands. (Tasks for Vegetation Science Ser.: No. 3). 480p. 1982. 115.00 (ISBN 90-6193-607-1, Pub. by Junk Pubs Netherlands). Kluwer Academic.
Sahu, B. N. Rauvolfia Serpentina (Sarpagandha) Vol. I: Botany, Ecology & Agronomy. 359p. 1979. 40.00 (ISBN 0-88065-186-5, Pub. by Messers Today & Tomorrows India). Scholarly Pubns.
Segelken, John G. The Plant Ecology of the Hazelwood Botanical Preserve. 1929. 1.00 (ISBN 0-86727-020-9). Ohio Bio Survey.
Sholars, Robert E. The Pygmy Forest. (Illus.). 50p. (Orig.). 1982. pap. 6.95 (ISBN 0-9611178-0-X). Sholars.
Silvertown, Jonathan. Introduction to Plant Population Ecology. LC 81-15595. 210p. (Orig.). 1982. pap. text ed. 17.95x (ISBN 0-582-44265-6). Longman.
Specht, R. J. & Roe, Ethel M. Conservation of Major Plant Communities in Australia & Papua New Guinea. (2 microfiches). 1974. 6.00 (ISBN 0-643-00094-1, C051, CSIRO). Unipub.
Stein, Norbert. Coniferen Im Westlichen: Malayischen Archipel. (Biogeographica Ser: No. 11). 1978. lib. bdg. 31.50 (ISBN 90-6193-212-2, Pub. by Junk Pubs Netherlands). Kluwer Academic.
Tansley, Arthur G. British Islands & Their Vegetation, 2 Vols. 1949. Set. 130.00 (ISBN 0-521-06600-X). Cambridge U Pr.
Van Der Maarel, Eddy & Werger, Marinus J., eds. Plant Species & Plant Communities. 1978. lib. bdg. 37.00 (ISBN 90-6193-591-1, Pub. by Junk Pubs Netherlands). Kluwer Academic.
Vickery, Margaret. Ecology of Tropical Plants. LC 83-6973. 170p. 1984. 27.95x (ISBN 0-471-90107-5, Pub. by Wiley-Interscience). Wiley.
Voigt, John W. & Mohlenbrock, Robert H. Plant Communities of Southern Illinois. LC 64-11168. (Illus.). 220p. 1964. 8.95x (ISBN 0-8093-0132-6). S Ill U Pr.
Walker, D. & West, R. G., eds. Studies in the Vegetation History of the British Isles. 89.50 (ISBN 0-521-07565-3). Cambridge U Pr.
Walter, H. Vegetation of the Earth: In Relation to Climate & the Eco-Physiological Conditions. 2nd ed. Wieser, J., tr. LC 72-85947. (Heidelberg Science Library: Vol. 15). (Illus.). xvi, 240p. 1979. pap. 19.00 (ISBN 0-387-90404-2). Springer-Verlag.
Warming, Eugenius & Vahl, Martin. Oecology of Plants: An Introduction to the Study of Plant-Communities. Egerton, Frank N., 3rd, ed. LC 77-74254. (History of Ecology Ser.). 1978. Repr. of 1909 ed. lib. bdg. 34.50x (ISBN 0-405-10423-5). Ayer Co Pubs.
Weimann, Reinhold. Fragen des Wasserhaushalts Mittelrheingebeit. 20.00 (ISBN 0-384-66530-6). Johnson Repr.
Wells, Bertram W. The Natural Gardens of North Carolina. Rev. ed. LC 33-1938. (Illus.). xix, 458p. 1967. 12.95 (ISBN 0-8078-1058-4). U of NC Pr.
Whittaker, Robert H., ed. Classification of Plant Communities. (Illus.). 1978. pap. 26.00 (ISBN 90-6193-566-0, Pub. by Junk Pubs Netherlands). Kluwer Academic.
Willson, Mary F. Plant Reproductive Ecology. LC 82-24826. 282p. 1983. 39.95 (ISBN 0-471-08362-3, Pub. by Wiley-Interscience). Wiley.
Woodbury, Angus, et al. Ecological Studies of the Flora & Fauna of Navajo Reservoir Basin, Colorado & New Mexico. (Upper Colorado Ser: No. 5). Repr. of 1961 ed. 34.50 (ISBN 0-404-60655-5). AMS Pr.
Woodbury, Angus M., et al. Ecological Studies of Flora & Fauna in Glen Canyon. (Glen Canyon Ser: No. 7). Repr. of 1959 ed. 42.00 (ISBN 0-404-60640-7). AMS Pr.
--Ecological Studies of the Flora & Fauna of the Curecanti Reservoir Basins, Western Colorado. (Upper Colorado Ser.: No. 8). Repr. of 1962 ed. 42.50 (ISBN 0-404-60659-8). AMS Pr.
Woodwell, George M., ed. The Role of Terrestrial Vegetation in the Global Carbon Cycle: Measurement by Remote Sensing. LC 83-10333. (SCOPE Ser. (Scientific Committee on Problems of thr Environment): SCOPE 23). 247p. 1984. 51.95 (ISBN 0-471-90262-4, 1-409, Pub. by Wiley-Interscience). Wiley.

BOTANY-EMBRYOLOGY
see also Botany-Morphology; Germination; Seeds
Bilgrami, K. S., et al. Changes in Nutritional Components of Stored Seeds Due to Fungal Association. (International Bioscience Monograph: No. 9). 90p. 1979. 8.00 (ISBN 0-88065-061-3, Pub. by Messers Today & Tomorrows Printers & Publishers India). Scholarly Pubns.
Evans, David A., et al, eds. Handbook of Plant Cell Culture, Vol. 2. LC 82-73774. 550p. 1983. 49.50 (ISBN 0-02-949780-9). Macmillan.
Johri, B. M., ed. Experimental Embryology of Vascular Plants. (Illus.). 265p. 1982. 49.50 (ISBN 0-387-10334-1). Springer-Verlag.
Noyes, Frederick B. Noyes' Oral Histiology & Embryology. rev., 7th ed. Schour, Isaac, ed. LC 53-9573. pap. 112.00 (ISBN 0-317-29248-X, 2055442). Bks Demand UMI.
Raghavan, V. Experimental Embroyognesis in Vascular Plants. (Experimental Botany Ser.). 1977. 95.00 (ISBN 0-12-575450-7). Acad Pr.

BOTANY-FIELD WORKS
see Botany-Laboratory Manuals

BOTANY-GEOGRAPHICAL DISTRIBUTION
see Phytogeography

BOTANY-HISTOLOGY
see Botany-Anatomy; Plant Cells and Tissues

BOTANY-HISTORY
Alcock, Randal H. Botanical Names for English Readers. LC 73-174935. xviii, 236p. 1971. Repr. of 1876 ed. 40.00x (ISBN 0-8103-3823-8). Gale.
Delaporte, Francois. Nature's Second Kingdom. Goldhammer, Arthur, tr. from Fr. (Illus.). 248p. 1982. pap. 8.95x (ISBN 0-262-54040-1). MIT Pr.
Greene, Edward L. Landmarks of Botanical History, 2 vols. Egerton, Frank N., ed. LC 79-66057. (Illus.). 1983. Vol. 1: 520p., Vol. 2: 640p. 100.00x set (ISBN 0-8047-1075-9). Stanford U Pr.
Harvey-Gibson, Robert J. Outlines of the History of Botany. Cohen, I. Bernard, ed. LC 80-2128. (Development of Science Ser.). (Illus.). 1981. lib. bdg. 25.00x (ISBN 0-405-13877-6). Ayer Co Pubs.
Hawks, Ellison & Boulger, George S. Pioneers of Plant Study. facs. ed. LC 75-86759. (Essay Index Reprint Ser). 1928. 19.00 (ISBN 0-8369-1139-3). Ayer Co Pubs.
Meyer, Bernard S. Botany at the Ohio State University: The First One Hundred Years, No. 2. Reese, Karen J. & Sciulli, Veda M., eds. (Bulletin New Ser.: Vol. 6). 177p. 1983. 10.00 (ISBN 0-86727-096-9). Ohio Bio Survey.
Morton, A. G. History of Botanical Science: An Account of the Development of Botany from the Ancient Time to the Present. LC 81-67891. 1981. 55.00 (ISBN 0-12-508380-7); pap. 27.00 (ISBN 0-12-508382-3). Acad Pr.
Rosemberg, Eugenia, ed. Gonadotropins Nineteen Sixty-Eight: Proceedings of the Workshop Conference Held at Vista Hermosa, Mor., Mexico, June 24-26, 1968. LC 68-59129. (Illus.). 1968. text ed. 12.00x (ISBN 0-87672-004-1). Geron-X.
Sutton, S. B. In China's Border Provinces. (Illus.). 1974. 10.95 (ISBN 0-8038-3396-2). Hastings.
Von Sachs, Julius. Geschichte der Botanik. 1875. 50.00 (ISBN 0-384-52870-8). Johnson Repr.
Whittle, Tyler & Cook, C. D. Curtis's Flower Garden Displayed. (Illus.). 1981. 52.00x (ISBN 0-19-217715-X). Oxford U Pr.
Wilkinson, Norman B. E. I. du Pont, Botaniste: The Beginning of a Tradition. LC 76-171485. (Illus.). 139p. 1972. 7.50x (ISBN 0-8139-0374-2, Eleutherian Mills-Hagley Foundation); pap. 4.95x (ISBN 0-8139-0398-X). U Pr of Va.

BOTANY-LABORATORY MANUALS
Alfieri, et al. Laboratory for General Botany. 1977. pap. text ed. 7.95 (ISBN 0-917962-00-1). Peek Pubns.
Balbach, M. K. & Bliss, L. C. Laboratory Manual for General Botany. 6th ed. LC 81-50369. 350p. 1982. 17.95 (ISBN 0-03-058514-7, HoltC). HR&W.

Balbach, Margaret & Bliss, Lawrence C. General Botany: Laboratory Manual. 6th ed. 350p. 1982. pap. text ed. 19.95x (ISBN 0-03-058514-7). SCP.

Barbour, M. Laboratory Studies in Botany. 6th ed. 263p. 1982. pap. text ed. 17.95 (ISBN 0-471-86185-5). Wiley.

Barrales, H., et al. The Plant Kingdom: A Laboratory Manual. 400p. 1981. pap. text ed. 17.95 (ISBN 0-8403-2372-7). Kendall-Hunt.

Biegert, E., ed. A Topical Guide to "Folia Primatologica", Volumes 1-30 (1963-1978) 160p. 1980. pap. 16.75 (ISBN 3-8055-0781-X). S Karger.

Cherry, Marlin O. Botany Laboratory Workbook. 4th ed. (Illus.). 140p. 1982. pap. text ed. 6.95x (ISBN 0-89641-077-3). American Pr.

Davis, William K., et al. Laboratory Exercises for General Botany. 4th ed. (Illus.). 94p. 1981. pap. text ed. 5.95x (ISBN 0-89641-067-6). American Pr.

Dean, Hank L. Biology of Plants: Laboratory Exercises. 5th ed. 288p. 1982. write for info. wire coil bdg (ISBN 0-697-04708-3). Wm C Brown.

DePoe, Charles E., et al. Laboratory Manual for General Botany. (Illus.). 176p. 1983. 10.95x (ISBN 0-88136-010-4). Jostens.

Foster, Virginia. The Botany Laboratory: A Manual for a First Course in Botany. 153p. 1981. pap. 8.95 lab manual (ISBN 0-89459-049-9). Hunter Textbks.

Hackbarth, Winston. Laboratory Study of Plants. 80p. (Orig.). 1981. lab manual 6.95x (ISBN 0-89459-150-9). Hunter Textbks.

Howell, G. Leon, et al. Botany Laboratory Manual. 173p. (Orig.). 1980. pap. 9.95x lab manual (ISBN 0-88725-015-7). Hunter Textbks.

Jackson, Dennis C. Laboratory Manual for Two Twenty-One General Botany. 1978. wire coil bdg. 6.95 (ISBN 0-88252-083-0). Paladin Hse.

Jain, S. K. & Rao, R. R. A Handbook of Field & Herbarium Methods. (Illus.). 150p. 1977. 7.00 (ISBN 0-88065-139-3, Pub. by Messers Today & Tomorrows Printers & Publishers India). Scholarly Pubns.

McClymont, John. Laboratory Manual for General Botany. 1978. wire coil bdg. 6.50 (ISBN 0-88252-079-2). Paladin Hse.

Moore, T. C. Research Experiences in Plant Physiology: A Laboratory Manual. 2nd ed. (Illus.). 348p. 1981. pap. 22.00 (ISBN 0-387-90606-1). Springer-Verlag.

Peterson, Curt M. Plant Biology Laboratory Manual. 2nd ed. 1976. pap. text ed. 9.95 (ISBN 0-8403-1405-1). Kendall-Hunt.

Sparling, S. R. Botany: A Laboratory Manual. 1966. write for info. (ISBN 0-02-414240-9). Macmillan.

Wilson, Peter. The Living Bush: A Naturalist's Guide to Australia. (Illus.). 112p. 1978. 9.95 (ISBN 0-241-89933-8, Pub. by Hamish Hamilton England). David & Charles.

Wochok, Zachary S., et al. Laboratory Manual: Plant Biology. 6th ed. 1981. pap. text ed. 13.95 (ISBN 0-8403-2530-4). Kendall-Hunt.

Zuerner, Frank & Camosy, Art, eds. Plants in the Laboratory. (Monograph Ser.: No. 1). (Illus.). 1984. 7.00 (ISBN 0-941212-03-3); members 5.00. Natl Assn Bio Tchrs.

BOTANY–MAPPING

see Vegetation Mapping

BOTANY–METHODOLOGY

Berlyn, Graeme P. & Miksche, Jerome P. Botanical Microtechnique & Cytochemistry. new ed. (Illus.). 326p. 1976. text ed. 16.50x (ISBN 0-8138-0220-2). Iowa St U Pr.

Cuthbert, Mabel J. & Verhoek, Susan. How to Know the Spring Flowers. 2nd ed. (Pictured Key Nature Ser.). 300p. 1982. write for info. wire coil (ISBN 0-697-04782-2). Wm C Brown.

Harborne, J. B. Phytochemical Methods. 1973. pap. 16.95x (ISBN 0-412-23050-X, NO. 2001, Pub. by Chapman & Hall). Methuen Inc.

Hellebust, J. A. & Craigie, J. S. Handbook of Phycological Methods. LC 73-79496. (Illus.). 1978. 54.50 (ISBN 0-521-21855-1). Cambridge U Pr.

Johansen, Donald A. Plant Microtechnique. (Botanical Sciences Ser.). 1940. text ed. 66.95 (ISBN 0-07-032540-5). McGraw.

BOTANY–MORPHOLOGY

see also Botany–Anatomy; Botany–Embryology

Adams, George & Whicher, Olive. The Plant Between Sun & Earth & the Science Physical & Ethereal Spaces. 2nd ed. (Illus.). 1980. pap. 33.95 (ISBN 0-85440-360-4, Pub. by Steinerbooks). Anthroposophic.

Bold, Harold C., et al. Morphology of Plants & Fungi. 4th ed. (Illus.). 1980. text ed. 35.95 scp (ISBN 0-06-040848-0, HarpC). Har-Row.

De Bary, Anton. Comparative Morphology & Biology of the Fungi, Mycetozoa, & Bacteria. Balfour, I. B., ed. Garnsey, E. H., tr. Repr. of 1887 ed. 50.00 (ISBN 0-384-11145-9). Johnson Repr.

Delevoryas, Theodore. Plant Diversification. 2nd ed. LC 76-30858. 144p. 1977. pap. text ed. 17.95x (ISBN 0-03-080133-8, HoltC). HR&W.

Eames, A. J. Morphology of the Angiosperms. LC 76-57780. 532p. 1977. Repr. of 1961 ed. 32.50 (ISBN 0-88275-527-7). Krieger.

Erdtman, G. Pollen & Spore Morphology & Plant Taxonomy. (Introduction to Polynology Ser.: Vol. 2). 1972. Repr. of 1957 ed. 17.95x (ISBN 0-02-844310-1). Hafner.

Foster, Adriance S. & Gifford, Ernest M. Comparative Morphology of Vascular Plants. 2nd ed. LC 73-22459. (Illus.). 751p. 1974. text ed. 37.95 (ISBN 0-7167-0712-8). W H Freeman.

Fowke, L. C. & Constabel, F., eds. Plant Protoplasts. 256p. 1985. price not set (ISBN 0-8493-6473-6). CRC Pr.

Guedes, M. Morphology of Seed Plants. (Plant Science Ser.: No. 2). (Illus.). 1979. lib. bdg. 16.80x (ISBN 3-7682-1195-9). Lubrecht & Cramer.

--Teratological Modifications & the Meaning of Flower Parts. (International Bioscience Monographs: No. 7). 62p. 1979. 8.00 (ISBN 0-88065-093-1, Pub. by Messers Today & Tomorrows Printers & Publishers India). Scholarly Pubns.

Harlow, William M. Art Forms from Plant Life. LC 75-25002. Orig. Title: Patterns of Life: The Unseen World of Plants. (Illus.). 1974. pap. 6.50 (ISBN 0-486-23262-X). Dover.

Khoshoo, T. N. & Nair, P. K., eds. Progress in Plant Research: Applied Morphology & Allied Subjects, Vol. 1. 320p. 1979. 50.00 (ISBN 0-88065-145-8, Pub. by Messers Today & Tomorrows Printers & Publishers India). Scholarly Pubns.

Li, Sui-Fong. Studies on the Tolerance to Elevated Temperatures in Pleurotus Ostreatus (Jacq. Ex Fr.) Kummer: A Contribution to Taxonomy & the Genetics of the Fruiting Process. (Bibliotheca Mycologica: No. 76). (Illus.). 88p. 1981. pap. text ed. 13.15x (ISBN 3-7682-1276-9). Lubrecht & Cramer.

Miller, Robert H. Root Anatomy & Morphology: A Guide to the Literature. viii, 271p. 1974. 22.50 (ISBN 0-208-01452-7, Archon). Shoe String.

Nair, P. K. Glimpses in Plant Research. (Botanical Lectures & Essays Ser.: Vol. IV). (Illus.). 1979. text ed. 27.50x (ISBN 0-7069-0727-2, Pub. by Vikas India). Advent NY.

--Glimpses in Plant Research, Vol. III. 1976. text ed. 20.00x (ISBN 0-7069-0432-X, Pub. by Vikas India). Advent NY.

Robinson, Harry. Morphology & Landscape. 1981. 25.00x (ISBN 0-7231-0756-4, Pub. by Univ Tutorial England). State Mutual Bk.

Ross, Juhan. The Radiation Regime & Architecture of Plant Stands. (Tasks for Vegetation Science Ser.: No. 3). 480p. 1982. 115.00 (ISBN 90-6193-607-1, Pub. by Junk Pubs Netherlands). Kluwer Academic.

Shah, J. J., ed. Form, Structure & Function in Plants, Pt. 2. (Current Trends in Life Sciences Ser.: Vol. 8). (Illus.). 150p. 20.00x (ISBN 0-88065-240-3, Pub. by Messers Today & Tommorrow Printers & Publishers). Scholarly Pubns.

--Form Structures & Function in Plant, Pt. I. iv, 148p. 1975. 22.50 (ISBN 0-88065-191-1, Pub. by Messers Today & Tomorrows Printers & Publishers India). Scholarly Pubns.

Shih, Gene & Kessel, Richard. Living Images: Biological Microstructures Revealed by Scanning Electron Microscopy. 155p. 1982. write for info. (ISBN 0-86720-006-5); pap. write for info. (ISBN 0-86720-008-1). Jones & Bartlett.

Shropshire, W., Jr., ed. Photomorphogenesis. Mohr, H. (Encyclopedia of Plant Physiology: Vol. 16, Pts. A & B). (Illus.). 900p. 1983. 150.00 (ISBN 0-387-12143-9). Springer-Verlag.

Sinnott, Edmund W. Plant Morphogenesis. LC 79-4660. 560p. 1979. Repr. of 1960 ed. lib. bdg. 34.50 (ISBN 0-88275-922-1). Krieger.

Sporne, K. R. Morphology of Pteridophytes: The Structure of Ferns & Allied Plants. 4th ed. 1975. pap. text ed. 13.75x (ISBN 0-09-123861-7, Hutchinson U Lib). Humanities.

Verghese, T. M., ed. Vistas in Plant Sciences: Special Volume in Plant Morphology, Vol. V. 146p. 1979. 14.00 (ISBN 0-88065-205-5, Pub. by Messers Today & Tomorrows Printers & Publishers India). Scholarly Pubns.

Von Humboldt, Alexander. Aspects of Nature in Different Lands & Different Climates. Sabine, Mrs., tr. LC 70-99251. 1970. Repr. of 1850 ed. 32.00 (ISBN 0-404-03385-7). AMS Pr.

Wood, Carroll E., Jr. A Student's Atlas of Flowering Plants: Some Dicotyledons of Eastern North America. 256p. 1974. pap. text ed. 10.95 scp (ISBN 0-06-047207-3, HarpC). Har-Row.

BOTANY–NOMENCLATORS

see Botany–Nomenclature

BOTANY–NOMENCLATURE

see also Botany–Terminology; Plant Names, Popular

Alcock, Randal H. Botanical Names for English Readers. LC 73-174935. xviii, 236p. 1971. Repr. of 1876 ed. 40.00x (ISBN 0-8103-3823-8). Gale.

Bailey, Liberty H. How Plants Get Their Names. (Illus.). 1933. pap. 3.95 (ISBN 0-486-20796-X). Dover.

--How Plants Get Their Names. LC 73-30611. 1975. Repr. of 1933 ed. 30.00x (ISBN 0-8103-3763-0). Gale.

--How Plants Get Their Names. (Illus.). 12.75 (ISBN 0-8446-1574-9). Peter Smith.

Coombes, Allen J. Timber Press Dictionary of Plant Names. 210p. 1985. 9.95 (ISBN 0-88192-023-1, Dist. by Intl Spec Bk). Timber.

Geiger, Walter E. Phytonymic Derivation Systems in the Romance Languages: Studies in Their Origin & Development. (Studies in the Romance Languages & Literatures: No.187). 240p. (Orig.). 1978. pap. 17.50x (ISBN 0-8078-9187-8). U of NC Pr.

Genaust, Helmut. Etymologisches Woertenbuch der Botanischen Pflanzennamen. (Ger.). 390p. 1976. 62.50 (ISBN 3-7643-0755-2, M-7368, Pub. by Birkhaeuser). French & Eur.

Gledhill, D. The Names of Plants. 150p. Date not set. price not set (ISBN 0-521-30549-7); pap. price not set (ISBN 0-521-31562-X). Cambridge U Pr.

Heller, John L. Studies in Linnaean Method & Nomenclature, Vol. 7. (Marburger Schriften zur Medicingeschichte). 328p. 1983. 31.05 (ISBN 3-8204-7344-0). P Lang Pubs.

Henry, A. N. An Aid to the International Code of Botanical Nomenclature. 98p. 1980. 6.00 (ISBN 0-88065-104-0, Pub. by Messers Today & Tomorrows Printers & Publishershers India). Scholarly Pubns.

Hill, A. W. Index Kewensis Supplement Vol. 9 (from 1931-1935) 305p. 1978. lib. bdg. 73.50 (ISBN 3-87429-134-0). Lubrecht & Cramer.

Hill, A. W. & Salisbury, E. J. Index Kewensis (From 1936 to 1940) Incl. Index Kewensis (From 1941 to 1950) Salisbury, E. J. 273p. 1978. lib. bdg. 59.50X (ISBN 3-87429-138-3); Index Kewensis (From 1951 to 1955) Taylor, George. 157p. 1980. lib. bdg. 42.00 (ISBN 3-87429-180-4); Index Kewensis (From 1966 to 1970) Heslop-Harrison, J. 151p. 1983. lib. bdg. 42.00 (ISBN 3-87429-209-6). 251p. 1980. lib. bdg. 63.00 (ISBN 3-87429-179-0). Lubrecht & Cramer.

Index Kewensis. Incl. Supplement Vol.1 (1886 to 1895) Durand, T. & Jackson, J. D. 519p. 1981. lib. bdg. 101.58X (ISBN 3-87429-190-1); Supplement Vol. 2 (1896-1900) Thiselton-Dyer, W. T., ed. 204p. 1981. 47.60; Supplement Vol. 3 (from 1901 to 1905) Prain, D. 193p. 1978. lib. bdg. 42.00X (ISBN 3-87429-133-2); Supplement Vol. 4 (1906 to 1910) Prain, D. 252p. lib. bdg. 54.60X (ISBN 3-87429-201-0). Repr. Lubrecht & Cramer.

Jackson, B. D., et al, eds. Index Kewensis Supplements. Incl. Vol. 1. 1866-1895. Durand, T. & Jackson, B. D., eds. 1901-06; Vol. 4. 1906-1910. Prain, D., ed. 1913; Vol. 6. 1916-1920. Hill, A. W., ed. 1926. 68.00x (ISBN 0-19-854315-8); Vol. 7. 1921-1925. Hill, A. W., ed. 1929. 63.00x (ISBN 0-19-854316-6); Vol. 8. 1926-1930. Hill, A. W., ed. 1933. 68.00x (ISBN 0-19-854317-4); Vol. 10. 1936-1940. Hill, A. W. & Salisbury, E. J., eds. 1947; Vol. 12. 1951-1955. Taylor, George, ed. 1959; Vol. 13. 1956-1960. Taylor, George, ed. 1966. 68.00x (ISBN 0-19-854354-9); Vol. 14. 1961-1965. Taylor, George, ed. 1970. 68.00x (ISBN 0-19-854370-0); Vol. 15. 1966-1970. Heslop-Harrison, J., compiled by. 1973; Vol. 16. 1971-1976. Brenan, J. P., ed. 1980. 140.00x (ISBN 0-19-854531-2). Oxford U Pr.

Kelly, Howard A. Some American Medical Botanists: Commemorated in Our Botanical Nomenclature. LC 77-3485. 1977. Repr. of 1913 ed. lib. bdg. 25.00 (ISBN 0-89341-145-0). Longwood Pub Group.

Lindsay, Thomas. Plant Names. LC 75-16423. viii, 93p. 1976. Repr. of 1923 ed. 40.00x (ISBN 0-8103-4160-3). Gale.

Merill, Elmer D. Index Rafinesquianus: The Plant Names Published by C. S. Rafinesque with Reductions, & a Consideration of His Methods, Objectives & Attainments. Cohen, I. Bernard, ed. LC 79-7984. 1980. Repr. of 1949 ed. lib. bdg. 25.50x (ISBN 0-405-12566-6). Ayer Co Pubs.

A Polyglot Dictionary of Plant Names. (Armenian, Latin, Rus., Eng., Fr. & Ger.). 180p. 1981. 32.00x (ISBN 0-686-44741-7, Pub. by Collets). State Mutual Bk.

Rafinesque, S. C. Precis de Descouvertes Somiologiques. 11.25 (ISBN 0-8446-1371-1). Peter Smith.

Stafleu, Frans A., ed. International Code of Botanical Nomenclature. (Regnum Vegetabile: Vol. 111). 472p. 1983. lib. bdg. 45.00x (ISBN 0-318-11898-X). Lubrecht & Cramer.

Stevens, John E. Discovering Wild Plant Names. (Discovering Ser.: No. 166). (Illus.). 64p. 1983. pap. 3.50 (ISBN 0-85263-213-4, Pub. by Shire Pubns England). Seven Hills Bks.

BOTANY–NOMENCLATURE (POPULAR)

see Plant Names, Popular

BOTANY–ORGANOGRAPHY

Robinson, Trevor. Organic Constituents of Higher Plants. 5th ed. 1983. 14.75 (ISBN 0-935118-02-0). Cordus Pr.

BOTANY–OUTLINES, SYLLABI, ETC.

Fuller, Harry J. & Ritchie, Donald D. General Botany. 5th ed. (Illus.). 1967. pap. 5.95 (ISBN 0-06-460033-5, CO 33, COS). B&N NY.

BOTANY–PATHOLOGY

see Plant Diseases

BOTANY–PERIODICALS

Lawrence, G., et al. B-P-H: Botanico-Periodicum-Huntianum. 1968. 20.00x (ISBN 0-913196-10-X). Hunt Inst Botanical.

Simonsen, R., ed. Bacillaria: International Journal for Diatom Research, Vol. 5. (Illus.). 256p. 1982. lib. bdg. 28.00x (ISBN 0-686-39500-X). Lubrecht & Cramer.

BOTANY–PHYSIOLOGY

see Plant Physiology

BOTANY–PHYTOGRAPHY

see Botany

BOTANY–PICTORIAL WORKS

Clusius, Carolus. Plant & Floral Woodcuts for Designers & Craftsmen: 419 Illustrations from the Renaissance Herbal of Clusius. 11.25 (ISBN 0-8446-5170-2). Peter Smith.

Daniels, G., ed. Artists from the Royal Botanic Gardens, Kew. (Illus.). 1974. pap. 3.00x (ISBN 0-913196-17-7). Hunt Inst Botanical.

Diment, Judith, et al. Catalogue of the Natural History Drawings Commissioned by Joseph Banks on the Endeavour Voyage 1768-1771 Held in the British Museum (Natural History) Botany - Australia, Pt. 1. 250p. 1984. lib. bdg. 75.00 (ISBN 0-930466-92-6). Meckler Pub.

Farr, Gerald G. Botany Illustrated. (Illus.). 52p. 1979. pap. text ed. 3.95x (ISBN 0-89641-055-2). American Pr.

Fourth International Exhibition of Twentieth Century Botanical Art & Illustration. Catalogue. Secrist, S. & Howard, N., eds. (Illus.). 1977. 12.00x (ISBN 0-913196-19-3). Hunt Inst Botanical.

House, Maria N. & Munro, Susan. Plantae Occidentalis: Two Hundred Years of Botanical Art in British Columbia. (Illus.). 117p. 1979. pap. 11.95x (ISBN 0-89955-413-X, Pub. by U BC Pr Canada). Intl Spec Bk.

King, Ronald. Botanical Illustration. (Illus.). 1979. 14.95 (ISBN 0-517-53525-4, C N Potter Bks); pap. 6.95 (ISBN 0-517-53526-2, C N Potter). Crown.

Korach, K., ed. Catalogue: Third International Exhibition of Twentieth Century Botanical Art & Illustration. (Illus.). 1972. 10.00x (ISBN 0-913196-14-2). Hunt Inst Botanical.

Kuck, Loraine E. & Tongg, Richard C. Hawaiian Flowers & Flowering Trees. LC 58-7494. (Illus.). 1958. boxed 19.50 (ISBN 0-8048-0237-8). C E Tuttle.

Linnaeus, C. Hortus Cliffortianus. (Illus.). 1968. Repr. of 1737 ed. 84.00 (ISBN 3-7682-0543-6). Lubrecht & Cramer.

Mohlenbrock, Robert H. Flowering Plants: Basswoods to Spurges. LC 81-8585. (Illustrated Flora of Illinois). (Illus.). 256p. 1982. 22.95x (ISBN 0-8093-1025-2). S Ill U Pr.

Ravenswaay, Charles van. Drawn from Nature: The Botanical Art of Joseph Prestele & His Sons. (Illus.). 360p. 1984. 45.00 (ISBN 0-87474-938-7, VRDN). Smithsonian.

Rix, Martyn. The Art of the Plant World: The Great Botanical Illustrators & Their Work. LC 80-14274. (Illus.). 224p. 1981. 85.00 (ISBN 0-87951-118-4); deluxe ed. 175.00 (ISBN 0-87951-139-7). Overlook Pr.

Second International Exhibition of Twentieth Century Botanical Art & Illustration. Catalogue. Lawrence, G., compiled by. (Illus.). 1968. 7.00x (ISBN 0-913196-11-8). Hunt Inst Botanical.

White, James J. & Wendel, D. E., eds. Catalogue: Fifth International Exhibition of Botanical Art & Illustration. 5th ed. (Illus.). 115p. 1983. softcover 15.00x (ISBN 0-913196-41-X). Hunt Inst Botanical.

Whittle, Tyler & Cook, C. D. Curtis's Flower Garden Displayed. (Illus.). 1981. 52.00x (ISBN 0-19-217715-X). Oxford U Pr.

BOTANY–PRE-LINNEAN WORKS

see also Herbs

Byers, Laura T. Hortus Librorum: Early Botanical Books at Bumbarton Oaks. LC 83-5697. (Illus.). 48p. 1983. pap. 6.00x (ISBN 0-88402-118-1). Dumbarton Oaks.

Clusius, Carolus. Plant & Floral Woodcuts for Designers & Craftsmen: 419 Illustrations from the Renaissance Herbal of Clusius. 11.25 (ISBN 0-8446-5170-2). Peter Smith.

Colden, J. Botanic Manuscript. Rickett, H. W. & Hall, E. C., eds. (Illus.). 1963. 10.00 (ISBN 0-934454-15-9). Lubrecht & Cramer.

Diment, J. A., et al. Catalogue of the Natural History Drawings Commissioned by Joseph Banks on the Endeavour Voyage, Part 1: Botany - Australia. (Illus.). 183p. 1984. pap. text ed. 60.00x (ISBN 0-565-09000-3, Pub. by Brit Mus Nat Hist England). Sabbot Natural Hist Bks.

Diment, Judith, et al. Catalogue of the Natural History Drawings Commissioned by Joseph Banks on the Endeavour Voyage 1768-1771 Held in the British Museum (Natural History) Botany - Australia, Pt. 1. 250p. 1984. lib. bdg. 75.00 (ISBN 0-930466-92-6). Meckler Pub.

Elliott, W. Rodger & Jones, David L. Encyclopedia of Australian Plants, Vol. 1. (Illus.). 336p. 40.00x (ISBN 0-85091-070-6, Pub. by Lothian). Intl Spec Bk.

Erickson, Rica. Plants of Prey. 1977. 15.00 (ISBN 0-85564-099-5, Pub. by U of W Austral Pr). Intl Spec Bk.

--Triggerplants. (Illus.). 229p. 1982. 22.95 (ISBN 0-85564-100-2, Pub. by U of W Austral Pr). Intl Spec Bk.

Etherington, Dan M. Multi-Period Budgeting & the Economic Assessment of Perennial Corporation Intercropping Systems. (Development Studies Centre - Occasional Paper: No. 26). 47p. (Orig.). 1982. pap. text ed. 2.00 (ISBN 0-909150-51-6, 1106, Pub. by ANUP Australia). Australia N U P.

Foged, N. Diatoms in Eastern Australia. (Bibliotheca Phycologica Ser.: No. 41). (Illus.). 1979. 21.00 (ISBN 3-7682-1203-3). Lubrecht & Cramer.

Gillison, A. N. & Anderson, D. J., eds. Vegetation Classification in Australia. 229p. 1981. 55.00x (ISBN 0-7081-1309-5, Pub. by CSIRO Australia). State Mutual Bk.

Groves, R. H., ed. Australian Vegetation. LC 80-40421. (Illus.). 350p. 1981. 75.00 (ISBN 0-521-23436-0). Cambridge U Pr.

Lands of the Alligator Rivers Area: Northern Territory. (Land Research Ser.: No. 38). (Illus.). 173p. 1976. pap. 13.50 (ISBN 0-643-00208-1, C019, CSIRO). Unipub.

Langley, Jean. Australian Bushflowers. (Illus.). 29.95x (ISBN 0-7018-0330-4, ABC). Sportshelf.

Mueller, Ferdinand Von. Fragmenta Phytographicae Australiae, Vols.1-11 & Suppl. 1974. 144.80 (ISBN 90-6123-311-9). Lubrecht & Cramer.

Petheram, R. J. & Kok, B. Plants of the Kimberly Region of Western Australia. (Illus.). 556p. (Orig.). 1983. pap. text ed. 35.00x (ISBN 0-85564-215-7, Pub. by U of W Austral Pr). Intl Spec Bk.

Sharr, F. A. Western Australian Plant Names & Their Meanings: A Glossary. 228p. 1978. pap. 24.95x (ISBN 0-85564-122-3, Pub. by U of W Austral Pr). Intl Spec Bk.

Smith, J. M. A History of Australian Vegetation. 216p. 1981. 18.50 (ISBN 0-07-072953-0). McGraw.

Specht, R. J. & Roe, Ethel M. Conservation of Major Plant Communities in Australia & Papua New Guinea. (2 microfiches). 1974. 6.00 (ISBN 0-643-00094-1, C051, CSIRO). Unipub.

Weber, W. A. & Wetmore, C. M. Catalogue of Lichens of Australia: Exclusive of Tasmania. 1972. 14.00 (ISBN 3-7682-5441-0). Lubrecht & Cramer.

Willis, J. H. A Handbook to Plants in Victoria, Vol. 1: Ferns, Conifers & Monocotyledons. 2nd ed. 481p. 1971. 25.00x (ISBN 0-522-83983-5, Pub. by Melbourne U Pr Australia). Intl Spec Bk.

--A Handbook to Plants in Victoria, Vol. 2: Dicotyledons. 1972. 40.00x (ISBN 0-522-84037-X, Pub by Melbourne U Pr Australia). Intl Spec Bk.

Wrigley, John W. & Fagg, Murray. Australian Native Plants. (Illus.). 448p. 1981. 48.95x (ISBN 0-00-216416-7, Pub. by W Collins Australia). Intl Spec Bk.

BOTANY–BAHAMAS

Correll, Donovan S. Flora of the Bahamian Archipelago. (Illus.). 1692p. 1982. lib. bdg. 105.00x (ISBN 3-7682-1289-0). Lubrecht & Cramer.

BOTANY–BRAZIL

Bicudo, C. E. & Samanez, I. M. Desmidioflorula Paulista III: Generos Bambu ina, Desmidium, Groenbladia, Nyalotheca, Onychonema, Phymatodos, Spondylosium, Teilingia. (Bibliotheca Phycologica Ser.: No. 68). (Port., Illus.). 138p. 1984. pap. text ed. 17.50x (ISBN 3-7682-1388-9). Lubrecht & Cramer.

Bicudo, Carlos M. Contribution to the Knowledge of the Desmids of the State of Sao Paulo. (Illus.). 1969. 10.00 (ISBN 3-7682-0653-X). Lubrecht & Cramer.

Cogniaux, Alfredus. Orchidaceae, 4 vols. (Flora Brasiliensis Ser.: Vol. 3, Pts. 4-6). (Lat., Illus.). 970p. 1975. Repr. Set. lib. bdg. 157.50x (ISBN 3-87429-080-8). Lubrecht & Cramer.

Leite Sant'Anna, C. Chlorococcales do Estado de Sao Paulo, Brazil. (Bibliotheca Phycologica Ser.: No. 67). (Port., Illus.). 348p. 1984. text ed. 52.50x (ISBN 3-7682-1387-0). Lubrecht & Cramer.

Mors, Walter B. & Rizzini, Carlos T. Useful Plants of Brazil. LC 66-17891. pap. 45.30 (ISBN 0-317-28317-0, 2016293). Bks Demand UMI.

BOTANY–CAMBODIA

Tixier, P. Bryogeographie-Du Mont Bokor (Cambodge) 1979. (Bryophytorum Bibliotheca 18). (Illus.). 1979. pap. text ed. 14.00x (ISBN 3-7682-1227-0). Lubrecht & Cramer.

BOTANY–CANADA

Bailey, Liberty H. Manual of Cultivated Plants. rev. ed. 1949. 37.95 (ISBN 0-02-505520-8). Macmillan.

Britton, Nathaniel L. & Brown, Addison. Illustrated Flora of the Northern United States & Canada, 3 Vols. (Illus.). 1970. pap. 12.95 ea.; Vol. 1. pap. (ISBN 0-486-22642-5); Vol. 2. pap. (ISBN 0-486-22643-3); Vol. 3. pap. (ISBN 0-486-22644-1). Dover.

Cody, William J. & Porsild, A. Erling. Vascular Plants of Continental Northwest Territories. (Illus.). 676p. 1980. lib. bdg. 85.00x (ISBN 0-660-00119-5, 56546-7, Pub. by Natl Mus Canada). U of Chicago Pr.

Cornut, Jacques P. Canadensium Plantarum. 1966. Repr. of 1635 ed. Facsimile Ed. 25.00 (ISBN 0-384-09835-5). Johnson Repr.

Gleason, H. A. New Britton & Brown Illustrated Flora of the Northeastern United States & Adjacent Canada, 3 Vols. rev. ed. (Illus.). 1975. Set. 115.00x (ISBN 0-02-845300-X). Hafner.

House, Maria N. & Munro, Susan. Plantae Occidentalis: Two Hundred Years of Botanical Art in British Columbia. (Illus.). 117p. 1979. pap. 11.95x (ISBN 0-89955-413-X, Pub. by U BC Pr Canada). Intl Spec Bk.

Hulten, Eric. Flora of Alaska & Neighboring Territories: A Manual of the Vascular Plants. LC 67-17302. (Illus.). 1016p. 1968. 65.00x (ISBN 0-8047-0643-3). Stanford U Pr.

Kuc, M. Bryogeography of Expedition Area, Axelberg Heiberg Island, N. W. T. Canada. 1973. 17.50 (ISBN 3-7682-0912-1). Lubrecht & Cramer.

Little, Elbert L. Forest Trees of the United States & Canada, & How to Identify Them. LC 79-52527. (Illus.). 1980. pap. text ed. 2.00 (ISBN 0-486-23902-0). Dover.

Montgomery, F. H. The Seeds & Fruits of Plants of Eastern Canada & Northeastern United States. LC 76-23241. 1976. 37.50x (ISBN 0-8020-5341-6). U of Toronto Pr.

Taylor, Ronald J. & Leviton, Alan E., eds. Mosses of North America. 170p. (Orig.). 1980. 11.95 (ISBN 0-934394-02-4). AAASPD.

Taylor, Roy L. & MacBryde, Bruce. Vascular Plants of British Columbia: A Descriptive Resource Inventory. (Illus.). 754p. (Orig.). 1977. pap. text ed. 28.00x (ISBN 0-7748-0054-2, Pub. by U of BC). Intl Spec Bk.

Turner, Nancy J. & Szczawinski, Adam F. Wild Green Vegetables of Canada. (Edible Wild Plants of Canada). (Illus.). 150p. 1980. pap. 9.95 spiral bdg. (ISBN 0-660-10342-7, 56325-1, Pub. by Natl Mus Canada). U of Chicago Pr.

Wade, L. Keith. Phenology of Cultivated Rhododendrons in Lower Mainland of British Columbia. (Illus.). 225p. (Orig.). 1979. pap. 8.25 (ISBN 0-89955-412-1, Pub. by U BC Pr Canada). Intl Spec Bk.

Walshe, Shan. Plants of Quetico & the Ontario Shield. (Illus.). 216p. 1980. 25.00 (ISBN 0-8020-3370-9); pap. 12.95 (ISBN 0-8020-3371-7). U of Toronto Pr.

BOTANY–CARIBBEAN AREA

Liogier, Henri A. & Martorell, Luis F. Flora of Puerto Rico & Adjacent Islands: A Systematic Synopsis. LC 82-16431. 342p. (Orig.). 1982. pap. 15.00 (ISBN 0-8477-2329-1). U of PR Pr.

BOTANY–CEYLON

Beddome, R. H. Handbook to the Ferns of British India, Ceylon & Malaysia: Peninsula with Supplement. 502p. 1977. 20.00 (ISBN 0-88065-054-0, Pub. by Messers Today & Tomorrows Printers & Publishers India). Scholarly Pubns.

Dassanayake, M. D., ed. A Handbook to the Flora of Ceylon, Vol. IV. rev. ed. 545p. 1983. lib. bdg. 25.00 (ISBN 90-6191-067-6, Pub. by Balkema RSA). IPS.

Trimen, Henry. Handbook to the Flora of Ceylon, 5 vols. 1978. Repr. of 1895 ed. Set. 375.00 (ISBN 0-89955-283-8, Pub. by Intl Bk Dist). Intl Spec Bk.

BOTANY–CHILE

Bahre, Conrad J. Destruction of the Natural Vegetation of North-Central Chile. LC 78-50836. (Publications in Geography Ser.: Vol. 23). 1979. 17.50x (ISBN 0-520-09594-4). U of Cal Pr.

Heusser, Calvin J. Pollen & Spores of Chile: Modern Types of Pteridophyta, Gymnospermae, & Angiospermae. LC 75-114322. 167p. 1971. 19.95x (ISBN 0-8165-0213-7). U of Ariz Pr.

Oberdorfer, E. Pflanzensoziologische Studien in Chile. (Illus.). 1960. 21.00 (ISBN 3-7682-0011-6). Lubrecht & Cramer.

Ruiz, H. & Pavon, J. Prodromus et Flora Peruviana et Chilensis, 4 vols. in 1. (Illus.). 1965. Repr. of 1802 ed. 210.00 (ISBN 3-7682-0283-6). Lubrecht & Cramer.

BOTANY–CHINA

Cheng-Yih, W. & H. Y. Hou, eds. The Vegetation of China, Vol. 1. 1983. 95.50 (ISBN 0-677-31080-3). Gordon.

Farrer, Reginald J. On the Eaves of the World, 2 Vols. LC 79-136386. (BCL Ser.: I). Repr. of 1917 ed. Set. 57.50 (ISBN 0-404-02368-1). AMS Pr.

Franchet, A. R. Plantae Davidiane Ex Sinarum Imperio, 2 pts. (Illus.). 1970. Repr. of 1884 ed. 105.00 (ISBN 3-7682-0670-X). Lubrecht & Cramer.

High Mountain Plants in China. Date not set. price not set (ISBN 0-442-20076-5). Sci Pr.

KitaGawa, Masao. Neo-Lineamenta Florae Manshuricae, Or: Enumeration of the Spontaneous Vascular Plants of Manchuria. (Flora et Vegetatio Mundi Ser.: No. 4). 1979. lib. bdg. 70.00 (ISBN 3-7682-1113-4). Lubrecht & Cramer.

Van Melle, P. J. Review of Juniperus Chinensis et al. (Illus.). 1947. pap. 5.00 (ISBN 0-934454-72-8). Lubrecht & Cramer.

Wilson, Ernest H. China, Mother of Gardens. LC 73-172555. (Illus.). Repr. of 1929 ed. 30.00 (ISBN 0-405-09081-1). Ayer Co Pubs.

--A Naturalist in Western China, 2 vols. LC 76-46620. 1977. Repr. of 1913 ed. write for info (ISBN 0-913728-17-9). Theophrastus.

BOTANY–EGYPT

Boulos, Loutfy & El-Hadidi, M. Nabil. The Weed Flora of Egypt: A Practical Guide. 1985. pap. 12.50x (ISBN 977-424-038-3, Pub. by Am Univ Cairo Pr). Columbia U Pr.

Fayed, A. A. Flora of Egypt. Hadidi, Nabil M., ed. (Taeckholmia Additional Ser.: No. 1: 93-97 (1980) Family 162. Globulariaceae). (Illus.). 5p. 1981. 6.75x (ISBN 0-686-34408-1). Lubrecht & Cramer.

Hadidi, Nabil E. Flora of Egypt. (Taeckholmia Additional Ser.: No. 1: 1-12: Outline of the Planned Flora of Egypt). 12p. 1981. pap. text ed. 6.75x (ISBN 0-686-32935-X). Lubrecht & Cramer.

--Flora of Egypt. Hadidi, Azz M., ed. (Taeckholmia Additional Ser.: No. 1: 13-92 Family 57: Amaranthaceae). (Illus.). 80p. 1981. pap. text ed. 18.00x (ISBN 0-686-34409-X). Lubrecht & Cramer.

Muschler, R. A Manual Flora of Egypt, 2 vols. in one. (Illus.). 1971. Repr. of 1912 ed. 105.00 (ISBN 3-7682-0678-5). Lubrecht & Cramer.

Tackholm, V. & Drar, M. Flora of Egypt, 4 vols. Set. pap. 178.50 (ISBN 3-87429-055-7). Lubrecht & Cramer.

BOTANY–EUROPE

Corillion, Robert. Les Charophycees de France et de l'Europe Occidentale. 1972. 61.60 (ISBN 3-87429-014-X). Lubrecht & Cramer.

Demuynck, M., et al, eds. Biogas Plants in Europe: A Practical Handbook. (Solar Energy in the European Community Ser.: No. E, Vol. 6). 1984. lib. bdg. 53.00 (Pub. by Reidel Holland). Kluwer Academic.

Dijkema, K. S. & Wolff, W. J., eds. Flora & Vegetation of the Wadden Sea Islands & Coastal Areas: Final Report of the Section "Flora & Vegetation of the Island's of the Wadden Sea Working Group, Report 9. 413p. 1983. lib. bdg. 28.00 (ISBN 90-6191-059-5, Pub. by Balkema RSA). IPS.

Henfrey, Arthur. The Vegetation of Europe, Its Conditions & Causes. Egerton, Frank N., 3rd, ed. LC 77-74227. (History of Ecology Ser.). 1978. Repr. of 1852 ed. lib. bdg. 30.00x (ISBN 0-405-10397-2). Ayer Co Pubs.

Heywood, V. H. & Clark, R. B., eds. Taxonomy in Europe: Final Report of the European Science Research Council's Ad Hoc Group on Biological Recording Systematics & Taxonomy. (European Science Research Council Review Ser.: Vol. 17). 170p. 1982. pap. 13.25 (ISBN 0-444-86363-X, North Holland). Elsevier.

Kibby, Geoffrey. Mushrooms & Toadstools: A Field Guide. (Illus.). 1979. text ed. 23.00x (ISBN 0-19-217688-9). Oxford U Pr.

Kuehner, R. & Romagnesi, H. Complements a la "Flore Analytique". (Bibliotheca Mycologica Ser.: No. 56). (Illus.). 1977. Repr. of 1954 ed. lib. bdg. 35.00x (ISBN 3-7682-1131-2). Lubrecht & Cramer.

Moser, Meinhard. Die Pilze Mitteleuropas: Vol. 4, Die Gattung Phlegmacium (Schleimkoepfe) (Illus.). 1960. 77.00 (ISBN 3-7682-0523-1). Lubrecht & Cramer.

Muller, F. M. Seedlings of the North-Western European Lowland. 1978. lib. bdg. 79.00 (ISBN 90-6193-588-1, Pub. by Junk Pubs Netherlands). Kluwer Academic.

Neuhoff, Walther. Die Pilze Mitteleuropas: Vol. 28, Die Milchlinge (Lactarii) (Illus.). 1956. 70.00 (ISBN 3-7682-0520-7). Lubrecht & Cramer.

Polunin, O. & Everard. Flowers of Europe: A Field Guide. 1981. 50.00x (ISBN 0-686-78775-7, Pub. by RHS Ent England). State Mutual Bk.

Polunin, Oleg. Flowers of Europe: A Field Guide. 1969. 55.00x (ISBN 0-19-217621-8). Oxford U Pr.

Polunin, Oleg & Walters, Martin. A Guide to the Vegetation of Britain & Europe. (Illus.). 1985. 26.95x (ISBN 0-19-217713-3). Oxford U Pr.

Punt, W. & Clarke, G. C., eds. The Northwest European Pollen Flora, Vol. 2. 266p. 1980. Repr. 68.00 (ISBN 0-444-41880-6). Elsevier.

Schaeffer, Julius. Die Pilze Mitteleuropas: Vol. 3, Russula-Monographie. (Illus.). 1970. Repr. of 1952 ed. 70.00 (ISBN 3-7682-0689-0). Lubrecht & Cramer.

Schroether, C. The Flora of the Alps with Two Hundred & Seven Varieties in Full Colours. (Illus.). 97p. 1984. 98.75 (ISBN 0-89266-482-7). Am Classical Coll Pr.

Singer, Rolf. Die Pilze Mitteleuropas: Vol. 5, Die Roehrlinge- Pt. 1, Die Boletaceae (Ohne Boletoideae) (Illus.). 1965. 42.00 (ISBN 3-7682-0526-6). Lubrecht & Cramer.

--Die Pilze Mitteleuropas: Vol. 5, Die Roehrlinge- Pt. 2, Die Boletoiceae una Strobilomycetaceae. (Illus.). 1967. 63.00 (ISBN 3-7682-0529-0). Lubrecht & Cramer.

Tutin, T. G., et al. Flora Europaea. Incl. Vol. 1. Lycopodiaceae to Plantanaceae. 1964. 120.00 (ISBN 0-521-06661-1); Vol. 2. Rosaceae to Umbelliferae. 1968. 120.00 (ISBN 0-521-06662-X); Vol. 3. Diapseniaceae to Myoporaceae. 120.00 (ISBN 0-521-08489-X); Vol. 4. Plantaginaceae to Compositae (& Rubiaceae) 1976. 120.00 (ISBN 0-521-08717-1); Vol. 5. Alismataceae to Orchidaceae. 1980. 125.00 (ISBN 0-521-20108-X). LC 64-24315. Set. 495.00 (ISBN 0-521-23205-8). Cambridge U Pr.

Welten, Max, ed. Vebreitungsatlas der Farn- und Blutenpflanzen der Schweiz, 2 Vols. 1982. Vol. 1, 704pp. text ed. 48.00; Vol. 2, 752pp. text ed. 103.95 (ISBN 0-8176-1308-0). Birkhauser.

BOTANY–FRANCE

Bornet, E. & Flahault, C. Revision Des Noostocacees Heterocystees: Contocacees Dans les Principaux Herbiers De France, Vol. 1. 1969. 21.00 (ISBN 3-7682-0002-7). Lubrecht & Cramer.

Cornut, Jacques P. Canadensium Plantarum. 1966. Repr. of 1635 ed. Facsimile Ed. 25.00 (ISBN 0-384-09835-5). Johnson Repr.

Duval, Marguerite. The King's Garden. Tomarken, Annette & Cowen, Claudine, trs. LC 81-15934. Orig. Title: La Planete Des Fleurs. (Fr., Illus.). 214p. 1982. 17.95x (ISBN 0-8139-0916-3). U Pr of Va.

Meriaux, J. Etude Analytique et Comparative de la Vegetation Aquatique D'Etangs et Marais du Nord de la France. (Valle de la Sensee et Bassin Houillier du Nord-Pas-de-Calais) (Offprint from Documents Phytosociolgique Ser.). (Fr.). 1979. pap. 17.50x (ISBN 3-7682-1238-6). Lubrecht & Cramer.

Peragallo, H & Peragallo, M. Les Diatomees Marines de France et des Districts Maririmes Voisins. (Gr., Illus.). 539p. 1984. Repr. of 1908 ed. lib. bdg. 133.00X (ISBN 3-87429-219-3). Lubrecht & Cramer.

Quelet, Lucien. Flore Mycologique de la France & Des Pays Limitrophes. 1962. Repr. of 1888 ed. 21.60 (ISBN 90-6123-123-X). Lubrecht & Cramer.

Rolland. Flore Populaire de la France: Historie Naturelle des Plantes dans leurs Rapports avec la Linguistique, 5 tomes. Set. 150.00 (ISBN 0-685-36690-1). French & Eur.

Roux, Claude. Etude Ecologique et Phytosociologique des Peuplements Licheniques Saxicoles-Calcicoles du Sud-Est de la France. (Bibliotheca Lichenologica: Vol. 15). (Fr., Illus.). 558p. 1981. text ed. 52.50x (ISBN 3-7682-1301-3). Lubrecht & Cramer.

BOTANY–GALAPAGOS ISLANDS

Schofield, Eileen K. Field Guide & Travel Journal: Plants of the Galapagos Islands. LC 83-40562. (Illus.). 128p. (Orig.). 1984. flexi-cover 10.95 (ISBN 0-87663-414-5). Universe.

Wiggins, Ira L. & Porter, Duncan M. Flora of the Galapagos Islands. LC 78-97917. (Illus.). 1040p. 1971. 65.00x (ISBN 0-8047-0732-4). Stanford U Pr.

BOTANY–FRENCH GUIANA

Aublet, J. B. Histoire des Plantes de la Guiane Francaise, 4 vols. bd. in one. (Historia Naturalis Classica Ser.: No. 100). 1977. Repr. of 1775 ed. lib. bdg. 175.00x (ISBN 3-7682-1105-3). Lubrecht & Cramer.

Roxburgh, W. Flora Indica: Description of Indian Plants. Carey, ed. (Illus.). lxiv, 775p. 1974. Repr. 50.00 (ISBN 0-88065-182-2, Pub. by Messers Today & Tomorrows Printers & Publishers India). Scholarly Pubns.

Royal Botanic Garden, Calcutta & Stapf, Otto. The Aconites of India: A Monograph by Otto Stabt, A Sketch of the Life of Francie Hamilton (Once Buchanan, Vol. X, Pt. 2. (Illus.). lxxv, 197p. 50.00 (ISBN 0-88065-014-1, Pub. by Messers Today & Tomorrows India). Scholarly Pubns.

Royal Botanic Garden, Calcutta, Annals, et al. A Century of New & Rare Indian Plants, Vol. V, Pt. II. (Illus.). 1971. Repr. of 1895 ed. 50.00 (ISBN 0-88065-011-7, Pub. by Messers Today & Tomorrows Printers & Publishers India). Scholarly Pubns.

Royal Botanic Garden, Calcutta, Annals of, et al. A Second Century of New & Rare Indian Plants, Vol. IX, Pt. 1. (Illus.). 80p. 1972. Repr. of 1901 ed. 50.00 (ISBN 0-88065-012-5, Pub. by Messers Today & Tomorrows Printers & Publishers India). Scholarly Pubns.

Royal Botanic Garden, Calcutta, Annals of & King, George. The Species of Artocarpus Indigenous to the British India: And the Indo-Malayan Species of Quercus & Castnopsis, 2 pts, Vol. II. (Illus.). 107p. 1979. Repr. of 1899 ed. 80.00 (ISBN 0-88065-010-9, Pub. by Messers Today & Tomorrows Printers & Publishers India). Scholarly Pubns.

Royal Botanic Garden, Calcutta, Annals of & Prain, D. The Species of Dalbargia of South Eastern Asia, Vol. X, Pt. 1. (Illus.). 114p. 1979. Repr. of 1904 ed. 100.00 (ISBN 0-88065-013-3, Pub. by Messers Today & Tomorrows Printers & Publishers India). Scholarly Pubns.

Royle, J. F. Illustrations of Botany & of the Himalayan Mountains & Flora of Cashmere - 1883, 2 vols. lxxviii, 468p. 1970. Repr. Vol. I: Text. 120.00 set (ISBN 0-88065-183-0, Pub. by Messers Today & Tomorrows Printers & Publishers India). Vol. II:plates. Scholarly Pubns.

Sahu, B. N. Rauvolfia Serpentina (Sarpagandha) Vol. I: Botany, Ecology & Agronomy. 359p. 1979. 40.00 (ISBN 0-88065-186-5, Pub. by Messers Today & Tomorrows India). Scholarly Pubns.

Saldanha, C. J. & Nicolson, D. H. Flora of Hasson District Karnataka India. 1978p. 79.00x (ISBN 0-686-84452-1, Pub. by Oxford & I B H India). State Mutual Bk.

Santha Devi. Spores of Indian Ferns. (Illus.). 129p. 1973. 15.00 (ISBN 0-88065-190-3, Pub. by Messers Today & Tomorrows Printers & Publishers India). Scholarly Pubns.

Sarma, Y. S. & Khan. Algal Taxonomy in India. (International Bio-Science Ser.: No. 6). 168p. 1980. 12.00 (ISBN 0-88065-184-9, Pub. by Messers Today & Tomorrows Printers & Publishers India). Scholarly Pubns.

Singh, Gurcharan & Kachroo, P. Forest Flora of Srinigar & Plants of the Neighbourhood. 1978. 23.75x (ISBN 0-89955-277-3, Pub. by Intl Bk Dist). Intl Spec Bk.

Smith, W. W. The Alpine & Sub-Alpine Vegetation of South-East Sikkim. (Records of the Botanical Survey of India Ser.: Vol. 4, No. 7). 1978. Repr. of 1913 ed. 15.00x (ISBN 0-89955-254-4, Pub. by Intl Bk Dist). Intl Spec Bk.

Srivastava, T. N. Flora Gorakhpurensis. 500p. 1976. 25.00 (ISBN 0-88065-196-2, Pub. by Messers Today & Tomorrow Printers & Publishers India). Scholarly Pubns.

Stewart, J. L. Punjab Plants: Compromising Botanical & Vernacular Names, & Uses of Most of the Trees, Shrubs, & Herbs of Economical Value, Growing Within the Province Intended As a Hand-Book for Officers & Residents in the Punjab. 1978. Repr. of 1869 ed. 37.50x (ISBN 0-89955-301-X, Pub. by Intl Bk Dist). Intl Spec Bk.

Survey & Cultivation of Edible Mushrooms in India, First National Symposium, Srinagar, 1976. Indian Mushroom Science I. Atal, C. K., et al, eds. (Current Trends in Life Sciences Ser.: Vol. 2). xxii, 532p. 1978. 25.00 (ISBN 0-88065-021-4, Pub. by Messers Today & Tomorrows Printers & Publishers India). Scholarly Pubns.

Swartz, O. Nova Genera of Species Plantarum Quae Sub Itinere in Indiam Occidentalem Digessit. 1962. Repr. of 1788 ed. 12.60 (ISBN 3-7682-0120-1). Lubrecht & Cramer.

Talbot, W. A. Forest Flora of the Bombay Presidency & Sind, 2 vols. 1978. Repr. of 1909 ed. Set. 87.50x set (ISBN 0-89955-279-X, Pub. by Intl Bk Dist). Intl Spec Bk.

Ward, Frank K. Plant Hunting on the Edge of the World. (Illus.). 1976. Repr. 12.50 (ISBN 0-913728-21-7). Theophrastus.

Wight, R. Icones Planatarum Indiae Orientalis, 6 Vols. in 3. 1936. 189.00 (ISBN 3-7682-0153-8). Lubrecht & Cramer.

Wright, Robert. Prodromus Florae Peninsulae Indiae Orientalis: Containing Abridged Descriptions of the Plants Found in the Peninsula of British India Arranged According to the Natural System, Vol. I. 1978. Repr. of 1834 ed. 37.50x (ISBN 0-89955-300-1, Pub. by Intl Bk Dist). Intl Spec Bk.

BOTANY–IRAQ

Guest, Evan, ed. Flora of Iraq: Introduction to the Flora, Vol. 1. (Illus.). 213p. 1983. pap. 10.00 (ISBN 0-8139-1016-1). U Pr of Va.

Rechinger, K. H. Flora of Lowland Iraq. 1964. 52.50 (ISBN 3-7682-0217-8). Lubrecht & Cramer.

Townsend, C. C. & Guest, Evan, eds. Flora of Iraq, Vol. 2. (Illus.). 184p. pap. 10.00x (ISBN 0-8139-1017-X). U Pr of Va.

--Flora of Iraq, Vol. 4, pts. 1 & 2. (Illus.). 1199p. 1980. pap. 40.00x (ISBN 0-8139-1019-6). U Pr of Va.

Townsend, C. C., et al, eds. Flora of Iraq: Gramineae, Vol. 9. (Illus.). 588p. 1983. pap. 20.00x (ISBN 0-8139-1020-X). U Pr of Va.

BOTANY–IRELAND

An Irish Florilegium: Wild & Garden Plants of Ireland. Walsh, Wendy, ed. LC 82-51213. (Illus.). 1983. 125.00 (ISBN 0-500-23363-2). Thames Hudson.

BOTANY–ISLANDS OF THE PACIFIC

Brown, F. B. Flora of Southeastern Polynesia: Bayard Dominick Expedition Publication Nos. 20, 21, & 22, 3 vols. (BMB). Repr. of 1931 ed. Vol. 1. 21.00 (ISBN 0-527-02190-3); Vol. 2. 19.00 (ISBN 0-527-02195-4); Vol. 3. 45.00 (ISBN 0-527-02236-5). Kraus Repr.

Brownlie, G. The Pteridophyte Flora of Fiji. (Beihefte Zur Nova Hedwigia 55). 1977. lib. bdg. 70.00x (ISBN 3-7682-5455-0). Lubrecht & Cramer.

Christensen, C. A Revision of the Pteridophyta of Samoa. (BMB Ser.). Repr. of 1943 ed. 19.00 (ISBN 0-527-02285-3). Kraus Repr.

Christophersen, E. Flowering Plants of Samoa, 2 Vols. (BMB). Repr. of 1938 ed. 46.00 set (ISBN 0-686-57457-5); Vol. 1. 31.00 (ISBN 0-527-02234-9); Vol. 2. 15.00 (ISBN 0-527-02262-4). Kraus Repr.

--Vegetation of Pacific Equatorial Islands. (BMB Ser.). Repr. of 1927 ed. 14.00 (ISBN 0-527-02147-4). Kraus Repr.

Clench, W. J. Cyclophoridae & Pupinidae of Caroline, Fijian, & Samoan Islands. (BMB Ser.). pap. 10.00 (ISBN 0-527-02304-3). Kraus Repr.

Copeland, E. B. Ferns of Fiji. (BMB Ser.). Repr. of 1929 ed. 14.00 (ISBN 0-527-02165-2). Kraus Repr.

--Pteridophytes of the Society Islands. (BMB Ser.). Repr. of 1932 ed. 12.00 (ISBN 0-527-02199-7). Kraus Repr.

Ducker, S. C. The Genus Chlorodesmis (Chlorophyta) in the Indo-Pacific Region. 1966. pap. 8.00 (ISBN 3-7682-0679-3). Lubrecht & Cramer.

Fosberg, F. R. Genus Gouldia. (BMB). Repr. of 1937 ed. 14.00 (ISBN 0-527-02255-1). Kraus Repr.

--Polynesian Species of Hedyotis. Repr. of 1943 ed. 12.00 (ISBN 0-527-02282-9). Kraus Repr.

Glassman, S. F. Flora of Ponape. (BMB). Repr. of 1952 ed. 19.00 (ISBN 0-527-02317-5). Kraus Repr.

Handy, E. S. Hawaiian Planter, Vol. 1. (BMB). Repr. of 1940 ed. 37.00 (ISBN 0-527-02269-1). Kraus Repr.

Kleinpell, R. M. Neogene Smaller Foraminifera from Lau, Fiji. (BMB Ser.). Repr. of 1954 ed. 14.00 (ISBN 0-527-02319-1). Kraus Repr.

Leenhouts, P. W. Genus Canarium in the Pacific. (BMB Ser.). pap. 10.00 (ISBN 0-527-02324-8). Kraus Repr.

MacDaniels, L. H. Study of the Fe'i Banana & Its Distribution with Reference to Polynesian Migrations. (BMB Ser.). 1947. 11.00 (ISBN 0-527-02298-5). Kraus Repr.

Miller, C. D. Food Values of Poi, Taro, & Limu. pap. 8.00 (ISBN 0-527-02140-7). Kraus Repr.

Miller, H. A., et al. Bryoflora of the Atolls of Micronesia. (Illus.). 1963. pap. 14.00 (ISBN 3-7682-5411-9). Lubrecht & Cramer.

--Prodromus Florae Muscorum Polynesiae. with a Key to Genera. 1978. lib. bdg. 35.00x (ISBN 3-7682-1115-0). Lubrecht & Cramer.

Moore, J. W. New & Critical Plants from Raiatea. (BMB Ser.). pap. 8.00 (ISBN 0-527-02208-X). Kraus Repr.

Oliver, W. R. Genus Coprosma. (BMB Ser.). Repr. of 1935 ed. 31.00 (ISBN 0-527-02238-1). Kraus Repr.

Parham, H. B. Fiji Native Plants, with Their Medicinal & Other Uses. LC 75-35146. Repr. of 1943 ed. 16.50 (ISBN 0-404-14162-5). AMS Pr.

Seemann, B. Flora Vitiensis. (Historia Naturalis Classica 103 Ser.). 1978. Repr. of 1865 ed. lib. bdg. 140.00x (ISBN 3-7682-1144-4). Lubrecht & Cramer.

Sherff, E. E. Revision of Tetramolopium, Lipochaeta, Dubautia, & Railliardia. (BMB). Repr. of 1935 ed. 12.00 (ISBN 0-527-02241-1). Kraus Repr.

Smith, A. C. Fijian Plant Studies. (BMB). Repr. of 1936 ed. 22.00 (ISBN 0-527-02247-0). Kraus Repr.

Walker, Egbert H. Flora of Okinawa & the Southern Ryukyu Islands. LC 75-34812. (Illus.). 1159p. 1976. 60.00x (ISBN 0-87474-145-9). Smithsonian.

Wilder, G. P. Breadfruit of Tahiti. (BMB). Repr. of 1928 ed. 18.00 (ISBN 0-527-02156-3). Kraus Repr.

--Flora of Makatea. (BMB). pap. 10.00 (ISBN 0-527-02226-8). Kraus Repr.

--Flora of Rarotonga. (BMB). Repr. of 1931 ed. 18.00 (ISBN 0-527-02192-X). Kraus Repr.

Yuncker, T. G. Flora of Niue Island. (BMB). Repr. of 1943 ed. 19.00 (ISBN 0-527-02286-1). Kraus Repr.

--Plants of the Manua Islands. (BMB). Repr. 11.00 (ISBN 0-527-02292-6). Kraus Repr.

--Plants of Tonga. (BMB). Repr. of 1959 ed. 34.00 (ISBN 0-527-02328-0). Kraus Repr.

--Revision of the Hawaiian Species of Peperomia. (BMB). Repr. of 1933 ed. 18.00 (ISBN 0-527-02218-7). Kraus Repr.

--Revision of the Polynesian Species of Peperomia. (BMB). Repr. of 1937 ed. 11.00 (ISBN 0-527-02251-9). Kraus Repr.

BOTANY–JAPAN

Hara, Hiroshi. Enumeratio Spermatophytum Japonicarum. 1972. 91.00 (ISBN 3-87429-040-9). Lubrecht & Cramer.

Hayami, Itaru, ed. A Systematic Survey of the Mesozoic Bivalvia from Japan. 249p. 1976. 38.00 (ISBN 0-86008-152-4, Pub. by U of Tokyo Japan). Columbia U Pr.

Kurata, Satoru, ed. A Bibliography of Forest Botany in Japan: 1940-1963. 146p. 1966. 20.00 (ISBN 0-86008-025-0, Pub. by U of Tokyo Japan). Columbia U Pr.

Kurata, Satoru & Nakaike, Toshiyuki, eds. Illustrations of Pteridophytes of Japan, Vol. 1. 628p. 1979. 60.00x (ISBN 0-86008-269-5, Pub. by U of Tokyo Japan). Columbia U Pr.

--Illustrations of Pteridophytes of Japan, Vol. 2. 648p. 1981. 65.00x (ISBN 0-86008-289-X, Pub. by U of Tokyo Japan). Columbia U Pr.

--Illustrations of Pteridophytes of Japan, Vol. 3. 728p. 1983. 70.00x (ISBN 0-86008-333-0, Pub. by U of Tokyo Japan). Columbia U Pr.

Numata, M., et al, eds. Studies in Conservation of Natural Terrestrial Ecosystems in Japan, Part II: Vegetation & Its Conservation, Vol. 8. (Japan International Biological Program Synthesis Ser.). 157p. 1975. 18.50x (ISBN 0-86008-218-0, Pub. by U of Tokyo Japan). Columbia U Pr.

--Studies in Conservation of Natural Terrestrial Ecosystems in Japan, Part II: Animal Communities, Vol. 9. (Japan International Biological Program Synthesis Ser.). 91p. 1975. 15.00x (ISBN 0-86008-219-9, Pub. by U of Tokyo Japan). Columbia U Pr.

Ohwi, Jisaburo. Flora of Japan. Meyer, Frederick G. & Walker, Egbert H., eds. LC 65-62683. (Illus.). 1984. Repr. of 1965 ed. 49.50x (ISBN 0-87474-708-2). Smithsonian.

Von Siebold, Philipp F. Flora Japonica. 1976. 1535.00 (ISBN 0-384-64940-8). Johnson Repr.

BOTANY–LATIN AMERICA

Bentham, G. The Botany of the Voyage of H. M. S. Sulphur, Under the Command of Captain Sir Edward Belcher 1832-42. (Illus.). 1968. 70.00 (ISBN 3-7682-0542-8). Lubrecht & Cramer.

Johnston, Marshall A. & Johnston, LaVerne A. Rhamnus. LC 78-16036. (Flora Neotropica Ser.: Vol. 20). 1978. pap. 10.00x (ISBN 0-89327-209-4). NY Botanical.

Leon, H. & Alain, Hermano. Flora de Cuba, 2 vols. (Span., Lat., Illus.). 2317p. 1979. Repr. of 1946 ed. lib. bdg. 182.00 five parts bound in 2 vols. (ISBN 3-87429-077-8). Lubrecht & Cramer.

Lundell, Cyrus L. The Vegetation of Peten. LC 77-11507. (Carnegie Institution of Washington. Publication: No. 478). Repr. of 1937 ed. 35.00 (ISBN 0-404-16270-3). AMS Pr.

Luteyn, James L. A Revision of the Mexican-Central American Species of Cavendishia (Vacciniaceae) LC 66-6394. (Memoirs of the New York Botanical Garden Ser.: Vol. 28, No. 3). 1976. pap. 19.00x (ISBN 0-89327-011-3). NY Botanical.

Maguire, B. The Botany of the Guyana Highland, Pt. XI. (Memoirs of the New York Botanical Garden Ser.: Vol. 32). (Illus.). 1981. pap. 40.00x (ISBN 0-89327-229-9). NY Botanical.

Skutch, Alexander F. The Imperative Call: A Naturalist's Quest in Temperate & Tropical America. LC 79-14701. (Illus.). x, 331p. 1979. 20.00 (ISBN 0-8130-0579-5). U Presses Fla.

Sleumer, H. O. Olacaceae. (Flora Neotropica Monograph: No. 38). 1984. 26.00x (ISBN 0-89327-254-X). NY Botanical.

Smith, Lyman B. & Downs, Robert J. Bromelioideae (Bromeliaceae) LC 79-14114. (Flora Neotropica Ser.: Vol. 14, No. 3). 1979. pap. 65.00x (ISBN 0-89327-210-8). NY Botanical.

Spichiger, R. & Loizeau, P. A. Trigoniaceae & Vochysiaceae. (Flora del Paraquay Ser.). (Spanish., Illus.). 36p. (Orig.). 1985. pap. 5.00 (ISBN 0-915279-04-5). Miss Botan.

Standley, Paul C. Flora of Costa Rica, 4 vols. 1980. Set. lib. bdg. 595.00 (ISBN 0-8490-3181-8). Gordon Pr.

Stotler, R. E. The Genus Frullania Subgenus Frullania in Latin America. 1970. 14.00 (ISBN 3-7682-0679-3). Lubrecht & Cramer.

Swails, L. F., Jr. The Genus Porella in Latin America. (Illus.). 1970. 14.00 (ISBN 3-7682-0674-2). Lubrecht & Cramer.

Villagran, M. C. Vegetationsgeschichtliche und Pflanzensoziologische Untersuchungen im Vicente Perez Nationalpark: Chile. (Dissertationes Botanicae Ser.: No. 54). (Ger., Illus.). 166p. 1981. pap. text ed. 17.50x (ISBN 3-7682-1265-3). Lubrecht & Cramer.

Wood, R. D. Charophytes of North America. 1967. 2.25 (ISBN 0-9603898-0-6). R D Wood.

BOTANY–LIBERIA

Johnston, Harry H. Liberia, 2 Vols. LC 71-78372. (Illus.). Repr. of 1906 ed. Set. 76.00x (ISBN 0-8371-3897-3, JOL&, Pub. by Negro U Pr). Greenwood.

BOTANY–MADAGASCAR

Cordenoy, E. Jacob De. Flore De l'Ile De la Reunion (Mascarene Islands) 1972. Repr. of 1895 ed. 52.50 (ISBN 3-7682-0758-7). Lubrecht & Cramer.

De La Bathie, H. Perrier. Flora of Madagascar: Orchids. Humbert, H., ed. Beckman, Steven D., tr. from French. LC 82-90881. (Illus.). 542p. 1982. 65.00x (ISBN 0-9609434-0-4). S D Beckman.

Jolly, A., et al, eds. Madagascar. LC 83-17394. (Key Environments Ser.). (Illus.). 250p. 1984. 19.50 (ISBN 0-08-028002-1). Pergamon.

BOTANY–MALAYA

Beddome, R. H. Handbook to the Ferns of British India, Ceylon & Malaysia: Peninsula with Supplement. 502p. 1977. 20.00 (ISBN 0-88065-054-0, Pub. by Messers Today & Tomorrows Printers & Publishers India). Scholarly Pubns.

Corner, E. J. Phylloporus Quel & Paxillus Fr. in Malaya & Borneo. (Illus.). 1971. pap. 10.50 (ISBN 3-7682-0741-2). Lubrecht & Cramer.

Ridley, Henry. The Flora of the Malay Peninsula, 5 vols. 1967. 115.00 (ISBN 90-6123-260-0). Lubrecht & Cramer.

BOTANY–MAURITUS

Baker, J. G. Flora of Mauritius & the Seychelles. 1971. Repr. of 1877 ed. 70.00 (ISBN 3-7682-0677-7). Lubrecht & Cramer.

BOTANY–MEXICO

Breedlove, Dennis E. Introduction to the Flora of Chiapas, Pt. 1. (Flora of Chiapas Ser.). (Illus., Orig.). 1981. pap. 2.50 (ISBN 0-940228-00-9). Calif Acad Sci.

Bright, Thomas & Pequegnat, Linda, eds. Biota of the West Flower Garden Bank. LC 74-10372. 436p. 1974. 19.95x (ISBN 0-87201-058-9). Gulf Pub.

Coyle, Jeanette & Roberts, Norman C. A Field Guide to the Common & Interesting Plants of Baja California. LC 74-24866. (Illus.). 224p. 1975. pap. 8.50 (ISBN 0-686-12112-0). Nat Hist Pub Co.

McVaugh, Rogers. Flora Novo-Galiciana: A Descriptive Account of the Vascular Plants of Western Mexico. Anderson, William R., ed. LC 82-13537. (Graminae Ser.: Vol. 14). (Illus.). 384p. 1983. text ed. 38.00x (ISBN 0-472-04814-7). U of Mich Pr.

--Flora Novo-Galiciana: A Descriptive Account of the Vascular Plants of Western Mexico-Compositae. Anderson, William R., ed. LC 82-13537. (Flora Novo-Galiciana Ser.: Vol. 12). (Illus.). 320p. 1985. pap. text ed. 125.00x (ISBN 0-472-04812-0). U of Mich Pr.

Shreve, Forrest & Wiggins, Ira L. Vegetation & Flora of the Sonoran Desert, 2 Vols. (Illus.). 1964. Set. 100.00x (ISBN 0-8047-0163-6). Stanford U Pr.

Standley, P. C. Trees & Shrubs of Mexico. (Contrib. U. S. Nat'l Herb. Ser.: No. 23, 1-5). 1722p. 1982. Repr. lib. bdg. 87.50 (ISBN 3-7682-1288-2). Lubrecht & Cramer.

BOTANY–NATAL

Wood, J. M. & Evans, M. S. Natal Plants: 1898-1912, 6 vols. in 2. (Illus.). 1970. Set. 140.00 (ISBN 3-7682-0671-8). Lubrecht & Cramer.

BOTANY–NEAR EAST

Daoud, Hazim S. Flora of Kuwait: Dicotyledoneae, Vol. I. Al-Rawi, Ali, rev. by. (Illus.). 288p. 1985. 75.00x (ISBN 0-7103-0075-1, Kegan Paul). Routledge & Kegan.

Kunkel, G. The Vegetation of Hormoz, Queshm & Neighbouring Islands (Southern Persian Gulf Area, No. 6) (Flora et Vegetatio Mundi Ser.). (Illus.). 186p. 1977. text ed. 21.00x (ISBN 3-7682-1120-7). Lubrecht & Cramer.

BOTANY–NETHERLANDS

La Billardiere, J. De & Stafleu, F. A. Novae Hollandiae Plantarum Specimen: 1894-06, 2 vols. in 1. 1966. 84.00 (ISBN 3-7682-0344-1). Lubrecht & Cramer.

Mennema, J., et al, eds. Atlas of the Netherlands Flora: Extinct & Very Rare Species, No. 1. (Illus.). 266p. 1980. lib. bdg. 65.00 (ISBN 90-6193-605-5, Pub. by Junk Pubs Netherlands). Kluwer Academic.

Wildemann, E. De. Prodrome De la Flore Algologique Des Indes Neerlandaises et Partie Des Territoires De Borneo Etc. 193p. 1978. lib. bdg. 38.50x (ISBN 3-87429-145-6). Lubrecht & Cramer.

BOTANY–NEW GUINEA

Paijmans, K. New Guinea Vegetation. 1982. 49.00x (ISBN 0-686-97904-4, Pub. by CSIRO Australia). State Mutual Bk.

Specht, R. J. & Roe, Ethel M. Conservation of Major Plant Communities in Australia & Papua New Guinea. (2 microfiches). 1974. 6.00 (ISBN 0-643-00094-1, C051, CSIRO). Unipub.

Van Royen, P. Alpine Flora of New Giunea, 4 vols. Incl. Vol. 1. General Part. 1980. lib. bdg. 35.00; Vol. 2. Taxonomic Part 1: Cupressaceae to Poaceae. 1980. lib. bdg. 105.00 (ISBN 3-7682-1244-0); Vol. 3. Taxonomic Part 2: Winteraceae to Polygonaceae. 1982. lib. bdg. 105.00 (ISBN 3-7682-1245-9); Vol. 4. Taxonomic Part 3: Fagaceae to Asteraceae. 1983. lib. bdg. 105.00 (ISBN 3-7682-1246-7). 350.00 set (ISBN 3-7682-1247-5). Lubrecht & Cramer.

Womersley, J. S., ed. Handbook to the Flora of Papua New Guinea, Vol. 1. 1977. 40.00x (ISBN 0-522-84095-7, Pub. by Melbourne U Pr Australia). Intl Spec Bk.

BOTANY–NEW ZEALAND

Brooker, S. G. & Cambie, R. C. New Zealand Medicinal Plants. (Illus.). 117p. 1983. 36.95 (ISBN 0-86863-382-8, Pub. by Heinemann Pubs New Zealand). Intl Spec Bk.

Druett, Joan. Exotic Intruders: The Introduction of Plants & Animals into New Zealand. (Illus.). 291p. 1984. 24.95x (ISBN 0-86863-397-6, Pub. by Heinemann Pub New Zealand). Intl Spec Bk.

Hooker, J. D. The Botany of the Antartic Voyage of H. M. Discovery Ships Erebus & Terror in the Years 1839-43, 3 vols. (Illus.). 1963. 336.00 (ISBN 3-7682-0196-1). Lubrecht & Cramer.

Moore, Lucy B. The Oxford Book of New Zealand Plants. (Illus.). 1978. text ed. 64.00x (ISBN 0-19-558035-4). Oxford U Pr.

Sarma, P. Freshwater Chaetophorales of New Zealand. (Freshwater Algae of New Zealand Ser.: Vol. 1). 1981. lib. bdg. 87.50x (ISBN 3-7682-5458-5). Lubrecht & Cramer.

BOTANY–NORTH AMERICA

see also Wild Flowers–North America

Barbour, Michael G., et al. Terrestrial Plant Ecology. 1980. 31.95 (ISBN 0-8053-0540-8). Benjamin-Cummings.

Batson, Wade T. Genera of the Eastern Plants. (Illus.). 203p. 1984. pap. 8.95 (ISBN 0-87249-450-0). U of SC Pr.

--Genera of the Western Plants. (Illus.). 210p. 1984. pap. 8.95 (ISBN 0-87249-451-9). U of SC Pr.

Cronquist, Arthur, et al. Composite. LC 78-17496. (North American Flora Ser. II: Pt. 10). 1978. pap. 25.00x (ISBN 0-89327-191-8). NY Botanical.

Crovello, Theodore J., et al. The Vascular Plants of Indiana: A Computer Based Checklist. LC 83-10024. 160p. 1983. text ed. 15.00x (ISBN 0-268-01923-1, 85-19233). U of Notre Dame Pr.

Crum, H. A. Sphagnophyta. (North American Flora Series II: Pt. II). 1984. 25.00x (ISBN 0-89327-252-3). NY Botanical.

Cushman, J. A. The American Species of Orthophragmina & Lepidocyclina. 1971. Repr. of 1928 ed. 15.60 (ISBN 0-934454-06-X). Lubrecht & Cramer.

Deganawidah. Ranger's Guide to Useful Plants of Eastern Wilds. (Illus.). 1964. 3.95 (ISBN 0-8158-0086-X). Chris Mass.

Elvander, Patrick E. & Wells, Elizabeth F. The Taxonomy of Saxifraga (Saxifragaceae) Section Boraphila Subsection Integrifoliae in Western North America: A Revision of The Genus Heuchera (Saxifrageae) in Eastern Norh America. Anderson, Christiane, ed. LC 84-393. (Systematic Botany Monographs Ser.). (Illus.). 121p. (Orig.). 1984. pap. 16.00 (ISBN 0-912861-03-7). Am Soc Plant.

Gleason, Henry A. & Cronquist, Arthur. Natural Geography of Plants. LC 64-15448. (Illus.). 420p. 1964. 55.00x (ISBN 0-231-02668-4). Columbia U Pr.

Harshberger, J. W. Phytogeographic Survey of North America: A Consideration of the Phytogeography of the North American Continent, Including Mexico, Central America & the West Indies, Together with the Evolution of North American Plant Distribution. (Illus.). 1958. Repr. of 1911 ed. 35.00 (ISBN 3-7682-0003-5). Lubrecht & Cramer.

Hitchcock, C. Leo & Cronquist, Arthur. Flora of the Pacific Northwest: An Illustrated Manual. LC 72-13150. (Illus.). 750p. 1973. 32.50x (ISBN 0-295-95273-3). U of Wash Pr.

Hitchcock, C. Leo, et al. Vascular Plants of the Pacific Northwest, 5 pts. Incl. Pt. 1. Vascular Cryptogams, Gymnosperms, & Monocotyledons. (Illus.). 925p. 1969. 40.00x (ISBN 0-295-73983-5); Pt. 2. Salicaceae to Saxifragaceae. (Illus.). 597p. 1964. 40.00x (ISBN 0-295-73984-3); Pt. 3. Saxifragaceae to Ericaceae. (Illus.). 614p. 1961. 40.00x (ISBN 0-295-73985-1); Pt. 4. Ericaceae Through Companulaceae. (Illus.). 516p. 1959. 40.00x (ISBN 0-295-73986-X); Pt. 5. Compositae. (Illus.). 349p. 1955. 40.00x (ISBN 0-295-73987-8). LC 56-62679. (Publications in Biology Ser.: No. 17). U of Wash Pr.

Howell, T. A. A Flora of Northwest America. (Reprints of U. S. Floras 9 Ser.: Vol. 1). 1978. Repr. lib. bdg. 28.00 (ISBN 3-7682-1170-3). Lubrecht & Cramer.

Hulten, E. The Amphi-Atlantic Plants & Their Phytogeographic Connections. (Illus.). 1973. 84.00 (ISBN 3-87429-041-7). Lubrecht & Cramer.

Kingsbury, John M. Poisonous Plants of the United States & Canada. 3rd ed. 1964. 38.95 (ISBN 0-13-685016-2). P-H.

Lawrence, George H. Introduction to Plant Taxonomy. (Illus.). 1955. text ed. write for info. (ISBN 0-02-368120-9). Macmillan.

McDougall, W. B. & Haskell, H. S. Seed Plants of Montezuma Castle National Monument, with Keys for the Identification of Species. (MNA Bulletin Ser.: No. 35). 1960. pap. 1.80 (ISBN 0-685-76473-7). Mus Northern Ariz.

Morley, Thomas. Memecyleae. LC 76-13371. (Flora Neotropica Monograph: Vol. 15). (Illus.). 1976. pap. 22.00x (ISBN 0-89327-000-8). NY Botanical.

Ott, Jonathan. Hallucinogenic Plants of North America. (Illus.). 15.00 (ISBN 0-914728-15-6); pap. 8.50 (ISBN 0-914728-16-4). Wingbow Pr.

Rafinesque, C. S. New Flora & Botony of North America, 4 pts. in 1 vol. 1946. pap. 10.00 (ISBN 0-934454-66-3). Lubrecht & Cramer.

Rogers, C. M. Linaceae. (North American Flora Series II: Pt. 12). 1984. 10.75x (ISBN 0-89327-260-4). NY Botanical.

Rollins, Reed C. & Shaw, Elizabeth A. Genus Lesquerella (Cruciferae) in North America. LC 72-87777. (Illus.). 385p. 1973. 20.00x (ISBN 0-674-34775-7). Harvard U Pr.

Rydberg, Per A. Flora of the Prairies & Plains of Central North America. (Illus.). 1965. Repr. of 1932 ed. 23.95x (ISBN 0-02-851240-5). Hafner.

Smith, Alexander H. North American Species of Psathyrella. LC 66-6394. (Memoirs of the New York Botanical Garden: Vol. 24). (Illus.). 1972. pap. 40.00x (ISBN 0-89327-012-1). NY Botanical.

Sterling, Keir B., ed. Development of Botany in Selected Regions of North America Before 1900: An Original Anthology. LC 77-81126. (Biologists & Their World Ser.). (Illus.). 1978. lib. bdg. 25.50x (ISBN 0-405-10722-6). Ayer Co Pubs.

Stevens, O. A. Handbook of North Dakota Plants. LC 63-14319. (Illus.). 330p. 1963. 8.75 (ISBN 0-911042-07-5). N Dak Inst.

Thomson, J. W. The Lichen Genus Physcia in North America. (Illus.). 1963. pap. 21.00 (ISBN 3-7682-5407-0). Lubrecht & Cramer.

Vankat, John L. The Natural Vegetation of North America: An Introduction. LC 78-31264. 261p. 1979. 21.95 (ISBN 0-471-01770-1). Wiley.

Vitt, Dale H. A Revision of the Genus Orthotricham in North America, North of Mexico. (Bryophytorum Bibliotheca: No. 1). (Illus.). 21.00 (ISBN 3-7682-0825-7). Lubrecht & Cramer.

Weidemann, Alfred M. Plants of the Oregon Coastal Dunes. 1969. pap. text ed. 6.20X (ISBN 0-88246-117-6). Oreg St U Bkstrs.

Welch, Winona H. Hookeriaceae. LC 76-21379. (North American Flora, Ser. II, Part 9). (Illus.). 1976. pap. 17.00x (ISBN 0-89327-006-7). NY Botanical.

Wolfe, C. B., Jr. Austroboletuc & Tylopilus Subgenus Porphyrellus, with Special Emphasis on North American Tax. (Bibliotheca Mycologica Ser.: No. 69). (Illus.). 1980. lib. bdg. 14.00x (ISBN 3-7682-1251-3). Lubrecht & Cramer.

Wood, Carroll E., Jr. A Student's Atlas of Flowering Plants: Some Dicotyledons of Eastern North America. 256p. 1974. pap. text ed. 10.95 scp (ISBN 0-06-047207-3, HarpC). Har-Row.

Wood, R. D. Charophytes of North America. 1967. 2.25 (ISBN 0-9603898-0-6). R D Wood.

BOTANY–NORWAY

Degelius, Gunnar. The Lichen Flora of the Island of Vega in Nordland, Northern Norway. (Acta Regiae Societatis Scientiarum et Litterarum Gothoburgensis, Botanica Ser.: No. 2). 127p. 1982. pap. text ed. 17.50x (ISBN 91-85252-30-1, Pub. by Acta Universitatis Sweden). Humanities.

Ronning, Olaf & Bjaerevoll, Olav. Flowers of Svalbard. (Illus.). 56p. 1981. pap. 14.00x (ISBN 82-00-05398-9). Universitet.

BOTANY–PANAMA

Standley, P. C. Flora of the Panama Canal Zone. 1968. pap. 21.00 (ISBN 3-7682-0578-9). Lubrecht & Cramer.

BOTANY–PERU

Ruiz, H. & Pavon, J. Prodromus et Flora Peruviana et Chilensis, 4 vols. in 1. (Illus.). 1965. Repr. of 1802 ed. 210.00 (ISBN 3-7682-0283-6). Lubrecht & Cramer.

BOTANY–PHILIPPINE ISLANDS

Merrill, E. D. A Flora of Manila. 1968. Repr. of 1912 ed. 42.00 (ISBN 3-7682-0548-7). Lubrecht & Cramer.

Merrill, Elmer D. An Enumeration of Philippine Flowering Plants, 4 vols. (Illus.). 1968. 136.50 (ISBN 90-6123-095-0). Lubrecht & Cramer.

BOTANY–SEYCHELLES

Baker, J. G. Flora of Mauritius & the Seychelles. 1971. Repr. of 1877 ed. 70.00 (ISBN 3-7682-0677-7). Lubrecht & Cramer.

Sauer, Jonathan D. Plants & Man on the Seychelles Coast: A Study in Historical Biogeography. (Illus.). 148p. 1967. U of Wis Pr.

BOTANY–SOUTH AMERICA

Acleto, Cesar O., et al, eds. Phycologia Latino-Americana, Vol. 1. (Span., Illus.). 186p. 1981. text ed. 21.00x (ISBN 3-7682-1297-1). Lubrecht & Cramer.

Chodat, R. & Fischer, W. La Vegetation du Paraguay: Resultats Scientifiques d'une Mission Botanquie au Paraguay. Repr. of 1977 ed. 42.00 (ISBN 3-7682-1106-1). Lubrecht & Cramer.

Cleef, A. M. The Vegetation of the Paramos of the Colombian Cordillera Oriental. (Dissertationes Botanicae Ser.: Vol. 61). (Illus.). 320p. 1981. text ed. 21.00x (ISBN 3-7682-1302-1). Lubrecht & Cramer.

Gilmartin, Jean. The Bromeliaceae of Ecuador. (Monographiae Phanerogamarum Ser.: No. 5). (Illus.). 1972. 42.00 (ISBN 3-7682-0725-0). Lubrecht & Cramer.

Goodspeed, T. Harper. Plant Hunters in the Andes. 2nd rev. & enl. ed. LC 61-7533. 1961. 33.00x (ISBN 0-520-00495-7). U of Cal Pr.

Hall, Norman. Botanists of the Eucalypts. 160p. 1982. 30.00x (ISBN 0-643-00271-5, Pub. by CSIRO Australia). State Mutual Bk.

Maguire, B., et al. The Botany of the Guyana Highland, Pt. XII. (Memoirs of the New York Botanical Garden Ser.: Vol. 38). 1985. 21.00x (ISBN 0-89327-255-8). NY Botanical.

Maguire, Bassett, et al. The Botany of the Guyana Highland: Part X. LC 78-9099. (Memoirs of the New York Botanical Garden Ser.: Vol. 29). 1978. pap. 25.00x (ISBN 0-89327-207-8). NY Botanical.

Moser, M. & Horak, E. Cortinarius Fr. und Nahe Verwandte Gottungen in Suedamerika. 1975. 87.50 (ISBN 3-7682-5452-6). Lubrecht & Cramer.

Poeppig, E. & Endlicher, S. Nova Genera Ac Species Plantarum Quas in Regno Chilensi, Peruviano & in Terra Amazonica Annis 1827-32: 1835-45. 1968. 196.00 (ISBN 3-7682-0549-5). Lubrecht & Cramer.

Spruce, Richard. Hepaticae of the Amazon & Andes of Peru & Ecuador. (Contributions from the New York Botanical Garden Ser.: Vol. 15). 1984. Repr. of 1884 ed. 40.00x (ISBN 0-89327-259-0). NY Botanical.

--Notes of a Botanist on the Amazon & Andes, 2 Vols. Wallace, A. R., ed. (Landmarks in Anthropology Ser). Repr. of 1908 ed. Set. 73.00 (ISBN 0-384-57200-6). Johnson Repr.

Weddell, H. A. Chloris Andina: Essai d'une Flore de la Region alpine des Cordilleres de l'Amerique du Sud, 2 vols. in 1. (Illus.). 1972. 87.50 (ISBN 3-7682-0729-3). Lubrecht & Cramer.

Wood, R. D. Charophytes of North America. 1967. 2.25 (ISBN 0-9603898-0-6). R D Wood.

BOTANY–SOVIET UNION

Ledebour, K. F. Icones Plantarum Novarum Vel Imperfecte Cognitarum Floram Rossicam, 5 Vols. in 1. 1968. 266.00 (ISBN 3-7682-0567-3). Lubrecht & Cramer.

BOTANY–SPAIN

Cavanilles, A. J. Icones & Descriptiones Plantarum Quae Aut Sponte in Hispania Crescunt Aut in Hortis Hospitantur 1791-1801, 6pts. in 2 vols. 1965. 280.00 (ISBN 3-7682-0292-5). Lubrecht & Cramer.

Knoche, H. Flora Balearica Etude Phytogeographique Sur les Iles Baleares, 4vols. (Illus.). 168.00 (ISBN 3-87429-061-1). Lubrecht & Cramer.

Willkomm, H. M. & Lange, J. M. Prodromus Florae Hispaniae: Seu Synopsis Methodica Omnium Plantarum in Hispania Sponte Nascentium, 3 vols. in 2. 1971. Repr. of 1880 ed. 175.00 (ISBN 3-510-65030-1). Lubrecht & Cramer.

BOTANY–SYRIA

La Billardiere, J. J. Icones Plantarum Syriae Rariorum: Descriptionibus & Observationibus Illustratar 1791-1812. (Illus.). 1968. 35.00 (ISBN 3-7682-0540-1). Lubrecht & Cramer.

BOTANY–TASMANIA

Curtis, Winifred. The Endemic Flora of Tasmania, 6 vols. 1981. 110.00x ea. (Pub. by RHS Ent England); Set. 550.00x (ISBN 0-686-78774-9). State Mutual Bk.

Hooker, J. D. The Botany of the Antartic Voyage of H. M. Discovery Ships Erebus & Terror in the Years 1839-43, 3 vols. (Illus.). 1963. 336.00 (ISBN 3-7682-0196-1). Lubrecht & Cramer.

BOTANY–TIBET

Stewart, Ralph R. The Flora of Ladak, Western Tibet. 1978. Repr. of 1917 ed. (Pub. by Intl Bk Dist). Intl Spec Bk.

BOTANY–TROPICS

Gates, Bronwen. Banisteriopsis & Diplopterys: Malpighiaceae. (Flora Neotropica Monograph 30). (Illus.). 238p. 1982. pap. 35.00x (ISBN 0-89327-238-8). NY Botanical.

Hall, J. B. & Swaine, M. D. Distribution & Ecology of Vascular Plants in a Tropical Rain Forest. (Geobotany Ser.: Vol. I). 392p. 1981. 112.00 (ISBN 90-6193-681-0, Pub. by Junk Pubs Netherlands). Kluwer Academic.

Hutchinson, J., et al. Flora of West Tropical Africa, Vols. I, II, & III. 2nd ed. (Illus.). 1982. Vol. I, 2 Pts., 828p. 55.00x (ISBN 0-8139-0954-6, Pub. by Brit Mus England); Vol. II, 544p. 35.00x (ISBN 0-8139-0963-5); Vol. III, 2 Pts., 574p. 37.50x (ISBN 0-8139-0964-3). U Pr of Va.

Larsen, Kai & Holm-Nielson, Lauritz, eds. Tropical Botany. LC 79-41003. 1980. 76.50 (ISBN 0-12-437350-X). Acad Pr.

Lauer, W., et al. Studien Zur Klima- und Vegetations Kunde der Tropen. 1952. 20.00 (ISBN 0-384-58675-9). Johnson Repr.

Mesa, Aldo. Nolanaceae. (Flora Neotropica Monograph: No. 26). 1981. pap. 12.00X (ISBN 0-89327-233-7). NY Botanical.

Pennington, T. D. Meliaceae. (Flora Neotropica Monograph 28). (Illus.). 1981. pap. 65.00x (ISBN 0-89327-235-3). NY Botanical.

Perry, Francis & Hay, Roy. Tropical & Subtropical Plants. 128p. 1981. 25.00x (ISBN 0-7063-5964-X, Pub. by Ward Lock Ed England). State Mutual Bk.

Poppendieck, Hans-Helmut. Cochlospermaceae. (Flora Neotropica Monograph 27). (Illus.). 1981. pap. 6.50x (ISBN 0-89327-231-0). NY Botanical.

BOTANY–TURKEY

Davis, P. H., ed. The Flora of Turkey, 6 vols. 60.00x ea., vols. 1-4 (Pub. by Edinburgh U Pr Scotland). Vol. 1, 1965 (ISBN 0-85224-159-3). Vol. 2, 1965 (ISBN 0-85224-000-7). Vol. 3, 1970 (ISBN 0-85224-154-2). Vol. 4, 1973 (ISBN 0-85224-208-5). Vol. 5, 1975. 100.00x (ISBN 0-85224-280-8, Pub. by Edinburgh U Pr Scotland); Vol. 6, 1979. 125.00x (ISBN 0-85224-336-7, Pub. by Edinburgh U Pr Scotland); Vol. 7. 125.00 (ISBN 0-85224-396-0). Columbia U Pr.

BOTANY–UNITED STATES

see also Botany–Alaska; Botany–Hawaii

Abrams, LeRoy. Illustrated Flora of the Pacific States, 4 vols. Incl. Vol. 1. Ferns to Birthworts. xi, 557p. 1923. 50.00x (ISBN 0-8047-0003-6); Vol. 2. Buckwheats to Kramerias. viii, 635p. 1944. 50.00x (ISBN 0-8047-0004-4); Vol. 3. Geraniums to Figworts. viii, 866p. 1951. 50.00x (ISBN 0-8047-0005-2); Vol. 4. Bignonias to Sunflowers. Ferris, Roxana S. v, 732p. (Contains index to vols. 1-4). 1960. 50.00x (ISBN 0-8047-0006-0). (Illus.). 200.00 set (ISBN 0-8047-1100-3). Stanford U Pr.

Ahmadjian, Vernon. Flowering Plants of Massachusetts. LC 78-19690. (Illus.). 608p. 1979. 22.50 (ISBN 0-87023-265-7). U of Mass Pr.

Anliot, Sture F. The Vascular Flora of Glen Helen, Clifton Gorge, & John Bryan State Parks. 1973. 3.50 (ISBN 0-86727-064-0). Ohio Bio Survey.

Arnberger, Leslie P. Flowers of the Southwest Mountains. 6th ed. Jackson, Earl, ed. LC 74-84444. (Popular Ser.: No. 7). 1974. pap. 7.50 (ISBN 0-911408-00-2). SW Pks Mnmts.

--Flowers of the Southwest Mountains. rev. ed. Priehs, T. J., ed. Dodson, Carolyn. LC 81-86380. 1983. pap. 7.95 (ISBN 0-911408-61-4). SW Pks Mnmts.

Axelrod, Daniel I. Middle Miocene Floras from the Middlegade Basin, West-Central Nevada: (Published in Geological Sciences, Vol. 129) 1985. 22.00x (ISBN 0-520-09695-9). U of Cal Pr.

Bailey, Liberty H. Manual of Cultivated Plants. rev. ed. 1949. 37.95 (ISBN 0-02-505520-8). Macmillan.

Barbour, Michael G. & Major, Jack, eds. Terrestrial Vegetation of California. LC 76-53769. 1002p. 1977. 99.95x (ISBN 0-471-56536-9, Pub. by Wiley-Interscience). Wiley.

Barkley, T. M. Field Guide to the Common Weeds of Kansas. LC 82-21914. (Illus.). 160p. 1983. 17.95x (ISBN 0-7006-0233-X); pap. 7.95 (ISBN 0-7006-0224-0). U Pr of KS.

Barnard, Carolyn & Potter, Loren D. New Mexico Grasses: A Vegetative Key. LC 83-21901. (Illus.). 160p. 1984. pap. 8.95 (ISBN 0-8263-0744-2). U of NM Pr.

Barneby, Rupert C. Daleae Imagines. LC 66-6394. (Memoirs of the New Botanical Garden Ser.: Vol. 27). 1977. pap. 50.00x (ISBN 0-89327-002-4). NY Botanical.

Bartel, Janice R. & Belt, Sage C. A Guide to Botanical Resources of Southern California. (Illus.). 88p. 1977. 2.00 (ISBN 0-938644-13-0). Nat Hist Mus.

Batson, Wade T. Landscape Plants for the Southeast: Botanical Sketch of Each Plant. LC 84-5267. (Illus.). xxi, 406p. 1984. 14.95 (ISBN 0-87249-433-0). U of SC Pr.

Becking, Rudolf W. A Pocket Flora of the Redwood Forest. (Illus.). 262p. (Orig.). 1982. pap. 15.00 (ISBN 0-933280-02-5). Island CA.

Belzer, Thomas J. Roadside Plants of Southern California. (Illus.). 172p. 1984. pap. 8.95 (ISBN 0-87842-158-0). Mountain Pr.

Benson, Lyman. The Cacti of Arizona. 3rd ed. LC 70-77802. (Illus.). 218p. 1969. pap. 12.50 (ISBN 0-8165-0509-8). U of Ariz Pr.

--The Native Cacti of California. LC 69-13176. (Illus.). 1969. 12.95 (ISBN 0-8047-0696-4). Stanford U Pr.

Blackwell, Will H., Jr. Guide to the Woody Plants of the Tri-State Area. (Illus.). 1976. pap. text ed. 7.95 (ISBN 0-8403-1581-3). Kendall-Hunt.

Braun, E. Lucy. Monocotyledoneae: Cat-Tails to Orchids. LC 66-25170. (Vascular Flora of Ohio: Vol. 1). (Illus.). 474p. 1967. 10.00 (ISBN 0-8142-0028-1). Ohio St U Pr.

--The Vegetation of the Mineral Springs Region of Adams County, Ohio. 1928. 3.00 (ISBN 0-86727-014-4). Ohio Bio Survey.

Britton, Nathaniel L. & Brown, Addison. Illustrated Flora of the Northern United States & Canada, 3 Vols. 2nd rev & enl. ed. (Illus.). Set. 49.50 (ISBN 0-8446-0514-X); 16.50 ea. Peter Smith.

Brown, Lauren. Grasses: An Identification Guide. (Peterson Native Library). 1979. 9.95 (ISBN 0-395-27624-1). HM.

Bruggen, Theodore Van. The Vascular Plants of South Dakota. 2nd ed. 476p. 1985. pap. text ed. 24.95x (ISBN 0-8138-0650-X). Iowa St U Pr.

Burt, Edward A. Thelephoraceae of North America, 15 Pts. (Illus.). 900p. 1966. Repr. of 1926 ed. lib. bdg. 25.00x (ISBN 0-02-842320-8). Lubrecht & Cramer.

Camburn, K. E., et al. The Haptobenthic Diatom Flora of Long Branch Creek, South Carolina. (Offprint from Nova Hedwigia Ser.: No. 30). (Illus.). 1979. 21.00x (ISBN 3-7682-1197-5). Lubrecht & Cramer.

Cannatella, Mary M. & Arnold, Rita E. Plants of the Texas Shore: A Beachcomber's Guide. LC 84-40553. (Illus.). 96p. 1985. pap. 5.95 (ISBN 0-89096-214-6). Tex A&M Univ Pr.

Chamberlin, Ralph V. Ethno-Botany of the Gosiute Indians of Utah. LC 14-11549. 1911. 11.00 (ISBN 0-527-00510-X). Kraus Repr.

Clewell, Andre F. Guide to the Vascular Plants of the Florida Panhandle. LC 84-29126. (Illus.). 608p. 1985. 30.00 (ISBN 0-8130-0779-8). U Presses Fla.

Colden, J. Botanic Manuscript. Rickett, H. W. & Hall, E. C., eds. (Illus.). 1963. 10.00 (ISBN 0-934454-15-9). Lubrecht & Cramer.

Creso, Irene, ed. Vascular Plants of Western Washington. LC 84-72043. (Illus.). 520p. (Orig.). 1984. pap. 14.95 (ISBN 0-9613916-0-X). Creso.

Cronquist, A., et al. Intermountain Flora: Vascular Plants of the Intermountain West, U.S.A. - the Monocotyledons, Vol. 6. LC 73-134298. 1977. 67.50x (ISBN 0-231-04120-9). Columbia U Pr.

Cronquist, Arthur. Vascular Flora of the Southeastern United States: Vol. 1-Asteraceae. Radford, Albert E., ed. LC 79-769. xv, 261p. 1980. 25.00x (ISBN 0-8078-1362-1). U of NC Pr.

Curtis, John T. Vegetation of Wisconsin: An Ordination of Plant Communities. (Illus.). 672p. 1959. 27.50 (ISBN 0-299-01940-3). U of Wis Pr.

Cusick, Allison W. & Silberhorn, Gene M. The Vascular Plants of Unglaciated Ohio. 1977. 9.00 (ISBN 0-86727-081-0). Ohio Bio Survey.

Czarnecki, D. B. & Blinn, D. W. Diatoms of Southwestern USA: Diatoms of the Colorado River in Grand Canyon National Park and Vicinity, Vol. 2. (Illus.). 1978. pap. text ed. 17.50 (ISBN 3-7682-1182-7). Lubrecht & Cramer.

Darrah, William C. A Critical Review of the Upper Pennsylvanian Floras of the Eastern United States. LC 74-113602. (Illus.). 224p. 1970. 36.00x (ISBN 0-913116-02-5). W C Darrah.

Deam, C. C. Flora of Indiana. 1981. Repr. of 1940 ed. 32.50 (ISBN 3-7682-0696-3). Lubrecht & Cramer.

--Flora of Indiana. (Reprints of U. S. Floras Ser.: Vol. 6). (Illus.). 1236p. 1984. lib. bdg. 35.00 (ISBN 3-7682-0696-3). Lubrecht & Cramer.

Dodge, Natt N. & Janish, Jeanne R. Flowers of the Southwest Deserts. 10th ed. LC 72-92509. (Popular Ser.: No. 4). (Illus.). 1976. pap. 2.50 (ISBN 0-911408-45-2). SW Pks Mnmts.

Egerton, Frank N., ed. American Plant Ecology, Eighteen Ninety-Seven to Nineteen Seventeen: An Original Anthology. LC 77-74202. (History of Ecology Ser.). (Illus.). 1978. lib. bdg. 59.50x (ISBN 0-405-10372-7). Ayer Co Pubs.

Eifert, Virginia L. Tall Trees & Far Horizons: Adventures & Discoveries of Early Botanists in America. LC 70-39100. (Essay Index Reprint Ser.). (Illus.). Repr. of 1965 ed. 27.50 (ISBN 0-8369-2686-2). Ayer Co Pubs.

Evans, Walter B., Jr. & Skardon, Mary A. Cedar Bog. (Annual Monograph Ser.). Orig. Title: Journal-Walter B. Evans. (Illus.). 54p. 1974. pap. 3.00 (ISBN 0-686-28231-0). Clark County Hist Soc.

Ewan, Joseph, ed. Short History of Botany in the United States. 174p. 1969. lib. bdg. 8.50 (ISBN 0-02-844360-8). Lubrecht & Cramert.

Farr, Marie L. Myxomycetes. LC 76-19370. (Flora Neotropica Monograph: No. 16). 1976. pap. 22.50x (ISBN 0-89327-003-2). NY Botanical.

Fassett, Norman C. Spring Flora of Wisconsin. 4th ed. LC 74-27307. (Illus.). 430p. 1976. 17.50x (ISBN 0-299-06750-5); pap. 9.50x (ISBN 0-299-06754-8). U of Wis Pr.

Ferlatte, William J. A Flora of the Trinity Alps. LC 72-635566. (Illus.). 1974. 26.50x (ISBN 0-520-02089-8). U of Cal Pr.

Flowers, Seville, et al. Ecological Studies of the Flora & Fauna of Flaming Gorge Reservoir Basin, Utah & Wyoming. (Upper Colorado Ser: No. 3). 42.00 (ISBN 0-404-60648-2). AMS Pr.

Geary, Ida. The Leaf Book: A Field Guide to Plants of Northern California. LC 78-188679. (Illus.). 388p. 1976. pap. 6.00 (ISBN 0-912908-01-7). Tamal Land.

Glassmann, S. F. A Revision of B. E. Dahlgren's Index of American Palms. (Phaneroga Marum Mongraphiae: No. 6). 1972. 42.00 (ISBN 3-7682-0765-X). Lubrecht & Cramer.

Gleason, H. A. New Britton & Brown Illustrated Flora of the Northeastern United States & Adjacent Canada, 3 Vols. rev. ed. (Illus.). 1975. Set. 115.00x (ISBN 0-02-845300-X). Hafner.

Godfrey, Robert K. & Wooten, Jean W. Aquatic & Wetland Plants of Southeastern United States: Dicotyledons. LC 80-16452. (Illus.). 944p. 1981. lib. bdg. 45.00x (ISBN 0-8203-0532-4). U of Ga Pr.

--Aquatic & Wetland Plants of Southeastern United States: Monocotyledons. LC 76-28924. 736p. 1979. 40.00x (ISBN 0-8203-0420-4). U of Ga Pr.

Goebel, K. Organopgraphy of Plants, Especially of the Archegoniatae & Spermatophyta, 2 Vols. Balfour, Issac B., tr. from Ger. (Illus.). 977p. 1969. Repr. of 1905 ed. lib. bdg. 35.00 (ISBN 0-02-845320-4). Lubrecht & Cramer.

Gordon, Robert B. The Natural Vegetation of Ohio in Pioneer Days. 1973. Repr. of 1969 ed. 4.00 (ISBN 0-86727-058-6). Ohio Bio Survey.

Great Plains Flora Assn. Atlas of the Flora of the Great Plains. 1977. text ed. 26.00x (ISBN 0-8138-0135-4). Iowa St U Pr.

Greene, Wilhelmina F. & Blomquist, Hugo L. Flowers of the South: Native & Exotic. xiv, 208p. 1953. 9.95 (ISBN 0-8078-0635-8). U of NC Pr.

Griggs, R. F. Botanical Survey of the Sugar Grove (Hocking Hills) Region. 1972. Repr. of 1914 ed. 3.50 (ISBN 0-86727-002-0). Ohio Bio Survey.

Gronoovius, J. F. Flora Virginica Exhibens Plantas Quas V. C. Johannes Clayton in Virginia Observavit Atque Collegit. pap. 10.00 (ISBN 0-934454-35-3). Lubrecht & Cramer.

Harris, Stuart K., et al. Flora of Essex County, Massachusetts. Snyder, Dorothy E., ed. 269p. 1975. 12.50 (ISBN 0-87577-049-5). Peabody Mus Salem.

Haughton, Claire S. Green Immigrants: The Plants That Transformed America. LC 79-24258. (Illus.). 464p. 1980. pap. 5.95 (ISBN 0-15-636492-1, Harv). HarBraceJ.

Hoover, Robert F. The Vascular Plants of San Luis Obispo County, California. LC 71-104883. 1970. 36.00x (ISBN 0-520-01663-7). U of Cal Pr.

Howell, John T. Marin Flora: Manual of the Flowering Plants & Ferns of Marin County, California. 2nd ed. LC 71-100608. (Supplement). 1970. 22.50 (ISBN 0-520-00578-3); pap. 12.95 (ISBN 0-520-05621-3, CAL 773). U of Cal Pr.

Irwin, H. S. & Barneby, R. C. Monographic Studies in Cassia (Leguminosae Caesalpinioideae) Sections Absus & Grimaldia, No. 3. LC 77-18919. (Memoirs of the New York Botanical Garden Ser.: Vol. 30). 1978. pap. 12.50x (ISBN 0-89327-197-7). NY Botanical.

Isely, Duane. Leguminosae of the United States Pt. III: Subfamily Papilionoideae-Tribes Sophoreae, Podalyreae, Loteae. (Memoirs of the New York Botanical Garden Ser.: Vol. 25, No. 3). (Illus.). 1981. pap. 35.00x (ISBN 0-89327-232-9). NY Botanical.

Jaeger, Edmund C. Desert Wild Flowers. rev. ed. LC 41-22485. (Illus.). 1941. 11.95 (ISBN 0-8047-0364-7); pap. 6.95 (ISBN 0-8047-0365-5, SP81). Stanford U Pr.

Jepson, W. L. Flora of California, Vols. 1, 2 & Vol. 3, Pts. 1 & 2. (Illus.). 1722p. 1979. Set. pap. 50.00x (ISBN 0-935628-00-2). Jepson Herbarium.

--Flora of California, Vol. 1: Pinaceae to Fumariaceae. (Illus.). 545p. 1922. pap. 16.00x (ISBN 0-935628-01-0). Jepson Herbarium.

--Flora of California, Vol. 2: Capparidaceae to Cornaceae. (Illus.). 684p. 1936. lib. bdg. 20.00x (ISBN 0-935628-03-7); pap. 14.00x (ISBN 0-935628-02-9). Jepson Herbarium.

--Flora of California, Vol. 3, Pt. 1: Lennoaceae to Convolvulaceae. (Illus.). 111p. 1939. pap. text ed. 7.00x (ISBN 0-935628-04-5). Jepson Herbarium.

--Flora of California, Vol. 3, Pt. 2: Convolvulaceae to Solanaceae. (Illus.). 335p. 1943. pap. text ed. 9.00 (ISBN 0-935628-05-3). Jepson Herbarium.

Jepson, Willis L. A Manual of the Flowering Plants of California. (Illus.). 1925. 42.50x (ISBN 0-520-00606-2). U of Cal Pr.

Kaczmarska & Rushforth, S. R. The Diatom Flora of Blue Lake Warm Soring, Utah, USA: A Contribution to the Freshwater Diatom Flora of the Hawaiian Islands. (Bibliotheca Diatomologica Ser.). (Illus.). 280p. 1983. text ed. 35.00X (ISBN 3-7682-1363-3). Lubrecht & Cramer.

Kearney, Thomas H., et al. Arizona Flora. 2nd rev. ed. (Illus.). 1960. 40.00x (ISBN 0-520-00637-2). U of Cal Pr.

Kirkbride, Joseph H., Jr. A Revision of the Genus Declieuxia (Rubiaceae) LC 66-6394. (Memoirs of the New York Botanical Garden Ser.: Vol. 28, No. 4). 1976. pap. 10.95x (ISBN 0-89327-010-5). NY Botanical.

Lakela, Olga. Flora of Northeastern Minnesota. LC 64-15424. (Illus.). 1965. 17.50x (ISBN 0-8166-0369-3). U of Minn Pr.

Lakela, Olga, et al. Plants of the Tampa Bay Area. rev. & supplemented ed. 1976. pap. 7.95 (ISBN 0-916224-10-4). Banyan Bks.

Lehr, J. Harry. A Catalogue of the Flora of Arizona. 1978. 4.75 (ISBN 0-9605656-0-4). Desert Botanical.

Lenz, Lee W. & Dourley, John. California Native Trees & Shrubs for Garden & Environmental Use in Southern California & Adjacent Areas. LC 81-50257. (Illus.). xiii, 232p. 1981. kivar flexible 23.50 (ISBN 0-9605808-1-6). Rancho Santa Ana.

Lleras, Eduardo. Trigoniaceae. LC 77-91706. (Flora Neotropica Monograph: No. 19). 1978. pap. 7.25x (ISBN 0-89327-198-5). NY Botanical.

Lloyd, Robert M. & Mitchell, Richard S. A Flora of the White Mountains, California & Nevada. LC 79-172393. (Illus.). 1973. 17.95 (ISBN 0-520-02119-3). U of Cal Pr.

McDougall, W. B. Seed Plants of Northern Arizona. 1973. 15.00 (ISBN 0-89734-009-4). Mus Northern Ariz.

MacKeever, Frank C. Native & Naturalized Plants of Nantucket. Ahles, Harry E., ed. LC 68-19673. 160p. 1968. 9.00x (ISBN 0-87023-037-9). U of Mass Pr.

MacNeal, Donald L. The Flora of the Upper Cretaceous Woodbine Sand in Denton County, Texas. (Monograph: No. 10). (Illus.). 152p. (Orig.). 1958. pap. 11.00 (ISBN 0-910006-17-2). Acad Nat Sci Phila.

Marr, C. D. Ramaria of Western Washington. 1973. 17.50 (ISBN 3-7682-0902-4). Lubrecht & Cramer.

Martin, Alexander C., et al. American Wildlife & Plants: A Guide to Wildlife Food Habits. 1951. pap. 7.50 (ISBN 0-486-20793-5). Dover.

--American Wildlife & Plants: A Guide to Wildlife Food Habits. 15.75 (ISBN 0-8446-2536-1). Peter Smith.

Mason, Herbert L. A Flora of the Marshes of California. LC 57-7960. (Illus.). 1957. 38.50x (ISBN 0-520-01433-2). U of Cal Pr.

Mass, P. J. M. Renealmia (Zingiberaceae-Zingiberoideae) Costoideae (Additions) (Zingiberaceae) LC 77-72241. (Flora Neotropica Monograph: No. 18). 1977. pap. 21.00x (ISBN 0-89327-192-6). NY Botanical.

Mohlenbrock, Robert H. Flowering Plants: Lilies to Orchids. LC 69-16118. (Illustrated Flora of Illinois Ser.). (Illus.). 304p. 1970. 22.95x (ISBN 0-8093-0408-2). S Ill U Pr.

--Guide to the Vascular Flora of Illinois. LC 75-22414. 506p. 1975. 22.95x (ISBN 0-8093-0704-9). S Ill U Pr.

Mohlenbrock, Robert H. & Ladd, Douglas M. Distribution of Illinois Vascular Plants. LC 77-15987. (Illus.). 289p. (Orig.). 1978. pap. 12.95x (ISBN 0-8093-0848-7). S Ill U Pr.

Mohr, C. Plant Life of Alabama. (Illus.). 1969. Repr. of 1901 ed. 28.00 (ISBN 3-7682-0622-X). Lubrecht & Cramer.

Montgomery, F. H. The Seeds & Fruits of Plants of Eastern Canada & Northeastern United States. LC 76-23241. 1976. 37.50x (ISBN 0-8020-5341-6). U of Toronto Pr.

Muir, John. Rambles of a Botanist among the Plants & Climates of California. Kimes, William F., intro. by. (Illus.). 43p. 1974. 10.00 (ISBN 0-87093-301-9). Dawsons.

--A Thousand Mile Walk to the Gulf. LC 16-23580. (Illus.). 220p. 1970. lib. bdg. 19.95 (ISBN 0-910220-18-2). Berg.

Munz, Philip A. A Flora of Southern California. (Illus.). 1974. 38.50x (ISBN 0-520-02146-0). U of Cal Pr.

--Supplement to a California Flora. 1968. pap. 16.50x (ISBN 0-520-00904-5). U of Cal Pr.

Munz, Philip A. & Keck, David D. A California Flora & Supplement. 1973. Repr. 38.50x (ISBN 0-520-02405-2). U of Cal Pr.

Navarro, J. Nelson. Marine Diatoms Associated with Mangrovew Prop Roots in the Indian River, Florida, USA. (Bibliotheca Phycologica 61 Ser.). (Illus.). 151p. (Orig.). 1982. pap. text ed. 15.70 (ISBN 3-7682-1337-4). Lubrecht & Cramer.

Neumann, J. J. The Polyporaceae of Wisconsin. 1971. Repr. of 1914 ed. 21.00 (ISBN 3-7682-0704-8). Lubrecht & Cramer.

Niehaus, Theodore F. A Biosystematic Study of the Genus Brodiaea (Amaryllidaceae) (U. C. Publications in Botany Ser.: Vol. 60). 1971. pap. 14.50x (ISBN 0-520-09390-9). U of Cal Pr.

Ornduff, Robert. Introduction to California Plant Life. (California Natural History Guides). (Illus.). 1974. 14.95x (ISBN 0-520-02583-0); pap. 4.95 (ISBN 0-520-02735-3). U of Cal Pr.

Patraw, Pauline M. & Janish, Jeanne R. Flowers of the Southwest Mesas. 5th ed. (Popular Ser.: No. 5). (Illus.). 1977. pap. 2.50 (ISBN 0-911408-47-9). SW Pks Mnmts.

Pennell, Francis W. The Scrophulariaceae of Eastern Temperate North America. (Monograph: No. 1). (Illus.). 650p. (Orig.). 1935. pap. 13.00 (ISBN 0-910006-08-3). Acad Nat Sci Phila.

Pennsylvania University Bicentennial Conference. Conservation of Renewable Natural Resources. Zon, Raphael & Cooper, William, eds. LC 68-26200. Repr. of 1941 ed. 19.50x (ISBN 0-8046-0356-1, Pub. by Kennikat). Assoc Faculty Pr.

Peterson, Lee. A Field Guide to Eastern Edible Wild Plants. (Peterson Field Guide Ser.). 1984. 16.95 (ISBN 0-395-20445-3); pap. 10.95 (ISBN 0-395-31870-X). HM.

Pound, Roscoe & Clements, Frederic E. The Phytogeography of Nebraska: General Survey. rev. ed. Egerton, Frank N., 3rd, ed. LC 77-74248. (History of Ecology Ser.). (Illus.). 1978. Repr. of 1900 ed. lib. bdg. 35.50x (ISBN 0-405-10417-0). Ayer Co Pubs.

Pursh, Frederick. Journal of a Botanical Excursion in the Northeastern Parts of the States of Pennsylvania & New York During the Year 1807. LC 79-101020. 1969. Repr. of 1869 ed. 13.00x (ISBN 0-87198-073-8). Friedman.

Radford, Albert E., et al. Manual of the Vascular Flora of the Carolinas. LC 68-28264. (Illus.). lxii, 1183p. 1968. 19.95x (ISBN 0-8078-1087-8). U of NC Pr.

Robichaud, Beryl & Buell, Marray F. The Vegetation of New Jersey. (Illus.). 208p. 1983. pap. 12.95 (ISBN 0-8135-0795-2). Rutgers U Pr.

Rogerson, Dr. Clark T., ed. This Issue Commemorating the 70th Birthday of Dr. Josiah L. Lowe. LC 66-6394. (Memoirs of the New York Botanical Garden Ser.: Vol. 28, No. 1). 1976. pap. 20.00x (ISBN 0-89327-004-0). NY Botanical.

Kaplan, H. & Dinar, N., eds. Boundary Layer Structure. 1984. lib. bdg. 69.50 (ISBN 90-277-1877-6, Pub. by Reidel Holland). Kluwer Academic.

McBean, G. A., ed. The Planetary Boundary Layer. (Technical Note Ser.: No. 165). (Illus.). 201p. 1980. pap. 20.00 (ISBN 92-63-10530-8, W460, WMO). Unipub.

McCave, I. N., ed. The Benthic Boundary Layer. LC 76-2641. (Illus.). 323p. 1976. 49.50x (ISBN 0-306-30886-X, Plenum Pr). Plenum Pub.

Schlichting, Hermann. Boundary Layer Theory. 7th ed. Kestin, J., tr. from Ger. (Mechanical Engineering Ser.). (Illus.). 1979. 48.00 (ISBN 0-07-055334-3). McGraw.

Weber, H. E., ed. Turbulent Boundary Layers. (Orig.). 1979. 30.00 (ISBN 0-685-96311-X, G00145). ASME.

BOUNDARY VALUE PROBLEMS

see also Scattering (Mathematics)

Agranovich, Z. S. & Marchenko, V. A. Inverse Problem of Scattering Theory. Seckler, B. D., tr. (Russian Monographs and Texts on the Physical Sciences Ser.). 304p. 1963. 80.95 (ISBN 0-677-20010-2). Gordon.

Alfsen, E. M. Compact Convex Sets & Boundary Integrals. LC 72-136352. (Ergebnisse der Mathematik und Ihrer Grenzgebiete: Vol. 57). (Illus.). 1971. 31.00 (ISBN 0-387-05090-6). Springer-Verlag.

Atkinson, F. V. Discrete & Continuous Boundary Problems. (Mathematics in Science & Engineering Ser.: Vol. 8). 1964. 80.00 (ISBN 0-12-065850-X). Acad Pr.

Bailey, Paul B., et al. Nonlinear Two Point Boundary Value Problems. (Mathematics in Science & Engineering Ser.: Vol. 4). 1968. 49.50 (ISBN 0-12-073350-1). Acad Pr.

Baiocchi, Claudio & Capelo, Antonio. Variational & Quasivariational Inequalities: Applications to Free Boundary Problems. 400p. 1984. 57.95x (ISBN 0-471-90201-2, Pub. by Wiley Interscience). Wiley.

Banerjee, P. K. & Butterfield, R. Boundary Element Methods in Engineering Science. 512p. 1982. text ed. 42.00 (ISBN 0-07-084120-9). McGraw.

Banerjee, P. K. & Mukherjee, S. Developments in Boundary Element Methods, Vol. 3. 328p. 1984. 70.50 (ISBN 0-85334-253-9, I-167-84, Pub. by Elsevier Applied Sci England). Elsevier.

Barro-Neto & Artino. Hypoelliptic Boundary-Value Problems. (Lecture Notes in Pure & Applied Mathematics: Vol. 53). 104p. 1980. 29.75 (ISBN 0-8247-6886-8). Dekker.

Berezanskii, Ju. M. Expansions in Eigenfunctions of Selfadjoint Operators. LC 67-22347. (Translations of Mathematical Monographs: Vol. 17). 1968. 67.00 (ISBN 0-8218-1567-9, MMONO-17). Am Math.

Bernfeld, Stephen R. & Lakshmikantham, V. An Introduction to Nonlinear Boundary Value Problems. (Mathematics in Science & Engineering: A Series of Monographs & Textbooks, Vol. 109). 1974. 60.00 (ISBN 0-12-093150-8). Acad Pr.

Boyce, W. E. & Diprima, R. C. Elementary Differential Equations & Boundary Value Problems. 4th ed. 1985. pap. text ed. write for info. (ISBN 0-471-87096-X). Wiley.

Brebbia, C. A. Boundary Element Techniques. (Illus.). 510p. 1984. 78.00 (ISBN 0-387-12484-5). Springer-Verlag.

Brebbia, C. A., ed. Boundary Elements VI. 900p. 1984. 55.50 (ISBN 0-387-13420-4). Springer-Verlag.

--Time-Dependent & Vibration Problems. (Topics in Boundary Element Research Ser.: Vol. 2). (Illus.). 280p. 1985. 59.00 (ISBN 0-387-13993-1). Springer-Verlag.

Brebbia, C. A., et al, eds. Boundary Elements. 104p. 1983. 112.00 (ISBN 0-387-12803-4). Springer-Verlag.

Carasso, Alfred & Stone, Alex P., eds. Improperly Posed Boundary Value Problems. (Research Notes in Mathematics Ser.: No. 1). 157p. 1975. pap. text ed. 20.50 (ISBN 0-273-00105-1). Pitman Pub MA.

Cercignani, Carlo. Mathematical Methods in Kinetic Theory. LC 69-15832. (Illus.). 227p. 1969. 29.50x (ISBN 0-306-30386-8, Plenum Pr). Plenum Pub.

Cesari, Lamberto, et al, eds. Nonlinear Functional Analysis & Differential Equations: Proceedings of the Michigan State University Conference. (Lecture Notes in Pure and Applied Math Ser.: Vol. 19). 1976. 65.00 (ISBN 0-8247-6452-8). Dekker.

Childs, B., et al, eds. Codes for Boundary-Value Problems in Ordinary Differential Equations. (Lecture Notes in Computer Science: Vol. 76). 388p. 1979. pap. 22.00 (ISBN 0-387-09554-3). Springer-Verlag.

Clements, David L. Boundary Value Problems Governed by Second Order Elliptic Systems. LC 80-20820. (Monographs & Studies: No. 12). 176p. 1981. text ed. 58.95 (ISBN 0-273-08502-6). Pitman Pub MA.

Coddington, E. A. & De Snoo, H. S. Regular Boundary Value Problems Associated with Pairs of Ordinary Differential Expressions. (Lecture Notes in Mathematics Ser.: Vol. 858). 225p. 1981. pap. 16.00 (ISBN 0-387-10706-1). Springer-Verlag.

Colton, D. L. Solution of Boundary Value Problems by the Method of Integral Operators. (Research Notes in Mathematics Ser.: No. 6). 148p. (Orig.). 1976. pap. text ed. 21.95 (ISBN 0-273-00307-0). Pitman Pub MA.

Crank, John. Free & Moving Boundary Problems. (Illus.). 1984. 64.00x (ISBN 0-19-853357-8). Oxford U Pr.

Cruse, T. A. & Rizzo, F. J., eds. Boundary-Integral Equation Method: Computational Applications in Applied Mechanics AMD, Vol. 11. 148p. 1975. pap. text ed. 14.00 (ISBN 0-685-78341-3, I00089). ASME.

Donaldson, Thomas. A Laplace Transform Calculus for Partial Differential Operators. LC 74-7370. (Memoirs: No. 143). 166p. 1974. pap. 11.00 (ISBN 0-8218-1843-0, MEMO-143). Am Math.

Engeli, M., et al. Refined Iterative Methods for Computation of the Solution & the Eigenvalues of Self-Adjoint Boundary Value Problems. (MIM Ser.: No. 8). (Illus.). 108p. 1959. pap. 20.95x (ISBN 0-8176-0098-1). Birkhauser.

Fortin, M. & Glowinski, R. Augmented Lagrangian Methods: Applications to the Numerical Solution of Boundary-Value Problems. (Studies in Mathematics & Its Applications: Vol. 15). 340p. 1983. 59.75 (ISBN 0-444-86680-9, I-168-83, North Holland). Elsevier.

Garnir, H. G., ed. Boundary Value Problems for Linear Evolution-Partial Differential Equations. (NATO Advanced Study Institutes Ser. C. Math & Phys. Sciences: No. 29). 1977. lib. bdg. 55.00 (ISBN 90-277-0788-X, Pub. by Reidel Holland). Kluwer Academic.

--Singularities in Boundary Value Problems. 370p. 1982. 49.50 (ISBN 90-277-1240-9, Pub. by Reidel Holland). Kluwer Academic.

Grisvard, P., et al, eds. Singularities & Constructive Methods for Their Treatment. (Lecture Notes in Mathematics: Vol. 1121). ix, 346p. 1985. pap. 23.50 (ISBN 0-387-15219-9). Springer-Verlag.

Hamilton, R. S. Harmonic Maps of Manifolds with Boundary. (Lecture Notes in Mathematics Ser.: Vol. 471). 168p. 1975. pap. 14.00 (ISBN 0-387-07185-7). Springer-Verlag.

Hanna, J. Ray. Fourier Series & Integrals of Boundary Value Problems. LC 81-16063. (Pure & Applied Mathematics Ser.). 271p. 1982. 37.50x (ISBN 0-471-08129-9, Pub. by Wiley-Interscience). Wiley.

Herrera, I. Boundary Methods: An Algebraic Theory. (Applicable Mathematics Ser.). 148p. 1984. text ed. 32.95 (ISBN 0-273-08635-9). Pitman Pub Ma.

Hromadka, T. V. The Complex Variable Boundary Element Method. (Lecture Notes in Engineering Ser.: Vol. 9). xi, 243p. 1984. pap. 15.50 (ISBN 0-387-13743-2). Springer-Verlag.

Kardestuncer, H., ed. Unification of Finite Element Methods. (Mathematics Studies: Vol. 94). 344p. 1984. 48.25 (ISBN 0-444-87519-0, I-265-84, North Holland). Elsevier.

Keller, Herbert B. Numerical Solution of Two Point Boundary Value Problems. (CBMS-NSF Regional Conference Ser.: No. 24). viii, 61p. (Orig.). 1976. pap. text ed. 10.00 (ISBN 0-89871-021-9). Soc Indus-Appl Math.

Knops, R. J. & Payne, L. E. Uniqueness Theorems in Linear Elasticity. LC 70-138813. (Springer Tracts in Natural Philosophy: Vol. 19). 1971. 28.00 (ISBN 0-387-05253-4). Springer-Verlag.

Kovach, Ladis D. Boundary Value Problems. (Illus.). 400p. 1984. 34.95 (ISBN 0-201-11728-2); tchrs' manual avail. (ISBN 0-201-11729-0). Addison-Wesley.

Ladyzhenskaya, O. A. The Boundary Value Problems of Mathematical Physics. Lohwater, J., tr. from Rus. (Applied Mathematical Sciences Ser.: Vol. 49). 350p. 1985. 58.00 (ISBN 0-387-90989-3). Springer-Verlag.

Ladyzhenskaya, O. A., ed. Boundary Value Problems of Mathematical Physics & Related Aspects of Function Theory, Part 3. LC 69-12506. (Seminars in Mathematics Ser.: Vol. 11). 79p. 1970. 25.00x (ISBN 0-306-18811-2, Consultants). Plenum Pub.

--Boundary Value Problems of Mathematical Physics & Related Aspects of Function Theory, Pt. 2. LC 69-12506. (Seminars in Mathematics Ser.: Vol. 7). 100p. 1970. 25.00x (ISBN 0-306-18807-4, Consultants). Plenum Pub.

Liggett, J. A. & Liu, Philip L. The Boundary Integral Equation Method for Porous Media Flow. 272p. 1983. text ed. 35.00x (ISBN 0-04-620011-8). Allen Unwin.

Mahwin, Jean. Topological Degree Methods in Non-Linear Boundary Value Problems. LC 78-31906. (CBMS Regional Conference Ser. in Mathematics: No. 40). 122p. 1981. pap. 11.00 (ISBN 0-8218-1690-X, CBMS-40). Am Math.

Miklowitz, J. The Theory of Elastic Waves & Waveguides. (Applied Mathematics & Mechanics Ser.: Vol. 22). 618p. 1978. 95.75 (ISBN 0-7204-0551-3, North-Holland). Elsevier.

Morawetz, Cathleen S. Notes on Time Decay & Scattering for Some Hyperbolic Problems. (CBMS-NSF Regional Conference Ser.: No. 19). v, 81p. (Orig.). 1975. pap. text ed. 13.00 (ISBN 0-89871-016-2). Soc Indus-Appl Math.

Na, T. Y. Computational Methods in Engineering: Boundary Value Problems. LC 79-51682. (Mathematics in Science & Engineering Ser.). 1979. 60.00 (ISBN 0-12-512650-6). Acad Pr.

Powers, David L. Boundary Value Problems. 2nd ed. 351p. 1979. 22.50i (ISBN 0-12-563760-8); instr's. manual 2.50i (ISBN 0-12-563762-4). Acad Pr.

--Elementary Differential Equations with Boundary Value Problems. 1985. text ed. write for info. (ISBN 0-87150-431-6, 33L2810, Prindle). PWS Pubs.

Rubenstein, L. I. Stefan Problem. LC 75-168253. (Translations of Mathematical Monographs: Vol. 27). 1971. 56.00 (ISBN 0-8218-1577-6, MMONO-27). Am Math.

Sakamoto, Reiko. Hyperbolic Boundary-Value Problems. LC 81-3865. 230p. 1982. 39.50 (ISBN 0-521-23568-5). Cambridge U Pr.

Schwabik, Stefan, et al. Differential & Integral Equations: Boundry Value Problems & Adjoints. 1979. 39.50 (ISBN 90-277-0802-9, Pub. by Reidel Holland). Kluwer Academic.

Seshadri, R & Na, T. Y. Group Invariance in Engineering Boundary Value Problems. (Illus.). 225p. 1985. 29.50 (ISBN 0-387-96128-3). Springer-Verlag.

Sigillito, V. G. Explicit A Priori Inequalities with Applications to Boundary Value Problems. (Research Notes in Mathematics: No. 13). (Orig.). 1977. pap. text ed. 16.95 (ISBN 0-273-01022-0). Pitman Pub MA.

Steklov Institute of Mathematics, Academy of Sciences, No. 125, U S S R. Boundary Value Problems of Mathematical Physics VIII: Proceedings. Ladyzenskaja, O. A., ed. LC 67-6187. (Proceedings of the Steklov Institute of Mathematics: No. 125). 1975. 65.00 (ISBN 0-8218-3025-2, STEKLO-125). Am Math.

Wilson, D. G., et al, eds. Moving Boundary Problems. 1978. 35.00 (ISBN 0-12-757350-X). Acad Pr.

BOUNDARY VALUE PROBLEMS–NUMERICAL SOLUTIONS

Albrecht, J. & Collatz, L., eds. Numerical Treatment of Free Boundary Value Problems. (International Series of Numerical Mathematics: Vol. 58). 350p. 1982. text ed. 36.95x (ISBN 0-8176-1277-7). Birkhauser.

Bensoussan, A., et al. Asymptotic Analysis for Periodic Structures. (Studies in Mathematics & Its Applications Ser.: Vol. 5). 700p. 1978. 70.25 (ISBN 0-444-85172-0, North-Holland). Elsevier.

Brebbia, C. Boundary Element Techniques in Engineering. new ed. (Illus.). 1980. text ed. 39.95 (ISBN 0-408-00340-5). Butterworth.

Brebbia, C. A., ed. Boundary Element Methods in Engineering, Southampton, England 1982: Proceedings. (Illus.). 649p. 1982. 66.00 (ISBN 0-387-11819-5). Springer-Verlag.

Collatz, Lothar, et al, eds. Constructive Methods for Nonlinear Boundary Value Problems & Nonlinear Oscillations. (International Series of Numerical Mathematics: Vol. 48). 192p. 1979. pap. 22.95x (ISBN 0-8176-1098-7). Birkhauser.

Conference, Oberwolfach, Germany, July 4-10, 1976. Numerical Treatment of Differential Equations: Proceedings. Bulirsch, R., et al, eds. (Lecture Notes in Mathematics Ser.: Vol. 631). (Eng. & Ger.). 1978. pap. 18.00 (ISBN 0-387-08539-4). Springer-Verlag.

Fairweather, Graeme. Finite Element Galerkin Methods for Differential Equations. (Lecture Notes in Pure & Applied Mathematics Ser.: Vol. 34). 1978. 45.00 (ISBN 0-8247-6673-3). Dekker.

Hall, G. & Watt, J. M., eds. Modern Numerical Methods for Ordinary Differential Equations. 1976. 42.50x (ISBN 0-19-853348-9). Oxford U Pr.

Ingham, D. B. & Kelmanson, M. A. Boundary Integral Equation Analysis of Singular, Potential & Biharmonic Problems. (Lecture Notes in Engineering Ser.: Vol. 7). (Illus.). iv, 173p. 1984. pap. 12.50 (ISBN 0-387-13646-0). Springer-Verlag.

Lattes, Robert. Methods of Resolution for Selected Boundary Problems in Mathematical Physics. (Documents on Modern Physics Ser.). 200p. 1969. 57.75x (ISBN 0-677-30060-3). Gordon.

--Quelques Methodes de Resolutions de Problemes aux Limites de la Physique Mathematiques. (Cours & Documents de Mathematiques & de Physique Ser.). 196p. (Orig.). 1967. 57.75x (ISBN 0-677-50060-2). Gordon.

Lee, E. Stanley. Quasilinearization & Invariant Imbedding. (Mathematics in Science & Engineering Ser.,: Vol. 41). 1968. 70.00 (ISBN 0-12-440250-X). Acad Pr.

Lions, J. L. & Magenes, E. Non-Homogeneous Boundary Value Problems & Applications, Vol. 1. Kenneth, P., tr. LC 71-151407. (Die Grundlehren der Mathematischen Wissenschaften: Vol. 181). 355p. 1972. 38.00 (ISBN 0-387-05363-8). Springer-Verlag.

--Non-Homogeneous Boundary Value Problems & Applications, Vol. 2. Kenneth, P., tr. LC 71-151407. (Die Grundlehren der Mathematischen Wissenschaften: Vol. 182). 242p. 1972. 28.00 (ISBN 0-387-05444-8). Springer-Verlag.

--Non-Homogeneous Boundary Value Problems & Applications, Vol. 3. Kenneth, P., tr. from Fr. LC 71-151407. (Die Grundlehren der Mathematischen Wissenschaften: Vol. 183). 330p. 1973. 55.00 (ISBN 0-387-05832-X). Springer-Verlag.

Oden, J. T. & Reddy, J. N. An Introduction to the Mathematical Theory of Finite Elements. LC 76-6953. (Pure & Applied Mathematics Ser.). 429p. 1976. 50.95x (ISBN 0-471-65261-X, Pub. by Wiley-Interscience). Wiley.

BOURBON WHISKEY

see Whiskey

BOUVIER D'FLANDRES (DOG)

see Dogs–Breeds–Bouvier D'Flandres

BOVERI, THEODOR, 1862-1915

Baltzer, Fritz. Theodor Boveri: The Life & Work of a Great Biologist, 1862-1915. Rudnick, Dorothea, tr. LC 67-21996. (Illus.). 1967. 34.00x (ISBN 0-520-00074-9). U of Cal Pr.

BOVIDAE, FOSSIL

Reynolds, S. H. Pleistocene Bovidae. Repr. of 1939 ed. 12.00 (ISBN 0-384-50400-0). Johnson Repr.

BOW AND ARROW

see also Crossbow

Barwick, Humphrey. Concerning the Force & Effect of Manual Weapons of Fire. LC 74-80163. (English Experience Ser.: No. 643). 86p. 1974. Repr. of 1594 ed. 8.00 (ISBN 90-221-0643-8). Walter J Johnson.

Hamilton, T. M. Native American Bows. 2nd ed. LC 82-81155. (Special Publications Ser.: No. 5). 1982. Repr. 10.00 (ISBN 0-943414-00-8). MO Arch Soc.

Loiselle, Emery J. Doctor Your Own Compound Bow. (Illus.). 148p. 1976. pap. 9.95 (ISBN 0-9613281-0-X). E J Loiselle.

Murdoch, John. Study of the Eskimo Bows in the U. S. National Museum. facs. ed. (Illus.). 24p. pap. 1.95 (ISBN 0-8466-4002-3, I2). Shorey.

BOXER (DOG)

see Dogs–Breeds–Boxers

BOYLE, ROBERT, 1627-1691

Boas, Marie. Robert Boyle & Seventeenth-Century Chemistry. LC 58-4386. Repr. of 1958 ed. 23.00 (ISBN 0-527-09250-9). Kraus Repr.

Jacob, J. R. Robert Boyle & the English Revolution: A Study in Social & Intellectual Change. LC 77-2997. (Studies in the History of Science). (Illus.). 1978. lib. bdg. 18.95 (ISBN 0-89102-072-1). B Franklin.

Shapin, Steven. Leviathan & the Air Pump: Hobbes, Boyle & the Experimental Life. Schaffer, Simon, ed. (Illus.). 475p. 1985. text ed. 60.00 (ISBN 0-691-08393-2). Princeton U Pr.

BRACHIOPODA

Carter, John L. & Carter, Ruth C. Bibliography & Index of North American Carboniferous Brachiopoda 1898-1968. LC 74-129146. (Geological Society of America Ser.: No. 128). pap. 98.00 (ISBN 0-317-27889-4, 2025460). Bks Demand UMI.

Cooper, G. Arthur. Brachiopods from the Caribbean Sea & Adjacent Waters. LC 75-4757. (Studies in Tropical Oceanography: No. 14). 1977. 29.95x (ISBN 0-87024-277-6). U Miami Marine.

Hertlein, Leo G. & Grant, U. S. Cenozoic Brachiopoda of Western North America. pap. 16.00 (ISBN 0-384-22688-4). Johnson Repr.

Muir-Wood, Helen M. A History of the Classification of the Phylum Brachipoda. (Illus.). vii, 124p. 1968. Repr. of 1955 ed. 22.50x (ISBN 0-565-00078-0, Pub. by Brit Mus Nat Hist England). Sabbot-Natural Hist Bks.

BRACHIOPODA, FOSSIL

Bassett, Michael G. & Cocks, Leonard R. A Review of Silvrian Brachiopods from Gotland. (Fossils & Strata Ser: No. 3). 1974. 10.50x (ISBN 8-200-09349-2, Dist. by Columbia U Pr). Universitet.

Davidson, Thomas. The Fossil Brachiopoda, 2 Vols. 1850-1856. pap. 83.00 (ISBN 0-384-10960-8). Johnson Repr.

Mattysse, S., ed. Psychiatry & the Biology of the Human Brain: A Symposium Dedicated to Seymour S. Kety. 310p. 1981. 62.75 (ISBN 0-444-00649-4, Biomedical Pr). Elsevier.

Minderhoud, J. M., ed. Cerebral Blood Flow. (The Jonxis Lectures: Vol. 7). 314p. 1982. 39.75 (ISBN 0-444-90207-4, Excerpta Medica). Elsevier.

Monro, Alexander. Three Treatises: On the Brain, the Eye, & the Ear. Bd. with Croonian Lectures on Cerebrqal Localization. Ferrier, D. (Contributions to the History of Psychology Ser., Vol. VII, Pt. E: Pysiological Psychology). 1980. Repr. of 1797 ed. 30.00 (ISBN 0-89093-326-X). U Pubns Amer.

Morihisa, John M. Brain Imaging in Psychiatry. LC 84-6303. (Clinical Insights Monograph). 112p. 1984. pap. text ed. 12.00x (ISBN 0-88048-052-1, 48-052-1). Am Psychiatric.

Motta, Marcella, ed. Endocrine Functions of the Brain. (Comprehensive Endocrinology Ser.). 493p. 1980. text ed. 78.00 (ISBN 0-89004-343-4). Raven.

Myslobodsky, Michael, ed. Hemisyndromes: Psychobiology, Neurology, Psychiatry. LC 83-2823. 1983. 55.00 (ISBN 0-12-512460-0). Acad Pr.

Needham, Charles W. Cerebral Logic: Solving the Problem of Mind & Brain. (Illus.). 232p. 1978. 23.50x (ISBN 0-398-03754-X). C C Thomas.

Neuberger, Max. The Historical Development of Experimental Brain & Spinal Cord Physiology Before Flourens. Clarke, Edwin, ed. & tr. from Ger. LC 81-47604. 424p. 1982. text ed. 32.50x (ISBN 0-8018-2380-3). Johns Hopkins.

Neumann, John Von. Computer & the Brain. LC 58-6542. (Silliman Lectures Ser.). 1958. pap. 4.95x (ISBN 0-300-02415-0). Yale U Pr.

Nicholson, J. P., ed. Interdisciplinary Investigations of the Brain. LC 72-91037. (Advances in Behavioral Biology Ser.: Vol. 5). 244p. 1973. 35.00x (ISBN 0-306-37905-8, Plenum Pr). Plenum Pub.

Nolte, John. The Human Brain: An Introduction to Its Functional Anatomy. LC 81-38337. (Illus.). 322p. 1981. pap. text ed. 19.95 (ISBN 0-8016-3702-3). Mosby.

Oakley, David A., ed. Brain & Mind. (Psychology in Progress Ser.). 320p. 1985. 33.00 (ISBN 0-416-31620-4, 9626); pap. 13.95 (ISBN 0-416-31630-1, 9627). Methuen Inc.

Oakley, David A. & Plotkin, H. C., eds. Brain, Behaviour, & Evolution. (Psychology in Progress Ser.). 1979. 12.95x (ISBN 0-416-71260-6, NO.2350). Methuen Inc.

Olszewsky, J. & Baxter, D. Cytoarchitecture of the Human Brain Stem. 2nd ed. (Illus.). 200p. 1981. 118.75 (ISBN 3-8055-2210-X). S Karger.

Orban, G. A. Neuronal Operations in the Visual Cortex. (Studies of Brain Function: Vol. 11). (Illus.). 385p. 1984. 38.00 (ISBN 0-387-11919-1). Springer-Verlag.

Ornstein, Robert & Thompson, Richard F. The Amazing Brain. (Illus.). 1984. 16.95 (ISBN 0-395-35486-2). HM.

Ostrander, Edgar A. Evidence That Ancient Mayan Cosmology Incorporated the Internal Functioning of the Human Brain. LC 83-72070. (Illus.). 56p. 1983. 10.00 (ISBN 0-9611638-0-1). Bks of New Univ.

Paoletti, R. & Davison, A. N., eds. Chemistry & Brain Development. LC 75-150494. (Advances in Experimental Medicine & Biology Ser.: Vol. 13). 467p. 1971. 59.50x (ISBN 0-306-39013-2, Plenum Pr). Plenum Pub.

Pearson, Ronald & Pearson, Lindsay. The Vertebrate Brain. 1976. 98.00 (ISBN 0-12-548060-1). Acad Pr.

Peiffer, Jurgen. Brain Aging: Human Destiny-Human Disease. (Illus.). 52p. 1981. pap. text ed. 9.00 (ISBN 3-456-81039-3, Pub. by Hans Huber Pubs). J K Burgess.

Peiper, Albrecht. Cerebral Function in Infancy & Childhood. LC 62-12856. 683p. 1964. 55.00x (ISBN 0-306-10514-4, Consultants). Plenum Pub.

Penfield, Wilder & Jasper, Herbert. Epilepsy & the Functional Anatomy of the Human Brain. 1954. 42.50 (ISBN 0-316-69833-4). Little.

Pontificia Academia Scientiarum, Study Week, 1964. Brain & Conscious Experience. Eccles, John C., ed. (Illus.). 1966. 69.50 (ISBN 0-387-03471-4). Springer-Verlag.

Powell, Graham. Brain & Personality. LC 79-87638. 122p. 1979. 33.95x (ISBN 0-03-052701-5). Praeger.

Powell, Graham E. Brain Function Therapy. 326p. 1981. 24.00x (ISBN 0-566-00315-5, 04112-2, Pub. by Gower Pub Co England). Lexington Bks.

Precht, W. Neuronal Operations in the Vestibular System. LC 77-16842. (Studies of Brain Functions: Vol. 2). (Illus.). 1978. pap. 29.00 (ISBN 0-387-08549-1). Springer-Verlag.

Purves, M. J. The Physiology of the Cerebral Circulation. LC 70-169577. (Physiological Society Monographs: No. 28). (Illus.). 40p. 1972. 95.00 (ISBN 0-521-08300-1). Cambridge U Pr.

Ramon y Cajal, Santiago. Studies on the Diencephalon. Ramon-Moliner, Enrique, tr. (Illus.). 248p. 1966. 24.75x (ISBN 0-398-01542-2). C C Thomas.

Ranly, Don M. Synopsis of Craniofacial Growth. (Illus.). 188p. 1980. pap. 19.95 (ISBN 0-8385-8779-8). ACC.

Reep, R., ed. Relationship Between Prefrontal & Limbic Cortex: A Comparative Anatomical Review. (Journal: Brain, Behavioral & Evolution: Vol. 25, Nos. 1-2). (Illus.). 80p. 1985. pap. 23.50 (ISBN 3-8055-4033-7). S Karger.

Reinis, Stanislav & Goldman, Jerome M. The Development of the Brain: Biological & Functional Perspectives. (Illus.). 416p. 1980. photocopy 41.75x (ISBN 0-398-03932-1). C C Thomas.

Restak, Richard M. The Brain. 1980. pap. 4.50 (ISBN 0-446-32282-2). Warner Bks.

Rockstroh, et al. Slow Brain Potentials & Behavior. LC 82-1939. 271p. 1982. text ed. 39.00 (ISBN 0-8067-0291-5). Urban & S.

Rosenfield, Israel. The Brain for Beginners. (Beginners Ser.). (Illus.). 1985. 14.95 (ISBN 0-86316-083-2); pap. 6.95 (ISBN 0-86316-084-0). Writers & Readers.

Routtenberg, Aryeh, ed. Biology of Reinforcement: Facet of Brain Stimulation Reward. (Behavioral Biology Ser.). 1980. 29.50 (ISBN 0-12-599350-1). Acad Pr.

Ruggiero, G., et al. Radiological Exploration of the Ventricles & Subarachnoid Space. LC 73-19548. (Illus.). 200p. 1974. 97.00 (ISBN 0-387-06572-5). Springer-Verlag.

Rumack. Perinatal & Infant Brain Imaging. 1984. 47.50 (ISBN 0-8151-7458-6). Year Bk Med.

Russell, I. Steele. Structure & Function of Cerebral Commissures. 520p. 1979. text ed. 50.00 (ISBN 0-8391-1391-9). Univ Park.

Russell, Peter. The Brain Book. 1979. 12.95 (ISBN 0-8015-0886-X, Hawthorn); pap. 9.95. Dutton.

Sagan, Carl. Broca's Brain: Reflections on the Romance of Science. LC 78-21810. (Illus.). 1979. 14.95 (ISBN 0-394-50169-1). Random.

Salamon, G. & Huang, Y. P. Radiologic Anatomy of the Brain. LC 75-45294. (Illus.). 1976. 199.00 (ISBN 3-540-07528-3). Springer-Verlag.

Schlesinger, Benno. Higher Cerebral Functions & Their Clinical Disorders: The Organic Basis of Psychology & Psychiatry. LC 59-10265. (Illus.). 576p. 1962. 81.00 (ISBN 0-8089-0413-2, 793890). Grune.

Scientific American Editors. The Brain: A Scientific American Book. LC 79-21012. (Illus.). 149p. 1979. pap. text ed. 11.95x (ISBN 0-7167-1151-6). W H Freeman.

Searle, John. Minds, Brains & Science. 112p. 1985. 10.00 (ISBN 0-674-57631-4). Harvard U Pr.

Sechenov, Ivan M. Reflexes of the Brain. 1965. pap. 6.95x (ISBN 0-262-69006-3). MIT Pr.

Seeger, W. Atlas of Topographical Anatomy of the Brain & Surrounding Structures for Neurosurgeons, Neuroradiologists, & Neuropathologists. LC 77-16683. (Illus.). 1978. 169.00 (ISBN 0-387-81447-7). Springer-Verlag.

Segalowitz, Sid J. Two Sides of the Brain. 292p. 1983. 14.95 (ISBN 0-13-935296-1); pap. 6.95 (ISBN 0-13-935304-6). P-H.

Shakhnovich, A. R. The Brain & Regulation of Eye Movement. LC 77-2209. (Illus.). 199p. 1977. 35.00x (ISBN 0-306-30980-7, Plenum Pr). Plenum Pub.

Siesjo, B. K. Brain Energy Metabolism. LC 77-2666. 607p. 1978. 119.95 (ISBN 0-471-99515-0). Wiley.

Sjolund, B. H., ed. Brain Stem Control of Spinal Mechanisms: Proceedings of the First Eric K. Fernstrom Symposium, Lund, Sweden, 10-13 November, 1981. Bjorklund, A. (Ferrnstrom Foundation Ser.: Vol. I). 519p. 1983. 110.75 (ISBN 0-444-80429-3, Biomedical Pr). Elsevier.

Smythies, J. R. Brain Mechanisms & Behaviour. 1970. 31.50 (ISBN 0-12-653240-0). Acad Pr.

Sommerhoff, Gerd. Logic of the Living Brain. LC 73-8198. 413p. 1974. 59.95 (ISBN 0-471-81305-2, Pub. by Wiley-Interscience). Wiley.

Spatz, M., et al, eds. Circulatory & Developmental Aspects of Brain Metabolism. LC 80-18746. 450p. 1980. 59.50x (ISBN 0-306-40542-3, Plenum Pr). Plenum Pub.

Stephan, H., et al. The Brain of the Common Marmoset (Callithrix Jacchus) (Illus.). 1980. 110.00 (ISBN 0-387-09782-1). Springer-Verlag.

Sterman, M. B., et al. Brain Development & Behavior. 1971. 77.50 (ISBN 0-12-666350-5). Acad Pr.

Symposium Held at the Mount Desert Island Biological Laboratory, Salisbury Cove, Maine, Sept. 1974. Fluid Environment of the Brain: Proceedings. Cserr, Helen F., et al, eds. 1975. 43.00 (ISBN 0-12-197450-2). Acad Pr.

Teyler. Brain, Mind, & Behavior. Chaput, Linda & Mauer, Jim, eds. 142p. 1984. write for info. instr's. manual (ISBN 0-7167-1642-9); telecourse instr's. manual avail. (ISBN 0-7167-1637-2); study guide 8.95 (ISBN 0-7167-1640-2); study guide for telecourse 8.95. W H Freeman.

Thompson, Richard F. The Brain: An Introduction to Neuroscience. LC 84-25872. 376p. 1985. 29.95 (ISBN 0-7167-1461-2); pap. 17.95 (ISBN 0-7167-1462-0). W H Freeman.

Thudichum, J. L. Treatise on the Chemical Constitution of the Brain. xxiii, 262p. 1962. Repr. of 1884 ed. 21.00 (ISBN 0-208-00575-7, Archon). Shoe String.

Torre, J. C. de la. Dynamics of Brain Monoamines. 215p. 1972. 23.50x (ISBN 0-306-30557-7, Plenum Pr). Plenum Pub.

Tower, Donald B. Hensing, Seventeen Nineteen: An Account of the First Chemical Examination of the Brain & the Discovery of Phosphorus Therein. 424p. 1983. text ed. 46.50 (ISBN 0-89004-884-3). Raven.

Unsoeld, R., et al. Computer Reformations of the Brain & Skull Base: Anatomy & Critical Applications. (Illus.). 250p. 1982. 129.00 (ISBN 0-387-11544-7). Springer-Verlag.

Verity, Robert. Subject & Object: As Connected with Our Double Brain, & a New Theory of Causation. LC 78-72828. (Brainedness, Handedness, & Mental Ability Ser.). Repr. of 1870 ed. 21.50 (ISBN 0-404-60896-5). AMS Pr.

Walsh, R. Toward an Ecology of the Brain. (Illus.). 285p. 1981. text ed. 25.00 (ISBN 0-89335-087-7). SP Med & Sci Bks.

Weidenreich, Franz. The Brain & Its Role in the Phylogenetic Transformation of the Human Skull. LC 78-72707. Repr. of 1941 ed. 19.50 (ISBN 0-404-18278-X). AMS Pr.

Weiner, Herbert, et al, eds. Brain, Behavior, & Bodily Disease. (Association of Research in Nervous & Mental Disease (ARNMD) Research Publications Ser.: Vol. 59). 388p. 1981. text ed. 62.50 (ISBN 0-89004-480-5). Raven.

Widroe, Harvey J. Human Behavior & Brain Function. (Illus.). 132p. 1975. 17.75x (ISBN 0-398-03271-8). C C Thomas.

Wiedemann, K. & Hoyer, S., eds. Brain Protection: Morphological, Patophysiological, & Clinical Aspects. (Illus.). 210p. 1983. 38.00 (ISBN 0-387-12532-9). Springer-Verlag.

Wilkenson, A. W., ed. Investigation of Brain Function. LC 81-10727. (Ettore Majorana International Science Series, Life Sciences: Vol. 7). 270p. 1981. 42.50 (ISBN 0-306-40811-2, Plenum Pr). Plenum Pub.

Winson, Jonathan. Brain & Psyche: The Biology of the Unconscious. LC 84-2802. (Illus.). 312p. 1985. 16.95 (ISBN 0-385-19425-0, Anchor Pr). Doubleday.

Wurtman, Richard J. & Wurtman, Judith J., eds. Control of Feeding Behavior, & Biology of the Brain in Protein-Calorie Malnutrition. LC 75-14593. (Nutrition & the Brain Ser: Vol. 2). 323p. 1977. 45.50 (ISBN 0-89004-046-X). Raven.

--Determinants of the Availability of Nutrients to the Brain. LC 75-14593. (Nutrition & the Brain Ser.: Vol. 1). 336p. 1977. 45.50 (ISBN 0-89004-045-1). Raven.

--Nutrition & the Brain, Vol. 7. 1985. text ed. price not set (ISBN 0-88167-142-8). Raven.

--Physiological & Behavioral Effects of Food Constituents. (Nutrition & the Brain Ser.: Vol. 6). 292p. 1983. text ed. 54.50 (ISBN 0-89004-733-2). Raven.

Young, John Z. Model of the Brain. 1964. 35.00x (ISBN 0-19-857333-2). Oxford U Pr.

BRAIN–ANALYSIS AND CHEMISTRY

see Brain Chemistry

BRAIN–ATLASES

Berman, Alvin L. Brain Stem of the Cat: A Cytoarchitectonic Atlas with Stereotaxic Coordinates. (Illus.). 192p. 1968. 250.00x (ISBN 0-299-04860-8). U of Wis Pr.

Emmers, Raimond & Akert, Konrad. Stereotaxic Atlas of the Brain of the Squirrel Monkey. (Illus.). 120p. 1963. 100.00x (ISBN 0-299-02690-6). U of Wis Pr.

Ford, D. H., et al. Atlas of the Human Brain. 3rd ed. 1978. 34.00 (ISBN 0-444-80008-5). Elsevier.

Heiss, W. D., et al. Atlas der Positonen-Emissions-Tomographie de Gehirns- Atlas of Position Emission Tomography of the Brain. (Illus.). 145p. 1985. 52.00 (ISBN 0-387-15636-4). Springer Verlag.

Manocha, S. L., et al. Macaca Mulatta Enzyme Histochemistry of the Nervous System. 1970. 60.00 (ISBN 0-12-469350-4). Acad Pr.

Seeger, W. Atlas of Topographical Anatomy of the Brain & Surrounding Structures. (Illus.). vii, 544p. 1985. pap. 45.00 (ISBN 0-387-81851-0). Springer-Verlag.

Sherwood, Nancy & Timiras, Paola. A Stereotaxic Atlas of the Developing Rat Brain. LC 70-103674. (Fr. & Ger., Illus.). 1970. 70.00x (ISBN 0-520-01656-4). U of Cal Pr.

Snider, Ray S. & Niemer, William T. Stereotaxic Atlas of the Cat Brain. LC 60-7244. (Illus.). Repr. of 1961 ed. 25.90 (ISBN 0-8357-9656-6, 2016990). Bks Demand UMI.

Strausfeld, N. J. Atlas of an Insect Brain. LC 75-19499. (Illus.). 214p. 1975. 150.00 (ISBN 0-387-07343-4). Springer-Verlag.

Urban, Ivan & Philippe, Richard. A Stereotaxic Atlas of the New Zealand Rabbit's Brain. (Illus.). 92p. 1972. photocopy ed. 12.75x (ISBN 0-398-02431-6). C C Thomas.

Waddington, Margaret M. Atlas of Human Intracranial Anatomy. LC 84-70458. (Illus.). 266p. 1984. text ed. 95.00 (ISBN 0-914960-46-6). Academy Bks.

Wilson, McClure. The Anatomic Foundation of Neuroradiology of the Brain. 2nd ed. 1972. 27.50 (ISBN 0-316-94413-0). Little.

Winters, W. D., et al. A Stereotaxic Brain Atlas for Macaca Nemestrina. LC 69-16743. (Illus.). 1969. 70.00x (ISBN 0-520-01445-6). U of Cal Pr.

Yoshikawa, Tetsuo. Atlas of the Brains of Domestic Animals. LC 67-27117. (Illus.). 1968. 60.00x (ISBN 0-271-73138-9). Pa St U Pr.

BRAIN–LOCALIZATION OF FUNCTIONS

Ardila, Alfredo. The Neurology & Neuropsychology of the Right Hemisphere. (Neuroscience Monographs: Vol. 1). 200p. 1984. 58.00 (ISBN 0-677-06320-2). Gordon.

Ciba Foundation. Cerebral Vascular Smooth Muscle & Its Control. LC 77-28855. (Ciba Foundation Symposium, New Ser.: 56). pap. 102.00 (ISBN 0-317-29773-2, 2022181). Bks Demand UMI.

Critchley, McDonald. Parietal Lobes. (Illus.). 1966. Repr. of 1953 ed. 52.95x (ISBN 0-02-843300-9). Hafner.

Denny-Brown. The Cerebral Control of Movement. 222p. 1982. 50.00x (ISBN 0-85323-001-3, Pub. by Liverpool Univ England). State Mutual Bk.

Dichgans, J., et al, eds. Cerebellar Functions. (Proceedings in Life Sciences Ser.). (Illus.). 350p. 1985. 48.50 (ISBN 0-387-13728-9). Springer-Verlag.

Dunaif-Hattis, Janet. Doubling the Brain: On the Evolution of Brain Lateralization & Its Implications for Language. LC 83-48765. (American University Studies XI (Anthropology & Sociology): Vol. 3). (Illus.). 215p. (Orig.). text ed. 27.00 (ISBN 0-8204-0056-4). P Lang Pubs.

Erlich, Y. H., et al, eds. Modulators, Mediators, & Specifiers in Brain Function. LC 79-14523. (Advances in Experimental Medicine & Biology Ser.: Vol. 116). 343p. 1979. 49.50x (ISBN 0-306-40173-8, Plenum Pr). Plenum Pub.

Fadely, Jack L. & Hosler, Virginia N. Case Studies in Left & Right Hemispheric Functioning. (Illus.). 182p. 1983. 19.50x (ISBN 0-398-04792-8). C C Thomas.

Fulton. The Frontal Lobes & Human Behaviour. 30p. 1982. 50.00x (ISBN 0-85323-311-X, Pub. by LIverpool Univ England). State Mutual Bk.

Goldstein, Menek, et al, eds. Ergot Compounds & Brain Function: Neuroendocrine & Neuropsychiatric Aspects. Calne, D. & Lieberman, A. (Advances in Biochemical Psychopharmacology Ser.: Vol. 23). 441p. 1980. text ed. 64.50 (ISBN 0-89004-450-3). Raven.

Jacobs, Barry L. & Gelperin, Alan, eds. Serotonin Neurotransmission & Behavior. 430p. 1981. text ed. 65.00x (ISBN 0-262-10023-1). MIT Pr.

Jakobson, Roman & Santilli, Kathy. Brain & Language: Cerebral Hemispheres & Linguistic Structure in Mutual Light. (New York University Slavic Papers: No. 4). 1980. 4.95 (ISBN 0-89357-068-0). Slavica.

Kertesz, Andrew, ed. Localization in Neuropsychology. LC 83-2537. 1983. 53.00 (ISBN 0-12-405050-6). Acad Pr.

Marangos, Paul J. & Cohen, Robert M. Brain Receptor Methodologies, Pt. A. (Neurobiological Research Ser.). 1984. 56.00 (ISBN 0-12-470350-X). Acad Pr.

Moore, Ernest, ed. Bases of Auditory Brain Stem Evoked Responses. 481p. 1983. 31.00 (ISBN 0-8089-1465-0, 792976). Grune.

Palm, G. Neural Assemblies: An Alternative Approach to Artificial Intelligence. (Studies of Brain Function: Vol. 7). (Illus.). 244p. 1982. 42.00 (ISBN 0-387-11366-5). Springer-Verlag.

Perecman, Ellen, ed. Cognitive Processing in the Right Hemisphere. (Perspectives in Neurolinguistics, Neuropsychology & Psycholinguistics Ser.). 1983. 39.00 (ISBN 0-12-550680-5). Acad Pr.

Pribram, Karl H. Languages of the Brain: Experimental Paradoxes & Principles in Neuropsychology. 5th ed. 432p. 1982. Repr. of 1971 ed. text ed. 35.00 (ISBN 0-913412-22-8). Brandon Hse.

Segalowitz, S. J., ed. Language Functions & Brain Organization. 1983. 45.00 (ISBN 0-12-635640-8). Acad Pr.

BRENT-GOOSE

Einarsen, Arthur S. Black Brant: Sea Goose of the Pacific Coast. LC 63-10796. (Illus.). 160p. 1965. 11.50x (ISBN 0-295-73730-1). U of Wash Pr.

BREWING

see also Ale; Beer; Enzymes; Liquors; Malt

Anderson, Stanley F. & Hull, Raymond. Art of Making Beer. rev. ed. 1971. pap. 5.95 (ISBN 0-8015-0380-9, 0578-170, Hawthorn). Dutton.

Barry, C. J. Home Brewed Beers & Stouts. 5th ed. (Illus.). 172p. Date not set. pap. 4.95 (ISBN 0-900841-58-3, Pub. by Aztex Corp). Argus Bks.

Beadle, Leigh P. The New Brew It Yourself: The Complete Guide to Home Brewing. 99p. 1981. 5.95 (ISBN 0-374-51536-0). FS&G.

Berry, C. J. Hints on Home Brewing. (Illus.). Date not set. pap. 1.95 (ISBN 0-900841-20-6, Pub. by Aztex Corp). Argus Bks.

Burch, Byron. Quality Brewing: A Guidebook for the Home Production of Fine Beers. pap. 2.50 (ISBN 0-9604284-0-2). Joby Bks.

European Brewery Convention. Elsevier's Dictionary of Brewing. 264p. 1983. 83.00 (ISBN 0-444-42131-9). Elsevier.

European Brewery Convention, ed. European Brewery Convention: Proceedings of the International Congress, 18th, Copenhagen, 1981. 740p. 80.00 (ISBN 0-904147-30-4). IRL Pr.

Hoigh, J. S., et al. Malting & Brewing Science, Vol. 2: Hopped Wort & Beer. 512p. 1982. 110.00x (ISBN 0-412-16590-2, Pub. by Chapman & Hall England). State Mutual Bk.

Hough, J. S., et al. Malting & Brewing Science, Vol. 1. 2nd ed. 300p. 1982. 42.00x (ISBN 0-412-16580-5, NO. 6550, Pub. by Chapman & Hall); Vol. 2, 1983. 65.00x (ISBN 0-412-16590-2, NO. 6511); Set. 95.00x (NO. 6877). Methuen Inc.

Hough, James S. Biotechnology of Malting & Brewing. (Cambridge Studies in Biotechnology 1). (Illus.). 168p. 1985. 39.50 (ISBN 0-521-25672-0). Cambridge U Pr.

Line, Dave. Beer Kits & Brewing. (Illus.). 154p. Date not set. pap. 4.95 (ISBN 0-900841-59-1, Pub. by Aztex Corp). Argus Bks.

--The Big Book of Brewing. (Illus.). 256p. Date not set. pap. 8.95 (ISBN 0-900841-34-6, Pub. by Aztex Corp). Argus Bks.

--Brewing Beers Like Those You Buy. (Illus.). 158p. Date not set. pap. 4.95 (ISBN 0-900841-51-6, Pub. by Aztex Corp). Argus Bks.

Lovett, Maurice. Brewing & Breweries. (Album Ser.: No. 72). (Illus.). 32p. 1985. pap. 3.50 (ISBN 0-85263-568-0, Pub. by Shire Pubns England). Seven Hills Bks.

McCall, Peter. Diabetic Brewing & Winemaking. 84p. Date not set. pap. 3.95 (ISBN 0-900841-60-5, Pub. by Aztex Corp). Argus Bks.

Miller, David. Home Brewing for Americans. (Illus.). 110p. Date not set. pap. 3.95 (ISBN 0-900841-61-3, Pub. by Aztex Corp). Argus Bks.

Newsom, Wilf. The Happy Brewer. (Illus.). 109p. Date not set. pap. 3.95 (ISBN 0-900841-49-4, Pub. by Aztex Corp). Argus Bks.

Orton, Vrest. The Homemade Beer Book. LC 72-89742. (Illus.). 1973. pap. 4.95 (ISBN 0-8048-1086-9). C E Tuttle.

Papazian, Charlie. The Complete Joy of Home Brewing. (Illus.). 352p. (Orig.). 1984. pap. 8.95 (ISBN 0-380-88369-4). Avon.

--Joy of Brewing. rev. ed. (Illus.). 88p. 1980. pap. 4.50 (ISBN 0-9604130-0-6). Log Boom.

Pollock, J. R., ed. Brewing Science, Vol. 1. (Food Science & Technology Ser.). 1979. 87.50 (ISBN 0-12-561001-7). Acad Pr.

--Brewing Science, Vol. 2. (Food Science & Technology Ser.). 1981. 98.50 (ISBN 0-12-561002-5). Acad Pr.

Pritchard, Bob. All about Beer & Home Brewing. (Illus.). 142p. Date not set. pap. 4.95 (ISBN 0-900841-72-9, Pub. by Aztex Corp). Argus Bks.

Reese, M. R. Better Beer & How to Brew It. LC 81-7003. (Illus.). 128p. 1981. pap. 6.95 (ISBN 0-88266-257-0). Garden Way Pub.

Shales, Ken. Brewing Better Beers. 2nd. ed. (Illus.). 92p. Date not set. pap. 4.95 (ISBN 0-900841-64-8, Pub. by Aztex Corp). Argus Bks.

Tritton, S. M. Tritton's Guide to Better Wine & Beer Making for Beginners. (Illus.). 160p. (Orig.). 1969. pap. 4.50 (ISBN 0-571-09171-7). Faber & Faber.

Turner, Ben. Home-Brewed Beer & Cider. (Illus.). 96p. (Orig.). 1981. pap. 6.95 (ISBN 0-7158-0638-6, Pub. by EP Publishing England). Sterling.

BREWING INDUSTRY

see also Ale; Beer

Baron, Stanley W. Brewed in America: A History of Beer & Ale in the United States. LC 72-5030. (Technology & Society Ser.). (Illus.). 424p. 1972. Repr. of 1962 ed. 33.00 (ISBN 0-405-04683-9). Ayer Co Pubs.

Breweries & Malsters in Europe, 1980. 69th ed. LC 46-33153. Orig. Title: Brauereien und Malzereien in Europa 1980. (Eng, Fr. & Ger.). 610p. (Orig.). 1980. 92.50x (ISBN 3-8203-0034-1). Intl Pubns Serv.

DeRasor, Roberto. Alcohol Distillers Manual. 205p. 1980. pap. 12.95 (ISBN 0-686-92650-1). Rutan Pub.

Donnachie, Ian. A History of the Brewing Industry in Scotland. 1979. text ed. 39.50x (ISBN 0-85976-032-4). Humanities.

Downard, William L. Dictionary of the History of the American Brewing & Distilling Industries. LC 79-6826. (Illus.). xxv, 268p. 1980. lib. bdg. 49.95 (ISBN 0-313-21330-5, DOD/). Greenwood.

EBC, ed. European Brewery Convention: Thesaurus, 2 vols. 2nd ed. 945p. 1983. Set. pap. 120.00 (ISBN 0-904147-39-8). IRL Pr.

European Brewery Convention, ed. European Brewery Convention: Proceedings of the International Congress, 19th, London, 1983. (Illus.). 728p. 1983. 90.00 (ISBN 0-904147-50-9). IRL Pr.

--European Brewery Convention: Proceedings of the International Congress, 17th, West Berlin, 1979. 874p. 1979. 70.00 (ISBN 9-070143-09-7). IRL Pr.

--European Brewery Convention: Proceedings of the International Congress, 16th, Amsterdam, 1977. 831p. 1977. 70.00 (ISBN 9-070143-03-8). IRL Pr.

Hawkins, K. H. & Pass, C. L. The Brewing Industry. 1979. pap. text ed. 17.50x (ISBN 0-435-84400-8). Gower Pub Co.

Hirt, Walter & Gutknecht, Vereina, eds. International Brewer's Directory, 1979. 8th ed. (Illus., Orig.). 1979. pap. 150.00x (ISBN 0-8002-0012-8). Intl Pubns Serv.

Keddie, James & Cleghorn, William. Brewing in Developing Countries. 200p. 1980. pap. 11.50x (ISBN 0-7073-0250-1, Pub. by Scottish Academic Pr Scotland). Columbia U Pr.

Modern Brewery Age Bluebook. 85.00 (ISBN 0-686-31373-9). Busn Journals.

Salem, Frederick W. Beer, Its History & Its Economic Value As a National Beverage. LC 72-5072. (Technology & Society Ser.). (Illus.). 292p. 1972. Repr. of 1880 ed. 19.00 (ISBN 0-405-04722-3). Ayer Co Pubs.

BRICK BUILDING

see Building, Brick

BRICKLAYING

see also Masonry

Brann, Donald R. Bricklaying Simplified. rev. ed. LC 77-140968. (Illus.). 1976. lib. bdg. 5.95 (ISBN 0-87733-068-9). Easi-Bild.

--Bricklaying Simplified. LC 77-140968. 1979. pap. 6.95 (ISBN 0-87733-668-7). Easi-Bild.

British Ceramic Society, ed. Load-Bearing Brickwork. 60.00x (ISBN 0-686-78853-2, Pub. by Brit Ceramic Soc England). State Mutual Bk.

Gilbreth, Frank B. Bricklaying System. LC 74-14805. (Management History Ser.: No. 31). 325p. 1974. Repr. of 1909 ed. 24.00 (ISBN 0-87960-034-9). Hive Pub.

Hendry, A. W., et al. An Introduction to Loadbearing Brickwork Design. LC 81-4121. (Series in Engineering Science: Civil Engineering). 184p. 1981. 54.95x (ISBN 0-470-27227-9). Halsted Pr.

Initial Skills in Bricklaying: A Practical Guide. LC 80-41756. (Illus.). 100p. 1981. 18.00 (ISBN 0-08-025424-1); pap. 10.00 (ISBN 0-08-025423-3). Pergamon.

Lloyd, Nathaniel. A History of English Brickwork. LC 72-87653. (Illus.). 1973. Repr. of 1925 ed. lib. bdg. 33.00x (ISBN 0-405-08750-0, Pub. by Blom). Ayer Co Pubs.

Rudman, Jack. Bricklayer. (Career Examination Ser.: C-110). (Cloth bdg. avail. on request). pap. 12.00 (ISBN 0-8373-0110-6). Natl Learning.

--Foreman Bricklayer. (Career Examination Ser.: C-2020). (Cloth bdg. avail. on request). pap. 10.00 (ISBN 0-8373-2020-8). Natl Learning.

U. S. Army. Concrete, Masonry & Brickwork: A Practical Handbook for the Homeowner & Small Builder. LC 75-12130. (Illus.). 204p. 1975. pap. 5.95 (ISBN 0-486-23203-4). Dover.

BRICKMAKING

see also Kilns

Boudreau, Eugene. Making the Adobe Brick. (Illus.). 1972. pap. 6.95 (ISBN 0-394-70617-X, Dist. by Random). Bookworks.

Brickmaking Plant: Industry Profile. (Development & Transfer of Technology Ser.). pap. 5.00 (ISBN 0-686-93193-9, UN78/2B9, UN). Unipub.

Hammond, Martin. Bricks & Brickmaking. (Albums Ser.: No. 75). (Illus.). 32p. (Orig.). 1981. pap. 2.95 (ISBN 0-85263-573-7, 3381289, Pub. by Shire Pubns England). Seven Hills Bks.

--Bricks & Brickmaking. (Shire Album Ser.: No. 75). (Illus.). 32p. 1985. pap. 3.50 (ISBN 0-317-20299-5, Pub. by Shire Pubns England). Seven Hills Bks.

Keddie, James & William, Cleghorn. Brick Manufacture in Developing Countries. 160p. 1980. pap. 11.50x (ISBN 0-686-91951-3, Pub. by Scottish Academic Pr Scotland). Columbia U Pr.

McCollam, C. Harold. The Brick & Tile Industry in Stark County, 1809-1976: A History. LC 76-17281. pap. 87.80 (ISBN 0-317-30443-7, 2024925). Bks Demand UMI.

BRICKS

see also Bricklaying; Clay

Beech, D. G. Testing Methods for Brick & Tile Manufacture. 1974. 35.00x (ISBN 0-900910-22-4, Pub. by Brit Ceramic Soc England). State Mutual Bk.

Brick & Tile Making: Procedure & Operating Practice in the Heavy Clay Industries. Bender, W. & Handle, F., eds. 831p. 1982. 180.00 (ISBN 0-9915000-0-8, Pub. by Brauverag Germany). Heyden.

British Ceramic Society, ed. Load-Bearing Brickwork, No. 6. 1982. 77.00x (ISBN 0-686-44604-6, Pub. by Brit Ceramic Soc England). State Mutual Bk.

Hammond, Martin. Bricks & Brickmaking. (Albums Ser.: No. 75). (Illus.). 32p. (Orig.). 1981. pap. 2.95 (ISBN 0-85263-573-7, 3381289, Pub. by Shire Pubns England). Seven Hills Bks.

--Bricks & Brickmaking. (Shire Album Ser.: No. 75). (Illus.). 32p. 1985. pap. 3.50 (ISBN 0-317-20299-5, Pub. by Shire Pubns England). Seven Hills Bks.

Load-Bearing Brickwork, No. 3. 1982. 40.00x (ISBN 0-686-44597-X, Pub. by Brit Ceramic Soc England). State Mutual Bk.

Load-Bearing Brickwork, No. 5. 1982. 77.00x (ISBN 0-686-44598-8, Pub. by Brit Ceramic Soc England). State Mutual Bk.

Stokoe, Jim. Decorative & Ornamental Brickwork: 175 Photographic Illustrations. (Illus.). 96p. 1982. pap. 6.00 (ISBN 0-486-24130-0). Dover.

Structural Ceramics Advisory Group of the Structural Ceramics Research Panel. Design Guide for Reinforced Brick & Prestressed Clay Brickwork. 1977. 30.00x (ISBN 0-900910-27-5, Pub. by Brit Ceramic Soc England). State Mutual Bk.

West, H. W., et al. The Resistance to Lateral Loads of Walls Built of Calcium Silicate Bricks. 1979. 20.00x (ISBN 0-900910-33-X, Pub. by Brit Ceramic Soc England). State Mutual Bk.

BRIDGE CIRCUITS

Kibble, B. P. & Rayner, G. H. Coaxial AC Bridge Networks. 1984. 42.00 (ISBN 0-9903001-2-9, Pub. by A Hilger England). Heyden.

BRIDGE CONSTRUCTION

see Bridges; Graphic Statics; Masonry; Scaffolding; Strains and Stresses

Podolny. Construction of Cable Stayed Bridges. 2nd ed. 1986. price not set (ISBN 0-471-82655-3). Wiley.

BRIDGES

see also Arches; Girders; Influence Lines; Trusses; also names of individual bridges

AASHTO Bridge Maintenance Manual. 7.00 (ISBN 0-686-20951-6, BM-1). AASHTO.

Bridge Aerodynamics. 140p. 1981. 90.00x (ISBN 0-7277-0135-5, Pub. by Tech Pr). State Mutual Bk.

Bridge Inspection. (Road Research Ser.). 1976. 6.00x (ISBN 92-64-11540-4). OECD.

Construction Manual for Highway Bridges & Incidental Structures, 1973. 66p. 1973. pap. 3.00 (ISBN 0-686-40564-1). AASHTO.

Cusens, A. R. & Pama, R. P. Bridge Deck Analysis. LC 74-3726. 278p. 1975. 64.95 (ISBN 0-471-18998-7, Pub. by Wiley-Interscience). Wiley.

Degenkolb, Oris H. Concrete Box Girder Bridges. (American Concrete Institute Monograph Ser: No. 10). (Illus.). 106p. 1977. text ed. 14.50x (ISBN 0-8138-1815-X). Iowa St U Pr.

Derucher & Heins. Bridges & Pier Protective Systems & Devices. (Civil Engineering Ser.: Vol. 1). 1979. 49.75 (ISBN 0-8247-6895-7). Dekker.

Farraday, R. V. & Charlton, F. G. Hydraulic Factors in Bridge Design. 110p. 1983. 29.75x (ISBN 0-946466-00-9). Am Soc Civil Eng.

George, Leland E. Exactness in Bridge Bidding. 1982. 6.95 (ISBN 0-8062-1909-2). Carlton.

Guide for Bridge Maintenance Management. 1980. 4.00 (ISBN 0-686-29461-0). AASHTO.

Guide Specifications for Fracture Critical Non-Redundant Steel Bridge Members. 34p. pap. 4.00 (ISBN 0-686-32349-1, GFC). AASHTO.

Guide Specifications for Horizontally Curved Highway Bridges. 160p. 1980. pap. 7.00 (ISBN 0-686-32348-3, GHC). AASHTO.

Guidelines for Developing a Bridge Maintenance Program. 28p. 10.00 (ISBN 0-917084-17-9). Am Public Works.

Henry, D. & Jerome, J. A. Modern British Bridges. (Illus.). 189p. 1965. 27.75 (ISBN 0-85334-058-7, Pub. by Elsevier Applied Sci England). Elsevier.

Howson, Elmer T., ed. Bridges & Trestles from Various Railway Engineering & Maintenance Cyclopedias from 1921, No. 54. (Train Shed Ser.). (Illus.). 1977. pap. 4.50 (ISBN 0-912318-89-9). N K Gregg.

Lee & Wood, L. J. Adjustment in the Urban System: The Tasman Bridge Collapse & Its Effects on Metropolitan Hobart. (Progress in Planning Ser.: Vol. 15, Pt. 2). 85p. 1981. pap. 14.75 (ISBN 0-08-026810-2). Pergamon.

Leliavsky, S. Arches & Short Span Bridges. (Design Textbooks in Civil Engineering: Vol. 7). (Illus.). 250p. 1982. 39.95 (ISBN 0-412-22560-3, NO. 6686, Pub. by Chapman & Hall England). Methuen Inc.

Long-Span Bridges: O.H. Centennial Conference, Nov. 13-14, 1979, Vol. 352 Of The Annals. LC 80-29312. (Annals of the New York Academy of Sciences). 281p. 1980. 56.00x (ISBN 0-89766-093-5). NY Acad Sci.

Loo, Yew C. & Cusens, Anthony R. The Finite-Strip Method in Bridge Engineering. (Viewpoint Publication Ser.). (Illus.). 1979. pap. text ed. 25.00x (ISBN 0-7210-1041-5). Scholium Intl.

Mair, George. Bridge Down: A True Story. LC 81-40335. (Illus.). 256p. 1982. 16.95 (ISBN 0-8128-2822-4). Stein & Day.

Manual for Maintenance Inspection of Bridges. 74p. 1983. pap. 4.00 (ISBN 0-686-40592-7). AASHTO.

Mathivat, Jacques. The Cantilever Construction of Prestressed Concrete Bridges. LC 82-23744. 341p. 1983. 69.95 (ISBN 0-471-10343-8, Pub. by Wiley-Interscience). Wiley.

Mock, Elizabeth B. The Architecture of Bridges. LC 70-169309. (Museum of Modern Art Publications in Reprint). (Illus.). 128p. 1972. Repr. of 1949 ed. 22.00 (ISBN 0-405-01568-2). Ayer Co Pubs.

Molof, Alan H. & Turkstra, Carl J., eds. Infrastructure: Maintenance & Repair of Public Works. (Annals of The New York Academy of Science Ser.: Vol. 431). 370p. 1984. lib. bdg. 20.00x (ISBN 0-89766-256-3); pap. 20.00x (ISBN 0-89766-257-1). NY Acad Sci.

OECD. Bridge Maintenance. (Road Research Ser.). 130p. (Orig.). 1981. pap. text ed. 8.50 (ISBN 92-64-12247-8). OECD.

OECD Staff. Bridge Rehabilitation & Strengthening. (Road Transport Research Ser.). 104p. 1983. pap. 15.00x (ISBN 92-64-12528-0). OECD.

Park, Sung H. Bridge Inspection & Structural Analysis: Handbook of Bridge Inspection. LC 80-81421. (Illus.). 312p. (Orig.). 1980. pap. text ed. 20.00x (ISBN 0-9604440-0-9). S H Park.

--Bridge Rehabilitation & Replacement (Bridge Repair Practice) LC 82-90094. (Illus.). 818p. 1984. text ed. 50.00x (ISBN 0-9604440-1-7). S H Park.

Peters, Tom F. The Development of Long-Span Bridge Building. (Eng, Fr. & Ger., Illus.). 188p. (Orig.). 1980. pap. text ed. 19.95 (ISBN 0-686-78178-3, Pub. by Verlag der Fachverein (ETH)). Interbk Inc.

Phillps, G. A. Thames Crossings: Bridges, Tunnels & Ferries. LC 81-65954. (Illus.). 288p. 1981. 37.50 (ISBN 0-7153-8202-0). David & Charles.

Report on Highway & Bridge Surveys. (Manual & Report on Engineering Practice Ser.: No. 44). 159p. 1962. pap. 7.50x (ISBN 0-87262-219-3). Am Soc Civil Eng.

Ruddock, E. C. Arch Bridges & Their Builders, 1735-1835. LC 77-82514. (Illus.). 1979. 95.00 (ISBN 0-521-21816-0). Cambridge U Pr.

Rudman, Jack. Assistant Bridge Operator. (Career Examination Ser.: C-26). (Cloth bdg. avail. on request). pap. 10.00 (ISBN 0-8373-0026-6). Natl Learning.

--Assistant Bridge Operator Trainee. (Career Examination Ser.: C-79). (Cloth bdg. avail. on request). pap. 10.00 (ISBN 0-8373-0079-7). Natl Learning.

--Bridge & Tunnel Lieutenant. (Career Examination Ser.: C-111). (Cloth bdg. avail. on request). pap. 12.00 (ISBN 0-8373-0111-4). Natl Learning.

--Bridge & Tunnel Maintainer. (Career Examination Ser.: C-94). (Cloth bdg. avail. on request). pap. 10.00 (ISBN 0-8373-0094-0). Natl Learning.

--Bridge & Tunnel Supervisor. (Career Examination Ser.: C-2222). (Cloth bdg. avail. on request). pap. 12.00 (ISBN 0-8373-2222-7). Natl Learning.

--Bridge Maintenance Supervisor. (Career Examination Ser.: C-2289). (Cloth bdg. avail. on request). 1977. pap. 12.00 (ISBN 0-8373-2289-8). Natl Learning.

--Bridge Mechanic. (Career Examination Ser.: C-1141). (Cloth bdg. avail. on request). pap. 10.00 (ISBN 0-8373-1141-1). Natl Learning.

--Bridge Operations Supervisor. (Career Examination Ser.: C-1142). (Cloth bdg. avail. on request). pap. 12.00 (ISBN 0-8373-1142-X). Natl Learning.

--Bridge Operator. (Career Examination Ser.: C-92). (Cloth bdg. avail. on request). pap. 10.00 (ISBN 0-8373-0092-4). Natl Learning.

--Bridge Operator-in-Charge. (Career Examination Ser.: C-91). (Cloth bdg. avail. on request). pap. 12.00 (ISBN 0-8373-0091-6). Natl Learning.

--Bridge Repair Supervisor. (Career Examination Ser.: C-2288). (Cloth bdg. avail. on request). 1977. pap. 12.00 (ISBN 0-8373-2288-X). Natl Learning.
--Senior Bridge & Tunnel Maintainer. (Career Examination Ser.: C-1472). (Cloth bdg. avail. on request). pap. 12.00 (ISBN 0-8373-1472-0). Natl Learning.
--Sergeant-Bridge & Tunnel Authority. (Career Examination Ser.: C-732). (Cloth bdg. avail. on request). pap. 12.00 (ISBN 0-8373-0732-5). Natl Learning.
Shank, W. H. Historic Bridges of Pennsylvania. 1980. 3.00 (ISBN 0-933788-33-9). Am Canal & Transport.
Standard Specifications for Highway Bridges. 1983. 25.00 (ISBN 0-686-23410-3, HB-13). AASHTO.
Standard Specifications for Movable Highway Bridges. 1979. pap. 5.00 (ISBN 0-686-27096-7, MHB-70). AASHTO.
Steinman, David B. The Builders of the Bridge: The Story of John Roebling & His Son. LC 72-5074. (Technology & Society Ser.). (Illus.). 462p. 1972. Repr. of 1950 ed. 35.50 (ISBN 0-405-04724-X). Ayer Co Pubs.
Swanson, Leslie C. Covered Bridges in Illinois, Iowa, & Wisconsin. rev. ed. (Illus., Orig.). 1970. pap. 3.00 (ISBN 0-911466-14-2). Swanson.
Troitsky, M. S. Cable-Stayed Bridges: Theory & Design. 385p. 1977. text ed. 76.00x (ISBN 0-258-97034-0, Pub. by Granada England). Brookfield Pub Co.
Turner, Dennis F. Building Sub-Contract Forms. 200p. 1984. cancelled (ISBN 0-246-11948-9, Pub. by Granada England). Sheridan.
Tytler, I. F., et al. Vehicles & Bridging. (Battlefield Weapons Systems & Technology Ser.: Vol. 1). (Illus.). 256p. 1985. 26.00 (ISBN 0-08-028322-5); pap. 16.00 (ISBN 0-08-028323-3). Pergamon.
Welt, Suzanne F. Covered Bridges of Oregon. (Illus.). 48p. 1982. 20.00 (ISBN 0-88014-044-5). Mosaic Pr OH.
White, et al. Bridge Maintenance, Inspection, & Evaluation. (Civil Engineering Ser.: Vol. 3). 272p. 1981. 39.75 (ISBN 0-8247-1086-X). Dekker.
Whitney, Charles S. Bridges: Their Art, Science & Evolution. (Illus.). 352p. 1983. 7.98 (ISBN 0-517-40244-0, Greenwich Hse). Outlet Bk Co.
Wittfoht, H. Building Bridges: History, Technology, Construction. 352p. 1984. 99.00 (ISBN 0-9908000-0-8, Pub. by Beton Bks W Germany). Heyden.
Wright, G. N. Bridges of Britain. 96p. 1981. 30.00x (ISBN 0-686-97139-6, Pub. by D B Barton England). State Mutual Bk.
Yilmas, Cetin, ed. Analysis & Design of Bridges. 1984. lib. bdg. 57.00 (ISBN 90-2472-932-7, Pub. by Martinus Nijhoff Netherlands). Kluwer Academic.

BRIDGES-HISTORY

Adams, Kramer. Covered Bridges of the West. LC 63-19906. (Illus.). 1963. 14.95 (ISBN 0-8310-7037-4). Howell-North.
Dillon, Richard, et al. High Steel. LC 78-72833. (Illus.). 1979. 25.00 (ISBN 0-89087-191-4). Celestial Arts.
Labovitz, Annette. Secrets of the Past, Bridges to the Future. Hershon, Jerome, ed. (Illus.). 190p. (Orig.). 1983. pap. text ed. 9.95x (ISBN 0-930029-00-3, TX1-317-473-TXV); tchr's. ed. 5.95x (ISBN 0-930029-01-1). Central Agency.
Shank, W. H. Historic Bridges of Pennsylvania. 1980. 3.00 (ISBN 0-933788-33-9). Am Canal & Transport.
Trachtenberg, Alan. Brooklyn Bridge: Fact & Symbol. 2nd ed. LC 78-68548. (Illus.). 1979. pap. 8.95 (ISBN 0-226-81115-8, P828, Phoen). U of Chicago Pr.

BRIDGES, CONCRETE

Aesthetics of Bridge Design. (PCI Journal Reprints Ser.). 20p. pap. 5.00 (ISBN 0-686-40001-1, JR62). Prestressed Concrete.
American Concrete Institute. Concrete Bridge Design: Papers Presented to the First International Symposium on Concrete Bridge Design, Toronto, 1967. LC 68-54701. (American Concrete Institute Publications: SP-23). (Illus.). pap. 160.00 (ISBN 0-317-10038-6, 2003079). Bks Demand UMI.
Applications of Stay-in-Place Prestressed Bridge Deck Panels. (PCI Journal Reprints Ser.). 8p. pap. 4.00 (ISBN 0-686-40119-0, JR211). Prestressed Concrete.
Beckett, Derrick. Concrete Bridges: An Introduction to Structural Design. (Illus.). 1973. 42.50x (ISBN 0-903384-01-9). Intl Ideas.
Degenkolb, Oris H. Concrete Box Girder Bridges. (Monograph No. 10). 1977. 29.25 (ISBN 0-685-85763-8) (ISBN 0-685-85764-6). ACI.
--Concrete Box Girder Bridges. (American Concrete Institute Monograph Ser: No. 10). (Illus.). 106p. 1977. text ed. 14.50x (ISBN 0-8138-1815-X). Iowa St U Pr.
Eleventh Street Bridge. (PCI Journal Reprints Ser.). 5p. pap. 4.00 (ISBN 0-686-40140-9, JR236). Prestressed Concrete.
Heins, Conrad P. Design of Modern Concrete Highway Bridges. Lawrie, Richard A., ed. 635p. 1983. text ed. 74.95x (ISBN 0-471-87544-9, Pub. by Wiley-Interscience). Wiley.
Mathivat, Jacques. The Cantilever Construction of Prestressed Concrete Bridges. LC 82-23744. 341p. 1983. 69.95 (ISBN 0-471-10343-8, Pub. by Wiley-Interscience). Wiley.
Pennells, Ernest. Concrete Bridge Designer's Manual. (Viewpoint Publication Ser.). (Illus.). 1978. text ed. 47.50x (ISBN 0-7210-1083-0). Scholium Intl.
Podolny, Walter & Muller, Jean M. Construction & Design of Prestressed Concrete Segmental Bridges. LC 81-13025. (Wiley Ser. of Practical Construction Guides). 561p. 1982. 82.50x (ISBN 0-471-05658-8, Pub. by Wiley Interscience). Wiley.
Rowe, R. E. Concrete Bridge Design. (Illus.). 268p. 1966. 53.75 (ISBN 0-85334-110-9, Pub. by Elsevier Applied Sci England). Elsevier.

BRIDGES, COVERED

see Covered Bridges

BRIDGES, ELECTRIC

see Bridge Circuits

BRIDGES, IRON AND STEEL

see also Steel, Structural

American Society of Civil Engineers, compiled by. Metal Bridges. 444p. 1974. pap. 49.00x (ISBN 0-87262-101-4). Am Soc Civil Eng.
Chatterjee, Sukhen. Design of Modern Steel Bridges. 300p. 1986. 50.00x (ISBN 0-246-11718-4, Pub. by Granada England). Sheridan.
Dillon, Richard, et al. High Steel. LC 78-72833. (Illus.). 1979. 25.00 (ISBN 0-89087-191-4). Celestial Arts.
Fisher, John W. Fatigue & Fracture in Steel Bridges: Case Studies. LC 83-23495. 315p. 1984. 45.95x (ISBN 0-471-80469-X, Pub. by Wiley-Interscience). Wiley.
Heins, C. P. & Firmage, D. A. Design of Modern Steel Highway Bridges. LC 78-9084. 463p. 1979. 52.95x (ISBN 0-471-04263-3, Pub. by Wiley-Interscience). Wiley.
Repair & Strengthening of Old Steel Truss Bridges. 144p. 1979. pap. 14.00x (ISBN 0-87262-194-4). Am Soc Civil Eng.

BRIDGES, SUSPENSION

Cassady, Stephen. Spanning the Gate: Building the Golden Gate Bridge. LC 77-83284. (Illus.). 132p. 1979. 20.00 (ISBN 0-916290-06-9). Squarebooks.
Construction of Trail Suspended Bridges in Nepal: An Application of Traditional Technology. 20p. 1981. pap. 5.00 (ISBN 92-808-0251-8, TUNU157, UNU). Unipub.
Gimsing, N. J. Cable Supported Bridges: Concepts & Design. 400p. 1983. 74.95 (ISBN 0-471-90130-X). Wiley.
Horton, Tom. Superspan. LC 82-17746. (Illus.). 96p. (Orig.). 1983. pap. 8.95 (ISBN 0-87701-277-6). Chronicle Bks.
Troitsky, M. S. Cable-Stayed Bridges: Theory & Design. 1977. 60.00x (ISBN 0-8464-0231-9). Beekman Pubs.

BRIDGES, WOODEN

see also Covered Bridges

American Wooden Bridges. 182p. 1976. pap. 24.75x (ISBN 0-87262-002-6). Am Soc Civil Eng.
Blaser, Werner. Wooden Bridges in Switzerland (Ponts de Bois en Suisse; Schweizer Holzbrucken) 184p. 1982. 52.95 (ISBN 0-8176-1334-X). Birkhauser.

BRIGHTNESS (ASTRONOMY)

see Photometry, Astronomical

BRINDLEY, JAMES, 1716-1772

Banks, A. G. & Schofield, R. B. Brindley at Wet Earth Colliery. LC 68-8316. (Illus.). 1968. 19.95x (ISBN 0-678-05578-5). Kelley.
Bode, H. James Brindley. (Clarendon Biography Ser.). (Illus.). 1973. pap. 3.50 (ISBN 0-912728-59-0). Newbury Bks.

BRINE

see Salt

BRISTOL AIRPLANES

Bruce, J. M. The Bristol Fighter. (Vintage Warbirds Ser.). (Illus.). 64p. (Orig.). 1985. pap. 5.95 (ISBN 0-85368-704-8, Pub. by Arms & Armour). Sterling.
Gilbert, James, ed. The Books of Miles, Westland & Bristol Aircraft: An Original Anthology, 3 vols. in 1. LC 79-7281. (Flight: Its First Seventy-Five Years Ser.). (Illus.). 1979. lib. bdg. 58.00x (ISBN 0-405-12190-3). Ayer Co Pubs.

BRITISH SCIENCE

see Science, British

BRITTANY SPANIEL

see Dogs-Breeds-Brittany Spaniel

BRITTLENESS

see also Fracture Mechanics; also subdivision Brittleness under special materials, e.g. Metals-Brittleness

Acquaviva, Samuel J. & Bortz, Seymour A., eds. Structural Ceramics & Testing of Brittle Materials. 232p. 1968. 93.75 (ISBN 0-677-12770-7). Gordon.
Fracture Mechanics Applied to Brittle Measurements: 11th Conference, STP 678. 232p. 1979. 25.00x (ISBN 0-8031-0365-4, 04-678000-30). ASTM.
Jayatilaka, Ayal De S. Fracture of Engineering Brittle Materials. (Illus.). 378p. 1979. 68.50 (ISBN 0-85334-825-1, Pub. by Elsevier Applied Sci England). Elsevier.
Lawn, B. R. & Wilshaw, T. R. Fracture of Brittle Solids. LC 74-12970. (Cambridge Solid State Science Ser.). (Illus.). 160p. 1975. pap. 21.95x (ISBN 0-521-09952-8). Cambridge U Pr.

BRITTLENESS OF METALS

see Metals-Brittleness

BROACHING MACHINES

Linsley, Horace E. Broaching: Tooling & Practice. LC 61-9128. pap. 56.00 (ISBN 0-317-10955-3, 2001909). Bks Demand UMI.

BROADCASTING

see also Radio Broadcasting; Television Broadcasting

Bittner, J. Broadcasting: An Introduction. 1980. 26.95 (ISBN 0-13-083535-8). P-H.
--Professional Broadcasting: A Brief Introduction. 1981. pap. 19.95 (ISBN 0-13-725465-2). P-H.
Browne, Donald R. International Radio Broadcasting: The Limits of the Limitless Medium. LC 81-22707. 384p. 1982. 34.95 (ISBN 0-03-059619-X). Praeger.
The Catalog of the Museum of Broadcasting, 2 vols. 1981. write for info. Ayer Co Pubs.
Clift, Charles, III & Greer, Archie, eds. Broadcast Programming, the Current Perspective. 7th ed. LC 81-40728. 260p. (Orig.). 1981. pap. text ed. 9.75 (ISBN 0-8191-1894-X). U Pr of Amer.
De Noriega, L. A. & Leach, F. Broadcasting in Mexico. (Case Studies on Broadcasting Systems). (Orig.). 1979. pap. 17.95x (ISBN 0-7100-0416-8). Routledge & Kegan.
Foster, Eugene S. Understanding Broadcasting. 2nd ed. (Illus.). 544p. 1982. pap. text ed. 25.95 (ISBN 0-394-35000-6, RanC). Random.
Halberstam, David. The Powers That Be. LC 78-20605. 1979. 17.95 (ISBN 0-394-50381-3). Knopf.
International Broadcasting Convention, 1982. (IEE Conference Publication Ser.: No. 220). 412p. 1982. pap. 75.00 (ISBN 0-85296-263-0, IC220). Inst Elect Eng.
International Broadcasting Convention '84. (IEE Conference Publications Ser.: No. 240). 418p. 1984. pap. 98.00 (ISBN 0-85296-295-9). Inst Elect Eng.
International Broadcasting Convention (1974: London) International Broadcasting Covention: 23-27 September, 1974. LC 75-308229. (Institution of Electrical Engineers Conference Publications Ser.: No. 119). pap. 84.80 (ISBN 0-317-10096-3, 2003626). Bks Demand UMI.
Johnson, Betty S. & Nagai, Gayle A. Triangle Broadcasting Company: A Word Information Processing Simulation. 192p. (Orig.). 1985. pap. text ed. 16.00scp (ISBN 0-672-98562-4); instr's guide 7.33scp (ISBN 0-672-98565-9); wkbk. 4.00scp (ISBN 0-672-98563-2); 3 tapes 66.00scp (ISBN 0-672-98564-0). Bobbs.
McCavitt, William E. Radio & Television: A Selected, Annotated Bibliography Supplement One: 1977-1981. LC 82-5743. 167p. 1982. 15.00 (ISBN 0-8108-1556-7). Scarecrow.
Palm, Rick, ed. FCC Rule Book. 1984. 3.00 (ISBN 0-87259-002-X). Am Radio.
Pepper, Robert M. The Formation of the Public Broadcasting Service. new ed. Sterling, Christopher H., ed. LC 78-21732. (Dissertations in Broadcasting Ser.). 1979. lib. bdg. 34.50x (ISBN 0-405-11769-8). Ayer Co Pubs.
Schiller, Herbert I. Mass Communications & American Empire. 1971. pap. 5.95x (ISBN 0-8070-6175-1, BP386). Beacon Pr.
Smith, F. Leslie. Perspectives on Radio & Television: An Introduction to Broadcasting in the United States. (Illus.). 1979. text ed. 23.95 scp (ISBN 0-06-046309-0, HarpC); inst. manual avail. (ISBN 0-06-366299-X). Har-Row.
Sprague, Michael. New Communications Technologies & Public Broadcasting: Impacts & Opportunities. 30p. 1981. pap. 25.00 (ISBN 0-941888-07-X). Comm Media.
Steiner, Peter O. Workable Competition in the Radio Broadcasting Industry. new ed. Sterling, Christopher H., ed. LC 78-21741. (Dissertations in Broadcasting Ser.). (Illus.). 1979. lib. bdg. 32.50x (ISBN 0-405-11777-9). Ayer Co Pubs.
Sterling, Christopher H. Electronic Media: A Guide to Trends in Broadcasting & Newer Technologies 1920-1983. LC 83-27019. 366p. 1984. 34.95 (ISBN 0-03-071468-0); pap. 17.95x (ISBN 0-03-054341-X). Praeger.
Sterling, Christopher H., ed. Dissertations in Broadcasting Series, 26 books. 1979. Set. lib. bdg. 739.50x set (ISBN 0-405-11754-X). Ayer Co Pubs.
Summers, Harrison B., et al. Broadcasting in the Public. 2nd ed. 1978. text ed. write for info (ISBN 0-534-00532-2). Wadsworth Pub.
Williford, Miriam, ed. Source Directory: Assistance to Third World Broadcasters. LC 79-3610. 200p. 1979. loose leaf 6.50 (ISBN 0-916584-14-3). Ford Found.

BROCADE

Tidball, Harriet. Brocade. LC 68-5499. (Shuttle Craft Guild Monographs: No. 22). (Illus.). 50p. 1967. pap. 8.75 (ISBN 0-916658-22-8). HTH Pubs.

BROMELIACIAE

Baker, J. G. Handbook of the Bromeliaceae. (Plant Monograph: No.8). 1972. Repr. of 1889 ed. 14.00 (ISBN 3-7682-0752-8). Lubrecht & Cramer.
Benzing, David H. Biology of the Bromeliads. 305p. (Orig.). 1980. pap. 14.95x (ISBN 0-916422-21-6). Mad River.
Gilmartin, Jean. The Bromeliaceae of Ecuador. (Monographiae Phanerogamarum Ser.: No. 5). (Illus.). 1972. 42.00 (ISBN 3-7682-0725-0). Lubrecht & Cramer.
Rauh, Werner. Bromeliads for Home, Garden & Greenhouse. Temple, Peter & Kendall, Harvey L., trs. from Ger. Orig. Title: Bromelien. (Illus.). 445p. 1979. text ed. 18.95x (ISBN 0-916422-44-5). Mad River.
Smith, Lyman B. & Downs, Robert J. Bromelioideae (Bromeliaceae) LC 79-14114. (Flora Neotropica Ser.: Vol. 14, No. 3). 1979. pap. 65.00x (ISBN 0-89327-210-8). NY Botanical.

BROMIDES

Bromophos. (Specifications for Plant Protection Products). 20p. 1977. pap. 7.50 (ISBN 0-686-64008-X, F1911, FAO). Unipub.

BRONZE

see also Founding; Metal-Work

American Society for Testing & Materials 0. The Microstructure of Bronze Sinterings. LC 62-20903. (American Society for Testing & Materials Ser.: Special Technical Publication, No. 323). pap. 20.00 (ISBN 0-317-10788-7, 2000130). Bks Demand UMI.
Curtis, Tony, ed. Bronze. (Illus.). 1978. 2.00 (ISBN 0-902921-40-1). Apollo.

BRONZING

see also Metals-Coloring

Hiorns, Arthur H. Metal-Colouring & Bronzing. 2nd ed. LC 79-8613. Repr. of 1911 ed. 33.50 (ISBN 0-404-18477-4). AMS Pr.

BROWN COAL

see Lignite

BROWNIAN MOVEMENTS

Chung, K. L. Lectures from Markov Processes to Brownian Motion. (Grundlehren der Mathematischen Wissenschaften). (Illus.). 256p. 1982. 39.50 (ISBN 0-387-90618-5). Springer-Verlag.
Durrett, Richard. Brownian Motion & Martingales in Analysis. 350p. 1984. text ed. write for info (ISBN 0-534-03065-3). Wadsworth Pub.
Einstein, Albert. Investigations on the Theory of the Brownian Movement. Furth, R., ed. Cowper, A. D., tr. 1926. pap. 3.50 (ISBN 0-486-60304-0). Dover.
Freedman, D. Brownian Motion & Diffusion. (Illus.). 231p. 1983. Repr. of 1971 ed. 26.00 (ISBN 0-387-90805-6). Springer-Verlag.
Harrison, J. M. & Kiver, E. P. Brownian Motion & Stochastic Flow Systems. 4th ed. (Probability & Mathematical Statistics Ser.). 160p. 1985. 29.95 (ISBN 0-471-81939-5). Wiley.
Hida, T. Brownian Motion. (Applications of Mathematics Ser.: Vol. 11). (Illus.). 1980. 43.00 (ISBN 0-387-90439-5). Springer-Verlag.
Ito, K. & McKean, H. P., Jr. Diffusion Processes & Their Sample Paths. (Grundlehren der Mathematischen Wissenschaften: Vol. 125). 1965. 39.00 (ISBN 0-387-03302-5). Springer-Verlag.
McConnell, James. Rotational Brownian Motion & Dielectric Theory. 1980. 56.50 (ISBN 0-12-481850-1). Acad Pr.
McKean, H. P., Jr. Stochastic Integrals. (Probability & Mathematical Statistics Ser,: Vol. 5). 1969. 39.50 (ISBN 0-12-483450-7). Acad Pr.
Port, Sidney C. & Stone, Charles J. Brownian Motion & Classical Potential Theory. LC 78-6772. (Probability & Mathematical Statistics Ser.). 1978. 49.50 (ISBN 0-12-561850-6). Acad Pr.
Wax, Nelson, ed. Selected Papers on Noise & Stochastic Processes. 1954. pap. 7.00 (ISBN 0-486-60262-1). Dover.

BRUCELLA
Olitzki, A. Immunological Methods in Brucellosis Research: Procedures, Pt. 2. (Bibliotheca Microbiologica: Vol 9). 1970. pap. 45.25 (ISBN 3-8055-0149-8). S Karger.
BRUNEL, ISAMBARD KINGDOM, 1806-1859
Beckett, Derrick. Brunels Britain. LC 80-66092. (Illus.). 256p. 1980. 25.00 (ISBN 0-7153-7973-9). David & Charles.
Pugsley, Alfred, ed. The Works of Isambard Kingdom Brunel: An Engineering Appreciation. LC 79-41470. (Illus.). 232p. 1980. 34.50 (ISBN 0-521-23239-2). Cambridge U Pr.
Tames, R. Isambard Brunel. (Clarendon Biography Ser.). (Illus.). 1973. pap. 3.50 (ISBN 0-912728-83-3). Newbury Bks.
BRUNELLIACEAE
Cuatrecasas, Jose. Brunelliaceae. (Flora Neotropica Monograph: No. 2). 1984. Repr. of 1970 ed. 15.00x (ISBN 0-89327-263-9). NY Botanical.
BRYOPHYTES
see also Liverworts; Mosses
Bruch, P., et al. Brvologie Europaea, Seu Genera Muscorum Europaeorum Monographice Illustrated: Collarium, Index & Supplement. Incl. Music Europaei Novi Vel Bryologiae Supplementum. Florschuetz, P. A., pref. by.. (Illus.). Repr. of 1866 ed. 502.00 (ISBN 90-6123-220-1). Lubrecht & Cramer.
Clarke, G. C. S. & Duckett, J. G., eds. Bryophyte Systematics, No. 14. LC 79-40897. (Systematics Association Special Ser.). 1980. 95.00 (ISBN 0-12-175050-7). Acad Pr.
Hebant, C. The Conducting Tissues of Bryophytes. 1977. 35.00 (ISBN 3-7682-1110-X). Lubrecht & Cramer.
International Association of Briologists, Taxonomic Workshop, 1979. Bryophyte Taxonomy: Methods, Practices & Floristic Exploration: Proceedings. Geissler, P. & Greene, S. W., eds. (Beiheft zu Nova Hedwigia Ser.: No. 71). (Illus.). 600p. 1982. 70.00 (ISBN 3-7682-5471-2). Lubrecht & Cramer.
Magill, R. E. & Schelpe, E. A. The Bryophytes of Southern Africa. (Illus.). 39p. 1983. pap. text ed. 10.00 (ISBN 0-621-04718-X, Pub. by Dept Agriculture & Fish S Africa). Intl Spec Bk.
Miller, H. A., et al. Bryoflora of the Atolls of Micronesia. (Illus.). 1963. pap. 14.00 (ISBN 3-7682-5411-9). Lubrecht & Cramer.
Schofield, Wilfred B. Introduction to Bryology. (Illus.). 480p. 1985. 42.50x (ISBN 0-02-949660-8). Macmillan.
Schultze-Motel, W., ed. Advances in Bryology: 1984, Vol. 2. (Illus.). 224p. 1985. lib. bdg. 28.00x (ISBN 3-7682-1406-0). Lubrecht & Cramer.
Sim, T. R. Bryophyta of South Africa. 1973. 61.60 (ISBN 3-87429-053-0). Lubrecht & Cramer.
Smith, A. J., ed. Bryophyte Ecology. (Illus.). 472p. 1982. 85.00 (ISBN 0-412-22340-6, NO. 6656, Pub. by Chapman & Hall). Methuen Inc.
Verdoorn, Fr., ed. Manual of Bryology. (Illus.). 1967. Repr. of 1932 ed. 27.90 (ISBN 90-6123-092-6). Lubrecht & Cramer.
Vitt, D. H. & Gradstein, S. R. Compendium of Bryology: A World Listing of Herbaria, Collectors, Bryologies & Current Research. (Bryphytorum Bibliotheca Ser.: No. 30). 356p. 1985. text ed. 21.00x (ISBN 3-7682-1434-6). Lubrecht & Cramer.
Watson, Eric V. Structure & Life of Bryopytes. 3rd ed. 1971. pap. text ed. 9.45x (ISBN 0-09-109301-5, Hutchinson U Lib). Humanities.
BRYOZOA
see Polyzoa
BSA MOTORCYCLE
Clew, Jeff. BSA A7 & A10 Twins '47 - '54. (Owners Workshop Manuals Ser.: No. 121). 1979. 10.50 (ISBN 0-85696-121-3, Pub. by J H Haynes England). Haynes Pubns.
Daniels, Marcus. BSA Unit Singles '58 - '72. new ed. (Owners Workshop Manuals Ser.: No. 127). 1979. 10.50 (ISBN 0-85696-127-2, Pub. by J H Haynes England). Haynes Pubns.
Darlington, Mansur. BSA Pre-unit Singles '54 - '61. new ed. (Owners Workshop Manuals Ser.: No. 326). 1979. 10.50 (ISBN 0-85696-326-7, Pub. by J H Haynes England). Haynes Pubns.
Jorgensen, Jeff, ed. BSA Service-Repair Handbook: 500 & 650cc Unit Construction Twins. (Illus.). pap. 13.95 (ISBN 0-89287-182-2, M302). Clymer Pubns.
Reynolds, Mark. BSA A50 & A65 Twins '61 - '68. new ed. (Owners Workshop Manuals Ser.: No. 155). 1979. 10.50 (ISBN 0-85696-155-8, Pub. by J H Haynes England). Haynes Pubns.
BUBBLE CHAMBER
Aleksandrov, Yu A. Bubble Chambers. Frisken, William R., tr. LC 66-14342. pap. 95.50 (ISBN 0-317-08533-6, 2055192). Bks Demand UMI.
Shutt, R. P., ed. Bubble & Spark Chambers: Principles & Use, 2 vols. (Pure & Applied Physics Ser.: Vol. 27). 1967. Vol. 1. 80.50 (ISBN 0-12-641001-1); Vol. 2. 80.50 (ISBN 0-12-641002-X). Acad Pr.
BUBBLES
Boys, C. V. Soap-Bubbles: Their Colours & the Forces Which Mold Them. LC 59-14223. 1959. lib. bdg. 11.50x (ISBN 0-88307-632-2). Gannon.
Boys, Charles V. Soap Bubbles. 3rd ed. (Illus.). 1959. pap. 3.50 (ISBN 0-486-20542-8). Dover.
Clift, Roland, et al. Bubbles, Drops & Particles. LC 77-6592. 1978. 58.50 (ISBN 0-12-176950-X). Acad Pr.
Eschenfelder, A. H. Magnetic Bubble Technology. (Springer Series in Solid State Sciences: Vol. 14). (Illus.). 360p. 1980. 49.80 (ISBN 0-387-09822-4). Springer-Verlag.
Lemlich, Robert. Adsorptive Bubble Separation Techniques. 1972. 71.50 (ISBN 0-12-443350-2). Acad Pr.
Malozemoff, A. P. & Slonczewski, J. C. Applied Solid State Science, Supplement I: Magnetic Domain Walls in Bubble Materials. (Serial Publication). 1979. 65.00 (ISBN 0-12-002951-0). Acad Pr.
BUBONIDAE
see Owls
BUCKLING (MECHANICS)
see also Structural Stability
Allen, H. G. & Bulson, P. S. Background to Buckling. (Illus.). 1980. text ed. 60.00x (ISBN 0-07-084100-4). McGraw.
Britvec, S. J. The Stability of Elastic Systems. 480p. 1973. text ed. 45.00 (ISBN 0-08-016859-0). Pergamon.
Chajes, Alexander. Principles of Structural Stability Theory. (Civil Engineering & Engineering Mechanics Ser.). (Illus.). 288p. 1974. 41.95 (ISBN 0-13-709964-9). P-H.
Kollar, L. & Dulacskai, E. Buckling of Shells for Engineers. LC 83-1697. 303p. 1984. text ed. 49.95x (ISBN 0-471-90328-0, Pub. by Wiley-Interscience). Wiley.
Litle, William A. Reliability of Shell Buckling Predictions. (Press Research Monographs: No. 25). 1964. 25.00x (ISBN 0-262-12013-5). MIT Pr.
Popov, Egor P. & Medwadowski, Stefan J., eds. Concrete Shell Buckling. LC 80-69968. (SP-67). 240p. (Orig.). 1981. pap. 39.95 (ISBN 0-686-95244-8). ACI.
Symposium in Cambridge, Mass, June 17-21, 1974. Buckling of Structures. Budiansky, B., ed. LC 75-31726. (International Union of Theoretical & Applied Mechanics). (Illus.). 420p. 1976. 99.20 (ISBN 0-387-07274-8). Springer-Verlag.
BUDGERIGARS
Binks, Gerald S. Best in Show: Breeding & Exhibiting Budgerigars. (Illus.). 176p. 1985. 12.95 (ISBN 0-668-06282-7). Arco.
De Grahl, Wolfgang. The Parrot Family: Parakeets-Budgerigars-Cockatiels-Lovebirds-Lories-Macaws. LC 83-17940. (Illus.). 176p. 1985. 12.95 (ISBN 0-668-06039-5); pap. 7.95 (ISBN 0-668-06043-3). Arco.
Dunigan, Opal. Training Budgerigars to Talk. (Illus.). 128p. 1981. 8.95 (ISBN 0-87666-845-7, PS-791). TFH Pubns.
Feyerabend, Cessa & Vriends, Matthew M., eds. Feeding Budgerigars. (Illus.). 1978. pap. 6.95 (ISBN 0-87666-971-2, AP-400). TFH Pubns.
Harris, Robbie. Grey-Cheeked Parakeets & Other Brotogeris. (Illus.). 160p. 1985. text ed. 9.95 (ISBN 0-86622-049-6, PS-830). TFH Pubns.
Howson, Ernest. The Book of the Budgerigar. 2nd ed. (Illus.). 180p. 1984. 14.95 (ISBN 0-946474-36-2). Triplegate.
Mackerness & Radford. Budgerigars. pap. 5.00x (ISBN 0-392-08314-0, SpS). Sportshelf.
Miller, Evelyn. The T.F.H. Book of Budgerigars. (Illus.). 80p. 6.95 (ISBN 0-87666-849-X, HP-004). TFH Pubns.
Radtke, Georg A. Encyclopedia of Budgerigars. Friese, U. Erich, tr. from Ger. 320p. 1981. 19.95 (ISBN 0-87666-899-6, H-1027). TFH Pubns.
Radtke, George A. Budgerigars. Orig. Title: Wellensittiche-Mein Hobby. (Illus.). 1979. 4.95 (ISBN 0-87666-984-4, KW-011). TFH Pubns.
Richmond, Howard. Joy of Budgerigars. (Illus.). 96p. 1983. 4.95 (ISBN 0-87666-553-9, PS-799). TFH Pubns.
Roberts, Mervin F. All about Breeding Budgerigars. (Illus.). 96p. 1984. 4.95 (ISBN 0-87666-568-7, PS-804). TFH Pubns.
Rogers, Cyril. Budgerigars. (Illus.). 93p. 1976. pap. 3.95 (ISBN 0-7028-1051-7). Avian Pubns.
Schneider, Earl & Vriends, Matthew M. Parakeets. (KW-036). (Illus.). 128p. 1984. Repr. of 1979 ed. 4.95 (ISBN 0-87666-749-3, KW-036). TFH Pubns.
Scoble, John. The Complete Book of Budgerigars. (Illus.). 144p. 1982. 19.95 (ISBN 0-7137-1262-7, Pub. by Blandford Pr England). Sterling.
Silva, Tony & Kotlar, Barbara. Conures. (Illus.). 96p. 1980. 4.95 (ISBN 0-87666-893-7, KW-121). TFH Pubns.
Teitler, Risa. Budgerigars, Taming & Training. (Illus.). 96p. 1979. 4.95 (ISBN 0-87666-887-2, KW-070). TFH Pubns.
--Starting Right with Budgerigars. (Illus.). 80p. 1983. 6.95 (ISBN 0-87666-556-3, PS-793). TFH Pubns.
--Taming & Training Ringneck Parakeets. (Illus.). 96p. 1981. 4.95 (ISBN 0-87666-822-8, KW-145). TFH Pubns.
Vriends, Matthew M. The Complete Budgerigar. LC 85-8324. (Illus.). 272p. 1985. 16.95 (ISBN 0-87605-822-5). Howell Bk.
--Parakeets of the World. (Illus.). 1979. 19.95 (ISBN 0-87666-999-2, H-101). TFH Pubns.
Vriends, Matthew M. & Feyerabend, Cessa. Breeding Budgerigars. (Illus.). 1978. 7.95 (ISBN 0-87666-790-6, PS-761). TFH Pubns.
Watmough, W. The Cult of the Budgerigar. (Illus.). 250p. 1984. pap. 11.95 (ISBN 0-947647-04-X, Pub. by Fanciers Supplies). Longwood Pub Group.
BUFFALO, AMERICAN
see Bison, American
BUFFALOES
Buffalo Reproduction & Artificial Insemination: Proceedings of the Seminar Sponsored by SIDA-Govt. of India, held at the National Dairy Research Institute, Karnal, India, Dec. 4-15, 1978. (Animal Production & Health Papers: No. 13). 370p. 1979. pap. 26.50 (ISBN 92-5-100743-8, F2086, FAO). Unipub.
Fahimuddin, M. Domestic Water Buffalo. 392p. 1981. 30.00x (ISBN 0-686-72948-X, Pub. by Oxford & IBH India). State Mutual Bk.
McHugh, Tom. The Time of the Buffalo. LC 78-24261. (Illus.). xxiv, 383p. 1979. pap. 9.95 (ISBN 0-8032-8105-6, BB 685, Bison). U of Nebr Pr.
Mloszewski, M. J. The Behavior & Ecology of the African Buffalo. LC 82-1153. (Illus.). 280p. 1983. 37.50 (ISBN 0-521-24478-1). Cambridge U Pr.
Rodney, William. Kootenai Brown. (Illus.). 251p. 1969. pap. 2.95 (ISBN 0-88826-045-8). Superior Pub.
BUFFETS (COOKERY)
St. Laurent, G. & Holden, C. Buffets: A Guide for Professionals. 29.95 (ISBN 0-471-81874-7). Wiley.
BUFFING
see Grinding and Polishing
BUGATTI (AUTOMOBILE)
see Automobiles, Foreign-Types-Bugatti
BUICK AUTOMOBILE
see Automobiles-Types-Buick
BUILDER'S PLANT
see Construction Equipment
BUILDING
see also Arches; Architecture; Bricklaying; Building Fittings; Building Sites; Building Trades; Carpentry; Concrete Construction; Construction Equipment; Construction Industry; Doors and Doorways; Environmental Engineering (Buildings); Floors; Foundations; Framing (Building); Garden Structures; Girders; House Construction; Masonry; Materials; Roofs; Scaffolding; Space Frame Structures; Trusses; Underground Construction; Walls; Windows
Architectural Record Magazine & Fischer, Robert, eds. Engineering for Architecture. (Architectural Record Book Ser.). (Illus.). 224p. 1980. 34.95 (ISBN 0-07-002353-0). McGraw.
Badzinski, Stanley. Home Construction & Estimating. (Illus.). 1979. ref. 20.95 (ISBN 0-13-392654-0). P-H.
Baker, G. Construction: Techniques. 1976. pap. 8.84 (ISBN 0-13-169409-X). P-H.
Ball, John E. Carpenters & Builders Library. 5th ed. LC 82-133279. 1983. 39.95 set (ISBN 0-672-23369-X); 10.95 ea. Vol. 1 (ISBN 0-672-23365-7). Vol. 2 (ISBN 0-672-23366-5). Vol. 3 (ISBN 0-672-23367-3). Vol. 4 (ISBN 0-672-23368-1). Audel.
Barry, R. Construction of Buildings, 5 vols. (Illus.). 508p. 1971. Set. spiral bdg. 40.00x (ISBN 0-8464-0276-9). Beekman Pubs.
--The Construction of Buildings: Foundations, Walls, Floors & Roofs. Incl. Vol. I. 3rd ed. 1969. pap. text ed. 12.50x (ISBN 0-258-96765-X); Vol. II. 2nd ed. 140p. 1970. pap. text ed. 13.50x (ISBN 0-258-96798-6); Vol. III. 2nd ed. 101p. 1972. pap. text ed. 13.50x (ISBN 0-258-96844-3); Vol. IV. 2nd ed. 120p. 1971. pap. text ed. 13.50x (ISBN 0-258-96829-X); Vol. V. 108p. 1978. pap. text ed. 13.50x (ISBN 0-258-97077-4). pap. (Pub. by Granada England). Brookfield Pub Co.
Barry, Robin. Barry: Construction of Building, Vol. 1. 4th ed. 128p. 1980. 9.95x (ISBN 0-246-11261-1, Pub. by Granada England). Sheridan.
--Barry: Construction of Building, Vol. 2. 3rd ed. 136p. 1982. 9.95x (ISBN 0-246-11263-8, Pub. by Granada England). Sheridan.
--Barry: Construction of Building, Vol. 3. 3th ed. 112p. 1972. 9.95x (ISBN 0-246-11950-0, Pub. by Granada England). Sheridan.
--Barry: Construction of Building, Vol. 4. 2nd ed. 128p. 1971. 9.95x (ISBN 0-246-11547-5, Pub. by Granada England). Sheridan.
--Barry: Construction of Building, Vol. 5. 112p. 1978. 9.95x (ISBN 0-246-11275-1, Pub. by Granada England). Sheridan.
Bentley, Howard B., ed. Building Construction Information Sources. LC 64-16502. (Management Information Guide Ser.: No. 2). 1964. 60.00x (ISBN 0-8103-0802-9). Gale.
Berk, Ronald A., ed. A Guide to Criterion-Referenced Test Construction. LC 84-47955. 1984. text ed. 32.50x (ISBN 0-8018-2417-6). Johns Hopkins.
Billington, N. S. & Roberts, B. M. Building Services Engineering: A Review of Its Development. LC 80-42036. (International Ser. on Building Environmental Engineering: Vol. 1). 537p. 1981. 88.00 (ISBN 0-08-026741-6); pap. 24.00 (ISBN 0-08-026742-4). Pergamon.
Boeminghaus, Dieter, ed. Pedestrian Areas & Dewing Elements. 288p. 1982. 110.00x (ISBN 0-686-45590-8, Pub. by L Brooks England). State Mutual Bk.
Boughton, Brian. Building & Civil Engineering Construction, Vol. 1. 192p. 1983. pap. 10.00x (ISBN 0-246-11966-7, Pub. by Granada England). Sheridan.
--Building & Civil Engineering Construction, Vol. 2. 173p. 1983. pap. 10.00x (ISBN 0-246-11967-5, Pub. by Granada England). Sheridan.
Boughton, Brian & Goodfellow, Denis. Construction Science, Vol. 1. 160p. 1984. pap. 10.00x (ISBN 0-246-12127-0, Pub. by Granada England). Sheridan.
--Construction Science, Vol. 2. 160p. 1984. pap. 10.00x (ISBN 0-246-12128-9, Pub. by Granada England). Sheridan.
Boyd, James S. Building for Small Acreages: Farm, Ranch & Recreation. LC 77-80716. 1978. text ed. 13.35 (ISBN 0-8134-1966-2); pap. text ed. 10.00x. Interstate.
Building in the Countryside. 88p. 1982. 40.00x (ISBN 0-686-45580-0, Pub. by L Brooks England). State Mutual Bk.
Butler, Robert B. Architectural & Engineering Calculations Manual. (Illus.). 384p. 1983. 21.95 (ISBN 0-07-009363-6). McGraw.
Ching, Francis D. Building Construction Illustrated. 1975. 21.95 (ISBN 0-442-21533-9). Van Nos Reinhold.
Cook, John P. Composite Construction Methods. LC 76-26020. (Practical Construction Guides Ser.). 330p. 1977. 51.50 (ISBN 0-471-16905-6, Pub by Wiley-Interscience). Wiley.
Council of American Building Officials. You Can Build It! pap. 1.50 (ISBN 0-318-00062-8). Intl Conf Bldg Off.
Di Valmarana, Mario, ed. Building by the Book I. (Palladian Studies in America: No. I). (Illus.). 110p. 1984. text ed. 20.00x (ISBN 0-8139-1022-6). U Pr of Va.
Fickes, Clyde P. & Groben, W. Ellis. Building with Logs. (Shorey Lost Arts Ser.). 56p. pap. 4.95 (ISBN 0-8466-6030-X, U30). Shorey.
Fitch, James M. American Building: The Historical Forces That Shaped It. (Illus.). 1966. 15.00 (ISBN 0-395-07680-3). HM.
Foster, Jack S. Structure & Fabric, 2 pts. LC 78-53853. (Mitchell's Building Construction Ser.). 1978. Pt. 1, 264p. pap. 17.95x (ISBN 0-470-26348-2). Halsted Pr.
Fullerton, R. L. Construction Technology, Level 2, Pt. 2. (Illus.). 144p. 1982. pap. text ed. 19.95x (ISBN 0-291-39654-2). Intl Ideas.
--Construction Technology: Level 2, Part 1. (Illus.). 144p. 1982. pap. 19.95x (ISBN 0-291-39653-4). Intl Ideas.
Fullerton, R. L. & Struct, M. I. Construction Technology Level 2, Pt. 1. 160p. 1981. 36.00x (ISBN 0-291-39653-4, Pub. by Tech Pr). State Mutual Bk.
--Construction Technology Level 2, Pt. 2. 160p. 1981. 36.00x (ISBN 0-291-39654-2, Pub. by Tech Pr). State Mutual Bk.
Fullman, James B. Construction Safety, Security, & Loss Prevention. LC 84-5077. (Wiley Practical Construction Guides Ser.: 1-344). 286p. 1984. text ed. 42.95x (ISBN 0-471-86821-3, Pub. by Wiley Interscience). Wiley.
Greene, Herb & Greene, Nanine H. Building to Last. (Illus.). 168p. 1981. 26.95 (ISBN 0-8038-0028-2). Hastings.
Hasenau, J. James. Build Your Own Home: A Guide to Subcontracting the Easy Way, a System to Save Time & Money. (Illus.). 1985. pap. 8.95 (ISBN 0-913042-10-2). Holland Hse Pr.
Hettema, Robert M. Mechanical & Electrical Building Construction. (Illus.). 400p. 1984. 35.95 (ISBN 0-13-569608-9). P-H.
Hilleborg, Arno. Strip Method of Design. 2nd ed. (C & CA Viewpoint Publication Ser.). (Illus.). 1976. pap. text ed. 26.50x (ISBN 0-7210-1012-1). Scholium Intl.
History of Real Estate, Building & Architecture in New York City. LC 67-23061. (Illus.). 1967. Repr. of 1898 ed. 14.95 (ISBN 0-405-00054-5). Ayer Co Pubs.

Standards for Concrete & Reinforced Concrete Works. (DIN Standards Ser.). 468.00 (ISBN 0-686-31839-0, 11294-3/78). Heyden.
Tomioka, Seishiro & Tomoika, Ellen M. Planned Unit Developments: Design & Regional Impact. LC 82-13419. 192p. 1984. 37.50x (ISBN 0-471-08595-2, Pub. by Wiley-Interscience). Wiley.
Traister, John. Mechanical Specifications for Building Construction. (Illus.). 224p. 1980. text ed. 23.95 (ISBN 0-8359-4318-6). Reston.
Vance, Mary. Architects' Contracts: A Bibliography. (Architecture Ser.: Bibliography A 1352). 1985. pap. 2.00 (ISBN 0-89028-322-2). Vance Biblios.
Walker, N., et al. Legal Pitfalls in Architecture, Engineering & Building Construction. 1979. 8.85 (ISBN 0-07-067851-0). McGraw.
Wallach, Paul & Hepler, Don. Reading Construction Drawings: Trade Edition. (Illus.). 320p. 1980. 29.95 (ISBN 0-07-067940-1). McGraw.
Willis, Arthur & Willis, Christopher. Practice & Procedure for the Quantity Surveyor. 8th ed. 272p. 1980. pap. 18.00x (ISBN 0-246-11242-5, Pub. by Granada England). Sheridan.
--Specification Writing: For Architects & Surveyors. 8th ed. 120p. 1983. 16.00x (ISBN 0-246-12228-5, Pub. by Granada England). Sheridan.

BUILDING–COSTS
see Building–Estimates

BUILDING–DATA PROCESSING

Adrian, James J. Microcomputers in the Construction Industry. 1984. text ed. 35.00 (ISBN 0-8359-4366-6). Reston.
Becker, William E. Minicomputer Checklist: A Guide for Builders in Selecting a Minicomputer. 31p. 1965. pap. 11.00 (SBN 0-86718-067-6); pap. 8.00 members. Natl Assn Home.
Bennett, Philip M. Construction Detail Banking: Systematic Storage & Retrieval. LC 83-14490. 174p. 1984. 34.95x (ISBN 0-471-88621-1, Pub. by Wiley-Interscience). Wiley.
Brandon, Peter S., et al. Computer Programs for Building Cost Appraisal. 200p. (Orig.). 1985. pap. text ed. 25.00x (ISBN 0-00-383043-8, Pub. by Collins England). Sheridan.
Halpin, Daniel W. & Woodhead, Ronald W. Constructo: A Heuristic Game for Construction Management. LC 73-76342. 195p. 1973. pap. 10.00x (ISBN 0-252-00337-3); computer program, non-profit institutions 250.00 (ISBN 0-252-00400-0); computer program 500.00 (ISBN 0-252-00399-3). U of Ill Pr.
--Design of Construction & Process Operations. LC 76-9784. 539p. 1976. 48.50 (ISBN 0-471-34565-2). Wiley.
Lee, Kaiman. Computer-Aided Building Code Checking: A Demonstration. 2nd ed. LC 74-308127. 34p. 1974. 12.00x (ISBN 0-915250-08-X). Environ Design.
--Computer Programs in Environmental Design, 5 vols. LC 74-169212. (Illus.). 1308p. 1974. Set. 210.00x (ISBN 0-915250-05-5). Environ Design.
Levin, Paul. Construction Computer Applications Directory. 2nd ed. 400p. 1985. 45.00 (ISBN 0-9605442-0-8). Constr Ind Pr.
O'Brien, J. J. CP-M in Construction Management. 3rd ed. 416p. 1984. 39.95 (ISBN 0-07-047663-2). McGraw.
Peters, Glen. Construction Project Management Using Small Computers. LC 83-8348. (Illus.). 160p. 1984. 29.50 (ISBN 0-89397-169-3). Nichols Pub.
Rathbone, Thomas B. Computers & Construction. 1984. text ed. 27.95 (ISBN 0-8359-0870-4). Reston.
Sclater, Neil. Introduction to Electronic Speech Synthesis. 112p. 1982. pap. 9.95 (ISBN 0-672-21896-8, 21896). Sams.

BUILDING–DETAILS

American National Standards Institute Staff, ed. ANSI A58: Minimum Design Loads for Buildings & Other Structures. 100p. 1982. pap. 12.00x (ISBN 0-87262-367-X). Am Soc Civil Eng.
Butcher, E. G. & Parnell, A. C. Designing for Fire Safety. 372p. 1983. 54.95 (ISBN 0-471-10239-3). Wiley.
Eastman, C. N., ed. Spatial Synthesis in Computer-Aided Building Design. (Illus.). 333p. 1975. 46.25 (ISBN 0-85334-611-9, Pub. by Elsevier Applied Sci England). Elsevier.
Gero, J. S. & Cowan, H. J. Design of Building Frames. (Illus.). 480p. 1976. 63.00 (ISBN 0-85334-644-5, Pub. by Elsevier Applied Sci England). Elsevier.
Greater London Council Department of Architecture & Civic Design. Detailing for Building Construction: A Designer's Manual of Over 350 Standard Details. (Illus.). 500p. 1980. pap. 37.75x (ISBN 0-85139-234-2). Nichols Pub.
Huth, Mark W. Basic Construction Blueprint Reading. 144p. 1980. 15.95 (ISBN 0-442-23874-6). Van Nos Reinhold.
Ketchum, Milo S. Handbook of Standard Structural Details for Buildings. 1956. text ed. 27.95 (ISBN 0-13-381822-5). P-H.
McNeill, Joseph. Common Defects in Residential Construction. 1986. cancelled (ISBN 0-442-23605-0). Van Nos Reinhold.
Martin, Leslie. Buildings & Ideas, Ninteen Thirty-Four to Nineteen Eighty-Three: From the Studio of Leslie Martin & His Associates. LC 82-4359. (Illus.). 233p. 1984. 89.50 (ISBN 0-521-23107-8). Cambridge U Pr.
Newman, Morton. Standard Structural Details for Building Construction. 1967. 55.50 (ISBN 0-07-046345-X). McGraw.
Traister. Blueprint Reading for the Building Trades. (Illus.). 1980. pap. 17.95 (ISBN 0-8359-0513-6). Reston.
Walker, Theodore D. Site Design & Construction Detailing. LC 77-18668. (Illus.). 467p. 1978. 29.95 (ISBN 0-914886-08-8); instr's manual 14.95 (ISBN 0-914886-25-8). PDA Pubs.
Wallach, Paul & Hepler, Don. Reading Construction Drawings: Trade Edition. (Illus.). 320p. 1980. 29.95 (ISBN 0-07-067940-1). McGraw.

BUILDING–DICTIONARIES

Abd-El-Gawad, Tawfik. Technical Dictionary: Archtiecture & Building. (Eng., Fr., Ger. & Arabic.). 1319p. 1976. 35.00x (ISBN 0-686-44745-X, Pub. by Collets). State Mutual Bk.
Barbier, Maurice. Diccionario Tecnico Ilustrado De Edificacion y Obras Publicas. (Span.). 177p. 1976. pap. 11.50 (ISBN 84-252-0327-9, S-50273). French & Eur.
Barry, W. R., ed. Architectural, Construction, Manufacturing & Engineering Glossary of Terms. 519p. 1979. pap. 40.00 (ISBN 0-930284-05-4). Am Assn Cost Engineers.
Benito Bacho, Jose. Diccionario de la Construccion y Obras Publicas Ingles-Espanol, 2 vols. (Span. & Eng.). 268p. 1975. Set. 38.95 (ISBN 84-85198-10-7, S-50117). French & Eur.
--Diccionario de la Construccion y Obras Publicas, Tomo 2: Span. (Span.). 110p. 1975. 18.95 (ISBN 84-85198-09-3, S-50119). French & Eur.
--Diccionario de la Construcion y de Obras Publicas, Tomo I: Ingles. (Span.). 168p. 1975. 18.95 (ISBN 84-85198-00-X, S-50118). French & Eur.
Brooks, Hugh. Encyclopedia of Building & Construction Terms. LC 82-21565. 416p. 1983. 50.00 (ISBN 0-13-275511-4). P-H.
Bucksch, Hector. Dictionnaire pour les Travaux Publics, le Batiment et l'Equipement des Chantiers de Construction. 7th ed. (Eng. & Fr.). 420p. 1979. 42.50 (ISBN 0-686-56930-X, M-6051). French & Eur.
Bucksch, Herbert & Galan e Hildalgo, Arturo. Diccionario Frances-Espanol de la Construccion y Obras Publicas. (Fr. & Span.). 564p. 1975. 35.95 (ISBN 84-7146-047-5, S-50133). French & Eur.
Chaballe, L. Y. & Vandenberghe, J. P. Elsevier's Dictionary of Building Tools & Materials. (Eng., Fr., Span., Ger. & Dutch.). 720p. 1982. 138.50 (ISBN 0-444-42047-9, I-261-82). Elsevier.
Cowan, Henry J. A Dictionary of Architectural Science. LC 73-15839. (Illus.). 354p. 1973. pap. 19.95x (ISBN 0-470-18070-6). Halsted Pr.
Dictionnaire Pour les Travaux Publics et l'Equipement des Chartiers de Construction, 2 vols. (Ger. & Fr.). 875p. 1976. leatherette, band I 112.00 (ISBN 3-7625-0379-6, M-7097). French & Eur.
Dictionnaire Pour les Travaux Publics et l'Equipement des Chartiers de Construction, 2 vols. (Ger. & Fr.). 911p. 1978. leatherette, band II 112.00 (ISBN 3-7625-0999-9, M-7098). French & Eur.
Encyclopedie Pratique De la Construction Du Batiment et Des Travaux Publics, 3 vols. (Fr.). 3587p. Set. 225.00 (ISBN 0-686-57165-7, M-6232). French & Eur.
English-Chinese Architectural Engineering Dictionary. (Eng. & Chinese.). 441p. 1973. 14.95 (ISBN 0-686-92620-X, M-9254). French & Eur.
Equipo Reactor de Ceac. Diccionario de la Construccion. (Span.). 650p. 1978. pap. 26.50 (ISBN 84-329-2608-6, S-50225). French & Eur.
Fullana Llompart, Miguel. Diccionario De L'art I Els Oficis De la Construccion. (Catalan.). 440p. 1974. 35.95 (ISBN 84-273-0372-6, S-50000). French & Eur.
Gaward, Abd El. Architecture & Building Dictionary: English-French-German-Arabic. (Eng., Fr., Ger. & Arabic.). 465p. 1976. Leatherette 45.00 (ISBN 0-686-92255-7, M-9753). French & Eur.
Hoshino, K. Encyclopedic Dictionary of Architecture & Building Construction. (Eng. & Japanese.). 535p. 1978. leatherette 75.00 (ISBN 0-686-92226-3, M-9332). French & Eur.
Illustrated Technical German for Builders. 183p. 1982. 39.00x (ISBN 0-686-45581-9, Pub. by L Brooks England). State Mutual Bk.
Krieger, Morris. Homeowner's Encyclopedia of House Construction. (Illus.). 1978. 31.95 (ISBN 0-07-035497-9). McGraw.
Lefebvre, Marcel. Nouveau Dictionnaire Du Batiment. (Fr.). 411p. 1971. pap. 25.00 (ISBN 0-686-57010-3, M-6351). French & Eur.
Lexique Des Termes Du Batiment. (Fr.). 212p. 1963. pap. 14.95 (ISBN 0-686-57014-6, M-6361). French & Eur.
Lexique Du Batiment. (Fr.). 14.95 (ISBN 0-686-57015-4, M-6364). French & Eur.
Machado, M. Diccionario Tecnico De la Construccion, Edificacion y Obras Publicas Frances-Espanol y Espanol-Frances. (Fr. & Span.). 576p. 1969. leatherette 35.95 (ISBN 84-283-0245-6, S-50242). French & Eur.
Mittag, M. Pratique De la Construction Des Batiments: Aide-Memoire Encyclopedique a L'usage Des Ingenieurs, Architectes et Entrepreneurs. (Fr.). 352p. 1977. 79.95 (ISBN 0-686-57052-9, M-6415). French & Eur.
Neve, Richard. City & Country Purchaser & Builder's Dictionary. LC 69-16762. Repr. of 1726 ed. 29.50x (ISBN 0-678-05616-1). Kelley.
Profor. Initiation Au Vocabulaire Du Batiment et Des Travaux Publics. (Fr.). 176p. 1979. 37.50 (ISBN 0-686-57088-X, M-6467). French & Eur.
Putnam, R. E. & Carlson, G. E. Architectural & Building Trades Dictionary. 3rd ed. 512p. 1983. 17.95 (ISBN 0-442-27461-0). Van Nos Reinhold.
Putnam, Robert. Builders Comprehensive Dictionary. 1984. text ed. 39.95 (ISBN 0-8359-0579-9). Reston.
Scott, John S. Dictionary of Building. rev. ed. (Reference Ser.). 392p. 1964. pap. 6.95 (ISBN 0-14-051015-X). Penguin.
Stein, J. Stewart. Construction Regulations Glossary: A Reference Manual. 930p. 1983. 66.95 (ISBN 0-471-89776-0, Pub. by Wiley Interscience). Wiley.
Wallnig, G. & Evered, H. L' Anglais Dans le Batiment: Text En Anglais Avec un Glossaire Illustre. (Eng., Fr. & Ger.). 100p. 1970. pap. 19.95 (ISBN 0-686-57255-6, M-6564). French & Eur.
--German for Building Specialists, (L'allemand Dans le Batiment, el Aleman En la Construccion) (Ger. & Eng.). 102p. 1979. 12.95 (ISBN 3-7625-0462-8, M-7420, Pub. by Bauverlag). French & Eur.
Wallnig, Gunter & Evered, H. L' Anglais Dans le Batiment: Texte En Anglais Avec un Glossaire Illustre, 2. (Eng., Fr. & Ger.). 192p. 1976. pap. 37.50 (ISBN 0-686-57256-4, M-6565). French & Eur.
Wallnig, Gunter & Evered, Harry. El Ingles en la Construccion. (Eng.-Span.). 104p. 1975. pap. 26.95 (ISBN 84-7146-082-3, S-50131). French & Eur.
Ware, Dora. Diccionario Manual Ilustrado De Arquitectura, Con los Terminos Mas Comunes Empleados En la Construccion. 6th ed. 224p. 1977. pap. 11.50 (ISBN 84-252-0021-0, S-50275). French & Eur.

BUILDING–EARLY WORKS TO 1800

Mudd, D. R. Estimating & Tendering for Construction Work. 200p. 1984. text ed. 59.95 (ISBN 0-408-01358-3); pap. text ed. 39.95 (ISBN 0-408-01359-1). Butterworth.
Neve, Richard. City & Country Purchaser & Builder's Dictionary. LC 69-16762. Repr. of 1726 ed. 29.50x (ISBN 0-678-05616-1). Kelley.

BUILDING–ESTIMATES

Adrian, James. Construction Estimating. 1982. text ed. 28.95 (ISBN 0-8359-0925-5); instrs'. manual avail. (ISBN 0-8359-0926-3). Reston.
Ahuja, Hira N. Successful Construction Cost Control. LC 80-10156. (Construction Management & Engineering Ser.). 388p. 1980. 56.95x (ISBN 0-471-05378-3, Pub. by Wiley-Interscience). Wiley.
Beeston, D. T. Statistical Methods for Building Price Data. 1983. 38.00x (ISBN 0-419-12270-2, NO. 6795, Pub. by E & FN Spon); pap. 19.00 (NO. 6794, Pub. by Chapman & Hall). Methuen Inc.
Berger & Associates Cost Consultants, Inc. Berger Building & Design Cost File, 1984: Mechanical, Electrical Trades, Vol. 2. 300 ed. LC 84-70008. (Illus.). 1984. pap. 32.50 (ISBN 0-942564-05-7). Building Cost File.
Bernstein, Levitt & Richardson, Anthony. Specification Clauses for Rehabilitation & Conversion Work. (Illus.). 128p. 1982. 27.50 (ISBN 0-85139-582-1). Nichols Pub.
Brandon, Peter S., et al. Computer Programs for Building Cost Appraisal. 200p. (Orig.). 1985. pap. text ed. 25.00x (ISBN 0-00-383043-8, Pub. by Collins England). Sheridan.
Brann, Donald R. How to Build a Low Cost House - Above or Below Ground. LC 81-69857. 226p. 1982. pap. 7.95 (ISBN 0-87733-832-9). Easi-Bild.
Brighty, S. Setting Out: A Guide for Site Engineers. (Illus.). 264p. 1975. text ed. 18.95x. Beekman Pubs.
Cardella, Carol A. Builders Guide to Merchandising. 55p. 1978. pap. 8.00 (ISBN 0-86718-012-9); pap. 6.00 members. Natl Assn Home.
Chrystal-Smith, G. Estimating for Alterations & Repairs. 128p. 1982. 29.00x (ISBN 0-7198-2545-8, Pub. by Northwood Bks). State Mutual Bk.
Collier, Keith. Estimating Construction Costs: A Conceptual Approach. text ed. 25.95 (ISBN 0-8359-1792-4). Reston.
--Fundamentals of Construction Estimating & Cost Accounting. (Illus.). 400p. 1974. 30.95 (ISBN 0-13-335604-3). P-H.
Cook, Paul J. Bidding for the General Contractor. Gardner, Michael, ed. 232p. 1985. text ed. 37.95 (ISBN 0-911950-77-X). R S Means.
--Estimating for the General Contractor. LC 82-208250. 225p. 1982. text ed. 35.95 (ISBN 0-911950-48-6); pap. 30.95 (ISBN 0-911950-49-4). R S Means.
Crespin, Vick S., et al. Walker's Manual for Construction Cost Estimating. Frank R. Walker Company, ed. (Illus.). 128p. 1981. pap. 12.95 (ISBN 0-911592-85-7). F R Walker.
Dell'Isola, Alphonse J. Value Engineering in the Construction Industry. 3rd ed. 376p. 1983. 38.50 (ISBN 0-442-26202-7). Van Nos Reinhold.
Engelsman, Coert. Heavy Construction Cost File, 1985: Unit Prices. 256p. 1985. pap. 39.95 (ISBN 0-442-26703-7). Van Nos Reinhold.
Enterkin, Hugh & Reynolds, Gerald. Estimating for Builders & Surveyors. 2nd ed. 1978. 27.50x (ISBN 0-434-90542-9). Intl Ideas.
Eppes, Bill G. & Whiteman, Daniel E. Cost Accounting for the Construction Firm. LC 83-21752. (Construction Management & Engineering Ser.: 1102). 174p. 1984. 32.95x (ISBN 0-471-88537-1, Pub. by Wiley-Interscience). Wiley.
Ferry, Douglas J. & Brandon, Peter S. Cost Planning of Buildings. 330p. 1980. 17.95x (ISBN 0-8464-1084-2). Beekman Pubs.
--Cost Planning of Buildings. 4th ed. 385p. 1980. pap. text ed. 17.00x (ISBN 0-246-11337-5, Pub. by Granada England). Brookfield Pub Co.
Foster, Norman. Construction Estimates from Take off to Bid. 2nd ed. (Modern Structure Ser.). (Illus.). 288p. 1973. 46.50 (ISBN 0-07-021632-0). McGraw.
Gallo, Frank J. & Campbell, Regis I. Small Residential Structures: Construction Practices & Material Take-off Estimates. LC 83-16911. 254p. 1984. 29.95 (ISBN 0-471-86914-7); 39.95 (ISBN 0-471-88359-X); student manual 12.95 (ISBN 0-471-86915-5). Wiley.
Goodacre, P. Worked Examples in Quantity Surveying Measurement. (Illus.). 175p. 1982. pap. 25.00 (ISBN 0-419-12340-7, NO. 6727, E & FN Spon). Methuen Inc.
Hardenbrook, Harry. Walker's Remodeling Estimator's Reference Book. (Illus.). 192p. 1981. pap. 19.95 (ISBN 0-911592-60-1). F R Walker.
--Walker's Remodeling Estimator's Reference Book. (Illus.). 325p. 1982. 25.00 (ISBN 0-911592-60-1, ScribT). Scribner.
Jackson, W. P. Estimating Home Building Costs. 320p. (Orig.). 1981. pap. 14.00 (ISBN 0-910460-80-9). Craftsman.
Jones, Jack P. Spec Builder's Guide. (Illus.). 448p. (Orig.). 1984. pap. 24.00 (ISBN 0-910460-38-8). Craftsman.
Kempen, Jay V. Construction Cost Estimating. 1983. text ed. 22.95 (ISBN 0-8359-0937-9). Reston.
Lewis, Jack R. Basic Construction Estimating. (Illus.). 176p. 1983. text ed. 24.95 (ISBN 0-13-058313-8). P-H.
Life Cycle Cost Analysis: A Guide for Architects. 1977. pap. 7.00x (ISBN 0-913962-21-X, 2-M708); pap. 6.00 members. Am Inst Arch.
National Association of Home Builders. Construction Cost Control. rev. ed. (Illus.). 64p. 1982. pap. 11.00 (ISBN 0-86718-153-2); pap. 8.00 members. Natl Assn Home.
Neil, James M. Construction Cost Estimating for Project Control. (Illus.). 336p. 1982. 32.95 (ISBN 0-13-168757-3). P-H.
Park, William R. Construction Bidding for Profit. LC 79-11451. (Practical Construction Guides Ser.). 293p. 1979. 36.595 (ISBN 0-471-04104-1, Pub. by Wiley-Interscience). Wiley.
Rudman, Jack. Construction Cost Specialist. (Career Examination Ser.: C-2060). (Cloth bdg. avail on request). 1977. pap. 14.00 (ISBN 0-8373-2060-7). Natl Learning.
Sarviel, E. Construction Estimating Reference Data. 368p. (Orig.). 1981. pap. 18.00 (ISBN 0-910460-89-2). Craftsman.
Spradlin, William H., Jr. The Building Estimator's Reference Book. 21st ed. (Illus.). 1270p. 1982. 29.95 (ISBN 0-911592-21-0). F R Walker.

Steinberg, J. & Stempel, M. Estimating for the Building Trades. 2nd ed. (Illus.). 1973. text ed. 15.75 (ISBN 0-8269-0537-4). Am Technical.
Stone, P. A. Building Economy: Design, Production & Organization. 3rd ed. 280p. text ed. 50.00 (ISBN 0-08-028677-1); pap. text ed. 17.00 (ISBN 0-08-028678-X). Pergamon.
Thomas, Paul I. How to Estimate Building Losses & Construction Costs. 4th ed. LC 83-3243. 474p. 1983. 32.95 (ISBN 0-13-405902-6). P-H.
Tumblin, Charles R. Construction Cost Estimates. LC 79-16376. (Ser. of Practical Construction Guides). 406p. 1980. 41.50x (ISBN 0-471-05699-5, Pub. by Wiley-Interscience). Wiley.
Tysoe, B. A. Construction Costs & Price Indices: Description & Use. 1981. 25.00x (ISBN 0-419-11930-2, NO.6492, Pub. by E & FN Spon). Methuen Inc.
Vance, Mary. Building Estimates & Costs: A Bibliography. (Architecture Ser.: Bibliography A 1327). 1985. pap. 4.50 (ISBN 0-89028-277-3). Vance Biblios.
Van Orman, H. A. Estimating for Residential Construction. LC 76-14083. 1978. pap. text ed. 16.80 (ISBN 0-8273-1605-4); instr.'s guide 4.80 (ISBN 0-8273-1606-2). Delmar.
Walker, Frank R., ed. Building Estimator's Reference Book with Pocket Estimator. rev. ed. (Illus.). 1270p. 1982. 34.95 (ISBN 0-911592-20-2); members 28.00. Natl Assn Home.
Ward, Sol A. & Litchfield, Thorndike. Cost Control in Design & Construction. (Illus.). 1980. 32.50 (ISBN 0-07-068139-2). McGraw.
Wass, Alonzo. Estimating Residential Construction. (Illus.). 1980. text ed. 30.95 (ISBN 0-13-289942-6). P-H.
Willis, Arthur & Willis, Christopher. Elements of Quantity Surveying. 7th ed. 254p. 1978. pap. 16.00x (ISBN 0-246-11471-1, Pub by Granada England). Sheridan.
Winslow, Taylor F. Construction Industry Production Manual. 192p. 1972. pap. 8.00 (ISBN 0-910460-04-3). Craftsman.

BUILDING–HANDBOOKS, MANUALS, ETC.
see also Building–Amateurs' Manuals
Adrian, James. Building Construction Handbook. 1982. text ed. 39.95 (ISBN 0-8359-0580-2). Reston.
Allen, Edward. The Professional Handbook of Building Construction. 608p. 1985. price not set (ISBN 0-471-82524-7). Wiley.
Ambrose, James. Simplified Design of Building Foundations. LC 80-39880. 338p. 1981. 34.95x (ISBN 0-471-06267-7, Pub. by Wiley-Interscience). Wiley.
American Institute of Architects. The Building Systems Integration Handbook. 1985. 84.95 (ISBN 0-471-86238-X). Wiley.
--Materials Components & Design: An Integrated Approach Handbook. Rush, Richard D., ed. 500p. 1985. 84.95x. Wiley.
American Institute of Timber Construction (AITC) Timber Construction Manual. 704p. 1985. 34.95 (ISBN 0-471-82758-4). Wiley.
Arnold, Christopher & Reitherman, Robert. Building Configuration & Seismic Design: The Architecture of Earthquake Resistance. 296p. 1982. 45.95 (ISBN 0-471-86138-3). Wiley.
Ball. Light Construction Techniques: From Foundation to Finish. (Illus.). 416p. 1980. ref. ed. 23.95 (ISBN 0-8359-4035-7). Reston.
Black, Leslie. The Builder's Reference Book. 11th ed. 432p. 1981. 40.00x (ISBN 0-7198-2810-4, Pub. by Northwood Bks). State Mutual Bk.
Bradshaw, Vaughn. Building Control Systems. 624p. 1985. 32.95 (ISBN 0-471-87166-4); slides avail. (ISBN 0-471-82652-9). Wiley.
Duell, J. & Lawson, F. Damp Proof Course Detailing. (Illus.). 64p. 1983. 18.80x (ISBN 0-85139-150-8, Pub. by Architectural Pr England); pap. text ed. 12.50x (ISBN 0-85139-149-4). Humanities.
Harris, Frank & McCaffer, Ronald. Worked Examples in Construction Management. 180p. 1978. pap. 14.00x (ISBN 0-246-11370-7, Pub. by Granada England). Sheridan.
Hodgkinson, Allan, ed. AJ Handbook of Building Structure. 2nd ed. (Illus.). 400p. 1980. (Pub. by Architectural); pap. 32.50 (ISBN 0-85139-273-3). Nichols Pub.
Hornbostel, Caleb & Hornung, William. Materials & Methods for Contemporary Construction. 2nd ed. (Illus.). 1982. 29.95 (ISBN 0-13-560904-6). P-H.
Hornung, William J. The Builders Vest Pocket Reference Book. 1982. pap. 6.95 (ISBN 0-13-085944-3). P-H.
Hornung, William J. Construction Drafter's Vest Pocket Reference Book. (Vest Pocket Reference Ser.). (Illus.). 240p. 1983. pap. 7.95 (ISBN 0-13-168823-5). P-H.
Insulation Techniques & Estimating Handbook. 120p. 1980. pap. 11.95 (ISBN 0-317-12697-0); pap. 7.00 members (ISBN 0-317-12698-9). Natl Assn Home.
Jackson, W. P. Building Layout. LC 79-21174. (Illus.). 1979. pap. 11.75 (ISBN 0-910460-69-8). Craftsman.
Kidder, Frank E. & Parker, Harry. Architects' & Builders' Handbook. 18th ed. 2315p. 1931. 117.95 (ISBN 0-471-47421-5, Pub. by Wiley-Interscience). Wiley.
LeFax Pub. Co. Editors. Builder's Data. (Lefax Data Bks.: No. 628). (Illus.). pap. 3.00 (ISBN 0-685-52848-0). LeFax.
Love, T. W. Stair Builders Handbook. LC 74-4298. (Illus.). 1974. pap. 12.75 (ISBN 0-910460-07-8). Craftsman.
Lytle, R. J. & Reschke, R. C. Component & Modular Techniques: A Builder's Handbook. 2nd ed. 1981. 31.50 (ISBN 0-07-039274-9). McGraw.
Merritt, Frederick S. Building Design Construction Handbook. 4th ed. 1408p. 1981. 84.50 (ISBN 0-07-041521-8). McGraw.
National Association of Home Builders. Form Builders Manual. (Illus.). 140p. 1979. Waterproof Edition 20.00; members 15.00; pap. 16.00; pap. 12.00 members. Natl Assn Home.
--Growth Issues & Answers. 51p. 1979. pap. 15.00 (ISBN 0-86718-051-X). Natl Assn Home.
--Manual of Lumber & Plywood Saving Techniques for Residential Light-Frame Construction. (Illus.). 88p. 1971. pap. 7.00 (ISBN 0-86718-066-8); pap. 5.00, members. Natl Assn Home.
--Production Manual for Superintendents & Foremen. 24p. 1979. pap. 5.50 (ISBN 0-86718-026-9); 4.00, members. Natl Assn Home.
--Productivity Improvement Manual. 36p. 1978. pap. 8.00 (ISBN 0-86718-027-7); 6.00, members. Natl Assn Home.
Olin, Harold B., et al. Construction Principles, Materials & Methods. 1208p. 1983. 59.95 (ISBN 0-317-12694-6); members 49.95 (ISBN 0-317-12695-4). Natl Assn Home.
Page, John S. Estimator's General Construction Man-Hour Manual. 2nd ed. LC 60-1386. (Estimator's Man-Hour Library). 250p. 1977. 39.95x (ISBN 0-87201-320-0). Gulf Pub.
Phelps, John & Philbin. Complete Building Construction. 2nd ed. LC 82-17780. (Audel Ser.). 1983. 19.95 (ISBN 0-672-23377-0). G K Hall.
Phelps, John & Philbin, Tom, eds. Complete Building Construction. 2nd ed. LC 82-17789. 1983. 19.95 (ISBN 0-672-23377-0). Audel.
Powers, J. Patrick. Construction Dewatering: A Guide to Theory & Practice. LC 80-18851. (Wiley Ser. of Practical Construction Guides). 484p. 1981. 49.95 (ISBN 0-471-69591-2, Pub. by Wiley-Interscience). Wiley.
A Primer for Builders: New Home Warranties & the Magnuson - Moss Act. 2nd. ed. 68p. 1978. pap. 3.50 (ISBN 0-86718-025-0). Natl Assn Home.
Richardson, John G. Formwork Construction & Practice. (Viewpoint Publication Ser.). (Illus.). 1978. pap. text ed. 50.00x (ISBN 0-7210-1058-X). Scholium Intl.
Russell, Barry. Building Systems, Industrialization & Architecture: Industrialization & Architecture. LC 80-41692. 758p. 1981. 83.95 (ISBN 0-471-27952-8, Pub. by Wiley-Interscience). Wiley.
Ryan, Anne. Low-Rise Domestic & Similar Framed Structures: Part 4. Supplementary Domestic Buildings for Built-up Areas. (Illus.). 42p. 1977. pap. 1.50x (ISBN 0-643-00160-3, Pub. by CSIRO). Intl Spec Bk.
Sanders, Gordon A. Light Building Construction. 1984. text ed. 29.95 (ISBN 0-8359-4032-2); instr's manual avail. (ISBN 0-8359-4033-0). Reston.
Schwolsky, Rick & Williams, James. The Builder's Guide to Solar Construction. 352p. 1982. 36.50x (ISBN 0-07-055786-1). McGraw.
Smith, R. C. & Andres, C. K. Principles & Practices of Heavy Construction. 3rd ed. (Illus.). 432p. 1986. text ed. 29.95 (ISBN 0-13-701939-4). P-H.
Smith, R. C. & Honkala, T. L. Principles & Practices of Light Construction. 4th ed. (Illus.). 480p. 1986. text ed. 33.95 (ISBN 0-13-702085-6). P-H.
Stoneback & Weisbecker. Three Hundred Thirty-Three Easy-to-Build Fun Projects for Your Home. 294p. 1981. 15.95; pap. 8.95 (ISBN 0-8306-1227-0, 1227). TAB Bks.
Sunset Editors. Garden & Patio Building Book. LC 82-83219. (Illus.). 1983. pap. 5.95 (ISBN 0-376-01216-1, Sunset Bks.). Sunset-Lane.
Vanderberg, Maritz & Elder, A. AJ Handbook of Building Enclosure. 388p. 1974. 28.50 (ISBN 0-85139-282-2). Nichols Pub.

BUILDING–HISTORY
Abernethy, Francis E., ed. Built in Texas. (Publications of the Texas Folklore Society Ser.: No. 42). (Illus.). 288p. 1979. 24.50 (ISBN 0-935014-00-4). E-Heart Pr.
Bassett, William B. Historic American Buildings Survey of New Jersey. (Illus.). 210p. 1977. 13.95 (ISBN 0-686-81818-0); pap. 9.95 (ISBN 0-686-81819-9). NJ Hist Soc.
Bowyer, Jack. History of Building. 275p. 1973. pap. text ed. 12.35x (ISBN 0-258-96854-0, Pub. by Granada England). Brookfield Pub Co.
Chesshire, Gustave. Analysis of Construction Techniques Used in the Building of Colonial Homes Prior to 1700. (Illus.). 134p. 1982. 145.75 (ISBN 0-86650-017-0). Gloucester Art.
Condit, Carl. American Building: Materials & Techniques from the Beginning of the Colonial Settlements to the Present. 2nd ed. (Illus.). xiv, 330p. 1982. lib. bdg. 25.00x (ISBN 0-226-11448-1); pap. 10.95x (ISBN 0-226-11450-3, CHAC25). U of Chicago Pr.
Powell, C. G. An Economic History of the British Building History: 1815-1979. LC 81-16830. 1982. pap. 10.95x (ISBN 0-416-32010-4, NO. 3593). Methuen Inc.

BUILDING–INSPECTION
see Building Inspection

BUILDING–MATERIALS
see Building Materials

BUILDING–PRICE BOOKS
see Building–Estimates

BUILDING–RESEARCH
see Building Research

BUILDING–SPECIFICATIONS
see Building–Contracts and Specifications

BUILDING–SUPERINTENDENCE
Barton, P. K. Building Services Integration. (Illus.). 1983. 27.00 (ISBN 0-419-12030-0, NO. 6830, Pub. by E & FN Spon). Methuen INc.
Building Research Advisory Board. Supervision & Inspection of Federal Construction. (Federal Construction Council Technical Report No. 54). 1968. pap. 5.00 (ISBN 0-309-01609-6). Natl Acad Pr.
Gower Publications, ed. Managing Buildings & Building Services in Great Britain. 1973. 19.95x (ISBN 0-8464-0595-4). Beekman Pubs.
Hurst, Rosemary. Services & Maintenance for Hotels & Residential Establishments. 152p. 1981. pap. 9.95 (ISBN 0-434-90793-6, Pub. by W Heinemann Ltd). David & Charles.
Lee, Reginald. Building Maintenance Management. 2nd ed. 372p. 1981. pap. 22.00x (ISBN 0-246-11608-0, Pub. by Granada England). Sheridan.
Rudman, Jack. Director of Custodial & Security Services. (Career Examination Ser.: C-2923). (Cloth bdg. avail. on request). pap. 14.00 (ISBN 0-8373-2923-X). Natl Learning.
--Principal Buildings Manager. (Career Examination Ser.: C-2719). (Cloth bdg. avail. on request). pap. 12.00 (ISBN 0-8373-2719-9). Natl Learning.
--Senior Building Rehabilitation Specialist. (Career Examination Ser.: C-1933). (Cloth bdg. avail. on request). pap. 14.00 (ISBN 0-8373-1933-1). Natl Learning.
--Senior Superintendent of Construction. (Career Examination Ser.). (Cloth bdg. avail. on request). pap. 14.00 (ISBN 0-8373-0541-1). Natl Learning.
--Structure Maintainer - Group F: Painting. (Career Examination Ser.: C-1776). (Cloth bdg. avail. on request). 1977. pap. 8.00 (ISBN 0-8373-1776-2). Natl Learning.
--Structure Maintainer - Groups A, B, C, D & E. (Career Examination Ser.: C-2064). (Cloth bdg. avail. on request). 1977. pap. 10.00 (ISBN 0-8373-2064-X). Natl Learning.
--Superintendent of Buildings & Grounds. (Career Examination Ser.: C-1773). (Cloth bdg. avail. on request). pap. 12.00 (ISBN 0-8373-1773-8). Natl Learning.
--Supervisor (Structures) (Career Examination Ser.: C-424). (Cloth bdg. avail. on request). pap. 12.00 (ISBN 0-8373-0424-5). Natl Learning.
--Supervisor (Structures - Group C) (Iron Work) (Career Examination Ser.: C-425). (Cloth bdg. avail. on request). pap. 12.00 (ISBN 0-8373-0425-3). Natl Learning.

BUILDING, ADOBE
Aller, Paul & Aller, Doris. Build Your Own Adobe. (Illus.). 1946. 10.95x (ISBN 0-8047-0993-9). Stanford U Pr.
Baer, Morley, et al. Adobes in the Sun. LC 72-85173. (Illus.). 144p. 1980. pap. 8.95 (ISBN 0-87701-168-0). Chronicle Bks.
Design Concept Associates. Homes in the Earth. (Illus.). 112p. 1980. pap. 7.95 (ISBN 0-87701-212-1). Chronicle Bks.
Gray, Virginia & Macrae, Alan. Mud, Space & Spirit: Handmade Adobes. Young, Noel, ed. LC 76-7958. (Illus.). 96p. (Orig.). 1976. pap. 9.95 (ISBN 0-88496-059-5). Capra Pr.
Groben, W. Ellis. Adobe Architecture: Its Design & Construction. facs. ed. (Shorey Lost Arts Ser.). 42p. pap. 4.95 (ISBN 0-8466-6042-3, U42). Shorey.
Hopson, Rex C. Adobe: A Comprehensive Bibliography. LC 79-64631. 1979. 15.00 (ISBN 0-89016-052-X); pap. 9.95 (ISBN 0-89016-051-1). Lightning Tree.
Hughes, Lenore H. Adobe Abodes. LC 84-82473. (Illus.). 190p. (Orig.). Date not set. pap. 10.95 (ISBN 0-9604772-0-9). Hughes Pub.
Iowa, Jerome. Ageless Adobe: History & Preservation in Southwestern Architecture. LC 84-16337. (Illus.). 158p. (Orig.). 1985. pap. 16.95 (ISBN 0-86534-034-X). Sunstone Pr.
McHenry, Paul G. Adobe & Rammed Earth Buildings: Design & Construction. LC 83-10397. 217p. 1984. 42.95x (ISBN 0-471-87677-1, Pub. by Wiley-Interscience). Wiley.
McHenry, Paul G., Jr. Adobe: Build It Yourself. LC 72-92105. 157p. 1973. pap. 12.50 (ISBN 0-8165-0370-2). U of Ariz Pr.
--Adobe: Build It Yourself. 2nd, rev. ed. LC 85-8432. (Illus.). 170p. 1985. pap. 18.50 (ISBN 0-8165-0948-4). U of Ariz Pr.
Newcomb, Duane. The Owner-Built Adobe House. (Illus.). 224p. 1980. pap. 8.95 (ISBN 0-684-17459-6). Scribner.
O'Connor, John F. The Adobe Book. LC 72-95653. (Illus.). 174p. 1973. 22.50 (ISBN 0-941270-06-8). Ancient City Pr.
Southwick, Marcia. Build with Adobe. 3rd rev. & enl. ed. LC 73-1504. (Illus.). 230p. 1974. pap. 7.95 (ISBN 0-8040-0634-2, 82-73443, Pub. by Swallow). Ohio U Pr.
Stedman, Myrtle. Adobe Fireplaces. rev. ed. LC 77-78520. (Illus., Orig.). 1977. pap. 2.50 (ISBN 0-913270-32-6). Sunstone Pr.
--Adobe Remodeling. (Illus.). 31p. (Orig.). 1976. pap. 3.45 (ISBN 0-913270-54-7). Sunstone Pr.

BUILDING, BRICK
Adams, J. T. The Complete Concrete Masonry & Brick Handbook. 1979. pap. 19.95 (ISBN 0-442-20830-8). Van Nos Reinhold.
Bicknell, A. J. Wooden & Brick Buildings with Details. (Architecture & Decorative Art Ser.). 1977. Repr. of 1875 ed. 85.00 (ISBN 0-306-70832-9). Da Capo.
Gravett, K. Timber & Brick Building in Kent. 1971. 50.00x (ISBN 0-85033-006-8, Pub. by Phillimore England). State Mutual Bk.
Handisyde, Cecil C. Hard Landscape in Brick. (Illus.). 74p. 1976. 17.95x (ISBN 0-85139-283-0, Pub. by Architectural Pr). Nichols Pub.
Hendry, A. W. Structural Brickwork. LC 80-26993. 209p. 1981. 59.95x (ISBN 0-470-27109-4). Halsted Pr.
Lloyd, Nathaniel. A History of English Brickwork. LC 72-87653. (Illus.). 1973. Repr. of 1925 ed. lib. bdg. 33.00x (ISBN 0-405-08750-0, Pub. by Blom). Ayer Co Pubs.
Svec, J. J. & Jeffers, P. E. Modern Masonry Panel Construction Systems. LC 72-83307. (Illus.). 144p. 1971. 19.95 (ISBN 0-8436-0114-0). Van Nos Reinhold.
Thurlimann, Bruno & Furler, Rene. Strength of Brick Walls Under Enforced End Rotation. (IBA Ser.: No. 89). 14p. 1979. pap. text ed. 4.95x (ISBN 3-7643-1108-8). Birkhauser.

BUILDING, CONCRETE
see Concrete Construction

BUILDING, EARTHQUAKE-PROOF
see Earthquakes and Building

BUILDING, FIREPROOF
see also Fireproofing
Aqua Group. Fire & Building: Guide for the Design Team. 190p. 1984. pap. 26.00x (ISBN 0-246-11878-4, Pub by Granada England). Sheridan.
Brannigan, Francis L. Building Construction for the Fire Service: A Fire Officer's Guide. McKinnon, Gordon, ed. (Get Ahead Ser). (Illus.). 87p. 1973. 8.50 (ISBN 0-87765-017-9, FSP-33). Natl Fire Prot.
Building Services Library, 15 bks. 1300p. includes protective case 38.70 (ISBN 0-685-58049-0, BSL-A). Natl Fire Prot.
Egan, M. David. Concepts in Building Fire Safety. LC 77-12184. 264p. 1978. 42.95x (ISBN 0-471-02229-2, Pub. by Wiley-Interscience). Wiley.
Fire Endurance of Prestressed Concrete Double-Tee Wall Assemblies. (PCI Journal Reprints Ser.). (Illus.). 11p. pap. 5.00 (ISBN 0-686-40046-1, JR115). Prestressed Concrete.
Fire Provisions to Model Building Codes Related to Prestressed Concrete Use. (PCI Journal Reprints Ser.). 69p. pap. 8.00 (ISBN 0-686-40074-7, JR153). Prestressed Concrete.
Ignition, Heat Release, & Noncombustibility of Materials - STP 502. 165p. 1972. 10.00 (ISBN 0-8031-0111-2, 04 502000 31). ASTM.
National Bureau of Standards. Detector Sensitivity & Siting Requirements for Dwellings. McKinnon, G. P. & Dean, A. E., eds. LC 76-48769. 1976. pap. 10.00 (ISBN 0-87765-086-1, SPP-43). Natl Fire Prot.
Standard Types of Building Construction. (Two Hundred Ser.). 1961. pap. 2.00 (ISBN 0-685-58037-7, 220). Natl Fire Prot.

BUILDING, HOUSE
see House Construction

BUILDING, IRON AND STEEL
see also Girders; Plates, Iron and Steel; Skyscrapers; Steel, Structural; Strength of Materials; Structures, Theory Of
Amon, Rene, et al. Steel Design for Engineers & Architects. 432p. 1982. 39.50 (ISBN 0-442-20297-0). Van Nos Reinhold.

Badger, D. D. & Bogardus, James. Origins of Cast Iron Architecture in America. LC 68-25760. (Architecture & Decorative Art Ser.: Vol. 13). (Illus.). 1970. Repr. of 1856 ed. lib. bdg. 55.00 (ISBN 0-306-71039-0). Da Capo.
Beedle, Lynn S. Plastic Design of Steel Frames. LC 58-13454. 406p. 1974. 56.95x (ISBN 0-471-06171-9, Pub. by Wiley-Interscience). Wiley.
Constructing in Steel: The User & the Maker. 158p. (Orig.). 1980. pap. text ed. 20.00x (ISBN 0-904357-27-9, Metals Soc). Brookfield Pub Co.
Crawley, Stanley W., et al. Steel Buildings: Analysis & Design. 3rd ed. 672p. 1984. text ed. 39.95 (ISBN 0-471-86414-5); write for info. solution (ISBN 0-471-89130-4). Wiley.
Disque, Robert O. Applied Plastic Design in Steel. LC 77-10512. 256p. 1978. Repr. of 1971 ed. lib. bdg. 16.50 (ISBN 0-88275-312-6). Krieger.
Dowling, P. J., et al, eds. Steel Plated Structures: An International Symposium. 1977. text ed. 50.00x (ISBN 0-8464-0884-8). Beekman Pubs.
Gaylord, Edwin H. & Gaylord, Charles N. Design of Steel Structures. 2nd ed. (Civil Engineering Ser.). (Illus.). 640p. 1972. text ed. 46.00 (ISBN 0-07-023110-9). McGraw.
Halperin, Don A. Building with Steel: Design Detailing & Erection. 2nd ed. LC 65-25450. (Illus.). pap. 69.80 (ISBN 0-317-10821-2, 2004576). Bks Demand UMI.
Hart, F., et al. Multi-Storey Buildings in Steel. 2nd ed. Godfrey, G. Bernard, tr. from Ger. (Illus.). 416p. 1985. 69.50 (ISBN 0-89397-224-X). Nichols Pub.
Johnson, R. P. Composite Structures of Steel & Concrete: Beams, Columns, Frames & Applications in Buildings, Vol. 1. 224p. 1982. pap. 18.00x (ISBN 0-246-11919-5, Pub. by Granada England). Sheridan.
Johnson, R. P. & Buckby, R. J. Composite Structures of Steel & Concrete, Vol. 11: Bridges with a Commentary on BS 5400, Pt. 5. 524p. 1979. text ed. 76.00x (ISBN 0-258-97104-5, Pub. by Granada England). Brookfield Pub Co.
Kirby, P. A. & Nethercot, D. A. Design for Structural Stability. LC 79-754. 165p. 1979. 53.95x (ISBN 0-470-26691-0). Halsted Pr.
Kloss, Hans. Application of Structural Steel Design. LC 77-18605. (Illus.). 1980. 16.00 (ISBN 0-8044-4554-0). Ungar.
Lothers, John E. Design in Structural Steel. 3rd ed. LC 71-160254. (Civil Engineering & Engineering Mechanics Ser). (Illus.). 1972. 38.95 (ISBN 0-13-201921-3). P-H.
MacGinley, T. J. Steel Structures: Practical Design Studies. 300p. 1981. 34.00x (ISBN 0-419-12560-4, NO. 6631, E & FN Spon England); pap. 17.95x (ISBN 0-419-11710-5, NO. 6598). Methuen Inc.
McGuire, William. Steel Structures. 1968. text ed. 45.00 (ISBN 0-13-846493-6). P-H.
Merritt, Frederick S., ed. Structural Steel Designer's Handbook. (Illus.). 1000p. 1972. 67.50 (ISBN 0-07-041507-2). McGraw.
Moy, S. S. Plastic Methods for Steel & Concrete Structures. 221p. 1981. pap. 29.95x (ISBN 0-470-27079-9). Halsted Pr.
Narayanan, R., ed. Steel-Framed Structures: Stability & Strength. 352p. 1985. 66.00 (ISBN 0-85334-329-2, Pub. by Elsevier Applied Sci England). Elsevier.
Tall, Lambert. Structural Steel Design. 2nd ed. Tall, Lambert, ed. LC 82-25853. 892p. 1983. Repr. of 1974 ed. text ed. 53.50 (ISBN 0-89874-602-7). Krieger.
Yu, Wei-Wen. Cold-Formed Steel Structures. LC 78-20815. 478p. 1979. Repr. of 1973 ed. lib. bdg. 26.50 (ISBN 0-88275-845-4). Krieger.

BUILDING, UNDERGROUND
see Underground Construction

BUILDING, WOODEN
Anderson, L. O. & Zornig, Harold F. Build Your Own Low Cost Home. 200p. 1972. pap. 9.95 (ISBN 0-486-21525-3). Dover.
Bicknell, A. J. Wooden & Brick Buildings with Details. (Architecture & Decorative Art Ser.). 1977. Repr. of 1875 ed. 85.00 (ISBN 0-306-70832-9). Da Capo.
Charles, F. W. B. The Conservation of Timber Buildings. LC 84-12984. (Illus.). 256p. 1984. 72.50 (ISBN 0-09-145090-X, Pub. by Hutchinson Educ). Longwood Pub Group.
Gravett, K. Timber & Brick Building in Kent. 1971. 50.00x (ISBN 0-85033-006-8, Pub. by Phillimore England). State Mutual Bk.
Langsner, Drew. A Logbuilder's Handbook. Warde, John, ed. (Illus.). 248p. 1982. 15.95 (ISBN 0-87857-416-6, 14-015-0); pap. 9.95 (ISBN 0-87857-419-0, 14-015-1). Rodale Pr Inc.
Parker, Harry & Hauf, Harold D. Simplified Design of Structural Wood. 3rd ed. LC 78-9888. 269p. 1979. 29.95x (ISBN 0-471-66630-0, Pub. by Wiley-Interscience). Wiley.
Timber Engineering Company. Timber Design & Construction Handbook. 1956. 58.00 (ISBN 0-07-064606-6). McGraw.
United Nations Economic Commission for Europe, Timber Committee. Behaviour of Wood Products in Fire: Proceedings, Oxford, 1977. 1977. pap. text ed. 35.00 (ISBN 0-08-021990-X). Pergamon.
Wolfe, Ralph, et al. Low-Cost Pole Building Construction. rev. ed. LC 80-10232. (Illus.). 176p. 1980. pap. 10.95 (ISBN 0-88266-170-1). Garden Way Pub.
Youngquist, Wally G. & Fleischer, Herbert O. Wood in American Life 1776-2076. LC 77-85427. 192p. 1977. 11.00 (ISBN 0-935018-00-X); members 9.00. Forest Prod.

BUILDING BLOCK DESIGN
see Unit Construction

BUILDING DYNAMICS
see Structural Dynamics

BUILDING FAILURES
see also Buildings–Protection
Addelson, L. Building Failures. 128p. 1982. pap. text ed. 27.25x (ISBN 0-85139-768-9, Pub. by Architectural Pr England). Humanities.
Davis, I., ed. Disasters & the Small Dwelling. 220p. 1981. 33.00 (ISBN 0-08-024753-9). Pergamon.
Feld, Jacob. Construction Failure. LC 68-30908. (Practical Construction Guides Ser.). 1968. 45.95x (ISBN 0-471-25700-1, Pub. by Wiley-Interscience). Wiley.
Hornstein, Marvin. The Sky Is Falling! Why Buildings Fail. LC 82-72602. (Illus.). 120p. (Orig.). 1982. pap. 7.95 (ISBN 0-89708-106-4). And Bks.
Ransom, W. H. Building Failures: Diagnosis & Avoidance. (Illus.). 176p. 1981. 22.00x (ISBN 0-419-11750-4, NO.6569, Pub. by E&FN Spon England); pap. 11.95 (ISBN 0-419-11760-1, NO. 6568). Methuen Inc.
Thompson, J. M. & Hunt, G. W. Collapse: The Buckling of Structures in Theory & Practice. LC 83-5190. 480p. 1984. 79.50 (ISBN 0-521-25102-8). CAmbridge U Pr.

BUILDING FITTINGS
see also Architectural Ironwork
Andrews, F. T. Building Mechanical Systems. 2nd ed. LC 75-11895. 412p. 1976. 24.50 (ISBN 0-88275-322-3). Krieger.
Bunce, J. W. The Integrity of Platform Superstructures: Analysis in Accordance with API RP2A. (Illus.). 200p. 1985. text ed. 40.00x (ISBN 0-00-383162-0, Pub. by Collins England). Sheridan.
Kaberlein, Joseph J. Air Conditioning Sheet Metal Layout. 3rd ed. 1973. 17.95 (ISBN 0-02-819360-1). Glencoe.
Kinzey, Bertram Y., Jr. & Sharp, H. M. Environmental Technologies in Architecture. (Illus.). 1963. ref. ed. 44.95 (ISBN 0-13-283226-7). P-H.

BUILDING INDUSTRY
see Construction Industry

BUILDING INSPECTION
American Society of Civil Engineers, compiled by. Reducing Risk & Liability Through Better Specifications & Inspections. LC 82-70874. 165p. 1982. pap. 18.75x (ISBN 0-87262-301-7). Am Soc Civil Eng.
Apartment Building Exterior Inspection Form. 1.50 (ISBN 0-686-46399-4, 981). Inst Real Estate.
Apartment Unit Interior Inspection Form. 1.50 (ISBN 0-686-46400-1, 982). Inst Real Estate.
Building Research Advisory Board. Supervision & Inspection of Federal Construction. (Federal Construction Council Technical Report No. 54). 1968. pap. 5.00 (ISBN 0-309-01609-6). Natl Acad Pr.
Civil-Structural Inspection, Course 29. (Illus.). 260p. 1979. spiral bdg. 41.00x (ISBN 0-87683-115-3). G P Courseware.
Clyde, James E. Construction Inspection: A Field Guide to Practice. 2nd ed. LC 83-6977. (Practical Construction Guides Ser.: I-344). 416p. 1983. 44.95x (ISBN 0-471-88861-3, Pub. by Wiley-Interscience). Wiley.
Engineering Fundamentals for Building Inspectors. 75.00 (ISBN 0-318-00067-9, BIT-104). Intl Conf Bldg Off.
Field Inspection Manual. 16.00 (ISBN 0-318-00053-9). Intl Conf Bldg Off.
Freedman, Daniel P. & Weinberg, Gerald M. Handbook of Walkthroughs, Inspections, & Technical Reviews. 3rd ed. 448p. 1982. text ed. 38.00 (ISBN 0-316-29282-6). Little.
Liebing, Ralph W. Systematic Construction Inspection. 119p. 1982. 32.50x (ISBN 0-471-08065-9, Pub. by Wiley-Interscience). Wiley.
McNeill, Joseph. Principles of Home Inspection: A Guide to Residential Construction, Inspection & Maintenance. 346p. 1979. 23.95 (ISBN 0-442-23606-9). Van Nos Reinhold.
O'Bannon, Robert E. Building Department Administration for Inspectors. 75.00 (ISBN 0-318-00057-1, BIT-118). Intl Conf Bldg Off.
O'Brien, James. Construction Inspection Handbook. 2nd ed. 684p. 1983. 44.50 (ISBN 0-442-25741-4). Van Nos Reinhold.
Office Building Exterior Inspection Form. 1.50 (ISBN 0-686-46407-9, 983). Inst Real Estate.
Rudman, Jack. Building Construction Inspector I. (Career Examination Ser.: C-1831). (Cloth bdg. avail. on request). pap. 12.00 (ISBN 0-8373-1831-9). Natl Learning.
--Building Construction Inspector II. (Career Examination Ser.: C-1832). (Cloth bdg. avail. on request). pap. 14.00 (ISBN 0-8373-1832-7). Natl Learning.
--Building Construction Inspector III. (Career Examination Ser.: C-1833). (Cloth bdg. avail. on request). pap. 14.00 (ISBN 0-8373-1833-5). Natl Learning.
--Building Inspector. (Career Examination Ser.: C-104). (Cloth bdg. avail. on request). pap. 12.00 (ISBN 0-8373-0104-1). Natl Learning.
--Building Plan Examiner. (Career Examination Ser.: C-1150). (Cloth bdg. avail. on request). pap. 12.00 (ISBN 0-8373-1150-0). Natl Learning.
--Chief Building Inspector. (Career Examination Ser.: C-2847). (Cloth bdg. avail. on request). 1980. pap. 14.00 (ISBN 0-8373-2847-0). Natl Learning.
--Chief Compliance Investigator. (Career Examination Ser.: C-2423). (Cloth bdg. avail. on request). pap. 14.00 (ISBN 0-8373-2423-8). Natl Learning.
--Chief Multiple Residence Inspector. (Career Examination Ser.: C-2844). (Cloth bdg. avail. on request). 1980. pap. 14.00 (ISBN 0-8373-2844-6). Natl Learning.
--Compliance Investigator. (Career Examination Ser.: C-2421). (Cloth bdg. avail. on request). pap. 12.00 (ISBN 0-8373-2421-1). Natl Learning.
--Construction Inspector. (Career Examination Ser.: C-164). (Cloth bdg. avail on request). pap. 12.00 (ISBN 0-8373-0164-5). Natl Learning.
--Housing Construction Inspector. (Career Examination Ser.: C-335). (Cloth bdg. avail. on request). pap. 10.00 (ISBN 0-8373-0335-4). Natl Learning.
--Inspector of Carpentry & Masonry. (Career Examination Ser.: C-365). (Cloth bdg. avail. on request). pap. 10.00 (ISBN 0-8373-0365-6). Natl Learning.
--Multiple Residence Inspector. (Career Examination Ser.: C-2842). (Cloth bdg. avail. on request). 1980. pap. 10.00 (ISBN 0-8373-2842-X). Natl Learning.
--Principal Building Inspector. (Career Examination Ser.: C-2853). (Cloth bdg. avail. on request). 1980. pap. 12.00 (ISBN 0-8373-2853-5). Natl Learning.
--Principal Construction Inspector. (Career Examination Ser.: C-1400). (Cloth bdg. avail. on request). pap. 12.00 (ISBN 0-8373-1400-3). Natl Learning.
--Senior Building Inspector. (Career Examination Ser.: C-2113). (Cloth bdg. avail. on request). 1977. pap. 14.00 (ISBN 0-8373-2113-1). Natl Learning.
--Senior Compliance Investigator. (Career Examination Ser.: C-2422). (Cloth bdg. avail. on request). pap. 12.00 (ISBN 0-8373-2422-X). Natl Learning.
--Senior Construction Inspector. (Career Examination Ser.: C-709). (Cloth bdg. avail. on reqeust). pap. 14.00 (ISBN 0-8373-0709-0). Natl Learning.
--Senior Electrical Inspector. (Career Examination Ser.: C-712). (Cloth bdg. avail. on request). pap. 14.00 (ISBN 0-8373-0712-0). Natl Learning.
--Senior Multiple Residence Inspector. (Career Examination Ser.: C-2843). (Cloth bdg. avail. on request). 1980. pap. 14.00 (ISBN 0-8373-2843-8). Natl Learning.
--Steel Construction Inspector. (Career Examination Ser.: C-765). (Cloth bdg. avail. on request). pap. 10.00 (ISBN 0-8373-0765-1). Natl Learning.
--Superintendent of Building Inspection. (Career Examination Ser.: C-2282). (Cloth bdg. avail. on request). 1977. pap. 12.00 (ISBN 0-8373-2282-0). Natl Learning.
--Supervising Building Inspector. (Career Examination Ser.: C-2840). (Cloth bdg. avail. on request). 1980. pap. 12.00 (ISBN 0-8373-2840-3). Natl Learning.
--Supervising Construction Inspector. (Career Examination Ser.: C-1043). (Cloth bdg. avail. on request). pap. 12.00 (ISBN 0-8373-1043-1). Natl Learning.
Schainblatt, Al & Koss, Margo. Fire Code Inspections & Fire Prevention: What Methods Lead to Success? (Illus.). 122p. (Orig.). 1979. pap. text ed. 6.95x. Urban Inst.
Structural Inspection: Concrete I. 69.00 (ISBN 0-318-00068-7, BIT-105). Intl Conf Bldg Off.
Tuck, Charles A., Jr., ed. NFPA Inspection Manual. 5th ed. LC 76-5194. (Illus.). 387p. 1982. 20.00 (ISBN 0-87765-239-2, SPP-11C). Natl Fire Prot.
Watts, John. The Supervision of Construction: A Guide to Site Inspection. (Illus.). 208p. 1980. 15.95 (ISBN 0-7134-2174-6, Pub. by Batsford England). David & Charles.

BUILDING MACHINERY
see also Construction Equipment
Hoerner, Thomas A. & Bear, W. Forrest. Micrometers Calipers & Gages. (Illus.). 21p. 1969. pap. text ed. 2.65x (ISBN 0-913163-03-1, 169). Hobar Pubns.

BUILDING MATERIALS
see also Asbestos; Bituminous Materials; Bricks; Cement; Ceramics; Concrete; Flooring; Insulating Materials; Plastics; Plastics in Building; Reinforced Concrete; Steel, Structural; Strength of Materials; Structural Engineering; Timber; Wood
Adhesives Used on Building Materials, 1970-April 1982. 71p. 1982. 78.00 (ISBN 0-686-48269-7, LS104). T-C Pubns CA.
Advances in Structural Composites Symposium: Proceedings, Anaheim CA, 10-12 October 1967. (Science of Advanced Materials & Process Engineering Ser., Vol. 12). 20.00 (ISBN 0-938994-12-3). Soc Adv Material.
AIAA-ASME Structures, Structural Dynamics & Material Conference (10th: 1969: New Orleans, Louisiana) Structures & Materials: Collection of Technical Papers, April 14-16, 1969. (Illus.). pap. 120.30 (ISBN 0-317-08388-0, 2016452). Bks Demand UMI.
American Institute of Architects. Materials Components & Design: An Integrated Approach Handbook. Rush, Richard D., ed. 500p. 1985. 84.95x. Wiley.
American Society for Metals. Materials Engineering in the Arctic: Proceedings of an International Conference, St. Jovite, Quebec, Canada, Sept. 27 - Oct. 1, 1976. LC 77-4214. (Illus.). pap. 85.80 (ISBN 0-317-08329-5, 2019499). Bks Demand UMI.
Astbury, N. F., et al. Gas Explosions in Load-Bearing Brick Structures. 1970. 10.00x (ISBN 0-900910-09-7, Pub. by Brit Ceramic Soc England). State Mutual Bk.
Bear, W. Forrest & Hoerner, Thomas A. Sawhorse Layout with the Framing Square. rev. ed. (Illus.). 8p. 1971. pap. text ed. 1.10x (ISBN 0-913163-01-5, 165). Hobar Pubns.
Blaser, W. Elemental Building Forms. 1982. 43.00 (ISBN 0-9908000-1-6, Pub. by Beton Bks W Germany). Heyden.
Bucksch, Herbert. Dictionary of Architecture, Building Construction & Materials, Vol. II. (Eng. & Ger.). 1137p. 1976. 175.00 (ISBN 3-7625-0714-7, M-7130). French & Eur.
--Dictionary of Architecture, Building Construction & Materials, Vol. I. (Eng. & Ger.). 942p. 1974. 175.00 (ISBN 3-7625-0357-5, M-7131). French & Eur.
--Dictionary of Architecture, Building Construction & Materials, 2 vols. 1974-76. plastic bdg.cancelled 120.00x ea. Vol. 1, Ger.-Eng (ISBN 3-7625-0357-5). Vol. 2, Eng.-Ger (ISBN 3-7625-0714-7). Intl Pubns Serv.
Building Material Industry. (UNIDO Monographs on Industrialization of Developing Countries: Problems & Prospects: Vol. 3). pap. 4.00 (ISBN 0-686-93196-3, UN69/2B/39V3, UN). Unipub.
Building Material Manufactures & Quarring. 1985. 150.00x (ISBN 0-317-07194-7, Pub. by Jordan & Sons UK). State Mutual Bk.
Cardella, Carol A. Builders Guide to Merchandising. 55p. 1978. pap. 8.00 (ISBN 0-86718-012-9); pap. 6.00 members. Natl Assn Home.
Corey, A. Raymond. The Development of Markets for New Materials: A Study of Building New End-Product Markets for Aluminum, Fibrous Glass, & the Plastics. LC 56-9764. pap. 69.80 (ISBN 0-317-29992-1, 2051840). Bks Demand UMI.
Dagostino, Frank. Materials of Construction. 1981. text ed. 26.95 (ISBN 0-8359-4286-4). Reston.
De Campoli, Giuseppe. Strength of Structural Materials: Understanding Basic Structural Design. LC 84-3569. 461p. 1984. text ed. 34.95 (ISBN 0-471-89082-0, Pub. by Wiley-Interscience). Wiley.
Derricott, R. & Chissick, Seymour S. Rebuild. LC 81-21942. (Properties of Materials Safety & Environmental Factors). 286p. 1982. 48.95x (ISBN 0-471-10173-7, Pub. by Wiley-Interscience). Wiley.
The Development Potential of Dimension Stone. pap. 8.50 (ISBN 0-686-94782-7, UN76/2A4, UN). Unipub.
Dictionnaire Pour l'Architecture, le Batiment et les Materiaux de Construction, 2 vols. (Ger. & Fr.). 820p. 1977. band I 236.00 (ISBN 3-7625-0786-4, M-7095). French & Eur.
Dictionnaire Pour l'Architecture, le Batiment et les Materiaux de Construction, 2 vols. (Ger. & Fr.). 688p. 1979. band II 236.00 (ISBN 3-7625-0787-2, M-7096). French & Eur.
Durability of Building Materials & Components, STP 691. 1034p. 1980. 74.95x (ISBN 0-8031-0325-5, 04-691000-10). ASTM.
Eldridge, H. J. Properties of Building Materials. (Illus.). pap. 30.30 (ISBN 0-317-08291-4, 2019627). Bks Demand UMI.

Everett, Alan. Finishes. (Mitchell's Building Ser.). (Illus.). 200p. 1971. pap. 14.95 (ISBN 0-7134-3335-3, Pub. by Batsford, Pub. by Batsford England). David & Charles.
Fabricated Structural Metal Products. 1982. 445.00 (ISBN 0-318-00508-5). Busn Trend.
Fire Retardant Treatments for Building Materials. (Seven Hundred Ser). 1961. pap. 2.00 (ISBN 0-685-58212-4, 703). Natl Fire Prot.
Foster, John S. & Harington, Raymond. Structure & Fabric. (Mitchell's Building Ser.). (Illus., Orig.). 1983. Vol. 1 288 pgs. pap. 16.95 (ISBN 0-7134-3863-0, Pub. by Batsford England); Vol. 2 456 pgs. pap. 21.00 (ISBN 0-7134-3865-7, Pub. by Batsford England). David & Charles.
Herubin, Charles & Marotta, Theodore. Basic Construction Materials. 2nd ed. 1981. text ed. 27.95 (ISBN 0-8359-0362-1); solutions manual avail. (ISBN 0-8359-0363-X). Reston.
Hornbostel, Caleb. Construction Materials: Types, Uses & Applications. LC 78-6278. 878p. 1978. 85.95 (ISBN 0-471-40940-5, Pub. by Wiley-Interscience). Wiley.
Hornbostel, Caleb & Hornung, William. Materials & Methods for Contemporary Construction. 2nd ed. (Illus.). 1982. 29.95 (ISBN 0-13-560904-6). P-H.
Hornung, W. Construction: Systems & Materials. 1976. pap. 8.84 (ISBN 0-13-169508-8). P-H.
Huntington, Whitney C. & Mickadeit, Robert E. Building Construction: Materials & Types of Construction. 5th ed. LC 79-24467. 471p. 1981. 31.95 (ISBN 0-471-05354-6). Wiley.
King, Harold. Components. (Mitchell's Building Ser.). (Illus.). 200p. 1971. (Pub. by Batsford England); pap. 17.50 (ISBN 0-7134-3333-7, Pub. by Batsford England). David & Charles.
Living with Marginal Aggregates - STP 597. 113p. 1976. pap. 5.50 (ISBN 0-8031-0391-3, 04-597000-07). ASTM.
Martin, John. Construction Materials. 1981. text ed. 27.95 (ISBN 0-8359-0933-6); instrs.' manual free (ISBN 0-8359-0934-4). Reston.
Mills, Adelbert P. Materials of Construction, Their Manufacture & Properties. 6th ed. LC 55-73681. (Illus.). pap. 120.00 (ISBN 0-317-08337-6, 2055132). Bks Demand UMI.
Mooney, Peter. Structural Foams. 1982. 1750.00 (ISBN 0-89336-196-8, P-006). BCC.
National Academy Of Sciences. Prefinishing of Exterior Building Components. 1962. 6.00. Natl Acad Pr.
National Association of Home Builders. Manual of Lumber & Plywood Saving Techniques for Residential Light-Frame Construction. (Illus.). 88p. 1971. pap. 7.00 (ISBN 0-86718-066-8); pap. 5.00, members. Natl Assn Home.
Parker, Harry, et al. Materials & Methods of Architectural Construction. 3rd ed. LC 58-8213. 724p. 1958. 49.95x (ISBN 0-471-66297-6, Pub. by Wiley-Interscience). Wiley.
Pavior Screeds. (Materials & Techniques in Building Practice: No. 1). pap. 20.00 (ISBN 0-317-08374-0, 2017713). Bks Demand UMI.
Pawley, Martin. Building for Tomorrow: Putting Waste to Work. LC 82-5821. (Illus.). 288p. 1982. 17.95 (ISBN 0-87156-324-X). Sierra.
Renfroe, O. S., ed. Building Materials from Solid Wastes. LC 79-16988. (Pollution Technology Rev. 61 Ser.). (Illus.). 275p. 1980. 36.00 (ISBN 0-8155-0771-2). Noyes.
Rosen, Harold J. & Bennett, Philip M. Construction Materials Evaluation & Selection: A Systematic Approach. LC 79-15885. (Practical Construction Guides Ser.). 163p. 1979. 34.95 (ISBN 0-471-73565-5, Pub. by Wiley-Interscience). Wiley.
Sluzas, Raymond & Ryan, Anne. A Graphic Guide to Industrialized Building Elements. LC 77-13121. (Illus.). 176p. 1977. 21.95 (ISBN 0-8436-0163-9); pap. 12.95 (ISBN 0-8436-0164-7). Van Nos Reinhold.
Smith, R. C. Materials of Construction. 3rd ed. (Illus.). 1979. text ed. 32.50 (ISBN 0-07-058497-4). McGraw.
Society of the Plastics Industry, Inc. Structural Foam '78 - Expanding Horizons. LC 78-67220. 1978. pap. text ed. 9.95 (ISBN 0-87762-257-4). Technomic.
Spence, Robin & Cook, David. Building Materials in Developing Countries. LC 82-17434. 360p. 1983. 39.95x (ISBN 0-471-10235-0). Wiley.
Spencer, Albert, et al. Materials of Construction. 1982. text ed. 26.95 (ISBN 0-8359-4291-0); solutions manual o.p. 0.00 (ISBN 0-8359-4292-9). Reston.
Stulz, Roland. Appropriate Building Materials: A Catalogue of Potential Solutions. (Illus.). 324p. 1983. pap. 19.50x (ISBN 0-903031-90-6, Pub. by Intermediate Tech England). Intermediate Tech.
Taylor, G. D. Materials of Construction. (Illus.). 254p. 1983. text ed. 24.00x (ISBN 0-582-41209-9). Longman.
Waddell, J. J. Construction Materials Ready-Reference Manual. 416p. 1984. 24.50 (ISBN 0-07-067649-6). McGraw.
Wass, Alonzo & Sanders, Gordon. Materials & Procedures for Residential Construction. (Illus.). text ed. 25.95 (ISBN 0-8359-4284-8). Reston.
Watson, Don A. Construction Materials & Processes. 2nd ed. LC 77-612. (Illus.). 1978. pap. text ed. 35.00 (ISBN 0-07-068471-5). McGraw.
Williams, Elizabeth & Williams, Robert. Building with Salvaged Lumber. (Illus.). 272p. 1983. 19.95 (ISBN 0-8306-0197-X); pap. 10.25 (ISBN 0-8306-0597-5, 1597). TAB Bks.

BUILDING MATERIALS–SPECIFICATIONS
see Building–Contracts and Specifications

BUILDING MATERIALS–TESTING

Method of Test of Surface Burning Characteristics of Building Materials. (Two Hundred Ser). 1972. pap. 2.00 (ISBN 0-685-58238-8, 255). Natl Fire Prot.
Smith, Brian J. Practical Construction Science. LC 79-40562. (Longman Technician Ser.: Construction & Civil Engineering). pap. 87.00 (ISBN 0-317-27785-5, 2025235). Bks Demand UMI.
Wilson, Forrest. Building Materials Evaluation Handbook. 368p. 1984. 34.50 (ISBN 0-442-29325-9). Van Nos Reinhold.

BUILDING REPAIR
see Buildings–Repair and Reconstruction; Dwellings–Maintenance and Repair

BUILDING RESEARCH

Building Research Advisory Board. Promotion of the Development & Use of the Subsystem Concept of Building Construction. LC 72-84109. 108p. 1972. pap. 5.25 (ISBN 0-309-02039-5). Natl Acad Pr.
International Council for Building Research Studies & Documentation. Directory of Building Research, Information & Development Organizations. 4th ed. 215p. 1981. pap. 42.00x (ISBN 0-419-12550-7, NO.6637, Pub by E&FN Spon England). Methuen Inc.
National Academy Of Sciences. Plastics in Building Illumination. 1958. pap. 3.00. Natl Acad Pr.

BUILDING SITES

Austin, Richard L. Site Graphics. (Illus.). 128p. 1984. text ed. 19.95 (ISBN 0-442-21077-9). Van Nos Reinhold.
Clayton, Christopher, et al. Site Investigation: A Handbook for Engineers. LC 81-21973. 448p. 1982. 54.95x (ISBN 0-470-27328-3). Halsted Pr.
Dike, R. Architectural Common Sense Site, Vol. 1. 1983. 22.95 (ISBN 0-442-21364-6); pap. 14.95 (ISBN 0-442-21805-2). Van Nos Reinhold.
Land Development Two. Orig. Title: Land Development Manual. (Illus.). 444p. 1981. pap. 27.00 (ISBN 0-86718-064-1); pap. 20.00, members. Natl Assn Home.
Parker, Harry & MacGuire, John W. Simplified Site Engineering for Architects & Builders. 250p. 1954. 32.50x (ISBN 0-471-66363-8, Pub. by Wiley-Interscience). Wiley.
Roberts, John M. The Building Site: Planning & Practice. LC 82-21931. 186p. 1983. 26.95 (ISBN 0-471-08868-4, Pub. by Wiley-Interscience). Wiley.
Robinette, Gary O., ed. Energy-Efficient Site Design. 176p. 1983. 25.45 (ISBN 0-442-22338-2). Van Nos Reinhold.
Roskind, Robert & Owner Builder Center. Before You Build. LC 81-51897. 192p. (Orig.). 1981. pap. 7.95 (ISBN 0-89815-036-1). Ten Speed Pr.
Walker, Theodore D. Site Design & Construction Detailing. LC 77-18668. (Illus.). 467p. 1978. 29.95 (ISBN 0-914886-08-8); instr's manual 14.95 (ISBN 0-914886-25-8). PDA Pubs.
Way, Douglas S. Terrain Analysis: A Guide to Site Selection Using Aerial Photographic Interpretation. 2nd ed. (Community Development Ser.: Vol. 1). (Illus.). 1978. 48.95 (ISBN 0-87933-318-9). Van Nos Reinhold.

BUILDING STONES
see also Masonry; Quarries and Quarrying; Stone-Cutting

Moen, Wayne S. Building Stone of Washington. (Bulletin Ser.: No. 55). (Illus.). 85p. 1967. 0.75 (ISBN 0-686-34710-2). Geologic Pubns.

BUILDING SUPERINTENDENCE
see Building–Superintendence

BUILDING TRADES
see also Building; Construction Industry; also Bricklayers, Carpenters, and similar headings

Arbor, Marilyn. Tools & Trades of America's Past: The Mercer Collection. 116p. 6.95 (ISBN 0-910302-12-X). Bucks Co Hist.
Fulcher, Alf, et al. Basic Building Craft Science. 164p. 1981. text ed. 14.50x (ISBN 0-246-11265-4, Pub. by Granada England). Brookfield Pub Co.
Greenman, Andrew B. Checklist of Shelter Marketing Requirements. rev. ed. 17p. 1977. pap. 3.50 (ISBN 0-86718-015-3); pap. 2.50 members. Natl Assn Home.
Langford, D. A. Direct Labour Organizations in the Construction Industry. 148p. 1982. text ed. 35.50x (ISBN 0-566-00542-5). Gower Pub Co.
National Association of Home Builders. Growth Issues & Answers. 51p. 1979. pap. 15.00 (ISBN 0-86718-051-X). Natl Assn Home.
Putnam, R. & Carlson, G. E. Architectural & Building Trades Dictionary. 3rd ed. (Illus.). 1974. 15.50 (ISBN 0-8269-0402-5). Am Technical.
Reid, D. A. Construction Principles. 1973. text ed. 24.95x (ISBN 0-7114-3305-4). Intl Ideas.
Rudman, Jack. Assistant Superintendent of Construction. (Career Examination Ser.: C-1114). (Cloth bdg. avail. on request). pap. 12.00 (ISBN 0-8373-1114-4). Natl Learning.
--Building Construction Estimator. (Career Examination Ser.: C-1145). (Cloth bdg. avail. on request). pap. 14.00 (ISBN 0-8373-1145-4). Natl Learning.
--Building Construction Inspector. (Career Examination Ser.: C-1146). (Cloth bdg. avail. on request). pap. 12.00 (ISBN 0-8373-1146-2). Natl Learning.
--Director of Engineering, Building & Housing. (Career Examination Ser.: C-2391). (Cloth bdg. avail. on request). pap. 14.00 (ISBN 0-8373-2391-6). Natl Learning.
--Foreman (Structures) (Career Examination Ser.: C-288). (Cloth bdg. avail. on request). pap. 8.00 (ISBN 0-8373-0288-9). Natl Learning.
--Gang Foreman (Structures-Group A) (Carpentry) (Career Examination Ser.: C-290). (Cloth bdg. avail. on request). pap. 12.00 (ISBN 0-8373-0290-0). Natl Learning.
--Gang Foreman (Structures-Group B) (Masonry) (Career Examination Ser.: C-291). (Cloth bdg. avail. on request). pap. 12.00 (ISBN 0-8373-0291-9). Natl Learning.
--Inspector of Carpentry & Masonry. (Career Examination Ser.: C-365). (Cloth bdg. avail. on request). pap. 10.00 (ISBN 0-8373-0365-6). Natl Learning.
--Sandblaster. (Career Examination Ser.: C-1461). (Cloth bdg. avail. on request). pap. 8.00 (ISBN 0-8373-1461-5). Natl Learning.
--Superintendent of Construction. (Career Examination Ser.: C-1500). (Cloth bdg. avail. on request). pap. 12.00 (ISBN 0-8373-1500-X). Natl Learning.
Schwicker, Angelo C. International Dictionary of Building Construction: English-French-German-Italian. (Eng., Fr., Ger. & Ital.). 1280p. 1975. lib. bdg. 65.00x (ISBN 0-87936-004-6). Scholium Intl.
Sundberg, E. W. Building Trades Blueprint Reading, Pt. 2. 2nd ed. (Illus.). 240p. pap. 14.50 spiral (ISBN 0-8269-0447-5). Am Technical.
Vallings, H. G. Mechanisation in Building. 2nd ed. (Illus.). 175p. 1976. 39.00 (ISBN 0-85334-651-8, Pub. by Elsevier Applied Sci England). Elsevier.
Van Orman, H. A. Estimating for Residential Construction. LC 76-14083. 1978. pap. text ed. 16.80 (ISBN 0-8273-1605-4); instr.'s guide 4.80 (ISBN 0-8273-1606-2). Delmar.
Wallnig, G. & Evered, H. L' Anglais Dans le Batiment: Text En Anglais Avec un Glossaire Illustre. (Eng., Fr. & Ger.). 100p. 1970. pap. 19.95 (ISBN 0-686-57255-6, M-6564). French & Eur.
Wallnig, Gunter & Evered, H. L' Anglais Dans le Batiment: Texte En Anglais Avec un Glossaire Illustre, 2. (Eng., Fr. & Ger.). 192p. 1976. pap. 37.50 (ISBN 0-686-57256-4, M-6565). French & Eur.

BUILDING TRADES–VOCATIONAL GUIDANCE

Choosing a Job: Building Trades. 80p. 1982. 25.00x (ISBN 0-85340-252-3, Pub. by Careers Con England). State Mutual Bk.
Construction Employment Guide in the National & International Field. 5th ed. 1979. pap. 15.00 (ISBN 0-8360-0022-6). World Trade.
Hahn, Lynn & Hahn, James. Aim for a Job in the Construction Industry. Rev. ed. (Aim High Ser.). 144p. 1982. lib. bdg. 8.97 (ISBN 0-8239-0427-X). Rosen Group.
Masonry: Equipment Planning Guides for Vocational & Technical Training & Education Programmes, Vol. 12. pap. 22.80 (ILO245, ILO). Unipub.
Neil, James M. Construction Cost Estimating for Project Control. (Illus.). 336p. 1982. 32.95 (ISBN 0-13-168757-3). P-H.
Rudman, Jack. Buildings Manager. (Career Examination Ser.: C-1153). (Cloth bdg. avail. on request). pap. 12.00 (ISBN 0-8373-1153-5). Natl Learning.
Smith, Hugh. Working in the Building Industry. 1982. 26.00x (ISBN 0-7134-2333-1, Pub. by Careers Con England). State Mutual Bk.
Spence, W. Construction: Industry & Careers. 1976. pap. 8.84 (ISBN 0-13-169466-9). P-H.
Winn, Charles S., et al. Exploring Construction Occupations. (Careers in Focus Ser.). 1975. text ed. 11.40 (ISBN 0-07-071021-X). McGraw.

BUILDINGS
see also Architecture; Basements; Building also names of particular types of building and construction e.g. Dwellings; School-houses; Concrete Construction

Aldous, Tony, ed. Trees & Buildings. 95p. 1980. pap. 11.25 (ISBN 0-900630-73-6, Pub. by RIBA). Intl Spec Bk.
American Society of Civil Engineers, compiled by. Seismic Performance of Low Rise Buildings: State-of-the-Art & Research Needs. LC 81-6930. 221p. 1981. pap. 20.50x (ISBN 0-87262-283-5). Am Soc Civil Eng.
Architectural Record Magazine. Public, Municipal & Community Buildings. 1980. 39.95 (ISBN 0-07-002351-4). McGraw.
Buildings: Their Uses & the Spaces About Them, Vol. 8. (Metropolitan America Ser.). 478p. 29.00x (ISBN 0-405-05421-1). Ayer Co Pubs.
Built in the U. S. A. American Buildings from Airports to Zoos. (Illus.). 192p. 1985. pap. 8.95 (ISBN 0-89133-118-2). Preservation Pr.
Bureau of Naval Personnel. Basic Construction Techniques for Houses & Small Buildings Simply Explained. (Illus.). 17.25 (ISBN 0-8446-4506-0). Peter Smith.
Business Communications Staff. Smart Buildings. 1985. pap. 1500.00 (ISBN 0-317-28177-1, GO89). BCC.
Dagostino, Frank. Mechanical & Electrical Systems in Building. 1982. text ed. 28.95 (ISBN 0-8359-4312-7). Reston.
Designing Buildings for Fire Safety. (Illus.). 125p. 1974. pap. 4.75 (ISBN 0-685-58197-7, SPP-24). Natl Fire Prot.
Eaton, K. J. & Eaton, K. J., eds. Proceedings of International Conference on Wind Effects on Buildings & Structures: Heathrow Nineteen Seventy-Five. LC 75-2730. 650p. 1976. 125.00 (ISBN 0-521-20801-7). Cambridge U Pr.
Gower Publications, ed. Managing Buildings & Building Services in Great Britain. 1973. 19.95x (ISBN 0-8464-0595-4). Beekman Pubs.
Harrison, John A. Old Stone Buildings: Extending & Renovating. (Illus.). 255p. 1980. 23.50 (ISBN 0-7153-8125-3). David & Charles.
Le Corbusier. Le Modulor & Other Buildings & Projects, 1944-1945, Vol. XV. Brooks, H. Allen, ed. LC 83-1580. (The Le Corbusier Archive Ser.). 504p. 1983. lib. bdg. 200.00 (ISBN 0-8240-5064-9). Garland Pub.
Macdonald, Argus J. Wind Loading on Buildings. LC 75-11988. 219p. 1975. 39.95x (ISBN 0-470-55976-4). Halsted Pr.
McGuinness, William J. & Stein, Benjamin. Building Technology: Mechanical & Electrical Systems. LC 76-14961. 1977. 39.95 (ISBN 0-471-58433-9); teacher's manual avail. (ISBN 0-471-01601-2). Wiley.
Maybeck, Edward, et al. U. S.-U.S.S.R. Joint Seminar on Internal Utility Systems in Buildings. Kosko, Louise A., et al, eds. (Illus.). 114p. (Orig.). 1981. pap. 10.00 (ISBN 0-939202-06-9). Delphi Pr WA.
Neufert, Ernst. Architect's Data: The Handbook of Building Types, 2nd (International) English Edition. LC 80-40644. 433p. 1980. 95.00x (ISBN 0-470-26947-2). Halsted Pr.
Pevsner, Nikolaus. A History of Building Types. LC 75-4459. (Bollingen Ser.: No. 35). (Illus., A. w. mellon lecture no. 19). 1976. 67.50 (ISBN 0-691-09904-9); pap. 19.50x (ISBN 0-691-01829-4). Princeton U Pr.
SITE: Buildings & Spaces. LC 80-16394. (Illus.). 48p. (Orig.). 1970. pap. 3.50 (ISBN 0-917046-10-2). Va Mus Arts.
Van Straaten, J. F. Thermal Performance of Buildings. (Illus.). 1967. text ed. 48.50x (ISBN 0-444-20011-8, Pub. by Applied Science). Burgess-Intl Ideas.
Waller, R. A. Building on Springs. 1969. 20.00 (ISBN 0-08-006399-3). Pergamon.
Witzel, S. A. Log Buildings. facs. ed. (Shorey Lost Arts Ser.). pap. 3.95 (ISBN 0-8466-6043-1, U43). Shorey.

BUILDINGS–ACOUSTICS
see Architectural Acoustics

BUILDINGS–DETAILS
see Architecture–Details; Building–Details

BUILDINGS–ENERGY CONSERVATION

American Institute of Architects. Architect's Handbook of Energy Practice: Building Envelope. (Illus.). 42p. 1982. pap. 7.50 (ISBN 0-913962-51-1). Am Inst Arch.
--Architect's Handbook of Energy Practice: Climate & Site. (Illus.). 55p. 1982. pap. 7.50 (ISBN 0-913962-50-3). Am Inst Arch.
--Architect's Handbook of Energy Practice: Daylighting. (Illus.). 48p. 1982. pap. 7.50 (ISBN 0-913962-52-X). Am Inst Arch.
--Architect's Handbook of Energy Practice: HVAC Systems. (Illus.). 54p. 1982. pap. 7.50 (ISBN 0-913962-53-8). Am Inst Arch.
--Architect's Handbook of Energy Practice: Photovoltaics. (Illus.). 56p. 1982. pap. 18.00x (ISBN 0-913962-56-2). Am Inst Arch.

--Architect's Handbook of Energy Practice: Shading & Sun Control. (Illus.). 48p. 1982. pap. 7.50 (ISBN 0-913962-49-X). Am Inst Arch.

--Architect's Handbook of Energy Practice: Thermal Transfer Through the Envelope. (Illus.). 51p. 1982. pap. 7.50 (ISBN 0-913962-55-4). Am Inst Arch.

Baird, George, et al, eds. Energy Performance of Buildings. 216p. 1984. 64.00 (ISBN 0-8493-5186-3). CRC Pr.

Burberry, Peter. Practical Thermal Design in Buildings. (Mitchell's Building Ser.). (Illus.). 192p. 1983. 45.00 (ISBN 0-7134-3514-3, Pub. by Batsford England). David & Charles.

Coad, William J. Energy Engineering & Management for Building Systems. 320p. 1981. text ed. 36.95 (ISBN 0-442-25467-9). Van Nos Reinhold.

Dubin, Fred S. & Long, Chalmers G., Jr. Energy Conservation Standards: For Building Design, Construction & Operation. 432p. 1982. 21.50 (ISBN 0-07-017884-4). McGraw.

Energyworks, Inc. Staff. Energy-Efficient Products & Systems: A Comparative Catalog for Architects & Engineers. 860p. 1983. incl. three 6 month updates 135.00 (ISBN 0-471-87336-5, Pub. by Wiley-Interscience); pap. Jan. 1983 update (ISBN 0-471-88223-2); pap. 1.00 2nd supplement (ISBN 0-471-87887-1); pap. Jan. 1984 update (ISBN 0-471-80697-8). Wiley.

Fisk, D. J. Thermal Control of Buildings. (Illus.). xvii, 245p. 1981. 69.95x (ISBN 0-85334-950-9). Intl Ideas.

Gopal, R., et al, eds. Energy Conservation in Building Heating & Air Conditioning Systems. 112p. 1978. 18.00 (ISBN 0-685-66798-7, H00116). ASME.

Holm, Dieter. Energy Conservation in Hot Climates. (Illus.). 160p. 1983. pap. 32.50 (ISBN 0-89397-159-6). Nichols Pub.

Lee, Kaiman. Encyclopedia of Energy-Efficient Building Design: 391 Practical Case Studies, 2 vols. LC 77-150686. 1977. Set. 150.00x (ISBN 0-915250-18-7). Environ Design.

Littler, John & Thomas, Randall. Design with Energy: The Conservation & Use of Energy in Buildings. (Cambridge Urban & Architectural Studies: 8). (Illus.). 320p. 1984. 49.50 (ISBN 0-521-24562-1); pap. 19.95 (ISBN 0-521-28787-1). Cambridge U Pr.

Meckler, Milton. Retrofitting of Commercial, Institutional, & Industrial Buildings for Energy Conservation. 432p. 1984. 42.50 (ISBN 0-442-26226-4). Van Nos Reinhold.

Meyer, William T. Energy Economics & Building Design. 352p. 1983. 29.95 (ISBN 0-07-041751-2). McGraw.

Model Energy Code, 1983. pap. 4.00 (ISBN 0-318-00047-4). Intl Conf Bldg Off.

O'Callaghan, P. W. Building for Energy Conservation. 1978. text ed. 36.00 (ISBN 0-08-022120-3). Pergamon.

Osborn, Peter D. Handbook of Energy Data & Calculations. 224p. 1985. text ed. 67.95 (ISBN 0-408-01327-3). Butterworth.

Palmquist, Roland. Refrigeration & Air Conditioning Library, 2 vols. (Illus.). 1977. Set. 21.95 (ISBN 0-672-23305-3); vol. I, air conditioning 10.95, home & commercial (ISBN 0-672-23288-X); vol. II refrigeration:home & commercial, 656pgs. 12.95 (ISBN 0-672-23286-3). Audel.

Robinette, Gary O., ed. Energy-Efficient Site Design. 176p. 1983. 25.45 (ISBN 0-442-22338-2). Van Nos Reinhold.

Seisler, Jeffrey M. & Londner, Henry D. Conserving Energy in Older Homes: A Do-It-Yourself Manual. (Illus.). 44p. (Orig.). 1982. pap. 4.95 (ISBN 0-9610932-0-X). Analytech.

Sherratt, A. F., ed. Energy Conservation & Energy Management in Buildings. (Illus.). 330p. 1976. 55.50 (ISBN 0-85334-684-4, Pub. by Elsevier Applied Sci England). Elsevier.

Sizemore, Michael, et al. Energy Planning for Buildings. (Illus.). 1979. 33.25 (ISBN 0-913962-08-2); members 26.75. Am Inst Arch.

Solar Energy Research Institute, ed. The Design of Energy-Responsive Commercial Buildings. LC 84-11864. 370p. 1985. text ed. 44.95 (ISBN 0-471-80463-0, Pub by Wiley-Interscience). Wiley.

Study of Regulations, Codes & Standards Related to Energy Use in Buildings. (ECE Committee on Housing, Building & Planning Ser.: No. 41). (Illus.). 54p. 1985. pap. 8.50 (UN84/2E7, UN). Unipub.

Thompson, Grant P. Building to Save Energy–Legal & Regulatory Approaches. LC 79-11754. (Environmental Law Institute State & Local Energy Conservation Project Ser.). (Illus.). 288p. 1980. prof ref 25.00 (ISBN 0-88410-059-6). Ballinger Pub.

Van Straaten, J. F. Thermal Performance of Buildings. (Illus.). 311p. 1967. 42.75 (ISBN 0-444-20011-8, Pub. by Elsevier Applied Sci England). Elsevier.

Watson, Donald. Energy Conservation Through Building Design. 1979. 29.50 (ISBN 0-07-068460-X). McGraw.

BUILDINGS–ENVIRONMENTAL ENGINEERING
see Environmental Engineering (Buildings)
BUILDINGS–FITTINGS
see Building Fittings
BUILDINGS–MATERIALS
see Building Materials
BUILDINGS–PROTECTION
see also Buildings–Repair and Reconstruction; Dampness in Buildings

Brannigan, Francis L. Building Construction for the Fire Service. 2nd ed. McKinnon, Gordon P. & Matson, Debra, eds. LC 78-178805. (Illus.). 392p. 1982. text ed. 20.00 (ISBN 0-87765-227-9, FSP-33A). Natl Fire Prot.

McGavin, Gary L. Earthquake Protection of Essential Building Equipment: Design, Engineering, Installation. LC 80-23067. 464p. 1981. 58.95x (ISBN 0-471-06270-7, Pub. by Wiley-Interscience). Wiley.

Mills, Edward D., ed. Building Maintenance & Preservation: A Guide for Design & Management. (Illus.). 192p. 1980. pap. text ed. 49.95 (ISBN 0-408-00470-3). Butterworth.

BUILDINGS–REPAIR AND RECONSTRUCTION
see also Architecture–Conservation and Restoration; Dwellings–Maintenance and Repair; Dwellings–Remodeling

Abrams, Lawrence & Abrams, Kathleen. Salvaging Old Barns & Houses: Tear it Down & Save Their Places. LC 82-19330. (Illus.). 128p. (Orig.). 1983. pap. 7.95 (ISBN 0-8069-7666-7). Sterling.

Architectural Record Magazine. New Life for Old Buildings. 200p. 1982. 38.50 (ISBN 0-07-002364-6). McGraw.

Bowyer, Jack. Vernacular Building Conservation. (Illus.). 176p. 1981. 65.00x (ISBN 0-85139-701-8). Nichols Pub.

Brann, Donald R. How to Remodel Buildings. LC 78-55239. 258p. 1978. pap. 7.95 (ISBN 0-87733-585-0). Easi-Bild.

Cantacuzino, Sherban & Brandt, Susan. Saving Old Buildings. (Illus.). 240p. 1981. 67.50x (ISBN 0-85139-498-1). Nichols Pub.

Chargar, William & Nunes, Morris A. The Property Maintenance Logbook. LC 84-17818. 612p. 1985. 39.95 (ISBN 0-13-731134-6, Busn). P-H.

Coad, William J. Energy Engineering & Management for Building Systems. 320p. 1981. text ed. 36.95 (ISBN 0-442-25467-9). Van Nos Reinhold.

Dibner, D. R. & Dibner-Dunlap, A. Building Additions Design. 256p. 1985. 39.95 (ISBN 0-07-016761-3). McGraw.

Evans, Barry. Housing Rehabilitation Handbook. (Illus.). 1980. 49.50 (ISBN 0-85139-293-8, Pub. by Architectural Pr). Nichols Pub.

Feirer, et al. Carpentry & Building Construction: Si Metric Edition. text ed. 31.80 (ISBN 0-02-662940-2). Bennett IL.

Gibson, E. J., ed. Developments in Building Maintenance, Vol. 1. (Illus.). 260p. 1979. 33.50 (ISBN 0-85334-801-4, Pub. by Elsevier Applied Sci England). Elsevier.

Graff, Arden. The Best Building on the Block. (Orig.). 1981. pap. 4.95 (ISBN 0-934892-01-6). Interiors.

Hardenbrook, Harry. Walker's Remodeling Estimator's Reference Book. (Illus.). 192p. 1981. pap. 19.95 (ISBN 0-911592-60-1). F R Walker.

--Walker's Remodeling Estimator's Reference Book. (Illus.). 325p. 1982. 25.00 (ISBN 0-911592-60-1, ScribT). Scribner.

Jones, Jack P. Manual of Professional Remodeling. 400p. (Orig.). 1982. pap. 18.75 (ISBN 0-910460-98-1). Craftsman.

Landry, Arthur W. Restoring Old Houses: A Guide for the Self-Builder & Building Professional. LC 83-6635. (Illus.). 160p. (Orig.). 1983. pap. 8.95 (ISBN 0-8069-7722-1). Sterling.

Lee, Reginald. Building Maintenance Management. 1976. 17.95x (ISBN 0-8464-0222-X). Beekman Pubs.

--Building Maintenance Management. 194p. 1976. pap. text ed. 17.50x (ISBN 0-258-96947-4, Pub. by Granada England). Brookfield Pub Co.

Lion, Edgar. Building Renovation & Recycling. LC 81-19464. 132p. 1982. 32.50x (ISBN 0-471-86444-7, Pub. by Wiley-Interscience). Wiley.

Markus, Thomas. Building Conversion & Rehabilitation. 1979. text ed. 69.95 (ISBN 0-408-00313-8). Butterworth.

Marsh, Paul. The Refurbishment of Commercial & Industrial Buildings. (Illus.). 144p. 1983. text ed. 38.00x (ISBN 0-86095-030-1, Construction Press). Longman.

Miles, Derek. A Manual on Building Maintenance: Management, Vol. 1. (Illus.). 78p. (Orig.). 1976. pap. 7.75x (ISBN 0-903031-28-0, Pub. by Intermediate Tech England). Intermediate Tech.

--A Manual on Building Maintenance: Methods, Vol. 2. rev. ed. (Illus.). 110p. (Orig.). 1979. pap. 7.75x (ISBN 0-903031-61-2, Pub. by Intermediate Tech England). Intermediate Tech.

Mills, Edward D., ed. Building Maintenance & Preservation: A Guide for Design & Management. (Illus.). 192p. 1980. pap. text ed. 49.95 (ISBN 0-408-00470-3). Butterworth.

Prudon, Theodore. Architectural Preservation & Conservation Handbook: A Color Reference. 1986. cancelled (ISBN 0-442-26641-3). Van Nos Reinhold.

Richardson, S. A. Protecting Buildings. 1977. 14.95 (ISBN 0-7153-7321-8). David & Charles.

Rudman, Jack. Building Maintenance. (Occupational Competency Examination Ser.: OCE-8). (Cloth bdg. avail. on request). pap. 13.95 (ISBN 0-8373-5708-X). Natl Learning.

--Building Rehabilitation Specialist. (Career Examination Ser.: C-1151). (Cloth bdg. avail. on request). pap. 12.00 (ISBN 0-8373-1151-9). Natl Learning.

--Building Repairman. (Career Examination Ser.: C-1152). (Cloth bdg. avail. on request). pap. 10.00 (ISBN 0-8373-1152-7). Natl Learning.

--Structure Maintainer. (Career Examination Ser.: C-772). (Cloth bdg. avail. on request). pap. 8.00 (ISBN 0-8373-0772-4). Natl Learning.

Sack, Thomas. Complete Guide to Building & Plant Maintenance. 2nd ed. LC 71-126828. (Illus.). 672p. 1971. 49.95 (ISBN 0-13-160101-6). P-H.

Schild, Erich, et al. Structural Failure in Residential Buildings, Vol. 4: Internal Walls, Ceilings & Floors. Orig. Title: Ger. 154p. 1981. 49.50x (ISBN 0-89397-100-6). Nichols Pub.

Shear, Mel A. Building Maintenance. 1985. text ed. 24.95 (ISBN 0-8359-0528-4). Reston.

Sinnott, Ralph. Safety & Security in Building Design. (Illus.). 258p. 1985. 29.50 (ISBN 0-442-28212-5). Van Nos Reinhold.

Williams, T. Jeff. All about Basic Home Repairs. Ortho Books Editorial Staff, ed. LC 79-52989. (Illus.). 112p. (Orig.). 1980. pap. 5.95 (ISBN 0-917102-82-7). Ortho.

BUILDINGS, DAMPNESS IN
see Dampness in Buildings
BUILDINGS, FARM
see Farm Buildings
BUILDINGS, INDUSTRIAL
see Industrial Buildings
BUILDINGS, PREFABRICATED
The Complete Guide to Factory-Made Houses. 2nd ed. 1984. 14.95 (ISBN 0-911749-00-4); pap. 8.95 (ISBN 0-911749-01-2). Caroline Hse.

Consumer Guide Editors. The Complete Book of Prefabs, Kits & Manufactured Houses. 160p. 1981. pap. 7.95 (ISBN 0-449-90051-7, Columbine). Fawcett.

Herbert, Gilbert. Pioneers of Prefabrication: The British Contribution in the Nineteenth Century. LC 76-47372. (Studies in Nineteenth-Century Architecture). (Illus.). 1978. text ed. 22.50x (ISBN 0-8018-1852-4). Johns Hopkins.

Lucke, Peggy. Outdoor Storage. Snow, Diane, ed. LC 83-62654. (Illus.). 96p. (Orig.). 1984. pap. 5.95 (ISBN 0-89721-022-0). Ortho.

Sluzas, Raymond & Ryan, Anne. A Graphic Guide to Industrialized Building Elements. LC 77-13121. (Illus.). 176p. 1977. 21.95 (ISBN 0-8436-0163-9); pap. 12.95 (ISBN 0-8436-0164-7). Van Nos Reinhold.

Svec, J. J. & Jeffers, P. E. Modern Masonry Panel Construction Systems. LC 72-83307. (Illus.). 144p. 1971. 19.95 (ISBN 0-8436-0114-0). Van Nos Reinhold.

BUILDINGS, RECONSTRUCTION OF
see Buildings–Repair and Reconstruction
BUILDINGS, RESTORATION OF
see Architecture–Conservation and Restoration
BUILT-IN TEST EQUIPMENT
see Automatic Checkout Equipment
BULBS
Bulbs. 2.25 (ISBN 0-686-21130-8). Bklyn Botanic.

Grey-Wilson, Christopher & Mathew, Brian. Bulbs: The Bulbous Plants of Europe & Their Allies. (Illus.). 1983. 32.95 (ISBN 0-00-219211-X, Collins Pub England). Greene.

McNair, James. All about Bulbs. ORTHO Books Editorial Staff, ed. LC 80-85222. (Illus.). 96p. (Orig.). 1982. pap. 5.95 (ISBN 0-917102-93-2). Ortho.

Mathew, Brian. The Larger Bulbs. 1978. 31.50 (ISBN 0-7134-1246-1, Pub. by Batsford England). David & Charles.

Rees, A. R. Growth of Bulbs: Applied Aspects of the Physiology of Ornamental Bulbous Plants. (Applied Botany Ser.: No. 1). 1972. 55.00 (ISBN 0-12-585450-1). Acad Pr.

Scott, George H. Bulbs: How to Select, Grow & Enjoy. 160p. 1982. pap. 7.95 (ISBN 0-89586-146-1). H P Bks.

Sunset Editors. Bulbs: How to Grow. 3rd ed. LC 73-75754. (Illus.). 80p. 1973. pap. 3.95 (ISBN 0-376-03085-2, Sunset Bks.). Sunset-Lane.

Wister, Gertrude S. Hardy Garden Bulbs. 1964. 5.95 (ISBN 0-525-12175-7). Dutton.

Wooldridge, M. J. Simultaneous Dry Bulb & Wet Bulb Temperature Data for Fourteen Australian Locations. 146p. 1980. 25.00 (ISBN 0-643-00343-6, Pub. by CSIRO Australia). State Mutual Bk.

BULK SOLIDS
see also Granular Materials; Powders
Colijn, Hendrik. Weighing & Proportioning of Bulk Solids. 2nd ed. LC 83-81909. (Illus.). 412p. 1984. 59.95x (ISBN 0-87201-914-4). Gulf Pub.

BULK SOLIDS FLOW
see also Fluidization
Thorton, Wendy A., ed. The Pneumotransport Bibliography. 1972. text ed. 26.00x (ISBN 0-900983-17-5, Dist. by Air Science Co.). BHRA Fluid.

BULK SOLIDS HANDLING
see also Earthwork; Silos
Cowin, S. C., ed. Mechanics Applied to the Transport of Bulk Materials AMD, Vol. 31, Bk. No. G00146. 140p. 1979. 20.00 (ISBN 0-686-58131-8). ASME.

International Conference in Bulk Materials Storage, Handling & Transportation. 396p. 1983. pap. text ed. 28.00x (ISBN 0-85825-209-0, Pub. by Inst Engineering Australia). Brookfield Pub Co.

Loeffler, F. J. & Proctor, C. R., eds. Unit & Bulk Materials Handling. 289p. 1980. 60.00 (ISBN 0-686-69864-9, H00163). ASME.

Marchello, J. M. & Gomezplata, A., eds. Gas-Solids Handling in the Process Industry. (Chemical Processing & Engineering: an International Ser.: Vol. 8). 336p. 1976. 65.00 (ISBN 0-8247-6302-5). Dekker.

Stepanoff, Alexely. Gravity Flow & Transportation of Solids in Suspension. LC 72-91156. (Materials Handling & Packaging Ser). 1969. text ed. 12.50 (ISBN 0-471-82202-7, Pub. by Wiley). Krieger.

Wohlbier, Reinhard H., ed. Stacking Blending Reclaiming of Bulk Materials. new ed. (Ser. on Bulk Materials Handling). 1977. 60.00x (ISBN 0-87849-018-3). Trans Tech.

BULL TERRIERS
see Dogs–Breeds–Bull Terriers
BULLDOGS
see Dogs–Breeds–Bulldogs
BULLION
see Precious Metals
BUMBLEBEES
Heinrich, Bernd. Bumblebee Economics. LC 78-23773. (Illus.). 1979. 17.50x (ISBN 0-674-08580-9); pap. 8.95 (ISBN 0-674-08581-7). Harvard U Pr.

Thorp, R. W. & Horning, D. S., Jr. Bumblebees & Cuckoo Bumblebees of California: Hymenoptera: Apidae. (Bulletin of the California Insect Survey Ser.: Vol. 23). 1982. pap. 20.00x (ISBN 0-520-09645-2). U of Cal Pr.

BUNDLES, FIBER (MATHEMATICS)
see Fiber Bundles (Mathematics)
BURBANK, LUTHER, 1849-1926
Clampett, Frederick W. Luther Burbank, Our Beloved Infidel, His Religion of Humanity. LC 73-109720. (Illus.). 144p. Repr. of 1926 ed. lib. bdg. 15.00x (ISBN 0-8371-4210-5, CLLB). Greenwood.

BURGLAR-ALARMS
Allen, Sam. Locks & Alarms. (Illus.). 352p. (Orig.). 1984. 21.95 (ISBN 0-8306-0359-X); pap. 15.95 (ISBN 0-8306-0259-3, 1559). TAB Bks.

Brann, Donald R. How to Install Protective Alarm Devices. rev ed. LC 72-89141. (Illus.). 1975. lib. bdg. 5.95 (ISBN 0-87733-095-6); pap. 5.95 (ISBN 0-87733-695-4). Easi-Bild.

Cole, Richard B. Protect Your Property: The Applications of Burglar Alarm Hardware. (Illus.). 192p. 1971. photo copy ed. 19.50x (ISBN 0-398-02262-3). C C Thomas.

Lewin, Tom. Security: Everyting You Need to Know about Household Alarm Systems. LC 82-61141. (Illus.). 99p. 1982. 16.95 (ISBN 0-9609362-0-3); pap. 7.95 (ISBN 0-9609362-1-1). Park Lane Ent.

Weber, Thad L. Alarm Systems & Theft Prevention. LC 73-78572. 384p. 1978. 22.95 (ISBN 0-913708-11-9). Butterworth.

BURGLARY PROTECTION
see also Burglar-Alarms; Locks and Keys; Security Systems
Forte, Robert. Stop Burglary, Prevent Home Break-Ins. (Illus.). 50p. (Orig.). 1983. 2.95 (ISBN 0-9609328-0-1). R Forte.

Nonte, George C., Jr. To Stop a Thief: The Complete Guide to House, Apartment & Property Protection. (Illus.). 244p. pap. 4.95 (ISBN 0-88317-028-0). Stoeger Pub Co.

Purpura, Philip. Security & Loss Prevention. LC 83-10044. 512p. 1983. text ed. 22.95 (ISBN 0-409-95075-0). Butterworth.

Stroik, J., ed. Building Security-STP 729. 210p. 1981. 25.00 (ISBN 0-8031-0606-8, 04-7290000-10). ASTM.

Weber, Thad L. Alarm Systems & Theft Prevention. LC 73-78572. 384p. 1978. 22.95 (ISBN 0-913708-11-9). Butterworth.

BURGUNDY (WINE)

Hanson, Anthony. Burgundy. (Wine Bks.). 354p. (Orig.). 1982. pap. 11.95 (ISBN 0-571-11798-8). Faber & Faber.

Simon, Andre L. All about Burgundy. (All About Wines, Vol. 5). 7.50. Shalom.

BURRO

see Mules

BUSES

see Motor Buses

BUSHINGS

see Bearings (Machinery); Electric Insulators and Insulation

BUSHNELL, DAVID, 1740-1826

Abbot, Henry L. Beginning of Modern Submarine Warfare, under Captain-Lieutenant David Bushnell, Sappers & Miners, Army of the Revolution. (Illus.). xiv, 68p. (Facsimile of 1881 ed.). 1966. 12.50 (ISBN 0-208-00031-3, Archon). Shoe String.

BUSINESS–DATA PROCESSING

Adamis, Eddie. Business BASIC for the Apple III: A Self Teaching Guide. LC 83-12328. 245p. 1984. pap. 16.95 (ISBN 0-471-88388-3, Pub. by Wiley Pr). Wiley.

Adams, David & Leigh, William E. Programming Business Systems with BASIC. 1984. text ed. 16.95 wkbk. (ISBN 0-538-10980-7, J98). SW Pub.

Advertising Agency Automation Market. 369p. 1984. 1550.00 (ISBN 0-86621-334-1, A1417). Frost & Sullivan.

Alves, Jeff & Curtin, Dennis. Planning & Budgeting for Higher Profits: An IBM-PC Business User's Guide. 156p. 1983. pap. 14.95 (ISBN 0-930764-61-7). Van Nos Reinhold.

Alves, Jeff, et al. Planning & Budgeting: A 1-2-3 Business User's Guide. 1983. pap. 16.95 (ISBN 0-930764-74-9); disk set 39.95 (ISBN 0-930764-93-5); disk 29.95 (ISBN 0-930764-94-3). Van Nos Reinhold.

Alves, Jeffrey & Curtin, Dennis. Planning & Budgeting-IBM Version. (Illus.). 224p. (Orig.). 1983. pap. 15.50 (ISBN 0-930764-61-7). Curtin & London.

Alves, Jeffrey R., et al. Planning & Budgeting for Higher Profits: A Multiplan Business User's Guide. (Illus.). 160p. 1984. pap. 16.95 (ISBN 0-930764-88-9). Van Nos Reinhold.

Amstutz, Arnold E. Computer Simulation of Competitive Market Response. (Illus.). 1967. pap. 12.50x (ISBN 0-262-51009-X). MIT Pr.

Amusement & Music Operators Association. Computers & Coin-Op. 1985. 7.00 (ISBN 0-318-04202-9). AMOA.

Apple Computer Personal Computers in Business Guide. Date not set. 2.95 (ISBN 0-317-04434-6, A2G0034). Apple Comp.

Aronofsky, Julius S., et al. Programmable Calculators Business Applications. 203p. 1978. pap. 11.95 (ISBN 0-317-06593-9). Tex Instr Inc.

Aschner, Katherine. The Word Processing Handbook: A Step-by-Step Guide to Automating the Office. 200p. 1983. pap. 19.95 (ISBN 0-442-21076-0). Van Nos Reinhold.

--Word Processing Handbook: A Step-by-Step Guide to Automating Your Office. 2nd ed. 1983. pap. 8.95 (ISBN 0-88908-913-2). Self Counsel Pr.

Asner, Michael. Up Your Computer: A Survival Handbook for Executives. 1984. text ed. 28.95 (ISBN 0-8359-8084-7); pap. text ed. 18.95 (ISBN 0-8359-8083-9). Reston.

Atre, Shakuntala. Data Base Structured Techniques for Design, Performance, & Management: With Case Studies. LC 80-14808. (Business Data Processing Ser.). 442p. 1980. 36.95x (ISBN 0-471-05267-1, Pub. by Wiley-Interscience). Wiley.

Authority List for Corporate Entries & Report Number Prefixes: Rev. 14. 499p. 1981. pap. 31.00 (ISBN 92-0-178181-4, IN6/R14, IAEA). Unipub.

Automated Education Center. Management Guide to Computer Programming. 1969. 25.00 (ISBN 0-403-04472-3). Scholarly.

--Management Systems & Programming. LC 78-79912. 17.50 (ISBN 0-403-04474-X). Scholarly.

Awad, Elias M. Business Data Processing. 5th ed. (Illus.). 1980. text ed. 28.95 (ISBN 0-13-093807-6); student guide 9.95 (ISBN 0-13-093757-6). P-H.

--Introduction to Computers. 2nd ed. (Illus.). 496p. 1983. text ed. 25.95 (ISBN 0-13-479444-3). P-H.

Baldwin, J. N. Microprocessors for Industry. 144p. 1982. text ed. 19.95 (ISBN 0-408-00517-3). Butterworth.

Barden, William, Jr. Microcomputers for Business Applications. LC 78-64984. 256p. 1979. pap. 9.95 (ISBN 0-672-21583-7, 21583). Sams.

Bates, Timothy & Wright, Judith. Evaluating Your Business Computer Needs. 150p. pap. 12.95 (6200). Hayden.

Becker, Jack D. Introduction to Business Data Processing: Supplement. 216p. 1982. pap. text ed. 13.95 (ISBN 0-8403-2829-X). Kendall-Hunt.

Becker, William E. & Harnett, Donald L. Business & Economics Statistics with Computer Applications. LC 85-9025. 1986. price not set (ISBN 0-201-10956-5). Addison-Wesley.

Beil, Don. Symphony: First Introduction to Business Software. 1984. cancelled (ISBN 0-8359-7440-5). Reston.

Bent, Robert J. & Sethares, George C. Business BASIC. 2nd ed. LC 83-19024. (Computer Science Ser.). 240p. 1984. pap. text ed. 18.25 pub net (ISBN 0-534-03179-X). Brooks-Cole.

Benton, F. Warren. Execucomp: Maximum Management with the New Computers. LC 83-17028. 261p. 1983. cloth 19.95x (ISBN 0-471-89828-7). Wiley.

Berg, Gary. Using Calculators for Business Problems. LC 78-10173. 1979. pap. text ed. 15.95 (ISBN 0-574-20565-9, 13-3565); instr's guide avail. (ISBN 0-574-20566-7, 13-3566). SRA.

Berner, Jeff. At Your Fingertips: Making the Most of the Micro. 202p. 1984. pap. 12.95 (ISBN 0-673-18049-2). Scott F.

Berst, Jessie. Computhink Guide to Spreadsheet. LC 83-82557. 168p. 1983. pap. 11.95 (ISBN 0-672-22164-0, 22164). Sams.

Birnbaum, Mark & Sickman, John. How to Choose Your Small Business Computer: Popular. LC 82-11665. (Microcomputer Bks.). 176p. 1983. pap. 9.95 (ISBN 0-201-10187-4). Addison-Wesley.

Bissett, Lesley D. Client Finder II. LC 84-9954. 1984. pap. 21.95 (ISBN 0-8359-0765-1). Reston.

Bittel, L. R., et al. Set for the Donut Franchise: A Microcomputer Simulation for Business in Action. 2nd ed. 48p. 1984. TRS S80 Version. 150.00 (ISBN 0-07-079357-3); Apple Version. 199.00. McGraw.

Bitter, Gary G. & Cook, Paul M. IBM BASIC for Business. (Illus.). 192p. 1986. pap. text ed. 19.95 (ISBN 0-13-448093-7). P-H.

Blumenthal, Susan. Understanding & Buying a Small Business Computer. LC 81-86553. 160p. 1982. pap. 9.95 (ISBN 0-672-21890-9, 21890). Sams.

Boillot, Michel. Understanding BASIC in Business. 1978. pap. text ed. 22.95 (ISBN 0-8299-0206-6). West Pub.

Bonelli, Robert A. Increasing Profitability with Minicomputers. (Illus.). 256p. 1981. text ed. 17.50 (ISBN 0-89433-175-2). Petrocelli.

Bosworth, Bruce. Business Programming Projects with BASIC. 256p. 1984. pap. text ed. 17.95 (ISBN 0-574-21480-1, 13-4480); tchr's ed. (ISBN 0-574-21481-X, 13-4481). SRA.

Brabb, George J. & McKean, Gerald. Business Data Processing: Concepts & Practices. LC 81-82556. 1982. 27.50 (ISBN 0-395-31684-7); instr's manual 2.00 (ISBN 0-395-31685-5); study guide 11.50 (ISBN 0-395-31686-3); test bank 2.00 (ISBN 0-395-31687-1); practice set 5.95 (ISBN 0-395-32018-6). HM.

Bradley, James. Introduction to Data-Base Management in Business. 642p. 1983. text ed. 37.95 (ISBN 0-03-061693-X). HR&W.

Brandon, Dick H. & Segelstein, Sidney. Boardroom's Complete Guide to Microcomputers. LC 83-15450. 302p. 1983. 50.00 (ISBN 0-932648-45-2). Boardroom.

Briefs, U., et al, eds. Computerization & Work. viii, 180p. 1985. pap. 22.00 (ISBN 0-387-15367-5). Springer-Verlag.

Brooner, E. G. BASIC Business Software. LC 80-52232. 144p. 1981. pap. 11.95 (ISBN 0-672-21751-1, 21751). Sams.

Brown, Gary D. Beyond COBOL: Survival in Business Applications Programming. LC 80-28650. 200p. 1981. 21.95 (ISBN 0-471-09030-1, Pub. by Wiley-Interscience); pap. 18.50 (ISBN 0-471-09949-X). Wiley.

Brown, Gary D. & Sefton, Donald. Surviving with Financial Application Packages for the Computer. 233p. 1983. 24.50 (ISBN 0-471-87065-X, Pub. by Wiley-Interscience). Wiley.

Brownstone, David M. & Carruth, Gorton. Where to Find Business Information: A Worldwide Guide for Everyone Who Needs the Answers to Business Questions. 2nd ed. LC 81-16439. 632p. 1982. Set. 70.00 (ISBN 0-471-08736-X, Pub. by Wiley-Interscience). Wiley.

Bui, X. T. Executive Planning with BASIC. LC 81-85954. (Illus.). 196p. 1982. pap. 15.95 (ISBN 0-89588-083-0, B380). SYBEX.

Burian, Barbara & Fink, Stuart. Business Data Processing. 2nd ed. LC 81-5207. (Illus.). 544p. 1982. text ed. 25.95 (ISBN 0-13-094045-3); study guide 8.95 (ISBN 0-13-094060-7). P-H.

Burns, Diane K. & Venit, Sharyn D. Mac at Work: Macintosh Windows on Business. 224p. 1985. pap. 17.95 (ISBN 0-471-82050-4); Book with program disk. 39.95 (ISBN 0-471-82737-1). Wiley.

Burrill, Claude & Quinto, Leon. Computer Model of a Growth Company. LC 79-162628. (Illus.). x, 224p. 1972. 46.25 (ISBN 0-677-00410-9). Gordon.

Business Programs Applications. 282p. 4.95 (ISBN 0-317-05257-8, 62-2074). Radio Shack.

Byers, Robert A. The dBASE II for Every Business. Thomson, Monet & Lincoln, Mary, eds. 339p. 1983. pap. 19.95 (ISBN 0-912677-03-1). Ashton-Tate Bks.

--The dBASE II for Every Business. 399p. 19.95 (ISBN 0-8359-1246-9). Reston.

Calmus, Lawrence P. The Business Guide to Small Computers. LC 82-10080. (Illus.). 192p. 1983. 23.50 (ISBN 0-07-009662-7). McGraw.

Canning, R. G. & Leeper, N. C. So You Are Thinking about a Small Business Computer. 203p. 1982. 22.95 (ISBN 0-13-823625-9); pap. 10.95 (ISBN 0-13-823617-8). P-H.

Cardoza, Anne, et al. One Hundred One Ways to Make Money with Application Software. 288p. 1985. pap. 9.95 (ISBN 0-671-50384-7, Pub. by Computer Bks). S&S.

Carlson, E. D., et al. Display Generation & Management Systems (DGMS) for Interactive Business Applications. 15.00 (ISBN 0-9940013-8-X, Pub. by Vieweg & Sohn Germany). Heyden.

Carver, D. K. Computers & Data Processing: Introduction with BASIC. 3rd ed. LC 78-19131. 366p. 1983. text ed. 24.95 (ISBN 0-471-09834-5). wkbk. 11.95 (ISBN 0-471-86252-5). Wiley.

Cecil, P. B. Word Processing in the Modern Office. 2nd ed. 1980. pap. 21.95 (ISBN 0-8053-1758-9); instrs manual 4.95 (ISBN 0-8053-1760-0); student wkbk 7.95 (ISBN 0-8053-1761-9). Benjamin-Cummings.

Chadwick, John W. Computing for Executives. (Illus.). 240p. (Orig.). 1984. 19.95 (ISBN 0-8306-0796-X); pap. 12.95 (ISBN 0-8306-1796-5, 1796). TAB Bks.

Champine, G. A. Computer Technology Impact on Management. 292p. 1978. 38.50 (ISBN 0-444-85179-8, North-Holland). Elsevier.

Chase, Cohrane & Barasch, Kenneth. Solving Marketing Problems with VisiCalc. LC 83-45392. 300p. (Orig.). 1984. pap. 14.95 (ISBN 0-8019-7423-2). Chilton.

Chaudhury, Jackie & Agley, Lyn. Simple Data Processing: A Practical Introduction to Business Information Technology. (Illus.). 60p. 1983. pap. 12.95x (ISBN 0-317-02460-4). Intl Ideas.

Clark, Ron. Fifty-five More Color Computer Programs for the Home, School & Office. (Illus.). 112p. (Orig.). 1982. pap. 9.95 (ISBN 0-86668-008-X). ARCsoft.

Clarke, Thursten. Evaluating Written Copy-Techniques for High-Tech Managers. 82p. Date not set. 19.95 (ISBN 0-935506-29-2). Carnegie Pr.

Clifford, Michael. The dBASE Book of Business Applications. (Illus.). 256p. 1984. pap. 19.95 (ISBN 0-8359-1242-6). Reston.

Clifton, H. D. Choosing & Using Computers: Assessing Data Processing Requirements for Smaller Companies. 1975. 22.00x (ISBN 0-8464-0247-5). Beekman Pubs.

Cobb, Douglas, et al. One-Two-Three for Business. 338p. 1984. pap. 16.95 (ISBN 0-88022-038-4, 34); IBM-PC format. disk 79.90 (240). Que Corp.

Cobb, Douglas F. & Cobb, Gena B. VisiCalc Models for Business. LC 82-42767. (Que's IBM-PC Library). (Illus.). 210p. (Orig.). 1983. pap. 16.95 (ISBN 0-88022-017-1, 7); software disk 79.90 ea. IBM-PC format (225). Apple II (226). Apple III format (227). Que Corp.

Cobb, Douglas F., et al. Multiplan Models for Business. (Illus.). 272p. 1983. pap. 15.95 (ISBN 0-88022-037-6, 33); software disk 79.90 ea. IBM-PC format (260). Eight-inch SS/SD format (263). Apple II format (262). Que Corp.

Cohen, Leo J. Creating & Planning the Corporate Data Base Project. 2nd ed. (Illus.). 323p. pap. 29.50 (ISBN 0-89435-116-8). QED Info Sci.

Cohen, William A. The Entrepreneur & Small Business Problem Solver: An Encyclopedia Reference & Guide. 655p. 1983. pap. text ed. 19.95 (ISBN 0-471-80795-8). Wiley.

Cole, Jim. Fifty Programs in BASIC for the Home, School & Office. 2nd ed. (Illus.). 96p. 1981. pap. 9.95 (ISBN 0-86668-502-2). ARCsoft.

Computer Strategies. The Beauty Salon Computer Handbook. 150p. 1983. looseleaf 45.00x (ISBN 0-913505-03-X). Computer Strat.

--The Distributor's Computer Handbook. 150p. 1983. looseleaf 45.00x (ISBN 0-913505-08-0). Computer Strat.

--The Motor Carrier's Computer Handbook. 150p. 1984. looseleaf 45.00x (ISBN 0-913505-15-3). Computer Strat.

--The Restaurant Computer Handbook. 150p. 1983. looseleaf 45.00x (ISBN 0-9603584-5-5). Computer Strat.

Computer Strategies Staff. The Oil & Gas Computer Handbook. 150p. 1983. looseleaf 45.00x (ISBN 0-913505-16-1). Computer Strat.

Condon, Robert. Data Processing with Applications. 2nd ed. (Illus.). 432p. 1980. text ed. 20.95 (ISBN 0-8359-1254-X); wkbk. 9.95 (ISBN 0-8359-1256-6); instrs.' manual avail. (ISBN 0-8359-1255-8). Reston.

--Data Processing with Applications. abr. ed. 1981. pap. text ed. 17.95 (ISBN 0-8359-1259-0). Reston.

Cortada, James W. Strategic Data Processing: Considerations for Management. (Illus.). 224p. 1984. text ed. 32.95 (ISBN 0-13-851246-9). P-H.

Couger, J. Daniel & McFadden, Fred R. First Course in Data Processing with BASIC. 2nd ed. (Computers & Information Processing Systems for Business Ser.). 595p. 1984. pap. 27.95 (ISBN 0-471-86945-7). Wiley.

--First Course in Data Processing with BASIC, COBOL, FORTRAN & RPG. 3rd ed. LC 83-17032. (Wiley Series in Computers & Information Processing Systems for Business: 1-661). 682p. 1984. text ed. 28.95 (ISBN 0-471-86946-5); write for info. tchr's ed. (ISBN 0-471-86952-X); pap. 15.95 student wkbk (ISBN 0-471-86951-1); write for info. tests (ISBN 0-471-88531-2); write for info. slides (ISBN 0-471-88493-6). Wiley.

Crop, Sheldon. Office Efficiency with Personal Computers. 175p. 1984. pap. cancelled (ISBN 0-89588-165-9). SYBEX.

Curtin, Dennis & Alves, Jeff. Controlling Financial Performance for Higher Profits: An Apple Business User's Guide. 160p. 1983. pap. 14.95 (ISBN 0-930764-58-7). Van Nos Reinhold.

--Controlling Financial Performance for Higher Profits: An IBM-PC Business User's Guide. 160p. 1983. pap. 14.95 (ISBN 0-930764-57-9); software disk 29.95 (ISBN 0-930764-68-4); bk. & disk 39.95 (ISBN 0-930764-78-1). Van Nos Reinhold.

Curtin, Dennis & Alves, Jefffey. Controlling Financial Performance: Apple Business Users Guide. (Illus.). 224p. (Orig.). 1983. pap. 15.50. Curtin & London.

Curtin, Dennis, et al. Controlling Financial Performance: A 1-2-3 Business User's Guide. 1983. 16.95 (ISBN 0-930764-73-0). Van Nos Reinhold.

Curtin, Dennis P. Manager's Guide to Framework: An Illustrated Short Course. 160p. 1985. pap. 18.95 (ISBN 0-13-550070-2). P-H.

Curtin, Dennis P., et al. Controlling Financial Performance for Higher Profits: A Multiplan Business User's Guide. (Illus.). 176p. 1984. pap. 19.50 (ISBN 0-930764-87-0); disk 29.95. Van Nos Reinhold.

Davis, W. S. Computers & Business Information Processing & BASIC: Getting Started. 1981. package 22.95 (ISBN 0-201-13299-0). Addison-Wesley.

--Computers & Business Information Processing & FORTRAN: Getting Started. 1981. package 22.95 (ISBN 0-201-13298-2). Addison-Wesley.

Davis, William S. Computer & Business Information Processing. 2nd ed. LC 82-6864. (Illus.). 448p. 1983. pap. text ed. 19.95 (ISBN 0-201-11118-7); instr's manual 2.95 (ISBN 0-201-11119-5); wkbk 6.95 (ISBN 0-201-11121-7); write for info. trans. masters. Addison-Wesley.

--Computers & Business Information Processing. LC 80-10946. 448p. 1981. pap. text ed. 17.95 (ISBN 0-201-03161-2); 7.95 (ISBN 0-201-03713-0). Addison-Wesley.

Deane, Barbara. Computer Power for the Business Woman. 250p. pap. cancelled (ISBN 0-89588-184-5). SYBEX.

Deighton, S., ed. Microprocessor Applications in Home & Office, 1977-1978: Bibliography. 1979. 23.00 (ISBN 0-85296-449-8). Inst Elect Eng.

Dembowski, Frederick L., ed. Administrative Uses for Microcomputers: Hardware, Vol. 2. 101p. 1983. 15.95 (ISBN 0-910170-28-2). Assn Sch Busn.

--Administrative Uses for Microcomputers: Software, Vol. 1. 143p. 1983. 15.95 (ISBN 0-910170-27-4). Assn Sch Busn.

DeRossi, Claude & Hopper, David. Software Interfacing: A User & Supplier Guide. (Illus.). 208p. 1984. 29.95 (ISBN 0-13-822353-X). P-H.

Dery, David. Computers in Welfare: The MIS-Match. LC 81-224. (Managing Information Ser.: Vol. 3). (Illus.). 264p. 1981. 25.00 (ISBN 0-8039-1610-8). Sage.

Didday, Rich L., et al. FORTRAN for Business People. (Illus.). 1978. pap. text ed. 21.95 (ISBN 0-8299-0101-9). West Pub.

Diebold, John. Business in the Age of Information. LC 84-45782. 144p. 1985. 14.95 (ISBN 0-8144-5792-4). Amacom.

Dinerstein, Nelson T. Creative Business Applications with dBASE II: A Beginner's Introduction. 160p. 1984. pap. 15.95 (ISBN 0-673-15957-4). Scott F.

Directories from InfoSource Inc. Business Software for the CP-M Computers: An Applications Directory. LC 83-45379. 256p. (Orig.). 1984. pap. 12.95 (ISBN 0-8019-7434-8). Chilton.

Directories from InfoSource, Inc. Micro Software for Business: An Applications Directory. LC 83-45396. 656p. (Orig.). 1984. pap. 19.95 (ISBN 0-8019-7430-5). Chilton.

Directories from InfoSource Inc. Staff. Business Software for the Apple II: An Applications Directory. LC 83-45382. 176p. (Orig.). 1984. pap. 12.95 (ISBN 0-8019-7431-3). Chilton.

Dock, V. Thomas. Structured BASIC: Programming for Business. 2nd ed. (Illus.). 144p. 1982. pap. text ed. 17.95 (ISBN 0-314-63167-4). West Pub.

--Structured BASIC Programming for Business. 3rd ed. (Illus.). 140p. 1984. pap. text ed. 18.95 (ISBN 0-314-85230-1). West Pub.

Dock, V. Thomas & Essick, Edward. Principles of Business Data Processing. 4th ed. 544p. 1981. text ed. 23.95 (ISBN 0-574-21295-7, 13-4295); instr's guide avail. (ISBN 0-574-21296-5, 13-4296); transparency masters avail. (ISBN 0-574-21303-1, 13-4303); study guide 10.95 (ISBN 0-574-21297-3, 13-4297). SRA.

--Principles of Business Data Processing with MIS...including BASIC: MIS Edition, Language Free. 4th ed. 544p. 1981. 25.95 (ISBN 0-574-21300-7, 13-4300). SRA.

Dolan, Kathleen. Business Computer Systems Design. 336p. 1984. pap. text ed. 13.95x (ISBN 0-938188-20-8). Mitchell Pub.

Dologite, Dorothy. Using Small Business Computers. (Illus.). 448p. 1984. text ed. 24.95 (ISBN 0-13-940156-3). P-H.

Dorf, Richard C. A Guide to the Best Business Software for the IBM PC. (Illus.). 192p. 1983. pap. 12.95 (ISBN 0-201-10256-0). Addison-Wesley.

Doswell, Andrew, ed. Foundations of Business Information Systems. (Approaches to Information Technology Ser.). 236p. 1985. pap. 18.95x (ISBN 0-306-41796-0). Plenum Pub.

Driscoll, Frederick F. Microprocessor-Microcomputer Technology. 520p. 1983. 29.95 (ISBN 0-442-21827-3). Van Nos Reinhold.

Dumpe, Bert. Using the Wang for Business: The Technician's Perspective. 346p. 1984. pap. text ed. 28.70 scp (ISBN 0-06-041801-X, HarpC); instr's. manual avail. (ISBN 0-06-361782-X). Har-Row.

Eckols, Steve. How to Design & Develop Business Systems: A Practical Approach to Analysis, Design & Implementation. LC 83-62380. (Illus.). 279p. (Orig.). 1983. pap. 20.00 (ISBN 0-911625-14-3). M Murach & Assoc.

Eliason, Alan & Kitts, Kent D. Business Computer Systems & Applications. 2nd ed. LC 78-18447. 384p. 1979. 16.95 (ISBN 0-574-21215-9, 13-4215); instr's guide 2.25 (ISBN 0-574-21216-7, 13-4216). SRA.

Eliason, Alan L. Mason Oaks: An Online Case Study in Business Systems Design. 128p. 1981. pap. text ed. 9.95 (ISBN 0-574-21310-4, 13-4310); instr's guide avail. (ISBN 0-574-21311-2, 13-4311). SRA.

--Online Business Computer Applications. 496p. 1983. pap. text ed. 16.95 (ISBN 0-574-21405-4, 13-4405); instr's. guide avail. (ISBN 0-574-21406-2, 13-4406). SRA.

--Royal Pines: An On-Line Case Study in Business Systems Design. 144p. (Orig.). 1984. pap. text ed. 9.95 (ISBN 0-574-21700-2, 13-4700); write for info. tchr's ed. (ISBN 0-317-03528-2, 13-4701). SRA.

Enockson, Paul G. A Guide for Selecting Computers & Software for Small Businesses. 1983. 21.95 (ISBN 0-8359-2642-7); pap. text ed. 14.95 (ISBN 0-8359-2641-9). Reston.

Erickson, Lawrence W. Microcomputer Activities for Office Procedures. 1984. pap. 4.80 (ISBN 0-538-11220-4, K22). SW Pub.

Ettlin, Walter A. Multiplan Made Easy. 14.95 (ISBN 0-07-881135-X, 135-X). Osborne-McGraw.

Falk, Howard. Handbook Computer Application for Small or Medium Business. LC 83-70782. 384p. 1983. 19.95 (ISBN 0-8019-7393-7). Chilton.

--Microcomputer Communications in Business. LC 84-45161. 400p. (Orig.). 1984. pap. 18.95 (ISBN 0-8019-7512-3). Chilton.

Finn, Nancy B. The Electronic Office. (Illus.). 160p. 1983. pap. 15.95 (ISBN 0-13-251819-8). P-H.

Fiske, Thomas S. Low Cost Costing: Product Costing with Your Microcomputer. (Illus.). 94p. (Orig.). 1984. pap. 24.95 spiral bound (ISBN 0-88006-084-0); Apple II, II Plus, IIe. spiral bound incl. disk 24.95 (ISBN 0-88006-067-0, CC7399); IBM-PC. spiral bound incl. disk 24.95 (ISBN 0-88006-071-9, CC7402); TRS-80 Model I, Model III. spiral bound incl. disk 24.95 (ISBN 0-88006-072-7, CC7403); spiral bound incl. disk 24.95 (ISBN 0-88006-092-1, CC7421). Green Pub Inc.

Fitzgerald, Jerry, et al. Fundamentals of Systems Analysis. 2nd ed. LC 80-11769. 590p. 1981. 35.45 (ISBN 0-471-04968-9, Pub. by Wiley Heyden); text ed. 29.50 members (ISBN 0-471-08117-5). Assn Inform & Image Mgmt.

Ford, Nelson. Business Graphics for the IBM PC. LC 83-51567. (Illus.). 259p. 1984. pap. 18.95 (ISBN 0-89588-124-1). SYBEX.

Forkner, Irvine F. BASIC Programming for Business. (Illus.). 288p. 1978. pap. text ed. 21.95x (ISBN 0-13-066423-5). P-H.

Forkner, Irvine H. Pascal Programming Business, Management Science, & Social Science Applications. 250p. 1984. pap. write for info. Wadsworth Pub.

Fry, Larry. BASIC Programming for Business: A Structured Approach. LC 84-14268. 352p. 1985. pap. text ed. 20.00 (ISBN 0-8273-2245-3); instr's. guide 4.10 (ISBN 0-8273-2246-1). Delmar.

Fry, Louis & Adams, Marsha T. The Business Microcomputer Handbook: Evaluation, Acquisition & Use. 1984. 19.45 (ISBN 0-03-071616-0). HR&W.

Fuchs, Jerome H. Computerized Cost Control Systems. 304p. 1976. 32.95 (ISBN 0-13-166223-6). P-H.

Fuori, William M. Introduction to the Computer: The Tool of Business. 3rd ed. (Illus.). 720p. 1981. text ed. 24.95 (ISBN 0-13-480343-4); pap. 8.95 study guide (ISBN 0-13-480368-X). P-H.

Gagliardi, Gary. How to Make Your Small Business Computer Pay Off: What the First Time Business System Buyer Must Know. 285p. 1983. 15.95 (ISBN 0-534-97926-2). Van Nos Reinhold.

--How to Make Your Small Computer Pay Off: What the First-Time Business System Buyer Must Know. (Data Processing Ser.). (Illus.). 279p. 1983. 14.95 (ISBN 0-534-97926-2). Lifetime Learn.

Gant, Wanda & Casale, James F., eds. Making Business Systems Effective: The Papers & Proceedings of Syntopican XIII. 500p. (Orig.). 1985. pap. text ed. 30.00 (ISBN 0-935220-13-5). Assn Info Sys.

Gershefski, George W. Using Lotus 1-2-3 to Solve Your Business Problems: Planning, Budgeting, Forecasting, Capital Investment Analysis A Practical Guide to Spreadsheet Planning. LC 84-10671. 156p. 1984. pap. text ed. 21.95x (ISBN 0-8476-7346-4). Rowman & Allanheld.

Gessford, John E. Modern Information Systems: Designed for Decision Support. LC 78-74684. 1980. text ed. 29.95 (ISBN 0-201-03099-3). Addison-Wesley.

Gillis, M. Arthur. Microcomputers in Financial Institutions. LC 84-73254. 1985. 25.00 (ISBN 0-87094-580-7). Dow Jones-Irwin.

Glau, Gregory R. Business Graphics for the Macintosh. 250p. 1985. pap. 19.95 (ISBN 0-87094-693-5). Dow Jones-Irwin.

--Business Power for Your Apple. 288p. 1984. 32.50 (ISBN 0-442-22779-5). Van Nos Reinhold.

Global Data-Processing System & Meteorological Service to Shipping. (World Weather Watch Planning Reports: No. 15). 26p. 1966. pap. 12.00 (ISBN 0-685-22305-1, W231, WMO). Unipub.

Gonzalez, Harvey J. & Fein, Lois. Datatran: A Comprehensive & Practical System for Developing & Maintaining Data Processing Systems. (Illus.). 432p. 1983. text ed. 41.95 (ISBN 0-13-196493-3). P-H.

Good, Phillip I. Computerize Your Business. LC 84-45159. 320p. (Orig.). 1984. pap. 17.95 (ISBN 0-8019-7519-0). Chilton.

--A Critical Guide to Software for the IBM PC & PC Compatible Computers: Computers for Professionals in Business, Agriculture, Law & Health. LC 83-17148. (Illus.). 284p. 1983. pap. 12.95 (ISBN 0-8019-7413-5). Chilton.

Gore, Marvin & Stubbe, John. Elements of Systems Analysis. 3rd ed. 568p. 1983. text ed. write for info. (ISBN 0-697-08169-9). instrs.' resource manual avail. (ISBN 0-697-08178-8); alternate casebook avail. (ISBN 0-697-00092-3); avail. solutions manual to alternate casebook (ISBN 0-697-00267-5). Wm C Brown.

Green, Rodney. Forecasting with Computer Models: Econometric, Population, & Energy Forecasting. LC 84-15934. 320p. 1985. 29.95 (ISBN 0-03-063788-0); pap. 12.95 (ISBN 0-03-063787-2). Praeger.

Greenwood, Frank. Profitable Small Business Computing. 176p. 1982. text ed. 21.95 (ISBN 0-316-32711-5); pap. 9.95 (ISBN 0-316-32712-3). Little.

Grelewicz, Richard M. Take It with You: The Complete Guide to Portable Business Computing. LC 84-5208. 246p. 1984. pap. 14.95 (ISBN 0-471-88198-8). Wiley.

Haden, Douglas. Total Business Systems: Computers in Business. (Illus.). 1978. text ed. 28.95 (ISBN 0-8299-0092-6). West Pub.

Hansen, Gladys O. Word Processing Systems Manual (1) for Originators & Support Staff. (Illus., Orig.). 1980. pap. text ed. 40.00 set (ISBN 0-936512-02-4). Telecom Lib.

Harris, Daniel. Lotus 1-2-3 Mastery: A Business Guide to 1-2-3 Productivity. 256p. incl. disk 38.95 (ISBN 0-13-540741-9). P-H.

Harvard Business Review. Catching Up with the Computer Revolution. Salerno, Lynn M., ed. LC 82-21899. (Harvard Business Review Executive Bk.). 531p. 1983. 24.95 (ISBN 0-471-87594-5, Pub. by Wiley-Interscience). Wiley.

Hattery, Lowell H. Executive Control & Data Processing. 1959. 10.00 (ISBN 0-910136-03-3). Anderson Kramer.

Hergert, Douglas. BASIC for Business. LC 81-85955. (Illus.). 223p. 1982. pap. 15.95 (ISBN 0-89588-080-6, B390). SYBEX.

--IBM PC Spreadsheets to Graphics. 250p. 1984. pap. 16.95 (ISBN 0-89588-163-2). SYBEX.

Hergert, Richard & Hergert, Douglas. Doing Business with Pascal. 371p. 17.95 (ISBN 0-317-00353-4). SYBEX.

Hildebrand. Business Programs for the IBM PC. 1983. 15.95 (ISBN 0-317-02367-5, 6351). Hayden.

Hildebrand, George. Using Microcomputers in Managerial Accounting. (Microcomputers in Business Ser.). (Illus.). 288p. 1985. lab manual 10.95 (ISBN 0-938188-27-5); instrs' guide & software avail. (ISBN 0-938188-28-3). Mitchell Pub.

Hindelang, Thomas J. & Dascher, Paul E. IBM PC Guide to Marginal Analysis: Business Thinking at the Cutting Edge. 320p. 1984. pap. cancelled (ISBN 0-88693-058-8). Banbury Bks.

Hirsch, Rudolph E. Computer Literacy for Middle Management. (Illus.). 224p. 1948. text ed. 27.50 (ISBN 0-13-164245-6). P-H.

Hodge, Bartow & Clements, James P. Business Systems Design. 1985. text ed. 26.95 (ISBN 0-8359-0519-5); tchr's. manual avail. (ISBN 0-8359-0520-9). Reston.

Hodges, William S. & Novak, Neal A. Applications of Software for Homes & Businesses. (Little, Brown Microcomputer Bookshelf Ser.). 350p. (Orig.). 1984. pap. 14.95 i (ISBN 0-316-36788-5). Little.

Holder, S. & Sherman, C. Elements of BASIC: A Problem Solving Approach for Business. 256p. 1984. pap. 10.45 (ISBN 0-471-80653-6). Wiley.

Holtz, Herman. Computer Work Stations: The Manager's Guide to Office Automation & Multi-Users Systems. 280p. 1985. 24.50 (ISBN 0-412-00711-8, NO. 9004, Pub. by Chapman & Hall). Methuen Inc.

Huber, Norman F. Data Communications: The Business Aspects. 356p. 1983. looseleaf bound 59.95 (ISBN 0-935506-05-5). Carnegie Pr.

Ingle, Marcus D., et al. Microcomputers in Development: A Manager's Guide. LC 83-19558. (K. P. Guideline Ser.). (Illus.). xi, 174p. (Orig.). 1983. pap. text ed. 12.75x (ISBN 0-931816-03-3). Kumarian Pr.

INIS: Authority List for Corporate Entries. (INIS Reference Ser.: No. 6). pap. 13.25 (IN6/R9, IAEA). Unipub.

International Computer Programs Staff. ICP Software Directory, Vol. 7: Microcomputer Systems, Specialized Business Applications, Pt. II. Hamilton, Dennis L., ed. 1985. pap. 95.00 (ISBN 0-88094-049-2). Intl Computer.

--ICP Software Directory, Vol. 7: Microcomputer Systems, Systems Software & General Business Applications, Pt. I. Hamilton, Dennis L., ed. 1985. pap. 95.00 (ISBN 0-88094-048-4). Intl Computer.

Jackson, Peter. Business Programming on Your BBC Micro. (Illus.). 192p. 1984. pap. 14.95 (ISBN 0-946576-20-3, Pub. by Phoenix Pub). David & Charles.

--Business Programming on Your Commodore 64. (Illus.). 192p. 1984. pap. 14.95 (ISBN 0-946576-19-X, Pub. by Phoenix Pub). David & Charles.

Jackson, Peter & Goode, Peter. Business Programming on Your Spectrum. 157p. 1984. pap. 13.95 (ISBN 0-946576-05-X, Pub. by Phoenix Pub). David & Charles.

Janossy, James. Software Engineering Techniques for Designing Business Data Processing Programs. 472p. 1985. 24.95 (ISBN 0-471-81576-4). Wiley.

Johnson, Rodney D. & Siskin, Bernard R. Quantitative Techniques for Business Decisions. (Illus.). 544p. 1976. 30.95 (ISBN 0-13-746990-X). P-H.

Jones, G. T. Data Capture in the Retail Environment. (Illus.). 1977. pap. 29.00x (ISBN 0-85012-168-X). Intl Pubns Serv.

Joslin, Edward O. Computer Selection: Augmented Edition. LC 77-78713. (Illus.). 1977. text ed. 25.00 (ISBN 0-89321-201-6). Tech Pr Inc.

Kahn, Robert E. & Vezza, Albert. Electronic Mail & Message Systems: Technical & Policy Perspectives. 223p. 1981. 25.00 (ISBN 0-88283-040-6). AFIPS Pr.

Kalthoff, Robert J. & Lee, Leonard S. Productivity & Records Automation. (Illus.). 400p. 1981. text ed. 37.95 (ISBN 0-13-725234-X). P-H.

Kenny, Donald P. Personal Computers in Business. LC 84-45204. 224p. 1985. 15.95 (ISBN 0-8144-7627-9). AMACOM.

Kepner, Terry & Robinson, Mark. Fifty-Eight Business Programs for the IBM PC. 1985. pap. 18.95 (ISBN 0-673-18286-X). Scott F.

--Fifty-Eight Business Programs for the Macintosh. 1985. pap. 18.95 (ISBN 0-673-18284-3). Scott F.

Kilgannon, Pete. Business Data Processing & Systems Analysts. 336p. 1980. pap. text ed. 19.95 (ISBN 0-7131-2755-4). E Arnold.

King, Richard A. & Trost, Stanley R. Doing Business with Multiplan. LC 84-51214. 250p. 1984. pap. 15.95 (ISBN 0-89588-148-9). SYBEX.

Kling, Bill. The ABC's of Lotus 1-2-3: A Step-by-Step Guide. 1985. pap. 18.95 (ISBN 0-673-15996-5). Scott F.

Klitzner, Carol & Plociak, Matthew J., Jr. Using VisiCalc: Getting Down to Business. LC 82-24764. 277p. 1983. pap. 16.95 (ISBN 0-471-89852-X, Pub. by Wiley Pr); additional for diskette 39.95; Apple II. software disk 39.95 (ISBN 0-471-89889-9); IBM-PC. software disk 39.95 (ISBN 0-471-88964-4); TRS-80 Modell III. software disk 39.95 (ISBN 0-471-88962-8). Wiley.

Koff, Richard M. Using Small Computers to Make Your Business Strategy Work. LC 83-27432. (Wiley Management Series on Problem Solving, Decision Making & Strategic Thinking: 1-578). 394p. 1984. pap. 19.95 (ISBN 0-471-87502-3). Wiley.

Konopasek, Milos & Jayaraman, Sundaresan. The TK! Solver Book: A Guide to Problem-Solving in Science, Engineering, Business & Education. 360p. (Orig.). 1984. pap. 19.95 (ISBN 0-07-881115-5, 115-5). Osborne-McGraw.

Kvanli, Alan H., et al. Introduction to Business Statistics: A Computer Integrated Approach. (Illus.). 1000p. 1986. text ed. 30.00 (ISBN 0-314-93192-9). West Pub.

LaPlante, Josephine M. An Introduction to Computer Analysis in the Social Sciences & Business Using SAS. (Learning Packages in the Policy Sciences Ser.: No. 21). (Illus.). 53p. (Orig.). 1981. pap. text ed. 3.50x (ISBN 0-936826-16-9). Pol Stud Assocs.

Laric, Michael V. & Stiff, Ronald. Marketing & Business Planning with the IBM PCs: A Guide to the Productive Use of Personal Computers for Business & Marketing Professionals. (Illus.). 224p. 1985. pap. 16.95 (ISBN 0-13-557067-0). P H.

Lehman, June M., ed. EDP: Applications for Employee Benefit Plans. 55p. (Orig.). 1985. pap. text ed. 10.00 (ISBN 0-89154-276-0). Intl Found Employ.

Lesser, M. L. Using the Microsoft Business BASIC Compiler on the IBM PC. 256p. 1985. price not set (ISBN 0-07-037299-3, BYTE Bks). McGraw.

Levine, Jack B. & Van Wijk, Alfons. Counting on Computers: The New Tool for Restaurant Management. LC 80-21289. 1980. 34.95 (ISBN 0-86730-230-5). Lebhar Friedman.

Lewis, Allen M. Structured DEC Basic for Business Using Files. (Illus.). 208p. 1986. pap. text ed. 18.95 (ISBN 0-13-854746-7). P H.

Lewis, Robert J. & Hart, David G. Business FORTRAN: A Structured Approach. 450p. 1981. pap. write for info. Wadsworth Pub.

Lewis, T. G. How to Profit from Your Personal Computer: Professional, Business, & Home Applications. 1978. pap. 13.95 (ISBN 0-8104-5761-X). Hayden.

Lewis, Ted G. The TRS-80 Means Business. LC 81-11384. 194p. 1982. pap. 14.95 (ISBN 0-471-08239-2); incl. disk 34.90 (ISBN 0-471-87565-1). Wiley.

Lohmuller, Keith. Introduction to Business Programming & Systems Analysis. (Illus.). 238p. (Orig.). 1983. 18.95 (ISBN 0-8306-0437-5, 1437); pap. 13.50 (ISBN 0-8306-1437-0). TAB Bks.

Lord, Kenniston, Jr. Using Apple Business Computer. 1983. 19.95 (ISBN 0-442-26016-4); pap. 13.95 (ISBN 0-442-25933-6). Van Nos Reinhold.

Software Projections, Inc. The Project Manager. (Professional Software Ser.). 1984. incl. disk 295.00 (ISBN 0-471-88196-1). Wiley.

Solomon, Sam. Business Applications Using the Compaq. 1984. 17.95 (ISBN 0-8359-0531-4). Reston.

Sorger, T. J. The Computer Buyer's Attorney. (Illus., Orig.). pap. 39.95 (ISBN 0-9604072-0-0). Sorger Assocs.

Sprenger, et al. Record Keeping Applications Using Microcomputer. 1986. text ed. price not set wkbk. & diskettes (ISBN 0-538-02000-8, B018). SW Pub.

Sprowls, R. Clay. Management Data Bases. LC 76-6100. 382p. 1976. (Pub. by Wiley Hamilton); TM Bases 5.50x (ISBN 0-471-02547-X). Wiley.

Stevens, William F. & Lind, Mary R. Programming with IBM PC BASIC with Business Applications. 1984. 23.95 (ISBN 0-8359-5674-1). Reston.

Stewart, Rosemary. How Computers Affect Management. 256p. 1972. 25.00x (ISBN 0-262-19105-9). MIT Pr.

Stone, M. David. Getting the Most from WordStar & Mailmerge: Things Micropro Never Told You. 128p. 1984. 20.95 (ISBN 0-13-354390-0); pap. 14.95 (ISBN 0-13-354382-X, Spec). P-H.

Struble, George. Business Information Processing with BASIC. LC 79-1423. 1980. text ed. 21.95 (ISBN 0-201-07640-3); wkbk. 7.95 (ISBN 0-201-07642-X); instr's. manual 2.95 (ISBN 0-201-07641-1); transparency avail. (ISBN 0-201-07643-8). Addison-Wesley.

Summer, Claire & Levy, Walter A. The Affordable Computer: Microcomputer Applications in Business & Industry. new ed. LC 78-24672. 1979. 13.95 (ISBN 0-8144-5493-3). AMACOM.

--Microcomputers for Business. 1980. pap. 7.95 (ISBN 0-8144-7539-6). AMACOM.

Svigals, Terome. Planning for Future Market Events Using Data Processing Support: A Five Step Growth Plan. LC 82-48765. 1983. 27.95x (ISBN 0-02-949740-X). Macmillan.

Swan. Pascal Programs for Business. 1983. 18.95 (ISBN 0-317-02343-8, 6270); disks & documentation 59.95 (7270). Hayden.

Taggart. Informations Systems: An Introduction to Computers in Organizations. 500p. 1980. text ed. 34.39 scp (ISBN 0-205-06908-8, 2069083); instrs' manual avail. (ISBN 0-205-06909-6). Allyn.

Taylor, et al. The Computerized Billing Clerk: Acme Electric Co. 1984. text ed. 6.95 (ISBN 0-538-25060-7, Y06). SW Pub.

Thierauf, Robert J. & Niehaus, John F. An Introduction to Data Processing for Business. LC 79-20568. 366p. 1980. 42.00 (ISBN 0-471-03439-8); tchrs' manual 9.00 (ISBN 0-471-03440-1); PP 227. study guide 17.45 (ISBN 0-471-07870-0). Wiley.

Tomeski, Edward A. Fundamentals of Computers in Business: A Systems Approach. LC 78-54208. 1979. text ed. 30.00x (ISBN 0-8162-8733-3); instructor's manual 6.00 (ISBN 0-8162-8734-1). Holden-Day.

Tomeski, Edward A. & Kleinschmidt, William. Fundamentals of Computers in Business: A Systems Approach (Student Study Guide) 1979. 10.95x (ISBN 0-8162-8735-X). Holden-Day.

Topping, Anne L. & Gibbons, Ian. Business Applications of Structured COBOL Programming. 600p. 1982. pap. text ed. 32.07 scp (ISBN 0-205-07750-1, 2077507); tchr's. ed. avail. (ISBN 0-205-07751-X). Allyn.

Tortorelli, Martens. BASIC Programming with Applications in Business. 176p. 1984. pap. text ed. 9.95 (ISBN 0-8403-3523-7). Kendall-Hunt.

Townsend, Kevin, ed. Choosing & Using Business Micro Software. 227p. 1984. text ed. 32.95x (ISBN 0-566-02496-9). Gower Pub Co.

Transnational Corporations & Transborder Data Flows: A Technical Paper. 149p. 1982. pap. 12.00 (ISBN 0-686-97595-2, UN82/2A4, UN). Unipub.

Trivette, Donald B. A BASIC Primer for the IBM Personal Computer: Programming Business Applications. 208p. 1984. pap. 18.95 (ISBN 0-673-15997-3). Scott F.

Trost, Stanley R. Advanced Business Models with 1- 2- 3. LC 84-51215. 250p. 1984. pap. 17.95 (ISBN 0-89588-159-4). SYBEX.

--Doing Business with VisiCalc. LC 82-50622. (Illus.). 259p. 1982. pap. 14.95 (ISBN 0-89588-086-5, V104). SYBEX.

Tymes, Elna R. Businessman's Guide to the Kaypro. (Illus.). 200p. 1984. 16.95 (ISBN 0-8359-0601-9). Reston.

VanDiver, Gerald. The IBM PC & XT Business Software Guide. 231p. 1984. 19.95 (ISBN 0-912603-12-7). Micro-Info.

Van Wolverton. VisiCalc Advanced Version: Worsheets for Business. (Illus.). 238p. (Orig.). 1984. pap. 18.95 (ISBN 0-912213-00-0, VisiPress). Random.

Veit, Stanely S. Using Microcomputers in Business: A Guide for the Perplexed. 192p. pap. 13.95 (6257). Hayden.

Veit, Stanley S. Using Microcomputers in Business: A Guide for the Perplexed. 2nd ed. 142p. 1983. pap. 13.95 (ISBN 0-8104-6257-5). Hayden.

Vichas, Robert P. New Encyclopedic Dictionary of Systems & Procedures. 700p. 1981. 39.95 (ISBN 0-13-612630-8). P-H.

Vitalari, Nicholas P. Structured BASIC for Business. (Illus.). 288p. 1985. pap. text ed. 21.95 (ISBN 0-13-854407-7). P-H.

Waite Group, et al. Microsoft MultiPlan: Of Mice & Menus: Models for Managing Your Business with the Apple Macintosh. 256p. 1985. pap. 16.95 (ISBN 0-914845-33-0). Microsoft.

Walden, Jeff B. The IBM PC in Your Corporation. (IBM PC Ser.). 320p. 1985. pap. 17.95 (ISBN 0-471-80849-0). Wiley.

Watson, Hugh H. & Carroll, Archie B. Computers for Business: A Book of Readings. 2nd ed. 1984. 16.95 (ISBN 0-256-03135-5). Business Pubns.

Watson, Hugh J. Computer Simulation in Business. LC 80-20612. 358p. 1981. 35.95x (ISBN 0-471-03638-2). Wiley.

Watson, Hugh J. & Carroll, Archie B. Computers for Business: A Managerial Emphasis. rev. ed. 1980. text ed. 22.50x (ISBN 0-256-02288-7). Business Pubns.

Weaver, David H. & Hanna, J. Marshall. Accounting Ten-Twelve, Part 3: Business Data Processing. 3rd ed. (Illus.). 1977. pap. text ed. 7.96 (ISBN 0-07-068903-2). McGraw.

Weber Systems Inc. Staff. Atari ST Business Software in BASIC. 330p. (Orig.). 1986. pap. 17.95 (ISBN 0-317-19095-4). Weber Systems.

Weber Systems, Inc. Staff. IBM PCjr Business Software in BASIC. (Applications Software Ser.). 300p. (Orig.). pap. cancelled; diskette 49.95. Weber Systems.

Weber Systems Inc. Staff. Lotus 1-2-3 Business Models. (Applications Software Models Ser.). 300p. pap. cancelled. Weber Systems.

--Sanyo MBC Business Software in BASIC. LC 85-5386. (Application Software Ser.). 330p. (Orig.). 1985. pap. 17.95 (ISBN 0-938862-37-5); incl. diskette 20.00 (ISBN 0-938862-38-3). Weber Systems.

--TK Solver Business Models. (Application Software Models Ser.). 300p. 1984. pap. cancelled. Weber Systems.

Weber Systems Staff. BASIC Business Package for TRS-80 Computers. LC 82-70599. (Applications Software Ser.). 210p. (Orig.). 1984. pap. 14.95 (ISBN 0-938862-27-8). Weber Systems.

Weinberger, Marvin & Howitt, Doran. Magazine's Databasics: Your Guide to Online Business Information. 608p. 1984. 28.00 (ISBN 0-8240-7290-1); pap. 22.00 (ISBN 0-8240-7287-1). Garland Pub.

Weldon, Jay-Louise. Data Base Administration. LC 80-20467. (Applications of Modern Technology in Business Ser.). 262p. 1981. 27.50x (ISBN 0-306-40595-4, Plenum Pr). Plenum Pub.

Whitbread, Martin, ed. Microprocessor Applications in Business & Industry. (Topics in Microprocessing Ser.: Book One). (Illus.). 153p. 1979. pap. text ed. 21.00 (ISBN 0-7194-0010-4, Pub. by Castle Hse England). J K Burgess.

Whitehouse, Gary E., ed. Software for Engineers & Managers: A Collection. 1984. pap. text ed. 24.95 (ISBN 0-89806-046-X). Inst Indus Eng.

Williams. Computer-Readable Databases, a Directory & Data Source Book: Business, Law, Humanities & Social Sciences. 4th ed. Date not set. write for info. (ISBN 0-444-87614-6). Elsevier.

Wilson, D. R. & Van Spronsen, C. J., eds. Microcomputers: Developments in Industry, Business & Education. 426p. 1984. 61.75 (ISBN 0-444-86742-2, North-Holland). Elsevier.

Woodwell, Donald R. Managing Personal Computer Workstations: A Corporate Resource. LC 84-70602. 270p. 1984. 27.50 (ISBN 0-87094-512-2). Dow Jones-Irwin.

Zarrella, John. High-Tech Consulting: A Guide to Making Money as a Computer Consultant. LC 83-17340. 167p. (Orig.). 1983. pap. 19.95 (ISBN 0-935230-08-4). Microcomputer Appns.

Zimmerman, Steven & Conrad, Leo. Osborne Business Applications. cancelled 17.95 (ISBN 0-89303-746-X). Brady Comm.

BUSINESS MACHINES

see Calculating-Machines; Electronic Office Machines; Office Equipment and Supplies

BUSINESS MATHEMATICS

see also Insurance–Mathematics; Ready-Reckoners

also subdivision Tables, etc. under economic subjects; also subdivision Tables and Ready-Reckoners under names of industries

Ackerman, Judy. Business Mathematics: Effective Problem Solving. 2nd ed. 1985. pap. text ed. 22.95 (ISBN 0-8359-0591-8). Reston.

Adams, William J. Calculus for Business & Social Science. LC 74-5524. 250p. 1975. text ed. 30.75 (ISBN 0-471-00988-1). Wiley.

Arya, Jagdish C. & Lardner, Robin. Mathematical Analysis for Business & Economics. 2nd ed. (Illus.). 704p. 1985. text ed. 31.95 (ISBN 0-13-561101-6); study guide 9.95 (ISBN 0-13-561176-8). P-H.

Arya, Jagdish C. & Lardner, Robin W. Applied Calculus for Business & Economics. (Illus.). 528p. 1981. text ed. 31.95 (ISBN 0-13-039255-3). P-H.

Ayres, Frank, Jr. Mathematics of Finance. (Schaum's Outline Ser.). (Orig.). 1963. pap. 8.95 (ISBN 0-07-002652-1). McGraw.

Barnett, Raymond A. Calculus for Management, Life, & Social Science. 3rd ed. (Illus.). 385p. 1984. text ed. 27.95 (ISBN 0-02-306130-8). Dellen Pub.

--College Mathematics for Management, Life, & Social Sciences. 3rd ed. LC 83-26147. (Illus.). 689p. 1984. text ed. 29.95 (ISBN 0-02-306220-7). Dellen Pub.

--Finite Mathematics for Management, Life & Social Science. 3rd ed. (Illus.). 487p. 1984. text ed. 28.95 (ISBN 0-02-306370-X). Dellen Pub.

Bassin, William M. Quantitative Business Analysis. LC 80-21090. 256p. 1981. text ed. 21.17 scp (ISBN 0-672-97696-X); scp tchr's. ed. 3.67 (ISBN 0-672-97697-8). Bobbs.

Beer, Gerald A. Applied Calculus for Business & Economics with an Introduction to Matrices. 1978. text ed. 21.95 (ISBN 0-316-08727-0); tchr's ed. avail. (ISBN 0-316-08728-9). Little.

Beighey, Clyde & Borchardt, Gordon C. Mathematics for Business, College Course. 5th ed. (Illus.). 256p. 1974. pap. text ed. 18.50 (ISBN 0-07-004370-1). McGraw.

Belstock, Alan & Smith, Gerald. Consumer Mathematics with Calculator Applications. Gafney, Leo, ed. 1980. text ed. 17.52x (ISBN 0-07-004436-8). McGraw.

Berenson, Mark & Levine, David. Basic Business Statistics: Concepts & Applications. 3rd ed. (Illus.). 816p. 1986. text ed. 31.95 (ISBN 0-13-057746-4). P-H.

Bierman, Harold, Jr., et al. Quantitative Analysis for Business Decisions. 6th ed. 1981. 31.95 (ISBN 0-256-02524-X). Irwin.

Bila, Dennis, et al. Mathematics for Business Occupations. (Orig.). 1978. pap. text ed. 21.95 (ISBN 0-316-09475-7); tchr's. ed. avail. (ISBN 0-316-09477-3); test bank avail. (ISBN 0-316-09476-5). Little.

Bittinger, M. L. & Crown, J. C. Mathematics for Business, Economics & Management. 1982. 31.95 (ISBN 0-201-10104-1); instrs' manual 2.50 (ISBN 0-201-10105-X). Addison-Wesley.

Booth, J. E. Textile Mathematics, Vol. 1. 162p. 1975. 40.00x (ISBN 0-686-63802-6). State Mutual Bk.

--Textile Mathematics, Vol. 3. 144p. 1977. 40.00x (ISBN 0-686-63804-2). State Mutual Bk.

Bowden, Aberdeen O. Consumers Uses of Arithmetic: An Investigation to Determine the Actual Uses Made of Arithmetic in Adult Social Life. LC 71-176583. (Columbia University. Teachers College. Contributions to Education: No. 340). Repr. of 1929 ed. 22.50 (ISBN 0-404-55340-0). AMS Pr.

Brooks, Lloyd D. Practical Business Mathematics. 464p. 1984. text ed. 19.95 (ISBN 0-574-20725-2, 13-3725); write for info. tchr's ed. (ISBN 0-574-20728-7, 13-3728); write for info. wkbk. resource manual (ISBN 0-574-20729-5, 13-3729). SRA.

Budnick, Frank S. Applied Mathematics for Business, Economics & the Social Sciences. 2nd ed. 832p. 1983. 31.95 (ISBN 0-07-008858-6). McGraw.

Burton & Shelton. Business Math Using Calculators. 1986. text ed. price not set (ISBN 0-538-13880-7, M88). SW Pub.

Busche, Don & Locke, Flora. College Mathematics for Business. LC 83-6640. 632p. 1984. text ed. 24.95 (ISBN 0-471-08995-8); wbk., 182 pgs. 9.95 (ISBN 0-471-08997-4). Wiley.

Business Graphs & Statistics - What They Say & How to Use Them. pap. 10.00 (ISBN 0-686-02523-7). Preston.

Business Mathematics. 2nd ed. (Illus.). 400p. 1979. pap. 14.95x (ISBN 0-7121-0282-5, Pub. by Macdonald & Evans England). Trans-Atlantic.

Chao, Lincoln L. Statistics for Management. 2nd ed. (Illus.). 752p. 1983. text ed. 28.75 (ISBN 0-89426-039-1); study guide 10.00 (ISBN 0-89426-040-5); Solutions Manual avail. (ISBN 0-89426-041-3). Scientific Pr.

Chernow, Fred. Business Mathematics Simplified & Self-Taught. LC 82-1713. 144p. 1982. pap. 4.95 (ISBN 0-668-05390-9, 5390). Arco.

Childress, Robert L. Calculus for Business & Economics. 2nd ed. LC 77-2855. (Illus.). 1978. text ed. 27.95 (ISBN 0-13-111534-0). P-H.

--Mathematics for Managerial Decisions. LC 73-17352. (Illus.). 656p. 1974. ref. ed. 29.95 (ISBN 0-13-562231-X). P-H.

Clar, Lawrence M. & Hart, James A. Mathematics for Business & Consumers. (Illus.). 1980. text ed. write for info. (ISBN 0-02-322540-8). Macmillan.

Clark, John J. & Clark, Margaret T. A Statistics Primer for Managers: How to Ask the Right Questions About Forecasting, Control & Investment. (Illus.). 272p. 19.95 (ISBN 0-02-905800-7). Macmillan.

Cleaves, Cheryl S., et al. Mathematics of the Business World. LC 78-18635. (Illus.). 1979. pap. text ed. 19.95 (ISBN 0-201-02773-9); instr's. manual 3.50 (ISBN 0-201-02774-7). Addison-Wesley.

Corbman, Bernard P. & Krieger, Murray. Mathematics of Retail Merchandising. 2nd ed. 450p. 1972. cloth 37.95x (ISBN 0-471-06587-0, Pub. by Ronald Pr). Wiley.

--Mathematics of Retail Merchandising. 2nd ed. LC 85-5161. 420p. 1985. Repr. of 1972 ed. lib. bdg. 32.50 (ISBN 0-89874-846-1). Krieger.

Cote, Raymond. Business Math Concepts. 336p. 1984. 19.75x (ISBN 0-89702-047-2); solution manual 18.10 (ISBN 0-89702-047-2). PAR Inc.

Crowdis, David G., et al. Concepts of Calculus with Applications to Business & Economics. 1975. text ed. write for info. (ISBN 0-02-473010-6); tchrs' manual free (ISBN 0-02-473020-3). Macmillan.

Decoster, D. T., et al. Accounting for Managerial Decision Making. 2nd ed. LC 77-15785. (Wiley Series Accounting & Information Systems). 438p. 1978. text ed. 28.45 (ISBN 0-471-02204-7). Wiley.

Dietrich, Frank H., II & Shafer, Nancy J. Business Statistics. (Illus.). 815p. 1984. 24.95 (ISBN 0-02-329510-4). Dellen Pub.

Dillon, William. Business Mathematics. LC 84-16987. 320p. 1985. pap. text ed. 14.80 spiral-bound (ISBN 0-8273-2346-8); instr's. guide 9.80 (ISBN 0-8273-2347-6); business simulation 8.80 (ISBN 0-8273-2349-2). Delmar.

Doe, Maryann & Warlum, Michael. Business Mathematics: A Positive Approach. 1982. pap. text ed. 20.60x (ISBN 0-673-16011-4). Scott F.

Downing, Douglas & Clark, Jeff. Business Statistics. (Business Review Ser.). 288p. 1985. pap. 8.95 (ISBN 0-8120-3576-3). Barron.

Duenas. Curso Basico de Matematicas Comerciales. 172p. 1982. 5.60 (ISBN 0-07-017994-8). McGraw.

Dyckman, Thomas & Thomas, L. Joseph. Algebra & Calculus for Business. (Illus.). 464p. 1974. text ed. 29.95 (ISBN 0-13-021758-1). P-H.

Ellis, John T. & Beam, Victoria R. Mastering Real Estate Math in One Day. 1983. pap. 11.95 (ISBN 0-13-559666-1). P-H.

Eppen, Gary D. & Gould, F. J. Quantitative Concepts for Management: Decision-Making Without Algorithms. 2nd ed. (Illus.). 768p. 1985. text ed. 31.95 (ISBN 0-13-746637-4). P-H.

Erdsneker, Barbara. Office Guide to Business Mathematics. LC 83-15900. 224p. 1984. 4.95 (ISBN 0-668-05801-3). Arco.

Ernest, John & Ernest, Charlotte. Basic Business Mathematics. 1977. text ed. write for info. (ISBN 0-02-472610-9). Macmillan.

Fairbank & Schultheis. Applied Business Math. 1980. text ed. 12.55 (ISBN 0-538-13450-X, M45). SW Pub.

Fairbank, Roswell E. & Schutheis, Robert. Mathematics for the Consumer. 1980. text ed. 9.80 (ISBN 0-538-13150-0, M15). SW Pub.

Fairbank, Roswell E., et al. Applied Business Mathematics. 12th ed. 1985. 12.95 (ISBN 0-317-18598-5, M46). SW Pub.

Fairbanks & Schultheis. Consumer Math. 1983. text ed. 10.60 (ISBN 0-538-13160-8, M16). SW Pub.

Felton, James J. Business Mathematics: A Basic Course. 528p. 1984. pap. text ed. 23.95 (ISBN 0-8403-3416-8). Kendall Hunt.

Fletcher, A. & Clark, G. Management & Mathematics. (Illus.). 1972. 29.95x (ISBN 0-8464-0589-X). Beekman Pubs.

Fogiel, Max, intro. by. Problem Solver in Business, Management & Finance. rev. ed. LC 78-64582. (Illus.). 1984. pap. text ed. 19.85 (ISBN 0-87891-516-8). Res & Educ.

Fowler, F. Parker, Jr. Basic Mathematics for Administration. LC 83-94. 358p. 1983. Repr. of 1962 ed. text ed. 24.95 (ISBN 0-89874-613-2). Krieger.

Fred R. Weber Co. Real Estate Math Using the Pocket Calculator-Computer. 1979. pap. 13.95 (ISBN 0-8359-6554-6). Reston.

Freilich, Gerald & Greenleaf, Frederick P. Algebraic Methods: In Business, Economics, & the Social Sciences - a Short Course. (Mathematics Ser.). (Illus.). 311p. 1977. pap. text ed. 8.50 (ISBN 0-7167-0470-6). W H Freeman.

Smith, Karl J. Business Mathematics. 512p. 1982. text ed. 30.00 (ISBN 0-205-07622-X, 5676223); tchr's. ed. avail. (ISBN 0-205-07623-8, 5676231); test & answer manual avail. (ISBN 0-205-07783-8, 5677831). Allyn.
Snyder, Llewellyn R. & Jackson, William F. Essential Business Mathematics. 7th ed. (Illus.). 1979. text ed. 26.95 (ISBN 0-07-059567-4). McGraw.
Stull, William A. Marketing Math. 2nd ed. 1985. text ed. 6.10 wkbk. (ISBN 0-538-04270-2, D27). SW Pub.
Swindle, Robert E. Business Math Basics. 2nd ed. LC 82-20326. 368p. 1983. pap. text ed. write for info. (ISBN 0-534-01323-6); write for info. tchr's ed. Kent Pub Co.
Taylor, Donald H. Handbook of Mathematic & Statistical Techniques for Accountants. (Illus.). 1977. 37.95 (ISBN 0-13-380345-7, Busn). P-H.
Tedder, Jake D. Practical Applications of Business Mathematics. (Illus.). 1978. text ed. 23.95 (ISBN 0-87909-652-7). Reston.
Tennant-Smith, J. Mathematics for the Manager. 1971. 23.95x (ISBN 0-17-761010-7). Intl Ideas.
Tepper, Bette & Godnick, Newton E. Mathematics for Retail Buying. 2nd ed. (Illus.). 224p. 1973. pap. 12.50 (ISBN 0-87005-215-2); answer manual 3.00 (ISBN 0-87005-216-0). Fairchild.
Tilley, M. R. Business Maths & Statistics. (Illus.). 1978. pap. text ed. 17.95x (ISBN 0-7131-0152-0). Intl Ideas.
Tolman, Ruth. Applied Mathematics for Merchandising. 1982. pap. 8.90 (ISBN 0-87350-330-9). Milady.
Troxell, Mary D. Retail Merchandising Mathematics: Principles & Procedures. 1980. pap. text ed. 21.95 (ISBN 0-13-775205-9). P-H.
Tuttle, Michael D. Practical Business Math: A Performance Approach. 3rd ed. 528p. 1982. pap. text ed. write for info. (ISBN 0-697-08187-7); instrs.' ed. avail. (ISBN 0-697-08188-5). Wm C Brown.
Vanhon-Acker, Wilfried R., ed. Business Statistics. (Core Business Program Ser.). (Illus.). 128p. Date not set. pap. 7.95 (ISBN 0-87196-805-3). Facts on File.
Vazquez-Cruz, Ruperto. Elementos de Matematica Comercial. 2nd ed. LC 76-7932. 1976. 8.00 (ISBN 0-8477-2623-1). U of PR Pr.
Vazsonyi, Andrew & Brunell, Richard. Business Mathematics for Colleges. 3rd ed. 1984. pap. 18.95x (ISBN 0-256-02989-X). Irwin.
Ventolo, William L., Jr., et al. Mastering Real Estate Mathematics: A Self-Instructional Text. 4th ed. LC 84-6838. (Illus.). 368p. 1984. pap. text ed. 19.95 (ISBN 0-88462-504-4, 1512-10, Real Estate Ed). Longman USA.
Weber, Jean E. Mathematical Analysis: Business & Economic Applications. 4th ed. (Illus.). 719p. 1982. text ed. 26.50 scp (ISBN 0-06-046977-3, HarpC); solutions manual avail. (ISBN 0-06-367027-5). Har-Row.
Wheeler, Ruric E. & Peeples, W. D., Jr. Finite Mathematics: With Applications to Business & the Social Sciences. LC 80-13916. 550p. 1980. text ed. 24.00 pub net (ISBN 0-8185-0418-8). Brooks-Cole.
Williams, Walter E. & Reed, James H. Fundamentals of Business Mathematics. 3rd ed. 736p. 1984. text ed. write for info (ISBN 0-697-08069-2); instrs.' manual avail. (ISBN 0-697-08237-7); wkbk. avail. (ISBN 0-697-08282-2). Wm C Brown.
Wilson, Guy M. A Survey of the Social & Business Usage of Arithmetic. LC 74-177633. (Columbia University. Teachers College. Contributions to Education: No. 100). Repr. of 1919 ed. 17.50 (ISBN 0-404-55100-9). AMS Pr.
Wilton, W. B. A-Z of Business Mathematics. 192p. 1980. pap. 12.50 (ISBN 0-434-92260-9, Pub. by W. Heinemann Ltd). David & Charles.
Wolfe, Jo Ann. Fundamentals of Real Estate Mathematics. 105p. (Orig.). 1984. pap. text ed. 7.95x (ISBN 0-88133-107-4). Waveland Pr.
Wood, M. Basic Mathematics: Skills & Applications. 592p. 1983. text ed. 18.48 (ISBN 0-07-071601-3). McGraw.
Zameeruddin, Qazi, et al. Business Mathematics. 600p. 1980. text ed. 25.00x (ISBN 0-7069-0752-3, Pub. by Vikas India). Advent NY.

BUTADIYNE
see Acetylene

BUTCHER SHOPS
see Butchers

BUTCHERING
see Slaughtering and Slaughter-Houses

BUTCHERS
see also Meat Cutting

Rudman, Jack. Butcher. (Career Examination Ser.: C-1156). (Cloth bdg. avail. on request). lib. bdg. 10.00 (ISBN 0-8373-1156-X). Natl Learning.

BUTTER
see also Oleomargarine

Hobson, Phyllis. Making Homemade Cheeses & Butter. LC 73-89125. (Country Skills Library). (Illus.). 48p. 1973. pap. 2.95 (ISBN 0-88266-019-5). Garden Way Pub.
Pabst, W. R., Jr. Butter & Oleomargarine. LC 70-76644. (Columbia University. Studies in the Social Sciences: No. 427). Repr. of 1937 ed. 15.00 (ISBN 0-404-51427-8). AMS Pr.

BUTTERFLIES
see also Caterpillars

Ackery, P. R. & Vane-Wright, R. I. Milkweed Butterflies. LC 83-7334. (Illus.). 450p. 1984. 75.00x (ISBN 0-8014-1688-4). Cornell U Pr.
Acworth, Bernard. Bird & Butterfly Mysteries. 1956. 10.00 (ISBN 0-8022-0004-4). Philos Lib.
Albrecht, Carl W. & Watkins, Reed A. Cross-Reference to Names of Ohio Skippers & Butterflies: Insecta, Lepidoptera, Hesperoidea & Papilionoidea. 1983. 4.00 (ISBN 0-86727-095-0). Ohio Bio Survey.
Arnold, Richard A. Ecological Studies of Six Endangered Butterflies, (Lepidoptera, Lycaenidae) Island Biogeography, Patch Dynamics & the Design of Habitat Preserves. (University of California Publications in Entomology: Vol. 99). 1983. pap. 15.00x (ISBN 0-520-09671-1). U of Cal Pr.
Baynes, E. S. Catalogue of Irish Macrolepidoptera. rev. ed. 120p. 1973. Repr. of 1964 ed. 50.00x (ISBN 0-317-07050-9, Pub. by EW Classey UK). State Mutual Bk.
Brewer, Jo. Butterflies. LC 74-23357. (Illus.). 1976. pap. 12.95 (ISBN 0-8109-2064-6). Abrams.
Brown, F. Martin & Heinemann, Bernard. Jamaica & Its Butterflies. 492p. 1972. 99.00x (ISBN 0-317-07104-1, Pub. by EW Classey UK). State Mutual Bk.
Carter, David & Phillips, Roger, eds. Butterflies & Moths of Britain & Europe. (Illus.). 192p. (Orig.). 1982. pap. text ed. 14.95x (ISBN 0-916422-37-2, Pub. by Pan Bks England). Mad River.
Check List of the Lepidoptera of American North of Mexico. 1983. 150.00x (ISBN 0-317-07055-X, Pub. by EW Classey UK). State Mutual Bk.
Christensen, James R. Field Guide to the Butterflies of the Pacific Northwest. LC 80-52967. (GEM Bks. - Natural History). (Illus.). 200p. (Orig.). 1981. pap. 16.95. U Pr of Idaho.
Comstock, W. P. Butterflies of the American Tropics: The Genus Anaea(Nymphalidae) 227p. 1961. 125.00x (ISBN 0-317-07043-6, Pub. by EW Classey UK). State Mutual Bk.
Curtis, Nelson. Butterflies of Idaho & the Northern Rockies. LC 84-50760. (Northwest Naturalist Ser.). (Illus.). 472p. (Orig.). 1986. pap. 24.95 (ISBN 0-89301-102-9). U Pr of Idaho.
D'Abrera, Bernard. Butterflies of the Afro-Tropical Region. 613p. 1980. 295.00x (ISBN 0-317-07042-8, Pub. by EW Classey UK). State Mutual Bk.
--Butterflies of the Neotropical Region. 188p. 1981. 370.00x (ISBN 0-317-07048-7, Pub. by EW Classey UK). State Mutual Bk.
--Butterflies of the Oriental Region. 265p. 1982. 370.00x (ISBN 0-317-07049-5, Pub. by EW Classey UK). State Mutual Bk.
Dornfeld, Ernst. Butterflies of Oregon. LC 80-51936. 275p. 1980. 24.95 (ISBN 0-917304-58-6). Timber.
Eliot, J. N. & Kawazoe, A. Blue Butterflies of the Lycaenopsis-group. (Illus.). 300p. 1983. 56.00x (ISBN 0-565-00860-9, Pub. by Brit Mus Nat Hist England). Sabbot-Natural Hist Bks.
Emmel, Thomas C. & Emmel, John F. The Butterflies of Southern California. (Science Ser.: No. 26). (Illus.). 148p. 1973. 7.00 (ISBN 0-938644-06-8); 4.00 (ISBN 0-938644-05-X). Nat Hist Mus.
Ferris, Clifford D. & Brown, F. Martin, eds. Butterflies of the Rocky Mountain States. LC 80-22274. (Illus.). 400p. 1981. 39.50 (ISBN 0-8061-1552-1); pap. 17.95 (ISBN 0-8061-1733-8). U of Okla Pr.
A Field Guide to the Butterflies Coloring Book. (A Peterson Field Guide Ser.). 1984. pap. 3.95 (ISBN 0-395-34675-4). HM.
Grote, A. R. An Illustrated Essay of the Noctuidae of North America: With a "Colony of Butterflies". 85p. 1971. Repr. of 1882 ed. 45.00x (ISBN 0-317-07097-5, Pub. by EW Classey UK). State Mutual Bk.
Hafernik, John E., Jr. Phenetics & Ecology of Hybridization in Buckeye Butterflies (Lepidoptera, Nymphalidae) (University of California Publications in Entomology: Vol. 96). 221p. 1982. 18.50x (ISBN 0-520-09649-5). U of Cal Pr.
Hall, C. Margaret. Field Notes: & Butterflies Beget Butterflies. LC 77-74865. 1978. 5.00 (ISBN 0-87212-084-8). Libra.
Harris, Lucien, Jr. Butterflies of Georgia. LC 73-160493. (Illus.). 1972. pap. 8.95 (ISBN 0-8061-1295-6). U of Okla Pr.
Hemming, F. Annotationes Leipidopterologicae. 187p. 1960-1964. 60.00x (ISBN 0-317-07026-6, Pub. by EW Classey UK). State Mutual Bk.
Hemming, Francis. The Generic Names of the Butterflies & Their Type-Species: Lepidoptera-Rhopalocera. 509p. 1967. pap. text ed. 55.00x (ISBN 0-686-27406-7, Pub. by Brit Mus Nat Hist England). Sabbot-Natural Hist Bks.
Hewitson, W. C. Hewitson on Butterflies. 216p. 1972. Repr. of 1877 ed. 40.00x (ISBN 0-317-07095-9, Pub. by EW Classey UK). State Mutual Bk.
Howe, William H. The Butterflies of North America. 648p. 1976. 39.95 (ISBN 0-385-04926-9); Limited edition 150.00 (ISBN 0-385-11435-4). Doubleday.
Klots, Alexander B. A Field Guide to the Butterflies of North America, East of the Great Plains. (Peterson Field Guide Ser.). 1977. 15.95 (ISBN 0-395-07865-2); pap. 7.95 (ISBN 0-395-25859-6). HM.
Larsen, Torben & Larsen, Kiki. Butterflies of Oman. 80p. 1980. 35.00x (ISBN 0-317-07040-1, Pub. by EW Classey UK). State Mutual Bk.
Larsen, Torben B. Butterflies of Lebanon. 272p. 1974. 47.00x (ISBN 0-317-07039-8, Pub. by EW Classey UK). State Mutual Bk.
Lorimer, R. J. Lepidoptera of the Orkney Islands. 96p. 1983. 35.00x (ISBN 0-317-07106-8, Pub. by EW Classey UK). State Mutual Bk.
Moeck, Arthur H. Geographic Variability in Speyeria: Comments, Records & Description of a New Subspecies (Nymphalidae) LC 75-4525. (Illus.). 48p. 1975. pap. 3.50 (ISBN 0-911836-08-X). Entomological Repr.
Opler, Paul A. & Krizek, George O. Butterflies East of the Great Plains: An Illustrated Natural History. LC 83-6197. (Illus.). 312p. 1984. 49.50 (ISBN 0-8018-2938-0). Johns Hopkins.
Poey, P. Centurie de Leipodpteres De L'Ise de Cuda. 62p. 1971. Repr. of 1832 ed. 75.00x (ISBN 0-317-07052-5, Pub. by EW Classey UK). State Mutual Bk.
Pyle, Robert M. Watching Washington Butterflies. LC 73-94500. (Trailside Ser). (Illus.). 1974. pap. 4.95 (ISBN 0-914516-03-5). Seattle Audubon Soc.
Riley. A Field Guide to the Butterflies of the West Indies. 27.95 (ISBN 0-00-219282-9, Collins Pub England). Greene.
Robinson, G. S. Macrolepidoptera of Fiji & Rotuma. (A Taxonomic & Biogeographic Study). 374p. 1975. 65.00x (ISBN 0-317-07108-4, Pub. by EW Classey UK). State Mutual Bk.
Romanoff, N. M. Memoirs sur les Lepidopteres. 295.00x (ISBN 0-317-07110-6, Pub. by EW Classey UK). State Mutual Bk.
Rothschild, W. & Jordan, K. American Papilios. Rev. ed. 343p. 1967. Repr. of 1906 ed. 90.00x (ISBN 0-317-07024-X, Pub. by EW Classey UK). State Mutual Bk.
Russwurm, A. D. Aberrations of British Butterflies. 80.00x (ISBN 0-317-07023-1, Pub. by EW Classey UK). State Mutual Bk.
Sbordoni, Valerio & Forestiero, Saverio. Butterflies of the World. LC 84-40101. (Illus.). 288p. 1985. 39.95 (ISBN 0-8129-1128-8). Times Bks.
Scott, James A. The Butterflies of North America: A Natural History & Field Guide. LC 82-60737. (Illus.). 684p. 1986. 45.00x (ISBN 0-8047-1205-0). Stanford U Pr.
Seguy, E. A. Seguy's Decorative Butterflies & Insects in Full Color. LC 77-83361. (Illus., Orig.). 1977. pap. 6.00 (ISBN 0-486-23552-1). Dover.
--Seguy's Decorative Butterflies & Insects in Full Color. (Illus.). 13.25 (ISBN 0-8446-5812-X). Peter Smith.
Turner, Bryan, ed. Illustrated Encyclopedia of Butterflies & Moths. (Illus.). 352p. 1979. 8.50 (ISBN 0-7064-0547-1, Mayflower Bks). Smith Pubs.
Tyler, Hamilton A. Swallowtail Butterflies of North America. LC 75-30569. (Illus.). 192p. (Orig.). 1975. 14.95 (ISBN 0-87961-039-5); pap. 8.95 (ISBN 0-87961-038-7). Naturegraph.
Valletta, A. The Butterflies of the Maltese Islands. 64p. 1976. 40.00x (ISBN 0-317-07047-9, Pub. by EW Classey UK). State Mutual Bk.
Weed, Clarence M. An Introduction to the Art & Science of Collecting Butterflies. (Illus.). 1980. Repr. of 1917 ed. 41.75 (ISBN 0-89901-003-2). Found Class Reprints.

BUTTERFLIES–AFRICA

Carcasson. The Butterflies of Africa. 29.95 (ISBN 0-00-219783-9, Collins Pub England). Greene.
Carcasson, R. H. The Swallowtail Butterflies of East Africa. 1984. 30.00x (ISBN 0-317-07177-7, Pub. by FW Classey UK). State Mutual Bk.
D'Abrera, Bernard. Butterflies of the Afro-Tropical Region. 613p. 1980. 295.00x (ISBN 0-317-07042-8, Pub. by EW Classey UK). State Mutual Bk.

BUTTERFLIES–AUSTRALIA

Common, I. F. & Waterhouse, D. F. Butterflies of Australia. 682p. 1972. 75.00x (ISBN 0-207-14236-X, Pub. by Angus & Robertson). State Mutual Bk.

BUTTERFLIES–EUROPE

Dal, Bjorn. The Butterflies of Northern Europe. Morris, Michael, ed. Littleboy, Roger, tr. (Illus.). 128p. 1982. 13.00 (ISBN 0-7099-0810-5, Pub. by Croom Helm Ltd). Longwood Pub Group.
Heslop, T. R., et al. Notes & Views of the Purple Emperor. 260p. 1964. 35.00x (ISBN 0-317-07165-3, Pub. by FW Classey UK). State Mutual Bk.
Higgins & Riley. A Field Guide to the Butterflies of Britain & Europe. 29.95 (ISBN 0-00-219241-1, Collins Pub England). Greene.
Tweedie & Wilkinson. The Butterflies & Moths of Britain & Europe. pap. 8.95 (ISBN 0-00-219770-7, Collins Pub England). Greene.

BUTTERFLIES–GREAT BRITAIN

Bradley, J. D. & Fletcher, D. S. British Butterflies & Moths. 1980. 75.00x (ISBN 0-902068-08-3, Pub. by Curwen England). State Mutual Bk.
Brooks, Margaret & Knight, Charles. Complete Guide to British Butterflies. (Illus.). 168p. 1982. 24.95 (ISBN 0-224-01958-9, Pub. by Jonathan Cape). Merrimack Pub Cir.
Carter, David. Butterflies & Moths in Britain & Europe. (Illus.). 192p. 1982. 31.50 (ISBN 0-434-10965-7, Pub. by W Heinemann Ltd). David & Charles.
Carter, David & Phillips, Roger, eds. Butterflies & Moths of Britain & Europe. (Illus.). 192p. (Orig.). 1982. pap. text ed. 14.95x (ISBN 0-916422-37-2, Pub. by Pan Bks England). Mad River.
Dennis, R. L. The British Butterflies: Their Origin & Establishment. 60.00x (ISBN 0-317-07035-5, Pub. by EW Classey UK). State Mutual Bk.
Eliot, J. N. & Kawazoe, A. Blue Butterflies of the Lycaenopsis-group. (Illus.). 300p. 1983. 56.00x (ISBN 0-565-00860-9, Pub. by Brit Mus Nat Hist England). Sabbot-Natural Hist Bks.
The Genitalia of the British Lepidoptera Geometridae. 50.00x (ISBN 0-317-07072-X, Pub. by EW Classey UK). State Mutual Bk.
Goater, B. The Butterflies & Moths of Hampshire & the Isle of Wight. 453p. 1974. 35.00x (ISBN 0-317-07037-1, Pub. by EW Classey UK). State Mutual Bk.
Goodden, Robert. British Butterflies: A Field Guide. 13.50 (ISBN 0-7153-7594-6). David & Charles.
Heath, John, ed. The Moths & Butterflies of Great Britain & Ireland, Vol. 1. 343p. (Orig.). 1976. text ed. 39.95x (ISBN 0-632-00331-6). Entomological Repr.
Higgins & Riley. A Field Guide to the Butterflies of Britain & Europe. 29.95 (ISBN 0-00-219241-1, Collins Pub England). Greene.
Petiver, James. Papilionum Britanniae Icones. 1984. 50.00x (ISBN 0-317-07167-X, Pub. by FW Classey UK). State Mutual Bk.
Pierce, F. N., et al. The Genitalia of the British Lepidoptera Noctuidae(Females) wrappers 40.00x (ISBN 0-317-07074-6, Pub. by EW Classey UK). State Mutual Bk.
--The Genitalia of the British Lepidoptera Noctuidae(Males) 39.00x (ISBN 0-317-07079-7, Pub. by EW Classey UK). State Mutual Bk.
Thomson, George. The Butterflies of Scotland: A Natural History. (Illus.). 272p. 1980. 50.00 (ISBN 0-7099-0383-9, Pub. by Croom Helm Ltd). Longwood Pub Group.
Tweedie & Wilkinson. The Butterflies & Moths of Britain & Europe. pap. 8.95 (ISBN 0-00-219770-7, Collins Pub England). Greene.

BUTTERFLIES–MALAYA

Corbet & Pendlebury. Butterflies of the Malay Peninsular. 3rd, rev. ed. Eliot, J. N., rev. by. 90.00x (ISBN 0-317-07045-2, Pub. by EW Classey UK). State Mutual Bk.

BUTTERFLIES–NEW ZEALAND

Gibbs, George W. New Zealand Butterflies. (Illus.). 208p. 1983. 45.00 (ISBN 0-00-216955-X, Pub. by W Collins New Zealand). Intl Spec Bk.

BUTTERFLIES–SAUDI ARABIA

Larsen, Torben B. Butterflies of Saudi Arabia & Its Neighbours. 160p. 1984. 100.00 (ISBN 0-905743-36-9, Pub. by Stacey Intl Pubs UK). State Mutual Bk.

BUTTERFLY-SHELL ROOFS
see Roofs, Shell

BUZZ BOMB
see V-One Bomb

BWR
see Boiling Water Reactors

BY-PRODUCTS
see Waste Products

BYTEC HYPERION (COMPUTER)

Bulmer, James. Your Hyperion Companion. cancelled 15.95 (ISBN 0-318-01429-7). Brady Comm.
Goldstein, Larry J. Getting Started with Your Hyperion. cancelled 17.95 (ISBN 0-89303-487-8). Brady Comm.

C

C ALGEBRAS

Dixmier, J. C Algebras. (Mathematical Library Studies: 15). 492p. 1977. 68.00 (ISBN 0-7204-0762-1, North-Holland). Elsevier.

Douglas, Ronald G. C-Algebra Extensions & K-Homology. LC 80-424. (Annals of Mathematics Studies: No. 95). (Illus.). 87p. 1980. 16.50x (ISBN 0-691-08265-0); pap. 7.95x (ISBN 0-691-08266-9). Princeton U Pr.

Dupre, M. J. The Classification & Structure of C-Algebra Bundles. LC 79-17975. (Memoirs Ser.: No. 222). 77p. 1979. pap. 10.00 (ISBN 0-8218-2222-5). Am Math.

Dupre, M. J. & Gillette, R. M. Banach Bundles: Banach Modules & Automorphisms of C-Algebras. (Research Notes in Mathematics: No. 92). 120p. 1983. pap. text ed. 16.95 (ISBN 0-273-08626-X). Pitman Pub MA.

Effros, E. G. & Hahn, Frank. Locally Compact Transformation Groups & C-Algebras. LC 52-42839. (Memoirs: No. 75). 93p. 1967. pap. 9.00 (ISBN 0-8218-1275-0, MEMO-75). Am Math.

Evans, Bruce D. C-Bundles & Compact Transformation Groups. LC 82-11544. (Memoirs of the American Mathematical Society Ser.: No. 269). 63p. 1982. pap. 9.00 (ISBN 0-8218-2269-1, MEMO/269). Am Math.

Goodearl, K. R. Notes on Real & Complex C-Algebras. 180p. 1982. 60.00x (ISBN 0-906812-16-X, Pub. by Shiva Pub England); pap. 40.00x (ISBN 0-906812-15-1). State Mutual Bk.

Goodearl, K. R., ed. Notes on Real & Complex C-Algebra. (Shiva Mathematics Ser.: 5). 180p. 1982. text ed. 28.95x (ISBN 0-906812-16-X). Birkhauser.

Hofmann, K. H. Duality of Compact Semigroups & C-Bigebras. LC 69-15931. (Lecture Notes in Mathematics: Vol. 129). 1970. pap. 10.70 (ISBN 0-387-04918-5). Springer-Verlag.

Hofmann, K. H. & Luikkonen, J., eds. Recent Advances in the Representation Theory of Rings & C-Algebras by Continuous Sections. LC 74-11237. (Memoirs: No. 148). 182p. 1974. pap. 12.00 (ISBN 0-8218-1848-1, MEMO-148). Am Math.

Pedersen, G. K. C-Algebras & Their Automorphism Groups. 1979. 80.00 (ISBN 0-12-549450-5). Acad Pr.

Sakai, S. C-Algebras & W-Algebras. LC 75-149121. (Ergebnisse der Mathematik und Ihrer Grenzgehiete: Vol. 60). 1971. 42.00 (ISBN 0-387-05347-6). Springer-Verlag.

C (COMPUTER PROGRAM LANGUAGE)

AT&T Technology Systems. The C Programmer's Handbook. 88p. 1985. pap. 14.95 (ISBN 0-13-110073-4). P-H.

Beam, Emmett. The Illustrated C Programming Book. Berliner, Thomas H., ed. LC 85-659. (Illus.). 240p. 1985. pap. 19.95 (ISBN 0-915381-65-6). WordWare Pub.

Berry, R. E. & Meekings, B. A. A Book on C. (Computer Science Ser.). (Illus.). 210p. (Orig.). 1984. pap. text ed. 22.50x (ISBN 0-333-36821-5). Scholium Intl.

Brand, Kim. Common C Functions. LC 84-61392. 292p. 1985. 17.95 (ISBN 0-88022-069-4, 148); disk 49.95. Que Corp.

Brown, Douglas. From Pascal to C: An Introduction to the C Programming Language. 176p. 1985. write for info. (ISBN 0-534-04602-9). Wadsworth Pub.

Chirlian, Paul M. Introduction to C. 300p. 1984. pap. 16.95 (ISBN 0-916460-37-1). Dilithium Pr.

Costales, Bryan. C: From A to Z. 244p. 1985. 21.95 (ISBN 0-13-110057-2); pap. 14.95 (ISBN 0-13-110040-8). P H.

Dahl, Bonnie. The Loran-C Users Guide. (Illus.). 220p. 1985. pap. 19.95 (ISBN 0-932647-00-6, 011-003). Richardsons Marine.

Feuer, Alan & Gehani, Narain. Comparing & Assessing Programming Languages: Ada, C & Pascal. (Software Ser.). (Illus.). 256p. 1984. text ed. 18.95; pap. text ed. write for info. (ISBN 0-13-154840-9). P-H.

Feuer, Alan R. The C Puzzle Book. (Illus.). 192p. 1982. text ed. 18.95 (ISBN 0-13-109934-5); pap. text ed. 14.95 (ISBN 0-13-109926-4). P-H.

Franz, Martin & Good, Phillip I. Writing Business Programs in C Language. LC 84-45695. 200p. (Orig.). 1985. spiral incl. disk o.p. 59.95 (ISBN 0-8019-7612-X); pap. 16.95 (ISBN 0-8019-7611-1). Chilton.

Gainsborough, John A. Personal Computing & C. 200p. 1985. pap. 19.95 (ISBN 0-912677-45-7). Ashton-Tate Bks.

Gehani, Narain. Advanced C: Food for the Educated Palate. LC 84-19851. 313p. 1984. pap. 19.95 (ISBN 0-88175-078-6). Computer Sci.

--C: An Advanced Introduction. LC 84-12145. 1984. text ed. 29.95 (ISBN 0-88175-053-0). Computer Sci.

Good, Phillip I. Increasing Your Business Effectiveness Through Computer Communications: PC Plus C Equals Productivity. LC 84-45691. 190p. (Orig.). 1985. pap. 17.95 (ISBN 0-8019-7559-X). Chilton.

Harbison, Samuel P. & Steele, Guy L., Jr. C: A Reference Manual. (Prentice-Hall Software Ser.). 272p. 1984. text ed. 24.95 (ISBN 0-13-110016-5); pap. text ed. 19.95 (ISBN 0-13-110008-4). P-H.

Hogan, Thom. The C Programmer's Handbook. 288p. 1984. pap. 19.95 (ISBN 0-89303-365-0). Brady Comm.

Hunter, Bruce H. Fifty C Programs. 200p. 1984. pap. cancelled (ISBN 0-89588-155-1). SYBEX.

--Understanding C. LC 83-51569. (Illus.). 352p. 1984. pap. 17.95 (ISBN 0-89588-123-3). SYBEX.

Kelley, Al & Pohl, Ira. A Book on C: An Introduction to Programming in C. (Illus.). 384p. 1984. pap. text ed. 29.95 (ISBN 0-8053-6860-4, 36860). Benjamin-Cummings.

Kernighan, Brian W. & Ritchie, Dennis M. The C Programming Language. LC 77-28983. (Software Ser.). 1978. pap. 22.50 ref. ed. (ISBN 0-13-110163-3). P-H.

--The C Programming Language: Convergent Technologies Edition. 240p. 1984. shrinkwrap 13.42 (ISBN 0-13-109984-1). P-H.

--The C Programming Language, Digital Equipment Coporation Edition. 240p. 1983. pap. 19.95 (ISBN 0-13-109950-7). P-H.

Kochan. Introduction to C Programming. 1984. 18.95 (ISBN 0-317-02384-5, 6261). Hayden.

Kochan, Stephen G. Programming in C. 384p. pap. 18.95 (6261). Hayden.

McNitt, Lawrence. Invitation to "C" Programming Language. (Illus.). 1985. text ed. 29.95 (ISBN 0-89433-280-5). Petrocelli.

--Invitation to "C" Programming Language. (Illus.). 300p. 1985. 29.95 (ISBN 0-89433-280-5). Van Nos Reinhold.

Miller. C Programming Language. 1985. pap. write for info. (ISBN 0-471-82560-3). Wiley.

Plum, Thomas. Learning to Program in C. (Illus.). 372p. (Orig.). 1983. pap. text ed. 25.00x (ISBN 0-911537-00-7). Plum Hall.

--Learning to Program in C. (Illus.). 368p. 1983. text ed. 32.95 (ISBN 0-13-527854-6); 25.00 (ISBN 0-13-527847-3). P-H.

--Reliable Data Structures in C. 200p. 1985. pap. text ed. 25.00x (ISBN 0-911537-04-X). Plum Hall.

Plum, Thomas & Brodie, Jim. Efficient C. 165p. 1985. pap. text ed. 25.00x (ISBN 0-911537-05-8). Plum Hall.

Pugh, Kenneth. C Language for Programmers. 1985. pap. 17.95 (ISBN 0-673-18034-4). Scott F.

Purdum, Jack. C Programming Guide. 2nd ed. LC 85-60689. 250p. 1985. pap. 19.95 (ISBN 0-88022-157-7, 188). Que Corp.

--C Self-Study Guide. LC 84-62752. 250p. 1985. pap. 16.95 (ISBN 0-88022-149-6, 176). Que Corp.

Purdum, Jack, et al. C Programmer's Library. 365p. 1984. pap. 19.95 (ISBN 0-88022-048-1, 45); disk 124.95 ea. IBM-PC format (270). Disk (271). Que Corp.

Schildt, Herbert. C Made Easy. 350p. (Orig.). 1985. pap. 18.95 (ISBN 0-07-881178-3, 178-3). Osborne-McGraw.

Schustack, Steve. Variations in C: Professional Programming Techniques for Developing Efficient Business Applications. 368p. 1985. pap. 19.95 (ISBN 0-914845-48-9). Microsoft.

Schwaderer. Master Programmers Reference Guide for C Programming Language. 1985. pap. price not set (ISBN 0-471-82641-3). Wiley.

Shrum, Carlton. Understanding C. 1984. pap. 3.50 (ISBN 0-88284-300-1). Alfred Pub.

Sidebottom, Thomas O. & Wortman, Leon. The C Programming Tutor. LC 83-21436. 288p. 1984. pap. 19.95 (ISBN 0-89303-364-2). Brady Comm.

Sobelman, Gerald E. & Krekelberg, David E. Advanced C: Techniques & Applications. LC 85-60694. 350p. 1985. pap. 19.95 (ISBN 0-88022-162-3, 179). Que Corp.

Stanley, Charles A. The C Language for Beginners. Dahl, Deanna & Colson, Elise, eds. 188p. (Orig.). 1985. pap. 20.00 (ISBN 0-9614857-0-1). Pressure Appli.

Stewart, Warren A. Surefire Programming in C. LC 84-26898. (Illus.). 288p. (Orig.). 1985. 21.95 (ISBN 0-8306-0873-7, 1873); pap. 16.95 (ISBN 0-8306-1873-2). TAB Bks.

Tondo, Clovis L. & Gimpel, Scott E. The C Answer Book. 224p. 1985. pap. text ed. 12.95 (ISBN 0-13-109877-2). P-H.

Traister, Robert J., Sr. Programming in C: For the Microcomputer. (Illus.). 176p. 1984. pap. 16.95 (ISBN 0-13-729641-X). P-H.

Troy, Doug. C Programming on the IBM PC. (Microcomputer Bookshelf Ser.). 350p. (Orig.). 1985. pap. 17.95 (ISBN 0-317-18225-0). Little.

Troy, Douglas A. C Language Programming on the IBM PC. (Microcomputer Bookshelf Ser.). 1985. pap. 17.95 (ISBN 0-316-85311-9). Little.

Waite, et al. C Primer Plus. LC 84-50060. 536p. 1984. pap. 19.95 (ISBN 0-672-22090-3, 22090). Sams.

Waite Group & Berry, John. Advanced C Programming. (Illus.). 320p. 1985. pap. 21.95 (ISBN 0-89303-473-8). Brady Comm.

Waldram, J. R. The Theory of Thermodynamics. (Illus.). 1985. 59.50 (ISBN 0-521-24575-3); pap. 24.95 (ISBN 0-521-28796-0). Cambridge U Pr.

Ward, Terry A. Applied Programming Techniques in C. 368p. 1985. pap. 19.95 (ISBN 0-673-18050-6). Scott F.

--Programming C on the Macintosh. 1985. pap. 19.95 (ISBN 0-673-18274-6). Scott F.

Weber Systems Staff. C Language User's Handbook. 336p. (Orig.). 1985. pap. 14.95 (ISBN 0-345-31998-2). Ballantine.

Wortman, Leon A. & Sidebottom, Thomas O. Business Programs in C. 200p. (Orig.). 1984. pap. cancelled (ISBN 0-89588-153-5). SYBEX.

Zahn, C. T. C Notes: A Guide to the C Programming Language. LC 78-63290. 112p. (Orig.). 1979. pap. 20.00 (ISBN 0-917072-13-8). Yourdon.

CABINET-WORK

see also Furniture Making; Veneers and Veneering; Woodwork

Blackie And Son. Victorian Cabinet-Maker's Assistant. (Illus.). 1970. pap. 10.00 (ISBN 0-486-22353-1). Dover.

Brann, Donald R. How to Build Bookcases & Stereo Cabinets. LC 79-56769. (Illus.). 194p. 1980. pap. 6.95 (ISBN 0-87733-804-3). Easi-Bild.

--How to Build Kitchen Cabinets, Room Dividers & Cabinet Furniture. rev. ed. LC 65-27708. 1978. lib. bdg. 5.95 (ISBN 0-87733-058-1); pap. 3.50 (ISBN 0-87733-658-X). Easi-Bild.

Burch, Monte. The Home Cabinetmaker: Woodworking Techniques, Furniture Building, & Installing Millwork. LC 79-4747. (A Popular Science Bk.). (Illus.). 640p. 1981. 26.83i (ISBN 0-06-014826-8, HarpT). Har-Row.

Calhoun, Ken. Cabinetmaking. (Illus.). 304p. 1984. 23.95 (ISBN 0-13-110064-5). P-H.

Cary, Jere. Building Your Own Kitchen Cabinets. LC 82-51260. (Illus.). 152p. 1983. pap. 11.95 (ISBN 0-918804-15-9, Dist. by W W Norton). Taunton.

Dahl, Alf A. & Wilson, J. Douglas. Cabinetmaking & Millwork: Tools, Materials, Layout. LC 53-11586. (Books of the Building Trade). pap. 89.80 (ISBN 0-317-09679-6, 2006111). Bks Demand UMI.

Demske, Dick. Carpentry & Woodworking. Roundtable Press, ed. LC 83-15094. (Illus.). 160p. (Orig.). 1983. 17.95 (ISBN 0-932944-63-9); pap. 6.95 (ISBN 0-932944-62-0). Creative Homeowner.

Feirer, John. Cabinetmaking & Millwork. 1982. text ed. 29.28 (ISBN 0-02-662760-4); student guide 6.64 (ISBN 0-02-662740-X); tchr's. guide 3.72 (ISBN 0-02-662770-1). Bennett IL.

--Furniture & Cabinet Making. 1983. text ed. 17.76 (ISBN 0-02-664050-3). Bennett Il.

Feirer, John L. Cabinetmaking & Millwork. 2nd, rev. ed. (Illus.). 1983. 42.50 (ISBN 0-684-17941-5, ScribT). Scribner.

--Furniture & Cabinet Making. (Illus.). 512p. 1983. pap. 19.95 (ISBN 0-684-17965-2, ScribT). Scribner.

Haynie, Paul J. Cabinetmaking. (Illus.). 272p. 1976. 23.95 (ISBN 0-13-110239-7). P-H.

Hayward, Charles H. Cabinet Making for Beginners. rev. ed. LC 78-24432. (Illus.). 218p. 1980. pap. 7.95 (ISBN 0-8069-8186-5). Sterling.

Hepplewhite, George. Cabinet-Maker & Upholsterer's Guide. 3rd ed. (Illus.). 1794. 15.25 (ISBN 0-8446-0693-6). Peter Smith.

Hopkinson, James. Victorian Cabinet Maker: The Memoirs of James Hopkinson, 1819-1894. Goodman, Jocelyne B., ed. LC 69-17113. (Illus.). 1969. 22.50x (ISBN 0-678-06526-8). Kelley.

Jenkins, Irving. Hawaiian Furniture & Hawaii's Cabinetmakers 1820-1940. LC 83-72242. (Illus.). 364p. 1983. 50.00 (ISBN 0-9607938-4-4); deluxe 100.00 (ISBN 0-9607938-5-2). Editions Ltd.

Jones, Peter. Start-to-Finish Cabinetmaking. 1980. pap. 9.95 (ISBN 0-8359-7062-0). Reston.

Lewis, Gaspar. Cabinetmaking, Patternmaking & Millwork. LC 79-50917. (Carpentry-Cabinetmaking Ser.). 438p. 1981. text ed. 19.00 (ISBN 0-8273-1814-6); instructor's guide 5.25 (ISBN 0-8273-1815-4). Delmar.

Moody, John A. American Cabinetmaker's Plane, Its Design & Development: 1700-1900. LC 81-67720. (Illus.). 250p. 1981. 34.50 (ISBN 0-9606548-0-1). Toolbox.

Peters, Alan. Cabinetmaking: The Professional Approach. (Illus.). 192p. 1985. 23.95 (ISBN 0-684-18520-2, ScribT). Scribner.

Philbin, Tom. Cabinets, Bookcases & Closets. Horowitz, Shirley M., ed. LC 80-69620. (Illus.). 160p. (Orig.). 1980. 19.95 (ISBN 0-932944-21-3); pap. 6.95 (ISBN 0-932944-22-1). Creative Homeowner.

Rowland, Amy Z. Handcrafted Shelves & Cabinets. Hilton, William, ed. (Illus.). 224p. 1984. 21.95 (ISBN 0-87857-481-6, 14-173-0); pap. 12.95 (ISBN 0-87857-482-4, 14-173-1). Rodale Pr Inc.

Scherer, George W. Designing, Building, & Installing Custom Cabinets for the Home. (Illus.). 384p. 1986. text ed. 29.95 (ISBN 0-13-200627-8). P-H.

Shelf Display Pack of Project Plan Book. 1984. 71.10 (ISBN 0-938708-10-4). L F Garlinghouse Co.

Sheraton, Thomas. The Cabinet-Maker & Upholsterer's Drawing Book. (Illus.). 18.00 (ISBN 0-8446-4637-7). Peter Smith.

Siegele, H. H. Cabinets & Built-Ins. LC 80-52589. (Home Craftsman Bk.). (Illus.). 104p. 1980. pap. 6.95 (ISBN 0-8069-8188-1). Sterling.

Sunset Editors. Bookshelves & Cabinets. LC 74-76541. (Illus.). 96p. (Orig.). 1974. pap. 5.95 (ISBN 0-376-01085-1, Sunset Bks). Sunset-Lane.

CABINET-WORKERS

Bjerkoe, Ethel H. Cabinetmakers of America. 2nd ed. LC 57-7278. (Illus.). 272p. 1978. 22.50 (ISBN 0-916838-14-5). Schiffer.

Burton, E. Milby. Charleston Furniture, Seventeen Hundred to Eighteen Twenty-Five. 2nd ed. LC 73-120917. Orig. Title: Contributions from the Charleston Museum: XII. (Illus.). xii, 200p. 1970. lib. bdg. 19.95 (ISBN 0-87249-198-6). U of SC Pr.

Chippendale, Thomas. Gentleman & Cabinet-Maker's Director. 3rd ed. (Illus.). 1966. pap. 8.95 (ISBN 0-486-21601-2). Dover.

--Gentleman & Cabinet-Makers Director. 3rd ed. (Illus.). 18.00 (ISBN 0-8446-1856-X). Peter Smith.

Connaissance des Arts Editors. Les Ebenistes du Huitieme Siecle Francais. Tr. of French Cabinetmakers of the Eighteenth Century. (Fr. & Eng., Illus., Avail. in Fr. & Eng. eds.). 75.00 (ISBN 0-685-11206-3). French & Eur.

Morningstar, Connie. Early Utah Furniture. LC 76-29637. (Illus.). 93p. 1976. 9.95 (ISBN 0-87421-088-7). Utah St U Pr.

Morse, John D., ed. Country Cabinetwork & Simple City Furniture. LC 77-114194. (Winterthur Conference Report 1969). (Illus.). 311p. 1970. 4.50 (ISBN 0-8139-0298-3, Pub. by Winterthur Museum). U Pr of Va.

CABLE RAILROADS

see Railroads, Cable

CABLE TELEVISION

see also Television Relay Systems

Babe, R. E. Cable Television & Telecommunications in Canada: An Economic Analysis. LC 75-620061. 338p. 1975. pap. 7.50 (ISBN 0-87744-129-4). Mich St U Pr.

Bretz, Rudy. Handbook for Producing Educational & Public-Access Programs for Cable Television. LC 75-44365. 160p. 1976. pap. 24.95 (ISBN 0-87778-089-7). Educ Tech Pubns.

Cable '83: International Conferences & Exhibtion on Satellite & Cable TV London - May 10-12, 1983. 400p. (Orig.). 1983. pap. text ed. 171.00x (ISBN 0-903796-96-1, Pub. by Online Conferences England). Brookfield Pub Co.

Cable '84: Proceedings of the Second European Conference on Satellite & Cable TV, London, July 1984. 373p. 1984. pap. text ed. 150.00x (ISBN 0-86353-011-7, Pub. by Online). Brookfield Pub Co.

CATV: End of a Dream. 1974. 2.00, institutions 5.00 (ISBN 0-686-09556-1). Network Project.

Chin, Felix. Cable Television: A Comprehensive Bibliography. LC 78-1526. 300p. 1978. 85.00x (ISBN 0-306-65172-6, Plenum Pr). Plenum Pub.

Crossed Wires (Cable TV) 100p. 1982. 12.50 (ISBN 0-686-81764-8). Ctr Analysis Public Issues.

Cunningham, John E. Cable Television. 2nd ed. LC 80-52937. 392p. 1980. pap. 13.95 (ISBN 0-672-21755-4). Sams.

Eastman, Susan Tyler & Klein, Robert. Strategies in Broadcast & Cable Promotion: Commercial Television, Radio, Cable, Pay Television, Public Television. 352p. 1982. pap. text ed. write for info. (ISBN 0-534-01156-X). Wadsworth Pub.

Glim, Jo Ann, ed. Lights! Camera! Action, Vol. 2. (How to Make Cable TV Work for You). 1985. write for info. (ISBN 0-9609790-1-8). Direct Market.

Harrell, Bobby. Cable Television Technology Handbook. 1985. text ed. 55.00 (ISBN 0-89006-157-2). Artech Hse.

Hollowell, Mary L., ed. Cable Broadband Communications Book, 1980-1981, Vol. 2. (Cable Broadband Communications Book Ser.). (Orig.). 1980. pap. 19.50x (ISBN 0-89461-031-7). Comm Pr Inc.

Horn, Frank W. Cable, Inside & Out, Vol. V. 1978. 7.95 (ISBN 0-686-98061-1). Telecom Lib.

Jacobs, Bruce D., et al. Own Your Own Cable System. 41p. 1983. 19.50 (ISBN 0-918943-00-0). Natl Con Coopera Bank.

Jeffers, Michael, ed. NCTA Recommended Practices for Measurements on Cable Television Systems. (Illus.). 200p. (Orig.). 1983. lab manual 40.00 (ISBN 0-940272-09-1). Natl Cable.

Kaatz, Ron. Cable: An Advertiser's Guide. LC 82-72511. 160p. 1982. pap. 15.95 (ISBN 0-87251-076-X). Crain Bks.

Kaatz, Ronald B. Cable: An Advertiser's Guide to the New Electronic Media. 2nd ed. LC 84-72915. 176p. 1985. pap. 15.95 (ISBN 0-87251-096-4). Crain Bks.

Mayer, Mary P. CATV: A History of Community Antenna Television. viii, 209p. 1972. 13.95 (ISBN 0-8101-0366-4). Northwestern U Pr.

Maynard, Jeff. Cable Television. (Illus.). 220p. 1985. pap. text ed. 27.50x (ISBN 0-00-383016-0, Pub. by Collins England). Sheridan.

Negrine, Ralph, ed. Cable Television & the Future of Broadcasting. 240p. 1985. 27.50 (ISBN 0-312-11318-8). St Martin.

Phillips Publishing Inc. Staff. The Interactive Cable TV Handbook. 4th ed. 360p. 1984. 147.00 (ISBN 0-317-27783-9). Knowledge Indus.

Regulating Cable Television Subscriber Rates. 57p. 1977. 15.00. Cable TV Info Ctr.

Rutkowski, Katherine, ed. Cable Delivers. (Technical Papers). (Illus.). 210p. (Orig.). 1982. pap. 10.00 (ISBN 0-940272-05-9). Natl Cable.

--Cable, Nineteen Eighty-One: The Future of Communications. (Technical Papers). (Illus.). 151p. (Orig.). 1981. 10.00 (ISBN 0-940272-01-6). Natl Cable.

Schreff, David J. How to Build a Career in Cable TV. 200p. (Orig.). 1983. pap. 9.95 (ISBN 0-911675-01-9). Skybridge Pub Inc.

Scott, James D. Cable Television: Strategy for Penetrating Key Urban Markets. LC 76-367151. (Michigan Business Reports Ser.: No. 58). pap. 36.00 (ISBN 0-317-28862-8, 2022081). Bks Demand UMI.

Seiden, Martin H. Cable Television U. S. A. An Analysis of Government Policy. LC 72-76453. (Special Studies in U. S. Economic, Social, & Political Issues). 1972. 39.50x (ISBN 0-275-28634-7). Irvington.

Selecting a Cable System Operator. 74p. 1975. 10.00. Cable TV Info Ctr.

Technical Standards & Specifications. 71p. 1973. 8.00. Cable TV Info Ctr.

Technological & Local Changes Which May Affect the CATV Industry. 50.00 (ISBN 0-686-32982-1). Info Gatekeepers.

Television Digest's Cable & Station Coverage Atlas. rev. ed. LC 67-118025. 1981-82. 115.50 (ISBN 0-911486-05-4). TV Factbk.

Television Digest's Cable & Station Coverage Atlas, 1983. rev. ed. 1983. 121.00 (ISBN 0-911486-09-7). TV Factbk.

Weinstein, S. B. Cable Television & Its Competitors. 150p. 1985. write for info. (ISBN 0-87942-197-5, PC-01891). Inst Electrical.

CABLES, ELECTRIC

see Cables, Submarine; Electric Cables; Telephone Cables

CABLES, SUBMARINE

Bright, Charles. Submarine Telegraphs: Their History, Construction & Working. LC 74-4669. (Telecommunications Ser). (Illus.). 744p. 1974. Repr. of 1898 ed. 57.50x (ISBN 0-405-06035-1). Ayer Co Pubs.

Field, Henry M. History of the Atlantic Telegraph. LC 76-38351. (Select Bibliographies Reprint Ser.). Repr. of 1866 ed. 21.00 (ISBN 0-8369-6768-2). Ayer Co Pubs.

Finn, Bernard & Sterling, Christopher, eds. Development of Submarine Cable Communications: An Original Anthology, 2 vols. LC 80-482. (Historical Studies in Telecommunications Ser.). (Illus.). 1980. Set. lib. bdg. 71.50x (ISBN 0-405-13192-5). Ayer Co Pubs.

Smith, Willouby. The Rise & Extension of Submarine Telegraphy. LC 74-4695. (Telecommunications Ser). (Illus.). 410p. 1974. Repr. of 1891 ed. 32.00x (ISBN 0-405-06058-0). Ayer Co Pubs.

CACAO

Here are entered works on the cacao tree and its culture only. Works dealing with the commercial product are entered under Chocolate and Cocoa.

Maclaren, W. A. Rubber, Tea & Cacao with Special Sections on Coffee, Spices & Tobacco. 1980. lib. bdg. 75.00 (ISBN 0-8490-3110-9). Gordon Pr.

Nigerian Cocoa Marketing Board, et al. Nigerian Cocoa Farmers. LC 70-142920. (Illus.). xxxix, 744p. Repr. of 1956 ed. lib. bdg. cancelled (ISBN 0-8371-5946-6, NCF&). Greenwood.

CACTUS

Andersohn, Gunter. Cacti & Succulents. (Illus.). 316p. 1983. 19.95 (ISBN 0-7158-0839-7, Pub by EP Publishing England). Sterling.

Anderson, Edward F. Peyote: The Divine Cactus. LC 79-20173. 248p. 1980. pap. 9.95 (ISBN 0-8165-0613-2). U of Ariz Pr.

Benson, Lyman. The Cacti of Arizona. 3rd ed. LC 70-77802. (Illus.). 218p. 1969. pap. 12.50 (ISBN 0-8165-0509-8). U of Ariz Pr.

--The Cacti of the United States & Canada. LC 73-80617. (Illus.). 1104p. 1982. 95.00x (ISBN 0-8047-0863-0). Stanford U Pr.

--The Native Cacti of California. LC 69-13176. (Illus.). 1969. 12.95 (ISBN 0-8047-0696-4). Stanford U Pr.

Britton, Nathaniel L. & Rose, J. N. Cactaceae: Descriptions & Illustrations of Plants of the Cactus Family, 4 Vols in 2. 2nd ed. (Illus.). 1937. 25.00 ea.; Vol. 1. (ISBN 0-486-21191-6); Vol. 2. (ISBN 0-486-21192-4). Dover.

Cabat, Erni. Arizona Cacti & Succulents, Bk. 2. 32p. Date not set. price not set (ISBN 0-913521-04-3). Cabat Studio Pubns.

Chapman, Peter & Martin, Margaret. An Illustrated Guide to Cacti & Succulents. LC 83-83423. (Illustrated Gardening Guides Ser.). (Illus.). 160p. 1984. 9.95 (ISBN 0-668-06194-4, 6194-4). Arco.

Chidamian, Claude. The Book of Cacti & Other Succulents. (Illus.). 260p. 1984. pap. 13.95 (ISBN 0-917304-90-X). Timber.

Craig, Robert T. The Mammillaria Handbook. (Illus.). 1945. 30.00 (ISBN 0-384-10090-2). Johnson Repr.

Dawson, E. Yale. Cacti of California. (California Natural History Guides: No. 18). (Illus.). 1966. pap. 3.95 (ISBN 0-520-00299-7). U of Cal Pr.

Earle, W. Hubert. Cacti of the Southwest. (Illus.). 210p. 1982. 17.50 (ISBN 0-935810-05-6); pap. 11.00. Primer Pubs.

Gick, James E. Cactus & Succulents from Mother Nature. (Illus.). 1977. pap. 2.50 (ISBN 0-918170-27-3, HP-503, Future Crafts Today). Gick.

Glass, Charles & Foster, Robert. Cacti & Succulents for the Amateur. (Illus.). 72p. 1980. pap. 4.95 (ISBN 0-7137-0834-4, Pub. by Blandford Pr England). Sterling.

Haage, Walther. Cacti from A to Z. cancelled (ISBN 0-8165-0819-4). U of Ariz Pr.

Haines, Ben M. Handbook of Cold Climate Cacti & Succulents: Plants That Can Take 20 to 40 Degrees Below Zero. rev. ed. LC 72-80198. (Illus.). 65p. 1977. pap. 5.50 (ISBN 0-9600586-1-3). B Haines.

Higgins, Vera. Cactus Growing for Beginners. (Illus.). 1964. 4.95 (ISBN 0-7137-0128-5, Pub by Blandford Pr England). Sterling.

Lamb, Edgar & Lamb, Brian. The Illustrated Reference on Cacti & Other Succulents in 5 Volumes. Incl. Vol. 1. 1955 (ISBN 0-7137-0681-3); Vol. 2. 1959 (ISBN 0-7137-0623-6); Vol. 3. 1965; Vol. 4. 1966 (ISBN 0-7137-0691-0). (Illus.). 20.95 ea. (Pub. by Blandford Pr England). Sterling.

--Illustrated Reference on Cacti & Succulents, Vol. 5. (Illus.). 1978. 20.95 (ISBN 0-7137-0852-2, Pub. by Blandford Pr England). Sterling.

Lamb, Edgar & Lamp, Brian. Pocket Encyclopedia of Cacti in Color. (Illus.). 217p. 1980. 9.95 (ISBN 0-7137-1197-3, Pub. by Blandford Pr England). Sterling.

Lawson, Harry C. Book of Cacti. (Illus.). 1969. pap. 2.00 (ISBN 0-685-09268-2). Educator Bks.

Pilbeam, John. Sulcorebutia & Weingartia. (Illus.). 144p. 1985. 32.95 (ISBN 0-88192-053-3). Timber.

Rayer, Guy. Flowering Cacti: A Color Guide. (Color Guides Ser.). (Illus.). 196p. 1984. 12.95 (ISBN 0-88254-938-3). Hippocrene Bks.

Schuster, Danny. An Introduction to Cacti. (Illus., Orig.). 1984. pap. 7.95 (ISBN 0-7137-1499-9, Pub. by Blandford Pr England). Sterling.

Sunset Editors. Cactus & Succulents. 2nd ed. LC 77-82873. (Illus.). 80p. 1978. pap. 4.95 (ISBN 0-376-03753-9, Sunset Bks.). Sunset-Lane.

Watson, Robert. Night-Blooming Cactus. LC 80-65999. 1980. 10.00 (ISBN 0-689-11090-1); pap. 5.95 (ISBN 0-689-11091-X). Atheneum.

Weniger, Del. Cacti of Texas & Neighboring States: A Field Guide. (Illus.). 366p. 1984. 24.95 (ISBN 0-292-71085-2); pap. 14.95 (ISBN 0-292-71063-1). U of Tex Pr.

CAD-CAM SYSTEMS

Allan, John J., 3rd. CAD Systems: Proceedings of the IFIP Working Conference on Computer Aided Design Systems, Austin, Texas, February 12-14, 1976. 458p. 1976. 64.00 (ISBN 0-7204-0472-X, North-Holland). Elsevier.

Autofact Five Conference on Computer-Integrated Manufacturing & the Automated Factory, Detroit, Mich., Nov. 1983. Autofact Five: Proceedings. xvi, 1048p. 1983. 60.00 (ISBN 0-444-86820-8). Elsevier.

Autofact Four Conference on Computer-Integrated Manufacturing & the Automated Factory, Philadelphia, Pa., Nov.-Dec. 1982. Autofact Four: Proceedings. 688p. 1983. 60.00 (ISBN 0-87263-093-5). Elsevier.

Barnhill, Robert E. & Boehm, Wolfgang, eds. Surfaces in Computer Aided Geometric Design: Proceedings of a Conference, Mathematisches Forschungsinstitut, Oberwolfach, F.R.G., April 25-30, 1982. xvi, 216p. 1983. 47.00 (ISBN 0-444-86550-0, I-32-83, North-Holland). Elsevier.

Barr, Paul, et al. CAD: Principles & Applications. (Illus.). 208p. 1985. text ed. 21.95 (ISBN 0-13-110198-6). P-H.

Begg, Vivienne. Developing Expert CAD Systems. (High Technology Modular Ser.). 128p. 1984. 19.95 (ISBN 0-89059-042-7, KP101, UPB). Unipub.

Besant, C. B. Computer-Aided Design & Manufacture. 2nd ed. LC 79-40971. (Engineering Science Ser.). (Illus.). 232p. 1982. 54.95x (ISBN 0-470-27372-0); pap. 26.95x (ISBN 0-470-27373-9). Halsted Pr.

Bo, Ketil & Lillehagen, Frank M., eds. CAD Systems Framework: Proceedings of the WG 5.2 Working Conference, Roros, June 1982. x, 342p. 1983. 49.00 (ISBN 0-444-86604-3, I-172-83, North Holland). Elsevier.

Bowman, Daniel J. The CAD-CAM Primer. LC 84-50904. 14.95 (ISBN 0-672-22187-X). Sams.

CAD-CAM Glossary. 19.25 (ISBN 0-686-40545-5). C I M Systems.

CAD-CAM Industry Directory. 164p. 1983. 35.00 (ISBN 0-910747-03-2). Tech Data TX.

CAM Systems. 30.00 (ISBN 0-318-02623-6). Print Indus Am.

Canadian CAD-CAM & Robotics: Conference Proceedings. 2nd ed. 200p. 1983. pap. 25.00 (ISBN 0-87263-119-2). ASME.

Carberry, Patrick R. CAD-CAM with Personal Computers. 189p. 1985. 21.95 (ISBN 0-8306-0852-4, 1852); pap. 14.95 (ISBN 0-8306-1852-X). TAB Bks.

Cassell, Douglas A. Introduction to Computer-Aided Manufacturing in Electronics. LC 73-177882. 248p. 1972. 21.50 (ISBN 0-471-14053-8, Pub. by Wiley). Krieger.

Chakraborty, J. & Dhande, S. G. Kinematics & Geometry of Planer & Spatial CAM Mechanisms. LC 76-50585. 162p. 1977. 18.95x (ISBN 0-470-15069-6). Halsted Pr.

Chasen, S. H. & Dow, J. W. The Guide for the Evaluation & Implementation of Cad-Cam Systems. 2nd ed. (Illus.). 461p. 1983. text ed. 250.00 (ISBN 0-938800-01-9). Cad Cam.

Computer-Aided Studies of Fishing Boat Hull Resistance. (Fisheries Technical Papers: No. 87). 127p. 1969. pap. 7.50 (ISBN 0-686-93179-3, F1741, FAO). Unipub.

Computers in Engineering, 1982, 4 Vols. Incl. Vol. 1. Computer-Aided Design, Manufacturing, & Simulation. 351p (G00215); Vol. 2. Robots & Robotics. 261p (G00216); Vol. 3. Mesh Generation, Finite Elements, Computers in Structural Optimization, Computers in the Engineering Workplace, Computers in Energy Systems, Personal Computing. 273p (G00217); Process Control, State-of-the-Art Printing Technology, Software Engineering & Management, Statistical Modeling & Reliability Techniques, Computers in Education. 305p (G00218). 1982. Set. 200.00 (ISBN 0-317-07007-X, G00219); 60.00 ea. ASME.

Conference on the HP-1000 International Users Group, 1st. Minicomputer Research & Applications: Proceedings. Brown, H. K., ed. LC 81-5134. (Illus.). 392p. 1981. 44.00 (ISBN 0-08-027567-2). Pergamon.

Desk Top Computing for Engineers. 58p. 1982. pap. 19.00 (ISBN 0-85298-503-7, MEP157). Soc Auto Engineers.

DeVries, W. R., ed. Computer Applications in Manufacturing Systems. 101p. 1980. 18.00 (ISBN 0-317-33464-6, G00194); members 9.00 (ISBN 0-317-33465-4). ASME.

--Computer Applications in Manufacturing Systems. (PED: Vol. 2). 101p. 1980. 18.00 (ISBN 0-317-06810-5, G00194). ASME.

Effective CADCAM. 125p. 1983. Nineteen papers. pap. 41.00 (ISBN 0-85298-517-7, MEP176). Soc Auto Engineers.

Encarnacao, J. & Schlechtendahl, E. G. Computer Aided Design: Fundamentals & System Architectures. (Symbolic Computation Ser.). (Illus.). 350p. 1983. 32.00 (ISBN 0-387-11526-9). Springer-Verlag.

Encarnacao, J., ed. File Structures & Data Bases for CAD: Proceedings of the IFIP-WG 5-2 Working Conference, Seeheim, Federal Republic of Germany, September 14-16, 1981. 372p. 1982. 47.00 (ISBN 0-444-86462-8, North Holland). Elsevier.

Encarnacao, J., et al, eds. CAD-CAM As a Basis for Development of Technology in Developing Nations: Proceedings of th IFIP WG 5.2 Working Conference, Sao Paulo, Brazil, October 1981. 437p. 1982. 76.75 (ISBN 0-444-86320-6). Elsevier.

European Conference on Electronic Design Automation, Brighton, UK, Sept. 1981. Electronic Design Automation. (IEE Conference Publication: No. 200). 290p. 1981. 98.00 (ISBN 0-85296-243-6). Inst Elect Eng.

European Congress on Electron Microscopy, 5th. Image Processing & Computer-Aided Design in Electronics: Proceedings. Hawkes, P. W., ed. 1973. 75.50 (ISBN 0-12-333365-2). Acad Pr.

Flora, Philip C. International CAD-CAM Software Directory. (Illus.). 140p. (Orig.). Date not set. pap. text ed. 35.00 (ISBN 0-910747-06-7). Tech Data TX.

--International Computer Aided Design Directory. (Illus.). 240p. (Orig.). pap. text ed. 35.00 (ISBN 0-910747-01-6). Tech Data TX.

Forrest, E. & Johnson, R. H. CAE, CAD, CAD-CAM Service Bureaus: Directory, Review, & Outlook, 1983. (Illus.). 130p. 1983. cancelled (ISBN 0-938484-09-5). Daratech.

Foundyller, Charles M. CAD-CAM, CAE: Evaluating Today's Systems. Jenkins, Bruce L., ed. (Series in CAD-CAM, CAE). (Illus.). 120p. 1984. 3-ring looseleaf 99.00x (ISBN 0-938484-18-4). Daratech.

--CAD-CAM, CAE: Survey, Review & Buyers' Guide. Jenkins, Bruce L., ed. (Daratech Series in CAD-CAM, CAE). (Illus.). 1985. 3-ring loose leaf 368.00x (ISBN 0-938484-16-8). Daratech.

--CAD-CAM, CAE: The Contemporary Technology. Jenkins, Bruce L., ed. (Series in CAD-CAM, CAE). (Illus.). 260p. 1984. 3-ring looseleaf 127.00x (ISBN 0-938484-17-6). Daratech.

--Contemporary CAD-CAM Technology. LC 80-129133. (Turnkey CAD-CAM Computer Graphics: A Survey & Buyer's Guide for Manufacturers, Pt. 1). (Illus.). 254p. 1980. cancelled (ISBN 0-938484-01-X). Daratech.

Gardan, Yvon & Lucas, Michel. Interactive Graphics in CAD. 256p. (Published in England by Kogan Page). 1984. 34.95 (ISBN 0-89059-036-2, KP100, UPB). Unipub.

Goetsch, David. Cad-Cam Workbook. 1983. text ed. 4.95 wkbk. (ISBN 0-538-33320-0, IE32). SW Pub.

Groover, Mikell P. Automation, Production Systems & Computer-Aided Manufacturing. 1980. text ed. 34.95 (ISBN 0-13-054668-2). P-H.

Groover, Mikell P., Jr. & Zimmers, Emory W., Jr. CAD-CAM: Computer-Aided Design & Manufacturing. LC 83-11132. (Illus.). 489p. 1984. text ed. 36.95 (ISBN 0-13-110130-7). P-H.

Gunn, Thomas G., Jr. Computer Applications in Manufacturing. LC 81-6544. (Illus.). 224p. 1981. 28.95 (ISBN 0-8311-1087-2). Indus Pr.

Harris, Roy D. & Maggard, Michael J. Computer Models in Operations Management: A Computer-Augmented System. 2nd ed. 1977. pap. text ed. 20.50 scp (ISBN 0-06-042664-0, HarpC); scp solutions manual 9.75 (ISBN 0-06-042666-7); source deck of all comp. progs. 30.00 (ISBN 0-06-042665-9). Har-Row.

Hatvany, J., et al. World Survey of CAM. (Illus.). viii, 141p. 1983. pap. 59.95 (ISBN 0-408-01255-2). Butterworth.

Hordeski, Michael. CAM Techniques. 1985. text ed. 37.95 (ISBN 0-8359-0620-5). Reston.

Hubbard, Stuart W. CAD-CAM Applications for Business. LC 84-42810. 144p. 1985. pap. 25.00 (ISBN 0-89774-167-6). Oryx Pr.

IFAC-IFIP Workshop, Kyoto, Japan, Aug. 31-Sept. 2, 1981. Real Time Programming, 1981: Proceedings. Hasegawa, T., ed. (Annual Review in Automatic Programming: Vol. 11). (Illus.). 150p. 1982. 50.00 (ISBN 0-08-027613-X). Pergamon.

International Computers in Engineering Conference & Exhibit, 1983. Computers in Engineering: Papers, 3 Vols. Incl. Vol. 1. Computer-Aided Design, Manufacturing, & Simulation, 55 papers. Cokonis, T. J., ed. 357p. 70.00 (GOO230); Vol. 2. Robotics Theory & Applications; Computers in Education, 47 papers. Ruoff, C. F. & Shoup, T. E., eds. 320p. 70.00 (GOO231); Vol. 3. Computer Software & Applications, 44 papers. Dietrich, D. E., ed. 263p. 70.00 (GOO232). 1983. Set. 180.00 (GOO233). ASME.

International Resource Development Inc. CAD-CAM Opportunities & Strategies. 161p. 1984. 985.00x (ISBN 0-88694-610-7). Intl Res Dev.

Knox, C. S. CAD-CAM Systems Implementation. (Mechanical Engineering Ser.). 352p. 1983. 39.75 (ISBN 0-8247-7041-2). Dekker.

Carafoli, E., ed. Membrane Transport of Calcium. LC 81-68980. 1982. 49.50 (ISBN 0-12-159320-7). Acad Pr.

Cheung, Wai Y., ed. Calcium & Cell Function, Vol. 4. (Molecular Biology Ser.). 1983. 70.00 (ISBN 0-12-171404-7). Acad Pr.

Cheung, Wai Yiu, ed. Calcium & Cell Function: Vol. 1, Calmodulin. LC 80-985. (Molecular Biology Ser.). 1980. 60.00 (ISBN 0-12-171401-2). Acad Pr.

Control of Bitter Pit & Breakdown by Calcium in the Apples Cox's Orange Pippin & Jonathan. (Agricultural Research Reports: No. 711). 43p. 1968. pap. 4.00 (ISBN 0-686-71855-0, PDC173, PUDOC). Unipub.

DeLuca, H. F. & Anast, C. S., eds. Pediatric Diseases Related to Calcium. 450p. 1980. 56.00 (ISBN 0-444-00361-4, Biomedical Pr). Elsevier.

Donowitz, Mark & Sharp, Geoffrey W. Mechanisms of Intestinal Electrolyte Transport & Regulation by Calcium: Proceedings of Kroc Foundation Conference, Santa Ynez Valley, California, September 26-30, 1983. LC 84-17127. (Kroc Foundation Ser.: Vol. 17). 388p. 1984. 78.00 (ISBN 0-8451-0307-5). A R Liss.

Godfraind, T. & Albertini, A., eds. Calcium Modulators: Proceedings of the International Symposium on Calcium Modulators, Venice, June 17-18, 1982. (Giovanni Lorenzini Foundation Ser.: Vol. 15). 380p. 1983. 68.00 (ISBN 0-444-80464-1, Biomedical Pr). Elsevier.

Grover, A. K. & Daniel, E. E., eds. Calcium & Contractility: Smooth Muscle. LC 84-28841. (Contemporary Biomedicine Ser.). (Illus.). 512p. 1985. 69.50 (ISBN 0-89603-066-0). Humana.

Marme, D., ed. Calcium & Cell Physiology. (Illus.). 415p. 1985. 45.00 (ISBN 0-387-13841-2). Springer-Verlag.

Mennear. Cadmium Toxicity. (Modern Pharmacology-Toxicology Ser.: Vol. 15). 1979. 45.00 (ISBN 0-8247-6766-7). Dekker.

Rahwan, Ralf G. & Witiak, Donald T. Calcium Regulation by Calcium Antagonists. LC 82-16451. (ACS Symposium Ser.: No. 201). 207p. 1982. lib. bdg. 34.95x (ISBN 0-8412-0744-5). Am Chemical.

Rubin, Ronald P. Calcium & Cellular Secretion. LC 82-7489. 287p. 1982. 39.50 (ISBN 0-306-40978-X, Plenum Pr). Plenum Pub.

Spiro, Thomas G. Calcium in Biology. LC 83-12564. (Metal Ions in Biology Ser.: No. 1-457). 278p. 1984. 75.00x (ISBN 0-471-88543-6, Pub. by Wiley-Interscience). Wiley.

Thomas, M. V. Techniques in Calcium Research. (Biological Techniques Ser.). 1982. 33.00 (ISBN 0-12-688680-6). Acad Pr.

Yiu Cheung, Wai, ed. Calcium & Cell Function, Vol. 2. (Molecular Biology Ser.). 1982. 66.00 (ISBN 0-12-171402-0). Acad Pr.

CALCIUM IN THE BODY

see also Calcification; Calcium Metabolism

Anghileri, Leopold J. & Tuffet-Anghileri, Anne M., eds. The Role of Calcium in Biological Systems, Vol. I. 288p. 1982. 81.00 (ISBN 0-8493-6280-6). CRC Pr.

Bronner, Felix & Peterlik, Meinrad. Epithelial Calcium & Phosphate Transport: Molecular & Cellular Aspects. LC 84-17149. (Progress in Clinical & Biological Research Ser.: Vol. 168). 416p. 1984. 68.00 (ISBN 0-8451-5018-9). A R Liss.

Calcium Requirements: Report of a WHO Expert Group, Rome, 1961. (Nutrition Meetings Reports: No. 30). 54p. 1962. pap. 4.75 (ISBN 0-686-93129-7, F86, FAO). Unipub.

Cheung, Wai Yiu. Calcium & Cell Function, Vol. 3. (Molecular Biology Ser.). 432p. 1983. 64.00 (ISBN 0-12-171403-9). Acad Pr.

Dacke, Christopher. Calcium Regulation in the Sub-Mammalian Vertebrates. 1979. 49.50 (ISBN 0-12-201050-7). Acad Pr.

Ebashi, Setsuro, et al, eds. Calcium Regulation in Biological Systems. 1985. 29.50 (ISBN 0-12-228650-2). Acad Pr.

Flaim, Stephen & Zelis, Robert F., eds. Calcium Blockers: Mechanisms of Action & Clinical Applications. LC 82-8548. (Illus.). 313p. 1982. text ed. 44.50 (ISBN 0-8067-0611-2). Urban & S.

Fleckenstein, Albrect. Calcium-Antagonism in Heart & Smooth Muscle: Experimental Facts & Therapeutic Prospects. LC 82-15990. 399p. 1983. 60.00x (ISBN 0-471-05435-6, Pub. by Wiley-Interscience). Wiley.

Mennear. Cadmium Toxicity. (Modern Pharmacology-Toxicology Ser.: Vol. 15). 1979. 45.00 (ISBN 0-8247-6766-7). Dekker.

Pak, Charles Y. Calcium Urolithiasis: Pathogenesis, Diagnosis, & Management. (Topics in Bone & Mineral Disorders Ser.). (Illus.). 174p. 1978. 29.50x (ISBN 0-306-31110-0, Plenum Pr). Plenum Pub.

Rasmussen, Howard. Calcium & Camp As Synarchic Messengers. LC 81-10482. 370p. 1981. 51.50 (ISBN 0-471-08396-8, Pub. by Wiley-Interscience). Wiley.

Rubin, Ronald. Calcium & the Secretory Process. LC 74-10557. (Illus.). 204p. 1974. 29.50x (ISBN 0-306-30778-2, Plenum Pr). Plenum Pub.

Rubin, Ronald P., et al, eds. Calcium in Biological Systems. 729p. 1985. 89.50x (ISBN 0-306-41747-2, Plenum Pr). Plenum Pub.

Scarpa, Antonio & Carafoli, Ernesto, eds. Calcium Transport & Cell Function. (Annals of the New York Academy of Sciences Ser.: Vol. 307). 655p. 1978. professional 70.00x (ISBN 0-89072-063-0). NY Acad Sci.

Singh. Calcium Channel Blockers. 1986. price not set (ISBN 0-88416-459-4). PSG Pub Co.

Weiss, G. B., ed. Calcium in Drug Action. LC 78-8517. 376p. 1978. 45.00 (ISBN 0-306-40015-4, Plenum Pr). Plenum Pub.

CALCIUM METABOLISM

Adams & Murray. Improving Your Health with Calcium & Phosphorus. 1978. 1.25x (ISBN 0-915962-25-X). Cancer Control soc.

Campbell, Anthony K. Intracellular Calcium: Its Universal Role As Regulator. LC 82-8656. (Monographs in Molecular Biophysics & Biochemistry). 540p. 1983. 82.95x (ISBN 0-471-10488-4, Pub. by Wiley-Interscience). Wiley.

Cohn, D. V., et al. Endocrine Control of Bone & Calcium Metabolism, Vol. 8A. (International Congress Ser.: Vol. 619). 1984. 107.50 (ISBN 0-444-80589-3). Elsevier.

--Endocrine Control of Bone & Calcium Metabolism, Vol. 8B. (International Congress Ser.: Vol. 635). 1984. 102.00 (ISBN 0-444-80590-7). Elsevier.

Cohn, D. V., et al, eds. Hormonal Control of Calcium Metabolism. (International Congress Ser.: No. 511). 506p. 1981. 98.75 (ISBN 0-444-90193-0, Excerpta Medica). Elsevier.

Corvilain, H. & Fuss, M., eds. Hormones & Calcium Metabolism. (Journal: HormoneResearch: Vol. 20, No. 1). 92p. 1984. pap. 16.75 (ISBN 3-8055-3888-X). S Karger.

Dacke, Christopher. Calcium Regulation in the Sub-Mammalian Vertebrates. 1979. 49.50 (ISBN 0-12-201050-7). Acad Pr.

European Symposium on Calcified Tissues, 10th, Hamburg, 1973. Calcium Metabolism, Bone & Metabolic Bone Diseases: Proceedings. Kuhlencordt, F. & Kruse, H. P., eds. (Illus.). xx, 381p. 1975. 42.00 (ISBN 0-387-06990-9). Springer-Verlag.

Flaim, Stephen & Zelis, Robert F., eds. Calcium Blockers: Mechanisms of Action & Clinical Applications. LC 82-8548. (Illus.). 313p. 1982. text ed. 44.50 (ISBN 0-8067-0611-2). Urban & S.

Harrison, Harold E. Disorders of Calcium & Phosphate Metabolism in Childhood Adolescence. LC 78-64712. (Major Problems in Clinical Pediatrics Ser.: Vol. 20). pap. 81.50 (ISBN 0-317-26439-7, 2024992). Bks Demand UMI.

Irving, James T. Calcium & Phosphoros Metabolism. 1973. 52.00 (ISBN 0-12-374350-8). Acad Pr.

Kenny, Alexander D., ed. Intestinal Calcium Absorption & Its Regulation. 176p. 1981. 56.00 (ISBN 0-8493-5701-2). CRC Pr.

Means, Anthony R. & O'Malley, Bert W. Methods in Enzymology: Hormone Action: Calmodulin & Calcium-Binding Proteins, Vol. 102, Pt. G. 1983. 47.50 (ISBN 0-12-182002-5). Acad Pr.

Nichols, George & Wasserman, R. H., eds. Cellular Mechanism for Calcium Transfer & Homeostasis. 1971. 59.50 (ISBN 0-12-518050-0). Acad Pr.

Norman, A. W. & Schaefer, K., eds. Vitamin D: Chemical, Biochemical & Clinical Endocrinology of Calcium Metabolism. (Illus.). 1288p. 1982. text ed. 114.00 (ISBN 3-11-008864-9). De Gruyter.

Rubin, Ronald P., et al, eds. Calcium in Biological Systems. 729p. 1985. 89.50x (ISBN 0-306-41747-2, Plenum Pr). Plenum Pub.

Siegel. Calcium Binding Proteins: Structure & Function. (Developments in Biochemistry Ser.: Vol. 14). 512p. 1980. 87.00 (ISBN 0-444-00565-X, Biomedical Pr). Elsevier.

U. S. -Japan International Symposium, East-West Center, Honolulu, Hawaii, August, 14-18, 1981 & Ohnishi, Tsuyoshi. Mechanism of Gated Calcium Transport Across Biological Membranes: Proceedings. LC 81-20578. 1982. 39.50 (ISBN 0-12-524980-2). Acad Pr.

CALCIUM SILICATES

West, H. W., et al. The Resistance to Lateral Loads of Walls Built of Calcium Silicate Bricks. 1979. 20.00x (ISBN 0-900910-33-X, Pub. by Brit Ceramic Soc England). State Mutual Bk.

CALCULATING BOARDS, NETWORK

see Electric Network Analyzers

CALCULATING-MACHINES

Here are entered works on calculators, as well as all mechanical computers of pre-1945 vintage. Works on modern electronic computers first developed after 1945 are entered under Computers.

see also Accounting Machines; Computation Laboratories; Computers; Cybernetics; Digital Counters; Programmable Calculators; Punched Card Systems; Slide-Rule; Tabulating Machines

Ash, Peter F. & Robinson, Edward E. Basic College Mathematics: A Calculator Approach. LC 80-15352. (Illus.). 544p. 1981. 23.95 (ISBN 0-201-00091-1); instrs' manual 3.00 (ISBN 0-201-00092-X). Addison-Wesley.

Babbage, Charles, et al. Charles Babbage: On the Principle & Development of the Calculator & Other Seminal Writings. 400p. 1984. pap. 7.95 (ISBN 0-486-24691-4). Dover.

Babbage, Henry. Babbage's Calculating Engines. (Charles Babbage Institute Reprint for the History of Computing Ser.: Vol. 2). (Illus.). 390p. 1984. Repr. of 1889 ed. text ed. 55.00x (ISBN 0-262-02200-1). MIT Pr.

--Babbage's Calculating Machines. (Charles Babbage Reprint Ser.). (Illus.). 390p. 1984. 55.00x. MIT Pr.

Ball, John A. Algorithms for RPN Calculators. LC 77-14977. 330p. 1977. 35.50 (ISBN 0-471-03070-8, Pub. by Wiley-Interscience). Wiley.

Beakley, George C. Electronic Hand Calculators. 4th ed. 1983. pap. 10.95 cancelled (ISBN 0-686-82939-5). Macmillan.

Beakley, George C. & Lovell, Robert E. Computation, Calculators & Computers: Tools of Engineering Problem Solving-Including FORTRAN. 368p. 1983. pap. text ed. write for info. (ISBN 0-02-307150-8). Macmillan.

Belstock, Alan & Smith, Gerald. Consumer Mathematics with Calculator Applications. Gafney, Leo, ed. 1980. text ed. 17.52x (ISBN 0-07-004436-8). McGraw.

Benedict, Howard M., et al. Calculator Techniques for Real Estate. LC 77-11252. 1977. 14.95 (ISBN 0-913652-10-5). Realtors Natl.

Bitter, Gary G. & Mikesell, Jeraldi L. Activities Handbook for Teaching with the Hand Held Calculator. 1979. text ed. 28.57 scp (ISBN 0-205-06713-1, 236713). Allyn.

Briggs, J. Robert & Kosy, Eugene J. Electronic Calculators. 1984. text ed. 8.95 (ISBN 0-538-13600-6, M60). SW Pub.

Burt, Bruce C., compiled by. Calculators: Readings from the Arithmetic Teacher & the Mathematics Teacher. LC 79-17365. (Illus.). 231p. 1979. pap. 6.25 (ISBN 0-87353-144-2). NCTM.

Business Communications Staff. Plastics in Business Machines. 1985. pap. 1950.00 (ISBN 0-89336-443-6, P-064R). BCC.

Butsch, Charlotte. Electronic Calculator: Student Guide. 1971. pap. text ed. 3.95 (ISBN 0-89420-055-0, 126877); cassette recordings 65.50 (ISBN 0-89420-143-3, 156780). Natl Book.

--The Printing Calculator: Student Guide. 2nd ed. 1971. pap. text ed. 3.85 (ISBN 0-89420-022-4, 126855); cassette recordings 50.20 (ISBN 0-89420-174-3, 156760). Natl Book.

Caravella, Joseph R. Minicalculators in the Classroom. LC 76-41213. 64p. 1977. pap. 4.40 (ISBN 0-8106-1812-5). NCTM.

--Minicalculators in the Classroom. 64p. 1977. pap. 4.95 (ISBN 0-8106-1812-5). NEA.

Carter, Juanita E. & Young, Darroch. Electronic Calculators: A Mastery Approach Year. 1981. 15.50 (ISBN 0-395-29621-8); instr's manual 1.00 (ISBN 0-395-29622-6). HM.

Carter, Juanita E. & Young, Darroch F. Calculating Machines: A Ten-Key Approach. 1975. pap. text ed. 19.95 (ISBN 0-395-18594-7); instrs.' manual 1.50 (ISBN 0-395-18805-9). HM.

Chinn, William G., et al. Arithmetic & Calculators: How to Deal with Arithmetic in the Calculator Age. LC 77-11111. (Illus.). 488p. 1978. pap. text ed. 17.95 (ISBN 0-7167-0015-8). W H Freeman.

Daryanani, Sital. Building Systems Design with Programmable Calculators. 1980. 44.95 (ISBN 0-07-015415-5). McGraw.

Dubisch, Roy. Basic Mathematics with Hand-Held Calculator. LC 78-57267. 1979. text ed. 29.95 (ISBN 0-8053-2341-4); instr's guide 4.95 (ISBN 0-8053-2344-9). Benjamin-Cummings.

Duffett-Smith, Peter. Practical Astronomy with Your Calculator. 2nd ed. LC 81-6191. 200p. 1981. 37.50 (ISBN 0-521-24059-X); pap. 10.95 (ISBN 0-521-28411-2). Cambridge U Pr.

Eckern, Gilbert & Hardin, Walt. The Ten-Key Touch System on Electronic Calculators: With Business & Industry Applications. (Illus.). 240p. 1983. pap. text ed. 14.95 (ISBN 0-89863-074-6). Star Pub CA.

Elich, Carlotta J. & Elich, Joseph. Trigonometry Using Calculators. LC 79-18934. (Illus.). 1980. text ed. 23.95 (ISBN 0-201-03186-8); instr's. manual 4.00 (ISBN 0-201-03187-6). Addison-Wesley.

Engineering Research Associates Staff. High-Speed Computing Devices, Vol. IV. (Charles Babbage Institute Reprint for the History of Computing Ser.). (Illus.). 451p. 1984. Repr. of 1950 ed. text ed. 38.00x (ISBN 0-262-05028-5). MIT Pr.

Giordano, Al. Basic Business Machine Calculations: A Complete Course. 2nd ed. (Illus.). 1978. pap. 22.95x ref. ed. (ISBN 0-13-057315-9). P-H.

Goldberg, Kenneth. Calculator Math Problems, Examples & Activities. 208p. 1982. 18.95 (ISBN 0-13-743310-7); pap. 8.95 (ISBN 0-13-743302-6). P-H.

Goldberg, Kenneth P. The Parent's Book on Calculators: Calculators & Your Child's Education. 1983. 17.50x (ISBN 0-19-503282-9, GB 731); pap. 6.95 (ISBN 0-19-503283-7, GB731). Oxford U Pr.

Green, D. R. & Lewis, J. Science with Pocket Calculators. (The Wykeham Science Ser.: No. 48). 300p. 1978. write for info (ISBN 0-85109-660-3); pap. cancelled (ISBN 0-85109-560-7). Taylor & Francis.

Green, David R. & Lewis, John. Science with Pocket Calculators. LC 78-57665. (Wykeham Science Ser.: No. 48). 220p. 1979. 27.50x (ISBN 0-8448-1361-3). Crane-Russak Co.

Groneman, Nancy J. Business Mathematics Using Electronic Calculators. (Illus.). 240p. 1982. 21.95 (ISBN 0-13-105205-5). P-H.

Harcharik, Kathleen & Armijo, Moses A. Business Computations. (Illus.). 320p. 1982. pap. 22.95 (ISBN 0-13-093104-7). P-H.

Hartree, Douglas. Calculating Machines: Recent & Prospective Developments & Their Impact on Mathematical Physics & Calculating Instruments & Machines. 1984. 30.00x (ISBN 0-262-08147-4). MIT Pr.

Hartres, Douglas R. Calculating Instruments & Machines. LC 49-6378. pap. 37.00 (ISBN 0-317-28432-0, 2019028). Bks Demand UMI.

Hempel, Marvin W. Ten-Key Adding Machine: Student Guide. 1970. pap. text ed. 5.55 (ISBN 0-89420-056-9, 126600); cassette recordings 142.40 (ISBN 0-89420-187-5, 156700). Natl Book.

Henrici, Peter. Computational Analysis with the HP-25 Pocket Calculator. LC 77-1182. 280p. 1977. pap. 26.50 (ISBN 0-471-02938-6, Pub. by Wiley-Interscience). Wiley.

Hestenes, Marshall & Hill, Richard. Algebra & Trigonometry with Calculators. (Illus.). 512p. 1981. text ed. 29.95 (ISBN 0-13-021857-X). P-H.

--College Algebra with Calculators. (Illus.). 416p. 1982. 28.95 (ISBN 0-13-140806-2). P-H.

Hestenes, Marshall D. & Hill, Richard O., Jr. Trigonometry with Calculators. (Illus.). 288p. 1982. text ed. 28.95 (ISBN 0-13-930859-8). P-H.

Horsburgh, E. M., ed. Handbook of the Napier Tercentary Celebration or Modern Instruments & Methods of Calculation. (The Charles Babbage Institute Reprint Series for the History of Computing: Vol. 3). (Illus.). 1983. Repr. of 1914 ed. 45.00x (ISBN 0-938228-10-2). Tomash Pubs.

--Handbook of the Napier Tercentenary Celebration of Modern Instruments & Methods of Calculation. (Charles Babbage Institute Reprint for the History of Computing Ser.: Vol. 3). (Illus.). 384p. 1984. Repr. of 1914 ed. text ed. 45.00x (ISBN 0-262-08141-5). MIT Pr.

Houston, Suzanne. Office Calculators & Adding Machines. 208p. 1981. pap. text ed. 10.95 (ISBN 0-8403-2519-3). Kendall-Hunt.

Hudson, Walter W. A Statistical Package for the Pocket Calculator: The SPPC Manual. 350p. 1982. pap. text ed. 14.95x (ISBN 0-942390-01-6). Walmyr.

Jacobs, Russell F. Problem Solving with the Calculator. 2nd ed. (Illus.). 160p. 1982. pap. text ed. 4.50 (ISBN 0-918272-08-4); ans. key & tchr's guide 1.25 (ISBN 0-918272-09-2). Jacobs.

James, Francisco J. The Pocket Calculator Boom. (Orig.). 1978. pap. 60.00 o.p (ISBN 0-933836-01-5); 6.25x (ISBN 0-933836-08-2). Simtek.

Kimmel, John. Using Ten-Key Electronic Desktop Calculators. 207p. 1983. pap. text ed. 9.75 (ISBN 0-89420-235-9, 126520); cassette recordings 94.95 (ISBN 0-89420-242-1, 126500). Natl Book.

Kinzey, Vera G. Mastering Ten-Key Calculators: Electronic & Mechanical. (Illus., Orig.). 1976. 14.95 (ISBN 0-15-555126-4, HC); instr's manual avail. (ISBN 0-15-555127-2). HarBraceJ.

Kohavi, Zvi & Paz, Azaria, eds. Theory of Machines & Computations: International Symposium on the Theory of Machines & Computations. 1971. 65.00 (ISBN 0-12-417750-6). Acad Pr.

Lavington, Simon. Early British Computers: The Story of Vintage Computers & The People Who Built Them. (Illus.). 140p. 1980. pap. 9.00 (ISBN 0-932376-08-8, EY-AX012-DP). Digital Pr.

LeBarre, James, et al. Machine Calculation of Business Problems. 233p. 1981. pap. 8.95 (ISBN 0-911744-75-4). Intl Educ Systems.

Levy, Lawrence S. Trigonometry with Calculators. 330p. 1983. text ed. write for info. (ISBN 0-02-370450-0). Macmillan.

Locke, Flora M. Electronic Calculators for Business Use. LC 78-1852. 264p. 1978. pap. text ed. 25.95 (ISBN 0-471-03579-3); pap. text ed. tchrs' manual avail. (ISBN 0-471-03766-4). Wiley.

McCarty, George. Calculator Calculus. rev. ed. LC 75-27363. (Illus.). xiv, 258p. 1980. pap. 19.95 (ISBN 0-936356-00-6). EduCALC Pubns.

McCready, Richard R. Office Machines: Electronic Calculators. 6th ed. LC 82-21337. 248p. 1983. pap. write for info. (ISBN 0-534-01285-X). Kent Pub Co.

McHale, Thomas J. & Witzke, Paul T. Calculation & Calculators. 1977. pap. text ed. 21.95 (ISBN 0-201-04771-3); tests avail. 3.95 (ISBN 0-201-04772-1). Addison-Wesley.

Meck, H. R. Scientific Analysis for Programmable Calculators. (Illus.). 160p. 1981. 15.95 (ISBN 0-13-796417-X, Spec); pap. 7.95 (ISBN 0-13-796409-9). P-H.

Merchant, Ronald. Basic Business Math & Electronic Calculators. 3rd ed. 306p. 1983. pap. text ed. 16.95x (ISBN 0-89863-069-X). Star Pub CA.

Morris, Janet. How to Develop Problem Solving Using a Calculator. LC 81-9569. (Illus.). 40p. 1981. pap. 4.00 (ISBN 0-87353-175-2). NCTM.

Moursund, David. Calculators in the Classroom: With Applications for Elementary & Middle School Teacher. LC 80-22165. 202p. 1981. pap. text ed. 17.45 (ISBN 0-471-08113-2). Wiley.

Mullish, Henry & Kestenbaum, Richard. Financial Analysis by Calculator: Problem-Solving Techniques With Applications. (Illus.). 157p. 1982. 17.95 (ISBN 0-13-316018-1); pap. 8.95 (ISBN 0-13-316000-9). P-H.

Mullish, Henry & Kochan, Stephen. Programmable Pocket Calculators. 264p. 1980. pap. 10.95 (ISBN 0-8104-5175-1). Hayden.

Muncaster, Barbara & Prescott, Susan L. Learning Basic Math & Business Math Using the Calculator. 1985. text ed. 7.95 wkbk. (ISBN 0-538-13540-9, M54). SW Pub.

Needles, Mark. Electronic Calculators in Business. 1982. pap. text ed. 21.70x (ISBN 0-673-16013-0). Scott F.

Pactor, Paul. Electronic Calculator. 1976. pap. 6.00 (ISBN 0-02-831010-1); key 1.60 (ISBN 0-02-831020-9). Glencoe.

Pactor, Paul & Johnson, Mina. Ten-Key Adding Machine Course. 2nd ed. 1976. pap. 6.00 (ISBN 0-02-830990-1); key 1.60 (ISBN 0-8224-2061-9). Glencoe.

Pasewark, William R. Electronic Display Calculator Course. 1984. 6.40 (ISBN 0-538-13650-2, M65). SW Pub.

--Electronic Display-Printing Calculator. 1984. text ed. 6.20 (ISBN 0-538-13630-8, M63). SW Pub.

--Electronic Printing Calculator. 1982. text ed. 5.80 (ISBN 0-538-13520-4, M52). SW Pub.

Pasewark, William R. & Cornelia, Nicholas. Calculating Machines Simulation. 1983. text ed. 6.30 wkbk. (ISBN 0-538-13560-3, M56). SW Pub.

Polisky, M. K. & Meehan, J. Solving Business Problems on the Electronic Calculator. 2nd ed. 256p. 1982. text ed. 11.40 (ISBN 0-07-041281-2). McGraw.

Price, Derek de Solla. Gears from the Greeks: The Antikythera Mechanism, a Calendar Computer from circa 80 B.C. LC 74-84369. (Transactions Ser.: Vol. 64, Pt. 7). (Illus.). 1974. pap. 8.00 (ISBN 0-87169-647-9). Am Philos.

Rhodes, George S. Numbers-a-Minute Timing Copy for Ten-Key Adding & Calculating Machines. 36p. (Orig.). 1980. pap. text ed. 4.25 (ISBN 0-89420-219-7, 126000); cassette 19.25 (ISBN 0-89420-226-X, 126004). Natl Book.

Ribera, Gilbert J. Machine Calculation for Business & Personal Use. 2nd ed. LC 79-83523. 1979. pap. text ed. 17.95x (ISBN 0-8162-7180-1); solutions manual 5.00x (ISBN 0-8162-7181-X). Holden-Day.

Rogoff, Mortimer. Calculator Navigation. (Illus.). 1980. 29.95 (ISBN 0-393-03192-6). Norton.

Saks, Mark. The Calculator Cookbook: Maximizing the Computational Power of Your Hand-Held Calculator. 286p. 1983. 22.95 (ISBN 0-13-110395-4); pap. 10.95 (ISBN 0-13-110387-3). P-H.

Salisbury, David F. Money Matters: Personal Financial Decision-Making with a Pocket Calculator. 228p. 1982. pap. 18.95 (ISBN 0-13-600528-4); pap. 9.95 (ISBN 0-13-600510-1). P-H.

Schmid, Hermann. Decimal Computation. LC 80-29514. 280p. 1983. Repr. of 1974 ed. lib. bdg. 27.50 (ISBN 0-89874-318-4). Krieger.

Seckler, Bernard. The Programmable Hand Calculator: A Teacher's Tool for Mathematics Classroom Lectures. 207p. (Orig.). 1982. handbk. 15.00 (ISBN 0-686-36869-X). Sigma Pr NY.

Shufeldt, H. H. & Newcomer, Kenneth. The Calculator Afloat. (Illus.). 225p. 1980. 16.95 (ISBN 0-87021-116-1); bulk rates avail. Naval Inst Pr.

--The Calculator Afloat: A Mariner's Guide to the Electronic Calculator. LC 80-81091. 256p. 1980. 16.95 (ISBN 0-87021-116-1). Naval Inst Pr.

Smith, J. R. Desk Calculators. (Illus.). 128p. 1973. pap. 9.95x (ISBN 0-8464-0323-4). Beekman Pubs.

Smith, Jon M. Scientific Analysis on the Pocket Calculator. 2nd ed. LC 77-6662. 445p. 1977. 29.95x (ISBN 0-471-03071-6, Pub. by Wiley-Interscience). Wiley.

Spikell, Mark A. & Snover, Stephen. Brain Ticklers: Timex-Sinclair 1000 Version. (Illus.). 208p. 1984. 13.95 (ISBN 0-13-081050-9); pap. 7.95 (ISBN 0-13-081000-2). P-H.

Stone, Jack. PIPESTAR 1: Pipe Stress Analysis for HP-41C-CV Calculators. 1984. manual & magnetic cards 99.00x (ISBN 0-87201-465-7). Gulf Pub.

Svoboda, Antonin & James, Hubert M. Computing Mechanisms & Linkages. (Illus.). 1948. pap. text ed. 4.95 (ISBN 0-486-61404-2). Dover.

Texas Instruments Learning Ser., et al. Understanding Calculator Math. Rev. ed. LC 78-50808. (Understanding Ser.). (Illus.). 224p. (Orig.). 1978. pap. 9.95 (ISBN 0-89512-016-X, LCB3321). Tex Instr Inc.

Tontsch, John W. Applied Electronic Math, with Calculators. 512p. 1982. pap. 26.95 (ISBN 0-574-21550-6, 13-4550); Instr's Guide Available (ISBN 0-574-21551-4, 13-4551). SRA.

Turck, J. A. Origin of Modern Calculating Machines. LC 72-5081. (Technology & Society Ser.). (Illus.). 200p. 1972. Repr. of 1921 ed. 17.00 (ISBN 0-405-04730-4). Ayer Co Pubs.

Vervoort & Mason. Calculator Math, 3 vols. (Makemaster Bk.). 1980. pap. 8.95 ea. Beginning Grades 5-7 (ISBN 0-8224-1200-4). Intermediate Grades 6-8 (ISBN 0-8224-1201-2). Advanced Grades 8-10 (ISBN 0-8224-1202-0). Pitman Learning.

Wadman, Ted & Coffin, Chris. An Easy Course in Using the HP-12C & Other Financial Calculators. (Easy Course Ser.). (Illus.). 1985. pap. 18.00 (ISBN 0-931011-01-9). Grapevine Pubns.

Warner, Joan. Business Calculator Operations. 2nd ed. LC 82-510. 1982. pap. text ed. 22.95 (ISBN 0-8359-0576-4); solutions manual avail. (ISBN 0-8359-0577-2). Reston.

CALCULATORS

see Calculating-Machines; Ready-Reckoners

CALCULATORS, PROGRAMMABLE

see Programmable Calculators

Patterson, G. A. Energy Analysis with a Pocket Calculator. 2nd ed. LC 77-88128. (Illus.). 138p. 1981. 16.95 (ISBN 0-917410-04-1). Basic Sci Pr.

CALCULUS

see also Curvature; Curves; Differential Equations; Fourier Series; Functions; Harmonic Analysis; Mathematical Analysis; Nonlinear Theories; Surfaces

Abbott, P. Calculus. (Teach Yourself Ser.). 1975. pap. 4.95 (ISBN 0-679-10391-0). McKay.

Adams, William J. Calculus for Business & Social Science. LC 74-5524. 250p. 1975. text ed. 30.75 (ISBN 0-471-00988-1). Wiley.

Allen, G. D. & Chui, Charles K. Elements of Calculus. LC 82-12874. (Mathematics Ser.). 512p. 1983. text ed. 23.50 pub net (ISBN 0-534-01188-8). Brooks-Cole.

Amazigo, John C. & Rubenfeld, Lester A. Advanced Calculus: And Its Applications to the Engineering & Physical Sciences. LC 80-283. 407p. 1980. text ed. 36.45 (ISBN 0-471-04934-4). Wiley.

Anton, H. Calculus: With Analytic Geometry. brief, 2nd ed. 738p. 1984. 32.95 (ISBN 0-471-88817-6); student's manual 10.95 (ISBN 0-471-80732-X). Wiley.

Anton, Howard. Calculus with Analytic Geometry. LC 79-11469. 1220p. 1980. 40.45 (ISBN 0-471-03248-4); solution manual 11.95 (ISBN 0-471-04498-9). Wiley.

--Calculus with Analytic Geometry. 2nd ed. LC 83-19778. 1239p. 1984. text ed. 40.45 (ISBN 0-471-08271-6); write for info. solution manual (ISBN 0-471-86901-5); pap. 15.95 students solution manual (ISBN 0-471-86902-3). Wiley.

Apostol, T. M. Calculus: Multi-Variable Calculus & Linear Algebra with Application, Vol. 2. 2nd ed. LC 67-14605. 673p. 1969. 44.00 (ISBN 0-471-00007-8); student solution 15.95 (ISBN 0-471-04498-9); calculus companion 12.95 (ISBN 0-471-88614-9). Wiley.

--Calculus: One-Variable Calculus with an Introduction to Linear Algebra, Vol. 1. 2nd ed. LC 73-20899. 666p. 1967. text ed. 44.00x (ISBN 0-471-00005-1); 15.95 (ISBN 0-471-86902-3); calculus companion 16.95 (ISBN 0-471-09230-4). Wiley.

Apostol, Tom, ed. Selected Papers in Precalculus. LC 77-792000079. (Raymond W. Brink Selected Mathematical Papers: Vol. 1). 21.00 (ISBN 0-88385-201-2). Math Assn.

Apostol, Tom, et al, eds. Selected Papers in Calculus. LC 76-102902. (Brink Selected Mathematical Papers: Vol. 2). 397p. 1969. 21.00 (ISBN 0-88385-202-0). Math Assn.

Arya, Jagdish C. & Lardner, Robin W. Applied Calculus for Business & Economics. (Illus.). 528p. 1981. text ed. 31.95 (ISBN 0-13-039255-3). P-H.

Ash, Robert & Ash, Carol. The Calculus Tutoring Book. 1985. write for info. (ISBN 0-87942-183-5, PC01776). Inst Electrical.

Ayres, Frank, Jr. Calculus. 2nd ed. (Schaum Outline Ser.). 1968. pap. 9.95 (ISBN 0-07-002653-X). McGraw.

Bahadur, R. R. Some Limit Theorems in Statistics. (CBMS-NSF Regional Conference Ser.: No. 4). v, 42p. 1971. pap. text ed. 8.00 (ISBN 0-89871-175-4). Soc Indus-Appl Math.

Barendregt, H. P. The Lambda Calculus: Its Syntax & Semantics. (Studies in Logic & the Foundation of Mathematics Ser.: Vol. 103). 616p. 1981. 95.75 (ISBN 0-444-85490-8, North-Holland). Elsevier.

Barnett, Raymond A. & Ziegler, Michael R. Applied Calculus. (Illus.). 674p. 1982. text ed. 28.95 (ISBN 0-89517-036-1). Dellen Pub.

Baues, H. J. Commutator Calculus & Groups of Homotopy Classes. (London Mathematical Society Lecture Note Ser.: No. 50). (Illus.). 220p. 1981. pap. 27.95 (ISBN 0-521-28424-4). Cambridge U Pr.

Baum, Alan, et al. Applied Calculus. LC 84-19316. 364p. 1985. 25.95 (ISBN 0-471-80306-5). Wiley.

Beer, Gerald A. Applied Calculus for Business & Economics with an Introduction to Matrices. 1978. text ed. 21.95 (ISBN 0-316-08727-0); tchr's ed. avail. (ISBN 0-316-08728-9). Little.

Beju, I. Spinor & Non-Euclidean Tensor Calculus with Applications. 267p. 1983. 44.00 (ISBN 0-9961006-8-7, Pub. by Abacus England). Heyden.

Benice, Daniel D. Precalculus Mathematics. 2nd ed. (Illus.). 512p. 1982. text ed. 29.95 (ISBN 0-13-694976-2). P-H.

Berkey, Dennis D. Calculus. LC 83-20046. 1194p. 1984. text ed. 42.95x (ISBN 0-03-059522-3). SCP.

Binmore, K. G. Calculus. LC 82-19728. (London School of Economics Mathematics Ser.). 450p. 1983. 52.50 (ISBN 0-521-24771-3); pap. 19.95 (ISBN 0-521-28952-1). Cambridge U Pr.

Bismut, Jean-Michel. Large Deviations & the Malliavin Calculus, Vol. 45. (Progress in Mathematics Ser.). 216p. 1984. 17.50 (ISBN 0-8176-3220-4). Birkhauser.

Bittinger, Marvin L. Calculus: Modeling Approach. 3rd ed. LC 83-6334. (Illus.). 544p. 1984. 32.95 (ISBN 0-201-11217-5); instr's manual 3.00 (ISBN 0-201-11219-1); student manual 9.95 (ISBN 0-201-11218-3). Addison-Wesley.

Blakeley, Walter R. Calculus for Engineering Technology. LC 67-29017. 441p. 1968. 31.95 (ISBN 0-471-07931-6). Wiley.

Boehm, C., ed. Calculus & Computer Science Theory: Proceedings of the Symposium Held in Rome, March 25-27, 1975. (Lecture Notes in Computer Science: Vol. 37). xiv, 370p. 1975. pap. 20.00 (ISBN 0-387-07416-3). Springer-Verlag.

Bonic, Robert, et al. Freshman Calculus. 2nd ed. 1976. text ed. 27.95 (ISBN 0-669-96727-0). Heath.

Boole, George. Treatise on the Calculus of Finite Differences. 5th ed. LC 76-119364. text ed. 13.95 (ISBN 0-8284-1121-2). Chelsea Pub.

Brady, Stephen W. & Farmer, Gale E. The Function Plotter: A Calculus Primer, Apple II Version. 1984. pap. text ed. 23.95 (ISBN 0-471-80189-5). Wiley.

Bressan, Aldo. A General Interpreted Modal Calculus. LC 77-151568. pap. 88.80 (ISBN 0-317-08253-1, 2011096). Bks Demand UMI.

Brown, Austin R., Jr. & Harris, Mark. Arbplot: A Computer Graphics Utility for Calculus. (A Software Microcomputer Program Ser.). 1982. scp Users guide manual 14.95 (ISBN 0-06-041027-2, HarpC); scp computer package 125.00 (ISBN 0-06-041026-4). Har-Row.

Bryant, Steven & Saltz, Daniel. Precalculus & Mathematics: Algebra & Trigonometry. (Illus.). 1980. text ed. 25.55x (ISBN 0-673-16242-7). Scott F.

Buck, R. C., ed. Studies in Modern Analysis. LC 62-11884. (MAA Studies: No. 1). 182p. 1962. 16.50 (ISBN 0-88385-101-6). Math Assn.

Buck, R. Creighton. Advanced Calculus. 3rd ed. LC 77-2859. (McGraw-Hill Intl. Series in Pure & Applied Mathematics). (Illus.). 1978. text ed. 38.95 (ISBN 0-07-008728-8). McGraw.

Burgmeier, James W. & Kost, Larry L. Epic: Exploration Programs in Calculus. (Illus.). 112p. 1985. pap. text ed. 29.95 (ISBN 0-13-283318-2). P-H.

Calter, Paul. Technical Mathematics with Calculus. (Illus.). 1008p. 1984. 31.95 (ISBN 0-13-898312-7). P-H.

Campbell, Howard E. & Dierker, Paul F. Calculus with Analytic Geometry. 3rd ed. 912p. 1982. text ed. write for info. (ISBN 0-87150-331-X, 2641, Prindle). PWS Pubs.

Caratheodory, Constantin. Calculus of Variations & Partial Differential Equations of the First Order. 2nd ed. LC 81-71519. (Illus.). 421p. 1982. text ed. 25.00 (ISBN 0-8284-0318-X). Chelsea Pub.

Carman & Saunders. Modern Technical Math with Calculus. write for info. (ISBN 0-534-04305-4). Wadsworth Pub.

Childress, Robert L. Calculus for Business & Economics. 2nd ed. LC 77-2855. (Illus.). 1978. text ed. 27.95 (ISBN 0-13-111534-0). P-H.

Christensen, Mark J. Computing for Calculus. 240p. 1981. pap. 7.75 (ISBN 0-12-304365-4). Acad Pr.

Clar, Lawrence & Hart, James. Calculus with Analytic Geometry for the Technologies. (Ser. in Technological Mathematics). (Illus.). 1980. text ed. 24.95 (ISBN 0-13-111856-0). P-H.

--Mathematics for the Technologies with Calculus. (P-H Series in Technical Mathematics). (Illus.). 1978. ref. ed. 29.95 (ISBN 0-13-562553-X). P-H.

Colombeau, J. F. Differential Calculus & Holomorphy. (Mathematical Studies: Vol. 64). 456p. 1982. 59.75 (ISBN 0-444-86397-4, North-Holland). Elsevier.

Connelly, James F. & Fratangelo, Robert A. Elementary Technical Mathematics with Calculus. 1979. write for info. (ISBN 0-02-324440-2). Macmillan.

Corwin & Szczarba. Calculus in Vector Spaces. (Pure & Applied Mathematics Ser.: Vol. 52). 1979. 95.00 (ISBN 0-8247-6832-9). Dekker.

Courant, R. Differential & Integral Calculus, 2 vols. Incl. Vol. 1. 630p. 1937. 43.95 (ISBN 0-471-17820-9); Vol. 2. 692p. 1936. 43.95x (ISBN 0-471-17853-5). Pub. by Wiley-Interscience). Wiley.

Courant, Richard & John, J. Fritz. Introduction to Calculus & Analysis, 2 vols. LC 65-16403. Vol. 2, 954p., 1974. 57.50x (ISBN 0-471-17862-4, Pub. by Wiley-Interscience). Wiley.

Crowdis, David G., et al. Concepts of Calculus with Applications to Business & Economics. 1975. text ed. write for info. (ISBN 0-02-473010-6); tchrs' manual free (ISBN 0-02-473020-3). Macmillan.

Crowell, Richard H. & Slesnick, William E. Calculus with Analytic Geometry. (Illus.). 1968. 26.95x (ISBN 0-393-09782-X). Norton.

Crowin, T. M. Elementary Calculus. (Mathematical Topics for Engineering & Science Students Ser.). (Illus.). 1976. 18.50x (ISBN 0-8464-0365-X); pap. 12.50x (ISBN 0-686-77141-9). Beekman Pubs.

Curtis, Philip C., Jr. Calculus with an Introduction to Vectors. LC 78-25618. 486p. 1979. Repr. of 1972 ed. text ed. 25.50 (ISBN 0-88275-822-5). Krieger.

Davidson, Ronald C. & Marion, Jerry B. Mathematical Methods for Introductory Physics with Calculus. 2nd ed. LC 79-19656. 232p. 1980. pap. text ed. 18.95x (ISBN 0-7216-2919-9). SCP.

Delillo, Nicholas T. Advanced Calculus with Applications. 1982. text ed. 31.95x (ISBN 0-02-328220-7). Macmillan.

De Sapio, Rodolfo. Calculus for the Life Sciences. LC 77-21312. (Illus.). 740p. 1978. text ed. 29.95x (ISBN 0-7167-0371-8). W H Freeman.

Dixon, Charles. Advanced Calculus. LC 80-41382. 147p. 1981. 39.95 (ISBN 0-471-27913-7, Pub. by Wiley-Interscience); pap. 25.95 (ISBN 0-471-27914-5). Wiley.

Downing, Douglas. Calculus. (The Easy Way Ser.). 1982. pap. 7.95 (ISBN 0-8120-2588-1). Barron.

Dressler, Robert E. & Stromberg, Karl. Techniques of Calculus. (Orig.). 1982. text ed. 25.00 (ISBN 0-87720-979-0); pap. text ed. 17.50 (ISBN 0-87720-978-2). AMSCO Sch.

Edelan, Dominic. Isovector Methods for Equations of Balans: With Programs for Computer Assistance in Operator Calculations and an Exposition of Practical Topics of the Exterior Calculus. 536p. 1980. 45.00x (ISBN 90-286-0420-0). Sijthoff & Noordhoff.

Edelen, Dominic G. Applied Exterior Calculus. LC 84-19575. 471p. 1985. pap. text ed. 44.95 (ISBN 0-471-80773-7, Pub. by Wiley-Interscience). Wiley.

Edwards, C. H. & Penney, David E. Calculus & Analytic Geometry. 1120p. 1982. 36.95 (ISBN 0-13-111609-6). P-H.

McBride, Adam C. Fractional Calculus & Integral Transforms of Generalized Functions. (Research in Mathematics Ser.: No. 31). 179p. (Orig.). 1979. pap. text ed. 22.50 (ISBN 0-273-08415-1). Pitman Pub MA.

McBrien, Vincent O. Introduction to Calculus. (Century Mathematics Ser.). (Illus.). 1969. 29.50x (ISBN 0-89197-237-4); pap. text ed. 14.00x (ISBN 0-89197-797-X). Irvington.

McCarty, George. Calculator Calculus. rev. ed. LC 75-27363. (Illus.). xiv, 258p. 1980. pap. 19.95 (ISBN 0-936356-00-6). EduCALC Pubns.

McKennon, Kelly. Multipliers, Positive Functionals, Positive-Definite Functions & Fourier-Stieltjes Transforms. LC 52-42839. (Memoirs: No. 111). 67p. 1971. pap. 9.00 (ISBN 0-8218-1811-2, MEMO-111). Am Math.

Maher, Richard. Beginning Calculus with Applications. LC 74-14793. (Illus.). 1976. 14.95x (ISBN 0-02-848730-3). Hafner.

Malvino, Albert P. Calculus for Electronics. LC 76-56805. (Illus.). 316p. 1977. Repr. of 1969 ed. lib. bdg. 21.50 (ISBN 0-88275-497-1). Krieger.

Marcus, Marvin. An Introduction to Pascal & Precalculus. 1984. 29.95 (ISBN 0-88175-009-3); tchr's diskette 17.00 (ISBN 0-88175-062-X); student's diskette 17.00 (ISBN 0-88175-061-1); solution manual 10.00 (ISBN 0-88175-063-8). Computer Sci.

Marsden, J. & Weinstein, A. Calculus I: Undergraduate Texts in Mathematics. 2nd ed. (Illus.). 300p. 1985. pap. 17.95 (ISBN 0-387-90974-5). Springer Verlag.

--Calculus II. 2nd ed. (Undergraduate Texts in Mathematics Ser.). (Illus.). 300p. 1985. pap. 17.95 (ISBN 0-387-90975-3). Springer-Verlag.

Mendelson, E. Schaum's Outline of Beginning Calculus. (Schaum's Outline Ser.). 384p. 1985. 8.65 (ISBN 0-07-041465-3). McGraw.

Men'Sov, D. E. Limits of Indeterminacy in Measure of T-Means of Subseries of a Trigonometric Sales. LC 81-14992. (Steklov Institute of Mathematics: No. 149). 23.00 (ISBN 0-8218-3043-0, STEKLO-149). Am Math.

Mett, C. L. & Smith, J. C. Calculus with Applications. LC 84-12517. 480p. 1984. 29.95 (ISBN 0-07-041687-7). McGraw.

Mikusinski, Jan. Operational Calculus, Vol. 1. 2nd ed. (International Series in Pure & Applied Mathematics: Vol. 109). (Illus.). 320p. 1982. 30.00 (ISBN 0-08-025071-8). Pergamon.

Miller, Kenneth S. Advanced Real Calculus. LC 74-7055. 196p. 1974. Repr. of 1957 ed. text ed. 14.00 (ISBN 0-88275-179-4). Krieger.

Millman, Richard S. & Parker, George D. Calculus: A Practical Introduction. (Illus.). 1979. text ed. 31.95 (ISBN 0-07-042305-9). McGraw.

Milne, W. E. Numerical Calculus. 1949. 40.00x (ISBN 0-691-08011-9). Princeton U Pr.

Milne-Thomson, L. M. The Calculus of Finite Difference. 2nd ed. LC 80-65906. xxiii, 558p. 1980. text ed. 22.50 (ISBN 0-8284-0308-2). Chelsea Pub.

Mizrahi & Sullivan. Calculus & Analytic Geometry. 2nd ed. 1985. text ed. write for info (ISBN 0-534-05454-4). Wadsworth Pub.

Mizrahi, Abe & Sullivan, Michael. Calculus with Applications to Business & Life Sciences. 2nd ed. LC 83-16946. 440p. 1984. 31.95 (ISBN 0-471-05484-4); solutions manual avail. (ISBN 0-471-88571-1). Wiley.

Mizrahi, Abshalom & Sullivan, Michael J. Calculus & Analytic Geometry. 1136p. 1982. text ed. write for info (ISBN 0-534-00978-6); write for info study guide (ISBN 0-534-00979-4). Wadsworth Pub.

Munen, M. & Yizze, James P. Precalculus. 4th ed. (Illus.). 1985. text ed. 27.95 (ISBN 0-87901-258-7); study guide 8.95 (ISBN 0-87901-259-5). Worth.

Natanson, I. P. Problemas Elementales de Maximo y Minimo y Suma de Cantidades Infintamente Pequenas. (Span.). 107p. 1977. pap. 1.95 (ISBN 0-8285-1690-1, Pub. by Mir Pubs USSR). Imported Pubns.

Newmark, Joseph. The Usefulness of Calculus: For the Behavioral, Life & Managerial Sciences. 1978. scp 26.50 (ISBN 0-06-385750-2, HarpC); solutions manual avail. (ISBN 0-06-375775-3). Har-Row.

Niven, Ivan. Calculus: An Introductory Approach. 2nd ed. 210p. 1968. Repr. of 1966 ed. 11.95 (ISBN 0-686-47386-8). Krieger.

Oakley, Cletus O. Calculus. rev. ed. (Orig.). 1957. pap. 5.50 (ISBN 0-06-460048-3, CO 48, COS). B&N NY.

--Calculus: A Modern Approach. (Illus., Orig.). 1971. pap. 6.95 (ISBN 0-06-460134-X, CO 134, COS). B&N NY.

Oberle, William F. Calculus and the Computer. 1986. pap. text ed. price not set (ISBN 0-201-15983-X). Addison-Wesley.

Oglesby, Francis C. Examination of a Decision Procedure. LC 52-42839. (Memoirs: No. 44). 148p. 1971. pap. 11.00 (ISBN 0-8218-1244-0, MEMO-44). Am Math.

Oldham, Keith B. & Spanier, Jerome. The Fractional Calculus: Theory & Applications, Differentiation & Integration to Arbitrary Order. 1974. 55.00 (ISBN 0-12-525550-0). Acad Pr.

Olmsted, John M. Advanced Calculus. (Illus.). 1961. text ed. 41.95 (ISBN 0-13-010983-5). P-H.

--Second Course in Calculus. LC 68-14041. (Century Mathematics Ser.). (Illus.). 1968. 39.50x (ISBN 0-89197-395-8); pap. text ed. 19.50x (ISBN 0-89197-932-8). Irvington.

Orth, D. L. Calculus in a New Key. (Illus., Orig.). 1976. pap. text ed. 9.25 (ISBN 0-917326-05-9). APL Pr.

Osserman, Robert. Two-Dimensional Calculus. LC 76-50613. 476p. 1977. Repr. of 1968 ed. lib. bdg. 26.50 (ISBN 0-88275-473-4). Krieger.

Paul, Richard S. & Haeussler, Ernest F., Jr. Calculus for Business. 1984. text ed. 24.95 (ISBN 0-8359-0635-3); instr's manual avail. (ISBN 0-8359-0636-1). Reston.

Paul, Richard S. & Shaevel, M. Leonard. Essentials of Technical Mathematics with Calculus. LC 77-17582. (P-H Series in Technical Mathematics). (Illus.). 1978. ref. ed. 29.95 (ISBN 0-13-289199-9). P-H.

Payne, Michael. Precalculus Mathematics: New Impressions. (Illus.). 1978. text ed. 29.95 (ISBN 0-7216-7126-8). HR&W.

Pease, Edward M. & Wadsworth, George P. Calculus: With Analytic Geometry. LC 68-56150. pap. 120.00 (ISBN 0-317-08689-8, 2012457). Bks Demand UMI.

Peluso, Ada. Background for Calculus. 1978. pap. text ed. 16.95 (ISBN 0-8403-2295-X, 40296301). Kendall-Hunt.

Peterson, Gordon M. & Graesser, R. F. Calculus. (Quality Paperback: No. 51). 321p. (Orig.). 1974. pap. 4.95 (ISBN 0-8226-0051-X). Littlefield.

Pine, Eli S. How to Enjoy Calculus: With Computer Applications. rev. ed. LC 83-60717. 158p. (Orig.). 1984. pap. 6.95 (ISBN 0-917208-02-1). Steinlitz-Hammacher.

Pinzon, Alvaro. Calculo, Bk. I. 2nd ed. (Span.). 1978. pap. text ed. 10.10 (ISBN 0-06-316986-X, Pub. by HarLA Mexico). Har-Row.

--Calculo, Bk. II. 2nd ed. (Span.). 1978. pap. text ed. 10.10 (ISBN 0-06-316987-8, Pub. by HarLA Mexico). Har-Row.

Piskunov, Nicholas. Differential & Integral Calculus for Engineers, 2 vols. 2nd ed. MIR Publishers, tr. from Rus. 1032p. 1974. text ed. 37.50x set (ISBN 0-8464-0334-X). Beekman Pubs.

Pownall, Malcolm. Functions & Graphs: Calculus Preparatory Mathematics. (Illus.). 592p. 1983. 29.95 (ISBN 0-13-332304-8). P-H.

Priestley, W. M. Calculus: An Historical Approach. (Undergraduate Texts in Mathematics Ser.). (Illus.). 1979. 24.00 (ISBN 0-387-90349-6). Springer-Verlag.

Protter, M. H. & Morrey, C. B., Jr. Intermediate Calculus. 2nd ed. (Undergraduate Texts in Mathematics Ser.). (Illus.). 600p. 1985. 38.00 (ISBN 0-387-96058-9). Springer-Verlag.

Protter, Murray H. & Morrey, Charles B., Jr. Calculus for College Students. 2nd ed. LC 72-3462. 1973. text ed. 31.95 (ISBN 0-201-05981-9). Addison-Wesley.

--Calculus with Analytic Geometry: A First Course. 3rd ed. LC 76-12801. (Mathematics Ser.). 1977. text ed. 27.95 (ISBN 0-201-06037-X); instr's manual 3.50 (ISBN 0-201-06031-0); student suppl. 9.95 (ISBN 0-201-06032-9). Addison-Wesley.

--Calculus with Analytic Geometry: A Second Course. LC 70-153066. (Mathematics Ser.). 1971. text ed. 27.95 (ISBN 0-201-06021-3). Addison-Wesley.

--College Calculus with Analytic Geometry. 3rd ed. LC 76-12800. (Mathematics Ser.). 1977. text ed. 39.95 (ISBN 0-201-06030-2); study guide 5.95 (ISBN 0-201-06036-1); study supplemental 9.95 (ISBN 0-201-06032-9). Addison-Wesley.

Purcell, Edwin J. & Varberg, Dale. Calculus with Analytic Geometry. 4th ed. (Illus.). 896p. 1984. text ed. 39.95 (ISBN 0-13-111807-2). P-H.

Ram, Michael. Essential Mathematics for College Physics with Calculus: A Self Study Guide. 418p. (Orig.). 1984. pap. text ed. 13.50 (ISBN 0-471-80876-8). Wiley.

Ratti, J. S. Elementary Applied Calculus. (Illus.). 445p. 1981. text ed. 24.50 (ISBN 0-936166-05-3). Mariner Pub.

Rees, Paul K. & Sparks, Fred W. Calculus with Analytic Geometry. LC 68-17508. (Illus.). 1969. text ed. 44.95 (ISBN 0-07-051675-8). McGraw.

Research & Education Association Staff. Advanced Calculus Problem Solver. rev. ed. (Illus.). 1056p. 1984. pap. text ed. 23.85 (ISBN 0-87891-533-8). Res & Educ.

--Pre-Calculus Problem Solver. LC 84-61812. (Illus.). 960p. 1984. pap. text ed. 19.85 (ISBN 0-87891-556-7). Res & Educ.

Rice, Bernard & Strange, Jerry. Technical Math with Calculus. LC 82-20445. 1983. text ed. write for info. (ISBN 0-87150-376-X, 2801, Prindle). PWS Pubs.

Rice, Harold S. & Knight, Raymond M. Technical Mathematics with Calculus. 3rd ed. (Illus.). 704p. 1974. text ed. 35.30 (ISBN 0-07-052205-7). McGraw.

Richmond, A. E. Calculus for Electronics. 3rd ed. LC 81-23642. 512p. 1982. text ed. 31.75 (ISBN 0-07-052353-3). McGraw.

Riddle, Douglas F. Calculus & Analytic Geometry. 1116p. 1974. text ed. write for info. (ISBN 0-534-01198-5). Wadsworth Pub.

--Calculus & Analytic Geometry. 4th ed. 1248p. write for info. (ISBN 0-534-01468-2). Wadsworth Pub.

Rodi, Stephen. Complete Solutions Manual to Accompany Swokowski's Calculus: Alternate Ed. 750p. 1982. pap. text ed. write for info. (ISBN 0-87150-342-5, 2733, Prindle). PWS Pubs.

Rodin, Burton. Basic Calculus with Applications. 1978. text ed. 27.70x (ISBN 0-673-16224-9). Scott F.

Rogers, Kenneth. Advanced Calculus. (Mathematics Ser.). 384p. 1976. text ed. 25.95x (ISBN 0-675-08651-5). Merrill.

Roman, Steven. The Umbral Calculus. LC 83-11940. (Pure & Applied Mathemnatics Ser.). 1983. 39.00 (ISBN 0-12-594380-6). Acad Pr.

Rosenberger, Noah B. The Place of the Elementary Calculus in the Senior High School Mathematics. LC 71-177209. (Columbia University. Teachers College. Contributions to Education: No. 117). Repr. of 1921 ed. 22.50 (ISBN 0-404-55117-3). AMS Pr.

Rosenstein, Joseph G. Linear Orderings. LC 80-2341. (Pure & Applied Mathematics Ser.). 1982. 67.50 (ISBN 0-12-597680-1). Acad Pr.

Ross, K. A. Elementary Analysis: The Theory of Calculus. Gehring, F. W. & Halmos, P. R., eds. LC 79-24806. (Undergraduate Texts in Mathematics Ser.). (Illus.). 350p. 1980. 24.00 (ISBN 3-540-90459-X). Springer-Verlag.

Rothenberg, Ronald I. Basic Computing for Calculus. 328p. 1985. 15.95 (ISBN 0-07-054011-X). McGraw.

Roubine, E., et al, eds. Mathematics Applied to Physics. (Illus.). 1970. 39.50 (ISBN 0-387-04965-7). Springer-Verlag.

Rudman, Jack. Calculus with Analytical Geometry. (College Level Examination Ser.: CLEP-43). (Cloth bdg. avail. on request). 1977. pap. 9.95 (ISBN 0-8373-5393-9). Natl Learning.

--Introductory Calculus. (College Level Examination Ser.: CLEP-21). 17.95 (ISBN 0-8373-5371-8); pap. 9.95 (ISBN 0-8373-5321-1). Natl Learning.

Salas, S. & Salas, C. Preparation for Calculus. 3rd ed. 477p. 1985. 28.95 (ISBN 0-471-87386-1); solutions manual 15.00 (ISBN 0-471-81894-1). Wiley.

Salas, S. L. & Hille, E. Calculus: One & Several Variables with Analytic Geometry, 2 pts. 4th ed. LC 81-21975. (Bahasa-Malaysia.). 1982. Pt. 1, 671p. text ed. 32.45 (ISBN 0-471-08055-1); Pt. 1, 600p. pap. text ed. 10.95 (ISBN 0-471-86622-9); Pt. 2, 613. text ed. 32.45 (ISBN 0-471-08054-3); Cloth combined, 1136p. text ed. 39.45 (ISBN 0-471-04660-4); student supplement 17.45 (ISBN 0-471-05383-X); student solutions manual 16.45 (ISBN 0-471-08008-X); transparencies 18.50 (ISBN 0-471-04698-1). Wiley.

Salas, S. L. & Hille, Einar. Calculus: One & Several Variables with Analytic Geometry - Bahasa-Malaysia. 4th ed. LC 81-19847. 1136p. 1982. 39.45 (ISBN 0-471-04660-4); avail. transparency supplement. Wiley.

Salas, Saturnino L. & Salas, Charles G. Precalculus. 2nd ed. LC 78-23236. 356p. 1979. text ed. 28.45 (ISBN 0-471-03124-0); solutions manual 12.45 (ISBN 0-471-05515-8). Wiley.

Sawyer, W. W. What is Calculus About? LC 61-6227. (New Mathematical Library: No. 2). 140p. 1975. pap. 7.50 (ISBN 0-88385-602-6). Math Assn.

Schachter, H. Calculus & Analytic Geometry. 1972. text ed. 35.50 (ISBN 0-07-055056-5). McGraw.

Schelin, Charles W. & Bange, David W. Calculus for Business & Economics. 1985. text ed. write for info. (ISBN 0-87150-863-X, 33L2960, Prindle). PWS Pubs.

Segal, S. L. Nine Introductions in Complex Analysis. (Mathematics Studies Ser.: Vol. 53). 716p. 1981. 55.00 (ISBN 0-444-86226-9, North Holland). Elsevier.

Seldin, J. P. & Hindley, R., eds. To H. B. Curry: Essays on Combinatory Logic, Lambda Calculus & Formalism. 1980. 69.00 (ISBN 0-12-349050-2). Acad Pr.

Selected Papers on Calculus. 397p. 1977. 24.00 (ISBN 0-88385-201-2, BSP-03). Math Assn.

Shenk, Al. Calculus & Analytic Geometry. 3rd ed. 1984. text ed. 39.30x (ISBN 0-673-16582-5). Scott F.

Shockley, James E. Calculus & Analytic Geometry. 1212p. 1982. text ed. 39.95x (ISBN 0-03-018886-5). SCP.

Simmons, G. F. Calculus with Analytic Geometry. LC 84-14359. 1056p. 1985. 40.95 (ISBN 0-07-057419-7). McGraw.

Simmons, George F. Precalculus Mathematics in a Nutshell. LC 81-8397. (Illus.). 127p. (Orig.). 1981. pap. text ed. 6.95x (ISBN 0-86576-009-8). W Kaufmann.

Simon, Arthur B. Calculus with Analytic Geometry. 1982. text ed. 39.30x (ISBN 0-673-16044-0). Scott F.

Smith, Sanderson M. & Griffin, Frank W. Calculus Simplified & Self-Taught. 256p. (Orig.). 1984. pap. 7.95 (ISBN 0-668-05756-4). Arco.

Soo Bong Chae. Holomorphy & Calculus in Normed Spaces. (Monographs & Textbooks in Pam). 400p. 1985. 65.00 (ISBN 0-8247-7231-8). Dekker.

Spiegel, Murray R. Advanced Calculus. (Orig.). 1963. pap. 9.95 (ISBN 0-07-060229-8). McGraw.

--Calculus of Finite Differences & Differential Equations. (Schaum's Outline Ser). pap. 8.95 (ISBN 0-07-060218-2). McGraw.

Spivak, Michael. Calculus. 2nd ed. LC 80-82517. (Illus.). 646p. 1980. text ed. 30.00x (ISBN 0-914098-77-2). Publish or Perish.

--Calculus on Manifolds: A Modern Approach to Classical Theorems of Advanced Calculus. (Orig.). 1965. pap. 20.95 (ISBN 0-8053-9021-9). Benjamin-Cummings.

Sprague, Atherton H. Calculus. LC 52-6205. Repr. of 1952 ed. 146.80 (ISBN 0-8357-9850-X, 2012416). Bks Demand UMI.

Stein, S. K. Calculus & Analytical Geometry. 3rd ed. (Illus.). 1248p. 1982. 44.95x (ISBN 0-07-061153-X). McGraw.

Stein, Sherman K. Calculus & Analytic Geometry. 2nd ed. (Illus.). 1977. text ed. 34.95 (ISBN 0-07-061008-8). McGraw.

Stockton, Doris S. Essential Precalculus. LC 77-75647. (Illus.). 1978. text ed. 29.50 (ISBN 0-395-25417-5); instr's. manual 1.85 (ISBN 0-395-25418-3). HM.

Strange & Rice. Technical Calculus with Analytic Geometry. 1986. text ed. write for info. Breton Pubs.

Strange, Jerry D. & Rice, Bernard J. Analytical Geometry & Calculus: With Technical Applications. 462p. 1970. 31.95 (ISBN 0-471-83190-5). Wiley.

Studer, Mailyn. Precalculus. 1981. text ed. 28.00x (ISBN 0-8162-8540-3); study guide. Holden-Day.

Swann, Howard & Johnson, John. Professor E. McSquared's Original, Fantastic, & Highly Edifying Calculus Primer. LC 77-7230. (Illus.). 216p. 1977. pap. 10.95 (ISBN 0-913232-47-5). W Kaufmann.

Swokowski, Earl W. Calculus with Analytic Geometry. 2nd ed. (Illus.). 1979. text ed. write for info. (ISBN 0-87150-268-2, PWS 2181, Prindle). PWS Pubs.

--Calculus with Analytic Geometry: Alternate Edition. 1008p. 1982. text ed. write for info. (ISBN 0-87150-341-7, 2731, Prindle). PWS Pubs.

--Elements of Calculus with Analytic Geometry. (Illus.). 636p. text ed. write for info. (ISBN 0-87150-504-5, Prindle); write for info. tchr's manual (ISBN 0-87150-507-X); write for info. calulator wkbk. (ISBN 0-686-64031-4); write for info. test bank (ISBN 0-686-64032-2); write for info. solutions manual (ISBN 0-87150-508-8). PWS Pubs.

Tan. Applied Calculus. 1986. text ed. write for info. (ISBN 0-87150-954-7, 33L4010, Prindle). PWS Pubs.

Taylor, Angus E. & Mann, Robert W. Advanced Calculus. 3rd ed. LC 81-16141. 732p. 1983. text ed. 39.00 (ISBN 0-471-02566-6); solutions avail. (ISBN 0-471-09918-X). Wiley.

Thomas, George B., Jr. & Finney, Ross L. Calculus & Analytic Geometry. 5th ed. LC 78-55832. (Illus.). 1979. Combined Ed. text ed. 38.95 (ISBN 0-201-07540-7); Pt. 1. o. p. 24.95 (ISBN 0-201-07541-5); Pt. 2. o. p. 26.95 (ISBN 0-201-07542-3); avail. student suppl. 10.95 (ISBN 0-201-07543-1); avail. self study guide 10.95 (ISBN 0-201-07655-1); solutions manual 13.95 (ISBN 0-201-07544-X). Addison-Wesley.

--Calculus & Analytic Geometry. 6th ed. LC 83-2569. (Illus.). 1100p. 1984. 39.95 (ISBN 0-201-16290-3); student suppl. 14.95 (ISBN 0-201-16298-9). Addison-Wesley.

--Calculus & Analytic Geometry: Functions of One Variable, Pt. 1. 6th ed. (Analytic Geometry & Infinite Ser.). 760p. 1984. 29.95 (ISBN 0-201-16291-1). Addison-Wesley.

--Calculus & Analytic Geometry: Vectors, Functions of Several Variables, Pt. 1. (Infinite Series & Differential). 520p. 1984. 27.95 (ISBN 0-201-16292-X). Addison-Wesley.

Thompson, J. E. Calculus for the Practical Worker. 4th ed. 280p. 1982. pap. 7.95 (ISBN 0-442-28274-5). Van Nos Reinhold.
Thompson, Silvanus P. Calculus Made Easy. 3rd ed. 1970. 6.95 (ISBN 0-312-11410-9, Papermac). St Martin.
Toeplitz, Otto. The Calculus: A Genetic Approach. Kothe, Gottfried, ed. Lange, Louise, tr. LC 63-9731. 206p. 1981. pap. 10.00x (ISBN 0-226-80667-7). U of Chicago Pr.
Trench, William F. Advanced Calculus. 1978. text ed. 29.50 scp (ISBN 0-06-046665-0, HarpC); ans. bk. avail. (ISBN 0-06-366680-4). Har-Row.
Troutman, J. L. Variational Calculus with Elementary Convexity. (Undergraduate Texts in Mathematics). (Illus.). 364p. 1983. 29.80 (ISBN 0-387-90771-8). Springer-Verlag.
Voxman, et al, eds. Advanced Calculus: An Introduction to Modern Analysis. (Pure & Applied Mathematics Ser.: Vol. 63). 1981. 55.00 (ISBN 0-8247-6949-X). Dekker.
Wallis, R. L. Differential & Integral Calculus. (Illus.). 152p. 1984. pap. 13.95 (ISBN 0-442-30579-6). Van Nos Reinhold.
Washington, Allyn J. Basic Technical Mathematics with Calculus, Metric. 4th ed. 1985. text ed. 33.95x (ISBN 0-8053-9545-8); instr's guide 5.95 (ISBN 0-8053-9546-6). Benjamin-Cummings.
--An Introduction to Calculus with Applications. LC 71-187928. 352p. 1972. text ed. 27.95 (ISBN 0-8465-8611-8). Benjamin-Cummings.
--Technical Calculus with Analytical Geometry. 2nd ed. 1980. 28.95 (ISBN 0-8053-9519-9); instr's. guide 4.95 (ISBN 0-8053-9533-4). Benjamin-Cummings.
Watanabe, S. Lectures on Stochastic Differential Equations & Malliavin Calculus. (Tata Institute Lectures on Mathematics Ser.). viii, 118p. 1984. pap. 9.50 (ISBN 0-387-12897-2). Springer-Verlag.
Whipkey, K. L. & Whipkey, Mary N. The Power of Calculus. 3rd ed. LC 78-24067. 373p. 1979. 32.00 (ISBN 0-471-03140-2); tchr's. manual avail. (ISBN 0-471-05500-X). Wiley.
Willard, Stephen. Calculus & Its Applications. 2nd ed. LC 80-28460. 350p. 1981. text ed. write for info. (ISBN 0-87150-305-0, 2431, Prindle). PWS Pubs.
Willcox, Alfred B., et al. Introduction to Calculus One & Two. 1971. text ed. 38.95 (ISBN 0-395-05543-1). HM.
Williams, Donald & Woods, Thomas J. Basic Calculus with Applications. 1979. text ed. write for info (ISBN 0-534-00685-X). Wadsworth Pub.
Wilson, R. L. Much Ado About Calculus: A Modern Treatment with Applications Prepared for Use with the Computer. LC 79-987. (Undergraduate Texts in Mathematics). (Illus.). 1979. 24.00 (ISBN 0-387-90347-X). Springer-Verlag.
Woods, Frederick S. Advanced Calculus: A Course Arranged with Special Reference to the Needs of Students of Applied Mathematics. pap. 101.80 (ISBN 0-317-08737-1, 2000161). Bks Demand UMI.
Woods, Frederick S. & Bailey, Frederick H. Elementary Calculus. pap. 98.80 (ISBN 0-317-08707-X, 2000159). Bks Demand UMI.
Youse, Bevan K. Calculus for the Managerial, Social, & Life Sciences. 135p. 1984. write for info. instr's manual & test bank (ISBN 0-314-77890-X); write for info. transparency masters (ISBN 0-314-77893-4). West Pub.
Zill, Dennis G. Calculus with Analytic Geometry. 939p. 1984. text ed. write for info. (ISBN 0-87150-432-4, 33L2820, Prindle). PWS Pubs.
Zill, Dennis G. & Dewar, Jacqueline M. Basic Mathematics for Calculus. 2nd ed. 448p. 1982. text ed. write for info (ISBN 0-534-01197-7). Wadsworth Pub.

CALCULUS–HISTORY

Boyer, Carl B. History of the Calculus & Its Conceptual Development. Orig. Title: Concepts of Calculus. 1959. pap. 5.95 (ISBN 0-486-60509-4). Dover.
--The History of the Calculus & Its Conceptual Development. LC 59-9673. 1959. lib. bdg. 15.00x (ISBN 0-88307-623-3). Gannon.

CALCULUS–PROBLEMS, EXERCISES, ETC.

Bluman, G. W. Problem Book for First Year Calculus. (Problem Books in Mathematics Ser.). (Illus.). 350p. 1984. 39.00 (ISBN 0-387-90920-6). Springer-Verlag.
Broadwin, Judith & Lenchner, George. Solution, A.P. Calculus Problems: Part II AB & BC, 1970-1984. 168p. (Orig.). 1984. pap. text ed. 6.50 (ISBN 0-9612940-2-7). Nassau Co Assn Mathematics Supv.
Delillo, Nicholas T. Advanced Calculus with Applications. 1982. text ed. 31.95x (ISBN 0-02-328220-7). Macmillan.
Downing, Douglas. Calculus by Discovery. 224p. 1982. 12.95 (ISBN 0-8120-5451-2). Barron.
Gelfand, S. I., et al. Learn Limits Through Problems. (Pocket Mathematical Library). 78p. 1968. 22.00 (ISBN 0-677-20720-4). Gordon.
Goodman, A. W. & Saff, Edward. Calculus: Concepts & Calculations. 1981. text ed. write for info. (ISBN 0-02-344740-0); Vol. 1. write for info. (ISBN 0-02-344750-8); Vol. 2. write for info. (ISBN 0-686-72521-2). Macmillan.
Hutchinngs, Mary H. & Cogswell, William R. Exercises in Calculus. 146p. 1981. pap. text ed. 5.95 (ISBN 0-88334-148-4). Ind Sch Pr.
Jones, Colin R. Problems in Calculus & Related Topics. LC 66-3023. pap. 50.00 (ISBN 0-317-09413-0, 2019396). Bks Demand UMI.
Lynch, Ransom, et al. Calculus, with Computer Applications. LC 72-86514. pap. 160.00 (ISBN 0-317-27946-7, 2055979). Bks Demand UMI.
McCarty, George. Calculator Calculus. rev. ed. LC 75-27363. (Illus.). xiv, 258p. 1980. pap. 19.95 (ISBN 0-936356-00-6). EduCALC Pubns.
Mansfield, Maynard J. Intermediate Real Analysis. LC 78-15379. 222p. 1979. Repr. of 1969 ed. lib. bdg. 16.50 (ISBN 0-88275-712-1). Krieger.
Miller, Eldon. Student Solutions for Calculus & Analytic Geometry, Vol. I. 208p. 1983. pap. text ed. write for info. (ISBN 0-534-00980-8). Wadsworth Pub.
Research & Education Association Staff. The Calculus Problem Solver. rev. ed. LC 74-17899. (Illus.). 1088p. 1984. pap. text ed. 19.85 (ISBN 0-87891-505-2). Res & Educ.
Spivak, Michael. Answer Book to Calculus. 2nd ed. 412p. 1984. text ed. 20.00 (ISBN 0-914098-78-0). Publish or Perish.
Thomas, George B., Jr. Calculus & Analytic Geometry with Supplementary Problems. LC 82-20754. 1983. 21.95 (ISBN 0-201-07779-5). Addison-Wesley.

CALCULUS–PROGRAMMED INSTRUCTION

Elich, Joseph & Elich, Carletta J. College Algebra with Calculus. (Math-Mallion Ser.). (Illus.). 480p. 1981. text ed. 25.95x (ISBN 0-201-13340-7); instr's. manual 2.50 (ISBN 0-201-13341-5); answer bk. 2.50 (ISBN 0-201-13342-3); student guide 6.95 (ISBN 0-201-13343-1). Addison-Wesley.
--Precalculus with Caculator Applications. (Math-Mallion Ser.). (Illus.). 576p. 1981. text ed. 26.95x (ISBN 0-201-13345-8); instr's. manual 3.00 (ISBN 0-201-13346-6); student solution bk. 6.95 (ISBN 0-201-13348-2); answer bk. 2.50. Addison-Wesley.

CALCULUS, ABSOLUTE DIFFERENTIAL

see Calculus of Tensors

CALCULUS, DIFFERENTIAL

Boltyansky, V. G. Differentiation Explained. 63p. 1977. pap. 1.95 (ISBN 0-8285-0716-3, Pub. by Mir Pubs USSR). Imported Pubns.
De Morgan, Augustus. Elementary Illustrations of the Differential & Integral Calculus. 152p. 16.95 (ISBN 0-87548-158-2). Open Court.
Ghosh, P. K. Mathematical Analysis: Differential Calculus, Vol. I. (A Modern Approach Ser.: Vol. 1). 484p. 1981. 30.00x (ISBN 0-86125-528-3, Pub. by Orient Longman India). State Mutual Bk.
Granville, William A. & Smith, Percey F. Elements of the Differential & Integral Calculus. rev. ed. pap. 142.00 (ISBN 0-317-08569-7, 2019890). Bks Demand UMI.
Hilton, P. J. Differential Calculus. (Library of Mathematics). 1968. pap. 5.00 (ISBN 0-7100-4341-4). Routledge & Kegan.
Keller, H. H. Differential Calculus in Locally Convex Spaces. LC 74-20715. (Lectures Notes in Mathematics Ser.: Vol. 417). xvi, 131p. 1974. pap. 13.00 (ISBN 0-387-06962-3). Springer-Verlag.
Korovkin, P. P. Differentiation. (Pocket Mathematical Library). 96p. 1968. 23.25 (ISBN 0-677-20750-6). Gordon.
Landau, Edmund. Differential & Integral Calculus. LC 65-4331. 372p. 1981. text ed. 16.95x (ISBN 0-8284-0078-4). Chelsea Pub.
McConnell, A. J. Applications of Tensor Analysis. pap. 6.50 (ISBN 0-486-60373-3). Dover.
Nachbin, Leopoldo. Introduction to Functional Analysis: Banach Spaces & Different Calculus. (Pure & Applied Mathematics: Monographs & Textbooks: Vol. 60). (Illus.). 184p. 1981. 35.00 (ISBN 0-8247-6984-8). Dekker.
Piskunov, Nikoloi. Differential & Integral Calculus. 896p. 1965. 121.50x (ISBN 0-677-20600-3). Gordon.
Rall, I. B. Automatic Differentiation: Techniques & Applications. (Lecture Notes in Computer Science Ser.: Vol. 120). 165p. 1981. pap. 14.00 (ISBN 0-387-10861-0). Springer Verlag.
Williams, Lloyd B. & Gray, Allan W. Calculus: Differential & Integral-Combined Syllabus. 1976. text ed. 16.00 (ISBN 0-89420-059-3, 122210); cassette recordings 140.95 (ISBN 0-89420-130-1, 350500). Natl Book.
--Calculus: Differential Syllabus, Pt. 1. 1976. text ed. 9.25 (ISBN 0-89420-057-7, 122202); cassette recordings 89.20 (ISBN 0-89420-131-X, 350510). Natl Book.
Yamamuro, S. Differential Calculus in Topological Linear Spaces. LC 73-21376. (Lecture Notes in Mathematics: Vol. 374). iv, 179p. 1974. pap. 13.00 (ISBN 0-387-06709-4). Springer-Verlag.

CALCULUS, INTEGRAL

see also Integrals; Integrals, Generalized

Crabill, Delmar C. & Neitzke, John J. Elementary Integral Calculus. (Illus.). 210p. 1983. pap. text ed. 12.25 (ISBN 0-8191-3516-X). U Pr of Amer.
De Morgan, Augustus. Elementary Illustrations of the Differential & Integral Calculus. 152p. 16.95 (ISBN 0-87548-158-2). Open Court.
Edwards, Joseph W. Integral Calculus, 2 Vols. LC 55-234. 45.00 ea. Vol. 1 (ISBN 0-8284-0102-0). Vol. 2 (ISBN 0-8284-0105-5). Chelsea Pub.
Ghosh, P. K. Mathematical Analysis: Integral Calculus (A Modern Approach) 356p. 1981. 30.00x (ISBN 0-86125-647-6, Pub. by Orient Longman India). State Mutual Bk.
Granville, William A. & Smith, Percey F. Elements of the Differential & Integral Calculus. rev. ed. pap. 142.00 (ISBN 0-317-08569-7, 2019890). Bks Demand UMI.
Landau, Edmund. Differential & Integral Calculus. LC 65-4331. 372p. 1981. text ed. 16.95x (ISBN 0-8284-0078-4). Chelsea Pub.
Ledermann, Walter. Integral Calculus. (Library of Mathematics). 1967. pap. 5.00x (ISBN 0-7100-4355-4). Routledge & Kegan.
Natanson, I. Summation of Infinitesimal Quantities. (Russian Tracts on the Physical Sciences Ser.). 74p. 1962. 19.75x (ISBN 0-677-20450-7). Gordon.
Piskunov, Nikoloi. Differential & Integral Calculus. 896p. 1965. 121.50x (ISBN 0-677-20600-3). Gordon.
Williams, Lloyd B. & Gray, Allan W. Calculus: Differential & Integral-Combined Syllabus. 1976. text ed. 16.00 (ISBN 0-89420-059-3, 122210); cassette recordings 140.95 (ISBN 0-89420-130-1, 350500). Natl Book.
--Calculus: Integral Syllabus, Pt. 2. 1976. text ed. 6.75 (ISBN 0-89420-058-5, 122208); cassette recordings 56.70 (ISBN 0-89420-132-8, 350516). Natl Book.

CALCULUS, OPERATIONAL

see also Laplace Transformation

Agranovich, Z. S. & Marchenko, V. A. Inverse Problem of Scattering Theory. Seckler, B. D., tr. (Russian Monographs and Texts on the Physical Sciences Ser.). 304p. 1963. 80.95 (ISBN 0-677-20010-2). Gordon.
Banach, Stefan. Theorie Des Operations Lineaires. 2nd ed. LC 63-21849. (Fr). 10.95 (ISBN 0-8284-0110-1). Chelsea Pub.
Conway, J. B. & Olin, R. F. A Functional Calculus for Subnormal Operators, II. LC 77-3937. (Memoirs Ser.: No. 184). 61p. 1977. pap. 12.00 (ISBN 0-8218-2184-9, MEMO-184). Am Math.
Krabbe, G. Operational Calculus. LC 77-79088. (Illus.). 1970. 45.00 (ISBN 0-387-04896-0). Springer-Verlag.
Krabbe, Gregors. Operational Calculus. LC 75-30722. 349p. 1976. 10.95x (ISBN 0-306-20017-1, Rosetta). Plenum Pub.
Taylor, Angus E. General Theory of Functions & Integration. 448p. 1985. pap. 10.95 (ISBN 0-486-64988-1). Dover.
Yosida, K. Operational Calculus, Vol. 55. (Applied Mathematical Sciences Ser.). 175p. 1984. pap. 22.00 (ISBN 0-387-96047-3). Springer-Verlag.

CALCULUS OF DIFFERENCES

see Difference Equations

CALCULUS OF OPERATIONS

see also Algebras, Linear

Kaplan, Wilfred. Operational Methods for Linear Systems. 1962. 30.95 (ISBN 0-201-03620-7). Addison-Wesley.
Pietsch, A. Operator Ideals. (Mathematical Library: Vol. 20). 432p. 1980. 93.75 (ISBN 0-444-85293-X, North Holland). Elsevier.
Vorobyev, Yu. V. Methods of Moments in Applied Mathematics. (Russian Monographs). (Illus.). 178p. 1965. 53.50x (ISBN 0-677-20340-3). Gordon.

CALCULUS OF SPINORS

see Spinor Analysis

CALCULUS OF TENSORS

see also Spaces, Generalized; Spinor Analysis

Abraham, R. & Marsden, J. E. Manifolds, Tensor Analysis, & Applications. LC 82-13737. 582p. 1983. text ed. 41.95 (ISBN 0-201-10168-8). Addison-Wesley.
Bishop, Richard & Goldberg, Samuel. Tensor Analysis on Manifolds. (Illus.). 1980. pap. 5.95 (ISBN 0-486-64039-6). Dover.
Borisenko, A. I. & Tarapov, I. E. Vector & Tensor Analysis with Applications. LC 79-87809. 1979. pap. 6.00 (ISBN 0-486-63833-2). Dover.
Corson, Edward M. Introduction to Tensors, Spinors, & Relativistic Wave Equations. 2nd ed. LC 80-85523. 222p. 1981. text ed. 15.95 (ISBN 0-8284-0315-5). Chelsea Pub.
Dodson, C. T. & Poston, T. Tensor Geometry: The Geometric Viewpoint & Its Uses. (Reference Works in Mathematics Ser.: No. 1). (Illus.). 620p. 1979. pap. 33.95 (ISBN 0-273-01040-9). Pitman Pub MA.
Erven, J. & Falkowski, B. J. Low Order Cohomology & Applications. (Lecture Notes in Mathematics Ser.: Vol. 877). 126p. 1981. pap. 12.00 (ISBN 0-387-10864-5). Springer-Verlag.
Fluegge, W. Tensor Analysis & Continuum Mechanics. LC 74-183541. (Illus.). vii, 207p. 1972. 29.00 (ISBN 0-387-05697-1). Springer-Verlag.
Golab, Stanislaw, ed. Tensor Calculus. 371p. 1974. 85.00 (ISBN 0-444-41124-0). Elsevier.
Goodbody, A. M. Cartesian Tensors: With Applications to Mechanics, Fluid Mechanics & Elasticity. (Mathematics & Its Applications Ser.). 298p. 1982. 84.95 (ISBN 0-470-27254-6). Halsted Pr.
Hay, George E. Vector & Tensor Analysis. 1953. pap. text ed. 4.00 (ISBN 0-486-60109-9). Dover.
Hermann, Robert. Energy Momentum Tensors. (Interdisciplinary Mathematics Ser.: No. 4). 153p. 1973. 14.00 (ISBN 0-915692-03-1, 99160024X). Math Sci Pr.
Hinchey, F. A. Vectors & Tensors for Engineers & Scientists. LC 76-21725. 298p. 1976. 17.95x (ISBN 0-470-15194-3). Halsted Pr.
Jaeger, L. G. Cartesian Tensors in Engineering Science. 1966. 28.00 (ISBN 0-08-011222-6); pap. 12.50 (ISBN 0-08-011221-8). Pergamon.
Jeffreys, Harold. Cartesian Tensors. (Orig.). 1931-1962. 19.95 (ISBN 0-521-05423-0); pap. 10.95 (ISBN 0-521-09191-8). Cambridge U Pr.
Klein, Felix. Famous Problems of Elementary Geometry & Other Monographs, 4 vols. in 1. Incl. From Determinant to Tensor. Sheppard, William F; Introduction to Combinatory Analysis. MacMahon, Percy A; Fermat's Last Theorem. Mordell, Louis J; Famous Problems of Elementary Geometry. Klein, Felix. 1956. 11.95 (ISBN 0-8284-0108-X). Chelsea Pub.
Krishnamurty, Karamcheti. Vector Analysis & Cartesian Tensors: With Selected Applications. LC 67-13843. (Holden-Day Series in Mathematical Physics). pap. 67.00 (ISBN 0-317-09182-4, 2016290). Bks Demand UMI.
Krogdahl, Wasley S. Tensor Analysis: Fundamentals & Applications. LC 78-62755. 1978. 21.75 (ISBN 0-8191-0594-5). U Pr of Amer.
Kyrala, A. Theoretical Physics: Applications of Vectors, Matrices, Tensors & Quaternions. LC 67-12810. (Studies in Physics & Chemistry: No. 5). pap. 93.00 (ISBN 0-317-08733-9, 2051978). Bks Demand UMI.
Lawden, D. F. An Introduction to Tensor Calculus: Relativity & Cosmology. 3rd ed. LC 81-14801. 1982. 205p. 44.95x, (ISBN 0-471-10082-X, Pub. by Wiley-Interscience); pap. 19.95, 235p. (ISBN 0-471-10096-X). Wiley.
Levi-Civita, Tullio. The Absolute Differential Calculus: Calculus of Tensors. Persico, Enrico, ed. Long, Marjorie, tr. from Italian. LC 76-27497. (Illus.). 480p. 1977. pap. text ed. 8.95 (ISBN 0-486-63401-9). Dover.
Parthasarathy, K. R. & Schmidt, K. Positive Definite Kernels, Continuous Tensor Products, & Central Limit Theorems of Probability Theory. LC 72-85400. (Lecture Notes in Mathematics: Vol. 272). 107p. 1972. pap. 9.00 (ISBN 0-387-05908-3). Springer-Verlag.
Penrose, Roger & Rindler, Wolfgang. Spinors & Space Time, Vol. 1: Two-Spinor Calculus & Relativistic Fields. 480p. 1984. 89.50 (ISBN 0-521-24527-3). Cambridge U Pr.
--Spinors & Space Time, Vol. 2: Spinor & Twistor Methods in Space-Time Geometry. 400p. Date not set. price not set (ISBN 0-521-25267-9). Cambridge U Pr.
Sokolnikoff, Ivan S. Tensor Analysis: Theory & Applications to Geometry & Mechanics of Continua. 2nd ed. LC 64-13223. (Applied Mathematics Ser.). pap. 93.30 (ISBN 0-317-08559-X, 2055264). Bks Demand UMI.
Synge & Schild. Tensor Calculus. 1978. pap. text ed. 6.00 (ISBN 0-486-63612-7). Dover.
Synge, John L. & Schild, A. Tensor Calculus. LC 75-323720. (Mathematical Expositions Ser.: No. 5). pap. 83.50 (ISBN 0-317-09117-4, 2014430). Bks Demand UMI.
Tyldesley, John R. An Introduction to Tensor Analysis for Engineers & Applied Scientists. LC 74-76860. pap. 31.50 (ISBN 0-317-08598-0, 2020978). Bks Demand UMI.
Williams, F. L. Tensor Products of Principal Series Representations, Reduction of Tensor Products of Principal Series Representations of Complex Semisimple Lie Groups. LC 73-19546. (Lecture Notes in Mathematics: Vol. 358). 132p. 1973. pap. 12.00 (ISBN 0-387-06567-9). Springer-Verlag.
Wrede, Robert C. Introduction to Vector & Tensor Analysis. 418p. 1972. pap. text ed. 7.50 (ISBN 0-486-61879-X). Dover.

CALCULUS OF VARIATIONS

see also Convex Domains; Functional Analysis

BOOKS - SUBJECT INDEX CAMBRIDGE UNIVERSITY–DEPARTMENT OF ENGINEERING

Adams. Single Variable Calculus. 624p. 1983. text ed. 24.95 (ISBN 0-201-10053-3). Addison-Wesley.

Arthurs, A. M. Complementary Variational Principles. 2nd ed. (Mathematical Monographs). 1980. 49.00x (ISBN 0-19-853532-5). Oxford U Pr.

Balakrishna, A. V., ed. Control Theory & the Calculus of Variations. LC 74-91431. 1969. 60.00 (ISBN 0-12-076953-0). Acad Pr.

Bensoussan, A. & Lions, J. L. Applications of Variational Inequalities in Stochastic Control. (Studies in Mathematics & Its Applications: Vol. 12). Orig. Title: Applications des Inequations Variationnelles en Controle Stochastique. 564p. 1982. 74.50 (ISBN 0-444-86358-3, North-Holland). Elsevier.

Besseling, J. F. & Van Der Heijden, A. M., eds. Trends in Solid Mechanics. 256p. 1980. 45.00x (ISBN 90-286-0699-8). Sijthoff & Noordhoff.

Bliss, Gilbert A. Calculus of Variations. (Carus Monograph: No. 1). 189p. 1925. 19.00 (ISBN 0-88385-001-X). Math Assn.

--Lectures on the Calculus of Variations. LC 46-5369. (Midway Reprints Ser.). 304p. 1980. 9.00x (ISBN 0-226-05896-4). U of Chicago Pr.

Bolza, Oskar. Lectures on the Calculus of Variations. 3rd ed. LC 73-16324. 12.95 (ISBN 0-8284-0145-4). Chelsea Pub.

--Vorlesungen Ueber Variationsrechnung. LC 62-8228. 23.95 (ISBN 0-8284-0160-8). Chelsea Pub.

Chicago University Department Of Mathematics. Contributions to the Calculus of Variations, 1930-41, 4 Vols. Bliss, G. A., ed. 1933-42. Set. 190.00 (ISBN 0-384-08750-7); 50.00 ea. Johnson Repr.

Corwin & Szczarba. Multivariable Calculus. (Pure and Applied Mathematics Ser.: Vol. 64). 544p. 1982. 59.75 (ISBN 0-8247-6962-7). Dekker.

Curtiss, J. H. Introduction to the Theory of Functions of a Complex Variable. (Pure & Applied Mathematics Ser.: Vol. 44). 1978. 29.75 (ISBN 0-8247-6501-X). Dekker.

Dreyfus, Stuart E. Dynamic Programming & the Calculus of Variations. (Mathematics in Science & Engineering Ser.: Vol. 21). 1965. 55.00 (ISBN 0-12-221850-7). Acad Pr.

Efimov, N. V., et al. Differential Geometry & Calculus of Variations. (Translations Ser.: No. 1 Vol. 6). 1970. Repr. of 1962 ed. 30.00 (ISBN 0-8218-1606-3, TRANS 1-6). Am Math.

Fisher, S. W. & Jerome, J. W. Minimum Norm Extremals in Function Spaces: With Applications to Classical & Modern Analysis. (Lecture Notes in Mathematics: Vol. 479). viii, 209p. (Orig.). 1975. pap. 16.00 (ISBN 0-387-07394-9). Springer-Verlag.

Friedman, A. Variational Principles & Free-Boundary Problems. (Pure & Applied Mathematics Ser.). 710p. 1982. text ed. 64.95x (ISBN 0-471-86849-3, Pub. by Wiley-Interscience). Wiley.

Gelfand, Izrail M. & Fomin, S. V. Calculus of Variations. Silverman, R., tr. (Illus.). 1963. ref. ed. 36.95 (ISBN 0-13-112292-4). P-H.

Goldstine, H. H. A History of the Calculus of Variations from the Seventeenth Through the Nineteenth Century. (Studies in the History of Mathematics & Physical Sciences: Vol. 5). (Illus.). 410p. 1980. 59.00 (ISBN 0-387-90521-9). Springer-Verlag.

Gould, Sydney H. Variational Methods for Eigenvalue Problems: An Introduction to the Weinstein Method of Intermediate Problems. 2nd ed. LC 66-76289. (Mathematical Expositions Ser.). 1966. 27.50x (ISBN 0-8020-1404-6). U of Toronto Pr.

Griffiths, P. Exterior Differential Systems & the Calculus of Variations. (Progress in Mathematics Ser.: Vol. 25). 349p. 1982. text ed. 30.00 (ISBN 0-8176-3103-8). Birkhauser.

Hermann, Robert. Diffferential Geometry & the Calculus of Variations. 2nd ed. LC 68-14664. (Intermath Ser.: No. 17). 724p. 1977. 52.00 (ISBN 0-915692-23-6, 991600320). Math Sci Pr.

Hestenes, Magnus R. Calculus of Variations & Optimal Control Theory. LC 79-25451. 418p. 1980. Repr. of 1966 ed. lib. bdg. 26.50 (ISBN 0-89874-092-4). Krieger.

Ioffe, A. D. & Tihomirov, V. M. Theory of Extremal Problems. (Studies in Mathematics & Its Applications: Vol. 6). 460p. 1979. 85.00 (ISBN 0-444-85167-4, North Holland). Elsevier.

Krasnov, M. L. Problems & Exercises in the Calculus of Variations. 222p. 1976. pap. 7.95 (ISBN 0-8285-2786-5, Pub. by Mir Pubs USSR). Imported Pubns.

Lang, Serge. Calculus of Several Variables. 2nd ed. LC 78-55822. (Mathematics Ser.). (Illus.). 1979. text ed. 34.95 (ISBN 0-201-04299-1). Addison-Wesley.

Leitmann, George. The Calculus of Variations & Optimal Control. LC 81-4582. (Mathematical Concepts & Methods in Science & Engineering Ser.: Vol. 24). 328p. 1981. 39.50x (ISBN 0-306-40707-8, Plenum Pr). Plenum Pub.

Ljusternik, L. A. Topology of the Calculus of Variations in the Large. LC 66-25298. (Translations of Mathematical Monographs: Vol. 16). 96p. 1982. pap. 21.00 (ISBN 0-8218-1566-0, MMONO-16). Am Math.

Logan, John D., ed. Invariant Variational Principles. 1977. 49.50 (ISBN 0-12-454750-8). Acad Pr.

Minkhlin, Solomon G. The Problem of the Minimum of a Quadratic Functional. Feinstein, A., tr. LC 64-24626. (Holden-Day Series in Mathematical Physics). pap. 41.00 (ISBN 0-317-09170-0, 2016292). Bks Demand UMI.

Morrey, Charles B. Multiple Integrals in the Calculus of Variations. (Grundlehren der Mathematischen Wissenschaften: Vol. 130). 1966. 51.00 (ISBN 0-387-03524-9). Springer-Verlag.

Morse, Marston. Calculus of Variations in the Large. LC 34-40909. (Colloquium Publications Ser.: Vol. 18). 368p. 1978. pap. 39.00 (ISBN 0-8218-1018-9, COLL-18). Am Math.

--Variational Analysis: Critical Extremals & Sturmian Extensions. LC 72-8368. (Pure & Applied Mathematics Ser.). Repr. of 1973 ed. 51.70 (ISBN 0-8357-9998-0, 2019523). Bks Demand UMI.

Pars, L. A. Introduction to the Calculus of Variations. 1962. text ed. 50.00x (ISBN 0-435-52691-X). Heinemann Ed.

Petrov, I. P. Variational Methods in Optimum Control Theory. Friedman, Morris D., tr. LC 68-18678. (Mathematics in Science & Engineering Ser.: Vol. 45). 1968. 60.00 (ISBN 0-12-552850-7). Acad Pr.

Quadling, D. A., ed. Four Extensions of Calculus (Draft Edition) LC 74-134617. (School Mathematics Project Ser.). (Illus.). 1971. text ed. 9.95x (ISBN 0-521-07929-2). Cambridge U Pr.

Reddy, J. N. Applied Functional Analysis & Variational Methods in Engineering. 560p. 1986. text ed. price not set (ISBN 0-07-051348-1). McGraw.

Rektorys, Karel. Variational Methods in Mathematics, Sciences & Engineering. new ed. SNTL, ed. LC 74-80530. 1976. lib. bdg. 71.00 (ISBN 90-277-0488-0, Pub. by Reidel Holland). Kluwer Academic.

Rund, Hanno. The Hamilton-Jacobi Theory in the Calculus of Variations: Its Role in Mathematics Theory & Application. LC 66-13030. 452p. 1973. Repr. of 1966 ed. 25.00 (ISBN 0-88275-063-1). Krieger.

Salinetti, G., ed. Multifunctions & Integrands. (Lecture Notes in Mathematics Ser.: Vol. 1091). v, 234p. 1984. pap. 13.50 (ISBN 0-387-13882-X). Springer-Verlag.

Smith, P. Convexity Methods in Variational Calculus. (Applied Engineering & Mathematical Sciences Ser.). 222p. 1985. 41.95 (ISBN 0-471-90679-4). Wiley.

Stacey, Weston M., Jr. Variational Methods in Nuclear Reactor Physics. (Nuclear Science & Technology Ser.). 1974. 56.50 (ISBN 0-12-662060-1). Acad Pr.

Symposium in Applied Mathematics - Chicago, 1956. Calculus of Variations & Its Applications: Proceedings. LC 50-1183. (Proceeding of the Symposia in Applied Mathematics: Vol.8). 153p. pap. 30.00 (PSAPM-8). Am Math.

Todhunter, Isaac. History of the Calculus of Variations in the Nineteenth Century. LC 61-18586. 18.50 (ISBN 0-8284-0164-0). Chelsea Pub.

Weinstein, Alexander & Stenger, William. Methods of Intermediate Problems for Eigenvalues. (Mathematics in Science & Engineering Ser.: Vol. 89). 1972. 60.00 (ISBN 0-12-742450-4). Acad Pr.

Weinstock, Robert. Calculus of Variations. LC 74-75706. pap. text ed. 6.50 (ISBN 0-486-63069-2). Dover.

Woodhouse, Robert. History of the Calculus of Variations in the Eighteenth Century. LC 64-20969. 11.50 (ISBN 0-8284-0177-2). Chelsea Pub.

Young, Laurence C. Lectures on the Calculus of Variations & Optimal Control Theory. 2nd ed. LC 79-57387. 1980. 16.95 (ISBN 0-8284-0304-X). Chelsea Pub.

CALENDAR

see also Chronology; Time

Bond, John J. Handy-Book of Rules & Tables for Verifying Dates with the Christian Era. LC 66-29473. 1966. Repr. of 1889 ed. 10.00x (ISBN 0-8462-1795-3). Russell.

Freeman-Grenville, G. S. The Muslim & Christian Calendars: Being Tables for the Conversion of Muslim & Christian Dates from the Hijra to the Year A. D. 2000. 2nd ed. 87p. 1977. 7.50x (ISBN 0-8476-1482-4). Rowman.

Nuttall, Zelia. Fundamental Principles of Old & New World Civilization. (HU PMP Ser.). 1901. 51.00 (ISBN 0-527-01190-8). Kraus Repr.

Schnippel, Emil. Die Englischen Kalenderstabe. pap. 8.00 (ISBN 0-384-54200-X). Johnson Repr.

CALENDAR–REFORM

see Calendar Reform

CALENDAR, ANGLO-SAXON

Henel, Heinrich. Studien Zum Altenglischen Computus. 1934. pap. 8.00 (ISBN 0-384-22300-1). Johnson Repr.

CALENDAR, ARAB

see Calendar, Islamic

CALENDAR, AZTEC

see Calendar, Mexican

CALENDAR, CHINESE

Hsueh, Chung-san. A Sino-Western Calendar for Two Thousand Years. lib. bdg. 90.00 (ISBN 0-87968-096-2). Krishna Pr.

CALENDAR, ISLAMIC

Freeman-Grenville, G. S. The Muslim & Christian Calendars: Being Tables for the Conversion of Muslim & Christian Dates from the Hijra to the Year A. D. 2000. 2nd ed. 87p. 1977. 7.50x (ISBN 0-8476-1482-4). Rowman.

CALENDAR, JEWISH

Burnaby, Sherrard B. Elements of the Jewish Muhammadan Calendars. 1976. lib. bdg. 59.95 (ISBN 0-8490-1757-2). Gordon Pr.

Langdon, Stephen H. Babylonian Menologies & the Semitic Calendars. LC 78-72744. (Ancient Mesopotamian Texts & Studies). Repr. of 1935 ed. 21.50 (ISBN 0-404-18192-9). AMS Pr.

CALENDAR, MAYA

Satterthwaite, Linton. Concepts & Structures of Maya Calendrical Arithmetics. LC 57-3294. (Museum of the University of Pennsylvania, The Philadelphia Anthropological Society Ser.). pap. 44.00 (ISBN 0-317-26205-X, 2052125). Bks Demand UMI.

Spinden, Herbert J. Reduction of Mayan Dates. (HU PMM). 1924. 24.00 (ISBN 0-527-01209-2). Kraus Repr.

Teeple, John, ed. Maya Astronomy. (Classics of Anthropology Ser.). 20.00 (ISBN 0-8240-9624-X). Garland Pub.

Thompson, J. E. Four Miscellaneous Papers on Mayans. (Chicago Field Museum of Natural History Fieldiana Anthropology Ser). 1927. 63.00 (ISBN 0-527-01877-5). Kraus Repr.

Thompson, J. Eric. Maya Hieroglyphic Writing: An Introduction. (Civilization of the American Indian Ser.: No. 56). (Illus.). 1975. pap. 21.95x (ISBN 0-8061-0958-0). U of Okla Pr.

CALENDAR, MEXICAN

Nuttall, Zelia. Fundamental Principles of Old & New World Civilization. (HU PMP Ser.). 1901. 51.00 (ISBN 0-527-01190-8). Kraus Repr.

Sahagun, Bernardino de. Florentine Codex, General History of the Things of New Spain, 13 bks. Anderson, Arthur J. & Dibble, Charles E., trs. Incl. Introductory Volume: Introductions, Sahaygun's Prologues & Interpolations, General Bibliography, General Indices. 35.00x (ISBN 0-87480-165-6); Bk. 1. Gods. 17.50 (ISBN 0-87480-000-5); Bk. 2. Ceremonies. 40.00x (ISBN 0-87480-194-X); Bk. 3. Origins of the Gods. 17.50x (ISBN 0-87480-002-1); Bks. 4 & 5. The Soothsayers, the Omens. 40.00x (ISBN 0-87480-003-X); Bk. 6. Rhetoric & Moral Philosophy. 40.00x (ISBN 0-87480-010-2); Bk. 7. Sun, Moon & Stars, & the Binding of the Years. 17.50 (ISBN 0-87480-004-8); Bk. 8. Kings & Lords. 20.00x (ISBN 0-87480-005-6); Bk. 9. Merchants. 20.00x (ISBN 0-87480-006-4); Bk. 10. People. 30.00x (ISBN 0-87480-007-2); Bk. 11. Earthly Things. 45.00x (ISBN 0-87480-008-0); Bk. 12. Conquest of Mexico. 27.50 (ISBN 0-87480-096-X). 1982. U of Utah Pr.

Shearer, Tony. Beneath the Moon & under the Sun. (Illus.). 164p. 1975. 8.50 (ISBN 0-89540-042-1, SB-042). Sun Pub.

CALENDAR, MUSLIM

see Calendar, Islamic

CALENDAR REFORM

Boudreau, Amy. Story of the Christian Year. 1971. 4.50 (ISBN 0-685-27196-X). Claitors.

CALENDAR STONE OF MEXICO

see Calendar, Mexican

CALF

see Calves

CALIFORNIA–CLIMATE

Bailey, Harry P. The Weather of Southern California. (California Natural History Guides: No. 17). (Illus., Orig.). 1966. pap. 2.65 (ISBN 0-520-00062-5). U of Cal Pr.

CALIFORNIA, UNIVERSITY OF–SCRIPPS INSTITUTION OF OCEANOGRAPHY

Shor, Elizabeth N. Scripps Institution of Oceanography: Probing the Oceans, 1936-1976. Rand, Elizabeth, ed. LC 78-52598. (Illus.). 1978. 17.95 (ISBN 0-914488-17-1); pap. 8.95 (ISBN 0-914488-18-X). Rand-Tofua.

CALIFORNIA CONDOR

Nash, Hugh, et al, eds. The Condor Question: Captive or Forever Free? LC 81-68548. (Illus.). 304p. (Orig.). 1981. pap. 0.95 (ISBN 0-913890-48-0). Brick Hse Pub.

Ricklefs, Robert E., ed. Audubon Conservation Report No. 6: Report of the Advisory Panel on the California Condor. (Audubon Conservation Report Ser.). 1978. pap. 1.50 (ISBN 0-930698-04-5). Natl Audubon.

CALIFORNIA GULL

Brusca, Richard C. Common Intertidal Invertebrates of the Gulf of California. rev. ed. LC 79-19894. (Illus.). 513p. 1980. pap. 26.95x (ISBN 0-8165-0682-5). U of Ariz Pr.

CALORIMETERS AND CALORIMETRY

see also Animal Heat; Specific Heat

Beezer, A. E., ed. Biological Microcalorimetry. LC 79-41236. 1980. 79.50 (ISBN 0-12-083550-9). Acad Pr.

Brown, H. D. Biochemical Microcalorimetry. 1969. 70.50 (ISBN 0-12-136150-0). Acad Pr.

Fredericks, Carlton. Calorie & Carbohydrate Guide. 1982. pap. 2.95 (ISBN 0-671-46941-X, 43059). PB.

Grime, G. K. Analytical Solution Calorimetry. (Chemical Analysis Ser.). 400p. 1985. 60.00 (ISBN 0-471-86942-2). Wiley.

Hemminger, Wolfgang & Hohne, Guenther. Calorimetry: Fundamentals and Practice. (Illus.). 250p. 1984. 60.00 (ISBN 0-89573-056-1). VCH Pubs.

Johnson, Julian F. & Gill, Phillip S., eds. Analytical Calorimetry, Vol. 5. 394p. 1984. 69.50x (ISBN 0-306-41507-0, Plenum Pr). Plenum Pub.

Lamprecht, I. & Schaarschmidt, B., eds. Application of Calorimetry in Life Sciences. 1977. 60.00 (ISBN 3-11-006919-9). De Gruyter.

Leisy, James. Calories in - Calories Out Calorie Counter: The Calorie Counter That Counts Both Ways. LC 80-24130. 96p. (Orig.). 1981. pap. 3.95 (ISBN 0-8289-0401-4). Greene.

Porter, R. S. & Johnson, J. F., eds. Analytical Calorimetry. Incl. Vol. 2. 460p. 1970. 69.50x (ISBN 0-306-30366-3); Vol. 3. 818p. 1974. 95.00x (ISBN 0-306-35243-5); Vol. 4. 251p. 1977. 49.50x (ISBN 0-306-35244-3). LC 68-8862 (Plenum Pr). Plenum Pub.

Pugh, Brinley. Fuel Calorimetry. 196p. 1966. 22.50x (ISBN 0-306-30654-9, Plenum Pr). Plenum Pub.

Sedacek, B. & Overberger, C. G. Microcalorimetry of Macromolecules. 112p. 1981. pap. 20.95 (ISBN 0-471-86313-0, Pub. by Wiley-Interscience). Wiley.

Sunner, Stig & Mansson, Margret, eds. Combustion Calorimetry: Experimental Chemical Thermodynamics I, Vol. 1. 1979. pap. text ed. 44.00 (ISBN 0-08-022385-0). Pergamon.

Webb, Paul. Human Calorimeters. 176p. 1985. 34.95 (ISBN 0-03-003008-0). Praeger.

Weinsier, Roland. Time Calorie Displacement. LC 83-61166. 1984. 9.50 (ISBN 0-89313-032-X). G F Stickley Co.

CALOTYPE

Brettell, Richard & Flukinger, Roy. Paper & Light: The Calotype in France & Great Britain, 1839-1870. (Illus.). 192p. 1983. 30.00 (ISBN 0-86559-053-2); pap. 18.95 (ISBN 0-686-44391-8). Art Inst Chi.

CALVES

Digestibility for Veal Calves of Fish Protein Concentrates. (Agricultural Research Reports: No. 819). 1974. pap. 5.00 (ISBN 90-220-0515-1, PDC194, PUDOC). Unipub.

Hobson, Phyllis. Raising a Calf for Beef. LC 76-20637. (Illus.). 120p. 1976. pap. 6.95 (ISBN 0-88266-095-0). Garden Way Pub.

Hoffmann, B. & Mason, I. L., eds. Calving Problems & Early Viability of the Calf. (Current Topics in Veterinary Medicine & Animal Science Ser.: No. 4). 1979. lib. bdg. 67.00 (ISBN 90-247-2195-4, Pub. by Martinus Nijhoff Netherlands). Kluwer Academic.

Roy, J. H. The Calf. 4th ed. LC 79-42840. (Studies in the Agricultural & Food Sciences). 1980. text ed. 89.95 (ISBN 0-408-70941-3). Butterworth.

--Calf: Nutrition & Health. 3rd ed. LC 71-119021. (Illus.). 1970. 22.75x (ISBN 0-271-00122-4). Pa St U Pr.

Signoret, J. P., ed. Welfare & Husbandry of Calves. 1982. lib. bdg. 34.50 (ISBN 90-247-2680-8, Pub. by Martinus Nijhoff Netherlands). Kluwer Academic.

Webster, John. Calf Husbandry, Health & Welfare. 250p. 1983. 20.00x (ISBN 0-86531-760-7). Westview.

CAMBRIAN PERIOD

see Geology, Stratigraphic–Cambrian

CAMBRIDGE UNIVERSITY–DEPARTMENT OF ENGINEERING

Hilken, Thomas J. Engineering at Cambridge University, 1783-1965. 1967. 29.95 (ISBN 0-521-05256-4). Cambridge U Pr.

CAMELLIA
Chidamian. Camellias & Common Sense. pap. 2.00 (ISBN 0-87505-277-0). Borden.
Durrant, Tom. The Camellia Story. 168p. 1983. 47.95 (ISBN 0-86863-395-X, Pub. by Heinemann Pub New Zealand). Intl Spec Bk.
Galle, Fred & Fell, Derek. All about Azaleas, Camellias & Rhododendrons. Beley, Jim, ed. LC 85-70879. (Illus.). 96p. (Orig.). 1985. pap. 5.95 (ISBN 0-89721-064-6). Ortho.
Hung Ta, Chang & Bartholomew, Bruce. Camellias. (Illus.). 240p. 1984. 29.95 (ISBN 0-917304-81-0). Timber.
Noble, Mary & Graham, Blanche. You Can Grow Camellias. (Illus.). 257p. 1976. pap. 6.95 (ISBN 0-486-23273-5). Dover.
Sunset Editors. Azaleas, Rhododendrons, Camellias. LC 81-82866. (Illus.). 96p. 1982. pap. 4.95 (ISBN 0-376-03020-8, Sunset Bks). Sunset-Lane.

CAMELS
Bulliet, Richard W. The Camel & the Wheel. LC 75-571. 352p. 1975. text ed. 22.50x (ISBN 0-674-09130-2). Harvard U Pr.
Fowler, Harlan D. Three Caravans to Yuma: The Untold Story of Bactrian Camels in Western America. LC 80-66268. (Illus.). 173p. 1980. 25.00 (ISBN 0-87062-131-9). A H Clark.
Gauthier-Pilters, Hilde & Dagg, Anne I. The Camel: Its Evolution, Behavior, & Relationship to Man. LC 80-23822. (Illus.). xii, 240p. 1981. pap. 8.95x (ISBN 0-226-28454-9). U of Chicago Pr.
Wilson, R. T. The Camel. (Intermediate Tropical Agriculture Ser.). (Illus.). 192p. 1983. pap. text ed. 70.00x (ISBN 0-582-77512-4). Longman.
Yagil, R. Camels & Camel Milk. (Animal Production & Health Papers: No. 26). 72p. 1982. pap. 7.50 (ISBN 92-5-101169-9, F2310, FAO). Unipub.

CAMERAS
see also Miniature Cameras; Moving-Picture Cameras; Single-Lens Reflex Cameras; View Cameras
Alesse, Craig. Basic Thirty-Five mm Photo Guide. LC 79-54311. (Illus.). 110p. (Orig.). 1980. pap. 9.95 (ISBN 0-936262-00-1). Amherst Media.
Association for Information & Image Management. All about Microfilm Cameras. (Consumer Ser.: No. C106). (Illus.). 24p. 1977. 5.00 (ISBN 0-89258-047-X, C106); member 3.75. Assn Inform & Image Mgmt.
Baczynsky, Mark. Camera Repair, Restoration & Adaptation. (Illus.). 52p. 1982. pap. 9.95 (ISBN 0-89816-009-X). Embee Pr.
Birnbaum, Hubert C. Amphoto Guide to Cameras. (Illus.). 184p. 1978. (Amphoto); pap. 7.95 (ISBN 0-8174-2117-3). Watson-Guptill.
--Photographing with Automatic Cameras. LC 81-67431. (The Kodak Workshop Ser.). (Illus.). 96p. 1981. pap. 8.95 (ISBN 0-87985-270-4, KW-11). Eastman Kodak.
Camera Reference Guide, 1983. 220p. 75.00 (ISBN 0-318-01044-5). Orion Res.
Choose Your Own Camera. (Choose Your Own Ser.). 1983. pap. 4.95 (ISBN 0-8120-2705-1). Barron.
Curtin, Dennis. Your Automatic Camera. (Your Automatic Camera Ser.). (Illus.). 128p. (Orig.). 1980. pap. 6.95 (ISBN 0-930764-17-X). Curtin & London.
DiSante, Theodore. How to Select & Use Medium-Format Cameras. 192p. 1981. 12.95 (ISBN 0-89586-046-5). H P Bks.
Durbin, Harold C. Camera Comparison Charts: 1984 Edition. 1984. pap. 25.00 (ISBN 0-936786-03-5). Durbin Assoc.
Emmanuel, W. D. Cameras: The Facts, a Collector's Guide, 1957-1964. Matheson, Andrew, ed. LC 80-41969. (Illus.). 528p. 1981. 54.95 (ISBN 0-240-51062-3). Focal Pr.
Gaunt, Leonard. Cameras. (Photographer's Library). (Illus.). 1985. pap. cancelled (ISBN 0-240-51187-5). Focal Pr.
Guide to Camera Equipment. (Petersen's Photographic Library: Vol. 6). 160p. 1981. softcover 9.95 (ISBN 0-8227-4055-9). Petersen Pub.
Hammond, John H. The Camera Obscura. 182p. 1981. 33.50 (ISBN 0-9960023-0-8, Pub. by A Hilger England). Heyden.
Hicks, Roger. A History of the 35MM Still Camera. (Illus.). 192p. 1984. 62.50 (ISBN 0-240-51233-2). Focal Pr.
Langford, Michael J., ed. Camera Book. (Illus.). 256p. 1980. 25.00 (ISBN 0-87165-073-8, Amphoto). Watson-Guptill.
Lothrop, Eaton S., Jr. A Century of Cameras. rev. ed. LC 73-88444. (Illus.). 196p. 1982. pap. 19.95 (ISBN 0-87100-163-2, 2163). Morgan.
McKeown, James M. & McKeown, Joan C. Dealer Blue Book of Cameras. 64p. 1982. pap. 8.95 (ISBN 0-931838-03-7). Centennial Photo Serv.
Model Releases. 1977. pap. 3.95 (ISBN 0-8174-1000-7, Amphoto). Watson-Guptill.
The Official Price Guide to Collectible Cameras. 3rd ed. LC 82-84645. 303p. 1985. 11.95 (ISBN 0-87637-295-7). Hse of Collectibles.
Permutt, Cyril. Collecting Old Cameras. LC 76-14888. (Photography Ser.). 1977. lib. bdg. 22.50 (ISBN 0-306-70855-8). Da Capo.
Ray, Sidney. Camera Systems. (Illus.). 240p. 1983. 37.95 (ISBN 0-240-51207-3). Focal Pr.
Reynolds, Clyde. Camera Movements. (Illus.). 1984. cancelled (ISBN 0-240-51143-3). Focal Pr.
Roberts, Fred M. Guide to the Ricoh Hi-Color 35 & Marine Capsule. (Illus., Orig.). 1972. pap. 4.50 (ISBN 0-912746-05-X). F M Roberts.
Society of Photographic Scientists & Engineers. International Symposium on Still Camera Technology: Advanced Printing of Paper Summaries, March 21-23,1983, the Dunes Hotel & Country Club, Las Vegas, Nevada. pap. 20.00 (ISBN 0-317-28846-6, 2020629). Bks Demand UMI.
Taylor, Herb, et al. How to Use Your 35mm Camera. LC 81-71227. (Modern Photo Guides). (Illus.). 120p. (Orig.). 1982. pap. 7.95 (ISBN 0-385-18144-2). Avalon Comm.
Wade, Glen, ed. Acoustic Imaging: Cameras, Microscopes, Phased Arrays & Holographic Systems. LC 76-21. 325p. 1976. 52.50x (ISBN 0-306-30914-9, Plenum Pr). Plenum Pub.
Wade, John. A Short History of the Camera. (Illus.). 144p. (Orig.). 1979. pap. 8.95 (ISBN 0-85242-640-2, 3640). Morgan.
Weber, Jeffrey R. Camera Repair Simplified. LC 80-65475. 112p. (Orig.). 1980. pap. text ed. 14.95 (ISBN 0-9604892-0-7). Weber Systems.
White, Robert. Discovering Old Cameras. (Discovering Ser.: No. 260). (Illus.). 48p. (Orig.). 1983. pap. 4.50 (ISBN 0-85263-691-1, Pub. by Shire Pubns England). Seven Hills Bks.

CAMERAS-TYPES-CANON
The Canon Camera Handbook. (Your Automatic Camera Ser.). 176p. (Orig.). 1981. pap. 9.95 (ISBN 0-930764-32-3). Curtin & London.
Gaunt, Leonard. Canon A Series Book. (Camera Bks.). 128p. 1983. pap. 9.95 (ISBN 0-240-51183-2). Focal Pr.
London, Barbara. A Short Course in Canon Photography. 1979. 14.95 (ISBN 0-930764-11-0); pap. 9.95 (ISBN 0-930764-01-3). Curtin & London.
--A Short Course in Canon Photography. rev. ed. 1983. pap. 11.95 (ISBN 0-930764-52-8). Van Nos Reinhold.
Michaels, Rick. Canon A-1: Amphoto Pocket Companion. (Illus.). 112p. 1981. pap. 4.95 (ISBN 0-8174-5522-1, Amphoto). Watson-Guptill.
--Canon AE1, AT-1: Amphoto Pocket Companion. (Illus.). 128p. 1981. pap. 4.95 (ISBN 0-8174-5523-X, Amphoto). Watson-Guptill.
Shipman, Carl. Canon SLR Cameras. LC 76-50430. (Illus.). 1977. pap. 12.95 (ISBN 0-912656-56-5). H P Bks.

CAMERAS-TYPES-HASSELBLAD
Freytag, H. The Hasselblad Way. 7th ed. (Camera Way Bks.). (Illus.). 424p. 1978. 28.95 (ISBN 0-240-50988-9). Focal Pr.
Wildi, Ernst. Hasselblad Manual. 2nd ed. (Camera Ways Bks.). (Illus.). 302p. 1982. 34.95 (ISBN 0-240-51186-7). Focal Pr.

CAMERAS-TYPES-KODAK
Handbook for Kodak Ultratec Products, Q-250. (Illus.). 44p. 1983. pap. text ed. 27.95 (ISBN 0-87985-342-5). Eastman Kodak.
McKeown, James M. & McKeown, Joan C. Collector's Guide to Kodak Cameras. (Illus.). 176p. (Orig.). 1981. pap. 12.95 (ISBN 0-931838-02-9). Centennial Photo Serv.

CAMERAS-TYPES-KONICA
Jacobs, Lou, Jr. The Konica Guide. rev. ed. (Modern Camera Guide Ser.). (Illus.). 128p. 1980. (Amphoto). pap. 7.95 (ISBN 0-8174-4125-5). Watson-Guptill.
--The Konica Guide. (Modern Camera Guides Ser.). (Illus.). 1978. 11.95 (ISBN 0-8174-2501-2, Amphoto); pap. 7.95 (ISBN 0-8174-4125-5). Watson-Guptill.

CAMERAS-TYPES-LEICA
Lager, James L. Leica Illustrated Guide III. LC 79-90513. 96p. (Orig.). 1979. pap. 18.95 (ISBN 0-87100-161-6, 2161). Morgan.
--Leica Literature. 512p. 1980. pap. 22.95 (ISBN 0-87100-174-8, 2174). Morgan.
Leica Manual (1935 First Edition) Facsimile. LC 35-14997. 512p. 1977. 12.95 (ISBN 0-87100-118-7, 2118). Morgan.
Leica 1928 Instruction Book. (Illus.). 19p. 1970. pap. 3.00 (ISBN 0-87100-107-1, 2107). Morgan.
Matheson, Andrew. The Leica Rangefinder Way. (Illus.). 272p. 1983. 36.95 (ISBN 0-240-51208-1). Focal Pr.

CAMERAS-TYPES-MAMIYA SEKOR
Borrell, Alexander. Mamiya M645 Book. 128p. 1983. pap. 9.95 (ISBN 0-240-51197-2). Focal Pr.
Reynolds, Clyde. Mamiya Twin Lens Book. (Camera Books). (Illus.). 104p. 1977. pap. 9.95 (ISBN 0-240-50974-9). Focal Pr.

CAMERAS-TYPES-MINOLTA
Cooper, J. The Minolta Systems Handbook. 1976. 29.95 (ISBN 0-13-584599-8, Spec). P-H.
--Minolta Systems Handbook. 2nd ed. 1979. 34.95 (ISBN 0-13-584581-5, Spec). P-H.
London, Barbara. A Short Course in Minolta Photography. 1979. 14.95 (ISBN 0-930764-12-9); pap. 9.95 (ISBN 0-930764-02-1). Curtin & London.
The Minolta Camera Handbook. (Your Automatic Camera Ser.). (Illus.). 176p. 1981. pap. 9.95 (ISBN 0-930764-31-5). Curtin & London.
Reynolds, Clyde. Minolta XD & XG Book. (Camera Book Series). (Illus.). 128p. 1980. pap. 9.95 (ISBN 0-240-51035-6). Focal Pr.
Sammon, Rick. Minolta SRT's. (Amphoto Pocket Companion Ser.). (Illus.). 1980. pap. 4.95 (ISBN 0-8174-4584-6, Amphoto). Watson-Guptill.
--Minolta XD's. (Amphoto Pocket Companion Ser.). (Illus.). 1980. pap. 4.95 (ISBN 0-8174-4582-X, Amphoto). Watson-Guptill.
--Minolta XG's. (Amphoto Pocket Companion Ser.). (Illus.). 1980. pap. 4.95 (ISBN 0-8174-4583-8, Amphoto). Watson-Guptill.
Shipman, Carl. How to Select & Use Minolta SLR Cameras. LC 80-81594. (Orig.). 1980. pap. 12.95 (ISBN 0-89586-044-9). H P Bks.
Wolf, John. The Minolta Guide. (Modern Camera Guide Ser.). (Illus.). 1979. (Amphoto); pap. 7.95 (ISBN 0-8174-2128-9). Watson-Guptill.

CAMERAS-TYPES-NIKON
Hayman, Rex. Nikon F-Three Book. (Camera Book Ser.). 128p. 1980. pap. 9.95 (ISBN 0-240-51073-9). Focal Pr.
Heiberg, Milton. Nikon F-Three: Amphoto Pocket Companion. (Illus.). 112p. 1981. pap. 4.95 (ISBN 0-8174-5532-9, Amphoto). Watson-Guptill.
Iocolano, Mark. Nikon F-Two. (Amphoto Pocket Companion Ser.). (Illus.). 128p. 1980. pap. 4.95 (ISBN 0-8174-2182-3, Amphoto). Watson-Guptill.
--Nikon FM & FE. (Amphoto Pocket Companion Ser.). (Illus.). 128p. 1980. pap. 4.95 (ISBN 0-8174-2181-5, Amphoto). Watson-Guptill.
Keppler, Herbert. The Nikon-Nikkormat Way. 3rd ed. (Camera Way Bks.). (Illus.). 512p. 1983. 32.95 (ISBN 0-240-51185-9). Focal Pr.
London, Barbara. A Short Course in Nikon Photography. 1979. 14.95 (ISBN 0-930764-10-2); pap. 9.95 (ISBN 0-930764-03-X). Curtin & London.
Reynolds, Clyde. Nikon FE FM EM Book. (Camera Book Ser.). (Illus.). 128p. 1980. pap. 9.95 (ISBN 0-240-51034-8). Focal Pr.
--The Nikon F2 & F Book. (Camera Books). 136p. 1977. pap. 9.95 (ISBN 0-240-50905-6). Focal Pr.
Shipman, Carl. How to Select & Use Nikon SLR Cameras Cameras. LC 78-52274. (Illus.). 1978. pap. 12.95 (ISBN 0-912656-77-8). H P Bks.
Wolf, John C. Nikon Guide. rev ed. (Modern Camera Guide Ser.). (Illus.). 1981. pap. 7.95 (ISBN 0-8174-5045-9, Amphoto). Watson-Guptill.

CAMERAS-TYPES-OLYMPUS
Gaunt, Leonard. The Olympus Book. (Camera Book Ser.). 136p. 1977. pap. 9.95 (ISBN 0-240-50942-0). Focal Pr.
Heiberg, Milton J. Olympus OM-Ten, OM-One & OM-Two. (Amphoto Pocket Companion Ser.). (Illus.). 1980. pap. 4.95 (ISBN 0-8174-2188-2, Amphoto). Watson-Guptill.
London, Barbara. A Short Course in Olympus Photography. 1979. 14.95 (ISBN 0-930764-13-7); pap. 9.95 (ISBN 0-930764-04-8). Curtin & London.
Mannheim, L. A. The Olympus OM Way. (Camera Way Bks.). (Illus.). 1979. 29.95 (ISBN 0-240-50985-4). Focal Pr.
Shipman, Carl. How to Select & Use Olympus SLR Cameras. LC 79-84702. (Illus.). 1979. pap. 12.95 (ISBN 0-89586-015-5). H P Bks.

CAMERAS-TYPES-PENTAX
Balsley, Gene. Pentax MX & ME. (Amphoto Pocket Companion Ser.). (Illus.). 1980. pap. 4.95 (ISBN 0-8174-2183-1, Amphoto). Watson-Guptill.
Keppler, Herbert. The Asahi Pentax Way. 11th ed. (Camera Way Bks.). (Illus.). 1979. 27.95 (ISBN 0-240-51018-6). Focal Pr.
London, Barbara. A Short Course in Pentax Photography. (Illus., Orig.). 1979. 14.95 (ISBN 0-930764-14-5); pap. 9.95 (ISBN 0-930764-05-6). Curtin & London.
Reynolds, Clyde. Asahi Pentax M Series Book. (Camera Bks). (Illus.). 1983. pap. 9.95 (ISBN 0-240-51194-8). Focal Pr.
Shipman, Carl. Pentax SLR Cameras. LC 76-51908. (Illus.). 1977. pap. 12.95 (ISBN 0-912656-57-3). H P Bks.
Swartz, Fred. The Pentax Guide. (Modern Camera Guide Ser.). (Illus.). 136p. 1980. (Amphoto); pap. 7.95 (ISBN 0-8174-2143-2). Watson-Guptill.

CAMERAS-TYPES-POLAROID LAND
Adams, Ansel. Polaroid Land Photography. LC 78-7069. 1978. 19.45 (ISBN 0-8212-0729-6, 712744). NYGS.
Olshaker, Mark. The Polaroid Story: Edwin Land & the Polaroid Experience. LC 77-15965. (Illus.). 292p. 1983. pap. 9.95 (ISBN 0-8128-6093-4). Stein & Day.

CAMERAS-TYPES-PRAKTICA
Gaunt, Leonard. Praktica Book. 2nd ed. (Camera Book Ser.). 120p. 1979. pap. 9.95 (ISBN 0-240-51052-6). Focal Pr.

CAMERAS-TYPES-YASHICA
Heiberg, Milton. Yashica FR, FR-I & FR-II: Amphoto Pocket Companion. (Illus.). 128p. 1981. pap. 4.95 (ISBN 0-8174-5534-5, Amphoto). Watson-Guptill.
--The Yashica Guide. (Modern Camera Guide Ser.). (Illus.). 1979. 12.95 (ISBN 0-8174-2479-2, Amphoto). Watson-Guptill.

CAMOUFLAGE (BIOLOGY)
Owen, Denis. Camouflage & Mimicry. LC 82-2566. (Phoenix Ser.). (Illus.). 160p. 1982. pap. 12.50 (ISBN 0-226-64188-0). U of Chicago Pr.

CAMPERS AND COACHES, TRUCK
see also Vans
Truscott, Lucian K. The Complete Van Book. (Illus.). 1976. (Dist. by Crown); pap. 6.95 (ISBN 0-517-52673-5). Crown.
Woodall's RV Owner's Handbook, Vol. 1. pap. 6.95 (ISBN 0-671-24614-3). Woodall.
Woodall's RV Owner's Handbook, Vol. 2. pap. 4.95 (ISBN 0-671-25163-5). Woodall.

CAMS
Chen, Fan Y. Mechanics & Design of Cam Mechanisms. LC 81-11927. (Illus.). 523p. 1982. 77.00 (ISBN 0-08-028049-8, A115). Pergamon.

CANADA-MANUFACTURES
Survey of Industrials, 1978. 52nd ed. (Orig.). 1978. pap. 25.00x (ISBN 0-88896-073-5). Intl Pubns Serv.

CANADIAN ARCTIC EXPEDITION, 1913-1918
Peacock, Donald. People, Peregrines, & Arctic Pipelines: The Critical Battle to Build Canada's Northern Gas Pipelines. LC 77-375197. (Illus.). 224p. 1977. pap. 5.95x (ISBN 0-295-95722-0). U of Wash Pr.

CANADIAN SCIENCE
see Science, Canadian

CANAL-BOATS
see also Barges
Smith, Peter L. Canal Barges & Narrow Boats. (Album Ser.: No. 8). (Illus.). 32p. 1983. pap. 2.95 (ISBN 0-85263-651-2, Pub. by Shire Pubns England). Seven Hills Bks.

CANALS
see also Intracoastal Waterways;
also names of canals, e.g. Erie canal; Stover Canal
Baer, Christopher T. Canals & Railroads of the Mid-Atlantic States, 1800-1860. 80p. 1981. pap. 15.00x (ISBN 0-914650-19-X). Eleutherian Mills-Hagley.
Boyes, John & Russell, Ronald. The Canals of Eastern England. 1977. 22.50 (ISBN 0-7153-7415-X). David & Charles.
Cameron, A. D. The Caledonian Canal. (Illus.). 1979. 20.00 (ISBN 0-900963-33-6, Pub. by Terence Dalton England). State Mutual Bk.
Cranmer, H. Jerome. The New Jersey Canals: State Policy & Private Enterprise, 1820-1832. LC 77-14768. (Dissertations in American Economic History Ser.). 1978. 34.50 (ISBN 0-405-11030-8). Ayer Co Pubs.
Darwin, Andrew. Canals & Rivers of Britain. (Illus.). 1977. 13.95 (ISBN 0-8038-1213-2). Hastings.
De Vries, Jan. Barges & Capitalism: Passenger Transportation in the Dutch Economy (1632-1839) 368p. 1981. pap. 19.00x (ISBN 90-6194-432-5, Pub. by Hes Pubs Netherlands). Benjamins North Am.
Duane, William J. Letters Addressed to the People of Pennsylvania. LC 68-18218. 1968. Repr. of 1811 ed. 25.00x (ISBN 0-678-00381-5). Kelley.
--Letters Addressed to the People of Pennsylvania Respecting the Internal Improvement of the Commonwealth: By Means of Roads & Canals. (American Classics in History & Social Science Ser.: No. 22). 1968. 16.00 (ISBN 0-8337-0923-2). B Franklin.
The Establishing Process of the Ogo & Yamuda Canals. 44p. 1981. pap. 5.00 (ISBN 92-808-0336-0, TUNU173, UNU). Unipub.
Facts & Arguments in Favour of Adopting Railways in Preference to Canals, in the State of Pennsylvania. 4th ed. LC 78-112543. (Rise of Urban America). 1970. Repr. of 1825 ed. 9.00 (ISBN 0-405-02452-5). Ayer Co Pubs.
Gallatin, Albert. Report of the Secretary of the Treasury on the Subject of Public Roads & Canals. LC 68-20392. Repr. of 1808 ed. 17.50x (ISBN 0-678-00368-8). Kelley.
Garrity, Richard. Canal Boatman: My Life on Upstate Waterways. LC 77-21909. (York State Bks.). (Illus.). 240p. 1984. pap. 12.95 (ISBN 0-8156-0191-3). Syracuse U Pr.

Giraldo, G. & Beth, E., eds. Role of Viruses in Human Cancer. 292p. 1980. 60.00 (ISBN 0-444-00440-8, Biomedical Pr). Elsevier.
Greenberg, Michael R. Urbanization & Cancer Mortality: The United States Experience, 1950-1975. (Monographs in Epidemiology & Biostatistics). (Illus.). 1983. 45.00x (ISBN 0-19-503173-3). Oxford U Pr.
Greenstein, Jesse P. Biochemistry of Cancer. 2nd ed. 1954. 77.00 (ISBN 0-12-300550-7). Acad Pr.
Gross, R., ed. Strategies in Clinical Hematology. (Recent Results in Cancer Research Ser.: Vol. 69). (Illus.). 1979. 32.00 (ISBN 0-387-09578-0). Springer-Verlag.
Gurchot, Charles. Trophoblast Theory of Cancer. 1.50x (ISBN 0-686-29932-9). Cancer Control Soc.
Halstead, Bruce. Amygdalin (Laetrile) Therapy. 2.75 (ISBN 0-686-29936-1). Cancer Control Soc.
Hartwell, Jonathan L. Plants Used Against Cancer. LC 81-85230. (Bio-Active Plants Ser.: Vol. 2). 754p. 1984. Repr. lib. bdg. 75.00x (ISBN 0-88000-130-5). Quarterman.
Hazra, Tapan A. & Beachley, Michael C., eds. Recent Advances in Clinical Oncology: Proceedings of a Conference Held in Williamsburg, Va., Feb.-March 1977. LC 78-14907. (Progress in Clinical & Biological Research: Vol. 25). (Illus.). 362p. 1978. 19.00x (ISBN 0-8451-0025-4). A R Liss.
Heinerman, John. Treatment of Cancer with Herbs. 1984. 9.95x (ISBN 0-89557-079-3). Cancer Control Soc.
Herfarth, C. & Schlag, P., eds. Gastric Cancer. (Illus.). 1979. pap. 51.00 (ISBN 0-387-09467-9). Springer-Verlag.
Hicks, Ron. Understanding Cancer. 141p. (Orig.). 1980. pap. 5.00 (ISBN 0-7022-1425-6). U of Queensland Pr.
Higby, Donald J., ed. The Cancer Patient & Supportive Care. (Cancer Treatment & Research Ser.). 1985. lib. bdg. 52.50 (ISBN 0-318-04537-0, Pub. by Martinus Nijhoff Netherlands). Kluwer Academic.
Hollander, Vincent P., ed. Hormonally Responsive Tumors. Edited Treatise ed. Date not set. price not set (ISBN 0-12-352560-8). Acad Pr.
Hornback, Ned B. & Shupe, Robert. Hyperthermia & Cancer: Human Clinical Trail Experience, Vol. II. 176p. 1984. 54.00 (ISBN 0-8493-5676-8). CRC Pr.
Hornback, Ned B. & Shupe, Robert E. Hyperthermia & Cancer: Human Clinical Trail Experience, Vol. I. 160p. 1984. 48.00 (ISBN 0-8493-5675-X). CRC Pr.
Hynes, R. & Fox, C. Fred, eds. Tumor Cell Surfaces & Malignancy: Proceedings. LC 80-7798. (Progress in Clinical & Biological Research Ser.: Vol. 41). 970p. 1980. 156.00 (ISBN 0-8451-0041-6). A R Liss.
Iacobelli, Stefano, et al, eds. Hormones & Cancer. (Progress in Cancer Research & Therapy Ser.: Vol. 14). 589p. 1980. text ed. 92.00 (ISBN 0-89004-486-4). Raven.
Institute of Medicine. Cancer Today: Origins, Prevention, & Treatment. (Illus.). 144p. 1984. 9.50 (ISBN 0-309-03436-1). Natl Acad Pr.
Javadpour, Nasser. Cancer of the Kidney. (Illus.). 192p. 1984. text ed. 34.00 (ISBN 0-86577-136-7). Thieme-Stratton.
Javor, George. The Challenge of Cancer. LC 79-29674. (Orion Ser.). 96p. 1980. pap. 3.50 (ISBN 0-8127-0275-1). Review & Herald.
Jeljackzewicz, Janusz, et al, eds. Bacteria & Cancer. 1983. 39.50 (ISBN 0-12-383820-7). Acad Pr.
Jung, T. & Sikora, K. Endocrine Problems in Cancer. 300p. 1984. 32.00 (ISBN 0-433-30277-1, Pub. by W Heinemann Med Bks). Sheridan Med Bks.
Kell, George. Laetrile vs. Cancer. 2.00x (ISBN 0-686-29766-0). Cancer Control Soc.
Klein, George & Weinhouse, Sidney, eds. Advances in Cancer Research, Vol. 24. 1977. 75.00 (ISBN 0-12-006624-6). Acad Pr.
--Advances in Cancer Research, Vol. 31. LC 52-13360. 1980. 65.00 (ISBN 0-12-006631-9). Acad Pr.
--Advances in Cancer Research, Vol. 32. 1980. 65.00 (ISBN 0-12-006632-7). Acad Pr.
Kramer, Marc B., ed. Forensic Audiology. (Perspectives in Audiology Ser.). (Illus.). 376p. 1982. text ed. 46.50 (ISBN 0-8391-1613-6). Univ Park.
Kurth, Karl H., et al. Progress & Controversies in Oncological Urology. LC 84-5658. (Progress in Clinical & Biological Research Ser.: Vol. 153). 626p. 1984. 86.00 (ISBN 0-8451-5003-0). A R Liss.
Kushi, Michio. Macrobiotic Approach to Cancer. 1981. 6.95x (ISBN 0-89529-209-2). Cancer Control Soc.
Kuss, Rene, et al. Bladder Cancer, Pt. A: Pathology, Diagnosis, & Surgery. LC 84-11237. (Progress in Clinical & Biological Research Ser.: Vol. 162A). 492p. 1984. 68.00 (ISBN 0-8451-0181-1). A R Liss.
--Bladder Cancer, Pt. B: Radiation, Local & Systemic Chemotherapy, & New Treatment Modalities. LC 84-11237. (Progress in Clinical & Biological Research Ser.: Vol. 162B). 482p. 1984. 68.00 (ISBN 0-8451-0182-X). A R Liss.
LaFond, Richard E., ed. Cancer: The Outlaw Cell. LC 78-2100. (Reprint of journal articles). 1978. 19.95 (ISBN 0-8412-0405-5); pap. 12.95 (ISBN 0-8412-0431-4). Am Chemical.
Leavitt, Wendell W., ed. Hormones & Cancer. LC 81-15743. (Advances in Experimental Medicine & Biology: Vol. 138). 432p. 1982. 57.50 (ISBN 0-306-40831-7, Plenum Pr). Plenum Pub.
Le Cam, L. & Neyman, J., eds. Probability Models & Cancer: Proceedings of an Interdisciplinary Cancer Study Conference. 310p. 1983. 40.00 (ISBN 0-444-86514-4, North Holland). Elsevier.
Lenoir, G., ed. Burkitt's Lymphoma: Human Cancer Model. (IARC Ser.). 450p. 1984. text ed. 35.00x (ISBN 0-19-723057-1). Oxford U Pr.
Le Serve, A., et al. Chemical, Work & Cancer. 1980. pap. 6.95 (ISBN 0-442-30705-5). Van Nos Reinhold.
Levi, S., ed. Ultrasound & Cancer: Invited Papers & Selected Free Communications Presented at the First International Symposium, Brussels, Belgium, July 23-24, 1982. (International Congress Ser.: No. 587). 384p. 1982. 81.00 (ISBN 0-444-90270-8, I-281-82, Excerpta Medica). Elsevier.
Levitt, Paul M. & Guralnick, Elissa S. The Cancer Reference Book: Direct & Clear Answers to Everyone's Questions. 271p. 1978. 14.95 (ISBN 0-87196-317-5). Facts on File.
Lilienfeld, A. M. Reviews in Cancer Epidemiology, Vol. 2. 456p. 1983. 54.00 (ISBN 0-444-00742-3, Biomedical Pr). Elsevier.
Livingston, Virginia. Microbiology of Cancer. 25.00x (ISBN 0-686-29788-1). Cancer Control Soc.
--Physician's Handbook to Microbiology of Cancer. 1977. 2.75x (ISBN 0-918816-06-8). Cancer Control Soc.
Lynch, H. T. Hereditary Factors in Carcinoma. (Recent Results in Cancer Research: Vol. 12). (Illus.). 1967. 21.00 (ISBN 0-387-03960-0). Springer-Verlag.
Lynch, Henry T. & Anton-Guirgis, Hoda. Biomarkers, Genetics & Cancer. (Illus.). 192p. 1985. 47.50 (ISBN 0-442-24958-6). Van Nos Reinhold.
Makita, Akira, et al, eds. Membrane Alterations in Cancer. (GANN Monographs on Cancer Research: No. 29). 311p. 1984. 55.00x (ISBN 0-306-41565-8, Plenum Pr). Plenum Pub.
Manner, Harold. Manner Therapy "C". 1982. 1.00 (ISBN 0-943080-06-1). Cancer Control Soc.
Marchalonis. Cancer Biology Reviews, Vol. 1. 368p. 1980. 55.00 (ISBN 0-8247-6856-6). Dekker.
--Cancer Biology Reviews, Vol. 3. 224p. 1982. 55.00 (ISBN 0-8247-1885-2). Dekker.
Marks, Paul A. Genetics, Cell Differentiation, & Cancer. (Bristol-Myers Cancer Symposia: Vol. 7). Date not set. 25.00 (ISBN 0-12-473060-4). Acad Pr.
Mastromarino, Anthony J. & Brattain, Michael G., eds. Large Bowel Cancer: Clinical & Basic Science Research. LC 84-15975. (Cancer Research Monographs: Vol. 3). 204p. 1985. 37.95 (ISBN 0-03-001529-4). Praeger.
Maugh, Thomas H., II & Marx, Jean L. Seeds of Destruction: The Science Report on Cancer Research. LC 75-15860. (Illus.). 250p. 1975. 29.50x (ISBN 0-306-30836-3, Plenum Pr). Plenum Pub.
Meleka, Fikri M. Dimensions of the Cancer Problem. xii, 144p. 1983. pap. 21.00 (ISBN 3-8055-3622-4). S Karger.
Menon, K. M. & Reel, Jerry R., eds. Steroid Hormone Action & Cancer. LC 76-25873. (Current Topics in Molecular Endocrinology Ser.: Vol. 4). 190p. 1976. 39.50x (ISBN 0-306-34004-6, Plenum Pr). Plenum Pub.
Mettlin, Curtis & Murphy, Gerald P. Issues in Cancer Screening & Communications. LC 82-15289. (Progress in Clinical & Biological Research Ser.: Vol. 83). 566p. 1982. 56.00 (ISBN 0-8451-0083-1). A R Liss.
Mihich, Enrico, ed. Biological Responses in Cancer: Progress Toward Potential Applications, Vol. 1. 324p. 1982. 37.50 (ISBN 0-306-41146-6, Plenum Pr). Plenum Pub.
Mihich, Enrico & Sakurai, Yoshio, eds. Biological Responses in Cancer: Progress Toward Potential Applications, Vol. 3. 232p. 1985. 39.50x (ISBN 0-306-41879-7, Plenum Pr). Plenum Pub.
Ming, Si-Chun, ed. Precursors of Gastric Cancer. LC 83-27025. 350p. 1984. 49.95 (ISBN 0-03-063969-7). Praeger.
Mitelman, F. Catalogue of Chromosome Aberrations in Cancer. (Journal: Cytogenetics & Cell Genetics: Vol. 36, No. 1-2). (Illus.). 516p. 1983. pap. 56.25 (ISBN 3-8055-3813-8). S Karger.
Morson, Bosil C. The Pathogenesis of Colorectal Cancer. LC 78-1792. (Major Problems in Pathology: Vol. 10). 1978. text ed. 21.00 (ISBN 0-7216-6558-6). Saunders.
Muggia, F. M. & Young, C. W. Anthracycline Antibiotics in Cancer Therapy. 1982. text ed. 69.50 (ISBN 0-686-37594-7, Pub. by Martinus Nijhoff Netherlands). Kluwer Academic.
Mulvihill, John J., et al, eds. Genetics of Human Cancer. LC 75-44924. (Progress in Cancer Research & Therapy Ser.: Vol. 3). 541p. 1977. 41.00 (ISBN 0-89004-110-5). Raven.
Murphy, Gerald, ed. Prostatic Cancer. LC 78-55284. (Illus.). 246p. 1979. 33.50 (ISBN 0-88416-190-0). PSG Pub Co.
Nass, G., ed. Modified Nucleosides & Cancer: Workshop, Freiburg, FRG, 1981. (Recent Results in Cancer Research: Vol. 84). (Illus.). 440p. 1983. 52.00 (ISBN 0-387-12024-6). Springer-Verlag.
Oppenheimer, Steven B. Cancer: A Biological & Clinical Introduction. 352p. 1982. text ed. 32.86 (ISBN 0-205-07652-1, 6776523); tchr's. ed. avail. (ISBN 0-205-07653-X, 6776531). Allyn.
Pauling, Linus. Cancer & Vitamin C. 9.95x (ISBN 0-446-97735-7). Cancer Control Soc.
Pavone-Macaluso, M., et al, eds. Testicular Cancer & Other Tumors of the Genitourinary Tract. (Ettore Majorana International Sciences Ser.: Life Sciences-Vol. 18). 526p. 1985. 85.00 (ISBN 0-306-41906-8, Plenum Pr). PLenum Pub.
Peto, Richard & Schneiderman, Marvin, eds. Banbury Report Nine: Quantification of Occupational Cancer. LC 81-10218. (Banbury Report Ser.: Vol. 9). 756p. 1981. 99.00x (ISBN 0-87969-208-1). Cold Spring Harbor.
Phillips. Viruses Associated with Human Cancer. 896p. 1983. 95.00 (ISBN 0-8247-1738-4). Dekker.
Pierce, G. Barry, et al. Cancer: A Problem of Developmental Biology. (Foundations of Developmental Biology Ser.). 1978. 27.95 (ISBN 0-13-113373-X). P-H.
Prescott, David & Flexer, Abraham S. Cancer: The Misguided Cell. LC 81-9033. (Illus.). 310p. 1981. pap. 16.95x (ISBN 0-87893-707-2). Sinauer Assoc.
Raven, Ronald W., ed. Outlook on Cancer. LC 77-8636. 328p. 1977. 42.50x (ISBN 0-306-31063-5, Plenum Pr). Plenum Pub.
Rein, Robert. Molecular Basis of Cancer: Macromolecular Structure, Carginogens, & Oncogenes, Pts. A & B. LC 84-23430. (PCBR Ser.: Vols. 172A-B). 608p. 1985. Set. 78.00 (ISBN 0-8451-5022-7); Vol. 172A, 608p. 78.00 (ISBN 0-8451-0186-2); Vol. 172B, 428p. 62.00 (ISBN 0-8451-0187-0). A R Liss.
Renneker, Mark & Presotto, Denise. Biology of Cancer Sourcebook. LC 78-72890. 1978. pap. text ed. 3.95 (ISBN 0-915950-30-8). Bull Pub.
Roe, Daphne A. Diet, Nutrition & Cancer. LC 83-9909. (Current Topics in Nutrition & Disease Ser.: Vol. 9). 304p. 1983. 38.00 (ISBN 0-8451-1608-8). A R Liss.
Rose, D. P. Endocrinology of Cancer, Vol. III. 208p. 1982. 62.00 (ISBN 0-8493-5339-4). CRC Pr.
Rosenbaum, Ernest, et al. Nutrition for the Cancer Patient. (Orig.). 1980. pap. 7.95 (ISBN 0-915950-38-3). Bull Pub.
Rowley, Janet D. & Ultman, John E., eds. Chromosomes & Cancer: From Molecules to Man (Symposium) (Bristol-Myers Cancer Symposium Ser.: Vol. 5). 1983. 44.50 (ISBN 0-12-600250-9). Acad Pr.
Salazar, Omar M., et al. Bronchogenic Carcinoma. (Onclogic Division of Radiation Oncology Ser.: Vol. 13). (Illus.). 384p. 1981. pap. 110.00 (ISBN 0-08-027464-1). Pergamon.
Sandberg, Avery A. The Chromosomes in Human Cancer & Leukemia. LC 79-22474. 776p. 1979. 155.00 (ISBN 0-444-00289-8, Biomedical Pr). Elsevier.
Sarma, R. H. & Sarma, M. H. DNA Double Helix & the Chemistry of Cancer. (Illus.). 450p. 1983. text ed. 24.50 (ISBN 0-940030-06-3); pap. text ed. 15.95 (ISBN 0-940030-08-X). Adenine Pr.
Sawicki, Eugene, ed. Handbook of Environmental Genotox, Vol. III: Cancer & Age. 528p. 1985. 96.00 (ISBN 0-8493-3403-9). CRC Pr.
Sax, N. Irving. Cancer Causing Chemicals. 400p. 1981. 42.95 (ISBN 0-442-21919-9). Van Nos Reinhold.
Schrauzer, G. N., ed. Inorganic & Nutritional Aspects of Cancer. LC 77-13974. (Advances in Experimental Medicine & Biology Ser.: Vol. 91). 362p. 1977. 49.50x (ISBN 0-306-32691-4, Plenum Pr). Plenum Pub.
Scott, Ronald B. Cancer: The Facts. (The Facts Ser.). 1979. text ed. 13.95x (ISBN 0-19-261149-6). Oxford U Pr.
Serrou, B. & Rosenfeld, C., eds. Current Concepts in Human Immunology & Cancer Immunomodulation: Proceedings of the International Symposium, Montpellier, France, January 18-20, 1982. (Developments in Immunology Ser.: Vol. 17). 664p. 1982. 84.75 (ISBN 0-444-80426-9, Biomedical Pr). Elsevier.
Shaw, Leslie M., et al, eds. Prostatic Acid Phosphatase Measurement: Detection & Management of Prostatic Cancer. (Annals of The New York Academy of Science Ser.: Vol. 390). 145p. 1982. lib. bdg. 30.00x (ISBN 0-89766-170-2); pap. 30.00x (ISBN 0-89766-171-0). NY Acad Sci.
Slaga, Thomas J., et al, eds. Mechanisms of Tumor Promotion & Cocarcinogenesis. LC 77-17752. (Carcinogenesis: a Comprehensive Survey Ser.: Vol. 2). 605p. 1978. 80.50 (ISBN 0-89004-208-X). Raven.
Slater, T. F. & Mc Brien, D., eds. Free Radicals, Lipid Peroxidation & Cancer. 1982. 55.00 (ISBN 0-12-481780-7). Acad Pr.
Sobel, Lester A., ed. Cancer & the Environment. 1979. lib. bdg. 19.95 (ISBN 0-87196-283-7). Facts on File.
Stening, Malcolm. Cancer & Related Lesions of the Vulva. (Illus.). 160p. 1980. 47.00 (ISBN 0-683-11022-5). Williams & Wilkins.
Studer, Kenneth E. & Chubin, Daryl E. The Cancer Mission: Social Contexts of Biomedical Research. LC 80-10312. (Sage Library of Social Research: Vol. 103). (Illus.). 319p. 1980. 28.00 (ISBN 0-8039-1423-7); pap. 14.00 (ISBN 0-8039-1424-5). Sage.
Sylvester, Edward J. Target: Cancer: The Latest Chapter in the Story of America's Most Important Crusade. 256p. 1986. 15.95 (ISBN 0-317-20294-4, ScribT). Scribner.
Symposium in Honor of the Jackson Laboratory's Fiftieth Anniversary, Bar Harbor, Maine, July 1979. Mammalian Genetics & Cancer: Proceedings. Russell, Elizabeth S., ed. LC 80-27531. (Progress in Clinical & Biological Research Ser.: Vol. 45). 342p. 1981. 46.00x (ISBN 0-8451-0045-9). A R Liss.
Szymendera, Janusz. Bone Mineral Metabolism in Cancer. LC 75-104194. (Recent Results in Cancer Research: Vol. 27). (Illus.). 1970. 26.00 (ISBN 0-387-04992-4). Springer-Verlag.
Tattersall, M. H. & Fox, R. M., eds. Nucleosides in Cancer Treatment: Rational Approaches to Antimetabolite Selectivity & Modulation. LC 80-70775. (Ludwig Symposia Ser.: Vol. 1). 1981. 49.50 (ISBN 0-12-683820-8). Acad Pr.
Vaeth, J. M., ed. Cancer & AIDS. (Frontiers of Radiation Therapy & Oncology Ser.: Vol. 19). (Illus.). x, 186p. 1985. 70.00 (ISBN 3-8055-3923-1). S Karger.
Vaeth, J. M. & Meyer, J., eds. Cancer & the Elderly. (Frontiers of Radiation Therapy & Oncology Ser.: Vol. 20). (Illus.). viii, 192p. 1985. 59.75 (ISBN 3-8055-4145-7). S Karger.
Winick, Myron. Nutrition & Cancer. LC 77-22650. (Current Concepts in Nutrition: Vol. 6). 184p. 1977. 54.95x (ISBN 0-471-03394-4, Pub. by Wiley-Interscience). Wiley.
Winters, Ruth. Cancer Causing Agents: Dictionary. 6.95x (ISBN 0-517-53601-3). Cancer Control Soc.
Zingg, E. & Wallace, D. M., eds. Bladder Cancer: Clinical Practice in Urology. (Clinical Practice in Urology Ser.). (Illus.). 302p. 1985. 59.50 (ISBN 0-387-13239-2). Springer-Verlag.

CANCER RESEARCH

Aisner, Joseph, ed. Cancer Treatment Research. Chang, Paul. (Developments in Oncology Ser.: Vol. 2). (Illus.). xvi, 272p. 1980. lib. bdg. 45.00 (ISBN 90-247-2358-2, Pub. by Martinus Nijhoff Netherlands). Kluwer Academic.
Burcheil, Scott W., et al, eds. Tumor Imaging: The Radioimmunochemical Detection of Cancer. (Illus.). 272p. 1981. 43.50x (ISBN 0-89352-156-6). Masson Pub.
Chirigos, Michael A., et al, eds. Mediation of Cellular Immunity in Cancer by Immune Modifiers. (Progress in Cancer Research & Therapy Ser.: Vol. 19). 288p. 1981. text ed. 45.50 (ISBN 0-89004-628-X). Raven.
Cornell. Statistical Methods for Cancer Studies. (Statistics: Textbooks & Monographs). 344p. 1984. Repr. of 1972 ed. 59.50 (ISBN 0-8247-7169-9). Dekker.
Davies, A. J. & Rudland, P. S. Medical & Biological Perspectives in Cancer Research. 1985. write for info. (ISBN 0-89573-423-0, Pub. by Ellis Horwood Ltd UK). VCH Pubs.
Engstorm, Paul F., et al. Advances in Cancer Control: Epidemiology & Research. LC 84-7894. (Progress In Clinical & Biological Research Ser.: Vol. 156). 482p. 1984. 58.00 (ISBN 0-8451-5006-5). A R Liss.
Goldman, Leon. Laser Cancer Research. (Recent Results in Cancer Research: Vol. 4). (Illus.). 1966. 15.00 (ISBN 0-387-03643-1). Springer-Verlag.
Greenstein, Jesse P. & Haddow, Alexander, eds. Advances in Cancer Research, Vol. 38. (Serial Publication). 1983. 60.00 (ISBN 0-12-006638-6). Acad Pr.

Homburger, F. & Trentin, J. J., eds. Oncogenesis & Natural Immunity in Syrian Hamsters. (Progress in Experimental Tumor Research: Vol. 23). (Illus.). 1978. 41.75 (ISBN 3-8055-2824-8). S Karger.

Inglis, J. R., ed. T Lymphocytes Today. 200p. 1983. 19.50 (ISBN 0-444-80524-9, I-331-83, Biomedical Pr). Elsevier.

Miwa, M. & Nishimura, S., eds. Primary & Tertiary Structure of Nucleic Acids & Cancer Research. (Illus.). 325p. 1983. 49.50x (ISBN 4-7622-6343-5, Pub. by Japan Sci Soc Japan). Intl Spec Bk.

Pincus, Gregory & Vollmer, E., eds. Biological Activities of Steroids in Relation to Cancer: Proceedings. 1960. 80.00 (ISBN 0-12-557068-6). Acad Pr.

Radiation-Induced Cancer. (Proceedings Ser.). (Illus.). 498p. 1969. pap. 35.75 (ISBN 92-0-010269-7, ISP228, IAEA). Unipub.

Szent-Gyhorgyi, Albert. Electronic Biology & Cancer: A New Theory of Cancer. LC 75-42797. pap. 30.00 (ISBN 0-317-28550-5, 2055011). Bks Demand UMI.

Van Zwieten, Matthew J. The Rat As an Animal Model in Breast Cancer Research. (Developments in Oncology Ser.). 300p. 1984. text ed. 52.00 (ISBN 0-89838-624-1, Pub. by Martinus Nijhoff Netherlands). Kluwer Academic.

Woolf, Charles M. Investigations on Genetic Aspects of Carcinoma of the Stomach & Breast. LC 55-9401. (University of California Publications in Public Health Ser.: Vol. 2, No. 4). pap. 22.50 (ISBN 0-317-29563-2, 2021211). Bks Demand UMI.

CANDLEMAKING

Guy, Gary V. Easy to Make Candles. (Illus.). 1980. pap. 2.50 (ISBN 0-486-23881-4). Dover.

Hobson, Phyllis. Making Homemade Soaps & Candles. LC 74-75461. (Country Skills Library). (Illus.). 48p. 1974. pap. 2.95 (ISBN 0-88266-026-8). Garden Way Pub.

Koch, Charles E. How to Make Candles & Money. (Illus., Orig.). pap. 2.95 (ISBN 0-87505-226-6). Borden.

CANDLES

see also Candlemaking

Faraday. Faraday's Chemical History of a Candle: Six Illustrated Lectures with Notes & Experiments. (Science Alive Ser.). (Illus.). 150p. 1980. cancelled 10.00x (ISBN 0-914090-86-0); pap. 6.95x (ISBN 0-914090-87-9). Chicago Review.

CANDY

see Confectionery

CANIDAE

Fox, M. W., ed. The Wild Canids: Their Systematics, Behavioral Ecology & Evolution. LC 83-268. 526p. 1984. Repr. of 1975 ed. text ed. 27.50 (ISBN 0-89874-619-1). Krieger.

Fox, Michael W. The Dog: Its Domestication & Behavior. LC 76-57852. 1978. 40.00 (ISBN 0-8240-9858-7). Garland Pub.

Nowak, Ronald M. North American Quarternary Canis. Wiley, E. O., ed. (U of KS Museum of Nat. Hist. Monograph: No. 6). (Illus.). 154p. 1979. pap. 10.00 (ISBN 0-89338-007-5). U of KS Mus Nat Hist.

CANNED FOOD

see Food, Canned

CANNING AND PRESERVING

see also Drying Apparatus; Food, Canned

Borella, Anne. The Home Canning Handbook: A Guide to Preserving Food at Home. pap. 1.95 (ISBN 0-87502-040-2). Benjamin Co.

--How to Book: Canning, Freezing, Drying. 1977. 1.95 (ISBN 0-87502-051-8). Benjamin Co.

Canning Industry. (UNIDO Guides to Information Sources: No. 19). pap. 4.00 (ISBN 0-686-94965-X, UN158, UN). Unipub.

Chioffi, Nancy & Mead, Gretchen. Keeping the Harvest. rev. ed. LC 80-19577. (Illus.). 208p. 1980. pap. text ed. 7.95 (ISBN 0-88266-247-3). Garden Way Pub.

Deeming, Sue & Deeming, Bill. Canning. (Illus.). 192p. 1983. pap. 7.95 (ISBN 0-89586-185-2). H P Bks.

Eastman, Wilbur F. The Canning, Freezing, Curing & Smoking of Meat, Fish, & Game. LC 75-16830. (Illus.). 220p. 1975. o. p. 11.95 (ISBN 0-88266-072-1); pap. 5.95 (ISBN 0-88266-045-4). Garden Way Pub.

Food Processors Institute. The A-to-Z of Container Corrosion: Another Path to Productivity. 48p. 1982. pap. text ed. 15.00 (ISBN 0-937774-06-5). Food Processor.

--Canned Foods: Principles of Thermal Process Control, Acidification & Container Closure Evaluation. 4th, rev. ed. 256p. 1982. pap. 40.00 (ISBN 0-937774-07-3). Food Processors.

Hersom, A. C. & Hulland, E. D. Canned Foods. 1981. text ed. 40.00 (ISBN 0-8206-0288-4). Chem Pub.

Kahn, Frederick E. Canning & Preserving Foods. (Preparing Food the Healthy Way Ser.). 1984. pap. 4.95. Caroline Hse.

Larsen, Norma S. Store Food. (Illus.). 174p. (Orig.). 1981. pap. 6.95 (ISBN 0-686-34387-5). Hens Pub.

MacRae, Norma M. Canning & Preserving Without Sugar. 168p. (Orig.). 1982. pap. 6.95 (ISBN 0-914718-71-1). Pacific Search.

National Food Processors Association, ed. Laboratory Manual for Food Canners & Processors, Vol. 2. Analysis, Sanitation & Statistics. 3rd ed. (Illus.). 1968. 50.00 (ISBN 0-87055-028-4). AVI.

Natural Convection Heating of Liquids, with Reference to Sterilization of Canned Food. (Agricultural Research Reports: No.839). 1975. pap. 24.00 (ISBN 90-220-0574-7, PDC57, PUDOC). Unipub.

Pyron, Cherry & Silitch, Clarissa M., eds. The Forgotten Arts: Making Old-Fashioned Pickles, Relishes, Chutneys, Sauces & Catsups, Mincemeats, Beverages & Syrups. LC 78-54880. (The Forgotten Arts Ser.). (Illus.). 64p. (Orig.). 1978. pap. 4.95 (ISBN 0-911658-84-X). Yankee Bks.

Seranne, Ann. The Home Canning & Preserving Book. 1975. pap. 5.95 (ISBN 0-06-463424-8, EH 424, EH). B&N NY.

Stumbo, C. R., et al. CRC Handbook of Lethality Guides for Low-Acid Canned Foods, 2 vols. 1982. Vol. 1, Conduction-Heating, 552pp. 75.50 (ISBN 0-8493-2961-2); Vol. 2, Conduction-Heating, 536pp. 77.50 (ISBN 0-8493-2962-0). CRC Pr.

Sunset Editors. Canning, Freezing & Drying. 2nd ed. LC 80-53480. (Illus.). 128p. 1981. pap. 4.95 (ISBN 0-376-02213-2, Sunset Books). Sunset-Lane.

Turgeon, Charlotte & Saturday Evening Post Editors. The Saturday Evening Post Small-Batch Canning & Freezing Cookbook. LC 78-53040. (Illus.). 160p. 1978. 8.95 (ISBN 0-89387-020-X, Co-Pub. by Sat Eve Post); pap. 4.95 (ISBN 0-686-36893-2). Curtis Pub Co.

United States Department of Agriculture. Complete Guide to Home Canning, Preserving & Freezing. LC 72-92754. (Illus.). 215p. 1973. pap. 3.95 (ISBN 0-486-22911-4). Dover.

U. S. Dept. of Agriculture. Home Canning of Fruits & Vegetables. (Shorey Lost Arts Ser.). (Illus.). 31p. pap. 1.95 (ISBN 0-686-70593-9). Shorey.

Walker, Charlotte. The Complete Book of Canning. ORTHO Books Editorial Staff, ed. LC 81-86184. (Illus.). 96p. (Orig.). 1982. pap. 5.95 (ISBN 0-89721-003-4). Ortho.

Wejman, Jacqueline & St. Peter, Genevieve. The Art of Preserving. rev. ed. (Illus.). 192p. 1983. pap. 7.95 (ISBN 0-89286-212-2). One Hund One Prods.

CANOES AND CANOEING

Adney, Edwin T. & Chapelle, Howard I. The Bark Canoes & Skin Boats of North America. 2nd ed. LC 64-62636. (Illus.). 242p. 1983. Repr. of 1964 ed. text ed. 19.95x (ISBN 0-87474-204-8). Smithsonian.

Buck, Peter & Hiroa, Te Rangi. Arts & Crafts of Hawaii: Canoes. (Special Pulbication Ser.: No. 45 (6)). (Illus.). 41p. 1957. pap. 3.00 (ISBN 0-910240-39-6). Bishop Mus.

Burton, Richard F. Explorations of the Highlands of Brazil, with a Full Account of the Gold & Diamond Mines. Incl. Canoeing Down Fifteen Hundred Miles of the Great River Sao Francisco, from Sabara to the Sea. LC 68-55181. (Illus.). 1968. Repr. of 1869 ed. Set. 2 Vols. lib. bdg. 32.75x (ISBN 0-8371-3793-4, BUHB). Greenwood.

Crowley, William, ed. Rushton's Rowboats & Canoes, 1903. LC 82-48169. (Illus.). 128p. 1983. pap. 8.95 (ISBN 0-87742-164-1). Intl Marine.

Hazen, David. The Stripper's Guide to Canoe-Building. LC 76-19972. 1982. 12.95 (ISBN 0-917436-00-8). Tamal Vista.

Parnes, Robert. Canoeing the Jersey Pine Barrens. Rev. ed. LC 81-9681. (Illus.). 286p. (Orig.). 1981. pap. 8.95 (ISBN 0-914788-44-2). East Woods.

Punola, John A. Fishing & Canoeing the Upper Delaware River. rev. for 1982 ed. (Illus.). 112p. (Orig.). 1981. pap. 4.95 (ISBN 0-939888-04-1). Path Pubns NJ.

Putz, G. Kayak Book. 1986. cancelled (ISBN 0-442-25867-4). Van Nos Reinhold.

Riviere, Bill. The Open Canoe. 1984. cancelled (ISBN 0-442-26955-2). Van Nos Reinhold.

CANON CAMERA

see Cameras–Types–Canon

CANS

see Containers

CAOUTCHOUC

see Rubber

CAP (COMPUTER)

Wilkes, M. V. & Needham, R. M. The Cambridge CAP Computer & Its Operating System. (Operating & Programming System Ser.: Vol. 6). 166p. 1979. 29.75 (ISBN 0-444-00357-6, Biomedical Pr); pap. 19.00 (ISBN 0-444-00358-4). Elsevier.

CAPACITORS

Campbell, D. S. Capacitors. Date not set. price not set (ISBN 0-677-05740-7). Gordon.

Frungel, Frank. High Speed Pulse Technology, 4 vols. Incl. Vol. 1. Capacitor Discharges, Magneto-Hydrodynamics, X-Rays, Ultrasonics. 1965. 83.00 (ISBN 0-12-269001-X); Vol. 2. Optical Pulses, Lasers, Measuring Techniques. 1965. 77.00 (ISBN 0-12-269002-8); Vol. 3. 1976. 83.00 (ISBN 0-12-269003-6); Vol. 4. 1980. 66.00 (ISBN 0-12-269004-4). Acad Pr.

Institution of Chemical Engineers. Condensers: Theory & Practice. 70.00 (ISBN 0-08-028772-7). Pergamon.

Marto, P. J. & Nunn, R. H. Power Condenser Heat Transfer Technology: Computer Modeling-Design-Fouling. 496p. 1981. 55.00 (ISBN 0-07-040662-6). McGraw.

CAPILLARIES

Hardaway, Robert M., III, ed. Capillary Perfusion in Health & Disease. LC 81-66551. (Illus.). 288p. 1981. 32.50 (ISBN 0-87993-163-9). Futura Pub.

Jules Gorin Club, 12th Meeting, Crans, Montana, March 1980. Choreocapillaries & Pigment Epithelium Involvements in Macular Diseases. Wessing, A., ed. (Journal: Opthamologica: Vol. 183, No. 1). (Illus.). ii, 52p. 1981. pap. 18.75 (ISBN 3-8055-3457-4). S Karger.

Krogh, August. Anatomy & Physiology of Capillaries. 1929. 75.00x (ISBN 0-685-89734-6). Elliots Bks.

Symposium on the Transfer of Molecules & Ions Between Capillary Blood & Tissue - Alfred Benzon Symposium 2. Capillary Permeability: Proceedings. Crone, C. Z. & Lassen, N. A., eds. 1970. 70.00 (ISBN 0-12-197650-5). Acad Pr.

Thwaites, C. J. Capillary Joining: Brazing & Soft-Soldering. (Materials Science Research Studies). 211p. 1982. 37.95 (ISBN 0-471-10167-2, Pub. by Res Stud Pr). Wiley.

CAPILLARITY

see also Brownian Movements; Hydrostatics; Permeability; Soil Capillarity; Surface Chemistry; Surface Tension

Laplace, Pierre S. Celestial Mechanics, Vols. 1-4. LC 69-11316. Set. text ed. 195.00 (ISBN 0-8284-0194-2). Chelsea Pub.

--Celestial Mechanics, Vol. 5. LC 63-11316. (Mecanique Celeste, Tome V, Fr). 1969. Repr. of 1832 ed. text ed. 20.00 (ISBN 0-8284-0214-0). Chelsea Pub.

Perfil'ev, Boris V., et al. Applied Capillary Microscopy: The Role of Microorganisms in the Formation of Iron-Manganese Desposits. LC 65-15003. pap. 32.50 (ISBN 0-317-10419-5, 2020669). Bks Demand UMI.

Rowlinson, J. S. & Widom, B. Molecular Theory of Capillarity. (International Ser. of Monographs on Chemistry). (Illus.). 1982. 59.00x (ISBN 0-19-855612-8). Oxford U Pr.

CARABIDAE

Noonan, Gerald R. South American Species of the Subgenus "Anistosarsus" Chaudoir (Genus "Notiobia" Party-Carabidae-Coleoptera) Part I: Taxonomy & Natural History. 1981. 5.75 (ISBN 0-89326-071-1). Milwaukee Pub Mus.

Thiele, H. U. Carabid Beetles in Their Environments: A Study on Habit Selection by Adaptations in Physiology & Behaviour. LC 77-9924. (Zoophysiology & Ecology: Vol. 10). (Illus.). 1977. 63.00 (ISBN 0-387-08306-5). Springer-Verlag.

CARATHEODORY MEASURE

Reay, John R. Generalizations of a Theorem of Caratheodory. LC 52-42839. (Memoirs: No. 54). 50p. 1965. pap. 9.00 (ISBN 0-8218-1254-8, MEMO-54). Am Math.

CARBANIONS

Bates, R. B. & Ogle, C. A. Carbanian Chemistry. (Reactivity & Structure Ser.: Vol. 17). 110p. 1983. 21.50 (ISBN 0-387-12345-8). Springer-Verlag.

Buncel, E. Carbanions: Mechanistic & Isotopic Aspects. (Reaction Mechanisms in Organic Chemistry Ser.: Vol. 9). 1974. 59.75 (ISBN 0-444-41190-9). Elsevier.

Cram, Donald J. Fundamentals of Carbanion Chemistry. (Organic Chemistry Ser.: Vol. 4). 1965. 57.50 (ISBN 0-12-196150-8). Acad Pr.

Stowell, John C. Carbanions in Organic Synthesis. LC 79-373. 247p. 1979. 39.95 (ISBN 0-471-02953-X, Pub. by Wiley-Interscience). Wiley.

CARBENES

Doetz, Karl H., et al. Transition Metal Carbene Complexes: Dedicated to Professor E. O. Fischer. 264p. 1983. 60.00x (ISBN 0-89573-073-1). VCH Pubs.

Ershov, V. V. & Nikiforov, G. A. Quinonediazides. (Studies in Organic Chemistry: Vol. 7). 302p. 1981. 74.50 (ISBN 0-444-42008-8). Elsevier.

Gilchrist, T. L. & Rees, C. W. Carbenes, Nitrenes, & Arynes. 131p. 1969. pap. 12.50x (ISBN 0-306-50026-4, Plenum Pr). Plenum Pub.

Kirmse, Wolfgang. Carbene Chemistry. 2nd ed. (Organic Chemistry Ser.: Vol. 1). 1971. 82.00 (ISBN 0-12-409956-4). Acad Pr.

Moss, Robert A., Jr. & Jones, Maitland, Jr. Carbenes, Vol. 2. LC 80-11836. (Reactive Intermediates in Organic Chemistry Ser.). 390p. 1983. Repr. of 1975 ed. lib. bdg. 29.50 each; lib. bdg. 55.00 set (ISBN 0-89874-160-2). Krieger.

Moss, Robert A., Jr. & Jones, Maitland, eds. Carbenes, Vol. 1. LC 80-11836. 368p. 1983. Repr. of 1973 ed. lib. bdg. 39.50 (ISBN 0-89874-216-1). Krieger.

CARBIDES

see also Silicon Carbide

Kosolapova, Tatiana Y. Carbides: Properties, Production, & Applications. LC 70-128507. 298p. 1971. 45.00x (ISBN 0-306-30496-1, Plenum Pr). Plenum Pub.

Storms, Edmund K. Refractory Carbides. 1967. 65.00 (ISBN 0-12-672850-X). Acad Pr.

CARBINES

see Rifles

CARBOHYDRATE METABOLISM

see also Phosphorylation

Beitner, R., ed. Regulation of Carbohydrate Metabolism, 2 vols. 240p. 1985. Set. 65.00 (ISBN 0-8493-5262-2); Set. 73.00 (ISBN 0-8493-5263-0). CRC Pr.

Birch, G. G. & Green, L. F., eds. Molecular Structure & Function of Food Carbohydrate. LC 73-16299. 308p. 1973. 58.95 (ISBN 0-470-07323-3). Halsted Pr.

Candy, David J. Biological Functions of Carbohydrates. LC 80-18668. (Tertiary Level Biology Ser.). 197p. 1980. 49.95x (ISBN 0-470-27038-1). Halsted Pr.

Cobelli, C. & Bergman, R. N., eds. Carbohydrate Metabolism: Quantitative Physiology & Mathematical Modelling. LC 80-41383. 440p. 1981. 82.95 (ISBN 0-471-27912-9, Pub. by Wiley Interscience). Wiley.

Colowick, S. & Ginsburg, Victor, eds. Methods in Enzymology: Complex Carbohydrates, Vol. 83, Pt. D. 1982. 69.50 (ISBN 0-12-181983-3). Acad Pr.

Colowick, Sidney & Wood, Willis, eds. Methods in Enzymology: Carbohydrate Metabolism. (Vol. 89. Pt. D). 656p. 1982. 66.00 (ISBN 0-12-181989-2). Acad Pr.

--Methods in Enzymology: Carbohydrate Metabolism, Vol. 90, Pt. E. 559p. 1982. 65.00 (ISBN 0-12-181990-6). Acad Pr.

Cornblath, Marvin & Schwartz, Robert. Disorders of Carbohydrate Metabolism in Infancy. LC 66-12410. (Major Problems in Clinical Pediatrics Ser.: Vol. 3). pap. 77.80 (ISBN 0-317-26428-1, 2024984). Bks Demand UMI.

Creutzfeldt, W., ed. Acarbose: Proceedings of the International Symposium on Acarbose Effects on Carbohydrate & Fat Metabolism, First, Montreux, October 8-10, 1981. (International Congress Ser.: No. 594). 588p. 1982. 81.00 (ISBN 0-444-90283-X, I-278-82, Excerpta Medica). Elsevier.

Dickens, Frank, et al, eds. Carbohydrate Metabolism & Its Disorders, 2 Vols. 1968. Vol. 1. 84.50 (ISBN 0-12-214901-7); Vol. 2. 66.50 (ISBN 0-12-214902-5). Acad Pr.

Duffus, C. M. & Duffus, J. H. Carbohydrate Metabolism in Plants. LC 82-22855. (Illus.). 192p. (Orig.). 1984. 13.95 (ISBN 0-582-44642-2). Longman.

Durlach, J. & Altura, B. M., eds. Magnesium, Diabetes & Carbohydrate Metabolism: Journal - Magnesium. (Vol. 2, Nos. 4-6). (Illus.). iv, 172p. 1984. pap. 41.75 (ISBN 3-8055-3865-0). S Karger.

Martin, Arthur W., ed. Comparative Physiology of Carbohydrate Metabolism in Heterothermic Animals. (Illus.). 155p. 1961. pap. 15.00x (ISBN 0-295-73748-4). U of Wash Pr.

Randle, P. J., et al, eds. Carbohydrate Metabolism & Its Disorders, Vol. 3. LC 68-17670. 1981. 83.50 (ISBN 0-12-579703-6). Acad Pr.

Roehrig. Carbohydrate Biochemistry & Metabolism. 1984. 45.00 (ISBN 0-87055-447-6). AVI.

Spoehr, Herman A. The Carbohydrate Economy of Cacti. Repr. of 1919 ed. 15.00 (ISBN 0-384-57140-9). Johnson Repr.

Stowers, H. Sutherland & Stowers, John. Carbohydrate Metabolism in Pregnancy & the Newborn. 2nd ed. (Illus.). 1984. text ed. 45.00 (ISBN 0-443-02859-1). Churchill.

Sutherland, H. W. & Stowers, John M., eds. Carbohydrate Metabolism in Pregnancy & the Newborn 1979. LC 79-10956. (Illus.). 1979. pap. 39.00 (ISBN 0-387-08798-2). Springer-Verlag.

CARBOHYDRATES

see also Dextran

also names of compounds belonging to this group, e.g. Cellulose, Dextrose

Birch, G. G., ed. Analysis of Food Carbohydrate. 288p. 1985. 60.00 (ISBN 0-85334-354-3, Pub. by Elsevier Applied Sci England). Elsevier.

Birch, G. G. & Shallenberger, R. S., eds. Developments in Food Carbohydrates, Vol. 1. 189p. 1977. 40.75 (ISBN 0-85334-733-6, Pub. by Elsevier Applied Sci England). Elsevier.

Birch, G. G., et al, eds. Glucose Syrups & Related Carbohydrates. (Illus.). 118p. 1971. 20.50 (ISBN 0-444-20103-3, Pub. by Elsevier Applied Sci England). Elsevier.

Brimacombe, J. S., ed. Carbohydrate Chemistry, Vols. 1-11. Incl. Vol. 1. 1967 Literature. 1968. 31.00 (ISBN 0-85186-002-8); Vol. 2. 1968 Literature. 1969. 31.00 (ISBN 0-85186-012-5); Vol. 3. 1969 Literature. 1970. 34.00 (ISBN 0-85186-022-2); Vol. 4. 1970 Literature. 1971. 34.00 (ISBN 0-85186-032-X); Vol. 5. 1971 Literature. 1972. 36.00 (ISBN 0-85186-042-7); Vol. 6. 1972 Literature. 1973. 38.00 (ISBN 0-85186-052-4); Vol. 7. 1973 Literature. 1975. 56.00 (ISBN 0-85186-062-1); Vol. 8. 1974 Literature. 1976. 61.00 (ISBN 0-85186-072-9); Vol. 9. 1975-76 Literature. 1977. 82.00 (ISBN 0-85186-082-6); Vol. 10. 1976-77 Literature. 1978. 82.00 (ISBN 0-85186-092-3); Vol. 11. LC 79-67610. 1979. 97.00 (ISBN 0-85186-102-4). LC 79-67610 (Pub. by Royal Soc Chem London). Am Chemical.

Cantor, Sidney M., ed. Use of Sugars & Other Carbohydrates in the Food Industry. LC 55-4135. (Advances in Chemistry Ser: No. 12). 1955. pap. 10.95 (ISBN 0-8412-0013-0). Am Chemical.

Carbohydrates in Human Nutrition: A Joint WHO Report. (Food & Nutrition Papers: No. 15). (Eng., Fr. & Span.). 89p. (2nd Printing 1983). 1980. pap. 7.50 (ISBN 92-5-100903-1, F2040, FAO). Unipub.

Carper, Jean & Krause, Patricia A. The All-in-One Carbohydrate Gram Counter. rev. ed. 304p. 1980. pap. 3.95 (ISBN 0-553-24475-2). Bantam.

Cheshire, M. V. Nature & Origin of Carbohydrates in Soils. LC 79-40898. 1980. 48.00 (ISBN 0-12-171250-8). Acad Pr.

Churms, Shirley C. CRC Handbook of Chromatography, Carbohydrates, Vol. I. 288p. 1982. 58.00 (ISBN 0-8493-3061-0). CRC Pr.

Colowick, S. & Ginsburg, Victor, eds. Methods in Enzymology: Complex Carbohydrates, Vol. 83, Pt. D. 1982. 69.50 (ISBN 0-12-181983-3). Acad Pr.

Devon, T. K. & Scott, A. I. Handbook of Naturally Occurring Compounds, 2 vols. Incl. Vol. 1. Acetogenins, Shikimates & Carbohydrates. 1975. 76.50 (ISBN 0-12-213601-2); Vol. 2. Terpenes. 1972. 77.00 (ISBN 0-12-213602-0). Acad Pr.

Deyl, Z., ed. Separation Methods. (New Comprehensive Biochemistry Ser.: No. 18). 534p. 1984. 75.00 (ISBN 0-444-80527-3). Elsevier.

Dufty, William. Sugar Blues. 256p. 1976. pap. 3.95 (ISBN 0-446-30512-X). Warner Bks.

El Khadem, Hassan S., ed. Synthetic Methods for Carbohydrates. LC 76-58888. (ACS Symposium Ser: No. 39). 1977. 29.95 (ISBN 0-8412-0365-2). Am Chemical.

Foster, A. B. Carbohydrate Chemistry, Vol. 9. 1979. 50.00 (ISBN 0-08-022354-0). Pergamon.

Fredericks, Carlton. Calorie & Carbohydrate Guide. 1982. pap. 2.95 (ISBN 0-671-46941-X, 43059). PB.

Ginsburg, Victor. Biology of Carbohydrates, Vol. 1. LC 80-20758. 336p. 1981. 70.95 (ISBN 0-471-03905-5, Pub. by Wiley-Interscience). Wiley.

Ginsburg, Victor & Robbins, Phillips W. Biology of Carbohydrates, Vol. 2. (Biology of Carbohydrates Ser.: 1-504). 342p. 1984. 80.00 (ISBN 0-471-03906-3, Pub. by Wiley-Interscience). Wiley.

Goldstein, Irwin J., ed. Carbohydrate-Protein Interaction. LC 78-25788. (ACS Symposium Ser.: No. 88). 1979. 26.95 (ISBN 0-8412-0466-7). Am Chemical.

Harmon, Robert E., ed. Cell Surface Carbohydrate Chemistry. 1978. 47.50 (ISBN 0-12-326150-3). Acad Pr.

Hill, R. D. & Munck, L., eds. New Approaches to Research on Cereal Carbohydrates: Proceedings of the Conference Held in Copenhagen, Denmark, June 24-29, 1984. (Progress in Biotechnology Ser.: Vol. 1). 416p. 1985. 102.00 (ISBN 0-444-42434-2). Elsevier.

Hood, Lamartine F. & Wardrip, E. K. Carbohydrates & Health. (Illus.). 1977. text ed. 30.00 (ISBN 0-87055-223-6). AVI.

Horton, Dereck & Tipson, R. Stuart. Advances in Carbohydrate Chemistry & Biochemistry, Vol. 38. 1981. 80.00 (ISBN 0-12-007238-6). Acad Pr.

Horton, Derek & Tipson, Stuart, eds. Advances in Carbohydrate Chemistry & Biochemistry, Vol. 37. LC 45-11351. 1980. 80.00 (ISBN 0-12-007237-8). Acad Pr.

Isbell, Horace S., ed. Carbohydrates in Solution. LC 73-81038. (Advances in Chemistry Ser.: No. 117). 1973. 32.95 (ISBN 0-8412-0178-1). Am Chemical.

Kennedy, J. F. & White, C. A. Bioactive Carbohydrates in Chemistry, Biochemistry & Biology. LC 82-9286. 331p. 1983. 84.95X (ISBN 0-470-27527-8). Halsted Pr.

Koivistoinen, Pekka & Hyvonen, Lea, eds. Carbohydrate Sweetners in Foods & Nutrition. LC 79-41549. 1980. 59.50 (ISBN 0-12-417050-1). Acad Pr.

Laskin, Allen I. & Lechevalier, Hubert, eds. Handbook of Microbiology, CRC, Vol. 4: Microbial Composition: Carbohydrates, Lipids & Minerals. 2nd ed. 744p. 1982. 72.50 (ISBN 0-8493-7204-6). CRC Pr.

Lee, C. K., ed. Developments in Food Carbohydrates, Vol. 2. (Illus.). 219p. 1980. 72.25 (ISBN 0-85334-857-X, Pub. by Elsevier Applied Sci England). Elsevier.

--Developments in Food Carbohydrates, Vol. 3. (Illus.). xii, 216p. 1982. 52.00 (ISBN 0-85334-996-7, Pub. by Elsevier Applied Sci England). Elsevier.

Lewis, D. H., ed. Storage Carbohydrates in Vascular Plants. (Society for Experimental Biology Seminar Ser.: No. 19). (Illus.). 256p. 1985. 69.50 (ISBN 0-521-23698-3). Cambridge U Pr.

Lineback, David R. & Inglett, George E. Food Carbohydrates. (Institute of Food Technologists Basic Symposia Ser.). (Illus.). 1982. lib. bdg. 55.00 (ISBN 0-87055-400-X). AVI.

Loewus, F. A. & Tanner, W., eds. Plant Carbohydrates I: Intracellular Carbohydrates. (Encyclopedia of Plant Physiology Ser.: Vol. 13 a). (Illus.). 880p. 1982. 145.00 (ISBN 0-387-11060-7). Springer-Verlag.

Marchesi, Vincent T., et al, eds. Cell Surface Carbohydrates & Biological Recognition: Proceedings of the ICN-UCLA Symposium Held at Keystone, Col., Feb. 1977. LC 78-417. (P.C.B.R.: VOl. 23). 690p. 1978. 91.00 (ISBN 0-8451-0023-8). A R Liss.

Netzer, Corinne T. Brand Name Carbohydrate Gram Counter. (Orig.). 1981. pap. 3.50 (ISBN 0-440-10658-3). Dell.

Pigman, W. Carbohydrates: Chemistry & Biochemistry, Vol. IB. 2nd ed. LC 68-26647. 1980. 76.50 (ISBN 0-12-556351-5); 65.00. Acad Pr.

Pigman, W. & Horton, D. The Carbohydrates. 2nd ed. Incl. Vol. 1A. 1972. 94.50 (ISBN 0-12-556301-9); Vol. 2A. 1970. 77.00 (ISBN 0-12-556302-7); Vol. 2B. 1970. 85.00 (ISBN 0-12-556352-3). Acad Pr.

Pigman, Ward & Horton, Derek, eds. Advances in Carbohydrate Chemistry & Biochemistry, Vol. 33. 1976. 90.00 (ISBN 0-12-007233-5). Acad Pr.

--Advances in Carbohydrate Chemistry & Biochemistry, Vol. 34. 1977. 90.00 (ISBN 0-12-007234-3). Acad Pr.

--Advances in Carbohydrate Chemistry & Biochemistry, Vol. 36. LC 45-11351. 1979. 80.00 (ISBN 0-12-007236-X). Acad Pr.

Pigman, Ward & Wolfrom, Melville, eds. Advances in Carbohydrate Chemistry & Biochemistry, Vol. 42. (Serial Publication Ser.). 1984. 65.00 (ISBN 0-12-007242-4). Acad Pr.

Pigman, Ward & Wolfrom, Melville L., eds. Advances in Carbohydrate Chemistry. Incl. Vol. 1. 1945 (ISBN 0-12-007201-7); Vol. 2. 1946 (ISBN 0-12-007202-5); Vol. 3. 1948 (ISBN 0-12-007203-3); Vol. 4. 1949 (ISBN 0-12-007204-1); Vol. 5. Hudson, C. S. & Cantor, S. M., eds. 1950 (ISBN 0-12-007205-X); Vol. 6. 1951 (ISBN 0-12-007206-8); Vol. 7. Hudson, C. S., et al, eds. 1952 (ISBN 0-12-007207-6); Vol. 8. Hudson, C. S. & Wolfrom, Melville, eds. 1953 (ISBN 0-12-007208-4); Vol. 9. Wolfrom, Melville L. & Tipson, R. Stuart, eds. 1954 (ISBN 0-12-007209-2); Vol. 10. 1955 (ISBN 0-12-007210-6); Vol. 11. 1956 (ISBN 0-12-007211-4); Vol. 12. 1957 (ISBN 0-12-007212-2); Vol. 13. 1958 (ISBN 0-12-007213-0); Vol. 14. 1959 (ISBN 0-12-007214-9); Vol. 15. 1960 (ISBN 0-12-007215-7); Vol. 16. 1962 (ISBN 0-12-007216-5); Vol. 17. 1963 (ISBN 0-12-007217-3); Vol. 18. 1963 (ISBN 0-12-007218-1); Vol. 19. 1964 (ISBN 0-12-007219-X); Vol. 20. 1965 (ISBN 0-12-007220-3); Vol. 21. 1967 (ISBN 0-12-007221-1); Vol. 22. 1967 (ISBN 0-12-007222-X); Vol. 23. 1968 (ISBN 0-12-007223-8); Vol. 24. 1970 (ISBN 0-12-007224-6); Vol. 25. 1971. 60.00 (ISBN 0-12-007225-4); Vol. 26. Tipson, Stuart R. & Horton, Derek, eds. 1971. 80.00 (ISBN 0-12-007226-2); Vol. 27. 1972. 80.00 (ISBN 0-12-007227-0); Vol. 28. 1973. 90.00 (ISBN 0-12-007228-9); Vol. 29. 1974. 90.00 (ISBN 0-12-007229-7). Vols. 1-27. 80.00 ea.; Vols. 20-24. 80.00 ea. Acad Pr.

--Advances in Carbohydrate Chemistry. Incl. Vol. 30. 1974. 90.00 (ISBN 0-12-007230-0); Vol. 31. 1975. 90.00 (ISBN 0-12-007231-9); Vol. 32. 1976. 90.00 (ISBN 0-12-007232-7). Acad Pr.

Shreeve, Walton W. Physiological Chemistry of Carbohydrates in Mammals. LC 73-88265. (Illus.). Repr. of 1974 ed. 65.40 (ISBN 0-8357-9553-5, 2016687). Bks Demand UMI.

Southgate, D. A. Determination of Food Carbohydrates. (Illus.). 1976. 37.00 (ISBN 0-85334-693-3, Pub. by Elsevier Applied Sci England). Elsevier.

Spoehr, Herman A. The Carbohydrate Economy of Cacti. Repr. of 1919 ed. 15.00 (ISBN 0-384-57140-9). Johnson Repr.

Sutherland, I. W., ed. Surface Carbohydrates of the Procaryotic Cell. 1978. 75.00 (ISBN 0-12-677850-7). Acad Pr.

Tipson, R. Stuart & Horton, Derek. Advances in Carbohydrate Chemistry & Biochemistry, Vol. 41. (Serial Publication Ser.). 1983. 70.00 (ISBN 0-12-007241-6); microfiche o.p. 39.50 (ISBN 0-12-007295-5). Acad Pr.

Tipson, R. Stuart & Horton, Derek, eds. Advances in Carbohydrate Chemistry & Biochemistry, Vol. 39. (Serial Publication Ser.). 1981. 80.00 (ISBN 0-12-007239-4). Acad Pr.

Tipson, Stuart & Horton, D., eds. Advances in Carbohydrate Chemistry & Biochemistry, Vol. 40. 402p. 1982. 75.00 (ISBN 0-12-007240-8); lib. ed. o.p. 84.50 (ISBN 0-12-007292-0); Microfiche o.p. 45.50 (ISBN 0-12-007293-9). Acad Pr.

Weber, Rudolf, ed. Biochemistry of Animal Development, 3 vols. Incl. Vol. 1. Descriptive Biochemistry of Early Development. 1965. 78.00 (ISBN 0-12-740601-8); Vol. 2. Biochemical Control Mechanisms & Adaptations in Development. 1967. 67.50 (ISBN 0-12-740602-6); Vol. 3. 1975. 73.50 (ISBN 0-12-740603-4). Set. 178.50. Acad Pr.

Whistler, Roy L. & Wolfrom, Melville L., eds. Methods in Carbohydrate Chemistry, 8 vols. Incl. Vol. 1. Analysis & Preparation of Sugars. 1962. 81.00 (ISBN 0-12-746201-5); Vol. 2. Reactions of Carbohydrates. 1963. 81.00 (ISBN 0-12-746202-3); Vol. 3. Cellulose. 1963. 75.00 (ISBN 0-12-746203-1); Vol. 4. Starch. 1964. 70.00 (ISBN 0-12-746204-X); Vol. 5. General Polysaccharides. 1965. 77.00 (ISBN 0-12-746205-8); Vol. 6. 1971. 81.00 (ISBN 0-12-746206-6); Vol. 7. 1976. 65.00 (ISBN 0-12-746207-4); Vol. 8. 1980. 60.00 (ISBN 0-12-746208-2). Acad Pr.

Williams, N. R., ed. Carbohydrate Chemistry, Vol. 16, Pt. I: Mono, Di, & Trisaccharides & Their Derivatives. 278p. 1985. 72.00 (ISBN 0-85186-162-8, 996194755, Pub. by Royal Soc Chem UK). Heyden.

CARBON

see also Charcoal; Coal; Coke; Diamonds; Graphite

American Society for Testing & Materials Staff. Specifications for Carbon & Alloy-Steel Plates for Pressure Vessels. pap. 46.50 (ISBN 0-317-28482-7, 2019125). Bks Demand UMI.

ASTM Standards on Manufactured Carbon & Graphite Products. 115p. 1981. pap. 3.50 (ISBN 0-8031-0821-4, 06-305001-00). ASTM.

Bewley, J. D. Nitrogen & Carbon Metabolism: Symposium on the Physiology & Bio-Chemistry of Plant Productivity. (Development in Plant & Soil Sciences Ser.: No. 3). 39.50 (ISBN 90-247-2472-4, Pub. by Junk Pubs Netherlands). Kluwer Academic.

Blair, John S. The Profitable Way: Carbon Plate Steel Specifying & Purchasing Handbook. (Illus.). 194p. 1978. 39.95x (ISBN 0-931690-08-0). Genium Pub.

--The Profitable Way: Carbon Sheet Steel Specifying & Purchasing Handbook. (Illus.). 158p. 1978. 39.95x (ISBN 0-931690-04-8). Genium Pub.

--The Profitable Way: Carbon Strip Steel Specifying & Purchasing Handbook. (Illus.). 194p. 1978. 39.95x (ISBN 0-931690-05-6). Genium Pub.

Bolin, B., et al, eds. The Global Carbon Cycle. LC 78-16261. (SCOPE Ser. (Scientific Committee on Problems of the Environment): Report 13). 491p. 1979. pap. 69.95 (ISBN 0-471-99710-2, Pub. by Wiley-Interscience). Wiley.

Bolin, Bert, ed. Carbon Cycle Modelling-Scope Report 16. (SCOPE Ser. (Scientific Committe on Problems of the Environment): Vol. 16). 390p. 1981. 57.95 (ISBN 0-471-10051-X, Pub. by Wiley-Interscience). Wiley.

Buncel, E. & Durst, T. Comprehensive Carbanion Chemistry: Selectivity in Carbon-Carbon Bond Formation Reactions, Pt. B. (Studies in Organic Chemistry: Vol. 5B). 1984. 75.00 (ISBN 0-444-42267-6). Elsevier.

Carbon & Graphite Fibers & Fiber Composites, March 1982-May 1983. 272p. 1983. 78.00 (ISBN 0-686-48273-5, LS108). T-C Pubns CA.

Davidson, H. W., et al. Manufactured Carbon. 1968. 18.00 (ISBN 0-08-012667-7); pap. 7.00 (ISBN 0-08-012666-9). Pergamon.

Delmonte, John. Technology of Carbon & Graphite Fiber Composites. (Illus.). 464p. 1981. 36.50 (ISBN 0-686-48237-9, 0213). T-C Pubns CA.

Fukui, K. Theory of Orientation & Stereoselection. LC 75-25597. (Reactivity & Structure: Vol. 2). (Illus.). 120p. 1975. 27.00 (ISBN 0-387-07426-0). Springer-Verlag.

Jenkins, Gwyn M. & Kawamura, K. Polymeric Carbons: Carbon Fibre, Glass & Char. LC 74-16995. pap. 46.50 (ISBN 0-317-29379-6, 2024480). Bks Demand UMI.

Khan, M. A. & Stanton, R. H., eds. Toxicology of Halogenated Hydrocarbons: Health & Ecological Effects. (Illus.). 350p. 1981. 66.00 (ISBN 0-08-027530-3). Pergamon.

Lexique International De Petrographie Des Charbons. 2nd ed. (Eng. & Fr.). 160p. 1963. 32.50 (ISBN 0-686-57016-2, M-6366). French & Eur.

Lexique International De Petrographie Des Charbon: Supplement. (Fr.). 250p. 1971. pap. 32.50 (ISBN 0-686-57017-0, M-6367). French & Eur.

Linnert, G. E. Metallurgy, Welding, Carbon & Alloy Steels- Fundamentals: WM1, Vol. 1. 3rd ed. 474p. 1965. 28.00 (ISBN 0-686-95602-8, WM1); member 21.00. Am Welding.

--Metallurgy, Welding, Carbon & Alloy Steels: Technology: WM2, Vol. 2. 3rd ed. 674p. 1967. 30.00 (ISBN 0-686-95605-2, WM2); member 22.50. Am Welding.

Mantell, Charles L. Carbon & Graphite Handbook. LC 78-21468. 548p. 1979. Repr. of 1968 ed. lib. bdg. 37.50 (ISBN 0-88275-796-2). Krieger.

Paxton, R. R. Manufactured Carbon: A Self-Lubricating Material for Mechanical Devices. 184p. 1979. 24.95 (ISBN 0-8493-5655-5). CRC Pr.

Perrich, Jerry R., ed. Activated Carbon Absorption for Wastewater Treatment. 272p. 1981. 82.00 (ISBN 0-8493-5693-8). CRC Pr.

Seigla, Donald C. & Smith, George W., eds. Particulate Carbon: Formation During Combustion. LC 81-15363. (General Motors Research Symposia Ser.). 516p. 1981. text ed. 69.50 (ISBN 0-306-40881-3, Plenum Pr). Plenum Pub.

Siegleman, H. W. & Hind, G., eds. Photosynthetic Carbon Assimilation. LC 78-11545. (Basic Life Sciences Ser.: Vol. 11). 455p. 1978. 57.50x (ISBN 0-306-40064-2, Plenum Pr). Plenum Pub.

Thrower. Chemistry & Physics of Carbon, Vol. 19. 440p. 1984. 79.50 (ISBN 0-8247-7245-8). Dekker.

Thrower, Peter A., ed. Chemistry & Physics of Carbon, Vol. 18. (Illus.). 208p. 1982. 79.00 (ISBN 0-8247-1740-6). Dekker.

Walker. Chemistry & Physics of Carbon: A Series of Advances, Vol. 17. 1981. 79.00 (ISBN 0-8247-1209-9). Dekker.

Walker & Thrower. Chemistry & Physics of Carbon: A Series of Advances, Vol. 15. 1979. 79.00 (ISBN 0-8247-6816-7). Dekker.

--Chemistry & Physics of Carbon: A Series of Advances, Vol. 16. 344p. 1981. 79.00 (ISBN 0-8247-6991-0). Dekker.

Walker, Philip L. Chemistry & Physics of Carbon, Vol. 4. LC 66-58302. pap. 102.80 (ISBN 0-317-08348-1, 2017695). Bks Demand UMI.

Walker, Philip L., ed. Chemistry & Physics of Carbon, Vol 2. LC 66-58302. pap. 100.00 (ISBN 0-317-08352-X, 2055058). Bks Demand UMI.

Walker, Philip L., Jr., ed. Chemistry & Physics of Carbon: A Series of Advances, Vol. 7. 1971. 79.00 (ISBN 0-8247-1762-7). Dekker.

Walker, Philip L., Jr. & Thrower, Peter A., eds. Chemistry & Physics of Carbon: A Series of Advances, Vol. 8. 334p. 1973. 79.00 (ISBN 0-8247-1755-4). Dekker.

--Chemistry & Physics of Carbon: A Series of Advances, Vol. 9. 312p. 1973. 79.00 (ISBN 0-8247-6019-0). Dekker.

--Chemistry & Physics of Carbon: A Series of Advances, Vol. 10. 288p. 1973. 79.00 (ISBN 0-8247-6072-7). Dekker.

--Chemistry & Physics of Carbon: A Series of Advances, Vol. 12. 216p. 1975. 79.00 (ISBN 0-8247-6304-1). Dekker.

Wolff, George T. & Klimisch, Richard L., eds. Particulate Carbon: Atmospheric Life Cycle. LC 81-21017. (General Motors Symposia Ser.). 421p. 1982. text ed. 55.00x (ISBN 0-306-40918-6, Plenum Pr). Plenum Pub.

Woodwell, George M., ed. The Role of Terrestrial Vegetation in the Global Carbon Cycle: Measurement by Remote Sensing. LC 83-10333. (SCOPE Ser. (Scientific Committee on Problems of thr Environment): SCOPE 23). 247p. 1984. 51.95 (ISBN 0-471-90262-4, 1-409, Pub. by Wiley-Interscience). Wiley.

Woodwell, George M. & Pecan, Erene, eds. Carbon & the Biosphere: Proceedings. LC 73-600092. (AEC Symposium Ser.). 399p. 1973. pap. 18.00 (ISBN 0-87079-006-4, CONF-720510); microfiche 4.50 (ISBN 0-87079-156-7, CONF-720510). DOE.

CARBON–ISOTOPES

see also Radiocarbon Dating

Fuchs, P. L. & Bunnell, C. A. Carbon-Thirteen NMR Based Organic Spectral Problems. LC 78-20668. 309p. 1979. pap. text ed. 20.95 (ISBN 0-471-04907-7). Wiley.

--How to Design an Effective Graphics Presentation, Vol. 17. (The Harvard Library of Computer Graphics, Mapping Collection). (Illus.). 86p. 1981. pap. 12.50 (ISBN 0-8122-1197-9). U of Pa Pr.
--Management's Use of Computer Graphics, Vol. 12. (The Harvard Library of Computer Graphics, Mapping Collection). (Illus.). 128p. 1981. pap. 12.50 (ISBN 0-8122-1192-8). U of Pa Pr.
--Management's Use of Maps: Commercial & Political Applications, Vol. 1. (The Harvard Library of Computer Graphics, Mapping Collection). (Illus.). 64p. 1979. pap. 12.50 (ISBN 0-8122-1181-2). U of Pa Pr.
--Management's Use of Maps: Including an Introduction to Computer Mapping for Executives, Vol. 7. (The Harvard Library of Computer Graphics, Mapping Collection). (Illus.). 103p. 1980. pap. 12.50 (ISBN 0-8122-1187-1). U of Pa Pr.
--Mapping Software & Cartographic Data Bases, Vol. 2. (The Harvard Library of Computer Graphics, Mapping Collection). (Illus.). 240p. 1979. pap. 12.50 (ISBN 0-8122-1182-0). U of Pa Pr.
--Thematic Map Design, Vol. 6. (The Harvard Library of Computer Graphics, Mapping Collection). (Illus.). 134p. 1979. pap. 12.50 (ISBN 0-8122-1186-3). U of Pa Pr.
--Urban, Regional, & State Applications: Plus a Special Section on Cadastral Systems, Vol. 3. (The Harvard Library of Computer Graphics, Mapping Collection). (Illus.). 195p. 1979. pap. 12.50 (ISBN 0-8122-1183-9). U of Pa Pr.
--Urban, Regional, & State Government Applications of Computer Mapping: Plus Computer Mapping in Education, Vol. 11. (The Harvard Library of Computer Graphics, Mapping Collection). (Illus.). 232p. 1980. pap. 12.50 (ISBN 0-8122-1191-X). U of Pa Pr.
Library of Congress, Geography & Map Division (Washington, D. C.) The Bibliography of Cartography, First Supplement. 1979. lib. bdg. 260.00 (ISBN 0-8161-0259-7, Hall Library). G K Hall.
Library of Congress, Washington, D.C. Geography & Map Division. The Bibliography of Cartography, 5 vols. 1973. Set. lib. bdg. 559.00 (ISBN 0-8161-1008-5, Hall Library). G K Hall.
Meynen, E. Multilingual Dictionary of Technical Terms in Cartography. (Eng. & Ger.). 572p. 1973. pap. 88.00 (ISBN 3-515-00127-1, M-7564, Pub. by F. Steiner). French & Eur.
Monkhouse, Francis & Wilkinson, Henry R. Maps & Diagrams: Their Compilation & Construction. 3rd, rev. & enl. ed. (University Paperbacks Ser.). (Illus.). 522p. 1971. pap. 14.95x (ISBN 0-416-07450-2, NO. 2326). Methuen Inc.
Monmonier, Mark S. Technological Transistion in Cartography. LC 84-40499. (Illus.). 320p. 1985. text ed. 25.00x (ISBN 0-299-10070-7). U of Wis Pr.
Paullin, Charles O. Atlas of the Historical Geography of the U. S. Wright, John K., ed. LC 75-14058. (Carnegie Institution of Washington Ser.: No. 4). (Illus.). 162p. 1975. Repr. of 1932 ed. lib. bdg. 135.25 (ISBN 0-8371-8208-5, PAHG). Greenwood.
Peters, Arno. The New Cartography. Kaiser, Ward & Smith, D. G., trs. from Ger. Orig. Title: Die Neue Kartographie. (Eng. & Ger., Illus.). 163p. 1984. 20.00 (ISBN 0-377-00147-3). Friend Pr.
Peuquet, Donna J. & Boyle, A. Raymond. Raster Scanning, Processing, & Plotting of Cartographic Documents. 130p. (Orig.). 1984. pap. text ed. 39.95x (ISBN 0-913913-01-4). Spad Sys.
Robinson, Arthur H. Look of Maps: An Examination of Cartographic Design. 118p. 1952. 11.50x (ISBN 0-299-00950-5). U of Wis Pr.
Rudman, Jack. Cartographer. (Career Examination Ser.: C-127). (Cloth bdg. avail. on request). pap. 12.00 (ISBN 0-8373-0127-0). Natl Learning.
--Cartographer-Draftsman. (Career Examination Ser.: C-1160). (Cloth bdg. avail. on request). pap. 12.00 (ISBN 0-8373-1160-8). Natl Learning.
--Chief Cartographer-Draftsman. (Career Examination Ser.: C-1169). (Cloth bdg. avail. on request). pap. 14.00 (ISBN 0-8373-1169-1). Natl Learning.
Smith, Thomas H. The Mapping of Ohio. LC 75-99081. (Illus.). 275p. 1977. 32.00x (ISBN 0-87338-054-1). Kent St U Pr.
Stibbe, Hugo L., ed. Cartographic Materials: A Manual of Interpretation for AACRZ. LC 82-11519. 268p. 1982. text ed. 40.00x, lib. bdg. (ISBN 0-8389-0363-0). ALA.
Taylor, D. R. Education & Training in Contemporary Cartography. (Progress in Contemporary Cartography Ser.). 1985. write for info. (ISBN 0-471-90305-1). Wiley.
--Graphic Communication & Design in Contemporary Cartography, Vol. 2. 314p. 1983. 67.95 (ISBN 0-471-10316-0). Wiley.
Tooley, R. V. Tooley's Dictionary of Mapmakers. LC 79-1936. 696p. 1979. 120.00x (ISBN 0-8451-1701-7). A R Liss.
--Tooley's Dictionary of Mapmakers: Supplement, No. 1. LC 84-29759. 128p. 1985. 39.50 (ISBN 0-8451-1703-3). A R Liss.
U. S. Library of Congress Map Division. A List of Maps of America in the Library of Congress, 2 vols. in 1. 1967. Repr. of 1902 ed. 46.50 (ISBN 0-8337-2739-7). B Franklin.
Westfall, Claude Z. Basic Graphics & Cartography. LC 84-51063. (Illus.). 422p. (Orig.). 1984. pap. text ed. 22.50 (ISBN 0-89101-061-0). U Maine Orono.
World Cartography. Incl. Vol. 12. pap. 3.50 (ISBN 0-686-94358-9, UN72/1/9); Vol. 13. pap. 5.00 (ISBN 0-686-99353-5, UN75/1/6); Vol. 15. (Illus.). 89p. 1979. pap. 7.00 (UN78/1/14); Vol. 16. 97p. 1980. pap. 9.00 (ISBN 0-686-72721-5, UN80/1/12). UN). Unipub.
Zogner, Lothar. Bibliographia Cartographica, Vol. 7. 244p. 1980. pap. 27.00 (ISBN 3-598-20622-4). K G Saur.

CARTOGRAPHY–DATA PROCESSING

International Cartographic Association. Glossary of Terms in Computer Assisted Cartography. 166p. 1980. 8.00 (ISBN 0-317-32457-8, C155). Am Congrs Survey.
Monmonier, Mark S. Computer-Assisted Cartography: Principles & Prospects. (Illus.). 256p. 1982. reference 33.95 (ISBN 0-13-165308-3). P-H.
Taylor, D. Fraser, ed. The Computer in Contemporary Cartography. LC 79-42727. (Progress in Contemporary Cartography Ser.: Vol. 1). pap. 67.00 (ISBN 0-317-30327-9, 2024806). Bks Demand UMI.
Vogel, Steven J., intro. by. Auto-Carto Seven: International Syposium on Computer Assisted Cartography. (Illus.). 599p. (Orig.). 1985. pap. 33.00 (ISBN 0-937294-65-9). ASP & RS.

CARTOGRAPHY–HISTORY

Christopher Saxton & Tudor Map-Making. 1981. pap. 12.00x (ISBN 0-686-72509-3, Pub. by Brit Lib England). State Mutual Bk.
Diamant, Lincoln. Bernard Romans: Forgotten Patriot of the American Revolution, Military Engineer & Cartographer of West Point & the Hudson Valley. LC 85-5421. (Illus.). 160p. 1985. 15.95 (ISBN 0-916346-56-0). Harbor Hill Bks.
Harrisse, Henry. Decouverte et Evolution Cartographique De Terre Neuve et Des Pays Circonvoisins Fourteen Ninety-Seven - Fifteen Hundred & One - Seventeen Sixty-Nine. (Illus.). 416p. 1968. Repr. of 1900 ed. 35.00 (ISBN 0-8398-0767-8). Parnassus Imprints.
Nordenskiold, A. E. Facsimile: Atlas to the Early History of Cartography. Ekelof, Johan & Markham, Clements, trs. (Illus.). 21.25 (ISBN 0-8446-5072-2). Peter Smith.
Nordenskiold, Adolf E. Facsimile Atlas to the Early History of Cartography: Reproductions of the Most Important Maps Printed in the Fifteenth & Sixteenth Centuries. (Illus.). 256p. 1973. pap. text ed. 15.95 (ISBN 0-486-22964-5). Dover.
Nordenskiold, Nils A. Periplus: An Essay on the Early History of Charts & Sailing Directions. Bather, Francis A., tr. from Swed. (Illus.). 1897. 189.00 (ISBN 0-8337-2572-6). B Franklin.
Robinson, Arthur H. Early Thematic Mapping in the History of Cartography. LC 81-11516. (Illus.). 1982. lib. bdg. 35.00x (ISBN 0-226-72285-6). U of Chicago Pr.
Tyacke, Sarah. Tudor Map-Making. 192p. 1982. 79.00x (ISBN 0-7123-0010-4, Pub. by Brit Lib England). State Mutual Bk.
Ware, John D. & Rea, Robert R. George Gauld: Surveyor & Cartographer of the Gulf Coast. LC 81-6341. (Illus.). 1982. 30.00 (ISBN 0-8130-0708-9). U Presses Fla.
Warner, Deborah J. The Sky Explored: Celestial Cartography, 1500-1800. LC 78-24737. 312p. 1979. 70.00x (ISBN 0-8451-1700-9). A R Liss.
Wilford, John N. The Mapmakers. LC 80-2716. (Illus.). 448p. 1981. 20.00 (ISBN 0-394-46194-0). Knopf.
--The Mapmakers: The Story of the Great Pioneer on Cartography from Antiquity to the Space Age. LC 81-52868. (Illus.). 448p. 1982. pap. 9.95 (ISBN 0-394-75303-8, Vin). Random.
Woodward, David. The Hermon Dunlap Smith Center for the History of Cartography: The First Decade. (Illus.). 24p. (Orig.). 1980. pap. 2.00 (ISBN 0-911028-28-5). Newberry.

CARTONS

see Paper Coatings

CARTRIDGES

Bartlett, W. A. & Gallatin, D. B. B & G Cartridge Manual. 2.00 (ISBN 0-913150-12-6). Pioneer Pr.
Datig, Fred A. Cartridges for Collectors, 3 Vols. Vol. I. 9.95 ea. (ISBN 0-87505-096-4). Vol. II (ISBN 0-87505-097-2). Vol. III (ISBN 0-87505-098-0). Borden.
Hogg, Ian V. The Cartridge Guide: The Small Arms Ammunition Identification Manual. LC 81-14485. (Illus.). 160p. 1982. 24.95 (ISBN 0-8117-1048-3). Stackpole.
Nonte, George. The Home Guide to Cartridge Conversions. rev. ed. 19.95 (ISBN 0-88227-005-2). Gun Room.
Suydam. American Cartridge. 10.95 (ISBN 0-87505-106-5). Borden.
Thomas, Gough. Shotguns & Cartridges for Game & Clays. 3rd ed. (Illus.). 254p. 1976. 25.00 (ISBN 0-7136-1583-4). Transatlantic.
Treadwell. Cartridges, Regulation & Experimental. 2.00 (ISBN 0-913150-13-4). Pioneer Pr.

CARTS

see Carriages and Carts

CARVER, GEORGE WASHINGTON, 1864?-1943

Clark, Glenn. Man Who Talks with the Flowers. pap. 0.95 (ISBN 0-910924-09-0). Macalester.
McMurry, Linda O. George Washington Carver: Scientist & Symbol. (Illus.). 1981. pap. 9.95 (ISBN 0-19-503205-5, GB 705, GB). Oxford U Pr.

CARYOCINESIS

see Karyokinesis

CASE HARDENING

American Society for Metals. Carburizing & Carbonitriding. LC 76-55702. pap. 58.30 (ISBN 0-317-20679-6, 2025145). Bks Demand UMI.
Diesburg, Daniel E., ed. Case-Hardened Steel: Microstructural & Residual Stress Effects; Proceedings, AIME Annual Meeting, Atlanta, Georgia, 1983. LC 83-63326. (Illus.). 237p. 1984. 54.00 (ISBN 0-89520-471-1). Metal Soc.
Parrish, G. & Harper, G. S. Production Gas Carburizing. (Materials Engineering Practice Ser.). (Illus.). 250p. 1985. 40.00 (ISBN 0-08-027312-2); pap. 15.75 (ISBN 0-08-027319-X). Pergamon.
TMS-AIME 112th Annual Meeting, Atlanta, March 9, 1983. Case-Hardened Steels: Microstructural & Residual Stress Effects. Diesburg, D. E., ed. 238p. 54.00 (ISBN 0-89520-471-1, 239); members 28.00 (ISBN 0-317-37191-6); student members 15.00 (ISBN 0-317-37192-4). Metal SOc.

CASIO (COMPUTER)

Cole, Jim. Thirty-Five Practical Programs for the Casio Pocket Computer. (Illus.). 96p. Date not set. 8.95 (ISBN 0-86668-014-4). ARCsoft.

CASSAVA

Cassava Cultural Practices. 152p. 1980. pap. 10.00 (ISBN 0-88936-245-9, IDRC151, IDRC). Unipub.
Cock, James H. Cassava. (IADS Development-Oriented Literature Ser.). 175p. 1984. 25.00x (ISBN 0-86531-356-3). Westview.
Delange, F. & Iteke, G. B. Nutritional Factors Involved in the Goitrogenic Action of Cassava. 100p. 1982. pap. 9.00 (ISBN 0-88936-315-3, IDRC184, IDRC). Unipub.
Ermans, A. M. & Mbulamonko, N. M. The Role of Cassava in the Etiology of Endemic Goitre & Cretinism. 182p. 1980. pap. 13.00 (ISBN 0-88936-220-3, IDRC136, IDRC). Unipub.
Grace, M. R. Cassava Processing. Rev. ed. (Plant Production & Protection Papers: No. 3). 155p. 1977. pap. 10.00 (ISBN 92-5-100171-5, F1453, FAO). Unipub.
Jones, William O. Manioc in Africa. 1959. 25.00x (ISBN 0-8047-0002-8). Stanford U Pr.
Nestel, B. & Cock, J. Cassava: The Development of an International Research Network. 70p. 1976. pap. 5.00 (ISBN 0-88936-076-6, IDRC59, IDRC). Unipub.
Nestel, B. & MacIntyre, R., eds. The International Exchange & Testing of Cassava Germ Plasm: Proceedings of an Interdisciplinary Worksop Held at CIAT, Palmira, Colombia, 4-6 Feb. 1975. (Illus.). 74p. 1977. pap. 6.00 (ISBN 0-88936-062-6, IDRC49, IDRC). Unipub.
Weber, E. & Nestel, B., eds. Intercropping with Cassava: Proceedings of an International Workshop Held at Trivandrum, India, 27 Nov. - 1 Dec. 1978. 144p. 1979. pap. 9.00 (ISBN 0-88936-231-9, IDRC142, IDRC). Unipub.

CASSIRER, ERNST, 1874-1945

Itzkoff, Seymour W. Ernest Cassirer: Scientific Knowledge & the Concept of Man. LC 79-159273. pap. 74.50 (ISBN 0-317-08062-8, 2022070). Bks Demand UMI.
Lipton, David R. & Cassirer, Ernst. Ernst Cassiver: The Dilemma of a Liberal Intellectual in Germany, 1914-33. LC 78-6945. 1978. 20.00x (ISBN 0-8020-5408-0). U of Toronto Pr.
Schilpp, Paul A., ed. Philosophy of Ernst Cassirer. LC 72-83947. (Library of Living Philosophers Ser.: Vol. VI). 954p. 1949. 39.95x (ISBN 0-87548-131-0); pap. 19.95 (ISBN 0-87548-146-9). Open Court.

CAST IRON

see also Founding; Iron-Founding

American Welding Society. Specification for Welding Rods & Covered Electrodes for Welding Cast Iron: A5.15. 10p. 1982. 10.00 (ISBN 0-87171-220-2); member 7.50. Am Welding.
Ames, Alex. Collecting Cast Iron. (Illus.). 143p. 1980. 19.95 (ISBN 0-86190-001-4). Schiffer.
Ammen, C. W. Casting Iron. (Illus.). 196p. 1984. o.p 15.95 (ISBN 0-8306-0210-0, 1610); pap. 10.25 (ISBN 0-8306-0610-6). TAB Bks.
Angus, H. T. Cast Iron: Physical & Engineering Properties. 2nd ed. 542p. 1976. 139.95 (ISBN 0-408-70933-2). Butterworth.
Arthur, Eric & Ritchie, Thomas. Iron: Cast & Wrought Iron in Canada from the Seventeenth Century to the Present. (Illus.). 256p. 1982. 27.50 (ISBN 0-8020-2429-7). U of Toronto Pr.
Building Research Advisory Board - Federal Construction Council. Criteria for the Acceptance of Cast Iron Soil Pipe. 1960. pap. 3.00 (ISBN 0-309-00836-0). Natl Acad Pr.
Continuous Casting: Fourth International Iron & Steel Congress, London 1982. 606p. 1984. text ed. 45.00x (ISBN 0-904357-47-3, Pub. by Metals Soc). Brookfield Pub Co.
Fredriksson, H. & Hillert, M., eds. Physical Metallurgy of Cast Iron: Materials Research Society Symposia Proceedings, Vol. 34. xxi, 500p. 1985. 95.00 (ISBN 0-444-00938-8, North-Holland). Elsevier.
Lux, B., et al, eds. The Metallurgy of Cast Iron. (Illus.). 1977. 265.00x (ISBN 2-604-00001-6). Brookfield Pub Co.
Merchant, Harish D. Recent Research on Cast Iron. LC 66-28072. 842p. 1968. 159.75x (ISBN 0-677-11000-6). Gordon.
Specification for Low-Alloy, Steel Covered Arc Welding Electrodes: A5.5. 29p. 1981. 10.00; member 7.50. Am Welding.

CASTING

see Founding; Iron-Founding; Plaster Casts; Plastics–Molding; Steel Castings

CASTINGS, METAL

see Metal Castings

CASTOR (RODENT)

see Beavers

CAT

see Cats

CATALOGS, ON-LINE

Cochrane, Pauline A. Redesign of Catalogs & Indexes for Improved Online Subject Access: Selected Papers of Pauline A. Cochrane. LC 85-42722. 384p. 1985. lib. bdg. 45.00 (ISBN 0-89774-158-7). Oryx Pr.
Coyle, Karen. RLIN II Processing for UC Online Catalog Input: Bibliographic Specifications. 1984. 5.00 (ISBN 0-317-18069-X). UCDLA.
Hunter, Eric. Computerized Cataloging. 186p. 1985. lib. bdg. 17.50 (ISBN 0-85157-377-0, Pub. by Bingley England). Shoe String.
MELVYL Reference Manual for the University of California Online Catalog. 1984. 10.00 (ISBN 0-317-03903-2). UCDLA.
Tolle, John E. Public Access Terminals: Determining Quantity Requirements. LC 84-164540. (OCLC Library Information & Computer Science Ser.). (Illus.). 161p. (Orig.). 1983. pap. 14.50 (ISBN 0-933418-51-5). OCLC Online Comp.

CATALOGS, STAR

see Stars–Catalogs

CATALYSIS

see also Fluidization; Platinum Catalysts

Afansiev, V. & Zaikov, G. In the Realm of Catalysis. 116p. 1979. pap. 3.95 (ISBN 0-8285-0822-4, Pub. by Mir Pubs USSR). Imported Pubns.
Anderson, J. R., ed. Catalysis-Science & Technology, Vol. 1. Boudart, M. (Illus.). 320p. 1981. 76.50 (ISBN 0-387-10353-8). Springer-Verlag.
Anderson, J. R. & Boudart, M., eds. Catalysis, Vol. 5. (Science & Technology Ser.). (Illus.). 280p. 1984. 54.00 (ISBN 0-387-12665-1). Springer-Verlag.
--Catalysis-Science & Technology, Vol. 2. (Illus.). 280p. 1981. 72.00 (ISBN 0-387-10593-X). Springer-Verlag.
--Catalysis: Science & Technology, Vol. 3. (Illus.). 290p. 1982. 58.00 (ISBN 0-387-11634-6). Springer-Verlag.
--Catalysis: Science & Technology, Vol. 6. (Illus.). 320p. 1984. 49.00 (ISBN 0-387-12815-8). Springer-Verlag.
Anderson, Robert B., ed. Experimental Methods in Catalytic Research. LC 68-18652. Vol. 1 1968. 91.50 (ISBN 0-12-058650-9); Vol. 2 1976. 70.00 (ISBN 0-12-058660-6); Vol. 3 1976. 75.00 (ISBN 0-12-058662-2). Acad Pr.
ASTM Standards on Catalysts. 64p. 1984. 19.00 (ISBN 0-8031-0202-X, 03-432084-12). ASTM.
Basolo, Fred & Burwell, Robert L., Jr., eds. Catalysis: Progress in Research. LC 73-81490. 193p. 1973. 35.00x (ISBN 0-306-30753-7, Plenum Pr). Plenum Pub.
Bell, Alexis T. & Hegedus, L. Louis, eds. Catalysis under Transient Conditions. LC 82-20639. (ACS Symposium Ser.: No. 178). 1982. 34.95 (ISBN 0-8412-0688-0). Am Chemical.

CATALYSTS

Stiles, Alvin B. Catalyst Manufacture: Laboratory & Commercial Preparations. (Chemical Industries Ser.: Vol. 14). (Illus.). 192p. 1983. 49.75 (ISBN 0-8247-7055-2). Dekker.

Tarhan, M. Orhan. Catalytic Reactor Design. (Illus.). 352p. 1983. 38.95 (ISBN 0-07-062871-8). McGraw.

Thomas, J. M. & Lambert, R. M. Characterization of Catalysts. LC 80-40961. 283p. 1981. 59.95 (ISBN 0-471-27874-2, Pub. by Wiley-Interscience). Wiley.

Whyte, Thaddeus E., Jr., et al, eds. Catalytic Materials: Relationship Between Structure & Reactivity. LC 84-2776. (ACS Symposium Ser.: No. 248). 465p. 1984. lib. bdg. 74.95x (ISBN 0-8412-0831-X). Am Chemical.

Yermakov, Y. I., et al. Catalysis by Supported Complexes. (Studies in Surface Science & Catalysis Ser.: Vol. 8). 522p. 1981. 100.00 (ISBN 0-444-42014-2). Elsevier.

CATAMOUNTS

see Pumas

CATAPHORESIS

see Electrophoresis

CATASTROPHES (GEOLOGY)

see also Geology–History

Arnold, V. I. Catastrophe Theory. Thomas, R. K., tr. (Illus.). 80p. 1984. pap. 9.80 (ISBN 0-387-12859-X). Springer-Verlag.

Berggren, W. A. & Van Couvering, John, eds. Catastrophes & Earth History: The New Uniformitarianism. LC 83-11026. (Series in Paleontology). (Illus.). 456p. 1983. 65.00x (ISBN 0-691-08328-2); pap. 19.50x (ISBN 0-691-08329-0). Princeton U Pr.

Poston, T. Catastrophe Theory & Its Applications. (Surveys & References Ser.: No. 2). 510p. 1979. text ed. 79.95 (ISBN 0-273-01029-8); pap. 30.95 o. p. (ISBN 0-273-08429-1). Pitman Pub MA.

Price, George M. Evolutionary Geology & the new Catastrophism. (Illus.). 352p. 1984. Repr. of 1926 ed. photocopy 16.95x (ISBN 0-915554-13-5). Sourcebook.

Scheidegger, A. E. Physical Aspects of Natural Catastrophes. 300p. 1975. 68.00 (ISBN 0-444-41216-6). Elsevier.

CATECHOLAMINES

Izumi, F. & Oka, M., eds. Synthesis, Storage & Secretion of Adrenal Catecholamines: Proceedings of a Satellite Symposium to the 8th International Congress of Pharmacology, 19-24 July 1981, Tokyo, Japan. (Illus.). 302p. 1982. 72.00 (ISBN 0-08-028012-9). Pergamon.

Knoll. Symposium on Pharmachaminergic & Serotonergic Mechanisms, Vol. 3. 1979. 14.00 (ISBN 0-9960007-6-3, Pub. by Akademiai Kaido Hungary). Heyden.

Kunos, George. Adrenoceptors & Catecholamine Action. LC 81-10431. (Neurotransmitter Receptors Ser.: Pt. B). 327p. 1983. 80.50 (ISBN 0-471-05726-6, Pub. by Wiley-Interscience). Wiley.

Lake, C. Raymond & Ziegler, Michael G. Catecholamines in Psychiatric & Neurological Disorders. 448p. 1985. pap. text ed. 35.95 (ISBN 0-409-95184-6). Butterworth.

Mason, Stephen T. Catecholamines & Behaviour. LC 83-7722. 400p. 1984. 59.50 (ISBN 0-521-24930-9); pap. 24.95 (ISBN 0-521-27082-0). Cambridge U Pr.

Riemersma, R. A. & Oliver, M. F., eds. Catecholamines in the Non-Ischaemic & Ischaemic Myocardium: Proceedings of the Sixth Argenteuil Symposiym, Waterloo, Belgium, 1981. (Argenteuil Symposia Ser.: Vol. 6). 260p. 1982. 81.00 (ISBN 0-444-80439-0, Biomedical Pr). Elsevier.

Robinsn, Ronald. Tumours That Secrete Catecholamines: Their Detection & Clinical Chemistry. LC 79-41731. pap. 36.00 (ISBN 0-317-29342-7, 2024034). Bks Demand UMI.

Usdin, Earl, et al. Catecholamines, Pt. A: Basic & Peripheral Mechanisms. LC 84-3967. (Neurology & Neurobiology Ser.: Vol. 8A). 420p. 1984. 120.00 (ISBN 0-8451-2707-1). A R Liss.

--Catecholamines. Pt. B: Neuropharmacology & Central Nervous System-Theoretical. (Neurology & Neurobiology Ser.: Vol. 8B). 520p. 1984. 140.00 (ISBN 0-8451-2708-X). A R Liss.

--Catecholamines, Pt. C: Neuropharmacology & Central Nervous System-Therapeutic Aspects. LC 84-3967. (Neurology & Neurobiology Ser.: Vol. 8C). 275p. 1984. 95.00 (ISBN 0-8451-2709-8). A R Liss.

CATEGORIES (MATHEMATICS)

see also Functor Theory

Adamek, Jiri. Theory of Mathematical Structures. 1983. lib. bdg. 59.50 (ISBN 90-277-1459-2, Pub. by Reidel Holland). Kluwer Academic.

Arbib, Michael A. & Manes, Ernest G., eds. Arrows, Structures & Functors: The Categorical Imperative. 1975. 33.50 (ISBN 0-12-059060-3). Acad Pr.

Banaschewski, B., ed. Categorical Aspects of Topology & Analysis, Ottawa 1981: Proceedings. (Lecture Notes in Mathematics Ser.: Vol. 915). 385p. 1982. pap. 22.00 (ISBN 0-387-11211-1). Springer-Verlag.

Barr, M. & Wells, C. Toposes, Triples & Theories. (Grundlehren der Mathematischen Wissenschaften Ser.: Vol. 278). (Illus.). xiii, 345p. 1985. 36.00 (ISBN 0-387-96115-1). Springer-Verlag.

Battelle Memorial Institute Conference - Seattle - 1968. Category Theory, Homology Theory & Their Applications, 1: Proceedings. Hilton, P. J., ed. LC 75-75931. (Lecture Notes in Mathematics: Vol. 86). 1969. pap. 14.70 (ISBN 0-387-04605-4). Springer-Verlag.

--Category Theory, Homology Theory & Their Applications, 2: Proceedings. Hilton, Peter J., ed. LC 75-75931. (Lecture Notes in Mathematics: Vol. 92). (Orig.). 1969. pap. 18.30 (ISBN 0-387-04611-9). Springer-Verlag.

--Category Theory, Homology Theory & Their Applications, 3: Proceedings. Hilton, Peter J., ed. LC 75-75931. (Lecture Notes in Mathematics: Vol. 99). (Orig.). 1969. pap. 21.90 (ISBN 0-387-04618-6). Springer-Verlag.

Dubuc, E. J. Kan Extensions in Enriched Category Theory. LC 77-131542. (Lecture Notes in Mathematics: Vol. 145). 1970. pap. 11.00 (ISBN 0-387-04934-7). Springer-Verlag.

Faith, Carl & Page, Stanley. FPF Ring Theory: Faithful Modules & Generators of Mod-R. LC 83-24067. (London Mathematical Society Lecture Note Ser.: No. 88). 176p. 1984. pap. text ed. 19.95 (ISBN 0-521-27738-8). Cambridge U Pr.

Gabriel, Pierre & Zisman, M. Calculus of Fractions & Homotopy Theory. (Ergebnisse der Mathematik und Ihrer Grenzgebiete: Vol. 35). (Illus.). 1967. 36.00 (ISBN 0-387-03777-2). Springer-Verlag.

Golan, Jonathan S. Decomposition & Dimension in Module Catagories, Vol. 33. (Lecture Notes in Pure & Applied Math Ser.). 1977. 45.00 (ISBN 0-8247-6643-1). Dekker.

Gray, J. Formal Category Theory: Adjointness for 2-Categories. LC 74-7910. (Lecture Notes in Mathematics: Vol. 391). xii, 282p. 1974. pap. 17.00 (ISBN 0-387-06830-9). Springer-Verlag.

Gray, John W., ed. Mathematical Applications of Category Theory. LC 84-9371. (Contemporary Mathematics Ser.: Vol. 30). 308p. 1984. pap. 28.00 (ISBN 0-8218-5032-6). Am Math.

Hartshorne, R. Residues & Duality. (Lecture Notes in Mathematics: Vol. 20). 1966. pap. 21.90 (ISBN 0-387-03603-2). Springer-Verlag.

Hofmann, K. H. Duality of Compact Semigroups & C-Bigebras. LC 69-15931. (Lecture Notes in Mathematics: Vol. 129). 1970. pap. 10.70 (ISBN 0-387-04918-5). Springer-Verlag.

Johnstone, P. T., et al. Indexed Categories & Their Application. (Lecture Notes in Mathematics: Vol. 661). (Illus.). 1978. pap. 17.00 (ISBN 0-387-08914-4). Springer-Verlag.

Kamps, K. H., et al, eds. Category Theory, Applications to Algebra, Logic, & Topology: Proceedings, Gummersbach, FRG, 1981. (Lecture Notes in Mathematics Ser.: Vol. 962). 322p. 1982. pap. 18.00 (ISBN 0-387-11961-2). Springer-Verlag.

Kelly, Gregory M. Basic Concepts of Enriched Category Theory. LC 81-18015. (London Mathematical Society Lecture Note Ser.: No. 64). 250p. 1982. pap. 29.95 (ISBN 0-521-28702-2). Cambridge U Pr.

Knutson, D. Algebraic Spaces. (Lecture Notes in Mathematics: Vol. 203). 1971. pap. 12.00 (ISBN 0-387-05496-0). Springer-Verlag.

Krishnan, Viaklathur S. An Introduction to Category Theory. LC 80-14055. (Illus.). 173p. 1980. 40.00 (ISBN 0-444-00383-5, North Holland). Elsevier.

Lambek, Joachim. Completions of Categories. (Lecture Notes in Mathematics: Vol. 24). (Orig.). 1966. pap. 10.70 (ISBN 0-387-03607-5). Springer-Verlag.

Lane, S. Mac, ed. Coherence in Categories. LC 72-87920. (Lecture Notes in Mathematics: Vol. 281). vii, 235p. 1972. pap. 11.00 (ISBN 0-387-05963-6). Springer-Verlag.

MacLane, S. Categories for the Working Mathematician. LC 78-166080. (Graduate Texts in Mathematics: Vol. 5). 272p. 1972. 22.00 (ISBN 0-387-90035-7). Springer-Verlag.

Magid, Andy R. Module Categories of Analytic Groups. LC 81-10215. (Cambridge Tracts in Mathematics: No. 81). 130p. 1982. 32.50 (ISBN 0-521-24200-2). Cambridge U Pr.

Makkai, M. & Reyes, G. First-Order Categorical Logic: Model-Theoretical Methods in the Theory of Topoi & Related Categories. LC 77-13221. (Lecture Notes in Mathematics: Vol. 611). 1977. pap. text ed. 22.00 (ISBN 0-387-08439-8). Springer-Verlag.

Michor, P. W. Functors & Categories of Banach Spaces: Tensor Products, Operator Ideals & Functors on Categories of Banach Spaces. (Lecture Notes in Mathematics: Vol. 651). 1978. pap. 12.00 (ISBN 0-387-08764-8). Springer-Verlag.

Midwest Category Seminar, 5th. Reports. Gray, J. W. & MacLane, S., eds. (Lecture Notes for Mathematics: Vol. 195). 1971. pap. 14.00 (ISBN 0-387-05442-1). Springer-Verlag.

Mitchell, Barry. Theory of Categories. (Pure & Applied Mathematics Ser.: Vol. 17). 1965. 49.50 (ISBN 0-12-499250-1). Acad Pr.

Moss, R. M. & Thomas, C. B. Algebraic K-Theory & Its Geometric Applications. LC 74-97991. (Lecture Notes in Mathematics Ser.). 1969. pap. 10.70 (ISBN 0-387-04627-5). Springer-Verlag.

Nivat, Maurice & Reynolds, John C., eds. Algebraic Methods in Semantics. (Illus.). 425p. 1985. write for info. Cambridge U Pr.

Scedrov, Andrej. Forcing & Classifying Topoi. Incl. Generalized Frobenius Partitions. Andrews, George E. (No. 301) (ISBN 0-8218-2302-7); The Structure of Shock Waves in Magnetohydrodynamics. Hesaaraki, Mahmud. (No. 302) (ISBN 0-8218-2303-5); Multipliers of Radical Banach Algebras of Power Series. Bade, W. G., et al. (Vol. 303) (ISBN 0-8218-2304-3); Measurable Selectors of PCA Multifunctions with Applications. Srebrny, Marian. LC 84-18464. (No. 311). 9.00; Dimensions of Spaces of Siegel Cusp Forms of Degree Two & Three. Eie, Minking. LC 84-10956. (Vol. 304). 10.00 (ISBN 0-8218-2305-1). (Memoirs: No. 295). 1984. write for info. Am Math.

Schubert, H. Categories. Gray, J., tr. from Ger. LC 72-83016. 390p. 1972. 48.00 (ISBN 0-387-05783-8). Springer-Verlag.

Seminar on Triples & Categorical Homology. Proceedings. Eckmann, B., ed. LC 68-59303. (Lecture Notes in Mathematics: Vol. 80). 1969. pap. 18.30 (ISBN 0-387-04601-1). Springer-Verlag.

Sidney Category Theory Seminar, 1972-1973. Category Seminar: Proceedings. Kelly, G. M., ed. (Lecture Notes in Mathematics Ser.: Vol. 420). 650p. 1974. pap. 21.00 (ISBN 0-387-06966-6). Springer-Verlag.

Stenstroem, B. Rings of Quotients: An Introduction to Methods of Ring Theory. LC 75-1003. (Grundlehren der Mathematischen Wissenschaften Ser.: Vol. 217). 315p. 1975. text ed. 56.00 (ISBN 0-387-07117-2). Springer-Verlag.

Strooker, J. R. Introduction to Categories, Homological Algebra & Sheaf Cohomology. LC 77-80849. 1978. 57.50 (ISBN 0-521-21699-0). Cambridge U Pr.

Tierney, Myles. Categorical Constructions in Stable Homotopy Theory. LC 70-77478. (Lecture Notes in Mathematics: Vol. 87). (Orig.). 1969. pap. 10.70 (ISBN 0-387-04606-2). Springer-Verlag.

Voreadou, R. Coherence & Non-Commutative Diagrams in Closed Categories. LC 76-50058. (Memoirs Ser.: No. 182). 1977. 13.00 (ISBN 0-8218-2182-2, MEMO-182). Am Math.

CATERPILLARS

see also Silkworms

Dethier, Vincent G. The World of the Tent-Makers: A Natural History of the Eastern Tent Caterpillar. LC 80-11361. (Illus.). 160p. 1980. lib. bdg. 13.50x (ISBN 0-87023-300-9); pap. 7.95 (ISBN 0-87023-301-7). U of Mass Pr.

Fracker, Stanley B. The Classification of Lepidopterous Larvae. (Illus.). Repr. of 1915 ed. 15.00 (ISBN 0-384-16670-9). Johnson Repr.

Ripley, Lewis B. The External Morphology & Postembryology of Noctuid Larvae. (Illinois Biological Monographs: Vol. 8, No. 4). pap. 8.00 (ISBN 0-384-50920-7). Johnson Repr.

Sargent, Theodore D. Legion of Night: The Underwing Moths. LC 75-8452. (Illus.). 224p. 1976. 15.00 (ISBN 0-87023-187-1). U of Mass Pr.

CATFISHES

Burr, Brooks M. & Mayden, Richard L. Life History of the Freckled Madtom, Noturus Nocturnus, in Mill Creek, Illinois: Pisces: Ictaluridae. (Occasional Papers: No. 98). 15p. 1982. 2.25 (ISBN 0-317-04823-6). U of KS Mus Nat Hist.

Eignmann, Carl H. A Revision of the South American Nematognathi or Catfishes. pap. 55.00 (ISBN 0-384-14040-8). Johnson Repr.

Emmens, Clifford W. & Axelrod, Herbert. Catfishes for the Advanced Hobbyist. 9.95 (ISBN 0-87666-018-9, PS-650). TFH Pubns.

Kindred, James E. Skull of Amiurus. (Illus.). 1919. 12.00 (ISBN 0-384-29415-4). Johnson Repr.

Lee, Jasper S. Commercial Catfish Farming. 2nd ed. (Illus.). 310p. 1981. text ed. 19.35 (ISBN 0-8134-2156-X, 2156); text ed. 14.50. Interstate.

Panayotou, Theodore, et al. The Economics of Catfish Farming in Central Thailand. (ICLARM Technical Reports: No. 4). (Illus.). 60p. (Orig.). 1983. pap. 10.00x (ISBN 0-89955-379-6, Pub. by ICLARM Philippines). Intl Spec Bk.

Simco, Bill A. & Cross, Frank B. Factors Affecting Growth & Production of Channel Catfish, Ictalurus Punctatus. (Museum Ser.: Vol. 17, No. 4). 66p. 1966. pap. 3.50 (ISBN 0-686-79830-9). U of KS Mus Nat Hist.

Will, Lawrence E. Okeechobee Catfishing. 1980. pap. 4.00 (ISBN 0-8200-1003-0). Great Outdoors.

CATHODE RAY OSCILLOSCOPE

Here are entered works on the test instrument in which the variations in an electrical quantity appear temporarily as a visible waveform on the screen of a cathode ray tube. works on the instrument combining a cathode ray oscilloscope and a camera to produce a permanent record of a waveform are entered under cathode ray oscillograph.

Bierman, et al. Practical Oscilloscope Handbook. 2nd ed. 184p. pap. 8.95 (ISBN 0-8104-0851-1). Hayden.

Brown, Gerald R. How to Read & Interpret Automotive Oscilloscope Patterns. LC 84-17900. 1984. text ed. 24.95 (ISBN 0-8359-2930-2); pap. text ed. 17.95 (ISBN 0-8359-2929-9). Reston.

Douglas-Young, John. Practical Oscilloscope Handbook. (Illus.). 1979. 14.95 (ISBN 0-13-693549-4, Parker). P-H.

Goodman, Robert L. Practical Troubleshooting with the Modern Oscilloscope. (Illus.). 1979. pap. 8.95 (ISBN 0-8306-1162-2, 1162). TAB Bks.

Hallmark, Clayton. Understanding & Using the Oscilloscope. LC 73-84546. 1973. pap. 9.95 (ISBN 0-8306-2664-6, 664). TAB Bks.

Lenk, John D. Handbook of Oscilloscopes: Theory & Application. rev., enl. ed. (Illus.). 320p. 1982. 27.95 (ISBN 0-13-380576-X). P-H.

Middleton, Robert G. Know Your Oscilloscope. 4th ed. LC 80-52230. 1980. pap. 11.95 (ISBN 0-672-21742-2). Sams.

--Troubleshooting with the Oscilloscope. 4th ed. LC 80-51719. 256p. 1980. 11.95 (ISBN 0-672-21738-4). Sams.

Prentiss. Oscilloscopes. (Illus.). 1980. text ed. 21.95 (ISBN 0-8359-5354-8); pap. text ed. 17.95 (ISBN 0-8359-5353-X). Reston.

Prentiss, Stan. The Complete Book of Oscilloscopes. (Illus.). 224p. 1983. pap. 12.95 (ISBN 0-8306-1532-6). TAB Bks.

Roth, Charles H., Jr. Use of the Dual-Trace Oscilloscope: A Programmed Text. rev. ed. 256p. 1982. 27.95 (ISBN 0-13-940031-1); pap. text ed. 22.95 (ISBN 0-13-940023-0). P-H.

Sinclair, Ian. The Oscilloscope in Use. 128p. 1980. 11.00x (ISBN 0-85242-471-X, Pub. by K Dickson). State Mutual Bk.

Van Erk, Rien. Oscilloscopes: Functional Operation & Measuring Examples. 1978. 39.50 (ISBN 0-07-067050-1). McGraw.

Whited, N. W. Automotive Oscilloscope. LC 76-3937. (Illus.). 99p. 1977. pap. 8.40 (ISBN 0-8273-1033-1). Delmar.

CATHODE RAY TUBES

see also Storage Tubes; Television Picture Tubes

Health Hazards of CRT's. 4.95 (ISBN 0-317-06061-9). Ryan Research.

Health Hazards of CRT's: A Comprehensive Bibliography on a Critical Issue of Workplace Health & Safety. 2nd ed. (Information Alert Ser.: No.3). 63p. 1983. pap. 8.95x (ISBN 0-942158-01-6). Ryan Research.

Kane, Gerry. The CRT Controller Handbook. 224p. (Orig.). 1980. pap. 9.95 (ISBN 0-07-931045-1, 45-1). Osborne-McGraw.

Kodak Films for Cathode-Ray Tube Recording. 1982. pap. 4.50 (ISBN 0-87985-128-7, P37). Eastman Kodak.

Nichols, Edward Leamington & Howes, H. L. Cathodo-luminescence & the Luminescence of Incandescent Solids. LC 28-21004. (Carnegie Institution of Washington. Publication: No. 384). pap. 89.50 (ISBN 0-317-08547-6, 2007882). Bks Demand UMI.

CATHODE RAYS

see also Electric Discharges through Gases; Electrons; X-Rays

Sherr, Sol. Electronic Displays. LC 78-10390. 1979. 66.95x (ISBN 0-471-02941-6, Pub. by Wiley-Interscience). Wiley.

CATHODIC PROTECTION

Cathodic Protection of Production Platforms in Cold Seawaters. 192p. 60.00 (ISBN 0-317-06640-4, 52122). Natl Corrosion Eng.

Cathodic Protection of Pulp & Paper Mill Effluent Clarifiers. 5.00 (ISBN 0-317-06637-4, 53043). Natl Corrosion Eng.

CATIONS

Baes, Charles F., Jr. & Mesmer, Robert E. The Hydrolysis of Cations. LC 75-44393. 489p. 1976. 63.95x (ISBN 0-471-03985-3, Pub. by Wiley-Interscience). Wiley.

--The Hydrolysis of Cations. 512p. 1986. Repr. of 1976 ed. lib. bdg. price not set (ISBN 0-89874-892-5). Krieger.

Boynton, Alton L. & McKeehan, Wallace L., eds. Ions, Cell Proliferation & Cancer. LC 82-20786. 1982. 50.00 (ISBN 0-12-123050-3). Acad Pr.

Nimmo, Joseph, Jr. Report in Regard to the Range & Ranch Cattle Business of the United States. LC 72-2860. (Use & Abuse of America's Natural Resources Ser.) 214p. 1972. Repr. of 1885 ed. 17.00 (ISBN 0-405-04524-7). Ayer Co Pubs.

Okediji, Florence A. The Cattle Industry in Northern Nigeria, 1900-1939. (African Humanities Ser.). (Illus., Orig.). 1973. pap. text ed. 2.00 (ISBN 0-941934-07-1). Indiana Africa.

CAUSALITY
see Causality (Physics)

CAUSALITY (PHYSICS)

AIP Conference. Causality & Physical Theories: Proceedings, No. 16. Rolnick, William B., ed. LC 73-93420. 177p. 1974. 12.00x (ISBN 0-88318-115-0). Am Inst Physics.

Armstrong, David & Malcolm, Norman. Consciousness & Causality. (Great Debates in Philosophy Ser.). 200p. 1984. 24.95x (ISBN 0-631-13212-0); pap. 9.95x (ISBN 0-631-13433-6). Basil Blackwell.

Bohm, David. Causality & Chance in Modern Physics. LC 57-28894. 1971. pap. 8.95x (ISBN 0-8122-1002-6, Pa Paperbks). U of Pa Pr.

Heise, David R. Causal Analysis. LC 75-20465. (A Wiley-Interscience Publication). pap. 79.30 (ISBN 0-317-26394-3, 2025173). Bks Demand UMI.

Swinburne, Richard. Space, Time & Causality. 1983. 39.50 (ISBN 90-277-1437-1, Pub. by Reidel Holland). Kluwer Academic.

CAVE FAUNA

Packard, Alpheus S. The Cave Fauna of North America: Remarks on the Anatomy of the Brain & Origin of the Blind Species. Egerton, Frank N., 3rd, ed. LC 77-74244. (History of Ecology Ser.). (Illus.). 1978. Repr. of 1888 ed. lib. bdg. 16.00x (ISBN 0-405-10413-8). Ayer Co Pubs.

CAVENDISH, HENRY, 1731-1810

Aykroyd, Wallace R. Three Philosophers: Lavoisier, Priestley & Cavendish. LC 77-98808. Repr. of 1935 ed. lib. bdg. 18.75 (ISBN 0-8371-2890-0, AYTB). Greenwood.

CAVES
see also Speleology
also names of caves, e.g. Lascaux Cave

Adams, William H. Famous Caves & Catacombs. facsimile ed. LC 70-37773. (Essay Index Reprint Ser.). Repr. of 1886 ed. 23.00 (ISBN 0-8369-2577-7). Ayer Co Pubs.

Aikens, C. Melvin. Hogup Cave. (Utah Anthropological Papers: No. 93). Repr. of 1970 ed. 24.00 (ISBN 0-404-60693-8). AMS Pr.

Brain, C. K. The Hunters or the Hunted? An Introduction to African Cave Taphonomy. LC 79-28104. 1981. lib. bdg. 40.00x (ISBN 0-226-07089-1); pap. 17.50x (ISBN 0-226-07090-5). U of Chicago Pr.

Buckland, William. Reliquiae Diluvianae: Observations on the Organic Remains Contained in Caves Fissures, & Diluvial Gravel. Albritton, Claude C., Jr., ed. LC 77-6510. (History of Geology Ser.). (Illus.). 1978. Repr. of 1823 ed. lib. bdg. 30.00x (ISBN 0-405-10433-2). Ayer Co Pubs.

Cosgrove, Cornelius B. Caves of the Upper Gila & Hueco Areas in New Mexico & Texas. (HU PMP Ser.). 1947. 37.00 (ISBN 0-527-01261-0). Kraus Repr.

Daunt-Mergens, Diana O., ed. Cave Research Foundation Personnel Manual. 3rd ed. (Illus.). 176p. 1981. pap. 5.00 (ISBN 0-939748-05-3). Cave Bks Mo.

Dougherty, Percy H., ed. Environmental Karst. LC 84-80188. (Illus.). 178p. (Orig.). 1984. text ed. 7.95 (ISBN 0-9613107-0-7). Geo Speleo Pubns.

Ford, T. D., ed. The Science of Speleology. 1976. 55.00 (ISBN 0-12-262550-1). Acad Pr.

Ford, Trevor D. Limestone & Caves of the Peak District. 469p. 1981. 50.00x (ISBN 0-86094-005-5, Pub. by GEO Abstracts England). State Mutual Bk.

Jennings, Jesse D. Cowboy Cave. (University of Utah Anthropological Papers Ser: No. 104). (Illus.). 224p. 1981. pap. 20.00x (ISBN 0-87480-182-6). U of Utah Pr.

--Danger Cave. LC 62-63182. (Utah Anthropological Papers: No. 27). Repr. of 1957 ed. 24.50 (ISBN 0-404-60627-X). AMS Pr.

Larson, Lane & Larson, Peggy. Caving: The Sierra Club Guide to Spelunking. LC 80-23110. (Sierra Club Outdoor Activities Guides Ser.). (Illus.). 320p. (Orig.). 1982. pap. 10.95 (ISBN 0-87156-246-4). Sierra.

Lavoie, Kathleen H., ed. Cave Research Foundation 1983 Annual Report. (Illus.). 42p. (Orig.). 1984. pap. 6.00 (ISBN 0-939748-15-0). Cave Bks MO.

Lawrence, Joe, Jr. & Brucker, Roger W. The Caves Beyond: The Story of the Floyd Collins' Crystal Cave Exploration. LC 73-34060. (Illus.). 320p. 1975. 10.95 (ISBN 0-914264-17-6); pap. 6.50 (ISBN 0-914264-18-4). Cave Bks MO.

Lindsley, Karen B., ed. Cave Research Foundation Annual Report, 1981. (Illus.). 55p. (Orig.). 1984. pap. 6.00 (ISBN 0-939748-04-5). Cave Bks MO.

Lovelock, Jim. A Caving Manual. (Illus.). 144p. 1981. 19.95 (ISBN 0-7134-1904-0, Pub. by Batsford England). David & Charles.

McClurg, David. Exploring Caves: A Guide to the Underground Wilderness. LC 80-14524. (Illus.). 224p. 1980. pap. 11.95 (ISBN 0-8117-2083-7). Stackpole.

Martin, Ronald L. Official Guide to Marvel Cave. LC 74-83031. (Illus.). 55p. (Orig.). 1974. pap. 3.95 (ISBN 0-915394-00-6). Ozark Mtn Pubs.

Massola, Aldo. Bunjil's Cave. (Illus.). 27.50x (ISBN 0-392-02447-0, ABC). Sportshelf.

Mercer, Henry C. The Hill-Caves of Yucatan: A Search for Evidence of Man's Antiquity in the Caverns of Central America. LC 75-12599. (Illus.). 227p. 1975. 11.95 (ISBN 0-914264-04-4); pap. 5.50 (ISBN 0-914264-05-2). Cave Bks MO.

Mitchell, Robert W. & Reddell, James R., eds. Studies on the Cavernicole Fauna of Mexico & Adjacent Regions. (Association for Mexican Cave Studies: Bulletin 5). 201p. 1973. 13.00 (ISBN 0-686-70406-1). Speleo Pr.

Moore, George W. & Sullivan, G. Nicholas. Speleology: The Study of Caves. (Illus.). pap. text ed. 5.95 (ISBN 0-939748-00-2). Cave Bks MO.

Packard, Alpheus S. The Cave Fauna of North America: Remarks on the Anatomy of the Brain & Origin of the Blind Species. Egerton, Frank N., 3rd, ed. LC 77-74244. (History of Ecology Ser.). (Illus.). 1978. Repr. of 1888 ed. lib. bdg. 16.00x (ISBN 0-405-10413-8). Ayer Co Pubs.

Palmer, Margaret V., ed. Cave Research Foundation: Annual Report, 1980. (Illus.). 51p. (Orig.). 1981. pap. 5.00 (ISBN 0-939748-03-7). Cave Bks MO.

Palmer, Margaret V. & Palmer, Arthur N., eds. Cave Research Foundation Annual Report, 1982. (Illus.). 45p. (Orig.). 1983. pap. 6.00 (ISBN 0-939748-06-1). Cave Bks MO.

Poulson, Thomas L. & Wells, Bethany J., eds. Cave Research Foundation 1979 Annual Report. (Illus.). 74p. (Orig.). 1981. pap. 5.00 (ISBN 0-939748-14-2). Cave Bks MO.

Preble, Jack. The Sinks of Gandy Creek. (Illus.). 1969. 3.00 (ISBN 0-87012-038-7). McClain.

Reddell, James R. A Preliminary Bibliography of Mexican Cave Biology with a Checklist of Published Records. (Association for Mexican Cave Studies: Bulletin 3). 184p. 1971. 10.00 (ISBN 0-686-70404-5). Speleo Pr.

Reddell, James R., ed. Studies on the Caves & Cave Fauna of the Yucatan Peninsula. (Association for Mexican Cave Studies: Bulletin 6). 296p. 1977. 13.00 (ISBN 0-686-70407-X). Speleo Pr.

Reddell, James R. & Mitchell, Robert W., eds. Studies on the Cavernicole Fauna of Mexico. (Association for Mexican Cave Studies: Bulletin 4). 239p. 1971. 13.00 (ISBN 0-686-70405-3). Speleo Pr.

Sloane, Bruce. Cavers, Caves, & Caving. 1977. 19.95 (ISBN 0-8135-0835-5). Rutgers U Pr.

Toigo, Angela. Caves & Canyons. 1st ed. LC 79-54772. (Illus.). 52p. 1979. 5.00 (ISBN 0-913180-02-5). Benedict Con Adoration.

Traister, Robert J. Cave Exploring. (Illus.). 192p. 1983. 16.95 (ISBN 0-8306-0266-6); pap. 10.95 (ISBN 0-8306-0166-X, 1566). TAB Bks.

Trimble, Stephen. Timpanogos Cave: A Window into the Earth. Priehs, T. J. & Dodson, Carolyn, eds. LC 82-61192. (Illus.). 48p. 1983. pap. 4.95 (ISBN 0-911408-64-9). SW Pks Mnmts.

Walsh, Frank K. & Halliday, William R. Oregon Caves: Discovery & Exploration. 3rd ed. (Illus.). 32p. 1982. pap. 2.95 (ISBN 0-913508-01-2). Te Cum Tom.

Watson, Richard A., ed. Cave Research Foundation: 1969-1973. (Illus.). 265p. (Orig.). 1984. pap. 11.00 (ISBN 0-939748-12-6). Cave Bks MO.

--Cave Research Foundation: 1974-1978. (Illus.). 341p. (Orig.). 1984. pap. 14.00 (ISBN 0-939748-13-4). Cave Bks MO.

CAVITATION

American Society of Mechanical Engineers. The Role of Nucleation in Boiling & Cavitation: Symposium Presented at Joint Fluids Engineering, Heat Transfer & Lubrication Conference, Detroit, Michigan, May 26-27, 1970. pap. 20.00 (ISBN 0-317-09023-2, 2016877). Bks Demand UMI.

Billet, M. L. & Arndt, R. E., eds. International Symposium on Cavitation Noise. 1982. 30.00 (H00231). ASME.

Characterization & Determination of Erosion Resistance - STP474. 440p. 1970. 28.75 (ISBN 0-8031-0029-9, 04-474000-29). ASTM.

Erosion, Wear & Interfaces with Corrosion, STP 567. 343p. 1974. 35.00 (ISBN 0-8031-0335-2, 04-567000-29). ASTM.

Hammitt, Frederick G. Cavitation & Multiphase Flow Phenomena. 448p. 1980. text ed. 80.00 (ISBN 0-07-025907-0). McGraw.

Hoyt, J. W., ed. Caviation & Multiphase Flow Forum. (FED Ser.: Vol. 2). 96p. 1983. pap. text ed. 20.00 (ISBN 0-317-02555-4). ASME.

--Cavitation & Polyphase Flow Forum - 1982. 65p. 1982. 20.00 (G00208). ASME.

Morgan, W. B. & Parkin, B. R., eds. International Symposium on Cavitation Inception. 238p. 1979. 30.00 (ISBN 0-686-59662-5, G00156). ASME.

Symposium on Cavity Flows (1975: Minneapolis). Cavity Flows: Presented at the Fluids Engineering Conference, Minneapolis, Minnisota, May 5-7, 1975. Parkin, Blaine R. & Morgan, W. B., eds. LC 75-8089. (Illus.). pap. 36.30 (ISBN 0-317-08133-0, 2016869). Bks Demand UMI.

Waid, Robert L., ed. Cavitation & Polyphase Flow Forum, 1977. pap. 20.00 (ISBN 0-317-08529-8, 2005689). Bks Demand UMI.

Waldron, R. A. Theory of Waveguides & Cavities. 134p. 1969. 37.25x (ISBN 0-677-61480-2). Gordon.

CAYAKS
see Canoes and Canoeing

CB RADIO
see Citizens Band Radio

CBM (COMPUTER)

Cassel, Don. BASIC 4.0 Programming for the Commodore PET-CBM. (Micropower Ser.). 224p. 1983. plastic comb 16.95 (ISBN 0-697-08265-2); incl. disk o.p. 29.95 (ISBN 0-697-09908-3). Wm C Brown.

Compute Magazine, ed. Compute's First Book of PET-CBM. (Illus.). 244p. (Orig.). 1981. pap. 12.95 (ISBN 0-942386-01-9). Compute Pubns.

Hallgren, Richard. Interface Projects for the PET-CBM. (Illus.). 200p. Date not set. cancelled (ISBN 0-13-469494-5); pap. cancelled (ISBN 0-13-469486-4). P-H.

Haskell, Richard. PET-CBM BASIC. (Illus.). 154p. 1982. 18.95 (ISBN 0-13-661769-7); pap. 12.95 (ISBN 0-13-661751-4). P-H.

Weber, Jeffrey R. User's Guide to PET-CBM Computers. LC 80-70466. (How to Use Your Personal Computer Ser.). 330p. 1983. pap. 13.95 (ISBN 0-9604892-8-2). Weber Systems.

CECIDOLOGY
see Galls (Botany)

CELESTIAL MECHANICS
see Mechanics, Celestial

CELESTIAL NAVIGATION
see Nautical Astronomy

CELL, VOLTAIC
see Electric Batteries

CELL CULTURE

Acton, Ronald T., ed. Cell Culture & Its Application. 1977. 60.00 (ISBN 0-12-043050-9). Acad Pr.

Adams, R. L. Cell Culture for Biochemists. Work, T. S. & Burdon, R. H., eds. (Laboratory Techniques in Biochemistry & Molecular Biology Ser.: Vol. 8, No. 1). 292p. 1980. 65.50 (ISBN 0-444-80248-7); pap. 27.00 (ISBN 0-444-80199-5). Elsevier.

Advances in Cell Culture, Vol. 2. (Serial Publication). 352p. 1982. 45.00 (ISBN 0-12-007902-X). Acad Pr.

Barnes, David W., et al. Methods for Preparation of Media Supplements, & Substrata for Serum-Free Animal Cell Culture. LC 84-7203. (Cell Culture Methods for Molecular & Cell Biology Ser.: Vol. 1). 378p. 1984. 49.50 (ISBN 0-8451-3800-6). A R Liss.

--Methods for Serum-Free Culture of Cells of the Endocrine System. LC 84-7202. (Cell Culture Methods for Molecular & Cell Biology Ser.: Vol. 2). 272p. 1984. 39.00 (ISBN 0-8451-3801-4). A R Liss.

--Methods for Serum-Free Culture of Neuronal & Lymphoid Cells. LC 84-7204. (Cell Culture Methods for Molecular & Cell Biology Ser.: Vol. 4). 280p. 1984. 39.50 (ISBN 0-8451-3803-0). A R Liss.

Bell, Paul B., Jr., ed. Scanning Electron Microscopy of Cells in Culture. (Illus.). vi, 314p. 1984. pap. 29.00 (ISBN 0-931288-31-2). Scanning Electron.

Bottenstein, Jane E. & Sato, Gordon, eds. Cell Culture in the Neurosciences. (Current Topics in Neurobiology Ser.). 404p. 1985. 49.50x (ISBN 0-306-41942-4, Plenum Pr). Plenum Pub.

Brown, S. A., ed. Cell-Culture Test Methods. LC 83-70421. (Special Technical Publications: No. 810). 157p. 1983. text ed. 30.00 (ISBN 0-8031-0249-6, 04-810000-54). ASTM.

Calcott, Peter H. Continuous Cultures of Cells, 2 vols. 1981. Vol. 1, 208 pgs. 67.00 (ISBN 0-8493-5377-7); Vol. 2, 224 pgs. 70.00 (ISBN 0-8493-5378-5). CRC Pr.

Cameron, Ivan L. & Pool, Thomas B., eds. The Transformed Cell. (Cell Biology Ser.). 1981. 65.00 (ISBN 0-12-157160-2). Acad Pr.

Chaleff, R. S. Genetics of Higher Plants: Applications of Cell Culture. (Development & Cell Biology Monographs: No. 9). 208p. 1981. 47.50 (ISBN 0-521-22731-3). Cambridge U Pr.

Evans, David P., et al, eds. Handbook of Plant Cell Culture, Vol. 1: Techniques for Propagation & Breeding. LC 82-73774. 1983. 53.00 (ISBN 0-02-949230-0). Macmillan.

Kuchler, Robert J. Biochemical Methods in Cell Culture & Virology. 1977. 70.00 (ISBN 0-12-786880-1). Acad Pr.

Kuchler, Robert J., ed. Animal Cell Culture & Virology. LC 74-833. (Benchmark Papers in Microbiology Ser.: Vol. 6). 461p. 1974. 57.95 (ISBN 0-87933-233-6). Van Nos Reinhold.

Littlefield, John W. & Commonwealth Fund. Variation, Senescence & Neoplasia in Cultured Somatic Cells. (Illus.). 147p. 1976. 8.95x (ISBN 0-674-93208-0). Harvard U Pr.

Luriya, E. A., ed. Hematopoietic & Lymphoid Tissue in Cultures. LC 76-55703. (Studies in Soviet Science: Life Science). (Illus.). 194p. 1977. 49.50 (ISBN 0-306-10934-4, Consultants). Plenum Pub.

McGarrity, G. J., et al, eds. Mycoplasma Infection of Cell Cultures. LC 77-25003. (Vol. 3). 352p. 1978. 42.50x (ISBN 0-306-32603-5, Plenum Pr). Plenum Pub.

Maramorosch, Karl. Advances in Cell Culture, Vol. 3. (Serial Publication Ser.). 1984. 60.00 (ISBN 0-12-007903-8). Acad Pr.

Maramorosch, Karl, ed. Advances in Cell Culture, Vol. 4. 1985. 49.50 (ISBN 0-12-007904-6). Acad Pr.

Maramorosh, Karl, ed. Advances in Cell Culture, Vol. I. (Serial Publication Ser.). 1981. 55.00 (ISBN 0-12-007901-1). Acad Pr.

Mather, Jennie P., ed. Mammalian Cell-Culture: The Use of Serum-Free Hormone-Supplemented Media. 302p. 1984. 39.50x (ISBN 0-306-41584-4, Plenum Pr). Plenum Pub.

Methods for Serum-Free Culture of Epithelial & Fibroblastic Cells. LC 84-7910. (Cell Culture Methods for Molecular & Cell Biology Ser.: Vol. 3). 306p. 1984. 49.50 (ISBN 0-8451-3802-2). A R Liss.

Middleton, C. A. & Sharp, J. A. Cell Locomotion "IN VITRO". Techniques & Observations. (Illus.). 176p. 1984. lib. bdg. 25.00x (ISBN 0-520-05209-9). U of Cal Pr.

Murphy, M. J., Jr., ed. In Vitro Aspects of Erythropoiesis. LC 78-16104. (Illus.). 1978. 49.50 (ISBN 0-387-90320-8). Springer-Verlag.

Nicolini, Claudio, ed. Cell Growth. LC 81-15732. (NATO ASI Series A, Life Sciences: Vol. 38). 837p. 1981. 89.50 (ISBN 0-306-40815-5, Plenum Pr). Plenum Pub.

Pfeiffer, Steven. Neuroscience Approached Through Cell Culture. 256p. 1982. 75.00 (ISBN 0-8493-6340-3). CRC Pr.

Pollack, Robert, ed. Readings in Mammalian Cell Culture. rev. ed. LC 75-15101. (Illus.). 884p. 1975. pap. text ed. 30.00x (ISBN 0-87969-116-6). Cold Spring Harbor.

Priest, Jean H. Human Cell Culture in Diagnosis of Disease. (Illus.). 300p. 1971. photocopy ed. 29.50x (ISBN 0-398-02384-0). C C Thomas.

Sato, Gordon, ed. Tissue Culture of the Nervous System. LC 73-79426. (Current Topics in Neurobiology Ser.: Vol. 1). (Illus.). 301p. 1973. 35.00x (ISBN 0-306-36701-7, Plenum Pr). Plenum Pub.

Sato, Gordon H., et al, eds. Growth of Cells in Hormonally Defined Media. LC 82-71652. (Cold Spring Harbor Conferences on Cell Proliferation Ser.: Vol. 9). 1213p. 1982. 2 bk set 177.00x (ISBN 0-87969-156-5). Cold Spring Harbor.

Sharp, William R. & Evans, David A., eds. Handbook of Plant Cell Culture: Crop Species, Vol. 2. 1984. 49.50 (ISBN 0-02-949780-9). Macmillan.

Uses & Standardization of Vertebrate Cell Cultures. (NCI Monograph: No. 5). 1984. 65.00 (ISBN 0-318-03390-9). Tissue Culture Assn.

Vasil, Indra K., ed. Cell Culture & Somatic Cell Genetics of Plants: Cell Growth, Cytodifferentiation, Cryopreservation, Vol. 2. Date not set. price not set (ISBN 0-12-715002-1). Acad Pr.

--Cell Culture & Somatic Cell Genetics of Plants, Vol. 1: Laboratory Procedures & Their Applications. LC 83-21538. 1984. 85.00 (ISBN 0-12-715001-3). Acad Pr.

CELL DIFFERENTIATION

Acosta, Enrique V. & Galina, Miguel A., eds. Eleventh International Congress of Anatomy, Part B: Advances in the Morphology of Cells & Tissues. LC 81-2778. (Progress in Clinical & Biological Research Ser.: Vol. 59B). 416p. 1981. 40.00 (ISBN 0-8451-0154-4). A R Liss.

Akoyunoglou, G. Cell Function & Differentiation, Pt. C. LC 82-21658. (Progress in Clinical & Biological Research Ser.: Vol. 102C). 382p. 1982. 42.00 (ISBN 0-8451-0167-6). A R Liss.

--Cell Function & Differentiation, Pt. B. LC 82-21658. (Progress in Clinical & Biological Research Ser.: Vol. 102B). 544p. 1982. 60.00 (ISBN 0-8451-0166-8). A R Liss.

Adolph, Edward F. Regulation of Size As Illustrated in Unicellular Organisms. (Illus.). 238p. 1931. 19.75x (ISBN 0-398-04184-9). C C Thomas.

Afzelius, Bjorn. Anatomy of the Cell. Satir, Birgit, tr. LC 66-13860. (Illus.). 1967. pap. 2.45x (ISBN 0-226-00851-7, P532, Phoen). U of Chicago Pr.

Akai, H. & King, R. C., eds. The Ultrastructure & Functioning of Insect Cells. (Illus.). 195p. 1983. 28.00x (ISBN 4-930813-00-X, Pub. by Japan Sci Soc Japan). Intl Spec Bk.

Alexandrov, V. Y. Cells, Macromolecules, & Temperature. (Ecological Studies Ser: Vol. 21). 1977. 51.00 (ISBN 0-387-08026-0). Springer-Verlag.

Allen, D. J., et al, eds. Three-Dimensional Microanatomy of Cells & Tissue Surfaces. 1981. 90.00 (ISBN 0-444-00607-9). Elsevier.

American Health Research Institute LTD. Genetic Engineering & Cell Intervention: Guidebook for Medicine, & Science. Bartone, John C., ed. LC 83-46106. 150p. 1984. 29.95 (ISBN 0-88164-146-4); pap. 21.95 (ISBN 0-88164-147-2). ABBE Pubs Assn.

Ankerst, Jaro, et al. Cell Surface Alteration As a Result of a Malignant Transformation. LC 72-13690. (Illus.). 237p. 1973. No. 2. text ed. 24.00x (ISBN 0-8422-7053-1); No. 1. text ed. 25.00x (ISBN 0-8422-7055-8). Irvington.

Appleton, D. R., et al. Cell Proliferation in the Gastrointestinal Tract. 428p. text ed. cancelled (ISBN 0-272-79597-6, Pub. by Pitman Bks Ltd UK). Pitman Pub MA.

Barigozzi, Claudio, ed. Origin & Natural History of Cell Lines: Proceedings of a Conference Held at Accademia Nazionale Dei Lincei, Rome, Italy, October 1977. LC 78-12805. (Progress in Clinical & Biological Research: Vol. 26). 208p. 1979. 29.00 (ISBN 0-8451-0026-2). A R Liss.

Beers, Roland F., Jr. & Bassett, Edward G., eds. Cell Fusion: Gene Transfer & Transformation. (Miles International Symposium Ser.: Vol. 14). (Illus.). 438p. 1984. 60.00 (ISBN 0-89004-941-6). Raven.

Bergsma, Daniel, ed. The Molecular Basis of Cell-Cell Interaction. (Alan R. Liss Ser.: Vol. 14, No. 2). 1978. 80.00 (ISBN 0-686-10131-6). March of Dimes.

Berns, Michael W. Cells. 2nd ed. 1983. pap. text ed. 17.95 (ISBN 0-03-061578-X, CBS C). SCP.

Bessis, M., et al, eds. Red Cell Rheology. (Illus.). 1978. pap. 68.00 (ISBN 0-387-09001-0). Springer-Verlag.

--Red Cell Shape: Physiology, Pathology, Ultrastructure. LC 73-77351. (Illus.). 180p. 1973. 29.00 (ISBN 0-387-06257-2). Springer-Verlag.

Biology Colloquium, 30th, Oregon State University, 1969. Biological Ultrastructure: The Origin of Cell Organelles: Proceedings. Harris, Patricia J., ed. LC 52-19235. (Illus.). 1971. 9.95x (ISBN 0-87071-169-5). Oreg St U Pr.

Bolis, Liana, et al, eds. Peptide Hormones, Biomembranes & Cell Growth. 304p. 1985. 49.50x (ISBN 0-306-41816-9, Plenum Pr). Plenum Pub.

Bonner, John T. Cells & Societies. 1955. 25.00x (ISBN 0-691-07919-6). Princeton U Pr.

Borek, Ernest. The Sculpture of Life. LC 73-6831. (Illus.). 181p. 1973. pap. 24.00x (ISBN 0-231-03425-3). Columbia U Pr.

Bowen, I. & Lockshin, R. Cell Death in Biology & Pathology. (Illus.). 450p. 1981. 75.00x (ISBN 0-412-16010-2, NO.6491, Pub. by Chapman & Hall). Methuen Inc.

Brachet, Jean & Mirsky, A. E., eds. The Cell: Biochemistry, Physiology, Morphology, 6 vols. Incl. Vol. 1. Methods: Problems of Cell Biology. 1959. 97.50 (ISBN 0-12-123301-4); Vol. 2. Cells & Their Component Parts. 1961. 97.50 (ISBN 0-12-123302-2); Vol. 3. Meiosis & Mitosis. 1961. 74.50 (ISBN 0-12-123303-0); Vol. 4. Specialized Cells, Part 1. 1960. 80.50 (ISBN 0-12-123304-9); Vol. 5. Specialized Cells, Part 2. 1961. 87.00 (ISBN 0-12-123305-7); Vol. 6. Supplementary Volume. 1964. 87.00 (ISBN 0-12-123306-5). Acad Pr.

Brewer, George J. The Red Cell: Sixth Ann Arbor Conference. (Progress in Clinical & Biological Research Ser.: Vol. 165). 608p. 1984. 86.00 (ISBN 0-8451-5015-4). A R Liss.

Brinkley, B. R. & Porter, Keith R., eds. International Cell Biology, 1976-1977. LC 77-79991. (Illus.). 694p. 1977. text ed. 15.00x (ISBN 0-87470-027-2). Rockefeller.

Brown, Harry D. Chemistry of the Cell Interface, 2 vols. 1971. Vol. 1. 72.00 (ISBN 0-12-136101-2); Vol. 2. 72.00 (ISBN 0-12-136102-0). Acad Pr.

Burgess, A. W. & Nicola, N. A. Growth Factors & Stem Cells. (Molecular Biology Ser.). 1984. 31.00 (ISBN 0-12-143750-7). Acad Pr.

Busch, Harris, ed. The Cell Nucleus, Vol. 9: Nuclear Particles, Pt.B. LC 81-9447. 1981. 65.00 (ISBN 0-12-147609-X). Acad Pr.

Cairnie, A. B., ed. Stems Cells: Renewing Cell Population. 1976. 57.50 (ISBN 0-12-155050-8). Acad Pr.

Campbell, P. N. The Structure & Function of Animal Cell Components. 1966. 25.00 (ISBN 0-08-011819-4); pap. 10.75 (ISBN 0-08-011818-6). Pergamon.

Carr, K. E. & Toner, P. G. Cell Structure: An Introduction to Biomedical Electron Microscopy. LC 81-67939. (Illus.). 388p. 1983. text ed. 48.00 (ISBN 0-443-02324-7). Churchill.

Catsimpoolas, Nicholas, ed. Methods of Cell Separation, 3 vols. LC 77-11018. (Biological Separations Ser.). (Illus.). Vol. 1, 375p, 1977. 39.50x (ISBN 0-306-34604-4, Plenum Pr); Vol. 2, 315p, 1979. 39.50x (ISBN 0-306-40094-4); Vol. 3, 215p, 1980. 35.00x (ISBN 0-306-40377-3). Plenum Pub.

Chang, Thomas M. Artificial Cells. (Illus.). 224p. 1972. photocopy ed. 25.50x (ISBN 0-398-02257-7). C C Thomas.

Cheng, Thomas C., ed. Structure of Membranes & Receptors. (Comparative Pathobiology Ser.: Vol. 5). 296p. 1984. 49.50x (ISBN 0-306-41503-8, Plenum Pr). Plenum Pub.

Cheung, Wai Yiu, ed. Calcium & Cell Function: Vol. 1, Calmodulin. LC 80-985. (Molecular Biology Ser.). 1980. 60.00 (ISBN 0-12-171401-2). Acad Pr.

Ciba Foundation. Cell Patterning. LC 78-304197. (Ciba Foundation Symposium: New Ser.: No. 29). pap. 91.00 (ISBN 0-317-29180-7, 2022157). Bks Demand UMI.

Cinader, Bernard, ed. Immunology of Receptors. (Immunology Ser.: Vol. 6). 544p. 1977. 79.75 (ISBN 0-8247-6674-1). Dekker.

Clemens, Michael J. Gene Expression, Vol. I. (Biochemistry of Cellular Regulation Ser.). 1980. 84.50 (ISBN 0-8493-5454-4). CRC Pr.

Cotman, C. W., et al, eds. Cell Surface & Neuron & Neuronal Function. Nicolson. (Cell Surface Reviews Ser.: Vol. 6). 546p. 1981. 121.75 (ISBN 0-444-80202-9, Biomedical Pr). Elsevier.

Cristofalo, V. J. & Holeckova, E., eds. Cell Impairment in Aging & Development. LC 75-1310. (Advances in Experimental Medicine & Biology Ser.: Vol. 53). 572p. 1975. 72.50x (ISBN 0-306-39053-1, Plenum Pr). Plenum Pub.

Crow, R., et al, eds. Experiments with Normal & Transformed Cells. 175p. 1979. lab manual 23.00x (ISBN 0-87969-123-9). Cold Spring Harbor.

Curtis, A. S. Cell Surface: Its Molecular Role in Morphogenesis. 1967. 76.50 (ISBN 0-12-199650-6). Acad Pr.

Cutts, J. H. Methods in Cell Separation Used in Hematology. 1970. 55.00 (ISBN 0-12-200050-1). Acad Pr.

Davidson, Richard L. & De La Cruz, Felix F. Somatic Cell Hybridization. LC 74-75725. 312p. 1974. 45.50 (ISBN 0-911216-75-8). Raven.

Dean, R. T. Cellular Degradative Processes. 1978. pap. 6.95 (ISBN 0-412-15190-1, NO.6082, Pub. by Chapman Hall). Methuen Inc.

De Duve, Christian. A Guided Tour of the Living Cell, Vols. I & II. (Illus.). 423p. Set. 55.95 (ISBN 0-7167-5002-3). W H Freeman.

--A Guided Tour of the Living Cell, Vols. I & II. (Scientific American Library). (Illus.). 463p. 1984. Set. 55.95. Vol. I (ISBN 0-7167-5002-3). Vol. II (ISBN 0-7167-5006-6). pap. 33.95 student ed. (ISBN 0-7167-6002-9). Sci Am Bks.

--A Guided Tour of the Living Cell. LC 84-29818. (Illus.). 433p. 1985. pap. 33.95 (ISBN 0-7167-6002-9). W H Freeman.

Demongeot, J., et al. Dynamical Systems & Cellular Automata. 1985. 39.50 (ISBN 0-12-209060-8). Acad Pr.

Drost-Hansen, W., ed. Cell-Associated Water. 1979. 55.00 (ISBN 0-12-222250-4). Acad Pr.

Dumont, J. E. & Nunez, J. Hormones & Cell Regulation. (European Symposium Ser.: Vol. 8). 1984. 68.00 (ISBN 0-444-80583-4, I-253-84). Elsevier.

Effects of Radiation on Cellular Proliferation & Differentiation. (Proceedings Ser.). (Illus.). 520p. 1968. pap. 35.75 (ISBN 92-0-010268-9, ISP186, IAEA). Unipub.

Elson, Elliot, et al, eds. Cell Membranes: Methods & Review, Vol. 2. 390p. 1984. 52.50x (ISBN 0-306-41761-8, Plenum Pr). Plenum Pub.

Fedoroff, S. & Hertz, Leif, eds. Cell, Tissue & Organ Cultures in Neurobiology. 1978. 60.00 (ISBN 0-12-250450-X). Acad Pr.

Freshney, Ian R., ed. Culture of Animal Cells: A Manual of Basic Technique. LC 82-24960. 310p. 1983. 49.50 (ISBN 0-8451-0223-0). A R Liss.

Frontiers in Cellular Surface Research: Boehringer Ingelheim Symposium. 1981. 27.95 (ISBN 0-915340-09-7). PJD Pubns.

Fujita, Tsuneo, et al. S.E.M. Atlas of Cells & Tissues. LC 80-85298. (Illus.). 338p. 1981. 90.00 (ISBN 0-89640-051-4). Igaku-Shoin.

Garland, P. B. & Mathias, A. P., eds. Biochemistry of the Cell Nucleus. (Symposia Ser.: No. 42). 244p. 1981. 30.00x (ISBN 0-904498-03-4, Pub. by Biochemical England). State Mutual Bk.

Garrod, D. R. Cellular Development. 1973. pap. 6.95 (ISBN 0-412-11410-0, NO.6117, Pub. by Chapman Hall). Methuen Inc.

Goldspink, G., ed. Differentiation & Growth of Cells in Vertebrate Tissues. 1974. 45.00x (ISBN 0-412-11390-2, NO.6128, Pub. by Chapman & Hall). Methuen Inc.

Golub, Edward S. The Cellular Basis of the Immune Response. rev. & 2nd ed. LC 80-28080. (Illus.). 325p. 1981. pap. text ed. 18.95x (ISBN 0-87893-212-7). Sinauer Assoc.

Gosh, Bijan, ed. Organization of Prokaryotic Cell Membranes, Vol. III. 288p. 1985. 87.00 (ISBN 0-8493-5659-8). CRC Pr.

Greaves, M. F. Cellular Recognition. 1975. pap. 6.95 (ISBN 0-412-13110-2, NO.6129, Pub. by Chapman & Hall). Methuen Inc.

Grinnell, Alan D. & Moody, William J., Jr. The Physiology of Excitable Cells. LC 83-12063. (Neurology & Neurobiology Ser.: Vol. 5). 620p. 1983. 72.00 (ISBN 0-8451-2704-7). A R Liss.

Haber, Edgar, ed. The Cell Membrane: Its Role in Interaction with the Outside World. 288p. 1984. 49.50x (ISBN 0-306-41827-4, Plenum Pr). Plenum Pub.

Hammerling, G. L., et al, eds. Monoclonal Antibodies & T-Cell Hybridomas: Perspectives & Technical Notes. (Research Monographs in Immunology: Vol. 3). 588p. 1982. 107.75 (ISBN 0-444-80351-3, Biomedical Pr). Elsevier.

Hampton, James C., ed. The Cell Cycle in Malignancy & Immunity: Proceedings. LC 74-600181. (ERDA Symposium Ser.). 614p. 1975. pap. 23.25 (CONF-731005); microfiche 4.50 (ISBN 0-87079-158-3, CONF-731005). DOE.

Hendry. Membrane Physiology & Cell Excitation. 1981. 14.50 (ISBN 0-8151-4267-6). Year Bk Med.

Hennessen, W., ed. Use of Heteroploid & Other Cell Substrates for the Production of Biologicals. (Developments in Biological Standardization: Vol. 50). (Illus.). x, 402p. 1982. pap. 36.25 (ISBN 3-8055-3472-8). S Karger.

Herberman, Ronald B., ed. NK Cells & Other Natural Effector Cells. LC 82-11406. 1566p. 1982. 79.50 (ISBN 0-12-341360-5). Acad Pr.

Hidaka, Hiroshi & Hartshorne, David L., eds. Calmodulin Antagonists & Cellular Physiology. Date not set. 79.00 (ISBN 0-12-347230-X). Acad Pr.

Hillman, H. & Sartory, P. The Living Cell. (Illus.). 112p. 1980. 23.50x (ISBN 0-906527-02-3); pap. 15.95x (ISBN 0-906527-01-5). Intl Ideas.

Hoagland, Mahlon B. The Roots of Life: A Layman's Guide to Genes, Evolution, & the Ways of Cells. 1978. 11.95 (ISBN 0-395-25811-1). HM.

Holtzman, Eric & Novikoff, Alex B. Cells & Organelles. 3rd ed. 544p. 1984. text ed. 32.95x (ISBN 0-03-049461-3). SCP.

Horecker, Bernard & Estabrook, Ronald, eds. Current Topics in Cellular Regulation: Biological Cycles, Vol. 18. (Serial Publication Ser.). 1981. 80.00 (ISBN 0-12-152818-9). Acad Pr.

Horecker, Bernard & Stadtman, E., eds. Current Topics in Cellular Regulation, Vol. 22. (Serial Publication). 1983. 49.00 (ISBN 0-12-152822-7). Acad Pr.

Horeker, Bernard & Stadtman, Earl L., eds. Current Topics in Cellular Regulation, Vol. 21. 306p. 1982. 60.00 (ISBN 0-12-152821-9). Acad Pr.

Hsie, Abraham W., et al, eds. Banbury Report 2: Mammalian Cell Mutagenesis: The Maturation of Test Systems. LC 79-21186. (Banbury Report Ser.). (Illus.). 504p. 1979. 52.00x (ISBN 0-87969-201-4). Cold Spring Harbor.

Humbert, James, et al. Neutrophil Physiology & Pathology. 200p. 1975. 56.00 (ISBN 0-8089-0917-7, 792080). Grune.

ICN-UCLA Symposium, Squaw Valley, Calif., 1976. Cell Shape & Surface Architecture: Proceedings. Revel, Jean P., et al, eds. LC 77-2483. (Progress in Clinical & Biological Research: Vol. 17). 630p. 1977. 67.00 (ISBN 0-8451-0017-3). A R Liss.

Inoue, S. & Stephens, R. E., eds. Molecules & Cell Movement. LC 75-16666. (Society of General Physiologists Ser.: Vol. 30). 460p. 1975. 52.00 (ISBN 0-89004-041-9). Raven.

Interdisciplinary Conference-5th. Cellular Dynamics, 4 Vols. Peachey, L. D., ed. 1969. Vols. 1 & 2, 446. 73.00x (ISBN 0-677-65010-8); Vols. 3 & 4, 310. 48.75x (ISBN 0-677-65020-5); Set, 756p. 116.95 (ISBN 0-677-13300-6). Gordon.

International Conference, la Jolla, Calif., Feb. 1977. The Molecular Basis of Cell-Cell Interaction: Papers. Lerner, Richard A. & Bergsma, Daniel, eds. LC 77-27909. (Birth Defects Original Article Ser.: Vol. 14, No. 2). 576p. 1978. 80.00 (ISBN 0-8451-1018-7). A R Liss.

International Pigment Cell Conference, 10th, Cambridge, Mass., October 1977, Pt. 1. Biologic Basis of Pigmentation. Klaus, S. N., ed. (Pigment Cell: Vol. 4). (Illus.). 1979. 67.75 (ISBN 3-8055-2972-4). S Karger.

International Pigment Cell Conference, 10th, Cambridge, Mass., October 1977, Pt. 2. Pathophysiology of Melanocytes. Klaus, S. N., ed. (Pigment Cell: Vol. 5). (Illus.). 1979. 59.25 (ISBN 3-8055-2973-2). S Karger.

International Symposium on Cell Biology & Cytopharmacology, First. Advances in Cytopharmacology, Vol. 1. Clementi, F. & Ceccarelli, B., eds. LC 70-84115. (Illus.). 493p. 1971. 69.50 (ISBN 0-911216-09-X). Raven.

International Symposium on Molecular Biology Staff. Cellular Modification & Genetic Transformation by Exogenous Nucleic Acids. LC 73-5909. (The John Hopkins Medical University Ser.: No. 2). pap. 87.50 (ISBN 0-317-28474-6, 2020738). Bks Demand UMI.

Jack, J. J. & Noble, D. Electric Current Flow in Excitable Cells. (Illus.). 1983. pap. 29.50x (ISBN 0-19-857527-0). Oxford U Pr.

Jackson, David. Cell System of Production. 170p. 1978. text ed. 29.00x (ISBN 0-220-66345-9, Pub. by Busn Bks England). Brookfield Pub Co.

Jasmin, G., ed. Cell Markers. (Methods & Achievements in Experimental Pathology: Vol. 10). (Illus.). xii, 296p. 1981. 70.75 (ISBN 3-8055-1736-X). S Karger.

Johnson, John E., Jr., ed. Aging & Cell Function. 300p. 1984. 42.50x (ISBN 0-306-41420-1, Plenum Pr). Plenum Pub.

--Aging & Cell Structure, Vol. 1. LC 81-17886. 401p. 1981. 59.50 (ISBN 0-306-40695-0, Plenum Pr). Plenum Pub.

--Aging & Cell Structure, Vol. 2. 240p. 1984. 42.50x (ISBN 0-306-41455-4, Plenum Pr). Plenum Pub.

Keebler, Catherine M. & Reagan, James W., eds. A Manual of Cytotechnology. 6th ed. LC 82-22818. (Illus.). 325p. 1984. text ed. 55.00 (ISBN 0-89189-168-4, 16-3-005-00). Am Soc Clinical.

Kemp, Brenda & Pillitteri, Adele. Fundamentals of Nursing: A Framework for Practice. 1984. text ed. 33.95 (ISBN 0-316-48818-6); tchr's. manual avail. (ISBN 0-316-48819-4). Little.

Kennedy, Donald, intro. by. Cellular & Organismal Biology: Readings from Scientific American. LC 74-775. (Illus.). 355p. 1974. text ed. 23.95 (ISBN 0-7167-0894-9); pap. text ed. 12.95 (ISBN 0-7167-0893-0). W H Freeman.

Kummerow, Fred A., et al, eds. Biomembranes & Cell Function, Vol. 414. 40.00x (ISBN 0-89766-222-9); pap. 40.00x (ISBN 0-89766-223-7). NY Acad Sci.

Kunnau, Wolfram. Live-Cell Therapy. 1983. 9.95x (ISBN 0-318-00142-X). Cancer Control Soc.

Kuo, Hyh-Fa, ed. Phospholipids & Cellular Regulation, Vols. I & II. 1985. Vol. I. price not set, 288p. (ISBN 0-8493-5537-0); Vol. II. price not set, 304p. (ISBN 0-8493-5538-9). CRC Pr.

Lapis, K. & Jenery, A., eds. Regulation & Control of Cell Proliferation. 506p. 1984. text ed. 63.00 (ISBN 0-9910001-5-3, Pub. by Akademiai Kaido Hungary). Heyden.

Lash, James & Burger, Max M., eds. Cell & Tissue Interactions. LC 77-83689. (Society of General Physiologists Ser: Vol. 32). 331p. 1977. 42.50 (ISBN 0-89004-180-6). Raven.

Leukocyte Culture Conference, 9th. Immune Recognition: Proceedings. Rosenthal, Alan S., ed. 1975. 68.50 (ISBN 0-12-597850-2). Acad Pr.

Levine, R. Current Topics in Cellular Regualtion, Vol. 26. Date not set. 89.95 (ISBN 0-12-152826-X). Acad Pr.

Locke, Michael & Locke, Michael, eds. Cellular Membranes in Development. 1964. 64.50 (ISBN 0-12-454168-2). Acad Pr.

Lucy, J. A., et al. Mammalian Cell Hybridization, II. (Illus.). 220p. 1973. text ed. 25.50x (ISBN 0-8422-7102-3). Irvington.

Manly, Richard S., ed. Adhesion in Biological Systems. 1970. 60.00 (ISBN 0-12-469050-5). Acad Pr.

Margulis, Lynn. Symbiosis in Cell Evolution: Life & Its Environment on the Early Earth. LC 80-26695. (Illus.). 419p. 1981. text ed. 30.95x (ISBN 0-7167-1255-5); pap. text ed. 18.95x (ISBN 0-7167-1256-3). W H Freeman.

Mason, Marion, et al. Nutrition & the Cell: The Inside Story. LC 72-95734. (Illus.). Repr. of 1973 ed. 17.50 (ISBN 0-8357-9636-1, 2013104). Bks Demand UMI.

Reader, Keith. Cultures on Celluloid. (Illus.). 232p. 1982. 24.95 (ISBN 0-7043-2272-2, Pub. by Quartet Bks). Merrimack Pub Cir.

Recent Developments in Cellulose: Ester Lacquers. 64p. 1976. 50.00x (ISBN 0-686-44699-2, Pub. by Chandler England). State Mutual Bk.

Rowell, R. M. & Youngs, R. Modified Cellulosics. 1978. 49.50 (ISBN 0-12-599750-7). Acad Pr.

Sarko. Proceedings of the Ninth Cellulose Conference. price not set (ISBN 0-471-88132-5). Wiley.

Shon, David N., ed. Graft Copolymerization of Lignocellulosic Fibers. LC 82-6717. (ACS Symposium Ser.: No. 187). 1982. 39.95 (ISBN 0-8412-0721-6). Am Chemical.

Symposium on International Developments in Cellulose, Papers, & Textiles (1976: New York) Cellulose Chemistry & Technology: A Symposium. Arthur, Jett C., Jr., ed. LC 77-6649. (ACS Symposium Ser.: No. 48). pap. 101.50 (ISBN 0-317-27809-6, 2015235). Bks Demand UMI.

Symposium on International Developments in Cellulose, Paper & Textiles. Cellulose Chemistry & Technology: A Symposium Sponsored by the Cellulose, Paper, & Textile Division at the Meeting of American Chemical Society, 171st, New York, N. Y., April 5-9, 1976. Arthur, Jett C., Jr., ed. LC 77-6649. (American Chemical Society. Symposium Ser.: No. 48). (Illus.). pap. 101.50 (ISBN 0-317-11051-9, 2015235). Bks Demand UMI.

Turbak, Albin F., ed. Cellulose Technology Research. LC 75-2021. (ACS Symposium Ser.: No. 10). 1975. 21.95 (ISBN 0-8412-0248-6). Am Chemical.

--Solvent Spun Rayon, Modified Cellulose Fibers & Derivatives. LC 77-12220. (ACS Symposium Ser.: No. 58). 1977. 26.95 (ISBN 0-8412-0388-1). Am Chemical.

Veal, F. J. Economics of Producing Certain Chemicals from Cellulose: A Review of Recent Literature, 1979. 1981. 80.00x (ISBN 0-686-97066-7, Pub. by W Spring England). State Mutual Bk.

Ward, Kyle. Chemical Modification of Papermaking Fibers. LC 72-92665. (Fiber Science Ser.: Vol. 4). (Illus.). pap. 63.50 (ISBN 0-317-07826-7, 2017691). Bks Demand UMI.

Weiner, Jack & Pollock, Vera. Analytical Methods: Cellulose & Pulp, Vol. 3. 1st supplement ed. LC 60-51407. (Bibliographic Ser.: No. 194). 1968. pap. 8.00 (ISBN 0-87010-002-5); supplement 2, 1973 10.00 (ISBN 0-87010-003-3). Inst Paper Chem.

Wilke, C. R., et al. Enzymatic Hydrolysis of Cellulose: Theory & Application. LC 83-2294. (Chemical Technology Review Ser.: No. 218). 164p. (Orig.). 1983. 24.00 (ISBN 0-8155-0945-6). Noyes.

Zhbankov, Rostislav G. Infrared Spectra of Cellulose & Its Derivatives. Stepanov, Academician B., ed. Densham, A. B., tr. from Rus. LC 65-25268. (Illus.). pap. 86.80 (ISBN 0-317-09373-8, 2020674). Bks Demand UMI.

CEMENT

see also Adhesives; Asbestos Cement; Concrete; Pavements; Portland Cement

ACI Committee 116. Cement & Concrete Terminology. 1978. pap. 17.75 (ISBN 0-685-85102-8, 116R-78). ACI.

Cedric Willson Symposium on Expansive Cement. 1980. 47.50 (ISBN 0-686-70071-6, SP-64). ACI.

Cembureau (European Cement Association), ed. Cement Standards of the World. 2nd ed. (Illus.). 177p. (Orig.). 1980. pap. 75.00x (ISBN 0-8002-2965-7). Intl Pubns Serv.

Cement & Concrete Thesaurus. 1969. pap. 19.95 (ISBN 0-685-85158-3, CCT). ACI.

Cement Standards: Evolution & Trends - STP 663. 119p. 1979. pap. 20.00 (ISBN 0-8031-0298-4, 04-663000-07). ASTM.

Clinker Storage Silo for Canada Cement Lafarge. (PCI Journal Reprints Ser.). 12p. pap. 5.00 (ISBN 0-686-40154-9, JR251). Prestressed Concrete.

Dipl-Ing, W. H. Cement Data Book: International Process Engineering in the Cement Industry, Vol. 2. (Illus.). 456p. 1983. 105.00 (ISBN 0-9915000-3-2, Pub. by Brauverag Germany). Heyden.

Dipl-Ing, W. H. & Czernin, W. H. C. Cement Chemistry & Physics for Civil Engineers. 2nd ed. (Illus.). 196p. 1980. 24.00 (ISBN 0-9915000-1-6, Pub. by Brauverag Germany). Heyden.

Duda, W. H. Cement Data Book. 2nd ed. (Ger. - Eng.). 1977. 160.00 (ISBN 0-686-56597-5, M-7317, Pub. by Bauverlag). French & Eur.

Fineness of Cement - STP 473. 109p. 1970. pap. 7.75 (ISBN 0-8031-0351-4, 04-473000-07). ASTM.

Ghosh, S. N., ed. Advances in Cement Technology: Critical Reviews & Case Studies on Manufacturing, Quality Control, Optimization & Use. (Illus.). 775p. 1982. 110.00 (ISBN 0-08-028670-4). Pergamon.

Grayson, Martin, ed. Encyclopedia of Glass, Ceramics, Clay & Cement. (Encyclopedia Reprint Ser.). 960p. 1985. 89.95x (ISBN 0-471-81931-X, Pub. by Wiley-Interscience). Wiley.

Hannant, D. J. Fibre Cements & Fibre Concretes. 219p. 1978. 59.95 (ISBN 0-471-99620-3, Pub. by Wiley-Interscience). Wiley.

Hirsch, Peter. Developments in Hydraulic Cements: Technology in the 1990's. (Philosophical Transactions of the Royal Society: Series A, Vol. 310). (Illus.). 207p. 1984. text ed. 72.00x (ISBN 0-85403-215-0, Pub. by Royal Soc London). Scholium Intl.

Klein Symposium on Expansive Cement Concretes 1972, Hollywood, Fl. Klein Symposium on Expansive Cement Concretes. LC 73-77948. (American Concrete Institute Publication Ser.: No. SP-38). pap. 125.80 (ISBN 0-317-27804-5, 2025079). Bks Demand UMI.

Kohlhaas, B., et al, eds. Cement Engineers Handbook. 4th ed. 790p. 1982. 90.00 (ISBN 0-9915000-2-4, Pub. by Brauverag Germany). Heyden.

Lea, F. M. Chemistry of Cement & Concrete. 1971. 58.75 (ISBN 0-8206-0212-4). Chem Pub.

Neville, Adam M. & Wainwright, P. High Alumina Cement Concrete. LC 76-354854. pap. 50.30 (ISBN 0-317-08024-5, 2016302). Bks Demand UMI.

Peray, K. Cement Manufacturer's Handbook. (Illus.). 1979. 32.50 (ISBN 0-8206-0245-0). Chem Pub.

--Rotary Cement Kiln. 2nd, rev. & enl. ed. (Illus.). 1985. 52.50 (ISBN 0-8206-0314-7). Chem Pub.

Popovics, Sandor. Concrete Making Materials. LC 78-1111. (Illus.). 1979. text ed. 45.00 (ISBN 0-07-050505-5). McGraw.

RILEM International Symposium. Testing & Test Methods of Fibre Cement Composites: RILEM Symposium held April 5-7, 1978. Swamy, R. N., ed. (Illus.). pap. 138.80 (ISBN 0-317-08289-2, 2019629). Bks Demand UMI.

Schleicher, C. & Wegener, B. Continuous Skew Slabs. 2nd ed. (Eng., Ger., & Rus., Illus.). 1971. 62.00x (ISBN 0-685-39794-7). Adlers Foreign Bks.

Schmid, P., tr. Microscopy of Cement Clinker: A Pictrure Atlas. 1965. 38.00 (ISBN 0-9960095-6-6, Pub. by Beton Bks W Germany). Heyden.

Skalny, Jan P. Cement Production & Use. 220p. (Orig.). 1980. pap. 20.00x (ISBN 0-939204-01-0, 79-08). Eng Found.

Soil-Cement Laboratory Handbook. 61p. 1971. pap. 5.00 (ISBN 0-89312-116-9, EB052S). Portland Cement.

Swamy, R. A., ed. Blended Cements. (Concrete Technology & Design Ser: Vol. 3). 224p. 47.00 (ISBN 0-317-14036-1, Pub. by Blackie & Son UK). Heyden.

University of Sheffield 8-9 April 1976 Conference. Hydraulic Cement Pastes, Their Structure & Properties: Proceedings. (Illus.). 1976. pap. 32.50x (ISBN 0-7210-1047-4). Scholium Intl.

Van Amerongen, C. Dictionary of Cement. (Ger. & Eng.). 202p. 1967. 44.00 (ISBN 3-7625-1171-3, M-7127). French & Eur.

Wicks, George G. & Ross, Wayne A., eds. Advances in Ceramics: Nuclear Waste Management. (Advances in Ceramics Ser.: Vol. 8). 1984. 90.00 (ISBN 0-916094-55-3). Am Ceramic.

CEMENT INDUSTRIES

Cembureau (European Cement Association) World Cement Directory 1980, 2 vols. 6th ed. LC 75-15776. (Illus.). 341p. (Orig.). 1980. Set. pap. 147.50x (ISBN 0-8002-2776-X). Intl Pubns Serv.

Cement & Concrete Industry. (UNIDO Guides to Information Sources: No. 2). pap. 4.00 (ISBN 0-686-94964-1, UN185, UN). Unipub.

Environmental Aspects of the Cement Industry. (Industry Overviews: Vol. 6). pap. 6.75 (UNEP003, UNEP). Unipub.

Francis. Cement Industry: 1796-1914. 1978. 25.00 (ISBN 0-7153-7386-2). David & Charles.

The Manufacture of Cement & Sulfuric Acid from Calcium Sulphate. pap. 2.00 (ISBN 0-686-94530-1, UN70/2B/29, UN). Unipub.

Verein Deutscher Zementwerke. Verfahrenstechnik der Zementherstellung. (Ger. Eng., Process Technology of Cement Manufacturing). 1979. 120.00 (ISBN 0-686-56472-3, M-7678, Pub. by Bauverlag). French & Eur.

CENOZOIC PERIOD

see Geology, Stratigraphic–Cenozoic

CENTIPEDES

Lewis, J. G. The Biology of Centipedes. (Illus.). 350p. 1981. 85.00 (ISBN 0-521-23413-1). Cambridge U Pr.

Williams, Stephen R. & Hefner, Robert A. Millipedes & Centipedes of Ohio. 1928. 1.00 (ISBN 0-86727-017-9). Ohio Bio Survey.

CENTRAL HEATING PLANTS

see Heating From Central Stations

CENTRIFUGAL COMPRESSORS

see Compressors

CENTRIFUGAL FORCE

see also Gravitation

Weissberger, Arnold & Hsu, Hsien-Wen. Separations by Centrifugal Phenomena. LC 81-4991. (Techniques of Chemistry Ser.: Vol. 16). 466p. 1981. 78.50x (ISBN 0-471-05564-6, Pub. by Wiley-Interscience). Wiley.

CENTRIFUGAL PUMPS

AIChe's Equipment Testing Procedures Committee. Centrifugal Pumps. 2nd ed. 1984. pap. 16.00 (ISBN 0-8169-0320-4). Am Inst Chem Eng.

Anderson, H. H. Centrifugal Pumps. 3rd ed. 480p. 1981. text ed. 92.00 (ISBN 0-85461-076-6, Pub by Trade & Tech England). Brookfield Pub Co.

Benaroya, Alfred. Fundamentals & Application of Centrifugal Pumps for the Practicing Engineer. 222p. 1978. 34.95x (ISBN 0-87814-040-9). Pennwell Bks.

Centrifugal Fire Pumps: Installation. (Twenty Ser.). 120p. 1974. pap. 3.75 (ISBN 0-685-46061-4, 20). Natl Fire Prot.

Church, Austin H. Centrifugal Pumps & Blowers. (Illus.). 320p. 1972. Repr. of 1944 ed. text ed. 20.50 (ISBN 0-88275-008-9). Krieger.

Karassik, I. J. Centrifugal Pump Clinic. (Mechanical Engineering Ser.: Vol. 6). 496p. 1981. 49.75 (ISBN 0-8247-1016-9). Dekker.

Liljestrand, Walter E. Understanding Centrifugal Pumps & Piping Systems. 416p. 1983. 71.95 (ISBN 0-87814-236-3, P4305). Pennwell Bks.

Lobanoff, Val S. & Ross, Robert R. Centrifugal Pumps: Design & Application. LC 84-15769. (Illus.). 350p. 1985. 41.95x (ISBN 0-87201-190-9). Gulf Pub.

Standard for the Installation of Centrifugal Fire Pumps. 134p. 5.00 (ISBN 0-686-68287-4). Natl Fire Prot.

Stepanoff, A. J. Centrifugal & Axial Flow Pumps: Theory, Design & Application. 2nd ed. LC 57-10815. 462p. 1957. 61.50x (ISBN 0-471-82137-3, Pub. by Wiley-Interscience). Wiley.

Trade & Technical Press Editors. Europump Terminology: Pump Applications. 900p. 1978. 107.00x (ISBN 0-85461-071-5, Pub by Trade & Tech England). Brookfield Pub Co.

Tramm, P. C. & Dean, R. C., Jr., eds. Centrifugal Compressor & Pump Stability, Stall & Surge. 202p. 1976. pap. 20.00 (ISBN 0-685-67493-2, I00098). ASME.

Yedidiah, S. Centrifugal Pump Problems. 229p. 1980. 51.95x (ISBN 0-87814-131-6). Pennwell Bks.

CENTRIFUGES

see also Human Centrifuge; Sedimentation Analysis

Beams, J. W., et al. Developments in the Centrifuge Separation Project: AEC Technical Information Center. (National Nuclear Energy Ser.: Div. X, Vol. 1). 269p. 1951. 22.00 (ISBN 0-87079-179-6, TID-5230); microfilm 10.00 (ISBN 0-87079-180-X, TID-5230). DOE.

Bingham, et al. Centrifuges. LC 83-161604. (Mud Equipment Manual Ser.: No. 8). 68p. (Orig.). 1983. pap. 17.95x (ISBN 0-87201-620-X). Gulf Pub.

European Conference on Mixing & Centrifugal Separation, 1st. Proceedings. 1975. text ed. 49.00x (ISBN 0-900983-39-6, Dist. by Air Science Co.). BHRA Fluid.

Fujita, Hiroshi. Foundations of Ultra-Centrifugal Analysis. LC 74-20899. 459p. 1975. 34.50 (ISBN 0-471-28582-X, Pub. by Wiley). Krieger.

McCall, J. S. & Potter, B. J. Ultracentrifugation. (Laboratory Monograph). (Illus.). 1973. text ed. 8.95 (ISBN 0-02-858470-8). Macmillan.

Price, C. A. Centrifugation in Density Gradients. LC 81-12693. 1982. 66.00 (ISBN 0-12-564580-5). Acad Pr.

Schachman, Howard K. Ultracentrifugation in Biochemistry. 1959. 60.00 (ISBN 0-12-621050-0). Acad Pr.

Sheeler, P. Centrifugation in Biology & Medical Science. 269p. 1981. 48.50 (ISBN 0-471-05234-5, Pub. by Wiley-Interscience). Wiley.

Svedberg, Theodor & Pedersen, Kai O. The Ultracentrifuge. Repr. of 1940 ed. 49.00 (ISBN 0-384-58890-5). Johnson Repr.

Williams, John W., ed. Ultracentrifugal Analysis in Theory & Experiment: Proceedings. 1963. 49.50 (ISBN 0-12-755150-6). Acad Pr.

CEPHALOPODA

see also Ammonoidea; Octopus

Boyle, Peter, ed. Cephalopod Life Cycles, Vol. 1. 1984.. 120.00 (ISBN 0-12-123001-5). Acad Pr.

Okutani, T. Stock Assessment of Cephalopod Resources Fished by Japan. (Fisheries Technical Papers: No. 173). 69p. 1977. pap. 7.50 (ISBN 92-5-100406-4, F1342, FAO). Unipub.

Philips, D. Catalogue of the Type & Figured Specimens of Fossil Cephalopląda (excluding Mesozoic Ammonoidea) in the British Museum (Natural History). 94p. 1982. pap. 25.00x (ISBN 0-565-00855-2, Pub. by Brit Mus Nat Hist England). Sabbot-Natural Hist Bks.

Phillips, D. Catalogue of the Type & Figured Specimens of Mesozoic Ammonoidea in the British Museum (Natural History) 1977. pap. 28.00x (ISBN 0-565-00790-4, Pub. by Brit Mus Nat Hist). Sabbot-Natural Hist Bks.

Report on Fishing for Squid & Other Cephalopods: Expert Consultation on Fishing, Tokyo & Hakodat, Japan, 1975. (Fisheries Reports: No. 170). 11p. 1976. pap. 7.50 (ISBN 0-685-66350-7, F817, FAO). Unipub.

Wright, C. W. & Wright, E. V. A Survey of the Fossil Cephalopoda of the Chalk of Great Britain. pap. 6.00 (ISBN 0-384-69440-3). Johnson Repr.

CEPHALOSPORIN

Flynn, Edwin H., ed. Cephalosporins & Penicillins: Chemistry & Biology. 1972. 76.50 (ISBN 0-12-261450-X). Acad Pr.

CEPHALOZIELLACEAE

Schuster, R. M. Studies in Cephaloziellaceae. (Illus.). 1977. 14.00 (ISBN 3-7682-0823-0). Lubrecht & Cramer.

CERAMBYCIDAE

Chemsak, John A. & Linsky, E. G. Checklist of Cerambycidae: The Longhorned Beetles. (Checklist of the Beetle of Canada United States, Mexico, Central America & the West Indies Ser.). 138p. (Orig.). 1982. pap. text ed. 18.00x (ISBN 0-937548-04-9). Plexus Pub.

Duffy, E. A. A Monograph of the Immature Stages of Australasian Timber Beetles - Cerambycidae. (Illus.). 235p. 1963. 34.00x (ISBN 0-565-00577-4, Pub. by Brit Mus Nat Hist England). Sabbot-Natural Hist Bks.

--A Monograph of the Immature Stages of Neotropical Timber Beetles (Cerambycidae) (Illus.). v, 327p. 1960. 42.00x (ISBN 0-565-00109-4, Pub. by Brit Mus Nat Hist). Sabbot-Natural Hist Bks.

Linsley, E. Gorton. The Cerambycidae of North America. Incl. Pt. I. Introduction. (U. C. Publ. in Entomology: Vol. 18). 1961; Pt. II. Taxonomy & Classification of the Parandrinae, Prioninae, Spondylinae, & Aseminae. (U. C. Publ. in Entomology: Vol. 19). 1962; Pt. III. Taxonomy & Classification of the Subfamily Cerambycinae, Tribes Opsimini Through Megaderini. (U. C. Publ. in Entomology: Vol. 20). 1962. pap. 14.00x (ISBN 0-520-09081-0); Pt. IV. Taxonomy & Classification of the Subfamily Cerambycinae, Tribes Elaphidionini Through Rhinotragini. (U. C. Publ. in Entomology: Vol. 21). 1963; Pt. V. Taxonomy & Classification of the Subfamily Cerambycinae, Tribes Callichromini Through Ancylocerini. (U. C. Publ. in Entomology: Vol. 22). 1964. pap. 14.00x (ISBN 0-520-09083-7). pap. U of Cal Pr.

CERAMIC COATING

see also Enamel and Enameling

American Welding Society. Flame Spraying of Ceramics: C2.13. 293p. 1970. 10.00 (ISBN 0-87171-141-9); members 7.50. Am Welding.

CERAMIC COLORING

see Color in the Ceramic Industries

CERAMIC FIBERS

British Ceramic Society, ed. Mechanical Properties of Ceramics. 1981. 50.00x (ISBN 0-686-78729-3, Pub. by Brit Ceramic Soc England). State Mutual Bk.

Rauch, H. W., et al. Ceramic Fibers & Fibrous Composite Materials. (Refractory Materials Ser: Vol. 3). 1968. 69.50 (ISBN 0-12-582850-0). Acad Pr.

CERAMIC INDUSTRIES

British Ceramic Society, ed. The Mechanical Engineering Properties & Applications of Ceramics. 50.00x (ISBN 0-686-78852-4, Pub. by Brit Ceramic Soc England). State Mutual Bk.

Frechette, V. D., et al, eds. Quality Assurance in Ceramic Industries. LC 79-14166. 275p. 1979. 49.50 (ISBN 0-306-40183-5, Plenum Pr). Plenum Pub.

Sekers, David. The Potteries. (Shire Album Ser.: No. 62). (Illus.). 32p. (Orig.). 1983. pap. 2.95 (ISBN 0-85263-564-8, Pub. by Shire Pubns England). Seven Hills Bks.

CERAMIC MATERIALS

see also Ceramic Metals

Acquaviva, Samuel J. & Bortz, Seymour A., eds. Structural Ceramics & Design. 240p. 1969. 69.50 (ISBN 0-677-13550-5). Gordon.

--Structural Ceramics & Testing of Brittle Materials. 232p. 1968. 93.75 (ISBN 0-677-12770-7). Gordon.

Baumgart, W., et al, eds. Process Mineralogy of Ceramic Materials. 229p. 1984. pap. 27.50 (ISBN 0-444-00963-9). Elsevier.

Bradt, Richard C. & Tressler, Richard E., eds. Deformation of Ceramic Materials. LC 75-4945. 577p. 1975. 85.00x (ISBN 0-306-30839-8, Plenum Pr). Plenum Pub.

CEREAL PRODUCTS
see also Flour
Barnes, Peter, ed. Lipids in Cereal Technology. (Food Science & Technology Ser.). 1984. 70.00 (ISBN 0-12-079020-3). Acad Pr.
Christensen, Edith A., ed. Approved Methods of the American Association of Cereal Chemists. 8th ed. LC 82-46081. 1200p. 1983. text ed. 140.00 member; text ed. 190.00 non member (ISBN 0-913250-31-7). Am Assn Cereal Chem.
Inglett, George E., ed. Cereals for Food & Beverages: Recent Progress in Cereal Chemistry & Technology. Munck, Lars. LC 80-10981. 1980. 56.50 (ISBN 0-12-370960-1). Acad Pr.
Jenkyn, J. F. & Plumb, R. T. Strategies for the Control of Cereal Disease: Organized by the British Plant Pathologist, Vol. 2. (Federation of British Plant Pathologists Ser.: Vol. 9). 219p. 1981. 57.95x (ISBN 0-470-27049-7). Halsted Pr.
Kent, N. L. Technology of Cereals: An Introduction for Students of Food Science & Agriculture. 3rd ed. LC 75-6654. (Illus.). 200p. 1983. 24.50 (ISBN 0-08-029801-X); pap. 13.50 (ISBN 0-08-029800-1). Pergamon.
Pomeranz, Y., ed. Cereals: A Renewable Resource, Theory & Practice. LC 81-71369. 728p. 1981. text ed. 49.00 member (ISBN 0-913250-22-8); text ed. 60.00 non-member. Am Assn Cereal Chem.
Rasper, Vladimir F., ed. Cereal Polysaccharides in Technology & Nutrition. 184p. 1984. pap. 23.00 (ISBN 0-913250-36-8). Am Assn Cereal Chem.
Royal Dublin Society. Cereal Production: Proceedings of the International Meeting on Production of Temperate Cereal Crops. Gallagher, E., ed. 304p. 1984. text ed. 89.95 (ISBN 0-407-00303-7). Butterworth.
Schneeweiss, R. Dictionary of Cereal Processing & Cereal Chemistry. (Eng., Fr., Ger., Lat., & Rus.). 520p. 1982. 121.50 (ISBN 0-444-42049-5, I-274-82). Elsevier.
Spiertz, J. H. & Kramer, T., eds. Crop Physiology & Cereal Breeding: Proceedings of a Eucarpia Workshop held in Wageningen, 13-16 November 1978. 193p. 1979. pap. 33.00 (ISBN 0-686-93150-5, PDC124, Pudoc). Unipub.
Vetter, James L., ed. Dairy Products for the Cereal Processing Industry. 202p. 1984. 24.00 (ISBN 0-913250-35-X). Am Assn Cereal Chem.

CEREALS
see Grain

CEREALS AS FOOD
Hunter, Beatrice T. Wheat, Millet & Other Grains. (Good Health Guide Ser.). 1982. pap. 1.45 (ISBN 0-87983-289-4). Keats.
Pomeranz, Y. Advances in Cereal Science & Technology, Vol. I. Incl. Advances in Cereal Science & Technology, Pomeranz, Y. LC 76-8695. (Vol. II). 463p. 1978. pap. text ed. 60.00 (ISBN 0-913250-08-2); pap. text ed. 49.00 members; Advances in Cereal Science & Technology. Pomeranz, Y. LC 76-645872. (Vol. III). 348p. 1980. pap. text ed. 60.00 (ISBN 0-913250-16-3); pap. text ed. 49.00 members; Advances in Cereal Science & Technology. Pomeranz, Y., ed. (Vol. IV). 342p. 1981. pap. text ed. 60.00 (ISBN 0-913250-21-X); pap. text ed. 49.00 members; Advances in Cereal Science & Technology. Pomeranz, Y., ed. LC 76-645872. (Vol. V). pap. text ed. 60.00 (ISBN 0-913250-28-7); pap. text ed. 49.00 members; Advances in Cereal Science & Technology. Pomeranz, Y., ed. LC 76-645872. (Vol. VI). pap. text ed. 60.00 (ISBN 0-913250-33-3); pap. text ed. 49.00 members; Advances in Cereal Science & Technology. Pomeranz, E., ed. (Vol. IIV). 362p. 1984. pap. text ed. 60.00 (ISBN 0-913250-39-2). LC 76-8695. 418p. 1976. text ed. 49.00 member (ISBN 0-913250-07-4); text ed. 60.00 non-member. Am Assn Cereal Chem.
Pomeranz, Y., ed. Cereals Seventy-Eight: Better Nutrition for the World's Millions. LC 78-69838. 272p. 1978. lib. bdg. 9.00 member (ISBN 0-913250-13-9). Am Assn Cereal Chem.

CEREBELLUM
Brodal, A. & Kawamura, K. The Olivocerebellar Projection: A Review. (Advances in Anatomy, Embryology & Cell Biology Ser.: Vol. 64). (Illus.). 144p. 1980. pap. 46.10 (ISBN 0-387-10305-8). Springer-Verlag.
Cooper, Irving, et al, eds. The Cerebellum, Epilepsy & Behavior. LC 73-21971. 413p. 1974. 39.50x (ISBN 0-306-30775-8, Plenum Pr). Plenum Pub.
Dichgans, J., et al, eds. Cerebellar Functions. (Proceedings in Life Sciences Ser.). (Illus.). 350p. 1985. 48.50 (ISBN 0-387-13728-9). Springer-Verlag.
Dow, Robert & Moruzzi, Giuseppe. The Physiology & Pathology of the Cerebellum. LC 58-8343. pap. 160.00 (ISBN 0-317-27914-9, 2055857). Bks Demand UMI.
Eccles, John C., et al. Cerebellum As a Neuronal Machine. (Illus.). 1967. 57.00 (ISBN 0-387-03762-4). Springer-Verlag.
Fields, William S., et al. The Cerebellum in Health & Disease. LC 78-78016. (Illus.). 588p. 1970. 37.50 (ISBN 0-87527-009-3). Green.
Frowein, R. A., ed. Head Injuries: Tumors of the Cerebellar Region. Proceedings of the 28th Annual Meeting of the German Society of Neurosurgery, Koeln, Sept. 18-21, 1977. LC 78-15592. (Advances in Neurosurgery Ser.: Vol. 5). (Illus.). 1978. pap. 61.00 (ISBN 0-387-08964-0). Springer-Verlag.
Hellige, Joseph B., ed. Cerebral Hemisphere Asymmetry: Method, Theory & Application. LC 82-16655. 528p. 1983. 54.95x (ISBN 0-03-058638-0). Praeger.
McHedlishvili. Regulation of Cerebral Circulation. 1979. 23.00 (ISBN 0-9960016-4-6, Pub. by Akademiai Kiado Hungary). Heyden.
Needham, Charles W. The Principles of Cerebral Dominance: The Evolutionary Significance of the Radical Deduplication of the Human Brain. (Illus.). 192p. 1982. 24.75x (ISBN 0-398-04700-6). C C Thomas.
Palay, S. L. & Chan-Palay, V. Cerebellar Cortex: Cytology & Organization. LC 73-77568. (Illus.). 400p. 1974. 96.00 (ISBN 0-387-06228-9). Springer-Verlag.
Palay, S. L. & Palay, V. Chan, eds. The Cerebellum: New Vistas. (Experimental Brain Research Supplementum: No. 6). (Illus.). 740p. 1982. 88.00 (ISBN 0-387-11472-6). Springer-Verlag.
Rohkamm, R. Degeneration & Regeneration in Neurons of the Cerebellum. (Advances in Anatomy Embryology & Cell Biology: Vol. 53, Part 6). (Illus.). 1977. pap. 33.00 (ISBN 0-387-08519-X). Springer-Verlag.
Thomas, Andre. Cerebellar Functions. Herring, W. C., tr. (Nervous & Mental Disease Monographs: No. 12). 19.00 (ISBN 0-384-60120-0). Johnson Repr.

CERIUM
Physical, Chemical, & Biological Properties of Radiocerium Relevant to Radiation Protection Guidelines. LC 79-84485. (NCRP Reports Ser.: No. 60). 1978. 9.00 (ISBN 0-913392-44-8). NCRP Pubns.

CERMETS
see Ceramic Metals

CERTHIOMORPHAE
see Nuthatches

CESIUM
Robinson, David B. Characteristics of Cesium. (Illus.). iv, 24p. 1978. pap. 4.00 (ISBN 0-9614845-0-0). Gemfield Assn.

CESIUM–ISOTOPES
Cesium-One Hundred Thirty-Seven from the Environment to Man: Metabolism & Dose. LC 77-77789. (NCRP Reports Ser.: No. 52). 1977. 7.00 (ISBN 0-913392-34-0). NCRP Pubns.

CESSNA (AIRPLANES)
All Those Cessna One Fifty's. 363p. 1980. pap. text ed. 12.95 (ISBN 0-939158-01-9). Flightshops.
Christy, Joe. The Complete Guide to Single-Engine Cessnas. 3rd ed. (Illus.). 1979. 10.95 (ISBN 0-8306-9800-0); pap. 7.95 (ISBN 0-8306-2268-3, 2268). TAB Bks.
National Flightshops. All Those Cessna 150's: Owners Manuals 1959-1977. 1980. pap. 12.95 (ISBN 0-939158-01-9, Pub. by National Flightshops). Aviation.

CESTODA
Arai, Hisao, ed. Biology of the Tapeworm Hymenolepis Diminuta. 1980. 66.00 (ISBN 0-12-058980-X). Acad Pr.
Arme, Christopher, ed. A Biology of the Eucestoda, Vol. 1. Pappas, Peter. 1984. 60.00 (ISBN 0-12-062101-0). Acad Pr.
Cooper, Arthur R. North American Pseudophyllidean Cestodes from Fishes. (Illus.). 1919. 19.00 (ISBN 0-384-09785-5). Johnson Repr.
Douthitt, Herman. Studies on the Cestode Family, Anoplocephalidae. (Illus.). 1915. pap. 8.00 (ISBN 0-384-12475-5). Johnson Repr.
Mayhew, Roy L. Studies on the Avian Species of the Cestode Family Hymenolepididae. (Illinois Biological Monographs: Vol. 10, No. 1). Repr. of 1925 ed. 12.00 (ISBN 0-384-36080-7). Johnson Repr.
Schmidt, Gerald D., ed. Handbook of Tapeworm Identification. 672p. 1985. 169.50 (ISBN 0-8493-3280-X). CRC Pr.
Smyth, J. D. The Physiology of Cestodes. (Illus.). 279p. 1969. 17.95x (ISBN 0-7167-0676-8). W H Freeman.
Upadhyay, H. P. A Monograph of Ceratocystis & Ceratocystiopsis. LC 80-6188. (Illus.). 290p. 1981. 30.00x (ISBN 0-8203-0539-1). U of Ga Pr.
Viru, Atko, ed. Hormones-Muscular Activity, Vol. I: Hormonal Ensemble in Exercise. 224p. 1985. 67.00 (ISBN 0-8493-5493-5). CRC Pr.
Wardle, Robert A., et al. Advances in the Zoology of Tapeworms, 1950-1970. LC 73-83728. (Illus.). 276p. 1974. 20.00x (ISBN 0-8166-0692-7). U of Minn Pr.

CETACEAE
see also Dolphins; Whales
Herman, L. M. Cetacean Behavior: Mechanisms & Functions. LC 80-11772. 463p. 1980. 56.50 (ISBN 0-471-37315-X). Wiley.
Leatherwood, Stephen & Reeves, Randall R. The Sierra Club Handbook of Whales & Dolphins. LC 83-388. (Sierra Club Paperback Library). (Illus.). 320p. 1983. 25.00 (ISBN 0-87156-341-X); pap. 12.95 (ISBN 0-87156-340-1). Sierra.
Mitchell, Edward. Porpoise, Dolphin & Small Whale Fisheries of the World: Status & Problems. (Illus.). 129p. 1975. pap. 12.00 (ISBN 2-88032-027-5, IUCN6, IUCN). Unipub.
Slijper, E. J. Die Cetaceen, Vergleichend-Anatomisch und Systematisch. (Illus.). 1973. Repr. of 1936 ed. lib. bdg. 55.80x (ISBN 90-6123-226-0). Lubrecht & Cramer.

CHAETOMIACEAE
Pickford, Grace. Contributions to a Study of South African Microchaetinae (Annelida Oligochaeta) (Connecticut Academy of Arts & Sciences Transaction Vol. 46, Pp. 13-76). (Illus., Orig.). 1975. pap. 10.50 (ISBN 0-208-01560-4, Archon). Shoe String.
Seth, H. K. A Monograph of the Genus Chaetomium. (Illus.). 1971. 35.00 (ISBN 3-7682-5437-2). Lubrecht & Cramer.

CHAETOPODA
see also Oligochaeta; Polychaeta
Ashworth, J. H. Catalogue of the Chaetopoda in the British Museum (Natural History) A. Polychaeta: Part I Arenicolidae. (Illus.). xii, 175p. 1912. 17.50x (ISBN 0-565-00102-7, Pub. by British Mus Nat Hist England). Sabbot-Natural Hist Bks.

CHAIN REACTION PILES
see Nuclear Reactors

CHAIN-TRACK VEHICLES
see Tracklaying Vehicles

CHAIRS
Armstrong, Richard. The Modern Chair: Its Origins & Evolution. LC 77-84973. (Illus.). 62p. 1977. pap. 7.00x (ISBN 0-934418-05-5). La Jolla Mus Contemp Art.
Denker, Bert & Denker, Ellen. The Rocking Chair Book. (Illus.). 1979. pap. 7.95 (ISBN 0-8317-7418-5, Mayflower Bks). Smith Pubs.
Dunbar, Michael. Make a Windsor Chair with Michael Dunbar. LC 83-50681. (Illus.). 176p. 1984. pap. 13.95 (ISBN 0-918804-21-3, Dist. by W W Norton). Taunton.
Hooton, Earnest A. Survey in Seating. Repr. of 1945 ed. lib. bdg. 15.00x (ISBN 0-8371-3952-X, HOSS). Greenwood.
Mason, J. W. & Co. Illustrated Catalog of Chairs & Furniture Manufactured by Joel W. Mason, 375 Pearl St., NYC. (Illus.). 116p. 1983. pap. 25.00 (ISBN 0-87556-495-X). Saifer.
Moser, Thos. Thos. Moser's Windsor Chairmaking. LC 82-50543. (Illus.). 192p. 1982. pap. 8.95 (ISBN 0-8069-5471-X). Sterling.
Perry, C. Seat Weaving. 1940. pap. 5.12 (ISBN 0-02-665670-1). Bennett IL.
Sparkes, Ivan. English Windsor Chairs. (Shire Album00946810x: No. 70). (Illus.). 32p. 1985. pap. 3.50 (ISBN 0-85263-562-1, Pub. by Shire Pubns England). Seven Hills Bks.
Workbench Magazine Staff. The Workbench Treasury of Chair Projects. LC 81-86464. (Illus.). 56p. 1982. pap. 4.95 (ISBN 0-86675-004-5, 45). Mod Handcraft.

CHALLENGER EXPEDITION, 1872-1876
Great Britain Challenger Office. Report on the Scientific Results of the Voyage of H. M. S. Challenger During the Years 1873-1876, 50 Vols. (Illus.). 1880-1895. Set. 5000.00 (ISBN 0-384-19750-7). Johnson Repr.
Moseley, Henry N. Notes by a Naturalist. new & rev. ed. LC 72-1710. Orig. Title: Notes by a Naturalist on the Challenger. (Illus.). Repr. of 1892 ed. 36.45 (ISBN 0-404-08159-2). AMS Pr.
Murray, John. Selections from the Report on the Scientific Results of the Voyage of H.M.S. Challenger During the Years 1872-76. Egerton, Frank N., 3rd, ed. LC 77-74242. (History of Ecology Ser.). (Illus.). 1978. Repr. of 1895 ed. lib. bdg. 19.00x (ISBN 0-405-10411-1). Ayer Co Pubs.

CHAMBERS, ROBERT, 1802-1871
Clyne, Norval. The Romantic Scottish Ballads & the Lady Wardlaw Heresy. LC 74-13040. 1974. Repr. of 1859 ed. lib. bdg. 15.00 (ISBN 0-88305-119-2). Norwood Edns.

CHAMBERS, SPACE
see Space Simulators

CHAMELEONS
Roberts, Mervin F. All about Chameleons & 'Anoles' (Illus.). 1977. 4.95 (ISBN 0-87666-772-8, PS-310). TFH Pubns.

CHAMPAGNE (WINE)
Simon, Andre L. All About Champagne. (All About Wines: Vol. 1). 7.50 (ISBN 0-87559-177-9). Shalom.

CHAMPIGNONS
see Mushrooms

CHANNELS (HYDRAULIC ENGINEERING)
see also Aqueducts; Canals; Harbors; Lakes; Reservoirs; Rivers
Chermisinoff, Nicholas P. Fluid Flow: Pumps, Pipes & Channels. LC 81-68034. (Illus.). 702p. 1981. 45.00 (ISBN 0-250-40432-X). Butterworth.
Chow Ven-Te. Open-Channel Hydraulics. (Civil Engineering Ser). 1959. 49.00 (ISBN 0-07-010776-9). McGraw.
French, R. H. Open-Channel Hydraulics. 704p. 1985. 49.95 (ISBN 0-07-022134-0). McGraw.
Henderson, Francis M. Open Channel Flow. 1966. write for info. (ISBN 0-02-353510-5). Macmillan.
Mahmood, K., et al, eds. Unsteady Flow in Open Channels, 3 vols. LC 75-9251. 1975. Set. 48.00 (ISBN 0-686-67936-9); Vol. 1. (ISBN 0-918334-09-8); Vol. 2. (ISBN 0-918334-10-1); Vol. 3. (ISBN 0-918334-11-X). WRP.
Schumm, S. A. & Watson, Harvey. Incised Channels. LC 83-50243. 220p. 1984. 20.00 (ISBN 0-918334-53-5). WRP.
Smith, K. V., ed. Channels & Channel Control Stuctures: Proceedings of the International Conference on Hydraulic Design in Water Resources Engineering - Channels & Control Structures, Univ. of Southampton, 1st, April 1984. (Illus.). 800p. 1985. 37.70 (ISBN 0-387-13192-2). Springer Verlag.
Stelczer, K. Bed-Load Transport: Theory & Practice. LC 80-54288. 1981. 22.00 (ISBN 0-918334-39-X). WRP.

CHAPARRAL COCK
see Road Runner (Bird)

CHARACEAE
Wood, R. D. Charophytes of North America. 1967. 2.25 (ISBN 0-9603898-0-6). R D Wood.
Wood, R. D. & Imahori, K. A Monograph & Iconograph of the Characeae, 2 vols. 1965. Set. 105.00 (ISBN 3-7682-0245-3). Lubrecht & Cramer.

CHARACINIDAE
Myers, George. Piranhas. 9.95 (ISBN 0-87666-771-X, M539). TFH Pubns.

CHARACTER RECOGNITION SYSTEMS
see Perceptrons

CHARCOAL
see also Carbon, Activated
Boutette, M. & Karch, G. E. Charcoal: Small Scale Production & Use. 60p. pap. 6.50 (ISBN 3-528-02009-1, 990400298, Pub. by Vieweg & Sohn Germany). Heyden.
Emrich, Walter. Handbook of Charcoal Making. 1985. lib. bdg. 39.50 (ISBN 0-318-04127-8, Pub. by Reidel Holland). Kluwer Academic.
ESCAP-FAO-UNEP Expert Group Meeting on Fuelwood & Charcoal: Proceedings. (Energy Resources & Development Ser.: No. 24). 120p. 1985. pap. 11.00 (UN82/2F10, UN). Unipub.
Gingery, David J. Charcoal Foundry. rev. ed. 80p. (Orig.). 1983. pap. 6.95 (ISBN 0-9604330-8-2). D J Gingery.
Proceedings of the ESCAP-FAO-UNEP Expert Group on Fuelwood & Charcoal. (Energy Resources Development Ser.: No. 24). 120p. 11.00 (ISBN 0-317-18752-X, E.82.II.F.10). UN.

CHARGED PARTICLE ACCELERATORS
see Particle Accelerators

CHARTS
see also Maps
Carroll, Phil. How to Chart Data. 2nd ed. LC 60-6963. pap. 67.50 (ISBN 0-317-10891-3, 2010381). Bks Demand UMI.
Durbin, Harold. Color Separation Scanner Comparison Charts: 1985 Edition. Date not set. write for info. (ISBN 0-936786-10-8). Durbin Assoc.
--Interactive Layout System Comparison Charts: 1985 Edition. Date not set. write for info. (ISBN 0-936786-09-4). Durbin Assoc.
--Offset Duplicator Press Comparison Charts: 1985 Edition. Date not set. pap. 25.00 (ISBN 0-936786-11-6). Durbin Assoc.
Graphs & Charts. (Basic Academic Ser.: Module 5). (Illus.). 110p. 1982. spiral bdg. 10.00x (ISBN 0-87683-229-X); instr's. manual 15.00 (ISBN 0-87683-240-0). G P Courseware.
Highsmith, Russell. How to Capture the Fine Points in Chart Reading. (Illus.). 171p. 1982. 69.85x (ISBN 0-86654-014-8). Inst Econ Finan.
Hostage, Jacqueline. Jackie's Kitchen Charts. LC 82-14680. (Illus.). 128p. (Orig.). 1982. pap. 5.95 plastic comb bdg (ISBN 0-932620-16-7). Betterway Pubns.
Lefferts, Robert. Elements of Graphics: How to Prepare Charts & Graphs for Effective Reports. (Illus.). 176p. (Orig.). 1982. pap. 4.76i (ISBN 0-06-463545-7, EH 545, EH). B&N NY.

--How to Prepare Charts & Graphs for Effective Reports. 1982. pap. 4.76 (ISBN 0-06-463545-7, EH-545). Har-Row.

Mulhearn, Henry J. Graphing, Charting Simplified. 105p. 1976. 6.00 (ISBN 0-87526-221-X). Gould.

Nordenskiold, Nils A. Periplus: An Essay on the Early History of Charts & Sailing Directions. Bather, Francis A., tr. from Swed. (Illus.). 1897. 189.00 (ISBN 0-8337-2572-6). B Franklin.

Wheat, James C. & Brun, Christian F. Maps & Charts Published in America Before Eighteen Hundred: A Bibliography, Vol. 3. rev. ed. (Illus.). 1979. 125.00 (ISBN 0-900470-89-5, Pub. by Holland Pr). W G Arader.

White, Jan V. Using Charts & Graphs: One Thousand Ideas for Getting Attention. 208p. 1984. pap. 24.95 (ISBN 0-8352-1894-5). Bowker.

CHARTS, NAUTICAL

see Nautical Charts

CHASSIS MOUNTED COACHES

see Campers and Coaches, Truck

CHEBYSHEV APPROXIMATION

Christensen, R. General Description of Entropy Minimax. (Entropy Minimax Sourcebook Ser.: Vol. I). 692p. 1981. text ed. 39.50 (ISBN 0-938876-06-6). Entropy Ltd.

--Multivariate Statistical Modeling. (Entropy Minimax Source Ser.: Vol. V). (Illus.). x, 724p. 1983. lib. bdg. 49.95 (ISBN 0-938876-14-7). Entropy Ltd.

Voronovskaja, E. V. Functional Method & Its Applications. LC 70-138816. (Translations of Mathematical Monographs: Vol. 28). 1970. 39.00 (ISBN 0-8218-1578-4, MMONO-28). Am Math.

CHEBYSHEV POLYNOMIALS

Rivlin, Theodore J. The Chebyshev Polynomials. LC 74-10876. (Pure & Applied Mathematics Ser). 186p. 1974. 39.95 (ISBN 0-471-72470-X, Pub. by Wiley-Interscience). Wiley.

CHEBYSHEV SYSTEMS

see also Approximation Theory

Salzer, Herbert E. & Levine, Norman. Tables for Converting Polynomial & Power Series into Chebyshev Series. LC 83-73685. Date not set. pap. 12.00 (ISBN 0-915061-01-5). Applied Sci Pubns.

Salzer, Herbert E., et al. Tables for Lagrangian Interpolation Using Chebyshev Points. LC 83-73684. Date not set. pap. 28.00 (ISBN 0-915061-00-7). Applied Sci Pubns.

Zielke, R. Discontinuous Cebysev Systems. Dold, A. & Eckmann, B., eds. (Lecture Notes in Mathematics: Vol. 707). 1979. pap. 13.00 (ISBN 0-387-09125-4). Springer-Verlag.

CHEESE

Carr, Sandy. The Simon & Schuster Pocket Guide to Cheese. (Illus.). 1981. 5.95 (ISBN 0-671-42475-0). S&S.

Carrol, Robert & Carrol, Ricki. Cheesemaking Made Easy: Sixty Delicious Varieties. LC 82-9300. (Illus.). 128p. 1982. pap. 6.95 (ISBN 0-88266-267-8). Garden Way Pub.

Courtine, Robert H. Dictionnaire des Fromages. (Fr.). 250p. 1972. pap. 6.95 (ISBN 0-686-56807-9, F-A16). French & Eur.

Ensrud, Barbara. The Pocket Guide to Cheese. 144p. 1981. pap. 4.95 (ISBN 0-399-50518-0, Perigee). Putnam Pub Group.

Kyle, Daryl. From Milk to Cheese: Make Your Own Country Kitchen Cheeses. (Illus.). 200p. Date not set. pap. 5.95 (ISBN 0-89496-000-8). Ross Bks.

Layton, T. A. The Cheese Handbook: A Guide to the World's Best Cheeses. rev. ed. 160p. 1973. pap. 3.50 (ISBN 0-486-22955-6). Dover.

Recommended International Standard for Cheeses & Government Acceptances. (Codex Alimentarius Commission Reports). 179p. (Orig.). 1974. pap. 4.50 (ISBN 92-5-101740-9, F626, FAO). Unipub.

Scott, R. Cheesemaking Practice. (Illus.). xix, 473p. 1981. 52.00x (ISBN 0-85334-927-4, Pub. by Elsevier Applied Sci England). Elsevier.

U. S. Department of Agriculture. Cheeses of the World. 1972. pap. 3.50 (ISBN 0-486-22831-2). Dover.

United States Department of Agriculture. Cheeses of the World. 12.00 (ISBN 0-8446-4524-9). Peter Smith.

Wilster, G. H. Practical Cheese Making. 1980. pap. text ed. 29.95x (ISBN 0-88246-127-3). Oreg St U Bkstrs.

CHEESE–BACTERIOLOGY

see also Dairy Bacteriology; Milk–Bacteriology

Davies, F. L. & Law, B. A., eds. Advances in Microbiology & Biochemistry of Cheese & Fermented Milk. 268p. 1984. 42.00 (ISBN 0-85334-287-3, Pub. by Elsevier Applied Sci England). Elsevier.

Hobson, Phyllis. Making Homemade Cheeses & Butter. LC 73-89125. (Country Skills Library). (Illus.). 48p. 1973. pap. 2.95 (ISBN 0-88266-019-5). Garden Way Pub.

CHEETAHS

Adamson, Joy. Spotted Sphinx. LC 77-85008. (Helen & Kurt Wolff Bk.). 313p. 1969. 9.50 (ISBN 0-15-184795-9). HarBraceJ.

Eaton, Randall L. The Cheetah: The Biology, Ecology, & Behavior of an Endangered Species. LC 81-18556. 192p. 1982. Repr. of 1974 ed. lib. bdg. 13.95 (ISBN 0-89874-451-2). Krieger.

Myers, Norman. The Cheetah (Acinonyx Jubatus) in Africa. (Illus.). 90p. 1975. pap. 12.00 (ISBN 2-88032-015-1, IUCN14, IUCN). Unipub.

CHEIROPTERA

see Bats

CHELATES

Ashmead, DeWayne. Chelated Mineral Nutrition. 186p. (Orig.). 1981. pap. 5.95 (ISBN 0-86664-002-9). Intl Inst Nat Health.

Ashmead, H. DeWayne, et al. Intestinal Absorbtion of Metal Ions & Chelates. (Illus.). 262p. 1985. 26.50x (ISBN 0-398-05047-3). C C Thomas.

Bell, Colin F. Principles & Applications of Metal Chelation. (Oxford Chemistry Ser.). (Illus.). 1977. 29.95x (ISBN 0-19-855485-0). Oxford U Pr.

Dwyer, F. P. & Mellor, D. P., eds. Chelating Agents & Metal Chelates. 1964. 76.00 (ISBN 0-12-225950-5). Acad Pr.

Martell, A. E., et al, eds. Development of Iron Chelators for Clinical Use. 312p. 1981. 75.50 (ISBN 0-444-00650-8, Biomedical Pr). Elsevier.

Zief, M., ed. Purification of Inorganic & Organic Materials: Techniques of Fractional Solidification. 1969. 75.00 (ISBN 0-8247-1823-2). Dekker.

CHELONETHIDA

Weygoldt, Peter. Biology of Pseudoscorpions. LC 78-82300. (Books in Biology Ser: No. 6). (Illus.). 1969. text ed. 11.00x (ISBN 0-674-07425-4). Harvard U Pr.

CHELONIA

see Turtles

CHEMICAL ABBREVIATIONS

see Chemistry–Abbreviations

CHEMICAL ADDITIVES IN FOOD

see Food Additives

CHEMICAL AFFINITY

see also Chemical Reaction, Rate Of; Valence (Theoretical Chemistry)

Benfey, O. Theodor. Classics in the Theory of Chemical Combination. LC 81-8300. 206p. 1981. Repr. of 1963 ed. 11.50 (ISBN 0-89874-368-0). Krieger.

Berthollet, Claude-Louis. Researches into the Laws of Chemical Affinity. 2nd ed. LC 65-23404. 1966. Repr. of 1809 ed. 27.50 (ISBN 0-306-70914-7). Da Capo.

Sundaram, P. V. & Eckstein, F., eds. Theory & Practice in Affinity Techniques. 1979. 79.50 (ISBN 0-12-677150-2). Acad Pr.

CHEMICAL ANALYSIS

see Chemistry, Analytic

CHEMICAL APPARATUS

see also Centrifuges; Chemistry–Manipulation; Glass Blowing and Working

Bockris, J. O'M., ed. Electrochemistry of Cleaner Environments. LC 72-179762. 296p. 1972. 39.50x (ISBN 0-306-30560-7, Plenum Pr). Plenum Pub.

Huber, J., ed. Instrumentation for High Performance Liquid Chromatography. (Journal of Chromatography Library: Vol. 13). 204p. 1978. 42.75 (ISBN 0-444-41648-X). Elsevier.

Ryan, T. H., ed. Electrochemical Detectors: Fundamental Aspects & Analytical Applications. 180p. 1984. 39.50x (ISBN 0-306-41727-8, Plenum Pr). Plenum Pub.

Shvartz, Galina L. & Kristal, M. M. Corrosion of Chemical Apparatus: Corrosion, Cracking & Methods of Protection Against It. LC 59-9233. pap. 64.00 (ISBN 0-317-10621-X, 2020646). Bks Demand UMI.

CHEMICAL BONDS

see also Molecular Orbitals

Augustine. Carbon-Carbon Bond Formation. (Techniques & Applications in Organic Synthesis Ser.: Vol. 6). 1979. 75.00 (ISBN 0-8247-6787-X). Dekker.

Boschke, F. L., ed. Bonding & Structure. (Topics in Current Chemistry: Vol. 63). (Illus.). 160p. 1976. 42.00 (ISBN 0-387-07605-0). Springer-Verlag.

Braterman, P. S., et al. Spectra & Chemical Interactions. LC 67-11280. (Structure & Bonding: Vol. 26). 1976. 36.00 (ISBN 0-387-07591-7). Springer-Verlag.

Carbon-Carbon Bond Formation Using Organometallic Compounds. LC 84-13078. (The Chemistry of Functional Groups Ser.: Vol. 3). 1985. 135.00 (ISBN 0-471-90557-7, Pub. by Wiley-Interscience). Wiley.

Chisholm, Malcolm, ed. Reactivity of Metal-Metal Bonds. LC 81-361. (ACS Symposium Ser.: No. 155). 1981. 41.95 (ISBN 0-8412-0624-4). Am Chemical.

Clark, Alfred. The Chemisorptive Bond: Basic Concepts. (Physical Chemistry: A Series of Monographs, Vol. 32). 1974. 57.50 (ISBN 0-12-175440-5). Acad Pr.

Clarke, M. J., et al, eds. Structure vs. Special Properties. (Structure & Bonding Ser.: Vol. 52). (Illus.). 204p. 1982. 50.00 (ISBN 0-387-11781-4). Springer-Verlag.

Companion, Audrey L. Chemical Bonding. 2nd ed. (Illus.). 1979. pap. text ed. 14.95 (ISBN 0-07-012379-9). McGraw.

Coppens, Philip & Hall, Michael B., eds. Electron Distributions & the Chemical Bond. LC 82-5390. 490p. 1982. 69.50x (ISBN 0-306-41000-1, Plenum Pr). Plenum Pub.

Daudel, Raymond. Quantum Theory of the Chemical Bond. LC 74-82700. Orig. Title: Theorie Quantique De la Liaison Chimique. 1974. lib. bdg. 26.00 (ISBN 90-277-0264-0, Pub. by Reidel Holland); pap. text ed. 14.00 (ISBN 90-277-0528-3, Pub. by Reidel Holland). Kluwer Academic.

DeKock, Roger L. & Gray, Harry B. Chemical Structure & Bonding. 1980. 36.95 (ISBN 0-8053-2310-4). Benjamin-Cummings.

Dimroth, K. Delocalized Phosphorus-Carbon Double Bonds: Phosphamethin-Cyanines Lambda to the Third Power - Phosphorins & Lambda to the Fifth Power - Phosphorins. LC 51-5497. (Topics in Current Chemistry: Vol. 38). (Illus.). 170p. 1973. pap. 30.70 (ISBN 0-387-06164-9). Springer-Verlag.

Dobias, B., et al. New Developments, Vol. 56. (Structure & Bonding). (Illus.). 160p. 1984. 34.00 (ISBN 0-387-13106-X). Springer-Verlag.

Douglas, Bodie & Hollingworth, Charles A. Introduction to Applications of Symmetry to Bonding & Spectra. 1985. 39.00 (ISBN 0-12-221340-8). Acad Pr.

Dunitz, J. D., et al, eds. Electrons in Oxygen & Sulphur-Containing Ligands. (Structure & Bonding: Vol. 28). (Illus.). 1976. 30.00 (ISBN 0-387-07753-7). Springer-Verlag.

--Inorganic Chemistry. (Structure & Bonding Ser.: Vol. 14). (Illus.). iii, 176p. 1973. pap. 38.00 (ISBN 0-387-06162-2). Springer-Verlag.

Epictis, N. B., et al. Unified Valence Bond Theory of Electronic Structure. (Lecture Notes in Chemistry: Vol. 29). 303p. 1982. pap. 23.40 (ISBN 0-387-11491-2). Springer-Verlag.

Gray, Harry B. Chemical Bonds: An Introduction to Atomic & Molecular Structure. LC 72-5014. 1973. pap. text ed. 21.95 (ISBN 0-8053-3402-5). Benjamin-Cummings.

Hameka, Hendrik F. Quantum Theory of the Chemical Bond. LC 74-14742. (Illus.). 1975. 23.95x (ISBN 0-02-845660-2). Hafner.

Holden, Alan. Bonds Between Atoms. (Illus.). 1971. pap. text ed. 4.95x (ISBN 0-19-501498-7). Oxford U Pr.

Jones, L. H. Inorganic Vibrational Spectroscopy, Vol. 1. LC 72-146803. pap. 58.00 (ISBN 0-8357-9083-5, 2055078). Bks Demand UMI.

Jorgensen, C. K., et al, eds. Chemical Bonding in Solids. (Structure & Bonding Ser.: Vol. 19). (Illus.). iv, 165p. 1974. text ed. 44.00 (ISBN 0-387-06908-9). Springer-Verlag.

Kettle, S. A. Symmetry & Structure. 1985. 34.95 (ISBN 0-471-90501-1). Wiley.

Kwart, H. & King, K. Delta-Orbital Involvement in the Organo-Chemistry of Silicon, Phosphorus & Sulfur. LC 77-1555. (Reactivity & Structure: Vol. 3). 1977. 56.00 (ISBN 0-387-07953-X). Springer-Verlag.

Levin, Alexander A. Solid State Quantum Chemistry: The Chemical Bond & Energy Bands in Tetrahedral Semiconductors. 1977. text ed. 43.95x (ISBN 0-07-037435-X). McGraw.

Margolis, Emil J. Bonding & Structure: A Review of Fundamental Chemistry. LC 68-12785. 175p. 1968. 18.50x (ISBN 0-306-50047-7, Plenum Pr). Plenum Pub.

Murrell, John N., et al. The Chemical Bond. LC 77-21728. 1978. 49.95 (ISBN 0-471-99577-0, Pub. by Wiley-Interscience); pap. 23.95 (ISBN 0-471-99578-9). Wiley.

New Concepts. (Structure & Bonding: Vol. 33). (Illus.). 1977. 49.00 (ISBN 0-387-08269-7). Springer-Verlag.

Pauling, Linus. The Nature of the Chemical Bond & the Structure of Molecules & Crystals: An Introduction to Modern Structural Chemistry. 3rd ed. (Baker Non-Resident Lectureship in Chemistry Ser.). (Illus.). 644p. 1960. 39.95x (ISBN 0-8014-0333-2). Cornell U Pr.

Phillips, James C. Covalent Bonding in Crystals, Molecules & Polymers. LC 74-104037. (Chicago Lectures in Physics Ser). 1970. pap. 8.00x (ISBN 0-226-66770-7). U of Chicago Pr.

Pimentel, George C. & Sprately, Richard D. Chemical Bonding Clarified Through Quantum Mechanics. LC 71-75914. 1969. 20.00x (ISBN 0-8162-6781-2). Holden-Day.

Radioassays & Non-Isotopic Ligand Assays Product Guide, Vol. 29, No. 5. 986p. 1983. 10.00 (ISBN 0-317-02266-0). Am Assn Clinical Chem.

Reid, K. F. Properties & Reactions of Bonds in Organic Molecules. LC 79-365421. pap. 142.50 (ISBN 0-317-09882-9, 2004551). Bks Demand Umi.

Rhodin, T. N. & Ertl, G., eds. Nature of the Surface Chemical Bond. 406p. 1979. 74.50 (ISBN 0-444-85053-8, North-Holland). Elsevier.

Ryschkewitsch, George E. Chemical Bonding & the Geometry of Molecules. LC 62-20784. (Selected Topics in Modern Chemistry Ser.). pap. 32.30 (ISBN 0-317-09188-3, 2005794). Bks Demand UMI.

Sirota, N. N., ed. Chemical Bonds in Semiconductors & Solids. LC 66-17188. 293p. 1968. 32.50x (ISBN 0-306-10779-1, Consultants). Plenum Pub.

--Chemical Bonds in Semiconductors & Thermodynamics. LC 66-17188. (Illus.). 293p. 1968. 37.50x (ISBN 0-306-10804-6, Consultants). Plenum Pub.

--Chemical Bonds in Solids, 4 vols. Incl. Vol. 1. General Problems & Electron Structure of Crystals. 163p (ISBN 0-306-17151-1); Vol. 2. Crystal Structure, Lattice Properties, & Chemical Bonds. 133p (ISBN 0-306-17152-X); Vol. 3. X-Ray & Thermodynamic Investigations. 200p (ISBN 0-306-17153-8); Vol. 4. Semiconductor Crystals, Glasses, & Liquids. 165p (ISBN 0-306-17154-6). LC 73-185456. 1972 (Consultants). 42.50 ea. (Consultants). Plenum Pub.

Spice, J. E. Chemical Binding & Structure. 1964. pap. 11.75 (ISBN 0-08-010567-X). Pergamon.

Steudel, Ralf. Chemistry of the Non-Metals: With an Introduction to Atomic Structure and Chemical Bonding. Nachod, E. C. & Zuckerman, J. J., trs. from Ger. (Illus.). 1977. 15.90x (ISBN 3-11-004882-5). De Gruyter.

Streitweiser, Andrew & Owens, Peter H. Orbital & Electron Density Diagrams: An Application of Computer Graphics. (Illus.). 150p. 1973. pap. text ed. write for info. (ISBN 0-02-418020-3). Macmillan.

Taylor, M. J. Metal to Metal Bonded States of the Main Group Elements. 1975. 44.00 (ISBN 0-12-684650-2). Acad Pr.

Vahrenkamp, H., et al. Novel Chemical Effects of Electronic Behavior. LC 67-11280. (Structure & Bonding: Vol. 32). 1977. 40.00 (ISBN 0-387-08014-7). Springer-Verlag.

Van Wazer, John R. & Absar, Ilyas. Electron Densities in Molecules & Molecular Orbitals. (Physical Chemistry Ser.). 1975. 40.00 (ISBN 0-12-714550-8). Acad Pr.

CHEMICAL BONDS–PROGRAMMED INSTRUCTION

Gray, Harry B. Electrons & Chemical Bonding. (Orig.). 1964. pap. 21.95 (ISBN 0-8053-3401-7). Benjamin-Cummings.

CHEMICAL COMPOSITION OF THE EARTH

see Geochemistry

CHEMICAL ELEMENTS

see also Actinide Elements; Atomic Weights; Periodic Law; Trace Elements; Valence (Theoretical Chemistry)

also names of elements

Bard & Lund. Encyclopedia of the Electrochemistry of the Elements. 328p. 1980. write for info. Dekker.

Bard, A. & Lund, Henning, eds. Encyclopedia of Electrochemicals of the Elements, Vol. 13. 1979. 119.50 (ISBN 0-8247-2513-1). Dekker.

Beck, Paul A., ed. Electronic Structure & Alloy Chemistry of the Transition Elements. LC 62-18701. pap. 65.30 (ISBN 0-317-08750-9, 2000679). Bks Demand UMI.

Bowen, H. J. Environmental Chemistry of the Elements. 1979. 50.00 (ISBN 0-12-120450-2). Acad Pr.

Brebbia, C. A. Progress in Bondary Element Methods. LC 81-6454. 325p. 1981. 58.95x (ISBN 0-470-27223-6). Halsted Pr.

Charlot, G. Colorimetric Determination of Elements. 449p. 1964. 64.00 (ISBN 0-444-40104-0). Elsevier.

Cherdyntsev, Viktor. Abundance of Chemical Elements. LC 61-11892. pap. 78.50 (ISBN 0-317-26166-5, 2024087). Bks Demand UMI.

Donohue, Jerry. The Structures of the Elements. LC 80-15363. 448p. 1982. Repr. of 1974 ed. lib. bdg. 29.50 (ISBN 0-89874-230-7). Krieger.

Encyclopedia of Electrochemistry of the Elements, Vol. 11. 119.50 (ISBN 0-8247-2511-5). Dekker.

Encyclopedia of Electrochemistry of the Elements, Vol. 14. 1980. 119.50 (ISBN 0-8247-2564-6). Dekker.

Fliszar, S. Charge Distributions & Chemical Effects. (Illus.). 225p. 1983. 42.80 (ISBN 0-387-90854-4). Springer-Verlag.

Fomenko, Vadim S. Handbook of Thermionic Properties: Electronic Work Functions & Richardson Constants of Elements & Compounds. LC 65-23385. 151p. 1966. 42.50x (ISBN 0-306-65117-3, IFI Plenum). Plenum Pub.

Friend, J. N. Man & the Chemical Elements. 354p. 1961. 19.50x (ISBN 0-85264-053-6, Pub. by Griffin England). State Mutual Bk.

Furman, N. Howell, ed. Standard Methods of Chemical Analysis: The Elements, Vol. 1. 6th ed. LC 74-23465. 1426p. 1975. Repr. of 1962 ed. 100.00 (ISBN 0-88275-254-5). Krieger.

Hamilton, E. I. The Chemical Elements & Man: Measurements, Perspectives, Applications. (Illus.). 512p. 1979. 44.75x (ISBN 0-398-03732-9). C C Thomas.

Hauschka, Rudolf. The Nature of Substance. Spock, Marjorie & Richards, Mary T., trs. from Ger. 225p. 1983. pap. 11.95 (ISBN 0-85440-424-4). Anthroposophic.

Holmes, Mike & Martin, L. H. Analysis & Design of Structural Connections: Reinforced Concrete & Steel. LC 82-15668. (Civil & Mechanical Engineering Ser.). 269p. 1983. 59.95x (ISBN 0-470-27365-8). Halsted Pr.

International Symposium on Superheavy Elements, March 9-11, 1978, Lubbock, Texas. Superheavy Elements: Proceedings. Lodhi, M. A., ed. 604p. 1979. 78.00 (ISBN 0-08-022946-8). Pergamon.

Key Elements: N, P, As, Sb, Bi, C. (Landolt-Boernstein Group Three: Vol. 7, Pt. C). 1979. 241.50 (ISBN 0-387-09039-8). Springer-Verlag.

Lavender, J. P., ed. Cultural & Experimental Applications of Krypton 81m. 1980. 75.00x (ISBN 0-686-69943-2, Pub. by Brit Inst Radiology England). State Mutual Bk.

Mazurs, Edward G. Graphic Representations of the Periodic System During One Hundred Years. new ed. LC 73-8051. (Illus.). 224p. 1974. 20.00 (ISBN 0-8173-3200-6). U of Ala Pr.

Norrie, Douglas & De Vries, Gerard. Finite Element Bibliography. LC 76-45615. 690p. 1976. 115.00x (ISBN 0-306-65167-X, IFI Plenum). Plenum Pub.

Petryanov, I. V. & Trifonov, D. N. Elementary Order: Mendeleev's Periodic System. 155p. 1985. pap. 3.95 (ISBN 0-8285-2870-5, Pub by Mir Pubs USSR). Imported Pubns.

Pies, W. & Weiss, A. Key Elements: N, P, As, Sb, Bi, C - 1: Key Element: N. LC 62-53136. (Landolt - Boernstein Group III: Vol. 7, Pt. C). (Illus.). 1978. 128.10 (ISBN 0-387-08674-9). Springer-Verlag.

Pizey, J. S. Synthetic Reagents, Vol. 5. LC 73-14417. (Synthetic Reagents Ser.). 261p. 1983. 79.95 (ISBN 0-470-27455-7). Halsted Pr.

Ruben, Samuel. Handbook of the Elements. 128p. 1985. pap. 9.95 (ISBN 0-87548-399-2). Open Court.

Samsonov, Gregory V. Handbook of the Physicochemical Properties of the Elements. LC 67-10536. 941p. 1968. 95.00x (ISBN 0-306-65126-2, IFI Plenum). Plenum Pub.

Schulz, Wallace W. & Benedict, Glen E. Neptunium-237 Production & Recovery. LC 72-600249. (AEC Critical Review Ser.). 94p. 1972. pap. 10.50 (ISBN 0-87079-001-3, TID-25955); microfiche 4.50 (ISBN 0-87079-465-5, TID-25955). DOE.

Sisler, Harry H. Electronic Structure, Properties, & the Periodic Law. 2nd ed. LC 72-9083. (Selected Topics in Modern Chemistry Ser.). pap. 32.00 (ISBN 0-317-08782-7, 2007241). Bks Demand UMI.

Stull, Daniel R. & Sinke, Gerard C., eds. Thermodynamic Properties of the Elements. LC 57-1340. (Advances in Chemistry Ser: No. 18). 1956. 24.95 (ISBN 0-8412-0019-X). Am Chemical.

Tayler, R. J. The Origin of the Chemical Elements. (Wykeham Science Ser.: No. 23). 176p. 1975. pap. cancelled (ISBN 0-85109-280-2). Taylor & Francis.

Tayler, R. J. & Everest, A. S. The Origin of the Chemical Elements. (Wykeham Science Ser.: No. 23). 176p. 1975. Repr. 9.95x (ISBN 0-8448-1150-5). Crane Russak Co.

Weeks, Mary E. Discovery of the Elements. 7th Rev. ed. LC 68-15217. (Illus.). pap. 160.00 (ISBN 0-317-09341-X, 2011897). Bks Demand UMI.

CHEMICAL EMBRYOLOGY

Jenne, Everett A., ed. Chemical Modeling in Aqueous Systems. LC 79-242. (ACS Symposium Ser.: No. 93). 1979. 69.95 (ISBN 0-8412-0479-9). Am Chemical.

Needham, Joseph. Biochemistry & Morphogenesis. 1942. 125.00 (ISBN 0-521-05797-3). Cambridge U Pr.

CHEMICAL ENGINEERING

see also Chemistry, Technical; Fluidization; Mechanical Engineering; Metallurgy; Mixing; Zone Melting

Abriola, L. M. Multiphase Migration of Organic Compounds in a Porous Medium: A Mathematical Model. (Lecture Notes in Engineering Ser.: Vol. 8). (Illus.). viii, 232p. 1984. pap. 15.00 (ISBN 0-387-13694-0). Springer-Verlag.

Agrawal, J. K. Practicals in Engineering Chemistry. 1981. 25.00x (ISBN 0-686-72962-5, Pub. by Oxford & IBH India). State Mutual Bk.

Akanazarova, S. L. & Kafarov, V. V. Experiment Optimization in Chemistry & Chemical Engineering. MAtskovsky, V. M. & Repyev, A. P., trs. from Rus. 312p. 1982. 9.95 (ISBN 0-8285-2305-3, Pub. by Mir Pubs USSR). Imported Pubns.

American Institute of Chemical Engineers National Meeting, Philadelphia June 8-12, 1980. Loss Prevention, Vol. 14. Chemical Engineering Progress, ed. 186p. 1981. Vol. 14. pap. 32.00 (ISBN 0-8169-0195-3, T-72); pap. 17.00 members (ISBN 0-317-03759-5). Am Inst Chem Eng.

American Institute Of Chemical Engineers. Twenty-Five Years of Chemical Engineering Progress. facs. ed. Kirkpatrick, S. D., ed. LC 68-55837. (Essay Index Reprint Ser). 1933. 20.00 (ISBN 0-8369-0149-5). Ayer Co Pubs.

Amundson, Neal R. Mathematical Methods in Chemical Engineering: Matrices & Their Application. 1966. ref. ed. 42.95 (ISBN 0-13-561084-2). P-H.

Anderson, Robert B. The Fischer-Tropsch Synthesis (Monograph) LC 83-15762. 1984. 55.00 (ISBN 0-12-058460-3). Acad Pr.

Aris, Rutherford & Varma, Arvind, eds. The Mathematical Understanding of Chemical Engineering Systems: Selected Papers of Neal R. Amundson. LC 79-40686. (Illus.). 1980. 155.00 (ISBN 0-08-023836-X). Pergamon.

Ayyangar, N. R., et al. A Course in Industrial Chemistry, Pt. 1. 204p. 1981. 30.00x (ISBN 0-86125-687-5, Pub. by Orient Longman India). State Mutual Bk.

Azbel, David. Chemical & Process Equipment Design: Vessel Design & Selection. LC 81-70863. 791p. 1982. 59.95 (ISBN 0-250-40478-8). Butterworth.

--Fundamentals of Heat Transfer for Process Engineering. LC 84-4213. (Illus.). 382p. 1984. 36.00 (ISBN 0-8155-0982-0). Noyes.

Baddour, Raymond F. & Timmins, Robert S., eds. Application of Plasmas to Chemical Processing. 1967. 32.50x (ISBN 0-262-02027-0). MIT Pr.

Baldeschwieler, John D., ed. Chemistry & Chemical Engineering in the People's Republic of China. LC 79-11217. 1979. pap. 12.95 (ISBN 0-8412-0502-7). Am Chemical.

Balzhiser, R. E., et al. Chemical Engineering Thermodynamics. (International Physical & Chemical Engineering Sciences Ser). (Illus.). 1972. ref. ed. 42.95 (ISBN 0-13-128603-X). P-H.

Belzer, Jack, ed. Encyclopedia of Computer Science & Technology, Vol. 11. 1978. 115.00 (ISBN 0-8247-2261-2). Dekker.

Benedict, Manson, et al. Nuclear Chemical Engineering. 2nd ed. (Illus.). 1008p. 1981. text ed. 49.00 (ISBN 0-07-004531-3). McGraw.

Biles, William E. & Swain, James J. Optimization & Industrial Experimentation. LC 79-9516. 368p. 1980. 56.95x (ISBN 0-471-04244-7, Pub. by Wiley-Interscience). Wiley.

Bloch. Compressors & Expanders: Selection & Application for the Process Industry. (Chemical Industries Ser.: Vol. 8). (Illus.). 328p. 1982. 49.50 (ISBN 0-8247-1854-2). Dekker.

Bridgwater, J., ed. Developments in Chemical Engineering: A Festschrift for P. V. Danckwerts. (Illus.). 190p. 1983. pap. 35.00 (ISBN 0-08-030251-3). Pergamon.

Bungay, Henry. Advanced Biochemical Engineering. 45.00 (ISBN 0-471-81279-X). Wiley.

Casper, Lawrence A. & Powell, Cedric J., eds. Industrial Applications of Surface Analysis. LC 82-16290. (ACS Symposium Ser.: No. 199). 438p. 1982. lib. bdg. 54.95x (ISBN 0-8412-0735-6). Am Chemical.

Chakrabarty, B. N. Industrial Chemistry. 1981. 40.00x (ISBN 0-686-72953-6, Pub. by Oxford & IBH India). State Mutual Bk.

Chalmers, L. & Bathe, P. Household & Industrial Chemical Specialties: Polishes, Disinfectants, Adhesives, Abrasives, Paints, Aerosols, Household Toiletries, Vol. 2. 1979. 32.50 (ISBN 0-8206-0250-7). Chem Pub.

Chandrasekaran, S. K., ed. Controlled Release Systems. LC 81-8019. (AICHE Symposium Ser.: Vol. 77). 85p. 1981. pap. 22.00 (ISBN 0-8169-0202-X, S-206); pap. 12.00 members (ISBN 0-686-47543-7). Am Inst Chem Eng.

Chaney & Putnam, eds. Electronic Properties Research Literature Retrieval Guide 1972-1976, 4 vols. LC 79-16082. 1374p. 1979. Set. 375.00x (ISBN 0-306-68010-6, IFI Plenum). Plenum Pub.

Chang, Huan-Yang & Over, Ira Earl. Selected Numerical Methods & Computer Programs for Chemical Engineers. 235p. (Orig.). 1980. pap. text ed. 11.95 (ISBN 0-88408-131-1). Sterling Swift.

Chemeca 83: Chemical Engineering Today Coping with Uncertainty. 812p. (Orig.). 1984. pap. text ed. 50.00x (ISBN 0-317-05744-8, Pub. by Inst. Engineering Australia). Brookfield Pub Co.

Chemical Engineering, Chemical Industry & Engineering Society of China & the American Institute of Chemical Engineers Joint Meeting, September 19-22, Beijing, China, 1982: Proceedings, 2 Vols. set. 926p. 1982. pap. 105.00 (ISBN 0-317-03767-6, P-34); pap. 65.00 members (ISBN 0-317-03768-4). Am Inst Chem Eng.

Chemical Engineering Magazine. Calculator Programs for Chemical Engineers, Vol 2. 300p. 1984. 37.50 (ISBN 0-07-010849-8). McGraw.

--Industrial Waste Water & Solid Waste Engineering. LC 80-12608. 376p. 1980. pap. 37.50 (ISBN 0-07-010694-0). McGraw.

--Physical Properties. 1977. 54.50 (ISBN 0-07-010715-7). McGraw.

--Process Heat Exchange. (Chemical Engineering Book Ser.). (Illus.). 624p. 1980. 47.50 (ISBN 0-07-010742-4). McGraw.

--Process Technology & Flowsheets. LC 79-12117. (Chemical Engineering Bks). 384p. 1980. 35.00 (ISBN 0-07-010741-6). McGraw.

Chemical Engineering Research in the UK. 60p. 1981. 15.00x (ISBN 0-85295-050-0, Pub. by Inst Chem Eng England). State Mutual Bk.

Clarke, Loyal & Davidson, R. Manual for Process Engineering Calculations. 2nd ed. (Chemical Engineering Ser). 39.50 (ISBN 0-07-011249-5). McGraw.

Clausen, Chris A., III & Mattson, Guy C. Principles of Industrial Chemistry. LC 78-9450. 412p. 1978. 45.00 (ISBN 0-471-02774-X, Pub. by Wiley-Interscience). Wiley.

The Commercial Development of Chemical Engineering Projects: Proceedings, No. 55. 214p. 1981. 75.00x (ISBN 0-85295-112-4, Pub. by Inst Chem Eng England). State Mutual Bk.

Coulson, J. M. Chemical Engineering: An Introduction to Design, Vol. 6. (Illus.). 720p. 1983. 75.00 (ISBN 0-08-022969-7); pap. 29.50 (ISBN 0-08-022970-0). Pergamon.

Coulson, J. M. & Richardson, J. F. Chemical Engineering, 6 vols. Incl. Vol. 1. text ed. 27.50, 3rd ed. 1978 (ISBN 0-08-020614-X); pap. text ed. 15.00 (ISBN 0-08-021015-5); pap. text ed. 13.00, 2nd ed. 1964 (ISBN 0-08-009017-6); Vol. 2. text ed. 25.00 (ISBN 0-08-022919-0); pap. text ed. 18.50, 1968 ed. (ISBN 0-08-013185-9); Vol. 3. 3rd ed. text ed. 17.50 (ISBN 0-08-016438-2); Vol. 4. Problems & Solutions (SI Units) 3rd ed. Backhurst, J. R. & Harker, J. H. text ed. 20.00 (ISBN 0-08-020926-2); pap. 10.50 (ISBN 0-08-020918-1). pap. write for info. Pergamon.

Coulson, J. M., et al. Chemical Engineering, Vol. 5: Solutions to the Problems in Volume Two. 3rd ed. LC 78-40923. (Chemical Engineering Technical Ser.). (Illus.). 1979. 40.00 (ISBN 0-08-022951-4); pap. 16.75 (ISBN 0-08-022952-2). Pergamon.

Coulson, J. R. & Peacock, D. G., eds. Chemical Engineering, Vol. 3. 2nd ed. (Chemical Engineering Ser.: Vol. 3). (Illus.). 1979. text ed. 83.75 (ISBN 0-08-023818-1); pap. text ed. 24.00 (ISBN 0-08-023819-X). Pergamon.

Cryogenics Committee of the BCC. Vacuum Insulated Cryogenic Pipe. 20p. 1981. 11.00x (ISBN 0-85295-066-7, Pub. by Inst Chem Eng England). State Mutual Bk.

Danckwerts, P. V. Insights into Chemical Engineering: Selected Papers of P. V. Danckwerts. LC 80-42316. (Illus.). 320p. 1981. 57.00 (ISBN 0-08-026250-3). Pergamon.

Daubert, T. E. Chemical Engineering Thermodynamics. (Chemical Engineering Ser.). 496p. 1985. 40.00 (ISBN 0-07-015413-9). McGraw.

Design Developments: Proceedings, No. 45, Birmingham, September 1976. 194p. 1981. 80.00x (ISBN 0-85295-104-3, Pub. by Inst Chem Eng England). State Mutual Bk.

Doraiswamy, L. K. & Mashelkar, R. A. Frontiers in Chemical Reaction Engineering. Vol. 1, 697p. 43.50 (ISBN 0-470-20038-3); Vol. 2, 463p. 43.50 (ISBN 0-470-20039-1); Set, 1160p. 87.00 (ISBN 0-470-20041-3). Halsted Pr.

Drew, Thomas B. & Hoopes, John W. Advances in Chemical Engineering, Vol. 10. (Serial Publication Ser.). 1978. 85.00 (ISBN 0-12-008510-0). Acad Pr.

Drew, Thomas B. & Hoopes, John W., Jr., eds. Advances in Chemical Engineering. Incl. Vol. 1. 1956. 85.00 (ISBN 0-12-008501-1); Vol. 2. 1958. 85.00 (ISBN 0-12-008502-X); Vol. 3. Drew, Thomas B., et al, eds. 1962. 85.00 (ISBN 0-12-008503-8); Vol. 4. 1964. 85.00 (ISBN 0-12-008504-6); Vol. 5. 1964. 85.00 (ISBN 0-12-008505-4); Vol. 6. 1966. 85.00 (ISBN 0-12-008506-2); Vol. 7. 1968. 85.00 (ISBN 0-12-008507-0); Vol. 8. 1970. 85.00 (ISBN 0-12-008508-9); Vol. 9. 1974. 85.00 (ISBN 0-12-008509-7). Acad Pr.

Drew, Thomas B., et al, eds. Advances in Chemical Engineering, Vol. 11. LC 56-6600. (Serial Publication Ser.). 1981. 85.00 (ISBN 0-12-008511-9). Acad Pr.

Ekerdt, John G., ed. Chemical Engineering Faculties, Nineteen Eighty-Four, Nineteen Eighty-Five, Vol. 10. 254p. 1984. 40.00 (ISBN 0-317-03749-8); pap. 20.00 members (ISBN 0-8169-0321-2). Am Inst Chem Eng.

Eurochem, 1980. Opportunities & Constraints: Proceedings. 436p. 1981. 90.00x (ISBN 0-85295-123-X, Pub. by Inst Chem Eng England). State Mutual Bk.

European Federation of Chemical Engineering. Particle Technology: Proceedings of the European Federation of Chemical Engineering, European Symposium, Amsterdam, Holland, June 3-5, 1980, Vols. A & B. Schonert, K., et al, eds. (E FCE Publication Ser.: No. 7). 1232p. 1980. text ed. 85.00x (ISBN 3-921567-27-0, Pub. by Dechema Germany). Scholium Intl.

Finlayson, Bruce A. Nonlinear Analysis in Chemical Engineering. (M-H Chemical Engineering Ser.). (Illus.). 384p. 1980. text ed. 52.00 (ISBN 0-07-020915-4). McGraw.

Franks, Roger G. Modeling & Simulation in Chemical Engineering. LC 72-39717. 411p. 1972. 54.95x (ISBN 0-471-27535-2, Pub. by Wiley-Interscience). Wiley.

Friedrichs, H. Melting & Dissolution. Hinds, G. & Minuth, K. P., trs. (Illus.). 179p. 1984. pap. 25.00 (ISBN 3-514-00319-X, Pub. by Verlag Stahlusen W Germany). Heyden.

Furter, William F., ed. A Century of Chemical Engineering. LC 81-23444. 471p. 1982. text ed. 59.50 (ISBN 0-306-40895-3, Plenum Pr). Plenum Pub.

--History of Chemical Engineering: Based on a Symposium Cosponsered by the ACS Divisions of History & Industrial & Engineering Chemistry at the ACS/CSJ Chemical Congress, Honolulu, Hawaii, April 2-6, 1979. LC 80-17432. (Advances in Chemistry Ser.: No. 190). (Illus.). 435p. 1980. 41.95 (ISBN 0-8412-0512-4). Am Chemical.

Gas Chromatography Institute, 3rd Annual Buffalo, N. Y. April 4-6, 1961. Progress in Industrial Gas Chromatography: Proceedings, Vol. 1. LC 61-15520. pap. 59.80 (ISBN 0-317-10634-1, 2020700). Bks Demand UMI.

Gmehling, J., et al. Vapor-Liquid Equilibrium Data Collection: Aldehydes, Ketones, Ethers, Vol. 1, Parts 3 & 4. Behrens, Dieter & Eckermann, Reiner, eds. LC 79-670289. (Dechema Chemistry Ser.). (Illus.). 1979. lib. bdg. 115.00x (ISBN 3-921-56714-9, Pub by Dechema Germany). Scholium Intl.

Grassman, Peter. Physical Principles of Chemical Engineering. 928p. 1971. text ed. 125.00 (ISBN 0-08-012817-3). Pergamon.

Hall. The Language of Chemical Engineering in English. (English for Careers Ser.). 1978. pap. text ed. 4.25 (ISBN 0-88345-348-7, 18515). Regents Pub.

Hazards: Vol. 11, Proceedings. (Symposium Ser.: No. 58). 304p. 1981. 80.00x (ISBN 0-85295-120-5, Pub. by Inst Chem Eng England). State Mutual Bk.

Heaton, C. A., ed. An Introduction to Industrial Chemistry. 384p. 1984. 24.00 (ISBN 0-249-44165-9, Pub. by Blackie & Son UK). Heyden.

Hegde, M. V., et al. A Course in Industrial Chemistry, Pt. 2. 264p. 1981. 35.00x (ISBN 0-86131-096-9, Pub. by Orient Longman India). State Mutual Bk.

Herman, Richard G., ed. Catalytic Conversions of Synthetic Gas & Alcohols to Chemicals. 488p. 1984. 69.50x (ISBN 0-306-41614-X, Plenum Pr). Plenum Pub.

High Temperature Chemical Reaction Engineering. 332p. 1981. 70.00x (ISBN 0-85295-001-2, Pub. by Inst Chem Eng England). State Mutual Bk.

High Temperature Chemical Reaction Engineering: Proceedings, No. 43, Harrogate, June 1975. 400p. 1981. 100.00x (ISBN 0-85295-017-9, Pub. by Inst Chem Eng England). State Mutual Bk.

Hill, Brenda W. Chemindustry Experiments. LC 79-10694. (Illus.). 1979. 8.95 (ISBN 0-89168-023-3); instr's manual 8.95 (ISBN 0-89168-024-1). L Erlbaum Assocs.

Himmelblau, David M. Basic Principles & Calculations in Chemical Engineering. 4th ed. (Illus.). 656p. 1982. text ed. 42.95 (ISBN 0-13-066498-7). P-H.

Hine, Fumio. Electrode Processes & Electrochemical Engineering. 428p. 1985. 55.00x (ISBN 0-306-41656-5, Plenum Pr). Plenum Pub.

Holland, Charles D. & Anthony, Raymond G. Fundamentals of Chemical Reaction Engineering. (International Series in the Physical & Chemical Engineering Sciences). (Illus.). 1979. text ed. 39.95 (ISBN 0-13-335596-9). P-H.

Homburger, F., ed. Safety Evaluation & Regulation of Chemicals, No. 3. (Illus.). 240p. 1985. 63.00 (ISBN 3-8055-4017-5). S Karger.

Wei, James & Georgakis, Christos, eds. Chemical Reaction Engineering: Boston. LC 82-11629. (ACS Symposium Ser.: No. 196). 614p. 1982. lib. bdg. 49.95x (ISBN 0-8412-0732-1). Am Chemical.

Wei, James, et al. The Structure of the Chemical Processing Industries: Function & Economics. (Chemical Engineering Ser.). (Illus.). 1978. text ed. 45.00 (ISBN 0-07-068985-7). McGraw.

Wei, James, et al, eds. Advances in Chemical Engineering, Vol. 12. (Serial Publication Ser.). 1983. 75.00 (ISBN 0-12-008512-7). Acad Pr.

Wittcoff, Harold & Reuben, Bryan G. Industrial Organic Chemicals in Perspective, Part 2: Technology, Formulation & Use. LC 79-19581. 502p. 1980. 69.95 (ISBN 0-471-05780-0, Pub. by Wiley-Interscience). Wiley.

Wittcoff, Harold A. & Reuben, Bryan G. Industrial Organic Chemicals in Perspective. (2 Pts.). 1983. Set. 84.50 (ISBN 0-471-10125-7). Wiley.

Yates, J. G. Fundamentals of Fluidized Bed Chemical Processes. 224p. 1983. text ed. 49.95. Butterworth.

CHEMICAL ENGINEERING–APPARATUS AND SUPPLIES

see also Heat Exchangers; Separators (Machines)

Brownell, Lloyd E. & Young, Edwin H. Process Equipment Design: Vessel Design. LC 59-5882. 408p. 1959. 74.95 (ISBN 0-471-11319-0, Pub by Wiley-Interscience). Wiley.

Klinov, I. Ya. Corrosion & Protection of Materials Used in Industrial Equipment. LC 61-15171. 228p. 1962. 37.50x (ISBN 0-306-10521-7, Consultants). Plenum Pub.

Lawrence, James F., ed. Liquid Chromatography in Environmental Analysis. LC 83-10711. (Contemporary Instrumentation & Analysis Ser.). 392p. 1984. 55.00 (ISBN 0-89603-045-8). Humana.

CHEMICAL ENGINEERING–COSTS

Allen, D. H. A Guide to the Economic Evaluation of Projects. 1981. 30.00x (ISBN 0-85295-131-0, Pub. by Inst Chem Eng England). State Mutual Bk.

Chemical Engineering Magazine. Modern Cost Engineering: Methods & Data, Vol. II. 2nd ed. 320p. 1984. 47.00 (ISBN 0-07-010851-X). McGraw.

CHEMICAL ENGINEERING–DATA PROCESSING

ALCHE Educational Services Dept. Annual Staff. Applications Software Survey for Personal Computers 1984. 191p. 1984. pap. 40.00 (ISBN 0-8169-0316-6); pap. 20.00 members (ISBN 0-317-17534-3). Am Inst Chem Eng.

Britz, B. Digital Simulation in Electrochemistry. (Lecture Notes in Chemistry Ser.: Vol. 23). 120p. 1981. pap. 16.50 (ISBN 0-387-10564-6). Springer-Verlag.

Chemical Engineering Magazine. Calculator Programs for Chemical Engineers, Vol. 1. (Chemical Engineering Ser.). 304p. 1981. 34.95 (ISBN 0-07-010793-9). McGraw.

--Calculator Programs for Chemical Engineers, Vol 2. 300p. 1984. 37.50 (ISBN 0-07-010849-8). McGraw.

--Microcomputer Programs for Chemical Engineers. Deutsch, David J., ed. LC 83-6386. 320p. 1984. 39.95 (ISBN 0-07-010852-8). McGraw.

Chemsoft Inc. Staff. CHEMCALC (TM) 6: Heat Exchanger Design (Shell & Tube) (CHEMCALC (TM) Software for Chemical Engineers Ser.). 80p. 1985. incl. floppy disk 995.00x (ISBN 0-87201-090-2). Gulf Pub.

--CHEMCALC (TM) 7: Physical Properties Databank. (CHEMCALC (TM) Software for Chemical Engineers Ser.). 40p. 1985. incl. floppy disk 495.00x (ISBN 0-87201-093-7). Gulf Pub.

Chen, Ning H. Process Reactor Design. 512p. 1983. scp 41.73 (ISBN 0-205-07903-2, 327903). Allyn.

Computers & Chemical Engineering: Case Histories in Design & Control. 71p. 1981. 60.00x (ISBN 0-686-75384-4, Pub. by Inst Chem Eng England). State Mutual Bk.

Davis, Mark E. Numerical Methods & Modeling for Chemical Engineers. LC 83-21590. 258p. 1984. 28.95 (ISBN 0-471-88761-7, Pub. by Wiley); solutions (Nonsaleable) 10.00 (ISBN 0-471-88252-6). Wiley.

European Symposium of the Working Party on Routine Computer Programs in Chemical Engineering, 5th, 1972. Decision, Design & the Computer: Proceedings, No. 35. 270p. 1981. 72.00x (ISBN 0-85295-076-4, Pub. by Inst Chem Eng England). State Mutual Bk.

Fang, C. S. CHEMCALC (TM) 2: Gas & Liquid Flow Calculations. LC 85-836. (CHEMCALC (TM) Software for Chemical Engineers Ser.). 1985. 3-ring binder with Floppy Disk 265.00x (ISBN 0-87201-086-4). Gulf Pub.

--CHEMCALC (TM) 3: Convective Heat Transfer. LC 85-837. (CHEMCALC (TM) Software for Chemical Engineers Ser.). 1985. 3-ring binder with Floppy Disk 265.00x (ISBN 0-87201-087-2). Gulf Pub.

Gordon, R., ed. Transport. (Computer Programs for Chemical Engineering Education Ser.). 1972. pap. 15.95 (ISBN 0-88408-031-5). Sterling Swift.

Henley, E., ed. Stoichiometry. (Computer Programs for Chemical Engineering Education Ser.). 1972. pap. 13.95 (ISBN 0-88408-028-5). Sterling Swift.

Institution of Chemical Engineers, Rugby UK, ed. Process Systems Engineering 1985: Computers in Chemical Engineering. Proceedings of the Symposium Held in Cambridge, UK, 31 March - 4 April 1985. (Institution of Chemical Engineers Symposium Ser.: Vol. 92). 708p. 1985. 63.50 (ISBN 0-08-031417-1, Pub by PPL). Pergamon.

Jelinek, R., ed. Design. (Computer Programs for Chemical Engineering Education Ser.). 1972. pap. 15.95 (ISBN 0-88408-033-1). Sterling Swift.

Keith, L. H. & Walters, D. B. Compendium of Safety Data Sheets for Research & Industrial Chemicals, 3 Vols. 1985. Set. 270.00 (ISBN 0-89573-313-7). VCH Pubs.

Luyben, W. L. Process Modeling, Simulation, & Control for Chemical Engineers. (Civil Engineering Ser.). (Illus.). 500p. 1972. text ed. 44.00 (ISBN 0-07-039157-2). McGraw.

OECD Staff. Confidentiality of Data & Chemical Control. 94p. 1982. pap. 10.00x (ISBN 92-64-12365-2). OECD.

Otar, Cemil. CHEMCALC (TM) 5: Heat Exchanger Network Optimization. LC 85-16856. (CHEMCALC (TM) Software for Chemical Engineers Ser.). 80p. 1985. incl. floppy disk 495.00x (ISBN 0-87201-089-9). Gulf Pub.

Reilly, M., ed. Kinetics. (Computer Programs for Chemical Engineering Education Ser.). 1972. pap. 15.95 (ISBN 0-88408-029-3). Sterling Swift.

Reklaitis, G. V. & Surola, J. J., eds. Data Base Implementation & Application. (AIChE Symposium Ser.: Vol. 79, No. 231). 79p. 1983. pap. 30.00 (ISBN 0-8169-0267-4). Am Inst Chem Eng.

Rippin, D. W. & Hughes, R. R., eds. Computer Applications in Chemical Engineering: Proceedings of the 12th Symposium of the European Federation of Chemical Engineering, Montreaux, April 1979. 639p. 1981. pap. 145.00 (ISBN 0-08-025022-X). Pergamon.

Sorensen, J. M. & Arlt, W. Liquid-Liquid Equilibrium Data Collection: Ternary & Quaternary Systems, Vol. V, Pt. 3. Behrens, D. & Eckermann, R., eds. (Dechema Chemistry Data Ser.). 605p. 1981. lib. bdg. 112.50x (ISBN 0-686-73456-4, Pub. by Dechema Germany). Scholium Intl.

--Liquid-Liquid Equilibrium Data Collection: Ternary Systems, Vol. V, Pt. 2. Behrens, D. & Eckermann, R., eds. (Dechema Chemistry Data Ser.). 1981. lib. bdg. 117.50x (ISBN 3-921-56718-1, Pub. by Dechema Germany). Scholium Intl.

Squires, Robert G. & Reklaitis, G. V., eds. Computer Applications to Chemical Engineering Process Design & Simulation. LC 79-27719. (ACS Symposium Ser.: No. 124). 1980. 49.95 (ISBN 0-8412-0549-3). Am Chemical.

Stagewise Computations. (Computer Programs for Chemical Engineering Education Ser.). 1972. pap. 15.95 (ISBN 0-88408-034-X). Sterling Swift.

Weber, James H. CHEMCALC (TM) 8: Physical Properties Calculations. (CHEMCALC (TM) Software for Chemical Engineers Ser.). 60p. 1986. incl floppy disk 195.00x (ISBN 0-87201-112-7). Gulf Pub.

Westerberg, A., ed. Control. (Computer Programs for Chemical Engineering Education Ser.). 1972. pap. 13.95 (ISBN 0-88408-030-7). Sterling Swift.

CHEMICAL ENGINEERING–DICTIONARIES

Carpovich, Eugene A. Russian-English Chemical Dictionary. 2nd ed. LC 61-11700. (Rus. & Eng.). 1963. 25.00 (ISBN 0-911484-03-5). Tech Dict.

Clason, W. Elsevier's Dictionary of Chemical Engineering, 2 Vols. (Eng., Fr., Span., Ital., Dutch, & Ger.). 1969. Set. 170.25 (ISBN 0-444-40736-7); Vol. 1. 98.00 (ISBN 0-444-40714-6); Vol. 2. 98.00 (ISBN 0-444-40715-4). Elsevier.

DeVries, Louis & Kolb, Helga. Dictionary of Chemistry & Chemical Engineering, 2 vols. 2nd ed. incl. Vol. 1. German-English. 1978. 150.00x; Vol. 2. English-German. LC 77-138815. 150.00x (ISBN 0-89573-025-1). (Ger. & Eng.). 1979. VCH Pubs.

Dictionary Industrial Chemistry: English-Chinese. (Eng. & Chinese.). 81p. 1977. pap. 1.95 (ISBN 0-686-92273-5, M-9585). French & Eur.

Dictionary of Industrial Chemistry. (Eng. & Chinese.). 24p. 1973. pap. 1.95 (ISBN 0-686-92145-3, M-9570). French & Eur.

Dictionary of Industrial Chemistry. (Chinese & Eng.). 164p. 1979. pap. 3.95 (ISBN 0-686-92529-7, M-9576). French & Eur.

Dictionary of Industrial Organic Chemistry. (Eng. & Chinese.). 56p. 1973. pap. 1.95 (ISBN 0-686-92279-4, M-9584). French & Eur.

Dictionnaire Technique Russe-Francais de la Preparation. (Fr. & Rus.). 129p. 1973. pap. 19.95 (ISBN 0-686-56771-4, M-6160). French & Eur.

English-Chinese Dictionary of Chemistry & Chemical Engineering. (Eng. & Chinese.). 1458p. 1978. leatherette 49.95 (ISBN 0-686-92360-X, M-9248). French & Eur.

Ernst, R. Dictionary of Chemical Terms, 2 vols. Vol. 1, Ger.-Eng. 33.70x (ISBN 3-8709-7011-1); Vol. 2, Eng-Ger. 41.20x (ISBN 3-8709-7012-X). Adlers Foreign Bks.

Vries, Louis de. Dictionary of Chemistry & Chemical Engineering, Vol. 1. (Eng. & Ger.). 1970. pap. 125.00 (ISBN 3-527-25303-3, M-7126). French & Eur.

--Dictionary of Chemistry & Chemical Engineering, Vol. 2. (Eng. & Ger.). 1972. pap. 125.00 (ISBN 3-527-25358-0, M-7125). French & Eur.

CHEMICAL ENGINEERING–EXAMINATIONS, QUESTIONS, ETC.

McComas, Stuart T., ed. Thermodynamics Exam File. LC 84-24688. (Exam File Ser.). 250p. (Orig.). 1985. pap. 9.95 (ISBN 0-910554-49-8). Engineering.

Rudman, Jack. Assistant Chemical Engineer. (Career Examination Ser.: C-31). (Cloth bdg. avail. on request). pap. 12.00 (ISBN 0-8373-0031-2). Natl Learning.

--Chemical Engineer. (Career Examination Ser.: C-134). (Cloth bdg. avail. on request). pap. 10.00 (ISBN 0-8373-0134-3). Natl Learning.

--Junior Chemical Engineer. (Career Examination Ser.: C-393). (Cloth bdg. avail. on research). pap. 12.00 (ISBN 0-8373-0393-1). Natl Learning.

CHEMICAL ENGINEERING–GRAPHIC METHODS

Austin, D. G. Chemical Engineering Drawing Symbols. 96p. 1979. 27.95x (ISBN 0-470-26601-5). Halsted Pr.

CHEMICAL ENGINEERING–PROBLEMS, EXERCISES, ETC.

Austin & Jeffreys. The Manufacture of Methyl-Ethyl-Ketone from 2 Butanol: A Worked Solution to a Problem in Chemical Engineering. 221p. 1981. 54.00x (ISBN 0-85295-115-9, Pub. by Inst Chem Eng England). State Mutual Bk.

Bird, R. Byron, et al. Transport Phenomena. LC 60-11717. 780p. 1960. 49.95x (ISBN 0-471-07392-X). Wiley.

Crockett, W. E. Chemical Engineering Review for PE Exam. 225p. 1985. 29.50 (ISBN 0-471-87874-X). Wiley.

Loebel, Arnold B. Chemical Problem Solving by Dimensional Analysis. 2nd ed. LC 77-78565. (Illus.). 1978. pap. text ed. 16.95 (ISBN 0-395-25516-3). HM.

Pavlov & Romankov. Examples & Problems to the Course of Unit Operations of Chemical Engineering. 616p. 1979. 10.80 (ISBN 0-8285-1533-6, Pub. by Mir Pubs USSR). Imported Pubns.

Ramkrishna, Doraiswami & Amundson, Neal R. Linear Operator Methods in Chemical Engineering with Applications to Transport & Reaction Systems Linear Operator Methods. (Illus.). 512p. 1985. text ed. 51.95 (ISBN 0-13-537341-7). P-H.

Sears, J. T., et al, eds. Problem Solving. LC 83-15515. (AIChE Symposium: Vol. 79). 63p. 1983. pap. 24.00 (ISBN 0-8169-0255-0, S-228); pap. 12.00 members (ISBN 0-317-03745-5). Am Inst Chem Eng.

CHEMICAL ENGINEERING–STATISTICAL METHODS

AICHE Design Institute for Physical Property Data Staff, ed. Predicting Chemical Process Design Data Manual: Data Prediction Manual. 1983. 150.00 (ISBN 0-8169-0233-X); 125.00 (ISBN 0-317-03747-1). Am Inst Chem Eng.

CHEMICAL ENGINEERING–TABLES, CALCULATIONS, ETC.

Jackson, A. T. & Lamb, J. Calculations in Food & Chemical Engineering: Theory, Worked Examples, & Problems. (Illus.). 221p. (Orig.). 1982. pap. text ed. 18.95x (ISBN 0-333-29423-8). Scholium Intl.

Kuong, Javier F. Applied Nomography, Vol. 2. LC 65-18920. 116p. 1968. 16.95x (ISBN 0-87201-586-6). Gulf Pub.

Schmidt, Joseph W. & Taylor, Robert E. Simulation & Analysis of Industrial Systems. LC 76-91792. (Irwin Series in Quantitative Analysis for Business). pap. 160.00 (ISBN 0-317-10878-6, 2050150). Bks Demand UMI.

Weber. Chemical Engineering Design Calculations. (Chemical Industries Ser.). 232p. 1984. 37.50 (ISBN 0-8247-7138-9). Dekker.

CHEMICAL ENGINEERING AS A PROFESSION

Alexander, Guy. Silica & Me: The Career of an Industrial Chemist. LC 73-75723. (Chemistry in Action Ser.). 111p. 1973. pap. 7.95 (ISBN 0-8412-0162-5). Am Chemical.

Bott, T. Reg. Chemical Engineering-Beating Pollution. 129p. 1982. 30.00x (ISBN 0-85225-747-3, Pub. by Careers Con England). State Mutual Bk.

Hagerty, D. Joseph, et al. Opportunities in Chemical Engineering. (VGM Career Bks.). (Illus.). 160p. 1983. 7.95 (ISBN 0-317-03437-5, 6588-4, Passport Bks.); pap. 5.95 (ISBN 0-317-03438-3). Natl Textbk.

CHEMICAL ENGINEERING LABORATORIES

Pinkava, J. Handbook of Laboratory Units Operations for Chemists & Chemical Engineers. 470p. 1971. 113.50 (ISBN 0-677-60600-1). Gordon.

CHEMICAL ENGINEERS

see also Chemists

Haynes, Williams. Chemical Pioneers. LC 74-99701. (Essay Index Reprint Ser.). 1939. 27.50 (ISBN 0-8369-1442-2). Ayer Co Pubs.

Miles, Wyndham D., ed. American Chemists & Chemical Engineers. LC 76-192. 1976. 29.95 (ISBN 0-8412-0278-8). Am Chemical.

Professional Directory of Chemists & Chemical Engineers. 25.00 (ISBN 0-686-39416-X). Amer Inst Chem.

CHEMICAL EQUATIONS

Chao, K. C. & Robinson, Robert, eds. Equations of State in Engineering & Research. LC 79-23696. (Advances in Chemistry Ser.: No. 182). 1979. 59.95 (ISBN 0-8412-0500-0). Am Chemical.

CHEMICAL EQUILIBRIUM

see also Linear Free Energy Relationship; Phase Rule and Equilibrium

Bard, Allen J. Chemical Equilibrium. (Illus.). 1968. pap. text ed. 13.50 scp (ISBN 0-06-040451-5, HarpC). Har-Row.

Baron, Robert E., et al. Chemical Equilibria in Carbon-Hydrogen-Oxygen Systems. LC 75-44374. (Energy Laboratory Ser.). 120p. 1976. 27.50x (ISBN 0-262-02121-8). MIT Pr.

Crynes, B. L. & Fogler, H. S., eds. Rate of Reaction, Sensitivity & Chemical Equilibrium. LC 80-25535. (AIChEMI Modular Instruction B. Ser.). 56p. 1981. pap. 30.00 (ISBN 0-8169-0180-5); pap. 15.00 members (ISBN 0-317-03844-3). Am Inst Chem Eng.

Denbigh, Kenneth G. The Principles of Chemical Equilibrium. 4th ed. (Illus.). 506p. 1981. 67.50 (ISBN 0-521-23682-7); pap. 21.95 (ISBN 0-521-28150-4). Cambridge U Pr.

Fischer, Robert B. Chemical Equilibrium. 1970. pap. text ed. 18.95 (ISBN 0-7216-3705-1, CBS C). SCP.

Garrels, Robert M. & Christ, Charles L. Solutions, Minerals & Equilibria. LC 65-12674. 1982. Repr. of 1965 ed. text ed. 25.00x (ISBN 0-87735-333-6). Freeman Cooper.

Gmehling, J. & Onken, U. Vapor-Liquid Equilibrium Data Collection Tables & Diagrams of Data for Binary & Multicomponent Mixtures up to Moderate Pressures; Constants of Correlation Equations for Computer Use: Part 2a: Organic Hydroxy Compounds: Alcohols, No. 1. LC 79-670289. (Dechema Chemistry Data Ser.). 1978. text ed. 110.00x (ISBN 3-921567-09-2). Scholium Intl.

--Vapor-Liquid Equilibrium Data Collection Tables & Diagrams of Data for Binary & Multicomponent Mixtures up to Moderate Organic Hydroxy Compounds: Alcohols & Phenols, Vol. I, Pt. 2b. (Dechema Chemistry Data Ser.). 1979. text ed. 103.50x (ISBN 3-921567-01-7). Scholium Intl.

Guenther, William B. Chemical Equilibrium: A Practical Introduction for the Physical & Life Sciences. LC 75-28028. (Illus.). 248p. 1975. 29.50 (ISBN 0-306-30850-9, Plenum Pr). Plenum Pub.

Henley, Ernest J. & Seader, J. D. Equilibrium-Stage Separation Operations in Chemical Engineering. LC 80-13293. 742p. 1981. text ed. 54.95 (ISBN 0-471-37108-4, Pub. by Wiley-Interscience). Wiley.

Hine, Jack. Structural Effects on Equilibria in Organic Chemistry. LC 80-11714. 362p. 1981. Repr. of 1975 ed. lib. bdg. 23.95 (ISBN 0-89874-144-0). Krieger.

Inczedy, J. Analytical Applications of Complex Equilibria. LC 75-25687. (Series in Analytical Chemistry). 415p. 1976. 104.95x (ISBN 0-470-42713-2). Halsted Pr.

International Union of Pure & Applied Chemistry. Equilibrium Constants of Liquid-Liquid Distribution Reactions, Pts. 1, 2 & 3. Marcus, Y., ed. Incl. Pt. 1. Organophosphorus Extractants. 184p. 39.00 (ISBN 0-08-020828-2); Pt. 2. Alkylammonium Salt Extractants. 96p. 24.00 (ISBN 0-08-020829-0). 1974. write for info. Pergamon.

--Stability Constants of Metal Complexes: Critical Survey of Stability Constants of EDTA Complexes, Vol. 14. Anderegg, G., ed. 1977. text ed. 14.25 (ISBN 0-08-022009-6). Pergamon.

Kragten, J. Atlas of Metal-Ligand Equilibria in Aqueous Solution. LC 77-12168. 781p. 1978. 174.95x (ISBN 0-470-99309-X). Halsted Pr.

Kuzanskaya, A. Calculations of Chemical Equilbria. 326p. 1978. 9.45 (ISBN 0-8285-0641-8, Pub. by Mir Pubs USSR). Imported Pubns.

Marcus, Y., et al, eds. Equilibrium Constants of Liquid-Liquid Distribution Reactions, Vol. 15, Pt. 3: Compound Forming Extractants, Solvating Solvents & Inert Solvents. 1977. pap. text ed. 14.50 (ISBN 0-08-022032-0). Pergamon.

Meites, L. An Introduction to Chemical Equilibrium & Kinetics. (Pergamon Ser. on Analytical Chemistry: Vol. 2). 1981. 83.00 (ISBN 0-08-023802-5); pap. 19.95 (ISBN 0-08-023803-3). Pergamon.

Morris, Kelso B. Fundamental Chemical Equilibria: Nonionic-Ionic. (Illus.). 120p. 1971. 32.50x (ISBN 0-677-03090-8). Gordon.

Poland, D. Cooperative Equilibria in Physical Biochemistry. (Monographs on Physical Biochemistry). (Illus.). 1978. text ed. 55.00x (ISBN 0-19-854622-X). Oxford U Pr.

Prausnitz, J. M., et al. Computer Calculations for Multicomponent Vapor-Liquid & Liquid-Liquid Equilibria. (P-H International Series in Physical & Chemical Engineering Sciences). (Illus.). 400p. 1980. text ed. 44.00 (ISBN 0-13-164962-0). P-H.

Ramette, Richard W. Chemical Equilibrium & Analysis. (Chemistry Ser). (Illus.). 672p. 1981. text ed. 33.95 (ISBN 0-201-06107-4); solutions manual 1.50 (ISBN 0-201-06109-0). Addison-Wesley.

Scatchard, George. Equilibrium in Solutions & Surface & Colloid Chemistry. Scheinberg, I. Herbert, ed. (Commonwealth Fund Ser). (Illus.). 384p. 1976. 30.00x (ISBN 0-674-26025-2). Harvard U Pr.

Smith, Buford D. Design of Equilibrium Stage Processes. (Chemical Engineering Ser.). 1963. text ed. 53.50 (ISBN 0-07-058637-3). McGraw.

Smith, William R. & Missen, Ronald W. Chemical Reaction Equilibrium Analysis: Theory & Algorithms. LC 82-6968. 364p. 1982. 46.95x (ISBN 0-471-09347-5, Pub. by Wiley-Interscience). Wiley.

Sorenson, J. M. & Arlt, W. Liquid-Liquid Equilibrium Data Collection: Binary Systems, Vol. V, Pt. 1. Behrens, Dieter & Eckermann, Reiner, eds. (Dechema Chemistry Data Ser.). (Illus.). 622p. 1980. text ed. 108.00x (ISBN 3-921-56717-3, Pub by Dechema Germany). Scholium Intl.

Stary, J., et al, eds. Critical Evaluation of Equilibrium Constants Involving Hydroxyquinoline & Its Metal Chelates: Critical Evaluation of Equilibrium Constants in Solutions: Pt. A: Stability Constants of Metal Complexes. (Chemical Data Ser.: Vol. 24). (Illus.). 1979. pap. 19.50 (ISBN 0-08-023929-3). Pergamon.

Steinhardt, J. & Reynolds, J. A. Multiple Equilibria in Proteins. 1970. 75.00 (ISBN 0-12-665450-6). Acad Pr.

CHEMICAL EVOLUTION

Biology Colloquium, 29th, Oregon State University 1968. Biochemical Coevolution: Proceedings. Chambers, Kenton L., ed. LC 52-19235. (Illus.). 128p. 1970. 9.95x (ISBN 0-87071-168-7). Oreg St U Pr.

Buvet, R. & Ponnamperuma, C., eds. Chemical Evolution & the Origin of Life. LC 75-146189. (Molecular Evolution Ser.: Vol. 1). (Illus.). 571p. 1971. 34.00 (ISBN 0-444-10093-8, North-Holland). Elsevier.

Dose, K., et al, eds. The Origin of Life & Evolutionary Biochemistry. LC 74-10703. 484p. 1974. 59.50x (ISBN 0-306-30811-8, Plenum Pr). Plenum Pub.

Ferguson, Andrew. Biochemical Systematics & Evolution. LC 79-20298. 194p. 1980. 64.95x (ISBN 0-470-26856-5). Halsted Pr.

Fourth International Conference on the Origin of Life, 1973, Invited Papers & Contributed Papers, et al. Cosmochemical Evolution & the Origins of Life, 2 vols. Oro, J. & Miller, S. L., eds. LC 74-77967. vii, 755p. 1974. Vol. 1. lib. bdg. 59.00 (ISBN 90-277-0519-4, Pub. by Reidel Holland); Vol. 2. lib. bdg. 36.00 (ISBN 9-0277-0518-6). Kluwer Academic.

Fox, J. L., et al, eds. Protein Structure & Evolution. 1976. 85.00 (ISBN 0-8247-6386-6). Dekker.

Fox, Sidney W. & Dose, Klaus. Molecular Evolution & the Origins of Life. 2nd expanded ed. LC 77-21434. (Biology-a Series of Textbooks: Vol. 2). 1977. 49.75 (ISBN 0-8247-6619-9). Dekker.

Gutfreund, H. Biochemical Evolution. 320p. 1981. text ed. 80.00 (ISBN 0-521-23549-9); pap. text ed. 27.95 (ISBN 0-521-28025-7). Cambridge U Pr.

Harborne, J. B., ed. Biochemical Aspects of Plant & Animal Coevolution. (Phytochemical Society Symposia Ser.). 1978. 77.00 (ISBN 0-12-324672-5). Acad Pr.

Holland, Heinrich D. The Chemical Evolution of the Atmosphere & Oceans. LC 83-43077. (Princeton Series in Geochemistry). (Illus.). 656p. 1984. 75.00x (ISBN 0-691-08348-7); pap. 24.50x (ISBN 0-691-02381-6). Princeton U Pr.

Kimura, Motoo. The Neutral Theory of Molecular Evolution. 384p. 1985. pap. 19.95 (31793-2). Cambridge U Pr.

Mani, G. S., ed. Evolutionary Dynamics of Genetic Diversity: Proceedings of a Symposium Held in Manchester, England, March 29-30, 1983. (Lecture Notes in Biomathematics: Vol. 53). vii, 312p. 1984. pap. 19.00 (ISBN 0-387-12903-0). Springer-Verlag.

Price, Charles C., ed. Synthesis of Life. (Benchmark Papers in Organic Chemistry: Vol. 1). 391p. 1974. 52.50 (ISBN 0-87933-131-3). Van Nos Reinhold.

Terzaghi, Eric, et al. Molecular Evolution. 450p. 1985. text ed. write for info. (ISBN 0-86720-021-9). Jones & Bartlett.

CHEMICAL FORMULAE

see Chemistry–Notation

CHEMICAL GENETICS

see also Molecular Biology

Clark, Peggy, et al. Isozymes: Biochemical & Genetic Studies. LC 73-10223. 242p. 1973. text ed. 27.50x (ISBN 0-8422-7126-0). Irvington.

Fishbein, Lawrence, et al. Chemical Mutagens: Environmental Effects on Biological Systems. LC 71-117078. (Environmental Science Ser). 1970. 75.00 (ISBN 0-12-257150-9). Acad Pr.

Gerrick, David J. Pharmacogenetics. (Illus.). 1978. 20.00 (ISBN 0-916750-43-4). Dayton Labs.

Loveless, Anthony. Genetic & Allied Effects of Alkylating Agents. LC 66-24944. (Illus.). 1966. 36.00x (ISBN 0-271-00047-3). Pa St U Pr.

New Biotechnology Comes to Market: A Booming Industry. 1985. 1750.00 (ISBN 0-89336-436-3, C-032R). BCC.

Weiner, J. S., ed. Physiological Variation & Its Genetic Basis. (Symposia of the Society for the Study of Human Biology Ser.: Vol. 17). 180p. 1977. cancelled (ISBN 0-85066-108-0). Taylor & Francis.

Yunis, Jorge, ed. Biochemical Methods in Red Cell Genetics. 1969. 76.00 (ISBN 0-12-775140-8). Acad Pr.

CHEMICAL GEOLOGY

see Geochemistry; Mineralogical Chemistry; Mineralogy, Determinative; Rocks–Analysis

CHEMICAL INDUSTRIES

Here are entered works on industries based largely on chemical processes. Material dealing with the manufacture of chemicals as such is entered under Chemicals–Manufacture and Industry.

see also Chemical Plants; Oil Industries; Paint Industry and Trade;

also names of specific industries, e.g. Soap and Soap Trade, Paper Making and Trade

Badaracco, Joseph A. Loading the Dice: A Five-Country Study of Vinyl Chloride Regulation. 208p. 1985. 19.95 (ISBN 0-317-19560-3). Harvard Busn.

Bader, Morton E. Practical Quality Management in the Chemical Process Industry. (Industrial Engineering Ser.: Vol. 7). (Illus.). 160p. 1983. 27.50 (ISBN 0-8247-1903-4). Dekker.

Baines, A. Research in the Chemical Industry: Environment Objective Strategy. (Illus.). 298p. 1971. 31.50 (ISBN 0-444-20035-5, Pub. by Elsevier Applied Sci England). Elsevier.

Baines, A., et al. Research in the Chemical Industry: The Environment, Objectives & Strategy. (Illus.). 1969. 33.60x (Pub. by Applied Science). Burgess-Intl Ideas.

Benn Publications Ltd. Chemical Industry Directory & Who's Who 1986. (Benn Directories). 1986. 98.50 (ISBN 0-86382-018-2). Nichols Pub.

Betts, G. G. & Plenard, F. J. Future Changes in the Chemical Industry. 34p. 1981. 32.00x (ISBN 0-85295-145-0, Pub. by IChemE). State Mutual Bk.

Bisio, Attilio & Kabel, Robert L. Scaleup in the Chemical Process Industries: Conversion from Laboratory Scale Tests to Successful Commercial Size Design. 704p. 1985. 75.00 (ISBN 0-471-05747-9). Wiley.

Cahiers de l Institut de Science Economique Appliquee; Propagation du Progres Technique: Industrie Chimique et Aeronautique. (Economies et Societes Serie AI: No. 1). 1962. 19.00 (ISBN 0-317-16521-6). Kraus Repr.

Chalmers, L. & Bathe, P. Household & Industrial Chemical Specialties: Soap, Detergents & Laundry Products, House Pest Control, Vol. 1. 1978. 25.50 (ISBN 0-8206-0222-1). Chem Pub.

Chemical Industry. (UNIDO Monographs on Industrialization of Developing Countries: Problems & Prospects: Vol. 8). pap. 4.00 (ISBN 0-686-94967-6, UN69/2B/39V8, UN). Unipub.

Chemistry in the Economy. LC 73-86535. 600p. 1973. pap. 9.95 (ISBN 0-8412-0321-0). Am Chemical.

Conservation of Energy in the Chemical Industry. 162p. 1981. pap. 14.00 (ISBN 0-686-79533-4, UN80/2E19, UN). Unipub.

Curry, Susan & Rich, Susan, eds. Kline Guide to the Chemical Industry. 4th ed. (Illus.). 590p. 1980. pap. 147.00 (ISBN 0-917148-13-4). Kline.

Davis, Lee N. The Corporate Alchemists: Profit Takers & Problem Makers in the Chemical Industry. LC 83-25014. 320p. 1984. 15.95 (ISBN 0-688-02187-5). Morrow.

A Directory of Ninety-Five Organic Chemical Plants in Ohio. Sperber, Sebastian, ed. LC 84-80590. 1984. pap. text ed. 15.00 (ISBN 0-918780-27-6). INFORM.

European Federation of Chemical Engineering, 2nd Intl. Conference on Phase Equilibria & Fluid Properties in the Chemical Industry, Berlin, 1980. Phase Equilibria & Fluid Properties in the Chemical Industry: Proceedings, Pts. 1 & 2. (EFCE Publication Ser.: No. 11). 1012p. 1980. text ed. 92.50x (ISBN 3-921567-35-1, Pub. by Dechema Germany). Scholium Intl.

Evans, Lee S. Chemical & Process Plant: A Guide to the Selection of Engineering Materials. 2nd ed. LC 80-20355. 190p. 1980. 44.95x (ISBN 0-470-27064-0). Halsted Pr.

Fawcett, Howard H., ed. Safety & Accident Prevention in Chemical Operations. 2nd ed. Wood, William S. LC 82-2623. 910p. 1982. 91.00 (ISBN 0-471-02435-X, Pub. by Wiley-Interscience). Wiley.

Gill, Colin, et al. Industrial Relations in the Chemical Industry. 276p. 1978. text ed. 41.95x (ISBN 0-566-00215-9). Gower Pub Co.

Grant, Colin D. Energy Consevation in the Chemical & Process Industries. 1979. 32.50x (ISBN 0-7114-5525-2). Intl Ideas.

Happel, J. & Jordan, D. Chemical Process Economics. 2nd rev. & expanded ed. (Chemical Processing & Engineering Ser: Vol. 1). 512p. 1975. 34.50 (ISBN 0-8247-6155-3). Dekker.

Haynes, William. American Chemical Industry: A History. LC 82-48307. (The World Economy Ser.). 3666p. 1982. lib. bdg. 440.00 (ISBN 0-8240-5362-1). Garland Pub.

Haynes, Williams. Southern Horizons. facsimile ed. LC 78-152174. (Essay Index Reprint Ser). Repr. of 1946 ed. 22.00 (ISBN 0-8369-2366-9). Ayer Co Pubs.

Hochheiser, Sheldon. Rohm & Haas: History of a Chemical Company. (Illus.). 300p. 1985. text ed. 19.95 (ISBN 0-8122-7940-9). U of Pa Pr.

Homburger, F., ed. Safety Evaluation & Regulation of Chemicals, No. 3. (Illus.). 240p. 1985. 63.00 (ISBN 3-8055-4017-5). S Karger.

Howells, E. R., ed. Technology of Chemicals & Materials for Electronics. (Chemical Industry Ser.). 363p. 1984. 57.00 (ISBN 0-470-20118-5). Halsted Pr.

Ingle, George W., ed. TSCA's Impact on Society & Chemical Industry. LC 83-2733. (Symposium Se.: No. 213). 244p. 1983. lib. bdg. 34.95 (ISBN 0-8412-0766-6). Am Chemical.

Louden, Louise. Recovery of Chemicals from Spent Pulping Liquors. LC 78-71464. (Bibliographic Ser.: No. 285). 1978. pap. 45.00 (ISBN 0-87010-043-2). Inst Paper Chem.

Miller, et al. Product Risk Reduction in the Chemical Industry. 1985. pap. 125.00 (ISBN 0-88057-294-9). Exec Ent Inc.

Miller, Richard K., et al. Noise Control Solutions for the Chemical & Petroleum Industries. 45.00 (ISBN 0-89671-010-6). Fairmont Pr.

Mining Chemicals Market. 217p. 1985. 1650.00 (ISBN 0-86621-319-8, A1402). Frost & Sullivan.

O'Connor, Charles J. & Lirtzman, Sidney I., eds. Handbook of Chemical Industry Labeling. LC 83-22108. (Illus.). 487p. 1984. 64.00 (ISBN 0-8155-0965-0, Noyes Pubns). Noyes.

OECD & Chemicals Control. 196p. (Orig.). 1982. pap. 9.00x (ISBN 0-686-37002-3). OECD.

Okochi, Akio & Uchida, Hoshimi, eds. The International Conferences on Business History: Development & Diffusion of Technology, Electrical & Chemical Industries, No. 6. 236p. 1980. 29.50x (ISBN 0-86008-270-9, Pub. by U of Tokyo Japan). Columbia U Pr.

O'Reilly, James T. & Gaynor, Kevin A. Federal Regulation of the Chemical Industry. LC 80-11488. (Regulatory Manual Ser.). 920p. 1980. 90.00 (ISBN 0-07-047728-0, Shepards-McGraw). McGraw.

Peck, Theodore P., ed. Chemical Industries Information Sources. LC 76-6891. (Management Information Guide Ser.: No. 29). 1979. 60.00x (ISBN 0-8103-0829-0). Gale.

Personnel Safety in Chemical & Allied Industries. LC 78-58303. 198p. 1979. pap. 24.25 (ISBN 0-87912-125-4, 129.96). Natl Safety Coun.

Rueben, B. G. & Burstall, M. L. The Chemical Economy: A Guide to the Technology & Economics of the Chemistry Industry. LC 73-85210. pap. 138.00 (ISBN 0-317-10562-0, 2019604). Bks Demand UMI.

Sharp, D. H. & West, T. F. The Chemical Industry. 600p. 1982. 103.00 (ISBN 0-470-27317-8). Halsted Pr.

The Specific Contribution of the Chemical Industries to the Vocational Training & Advanced Training of Manpower in Developing Countries: Report 2. Chemical Industries Committee, Ninth Session, Geneva September 21-30, 1982. iv, 1982p. 1982. 8.55 (ISBN 92-2-103055-5). Intl Labour Office.

Taylor, Graham D. & Sudnik, Patricia E. Du Pont & the International Chemical Industry. (The Evolution of American Business: Industries, Institutions & Entrepreneurs Ser.). 1984. lib. bdg. 18.95 (ISBN 0-8057-9805-6, Twayne). G K Hall.

Water & Wastewater Treatment Chemicals (U. S.) 1985. write for info. (ISBN 0-86621-420-8, A1495). Frost & Sullivan.

Wei, James, et al. The Structure of the Chemical Processing Industries: Function & Economics. (Chemical Engineering Ser.). (Illus.). 1978. text ed. 45.00 (ISBN 0-07-068985-7). McGraw.

Weissermel, K. & Arpe, H-J. Industrial Organic Chemistry: Important Raw Materials & Intermediates. 404p. 1978. 43.60x (ISBN 0-89573-005-7). VCH Pubs.

Wilkinson, Norman B. Lammot DuPont & the American Explosives Industry, 1850-1884. 1983. write for info. U Pr of Va.

CHEMICAL INDUSTRIES–EUROPE

Chemical Directory of Northern Europe: Denmark, Finland, Iceland, Norway, Sweden 1977-79 Ed. 4th ed. 320p. 1977. 60.00x (ISBN 0-8002-0292-9). Intl Pubns Serv.

IPC Business Press, ed. Chemfacts Belgium. 1984. 150.00x (ISBN 0-617-00258-4, Pub. by IPC Busn England). State Mutual Bk.

--Chemfacts Federal Republic of Germany. 1984. 150.00x (ISBN 0-617-00317-3, Pub. by IPC Busn England). State Mutual Bk.

--Chemfacts France. 1984. 150.00x (ISBN 0-617-00260-6, Pub. by IPC Business Press). State Mutual Bk.

--Chemfacts Italy. 150.00x (ISBN 0-617-00300-9, Pub. by IPC Busn England). State Mutual Bk.

--Chemfacts Netherlands. 1984. 150.00x (ISBN 0-617-00259-2, Pub. by IPC Busn England). State Mutual Bk.

--Chemfacts Spain. 1984. 150.00x (ISBN 0-617-00261-4, Pub. by IPC Busn England). State Mutual Bk.

--European Chemical Buyers' Guide. 1984. 195.00x (ISBN 0-617-00255-X, Pub. by IPC Busn England). State Mutual Bk.

Smith, John G. The Origin & Early Development of the Heavy Chemical Industry in France. (Illus.). 1979. 98.00x (ISBN 0-19-858136-X). Oxford U Pr.

CHEMICAL INDUSTRIES–EUROPE (EASTERN)

Rajana, Cecil. The Chemical & Petro-Chemical Industries of Russia & Eastern Europe, 1960-1980. 1975. 62.50x (ISBN 0-85621-040-4, Pub. by Scottish Academic Pr Scotland). Columbia U Pr.

CHEMICAL INDUSTRIES–GERMANY

Hufbauer, Karl. The Formation of the Chemical Community (1720-1795) LC 81-2988. 288p. 1982. 45.00x (ISBN 0-520-04318-9); pap. 14.95x (ISBN 0-520-04415-0, CAMPUS 299). U of Cal Pr.

Wunder, Dietrich, intro. by. Directory of the West German Chemical Industry: (Firmenhandbuch Chemische Industrie, 2 vols. 10th ed. 512p. 1979. 115.00x (ISBN 3-430-12758-0). Intl Pubns Serv.

CHEMICAL INDUSTRIES–GREAT BRITAIN

British Chemical (Industrial) Companies. 1985. 125.00x (ISBN 0-317-07193-9, Pub. by Jordan & Sons UK). State Mutual Bk.

Institution of Chemical Engineers, Annual Research Meeting, 7th, 1980. Collected Papers. 82p. 1981. 30.00x (ISBN 0-686-75390-9, Pub. by Inst Chem Eng England). State Mutual Bk.

IPC Business Press, ed. Chemfacts United Kingdom. 1984. 150.00x (ISBN 0-617-00318-1, Pub. by IPC Busn England). State Mutual Bk.

Jordans, ed. The British Chemical Industry. 100p. 1985. 275.00 (ISBN 0-85938-150-1, Pub. by Jordans). State Mutual Bk.

Market Research & Corporate Planning in the Chemical Manufacturing & Plant Supply Industries: Proceedings. 1981. 11.00x (ISBN 0-686-75391-7, Pub. by Inst Chem Eng England). State Mutual Bk.

Warren, Kenneth. Chemical Foundations: The Alkali Industry in Britain to Nineteen Twenty-Six. (Oxford Research Studies in Geography). (Illus.). 1980. text ed. 54.00x (ISBN 0-19-823231-4). Oxford U Pr.

CHEMICAL INDUSTRIES–JAPAN

Japan Chemical Directory. 1984. 210.00x (ISBN 0-8002-3620-3). Intl Pubns Serv.

Japan Chemical Directory, 1982. LC 68-51873. 598p. 1982. 132.50x (ISBN 0-8002-2985-1). Intl Pubns Serv.

CHEMICAL INDUSTRIES–SOVIET UNION

Dienes, Leslie. Locational Factors & Locational Developments in the Soviet Chemical Industry. LC 69-18023. (Research Papers: No. 119). 285p. 1969. pap. 10.00 (ISBN 0-89065-027-6). U Chicago Dept Geog.

Rajana, Cecil. The Chemical & Petro-Chemical Industries of Russia & Eastern Europe, 1960-1980. 1975. 62.50x (ISBN 0-85621-040-4, Pub. by Scottish Academic Pr Scotland). Columbia U Pr.

CHEMICAL INSTRUMENTS

see Chemical Apparatus

CHEMICAL KINETICS

see Chemical Reaction, Rate of

CHEMICAL LABORATORIES

see also Chemical Engineering Laboratories

Arnold O. Beckman Conference in Clinical Chemistry, 1st & Young, Donald. Clinician & Chemist: The Relationship of the Laboratory to the Physician. LC 78-72880. 375p. 1979. 35.00 (ISBN 0-915274-08-6); members 25.00. Am Assn Clinical Chem.

Castegnaro, M., et al, eds. Laboratory Decontamination & Destruction of Aflatoxins, B1, B2, G1, G2 in Laboratory Wastes. (IARC Ser.). (Illus.). 68p. 1980. pap. 9.95x (ISBN 0-19-723037-7). Oxford U Pr.

--Laboratory Decontamination & Destruction of Carcinogens in Laboratory Wastes: Some N-Nitrosamines. (IARC). (Illus.). 82p. 1982. text ed. 10.95x (ISBN 0-19-723043-1). Oxford U Pr.

--Laboratory Decontamination & Destruction of Carcinogens in Laboratory Wastes: Some N-Nitrosamines. (IARC Ser.). (Illus.). 74p. 1983. pap. 12.95x (ISBN 0-19-723054-7). Oxford U Pr.

--Laboratory Decontamination & Destruction of Carcinogens in Laboratory Wastes: Some Polycyclic Aromatic Hydrocarbons. (IARC Ser.). (Illus.). 86p. 1983. pap. 12.95x (ISBN 0-19-723049-0). Oxford U Pr.

Frazer, J. W. & Kunz, F. W., eds. Computerized Laboratory Systems, STP 578. LC 75-2512. (Special Technical Publications Ser.: No. 578). 278p. 1984. 24.00 (ISBN 0-8031-0268-2, 04-578000-34). ASTM.

Gaston, P. J. Care, Handling & Disposal of Dangerous Chemicals. rev. & enl. ed. 1970. pap. 15.00 (ISBN 0-685-11997-1). Heinman.

Green, Michael E. & Turk, Amos. Safety in Working with Chemistry. (Illus.). 1978. pap. text ed. write for info. (ISBN 0-02-346420-8). Macmillan.

Guilbault, George G. & Hargis, Larry G. Instrumental Analysis Manual: Modern Experiments for the Laboratory. LC 78-126311. pap. 113.00 (ISBN 0-317-08385-6, 2055039). Bks Demand UMI.

Health & Safety in the Chemical Laboratory. 208p. 1984. 30.00 (ISBN 0-85186-945-9, Pub. by Royal Soc Chem UK). Heyden.

Heasley, Victor L. & Christensen, Val J. Chemistry & Life in the Laboratory: Experiments in General, Organic & Biological Chemistry. 2nd ed. 264p. 1983. pap. text ed. 15.95x (ISBN 0-8087-4716-9). Burgess.

Massart, D. L., et al. Evaluation & Optimization of Laboratory Methods & Analytical Procedures. (Techniques & Instrumentation in Analytical Chemistry Ser.: Vol. 1). 596p. 1978. 72.50 (ISBN 0-444-41743-5). Elsevier.

Meloan, Clifton E. Instrumental Analysis Using Spectroscopy. LC 68-20179. (Medical Technology Ser.: No. 1). pap. 44.50 (ISBN 0-317-09062-3, 2050349). Bks Demand UMI.

Renfrew, Malcolm M., ed. Safety in the Chemical Laboratory, Vol. 4. 1981. pap. 12.50 (ISBN 0-910362-06-8). Chem Educ.

Steere, Norman V. Safety in the Chemical Laboratory, 2 vols. o. p. 10.35 (ISBN 0-910362-03-3); Vol. 2. 1971. 10.90; Vol. 3. 1973. 10.90 (ISBN 0-910362-05-X). Chem Educ.

Walmsley, Judith A. & Walmsley, Frank. Chemical Principles, Properties, & Reactions in the Laboratory. 400p. 1985. pap. 12.95 (ISBN 0-201-08110-5). Addison-Wesley.

Walters, Douglas & Jameson, C. W. Health & Safety for Toxicity Testing. 352p. 1984. text ed. 39.95 (ISBN 0-250-40546-6). Butterworth.

CHEMICAL LITERATURE

see also Information Storage and Retrieval Systems–Chemistry

Selected Titles in Chemistry. 4th ed. 1977. pap. 1.25 (ISBN 0-8412-0413-6). Am Chemical.

Singer, T. E., ed. Searching the Chemical Literature. LC 61-11330. (Advances in Chemistry Ser: No. 30). 1961. 29.95 (ISBN 0-8412-0031-9). Am Chemical.

Woodburn, Henry M. Using the Chemical Literature: A Practical Guide. (Library & Information Science Ser.: Vol. 11). 312p. 1974. pap. 29.75 (ISBN 0-8247-7455-8). Dekker.

CHEMICAL MANIPULATION

see Chemistry–Manipulation

CHEMICAL MICROSCOPY

Chamot, Emile & Mason, Clyde W. Handbook of Chemical Microscopy, Vol. 1. 3rd ed. LC 58-12706. pap. 125.50 (ISBN 0-317-28588-2, 2055183). Bks Demand UMI.

Fryer, J. R. The Chemical Applications of Transmission Electron Microscopy. 1979. 55.00 (ISBN 0-12-269350-7). Acad Pr.

Mason, C. W. Handbook of Chemical Microscopy, Vol. 1. 4th ed. LC 82-11040. 505p. 1983. 80.50x (ISBN 0-471-57531-3). Wiley.

CHEMICAL MODELS

The Allyn & Bacon Molecular Model Set for General Chemistry. 1985. 9.93 (ISBN 0-205-08281-5, 688281). Allyn.

The Allyn & Bacon Molecular Model Set for Organic Chemistry. 1985. 19.29 (ISBN 0-205-08136-3, 688136). Allyn.

Jenne, Everett A., ed. Chemical Modeling in Aqueous Systems. LC 79-242. (ACS Symposium Ser.: No. 93). 1979. 69.95 (ISBN 0-8412-0479-9). Am Chemical.

Kalashnikov, N. P. & Remizovich, V. S. Collisions of Fast Charged Particles in Solids. Erastov, Konstantin, tr. from Rus. 438p. 1985. text ed. 145.00 (ISBN 0-677-06080-7). Gordon.

Nicholas, J. F. An Atlas of Models of Crystal Surfaces. 238p. 1965. 92.50x (ISBN 0-677-00580-6). Gordon.

Suckling, Colin J., et al. Chemistry Through Models. LC 77-71429. (Illus.). 1978. 57.50 (ISBN 0-521-21661-3). Cambridge U Pr.

--Chemistry Through Models. LC 77-71429. (Illus.). 321p. 1980. pap. 16.95x (ISBN 0-521-29932-2). Cambridge U Pr.

Wells, A. F. Models in Structural Inorganic Chemistry. 1970. text ed. 12.95x (ISBN 0-19-501278-X). Oxford U Pr.

CHEMICAL NOMENCLATURE

see Chemistry–Nomenclature

CHEMICAL OCEANOGRAPHY

see also Water Chemistry

Burton, J. D. & Liss, P. S., eds. Estuarine Chemistry. 1977. 47.50 (ISBN 0-12-147350-3). Acad Pr.

Chemical Oceanography in Canada. (Fisheries Research Board of Canada Reports). 19p. 1978. pap. 5.50 (ISBN 0-660-00532-8, SSC93, SSC). Unipub.

Church, Thomas M., ed. Marine Chemistry in the Coastal Environment. (ACS Symposium Ser.: No. 18). 1979. pap. 34.95 (ISBN 0-8412-0531-0). Am Chemical.

Duursma, E. K. & Dawson, R., eds. Marine Organic Chemistry: Evolution, Composition, Interactions & Chemistry of Organic Matter in Seawater. (Oceanography Ser.: Vol. 31). 522p. 1981. 98.00 (ISBN 0-444-41892-X). Elsevier.

Faulkner, D. J. & Fenical, W. H., eds. Marine Natural Products Chemistry. LC 76-58470. (NATO Conference Ser. IV, Marine Sciences: Vol. 1). 433p. 1977. 55.00x (ISBN 0-306-32921-2, Plenum Pr). Plenum Pub.

Ferronsky, V. I. & Polyakov, V. A. Environmental Isotopes in the Hydrosphere. 466p. 1982. 79.95x (ISBN 0-471-10114-1, Pub. by Wiley-Interscience). Wiley.

Head, P. C., ed. Practical Estuarine Chemistry: A Handbook. (Estuarine & Brackish-Water Sciences Association Handbook). 350p. 1985. 54.50 (ISBN 0-521-30165-3). Cambridge U Pr.

Holland, Heinrich D. The Chemical Evolution of the Atmosphere & Oceans. LC 83-43077. (Princeton Series in Geochemistry). (Illus.). 656p. 1984. 75.00x (ISBN 0-691-08348-7); pap. 24.50x (ISBN 0-691-02381-6). Princeton U Pr.

Horne, R. A. Marine Chemistry: The Structure of Water & the Chemistry of the Hydrosphere. LC 69-16120. 568p. 1969. 66.95 (ISBN 0-471-40942-1, Pub. by Wiley-Interscience). Wiley.

Martin, Dean F. Marine Chemistry, Vol. 1. 2nd ed. LC 76-169633. (Illus.). pap. 100.30 (ISBN 0-317-07993-X, 2055069). Bks Demand UMI.

--Marine Chemistry, Vol. 2: Theory & Applications. 1970. 35.00 (ISBN 0-8247-1458-X). Dekker.

Riley, J. P. & Chester, R. Introduction to Marine Chemistry. 1971. 35.00 (ISBN 0-12-588750-7). Acad Pr.

Riley, J. P. & Chester, R., eds. Chemical Oceanography, Vol. 8. 1983. 75.00 (ISBN 0-12-588608-X). Acad Pr.

Riley, J. P. & Skirrow, G., eds. Chemical Oceanography, Vol. 7. 2nd ed. 1979. 75.00 (ISBN 0-12-588607-1). Acad Pr.

Sigleo, Anne C. & Hattori, Akihiko, eds. Marine & Estuarine Geochemistry. (Illus.). 340p. 1985. 39.00 (ISBN 0-87371-007-X). Lewis Pubs Inc.

Whitfield, M. & Jagner, D. Marine Electrochemistry: A Practical Introduction. LC 80-42023. 529p. 1981. 84.95x (ISBN 0-471-27976-5, Pub. by Wiley-Interscience). Wiley.

Zirino, Alberto, ed. Mapping Strategies in Chemical Oceanography. LC 85-20265. (Advances in Chemistry Ser.: No. 209). 468p. 1985. lib. bdg. 89.95x (ISBN 0-8412-0862-X). Am Chemical.

CHEMICAL PLANTS

see also Chemical Engineering–Apparatus and Supplies

Aitio, Antero, et al, eds. Biological Monitoring & Surveillance of Workers Exposed to Chemicals. LC 82-2946. (Illus.). 403p. 1983. text ed. 64.50 (ISBN 0-89116-253-4). Hemisphere Pub.

Backhurst, J. R. & Harker, J. H. Process Plant Design. LC 72-12561. 411p. 1973. 46.95 (ISBN 0-444-19566-1). Elsevier.

Benedek, P., ed. Steady-State Flow-Sheeting of Chemical Plants. (Chemical Engineering Monographs: Vol. 12). 410p. 1981. 72.50 (ISBN 0-444-99765-2). Elsevier.

Business Communications Staff. Oil & Gas Field Chemicals. 1983. 1500.00 (ISBN 0-89336-373-1, C-048). BCC.

Chemical Process Hazards with Special Reference to Plant Design, Vol. 6: Proceedings, No. 49, Manchester, April 1977. 152p. 1981. 80.00x (ISBN 0-85295-100-0, Pub. by Inst Chem England). State Mutual Bk.

Chemical Process Hazards with Special Reference to Plant Design: Proceedings, No. 39 Manchester, April 1974, Vol. 5. 350p. 1981. 80.00x (ISBN 0-85295-002-0, Pub. by Inst Chem Eng England). State Mutual Bk.

Clayton, P. & Wallin, S. C. An Environmental Study of an Activated Carbon Plant, 1978. 1981. 60.00x (ISBN 0-686-97068-3, Pub. by W Green England). State Mutual Bk.

Cook, T. M. & Cullen, D. J. Chemical Plant & Its Operation (Including Safety & Health Aspects) 2nd ed. (Illus.). 1980. text ed. 22.00 (ISBN 0-08-023812-2); pap. text ed. 10.00 (ISBN 0-08-023813-0). Pergamon.

Davidson Pratt, J. & West, T. F. Services for the Chemical Industry. 1968. pap. 11.50 (ISBN 0-08-012664-2). Pergamon.

Froment, G. F., ed. Large Chemical Plants. (Chemical Engineering Monographs: Vol. 10). 190p. 1979. 53.25 (ISBN 0-444-41837-7). Elsevier.

Inform Inc. A Directory of Eighty-Two Organic Chemical Plants in New York. Sperber, Sebastian & Rohmann, Steven O., eds. LC 84-81260. 1984. pap. text ed. 15.00 (ISBN 0-918780-28-4). Inform.

Kumar, Anil. Chemical Process Synthesis & Engineering Design. 556p. 1982. 29.95x (ISBN 0-07-096470-X). McGraw.

Larinkari, J., ed. Computer Applications in the Analysis of Chemical Data & Plants. LC 77-5201. (Illus.). 1977. pap. 25.00 (ISBN 0-89500-028-8). Sci Pr.

Levine, Adeline G. Love Canal: Science, Politics, & People. LC 80-8361. 288p. 1982. 26.50x (ISBN 0-669-04034-7); pap. 10.00x (ISBN 0-669-05411-9). Lexington Bks.

Opportunities for Chemical Plant Growth Regulation. (Monograph Ser.: No. 21). 222p. (Orig.). 1978. pap. 28.00x (Pub. by B C P C England). Intl Spec Bk.

Pilborough, L. Inspection of Chemical Plants. 392p. 1977. 29.95x (ISBN 0-87201-388-X). Gulf Pub.

Sarokin, David & Sperber, Sebastian, eds. A Directory of Eighty-Four Organic Chemical Plants in California. LC 83-83002. (Illus.). 1983. pap. 15.00 (ISBN 0-918780-24-1). INFORM.

Shumaker, Terrence M. Process Piping Blueprint Reading. (Illus.). 176p. 1982. 19.95 (ISBN 0-13-723502-X). P-H.

Sittig, M. Pollution Control in the Organic Chemical Industry. LC 74-77220. (Pollution Technology Review Ser: No. 9). (Illus.). 305p. 1974. 36.00 (ISBN 0-8155-0536-1). Noyes.

CHEMICAL PLANTS–TABLES, CALCULATIONS, ETC.

Quarantelli, E. L. Chemical Disasters: Preparations & Responses at the Local Level. 170p. 1985. text ed. 27.50x (ISBN 0-8290-1289-3). Irvington.

Shumaker. Process Pipe Drafting. 8.00 (ISBN 0-87006-512-2). Goodheart.

CHEMICAL POLISHING OF METALS

see Metals–Pickling

CHEMICAL PROCESS CONTROL

Aerstin, Frank & Street, Gary. Applied Chemical Process Design. LC 78-9104. (Illus.). 312p. 1978. 32.00x (ISBN 0-306-31088-0, Plenum Pr). Plenum Pub.

Box, George E. & Draper, Norman R. Evolutionary Operation: A Statistical Method for Process Improvement. LC 68-56159. (Applied Probability & Mathematical Statistics Ser). 237p. 1969. 42.50x (ISBN 0-471-09305-X, Pub. by Wiley-Interscience). Wiley.

Chemical Process Hazards with Special Reference to Plant Design, Vol. 6: Proceedings, No. 49, Manchester, April 1977. 152p. 1981. 80.00x (ISBN 0-85295-100-0, Pub. by Inst Chem England). State Mutual Bk.

Chemical Process Hazards with Special Reference to Plant Design: Proceedings, No. 39 Manchester, April 1974, Vol. 5. 350p. 1981. 80.00x (ISBN 0-85295-002-0, Pub. by Inst Chem Eng England). State Mutual Bk.

Edgar, T. F., ed. Advanced Control & Modeling Techniques. LC 80-20826. (Alchemi Series A: Process Control: Vol 4). 82p. 1984. pap. 30.00 (ISBN 0-8169-0236-4); pap. 15.00 members (ISBN 0-317-17539-4). Am Inst Chem Eng.

Edgar, Thomas F. & Seborg, Dale E., eds. Chemical Process Control: Proceedings of the Engineering Foundation Conference, Jan. 18-23, 1981, Sea Island, Ga, Vol. 2. LC 81-71594. 649p. 1982. text ed. 60.00 (ISBN 0-8169-0203-8); text ed. 45.00 (ISBN 0-317-03783-8). Am Inst Chem Eng.

Huskins, D. J. Quality Measuring Instruments in On-Line Process Analysis. 455p. 1982. 119.00x (ISBN 0-470-27521-9). Halsted Pr.

Institution of Chemical Engineers & Linhoff, B. User Guide on Process Integration for the Efficient Use of Energy. (Illus.). 252p. 1983. 25.00 (ISBN 0-08-030245-9). Pergamon.

Stephanopoulos, George. Chemical Process Control: An Introduction to Theory & Practice. (Illus.). 704p. 1984. 41.95 (ISBN 0-13-128629-3). P-H.

Whitaker, Norman. Process Instrumentation Primer. 117p. 1980. 39.95x (ISBN 0-87814-128-6). Pennwell Bks.

CHEMICAL PROCESSES

see also Chemical Reactions

AICHE Design Institute for Physical Property Data Staff, ed. Predicting Chemical Process Design Data Manual: Data Prediction Manual. 1983. 150.00 (ISBN 0-8169-0233-X); 125.00 (ISBN 0-317-03747-1). Am Inst Chem Eng.

Belzer, Jack, ed. Encyclopedia of Computer Science & Technology, Vol. 11. 1978. 115.00 (ISBN 0-8247-2261-2). Dekker.

Brian, P. L. Staged Cascades in Chemical Processing. (International Series in the Physical & Chemical Engineering Sciences). (Illus.). 272p. 1972. ref. ed. 38.95 (ISBN 0-13-840280-9). P-H.

Felder, Richard M. & Rousseau, Ronald W. Elementary Principles of Chemical Processes. LC 77-12043. 571p. 1978. text ed. 44.00x (ISBN 0-471-74330-5); solutions manual 10.95 (ISBN 0-471-03680-3). Wiley.

Gupte, Parag A., et al, eds. Documentation of the Basis for Selection of the Contents of Chapter 3 Vapor Pressure in Manual for Predicting Chemical Process Design Data. 130p. 1984. pap. 90.00 spiral (ISBN 0-8169-0313-1). Am Inst Chem Eng.

Institution of Chemical Engineers. Chemical Process Hazards, Vol. VII. 52.50 (ISBN 0-08-028756-5). Pergamon.

Institution of Chemical Engineers, London & South-Eastern Branch & Process Engineering Group of the Society of Chemical Industry. Processes for Chemicals from Some Renewable Raw Materials: Proceedings, 1979. 47p. 1981. 50.00x (ISBN 0-686-75392-5, Pub. by Inst Chem Eng England). State Mutual Bk.

Jordan, Donald G. Chemical Process Development, 2 pts. LC 78-23432. 1979. Repr. of 1968 ed. Pt. 1 428p. lib. bdg. 39.50 (ISBN 0-88275-805-5); Pt. 2 628p. lib. bdg. 45.50 (ISBN 0-88275-806-3); Set 1056p. lib. bdg. 76.50 (ISBN 0-89874-064-9). Krieger.

Kallianpur, Chiatanya, et al, eds. Documentation of the Basis for Selection of the Contents of Chapter 2 Critical Properties in Manual for Predicting Chemical Process Design Data. 102p. 1984. pap. 90.00 spiral (ISBN 0-8169-0312-3, 04-015040-34). Am Inst Chem Eng.

McKetta. Encyclopedia of Chemical Processing & Design, Vol. 13. 1981. 115.00 (ISBN 0-8247-2463-1). Dekker.

--Encyclopedia of Chemical Processing & Design, Vol. 14. 1982. 115.00 (ISBN 0-8247-2464-X). Dekker.

--Encyclopedia of Chemical Processing & Design, Vol. 16. 1982. 115.00 (ISBN 0-8247-2466-6). Dekker.

--Encyclopedia of Chemical Processing & Design, Vol. 18. 1983. 115.00 (ISBN 0-8247-2468-2). Dekker.

--Encyclopedia of Chemical Processing & Design, Vol. 19. 1983. 115.00 (ISBN 0-8247-2469-0). Dekker.

--Encyclopedia of Chemical Processing & Design, Vol. 20. 1984. 115.00 (ISBN 0-8247-2470-4). Dekker.

Beynon, J. H. & Gilbert, J. R. Application of Transition State Theory to Unimolecular Reactions: An Introduction. LC 83-17016. 85p. 1984. 26.95x (ISBN 0-471-90316-7, Pub. by Wiley-Interscience). Wiley.

Bowden, Frank P. & Yoffa, A. D. Fast Reactions in Solids. pap. 44.00 (ISBN 0-317-09010-0, 2051338). Bks Demand UMI.

Breslow, Ronald. Organic Reaction Mechanisms: An Introduction. 2nd ed. (Organic Chemistry Monograph Ser.). 1969. pap. 18.95 (ISBN 0-8053-1253-6). Benjamin-Cummings.

Bretherick, L. Handbook of Reactive Chemical Hazards, CRC. 996p. 1975. 49.95 (ISBN 0-685-69893-9). CRC Pr.

Budnikov, P. P. & Ginstling, A. M. Principles of Solid State Chemistry. 468p. 1970. 119.50 (ISBN 0-677-61250-8). Gordon.

Butler, A. R. & Perkins, M. J., eds. Organic Reaction Mechanisms, 1973: An Annual Survey Covering the Literature Dated December 1972 Through November 1973. LC 66-23143. pap. 146.80 (ISBN 0-317-29325-7, 2024016). Bks Demand UMI.

--Organic Reaction Mechanisms, 1974: An Annual Survey Covering the Literature Dated December 2973 Through November 1974. LC 66-23143. pap. 160.00 (ISBN 0-317-29326-5, 2024017). Bks Demand UMI.

--Organic Reaction Mechanisms, 1975: An Annual Survey Covering the Literature Dated December 1974 Through November 1975. LC 66-23143. pap. 157.50 (ISBN 0-317-29327-3, 2024018). Bks Demand UMI.

--Organic Reaction Mechanisms, 1976: An Annual Survey Covering the Literature Dated December 1975 Through November 1976. LC 66-23143. pap. 160.00 (ISBN 0-317-29328-1, 2024019). Bks Demand UMI.

Capon, B. & Rees, C. W., eds. Organic Reaction Mechanisms, 1969: An Annual Survey Covering the Literature Dated December 1968 Through November 1969. LC 66-23143. pap. 160.00 (ISBN 0-317-28687-0, 2051618). Bks Demand UMI.

Capon, Brian, ed. Neighboring Group Participation, Vol. 1. LC 76-17812. (Illus.). 280p. 1976. 42.50x (ISBN 0-306-35027-0, Plenum Pr). Plenum Pub.

Carberry, James J. Chemistry & Catalytic Reaction Engineering. (Chemical Engineering Ser.). (Illus.). 1976. 45.00 (ISBN 0-07-009790-9). McGraw.

Christoph, S. G. Collision Theory & Statistical Theory of Chemical Reactions. (Lectures Notes in Chemistry: Vol. 18). (Illus.). 322p. 1980. pap. 32.00 (ISBN 0-387-10012-1). Springer-Verlag.

Dauben, William G. Organic Reactions, Vol. 29. LC 42-20265. 457p. 1983. 49.50 (ISBN 0-471-87490-6, Pub. by Wiley-Interscience). Wiley.

--Organic Reactions, Vol. 30. (Organic Reactions Ser.). 592p. 1984. 54.50 (ISBN 0-471-89013-8, 2201, Pub. by Wiley-Interscience). Wiley.

--Organic Reactions, Vol. 32. LC 42-20265. (Organic Reactions Ser.: 2201). 533p. 1984. 54.95 (ISBN 0-471-88101-5, Pub. by Wiley-Interscience). Wiley.

Dauben, William G., ed. Organic Reactions, Vol. 23. LC 42-20265. 528p. 1984. Repr. of 1976 ed. 42.50 (ISBN 0-89874-796-1). Krieger.

--Organic Reactions, Vol. 25. LC 42-20265. 518p. 1984. Repr. of 1977 ed. 42.50 (ISBN 0-89874-798-8). Krieger.

Daudel, R. & Pullman, A., eds. Quantum Theory of Chemical Reactions. 1982. lib. bdg. 32.50 (ISBN 90-277-1467-3, Pub. by Reidel Holland). Kluwer Academic.

Daudel, Raymond, et al, eds. Quantum Theory of Chemical Reactions: Collision Theory, Reaction Path, Static Indices, Vol. 1. 1980. lib. bdg. 34.00 (ISBN 90-277-1047-3, Pub. by Reidel Holland). Kluwer Academic.

--Quantum Theory of Chemical Reactions: Solvent Effect, Reaction Mechanisms, Photochemical Processes, Vol. 11. 340p. 1980. PLB 42.00 (ISBN 90-277-1182-8, Pub. by Reidel Holland). Kluwer Academic.

Doraiswamy, L. K. & Mashelkar, R. A. Frontiers in Chemical Reaction Engineering. Vol. 1, 697p. 43.50 (ISBN 0-470-20038-3); Vol. 2, 463p. 43.50 (ISBN 0-470-20039-1); Set, 1160p. 87.00 (ISBN 0-470-20041-3). Halsted Pr.

Doraiswamy, L. K. & Sharma, M. M. Heterogeneous Reactions: Analysis, Examples & Reactor Design, 2 vols. LC 82-19968. 538p. 1984. Vol. 1, Gas-solid & Solid-solid reactions, 624pgs. 66.95x (ISBN 0-471-05368-6, Pub. by Wiley-Interscience); Vol. 2, Fluid-Fluid-Solid Reactions, 650pgs. 59.95x (ISBN 0-471-05367-8, Pub. by Wiley-Interscience). Wiley.

Doraiswamy, L. K., ed. Recent Advances in the Engineering Analysis of Chemically Reacting Systems. 611p. 1984. 49.95 (ISBN 0-470-20026-X). Halsted Pr.

Ebert, K. H., ed. Modelling of Chemical Reaction Systems: Proceedings. (Springer Series in Chemical Physics: Vol. 18). (Illus.). 389p. 1981. 39.00 (ISBN 0-387-10983-8). Springer Verlag.

Eliel, Ernest L. & Otsuka, Sei, eds. Asymmetric Reactions & Processes in Chemistry. LC 82-3908. (ACS Symposium Ser.: No. 185). 1982. 39.95 (ISBN 0-8412-0717-8). Am Chemical.

Fackler, J. P., Jr., ed. Symmetry in Chemical Theory: Application of Group Theoretical Techniques to the Solution of Chemical Problems. LC 73-12620. (Benchmark Papers in Inorganic Chemistry: Vol. 4). 508p. 1974. 56.00 (ISBN 0-87933-018-X). Van Nos Reinhold.

Fiechter, A., ed. Reactors & Reactions. (Advances in Biochemical Engineering Ser.: Vol. 19). (Illus.). 250p. 1981. 59.50 (ISBN 0-387-10464-X). Springer-Verlag.

Folger, H. Scott & Brown, Lee F. Fundamentals of Chemical Reaction Engineering. (Illus.). 752p. 1986. text ed. 42.95 (ISBN 0-13-334558-0). P-H.

Gurel, O. Oscillations in Chemical Reactions. (Topics in Current Chemistry: Vol. 118). (Illus.). 130p. 1983. 28.00 (ISBN 0-387-12575-2). Springer-Verlag.

Hague, David N. Fast Reactions. LC 74-149571. (Illus.). pap. 41.80 (ISBN 0-317-09314-2, 2016970). Bks Demand UMI.

Hammes, G. G. Techniques of Chemistry: Investigation of Rates & Mechanisms of Reactions, Vol. 6. 3rd ed. 665p. 1974. 95.95 (ISBN 0-471-93127-6, Pub. by Wiley-Interscience). Wiley.

Hazardous Chemical Reactions. rev. ed. (Forty Ser.). 1971. pap. 3.25 (ISBN 0-685-58151-9, 491M). Natl Fire Prot.

High Temperature Chemical Reaction Engineering. 332p. 1981. 70.00x (ISBN 0-85295-001-2, Pub. by Inst Chem Eng England). State Mutual Bk.

Hill, Charles G., Jr. An Introduction to Chemical Engineering Kinetics & Reactor Design. LC 77-8280. 594p. 1977. 48.50 (ISBN 0-471-39609-5); Solutions Manual avail. (ISBN 0-471-05258-2). Wiley.

Holland, Charles D. & Anthony, Raymond G. Fundamentals of Chemical Reaction Engineering. (International Series in the Physical & Chemical Engineering Sciences). (Illus.). 1979. text ed. 39.95 (ISBN 0-13-335596-9). P-H.

House, Herbert O. Modern Synthetic Reactions. 2nd ed. LC 78-173958. 1972. text ed. 39.95 (ISBN 0-8053-4501-9). Benjamin-Cummings.

Hudlicky, Milos. Chemistry of Organic Fluorine Compounds. LC 73-14377. 903p. 1976. text ed. 172.95x (ISBN 0-470-41835-4). Halsted Pr.

Institution of Chemical Engineers. Runaway Reactions. 58.50 (ISBN 0-08-028766-2). Pergamon.

Institution of Chemical Engineers, ed. Chemical Reaction Engineering: Proceedings of the 8th International Symposium, Held in Edinburgh, UK, 10-13 September 1984. (Institution of Chemical Engineers Symposium Ser.: Vol. 87). 810p. 1984. 77.00 (ISBN 0-08-030283-1). Pergamon.

Jacobson, Carl A. Encyclopedia of Chemical Reactions, Vol. 8; Index. Hampel, Clifford A., ed. LC 46-822. pap. 135.80 (ISBN 0-317-09757-1, 2051540). Bks Demand UMI.

Jennings, K. R. & Cundall, R. B., eds. Progress in Reaction Kinetics: Vol. 9 Complete. 368p. 1980. 84.00 (ISBN 0-08-020343-4). Pergamon.

Kapila, Ashwani K. Asymptotic Treatment of Chemically Reacting Systems. (Applicable Math Ser.). 128p. 1983. text ed. 35.95 (ISBN 0-273-08513-1). Pitman Pub MA.

Kende, Andrew S., ed. Organic Reactions, Vol. 33. LC 42-20265. (Organic Reactions Ser.: 2201). 352p. 1984. 45.00 (ISBN 0-471-80229-8, Pub. by Wiley-Interscience); Vol. 34, 412p. 49.95 (ISBN 0-471-80673-0). Wiley.

Kleinberg, Jacob, ed. Mechanisms of Inorganic Reactions. LC 65-26226. (Advances in Chemistry Ser: No. 49). 1965. 23.95 (ISBN 0-8412-0050-5). Am Chemical.

Klopman, Gilles, ed. Chemical Reactivity & Reaction Paths. LC 73-17325. 382p. 1974. 29.50 (ISBN 0-471-49355-4). Krieger.

Knipe, A. C. & Watts, W. E. Organic Reaction Mechanisms, 1978, Vol. 14. LC 66-23143. 719p. 1980. 241.00 (ISBN 0-471-27613-8). Wiley.

--Organic Reaction Mechanisms, 1981, Vol. 17. 700p. 1983. 155.00 (ISBN 0-471-10459-0). Wiley.

Knipe, A. C. & Watts, W. E., eds. Organic Reaction Mechanisms, 1979, Vol. 15. LC 66-23143. 759p. 1981. 197.95 (ISBN 0-471-27818-1). Wiley.

Latham, J. L. Elementary Reaction Kinetics. 2nd ed. (Illus.). 1970. limpbinding 3.75 (ISBN 0-8088-4610-8). Davey.

Levine, R. D. & Bernstein, R. B. Molecular Reaction Dynamics. (Illus.). 1974. text ed. 13.95x (ISBN 0-19-855477-X). Oxford U Pr.

Liler, M. Reaction Mechanisms in Sulphuric Acid & Other Strong Acid Solutions. (Organic Chemistry Ser.). 1971. 68.50 (ISBN 0-12-450050-1). Acad Pr.

Luss, Dan & Weekman, Vern W., Jr., eds. Chemical Reaction Engineering Reviews--Houston. LC 78-8477. (ACS Symposium Ser.: No. 72). 1978. 32.95 (ISBN 0-8412-0432-2). Am Chemical.

Manual of Hazardous Chemical Reactions. (Fourty Ser.). 312p. 1971. pap. 3.25 (ISBN 0-685-46067-3, 491M). Natl Fire Prot.

Marchand, Alan P. & Lehr, Roland E., eds. Pericyclic Reactions. (Organic Chemistry Series). 1977. Vol. 1. 70.00 (ISBN 0-12-470501-4); Vol. 2. 80.00 (ISBN 0-12-470502-2). Acad Pr.

Nikitin, E. E. & Umanskii, S. Y. Theory of Slow Atomic Collisions. (Series in Chemical Physics: Vol. 30). (Illus.). 440p. 1984. 49.00 (ISBN 0-387-12414-4). Springer-Verlag.

Nikitin, Evengii. Theory of Thermally Induced Gas Phase Reactions. Schlag, E. W., tr. LC 66-12733. pap. 41.80 (ISBN 0-317-09605-2, 2050961). Bks Demand UMI.

Olah, George A. & Schleyer, Paul, eds. Reactive Intermediates in Organic Chemistry: Carbonium Ions. Set. 188.00 (ISBN 0-686-75231-7); Vol. 2 Methods Of Formation & Major Types 500p. 35.25 (ISBN 0-471-65333-0); Vol. 3 Major Types 536p. 46.00 (ISBN 0-471-65334-9); Vol. 4 Major Types. 46.50 (ISBN 0-471-65337-3). Krieger.

Organic Reactions, Vols. 1-20. Incl. Vol. 1. Adams, Roger, ed. 400p. 1978. Repr. of 1942 ed (ISBN 0-88275-729-6); Vol. 2. Adams, Roger, ed. 470p. 1981. Repr. of 1944 ed (ISBN 0-89874-375-3); Vol. 3. Adams, Roger, ed. 468p. 1975. Repr. of 1946 ed (ISBN 0-88275-875-6); Vol. 4. Adams, Roger, ed. 438p. 1979. Repr. of 1948 ed (ISBN 0-88275-780-6); Vol. 5. Adams, Roger, ed. 454p. 1977. Repr. of 1949 ed (ISBN 0-88275-249-9); Vol. 6. Adams, Roger, ed. 526p. 1975. Repr. of 1951 ed (ISBN 0-88275-876-4); Vol. 7. Adams, Roger, ed. 448p. 1975. Repr. of 1953 ed (ISBN 0-88275-877-2); Vol. 8. Adams, Roger, ed. 446p. 1975. Repr. of 1954 ed (ISBN 0-88275-878-0); Vol. 9. Adams, Roger, ed. 476p. 1975. Repr. of 1957 ed (ISBN 0-88275-879-9); Vol. 10. Adams, Roger, ed. 572p. 1975. Repr. of 1959 ed (ISBN 0-88275-880-2); Vol. 11. Cope, Arthur C., ed. 510p. 1975. Repr. of 1960 ed (ISBN 0-88275-881-0); Vol. 12. Cope, Arthur C., ed. 546p. 1975. Repr. of 1962 ed (ISBN 0-88275-882-9); Vol. 13. Cope, Arthur C. 390p. 1979. Repr. of 1962 ed (ISBN 0-88275-836-5); Vol. 14. Cope, Arthur C., ed. 506p. 1978. Repr. of 1965 ed (ISBN 0-88275-730-X); Vol. 15. Cope, Arthur C., ed. 616p. 1978. Repr. of 1967 ed (ISBN 0-88275-731-8); Vol. 16. Cope, Arthur C., ed. 456p. 1975. Repr. of 1968 ed (ISBN 0-88275-883-7); Vol. 17. Dauben, William G., ed. 346p. 1975. Repr. of 1969 ed (ISBN 0-88275-884-5); Vol. 18. Dauben, Wlliam G., ed. 476p. 1978. Repr. of 1970 ed (ISBN 0-88275-732-6); Vol. 19. Dauben, William G., ed. 446p. 1975. Repr. of 1972 ed (ISBN 0-88275-885-3); Vol. 20. Dauben, William G., ed. 506p. 1981. Repr. of 1973 ed (ISBN 0-89874-390-7). LC 42-20265. Vols. 1-19. 31.50 ea.; Vol. 20. 39.50. Krieger.

Pearson, Ralph G. Symmetry Rules for Chemical Reactions: Orbital Topology & Elementary Processes. LC 76-10314. pap. 139.30 (ISBN 0-317-28061-9, 2055771). Bks Demand UMI.

Pietschmann, H. Weak Interactions: Formulas, Results & Derivations. (Illus.). 202p. 1983. 29.50 (ISBN 0-387-81783-2). Springer-Verlag.

Poland, Alan & Kimbrough, Renate D., eds. Biological Mechanisms of Dioxin Action. LC 84-22955. (Banbury Reports: Vol. 18). 600p. 1985. 75.00 (ISBN 0-87969-218-9). Cold Spring Harbor.

Ranganathan, Darshan & Ranganathan, Subramania. Further Challenging Problems in Organic Reaction Mechanisms. LC 79-24608. 1980. 21.50 (ISBN 0-12-580060-6). Acad Pr.

Salem, Lionel. Electrons in Chemical Reactions: First Priciples. LC 81-19833. 260p. 1982. 37.50 (ISBN 0-471-08474-3, Pub. by Wiley-Interscience). Wiley.

Schaal, R., ed. Chemical Kinetics of Homogeneous Systems. Edward, John T., tr. from Fr. LC 73-94455. Orig. Title: La Cinetique Chimique Homogene. 200p. 1974. lib. bdg. 31.50 (ISBN 90-277-0446-5, Pub. by Reidel Holland). Kluwer Academic.

Schafer, Harald. Chemical Transport Reactions. Frankfort, Hans, tr. 1964. 40.00 (ISBN 0-12-621750-5). Acad Pr.

Society for Industrial & Applied Mathematical - American Mathematical Society Symposia - New York - April, 1974. Mathematical Aspects of Chemical & Biochemical Problems & Quantum Chemistry: Proceedings. Cohen, Donald S, ed. LC 74-26990. (SIAM-AMS Proceedings Ser.: Vol. 8). 1974. 33.00 (ISBN 0-8218-1328-5, SIAMS-8). Am Math.

Sykes, Peter. A Guidebook to Mechanism in Organic Chemistry. 5th ed. (Illus.). 416p. (Orig.). pap. text ed. 16.95x (ISBN 0-582-44121-8). Longman.

Tamaru, K. Dynamic Heterogeneous Catalysis. 1978. 35.00 (ISBN 0-12-684150-0). Acad Pr.

Thyagarajan, B. S. Selective Organic Transformations, Vol. 2. 352p. 1972. 37.50 (ISBN 0-471-86688-1, Pub. by Wiley). Krieger.

Twigg, M. V., ed. Mechanisms of Organometallic & Inorganic Reactions, Vol. 1. 389p. 1983. 55.00x (ISBN 0-306-41142-3, Plenum Press). Plenum Pub.

Tyson, J. J. The Belousov-Zhabotinskii Reaction. Levin, S., ed. (Lecture Notes in Biomathematics: Vol. 10). 1976. soft cover 13.00 (ISBN 0-387-07792-8). Springer-Verlag.

Villermaux, J. & Trambouze, P., eds. Chemical Reaction Engineering: International Symposium on Chemical Reaction Engineering, Nice, France, March 25-27, 1980, Vol. 1, Contributed Papers. LC 79-41749. 540p. 1980. 85.00 (ISBN 0-08-024018-6). Pergamon.

--Chemical Reaction Engineering: Sixth International Symposium on Chemical Reaction Engineering--Plenary Lectures, Vol. 2. LC 79-41749. (Illus.). 259p. 1980. pap. 44.00 (ISBN 0-08-026234-1). Pergamon.

Weekman, Vern W., Jr & Luss, Dan, eds. Chemical Reaction Engineering - Houston. LC 77-25340. (ACS Symposium Ser.: No. 65). 1978. 44.95 (ISBN 0-8412-0401-2). Am Chemical.

Wei, James & Georgakis, Christos, eds. Chemical Reaction Engineering: Boston. LC 82-11629. (ACS Symposium Ser.: No. 196). 614p. 1982. lib. bdg. 49.95x (ISBN 0-8412-0732-1). Am Chemical.

--Chemical Reaction Engineering: Plenary Lectures. LC 83-11876. (ACS Symposium Ser.: No. 226). 202p. 1983. lib. bdg. 31.95x (ISBN 0-8412-0793-3). Am Chemical.

Weiss, Howard D. Guide to Organic Reactions. LC 78-105323. pap. 63.30 (ISBN 0-317-08980-3, 2051511). Bks Demand UMI.

Willett, P., ed. Modern Approaches to Chemical Reaction Searching. 250p. 1986. text ed. write for info. (ISBN 0-566-03550-2). Gower Pub Co.

CHEMICAL REACTORS

Crynes, B. L. & Fogler, H. S., eds. Reactors & Rate Data. LC 80-24435. (AIChEMI Modular Instruction E. Ser.: Vol. 2). 94p. 1981. pap. 30.00 (ISBN 0-8169-0180-5, J-11); pap. 15.00 members (ISBN 0-317-03846-X). Am Inst Chem Eng.

Denbigh, K. G. & Turner, J. C. Chemical Reactor Theory: An Introduction. 3rd ed. LC 83-7557. 250p. 1984. 42.50 (ISBN 0-521-25645-3); pap. 15.95 (ISBN 0-521-27630-6). Cambridge U Pr.

Denbigh, Kenneth G. & Turner, J. C. Chemical Reactor Theory: An Introduction. LC 76-123661. pap. 59.00 (ISBN 0-317-10504-3, 2013219). Bks Demand UMI.

Dudukovic, Milorad P. & Mills, Patrick L., eds. Chemical & Catalytic Reactor Modeling. LC 83-22378. (ACS Symposium Ser.: No. 237). 426p. 1983. lib. bdg. 59.95 (ISBN 0-8412-0815-8). Am Chemical.

Fahidy, T. Z. Principles of Electrochemical Reactor Analysis. (Chemical Engineering Monographs: Vol. 18). 1985. 68.75 (ISBN 0-444-42451-2). Elsevier.

Fiechter, A., ed. Reactors & Reactions. (Advances in Biochemical Engineering Ser.: Vol. 19). (Illus.). 250p. 1981. 59.50 (ISBN 0-387-10464-X). Springer-Verlag.

Fogler, H. Scott, ed. Chemical Reactors. LC 81-12672. (ACS Symposium Ser.: No. 168). 1981. 39.95 (ISBN 0-8412-0658-9). Am Chemical.

Froment, Gilbert F. & Bischoff, Kenneth B. Chemical Reactor Analysis & Design. LC 78-12465. 765p. 1979. text ed. 55.50x (ISBN 0-471-02447-3). Wiley.

Gianetto, Agostino & Silveston, Peter L., eds. Multiphase Chemical Reactors: Theory, Design, Scale-up. 1985. 110.00 (ISBN 0-89116-415-4). Hemisphere Pub.

Levenspiel, Octave. Chemical Reaction Engineering. 2nd ed. LC 72-178146. 578p. 1972. text ed. 46.50 (ISBN 0-471-53016-6). Wiley.

--Chemical Reactor Omnibook Plus. 1984. 24.00x (ISBN 0-88246-069-2). Oreg St U Bkstrs.

--Chemical Reactors Minibook. pap. text ed. 7.50x (ISBN 0-88246-068-4). Oreg St U Bkstrs.

Ramachandran, P. A. & Chaudhari, R. V. Three-Phase Catalytic Reactors. LC 81-23521. (Topics in Chemical Engineering Ser.: Vol. 2). (Illus.). 440p. 1983. 79.50 (ISBN 0-677-05650-8). Gordon.

Rase, Howard F. Chemical Reactor Design for Process Plants, 2 vols. Incl. Vol. 1. Principles & Techniques. 78.50 (ISBN 0-471-01891-0); Vol. 2. Case Studies & Design Data. 36.50 (ISBN 0-471-01890-2). LC 77-1285. 1977 (Pub. by Wiley-Interscience). Wiley.

Rodrigues, A. & Calo, J. Multiphase Chemical Reactors: Design Methods, Vol. II. 1981. 57.00 (ISBN 90-286-2821-5, Pub. by Martinus Nijhoff Netherlands). Kluwer Academic.

Rose, L. M., ed. Chemical Reactor Design in Practice. (Chemical Engineering Monographs: Vol. 13). 378p. 1981. 74.50 (ISBN 0-444-42018-5). Elsevier.

Tarhan, M. Orhan. Catalytic Reactor Design. (Illus.). 352p. 1983. 38.95 (ISBN 0-07-062871-8). McGraw.

Wen, C. Y. & Fan, L. T. Models for Flow Systems & Chemical Reactors. (Chemical Processing & Engineering: an International Ser.: Vol. 3). 584p. 1975. 75.00 (ISBN 0-8247-6346-7). Dekker.

Westerterp, K. R. & Van Swaaij, W. P. Chemical Reactor Design & Operation. 2nd ed. LC 83-5769. 800p. 1984. 100.00x (ISBN 0-471-90183-0, Pub. by Wiley-Interscience). Wiley.

CHEMICAL REAGENTS

see Chemical Tests and Reagents

CHEMICAL REDUCTION

see Reduction, Chemical

CHEMICAL RESEARCH

ACS Directory of Graduate Research. 1230p. 1983. 43.00 (ISBN 0-8412-0797-6). Am Chemical.

Baines, A., et al. Research in the Chemical Industry: The Environment, Objectives & Strategy. (Illus.). 1969. 33.60x (Pub. by Applied Science). Burgess-Intl Ideas.

Bernstein, R. B. Chemical Dynamics Via Molecular & Laser Techniques. (Illus.). 1982. 59.00x (ISBN 0-19-855154-1); pap. 24.95x (ISBN 0-19-855169-X). Oxford U Pr.

Braun, T., et al, eds. Polyurethane Foam Sorbents in Separation Science & Tech. 224p. 1985. 70.00 (ISBN 0-8493-6597-X). CRC Pr.

Brebbia, C. A., ed. Basic Principles & Applications. (Topics in Boundary Elements Research Ser.: Vol. 3). (Illus.). 280p. 1984. 49.50 (ISBN 0-387-13097-7). Springer-Verlag.

Brown, A. G. & Roberts, S. M., eds. Recent Advances in the Chemistry of B-Lactum Antibiotics: Third International Symposium, 1984. 398p. 1985. pap. 48.00 (ISBN 0-85186-955-6, 996104712, Pub. by Royal Soc Chem UK). Heyden.

Contis & Phillips, Donald. Investigating Chemistry: Up'N Atom. 176p. 1982. pap. text ed. 13.95 (ISBN 0-8403-2640-8). Kendall-Hunt.

Directory of Graduate Research. 1977. 25.00 (ISBN 0-8412-0414-4). Am Chemical.

Fujiwara, Shizuo & Mark, Harry B., Jr., eds. Information Chemistry: Computer-Assisted Chemical Research Design. (Illus.). 386p. 1976. 65.00x (ISBN 0-86008-150-8, Pub. by Japan Sci Soc Japan). Intl Spec Bk.

Hepple, Peter, ed. The Applications of Computer Techniques in Chemical Research: Proceedings, Manchester, 15-17 November, 1971. LC 73-151797. pap. 71.50 (ISBN 0-317-29021-5, 2023687). Bks Demand UMI.

Maynard, John T. Understanding Chemical Patents: A Guide for the Inventor. LC 77-28097. 1978. 19.95 (ISBN 0-8412-0347-4). Am Chemical.

Paquette, L. A. Recent Synthetic Developments in Polyquinine Chemistry. (Topics in Current Chemistry Ser.: Vol. 119). 160p. 1984. 28.50 (ISBN 0-387-12766-6). Springer-Verlag.

Paquette, Leo A. The Renaissance in Cyclooctatetraene Chemistry. Barton, et al, eds. 1976. pap. text ed. 14.00 (ISBN 0-08-020479-1). Pergamon.

Pollock, Gisella L., ed. Chemical Research Faculties: An International Directory. LC 83-22323. 532p. 1984. lib. bdg. 129.95x (ISBN 0-8412-0817-4). Am Chemical.

Runser, Dennis J., ed. Industrial-Academic Interfacing. LC 83-27558. (ACS Symposium Ser.: No. 244). 164p. 1984. lib. bdg. 34.95 (ISBN 0-8412-0825-5). Am Chemical.

CHEMICAL STRUCTURE

see also Chemical Bonds; Molecular Structure; Stereochemistry; Valence (Theoretical Chemistry)

Barnard, John M., ed. Computer Handling of Generic Chemical Structures. LC 84-13725. 242p. 1984. text ed. 53.95x (ISBN 0-566-03515-4). Gower Pub Co.

Barron, L. D., et al. Structural Chemistry. (Topics in Current Chemistry. Fortschritte der Chemischen Forschung: Vol. 123). (Illus.). 200p. 1984. 36.50 (ISBN 0-387-13099-3). Springer Verlag.

Bonchev, Danail. Information Theoretic Indices for Characterization of Chemical Structures. (Chemotrics Research Studies Ser.). 264p. 1983. 58.95 (ISBN 0-471-90087-7, Pub. by Res Stud Pr). Wiley.

Boschke, F. L., ed. Bonding & Structure. (Topics in Current Chemistry: Vol. 63). (Illus.). 160p. 1976. 42.00 (ISBN 0-387-07605-0). Springer-Verlag.

Clarke, M. J., et al, eds. Structure vs. Special Properties. (Structure & Bonding Ser.: Vol. 52). (Illus.). 204p. 1982. 50.00 (ISBN 0-387-11781-4). Springer-Verlag.

DeKock, Roger L. & Gray, Harry B. Chemical Structure & Bonding. 1980. 36.95 (ISBN 0-8053-2310-4). Benjamin-Cummings.

Dewar, M. J., et al, eds. Synthetic & Structural Problems. (Topics in Current Chemistry Ser.: Vol. 106). (Illus.). 170p. 1982. 41.00 (ISBN 0-387-11766-0). Springer-Verlag.

Division of Chemistry & Chemical Technology. Critical Evaluation of Chemical & Physical Structural Information. LC 74-4164. (Illus.). 624p. 1974. pap. 37.95 (ISBN 0-309-02146-4). Natl Acad Pr.

Dobias, B., et al. New Developments, Vol. 56. (Structure & Bonding). (Illus.). 160p. 1984. 34.00 (ISBN 0-387-13106-X). Springer-Verlag.

Kettle, S. A. Symmetry & Structure. 1985. 34.95 (ISBN 0-471-90501-1). Wiley.

Koetzle, T. F., ed. Structure & Bonding: Relationships Between Quantum Chemistry & Crystallography. (Transactions of the ACA: Vol. 16). 95p. 1980. pap. 15.00 (ISBN 0-937140-25-2). Polycrystal Bk Serv.

Margolis, Emil J. Bonding & Structure: A Review of Fundamental Chemistry. LC 68-12785. 175p. 1968. 18.50x (ISBN 0-306-50047-7, Plenum Pr). Plenum Pub.

Moskowitz, H. R. & Warren, Craig, eds. Odor Quality & Chemical Structure. LC 80-28633. (ACS Symposium Ser.: No. 148). 1981. 34.95 (ISBN 0-8412-0607-4). Am Chemical.

Van Wazer, John R. & Absar, Ilyas. Electron Densities in Molecules & Molecular Orbitals. (Physical Chemistry Ser.). 1975. 40.00 (ISBN 0-12-714550-8). Acad Pr.

CHEMICAL SYMBOLS

see Chemistry–Nomenclature; Chemistry–Notation

CHEMICAL TECHNOLOGY

see Chemistry, Technical

CHEMICAL TESTS AND REAGENTS

see also Ozone; Spot Tests (Chemistry)

Cadogan, J. I., ed. Organophosphorus Reagents in Organic Synthesis. LC 79-50307. (Organic Chemistry Ser.). 1980. 95.00 (ISBN 0-12-154350-1). Acad Pr.

Fieser & Fieser's. Reagents for Organic Synthesis, Vol. 11. (Fieser's Reagents for Organic Synthesis Ser.). 669p. 1984. 45.00x (ISBN 0-471-88628-9, Pub. by Wiley-Interscience). Wiley.

Fieser, Louis F. & Fieser, Mary. Reagents for Organic Synthesis, 8 vols. Vol. 1, 1967, 1457p. 74.95 (ISBN 0-471-25875-X); Vol. 2, 1969, 538p. 49.95 (ISBN 0-471-25876-8); Vol. 3, 1972, 401p. 45.95x (ISBN 0-471-25879-2); Vol. 4, 1974, 660p. 51.95 (ISBN 0-471-25881-4); Vol. 5, 1975, 864p. 55.95 (ISBN 0-471-25882-2); Vol. 6, 1977, 765p. 53.50 (ISBN 0-471-25873-3); Vol. 7, 1979, 487p. 49.95 (ISBN 0-471-02918-1); Vol. 8, 1980, 602p. 54.50 (ISBN 0-471-04834-8). Wiley.

Fieser, Mary. Fieser & Fieser's Reagents for Organic Synthesis, Vol. 10. (Reagents for Organic Synthesis Ser.). 528p. 1982. 44.50 (ISBN 0-471-86636-9, Pub. by Wiley-Interscience). Wiley.

Fieser, Mary, et al. Reagents for Organic Synthesis, Vol. 9. (Reagents for Organic Synthesis Ser.). 596p. 1981. 51.95 (ISBN 0-471-05631-6, Pub. by Wiley-Interscience). Wiley.

Gabb, M. H. & Latcham, W. E. Handbook of Laboratory Solutions. 1968. 15.00 (ISBN 0-8206-0055-5). Chem Pub.

Holzbecher, Z., et al. Organic Reagents in Inorganic Analysis. LC 75-34459. (Ser. in Analytical Chemistry). 734p. 1976. 117.95x (ISBN 0-470-01396-6). Halsted Pr.

Linscott, William D. Linscott's Directory of Immunological & Biological Reagents. 3rd ed. 176p. 1984. 30.00x (ISBN 0-9604920-2-X). W D Linscott.

OECD Staff. OECD Guidelines for Testing of Chemicals. 700p. (Orig.). 1981. pap. text ed. 80.00x (ISBN 92-64-12221-4). OECD.

Perrin, D. D. Organic Complexing Reagents: Structural Behavior & Application to Inorganic Analysis. LC 77-16083. 378p. 1978. Repr. of 1964 ed. lib. bdg. 24.50 (ISBN 0-88275-574-9). Krieger.

Pizey, J. S. Synthetic Reagents, Vols. 1-2. LC 73-14417. (Ellis Horwood Synthetic Reagents Ser.). 353p. 1974. Vol. 1, 411p. 94.95 (ISBN 0-470-69104-2); Vol. 2, 353p. 94.95 (ISBN 0-470-69107-7). Halsted Pr.

--Synthetic Reagents: Chloramine-T; Hydrogen Peroxide; Polyphosphoric Acid, Vol. 6. (Synthetic Reagents Ser.). 81.95 (ISBN 0-470-20152-5). Halsted Pr.

--Synthetic Reagents Vol. 4: Mercuric Acetate Periodic Acid & Periodates Sulfuryl Chloride. LC 80-41742. 426p. 1981. 124.95 (ISBN 0-470-27133-7). Halsted Pr.

Pizey, J. S., ed. Synthetic Reagents, Vol. 3. LC 73-14417. 447p. 1977. 79.95 (ISBN 0-470-99118-6). Halsted Pr.

Pribil, F. Analytical Application of EDTA & Related Compounds. 368p. 1972. text ed. 99.00 (ISBN 0-08-016363-7). Pergamon.

Sievers, Robert E. Nuclear Magnetic Resonance Shift Reagents. 1973. 44.00 (ISBN 0-12-643050-0). Acad Pr.

Specifications for Reagents Mentioned in the International Pharmacopoeia. (Also avail. in French). 1963. 8.00 (ISBN 92-4-154002-8). World Health.

Walter. Dry Reagent Chemistries in Chemical Analysis. (Chemical Analysis-A Series of Monographs on Analytical Chemistry & Its Applications). Date not set. price not set (ISBN 0-471-82494-1). Wiley.

Welcher, Frank. Chemical Solutions: Reagent Useful to the Chemist, Biologist & Bacteriologist. 412p. 1966. pap. 5.50 (ISBN 0-442-09280-6). Krieger.

Welcher, Frank J. & Boschmann, Erwin. Organic Reagents for Copper. LC 76-18141. 632p. (Orig.). 1979. 41.50 (ISBN 0-88275-440-8). Krieger.

CHEMICAL WARFARE

see also Decontamination (From Gases, Chemicals, etc.)

Alexander, A., et al. Control of Chemical & Biological Weapons. LC 73-151279. 1971. pap. 1.50 (ISBN 0-87003-016-7). Carnegie Endow.

Brown, Frederic J. Chemical Warfare: A Study in Restraints. LC 80-27993. xix, 355p. 1981. Repr. of 1968 ed. lib. bdg. 37.50x (ISBN 0-313-22823-X, BRCHW). Greenwood.

Cookson, John & Nottingham, Judith. Survey of Chemical & Biological Warfare. LC 79-128595. 432p. pap. 3.95 (ISBN 0-85345-223-7). Monthly Rev.

Evans, Grant. The Yellow Rainmakers: Are Chemical Weapons Being Used in Southeast Asia? 160p. 1983. 24.00 (ISBN 0-8052-7164-3, Pub. by NLB England); pap. 7.50 (ISBN 0-8052-7165-1). Schocken.

Haldane, John B. Callinicus: A Defence of Chemical Warfare. LC 78-148366. (Library of War & Peace; the Character & Causes of War). lib. bdg. 46.00 (ISBN 0-8240-0461-2). Garland Pub.

Health Aspects of Chemical & Biological Weapons: Report of a WHO Group of Consultants. 132p. 1970. pap. 5.60 (ISBN 92-4-156034-7, 188). World Health.

Hoeber, Amoretta M. The Chemistry of Defeat: Asymmetries in U. S. & Soviet Chemical Warfare Postures. LC 81-84989. (Special Report Ser.). 91p. 1981. 6.50 (ISBN 0-89549-037-4). Inst Foreign Policy Anal.

Livingstone, Neil C. & Douglass, Joseph D. CBW: The Poor Man's Atomic Bomb. LC 84-47502. (National Security Papers: No. 1). 36p. 1984. pap. 5.00 (ISBN 0-89549-057-9, IFPA35, IFPA). Unipub.

--CBW: the Poor Man's Atomic Bomb. Toner, John, tr. LC 84-47502. (National Security Paper Ser.). 36p. 1984. 5.00 (ISBN 0-89549-057-9). Inst Foreign Policy Anal.

McNaught, L. W. Nuclear, Biological & Chemical Warfare. (Brassey's Battlefield Weapons Systems & Technology Ser.: Vol. 4). 60p. 1984. 27.00 (ISBN 0-08-028328-4); pap. 12.50 (ISBN 0-08-028329-2). Pergamon.

Meselson, Matthew, ed. Chemical Weapons & Chemical Arms Control. LC 77-93266. 1978. pap. text ed. 3.00 (ISBN 0-87003-010-8). Carnegie Endow.

Murphy, Sean, et al. No Fire, No Thunder: The Threat of Chemical & Biological Weapons. LC 84-20579. 160p. 1984. 23.00 (ISBN 0-85345-661-5); pap. 7.50 (ISBN 0-85345-662-3). Monthly Rev.

Robinson, Julian P. Chemical Warfare Arms Control: A Framework for Considering Policy Alternatives. (Chemical & Biological Warfare Studies: No. 2). 1985. write for info. (S I P R I). Taylor & Francis.

Seagrave, Sterling. Yellow Rain: A Journey Through the Terror of Chemical Warfare. LC 81-12645. 324p. 1981. 11.95 (ISBN 0-87131-349-9). M Evans.

SIPRI Staff & Thomas. Chemical & Biological Warfare Studies, Vol. 1: Effect of Chemical Warfare: a Selective Review & Bibliography of British State Papers. 1985. pap. 17.00 (ISBN 0-85066-307-5). Taylor & Francis.

Storella, Mark C. Poisoning Arms Control: The Soviet Union & Chemical-Biological Weapons. LC 84-10832. (Special Report Ser.). 99p. 1984. 7.50 (ISBN 0-89549-063-3). Inst Foreign Policy Anal.

Taylor & Francis, Ltd., ed. Chemical Weapons: Destruction & Conversion. 210p. 1980. pap. 15.00x (ISBN 0-85066-199-4). Taylor & Francis.

Thomas, Andy. Effects of Chemical Welfare: A Selective Review & Bibliography of British State Papers. (Chemical & Biological Warfare Studies). 19.00 (ISBN 0-85066-307-5, S I P R I). Taylor & Francis.

Thomas, Ann V. & Thomas, A. J., Jr. Legal Limits on the Use of Chemical & Biological Weapons. LC 78-128123. 1970. 15.95 (ISBN 0-87074-111-X). SMU Press.

Trapp, Ralf. The Detoxification & Natural Degradation of Chemical Warfare Agents. (Chemical & Biologocal Warfare Agents Studies: No. 3). 1985. write for info. (SIPRI). Taylor & Francis.

CHEMICAL WORKERS

see also Chemists

Halle, David. America's Working Man: Work, Home, & Politics among Blue-Collar Property Owners. LC 84-2566. (Illus.). 288p. 1984. 24.95 (ISBN 0-226-31365-4). U of Chicago Pr.

Rilhimaki, Aitio. Biological Monitoring & Surveillance of Workers Exposed to Chemicals. 1983. text ed. 69.50 (ISBN 0-07-000737-3). McGraw.

CHEMICAL WORKS

see Chemical Plants

CHEMICALS

see also groups of chemicals, e.g. Acids, Explosives, and individual chemical substances, e.g. Carbolic Acid

Bahme, Charles W. Fire Officers Guide to Dangerous Chemicals. (Get Ahead Ser.). 250p. 1972. 8.50 (ISBN 0-685-46048-7, FSP#36). Natl Fire Prot.

Business Communications Staff. Specialty Water Treatment Chemicals. 1985. pap. 1750.00 (ISBN 0-89336-433-9, C-002N). BCC.

Chalmers, L. & Bathe, P. Household & Industrial Chemical Specialties: Polishes, Disinfectants, Adhesives, Abrasives, Paints, Aerosols, Household Toiletries, Vol. 2. 1979. 32.50 (ISBN 0-8206-0250-7). Chem Pub.

Chemical Resistance Data Handbook. 85.00 (ISBN 0-686-48133-X, 0302). T-C Pubns CA.

Conway, Richard A. Environmental Risk Analysis of Chemicals. (Environmental Engineering Ser.). 640p. 1981. 42.50 (ISBN 0-442-21650-5). Van Nos Reinhold.

Cooke, Edward I., ed. Handbook of Chemical Synonyms & Trade Names. 8th ed. 776p. 1978. 66.00 (ISBN 0-685-56918-7). CRC Pr.

Daly, John W., et al, eds. Physiology & Pharmacology of Adenosine Derivatives. (Illus.). 314p. 1983. text ed. 76.00 (ISBN 0-89004-833-9). Raven.

Follweiler, Joanne M. & Sherma, Joseph, eds. Handbook of Chromatography, Pesticides & Related Organic Chemicals. 368p. 1984. 67.00 (ISBN 0-8493-4010-1). CRC Pr.

Fomenko, Vadim S. Handbook of Thermionic Properties: Electronic Work Functions & Richardson Constants of Elements & Compounds. LC 65-23385. 151p. 1966. 42.50x (ISBN 0-306-65117-3, IFI Plenum). Plenum Pub.

Hollaender, A., et al, eds. Trends in the Biology of Fermentations for Fuels & Chemicals. LC 81-5928. (Basic Life Sciences Ser.). 604p. 1981. 85.00x (ISBN 0-306-40752-3, Plenum Pr). Plenum Pub.

International Conference on Chemical Vapor Deposition. Chemical Vapor Deposition: Papers of the International Conference, 4th, Boston, 1973. Wakefield, Gene F. & Blocher, John M., Jr., eds. LC 73-86873. pap. 152.00 (ISBN 0-317-10740-2, 2050866). Bks Demand UMI.

--Chemical Vapor Deposition: Proceedings of the International Conference, 5th, Slough England, 1975. Blocher, John, et al, eds. LC 75-21170. (Illus.). pap. 160.00 (ISBN 0-317-11030-6, 2051507). Bks Demand UMI.

--Chemical Vapor Deposition: Proceedings of the International Conference, 6th, Atlanta, GA, 1977. Donaghey, Lee F., et al, eds. LC 77-84949. (Illus.). pap. 148.30 (ISBN 0-317-11098-5, 2051324). Bks Demand UMI.

IPC Business Press, ed. European Chemical Buyers' Guide. 1984. 195.00x (ISBN 0-617-00255-X, Pub. by IPC Busn England). State Mutual Bk.

Kenworthy, L., ed. Chemicals in Ships. LC 79-670116. 1979. 35.00x (ISBN 0-900976-72-1, Pub. by Inst Marine Eng). Intl Spec Bk.

Kilian, M., et al, eds. Haemophilus, Pasteurella & Actinobacillus. 1981. 44.00 (ISBN 0-12-406780-8). Acad Pr.

Kuhns, John F., ed. Codex of Fishery Chemicals. 1983. looseleaf 50.00X (ISBN 0-318-00766-5). Written Word.

Lyman, W. J. & Reehl, W. F. Handbook of Chemical Property Estimation Methods. 976p. 1982. 52.50 (ISBN 0-07-039175-0). McGraw.

McGraw-Hill Editors. Dictionary of Chemical Terms. 480p. 1985. write for info. (ISBN 0-07-045417-5). McGraw.

McKetta, John, ed. Encyclopedia of Chemical Processing & Design, Vol. 10. 1979. 115.00 (ISBN 0-8247-2410-0). Dekker.
Neely. Chemicals in the Environment. (Pollution Engineering & Technology Ser.: Vol. 7). 1980. 39.75 (ISBN 0-8247-6975-9). Dekker.
Newman, Paul. Optical Resolution Procedures for Chemical Compounds, Vol. 1: Amines & Related Compounds. 1981. 52.50 (ISBN 0-9601918-0-1). Optical Resolution.
Nicolis, G. & Baras, F., eds. Chemical Instabilities: Applications in Chemistry, Engineering, Geology, & Materials Science. 1984. lib. bdg. 58.00 (ISBN 90-277-1705-2, Pub. by Reidel Holland). Kluwer Academic.
Perrin, D. D., et al. Purification of Laboratory Chemicals. 2nd ed. LC 79-41708. 580p. 1980. 85.00 (ISBN 0-08-022961-1). Pergamon.
Saxena, J. Hazard Assessment of Chemicals: Current Developments, Vol. 3. (Serial Publication). 1984. 65.00 (ISBN 0-12-312403-4). Acad Pr.
Saxena, Jitendra, ed. Hazard Assessment of Chemicals, Vol. 2. (Serial Publication). 332p. 1983. 47.50 (ISBN 0-12-312402-6). Acad Pr.
Swann, Robert L. & Eschenroeder, Alan, eds. Fate of Chemicals in the Environment. LC 83-12209. (ACS Symposium Ser.: No. 225). 320p. 1983. lib. bdg. 49.95 (ISBN 0-8412-0792-5). Am Chemical.
Thibodeaux, Louis J. Chemodynamics: Environmental Movement of Chemicals in Air, Water, & Soil. LC 78-31637. 501p. 1979. 54.95x (ISBN 0-471-04720-1, Pub. by Wiley-Interscience). Wiley.
Twigg, John. The Chemicals We Use. (Science in Today's World Ser.). (Illus.). 72p. 1984. 14.95 (ISBN 0-7134-4483-5, Pub. by Batsford England). David & Charles.
Walker, Colin. Environmental Pollution by Chemicals. 1980. pap. text ed. 8.25x (ISBN 0-09-123891-9, Hutchinson U Lib). Humanities.
Wolman, Yecheskel. Chemical Information: A Practical Guide to Utilization. LC 82-2763. 250p. 1983. 26.95x (ISBN 0-471-10319-5, Pub. by Wiley-Interscience). Wiley.

CHEMICALS–MANUFACTURE AND INDUSTRY

see also Chemical Industries; Chemical Workers; Chemistry, Technical; Electrochemistry, Industrial;
also specific chemical industries

Annual Bullentin of Exports of Chemical Products: 1973, Vol. 1. (Eng., Fr & Rus.). pap. 9.50 (ISBN 0-686-94848-3, UN75/2E/10, UN). Unipub.
Annual Bulletin of Trade in Chemical Products: 1974-1978, Vols. 1-5. Incl. Vol. 6. 1979. 285p. 1981. pap. 19.00 (UN812E3); Vol. 8. 1981. 284p. 1983. pap. text ed. 30.00 (UN83/2E5); Vol. 9. 1982. (Eng., Fr & Rus., Illus.). 285p. 1985. pap. 33.00 (UN84/2E3). (Eng., Fr. & Rus.). pap. 19.00 ea. (UN76/2E16, UN). Vol. 1, 1974 (UN74/2E16). Vol. 2, 1975 (UN76/2E22). Vol. 3, 1976 (UN77/2E22). Vol. 4, 1977 (UN78/2E23). Vol. 5, 1978 (UN79/2E29). Unipub.
Benninghoff, H. Index of Chemicals. (Eng., Ger., & Fr.). 1974. 128.00 (ISBN 0-444-41075-9). Elsevier.
Betts, G. G. & Plenard, F. J. Future Changes in the Chemical Industry. 34p. 1981. 32.00x (ISBN 0-85295-145-0, Pub. by IChemE). State Mutual Bk.
Chem Sources-U. S. A. 26th ed. 1985. 180.00 (ISBN 0-937020-06-0). Directories Pub.
Chemical Manufacturers Association. Risk Management of Existing Chemicals. LC 84-80974. (Illus.). 192p. 1984. pap. 28.00 (ISBN 0-86587-065-9). Gov Insts.
Control of Chemicals in Importing Countries. 196p. (Orig.). 1982. pap. 12.00x (ISBN 92-64-12272-9). OECD.
Derz, Friedrich W., ed. ChemBUYdirect: International Chemical Buyers Directory, 3 vols. 1974-76. Set. 259.00x (ISBN 3-11-004688-1). De Gruyter.
European Federation of Chemical Engineering, 2nd Intl. Conference on Phase Equilibria & Fluid Properties in the Chemical Industry, Berlin, 1980. Phase Equilibria & Fluid Properties in the Chemical Industry: Proceedings, Pts. 1 & 2. (EFCE Publication Ser.: No. 11). 1012p. 1980. text ed. 92.50x (ISBN 3-921567-35-1, Pub. by Dechema Germany). Scholium Intl.
Flick, Ernest W. Household, Automotive & Industrial Chemical Formulations. 2nd ed. LC 83-22115. 360p. 1984. 48.00 (ISBN 0-8155-0970-7). Noyes.
Furbush, S. A. Energy-Conservation Opportunities in the Chemical Industry. Gyftopoulos, Elias P. & Cohen, Karen C., eds. (Industrial Energy-Conservation Manuals Ser.: No. 14). (Illus.). 136p. 1982. loose-leaf 20.00x (ISBN 0-262-06081-7). MIT Pr.
Goldfarb, Alan S., et al. Organic Chemicals Manufacturing Hazards. LC 81-65889. 430p. 1981. text ed. 59.95 (ISBN 0-250-40409-5). Butterworth.
Goldstein, Irving S. Organic Chemicals from Biomass. 320p. 1981. 92.00 (ISBN 0-8493-5531-1). CRC Pr.
Hardie, D. W. & Davidson Pratt, J. A History of the Modern British Chemical Industry. 1966. pap. 11.75 (ISBN 0-08-011686-8). Pergamon.
Hart, J. Roger. Effective Chemical Marketing, Advertising & Promotion: A Practical Guide for the Chemical Marketing Professional. LC 83-12179. (Illus.). 121p. 1984. 24.00 (ISBN 0-8155-0954-5, Noyes Pubns). Noyes.
Haynes, Williams. Chemical Pioneers. LC 74-99701. (Essay Index Reprint Ser.). 1939. 27.50 (ISBN 0-8369-1442-2). Ayer Co Pubs.
Lexique des Termes Techniques Concernant le Material d'Une Usine d'Acetylene Dissous. (Fr.). 78p. (Lexicon of Technical Terms Concerning the Materials of Dissolved Acetylene Manufacturing). 1970. pap. 29.95 (ISBN 0-686-56759-5, M-6363). French & Eur.
Louden, Louise. Recovery of Chemicals from Spent Pulping Liquors. LC 78-71464. (Bibliographic Ser.: No. 285). 1978. pap. 45.00 (ISBN 0-87010-043-2). Inst Paper Chem.
McKetta. Encyclopedia of Chemical Processing & Design, Vol. 23. 1985. 125.00 (ISBN 0-8247-2473-9). Dekker.
McKetta, J., ed. Encyclopedia of Chemical Processing & Design, Vol. 6. 1978. 115.00 (ISBN 0-686-80400-7). Dekker.
--Encyclopedia of Chemical Processing & Design, Vol. 9. 1979. 115.00 (ISBN 0-8247-2409-7). Dekker.
McKetta, John J., Jr., intro. by. Chemical Technology: An Encyclopedic Treatment, 7 vols. Incl. Vol. 1. Air, Water, Inorganic Chemicals & Nucleonics. 1968; Vol. 2. Non-Metallic Ores, Silicate Industries & Solid Minerals Fuels. (Illus.). 828p. 1971. Pgs. 828 (ISBN 0-06-491103-9). (06296); Vol. 3. Metals & Ores. (Illus.). 918p. 1970. Pgs. 918 (ISBN 0-06-491104-7). (06297); Vol. 4. Petroleum & Organic Chemicals. (Illus.). 792p. 1972. Pgs. 792 (ISBN 0-06-491105-5). (06298); Vol. 5. Natural Organic Materials & Related Synthetic Products. (Illus.). 898p. 1972. Pgs. 898 (ISBN 0-06-491106-3). (06299); Vol. 6. Wood, Paper, Textiles, Plastics & Photographic Materials. (Illus.). 686p. 1973 (ISBN 0-06-491107-1). (06300); Vol. 7. Vegetable Food Products & Luxuries. (Illus.). 905p. 1975. Pgs. 905 (ISBN 0-06-491108-X). (06301); Vol. 8. Edible Oils & Fats & Animal Food Products: Material Resources. (Illus.). 600p. 1975. Pgs. 600 (ISBN 0-06-491109-8). (06302). (Illus.). 45.00x ea. B&N Imports.
NFPA Forest Committee. Chemicals for Forest Fire Fighting. 2nd ed. 112p. 1967. 3.00 (ISBN 0-685-46049-5). Natl Fire Prot.
OPD Chemical Buyers Directory, 1985. 72nd ed. 830p. 1984. pap. 60.00 (ISBN 0-9606454-3-8). Schnell Pub.
Rich, Susan, ed. Profiles of U.S. Chemical Distributors. LC 81-83812. 265p. 1981. pap. 277.00 (ISBN 0-917148-77-0). Kline.
Sittig, Marshall. Manufacturing Processes for New Pharmaceuticals. LC 83-13074. (Chemical Technology Review Ser.: No. 220). (Illus.). 612p. 1984. 84.00 (ISBN 0-8155-0952-9, Noyes Pubns). Noyes.
Stratton, Andrew. Energy & Feedstocks in the Chemical Industry. 403p. 1983. 96.95 (ISBN 0-470-27396-8). Halsted Pr.
Valle-Riestra, J. Frank. Project Evaluation in the Chemical Process Industries. (Chemical Engineering Ser.). (Illus.). 752p. 1983. text ed. 46.00 (ISBN 0-07-066840-X). McGraw.
Veal, F. J. Economics of Producing Certain Chemicals from Cellulose: A Review of Recent Literature, 1979. 1981. 80.00x (ISBN 0-686-97066-7, Pub. by W Spring England). State Mutual Bk.

CHEMICALS–PHYSIOLOGICAL EFFECTS

Brooke, L. T., et al, eds. Acute Toxicities of Organic Chemicals to Fathead Minnows (Pimephales Promelas, Vol. 1. (Toxicity of Organic Chemicals Ser.). (Illus.). 414p. (Orig.). 1984. pap. 62.95 (ISBN 0-9614968-0-0). U of WI-Superior.

CHEMICALS–SAFETY MEASURES

Bartone, John C., II. Health & Medical Aspects of Chemical Industries: Subject Analysis & Research Guide. LC 83-45536. 153p. 1984. 29.95 (ISBN 0-88164-104-9); pap. 21.95 (ISBN 0-88164-105-7). ABBE Pubs Assn.
Bretherick, L. Handbook of Reactive Chemical Hazards. 2nd ed. 1979. text ed. 175.00 (ISBN 0-408-70927-8). Butterworth.
--Handbook of Reactive Chemical Hazards, CRC. 996p. 1975. 49.95 (ISBN 0-685-69893-9). CRC Pr.
Bretherick, Leslie. Handbook of Reactive Chemical Hazards. 3rd ed. 1280p. 1985. text ed. 139.95 (ISBN 0-408-01388-5). Butterworth.
Brock, Neely W. & Gary, Blau, eds. Environmental Exposure From Chemicals, Vol. 2. 192p. 1985. 60.00 (ISBN 0-8493-6166-4). CRC Pr.
Garcia, Eugene N. & Spencer, Wanda. Safety for People & for Chemicals. LC 79-90457. (Illus.). 80p. (Orig.). 1979. pap. 4.50x (ISBN 0-87881-096-X); incl. 2 tests. Mojave Bks.
Homburger, F., ed. Safety Evaluation & Regulation of Chemicals. (Illus.). xiv, 294p. 1983. 84.25 (ISBN 3-8055-3578-3). S Karger.
Kruus, P., et al, eds. Controversial Chemicals: A Citizen's Guide. 232p. 1984. pap. text ed. 14.50 (ISBN 0-919868-22-3, Pub. by Multisci Pubns Ltd). Brookfield Pub Co.
Media Institute. Chemical Risks: Fears, Facts, & the Media. LC 85-60247. (Illus.). 72p. (Orig.). 1985. pap. 12.95 (ISBN 0-937790-28-1). Media Inst.
National Research Council. Disposal of Chemical Munitions & Agents. 216p. 1984. pap. text ed. 16.40 (ISBN 0-309-03527-9). Natl Acad Pr.
OECD Staff. Economic Aspects of International Chemicals Control. 96p. (Orig.). 1983. pap. 11.00x (ISBN 92-64-12508-6). OECD.
Pipitone, David A. Safe Storage of Laboratory Chemicals. LC 83-21641. 280p. 1984. 60.00 (ISBN 0-471-89610-1, Pub. by Wiley-Interscience). Wiley.
Prudent Practices for Disposal of Chemicals from Laboratories. 304p. 1983. 16.50 (ISBN 0-309-03390-X). Natl Acad Pr.
Regenstein, Lewis. America the Poisoned: How Deadly Chemicals are Destroying our Environment, our Wildlife, Our selves & How We can Survive! LC 82-1813. (Illus.). 1982. 16.95 (ISBN 0-87491-486-8); pap. 8.95 (ISBN 0-87491-605-4). Acropolis.
Rilhimaki, Aitio. Biological Monitoring & Surveillance of Workers Exposed to Chemicals. 1983. text ed. 69.50 (ISBN 0-07-000737-3). McGraw.
Rodricks, Joseph V. & Tardiff, Robert C., eds. Assessment & Management of Chemical Risks. LC 83-25851. (ACS Symposium Ser.: No. 239). 184p. 1984. lib. bdg. 39.95x (ISBN 0-8412-0821-2). Am Chemical.
Saxen, Jitendra, ed. Hazard Assessments of Chemicals, Vol. 4. 1985. 69.50 (ISBN 0-12-312404-2). Acad Pr.
Sheenan, P. J. Appraisal of Tests to Predict the Environmental Behavior of Chemicals: Scope 25. (Scope Ser.). 1984. 59.95 (ISBN 0-471-90545-3). Wiley.
Smith, Al J. Managing Hazardous Substances Accidents. (Illus.). 224p. 1981. 29.50 (ISBN 0-07-058467-2). McGraw.
Toxic Chemical & Explosives Facilities: Safety & Engineering Design. LC 79-9760. (Symposium Ser.: No. 96). 1979. 39.95 (ISBN 0-8412-0481-0). Am Chemical.
Worobec, Mary D. Toxic Substances Controls Primer: Federal Regulation of Chemicals in the Environment. 236p. 1984. 20.00 (ISBN 0-87179-458-6). BNA.

CHEMICULTURE

see Hydroponics

CHEMILUMINESCENCE

Burr. Chemi-& Bioluminescence. (Clinical & Biochemical Analysis Ser.). 658p. 1985. 85.00 (ISBN 0-8247-7277-6). Dekker.
Cormier, M. J., et al, eds. Chemiluminescence & Bioluminescence. LC 73-76169. 515p. 1973. 55.00x (ISBN 0-306-30733-2, Plenum Pr). Plenum Pub.
Deluca, Marlene & McElroy, William, eds. Bioluminescience & Chemiluminescence: Basic Chemistry & Analytical Applications. 1981. 59.50 (ISBN 0-12-208820-4). Acad Pr.
Dyke, Knox V., ed. Bioluminesence & Chemiluminesence Instruments & Applications, Vols. I & II. 1985. Vol. I, 288 pgs. 83.00 (ISBN 0-8493-5863-9); Vol. II, 320 pgs. 93.00 (ISBN 0-8493-5864-7). CRC Pr.
Fontijn, A., ed. Gas-Phase Chemiluminescence & Chemi-Ionization. 370p. 1985. 40.75 (ISBN 0-444-86950-6, North-Holland). Elsevier.
Kricka. Analytical Applications of Bioluminescence & Chemiluminescence. 1984. 49.00 (ISBN 0-12-426290-2). Acad Pr.

CHEMISTRY

see also Acids; Agricultural Chemistry; Alchemy; Assaying; Bases, Chemistry; Biological Chemistry; Botanical Chemistry; Catalysis; Color; Combustion; Cosmochemistry; Crystallization; Crystallography; Decomposition (Chemistry); Electrochemistry; Evaporation; Explosives; Fermentation; Fire; Gases–Liquefaction; Geochemistry; Immunochemistry; Microchemistry; Pharmacy; Photochemistry; Photographic Chemistry; Physiological Chemistry; Poisons; Solution (Chemistry); Spectrum Analysis; Stereochemistry; Water Chemistry
also headings beginning with the word Chemical

Abbott, David. Basic Notes on Advanced Level Chemistry. pap. 6.50x (ISBN 0-392-08409-0, SpS). Sportshelf.
Abraham, Michael R. & Pavelich, Michael J. Inquiries into Chemistry. (Illus.). 1979. 10.95x (ISBN 0-917974-32-8). Waveland Pr.
Abrash, Henry & Hardcastle, Kenneth. Chemistry. 1981. Repr. text ed. write for info. (ISBN 0-02-471100-4); lab. manual avail. (ISBN 0-02-471170-5); study guide avail. (ISBN 0-686-72522-0). Macmillan.
Acharya, K. R., et al. Pre-University Chemistry, Vol. 1. 2nd & rev. ed. 267p. 1985. 15.95x (ISBN 0-7069-2665-X, Pub. by Vikas India). Advent NY.
Acquaah, Samuel O. A New Certificate Practical Chemistry. LC 83-82066. 112p. 1983. write for info (ISBN 0-8187-0054-8). Harlo Pr.
Akanazarova, S. L. & Kafarov, V. V. Experiment Optimization in Chemistry & Chemical Engineering. MAtskovsky, V. M. & Repyev, A. P., trs. from Rus. 312p. 1982. 9.95 (ISBN 0-8285-2305-3, Pub. by Mir Pubs USSR). Imported Pubns.
Akhmetov, N. General & Inorganic Chemistry. 670p. 1983. 13.95 (ISBN 0-8285-2567-6, Pub. by Mir Pubs USSR). Imported Pubns.
Albright, Thomas A. Orbital Interactions in Chemistry. LC 84-15310. 447p. 1985. 49.95 (ISBN 0-471-87393-4, Pub. by Wiley-Interscience). Wiley.
Allen, Thomas L. & Keefer, Raymond M. Chemistry: Experiment & Theory. 2nd ed. 742p. 1982. text ed. 31.95 scp (ISBN 0-06-040209-1, HarpC); solution manual scp 3.95 (ISBN 0-06-040211-3); instr's. manual avail. (ISBN 0-06-360203-2). Har-Row.
Anderson, Curtis B., et al. Chemistry: Principles & Applications. 1973. text ed. 24.95x (ISBN 0-669-73833-6); instructors' manual free (ISBN 0-669-81919-0). Heath.
Ash, M. & Ash, I. Encyclopedia of Industrial Chemical Additives, Vol. 1, A-F. 1984. 75.00 (ISBN 0-8206-0299-X). Chem Pub.
Bailar, John C., Jr., et al. Chemistry. 2nd ed. 1984. 28.00i (ISBN 0-12-072855-9); instrs' manual 10.00i (ISBN 0-12-072857-5); student solutions manual 7.25i (ISBN 0-12-072858-3); study guide 9.25i (ISBN 0-12-072859-1); transparency masters 50.00i (ISBN 0-12-072860-5). Acad Pr.
Baker, Jeffrey J. W. & Allen, Garland E. Matter, Energy, & Life: An Introduction to Chemical Concepts. 4th ed. LC 80-17946. (Life Sciences Ser.). 256p. 1981. 15.95 (ISBN 0-201-00169-1). Addison-Wesley.
Balahura, Robert. Test Bank to Accompany General Chemistry. LW, LC & GLH, eds. 214p. 1984. pap. write for info. (ISBN 0-7167-1696-8). W H Freeman.
Baldeschwieler, John D., ed. Chemistry & Chemical Engineering in the People's Republic of China. LC 79-11217. 1979. pap. 12.95 (ISBN 0-8412-0502-7). Am Chemical.
Banerjea, D. Coordination Chemistry: Twentieth International Conference on Coordination Chemistry, Calcutta, India, 10-14 Dec. 1979, Proceedings, Vol. 20. LC 80-41163. 286p. 1980. 88.00 (ISBN 0-08-023942-0). Pergamon.
Bates, R. B. & Ogle, C. A. Carbanian Chemistry. (Reactivity & Structure Ser.: Vol. 17). 110p. 1983. 21.50 (ISBN 0-387-12345-8). Springer-Verlag.
Baum, Stuart J. & Scaife, Charles W. Chemistry: A Life Science Approach. 2nd ed. (Illus.). 1980. text ed. write for info. (ISBN 0-02-306610-5). Macmillan.
Beck, Curt W., ed. Archeological Chemistry. LC 74-22372. (Advances in Chemistry Ser: No. 138). 1974. 39.95 (ISBN 0-8412-0211-7). Am Chemical.
Belov, Nikolai V. Crystal Chemistry of Large-Cation Silicates. LC 63-17642. pap. 42.00 (ISBN 0-317-08935-8, 2003357). Bks Demand UMI.
Bennett, H. Chemical Specialties. 1978. 28.50 (ISBN 0-8206-0210-8). Chem Pub.
Bertini & Drago. The Coordination Chemistry of Metalloenzymes: The Role of Metals in Reaction Involving Water, Dioxygen & Related Species. 1983. lib. bdg. 56.00 (ISBN 90-277-1530-0, Pub. by Reidel Holland). Kluwer Academic.
Bettelheim, Frederick A. & March, Jerry. Introduction to General, Organic & Biochemistry. LC 83-20124. 708p. 1984. text ed. 33.95x (ISBN 0-03-061548-8); study guide 12.95 (ISBN 0-03-064122-5). SCP.
Bhave, W. N. & King, W. R. New Secondary Chemistry. 292p. 1981. 30.00x (ISBN 0-86131-015-2, Pub. by Orient Longman India). State Mutual Bk.
Binford, Jesse S., Jr. Foundation of Chemistry. 1977. write for info. (ISBN 0-02-309880-5, 30988). Macmillan.
--Foundations of Chemistry. (Illus.). 334p. 1985. pap. text ed. 23.95 (ISBN 0-931541-03-4). Bk Pubs.
Bochnovic, John. The Inventive Step: Its Evolution in Canada, the United Kingdom, & the United States. Beier, Freidrich & Schricker, Gerhard, eds. (I I C Studies, Vol. 5). 90p. 1982. 25.30x (ISBN 0-89573-058-8). VCH Pubs.

Boikess, Robert, et al. Elements of Chemistry: General, Organic & Biological. (Illus.). 704p. 1986. text ed. 35.95 (ISBN 0-13-263583-6). P-H.

Boikess, Robert S. & Edelson, Edward. Chemical Principles. 3rd ed. 866p. 1985. text ed. 36.50 scp (ISBN 0-06-040805-7, HarpC); instr's. manual avail. (ISBN 0-06-360795-6); solutions manual avail. (ISBN 0-06-040813-8); answer book avail. (ISBN 0-06-360796-4). Har-Row.

Boikess, Robert S., et al. Chemical Principles. 2nd ed. (Illus.). 1981. text ed. 33.95 scp (ISBN 0-06-040808-1, HarpC); pap. text ed. 18.50 scp lab manual (ISBN 0-06-040811-1); study guide scp 8.50 (ISBN 0-06-040809-X); scp solutions manual 6.75 (ISBN 0-06-040812-X); instr. manual avail. (ISBN 0-06-360792-1); ans. bk. avail. (ISBN 0-06-360793-X). Har-Row.

Boldyrev, V. V., et al, eds. Control of the Reactivity of Solids. (Studies in Surface Science & Catalysts: Vol. 2). 226p. 1979. 64.00 (ISBN 0-444-41800-8). Elsevier.

Boschke, F. L., ed. Van der Waals Systems. (Topics in Current Chemistry: Vol. 93). (Illus.). 140p. 1980. 42.00 (ISBN 0-387-10058-X). Springer-Verlag.

Boschmann, E. & Wells, N. Chemistry in Action: A Laboratory Manual for General, Organic, & Biological Chemistry. 2nd ed. 320p. 1984. 17.95 (ISBN 0-07-006529-2). McGraw.

Bowers, Michael, ed. Gas Phase Ion Chemistry. 1979. Vol. 1. 49.50 (ISBN 0-12-120801-X); Vol. 2. 52.50 (ISBN 0-12-120802-8). Acad Pr.

Bradley, J. N., et al, eds. Essays in Chemistry. Incl. Vol. 1. 1970. pap. 24.50 (ISBN 0-12-124101-7); Vol. 2. 1971. pap. 24.50 (ISBN 0-12-124102-5); Vol. 3. 1972. pap. 25.00 (ISBN 0-12-124103-3); Vol. 4. 1973. pap. 25.00 (ISBN 0-12-124104-1); Vol. 5. 1974. pap. 25.00 (ISBN 0-12-124105-X); Vol. 6. 1978. pap. 25.00 (ISBN 0-12-124106-8); Vol. 7. 1978. pap. 25.00 (ISBN 0-12-124107-6). pap. Acad Pr.

Brady. General Chemistry: Principles & Structure, Vol. 2. 2nd ed. 500p. 1985. pap. text ed. write for info. (ISBN 0-471-89534-2). Wiley.

Brady, J. E. & Humiston, J. R. General Chemistry: Principles & Structure, 2 vols. 2nd ed. (Bahasa-Malaysia.). 900p. 1985. Set. text ed. write for info. (ISBN 0-471-80156-9); Vol. 1, 500p. pap. text ed. 16.00 (ISBN 0-471-86617-2); Vol. 2, 500p. pap. text ed. 16.00 (ISBN 0-471-86618-0). Wiley.

Brady, James E. & Holum, John R. Fundamentals of Chemistry. 2nd ed. LC 83-21796. 960p. 1984. text ed. 39.50 (ISBN 0-471-87548-1); write for info. tchr's lab (ISBN 0-471-87894-4); study guide 15.50 (ISBN 0-471-87891-X); lab. manual 20.50 (ISBN 0-471-89007-3); sol. manual 13.95 (ISBN 0-471-87947-9); write for info. transparency (ISBN 0-471-87946-0). Wiley.

Brady, James E. & Humiston, Gerard E. General Chemistry: Principles & Structure. 3rd ed. 831p. 1982. 38.50 (ISBN 0-471-07806-9); text ed. 35.95 SI version (ISBN 0-471-86739-X); exam manager 10.95 (ISBN 0-471-80509-2); solutions manual 12.95 (ISBN 0-471-09964-3); solutions manual, SI version 9.50 (ISBN 0-471-86968-6); study guide 13.95 (ISBN 0-471-08354-2). Wiley.

--General Chemistry: Principles & Structure. 2nd ed. LC 77-11045. 800p. 1978. text ed. 27.95 (ISBN 0-471-01910-0). wkbk. 8.25x (ISBN 0-471-03498-3). Wiley.

Bragg, William L. & Porter, George, eds. Physical Sciences: The Royal Institution Library of Science, 10 vols. plus index. (Illus.). 5300p. 1971. Set. 185.00 (ISBN 0-444-20048-7, Pub. by Elsevier Applied Sci England). Set. pap. 74.00 (ISBN 0-85334-615-1). Elsevier.

Breck, Donald W. Zeolite Molecular Sieves: Structure, Chemistry & Use. LC 83-26809. 784p. 1984. Repr. of 1974 ed. lib. bdg. 72.50 (ISBN 0-89874-648-5). Krieger.

Brescia, Frank & Mehlman, Stanley. Chemistry: A Modern Introduction. 2nd ed. 1978. text ed. 37.95 (ISBN 0-7216-1984-3, CBS C); instr's manual 9.95 (ISBN 0-03-057156-1); study guide 11.95 (ISBN 0-7216-2076-0). SCP.

Brown, Theodore L. & Le May, H. Eugene, Jr. Chemistry: The Central Science. 3rd ed. (Illus.). 896p. 1985. text ed. 37.95 (ISBN 0-13-128950-0); solutions manual, 536 pp. 8.95. P-H.

Browning, Bertie L. Methods of Wood Chemistry, 2 vols. LC 66-28537. (Illus.). Vol. 1. pap. 101.50 (ISBN 0-317-10830-1, 2006346); Vol. 2. pap. 130.30 (ISBN 0-317-10831-X). Bks Demand UMI.

Bud, Robert F. & Roberts, Gerrylynn K. Science Versus Practice: Chemistry in Victorian Britain. LC 84-853. 256p. 1984. 35.00 (ISBN 0-7190-1070-5, Pub. by Manchester Univ Pr). Longwood Pub Group.

Buncel, E., et al. Electron Deficient Aromatic & Heteroaromatic-Base Interactions: Chemistry of Anionic Sigma Complexes. (Studies in Organic Chemistry: No. 14). 350p. 1984. 115.50 (ISBN 0-444-42305-2). Elsevier.

Bunger, James, ed. Chemistry of Asphaltenes. Li, Norman C. LC 81-19053. (Advances in Chemistry Ser.: No. 195). 1981. 49.95 (ISBN 0-8412-0592-2). Am Chemical.

Bushman, Eva M. Introductory Chemistry. 130p. pap. text ed. 7.95 (ISBN 0-89420-217-0, 236025); cassettes 165.95 (ISBN 0-89420-216-2, 236000). Natl Book.

Caglioti, Luciano & Giacconi, Mirella. The Two Faces of Chemistry: The Benefits & the Risks of Chemical Technology. LC 82-12706. 240p. 1985. 22.50 (ISBN 0-262-03088-8); pap. 8.95 (ISBN 0-262-53064-3). MIT Pr.

Callewaert, Denis M. & Genyea, Julien. Basic Chemistry: General, Organic, Biological. 1980. text ed. 28.95x (ISBN 0-87901-130-0). Worth.

--Fundamentals of College Chemistry. 1980. text ed. 24.95x (ISBN 0-87901-125-4). Worth.

Canham, Geoffrey R. Foundations of Chemistry. 320p. 1983. pap. 10.95 lab manual (ISBN 0-201-10416-4); instr's. guide 2.50 (ISBN 0-201-10418-0). Addison-Wesley.

Cantow, H. J., et al, eds. Chemistry. LC 61-642. (Advances in Polymer Science: Vol. 31). (Illus.). 1979. 54.00 (ISBN 0-387-09200-5). Springer-Verlag.

Chang, Raymond. Chemistry. 2nd ed. 832p. 1985. text ed. 35.00 (ISBN 0-394-32983-X, RanC); wkbk. 11.95 (ISBN 0-394-33475-2); solutions manual 9.95 (ISBN 0-394-33538-4). Random.

--Introduction to Chemistry. 1981. text ed. 35.00x (ISBN 0-394-32983-X, RanC); wkbk. 11.95 (ISBN 0-394-33475-2). Random.

Chapuisat, X., et al, eds. Theory. (Topics in Current Chemistry Ser: Vol. 68). 1976. 34.00 (ISBN 0-387-07932-7). Springer-Verlag.

Chemistry. (Undergraduate Program Field Test Ser.: UPFT-4). (Cloth bdg. avail. on request). pap. 9.95 (ISBN 0-8373-6004-8). Natl Learning.

Chemistry. (The Pocket Professor Ser.). 1984. pap. 2.95 (ISBN 0-946913-07-2, Pub. by Coll Lane Pubs). Kampmann.

Chemistry Fundamentals. (Illus.). 545p. 1981. looseleaf 60.00x (ISBN 0-87683-331-8); lessons plans 1250.00x (ISBN 0-87683-332-6); transparencies 275.00x (ISBN 0-87683-333-4); question bank 210.00x (ISBN 0-87683-334-2); training package 1615.00x (ISBN 0-87683-330-X). G P Courseware.

Chemistry of Art. 1980. 3.90 (ISBN 0-910362-13-0). Chem Educ.

The Chemistry of Art: A Sequel. 1981. pap. 5.50 (ISBN 0-910362-16-5). Chem Educ.

The Chemistry of Powder & Explosives. 1982. lib. bdg. 75.00 (ISBN 0-87700-430-7). Revisionist Pr.

Chen, Philip S. Chemistry: Inorganic, Organic & Biological. 2nd ed. (College Outline Ser.). 288p. 1980. pap. 6.50 (ISBN 0-06-460182-X, CO 182, COS). B&N NY.

Clark, Ronald D. & Amai, Robert L. Chemistry: The Science & the Scene. LC 74-22969. 356p. 1975. 21.50 (ISBN 0-471-15857-7). Krieger.

Clarke, John S. Teach Yourself Chemistry. 1979. pap. text ed. 5.95 (ISBN 0-679-12055-6). McKay.

Compton, Charles. Inside Chemistry. (Illus.). 1979. text ed. 29.95 (ISBN 0-07-012350-0). McGraw.

Crout, D. H. Chemistry of Natural Products. Date not set. 35.00 (ISBN 0-87735-213-5). Freeman Cooper.

Current Topics in Chinese Science: Section B: Chemistry, Vol. 3. 575p. 1984. pap. text ed. 68.00 (ISBN 0-677-40385-2). Gordon.

Daly, John W., et al, eds. Physiology & Pharmacology of Adenosine Derivatives. (Illus.). 314p. 1983. text ed. 76.00 (ISBN 0-89004-833-9). Raven.

Darlington, C. LeRoy & Eigenfeld, Neil. The Chemical World: Activities & Explorations. LC 76-4597. (Illus.). 1977. text ed. 20.20 (ISBN 0-395-24070-0); tchr's annotated ed. 24.68 (ISBN 0-395-24071-9). HM.

D Auria, John M. & Gilchrist, Alan B. Chemistry & the Environment: Laboratory Experience. LC 72-82803. pap. 42.60 (ISBN 0-317-08680-4, 2013067). Bks Demand UMI.

Davis, Raymond E., et al. Principles of Chemistry. LC 83-19271. 884p. 1984. text ed. 38.95x (ISBN 0-03-060458-3). SCP.

Davison, A., et al, eds. New Concepts Two. (Topics in Current Chemistry: Vol. 42). (Illus.). iv, 158p. 1973. 35.00 (ISBN 0-387-06399-4). Springer-Verlag.

Deutsch, R. W. & Whitney, J. W., eds. Chemistry, Health Physics, & Nuclear Instrumentation. (Academic Program for Nuclear Power Plant Personnel Ser.: Vol. IV). (Illus.). 454p. 1972. looseleaf 60.00x (ISBN 0-87683-150-1); lessons palns 500.00x (ISBN 0-87683-157-9); exercise solutions 25.00x (ISBN 0-87683-164-1); quizzes & examinations 25.00x (ISBN 0-87683-171-4). G P Courseware.

De Voe, James R., ed. Validation of the Measurement Process. LC 77-15555. (ACS Symposium Ser.: No. 63). 1977. 29.95 (ISBN 0-8412-0396-2). Am Chemical.

Devon, T. K. & Scott, A. I. Handbook of Naturally Occurring Compounds, 2 vols. Incl. Vol. 1. Acetogenins, Shikimates & Carbohydrates. 1975. 76.50 (ISBN 0-12-213601-2); Vol. 2. Terpenes. 1972. 77.00 (ISBN 0-12-213602-0). Acad Pr.

Dewar, M. J., et al, eds. Wittig Chemistry: Dedicated to Professor Dr. G. Wittig. (Topics in Current Chemistry Ser.: Vol. 109). (Illus.). 220p. 1983. 43.50 (ISBN 0-387-11907-8). Springer-Verlag.

Dickson, T. R. Introduction to Chemistry. 4th ed. LC 82-10856. 540p. 1983. text ed. 30.95x (ISBN 0-471-09954-6). lab experiments 16.95 (ISBN 0-471-87192-3); transparencies o.p. 8.00 (ISBN 0-471-04757-0); study guide 12.95 (ISBN 0-471-87191-5); tchrs. manual o.p. 10.00 (ISBN 0-471-04750-3). Wiley.

Dillard, Clyde R. & Goldberg, David E. Chemistry: Reactions, Structure, & Properties. 2nd ed. (Illus.). 1978. write for info. (ISBN 0-02-329580-5). Macmillan.

Dollberg, Donald D. & Verstuyft, Allen W., eds. Analytical Techniques in Occupational Health Chemistry. LC 79-28460. (ACS Symposium Ser.: No. 120). 1980. 39.95 (ISBN 0-8412-0539-6). Am Chemical.

Dolphin, David, et al, eds. Biomimetic Chemistry. LC 80-22864. (ACS Advances in Chemistry Ser.: No. 191). 1980. 59.95 (ISBN 0-8412-0514-0). Am Chemical.

Dorn, James M. & Hopkins, Barbara. Thanatochemistry: A Survey of General, Organic & Biochemistry for Funeral Service Professionals. 1985. text ed. 38.95 (ISBN 0-8359-7640-8). Reston.

Ebbing, Darrell. General Chemistry. 928p. 1983. text ed. 34.95 (ISBN 0-395-31489-5); instr's. manual 2.00 (ISBN 0-395-31490-9); solns. manual 9.95 (ISBN 0-395-31491-7); study guide 13.95 (ISBN 0-395-31493-3); lab manual 19.95 (ISBN 0-395-31492-5); transparencies 125.00 (ISBN 0-395-34457-3). HM.

Eblin, Lawrence P. Elements of Chemistry in the Laboratory. 2nd ed. (Illus.). 178p. (Orig.). 1970. spiral bdg. 13.95 (ISBN 0-15-522073-X, HC). HarBraceJ.

Elementos Encadenados. (Serie De Quimica: No. 5). (Span.). pap. 3.50 (ISBN 0-8270-6340-7). OAS.

Eriksson, Erik. Principles & Applications of Hydrochemistry. 200p. 1985. 37.00 (ISBN 0-412-25040-3, 9671). Methuen Inc.

Eubanks, I. Dwaine & Derner, Otis C. Chemistry in Civilization. LC 74-80913. pap. 68.10 (ISBN 0-317-08908-0, 2055101). Bks Demand UMI.

Eyring, H., et al, eds. Physical Chemistry: An Advanced Treatise in Eleven Volumes. Incl. Vol. 1. Thermodynamics. Jost, W., ed. 1971. 95.00 (ISBN 0-12-245601-7); Vol. 2, Statistical Mechanics. Eyring, H., ed. 1967. 87.00, by subscription 70.50 (ISBN 0-12-245602-5); Vol. 3. Electronic Structure of Atoms & Molecules. Henderson, D., ed. 1969. 95.00 (ISBN 0-12-245603-3); Vol. 4. Molecular Properties. Henderson, D., ed. 1970. 99.50 (ISBN 0-12-245604-1); Vol. 5. Valency. Eyring, H., ed. 1970. 99.50 (ISBN 0-12-245605-X); Vol. 6A. General Introduction & Gas Reactions. Jost, W., ed. 1974. Pt. A. 95.00 (ISBN 0-12-245606-8); Pt. B, 1975. 95.00 (ISBN 0-12-245656-4); Vol. 7. Reactions in Condensed Phases. Eyring, H., ed. 1975. 95.00 (ISBN 0-12-245607-6); Vol. 8. Liquid State. Henderson, D., ed. Pt. A, 1971. 70.00 (ISBN 0-12-245608-4); Pt. B. 87.00 (ISBN 0-12-245658-0); Vol. 9. Electrochemistry. Eyring, H., ed. 1970. Pt. A. 87.00 (ISBN 0-12-245609-2); Pt. B. 87.00 (ISBN 0-12-245659-9). Pt. B; Vol. 10. Solid State Chemistry. Jost, W., ed. 1970. 95.00 (ISBN 0-12-245610-6); Vol. 11 Pt. A. Mathematical Applications. Henderson, D., ed. 1975. 95.00 (ISBN 0-12-245611-4); Pt. B. 101.50 (ISBN 0-12-245661-0). Acad Pr.

Feigl, Dorothy M. & Hill, John W. General, Organic, & Biological Chemistry: Foundations of Life. 2nd, rev. ed. (Illus.). 544p. 1985. text ed. price not set (ISBN 0-8087-3026-6); price not set student guide (ISBN 0-8087-3027-4). Burgess.

Fessenden, Ralph J. & Fessenden, Joan S. Basic Chemistry for the Health Sciences. 3rd ed. 1984. text ed. 37.14 (ISBN 0-205-08016-2, 688016); write for info. instr's. manual (ISBN 0-205-08029-4); student guide 10.22 (ISBN 0-205-08017-0, 688017). Allyn.

--Chemical Principles for the Life Sciences. 2nd ed. 1979. text ed. 32.74 (ISBN 0-205-06506-6, 686506); instr's manual (ISBN 0-205-06533-3). Allyn.

Fine, Leonard W. Chemistry. 2nd ed. LC 77-12000. 840p. 1978. 22.50 (ISBN 0-683-03210-0). Krieger.

Fotoquimica de los Gases. (Serie De Quimica: No. 7). (Span.). 64p. 1972. pap. 3.50 (ISBN 0-8270-6355-5). OAS.

Fountain, Robert L. Chemistry Manual for Operators. LC 81-68897. (Illus.). 148p. 1981. pap. text ed. 19.95 (ISBN 0-250-40504-0). Butterworth.

Garland, John K. Chemistry of Our World. (Illus.). 768p. 1975. text ed. 19.95 (ISBN 0-02-340520-1, 34052). Macmillan.

Geffner, Saul L. & Kass, Gerard A. Contemporary Chemistry. (Orig.). 1981. pap. text ed. 8.92 (ISBN 0-87720-100-5). AMSCO Sch.

Giddings, J. Calvin. Chemistry, Man, & Environmental Change: An Integrated Approach. (Illus.). 450p. 1973. text ed. 25.30 scp (ISBN 0-06-382790-5, HarpC). Har-Row.

Gilleland, Martha J. Introduction to General, Organic & Biological Chemistry. (Illus.). 832p. 1982. text ed. 31.95 (ISBN 0-314-63173-9). West Pub.

Ginsburg, David. Propellanes: Structure & Reactions. (Monographs in Modern Chemistry: Vol. 7). 272p. 1975. 81.20x (ISBN 3-527-25602-4). VCH Pubs.

Glinka, N. General Chemistry. Sobolev, D., tr. (Russian Monographs). (Illus.). 694p. 1965. 92.50 (ISBN 0-677-20560-0). Gordon.

Glinka, N. L. General Chemistry, 2 vols. 768p. 1981. 16.50 set (ISBN 0-8285-2119-0, Pub. by Mir Pubs USSR). Imported Pubns.

Goates, J. Rex, et al. General Chemistry: Theory & Description. 788p. 1981. text ed. 28.95 (ISBN 0-15-529535-7, HC); solutions manual avail. (ISBN 0-15-529536-5). HarBraceJ.

Goel, D. P. & Mittal, S. P. Revision in Chemistry, No. I. (Illus.). vi, 91p. (Orig.). 1983. pap. text ed. 5.95x (ISBN 0-86131-378-X, Pub. by Orient Longman Ltd India). Apt Bks.

Goldberg, E. D., ed. Atmospheric Chemistry, Berlin, 1982. (Dahlem Workshop Reports, Physical & Chemical: Vol. 4). (Illus.). 400p. 1982. 25.00 (ISBN 0-387-11651-6). Springer-Verlag.

Golloch, Alfred, et al. Anorganisch-Chemische Praparate: Darstellung und Charakterisierung Ausgewahlter Vernindungen. (Ger., Illus.). xvi, 324p. 1985. 19.20x (ISBN 3-11-004821-3). De Gruyter.

Gorbaty, Martin L. & Harney, Brian M., eds. Refining of Synthetic Crudes. LC 79-21098. (Advance in Chemistry: No. 179). 1979. 39.95 (ISBN 0-8412-0456-X). Am Chemical.

Grant, R. A., ed. Applied Protein Chemistry. (Illus.). 332p. 1980. 52.00 (ISBN 0-85334-865-0, Pub. by Elsevier Applied Sci England). Elsevier.

Greenwood, N. N. & Earnshaw, A. Chemistry of the Elements. LC 83-13346. (Illus.). 1542p. 1984. 120.00 (ISBN 0-08-022056-8); flexi-cover 34.95 (ISBN 0-08-022057-6). Pergamon.

Grillot, Gerald F. A Chemical Background for the Paramedical Sciences. 2nd ed. (Illus.). 1974. text ed. 27.50 scp (ISBN 0-06-042511-3, HarpC). Har-Row.

Gross, Helmut. Chemie und Chemische Technik. 2nd ed. (Eng. -Ger., Chemistry and Chemical Engineering). 1978. 55.00 (ISBN 0-686-56598-3, M-7319, Pub. by VEB Verlag Technik). French & Eur.

Grunewald, H., ed. Chemistry for the Future: Proceedings of the 29th IUPAC Congress, Cologne, Federal Republic of Germany, 5-10 June 1983. LC 83-23825. (IUPAC Symposium Ser.). 268p. 1984. 95.00 (ISBN 0-08-029249-6). Pergamon.

Gunther, F. A., ed. Residue Reviews, Vol. 77. (Illus.). 364p. 1981. 44.00 (ISBN 0-387-90538-3). Springer-Verlag.

Gymer, Roger G. Chemistry in the Natural World. 1976. text ed. 22.95 (ISBN 0-669-00343-3); instructor's manual free (ISBN 0-669-00352-2). Heath.

Hall, A. O. Chemistry for Beginners. 1978. pap. text ed. 7.50x (ISBN 0-435-64310-X). Heinemann Ed.

Hardwick, E. Russell. Introduction to Chemistry. (Illus.). 654p. 1984. text ed. 29.95x (ISBN 0-8087-4740-1); study guide 8.95x (ISBN 0-8087-4936-6). Burgess.

Harris, Frank E. Principles of Chemistry. 1977. pap. text ed. 15.00 each incl. 8 texts (ISBN 0-8449-0400-7); tchrs' manual 6.00; test 8.00. Learning Line.

Harrison, T. & Murphy, M. Mixtures in Chemistry. 1972. text ed. 1.05 (ISBN 0-13-586008-3). P-H.

Hearst, John E. & Ifft, James B. Contemporary Chemistry. LC 75-28230. (Illus.). 753p. 1976. text ed. 29.95 (ISBN 0-7167-0172-3). W H Freeman.

Hein, Morris. Foundations of College Chemistry. 5th ed. LC 81-18003. (Chemistry Ser.). 600p. 1982. text ed. 24.50 pub net (ISBN 0-8185-0476-5). Brooks-Cole.

--Foundations of College Chemistry: The Alternate Second Edition. LC 83-9999. 1984. text ed. 19.50 pub net (ISBN 0-534-03026-2). Brooks-Cole.

Herron, J. Dudley. Understanding Chemistry. 515p. 1981. text ed. 26.00x (ISBN 0-394-32087-5, RanC); wkbk, by Elizabeth Kean 10.00 (ISBN 0-394-32423-4); lab manual, by Jane Copes 12.00 (ISBN 0-394-32437-4). Random.

--Understanding Chemistry. 2nd ed. 515p. 1986. text ed. 27.95 (ISBN 0-394-34043-4, RanC). Random.

Heslop, R. B. & Wild, Gillian M. SI Units in Chemistry: An Introduction. (Illus.). 1971. text ed. 13.00 (ISBN 0-85334-650-X, Pub. by Applied Sci England); pap. text ed. 12.00x (ISBN 0-85334-515-5). Burgess-Intl Ideas.

Hess, Fred C. Chemistry Made Simple. Thomas, Arthur L., rev. by. LC 82-46054. (Made Simple Ser.). (Illus.). 224p. 1984. pap. 4.95 (ISBN 0-385-18850-1). Doubleday.

Higgins, I. J. & Burns, R. G. The Chemistry & Microbiology of Pollution. 1975. 46.00 (ISBN 0-12-347950-9). Acad Pr.

Hill, James C. Chemistry: The Central Science. 3rd ed. (Illus.). 30p. 1985. pap. text ed. 9.95 solutions manual (ISBN 0-13-127499-6). P-H.

Hill, John W. & Feigl, Dorothy M. Chemistry & Life: An Introduction to General, Organic, & Biological Chemistry. 2nd ed. 1983. pap. text ed. 28.95x (ISBN 0-8087-3109-2). Burgess.

Holleman, A. F. & Wiberg, Egon. Lehrbuch der Anorganischen Chemie. (Ger., Illus.). xxx, 1451p. 1984. 48.00x (ISBN 3-11-007511-3). De Gruyter.

Holtclaw, Henry, Jr., et al. General Chemistry. 7th ed. 928p. 1984. text ed. 33.95 (ISBN 0-669-06335-5). Heath.

Holtzclaw, Henry, Jr., et al. College Chemistry with Qualitative Analysis. 7th ed. 944p. text ed. 33.95 (ISBN 0-669-06333-9). Heath.

Holum, J. R. Elements of General & Biological Chemistry. 6th ed. LC 82-11046. 523p. 1983. 31.95 (ISBN 0-471-09935-X); pap. 18.50 (ISBN 0-471-08236-8); tchr's. manual 10.95 (ISBN 0-471-87194-X); pap. 13.50 study guide (ISBN 0-471-89033-2). Wiley.

Hopp, V. & Hennig, I. Handbook of Applied Chemistry: Facts for Engineers, Scientists, Technicians, & Technical Managers. 840p. 1983. 49.95 (ISBN 0-07-030320-7). McGraw.

Horne, R. A. The Chemistry of Our Environment. LC 77-1156. 869p. 1978. 93.95 (ISBN 0-471-40944-8, Pub. by Wiley-Interscience). Wiley.

Horrigan, Philip A. The Challenge of Chemistry. rev. ed. 1980. pap. text ed. 15.95x (ISBN 0-941512-01-0). Marshland Pub.

--The New Challenge of Chemistry. (Orig.). 1985. pap. 24.95x (ISBN 0-941512-02-9). Marshland Pub.

Houk, C. C. & Post, R. Chemistry: Concepts & Problems. (Self-Teaching Guides Ser.). 370p. 1977. pap. text ed. 9.95 (ISBN 0-471-41500-6, Pub. by Wiley). Wiley.

Hughes, Tom. Chemistry Connections: Ideas to Interpret Your Changing World. 512p. 1983. pap. text ed. 16.95 (ISBN 0-8403-2942-3). Kendall-Hunt.

Hutzinger, O., ed. Reactions & Processes. (Handbook of Environmental Chemistry Ser.: Vol. II, Pt. B). (Illus.). 232p. 1982. 47.00 (ISBN 0-387-11107-7). Springer-Verlag.

Ihde, Aaron J. The Development of Modern Chemistry. (Illus.). 851p. 1983. pap. 14.95 (ISBN 0-486-64235-6). Dover.

Inagaki, Yoshio & Okazaki, Renji. Chemistry of N-Thiosulfinylamines. (Sulfur Reports: Vol. 2, No. 4). 40p. 1982. 24.50 (ISBN 3-7186-0126-5). Harwood Academic.

International Congress of Pure & Applied Chemistry 28th, Vancouver, BC, Canada, 16-22 August 1981. Frontiers in Chemistry: Proceedings. Laidler, ed. (IUPAC Symposium Ser.). (Illus.). 350p. 1982. 94.00 (ISBN 0-08-026220-1). Pergamon.

International Congress of Pure & Applied Chemistry, 27th, Helsinki, Finland, Aug. 27-31, 1979. International Congress of Pure & Applied Chemistry, 27th. Varmavuori, A., ed. LC 79-42639. 396p. 1980. 140.00 (ISBN 0-08-023936-6). Pergamon.

International Union of Pure & Applied Chemistry. Chemistry International: 1980 Supplement. (Biennial Supplement to Chemistry International Ser.). 162p. 1980. 11.75 (ISBN 0-08-026186-8). Pergamon.

Izatt. Progress in Macrocyclic Chemistry: Synthesis of Marcocycles: Design of Selective Complexing Agent, Vol. 3. 1985. write for info. (ISBN 0-471-82589-1). Wiley.

James, M. Lynn & Schreck, James O. General, Organic & Biological Chemistry: A Brief Introduction. 560p. 1982. text ed. 27.95 (ISBN 0-669-03862-8); lab guide 11.95 (ISBN 0-669-03864-4); student guide 9.95 (ISBN 0-669-03865-2); instr's guide 1.95 (ISBN 0-669-03866-0). Heath.

Jenson, J. T. & Ferren, William P. College General Chemistry. LC 70-97561. 1971. text ed. 21.95x (ISBN 0-675-09400-3). Merrill.

Jones, Mark M., et al. Chemistry, Man & Society. 4th ed. 1983. text ed. 32.95 (ISBN 0-03-063032-0, CBS C); instructor's manual 19.95 (ISBN 0-03-062892-X). SCP.

Jortner, Joshua, et al, eds. Photoselective Chemistry, Pt. 1, Vol. 47. (Advances in Chemical Physics Ser.). 769p. 1981. 120.00 (ISBN 0-471-06275-8, Pub. by Wiley-Interscience). Wiley.

--Photoselective Chemistry, Pt. 2, Vol. 47. (Advances in Chemical Physics Ser.). 718p. 1981. 108.00 (ISBN 0-471-06274-X, Pub. by Wiley-Interscience). Wiley.

Kaiser, Carl & Kebabian, John W. Dopamine Receptors. LC 83-6433. (AGS Symposium Ser.: No. 224). 289p. 1983. lib. bdg. 34.95x (ISBN 0-8412-0781-X). Am Chemical.

Katritzky, Alan R., ed. Advances in Heterocyclic Chemistry, Vol. 33. (Serial Publication Ser.). 1983. 65.00 (ISBN 0-12-020633-1). Acad Pr.

Keenan, Charles W., et al. General College Chemistry. 6th ed. 1980. text ed. 31.95 scp (ISBN 0-06-043616-6, HarpC); scp lab manual 18.95 (ISBN 0-06-046298-1); instr's manual avail. (ISBN 0-06-363613-1); scp study guide 13.50 (ISBN 0-06-043706-5); instr's manual & storeroom guide for lab manual avail. (ISBN 0-06-366308-2). Har-Row.

Keim. Catalysis in C-Chemistry. 1983. PLB 58.50 (ISBN 90-277-1527-0, Reidel Holland). Kluwer Academic.

Kieffer, William F. Chemistry Today. 1976. text ed. 27.50 scp (ISBN 0-06-384550-4, HarpC); instr's. manual avail. (ISBN 0-06-373575-X). Har-Row.

King, Edward L. Chemistry. 1100p. 1981. text ed. 34.00 (ISBN 0-394-32761-6, RanC). Random.

Kirk & Othmer. Encyclopedia of Chemical Technology, 24 vols. 3rd ed. Incl. Vol. 1. A-Alkanolamines. 967p (ISBN 0-471-02037-0); Vol. 2. Alkoxides, Metals & Antibiotics (Peptides) 1036p (ISBN 0-471-02038-9); Vol. 3. Antibiotics (Phenazines) to Bleaching Agents. 958p (ISBN 0-471-02039-7); Vol. 4. Blood, Coagulants & Anticoagulants to Cardiovascular Agents. 3rd ed. LC 77-15820. 930p. 1978. 195.00 (ISBN 0-471-02040-0, Wiley); Vol. 5. Castor Oil to Chlorosulfuric Acid. 3rd ed. LC 78-15820. 880p. 1979. 195.00 (ISBN 0-471-02041-9, Wiley); Vol. 6. Chocolate & Cocoa to Copper. 869p. 1979. 195.00 (ISBN 0-471-02042-7); Vol. 7. Copper Alloys to Distillations. 3rd ed. LC 77-15820. 891p. 1979. 195.00 (ISBN 0-471-02043-5, Wiley); Vol. 8. Diuretics to Emulsions. 930p. 1979. 195.00 (ISBN 0-471-02044-3); Vol. 9. Enamels, Porcelain or Vitreous to Ferrites. 902p. 1980. 195.00 (ISBN 0-471-02062-1); Vol. 10. Ferroelectrics to Fluorine Compounds. 962p. 1980. 195.00 (ISBN 0-471-02063-X); Vol. 11. Fluorine Compounds to Gold & Gold Compounds. 995p. 1980. 195.00 (ISBN 0-471-02064-8); Vol. 12. Gravity Concentration to Hydrogen Energy. 1037p. 1980. 195.00 (ISBN 0-471-02065-6); Vol. 13. Hydrogen-Ion Activity to Laminated Materials, Glass. 993p. 1981 (ISBN 0-471-02066-4); Vol. 14. Laminated Wood-based Composites to Mass Transfer. 981p. 1981 (ISBN 0-471-02067-2); Vol. 15. Matches to Nitrosamines. 996p. 1981 (ISBN 0-471-02068-0); Vol. 16. Noise Pollution to Perfumes. 971p. 1981 (ISBN 0-471-02069-9); Vol. 17. Peroxides & Peroxy Compounds, Inorganic to Piping Systems. 957p. 1982 (ISBN 0-471-02070-2); Vol. 18. Plant-Growth Substances to Potassium Compounds. 950p. 1982 (ISBN 0-471-02071-0); Vol. 19. Powder Coating to Recycling Rubber. 1010p. 1982 (ISBN 0-471-02072-9); Vol. 20. Refractories-Silk. 981p. 1983 (ISBN 0-471-02073-7); Vol. 21. Silver & Silver Alloys-Sulfonic Acids. 968p. 1983 (ISBN 0-471-02074-5); Vol. 22. Sulfonation & Sulfation - Thorium & Thorium Compounds. 1002p. 1983 (ISBN 0-471-02075-3); Vol. 23. Thyroid & Antithyroid Preparations to Vinyl Polymers. 1008p. 1983 (ISBN 0-471-02076-1); Vol. 24. Vitamin-Zone Refining. 917p. 1983 (ISBN 0-471-02077-X). 1978-80. 195.00 ea. (Pub. by Wiley-Interscience); Twenty-six vol. set & supplement. 4550.00 (ISBN 0-471-80104-6). Wiley.

Kolisko, Eugen. Elementary Chemistry. 1979. pap. 3.95 (ISBN 0-906492-02-5, Pub. by Kolisko Archives). St George Bk Serv.

Konigsberg-Kerner, Nancy. Chemical Investigations. (Illus.). 500p. 1985. pap. 19.95x (ISBN 0-8053-5410-7). Benjamin-Cummings.

Kostiner, Edward & Rea, Jesse R. Fundamentals of Chemistry. 480p. 1979. text ed. 22.95 (ISBN 0-15-529430-X, HC); instructor's manual avail. (ISBN 0-15-529431-8); study guide. pap. 8.95 (ISBN 0-15-529433-4); lab manual 9.95 (ISBN 0-15-529432-6). HarBraceJ.

Kroschwitz, J. I. & Winokur, M. Chemistry: General, Organic, Biological. LC 84-12224. 800p. 1985. 35.95 (ISBN 0-07-035535-5); study guide 13.95 (ISBN 0-07-035537-1). McGraw.

Kroschwitz, Jacqueline I. & Winokur, Melvin. Chemistry: A First Course. (Illus.). 1980. text ed. 29.95x (ISBN 0-07-035531-2). McGraw.

Kuroda, Paul K. The Origin of the Chemical Elements & the Oklo Phenomenom. (Illus.). 196p. 1982. 41.00 (ISBN 0-387-11679-6). Springer-Verlag.

Larson, Dewey B. Nothing but Motion. LC 79-88078. (Illus.). 1979. 9.50 (ISBN 0-913138-07-X). North Pacific.

Lavoisier, Antoine. Elements of Chemistry. 539p. 1984. pap. 11.95 (ISBN 0-486-64624-6). Dover.

Lebedev, N. N. Chemistry & Technology of Basic Organic & Petrochemical Synthesis, 2 vols. 638p. 1984. Set. 16.00 (ISBN 0-8285-2784-9, Pub. by Mir Pubs USSR). Imported Pubns.

Lee, Jessie C. & Bettelheim, Frederick A. Introduction to General, Organic & Biochemistry: Laboratory Manual. 384p. 1984. pap. 18.95x (ISBN 0-03-063307-9). SCP.

Lefax Pub. Co. Editors. Chemical Handbook. (Lefax Technical Manuals: No. 777). (Illus.). looseleaf bdg. 8.50 (ISBN 0-685-14125-X). LeFax.

Leisinger, T., et al, eds. Microbial Degradation of Xenobiotics & Recalcitrant Compounds. LC 81-67908. 1982. 69.50 (ISBN 0-12-442920-3). Acad Pr.

Lessing, Lawrence P. Understanding Chemistry. LC 59-14418. pap. 48.00 (ISBN 0-317-08764-9, 2007397). Bks Demand UMI.

Lewis, John R. First-Year College Chemistry. 9th ed. (Illus., Orig.). 1971. pap. 6.50 (ISBN 0-06-460005-X, CO 5, COS). B&N NY.

Lingren, Wesley E. Essentials of Chemistry. (Illus.). 640p. 1986. text ed. 31.95 (ISBN 0-13-284316-1). P-H.

Lippincott, W. T., et al. Experimental General Chemistry. 490p. 1984. pap. text ed. 21.95x (ISBN 0-03-060463-X). SCP.

Lippy, John. Chemical Magic. 164p. pap. 4.00 (ISBN 0-913022-32-2). Angriff Pr.

Loebel, Arnold B. Chemistry: Concepts & Calculations. LC 77-26720. pap. 144.00 (ISBN 0-317-09888-8, 2022508). Bks Demand UMI.

Loewenthal, R. E. & Marais, G. V. Carbonate Chemistry of Aquatic Systems: Theory & Application, Vol. 1. LC 76-24963. 1976. 39.95 (ISBN 0-250-40141-X). Butterworth.

Lowman, Robert G., et al. Experimental Introductory Chemistry: Inorganic, 2 Pts. (Illus.). 195p. 1981. pap. text ed. 6.95x (ISBN 0-89641-096-X). American Pr.

Maciel, Gary E., et al. Chemistry. 1978. text ed. 31.95 (ISBN 0-669-84830-1); instr's manual 1.95 (ISBN 0-669-99945-8); lab manual 13.95 (ISBN 0-669-00999-7); study guide 10.95 (ISBN 0-669-01000-6). Heath.

McNair, Harold M. Cromatografia de Gases. Dominguez, Xorge A., tr. from Sp. (Quimica Monografia: No. 23). 90p. 1981. pap. 3.50 (ISBN 0-8270-1360-4). OAS.

McOmie, J. F., ed. Protective Groups in Organic Chemistry. LC 72-91038. 418p. 1973. 49.50 (ISBN 0-306-30717-0, Plenum Pr). Plenum Pub.

McQuarrie, Donald A. & Rock, Peter. Descriptive Chemistry. LC 84-21078. (Illus.). 176p. 1985. pap. text ed. 12.95 (ISBN 0-7167-1706-9). W H Freeman.

McQuarrie, Donald A. & Rock, Peter A. General Chemistry. 832p. 1984. text ed. 31.95 (ISBN 0-7167-1499-X). W H Freeman.

McTigue, P. T., ed. Chemistry: Key to the Earth. 2nd ed. (Illus.). 1983. pap. 30.00x (ISBN 0-522-84257-7, Pub. by Melbourne U Pr). Intl Spec Bk.

Mager, Peter P. Multidimensional Pharmacochemistry: Design of Safer Drugs. LC 82-24362. (Medicinal Chemistry Ser.). 1985. 89.00 (ISBN 0-12-465020-1). Acad Pr.

Mahan, Bruce H. College Chemistry. 1966. text ed. 33.95 (ISBN 0-201-04404-8). Addison-Wesley.

Maier, Mary & Rodriguez, Nelson. Elements of General, Organic & Biochemistry. 600p. 1984. text ed. write for info (ISBN 0-87150-782-X, 4551). Brooks-Cole.

Maizell, Robert E. How to Find Chemical Information: A Guide for Practicing Chemists, Teachers & Students. LC 78-23222. 261p. 1979. 34.00x (ISBN 0-471-56531-8, Pub. by Wiley-Interscience). Wiley.

Makarov, Evgeniis S. Crystal Chemistry of Simple Compounds of Uranium, Thorium, Plutonium, Neptunium. Uvarov, E. B., tr. from Rus. LC 59-14486. pap. 38.30 (ISBN 0-317-08925-0, 2003366). Bks Demand UMI.

Malinowski, Edmund R. & Howery, Darryl G. Factor Analysis in Chemistry. LC 79-27081. 251p. 1980. 43.50x (ISBN 0-471-05881-5, Pub. by Wiley Interscience); teachers manual avail. (ISBN 0-471-08728-9); study guide avail. (ISBN 0-471-08292-9). Wiley.

Malone. Basic Concepts of Chemistry: Computerized Version. 2nd ed. 624p. 1984. 34.95 (ISBN 0-471-82564-6). Wiley.

Malone, Leo J. Basic Concepts of Chemistry. LC 80-19501. 454p. 1981. text ed. 31.45 (ISBN 0-471-06381-9); study guide 9.50 (ISBN 0-471-08292-9); write for info. tchr's manual (ISBN 0-471-08728-9). Wiley.

--Basic Concepts of Chemistry. 2nd ed. LC 84-19476. 603p. 1985. text ed. 29.95 (ISBN 0-471-88600-9); study guide 13.95 (ISBN 0-471-80208-5). Wiley.

Manahan, Stanley. Environmental Chemistry. 4th ed. 560p. 1983. text ed. 23.00 pub net (ISBN 0-87150-764-1, 4481). Brooks-Cole.

Manahan, Stanley E. General Applied Chemistry. 2nd ed. 1982. text ed. 20.00 pub net (ISBN 0-87150-750-1, 4361). Brooks-Cole.

March, Jerry & Windwer, Stanley. General Chemistry. (Illus.). 1979. text ed. write for info. (ISBN 0-02-375860-0); students' solution suppl. avail.; instrs'. manual avail. Macmillan.

Martell, Arthur E. & Smith, Robert M., eds. Critical Stability Constants, Vols.1-4. Incl. Vol. 1. Amino Acids. 469p. 1974. 59.50x (ISBN 0-306-35211-7); Vol. 2. Amines. 415p. 1975. 59.50x (ISBN 0-306-35212-5); Vol. 3. Other Organic Ligands. 495p. 1977. 65.00x (ISBN 0-306-35213-3); Vol. 4. Inorganic Complexes. 257p. 1976. 49.50x (ISBN 0-306-35214-1). LC 74-10610. (Illus., Plenum Pr). Plenum Pub.

Mascetta, Joseph A. Chemistry. (Easy Way Ser.). 320p. 1983. pap. 7.95 (ISBN 0-8120-2624-1). Barron.

Masterton, William & Cherim, Stanley M. Introduction to Chemistry. LC 83-17244. 489p. 1984. text ed. 33.95x (ISBN 0-03-059676-9); lab manual 18.95x (ISBN 0-03-069571-6). SCP.

Masterton, William & Slowinski, Emil. Chemical Principles. 5th ed. 1981. text ed. 35.95 (ISBN 0-03-057804-3, CBS C); Instr's manual 11.95 (ISBN 0-03-058126-5); study guide 14.95 (ISBN 0-03-058276-8); overhead transparency 400.00 (ISBN 0-03-059298-4); test bank 100.00 (ISBN 0-03-058261-X). SCP.

--Chemical Principles, with Qualitative Analysis. 1986. text ed. 39.95 (ISBN 0-03-062646-3, CBS C). SCP.

Masterton, William, et al. Chemical Principles, Using S. I. Units. 5th ed. 1981. text ed. 39.95 (ISBN 0-03-057886-8, CBS C). SCP.

Melchiorre, C. & Giannella, M. Highlights in Receptor Chemistry. 1984. 67.50 (ISBN 0-444-80569-9, I-175-84). Elsevier.

Mendeleev, D. I. Principles of Chemistry, 4 pts. in 2 vols. 3rd ed. Pope, Thomas H., ed. Kamensky, G., tr. 1905. Set. 70.00 (ISBN 0-527-63100-0). Kraus Repr.

Messer, Melanie, et al. Introductory Experimental Chemistry. 1977. P-H.

Miall, Stephen & Miall, Laurence M. Chemistry, Matter, & Life. LC 70-39099. (Essay Index Reprint Ser.). Repr. of 1937 ed. 21.00 (ISBN 0-8369-2703-6). Ayer Co Pubs.

Mierzejewski, D. L. Fundamentals of Chemistry. (Illus.). 410p. 1982. pap. text ed. 66.00x looseleaf (ISBN 0-87683-212-5). G P Courseware.

Miller. Chemistry: A Basic Introduction. 3rd ed. 653p. Date not set. write for info. lab manual; write for info. study guide. Watts.

Miller, Glenn H. & Augustine, Frederick. Basic Chemistry. 2nd ed. 1979. scp 20.50 (ISBN 0-06-385476-7, HarpC); instructor's manual avail. (ISBN 0-06-375620-X). Har-Row.

Monroe, Manus & Abrams, Karl. A Course in Experimental Chemistry: Book I. 1983. 13.60x (ISBN 0-87735-210-0). Freeman Cooper.

Moore, John W. & Moore, Elizabeth A. Environmental Chemistry. 1976. 21.75i (ISBN 0-12-505050-X). Acad Pr.

Moore, John W., et al. Chemistry. (Illus.). 1978. text ed. 37.95 (ISBN 0-07-042925-1). McGraw.

Moreau, Nancy & Romano, Nicholas. A General Chemistry Review. 3rd ed. (Illus.). 189p. 1985. pap. text ed. 4.00 (ISBN 0-9606036-4-6). N & N Pub.

Morris, Kelso B. Fundamental Chemical Equilibria: Nonionic-Ionic. (Illus.). 120p. 1971. 32.50x (ISBN 0-677-03090-8). Gordon.

Mortimer. Chemistry. 6th ed. 1986. text ed. write for info. (ISBN 0-534-05670-9). Wadsworth Pub.

Murphy, Daniel B. & Rousseau, Viateur. Foundations of College Chemistry. 3rd ed. LC 79-17521. 767p. 1980. text ed. 36.95x (ISBN 0-471-04621-3); study guide 12.50 (ISBN 0-471-07881-6). Wiley.

Nebergall, William H., et al. College Chemistry with Qualitative Analysis. 6th ed. 1980. text ed. 31.95 (ISBN 0-669-02217-9); instr's. manual 1.95 (ISBN 0-669-02475-9); study guide 9.95 (ISBN 0-669-02474-0); basic laboratory studies 12.95 (ISBN 0-669-02473-2); problems & solutions guide 9.95 (ISBN 0-669-02472-4); problems & sol. supp 1.95 (ISBN 0-669-04364-8). Heath.

Suckling, Colin J. & Suckling, Keith E. Biological Chemistry. LC 79-51830. (Cambridge Texts in Chemistry & Biochemistry Ser.). (Illus.). 350p. 1980. 69.50 (ISBN 0-521-22852-2); pap. 22.95 (ISBN 0-521-29678-1). Cambridge U Pr.

Summerlin, Lee R. Chemistry for the Life Sciences. Incl. P. S. Associates. wkbk. 8.00 (ISBN 0-394-32457-9); Hendrickson, William & Healy, Juanita. lab manual 10.00 (ISBN 0-394-32520-6). 631p. 1981. text ed. 25.00 (ISBN 0-394-32215-0, RanC). Random.

Summers, Donald B. The Chemistry Handbook. 2nd ed. 1975. pub net 7.00 (ISBN 0-87150-715-3, WG 4181). Brooks-Cole.

Symons. Chemical & Biological Aspect. 1978. 13.95 (ISBN 0-442-30228-2). Van Nos Reinhold.

Szmant, H. Harry & Kauffman, George B., eds. The Central Science: Essays on the Uses of Chemistry. LC 83-18054. 181p. 1984. 15.00x (ISBN 0-912646-84-5). Tex Christian.

Tamminen, Mildred & Gregg, Sylvia J. Problem Solving for General Chemistry. 1977. write for info. (ISBN 0-87150-721-8, WG 4151). Brooks-Cole.

Tarrant, Paul, ed. Fluorine Chemistry Reviews, Vol. 6. 216p. 1973. 65.00 (ISBN 0-8247-1650-7). Dekker.

Taylor, William I. & Farnsworth, Norman, eds. The Vinca Alkaloids: Botany, Chemistry, & Pharmacology. LC 73-83859. pap. 94.30 (ISBN 0-317-28688-9, 2055284). Bks Demand UMI.

Thomas, Ursula & Twaddell, Freeman. Lesestoff. Incl. Physik & Chemie. LC 76-11313 (ISBN 0-299-07194-4); Mensch & Gesellschaft. LC 46-1323 (ISBN 0-299-07184-7); Literatur. LC 76-11317 (ISBN 0-299-07174-X); Biologie. LC 76-11322 (ISBN 0-299-07164-2). 1977. pap. text ed. 6.00x ea. U of Wis Pr.

Timberlake, Karen C. Chemistry. 3rd ed. 557p. 1983. text ed. 28.50 scp (ISBN 0-06-046632-4, HarpC); instr's manual & test items avail. (ISBN 0-06-366621-9); scp lab manual 12.50 (ISBN 0-06-046631-6); scp study guide 8.50 (ISBN 0-06-046629-4). Har-Row.

Tobolsky, Arthur V., ed. The Chemistry of Sulfides. LC 67-29545. pap. 72.80 (ISBN 0-317-09194-8, 2006362). Bks Demand UMI.

Tonnis, John & Rausch, Gerald. Chemical Investigations for the Nonscientist. 1980. coil binding 7.95 (ISBN 0-88252-109-8). Paladin Hse.

Toon, Ellis. Foundations of Chemistry: (Si Edition) 1978. text ed. 16.25 (ISBN 0-03-920066-3, Pub. by HR&W Canada); write for info. (ISBN 0-685-10139-8); lab. experiments 5.95 (ISBN 0-03-920067-1). HR&W.

Ucko, David. Living Chemistry. 1977. text ed. 21.75i (ISBN 0-12-705950-4); lab manual 8.00i (ISBN 0-12-705956-3); transparency masters 10.00i (ISBN 0-12-705958-X); tchr's. guide 10.00i (ISBN 0-12-705957-1); 7.25i (ISBN 0-12-705955-5). Acad Pr.

Ucko, David A. Experiments for Living Chemistry: An Introduction to General, Organic, & Biological Chemistry. 2nd ed. Date not set. text ed. price not set (ISBN 0-12-705967-9). Acad Pr.

Ucko, David A. & Ucko, Barbara. Living Chemistry: An Introduction to General, Organic, & Biological Chemistry. 2nd ed. Date not set. price not set (ISBN 0-12-705965-2); price not set study guide (ISBN 0-12-705966-0). Acad Pr.

Van Kampen, N. G. Stochastic Processes in Physics & Chemistry. 420p. 1982. 76.75 (ISBN 0-444-86200-5, North-Holland); pap. 28.00 (ISBN 0-444-86650-7). Elsevier.

Veprek, S. & Venugopalan, M., eds. Plasma Chemistry, Vol. IV. (Topics in Current Chemistry Ser.: Vol. 107). (Illus.). 186p. 1983. 36.00 (ISBN 0-387-11828-4). Springer-Verlag.

Voegtle, F., ed. Cyclophanes I. (Topics in Current Chemistry Ser.: Vol. 113). (Illus.). 210p. 1983. 39.00 (ISBN 0-387-12397-0). Springer-Verlag.

Voegtle, F. & Boschke, F. L., eds. Host Guest Complex Chemistry, No. II. (Topics in Current Chemistry Ser.: Vol. 101). (Illus.). 220p. 1982. 39.50 (ISBN 0-387-11103-4). Springer-Verlag.

Voegtle, P., ed. Cyclophanes II. (Topics in Current Chemistry: Vol. 115). (Illus.). 170p. 1983. 34.00 (ISBN 0-387-12478-0). Springer-Verlag.

Vol'Pin, E., ed. Chemistry Reviews, Vol. 2. (Soviet Scientific Reviews Ser.: Section B). 480p. 1980. 170.00 (ISBN 3-7186-0018-8). Harwood Academic.

Vol'Pin, M. E., ed. Chemistry Reviews, Vol. 3. (Soviet Scientific Reviews Ser.: Section B). 307p. 1981. 170.00 (ISBN 3-7186-0057-9). Harwood Academic.

Vowles, P. D. & Connell, D. W. Experiments in Environmental Chemistry: A Laboratory Manual. LC 80-40270. (Pergamon Ser. on Environmental Science: Vol. 4). (Illus.). 108p. 1980. pap. 9.95 (ISBN 0-08-024009-7). Pergamon.

Walmsley, Judith A. & Walmsley, Frank. Chemical Principles, Properties, & Reactions in the Laboratory. 400p. 1985. pap. 12.95 (ISBN 0-201-08110-5). Addison-Wesley.

Wartell, Michael & Cummins, Jack. Fundamentals of Chemistry. 450p. 1980. 20.00, pub net (ISBN 0-87150-736-6, W6 4271). Brooks-Cole.

Waser, Jurg, et al. Chem One. 2nd ed. Ricci, Jay, ed. (Illus.). 1980. 38.95 (ISBN 0-07-068432-4). McGraw.

Watt, George W., et al. Chemistry in the Laboratory. (Illus., Orig.). 1964. 15.95x (ISBN 0-393-09511-8, NortonC); pap. text ed. 9.95x (ISBN 0-393-09626-2). Norton.

Weast, Robert C. Handbook of Chemistry & Physics. 63rd ed. 2432p. 1982. 59.95 (ISBN 0-8493-0463-6). CRC Pr.

Weiner, Susan A. & Peters, Edward I. Introduction to Chemical Principles: A Laboratory Approach. 3rd ed. 1986. pap. 19.95 (ISBN 0-03-002923-6, CBS C); instr's manual 6.95 (ISBN 0-03-002924-4). SCP.

Weissberger. Techniques of Chemistry: Physical Methods of Chemistry, Vol. 1, Pt. 2. 5th ed. 1985. write for info. (ISBN 0-471-82515-8). Wiley.

Weissberger, Arnold, et al. Techniques of Chemistry: Microwave Molecular Spectra, Vol. 18. 3rd ed. (Techniques of Chemistry Ser.: 1-284). 944p. 1984. 175.00x (ISBN 0-471-08681-9, Pub. by Wiley-Interscience). Wiley.

West, Michael A., ed. Lasers in Chemistry. 438p. (Proceedings). 1977. 85.00 (ISBN 0-444-41630-7). Elsevier.

White, D. A Modern Introduction to Chemistry. 1979. pap. 4.10 (ISBN 0-08-022620-5). Pergamon.

Whitman, R. & Zinck, E. Chemistry Today. 1976. text ed. 19.90 (ISBN 0-13-129486-5); lab. manual 7.60 (ISBN 0-13-129502-0); 11.40 (ISBN 0-13-129494-6). P-H.

Whitten, Kenneth W. & Gailey, Kenneth D. General Chemistry with Qualitative Analysis. 2nd ed. 1984. text ed. 39.95 (ISBN 0-03-063827-5, CBS C); instr's. manual 19.95 (ISBN 0-03-069574-0); study guide 13.95 (ISBN 0-03-063569-1); lecture outline 13.95 (ISBN 0-03-063577-2); solution manual 12.95 (ISBN 0-03-063573-X); problems bk. 13.95 (ISBN 0-03-063576-4). SCP.

Whittingham, M. Stanley & Jacobson, Allen J., eds. Intercalation Chemistry. 627p. 1982. 87.50 (ISBN 0-12-747380-7). Acad Pr.

Widom, Joanne M. & Edelstein, Stuart J. Chemistry: An Introduction to General, Organic, & Biological Chemistry. LC 80-23816. (Illus.). 743p. 1981. text ed. 29.95x (ISBN 0-7167-1224-5); instr's. manual avail.; study guide 9.95x (ISBN 0-7167-1314-4); transparencies masters avail. W H Freeman.

Wight, H. & Williamson, D. Preparation for General Chemistry. 1974. 29.95 (ISBN 0-07-070165-2). McGraw.

Williams, G. H., ed. Advances in Free Radical Chemistry, Vol. 6. 304p. 1980. 94.95x (ISBN 0-471-26087-8, Pub. by Wiley Heyden). Wiley.

Wilson, James G. & Newall, A. B. General & Inorganic Chemistry. 2nd ed. (Illus.). 1971. text ed. 24.95x (ISBN 0-521-07073-2). Cambridge U Pr.

Wiseman, F. L. Chemistry in the Modern World. 544p. 1985. 31.95 (ISBN 0-07-071150-X). McGraw.

Withers, G. R. & Stranks, D. R. Chemistry: A Structural View: Practical Manual. pap. 28.00 (ISBN 0-317-08971-4, 2051417). Bks Demand UMI.

Wolfe, D. H. Essentials of General, Organic & Biological Chemistry. 640p. 1985. price not set (ISBN 0-07-071415-0); price not set study guide (ISBN 0-07-071417-7). McGraw.

--Introduction to College Chemistry. 32.95 (ISBN 0-07-071410-X); study guide 13.95 (ISBN 0-07-071412-6). McGraw.

Wolka, R. Introduction to Chemistry. 1980. 17.95. P-H.

Wolke, Robert L. Chemistry Explained. (Illus.). 1980. text ed. 30.95 (ISBN 0-13-129163-7). P-H.

Wood, E. J., ed. Structure & Function of Invertebrate Respiratory Proteins. (Life Chemistry Reports Ser.: Supplement). 416p. 1983. 55.00 (ISBN 3-7186-0155-9). Harwood Academic.

Wood, Jesse H. & Keenan, Charles. Quimica General. (Span.). 1970. 13.30 (ISBN 0-06-317050-7, IntlDept). Har-Row.

Yoder, Claude H., et al. Chemistry. 2nd ed. 876p. 1980. text ed. 28.95 (ISBN 0-15-506470-3, HC); instr's manual avail. (ISBN 0-15-506471-1). HarBraceJ.

Young, Jay A. Chemistry: A Human Concern. (Illus.). 1978. text ed. write for info. (ISBN 0-02-431160-X). Macmillan.

Zahradnik, R. & Hartmann, H. New Concepts Three. (Topics in Current Chemistry: Vol. 43). (Illus.). 145p. 1973. 33.00 (ISBN 0-387-06400-1). Springer-Verlag.

CHEMISTRY–ABBREVIATIONS

Wohlauer, Gabriele E. & Gholston, H. D. German Chemical Abbreviations. pap. 20.00 (ISBN 0-317-09828-4, 2012005). Bks Demand UMI.

CHEMISTRY–ADDRESSES, ESSAYS, LECTURES

Asimov, Isaac. Asimov on Chemistry. LC 73-15322. (Illus.). 288p. 1974. 8.95 (ISBN 0-385-04100-4); (Anch). Doubleday.

Black, Joseph. Lectures on the Elements of Chemistry, 3 vols. LC 78-72776. Repr. Set. 145.00 (ISBN 0-404-17625-9). AMS Pr.

Boschke, F., ed. Reactive Intermediates. LC 51-5497. (Topics in Current Chemistry: Vol. 16, Pt. 1). (Illus.). 1970. pap. 48.40 (ISBN 0-387-05103-1). Springer-Verlag.

Boschke, F. L., ed. Micelles. (Topics in Current Chemistry: Vol. 87). (Illus.). 1980. 56.00 (ISBN 0-387-09639-6). Springer-Verlag.

Bradley, J. N., et al, eds. Essays in Chemistry. Incl. Vol. 1. 1970. pap. 24.50 (ISBN 0-12-124101-7); Vol. 2. 1971. pap. 24.50 (ISBN 0-12-124102-5); Vol. 3. 1972. pap. 25.00 (ISBN 0-12-124103-3); Vol. 4. 1973. pap. 25.00 (ISBN 0-12-124104-1); Vol. 5. 1974. pap. 25.00 (ISBN 0-12-124105-X); Vol. 6. 1978. pap. 25.00 (ISBN 0-12-124106-8); Vol. 7. 1978. pap. 25.00 (ISBN 0-12-124107-6). pap. Acad Pr.

Emmett, J. C., ed. Second SCI-RSC: Medical Chemistry Symposium. 332p. 1984. 43.00 (ISBN 0-85186-935-1, Pub. by Royal Soc Chem UK). Heyden.

Goldman, I. David, ed. Proceedings of the Second Workshop on Folyl & Antifolyl Polyglumates. LC 85-3531. 416p. 1985. 45.00 (ISBN 0-03-002033-6). Praeger.

Haken, H. Evolution of Order & Chaos in Physics, Chemistry, & Biology: Schloss Elmau, FRG, 1982 Proceedings. (Springer Series in Synergetics: Vol. 17). (Illus.). 287p. 1982. 35.00 (ISBN 0-387-11904-3). Springer-Verlag.

In Memory of H. L. Meerwein. (Topics in Current Chemistry: Vol. 80). (Illus.). 1979. 81.00 (ISBN 0-387-09309-5). Springer-Verlag.

International Symposium on Macromolecular Chemistry (1961: Montreal) Macromolecular Chemistry: Special Lectures Presented at the International Symposium on Macromolecular Chemistry Held in Montreal, Canada, 27th July-1st August, 1961, Vol. 1. pap. 86.30 (ISBN 0-317-09293-6, 2020710). Bks Demand UMI.

International Symposium on Macromolecular Chemistry (1965: Prague) Macromolecular Chemistry, Vol. 2: Special Lectures Presented at the International Symposium on Macromolecular Chemistry Held in Prague, Czechoslovakia, 30 August-4 September 1965. LC 67-83242. (Illus.). pap. 160.00 (ISBN 0-317-09710-5, 2020711). Bks Demand UMI.

International Symposium on Macromolecular Chemistry (1967: Brussels & Louvain) Macromolecular Chemistry, Vol. 4: Plenary & Main Lectures Presented at the International Symposium on Macromolecular Chemistry Held in Brussels-Louvain, Belgium 12-16 June 1967. LC 68-54464. (Illus.). pap. 80.30 (ISBN 0-317-09693-1, 2020712). Bks Demand UMI.

International Union of Pure & Applied Chemistry. The Chemistry of Natural Products: Proceedings. Incl. No. 1. Melbourne, Canberra & Sydney, 1960. 1961; No. 2. Prague, 1962. 1963; No. 3. Kyoto, 1964. 1964; No. 4. Stockholm, 1966. 1967; No. 5. London, 1968. 1968; No. 6. Mexico City, 1969. 1970. 25.00 (ISBN 0-08-020743-X); No. 7. Riga, USSR, 1970. 1970. 36.00 (ISBN 0-08-020744-8); No. 8. New Delhi, India, 6-12 Feb., 1972. 1973. 25.00 (ISBN 0-08-020745-6); No. 9. Ottawa, 1974. Bishop, C. T. & Edwards, O. E., eds. 1975. 33.00 (ISBN 0-08-020972-6); 59.00 (ISBN 0-08-021198-4). write for info. Pergamon.

Lavoisier, Antoine. Essays, Physical & Chemical. Thomas, H., tr. 511p. 1970. Repr. of 1776 ed. 45.00x (ISBN 0-7146-1604-4, F Cass Co). Biblio Dist.

Marcus, Y. & Ben-Dor, L., eds. International Congress of Pure & Applied Chemistry, 25th, Jerusalem, 1975: Proceedings. 1977. text ed. 37.00 (ISBN 0-08-020952-1). Pergamon.

Meier, Dale J., ed. Block Copolymers: Science & Technology. (MMI Press Symposium Ser.). 210p. 1983. 75.00 (ISBN 3-7186-0144-3). Harwood Academic.

Mulder, G. J. & Caldwell, J., eds. Sulfate Metabolism & Sulfate Conjugation. 312p. 1982. 42.00x (ISBN 0-85066-233-8). Taylor & Francis.

Mulvaney, J. E. Macromolecular Syntheses, Vol. 6. LC 78-648294. (Illus.). pap. 32.00 (ISBN 0-317-09959-0, 2055602). Bks Demand UMI.

Nichols, James R. Chemistry of the Farm & the Sea. LC 73-125755. (American Environmental Studies). 1970. Repr. of 1867 ed. 12.00x (ISBN 0-405-02681-1). Ayer Co Pubs.

Scott, Arthur F., ed. Survey of Progress in Chemistry, 8 vols. Incl. Vol. 1. 1963. 59.50 (ISBN 0-12-610501-4); Vol. 2. 1965. 59.50 (ISBN 0-12-610502-2); Vol. 3. 1966. 59.50 (ISBN 0-12-610503-0); Vol. 4. 1968. 59.50 (ISBN 0-12-610504-9); Vol. 5. 1969. 59.50 (ISBN 0-12-610505-7); Vol. 6. 1974. 75.00 (ISBN 0-12-610506-5); Vol. 7. 1976. 59.50 (ISBN 0-12-610507-3); Vol. 8. 1978. 65.00 (ISBN 0-12-610508-1); Vol. 9. 1980. 49.50 (ISBN 0-12-610509-X). Acad Pr.

Technical Association of the Pulp & Paper Industry. International Chemical Recovery Conference, 1985: Proceedings of TAPPI, New Orleans Marriott, New orleans, LA, April 28-May 1. Bk. 1. pap. 47.50 (ISBN 0-317-26864-3, 2025292); Bk. 2. pap. 32.50 (ISBN 0-317-26865-1); Bk. 3. pap. 42.30 (ISBN 0-317-26866-X). Bks Demand UMI.

Tsuruta, T., ed. International Congress of Pure & Applied Chemistry, XXVI: Chemistry for the Welfare of Mankind, Vol. 1. (IUPAC Symposia Ser.). 1979. text ed. 140.00 (ISBN 0-08-022007-X). Pergamon.

Tsuruta, T. F., ed. Chemistry for the Welfare of Mankind: Proceedings of the 26th International Congress of Pure & Applied Chemistry, Tokyo, 1977, 5 Vols. 26th ed. (IUDAC-TOK). (Illus.). 1979. Set. 240.00 (ISBN 0-08-022040-1). Pergamon.

Varmuza, K. Pattern Recognition in Chemistry. (Lecture Notes in Chemistry Ser.: Vol. 21). (Illus.). 217p. 1980. pap. 25.00 (ISBN 0-387-10273-6). Springer-Verlag.

Vol'pin, M. E. Chemistry Reviews. (Soviet Scientific Reviews Ser.: Section B, Vol. 6). 452p. 1984. text ed. 170.00 (ISBN 3-7186-0139-7). Harwood Academic.

Volpin, M. E., ed. Chemistry Reviews, Vol. 4. (Soviet Scientific Reviews Ser.: Section B). 382p. 1982. 170.00 (ISBN 3-7186-0114-1). Harwood Academic.

CHEMISTRY–APPARATUS

see Chemical Apparatus

CHEMISTRY–BIBLIOGRAPHY

see also Chemical Literature

Bolton, H. C. A Select Bibliography of Chemistry. Incl. 1492-1892. 1893. 128.00 (ISBN 0-527-09400-5); First Supplement, 1492-1897, Section 1-7. 1899. 35.00 (ISBN 0-527-09420-X); First Supplement, 1492-1897, Section 8: Academic Dissertations. 1901. 35.00 (ISBN 0-527-09426-9); Second Supplement, 1492-1902. 1904. 35.00 (ISBN 0-527-09432-3). (Smithsonian Miscellaneous Collections Ser: No. 36). Kraus Repr.

Burman, C. R. How to Find Out in Chemistry. 2nd ed. LC 67-549. 1967. pap. 7.75 (ISBN 0-08-011880-1). Pergamon.

Kieffer, W. F. & Rakestraw, eds. Cumulative Index to Journal of Chemical Education, 3 vols. index 9.90 ea. Vol. 1 (ISBN 0-910362-10-6, 1924-1949). Vol. 2 (ISBN 0-910362-11-4, 1949-1958). Vol. 3 (ISBN 0-910362-12-2, 1958-1968). Chem Educ.

Mellon, M. G. Chemical Publications. 5th ed. 352p. 1982. text ed. 34.95x (ISBN 0-07-041514-5). McGraw.

Neu, John, et al, eds. Chemical, Medical, & Pharmaceutical Books Printed Before 1800: In the Collections of the University of Wisconsin Libraries. 288p. 1965. 27.50x (ISBN 0-299-03680-4). U of Wis Pr.

Selected Titles in Chemistry. 4th ed. 1977. pap. 1.25 (ISBN 0-8412-0413-6). Am Chemical.

CHEMISTRY–COLLECTED WORKS

Flory, Paul J. Selected Works of Paul J. Flory, 3 vols. Mandelkern, Leo, et al, eds. LC 84-51712. 2644p. 1985. Set. 165.00x (ISBN 0-8047-1277-8). Stanford U Pr.

Kochetkov, N. K. & Vol'pin, M. E. Chemistry Reviews. (Soviet Scientific Reviews Ser.: Section B, Vol. 7). 375p. 1985. pap. text ed. 170.00 (ISBN 3-7186-0154-0). Harwood Academic.

Lavoisier, Antoine-L. Oeuvres de Lavoisier, 6 Vols. (Illus.). Repr. of 1893 ed. Set. 210.00 (ISBN 0-384-31677-8). Johnson Repr.

Priestley, Joseph. Scientific Correspondence: Ninety-Seven Letters. LC 5-5452. 1968. Repr. of 1892 ed. 22.00 (ISBN 0-527-72728-8). Kraus Repr.

CHEMISTRY–DATA PROCESSING

Abraham, F. & Tiller, W. A., eds. An Introduction to Computer Simulation in Applied Science. LC 72-83047. 220p. 1972. 29.50 (ISBN 0-306-30579-8, Plenum Pr). Plenum Pub.

Allendoerfer, Robert D. Explorations in Chemistry. 64p. 1985. pap. text ed. 35.00 (ISBN 0-13-295866-X). P-H.

Barker, P. G. Computers in Analytical Chemistry. LC 82-22276. (Pergamon Ser. in Analytical Chemistry: Vol. 6). (Illus.). 472p. 1983. 75.00 (ISBN 0-08-024008-9). Pergamon.

Barnard, John M., ed. Computer Handling of Generic Chemical Structures. LC 84-13725. 242p. 1984. text ed. 53.95x (ISBN 0-566-03515-4). Gower Pub Co.

CHEMISTRY–DICTIONARIES

CHEMISTRY–DIRECTORIES

CHEMISTRY–EARLY WORKS TO 1800

Grew, Nehemiah. The Anatomy of Plants, with an Idea of a Philosophical History of Plants & Several Other Lectures. 1965. Repr. of 1682 ed. Facsimile Ed. 60.00 (ISBN 0-384-19950-X). Johnson Repr.

CHEMISTRY–EXAMINATIONS, QUESTIONS, ETC.

Boxer, Robert. Graduate Record Examination in Chemistry. 3rd Ed. ed. LC 83-15742. 256p. (Orig.). 1984. pap. 7.95 (ISBN 0-668-05741-6). Arco.

Davey, L. E. & Verstraeten, A. Indian Certificate Chemistry. 374p. 1981. 30.00x (ISBN 0-86125-663-8, Pub. by Orient Longman India). State Mutual Bk.

Liska, Ken & Pryde, Lucy T. Student Study Guide to Accompany Introductory Chemistry for Health Professionals. 272p. 1984. pap. text ed. write for info. study guide (ISBN 0-02-371010-1). Macmillan.

Mascetta, Joseph. Barron's How to Prepare for the College Board Achievement Tests -- Chemistry. 2nd ed. LC 81-887. 1981. pap. text ed. 7.95 (ISBN 0-8120-2069-3). Barron.

Nyman, C. J., et al. Problems for General Chemistry & Qualitative Analysis. 4th ed. LC 79-24489. 342p. 1980. pap. text ed. 13.95 (ISBN 0-471-05299-X). Wiley.

Powers, Samuel R. A Diagnostic Study of the Subject Matter of High School Chemistry. LC 79-177164. (Columbia University. Teachers College. Contributions to Education: No. 149). Repr. of 1924 ed. 22.50 (ISBN 0-404-55149-1). AMS Pr.

Practicing to Take the GRE Chemistry Test. (Orig.). 1983. pap. 6.95 (ISBN 0-88685-002-9). Educ Testing Serv.

Romano, Nick. A Regents Chemistry Review. Garnsey, Wayne, ed. (Illus.). 220p. 1985. pap. text ed. 2.50 (ISBN 0-9606036-7-0). N & N Pub.

Rudman, Jack. Assistant Chemist. (Career Examination Ser.: C-32). (Cloth bdg. avail. on request). pap. 12.00 (ISBN 0-8373-0032-0). Natl Learning.

--Chemist. (Career Examination Ser.: C-135). (Cloth bdg. avail. on request). pap. 12.00 (ISBN 0-8373-0135-1). Natl Learning.

--Chemistry. (College Proficiency Examination Ser.: CPEP-6). (Cloth bdg. avail. on request). pap. 9.95 (ISBN 0-8373-5406-4). Natl Learning.

--Chemistry. (Graduate Record Examination Ser.: GRE-2). (Cloth bdg. avail. on request). pap. 13.95 (ISBN 0-8373-5202-9). Natl Learning.

--Chemistry & General Sciences - Sr. H.S. (Teachers License Examination Ser.: T-6). (Cloth bdg. avail. on request). pap. 13.95 (ISBN 0-686-66502-3). Natl Learning.

--Chemistry, Physics & General Science. (National Teachers Examination Ser.: NT-7). (Cloth bdg. avail. on request). pap. 11.95 (ISBN 0-8373-8417-6). Natl Learning.

--General Chemistry. (College Level Examination Ser.: CLEP-13). (Cloth bdg. avail.on request). 9.95 (ISBN 0-8373-5313-0). Natl Learning.

--Junior Chemist. (Career Examination Ser,.: C-394). (Cloth bdg. avail on request). pap. 12.00 (ISBN 0-8373-0394-X). Natl Learning.

--Laboratory Aide. (Career Examination Ser.: C-430). (Cloth bdg. avail. on request). pap. 10.00 (ISBN 0-8373-0430-X). Natl Learning.

--Laboratory Assistant (Chemistry) (Career Examination Ser.: C-432). (Cloth bdg. avail. on request). pap. 10.00 (ISBN 0-8373-0432-6). Natl Learning.

--Principal Chemist. (Career Examination Ser.: C-2403). (Cloth bdg. avail. on request). pap. 12.00 (ISBN 0-8373-2403-3). Natl Learning.

--Senior Chemist. (Career Examination Ser.: C-2402). (Cloth bdg. avail. on request). pap. 14.00 (ISBN 0-8373-2402-5). Natl Learning.

Solomon, Lawrence. College Board Achievement Test in Chemistry. 288p. 1984. pap. 7.95 (ISBN 0-668-06168-5, 6168). Arco.

Walsh, Michael, et al, eds. Barron's Regents Exams & Answers Chemistry. rev. ed. LC 57-58729. 300p. 1982. pap. text ed. 4.50 (ISBN 0-8120-3163-6). Barron.

CHEMISTRY–EXPERIMENTS

see also Chemistry, Organic–Experiments

Alyea, Hubert N. & Dutton, F. B. Tested Demonstrations in Chemistry. 6th ed. 1962. 10.90 (ISBN 0-910362-07-6). Chem Educ.

Artz, Robert J. Experimental Chemistry: An Introduction. 1982. 11.95 (ISBN 0-316-05278-7); pap. avail. instrs' manual (ISBN 0-316-05279-5). Little.

Block, Toby F. Experiments in General Chemistry. 240p. 1983. pap. text ed. 11.50 (ISBN 0-8403-3103-7). Kendall-Hunt.

Geanangel, Russell A. & Wendlandt, Wesley W. Experimental Chemistry. 5th ed. 1979. 11.95 (ISBN 0-8403-2355-7). Kendall-Hunt.

Gilleland, Martha J. Basic Experiments for General, Organic, & Biological Chemistry. new ed. 226p. 1982. 13.95 (ISBN 0-314-63239-5). West Pub.

Goldschmiedt, Henry. Practical Formulas for Hobby or Profit. (Illus.). 1973. 17.00 (ISBN 0-8206-0235-3). Chem Pub.

Grew, N. Experiments in Consort of the Luctation Arising from the Affusion of Several Menstrums upon All Sorts of Bodies, etc. 118p. 1985. 12.50 (ISBN 0-87556-632-4); pap. write for info. (ISBN 0-87556-114-4). Saifer.

Guttman, Michael. Experiments for Chemistry: 1046L. 1976. coil bdg. 4.95 (ISBN 0-88252-047-4). Paladin Hse.

Hentz, F. C., Jr. & Long, G. Gilbert. Experiments with Chemical Reactions. 1979. coil bdg. 9.50 (ISBN 0-88252-035-0). Paladin Hse.

Hill, John W., et al. Chemistry for Changing Times. 4th ed. 576p. 1984. text ed. 27.95x (ISBN 0-8087-4738-X); study guide 9.95x (ISBN 0-8087-5038-0). Burgess.

Horrigan, P. & Kelly, J. Challenging Experiments in Chemistry. rev. ed. 1982. pap. 13.95x (ISBN 0-941512-00-2). Marshland Pub.

Jolly, William L. Encounters in Experimental Chemistry. 2nd ed. (Illus.). 143p. 1985. spiral bound 12.95x (ISBN 0-15-522598-7, HC); instr's. manual avail. (ISBN 0-15-522599-5). HarBraceJ.

Kistner, C. Richard. Experiments in Second Semester General Chemistry. 1979. coil bdg. 5.95 (ISBN 0-88252-026-1). Paladin Hse.

Kistner, Richard C. Experiments in First Semester General Chemistry. 1930. coil bdg. 8.50 (ISBN 0-88252-029-6). Paladin Hse.

Lowry, George, et al. Lab Experiments in General Chemistry. 1981. 17.95 (ISBN 0-88252-111-X). Paladin Hse.

Mercer, Edward, et al. Experiments in General Chemistry. 1978. coil bdg. 7.95 (ISBN 0-88252-076-8). Paladin Hse.

Messer, Melanie, et al. Introductory Experimental Chemistry. 1977. P-H.

Mills, Jerry L. & Mitchell, Roy E. General Chemistry Experiments. (Illus.). 1979. lab manual 11.95x (ISBN 0-89582-012-9). Morton Pub.

Sawyer, Donald T., et al. Chemistry Experiments for Instrumental Methods. LC 83-23297. 350p. 1984. pap. text ed. 20.95x (ISBN 0-471-89303-X). Wiley.

Segal, B. G. Chemistry: Experiment & Theory. 999p. 1985. 34.95 (ISBN 0-471-80811-3); write for info., study guide (ISBN 0-471-80972-1); write for info. solutions manual (ISBN 0-471-80974-8). Wiley.

Shah, Dinesh O., ed. Macro & Microemulsions: Theory & Applications. LC 84-28358. (ACS Symposium Ser.: No. 272). 488p. 1985. lib. bdg. 84.95x (ISBN 0-8412-0896-4). Am Chemical.

Shakhashiri, Bassam Z., et al. Chemical Demonstrations: A Handbook for Teachers of Chemistry, Vol. 1. LC 81-70016. (Illus.). 368p. 1983. 25.00x (ISBN 0-299-08890-1). U of Wis Pr.

Sienko, Michael J. & Plane, Robert A. Experimental Chemistry. 5th ed. 1976. text ed. 21.95 (ISBN 0-07-057331-X). McGraw.

Tocci, Salvatore. Experiments & Projects in Consumer Chemistry. (Illus.). 160p. 12.95 (ISBN 0-668-06026-3); pap. 6.95 (ISBN 0-668-06033-6). Arco.

University of Iowa Chemistry Staff. Experiments in Chemistry. 1981. spiral bdg. 6.80x (ISBN 0-87563-210-6). Stipes.

Weiss, Gerald S. & Wismer, Robert K. Experiments in General Chemistry. 4th ed. 368p. 1985. text ed. write for info. (ISBN 0-02-394810-8). Macmillan.

Wells, Norman, et al. Chemistry in Action: Novel & Classical Approaches. 2nd ed. (Illus.). 1980. lab manual 10.95 (ISBN 0-930116-02-X). Sci Ent.

CHEMISTRY–HISTORY

see also Alchemy; Chemical Literature

Anderson, Wilda C. Between the Library & the Laboratory: The Language of Chemistry in Eighteenth-Century France. LC 84-47942. 1985. text ed. 22.50x (ISBN 0-8018-3229-2). Johns Hopkins.

Asimov, Isaac. A Short History of Chemistry. LC 78-25789. (Illus.). 1979. Repr. of 1965 ed. lib. bdg. 29.50x (ISBN 0-313-20769-0, ASSH). Greenwood.

Beguinus, Jean. Tyrocinium Chymicum. Russell, Richard, tr. from Lat. LC 83-80335. xxiv, 135p. 1983. Repr. of 1669 ed. 15.00 (ISBN 0-935214-05-4). Heptangle.

Boas, Marie. Robert Boyle & Seventeenth-Century Chemistry. LC 58-4386. Repr. of 1958 ed. 23.00 (ISBN 0-527-09250-9). Kraus Repr.

Browne, Charles A. A Source Book of Agricultural Chemistry. Egerton, Frank N., 3rd, ed. LC 77-74205. (History of Ecology Ser.). 1978. Repr. of 1944 ed. lib. bdg. 23.50x (ISBN 0-405-10375-1). Ayer Co Pubs.

Bud, Robert F., et al. Chemistry in America, 1876-1976. 1984. lib. bdg. 79.50 (ISBN 90-277-1720-6, Pub. by Reidel Holland). Kluwer Academic.

Cohen, I. Bernard, ed. Andrew N. Meldrum. LC 80-2096. (Development of Science Ser.). (Illus.). lib. bdg. 45.00x (ISBN 0-405-13861-X). Ayer Co Pubs.

Crosland, Maurice P. Historical Studies in the Language of Chemistry. 1982. 16.50 (ISBN 0-8446-5881-2). Peter Smith.

Firth, Grace. Secrets of the Still: A Zesty History & How-To for Making Spirits, Fragrances, Curables, Gasahol & Other Products of the Stillroom. 1983. 17.95 (ISBN 0-914440-66-7). EPM Pubns.

Hannaway, Owen. The Chemists & the Word: The Didactic Origins of Chemistry. LC 74-24380. (Illus.). 182p. 1975. 17.50x (ISBN 0-8018-1666-1). Johns Hopkins.

Hufbauer, Karl. The Formation of the Chemical Community (1720-1795) LC 81-2988. 288p. 1982. 45.00x (ISBN 0-520-04318-9); pap. 14.95x (ISBN 0-520-04415-0, CAMPUS 299). U of Cal Pr.

Jaffe, Bernard. Crucibles: The Story of Chemistry from Ancient Alchemy to Nuclear Fission. LC 75-38070. (Illus.). 1976. pap. text ed. 6.50 (ISBN 0-486-23342-1). Dover.

--Crucibles: The Story of Chemistry from Ancient Alchemy to Nuclear Fission. 4th rev. ed. 15.25 (ISBN 0-8446-5486-8). Peter Smith.

Kendall, James. Young Chemists & Great Discoveries. facs. ed. LC 76-76907. (Essay Index Reprint Ser). 1939. 19.00 (ISBN 0-8369-0023-5). Ayer Co Pubs.

Kopp, Hermann F. Die Entwickelung der Chemie in der Neueren Zeit. Repr. of 1873 ed. 50.00 (ISBN 0-384-30200-9). Johnson Repr.

Leicester, Henry. Source Book in Chemistry, Nineteen Hundred to Nineteen Fifty. (Source Books in History of Science). text ed. 18.50x (ISBN 0-674-82231-5). Harvard U Pr.

Leicester, Henry M. Historical Background of Chemistry. LC 79-166426. (Illus.). 1971. pap. text ed. 4.50 (ISBN 0-486-61053-5). Dover.

--The Historical Background of Chemistry. (Illus.). 14.50 (ISBN 0-8446-4569-9). Peter Smith.

Leonard, Jonathan N. Crusaders of Chemistry. LC 72-8533. (Essay Index Reprint Ser.). 1972. Repr. of 1930 ed. 24.50 (ISBN 0-8369-7320-8). Ayer Co Pubs.

Li Ch'iao-P'ing. The Chemical Arts of Old China. LC 75-36234. Repr. of 1948 ed. 24.50 (ISBN 0-404-14482-9). AMS Pr.

McCann, H. Gilman. Chemistry Transformed: The Paradigmatic Shift from Phlogiston to Oxygen. LC 78-19173. (Modern Sociology: a Series of Monographs, Treatises & Texts). 1978. 24.50x (ISBN 0-89391-004-X). Ablex Pub.

Mauskopf, Seymour. Crystals & Compounds: Molecular Structure & Composition in Nineteenth-Century French Science. LC 76-3197. (Transactions Ser.: Vol. 66, Pt. 3). (Illus.). 1976. pap. 7.00 (ISBN 0-87169-663-0). Am Philos.

Muhammad Ibn Zakariya. Practical Chemistry in the Twelfth Century. Steele, Robert R., ed. Gerard Of Cremona, tr. LC 79-8590. Repr. of 1929 ed. 19.50 (ISBN 0-404-18444-8). AMS Pr.

Muir, M. M. A History of Chemical Theories & Laws. LC 74-26279. (History, Philosophy & Sociology of Science Ser.). 1975. Repr. 38.00x (ISBN 0-405-06606-6). Ayer Co Pubs.

Multhauf, Robert P. The Origins of Chemistry. 1967. lib. bdg. 15.00 (ISBN 0-685-52442-6). Watson Pub Intl.

Neubauer, Alfred. Chemistry Today: The Portrait of a Science. (Illus.). 214p. 1983. 12.95 (ISBN 0-668-05838-2, 5838). Arco.

Partington, James R. Origins & Development of Applied Chemistry. LC 74-26284. (History, Philosophy & Sociology of Science Ser.). 1975. Repr. 45.50x (ISBN 0-405-06611-2). Ayer Co Pubs.

Reese, Kenneth M., ed. A Century of Chemistry: The Role of Chemists & the American Chemical Society. LC 76-6126. 1976. 15.95 (ISBN 0-8412-0307-5). Am Chemical.

Rocke, Alan J. Chemical Atomism in the Nineteenth Century: From Dalton to Cannizzaro. LC 83-25082. 404p. 1984. 27.50 (ISBN 0-8142-0360-4). Ohio St U Pr.

Sivin, Nathan. Chinese Alchemy: Preliminary Studies. LC 67-27093. (Monographs in the History of Science Ser). 1968. 22.50x (ISBN 0-674-12150-3). Harvard U Pr.

Smith, Edgar F. Chemistry in America: Chapters from the History of the Science in the United States. LC 72-5073. (Technology & Society Ser.). Repr. of 1914 ed. 23.00 (ISBN 0-405-04723-1). Ayer Co Pubs.

Stillman, John M. Story of Alchemy & Early Chemistry. 16.00 (ISBN 0-8446-3016-0). Peter Smith.

Sturchild, Jeffrey L. The History of Chemistry: A Critical Bibliography. LC 84-45399. 250p. 1985. lib. bdg. 35.00 (ISBN 0-8240-8950-2). Garland Pub.

Symposium on Teaching Chemistry, San Francisco, 1968. Teaching the History of Chemistry. Kaufmann, G. B., ed. 1968. 21.75x (ISBN 0-685-27537-X). Adlers Foreign Bks.

Thackray, Arnold. Atoms & Power: An Essay on Newtonian Matter-Theory & the Development of Chemistry. LC 72-99521. (Harvard Monographs in the History of Science Ser.). (Illus.). pap. 66.90 (ISBN 0-8357-9153-X, 2017756). Bks Demand UMI.

Thomson, Thomas. The History of Chemistry, 2 vols. in 1. 2nd ed. LC 74-26298. (History, Philosophy & Sociology of Science Ser). 1975. Repr. 46.50x (ISBN 0-405-06623-6). Ayer Co Pubs.

Tilden, William A. Famous Chemists. facs. ed. LC 68-20344. (Essay Index Reprint Ser). 1921. 18.00 (ISBN 0-8369-0944-5). Ayer Co Pubs.

University of Pennsylvania. Catalog of the Edgar Fahs Smith Memorial Collection in the History of Chemistry. 1960. 89.00 (ISBN 0-8161-0522-7, Hall Library). G K Hall.

Vlasov, L. G. & Trifonov, D. N. One Hundred & Seven Stories About Chemistry. Sobolev, David, tr. (Illus.). 1977. pap. 3.95 (ISBN 0-8285-5067-0, Pub. by Mir Pubs USSR). Imported Pubns.

Von Meyer, Ernst. A History of Chemistry from Earliest Times to the Present Day: Introduction to the Study of the Science. M'Gowan, George, tr. LC 74-26303. (History, Philosophy & Sociology of Science Ser.). 1975. Repr. 42.00x (ISBN 0-405-06627-9). Ayer Co Pubs.

Wells, Horace L. Studies from the Chemical Laboratory of the Sheffield Scientific School (Yale University, 2 vols. 1901. 100.00x set (ISBN 0-685-89786-9). Elliots Bks.

Wurtz, Adolf. A History of Chemical Theory from the Age of Lavoisier to the Present Time. Cohen, I. Bernard & Watts, Henry, eds. LC 80-215. (Development of Science Ser.). (Illus.). 1981. Repr. of 1869 ed. Ayer Co Pubs.

CHEMISTRY–LABORATORIES

see Chemical Laboratories

CHEMISTRY–LABORATORY MANUALS

see also Chemistry, Analytic–Laboratory Manuals; Chemistry, Clinical–Laboratory Manuals; Chemistry, Inorganic–Laboratory Manuals; Chemistry, Organic–Laboratory Manuals; Chemistry, Physical and Theoretical–Laboratory Manuals; Glass Blowing and Working; Physiological Chemistry–Laboratory Manuals

Ahner, Walter. Laboratory Manual in Chemistry. 1964. pap. 7.75 (ISBN 0-87720-123-4). AMSCO Sch.

Ahner, Walter L. Workbook & Laboratory Manual in Chemistry. rev. ed. (Illus.). 1964. pap. 8.92 (ISBN 0-87720-125-0). AMSCO Sch.

Aikens, David A., et al. Principles & Techniques for an Integrated Chemistry Laboratory. (Illus.). 420p. 1984. pap. text ed. 14.95x (ISBN 0-88133-102-3). Waveland Pr.

Alexander, John J. & Steffel, Margaret J. Chemistry in the Laboratory. 374p. 1976. pap. text ed. 15.95 (ISBN 0-15-506466-5, HC); instructor's manual (ISBN 0-15-506469-X). HarBraceJ.

Allen, Thomas & Keefer, Raymond. General Chemistry Experiments. 1982. wire coil bdg. 5.95 (ISBN 0-88252-085-7). Paladin Hse.

Anderson, Christian & Hawes, J. L. Basic Experimental Chemistry: A Laboratory Manual for Beginning Students. rev. ed. 1971. pap. 21.95 (ISBN 0-8053-0222-0). Benjamin-Cummings.

Bobrik, Michael A. General Chemistry Laboratory Manual. 94p. 1982. pap. text ed. 8.95 (ISBN 0-8403-2653-X). Kendall-Hunt.

Bramwell, Fitzgerald B., et al. Investigations in General Chemistry: Quantitative Techniques and Basic Principles. 1977. spiral bdg. 14.95x (ISBN 0-8087-2803-2). Burgess.

Cain, H. W. & Hunt, R. L. Principles of Chemistry Laboratory: Manual for CH 111A & 112A. 1984. pap. text ed. 16.25 (ISBN 0-89917-431-0). Tichenor Pub.

Cassen, Thomas. Chemistry Laboratory Manual for Nurses. 1983. Paladin Hse.

--Chemistry 101 L Lab Manual. 1981. coil binding 15.95 (ISBN 0-88252-092-X). Paladin Hse.

Conroy, Lawrence E., et al. General Chemistry Laboratory Operation. 3rd ed. 1977. pap. write for info. (ISBN 0-02-324330-9, 32433). Macmillan.

Corwin, Charles H. Basic Chemistry: Laboratory Experiments. 4th ed. (Illus.). 272p. 1985. lab manual 19.95 (ISBN 0-13-057845-2). P-H.

Dondes, Seymour & Lurie, Steven W. General Chemistry Laboratory Manual. 3rd ed. (Illus.). 1981. 13.95 (ISBN 0-89529-154-1). Avery Pub.

Long, Gilbert G. & Hentz, Forrest C. Problem Exercises for General Chemistry. 2nd ed. LC 81-19686. 351p. 1982. pap. text ed. 14.95 (ISBN 0-471-08251-1). Wiley.

Margolis, Emil J. Formulation & Stoichiometry: A Review of Fundamental Chemistry. LC 67-28063. 225p. 1968. 19.50x (ISBN 0-306-50048-5, Plenum Pr). Plenum Pub.

Rinehart, Frank P. The Chemistry Tutor: Pt. 1-Balancing Equations & Stoichiometry Part II Oxidation Reduction. 1984. disk 25.00 (ISBN 0-471-80274-3); pap. text ed. 25.00 redox (ISBN 0-471-80339-1). Wiley.

Sasin, George S., et al. Chemistry Computations & Reactions. pap. 4.95 (ISBN 0-914770-06-3). Littoral Develop.

Sienko, Michael J. Chemistry Problems. 2nd ed. LC 70-151306. (Chemistry Ser). 1972. pap. text ed. 21.95 (ISBN 0-8053-8808-7). Benjamin-Cummings.

Sisler, Harry H., et al. Chemistry: A Systematic Approach. (Illus.). 1980. text ed. 28.95x (ISBN 0-19-502630-6); pap. text ed. 8.95x study guide (ISBN 0-19-502719-1); text ed. 4.95x instructor's manual (ISBN 0-19-502718-3). Oxford U Pr.

Smith, R. Nelson & Pierce, Conway. Solving General Chemistry Problems. 5th ed. LC 79-23677. (Illus.). 474p. 1980. pap. text ed. 11.95x (ISBN 0-7167-1117-6); answers to b group avail. W H Freeman.

Sonntag, Wendy W. & Rothenbuhler, Claire. Problems & Solutions to Accompany Quellette's Introduction to General, Organic, & Biological Chemistry. 304p. 1984. pap. write for info. (ISBN 0-02-413780-4). Macmillan.

Stoker, Owen C. & Stoker, H. Stephen. Introduction to Chemical Principles. (Illus.). 400p. 1983. write for info. student guide (ISBN 0-02-417610-9). Macmillan.

Wheeler, James W. Chemistry Problem Solving: Student Guide. 144p. 1979. pap. text ed. 7.50 (ISBN 0-89420-061-5, 237050); cassette recordings 342.20 (ISBN 0-89420-133-6, 237000). Natl Book.

Willis, Christopher. Problem-Solving in General Chemistry. LC 76-14004. (Illus.). 1977. pap. text ed. 16.50 (ISBN 0-395-24532-X). HM.

CHEMISTRY–PROGRAMMED INSTRUCTION

Banks, James E. Naming Organic Compounds: A Programmed Introduction to Organic Chemistry. 2nd ed. LC 75-291. 1976. pap. text ed. 18.95 (ISBN 0-7216-1536-8, CBS C). SCP.

Beatty, James W. & Beatty, James J. The Elements of Style in Chemistry: A Computer Assisted Instruction Supported Text. LC 81-40530. 116p. (Orig.). 1982. pap. text ed. 8.50 (ISBN 0-8191-1941-5). U Pr of Amer.

Hess, Fred C. Chemistry Made Simple. Thomas, Arthur L., rev. by. LC 82-46054. (Made Simple Ser.). (Illus.). 224p. 1984. pap. 4.95 (ISBN 0-385-18850-1). Doubleday.

Loebel, Arnold. Programmed Problem Solving for First Year Chemistry. LC 82-83359. 512p. 17.95 (ISBN 0-395-32626-5). HM.

Mentwig, Joachim & Kreuder, Manfred. Chemistry Made Easy, Part II: A Programmed Course for Self-Instruction. Rouvray, D. H., tr. from Ger. (Illus.). 691p. 1983. pap. 22.50x (ISBN 0-89573-050-2). VCH Pubs.

Nentwig, Joachim & Kreuder, Manfred. Chemistry Made Easy, Part I: A Programmed Course for Self-Instruction. Roureay, D. H., tr. from Ger. (Illus.). 652p. 1983. pap. 19.00x (ISBN 0-89573-049-9). VCH Pubs.

Peters, Edward I. Problem Solving for Chemistry. 2nd ed. LC 75-12493. (Illus.). 300p. 1976. pap. text ed. 16.95 (ISBN 0-7216-7206-X, CBS C). SCP.

Wiseman, Frank L. Chemistry Skills Series: Programmed Learning, Units 1-10. 201p. 1983. pap. text ed. 14.95x (ISBN 0-89917-400-0). Tichenor Pub.

CHEMISTRY–RESEARCH

see Chemical Research

CHEMISTRY–STUDY AND TEACHING

Bailey, Philip S. & Bailey, Christina A. Organic Chemistry: A Brief Survey of Concepts & Applications. 3rd ed. 1985. text ed. 34.30 (ISBN 0-205-08195-9, 688195); net 14.29 (ISBN 0-205-08197-5, 688197); study guide avail. Allyn.

Bandtock, John & Hanson, Paul. Success in Chemistry. (Success Studybooks Ser.). (Illus.). 380p. 1975. pap. 12.00 (ISBN 0-7195-2914-X). Transatlantic.

Basic Chemistry. (Basic Academics Ser.: Module 6). (Illus.). 60p. 1982. spiral bdg. 10.00x (ISBN 0-87683-230-3); instr's. manual 15.00x (ISBN 0-87683-241-9). G P Courseware.

Bouillon, Joan. Principles of College Chemistry. 160p. 1984. study guide 8.95x (ISBN 0-8087-4920-X). Burgess.

Carpenter, William W. Certain Phases of the Administration of High School Chemistry. LC 70-176627. (Columbia University. Teachers College. Contributions to Education: No. 191). Repr. of 1925 ed. 22.50 (ISBN 0-404-55191-2). AMS Pr.

Chemistry Curriculum & Teaching Materials: Report of a Regional Design Workshop. 47p. 1983. pap. text ed. 7.00 (ISBN 0-686-46349-8, UB135, UNESCO). Unipub.

Clouser, Joseph L. Keller Plan for Self-Paced Study Using Masterton & Slowinski's Chemical Principles. pap. text ed. cancelled (ISBN 0-8290-0633-8). Irvington.

College Chemistry Seniors: 1977-78. 1977. pap. 30.00 (ISBN 0-8412-0415-2). Am Chemical.

Daley, Henry O. & O'Malley, Robert F. Problems in Chemistry. rev. ed. (Undergraduate Chemistry Ser: Vol. 3). 512p. 1974. 25.00 (ISBN 0-8247-6107-3). Dekker.

Ensenanza De La Quimica Experimental. (Serie De Quimica: No. 6). (Span.). 1969. pap. 3.50 (ISBN 0-8270-6350-4). OAS.

Gillson, Margery. Developing a High School Chemistry Course Adapted to the Differentiated Needs of Boys & Girls. LC 75-176805. (Columbia University. Teachers College. Contributions to Education Ser.: No. 709). Repr. of 1937 ed. 22.50 (ISBN 0-404-55709-0). AMS Pr.

Hackert, Marvin L. Chemistry & Life: Study Guide. 2nd ed. 1983. pap. text ed. 9.95x (ISBN 0-317-16466-X). Burgess.

Horton, Ralph E. Measurable Outcomes of Individual Laboratory Work in High School Chemistry. LC 70-176879. (Columbia University. Teachers College. Contributions to Education Ser.: No. 303). Repr. of 1928 ed. 22.50 (ISBN 0-404-55303-6). AMS Pr.

Isenhour, T. L. & Pedersen, L. G. Passing Freshman Chemistry: Prerequesite Skills & Concepts. 177p. (Orig.). 1981. pap. text ed. 10.95 spiralbound (ISBN 0-15-568230-X, HC); instr's. manual avail. (ISBN 0-15-568231-8). HarBraceJ.

Kornhauser, A., et al. Chemical Education in the Seventies. (An IUPAC Publication). 338p. 1981. pap. 19.25 (ISBN 0-08-026208-2). Pergamon.

Ludena, E. V., et al, eds. Computers in Chemical Education & Research. LC 77-9473. 488p. 1977. 65.00x (ISBN 0-306-31071-6, Plenum Pr). Plenum Pub.

Mahan, Bruce H. University Chemistry. 3rd ed. LC 74-19696. 1975. text ed. 35.95 (ISBN 0-201-04405-6). Addison-Wesley.

Mascetta, Joseph. Barron's How to Prepare for the College Board Achievement Tests -- Chemistry. 2nd ed. LC 81-887. 1981. pap. text ed. 7.95 (ISBN 0-8120-2069-3). Barron.

Moore, John W., ed. Iterations: Computing in the Journal of Chemical Education. 1981. 12.50 (ISBN 0-910362-17-3). Chem Educ.

New Trends in Chemistry Teaching, 5 vols. (Teaching of Basic Sciences Ser.). Vol. 1, 1964. pap. 19.75 (ISBN 92-3-000672-6, U1172, UNESCO); Vol. 3, 1972. pap. 12.25 (ISBN 92-3-001001-4, U415); Vol. 4, 1979. pap. 7.50 (ISBN 92-3-101241-X, U416); Vol. 5, 1981. pap. 19.75 (ISBN 92-3-101907-4, U1172). Unipub.

Powers, Samuel R. A Diagnostic Study of the Subject Matter of High School Chemistry. LC 79-177164. (Columbia University. Teachers College. Contributions to Education: No. 149). Repr. of 1924 ed. 22.50 (ISBN 0-404-55149-1). AMS Pr.

Sackheim, George I. Introduction to Chemistry for Biology Students. 3rd ed. (Programed Biology Studies). (Illus.). 135p. (Orig., Prog. Bk.). 1983. pap. text ed. 6.95 (ISBN 0-88462-016-6, 3304-01, Ed Methods). Longman USA.

Santiago, Paul. An Audio-Tutorial Introduction to Chemistry: Workbook. (Illus.). 192p. 1985. pap. text ed. 15.95x (ISBN 0-88133-159-7). Waveland Pr.

Schmid, George H. & Dean, Coleen L. Study Guide for Schmid's the Chemical Basis of Life. 1982. pap. 12.95 (ISBN 0-316-77375-1). Little.

Shakhashiri, Bassam Z., et al. Chemical Demonstrations: A Handbook for Teachers of Chemistry, Vol. 1. LC 81-70016. (Illus.). 368p. 1983. 25.00x (ISBN 0-299-08890-1). U of Wis Pr.

Shea, Richard. Shea Lectures: Solving General Chemistry Problems. 160p. 1982. 15.00 (ISBN 0-682-49871-8, University). Exposition Pr FL.

Shulz, William D. & Powell, Howard B. Laboratory Manual for Schnid's the Chemical Basis of Life. 1982. pap. write for info. (ISBN 0-316-77375-1). Little.

Smith, Maurice T., ed. New Movements in the Study & Teaching of Chemistry. 272p. 1982. 30.00x (ISBN 0-85117-077-3, Pub. by M Temple Smith). State Mutual Bk.

Wilson, James G. & Newall, A. B. General & Inorganic Chemistry. 2nd ed. (Illus.). 1971. text ed. 24.95x (ISBN 0-521-07073-2). Cambridge U Pr.

Wood, E. J., ed. Microcomputers in Biochemical Education: Proceedings of the FEBS Meeting, Brussels, July 1983. 220p. 1984. 36.00 (ISBN 0-85066-288-5); pap. 20.00x (ISBN 0-85066-289-3). Taylor & Francis.

Zollinger, Heinrich. Chemie und Hochschule. (Poly: No. 11). (Ger., Illus.). 163p. 1978. pap. 16.95x (ISBN 0-8176-1044-8). Birkhauser.

CHEMISTRY–TABLES, ETC.

see also Chemistry, Organic–Tables, etc.

Bauer, Edward L. Statistical Manual for Chemists. 2nd ed. 1971. 39.00 (ISBN 0-12-082756-5). Acad Pr.

Cheronis, Nicholas D. & Entrikin, John B. Identification of Organic Compounds: A Students Text Using Semimicro Techniques. 1963. 55.00 (ISBN 0-470-15279-6, Pub. by Wiley-Interscience). Wiley.

Fischbeck, H. J. & Fishbeck, K. H. Formulas, Facts, & Constants for Students & Professionals in Engineering, Chemistry, & Physics. 270p. 1982. pap. 16.00 (ISBN 0-387-11315-0). Springer-Verlag.

Gmehling, et al, eds. Vapor-Liquid Equilibrium Data Collection Tables & Diagrams of Data for Binary & Multicomponent Mixtures up to Moderate Pressures; Constants of Correlation Equations for Computer Use: Part 2b: Organic Hydroxy Compounds: Alcohols & Phenols. LC 79-670289. (Dechema Chemistry Data Ser.: Vol. 1). 1978. text ed. 103.50x (ISBN 3-921567-12-2, Pub. by Dechema Germany). Scholium Intl.

Helbing, Wolfgang & Burkart, Adolf. Chemical Tables for Laboratory & Industry. LC 79-26137. 272p. 1980. 29.95x (ISBN 0-470-26910-3). Halsted Pr.

Hellwege, K. H., ed. Landolt-Boernstein Numerical Data & Functional Relationships in Science & Technology, New Series, Group 4: Macroscopic & Technical Properties of Matter, Vol. 1, Densities Of Nonaquesous Solutions: Phosphorescence Of Inorganic Substances. 1974. 249.90 (ISBN 0-387-06269-6). Springer-Verlag.

--Landolt-Boernstein Numerical Data & Functional Relationships in Science & Technology, New Series, Group 1: Nuclear Particle & Physics, Vols. 1-8. Incl. Vol. 1. Energy Levels of Nuclei. (Illus.). 814p. 1961. 149.10 (ISBN 0-387-02715-7); Vol. 2. Nuclear Radii. Collard, H. R., et al. Schopper, H., ed. (Illus.). viii, 54p. 1967. 25.20 (ISBN 0-387-03894-9); Vol. 3. Numerical Tables for Angular Correlation Computations in Alpha, Beta & Gamma Spectroscopy. Appel, H. Schopper, H., ed. vi, 1202p. 1968. 226.80 (ISBN 0-387-04218-0); Vol. 4. Numerical Tables for Beta-Decay & Electron Capture. Behrens, H. & Jaenecke, J. Schopper, H., ed. (Illus.). viii, 316p. 1968. 75.60 (ISBN 0-387-04593-7); Vol. 5, Pt. A. Q-Values & Excitation Functions of Nuclear Reactions, Pt.A: Q-Values. Keller, K. A., et al. 1972. 247.80 (ISBN 0-387-06031-6); Vol. 5, Pt. B. Q-Values & Excitation Functions of Nuclear Reactions, Pt. B: Excitation Functions for Charged-Particle Induced Nuclear Reactions. Keller, K. A., et al. 1973. 153.30 (ISBN 0-387-06167-3); Vol. 5, Pt. C. Estimation of Unknown Excitation Functions & Thick-Target Yields for p, d, He & Reactions. Diddens, A. N., et al. 1974. 79.80 (ISBN 0-387-06723-X); Vol. 6. Properties & Production Spectra of Elementary Particles. Diddens, A. N., et al. Schopper, H., ed. 1972. 75.60 (ISBN 0-387-06047-2); Vol. 7. Elastic & Charge Exchange Scattering of Elementary Particles. Schopper, H., ed. 210.00 (ISBN 0-387-06248-3); Vol. 8. Photoproduction of Elementary Particles. Genzel, H. & Joos, P. J. 142.80 (ISBN 0-387-06249-1). Springer-Verlag.

--Landolt-Boernstein Numerical Data & Functional Relationships in Science & Technology, New Series, Group 3: Crystal & Solid State Physics, Vols. 1-6. Incl. Vol. 1. Elastic, Piezoelectric, Piezooptic & Electrooptic Constants of Crystals. Bechman, R. & Hearmon, R. F. x, 160p. 1966; Vol. 2. Elastic, Piezoelectric, Piezooptic, Electrooptic Constants, & Non-Linear Dielectric Susceptibilities of Crystals. Bechman, R., et al. (Illus.). ix, 232p. 1969; Vol. 3. Ferro- & Antiferroelectric Substances. Mitsui, T., et al. (Illus.). viii, 584p. 1969; Vol. 4, Pt. A. Magnetic & Other Properties of Oxides & Related Compounds. Goodenough, J. B., et al. (Illus.). xv, 367p. 1970. 130.20 (ISBN 0-387-04898-7); Vol. 4, Pt. B: Magnetic & Other Properties of Oxides & Related Compounds. Bonnenberg, F., et al. (Illus.). xvi, 666p. 1970. 235.20 (ISBN 0-387-05176-7); Vol. 5. Structure Data of Organic Crystals, 2 vols. Schudt, E. & Weitz, G. (Illus.). 1971. Set. 428.40 (ISBN 0-387-05177-5); Vol. 6. Structure Data of Elements & Intermetallic Phases. Eckerlin, P. & Kandler, H. 1971. 346.50 (ISBN 0-387-05500-2). LC 62-53136. Springer-Verlag.

Hellwege, K. H. & Hellwege, A. M., eds. Landolt-Boernstein Numerical Data & Functional Relationships in Science & Technology, New Series, Group 2: Atomic & Molecular Physics, Vols. 1-6. Incl. Vol. 1. Magnetic Properties of Free Radicals. Fischer, H. x, 154p. 1965. 46.20 (ISBN 0-387-03346-7); Vol. 2. Magnetic Properties of Coordination & Organo-Metallic Transition Metal Compounds. Koenig, E. xii, 578p. 1966. 161.70 (ISBN 0-387-03593-1); Vol. 3. Luminescence of Organic Substances. Schmillen, A. & Legler, R. (Illus.). viii, 416p. 1967. 136.50 (ISBN 0-387-03895-7); Vol. 4. Molecular Constants from Microwave Spectroscopy. Starck, B. (Illus.). x, 225p. 1967. 75.60 (ISBN 0-387-03896-5); Vol. 5. Molecular Acoustics. Schaaffs, W. (Illus.). xii, 286p. 1967. 111.30 (ISBN 0-387-03897-3); Vol. 6. Molecular Constants from Microwave-, Molecular Beam- & ESR-Spectroscopy. De Maison, J., et al. 1974. 239.40 (ISBN 0-387-05977-6). Springer-Verlag.

Kaye, G. W. & Laby, T. H. Tables of Physical & Chemical Constants. 14th rev. ed. Bailey, A. E., et al, eds. LC 73-85205. (Illus.). 320p. 1973. text ed. 25.00x (ISBN 0-582-46326-2). Longman.

Lefax Pub. Co. Editors. Chemical Tables. (Lefax Technical Manuals.: No. 779). (Illus.). looseleaf bdg. 9.50 (ISBN 0-685-14127-6). LeFax.

Petryanov, I. V. & Trifonov, D. N. Elementary Order: Mendeleev's Periodic System. 155p. 1985. pap. 3.95 (ISBN 0-8285-2870-5, Pub by Mir Pubs USSR). Imported Pubns.

CHEMISTRY–TERMINOLOGY

Bennett, H. Encyclopedia of Chemical Trademarks & Synonyms, Vol. 1 A-E. 1981. 65.00 (ISBN 0-8206-0286-8). Chem Pub.

Cooke, E. I. & Cooke, R. W. Gardner's Chemical Synonyms & Trade Names: A Dictionary & Commercial Handbook Containing Over 35,500 Definitions & Identifications. 8th ed. 776p. 1980. 150.00x (ISBN 0-291-39678-X, Pub. by Tech Pr). State Mutual Bk.

Fromherz, H. & King, A. English-German Chemical Terminology: An Introduction to Chemistry in English & German. 5th rev. ed. (Eng. & Ger.). 588p. 1968. 55.00 (ISBN 0-686-56603-3, M-7362, Pub. by Vlg. Chemie). French & Eur.

Fromherz, Hans & King, Alexander. English-German Chemical Terminology: An Introduction to Chemistry in English & German. 5th ed. LC 68-26705. (Eng. & Ger.). 588p. 1968. 46.30x (ISBN 3-527-25093-X). VCH Pubs.

--French-English Chemical Terminology: An Introduction to Chemistry in French & English. (Fr. & Eng.). 561p. 1968. 46.30x (ISBN 3-527-25095-6). VCH Pubs.

--French-German Chemical Terminology: An Introduction to Chemistry in French & German. LC 68-54575. (Fr. & Ger.). 588p. 1969. 46.30x (ISBN 3-527-25094-8). VCH Pubs.

Godman, Arthur. Barnes & Noble Thesaurus of Chemistry. (Illus.). 256p. 1983. 13.41i (ISBN 0-06-015175-7); pap. 6.68i (ISBN 0-06-463578-3, EH 578). B&N NY.

Hampel, Clifford A. & Hawley, Gessner G. Glossary of Chemical Terms. 2nd ed. 1982. 21.95 (ISBN 0-442-23871-1). Van Nos Reinhold.

Hawley, Gessner. Condensed Chemical Dictionary. 10th ed. 1150p. 1981. text ed. 46.75 (ISBN 0-442-23244-6). Van Nos Reinhold.

Schoenfeld, R. The Chemist's English. 200p. 1985. 20.00 (ISBN 0-89573-436-2). VCH Pubs.

CHEMISTRY–VOCATIONAL GUIDANCE

see Chemistry As a Profession

CHEMISTRY, AGRICULTURAL

see Agricultural Chemistry

CHEMISTRY, ANALYTIC

see also Chromatographic Analysis; Electrolysis; Fluorimetry; Instrumental Analysis; Mineralogy, Determinative; Phosphorimetry; Polarograph and Polarography; Radioactivation Analysis; Spectrophotometry;

also subdivision analysis under special subjects, e.g. Gases–Analysis; Rocks–Analysis

Ahuja, Sut, et al, eds. Chemical Analysis of the Environment & Other Techniques. LC 73-82575. 384p. 1973. 49.50x (ISBN 0-306-39305-0, Plenum Pr). Plenum Pub.

Alyea, Elmer C. & Meek, Devon W., eds. Catalytic Aspects of Metal Phosphine Complexes. LC 81-12903. (Advances in Chemistry Ser.: No. 196). 1981. 69.95 (ISBN 0-8412-0601-5). Am Chemical.

Klimova, V. A. Basic Methods of Organic Microanalysis. 228p. 1977. 5.95 (ISBN 0-8285-0641-8, Pub. by Mir Pubs USSR). Imported Pubns.

Knapp, Daniel R. Handbook of Analytical Derivatization Reactions. LC 78-12944. 741p. 1979. 86.00x (ISBN 0-471-03469-X, Pub. by Wiley-Interscience). Wiley.

Kolthoff, I. & Elving, P. Treatise on Analytical Chemistry, Vol. 7. 2nd ed. LC 78-1707. (Theory & Practice Ser.: Pt. 1). 816p. 1981. 92.50 (ISBN 0-471-07996-0, Pub. by Wiley-Interscience). Wiley.

Kolthoff, I. M. & Elving, P. J. Treatise on Analytical Chemistry, 3 pts. Incl. Vols. 10-12. Theory & Practice of Analytical Chemistry. (Pt. 1); Vols. 15. Analytical Chemistry of the Elements & of Inorganic & Organic Compounds. Kolthoff, I. M. & Elving, Phillip J. (Pt. 2). Vol. 10, 1978. 85.50 (ISBN 0-471-49998-6). Vol. 14, 1971. 51.00 (ISBN 0-471-50005-4); Vol. 15, 1976. 83.00 (ISBN 0-471-50009-7); Vols. 3. Analytical Chemistry in Industry. Kolthoff, I M. & Stross, F H., eds. (Pt. 3). 598p. 1976. 110.00 (ISBN 0-471-50012-7); 96.00 (ISBN 0-471-02765-0). LC 59-12439 (Pub. by Wiley-Interscience). Wiley.

--Treatise on Analytical Chemistry: Analytical Chemistry of Inorganic & Organic Compounds, Vol. 16, Pt. 2. (Analytical Chemistry Ser.). 560p. 1980. 87.50 (ISBN 0-471-05857-2). Wiley.

--Treatise on Analytical Chemistry: Analytical Chemistry of Inorganic & Organic Compounds, Vol. 17, Pt. 2. (Analytical Chemistry Ser.). 388p. 1980. 88.95 (ISBN 0-471-06481-5). Wiley.

--Treatise on Analytical Chemistry: Theory & Practice, Vol. 2, Pt. 1. 2nd ed. (Analytical Chemistry Ser.). 815p. 1979. 107.50 (ISBN 0-471-05510-7). Wiley.

Kolthoff, I. M. & Elving, Philip J. Treatise on Analytical Chemistry, Vol. 3. 2nd ed. LC 78-1707. (Theory & Practice Ser.: Pt. 1). 592p. 1983. 82.00x (ISBN 0-471-49969-2, Pub. by Wiley-Interscience). Wiley.

--Treatise on Analytical Chemistry, Vol. 10. 2nd ed. (Pt. 1). 533p. 1983. 70.00x (ISBN 0-471-89688-8, Pub. by Wiley-Interscience). Wiley.

--Treatise on Analytical Chemistry: Theory & Practice, Vol. 5. 2nd ed. (Pt. 1). 668p. 1982. 91.95x (ISBN 0-471-01837-6, Pub. by Wiley-Interscience). Wiley.

Kolthoff, I. M., et al, eds. Treatise on Analytical Chemistry: Theory & Practice, Vol. 4. 2nd ed. (1-299). 688p. 1984. Pt. 1. 75.00 (ISBN 0-471-01836-8, Pub. by Wiley-Interscience). Wiley.

Kolthoff, P. J. & Elving, P. J. Treatise on Analytical Chemistry: Theory & Practice, Vol. 8, Pt. 1. 2nd ed. (Analytical Chemistry Ser.). 1985. 85.00 (ISBN 0-471-07995-2). Wiley.

--Treatise on Analytical Chemistry: Theory & Practice, Vol. 14, Pt. 1. 2nd ed. (Analytical Chemistry Ser.). 1985. 80.00 (ISBN 0-471-80648-X). Wiley.

Kotrly, Stanislav & Sucha, Ladislav. Handbook of Chemical Equilibria in Analytical Chemistry. (Ellis Horwood Analytical Chemistry Ser.: I-118). 414p. 1985. 97.00x (ISBN 0-470-27479-4). Halsted Pr.

Kuwana, Ted & Osa, Tetsuo, eds. Physical Methods in Modern Chemical Analysis, Vol. 1. 1978. 46.00 (ISBN 0-12-430801-5). Acad Pr.

Kuwana, Theodore, ed. Physical Methods in Modern Chemical Analysis, Vol. 2. LC 77-92242. 1980. 45.00 (ISBN 0-12-430802-3). Acad Pr.

Lambert, Joseph B. & Riddell, Frank G., eds. The Multinuclear Approach to NMR Spectroscopy. 1983. lib. bdg. 72.00 (ISBN 90-277-1582-3, Pub. by Reidel Holland). Kluwer Academic.

Lambert, Joseph B., et al. Organic Structural Analysis. (Illus.). 640p. 1976. text ed. write for info. (ISBN 0-02-367290-0). Macmillan.

Lawrence, James F. Trace Analysis, Vol. 1. 1981. 47.50 (ISBN 0-12-682101-1). Acad Pr.

Lawrence, James F., ed. Liquid Chromatography in Environmental Analysis. LC 83-10711. (Contemporary Instrumentation & Analysis Ser.). 392p. 1984. 55.00 (ISBN 0-89603-045-8). Humana.

Lefax Pub. Co. Editors. Chemical Analysis. (Lefax Data Bks.: No. 656). (Illus.). looseleaf bdg. 3.00 (ISBN 0-685-14124-1). LeFax.

Liang, et al. Analytical Chemistry. (Illus.). 368p. 1985. 39.00 (ISBN 0-87371-053-3). Lewis Pubs Inc.

Liteanu, C. & Rica, I. Statistical Theory & Methodlogy of Trace Analysis. (Ellis Horwood Ser. in Analytical Chemistry). 446p. 1980. 109.95x (ISBN 0-470-26797-6). Halsted Pr.

Lyalikov, Y. S. & Klyachko, Y. A. Theoretical Foundations of Modern Chemical Analysis. 1980. 8.45 (ISBN 0-8285-1777-0, Pub. by Mir Pubs USSR). Imported Pubns.

Lynn, J. Daniel, et al. New Methods of Automated Sequence Analysis of Proteins. (Illus.). 220p. 1973. text ed. 39.50x (ISBN 0-8422-7099-X). Irvington.

Lyon, William S., ed. Analytical Chemistry in Nuclear Fuel Reprocessing. LC 77-16721. (Illus.). 1978. lib. bdg. 35.00 (ISBN 0-89500-006-7). Sci Pr.

Ma, Tsu S. & Horak, V. Microscale Manipulations in Chemistry. LC 75-20093. (Chemical Analysis: Vol. 44). pap. 126.00 (ISBN 0-317-09305-3, 2022487). Bks Demand UMI.

McBryde, W. A., ed. A Critical Review of Equilibrium Data for Proton-and Metal Complexes of 1,10-Phenanthroline, 2,2'-Bipyridyl & Related Compounds: Critical Evaluation of Equilibrium Const. in Solution; Part A: Stability Const. of Metal Complexes, Vol. 17. 1978. pap. text ed. 22.00 (ISBN 0-08-022344-3). Pergamon.

Marcus, Y., et al, eds. Equilibrium Constants of Liquid-Liquid Distribution Reactions, Vol. 15, Pt. 3: Compound Forming Extractants, Solvating Solvents & Inert Solvents. 1977. pap. text ed. 14.50 (ISBN 0-08-022032-0). Pergamon.

Marr, Ian & Cresser, Malcolm S. Environmental Chemical Analysis. 224p. 1983. 42.00 (ISBN 0-412-00201-9, NO. 5023, Pub. by Chapman & Hall England). Methuen Inc.

Massart, D. L., et al. Evaluation & Optimization of Laboratory Methods & Analytical Procedures. (Techniques & Instrumentation in Analytical Chemistry Ser.: Vol. 1). 596p. 1978. 72.50 (ISBN 0-444-41743-5). Elsevier.

Mathur, N. K. & Narang, C. K. Determination of Organic Compounds with N-Bromosuccinimide & Allied Reagents. (Analysis of Organic Materials Ser.). 1975. 39.00 (ISBN 0-12-479750-4). Acad Pr.

Mattson, James, ed. Laboratory Systems & Spectroscopy. (Computers in Chemistry & Instrumentation: Vol. 5). 1977. 69.75 (ISBN 0-8247-6207-X). Dekker.

Melson, G. A., ed. Coordination Chemistry of Macrocyclic Compounds. LC 78-27023. (Illus.). 678p. 1979. 85.00x (ISBN 0-306-40140-1, Plenum Pr). Plenum Pub.

Miller, James M. Separation Methods in Chemical Analysis. LC 74-13781. 309p. 1975. 45.00x (ISBN 0-471-60490-9, Pub. by Wiley-Interscience). Wiley.

Minczewski, J., et al. Separation & Preconcentration Methods in Inorganic Trace Analysis. (Analytical Chemistry Ser.). 550p. 1982. 102.00 (ISBN 0-470-27169-8). Halsted Pr.

Mix, Paul E. The Design & Application of Process Analyzer Systems. LC 83-21915. (Chemical Analysis: A Series of Monographs on Analytical Chemistry & Its Applications: 1-075). 312p. 1984. 55.00x (ISBN 0-471-86518-4, Pub. by Wiley-Interscience). Wiley.

Moeller, Therald, et al, eds. Chemistry with Qualitative Analysis. 2nd ed. 1984. 29.50i (ISBN 0-12-503360-5). Acad Pr.

Morf, W. E. Principles of Ion-Selective Electrodes & of Membrane Transport. (Studies in Analytical Chemistry: Vol. 2). 434p. 1981. 81.00 (ISBN 0-444-99749-0). Elsevier.

Moses, A. J. Nuclear Techniques in Analytical Chemistry. LC 64-15736. (International Series on Analytical Chemistry: Vol. 20). 1965. 11.30 (ISBN 0-08-010695-1). Pergamon.

Mukhedkar, A. J. & Pol, P. G. A Course in Chemical Analysis. 364p. 1981. 30.00x (ISBN 0-686-72269-8, Pub. by Orient Longman India). State Mutual Bk.

Murt, E. M. & Guldner, W. G., eds. Physical Measurement & Analysis of Thin Films. LC 68-13392. (Illus.). 194p. 1969. 35.00 (ISBN 0-306-39302-6, Plenum Pr). Plenum Pub.

Natusch, David F. S. & Hopke, Philip K. Analytical Aspects of Environmental Chemistry. LC 82-13518. (Chemical Analysis Monographs). 267p. 1983. 47.00x (ISBN 0-471-04324-9, Pub. by Wiley Interscience). Wiley.

Parker, G. A. Analytical Chemistry of Molybdenum. (Illus.). 175p. 1983. 44.50 (ISBN 0-387-12235-4). Springer-Verlag.

Pataki, L. & Zapp, E. Basic Analytical Chemistry. (Analytical Chemistry Ser.: Vol. 2). (Illus.). 1981. 61.00 (ISBN 0-08-023850-5). Pergamon.

Pecsok, Robert L., et al. Modern Methods of Chemical Analysis. 2nd ed. LC 76-13894. 1976. 37.50x (ISBN 0-471-67662-4). Wiley.

Perrin, D. D. Organic Complexing Reagents: Structural Behavior & Application to Inorganic Analysis. LC 77-16083. 378p. 1978. Repr. of 1964 ed. lib. bdg. 24.50 (ISBN 0-88275-574-9). Krieger.

Peters, Dennis G., et al. Chemical Separations & Measurements: Theory & Practice of Analytical Chemistry. LC 73-87385. (Illus.). 749p. 1974. text ed. 39.95 (ISBN 0-7216-7203-5, CBS C). SCP.

Physical Methods in Modern Chemical Analysis, Vol. 3. Kuwana, Theodore, ed. 320p. 1983. 55.00 (ISBN 0-12-430803-1). Acad Pr.

Pietrzyk, Donald J. & Frank, Clyde. Analytical Chemistry. 2nd ed. 700p. 1979. 24.00i (ISBN 0-12-555160-6); pap. text ed. 10.00 instr's. manual (ISBN 0-12-555162-2). Acad Pr.

Plambeck, James A. Electroanalytical Chemistry: Basic Principles & Applications. LC 82-2803. 404p. 1982. 42.95 (ISBN 0-471-04608-6, Pub. by Wiley-Interscience). Wiley.

Pribil, R. Applied Complexometry, Vol.5. Stulikova, M., et al, trs. (Analytical Chemistry Ser.). (Illus.). 425p. 1982. 83.00 (ISBN 0-08-026277-5). Pergamon.

Price, J. W. & Smith, R. Tin. (Handbook of Analytical Chemistry: Vol. 4, Pt. 3, Section A, Y). (Illus.). 1978. 86.20 (ISBN 0-387-08234-4). Springer-Verlag.

Ramette, Richard W. Chemical Equilibrium & Analysis. (Chemistry Ser). (Illus.). 672p. 1981. text ed. 33.95 (ISBN 0-201-06107-4); solutions manual 1.50 (ISBN 0-201-06109-0). Addison-Wesley.

Royal Society of London. Recent Advances in Analytical Chemistry: Proceedings of a Royal Society Discussion Meeting held on 9 & 10 December 1981. Thomas, J. M., et al, eds. (Illus.). 219p. 1982. text ed. 70.00x (ISBN 0-85403-191-X, Pub. by Royal Soc London). Scholium Intl.

Sampling, Standards & Homogeneity, STP 540. 136p. 1973. 12.50 (ISBN 0-8031-0561-4, 04-540000-34). ASTM.

Samuelson, Olof. Ion Exchange Separations in Analytical Chemistry. LC 63-2330. pap. 118.50 (ISBN 0-317-10491-8, 2007396). Bks Demand UMI.

Sawicki, Eugene. Photometric Organic Analysis: Basic Principles with Applications. LC 70-116768. (Chemical Analysis Ser.: Vol. 31). pap. 160.00 (ISBN 0-317-08871-8, 2006491). Bks Demand UMI.

Schramel, P., ed. Trace Element Analytical Chemistry in Medicine & Biology. 1000p. 1980. 100.00 (ISBN 3-11-008357-4). De Gruyter.

Schuetzle, Dennis, ed. Monitoring Toxic Substances. LC 78-27490. (ACS Symposium Ser.: No. 94). 1979. 44.95 (ISBN 0-8412-0480-2) (ISBN 0-8412-0656-2). Am Chemical.

Shapiro, Bernard L. New Directions in Chemical Analysis: Proceedings of the Annual Symposia of the Industry University Cooperative Chemistry Program (IUCCP) of the Texas A&M Univ. Chemistry Department, No. 3. LC 85-40053. 450p. 1985. lib. bdg. 45.00x (ISBN 0-89096-255-3). Tex A&M Univ Pr.

Shepherd, P. T. Trac-Trends in Analytical Chemistry: Reference Edition, 1981-1982. (Trac Compendium Ser.: Vol. 1). 1984. 89.50 (ISBN 0-317-11476-X). Elsevier.

Simmons, Ivor L. & Ewing, Galen W., eds. Progress in Analytical Chemistry, Vol. 8. LC 76-14896. 336p. 1976. 49.50 (ISBN 0-306-39308-5, Plenum Pr). Plenum Pub.

Skoog, Douglas A. Analytical Chemistry. 4th ed. 704p. 1986. text ed. 40.95x (ISBN 0-03-002954-6); solns. manual o.s.i. 11.95 (ISBN 0-03-002924-4). SCP.

Skoog, Douglas A. & West, Donald M. Fundamentals of Analytical Chemistry. 4th ed. 1982. text ed. 42.95x (ISBN 0-03-058459-0, CBS C); solns. manual 11.95 (ISBN 0-03-058461-2). SCP.

Slavin, Morris. Emission Spectrochemical Analysis. LC 78-15394. 266p. 1978. Repr. of 1971 ed. lib. bdg. 26.50 (ISBN 0-88275-724-5). Krieger.

Smith, A. Lee. Analysis of Silicones in Chemical Analysis. LC 83-8421. (Vol. 41). 416p. 1983. Repr. of 1974 ed. text ed. 49.50 (ISBN 0-89874-640-X). Krieger.

Snell, Forster D. Photometric & Fluorometric Methods of Analysis: Metals, 2 pts. LC 77-25039. 2192p. 1978. Set. 395.95 (ISBN 0-471-81014-2, Pub. by Wiley-Interscience). Wiley.

Sokolov, Igor' I. Tables & Nomograms of Hydrochemical Analysis. LC 60-13952. pap. 22.30 (ISBN 0-317-09355-X, 2020662). Bks Demand UMI.

Strasheim, A. & Steele, T. W., eds. Analytical Chemistry in the Exploration, Mining & Processing of Materials. 1978. text ed. 65.00 (ISBN 0-08-021199-2). Pergamon.

Svehla, G., ed. Comprehensive Analytical Chemistry: Thermal Methods in Analytical Chemistry Substoichiometric Analytical Chemistry, Vol. 7. 322p. 1976. 106.50 (ISBN 0-444-41166-6). Elsevier.

--Comprehensive Analytical Chemistry, Vol. 16: Chemical Microscopy, Thermomicroscopy of Organic Compounds. 514p. 1982. 140.50 (ISBN 0-444-41950-0). Elsevier.

--Comprehensive Analytical Chemistry, Vol. 18: Kinetic Methods of Analytical Chemistry, & Application of Computers in Analytical Chemistry. 446p. 1983. 117.00 (ISBN 0-444-99685-0). Elsevier.

Svehla, G. & Mazor, M., eds. Comprehensive Analytical Chemistry: Methods of Organic Analysis, Vol. 15. 1983. 140.50 (ISBN 0-444-99704-0). Elsevier.

Svehla, G. & Wilson, C., eds. Comprehensive Analytical Chemistry: Analysis of Complex Hydrocarbon Mixtures, 2 pts, Vol.13A. 1982. Pt. A: Separation Methods. 110.75 (ISBN 0-444-99736-9); Pt. B: Group Analysis & Detailed Analysis. 110.75 (ISBN 0-444-99735-0). Elsevier.

--Comprehensive Analytical Chemistry: Applications of Mathematical Statistics in Analytical Chemistry, Vol. 11. 408p. 1981. 110.75 (ISBN 0-444-41886-5). Elsevier.

--Comprehensive Analytical Chemistry: Enzyme Electrodes in Analytical Chemistry, Vol. 8. LC 58-10158. 590p. 1977. 123.50 (ISBN 0-444-41523-8). Elsevier.

--Comprehensive Analytical Chemistry: Ion Exchangers in Analytical Chemistry, Vol. 14. 586p. 1982. 123.50 (ISBN 0-444-99717-2). Elsevier.

--Comprehensive Analytical Chemistry: Organic Spot Test Analysis: The History of Analytical Chemistry, Vol. 10. 304p. 1980. 95.75 (ISBN 0-444-41859-8). Elsevier.

--Comprehensive Analytical Chemistry: Thermal Analysis; Simultaneous Thermoanalytical Examinations by Means of the Derivatograph, Vol. 12A. 278p. 1981. 78.75 (ISBN 0-444-41949-7). Elsevier.

--Comprehensive Analytical Chemistry: Ultraviolet Photoelectron & Photoion Spectroscopy; Auger Electron Spectroscopy; Plasma Excitation in Spectrochemical Analysis, Vol. 9. 306p. 1979. 95.75 (ISBN 0-444-41732-X). Elsevier.

--Comprehensive Analytical Chemisty: Analytical Infrared Spectroscopy, Vol. 6. 556p. 1976. 119.25 (ISBN 0-444-41165-8). Elsevier.

Takeuchi. Analytical Chemistry, Vol. 3. (Organic Synthesis--Today & Tomorrow). 39.00 (ISBN 0-08-022037-1). Pergamon.

Talmi, Yair, ed. Multichannel Image Detectors. LC 79-12441. (ACS Symposium Ser.: No. 102). 1979. 39.95 (ISBN 0-8412-0504-3). Am Chemical.

Thomas, J. D. Ion-Selective Electrode Reviews, Vol. 1. (Illus.). 280p. 1980. 47.00 (ISBN 0-08-026044-6). Pergamon.

Tugarinov, A. I., ed. Recent Contributions to Geochemistry & Analytical Chemistry. Slutzkin, D., tr. LC 74-8165. 694p. 1975. 98.95x (ISBN 0-470-89228-5). Halsted Pr.

Upor, E., et al. Wilson & Wilson's Comprehensive Analytical Chemistry, Vol. XX: Photometric Methods in Inorganic Trace Analysis. Svehla, G., ed. 208p. 1985. 115.50 (ISBN 0-444-99588-9). Elsevier.

Vidal, C. & Pacault, A., eds. Nonlinear Phenomena in Chemical Dynamics: Proceedings. (Springer Series in Synergetics: Vol. 12). (Illus.). 280p. 1981. 36.00 (ISBN 0-387-11294-4). Springer-Verlag.

Vinson, Joseph A., ed. Cannabinoid Analysis in Physiological Fluids. LC 79-10934. (ACS Symposium Ser.: No. 98). 1979. 29.95 (ISBN 0-8412-0488-8). Am Chemical.

Vogel, A. I. Vogel's Textbook of Practical Organic Chemistry. 4th ed. Furniss, B. S., et al, eds. LC 77-23559. (Illus.). 1978. text ed. 60.00x (ISBN 0-582-44250-8). Longman.

Vogtle, F. & Weber, E., eds. Host Guest Complex Chemistry: Macrocycles. (Illus.). 420p. 1985. pap. 18.00 (ISBN 0-387-13950-8). Springer-Verlag.

Wainerdi, Richard E. & Uken, Ernst A., eds. Modern Methods of Geochemical Analysis. LC 75-157148. 397p. 1971. 55.00x (ISBN 0-306-30474-0, Plenum Pr). Plenum Pub.

Weissberger, A. & Rossiter, B. W., eds. Techniques of Chemistry: Optical, Spectroscopic & Radioactivity Methods: Iternferometry, Light Scattering, Microscopy, Microwave & Magnetic Resonance Spectroscopy, Vol. 1, Pt. 3A. 732p. 1972. 60.00 (ISBN 0-471-92729-5). Krieger.

Welcher, Frank J., ed. Standard Methods of Chemical Analysis: Instrumental Methods, Vol. IIIA. 6th ed. LC 74-23465. 996p. 1975. Repr. of 1966 ed. 70.00 (ISBN 0-88275-342-8). Krieger.

--Standard Methods of Chemical Analysis: Vol. IIA Industrial & Natural Products & Noninstrumental Methods. 6th ed. LC 74-23465. 1372p. 1975. Repr. of 1963 ed. 96.00 (ISBN 0-88275-340-1). Krieger.

--Standard Methods of Chemical Analysis: Vol. IIB, Industrial & Natural Products & Non Instrumental Methods. 6th ed. LC 74-23465. 1348p. 1975. Repr. of 1963 ed. 72.50 (ISBN 0-88275-333-9). Krieger.

--Standard Methods of Chemical Analysis: Vol. IIIB, Instrumental Methods. 6th ed. LC 74-23465. 1060p. 1975. Repr. of 1966 ed. 74.00 (ISBN 0-88275-253-7). Krieger.

Wilson, C. L. & Wilson, D. W., eds. Comprehensive Analytical Chemistry: Emission Spectroscopy, Vol. 5. LC 58-10158. 383p. 1975. 106.50 (ISBN 0-444-41164-X). Elsevier.

--Comprehensive Analytical Chemistry: Instrumentation for Spectroscopy, Vol. 4. LC 58-10158. 374p. 1975. 106.50 (ISBN 0-444-41163-1). Elsevier.

--Comprehensive Analytical Chemistry, Vols. 1 & 2. Incl. Vol 1: Classical Analysis, 3 Pts. 1959-62. Pt. A. 106.50 (ISBN 0-444-40647-6); Pt. B. 123.50 (ISBN 0-444-40648-4); Pt. C. 123.50 (ISBN 0-444-40649-2); Vol. 2: Electrical Methods & Physical Separation Methods, 4 pts. 1968. Pt. A. 78.75 (ISBN 0-444-40650-6); Pt. B. 106.50 (ISBN 0-444-40651-4); Pt. C. 106.50; Pt. D: Coulometric Analysis. 1975. 123.50 (ISBN 0-444-41044-9). Elsevier.

Wilson, C. L., et al, eds. Comprehensive Analytical Chemistry: Elemental Analysis, Vol. 3. LC 58-10158. 399p. 1975. 106.50 (ISBN 0-444-41162-3). Elsevier.

Wilson, H. N. An Approach to Chemical Analysis. 1966. Set. 30.00 (ISBN 0-08-011543-8). Pergamon.

Windawi, H. & Ho, F. L. Applied Electron Spectroscopy for Chemical Analysis, Vol. 63. (Chemical Analysis Ser.). 213p. 1982. 51.50 (ISBN 0-471-09051-4). Wiley.

Woodburn, John H. Taking Things Apart & Puttings Things Together. LC 76-20448. 1976. pap. 7.95. Am Chemical.

Yaroslarisev & Kreshkov. A Course in Analytical Chemistry, 2 vols. 738p. 1977. Set. 11.25 (ISBN 0-8285-0645-0, Pub. by Mir Pubs USSR). Imported Pubns.

Zweig, Gunter, ed. Analytical Methods for Pesticides, Plant Growth Regulators & Food Additives, 11 vols. Incl. Vol. 1. Principles, Methods & General Applications. 1963. 86.50 (ISBN 0-12-784301-9); Vol. 2. Insecticides. 1964.. 86.50 (ISBN 0-12-784302-7); Vol. 3. Fungicides, Nematocides & Soil Fumigants, Rodenticides, & Food & Feed Additives. 1964; Vol. 4. Herbicides (Plant Growth Regulators) 1964. 50.50 (ISBN 0-12-784304-3); Vol. 5. 1967. 82.50 (ISBN 0-12-784305-1); Vol. 6. 1970. 89.50 (ISBN 0-12-784306-X); Vol. 7. Thin-Layer & Liquid Chromatography & Analysis of Pesticides of International Importance. 1973. 89.50 (ISBN 0-12-784307-8); Vol. 8. Government Regulations, Pheromone Analyses, Additional Pesticides. Zweig, Gunter & Sharma, Joseph, eds. 1976. 86.50 (ISBN 0-12-784308-6); Vol. 10. Newer & Updated Methods. Zweig, Gunter & Sharma, Joseph, eds. 1978. 73.50 (ISBN 0-12-784310-8); Vol. 11. 1980. 66.00 (ISBN 0-12-784311-6). Acad Pr.

CHEMISTRY, ANALYTIC–BIBLIOGRAPHY

Cumulative Indexes to Analytical Chemistry, 4 bks. Incl. 1964-68. 10.00 (ISBN 0-685-55716-2); 1959-63. 7.00 (ISBN 0-685-55717-0); 1944-58. 9.00 (ISBN 0-685-55718-9); 1929-58. 11.50 (ISBN 0-685-55719-7). Am Chemical.

CHEMISTRY, ANALYTIC–LABORATORY MANUALS

Alexander, P., et al, eds. A Laboratory Manual of Analytical Methods of Protein Chemistry (Including Polypeptides, Vols. 2-5. Incl. Vol. 2. Composition, Structure & Reactivity of Protein. 1960. lib. bdg. 16.50 (ISBN 0-08-011398-2); Vol. 3. Determination of the Size & Shape of Protein in Molecules. 1961; Vol. 4. Protein Analysis. 1965; Vol. 5. 1968. 18.00 (ISBN 0-08-012677-4). Pergamon.

Dux, James P. Handbook of Quality Assurance for the Analytical Chemistry Laboratory. 160p. 1985. 24.50 (ISBN 0-442-21972-5). Van Nos Reinhold.

Ewing, Galen W. Analytical Instrumentation: A Laboratory Guide for Chemical Analysis. LC 66-5557. (Illus.). pap. 42.80 (ISBN 0-317-09110-7, 2019392). Bks Demand UMI.

Food & Drug Administration. Macroanalytical Procedures Manual. rev. ed. (FDA Technical Bulletin Ser.: No. 5). (Illus.). 176p. 1984. three hole drill with binder 29.00 (ISBN 0-935584-28-5); foreign 30.50. Assoc Official.

Gilreath, Esmarch S. Experimental Procedures in Elementary Qualitative Analysis. 1968. text ed. 20.95 (ISBN 0-07-023213-X). McGraw.

King, Edward J. Ionic Reactions & Separations: Experiments in Qualitative Analysis. 254p. 1973. spiral bdg. 14.95 (ISBN 0-15-547041-8, HC). HarBraceJ.

Massart, D. L., et al. Evaluation & Optimization of Laboratory Methods & Analytical Procedures. (Techniques & Instrumentation in Analytical Chemistry Ser.: Vol. 1). 596p. 1978. 72.50 (ISBN 0-444-41743-5). Elsevier.

Swift, Ernest H. & Butler, Eliot A. Quantitative Measurements & Chemical Equilibria. LC 78-161009. (Chemistry Ser.). (Illus.). 719p. 1972. text ed. 35.95x (ISBN 0-7167-0170-7); tchr's. manual avail. W H Freeman.

CHEMISTRY, ANALYTIC–PROBLEMS, EXERCISES, ETC.

Brewer, Stephen. Solving Problems in Analytical Chemistry. LC 79-17164. 528p. 1980. pap. text ed. 20.95x (ISBN 0-471-04098-3). Wiley.

Nakon, Robert. Chemical Problem Solving Using Dimensional Analysis. (Illus.). 1978. pap. 18.95 (ISBN 0-13-128645-5). P-H.

Stoker, Owen C. & Stoker, H. Stephen. Introduction to Chemical Principles. (Illus.). 400p. 1983. write for info. student guide (ISBN 0-02-417610-9). Macmillan.

CHEMISTRY, ANALYTIC–QUALITATIVE

see also Spectrum Analysis; Spot Tests (Chemistry)

Atkins, P. W. Molecular Quantum Mechanics. 2nd ed. (Illus.). 1983. pap. 27.95x (ISBN 0-19-855170-3). Oxford U Pr.

--Molecular Quantum Mechanics: Solutions Manual. (Illus.). 1983. pap. 14.95x (ISBN 0-19-855180-0). Oxford U Pr.

Benedetti-Pichler, A. A. Identification of Materials Via Physical Properties, Chemical Testing & Microscopy. (Illus.). 1964. 42.00 (ISBN 0-387-80670-9). Springer-Verlag.

Brumblay, Ray U. Qualitative Analysis. (Illus., Orig). 1964. pap. 5.95 (ISBN 0-06-460116-1, CO 116, COS). B&N NY.

Carney, Robert J. Outline of the Methods of Qualitative Chemical Analysis. 1947. 1.00x (ISBN 0-685-21795-7). Wahr.

Cheronis, Nicholas D. & Entrikin, John B. Identification of Organic Compounds: A Students Text Using Semimicro Techniques. 1963. 55.00 (ISBN 0-470-15279-6, Pub. by Wiley-Interscience). Wiley.

Day, R. A., Jr. & Underwood, Arthur L. Quantitative Analysis. 4th ed. (Illus.). 1980. text ed. 37.95 (ISBN 0-13-746545-9); pap. 9.95 solutions manual (ISBN 0-13-746560-2); lab manual 14.95 (ISBN 0-13-746552-1). P-H.

Fales, Harold A. & Kenny, Frederic. Inorganic Quantitative Analysis. (Illus.). 1955. 37.50x (ISBN 0-89197-501-2). Irvington.

Feigl, Fritz & Anger, Y. Spot Tests in Organic Analysis. 7th ed. 772p. 1966. 117.00 (ISBN 0-444-40209-8). Elsevier.

Gilreath, Esmarch S. Experimental Procedures in Elementary Qualitative Analysis. 1968. text ed. 20.95 (ISBN 0-07-023213-X). McGraw.

Haberman, Shelby. Analysis of Qualitative Data: Vol. I - Introductory Topics (TXX) LC 77-25731. 1978. 33.00 (ISBN 0-12-312501-4). Acad Pr.

Kennedy, John J. Analyzing Qualitative Data: Introductory Log-Linear Analysis for Behavioral Research. LC 82-18040. 284p. 1983. 32.95x (ISBN 0-03-060422-2). Praeger.

King, Edward J. Ionic Reactions & Separations: Experiments in Qualitative Analysis. 254p. 1973. spiral bdg. 14.95 (ISBN 0-15-547041-8, HC). HarBraceJ.

Ma, Tsu-Sheng. Quantitative Analysis of Organic Mixtures: General Principles, Pt. 1. LC 78-23202. pap. 96.00 (ISBN 0-317-08874-2, 2055601). Bks Demand UMI.

Moseley, W. David. Qualitative Analysis: An Introduction. 128p. 1984. pap. text ed. 8.50 (ISBN 0-8403-3453-2). Kendall-Hunt.

Nebergall, William H., et al. College Chemistry with Qualitative Analysis. 1088p. 18.95x (ISBN 0-669-91355-3); instructor's manual free (ISBN 0-669-98004-8); lab manual 7.95x (ISBN 0-669-97980-5); study guide 5.95x (ISBN 0-669-97972-4); problems & solutions manual 3.95x (ISBN 0-669-97998-8). Heath.

Nyman, C. J., et al. Problems for General Chemistry & Qualitative Analysis. 4th ed. LC 79-24489. 342p. 1980. pap. text ed. 13.95 (ISBN 0-471-05299-X). Wiley.

Openshaw, Harry T. Laboratory Manual of Qualitative Organic Analysis. 3rd ed. 1955. pap. 11.95x (ISBN 0-521-29112-7). Cambridge U Pr.

Rodriguez, Esther. Selected Experiments in General Chemistry & Qualitative Analysis. 1976. coil bdg. 11.95 (ISBN 0-88252-050-4). Paladin Hse.

Schenk, George H. & Ebbing, Darell D. Qualitative Analysis & Ionic Equilibrium. LC 84-81935. 256p. 1984. pap. text ed. 7.95 (ISBN 0-395-36517-1). HM.

Schneider, Frank L. Qualitative Organic Microanalysis. 1964. 77.50 (ISBN 0-12-627750-8). Acad Pr.

Slowinski, Emil & Masterton, William. Qualitative Analysis & the Properties of Ions in Aqueous Solution. LC 75-145567. 1971. 18.95 (ISBN 0-7216-8369-X, CBS C). SCP.

Slowinski, Emil, et al. Chemical Principles in the Lab with Qualitative Analysis. alternate ed. 1983. pap. text ed. 21.95 (ISBN 0-03-062649-8, CBS C); instructor's manual 20.00 (ISBN 0-03-062651-X). SCP.

Snell, Foster D. & Snell, Cornelia T. Colorimetric Methods of Analysis. Incl. Vol. 4A. Organic Compounds of Noncyclic Nitrogen. 1967. 24.95x (ISBN 0-442-37848-3); Vol. 4AA. 1970. 24.95x (ISBN 0-442-07849-8); Vol. 4AAA. 1971. 24.95x (ISBN 0-442-27853-5). Van Nos Reinhold.

Sorum, Harvey & Lagowski, Joseph. Introduction to Semimicro Qualitative Analysis. (Illus.). 368p. 1983. pap. text ed. 18.95 (ISBN 0-13-496067-X). P-H.

Thompson, Donald O. & Chimenti, Dale E., eds. Review of Progress in Quantitative Nondestructive Evaluation, Vol. 1. LC 82-9140. 832p. 1982. 95.00x (ISBN 0-306-41024-9, Plenum Pr). Plenum Pub.

Tremillon, B. Chemistry in Non-Aoueous Solvents. Corcoran, N., tr. LC 73-86094. 1974. lib. bdg. 41.00 (ISBN 90-277-0389-2, Pub. by Reidel Holland). Kluwer Academic.

Vecera, Miroslov & Gasparic, Jiri. Detection & Identification of Organic Compounds. LC 72-11065. 423p. 1971. 55.00x (ISBN 0-306-30476-7, Plenum Pr). Plenum Pub.

Vogel, A. I. & Svehla, G., eds. Vogel's Textbook of Macro & Semimicro Qualitative Inorganic Analysis. 5th ed. LC 77-8290. 1979. text ed. 42.00x (ISBN 0-582-44367-9). Longman.

Weisz, H. Microanalysis by the Ring Oven Technique. 2nd ed. 1970. 30.00 (ISBN 0-08-015702-5). Pergamon.

CHEMISTRY, ANALYTIC–QUANTITATIVE

see also Distillation, Fractional; Electrochemical Analysis; Volumetric Analysis

Alexeyev, Vladimir. Quantitative Analysis. MIR Publishers, tr. from Rus. (Illus.). 563p. 1975. text ed. 17.95x (ISBN 0-8464-0774-4). Beekman Pubs.

--Quantitative Analysis. (Russian Monographs & Texts on the Physical Sciences). 501p. 1969. 67.25 (ISBN 0-677-20860-X). Gordon.

Birman, M. S. & Solomjak, M. Z. Quantitative Analysis in Sobolev Imbedding Theorems & Applications to Spectral Theory. (Translations Ser. 2: Vol. 114). 1980. 34.00 (ISBN 0-8218-3064-3, TRANS2-114). Am Math.

Brown, Theodore & Le May, Eugene. Qualitative Inorganic Analysis. (Illus.). 160p. 1983. pap. 7.95 (ISBN 0-13-744946-1). P H.

Brumblay, Ray U. Quantitative Analysis. 2nd ed. (Orig.). 1972. pap. 4.95 (ISBN 0-06-460050-5, CO 50, COS). B&N NY.

Collier, Francis, et al. Quantitative Laboratory Experiments in General Chemistry. LC 75-26087. (Illus.). 288p. 1976. spiral bdg. 17.50 (ISBN 0-395-18982-9). HM.

Day, R. A. & Underwood, Arthur L. Quantitative Analysis. 5th ed. (Illus.). 704p. 1986. text ed. 38.95 (ISBN 0-13-746728-1). P-H.

Fichera, G. Numerical & Quantitative Analysis. (Surveys & References Ser.: No. 3). 218p. 1978. text ed. 49.95 (ISBN 0-273-00284-8). Pitman Pub MA.

Flaschka, H. A., et al. Quantitative Analytical Chemistry: An Introduction to Practice. 2nd ed. 225p. 1981. pub net Lab manual. 12.00 (ISBN 0-87150-731-5, 4252). Brooks-Cole.

Fritz, James S. & Schenk, George H., Jr. Quantitative Analytical Chemistry. 4th ed. (Illus.). 1979. text ed. 40.00 (ISBN 0-205-06527-9, 6865275); instr's. manual avail. (ISBN 0-205-06544-9, 686544). Allyn.

Gibbons, Jean D. Nonparametric Methods for Quantitative Analysis. 2nd. ed. LC 84-73390. (American Sciences Press Series in Mathematical & Management Sciences Ser.: Vol. 2). 1985. 34.50 (ISBN 0-935950-09-5). Am Sciences Pr.

Guilbault, G. G. Modern Quantitative Analysis: Experiments for Non-Chemistry Majors. 256p. 1974. 22.75 (ISBN 0-8247-6106-5). Dekker.

Harris, Daniel C. Quantitative Chemical Analysis. LC 82-7421. (Illus.). 748p. 1982. text ed. 34.95 (ISBN 0-7167-1347-0). W H Freeman.

--Quantitative Chemical Analysis: Solutions Manual. Walters, Lee & Maurer, Jim, eds. (Illus.). 145p. 1984. write for info. (ISBN 0-7167-1531-7). W H Freeman.

Holderness, A. & Lambert, J. The Essentials of Qualitative Analysis. 3rd ed. 1974. pap. text ed. 4.50x (ISBN 0-435-65535-3). Heinemann Ed.

Kasler, F. Quantitative Analysis by NMR Spectroscopy. 1973. 39.00 (ISBN 0-12-400850-X). Acad Pr.

Keattch, C. J. & Dollimore, D. An Introduction to Thermogravimetry. 1975. 35.95 (ISBN 0-471-25834-2, Wiley Heyden). Wiley.

Kenner, Charles T. & Busch, Kenneth W. Quantitative Analysis. 1979. text ed. write for info. (ISBN 0-02-362490-6). Macmillan.

Klecka, William R. Discriminant Analysis. LC 80-50927. (Quantitative Applications in the Social Sciences Ser.: No. 19). (Illus.). 71p. 1980. pap. 5.00 (ISBN 0-8039-1491-1). Sage.

Kolthoff, Isaak M., et al. Quantitative Chemical Analysis. 4th ed. (Illus.). 1969. text ed. write for info. (ISBN 0-02-366000-7). Macmillan.

Korenman, I. M. Introduction to Quantitative Ultramicroanalysis. 1965. 59.50 (ISBN 0-12-420550-X). Acad Pr.

Kumar, Vinay. Experimental Techniques in Quantitative Chemical Analysis. LC 80-69043. 183p. (Orig.). 1981. pap. text ed. 12.00 (ISBN 0-8191-1509-6). U Pr of Amer.

Laitinen, Herbert A. & Harris, Walter E. Chemical Analysis. 2nd ed. (Advanced Chemistry Ser.). (Illus.). 611p. 1975. text ed. 53.95 (ISBN 0-07-036086-3). McGraw.

Lucey, T. Quantitative Techniques. 352p. 1979. 37.00x (ISBN 0-905435-09-5, Pub. by DP Pubns). State Mutual Bk.

Miller. Statistics for Analytical Chemistry. (Analytical Chemistry Ser.). 1984. 39.95 (ISBN 0-470-20128-2). Wiley.

Novak, Josef. Quantitative Analysis by Gas Chromatography. (Chromatographic Science Ser.: Vol. 5). 224p. 1975. 38.50 (ISBN 0-8247-6311-4). Dekker.

Pickering, W. F. Modern Analytical Chemistry. LC 77-138500. Repr. of 1971 ed. 120.00 (ISBN 0-8357-9087-8, 2055008). Bks Demand UMI.

Pierce, W. C., et al. Quantitative Analysis. 4th ed. LC 58-7905. 497p. 1958. 38.50 (ISBN 0-471-68904-1); answer guide 12.95 (ISBN 0-471-68937-8). Wiley.

Schmidt, Joseph W. & Taylor, Robert E. Simulation & Analysis of Industrial Systems. LC 76-91792. (Irwin Series in Quantitative Analysis for Business). pap. 160.00 (ISBN 0-317-10878-6, 2050150). Bks Demand UMI.

Serjeant, E. P. Potentiometry & Potentiometric Titrations. LC 83-21903. (Chemical Analysis: A Series of Monographs on Analytical Chemistry & it Applications). 725p. 1984. 75.00x (ISBN 0-471-07745-3, 1-075, Pub. by Wiley-Interscience). Wiley.

Siggia, Sidney & Hanna, J. Gordon. Quantitative Organic Analysis via Functional Groups. 4th ed. LC 78-5940. 883p. 1979. 103.00 (ISBN 0-471-03273-5, Pub. by Wiley-Interscience). Wiley.

Steyermark, Al. Quantitative Organic Microanalysis. 2nd ed. 1961. 65.00 (ISBN 0-12-670450-3). Acad Pr.

Swift, Ernest H. & Butler, Eliot A. Quantitative Measurements & Chemical Equilibria. LC 78-161009. (Chemistry Ser.). (Illus.). 719p. 1972. text ed. 35.95x (ISBN 0-7167-0170-7); tchr's. manual avail. W H Freeman.

Vogel, A. I. Vogel's Textbook of Quantitative Inorganic Analysis. 4th ed. Bassett, J., et al, eds. LC 77-5545. (Illus.). 1978. text ed. 55.00x (ISBN 0-582-46321-1). Longman.

CHEMISTRY, ANIMAL

see Physiological Chemistry

CHEMISTRY, BIOLOGICAL

see Biological Chemistry

CHEMISTRY, BOTANICAL

see Botanical Chemistry

CHEMISTRY, CLINICAL

Beeler, Myrton F. Interpretations in Clinical Chemistry. 1st. ed. LC 77-95105. (Illus.). 580p. 1978. text ed. 27.50 softbound (ISBN 0-89189-045-9, 45-2-036-00). Am Soc Clinical.

Bishop, Michael L., et al. Clinical Chemistry: Principles, Procedures, Correlations. (Illus.). 624p. 1985. text ed. 42.50 (ISBN 0-397-50662-7, Lippincott Medical). Lippincott.

Blick, K. E. & Liles, S. M. Principles of Clinical Chemistry. 650p. 1985. 22.95 (ISBN 0-471-88502-9). Wiley.

Braetter, P. & Schramel, P., eds. Trace Element Analytical Chemistry in Medicine & Biology, Vol. 3: Proceedings of the 3rd International Workshop. LC 80-26803. (Illus.). xvi, 763p. 1984. 109.00X (ISBN 3-11-009821-0). De Gruyter.

Breccia, A. & Cavalleri, B., eds. Nitroimidazoles: Chemistry, Pharmacology & Clinical Application. (NATO ASI Series A, Life Science: Vol. 42). 225p. 1982. 37.50 (ISBN 0-306-40916-X, Plenum Pr). Plenum Pub.

Brewster, Marge A. Clinical Chemistry Self-Assessment: Five Hundred Multiple-Choice Questions with Answers Explained. 155p. 1982. pap. 15.00 (ISBN 0-915274-18-3, 306); pap. 12.00 member. Am Assn Clinical Chem.

Brown, S. S., ed. Clinical Chemistry & Chemical Toxicology. 1977. 47.00 (ISBN 0-444-41601-3). Elsevier.

Buttner, J., ed. History of Clinical Chemistry. LC 83-1968. (Illus.). 91p. 1983. 49.00 (ISBN 3-11-008912-2). De Gruyter.

Chenault, V. Michele. Clinical Chemistry Lab Manual for the Medical Technology Student. 1979. pap. text ed. 10.95x (ISBN 0-89917-014-5). TIS Inc.

Clinical Chemistry: Laboratory Diagnosis & Patient Monitoring. 1984. 27.95 (ISBN 0-87489-265-1). Med Economics.

Clinical Chemistry: Reference Edition. 95.00 (ISBN 0-317-17665-X, 108). Am Assn Clinical Chem.

Clinical Chemistry: 1973-1980 Cumulative Index with Citations. 1981. pap. 15.00 AACA members, 25.00 for non-members (ISBN 0-317-17662-5, 102). Am Assn Clinical Chem.

Cooper, Gerald. Selected Methods of Clinical Chemistry, Vol. 8. LC 53-7099. 209p. 1977. 30.00 (ISBN 0-915274-05-1); members 20.00. Am Assn Clinical Chem.

Cooper, Gerald R., ed. Selected Methods of Clinical Chemistry, Vol. 10. 234p. 1983. AACC member 40.00 (ISBN 0-915274-21-3); non-member 30.00. Am Assn Clinical Chem.

Cox, Kenneth R. Planning Clinical Experiments. (Illus.). 344p. 1968. 28.50x (ISBN 0-398-00353-X). C C Thomas.

Dietz, A. A. & Grannis, G. F., eds. Aging - Its Chemistry: Proceedings of the Third Arnold O. Beckman Conference in Clinical Chemistry. LC 80-65825. 448p. 1980. AACC members 25.00 (ISBN 0-915274-10-8); non-members 35.00. Am Assn Clinical Chem.

Fleisher, Martin, ed. The Clinical Biochemistry of Cancer: Proceedings of the Second Arnold O. Beckman Conference in Cliniical Chemistry. LC 79-14027. 405p. 1979. 30.00 (ISBN 0-915274-09-4); members 20.00. Am Assn Clinical Chem.

Glickson. Bleomycin: Chemistry & Clinical Applications. write for info. (ISBN 0-8247-1289-7). Dekker.

Grant, J. K. & Beastall, G. H. Clinical Biochemistry of Steroid Hormones: Methods & Applications. 320p. 1984. 45.00 (ISBN 0-444-00849-7). Elsevier.

Hercules, D. M., et al, eds. Contemporary Topics in Analytical & Clinical Chemistry. LC 77-8099. (Illus.). Vol. 1, 1977, 327p. 49.50x (ISBN 0-306-33521-2, Plenum Pr); Vol. 2, 1978, 296p. 49.50x (ISBN 0-306-33522-0). Plenum Pub.

Hercules, David M. & Hieftje, Gary M., eds. Contemporary Topics in Analytical & Clinical Chemistry, Vol. 4. LC 79-640979. (Illus.). 396p. 1982. 57.50 (ISBN 0-306-40943-7, Plenum Pr). Plenum Pub.

Hicks, Jocelyn M. & Parker, K. Michael. Selected Analyses in Clinical Chemistry. 1984. 22.00 (ISBN 0-915274-25-6); members 19.50 (ISBN 0-317-13767-0). Am Assn Clinical Chem.

Hood, W. A-Z of Clinical Chemistry. LC 80-23908. 386p. 1980. 29.95x (ISBN 0-470-27029-2). Halsted Pr.

International Symposium on Quantitative Mass Spectrometry in Life Sciences, 1st, State University of Ghent Belgium June 16-18 1976. Quantitative Mass Spectrometry in Life Sciences: Proceedings. DeLeenheer, A. P. & Roncucci, Romeo R, eds. LC 77-3404. 254p. 1977. 64.00 (ISBN 0-444-41557-2). Elsevier.

International Symposium, 6th, Geneva, Apr 23-25, 1975, et al. Quality Control in Clinical Chemistry: Proceedings. Anido, A. & Van Kampen, E. J., eds. (Illus.). 640p. 1975. 44.00x (ISBN 3-11-006692-0). De Gruyter.

Kaiser, E. & Gabl, F., eds. Eleventh International Congress of Clinical Chemistry. (Illus.). xx, 1575p. 1982. 128.00x (ISBN 3-11-008447-3). De Gruyter.

Kaneko, J. J. & Cornelius, C. E., eds. Clinical Biochemistry of Domestic Animals, Vols. 1 & 2. 2nd ed. 1970. Vol. 1. 60.00 (ISBN 0-12-396301-X); Vol. 2, 1971. 58.00 (ISBN 0-12-396302-8). Acad Pr.

Kaplan, Alex & Szabo, Laverne. Clinical Chemistry: Interpretation & Techniques. 2nd ed. LC 82-17249. (Illus.). 427p. 1983. text ed. 28.50 (ISBN 0-8121-0873-6). Lea & Febiger.

King, J. Stanton, ed. Clinical Chemistry: Cumulative Index with Citations. 227p. 1981. 10.00 (ISBN 0-686-78714-5). Am Assn Clinical Chem.

--Two-Dimensional Gel Electrophoresis: A Special Issue of Clinical Chemistry, Vol. 28, No. 4. Pt. 2. 1092p. 1982. pap. 25.00 (ISBN 0-686-91956-4, 101). Am Assn Clinical Chem.

Knowles, Derek. MCQ Tutor for Students of Clinical Chemistry. 1979. pap. text ed. 17.95 (ISBN 0-8151-5113-6). Year Bk Med.

Kricka, L. J., ed. Analytical Methods in Clinical Chemistry. (Illus.). 96p. 1984. pap. 25.50 (ISBN 0-08-031453-8). Pergamon.

Latner, A. L. & Schwartz, M., eds. Advances in Clinical Chemistry, Vol. 23. (Serial Publication). 1983. 44.00 (ISBN 0-12-010323-0). Acad Pr.

Latner, A. L. & Schwartz, M. K., eds. Advances in Clinical Chemistry, Vol. 22. (Serial Publication Ser.). 1981. 55.00 (ISBN 0-12-010322-2). Acad Pr.

Latner, A. L. & Schwartz, Morton K., eds. Advances in Clinical Chemistry, Vol. 21. LC 58-12341. (Serial Publication Ser.). 1980. 60.00 (ISBN 0-12-010321-4). Acad Pr.

Lijnen, H. R., et al, eds. Synthetic Substrates in Clinical Blood Coagulation Assays. (Developments in Hematology Ser.: No. 1). 142p. 1981. PLB 23.50 (ISBN 90-247-2409-0, Pub. Bymartinus Nijhoff). Kluwer Academic.

Medway, William, et al. Textbook of Veterinary Clinical Pathology. LC 69-13696. 536p. 1969. 24.50 (ISBN 0-686-74094-7). Krieger.

Meites, Samuel, ed. Pediatric Clinical Chemistry. rev. ed. LC 80-66259. 513p. 1981. 35.00 (ISBN 0-915274-12-4); members 30.00. Am Assn Clinical Chem.

Natelson, Samuel & Natelson, Ethan A., eds. Principles of Applied Clinical Chemistry: Chemical Background & Medical Applications, 2 vols. Incl. Vol. 1, Maintenance of Fluid & Electrolyte Balance. 393p. 1975. 45.00 (ISBN 0-306-35231-1); Vol. 2, The Erythrocyte Chemical Composition, Normal & Aberrant Metabolism. 584p. 1978. 69.50 (ISBN 0-306-35232-X). LC 75-4798. (Illus., Plenum Pr). Plenum Pub.

Pasternak, Charles A., ed. Radioimmunoassay in Clinical Biochemistry. LC 76-675546. pap. 79.30 (ISBN 0-317-29335-4, 2024025). Bks Demand UMI.

Price, Christopher P. & Spencer, Kevin, eds. Centrifugal Analysers in Clinical Chemistry. LC 80-81330. (Illus.). 520p. 1980. 79.95x (ISBN 0-03-058854-5). Praeger.

Rapporport, A. E. Quality Control in Clinical Chemistry. 338p. 1972. 90.00 (ISBN 3-456-00299-8, Pub. by Holdan Bk Ltd UK). State Mutual Bk.

Reiner, Miriam, et al, eds. Standard Methods of Clinical Chemistry. Incl. Vol. 1. Reiner, Miriam, ed. 1953. 39.00 (ISBN 0-12-609101-3); Vol. 2. Seligson, David, ed. 1958. 41.50 (ISBN 0-12-609102-1); Vol. 3. 1961; Vol. 4. 1964. 41.50 (ISBN 0-12-609104-8); Vol. 5. Meites, S., ed. 1965. 41.50 (ISBN 0-12-609105-6); Vol. 6. MacDonald, R. P., ed. 1970. 55.00 (ISBN 0-12-609106-4); Vol. 7. 1972. 59.50 (ISBN 0-12-609107-2). Acad Pr.

Richterich, R. Clinical Chemistry: Theory, Practice & Interpretation. Colombo, J. P., ed. LC 80-40286. 766p. 1981. 55.95 (ISBN 0-471-27809-2, Pub. by Wiley-Interscience). Wiley.

Richterich, R. & Colombo, Jean-Pierre, eds. Klinische Chemie. Theorie, Praxis, Interpretation, 4: Vollstaendig neu bearbeitete Auflage. (Illus.). 1978. 35.00 (ISBN 3-8055-2796-9). S Karger.

Robinsn, Ronald. Tumours That Secrete Catecholamines: Their Detection & Clinical Chemistry. LC 79-41731. pap. 36.00 (ISBN 0-317-29342-7, 2024034). Bks Demand UMI.

Robinson, R. Clinical Chemistry & Automation: A Study in Laboratory Proficiency. 188p. 1971. 21.95x (ISBN 0-85264-204-0, Pub. by Griffin England). State Mutual Bk.

Rosenfeld, Louis, ed. The Origins of Clinical Chemistry: The Evolution of Protein Analysis. 1982. 46.50 (ISBN 0-12-597580-5). Acad Pr.

Rudman, Jack. Clinical Chemistry. (College Level Examination Ser.: CLEP-32). (Cloth bdg. avail. on request). pap. 11.95 (ISBN 0-8373-5332-7). Natl Learning.

Saris, Nils-Erik, ed. International Federation of Clinical Chemistry: Recommendations & Related Documents, Volume 1, 1978-1983. LC 84-16994. 146p. 1984. pap. 44.00x (ISBN 3-11-008766-9). De Gruyter.

Scimone, John & Rothstein, Robert. Clinical Chemistry: Functional Medical Laboratory Manual. (Illus.). 1978. lab. manual 10.50 (ISBN 0-87055-271-6). AVI.

Serio, M. & Pazzagli, M., eds. Luminescent Assays: Perspectives in Endocrinology & Clinical Chemistry. (Serono Symposia Publications from Raven Press Ser.: Vol. I). 304p. 1982. text ed. 51.00 (ISBN 0-89004-740-5). Raven.

Simmons, Ivor L. & Ewing, Galen W., eds. Methods in Radioimmunoassay, Toxicology & Related Areas. LC 74-23819. 183p. 1974. 45.00x (ISBN 0-306-39307-7, Plenum Pr). Plenum Pub.

Symposium of Beta-Carbolines & Tetrahydroisoquinolines, La Jolla, Ca., December, 12-13, 1981 & Bloom, Floyd. Beta-Carbolines & Tetrahydroisoquinolines: Proceedings. LC 82-7789. (Progress In Clinical & Biological Research Ser.: Vol. 90). 454p. 1982. 44.00 (ISBN 0-8451-0090-4). A R Liss.

Tietz, Norbert W. Textbook of Clinical Chemistry. (Illus.). 1500p. Date not set. price not set (ISBN 0-7216-8886-1). Saunders.

Tietz, Norbert W., ed. Fundamentals of Clinical Chemistry. 2nd ed. LC 73-91279. (Illus.). 1100p. 1976. text ed. 39.50x (ISBN 0-7216-8866-7). Saunders.

Toro, Gelson & Ackermann, Philip G. Practical Clinical Chemistry. LC 74-4945. 1975. text ed. 29.95 (ISBN 0-316-85057-8). Little.

Weisbrot. Statistics for the Clinical Laboratory. 1984. 29.50 (ISBN 0-397-50620-1, 65-07859, Lippincott Medical). Lippincott.

Werner, Mario, ed. CRC Handbook of Clinical Chemistry. (CRC Series in Clinical Lab Science). 576p. 1982. 98.00 (ISBN 0-8493-7081-7). CRC Pr.

White, Wilma, et al. Chemistry for the Clinical Laboratory. 4th ed. LC 75-31617. (Illus.). 756p. 1976. 25.95 (ISBN 0-8016-5432-7). Mosby.

Whitehead, T. P. Quality Control in Clinical Chemistry. LC 76-44522. (Quality Control Methods in the Clinical Laboratory Ser.). 130p. 1977. text ed. 42.00 (ISBN 0-471-94075-5, Pub. by Wiley Medical). Wiley.

CHEMISTRY, CLINICAL–LABORATORY MANUALS

Hanok, Albert. Manual for Laboratory Clinical Chemistry. 1969. 12.00x (ISBN 0-87672-002-5). Geron-X.

Lauber, K. Chemie im Laboratorium. 4th ed. (Illus.). viii, 376p. 1983. softcover 33.25 (ISBN 3-8055-3547-3). S Karger.

Loeb, Walter F., ed. Clinical Chemistry of Laboratory Animals. Quimby, Fred W. 1985. pap. text ed. 30.00 (ISBN 0-8391-1901-1, 21041). Univ Park.

Noe, Dennis A. The Logic of Laboratory Medicine: Principles for Use of the Clinical Laboratory. (Illus.). 336p. (Orig.). 1985. pap. 21.50 (ISBN 0-8067-1371-2). Urban & S.

CHEMISTRY, DAIRY

see Dairy Bacteriology

CHEMISTRY, FORENSIC

see also Poisons

Brunelle, Richard L. & Reed, Robert W. Forensic Examination of Ink & Paper. LC 83-18039. (Illus.). 302p. 1984. 49.50x (ISBN 0-398-04935-1). C C Thomas.

Crown, David A. Forensic Examination of Paints & Pigments. 276p. 1968. 24.75x (ISBN 0-398-00372-6). C C Thomas.

Gerber, Samuel M., ed. Chemistry & Crime: From Sherlock Holmes to Today's Courtroom. (Other Technical Bks.). 135p. 1983. lib. bdg. 19.95 (ISBN 0-8412-0784-4). Am Chemical.

JCPDS-International Centre for Diffraction Data. Selected Powder Diffraction Data for Forensic Materials. write for info (83-192712). Amer Bar Assn.

Lasslo, A., ed. Blood Platelet Function & Medicinal Chemistry. 336p. 1984. 49.50 (ISBN 0-444-00790-3, Biomedical Pr). Elsevier.

Louden, Louise. Forensic Paper Examination & Analysis. LC 79-55266. (Bibliographic Ser.: No. 286). 1979. pap. 10.00 (ISBN 0-87010-057-2). Inst Paper Chem.

Lurie & Wittwer. HPLC in Forensic Chemistry. (Chromatographic Science Ser.). 560p. 1983. 75.00 (ISBN 0-8247-1756-2). Dekker.

Maehly, A. & Stroemberg, L. Chemical Criminalistics. (Illus.). 320p. 1981. 84.50 (ISBN 0-387-10723-1). Springer-Verlag.

Miller, Larry S., et al. Human Evidence in Criminal Justice. 2nd ed. LC 83-221811. vii, 190p. 1985. 13.95 (ISBN 0-932930-56-5). Pilgrimage INC.

Murray, R. C. & Tedrow, John C. Forensic Geology: Earth Sciences & Criminal Investigation. 1975. 22.50x (ISBN 0-8135-0794-4). Rutgers U Pr.

Saferstein, Richard. Criminalistics: An Introduction to Forensic Science. 2nd ed. (Criminal Justice Ser.). 1981. 28.95 (ISBN 0-13-193300-0). P-H.

Vom Ende, Rudolf, ed. Criminology & Forensic Sciences: An International Bibliography 1950-1980, 3 vols. 2389p. 1982. lib. bdg. 175.00 (ISBN 3-598-10374-3). K G Saur.

CHEMISTRY, INDUSTRIAL

see Chemical Engineering; Chemistry, Technical

CHEMISTRY, INORGANIC

see also Earths, Rare; Electric Furnaces; Metals; Platinum Group;

also names and classes of inorganic compounds

Adams, David M. Inorganic Solids: An Introduction to Concepts in Solid-State Structural Chemistry. LC 73-16863. pap. 88.00 (ISBN 0-317-09025-9, 2051237). Bks Demand UMI.

--Inorganic Solids: An Introduction to Concepts in Solid-Stte Sructural Chemistry. LC 73-16863. pap. 88.00 (ISBN 0-317-30437-2, 2024928). Bks Demand UMI.

Addison, A. W. & Cullen, W. R. Biological Aspects of Inorganic Chemistry. LC 76-44225. 410p. 1977. text ed. 35.00 (ISBN 0-471-02147-4). Krieger.

Addison, C. C., ed. Inorganic Chemistry of the Main Group Elements, Vols. 1-5. LC 72-95028. Vol. 1 1973. 1971-72 literature 43.00 (ISBN 0-85186-752-9); Vol. 2 1974. 1972-73 literature 61.00 (ISBN 0-85186-762-6); Vol. 3 1976. 1973-74 literature 73.00 (ISBN 0-85186-772-3); Vol. 4 1977. 1974-75 literature 66.00 (ISBN 0-85186-782-0); Vol. 5 1978. 1975-76 literature 86.00 (ISBN 0-85186-792-8). Am Chemical.

Addison, W. E. Structural Principles in Inorganic Compounds. pap. 50.00 (ISBN 0-317-08948-X, 2006383). Bks Demand UMI.

Ahrens, L. H. Physics & Chemistry of the Earth, Vol. 10. (Illus.). 270p. 1980. 105.00 (ISBN 0-08-020287-X). Pergamon.

Akhemtov, N. Inorganic Chemistry. 640p. 1975. 19.95x (ISBN 0-8464-1262-4). Beekman Pubs.

Akhmetov, N. General & Inorganic Chemistry. 670p. 1983. 13.95 (ISBN 0-8285-2567-6, Pub. by Mir Pubs USSR). Imported Pubns.

Akhmetov, Nail. Inorganic Chemistry. 565p. text ed. cancelled (ISBN 0-8290-1479-9). Irvington.

American Society for Testing & Materials. Symposium on the Chemical & Physical Effects of High-Energy Radiation on Inorganic Substances. LC 64-14646. (American Society for Testing & Materials Special Technical Publication Ser.: No. 359). pap. 29.80 (ISBN 0-317-09795-4, 2000748). Bks Demand UMI.

Anthropogenic Compounds, Pt. A. (Handbook of Environmental Chemistry Ser.: Vol. 3). (Illus.). 290p. 1980. 64.00 (ISBN 0-387-09690-6). Springer-Verlag.

Aylett, B. J. Fundamentals of Inorganic Chemistry: A Programmed Introduction. Billing, D. E., ed. pap. 27.00 (ISBN 0-317-29354-0, 2024006). Bks Demand UMI.

Aylett, B. J. & Smith, B. C. Problems in Inorganic Chemistry. LC 66-18189. pap. 40.00 (ISBN 0-317-09068-2, 2007643). Bks Demand UMI.

Bailar, J. C., et al, eds. Comprehensive Inorganic Chemistry, 5 vols. Incl. Vol. 1. H, Noble Gases, Group 1A, Group 11A, Group 111B, C, & Si. 215.00 (ISBN 0-08-016987-2); Vol. 2: Ge, Sn, Pb, Group VB, Group VIB, Group VIIB. 215.00 (ISBN 0-08-016988-0); Vol. 3: Lanthanides, Transition Metal Compounds. 215.00 (ISBN 0-08-016989-9); Vol. 4: Actinides, Master Index. 215.00 (ISBN 0-08-016990-2). 1973. Set. text ed. 900.00 (ISBN 0-08-017275-X). Pergamon.

Basolo, Fred. Inorganic Syntheses, Vol. 16. LC 79-642684. 270p. 1982. Repr. of 1976 ed. lib. bdg. cancelled (ISBN 0-89874-540-3). Krieger.

Basolo, Fred & Pearson, R. G. Mechanisms of Inorganic Reactions. 2nd ed. LC 66-28755. 701p. 1967. 55.00x (ISBN 0-471-05545-X, Pub. by Wiley-Interscience). Wiley.

Bassett, J. Inorganic Chemistry. 1965. text ed. 28.00 (ISBN 0-08-011207-2). Pergamon.

Berezhnoi, A. I. Glass-Ceramics & Photo-Sitalls. LC 69-12509. 444p. 1970. 45.00x (ISBN 0-306-30400-7, Plenum Pr). Plenum Pub.

Berndt, A., et al. Organic C-Centered Radicals. LC 62-53136. (Landolt-Boernstein,Group II: Vol. 9, Pt. 8). (Illus.). 1977. 327.60 (ISBN 0-387-08152-6). Springer-Verlag.

Boschke, F., ed. Inorganic & Analytical Chemistry. LC 51-5497. (Topics in Current Chemistry: Vol. 26). (Illus.). 125p. 1972. pap. 26.00 (ISBN 0-387-05589-4). Springer-Verlag.

Boschke, F. L., ed. Inorganic & Physical Chemistry. (Topics in Current Chemistry Ser.: Vol. 77). (Illus.). 1978. 59.00 (ISBN 0-387-08987-X). Springer-Verlag.

--Inorganic Chemistry. (Topics in Current Chemistry Ser.: Vol. 96). (Illus.). 155p. 1981. 52.00 (ISBN 0-387-10425-9). Springer-Verlag.

--Instrumental Inorganic Chemistry. LC 79-14180. (Topics in Current Chemistry: Vol. 85). (Illus.). 1979. 58.00 (ISBN 0-387-09338-9). Springer-Verlag.

Brenauer, K., et al. Theoretical Inorganic Chemistry: No. 2. (Topics in Current Chemistry: Vol. 65). 1976. 34.00 (ISBN 0-387-07637-9). Springer-Verlag.

Broul, M. & Hyvit, J. Solubility in Inorganic Two-Component Systems. (Physical Sciences Data Ser.: Vol. 6). 574p. 1981. 85.00 (ISBN 0-444-99763-6). Elsevier.

Brown, Theodore & LeMay, Eugene. Chemistry: The Central Science, Qualitative Inorganic Analysis. 3rd ed. (Illus.). 160p. 1985. pap. text ed. 7.95 (ISBN 0-13-127549-6). P-H.

Burdett, Jeremy K. Molecular Shapes: Theoretical Models of Inorganic Stereochemistry. LC 80-15463. 287p. 1980. 42.95 (ISBN 0-471-07860-3, Pub. by Wiley-Interscience). Wiley.

Burns, D. T. & Townshend, A. Inorganic Reaction Chemistry: Reactions of the Elements & Their Compounds, Vol. 2A. Carter, A. H., ed. (Ser. in Analytical Chemistry). 300p. 1981. 84.95x (ISBN 0-470-27105-1). Halsted Pr.

Burns, D. T., et al. Inorganic Reaction Chemistry: Systematic Chemical Separation, Vol. 1. (Analytical Chemistry Ser.). 248p. 1980. pap. 29.95 (ISBN 0-470-27237-6). Halsted Pr.

Carlin, Richard L., ed. Transition Metal Chemistry: A Series of Advances, Vol. 5. 1969. 75.00 (ISBN 0-8247-1080-0). Dekker.

--Transition Metal Chemistry: A Series of Advances, Vol. 6. LC 65-27431. 1970. 75.00 (ISBN 0-8247-1081-9). Dekker.

Chisholm, Malcolm H., ed. Inorganic Chemistry: Toward the Twenty-First Century. LC 82-24505. (ACS Symposium Ser.: No. 211). 566p. 1983. lib. bdg. 59.95x (ISBN 0-8412-0763-1). Am Chemical.

Chvalovsky, Vaclav & Bellama, J. M., eds. Carbon-Functional Organosilicon Compounds. (Modern Inorganic Chemistry Ser.). 318p. 1984. 45.00x (ISBN 0-306-41671-9, Plenum Pr). Plenum Pub.

Clarke, M. J., et al, eds. Inorganic Chemistry. (Structure & Bonding Ser.: Vol. 46). (Illus.). 190p. 1981. 44.00 (ISBN 0-387-10655-3). Springer-Verlag.

--Topics in Inorganic & Physical Chemistry. (Structure & Bonding Ser.: Vol. 50). (Illus.). 178p. 1982. 46.00 (ISBN 0-387-11454-8). Springer-Verlag.

--A Comprehensive Treatise on Inorganic & Theoretical Chemistry, Vols. 2-6, 8-9, 14-16. Incl. Vol. 2. pap. 160.00 (ISBN 0-317-10323-7); Vol. 3. pap. 160.00 (ISBN 0-317-10324-5); Vol. 4. pap. 160.00 (ISBN 0-317-10325-3); Vol. 5, Pt. 1. pap. 160.00 (ISBN 0-317-10326-1); Vol. 6, Pt. 2. pap. 160.00 (ISBN 0-317-10327-X); Vol. 8. pap. 160.00 (ISBN 0-317-10328-8); Vol. 9. pap. 160.00 (ISBN 0-317-10329-6); Vol. 14. pap. 160.00 (ISBN 0-317-10330-X); Vol. 15. pap. 160.00 (ISBN 0-317-10331-8); Vol. 16. pap. 160.00 (ISBN 0-317-10332-6). LC 22-7753. Repr. of 1922 ed. (2004548). Bks Demand UMI.

Mellor, Parta. Mellor's Comprehensive Treatise on Inorganic & Theoretical Chemistry, Vol. 5, Pt. A. LC 79-40444. (Illus.). 825p. 1980. 170.00x (ISBN 0-582-46277-0). Longman.

Melson, G. A., ed. Coordination Chemistry of Macrocyclic Compounds. LC 78-27023. (Illus.). 678p. 1979. 85.00x (ISBN 0-306-40140-1, Plenum Pr). Plenum Pub.

Miller, Joel S., ed. Extended Linear Chain Compounds, Vol. 1. LC 81-17762. 497p. 1981. 65.00x (ISBN 0-306-40711-6, Plenum Pr). Plenum Pub.

--Extended Linear Chain Compounds, Vol. 2. LC 81-17762. 532p. 1981. 65.00x (ISBN 0-306-40712-4, Plenum Pr). Plenum Pub.

Mizuike, A. Enrichment Techniques for Inorganic Trace Analysis. (Chemical Laboratory Practice). (Illus.). 144p. 1983. 32.00 (ISBN 0-387-12051-3). Springer-Verlag.

Moeller, Therald. Inorganic Chemistry: A Modern Introduction. LC 81-16455. 846p. 1982. 39.95x (ISBN 0-471-61230-8, Pub. by Wiley-Interscience). Wiley.

Monceau, Pierre. Electronic Properties of Inorganic Quasi-One-Dimensional Compounds. 1985. Part I Experimental. 89.00 (ISBN 90-277-1801-6, Pub. by Reidel Holland); Part II Experimental. lib. bdg. 58.00 (ISBN 90-277-1800-8); Part I, Theoretical. lib. bdg. 48.00 (ISBN 0-318-03895-1). Kluwer Academic.

Moser, William R. & Happel, John R., eds. Catalytic Chemistry of Solid-State Inorganics, Vol. 272. (Annals of the New York Academy of Sciences). 1976. 10.00x (ISBN 0-89072-013-4). NY Acad Sci.

Mukhedkar, A. J., et al. A Course in Inorganic Chemistry. 252p. 1981. 30.00x (ISBN 0-86125-686-7, Pub. by Orient Longman India). State Mutual Bk.

Murray, Peter S. & Dawson, P. R. Structural & Comparative Inorganic Chemistry. 1976. pap. text ed. 11.95x (ISBN 0-435-65644-9). Heinemann Ed.

NATO Advanced Study Institute, Inorganic Laboratory, St. John's College, Oxford, September 8-18, 1974. Electronic States of Inorganic Compounds: New Experimental Techniques. Day, P., ed. LC 75-17752. (NATO Advanced Study Institute Ser: No. C20). 541p. 1975. 66.00 (ISBN 90-277-0627-1, Pub. by Reidel Holland). Kluwer Academic.

New Concepts. (Structure & Bonding: Vol. 33). (Illus.). 1977. 49.00 (ISBN 0-387-08269-7). Springer-Verlag.

New Theoretical Aspects. LC 67-11280. (Structure & Bonding: Vol. 35). (Illus.). 1978. 48.00 (ISBN 0-387-08887-3). Springer-Verlag.

Nicholls, D. Inorganic Chemistry in Liquid Ammonia. (Topics in Inorganic & General Chemistry Ser.: Vol. 17). 238p. 1979. 55.50 (ISBN 0-444-41774-5). Elsevier.

Niedenzu, Kurt & Zimmer, Hans, eds. Annual Reports in Inorganic & General Syntheses, Vol. 1. 1973. 49.00 (ISBN 0-12-040701-9). Acad Pr.

Nyquist, R. A. & Kegel, R. O. Infrared Spectra of Inorganic Compounds. 1971. 71.00 (ISBN 0-12-523450-3). Acad Pr.

Pass, G. & Sutcliffe, H. Practical Inorganic Chemistry: Preparations, Reactions & Instrumental Methods. 2nd ed. 256p. 1979. pap. 12.95x (ISBN 0-412-16150-8, NO. 6214, Pub. by Chapman & Hall England). Methuen Inc.

Pies, W. & Weiss, A. Crystal Structure Data of Inorganic Compounds: Part B: Key Elements O, S, Se, Te. Part B2: Substance Numbers B1818...2804. (Landolt-Boernstein: Group III, Vol. 7). 1980. 117.60 (ISBN 0-387-09593-4). Springer-Verlag.

--Crystal Structure Data of Inorganic Compounds, Part B: Key Elements O, S, Se, Te; 3 - Key Elements S, Se, Te. (Landolt-Boernstein Numerical Data & Functional Relationships in Science & Technology Ser.: Vol. 7, Pt. b). 460p. 1982. 287.20 (ISBN 0-387-11622-2). Springer-Verlag.

--Landolt-Boernstein Numerical Data & Functional Relationships in Science & Technology, New Series, Group 3: Crystal & Solid State Physics, Vol. 7a, Structure Data Of Inorganic Compounds. LC 62-53136. 647p. 1973. 252.00 (ISBN 0-387-06166-5). Springer-Verlag.

Porterfield, William W. Inorganic Chemistry. LC 82-18485. (Illus.). 650p. 1983. text ed. 36.95 (ISBN 0-201-05660-7); solutions guide 7.95 (ISBN 0-201-05661-5). Addison-Wesley.

Pregosin, P. S. & Kunz, R. W. P & C NMR of Transition Metal Phosphine Complexes. (NMR Ser.: Vol. 16). (Illus.). 1979. 47.00 (ISBN 0-387-09163-7). Springer-Verlag.

Purcell, Keith F. & Kotz, John C. An Introduction to Inorganic Chemistry. 1980. text ed. 40.95 (ISBN 0-03-056768-8, CBS C); tchr's ed. 9.95 (ISBN 0-03-056769-6). SCP.

Raiswell, R. W., et al. Environmental Chemistry. LC 80-12132. (Resource & Environmental Science Ser.). 184p. 1980. pap. text ed. 21.95x (ISBN 0-470-26968-5). Halsted Pr.

Rao, A. P., et al. Topics in Inorganic Chemistry. 388p. 1981. 34.00x (ISBN 0-86125-187-3, Pub. by Orient Longman India). State Mutual Bk.

Rao, C. N. & Ferraro, J. R. Spectroscopy in Inorganic Chemistry. 1970-1971. Vol. 1. 71.50 (ISBN 0-12-580201-3); Vol. 2. 71.50 (ISBN 0-12-580202-1). Acad Pr.

Rawcliffe, C. T. & Rawson, D. H., eds. Principles of Inorganic & Theoretical Chemistry. 1974. pap. text ed. 15.95x (ISBN 0-435-66747-5). Heinemann Ed.

Remy, H. Treatise on Inorganic Chemistry, 2 vols. Kleinberg, J., ed. Incl. Vol. 1: Introduction & Main Groups of the Periodic Tables. 866p. 83.00 (ISBN 0-444-40470-8); Vol. 2: Subgroups of the Periodic Table & General Topics. 798p. 83.00 (ISBN 0-444-40471-6). 1956. Elsevier.

Rickert, Hans. Electrochemistry of Solids: An Introduction. (Inorganic Chemistry Concepts Ser.: Vol. 7). (Illus.). 260p. 1982. 71.00 (ISBN 0-387-11116-6). Springer-Verlag.

Riedel, Erwin. Allgemeine und Anorganische Chemie: Ein Lehrbuch fuer Studenten mit Nebenfach Chemie. 3rd ed. (Ger., Illus.). x, 346p. 1985. pap. text ed. 19.60x (ISBN 3-11-010269-2). De Gruyter.

Rochow, Eugene G. Inorganic Synthesis, Vol. 6. LC 79-642684. 272p. 1985. Repr. of 1960 ed. lib. bdg. write for info (ISBN 0-89874-539-X). Krieger.

Rodymans, C. & Rabenau, A., eds. Crystal Structure & Chemical Bonding in Inorganic Chemistry. 1975. 42.75 (ISBN 0-444-10961-7). Elsevier.

Rorabacher, David B. & Endicott, John F., eds. Mechanistic Aspects of Inorgnic Reactions. LC 82-13817. (ACS Symposium Ser.: No. 198). 486p. 1982. 54.95 (ISBN 0-8412-0734-8). Am Chemical.

Royal Society Discussion Meeting, May 20-21, 1982. Metal Clusters in Chemistry: Proceedings. Lewis, Jack & Green, M. L., eds. (Phil. Trans. Royal Society Series A: Vol. 308). (Illus.). 166p. 1983. text ed. 51.00x (ISBN 0-85403-204-5, Pub. by Royal Soc London). Scholium Intl.

Saito, Y. Inorganic Molecular Dissymmetry. (Inorganic Chemistry Concepts: Vol. 4). (Illus.). 1979. 51.00 (ISBN 0-387-09176-9). Springer-Verlag.

Sharpe, A. G. Inorganic Chemistry. LC 79-41765. (Illus.). 704p. 1981. 50.00x (ISBN 0-582-45064-0); pap. text ed. 25.00x (ISBN 0-582-45080-2). Longman.

Sharpe, A. G. & Emeleus, H. J., eds. Advances in Inorganic Chemistry & Radiochemistry, Vol. 26. (Serial Publication Ser.). 1983. 64.50 (ISBN 0-12-023626-5). Acad Pr.

Slowinski, Emil & Masterton, William. Qualitative Analysis & the Properties of Ions in Aqueous Solution. LC 75-145567. 1971. 18.95 (ISBN 0-7216-8369-X, CBS C). SCP.

Sohnel, O. & Novotny, P. Densities of Aqueous Solutions of Inorganic Substances. (Physical Sciences Data Ser.: No. 22). 336p. 1984. 65.00 (ISBN 0-444-99596-X). Elsevier.

Sykes, A. G. Advances in Inorganic & Bioorganic Mechanisms, Vol. 3. 1984. 95.00 (ISBN 0-12-023803-9). Acad Pr.

Sykes, A. G., ed. Advances in Inorganic & Bioinorganic Mechanisms, Vol. I. (Serial Publication Ser.). 1982. 75.00 (ISBN 0-12-023801-2). Acad Pr.

--Advances in Inorganic & Bioinorganic Mechanisms, Vol. 4. (Serial Publication). Date not set. price not set (ISBN 0-12-023804-7). Acad Pr.

Szantay, C., et al, eds. Chemistry & Biotechnology of Biologically Active Natural Products: Proceedings of the International Conference, 2nd, Budapest, 15-19 Aug., 1983. (Studies in Organic Chemistry: No. 17). 378p. 1984. 74.00 (ISBN 0-444-99608-7, I-232-84). Elsevier.

Thompson, R., ed. Mellor's Comprehensive Treatise on Inorganic & Theoretical Chemistry: Supplement to Vol. V, Boron, Pt. B1. LC 22-7753. (Illus.). xii, 616p. 1982. text ed. 175.00x (ISBN 0-582-46278-9). Longman.

Tofield, B. C. & Fricke, B. Recent Impact of Physics on Inorganic Chemistry. LC 67-11280. (Structure & Bonding Ser.: Vol. 21). (Illus.). 150p. 1975. text ed. 36.00 (ISBN 0-387-07109-1). Springer-Verlag.

Twigg, M. V., ed. Mechanisms of Organometallic & Inorganic Reactions, Vol. 1. 389p. 1983. 55.00x (ISBN 0-306-41142-3, Plenum Press). Plenum Pub.

--Mechanisms of Organometallic & Inorganic Reactions, Vol. 2. 422p. 1984. 59.50x (ISBN 0-306-41404-X, Plenum Pr). Plenum Pub.

Upadhyaya, K. N. A Textbook of Inorganic Chemistry: The Representative Elements, Vol. 2. 256p. 1985. pap. text ed. 15.95x (ISBN 0-7069-2666-8, Pub. by Vikas India). Advent NY.

Vogel, A. I. Vogel's Textbook of Quantitative Inorganic Analysis. 4th ed. Bassett, J., et al, eds. LC 77-5545. (Illus.). 1978. text ed. 55.00x (ISBN 0-582-46321-1). Longman.

Wells, A. F. Models in Structural Inorganic Chemistry. 1970. text ed. 12.95x (ISBN 0-19-501278-X). Oxford U Pr.

--Structural Inorganic Chemistry. 5th ed. (Illus.). 1983. text ed. 98.00x (ISBN 0-19-855370-6). Oxford U Pr.

Williams, A. F. A Theoretical Approach to Inorganic Chemistry. (Illus.). 1979. 60.00 (ISBN 0-387-09073-8). Springer-Verlag.

Williams, R. J. & Da Silva, J. R., eds. New Trends in Bio-Inorganic Chemistry. 1979. 49.50 (ISBN 0-12-755050-X). Acad Pr.

Wyckoff, Ralph W. Crystal Structures, Vol. 2: Inorganic Compounds Rxn, Rnmx2, Rnmx3-Crystal Structures. LC 78-23589. 596p. 1985. Repr. of 1964 ed. lib. bdg. write for info. (ISBN 0-89874-388-5). Krieger.

Zuckerman, J. J., ed. The Formation of the Bond to Hydrogen, Pt. 1. (Inorganic Reactions & Methods Ser.: Vol. 1). 288p. 1985. lib. bdg. 92.00 (ISBN 0-89573-251-3). VCH Pubs.

Zuckerman, Jerold J., ed. Organotin Compounds: New Chemistry & Applications; A Symposium Sponsored by the Division of Inorganic Chemistry, at the 171st Meeting of the American Chemical Society, New York, N. Y., April 6-7, 1976. LC 76-54338. (Advances in Chemistry Ser.: No. 157). pap. 77.30 (ISBN 0-317-26307-2, 2024238). Bks Demand UMI.

CHEMISTRY, INORGANIC–BIBLIOGRAPHY

Holzbecher, Z., et al. Organic Reagents in Inorganic Analysis. LC 75-34459. (Ser. in Analytical Chemistry). 734p. 1976. 117.95x (ISBN 0-470-01396-6). Halsted Pr.

Nagy, Zoltan, ed. Electrochemical Synthesis of Inorganic Compounds: A Bibliography. 488p. 1985. 75.00x (ISBN 0-306-41938-6, Plenum Pr). Plenum Pub.

CHEMISTRY, INORGANIC–LABORATORY MANUALS

Akhmetov, N. Problems & Laboratory Experiments in Inorganic Chemistry. 256p. 1982. 8.95 (ISBN 0-8285-2443-2, Pub. by Mir Pubs USSR). Imported Pubns.

Nicholls, D. Inorganic Chemistry in Liquid Ammonia. (Topics in Inorganic & General Chemistry Ser.: Vol. 17). 238p. 1979. 55.50 (ISBN 0-444-41774-5). Elsevier.

CHEMISTRY, INORGANIC–SYNTHESIS

Angelici, Robert J. Synthesis & Technique in Inorganic Chemistry. 2nd ed. 1977. text ed. 32.95 (ISBN 0-7216-1281-4, CBS C). SCP.

Armitage, D. A. Inorganic Rings & Cages. LC 72-76951. 387p. 1972. 52.50x (ISBN 0-8448-0004-X). Crane-Russak Co.

Basolo, Fred, ed. Inorganic Syntheses, Vol. 16. LC 79-642684. (Inorgnic Syntheses Ser.). 256p. 1975. Repr. lib. bdg. 25.00 (ISBN 0-07-004015-X). Krieger.

Busch, Daryle H. Inorganic Syntheses, Vol. 20. LC 39-23015. (Inorganic Synthesis Ser.). 303p. 1980. 45.50x (ISBN 0-471-07715-1, Pub. by Wiley-Interscience). Wiley.

Dewar, M. J., et al, eds. Synthetic & Structural Problems. (Topics in Current Chemistry Ser.: Vol. 106). (Illus.). 170p. 1982. 41.00 (ISBN 0-387-11766-0). Springer-Verlag.

Douglas, Brodie E., ed. Inorganic Syntheses, Vol. 18. LC 39-23015. (Inorganic Syntheses Ser.). 238p. 1977. 45.95x (ISBN 0-471-03393-6, Pub. by Wiley-Interscience). Wiley.

Fackler, John P., ed. Inorganic Syntheses, Vol. 21. LC 39-23015. (Inorganic Synthesis Ser.). 215p. 1982. 40.50x (ISBN 0-471-86520-6, Pub. by Wiley-Interscience). Wiley.

Hagenmuller, Paul, ed. Preparative Methods in Solid State Chemistry. 1972. 95.00 (ISBN 0-12-313350-5). Acad Pr.

Holt, Smith L., Jr. Inorganic Syntheses, Vol. 22. (Inorganic Syntheses Ser.: 2-146). 278p. 1983. 45.50x (ISBN 0-471-88887-7, Pub. by Wiley-Interscience). Wiley.

Inorganic Synthesis, Vols. 1, 2, 4, 5, 7, 11. Incl. Vol. 1. Booth, H. S., ed. 1978. Repr. of 1939 ed (ISBN 0-88275-630-3); Vol. 2. Fernelius, W. C., ed. 1978. Repr. of 1946 ed (ISBN 0-88275-867-5); Vol. 4. Bailar, J. C., ed. 1978. Repr. of 1953 ed (ISBN 0-88275-868-3); Vol. 5. Moeller, T., ed. 1978. Repr. of 1957 ed (ISBN 0-88275-869-1); Vol. 7. Kleinberg, J., ed. 1978. Repr. of 1963 ed (ISBN 0-88275-870-5); Vol. 11. Jolly, W. L., ed. 1978. Repr. of 1968 ed (ISBN 0-88275-871-3). 1978. 25.00 ea. Krieger.

Kirschner, S. Inorganic Syntheses, Vol. 23. 256p. 1985. 39.95 (ISBN 0-471-81873-9). Wiley.

MacDairmid, Alan G., ed. Inorganic Synthesis, Vol. 17. LC 39-23015. 255p. 1977. 25.00 (ISBN 0-07-044327-0). Krieger.

McMurrary, John, et al, eds. Annual Reports in Organic Synthesis, Vol. 12. (Serial Publication). 1982. 39.50 (ISBN 0-12-040812-0). Acad Pr.

Morrison, James D. & Scott, John W. Asymetric Synthesis, Vol. 4: The Chiral Carbon Pool & Chiral Sulfur, Nitrogen, Phosphorus & Silicon Centers. 1984. 85.00 (ISBN 0-12-507704-1). Acad Pr.

Nagy, Zoltan, ed. Electrochemical Synthesis of Inorganic Compounds: A Bibliography. 488p. 1985. 75.00x (ISBN 0-306-41938-6, Plenum Pr). Plenum Pub.

New Synthetic Methods, 6 vols. 270p. 1975. Vol. 1, 169p. 31.80x (ISBN 3-527-25640-7); Vol. 2, 172p. 31.80x (ISBN 3-527-25641-5); Vol. 3, 244p. 40.00x (ISBN 3-527-25642-3); Vol. 4, 1979, 270p. 40.00x (ISBN 0-89573-019-7); Vol. 5, 1979, 278p. 40.00x (ISBN 0-89573-020-0); Vol. 6, 1979, 247p. 40.00x (ISBN 0-89573-021-9). VCH PUbs.

Parry, Robert W., ed. Inorganic Synthesis, Vol. 12. 362p. 1985. Repr. of 1970 ed. lib. bdg. write for info. (ISBN 0-89874-384-2). Krieger.

Parshall, George W. Inorganic Syntheses, Vol. 15. 298p. 1983. Repr. of 1974 ed. lib. bdg. 25.00 (ISBN 0-89874-386-9). Krieger.

Wade, L. G. & O'Donnell, M. J., eds. Annual Reports in Organic Synthesis, Vol. 11. (Serial Publication). 1981. 39.50 (ISBN 0-12-040811-2). Acad Pr.

Zimmer, Hans, ed. Annual Reports in Inorganic & General Syntheses, Vol. 5. 1977. 59.50 (ISBN 0-12-040705-1). Acad Pr.

CHEMISTRY, MEDICAL AND PHARMACEUTICAL

see also Chemistry, Clinical; Disinfection and Disinfectants; Drugs; Pharmacy; Poisonous Plants; Poisons

Abramovitch, R. A., ed. Reactive Intermediates, Vol. 1. LC 79-344. (Illus.). 536p. 1980. 69.50x (ISBN 0-306-40220-3, Plenum Pr). Plenum Pub.

Albert, Adrien. Selective Toxicity: The Physico-Chemical Basis of Theory. 6th ed. LC 78-15491. 1979. pap. text ed. 19.95x (ISBN 0-412-23650-8). Halsted Pr.

Bailey. Annual Reports in Medicinal Chemistry, Vol. 19. 1984. 35.00 (ISBN 0-12-040519-9). Acad Pr.

Bauer, R. & Loeschen, R. Chemistry for the Allied Health Sciences. 1980. 28.95 (ISBN 0-13-129205-6); lab manual 16.95 (ISBN 0-13-129213-7); student guide 10.95 (ISBN 0-13-129197-1). P-H.

Baum, H. & Gergely, J., eds. Molecular Aspects of Medicine, Vol. 2. LC 80-40473. (Illus.). 453p. 1980. 77.00 (ISBN 0-08-026355-0). Pergamon.

Baum, H., et al, eds. Molecular Aspects of Medicine, Vol. 6. (Illus.). 584p. 1984. 162.00 (ISBN 0-08-031724-3). Pergamon.

Berti, F., et al, eds. Cyclooxygenase & Lipoxygenase Modulators in Lung Reactivity. (Progress in Biochemical Pharmacology: Vol. 20). (Illus.). x, 146p. 1985. 56.75 (ISBN 3-8055-3974-6). S Karger.

Borchardt, Ronald T., et al, eds. Directed Drug Delivery. LC 85-2291. (Experimental Biology & Medicine Ser.). (Illus.). 384p. 1975. 59.50 (ISBN 0-89603-089-X). Humana.

Boschke, F. L., ed. Medicinal Chemistry. LC 77-24573. (Topics in Current Chemistry: Vol. 72). (Illus.). 1977. 43.00 (ISBN 0-387-08366-9). Springer-Verlag.

Burger, Alfred. A Guide to the Chemical Basis of Drug Design. LC 83-3575. 300p. 1983. 50.00x (ISBN 0-471-86828-0, Pub. by Wiley-Interscience). Wiley.

Cain, Cornelius K., ed. Annual Reports in Medicinal Chemistry. 1973. Vol. 8 1973. 51.00 (ISBN 0-12-040508-3); Vol. 9 1974. 51.00 (ISBN 0-12-040509-1); Vol. 10 1975. 51.00 (ISBN 0-12-040510-5); Vol. 11 1976. 51.00 (ISBN 0-12-040511-3); Vol. 12 1977. 48.00 (ISBN 0-12-040512-1). Acad Pr.

--Annual Reports in Medicinal Chemistry, Vol. 17. (Serial Publication). 400p. 1982. 45.00 (ISBN 0-12-040517-2). Acad Pr.

--Annual Reports in Medicinal Chemistry, Vol. 18. (Serial Publication Ser.). 1983. 42.50 (ISBN 0-12-040518-0). Acad Pr.

Bamford, C. H. & Tipper, C. F., eds. Comprehensive Chemical Kinetics, Vols. 1-18. Incl. Vol. 1. Practice of Kinetics. 450p. 1969. 102.25 (ISBN 0-444-40673-5); Vol. 2. Theory of Kinetics. 486p. 1969. 102.25 (ISBN 0-444-40674-3); Vol. 3. Formation & Decay of Excited Species: Formation & Decay of Excited Species. 300p. 1970. 87.25 (ISBN 0-444-40802-9); Vol. 4. Decomposition of Inorganic & Organometallic Compounds. 272p. 1972. 87.25 (ISBN 0-444-40936-X); Vol. 5. Decomposition & Isomerization of Organic Compounds. 779p. 1972. 149.00 (ISBN 0-444-40861-4); Vol. 6. Reactions of Non-Metallic Inorganic Compounds. 517p. 1972. 127.75 (ISBN 0-444-40944-0); Vol. 7. Reactions of Metallic Salts & Complexes & Organometallic Compounds. 615p. 1972. 136.25 (ISBN 0-444-40913-0); Vol. 8. Proton Transfer of Related Reactions. 262p. 1977. 87.25 (ISBN 0-444-41512-2); Vol. 9. Addition & Elimination Reactions of Aliphatic Compounds. 515p. 1973. 127.75 (ISBN 0-444-41051-1); Vol. 10. Ester Formation & Hydrolysis & Related Reactions. 309p. 1972. 87.25 (ISBN 0-444-40957-2); Vol. 12. Electrophilic Substitution at a Saturated Carbon Atom. 256p. 1973. 87.25 (ISBN 0-444-41052-X); Vol. 13. Reactions of Aromatic Compounds. 508p. 1972. 127.75 (ISBN 0-444-40937-8); Vol. 14. Degradation of Polymers. 564p. 1975. 136.25 (ISBN 0-444-41155-0); Vol. 14A. Free Radical Polymerization. 594p. 1977. 136.25 (ISBN 0-444-41486-X); Vol. 15. Nonradial Polymerization. 660p. 1976. 144.25 (ISBN 0-444-41252-2); Vol. 16. Liquid Phase Oxidation. 264p. 1980. 87.25 (ISBN 0-444-41860-1); Vol. 17. Gas Phase Combustion. 520p. 1977. 136.25 (ISBN 0-444-41513-0); Vol. 18. Selected Elementary Reactions. 486p. 1976. 136.25 (ISBN 0-444-41294-8). Elsevier.

Barkash, V. A. & Shubin, V. G. Contemporary Problems in Carbonium Ion Chemistry I-II, 2 Vols. (Topics in Current Chemistry Ser.: Vols. 116-117). (Illus.). 320p. 1984. Set. 45.50 (ISBN 0-387-12555-8). Springer Verlag.

Barton, D. H., et al. Comprehensive Organic Chemistry. Incl. Vol. 1: Stereochemistry, Hydrocarbons, Halo Compounds, & Oxygen Compounds. 230.00x (ISBN 0-08-021313-8); Vol. 2: Nitrogen Compounds, Carboxylic Acids, & Phosphorus Compounds. 230.00x (ISBN 0-08-021314-6); Vol. 3: Sulphur, Selenium, Boron, & Organometallic Compounds. 230.00x (ISBN 0-08-021315-4); Vol. 4: Heterocyclic Compounds. 230.00x (ISBN 0-08-021316-2); Vol. 5: Biological Compounds. 230.00x (ISBN 0-08-021317-0); Vol. 6: Formula, Subject, Author, Reaction & Reagent Indexes. 230.00x (ISBN 0-08-022931-X); Vols. 1-3. half set 687.50; Vols. 4-6. half set 687.50 (ISBN 0-08-023815-7). Vol. 1-3. half set 687.50 (ISBN 0-08-021319-7); Vol. 4-6. half set 687.50 (ISBN 0-08-023815-7). Pergamon.

Barton, F. R., ed. R. B. Woodward Remembered: A Collection of Papers in Honour of Robert Burns Woodward 1917-1979. (Illus.). 542p. 1982. 83.00 (ISBN 0-08-029238-0). Pergamon.

Bassindale, A., ed. The Third Dimension in Organic Chemistry. 1983. pap. 15.00x (ISBN 0-686-90154-1, Pub. by Open Univ Pr). Taylor & Francis.

Bassindale, Alan. The Third Dimension in Organic Chemistry. 242p. 1984. pap. 17.95x (ISBN 0-471-90189-X, Pub. by Wiley Interscience). Wiley.

Baum, Stuart, et al. Exercises in Organic & Biological Chemistry. 2nd ed. 1981. write for info. (ISBN 0-02-306540-0). Macmillan.

Baum, Stuart J. Introduction to Organic & Biological Chemistry. 3rd ed. 1981. write for info. (ISBN 0-02-306640-7); pap. write for info. (ISBN 0-02-306580-X). Macmillan.

Baumgarten, H. E. Organic Syntheses: Collective Volumes, Vol. 5. 1234p. 1973. Vols. 40-49. 59.50 (ISBN 0-471-05707-X). Wiley.

Beilstein Institute for Literature of Organic Chemistry. Acyclische Kohlenwasserstoffe, Hydroxy-Verbindungen und Oxo-Verbindungen. (Beilsteins Handbuch der Organischen Chemie, 4th Ed., 4th Suppl.: Vol. 1, Pt. 6). 569p. 1975. 348.60 (ISBN 0-387-07221-7). Springer-Verlag.

--Acyclische Verbindungen. Boit, H. G., ed. LC 72-95756. (Beilsteins Handbuch der Organischen Chemie, Ser., 4th Ed., 4th Suppl.: Vol. 2, Pt. 1). 692p. 1975. 404.90 (ISBN 0-387-07311-6). Springer-Verlag.

--Beilstein-Leitfaden: Eine Anleitung Zur Benutzung Von Beilsteins Handbuch der Organischen Chemie. 56p. 1975. pap. 257.10 (ISBN 0-387-07431-7). Springer-Verlag.

--Isocyclische Oxoamine, Aminocarbonsauren, Aminossulfinsauren, Aminosulfonsauren. (Beilsteins Handbuch der Organischen Chemie, 4th Ed., 3rd Suppl.: Vol. 14, Pt. 5). 878p. 1975. 215.10 (ISBN 0-387-07099-0). Springer-Verlag.

Belcher, R., ed. Instrumental Organic Elemental Analysis. 1978. 59.50 (ISBN 0-12-085950-5). Acad Pr.

Bender, M. L. & Domiyama, M. Cyclodextrin Chemistry. (Relativity & Structure Ser.: Vol. 6). (Illus.). 1978. 30.00 (ISBN 0-387-08577-7). Springer-Verlag.

Bender, Myron L., et al. The Bioorganic Chemistry of Enzymatic Catalysis. LC 83-19857. 312p. 1984. 39.50x (ISBN 0-471-05991-9, Pub. by Wiley Interscience). Wiley.

Benfey, O. Theodor. From Vital Force to Structural Formulas. LC 74-32607. 115p. 1975. pap. 7.95 (ISBN 0-8412-0273-7). Am Chemical.

Benfey, Otto T. The Names & Structures of Organic Compounds. LC 82-10012. 228p. 1982. pap. text ed. 9.50 (ISBN 0-89874-520-9). Krieger.

Bergman, E. D. & Pullman, Bernard, eds. Conformation of Biological Molecules & Polymers. 1973. 90.00 (ISBN 0-12-091065-9). Acad Pr.

Bernardi, F. & Mangini, A. Organic Sulfur Chemistry: Theoretical & Experimental Advances. (Studies in Organic Chemistry: Vol. 19). 1985. 146.50 (ISBN 0-444-42453-9). Elsevier.

Berndt, A., et al. Organic C-Centered Radicals. LC 62-53136. (Landolt-Boernstein,Group II: Vol. 9, Pt. 8). (Illus.). 1977. 327.60 (ISBN 0-387-08152-6). Springer-Verlag.

Bettelheim, Frederick A. & March, Jerry. Introduction to General, Organic & Biochemistry. LC 83-20124. 708p. 1984. text ed. 33.95x (ISBN 0-03-061548-8); study guide 12.95 (ISBN 0-03-064122-5). SCP.

Beynon, J. H., et al. The Mass Spectra of Organic Molecules. (Illus.). 510p. 1968. 81.00 (ISBN 0-444-40046-X). Elsevier.

Bible, Roy H., Jr. Interpretation of NMR Spectra: An Empirical Approach. LC 64-20741. 150p. 1965. 29.50x (ISBN 0-306-30187-3, Plenum Pr). Plenum Pub.

Bigley, D. B. & Talbot, R. J., eds. Introduction to Organic Chemistry. (Illus.). 400p. 1971. 20.50 (ISBN 0-444-20036-3, Pub. by Elsevier Applied Sci England). Elsevier.

Biomimetic & Bioorganic Chemistry: Topics in Current Chemistry. (Topics in Current Chemistry Ser.: Vol. 128). (Illus.). 270p. 1985. 49.50 (ISBN 0-387-15136-2). Springer-Verlag.

Birkofer, L. Organic Chemistry: Syntheses & Reactivity. (Topics in Current Chemistry Ser.: Vol. 88). (Illus.). 200p. 1980. 61.00 (ISBN 0-387-09817-8). Springer-Verlag.

Blatt, A. H., ed. Organic Syntheses: Collective Volumes, Vol. 2. 654p. 1943. Vols. 10-19. 45.95 (ISBN 0-471-07986-3). Wiley.

Boschke, F., et al, eds. Structure & Transformations of Organic Molecules. (Topics in Current Chemistry: Vol. 32). (Illus.). 110p. 1972. pap. 29.50 (ISBN 0-387-05936-9). Springer-Verlag.

Boschke, F. L., ed. Organic Chemistry. (Topics in Current Chemistry: Vol. 92). 190p. 1980. 60.00 (ISBN 0-387-10048-2). Springer-Verlag.

--Organic Chemistry. LC 77-14137. (Topics in Current Chemistry: Vol. 73). 1978. 63.00 (ISBN 0-387-08480-0). Springer-Verlag.

--Organic Chemistry & Theory. (Topics in Current Chemistry Ser.: Vol. 75). (Illus.). 1978. 47.00 (ISBN 0-387-08834-2). Springer-Verlag.

Braun, D., et al. Practical Macromolecular Organic Chemistry. Ivin, Kenneth J., tr. from Ger. (MMI Press Polymer Monograph: Vol. 4). 1984. 96.00 (ISBN 3-7186-0059-5). Harwood Academic Pubs.

Breslow, Ronald. Organic Reaction Mechanisms: An Introduction. 2nd ed. (Organic Chemistry Monograph Ser.). 1969. pap. 18.95 (ISBN 0-8053-1253-6). Benjamin-Cummings.

Brevard, C. & Granger, P. Handbook of High Resolution Multinuclear NMR. LC 81-8603. 229p. 1981. 30.95 (ISBN 0-471-06323-1, Pub. by Wiley-Interscience). Wiley.

Brossi, Arnold & Benson, Richard E., eds. Organic Syntheses: An Annual Publication of Satisfactory Methods for the Preparation of Organic Chemicals, Vol. 53. LC 21-17747. pap. 51.80 (ISBN 0-317-28689-7, 2055283). Bks Demand UMI.

Brown, Roger F. Pyrolytic Methods in Organic Chemistry: Applications of Flow & Flash Vacuum Pyrolytic Techniques. LC 79-52787. (Organic Chemistry Ser.). 1980. 55.00 (ISBN 0-12-138050-5). Acad Pr.

Brugel, Werner. Nuclear Magnetic Resonance Spectra & Chemical Structure. 1968. 58.50 (ISBN 0-12-137450-5). Acad Pr.

Buckingham, J. Heilbron's Dictionary of Organic Compounds: Second Supplement. 5th ed. 700p. 1984. 199.00 (ISBN 0-412-17020-5, NO. 6800, Pub. by Chapman & Hall). Methuen Inc.

Buckingham, J., ed. Dictionary of Organic Compounds: Third Supplement. 5th ed. 800p. 1985. 230.00 (ISBN 0-412-17030-2, 9553, Pub. by Chapman & Hall England). Methuen Inc.

Buckingham, J., et al, eds. Dictionary of Organic Compounds, 7 Vols. 5th ed. 1982. Set. 1950.00x (ISBN 0-412-17000-0, NO.6611, Pub. by Chapman & Hall). Methuen Inc.

Buckingham, J. B., ed. Heilbron's Dictionary of Organic Compounds, 7 vols. 5th ed. 7848p. 1982. 2150.00 (ISBN 0-412-17000-0, NO. 6611). Methuen Inc.

Budzikiewicz, Herbert & Djerassi, Carl. Interpretation of Mass Spectra of Organic Compounds. LC 64-14625. (Holden-Day Series in Physical Techniques in Chemistry). pap. 72.00 (ISBN 0-317-09615-X, 2051040). Bks Demand UMI.

Buncel, E. & Durst, T., eds. Comprehensive Carbanion Chemistry. (Studies in Organic Chemistry: Vol. 5, Pt. A). 400p. 1980. 78.75 (ISBN 0-444-41913-6). Elsevier.

Buncel, E. & Lee, C. C., eds. Carbon-Thirteen in Organic Chemistry. (Isotopes in Organic Chemistry Ser.: Vol. 3). 288p. 1977. 70.25 (ISBN 0-444-41472-X). Elsevier.

--Isotopes in Organic Chemistry: Isotopic Effects - Recent Developments in Theory & Experiment, Vol. 6. 266p. 1984. 85.25 (ISBN 0-444-42368-0, I-236-84). Elsevier.

Butler, A. R. & Perkins, M. J., eds. Organic Reaction Mechanisms, 1973: An Annual Survey Covering the Literature Dated December 1972 Through November 1973. LC 66-23143. pap. 146.80 (ISBN 0-317-29325-7, 2024016). Bks Demand UMI.

--Organic Reaction Mechanisms, 1974: An Annual Survey Covering the Literature Dated December 2973 Through November 1974. LC 66-23143. pap. 160.00 (ISBN 0-317-29326-5, 2024017). Bks Demand UMI.

--Organic Reaction Mechanisms, 1975: An Annual Survey Covering the Literature Dated December 1974 Through November 1975. LC 66-23143. pap. 157.50 (ISBN 0-317-29327-3, 2024018). Bks Demand UMI.

--Organic Reaction Mechanisms, 1976: An Annual Survey Covering the Literature Dated December 1975 Through November 1976. LC 66-23143. pap. 160.00 (ISBN 0-317-29328-1, 2024019). Bks Demand UMI.

Butler, George B. & Berlin, K Darrell. Fundamentals of Organic Chemistry: Theory & Application. LC 79-128351. pap. 160.00 (ISBN 0-317-08668-5, 2012449). Bks Demand UMI.

Callewaert, Denis M. & Genyea, Julien. Fundamentals of Organic & Biological Chemistry. 1980. text ed. 25.95x (ISBN 0-87901-129-7). Worth.

Calvin, Melvin, ed. Organic Chemistry of Life: Readings from Scientific American. LC 73-12475. (Illus.). 452p. 1973. text ed. 23.95 (ISBN 0-7167-0884-1); pap. text ed. 12.95 (ISBN 0-7167-0883-3). W H Freeman.

Capon, B. & Rees, C. W., eds. Organic Reaction Mechanisms, 1969: An Annual Survey Covering the Literature Dated December 1968 Through November 1969. LC 66-23143. pap. 160.00 (ISBN 0-317-28687-0, 2051618). Bks Demand UMI.

Carey, Francis A. Advanced Organic Chemistry, 2 Pts. LC 76-54956. Pt. A - Structure & Mechanisms. pap. 152.30 (ISBN 0-317-30351-1, 2024720); Pt. B - Reactions & Synthesis. pap. 136.80 (ISBN 0-317-30352-X). Bks Demand UMI.

Carey, Francis A. & Sundberg, Richard J. Advanced Organic Chemistry, Part A: Structure & Mechanisms. LC 76-26090. (Illus.). 583p. 1977. 49.50x (ISBN 0-306-35116-1, Plenum Pr). Plenum Pub.

--Advanced Organic Chemistry, Part B: Reactions & Synthesis. LC 76-54956. (Illus.). 521p. 1977. 49.50x (ISBN 0-306-35117-X, Plenum Pr). Plenum Pub.

--Advanced Organic Chemistry: Structure & Mechanism, Pt. A. 2nd ed. 744p. 1984. 59.50x (ISBN 0-306-41087-7, Plenum Pr); pap. 19.95x (ISBN 0-306-41198-9). Plenum Pub.

Castle, Raymond N., ed. Topics in Heterocyclic Chemistry. LC 71-78478. pap. 69.00 (ISBN 0-317-08776-2, 2011959). Bks Demand UMI.

Chambers, Richard D. Fluorine in Organic Chemistry. LC 73-7824. (Interscience Monographs on Organic Chemistry). pap. 101.50 (ISBN 0-317-26348-X, 2055982). Bks Demand UMI.

Chapman, O. L., ed. Organic Photochemistry, Vol. 3. 320p. 1973. 69.75 (ISBN 0-8247-1096-7). Dekker.

Chapman, Orville L. Organic Syntheses, Vol. 60. LC 21-17747. (Organic Syntheses Ser.). 156p. 1981. 26.50 (ISBN 0-471-09359-9, Pub. by Wiley-Interscience). Wiley.

Cheng, K. L. & Ueno, Keihei. CRC Handbook of Organic Analytical Reagents. 544p. 1982. 78.00 (ISBN 0-8493-0771-6). CRC Pr.

Cheronis, Nicholas & Entrikin, John B. Identification of Organic Compounds: A Student's Text Using Semimicro Techniques. LC 62-21450. pap. 122.30 (ISBN 0-317-26179-7, 2025183). Bks Demand UMI.

Cheronis, Nicholas D. & Entrikin, John B. Identification of Organic Compounds: A Students Text Using Semimicro Techniques. 1963. 55.00 (ISBN 0-470-15279-6, Pub. by Wiley-Interscience). Wiley.

Cheronis, Nicholas D., et al. Semimicro Qualitative Organic Analysis: The Systematic Identification of Organic Compounds. 3rd ed. LC 80-461. 1072p. 1983. Repr. of 1965 ed. lib. bdg. 62.50 (ISBN 0-89874-124-6). Krieger.

Chien, James C. Polyacetylene: Chemistry, Physics, & Material Science. LC 83-7237. 1984. 89.00 (ISBN 0-12-172460-3). Acad Pr.

Choudhry, G. G. & Hutzinger, O. Mechanistic Aspects of the Thermal Formation of Halogenated Organic Compounds Including Polychlorinated Dibenzo-p-Dioxins. LC 83-1640. (Current Topics in Environmental & Toxicological Chemistry Ser.: Vol. 4). (Illus.). 210p. 1983. 39.00 (ISBN 0-677-06130-7). Gordon.

Chung, C. S. Practical Organic Chemistry. (Orig.). 1973. pap. text ed. 3.95x (ISBN 0-686-71781-3, 00127). Heinemann Ed.

Ciba Foundation Staff. Further Perspectives in Organic Chemistry. (Ciba Foundation Symposium: New Ser. 53). pap. 55.00 (ISBN 0-317-08911-0, 2022178). Bks Demand UMI.

Clarke, H. T. A Handbook of Organic Analysis: Qualitative & Quantitative. 5th ed. Haynes, B., ed. LC 74-83479. 320p. 1975. pap. 20.50x (ISBN 0-8448-0662-5). Crane-Russak Co.

Cook, J. & Carruthers, W. Progress in Organic Chemistry, Vol. 7. 176p. 1968. 32.50x (ISBN 0-306-30637-9, Plenum Pr). Plenum Pub.

Coulson, C. A., et al. Huckell Theory for Organic Chemists. 1978. 44.00 (ISBN 0-12-193250-8). Acad Pr.

Coxon, J. M. & Halton, B. Organic Photochemistry. LC 73-82447. (Chemistry Texts Ser). (Illus.). 270p. 1974. pap. 18.95 (ISBN 0-521-09824-6). Cambridge U Pr.

Cram, Jane M. & Cram, Donald J. Essence of Organic Chemistry. LC 77-73957. (Chemistry Ser.). 1978. text ed. 29.95 (ISBN 0-201-01031-3); study guide 6.95 (ISBN 0-201-01032-1). Addison-Wesley.

Creswell, Clifford J., et al. Spectral Analysis of Organic Compounds: An Introductory Programmed Text. 2nd ed. LC 72-77099. 1972. pap. 14.95x (ISBN 0-8087-0335-8). Burgess.

Csizmadia, I. G. Molecular Structure & Conformation: Recent Advances. (Progress in Theoretical Organic Chemistry Ser.: Vol. 3). 344p. 1982. 93.75 (ISBN 0-444-42089-4, I-260-82). Elsevier.

Dalton, David. Organic Chemistry Experiments. 1986. cancelled. Van Nos Reinhold.

Dauben, William G. Organic Reactions, Vol. 29. LC 42-20265. 457p. 1983. 49.50 (ISBN 0-471-87490-6, Pub. by Wiley-Interscience). Wiley.

--Organic Reactions, Vol. 30. (Organic Reactions Ser.). 592p. 1984. 54.50 (ISBN 0-471-89013-8, 2201, Pub. by Wiley-Interscience). Wiley.

--Organic Reactions, Vol. 32. LC 42-20265. (Organic Reactions Ser.: 2201). 533p. 1984. 54.95 (ISBN 0-471-88101-5, Pub. by Wiley-Interscience). Wiley.

Dauben, William G., ed. Organic Reactions, Vol. 21. LC 42-20265. (Organic Reactions Ser.). 428p. 1984. Repr. of 1974 ed. lib. bdg. 42.50 (ISBN 0-89874-777-5). Krieger.

--Organic Reactions, Vol. 22. LC 42-20265. 486p. 1984. Repr. of 1975 ed. 42.50 (ISBN 0-89874-795-3). Krieger.

--Organic Reactions, Vol. 23. LC 42-20265. 528p. 1984. Repr. of 1976 ed. 42.50 (ISBN 0-89874-796-1). Krieger.

--Organic Reactions, Vol. 24. LC 42-20265. 444p. 1984. Repr. of 1976 ed. 42.50 (ISBN 0-89874-797-X). Krieger.

--Organic Reactions, Vol. 25. LC 42-20265. 518p. 1984. Repr. of 1977 ed. 42.50 (ISBN 0-89874-798-8). Krieger.

--Organic Reactions, Vol. 26. LC 42-20265. (Organic Reactions Ser.). 496p. 1984. Repr. of 1979 ed. lib. bdg. 42.50 (ISBN 0-89874-778-3). Krieger.

--Organic Reactions, Vol. 31. LC 42-20265. (Organic Reactions Ser.: 2-201). 376p. 1984. 44.50 (ISBN 0-471-88671-8, Pub by Wiley Interscience). Wiley.

Dauben, William G., et al, eds. Organic Reactions, Vol. 22. LC 42-20265. 486p. 1984. Repr. of 1975 ed. 42.50 (ISBN 0-89874-795-3). Krieger.

Davis, R. & Wells, C. H. J. Spectral Problems in Organic Chemistry. (Illus.). 200p. 1984. pap. text ed. 10.95 (ISBN 0-412-00561-1, 9019, Pub. by Chapman & Hall England). Methuen Inc.

Dazeley, G. H. Organic Chemistry. LC 69-10061. 1969. text ed. 19.95x (ISBN 0-521-07171-2). Cambridge U Pr.

Jones, J. B., et al. Techniques of Chemistry: Vol. 10, Applications of Biochemical Systems in Organic Chemistry, 2 pts. 522p. 1976. Set. 117.95x (ISBN 0-471-02279-9). Wiley.

Jones, Maitland, Jr. & Moss, Robert A., eds. Reactive Intermediates: A Serial Publication, 2 vols. (Reactive Intermediates: A Serial Publication). 1981. (Pub. by Wiley-Interscience); Vol. 2, 396p. 63.50 (ISBN 0-471-01875-9). Wiley.

Jorgensen, William L. & Salem, Lionel. The Organic Chemist's Book of Orbitals. 1973. 47.50 (ISBN 0-12-390250-9); pap. 29.50 (ISBN 0-12-390256-8). Acad Pr.

Kas, J., et al. Preparative Organic Chemistry. (Topics in Current Chemistry Ser.: Vol. 112). (Illus.). 230p. 1983. 42.00 (ISBN 0-387-12396-2). Springer-Verlag.

Katritzky, A. R., ed. Advances in Heterocyclic Chemistry, Vol. 37. 1984. 85.00 (ISBN 0-12-020637-4). Acad Pr.

Katritzky, Alan. Advances in Heterocyclic Chemistry, Vol. 31. (Serial Publication). 1982. 80.00 (ISBN 0-12-020631-5). Acad Pr.

Katritzky, Alan R., ed. Advances in Heterocyclic Chemistry, Vol. 25. 1980. 70.00 (ISBN 0-12-020625-0). Acad Pr.

--Advances in Heterocyclic Chemistry, Vol. 30. (Serial Publication Ser.). 1982. 85.00 (ISBN 0-12-020630-7). Acad Pr.

Kemp, Daniel S. & Vellaccio, Frank. Organic Chemistry. 1980. 38.95 (ISBN 0-87901-123-8); wkbk. & solutions manual 17.95 (ISBN 0-87901-124-6). Worth.

Kende, Andrew S., ed. Organic Reactions, Vol. 33. LC 42-20265. (Organic Reactions Ser.: 2201). 352p. 1984. 45.00 (ISBN 0-471-80229-8, Pub. by Wiley-Interscience); Vol. 34, 412p. 49.95 (ISBN 0-471-80673-0). Wiley.

Kennett, B. H., et al. Mass Spectra of Organic Compounds: Pt. 2. 158p. 1981. 60.00x (ISBN 0-643-00273-1, Pub. by CSIRO Australia). State Mutual Bk.

Kirsten, Wolfgang J. Organic Elemental Analysis: Ultramicro, Micro, & Trace Methods. 1983. 27.50 (ISBN 0-12-410280-8). Acad Pr.

Klimova, V. A. Basic Methods of Organic Microanalysis. 228p. 1977. 5.95 (ISBN 0-8285-0641-8, Pub. by Mir Pubs USSR). Imported Pubns.

Klumpp, Gerhard W. Reactivity in Organic Chemistry. LC 81-16437. 502p. 1982. 53.50x (ISBN 0-471-06285-5, Pub. by Wiley-Interscience). Wiley.

Knipe, A. C. & Watts, W., eds. Organic Reaction Mechanisms 1980: An Annual Survey Covering the Literature Dated December 1979 Through November 1980, Vol. 16. LC 66-23143. 718p. 1982. 201.00 (ISBN 0-471-10004-8, Pub. by Wiley-Interscience). Wiley.

Knipe, A. C. & Watts, W. E., eds. Organic Reaction Mechanisms, Vol. 19. 1985. 130.00 (ISBN 0-471-90503-8). Wiley.

--Organic Reaction Mechanisms 1977: An Annual Survey Covering the Literature Dated December 1976 Through November 1977, Vol. 13. LC 66-23143. 741p. 1979. 210.95 (ISBN 0-471-99666-1, Pub. by Wiley-Interscience). Wiley.

Kochi, Jay. Organometallic Mechanism & Catalysis: The Role of Reactive Intermediates Organic Processes. 1979. 61.50 (ISBN 0-12-418250-X). Acad Pr.

Konstandt, F. Organic Coatings: Properties & Evaluation. (Illus.). 1985. 45.00 (ISBN 0-8206-0306-6). Chem Pub.

Kosak. Catalysis of Organic Reactions (TBC) (Chemical Industries Ser.). 504p. 1984. 75.00 (ISBN 0-8247-7153-2). Dekker.

Kvenvolden, K. A., ed. Geochemistry & the Origin of Life. LC 74-24685. (Benchmark Papers in Geology Ser: Vol. 14). 500p. 1975. 65.00 (ISBN 0-12-786895-X). Acad Pr.

Landor, Stephen R., ed. The Chemistry of the Allenes: Vol. 1, Synthesis of Allenes. 1983. 66.00 (ISBN 0-12-436101-3). Acad Pr.

--The Chemistry of the Allenes: Vol. 2, Reactions of Allenes. 1983. 86.00 (ISBN 0-12-436102-1). Acad Pr.

--The Chemistry of the Allenes: Vol. 3, Stereochemical, Spectroscopic & Special Aspects. 1983. 86.00 (ISBN 0-12-436103-X). Acad Pr.

Lednicer, Daniel & Mitscher, Lester A. Organic Chemistry of Drug Synthesis, 2 vols. LC 76-28387. Vol. 1, 1977, 471p. 40.95x (ISBN 0-471-52141-8, Pub. by Wiley-Interscience); Vol. 2, 1980, 526p. 42.95x (ISBN 0-471-04392-3). Wiley.

Lee, Donald G. Oxidation of Organic Compounds by Permanganate Ion & Hexavalent Chromium. 176p. 1980. 15.00 (ISBN 0-87548-351-8). Open Court.

Lee, Jessie C. & Bettelheim, Frederick A. Introduction to General, Organic & Biochemistry: Laboratory Manual. 384p. 1984. pap. 18.95x (ISBN 0-03-063307-9). SCP.

Leffler, John F. Short Course in Modern Organic Chemistry. Smith, James, ed. 366p. 1973. text ed. write for info. (ISBN 0-02-369320-7). Macmillan.

Le Noble, William J. Highlights of Organic Chemistry: An Advanced Textbook. (Studies in Organic Chemistry: Vol. 3). 1000p. 1974. 35.00 (ISBN 0-8247-6210-X). Dekker.

Lenox, Ronald S. & Crissman, Jack K. Laboratory Manual for Organic Chemistry. 138p. 1979. pap. 13.25 (ISBN 0-534-00690-6); pap. 6.00 instr's manual, 34p. Krieger.

Levsen, K. Fundamental Aspects of Organic Mass Spectrometry. (Progress in Mass Spectroscopy Ser.: Vol. 4). (Illus.). 312p. 1978. 60.00x (ISBN 0-89573-009-X). VCH Pubs.

Levy, George C., et al. Carbon-Thirteen Nuclear Magnetic Resonance. 2nd ed. LC 80-17289. 338p. 1980. 37.50 (ISBN 0-471-53157-X, Pub. by Wiley-Interscience). Wiley.

Linstromberg, Walter W. & Baumgarten, Henry E. Organic Chemistry: A Brief Course. 5th ed. 448p. lib. bdg. 25.95 (ISBN 0-669-05525-5); pap. text ed. 9.95 Problems & Solutions Guide (ISBN 0-669-05526-3). Heath.

Lippard, Stephen J., ed. Progress in Inorganic Chemistry, Vols. 11, 14, 16. Vol. 11, 1970, 404p. 29.50 (ISBN 0-471-54081-1); Vol. 14, 1971, 492p. 36.00 (ISBN 0-471-54084-6); Vol. 16, 1972, 630p. 34.50 (ISBN 0-471-54086-2, Pub. by Wiley). Krieger.

Lloyd, Douglas. Non-Benzenoid Conjugated Carbocyclic Compounds. (Studies in Organic Chemistry: No. 16). 432p. 1984. 96.50 (ISBN 0-444-42346-X, I-254-84). Elsevier.

Loudon, G. Marc. Organic Chemistry. LC 83-7075. (Chemistry Ser.). 1150p. 1984. text ed. 41.95 (ISBN 0-201-14438-7); study guide 19.95 (ISBN 0-201-14436-0); transparencies 150.00 (ISBN 0-201-14442-5). Addison-Wesley.

Lowman, Robert G., et al. Experimental Introductory Chemistry: Organic & Biochemistry. (Illus.). 84p. 1983. pap. text ed. 4.95x (ISBN 0-89641-125-7). American Pr.

Ma & Ritner. Modern Organic Elemental Analysis. 1979. 85.00 (ISBN 0-8247-6786-1). Dekker.

Ma, T. S. & Hassan, S. S. Organic Analysis Using Ion-Selective Electrodes. (Analysis of Organic Materials Ser.). 1982. Vol. 1. 45.00 (ISBN 0-12-462901-6); Vol. 2. 59.50 (ISBN 0-12-462902-4). Acad Pr.

Ma, Tis & Ladas, A. S. Organic Functional Group Analysis by Gas Chromatography. (Analyses of Organic Materials Ser.). 1976. 49.50 (ISBN 0-12-462850-8). Acad Pr.

McClure, Thomas A., ed. Resource Materials. Lipinsky, Edward S. (Handbook of Biosolar Resources Ser.: Vol. 2). 608p. 1981. 83.00 (ISBN 0-8493-3473-X). CRC Pr.

Mackay, K. M. & Mackay, R. A. Introduction to Modern Inorganic Chemistry. 3rd ed. (Illus.). 349p. 1982. pap. text ed. 26.50x (ISBN 0-7002-0278-1). Intl Ideas.

Mackie, R. K. & Smith, D. M. Guidebook to Organic Synthesis. LC 80-41904. (Illus.). 336p. (Orig.). 1982. pap. text ed. 19.95x (ISBN 0-582-45592-8). Longman.

McLafferty, F. W., ed. Mass Spectrometry of Organic Ions. 1963. 98.50 (ISBN 0-12-483650-X). Acad Pr.

Mc Manus, Samuel P., ed. Organic Reactive Intermediates. (Organic Chemistry Ser.). 1973. 67.00 (ISBN 0-12-485450-8). Acad Pr.

McMurry, John. Organic Chemistry. LC 83-7744. 1051p. 1983. text ed. 30.75 pub net (ISBN 0-534-01204-3); study guide 14.00 (ISBN 0-534-02675-3). Brooks-Cole.

McMurry, John & Miller, R. Bryan, eds. Annual Reports in Organic Synthesis, Vols. 1-3. 49.50 (ISBN 0-12-040801-5); Vol. 2. 1972. 49.50 (ISBN 0-12-040802-3); Vol. 3, 1973. 49.50 (ISBN 0-12-040803-1). Acad Pr.

Maier, Mary & Rodriguez, Nelson. Elements of General, Organic & Biochemistry. 600p. 1984. text ed. write for info (ISBN 0-87150-782-X, 4551). Brooks-Cole.

Maitlis, Peter. Organic Chemistry of Palladium, 2 Vols. 1971. Vol. 1. 75.00 (ISBN 0-12-465801-6); Vol. 2. 60.00 (ISBN 0-12-465802-4); Set. 115.00. Acad Pr.

Mamantov, Glen & Braunstein, J., eds. Advances in Molten Salt Chemistry, Vol. 4. 456p. 1981. 65.00x (ISBN 0-306-40833-3, Plenum Pr). Plenum Pub.

Mann, Frederick G. & Saunders, Bernard C. Introduction to Practical Organic Chemistry. 2nd ed. LC 66-84573. pap. 54.80 (ISBN 0-317-08940-4, 2003647). Bks Demand UMI.

March, Jerry. Advanced Organic Chemistry. 3rd ed. 1346p. 1985. 39.95 (ISBN 0-471-88841-9, Pub. by Wiley-Interscience). Wiley.

Marvel, Elliot N. Thermal Electrocyclic Reactions. (Organic Chemistry Ser.). 1980. 65.00 (ISBN 0-12-476250-6). Acad Pr.

Maskill, Howard. The Physical Basis of Organic Chemistry. (Illus.). 480p. 1985. 37.50 (ISBN 0-19-855192-4); pap. 21.95 (ISBN 0-19-855199-1). Oxford U Pr.

Mass Spectra of Organic Compounds, Pts. 1-8. 1982. Set. 480.00x (ISBN 0-686-97909-5, Pub. by CSIRO Australia). State Mutual Bk.

Mathur, N. K. & Narang, C. K. Determination of Organic Compounds with N-Bromosuccinimide & Allied Reagents. (Analysis of Organic Materials Ser.). 1975. 39.00 (ISBN 0-12-479750-4). Acad Pr.

Mathur, N. K., et al. Polymers As Aids in Organic Chemistry. LC 79-52789. 1980. 37.50 (ISBN 0-12-479850-0). Acad Pr.

Matteson, B. S. Organometallic Reaction Mechanisms of the Nontransition Elements. 1974. 70.00 (ISBN 0-12-481150-7). Acad Pr.

Mazor, L. Analytical Chemistry of Organic Halogen Compounds. LC 75-5934. 400p. 1976. text ed. 59.00 (ISBN 0-08-017903-7). Pergamon.

Mecanismos De las Reacciones Organicas. (Serie De Quimica: No. 4). (Span.). 1977. pap. 2.00 (ISBN 0-8270-6420-9). OAS.

Meier, H. Organic Semiconductors: Dark & Photoconductivity of Organic Solids. LC 74-76846. (Monographs in Modern Chemistry: Vol. 2). (Illus.). 676p. 1974. 81.20x (ISBN 3-527-25438-2). VCH Pubs.

Meislich, Herbert, et al. Schaum's Outline of Organic Chemistry. 1977. pap. 9.95 (ISBN 0-07-041457-2). McGraw.

Meites, Louis & Zuman, Petr. CRC Handbook Series in Organic Electrochemistry, Vol. VI. 552p. 1983. 83.00 (ISBN 0-8493-7226-7). CRC Pr.

Menger, F. M. & Mandell, L. Electronic Interpretation of Organic Chemistry: A Problems-Oriented Text. LC 79-21718. 223p. 1980. text ed. 29.50x (ISBN 0-306-40379-X, Plenum Pr); pap. text ed. 14.50x (ISBN 0-306-40391-9, Plenum Pr). Plenum Pub.

Menger, Frederic M., et al. Organic Chemistry: A Concise Approach. 2nd ed. 1975. 36.95 (ISBN 0-8053-3281-2). Benjamin-Cummings.

Miller, B. Organic Chemistry: The Basis of Life. 1980. 32.95 (ISBN 0-8053-7071-4). Addison-Wesley.

Miller, John A. & Neuzil, E. F. General Organic Chemistry. 1979. text ed. 26.95 (ISBN 0-669-01885-6); lab manual 14.95 (ISBN 0-669-01886-4); study guide 10.95 (ISBN 0-669-01887-2). Heath.

Minisci, F., et al. Synthetic & Mechanistic Organic Chemistry. (Topics in Current Chemistry: Vol. 62). 1976. 53.00 (ISBN 0-387-07525-9). Springer-Verlag.

Molecular Crystals & Liquid Crystals Special Topics: Proceedings of the Eighth International Liquid Crystals Conference, Kyoto, Japan, June 30-July 4, 1980, 6 vols. 1955p. 1981. pap. 698.95x (ISBN 0-677-40295-3). Gordon.

Moore, James A. & Barton, Thomas. Organic Chemistry. 1978. text ed. 32.95 (ISBN 0-7216-6516-0, CBS C); overhead transparency 200.00 (ISBN 0-7216-9949-9); study guide 10.95 (ISBN 0-7216-6518-7). SCP.

Moore, James A. & Barton, Thomas J. Organic Chemistry: An Overview. LC 77-72792. (Illus.). 1978. text ed. 32.95 (ISBN 0-7216-6516-0). HR&W.

Morrison, James D. Student Guide & Solutions Manual for Organic Chemistry. 176p. 1984. pap. 11.00 (ISBN 0-534-00720-1). Krieger.

Morrison, James D. & Mosher, Harry S. Asymmetric Organic Reactions. corr. ed. LC 75-21608. 1976. pap. 12.95 (ISBN 0-8412-0296-6). Am Chemical.

Morrison, Robert T. & Boyd, Robert N. Organic Chemistry. 4th ed. 1408p. 1983. scp 43.16 (ISBN 0-205-05838-8, EDP 685838); scp student guide 22.41 (ISBN 0-205-05839-6, EDP 685839). Allyn.

Mosnaim & Wolf. Noncatecholic Phenylethylamines. (Pharm-Toxicology Ser.: Vol. 12, Pt. 1). 1978. 85.00 (ISBN 0-8247-6616-4). Dekker.

Mukaiyama. Organic Chemistry, Vol. 4. (Organic Synthesis--Today & Tomorrow). 39.00 (ISBN 0-08-022038-X). Pergamon.

Murray, Peter R. Principles of Organic Chemistry. 2nd ed. 1977. pap. text ed. 16.50x (ISBN 0-435-65643-0). Heinemann Ed.

Nachod, F. C. & Zuckerman, J. J., eds. Determination of Organic Structures by Physical Methods. 1971. Vol. 3. 82.00 (ISBN 0-12-513403-7); Vol. 4. 73.50 (ISBN 0-12-513404-5); Vol. 5 1973. 78.00 (ISBN 0-12-513405-3). Acad Pr.

Nakanishi, Koji & Solomon, Philippa H. Infrared Absorption Spectroscopy. 2nd ed. LC 76-27393. 1977. pap. 24.00x (ISBN 0-8162-6251-9). Holden-Day.

Nakanishi, Koji, et al. Natural Products Chemistry. LC 74-6431. (Vol. III). (Illus.). 700p. 1984. 90.00x (ISBN 0-935702-14-8). Univ Sci Bks.

Natori, Shinsaku, et al. Advances in Natural Products Chemistry: Extraction & Isolation of Biologically Active Components. LC 81-6637. 685p. 1981. 94.95 (ISBN 0-470-27245-7). Halsted Pr.

Neckers, D. C. & Doyle, M. P. Organic Chemistry. 1147p. 1977. 44.50 (ISBN 0-471-63091-8); pap. 17.45 study guide 445p (ISBN 0-471-63092-6); pap. 16.45 solutions manual 296p (ISBN 0-471-02385-X); transp. avail. (ISBN 0-471-03412-6). Wiley.

Neely. Organic Chemicals in the Environment. (Pollution Engineering & Technology Ser.: Vol. 13). 424p. 1980. 39.75 (ISBN 0-8247-6975-9). Dekker.

Negwer, Martin. Organic Chemical Drugs & Their Synonyms, 3 vols. 5th ed. 1863p. 1978. Set. 125.00x (ISBN 0-89573-100-2). VCH Pubs.

Nesmeyanov, A. N. & Nesmeyanov, N. A. Fundamentals of Organic Chemistry, 4 Vols. 1810p. 1978. 35.00 (ISBN 0-8285-2542-0, Pub. by Mir Pubs USSR). Imported Pubns.

Nesmeyanov, N. A. & Nesmeyanov, A. N. Fundamentals of Organic Chemistry, Vol. 1. 484p. 1976. 10.00 (ISBN 0-8285-0650-7, Pub. by Mir Pubs USSR). Imported Pubns.

--Fundamentals of Organic Chemistry, Vol. 2. 353p. 1977. 8.45 (ISBN 0-8285-0651-5, Pub. by Mir Pubs USSR). Imported Pubns.

--Fundamentals of Organic Chemistry, Vol. 3. 468p. 1977. 8.95 (ISBN 0-8285-0652-3, Pub. by Mir Pubs USSR). Imported Pubns.

New Concepts. (Structure & Bonding: Vol. 33). (Illus.). 1977. 49.00 (ISBN 0-387-08269-7). Springer-Verlag.

Newman, Paul. Optical Resolution Procedures for Chemical Compounds: Alcohols, Phenols, Thiols, Aldehydes & Ketones, Vol. 3. 738p. 1984. lib. bdg. 57.50x (ISBN 0-9601918-4-4). Optical Resolution.

--Optical Resolution Procedures for Chemical Compounds, Vol. 2: Acids, 2 pts. LC 78-61452. 1981. Set. 79.00 (ISBN 0-9601918-3-6). Pt. I, 566p (ISBN 0-9601918-1-X). Pt. II, 580p (ISBN 0-9601918-2-8). Optical Resolution.

Norman, R. O. Principles of Organic Synthesis. 2nd ed. 1978. pap. 29.95x (ISBN 0-412-15520-6, NO. 6210, Pub. by Chapman & Hall). Methuen Inc.

Nucleic Acids Chemistry Eighth Symposium, Japan 1980: Proceedings. (Nucleic Acids Symposium Ser.: No. 8). 208p. 1980. 20.00 (ISBN 0-904147-28-2). IRL Pr.

Oja, Simo S., et al. Taurine: Biological Actions & Clinical Perspectives. LC 84-4303. (Progress in Clinical & Biological Research Ser.: Vol. 179). 500p. 1985. 68.00 (ISBN 0-8451-5029-4). A R Liss.

Olah, George A. & Schleyer, Paul, eds. Reactive Intermediates in Organic Chemistry: Carbonium Ions. Set. 188.00 (ISBN 0-686-75231-7); Vol. 2 Methods Of Formation & Major Types 500p. 35.25 (ISBN 0-471-65333-0); Vol. 3 Major Types 536p. 46.00 (ISBN 0-471-65334-9); Vol. 4 Major Types. 46.50 (ISBN 0-471-65337-3). Krieger.

O'Leary, M. Contemporary Organic Chemistry. 1975. text ed. 34.95 (ISBN 0-07-047694-2). McGraw.

O'Neill, Peter. Environmental Chemistry. (Illus.). 176p. 1985. text ed. 25.00x (ISBN 0-04-551085-7); pap. text ed. 11.95x (ISBN 0-04-551086-5). Allen Unwin.

Orchin, Milton, et al. The Vocabulary of Organic Chemistry. LC 79-25930. 609p. 1980. 49.50 (ISBN 0-471-04491-1, Pub. by Wiley-Interscience). Wiley.

Organic Chemistry. LC 79-924. 584p. 1979. 27.00 (ISBN 0-534-00605-1). Krieger.

Organic Chemistry. (Topics in Current Chemistry: Vol. 127). (Illus.). 220p. 1985. 45.00 (ISBN 0-387-15088-9). Springer-Verlag.

Organic Compounds: Syntheses, Stereochemistry, Reactivity. (Topics in Current Chemistry: Vol. 74). (Illus.). 1978. 37.00 (ISBN 0-387-08633-1). Springer-Verlag.

Organic Synthesis. Incl. New Directions in Aromatic Nucleophilic Substitution. Zoltewicz, J. A; Formation & Reactions of Aminyloxides. Aurich, H. G. & Weiss, W.; Cylobutadienoids. Vollhardt, K. P. (Topics in Current Chemistry: Vol. 59). (Illus.). 160p. 1975. 36.00 (ISBN 0-387-07440-6). Springer-Verlag.

Ouellette, Robert J. Introduction to General, Organic, & Biological Chemistry. (Illus.). 720p. 1984. text ed. write for info. (ISBN 0-02-389880-1); write for info. test bank (ISBN 0-02-390220-5). Macmillan.

Ovchinnikov, Yu, ed. Frontiers in Bio-Organic Chemistry & Molecular Biology. (ICSU Press Symposium Ser.: No. 4). 1984. write for info. (ISBN 0-444-80643-1). ICSU Pr.

Owen, E. D. Degradation & Stabilisation of PVC. (Illus.). 314p. 1984. 64.75 (ISBN 0-85334-265-2, I-219-84, Pub. by Elsevier Applied Sci England). Elsevier.

Padwa, Albert. Organic Photochemistry, Vol. 6. 1983. 79.75 (ISBN 0-8247-7003-X). Dekker.

Palmer, William G. Experimental Inorganic Chemistry. pap. 153.00 (ISBN 0-317-27574-7, 2024514). Bks Demand UMI.

Verschueren, Karel. Handbook of Environmental Data on Organic Chemicals. 2nd ed. 1336p. 1983. 99.50 (ISBN 0-442-28802-6). Van Nos Reinhold.

Vishnoi, N. K. Advanced Practical Organic Chemistry. 1979. text ed. 25.00x (ISBN 0-7069-0706-X, Pub. by Vikas India). Advent NY.

Vlahov, R., ed. Chemistry of Natural Products, Eleven: International Symposium on Chemistry of Natural Products, 11th, Golden Sands, Bulgaria, 17-23 September, 1978. 1979. 45.00 (ISBN 0-08-022366-4). Pergamon.

Voelter, W., et al, eds. Chemistry of Peptides & Proteins: Proceeding of the Fourth USSR-FRG Symposium Tubingen, F. R. of Germany, June 8-12, 1982, Vol. 2. LC 84-4294. (Illus.). xii, 497p. 1984. 74.00x (ISBN 3-11-009580-7). De Gruyter.

Vogel, A. I. Vogel's Textbook of Practical Organic Chemistry. 4th ed. Furniss, B. S., et al, eds. LC 77-23559. (Illus.). 1978. text ed. 60.00x (ISBN 0-582-44250-8). Longman.

Voronkov, Mikhail G., et al. Reactions of Sulphur with Organic Compounds. 421p. 1984. 69.50x (ISBN 0-306-10978-6, Consultants). Plenum Pub.

Wade, L. G., Jr. & O'Donnell, Martin J., eds. Annual Reports in Organic Synthesis, Vol. 9. LC 71-167779. 1979. 39.50 (ISBN 0-12-040809-0). Acad Pr.

Wadia, M. S., et al. A Course in Organic Chemistry. 244p. 1981. 30.00x (ISBN 0-86131-055-1, Pub. by Orient Longman India). State Mutual Bk.

Walker, Ruth A. Organic Chemistry: How to Solve It. LC 70-148030. (Illus.). 251p. (Orig.). 1972. wkbk 5.00x (ISBN 0-87735-208-9). Freeman Cooper.

Weast, Robert C., ed. CRC Handbook of Data of Organic Compounds, 2 vols. 2000p. 1985. Vol. I. 100.00 (ISBN 0-8493-0401-6); Vol. II. 100.00 (ISBN 0-8493-0402-4); Set. 200.00 (ISBN 0-8493-0400-8). CRC Pr.

Weingand, Darlene E. The Organic Public Library: Alive with Change. 1984. lib. bdg. 23.50 (ISBN 0-87287-429-X). Libs Unl.

Weininger, Stephan & Stermitz, Frank R., eds. Organic Chemistry. 1984. text ed. 31.00i (ISBN 0-12-742360-5). Acad Pr.

Weiss, Howard D. Guide to Organic Reactions. LC 78-105323. pap. 63.30 (ISBN 0-317-08980-3, 2051511). Bks Demand UMI.

Weissermel, K. & Arpe, H-J. Industrial Organic Chemistry: Important Raw Materials & Intermediates. 404p. 1978. 43.60x (ISBN 0-89573-005-7). VCH Pubs.

Welcher, Frank J. & Boschmann, Erwin. Organic Reagents for Copper. LC 76-18141. 632p. (Orig.). 1979. 41.50 (ISBN 0-88275-440-8). Krieger.

Wender, Irving & Pino, Piero, eds. Organic Synthesis via Metal Carbonyls, Vol. 1. LC 67-13965. pap. 132.80 (ISBN 0-317-09953-1, 2006314). Bks Demand UMI.

Whitaker, Robert, et al. Concepts of General, Organic, & Biological Chemistry. LC 80-82738. (Illus.). 704p. 1981. text ed. 35.95 (ISBN 0-395-29273-5); study guide 10.95 (ISBN 0-395-29275-1); manual 1.00instr's (ISBN 0-395-29274-3); lab manual by Aandra Kotin 16.95 (ISBN 0-395-29276-X); instr's manual to lab excercises 1.50. (ISBN 0-395-30518-7). HM.

Widom, Joanne M. & Edelstein, Stuart J. Chemistry: An Introduction to General, Organic, & Biological Chemistry. LC 80-23816. (Illus.). 743p. 1981. text ed. 29.95x (ISBN 0-7167-1224-5); instr's. manual avail.; study guide 9.95x (ISBN 0-7167-1314-4); transparencies masters avail. W H Freeman.

Wilbraham, Antony & Matta, Michael. Introduction to Organic & Biological Chemistry. 1984. 27.95 (ISBN 0-8053-9651-9); instr's guide 6.95 (ISBN 0-8053-9652-7); study guide 8.95 (ISBN 0-8053-9654-3). Benjamin-Cummings.

Wilcox, Charles F. Experimental Organic Chemistry: Theory & Practice. 544p. 1984. text ed. write for info. (ISBN 0-02-427600-6). Macmillan.

Williams, D. H. & Fleming, I. Spectroscopic Methods in Organic Chemistry. 3rd ed. (Illus.). 1980. pap. text ed. 28.95 (ISBN 0-07-084108-X). McGraw.

Williams, G. H. Organic Chemistry: A Conceptual Approach. 1977. 14.00x (ISBN 0-435-65930-8). Heinemann Ed.

Williams, Hugh J. Introduction to Organic Chemistry. LC 81-21931. 200p. 1982. (Pub. by Wiley-Interscience); pap. write for info. (ISBN 0-471-10207-5). Wiley.

Wingrove & Caret. Quimica Organica. (Span.). 1983. pap. text ed. write for info. (ISBN 0-06-319450-3, Pub. by HarLA Mexico). Har-Row.

Wingrove, Alan S. & Caret, Robert L. Organic Chemistry. 1334p. 1981. text ed. 35.50scp (ISBN 0-06-163400-X, HarpC); scp study guide & answer bk. 16.50 (ISBN 0-06-163413-1). Har-Row.

Wintner, Claude E. Strands of Organic Chemistry: A Series of Lectures. LC 78-60358. 1978. pap. text ed. 12.95x (ISBN 0-8162-9661-8). Holden-Day.

Wise. Organic Chemicals from Biomass. 1983. 45.95 (ISBN 0-201-09040-6). Benjamin-Cummings.

Wiseman, P. Introduction to Industrial Organic Chemistry. 2nd ed. (Illus.). 336p. 1979. 40.75 (ISBN 0-85334-795-6, Pub. by Elsevier Applied Sci England); pap. 24.00 (ISBN 0-85334-850-2). Elsevier.

Wittcoff, Harold A. & Reuben, Bryan G. Industrial Organic Chemicals in Perspective, Part 1: Raw Materials & Manufacture. LC 79-19581. 298p. 1980. 43.00 (ISBN 0-471-03811-3, Pub. by Wiley-Interscience). Wiley.

Wolf, E. J. Separation Methods in Organic Chemistry & Biochemistry. 1969. 49.50 (ISBN 0-12-761650-0). Acad Pr.

Wu. Modern Organic Chemistry, 2 vols. (College Outline Ser.). Vol. 1. pap. 5.95 (ISBN 0-06-460172-2, CO 172, COS); Vol. 2. pap. 4.95 (ISBN 0-06-460173-0, CO 173). B&N NY.

Wyckoff, Ralph W. Crystal Structures, Vol. 3. LC 78-23589. 989p. 1981. Repr. of 1965 ed. lib. bdg. 59.50 (ISBN 0-88275-800-4). Krieger.

Yearbook 1981: With Reaction Titles Vol. 31 to 35 & Cumulative Index; Mit Deutschem Registerschluessel. (Synthetic Methods of Organic Chemistry Series: Vol. 35). xviii, 838p. 1981. 297.25 (ISBN 3-8055-1607-X). S Karger.

Zahradnik, Rudolph & Pancir, Jiri. HMO Energy Characteristics. LC 75-130314. 120p. 1970. 37.50x (ISBN 0-306-65152-1, IFI Plenum). Plenum Pub.

Zlatkis, Albert, et al. A Concise Introduction to Organic Chemistry. 624p. 1973. text ed. 41.95 (ISBN 0-07-072850-X). McGraw.

Zubrick, James W. Work in the Hood: The First Entertaining Organic Chemistry Laboratory Guide. LC 80-69113. (Illus.). 120p. (Orig.). 1980. pap. 4.50 (ISBN 0-937926-00-0). Scienspot.

Zuman, P. Elucidation of Organic Electrode Processes. (Current Chemical Concepts Ser.). 1969. 49.50 (ISBN 0-12-782750-1). Acad Pr.

CHEMISTRY, ORGANIC–EXPERIMENTS

Brabson, G. Dana. Introductory Organic & Biochemistry Experiments for Students in the Health Professions. 1984. pap. text ed. 10.95 (ISBN 0-89917-429-9). Tichenor Pub.

Fessenden, Ralph J. & Fessenden, Joan S. Techniques & Experiments for Organic Chemistry. 480p. 1983. text ed. write for info. (ISBN 0-87150-755-2, 4401). Brooks-Cole.

Fieser, Louis F. & Williamson, Kenneth L. Organic Experiments. 448p. 1983. 26.95 (ISBN 0-669-05890-4). Heath.

Helmkamp, George K. & Johnson, Harry, Jr. Selected Experiments in Organic Chemistry. 2nd ed. (Illus.). 1968. lab manual 13.95 (ISBN 0-7167-0138-3); teacher's manual avail.; indiv. experiments 0.75 ea. W H Freeman.

Helmkamp, George K. & Johnson, Harry W., Jr. Selected Experiments in Organic Chemistry. 3rd ed. (Illus.). 208p. 1983. lab manual 13.95 (ISBN 0-7167-1449-3). W H Freeman.

Linstromberg, Walter W. & Baumgarten, Henry E. Organic Experiments. pap. text ed. 14.95 (ISBN 0-669-05524-7). Heath.

Loewenthal, H. J. Guide for the Perplexed Organic Expermentalist. 184p. 1978. pap. 23.95 (ISBN 0-471-25862-8, Pub. by Wiley Heyden). Wiley.

Moore, James A., et al. Experimental Methods in Organic Chemistry. 3rd ed. 1982. text ed. 31.95 (ISBN 0-03-056896-X, CBS C); instr's manual 10.95 (ISBN 0-03-058401-9). SCP.

Roberts, Royston M., et al. Modern Experimental Organic Chemistry. 4th ed. 1985. text ed. 32.95 (ISBN 0-03-063018-5, CBS C); instr's manual 10.95 (ISBN 0-03-063019-3). SCP.

CHEMISTRY, ORGANIC–LABORATORY MANUALS

Burnett, Thomas & Newkome, George. Lab Course in Organic Chemistry. 1979. wire coil bdg. 11.95 (ISBN 0-88252-099-7). Paladin Hse.

Cason, James & Rapoport, Henry. Laboratory Text in Organic Chemistry. 3rd ed. (Chemistry Ser). 1970. pap. 26.95 ref. ed. O.P. (ISBN 0-13-521435-1). P-H.

Gortler, Leon B. & Tripp, Robert C., eds. Techniques & Experiments in Organic Chemistry. 2nd ed. (Illus.). 1978. lab manual 9.95 (ISBN 0-89529-016-2). Avery Pub.

Helmkamp, George K. & Johnson, Harry, Jr. Selected Experiments in Organic Chemistry. 2nd ed. (Illus.). 1968. lab manual 13.95 (ISBN 0-7167-0138-3); teacher's manual avail.; indiv. experiments 0.75 ea. W H Freeman.

Landgrebe, John A. Theory & Practice in the Organic Laboratory. 3rd ed. 576p. 1982. pap. text ed. 26.95 (ISBN 0-669-04494-6). Heath.

--Theory & Practice in the Organic Laboratory. pap. text ed. 17.95x (ISBN 0-669-99937-7). Heath.

Lehman, John W. Operational Organic Chemistry: A Laboratory Course. new ed. 640p. 1981. text ed. 35.72 (ISBN 0-205-07146-5, 687146-1); tchr's. ed. free (ISBN 0-205-07147-3). Allyn.

Marmor, Solomon. Laboratory Methods in Organic Chemistry. LC 81-65304. 1981. text ed. 26.95x (ISBN 0-8087-3997-2). Burgess.

Miller, John A. & Neuzil, E. F. Modern Experimental Organic Chemistry. 736p. 1982. pap. text ed. 26.95 (ISBN 0-669-03174-7); instr's. guide 0699061603 1.95. Heath.

Openshaw, Harry T. Laboratory Manual of Qualitative Organic Analysis. 3rd ed. 1955. pap. 11.95x (ISBN 0-521-29112-7). Cambridge U Pr.

Pasto, Daniel J. & Johnson, Carol R. Laboratory Text for Organic Chemistry: A Source Book of Chemical & Physical Techniques. 1979. pap. 26.95 (ISBN 0-13-521302-9). P-H.

Pavia, Donald. Introduction to Organic Lab Techniques. 2nd ed. 1982. text ed. 34.95x (ISBN 0-03-058424-8, CBS C); instr's manual 10.95 (ISBN 0-03-058426-4). SCP.

Roberts, Royston M., et al. Modern Experimental Organic Chemistry. 3rd ed. LC 78-10752. (Illus.). 1979. text ed. 30.95 (ISBN 0-03-044391-1, HoltC); instr's manual 10.95 (ISBN 0-03-044396-2). HR&W.

Sabel, W. Basic Techniques of Preparative Organic Chemistry. 1967. pap. 7.00 (ISBN 0-08-012307-4). Pergamon.

Swinehart, James. Organic Chemistry: An Experimental Approach. (Illus., Orig.). 1969. pap. 30.95 (ISBN 0-13-640649-1). P-H.

Ticknor-Gabrielsen. Organic Chemistry in the Laboratory. 336p. 1983. pap. text ed. 15.95 (ISBN 0-8403-3050-2). Kendall-Hunt.

Wawzonek, Stanley, et al. Laboratory Manual of Organic Chemistry: Experiments on a Semimacro Scale. 3rd ed. 1976. wire coil bdg. 11.95 (ISBN 0-8403-0867-1). Kendall-Hunt.

Zubrick, James W. The Organic Chemistry Labroatory Survival Manual: A Student's Guide to Techniques. LC 83-21808. 244p. 1984. pap. text ed. 11.95 (ISBN 0-471-87131-1). Wiley.

CHEMISTRY, ORGANIC–OUTLINES, SYLLABI, ETC.

Banks, James E. Naming Organic Compounds: A Programmed Introduction to Organic Chemistry. 2nd ed. LC 75-291. 1976. pap. text ed. 18.95 (ISBN 0-7216-1536-8, CBS C). SCP.

Degering, F., ed. Organic Chemistry. 6th ed. 1965. pap. 5.50x (ISBN 0-06-460006-8, CO 7000, COS). B&N NY.

Simpson, J. Ernest, et al. An Outline of Organic Chemistry. 3rd ed. (Illus.). 448p. 1975. pap. text ed. 25.95 (ISBN 0-07-057436-7). McGraw.

CHEMISTRY, ORGANIC–PROBLEMS, EXERCISES, ETC.

Agronomov, A., et al. Problems & Exercises in Organic Chemistry. MIR Publishers, tr. 400p. 1975. 17.50x (ISBN 0-8464-0756-6). Beekman Pubs.

Bulter, Anthony R. Problems in Physical Organic Chemistry. LC 72-617. pap. 28.80 (ISBN 0-317-09092-5, 2016972). Bks Demand UMI.

Finar, Ivor L. Problems & Their Solutions in Organic Chemistry. LC 73-166074. pap. 92.30 (ISBN 0-317-09079-8, 2010050). Bks Demand UMI.

Geissman, T. A. Workbook in Organic Chemistry: Exercises in the Properties, Behavior, & Synthesis of Organic Compounds. (Illus.). 245p. 1972. pap. text ed. 10.95x (ISBN 0-7167-0167-7). W H Freeman.

Gibson, Gerald W. Mastering Organic Chemistry: A Problem Solving Approach. LC 77-78569. 1979. pap. text ed. 18.95 (ISBN 0-7216-4111-3, CBS C). SCP.

Gronomov, A. Problems & Exercises in Organic Chemistry. 341p. 1974. 7.45 (ISBN 0-8285-0663-9, Pub. by Mir Pubs USSR). Imported Pubns.

Horn, David E. & Strauss, Michael J. Problems in Organic Chemistry. 1985. pap. text ed. 9.95 (ISBN 0-471-81649-3). Wiley.

Maire, J. & Waegell, B. Structures, Mecanismes et Spectroscopie. (Cours & Documents de Chimie Ser.). 312p. (Fr). 1969. 80.95x (ISBN 0-677-50160-9). Gordon.

Maire, J. C. & Waegell, B. Structures, Mechanisms & Spectroscopy: 120 Problems, 60 Solutions for the Organic Chemist. LC 70-146808. (Documents in Chemistry Ser.). (Illus.). 312p. 1971. 77.00x (ISBN 0-677-30160-X). Gordon.

March, J. Problems in Advanced Organic Chemistry. LC 70-176119. Repr. of 1971 ed. 81.90 (ISBN 0-8357-9093-2, 2055049). Bks Demand UMI.

Meislich, Herbert, et al. Schaum's Outline of Organic Chemistry. 1977. pap. 9.95 (ISBN 0-07-041457-2). McGraw.

Ranganathan, D. Challenging Problems in Organic Reaction Mechanisms. 1972. 35.00 (ISBN 0-12-580050-9). Acad Pr.

Research & Education Association Staff. The Organic Chemistry Problem Solver. rev. ed. LC 78-51952. 1408p. 1984. pap. text ed. 24.85 (ISBN 0-87891-512-5). Res & Educ.

Ryles, A. P. & Smith, K. Worked Examples in Essential Organic Chemistry. LC 80-42022. 161p. 1981. 37.95x (ISBN 0-471-27972-2, Pub. by Wiley-Interscience); pap. text ed. 14.95x (ISBN 0-471-27975-7). Wiley.

Ueselorskaya, T. K. Problems & Exercises in Organic Chemistry. 311p. 1979. 8.95 (ISBN 0-8285-1530-1, Pub. by Mir Pubs USSR). Imported Pubns.

Zahradnik, R. & Carsky, P. Organic Quantum Chemistry Problems. LC 75-186258. 222p. 1973. 32.50 (ISBN 0-306-30516-X, Plenum Pr); pap. 8.95 (ISBN 0-306-20003-1). Plenum Pub.

CHEMISTRY, ORGANIC–SYNTHESIS

see also Biosynthesis; Plastics; Polymers and Polymerization; Synthetic Products

Apsimon, John. The Total Synthesis of Natural Products, Vol. 6. LC 72-4075. 291p. 1984. 44.00 (ISBN 0-471-09900-7, Pub. by Wiley-Interscience). Wiley.

Apsimon, John W., ed. The Total Synthesis of Natural Products, 3 vols. LC 72-4075. 1973. Vol. 1, 603p. 59.95x (ISBN 0-471-03251-4); Vol. 2, 754p. 64.50x (ISBN 0-471-03252-2); Vol. 3, 566p. 64.50x (ISBN 0-471-02392-2, Pub. by Wiley-Interscience). Wiley.

Augustine. Carbon-Carbon Bond Formation. (Techniques & Applications in Organic Synthesis Ser.: Vol. 6). 1979. 75.00 (ISBN 0-8247-6787-X). Dekker.

Bindra, Jasjit S. & Bindra, Ranjna. Creativity in Organic Synthesis, Vol. 1. 1975. 45.00 (ISBN 0-12-099450-X). Acad Pr.

Bird, C. W. Transition Metal Intermediates in Organic Synthesis. 1967. 62.50 (ISBN 0-12-099750-9). Acad Pr.

Birkofer, L. Organic Chemistry: Syntheses & Reactivity. (Topics in Current Chemistry Ser.: Vol. 88). (Illus.). 200p. 1980. 61.00 (ISBN 0-387-09817-8). Springer-Verlag.

Blackborow, J. R. & Young, D. Metal Vapour Synthesis in Organometallic Chemistry. LC 79-9844. (Reactivity & Structure Ser.: Vol. 9). (Illus.). 1979. 63.00 (ISBN 0-387-09330-3). Springer-Verlag.

Blatt, A. H. Organic Synthesis Collective Volumes, Vol. 2. 654p. 1943. 42.95 (ISBN 0-471-07986-3). Wiley.

Brown, Herbert C. Boranes in Organic Chemistry. LC 79-165516. (Baker Lecture Ser.). (Illus.). 464p. 1972. 52.50x (ISBN 0-8014-0681-1). Cornell U Pr.

Brown, Herbert C., et al. Organic Syntheses Via Boranes. LC 74-20520. 283p. 1975. 45.50 (ISBN 0-471-11280-1, Pub. by Wiley-Interscience). Wiley.

Buehler, Calvin A. & Pearson, Donald E. Survey of Organic Syntheses, 2 vols. LC 73-112590. Vol. 1, 1970, 1166p. 95.00 (ISBN 0-471-11670-X); Vol. 2, 1977, 1105p. 56.50 (ISBN 0-471-11671-8, Pub. by Wiley-Interscience). Wiley.

Carruthers, W. Some Modern Methods of Organic Synthesis. 2nd ed. LC 77-77735. (Cambridge Texts in Chemistry & Biochemistry Ser.). (Illus.). 1978. pap. 24.95 (ISBN 0-521-29241-7). Cambridge U Pr.

Coates, Robert M., ed. Organic Syntheses, Vol. 59. LC 21-17747. (Series on Organic Synthesis). 1980. 26.95 (ISBN 0-471-05963-3, Pub. by Wiley-Interscience). Wiley.

Colquhoun, H. M., et al. New Pathways for Organic Synthesis: Practical Applications of Transition Metals. 430p. 1983. 59.50x (ISBN 0-306-41318-3, Plenum Pr). Plenum Pub.

Cragg, Gordon. Organoboranes in Organic Synthesis. (Studies in Organic Chemistry: Vol. 1). 440p. 1973. 75.00 (ISBN 0-8247-6018-2). Dekker.

Davies, S. G., ed. Organotransition Metal Chemistry: Applications to Organic Synthesis. (Organic Chemistry Ser.: Vol. 2). (Illus.). 428p. 1982. 85.00 (ISBN 0-08-026202-3). Pergamon.

Desimoni, Giovanni, et al, eds. Natural Products Synthesis through Pericyclic Reactions. LC 83-12303. (ACS Monographs: No. 180). 443p. 1983. lib. bdg. 89.95 (ISBN 0-8412-0757-7). Am Chemical.

Dewar, M. J., et al, eds. Synthetic & Structural Problems. (Topics in Current Chemistry Ser.: Vol. 106). (Illus.). 170p. 1982. 41.00 (ISBN 0-387-11766-0). Springer-Verlag.

Duffy, J. I., ed. Chemicals by Enzymatic & Microbial Processes: Recent Advances. LC 80-16150. (Chemical Technology Review: No. 161). (Illus.). 386p. 1980. 48.00 (ISBN 0-8155-0805-0). Noyes.

Elliott, Michael, ed. Synthetic Pyrethroids. LC 77-1810. (ACS Symposium Ser.: No. 42). 1977. 29.95 (ISBN 0-8412-0368-7). Am Chemical.

Falbe, J. Carbon Monoxide in Organic Synthesis. Adams, C. R., tr. LC 77-108917. (Illus.). 1970. 44.00 (ISBN 0-387-04814-6). Springer-Verlag.

Fieser & Fieser's. Reagents for Organic Synthesis, Vol. 11. (Fieser's Reagents for Organic Synthesis Ser.). 669p. 1984. 45.00x (ISBN 0-471-88628-9, Pub. by Wiley-Interscience). Wiley.

Finch, A. F., ed. Yearbook Nineteen, 1983. (Theilheimer's Synthetic Methods of Organic Chemistry: Vol. 37). xxiv, 576p. 1983. 227.25 (ISBN 3-8055-3600-3). S Karger.

--Yearbook, 1985. (Theilheimer's Synthetic Methods of Organic Chemistry Ser.: Vol. 39). xxiv, 548p. 1985. 243.75 (ISBN 3-8055-3987-8). S Karger.

Finch, Alan, ed. Yearbook, 1984. (Theilheimer's Synthetic Methods of Organic Chemistry: Vol. 38). (Illus.). xxiv, 624p. 1984. 246.00 (ISBN 3-8055-3817-0). S Karger.

Fitton, A. O. & Smalley, R. K. Practical Heterocyclic Chemistry. LC 68-19255. 1968. 26.00 (ISBN 0-12-257850-3). Acad Pr.

Fleming, Ian. Selected Organic Syntheses: A Guidebook for Organic Chemists. LC 72-615. 227p. 1973. 49.95x (ISBN 0-471-26390-7); pap. 32.95 (ISBN 0-471-26391-5, Pub. by Wiley-Interscience). Wiley.

Freifelder, Morris. Catalytic Hydrogenation in Organic Synthesis: Procedures & Commentary. LC 78-9458. 191p. 1978. 34.95 (ISBN 0-471-02945-9, Pub. by Wiley-Interscience). Wiley.

Gilman, H. Organic Syntheses Collective Volumes: Vols. 1-9, Vol. 1. 580p. 1941. 42.95 (ISBN 0-471-30030-6, Pub. by Wiley-Interscience). Wiley.

Hanessian, S. Total Synthesis of Natural Products: The 'Chiron' Approach. LC 83-19307. (Organic Chemistry Ser.: Vol. 3). 310p. 1983. 40.00 (ISBN 0-08-029247-X); pap. 20.00 (ISBN 0-08-030715-9). Pergamon.

Harrison, Ian T. & Harrison, Shuyan. Compendium of Organic Synthetic Methods, 2 vols. LC 71-162800. 1971. Vol. 1, 529p. 38.50 (ISBN 0-471-80966-7); Vol. 2, 437p. 32.50 (ISBN 0-471-35551-8); Five vol. set. 155.00 (Pub by Wiley-Interscience). Wiley.

Heck, Richard F. Palladium Reagents in Organic Synthesis. (Best Synthetic Methods Ser.). Date not set. 99.00 (ISBN 0-12-336140-0). Acad Pr.

Hegedus, Louis S. & Wade, Leroy. Compendium of Organic Synthetic Methods, Vol. 3. LC 71-162800. 495p. 1977. 32.50 (ISBN 0-471-36752-4, Pub by Wiley-Interscience). Wiley.

Hodge, P. & Sherrington, D. C. Polymer-Supported Reactions in Organic Sythesis. 484p. 1980. 106.95 (ISBN 0-471-27712-6). Wiley.

Horning, E. C. Organic Synthesis: Collective Volumes, Vol. 3, Vols. 20-29. 890p. 1955. 53.95 (ISBN 0-471-40953-7). Wiley.

Horspool, William M., ed. Synthetic Organic Photochemistry. LC 84-10480. 552p. 1984. 75.00x (ISBN 0-306-41449-X, Plenum Pr). Plenum Pub.

House, Herbert O. Modern Synthetic Reactions. 2nd ed. LC 78-173958. 1972. text ed. 39.95 (ISBN 0-8053-4501-9). Benjamin-Cummings.

Kazanskii, B. A., et al. Organic Compounds: Reactions & Methods, Vol. 22. LC 73-16109. (Illus.). 366p. 1973. 65.00x (ISBN 0-306-67122-0, IFI Plenum). Plenum Pub.

Kazanskii, B. A., et al, eds. Organic Compounds: Reaction & Methods, Vol. 21. LC 73-79432. (Illus.). 329p. 1973. 59.50x (ISBN 0-306-67121-2, IFI Plenum). Plenum Pub.

--Organic Compounds: Reactions & Methods, Vol. 23. LC 73-79432. 492p. 1975. 89.50x (ISBN 0-306-67123-9, IFI Plenum). Plenum Pub.

Knunyants, I. L. & Yakobson, G. G., eds. Syntheses of Fluororganic Compounds. 260p. 1985. 69.00 (ISBN 0-387-15077-3). Springer-Verlag.

Larock, R. C. Organomercury Compounds in Organic Synthesis. (Reactivity & Structure Ser.: Vol. 22). 420p. 1985. 94.00 (ISBN 0-387-13749-1). Springer-Verlag.

Lednicer, Daniel & Mitscher, Lester A. Organic Chemistry of Drug Synthesis, Vol. 3. LC 76-28387. 284p. 1984. 29.95x (ISBN 0-471-09250-9, Pub. by Wiley-Interscience). Wiley.

Lindberg, Thomas. Strategies & Tactics of Organic Synthesis. LC 83-15674. 1984. 60.00 (ISBN 0-12-450280-6). Acad Pr.

Lukevits, E. Ya. & Voronkov, M. G. Organic Insertion Reactions of Group IV Elements. LC 65-22184. 413p. 1966. 45.00x (ISBN 0-306-10745-7, Consultants). Plenum Pub.

Mikhailov, B. M. & Bubnov, Yu N. Organoboron Compounds in Organic Synthesis. 560p. 1984. 224.00 (ISBN 3-7186-0113-3). Harwood Academic.

Miller, R. Bryan & Wade, L. G., Jr. Annual Reports in Organic Synthesis, 1977, Vol. 8. 1978. 45.00 (ISBN 0-12-040808-2). Acad Pr.

Millich, Frank & Carraher, Charles E. Interfacial Synthesis: Vol. 1, Fundamentals. 1977. 85.00 (ISBN 0-8247-6372-6). Dekker.

Milller, R. Bryan & Wade, L. G., Jr., eds. Annual Reports in Organic Synthesis 1976, Vol. 7. 1977. 49.50 (ISBN 0-12-040807-4). Acad Pr.

Morrison, James D., ed. Asymmetric Synthesis: Analytical Methods, Vol. 1. LC 83-4620. 1983. 35.00 (ISBN 0-12-507701-7). Acad Pr.

--Asymmetric Synthesis: Stereodifferentiating Addition Reactions, Part A, Vol. 2. LC 83-6423. 1983. 49.50 (ISBN 0-12-507702-5). Acad Pr.

Muccino, Richard R. Organic Synthesis with Carbon-Fourteen. 608p. 1983. 59.50 (ISBN 0-471-05165-9, Pub. by Wiley-Interscience). Wiley.

Mundy, B. Concepts of Organic Chemistry. (Studies in Organic Chem Ser.: Vol. 8). 1979. 34.50 (ISBN 0-8247-7448-5). Dekker.

New Synthetic Methods, 6 vols. 270p. 1975. Vol. 1, 169p. 31.80x (ISBN 3-527-25640-7); Vol. 2, 172p. 31.80x (ISBN 3-527-25641-5); Vol. 3, 244p. 40.00x (ISBN 3-527-25642-3); Vol. 4, 1979, 270p. 40.00x (ISBN 0-89573-019-7); Vol. 5, 1979, 278p. 40.00x (ISBN 0-89573-020-0); Vol. 6, 1979, 247p. 40.00x (ISBN 0-89573-021-9). VCH PUbs.

Nozaki, H., ed. Current Trends in Organic Synthesis: Proceedings of the Fourth International Conference on Organic Synthesis, Tokyo, Japan, August 22-27, 1982. LC 82-22445. (IUPAC Symposium Ser.). (Illus.). 442p. 1983. 90.00 (ISBN 0-08-029217-8). Pergamon.

Organic Compounds: Syntheses, Stereochemistry, Reactivity. (Topics in Current Chemistry: Vol. 74). (Illus.). 1978. 37.00 (ISBN 0-387-08633-1). Springer-Verlag.

Parham, William E. Syntheses & Reactions in Organic Chemistry. LC 74-1410. 558p. 1974. pap. text ed. 12.50 (ISBN 0-88275-171-9). Krieger.

Photochemistry & Organic Synthesis. (Topics in Current Chemistry Ser.: Vol. 129). (Illus.). 280p. 1985. 49.50 (ISBN 0-387-15141-9). Springer-Verlag.

Posner, Gary H. Introduction to Synthesis Using Organocopper Reagents. LC 80-13538. 140p. 1980. 32.50x (ISBN 0-471-69538-6, Pub. by Wiley-Interscience). Wiley.

--An Introduction to Synthesis Using Organocopper Reagents. LC 85-4744. 160p. 1985. Repr. of 1980 ed. lib. bdg. 24.50 (ISBN 0-89874-853-4). Krieger.

Sandler, Stanley R. Organic Functional Group Preparations, Vol. I. 2nd ed. (Organic Chemistry Ser.). 1983. lib. bdg. 75.00 (ISBN 0-12-618601-4). Acad Pr.

Sandler, Stanley R. & Karo, Wolf. Organic Functional Group Preparations, 4 vols. (Organic Chemistry Ser.: Vol. 12). Vol.1. 1969. 77.00 (ISBN 0-12-618550-6); Vol.2. 1971. 75.00 (ISBN 0-12-618552-2); Vol. 3. 1972. 75.00 (ISBN 0-12-618553-0). Acad Pr.

Sarel, S., ed. Organic Synthesis Two: Second IUPAC Symposium on Organic Synthesis, Jerusalem & Haifa, Israel, 10-15 September, 1978. (IUPAC Symposia Ser.). (Illus.). 1979. 39.00 (ISBN 0-08-022363-X). Pergamon.

Scheffold, R. Modern Synthetic Methods 1983: Transition Metals in Organic Synthesis, Vol. 3. 2440p. 1983. 36.95 (ISBN 0-471-90190-3, Pub. by Wiley-Interscience). Wiley.

Schoenberg, A. Preparative Organic Photochemistry. 2nd ed. LC 67-16134. (Illus.). 1968. 98.00 (ISBN 0-387-04325-X). Springer-Verlag.

Schuster, Herbert F. & Coopola, Gary M. Allenes in Organic Synthesis. 358p. 1984. text ed. 47.50x (ISBN 0-471-87284-9, Pub by Wiley-Interscience). Wiley.

Shriner, R. L. & Shriner, R. H. Organic Syntheses Collective Volumes Cumulative Indices for Collective Volumes 1-5. 432p. 1975. 39.50 (ISBN 0-471-78885-6, Pub. by Wiley-Interscience). Wiley.

Smith, Gerard V., ed. Catalysis in Organic Synthesis, 1977. 1978. 39.50 (ISBN 0-12-650550-0). Acad Pr.

Stevens, Robert V. Organic Syntheses, Vol. 61. LC 21-17747. (Organic Syntheses Ser.). 165p. 1983. 28.50 (ISBN 0-471-87038-2, Pub. by Wiley-Interscience). Wiley.

Theilheimer, W., ed. Synthetic Methods of Organic Chemistry: Synthetische Methoden der Organischen Chemie, 32 vols. Incl. Vol. 1. A Thesaurus. 2nd ed. Wynberg, H., tr. from Ger. 1975. 45.50 (ISBN 3-8055-2226-6); Vol. 2. A Thesaurus. 2nd ed. Ingberman, A., tr. from Ger. 1975. 58.25 (ISBN 3-8055-2227-4); Repertorium. (With Eng. index key). Vol. 3. 1975. 85.25 (ISBN 3-8055-2228-2); Vol. 4. 1966. 75.50 (ISBN 3-8055-0640-6); Vol. 5. Annual Survey, 1951. 2nd ed. 1966. 125.25 (ISBN 3-8055-0641-4); Annual Survey, 1952. 2nd ed. 1975. Vol. 6 1952. 72.00 (ISBN 3-8055-2229-0); Vol. 7 1953. 81.00 (ISBN 3-8055-2230-4); Vol. 8. Annual Survey, 1954. 2nd ed. (With cumulative index to vols. 6-8). 1975. 91.25 (ISBN 3-8055-2230-4); Vol. 9. Annual Survey, 1955. 1955. 56.50 (ISBN 3-8055-0643-0); Vol. 10. Yearbook, 1956. 2nd ed. (With Reaction titles & cumulative index to vols. 6-10). 1975. 133.75 (ISBN 3-8055-2232-0); Yearbooks, 1957. 2nd ed. 1975. Vol. 11. 1957. 88.75 (ISBN 3-8055-2233-9); Vol. 12. 1958. 97.75 (ISBN 3-8055-2234-7); Vol. 13. 1959. 108.00 (ISBN 3-8055-2235-5); Vol. 14. 1960. 98.25 (ISBN 3-8055-2236-3); Vol. 15. Yearbook, 1961. (With Reaction titles & cumulative index to vols. 11-15; Ger. word key). 1961. 129.50 (ISBN 3-8055-0646-5); Yearbook, 1962. (With ger. word key). Vol. 16. 1962. 108.00 (ISBN 3-8055-0647-3); Vol. 17. 1963. 108.00 (ISBN 3-8055-0648-1); Vol. 18. 1964. 122.25 (ISBN 3-8055-0650-3); Vol. 19. 1965. 122.25 (ISBN 3-8055-0651-1); Vol. 20. Yearbook, 1966. (With Reaction titles & cumulative index to vols. 16-20; Ger. word key). 1966. 176.75 (ISBN 3-8055-0653-8); Yearbooks, 1967. (With Ger. word key). Vol. 21. 1967. 140.25 (ISBN 3-8055-0654-6); Vol. 22. 1968. 163.00 (ISBN 3-8055-0655-4); Vol. 23. 1969. 190.00 (ISBN 3-8055-0656-2); Vol. 24. 1970. 179.75 (ISBN 3-8055-0657-0); Vol. 25. Yearbook, 1971. (With Reaction titles & cumulative index to vols. 21-25; Ger. word key). 1971. 177.25 (ISBN 3-8055-1198-1); Yearbooks, 1972. (With Ger. word key). Vol. 26. 1972. 170.75 (ISBN 3-8055-1390-9); Vol. 27. 1973. 191.25 (ISBN 3-8055-1565-0); Vol. 28. 1974. 293.50 (ISBN 3-8055-1680-0); Vol. 29. 1975. 175.50 (ISBN 3-8055-2095-6); Vol. 30. Yearbook, 1976. (With Reaction titles & cumulative index to vols. 26-30; Ger. word key). 314.50 (ISBN 3-8055-2256-8); Yearbooks, 1977. (With Ger. word key). Vol. 31, 1977. 298.25 (ISBN 3-8055-2432-3); Vol. 32. 1978. 293.50 (ISBN 3-8055-2818-3). S Karger.

Thyagarajan, B. S. Selective Organic Transformations, Vol. 2. 352p. 1972. 37.50 (ISBN 0-471-86688-1, Pub. by Wiley). Krieger.

Trost, Barry M. & Melvin, Lawrence S., Jr. Sulfer Ylides: Emerging Synthetic Intermediates. (Organic Chemistry Ser.). 1975. 75.00 (ISBN 0-12-701060-2). Acad Pr.

Trost, Barry M. & Hutchinson, C. R., eds. Organic Synthesis - Today & Tomorrow: Third IUPAC Symposium on Organic Synthesis, Madison, Wisconsin, U.S.A., 15-20 June 1980. (IUAC Symposium Ser.). (Illus.). 360p. 1981. 99.00 (ISBN 0-08-025268-0). Pergamon.

Tsuji, J. Organic Synthesis by Means of Transition Metal Complexes. LC 72-14259. (Reactivity & Structure Ser.: Vol. 1). 200p. 1975. 42.00 (ISBN 0-387-07227-6). Springer-Verlag.

Wade, L. G., Jr. & O'Donnell, Martin J., eds. Annual Reports in Organic Synthesis, Vol. 10. 1980. 41.50 (ISBN 0-12-040810-4). Acad Pr.

Wade, Leroy G. Compendium of Organic Synthetic Methods, Vol. 4. LC 71-162800. 497p. 1980. 32.50 (ISBN 0-471-04923-9, Pub. by Wiley-Interscience). Wiley.

Wade, Leroy G., Jr. Compendium of Organic Synthetic Methods, Vol. 5. (Compendium of Organic Synthetic Methods Ser.: 1-101). 552p. 1984. 37.50x (ISBN 0-471-86728-4, Pub. by Wiley-Interscience). Wiley.

Warren, Stuart. Designing Organic Syntheses: A Programmed Introduction to the Synthon Approach. LC 77-15479. 285p. 1978. 15.95x (ISBN 0-471-99612-2, Pub. by Wiley-Interscience). Wiley.

--Organic Synthesis: The Disconnection Approach. LC 81-19694. 391p. 1984. text ed. 39.95x (ISBN 0-471-10160-5); pap. text ed. 19.95x (ISBN 0-471-10161-3); wkbk. 17.95 (ISBN 0-471-90082-6). Wiley.

Weber, W. P. & Gokel, G. W. Phase Transfer Catalysis in Organic Synthesis. LC 77-22798. (Reactivity & Structure: Vol. 4). 1977. 39.50 (ISBN 0-387-08377-4). Springer-Verlag.

Weissberger, N. L. & Tilak, B. V. Technique of Electroorganic Synthesis: Scale-up & Engineering Aspects, Vol.5, Pt.3. LC 75-18447. (Techniques of Chemistry Ser.). 536p. 1982. 108.50 (ISBN 0-471-06359-2, Pub. by Wiley-Interscience). Wiley.

Wipke, W. Todd & Howe, W. Jeffrey, eds. Computer-Assisted Organic Synthesis. LC 77-13629. (ACS Symposium Ser.: No. 61). 1977. 27.95 (ISBN 0-8412-0394-6); pap. 29.95 (ISBN 0-8412-0654-6). Am Chemical.

Zorback, W. Werner & Tipson, R. Stuart, eds. Synthetic Procedures in Nucleic Acid Chemistry: Vol. 1. 570p. (Orig.). 1968. 31.00 (ISBN 0-470-98415-5). Krieger.

--Synthetic Procedures in Nucleic Acid Chemistry: Vol. 2. 686p. (Orig.). 1973. 54.25 (ISBN 0-471-98418-3). Krieger.

CHEMISTRY, ORGANIC–TABLES, ETC.

Beynon, J. H. & Williams, A. E. Mass & Abundance Tables for Use in Mass Spectrometry. 570p. 1963. 117.00 (ISBN 0-444-40044-3). Elsevier.

Buckingham, J. B., et al, eds. Dictionary of Organic Compounds: First Supplement. 1983. 175.00 (ISBN 0-412-17010-8, NO. 6798, Pub. by Chapman & Hall). Methuen Inc.

Dreisbach, Robert R. Physical Properties of Chemical Compounds, 3 vols. Incl. Vol. 1. 536p. 1955; Vol. 2. 491p. 1959. 37.95 (ISBN 0-8412-0023-8); Vol. 3. 489p. 1961. 39.95 (ISBN 0-8412-0030-0). LC 55-2887. (Advances in Chemistry Ser: Nos. 15, 22, 29). Am Chemical.

Gebhardt, M. & Neuhaus, A. Landolt-Boernstein Numerical Data & Functional Relationships in Science & Technology, New Series, Group 3: Crystal & Solid State Physics, Vol. 8, Structure Data Of Organic Compounds. Hellwege, K. H., ed. 1972. 75.60 (ISBN 0-387-05732-3). Springer-Verlag.

Grasselli, J. & Ritchey, W., eds. Atlas of Spectral Data & Physical Constants for Organic Compounds, 6 vols. 2nd ed. LC 72-2452. 4688p. 1975. Set. 725.00 (ISBN 0-87819-317-0). CRC Pr.

Hirayama, Kenzo. Handbook of Ultraviolet & Visible Absorption Spectra of Organic Compounds. LC 66-24948. 645p. 1967. 75.00x (ISBN 0-306-65123-8, IFI Plenum). Plenum Pub.

Pedley, J. B., et al. Thermochemical Data of Organic Compounds. 450p. 1985. text ed. 99.00 (ISBN 0-412-27100-1, 9570, Pub. by Chapman & Hall). Methuen Inc.

Pretsch, E., et al. Tables of Spectral Data for Structure Determination of Organic Compounds. (Chemical Laboratory Practice). 335p. 1983. pap. 14.50 (ISBN 0-387-12406-3). Springer-Verlag.

Rappoport, Zvi, ed. Handbook of Tables for Organic Compound Identification, CRC. 3rd ed. LC 63-19660. (Handbook Ser.). 1967. 49.95 (ISBN 0-8493-0303-6). CRC Pr.

CHEMISTRY, PATHOLOGICAL

see Chemistry, Medical and Pharmaceutical; Physiological Chemistry

CHEMISTRY, PHARMACEUTICAL

see Chemistry, Medical and Pharmaceutical

CHEMISTRY, PHOTOGRAPHIC

see Photographic Chemistry

CHEMISTRY, PHYSICAL AND THEORETICAL

see also Adsorption; Atomic Mass; Atomic Theory; Atomic Weights; Atoms; Catalysis; Chemical Affinity; Chemical Bonds; Chemical Equilibrium; Chemical Reaction, Rate of; Chemical Structure; Chemistry, Physical Organic; Colloids; Coordination Compounds; Crystallization; Crystallography; Dipole Moments; Electrochemistry; Electrolysis; Electrolytes; Flocculation; Gases–Liquefaction; Hydrogen Bonding; Instrumental Analysis; Isomerism; Mass Transfer; Melting Points; Molecular Theory; Molecular Weights; Nuclear Chemistry; Nuclear Physics; Nucleation; Periodic Law; Phase Rule and Equilibrium; Photochemistry; Polymers and Polymerization; Quantum Chemistry; Quantum Theory; Radiation Chemistry; Radiochemistry; Solid State Chemistry; Solubility; Solution (Chemistry); Stereochemistry; Sulphur Bonding; Surface Chemistry; Thermochemistry; Thermodynamics; Valence (Theoretical Chemistry)

Adamson, Arthur. A Textbook of Physical Chemistry. 2nd ed. 953p. 1979. 27.25i (ISBN 0-12-044260-4); solutions manual 5.75i (ISBN 0-12-044265-5). Acad Pr.

Adamson, Arthur W. A Textbook of Physical Chemistry. 3rd ed. Date not set. text ed. price not set (ISBN 0-12-044255-8). Acad Pr.

--Understanding Physical Chemistry. 3rd ed. 1980. 21.95 (ISBN 0-8053-0128-3). Benjamin Cummings.

Advances in Chemical Radio-Sensitization. (Panel Proceedings Ser.). (Illus.). 156p. (Orig.). 1975. pap. 13.00 (ISBN 92-0-111474-5, ISP368, IAEA). Unipub.

Akhadov, Ya Y. Dielectric Properties of Binary Solutions: A Data Handbook. 400p. 1981. 125.00 (ISBN 0-08-023600-6). Pergamon.

Alberty. Physical Chemistry. 7th ed. Date not set. price not set (ISBN 0-471-82577-8). Wiley.

Alberty, Robert A. Physical Chemistry. 6th ed. LC 82-11058. 824p. 1983. text ed. 45.00 (ISBN 0-471-09284-3); solutions manual 14.95 (ISBN 0-471-87208-3). Wiley.
Alberty, Robert A. & Daniels, Farrington. Physical Chemistry SI Version. LC 78-14876. 692p. 1980. text ed. 38.00 (ISBN 0-471-05716-9); solutions manual 16.45 (ISBN 0-471-06376-2). Wiley.
Arnikar, H. J. & Kulharni, R. A. Topics in Physical Chemistry. 246p. 1981. 30.00x (ISBN 0-86125-417-1, Pub. by Orient Longman India). State Mutual Bk.
Arnikar, H. J. & Kulkarni, R. A. A Course in Physical Chemistry. 126p. 1981. 30.00x (ISBN 0-86125-404-X, Pub. by Orient Longman India). State Mutual Bk.
Atkins, P. W. Physical Chemistry. 2nd ed. LC 81-15260. (Illus.). 1095p. 1982. text ed. 35.95 (ISBN 0-7167-1381-0); solutions manual 10.95. W H Freeman.
--Physical Chemistry. LC 77-21208. (Illus.). 1008p. 1978. text ed. 29.95x (ISBN 0-7167-0187-1); solutions manual o.p. 7.95x (ISBN 0-7167-1071-4). W H Freeman.
Atkins, Peter W. Physical Chemistry. 3rd ed. LC 85-7048. (Illus.). 528p. 1985. text ed. write for info. (ISBN 0-7167-1749-2). W H Freeman.
Atwood, Jerry L., et al. Inclusion Compounds, Vol. 2. 1984. 72.00 (ISBN 0-12-067102-6). Acad Pr.
--Inclusion Compounds, Vol. 3. 1985. 98.00 (ISBN 0-12-067103-4). Acad Pr.
Balta, P. & Balta, E. An Introduction to the Physical Chemistry of the Vitreous State. 1976. 39.00 (ISBN 0-9961001-4-8, Pub. by Abacus England). Heyden.
Barrante, James R. Applied Mathematics for Physical Chemistry. (Illus.). 160p. 1974. pap. text ed. 23.95 (ISBN 0-13-041384-4). P-H.
Barrow, Gordon. Physical Chemistry. 4th ed. (Illus.). 1979. text ed. 34.95 (ISBN 0-07-003825-2). McGraw.
--Physical Chemistry for the Life Sciences. 2nd ed. (Illus.). 448p. 1981. text ed. 34.95 (ISBN 0-07-003858-9). McGraw.
Benfey, O. Theodor. Classics in the Theory of Chemical Combination. LC 81-8300. 206p. 1981. Repr. of 1963 ed. 11.50 (ISBN 0-89874-368-0). Krieger.
--From Vital Force to Structural Formulas. LC 74-32607. 115p. 1975. pap. 7.95 (ISBN 0-8412-0273-7). Am Chemical.
Ben-Shaul, A., et al. Lasers & Chemical Change. (Springer Ser. in Chemical Physics: Vol. 10). (Illus.). 497p. 1981. 49.00 (ISBN 0-387-10379-1). Springer-Verlag.
Berliner, L. J. & Reuben, J., eds. Biological Magnetic Resonance, Vol. 2. LC 78-16035. (Illus.). 352p. 1980. 52.50x (ISBN 0-306-40264-5, Plenum Pr). Plenum Pub.
Bernstein, R. B., ed. Atom-Molecule Collision Theory: Guide for the Experimentalist. LC 78-27380. (Physics of Atoms & Molecules Ser.). (Illus.). 1979. 95.00x (ISBN 0-306-40121-5, Plenum Pr). Plenum Pub.
Berry, R. Stephen, et al. Physical Chemistry. LC 79-790. 1281p. 1980. text ed. 51.50 comb. cloth (ISBN 0-471-04829-1); pap. 17.95 solutions manual (ISBN 0-471-04844-5). Wiley.
--Physical Chemistry, 3 pts. Incl. Pt. 1. The Structure of Matter. 521p. 1980. pap. text ed. 29.50 (ISBN 0-471-05824-6); Pt. 2. Matter in Equilibrium Statistical Mechanics & Thermodynamics. 585p. 1980. pap. text ed. 30.00 (ISBN 0-471-05825-4); Pt. 3. Physical & Chemical Kinetics. 281p. 1980. pap. text ed. 24.95 (ISBN 0-471-05823-8). 1980. Wiley.
Bersuker, I. B. The Jahn-Teller Effect: A Bibliographic Review. 600p. 1983. 85.00x (ISBN 0-306-65206-4, IFI-Plenum). Plenum Pub.
Berthollet, Claude L. Essai De Statique Chimique, 2 Vols. Repr. of 1803 ed. Set. 70.00 (ISBN 0-384-04079-9). Johnson Repr.
Berzelius, Jons J. Essai sur la Theorie Des Proportions Chimiques et Sur L'influence Chimique De L'electricite. (Fr). Repr. of 1819 ed. 36.00 (ISBN 0-384-04082-9). Johnson Repr.
Bienkiewicz, Krzysztof J. Physical Chemistry of Leather Making. LC 80-27191. 556p. 1983. 46.50 (ISBN 0-89874-304-4). Krieger.
Bishop, David M. Group Theory & Chemistry. (Illus.). 1973. 49.00x (ISBN 0-19-855140-1). Oxford U Pr.
Boschke, F., ed. New Concepts One. LC 51-5497. (Topics in Current Chemistry: Vol. 41). (Illus.). 150p. 1973. 31.00 (ISBN 0-387-06333-1). Springer-Verlag.
--Stereo- & Theoretical Chemistry. LC 51-5497. (Topics in Current Chemistry: Vol. 31). (Illus.). 160p. 1972. pap. 27.20 (ISBN 0-387-05841-9). Springer-Verlag.
Boschke, F. L., ed. Inorganic & Physical Chemistry. (Topics in Current Chemistry Ser.: Vol. 77). (Illus.). 1978. 59.00 (ISBN 0-387-08987-X). Springer-Verlag.
--New Trends in Chemistry. (Topics in Current Chemistry Ser.: Vol. 100). (Illus.). 213p. 1982. 48.00 (ISBN 0-387-11287-1). Springer-Verlag.
Brown, Harry D. Chemistry of the Cell Interface, 2 vols. 1971. Vol. 1. 72.00 (ISBN 0-12-136101-2); Vol. 2. 72.00 (ISBN 0-12-136102-0). Acad Pr.
Cassidy, Harold G. Science Restated: Physics & Chemistry for the Non-Scientist. LC 72-119371. (Illus.). 538p. 1970. text ed. 12.00x (ISBN 0-87735-007-8). Freeman Cooper.
Chang, Raymond. Physical Chemistry with Applications to Biological Systems. 2nd ed. (Illus.). 1981. text ed. 29.95 (ISBN 0-02-321040-0). Macmillan.
Chemistry Research & Chemical Techniques Based on Research Reactors. (Technical Reports Ser.: No. 17). (Illus.). 264p. (Orig.). 1963. pap. 17.00 (ISBN 92-0-045063-6, IDC17, IAEA). Unipub.
Clarke, M. J., et al, eds. Topics in Inorganic & Physical Chemistry. (Structure & Bonding Ser.: Vol. 50). (Illus.). 178p. 1982. 46.00 (ISBN 0-387-11454-8). Springer-Verlag.
Committee for the Survey of Chemistry. Theoretical Chemistry. 1966. pap. 3.00 (ISBN 0-309-01292-9). Natl Acad Pr.
Conway, B. E. Ionic Hydration in Chemistry & Biophysics. (Studies in Physical & Theoretical Chemistry: Vol. 12). 774p. 1981. 132.00 (ISBN 0-444-41947-0). Elsevier.
D'Ans, J., et al. Densities of Binary Aqueous Systems & Heat Capacities of Liquid Systems. LC 62-53136. (Landolt-Boernstein Group IV: Vol. 1, Pt. B). (Illus.). 1977. 134.40 (ISBN 0-387-08272-7). Springer-Verlag.
Dasent, W. E. Nonexistent Compounds: Compounds of Low Stability. LC 65-27436. pap. 47.80 (ISBN 0-317-08402-X, 2055035). Bks Demand UMI.
Davis, Jeff C., Jr. Advanced Physical Chemistry: Molecules, Structure, & Spectra. (Illus.). 632p. 1965. 39.95x (ISBN 0-471-06719-9, Pub. by Wiley-Interscience). Wiley.
Davison, A., ed. Physical & Inorganic Chemistry. (Topics in Current Chemistry Ser.: Vol. 111). (Illus.). 194p. 1983. 39.50 (ISBN 0-387-12065-3). Springer-Verlag.
Delone, N. B. & Krainov, V. P. Atoms in Strong Light Fields. (Springer Series in Chemical Physics: Vol. 28). (Illus.). 350p. 1985. 49.00 (ISBN 0-387-12412-8). Springer-Verlag.
Denisov, E. T., et al. Liquid-Phase Oxidation of Oxygen-Containing Compounds. (Studies in Soviet Science-Physical Sciences Ser.). (Illus.). 369p. 1978. 59.50x (ISBN 0-306-10936-0, Consultants). Plenum Pub.
DeTar, Delos F., ed. Molecular Mechanics: A Symposium. LC 77-14614. 1978. pap. text ed. 36.00 (ISBN 0-08-022070-3). Pergamon.
Dickerson, et al. Chemical Principles. 4th ed. 1984. 37.95 (ISBN 0-8053-2422-4); By Samuels. study guide 13.95 (ISBN 0-8053-2424-0); Relevant Problems by Butler & Grosser. 13.95 (ISBN 0-8053-1230-7). By Chastain. instrs' guide 6.95 (ISBN 0-8053-2423-2). Benjamin-Cummings.
Diehl, P., et al, eds. Van der Waals Forces & Schielding Effects. LC 75-15821. (NMR - Basic Principles & Progress: Vol. 10). (Illus.). 140p. 1975. 36.00 (ISBN 0-387-07340-X). Springer-Verlag.
Dixon, R. N. & Thomson, C., eds. Theoretical Chemistry, Vols. 1-3. LC 73-92911. Vol. 1 1974. 1973 literature 29.00 (ISBN 0-85186-754-5); Vol. 2 1975. 32.00 (ISBN 0-85186-764-2); Vol. 3 1978. 34.00 (ISBN 0-85186-774-X). Am Chemical.
Dolphin, David, ed. The Porphyrins. Incl. Vol. 1, Pt. A. 1978. 78.00 (ISBN 0-12-220101-9); Physical Chemistry. 1978. Vol. 3, Pt. A. 90.00 (ISBN 0-12-220103-5); Vol. 4, Pt. B, 1979. 65.00 (ISBN 0-12-220104-3); Vol. 5, Pt. C. 77.50 (ISBN 0-12-220105-1). LC 77-14197. 1978-79. Acad Pr.
Dorio, M. M. & Freed, J. A., eds. Multiple Electron Resonance Spectroscopy. LC 78-27381. (Illus.). 524p. 1979. 69.50x (ISBN 0-306-40123-1, Plenum Pr). Plenum Pub.
Edsall, John T. & Wyman, Jeffries. Biophysical Chemistry, Vol. 1: Thermodynamics, Electrostatics & the Biological Significance of the Properties of Matter. 1958. 72.00 (ISBN 0-12-232201-0). Acad Pr.
Eisenberg, David & Crothers, Donald M. Physical Chemistry with Applications to the Life Sciences. 1979. 38.95 (ISBN 0-8053-2402-X); instrs'. guide 6.95 (ISBN 0-8053-2403-8). Benjamin-Cummings.
Eland, J. H. Photoelectron Spectroscopy. LC 73-17763. 1974. 42.95x (ISBN 0-470-23485-7). Halsted Pr.
Elliott, John F., ed. Steelmaking: The Chipman Conference. 1965. 40.00x (ISBN 0-262-05003-X). MIT Pr.
Ernst, R. D., et al. Complex Chemistry. (Structure & Bonding Ser.: Vol. 57). (Illus.). 210p. 1984. 45.00 (ISBN 0-387-13411-5). Springer-Verlag.
Evans, Robert C. Introduction to Crystal Chemistry. 2nd ed. (Illus.). 1964. pap. text ed. 29.95 (ISBN 0-521-09367-8). Cambridge U Pr.
Everdell, M. H. Statistical Mechanics & Its Chemical Applications. 1975. 55.00 (ISBN 0-12-244450-7). Acad Pr.
Eyring, H., et al, eds. Physical Chemistry: An Advanced Treatise in Eleven Volumes. Incl. Vol. 1. Thermodynamics. Jost, W., ed. 1971. 95.00 (ISBN 0-12-245601-7); Vol. 2, Statistical Mechanics. Eyring, H., ed. 1967. 87.00, by subscription 70.50 (ISBN 0-12-245602-5); Vol. 3. Electronic Structure of Atoms & Molecules. Henderson, D., ed. 1969. 95.00 (ISBN 0-12-245603-3); Vol. 4. Molecular Properties. Henderson, D., ed. 1970. 99.50 (ISBN 0-12-245604-1); Vol. 5. Valency. Eyring, H., ed. 1970. 99.50 (ISBN 0-12-245605-X); Vol. 6A. General Introduction & Gas Reactions. Jost, W., ed. 1974. Pt. A. 95.00 (ISBN 0-12-245606-8); Pt. B, 1975. 95.00 (ISBN 0-12-245656-4); Vol. 7. Reactions in Condensed Phases. Eyring, H., ed. 1975. 95.00 (ISBN 0-12-245607-6); Vol. 8. Liquid State. Henderson, D., ed. Pt. A, 1971. 70.00 (ISBN 0-12-245608-4); Pt. B. 87.00 (ISBN 0-12-245658-0); Vol. 9. Electrochemistry. Eyring, H., ed. 1970. Pt. A. 87.00 (ISBN 0-12-245609-2); Pt. B. 87.00 (ISBN 0-12-245659-9). Pt. B; Vol. 10. Solid State Chemistry. Jost, W., ed. 1970. 95.00 (ISBN 0-12-245610-6); Vol. 11 Pt. A. Mathematical Applications. Henderson, D., ed. 1975. 95.00 (ISBN 0-12-245611-4); Pt. B. 101.50 (ISBN 0-12-245661-0). Acad Pr.
Eyring, Henry & Henderson, Douglas, eds. Theoretical Chemistry: Advances in Perspectives, Vol. 2. 1976. 72.00 (ISBN 0-12-681902-5). Acad Pr.
Eyring, Henry, et al, eds. Annual Review of Physical Chemistry, Vol. 23. LC 51-1658. (Illus.). 1972. text ed. 20.00 (ISBN 0-8243-1023-3). Annual Reviews.
--Annual Review of Physical Chemistry, Vol. 24. LC 51-1658. (Illus.). 1973. text ed. 20.00 (ISBN 0-8243-1024-1). Annual Reviews.
--Annual Review of Physical Chemistry, Vol. 26. LC 51-1658. (Illus.). 1975. text ed. 20.00 (ISBN 0-8243-1026-8). Annual Reviews.
--Annual Review of Physical Chemistry, Vol. 25. LC 51-1658. (Illus.). 1974. text ed. 20.00 (ISBN 0-8243-1025-X). Annual Reviews.
Field, Richard J. & Burger, Maria. Oscillations & Traveling Waves in Chemical Systems. LC 84-15382. 688p. 1984. text ed. 85.00x (ISBN 0-471-89384-6, Pub. by Wiley Interscience). Wiley.
Findlay, Alexander. Introduction to Physical Chemistry. 3rd, rev. ed. LC 53-8678. pap. 150.50 (ISBN 0-317-08883-1, 2003640). Bks Demand UMi.
Fischer, Gad. Vibronic Coupling. (Theoretical Chemistry Ser.). 1984. 42.00 (ISBN 0-12-257240-8). Acad Pr.
Fluck, E. & Goldanskii, V. I. Modern Physics in Chemistry, Vol. 1. 1977. 67.00 (ISBN 0-12-261201-9). Acad Pr.
--Modern Physics in Chemistry, Vol. 2. 1980. 99.50 (ISBN 0-12-261202-7). Acad Pr.
Forst, Wendell. Theory of Unimolecular Reactions. (Physical Chemistry Ser.). 1973. 81.00 (ISBN 0-12-262350-9). Acad Pr.
Freifelder, David. Principles of Physical Chemistry with Applications to the Biological Sciences. 2nd ed. 809p. 1985. text ed. write for info. (ISBN 0-86720-046-4). Jones & Bartlett.
Fried, Vojtech, et al. Physical Chemistry. 1977. write for info. (ISBN 0-02-339760-8, 33976). Macmillan.
Gerasimov, Ya., ed. Physical Chemistry, 2 vols. 1233p. 1974. Set. 12.40 (ISBN 0-8285-0657-4, Pub. by Mir Pubs USSR). Imported Pubns.
Goddard, Frederick W. & James, Eric J. The Elements of Physical Chemistry. LC 67-105999. pap. 135.00 (ISBN 0-317-09843-8, 2004943). Bks Demand UMI.
Gold, V., ed. Advances in Physical Organic Chemistry, Vol. 20. LC 62-22125. (Serial Publication Ser.). 1984. 50.00 (ISBN 0-12-033520-4). Acad Pr.
Goodisman, Jerry. Diatomic Interaction Potential Theory, 2 vols. Incl. Vol. 1. Fundamentals. 1973. 73.50 (ISBN 0-12-290201-7); Vol. 2. Applications. 1973. 78.00 (ISBN 0-12-290202-5). (Physical Chemistry Ser.). Acad Pr.
Googenough, J. B. & Jorgensen, C. K., eds. Cation Ordering & Electron Transfer. (Structure & Bonding Ser.: Vo. 61). (Illus.). 170p. 1985. 35.00 (ISBN 0-387-15446-9). Springer-Verlag.
Grassman, Peter. Physical Principles of Chemical Engineering. 928p. 1971. text ed. 125.00 (ISBN 0-08-012817-3). Pergamon.
Greene, Edward F. & Toennies, J. Peter. Chemical Reactions in Shock Waves. 1964. 56.00 (ISBN 0-12-299850-2). Acad Pr.
Henderson, Douglas, ed. Theoretical Chemistry: Theory of Scattering-Papers in Honor of Henry Eyring, Vol. 6a. (Serial Publication). 1981. 59.50 (ISBN 0-12-681906-8). Acad Pr.
--Theoretical Chemistry: Theory of Scattering: Papers in Honor of Henry Eyring, Vol. 6B. (Serial Publications). 1981. 58.50 (ISBN 0-12-681907-6). Acad Pr.
Henderson, Douglas & Eyring, Henry, eds. Theoretical Chemistry: Advances & Perspectives, Vol. 3. 1978. 59.50 (ISBN 0-12-681903-3). Acad Pr.
Herberhold, M. Metal Pi Complexes, 2 Pts, Vol. 2. LC 65-13231. 1972-74. Pt. 1: General Survey. 127.75 (ISBN 0-444-40899-1); Vol. 2: Specific Aspects. 127.75 (ISBN 0-444-41061-9). Elsevier.
Hirtzel, C. S. & Rajagopalan, Raj. Colloidal Phenomena: Advanced Topics. LC 84-22630. (Illus.). 318p. 1985. 36.00 (ISBN 0-8155-1011-X). Noyes.
Hobza, P. & Zahradnik, R. Weak Intermolecular Interactions in Chemistry & Biology. (Studies in Physical & Theoretical Chemistry: Vol. 3). 246p. 1980. 51.00 (ISBN 0-444-99785-7). Elsevier.
Holum, John R. Principles of Physical, Organic, & Biological Chemistry: An Introduction to the Molecular Basis of Life. LC 68-9249. (Illus.). pap. 120.00 (ISBN 0-317-09458-0, 2055142). Bks Demand UMI.
Horvath, A. L. Physical Properties of Inorganic Compounds. LC 74-81574. 466p. 1975. 79.50x (ISBN 0-8448-0523-8). Crane-Russak Co.
Hougen, O. A., et al. Chemical Process Principles, 3 pts. Incl. Pt. 1. Material & Energy Balances. 2nd ed. 525p. 1954; Pt. 2. Thermodynamics. 2nd ed. 624p. 1959. 57.50 (ISBN 0-471-41382-8); Pt. 3. Kinetics & Catalysis. 303p. 1947. LC 54-13512. Wiley.
Isaacs, Neil S. Liquid Phase High Pressure Chemistry. LC 80-40844. 414p. 1981. 114.95 (ISBN 0-471-27849-1, Pub. by Wiley-Interscience). Wiley.
IUPAC (International Union of Pure & Applied Chemistry) IUPAC Handbook Nineteen Eighty-Three to Nineteen Eighty-Five. 202p. 1984. pap. 15.00 (ISBN 0-08-031437-6). Pergamon.
James, Arthur M. & Prichard, F. E. Practical Physical Chemistry. 3rd ed. LC 73-85687. pap. 89.50 (ISBN 0-317-27847-9, 2025254). Bks Demand UMI.
Johnson. Numerical Methods in Chemistry. (Undergraduate Chemistry--a Ser. of Textbooks: Vol. 7). 1980. 33.75 (ISBN 0-8247-6818-3). Dekker.
Jones, Richard A. Physical & Mechanistic Organic Chemistry. 2nd ed. LC 78-27739. (Texts in Chemistry & Biochemistry Ser.). (Illus.). 425p. 1984. 69.50 (ISBN 0-521-25863-4); pap. 27.95 (ISBN 0-521-27886-4). Cambridge U Pr.
Jordan, Peter C. Chemical Kinetics & Transport. LC 78-20999. (Illus.). 1979. 29.50x (ISBN 0-306-40122-3, Plenum Pr). Plenum Pub.
Judd, Brian R. Angular Momentum Theory for Diatomic Molecules. 1975. 59.50 (ISBN 0-12-391950-9). Acad Pr.
Karplus, M. & Porter, R. N. Atoms & Molecules: An Introduction for Students of Physical Chemistry. 1970. pap. text ed. 27.95 (ISBN 0-8053-5218-X). Benjamin-Cummings.
Katritsky. Physical Methods in Heterocyclic Chemistry, Vol. 6. 1974. 68.50 (ISBN 0-12-401106-3). Acad Pr.
Katritzky, A. R. & Boulton, A. J., eds. Theoretical Chemistry: Advances & Perspectives, Vol. 5. LC 75-21963. 1980. 60.00 (ISBN 0-12-681905-X). Acad Pr.
Kauffman, George B., ed. Classics in Coordination Chemistry: Twentieth-Century Papers (1904-1935, Pt. III. LC 67-26870. (Classics of Science Ser.). (Illus.). 1978. pap. text ed. 6.95 (ISBN 0-486-63496-5). Dover.
Kemp. Physical Chemistry: A Step by Step Approach. (Undergraduate Chemistry - A Series of Textbooks: Vol. 6). 1979. 34.75 (ISBN 0-8247-6640-7). Dekker.
King, D. A. & Woodruff, D. P. Chemisorption Systems, 2 pts. (Chemical Physics of Solid Surfaces & Heterogeneous Catalysis Ser.: Vol. 3). 1984. write for info. (ISBN 0-444-42027-4). Elsevier.
King, D. A. & Woodruff, D. P., eds. Chemisorption Systems: Chemical Physics of Solid Surfaces & Hetergeneous Catalysis, Vol. 3B. 320p. 1984. 92.75 (ISBN 0-444-42178-5, I-233-84). Elsevier.
Kireev, V. Physical Chemistry. MIR Publishers, tr. from Rus. (Illus.). 640p. 1975. 21.00x (ISBN 0-8464-0716-7). Beekman Pubs.
--Physical Chemistry. 572p. 1977. 8.45 (ISBN 0-8285-0660-4, Pub. by Mir Pubs USSR). Imported Pubns.
Kittsley, Scott L. Physical Chemistry. 3rd ed. LC 68-26399. (Orig.). 1955. pap. 4.95 (ISBN 0-06-460097-1, COS CO 97). B&N NY.

Technical Association of the Pulp & Paper Industry. Introduction to the Practical Aspects of Wet End Chemistry, 1984: Paper Valley Hotel, Appleton, Wi., October 29-31. pap. 99.80 (ISBN 0-317-20783-0, 2024787). Bks Demand UMI.

Thompson, R., ed. Mellor's Comprehensive Treatise on Inorganic & Theoretical Chemistry: Supplement to Vol. V, Boron, Pt. B1. LC 22-7753. (Illus.). xii, 616p. 1982. text ed. 175.00x (ISBN 0-582-46278-9). Longman.

Tinoco, Ignacio, Jr., et al. Physical Chemistry: Principles & Applications in Biological Sciences. LC 77-25417. 1978. solutions 9.95. P-H.

--Physical Chemistry: Principles & Applications in Biological Sciences. 2nd ed. (Illus.). 656p. 1985. text ed. 34.95 (ISBN 0-13-666280-3). P-H.

Tolk, N. H., et al, eds. Desorption Induced by Electron Transitions, DIET I. (Springer Series in Chemical Physics: Vol. 24). (Illus.). 269p. 1983. 33.00 (ISBN 0-387-12127-7). Springer-Verlag.

Tsuchida, E., et al. Molecular Properties. LC 61-642. (Advances in Polymer Science: Vol. 24). (Illus.). 1977. 53.00 (ISBN 0-387-08124-0). Springer-Verlag.

Van Olphen, H. & Mysels, Karol J. Physical Chemistry: Enriching Topics from Colloid & Surface Science. LC 75-23217. (Illus.). xvi, 404p. 1975. lib. bdg. 17.00x (ISBN 0-916004-03-1); pap. text ed. 7.50x (ISBN 0-916004-01-5). Theorex.

Vidal, C. & Pacault, A., eds. Non-Equilibrium Dynamics in Chemical Systems. (Springer Series in Synergetics: Vol. 27). (Illus.). x, 255p. 1984. 26.00 (ISBN 0-387-15065-X). Springer-Verlag.

Villani, S., ed. Uranium Enrichment. (Topics in Applied Physics Ser.: Vol. 35). (Illus.). 1979. 59.00 (ISBN 0-387-09385-0). Springer-Verlag.

Vincent, Alan. Molecular Symmetry & Group Theory: A Programmed Introduction to Chemical Application. LC 76-26095. 156p. 1977. pap. 15.95x (ISBN 0-471-01868-6, Pub. by Wiley-Interscience). Wiley.

Ward, Charlotte R. This Blue Planet: Introduction to Physical Science. 417p. 1972. text ed. 24.95 (ISBN 0-316-92230-7); instuctor's Manual avail. (ISBN 0-316-92222-6). Little.

Weissberger, Arnold, et al, eds. Techniques of Chemistry: Vol. I, Pt. 3C, Physical Methods of Chemistry: Polarimetry. LC 49-48584. 528p. 1972. 47.95 (ISBN 0-471-92732-5). Krieger.

--Techniques of Chemistry: Vol. I, Pt. 6, Physical Methods of Chemistry. LC 75-29544. 336p. 1977. 36.00 (ISBN 0-471-92899-2). Krieger.

--Techniques of Chemistry: Vol. I, Pt. 3D Physical Methods of Chemistry: X-Ray Nuclear, Molecular Beam & Radioactivity Methods. 706p. 1972. 62.50 (ISBN 0-471-92733-3). Krieger.

Williams, Virginia R., et al. Basic Physical Chemistry for the Life Sciences. 3rd ed. LC 77-13374. (Illus.). 553p. 1978. text ed. 30.95x (ISBN 0-7167-0027-1); answer bk. avail. W H Freeman.

Wilson, J. R., et al, eds. Experiments in Physical Chemistry. 2nd rev. ed. Rickett, R. M. W. LC 68-18536. 1978. 16.25 (ISBN 0-08-023798-3). Pergamon.

Woolley, R. G., ed. Quantum Dynamics of Molecules: The New Experimental Challenge to Theorists. LC 80-16321. (NATO ASI Series B, Physics: Vol. 57). 571p. 1980. 85.00 (ISBN 0-306-40462-1, Plenum Pr). Plenum Pub.

Wyatt, P. A. Energy & Entropy in Chemistry. (Topics in Physics & Chemistry Ser.). 1967. 25.00x (ISBN 0-312-25130-0). St Martin.

Wyn-Jones, E. & Gormally, J., eds. Aggregation Processes in Solution. (Studies in Physical & Theoretical Chemistry: Vol. 26). 632p. 1983. 138.50 (ISBN 0-444-42187-4). Elsevier.

Zuman, Petr & Patel, Rmesh. Techniques in Organic Reaction Kinetics. LC 84-7450. 380p. 1984. text ed. 49.50 (ISBN 0-471-03556-4, Pub by Wiley-Interscience). Wiley.

CHEMISTRY, PHYSICAL AND THEORETICAL–LABORATORY MANUALS

Crockford, H. D., et al. Laboratory Manual of Physical Chemistry. 2nd ed. 352p. 1976. text ed. 25.50 (ISBN 0-471-18844-1). Wiley.

Daniels, Farrington, et al. Experimental Physical Chemistry. 7th ed. 1970. text ed. 40.95 (ISBN 0-07-015339-6). McGraw.

Shoemaker, David, et al. Experiments in Physical Chemistry. 4th ed. (Illus.). 736p. 1980. text ed. 36.95 (ISBN 0-07-057005-1). McGraw.

CHEMISTRY, PHYSICAL AND THEORETICAL–PROBLEMS, EXERCISES, ETC.

Dogra, Sneh Kumar & Dogra, Sulekha. Physical Chemistry Through Problems. LC 83-12819. 674p. 1984. 29.95x (ISBN 0-470-27491-3). Halsted Pr.

Riter, J. R. Exercises in Chemical Physics. 328p. 1972. 67.25x (ISBN 0-677-02350-2). Gordon.

CHEMISTRY, PHYSICAL AND THEORETICAL–PROGRAMMED INSTRUCTION

Hoare, Derrick E. Programmed Introduction to General & Physical Chemistry. LC 67-27670. (Illus.). Repr. of 1967 ed. 28.40 (ISBN 0-8357-9965-4, 2013982). Bks Demand UMI.

CHEMISTRY, PHYSICAL ORGANIC

Abramovitch, R. A., ed. Reactive Intermediates, Vol. 3. LC 82-15139. 644p. 1983. 79.50x (ISBN 0-306-40970-4, Plenum Pr). Plenum Pub.

Boschke, F., ed. Dynamic Chemistry. LC 51-5497. (Topics in Current Chemistry: Vol. 45). (Illus.). 250p. 1974. 38.00 (ISBN 0-387-06471-0). Springer-Verlag.

Buckingham, A. D., et al. Organic Liquids: Structure, Dynamics & Chemical Properties. LC 78-8462. 352p. 1978. 87.95 (ISBN 0-471-99673-4, Pub. by Wiley-Interscience). Wiley.

Cantor, Charles R. & Schimmel, Paul R. Biophysical Chemistry, Part III: The Behavior of Biological Macromolecules. LC 79-27860. (Illus.). 597p. 1980. 49.95 (ISBN 0-7167-1191-5); pap. text ed. 29.95 (ISBN 0-7167-1192-3). W H Freeman.

Carpenter, Barry K. Determination of Organic Reaction Mechanisms. 247p. 1984. 34.95x (ISBN 0-471-89369-2, Pub. by Wiley-Interscience). Wiley.

Csizmadia, I. G., ed. Applications of MO Theory in Organic Chemistry. (Progress in Theoretical Organic Chemistry Ser.: Vol. 2). 626p. 1977. 106.50 (ISBN 0-444-41565-3). Elsevier.

Fisher, H., et al. Electronic Structure of Organic Compounds. (Topics in Current Chemistry: Vol. 24). 1971. pap. 18.90 (ISBN 0-387-05540-1). Springer-Verlag.

Gilchrist, T. L. & Storr, R. C. Organic Reactions & Orbital Symmetry. 2nd ed. LC 78-54578. (Cambridge Texts in Chemistry & Biochemistry Ser.). (Illus.). 1979. 75.00 (ISBN 0-521-22014-9); pap. 24.95 (ISBN 0-521-29336-7). Cambridge U Pr.

Gold, V. Advances in Physical Organic Chemistry, Vol. 19. (Serial Publication). 1983. 69.50 (ISBN 0-12-033519-0). Acad Pr.

Gold, V., ed. Advances in Physical Organic Chemistry. Incl. Vol. 11. 1975. 70.00 (ISBN 0-12-033511-5); Vol. 12. 1975. 65.00 (ISBN 0-12-033512-3); Vol. 13. 1976. 80.00 (ISBN 0-12-033513-1); Vol. 14. 1977. 70.00 (ISBN 0-12-033514-X). (Serial Publication). Acad Pr.

--Advances in Physical Organic Chemistry, Vol. 16. 1979. 60.00 (ISBN 0-12-033516-6). Acad Pr.

Gold, V. & Bethell, D., eds. Advances in Physical Organic Chemistry, Vol. 15. 1978. 65.00 (ISBN 0-12-033515-8). Acad Pr.

--Advances in Physical Organic Chemistry, Vol. 18. (Serial Publication). 1982. 70.00 (ISBN 0-12-033518-2). Acad Pr.

--Advances in Physical Organic Chemistry, Vol. 21. (Serial Publication). 1985. 51.50 (ISBN 0-12-033521-2). Acad Pr.

Gold, Victor, ed. Advances in Physical Organic Chemistry. Incl. Vol. 1. 1963. 80.00 (ISBN 0-12-033501-8); Vol. 2. 1964. 60.00 (ISBN 0-12-033502-6); Vol. 3. 1965. 55.00 (ISBN 0-12-033503-4); Vol. 4. 1966. 70.00 (ISBN 0-12-033504-2); Vol. 5. 1967. 75.00 (ISBN 0-12-033505-0); Vol. 6. 1968. 70.00 (ISBN 0-12-033506-9); Vol. 7. 1969. 70.00 (ISBN 0-12-033507-7); Vol. 8. 1970. 80.00 (ISBN 0-12-033508-5); Vol. 9. 1972. 60.00 (ISBN 0-12-033509-3); Vol. 10. 1973. 50.00 (ISBN 0-12-033510-7). Acad Pr.

Gordon, John E. The Organic Chemistry of Electrolyte Solutions. LC 75-16139. 576p. 1975. 38.50 (ISBN 0-471-31620-2). Krieger.

Hanzlik, Robert P., ed. Inorganic Aspects of Biological & Organic Chemistry. 1976. 52.50 (ISBN 0-12-324050-6). Acad Pr.

Harris, J. Milton & Wamser, Carl C. Fundamentals of Organic Reaction Mechanisms. LC 75-40275. 384p. 1976. 42.95 (ISBN 0-471-35400-7). Wiley.

Horspool, W. M. Aspects of Organic Photochemistry. 1976. 55.00 (ISBN 0-12-356650-9). Acad Pr.

Jones, Maitland, Jr. & Moss, Robert A. Reactive Intermediates: A Serial Publication, Vol. 3. (Reactive Intermediates: A Serial Publication: 1-397). 435p. 1985. text ed. 79.50x (ISBN 0-471-01893-7, Pub. by Wiley-Interscience). Wiley.

Lambert, Joseph B. Physical Organic Chemistry Through Solved Problems. 1978. pap. text ed. 19.95x (ISBN 0-8162-4921-0). Holden-Day.

Lowry, Thomas H. & Richardson, Kathleen S. Mechanism & Theory in Organic Chemistry. 2nd ed. 991p. 1981. text ed. 40.00 scp (ISBN 0-06-044083-X, HarpC); ans. bk. avail. (ISBN 0-06-364043-0). Har-Row.

Minkin, V. I., et al. Dipole Moments in Organic Chemistry. LC 69-17901. (Physical Methods in Organic Chemistry Ser). 288p. 1970. 32.50x (ISBN 0-306-30408-2, Plenum Pr). Plenum Pub.

Pasto, Daniel & Johnson, Carl. Organic Structure Determination. 1969. ref. ed. 37.95 (ISBN 0-13-640854-0). P-H.

Peacocke, A. R. An Introduction to the Physical Chemistry of Biological Organization. (Illus.). 1983. 65.00x (ISBN 0-19-855359-5). Oxford U Pr.

Ritchie, C. D. Physical Organic Chemistry. (Organic Chemical Ser.: Vol. 4). 34.50 (ISBN 0-8247-6323-8). Dekker.

Ross, Sidney, et al. Anodic Oxidation. (Organic Chemistry Ser.). 1975. 80.00 (ISBN 0-12-597650-X). Acad Pr.

Streitwieser, A. & Taft, R. W., eds. Progress in Physical Organic Chemistry, Vol. 11. LC 63-19364. 440p. 1974. 33.00 (ISBN 0-471-83357-6). Krieger.

Sykes, Peter. A Guidebook to Mechanism in Organic Chemistry. 5th ed. (Illus.). 416p. (Orig.). pap. text ed. 16.95x (ISBN 0-582-44121-8). Longman.

Taft, Robert W. Progress in Physical Organic Chemistry, Vol. 14. LC 63-19364. (Progress in Physical Organic Chemistry Ser.). 374p. 1983. 75.00 (ISBN 0-471-86882-5, Pub. by Wiley-Interscience). Wiley.

Zimmerman, Howard E. Quantum Mechanics for Organic Chemists. 1975. 29.50 (ISBN 0-12-781650-X); pap. 19.50 (ISBN 0-12-781651-8). Acad Pr.

CHEMISTRY, PHYSIOLOGICAL

see Physiological Chemistry

CHEMISTRY, QUANTUM

see Quantum Chemistry

CHEMISTRY, SOIL

see Soil Chemistry

CHEMISTRY, SOLID STATE

see Solid State Chemistry

CHEMISTRY, SURFACE

see Surface Chemistry

CHEMISTRY, SYNTHETIC

see Chemistry, Inorganic–Synthesis; Chemistry, Organic–Synthesis

CHEMISTRY, TECHNICAL

see also Alloys; Animal Products; Biochemical Engineering; Bleaching; Canning and Preserving; Ceramics; Chemical Engineering; Chemical Industries; Chemical Reactors; Chemicals–Manufacture and Industry; Chemurgy; Cleaning Compounds; Corrosion and Anti-Corrosives; Cracking Process; Electrochemistry; Extraction (Chemistry); Food–Analysis; Gums and Resins; High Pressure (Technology); Oxygen–Industrial Applications; Tanning; Textile Chemistry; Wood–Chemistry

also particular industries and products, e.g. Clay Industries; Dyes and Dyeing; Petroleum Products

Abd-El-Wahed, A. M. Chemical Technology Dictionary: English, French-German-Arabic. (Eng., Fr., Ger. & Arabic.). 383p. 1974. 45.00 (ISBN 0-686-92502-5, M-9759). French & Eur.

American Institute Of Chemical Engineers. Twenty-Five Years of Chemical Engineering Progress. facs. ed. Kirkpatrick, S. D., ed. LC 68-55837. (Essay Index Reprint Ser). 1933. 20.00 (ISBN 0-8369-0149-5). Ayer Co Pubs.

Ash, M. & Ash, I. Encyclopedia of Industrial Chemical Additives, Vol. 2, G-O. 1984. 75.00 (ISBN 0-8206-0308-2). Chem Pub.

--Encyclopedia of Industrial Chemical Additives, Vol. 3, P-Z. 1984. 75.00 (ISBN 0-8206-0309-0). Chem Pub.

Bamford, C. H., et al. Kinetics & Chemical Technology. (Comprehensive Chemical Kinetics Ser.: Vol. 23). Date not set. write for info. (ISBN 0-444-42441-5). Elsevier.

Breck & Brown. Chemistry for Science & Engineering. 450p. 1982. 29.95 (ISBN 0-07-092372-8). McGraw.

Chakrabarty, B. N. Industrial Chemistry. 1981. 40.00x (ISBN 0-686-72953-6, Pub. by Oxford & IBH India). State Mutual Bk.

Choudhary, G. & Keith, L. H., eds. Chlorinated Dioxins & Dibenzofurane. 1983. text ed. 42.50 (ISBN 0-250-40604-7). Butterworth.

Clausen, Chris A., III & Mattson, Guy C. Principles of Industrial Chemistry. LC 78-9450. 412p. 1978. 45.00 (ISBN 0-471-02774-X, Pub. by Wiley-Interscience). Wiley.

Cox. Natural Gas Hydrates. 1983. text ed. 29.95 (ISBN 0-250-40631-4). Butterworth.

Gillies, M. T., ed. Water-Based Industrial Finishes: Recent Developments. LC 80-17520. (Chemical Technology Review Ser.: No. 167). 435p. 1980. 48.00 (ISBN 0-8155-0812-3). Noyes.

Goodman, Murray & Morehouse, Frank. Organic Molecules in Action. LC 72-85025. (Illus.). 368p. 1973. 24.50x (ISBN 0-677-01810-X). Gordon.

Halpern, M. G., ed. Polishing & Waxing Compositions: Recent Developments. LC 82-7691. (Chemical Technology Rev. 213). (Illus.). 301p. 1983. 36.00 (ISBN 0-8155-0916-2). Noyes.

Hastie, John W. High Temperature Vapors: Science & Technology. (Materials Science & Technology Ser.). 1975. 76.50 (ISBN 0-12-331950-1). Acad Pr.

Henrici-Olive, G. & Olive, S. The Chemistry of the Catalyzed Hydrogenation of Carbon Monoxide. (Illus.). 230p. 1984. 56.00 (ISBN 0-387-13292-9). Springer-Verlag.

Hickson, John L., ed. Sucrochemistry. LC 77-1296. (ACS Symposium Ser.: No. 41). 1977. 34.95 (ISBN 0-8412-0290-7). Am Chemical.

Hocking, M. B. Modern Chemical Technology & Emission Control. (Illus.). 530p. 1985. 38.50 (ISBN 0-387-13466-2). Springer-Verlag.

Hopp, V. & Hennig, I. Handbook of Applied Chemistry: Facts for Engineers, Scientists, Technicians, & Technical Managers. 840p. 1983. 49.95 (ISBN 0-07-030320-7). McGraw.

International Union of Pure & Applied Chemistry. International Congress of Pure & Applied Chemistry, 24th, Hamburg, 1973: Proceedings, 7 vols. Incl. Vol. 1. High Polymers. 208p. 27.00 (ISBN 0-08-020770-7); Vol. 2. Chemistry of Organic Natural Products. 196p. 27.00 (ISBN 0-08-020771-5); Vol. 3. Solid-State Chemistry. 180p. 27.00 (ISBN 0-08-020772-3); Vol. 4. Compounds of Non-Metals. 156p. 22.00 (ISBN 0-08-020773-1); Vol. 5. Applied Electrochemistry. 190p. 27.00 (ISBN 0-08-020774-X); Vol. 6. Radiochemistry. 174p. 27.00 (ISBN 0-08-020775-8); Vol. 7. Symposium on Information & Communication in Chemistry. 128p. 22.00 (ISBN 0-08-020776-6). 1974. write for info. Pergamon.

Ishida, Hatsuo & Kumar, Ganesh, eds. Molecular Characterization of Composite Interfaces. (Polymer Science & Technology Ser.: Vol. 27). 444p. 1985. 75.00x (ISBN 0-306-41837-1, Plenum Pr). Plenum Pub.

Jones, Reanta, ed. Modern Chemical Technology. 2nd ed. Vol. 1, 1979. 16.00 (ISBN 0-8412-0490-X); Vol. 2, 1979. 16.00 (ISBN 0-8412-0491-8); Vol. 3,1979. 16.00 (ISBN 0-8412-0492-6); Guidebook, 1972. 16.00 (ISBN 0-8412-0497-7); Tchr's. Manual, 1981. 16.00 (ISBN 0-8412-0714-3). Am Chemical.

Kent, James A., ed. Riegel's Handbook of Industrial Chemistry. 8th ed. 1008p. 1983. 62.50 (ISBN 0-442-20164-8). Van Nos Reinhold.

Kirk & Othmer. Concise Encyclopedia of Chemical Technology. 1318p. 1985. 99.95 (ISBN 0-471-86977-5, Pub. by Wiley-Interscience). Wiley.

Leeson, Lewis J. & Carstenpen, J. Thuro. Dissolution Technology. 1974. 21.00 (ISBN 0-917330-15-3). Am Pharm Assn.

Leidheiser, Henry, Jr. The Corrosion of Copper, Tin, & Their Alloys. LC 78-12566. (Illus.). 426p. 1979. Repr. of 1971 ed. lib. bdg. 35.00 (ISBN 0-88275-752-0). Krieger.

Lowenheim, Frederick A. & Moran, Marguerite K. Faith, Keyes, & Clark's Industrial Chemicals. 4th ed. LC 75-17951. 904p. 1975. 120.00 (ISBN 0-471-54964-9, Pub. by Wiley-Interscience). Wiley.

McKetta, J., ed. Encyclopedia of Chemical Processing & Design, Vol. 7. 1978. 115.00 (ISBN 0-8247-2407-0). Dekker.

McKetta, John, ed. Encyclopedia of Chemical Processing & Design, Vol.5. 1977. 115.00 (ISBN 0-8247-2405-4). Dekker.

McKetta, John J. Encyclopedia of Chemical Processing & Design, Vol. 3. 1977. 115.00 (ISBN 0-8247-2403-8). Dekker.

McKetta, John J., ed. Encyclopedia of Chemical Processing & Designs, Vol. 1. 1976. 115.00 (ISBN 0-8247-2401-1). Dekker.

--Encyclopedia of Chemical Processing & Design, Vol. 2. 1977. 115.00 (ISBN 0-8247-2402-X). Dekker.

--Encyclopedia of Chemical Processing & Design, Vol. 4. 1977. 115.00 (ISBN 0-8247-2404-6). Dekker.

Modern Chemical Technology. 2nd ed. 1980. Vol. 4. pap. 16.00 (ISBN 0-8412-0493-4); Vol. 5. pap. 16.00 (ISBN 0-8412-0494-2); Vol. 6. pap. 16.00 (ISBN 0-8412-0495-0). Am Chemical.

Mukhlyonov, I., ed. Chemical Technology, 2 vols. 647p. 1979. 13.00 (ISBN 0-8285-1547-6, Pub. by Mir Pubs USSR). Imported Pubns.

Mukhlyonov, I. P., ed. Calculations of Chemical Technological Processes. 276p. 1979. 9.00 (ISBN 0-8285-2116-6, Pub. by Mir Pubs USSR). Imported Pubns.

Newman, Paul. Optical Resolution Procedures for Chemical Compounds: Alcohols, Phenols, Thiols, Aldehydes & Ketones, Vol. 3. 738p. 1984. lib. bdg. 57.50x (ISBN 0-9601918-4-4). Optical Resolution.

Peacocke, T. A. Radiochemistry: Theory & Experiment. LC 78-57666. (Wykeham Science Ser.: No. 50). 274p. 1979. pap. 14.00x (ISBN 0-8448-1360-5). Crane-Russak Co.

Pecsok, Robert L., et al, eds. Chemical Technology Handbook. new ed. LC 75-22497. 1975. 24.95 (ISBN 0-8412-0242-7); pap. 14.95 (ISBN 0-8412-0578-7). Am Chemical.

Nowlis, Vincent. Companionship Preference & Dominance in the Social Interaction of Young Chimpanzees. (Comp Psych Monographs). 1941. pap. 5.00 (ISBN 0-527-24920-3). Kraus Repr.

Plooij, Frans X. The Behavioral Development of Free-Living Chimpanzee Babies & Infants. Lipsitt, Lewis P., ed. LC 83-25804. (Monographs on Infancy: Vol. 4). (Illus.). 208p. (Orig.). 1984. text ed. 27.50 (ISBN 0-89391-114-3). Ablex Pub.

Riesen, Austin H. & Kinder, E. F. Postural Development of Infant Chimpanzees. 1952. 59.50x (ISBN 0-685-69858-0). Elliots Bks.

Susman, Randall L. The Pygmy Chimpanzee: Evolutionary Biology & Behavior. LC 84-13236. 419p. 1984. 59.50x (ISBN 0-306-41595-X, Plenum Pr). Plenum Pub.

Teleki, Geza. Predatory Behavior Among Wild Chimpanzees. LC 70-124442. (Illus.). 232p. 1973. 28.50 (ISBN 0-8387-7747-3). Bucknell U Pr.

Terrace, Herbert. Nim: A Chimpanzee Who Learned Sign Language. 448p. 1981. pap. 3.95 (ISBN 0-671-42041-0). WSP.

Terrace, Herbert S. Nim: A Chimpanzee Who Learned Sign Language. LC 79-2157. (Illus.). 1979. 15.00 (ISBN 0-394-40250-2). Knopf.

Williams, Leonard. The Dancing Chimpanzee. LC 80-40598. 95p. 1980. 11.95 (ISBN 0-8052-8057-X, Pub. by Allison & Busby England); pap. 5.95 (ISBN 0-8052-8056-1). Schocken.

Yerkes, Robert M. Chimpanzees: A Laboratory Colony. Repr. of 1943 ed. 32.00 (ISBN 0-384-70148-5). Johnson Repr.

CHINCHILLAS

Denham, Ken. Guinea Pigs & Chinchillas. (Illus.). 93p. 1977. pap. 3.95 (ISBN 0-7028-1075-4). Avian Pubns.

Parker. Modern Chinchilla Fur Farming. 30.00 (ISBN 0-87505-126-X). Borden.

CHINESE ASTRONOMY

see Astronomy, Chinese

CHINESE CALENDAR

see Calendar, Chinese

CHINESE MATHEMATICS

see Mathematics, Chinese

CHINONE

see Quinone

CHIPMUNKS

White, John A. The Balcum of the Chipmunks of Western North America. (Museum Ser.: Vol. 5, No.35). 21p. 1953. pap. 1.25 (ISBN 0-317-04972-0). U of KS Mus Nat Hist.

--Genera & Subgenera of Chipmunks. (Museum Ser.: Vol. 5, No. 32). 19p. 1953. pap. 1.25 (ISBN 0-317-04969-0). U of KS Mus Nat Hist.

--Geographic Distribution & Taxonomy of the Chipmunks of Wyoming. (Museum Ser.: Vol. 5, No. 34). 28p. 1953. pap. 1.50 (ISBN 0-317-04971-2). U of KS Mus Nat Hist.

--A New Chipmunk (Genus Eutamias) from the Black Hills. (Museum Ser.: Vol. 5, No. 19). 4p. 1952. pap. 1.25 (ISBN 0-317-04968-2). U of KS Mus Nat Hist.

--Taxonomy of the Chipmunks: Eutamias Quadrivittatus & Eutamias Umbrinus. (Museum Ser.: Vol. 5, No. 33). 20p. 1953. pap. 1.25 (ISBN 0-317-04970-4). U of KS Mus Nat Hist.

CHIROPTERA

see Bats

CHITTAHS

see Cheetahs

CHLAMYDOPHORIDAE

see Armadillos

CHLORIDES

see also specific chlorides

Chlorine Institute. Properties of Chlorine in SI Units. LC 81-67483. (Illus.). 64p. 1981. pap. text ed. 23.00x (ISBN 0-940230-02-X). Chlorine Inst.

Gerencser, George A. Chloride Transport Coupling in Biological Membranes & Epithelia. 1984. 113.50 (ISBN 0-444-80522-2, I-182-84). Elsevier.

Jackson, C., ed. Modern Chlor-Alkali Technology, Vol. 2. LC 81-131882. 389p. 1983. 95.00 (ISBN 0-470-27471-9). Halsted Pr.

Smith, Ralph G. Chlorine: An Annotated Bibliography. LC 72-75586. 168p. 1971. pap. text ed. 12.00 (ISBN 0-686-32455-2). Chlorine Inst.

Stender, V. V., ed. Electrometallurgy of Chloride Solutions. LC 65-17786. 138p. 1965. 30.00x (ISBN 0-306-10731-7, Consultants). Plenum Pub.

CHLORINE

see also Organochlorine Compounds

Angus, S., et al, eds. International Thermodynamic Tables of the Fluid State 8. Chlorine (Tentative Tables) (Chemical Data Ser.: No. 31). (Illus.). 168p. 1984. 47.50 (ISBN 0-08-030713-2). Pergamon.

Breisch, Linda L. & Wright, David A. Chlorine & the Chesapeake Bay: A Review of Research Literature. 6.00 (ISBN 0-943676-17-7). MD Sea Grant Col.

Division of Medical Sciences, Assembly of Life Sciences, National Research Council. Chlorine & Hydrogen Chloride. LC 76-39940. (Medical & Biological Effects of Environmental Pollutants Ser.). 282p. 1976. pap. 11.50 (ISBN 0-309-02519-2). Natl Acad Pr.

Easton, A. J., et al. Analysis of Chondritic Material Using Selective Attack by Chlorine. (Illus.). 1981. spiral bdg. 21.50x (ISBN 0-565-00837-4, Pub. by Brit Mus Nat Hist England). Sabbot-Natural Hist Bks.

Price, J. M. Coronaries, Cholesterol & Chlorine. 100p. 1984. pap. 2.25 (ISBN 0-515-08160-4, 06107-7). Jove Pubns.

Rice, Rip G. & Cotruvo, Joseph A., eds. Ozone Chlorine-Dioxide Oxidation Products of Organic Materials. LC 78-53924. (Illus.). 1978. text ed. 50.00 (ISBN 0-918650-02-X). Intl Ozone.

Robinson, J. S., ed. Chlorine Production Processes: Recent & Energy Saving Developments. LC 81-2361. (Chemical Technology Review: No. 185, Energy Technology Review: No. 64). (Illus.). 388p. 1981. 48.00 (ISBN 0-8155-0842-5). Noyes.

Sconce, J. S., ed. Chlorine: Its Manufacture, Properties & Uses. LC 62-20781. 912p. 1972. Repr. of 1962 ed. 59.50 (ISBN 0-88275-075-5). Krieger.

Smith, Ralph G. Chlorine: An Annotated Bibliography Supplement. 1983. pap. 12.00 (ISBN 0-940230-03-8). Chlorine Inst.

Young, A. S. Sulfur Dioxide, Chlorine, Fluorine & Chlorine Oxides. 1983. 100.00x (ISBN 0-08-026218-X). Pergamon.

CHLORINE COMPOUNDS

see also Organochlorine Compounds

Hutzinger, O., et al, eds. Chlorinated Dioxins & Related Compounds-Impact on the Environment: Proceedings of a Workshop Held October 22-24 1980, Istituto Superiore Di Sanita, Rome, Italy. (Pergamon Series on Environmental Science: Vol. 5). (Illus.). 624p. 1982. 83.00 (ISBN 0-08-026256-2). Pergamon.

Suschitzky, H., ed. Polychloroaromatic Compounds. LC 74-1617. 540p. 1975. 75.00x (ISBN 0-306-30795-2, Plenum Pr). Plenum Pub.

Young, A. S. Sulfur Dioxide, Chlorine, Fluorine & Chlorine Oxides. 1983. 100.00x (ISBN 0-08-026218-X). Pergamon.

CHLORINE ORGANIC COMPOUNDS

see Organochlorine Compounds

CHLORODESMIS

Ducker, S. C. The Genus Chlorodesmis (Chlorophyta) in the Indo-Pacific Region. 1966. pap. 8.00 (ISBN 3-7682-0679-3). Lubrecht & Cramer.

CHLOROFORM

Environmental Studies Board. Chloroform, Carbon Tetrachloride & Other Halomethanes: An Enviromental Assessment. 304p. 1978. pap. 10.25 (ISBN 0-309-02763-2). Natl Acad Pr.

CHLOROPHYCEAE

Barrientos, Parra O. Revision der Gattung Pediastrum Meyen (Chlorophyta) (Bibliotheca Phycologica: No. 48). (Illus.). 1979. 21.00x (ISBN 3-7682-1254-8). Lubrecht & Cramer.

CHLOROPHYLL

see also Porphyrin and Porphyrin Compounds

Jensen, Bernard. Health Magic Through Chlorophyll: From Living Plant Life, Book 1. (Magic Survival Kit Ser.). 4.95 (ISBN 0-89557-024-6). Bi World Indus.

Vernon, Leo P. & Seely, G. R. Chlorophylls: Physical, Chemical & Biological Properties. 1966. 92.50 (ISBN 0-12-718650-6). Acad Pr.

CHLOROPLASTIDS

see Chromatophores

CHLOROPLASTS

see also Chromatophores

Akoyunoglou, George, ed. Chloroplast Development, Vol. 5. 1104p. 1981. 102.00 (ISBN 0-86689-010-6, 992200075). Balaban Intl Sci Serv.

Baker, N. R. & Barber, J., eds. Chloroplast Biogenesis. (Topics in Photosynthesis Ser.: Vol. 5). 380p. 1984. 96.00 (ISBN 0-444-80548-6). Elsevier.

Barber, J., ed. The Intact Chloroplast. (Topics in Photosynthesis: Vol. 1). 476p. 1976. 95.75 (ISBN 0-444-41451-7, North Holland). Elsevier.

Birky, C. William, Jr., et al, eds. Genetics & Biogenesis of Mitochondria & Chloroplasts. LC 75-20271. (Ohio State University Biosciences Colloquia: No.1). (Illus.). 371p. 1976. 15.00x (ISBN 0-8142-0236-5). Ohio St U Pr.

Butterfass, T. Patterns of Chloroplast Reproduction. (Cell Biology Monographs: Vol. 6). (Illus.). 1979. 69.00 (ISBN 0-387-81541-4). Springer-Verlag.

Edelman, M., et al, eds. Methods in Chloroplast Molecular Biology. 1152p. 1983. 183.00 (ISBN 0-444-80368-8, I-518-82, Biomedical Pr). Elsevier.

Ellis, R. J., ed. Chloroplast Biogenesis. (Society for Experimental Biology Seminar Ser.: No. 21). 288p. 1985. 70.00 (ISBN 0-521-24816-7). Cambridge U Pr.

Halliwell, Barry. Chloroplast Metabolism: The Structure & Function of Chloroplasts in Green Leaf Cells. (Illus.). 1981. 50.00x (ISBN 0-19-854549-5); pap. 15.95 (ISBN 0-19-854585-1). Oxford U Pr.

Hoober, J. Kenneth. Chloroplasts. LC 84-9934. (Cellular Organelles Ser.). 292p. 1984. 42.50x (ISBN 0-306-41643-3, Plenum Pr). Plenum Pub.

Prebble, J. N. Mitochondria, Chloroplasts & Bacterial Membranes. (Illus.). 1981. text ed. 26.00x (ISBN 0-582-44133-1). Longman.

Reinert, J., ed. Chloroplasts. (Results & Problems in Cell Differentiation Ser.: Vol. 10). (Illus.). 280p. 1977. 51.00 (ISBN 0-387-10082-2). Springer-Verlag.

Sager, Ruth. Cytoplasmic Genes & Organelles. 1972. 37.50 (ISBN 0-12-614650-0). Acad Pr.

Schapedonk, A. H. Electrical Events Associated with Primary Photosynthetic Reactions in Chloroplast Membranes. (Agricultural Research Reports: No. 905). 103p. 1980. pap. 16.75 (ISBN 90-220-0756-1, PDC218, PUDOC). Unipub.

Schiff, J. A., ed. On the Origins of Chloroplasts. 336p. 1982. 100.00 (ISBN 0-444-00573-0, Biomedical Pr). Elsevier.

CHOCOLATE

see also Cocoa

Lawrence, Paul A. In Praise of Chocolate. LC 81-80700. (Positive Health Ser.). (Illus.). 80p. (Orig.). 1981. pap. 5.95 (ISBN 0-938034-03-0). PAL Pr.

Minifie, Bernard W. Chocolate, Cocoa & Confectionery: Science & Technology. 2nd ed. (Illus.). 1980. lib. bdg. 62.50 (ISBN 0-87055-330-5). AVI.

Olney, Judith. Joy of Chocolate. LC 82-11356. 1982. 14.95 (ISBN 0-8120-5435-0). Barron.

CHOLESTEROL

Abraham, Sidney, et al. Serum Cholesterol Level of Adults 18-74 Years in the United States, 1971-1974. Stevenson, Taloria, ed. (Series Eleven: No. 205). 1977. pap. text ed. 1.50 (ISBN 0-8406-0111-5). Natl Ctr Health Stats.

Dupont, Jacqueline. Cholesterol Systems in Insects & Animals. 160p. 1982. 55.00 (ISBN 0-8493-5315-7). CRC Pr.

Gibbons, G. F., et al. Biochemistry of Cholesterol. 370p. 1982. 102.25 (ISBN 0-444-80348-3, Biomedical Pr). Elsevier.

Hausman, Patricia. Jack Sprat's Legacy: The Science & Politics of Fat & Cholesterol. 288p. 1982. 6.95 (ISBN 0-399-90111-6, Pub. by Richard Marek). Ctr Sci Public.

Isbit, Arthur & Buckner, Nancy. Cholesterols: Causing Cancers & a Whole Lot More. 50p. (Orig.). 1984. pap. 5.50 (ISBN 0-917591-01-1). Health Pub Co.

Kaufman, W. I. Cholesterol Control Gram Counter. (Orig.). 1985. pap. 2.50 (ISBN 0-515-07742-9). Jove Pubns.

Kraus, Barbara. Dictionary of Sodium, Fats & Cholesterol. LC 72-90848. (Illus.). 256p. 1974. 9.95 (ISBN 0-448-01371-1); pap. 6.95 (ISBN 0-399-50945-3, G&D). Putnam Pub Group.

Paumgartner, G. & Gerok, W., eds. Bile Acids & Cholesterol in Health & Disease. 350p. 1983. text ed. write for info. (ISBN 0-85200-729-9, Pub. by MTP Pr England). Kluwer Academic.

Price, J. M. Coronaries, Cholesterol & Chlorine. 100p. 1984. pap. 2.25 (ISBN 0-515-08160-4, 06107-7). Jove Pubns.

Sabine, John R. Cholesterol. LC 76-28905. 1977. 75.00 (ISBN 0-8247-6516-8). Dekker.

Shipp, Audrey, ed. Serum Cholesterol Levels of Persons Aged 4-74 Years by Socioeconomic Characteristics, United States, 1971-74. (Series 11: No. 217). 1979. pap. text ed. 1.75 (ISBN 0-8406-0180-8). Natl Ctr Health Stats.

Smith, L. L. Cholesterol Autoxidation. LC 81-10616. 692p. 1981. text ed. 85.00x (ISBN 0-306-40759-0, Plenum Pr). Plenum Pub.

Sodhi, H. S., et al. Clinical Methods in Study of Cholesterol Metabolism. (Monographs on Atherosclerosis: Vol. 9). (Illus.). 1979. pap. 35.00 (ISBN 3-8055-2986-4). S Karger.

Strauss, Jerome F., III & Menon, K. M., eds. Lipoprotein & Cholesterol Metabolism in Steroidogenic Tissues. 350p. 1985. pap. text ed. 35.00 (ISBN 0-89313-069-9). G F Stickley Co.

Wade, Carlson. Fact-Book on Fats, Oils & Cholesterol. LC 73-80029. (Pivot Original Health Book). 160p. 1973. pap. 1.50 (ISBN 0-87983-051-4). Keats.

CHONDRIOSOMES

see Mitochondria

CHORDATA

see also Tunicata; Vertebrates

Alexander, R. McNeill. The Chordates. 2nd. ed. (Illus.). 500p. 1981. text ed. 75.00 (ISBN 0-521-23658-4); pap. text ed. 24.95 (ISBN 0-521-28141-5). Cambridge U Pr.

Bracegirdle, Brian & Miles, Patricia H. An Atlas of Chordate Structure. (Heinemann Biology Atlases Ser.). 1978. text ed. 15.50x (ISBN 0-435-60316-7). Heinemann Ed.

Jollie, Malcolm. Chordate Morphology. LC 62-17800. 492p. 1973. Repr. of 1962 ed. 24.50 (ISBN 0-88275-090-9). Krieger.

Lehman, H. Eugene. Chordate Development. 2nd ed. LC 77-83249. (Illus.). 358p. 1983. pap. text ed. 21.95 (ISBN 0-89459-160-6). Hunter Textbks.

Weichert, Charles K. Anatomy of the Chordates. 4th ed. LC 70-121668. 1970. text ed. 44.95 (ISBN 0-07-069007-3). McGraw.

Weichert, Charles K. & Presch, William. Elements of Chordate Anatomy. 4th ed. (Illus.). 608p. 1975. text ed. 43.95 (ISBN 0-07-069008-1). McGraw.

CHOW CHOWS (DOGS)

see Dogs–Breeds–Chow Chows

CHROMATIC ABERRATION (OPTICS)

see Lenses

CHROMATICS

see Color

CHROMATIN

Busch, Harris, ed. The Cell Nucleus, 7 vols. Incl. Vol. 1, 1974. 85.00 (ISBN 0-12-147601-4); Vol. 2, 1974. 85.00 (ISBN 0-12-147602-2); Vol. 3, 1974. 85.00 (ISBN 0-12-147603-0); Chromatin, Pt. A. Vol. 4, 1978. 70.00 (ISBN 0-12-147604-9); Chromatin, Pt. B. Vol. 5, 1978. 70.00 (ISBN 0-12-147605-7); Chromatin, Pt. C. Vol. 6, 1978. 70.00 (ISBN 0-12-147606-5); Chromatin, Pt. D. Vol. 7, 1979. 80.00 (ISBN 0-12-147607-3). LC 73-18944. Acad Pr.

Ciba Foundation. The Structure & Function of Chromatin. LC 76-357416. (Ciba Foundation Symposium: New Ser.: No. 28). pap. 94.50 (ISBN 0-317-29182-3, 2022156). Bks Demand UMI.

Cold Spring Harbor Symposia on Quantitative Biology: Chromatin, Vol. 42. LC 34-8174. (Illus.). 1260p. 1978. 139.00x (ISBN 0-87969-041-0). Cold Spring Harbor.

Nagl, W. & Ehrendorfer, F., eds. Genome & Chromatin - Organization, Evolution, Function: Symposium, Kaiserslautern, October 13-15, 1978. (Plant Systematics & Evolution: Supplement 2). (Illus.). 1979. 87.40 (ISBN 0-387-81539-2). Springer-Verlag.

Nicolini, Claudio, ed. Chromatin Structure & Function, Pt. A: Molecular & Cellular Biophysical Methods. (NATO ASI Series A, Life Sciences: Vol. 21A). 398p. 1979. 49.50x (ISBN 0-306-40075-8, Plenum Pr). Plenum Pub.

--Chromatin Structure & Function, Pt. B: Levels of Organization & Cell Function. (NATO ASI Series A, Life Sciences: Vol. 21B). 529p. 1979. 59.50x (ISBN 0-306-40076-6, Plenum Pr). Plenum Pub.

Samal, Babrubahan. Transcription of the Eukaryotic Genome, Vol. 1. Horrobin, D. F., ed. (Annual Research Reviews). 1980. 38.00 (ISBN 0-88831-063-3, Dist. by Pergamon). Eden Pr.

Simon, Melvin & Hershkowitz, Ira. Genome Rearrangement. LC 84-29716. (UCLA Ser.: Vol. 20). 350p. 1985. 48.00 (ISBN 0-8451-2619-9). A R Liss.

Wolff, Sheldon. Sister Chromatid Exchange. LC 81-13102. 306p. 1982. 80.50x (ISBN 0-471-05987-0, Pub. by Wiley-Interscience). Wiley.

CHROMATOGRAPHIC ANALYSIS

see also Gas Chromatography; Gel Permeation Chromatography; Liquid Chromatography; Paper Chromatography; Thin Layer Chromatography

Ahuja, Satinder, ed. Ultrahigh Resolution Chromatography. LC 84-2792. (ACS Symposium Ser.: No. 250). 231p. 1984. lib. bdg. 44.95x (ISBN 0-8412-0835-2). Am Chemical.

Alexander, Guy B. Chromatography: An Adventure in Graduate School. LC 77-8637. (Chemistry in Action Ser.). 1977. pap. 5.95. Am Chemical.

Alonso, J. L. & Tarrach, R., eds. Quantum Chromodynamics: Proceedings. (Lecture Notes in Physics: Vol. 113). 306p. 1980. pap. 26.00 (ISBN 0-387-09731-7). Springer-Verlag.

Altgelt & Gouw. Chromatography in Petroleum Analysis. (Chromatographic Science Ser.: Vol. 11). 1979. 85.00 (ISBN 0-8247-6790-X). Dekker.

ASTM Standards on Chromatography. 764p. 1981. 40.00 (ISBN 0-8031-0613-0, 03-519081-39). ASTM.

Chromatographic Sterol Analysis as Applied to Investigation of Milkfat & Other Oils. 1963. pap. 11.50 (ISBN 90-220-0091-5, PDC161, PUDOC). Unipub.

Churms, Shirley C. CRC Handbook of Chromatography, Carbohydrates, Vol. I. 288p. 1982. 58.00 (ISBN 0-8493-3061-0). CRC Pr.

Denney, Ronald C. Dictionary of Chromatography. 2nd ed. 229p. 1982. 50.95 (ISBN 0-471-87477-9, Pub. by Wiley-Interscience). Wiley.

German, James. Chromosome Mutation & Neoplasia. LC 82-21697. 486p. 1983. 96.00 (ISBN 0-8451-0220-6). A R Liss.

Grouchy, J. & Turleau, C. Atlas de las Enfermedades Cromosomicas. (Span.). 356p. 1978. 97.50 (ISBN 84-7102-959-6, S-31931). French & Eur.

Klinger, H. P., et al, eds. Chromosome Mutations: Their Potential Relevance to the Genetic Risks in Man. (Journal: Cytogenetics & Cell Genetics: Vol. 33, No. 1-2). (Illus.). 202p. 1982. pap. 54.50 (ISBN 3-8055-3569-4). S Karger.

Mitelman, F. Catalogue of Chromosome Aberrations in Cancer. (Journal: Cytogenetics & Cell Genetics: Vol. 36, No. 1-2). (Illus.). 516p. 1983. pap. 56.25 (ISBN 3-8055-3813-8). S Karger.

Montagu, M. F. Genetic Mechanisims in Human Disease: Chromosomal Aberrations. (Illus.). 616p. 1961. photocopy ed. 59.50x (ISBN 0-398-01331-4). C C Thomas.

Sybenga, J. Meiotic-Configurations. LC 75-17562. (Monographs on Theoretical & Applied Genetics: Vol. 1). (Illus.). 270p. 1975. 42.00 (ISBN 0-387-07347-7). Springer-Verlag.

Yunis, G. J. New Chromosomal Syndromes. 1977. 70.00 (ISBN 0-12-775165-3). Acad Pr.

CHROMOSOME NUMBERS

see also Polyploidy

Makino, Sajiro. Atlas of the Chromosome Numbers in Animals. facsimile ed. 290p. 1951. pap. 11.95x (ISBN 0-8138-2220-3). Iowa St U Pr.

Robinson, Arthur, et al, eds. Sex Chromosome Aneuploidy: Prospective Studies on Children. LC 78-13921. (Alan R. Liss Ser.: Vol. 15, No. 1). 1979. 38.00 (ISBN 0-8451-1024-1). March of Dimes.

CHROMOSOMES

see also Chromosome Abnormalities; Chromosome Numbers; Genetics; Human Chromosomes; Karyotypes; Karyokinesis; Linkage (Genetics); Sex Chromosomes

Allfrey, V. G., et al, eds. Organization & Expression of Chromosomes, LSRR 4. (Dahlem Workshop Reports Ser.: L.S.R.R. No. 4). 349p. 1976. pap. 36.50x (ISBN 0-89573-088-X). VCH Pubs.

Beermann, W., ed. Developmental Studies on Giant Chromosomes. LC 74-189387. (Results & Problems in Cell Differentiation Ser.: Vol. 4). (Illus.). 220p. 1972. 28.00 (ISBN 0-387-05748-X). Springer-Verlag.

Bennett, D. M., et al, eds. Chromosomes Today: Vol. VII. (Illus.). 336p. 1981. text ed. 38.50x (ISBN 0-04-575021-1). Allen Unwin.

Bennett, M. D., et al, eds. Chromosomes Today. (Chromosomes Today Ser.: Vol. VIII). (Illus.). 400p. 1984. text ed. 50.00x (ISBN 0-04-575023-8). Allen Unwin.

Biology Colloquium, 35th, Oregon State University,1974. Chromosomes - from Simple to Complex: Proceedings. Roberts, Paul, ed. LC 76-5880. (Illus.). 96p. 1977. pap. text ed. 9.95x (ISBN 0-87071-174-1). Oreg St U Pr.

Bonne-Tamir, Batsheva & Cohen, Tirza, eds. Human Genetics, Part A: The Unfolding Genome. LC 82-17230. (Progress in Clinical & Biological Research Ser.: Vol. 103A). 584p. 1982. 88.00 (ISBN 0-8451-0168-4). A R Liss.

Bostock, C. J. & Summer, A. The Eukaryotic Chromosome. xviii, 526p. 1978. 89.75 (ISBN 0-444-80003-4, Biomedical Pr). Elsevier.

Boyce, A. J. Chromosome Variation in Human Evolution. LC 75-25643. (Symposia for the Study of Human Biology Ser: Vol. 14). 131p. 1976. 34.95x (ISBN 0-470-09330-7). Halsted Pr.

Brandham, P. E. & Bennett, M. D., eds. Kew Chromosome Conference, Vol. II. 408p. 1983. text ed. 35.00x (ISBN 0-04-575022-X). Allen Unwin.

Cold Spring Harbor Symposia on Quantitative Biology: Genes & Chromosomes, Vol. 9. LC 34-8174. (Illus.). 325p. 1941. 38.00x (ISBN 0-87969-008-9). Cold Spring Harbor.

Darlington, C. D. Chromosome Botany & the Origins of Cultivated Plants. rev. ed. 1973. 18.95x (ISBN 0-02-843670-9). Hafner.

Darlington, C. D. & Lewis, K. R., eds. Chromosomes Today, Vol. 2. LC 65-5655. 275p. 1969. 30.00x (ISBN 0-306-37662-8, Plenum Pr). Plenum Pub.

Denton, T. E. Fish Chromosome Methodology. (Illus.). 176p. 1973. 17.50x (ISBN 0-398-02831-1). C C Thomas.

Epstein, Henry F. & Wolf, Stewart, eds. Genetic Analysis of the Chromosome: Studies of Duchenne Muscular Dystrophy & Related Disorders. (Advances in Experimental Medicine & Biology: Vol. 154). 344p. 1982. 37.50x (ISBN 0-306-41129-6, Plenum Pr). Plenum Pub.

Haskell, G. & Willis, A. B. Primer of Chromosome Practice. 196p. 1970. 57.75 (ISBN 0-677-61770-4). Gordon.

Hnilica, Lubomir S., ed. Chromosomal Nonhistone Proteins: Structural Association, Vol. IV. 320p. 1984. 92.00 (ISBN 0-8493-5514-1). CRC Pr.

Hsu, T. C. & Benirschke, K. An Atlas of Mammalian Chromosomes, Vol. 8. (Illus.). xl, 252p. 1974. boxed loose-leaf 32.00 (ISBN 3-540-06755-8). Springer-Verlag.

--An Atlas of Mammalian Chromosomes, Vol. 9. (Illus.). 280p. 1975. boxed loose-leaf 29.00 (ISBN 0-387-07365-5). Springer-Verlag.

--An Atlas of Mammalian Chromosomes, Vol. 10. (Illus.). 1977. loose leafs 47.00 (ISBN 0-387-90273-2). Springer-Verlag.

Jones, R. N. & Rees, H. B Chromosomes. 1982. 49.00 (ISBN 0-12-390060-3). Acad Pr.

Kolber, Alan & Kohiyama, Masamichi, eds. Mechanism & Regulation of DNA Replication. LC 74-14571. 469p. 1974. 49.50 (ISBN 0-306-30818-5, Plenum Pr). Plenum Pub.

Lee, Sherry, et al. Chromosomes & Genes: An Interracial Anthology. 54p. (Orig.). 1982. pap. 4.25x (ISBN 0-940248-12-3). Guild Pr.

Lewin, Benjamin. Gene Expression: Eucaryotic Chromosomes, 1 of 3 vols, Vol. 2. 2nd ed. LC 80-10849. 1160p. 1980. 59.95x (ISBN 0-471-01977-1, Pub. by Wiley-Interscience); pap. 34.50x (ISBN 0-471-01976-3, Pub. by Wiley-Interscience). Wiley.

M. D. Anderson Symposia on Fundamental Cancer Research, 33rd. Genes, Chromosomes, & Neoplasia. Arrighi, Frances E., et al, eds. 550p. 1981. 88.00 (ISBN 0-89004-532-1). Raven.

MacGregor, Herbert C. & Varley, Jennifer M. Working with Animal Chromosomes. LC 82-23788. 250p. 1983. 44.95x (ISBN 0-471-10295-4, Pub. by Wiley-Interscience). Wiley.

Morgan, Thomas H. The Mechanism of Mendelian Heredity. 1972. Repr. of 1915 ed. 35.00 (ISBN 0-384-40136-8). Johnson Repr.

Rao, Potu, et al, eds. Premature Chromosome Condensation: Application in Basic, Clinical & Mutation Research. (Cell Biology Ser.). 1982. 55.00 (ISBN 0-12-580450-4). Acad Pr.

Sandberg, Avery A. The Chromosomes in Human Cancer & Leukemia. LC 79-22474. 776p. 1979. 155.00 (ISBN 0-444-00289-8, Biomedical Pr). Elsevier.

--Cytogenetics of the Mammalian X Chromosome, Pt. A: Basic Mechanisms of X Chromosome BEH. LC 83-19992. (Progress & Topics in Cytogenetics Ser.: Vol 3A). 522p. 1983. 98.00 (ISBN 0-8451-2402-1). A R Liss.

--Cytogenetics of the Mammalian X Chromosome, PT. B: X Chromosome Anomalies & Their Clinical Manifestations. LC 83-19992. (Progress & Topics in Cytogenetics: Vol. 3B). 532p. 1983. 98.00 (ISBN 0-8451-2403-X). A R Liss.

--The Y Chromosome: Basic Characteristics of the Y Chromosome, Pt. A. (PTC Ser.). 552p. 1985. write for info. A R Liss.

Schwarzacher, H. G., ed. Chromosomes in Mitosis & Interphase. (Handbuch der Mikroskopischen Anatomie Des Menschen: Vol. 1, Pt 3). (Illus.). 200p. 1976. 80.30 (ISBN 0-387-07456-2). Springer-Verlag.

Searle, A. G. & De Boer, P., eds. Workshops on Chromosomal Aspects of the Male Sterility in Mammals: Abstracts. (Journal; Cytogenetics & Cell Genetics: Vol. 27; No. 4). (Illus.). 84p. 1980. pap. 4.75 (ISBN 3-8055-1610-X). S Karger.

Seeberg, Erling & Kleppe, Kjell, eds. Chromosome Damage & Repair. LC 81-19871. (NATO ASI Series A, Life Sciences: Vol. 40). 638p. 1982. text ed. 79.50 (ISBN 0-306-40886-4, Plenum Pr). Plenum Pub.

Sevanez, H. The Phylogeny of Human Chromosomes. (Illus.). 1979. pap. 28.00 (ISBN 0-387-09303-6). Springer-Verlag.

Sharma & Sharma. Chromosome Techniques. 3rd ed. LC 79-41279. 1980. 165.00 (ISBN 0-408-70942-1). Butterworth.

Sharma, Archana. The Chromosomes. 286p. 1976. 50.00x (ISBN 0-686-84450-5, Pub. by Oxford & I B H India). State Mutual Bk.

Sharma, Arun K. Chromosomes in Evolution of Eukaryotic Groups, Vol. I. 304p. 1983. 89.00 (ISBN 0-8493-6496-5). CRC Pr.

Sharma, Arun K. & Sharma, Archana, eds. Chromosomes in Evolution of Eukaryotic Groups, Vol. II. 208p. 1984. 89.00 (ISBN 0-8493-6497-3). CRC Pr.

Slavkin, Harold C. & Grevlich, Richard C., eds. Extracellular Matrix Influences on Gene Expression. 1975. 79.50 (ISBN 0-12-648360-4). Acad Pr.

Society for the Study of Development & Growth - 23rd Symposium. The Role of Chromosomes in Development: Proceedings. Locke, M., ed. 1964. 52.00 (ISBN 0-12-454150-X). Acad Pr.

Stock, R. & Rice, C. B. Chromatographic Methods. 3rd ed. 1974. pap. 15.95x (ISBN 0-412-20810-5, NO.6276, Pub. by Chapman & Hall). Methuen Inc.

Sutherland, Grant R. & Hecht, Frederick. Fragile Sites on Human Chromosomes. (Illus.). 1985. 45.00 (ISBN 0-19-503542-9). Oxford U Pr.

Sybenga, J. Meiotic-Configurations. LC 75-17562. (Monographs on Theoretical & Applied Genetics: Vol. 1). (Illus.). 270p. 1975. 42.00 (ISBN 0-387-07347-7). Springer-Verlag.

Therman, E. Human Chromosomes. (Illus.). 235p. 1980. 25.00 (ISBN 0-387-90509-X). Springer-Verlag.

Tice, Raymond R. & Hollaender, Alexander, eds. Sister Chromatid Exchanges: Twenty-Five Years of Experimental Research, 2 vols, Pts. A & B. Incl. Pt. A. The Nature of the SCEs. 560p. 75.00x (ISBN 0-306-41881-9, Plenum Pr); Pt. B. Genetic Toxicology & Human Studies. 560p. 75.00x (ISBN 0-306-41882-7, Plenum Pr). (Basic Life Sciences Ser.: Vols. 29A & 29B). 1120p. 1984. Set. 135.00 (ISBN 0-317-17199-2, Plenum Pr). Plenum Pub.

Uebele-Kallhardt, B. M. Human Oocytes & Their Chromosomes: An Atlas. (Illus.). 1978. 35.00 (ISBN 0-387-08879-2). Springer-Verlag.

Voeller, Bruce R., ed. The Chromosome Theory of Inheritance: Classic Papers in Development & Heredity. LC 68-19963. pap. 61.50 (ISBN 0-317-26284-X). Bks Demand UMI.

Zellweger, Hans & Simpson, Jane. Chromosomes of Man. (Clinics in Developmental Medicine Ser.: Vols. 65 & 66). 228p. 1977. text ed. 26.50 (ISBN 0-433-39886-8, Pub. by Spastics Intl England). Lippincott.

CHROMOSPHERIC ERUPTIONS

see Solar Flares

CHRONOLOGY

see also Almanacs; Calendar; Clocks and Watches; Dendrochronology; Geological Time; Radioactive Dating; Time

Beda. Bedae Opera De Temporibus. Jones, C. W., ed. 1966. Repr. of 1943 ed. 12.50x (ISBN 0-910956-17-0). Medieval Acad.

Bond, John J. Handy-Book of Rules & Tables for Verifying Dates with the Christian Era. LC 66-29473. 1966. Repr. of 1889 ed. 10.00x (ISBN 0-8462-1795-3). Russell.

Chesnel De La Charbouclais, L. P. Dictionnaire de Geologie... et Dictionnaire de Chronologie Universelle par M. Champagnac, Vol. 50. Migne, J. P., ed. (Encyclopedie Theologique Ser.). (Fr.). 728p. Repr. of 1849 ed. lib. bdg. 192.50x (ISBN 0-89241-253-4). Caratzas.

Langdon, Stephen H. Babylonian Menologies & the Semitic Calendars. LC 78-72744. (Ancient Mesopotamian Texts & Studies). Repr. of 1935 ed. 21.50 (ISBN 0-404-18192-9). AMS Pr.

CHRONOMETER

Gould, Rupert. Marine Chronometer. (Illus.). 45.00x (ISBN 0-87556-106-3). Saifer.

Whitney, Marvin E. The Ships Chronometer. (Illus.). 490p. 1984. 49.95 (ISBN 0-918845-08-4). Am Watchmakers.

CHRONOPHOTOGRAPHY

see Cinematography

CHRYSANTHEMUMS

Beijing Bureau of Parks & Gardens, Staff. Chinese Chrysanthemums. (Illus.). 74p. (Orig.). 1981. pap. 13.95 (ISBN 0-8351-0965-8). China Bks.

Brook, Wallace. Growing & Showing Chrysanthemums. (Growing & Showing Ser.). (Illus.). 68p. 1984. 9.95 (ISBN 0-7153-8574-7). David & Charles.

Machin, B. & Scopes, N. Chrysanthemums: Year Round Growing. 1981. 40.00x (ISBN 0-686-78767-6, Pub. by RHS Ent England). State Mutual Bk.

Masters, Margaret. Australian House & Garden Book of Chrysanthemums. pap. 8.50x (ISBN 0-392-06885-0, ABC). Sportshelf.

Nutritional Disorders in Chrysanthemums. 42p. 1980. pap. 13.50 (ISBN 90-220-0718-9, PDC174, Pudoc). Unipub.

CHRYSLER CORPORATION

Dammann, George H. Seventy Years of Chrysler. LC 74-75795. (Automotive Ser.). (Illus.). 384p. 1974. 29.95 (ISBN 0-912612-06-1). Crestline.

Stuart, Reginald. Bailout: America's Billion Dollar Gamble on the "New" Chrysler Corporation. LC 80-70279. (Illus.). 210p. (Orig.). 1981. pap. 6.95 (ISBN 0-89708-050-5). And Bks.

CHRYSOPHYCEAE

Bourrelly, P. Recherches Sur les Chrysophycees: Morphologie, Phylogenie, Systematique. (Illus.). 1971. Repr. of 1957 ed. 28.00 (ISBN 3-7682-0703-X). Lubrecht & Cramer.

CHURCH WORK–DATA PROCESSING

Bedell, Kenneth. Using Personal Computers in the Church. 112p. 1982. pap. 7.95 (ISBN 0-8170-0948-5). Judson.

Bedell, Kenneth & Rossman, Parker. Computers: New Opportunities for Personalized Ministry. 128p. 1984. pap. 7.95 (ISBN 0-8170-1039-4). Judson.

Brown, Lowell & Haystead, Wes. The Church Computer Manual. 160p. (Orig.). 1985. pap. 12.95 (ISBN 0-8423-0271-9). Tyndale.

Computer Strategies. The Church Computer Handbook. 150p. 1983. looseleaf 45.00x (ISBN 0-913505-04-8). Computer Strat.

Dilday, Russell H., Jr. Personal Computer: A New Tool for Ministers. 1985. pap. 8.95 (ISBN 0-8054-3111-X). Broadman.

Houk, Neil B. Pasor Goode & His Marvelous Micro. 59p. (Orig.). 1984. pap. 5.95 (ISBN 0-9615086-0-4). Church Bytes.

Hughes, John. Bits, Bytes, & Biblical Studies. 175p. 1986. pap. 6.95 (ISBN 0-8407-5970-3). Nelson.

Iles, Robert H. & Callison, William L. Selecting Computers for Ministry. LC 84-62333. (Illus.). 160p. (Orig.). 1985. pap. 13.95 (ISBN 0-932489-00-1). New Begin Co.

Johnson, William R. The Pastor & the Personal Computer: Information Management for Ministers. 224p. (Orig.). 1985. pap. 10.50 (ISBN 0-687-30134-3). Abingdon.

--Selecting the Church Computer. 160p. (Orig.). 1984. pap. 8.95 (ISBN 0-687-37135-X). Abingdon.

CICADA

Hearn, Lafcadio. Shadowings. LC 77-138070. (Illus.). 1971. pap. 6.75 (ISBN 0-8048-0967-4). C E Tuttle.

Young, Allen M. Seasonal Adult Emergences of Cicadas (Homoptera: Cicadidae) in Northwestern Costa Rica. 29p. 1980. 3.00 (ISBN 0-89326-067-3). Milwaukee Pub Mus.

CICHLIDAE

Axelrod, Herbert R. African Cichlids of Lakes Malawi & Tanganyika. (Illus.). 224p. 1973. 19.95 (ISBN 0-87666-792-2, PS-703). TFH Pubns.

Goldstein, Robert J. Cichlids of the World. (Illus.). 382p. 1973. 29.95 (ISBN 0-87666-032-4, H-945). TFH Pubns.

Greenwood, P. H. The Haplochromine Fishes of the East African Lakes. 839p. 1981. lib. bdg. 70.00 (ISBN 3-601-00483-6). Kraus Intl.

CICS-VS (COMPUTER SYSTEM)

Ashley. CICS-VS Command Level Programming, Bk. 3. (Data Processing Training Ser.). 1985. pap. price not set (ISBN 0-471-82367-8). Wiley.

--CICS-VS Command Level Programming Introduction, Bk. 1. (Data Processing Training Ser.). 1985. pap. write for info. (ISBN 0-471-82366-X). Wiley.

Lim, Pacifico A. CICS-VS Command Level with ANS COBOL Examples. (VNR Data Processing Ser.). (Illus.). 416p. 1982. 32.95 (ISBN 0-442-22607-1); disks for apple II & IBM-PC 59.50 ea. Van Nos Reinhold.

OSI Publications Ltd. CICS-VS Reference Handbook. rev. ed. (Illus.). 325p. 1984. pap. 35.00 spiral bound (ISBN 0-918317-00-2). OSI Pubns.

CIDER

see also Wine and Wine Making

Harrison, Shirley. A Taste of Cider. (Illus.). 96p. 1982. 11.50 (ISBN 0-7153-8216-0). David & Charles.

Orton, Vrest. The American Cider Book. 136p. 1973. pap. 3.25 (ISBN 0-374-51076-8). FS&G.

Scott, Cyril. Cider Vinegar. 1982. pap. 2.95 (ISBN 0-87904-011-4). Lust.

CIGARETTES

Curtis, Lindsay R. Cigarrillo: Contaminante, No. 1. 48p. pap. 1.10 (ISBN 0-311-46073-9). Casa Bautista.

CILIA AND CILIARY MOTION

see also Epithelium; Flagella (Microbiology)

Brain, et al. Respiratory Defense Mechanisms, Pt. 1. (Lung Biology in Health & Disease Ser.: Vol. 5). 1977. 75.00 (ISBN 0-8247-6381-5). Dekker.

International Meeting of the Mechanism & Control of Ciliary Movement, Friday Hárbor, Washington, September 9-12, 1981. Mechanisms & Control of Ciliary Movement: Proceedings. Brokaw, Charles J. & Verdugo, Pedro, eds. LC 81-20860. (Progress in Clinical & Biological Research Ser.: Vol. 80). 264p. 1982. 44.00 (ISBN 0-8451-0080-7). A R Liss.

Satir, Peter. Cilia & Related Organelles. Head, J. J., ed. LC 81-67984. (Carolina Biology Readers Ser.). (Illus.). 16p. 1983. pap. 1.60 (ISBN 0-89278-323-0, 45-9723). Carolina Biological.

CILIATA

Bick, H. Ciliated Protozoa: An Illustrated Guide to the Species Used As Biological Indicators in Fresh Water Biology. 198p. 1972. pap. 9.60 (ISBN 92-4-154028-1, 1308). World Health.

Elliot, Alfred M. Biology of Tetrahymena. LC 73-12911. 508p. 1973. 65.00 (ISBN 0-87933-013-9). Van Nos Reinhold.

Jones, Alick R. The Ciliates. LC 73-87077. (Illus.). 160p. 1974. 22.50 (ISBN 0-312-13860-1). St Martin.

Nanney, D. L. Experimental Ciliatology: An Introduction to Genetic & Developmental Analysis in Ciliates. LC 79-21918. 304p. 1980. 35.50x (ISBN 0-471-06008-9, Pub. by Wiley-Interscience). Wiley.

CINEMATOGRAPHY

see also Amateur Moving-Pictures; Cinematography, Trick; Kinetoscope; Microcinematography; Moving-Picture Cameras; Television Film

Art of Cinema. (Yale French Studies: No. 17). 1956. pap. 9.00 (ISBN 0-527-01725-6). Kraus Repr.

Lieberman, Jethro K. & Rhodes, Neil S. The Complete Nineteen Eighty CB Handbook. 1980. pap. 2.95 (ISBN 0-380-48587-7, 48587). Avon.

Oldham, Joseph, ed. Motor CB Radio Handbook. new ed. (Illus.). 1978. pap. 2.95 (ISBN 0-910992-86-X). Hearst Bks.

Schultz, Lawrence. How to Repair CB Radios. Haas, Mark, ed. (Electro Skills Ser.). (Illus.). 176p. 1980. pap. 11.30 (ISBN 0-07-055638-5). McGraw.

Schwartz, Martin. Citizens Band Radio Rules & Regulations, Pt. 95. LC 77-82143. 1979. pap. 1.00 (ISBN 0-912146-14-1). AMECO.

Smelser, Newt. Beginner's CB & Two-Way Radio Repairing. LC 80-23818. (Illus.). 242p. 1981. text ed. 33.95x (ISBN 0-88229-573-X); pap. text ed. 17.95x (ISBN 0-88229-763-5). Nelson-Hall.

CITIZENS RADIO SERVICE

see Citizens Band Radio

CITRUS FRUIT INDUSTRY

Citrus Fruit. (International Standardisation of Fruit & Vegetables Ser.). 103p. (Orig.). 1980. pap. 17.50x (ISBN 9-2640-2112-4). OECD.

Compendium of Citrus Statistics. (Commodity Reference Ser.: No. 4). 169p. 1967. pap. 12.25 (ISBN 92-5-001738-3, F97, FAO). Unipub.

International Organization of Citrus Virologists - 5th Conference. Proceedings. Price, W. C., ed. LC 59-63553. 1972. 11.50 (ISBN 0-8130-0327-X). U Presses Fla.

Reuther, Walter, et al, eds. The Citrus Industry, Vol. IV: Crop Protection. LC 67-63041. 1978. 20.00x (ISBN 0-931876-24-9, 4088). Ag & Nat Res.

Ziegler, Louis W. & Wolfe, Herbert S. Citrus Growing in Florida. rev. ed. LC 75-5664. 1975. 12.00 (ISBN 0-8130-0488-8). U Presses Fla.

CITRUS FRUITS

see also Citrus Fruit Industry; Lemon; Orange; Pectin

Citrus Fruit. (Commodity Projections: 1985). 41p. 1979. pap. 7.50 (ISBN 0-686-59424-X, F1616, FAO). Unipub.

Compendium of Citrus Statistics. (Commodity Reference Ser.: No. 4). 169p. 1967. pap. 12.25 (ISBN 92-5-001738-3, F97, FAO). Unipub.

Cooper, William C. In Search of the Golden Apple: An Adventure in Citrus Science & Travel. 1981. 14.95 (ISBN 0-533-04803-6). Vantage.

Hopkins, James T. Fifty Years of Citrus: The Florida Citrus Exchange, 1909-1959. LC 60-10227. (Illus.). 1960. 6.00 (ISBN 0-8130-0114-5). U Presses Fla.

International Organization of Citrus Virologists - 3rd Conference. Proceedings. Price, W. C., ed. LC 61-64183. 1965. 11.50 (ISBN 0-8130-0190-0). U Presses Fla.

International Organization of Citrus Virologists - 2nd Conference. Proceedings. Price, W. C., ed. LC 61-64183. 1961. 11.50 (ISBN 0-8130-0189-7). U Presses Fla.

Krehl, Willard A. The Role of Citrus in Health & Disease. LC 76-4502. 1976. 6.50 (ISBN 0-8130-0532-9). U Presses Fla.

Nagy, Steven & Attaway, John, eds. Citrus Nutrition & Quality. LC 80-22562. (ACS Symposium Ser.: No. 143). 1980. 38.95 (ISBN 0-8412-0595-7). Am Chemical.

Ray, Richard & Walheim, Lance. Citrus. LC 80-82383. (Gardening Ser.). (Orig.). 1980. pap. 7.95 (ISBN 0-89586-076-7). H P Bks.

Sinclair, Walton B. The Grapefruit: Its Composition, Physiology & Products. LC 72-619646. 1972. 15.00x (ISBN 0-931876-11-7, 4029). Ag & Nat Res.

Van Brussel, E. W. Interrelations Between Citrus Rust Mite, Hirsutella, Thompsonii & Greasy Spot on Citrus in Surinam. (Illus.). 80p. 1975. pap. 16.00 (ISBN 90-220-0575-5, PDC45, PUDOC). Unipub.

Ziegler, Louis W. & Wolfe, Herbert S. Citrus Growing in Florida. rev. ed. LC 75-5664. 1975. 12.00 (ISBN 0-8130-0488-8). U Presses Fla.

CITY PLANNING

see also Garden Cities; Urban Transportation

Adams, Robert M., et al. The Fitness of Man's Environment. LC 68-20988. (Smithsonian Annual, No. 2). 205p. 1968. 17.50x (ISBN 0-87474-058-4). Smithsonian.

Adams, Thomas. The Design of Residential Areas: Basic Considerations, Principles & Methods. LC 73-2900. (Metropolitan America Ser.: Vol. 6). 334p. 1974. Repr. of 1934 ed. 33.00x (ISBN 0-405-05381-9). Ayer Co Pubs.

Alexander, Laurence, ed. Downtown Planning & Development Annual, 1977. LC 77-641768. (Planning & Development Ser.). 1977. pap. 11.00 (ISBN 0-915910-08-X). Downtown Res.

Alexander, Laurence A., ed. Downtown Mall Annual & Urban Design Report, Vol. 3. LC 75-646900. (Design Ser). (Illus.). 1977. pap. 11.00 (ISBN 0-915910-09-8). Downtown Res.

--Public Attitudes Toward Downtown Malls: A National Opinion Research Survey. LC 75-21099. (Illus.). 84p. 1975. pap. 17.50 (ISBN 0-915910-05-5). Downtown Res.

--Winning Downtown Projects: A Photographic Case Study Report of Outstanding Downtown Developments. LC 81-66891. (Illus., Orig.). 1981. pap. 25.00 (ISBN 0-915910-18-7). Downtown Res.

American Society of Civil Engineers, compiled By. Bicycle-Pedestrian Planning & Design. 708p. 1974. pap. 22.50x (ISBN 0-87262-065-4). Am Soc Civil Eng.

--Dynamic Planning for Environmental Quality in the 1980's. 281p. 1978. pap. 19.75x (ISBN 0-87262-098-0). Am Soc Civil Eng.

American Society of Planning Officials. Planned Unit Development Ordinances. 1973. 6.00 (ISBN 0-685-71649-X). Urban Land.

Andrews, Richard B., ed. Urban Land Use Policy. LC 70-169230. 1972. 22.95 (ISBN 0-02-900700-3). Free Pr.

Anglin, R. L., Jr., ed. Energy in the Man-Built Environment. LC 81-67745. 728p. 1982. pap. 47.00x (ISBN 0-87262-297-5). Am Soc Civil Eng.

Appleyard, Donald. Planning a Pluralist City: Conflicting Realities in Ciudad Guayana. LC 75-40026. 350p. 1976. text ed. 37.50x (ISBN 0-262-01044-5). MIT Pr.

Argan, Giulio. The Renaissance City. LC 70-90409. (Planning & Cities Ser). (Illus.). 1969. pap. 7.95 (ISBN 0-8076-0521-2). Braziller.

Ashihara, Yoshinobu. The Aesthetic Townscape. Riggs, Lynne E., tr. from Japanese. (Illus.). 196p. 1983. 24.75 (ISBN 0-262-01069-0); pap. 9.95 (ISBN 0-262-51031-6). MIT Pr.

Attoe, Wayne. Skylines: Understanding & Molding Urban Silhouettes. LC 80-41684. 128p. 1981. 48.95x (ISBN 0-471-27940-4, Pub. by Wiley-Interscience). Wiley.

Ayeni, Bola. Concepts & Techniques in Urban Analysis. LC 78-19219. 1979. 32.50 (ISBN 0-312-16044-5). St Martin.

Bacon, Edmund N. Design of Cities. rev ed. (Illus.). 336p. 1976. pap. 22.95 (ISBN 0-14-004236-9). Penguin.

Baglivo, Jenny A. & Graver, Jack E., eds. Incidence & Symmetry in Design & Architecture. LC 81-18160. (Cambridge Urban & Architectural Studies: No. 7). 400p. 1983. 57.50 (ISBN 0-521-23043-8); pap. 16.95 (ISBN 0-521-29784-2). Cambridge U Pr.

Barnett, Jonathan. An Introduction to Urban Design. LC 81-47792. (Icon Editions Ser.). (Illus.). 1982. 20.14i (ISBN 0-06-430376-4, HarpT). Har-Row.

Basile, Ralph J., et al. Downtown Development Handbook. LC 80-50928. (Community Builder Handbook Ser.). (Illus.). 264p. 1980. 48.00 (ISBN 0-87420-591-3, D12); members 36.00. Urban Land.

Batty, M. Urban Modelling. (Urban & Architectural Studies). (Illus.). 384p. 1976. 75.00 (ISBN 0-521-20811-4). Cambridge U Pr.

Batty, Michael & Hutchinson, Bruce, eds. Systems Analysis in Urban Policy-Making & Planning. (NATO Conference Series II, Systems Science: Vol. 12). 605p. 1983. 85.00x (ISBN 0-306-41118-0). Plenum Pub.

Baxter, Richard, et al, eds. Urban Development Models. LC 79-301020. (Cambridge University Centre for Land Use & Built Form Studies Conference Proceedings: No. 3). pap. 85.80 (ISBN 0-317-27680-8, 2025216). Bks Demand UMI.

Berk, Emanuel. Downtown Improvement Manual. (APA Planners Press Ser.). 780p. 1976. pap. 28.95. Planners Pr.

Berry, Brian J., et al. Land Use, Urban Form & Environmental Quality. LC 73-87830. (Research Papers Ser.: No. 155). (Illus.). 440p. 1974. pap. 10.00 (ISBN 0-89065-062-4). U Chicago Dept Geog.

Bhargava, Gopal, ed. Urban Problems & Policy Perspectives. 1981. 38.00x (ISBN 0-8364-0720-2, Pub. by Abhinav India). South Asia Bks.

Blair, Thomas L., ed. Urban Innovation Abroad: Problem Cities in Search of Solutions. 424p. 1984. 55.00x (ISBN 0-306-41492-9, Plenum Pr). Plenum Pub.

Blumenfeld, Hans. Modern Metropolis: Its Origins, Growth, Characteristics, & Planning, Selected Essays. Spreiregen, Paul, ed. 1971. pap. 5.95x (ISBN 0-262-52028-1). MIT Pr.

Bookchin, Murray. The Limits of the City. LC 73-17852. 192p. (Orig.). 1974. pap. 4.50xi (ISBN 0-06-131944-9, TB 1944, Torch). Har-Row.

Branch, Melville C. Comparative Urban Design-Rare Engravings: 1830-1843. 108p. 49.50 (ISBN 0-686-69145-8, Co Pub by U of Cal Pr). Ayer Co Pubs.

--Comprehensive City Planning. LC 85-70970. (Illus.). 238p. 1985. pap. 21.95 (ISBN 0-918286-41-7). Planners Pr.

--Continuous City Planning: Integrating Municipal Management & City Planning. 181p. 1980. 31.95x (ISBN 0-471-08943-5, Pub. by Wiley-Interscience). Wiley.

Brecher, Charles & Horton, Raymond D., eds. Setting Municipal Priorities, 1982. LC 81-66978. 464p. 1981. text ed. 29.95x (ISBN 0-87154-137-8). Russell Sage.

Breese, Gerald W. & Whiteman, Dorothy E. Approach to Urban Planning. LC 73-90474. Repr. of 1953 ed. lib. bdg. 15.00x (ISBN 0-8371-2284-8, BRUP). Greenwood.

Breheny, M. & Hooper, A., eds. Rationality in Planning: Critical Essays on the Role of Rationality in Urban & Regional Planning. 252p. 1985. 25.95x (ISBN 0-85086-112-8, 9130, Pub. by Pion England). Methuen Inc.

Bromley, R., ed. Planning for Small Enterprises in Third World Cities. (Urban & Regional Planning Ser.: Vol. 34). 360p. 1984. 50.00 (ISBN 0-08-025236-2); pap. 29.50 (ISBN 0-08-031333-7). Pergamon.

Brotchie, John, ed. The Future of Urban Form: The Impact of New Technology. 250p. 1985. 43.50 (ISBN 0-89397-213-4). Nichols Pub.

Burchell, Robert W. & Sternlieb, George, eds. Planning Theory in the Nineteen Eighties: A Search for Future Directions. LC 78-12929. 1978. pap. text ed. 12.95 (ISBN 0-88285-048-2). Ctr Urban Pol Res.

Burke, Edmund M. A Participatory Approach to Urban Planning. LC 78-31107. 304p. 1979. text ed. 29.95 (ISBN 0-87705-393-6). Human Sci Pr.

Calsat, Jean-Henri & Sydler, Jean P. Vocabulaire International des Termes d'Urbanisme et d'Architecture. (Fr., Ger. & Eng.). 350p. 1970. 95.00 (ISBN 0-686-56935-0, M-6057). French & Eur.

Caputo, David A. Urban America: The Policy Alternatives. LC 76-7351. (Illus.). 1976. text ed. 22.95 (ISBN 0-7167-0556-7). W H Freeman.

Catanese, Anthony J., et al. Urban Planning: A Guide to Information Sources. LC 78-13462. (Urban Studies Information Guide Ser.: Vol. 2). 165p. 1979. 60.00x (ISBN 0-8103-1399-5). Gale.

Chermayeff, Serge & Alexander, Christopher. Community & Privacy: Toward a New Architecture of Humanism. LC 63-10704. 1963. pap. 2.50 (ISBN 0-385-03476-8, Anch). Doubleday.

Cherry, Gordon E., ed. Shaping an Urban World: Planning in the Twentieth Century. LC 80-17276. 1980. 30.00 (ISBN 0-312-71618-4). St Martin.

Choay, Francoise. Modern City: Planning in the Nineteenth Century. LC 77-90408. (Planning & Cities Ser). (Illus.). 1969. 7.95 (ISBN 0-8076-0516-6); pap. 7.95 (ISBN 0-8076-0520-4). Braziller.

Clark, Colin. Regional & Urban Location. LC 81-21510. 1982. 32.50x (ISBN 0-312-66903-8). St Martin.

Clark, Terry N. Research in Urban Policy, Vol. 1. 47.50 (ISBN 0-89232-325-6). Jai Pr.

--Urban Policy Analysis: Directions for Future Research. (Urban Affairs Annual Reviews: Vol. 21). 400p. 1981. 28.00 (ISBN 0-8039-1627-2); pap. 14.00 (ISBN 0-8039-1628-0). Sage.

Coates, D. R. Geology & Society: A New York Publication. 275p. 1985. 49.95 (ISBN 0-412-25160-4, NO. 5061, Pub. by Chapman & Hall England); pap. 22.50 (ISBN 0-412-25170-1, NO. 5062, Pub. by Chapman & Hall England). Methuen Inc.

Colvin, Brenda. Land & Landscape: Evolution, Design & Control. 2nd ed. (Illus.). 1971. 28.00 (ISBN 0-7195-1800-8). Transatlantic.

Committee on Urban Waterfront Lands. Urban Waterfront Lands. xii, 243p. 1980. pap. text ed. 12.95 (ISBN 0-309-02940-6). Natl Acad Pr.

Cook, Charles C., intro. by. Land Valuation Methods: Urban Land. (Lincoln Institute Monograph: No. 80-1). (Illus.). 200p. 1980. pap. text ed. 10.00 (ISBN 0-686-29505-6). Lincoln Inst Land.

Cook, Theodore S. City Planning Theory. 5.00 (ISBN 0-685-28344-5). Philos Lib.

Cowan, Peter, ed. The Future of Planning. LC 73-80439. (Centre for Environmental Studies Ser.: Vol. 1). pap. 47.50 (ISBN 0-317-29598-5, 2021882). Bks Demand UMI.

Cram, Ralph A. Walled Towns. 59.95 (ISBN 0-8490-1271-6). Gordon Pr.

Creighton, Thomas H., ed. Building for Modern Man. facs. ed. LC 74-80385. (Essay Index Reprint Ser). 1949. 17.50 (ISBN 0-8369-1029-X). Ayer Co Pubs.

Cullen, Gordon. Concise Townscape. (Illus.). 1961. pap. 10.95 (ISBN 0-442-21770-6). Van Nos Reinhold.

Cutler, Laurence S. & Cutler, Sherrie S. Recycling Cities for People. 2nd ed. 314p. 1982. pap. 29.95 (ISBN 0-8436-0170-1); 16.95 (ISBN 0-442-21604-1). Van Nos Reinhold.

Darin-Drabkin, H. Land Policy & Urban Growth. LC 76-39912. 1977. text ed. 28.00 (ISBN 0-08-020401-5). Pergamon.

Davenport, Roxanne W., ed. Model Cities Reports: A Bibliographic Guide to the Microfiche Collection. 98p. 1981. pap. text ed. 50.00 (ISBN 0-667-00589-7). Microfilming Corp.

De Blij, Harm J. Dar es Salaam: A Study in Urban Geography. LC 63-18014. pap. 25.30 (ISBN 0-317-27599-2, 2014769). Bks Demand UMI.

DeChiara, Joseph & Koppelman, Lee. Urban Planning & Design Criteria. 3rd ed. 702p. 1982. 69.50 (ISBN 0-442-21946-6). Van Nos Reinhold.

De La Croix, Horst. Military Considerations in City Planning: Fortifications. LC 72-143398. (Planning & Cities Ser). (Illus.). 1971. 7.95 (ISBN 0-8076-0585-9); pap. 3.95 (ISBN 0-8076-0584-0). Braziller.

Dendrinos, Dimitrios S. Urban Revolution: Studies in the Mathematical Ecology of Cities. (Illus.). 1985. 27.95 (ISBN 0-19-823249-7). Oxford U Pr.

Derthick, Martha. New Towns in-Town: Why a Federal Program Failed. LC 73-187564. 102p. 1972. pap. 6.95x (ISBN 0-87766-022-0, 70006). Urban Inst.

DeSouza, Alfred, ed. Urban Growth & Urban Planning: Political Context & People's Priorities. 1984. pap. 6.00 (ISBN 0-8364-1242-7, Pub. by Indian Soc Inst). South Asia Bks.

Diamond, D. R. & McLoughlin, J. B., eds. Progress in Planning, Vol. 7. (Illus.). 1979. 55.00 (ISBN 0-08-020333-7). Pergamon.

--Progress in Planning, Vol. 9. 300p. 1979. 55.00 (ISBN 0-08-025221-4). Pergamon.

--Progress in Planning, Vol. 11. (Illus.). 280p. 1980. 55.00 (ISBN 0-08-025802-6). Pergamon.

--Progress in Planning, Vol. 18. (Illus.). 384p. 1983. 60.00 (ISBN 0-08-030415-X). Pergamon.

Doherty, Joseph C. Growth Management in Countryfied Cities, Vol. 1: Change & Response. Doherty, Kristan & Grieg, Margot, eds. LC 84-51900. (Illus.). 100p. (Orig.). 1984. pap. 6.95 (ISBN 0-9613980-1-9). Vert Milon Pr.

Downs, Anthony. Neighborhoods & Urban Development. LC 81-66190. 250p. 1981. 26.95 (ISBN 0-8157-1920-5); pap. 9.95 (ISBN 0-8157-1919-1). Brookings.

Doxiadis, C. A. Anthropopolis: City for Human Development. (Illus.). 398p. 1975. pap. 5.95x (ISBN 0-393-08737-9). Norton.

Dubeck, Paula J & Miller, Zane L., eds. Urban Professionals & the Future of the Metropolis. (National University Publications, Interdisciplinary Urban Ser.). 134p. 1980. 13.50x (ISBN 0-8046-9261-0, Pub by Kennikat). Assoc Faculty Pr.

Duncan, Otis D. An Examination of the Problem of Optimum City Size. Zuckerman, Harriet & Merton, Robert K., eds. LC 79-8994. (Dissertations on Sociology). (Illus.). 1980. lib. bdg. 25.50x (ISBN 0-405-12965-3). Ayer Co Pubs.

Dunkerley, Harold B. & Whitehead, Christine M. E. Urban Land Policy: Issues & Opportunities. LC 82-20247. 224p. 1983. 22.50 (ISBN 0-19-520403-4, OX 520403). World Bank.

Eckbo, Garrett. Urban Landscape Design. (Illus.). 1964. 41.50 (ISBN 0-07-018880-7). McGraw.

Edwards, Arthur. The Design of Suburbia: A Critical Study in Environmental History. (Illus.). 281p. 1981. 32.50 (ISBN 0-686-72349-X, Pub. by Pembridge England). Shoe String.

Elias, Thomas S., et al. Trees & the Community. 1973. pap. 4.00x (ISBN 0-89327-051-2). NY Botanical.

Enviromental Design Press. How to Make Cities Liveable: Design Guidelines for Urban Homesteading. Robinette, Gary O., ed. 149p. 1984. 27.50 (ISBN 0-442-22203-3). Van Nos Reinhold.

Eulenberger, Peter. Anwendung des Simulationsmodells BAYMO 70 auf die Stadtentwicklungsplanung, Vol. 2. (Interdisciplinary Systems Research Ser.: No. 44). (Ger.). 94p. 1980. pap. 18.95x (ISBN 0-8176-0969-5). Birkhauser.

Evans, Alan & Eversley, David, eds. The Inner City: Employment & Industry. (Centre for Environmental Studies Ser.). 1980. text ed. 80.00x (ISBN 0-435-84355-9). Gower Pub Co.

Everett, Robinson O. & Leach, Richard H. Urban Problems & Prospects. LC 65-28034. (Library of Law & Contemporary Problems). 240p. 1965. 10.00 (ISBN 0-379-11506-9). Oceana.

Exline, Christopher H., et al. The City: Patterns & Processes in the Urban Ecosystem. (Illus.). 300p. (Orig.). 1981. lib. bdg. 34.00x (ISBN 0-89158-904-X); pap. 15.00 (ISBN 0-89158-905-8). Westview.

Expert Group Meeting on the Role of Small & Intermediate-Sized Cities in National Development: Nagoya, Japan, 26 Jan. - Feb. 1982. (Meeting Report Ser.: No. 9). 99p. 1982. pap. 6.75 (ISBN 0-686-97542-1, CRD123, UNCRD). Unipub.

Fabos, Julius Gy. Land Use Planning: From Global to Local Challenge. 300p. 1985. 39.95 (ISBN 0-412-25200-7, 5068, Pub. by Chapman & Hall England); pap. 18.95 (ISBN 0-412-25210-4, 5069). Methuen Inc.

Feldt, Allan. CLUG: Community Land Use Game. LC 78-190151. Orig. Title: Clug Players Manual. 1972. pap. text ed. 15.95 (ISBN 0-02-910090-9). Free Pr.

Ferris, John. Participation in Urban Planning. 95p. 1972. pap. text ed. 6.25 (ISBN 0-7135-1714-X, Pub. by Bedford England). Brookfield Pub Co.

Ford, Kristina, ed. Remote Sensing for Planners. LC 78-31594. (Illus.). 272p. 1979. text ed. 25.00 (ISBN 0-88285-058-X). Ctr Urban Pol Res.

Fraser, Derek, ed. Municipal Reform & the Industrial City. LC 81-21302. 1982. 32.50 (ISBN 0-312-55268-8). St Martin.

Gallion, Arthur B. & Eisner, Simon. The Urban Pattern, City Planning & Design. 4th ed. 528p. 1980. 14.95x (ISBN 0-442-26261-2). Van Nos Reinhold.

Gemmill, Daphne. City Air. 35p. 1975. 6.00 (ISBN 0-916450-05-8). Coun on Municipal.

Giedion, Sigfried. Space, Time & Architecture: The Growth of a New Tradition. 5th rev. & enl. ed. LC 67-17310. (Charles Eliot Norton Lectures Ser: 1938-1939). (Illus.). lvi, 897p. 35.00 (ISBN 0-674-83040-7). Harvard U Pr.

Gill, Don & Bonnett, Penelope. Nature in the Urban Landscape: A Study of City Ecosystems. LC 73-76409. (Illus.). 209p. 1973. 12.00x (ISBN 0-912752-03-3). York Pr.

Gillie, F. B. An Approach to Town Planning. (Publications of the Institute of Social Studies Paperback Ser.: No. 3). 164p. 1971. pap. text ed. 8.80x (ISBN 90-2791-760-4). Mouton.

Gluck, Peter R. & Meister, Richard J. Cities in Transition: Social Change & Institutional Responses in Urban Development. LC 79-12217. 1979. pap. text ed. 8.95x (ISBN 0-317-30662-6). Wiener Pub Inc.

Golany, Gideon, ed. Urban Planning for Arid Zones: American Experiences & Directions. LC 77-10472. pap. 66.80 (ISBN 0-317-28052-X, 2055775). Bks Demand UMI.

Grandjean, E. & Gilgen, A. Environmental Factors in Urban Planning. 206p. 1976. text ed. 42.50x (ISBN 0-8290-0943-4). Irvington.

Grava, Sigurd. Urban Planning Aspects of Water Pollution Control. LC 72-87147. (Illus.). 223p. 1969. 30.00x (ISBN 0-231-03280-3). Columbia U Pr.

Guggenheimer, Elinor C. Planning for Parks & Recreation Needs in Urban Areas. LC 68-31141. (Illus.). 261p. 1969. text ed. 29.00x (ISBN 0-8290-0192-1). Irvington.

Hagman, Donald G. Public Planning & Control of Urban & Land Development Cases & Materials. 2nd ed. LC 80-36684. (American Casebook Ser.). 1301p. 1980. text ed. 28.95 (ISBN 0-8299-2100-1). West Pub.

Hartshorn, Truman A. Interpreting the City: Urban Geography. LC 79-19544. 498p. 1980. text ed. 34.00 (ISBN 0-471-05637-5). Wiley.

Heinonen, Sirkka & Kolm, Arno. Urban & Regional Planning Glossary: English-French & Finnish-Russian. 163p. (Orig.). 1984. pap. 25.00 (ISBN 951-682-092-1, Pub. by Rahennuskirya Oy Finland). Heinman.

Hengeveld, H. & De Vocht, C., eds. Role of Water in Urban Ecology. (Developments in Landscape Management & Urban Planning Ser.: Vol. 5). 362p. 1982. 78.75 (ISBN 0-444-42078-9). Elsevier.

Herfindahl, Orris C. & Kneese, Allen V. Quality of the Environment: An Economic Approach to Some Problems in Using Land, Water & Air. (Resources for the Future Ser). 104p. (Orig.). 1965. pap. 4.50x (ISBN 0-8018-0268-7). Johns Hopkins.

Houghton-Evans, W. Planning Cities: Legacy & Portent. (Illus.). 1976. 23.00x (ISBN 0-8464-0722-1). Beekman Pubs.

Hoyle, B. & Pinder, D., eds. Cityport Industrialization & Regional Development: Spatial Analysis & Planning Strategies. (The Urban & Regional Planning Ser.: Vol. 24). 1981. 60.00 (ISBN 0-08-025815-8). Pergamon.

IFAC Workshop, Kyoto, Japan, Aug. 1977. Urban, Regional & National Planning: Environmental Aspects: Proceedings. Hasegawa, T. & Inoue, K., eds. LC 78-40573. 238p. 1978. text ed. 59.00 (ISBN 0-08-022013-4). Pergamon.

Implementation of Urban Plans. (OECD Urban Management Studies: No. 3). 133p. 1979. 9.50x (ISBN 92-64-11982-5). OECD.

International City Management Association in Cooperation with APA. The Practice of Local Government Planning. 5th ed. So, Frank S., et al, eds. 700p. 1979. 37.50. Planners Pr.

International Conference on Social Welfare. Urban Development: Its Implications for Social Welfare. 458p. 1967. pap. 20.00x (ISBN 0-231-08624-5). Columbia U Pr.

Jackson, John N. Surveys for Town & Country Planning. LC 76-7580. 1976. Repr. of 1963 ed. lib. bdg. 18.00x (ISBN 0-8371-8866-0, JAST). Greenwood.

Jensen, David. Zero Lot Line Housing. LC 81-40469. (Illus.). 160p. 1981. pap. 28.00 (ISBN 0-87420-600-6, B10); pap. 21.00 members. Urban Land.

Jensen, Rolf. Cities of Vision. (Illus.). 382p. 1974. 44.50 (ISBN 0-85334-569-4, Pub. by Elsevier Applied Sci England). Elsevier.

Johnston, Norman J. Cities in the Round. LC 81-21984. (Illus.). 144p. 1983. 29.95x (ISBN 0-295-95918-5). U of Wash Pr.

Joint Report on the Expert Consultations on Policies & Institutions for Integrated Rural Development, 2 vols. 1977. Set. pap. 27.25 (ISBN 92-5-100265-7, F1001, FAO). Unipub.

Joyce, Frank. Local Government, Environmental Planning & Control. 320p. 1981. text ed. 39.00x (ISBN 0-566-00440-2). Gower Pub Co.

Kaplan, Harold. Reform, Planning & City Politics: Montreal, Winnipeg, Toronto. 768p. 1981. 47.50x (ISBN 0-8020-5543-5). U of Toronto Pr.

Karvel, George & Petry, Glenn H. Optimal City Size. 66p. 10.00 (ISBN 0-686-64197-3). U CO Busn Res Div.

Kinkead, Eugene. A Concrete Look at Nature. (Illus.). 242p. 1974. 8.00 (ISBN 0-8129-0471-0, QH105.N7K55). E Kinkead.

--Wildness Is All Around Us. (Illus.). 178p. 1978. 10.00x (ISBN 0-87690-277-8, QH541.5.C6K56). E Kinkead.

Kirchenmann, Jorg C. & Muschalek, Christian. Residential Districts. (Illus.). 192p. 1980. 32.50 (ISBN 0-8230-7491-9, Whitney Lib). Watson-Guptill.

Klaassen, W. T., et al, eds. The Dynamics of Urban Development. 1981. 35.00x (ISBN 0-312-22373-0). St Martin.

Krieger, Martin H. Advice & Planning. 256p. 1981. 29.95 (ISBN 0-87722-217-7). Temple U Pr.

Krier, Rob. Urban Space. LC 79-64347. (Illus.). 174p. 1979. pap. 19.95 (ISBN 0-8478-0236-1). Rizzoli Intl.

Krueckeberg, Donald A. & Silvers, Arthur L. Urban Planning Analysis: Methods & Models. LC 74-7087. 486p. 1974. 41.50x (ISBN 0-471-50858-6). Wiley.

Kuenzlen, Martin. Playing Urban Games: The Systems Approach to Planning. LC 75-189032. 1978. 16.50x (ISBN 0-262-11069-5); pap. 6.95x (ISBN 0-262-61028-0). MIT Pr.

LaConte, P. & Gibson, J. E. Human & Energy Factors: Factors in Urban Planning; A Systems Approach. 1982. 50.00 (ISBN 90-247-2688-3, Pub. by Martinus Nijhoff Netherlands). Kluwer Academic.

Lapatra, Jack W. Applying the Systems Approach to Urban Development. LC 73-11942. (Community Development Ser.: Vol. 5). 296p. 1973. pap. 21.95 (ISBN 0-87933-298-0). Van Nos Reinhold.

Larson, R. & Odoni, A. Urban Operations Research. 1981. 39.95 (ISBN 0-13-939447-8). P-H.

Laurie, Ian C., ed. Nature in Cities: The Natural Environment in the Design & Development of Urban Green Space. LC 77-20987. 428p. 1979. 82.95x (ISBN 0-471-99605-X, Pub. by Wiley-Interscience). Wiley.

Le Corbusier. Le Corbusier: City of Tomorrow. (Illus.). 1971. pap. 9.95x (ISBN 0-262-62017-0). MIT Pr.

--City of Tomorrow. 1971. pap. 9.95x (ISBN 0-262-62017-0). MIT Pr.

Lee, Colin. Models in Planning. LC 72-8442. 152p. 1973. text ed. 25.00 (ISBN 0-08-017020-X); pap. text ed. 10.75 (ISBN 0-08-017021-8). Pergamon.

Leibbrand, Kurt. Stadt und Verkehr: Theorie und Praxis der Stadtischen Verkehrsplanung. (Ger.). 404p. 1980. 75.95x (ISBN 0-8176-1072-3). Birkhauser.

Lottman, Herbert R. How Cities Are Saved. LC 75-11142. (Illus.). 1976. 12.50x (ISBN 0-87663-260-6). Universe.

McKay, David & Cox, Andrew W. The Politics of Urban Change. 297p. 1979. pap. 10.75 (ISBN 0-85664-847-7, Pub. by Croom Helm Ltd). Longwood Pub Group.

McNulty & Kliment. Neighborhood Conversation: A Handbook of Methods & Techniques. (Illus.). 256p. 1976. 21.95 (ISBN 0-8230-7380-7, Whitney Lib). Watson-Guptill.

Malamud, Gary W. Boomtown Communities. 264p. 1984. 29.95 (ISBN 0-442-26399-6). Van Nos Reinhold.

Marsh, Benjamin Clark. An Introduction to City Planning: Democracy's Challenge to the American City. LC 73-11939. (Metropolitan America Ser). 1974. Repr. 14.00x (ISBN 0-405-05401-7). Ayer Co Pubs.

Marsh, G., ed. The Local Plan Inquiry: The Role in Local Plan Preparation, Vol. 19/2. (Illus.). 80p. 1983. pap. 20.00 (ISBN 0-08-030442-7). Pergamon.

Meltsner, Arnold J. The Politics of City Revenue. LC 70-129610. (Oakland Project Ser.). 1971. 30.00x (ISBN 0-520-01812-5); pap. 8.95x (ISBN 0-520-02773-6). U of Cal Pr.

Meltzer, Jack. Metropolis to Metroplex: The Social & Spatial Planning of Cities. LC 83-49195. 216p. 1984. text ed. 22.50x (ISBN 0-8018-3152-0); pap. text ed. 8.95x (ISBN 0-8018-3153-9). Johns Hopkins.

Merriam, Dwight, et al, eds. Inclusionary Zoning Moves Downtown. LC 84-61997. 223p. (Orig.). 1985. pap. write for info. (ISBN 0-918286-37-9). Planners Pr.

Michelson, William, ed. Behavioral Research Methods in Environmental Design. LC 74-10937. (Community Development Ser: Vol. 8). 307p. 1975. 29.95 (ISBN 0-87933-174-7). Van Nos Reinhold.

Miller, Brown, et al. Innovation in New Communities. 392p. 1972. 32.50x (ISBN 0-262-13082-3). MIT Pr.

Miller, Christopher & Wood, Christopher. Planning & Pollution: An Examination of the Role of Land Planning in the Protection of Environmental Quality. (Illus.). 1983. text ed. 32.50x (ISBN 0-19-823245-4). Oxford U Pr.

Miller, Ronald J. The Demolition of Skid Row. LC 81-47182. 160p. 1981. 22.00x (ISBN 0-669-04563-2). Lexington Bks.

Moriarty, Barry M. Industrial Location & Community Development. LC 79-16029. xvii, 381p. 1980. 27.50 (ISBN 0-8078-1400-8); pap. 9.95x (ISBN 0-8078-4064-5). U of NC Pr.

Morris, David. Self-Reliant Cities: Energy & the Transformation of Urban America. LC 81-18301. (Illus.). 256p. 1982. 19.95 (ISBN 0-87156-296-0); pap. 8.95 (ISBN 0-87156-309-6). Sierra.

Mumford, Lewis. The Culture of Cities. LC 80-23130. (Illus.). xviii, 586p. 1981. Repr. of 1970 ed. lib. bdg. 45.00x (ISBN 0-313-22746-2, MUCC). Greenwood.

--From the Ground Up: Observations on Contemporary Architecture, Housing, Highway Building, & Civic Design. LC 56-13736. (Orig.). 1956. pap. 3.50 (ISBN 0-15-634019-4, Harv). HarBraceJ.

Municipal Art Society of New York. Design Arts Two. 112p. 1981. 7.50 (ISBN 0-317-14548-7, D30). Urban Land.

New York City Planning Commission. Plan for New York City. Richards, Peter, ed. Incl. Vol. 1. Critical Issues. 1970. pap. 24.00x (ISBN 0-262-64004-X); Vol. 2. Bronx. 1970. pap. 22.00x (ISBN 0-262-64005-8); Vol. 3. Brooklyn. 1970. pap. 22.00xo. p. (ISBN 0-262-64006-6); Vol. 4. Manhattan. 1970. o. p. (ISBN 0-262-64007-4); Vol. 5. Queens; Vol. 6. Staten Island. 22.50x (ISBN 0-262-64009-0). pap. MIT Pr.

OECD. Urban Environmental Indicators. 274p. (Orig.). 1978. pap. 14.00x (ISBN 92-64-11754-7). OECD.

OECD Staff. Energy Statistics & Main Historical Series 1981-1982. 146p. 1984. pap. 16.00x (ISBN 92-64-02496-4). OECD.

O'Harrow, Dennis. Dennis O'Harrow: Plan Talk & Plain Talk. Berger, Marjorie S., ed. LC 81-68158. 360p. 1981. 19.95 (ISBN 0-918286-22-0). Planners Pr.

Olmsted, Frederick L. Public Parks & the Enlargement of Towns. LC 76-112564. (Rise of Urban America). 1970. Repr. of 1870 ed. 12.00 (ISBN 0-405-02469-X). Ayer Co Pubs.

Oosterbaan, John. Population Dispersal: A National Imperative. LC 79-9672. 160p. 1980. 23.00x (ISBN 0-669-03615-3). Lexington Bks.

Orchard, W. R. & Sherratt, A. F., eds. Combined Heat & Power: Whole City Heating, Planning Tomorrow's Energy Economy. LC 80-41444. 1980. pap. 62.00 (ISBN 0-317-27696-4, 2025214). Bks Demand UMI.

O'Riordan, T. & Turner, K., eds. An Annotated Reader in Environmental Planning & Management. LC 82-7569. (Urban & Regional Planning Ser.: Vol. 30). (Illus.). 484p. 1983. 45.00 (ISBN 0-08-024669-9); pap. 20.00 (ISBN 0-08-024668-0). Pergamon.

Pacione, Michael. Urban Problems & Planning in the Developed World. 1981. 35.00x (ISBN 0-312-83465-9). St Martin.

Pacione, Michael, ed. Problems & Planning in Third World Cities. 1981. 30.00 (ISBN 0-312-64737-9). St Martin.

Palen. City Scenes: Problems & Prospects. 2nd ed. 1981. pap. text ed. 13.95 (ISBN 0-316-68871-1). Little.

Patel, Dinker I. Exurbs: Urban Residential Developments in the Countryside. LC 79-48040. 151p. 1980. text ed. 20.50 (ISBN 0-8191-1001-9); pap. text ed. 9.50 (ISBN 0-8191-1002-7). U Pr of Amer.

Peace, David. Historic Buildings & Planning Policies. 27p. 1979. pap. text ed. 5.00x (ISBN 0-900312-91-2, Pub. by Coun Brit Archaeology). Humanities.

Penne, R. Leo, et al. The Economics of Amenity: Community Futures & Quality of Life. LC 85-6545. (Illus.). 160p. (Orig.). 1985. pap. 12.95 (ISBN 0-941182-15-0). Partners Livable.

Perraton, Jean & Baxter, Richard, eds. Models, Evaluations & Information Systems for Planners. LC 75-326945. (Cambridge University Centre for Land Use & Built Form Studies Conference Proceedings: No. 1). pap. 79.00 (ISBN 0-317-27672-7, 2025215). Bks Demand UMI.

Portugali. Distribution, Allocation, Social Structure & Spatial Form: Elements of Planning Theory. (Progress in Planning Ser.: Vol. 14, Part 3). (Illus.). 83p. 1980. pap. 14.75 (ISBN 0-08-026808-0). Pergamon.

Priest, Donald E. & Black, J. Thomas. Joint Development: Making the Real Estate-Transit Connection. LC 79-66189. (Illus.). 216p. 1979. pap. 32.00 (ISBN 0-87420-588-3, L57); pap. 24.00 members. Urban Land.

Pushkarev, Boris S. & Zupan, Jeffrey M. Urban Space for Pedestrians: A Quantitative Approach: a Report of the Regional Plan Association. LC 75-29242. 272p. 1975. text ed. 35.00x (ISBN 0-262-16063-3). MIT Pr.

Rabinowitz, Harvey Z. Building in Use Study, 3 pts. Incl. Pt. 1. Technical Factors; Pt. 2. Functional Factors. (Publications in Architecture & Urban Planning Ser.). (Illus.). v, 258p. 1975. 12.00 ea. (ISBN 0-938744-02-X, R75-1). U of Wis Ctr Arch-Urban.

Ransom, Harry, ed. People's Architects. LC 64-15812. pap. 29.70 (ISBN 0-8357-9652-3, 2016991). Bks Demand UMI.

Rao, A. G. Madhava, ed. Modern Trends in Housing in Developing Countries. (Illus.). 400p. 1984. 55.00 (ISBN 0-419-13290-2, 6883, Pub. by E & FN Spon England). Methuen Inc.

Ravetz, Alison. Remaking Cities: Contradictions of the Recent Urban Environment. 375p. 1980. 29.95 (ISBN 0-85664-293-2, Pub. by Croom Helm Ltd); pap. 13.00 (ISBN 0-7099-2220-5). Longwood Pub Group.

Rein, Martin. From Policy to Practice. 272p. 1983. 30.00 (ISBN 0-87332-194-4); pap. 14.95 (ISBN 0-87332-219-3). M E Sharpe.

Relph, E. Place & Placelessness. (Pion Research in Planning & Design Ser.). (Illus.). 156p. 1984. pap. 7.50x (ISBN 0-85086-111-X, NO. 5074). Methuen Inc.

Riddick, William. Charrette Processes: A Tool in Urban Planning. LC 74-14257. (Illus.). 110p. 1971. softbound 7.50 (ISBN 0-87387-041-7). Shumway.

Roberts, Philip J. Valuation of Development Land in Hong Kong. LC 76-369546. pap. 24.30 (ISBN 0-317-27920-3, 2025128). Bks Demand UMI.

Rodwin, Lloyd. Cities & City Planning. LC 81-13956. (Environment, Development, & Public Policy - Cities & Development Ser.). 317p. 1981. 29.50 (ISBN 0-306-40666-7, Plenum Pr). Plenum Pub.

Rohe, William M. & Gates, Lauren B. Planning with Neighborhoods. LC 84-17221. (Urban & Regional Policy & Development Studies). 260p. 1985. 35.00x (ISBN 0-8078-1638-8); pap. 12.95 (ISBN 0-8078-4133-1). U of NC Pr.

Rosenbloom, Richard S. & Russell, John R. New Tools for Urban Management. 1971. text ed. 18.50x (ISBN 0-87584-093-0). Harvard U Pr.

Rosenthal, Donald B., ed. Urban Revitalization. LC 79-27881. (Urban Affairs Annual Reviews: Vol. 18). (Illus.). 308p. 1980. 28.00 (ISBN 0-8039-1190-4); pap. 14.00 (ISBN 0-8039-1191-2). Sage.

Rothenberg, Jerome. Economic Evaluation of Urban Renewal: Conceptual Foundation of Benefit-Cost Analysis. LC 67-19190. (Studies of Government Finance Ser.). pap. 72.80 (ISBN 0-317-28184-4, 2022559). Bks Demand UMI.

Rubenstein, Harvey M. Central City Malls. LC 78-7536. 191p. 1978. 57.50 (ISBN 0-471-03098-8, Pub. by Wiley-Interscience). Wiley.

Rudman, Jack. Assistant Urban Designer. (Career Examination Ser.: C-1120). (Cloth bdg. avail. on request). pap. 12.00 (ISBN 0-8373-1120-9). Natl Learning.

--Housing, Planning & Redevelopment Aide. (Career Examination Ser.: C-343). (Cloth bdg. avail. on request). pap. 10.00 (ISBN 0-8373-0343-5). Natl Learning.

--Planner. (Career Examination Ser.: C-588). (Cloth bdg. avail. on request). pap. 10.00 (ISBN 0-8373-0588-8). Natl Learning.

--Urban Designer. (Career Examination Ser.). (Cloth bdg. avail. on request). pap. 12.00 (ISBN 0-8373-1527-1, C-1527). Natl Learning.

--Urban Planner. (Career Examination Ser.: C-854). (Cloth bdg. avail. on request). pap. 12.00 (ISBN 0-8373-0854-2). Natl Learning.

Saroff, Jerome R. & Levitan, Alberta Z. Survey Manual for Comprehensive Urban Planning: The Use of Opinion Surveys & Sampling Techniques in the Planning Process. LC 73-628164. (Joint Institute of Social & Economic Research Ser.: No. 19). (Illus.). 154p. 1969. pap. 10.00x (ISBN 0-295-95116-8). U of Wash Pr.

Schnidman, Frank, et al, eds. Management & Control of Growth: Techniques in Application. LC 78-73139. (Management & Control of Growth Ser.: Vol. 4). 335p. 1978. pap. 24.00 (ISBN 0-87420-578-6, M11); pap. 18.00 members. Urban Land.

Schuclein, Werner & Eulenberger, Peter. Anwendung des Simulationsmodells BAYMO 70 auf die Stadtentwicklungsplanung, Vol. 3. (Interdisciplinary Systems Research Ser.: No. 45). (Ger.). 138p. 1980. pap. 20.95x (ISBN 0-8176-0970-9). Birkhauser.

Schulein, Werner. Anwendung des Simulationsmodells BAYMO 70 auf die Stadtentwicklungsplanung, Vol. 1. (Interdisciplinary Systems Research Ser.: No. 43). (Ger.). 136p. 1980. pap. 20.95x (ISBN 0-8176-0968-7). Birkhauser.

Scott, A. J. The Urban Land Nexus & the State. 256p. 1980. 24.00x (ISBN 0-85086-079-2, NO. 6390, Pub. by Pion England). Methuen Inc.

Sewell, W. Derrick & Coppock, J. T., eds. Public Participation in Planning. LC 76-56800. pap. 57.80 (ISBN 0-317-30323-6, 2024804). Bks Demand UMI.

Shirvani, Hamid. Urban Design Review: A Guide for Planners. LC 81-68161. (Illus.). 230p. (Orig.). 1981. pap. 21.95 (ISBN 0-918286-23-9). Planners Pr.

Smith, David L. Amenity & Urban Planning: The Origin & Role of the Aesthetic Element in Modern Practice. (Illus.). 247p. 1974. 18.00x (ISBN 0-8464-0038-3). Beekman Pubs.

Smith, Halbert C., et al. Real Estate & Urban Development. 3rd ed. 1981. 28.95x (ISBN 0-256-02445-6). Irwin.

Soleri, Paolo. Arcology: The City in the Image of Man. 1970. pap. 17.50 (ISBN 0-262-69041-1). MIT Pr.

Solesbury, William. Policy in Urban Planning: Structure Plans, Local Plans, & Urban Development. 1974. 21.00 (ISBN 0-08-017758-1). Pergamon.

Spreiregen, Paul D. Urban Design: The Architecture of Towns & Cities. LC 81-8177. 256p. 1981. Repr. of 1965 ed. lib. bdg. 29.50 (ISBN 0-89874-300-1). Krieger.

Stalley, Marshall, ed. Patrick Geddes: Spokesman for Man & the Environment. LC 75-163963. 1972. 37.50x (ISBN 0-8135-0697-2). Rutgers U Pr.

Stave, Bruce M., ed. Modern Industrial Cities: History, Policy, & Survival. (Sage Focus Editions Ser.). 320p. 1981. 28.00 (ISBN 0-8039-1760-0); pap. 14.00 (ISBN 0-8039-1761-9). Sage.

Suedfeld, Peter & Russell, James A., eds. The Behavioral Basis of Design: Selected Papers, Bk. 1. LC 76-11594. (Community Development Ser.: Vol. 28). 1976. 34.50 (ISBN 0-87933-248-4). Van Nos Reinhold.

Suedfeld, Peter, et al, eds. The Behavioral Basis of Design: Bk. 2, Session Summaries & Papers. LC 76-11594. (Community Development Ser.: Vol. 36). (Illus.). 1977. 41.95 (ISBN 0-87933-293-X). Van Nos Reinhold.

Sullivan, John J., ed. Explorations in Urban Land Economics. LC 79-119693. 122p. 1970. pap. 2.50 (ISBN 0-686-01014-0). Lincoln Inst Land.

A Survey of Urban Arterial Design Standards. (Illus.). 91p. 1969. 10.00x (ISBN 0-917084-21-7). Am Public Works.

Sutcliffe, Anthony. Towards the Planned City. 1981. 27.50 (ISBN 0-312-81039-3). St Martin.

Szanton, Peter. Not Well Advised. LC 80-69174. 185p. 1981. 11.95x (ISBN 0-87154-874-7). Russell Sage.

Taeuber, Conrad & Ylvisaker, Paul N. Density: Five Perspectives. LC 72-79134. (Special Report Ser.). (Illus.). 63p. 1972. pap. 10.50 (ISBN 0-87420-556-5); pap. 8.00 members. Urban Land.

Taylor, John L. & Williams, David G. Urban Planning Practice in Developing Countries. LC 81-81224. (Urban & Regional Planning Ser.: Vol. 25). (Illus.). 365p. 1982. 49.50 (ISBN 0-08-022225-0). Pergamon.

Taylor, Lisa, ed. Urban Open Spaces. (Illus.). 128p. 1980. pap. 9.95 (ISBN 0-8478-0304-X). Rizzoli Intl.

Todaro, Michael P. & Stilkind, Jerry. City Bias & Rural Neglect: The Dilemma of Urban Development. LC 80-26071. (Public Issues Papers). 93p. (Orig.). 1981. pap. text ed. 3.50 (ISBN 0-87834-042-4). Population Coun.

Unwin, Raymond. Legacy of Raymond Unwin: A Human Pattern for Planning. Creese, Raymond, ed. 1967. 32.50x (ISBN 0-262-03022-5). MIT Pr.

--Town Planning in Practice. 2nd ed. LC 68-56507. (Illus.). 1969. Repr. of 1934 ed. 33.00 (ISBN 0-405-09036-6). Ayer Co Pubs.

Urban Land Institute. A Directory of Mixed-Use Developers. LC 83-145296. pap. 20.00 (ISBN 0-317-30050-4, 2025041). Bks Demand UMI.

Urban Land Policies & Land-Use Control Measures, 7 Vols. Incl. Vol. 1. Africa. pap. 3.00 (ISBN 0-686-93558-6, UN73/4/5); Vol. 2. Asia & the Far East. pap. 4.00 (ISBN 0-686-93559-4, UN73/4/6); Vol. 3. Western Europe. pap. 6.00 (ISBN 0-686-93560-8, UN73/4/7); Vol. 4. Latin America. pap. 3.00 (ISBN 0-686-93561-6, UN73/4/8); Vol. 5. Middle East. pap. 2.50 (ISBN 0-686-93562-4, UN73/4/9); Vol. 6. Northern America. pap. 5.00 (ISBN 0-686-93563-2, UN73/4/10); Vol. 7. Global Review. pap. 11.00 (ISBN 0-686-93564-0, UN73/4/11). UN). Unipub.

Urban Planning Guide. (Manual & Report on Engineering Practice Ser.: No. 49). 305p. 1969. pap. 8.00x (ISBN 0-87262-223-1). Am Soc Civil Eng.

Vance, Mary. Planning in the Netherlands: Monographs. (Architecture Ser.: Bibliography A-1302). 42p. 1985. pap. 6.00 (ISBN 0-89028-232-3). Vance Biblios.

Van Der Knaap, G. A. Population Growth & Urban Systems Development. (Studies in Applied Regional Science: Vol. 18). 245p. 1980. lib. bdg. 16.00 (ISBN 0-89838-024-3, Pub. by Martinus Nijhoff Netherlands). Kluwer Academic.

Van Lierop, F. J. & Nijkamp, Peter. Locational Developments & Urban Planning. (NATO Advanced Study Behavioral & Social Sciences Ser.: No. 5). 549p. 1981. 60.00 (ISBN 90-286-2651-4). Sijthoff & Noordhoff.

Walker, Mabel L. Urban Blight & Slums: Economic & Legal Factors in Their Origin, Reclamation & Prevention. LC 70-139943. (Illus.). 1971. Repr. of 1938 ed. 20.00x (ISBN 0-8462-1546-2). Russell.

Wallace, Samuel E. The Urban Environment. 1980. pap. 18.00x (ISBN 0-256-02218-6). Dorsey.

Webber, M. J. Information Theory & Urban Spatial Structure. 394p. 1979. 80.00 (ISBN 0-85664-665-2, Pub. by Croom Helm Ltd). Longwood Pub Group.

Whittick, Arnold, ed. Encyclopedia of Urban Planning. LC 79-23480. 1248p. 1980. Repr. of 1974 ed. lib. bdg. 59.50 (ISBN 0-89874-104-1). Krieger.

WHO Scientific Group. Geneva, 1971. Development of Environmental Health Criteria for Urban Planning: Report. (Technical Report Ser.: No. 511). (Also avail. in French & Spanish). 1972. pap. 1.60 (ISBN 92-4-120511-3). World Health.

WHO-WMO Symposium on Urban Climates & Building Climatology: Proceedings, Brussels, Oct. 1968. (Technical Note Ser.: No. 108). (Eng. & Fr.). 390p. 1970. pap. 50.00 (ISBN 0-686-93905-0, WMO). Unipub.

Wiebenson, Dora. Tony Garnier: The Cite Industrielle. LC 79-78051. (Planning & Cities Ser.). (Illus.). 1969. 7.95 (ISBN 0-8076-0515-8). Braziller.

Wiedenhoeft, Ronald V. Cities for People. 1981. 24.95 (ISBN 0-442-29429-8). Van Nos Reinhold.

Williams, Ken. Statistics & Urban Planning. LC 75-23011. 189p. 1975. 21.50 (ISBN 0-470-94870-1, Pub. by Wiley). Krieger.

Willis, K. G. The Economics of Town & Country Planning. 281p. 1980. text ed. 30.00x (ISBN 0-246-11342-1, Pub. by Granada England). Brookfield Pub Co.

--Economics of Town & Country Planning. 290p. 1980. 24.00x (ISBN 0-246-11342-1, Pub by Granada England). Sheridan.

Willson, John S., et al. Comprehensive Planning & the Environment: A Manual for Planners. LC 78-66683. 1979. text ed. 25.00 (ISBN 0-89011-515-X). Abt Bks.

Wilson, Alan G. Urban & Regional Models in Geography & Planning. LC 73-8200. pap. 108.00 (ISBN 0-317-30329-5, 2024807). Bks Demand UMI.

Wingo, Lowdon, Jr. Transportation & Urban Land. LC 77-86416. (Resources for the Future Ser.). 144p. Repr. of 1961 ed. 25.00 (ISBN 0-404-60346-7). AMS Pr.

WMO Symposium on Meteorology as Related to Urban & Regional Land-Use Planning: Proceedings. (Illus.). 1977. pap. text ed. 22.50 (ISBN 92-63-10444-1, WMO). Unipub.

Woodbury, Coleman, ed. Future of Cities & Urban Redevelopment. LC 53-7679. (Midway Reprint Ser.). 1975. pap. 24.75x (ISBN 0-226-90650-7). U of Chicago Pr.

Wrather, Christopher. Two Programs for the Delimitation of Functional & Nodal Regions from an Intercity Flow Matrix. (Research Report Ser.: 1977-2). 1977. pap. 4.00 (ISBN 0-87755-270-3). Bureau Busn UT.

Wright, Frank L. Living City. pap. 6.95 (ISBN 0-452-00639-2, F639, Mer). NAL.

Zucker, Paul, ed. New Architecture & City Planning. facs. ed. LC 76-128337. (Essay Index Reprint Ser). 1944. 42.00 (ISBN 0-8369-2035-X). Ayer Co Pubs.

CITY PLANNING–BIBLIOGRAPHY

Bergquist, Charles W. Alternative Approaches to the Problem of Development: A Selected & Annotated Bibliography. LC 77-88665. 264p. 1979. lib. bdg. 19.95 (ISBN 0-89089-081-1); pap. 9.95 (ISBN 0-89089-083-8). Carolina Acad Pr.

Branch, Melville C. & Mazza, Eliane G. Selected Annotated Bibliography on New Town Planning & Development. (Architecture Ser.: Bibliography A-216). 133p. 1980. pap. 14.00 (ISBN 0-88066-061-9). Vance Biblios.

Casper, Dale E. The English Urban Environment: Recent Writings, 1980-1983. (Public Administration Ser.: Bibliography P 1643). 1985. pap. 2.00 (ISBN 0-89028-333-8). Vance Biblios.

City Planning Bibliography: A Basic Bibliography of Sources & Trends. 3rd ed. 534p. 1972. pap. 16.75x (ISBN 0-87262-036-0). Am Soc Civil Eng.

Colokathis, Jane. Comprehensive Index to CPL Exchange Bibliographies, No. 1-1565: A Numerical Index. (CPL Bibliographies: No. 3). 89p. 1979. pap. 9.00 (ISBN 0-86602-003-9). CPL Biblios.

--Comprehensive Index to CPL Exchange Bibliographies, No. 1-1565: A Subject Index. (CPL Bibliographies: No. 1). 119p. 1979. pap. 12.00 (ISBN 0-86602-001-2, Z5942). CPL Biblios.

--Comprehensive Index to CPL Exchange Bibliographies, Nos. 1-1565: An Author Index. (CPL Bibliographies: No. 2). 100p. 1979. pap. 10.00 (ISBN 0-86602-002-0). CPL Biblios.

Dowall, David E. & Mingilton, Jesse. Effects of Environmental Regulations on Housing Costs. (CPL Bibliographies: No. 6). 67p. 1979. pap. 7.00 (ISBN 0-86602-006-3). CPL Biblios.

Filipovitch, Anthony & Reeves, Earl, eds. Urban Community: A Guide to Information Sources. LC 78-13171. (The Urban Studies Information Guide Ser.: Vol. 4). 1978. 60.00x (ISBN 0-8103-1429-0). Gale.

Goehlert, Robert. City & Regional Planning: A Bibliography of Journal Literature 1945-1975. (Public Administration Ser.: P 124). 1978. pap. 5.50 (ISBN 0-88066-009-0). Vance Biblios.

Harvard University - Graduate School Of Design. Catalogue of the Library of the Graduate School of Design, 44 Vols. 1968. Set. 3725.00 (ISBN 0-8161-0812-9, Hall Library). G K Hall.

International Institute for Environment & Development (I.I.E.D.) Human Settlements, an Annotated Bibliography. Anglemyer, Mary & Ottersen, Signe R., eds. LC 76-10832. 1976. pap. text ed. 44.00 (ISBN 0-08-021243-3). Pergamon.

Murphy, Thomas P., ed. Urban Indicators: A Guide to Information Sources. LC 80-13333. (Urban Studies Information Guide Ser.: Vol. 10). 1980. 60.00x (ISBN 0-8103-1451-7). Gale.

Otness, Harold M. Index to Early Twentieth Century City Plans Appearing in Guidebooks: Baedeker, Muirhead-Blue Guides, Murray, I. J. G. R., Etc., Plus Selected Other Works to Provide Worldwide Coverage of Over 2,000 Plans to Over 1,200 Communities, Found in 74 Guidebooks. LC 78-15094. (Western Association of Map Libraries: Occasional Paper; No. 4). (Illus.). 124p. (Orig.). 1978. pap. 6.00x (ISBN 0-939112-05-1). Western Assn Map.

--Index to Nineteenth Century City Plans Appearing in Guidebooks: Baedeker, Murray, Joanne, Black, Appleton, Meyer, Plus Selected Other Works to Provide Coverage of Over 1,800 Plans to Nearly 600 Communities Found in 164 Guidebooks. LC 80-24483. (Western Association of Map Libraries: Occasional Paper; No. 7). (Illus.). 108p. (Orig.). 1980. pap. 6.00x (ISBN 0-939112-08-6). Western Assn Map.

Palumbo, Dennis & Taylor, George A., eds. Urban Policy: A Guide to Information Sources. LC 78-25957. (Urban Studies Information Guide Ser.: Vol. 6). 1979. 60.00x (ISBN 0-8103-1428-2). Gale.

Peterson-Hunt, William S. & Woodruff, Evelyn L. Union List of Sanborn Fire Insurance Maps Held by Institutions in the United States & Canada: Volume 2 (Montana to Wyoming, Canada & Mexico, with a Supplement & Corrigenda to Volume 1. rev. ed. LC 76-6129. (Western Association of Map Libraries: Occasional Paper; No. 3). (Illus.). 216p. (Orig.). 1977. pap. 6.00x (ISBN 0-939112-03-5); pap. 10.00x Vols. 1 & 2 (ISBN 0-939112-04-3). Western Assn Map.

Shillaber, Caroline. A Library Classification for City & Regional Planning: A Revision of Pray & Kimball's City Planning Classification of 1913. LC 72-95456. (City Planning Studies: No. 18). 1973. 8.95x (ISBN 0-674-53055-1). Harvard U Pr.

Tilton, Doreen B., ed. Housing & Urban Affairs, 1965-1976: A Bibliographic Guide to the Microform Collection. 342p. 1978. 50.00 (ISBN 0-667-00519-6). Microfilming Corp.

U. S. Department of Housing & Urban Development, Washington, D. C. Dictionary Catalog of the United States Department of Housing & Urban Development Library & Information Division, 19 vols. 1972. Set. lib. bdg. 1880.00 (ISBN 0-8161-1007-7, Hall Library). G K Hall.

Viet, Jean, compiled by. New Towns: A Selected Annotated Bibliography. Bd. with Selected Documentation on Criminology. International Society of Criminology, compiled by.; International Co-Operation & Programmes of Economic & Social Development: An Annotated Bibliography. Viet, Jean. Repr. of 1961 ed. (UNESCO Scholarship Reprint Ser.: Nos. 12 & 15). pap. 49.00 (ISBN 0-317-16301-9). Kraus Repr.

Wheater, Delma J. Environmental Design: An Analysis of the Field, Its Implication for Libraries & a Guide to the Literature, Nos. 747-748. 1975. 8.50 (ISBN 0-686-20341-0). CPL Biblios.

CITY PLANNING–DATA PROCESSING

Batty, Michael & Hutchinson, Bruce, eds. Systems Analysis in Urban Policy-Making & Planning. (NATO Conference Series II, Systems Science: Vol. 12). 605p. 1983. 85.00x (ISBN 0-306-41118-0). Plenum Pub.

Baxter, Richard S. Computer & Statistical Techniques for Planners. 1976. pap. 22.00x (ISBN 0-416-84630-0, NO.2613). Methuen Inc.

Eulenberger, Peter. Anwendung des Simulationsmodells BAYMO 70 auf die Stadtentwicklungsplanung, Vol. 2. (Interdisciplinary Systems Research Ser.: No. 44). (Ger.). 94p. 1980. pap. 18.95x (ISBN 0-8176-0969-5). Birkhauser.

Forrester, Jay W. Urban Dynamics. 1969. 35.00x (ISBN 0-262-06026-4). MIT Pr.

Negroponte, Nicholas. The Architecture Machine. (Illus.). 164p. 1970. pap. 4.95x (ISBN 0-262-64010-4). MIT Pr.

Nijkamp, Peter. Multidimensional Spatial Data & Decision Analysis. LC 79-40518. 322p. 1979. 73.95x (ISBN 0-471-27603-0, Pub. by Wiley-Interscience). Wiley.

Ottensmann, John R. BASIC Microcomputer Programs for Urban Analysis & Planning. 230p. (Orig.). 1985. 28.50 (ISBN 0-412-00741-X, 9197, Pub. by Chapman & Hall England); pap. 18.50 (ISBN 0-412-00871-8, 9198). Methuen Inc.

Patterson, Phillip D., ed. Recent Developments in Urban Gaming. (SCS Simulation Ser.: Vol. 2, No. 2). 1972. 30.00 (ISBN 0-686-36659-X). Soc Computer Sim.

Schuclein, Werner & Eulenberger, Peter. Anwendung des Simulationsmodells BAYMO 70 auf die Stadtentwicklungsplanung, Vol. 3. (Interdisciplinary Systems Research Ser.: No. 45). (Ger.). 138p. 1980. pap. 20.95x (ISBN 0-8176-0970-9). Birkhauser.

Schulein, Werner. Anwendung des Simulationsmodells BAYMO 70 auf die Stadtentwicklungsplanung, Vol. 1. (Interdisciplinary Systems Research Ser.: No. 43). (Ger.). 136p. 1980. pap. 20.95x (ISBN 0-8176-0968-7). Birkhauser.

Steinitz, Carl & Rogers, Peter. Systems Analysis Model of Urbanization & Change: An Experiment in Interdisciplinary Education. 1970. 25.00x (ISBN 0-262-19074-5). MIT Pr.

Stuart, Darwin E. Information Systems in Urban Planning: A Review. (PAS Reports: No. 260). 60p. 1970. 6.00 (ISBN 0-318-13010-6). Am Plan Assn.

CITY PLANNING–HISTORY

Benevolo, Leonardo. Origins of Modern Town Planning. Landry, Judith, tr. from It. 1971. pap. 7.95x (ISBN 0-262-52018-4). MIT Pr.

Bjork, Gordon C. Life, Liberty & Property: The Economics & Politics of Land-Use Planning & Environmental Controls. LC 80-8038. 160p. 1980. 22.00x (ISBN 0-669-03952-7). Lexington Bks.

Chalklin, C. W. The Provincial Towns of Georgian England: A Study of the Building Process, 1740-1820. (Studies in Urban History: No. 3). (Illus.). 416p. 1974. 25.00x (ISBN 0-7735-0200-9). McGill-Queens U Pr.

Churchill, Henry S. City Is the People. 1962. pap. 1.95x (ISBN 0-393-00174-1, Norton Lib). Norton.

Cullen, Gordon. Concise Townscape. (Illus.). 1961. pap. 10.95 (ISBN 0-442-21770-6). Van Nos Reinhold.

Gutkind, Erwin A. International History of City Development, 8 vols. Incl. Vol. 1. Urban Development in Central Europe. 1964; Vol. 2. Urban Development in Alpine & Scandinavian Countries. 1965. 50.00 (ISBN 0-02-913260-6); Vol. 3. Urban Development in Southern Europe; Spain & Portugal. 1967. 50.00 (ISBN 0-02-913270-3); Vol. 4. Urban Development in Southern Europe; Italy & Greece. 1969. 50.00 (ISBN 0-02-913280-0); Vol. 5. Urban Development in Western Europe; France & Belgium. 1970. 50.00 (ISBN 0-02-913300-9); Vol. 6. Urban Development in Western Europe: The Netherlands & Great Britain. 1971. 50.00 (ISBN 0-02-913310-6); Vol. 7. Urban Development in East-Central Europe: Poland, Czechoslavia, & Hungary. 1972. 45.00 (ISBN 0-02-913320-3); Vol. 8. Urban Development in Eastern Europe: Bulgaria, Romania, & U.S.S.R. 1972. 50.00 (ISBN 0-02-913330-0). LC 64-13231. 300.00 (ISBN 0-02-913340-8). Free Pr.

Lynch, Kevin. Site Planning. 3rd ed. 1971. 19.95x (ISBN 0-262-12106-9). MIT Pr.

Rasmussen, Steen E. Towns & Buildings. 1969. pap. 10.95s (ISBN 0-262-68011-4). MIT Pr.

Sanderson, Warren, ed. International Handbook of Contemporary Developments in Architecture. LC 80-24794. (Illus.). 600p. 1981. lib. bdg. 85.00 (ISBN 0-313-21439-5, SIH/). Greenwood.

Strong, Ann L. Planned Urban Environments: Sweden, Finland, Israel, The Netherlands, France. LC 73-134204. (Illus.). 416p. 1971. 36.00x (ISBN 0-8018-1245-3). Johns Hopkins.

Sutcliffe, Anthony. The History of Urban & Regional Planning. 300p. 1980. 35.00x (ISBN 0-87196-303-5). Facts on File.

Ward-Perkins, J. B. Cities of Ancient Greece & Italy. (Planning & Cities Ser). (Illus.). 128p. 1974. pap. 7.95 (ISBN 0-8076-0678-2). Braziller.

Westfall, Carroll. In This Most Perfect Paradise: Alberti, Nicholas V, and the Invention of Conscious Urban Planning in Rome, 1447-55. 1974. 36.75x (ISBN 0-271-01175-0). Pa St U Pr.

White, Morton & White, Lucia. The Intellectual Versus the City: From Thomas Jefferson to Frank Lloyd Wright. LC 81-1755. xiv, 270p. 1981. Repr. of 1977 ed. lib. bdg. 25.00x (ISBN 0-313-22786-1, WHIV). Greenwood.

CITY PLANNING—IRELAND

Curriculum Development Unit, ed. Urban Ireland: Development of Towns & Villages. (Illus.). 128p. 1982. 14.95 (ISBN 0-86278-017-9, XPub. by O'Brien Pr Ireland); pap. 6.95 (ISBN 0-86278-018-7, Pub. by O'Brien Pr Ireland). Irish Bks Media.

CITY PLANNING—UNITED STATES

Bjork, Gordon C. Life, Liberty & Property: The Economics & Politics of Land-Use Planning & Environmental Controls. LC 80-8038. 160p. 1980. 22.00x (ISBN 0-669-03952-7). Lexington Bks.

Bryce, Herrington J., ed. Cities & Firms. LC 80-8367. (The Urban Roundtable Ser.). 272p. 1980. 25.00x (ISBN 0-669-04042-8). Lexington Bks.

Caminos, Horacio & Goethert, Reinhard. Urbanization Primer: Project Assessment, Site Analysis, Design Criteria for Site & Services & Similar Dwelling Environments in Developing Areas, with a Documentary Collection of Photographs on Urbanization. (Illus.). 1978. text ed. 42.50x (ISBN 0-262-03066-7). MIT Pr.

Catanese, Anthony J. & Snyder, James C. Introduction to Urban Planning. (Illus.). 1979. text ed. 39.00 (ISBN 0-07-010228-7). McGraw.

Committee On Urban Technology - Division Of Engineering. Long-Range Planning for Urban Research & Development: Technological Considerations. (Illus., Orig.). 1969. pap. 5.75 (ISBN 0-309-01729-7). Natl Acad Pr.

Drennan, Mathew P. Modeling Metropolitan Economies for Forecasting & Policy Analysis. 256p. text ed. 40.00x (ISBN 0-8147-1781-0). NYU Pr.

Eichler, Edward P. & Kaplan, Marshall. The Community Builders. LC 67-13601. (California Studies in Urbanization & Environmental Design). 1967. 26.00x (ISBN 0-520-00380-2). U of Cal Pr.

Everett, Robinson O. & Leach, Richard H. Urban Problems & Prospects. LC 65-28034. (Library of Law & Contemporary Problems). 240p. 1965. 10.00 (ISBN 0-379-11506-9). Oceana.

Ewald, William R., Jr., ed. Environment for Man: The Next Fifty Years. LC 67-14215. (Midland Bks.: No. 102). (Illus.). Repr. of 1967 ed. 60.50 (ISBN 0-8357-9207-2, 2017619). Bks Demand UMI.

Ferri, Roger C. Pedestrian City: A Proposal for an American Architecture & Urbanism in the Post-Petroleum Age. (Illus.). 24p. (Orig.). 1981. pap. text ed. 2.50 (ISBN 0-9605928-0-6). Ferri.

Foster, Mark S. From Streetcar to Superhighway: American City Planners & Urban Transportation, 1900-1940. LC 80-27202. (Technology & Urban Growth Ser.). (Illus.). 263p. 1981. 34.95 (ISBN 0-87722-210-X). Temple U Pr.

Geller, Evelyn, ed. Saving America's Cities. (Reference Shelf Ser.). 1979. 8.00 (ISBN 0-8242-0631-2). Wilson.

Gibson, J. E. Designing the New City: A Systematic Approach. LC 76-44899. (Systems Engineering & Analysis Ser.). 288p. 1977. 46.95x (ISBN 0-471-29752-6, Pub. by Wiley-Interscience). Wiley.

Gordon, Stuart. Gordonstown, a New Design for America. (Illus.). 288p. 1980. pap. 5.95 (ISBN 0-9603942-0-6). Gordonstown.

Gutheim, Frederick. Worthy of the Nation: The History of Planning for the National Capital. LC 77-120. (Illus.). 416p. 1977. 29.95x (ISBN 0-87474-496-2). Smithsonian.

Hagman, Donald G. Public Planning & Control of Urban & Land Development-Cases & Materials: 1982 Supplement to Teacher's Manual. 2nd ed. (American Casebook Ser.). 51p. 1982. pap. text ed. write for info. (ISBN 0-314-66383-5). West Pub.

Holy, R. A. Relationship of City Planning to School Plant Planning. LC 73-176877. (Columbia University. Teachers College. Contributions to Education Ser.: No. 662). Repr. of 1935 ed. 22.50 (ISBN 0-404-55662-0). AMS Pr.

Jacob, Bernard & Morphew, Carol. Skyway Typology. 1984. 10.25 (ISBN 0-317-06678-1). Am Inst Arch.

Lang, Michael. Gentrification amid Urban Decline. 168p. 1982. prof ref 29.95 (ISBN 0-88410-697-7). Ballinger Pub.

Lapatra, Jack W. Applying the Systems Approach to Urban Development. LC 73-11942. (Community Development Ser.: Vol. 5). 296p. 1973. pap. 21.95 (ISBN 0-87933-298-0). Van Nos Reinhold.

Martin, Robert L. The City Moves West: Economic & Industrial Growth in Central West Texas. 200p. 1969. 12.50x (ISBN 0-292-78412-0). U of Tex Pr.

Mayer, Harold M. & Hayes, Charles R. Land Uses in American Cities. LC 82-81036. (Illus.). 200p. (Orig.). 1983. pap. text ed. 9.95 (ISBN 0-941226-02-6). Park Pr Co.

Moriarty, Barry M. Industrial Location & Community Development. LC 79-16029. xvii, 381p. 1980. 27.50 (ISBN 0-8078-1400-8); pap. 9.95x (ISBN 0-8078-4064-5). U of NC Pr.

Mumford, Lewis. The Highway & the City. LC 80-22641. viii, 246p. 1981. Repr. of 1953 ed. lib. bdg. 25.00x (ISBN 0-313-22747-0, MUHC). Greenwood.

Neighborhood & Community Planning, Vol. 9. (Metropolotian America Ser.). 370p. 1974. 23.00x (ISBN 0-405-05422-X). Ayer Co Pubs.

New York City Planning Commission. Plan for New York City. Richards, Peter, ed. Incl. Vol. 1. Critical Issues. 1970. pap. 24.00x (ISBN 0-262-64004-X); Vol. 2. Bronx. 1970. pap. 22.00x (ISBN 0-262-64005-8); Vol. 3. Brooklyn. 1970. pap. 22.00xo. p (ISBN 0-262-64006-6); Vol. 4. Manhattan. 1970. o. p (ISBN 0-262-64007-4); Vol. 5. Queens; Vol. 6. Staten Island. 22.50x (ISBN 0-262-64009-0). pap. MIT Pr.

Palley, Marian L. & Palley, Howard A. Urban America & Public Policies. 2nd ed. 336p. 1981. pap. text ed. 11.95 (ISBN 0-669-04004-5). Heath.

Perloff, Harvey S. Planning the Post-Industrial City. LC 80-67753. (Illus.). 327p. (Orig.). 1980. 25.95 (ISBN 0-918286-21-2). Planners Pr.

Perloff, Harvey S., ed. The Quality of the Urban Environment: Essays on "New Resources" in an Urban Age. LC 69-16858. (Rff Research Report Ser). (Illus.). 332p. (Orig.). 1969. pap. 7.50x (ISBN 0-8018-1028-0). Johns Hopkins.

Platt, Rutherford H. Open Land in Urban Illinois: Roles of the Citizen Advocate. LC 78-146641. 132p. 1971. pap. 5.00 (ISBN 0-87580-506-X). N Ill U Pr.

Ransom, Harry, ed. People's Architects. LC 64-15812. pap. 29.70 (ISBN 0-8357-9652-3, 2016991). Bks Demand UMI.

Reps, John W. Cities of the American West: A History of Frontier Urban Planning. LC 78-51187. (Illus.). 1979. 110.00x (ISBN 0-691-04648-4). Princeton U Pr.

Roeseler, W. G. Successful American Urban Plans. LC 81-47028. 224p. 1981. 30.50x (ISBN 0-669-04540-3). Lexington Bks.

Rosen, George. Decision-Making Chicago-Style: The Genesis of a University of Illinois Campus. LC 79-25643. (Illus.). 224p. 1980. 17.50x (ISBN 0-252-00803-0). U of Ill Pr.

Rosenthal, Donald B., ed. Urban Revitalization. LC 79-27881. (Urban Affairs Annual Reviews: Vol. 18). (Illus.). 308p. 1980. 28.00 (ISBN 0-8039-1190-4); pap. 14.00 (ISBN 0-8039-1191-2). Sage.

Schaffer, Daniel. Garden Cities for America: The Radburn Experience. 276p. 1982. 34.95 (ISBN 0-87722-258-4). Temple U Pr.

Sears, Joan N. The First One Hundred Years of Town Planning in Georgia. LC 78-74091. (Illus.). 240p. 1979. bds. 15.00 (ISBN 0-87797-046-7). Cherokee.

Solomon, Arthur P., ed. The Prospective City: Economic, Population, Energy, & Environmental Developments Shaping Our Cities & Suburbs. (MIT-Harvard Joint Center for Urban Studies). 1979. text ed. 37.50x (ISBN 0-262-19182-2); pap. 10.95x (ISBN 0-262-69071-3). MIT Pr.

Stein, Clarence S. Toward New Towns for America. (Illus.). 1966. pap. 10.95x (ISBN 0-262-69009-8). MIT Pr.

Untermann, Richard K. Accommodating the Pedestrian: Adapting Towns & Neighborhoods for Walking & Biking. (Illus.). 256p. 1984. 34.50 (ISBN 0-442-28823-9). Van Nos Reinhold.

Urban Development Strategies in the Context of Regional Development: Report of the Seminar Held at Nagoya, Japan, 28 Oct. - 8 Nov. 1974. 66p. 1975. pap. 5.00 (ISBN 0-686-75158-2, CRD002, UNCRD). Unipub.

Vasu, Michael L. Politics & Planning: A National Study of American Planners. LC 78-10440. (Institute for Research in Social Science Ser.). xv, 236p. 1979. 20.00 (ISBN 0-8078-1342-7). U of NC Pr.

Willis, F. Roy. Western Civilization: An Urban Perspective, 2 vols. 3rd ed. (Vol. 1, 688 pp.:vol. 2, 560 pp.). 1981. Vol. 1. pap. text ed. 17.95 (ISBN 0-669-03364-2); Vol. 2. pap. text ed. 17.95 (ISBN 0-669-03365-0); instr's guide 1.95 (ISBN 0-669-03366-9). Heath.

CITY SURVEYING

see Surveying

CITY TRAFFIC

Levine, W. S. & Lieberman, E., eds. Issues in Control of Urban Traffic Systems. LC 81-71830. 268p. 1982. pap. write for info. (ISBN 0-939204-07-X). Eng Found.

Mitchell, Robert B. & Rapkin, Chester. Urban Traffic, a Function of Land Use. LC 74-12851. (Columbia Institute for Urban Land Use & Housing Studies). (Illus.). 226p. 1974. Repr. of 1954 ed. lib. bdg. 15.00 (ISBN 0-8371-7766-9, MIUT). Greenwood.

Taebel, Delbert A. & Cornehls, James V. The Political Economy of Urban Transportation. LC 77-23150. (National University Publications Interdisciplinary Urban Ser). (Illus.). 1977. 21.00 (ISBN 0-8046-9178-9, Pub. by Kennikat). Assoc Faculty Pr.

Vehicle Modifications for Urban Survival. (Economic & Survival Ser.). (Illus.). 50p. (Orig.). 1981. pap. 10.00 (ISBN 0-939856-18-2). Tech Group.

CITY TRANSPORTATION

see Urban Transportation

CIVIL ENGINEERING

see also Aqueducts; Arches; Bridges; Canals; Dams; Curves in Engineering; Docks; Drainage; Earthwork; Excavation; Foundations; Hydraulic Engineering; Irrigation; Marine Engineering; Masonry; Mechanical Engineering; Mining Engineering; Piers; Piling (Civil Engineering); Railroad Engineering; Railroads–Construction; Reclamation of Land; Rivers; Roads; Sanitary Engineering; Steel, Structural; Streets; Strength of Materials; Structural Dynamics; Surveying; Tunnels and Tunneling; Walls; Water-Supply Engineering; Wharves

also subdivision Public Works under names of countries, cities, etc. e.g. United States–Public Works

Abbett, R. W. American Civil Engineering Practice, Vol. 3. LC 56-11255. Repr. of 1973 ed. 120.00 (ISBN 0-8357-9835-6, 2055091). Bks Demand UMI.

Acid Rain. 174p. 1979. pap. 17.50x (ISBN 0-87262-202-9). Am Soc Civil Eng.

Aguilar, Rodolfo J. Systems Analysis & Design in Engineering, Architecture, Construction, & Planning. (Civil Engineering & Engineering Mechanics Ser). (Illus.). 448p. 1973. ref. ed. 33.95 (ISBN 0-13-881458-9). P-H.

Allen, H. G. & Bulson, P. S. Background to Buckling. (Illus.). 1980. text ed. 60.00x (ISBN 0-07-084100-4). McGraw.

American Society of Civil Engineers, Conference, North Carolina State Univ., May 1977. Advances in Civil Engineering Through Engineering Mechanics: Proceedings. 634p. 1977. pap. 36.00x (ISBN 0-87262-087-5). Am Soc Civil Eng.

American Society of Civil Engineers, compiled By. Applied Techniques for Cold Environments, 2 vols. 1183p. 1978. pap. 64.00x (ISBN 0-87262-182-0). Am Soc Civil Eng.

--ASCE-ICE-CSCE: Predicting & Designing for Natural & Man Made Hazards, 1978. 300p. 1979. pap. 30.00x (ISBN 0-87262-187-1). Am Soc Civil Eng.

--Case Studies of Applied Advanced Data Collection & Management. LC 80-65303. 416p. 1980. pap. 29.00x (ISBN 0-87262-037-9). Am Soc Civil Eng.

American Society of Civil Engineers & Norris, G. M., eds. Cone Penetration Testing & Experience. LC 81-69229. 485p. 1981. pap. 34.75x (ISBN 0-87262-284-3). Am Soc Civil Eng.

American Society of Civil Engineers, compiled by. Converting Existing Hydro-Electric Dams & Reservoirs into Pumped Storage Facilities. 607p. 1975. pap. 19.00x (ISBN 0-87262-120-0). Am Soc Civil Eng.

American Society of Civil Engineers. Cumulative Index to ASCE Publications: 1975-1979. 1192p. 1979. 40.00x (ISBN 0-87262-175-8). Am Soc Civil Eng.

--Cumulative Index to ASCE Publications 1960-1969. 928p. 1970. 20.00x (ISBN 0-87262-232-0). Am Soc Civil Eng.

--Cumulative Index to ASCE Publications 1970-1974. 1066p. 1974. 24.00x (ISBN 0-87262-233-9). Am Soc Civil Eng.

American Society of Civil Engineers, compiled By. Engineering Ethics. 118p. 1975. pap. 7.00x (ISBN 0-87262-173-1). Am Soc Civil Eng.

American Society of Civil Engineers Staff, compiled By. Environmental Impacts of International Civil Engineering Projects & Practices. 263p. 1978. pap. 18.00x (ISBN 0-87262-129-4). Am Soc Civil Eng.

American Society of Civil Engineers, compiled by. Evaluation, Maintenance & Upgrading of Wood Structures: A Guide & Commentary. LC 82-72779. 434p. 1982. pap. 13.00x (ISBN 0-87262-317-3). Am Soc Civil Eng.

--Guide for The Field Testing of Bridges. LC 80-69154. 76p. 1980. pap. 12.00x (ISBN 0-87262-255-X). Am Soc Civil Eng.

American Society of Civil Engineers & Klohn, Charles H., eds. Joint Usage of Utility & Transportation Corridors. LC 81-68750. 127p. 1981. pap. 15.50x (ISBN 0-87262-277-0). Am Soc Civil Eng.

American Society of Civil Engineers & Smith, D. J., Jr., eds. Lifeline Earthquake Engineering: The Current State of Knowledge. LC 81-67748. 360p. 1981. pap. 28.00x (ISBN 0-87262-274-6). Am Soc Civil Eng.

American Society of Civil Engineers & Yong, R. N., eds. Limit Equilibrium, Plasticity & Generalized Stress-Strain in Geotechnical Engineering. LC 81-69233. 875p. 1981. pap. 55.75x (ISBN 0-87262-282-7). Am Soc Civil Eng.

American Society of Civil Engineers. Placement & Improvement of Soil to Support Structures: Specialty Conference held at Cambridge, MA, August 26-28, 1968. LC 72-185397. (Illus.). pap. 111.50 (ISBN 0-317-08328-7, 2019535). Bks Demand UMI.

American Society of Civil Engineers, compiled by. Quality System in Construction. 210p. 1974. pap. 11.00x (ISBN 0-87262-073-5). Am Soc Civil Eng.

American Society of Civil Engineers, Engineering Mechanics Division. The Relation of Engineering Mechanics Research to the Practice of Civil Engineering: Engineering Mechanics Division Specialty Conference, Washington, D.C., October 12-14, 1966. LC 67-1660. (Illus.). pap. 160.00 (ISBN 0-317-11018-7, 2004904). Bks Demand UMI.

American Society of Civil Engineers, compiled by. Site Characterization & Exploration. 401p. 1979. pap. 15.00x (ISBN 0-87262-186-3). Am Soc Civil Eng.

American Society of Civil Engineers. Transactions of the American Society of Civil Engineers, Vol. 144. 1979. 22.50x (ISBN 0-87262-236-3). Am Soc Civil Eng.

American Society of Civil Engineers, compiled by. Transactions of the American Society of Civil Engineers, Vol. 146, 1981. 1056p. 1982. 52.50x (ISBN 0-87262-309-2). Am Soc Civil Eng.

Appropriate Technologies in Civil Engineering Works in Developing Countries. pap. 3.50 (ISBN 0-686-94717-7, UN76/2A2, UN). Unipub.

ASCE Combined Index. Incl. ASCE Combined Index, 1980. 528p. 1981 (ISBN 0-87262-349-1); ASCE Combined Index, 1981. 209p. 1982 (ISBN 0-87262-314-9); ASCE Combined Index, 1982. 304p. 1983 (ISBN 0-87262-350-5). 528p. pap. 20.00 ea. Am Soc Civil Eng.

ASCE Committee on Engineering Management, Aug. 1976. Civil Engineer's Role in Productivity in the Construction Industry, 2 vols. 402p. 1976. Set. pap. 17.75x (ISBN 0-87262-075-1). Am Soc Civil Eng.

ASCE Conference, Construction Division, 1979. Construction Risks & Liability Sharing, 2 vols. LC 80-65819. 427p. 1979. pap. 42.00x (ISBN 0-87262-048-4). Am Soc Civil Eng.

ASCE Conference, San Francisco, May 1978. Coastal Zone '78: 1978, 4 vols. 3195p. 1978. Set. pap. 118.00x (ISBN 0-87262-134-0). Am Soc Civil Eng.

ASCE Conference, Surveying & Mapping Division, 1980. The Planning & Engineering Interface with a Modernized Land Data System. Marks, G. Warren, ed. LC 80-66123. 269p. 1980. pap. 26.50x (ISBN 0-87262-243-6). Am Soc Civil Eng.

ASCE Conference, Waterway, Port, Coastal & Ocean Division, 1980. Ports '80. Mascenik, John, ed. LC 80-65719. 849p. 1980. pap. 50.00x (ISBN 0-87262-108-1). Am Soc Civil Eng.

ASCE Guide to Employment Conditions for Civil Engineers. (Manual & Report on Engineering Practice Ser.: No. 55). 24p. 1980. pap. 7.00x (ISBN 0-87262-229-0). Am Soc Civil Eng.

ASCE Professional Activities Committee Conference, March 1977. Ethics, Professionalism, & Maintaining Competence. American Society of Civil Engineers, compiled By. 357p. 1977. pap. 18.50x (ISBN 0-87262-076-X). Am Soc Civil Eng.

ASCE, Technical Council on Computer Practices, 1980. Computing in Civil Engineering 1980. Schelling, David R., ed. LC 80-66141. 739p. 1980. pap. 34.00x (ISBN 0-87262-246-0). Am Soc Civil Eng.

ASCE Waterway, Port Coastal & Ocean Division Conference, Charleston, Nov. 1977. Coastal Sediments: 1977. American Society of Civil Engineers, compiled By. 1143p. 1977. pap. 47.00x (ISBN 0-87262-090-5). Am Soc Civil Eng.

Bache, David H. & MacAskill, Ian A. Vegetation in Civil & Landscape Engineering. (Illus.). 320p. 1984. text ed. 40.00x (ISBN 0-246-11507-6, Pub. by Granada England). Sheridan.

Baguelin, F., et al. The Pressuremeter & Foundation Engineering. (Rock & Soil Mechanics Ser.). (Illus.). 1978. 58.00x (ISBN 0-87849-019-1). Trans Tech.

Beards, C. F. Vibration Analysis & Control System Dynamic. LC 81-6646. (Ser. in Engineering Science: Civil Engineering). 169p. 1981. 54.95x (ISBN 0-470-27255-4). Halsted Pr.

Blake, L. S., ed. Civil Engineer's Reference Book. 3rd ed. 1800p. 1977. 119.95 (ISBN 0-408-70475-6). Butterworth.

Boughton, Brian. Building & Civil Engineering Construction, Vol. 1. 192p. 1983. pap. 10.00x (ISBN 0-246-11966-7, Pub. by Granada England). Sheridan.

--Building & Civil Engineering Construction, Vol. 2. 173p. 1983. pap. 10.00x (ISBN 0-246-11967-5, Pub. by Granada England). Sheridan.

Boughton, Brian W. Building & Civil Engineering Construction, Vol. 2. 168p. 1983. pap. text ed. 12.50x (Pub. by Granada England). Brookfield Pub Co.

Brandon, Peter S. & Powell, James A, eds. Quality & Profit in Building Design. 400p. 1985. 52.00 (ISBN 0-419-13390-9, NO. 9191, Pub. by E & FN Spon England). Methuen Inc.

Braun, Gerhard. Planning & Engineering of Shortwave Links. 252p. 1982. 44.95 (ISBN 0-471-26213-7, Pub. by Wiley Heyden). Wiley.

Brown, Roger J. Permafrost in Canada: Its Influence on Northern Development. LC 70-464841. (Illus.). 1970. 27.50x (ISBN 0-8020-1602-2). U of Toronto Pr.

Caldwell, Stan R. & Crissman, Randy D., eds. Design for Ice Forces. LC 83-70400. 224p. 1983. pap. 21.25x (ISBN 0-87262-356-4). Am Soc Civil Eng.

Chen, W. F. & Lewis, A. D., eds. Recent Advances in Engineering Mechanics & Their Impact on Civil Engineering Practice, 2 Vols. 1378p. 1983. pap. 106.00x (ISBN 0-87262-358-0). Am Soc Civil Eng.

Chen, W. F. & Ting, E. C., eds. Fracture in Concrete. LC 80-69656. 114p. 1980. pap. 12.00x (ISBN 0-87262-259-2). Am Soc Civil Eng.

Christian, Anthony J. Management, Machines & Methods in Civil Engineering. LC 81-2434. (Construction Management & Engineering Ser.). 360p. 1981. 45.95x (ISBN 0-471-06334-7, Pub. by Wiley-Interscience). Wiley.

Civil & Environmental Engineering Aspects of Energy Complexes: Proceedings of the Engineering Foundation Conference, August 1975. 456p. 1976. pap. 14.00x (ISBN 0-87262-153-7). Am Soc Civil Eng.

The Civil Engineer: His Origins. 122p. 1970. pap. 6.50x (ISBN 0-87262-024-7). Am Soc Civil Eng.

Civil Engineering Classics: Outstanding Papers of Thomas R. Camp. 418p. 1973. pap. 16.00x (ISBN 0-87262-053-0). Am Soc Civil Eng.

Civil Engineering Education, 2 vols. 1119p. 1979. Set. pap. 48.00x (ISBN 0-87262-195-2). Am Soc Civil Eng.

Civil Engineering Education: Related to Engineering Practice & to the Nation's Needs, 2 Vols. 1545p. 1974. Set. pap. 48.00x (ISBN 0-87262-110-3). Am Soc Civil Eng.

Civil Engineering Procedure. 3rd ed. 112p. 1979. pap. 8.00x (ISBN 0-7277-0113-4). Am Soc Civil Eng.

Civil Engineering Work: A Compendium of Occupational Safety Practice. (Occupational Safety & Health Ser.: No. 45). vii, 153p. 1981. pap. 11.40 (ISBN 92-2-102577-2, ILO180, ILO). Unipub.

Civil Engineers in the World Around Us. 299p. 1974. pap. 13.50x (ISBN 0-87262-069-7). Am Soc Civil Eng.

Coastal Engineering International Conference, 15th, Honolulu, Hawaii, July 1976 & American Society of Civil Engineers. Coastal Engineering: 1976, 4 vols. 2242p. 1977. Set. pap. 110.00x (ISBN 0-87262-083-2). Am Soc Civil Eng.

Coastal Engineering International Conference, 16th, Hamburg, Germany, Aug. 1978. Coastal Engineering: 1978, 3 vols. American Society of Civil Engineers, compiled By. 3096p. 1979. pap. 110.00x (ISBN 0-87262-190-1). Am Soc Civil Eng.

Coastal Engineering: Proceedings of the 13th Coastal Engineering International Conference, Vancouver, BC, Canada, July 1972, 3 vols. American Society of Civil Engineers, compiled By. 3476p. 1973. Set. pap. 99.00x (ISBN 0-87262-049-2). Am Soc Civil Eng.

Cost Control & Accounting for Civil Engineers. (Manual & Report on Engineering Practice Ser.: No. 33). 34p. 1971. pap. 4.00x (ISBN 0-87262-210-X). Am Soc Civil Eng.

Council on Tall Buildings & Urban Habitat. Tall Building Criteria & Loading. LC 79-56002. (Monographs on the Planning & Design of Tall Buildings: No. 5). 900p. 1980. 50.00x (ISBN 0-87262-237-1). Am Soc Civil Eng.

Currie, B. & Sharpe, R. A. Design of Structural Elements Level IV. (Illus.). 176p. 1984. pap. text ed. 23.95x (ISBN 0-7121-0443-7). Trans-Atlantic.

Derucher, Kenneth & Heins, Conrad. Materials for Civil & Highway Engineers. (Illus.). 416p. 1981. text ed. 37.95 (ISBN 0-13-560490-7). P-H.

Edge, Billy L., ed. Coastal Zone '80: 1980, 4 vols. LC 80-69152. 3302p. 1980. Set. pap. 110.00x (ISBN 0-87262-258-4). Am Soc Civil Eng.

Electric Power & the Civil Engineer. 688p. 1974. pap. 39.50x (ISBN 0-87262-070-0). Am Soc Civil Eng.

Engineering Foundation Conference, Jan. 1978. Evaluation & Prediction of Subsidence. American Society of Civil Engineers, compiled By. 600p. 1979. pap. 36.00x (ISBN 0-87262-137-5). Am Soc Civil Eng.

Engineering Foundation Conference, Nov. 1974. The Constructed Environment with Man as the Measure. 322p. pap. 22.00x (ISBN 0-87262-157-X). Am Soc Civil Eng.

Friedlander, S. K. Smoke, Dust & Haze: Fundamentals of Aerosol Behavior. LC 76-26928. 317p. 1977. 46.50x (ISBN 0-471-01468-0, Pub. by Wiley Interscience). Wiley.

Fuller, Frank. Deep Foundations. LC 80-69155. 544p. 1980. pap. 25.00x (ISBN 0-87262-256-8). Am Soc Civil Eng.

Gach, Gary. Preparing the Ground. 48p. (Orig.). 1975. pap. text ed. 3.00 (ISBN 0-915970-02-3). Heirs Intl.

Gheorghiu, A. & Dragomir, V. Geometry of Structural Forms. (Illus.). 319p. 1978. 44.50 (ISBN 0-85334-683-6, Pub. by Elsevier Applied Sci England). Elsevier.

Gilmore, Robert. Catastrophe Theory for Scientists & Engineers. LC 80-22154. 666p. 1981. 58.95x (ISBN 0-471-05064-4, Pub. by Wiley-Interscience). Wiley.

Gregory, C. E. Explosives for North American Engineers. 3rd ed. (Rock & Soil Mechanics Ser.). (Illus.). 1983p. 1979. 29.50x (ISBN 0-87849-025-6); 38.00x (ISBN 0-87849-051-5). Trans Tech.

Hagerty, D. Joseph & Heer, John E., Jr. Opportunities in Civil Engineering. (VGM Career Bks.). (Illus.). 160p. 1983. 7.95 (ISBN 0-317-03472-3, 6569-0, Passport Bks.); pap. 5.95 (ISBN 0-317-03473-1, 6570-8). Natl Textbk.

Hall. The Language of Civil Engineering in English. (English for Careers Ser.). 1977. pap. text ed. 4.25 (ISBN 0-88345-282-0, 18516). Regents Pub.

Hanna, T. H. Foundation Instrumentation. new ed. LC 72-90015. (Rock & Soil Mechanics Ser.). (Illus.). 400p. 1973. 35.00 (ISBN 0-87849-006-X). Trans Tech.

Hardy, H. Reginald & Leighton, Frederick W. Proceedings of the Second Conference on Acoustic Emission: Microseismic Activity in Geologic Structures & Materials. (Rock & Soil Mechanics Ser.). (Illus.). 500p. 1980. 45.00x (ISBN 0-87849-032-9). Trans Tech.

Harris, Robert B. Precedence & Arrow Networking Techniques for Construction. LC 78-5786. 429p. 1978. text ed. 46.75 (ISBN 0-471-04123-8). Wiley.

Hart, Gary. Dynamic Response of Structures: Experimentation, Observation, Prediction & Control. LC 80-70135. 960p. 1980. pap. 65.00x (ISBN 0-87262-261-4). Am Soc Civil Eng.

Holm, Dieter. Energy Conservation in Hot Climates. (Illus.). 160p. 1983. pap. 32.50 (ISBN 0-89397-159-6). Nichols Pub.

Horner, P. C. Earthworks. 54p. 1981. pap. 6.50x (ISBN 0-7277-0091-X). Am Soc Civil Eng.

Institution of Civil Engineers Staff, ed. Corrosion in Civil Engineering. 186p. 1979. 26.50x (ISBN 0-7277-0079-0). Am Soc Civil Eng.

International Conference, 14th, Copenhagen, Denmark, June 1974. Coastal Engineering: 1974, 3 vols. American Society of Civil Engineers, compiled by. 2705p. 1975. pap. 110.00x (ISBN 0-87262-113-8). Am Soc Civil Eng.

International Conference, 17th on Costal Engineering, Australia, March, 1980. Coastal Engineering: 1980, 3 vols. LC 81-69156. 3249p. 1981. pap. 150.00x (ISBN 0-87262-264-9). Am Soc Civil Eng.

International Labour Office Staff. Civil Engineering Work: A Compendium of Occupational Safety Practice. (Occupational Safety & Health Ser.: No. 45). viii, 153p. (Orig.). 1981. pap. 11.40 (ISBN 92-2-102577-2). Intl Labour Office.

International Symposium on Stratified Flows. 756p. 1973. pap. 32.50x (ISBN 0-87262-059-X). Am Soc Civil Eng.

Jackson, N. Civil Engineering Materials. 3rd ed. (Illus.). 429p. 1984. 39.50x (ISBN 0-333-34791-9, Pub. by Macmillan England). Scholium Intl.

Jeremic, M. L. Elements of Hydraulic Coal Mine Design. LC 83-10762. 160p. 1983. 30.95x (ISBN 0-87201-444-4). Gulf Pub.

Jones, R. Construction Estimating. 152p. 1967. pap. 17.00 (ISBN 0-8273-0108-1); pads 2.00 (ISBN 0-8273-0110-3). Delmar.

Jude, D. V. Civil Engineering Drawing. 2nd ed. 151p. 1983. pap. text ed. 19.95 (ISBN 0-246-11752-4, Granada England). Brookfield Pub Co.

Judson, David, ed. Caving Practice & Equipment. (Illus.). 224p. 1984. 27.00 (ISBN 0-7153-8155-5). David & Charles.

Keen, C. E., ed. Crustal Properties Across Passive Margins. (Developments in Grotectonics Ser.: Vol. 15). 390p. 1980. 93.50 (ISBN 0-444-41852-0). Elsevier.

Kennie. Remote Sensing in Civil Engineering. 1985. 75.00 (ISBN 0-470-20135-5). Wiley.

Krausz, A S. Time Dependent Fracture. 1985. lib. bdg. 39.50 (ISBN 90-247-3132-1, Pub. by Martinus Nijhoff Neatherlands). Kluwer Academic.

Laithwaite, E. R. Linear Motor & Its Application to Tracked Hovercraft. 12p. 1971. pap. 2.25x (ISBN 0-317-03988-1). Am Soc Civil Eng.

Lama, R. D. & Vutukuri, V. S. Handbook on Mechanical Properties of Rocks, Vol. III. (Rock & Soil Mechanics Ser.). (Illus.). 1978. 65.00x (ISBN 0-87849-022-1). Trans Tech.

--Handbook on Mechanical Properties of Rocks, Vol. IV. (Rock & Soil Mechanics Ser.). (Illus.). 1978. 65.00x (ISBN 0-87849-023-X). Trans Tech.

Lee, Ian K., et al. Geotechnical Engineering. LC 81-13787. 512p. 1982. text ed. 38.95 (ISBN 0-273-01755-1). Pitman Pub MA.

Leliavsky, S. Arches & Short Span Bridges. (Design Textbooks in Civil Engineering: Vol. 7). (Illus.). 250p. 1982. 39.95 (ISBN 0-412-22560-3, NO. 6686, Pub. by Chapman & Hall England). Methuen Inc.

McCaffrey, R. G., et al. The Civil Engineering Standard Method of Measurement in Practice. 250p. 1983. pap. text ed. 29.95x (ISBN 0-246-11928-4, Pub. by Granada England). Brookfield Pub Co.

McGuire, William & Gallagher, Richard H. Matrix Structural Analysis. LC 78-8471. 460p. 1979. text ed. 51.75 (ISBN 0-471-03059-7); solutions manual avail. (ISBN 0-471-05535-2). Wiley.

McLean, Adam C. & Gribble, Colin D. Geology for Civil Engineers. (Illus.). 1979. text ed. 30.00x (ISBN 0-04-624001-2); pap. text ed. 15.95x. Allen Unwin.

Major. Dynamics in Civil Engineering, 4 vols. 1981. Set. 124.00 (ISBN 0-9960070-5-9, Pub. by Akademiai Kaido Hungary); 35.00 ea. Vol. 1 (ISBN 0-9960071-3-X). Vol. 2 (ISBN 0-9960071-4-8). Vol. 3 (ISBN 0-9960071-5-6). Vols.4 (ISBN 0-9960071-6-4). Heyden.

Major, A. Dynamic Civil Engineering, 4 Vols. 1981. price 124.00 set (ISBN 0-9960070-5-9, Pub. by Akademiai Kaido Hungary); Vol. 1. 35.00 (ISBN 0-9960071-3-X); Vol. 2. 35.00 (ISBN 0-9960071-4-8); Vol. 3. 35.00 (ISBN 0-9960071-5-6); Vol. 4. 35.00 (ISBN 0-9960071-6-4). Heyden.

Marks, R. J., et al. Aspects of Civil Engineering Contract Procedure. 2nd ed. 1978. text ed. 30.00 (ISBN 0-08-021013-9); pap. text ed. 14.00 (ISBN 0-08-021012-0). Pergamon.

Merritt, Frederick S., ed. Standard Handbook for Civil Engineers. 3rd ed. 1664p. 1983. 83.40 (ISBN 0-07-041515-3). McGraw.

Meyer, Carl F. & Gibson, David W. Route Surveying & Design. 5th ed. (Illus.). 1980. text ed. 28.50 scp (ISBN 0-7002-2524-2, HarpC). Har-Row.

Modeling Techniques, 2 vols. 1709p. 1975. pap. 67.00x (ISBN 0-87262-124-3). Am Soc Civil Eng.

Monismith, Carl L. Addressing Societal Needs of the 1980's Through Civil Engineering Research. LC 82-70765. 335p. 1982. pap. 34.75x (ISBN 0-87262-300-9). Am Soc Civil Eng.

Munson, Albe E. Construction Design for Landscape Architects. (Illus.). 212p. 1974. 44.50 (ISBN 0-07-044046-8). McGraw.

Nelson, John. Drafting for Trades & Industry - Civil. LC 77-91450. (Drafting Ser.). 942p. 1979. pap. text ed. 8.80 (ISBN 0-8273-1844-8); instructor's guide 5.25 (ISBN 0-8273-1641-0). Delmar.

Newmark, Nathan M. Selected Papers by Nathan M. Newmark. LC 76-25684. (Civil Engineering Classics Ser.). (Illus.). pap. 160.00 (ISBN 0-317-08325-2, 2019537). Bks Demand UMI.

O'Neill, Michael W. & Dobry, Ricardo, eds. Dynamic Response of Pile Foundations: Analytical Aspects. LC 80-69151. 118p. 1980. pap. 12.00x (ISBN 0-87262-257-6). Am Soc Civil Eng.

O'Reilly, Arthur T. Civil Engineering Claims. 300p. 1986. 40.00x (ISBN 0-246-12121-1, Pub. by Granada England). Sheridan.

Paxton, J. M. Manual of Civil Engineering Plant & Equipment. 2nd ed. (Illus.). 592p. 1977. 111.00 (ISBN 0-85334-500-7, Pub. by Elsevier Applied Sci England). Elsevier.

Pinfold, Geoffrey M. Reinforced Concrete Chimneys & Towers. (C & CA Viewpoint Publication Ser.). (Illus.). 1976. text ed. 24.50x (ISBN 0-7210-0993-X). Scholium Intl.

Planning, Engineering & Constructing the Superprojects. 537p. 1979. pap. 27.00x (ISBN 0-87262-178-2). Am Soc Civil Eng.

Plastic Design in Steel: A Guide & Commentary. (Manual & Report of Engineering Practice Ser.: No. 41). 348p. 1971. pap. 15.00x (ISBN 0-87262-217-7). Am Soc Civil Eng.

Plate, E., ed. Engineering Meteorology. (Studies in Wind Engineering & Industrial Aerodynamics: Vol. 1). 740p. 1982. 149.00 (ISBN 0-444-41972-1, I-272-82). Elsevier.

Powell, James A. & Cooper, Ian, eds. Designing For Building Utilisation. 400p. 1985. 47.50 (ISBN 0-419-13470-0, NO. 7337, Pub. by E & FN Spon England). Methuen Inc.

Pumping Manual. 7th ed. LC 83-82524. 650p. 1984. 59.95x (ISBN 0-87201-751-6). Gulf Pub.

Rankilor, P. R. Membranes in Civil Engineering. LC 80-40504. 377p. 1981. 69.95 (ISBN 0-471-27808-4, Pub. by Wiley-Interscience). Wiley.

Reynolds, G. J. Measurement of Civil Engineering Work. 132p. 1980. pap. text ed. 14.50x (ISBN 0-246-11376-6, Pub. by Granada England). Brookfield Pub Co.

Safety & Health in Building & Civil Engineering Work: ILO Code of Practice. 1981. 17.10 (ISBN 92-2-100974-2). Intl Labour Office.

Salt, Harriet. Mighty Engineering Feats. facs. ed. LC 71-86782. (Essay Index Reprint Ser). 1937. 20.00 (ISBN 0-8369-1193-8). Ayer Co Pubs.

Schultz, John R. & Cleaves, A. B. Geology in Engineering. LC 55-7317. 592p. 1955. text ed. 47.50 (ISBN 0-471-76461-2). Wiley.

Schwartz, Max. Civil Engineering for the Plant Engineer. 2nd ed. LC 79-21884. 416p. 1984. lib. bdg. 29.50 (ISBN 0-317-19767-3) (ISBN 0-89874-050-9). Krieger.

Selected Papers by Alfred M. Freudenthal: Civil Engineering Classics. 813p. 1981. pap. 54.00x (ISBN 0-87262-263-0). Am Soc Civil Eng.

Sharp, B. B. Water Hammer: Problems & Solutions. 152p. 1981. text ed. 34.50 (ISBN 0-7131-3427-5). E Arnold.

Simiu, Emil & Scanlan, Robert H. Wind Effects on Structures: An Introduction to Wind Engineering. LC 77-21192. 458p. 1978. 48.50x (ISBN 0-471-02175-X, Pub. by Wiley-Interscience). Wiley.

Smith, Alan A., et al. Civil Engineering Systems Analysis & Design. LC 82-13640. 473p. 1983. text ed. write for info. (ISBN 0-471-90059-1, Pub. by Wiley-Interscience); pap. text ed. 31.95 (ISBN 0-471-90060-5). Wiley.

Smith, G. N. Introduction to Matrix & Finite Elements in Civil Engineering. (Illus.). 222p. 1971. 20.50 (ISBN 0-85334-502-3, Pub. by Elsevier Applied Sci England). Elsevier.

Snethen, Donald. Expansive Soils, 2 vols. LC 66-140. 935p. 1980. pap. 46.00x (ISBN 0-87262-245-2). Am Soc Civil Eng.

Stark, R. M. & Nichols, R. L. Mathematical Foundation for Design. 1972. text ed. 48.00 (ISBN 0-07-060857-1). McGraw.

Stopher, Peter R., et al, eds. New Horizons in Travel-Behavior Research. LC 78-24830. 784p. 1981. 45.00 (ISBN 0-669-02850-9). Lexington Bks.

Storr, Eric D., ed. Hydraulics in Civil Engineering. 300p. 1984. pap. text ed. 20.00x (ISBN 0-85825-211-2, Pub. by Inst Engineers Australia). Brookfield Pub Co.

Teeni, M., ed. Structure, Solid Mechanics & Engineering Design, the Proceedings of the Southampton 1969 Civil Engineering Materials Conference, Pts. 1 & 2. LC 71-149573. Pt. 1. pap. 160.00 (ISBN 0-317-29877-1, 2016150); Pt. 2. pap. 147.00 (ISBN 0-317-29878-X). Bks Demand UMI.

Templeman, Andrew B. Civil Engineering Systems. (Illus.). 375p. 1983. text ed. 47.50x (ISBN 0-333-28509-3); pap. text ed. 24.95x (ISBN 0-333-28510-7). Scholium Intl.

Transactions Nineteen Seventy-Eight. 1979. text ed. 18.00 (ISBN 0-87262-235-5). Am Soc Civil Eng.

Transactions Nineteen Seventy-Seven. 808p. 1978. text ed. 12.00 (ISBN 0-87262-234-7). Am Soc Civil Eng.

Urquhart, Leonard C. Civil Engineering Handbook. 4th ed. 1959. 69.50 (ISBN 0-07-066148-0). McGraw.

Vanmarcke, Erik. Random Fields: Analysis & Synthesis. (Illus.). 416p. 1983. 47.50x (ISBN 0-262-22026-1). MIT Pr.

Vine, G. B. Structural Analysis. LC 80-42209. (Constructions & Civil Engineering Sector: Technician Ser.). (Illus.). 288p. (Orig.). 1982. pap. text ed. 10.95 (ISBN 0-582-41618-3). Longman.

Wang, Lawrence & Pereira, Norman, eds. Handbook of Environmental Engineering, Vol. 4. (Handbook of Environmental Engineering Ser.). 480p. 1985. 74.50 (ISBN 0-89603-059-8). Humana.

Warring, R. H. Pumps: Selection, Systems, & Applications. 2nd ed. LC 83-82095. 280p. 1984. 49.95x (ISBN 0-87201-736-2). Gulf Pub.

Wisely, William H. The American Civil Engineer: 1852 - 1974: The History, Traditions & Development of the ASCE. LC 74-17792. 474p. 1974. 20.00x (ISBN 0-87262-000-X). Am Soc Civil Eng.

Yu, Wei-Wen. Cold-Formed Steel Structures. LC 78-20815. 478p. 1979. Repr. of 1973 ed. lib. bdg. 26.50 (ISBN 0-88275-845-4). Krieger.

Zaruba, Q. & Mencl, V. Engineering Geology. (Developments in Geotechnical Engineering: Vol. 10). 504p. 1976. text ed. 51.00 (ISBN 0-444-99877-2). Elsevier.

Zienkiewicz, O. C. The Finite Element Method. 3rd ed. (Illus.). 1978. text ed. 49.00 (ISBN 0-07-084072-5). McGraw.

Zilly, Robert G., ed. Handbook of Environmental Civil Engineering. LC 74-26993. pap. 160.00 (ISBN 0-317-08181-0, 2014901). Bks Demand UMI.

CIVIL ENGINEERING–BIBLIOGRAPHY

Palyza, M. M. Useful Books of Reference for Designers (1926-1983) Held by the Science Reference Library: Pt 1 Units in Physics, Metrication, Mettallurgy, Computers in Engineering, Civil Engineering. 168p. (Orig.). 1984. pap. 7.50 (ISBN 0-7123-0712-5, Pub. by British Lib). Longwood Pub Group.

CIVIL ENGINEERING–DATA PROCESSING

American Society of Civil Engineers. Computing in Civil Engineering: Conference. (Illus.). pap. 160.00 (ISBN 0-317-08312-0, 2019544). Bks Demand UMI.

American Society of Civil Engineers, ed. Introductory Manual on Computer Services. (Manual & Report on Engineering Practice Ser.: No. 61). 92p. 1983. pap. 16.00x (ISBN 0-87262-366-1). Am Soc Civil Eng.

ASCE Technical Council on Computer Practices, New York, May, 1981. International Conference on Computing in Civil Engineering. LC 81-66346. 1222p. 1981. pap. 75.50x (ISBN 0-87262-270-3). Am Soc Civil Eng.

Cope, R. & Sawko, F. Computer Methods for Civil Engineering. 336p. 1982. 19.00 (ISBN 0-07-084129-2). McGraw.

Engineering Equipment & Automation Means for Waste-Water Management in ECE Countries, Pt. 1. 111p. 12.50 (ISBN 0-317-18703-1, E.84.II.E.13). UN.

Hromadka, T. V., II & Clements, J. Computer Methods in Urban Watershed Hydraulics. Hromadka, Laura, ed. LC 83-82787. (Illus.). 296p. (Orig.). 1984. pap. text ed. 38.50 (ISBN 0-914055-02-X). Lighthouse Pubns.

Hromadka, T. V., II & Durban, T. J. Computer Methods in Water Resources. Hromadka, Laura, ed. LC 83-82824. (Illus.). 318p. (Orig.). 1984. pap. text ed. 37.50 (ISBN 0-914055-01-1). Lighthouse Pubns.

Jenkins. Basic Computing for Civil Engineers. 1983. 13.95 (ISBN 0-442-30558-3). Van Nos Reinhold.

McCuen, R. FORTRAN Programming for Civil Engineers. 1975. pap. 26.95 (ISBN 0-13-329417-X). P-H.

Medearis, Kenneth. Report on an Investigation of the Feasibility of Establishing a National Civil Engineering Software Center to the American Society of Civil Engineers for the Research Council on Computer Practices. LC 79-302366. pap. 32.00 (ISBN 0-317-20732-6, 2023822). Bks Demand UMI.

National Computing Centre Ltd., ed. Computers in Civil Engineering Design. 160p. 1972. pap. 40.00x (ISBN 0-85012-105-1). Intl Pubns Serv.

CIVIL ENGINEERING–DICTIONARIES

American Society of Civil Engineers, compiled by. Definitions of Surveying & Associated Terms. (Manual & Report on Engineering Practice Ser.: No. 34). 218p. 1978. pap. 8.00x (ISBN 0-87262-211-8). Am Soc Civil Eng.

Bucksch, H. Woerterbuch fuer Bautechnik und Baumaschinen. 4th ed. (Ger. & Fr.). 1976. pap. 112.00 (ISBN 0-686-56607-6, M-6922). French & Eur.

Bucksch, Herbert. Dictionary of Civil Engineering & Construction Machinery & Equipment, Vol. 1. 5th ed. (Fr. & Eng.). 420p. 1976. 30.00 (ISBN 3-7625-0533-0, M-7120). French & Eur.

--Dictionary of Civil Engineering & Construction Machinery & Equipment, Vol. 1. 7th ed. (Eng. & Ger.). 1978. leatherette 135.00 (ISBN 3-7625-0950-6, M-7122). French & Eur.

--Dictionary of Civil Engineering & Construction Machinery & Equipment, Vol. 2. 5th ed. (Fr. & Eng.). 548p. 1976. 40.00 (ISBN 3-7625-0534-9, M-7119). French & Eur.

--Dictionary of Civil Engineering & Construction Machinery & Equipment, Vol. 2. 7th ed. (Eng. & Ger.). 1978. leatherette 135.00 (ISBN 3-7625-0951-4, M-7121). French & Eur.

Building Industry & Civil Engineering Society. Dictionary of Technical Information, Vol. 41. 210p. 1980. 15.00x (ISBN 0-569-08243-9, Pub. by Collet's). State Mutual Bk.

English-Chinese Dictionary of Civil & Architectural Engineering Terms. (Eng. & Chinese.). 706p. 1979. 29.95 (ISBN 0-686-97359-3, M-9271). French & Eur.

Gerecke, Karl. Vademekum Technische Werte der Getreidemittelverarbeitung und Futtermitteltechnik. (Ger.). 160p. 1970. 20.00 (ISBN 3-87696-106-8, M-7133). French & Eur.

Huerlimann, Ernst. Lexikon Feurden Bauherrn. (Ger.). 1975. 28.50 (ISBN 3-478-04250-X, M-7202). French & Eur.

Research & Education Association. Technical Dictionary for Civil Engineers. 1408p. 1981. 32.65 (ISBN 0-87891-531-1). Res & Educ.

Robb, Louis A. Engineers' Dictionary, Spanish-English, English-Spanish. 2nd ed. LC 40-50261. (Span. & Eng.). 664p. 1949. 56.95 (ISBN 0-471-72501-3, Pub. by Wiley-Interscience). Wiley.

Scott, John S. Dictionary of Civil Engineering. 3rd ed. LC 80-24419. 308p. 1981. 24.95x (ISBN 0-470-27087-X). Halsted Pr.

--The Penguin Dictionary of Civil Engineering. (Reference Ser.). 312p. 1984. pap. 7.95 (ISBN 0-14-051011-7). Penguin.

Steinig, Karl. Woerterbuch fuer Strassenbau und Strassenverkehe. (Fr. & Ger.). 1970. 92.00 (ISBN 3-7812-0560-6, M-6921). French & Eur.

Wittke, Heinz. Vademekum fuer Vermessungstechnik. (Ger.). 334p. 1948. 15.95 (ISBN 3-476-40017-4, M-7134). French & Eur.

CIVIL ENGINEERING–ESTIMATES AND COSTS

see Engineering–Estimates and Costs

CIVIL ENGINEERING–EXAMINATIONS, QUESTIONS, ETC.

Brungraber, Robert L. Timber Design for the Civil Professional Engineering Exam. 175p. 1984. pap. 15.95 (ISBN 0-932276-38-5). Prof Engine.

Calder, Clarence A., ed. Mechanics of Materials Exam File. LC 84-24702. (Exam File Ser.). 378p. (Orig.). 1985. pap. 9.95 (ISBN 0-910554-46-3). Engineering.

Klemetson, Stanley L., ed. Fluid Mechanics Exam File. LC 84-24693. (Exam File Ser.). 218p. (Orig.). 1985. pap. 9.95 (ISBN 0-910554-48-X). Engineering.

Newnan, Donald G. & Lindskog, Robert E. Civil Engineering License Exam File. 9th ed. (Exam File Ser.). 316p. 1985. pap. 23.95 (ISBN 0-910554-50-1). Engineering.

Raphael, Coleman & Lindskog, Robert. Preparing for the Civil Engineering Professional Examination. LC 82-24270. 248p. 1983. pap. 21.95 (ISBN 0-910554-41-2). Engineering.

Rudman, Jack. Assistant Civil Engineer. (Career Examination Ser.: C-33). (Cloth bdg. avail. on request). pap. 12.00 (ISBN 0-8373-0033-9). Natl Learning.

--Bridge Maintenance Supervisor I. (Career Examination Ser.: C-855). (Cloth bdg. avail. on request). pap. 12.00 (ISBN 0-8373-0855-0). Natl Learning.

--Bridge Maintenance Supervisor II. (Career Examination Ser.: C-856). (Cloth bdg. avail. on request). pap. 12.00 (ISBN 0-8373-0856-9). Natl Learning.

--Bridge Maintenance Supervisor III. (Career Examination Ser.: C-857). (Cloth bdg. avil. on request). pap. 14.00 (ISBN 0-8373-0857-7). Natl Learning.

--Chief Civil Engineer. (Career Examination Ser.: C-1170). (Cloth bdg. avail. on request). pap. 14.00 (ISBN 0-8373-1170-5). Natl Learning.

--Civil Engineer. (Career Examination Ser.: C-136). (Cloth bdg. avail. on request). pap. 12.00 (ISBN 0-8373-0136-X). Natl Learning.

--Civil Engineer Five. (Career Examination Ser.: C-2162). (Cloth bdg. avail. on request). 1976. pap. 14.00 (ISBN 0-8373-2162-X). Natl Learning.

--Civil Engineer Four. (Career Examination Ser.: C-2161). (Cloth bdg. avail. on request). 1976. pap. 14.00 (ISBN 0-8373-2161-1). Natl Learning.

--Civil Engineer One. (Career Examination Ser.: C-2158). (Cloth bdg. avail. on request). 1976. pap. 12.00 (ISBN 0-8373-2158-1). Natl Learning.

--Civil Engineer: One to Five. (Career Examination Ser.: C-2000). (Cloth bdg. avail. on request). pap. 16.00 (ISBN 0-8373-2000-3). Natl Learning.

--Civil Engineer Three. (Career Examination Ser.: C-2160). (Cloth bdg. avail. on request). 1976. pap. 12.00 (ISBN 0-8373-2160-3). Natl Learning.

--Civil Engineer Two. (Career Examination Ser.: C-2159). (Cloth bdg. avail. on request). 1976. pap. 12.00 (ISBN 0-8373-2159-X). Natl Learning.

--Civil Engineering Draftsman I. (Career Examination Ser.: C-2154). (Cloth bdg. avail. on request). 1976. pap. 12.00 (ISBN 0-8373-2154-9). Natl Learning.

--Civil Engineering Draftsman II. (Career Examination Ser.: C-2155). (Cloth bdg. avail. on request). 1976. pap. 12.00 (ISBN 0-8373-2155-7). Natl Learning.

--Civil Engineering Draftsman III. (Career Examination Ser.: C-2156). (Cloth bdg. avail. on request). 1976. 14.00 (ISBN 0-8373-2156-5). Natl Learning.

--Civil Engineering Trainee. (Career Examination Ser.: C-945). (Cloth bdg. avail. on request). pap. 10.00 (ISBN 0-8373-0945-X). Natl Learning.

--Junior Civil Engineer. (Career Examination Ser.: C-395). (Cloth bdg. avail. on request). pap. 12.00 (ISBN 0-8373-0395-8). Natl Learning.

--Junior Civil Engineer Trainee. (Career Examination Ser.: C-212). (Cloth bdg. avail. on request). pap. 10.00 (ISBN 0-8373-0212-9). Natl Learning.

--Senior Civil Engineer. (Career Examination Ser.: C-998). (Cloth bdg. avail. on request). pap. 12.00 (ISBN 0-8373-0998-0). Natl Learning.

--Senior Civil Engineer (Structures) (Career Examination Ser.: C-1917). (Cloth bdg. avail. on request). pap. 14.00 (ISBN 0-8373-1917-X). Natl Learning.

--Town Engineer. (Career Examination Ser.: C-2001). (Cloth bdg. avail. on request). pap. 12.00 (ISBN 0-8373-2001-1). Natl Learning.

Smith, Charles E., ed. Dynamics Exam File. LC 84-24699. (Exam File Ser.). 346p. (Orig.). 1985. pap. 9.95 (ISBN 0-910554-44-7). Engineering.

--Statics Exam File. LC 84-21141. (Exam File Ser.). 346p. (Orig.). 1985. pap. 9.95 (ISBN 0-910554-47-1). Engineering.

CIVIL ENGINEERING–HANDBOOKS, MANUALS, ETC.

American Society of Civil Engineers, compiled by. Consulting Engineering: A Guide for the Engagement of Engineering Services. (Manual & Report on Engineering Practice Ser.: No. 45). 96p. 1975. pap. 8.00x (ISBN 0-87262-276-2). Am Soc Civil Eng.

American Society of Civil Engineers. Engineering & Contracting Procedure for Foundations: Responsibilities of the Contracting Parties. LC 42-229. (American Society of Civil Engineers Manuals of Engineering Practice Ser.: No. 8). pap. 20.00 (ISBN 0-317-08381-3, 2016450). Bks Demand UMI.

Lindeburg, Michael R. Civil Engineering Review Manual. 3rd ed. LC 81-81682. (Engineering Review Manual Ser.). (Illus.). 784p. (Orig.). 1981. pap. 37.95 (ISBN 0-932276-28-8); wkbk. o.p. 4.00 (ISBN 0-932276-17-2). Prof Engine.

Seeylye, E. E. Data Book for Civil Engineers, 2 vols. 3rd ed. Incl. Vol.1. Design. 670p. 1960. 97.95 (ISBN 0-471-77286-0); Vol.2. Specification & Costs. 566p. 1957. 91.95 (ISBN 0-471-77319-0). Wiley.

Stephens, W. B. Civil Engineering Technician's Ready Reference Manual. 408p. 1984. 29.95 (ISBN 0-07-061187-4). McGraw.

CIVIL ENGINEERING–HISTORY

The History of Civil Engineering Since 1600: An Annotated Bibliography. LC 84-45400. 250p. 1985. lib. bdg. 35.00 (ISBN 0-8240-8948-0). Garland Pub.

Upton, Neil. An Illustrated History of Civil Engineering. LC 76-41092. 191p. 1976. 17.50x (ISBN 0-8448-1032-0). Crane-Russak Co.

CIVIL ENGINEERING–MANAGEMENT

see Engineering–Management

CIVIL ENGINEERING–STUDY AND TEACHING

see Engineering–Study and Teaching

CIVIL ENGINEERING–TABLES, CALCULATIONS, ETC.

Barnes, Martin. Civil Engineering Standard Method of Measurement: Examples. 106p. 1977. pap. 6.50x (ISBN 0-7277-0035-9). Am Soc Civil Eng.

Civil Engineering Standard Method of Measurement. 62p. 1976. pap. 9.25x (ISBN 0-7277-0027-8). Am Soc Civil Eng.

Davis, Raymond E., et al. Surveying Theory & Practice. 6th ed. (Illus.). 1120p. 1981. text ed. 46.00 (ISBN 0-07-015790-1). McGraw.

CIVIL ENGINEERS

Davis, E. H. & Campbell-Allen, D. The Profession of a Civil Engineer: Studies in Honour of John Roderick. LC 79-670361. 1979. 29.00x (ISBN 0-424-00064-4, Pub. by Sydney U Pr). Intl Spec Bk.

Davis, Patricia. End of the Line: Alexander J. Cassatt & Pennsylvania Railroad. LC 78-977. 1978. 20.00 (ISBN 0-88202-181-8). Watson Pub Intl.

Lipinski, Martha E., ed. Role of the Civil Engineer in Highway Safety. 216p. 1983. pap. 23.00x (ISBN 0-87262-374-2). Am Soc Civil Eng.

CIVILIZATION AND ASTRONAUTICS

see Astronautics and Civilization

CIVILIZATION AND MACHINERY

see Technology and Civilization

CIVILIZATION AND SCIENCE

see Science and Civilization

CIVILIZATION AND TECHNOLOGY

see Technology and Civilization

CLADOSPORIUM

De Vries, G. A. Contribution to the Knowledge of the Genus Cladosporium Linx Ex Fries: Thesis. (Illus.). 1967. 16.00 (ISBN 3-7682-0458-8). Lubrecht & Cramer.

Van den Hoek, C. A Taxonomic Revision of the American Species of Cladophora (Chlorophyceae) in the North Atlantic. (Oceans & Their Geographic Distribution Ser.). Date not set. price not set (ISBN 0-444-85541-6). Elsevier.

CLARET

Simon, Andre L. All about Claret. (All About Wines: Vol. 7). 7.50 (ISBN 0-87559-179-5). Shalom.

CLASS FIELD THEORY

Cohn, Harvey. Introduction to the Construction of Class Fields. (Cambridge Studies in Advanced Mathematics: No. 6). (Illus.). 225p. 1985. 44.50 (ISBN 0-521-24762-4). Cambridge U Pr.

Frohlich, A. Central Extensions, Galois Groups, & Ideal Class Groups of Numbers Fields. LC 83-19685. (Contemporary Mathematics Ser.: Vol. 24). 86p. 1983. pap. 17.00 (ISBN 0-8218-5022-9). Am Math.

Seminar on Complex Multiplication, Institute for Advanced Study, Princeton & Borel, A. Proceedings. (Lecture Notes in Mathematics: Vol. 21). 1966. pap. 10.70 (ISBN 0-387-03604-0). Springer-Verlag.

Weil, A. Basic Number Theory. 3rd ed. LC 74-13963. (Die Grundlehren der Mathematischen Wissenschaften Ser.: Vol. 144). xviii, 325p. 1974. 33.00 (ISBN 0-387-06935-6). Springer-Verlag.

CLASSES (MATHEMATICS)

see Set Theory

CLASSICAL FIELD THEORY

see Field Theory (Physics)

CLASSIFICATION–BOOKS–MILITARY ART AND SCIENCE

Pohler, Johann. Bibliotheca Historico-Militaris, 4 Vols. 1899. 271.00 (ISBN 0-8337-2793-1). B Franklin.

CLASSIFICATION–BOOKS–SCIENCE

Lancaster, F. Wilfrid. Libraries & Librarians in on Age of Electronics. LC 82-81403. (Illus.). ix, 229p. 1982. text ed. 26.50 (ISBN 0-87815-040-4). Info Resources.

CLASSIFICATION–BOTANY

see Botany–Classification

CLASSIFICATION–PLANTS

see Botany–Classification

CLASSIFICATION–ROCKS

see Rocks–Classification and Nomenclature

CLASSIFICATION–ZOOLOGY

see Zoology–Classification

CLASSIFICATION OF SCIENCES

Cassiodorus. Introduction to Divine & Human Readings. Jones, L. W., tr. 1966. lib. bdg. 20.50x (ISBN 0-374-94275-7). Octagon.

Flint, Robert. Philosophy As Scientia Scientiarum: A History of Classifications of the Sciences. LC 74-26261. (History, Philosophy & Sociology of Science Ser). 1975. Repr. 25.00x (ISBN 0-405-06589-2). Ayer Co Pubs.

Slaughter, Mary. Universal Languages & Scientific Taxonomy in the Seventeenth Century. LC 81-20147. 304p. 1982. 52.50 (ISBN 0-521-24477-3). Cambridge U Pr.

Tennant, F. R. The Philosophy of the Sciences; or, the Relations Between the Departments of Knowledge. ix, 191p. 1973. Repr. of 1932 ed. 18.00 (ISBN 0-208-01317-2, Archon). Shoe String.

CLAY

see also Bricks; Ceramics; Particles

Anaejionu, Paul. X-Ray Diffraction Study to Assess the Potential Economic-Pharmaceutical Uses for Nigerian Clays. (Science & Development in Africa Ser.). 1979. pap. 10.00x (ISBN 0-914970-22-4). Conch Mag.

Bennett, Richard & Hulbert, Matthew H. Clay Microstructure. (Illus.). 218p. 1986. text ed. write for info. (ISBN 0-88746-065-8). Intl Human Res.

Beutelspacher, H. & Van Der Marel, H. Atlas of Electron Mic oscopy of Clay Minerals & Their Admixtures. 333p. 1968. 132.00 (ISBN 0-444-40041-9). Elsevier.

Brindley, G. W. & Brown, G., eds. Crystal Structures of Clay Minerals & Their X-Ray Identification. 495p. 1982. text ed. 70.00x (ISBN 0-903056-08-9, Mineralogical). Brookfield Pub Co.

Brownell, W. E. Structural Clay Products. LC 76-40216. (Applied Mineralogy Ser: Vol. 9). 1976. 61.00 (ISBN 0-387-81382-9). Springer-Verlag.

Campana, A. M. Teacher of Pottery, Clay Modeling, Casting, Sculpturing, Wood Carving. (Illus.). 1962. 5.40 (ISBN 0-939608-10-3). Campana Art.

Chappel, James. The Potter's Complete Book of Clay & Glazes. 448p. 1977. 27.50 (ISBN 0-8230-4202-2). Watson-Guptill.

Clay Fills. 330p. 1979. 47.50x (ISBN 0-7277-0069-3). Am Soc Civil Eng.

Clay Flowers Techniques, Bk. II. (Illus.). 1984. 12.00 (ISBN 0-916809-06-4). Scott Pubns MI.

Creer, K. M., et al, eds. Geomagnetism of Baked Clays & Recent Sediments. 324p. 1983. 53.25 (ISBN 0-444-42231-5, I-268-83). Elsevier.

Fowden, Leslie, et al, eds. Clay Minerals: Their Structure, Behavior & Use. (Illus.). 212p. 1984. lib. bdg. 70.00x (ISBN 0-85403-232-0, Pub. by Royal Soc London). Scholium Intl.

Grayson, Martin, ed. Encyclopedia of Glass, Ceramics, Clay & Cement. (Encyclopedia Reprint Ser.). 960p. 1985. 89.95x (ISBN 0-471-81931-X, Pub. by Wiley-Interscience). Wiley.

Grim, Ralph E. Applied Clay Mineralogy. LC 61-12035. (International Earth Science Ser.). pap. 105.50 (ISBN 0-317-28224-7, 2055970). Bks Demand UMI.

--Clay Mineralogy. 2nd ed. LC 67-24951. (McGraw-Hill International Earth & Planetary Science Ser.). pap. 149.00 (ISBN 0-317-28217-4, 2055969). Bks Demand UMI.

Hasruddin Siddiqui, M. K. Bleaching Earths. 1968. text ed. 23.00 (ISBN 0-08-012738-X). Pergamon.

The Infrared Spectra Handbook of Minerals & Clays. 1982. 265.00 (ISBN 0-8456-0080-X). Sadtler Res.

Structural Ceramics Advisory Group of the Structural Ceramics Research Panel. Design Guide for Reinforced Brick & Prestressed Clay Brickwork. 1977. 30.00x (ISBN 0-900910-27-5, Pub. by Brit Ceramic Soc England). State Mutual Bk.

Swineford, A., ed. National Conference on Clays & Minerals, 8th: Proceedings. 1961. write for info. (ISBN 0-08-009351-5). Pergamon.

Theng, B. K. The Chemistry of Clay-Organic Reactions. LC 74-12524. pap. 88.80 (2020262). Bks Demand UMI.

Theng, B. K. G. Formation & Properties of Clay-Polymer Complexes. (Developments in Soil Science: Vol. 9). 362p. 1979. 76.75 (ISBN 0-444-41706-0). Elsevier.

Van Olphen, H. An Introduction to Clay Colloid Chemistry. 2nd ed. LC 77-400. 1977. 55.00x (ISBN 0-471-01463-X, Pub. by Wiley-Interscience). Wiley.

Van Olphen, H., ed. International Clay Conference, 1981: Proceedings of the VII International Clay Conference, Bologna & Pavia, Italy, September 6-12, 1981. (Developments in Sedimentology Ser.: No. 35). 828p. 1982. 85.00 (ISBN 0-444-42096-7, I-295-82). Elsevier.

Van Olphen, H. & Fripiat, J. J., eds. Data Handbook for Clay Materials & Other Non-Metallic Minerals. (Illus.). 1979. text ed. 90.00 (ISBN 0-08-022850-X). Pergamon.

Velde, B. Clay Minerals: A Physico-Chemical Explanation of Their Occurrence. (Developments in Sedimentology Ser.: Vol. 40). 428p. 1985. 59.25 (ISBN 0-444-42423-7). Elsevier.

Zvyagin, B. B. Electron-Diffraction Analysis of Clay Mineral Structures. LC 65-17783. (Monographs in Geoscience Ser.). 264p. 1967. 42.50x (ISBN 0-306-30273-X, Plenum Pr). Plenum Pub.

CLAY INDUSTRIES

see also Bricks; Pottery

Clays & Other Collodial Systems in Ceramics. 1982. 35.00x (ISBN 0-686-44605-4, Pub. by Brit Ceramic Soc England). State Mutual Bk.

International Clay Conference, 1975. Proceedings. Bailey, Sturges W., ed. LC 75-32132. (Illus.). 1976. 55.00x (ISBN 0-915834-02-2). Applied Pub.

CLAYTON, JOHN, 1685-1773

Gaston, Georg M. Jack Clayton: A Guide to References & Resources. 1981. lib. bdg. 26.00 (ISBN 0-8161-8524-7, Hall Reference). G K Hall.

CLEAN ROOMS

see also Dust–Removal; Environmental Engineering

Austin, Philip R. Design & Operation of Clean Rooms. rev. ed. LC 79-103628. (Illus.). 462p. 1970. 59.95 (ISBN 0-912524-00-6). Busn News.

Phillips, G. B. & Runkle, R. S. Biomedical Applications of Laminar Airflow. LC 72-95698. (Uniscience Ser.). 1973. 50.00 (ISBN 0-8493-5006-9). CRC Pr.

CLEANING

see also Bleaching; Cleaning Compounds; Dry Cleaning; House Cleaning

Johnson, Mary P. Everything You Need to Know to Start a House Cleaning Service. 1979. pap. text ed. 14.95x (ISBN 0-9601054-0-9). Cleaning Consul.

Rudman, Jack. Cleaner (Men) (Career Examination Ser.: C-946A). (Cloth bdg. avail. on request). pap. 10.00 (ISBN 0-8373-0946-8). Natl Learning.

--Cleaner (Women) (Career Examination Ser.: C-946B). (Cloth bdg. avail. on request). pap. 10.00. Natl Learning.

CLEANING COMPOUNDS

see also Detergents, Synthetic; Soap and Soap Trade

Ash, M. & Ash, I. Formulary of Detergents & Other Cleaning Agents. 1980. 35.00 (ISBN 0-8206-0247-7). Chem Pub.

Cleaning, Polishing & Sanitation Products. 260p. 1984. 550.00 (ISBN 0-686-32750-0). Busn Trend.

Cold Cleaning with Halogenated Solvents - STP 403A. 52p. 1981. pap. 7.25 (ISBN 0-8031-0758-7, 04-403010-15). ASTM.

Cutler, W. G. & Davis, R. C., eds. Detergency: Theory & Test Methods, Pt. 1. (Surfactant Science Ser.: Vol. 5). 464p. 1972. 85.00 (ISBN 0-8247-1113-0). Dekker.

--Detergency: Theory & Test Methods, Part 2. (Surfactant Science Ser.: Vol. 5). 296p. 1975. 85.00 (ISBN 0-8247-1114-9). Dekker.

Environment Resources Ltd. Cleaning & Conditioning Agents: Their Impact on the Environment in the EEC. 138p. 1978. 33.00x (ISBN 0-86010-108-8, Pub. by Graham & Trotman England). State Mutual Bk.

Flick, Ernest W. Institutional & Industrial Cleaning Product Formulations. LC 85-4961. (Illus.). 338p. 1985. 48.00 (ISBN 0-8155-1026-8). Noyes.

List of Fluorescent Whitening Agents for the Soap & Detergent Industry DS 53A. 10p. 1976. 3.50 (ISBN 0-8031-0819-2, 05-053010-15). ASTM.

Longman, G. F. The Analysis of Detergents & Detergent Products. LC 75-4649. 625p. 1975. 109.95x (ISBN 0-471-54457-4, Pub. by Wiley-Interscience). Wiley.

McGowan, Ellen A. A Comparative Study of Detergents, with Special Reference to the Teaching of the Subject. LC 75-177025. (Columbia University. Teachers College. Contributions to Education: No. 441). Repr. of 1930 ed. 22.50 (ISBN 0-404-55441-5). AMS Pr.

Polanyi, George. Detergents: A Question of Monopoly. (Institute of Economic Affairs, Research Monographs: No. 24). 1972. pap. 2.50 technical (ISBN 0-255-35988-8). Transatlantic.

Soap & Detergrent Industry. (UNIDO Guides to Information Sources: No. 24). pap. 4.00 (ISBN 0-686-93278-1, UNID181, UN). Unipub.

U. K. Household Chemical Markets. 1985. 150.00x (ISBN 0-686-71961-1, Pub. by Euromonitor). State Mutual Bk.

CLEANING MACHINERY AND APPLIANCES

see also Dust–Removal

American Institute of Maintenance. Selection & Care of Cleaning Equipment. 86p. 1982. pap. 3.00 (ISBN 0-9609052-3-5). Am Inst Maint.

CLEANING PREPARATIONS

see Cleaning Compounds

CLEANSERS (COMPOUNDS)

see Cleaning Compounds

CLIMATE

see Climatology

CLIMATE, INFLUENCE OF

see Architecture and Climate; Man–Influence of Environment

CLIMATOLOGY

see also Architecture and Climate; Atmospheric Pressure; Atmospheric Temperature; Bioclimatology; Dendrochronology; Meteorology; Numerical Weather Forecasting; Paleoclimatology; Rain and Rainfall; Seasons; Vegetation and Climate; Weather; also names of countries, cities, etc. with or without the subdivision Climate

American Association for the Advancement of Science. Ground Level Climatology: A Symposium Presented at the Berkeley Meeting of the American Association for the Advancement of Science. Shaw, Robert H., ed. LC 67-29427. (American Association for the Advancement of Science Publication: No. 86). pap. 101.80 (ISBN 0-317-09580-3, 2015168). Bks Demand UMI.

Ausebel, J. & Biswas, A. K. Climatic Constraints & Human Activities. LC 80-41073. (IIASA Proceedings: Vol. 10). (Illus.). 215p. 1980. 35.00 (ISBN 0-08-026721-1). Pergamon.

Bach, W., ed. Interactions of Food & Climate. 1982. 58.50 (ISBN 90-277-1353-7, Pub. by Reidel Holland); pap. 28.50 (ISBN 90-277-1354-5, Pub. by Reidel Holland). Kluwer Academic.

Bach, Wilfrid. Our Threatened Climate. 1983. lib. bdg. 29.00 (ISBN 90-277-1680-3, Pub. by Reidel Holland). Kluwer Academic.

Bach, Wilfrid, et al, eds. Interactions of Energy & Climate. 568p. 1980. lib. bdg. 58.00 (ISBN 90-277-1179-8, Pub. by Reidel Holland); pap. 26.50 (ISBN 90-277-1177-1, Pub. by Reidel Holland). Kluwer Academic.

Bandyopadhyaya, J. Climate & World Order. 180p. 1983. text ed. 17.75x (ISBN 0-391-02893-6). Humanities.

Barrett, E. C. Climatology from Satellites. (Illus.). 418p. 1974. pap. 17.00x (ISBN 0-416-72150-8, NO.2614). Methuen Inc.

Barry, Roger G. Mountain Weather & Climate. LC 80-42348. (Illus.). 313p. 1981. 43.00x (ISBN 0-416-73730-7, NO. 3464). Methuen Inc.

Barry, Roger G. & Chorley, R. J. Atmosphere, Weather & Climate. 4th ed. 425p. 1982. 33.00x (ISBN 0-416-33690-6, NO. 3748); pap. 14.95x (ISBN 0-416-33700-7, 3740). Methuen Inc.

Berger, A. L. & Nicolis, C. New Perspectives in Climate Modelling, Vol. 16. (Developments in Atmospheric Sciences Ser.). 404p. 1984. 57.75 (ISBN 0-444-42295-1, I-093-84). Elsevier.

Berger, A. L., et al, eds. Milankovitch & Climate: Understanding the Response to Astronomical Forcing, 2 vol. set. 1984. lib. bdg. 117.00 2 volume set, not sold separately (Pub. by Reidel Holland). Kluwer Academic.

Berggren, R. Economic Benefits of Climatological Services. (Technical Note Ser.: No. 145). 43p. 1975. pap. 15.00 (ISBN 92-63-10424-7, W189, WMO). Unipub.

Blaxter, K., ed. Food, Nutrition & Climate. Fowden, L. (Illus.). 422p. 1982. 72.25 (ISBN 0-85334-107-9, Pub. by Elsevier Applied Sci England). Elsevier.

Board on Agriculture & Renewable Resources, National Research Council. Climate & Food: Climatic Fluctuation & U. S. Agricultural Production. LC 76-46195. 1976. pap. 9.25 (ISBN 0-309-02522-2). Natl Acad Pr.

Bolin, B. Climatic Changes & Their Effects on the Biosphere. 49p. (4th IMO Lecture). 1980. pap. 30.00 (ISBN 92-63-10542-1, W481, WMO). Unipub.

Borisov, P. Can Man Change the Climate? 175p. 1973. pap. 3.45 (ISBN 0-8285-0816-X, Pub. by Progress Pubs USSR). Imported Pubns.

Bourke, P. Climatic Aspects of the Possible Establishment of the Japanese Beetle in Europe. (Technical Note Ser.: No. 41). 9p. 1961. pap. 11.00 (ISBN 0-685-57275-7, W16, WMO). Unipub.

Brooks, C. E. Climate Through the Ages: A Study of the Climatic Factors & Their Variations. 2nd ed. 13.25 (ISBN 0-8446-0516-6). Peter Smith.

Brooks, Charles E. Climate in Everyday Life. LC 75-36507. (Illus.). 314p. 1976. Repr. of 1950 ed. lib. bdg. 19.25x (ISBN 0-8371-8647-1, BRCEL). Greenwood.

--The Evolution of Climate. LC 77-10221. Repr. of 1922 ed. 18.00 (ISBN 0-404-16201-0). AMS Pr.

Brown, Lester R. U.S. & Soviet Agriculture: The Shifting Balance. (Worldwatch Institute Papers: No. 51). 48p. 1982. pap. 2.95 (ISBN 0-916468-51-8, WW51, WMO). Unipub.

Budyko, M. I. Climate Changes. Zolina, R., tr. from Rus. (Illus.). 261p. 1977. 24.00 (ISBN 0-87590-206-5). Am Geophysical.

--The Earth's Climate: Past & Future. LC 81-17673. (International Geophysics Ser.). 1982. 43.00 (ISBN 0-12-139460-3). Acad Pr.

Calder, Nigel. The Weather Machine. (Illus.). 144p. 1977. pap. text ed. 4.95 (ISBN 0-14-004489-2). Penguin.

--The Weather Machine. (Illus.). 1975. PLB 14.95 (ISBN 0-670-75425-0). Viking.

Chandler, T. J. Selected Bibliography on Urban Climate. 383p. (Orig.). 1970. pap. 35.00 (ISBN 0-685-04924-8, W90, WMO). Unipub.

--Urban Climatology & Its Relevance to Urban Design. (Technical Note Ser.: No. 149). (Illus.). 61p. 1976. pap. 15.00 (ISBN 0-685-68977-8, W198, WMO). Unipub.

Commission for Special Applications of Meteorology & Climatology: Abridged Final Report of the Seventh Session. 113p. 1978. pap. 25.00 (ISBN 0-685-93702-X, W413, WMO). Unipub.

Commission for Special Applications of Meteorology & Climatology, 6th Session, 1973. Report. pap. 25.00 (ISBN 0-686-93925-5, W142, WMO). Unipub.

Cooper, W. Warm Air Heating for Climate Control. 1980. 29.95 (ISBN 0-13-944231-6). P-H.

Court, Arnold, ed. Eclectic Climatology: Association of Pacific Coast Geographers, Vol. 30. LC 37-13376. (Illus.). 1968. 8.00x (ISBN 0-87071-312-4). Oreg St U Pr.

CO2-Climate Review Panel Climate Research Committee National Research Council. Carbon Dioxide & Climate: A Second Assessment. 72p. 1982. pap. text ed. 7.25 (ISBN 0-309-03285-7). Natl Acad Pr.

Critchfield, Howard J. General Climatology. 4th ed. (Illus.). 464p. 1983. text ed. 33.95 (ISBN 0-13-349217-6). P-H.

Crowe, P. R. Concepts in Climatology. LC 77-174727. 355p. 1972. 37.50 (ISBN 0-312-16065-8). St Martin.

Crowe, Percy R. Concepts in Climatology. LC 72-176213. (Geographies for Advanced Study Ser.). pap. 152.30 (ISBN 0-317-08860-2, 2019601). Bks Demand UMI.

Derbyshire, Edward, ed. Geomorphology & Climate. LC 75-4523. Repr. of 1976 ed. 99.80 (ISBN 0-8357-9899-2, 2016026). Bks Demand UMI.

Dickson, H. Climate & Weather. 1976. lib. bdg. 59.95 (ISBN 0-8490-1638-X). Gordon Pr.

Flohn, H. General Climatology. Landsberg, H. E., ed. (World Survey of Climatology Ser.: Vol. 2). 266p. 1970. 102.25 (ISBN 0-444-40702-2). Elsevier.

Flohn, Hermann & Fantachi, Roberto, eds. The Climate of Europe: Past, Present & Future. 1984. lib. bdg. 49.00 (ISBN 90-277-1745-1, Pub. by Reidel Holland). Kluwer Academic.

Flohn, N. Climate & Weather. (Illus., Orig.). 1968. pap. 3.95 (ISBN 0-07-021325-9). McGraw.

Ford, Michael J. The Changing Climate: Responses of the Natural Flora & Fauna. (Illus.). 192p. 1982. text ed. 27.50x (ISBN 0-04-574017-8). Allen Unwin.

Forry, Samuel. The Climate of the United States & Its Endemic Influences. LC 77-10224. Repr. of 1842 ed. 27.50 (ISBN 0-404-16205-3). AMS Pr.

Frakes, L. A. Climates Throughout Geologic Time. 310p. 1980. 38.50 (ISBN 0-444-41925-X). Elsevier.

Frenzel, Burkhard. Climatic Fluctuations of the Ice Age. Nairn, A. E., tr. from Ger. LC 70-170788. (Illus.). 252p. 1973. text ed. 22.50 (ISBN 0-8295-0226-2). UPB.

Fritts, H. C. Tree Rings & Climate. 1977. 88.50 (ISBN 0-12-268450-8). Acad Pr.

Gates, Ernest S. Meteorology & Climatology. 4th ed. (Illus.). 1972. pap. text ed. 24.95x (ISBN 0-245-52869-5). Intl Ideas.

Gentilli, J., ed. Climates of Australia & New Zealand. (World Survey of Climatology Ser.: Vol. 13). 405p. 1971. 134.00 (ISBN 0-444-40827-4). Elsevier.

Gentilli, Joseph. A Geography of Climate. LC 77-10225. Repr. of 1952 ed. 13.50 (ISBN 0-404-16206-1). AMS Pr.

Geophysics Research Board. Climate, Climatic Change & Water Supply. 1977. pap. 9.25 (ISBN 0-309-02625-3). Natl Acad Pr.

Geophysics Research Board, National Research Council. Climate in Earth History. 1982. pap. text ed. 16.25 (ISBN 0-309-03329-2). Natl Acad Pr.

Gibson, T. E., ed. Weather & Parasitic Animal Disease. (Technical Note Ser.: No. 159). 174p. 1978. pap. 30.00 (ISBN 92-63-10497-2, W410, WMO). Unipub.

Gribbin, J., ed. Climatic Change. LC 76-52185. 1978. 77.50 (ISBN 0-521-21594-3); pap. 24.95x (ISBN 0-521-29205-0). Cambridge U Pr.

CLIMATOLOGY, AGRICULTURAL
see Crops and Climate

CLIMBING PLANTS

Beckett, Kenneth A. Climbing Plants. (Illus.). 178p. 1983. 17.95 (ISBN 0-917304-76-4). Timber.

Darwin, Charles. The Movements & Habits of Climbing Plants. 1977. Repr. of 1891 ed. lib. bdg. 40.00 (ISBN 0-8492-0621-9). R West.

Darwin, Charles R. The Movements & Habits of Climbing Plants. LC 72-3896. (Illus.). viii, 208p. 42.50 (ISBN 0-404-08411-7). AMS Pr.

Galet, Pierre. A Practical Ampelography: Grapevine Indentification. Morton, Lucie, tr. LC 78-59631. (Illus.). 192p. 1979. 39.95x (ISBN 0-8014-1240-4). Comstock.

Ground Covers & Vines. 1978. 2.25 (ISBN 0-686-00615-1). Bklyn Botanic.

Ivies. 1982. 20.00x (ISBN 0-906603-09-9, Pub. by RHS Ent England). State Mutual Bk.

Jones, L. R. & Rand, F. V. The Handbook of Vermont Shrubs & Woody Vines. LC 79-84806. pap. 3.95 (ISBN 0-8048-1316-7). C E Tuttle.

Newcomb, Lawrence. Newcomb's Wildflower Guide: An Ingenious New Key System for Quick Positive Field Identification of the Wildflowers, Flowering Shrubs & Vines of Northeastern & North-Central North America. (Illus.). 1977. 18.45i (ISBN 0-316-60441-0). Little.

Pearkes, Gillian. Vine Growing in the British Isles. 224p. 1980. 39.00x (Pub. by J M Dent England). State Mutual Bk.

Phillips, C. E. Climbing Plants for Walls & Gardens. (Illus.). 1967. 27.50x (ISBN 0-89563-038-9). Intl Ideas.

Stokes, Donald. The Natural History of Wild Shrubs & Vines. LC 80-8219. (Illus.). 256p. 1981. 17.26i (ISBN 0-06-014163-8, HarpT). Har-Row.

Symonds, George W. The Shrub Identification Book. LC 63-7388. 1963. 17.95 (ISBN 0-688-00040-1); pap. 12.95 (ISBN 0-688-05040-9). Morrow.

Top Rated Trellises & Espaliers. (Golden Gardening Ser.). (Illus.). 64p. 1984. pap. 3.95 (ISBN 0-307-46642-6, Golden Pr). Western Pub.

CLINICAL CHEMISTRY

see Chemistry, Clinical

CLINICAL ENGINEERING

see Biomedical Engineering

CLINICAL LABORATORY TECHNICIANS

see Medical Technologists

CLIPPER-SHIPS

Anderson, Romola & Anderson, R. C. The Sailing Ship: Six Thousand Years of History. LC 79-177507. 22.00 (ISBN 0-405-08205-3). Ayer Co Pubs.

Clark, Admont G. They Built Clipper Ships in Their Back Yard. 32p. 1963. pap. 1.95 (ISBN 0-940160-00-5). Parnassus Imprints.

Howe, Octavius & Mathews, F. C. American Clipper Ships, 1833-1858, 2 vols. (Illus.). 1967. Repr. of 1926 ed. boxed 37.50 (ISBN 0-87266-016-8). Argosy.

Lubbock, Basil. The China Clippers. 1981. 45.00x (ISBN 0-85174-109-6, Pub. by Nautical England). State Mutual Bk.

--The Colonial Clippers. 1981. 40.00x (ISBN 0-85174-110-X, Pub. by Nautical England). State Mutual Bk.

MacGregor, David. The Tea Clippers. 224p. 1982. 55.00x (ISBN 0-85177-256-0, Pub. by Conway Marit England). State Mutual Bk.

Underhill, H. A. Masting & Rigging: The Clipper Ship & Ocean Carrier. (Illus.). 1946. 30.00 (ISBN 0-85174-173-8). Heinman.

Whipple, A. B. The Clipper Ships. Time-Life Bks, ed. (The Seafarers Ser.). (Illus.). 176p. 1980. 13.95 (ISBN 0-8094-2677-3). Time-Life.

CLOCK AND WATCH MAKERS

American Watch Co. New Orleans Exposition 1884-1885. 1972. 3.00 (ISBN 0-913602-02-7). K Roberts.

Ansonia Clock Co., Eighteen Eighty-Six to Eighteen Eighty-Seven Price Guide. (Illus.). 1979. paper-plastic bdg. 10.00 (ISBN 0-915706-21-0). Am Reprints.

Elgin Reminiscenes: Making Watches by Machinery 1869. 1972. 3.00 (ISBN 0-913602-01-9). K Roberts.

Hoopes, Penrose R. Connecticut Clockmakers of the Eighteenth Century. LC 75-28975. (Illus.). 200p. 1975. Repr. of 1930 ed. 12.50 (ISBN 0-8048-1152-0). C E Tuttle.

Kochmann, K. Gustav Becker Story: European Industrial Clockmaking 1847-1926. 4th ed. (Illus.). 112p. 1983. pap. 9.75 (ISBN 0-686-47041-9). Antique Clocks.

Loomes, Brian. Watchmakers & Clockmakers of the World, Vol. 2. 300p. 1982. 52.00x (ISBN 0-7198-0120-6, Pub. by Northwood Bks). State Mutual Bk.

Nutting, Wallace. The Clock Book. LC 70-178648. (Illus.). 1975. Repr. of 1924 ed. 47.00x (ISBN 0-8103-4145-X). Gale.

--Furniture Treasury, 3 Vols. (Illus.). Vols. 1 & 2 In 1. 29.95 (ISBN 0-02-590980-0); Vol. 3. 24.95 (ISBN 0-02-591040-X). Macmillan.

Roberts, Kenneth D. Contributions of Joseph Ives to Connecticut Clock Technology, 1810-1862. LC 77-118414. 1970. 25.00 (ISBN 0-913602-00-0). K Roberts.

Smith, Bede. The Lancashire Watch Company, Prescott, Lancashire, England 1889-1910. 1973. 7.50 (ISBN 0-913602-08-6). K Roberts.

Tardy. Dictionaire des Horlogers Francais. (Fr.). 350p. 1977. pap. 79.95 (ISBN 0-686-56726-9, M-6528). French & Eur.

CLOCK AND WATCH MAKING

see also Clocks and Watches

Baier, Joseph, et al. Questions & Answers of & for the Clockmaking Profession. 1982. (ISBN 0-918845-04-1). Am Watchmakers.

Daniele, Joseph. How to Build Thirty-Five Great Clocks. Schnell, Judith, ed. (Illus.). 172p. 1984. 29.95 (ISBN 0-8117-1816-6). Stackpole.

Daniele, Joseph W. How to Build a Clock-With Thirty Five Plans & Complete Instructions. (Illus.). 224p. 1982. pap. 12.95 (ISBN 0-940166-01-1). Old Main Bks.

Daniels, George. Watchmaking. (Illus.). 440p. 1981. 65.00x (ISBN 0-85667-150-9, Pub. by Sotheby Pubns Englabd). Biblio Dist.

Ehrhardt, Roy. Pocket Watch Price Indicator,1979. (Illus.). 1979. plastic ring bdg. 10.00 (ISBN 0-913902-29-2). Heart Am Pr.

Electric Clocks & Chimes. (Illus.). 160p. 1979. pap. 4.95 (ISBN 0-85242-474-4). Aztex.

Elgin Reminiscenes: Making Watches by Machinery 1869. 1972. 3.00 (ISBN 0-913602-01-9). K Roberts.

Fried, Henry B. Bench Practices for Watch-Clockmakers. 1984. 9.00 (ISBN 0-317-17083-X). Am Watchmakers.

Glasgow, David. Watch & Clock Making. (Illus.). 1977. Repr. of 1885 ed. 25.00 (ISBN 0-7158-1215-7). Charles River Bks.

Hoopes, Penrose R. Connecticut Clockmakers of the Eighteenth Century. LC 75-28975. (Illus.). 200p. 1975. Repr. of 1930 ed. 12.50 (ISBN 0-8048-1152-0). C E Tuttle.

Hope-Jones, F. Electric Clocks & How to Make Them. (Illus.). 208p. 1979. pap. 4.95 (ISBN 0-85242-533-3). Aztex.

Hughes, Billy G., Jr. You Can Make Horseman Clocks. 52p. 1980. pap. 4.00 (ISBN 0-914208-08-X). Longhorn Pr.

Kochmann, K. Gustav Becker Story: European Industrial Clockmaking 1847-1926. 4th ed. (Illus.). 112p. 1983. pap. 9.75 (ISBN 0-686-47041-9). Antique Clocks.

Ohlson, Olof. Helpful Information for Watchmakers. LC 84-16877. (Illus.). 37p. 1985. pap. 6.95 (ISBN 0-930163-21-4). Arlington Bk.

Questions & Answers of & for the Watchmaking Profession. 1977. write for info. (ISBN 0-918845-01-7). Am Watchmakers.

Radiation Protection Standards for Radioluminous Timepieces. (Safety Ser.: No. 23). 37p. 1967. pap. 6.25 (ISBN 92-0-123467-8, ISP167, IAEA). Unipub.

Reeve, Claude. Clockmaking for the Amateur. (Illus.). 136p. 1980. pap. 8.50 (ISBN 0-85242-423-X). Aztex.

Roberts, Kenneth D., frwd. by. Precision Machinery of American Watch Tool Co., Waltham, Mass. 56p. 1980. pap. 4.50 (ISBN 0-913602-33-7). K Roberts.

Way, R. Bernard. How to Make an Electric Clock. (Illus.). 64p. 1979. pap. 3.95 (ISBN 0-85242-473-6). Aztex.

Winterhalden & Hofmeier. The Lenzkirch Clocks: European Industrial Clockmaking, 1866-1933. (Illus.). 133p. 1985. ltd. ed. softcover 12.50 (ISBN 0-933396-13-9). Antique Clocks.

CLOCKS AND WATCHES

see also Chronometer; Clock and Watch Making; Time Measurements

Ansonia Clock Co., Eighteen Eighty-Six to Eighteen Eighty-Seven Price Guide. (Illus.). 1979. paper-plastic bdg. 10.00 (ISBN 0-915706-21-0). Am Reprints.

Antique Collector's Club. Britten's Old Clock & Watches & Their Makers. 3rd ed. (Illus.). 517p. 1978. Repr. of 1911 ed. 49.50 (ISBN 0-902028-69-3). Antique Collect.

Baier, Joseph. Striking Clocks: A Hands-On Survey for the Clockmaker. 1983. write for info. (ISBN 0-918845-07-6). Am Watchmakers.

Britten, F. J. Old Clocks & Watches. 1932. 70.00x (ISBN 0-686-45467-7, Pub. by EP Pub England). State Mutual Bk.

--Watch & Clockmakers' Handbook. (Illus.). 1976. 29.50 (ISBN 0-902028-46-4). Apollo.

--Watch & Clockmakers' Handbook, Dictionary & Guide. (Illus.). 499p. 1976. Repr. of 1907 ed. 29.50 (ISBN 0-902028-46-4). Antique Collect.

Britten, F. W. Horological Helps & Hints. (Illus.). 375p. 1977. Repr. of 1929 ed. 29.50 (ISBN 0-902028-64-2). Antique Collect.

Brown, H. Miles. Cornish Clocks & Clockmakers. (Illus.). 102p. 1980. Repr. 14.95 (ISBN 0-7153-4999-6). David & Charles.

Bruton, Eric. The Longcase Clock. (Illus.). 1977. 29.95x (ISBN 0-8464-0578-4). Beekman Pubs.

Bruton, Eric & Scribner Press. The Longcase Clock. 2nd ed. (Illus.). 1979. 22.95 (ISBN 0-684-16247-4, ScribT). Scribner.

Cipolla, Carlo M. Clocks & Culture, 1300-1700. (Illus.). 1978. pap. 5.95 (ISBN 0-393-00866-5, N866, Norton Lib). Norton.

Clutton, Cecil & Daniels, George. Watches: A Complete History of the Technical & Decorative Development of the Watch. 3rd rev. & enlarg. ed. (Illus.). 312p. 1979. 95.00 (ISBN 0-85667-058-8, Pub by Sotheby Pubns England). Biblio Dist.

Cunynghame, Henry H. Time & Clocks: A Description of Ancient & Modern Methods of Measuring Time. LC 77-78127. (Illus.). 208p. 1970. Repr. of 1906 ed. 35.00x (ISBN 0-8103-3576-X). Gale.

Cutmore, M. The Watch Collector's Handbook. LC 75-42563. (Illus.). 160p. 1976. 14.50 (ISBN 0-8048-1174-1). C E Tuttle.

Daniels, George & Clutton, Cecil, eds. Clocks & Watches: The Collection of the Worshipful Company of Clockmakers. (Illus.). 160p. 1975. 52.50 (ISBN 0-85667-019-7, Pub. by Sotheby Pubns England). Biblio Dist.

Ehrhardt, Roy. American Pocket Watch Production Totals & Dates, Plus Inventory Pages. 56p. 1979. 3.00 (ISBN 0-913902-30-6). Heart Am Pr.

--Pocket Watch Price Indicator. (Illus.). 1980. plastic ring bdg. 12.00 (ISBN 0-913902-32-2). Heart Am Pr.

Ehrhardt, Roy, illus. American Pocket Watches Encyclopedia & Price Guide, Vol. 1. 1982. plastic ring bdg 25.00x (ISBN 0-913902-33-0). Heart Am Pr.

Fried, Henry B. Bench Practices for Watch-Clockmakers. 1984. 9.00 (ISBN 0-317-17083-X). Am Watchmakers.

Hagans, Orville R. Watch & Clock Information, Please. 1981. write for info. (ISBN 0-918845-03-3). Am Watchmakers.

Harris, H. G. Collecting & Identifying Old Clocks. (Illus.). 256p. 12.95. Wallace-Homestead.

Harris, H. R. Nineteenth Century American Clocks. (Illus.). 256p. 1981. 12.95 (ISBN 0-87523-197-7). Emerson.

Holtz, Frederick C. & Ridgely, Frances S. Clocks from the Hunter Collection. (Scientific Papers Ser.: Vol. IX). (Illus.). 64p. 1957. pap. 2.00 (ISBN 0-89792-017-1). Ill St Museum.

Hyltin, Tom M. Digital Electronic Watch. 1978. pap. 19.95 (ISBN 0-442-22596-2). Van Nos Reinhold.

--It's About Time: The Digital Electronic Watch. (Illus.). 224p. 1984. 21.95 (ISBN 0-317-17088-0). Am Watchmakers.

Kadar, Wayne L. Clock Making for the Woodworker. (Illus.). 192p. 1984. 16.95 (ISBN 0-8306-0648-3); pap. 11.50 (ISBN 0-8306-1648-9, 1648). TAB Bks.

Kochmann, K. The Hamburg-American Clock Company. (Illus.). 176p. 1980. soft cover 10.20 (ISBN 0-933396-10-4). Antique Clocks.

Landes, David S. Revolution in Time: Clocks & the Making of the Modern World. (Illus.). 544p. 1985. pap. 8.95 (ISBN 0-674-76802-7, Belknap Pr). Harvard U Pr.

Loomes, Brian. Complete British Clocks. LC 78-66804. (Illus.). 1978. 24.00 (ISBN 0-7153-7567-9). David & Charles.

--White Dial Clocks: The Complete Guide. (Illus.). 192p. 1981. 32.00 (ISBN 0-7153-8073-7). David & Charles.

Macey, Samuel L. Clocks & the Cosmos: Time in Western Life & Thought. (Illus.). 256p. 1980. 21.00 (ISBN 0-208-01773-9, Archon). Shoe String.

Maurice, Klaus & Mayr, Otto. The Clockwork Universe: German Clocks & Automata 1550-1650. LC 80-16780. (Illus.). 332p. 1980. 19.95 (ISBN 0-88202-188-5). Smithsonian.

Nutting, Wallace. The Clock Book. LC 70-178648. (Illus.). 1975. Repr. of 1924 ed. 47.00x (ISBN 0-8103-4145-X). Gale.

--Furniture Treasury, 3 Vols. (Illus.). Vols. 1 & 2 In 1. 29.95 (ISBN 0-02-590980-0); Vol. 3. 24.95 (ISBN 0-02-591040-X). Macmillan.

Penman, Laurie. Clock Design & Construction. (Illus.). 128p. (Orig.). 1984. pap. 15.95 (ISBN 0-85242-825-1, Pub. by Argus). Aztex.

Ponsford, Clive. Devon Clocks & Clockmakers. (Illus.). 320p. 1985. 50.00 (ISBN 0-7153-8332-9). David & Charles.

Roberts, Deryck. The Bracket Clock. (Illus.). 192p. 1982. 26.50 (ISBN 0-7153-8261-6). David & Charles.

Rudolph, James S. Make Your Own Working Clock. LC 83-47570. 40p. 1983. pap. 7.64i (ISBN 0-06-091066-6, CN1066, CN). Har-Row.

St. Louis Clock Company 1904. 1983. pap. 7.95 (ISBN 0-915706-08-3). Am Reprints.

Seth Thomas Clock Company, 1879. 1983. pap. 7.95 (ISBN 0-915706-04-0). Am Reprints.

Seth Thomas Clock Company, 1884-1885. 1983. pap. 7.95 (ISBN 0-915706-05-9). Am Reprints.

Smith, Eric. Striking & Chiming Clocks: Their Working & Repair. (Illus.). 192p. 1985. 19.95 (ISBN 0-668-06422-6). Arco.

Tait, Hugh. Clocks & Watches. (Illus.). 72p. 1983. pap. 6.95 (ISBN 0-674-13571-7). Harvard U Pr.

Taylor, Snowden. The Developmental Era of Eli Terry & Seth Thomas Shelf Clocks. (Illus.). 64p. 1985. pap. 7.75 (ISBN 0-913602-60-4). K Roberts.

Turner, Anthony. Time Museum Catalogue of the Collection; Volume I: Time Measuring Instruments, Part 3: Water-Clocks, Sand-Glasses, Fire-Clocks. Chandler, Bruce, ed. (Illus.). 183p. 1984. 95.00 (ISBN 0-912947-01-2). Time Museum.

Watch & Clockmakers Buyer's Guide, 1985. 1985. write for info. (ISBN 0-918845-09-2). Am Watchmakers.

Waterbury Clock Company 1867. 1976. pap. 7.95 (ISBN 0-915706-09-1). Am Reprints.

Weaver. Electrical & Electronic Clocks & Watches. 1982. text ed. 39.95 (ISBN 0-408-01140-8). Butterworth.

Whitton, Blair. American Clockwork Toys. LC 81-51443. (Illus.). 224p. 1981. 25.00 (ISBN 0-916838-55-2). Schiffer.

Wood, Edward J. Curiosities of Clocks & Watches from the Earliest Times. LC 70-174149. (Illus.). x, 443p. 1974. Repr. of 1866 ed. 43.00x (ISBN 0-8103-3984-6). Gale.

Wyke, John. A Catalogue of Tools for Watch & Clock Makers. LC 77-12219. (Illus.). 153p. 1978. 17.50x (ISBN 0-8139-0751-9, Winterthur Museum). U Pr of Va.

CLOCKS AND WATCHES–REPAIRING AND ADJUSTING

DeCarle, Don. Practical Clock Repairing. 18.95x (ISBN 0-685-22074-5). Wehman.

--Practical Watch Repairing. 18.95x (ISBN 0-685-22078-8). Wehman.

Harris, H. G. Advanced Watch & Clock Repair. LC 73-81498. (Illus.). 272p. 1973. 11.95 (ISBN 0-87523-181-0). Enslow Pubs.

--Advanced Watch & Clock Repair. 272p. 1985. 10.95 (ISBN 0-87523-181-0). Wallace-Homestead.

--Handbook of Watch & Clock Repairs. rev. ed. LC 63-9747. (Illus.). 181p. 1982. 10.95 (ISBN 0-87523-141-1). Enslow Pubs.

--Handbook of Watch & Clock Repairs. (Illus.). 192p. 1984. pap. 4.76i (ISBN 0-06-463591-0, EH 591). B&N NY.

Harris, P. Buford. Modern Watch & Clock Repairing. LC 73-77479. (Illus.). 250p. 1972. 16.95 (ISBN 0-911012-05-2). Nelson-Hall.

Kelly. Clock Repair As a Hobby. LC 81-85509. 1972. pap. 5.95 (ISBN 0-8329-1118-6). New Century.

Rudman, Jack. Clock Repairer. (Career Examination Ser.: C-151). (Cloth bdg. avail on request). pap. 10.00 (ISBN 0-8373-0151-3). Natl Learning.

Smith, Eric. How to Repair Clocks. (Illus.). 1979. 10.95 (ISBN 0-8306-9723-3); pap. 7.95 (ISBN 0-8306-1168-1, 1168). TAB Bks.

CLONING

see also Plant Propagation

Carmen, Ira H. Cloning & the Constitution: An Inquiry into Govermental Policy Making & Genetic Engineering. LC 85-40363. (Illus.). 240p. 1985. text ed. 22.50x (ISBN 0-299-10340-4). U of Wis Pr.

Conger, B. V., ed. Cloning Agricultural Plants via In Vitro Techniques. LC 80-23852. 280p. 1981. 85.00 (ISBN 0-8493-5797-7). CRC Pr.

Drlica, Karl. Understanding DNA & Gene Cloning: A Guide for the Curious. LC 84-3518. 205p. 1984. pap. text ed. 12.50 (ISBN 0-471-87942-8). Wiley.

Evatt, B. L., et al, eds. Megakaryocyte Biology & Precursors: In Vitro Cloning & Cellular Properties. 350p. 1981. 93.00 (ISBN 0-444-00585-4, Biomedical Pr). Elsevier.

Glover, D. M., ed. DNA Cloning, 2 vols, Vols. 1 & 2. (Practical Approach Ser.). (Illus.). 250p. (Orig.). 1985. Vol. 1. pap. text ed. 25.00 ea. (ISBN 0-947946-18-7). Vol. 2 (ISBN 0-947946-19-5). IRL Pr.

Hyde, Margaret O. & Hyde, Lawrence E. Cloning & the New Genetics. LC 83-20727. (Illus.). 128p. 1984. PLB 11.95 (ISBN 0-89490-084-6). Enslow Pubs.

Lester, Lane P. & Hefley, James C. Cloning: Miracle or Menace. 1980. pap. 4.95 (ISBN 0-8423-0294-8). Tyndale.

McKinnell, Robert G. Cloning: Of Frogs, Mice & Other Animals. rev. ed. LC 84-7514. (Illus.). 152p. Date not set. 12.95 (ISBN 0-8166-1360-5). U of Minn Pr.

Maniatis, T., et al. Molecular Cloning: A Laboratory Manual. LC 81-68891. (Illus.). 545p. 1982. 40.00 (ISBN 0-87969-136-0). Cold Spring Harbor.

Menditto, Joseph & Kirsch, Debbie. Genetic Engineering, DNA & Cloning: A Bibliography in the Future of Genetics. LC 82-50417. 790p. 1982. 50.00 (ISBN 0-87875-241-2). Whitston Pub.

Coal-Chem Two Thousand: Proceedings. (Symposium Ser.: No. 62). 250p. 1981. 80.00x (ISBN 0-85295-124-8, Pub. by Inst Chem Eng England). State Mutual Bk.

Coal Utilization: An International Forum on New Technologies. (Illus.). 134p. 1984. pap. 15.00 (ISBN 92-3-102081-1, U1313, UNESCO). Unipub.

Congressional Office of Technology Assessment. The Direct Use of Coal: Prospects & Problems of Production & Combustion. 432p. 1981. prof ref. 35.00x (ISBN 0-88410-648-9). Ballinger Pub.

Cooper, B. R. & Petrakis, L., eds. Chemistry & Physics of Coal Utilization - 1980 (APS, Morgantown) LC 81-65106. (AIP Conference Proceedings: No. 70). 472p. 1981. lib. bdg. 34.50 (ISBN 0-88318-169-X). Am Inst Physics.

Cooper, Bernard R., ed. Scientific Problems of Coal Utilization: Proceedings. LC 78-9553. (DOE Symposium Ser.). 424p. 1978. pap. 18.50 (ISBN 0-87079-400-0, CONF-770509); microfiche 4.50 (ISBN 0-87079-378-0, CONF-770509). DOE.

Cooper, Bernard R. & Ellingson, William A., eds. The Science & Technology of Coal & Coal Utilization. 682p. 1984. 85.00x (ISBN 0-306-41436-8, Plenum Pr). Plenum Pub.

Cusumano, James A. & Farkas, Adalbert, eds. Catalysis in Coal Conversion. LC 77-25620. 1978. 47.50 (ISBN 0-12-199935-1). Acad Pr.

The Direct Use of Coal: Prospects & Problems of Production & Combustion. (Illus.). 1981. Repr. 60.00x (ISBN 0-8103-1022-8). Gale.

DOE Technical Information Center Staff. Coal Processing: Gasification, Liquefaction, Desulfurization. A Bibliography, 1930-1974. 763p. 1974. pap. 32.00 (ISBN 0-87079-165-6, TID-3349); microfiche 4.50 (ISBN 0-87079-409-4, TID-3349). DOE.

Dryden, I. G., ed. Coal Science, Vol. 1. (Serial Publication). 304p. 1982. 44.00 (ISBN 0-12-150701-7). Acad Pr.

Edgar, Thomas F. Coal Processing & Pollution Control. LC 83-10725. 576p. 1983. 49.95x (ISBN 0-87201-122-4). Gulf Pub.

Eliot, R. C., ed. Coal Desulfurization Prior to Combustion. LC 78-56014. (Chemical Technology Review Ser., Pollution Tech. Rev. 45: No. 113). 113p. 1978. 42.00 (ISBN 0-8155-0712-7). Noyes.

Ellington, R. T., ed. Liquid Fuels from Coal. 1977. 42.50 (ISBN 0-12-237250-6). Acad Pr.

Elliott, Martin A., ed. Chemistry of Coal Utilization, Vol. 2. LC 80-13296. 2374p. 1981. 246.50 (ISBN 0-471-07726-7, Pub. by Wiley-Interscience). Wiley.

Evans, T. J. Bituminous Coal in Texas. (Illus.). 65p. 1974. Repr. 3.50 (ISBN 0-686-29325-8, HB 4). Bur Econ Geology.

Falbe, Jurgen, ed. Chemical Feedstocks from Coal. LC 81-3022. 647p. 1982. 115.95 (ISBN 0-471-05291-4, Pub. by Wiley-Interscience). Wiley.

Fettweis, G. B. World Coal Resources: Methods of Assessment & Results. (Developments in Economic Geology Ser.: Vol. 10). 416p. 1979. 87.25 (ISBN 0-444-99779-2). Elsevier.

Field Description of Coal STP 661. 76p. 1978. pap. 7.50x (ISBN 0-8031-0349-2, 04-661000-13). ASTM.

Fuerstenau, Maurice C. & Palmer, R. B., eds. Gold, Silver, Uranium & Coal - Geology, Mining, Extraction, & Environment. LC 82-73914. (Illus.). 526p. 1983. pap. text ed. 40.00x (ISBN 0-89520-406-1, 406-1). Soc Mining Eng.

Fuller, E. L., Jr., ed. Coal & Coal Products: Analytical Characterization Techniques. LC 82-18442. (ACS Symposium Ser.: No. 205). 326p. 1982. lib. bdg. 49.95 (ISBN 0-8412-0748-8). Am Chemical.

Gaines, Linda, et al. TOSCA: The Total Social Cost of Coal & Nuclear Power. LC 78-26240. 144p. 1979. prof ref 29.95 (ISBN 0-88410-086-3). Ballinger Pub.

Given, P. H. & Cohen, A. D., eds. Interdisciplinary Studies of Peat & Coal Origins. LC 77-71662. (Microform Publication: No. 7). (Illus.). 1977. 4.00 (ISBN 0-8137-6007-0). Geol Soc.

Goplerud, C. Peter, III. Coal Development & Use: The Legal Constraints & Incentives. LC 80-8890. 320p. 1982. 31.50x (ISBN 0-669-04403-2). Lexington Bks.

Gorbaty, Martin L. & Ouchi, K., eds. Coal Structure. LC 80-24104. (ACS Advances in Chemistry Ser.: No. 192). 1981. 39.95 (ISBN 0-8412-0524-8). Am Chemical.

Gorbaty, Martin L., et al, eds. Coal Science, Vol. 3. LC 82-179203. (Serial Publication Ser.). 1984. 90.00 (ISBN 0-12-150703-3). Acad Pr.

Grainger, L. Coal: Modern Technology & Economics. 300p. 1980. 33.00x (ISBN 0-86010-213-0, Pub. by Graham & Trotman England). State Mutual Bk.

Grainger, L. & Gibson, J. Coal Utilisation: Technology, Economics & Policy. LC 81-7249. 503p. 1982. 53.95 (ISBN 0-470-27272-4). Halsted Pr.

Hall, Vivian S. A Bibliography of the Geology of Kentucky Coal, 1835-1983. LC 83-51254. 160p. (Orig.). 1984. pap. 35.00 (ISBN 0-938376-03-9). Willowood Pr.

Harvey, Curt. Regional Demand & Supply Behavior by Sectors of the U. S. Coal Industry. 45p. 1982. pap. text ed. 5.00 (ISBN 0-86607-009-5). KY Ctr Energy Res.

Hellman, Caroline J. C. & Hellman, Richard. The Competitive Economics of Nuclear & Coal Power. LC 82-47500. 208p. 1982. 26.50x (ISBN 0-669-05533-6). Lexington Bks.

Hesketh, H. E., ed. Second Symposium on Integrated Environmental Controls for Coal Fired Power Plants. 139p. 1983. pap. text ed. 25.00 (ISBN 0-317-02646-1, H00252). ASME.

Hoffman, E. J. Coal Conversion. LC 77-93533. (Illus.). 464p. 1978. 65.00x (ISBN 0-9601552-1-X). Energon Co.

Howard-Smith, I. & Werner, G. J. Coal Conversion Technology. LC 76-1387. (Chemical Technology Review Ser.: No. 66). (Illus.). 133p. 1976. 24.00 (ISBN 0-8155-0614-7). Noyes.

Hower, James & Wild, Gerry. Petrography of Kentucky Coals in the Princess Reserve District. (Resource Characterization Ser.). 27p. (Orig.). 1981. pap. 4.00 (ISBN 0-86607-004-4). KY Ctr Energy Res.

Hutton, Cynthia A. & Gould, Robert N. Cleaning up Coal: A Study of the Technology & Use of Coal Cleaning. LC 82-81548. (Orig.). 1982. 37.50 (ISBN 0-918780-18-7). INFORM.

Ide, Arthur F. Coal: Yesterday's Energy Today, Vol. 2. LC 81-20012. (Illus.). 60p. 1982. lib. bdg. 8.00 (ISBN 0-86663-804-0); pap. text ed. 0.95 (ISBN 0-86663-805-9). Ide Hse.

--Coal: Yesterday's Energy Tomorrow. (Energy: Management, Conservation & Communication Ser.: Vol. 2). (Illus.). 60p. (Orig.). 1981. lib. bdg. 8.50 (ISBN 0-86663-808-3); pap. text ed. 0.95 (ISBN 0-86663-809-1). Ide Hse.

Institution of Chemical Engineers Staff, ed. Coal Liquid Mixtures: First European Conference, Proceedings, October 5-6, 1983, Cheltenham, U.K. (Institution of Chemical Engineers Symposium Ser.: Vol. 83). 250p. 1983. 48.50 (ISBN 0-08-031397-3, 1902, 1903, 1502, 1100). Pergamon.

International Technical Conference on Slurry Transportation, 3rd: Proceedings. LC 78-52717. (Illus.). 224p. 1978. pap. 50.00 (ISBN 0-932066-03-8). Slurry Tech.

Iron & Steel Society of AIME. The Mining & Coking of Coal: Proceedings of the 2nd Conference, Pittsburgh Meeting, October 6-7, 1980, Vol. 1- 1980. LC 81-109760. pap. 20.00 (ISBN 0-317-29822-4, 2019696). Bks Demand UMI.

James, Peter. The Future of Coal. 296p. 1982. 19.50x (ISBN 0-8448-1412-1). Crane-Russak Co.

Javalas, G. S. Coal Pyrolysis. (Coal Science & Technology Ser.: No. 4). 168p. 1982. 53.25 (ISBN 0-444-42107-6). Elsevier.

Kaiser, W. R., et al. Lignite Resources in Texas. (Report of Investigations: RI 104). (Illus.). 52p. 1980. 2.00 (ISBN 0-318-03244-9). Bur Econ Geology.

Karr, Clarence, Jr., ed. Analytical Methods for Coal & Coal Products, 2 vols. LC 78-4928. 80.00 ea. Vol. 1, 1978 (ISBN 0-12-399901-4). Vol. 2, 1979 (ISBN 0-12-399902-2). Acad Pr.

Kasem, A., ed. Three Clean Fuels from Coal-Technology & Economics: Synthetic Natural Gas, Methanol, & Medium Btu Gas. 1979. 435.00 (ISBN 0-8247-6923-6). Dekker.

Komanoff, Charles. Power Plant Cost Escalation: Nuclear & Coal Capital Costs, Regulation, & Economics. 336p. 1982. 28.50 (ISBN 0-442-24903-9). Van Nos Reinhold.

Leonard, Joseph W., ed. Coal Preparation. 4th ed. LC 79-52245. (Illus.). 1204p. 1979. text ed. 46.00x (ISBN 0-89520-258-1). Soc Mining Eng.

Liu. Physical Cleaning of Coal. (Energy, Power & Environment Ser.). 664p. 1982. 75.00 (ISBN 0-8247-1862-3). Dekker.

Lloyd, William G. Development of Methods of Characterizing Coal in its Plastic State. 87p. 1980. pap. text ed. 7.00 (ISBN 0-86607-002-8). KY Ctr Energy Res.

Lowry, H. H. & Elliott, Martin A. The Chemistry of Coal Utilization, Vols. 1 & 2. LC 45-5498. 2084p. 1981. Set. 108.00 (ISBN 0-471-02494-5, Pub. by Wiley-Interscience); suppl. vol. (1963) 122.00 (ISBN 0-471-55158-9); 4 vols. set 405.00 (ISBN 0-471-07816-6). Wiley.

Mahlum, Dennis D., et al, eds. Coal Conversion & the Environment: Chemical, Biomedical, & Ecological Considerations. LC 81-607088. (DOE Symposium Ser.: Proceedings). 620p. 1981. pap. 24.75 (ISBN 0-87079-128-1, CONF-801039); microfiche 4.50 (ISBN 0-87079-401-9, CONF-801039). DOE.

Meadowcroft, D. B. & Manning, M. I., eds. Corrosion Resistant Materials for Coal Conversion Systems. 612p. 1983. 100.00 (ISBN 0-85334-198-2, I-208-83, Pub. by Elsevier Applied Sci England). Elsevier.

Merrick, D. Coal Combustion & Conversion Technology. 1984. 74.50 (ISBN 0-444-00933-7). Elsevier.

Merrit, Roy D. Coal Overburden: Geological Characterization & Premine Planning. LC 83-13093. (Energy Technology Review No. 88). (Illus.). 343p. 1984. 39.00 (ISBN 0-8155-0964-2). Noyes.

Meyers. Coal Handbook. (Energy, Power, & Environment Ser.: Vol. 11). 840p. 1981. 79.75 (ISBN 0-8247-1270-6). Dekker.

Meyers, Robert A. Coal Structure. 318p. 1982. 55.00 (ISBN 0-12-493080-8). Acad Pr.

Milsom, C. H. The Coal Was There for Burning. (Illus.). 88p. 1976. 13.50x (ISBN 0-900976-50-0, Pub. by Inst Marine Eng). Intl Spec Bk.

Moyers, J. C., et al. Coal Preparation Plant Automation. LC 83-2392. (Energy Tech. Rev. 83). (Illus.). 300p. (Orig.). 1983. 39.00 (ISBN 0-8155-0942-1). Noyes.

Nangia, Vinod K. Materials of Construction for Advanced Coal Conversion Systems. LC 81-18938. (Energy Technology Review Ser.: No. 75). (Illus.). 511p. 1982. 48.00 (ISBN 0-8155-0884-0). Noyes.

The National Coal Policy Project. 83p. 1979. pap. 10.00 (ISBN 0-686-68797-3, CSIS016, CSIS). Unipub.

Nettleton, M. A., et al. Coal: Current Advances in Coal Chemistry & Mining Techniques, Vol. 2. 1976. text ed. 28.00x (ISBN 0-8422-7283-6). Irvington.

Nowacki, Perry. Coal Liquefaction Processes. LC 79-14384. (Chemical Technology Review Ser.: No. 131; Energy Technology Review, No. 45). (Illus.). 1979. 48.00 (ISBN 0-8155-0756-9). Noyes.

Noyes, R., ed. Coal Resources, Characteristics & Ownership in the U.S.A. LC 77-94231. (Illus.). 346p. 1978. 45.00 (ISBN 0-8155-0698-8). Noyes.

OECD. The Clean Use of Coal: A Technology Review. 166p. (Orig.). 1985. pap. 25.00x (ISBN 92-64-12657-0). OECD.

--Coal Liquefaction: A Technology Review. 70p. (Orig.). 1982. pap. 9.25x (ISBN 92-64-12377-6). OECD.

OECD Staff. Coal & Environmental Protection: Costs & Costing Methods. 132p. (Orig.). 1983. pap. 12.00x (ISBN 92-64-12513-2). OECD.

--The Use of Coal in Industry. 445p. (Orig.). 1982. pap. 44.00x (ISBN 92-64-12308-3). OECD.

OECD Staff & IEA Staff. Coal Use & the Environment. 87p. (Orig.). 1983. pap. 14.00x (ISBN 92-64-12421-7). OECD.

Patterson, Walter C. & Griffin, Richard F. Fluidized Bed Energy Technology: Coming to a Boil. LC 78-60484. (Orig.). 1978. pap. 25.00 (ISBN 0-918780-10-1). INFORM.

Pelofsky, Arnold, ed. Coal Conversion Technology: Problems & Solutions. LC 79-17936. (ACS Symposium Ser.: No. 110). 1979. 32.95 (ISBN 0-8412-0516-7). Am Chemical.

Pitt, G. J. & Milward, G. R., eds. Coal & Modern Coal Processing: An Introduction. 1979. 27.50 (ISBN 0-12-557850-4). Acad Pr.

Rahmani, Ray A. & Flores, Romeo M., eds. Sedimentology of Coal & Coal-Bearing Sequences. 396p. 1985. pap. 56.00x (ISBN 0-632-01286-2). Blackwell Pubns.

Rose, Jerry, ed. Proceedings: Seventh Kentucky Coal By-Products Seminar. 55p. (Orig.). 1982. pap. text ed. 10.00x (ISBN 0-86607-006-0). KY Ctr Energy Res.

Rose, Jerry G., ed. Proceedings: Fifth Kentucky Coal Refuse Disposal & Utilization Seminar & Stability Analysis of Refuse Dams Workshop. 75p. 1980. pap. text ed. 10.00 (ISBN 0-686-94732-0). KY Ctr Energy Res.

Schmidt, R. A. Coal in America: Reserves, Production & Use. 1979. 69.95 (ISBN 0-07-055347-5). McGraw.

Schuler & Hull. Coal Heat. LC 80-53155. (Illus.). 158p. pap. 5.95 (ISBN 0-916838-37-4). Schiffer.

Schultz, H. D. Coal Liquefaction Products: NMR Spectroscopic Characterization & Production Processes, Vol. 1. LC 83-3511. 432p. 1983. 69.95 (ISBN 0-471-89232-7, Pub. by Wiley-Interscience). Wiley.

Shannon, Robert H. Handbook of Coal-Based Electric Power Generation: The Technology, Utilization, Application & Economics of Coal for Generating Electric Power. LC 82-7916. (Illus.). 372p. 1983. 45.00 (ISBN 0-8155-0907-3). Noyes.

Simeons, C. Coal: Its Role in Tomorrow's Technology. 1978. text ed. 125.00 (ISBN 0-08-022712-0). Pergamon.

Singer, Stanley. Pulverized Coal Combustion: Recent Developments. LC 84-4082. (Energy Technology Review Ser.: No. 90). (Illus.). 184p. 1984. 32.00 (ISBN 0-8155-0992-8). Noyes.

Singh, Jag J. & Deepak, Adarsh, eds. Environmental & Climatic Impact of Coal Utilization. LC 79-28681. 1980. 49.50 (ISBN 0-12-646360-3). Acad Pr.

South African Coal Processing Society. Coal Preparation for Plant Operators. 3rd ed. (Illus.). 360p. 1980. 135.00 (ISBN 0-620-04757-7). Miller Freeman.

Speight. The Chemistry & Technology of Coal. (Chemical Industries Ser.). 576p. 1983. 75.00 (ISBN 0-8247-1915-8). Dekker.

Spinks, A., et al, eds. New Coal Chemistry. (The Royal Society of London Ser.: Vol. 300). 215p. 1981. Repr. text ed. 74.00x (ISBN 0-85403-159-6, Pub. by Royal Soc London). Scholium Intl.

Steam Coal: Prospects to 2000. 1978. 12.00x (ISBN 92-64-11867-5). OECD.

Stone, J. F. Palynology of the Eddleman Coal (Pennsylvanian) of North-Central Texas. (Illus.). 55p. 1969. 1.50 (ISBN 0-318-03165-5). Bur Econ Geology.

Sullivan, Richard F., ed. Upgrading Coal Liquids. LC 81-1277. (ACS Symposium Ser.: No. 156). 1981. 31.95 (ISBN 0-8412-0629-5). Am Chemical.

Swann, Philip D., et al. Extraction of Useful Chemical Derivatives from Coal. LC 74-26746. (Energy Ser.: Vol. 2). 188p. 1976. text ed. 38.00x (ISBN 0-8422-7263-1). Irvington.

Tatsch, J. H. Coal Deposits: Origin, Evolution, & Present Characteristics. LC 76-28096. (Illus.). 590p. 1980. 156.00 (ISBN 0-912890-13-4). Tatsch.

Tewalt, S. J., et al. Estimation of Coal Resources in Texas Gulf Coast, Ohio Northern Appalachian, & Wyoming Powder River Basins: A Comparison of Statistical Approaches. (Report of Investigations Ser.: RI 136). (Illus.). 137p. 1983. 5.50 (ISBN 0-318-03295-3). Bur Econ Geology.

Torrey, S., ed. Trace Contaminants from Coal. LC 78-61890. (Pollution Technology Review: No. 50). 249p. 1979. 39.00 (ISBN 0-8155-0724-0). Noyes.

Tsai, S. C. Fundamentals of Coal Benefication & Utilization. (Coal Science & Technology Ser.: Vol. 2). 376p. 1982. 83.00 (ISBN 0-444-42082-7, I-174-82). Elsevier.

Van Krevelen. Coal: Topology, Chemistry, Physics & Constitution. (Coal Science & Technology Ser.: Vol. 3). 514p. 1981. 106.50 (ISBN 0-444-40600-X). Elsevier.

VDI. Synthetic Fuels from Coal. (Progress Report of the VDI-Z, Series 3: No. 79). 226p. (Orig.). 1983. pap. 62.00 (ISBN 0-9907000-0-3, Pub. by VDI W Germany). Heyden.

Walker, Flora K. Bibliography & Index of U. S. Geological Survey Publications Relating to Coal: January 1971 Through June 1978. 80p. (Orig.). 1980. pap. 4.00 (ISBN 0-913312-44-4). Am Geol.

Wheelock, Thomas D., ed. Coal Desulfurization: Chemical & Physical Methods. LC 77-17216. (ACS Symposium Ser.: No. 64). 1977. 35.95 (ISBN 0-8412-0400-4). Am Chemical.

Wilson, Carroll L., ed. Coal-Bridge to the Future. (World Coal Study Ser.: Vol. 1). 276p. 1980. prof ref 25.00 (ISBN 0-88410-099-5). Ballinger Pub.

Winans, Randall E. & Crelling, John C. Chemistry & Characterization of Coal Macerals. LC 84-6260. (ACS Symposium Ser.: No. 252). 184p. 1984. lib. bdg. 36.95x (ISBN 0-8412-0838-7). Am Chemical.

World Coal Study. Coal: A Bridge to the Future. LC 81-47090. (Illus.). 280p. 1985. pap. 5.72icancelled (ISBN 0-06-090883-1, CN 883, CN). Har-Row.

Zimmerman, Raymond E. Evaluating & Testing the Coking Properties of Coal. LC 79-84399. (A World Coal Book). (Illus.). 1979. 75.00 (ISBN 0-87930-111-2). Miller Freeman.

COAL–COMBUSTION
see Combustion

COAL–DESULPHURIZATION
DOE Technical Information Center. Coal Desulfurization: A Bibliography. 510p. 1983. pap. 24.75 (ISBN 0-87079-514-7, DOE/TIC-3400); microfiche 4.50 (ISBN 0-87079-515-5, DOE/TIC-3400). DOE.

COAL–DICTIONARIES
Todd, A. H. Lexicon of Terms Relating to the Assessment & Classification of Coal Resources. 140p. 1983. 55.00x (ISBN 0-8448-1438-5). Crane-Russak Co.

COAL–LIQUEFACTION
see Coal Liquefaction

COAL–GREAT BRITAIN
Jevons, William S. Coal Question. 3rd ed. LC 65-24371. Repr. of 1906 ed. 37.50x (ISBN 0-678-00107-3). Kelley.

Manners, Gerald. Coal in Britain. (The Resource Management Ser., No 4.). (Illus.). 1981. text ed. 25.00x (ISBN 0-04-333018-5); pap. text ed. 11.95x (ISBN 0-04-333019-3). Allen Unwin.

Schwieder, Dorothy. Black Diamonds: Life & Work in Iowa's Coal Mining Communities, 1895-1925. (Illus.). 204p. 1983. 18.95 (ISBN 0-8138-0991-6). Iowa St U Pr.
Shaw, Alan & Bruns, G. R. Australian Coal Industry. 1947. pap. 8.50x (ISBN 0-522-83741-7, Pub. by Melbourne U Pr). Intl Spec Bk.
Sinclair, Upton. The Coal War. Graham, John, ed. & intro. by. LC 75-40885. 335p. 1976. text ed. 19.50x (ISBN 0-87081-067-7). Colo Assoc.
Spearman, James E. United States Metallurgical Coal Industry. 209p. 1980. 12.50 (ISBN 0-937058-00-9). West Va U Pr.
Stefanko, Robert. Coal Mining Technology: Theory & Practice. Bise, Christopher J., ed. LC 82-71995. (Illus.). 410p. 1983. 45.00x (ISBN 0-89520-404-5, 404-5). Soc Mining Eng.
Strip-Mineable Coals Guidebook. LC 80-81269. 1980. 103.00 (ISBN 0-942218-08-6). Minobras.
Technology & Labour in Japanese Coal Mining. 65p. 1980. pap. 5.00 (ISBN 92-808-0082-5, TUNU090, UNU). Unipub.
Todd, A. H. Lexicon of Terms Relating to the Assessment & Classification of Coal Resources. 140p. 1982. 99.00x (ISBN 0-86010-403-6, Pub. by Graham & Trotman England). State Mutual Bk.
Tompkins, Dorothy C. Strip Mining for Coal. LC 73-919. (Public Policy Bibliographies: No. 4). 86p. (Orig.). 1973. pap. 5.00x (ISBN 0-87772-166-1). Inst Gov Stud Berk.
Trace Element Geochemistry of Coal Resource Development Related to Environmental Quality & Health. 1980. 12.50 (ISBN 0-309-03048-X). Natl Acad Pr.
The Transfer of Coal-Mining Technology from Japan to Manchuria & Manpower Problems-Focusing on the Development of the Fushun Coal Mines. (Project on Technology Transfer, Transformation & Development: The Japanese Experience). 92p. 1981. pap. 5.00 (ISBN 92-808-0225-9, TUNU167, UNU). Unipub.
Vietor, Richard H. Environmental Politics & the Coal Coalition. LC 79-5277. (Environmental History Ser.: No. 2). 304p. 1980. 23.50x (ISBN 0-89096-094-1). Tex A&M Univ Pr.
Wang, Y. J. & Sanford, Richard L., eds. First Conference on Use of Computers in the Coal Industry: Proceedings. LC 83-71931. (Illus.). 702p. 1983. 50.00x (ISBN 0-89520-416-9, 416-9). Soc Mining Eng.
Ward, Colin R., ed. Coal Geology & Coal Technology: Exploration, Mining Preparation & Use. (Illus.). 352p. 1985. 75.00x (ISBN 0-86793-208-2); pap. 40.00 (ISBN 0-86793-096-9). Blackwell Pubns.
Wiener, Daniel P., et al. Reclaiming the West: The Coal Industry & Surface-Mined Lands. LC 80-81777. 1980. pap. 20.00x (ISBN 0-918780-16-0). INFORM.
Wilson, Carroll L., ed. Future Coal Prospects: Country & Regional Assessments. (World Coal Study: Vol. II). 608p. 1980. prof ref 50.00x (ISBN 0-88410-098-7). Ballinger Pub.
Zimmerman, Martin B. The U. S. Coal Industry: The Economics of Policy Choice. 256p. 1981. text ed. 37.50x (ISBN 0-262-24023-8). MIT Pr.

COAL MINES AND MINING–SAFETY REGULATIONS

Coal Mines Committee, 11th Session, Geneva 1982. Employment & Training With Reference to Health & Safety at Coal Mines, Report II. International Labour Office, ed. iv, 75p. (Orig.). 1982. pap. 7.15 (ISBN 0-686-87162-6). Intl Labour Office.
Hesketh, H. E., ed. Integrated Environmental Control for Coal-Fired Power Plants. 158p. 1981. 30.00 (ISBN 0-686-34498-7, H00181). ASME.

COAL MINES AND MINING–AUSTRALIA

Shaw, Alan & Bruns, G. R. Australian Coal Industry. 1947. pap. 8.50x (ISBN 0-522-83741-7, Pub. by Melbourne U Pr). Intl Spec Bk.

COAL MINES AND MINING–CHINA

Carlson, Ellsworth C. Kaiping Mines, Eighteen Seventy-Seven to Nineteen Twelve. rev. 2nd ed. LC 71-148943. (East Asian Monographs Ser: No. 3). 1971. pap. 11.00x (ISBN 0-674-49700-7). Harvard U Pr.

COAL MINES AND MINING–GREAT BRITAIN

Benson, John. Bibliography of the British Coal Industry. Neville, Robert & Thompson, Charles, eds. 1981. 105.00x (ISBN 0-19-920120-X). Oxford U Pr.
Buxton, Neil. The Economic Development of the British Coal Industry. 1979. 48.00 (ISBN 0-7134-1994-6, Pub. by Batsford England). David & Charles.
Coal: A Pictorial History of the British Coal Industry. (Illus.). 96p. 1982. 12.50 (ISBN 0-7153-8242-X). David & Charles.
Galloway, Robert L. History of Coal Mining in Great Britain. LC 69-10851. Repr. of 1882 ed. 35.00x (ISBN 0-678-05598-X). Kelley.
Hair, T. H. Series of Views of the Collieries in the Counties of Northcumberland & Durham. LC 69-11240. (Illus.). Repr. of 1844 ed. lib. bdg. 35.00x (ISBN 0-678-05581-5). Kelley.
Holland, John. History & Description of Fossil Fuel, the Collieries & Coal Trade of Great Britain. 486p. 1968. Repr. of 1841 ed. 35.00x (ISBN 0-7146-1398-3, F Cass Co). Biblio Dist.
Jevons, H. Stanley. British Coal Trade. LC 68-58858. (Illus.). Repr. of 1915 ed. 57.50x (ISBN 0-678-05559-9). Kelley.
Langton, J. Geographical Change & Industrial Revolution. LC 78-67428. (Cambridge Geographical Studies: No. 11). (Illus.). 1980. 67.00 (ISBN 0-521-22490-X). Cambridge U Pr.
Leifchild, J. R. Our Coal & Coal-Pits. (Illus.). 243p. 1968. Repr. of 1856 ed. 28.50x (ISBN 0-7146-1401-7, F Cass Co). Biblio Dist.
--Our Coal & Our Coal-Pits. 2nd ed. LC 68-58856. Repr. of 1856 ed. 27.50x (ISBN 0-678-05065-1). Kelley.
Nef, John U. The Rise of the British Coal Industry, 2 vols. facsimile ed. LC 71-37902. (Select Bibliographies Reprint Ser). Repr. of 1932 ed. Set. 81.50 (ISBN 0-8369-6740-2). Ayer Co Pubs.
--Rise of the British Coal Industry, 2 vols. (Illus.). 1966. Repr. of 1932 ed. 85.00x set (ISBN 0-7146-1346-0, BHA-01346, F Cass Co). Biblio Dist.
Whitmore, R. L. Coal in Queensland: The First Fifty Years. (Illus.). xvii, 185p. 1982. text ed. 24.50x (ISBN 0-7022-1619-4). U of Queensland Pr.

COAL OIL

see Petroleum

COAL TAR

Gardner, Walter M. The British Coal-Tar Industry. Cohen, I. Bernard, ed. LC 80-2122. (Development of Science Ser.). (Illus.). 1981. lib. bdg. 40.00x (ISBN 0-405-13845-8). Ayer Co Pubs.

COAL-TAR PRODUCTS

see also Mineral Oils; Oils and Fats

Gesner, Abraham. Practical Treatise on Coal, Petroleum & Other Distilled Oils. 2nd ed. Gesner, George W., ed. LC 67-29511. Repr. of 1865 ed. 25.00x (ISBN 0-678-00440-4). Kelley.
Hydrogenation of Coal & Coal Tars. pap. 2.50 (ISBN 0-686-94563-8, UN72/2B27, UN). Unipub.

COAL TRADE

Annual Bulletin of Coal Statistics for Europe, Vol. XVIII: 1983. 90p. 11.00 (ISBN 0-317-18749-X, E/F/R.84.II.E.16). UN.
Bakerman, Theodore. Anthracite Coal: A Study in Advanced Industrial Decline. Bruchey, Stuart, ed. LC 78-22656. (Energy in the American Economy Ser.). (Illus.). 1979. lib. bdg. 23.00x (ISBN 0-405-11960-7). Ayer Co Pubs.
The Environmental Impact of Future Coal Production & Use in the EEC. 164p. 1982. 90.00x (ISBN 0-86010-446-X, Pub. by Order Dept Graham Trotman England). State Mutual Bk.
Jevons, H. Stanley. British Coal Trade. LC 68-58858. (Illus.). Repr. of 1915 ed. 57.50x (ISBN 0-678-05559-9). Kelley.
Johnson, James P. A New Deal for Soft Coal: The Attempted Revitalization of the Bituminous Coal Industry Under the New Deal. Bruchey, Stuart, ed. LC 78-22690. (Energy in the American Economy Ser.). 1979. lib. bdg. 25.50x (ISBN 0-405-11993-3). Ayer Co Pubs.
--The Politics of Soft Coal: The Bituminous Industry from World War I through the New Deal. LC 78-31555. 280p. 1979. 16.50x (ISBN 0-252-00739-5). U of Ill Pr.
Landis, Robin C. Sulfur Emissions Policies, Oil Prices, & the Appalachian Coal Industry. LC 80-8625. (Outstanding Dissertations in Economics Ser.). 270p. 1984. lib. bdg. 36.00 (ISBN 0-8240-4182-8). Garland Pub.
Langton, J. Geographical Change & Industrial Revolution. LC 78-67428. (Cambridge Geographical Studies: No. 11). (Illus.). 1980. 67.00 (ISBN 0-521-22490-X). Cambridge U Pr.
Nef, John U. The Rise of the British Coal Industry, 2 vols. facsimile ed. LC 71-37902. (Select Bibliographies Reprint Ser). Repr. of 1932 ed. Set. 81.50 (ISBN 0-8369-6740-2). Ayer Co Pubs.
Novak, Thomas, et al, eds. Use of Computers in the Coal Industry Conference, 2nd: Proceedings. LC 85-70438. (Illus.). 475p. 1985. 50.00X (ISBN 0-89520-437-1, 437-1). Soc Mining Eng.
OECD Staff & IEA Staff. Coal Prospects & Policies in IEA Countries, 1981 Review. 170p. (Orig.). 1982. pap. 17.00x (ISBN 92-64-12336-9). OECD.
South African Coal Processing Society. Quality & Quantity Control in Coal Trading. (Illus.). 137p. 1980. pap. 77.00 (ISBN 0-620-05879-X). Miller Freeman.
Striner, Herbert E. An Analysis of the Bituminous Coal Industry in Terms of Total Energy Supply & a Synthetic Oil Program. Bruchey, Stuart, ed. LC 78-22752. (Energy in the American Economy Ser.). (Illus.). 1979. lib. bdg. 24.50x (ISBN 0-405-12016-8). Ayer Co Pubs.
United Nations Economic Commission for Europe. Coal: Nineteen Eighty-Five & Beyond A Perspective Study. LC 77-30437. 1978. pap. text ed. 30.00 (ISBN 0-08-022409-1). Pergamon.

COAST CHANGES

see also Beach Erosion; Sedimentation and Deposition; Shore Lines; Shore Protection

Bird, Eric C. Coastline Changes: A Global Review. LC 84-22064. 1985. 39.95 (ISBN 0-471-90646-8). Wiley.
Komar, Paul D. Beach Processes & Sedimentation. (Illus.). 464p. 1976. 43.95 (ISBN 0-13-072595-1). P-H.
Komar, Paul D., ed. Handbook of Coastal Process & Erosion. 320p. 1983. 70.00 (ISBN 0-8493-0225-0). CRC Pr.
Lind, Aulis O. Coastal Landforms of Cat Island, Bahamas: A Study of Holocene Accretionary Topography & Sea Level Change. LC 76-77892. (Research Papers Ser.: No. 122). 156p. 1969. pap. 10.00 (ISBN 0-89065-029-2). U Chicago Dept Geog.
Mitchell, James K. Community Response to Coastal Erosion: Individual & Collective Adjustments to Hazard on the Atlantic Shore. LC 73-92652. (Research Papers Ser.: No. 156). 209p. 1974. 10.00 (ISBN 0-89065-063-2). U Chicago Dept Geog.
Steers, J. A., ed. Introduction to Coastline Development. 1st U.S. ed. 1971. 25.00x (ISBN 0-262-19089-3). MIT Pr.
Williams, William W. Coastal Changes. LC 75-3873. (Illus.). 220p. 1975. Repr. of 1960 ed. lib. bdg. 16.00x (ISBN 0-8371-8088-0, WICOC). Greenwood.

COAST-PILOT GUIDES

see Pilot Guides

COAST PROTECTIVE WORKS

see Shore Protection

COASTAL ECOLOGY

see Seashore Ecology

COASTAL FLORA

see also Halophytes; Marine Flora

Chapman, V. J. Coastal Vegetation. 2nd ed. 1976. pap. text ed. 18.75 (ISBN 0-08-019687-X). Pergamon.
Dawson, E. Yale. Seashore Plants of Northern California. (California Natural History Guides: No. 20). 1966. pap. 3.25 (ISBN 0-520-00301-2). U of Cal Pr.
--Seashore Plants of Southern California. (California Natural History Guides: No. 19). 1966. pap. 2.95 (ISBN 0-520-00300-4). U of Cal Pr.
Dawson, E. Yale & Foster, Michael S. Seashore Plants of California. LC 81-19690. (California Natural History Guides Ser.: No. 47). (Illus.). 226p. 1983. 15.95 (ISBN 0-520-04138-0); pap. 7.95 (ISBN 0-520-04139-9). U of Cal Pr.
Lewis, Roy R., III, ed. Creation & Restoration of Coastal Plant Communities. 232p. 1982. 69.50 (ISBN 0-8493-6573-2). CRC Pr.

COASTAL SIGNALS

see Signals and Signaling

COASTAL WATERWAYS

see Intracoastal Waterways

COASTAL ZONE MANAGEMENT

see also Marine Pollution; Shore Protection

ASCE Conference, San Francisco, May 1978. Coastal Zone '78: 1978, 4 vols. 3195p. 1978. Set. pap. 118.00x (ISBN 0-87262-134-0). Am Soc Civil Eng.
ASCE Waterway, Port Coastal & Ocean Division Conference, Charleston, Nov. 1977. Coastal Sediments: 1977. American Society of Civil Engineers, compiled By. 1143p. 1977. pap. 47.00x (ISBN 0-87262-090-5). Am Soc Civil Eng.
Barnes, R. S. Coastal Lagoons. LC 80-40041. (Cambridge Studies in Modern Biology: No. 1). (Illus.). 130p. 1980. 37.50 (ISBN 0-521-23422-0); pap. 13.95 (ISBN 0-521-29945-4). Cambridge U Pr.
Bird, Eric C. Jakarta Workshop on Coastal Resources Management: Proceedings. Soegiarto, Aprilani, ed. 106p. 1980. pap. 15.00 (TUNU100, UNU). Unipub.
Center for Ocean Management Studies, ed. Comparative Marine Policy: Perspectives from Europe, Scandinavia, Canada & the United States. LC 80-21455. 336p. 1981. 42.95x (ISBN 0-03-058307-1). Praeger.
Clark, John R. Coastal Ecosystem Management. LC 81-18650. 940p. 1983. Repr. of 1977 ed. lib. bdg. 59.50 (ISBN 0-89874-456-3). Krieger.
Coastal Engineering International Conference, 15th, Honolulu, Hawaii, July 1976 & American Society of Civil Engineers. Coastal Engineering: 1976, 4 vols. 2242p. 1977. Set. pap. 110.00x (ISBN 0-87262-083-2). Am Soc Civil Eng.
Coastal Engineering International Conference, 16th, Hamburg, Germany, Aug. 1978. Coastal Engineering: 1978, 3 vols. American Society of Civil Engineers, compiled By. 3096p. 1979. pap. 110.00x (ISBN 0-87262-190-1). Am Soc Civil Eng.
Coastal Engineering: Proceedings of the 13th Coastal Engineering International Conference, Vancouver, BC, Canada, July 1972, 3 vols. American Society of Civil Engineers, compiled By. 3476p. 1973. Set. pap. 99.00x (ISBN 0-87262-049-2). Am Soc Civil Eng.
Coastal Lagoon Survey. (Technical Papers in Marine Science: No. 31). 280p. 1980. pap. 17.75 (ISBN 0-686-74026-2, U1085, UNESCO). Unipub.
Devanney, J. W., et al. Parable Beach: A Primer in Coastal Zone Management. 1976. text ed. 15.00x (ISBN 0-262-04052-2). MIT Pr.
Edge, Bill L., ed. Coastal Engineering: 1982, 3 Vols. 18th ed. 2844p. 1983. pap. 165.00 (ISBN 0-87262-373-4). Am Soc Civil Eng.
Griggs, Gary B. & Savoy, Lauret E., eds. Living with the California Coast. (Living with the Shore Ser.). (Illus.). 424p. 1985. 27.95 (ISBN 0-8223-0632-8); pap. 14.95 (ISBN 0-8223-0633-6). Duke.
Heikoff, Joseph M., ed. Shorelines & Beaches in Coastal Management: A Bibliography, No. 876. 1975. 6.50 (ISBN 0-686-20368-2). CPL Biblios.
Horikawa, K. Coastal Engineering: An Introduction to Ocean Engineering. LC 78-17979. 402p. 1978. 57.95x (ISBN 0-470-26449-7). Halsted Pr.
Hydraulics in the Coastal Zone. 372p. 1977. pap. 19.75x (ISBN 0-87262-085-9). Am Soc Civil Eng.
International Conference, 14th, Copenhagen, Denmark, June 1974. Coastal Engineering: 1974, 3 vols. American Society of Civil Engineers, compiled by. 2705p. 1975. pap. 110.00x (ISBN 0-87262-113-8). Am Soc Civil Eng.
Lewis, Roy R., III, ed. Creation & Restoration of Coastal Plant Communities. 232p. 1982. 69.50 (ISBN 0-8493-6573-2). CRC Pr.
Magoon, Orville T. & Converse, Hugh, eds. Coastal Zone '83: 1983, 3 Vols. 2990p. 1983. Set. pap. 180.00x (ISBN 0-87262-359-9). Am Soc Civil Eng.
Saila, Saul B., ed. Coastal & Offshore Environmental Inventory: Cape Hatteras to Nantucket Shoals. LC 72-619712. (Marine Publications Ser.). 1973. No. 2. pap. 10.00 (ISBN 0-938412-04-3); No. 3. pap. 5.00, complementary vol. (ISBN 0-938412-20-5). URI MAS.
Scott, Stanley, ed. Coastal Conservation: Essays on Experiments in Governance. LC 79-25504. 56p. 1981. pap. text ed. 5.50x (ISBN 0-87772-270-6). Inst Gov Stud Berk.
Seavey, George L. Rhode Island's Coastal Natural Areas: Priorities for Protection & Management. (Marine Technical Report Ser.: No. 43). 1975. pap. 2.00 (ISBN 0-938412-13-2). URI MAS.
Teas, H. J., ed. Physiology & Management of Mangroves. (Task for Vegetation Science). 1984. lib. bdg. 38.00 (ISBN 90-6193-949-6, Pub. by Junk Pubs Netherlands). Kluwer Academic.
Technologies for Coastal Erosion Control. 132p. 1983. pap. 14.00 (ISBN 0-686-44457-4, UN82/2A19, UN). Unipub.
United Nations Department of International Economic & Social Affairs, Ocean Economics & Technology Branch. Coastal Area Management & Development. 196p. 1982. 44.00 (ISBN 0-08-023393-7). Pergamon.
Valencia, Mark J., ed. Proceedings of the Workshop on Coastal Area Development & Management in Asia & the Pacific: Manila, Philippines, Three to Twelve December Nineteen Seventy-Nine. ix, 202p. (Orig.). 1981. pap. text ed. 5.00 (ISBN 0-86638-037-X). E W Center HI.
Weggel, J. Richard, ed. Coastal Structures: 1983. LC 82-84759. 1020p. 1983. pap. 76.00x (ISBN 0-87262-353-X). Am Soc Civil Eng.
Wong, Kong, ed. Ports '83. 842p. 1983. pap. 59.75x (ISBN 0-87262-352-1). Am Soc Civil Eng.

COASTS

see also Coast Changes; Coastal Flora; Coastal Zone Management; Estuaries; Fjords; Ocean Waves; Seashore; Shore Protection

Beer, T. Environmental Oceanography: An Introduction to the Behaviour of Coastal Waters. LC 82-18099. (PIL Ser.). (Illus.). 109p. 1983. 30.00 (ISBN 0-08-026291-0); pap. 13.00 (ISBN 0-08-026290-2). Pergamon.
Bennett, R. F. The Coast Guardsman's Manual. 7th. ed. (Illus.). 656p. 1983. text ed. 10.95x (ISBN 0-87021-118-8). Naval Inst Pr.
Bird, Eric. Coasts. 3rd ed. (Illus.). 320p. 1984. 34.95x (ISBN 0-631-13567-7); pap. 11.95x (ISBN 0-631-13568-5). Basil Blackwell.
Bird, Eric C. & Schwartz, Maurice L., eds. The World's Coastline. (Illus.). 1184p. 1985. 97.50 (ISBN 0-442-21116-3). Van Nos Reinhold.

Ledgard, Henry F. & Chmura, Louis J., Jr. COBOL with Style: Programming Proverbs. (Computer Programming Ser.). 1976. pap. text ed. 10.95 (ISBN 0-8104-5781-4). Hayden.
Ledin, George, Jr. & Kudlick, Michael D. The COBOL Programmer's Book of Rules. (Computer Technology Ser.). (Illus.). 221p. 1983. pap. 14.95 (ISBN 0-534-97923-8). Lifetime Learn.
Ledin, George, Jr., et al. The COBOL Programmer's Book of Rules. 221p. 1983. pap. 15.95. Van Nos Reinhold.
Lim, Pacifico A. CICS-VS Command Level with ANS COBOL Examples. (VNR Data Processing Ser.). (Illus.). 416p. 1982. 32.95 (ISBN 0-442-22607-1); disks for apple II & IBM-PC 59.50 ea. Van Nos Reinhold.
--A Guide to Structured COBOL with Efficiency Techniques & Special Algorithms. (Data Processing Ser.). 272p. 1980. 24.95 (ISBN 0-442-24585-8). Van Nos Reinhold.
--A Guide to Structured COBOL with Efficiency Techniques & Special Algorithms. 286p. 1982. pap. 13.95 (ISBN 0-442-24589-0). Van Nos Reinhold.
Lowe, Doug. CICS for the COBOL Programmer: Instructor's Guide. 250p. 1985. price not set binder (ISBN 0-911625-27-5). M Murach & Assoc.
--CICS for the COBOL Programmer, Part 1: An Introductory Course. LC 83-62724. (Illus.). 326p. 1984. 25.00 (ISBN 0-911625-15-1). M Murach & Assoc.
--CICS for the COBOL Programmer, Part 2: An Advanced Course. LC 83-62724. (Illus.). 322p. (Orig.). 1985. 25.00 (ISBN 0-911625-16-X). M Murach & Assoc.
--VSAM for the COBOL Programmer. (Illus.). 150p. 1982. pap. 15.00 (ISBN 0-911625-12-7). M Murach & Assoc.
McCalla, Richard. Structured COBOL Programming & Data Processing Methods. LC 84-21367. (Computer Science Ser.). 450p. 1985. pap. text ed. 20.00 pub net (ISBN 0-534-04488-3). Brooks-Cole.
McCalla, Thomas R. Introduction to Structured COBOL: With Business Applications. 500p. 1984. write for info. tchr's manual. Wadsworth Pub.
McCameron, Fritz A. COBOL Logic & Programming. 4th ed. 1981. pap. 18.75x (ISBN 0-256-02483-9). Irwin.
--COBOL Logic & Programming. 5th ed. LC 84-18730. (Information & Decision Sciences Ser.). 451p. 1985. text ed. 22.95x (ISBN 0-256-03210-6). Irwin.
McCracken, D. D. & Garbassi, U. A Guide to COBOL Programming. 2nd ed. 209p. 1970. pap. 22.50x (ISBN 0-471-58243-3). Wiley.
McCracken, Daniel. A Simplified Guide to Structured COBOL Programming. LC 75-44339. 390p. 1976. 27.95 (ISBN 0-471-58284-0). Wiley.
McNitt, Lawrence. Invitation to COBOL for the TRS-80. (Illus.). 240p. 1983. pap. text ed. 15.00 (ISBN 0-89433-209-0). Petrocelli.
Manning, Gerry. Advanced COBOL: A Structured Approach. 480p. 1984. pap. text ed. 25.95 (ISBN 0-394-33071-4, RanC). Random.
--COBOL Basics. 2nd ed. 400p. 1984. pap. text ed. 23.00 (ISBN 0-394-33572-4, RanC). Random.
Medley, Don B. & Eaves, Ronald W. Programming Principles with COBOL I. 1984. text ed. 16.30 wkbk. (ISBN 0-538-10420-1, J42). SW Pub.
Minkler, Dwight. Structured COBOL Workbench. 16.95 (ISBN 0-13-854258-9). P-H.
Mullish, Henry. A Business-Like Approach to COBOL. 1979. pap. text ed. 18.50 scp (ISBN 0-7002-2506-4, HarpC). Har-Row.
--Structured COBOL: A Modern Approach. 365p. 1982. pap. text ed. 21.95 scp (ISBN 0-06-044652-8, HarpC); instr's. manual avail. (ISBN 0-06-364640-4). Har-Row.
Murach, Mike. Standard COBOL. 2nd ed. LC 74-34184. (Illus.). 400p. 1975. pap. text ed. 20.95 (ISBN 0-574-18401-5, 13-4010); instr's guide avail. (ISBN 0-574-18402-3, 13-4011). SRA.
--Structured COBOL. 1980. pap. text ed. 22.95 (ISBN 0-574-21260-4, 13-4260); instr's guide avail. (ISBN 0-574-21261-2, 13-4261); os supplement 6.95 (ISBN 0-574-21263-9, 13-4263); dos supplement 6.95 (ISBN 0-574-21264-7, 13-4264). SRA.
Murach, Mike & Noll, Paul. Structured ANS COBOL, 2 pts. Incl. Pt. 1. A Course for Novices. 498p; Pt. 2. An Advanced Course. 458p. (Illus.). 1979. pap. 20.00 ea. (ISBN 0-911625-13-5). M Murach & Assoc.
--Structured ANS COBOL, Pt. 1: A Course for Novices. LC 78-69920. (Illus.). 498p. 1979. pap. 20.00 (ISBN 0-911625-05-4). M Murach & Assoc.
--Structured ANS COBOL, Pt. 2: An Advanced Course. LC 78-69920. (Illus.). 458p. 1979. pap. 20.00 (ISBN 0-911625-06-2). M Murach & Assoc.
Murach, Mike, et al. Structured ANS COBOL Advisor's Guide. Taylor, Judy, ed. 320p. (Orig.). 1980. 3 ring bdr. 100.00 (ISBN 0-911625-09-7). M Murach & Assoc.
Naps, Thomas & Singh, Bhaghat. COBOL: A Comprehensive Treatment. (Illus.). 432p. 1982. pap. text ed. 20.95 (ISBN 0-8359-0830-5); solutions manual avail. (ISBN 0-8359-0832-1). Reston.
National Computing Center. Structured COBOL Reference Summary. 100p. 1984. pap. text ed. 15.00 (ISBN 0-471-81056-8). Wiley.
National Computing Centre. COBOL Reference Summary. 100p. (Orig.). 1981. pap. 17.50x (ISBN 0-85012-318-6). Intl Pubns Serv.
--COBOL Reference Summary. 95p. 1981. 16.40 (ISBN 0-471-89496-6, Pub. by Wiley-Interscience). Wiley.
Noll, Paul. Structured Programming for the COBOL Programmer. LC 77-85445. (Illus.). 239p. (Orig.). 1977. pap. text ed. 15.00 (ISBN 0-911625-03-8). M Murach & Assoc.
Noll, Paul & Murach, Mike. The COBOL Programmer's Handbook. LC 84-61555. (Illus.). 325p. 1985. pap. 20.00 (ISBN 0-911625-21-6). M Murach & Assoc.
--How to Design & Develop COBOL Programs. LC 84-61556. (Illus.). 536p. 1985. pap. 20.00 (ISBN 0-911625-20-8). M Murach & Assoc.
Overbeek, Ross A. & Singletary, Wilson E. Introduction to COBOL: A Primer & a Programmer's Guide. LC 84-14491. 408p. 1985. pap. write for info. (ISBN 0-201-16310-1); write for info. tchr's manual (ISBN 0-201-16315-2); write for info. trans. master (ISBN 0-201-16317-9). Addison-Wesley.
Paquette, Gerard A. Structured COBOL: A Problem-Solving Approach. 624p. 1984. pap. text ed. write for info. (ISBN 0-87150-697-1, 8300). PWS Pubs.
Parkin, Andrew. COBOL for Students. 2nd ed. 224p. 1982. pap. text ed. 14.95 (ISBN 0-7131-3477-1). E Arnold.
Patmore, Ruth & Ross, Elizabeth. Rossmore Appliances. 50p. 1972. 5.50 (ISBN 0-686-66706-9). Macmillan.
Philippakis, A. S. & Kazmier, L. J. Advanced COBOL for Information Systems. (Illus.). 608p. 1982. 35.95x (ISBN 0-07-049806-7). McGraw.
Philippakis, Andreas & Kazmier, Leonard. Program Design Concepts with Application in COBOL. (Illus.). 240p. 1983. text ed. 30.95 (ISBN 0-07-049808-3). McGraw.
Philippakis, Andreas S. & Kazmier, Leonard J. Information Systems Through COBOL. 2nd ed. (Illus.). 1978. text ed. 33.95 (ISBN 0-07-049791-5). McGraw.
--Structured COBOL. 2nd ed. Stewart, Charles E., ed. (Illus.). 448p. 1981. pap. text ed. 25.95 (ISBN 0-07-049801-6). McGraw.
Pierson, J. K. & Horn, Jeretta. Structured COBOL Programming. 1986. pap. text ed. 23.95x (ISBN 0-673-15913-2). Scott F.
Pitts, Gerald N. & Bateman, Barry L. Essentials of COBOL Programming: A Structured Approach. LC 82-12530. 145p. 1982. pap. text ed. 15.95 (ISBN 0-914894-34-X). Computer Sci.
Pollack, Morris & Geist, Harry. Structured COBOL Programming. 340p. (Orig.). 1982. pap. text ed. 24.15 scp (ISBN 0-672-97690-0). Bobbs.
Pollock, Morris & Geist, Harry. Structural COBOL Programming. 340p. 1982. pap. text ed. write for info. (ISBN 0-02-384150-8). Macmillan.
Popkin, Gary S. Advanced Structured COBOL. LC 82-21278. 512p. 1983. pap. text ed. write for info. (ISBN 0-534-01394-5). Kent Pub Co.
--Comprehensive Structured COBOL. LC 83-25596. 560p. 1984. write for info. (ISBN 0-534-03112-9). Kent Pub Co.
--Introductory Structured COBOL Programming. 480p. 1981. 21.95 (ISBN 0-442-26771-1). Van Nos Reinhold.
--Introductory Structured COBOL Programming. 2nd ed. LC 85-234. 368p. 1985. pap. text ed. write for info. (ISBN 0-534-04566-9). Kent Pub Co.
Price, Wilson T. & Olson, Jack. Elements of COBOL Programming. 384p. 1981. text ed. 23.95 (ISBN 0-03-058052-8, HoltC). HR&W.
Prince, Anne & Murach, Mike. How to Design & Develop COBOL Programs: Case Studies. LC 85-61543. 75p. 1985. price not set (ISBN 0-911625-22-4). M Murach & Assoc.
--How to Design & Develop COBOL Programs: Instructor's Guide. 250p. 1985. price not set binder (ISBN 0-911625-23-2). M Murach & Assoc.
Priscoe. Structured COBOL: A Beginners Guide. 7.95 (ISBN 0-07-050888-7). McGraw.
Pugh, John & Bell, Doug. Modern Methods for COBOL Programmers. LC 82-22978. (Illus.). 216p. 1983. 21.95 (ISBN 0-13-595215-8). P-H.
Richards, Thomas C. COBOL: An Introduction. (Data Processing Ser.). 350p. 1981. pap. text ed. 19.95 (ISBN 0-675-08041-X). Merrill.
Robinson, P. B. Advanced COBOL: ANS 74. 216p. 1976. 32.50 (ISBN 0-444-19453-3). Elsevier.
Rogers. The COBOL Programmer Design Book. 1985. price not set (ISBN 0-471-82666-9). Wiley.
Rosendorf, Beverly. Computer Programming in COBOL the Easy Way. (Easy Way Ser.). 256p. 1984. pap. 8.95 (ISBN 0-8120-2801-5). Barron.
Russell, Christopher. A COBOL Handbook. 176p. 1984. 11.95 (ISBN 0-201-14650-9). Addison-Wesley.
Saxon, J. & Englander, W. ANSI COBOL Programming. 2nd ed. 1978. pap. text ed. 21.95 (ISBN 0-13-037770-8). P-H.
Schwartz, Floyd C. Advanced COBOL Techniques: A Lab Manual. 160p. 1984. pap. text ed. 14.95 (ISBN 0-8403-3326-9). Kendall Hunt.
Seidel, Ken. Microsoft COBOL. 200p. 1983. pap. 15.95 (ISBN 0-88056-117-3). Dilithium Pr.
Shank, Thayne A. The Structured COBOLer's Guide. (Illus.). 144p. 1984. pap. 19.95 (ISBN 0-13-854448-4). P-H.
Shelly, Gary B. & Cashman, Thomas J. Advanced ANSI, COBOL Disk-Tape Programming Efficiencies. LC 74-21838. 378p. 1974. pap. text ed. 24.95 (ISBN 0-88236-105-8). Anaheim Pub Co.
--Advanced Structured COBOL Program Design & File Processing. LC 78-62480. (Illus.). 525p. 1978. pap. text ed. 24.95 (ISBN 0-88236-112-0). Anaheim Pub Co.
--ANSI COBOL Workbook, Testing & Debugging Techniques. 237p. 1973. pap. 10.95 (ISBN 0-88236-104-X). Anaheim Pub Co.
--DOS Job Control for COBOL Programmers. (Illus.). 311p. 1971. pap. text ed. 22.95 (ISBN 0-88236-265-8). Anaheim Pub Co.
Shelly, Gary B & Cashman, Thomas J. Introduction to Computer Programming ANSI COBOL. (Illus.). 382p. 1973. pap. text ed. 24.95 (ISBN 0-88236-103-1). Anaheim Pub Co.
Shelly, Gary B. & Cashman, Thomas J. Introduction to Computer Programming Structured COBOL. LC 77-89824. 583p. 1977. pap. 24.95 (ISBN 0-88236-111-2). Anaheim Pub Co.
Shelly, Gary B., et al. Structured COBOL: Flowcharting Edition. 544p. 1985. pap. text ed. 24.95 (ISBN 0-88236-128-7). Anaheim Pub Co.
--Structured COBOL: Pseudocode Edition. 544p. 1985. pap. text ed. 24.95 (ISBN 0-88236-127-9). Anaheim Pub Co.
Shyh-Yuan, David L. CICS-VS Command Level Programming with COBOL Examples. 295p. 1983. perfect bdg. 29.95 (ISBN 0-9611810-1-X). D L Shyh Yuan.
Smith, Marilyn Z. Standard COBOL: A Problem-Solving Approach. 308p. 1974. pap. text ed. 23.50 (ISBN 0-395-17091-5). HM.
Sordillo, Donald A. The Programmer's ANSI COBOL Reference Manual. (Illus.). 1978. ref. 37.95 (ISBN 0-13-729491-3). P-H.
Spence, J. Wayne. COBOL for the Eighties. 2nd ed. (Illus.). 625p. (Orig.). 1985. pap. text ed. 24.95 (ISBN 0-314-85303-0). West Pub.
--COBOL for the 80's. (Illus.). 608p. 1982. pap. 22.95 (ISBN 0-314-63290-5). West Pub.
Stern, Nancy & Stern, Robert A. Structured COBOL Programming. 3rd ed. LC 79-18434. 571p. 1980. pap. 30.45 (ISBN 0-471-04913-1). Wiley.
--Structured COBOL Programming. 4th ed. 800p. 1985. pap. text ed. 26.95 (ISBN 0-471-87150-8); Study guide, 4th ed., 313p. pap. 10.95 (ISBN 0-471-88067-1). Wiley.
Teach Yourself Computer Programming in COBOL. 1983. pap. 5.95 (ISBN 0-679-10259-0). Mckay.
Topping, Anne L. & Gibbons, Ian. Business Applications of Structured COBOL Programming. 600p. 1982. pap. text ed. 32.07 scp (ISBN 0-205-07750-1, 2077507); tchr's. ed. avail. (ISBN 0-205-07751-X). Allyn.
Triance, J. M. COBOL Programming. (Illus.). 178p. (Orig.). 1981. pap. 25.00x (ISBN 0-85012-249-X). Intl Pubns Serv.
--COBOL Programming. 180p. 1981. pap. 22.95 (ISBN 0-471-89495-8). Wiley.
--Structured COBOL Programming. 178p. 1984. pap. text ed. 21.55 (ISBN 0-471-81053-3, Pub by Wiley-Interscience). Wiley.
Viands, Leon. CICS Command Level Reference Guide for COBOL Programmers. LC 83-72642. 140p. 1983. QED Info Sci.
Walstrom, John A. & Lindahl, Tate F. Advanced Structured COBOL. 432p. 1985. pap. text ed. write for info. (ISBN 0-02-424250-0). Macmillan.
Watters, John. COBOL Programming: A Complete Guide in Writing COBOL Programs. LC 73-154624. pap. 85.80 (ISBN 0-317-09174-3, 2051303). Bks Demand UMI.
Weinberg, Gerald M., et al. High Level COBOL Programming. 252p. 1977. pap. 26.50 (ISBN 0-89435-126-5). QED Info Sci.
Weiner, Howard D. Introductory Structured COBOL: A Programming Skills Approach. 344p. 1983. pap. text ed. write for info. (ISBN 0-697-08149-4); instr's manual avail. (ISBN 0-697-08170-2); write for info. casebook (ISBN 0-697-08171-0). Wm C Brown.
Welburn, Tyler. Advanced Structured COBOL: Batch, On Line, & Data-Base Concepts. LC 82-73737. (Illus.). 654p. (Orig.). 1983. pap. text ed. 27.95 (ISBN 0-87484-558-0, 558). Mayfield Pub.
--Structured COBOL: Fundamentals & Style. LC 80-84013. (Illus.). 536p. 1981. pap. text ed. 23.95 (ISBN 0-87484-543-2); instructor's manual avail. Mayfield Pub.
Welland, Ray. COBOL Programming for Microcomputers: Using CIS COBOL. 200p. 1983. write for info. (ISBN 0-201-14639-8). Addison-Wesley.
Wohl, Gerald. Structured COBOL: A Direct Approach. 1979. 22.95 (ISBN 0-574-21230-2, 13-4230); student manual 7.95 (ISBN 0-574-21232-9, 13-4232); student solutions manual avail. (ISBN 0-574-21233-7, 13-4233); instr's guide avail. (ISBN 0-574-21231-0, 13-4231). SRA.
Worth, Thomas. COBOL for Beginners. (Illus.). 1977. pap. text ed. 23.95 (ISBN 0-13-139378-2). P-H.
Yourdon, Edward, et al. Learning to Program in Structured COBOL, Pt. 1. 2nd ed. LC 78-63350. 280p. 1978. pap. 14.50 (ISBN 0-917072-12-X). Yourdon.
--Learning to Program in Structured COBOL, Pts. 1 & 2. (Software Ser.). 1979. text ed. 23.95 (ISBN 0-13-527713-2). P-H.

COBORDISM THEORY

Sanders, Jack P. The Category of H-Modules Over a Spectrum. LC 73-22409. (Memoirs: No. 141). 136p. 1974. pap. 11.00 (ISBN 0-8218-1841-4, MEMO-141). Am Math.

COBRA (AUTOMOBILE)

see Automobiles–Types–Cobra

COCAINE

American Health Research Institute Ltd. Medical Subject Research Index of International Bibliography Concerning Cocaine. Bartone, J. C., ed. LC 81-71267. 198p. 1982. 34.95 (ISBN 0-941864-16-2); pap. 29.95 (ISBN 0-941864-17-0). ABBE Pubs Assn.
Cohen, Sidney. Cocaine Today. LC 82-198608. 44p. 1981. pap. 2.50 (ISBN 0-942348-02-8). Am Council Drug Ed.
Cohen, Sidney & Lessin, Phyllis J. Marijuana & Alcohol. LC 82-73281. 28p. 1982. pap. 2.50 (ISBN 0-942348-09-5). Am Council Drug Ed.
The Coke Book: The Complete Reference to the Users & Abuses of Cocaine. 224p. 1984. pap. 3.50 (ISBN 0-425-07117-0). Berkley Pub.
Ellinwood, Everett M., Jr. & Kilbey, M., eds. Cocaine & Other Stimulants. LC 76-47488. (Advances in Behavioral Biology Ser.: Vol. 21). 731p. 1977. 75.00x (ISBN 0-306-37921-X, Plenum Pr). Plenum Pub.
Lee, David. Cocaine Handbook. LC 81-10865. (Illus.). 208p. 1981. 34.95 (ISBN 0-915904-68-3); pap. 19.95 (ISBN 0-915904-56-X). And-Or Pr.
Peterson, Robert C., et al. Cocaine: A Second Look. Smith, David E. & Dogoloff, Lee, eds. LC 83-70823. 46p. (Orig.). 1983. pap. 2.50 (ISBN 0-942348-13-3). Am Council Drug Ed.
Phillips, Joel & Wynne, Ronald D. Cocaine: The Mystique & the Reality. 1980. pap. 3.95 (ISBN 0-380-48678-4, 58248-1, Discus). Avon.

COCCIDAE

see Scale-Insects

COCCIDIA

Board of Education & Training. Identification of Aerobic Gram-Positive & Gram-Negative Cocci. 3rd ed. (Continuing Education Manual Ser.). 1981. 9.00 (ISBN 0-686-95651-6). Am Soc Microbio.
Ghani, M. A. & Mugaffar, N. Relations between the Parasitic Predator Complex & the Host-Plants of Coccids in Pakistan. 60p. 1974. 39.00x (ISBN 0-85198-288-3, Pub. by CAB Bks England). State Mutual Bk.
Long, Peter L., ed. The Biology of the Coccidia. 512p. 1982. text ed. 78.50 (ISBN 0-8391-1680-2). Univ Park.

COCCINELLIDAE

see Ladybirds

COCKATEELS

Alderton, David. Parrots, Lories & Cockatoos. 200p. 1982. 21.95 (ISBN 0-86230-041-X). Triplegate.
Allen, Gerald R. & Allen, Connie J. All about Cockatiels. (Illus.). 1977. 7.95 (ISBN 0-87666-757-4, PS-746). TFH Pubns.
Bulger, Dorothy. All about Breeding Cockatiels. (Illus.). 96p. 1983. 4.95 (ISBN 0-87666-942-9, PS-801). TFH Pubns.
Curtis, Nancy. Cockatiels. (Orig.). pap. 3.95 (ISBN 0-87666-420-6). TFH Pubns.
Decoteau, A. E. Handbook of Cockatoos. (Illus.). 159p. 1981. 19.95 (ISBN 0-87666-826-0, H-1030). TFH Pubns.

Bubel, Mike & Bubel, Nancy. Root Cellaring the Simple no-Processing Way to Store Fruits & Vegetables. (Illus.). 320p. 1979. 12.95 (ISBN 0-87857-277-5). Rodale Pr Inc.

Design & Operation of Cold Stores in Developing Countries. (Agricultural Services Bulletin Ser.: No. 19/2). 80p. 1985. pap. 7.50 (ISBN 92-5-101373-X, F2691 5071, FAO). Unipub.

Tressler, Donald K., et al. Freezing Preservation of Foods, 4 vols. 4th ed. Incl. Vol. 1. Principles of Refrigeration; Equipment for Freezing & Transporting Food. 50.00 (ISBN 0-87055-044-6); Vol. 2. Factors Affecting Quality in Frozen Foods. 55.00 (ISBN 0-87055-045-4); Vol. 3. Commercial Freezing Operations; Fresh Foods; Vol. 4. Freezing of Precooked & Prepared Foods. (Illus.). 1968. AVI.

World Petroleum Congress. Proceedings of the Ninth World Petroleum Congress: Processing & Storage, Vol. 5. 130p. 1975. 111.00 (ISBN 0-85334-667-4, Pub. by Elsevier Applied Sci England). Elsevier.

COLD STRESS (BIOLOGY)

see Cold–Physiological Effect

COLD WELDING

American Society for Metals. Source Book on Cold Forming: A Discriminative Selection of Outstanding Articles from the Periodical Literature. LC 75-6855. (American Society for Metals. Engineering Bookshelf Ser.). (Illus.). pap. 93.80 (ISBN 0-317-11151-5, 2019501). Bks Demand UMI.

COLD WORKING OF METALS

see Metals–Cold Working

COLEOPTERA

see Beetles

COLINAE

see Quails

COLLAGEN

Furthmayr, Heinz, ed. Immunochemistry of the Extracellular Matrix, 2 Vols. 208p. 1982. Vol. I, 288pp. 75.00 (ISBN 0-8493-6196-6); Vol. II, 208 pp. 59.50 (ISBN 0-8493-6197-4). CRC Pr.

Longacre, J. J. The Ultrastructure of Collagen: Its Relation to the Healing of Wounds & to the Management of Hypertrophic Scars. (Illus.). 538p. 1976. 54.75x (ISBN 0-398-03254-8). C C Thomas.

Mandl, Ines, ed. Collagenase. LC 73-173997. (Illus.). 222p. 1972. 57.75x (ISBN 0-677-15190-X). Gordon.

Prockop, D. J. & Champe, P. C., eds. Gene Families of Collagen & Other Proteins. (Developments in Biochemistry Ser.: Vol. 15). 242p. 1980. 49.75 (ISBN 0-444-00567-6, Biomedical Pr). Elsevier.

Ramachandran, G. N. & Reddi, A. H., eds. Biochemistry of Collagen. LC 76-7075. (Illus.). 536p. 1976. 69.50x (ISBN 0-306-30855-X, Plenum Pr). Plenum Pub.

Veis, Arthur. Macromolecular Chemistry of Gelatin. (Molecular Biology: Vol. 5). 1964. 75.00 (ISBN 0-12-715450-7). Acad Pr.

Viidik, Andrus & Vuust, Jens, eds. Biology of Collagen. 1980. 84.00 (ISBN 0-12-721750-9). Acad Pr.

Woodhead-Galloway, John. Collagen: The Anatomy of Protein. (Studies in Biology: No. 117). 64p. 1979. pap. text ed. 8.95 (ISBN 0-7131-2783-X). E Arnold.

Woolley, David E. & Evanson, John M. Collagenase in Normal & Pathological Connective Tissues. LC 79-40821. 292p. 1980. 69.95x (ISBN 0-471-27668-5, Pub. by Wiley-Interscience). Wiley.

COLLAPSE OF BUILDINGS

see Building Failures

COLLEGE RADIO STATIONS

see Radio Stations

COLLEMBOLA

Christiansen, Kenneth & Bellinger, Peter. The Collembola of North America, North of the Rio Grande: A Taxonomic. (Illus.). 1322p. 1981. 35.00 (ISBN 0-686-34383-2). Grinnell Coll.

COLLIE (DOG)

see Dogs–Breeds–Collies

COLLINEATION

Belsley, David A., et al. Regression Diagnostics: Identifying Influential Data & Sources of Collinearity. LC 79-19876. (Ser. in Probability & Mathematical Statistics: Applied Probability & Statistics). 292p. 1980. 36.95x (ISBN 0-471-05856-4, Pub. by Wiley-Interscience). Wiley.

Kallaher, M. J., ed. Affine Planes with Transitive Collineation Groups. 156p. 1981. 47.25 (ISBN 0-444-00620-6, North-Holland). Elsevier.

Ostrom, T. G. Finite Translation Planes. LC 73-139732. (Lecture Notes in Mathematics: Vol. 158). 1970. pap. 11.00 (ISBN 0-387-05186-4). Springer-Verlag.

COLLISIONS (NUCLEAR PHYSICS)

see also Ion Bombardment; Ionization; Nuclear Reactions; Radiation; Scattering (Physics); also names of particles, e.g. Electrons, Neutrons, Protons

AIP Conference. Experiments on High Energy Particle Collisions-1973: Proceedings, No. 12. Panvini, R. S., ed. LC 73-81705. 419p. 1973. 15.00 (ISBN 0-88318-111-8). Am Inst Physics.

--High Energy Collisions-1973: Proceedings, No. 15. Quigg, Chris, ed. LC 73-92324. 314p. 1973. 13.75x (ISBN 0-88318-114-2). Am Inst Physics.

Andersen, Hans H. & Ziegler, James F., eds. Hydrogen Stopping Powers & Ranges in All Elements, Vol. 3. LC 77-3068. 1977. text ed. 47.00 (ISBN 0-08-021605-6). Pergamon.

Andersen, S., et al, eds. Atomic Collisions in Solids: Conference, No. IV. 476p. 1972. 132.95 (ISBN 0-677-04660-X). Gordon.

Anisovich, V. V., et al. Quark Model & High Energy Collisions. 280p. 1984. 35.00x (ISBN 9971-966-68-9, Pub. by World Sci Singapore). Taylor & Francis.

Arifov, U. A. Interaction of Atomic Particles with a Solid Surface. LC 79-76223. 374p. 1969. 45.00x (ISBN 0-306-10831-3, Consultants). Plenum Pub.

Balian, R. & Iagolnitzer, D., eds. Structural Analysis of Collision Amplitudes: Proceedings, les Houches June Institute of Physics, June 2-27, 1975. LC 76-17583. 1976. 95.75 (ISBN 0-7204-0506-8, North-Holland). Elsevier.

Berenyi, D. & Hock, G., eds. High-Energy Ion-Atom Collisions: Proceedings of the International Seminar on High-Energy Ion-Atom Collision Processes, Debrecen, Hungary, Mar. 17-19, 1982. (Nuclear Methods Monographs: Vol. 2). 276p. 1982. 68.00 (ISBN 0-444-99703-2). Elsevier.

Bock, R., ed. Heavy Ion Collisions: Heavy Ion Reactors & Microscopic Properties of Nuclear States, Vol. 1. 676p. 1979. 121.50 (ISBN 0-7204-0738-9, North Holland). Elsevier.

Bowman, J. M., ed. Molecular Collision Dynamics. (Topics in Current Physics Ser.: Vol. 33). (Illus.). 158p. 1983. 22.00 (ISBN 0-387-12014-9). Springer-Verlag.

Bransden, B. H. Atomic Collision Theory. 2nd ed. (Illus.). 500p. 1970. text ed. 39.95 (ISBN 0-8053-1181-5). Benjamin-Cummings.

Brouillard, F., ed. Physics of Ion-Ion & Electron-Ion Collisions. (NATO ASI Series B, Physics: Vol. 83). 550p. 1983. 79.50 (ISBN 0-306-41105-9, Plenum Pr). Plenum Pub.

Burke, P. G. & Moiseiwitsch, B. L., eds. Atomic Processes & Applications. 1976. 76.75 (ISBN 0-7204-0444-4, North-Holland). Elsevier.

Carlson, Per & Trower, W. Peter, eds. Physics in Collision: High ee-ep-pp Interactions, Vol. 2. 430p. 1983. 69.50 (ISBN 0-306-41249-7, Plenum Press). Plenum Pub.

Child, M. S. Molecular Collision Theory. 1974. 56.00 (ISBN 0-12-172650-9). Acad Pr.

Christophorou, L. G. Electron Molecule Interactions & Their Applications. LC 83-7648. 1984. Vol. 1. 80.00 (ISBN 0-12-174401-9); Vol. 2. 85.00 (ISBN 0-12-174402-7). Acad Pr.

Datz, S., ed. Physics of Electronic & Atomic Collisions: Abstracts of Contributed Papers, 2 Vols. 1220p. 1981. Set. pap. 138.50 (ISBN 0-444-86322-2, North-Holland). Elsevier.

Ehrenberg, W. & Gibbons, D. J. Electron Bombardment Induced Conductivity & Its Applications. LC 81-66385. 1981. 96.00 (ISBN 0-12-233350-0). Acad Pr.

Eichler, J., et al, eds. Electronic & Atomic Collisions. 900p. 1985. 122.25 (North-Holland); pap. 86.75 (ISBN 0-444-86844-5). Elsevier.

Field, F. H. & Franklin, J. L. Electron Impact Phenomena. rev. ed. (Pure & Applied Physics Ser.: Vol. 1). 1957. 76.50 (ISBN 0-12-255450-7). Acad Pr.

Geltman, Sydney. Topics in Atomic Collision Theory. (Pure & Applied Physics Ser: Vol. 32). 1969. 67.50 (ISBN 0-12-279650-0). Acad Pr.

Gianturco, F. The Transfer of Molecular Energies by Collision: Recent Quantum Treatments. (Lecture Notes in Chemistry: Vol. 11). (Illus.). 327p. 1979. pap. 25.00 (ISBN 0-387-09701-5). Springer-Verlag.

Gianturco, Franco A., ed. Atomic & Molecular Collision Theory. LC 81-15362. (NATO ASI Series B, Physics: Vol. 71). 525p. 1982. 75.00x (ISBN 0-306-40807-4, Plenum Pr). Plenum Pub.

Goldberger, M. L. Collision Theory. rev ed. LC 75-15669. 930p. 1975. Repr. of 1964 ed. 52.50 (ISBN 0-88275-313-4). Krieger.

Groeneveld, K. O., et al, eds. Forward Electron Ejection in Ion Collisions. (Lecture Notes in Physics Ser.: Vol. 213). vii, 165p. 1984. pap. 12.00 (ISBN 0-387-13887-0). Springer-Verlag.

Hinze, Juergen, ed. Electron-Atom & Electron-Molecule Collisions. LC 82-18927. (Physics of Atoms & Molecules Ser.). 362p. 1983. 52.50x (ISBN 0-306-41188-1, Plenum Pr). Plenum Pub.

Johnson, R. E. Introduction to Atomic & Molecular Collisions. LC 82-3776. 300p. 1982. text ed. 32.50x (ISBN 0-306-40787-6, Plenum Pr). Plenum Pub.

Kaminsky, Manfred. Atomic & Ionic Impact Phenomena on Metal Surfaces. (Illus.). 1965. 50.80 (ISBN 0-387-03410-2). Springer-Verlag.

Kleinpoppen, H. & Williams, J. F., eds. Coherence & Correlation in Atomic Collisions. LC 79-15977. (Physics of Atoms & Molecules Ser.). (Illus.). 720p. 1980. 85.00x (ISBN 0-306-40250-5, Plenum Pr). Plenum Pub.

Lambert, J. D. Vibrational & Rotational Relaxation in Gases. (International Series of Monographs on Chemistry). (Illus.). 1977. 47.50x (ISBN 0-19-855605-5). Oxford U Pr.

McKoy, Vincent & Suzuki, H., eds. Electron-Molecule Collisions & Photoionization Processes. (Illus.). 244p. 1984. 24.95x (ISBN 0-89573-134-7). VCH Pubs.

Madurga, G. & Lozano, M. Heavy-Ion Collision, La Rabida, Spain, 1982: Proceedings. (Lecture Notes in Physics: Vol. 168). 429p. 1982. pap. 23.00 (ISBN 0-387-11945-0). Springer-Verlag.

Massey, H. S., ed. Applied Atomic Collision Physics. (Pure & Applied Physics Ser.: Vol. 4). 1983. 79.00 (ISBN 0-12-478804-1). Acad Pr.

Massey, H. S. & McDaniel, Earl, eds. Applied Atomic Collision Physics: Gas Laser, Vol. 3. (Pure & Applied Physics Ser.). 544p. 1982. 72.50 (ISBN 0-12-478803-3). Acad Pr.

Massey, H. S., et al, eds. Applied Atomic Collision Physics, Vol. 5. (Pure & Applied Physics Ser.). 426p. 1982. 69.50 (ISBN 0-12-478805-X). Acad Pr.

Massey, Harrie. Atomic & Molecular Collisions. LC 79-11716. 309p. 1979. 48.95x (ISBN 0-470-26742-9). Halsted Pr.

Massey, Harrie, et al. Applied Atomic Collision Physics: Atmospheric Physics & Chemistry, Vol. 1. (Pure & Applied Physics Ser.). 482p. 1982. 67.50 (ISBN 0-12-478801-7). Acad Pr.

Morgan, B. L., ed. Advances in Electronics & Electron Physics, Vol. 64. 1985. 65.00 (ISBN 0-12-014664-9). Acad Pr.

Norenberg, W. & Weidenmuller, H. A. Introduction to the Theory of Heavy-Ion Collisions. (Lecture Notes in Physics: Vol. 51). (Illus.). 1980. soft cover 23.00 (ISBN 0-387-09753-8). Springer-Verlag.

Rahman, N. K. & Guidotti, C., eds. Photon-Assisted Collisions & Related Topics. 377p. 1982. 63.50 (ISBN 3-7186-0130-3). Harwood Academic.

Risley, John S. & Geballe, Ronald, eds. Electronic & Atomic Collisions: Abstracts of Papers of the 9th International Conference on the Physics of Electronic & Atomic Collisions, 2 vols. LC 75-15451. 1198p. 1975. Set. pap. 50.00x (ISBN 0-295-95456-6). U of Wash Pr.

--The Physics of Electronic & Atomic Collisions: Invited Lectures, Review Papers & Progress Reports of the Nineth International Conference on the Physics of Electronic & Atomic Collisions. LC 75-39962. 916p. 1976. 50.00x (ISBN 0-295-95455-8). U of Wash Pr.

Skobel'tsyn, D. V., ed. Physics of Atomic Collisions. LC 79-157934. (P. N. Lebedev Physics Institute Ser.: Vol. 51). 188p. 1971. 42.50 (ISBN 0-306-10863-1, Consultants). Plenum Pub.

Smith, Kenneth. The Calculation of Atomic Collision Processes. LC 78-168645. 230p. 1971. 23.50 (ISBN 0-471-80000-7). Krieger.

Williams, Brian G. Compton Scattering: A Tool for the Investigation of Electron Momentum Distribution. LC 76-42261. (Illus.). 1977. text ed. 70.95x (ISBN 0-07-070360-4). McGraw.

COLLISIONS, AIRCRAFT

see Aeronautics–Accidents

COLLOIDS

see also Particles; Rheology

Andrade, Joseph D., ed. Hydrogels for Medical & Related Applications. LC 76-28170. (ACS Symposium Ser: No. 31). 1976. 29.95 (ISBN 0-8412-0338-5). Am Chemical.

Buscall, R., et al, eds. Science & Technology of Polymer Colloids. (Illus.). 336p. 1985. 57.00 (ISBN 0-85334-312-8, Pub. by Elsevier Applied Sci England). Elsevier.

Dickinson, E. & Stainsby, G. Colloids in Food. (Illus.). xiv, 532p. 1982. 92.50 (ISBN 0-85334-153-2, I-357-82, Pub. by Elsevier Applied Sci England). Elsevier.

Everett, D. H. Colloid Science, Vols. 1-2. LC 72-95096. Vol. 1 1970-71 Literature. 1973 36.00 (ISBN 0-85186-508-9, Pub. by Royal Soc Chem London); Vol. 2 1972-74 Literature. 1976 47.00. Am Chemical.

Fitch, Robert M., ed. Polymer Colloids, I. LC 70-153721. 187p. 1971. 39.50 (ISBN 0-306-30536-4, Plenum Pr). Plenum Pub.

Glicksman, Martin. Food Hydrocolloids. 232p. 1982. 65.00 (ISBN 0-8493-6041-2). CRC Pr.

Good, R. J. & Stromberg, R., eds. Surface & Colloid Science, Vol. 11. LC 67-29459. (Illus.). 360p. 1979. 49.50x (ISBN 0-306-40108-8, Plenum Pr). Plenum Pub.

Graham, H. D. Food Colloids. (Illus.). 1977. lib. bdg. 57.50 (ISBN 0-87055-201-5). AVI.

Gronwall, Anders. Dextran & Its Use in Colloidal Infusion Solutions. (Illus.). 1957. 39.00 (ISBN 0-12-304050-7). Acad Pr.

Hair, Michael & Croucher, Melvin D., eds. Colloids & Surfaces in Reprographic Technology. LC 82-13931. (ACS Symposium Ser.: No. 200). 594p. 1982. lib. bdg. 64.95x (ISBN 0-8412-0737-2). Am Chemical.

Hames, B. D. & Rickwood, D., eds. Gel Electrophoresis of Proteins: A Practical Approach. (Practical Approach Ser.). 308p. 1981. pap. 20.00 (ISBN 0-904147-22-3). IRL Pr.

Heicklein, Julian. Colloid Formation & Growth: A Chemical Kinetic Approach. 1976. 41.00 (ISBN 0-12-336750-6). Acad Pr.

Heimenz, Paul C. Principles of Colloids & Surface Chemistry. (Undergraduate Chemistry Textbooks Ser.: Vol. 4). 1977. 34.50 (ISBN 0-8247-6573-7). Dekker.

Henisch, Heinz K. Crystal Growth in Gels. LC 77-86379. (Illus.). 1970. text ed. 14.75 (ISBN 0-271-00104-6). Pa St U Pr.

Hirtzel, C. S. & Rajagopalan, Raj. Colloidal Phenomena: Advanced Topics. LC 84-22630. (Illus.). 318p. 1985. 36.00 (ISBN 0-8155-1011-X). Noyes.

Hunter, R. J. Zeta Potential in Colloid Science. LC 80-42268. 1981. 84.00 (ISBN 0-12-361960-2). Acad Pr.

Iler, Ralph K. The Chemistry of Silica: Solubility, Polymerization, Colloid & Surface Properties & Biochemistry. LC 78-23960. 866p. 1979. 115.00 (ISBN 0-471-02404-X, Pub. by Wiley-Interscience). Wiley.

International Conference on Colloid & Surface Science. Proceedings of International Conference on Colloid & Surface Science. Wolfram, ed. 1976. 11.50 (ISBN 0-9960003-7-2, Pub. by Akademiai Kaido Hungary). Heyden.

Israelachvili, Jacob N. Intermolecular & Surface Forces. (Colloid Science Ser.). 1985. 65.00 (ISBN 0-12-375180-2). Acad Pr.

Jennings, B. R., ed. Electro-Optics & Dielectrics of a Macromolecules & Colloids. LC 79-10117. 423p. 1979. 65.00x (ISBN 0-306-40169-X, Plenum Pr). Plenum Pub.

Kerker, Milton, ed. Colloid & Interface Science, Vols. 2-5. Incl. Vol. 2. Aerosols, Emulsions & Surfactants. 1976. 59.50 (ISBN 0-12-404502-2); Vol. 3. Adsorption, Catalysis, Solid Surfaces, Wetting, Surface Tension & Water. 1976. 65.00 (ISBN 0-12-404503-0); Vol. 4. Hydrosols & Rheology. 60.00 (ISBN 0-12-404504-9); Vol. 5. Biocolloids, Polymers, Monolayers, Membranes & General Papers. 60.00 (ISBN 0-12-404505-7). 1976. Acad Pr.

Kruyt, Hugo R., ed. Colloid Science, 2 vols. Incl. Vol. 1: Irreversible Systems. 389p. 1952. 106.50 (ISBN 0-444-40343-4); Vol. 2: Reversible Systems. 1949. 73.25 (ISBN 0-444-40344-2). Elsevier.

Lebedev, L. M. Metacolloids in Endogenic Deposits. LC 65-25241. (Monographs in Geoscience Ser.). 1967. 42.50x (ISBN 0-306-30295-0, Plenum Pr). Plenum Pub.

Matijevic, E., ed. Surface & Colloid Science, Vol. 10. LC 67-29459. (Illus.). 360p. 1978. 49.50x (ISBN 0-306-38260-1, Plenum Pr). Plenum Pub.

Matijevic, Egon, ed. Surface & Colloid Science, Vol. 12. LC 67-29459. 484p. 1982. 65.00x (ISBN 0-306-40616-0, Plenum Pr). Plenum Pub.

Matijevic, Egon & Good, Robert J., eds. Surface & Colloid Science, Vol. 13. 287p. 1984. 45.00x (ISBN 0-306-41322-1, Plenum Pr). Plenum Pub.

Mittal, K. L., ed. Colloidal Dispersions & Micellar Behavior: Papers from A Symposium Honoring Robert D. Vold & Marjorie J. Vold. LC 74-34072. (American Chemical Society ACS Symposium Ser.: No. 9). (Illus.). pap. 90.50 (ISBN 0-317-09351-7, 2015233). Bks Demand UMI.

--Solution Chemistry of Surfactants, 2 vols. LC 79-15067. 1979. Set. 120.00x (Plenum Pr); Vol. 1, 69.50x (ISBN 0-306-40174-6); Vol. 2, 460p. 69.50x (ISBN 0-306-40175-4). Plenum Pub.

Mysels, Karol J. Introduction to Colloid Chemistry. LC 77-13916. 492p. 1978. Repr. of 1959 ed. lib. bdg. 28.50 (ISBN 0-88275-628-1). Krieger.

Napper, Don H. Polymeric Stabilization of Colloidal Dispersions, Vol. 1. (Colloid Science Ser.). 1984. 65.00 (ISBN 0-12-513980-2). Acad Pr.

Popiel, W. J. Introduction to Colloid Science. 1978. 12.50x (ISBN 0-682-48737-6, University). Exposition Pr FL.

Scatchard, George. Equilibrium in Solutions & Surface & Colloid Chemistry. Scheinberg, I. Herbert, ed. (Commonwealth Fund Ser). (Illus.). 384p. 1976. 30.00x (ISBN 0-674-26025-2). Harvard U Pr.

COLOR TELEVISION

Kazan, B. Color Television Picture Tubes: Advances in Image Pick up Supplement I. Merrill. 1974. 69.50 (ISBN 0-12-022151-9). Acad Pr.

Priestley, A. C. Receiving Pal Colour Television. 256p. 1980. 30.00x (ISBN 0-85242-371-3, Pub. by J Dickson). State Mutual Bk.

Ross, Rodger J. Color Film for Color Television. (Library of Image & Sound Technology). 13.95 (ISBN 0-8038-1137-3). Hastings.

Rzeszewski, T. Color Television. LC 83-7894. 1983. 44.95 (ISBN 0-87942-168-1, PC01610). Inst Electrical.

Rzeszewski, T. & Troiano, A. Color Television. 473p. 1983. 44.95x (ISBN 0-471-88177-5, Pub. by Wiley-Interscience). Wiley.

Wilding, G. R. Solid-State Color Television Circuits. 18.85 (ISBN 0-408-00228-X, NB 54, Pub. by Newnes-Butterworth). Hayden.

COLOR TELEVISION–REPAIRING

ET D Staff. Color TV Trouble Factbook: Problems & Solutions. 3rd ed. LC 76-21178. 1976. pap. 14.95 (ISBN 0-8306-1119-3). TAB Bks.

Goodman, Robert. Color TV Case Histories Illustrated: Photo Guide to Troubles & Cures. LC 74-33619. (Illus.). 238p. 1975. pap. 7.95 (ISBN 0-8306-2302-7, 2302). TAB Bks.

Goodman, Robert L. Color TV Case Histories Illustrated: Photo Guide to Trouble Cures, Vol. 2. 2nd ed. (Illus.). 1977. pap. 7.95 (ISBN 0-8306-6876-4, 876). TAB Bks.

King, Gordon J. Color Television Servicing. 2nd ed. 18.95 (ISBN 0-408-00137-2, NB 34, Pub. by Newnes-Butterworth). Hayden.

RCA Staff. RCA Color-TV Service Handbook, Vol. 4. (Illus.). 284p. 1972. pap. 2.95 (ISBN 0-913970-15-8, 1A1973). RCA Dist Spec Prods.

COLOR VISION

Buckley, Mary & Baum, David, eds. Color Theory: A Guide to Information Sources. LC 73-17517. (Art & Architecture Information Guide Ser.: Vol. 2). x, 173p. 1975. 60.00x (ISBN 0-8103-1275-1). Gale.

Fletcher, R. & Voke, J. Detective Color Vision. 580p. 1985. 72.00 (ISBN 0-85274-395-5, 990300269, Pub. by A Hilger England). Heyden.

Ichikawa, Hiroshi & Hukami, Kaitiro. Standard Pseudoisochromatic Plates: For Acquired Color Vision Defects, Part II. (Illus.). 1983. spiral bound monograph 42.50 (ISBN 0-89640-081-6). Igaku-Shoin.

Katz, David. World of Colour. MacLeod, R. B., tr. from Ger. LC 35-9364. (Psychology Ser). 1970. Repr. of 1935 ed. 23.00 (ISBN 0-384-28750-6). Johnson Repr.

MacAdam, D. L. Color Measurement: Theme & Variation. (Springer Ser. in Optical Sciences: Vol. 27). (Illus.). 250p. 1981. 43.00 (ISBN 0-387-10773-8). Springer-Verlag.

Mollon, John & Sharpe, L. Ted, eds. Colour Vision: Physiology & Psychophysics. 1983. 49.00 (ISBN 0-12-504280-9). Acad Pr.

Motokawa, K. Physiology of Color & Pattern Vision. (Illus.). 1970. 45.00 (ISBN 0-387-04977-0). Springer-Verlag.

Ottoson, David & Zeki, Semir, eds. Central & Peripheral Mechanisms of Colour Vision. (Wenner-Gren International Symposium Ser.: Vol. 43). 320p. 1985. text ed. 85.00x (ISBN 0-333-39321-X, Pub. by Macmillan Educ Ltd UK). Sheridan Med Bks.

Rand, Gertrude. The Factors That Influence the Sensitivity of the Retina to Color. Bd. with Learning in Dementia Praecox. Boring, E. G. Repr. of 1913 ed; An Experiment in Linear Space Perception. Maxfield, F. N. Repr. of 1913 ed; The Form Board Test. Sylvester, R. H. Repr. of 1913 ed; The Influence of Stimulus Duration on Reaction Time. Wells, G. R. Repr. of 1913 ed. (Psychology Monographs General & Applied: Vol. 15). pap. 36.00 (ISBN 0-317-15615-2). Kraus Repr.

Stiles, W. S. Mechanisms of Color Vision. 1978. 59.00 (ISBN 0-12-671350-2). Acad Pr.

Verriest, G. Colour Vision Deficiencies VI. 1982. text ed. 99.50 (ISBN 90-6193-729-9, Pub. by Junk Pubs Netherlands). Kluwer Academic.

Wasserman, Gerald S. Color Vision: An Historical Introduction. LC 78-5346. (Behavior Ser.). 224p. 1978. 42.95x (ISBN 0-471-92128-9, Pub. by Wiley-Interscience). Wiley.

Zrenner, E. Neurophysiological Aspects of Color Vision in Primates. (Studies of Brain Function: Vol. 9). (Illus.). 218p. 1983. 39.00 (ISBN 0-387-11653-2). Springer-Verlag.

COLORIMETRY

see also Chemical Tests and Reagents; Chemistry, Analytic

Bartos, J. & Pesez, M. Colormetric & Fluorimetric Analysis of Steroids. 1977. 55.00 (ISBN 0-12-080150-7). Acad Pr.

Boltz, David F. & Howell, James A. Colorimetric Determination of Nonmetals. 2nd ed. LC 77-12398. (Chemical Analysis Ser.: Vol. 8). 543p. 1978. 92.00 (ISBN 0-471-08750-5, Pub by Wiley-Interscience). Wiley.

Chamberlin, G. J. & Chamberlin, D. G. Colour: Its Measurement, Computation, & Application. (International Topics in Science Ser.). 148p. 1980. 34.95 (ISBN 0-471-25625-0, Pub. by Wiley Heyden). Wiley.

Charlot, G. Colorimetric Determination of Elements. 449p. 1964. 64.00 (ISBN 0-444-40104-0). Elsevier.

Francis, F. J. & Clydesdale, F. M. Food Colorimetry: Theory & Applications. (Illus.). 1975. text ed. 60.00 (ISBN 0-87055-183-3). AVI.

Hardy, Arthur C., ed. Handbook of Colorimetry. (Illus.). 1936. 45.00x (ISBN 0-262-08001-X). MIT Pr.

Pesez, M. & Bartos, J. Colorimetric & Fluorimetric Analysis of Organic Compounds & Drugs. (Clinical & Biochemical Analysis Ser.: Vol. 1). 688p. 1974. 99.75 (ISBN 0-8247-6105-7). Dekker.

Practical Guide to Colorimetry. (Measurement & Testing Guides Ser.). 1976. 4.50 (ISBN 0-686-96239-7, LM-16); member 2.25 (ISBN 0-686-99742-5). Illum Eng.

Practical Guide to Colorimetry of Light Sources. 4.50 (ISBN 0-686-47881-9). Illum Eng.

Sandell, E. B. & Onishi, Hiroshi. Photometric Determination of Traces of Metals: General Aspects, Vol. 3. 4th ed. LC 77-18937. (Chemical Analysis Ser.). 1085p. 1978. 122.00 (ISBN 0-471-03094-5, Pub. by Wiley-Interscience). Wiley.

Snell, Foster D. & Snell, Cornelia T. Colorimetric Methods of Analysis. Vol. 4A, 1970. 30.00; Vol. 4AA, 1971. 31.50 (ISBN 0-442-27853-5); Vol. 4AAA. 26.50 (Pub. by Van Nos Reinhold). Krieger.

--Colorimetric Methods of Analysis. Incl. Vol. 4A. Organic Compounds of Noncyclic Nitrogen. 1967. 24.95x (ISBN 0-442-37848-3); Vol. 4AA. 1970. 24.95x (ISBN 0-442-07849-8); Vol. 4AAA. 1971. 24.95x (ISBN 0-442-27853-5). Van Nos Reinhold.

COLORING MATTER

see also Pigments

Gore, T. S., et al, eds. Recent Progress in the Chemistry of Natural & Synthetic Colouring Matters & Related Fields. 1962. 81.00 (ISBN 0-12-291650-6). Acad Pr.

COLORING OF CERAMICS

see Color in the Ceramic Industries

COLORING OF METALS

see Metals–Coloring

COLORS

see also Color

Boyle, Robert. Experiments & Considerations Touching Colours. (Illus.). Repr. of 1664 ed. 25.00 (ISBN 0-384-05350-5). Johnson Repr.

Bullrich, Kurt. Die Farbigen Dammerungserscheinngen. 100p. 1982. 17.95 (ISBN 0-8176-1355-2). Birkhauser.

Colour Index. 3rd, Rev. ed. 1982. 900.00x (ISBN 0-686-81698-6, Pub. by Soc Dyers & Colour). State Mutual Bk.

Colour Index: Supplement, Vol. 5. Rev. ed. 1982. 210.00x (ISBN 0-686-81697-8, Pub. by Soc Dyers & Colour). State Mutual Bk.

Goethe, Johann W. Goethe's Theory of Colours. lib. bdg. 79.95 (ISBN 0-87968-196-9). Gordon Pr.

Katz, David. World of Colour. MacLeod, R. B., tr. from Ger. LC 35-9364. (Psychology Ser). 1970. Repr. of 1935 ed. 23.00 (ISBN 0-384-28750-6). Johnson Repr.

Kornerup, A. & Wanscher, J. H. Methuen Handbook of Colour. 3rd rev. ed. (Illus.). 1984. 32.95 (ISBN 0-8038-3065-3). Hastings.

COLT REVOLVER

Bady, Donald B. Colt Automatic Pistols. rev. ed. 1973. 18.50 (ISBN 0-87505-099-9). Borden.

Shumaker, P. L. Colt's Variations of the Old Model Pocket Pistol. 1957. 10.95 (ISBN 0-87505-100-6). Borden.

Whittington, Robert D., III. The Colt Whitneyville-Walker Pistol. LC 83-73228. (Illus.). 96p. 1984. 20.00 (ISBN 0-9613049-0-1). Brownlee Books.

COLUMBAE

see Pigeons

COLUMBIDAE

see Pigeons

COLUMBIUM

see Niobium

COLUMNS

see also Strength of Materials

Johnston, Bruce G. Guide to Stability Design Criteria for Metal Structures. 3rd ed. LC 75-40155. 616p. 1976. 68.50x (ISBN 0-471-44629-7, Pub. by Wiley-Interscience). Wiley.

COLUMNS, CONCRETE

Biaxial & Uniaxial Capacity of Rectangular Columns. 31p. 1967. pap. 5.00 (ISBN 0-89312-005-7, EB031D). Portland Cement.

Capacity of Restrained Eccentrically Loaded Long Columns. 49p. 1965. pap. 5.00 (ISBN 0-89312-006-5, EB027D). Portland Cement.

Czerniak, Eli. Reinforced Concrete Columns, 2 vols. Incl. Vol. 1. Working Stress Design for Concrete Columns. (Illus.). 424p. 18.00 (ISBN 0-8044-4166-9); Vol. 2. Working Stress Design Charts for Spiral Columns. (Illus.). 320p. 15.00 (ISBN 0-8044-4167-7). Set. 33.00 (ISBN 0-8044-4165-0). Ungar.

Effects of Column Exposure in Tall Structures. 97p. 1965. pap. 6.75 (ISBN 0-89312-065-0, EB018D). Portland Cement.

Nishkin, V. S. Thermal Stresses in a Composite Cylinder with an Arbitrary Temperature Distribution Along Its Length. 119p. 1966. 49.50x (ISBN 0-306-65116-5, IFI Plenum). Plenum Pub.

Ultimate Strength Design of Reinforced Concrete Columns. 50p. 1969. pap. 4.00 (ISBN 0-89312-124-X, EB009D). Portland Cement.

COMAL (COMPUTER PROGRAM LANGUAGE)

Bramer, Max A. Adding Structure to BASIC with Comal 80. 288p. 1983. write for info (ISBN 0-201-14632-0). Addison-Wesley.

Christensen, Borge. COMAL from A to Z. (The Amazing Adventures of Captain COMAL Ser.). (Illus.). 64p. 1984. pap. 6.95 (ISBN 0-928411-00-1). COMAL Users.

Gratte, Ingvar. Starting with COMAL. 224p. 1985. pap. 15.95 (ISBN 0-13-843003-9). P-H.

Lindsay, Len. Captain COMAL Gets Organized. (The Amazing Adventures of Captain COMAL Ser.). (Illus.). 102p. 1984. pap. 19.95 (ISBN 0-928411-01-X). COMAL Users.

COMBINATIONS

see also Probabilities

Anderson, I., ed. Surveys in Combinatorics, 1985. (London Mathematical Society Lecture Note Ser.: No. 103). 180p. 1985. pap. 18.95 (ISBN 0-521-31524-7). Cambridge U Pr.

Combinational Theory Seminar, Eindhoven University of Technology. Proceedings. Van Lint, J. H., ed. (Lecture Notes in Mathematics: Vol. 382). vi, 131p. 1974. pap. text ed. 13.00 (ISBN 0-387-06735-3). Springer-Verlag.

Gelfand, S. I., et al. Sequences & Combinatorial Problems. (Pocket Mathematical Library). 92p. 1968. 24.50 (ISBN 0-677-20730-1). Gordon.

Lovasz, L. Combinatorial Problems & Exercises. LC 78-12133. 450p. 1979. pap. 38.50 (ISBN 0-444-85242-5, North Holland); 76.75 (ISBN 0-444-85219-0, North Holland). Elsevier.

Mendelsohn, E., ed. Algebraic & Geometric Combinatorics. 378p. 1982. 81.00 (ISBN 0-444-86365-6, I-194-82, North-Holland). Elsevier.

Rosa, A. & Sabidussi, G. Theory & Practice of Combinatorics. (Mathematics Studies Ser.: Vol. 60). 264p. 1982. 59.00 (ISBN 0-444-86318-4, North Holland). Elsevier.

Symposium in Pure Mathematics, Los Angeles. 1968. Combinatorics. Motzkin, T. S., ed. LC 74-153879. (Proceedings of Symposia in Pure Mathematics: Vol. 19). 1971. 43.00 (ISBN 0-8218-1419-2, PSPUM-19). Am Math.

Wall, C. T., ed. Homological Groups Theory. LC 78-74013. (London Mathematical Society Lecture Note: No. 36). 1980. pap. 49.50 (ISBN 0-521-22729-1). Cambridge U Pr.

Whitworth, William A. Choice & Chance with One Thousand Exercises. 5th ed. 1965. Repr. of 1901 ed. 8.95x (ISBN 0-02-854750-0). Hafner.

COMBINATORIAL ANALYSIS

see also Combinations; Graph Theory; Permutations

Aigner, M. Combinatorial Theory. (Grundlehren der Mathemtischen Wissenschaften Ser.: Vol. 234). (Illus.). 1979. 53.50 (ISBN 0-387-90376-3). Springer-Verlag.

Anderson, Ian. A First Course in Combinatorial Mathematics. (Illus.). 1979. pap. text ed. 12.95x (ISBN 0-19-859617-0). Oxford U Pr.

Australian Conference on Combinational Mathematics, Sixth, Armidale, Australia, August 1978. Combinatorial Mathematics VI: Proceedings. Horadam, A. F. & Wallis, W. D., eds. (Lecture Notes in Mathematics: Vol. 748). 1979. pap. 17.00 (ISBN 0-387-09555-1). Springer-Verlag.

Australian Conference on Combinatorial Mathematics. Proceedings. Holton, D. A., ed. (Lecture Notes in Mathematics Ser.: Vol. 403). viii, 148p. 1974. pap. 13.00 (ISBN 3-540-06903-8). Springer-Verlag.

Australian Conference, 3rd, Queensland, 1974. Combinatorial Mathematics Three: Proceedings. Street, A. P. & Wallis, W. D., eds. (Lecture Notes in Mathematics Ser.: Vol. 452). ix, 233p. 1975. pap. 16.00 (ISBN 0-387-07154-7). Springer-Verlag.

Bachem, A., et al, eds. Bonn Workshop on Combinatorial Optimization. (Mathematics Studies: Vol. 66). 312p. 1982. pap. 51.00 (ISBN 0-444-86366-4, I-320-82, North Holland). Elsevier.

Barlotti, A. Combinatorial & Geometric Structures & Their Applications. (Mathematical Studies: Vol. 63). 294p. 1982. 40.50 (ISBN 0-444-86384-2, I-97-82, North Holland). Elsevier.

Baumert, L. Cyclic Difference Sets. LC 73-153466. (Lecture Notes in Mathematics: Vol. 182). 1971. pap. 11.00 (ISBN 0-387-05368-9). Springer-Verlag.

Beckenbach, Edwin F., ed. Applied Combinatorial Mathematics. LC 80-12457. 630p. 1981. Repr. of 1964 ed. lib. bdg. 42.50 (ISBN 0-89874-172-6). Krieger.

Berge, C. & Bresson, D., eds. Combinatorial Mathematics: Proceedings of the International Colloquium on Graph Theory & Combinatorics, Marseille-Luminy, June, 1981. (Mathematics Studies: Vol. 75). 660p. 1983. 96.00 (ISBN 0-444-86512-8, I-419-83, North Holland). Elsevier.

Berge, Claude. Principles of Combinatorics. (Mathematics in Science & Engineering Ser.: Vol. 72). 1971. 45.00 (ISBN 0-12-089750-4). Acad Pr.

Berman, Gerald & Fryer, K. D. Introduction to Combinatorics. 1972. text ed. 22.50i (ISBN 0-12-092750-0). Acad Pr.

Billington, E. J., et al, eds. Combinatorial Mathematics IX, Brisbane, Australia: Proceedings, 1981. (Lecture Notes in Mathematics: Vol. 952). 443p. 1982. pap. 25.00 (ISBN 0-387-11601-X). Springer-Verlag.

Bogart, Kenneth P. Introductory Combinatorics. 400p. 1983. text ed. 29.95 (ISBN 0-273-01923-6). Pitman Pub MA.

Bollobas. Graph Theory & Combinatorics. 1984. 50.00 (ISBN 0-12-111760-X). Acad Pr.

Bollobas, Bella, ed. Survey in Combinatorics. LC 79-51596. (London Mathematical Society Lecture Note Ser.: No. 38). 1979. pap. 27.95x (ISBN 0-521-22846-8). Cambridge U Pr.

Boltjansky, Vladimir G., et al. Results & Problems in Combinatorial Geometry. Bollobas, B. & Harris, A., trs. (Illus.). 112p. Date not set. price not set (ISBN 0-521-26298-4); pap. price not set (ISBN 0-521-26923-7). Cambridge U Pr.

Bose, R. C. & Manuel, B. Introduction to Combinatorial Theory. (Probability & Mathmatical Statistics Ser.: 1-345). 237p. 1984. 29.95x (ISBN 0-471-89614-4, 1-345, Pub by Wiley Interscience). Wiley.

British Combinatorial Conference, Sixth. Combinatorial Surveys: Proceedings. Cameron, Peter, ed. 1977. 47.00 (ISBN 0-12-157150-5). Acad Pr.

Cameron, P. J. Parallelisms of Complete Designs. LC 75-32912. (London Mathematical Society Lecture Note Ser.: No. 23). (Illus.). 1976. 22.95 (ISBN 0-521-21160-3). Cambridge U Pr.

Capital Conference on Graph Theory & Combinatorics, George Washington University, June 18-22, 1973. Graphs & Combinatorics: Proceedings. Bari, R. A. & Harary, F., eds. LC 74-13955. (Lecture Notes in Mathematics: Vol. 406). viii, 355p. 1974. pap. 20.00 (ISBN 0-387-06854-6). Springer-Verlag.

Casse, L. R., ed. Combinatorial Mathematics X. (Lecture Notes in Mathematics: Vol. 1036). xi, 419p. 1983. pap. 20.00 (ISBN 0-387-12708-9). Springer-Verlag.

Chandler, B. & Magnus, W. History of Combinatorial Group Theory: A Case Study of the History of Ideas. (Studies in the History of Mathematics & Physical Sciences: Vol. 9). (Illus.). 234p. 1982. 52.00 (ISBN 0-387-90749-1). Springer-Verlag.

Christofides, Nicos, et al, eds. Combinatorial Optimization. LC 78-11131. 425p. 1979. 84.95 (ISBN 0-471-99749-8, Pub. by Wiley-Interscience). Wiley.

CISM (International Center for Mechanical Sciences) Dept. of Automation & Information. Combinatorial Search Problems. Katona, G., ed. (CISM Pubns. Ser: No. 145). 57p. 1973. pap. 8.60 (ISBN 0-387-81169-9). Springer-Verlag.

Colbourn, C. J. & Colbourn, M. J., eds. Algorithms in Combinatorial Design Theory. (Mathematics Studies: Vol. 114). 334p. 1985. 45.00 (ISBN 0-444-87802-5, North-Holland). Elsevier.

Crapo, Henry H. & Rota, Gian-Carlo. On the Foundations of Combinatorial Theory: Combinatorial Geometries. 1970. pap. 10.00x (ISBN 0-262-53016-3). MIT Pr.

Crossley, J. N. & Nerode, A. Combinatorial Factors. LC 73-10783. (Ergebnisse der Mathematik und Ihrer Grenzgebiete: Vol. 81). (Illus.). 160p. 1974. 25.00 (ISBN 0-387-06428-1). Springer-Verlag.

Egorychev, G P. Integral Representation & the Computation of Combinatorial Sums. LC 83-22393. (Translations of Mathematical Monographs: No. 59). 286p. 1984. 90.00 (ISBN 0-8218-4512-8). Am Math.

Eisen, M. Elementary Combinatorial Analysis. (Notes on Mathematics & Its Applications Ser.). 248p. 1969. 49.95 (ISBN 0-677-02260-3). Gordon.

Erdos, P., et al, eds. Combinatorial Theory & its Applications. (Colloquia Mathematica Societatis Janos Bolyai: Vol. 4). 1202p. 1970. 127.50 (ISBN 0-7204-2038-5, North Holland). Elsevier.

Fitch, Frederick B. Elements of Combinatory Logic. LC 73-86892. pap. 32.30 (ISBN 0-317-08731-2, 2013383). Bks Demand UMI.
Fourth Australian Conference, University of Adelaide, 27-29 Aug. 1976. Combinatonal Mathematics, IV: Proceedings. Casse, L. R. & Wallis, W. D., eds. (Lecture Notes in Mathematics Ser.: Vol. 560). 1976. soft cover 17.00 (ISBN 3-540-08053-8). Springer-Verlag.
Furstenberg, H. Recurrence in Ergodic Theory & Combinatorial Number Theory. LC 80-7518. (Rice University, Dept. of Mathematics, M. B. Porter Lectures). 228p. 1981. 27.50 (ISBN 0-691-08269-3). Princeton U Pr.
Goulden, I. P. & Jackson, D. M. Combinatorial Enumeration. 569p. 1983. 54.95x (ISBN 0-471-86654-7, Pub. by Wiley-Interscience). Wiley.
Graver, J. E. & Watkins, M. E. Combinatorics: With Emphasis on the Theory of Graphs. LC 77-1200. (Graduate Texts in Mathematics: Vol. 54). (Illus.). 1977. pap. text ed. 36.00 (ISBN 0-387-90245-7). Springer-Verlag.
Grimaldi, Ralph P. & Rose-Hulman. Discrete & Combinatorial Mathematics. LC 84-9359. 1985. text ed. 32.95 (ISBN 0-201-12590-0). Addison-Wesley.
Guy, et al, eds. Combinatorial Structures & Their Applications. 524p. 1970. 104.50 (ISBN 0-677-13890-3). Gordon.
Hall, M. Combinatorial Theory. LC 67-11108. 1967. text ed. 48.50 (ISBN 0-471-00228-3). Wiley.
--Combinatorial Theory. 2nd ed. (Discrete Mathematics Ser.). 1985. 25.95 (ISBN 0-471-09138-3). Wiley.
Hindley, R. & Seldin, J. P. Introduction to Combinators & Lambda-Calculus. (London Mathematical Society Students Texts: No. 1). 300p. Date not set. price not set (ISBN 0-521-26896-6); pap. price not set (ISBN 0-521-31839-4). Cambridge U Pr.
Holroyd & Wilson. Geometrical Combinatorics. (Research Notes in Mathematics Ser.: No. 114). 112p. 1984. pap. text ed. 15.95 (ISBN 0-273-08675-8). Pitman Pub MA.
Holton, D. A. & Seberry, J., eds. Combinatorial Mathematics: Proceedings, International Conference on Combinatorial Theory, Canberra August 16-27, 1977. (Lecture Notes in Mathematics: Vol. 686). 1978. pap. 25.00 (ISBN 0-387-08953-5). Springer-Verlag.
Hu, T. C., et al. Combinatorial Algorithms. LC 81-15024. (Computer Science Ser.). 500p. 1981. text ed. 28.95 (ISBN 0-201-03859-5); program manual 15.00 (ISBN 0-201-11469-0). Addison-Wesley.
Jacobs, Konrad. Einfuhrung in die Kombinatorik. (Ger.). 274p. 1983. 21.60 (ISBN 3-11-008736-7). De Gruyter.
Jungnickel, D. H. & Vedder, K., eds. Combinatorial Theory: Proceedings, Schloss Rauischholzhausen, Federal Republic of Germany, 1982. (Lecture Notes in Mathematics Ser.: Vol. 969). 326p. 1982. pap. 18.00 (ISBN 0-387-11971-X). Springer-Verlag.
Kay, D. C. Convexity & Related Combinatorial Geometry. 1982. 35.00 (ISBN 0-8247-1278-1). Dekker.
Kim, A. C. & Neumann, B. H., eds. Groups-Korea 1983. (Lecture Notes in Mathematics Ser.: Vol. 1098). vii, 183p. 1984. pap. 9.50 (ISBN 0-387-13890-0). Springer-Verlag.
Kung, Joseph P., ed. Young Tableaux in Combinatorics, Invariant Theory, & Algebra: An Anthology of Recent Work. LC 82-11330. 347p. 1982. 32.00 (ISBN 0-12-428780-8). Acad Pr.
Lander, Eric. Symmetric Designs: An Algebraic Approach. LC 82-9705. (London Mathematical Society Lecture Note Ser.: Note 74). 175p. 1983. pap. 32.50 (ISBN 0-521-28693-X). Cambridge U Pr.
Ledermann, W. & Vajda, S. Handbook of Applicable Mathematics: Geometry & Combinatorics, 2 pts. (Handbook of Applicable Mathematics Ser.). 550p. 1985. Set. 170.00 (ISBN 0-471-90023-0); Pt. A. 85.00 (ISBN 0-471-90567-4); Pt. B. 85.00 (ISBN 0-471-90568-2). Wiley.
Little, C., ed. Combinatorial Mathematics V. LC 77-26173. (Lecture Notes in Mathematics: Vol. 622). 1977. pap. text ed. 18.00 (ISBN 0-387-08524-6). Springer-Verlag.
Liu, Chung L. Introduction to Applied Combinatorial Mathematics. 1968. text ed. 48.95 (ISBN 0-07-038124-0). McGraw.
Lloyd, Keith E., ed. Surveys in Combinatorics: Invited Papers for the 9th British Combinatorial Conference 1983. LC 83-10078. (London Mathematical Society Lecture Note Ser. No. 82). 256p. 1983. pap. 29.95 (ISBN 0-521-27552-0). Cambridge U Pr.
Lothaire, M. Encyclopedia of Mathematics & Its Applications: Combinatorics on Words, Vol. 17. 1984. 34.50 (ISBN 0-317-14395-6, 30237-4). Cambridge U Pr.
Lyndon, R. & Schapp, P. E. Combinatorial Group Theory. (Ergebnisse der Mathematik und Ihrer Grenzgebiete: Vol. 89). 1977. 48.00 (ISBN 0-387-07642-5). Springer-Verlag.
McAvaney, K L., ed. Combinatorial Mathematics: Proceedings, Vol. VIII. (Lecture Notes in Mathematics Ser.: Vol. 884). 359p. 1981. pap. 22.00 (ISBN 0-387-10883-1). Springer-Verlag.
MacMahon, Percy A. Combinatory Analysis, 2 Vols. in 1. LC 59-10267. 29.50 (ISBN 0-8284-1137-9). Chelsea Pub.
Moore, Patrick. Science & Fiction. 1957. lib. bdg. 20.00 (ISBN 0-8414-6347-6). Folcroft.
Narayana, T. V. Lattice Path Combinatorics with Statistical Applications. LC 78-6710. (Mathematical Expositions Ser.). 1979. 20.00x (ISBN 0-8020-5405-6). U of Toronto Pr.
NATO Advanced Study Institute, Versailles, France, September 2-13, 1974. Combinatorial Programming: Methods & Application, Proceedings. Roy, B., ed. (NATO Advanced Study Institutes: No. C19). 386p. 1975. 47.50 (ISBN 9-0277-0506-2, Pub. by Reidel Holland). Kluwer Academic.
Neofields & Combinatorial Designs. Hsu, Frank D., ed. (Advances in Discrete Mathematics & Computer Science Ser.). 401p. 1984. pap. 60.00 (ISBN 0-911767-27-4). Hadronic Pr Inc.
O'Heigeartaigh, M., et al. Combinatorial Optimization: Annotated Bibliographies. Kan, Rinnooy, ed. 1984. pap. text ed. 24.95 (ISBN 0-471-90490-2). Wiley.
Padberg, M. W. Combinatorial Optimization. (Mathematical Programming Studies: Vol. 12). 222p. 1980. pap. 34.00 (ISBN 0-444-85489-4). Elsevier.
Page, E. S. & Wilson, L. B. An Introduction to Computational Combinatorics. LC 78-54722. (Cambridge Computer Science Texts Ser.: No. 9). (Illus.). 1979. 42.50 (ISBN 0-521-22427-6); pap. 15.95x (ISBN 0-521-29492-4). Cambridge U Pr.
Percus, J. K. Combinatorial Methods. LC 78-152001. (Applied Mathematical Sciences Ser.: Vol. 4). (Illus.). 208p. 1971. pap. 21.95 (ISBN 0-387-90027-6). Springer-Verlag.
Pultr, A. & Trnkova, V. Combinatorial, Algebraic & Topological Representation of Groups, Semigrous & Categories. (Mathematical Library Ser.: Vol. 22). 372p. 1980. 59.75 (ISBN 0-444-85083-X, North-Holland). Elsevier.
Rayward-Smith. Combinatorial Optimization II. (Mathematical Programming Studies: Vol. 13). 142p. 1980. pap. 25.75 (ISBN 0-444-86040-1, North-Holland). Elsevier.
Reingold, et al. Combinatorial Algorithms: Theory & Practice. 1977. text ed. 36.95 (ISBN 0-13-152447-X). P-H.
Riordan, John. Combinatorial Identities. LC 78-26915. 270p. 1979. Repr. of 1968 ed. 19.50 (ISBN 0-88275-829-2). Krieger.
--An Introduction to Combinatorial Analysis. LC 80-337. 260p. 1980. 26.50 (ISBN 0-691-08262-6); pap. 13.50 (ISBN 0-691-02365-4). Princeton U Pr.
Roberts, Fred S. Applied Combinatorics. (Illus.). 672p. 1984. text ed. 40.95. P-H.
Rota, Gian-Carlo, ed. Studies in Foundations & Combinatorics: Advances in Mathematics Supplementary Studies, Vol. 1. 1978. 70.00 (ISBN 0-12-599101-0). Acad Pr.
Rota, Gian-Carol, ed. Studies in Combinatorics. LC 78-60730. (Studies in Mathematics: No. 17). 1979. 21.00 (ISBN 0-88385-117-2). Math Assn.
Srivastava, J. Combinatorial Mathematics Optical Designs & Their Applications. (Annals of Discreet Mathematics Ser.: Vol. 6). 392p. 1980. 78.75 (ISBN 0-444-86048-7, North-Holland). Elsevier.
Stanley, Richard. Ordered Structures & Partitions. LC 52-42839. (Memoirs: No. 119). 104p. 1972. pap. 9.00 (ISBN 0-8218-1819-8, MEMO-119). Am Math.
Steiglitz, Kenneth & Papadimitriou, Christos. Combinatorial Optimization: Algorithm & Complexity. (Illus.). 512p. 1982. 43.95 (ISBN 0-13-152462-3). P-H.
Stillwell, J. Classical Topology & Combinatorial Group Theory. (Graduate Texts in Mathematics Ser.: Vol. 72). (Illus.). 301p. 1980. 39.50 (ISBN 0-387-90516-2). Springer-Verlag.
Symposium in Applied Mathematics-New York - 1958. Combinatorial Analysis: Proceedings, Vol. 10. Bellman, R. & Hall, M., Jr., eds. LC 50-1183. (Proceedings of Symposia in Applied Mathematics: Vol. 10). 311p. 1979. pap. 35.00 (ISBN 0-8218-1310-2, PSAPM-10). Am Math.
Takacs, Lajos. Combinatorial Methods in the Theory of Stochastic Processes. LC 76-55801. 276p. 1977. Repr. of 1967 ed. lib. bdg. 19.50 (ISBN 0-88275-491-2). Krieger.
Tomescu, I. & Melter, R. A. Problems in Combinatorics & Graph Theory. (Discrete Mathematics Ser.). 368p. 1985. 31.95 (ISBN 0-471-80155-0). Wiley.
Tomescu, Ioan. Introduction to Combinatorics. Lloyd, E. Keith, ed. Rudeanu, S., tr. from Romanian. Tr. of Introducere in Combinatorica. (Illus.). 250p. 1975. text ed. 30.00x (ISBN 0-569-08057-6, Pub. by Collets England). Scholium Intl.
Tutte, W. T., ed. Recent Progress in Combinatorics: Proceedings. 1969. 76.50 (ISBN 0-12-705150-3). Acad Pr.
Vilenkin, N. Y. Combinatorics. 1971. 55.00 (ISBN 0-12-721940-4). Acad Pr.
Wallis, W. D., et al. Combinatorics: Room Squares, Sum-Free Sets, Hadamard Matrices. LC 72-90443. (Lecture Notes in Mathematics: Vol. 292). 508p. 1972. pap. 23.00 (ISBN 0-387-06035-9). Springer-Verlag.
Williamson, Stanley G. Combinatorics for Computer Science. LC 84-17018. 1985. text ed. 39.95 (ISBN 0-88175-020-4). Computer Sci.
Wilson, R. J., ed. Applications of Combinatorics. (Shiva Mathematics Ser.: 6). 140p. 1982. pap. 13.95 (ISBN 0-906812-13-5). Birkhauser.
--Graph Theory & Combinatorics. (Research Notes in Mathematics: No. 34). 148p. (Orig.). 1979. pap. text ed. 24.95 (ISBN 0-273-08435-6). Pitman Pub MA.
Zimmermann, U. Linear & Combinatorial Optimization in Ordered Algebraic Structures. (Annals of Discreet Mathematics Ser.: Vol. 10). 380p. 1981. 78.75 (ISBN 0-444-86153-X, North-Holland). Elsevier.

COMBINATORIAL TOPOLOGY

Brualdi, R. A. Introductory Combinatorics. 374p. 1977. text ed. 30.50 (ISBN 0-7204-8610-6, North-Holland). Elsevier.
Cairns, S. S., ed. Differential & Combinatorial Topology: A Symposium in Honor of Marston Morse. (Princeton Mathematical Ser.: No. 27). 1965. 32.00 (ISBN 0-691-07945-5). Princeton U Pr.
Cohen, D. I. Basic Techniques of Combinatorial Theory. 297p. 1978. 35.50 (ISBN 0-471-03535-1). Wiley.
Deza, M. & Rosenberg, I. G., eds. Combinatorics 79, 2 pts. (Annals of Discrete Mathematics: Vols. 8 & 9). 1981. Set. (ISBN 0-444-86112-2); Pt. 1. 74.50 (ISBN 0-444-86110-6); Pt. 2. 74.50 (ISBN 0-444-86111-4). Elsevier.
Hersch, Joseph & Rota, Gian-Carlo, eds. George Polya - Collected Papers: Probability; Combinatories; Teaching & Learning in Mathematics, Vol. IV. (Mathematicians of Our Time Ser.: No. 23). 676p. 1984. 65.00 (ISBN 0-262-16097-8). MIT Pr.
Lundell, A. T. & Weingram, S. The Topology of CW Complexes. LC 68-26689. (Illus.). vii, 216p. 1969. 21.00 (ISBN 0-387-90128-0). Springer-Verlag.
Magnus, Wilhelm. Noneuclidian Tesselations & Their Groups. 1974. 44.00 (ISBN 0-12-465450-9). Acad Pr.
NATO Advanced Study Institute, Breukelen, the Netherlands, 1974. Combinatorics: Proceedings, C16. Hall, M., Jr. & Van Lint, J. H., eds. LC 75-8819. (NATO Advanced Studies Institute Ser: No. C-16). 480p. 1975. lib. bdg. 58.00 (ISBN 90-277-0593-3, Pub. by Reidel Holland). Kluwer Academic.
Pontryagin, Lev S. Foundations of Combinatorial Topology. LC 52-14408. 1952. 10.50x (ISBN 0-910670-10-2). Graylock.
Practical Engineering Applications Software. Column Design. 1985. IBM-PC Version. incl. disk 125.00 (ISBN 0-471-80295-6); Apple Version. incl. disk 125.00 (ISBN 0-471-88425-1). Wiley.
Pultr, A. & Trnkova, V. Combinatorial, Algebraic & Topological Representation of Groups, Semigrous & Categories. (Mathematical Library Ser.: Vol. 22). 372p. 1980. 59.75 (ISBN 0-444-85083-X, North-Holland). Elsevier.
Reichmeider, Philip. The Equivalence of Some Combinatorial Matching Theorems. LC 84-11746. (Illus.). 127p. 1985. 15.50x (ISBN 0-936428-09-0). Polygonal Pub.
Temperley, H. N., ed. Combinatorics: Proceedings of the British Combinatorial Conference, 8th, University College, Swansea, 1981. LC 81-10007. (London Mathematical Society Lecture Note Ser.: No. 52). (Illus.). 200p. 1981. pap. 29.95 (ISBN 0-521-28514-3). Cambridge U Pr.
Williamson, Stanley G. Combinatorics for Computer Science. LC 84-17018. 1985. text ed. 39.95 (ISBN 0-88175-020-4). Computer Sci.

COMBUSTION

see also Chemical Warfare; Fire; Flame; Fuel; Heat; Propellants; Smoke

Badin, E. J. Coal Combustion Chemistry: Correlation Aspects. (Coal Science & Technology Ser.: Vol. 6). 260p. 1984. 61.75 (ISBN 0-444-42318-4, I-132-84). Elsevier.
Barnard, J. A & Bradley, J. N. Flame & Combustion. 2nd ed. 344p. 1985. text ed. 55.00 (ISBN 0-412-23030-5, NO. 9254, Pub. by Chapman & Hall England); pap. text ed. 27.00 (ISBN 0-412-23040-2, NO. 9255, Pub. by Chapman & Hall England). Methuen Inc.
Bartok, William, ed. Combustion of Synthetic Fuels. LC 83-2822. (ACS Symposium Ser.: No. 217). 246p. 1983. lib. bdg. 34.95x (ISBN 0-8412-0773-9). Am Chemical.
Benjamin-Clarke Associates, Inc. Fire Deaths - Causes & Strategies for Control. LC 84-51634. 77p. 1984. pap. 20.00 (ISBN 0-87762-370-8). Technomic.
Broeze, J. J. Combustion in Piston Engines. 216p. 1963. 50.00x (ISBN 0-85950-036-5, Pub. by Stam Pr England). State Mutual Bk.
Buckmaster, J. D. & Ludford, G. S. S. Lectures on Mathematical Combustion. LC 83-61375. (CBMS-NSF Regional Conference Ser.: No. 43). viii, 126p. 1983. pap. text ed. 14.50 (ISBN 0-89871-186-X). Soc Indus-Appl Math.
Buckmaster, John D., ed. The Mathematics of Combustion. LC 85-50339. (Frontiers in Applied Mathematics: No. 2). xii, 288p. 1985. 32.50 (ISBN 0-89871-053-7). Soc Indus-Appl Math.
Chigier, N. A. Progress in Energy & Combustion Science, Vol. 4. 224p. 1980. 125.00 (ISBN 0-08-024257-X). Pergamon.
Chigier, N. A., ed. Energy & Combustion Science: Selected Papers from Progress in Energy & Combustion Science. LC 79-40860. (Illus.). 1979. 48.00 (ISBN 0-08-024781-4); pap. 15.75 (ISBN 0-08-024780-6). Pergamon.
--Progress in Energy & Combustion Science, Vol. 6. (Illus.). 388p. 1981. 130.00 (ISBN 0-08-027153-7). Pergamon.
--Progress in Energy & Combustion Science, Vol. 6, Pt. 2. 102p. 1980. pap. 27.00 (ISBN 0-08-026059-4). Pergamon.
--Progress in Energy & Combustion Science, Vol. 7. (Illus.). 316p. 1982. 145.00 (ISBN 0-08-029124-4). Pergamon.
--Progress in Energy & Combustion Science, Vol. 8. 354p. 1983. 144.00 (ISBN 0-08-031041-9). Pergamon.
--Progress in Energy & Combustion Science, Vol. 9. (Illus.). 378p. 1984. 144.00 (ISBN 0-08-031727-8). Pergamon.
Chigier, Norman A., ed. Progress in Energy & Combustion Science, Vols. 1-2. Incl. Vol. 1, Pt. 1. pap. 15.50 (ISBN 0-08-019931-3); Vol. 1, Pts. 2-3. pap. 25.00 (ISBN 0-08-021023-6); Vol. 1, Pt. 4. pap. 22.00 (ISBN 0-08-021041-4); Vol. 1, Complete. Pollution Formation & Destruction in Flames. 97.50 (ISBN 0-08-020307-8); Vol. 2, Pt. 1. pap. 14.00 (ISBN 0-08-021211-5); Vol. 2, Pt. 2. pap. 14.00 (ISBN 0-08-021213-1); Vol. 2, Pt. 3. pap. 12.50 (ISBN 0-08-021215-8); Vol. 2, Pt. 4. 97.50 (ISBN 0-08-021217-4); Vol. 2 Complete, 1978. 50.00 (ISBN 0-08-021219-0). LC 75-24822. 1976-78. pap. write for info. Pergamon.
Correlations Between Ash Compositions from Coal Combustion & Tendencies Toward Slagging, Fouling & Incomplete Combustion. 1984. write for info. Elsevier.
Crosley, David R., ed. Laser Probes for Combustion Chemistry. LC 80-17137. (ACS Symposium Ser.: No. 134). 1980. 49.95 (ISBN 0-8412-0570-1). Am Chemical.
Dussourd, J. L., et al, eds. Fluid Mechanics of Combustion. 267p. 1974. pap. text ed. 20.00 (ISBN 0-685-41500-7, 100034). ASME.
Ebert, Lawrence B., ed. Chemistry of Engine Combustion Deposits. 388p. 1985. 69.50x (ISBN 0-306-41936-X, Plenum Pr). Plenum Pub.
Eckbreth, A. C. Spatially Precise Laser Diagnostics for Combustion Temperature & Species. (Energy & Engineering Science Ser.). 1985. 35.00 (ISBN 0-9961006-6-0, Pub. by Abacus England). Heyden.
Energy Commission of the European Communities. Energy Conservation in Industry, 3 vols. Bd. with Combustion & Heat Recovery. 47.00; Engines & Batteries. 27.00; Applications & Technologies. 38.00. 1984. Set. 105.00 (ISBN 3-18-419095-1, 990700062, Pub. by VDI Verlag Gmbh Dusseldorf). Heyden.
Engine Combustion Analysis: New Approaches. 1985. 22.00 (ISBN 0-89883-717-0, P156). Soc Auto Engineers.
Fuels & Combustion. (Principles of Steam Generation Ser.: Module 6). (Illus.). 70p. 1982. spiral bdg. 10.00x (ISBN 0-87683-256-7); instr's. manual 15.00x (ISBN 0-87683-277-X). G P Courseware.
Gardiner, W. C., ed. Combustion Chemistry. (Illus.). 550p. 1984. 57.50 (ISBN 0-387-90963-X). Springer-Verlag.
Graham & Trotman Ltd., ed. Fluidised Combustion: Systems & Applications. 512p. 1981. 85.00x (ISBN 0-686-80925-4, Pub. by Graham & Trotman England). State Mutual Bk.
Hilado, Carlos J., ed. Smoke & Products of Combustion, Part 2, Vol. 15. LC 73-82115. (Fire & Flammability Ser.). (Illus.). 1976. pap. 9.95 (ISBN 0-87762-175-6). Technomic.
Hucknall, David. J. Chemistry of Hydrocarbon Combustion. 448p. 1985. text ed. 85.00 (ISBN 0-412-26110-3, NO. 9333, Pub. by Chapman & Hall England). Methuen Inc.

Industrial Heating Equipment Assn. The Directory of Industrial Heat Processing & Combustion Equipment, 1984. Miller, Richard K., ed. 150p. 1984. pap. text ed. 25.00 (ISBN 0-915586-80-0). Fairmont Pr.

Institute of Energy. Fluidised Combustion: Systems & Applications. (Institute of Energy Symposium Ser.: No. 4). 450p. 1982. pap. 66.00x (ISBN 0-8448-1418-0). Crane-Russak Co.

Kanury, A. M. Introduction to Combustion Phenomena. (Combustion Science & Technology Ser.). 430p. 1975. 59.95x (ISBN 0-677-02690-0). Gordon.

Khalil, E. E. Modelling of Furnaces & Combustors. 1982. 41.00 (ISBN 0-9961005-3-9, Pub. by Abacus England). Heyden.

Kuo, Kenneth. Fundamentals of Combustion. Date not set. 50.00 (ISBN 0-471-09852-3). Wiley.

Lewis, Bernard & Von Elbe, Guenther. Combustion, Flames, & Explosions of Gases. 2nd ed. 1961. 91.50 (ISBN 0-12-446750-4). Acad Pr.

McCarthy, Gregory J. & Lauf, Robert J., eds. Fly Ash Coal & Conversion By-Products: Characterization, Utilization & Disposal I, Vol. 43. LC 85-7248. 1985. text ed. 30.00 (ISBN 0-931837-08-1). Materials Res.

Macek, A. Coal Research. 140p. 1977. pap. 74.25 (ISBN 0-677-40255-4). Gordon.

Morel, T., et al, eds. Fluid Mechanics of Combustion Systems. 266p. 1981. 40.00 (ISBN 0-686-34487-1, G00197). ASME.

National Fire Protection Association. Flammable & Combustible Liquids Code: 1981. 1981. 10.00 (ISBN 0-317-07372-9, NFPA 30). Natl Fire Prot.

Odgers, J. & Kretschmer, D. Gas Turbine Fuels & Their Influence on Combustion. (Energy & Engineering Science Ser.). 1984. 40.00 (ISBN 0-9901004-7-2, Pub. by Abacus England). Heyden.

Osbourne, Alan & Neild, A. B., eds. Modern Marine Engineer's Manual, Vol. 1. 2nd ed. LC 65-18208. (Illus.). 1965. Vol. 1. 30.00x (ISBN 0-87033-063-2). Cornell Maritime.

Palmer, H. B. & Beer, J. M., eds. Combustion Technology: Some Modern Developments. 1974. 81.00 (ISBN 0-12-544750-7). Acad Pr.

Patankar, S. V., et al, eds. Numerical Prediction of Flow, Heat Transfer Turbulence, & Combustion: Selected Works of Professor D. Brian Spalding. LC 83-12172. 444p. 1983. 100.00 (ISBN 0-08-030937-2, 11). Pergamon.

Patterson, Walter C. & Griffin, Richard F. Fluidized Bed Energy Technology: Coming to a Boil. LC 78-60484. (Orig.). 1978. pap. 25.00 (ISBN 0-918780-10-1). INFORM.

Penner, S. S. Chemical Rocket Propulsion & Combustion Research. (Illus.). 170p. 1962. 45.25x (ISBN 0-677-00710-8). Gordon.

Pincus, Alexis G. Combustion Melting in the Glass Industry. LC 78-55358. (Processing in the Glass Industry Ser.). 300p. 1980. 29.95 (ISBN 0-911993-11-8). Ashlee Pub Co.

Podolski, W. F., et al. Pressurized Fluidized Bed Combustion Technology. LC 83-13215. (Energy Tech. Rev. 87; Pollution Tech. Rev. 103). (Illus.). 429p. 1984. 45.00 (ISBN 0-8155-0960-X). Noyes.

Priestley, Joseph. Considerations on the Doctrine of Phlogiston, & the Decomposition of Water. Foster, William, ed. LC 30-8577. 1968. Repr. of 1929 ed. 15.00 (ISBN 0-527-72700-8). Kraus Repr.

Project Squid Workshop on Combustion Measurement in Jet Propulsion System. Combustion Measurements: Modern Techniques & Instrumentation Proceedings. Goulard, Robert J., ed. LC 76-25999. pap. 123.80 (ISBN 0-317-08914-5, 2055326). Bks Demand UMI.

Raask, Erich. Mineral Impurities in Coal Combustion: Behavior, Problems, & Remedial Measures. LC 83-26400. (Illus.). 500p. 1985. 69.50 (ISBN 0-89116-362-X). Hemisphere Pub.

Remenyi. Combustion Stability. 1981. 18.00 (ISBN 0-9960070-3-2, Pub. by Akademiai Kaido Hungary). Heyden.

Schumacher, M. M., ed. Coal-Oil Mixture Combustion Technology. (Energy Technical Review: No. 73). (Illus.). 481p. 1982. 48.00 (ISBN 0-8155-0878-6). Noyes.

Schwieger, Robert G., ed. Fluidized Bed Combustion & Applied Technology. (Illus.). 636p. 1984. text ed. 95.00 (ISBN 0-89116-383-2). Hemisphere Pub.

Sheahan, Richard T. Fluidized Bed Combustion: Technical, Financial & Regulatory Issues. (Illus.). 281p. 1983. 3-ring binder 48.00 (ISBN 0-86587-105-1). Gov Insts.

Singer, Stanley. Pulverized Coal Combustion: Recent Developments. LC 84-4082. (Energy Technology Review Ser.: No. 90). (Illus.). 184p. 1984. 32.00 (ISBN 0-8155-0992-8). Noyes.

Sloane, Thompson M., ed. The Chemistry of Combustion Processes. LC 84-2816. (ACS Symposium Ser.: No. 249). 287p. 1984. lib. bdg. 49.95x (ISBN 0-8412-0834-4). Am Chemical.

Smoot, L. D. & Pratt, D. T., eds. Pulverized Coal Combustion & Gasification: Theory & Applications for Continuous Flow Processes. LC 78-12564. 352p. 1978. 49.50 (ISBN 0-306-40084-7, Plenum Pr). Plenum Pub.

Smoot, L. Douglas & Smith, Philip J. Coal Combustion & Gasification. (Chemical Engineering Ser.). 460p. 1985. 59.50x (ISBN 0-306-41750-2, Plenum Pr). Plenum Pub.

Stavitskiy, M. G., et al. Hazard Analysis & Behavior of Combustible Materials. LC 83-1763. (Fire Fighting Aboard Ships Ser.: Vol. I). 250p. (Orig.). 1983. pap. 59.95x (ISBN 0-87201-306-5). Gulf Pub.

Strehlow, R. A. Combustion Fundamentals. (Energy, Combustion & Environment). 576p. 1984. 41.95 (ISBN 0-07-062221-3). McGraw.

Strehlow, Roger A. Fundamentals of Combustion. LC 77-5368. 480p. 1979. Repr. of 1968 ed. 31.50 (ISBN 0-88275-539-0). Krieger.

Sunner, Stig & Mansson, Margret, eds. Combustion Calorimetry: Experimental Chemical Thermodynamics I, Vol. 1. 1979. pap. text ed. 44.00 (ISBN 0-08-022385-0). Pergamon.

Teague, Paul E., ed. Smoke & Other Products of Combustion. LC 76-47957. (Illus.). 1977. pap. text ed. 5.00 (ISBN 0-87765-085-3, SPP-41). Natl Fire Prot.

Tillman, David, et al. Wood Combustion: Principles, Processes & Economics. LC 81-10907. 1981. 21.50 (ISBN 0-12-691240-8). Acad Pr.

Tipper, C. F., ed. Oxidation & Combustion Reviews, Vol. 6. LC 65-12562. 240p. 1973. 34.00 (ISBN 0-444-41104-6). Elsevier.

Westbrook, Charles & Miller, James A. Laminar Flame Propagation in Premixed Gases. (Combustion Science & Technology Ser.). 365p. 1984. pap. text ed. 90.00 (ISBN 0-677-06545-0). Gordon.

Williams, Forman A. Combustion Theory. 2nd ed. 704p. 1985. text ed. 49.95x (ISBN 0-8053-9801-5, 38901). Benjamin-Cummings.

Zeldovich, Ya. B., et al. The Mathematical Theory of Combustion & Explosions. 620p. 1985. 95.00x (ISBN 0-306-10974-3, Plenum Pr). Plenum Pub.

COMBUSTION GASES

see also Automobiles–Motors–Exhaust Gas

Ash Deposit & Corrosion from Impurities in Combustion Gases Symposium, June 26-July 1, 1977, New England College, Henniker, New Hampshire. Ash Deposits & Corrosion Due to Impurities in Combustion Gases: Proceedings. Bryers, R. W., ed. LC 78-7001. (Illus.). 691p. 1978. text ed. 89.95 (ISBN 0-89116-074-4). Hemisphere Pub.

Bryers, Richard W., ed. Fouling & Slagging Resulting from Impurities in Combustion Gases. LC 83-80600. 550p. 1983. text ed. 45.00 (ISBN 0-939204-18-5, 81-18). Eng Found.

Cheremisinoff, Paul & Young, Richard, eds. Air Pollution Control & Design Handbook, Pt. 1. (Pollution Engineering & Technology Ser.: Vol. 2). 1977. 85.00 (ISBN 0-8247-6444-7). Dekker.

Cornelius, W. & Agnew, W. G., eds. Emissions from Continuous Combustion Systems. LC 72-80343. (General Motors Symposia Ser.). 479p. 1972. 69.50x (ISBN 0-306-30702-2, Plenum Pr). Plenum Pub.

Hudson, John L. & Rochelle, Gary T., eds. Flue Gas Desulfurization. LC 82-6818. (ACS Symposium Ser.: No. 188). 1982. 44.95 (ISBN 0-8412-0722-4). Am Chemical.

Kaplan, Harold K., et al. Combustion Toxicology: Principles & Test Methods. LC 83-70043. 167p. 1983. pap. 22.00 (ISBN 0-87762-321-X). Technomic.

Ladenburg, R. W., et al, eds. Physical Measurements in Gas Dynamics & Combustion. LC 54-13127. pap. 151.50 (ISBN 0-317-09134-4, 2000097). Bks Demand UMI.

Lewis, Bernard & Von Elbe, Guenther. Combustion, Flames, & Explosions of Gases. 2nd ed. 1961. 91.50 (ISBN 0-12-446750-4). Acad Pr.

Mattavi, James N. & Amann, Charles A., eds. Combustion Modeling in Reciprocating Engines. LC 80-10451. (General Motors Research Symposia Ser.). 714p. 89.50x (ISBN 0-306-40431-1, Plenum Pr). Plenum Pub.

Niessen, Walter R. Combustion & Incineration. (Pollution Engineering & Technology Ser.: Vol. 7). 1978. 75.00 (ISBN 0-8247-6656-3). Dekker.

Research Committee on Industrial & Municipal Wastes, ASME & A. D. Little, Inc., eds. Study on State-of-the-Art of Dioxin from Combustion Sources. 1981. 20.00 (ISBN 0-686-34520-7, H00180). ASME.

Turner, Roger N. & Low, Royston. Moxibustion: Its Principles & Practice. 96p. 1981. 30.00x (ISBN 0-7225-0675-9, Pub. by Thorsons England). State Mutual Bk.

COMETS

Periodic comets are entered under the name of the discoverer, e.g. Halley's Comet.

Bainbridge, John. Astronomical Description of the Late Comet from the 18. of Novemb. 1618 to the 16. of December Following. LC 74-28828. (English Experience Ser.: No. 710). 1975. Repr. of 1619 ed. 6.00 (ISBN 90-221-0710-8). Walter J Johnson.

Brandt, John C. & Chapman, Robert D. Introduction to Comets. LC 76-47207. (Illus.). 256p. 1981. 52.50 (ISBN 0-521-23906-0). Cambridge U Pr.

--Introduction to Comets. LC 76-47207. 256p. 1982. pap. 13.95 (ISBN 0-521-27218-1). Cambridge U Pr.

Brandt, John C., ed. Comets: Readings from Scientific American. LC 81-4562. (Illus.). 92p. 1981. text ed. 17.95 (ISBN 0-7167-1319-5); pap. text ed. 10.95 (ISBN 0-7167-1320-9). W H Freeman.

Carusi, Andrea & Valsecchi, Giovanni B., eds. Dynamics of Comets: Their Origin & Evolution. (Astrophysics & Space Science Library). 1985. lib. bdg. 59.00 (ISBN 90-277-2047-9, Pub. by Reidel Holland). Kluwer-Academic.

Cristescu, Cornelia & Klepczynski, W. J., eds. Asteroids, Comets, Meteoric Matter: Proceedings. (Illus.). 333p. 1975. text ed. 60.00x (ISBN 0-87936-008-9). Scholium Intl.

Edberg, Stephen J. International Halley Watch Amateur Observers' Manual for Scientific Comet Studies. LC 85-20591. (Illus.). 192p. 1983. pap. 9.95 (ISBN 0-89490-102-8). Enslow Pubs.

Gibilisco, Stan. Comets, Meteors & Asteroids: How They Affect Earth. (Illus.). 208p. (Orig.). 1985. pap. 12.95 (ISBN 0-8306-1905-4, 1905). TAB Bks.

Gregory, David. The Elements of Physical & Geometrical Astronomy, 2 vols. 1972. Repr. of 1726 ed. Set. 70.00 (ISBN 0-384-19920-8). Johnson Repr.

Hoegner, W. & Richter, N. Isophotometric Atlas of Comets, 2 pts. (Illus.). 1980. Pt. 1. 62.60 (ISBN 0-387-09171-8); Pt. 2. 52.00 (ISBN 0-387-09172-6). Springer-Verlag.

I.A.U. Symposium, No. 45, Leningrad, U.S.S.R., August 4-11, 1970. Motion, Evolution of Orbits & Origins of Comets: Proceedings. Chebotarev, ed. LC 73-179895. (I.A.U. Symposia). 521p. 1972. lib. bdg. 63.00 (ISBN 90-277-0207-1, Pub. by Reidel Holland). Kluwer Academic.

Irwin, Christopher O. Comets. (Illus.). 48p. 1981. 21.00 (ISBN 0-88014-033-X). Mosaic Pr OH.

Jervis, Jane L. Cometary Theory in Fifteenth-Century Europe. 1985. lib. bdg. 39.00 (ISBN 0-318-04126-X, Pub. by Reidel Holland). Kluwer Academic.

Kronk, Gary W. Comets: A Descriptive Catalog. LC 82-20971. 344p. 1984. pap. text ed. 22.50x (ISBN 0-89490-071-4). Enslow Pubs.

Kuiper, Gerard P. & Middlehurst, Barbara M., eds. Moon, Meteorites & Comets. LC 62-18117. (Solar System Ser: Vol. 4). 1963. 60.00x (ISBN 0-226-45928-4). U of Chicago Pr.

McDonnell, J. A., ed. Cosmic Dust. LC 77-2895. 693p. 1978. text ed. 176.95x (ISBN 0-471-99512-6, Pub. by Wiley-Interscience). Wiley.

Marsden, Brian G. Catalog of Cometary Orbits. LC 83-1739. 100p. 1983. pap. text ed. 10.95x (ISBN 0-89490-095-1). Enslow Pubs.

Meadows, Jack. Space Garbage: Comets, Meteors & other Solar-System Debris. (Illus.). 160p. 1985. pap. 17.95 (ISBN 0-540-01087-1, Pub. by G Philip UK). Sheridan.

Olsen, Roberta J. Fire & Ice: A History of Comets in Art. LC 85-7295. (Illus.). 134p. 1985. 24.95 (ISBN 0-8027-0855-2); pap. 14.95 (ISBN 0-8027-7283-8). Walker & Co.

Ponnamperuma, Cyril, ed. Comets & the Origin of Life. 292p. 1981. 39.50 (ISBN 90-277-1318-9, Pub. by Reidel Holland). Kluwer Academic.

Sagan, Carl. Comet. 1985. 24.95 (ISBN 0-317-20762-8). Random.

Schiaparelli, G. V. Le Opere Publicate per Cura Della Reale Specola Di Brera, Vols. 1-11. (Sources of Science Ser). (It). Repr. of 1930 ed. Set. 440.00 (ISBN 0-384-53780-4). Johnson Repr.

Schove, D. J. Chronology of Eclipses & Comets AD1-1000. (Illus.). 356p. 1985. 29.50 (ISBN 0-85115-406-9, Pub. by Boydell & Brewer). Longwood Pub Group.

Seargent, David A. Comets: Vagabonds of Space. LC 81-43636. (Illus.). 256p. 1982. 15.95 (ISBN 0-385-17869-7). Doubleday.

Stasiuk, Garry & Gruber, Dwight. The Comet Handbook. (Illus.). 32p. (Orig.). 1984. pap. 5.00 (ISBN 0-932421-00-8). Stasiuk Ent.

Whipple, Fred L. The Mystery of Comets. LC 85-8343. (Library of the Solar System). (Illus.). 208p. (Orig.). 1985. 24.95 (ISBN 0-87474-968-9, WHMC); pap. 12.50 (ISBN 0-87474-971-9, WHMCP). Smithsonian.

Wilkening, Laurel L, ed. Comets. LC 81-21814. 766p. 1982. 29.95x (ISBN 0-8165-0769-4). U of Ariz Pr.

COMMENSALISM

see Symbiosis

COMMERCIAL CORRESPONDENCE–COPYING PROCESSES

see Copying Processes

COMMERCIAL VEHICLES

see also Motor Buses; Motor-Trucks

Baldwin, Nick. Observer's Book of Commercial Vehicles 1981. (Illus.). 192p. 1980. 4.95 (ISBN 0-7232-1619-3, Pub. by Frederick Warne England). Motorbooks Intl.

Georgano, G. N. The Complete Encyclopedia of Commercial Vehicles. LC 79-88062. (Illus.). 1979. 35.00 (ISBN 0-87341-024-6). Krause Pubns.

--The Complete Encyclopedia of Commercial Vehicles. 1979. 35.00. Motorbooks Intl.

Hannay, R. N. Guy Motors & the Wulfrunian. 76p. 1981. 20.00x (ISBN 0-903839-26-1, Pub. by Transport). State Mutual Bk.

COMMODORE COMPUTERS

see also Commodore 64 (Computer)

Bartel, Ranier. Ideas for Use on Your Commodore. Dykema, Greg, tr. from Ger. 225p. (Orig.). 1984. pap. text ed. 12.95 (ISBN 0-916439-07-0). Abacus Soft.

--Science & Engineering for the Commodore. Dykema, Greg, tr. from Ger. 343p. (Orig.). 1985. pap. text ed. 19.95 (ISBN 0-916439-09-7). Abacus Soft.

The Blue Book for the Commodore 64 Computer. 2nd ed. 17.95 (ISBN 0-927853-04-3). WIDL Video.

Brain Bank. The BASIC Conversions Handbook for Apple, Commodore, TRS-80, & Atari Users. write for info. Hayden.

Callery, Michael. Commodore Magic. (Illus.). 256p. 1984. pap. 12.95 (ISBN 0-525-48120-6, 01258-370). Dutton.

Cane, Mike. Computer Phone Book Online Guide for the Commodore Computers. 496p. 1984. pap. 9.95 (ISBN 0-451-82084-3, Sig). NAL.

Commodore Computer Staff. Commodore Software Encyclopedia. 3rd ed. 896p. 1983. pap. text ed. 19.95 (ISBN 0-672-22091-1, 22091). Sams.

The Commodore Software Guide & Handbook. 300p. 1985. 24.95 (ISBN 0-912603-45-3). Micro Info.

Compute Editors. Compute's Commodore Collection, Vol. 2. (Orig.). 1984. pap. 12.95 (ISBN 0-942386-70-1). Compute Pubns.

Computer Publishers & Publications, 1985-86: An International Directory & Yearbook. 2nd ed. 450p. 1985. 95.00x (ISBN 0-88709-009-5). Comm Trends Inc.

Consumers Guide Editors, ed. The User's Guide to Commodore. (Orig.). 1983. pap. 3.95 (ISBN 0-671-49505-4). PB.

Foster, Dennis L. & D. L. Foster Book Company Editors. The Addison-Wesley Book of Commodore Software 1985. 416p. 1985. pap. 19.95 (ISBN 0-201-12020-8). Addison-Wesley.

Gerits, Klaus, et al. Tricks & Tips for the Commodore. Dykema, Greg, tr. (Ger.). 276p. (Orig.). 1984. pap. text ed. 19.95 (ISBN 0-916439-03-8). Abacus Soft.

Goldstein, Lou & Softsync, Inc. Commodore LOGO from A to Z: The Complete Book of the LOGO Language. 256p. pap. cancelled (ISBN 0-89303-465-7). Brady Comm.

Grubbs, Jim. The Commodore Ham's Companion. Grubbs, Jon, ed. LC 85-61585. 100p. (Orig.). 1985. pap. 19.95 (ISBN 0-931387-24-8). Qsky Pub.

Heller, Dave & Heller, Dorothy. Free Software for Your Commodore. (Free Software Ser.). (Illus.). 224p. 1984. pap. text ed. 8.95 (ISBN 0-86582-122-4, EN79212). Enrich.

Heller, David & Johnson, John. Dr. C. Wacko Presents Commodore BASIC & the Whiz-Bang Miracle Machine. 1245p. 1984. pap. 12.95 (ISBN 0-201-11494-1). Addison-Wesley.

Knott, Julie & Prochnow, David. Commodore Peripherals: A User's Guide. (Orig.). 1984. pap. 9.95 (ISBN 0-942386-56-6). Compute Pubns.

Krute, Stan. Commodore LOGO for Beginners. cancelled 14.95 (ISBN 0-89303-377-4). Brady Comm.

Liesert, H. J. Peeks & Pokes for the Commodore. Traas, Gene, tr. from Ger. 204p. (Orig.). 1985. pap. text ed. 14.95 (ISBN 0-916439-13-5). Abacus Soft.

Plenge, Axel. The Graphics Book for the Commodore. Dykema, Greg, tr. from Ger. 350p. (Orig.). 1984. pap. text ed. 19.95 (ISBN 0-916439-05-4). Abacus Soft.

Heeb, Dan. Compute'S VIC-20 & Commodore 64 Tool Kit: Kernal. Compute Editors, ed. (Orig.). 1985. 16.95 (ISBN 0-942386-33-7). Compute Pubns.
--Compute's VIC-20 & Commodore 64 Tool Kit: BASIC. 16.95 (ISBN 0-942386-32-9). Compute Pubns.
Heil, John A. & Martin, Jack. Commodore 64: The Intelligent & Intelligible Guide for the Inquisitive Adult. 208p. 1983. pap. 14.95 (ISBN 0-88693-067-7). Banbury Bks.
Heilborn, John. Compute's Beginner's Guide to Commodore 64 Sound. Compute, ed. 256p. (Orig.). 1984. pap. 12.95 (ISBN 0-942386-54-X). Compute Pubns.
--Compute's Reference Guide to Commodore 64 Graphics. 218p. (Orig.). 1983. pap. 12.95 (ISBN 0-942386-29-9). Compute Pubns.
Heilborn, John & Talbott, Ran. Your Commodore 64: A Guide to the Commodore 64 Computer. 464p. (Orig.). 1983. pap. 14.95 (ISBN 0-88134-114-2, 114-2). Osborne-McGraw.
Heiserman, David L. One Hundred One Programming Surprises & Tricks for Your Commodore 64 Computer. (Illus.). 208p. (Orig.). 1985. 18.95 (ISBN 0-8306-0951-2); pap. 11.95 (ISBN 0-8306-1951-8). TAB Bks.
Held, Gilbert. Commodore 64 BASIC: A Quick Reference Guide. 1983. pap. 2.95 (ISBN 0-471-88240-2, Pub. by Wiley Pr); pap. 29.50 prepack of 10 (ISBN 0-471-88250-X). Wiley.
Hergert, Douglas. The Commodore 64-VIC-20 BASIC Handbook. LC 83-50718. (Illus.). 185p. 1983. pap. 14.95 (ISBN 0-89588-116-0). SYBEX.
Herriott, John. Using & Programming the Commodore 64: Including Ready-to-Run Programs. 176p. (Orig.). 1984. 13.95 (ISBN 0-8306-0712-9, 1712); pap. 9.25 (ISBN 0-8306-1712-4); incl. disk 24.50 (ISBN 0-8306-5056-3). TAB Bks.
--Using & Programming the VIC-20, Including Ready-to-Run Programs. 192p. (Orig.). 1984. 15.95 (ISBN 0-8306-0702-1, 1702); pap. 10.25 (ISBN 0-8306-1702-7). TAB Bks.
Highmore, David & Page, Liz. Programming Tips for the Commodore 64. LC 84-17395. 160p. 1984. pap. 14.95 (ISBN 0-471-81553-5, Pub. by Wiley Pr). Wiley.
Hime, Robert. QuickWrite: Commodore Sixty-Four. 128p. 1984. pap. cancelled (ISBN 0-88056-220-X). Dilithium Pr.
How to Program Your Commodore 64: BASIC for Beginners. 1984. pap. 9.95 (ISBN 0-318-01973-6). WSP.
Hunter, James & Guntle, Gregory. Commodore 64 Trivia Data Base. LC 84-51504. 112p. 1984. 8.95 (ISBN 0-672-22396-1, 22396). Sams.
Jackson, Peter. Business Programming on Your Commodore 64. (Illus.). 192p. 1984. pap. 14.95 (ISBN 0-946576-19-X, Pub. by Phoenix Pub). David & Charles.
Jeffries, Ron & Fisher, Glen. Commodore 64 Fun & Games, Vol. 2. (Orig.). 1984. pap. 12.95 (ISBN 0-446-38183-7). Warner Bks.
Jeffries, Ronald, et al. Commodore 64 Fun & Games. 180p. (Orig.). 1983. pap. 11.95 (ISBN 0-88134-116-9). Osborne-McGraw.
Jones, A. J. & Carpenter, G. Mastering the Commodore 64. (Professional Software Ser.). 383p. 1984. pap. text ed. 14.95 (ISBN 0-471-80755-9, 1-999); incl. disk 39.90 (ISBN 0-471-80751-6, 1-598). Wiley.
Jones, Aubrey B., Jr. I Speak BASIC to My Commodore 64. student text 9.75 (6172); tchr's manual 18.75 (6162); exam 15.00 (6182); Tchr's Manual, 20 Student Texts, & Exam. classroom set 200.00 (6152). Hayden.
Kascmer, Joseph. The Easy Guide to Your Commodore 64. LC 83-40232. (Illus.). 130p. 1983. pap. 9.95 (ISBN 0-89588-126-8). SYBEX.
Kassab, Vincent. Commodore 64 BASIC Programming with Technical Applications. (Illus.). 256p. 1984. pap. text ed. 15.95 (ISBN 0-13-152166-7). P-H.
Kelly, Tim. Using the Commodore 64 Without Learning BASIC. 1984. 15.95 (ISBN 0-8359-8128-2). P-H.
--Using the Commodore 64 Without Using BASIC. pap. text ed. 15.95 (ISBN 0-8359-8128-2). Reston.
Kidd, Kathy H. & Kidd, Clark. Commodore 64 Games for Kids. 267p. (Orig.). 1984. 12.95 (ISBN 0-942386-37-X). Compute Pubns.
King, Richard A. & Trost, Stanley R. Multiplan on the Commodore 64. 225p. 1985. pap. 15.95 (ISBN 0-89588-231-0). SYBEX.
Klein, Mike. The Commodore 64 Experience. 220p. (Orig.). 1983. pap. text ed. 14.95 (ISBN 0-88190-230-6, BO230). Datamost.
Knapp, Jeff. Graphics for the Commodore 64 Computer. (Illus.). 144p. 1984. pap. 12.95 (ISBN 0-13-363094-3); incl. disk 29.95 (ISBN 0-13-363102-8). P-H.
Knight, Timothy & LaBatt, Darren. Commodore 64 BASIC Programs. 2nd ed. LC 83-50832. 9.95 (ISBN 0-672-22402-X). Sams.
Knott, Julie & Prochnow, Dave. Commodore 64 Tutor for Home & School: How to Program in LOGO, PILOT, & BASIC. 1985. pap. 15.95 (ISBN 0-673-18074-3). Scott F.
Knottingham, Ken E. & Vander Waal, Scott. The World of the Commodore 64. (Illus.). 272p. (Orig.). 1983. pap. 14.95 (ISBN 0-913049-01-8); 29.95 (ISBN 0-913049-02-6). Impress Pub.
Kohl, Herb & Kahn, Ted. Commodore 64 Games & Recreation. (Illus.). 225p. 16.95 (ISBN 0-8359-0773-2). Reston.
Kokinski, Mathieu. Commodore 64 Roadmap. (Illus.). 192p. 1985. pap. cancelled (ISBN 0-88056-341-9). Dilithium Pr.
Kreutner, Donald C. Commodore 64 Favorite Programs Explained. LC 83-63254. 194p. 1984. pap. 12.95 (ISBN 0-88022-073-2, 113). Que Corp.
Krute, Stan. Inside the Commodore 64. 1985. cancelled (ISBN 0-318-01426-2). Brady Comm.
--Introduction to Assembly Language for the Commodore 64. cancelled 17.95 (ISBN 0-89303-572-6). Brady Comm.
Lane, John M. Programming Commodore Graphics with Your 64 or 128. 1985. pap. 14.95 (ISBN 0-673-18084-0). Scott F.
Laric, Michael V. & Stiff, M. Ronald. Multiplan for the Commodore 64. (Microcomputer Power Series). 150p. 1985. 16.95 (ISBN 0-697-00424-4); incl. diskette 27.95 (ISBN 0-697-00425-2). Wm C Brown.
Larsen, Sally G. Sprite Graphics for the Commodore 64. 184p. 1983. 21.95 (ISBN 0-13-838144-5); pap. 15.95 (ISBN 0-13-838136-4). P-H.
LaVarta, Marlene. Commodore 64: Programs for the Home. 224p. 1985. pap. 14.95 (ISBN 0-471-81151-3, Pub. by Wiley Pr). Wiley.
Lawrence, David. The Working Commodore 64. (The Working Ser.: No. 1). 192p. (Orig.). 1984. pap. 9.95 (ISBN 0-916688-64-X, 64-X). Creative Comp.
Lawrence, David & England, Mark. Commodore 64 Machine Code Master. (Illus.). 250p. 16.95 (ISBN 0-8359-0879-8). Reston.
Leemon, Sheldon. Mapping the Commodore 64. 268p. (Orig.). 1984. pap. 14.95 (ISBN 0-942386-23-X). Compute Pubns.
Librach, Hank & Behrendt, William. Using the Commodore 64 in the Home. (Illus.). 100p. 1984. pap. 10.95; incl. disk 29.95 (ISBN 0-13-940099-0). P-H.
Lien, David A. Learning Commodore 64 BASIC. LC 84-71389. (CompuSoft Learning Ser.). (Illus.). 360p. 1984. pap. 14.95 (ISBN 0-932760-22-8). CompuSoft.
Lindsay, Len. Comal Handbook: Commodore 64 Version (2.00) 1984. incl. disk 34.95 (ISBN 0-8359-0785-6); pap. 16.95 (ISBN 0-8359-0784-8). Reston.
Lippman, Gary. Your Second Commodore 64 Program. LC 84-50356. (Illus.). 240p. 1984. pap. 13.95 (ISBN 0-89588-152-7). SYBEX.
Ludinski, G. Brainteasers for the Commodore 64. 143p. 1984. pap. 12.95 (ISBN 0-946576-09-2, Pub. by Phoenix Pub). David & Charles.
Lyons, Len. The Commodore 64 Connection. 256p. 1985. pap. 16.95 (ISBN 0-201-17631-9). Addison-Wesley.
Lyons, Len, et al. Using the Commodore 64: A Hand Guide to Getting the Most from the Bestselling Microcomputer. LC 84-2847. 1438p. 1984. pap. 14.95 (ISBN 0-201-05156-7). Addison-Wesley.
The Machine Language Book for the Commodore 64. Dykema, G., tr. from German. 215p. 1984. pap. 19.95 (ISBN 0-916439-02-X). Abacus Soft.
Mandell, Steven L. Beginning BASIC for the Commodore 64. (Illus.). 150p. (Orig.). 1985. pap. text ed. 13.95 (ISBN 0-314-85264-6). West Pub.
--The Commodore 64 Guidebook. (Illus.). 150p. (Orig.). 1985. pap. text ed. 13.95 (ISBN 0-314-85261-1). West Pub.
Margolis, Art. Troubleshooting & Repairing Your Commodore 64. (Illus.). 288p. (Orig.). 1985. 22.95 (ISBN 0-8306-0889-3, 1889); pap. 14.95 (ISBN 0-8306-1889-9). TAB Bks.
Matthews, Toby & Smith, Paul. Winning Games on the Commodore 64. 302p. 1984. pap. text ed. 14.95 (ISBN 0-471-81531-4, Pub. by Wiley Pr). Wiley.
Matthews, Toby, et al. Winning Strategy Games on the Commodore 64. Date not set. incl. disk 39.90 (ISBN 0-471-82521-2); disk 24.95 (ISBN 0-471-82519-0). Wiley.
Maurer, W. Douglas. Commodore 64 Assembly Language. LC 84-16981. 420p. 1985. pap. 19.95 (ISBN 0-88175-040-9); diskette 15.00 (ISBN 0-88175-041-7). Computer Sci.
Mellin, Michael, et al, eds. The Book of Commodore 64 Software 1985. 300p. 1984. pap. 19.95 (ISBN 0-912003-21-9). Bk Co.
Milewski, Richard A. & InfoWorld Editors. InfoWorld's Essential Guide to the Commodore 64. (InfoWorld's Essential Guide Ser.). 250p. (Orig.). 1984. pap. 16.30i (ISBN 0-06-669005-6). Har Row.
Miller, Deborah. Teach Yourself BASIC with the Commodore 64: A Beginner's Guide to Writing Programs. (Illus.). 192p. pap. cancelled (ISBN 0-89303-876-8). Brady Comm.
Money, Steve. Commodore 64 Graphics & Sound. 1985. 12.95 (ISBN 0-13-152034-2). P H.
Moore, Herb. Sound & Graphics for the Commodore 64. 240p. 1985. pap. 14.95 (ISBN 0-471-80556-4, Pub by Wiley Pr). Wiley.
Mosher, Frederick E. & Schneider, David I. Handbook of BASIC for the Commodore 64. LC 83-26618. 354p. 1984. pap. 14.95 (ISBN 0-89303-505-X). Brady Comm.
Mowe, Richard & Ronald, Mummaw. The Academic Commodore 64. 1984. pap. text ed. 15.95 (ISBN 0-8359-0017-7). Reston.
Mullish, Henry & Cooper, Herbert. Zappers for the Commodore 64. 224p. 1984. pap. 9.95 spiral bd (ISBN 0-671-50714-1, Pub. by Computer Bks). S&S.
Mullish, Henry & Kruger, Dov. At Home with BASIC: The Simon & Schuster Guide to Programming the Commodore 64. 192p. 1984. pap. 12.95 spiral bdg. (ISBN 0-671-49861-4, Pub. by Computer Bks). S&S.
Music Made Easy: Commodore 64. 1984. incl. disk 29.95 (ISBN 0-88284-292-7). Alfred Pub.
Nadler, Bob. The Commodore 64 Illustrated. 176p. pap. 10.95 (6453). Hayden.
Nickles, Herbert & Culp, George. Instructional Computing Fundamentals for the Commodore 64. LC 84-29222. (Computer Science Ser.). 250p. 1985. pap. text ed. 15.00 pub net (ISBN 0-534-04662-2). Brooks-Cole.
Noble, Tony. Learning Is Fun: Programs for the Commodore 64. 1985. pap. 14.95 (ISBN 0-471-81558-6). Wiley.
O'Malley, Timothy J. Artificial Intelligence Projects for the Commodore 64. LC 84-26749. (Illus.). 160p. (Orig.). 1985. 12.95 (ISBN 0-8306-0883-4, 1883); pap. 12.45 (ISBN 0-8306-1883-X). TAB Bks.
Onosko, Tim. Commodore 64: Getting the Most from It. LC 83-14127. 384p. 1983. 14.95 (ISBN 0-89303-380-4). Brady Comm.
--Commodore 64 User's Guide. cancelled (ISBN 0-317-04670-5). Brady Comm.
Peckham, H. D. Hands-on BASIC for the Commodore 64. 344p. 1984. 23.95 (ISBN 0-07-049154-2). McGraw.
Peddicord, Richard G. Beginning BASIC on the Commodore 64. 187p. 1984. 19.95 (ISBN 0-88284-306-0). Alfred Pub.
--Creating Graphics & Music on the Commodore 64. 128p. 1985. incl. disk 19.95 (ISBN 0-88284-305-2). Alfred Pub.
--Everything You Can Do with Your Commodore 64. (Everything You Can Do with Your... Ser.). 1984. pap. 9.95 (ISBN 0-88284-278-1). Alfred Pub.
--How to Use the Commodore 64. (Handy Guide Ser.). 64p. (Orig.). 1983. pap. 3.50 (ISBN 0-88284-247-1). Alfred Pub.
--Understanding Commodore 64 BASIC. (Handy Guide Ser.). 64p. (Orig.). 1984. pap. 3.50. Alfred Pub.
--Understanding Commodore 64 Graphics. (Handy Guide Ser.). 64p. (Orig.). 1984. pap. 3.50 (ISBN 0-88284-282-X). Alfred Pub.
Perry, Gregory. Graphics & Sound on the Commodore 64. (Illus.). 304p. 1985. pap. text ed. 29.95 incl. disk (ISBN 0-13-363151-6); pap. text ed. 15.95 (ISBN 0-13-363144-3); disk 14.85 (ISBN 0-13-363169-9). P-H.
Phillips, Gary. Commodore 64 Expansion Guide. LC 84-23999. (Illus.). 277p. 1985. pap. 22.95 (ISBN 0-8306-0961-X); pap. 16.95 (ISBN 0-8306-1961-5). TAB Bks.
--Commodore 64 Free Software. 300p. pap. cancelled (ISBN 0-89588-201-9). SYBEX.
--Commodore 64 Software Buyers Guide. (Illus.). 496p. 1984. pap. 16.95 (ISBN 0-89303-382-0). Brady Comm.
Phillips, Gary, et al. The Commodore 64 User's Encyclopedia. 2nd ed. Mellin, Michael F. & McCroskey, Mia, eds. 270p. (Orig.). 1984. pap. 14.95 (ISBN 0-912003-37-5). Bk Co.
Platt, Charles. Graphics Guide to the Commodore 64. LC 83-51570. (Illus.). 261p. (Orig.). 1984. pap. 15.95 (ISBN 0-89588-138-1). SYBEX.
Porter, Kent. Mastering Sight & Sound on the Commodore 64. (Plume Computer Bks.). (Illus.). 224p. 1984. pap. 9.95 (ISBN 0-452-25490-6, Plume). NAL.
--Porter's Programs for the Commodore 64. 1984. pap. 6.95 (ISBN 0-451-82090-8, Sig). NAL.
Presley & Deckel. Beginner's Guide to the Commodore 64. 312p. 1984. pap. 16.50 (ISBN 0-931717-01-9); 3 ring binder tchr's guide 19.95 (ISBN 0-931717-03-5). Lawrenceville Pr.
Renko, Hal & Edwards, Sam. Crazy Games for Your Commodore 64. (Illus.). 144p. 1984. pap. 5.95 (ISBN 0-201-16483-3). Addison-Wesley.
Renko, Hal, et al. The Antagonists: A Complete Microworld Adventure for the Commodore 64. 128p. 1985. pap. 8.95 (ISBN 0-201-16491-4). Addison-Wesley.
--The Secret of Arendarvon Castle: A Complete Microworld Adventure for the Commodore 64. (Illus.). 128p. 1984. pap. 8.95 (ISBN 0-201-16485-X). Addison-Wesley.
Rice, Jean & Henke, James. Friendly BASIC: Commodore 64 Version. 1984. cancelled. Reston.
Richter, Michael. Advanced BASIC Programming for the Commodore 64 & Other Commodore Computers. LC 83-15604. 134p. 1983. pap. 12.95 (ISBN 0-89303-302-2); diskette 25.00 (ISBN 0-89303-299-9). Brady Comm.
Rienhardt, Mona. Programmer's Desk Reference for Commodore 64 BASIC. (Illus.). 176p. 1985. pap. 15.95 (ISBN 0-89303-770-2). Brady Comm.
Rinder, Robert. Cookbook of Creative Programs for the Commodore 64. 1984. pap. 12.95 (ISBN 0-452-25571-6, Plume). NAL.
Rosch, Winn L. The Commodore 64 Survival Manual. 256p. (Orig.). 1984. pap. 12.95 (ISBN 0-553-34254-1). Bantam.
Rugg, Tom & Feldman, Phil. Mind Moves: Strategic Games for the Commodore 64. 160p. 1984. pap. 9.95 (ISBN 0-88056-054-1); incl. disk 24.95 (ISBN 0-88056-225-0); incl. cassette 24.95 (ISBN 0-88056-228-5). Dilithium Pr.
--More Than Thirty-Two BASIC Programs for the Commodore 64. (Illus.). 350p. 1983. pap. 19.95 (ISBN 0-88056-112-2); incl. disk 39.95 (ISBN 0-88056-180-7); incl. cassette 39.95 (ISBN 0-88056-183-1). Dilithium Pr.
Rupp, William & Hartman, Patricia A. Commodore 64 Game Construction Kit. 446p. (Orig.). 1984. pap. 14.95 (ISBN 0-88190-293-4, BO293). Datamost.
Salkind, Neil. A Guide to Commodore 64 Software & Hardware. cancelled (ISBN 0-317-07075-4). Datamost.
Sanders, William B. The Elementary Commodore 64. (Elementary Ser.). (Illus.). 211p. (Orig.). 1983. pap. text ed. 14.95 (ISBN 0-88190-001-X, B0034). Datamost.
Sawusch, Mark R. & Summers, Tan A. One Thousand & One Things to Do with Your Commodore 64. (Illus.). 256p. (Orig.). 1984. 15.95 (ISBN 0-8306-0836-2, 1836); pap. 10.95 (ISBN 0-8306-1836-8). TAB Bks.
Schaffer & Schaffer. Commodore 64 Color Graphics: An Advanced Guide. (Illus.). 220p. 1984. pap. 14.95 (ISBN 0-8359-0787-2). Reston.
Schechter, Gil. Learn BASIC Programming in Fourteen Days on Your Commodore 64. LC 84-50052. 12.95 (ISBN 0-672-22279-5). Sams.
Schwenk, George A. & Schwenk, Nancy E. Commodore 64 Advanced Game Design. (Illus.). 144p. (Orig.). 1985. 15.95 (ISBN 0-8306-0923-7); pap. 10.95 (ISBN 0-8306-1923-2). TAB Bks.
Scott, Allan. The Complete Spectrum. (Illus.). 190p. (Orig.). 1984. pap. 19.95 (ISBN 0-246-12569-1, Pub. by Granada England). Sheridan.
Scott, Allan, ed. The Complete Commodore 64. 198p. (Orig.). 1984. pap. 19.95 (ISBN 0-246-12580-2, Pub. by Granada England). Sheridan.
Severin, Ranier. Commodore 64 for Scientists & Engineers. Dykema, Greg, tr. from Ger. 250p. 1984. pap. text ed. 19.95 (ISBN 0-916439-09-7). Abacus Soft.
Shaffer & Shaffer. Commodore 64 Color Graphics: A Beginner's Guide. (Illus.). 1984. pap. 14.95 (ISBN 0-8359-0786-4). Reston.
Shaffer & Shaffer Applied Research & Development. Commodore 64 Color Graphics: A Beginner's Guide. 1983. pap. 14.95 (ISBN 0-912003-06-5). Bk Co.
--Commodore 64 Color Graphics: An Advanced Guide. 300p. (Orig.). 1983. pap. 14.95 (ISBN 0-912003-07-3). Bk Co.
Sharpe, Roger C., ed. The Commodore 64 & Executive 64 User's Guide. (Easy Home Computer Ser.). 1983. 5.95 (ISBN 0-02-008690-3). Macmillan.
Shipman, Carl. How to Program Your Commodore 64: BASIC for Beginners. 336p. 1984. pap. 12.95 (ISBN 0-89586-310-3). H P Bks.
Shneiderman, Ben. Let's Learn BASIC: An Introduction to Programming the Commodore 64. (Microcomputer Bookself Ser.). 175p. (Orig.). 1984. pap. 8.95 (ISBN 0-316-78725-6). Little.
Simpson, Henry. Serious Programming for the Commodore 64. (Illus.). 176p. (Orig.). 1984. 15.95 (ISBN 0-8306-0821-4, 1821); pap. 9.95 (ISBN 0-8306-1821-X). TAB Bks.
Sinclair, Ian. Commodore 64 Computing. 133p. 1983. 19.95 (ISBN 0-13-152314-7); pap. 12.95 (ISBN 0-13-152306-6). P-H.
--Introducing Commodore 64 Machine Code. 1984. 19.95 (ISBN 0-13-477324-1); pap. 12.95 (ISBN 0-13-477316-0). P-H.
--Useful Subroutines & Utilities for the Commodore 64. (Illus.). 160p. (Orig.). 1985. pap. 13.95 (ISBN 0-00-383012-8, Pub. by Collins England). Sheridan.

Introduction to Communication Systems: Arabic Edition. Date not set. pap. price not set (ISBN 0-471-82529-8). Wiley.

Jackins, Harvey. Communication of Important Ideas. 1963. pap. 0.50 (ISBN 0-911214-09-7). Rational Isl.

Jain, Nemi C., ed. International & Intercultural Communication Annual, Vol. VI. 120p. (Orig.). 1982. pap. text ed. 10.50x (ISBN 0-933662-22-X). Intercult Pr.

Janowitz, Morris & Hirsch, Paul, eds. Reader in Public Opinion & Mass Communication. 3rd ed. LC 80-2444. 448p. 1981. pap. text ed. 13.95 (ISBN 0-02-916020-0). Free Pr.

Jefferson, George. Communications Getting It All Together: The British Computer Society Lecture, No. 4. (British Computer Society). 14p. 1983. 11.95x (ISBN 0-471-26269-2, Wiley Heyden). Wiley.

Johnston, James W., Jr., et al, eds. Communication by Chemical Signals. LC 74-92664. 412p. 1970. 37.50x (ISBN 0-306-50037-X, Plenum Pr). Plenum Pub.

Jordan, Larry E. Communications with the IBM PCjr. (Illus.). 256p. Date not set. pap. 14.95 (ISBN 0-89303-386-3). Brady Comm.

Junckerstorff, Kurt. Antidumping-Recht. 462p. 1974. 132.00 (ISBN 3-11-004798-5). De Gruyter.

Jussawalla, Meheroo & Lamberton, D. M., eds. Communication Economics & Development: Proceedings of an East-West Communication Institute Workshop, Honolulu, Hawaii, June 1980. LC 81-13826. (Pergamon Policy Studies on International Development). 356p. 1982. 33.00 (ISBN 0-08-027520-6). Pergamon.

Kates, Linda & Schein, Jerome. A Complete Guide to Communication with Deaf Blind Persons. (Illus.). 108p. 1981. pap. text ed. 3.95 (ISBN 0-913072-40-0). Natl Assn Deaf.

Kazakos, D. & Papantoni-Kazakos, P. Nonparametric Methods in Communications. (Electrical Engineering & Electronics Ser.: Vol. 2). 1977. 65.00 (ISBN 0-8247-6660-1). Dekker.

Kline, F. Gerald & Tichenor, Phillip J., eds. Current Perspectives in Mass Communication Research. LC 72-84051. (Sage Annual Reviews of Communication Research Ser.: Vol. 1). 320p. 1974. 25.00 (ISBN 0-8039-0171-2); pap. 12.50 (ISBN 0-8039-0493-2). Sage.

Klinzing, Dennis & Klinzing, Dene. Communication for Allied Health Professionals. 272p. 1985. pap. text ed. write for info. (ISBN 0-697-00075-3). Wm C Brown.

Krippendorff, Klaus. Content Analysis: An Introduction to Its Methodology. LC 80-19166. (The Sage Commtext Ser.: Vol. 5). (Illus.). 191p. 1980. 17.50 (ISBN 0-8039-1497-0); pap. 9.95 (ISBN 0-8039-1498-9). Sage.

Lane, J. E. Communicating with Microcomputers. 66p. 1981. pap. 10.95 (ISBN 0-471-89497-4). Wiley.

Larson, Charles U. Communication: Everyday Encounters. 240p. 1981. pap. text ed. 11.95x (ISBN 0-917974-60-3). Waveland Pr.

Lederman, Linda C. New Dimensions: An Introduction to Human Communication. 414p. 1977. pap. text ed. write for info. (ISBN 0-697-04118-2); instr's manual avail. (ISBN 0-697-04236-7). Wm C Brown.

Lee, John A. Toward Realistic Communication Policies: Recent Trends & Ideas Compiled & Analysed. (Reports & Papers on Mass Communication: No. 76). 60p. 1975. pap. 5.00 (ISBN 92-3-101295-9, U683, UNESCO). Unipub.

Lehman, Maxwell, ed. Communication Technologies & Information Flow. (PPS on Science & Technology Ser.). (Illus.). 175p. 1981. 22.00 (ISBN 0-08-027169-3); pap. 10.95 (ISBN 0-08-027528-1). Pergamon.

Lewis, D. B. & Gower, D. M. Biology of Communication. LC 79-20920. (Tertiary Level Biology Ser.). 239p. 1980. 44.95x (ISBN 0-470-26859-X). Halsted Pr.

Lindell, Anne. Intensive English for Communication, Bk. 2. (Illus.). 294p. 1980. pap. text ed. 7.95x (ISBN 0-472-08572-7). U of Mich Pr.

Lionberger, Herbert F. & Gwin, Paul. Communication Strategies: A Guide for Agricultural Change Agents. 239p. 1982. pap. text ed. 9.75x (ISBN 0-8134-2236-1). Interstate.

Little, Florence. Communication at Work. 1981. 20.00 (ISBN 0-340-25264-2, Pub. by Hodder & Stoughton England). State Mutual Bk.

MacBride, Sean, et al, eds. Many Voices, One World: Communication & Society Today & Tomorrow. 312p. (2nd Printing 1983. Co-published by Kogan-Page, London; & Unipub, New York). 1980. pap. 13.50 (ISBN 92-3-101802-7, U1034, UNESCO). Unipub.

McCabe & Bender. Speaking Is a Practical Matter. 4th ed. 384p. 1981. pap. text ed. 21.43 (ISBN 0-205-07230-5, 4872304); free tchr's ed. (ISBN 0-205-07231-3). Allyn.

McIntyre, Ron L. The Jelly Bean Principle: Cybericonics. LC 81-69380. (Illus.). 268p. 1981. 14.95. Cybericonics.

MacKay, Donald M. Information, Mechanism & Meaning. 1970. pap. 5.95x (ISBN 0-262-63032-X). MIT Pr.

McLuhan, Marshall. Understanding Media: The Extensions of Man. 1964. pap. 4.95 (ISBN 0-07-045436-1). McGraw.

Maid, Amy. Communication As a Second Language, 5 pts. Incl. Pt. 1. Language. 1978. pap. 4.95 (ISBN 0-916250-28-8); Pt. 2. Ideas. 1978. pap. 4.95 (ISBN 0-916250-29-6); Pt. 3. Mass Communication. 1978. pap. 4.95 (ISBN 0-916250-30-X); Pt. 4. Print. 1978. pap. 4.95 (ISBN 0-916250-31-8); Pt. 5. Airwaves & Beyond. 1978. pap. 4.95 (ISBN 0-916250-32-6). (Mandala Series in Education). (Illus.). Set. pap. 22.95 (ISBN 0-916250-27-X). Irvington.

Media Institute Staff. The New Technologies: Changes & Challenges in Public Relations. 60p. (Orig.). 1983. pap. 20.00 (ISBN 0-937790-10-9). Media Inst.

Melody, William H., et al. Culture, Communication, & Dependency: The Tradition of H. A. Innis. LC 80-21189. (Communication & Information Science Ser.). 288p. 1981. text ed. 29.50 (ISBN 0-89391-065-1); pap. 18.95 (ISBN 0-89391-079-1). Ablex Pub.

Michaels, Claire F. & Carello, Claudia A. Direct Perception. (Illus.). 224p. 1981. text ed. 26.95 (ISBN 0-13-214791-2). P-H.

Middleton, John, ed. Approaches to Communication Planning. (Monographs on Communication Planning: No. 1). (Illus.). 300p. 1981. pap. 23.25 (ISBN 92-3-101801-9, U1070, UNESCO). Unipub.

Middleton, Karen P. & Jussawalla, Meheroo. The Economics of Communication: A Selected Bibliography with Abstracts Published in Cooperation with the East-West Center, Hawaii. LC 80-20505. (Pergamon Policy Studies on International Development). 1981. 28.00 (ISBN 0-08-026325-9). Pergamon.

Miller, Gary M. Modern Electronic Communications. 2nd ed. (Illus.). 592p. 1983. text ed. 34.95 (ISBN 0-13-593152-5). P-H.

Mobile Telecommunications-84. 1984. 95.00 (Pub. by Online). Taylor & Francis.

Mortensen, C. David. Communication: The Study of Human Interaction. 480p. 1972. text ed. 31.95 (ISBN 0-07-043395-X). McGraw.

Murphy, Brian. The World Wired Up: Unscrambling the New Communications Puzzle. (Comedia Ser.). 192p. 1983. 15.00 (ISBN 0-906890-25-X, Dist. by Scribner); pap. 6.95 (ISBN 0-906890-24-1). M Boyars.

Mytton, Graham. Mass Communication in Africa. 220p. 1983. pap. text ed. 14.95 (ISBN 0-7131-8140-0). E Arnold.

Nadin, Mihai, ed. New Elements in the Semiotics of Communication. 190p. 1984. pap. 19.00x (ISBN 3-87808-560-5). Benjamins North Am.

Naimark & Barba. Communications on Communication. 3rd ed. 85p. 1985. 16.95 (ISBN 0-911204-03-2). Rajah.

Narasimham, R. Modelling Language Behavior. (Springer Series in Language & Communication: Vol. 10). (Illus.). 220p. 1981. 32.00 (ISBN 0-387-10513-1). Springer-Verlag.

Nimmo, Dan, ed. Communication Yearbook, No. 3. 704p. 1979. 29.95 (ISBN 0-87855-341-X). Transaction Bks.

OECD. Handbook of Information, Computer & Communications Activities of Major International Organizations. (Information Computer Communications Policy (ICCP) Ser.: No. 4). 233p. (Orig.). 1980. pap. 14.50x (ISBN 92-64-12035-1, 93-80-01-1). OECD.

OECD Staff. An Exploration of Legal Issues in Information & Communication Technologies. (Info. Computer Communication Policy Ser.: No. 8). 136p. (Orig.). 1984. pap. 14.00x (ISBN 92-64-12527-2). OECD.

Optoelectronics: Growth G-062. 1982. 1250.00 (ISBN 0-89336-286-7). BCC.

Pearson, Judy C. Gender & Communication. 416p. 1984. pap. text ed. write for info. (ISBN 0-697-00115-6); instr's. manual avail. (ISBN 0-697-00264-0). Wm C Brown.

Penman, Robyn. Communication Processes & Relationship. 1980. 33.00 (ISBN 0-12-550380-6). Acad Pr.

Peterson, Brent D., et al. Communication Probes. 3rd ed. 264p. 1982. pap. text ed. 17.95 (ISBN 0-574-22575-7, 13-5575); instr. guide avail. (ISBN 0-574-22576-5, 13-5576). SRA.

Pierce, John R. Signals: The Telephone & Beyond. LC 81-3195. (Illus.). 181p. 1981. pap. text ed. 9.95x (ISBN 0-7167-1336-5). W H Freeman.

Rahim, Syed A. & Middleton, John, eds. Perspectives in Communication Policy & Planning. (Communications Monographs: No.3). 373p. 1978. pap. text ed. 7.00x (ISBN 0-8248-0581-X, Eastwest Ctr). UH Pr.

Ramo, Simon & Whinnery, John R. Fields & Waves in Communication Electronics. 2nd ed. LC 84-7355. 817p. 1984. text ed. 39.95 (ISBN 0-471-87130-3). Wiley.

Reinsch, Lamar & Stano, Michael. Communications in Interviews. 256p. 1982. pap. 18.95 (ISBN 0-13-153502-1). P-H.

Research & Education Association Staff. Electronic Communications Problem Solver. LC 84-61814. (Illus.). 1056p. 1984. pap. text ed. 23.85 (ISBN 0-87891-558-3). Res & Educ.

Robb, Scott H. Television-Radio Age Communications Coursebook. 1981. pap. 16.50 looseleaf (ISBN 0-686-12159-7); 29.00 (ISBN 0-686-12160-0). CRI.

Rogers, Everett M. & Kincaid, D. Lawrence. Communication Networks: Towards a New Paradigm for Research. LC 80-65202. (Illus.). 1981. 24.95 (ISBN 0-02-926740-4). Free Pr.

Rosenfield, Lawrence W. Aristotle & Information Theory: A Comparison of the Influence of Causal Assumptions on Two Theories of Communication. (Janua Linguarum, Ser. Major: No. 35). 1971. text ed. 20.00x (ISBN 0-686-22490-6). Mouton.

Rudman, Jack. Communications Aide. (Career Examination Ser.: C-1201). (Cloth bdg. avail. on request). pap. 10.00 (ISBN 0-8373-1201-9). Natl Learning.

--Communications Analyst. (Career Examination Ser.: C-1202). (Cloth bdg. avail. on request). pap. 12.00 (ISBN 0-8373-1202-7). Natl Learning.

--Communications Operator. (Career Examination Ser.: C-2296). (Cloth bdg. avail. on request). 1977. pap. 10.00 (ISBN 0-8373-2296-0). Natl Learning.

--Electronics Communication. (Occupational Competency Examination Ser.: OCE-19). (Cloth bdg. avail. on request). pap. 13.95 (ISBN 0-8373-5719-5). Natl Learning.

--Principal Communications Technician. (Career Examination Ser.: C-2413). (Cloth bdg. avail. on request). pap. 12.00 (ISBN 0-8373-2413-0). Natl Learning.

--Senior Communications Technician. (Career Examination Ser.: C-2412). (Cloth bdg. avail. on request). pap. 12.00 (ISBN 0-8373-2412-2). Natl Learning.

Saugatad, Per. A Theory of Communication & Use of Language. 1977. 16.00x (ISBN 82-00-01631-5). Universitet.

Schramm, Wilbur & Lerner, Daniel, eds. Communication & Change: The Last Ten Years - & the Next. LC 76-18893. 1976. pap. text ed. 8.95x (ISBN 0-8248-0645-X, Eastwest Ctr). UH Pr.

Sebeok, Thomas A. & Rosenthal, Robert, eds. The Clever Hans Phenomenon: Communication with Horses, Whales, Apes, & People. LC 81-2806. 311p. 1981. 62.00x (ISBN 0-89766-113-3, VOL. 364C); pap. 62.00x (ISBN 0-89766-114-1, VOL. 364P). NY Acad Sci.

Sereno, Kenneth K. & Mortensen, C. David, eds. Foundations of Communication Theory. (Harper's Series in Speech). (Illus., Orig.). 1970. pap. text ed. 17.95 scp (ISBN 0-06-044623-4, HarpC). Har-Row.

Shave, David W. Communication Breakdown: Cause & Cure. LC 73-377. 320p. 1975. 18.50 (ISBN 0-87527-125-1). Green.

Sherif, Muzafer & Hovland, Carl I. Social Judgment: Assimilation & Contrast Effects in Communication & Attitude Change. LC 80-21767. (Yale Studies in Attitude & Communication: Vol. 4). xii, 218p. 1981. Repr. of 1961 ed. lib. bdg. 25.00x (ISBN 0-313-22438-2, SHSO). Greenwood.

Siegman, Aron Wolfe & Pope, Benjamin. Studies in Dyadic Communication: Proceedings of a Research Conference on the Interview. 356p. 1972. text ed. 25.00 (ISBN 0-08-015867-6). Pergamon.

Skwirzynski, J. K., ed. Communication Systems & Random Process Theory, No. 12. (Nato Advanced Study Institute Ser.,Applied Science Ser.). 996p. 1978. 75.00x (ISBN 90-286-0568-1). Sijthoff & Noordhoff.

Smythe, Dallas W. Dependency Road: Communications, Capitalism, Consciousness & Canada. 300p. 1981. text ed. 34.50 (ISBN 0-89391-067-8); pap. 17.95 (ISBN 0-89391-088-0). Ablex Pub.

Society for Technical Communication, Symposium on the State of the Art in Communication, Point Mugu, Calif., Oct., 1975. Proceedings. 1975. 15.00 (ISBN 0-87703-123-1). Univelt Inc.

Sommerlad, Lloyd E. National Communications Systems: Some Policy Issues & Options. (Reports & Papers on Mass Communication: No. 74). 35p. 1975. pap. 5.00 (ISBN 92-3-101248-7, U398, UNESCO). Unipub.

Steinfatt, Thomas. Human Communication: An Interpersonal Introduction. LC 76-18065. 1977. pap. 14.47 scp (ISBN 0-672-61359-X). Bobbs.

Theobald, Robert. Beyond Despair: A Policy Guide to the Communications Era. rev. ed. LC 81-5348. 220p. 1981. pap. 8.95 (ISBN 0-932020-05-4). Seven Locks Pr.

Thomas, Sari, ed. Studies in Mass Communication & Technology. LC 83-25746. (Studies in Communication: Vol. 1). 272p. 1984. text ed. 35.00 (ISBN 0-89391-133-X). Ablex Pub.

Tribolet, Leslie B. The International Aspects of Electrical Communications in the Pacific Area. LC 78-64275. (Johns Hopkins University. Studies in the Social Sciences. Extra Volumes-New Ser.: 4). Repr. of 1929 ed. 14.50 (ISBN 0-404-61376-4). AMS Pr.

Truax, Barry. Acoustic Communication. Voigt, Melvin J., ed. LC 84-20372. (Communication & Information Science Ser.). 288p. 1985. text ed. 29.50 (ISBN 0-89391-263-8); pap. 18.95 (ISBN 0-89391-307-3). Ablex Pub.

Twyford, John. Graphic Communication. (Illus.). 120p. 1981. 17.50 (ISBN 0-7134-3388-4, Pub. by Batsford England). David & Charles.

Tzannes, Nicolaos S. Communication & Radar Systems. (Illus.). 464p. 1985. text ed. 38.95 (ISBN 0-13-153545-5). P-H.

Vallee, Jacques, et al. Pragmatics & Dynamics. (Group Communication Through Computers: Vol. 3). 204p. 1975. 18.00 (ISBN 0-318-14419-0, R35). Inst Future.

Vanderheiden, Gregg C. & Grilley, Kate, eds. Non-Vocal Communication Techniques & Aids for the Severely Physically Handicapped. (Illus.). 246p. 1976. pap. 19.95 (ISBN 0-8391-0952-0). Univ Park.

Voigt, Melvin J. & Hanneman, Gerhard J., eds. Progress in Communication Sciences, Vol. 1. (Communication & Information Science Ser.). 1979. 35.00x (ISBN 0-89391-010-4). Ablex Pub.

Watzlawick, Paul, et al. Pragmatics of Human Communication. (Illus.). 1967. 15.95x (ISBN 0-393-01009-0, NortonC). Norton.

Williams, Frederick. The Communications Revolution. (Illus.). 288p. 1982. 25.00 (ISBN 0-8039-1782-1); pap. 12.50 (ISBN 0-8039-1783-X). Sage.

Williams, Raymond, ed. Contact: Human Communication & Its History. (Illus.). 1981. 29.95 (ISBN 0-500-01239-3). Thames Hudson.

Wilson, D. The Communicators & Society. 1968. pap. 3.50 (ISBN 0-08-012977-3). Pergamon.

Wilson, Howard. Communications. 1976. pap. 1.50 (ISBN 0-910022-14-3). ARA.

Woods, David L. A History of Tactical Communications Techniques. LC 74-4700. (Telecommunications Ser). (Illus.). 310p. 1974. 27.00x (ISBN 0-405-06063-7). Ayer Co Pubs.

Wrangham, Elizabeth. The Communications Revolution. Yapp, Malcolm, et al, eds. (World History Ser.). (Illus.). 32p. 1980. lib. bdg. 6.95 (ISBN 0-89908-134-7); pap. text ed. 2.45 (ISBN 0-89908-109-6). Greenhaven.

Zacharis, John. Exploring Careers in Communications & Telecommunications. 1985. 8.97 (ISBN 0-8239-0644-2). Rosen Group.

Zannes, Estelle. Communication: The Widening Circle. 288p. 1981. pap. text ed. 14.95 (ISBN 0-394-34998-9, RanC). Random.

Ziemer, Rodger E. & Tranter, William. Principles of Communciations: Systems Modulation & Noise. LC 75-25015. (Illus.). 736p. 1976. text ed. 39.95 (ISBN 0-395-20603-0); solutions manual 10.50 (ISBN 0-395-20604-9). HM.

COMMUNICATION–CONTENT ANALYSIS

see Content Analysis (Communication)

COMMUNICATION–ECONOMIC ASPECTS

Van Houten, H., ed. The Competitive Strength of the Information & Communication Industry in Europe. 1983. lib. bdg. 32.50 (ISBN 90-247-2860-6, Pub. by Martinus Nijhoff Netherlands). Kluwer Academic.

COMMUNICATION–RESEARCH

see Communications Research

COMMUNICATION AMONG ANIMALS

see Animal Communication

COMMUNICATION IN RESEARCH

see Communication in Science

COMMUNICATION IN SCIENCE

see also Communication of Technical Information; Exchanges, Literary and Scientific; Science–Information Services; Science News; Scientific Libraries

Anderson, Paul & Brockmann, John, eds. New Essays in Technical & Scientific Communications: Theory, Research, & Practice. (Baywood Technical Communication Ser.: Vol 2). 272p. (Orig.). 1983. pap. text ed. 18.00x (ISBN 0-89503-036-5). Baywood Pub.

Balaban, Miriam, ed. Scientific Information Transfer: The Editor's Role. 1978. lib. bdg. 37.00 (ISBN 90-277-0917-3, Pub. by Reidel Holland). Kluwer Academic.

Booth, Vernon. Communicating in Science: Writing & Speaking. 80p. 1985. pap. 6.95 (ISBN 0-521-27771-X). Cambridge U Pr.

--Writing a Scientific Paper & Speaking at Scientific Meetings. 5th ed. 1981. 25.00x (ISBN 0-686-81318-9, Pub. by Biochemical England). State Mutual Bk.

Burger, Henry G. Wordtree: A Transitive Cladistic for Solving Physical & Social Problems. LC 84-13007. 380p. 1984. 149.00 (ISBN 0-936312-00-9). Wordtree.

Chubin, Daryl E. Sociology of Sciences: An Annotated Bibliography on Invisible Colleges, 1972-1981. LC 82-48773. 216p. 1983. lib. bdg. 33.00 (ISBN 0-8240-9223-6). Garland Pub.

Clements, W. & Berlo, R. The Scientific Report: A Guide for Authors. Society for Technical Communication, ed. 52p. (Orig.). pap. text ed. 15.00x (ISBN 0-914548-39-5). Soc Tech Comm.

Committee On Data For Science And Technology Of The International Council Of Scientific Unions. International Compendium of Numerical Data Projects. 1969. 38.00 (ISBN 0-387-04570-8). Springer-Verlag.

Crane, Diana. Invisible Colleges: Diffusion of Knowledge in Scientific Communities. LC 77-182088. 1972. 10.50x (ISBN 0-226-11857-6). U of Chicago Pr.

--Invisible Colleges: Diffusion of Knowledge in Scientific Communities. LC 77-182088. x, 214p. 1975. Repr. of 1972 ed. pap. 2.95 (ISBN 0-226-11858-4, P623, Phoen). U of Chicago Pr.

Dixon, Diana & Hills, Philip. Talking about Your Research. 1981. 25.00x (ISBN 0-906083-19-2, Pub. by Primary Com England). State Mutual Bk.

Dudley, Hugh. The Presentation of Original Work in Medicine & Biology. LC 76-30629. (Illus.). 1977. pap. text ed. 10.75 (ISBN 0-443-01583-X). Churchill.

Garvey, William D. Communication: The Essence of Science Facilitating Information Exchange Among Librarians, Scientists, Engineers, & Students. 1979. pap. text ed. 19.50 (ISBN 0-08-023344-9). Pergamon.

Gordon, Michael. The Evaluation of Research Papers by Primary Journals in the U. K. 76p. 1978. 25.00x (ISBN 0-906083-03-6, Pub. by Primary Com England). State Mutual Bk.

Hart, Stuart L., et al, eds. Improving Impact Assessment: Increasing the Relevance & Utilization of Technical & Scientific Information. (Replica Edition). 410p. 1985. softcover 30.00x (ISBN 0-86531-865-4). Westview.

Hawkins, C. & Sorgi, M., eds. Research. (Illus.). 195p. 1985. pap. 18.00 (ISBN 0-387-13992-3). Springer-Verlag.

Jones, Greta, et al. The Presentation of Science by the Media. 1978. 25.00x (ISBN 0-686-96959-6, Pub. by Primary Com England). State Mutual Bk.

Large, J. A. The Foreign-Language Barrier: Problems in Scientific Communication. (Language Library). 202p. 1983. 24.95 (ISBN 0-233-97488-1). Basil Blackwell.

Meadows, Jack. New Technology & Developments in the Communication of Research During the 1980's. 1981. 25.00x (ISBN 0-906083-12-5, Pub. by Primary Com England). State Mutual Bk.

Olsen, Leslie & Huchin, Thomas. Principles of Communications for Science & Technology. (Illus.). 432p. 1983. 21.95 (ISBN 0-07-047821-X). McGraw.

Rock, Fern. Slaying the English Jargon. 42p. 1983. pap. text ed. 8.00x (ISBN 0-914548-43-3). Soc Tech Comm.

Singleton, Alan. Learned Societies, Journals & Collaboration with Publishers. 164p. 1981. 40.00x (ISBN 0-906083-14-1, Pub. by Primary Com England). State Mutual Bk.

Society for Technical Communication & Stoner, Russell, eds. Proceedings of the International Technical Communication Conference, 30th, St. Louis, May 1-4, 1983. (Spirit of Technical Communication Ser.). 450p. 1983. pap. 45.00x (ISBN 0-914548-39-5, Dist. by Univelt Inc). Soc Tech Comm.

Society for Technical Communication & Barnow, Renee, eds. Proceedings of the International Technical Communication Conference, 31st, 1984. 600p. 1984. pap. text ed. 45.00x (ISBN 0-914548-46-8, Dist. by Univelt Inc). Soc Tech Comm.

COMMUNICATION IN SCIENCE–BIBLIOGRAPHY

Carlson, Helen V., et al, eds. An Annotated Bibliography of Technical Writing, Editing, Graphics, & Publishing 1966-1980. 500p. 1983. text ed. 40.00x (ISBN 0-914548-45-X). Soc Tech Comm.

COMMUNICATION OF TECHNICAL INFORMATION

see also Technical Libraries; Technical Writing; Technology–Information Services

Agricultural Communicators in Education. Communications Handbook. 4th ed. (Illus.). 224p. 1983. pap. text ed. 14.95x (ISBN 0-8134-2226-4, 2226). Interstate.

Anderson, Paul & Brockmann, John, eds. New Essays in Technical & Scientific Communications: Theory, Research, & Practice. (Baywood Technical Communication Ser.: Vol. 2). 272p. (Orig.). 1983. pap. text ed. 18.00x (ISBN 0-89503-036-5). Baywood Pub.

Anderson, W. Steve & Cox, Don R. The Technical Reader: Readings in Technical Business & Scientific Communication. 2nd ed. LC 83-26410. 357p. 1984. pap. text ed. 14.95 (ISBN 0-03-062396-0, HoltC). HR&W.

Burger, Henry G. Wordtree: A Transitive Cladistic for Solving Physical & Social Problems. LC 84-13007. 380p. 1984. 149.00 (ISBN 0-936312-00-9). Wordtree.

Campbell, John S. Improve Your Technical Communication. LC 76-8493. 216p. 1976. pap. text ed. 9.95x (ISBN 0-915668-26-2). G S E Pubns.

Carlsen, D. & Tryon, V. Communication: Graphic Arts. 1976. pap. 8.84 (ISBN 0-13-153189-1). P-H.

Carosso. Technical Communications. 1986. text ed. write for info. Wadsworth Pub.

Casagrande, Diane O. & Casagrande, Roger D. Oral Communication: A Tool for Technical Success. 300p. 1985. pap. text ed. write for info. (ISBN 0-534-05532-X). Wadsworth Pub.

Clements, W. & Berlo, R. The Scientific Report: A Guide for Authors. Society for Technical Communication, ed. 52p. (Orig.). pap. text ed. 15.00x (ISBN 0-914548-39-5). Soc Tech Comm.

Clements, W. & Waite, R. G. Guide for Beginning Technical Editors. Society for Technical Communication, ed. 54p. 1983. pap. text ed. 15.00x (ISBN 0-914548-40-9). Soc Tech Comm.

Communication Science & Technology, 4 vols. Incl. Vol. 1. Communication Science & Technology: An Introduction. Penland, P. 220p. 24.25 (ISBN 0-8247-6142-1); Vol. 3. Group Dynamics & Individual Development. Penland, P. & Fine, S. 168p. 28.75 (ISBN 0-8247-6143-X); Vol. 4. Community Psychology & Coordination. Penland, P. & Williams, J. 200p. 24.75 (ISBN 0-8247-6144-8). 1974. Dekker.

Dagher, Joseph P. Technical Communication: A Practical Guide. (Illus.). 1978. pap. text ed. 19.95 (ISBN 0-13-898247-3). P-H.

Fear, David E. Technical Communication. 2nd ed. 1981. pap. text ed. 17.35x (ISBN 0-673-15401-7). Scott F.

Gerace, P. & Mangione, S. Communication: Photography. 1976. pap. 8.84 (ISBN 0-13-153239-1). P-H.

Giuliano, Vincent, et al. Into the Information Age: A Perspective for Federal Action on Information. 142p. 1979. pap. text ed. 9.00x (ISBN 0-8389-0283-9). ALA.

Gould, Jay R., ed. Directions in Technical Writing & Communication. LC 77-75832. (Technical Writing & Communications Ser.: Vol. 1). 1978. pap. 7.95x (ISBN 0-89503-006-3). Baywood Pub.

Hart, Stuart L., et al, eds. Improving Impact Assessment: Increasing the Relevance & Utilization of Technical & Scientific Information. (Replica Edition). 410p. 1985. softcover 30.00x (ISBN 0-86531-865-4). Westview.

International Technical Communications Conference, 23rd, Washington, D. C., May 1976. Meeting the Challenge of Reality: Proceedings. lib. bdg. 25.00x (ISBN 0-914548-20-4, Pub. by Soc Tech Comm). Univelt Inc.

International Technical Communication Conference, 27th. Proceedings: Bridge of Understanding. Blakely, J. Paul, ed. 1980. microfiche 30.00x (ISBN 0-914548-32-8, Pub. by Soc Tech Comm). Univelt Inc.

International Technical Communication Conference, 28th, Pittsburgh, Pennsylvania, May 20-23, 1981. Theme Communications for the Eighties, Getting to the Point: Proceedings. Whittaker, Della A., ed. 450p. 45.00x (ISBN 0-914548-34-4, Pub. by Soc Tech Comm). Univelt Inc.

Kim, Wan-hui & Chien, Robert T. Topological Analysis & Synthesis of Communication Networks. LC 62-14636. (Illus.). pap. 80.50 (ISBN 0-317-08767-3, 2010965). Bks Demand UMI.

McGraw Hill-Chemical Engineering Editors. Effective Communication for Engineers. 216p. 1975. pap. text ed. 28.00 (ISBN 0-07-045032-3). McGraw.

Manko, Howard H. Effective Technical Speeches & Sessions: A Guide for Speakers & Program Chairmen. LC 69-18731. (Illus.). 1969. 28.95 (ISBN 0-07-039896-8). McGraw.

Mattelart, Armand & Schmucler, Hector. Communication & Information Technologies. Voigt, Melvin J., ed. Buxton, David, tr. from Fr. (Communication & Information Science Ser.). 200p. 1985. text ed. 24.50 (ISBN 0-89391-214-X). Ablex Pub.

Miller, Gary M. Modern Electronic Communications. 2nd ed. (Illus.). 592p. 1983. text ed. 34.95 (ISBN 0-13-593152-5). P-H.

Miller, R. Communication: Electricity & Electronics. 1976. 7.69 (ISBN 0-13-153098-4); pap. text ed. 8.84 (ISBN 0-13-153072-0). P-H.

Moran, Michael G. & Journet, Debra, eds. Research in Technical Communication: A Bibliographic Sourcebook. LC 84-8977. xxviii, 512p. 1985. lib. bdg. 57.50 (ISBN 0-313-23431-0, MRT/). Greenwood.

New Communications & Information Technologies. 1979. pap. 5.00 (ISBN 0-9603466-1-9). T R A C.

Olsen, Leslie & Huchin, Thomas. Principles of Communications for Science & Technology. (Illus.). 432p. 1983. 21.95 (ISBN 0-07-047821-X). McGraw.

Pearsall, Thomas E. & Sullivan, Frances J. Academic Programs in Technical Communication. 1976. pap. 8.00 (ISBN 0-914548-27-1). Soc Tech Comm.

Proposals & Their Preparation, Vol. 1. (Anthology). 25.00x (ISBN 0-914548-06-9). Soc Tech Comm.

Puzman, Josef & Porizek, Radoslav. Communication Control in Computer Networks. LC 80-41259. (Wiley Series in Computing). 296p. 1980. 54.95 (ISBN 0-471-27894-7, Pub. by Wiley Interscience). Wiley.

Sherlock. Guide to Technical Communication. 1985. 19.29 (ISBN 0-205-07790-0, 177790). Allyn.

Society for Technical Communication, ed. International Technical Communications Conference, Washington, D.C., May, 1976: Proceedings, Vol. 23. (Illus.). 1976. 25.00x (ISBN 0-914548-20-4). Univelt Inc.

--Proceedings of the International Technical Communication Conference, 28th, Pittsburgh, May 1981. 45.00x (ISBN 0-914548-34-4, Dist. by Univelt Inc). Soc Tech Comm.

Society for Technical Communication. Proceedings of the International Technical Communication Conference, 23rd, Washington, D. C., May 12-15, 1976. 376p. 1976. 25.00 (ISBN 0-317-20400-9). Soc Tech Comm.

Society for Technical Communication, ed. Proceedings of the International Technical Communication Conference, 32nd, Houston, TX, May 19-22, 1985. (Illus.). 500p. 1985. pap. text ed. 45.00 (ISBN 0-914548-48-4, Dist. by Univelt Inc). Soc Tech Comm.

Society for Technical Communication. A Symposium on the State of the Art in Communiction: October 1975, Point Mugu, California. 1975. 15.00 (ISBN 0-87703-123-1). Soc Tech Comm.

Sparrow, W. Keats & Pickett, Nell Ann, eds. Technical & Business Communication in Two-Year Programs. 205p. (Orig.). 1983. pap. 8.95 (ISBN 0-8141-5298-8); members 7.75. NCTE.

Stanley, William. Electronic Communication Systems. 1982. text ed. 29.95 (ISBN 0-8359-1666-9); instrs'. manual avail. (ISBN 0-8359-1667-7). Reston.

Turner, Barry T. Effective Technical Writing & Speaking. 2nd ed. 220p. 1978. text ed. 31.50x (ISBN 0-220-66344-0, Pub. by Busn Bks England). Brookfield Pub Co.

Uyehara, Cecil H., ed. United States-Japan Technological Exchange Symposium: Sponsored by the Japan-American Society of Washington, 1981. LC 82-40064. 142p. (Orig.). 1982. PLB 21.75 (ISBN 0-8191-2423-0); pap. text ed. 9.25 (ISBN 0-8191-2424-9). U Pr of Amer.

Wischerth, G. E. Interim Standards: Technical Manual & Report Formats. Society for Technical Communication, ed. (Illus.). 76p. 1981. pap. text ed. 15.00x (ISBN 0-317-17136-4). Soc Tech Comm.

--Interim Standards: Technical Manual & Report Formats. 76p. 1981. pap. 15.00 (STC-106-81). Soc Tech Comm.

COMMUNICATION SYSTEMS

see Telecommunication Systems

COMMUNICATION TRANSMISSION LINES

see Telecommunication Lines

COMMUNICATIONS, MILITARY

see also Signals and Signaling

National Academy of Science. Scientific Communications & National Security. 188p. 1982. 14.50 (ISBN 0-309-03332-2). Natl Acad Pr.

COMMUNICATIONS RELAY SYSTEMS

see Artificial Satellites in Telecommunication

COMMUNICATIONS RESEARCH

see also Content Analysis (Communication)

Akin, Johnnye, et al, eds. Language Behavior: A Book of Readings in Communication. LC 77-110948. (Janua Linguarum, Ser. Major: No. 41). 1970. text ed. 38.40x (ISBN 90-2791-244-0). Mouton.

Bustanoby, Andre & Bustanoby, Fay. Just Talk to Me. 192p. (Orig.). 1981. pap. text ed. 5.95 (ISBN 0-310-22181-1). Zondervan.

Campbell, Joe. Mastering Serial Communications. 250p. 1985. pap. 19.95 (ISBN 0-89588-180-2). SYBEX.

Carswell, E. A. & Rommetveit, R. Social Context of Messages. (European Monographs in Social Psychology). 1972. 31.50 (ISBN 0-12-161250-3). Acad Pr.

Cragan, John F. & Shields, Donald C. Applied Communication Research: A Dramatistic Approach. 432p. 1981. text ed. 18.95x (ISBN 0-917974-53-0). Waveland Pr.

Dervin, Brenda & Voigt, Melvin J., eds. Progress in Communication Sciences, Vol. 4. (Communication & Information Science Ser.). 304p. 1983. text ed. 35.00 (ISBN 0-89391-102-X). Ablex Pub.

Dexter, Lewis A. & White, David M., eds. People, Society & Mass Communications. LC 64-11222. 1964. text ed. 17.95 (ISBN 0-02-907400-2). Free Pr.

Klapper, Joseph T. Effects of Mass Communication. LC 60-14402. 1960. text ed. 14.95 (ISBN 0-02-917380-9). Free Pr.

Kline, F. Gerald & Tichenor, Phillip J., eds. Current Perspectives in Mass Communication Research. LC 72-84051. (Sage Annual Reviews of Communication Research Ser.: Vol. 1). 320p. 1974. 25.00 (ISBN 0-8039-0171-2); pap. 12.50 (ISBN 0-8039-0493-2). Sage.

Lapatine, Sol. Electronics in Communications. LC 77-17573. (Electronic Technology Ser.). 341p. 1978. text ed. 31.95x (ISBN 0-471-01842-2); solutions manual 3.00 (ISBN 0-471-03713-3). Wiley.

Longo, G., ed. The Information Theory Approach to Communications. (CISM-Courses & Lectures: Vol. 229). (Illus.). 1978. pap. 49.60 (ISBN 0-387-81484-1). Springer-Verlag.

Mander, Mary S., ed. Communications in Transition: Issues & Debates in Current Research. 352p. 1983. 35.95x (ISBN 0-03-062938-1). Praeger.

Mann, Margaret. Primary Communications: An Annotated Review of the Literature Since 1970. 75p. 1982. 50.00x (ISBN 0-906083-20-6, Pub. by Primary Com England). State Mutual Bk.

Mass Media in Society: The Need of Research. (Reports & Papers on Mass Communication: No. 59). 33p. (Orig.). 1970. pap. 5.00 (ISBN 92-3-100953-2, U372, UNESCO). Unipub.

Monge, Peter R. & Capella, Joseph N., eds. Multivariate Techniques in Human Communications Research. LC 79-28430. (Human Communication Research Ser.). 1980. 57.50 (ISBN 0-12-504450-X). Acad Pr.

Nafziger, Ralph O. & White, David M., eds. Introduction to Mass Communications Research. 2nd ed. LC 63-8223. (Journalism Monographs, Vol. 6). 1963. text ed. 17.50x (ISBN 0-8071-0626-7). La State U Pr.

Robinson, Glen O., ed. Communications for Tomorrow: Policy Perspectives for the 1980's. 512p. 1978. 17.95x (ISBN 0-03-046546-X); pap. 17.95x o. p. student ed. (ISBN 0-03-046541-9). Praeger.

Rubin, Rebecca B., et al. Communication Research: Strategies & Sources. 190p. 1985. pap. text ed. write for info (ISBN 0-534-05514-1). Wadsworth Pub.

Rybak, B., ed. Bio-Informatics & Bio-Process Studies in the Physiology of Communication. (Health Communications & Informatics Biosciences Communications: Vol. 4, No. 3). (Illus.). 1978. 8.25 (ISBN 3-8055-2856-6). S Karger.

Schiller, Herbert I. Mass Communications & American Empire. 1971. pap. 5.95x (ISBN 0-8070-6175-1, BP386). Beacon Pr.

Singh, Indu, ed. Telecommunications in the Year Two Thousand. LC 82-13800. (Communication & Information Science Ser.). 224p. 1983. text ed. 29.50 (ISBN 0-89391-137-2). Ablex Pub.

Stempel, Guido H., III & Westley, Bruce H. Research Methods in Mass Communication. (Illus.). 550p. 1981. text ed. 30.95 (ISBN 0-13-774240-1). P-H.

Tucker, Raymond, et al. Research in Speech Communication. (Series in Speech Communication). (Illus.). 352p. 1981. text ed. 31.95 (ISBN 0-13-774273-8). P-H.

COMMUNICATIONS RESEARCH–DATA PROCESSING

Edelstein, Alex S., et al, eds. Information Societies: Comparing the Japanese & American Experiences. LC 78-71366. (Illus.). 1978. pap. 10.95 (ISBN 0-933236-00-X). Intl Comm Ctr.

Hirsch, Paul M., et al, eds. Strategies for Communication Research. LC 77-88630. (Sage Annual Reviews of Communication Research: Vol. 6). 288p. 1977. 25.00 (ISBN 0-8039-0891-1); pap. 12.50 (ISBN 0-8039-0892-X). Sage.

Shuchman, Hedvah L. Information Transfer in Engineering. (Illus.). 300p. (Orig.). 1981. pap. 45.00 (ISBN 0-9605196-0-2). Futures Group.

COMMUNICATION SYSTEMS, COMPUTER

see Computer Networks

Feher, Kamilo. Digital Communications: Satellite-Earth Station Engineering. (Illus.). 496p. 1983. 41.95 (ISBN 0-13-212068-2). P-H.

Torrieri, Don J. Principles of Military Communication Systems. LC 81-67379. (Artech Telecommunication Library). (Illus.). 300p. 1981. 29.00x (ISBN 0-89006-102-5). Artech Hse.

COMMUNITY ANTENNA TELEVISION
see Cable Television

COMMUTATIVE RINGS

Bass, H., ed. Algebraic K-Theory 3: Hermitian K-Theory & Geometric Applications. LC 73-13421. (Lecture Notes in Mathematics: Vol. 343). xv, 572p. 1973. pap. 27.00 (ISBN 0-387-06436-2). Springer-Verlag.

Brandal, W. Commutative Rings Whose Finitely Generated Modules Decompose. (Lecture Notes in Mathematics: Vol. 723). 1979. pap. 13.00 (ISBN 0-387-09507-1). Springer-Verlag.

Faith, C. & Wiegand, S., eds. Module Theory: Proceedings, Seattle, August 15-18, 1977. LC 79-4636. (Lecture Notes in Mathematics: Vol. 700). 1979. pap. 17.00 (ISBN 0-387-09107-6). Springer-Verlag.

Fossum, R. M. The Divisor Class Group of a Krull Domain. LC 72-918901. (Ergebnisse der Mathematik und Ihrer Grenzgebiete: Vol. 74). (Illus.). 148p. 1973. 31.00 (ISBN 0-387-06044-8). Springer-Verlag.

Fossum, R. M., et al. Trivial Extensions of Abelian Categories: Homological Algebra of Trivial Extensions of Abelian Categories with Applications to Ring Theory. (Lecture Notes in Mathematics Ser.: Vol. 456). xi, 122p. (Orig.). 1975. pap. 13.00 (ISBN 0-387-07159-8). Springer-Verlag.

Frohlich, A. Central Extensions, Galois Groups, & Ideal Class Groups of Numbers Fields. LC 83-19685. (Contemporary Mathematics Ser.: Vol. 24). 86p. 1983. pap. 17.00 (ISBN 0-8218-5022-9). Am Math.

Gilmer, Robert. Commutative Semigroup Rings. LC 83-51596. (Chicago Lectures in Mathematics Ser.). xii, 380p. 1984. lib. bdg. 30.00x (ISBN 0-226-29391-2); pap. 12.00x (ISBN 0-226-29392-0). U of Chicago Pr.

Gordon, Robert & Robson, J. C. Krull Dimension. LC 73-6825. (Memoirs: No. 133). 78p. 1978. pap. 12.00 (ISBN 0-8218-1833-3, MEMO-133). Am Math.

Hutchins, Harry C. Examples of Commutative Rings. LC 81-13780. (Examples of Mathematical Structures Ser.: Vol. 2). 176p. 1981. 17.75x (ISBN 0-936428-05-8). Polygonal Pub.

Knutson, D. Lambda-Rings & the Representation Theory of the Symmetric Group. LC 73-75663. (Lecture Notes in Mathematics: Vol. 308). iv, 203p. 1973. pap. 14.00 (ISBN 0-387-06184-3). Springer-Verlag.

Magid, A. R. Separable Galois Theory of Commutative Rings. (Pure & Applied Mathematics Ser.: Vol. 27). 1974. 35.00 (ISBN 0-8247-6163-4). Dekker.

Matlis, E. One-Dimensional Cohen-Macaulay Rings. (Lecture Notes in Mathematics Ser.: Vol. 327). xii, 157p. 1973. pap. 14.00 (ISBN 0-387-06327-7). Springer-Verlag.

Vasconcelos, Wolmer V., ed. The Rings of Dimension II. (Lecture Notes in Pure & Applied Mathematics Ser.: Vol. 22). 1976. 29.75 (ISBN 0-8247-6447-1). Dekker.

COMOPODA
see Lamellibranchiata

COMPACTING
see also Centrifuges; Vibratory Compacting

Walker, R. C. The Stone Cech Compactification. (Ergebnisse der Mathematik und Ihrer Grenzgebiete Ser.: Vol. 83). x, 332p. 1974. 44.00 (ISBN 0-387-06699-3). Springer-Verlag.

COMPACTION OF SOILS
see Soil Stabilization

COMPAQ PORTABLE COMPUTER

Arnold, William. The Compaq Portable Computer: Use, Applications & BASIC. LC 84-19219. 1985. pap. text ed. 18.45 (ISBN 0-03-064119-5). HR&W.

Chambers, Harold C. The Compaq Compatible Software Guide. 1984. 21.95 (ISBN 0-317-06185-2). P-H.

Fregel, Louis E., Jr. & Fregel, Louis E. Compaq Users Handbook. LC 84-50647. 15.95 (ISBN 0-672-22037-7). Sams.

Goldstein, Larry J. & Rensin, Joseph K. Compaq Portable Computer User's Guide. LC 83-17140. (Illus.). 400p. 1983. pap. 18.95 (ISBN 0-89303-389-8). Brady Comm.

Lord, Kenniston W., Jr. Using the Compaq Portable Computer. 464p. 1984. 23.45 (ISBN 0-442-25947-6); pap. 13.95 (ISBN 0-442-25949-2). Van Nos Reinhold.

Schwieder, Pete H. How to Repair Your Own Compaq Portable PC. (Illus.). 186p. 1985. pap. 24.95 (ISBN 0-915097-05-2). Personal Sys Pubns.

Solomon, Sam. Business Applications Using the Compaq. 1984. 17.95 (ISBN 0-8359-0531-4). Reston.

Uston, Ken. Ken Uston's Illustrated Guide to the Compaq. (Illustrated Guides Ser.). 1984. 12.95 (ISBN 0-13-514696-8). P-H.

Weber Systems, Inc. Staff. Compaq User's Handbook. LC 84-2255. (WSI's How to Use Your Personal Computer Ser.). 350p. 1983. pap. cancelled (ISBN 0-938862-11-1). Weber Systems.

--Compaq User's Handbook. 1984. pap. 9.95 (ISBN 0-345-31841-2). Ballantine.

COMPARATIVE ANATOMY
see Anatomy, Comparative

COMPARATIVE MORPHOLOGY
see Anatomy, Comparative; Morphology

COMPARATIVE PHYSIOLOGY
see Physiology, Comparative

COMPASS
see also Magnetism, Terrestrial

Borough, William. A Discourse of the Variation of the Cumpas. LC 73-6102. (English Experience Ser.: No. 571). 60p. 1973. Repr. of 1581 ed. 21.00 (ISBN 90-221-0571-7). Walter J Johnson.

Denne, W. Magnetic Compass Deviation & Correction. 3rd ed. 165p. 1979. 17.50x (ISBN 0-85174-332-3). Sheridan.

Farrar, R. A. Survey by Prismatic Compass. 16p. 1980. pap. text ed. 4.00x (ISBN 0-900312-96-3, Pub. by Coun Brit Archaeology). Humanities.

Fleming, June. Staying Found: The Complete Map & Compass Handbook. LC 81-52429. (Illus.). 192p. (Orig.). 1982. pap. 4.95 (ISBN 0-394-75152-3, Vin). Random.

Galilei, Galileo. Galileo Galilei: Operations of the Geometric & Military Compass. Drake, Stillman, tr. from Ital. & intro. by. LC 78-606002. (Illus.). 1978. pap. text ed. 6.95x (ISBN 0-87474-383-4). Smithsonian.

Kemp, J. F. & Young, P. Notes on Compass Work. (Kemp & Young Ser.). 112p. 1972. pap. 9.95x (ISBN 0-540-00362-X). Sheridan.

Sipe, F. Henry. Compass Land Surveying. new ed. 1979. 12.00 (ISBN 0-87012-084-0). McClain.

COMPASS, GYROSCOPIC
see Gyro Compass

COMPENSATION (PHYSIOLOGY)
see Adaptation (Physiology)

COMPILING (ELECTRONIC COMPUTERS)
see also Electronic Data Processing; Electronic Digital Computers–Programming

Aho, Alfred V. & Ullman, Jeffrey D. Principles of Compiler Design. LC 77-73953. (Illus.). 1977. text ed. 34.95 (ISBN 0-201-00022-9). Addison-Wesley.

--Theory of Parsing, Translation & Compiling: Vol. 1, Parsing. (Illus.). 592p. 1972. ref. ed. 40.95 (ISBN 0-13-914556-7). P-H.

Automated Education Center. The Decision Module Compiler. LC 78-120097. 29.00 (ISBN 0-403-04463-4). Mgmt Info Serv.

Barrett, William A. & Couch, John D. Compiler Construction: Theory & Practice. LC 78-26183. 512p. 1979. text ed. 33.95 (ISBN 0-574-21335-X, 13-4335). SRA.

Bauer, F. L., et al. Compiler Construction: An Advanced Course. 2nd ed. (Lecture Notes in Computer Science: Vol. 21). 1977. 17.00 (ISBN 0-387-08046-5). Springer-Verlag.

Berry, R. E. Programming Language Translation. (Computers & Their Applications Ser.). 175p. 1983. pap. 28.95x (ISBN 0-470-27468-9). Halsted Pr.

Bolc, L., ed. The Design of Interpreters, Compilers, & Editors, for Augmented Transition Networks. (Symbolic Computation). (Illus.). 214p. 1983. 31.00 (ISBN 0-387-12789-5). Springer-Verlag.

Branquart, P., et al. An Optimized Translation Process & Its Application to ALGOL 68. LC 75-45092. (Lecture Notes in Computer Science: Vol. 38). 1976. pap. 20.00 (ISBN 0-387-07545-3). Springer-Verlag.

Brown, P. J. Writing Interactive Compilers & Interpreters. LC 79-40513. (Computing Ser.). 265p. 1981. pap. 17.95x (ISBN 0-471-10072-2, Pub. by Wiley-Interscience). Wiley.

--Writing Interactive Compilers & Interpreters. LC 79-40513. (Wiley Series in Computing). 265p. 1979. 44.95 (ISBN 0-471-27609-X, Pub. by Wiley-Interscience). Wiley.

Calingaert, Peter. Assemblers, Compilers, & Program Translation. LC 78-21905. 270p. 1979. 28.95 (ISBN 0-914894-23-4). Computer Sci.

Cattell, R. G. Formalization & Automatic Derivation of Code Generators. Stone, Harold S., ed. LC 82-4802. (Computer Science: Systems Programming Ser.: No. 3). 158p. 1982. 34.95 (ISBN 0-8357-1316-4). UMI Res Pr.

Davie, J. T. & Morrison, R. Recursive Descent Compiling. LC 81-6778. (Computers & Their Applications). 195p. 1981. pap. 29.95x (ISBN 0-470-27361-5). Halsted Pr.

Fabri, Janet. Automatic Storage Optimization. Stone, Harold, ed. LC 82-6995. (Computer Science: Systems Programming Ser.: No. 9). 306p. 1982. 49.95 (ISBN 0-8357-1346-6). UMI Res Pr.

Foster, J. M. Automatic Syntactic Analysis. (Computer Monograph Ser.: Vol. 7). 65p. 1970. 40.00 (ISBN 0-444-19725-7). Elsevier.

Gries, David. Compiler Construction for Digital Computers. 493p. 1971. 42.50 (ISBN 0-471-32776-X). Wiley.

Halstead, M. H., ed. A Laboratory Manual for Compiler & Operating System Inplementation. (Operating & Programming Systems Ser). 130p. 1974. 18.75 (ISBN 0-444-00142-5, North Holland). Elsevier.

Hansen, B. Brinch Hansen on Pascal Compilers. (Illus.). 256p. Date not set. text ed. 27.95 (ISBN 0-13-083098-4). P-H.

Hartmann, A. C. A Concurrent Pascal Compiler for Minicomputers. Goos, G. & Hartmanis, J., eds. (Lecture Notes in Computer Science Ser.: Vol. 50). 1977. pap. 11.95 (ISBN 0-387-08240-9). Springer-Verlag.

Hunter, R. Compilers: Their Design & Construction Using Pascal. (Computing Ser.). 1985. write for info. (ISBN 0-471-90720-0). Wiley.

Hunter, Robin. The Design & Construction of Compilers. (Wiley Computing Ser.). 272p. 1982. 29.95x (ISBN 0-471-28054-2, Pub. by Wiley-Interscience); pap. write for info. (ISBN 0-471-09979-1). Wiley.

Kastens, U., et al. GAG: A Practical Compiler Generator. (Lecture Notes in Computer Science: Vol. 141). 156p. 1982. pap. 12.00 (ISBN 0-387-11591-9). Springer-Verlag.

Leverett, Bruce W. Register Allocation in Optimizing Compilers. Stone, Harold, ed. LC 83-18297. (Computer Science Ser.: Systems Programming: No. 19). 234p. 1983. 39.95 (ISBN 0-8357-1530-2). UMI Res Pr.

Lewi, J., et al, eds. A Programming Methodology in Compiler Construction: Concepts, 2 pts. 1979-82. Pt. 1: Concepts, 1979. 44.75 (ISBN 0-444-85288-3, North Holland); Pt. 2 Implementation. 57.50 (ISBN 0-444-86339-7). Elsevier.

Lewis, Philip M., 2nd, et al. Compiler Design Theory. LC 75-9012. (Illus.). 672p. 1976. text ed. 36.95 (ISBN 0-201-14455-7). Addison-Wesley.

Lorho, B. Methods & Tools for Compiler Construction. 350p. 1984. 49.50 (ISBN 0-521-26843-5). Cambridge U Pr.

Moore, J. WATFIV. 1975. pap. 19.95 (ISBN 0-87909-876-7). Reston.

Polak, W. Compiler Specification & Verification. (Lecture Notes in Computer Science Ser.: Vol. 124). 269p. 1981. pap. 19.00 (ISBN 0-387-10886-6). Springer-Verlag.

Pyster, Arthur B. Compiler Design & Construction. (Electrical-Computer Science & Engineering Ser.). 384p. 1980. 26.95 (ISBN 0-442-24394-4). Van Nos Reinhold.

--Compiler Design & Construction. 357p. 1983. pap. text ed. write for info. (ISBN 0-87150-428-6, 8060). PWS Pubs.

Schreiner, Axel T. & Friedman, H. George, Jr. Introduction to Compiler Construction with UNIX. 224p. 1985. text ed. 25.00 (ISBN 0-13-474396-2). P-H.

Steele, D. R. An Introduction to Elementary Computer & Compiler Design. 152p. 1978. 25.25 (ISBN 0-444-00243-X, North-Holland). Elsevier.

Tremblay, J. P. & Sorenson, P. G. The Theory & Practice of Compiler Writing. 816p. 1984. 35.95 (ISBN 0-07-065161-2). McGraw.

Waite, W. M. & Goos, G. Compiler Construction. LC 83-14714. (Texts & Monographs in Computer Science). (Illus.). 446p. 1984. 26.50 (ISBN 0-387-90821-8). Springer Verlag.

Weingarten, Frederick W. Translation of Computer Languages. LC 72-83240. 330p. 1973. text ed. 21.95x (ISBN 0-8162-9423-2). Holden-Day.

Wichmann, Brian A. & Ciechanowicz, Z. J., eds. Pascal Compiler Validation. LC 82-23882. 176p. 1983. 26.95 (ISBN 0-471-90133-4, Pub. by Wiley-Interscience). Wiley.

Wulf, William, et al. The Design of an Optimizing Compiler. LC 74-21789. (Programming Languages Ser.). 165p. 1975. (North Holland); pap. text ed. 19.00 (ISBN 0-444-00158-1, North Holland). Elsevier.

COMPLEX COMPOUNDS
see also Complex Ions; Coordination Compounds

Aizenberg, L A. & Yuzhakov, A P. Integral Representations & Residues in Multidimensional Complex Analysis. LC 83-15549. (Translations of Mathematical Monographs: No. 58). 283p. 1983. 68.00 (ISBN 0-8218-4511-X). Am Math.

Boschke, G., et al. PI Complexes of Transition Metals. (Topics in Current Chemistry: Vol. 28). (Illus.). 205p. 1972. pap. 27.20 (ISBN 0-387-05728-5). Springer-Verlag.

Choudhary, B. The Elements of Complex Analysis. LC 83-12820. 262p. 1983. 19.95x (ISBN 0-470-27492-1). Halsted Pr.

Foster, R. Organic Charge-Transfer Complexes. (Organic Chemistry Ser.). 1969. 79.00 (ISBN 0-12-262650-8). Acad Pr.

Hartley, F. R. Supported Metal Complexes: A New Generation of Catalysts. 1985. lib. bdg. 59.00 (ISBN 90-277-1855-5, Pub. by Reidel Holland). Kluwer Academic.

Holland, A. S. Complex Function Theory. 304p. 1980. 39.25 (ISBN 0-444-00342-8, North-Holland). Elsevier.

Houghton, R. P. Metal Complexes in Organic Chemistry. LC 78-51685. (Cambridge Texts in Chemistry & Biochemistry). 1979. 67.50 (ISBN 0-521-21992-2); pap. 23.95 (ISBN 0-521-29331-6). Cambridge U Pr.

Perrin, D. D. Organic Complexing Reagents: Structural Behavior & Application to Inorganic Analysis. LC 77-16083. 378p. 1978. Repr. of 1964 ed. lib. bdg. 24.50 (ISBN 0-88275-574-9). Krieger.

Steinhardt, J. & Reynolds, J. A. Multiple Equilibria in Proteins. 1970. 75.00 (ISBN 0-12-665450-6). Acad Pr.

Tsutsui, M., et al. Introduction to Metal Pi-Complex Chemistry. LC 70-81164. 210p. 1970. 35.00x (ISBN 0-306-30410-4, Plenum Pr). Plenum Pub.

Yarwood, J., ed. Spectroscopy & Structure of Molecular Complexes. LC 73-77125. 594p. 1974. 85.00x (ISBN 0-306-30742-1, Plenum Pr). Plenum Pub.

Yatsimirskii, K. B. & Vasil'ev, V. P. Instability Constants of Complex Compounds. LC 60-10560. 214p. 1960. 32.50x (ISBN 0-306-10543-8, Consultants). Plenum Pub.

Yen, Teh Fu, ed. Electron Spin Resonance of Metal Complexes. LC 69-19169. 204p. 1969. 32.50x (ISBN 0-306-30394-9, Plenum Pr). Plenum Pub.

COMPLEX IONS
see also Complex Compounds; Transition Metals

Phariseau, P. & Temmerman, W. T., eds. The Electronic Structure of Complex Systems. (NATO ASI Series B, Physics: Vol. 113). 812p. 1985. 120.00x (ISBN 0-306-41824-X, Plenum Pr). Plenum Pub.

Taube, H. Electron Transfer Reactions of Complex Ions in Solution. (Current Chemical Concepts Ser.). 1970. 37.50 (ISBN 0-12-683850-X). Acad Pr.

COMPLEX MANIFOLDS
see also Almost Complex Manifolds

Friedman, Robert & Morrison, David, eds. The Birational Theory of Degenerations. (Progress in Mathematics Ser.: Vol. 29). 386p. 1983. text ed. 27.50x (ISBN 0-8176-3111-9). Birkhauser.

Gunning, Robert C. On Uniformization of Complex Manifolds. LC 78-55534. (Mathematical Notes Ser: 22). 1978. pap. 16.50 (ISBN 0-691-08176-X). Princeton U Pr.

Henkin, Gennadi M. & Leiterer, Jurgen. Theory of Functions on Complex Manifolds. (Monographs in Mathematics). 240p. 1983. text ed. 29.95 (ISBN 3-7643-1477-X). Birkhauser.

Lerner, D. E. & Sommers, P. D., eds. Complex Manifold Techniques in Theoretical Physics. (Research Notes in Mathematics Ser.: No. 32). 320p. (Orig.). 1979. pap. text ed. 28.50 (ISBN 0-273-08437-2). Pitman Pub MA.

Popp, H., ed. Classification of Algebraic Varieties & Compact Complex Manifolds. (Lecture Notes in Mathematics Ser.: Vol. 412). v, 333p. 1974. pap. 20.00 (ISBN 0-387-06951-8). Springer-Verlag.

Shiffman, Bernard & Sommese, Andrew J. Vanishing Theorems on Complex Manifolds. (Progress in Mathematics Ser.: Vol. 56). 1985. text ed. write for info. (ISBN 0-8176-3288-3). Birkhauser.

Sorani, Giuliano. An Introduction to Real & Complex Manifolds. (Notes on Mathematics & Its Applications Ser.). 212p. 1969. 40.50x (ISBN 0-677-02150-X). Gordon.

Veno, K. Classification Theory of Algebraic Varieties & Compact Complex Spaces. LC 75-1211. (Lecture Notes in Mathematics Ser.: Vol. 439). xix, 278p. 1975. pap. 19.00 (ISBN 0-387-07138-5). Springer-Verlag.

Wells, R. O. Differential Analysis on Complex Manifolds. LC 79-11893. (Graduate Texts in Mathematics: Vol. 65). 1980. 26.00 (ISBN 0-387-90419-0). Springer-Verlag.

COMPLEX NUMBERS
see Numbers, Complex

COMPLEXES
see also Combinatorial Topology

Andreotti, Aldo. Complexes of Partial Differential Operators. LC 75-8440. (Yale Mathematical Monographs: No. 6). pap. 15.00 (ISBN 0-8357-9106-8, 2016793). Bks Demand UMI.

Cazacu, C. A., et al, eds. Romanian-Finnish Seminar on Complex Analysis. (Lecture Notes in Mathematics: Vol. 743). 713p. 1979. pap. 40.00 (ISBN 0-387-09550-0). Springer-Verlag.

--Complex Analysis-Fifth Romanian--Finnish Seminar, Pt. I. (Lecture Notes in Mathematics: Vol. 1013). 393p. 1983. pap. 21.00 (ISBN 0-387-12682-1). Springer-Verlag.

--Complex Analysis-Fifth Romanian--Finnish Seminar, Pt. II. (Lecture Notes in Mathematics: Vol. 1014). 338p. 1983. 19.00 (ISBN 0-387-12683-X). Springer-Verlag.

Vinson, Jack R. & Taya, Minoru, eds. Recent Advances in Composites in the United States & Japan - STP 864. LC 85-6119. (Illus.). 740p. 1985. text ed. 75.00 (ISBN 0-8031-0436-7, 04864000-33). ASTM.

Whitney, J. M. & Pipes, R. B. Experimental Mechanics of Fiber Reinforced Composite Materials. (Illus.). 256p. 1982. 32.00 (ISBN 0-686-48254-9, 2301). T-C Pubns CA.

COMPOSITES, FIBROUS

see Fibrous Composites

COMPOSITION (PRINTING)

see Type-Setting

COMPOST

see also Humus

Appelhof, Mary. Vermicomposting: Selected Articles. 32p. 1982. 10.00x (ISBN 0-942256-04-2). Flower Pr.

Bunt, A. C. Modern Potting Composts. 1976. 23.75x (ISBN 0-271-01221-8, 75-42969). Pa St U Pr.

Ecology of Compost. 1976. 0.25 (ISBN 0-686-20727-0). SUNY Environ.

Gotaas, H. B. Composting: Sanitary Disposal & Reclamation of Organic Wastes. (Monograph Ser: No. 31). (Eng. & Fr., Illus.). 205p. 1956. 14.00 (ISBN 92-4-140031-5). World Health.

Handreck, K. A. Composting: Making Soil Improver from Rubbish. 19p. 1978. pap. 6.00 (ISBN 0-686-71825-9, C046, CSIRO). Unipub.

Handreck, Kevin. Composting. 19p. 1981. pap. 1.75x (ISBN 0-643-02168-X, Pub. by CSIRO). Intl Spec Bk.

Krishnamurthy, R. A Manual on Compost & Other Organic Manures. (Illus.). 150p. 1977. 4.00 (ISBN 0-88065-148-2, Pub. by Messers Today & Tomorrows Printers & Publishers India). Scholarly Pubns.

Organic Gardening & Minnich, Jerry. The Rodale Guide to Composting. (Illus.). 1979. 14.95 (ISBN 0-87857-212-0). Rodale Pr Inc.

Shewell-Cooper, W. E. Compost Gardening. LC 74-18416. (Illus.). 1975. 12.95x (ISBN 0-02-852110-2). Hafner.

COMPOUNDS, UNSATURATED

American Society for Testing & Materials. Determination of Nonmetallic Compounds in Steel: A Symposium. LC 66-12290. (American Society for Testing & Materials Special Technical Publication Ser.: No. 393). pap. 25.80 (ISBN 0-317-09781-4, 2000967). Bks Demand UMI.

Breitmaier, E., et al. Atlas of Carbon-13 NMR Data, Vol. 1: Compounds 1-1003. LC 76-2126. pap. 59.00 (ISBN 0-317-26279-3, 2055699). Bks Demand UMI.

Devon, T. K. & Scott, A. I. Handbook of Naturally Occurring Compounds, 2 vols. Incl. Vol. 1. Acetogenins, Shikimates & Carbohydrates. 1975. 76.50 (ISBN 0-12-213601-2); Vol. 2. Terpenes. 1972. 77.00 (ISBN 0-12-213602-0). Acad Pr.

COMPRESSED GAS

see Gases, Compressed

COMPRESSIBILITY

see also Elasticity; Shock Waves

Anderson. Modern Compressible Flow: With Historical Perspective. (Mechanical Engineering Ser.). 1982. 45.00 (ISBN 0-07-001654-2). McGraw.

Pekalski, A. & Przystawa, J. A., eds. Modern Trends in the Theory of Condensed Matter: Proceedings. (Lecture Notes in Physics: Vol. 115). 587p. 1980. pap. 45.00 (ISBN 0-387-09752-X). Springer-Verlag.

Yahya, S. M. Fundamentals of Compressible Flow. LC 81-13390. 358p. 1982. 21.95x (ISBN 0-470-27282-1). Halsted Pr.

COMPRESSORS

see also Refrigeration and Refrigerating Machinery

Ferguson, Thomas B. The Centrifugal Compressor Stage. LC 64-9032. pap. 40.50 (ISBN 0-317-08541-7, 2051728). Bks Demand UMI.

Greene, R. W. The Chemical Engineering to Compressors. 250p. 1984. 37.50 (ISBN 0-07-024312-3). McGraw.

Hawthorne, W. R., ed. Aerodynamics of Turbines & Compressors. (High Speed Aerodynamics & Jet Propulsion Ser.: Vol. 10). 1964. 63.00 (ISBN 0-691-07904-8). Princeton U Pr.

Horlock, J. H. Axial Flow Compressors. LC 73-75588. 222p. 1973. Repr. of 1958 ed. 14.50 (ISBN 0-88275-096-8). Krieger.

--Axial Flow Turbines: Fluid Mechanics & Thermodynamics. LC 73-75589. 286p. 1973. Repr. of 1966 ed. 19.50 (ISBN 0-88275-097-6). Krieger.

Lapina, Ronald P. Estimating Centifugal Compressor Performance. LC 82-3124. (Process Compressor Technology Ser.: Vol. 1). 208p. 1982. 39.95x (ISBN 0-87201-101-1). Gulf Pub.

McMillan, G. K. Centrifugal & Axial Compressor Control. 1983. Instr's Guide: 24p. pap. text ed. 10.00x (ISBN 0-87664-745-X); Student Text: 144p. pap. text ed. 24.95x (ISBN 0-87664-744-1). Instru Soc.

Narayanan, R., ed. Axially Compressed Structures: Stability & Strength. (Illus.). 316p. 1982. 61.00 (ISBN 0-85334-139-7, I-302-82, Pub. by Elsevier Applied Sci England). Elsevier.

Nisenfeld, A. Eli. Centrifugal Compressors: Principles of Operation & Control. LC 82-80223. (ISA Monograph: No. 3). 254p. 1982. text ed. 34.95x (ISBN 0-87664-564-3). Instru Soc.

Portable Compressor Market. 252p. 1983. 1300.00 (ISBN 0-86621-176-4). Frost & Sullivan.

Pumps & Compressors. 1984. 595.00 (ISBN 0-686-38424-5, A210). Busn Trend.

Stepanoff, Alexey J. Pumps & Blowers. LC 75-11894. 324p. 1978. Repr. of 1965 ed. 19.50 (ISBN 0-88275-306-1). Krieger.

Tramm, P. C. & Dean, R. C., Jr., eds. Centrifugal Compressor & Pump Stability, Stall & Surge. 202p. 1976. pap. 20.00 (ISBN 0-685-67493-2, I00098). ASME.

COMPUTABILITY THEORY

see Recursive Functions

COMPUTABLE FUNCTIONS

see Recursive Functions

COMPUTATION LABORATORIES

Graef, Martin, et al. Organization & Operation of a Computer Center. Goldman, Abram F., tr. from Ger. 406p. 1985. text ed. 34.95x (ISBN 0-02-949990-9). Macmillan.

Hoie, T. A. Performance Control: Service & Resource Control in Complex IBM Computing Centres. (Illus.). 252p. 1983. 42.75 (ISBN 0-444-86517-9, North Holland). Elsevier.

Price, Shirley & Price, Merle. The Primary Math Lab. LC 78-7984. (Illus.). 1978. 14.95 (ISBN 0-673-16414-4); pap. 12.95 (ISBN 0-673-16415-2). Scott F.

Swetz, Frank. The Mathematics Laboratory in the Elementary School: What? Why? & How? Valenza, Samuel W., Jr., ed. LC 80-81349. (Illus., Orig.). 1981. pap. 7.95 (ISBN 0-936918-03-9). Intergalactic NJ.

COMPUTATIONAL LINGUISTICS

see Linguistics–Data Processing; Mathematical Linguistics; Programming Languages (Electronic Computers)

COMPUTER AIDED DESIGN OF SCIENTIFIC AND ENGINEERING SYSTEMS (COMPUTER PROGRAMS)

see Cadses (Computer Programs)

COMPUTER ARCHITECTURE

see also Computer Engineering

Atwood, Jerry W. The Systems Analyst: How to Design Computer-Based Systems. 240p. 17.50 (5102). Hayden.

Baer, Jean-Loup. Computer Systems Architecture. LC 72-27039. (Illus.). 626p. 1980. text ed. 34.95 (ISBN 0-914894-15-3). Computer Sci.

Beizer, Boris. The Architecture & Engineering of Digital Computer Computers, Vols. 1 & 2. LC 71-141244. 1971. Vol. 1, 394p. 59.50x (ISBN 0-306-37151-0, Plenum Pr); Vol. 2, 453 P. 65.00x (ISBN 0-306-37152-9). Plenum Pub.

Boon. Microprogramming & Systems Architecture. (Infotech Computer State of the Art Reports). 644p. 1975. 85.00 (ISBN 0-08-028547-3). Pergamon.

Bormann, J., ed. Programming Languages & System Design. 252p. 1984. 32.75 (ISBN 0-444-86794-5, I-535-83, Pub. by North Holland). Elsevier.

Boulaye, G. & Lewin, Douglas, eds. Computer Architecture. (NATO Advanced Study Institute Ser. C, Math & Physical Sciences: No. 32). (Illus.). 1977. lib. bdg. 37.00 (ISBN 90-277-0803-7, Pub. by Reidel Holland). Kluwer Academic.

Chen, Peter. The Entity-Relationship Approach to Logical Data Base Design. Curtice, Robert M., ed. (Data Base Monograph Ser.: No. 6). 1977. pap. text ed. 15.00 (ISBN 0-89435-020-X). QED Info Sci.

Chinitz, M. Paul. Logic Design of Computers: An Introduction. LC 81-50566. 416p. 1981. pap. 15.95 (ISBN 0-672-21800-3, 21800). Sams.

Chu, Yaohan. High-Level Language Computer Architecture. 1975. 74.50 (ISBN 0-12-174150-8). Acad Pr.

Cypser, R. J. Communications Architecture for Distributed Systems. LC 76-52673. (Illus.). 1978. text ed. 38.95 (ISBN 0-201-14458-1). Addison-Wesley.

--Communications Architecture for Distributed Systems. 711p. 1978. 21.95 (ISBN 0-686-98122-7). Telecom Lib.

D'Angelo, Henry. Microcomputer Structures. 1981. 24.95 (ISBN 0-07-015294-2, BYTE Bks). McGraw.

Dasgopta. Computer Architecture: A Synthesis. 1986. price not set (ISBN 0-471-82310-4). Wiley.

Dasgupta, Subrata. The Design & Description of Computer Architectures. LC 83-21826. 300p. 1984. 40.95x (ISBN 0-471-89616-0, Pub. by Wiley-Interscience). Wiley.

Davis, M. I. IBM Series One Design Decisions: Architecture. (Illus.). 48p. (Orig.). 1979. pap. text ed. 5.20 (ISBN 0-933186-01-0, G360-0060). IBM Armonk.

Doran, R. W. Computer Architecture: A Structured Approach. (A. P. I. C. Studies in Data Processing Ser.). 1979. 49.50 (ISBN 0-12-220850-1). Acad Pr.

Dudewicz, Edward J. & Karian, Zaven A. Tutorial: Modern Design & Analysis of Discrete-Event Computer Simulations. 500p. 1985. 45.00 (ISBN 0-8186-0597-9); prepub. 36.00 (ISBN 0-317-31782-2). IEEE Comp Soc.

Fitzgerald, Jerry. Business Data Communications: Basic Concepts, Security & Design. LC 83-14798. (Wiley Series in Computers & Information Processing Systems for Business: 1-661). 502p. 1984. 33.45x (ISBN 0-471-89549-0); tchr's. ed. avail. (ISBN 0-471-88327-1). Wiley.

Foster, Caxton C. & Iberall, Thea. Computer Architecture. 3rd ed. (Illus.). 384p. 1985. 38.95 (ISBN 0-442-27219-7). Van Nos Reinhold.

Foundyller, Charles M. CAD-CAM Minisystem Report: A Guide to Ready-to-Use Design & Drafting Systems under 100,000 Dollars. (Illus.). 275p. 1983. cancelled (ISBN 0-938484-05-2). Daratech.

Fu, K. S. & Ichikawa, T., eds. Special Computer Architectures for Pattern Processing. 272p. 1981. 79.50 (ISBN 0-8493-6100-1). CRC Pr.

Garside, R. G. The Architecture of Digital Computers. (Oxford Applied Mathematics & Computing Science Ser.). (Illus.). 1980. text ed. 74.00x (ISBN 0-19-859627-8); pap. text ed. 34.50x (ISBN 0-19-859638-3). Oxford U Pr.

Gee, K. C. Proprietary Network Architectures. 250p. 1981. pap. 109.25 (ISBN 0-471-89423-0). Wiley.

Georgiou, Vassilios J. A Parallel Pipeline Computer Architecture for Speech Processing. Stone, Harold, ed. LC 83-18133. (Computer Science: Computer Architecture & Design Ser.: No. 2). 100p. 1984. 34.95 (ISBN 0-8357-1524-8). UMI Res Pr.

Gero, J. S., ed. Optimization in Computer-Aided Design: Proceedings of the IFIP WG 5.2. Working Conference on Optimization of Computer-Aided Design, Lyon, France, 24-26 October, 1983. 382p. 1985. 50.00 (ISBN 0-444-87690-1, North-Holland). Elsevier.

Giloi, W. K. & Shriver, B. D., eds. Methodologies for Computer System Design: Proceedings of the IFIP WG 10.1 Working Conference on Methodologies for Computer System Design, Lille, France, 15-17 September, 1983. 344p. 1985. 55.75 (ISBN 0-444-87687-1, North-Holland). Elsevier.

Green, Paul E., Jr., ed. Computer Network Architectures & Protocols. LC 82-5227. (Applications of Communications Theory Ser.). 735p. 1982. 65.00x (ISBN 0-306-40788-4, Plenum Pr). Plenum Pub.

Greenfield, S. E. The Architecture of Microcomputers. 366p. 1980. text ed. 27.95 (ISBN 0-316-32669-0). Little.

--The Architecture of Microcomputers, Vol. II. 1983. pap. text ed. 12.95 (ISBN 0-316-32675-5). Little.

--The Architecture of Microcomputers: Fundamentals, Vol. I. 1983. 15.95 (ISBN 0-316-32674-7). Little.

Hamacher, V. Carl, et al. Computer Organization. 2nd ed. (Computer Science Ser.). (Illus.). 608p. 1984. text ed. 38.95 (ISBN 0-07-025683-7). McGraw.

Hill, Frederick J. & Peterson, Gerald R. Digital Systems: Hardware Organization & Design. 2nd ed. LC 78-7209. 701p. 1978. text ed. 46.75 (ISBN 0-471-39608-7); write for info. tchrs. ed. (ISBN 0-471-03694-3). Wiley.

Hockney, R. W. & Jesshope, C. R. Parallel Computers: Architecture, Programming & Algorithms. 1981. 49.00 (ISBN 0-9960022-8-6, Pub. by A Hilger England); pap. 18.00 (ISBN 0-9960025-5-3). Heyden.

Hoie, T. A. Central Systems Architecture: Planning & Controlling Complex IBM Computing Centres. 636p. 1981. 74.50 (ISBN 0-444-86163-7, North-Holland). Elsevier.

Hsiao, David K., ed. Advanced Database Machine Architecture. (Illus.). 464p. 1983. text ed. 43.95 (ISBN 0-13-011262-3). P-H.

Hunter, Colin & Ready, Jim. IAPX 432 Architecture. 1982. text ed. 19.95 (ISBN 0-8359-3015-7). Reston.

Hwang, Kai & Briggs, Faye A. Computer Architecture & Parallel Processing. 848p. 1984. 45.95 (ISBN 0-07-031556-6). McGraw.

Intel Staff. IAPX 286 Architecture Extension Kernal K286 User's Guide. 180p. (Orig.). pap. 29.00 (ISBN 0-917017-08-0, 121961-001). Intel Corp.

--An Introduction to the Intel 286 Concepts & Architecture. 560p. (Orig.). 1985. pap. 16.95 (ISBN 0-917017-23-4, 230980-001). Intel Corp.

Kapps & Stafford. Vax Assembly Language & Architecture. 1985. text ed. write for info. (ISBN 0-87150-837-0, 37L8500). PWS Pubs.

Kartashev, Svetland & Kartashev, Steven. Designing & Programming Modern Computers & Systems. (LSI Modular Computer Systems Ser.: Vol. I). (Illus.). 736p. 1982. text ed. 47.50 (ISBN 0-13-201343-6). P-H.

Katevenis, Manolis G. Reduced Instruction Set Computer Architectures For VLSI. (Association for Computing Machinery Doctoral Dissertation Award Ser.). (Illus.). 225p. 1985. text ed. 30.00x (ISBN 0-262-11103-9). MIT Pr.

Khambata, Adi J. Microprocessors-Microcomputers: Architecture, Software & Systems. LC 81-11360. (Electronic Technology Ser.). 577p. 1982. 32.95x (ISBN 0-471-06490-4); tchr's. manual 20.00x (ISBN 0-471-86316-5). Wiley.

Kogge, Peter M. The Architecture of Pipelined Computers. LC 80-26122. (Advanced Computer Science Ser.). (Illus.). 352p. 1981. text ed. 49.95 (ISBN 0-07-035237-2). McGraw.

Kraft, George D. & Toy, Wing N. Microprogrammed Control & Reliable Design of Small Computers. (Illus.). 248p. 1981. text ed. 40.00 (ISBN 0-13-581140-6). P-H.

Kuck, David L. The Structure of Computers & Computations, Vol. 1. LC 78-5412. 1978. 45.50 (ISBN 0-471-02716-2); tchr's manual avail. (ISBN 0-471-05294-9). Wiley.

Kyle, Garland R. Images in Print. Kitz, Linda, ed. LC 85-61516. 200p. (Orig.). 1986. pap. text ed. 8.95 (ISBN 0-9614055-1-1). Modern Wrds.

Langdon, Glen G., Jr. Computer Design. LC 81-71785. (Illus.). 575p. 1982. 36.00 (ISBN 0-9607864-0-6). Computeach.

Lavington, S. H. Processor Architecture. (Illus.). 136p. 1976. pap. 15.50x (ISBN 0-85012-154-X). Intl Pubns Serv.

Lavington, Simon H. Logical Design of Computers: A Course of Twelve Television Lectures. 2nd ed. 58p. 1969. pap. 10.00 (ISBN 0-7190-0480-2, Pub. by Manchester Univ Pr). Longwood Pub Group.

Leben, J. & Arnold, J. IBM CPU & Storage Architecture: System-370-Mode & 370-XA Mode. (Data Processing Training Ser.). 256p. 1984. pap. 49.95 (ISBN 0-471-80142-9). Wiley.

Leben, Joe & Arnold, Jim. IBM I-O Architecture & Virtual Storage Concepts: Systems-370-Mode & 370-XA-Mode Processors. LC 84-7589. (Data Processing Training Ser.). 250p. 1984. 49.95 (ISBN 0-471-80141-0, 1-615). Wiley.

Lekstrom, Len & Sachs, Arline. Introduction to Computer System Architecture. 200p. 1983. pap. text ed. 12.95 (ISBN 0-8403-2937-7). Kendall-Hunt.

Levy, Henry M. Capability-Based Computer Systems. 250p. 1983. 28.00 (ISBN 0-932376-22-3, EY-00011-DP). Digital Pr.

Lippiatt, Arthur & Wright, Graham. Architecture of Small Computer Systems. 2nd ed. (Illus.). 240p. 1986. pap. text ed. 10.95 (ISBN 0-13-044744-7). P-H.

Liu, Yu-Cheng & Gibson, Glenn A. Microcomputer Systems: The 8086-8088 Family, Architecture, Programming, & Design. LC 83-4552. (Illus.). 544p. 1984. 39.95 (ISBN 0-13-580944-4). P-H.

Lloyd, Don. Computer Architecture & Assembly Language. LC 83-43296. 192p. (Orig.). pap. cancelled (ISBN 0-8019-7446-1). Chilton.

Lorin, Harold. Introduction to Computer Architecture & Organization. LC 82-8640. 311p. 1982. 28.95 (ISBN 0-471-86679-2, Pub. by Wiley-Interscience). Wiley.

Mano, Morris. Computer System Architecture. 2nd ed. (Illus.). 544p. 1982. 40.90 (ISBN 0-13-166611-8). P-H.

Marino, Leonard R. Principles of Computer Design. LC 84-23812. 592p. 1985. text ed. 37.95. Computer Sci.

Meyer, Theodore H. Computer Architecture & Organization - with Examples Using the PPD-11. (Illus.). 210p. 1982. pap. 16.95 (ISBN 0-918398-55-X). Dilithium Pr.

Mueller, Robert A. Automated Microcode Synthesis. Stone, Harold, ed. LC 83-24095. (Computer Science: Computer Architecture & Design Ser.: No. 1). 134p. 1984. 39.95 (ISBN 0-8357-1498-5). UMI Res Pr.

Myers, Glenford J. Advances in Computer Architecture. 2nd ed. LC 81-11374. 545p. 1982. 53.50x (ISBN 0-471-07878-6, Pub. by Wiley Interscience). Wiley.

Nadler, Gerald, et al. Design Concepts for Information Systems. Rev. ed. 1983. 13.00 (ISBN 0-89806-015-X, 107). Inst Indus Eng.

Nicoud, J. D., et al, eds. Microcomputer Architectures: Proceedings of the Third EUROMICRO Symposium on Microprocessing Microprogramming, October 1977, Amsterdam. 284p. 1978. 64.00 (ISBN 0-444-85097-X, North-Holland). Elsevier.

Ogdin, Carol A. Microcomputer Design. (Illus.). 1978. ref. ed. 32.95 (ISBN 0-13-580977-0); pap. 24.95 (ISBN 0-13-580985-1). P-H.

--Microcomputer System Design & Techniques. (Tutorial Texts Ser.). 374p. 1980. 24.00 (ISBN 0-8186-0259-7, Q259). IEEE Comp Soc.

Operation Update Series in Microprocessors & Micro-Minicomputers: Design & Application, 8 bks. 1981. Set. 95.00 (ISBN 0-07-079299-2). McGraw.

Osaki, S. & Nishio, T. Reliability Evaluation of Some Fault-Tolerant Computer Architectures. (Lecture Notes in Computer Science Ser.: Vol. 97). 129p. 1980. pap. 13.00 (ISBN 0-387-10274-4). Springer-Verlag.

PDP-11 Architecture Handbook. 272p. 1983. pap. 15.00 (ISBN 0-932376-37-1, EB-23657-DP). Digital Pr.

Peatman, J. B. Microcomputer-Based Design. 1977. 43.95 (ISBN 0-07-049138-0). McGraw.

Prasad, N. S. Architecture & Implementation of Large Scale IBM Processors. 334p. 1981. 29.50 (ISBN 0-89435-051-X). QED Info Sci.

Salisbury, Alan B. Microprogrammable Computer Architectures. 2nd ed. LC 75-26337. (Computer Design & Architecture Ser.: Vol. 1). 162p. 1976. 31.50 (ISBN 0-444-00175-1, North Holland); pap. 17.25 (ISBN 0-444-00174-3). Elsevier.

Shiva, Sajjan G. Computer Design & Architecture. 1984. text ed. 37.95 (ISBN 0-316-78714-0); tchr's. ed. avail. (ISBN 0-316-78715-9). Little.

Siewiorek, D., et al. Computer Structures: Principles & Examples. (Computer Science Ser.). 1982. 42.95 (ISBN 0-07-057302-6). McGraw.

Siewiorek, Daniel P. & Barbacci, Mario. The Design & Analysis of Instruction Set Processors. Vastyan, James E., ed. 320p. 1982. 18.95x (ISBN 0-07-057303-4). McGraw.

Stallings, William. Computer Communications: Architectures, Protocols, & Standards. 1984. write for info. IEEE Comp Soc.

Stallings, William, ed. Tutorial: Computer Communication: Architectures, Protocols, & Standards. LC 85-60383. (Tutorial Text Ser.). 485p. (Orig.). 1985. 36.00 (ISBN 0-8186-0604-5, 604); microfiche 36.00 (ISBN 0-8186-4604-7). IEEE Comp Soc.

Stone, Harold S. Introduction to Computer Architecture. 2nd, rev. ed. 640p. 1980. text ed. 32.95 (ISBN 0-574-21225-6, 13-4225). SRA.

Subbarao, Wunnava. Microprocessors: Hardware, Software, & Design Applications. 1984. text ed. 29.95 (ISBN 0-8359-4394-1); solutions manual avail. (ISBN 0-8359-4395-X). Reston.

Thirty-Twenty GHz Mixed User Architecture Development Study. Exec. Study. 20.00 (ISBN 0-686-33007-2); Final Report. 100.00 (ISBN 0-686-33008-0). Info Gatekeepers.

Thurber, Kenneth J. Distributed Processor Communication Architecture. (Tutorial Texts Ser.). 517p. 1979. 30.00 (ISBN 0-8186-0258-9, Q258). IEEE Comp Soc.

Thurber, Kenneth J. & Masson, G. M. Distributed Processor Communication Architecture. LC 79-1563. (Illus.). 288p. 1979. 30.00x (ISBN 0-669-02914-9). Lexington Bks.

Thurber, Kenneth J. & Patton, Peter C. Computer-System Requirements: Techniques & Examples. LC 79-7184. 128p. 1982. 19.00x (ISBN 0-669-02958-0). Lexington Bks.

Tiberghien, Jaques, ed. New Computer Architectures. (International Lecture Series Computer Science). 1984. 28.50 (ISBN 0-12-690980-6). Acad Pr.

Tomek, Ivan. Introduction to Computer Organization. LC 80-24238. (Illus.). 456p. 1981. text ed. 29.95 (ISBN 0-914894-08-0). Computer Sci.

Wakerly, John F. Microcomputer Architecture & Programming, Vol. 1. LC 80-29060. 692p. 1981. 43.50 (ISBN 0-471-05232-9); tchr's manual avail. (ISBN 0-471-86574-5). Wiley.

Weiland, Richard J. The Programmer's Craft: Program Construction, Computer Architecture, & Data Management. Bauer, Charles R., ed. LC 82-23018. (Illus.). 160p. 1983. 23.95 (ISBN 0-8359-5645-8). Reston.

Yakubaitis, Eduard A. Network Architectures for Distributed Computing. Morell, Martin, tr. from Rus. LC 83-70666. x, 415p. 1983. 45.00 (ISBN 0-89864-005-9). Allerton Pr.

Zarrella, John. System Architecture. LC 80-82932. (Microprocessor Software Engineering Concepts Ser.). (Illus.). 240p. (Orig.). 1980. pap. 18.95 (ISBN 0-935230-02-5). Microcomputer Appns.

COMPUTER ART

Angell, Ian O. Computer Geometric Art. (Dover Design Library). 48p. 1985. pap. 2.95 (ISBN 0-486-24855-0). Dover.

Applied Research & Development Inc. Staff & Shaffer. Electric Art Gallery. 1985. pap. 29.95 incl. disk (ISBN 0-912677-68-6). Ashton-Tate Bks.

Bedworth. Computer Animation. 1984. write for info. (ISBN 0-07-004269-1). McGraw.

Cohen, Harold, et al. Art & Computers: The First Artificial Intelligence Coloring Book. (Illus.). 1984. 19.95 (ISBN 0-86576-060-8). W Kaufmann.

Deken, Joseph. Computer Images: State of the Art. (Illus.). 200p. 1983. pap. 16.95 (ISBN 0-941434-40-0). Stewart Tabori & Chang.

Flanagan, Floyd. MacCats: Ninety Nine Ways to Paint a Cat with MacPaint. 1985. pap. 9.95 (ISBN 0-673-18143-X). Scott F.

Franke, H. W. Computer Graphics - Computer Art. 2nd, rev. ed. Metzger, G. & Schrack, A., trs. from Ger. (Illus.). 200p. 1985. Repr. of 1971 ed. 48.00 (ISBN 0-387-15149-4). Springer-Verlag.

Gonick, Larry & Hosler, Jay. Cartoon Guide to Computer Science. (Illus.). 224p. (Orig.). 1983. pap. 4.76i (ISBN 0-06-460417-9, COS CO 417). B&N NY.

Hayward, S. Computers for Animation. (Illus.). 176p. 1984. 37.50 (ISBN 0-240-51049-6). Focal Pr.

Heiserman, David. Computer Art & Animation for the TRS-80. (Illus.). 288p. 1983. text ed. 20.95 (ISBN 0-13-164749-0); pap. text ed. 15.95 (ISBN 0-13-164731-8). P-H.

Lamis, Leroy. PC Art. 50p. (Orig.). 1983. pap. 50.00 disk & booklet (ISBN 0-925999-27-X). PC Art.

Malina, Frank J., ed. Visual Art, Mathematics & Computers: Selections from the Journal Leonardo. 1979. text ed. 76.00 (ISBN 0-08-021854-7). Pergamon.

Person, Ron. Animation Magic with Your Apple IIe & IIc. 224p. (Orig.). 1985. pap. 15.95 (ISBN 0-07-881161-9, 161-9). Osborne McGraw.

Pinchot Publications. Computer Photography. 60.00 (ISBN 0-8359-0821-6). Reston.

Prueitt, Melvin L. Art & the Computer. 256p. 1984. pap. 29.95 (ISBN 0-07-050899-2); 39.95 (ISBN 0-07-050894-1). McGraw.

Thornburg, David D. Computer Art & Animation: A User's Guide to TRS-80 Color LOGO. (Illus.). 160p. 1984. write for info. (ISBN 0-201-07959-3). Addison-Wesley.

--Computer Art & Animation: A User's Guide to TI 99-4A Color LOGO. (Illus.). 224p. 1983. pap. 12.95 (ISBN 0-201-07958-5). Addison-Wesley.

Wadsworth, Nat. Introduction to Computer Animation. 80p. 1983. pap. 10.95 (ISBN 0-317-00364-X). Hayden.

Whitney, John. Digital Harmony: On the Complementarity of Music & Visual Art. (Illus.). 200p. 1981. 24.95 (ISBN 0-07-070015-X, BYTE Bks). McGraw.

Wilson, Stephen. Using Computers to Create Art. (Illus.). 416p. 1986. pap. text ed. 24.95 (ISBN 0-13-938341-7). P H.

COMPUTER-ASSISTED INSTRUCTION

Abelson, Harold & DiSessa, Andrea. Turtle Geometry: The Computer As a Medium for Exploring Mathematics. (Artificial Intelligence Ser.). (Illus.). 477p. 1981. text ed. 27.00x (ISBN 0-262-01063-1). MIT Pr.

Abelson, Robert B., ed. Using Microcomputers in the Social Studies Classroom. LC 83-14925. (Orig.). 1983. pap. 9.95 (ISBN 0-89994-282-2). Soc Sci Ed.

The Arithmetic Classroom: Addition, 3 pts. (Courses by Computers Ser.). Apple. 49.95 (ISBN 0-88408-196-6); IBM-PC, PCjr. 49.95 (ISBN 0-88408-284-9); Acom. 49.95 (ISBN 0-88408-340-3). Sterling Swift.

The Arithmetic Classroom: Decimals. (Courses by Computers Ser.). Apple. 49.95 (ISBN 0-88408-203-2); IBM-PC, PCjr. 49.95 (ISBN 0-88408-291-1); 49.95 (ISBN 0-88408-348-9). Sterling Swift.

The Arithmetic Classroom: Division, 3 pts. (Courses by Computers Ser.). Apple. 49.95 (ISBN 0-88408-199-0); IBM-PC, PCjr. 49.95; Acom. 49.95 (ISBN 0-88408-344-6). Sterling Swift.

The Arithmetic Classroom: Fraction - Addition & Subtraction. (Courses by Computers Ser.). Apple. 49.95 (ISBN 0-88408-201-6); IBM-PC, PCjr. 49.95; Acom. 49.95 (ISBN 0-88408-346-2). Sterling Swift.

The Arithmetic Classroom: Fraction - Multiplication & Division, 3 pts. (Courses by Computers Ser.). Apple. 49.95 (ISBN 0-88408-202-4); IBM-PC, PCjr. 49.95 (ISBN 0-88408-290-3); Acom. 49.95 (ISBN 0-88408-347-0). Sterling Swift.

The Arithmetic Classroom: Fractions - Basic Concepts, 3 pts. (Courses by Computers Ser.). Apple. 49.95 (ISBN 0-88408-200-8); IBM-PC, PCjr. 49.95 (ISBN 0-88408-293-8); Acom. 49.95 (ISBN 0-88408-345-4). Sterling Swift.

The Arithmetic Classroom: Games, 3 pts. (Courses by Computers Ser.). Apple. 29.95 (ISBN 0-88408-204-0); IBM-PC, PCjr. 29.95 (ISBN 0-88408-294-6); Acom. 29.95 (ISBN 0-88408-349-7). Sterling Swift.

The Arithmetic Classroom: Multiplication, 3 pts. (Courses by Computers Ser.). Apple. 49.95 (ISBN 0-88408-198-2); IBM-PC, PCjr. 49.95 (ISBN 0-88408-286-5); Acom. 49.95 (ISBN 0-88408-343-8). Sterling Swift.

The Arithmetic Classroom: Subtraction, 3 pts. (Courses by Computers Ser.). Apple. 49.95 (ISBN 0-88408-197-4); Acom. 49.95 (ISBN 0-88408-341-1); IBM-PC, PCjr. 49.95 (ISBN 0-88408-285-7). Sterling Swift.

Automated Education Center. Computer-Assisted Instructions. LC 76-121257. 25.00 (ISBN 0-403-04458-8). Scholarly.

Bailey, Daniel E., ed. Computer Science in Social & Behavioral Science Education. LC 77-25087. (Illus.). 520p. 1978. 32.95 (ISBN 0-87778-101-X). Educ Tech Pubns.

Baker, Justine. Microcomputers in the Classroom. LC 82-60799. (Fastback Ser.: No. 179). 50p. 1982. pap. 1.50 (ISBN 0-87367-179-1). Phi Delta Kappa.

Barrette, Pierre. Microcomputers in K-Twelve Education: Second Annual Conference Proceedings. LC 83-2101. 141p. 1983. 30.00 (ISBN 0-914894-87-0). Computer Sci.

Barrette, Pierre, ed. Microcomputers in K-Twelve Education, First Annual Conference Proceedings. LC 82-2522. 123p. 1982. pap. text ed. 30.00 (ISBN 0-914894-32-3). Computer Sci.

Beatty, James W. & Beatty, James J. The Elements of Style in Chemistry: A Computer Assisted Instruction Supported Text. LC 81-40530. 116p. (Orig.). 1982. pap. text ed. 8.50 (ISBN 0-8191-1941-5). U Pr of Amer.

Beech, G., ed. Computer Assisted Learning in Science Education. LC 78-40566. 1979. pap. text ed. 50.00 (ISBN 0-08-023010-5). Pergamon.

Behrmann, Michael. Handbook of Microcomputers in Special Education. (Illus.). 250p. 1984. pap. 25.00 (ISBN 0-933014-35-X). College-Hill.

Behrmann, Michael M., ed. Handbook of Microcomputers in Special Education. 281p. 1984. 22.95 (ISBN 0-933014-35-X). Coun Exc Child.

Besag, Frank P. & Levine, Leonard P. BASIC for Teachers. 1984. pap. 14.95 (ISBN 0-8039-2329-5). Sage.

--Computer Literacy for Teachers. LC 84-6954. 112p. (Orig.). 1984. pap. 9.95 (ISBN 0-8039-2330-9). Sage.

Bitter, Gary G. & Gore, Kay. The Best of Educational Software for Apple II Computers. 375p. 1984. pap. 12.95 (ISBN 0-89588-206-X). SYBEX.

--The Best of Educational Software for the Commodore 64. 250p. 1984. pap. 16.95 (ISBN 0-89588-223-X). SYBEX.

Bork, A., ed. Computer Assisted Learning in Physics Education. LC 80-41129. (Illus.). 80p. 1980. 36.00 (ISBN 0-08-025812-3). Pergamon.

Bork, Alfred. Learning with Computers. (Illus.). 286p. 1981. 28.00 (ISBN 0-932376-11-8, EY-AX014-DP). Digital Pr.

Briefs, U. & Tagg, E. D., eds. Education for System Designer-User Cooperation. 1985. 28.00 (ISBN 0-444-87716-9). Elsevier.

Browning, Ruth & Durbin, Sandra. Computers in the Home Economics Classroom. 1985. 6.00 (ISBN 0-318-04256-8). Home Econ Educ.

Budoff, Milton, et al. Microcomputers in Special Education: An Introduction to Instructional Applications. LC 84-7596. 237p. 1984. 19.95 (ISBN 0-914797-07-7). Brookline Book.

Burke, Robert L. CAI Sourcebook. (Illus.). 160p. 1982. text ed. 19.95 (ISBN 0-13-110155-2). P-H.

--CAI Sourcebook. (Illus.). 224p. 1982. pap. text ed. 12.95 (ISBN 0-13-110148-X). P-H.

Burris, Russell. Computer Network Experiments in Teaching Law. 65p. 1980. 10.00 (ISBN 0-318-14010-1); members 5.00 (ISBN 0-318-14011-X). Educom.

Callison, William L. Using Computers in the Classroom. (Illus.). 192p. 1985. pap. 16.95 (ISBN 0-13-940214-4). P-H.

Carlson, Marthena, et al. A Computer-Assisted Instructional System for Elementary Mathematics. 78p. 1974. 1.00 (ISBN 0-318-14702-5, ED 104 667). Learn Res Dev.

Chambers, Jack & Sprecher, Jerry. Computer Assisted Instruction: Its Use in the Classroom. (Illus.). 240p. 1983. 19.95 (ISBN 0-13-164384-3); pap. 13.95 (ISBN 0-13-164376-2). P-H.

Chan, Julie M. & Korostoff, Marilyn. Teachers' Guide to Designing Classroom Software. LC 84-6962. 95p. (Orig.). 1984. pap. 9.95 (ISBN 0-8039-2313-9). Sage.

Charp, Sylvia, et al. Laymens Guide to the Use of Computers in Education. 2nd Ed. ed. 61p. 1982. pap. 4.00 (ISBN 0-318-16884-7). Assn Educ Data.

Chaya, Ruth K. & Miller, Joan M. More BASIC Programming for the Classroom & Home Teacher (IBM PC, IBM PCjr, Commodore, Apple, Macintosh) 262p. (Orig.). 1985. pap. text ed. 17.95X (ISBN 0-8077-2780-6). Tchrs Coll.

Chew, Charles R., ed. Computers in the English Classroom: Promises & Pitfalls. 148p. 1984. pap. text ed. 5.00 (ISBN 0-930348-11-7). NY St Eng Coun.

Clark, Ron. Fifty-Five Color Computer Programs for the Home, School & Office. 128p. (Orig.). 1982. pap. 9.95 (ISBN 0-86668-005-5). ARCsoft.

Classroom Computer Learning Directory of Educational Resources, 1983-1984. cancelled. Pitman Pub MA.

Clay, Katherine, ed. Microcomputers in Education: A Handbook of Resources. LC 82-12596. 80p. 1982. pap. 27.50 (ISBN 0-89774-064-5). Oryx Pr.

Clements, Douglas H. Computers in Early & Primary Education. (Illus.). 352p. 1985. text ed. 17.95 (ISBN 0-13-164013-5). P-H.

Cline, Hugh F., et al, eds. The Electronic Schoolhouse. 148p. 1985. text ed. 16.50 (ISBN 0-89859-649-1). L Erlbaum Assocs.

Closing the Gap Between Technology & Application: Proceedings. 215p. 20.00 (ISBN 0-318-14008-X); members 10.00 (ISBN 0-318-14009-8). Educom.

Collins, James L. & Sommers, Elizabeth A., eds. Writing-on-Line: Using Computers in the Teaching of Writing. 176p. 1985. pap. text ed. 9.75x (ISBN 0-317-19861-0). Boynton Cook Pubs.

Computers & Students Activities Handbook. 52p. 1985. pap. text ed. write for info. (ISBN 0-88210-163-3). Natl Assn Principals.

Computers in the Learning Environment, 1974. 16.00x (ISBN 0-85012-098-5). Intl Pubns Serv.

Culp, George & Nickles, Herbert N. An Apple for the Teacher: Fundamentals of Instructional Computing. 256p. 1983. pap. text ed. 14.00 pub net (ISBN 0-534-01378-3, 82-24506). Brooks-Cole.

Culp, George H. & Nickles, Herbert L. An Apple for the Teacher: Fundamentals of Instructional Computing. 2nd ed. 275p. 1986. pap. text ed. 15.00 (ISBN 0-534-05832-9). Brooks-Cole.

David, Elaine. A Teacher's Guide to Teaching BASIC in the Elementary Schools. 1982. 5.95 (ISBN 0-318-01731-8). E David Assoc.

Davisson, William I. & Bonello, Frank J. Computer-Assisted Instruction in Economics. LC 76-642. 208p. 1976. text ed. 22.95 (ISBN 0-268-00715-2). U of Notre Dame Pr.

Dean, Chris & Whitlock, Quentin. The Handbook of Computer-Based Training. 250p. 1982. 26.50 (ISBN 0-89397-132-4). Nichols Pub.

Dennis, J. Richard & Kansky, Robert. Instructional Computing: An Action Guide for Educators. 1984. pap. 15.50x (ISBN 0-673-16606-6). Scott F.

Dickson. Apple Teaches Language Arts. (Illus.). 250p. 1984. 17.95 (ISBN 0-8359-0077-0). Reston.

Dickson, Wayne & Raymond, Mike. The Language Arts-Computer Book: A How-to Guide for Teachers. (Illus.). 1983. text ed. 21.95 (ISBN 0-8359-3942-1); pap. 17.95 (ISBN 0-8359-3941-3). Reston.

Digit Magazine Editors. Ace Your Grades with Your Computer. 1985. pap. 8.95 (ISBN 0-671-53060-7, Pub. by Computer Bks). S&S.

Douglas, Shawhan. Physics with the Computer: Teacher's Edition. 288p. (Orig.). 1981. 24.95 (ISBN 0-87567-037-7). Entelek.

Eisele, James E., et al. Computer Assisted Planning of Curriculum & Instruction: How to Use Computer Based Resource Units to Individualize Instruction. LC 78-157844. 144p. 1971. pap. 11.95 (ISBN 0-87778-018-8). Educ Tech Pubns.

EPIE Institute. The Educational Software Selector. 2nd ed. 800p. 1985. 59.95x (ISBN 0-8077-2779-2). Tchrs Coll.

Favaro, P. J. An Educator's Guide to Microcomputers & Learning. (Illus.). 192p. 1985. 19.95 (ISBN 0-13-240839-2); pap. 14.95 (ISBN 0-13-240821-X). P-H.

Ferguson, Richard L. Computer Assistance for Individualizing Measurement. 81p. 1971. 1.50 (ISBN 0-318-14701-7). Learn Res Dev.

Forseth, Sonia D., et al. E-Z Microcomputer Handbook for Elementary Teachers: Programs in BASIC for Mathematics, Science & Reading-Language Arts. 256p. 1984. pap. 24.95 (ISBN 0-13-298415-6). P-H.

Frank, Mary, ed. Young Children in a Computerized Environment. LC 81-20028. (Journal of Children in Contemporary Society Ser.: Vol. 14, No. 1). 96p. 1981. text ed. 20.00 (ISBN 0-86656-108-0, B108). Haworth Pr.

Futrell, Mynga K. & Geisert, Paul. The Well-Trained Computer: Designing Systematic Instructional Materials for the Classroom Microcomputer. LC 84-1629. (Illus.). 290p. 1984. 26.95 (ISBN 0-87778-190-7). Educ Tech Pubns.

Gage, Jennifer. Directory of Computerized Resources in Bilingual Education. 52p. 1982. 5.65 (ISBN 0-317-14965-2). Natl Clearinghse Bilingual Ed.

Geoffrion, Leo D. & Geoffrion, Olga P. Computers & Reading Instruction. LC 83-8727. (Computers in Education). (Illus.). 224p. 1983. pap. 14.95 (ISBN 0-201-10566-7). Addison-Wesley.

Gerver, Elisabeth. Computers & Adult Learning. 128p. 1984. 34.00x (ISBN 0-335-10577-7, Pub. by Open Univ Pr); pap. 13.00x (ISBN 0-335-10423-1, Pub. by Open Univ Pr). Taylor & Francis.

Gill, Peter. Microcomputer Assisted Learning in the Primary School. (Ward Lock Educational Ser.). 29.00x (ISBN 0-7062-4241-6, Pub. by Ward Lock Educational). State Mutual Bk.

Grayson, Fred N. Household Budgeting & Accounting on Your Home Computer. LC 83-26235. (Illus.). 96p. 1984. pap. 5.95 (ISBN 0-399-50986-0, G&D). Putnam Pub Group.

Grubb, R. E. A Design Language for Computer-Assisted Instruction. (Illus.). 155p. 1974. pap. text ed. 20.00 (ISBN 0-87567-103-9). Entelek.

Hagen, Dolores. Microcomputer Resource Book for Special Education: How to Use the Microcomputer with Handicapped Children. 1984. text ed. 21.95 (ISBN 0-8359-4345-3); pap. text ed. 16.95 (ISBN 0-8359-4344-5). Reston.

--Microcomputer Resource Book for Special Education. 224p. 1984. 15.95 (ISBN 0-8359-4344-5). Coun Exc Child.

Hamblen, John W. & Baird, Thomas B. Fourth Inventory of Computing in Higher Education: Statistical Report. 400p. 1979. 25.00 (ISBN 0-318-14024-1); members 15.00 (ISBN 0-318-14025-X). Educom.

Hansen, Viggo P., ed. Computers in Mathematics Education: 1984 Yearbook. LC 84-2037. (Illus.). 256p. 1984. 14.50 (ISBN 0-87353-210-4). NCTM.

Harris, Diana & Nelson-Heern, Laurie, eds. Proceedings of NECC 1981. (Illus., Orig.). 1981. pap. 15.00 (ISBN 0-937114-01-4). Weeg Comp.

Harris, JoAnn, ed. Tested Practices: Computer Assisted Guidance Systems. pap. text ed. 6.00 pkg. of 5 (ISBN 0-686-05000-2). Am Assn Coun Dev.

Heines, Jesse M. Screen Design Strategies for Computer-Assisted Instruction. 196p. 1983. 28.00 (ISBN 0-932376-28-2, EY-00028-DP). Digital Pr.

Hernandez-Logan, Carmella, et al. Computer Support for Education. Reed, R., ed. LC 81-84976. 90p. (Orig.). 1982. 10.95 (ISBN 0-88247-645-9); pap. 6.95 (ISBN 0-88247-635-1). R & E Pubs.

Hickey, A. E. Research Guidelines for Computer-Assisted Instruction. 115p. 1974. 20.00 (ISBN 0-87567-102-0). Entelek.

Hickey, Albert E. Computer-Assisted Instruction: A Summary of Research in Selected Areas. 1975. pap. text ed. 15.00 (ISBN 0-87567-067-9). Entelek.

Hively, Wells, et al, eds. Hively's Choice: A Curriculum Guide to Outstanding Educational Microcomputer Programs for Preschool Through Grade 9 - School Year 1983-84. LC 83-73030. 1983. pap. 19.95 (ISBN 0-8454-8100-2). Continental Pr.

Hoffman, Ruth. Microcomputers & Teachers. 148p. 1983. pap. text ed. 9.95 (ISBN 0-89108-119-4). Love Pub Co.

Hofmeister, Alan. Microcomputer Applications in the Classroom. 1984. pap. text ed. 18.95 (ISBN 0-03-063637-X). HR&W.

Holton, Felicia A. Compukids: A Parent's Guide to Computers & Learning. 1985. 9.95 (ISBN 0-452-25560-0, Plume). NAL.

Hudson, Keith. Introducing CAL: A Practical Guide to Writing Computer Assisted Learning Programs. 200p. 1984. 39.95 (ISBN 0-412-26230-4, NO. 9315, Pub. by Chapman & Hall); pap. 19.95 (ISBN 0-412-26240-1, NO. 9190, Pub. by Chapman & Hall). Methuen Inc.

Human Resources Research Organization. Academic Computing Directory: A Search for Exemplary Institutions Using Computers for Learning & Teaching. (Orig.). 1977. pap. write for info (ISBN 0-686-26204-2). Human Resources.

Hunter, Beverly, et al. Learning Alternatives in U. S. Education: Where Student & Computer Meet. LC 74-31417. 424p. 1975. 29.95 (ISBN 0-87778-078-1). Educ Tech Pubns.

Huntington, John F. Computer-Assisted Instruction Using BASIC. LC 79-539. (Illus.). 240p. 1979. 26.95 (ISBN 0-87778-135-4). Educ Tech Pubns.

International Council for Computers in Education. LOGO in the Classroom. 1984. write for info. Intl Coun Comp.

Jacobson, Eric. The Learning of Number Facts Through Computer Instruction. 60p. 1976. 1.50 (ISBN 0-318-14719-X). Learn Res Dev.

Johansen, Robert, et al. Electronic Education: Using Teleconferencing in Postsecondary Organizations. 176p. 1978. 12.00 (ISBN 0-318-14414-X, R42). Inst Future.

Johnson, Barbara & Johnson, Ronald D. Computer Courseware: Spelling. 41p. (Orig.). 1984. pap. text ed. 39.95 (ISBN 0-88450-900-1, 7093-B). Communication Skill.

Johnson, Cynthia. Microcomputer & the School Counselor. 125p. 1982. pap. text ed. 13.95 (ISBN 0-911547-55-X, 72245W34). Am Assn Coun Dev.

Jones, A. & Weinstock, H. Computer-Based Science Instruction. 376p. 1978. 37.50x (ISBN 90-286-0248-8). Sijthoff & Noordhoff.

Judd, Dorothy H. & Judd, Robert. Mastering the Micro: Using the Microcomputer in the Elementary Classroom. (YA) 1984. pap. 9.95 (ISBN 0-673-15909-4). Scott F.

Kelly, A. V. Microcomputers & the Curriculum. 1984. pap. text ed. 11.00i (ISBN 0-06-318273-4). Har-Row.

Kelly, J. Terence & Anandam, Kamala. Teaching Writing with the Computer as Helper. (Pocket Reader Ser.: No. 2). 56p. 1982. pap. 5.00 ea. (ISBN 0-87117-115-5); pap. 25.00 12 copies. Am Assn Comm Jr Coll.

Kenning, M. J. & Kenning, M-M. An Introduction to Computer Assisted Language Teaching. 1983. pap. 10.95x (ISBN 0-19-437090-9). Oxford U Pr.

Kirby, Dale & Kirby, Sandy. How to Help Your Child Earn Better Grades with Your Home Computer: A Parent's Handbook. 280p. 1984. pap. 9.95 (ISBN 0-88693-152-5). Banbury Bks.

Kleiman, Glenn. Brave New Schools: How Computers Can Change Education. 1984. text ed. 18.95 (ISBN 0-8359-0527-6); pap. text ed. 14.95 (ISBN 0-8359-0526-8). Reston.

Last, Rex W. Language Teaching & the Microcomputer. 192p. 1984. pap. 9.95x (ISBN 0-631-13413-1). Basil Blackwell.

Lathrop, Ann & Goodson, Bobby. Courseware in the Classroom: Selecting, Organizing, & Using Educational Software. 1983. pap. 9.95 (ISBN 0-201-20007-4, Sch Div). Addison-Wesley.

Lawrence, Jackie L. Using the Computer to Learn about Computers. (Illus.). 300p. 1984. 24.95 (ISBN 0-89433-254-6, Dist. by Van Nos Reinhold). Petrocelli.

Learning Achievements. Learning Achievements: Proofamatics Instructors Guide Binder. 1983. 150.00 (ISBN 0-07-054522-7); participants kit 40.00 (ISBN 0-07-054530-8). software 145.00. McGraw.

Lewis, B. & Tagg, E. D., eds. Computers in Education. 876p. 1982. 95.75 (ISBN 0-444-86255-2, North-Holland). Elsevier.

Lewis, R., ed. Involving Micros in Education: Proceedings of the IFIP TC 3 & University of Lancaster Joint Working Conference, Lancaster, England, March 24-26, 1982. 240p. 1982. 36.25 (ISBN 0-444-86459-8, North-Holland). Elsevier.

Lewis, R. & Tagg, E. D., eds. Computer Assisted Learning: Scope, Progress & Limits. vii, 223p. 1981. pap. text ed. 16.00x (ISBN 0-435-77700-9). Heinemann Ed.

Lindelow, John. Administrator's Guide to Computers in the Classroom. LC 83-80834. x, 54p. (Orig.). 1983. pap. 5.50 (ISBN 0-86552-084-4). U of Oreg ERIC.

Logan, Robert. Instructional Systems Development: An International View of Theory & Practice. (Educational Technology Ser.). 304p. 1982. 39.50 (ISBN 0-12-455450-4). Acad Pr.

McKenzie, J., et al, eds. Interactive Computer Graphics in Science Teaching. LC 78-40598. (Computers & Their Applications Ser.). 247p. 1978. 42.95x (ISBN 0-470-26419-5). Halsted Pr.

Maddison, John. Education in the Microelectronics Era. LC 99-943832. 208p. 1983. pap. 13.00x (ISBN 0-335-10182-8, Pub. by Open Univ Pr). Taylor & Francis.

--Information Technology & Education. 320p. 1982. 38.00x (ISBN 0-335-10183-6, Pub. by Open Univ Pr). Taylor & Francis.

Masie, Elliott & Stein, Michele. Using Computers in College Student Activities. (National Student Leadership Center Ser.). 104p. 1984. pap. 12.95 (ISBN 0-913393-16-9). Sagamore.

Mason, George E. & Blanchard, Jay S. Computer Applications in Reading. 2nd ed. 215p. (Orig.). 1983. pap. 8.00 (ISBN 0-87207-936-8, 936). Intl Reading.

Megarry, Jacquetta, et al, eds. World Yearbook of Education, 1982-83: Computers & Education. LC 82-12414. (Illus.). 350p. 1983. 36.00 (ISBN 0-89397-138-3). Nichols Pub.

Meredith, Joseph C. The CAI Author-Instructor: An Introduction & Guide to the Preparation of Computer-Assisted Instruction Materials. LC 70-125876. 144p. 1971. 19.95 (ISBN 0-87778-014-5). Educ Tech Pubns.

Metzger, Daniel L. Twenty-Two Microcomputer Projects to Build, Use & Learn. (Illus.). 272p. text ed. 24.95 (ISBN 0-13-934720-8); pap. text ed. 25.95 (ISBN 0-13-934712-7). P-H.

Microcomputers & Health Education. 1983. 6.00 (ISBN 0-317-06642-0, 240-27112). AAHPERD.

Microcomputers & Special Education. 1984. 84.00 (ISBN 0-89568-458-6). Spec Learn Corp.

Microcomputers Directory: Applications in Educational Settings. 1983. write for info. Harvard U Pr.

Microcomputers Go to School. LC 84-123. 180p. 1984. pap. text ed. 16.95 (ISBN 0-931028-53-1). Teach'em.

Microcomputers in Education: Papers of the Online Conference, Mersey Micro Shoe, 1980. 55p. 1980. softcover 23.00x (ISBN 0-903796-64-3). Taylor & Francis.

Microcomputers in Primary Education, Univ. of Exeter, April 1981. Microcomputers & Children in the Primary School: Papers. Garland, Roy, ed. 226p. 1982. text ed. 30.00x (ISBN 0-905273-33-8, Pub. by Falmer Pr); pap. 16.00x (ISBN 0-905273-32-X, Pub. by Falmer Pr). Taylor & Francis.

Miller, Joan M. & Chaya, Ruth K. BASIC Programming for the Classroom & Home Teacher. 262p. 1982. pap. text ed. 17.95x (ISBN 0-8077-2728-8). Tchrs Coll.

Milner, Joseph O., ed. Micro to Main Frame Computers in English Education. 41p. 1982. pap. 3.00 (ISBN 0-8141-3156-5). NCTE.

Mosmann, Charles. Evaluating Instructional Computing: Measuring Needs & Resources for Computing in Higher Education. 88p. 1977. 12.00 (ISBN 0-318-14018-7); members 6.00 (ISBN 0-318-14019-5). Educom.

Mowe, Richard & Ronald, Mummaw. The Academic Commodore 64. 1984. pap. text ed. 15.95 (ISBN 0-8359-0017-7). Reston.

Nathan, Joe. Micro-Myths: Exploring the Limits of Learning with Computers. 144p. (Orig.). 1985. pap. 7.95 (ISBN 0-86683-967-4, AY8542). Winston Pr.

National Council of Teachers of Mathematics. Teaching with Microcomputers. 88p. 1983. pap. 4.00 (ISBN 0-686-46853-8). NCTM.

Newman, Isadore, ed. Computer-Assisted Instructions. Four Selected Articles & a Cross Referenced, Annotated Bibliography. 141p. 1975. pap. text ed. 4.00 (ISBN 0-917180-03-8). I Newman.

Nickles, Herbert & Culp, George. Instructional Computing with the TRS-80. 300p. 1984. pap. write for info. Wadsworth Pub.

Nickles, Herbert & Culp, George H. Instructional Computing with the TRS-80. LC 83-10160. 288p. 1983. pap. text ed. 14.00 pub net (ISBN 0-534-02966-3). Brooks-Cole.

Nievergelt, Jurg & Ventura, Andrea. Small Programs for Small Machines: Computers & Education. LC 84-28338. 240p. 1985. pap. write for info. (ISBN 0-201-11129-2). Addison-Wesley.

North American Perspective: Computing & Networks in Canada & the United States: Proceedings. 222p. 12.00 (ISBN 0-318-14026-8); members 6.00 (ISBN 0-318-14027-6). Educom.

Oettinger, Anthony G. & Marks, Sema. Run, Computer, Run: The Mythology of Educational Innovation-An Essay. LC 71-78522. (Studies in Technology & Society). 1969. 20.00x (ISBN 0-674-78041-8). Harvard U Pr.

O'Neil, Harold F., ed. Computer-Based Instruction: A State-of-the-Art Assessment. (Educational Technology Ser.). 1981. 35.00 (ISBN 0-12-526760-6). Acad Pr.

--Procedures for Instructional Systems Development. LC 79-12002. (Educational Technology Ser.). 1979. 32.50 (ISBN 0-12-526660-X). Acad Pr.

O'Neill, Harold F. Effects of Stress on State Anxiety & Performance in Computer-Assisted Learning. LC 79-136729. 1970. 25.00 (ISBN 0-403-04525-8). Scholarly.

Orwig, Gary. Creating Computer Programs for Learning: A Guide for Trainers, Parents & Teachers. 1983. pap. 15.95 (ISBN 0-8359-1168-3). Reston.

O'Shea, Tim & Self, John. Learning & Teaching with Computers: The Artificial Intelligence Revolution. 336p. 1983. 18.95 (ISBN 0-13-527770-1); pap. 12.95 (ISBN 0-13-527762-0). P-H.

Pantiel, Mindy & Petersen, Becky. The Senior High Computer Connection. LC 85-3660. (Illus.). 272p. 1985. pap. 18.95 (ISBN 0-13-806530-6). P-H.

Papert, Seymour. Mindstorms: Children, Computers, & Powerful Ideas. LC 79-5200. 1982. 15.95x (ISBN 0-465-04627-4); pap. 6.95 (ISBN 0-465-04629-0). Basic.

Parent-Teacher's Microcomputing Sourcebook for Children, 1985. 846p. 1985. pap. 19.95 (ISBN 0-8352-1959-3). Bowker.

Park, Roger & Burris, Russell. Computer-Aided Instruction in Law: Theories, Techniques, & Trepidations. 50p. (Reprinted from 1978 ABF Res. J., No. 1). 1978. 2.50 (ISBN 0-317-33322-4). Am Bar Foun.

Park, Roger C. Computer-Aided Exercises in Civil Procedure. 2nd ed. LC 83-16815. (Misc. Ser.). 167p. 1983. pap. text ed. 9.95 (ISBN 0-314-76495-X). West Pub.

Paterson, Dale. Intelligent Schoolhouse: Readings on Computers & Learning. 1984. text ed. 18.95 (ISBN 0-8359-3108-0); pap. text ed. 14.95 (ISBN 0-8359-3107-2). Reston.

Planning for Computing in Higher Education: Proceedings. 240p. 25.00 (ISBN 0-318-14028-4); members 15.00 (ISBN 0-318-14029-2). Educom.

Pogrow, Stanley. Education in the Computer Age. LC 83-11213. 232p. 1983. 25.00 (ISBN 0-8039-1992-1). Sage.

Poirot, James & Norris, Cathleen. Computers & Mathematics. 2nd ed. (Illus.). 1985. text ed. 27.95 (ISBN 0-88408-424-8). Sterling Swift.

Policies, Strategies & Plans for Computing in Higher Education: Proceedings. 200p. 12.00 (ISBN 0-318-14030-6); members 6.00 (ISBN 0-318-14031-4). Educom.

Radin, Stephen & Greenberg, Harold M. Computer Literacy for School Administrators. LC 82-48597. 288p. 1983. 28.00x (ISBN 0-669-06330-4). Lexington Bks.

Radin, Stephen & Lee, Fayvian. Computers in the Classroom: A Survival Guide for Teachers. 296p. 1984. pap. text ed. 16.95 (ISBN 0-574-23105-6, 13-6105). SRA.

Razik, Taher A., ed. Bibliography of Programmed Instruction & Computer Assisted Instruction. LC 76-125875. (Educational Technology Bibliography Ser.: Vol.1). 288p. 1971. 26.95 (ISBN 0-87778-013-7). Educ Tech Pubns.

Readings in Microcomputers & Individualized Educational Programs. 1984. 16.00 (ISBN 0-89568-418-7). Spec Learn Corp.

Readings in Microcomputers & the Gifted Child. 1984. 16.00 (ISBN 0-89568-404-7). Spec Learn Corp.

The Reality of National Computer Networking for Higher Education. 200p. 16.00 (ISBN 0-318-14032-2); members 9.00 (ISBN 0-318-14033-0). Educom.

Reidesel, C. Alan & Clements, Douglas. Coping with Computers in the Elementary & Middle Schools. (Illus.). 384p. 1985. pap. text ed. 22.95 (ISBN 0-13-172420-7). P-H.

Reynolds, Angus & Davis, Dick. Computer-Based Learning: A Self-Teaching Guide. 256p. 1985. pap. 15.95 (ISBN 0-471-80227-1, Pub. by Wiley Pr). Wiley.

Riley, John T. & Hurtz, Judie. Organizing Your Computer Program: Lab vs Classroom Usage. (Illus.). 26p. 1983. pap. 7.95 (ISBN 0-912007-04-4). Computer Direct.

Riley, John T. & Hurtz, Judie L. Student Involvement-Implementing: A Computer Tutor Program. 21p. (Orig.). 1983. pap. 7.95 (ISBN 0-912007-01-X). Computer Direct.

Roman, Richard A. Teaching Problem Solving & Mathematics by Computer: An Interim Report. 63p. 1974. 1.50 (ISBN 0-318-14743-2, ED 101 690). Learn Res Dev.

Rushby, N. J., ed. Computer Based Learning. (Infotech Computer State of the Art Reports: Vol. 11, No. 4). 400p. 1983. 445.00 (ISBN 0-08-028575-9). Pergamon.

--Selected Readings in Computer-Based Learning. 220p. 1981. 32.50x (ISBN 0-89397-101-4). Nichols Pub.

Russell, Terry. Computers in the Primary School. (Illus., Orig.). 1985. pap. 19.95 (ISBN 0-7121-0451-8). Trans Atlantic.

Sagan, Hans. Calculus Accompanied by the Apple. 1984. pap. 16.95 (ISBN 0-8359-0633-7). Reston.

Sage, Edwin R. Problem Solving with the Computer. (Illus.). 244p. (Orig.). 1969. pap. 14.95 (ISBN 0-87567-030-X). Entelek.

Sarapin, Marvin I. & Post, Paul E. Computer Programs for Industrial Arts-Technology Education. LC 83-25464. 192p. (Orig.). 1984. 12.50 (ISBN 0-87006-460-6); pap. 16.00 ref. ed. Goodheart.

Sass, Richard E. A Computer-Based Instructional Management Program for Classroom Use. 70p. 1971. 1.50 (ISBN 0-318-14703-3, E D 052 621). Learn Res Dev.

Sauve, Deborah A. & Schnuer, Susan. Computer-Assisted Instruction: Learning Online. 103p. 1984. 7.40 (ISBN 0-89763-103-X). Natl Clearinghse Bilingual Ed.

Sedlik, Jay M. Systems Engineering of Education: Systems Techniques for Pretesting Mediated Instructional Materials, No. 14. LC 79-162916. (Illus.). 1971. text ed. 18.00 (ISBN 0-87657-112-7). Ed & Training.

Self, John. Microcomputers in Educations: A Critical Evaluation of Educational Software. 192p. 1985. 18.50 (ISBN 0-7108-0936-0, Pub. by Salem Acad). Merrimack Pub Cir.

Shockley, Robert & Cutlip, Glen. Excelling: Raising Your Grades with High Tech. 1985. 8.97 (ISBN 0-8239-0646-9). Rosen Group.

Siegel, Martin, et al. Computer As a Teacher. Rothman, J., ed. 250p. 1985. text ed. 11.95 (ISBN 0-394-33474-4). Random.

Silvern, Leonard C. Fundamentals of Teaching Machine & Programmed Learning Systems Guide. LC 64-20647. (Illus.). 1964. 10.00 (ISBN 0-87657-118-6). Ed & Training.

Chang, S. L. Fundamentals Handbook of Electrical & Computer Engineering, 3 Vols. 1983. 189.95 (ISBN 0-471-89690-X). Wiley.

Chang, Sheldon S. L. Fundamentals Handbook of Electrical & Computer Engineering: Communications, Control, Devices & Systems, Vol. 2. LC 82-4872. 737p. 1983. 74.95x (ISBN 0-471-86213-4). Wiley.

--Fundamentals Handbook of Electrical & Computer Engineering: Vol. 1: Circuits, Fields, & Electronics. LC 82-4872. 707p. 1982. 74.95x (ISBN 0-471-86215-0, Pub. by Wiley-Interscience). Wiley.

--Fundamentals Handbook of Electrical & Computer Engineering: Vol. 3: Computer Hardware, Software & Applications. LC 82-4872. 507p. 1982. 71.50 (ISBN 0-471-86214-2, Pub. by Wiley-Interscience). Wiley.

Chen, Peter. The Entity-Relationship Approach to Logical Data Base Design. Curtice, Robert M., ed. (Data Base Monograph Ser.: No. 6). 1977. pap. text ed. 15.00 (ISBN 0-89435-020-X). QED Info Sci.

Chinitz, M. Paul. Logic Design of Computers: An Introduction. LC 81-50566. 416p. 1981. pap. 15.95 (ISBN 0-672-21800-3, 21800). Sams.

Cogdell, J. R. An Introduction to Circuits & Electronics. (Illus.). 560p. 1986. text ed. 38.95 (ISBN 0-13-479346-3). P-H.

Cohoon, James P. Algorithms for Some Design Automation Problems. Stone, Harold, ed. LC 84-24101. (Computer Science: Computer Architecture & Design Ser.: No. 3). 113p. 1985. 34.95 (ISBN 0-8357-1615-5). UMI Res Pr.

Cole, A. J. Macro Processors. 2nd ed. LC 81-10068. (Cambridge Computer Science Texts Ser.: No. 4). 240p. 1982. 29.95 (ISBN 0-521-24259-2); pap. 14.95 (ISBN 0-521-28560-7). Cambridge U Pr.

Colloms, Martin. Computer Controlled Testing & Instrumentation: An Introduction to the IEC-625: IEEE-488 Bus. 151p. 1983. 27.95x (ISBN 0-470-27406-9). Halsted Pr.

Computer & Business Equipment Manufacturers Association. The Computer & Business Equipment Industry Marketing Data Book. 177p. (Orig.). 1983. pap. 55.50 (ISBN 0-912797-02-9). CBEMA.

Computer FX 'Eighty-Four: Computer Animation & Digital Effects. 213p. 1984. pap. text ed. 100.00x (ISBN 0-86353-013-3, Pub. by Online). Brookfield Pub Co.

Configuring Distributed Computer Systems. 1981. pap. 5.00 (ISBN 0-918734-28-2). Reymont.

Cullingford, Richard E. Natural Language Processing: A Knowledge Engineering Approach. (Computer Science Ser.). 400p. 1985. 29.95x (ISBN 0-8476-7358-8). Rowman & Allanheld.

Deasington, R. J. A Practical Guide to Computer Communications & Networking. LC 84-4617. (Computers & Their Applications Ser.: 1-403). 126p. 1984. pap. text ed. 24.95x (ISBN 0-470-20078-2). Halsted Pr.

Director, S. W., ed. Computer-Aided Circuit Design: Simulation & Optimization. LC 73-16060. (Benchmark Papers in Electrical Engineering & Computer Science: Vol. 5). 380p. 1974. 51.95 (ISBN 0-87933-068-6). Van Nos Reinhold.

Dobelis, M. C. Bridging the Gap Between Computer Technicians & Users. (Illus.). 1976. pap. 0.50 (ISBN 0-918230-05-5). Barnstable.

Dolan, Kathleen. Business Computer Systems Design. 336p. 1984. pap. text ed. 13.95x (ISBN 0-938188-20-8). Mitchell Pub.

Doll, Dixon R. Data Communications: Facilities, Networks & System Design. 493p. 1978. 34.50 (ISBN 0-686-98099-9). Telecom Lib.

Dudewicz, Edward J. & Karian, Zaven A. Tutorial: Modern Design & Analysis of Discrete-Event Computer Simulations. 500p. 1985. 45.00 (ISBN 0-8186-0597-9); prepub. 36.00 (ISBN 0-317-31782-2). IEEE Comp Soc.

Eckols, Steve. How to Design & Develop Business Systems: A Practical Approach to Analysis, Design & Implementation. LC 83-62380. (Illus.). 279p. (Orig.). 1983. pap. 20.00 (ISBN 0-911625-14-3). M Murach & Assoc.

Eliason, Alan L. Mason Oaks: An Online Case Study in Business Systems Design. 128p. 1981. pap. text ed. 9.95 (ISBN 0-574-21310-4, 13-4310); instr's guide avail. (ISBN 0-574-21311-2, 13-4311). SRA.

--Royal Pines: An On-Line Case Study in Business Systems Design. 144p. (Orig.). 1984. pap. text ed. 9.95 (ISBN 0-574-21700-2, 13-4700); write for info. tchr's ed. (ISBN 0-317-03528-2, 13-4701). SRA.

Engineering Computer Forum 1980. 502p. 1981. 10.00 (ISBN 0-317-34105-7, 04068010). Edison Electric.

Engineering Staff of Archive. Streaming. (Illus.). 196p. (Orig.). pap. 14.95 (ISBN 0-9608810-0-X). Archive Corp.

Flynn, M. J., et al, eds. Microcomputer System Design: An Advanced Course, Dublin, 1981. 2nd ed. (Springer Study Edition). vii, 397p. 1984. pap. 19.95 (ISBN 0-387-13545-6). Springer-Verlag.

Foundyller, Charles M. CAD-CAM Minisystem Report: A Guide to Ready-to-Use Design & Drafting Systems under 100,000 Dollars. (Illus.). 275p. 1983. cancelled (ISBN 0-938484-05-2). Daratech.

Fujiwara, Hideo. Logic Testing & Design for Testability. (Series in Computer Systems). (Illus.). 304p. 1985. text ed. 35.00x (ISBN 0-262-06096-5). MIT Pr.

Gallawa, Robert L. On the Viability of 1300 Operation in the MX-C3 Program. 1980. 50.00 (ISBN 0-686-39231-0). Info Gatekeepers.

Giloi, W. K. & Shriver, B. D., eds. Methodologies for Computer System Design: Proceedings of the IFIP WG 10.1 Working Conference on Methodologies for Computer System Design, Lille, France, 15-17 September, 1983. 344p. 1985. 55.75 (ISBN 0-444-87687-1, North-Holland). Elsevier.

Glover, Fred, et al. Improved Computer-Based Planning Techniques. 1977. 2.50 (ISBN 0-686-64189-2). U CO Busn Res Div.

Gorsline, George W. Computer Organization: Hardware-Software. (Illus.). 400p. 1986. text ed. 36.95 (ISBN 0-13-165325-3). P-H.

Gunther, Richard C. A Management Methodology for Software Product Engineering. LC 78-711. 379p. 1978. 43.95x (ISBN 0-471-33600-9, Pub. by Wiley-Interscience). Wiley.

Haralick, R. M., ed. Pictorial Data Analysis. (NATO ASI Series F: Computer & Systems Sciences, No. 4). 480p. 1983. 49.70 (ISBN 0-387-12288-5). Springer-Verlag.

Harper, Dennis O. & Stewart, James H. Run: Computer Education. 1983. pub net 14.00 (ISBN 0-534-01265-5, 82-12933). Brooks-Cole.

Haueisen, William D. & Camp, James L. Business Systems for Microcomputers: Concept, Design & Implications. (Series in Data Processing Management). (Illus.). 480p. 1982. text ed. 31.95 (ISBN 0-13-107805-4). P-H.

Hayes, John. Computer Organization & Architecture. (Illus.). 1978. text ed. 41.95 (ISBN 0-07-027363-4). McGraw.

Hayes-Roth, Frederick, et al. Building Expert Systems. LC 82-24511. (Teknowledge Ser.). (Illus.). 1983. 36.95 (ISBN 0-201-10686-8). Addison-Wesley.

Heath, F. G. Computer Engineering: A Guide to the Study of Paper 346 of the CEI Examinations. (PPL Study Guide Ser.: No. 6). (Illus.). pap. 20.00 (ISBN 0-317-09258-8, 2011895). Bks Demand UMI.

Heinlein, Robert. The Past Through Tomorrow. 832p. 1984. pap. 3.95 (ISBN 0-425-07994-5). Berkley Pub.

Henderson. System Design. (Infotech Computer State of the Art Reports). 1981. 405.00 (ISBN 0-08-028559-7). Pergamon.

Hill, Frederick J. & Peterson, Gerald R. Digital Systems: Hardware Organization & Design. 2nd ed. LC 78-7209. 701p. 1978. text ed. 46.75 (ISBN 0-471-39608-7); write for info. tchrs. ed. (ISBN 0-471-03694-3). Wiley.

Hoernes, G. & Heilweil, M. Introduction to Boolean Algebra & Logic Design: A Program for Self-Instruction. 1964. pap. text ed. 27.95 (ISBN 0-07-029183-7). McGraw.

Hosier. Structured Analysis & Design, 2 vols. (Infotech Computer State of the Art Reports). 646p. 1978. Set. 125.00 (ISBN 0-08-028543-0). Pergamon.

Hufault, J. R. OP AMP Network Design Manual. 448p. 1985. 37.00 (ISBN 0-471-81327-3). Wiley.

Hugo. Fourth Generation. (Infotech Computer State of the Art Reports). 501p. 1971. 310.00 (ISBN 0-08-028550-3). Pergamon.

Hurley, Richard B. Decision Tables in Software Engineering. (VNR Data Processing Ser.). 184p. 1982. text ed. 22.95 (ISBN 0-442-23599-2); disks for Apple II & IBM-PC 59.50 ea. (ISBN 0-442-23666-2). Van Nos Reinhold.

IEEE Standard 729-1983: IEEE Standard Glassary of Software Engineering Terminology. 1983. 7.50 (ISBN 0-317-03952-0, SHO8920). IEEE Comp Soc.

Iliffe, J. Advanced Computer Design. 41.95 (ISBN 0-13-011254-2). P-H.

Infotech. International Survey, 3 vols. (Infotech Computer State of the Art Reports). 466p. 1978. Set. 835.00 (ISBN 0-08-028532-5). Pergamon.

--Structured Software Development, 2 vols. (Infotech Computer State of the Art Reports). 580p. 1979. 145.00 (ISBN 0-08-028529-5). Pergamon.

Ingels. What Every Engineer Should Know about Computer Modeling & Simulation. (What Every Engineer Should Know Ser.). 256p. 1985. 27.50 (ISBN 0-8247-7444-2). Dekker.

Ingevaldsson, Leif. Jackson Structured Programming: A Practical Method of Program Design. 194p. (Orig.). 1979. pap. text ed. 19.95x (ISBN 0-317-02803-0, Pub. by Chartwell-Bratt England). Brookfield Pub Co.

Interface Workshop. Software Engineering Education: Needs & Objectives. Wasserman, A. I. & Freeman, P., eds. (Illus.). 1976. pap. 18.00 (ISBN 0-387-90216-3). Springer-Verlag.

Jackson, Herbert. Introduction to Electric Circuits. 6th ed. (Illus.). 800p. 1986. text ed. 37.95 (ISBN 0-13-481425-8). P-H.

Kableshkov, Stoyan O. The Anthropocentric Approach to Computing & Reactive Machines. LC 82-24836. (Computer Engineering Research Ser.). 144p. 1983. 42.95x (ISBN 0-471-90140-7, Res Stud Pr). Wiley.

Kartashev, Svetland & Kartashev, Steven. Designing & Programming Modern Computers & Systems. (LSI Modular Computer Systems Ser.: Vol. I). (Illus.). 736p. 1982. text ed. 47.50 (ISBN 0-13-201343-6). P-H.

Kidder, Tracy. The Soul of a New Machine. Large Print ed. LC 81-23223. 471p. 1982. Repr. 13.95x (ISBN 0-89621-342-0). Thorndike Pr.

--The Soul of a New Machine. 304p. 1982. pap. 3.95 (ISBN 0-380-59931-7, 60029-3). Avon.

Kolence, Kenneth W., ed. CPU Power Analysis Report. LC 76-12687. 300p. 1977. 275.00 (ISBN 0-931900-02-6). Inst Info Mgmt.

Kulp, Russel C., ed. EMS Communications: Utilizing the New Hardware & Systems Technology. (Emergency Health Services Quarterly Ser.: Vol. 1, No. 2). (Illus.). 67p. 1982. pap. text ed. 15.00 (ISBN 0-917724-56-9, B56). Haworth Pr.

Laden, Hyman N. & Gildersleeve, T. R. System Design for Computer Applications. LC 63-17363. pap. 84.00 (ISBN 0-317-09782-2, 2007075). Bks Demand UMI.

Lavington, S. H. Processor Architecture. (Illus.). 136p. 1976. pap. 15.50x (ISBN 0-85012-154-X). Intl Pubns Serv.

Lavington, Simon H. Logical Design of Computers: A Course of Twelve Television Lectures. 2nd ed. 58p. 1969. pap. 10.00 (ISBN 0-7190-0480-2, Pub. by Manchester Univ Pr). Longwood Pub Group.

Liao, Thomas T. & Miller, David C., eds. Systems Approach to Instructional Design. LC 77-86497. (Technology of Learning Systems Ser.: Vol. 1). (Illus.). 1978. pap. 10.00x (ISBN 0-89503-004-7). Baywood Pub.

Mariani, Michael P. & Palmer, David F. Distributed System Design. (Tutorial Texts Ser.). 409p. 1979. 27.00 (ISBN 0-8186-0267-8, Q267). IEEE Comp Soc.

Mazda, F. F. Components of Computers. 100p. 1980. 75.00x (ISBN 0-901150-04-5, Pub. by Electrochemical Scotland). State Mutual Bk.

Miller, Webb. The Engineering of Numerical Software. LC 84-9830. (Computational Mathematics Ser.). (Illus.). 192p. 1985. text ed. 33.95 (ISBN 0-13-279043-2). P-H.

Murray. User Friendly Systems. (Infotech Computer State of the Art Reports). 439p. 1981. 405.00 (ISBN 0-08-028557-0). Pergamon.

Nadler, Gerald, et al. Design Concepts for Information Systems. Rev. ed. 1983. 13.00 (ISBN 0-89806-015-X, 107). Inst Indus Eng.

Nashelsky, Louis. Introduction to Digital Computer Technology. 3rd ed. LC 82-13377. 536p. 1983. 29.95 (ISBN 0-471-09646-6, VT30); tchrs.' manual avail. (ISBN 0-471-89528-8). Wiley.

Newkirk, John A. & Mathews, Robert G. The VLSI Designer's Library. (VLSI Systems Ser.). (Illus.). 200p. 1983. pap. 32.95 (ISBN 0-201-05444-2). Addison-Wesley.

Nordbotten, Joan C. The Analysis & Design of Computer-Based Information Systems. LC 84-80455. 650p. 1985. text ed. 25.00 (ISBN 0-395-35707-1); instr's manual 2.00 (ISBN 0-395-37806-0). HM.

Ogdin, Carol A. Microcomputer System Design & Techniques. (Tutorial Texts Ser.). 374p. 1980. 24.00 (ISBN 0-8186-0259-7, Q259). IEEE Comp Soc.

Operation Update Series in Microprocessors & Micro-Minicomputers: Design & Application, 8 bks. 1981. Set. 95.00 (ISBN 0-07-079299-2). McGraw.

Ort, Harry H. Structured Data Processing Design. LC 84-14506. 224p. 1985. pap. 16.95 (ISBN 0-201-05425-6). Addison-Wesley.

Overmars, M. H. The Design of Dynamic Data Structures. (Lecture Notes in Computer Science: Vol. 156). 181p. 1983. pap. 12.00 (ISBN 0-387-12330-X). Springer-Verlag.

Peatman, J. B. Microcomputer-Based Design. 1977. 43.95 (ISBN 0-07-049138-0). McGraw.

Powers, Michael J., et al. Computer Information Systems Development: Analysis & Design. 1984. text ed. 21.95 (ISBN 0-538-10820-7, J82). SW Pub.

Preparata, Franko. Introduction to Computer Engineering. 315p. 1984. text ed. 35.50 scp (ISBN 0-06-045271-4, HarpC). Har-Row.

Ralston, Anthony & Reilly, Edwin D., Jr. Encyclopedia of Computer Science & Engineering. 2nd ed. (Illus.). 1678p. 1982. 87.50 (ISBN 0-442-24496-7). Van Nos Reinhold.

Rudman, Jack. Computer Technician. (Teachers License Examination Ser.: T-67). (Cloth bdg. avail. on request). pap. 13.95 (ISBN 0-8373-8087-1). Natl Learning.

Sangiovanni-Vincentelli, Alberto, ed. Advances in Computer-Aided Engineering Design, Vol. 1. 1983. 45.00 (ISBN 0-89232-400-7). Jai Pr.

Sargent, Murray, III & Shoemaker, Richard. The IBM PC from the Inside Out. 288p. 1983. pap. 16.95 (ISBN 0-201-06896-6). Addison-Wesley.

Sherwood. Interactive Computing. (Infotech Computer State of the Art Reports). 548p. 1972. 85.00s (ISBN 0-08-028536-8). Pergamon.

Shiva, Sajjan G. Computer Design & Architecture. 1984. text ed. 37.95 (ISBN 0-316-78714-0); tchr's. ed. avail. (ISBN 0-316-78715-9). Little.

Siebert, William. Circuits, Signals & Systems. (Electrical Engineering Computer Science Dept. Textbook Ser.). (Illus.). 600p. 1984. text ed. 35.00x (ISBN 0-262-19229-2). MIT Pr.

Smith, William V. Electronic Information Processing. LC 73-81245. (Modern Frontiers in Applied Science). (Illus.). 138p. 1974. 20.00 (ISBN 0-89006-038-X). Artech Hse.

Swann, Gloria H. Top Down Structured Design Techniques. LC 77-27092. (PBI Series for Computer & Data Processing Professionals). 1978. text ed. 15.00 (ISBN 0-89433-094-2); pap. 11.50 (ISBN 0-89433-019-5). Petrocelli.

Teja, Edward R. Teaching Your Computer to Talk: A Manual of Command & Response. (Illus.). 208p. pap. 8.95 (ISBN 0-8306-1330-7, 1330). TAB Bks.

Thorin, Marc. Software Engineering. (Illus.). 136p. 1985. pap. text ed. 18.95 (ISBN 0-408-01426-1). Butterworth.

Tomek, Ivan. Introduction to Computer Organization Workbook. (Illus., Orig.). 1981. pap. text ed. 9.95 (ISBN 0-914894-70-6). Computer Sci.

Townsend. Digital Computer & Design. 2nd ed. 1982. pap. text ed. 24.95 (ISBN 0-408-01155-6). Butterworth.

Toy, Wing & Zee, Benjamin. Computer Hardware-Software Architecture. (Illus.). 464p. 1986. text ed. 35.00 (ISBN 0-13-163502-6). P-H.

Turner, Ray. Software Engineering Methodology. 1984. text ed. 21.95 (ISBN 0-8359-7022-1). Reston.

U. S. Third-Party Maintenance Market for Computer Datacom Equipment. (Reports Ser.: No. 512). 145p. 1982. 985.00x (ISBN 0-88694-512-7). Intl Res Dev.

Utley, B. G. IBM System-38: Technical Developments. (IBM Systems Design & Development Ser.). (Illus.). 109p. 1980. pap. 6.60 (ISBN 0-933186-03-7, G-580-0237-1). IBM Armonk.

Vick, Charles R., ed. Handbook of Software Engineering. Ramamoorthy, C. V. 768p. 1983. 62.50 (ISBN 0-442-26251-5). Van Nos Reinhold.

Vince. Computer Operations. (Infotech Computer State of the Art Reports). 314p. 1982. 445.00 (ISBN 0-08-028567-8). Pergamon.

Warman, E. A. Computer Applications in Production & Engineering. 1983. 95.00 (ISBN 0-444-86614-0, I-406-83). Elsevier.

Wasserman, Anthony I. Programming Language Design. (Tutorial Texts Ser.). 527p. 1980. 30.00 (ISBN 0-8186-0312-7, Q312); members 18.00. IEEE Comp Soc.

--Software Development Environments. (Tutorial Texts Ser.). 476p. 1981. 30.00 (ISBN 0-8186-0385-2, Q385). IEEE Comp Soc.

Weiner, Roberta, ed. Computers, Productivity & Management in Construction. 3rd ed. 117.00 (ISBN 0-686-42716-5). Constr Ind Pr.

Wells, M. Computing Systems Hardware. LC 75-27263. (Cambridge Computer Science Texts Ser.: No. 6). (Illus.). 225p. 1976. 18.95x (ISBN 0-521-29034-1). Cambridge U Pr.

White. Future Systems, 2 vols. 700p. 1972. Set. pap. 105.00fs (ISBN 0-08-028534-1). Pergamon.

--System Tuning. (Infotech Computer State of the Art Reports). 510p. 1977. 85.00 (ISBN 0-08-028520-1). Pergamon.

Whitney, Patrick F. & Kent, Cheryl, eds. Design in the Information Environment: How Computing Is Changing the Problems, Processes & Theories of Design. 192p. 1986. pap. text ed. 10.95 (ISBN 0-317-18603-5, KnopfC). Knopf.

Wiatrowski, Claude A. & House, Charles H. Logic Circuits & Microcomputer Systems. Cerra, Frank J., ed. (McGraw-Hill Series in Electrical Engineering: Computer Engineering & Switching Theory-Electronics & Electronic Circuits). (Illus.). 512p. 1980. text ed. 42.00 (ISBN 0-07-070090-7). McGraw.

Williams, Bernard O. & Burch, John L., eds. Human Foundations of Advanced Computing Technology: The Guide to the Select Literature. LC 85-60628. (Orig.). 1985. pap. 75.00 (ISBN 0-916313-09-3). Report.

Y-Fourteen Report, No. 3: Guideline for Documenting of Computer Systems in Computer - Aided Preparation of Product Definition Data - Design Requirements Book No. N00079. 1977. pap. text ed. 2.50 (ISBN 0-685-81930-2). ASME.

Yao, S. B. & Kunii, T. L., eds. Data Base Design Techniques II: Physical Structures & Applications Tokyo 1979: Proceedings. (Lecture Notes in Computer Sciences: Vol. 133). 170p. 1982. pap. 14.00 (ISBN 0-387-11215-4). Springer-Verlag.

Yao, S. B., et al, eds. Data Base Design Technique I: Requirements & Logical Structures New York 1978: Proceedings. (Lecture Notes in Computer Sciences: Vol. 132). 227p. 1982. pap. 16.00 (ISBN 0-387-11214-6). Springer-Verlag.

Young, S. J. Real Time Language Design & Development. (Computers & Their Applications Ser.). 352p. 1982. 85.95 (ISBN 0-470-27343-7). Halsted Pr.

COMPUTER GAMES

Here are entered works on games played on a computer. works on the application of computers and data processing techniques to games in general, including recording statistics, setting up tournaments, etc., are entered under games–data processing.

Ahl, David H. & North, Steve. More BASIC Computer Games. LC 78-74958. (Illus.). 186p. 1979. pap. 7.95 (ISBN 0-916688-09-7, 6C2). Creative Comp.

Ahl, David H., ed. BASIC Computer Games: Microcomputer Edition. LC 78-50028. (Illus.). 180p. 1978. pap. 7.95 (ISBN 0-916688-07-0, 6C). Creative Comp.

--BASIC Computer Games: Microcomputer Edition. LC 78-17624. (Illus.). 188p. 1978. pap. 7.95 (ISBN 0-89480-052-3, 215). Workman Pub.

--The Best of Creative Computing, Vol. 1. LC 76-438. (Illus.). 326p. 1976. pap. 12.95 (ISBN 0-916688-01-1, 6A). Creative Comp.

--Big Computer Games. 160p. 1984. pap. 9.95 (ISBN 0-916688-40-2, 13C). Creative Comp.

--More BASIC Computer Games. LC 80-57619. (Illus.). 188p. 1980. pap. 8.95 (ISBN 0-89480-137-6, 438). Workman Pub.

--More BASIC Computer Games: TRS-80. LC 78-50028. (Illus.). 196p. (Orig.). 1980. pap. 7.95 (ISBN 0-916688-19-4, 6C4). Creative Comp.

Alberts, Cecil D. Game Power for Phonics, Plus. 1981. 75.00 (ISBN 0-915048-04-3). Spin-A-Test Pub.

Allston, Aaron. Trail of the Gold Spike. Mallonee, Dennis, ed. (Hero System Ser.). (Illus.). 32p. (Orig.). 1984. pap. 5.95 (ISBN 0-917481-51-8). Hero Games.

Anstis, Stuart. Write Your Own Apple Games. (Illus.). 174p. 1983. 12.95 (ISBN 0-916688-49-6, 2W). Creative Comp.

Bangley, Bernard K. Bible BASIC: Bible Games for Personal Computers. LC 83-48461. 128p. (Orig.). 1983. pap. 9.57 (ISBN 0-06-250042-2, CN 4092, HarpR). Har-Row.

Banse, Timothy P. Home Applications & Games. (Microcomputer Bookshelf Ser.). 1985. IBM. pap. 14.50 (ISBN 0-316-08049-7); Commodore 64. pap. 14.50 (ISBN 0-316-08048-9); Coleco ADAM 600. pap. 14.50 (ISBN 0-316-08047-0). Little.

--Home Applications & Games for Atari Home Computers. (Microcomputer Bookshelf Ser.). 134p. 1983. pap. text ed. 14.50 (ISBN 0-316-08044-6). Little.

--Home Applications & Games for the Apple II, II Plus & IIe Computers. (Microcomputer Bookshelf Ser.). 170p. (Orig.). 1984. pap. 14.50 (ISBN 0-316-08045-4). Little.

--Home Applications & Games for the Coleco Adam. 132p. 1985. lib. bdg. 15.95 (ISBN 0-934523-00-2); pap. 14.95 (ISBN 0-934523-01-0). Version One Point-Zero.

Barrett, Terry P. & Jones, Antonia J. Winning Games on the VIC-20. (Recreational Computing Ser.: No. 1-704). 143p. (Orig.). 1983. pap. 12.95 (ISBN 0-471-80601-3, 1-704, Pub. by Wiley Pr). Wiley.

Behrendt, Bill. Pocket Magic: Twenty-Five Intriguing, Animated Games for the TRS-80 PC & the Sharp PC-1211. 96p. 1982. 17.95 (ISBN 0-13-683847-2); pap. 9.95 (ISBN 0-13-683839-1). P-H.

Behrendt, Bill L. Conquering the Commodore 64 Kingdom: 25 Original Games in Dazzling Sight & Sound. 170p. 1984. pap. 14.95 (ISBN 0-13-167917-1); incl. disk 29.95. P-H.

--Conquering the PCjr Kingdom: 25 Original Games in Dazzling Sight & Sound. 180p. 1984. pap. 14.95 (ISBN 0-13-167891-4); incl. disk 29.95 (ISBN 0-13-167909-0). P-H.

--Thirty Games for the Timex-Sinclair Computer. 1983. write for info. P-H.

Behrendt, William. Thirty Games for the Timex-Sinclair 1000. 84p. 1983. 9.95 (ISBN 0-13-918904-1); pap. 4.95 (ISBN 0-13-918896-7). P-H.

Bishop, Owen. Commodore 64 Wargaming. (Illus.). 160p. (Orig.). 1985. pap. 17.95 (ISBN 0-00-383010-1, Pub. by Collins England). Sheridan.

Bradbeer, Robin & Gale, Harold, eds. The Times Book of Computer Puzzles & Games for the Commodore 64. (Illus.). 144p. 1985. pap. 11.95 (ISBN 0-283-99163-1, Pub. by Sidgwick & Jackson). Merrimack Pub Cir.

Bradbury, A. J. Adventure Games for the Commodore 64. 194p. 1985. pap. 10.95 (ISBN 0-13-014002-3). P H.

Bramer, M. A. Computer Game-Playing: Theory & Practice. LC 83-10678. (Artificial Intelligence Ser.). 306p. 1983. 61.95x (ISBN 0-470-27466-2). Halsted Pr.

Bridges, George. IBM PCjr Games Programs. 96p. 1984. 7.95 (ISBN 0-86668-036-5). ARCsoft.

Buchsbaum, W. H. & Mauro, R. Microprocessor-Based Electronic Games. 350p. 1983. pap. 9.95 (ISBN 0-07-008722-9, BYTE Bks). McGraw.

Burns, Edward. VIC-20: Fifty Easy-to-Run Computer Games. LC 83-50375. 128p. 1983. pap. 5.95 (ISBN 0-672-22188-8, 22188); incl. tape 12.95 (ISBN 0-672-26170-7, 26170). Sams.

Buscaino, Dale & Daniel, Scott. Superzap: IBM-PC Version 1.0. Moore, David & Trapp, Charles, eds. (Illus.). 104p. 1985. softcover & disk 49.95 (ISBN 0-932679-00-5). Blue Cat.

Busch, David. BASIC Games for Your Commodore 64. cancelled 14.95 (ISBN 0-89303-909-8). Brady Comm.

--BASIC Games for Your IBM Peanut. cancelled 9.95 (ISBN 0-89303-908-X). Brady Comm.

--BASIC Games for Your VIC-20 Computer. 9.95 (ISBN 0-89303-910-1). Brady Comm.

Busch, David D. Twenty-Five Games for Your TRS-80 Model 100. (Illus.). 160p. (Orig.). 1984. 15.95 (ISBN 0-8306-0698-X, 1698); pap. 10.25 (ISBN 0-8306-1698-5). TAB Bks.

California State University. Ten Common Inferences: Oscar-The Big Escape for Use with Apple II. 1984. write for info. (ISBN 0-07-831014-8). McGraw.

Camp, Robert. Creating Arcade Games on the Commodore 64. 357p. 1984. 14.95 (ISBN 0-942386-36-1). Compute Pubns.

--Creating Arcade Games on the VIC. 185p. 1984. pap. 12.95 (ISBN 0-942386-25-6). Compute Pubns.

Capelia, M. E. & Wienstock, M. Games Ti's Plays. 14.95 (ISBN 0-317-05649-2). P-H.

Capella, Mark & Weinstock, Mike. Games Commodore 64s Play. (Games Computers Play Ser.). pap. 14.95 (ISBN 0-88190-121-0). Datamost.

Chance, David. Thirty-Three Challenging Computer Games for the TRS-80, Apple & PET. (Illus.). 252p. 15.95 (ISBN 0-8306-9703-9, 1275); pap. 9.25 (ISBN 0-8306-1275-0). TAB Bks.

Chance, David W. Thirty-Three Adult Computer Games in BASIC for the IBM PC, Apple II, IIe & TRS-80. (Illus.). 378p. 1983. 18.95 (ISBN 0-8306-0627-0, 1627); pap. 13.50 (ISBN 0-8306-1627-6). TAB Bks.

--Twenty-Five Exciting Computer Games in BASIC for All Ages. LC 82-19286. (Illus.). 288p. 1983. o.p 21.95 (ISBN 0-8306-0427-8, 1427); pap. 12.95 (ISBN 0-8306-1427-3). TAB Bks.

Chiu, Y. & Mullish, H. Crunchers: Twenty-One Games for the Timex-Sinclair 1000 (2k) (McGraw-Hill VTX Ser.). 144p. 1983. pap. 8.95 (ISBN 0-07-010831-5, BYTE Bks). McGraw.

--Munchers: Twenty-Five Simple Games for the Texas Instruments 99-2 Basic Computer. (Illus.). 160p. 1984. pap. 9.95 (ISBN 0-07-010839-0, BYTE Bks). Mcgraw.

Clarke, M. R. Advances in Computer Chess II. 142p. 1980. 16.00x (ISBN 0-85224-377-4, Pub. by Edinburgh U Pr Scotland). Columbia U Pr.

Cole, Jim. Murder in the Mansion & Other Computer Adventures. 2nd ed. (Illus.). 96p. (Pocket BASIC for the TRS-80). 1981. pap. 6.95 (ISBN 0-86668-501-4). ARCsoft.

Coletta, P. Multiploy. 1982. lib. bdg. 24.95 (ISBN 0-8359-4742-4). Reston.

Coletta, Paul. Apple Graphics Games. LC 82-23161. 1983. 16.95 (ISBN 0-8359-0325-7); disk 15.00 (ISBN 0-8359-0313-3); bk. & disk o.p. 34.95 (ISBN 0-8359-0326-5). Reston.

Commodore 64 Games Book. 14.95 (ISBN 0-318-00661-8). Melbourne Hse.

Compute Editors, ed. Compute's Commodore 64-128 Collection. (Orig.). 1985. pap. 12.95 (ISBN 0-942386-97-3). Compute Pubns.

Compute! Magazine Staff. Compute's First Book of Atari Games. 232p. (Orig.). 1983. pap. 12.95 (ISBN 0-942386-14-0). Compute Pubns.

--Compute's First Book of Commodore 64 Games. 217p. (Orig.). 1983. pap. 12.95 (ISBN 0-942386-34-5). Compute Pubns.

--Compute's First Book of TI Games. Regena, C., ed. 211p. (Orig.). 1983. pap. 12.95 (ISBN 0-942386-17-5). Compute Pubns.

--Compute's First Book of VIC. (Illus.). 212p. (Orig.). 1982. pap. 12.95 (ISBN 0-942386-07-8). Compute Pubns.

--Compute's First Book of VIC Games. 201p. 1983. 12.95 (ISBN 0-942386-13-2). Compute Pubns.

Compute! Magazine Staff, ed. Compute's Second Book of Commodore 64 Games. (Orig.). 1984. pap. 12.95 (ISBN 0-942386-64-7). Compute Pubns.

Computer Games. 152p. 7.95 (ISBN 0-317-05255-1, 62-2068). Radio Shack.

Conklin, Dick. PC Graphics: Charts, Graphs, Games, & Art on the IBM-PC. LC 83-5797. (IBM Personal Computer Ser.). 182p. 1983. pap. text ed. 15.95 (ISBN 0-471-89207-6, 1-646, Pub. by Wiley Pr); book & program disk 40.90 (ISBN 0-471-88541-X). Wiley.

Conrod, J. Computer Bible Games, Bk. 1. 192p. (Orig.). 1983. pap. 6.95 (ISBN 0-89636-126-8). Accent Bks.

Consumer Digest Editors, ed. How to Win at Apple Computer Games. 64p. 1984. spiral bound 8.95 (ISBN 0-671-49559-3). S&S.

Consumer Guide Editors. Book of Personal Computers & Games. 54p. 1984. spiral bdg. 3.98 (ISBN 0-517-41595-X, Pub. by Beekman Hse). Outlet Bk Co.

--How to Win at Atari Computer Games. (Illus.). 64p. 1983. pap. 8.95 spiral bound cancelled (ISBN 0-671-49558-5, Fireside). S&S.

Crawford, Chris. The Art of Computer Game Design: Reflections of a Master Game Designer. 120p. (Orig.). 1984. pap. 14.95 (ISBN 0-07-881117-1, 117-1). Osborne-McGraw.

Cuellar, Gabriel. Games for the IBM-PC. 1984. 19.95 (ISBN 0-8359-2420-3). Reston.

Curnow, Ray & Curnou, Susan. Games, Graphics & Sound. (Clear & Simple Home Computer Ser.: Vol. III). (Illus.). 128p. 1984. 9.95 (ISBN 0-671-49444-9, Fireside). S&S.

DaCosta, Frank. Writing BASIC Adventure Programs for the TRS-80. LC 82-5945. (Illus.). 228p. 1982. 14.95 (ISBN 0-8306-2422-8, 1422); pap. 10.25 (ISBN 0-8306-1422-2, 1422). TAB Bks.

Davis, Ian A. Forty-Four Dynamic ZX-81 Games & Recreations. (Illus.). 1984. pap. 13.95 (ISBN 0-13-329144-8). P-H.

Dempsey, Tom. The TRS-80 Beginner's Guide to Games & Graphics. 1984. 16.95 (ISBN 0-317-06048-1); pap. 16.95 (ISBN 0-936200-10-3). Blue Cat.

Ende, Franz. The Great Book of Games. 144p. 9.95 (ISBN 3-88963-182-7). Blue Cat.

--Great Book of Games, Vol. 1. 144p. 9.95 (ISBN 3-88963-182-7). Elcomp.

Engel Enterprises & Engel, C. W. Stimulating Simulations. 2nd ed. 112p. 1979. pap. 7.50 ea. (ISBN 0-8104-5170-0). Atari Version (ISBN 0-8104-5197-2, 5197). Microsoft Version (5170). VIC Version (5173). Apple Version (6317). Commodore 64 Version (5201). TI-99-4A Version (6404). Hayden.

Ewban, Kay, et al. BBC Micro Gamemaster. (Illus.). 159p. (Orig.). 1984. pap. 11.95 (ISBN 0-246-12581-0, Pub. by Granada England). Sheridan.

Ewbank, Kay, et al. Electron Gamemaster. (Illus.). 162p. (Orig.). 1984. pap. 11.95 (ISBN 0-246-12514-4, Pub. by Granada England). Sheridan.

Fabbri, Tony. Animation, Games, & Sound for the Apple II-IIe. (P-H Personal Computing Ser.). (Illus.). 144p. 1984. pap. text ed. 17.95 incl. cassette (ISBN 0-13-037284-6); incl. disk 31.95 (ISBN 0-13-037276-5). P-H.

--Animation, Games & Sound for the IBM Personal Computer. (Illus.). 224p. 1983. pap. text ed. 19.50 (ISBN 0-13-037689-2). P-H.

--Animation, Games & Sound for the TI 99-4A. (Prentice-Hall Personal Computing Ser.). (Illus.). 224p. 1985. pap. text ed. 17.95 (ISBN 0-13-037227-7). P-H.

--Animation, Games, & Sounds for the Commodore 64. (Prentice-Hall Personal Computing Ser.). (Illus.). 224p. 1984. pap. text ed. 16.95 (ISBN 0-13-037375-3). P-H.

Farvour, James. Commodore 64 Arcade Game Design. (Illus.). 200p. (Orig.). Date not set. pap. 16.95 (ISBN 0-912003-45-6). Bk Co.

Fox, Michael. Quick 'n Fun Games for the IBM Personal Computer. 96p. 1984. 8.95 (ISBN 0-86668-044-6). ARCsoft.

Franklin, Howard M., et al. Golden Delicious Games for the Apple Computer. LC 81-23074. (Self Teaching Guides Ser.: No. 1-704). 150p. 1982. pap. 12.95 (ISBN 0-471-09083-2); Avail. software disk set 47.90 (ISBN 0-471-89842-2); disk 34.95 (ISBN 0-471-86837-X). Wiley.

Gabriele, Peter & Gabriele, Rosemarie. Game Techniques in Applesoft BASIC. (Illus.). 148p. 1985. pap. cancelled (ISBN 0-8159-5617-7). Devin.

Gutman, Dan & Adams, Shay. The Greatest Games: The Ninety-Three Best Computer Games of All Time. Compute Editors, ed. (Orig.). 1985. pap. 9.95 (ISBN 0-942386-95-7). Compute Pubns.

Hartnell, Tim. Creating Adventure Games on Your Computer. (Orig.). 1984. 9.95 (ISBN 0-345-31883-8). Ballantine.

--Fifty-One Game Programs for the Timex-Sinclair 1000 & 1500. 1983. pap. 2.50 (ISBN 0-451-12598-3, Sig). NAL.

--Getting Acquainted with Your ZX-81. 3rd ed. 120p. 1981. pap. 9.95 (ISBN 0-916688-33-X, 15Y). Creative Comp.

--Seventy Games for the Timex-Sinclair 1000. 144p. 1983. pap. 9.95 (ISBN 0-201-11064-4). Addison-Wesley.

--Tim Hartnell's Executive Games for the IBM PC & XT. 288p. (Orig.). 1984. pap. 9.95 (ISBN 0-345-31940-0). Ballantine.

--Tim Hartnell's Giant Book of Computer Games. 400p. 1984. pap. 7.95 (ISBN 0-345-31609-6). Ballantine.

--Tim Hartnell's Second Giant Book of Computer Games. 1984. 9.95 (ISBN 0-345-32245-2). Ballantine.

Hartnell, Tim & Ramshaw, Mark. Zap! Pow! Boom! Arcade Games for the VIC-20. 1983. text ed. 17.95 (ISBN 0-8359-9539-9); pap. text ed. 12.95 (ISBN 0-8359-9538-0). Reston.

Haywood, Daniel. Creating Arcade Games on Your Timex-Sinclair 2068. 1984. pap. cancelled (ISBN 0-8359-1143-8). Reston.

Heiserman, David L. How to Design & Build Your Own Custom TV Games. (Illus.). 1979. pap. 13.95 (ISBN 0-8306-9815-9, 1101). TAB Bks.

Heller, David, et al. Dr. C. Wacko's Miracle Guide to Designing & Programming Your Own Atari Computer Arcade Games. 1983. pap. 12.95 (ISBN 0-201-11488-7); book & software 24.95 (ISBN 0-201-11490-9). Addison-Wesley.

Hergert, Douglas & Kalash, Joseph T. Apple Pascal Games. LC 81-16577. (Illus.). 371p. 1981. pap. 15.95 (ISBN 0-89588-074-1, P360). SYBEX.

Holtz, Frederick. TI 99-4A Game Programs. (Illus.). 240p. 1983. 17.95 (ISBN 0-8306-0730-7); pap. 11.50 (ISBN 0-8306-1630-6, 1630). TAB Bks.

Horn, Delton. Golden Flutes & Great Escapes Book. 200p. 1984. Apple Version. incl. disk 29.95 (ISBN 0-88056-206-4). Dilithium Pr.

--Golden Flutes & Great Escapes: Writing Adventure Games for Your Computer Book-Software Package. 175p. 1984. pap. 9.95 (ISBN 0-88056-089-4); TRS Model III & IV. incl. disk 29.95 (ISBN 0-88056-194-7); TRS-80 Model III & IV. incl. diskette 29.95 (ISBN 0-88056-193-9). Dilithium Pr.

Horn, Delton T. Thirty-Four More Tested, Ready-to-Run Game Programs in BASIC. (Illus.). 224p. pap. 9.25 (ISBN 0-8306-1228-9). TAB Bks.

How to Get the Most from Your Chess Computer. pap. 9.95 (ISBN 0-686-79080-4). R H M Pr.

Hunt, Greg. Great Games for the IBM PC: A Buyer's Guide to Challenging Games of Strategy & Skill. 320p. 1984. pap. 7.95 (ISBN 0-88693-100-2). Banbury Bks.

--Great Games for the IBM PCjr: A Buyer's Guide for Families. 280p. 1984. pap. 7.95 (ISBN 0-88693-155-X). Banbury Bks.

Ingalls, Robert. TI Games for Kids. 178p. 1984. pap. 12.95 (ISBN 0-942386-39-6). Compute Pubns.

Inman, Don. TRS-80 Color Computer Graphics. 1984. 14.95 (ISBN 0-317-06049-X). Micro Works.

International Conference on Advances in Computer Chess, London, UK, April 1981. Advances in Computer Chess III: Proceedings. Clarke, M. R., ed. LC 78-309646. (Pergamon Chess Ser.). 182p. 1982. 25.00 (ISBN 0-08-026898-6). Pergamon.

James, Mike, et al. The Atari Book of Games. 156p. 1984. pap. 12.95 (ISBN 0-07-881159-7, 159-7). Osborne-McGraw.

--Timex-Sinclair 2000 Book of Games. 128p. 1983. 16.95 (ISBN 0-13-921791-6); pap. 9.95 (ISBN 0-13-921783-5). P-H.

Jeffries, Ron & Fisher, Glen. Commodore 64 Fun & Games, Vol. 2. (Orig.). 1984. pap. 12.95 (ISBN 0-446-38183-7). Warner Bks.

Jeffries, Ronald, et al. Commodore 64 Fun & Games. 180p. (Orig.). 1983. pap. 11.95 (ISBN 0-88134-116-9). Osborne-McGraw.

Jones, Robin & Stewart, Ian. Timex-Sinclair 1000: Programs, Games, & Graphics. 100p. 1982. pap. 10.95 (ISBN 0-8176-3080-5). Birkhauser.

Kaplan, E. L. Mathematical Programming & Games, Vol. 1. LC 81-2990. 588p. 1982. 44.00 (ISBN 0-471-03632-3). Wiley.

Keogh, James E. Create-a-Game for Your IBM PCjr. (Orig.). pap. cancelled (ISBN 0-440-51625-0, Dell Trade Pbks). Dell.
Kidd, Clark & Kidd, Kathy. Compute's Apple Games for Kids. Compute Editors, ed. 320p. (Orig.). 1985. pap. 12.95 (ISBN 0-942386-91-4). Compute Pubns.
Kidd, Kathy H. & Kidd, Clark. Commodore 64 Games for Kids. 267p. (Orig.). 1984. 12.95 (ISBN 0-942386-37-X). Compute Pubns.
Kohl, Herb & Kahn, Ted. Adam Games & Recreation. 15.95 (ISBN 0-8359-0094-0). Reston.
--Commodore 64 Games & Recreation. (Illus.). 225p. 16.95 (ISBN 0-8359-0773-2). Reston.
Kosniowski, Czes. Fun Mathematics on Your Microcomputer. LC 83-1811. 1983. pap. 10.95 (ISBN 0-521-27451-6). Cambridge U Pr.
Levy, David. Computer Gamesmanship: The Complete Guide to Creating & Structuring Intelligent Game Programs. 288p. 1984. pap. 12.95 (ISBN 0-671-49532-1, Pub. by Computer Bks). S&S.
--The Joy of Computer Chess. (Illus.). 160p. 1984. 14.95 (ISBN 0-13-511627-9); pap. 7.95 (ISBN 0-13-511619-8). P-H.
--U. S. Computer Chess Championship, 1976. (Computer Chess Series). (Illus.). 1977. pap. 6.95x (ISBN 0-914894-04-8). Computer Sci.
Levy, David & Newborn, Monroe. All about Chess & Computers. LC 82-12497. (Computer Chess Ser.). 146p. 1982. pap. text ed. 21.95 (ISBN 0-914894-75-7). Computer Sci.
--More Chess & Computers: The Microcomputer Revolution, the Challenge Match. LC 80-16057. (Illus.). 1980. pap. 12.95x (ISBN 0-914894-07-2). Computer Sci.
Macaluso, Pat. Learning Simulation Techniques on a Microcomputer Playing Blackjack & Other Monte Carlo Games. (Illus.). 154p. (Orig.). 1983. 16.95 (ISBN 0-8306-0535-5, 1535); pap. 10.95 (ISBN 0-8306-1535-0). TAB Bks.
McEvoy, Seth. Create-a-Game for Your VIC-20. (Orig.). pap. cancelled (ISBN 0-440-51624-2, Dell Trade Pbks). Dell.
--Creating Arcade Games on the TI 99-4A. 200p. 1984. pap. 12.95 (ISBN 0-942386-27-2). Compute Pubns.
--Creating Arcade Games on the Timex-Sinclair. 192p. (Orig.). 1984. 12.95 (ISBN 0-942386-26-4). Compute Pubns.
McGath, Gary. Compute's Guide to Adventure Games. (Orig.). 1984. pap. 12.95 (ISBN 0-942386-67-1). Compute Pubns.
McIntire, Thomas C. The A to Z Book of Computer Games. (Illus.). 1979. 14.95 (ISBN 0-8306-9809-4); pap. 10.25 (ISBN 0-8306-1062-6, 1062). TAB Bks.
Mateosian, Richard. Inside BASIC Games. LC 80-53281. (Illus.). 347p. 1981. pap. 14.95 (ISBN 0-89588-055-5, BX255). SYBEX.
Matthews, Toby & Smith, Paul. Winning Games on the Commodore 64. 302p. 1984. pap. text ed. 14.95 (ISBN 0-471-81531-4, Pub. by Wiley Pr). Wiley.
Maunder, Robert. Creative Games for the Timex-Sinclair 2068. 128p. 1984. pap. 7.95 (ISBN 0-916688-24-0). Creative Comp.
Minter, Greg & Ruffner, John. Designing Apple Games with Pizazz! (Illus.). 328p. (Orig.). 1984. pap. 14.95 (ISBN 0-88190-387-6, BO387). Datamost.
Mullish, Henry & Cooper, Herbert. Zappers for the Commodore 64. 224p. 1984. pap. 9.95 spiral bd (ISBN 0-671-50714-1, Pub. by Computer Bks). S&S.
Mullish, Henry & Kruger, Dov. Zappers: Having Fun Programming & Playing Twenty-Three Games for the TI 99-4A. 128p. 1984. pap. 9.95 (ISBN 0-671-49862-2, Pub. by Computer Bks). S&S.
Nahigian, J. Victor & Hodges, William S. Computer Games for Businesses, Schools, & Homes. (Orig.). 1979. pap. text ed. 12.95 (ISBN 0-316-59692-2). Little.
--Computer Games for the TRS-80. 151p. (Orig.). 1981. pap. text ed. 10.95 (ISBN 0-316-59691-4). Little.
Newborn, Monroe. Computer Chess. (A.C.M. Monograph Ser). 1975. 41.00 (ISBN 0-12-517250-8). Acad Pr.
Olson, Nancy B. A Manual of AACR 2 Examples for Microcomputer Software. 2nd ed. Swanson, Edward, ed. 1985. pap. text ed. 17.50 (ISBN 0-936996-20-X). Soldier Creek.
One Hundred One BASIC Computer Games. (DECbooks). 249p. 1975. pap. 10.00 (ISBN 0-932376-24-X, EB-04873-DP). Digital Pr.
Page, Edward. Timex-Sinclair Computer Games Programs. 96p. 1983. 7.95 (ISBN 0-86668-026-8). ARCsoft.
Pellier, P. Programming Real Time Games on the TRS-80. Martres, Laurent, tr. from Fr. 112p. Date not set. price not set. Blue Cat.
Person, Ron. Macintosh Game Animation. 280p. (Orig.). 1985. pap. 15.95 (ISBN 0-07-881127-9). Osborne-McGraw.
Reid-Green, Keith. Create Your Own: Games Computers Play. (Illus.). 256p. 1984. pap. 21.00 (ISBN 0-932376-29-0, EY-00025-DP). Digital Pr.
Renko, Hal & Edwards, Sam. Cosmic Games for the Commodore VIC-20. (Illus.). 192p. 1983. pap. 5.95 (ISBN 0-201-16476-0). Addison-Wesley.
--Crazy Games for Your Commodore 64. (Illus.). 144p. 1984. pap. 5.95 (ISBN 0-201-16483-3). Addison-Wesley.
--Tantalizing Games for the Timex-Sinclair 2000. (Illus.). 192p. 1983. pap. 5.95 (ISBN 0-201-16479-5). Addison-Wesley.
--Tantalizing Games for the Timex-Sinclair 1000. cancelled (ISBN 0-201-16478-7). Benjamin-Cummings.
Renko, Hal & Sandra, Emerson. Astounding Games for Your Apple Computer. pap. 5.95 (ISBN 0-201-16482-5). Addison-Wesley.
Renko, Hal, et al. The Antagonists: A Complete Microworld Adventure for the Apple II. 128p. 1985. pap. 8.95 (ISBN 0-201-16490-6). Addison-Wesley.
--The Antagonists: A Complete Microworld Adventure for the Commodore 64. 128p. 1985. pap. 8.95 (ISBN 0-201-16491-4). Addison-Wesley.
--The Antagonists: A Complete Microworld Adventure for the IBM-PC. 128p. 1985. pap. 8.95 (ISBN 0-201-16492-2). Addison-Wesley.
--The Secret of Arendarvon Castle: A Complete Microworld Adventure for the Apple II. 128p. 1984. pap. 8.95 (ISBN 0-201-16484-1). Addison-Wesley.
--The Secret of Arendarvon Castle: A Complete Microworld Adventure for the Commodore 64. (Illus.). 128p. 1984. pap. 8.95 (ISBN 0-201-16485-X). Addison-Wesley.
--The Secret of Arendarvon Castle: A Complete Microworld Adventure for the IBM-PC. 128p. 1984. pap. 8.95 (ISBN 0-201-16486-8). Addison-Wesley.
Ritchie, David. Designing Your Own Computer Games. LC 84-61112. 128p. (Orig.). 1984. pap. 6.95 (ISBN 0-688-03928-6, Quill NY). Morrow.
Roberts, Sam. Games for the Atari. 1982. pap. 7.95 (ISBN 0-936200-36-7). Blue Cat.
Rosenberg, R. C. Software Toolkit: Apple II Plus Version. 1984. write for info. (ISBN 0-07-053912-X); IBM-PC software toolkit 1100.00 (ISBN 0-07-053914-6). McGraw.
Rugg, Tom & Feldman, Phil. Mind Moves: Strategic Games for the Commodore 64. 160p. 1984. pap. 9.95 (ISBN 0-88056-054-1); incl. disk 24.95 (ISBN 0-88056-225-0); incl. cassette 24.95 (ISBN 0-88056-228-5). Dilithium Pr.
Rupp, William & Hartman, Patricia A. Commodore 64 Game Construction Kit. 446p. (Orig.). 1984. pap. 14.95 (ISBN 0-88190-293-4, BO293). Datamost.
Sage, Edwin R. Fun & Games with the Computer. 351p. 1975. pap. text ed. 14.95 (ISBN 0-87567-075-X). Entelek.
Schuette, Kim. The Book of Adventure Games. (Illus.). 350p. 1984. pap. 19.95 (ISBN 0-912003-08-1). Bk Co.
Schwenk, George A. & Schwenk, Nancy E. Commodore 64 Advanced Game Design. (Illus.). 144p. (Orig.). 1985. 15.95 (ISBN 0-8306-0923-7); pap. 10.95 (ISBN 0-8306-1923-2). TAB Bks.
Shafer, Dan & Blanchard, Chuck. Games & Utilities for the Macintosh. (Illus.). 1985. 18.95 (ISBN 0-452-25641-0, Plume). NAL.
Solomon, Eric. Games Programming. LC 83-26292. (Illus.). 250p. 1984. pap. 14.95 (ISBN 0-521-27110-X). Cambridge U Pr.
Spangenburg, Ray & Moser, Dian. The Survival Kit for Apple Computer Games. LC 82-17912. (Illus.). 162p. 1983. pap. write for info. (ISBN 0-534-01432-1). Wadsworth Pub.
Spencer, Donald. Sixty Challenging Problems with BASIC Solutions. LC 79-50793. 1979. pap. 9.95 (ISBN 0-8104-5180-8). Hayden.
Spencer, Donald D. Game Playing with BASIC. 1977. pap. 12.50 (ISBN 0-8104-5109-3). Hayden.
--Game Playing with Computers. rev., 2nd ed. 320p. 1975. 21.95 (ISBN 0-8104-5103-4). Hayden.
Stanton, Jeffrey. Apple Graphics & Arcade Game Design. 288p. 1982. pap. 19.95 (ISBN 0-912003-01-4). Bk Co.
Stephenson, J. W., et al. Brain Games for Kids & Adults Using the Apple II, IIe, & IIc. (Illus.). 256p. 1984. pap. 13.95 (ISBN 0-89303-362-6); diskett 20.00 (ISBN 0-89303-366-9). Brady Comm.
Stephenson, John W. Brain Games for Kids & Adults Using the Commodore 64. (Illus.). 224p. 1984. pap. 12.95 (ISBN 0-89303-349-9); bk. & diskette 27.95 (ISBN 0-89303-350-2); bk. diskette 15.00 (ISBN 0-89303-353-7). Brady Comm.
Stewart, Ian & Jones, Robin. Introducing the Timex-Sinclair 2000: Programs, Games, & Graphics. cancelled. Birkhauser.
Swan. Pascal Programs for Games & Graphics. 224p. 1983. 15.95 (ISBN 0-317-02344-6, 6271); disks & documentation 49.94 (7271). Hayden.
Targ, Joan & Levinsky, Jeff. Ready, Run, Fun: Apple II-IIe Edition, Vol. I. (Illus.). 150p. 1984. pap. 14.95 (ISBN 0-13-762204-X). P-H.
--Ready, Run, Fun: IBM-PC Edition, Vol. I. (Illus.). 150p. 1983. pap. 14.95 (ISBN 0-13-762220-1). P-H.
Thompson, Thomas, Jr. Games & Graphics for the TI 99-4A. 128p. pap. 8.95 (6407). Hayden.
Throop, Thomas. Computer Bridge. 160p. 1983. pap. 10.95 (ISBN 0-317-00356-9). Hayden.
Tobey, Peter W. & Kelley, James E., Jr. Cage's Secret: A Microcomputer Enigma. 352p. 1984. 14.95 (ISBN 0-88693-169-X). Banbury Bks.
Ton & Ton. Entertainment Games in TI BASIC & Extended BASIC Programs. LC 83-50493. 176p. pap. 8.95 (ISBN 0-672-22204-3, 22204). book & tape 15.95 (ISBN 0-672-26169-3, 26169). Sams.
Townsend, Carl. Conquering Adventure Games. (Illus.). 256p. 1984. pap. 14.95 (ISBN 0-88056-350-8). Dilithium Pr.
Tracton, Ken. Fifty-Seven Practical Programs & Games in BASIC. (Illus.). 210p. 1978. 13.95 (ISBN 0-8306-9987-2); pap. 8.25 (ISBN 0-8306-1000-6, 1000). TAB Bks.
Traister, Robert J. Thirty-Three Games of Skill & Chance for the IBM PC. (Illus.). 256p. 1983. 18.95 (ISBN 0-8306-0126-0); pap. 12.95 (ISBN 0-8306-1526-1, 1526); incl. disk 29.95. TAB Bks.
Traister, Robert S. How to Write Picture Programs for the Commodore VIC-20. 96p. 1984. pap. 11.95 (ISBN 0-13-441536-1). P-H.
Turner, Len. Texas Instruments Home Computer Games Programs. 96p. 1983. 8.95 (ISBN 0-86668-032-2). ARCsoft.
Volkstorf, J. Edward, Jr. Fun & Games on the IBM PCjr. 1984. pap. 16.95 (ISBN 0-13-332461-3); disk 22.95 (ISBN 0-13-332479-6); incl. disk 49.95 (ISBN 0-13-332453-2). P-H.
--Fun & Games on the IBM PCjr. (Illus.). 256p. 1985. pap. 16.95 (ISBN 0-13-332487-7). P-H.
Waterford, Van. Microcomputer-Controlled Toys & Games & How They Work. (Illus.). 240p. (Orig.). 1983. 17.95 (ISBN 0-8306-0407-3); pap. 10.25 (ISBN 0-8306-1407-9, 1407). TAB Bks.
Weinstock, Mike & Capella, Mark. Games Panasonics Play. (Games Computers Play Ser.). pap. cancelled (ISBN 0-317-06137-2). Datamost.
--Games VIC's Play. 1984. cancelled (ISBN 0-317-07020-7). Datamost.
Welsh, David. Computer Chess. 309p. 1983. pap. 11.95 (ISBN 0-697-09900-8). Wm C Brown.
Wilcox, Clifford M. Apple Fun & Games. 194p. (Orig.). 1985. pap. 13.95 (ISBN 0-07-881168-6, 168-6). Osborne McGraw.
Wiley, Larry. The Fermi-Pico-Bagels LOGO Game: Developing Thinking Skills Using Words & List. 34p. 1984. 5.00 (ISBN 0-89824-109-X); bk. & Apple disk 19.95 (ISBN 0-89824-110-3); bk. & Commodore disk 19.95 (ISBN 0-89824-111-1); bk. & IBM disk 19.95 (ISBN 0-89824-112-X); bk. Terrapin disk 19.95 (ISBN 0-89824-113-8). Trillium Pr.
Williams, Phillip. MSX Games Book. 200p. 1984. pap. 14.95 (ISBN 0-86161-172-1). Melbourne Hse.
Witham, Joan, ed. The Softside Sampler: TRS-80 Entertainment Programs. 128p. 1983. pap. 10.95 (ISBN 0-317-00366-6). Hayden.
Wyatt, Allen. Apple Games. LC 84-51166. 8.95 (ISBN 0-672-22394-5). Sams.
--TI-99 4A Games. LC 84-51462. 8.95 (ISBN 0-672-22398-8). Sams.
Zimmerman, S. Scott & Zimmerman, Beverly B. Action Games for the Apple: How to Design Computer Games. 1985. pap. 12.95 (ISBN 0-673-18091-3). Scott F.

COMPUTER GRAPHICS

Albrecht, Robert L. & Inman, Don. BASIC for Your TRS-80 Super. LC 81-16286. (Self-Teaching Guides Ser.: No. 1-581). 374p. 1982. pap. text ed. 10.95 (ISBN 0-471-09644-X, Pub. by Wiley Pr). Wiley.
American Society of Mechanical Engineers. Interactive Computer Graphics in Engineering: Presented at the Winter Annual Meeting of the American Society of Mechanical Engineers, New York, N.Y. December 5-10-, 1976. Hulbert, L. E., ed. LC 77-77033. pap. 21.00 (ISBN 0-317-07994-8, 2051328). Bks Demand UMI.
Angell, I. O. Advanced Graphics with the IBM Personal Computer. 1985. pap. 24.95 (ISBN 0-470-20134-7). Wiley.
Angell, Ian O. A Practical Introduction to Computer Graphics. LC 81-11361. (Computers & Their Applications Ser.). 143p. 1981. pap. 19.95x (ISBN 0-470-27251-1). Halsted Pr.
Artwick, Bruce. Applied Concepts in Microcomputer Graphics. (Illus.). 400p. 1984. text ed. 34.95 (ISBN 0-13-039322-3). P-H.
Artwick, Bruce A. Microcomputer Displays, Graphics, & Animation. LC 84-61429. (Illus.). 384p. 1985. pap. text ed. 18.95 (ISBN 0-13-580226-1). P-H.
Automated Education Center. Digital Computer Graphics, 2 vols. 69.00 (ISBN 0-403-04465-0). Scholarly.
Avante-Garde Publishing Corporation Staff, et al. Getting Graphic on the Apple. 204p. 1985. pap. 14.95 (ISBN 0-13-354044-8). P-H.
--Getting Graphic on the Commodore 64. (Illus.). 208p. 1985. pap. 14.95 (ISBN 0-13-354051-0). P-H.
Avante-Garde Publishing Corporation Staff & Thiel, James R. Getting Graphic on the IBM-PC. 192p. 1985. pap. 14.95 (ISBN 0-13-354069-3). P-H.
Bailey, Harold & Kerlin, Edward. Apple Graphics: Activities Handbook for the Beginner. LC 83-21406. 432p. 1984. 16.95 (ISBN 0-89303-308-1); bk. & diskette 36.95 (ISBN 0-89303-309-X); diskette 20.00 (ISBN 0-89303-310-3). Brady Comm.
--Commodore 64 Graphics: Activities Handbook. 14.95 (ISBN 0-89303-379-0). Brady Comm.
Barnett, Michael & Barnett, Gabrielle. Beginning Graphics for the Commodore 64. 1984. cancelled. Reston.
Barnett, Michael P. & Barnett, Graham K. Personal Graphics for Profit & Pleasure on the Apple II Plus and IIe Personal Computers. (Microcomputer Bookshelf Ser.). 208p. 1982. pap. text ed. 14.50 (ISBN 0-316-08164-7). Little.
--Personal Graphics for Profit & Pleasure on the IBM Personal Computer. (Little, Brown Microcomputer Bookshelf Ser.). 225p. (Orig.). 1984. pap. 14.50 (ISBN 0-316-08220-1). Little.
Beatty, John C. & Booth, Kellogg S. Computer Graphics. 2nd ed. (Tutorial Texts Ser.). 570p. 1982. 39.00 (ISBN 0-8186-0425-5, Q425). IEEE Comp Soc.
Biegen, Joseph R. & Beston, William C. Introduction to Computer Graphics: CADDS-3. (Illus.). 210p. 1984. 16.50 (ISBN 0-911597-00-X). Redcomp Servs.
Boom, Michael. Understanding Atari Graphics. LC 82-18463. (An Alfred Handy Guide Ser.). 48p. 1982. pap. 3.50 (ISBN 0-88284-224-2). Alfred Pub.
Boyd, Alan. Techniques of Interactive Computer Graphics. 240p. 1985. pap. text ed. 25.95x (ISBN 0-86238-024-3, Pub. by Chartwell-Bratt England). Brookfield Pub Co.
Brodie, K. Mathematical Methods in Computer Graphics & Design. LC 79-50302. 1980. 33.00 (ISBN 0-12-134880-6). Acad Pr.
Butler, ed. International Conference on Computer Communication, 1974: Computer Communication Today & Up to 1985. 610p. 1974. 42.50 (ISBN 0-444-86194-7, North-Holland). Elsevier.
Cassel, Don. Graphics, Sound, & Music for the Commodore 64. (Microcomputer Power Ser.). 140p. 1984. deluxe ed. 27.95 plastic comb bdg. (ISBN 0-697-00422-8); pap. 15.95 (ISBN 0-697-00423-6); incl. diskette 27.95. Wm C Brown.
Chambers, John M. & Cleveland, William S. Graphical Methods for Data Analysis. LC 83-3660. (Statistics-Probability Ser.). 395p. 1983. write for info. (ISBN 0-534-98052-X). Wadsworth Pub.
Chambers, John M., et al. Graphical Methods for Data Analysis. 416p. 1983. pap. text ed. write for info (ISBN 0-87150-413-8, 5020, Duxbury Pr). PWS Pubs.
Chance. Computer Graphics with 29 Ready-to-Run Programs. 280p. 1981. o.p 15.95 (ISBN 0-8306-9636-9); pap. 10.25 (ISBN 0-8306-1276-9, 1276). TAB Bks.
Chasen, Sylvan H. Geometric Principles & Procedures for Computer Graphic Applications. LC 78-7998. (Illus.). 1978. 37.50 (ISBN 0-13-352559-7). P-H.
Chien, Y. T. Interactive Pattern Recognition. (Electrical Engineering & Electronics Ser.: Vol. 3). 1978. 55.00 (ISBN 0-8247-6631-8). Dekker.
Clark, David R. Computers for Image-Making. (Audio-Visual Media for Education & Research Ser.: Vol. 2). (Illus.). 166p. 1980. 34.00 (ISBN 0-08-024058-5); pap. 17.00 (ISBN 0-08-024059-3). Pergamon.
Clark, Ron. Color Computer Graphics. (Illus.). 128p. 1983. 9.95 (ISBN 0-86668-012-8). ARCsoft.
Clarke, Frank H. & Henkel, James G., eds. Molecular Graphics on the Apple Microcomputer. 1985. 129.50 (ISBN 0-12-175780-3). Acad Pr.
Coletta, Paul. Apple Graphics Games. LC 82-23161. 1983. 16.95 (ISBN 0-8359-0325-7); disk 15.00 (ISBN 0-8359-0313-3); bk. & disk o.p. 34.95 (ISBN 0-8359-0326-5). Reston.
Collins, Joseph W. Atari Color Graphics: A Beginner's Workbook. pap. 12.95 (ISBN 0-912003-19-7). Bk Co.
Color Computer Graphics. 256p. 5.95 (ISBN 0-317-05264-0, 62-2076). Radio Shack.

--Computer Mapping of Natural Resources & the Environment: Plus Satellite-Derived Data Applications, Vol. 15. (The Harvard Library of Computer Graphics, Mapping Collection). (Illus.). 180p. 1981. pap. 12.50 (ISBN 0-8122-1195-2). U of Pa Pr.
--The Harvard Library of Computer Graphics, Mapping Collection, 19 vols. (Illus.). 1981. Set. pap. 99.50 (ISBN 0-8122-1180-4). U of Pa Pr.
--How to Design an Effective Graphics Presentation, Vol. 17. (The Harvard Library of Computer Graphics, Mapping Collection). (Illus.). 86p. 1981. pap. 12.50 (ISBN 0-8122-1197-9). U of Pa Pr.
--Management's Use of Computer Graphics, Vol. 12. (The Harvard Library of Computer Graphics, Mapping Collection). (Illus.). 128p. 1981. pap. 12.50 (ISBN 0-8122-1192-8). U of Pa Pr.
--Management's Use of Maps: Commercial & Political Applications, Vol. 1. (The Harvard Library of Computer Graphics, Mapping Collection). (Illus.). 64p. 1979. pap. 12.50 (ISBN 0-8122-1181-2). U of Pa Pr.
--Management's Use of Maps: Including an Introduction to Computer Mapping for Executives, Vol. 7. (The Harvard Library of Computer Graphics, Mapping Collection). (Illus.). 103p. 1980. pap. 12.50 (ISBN 0-8122-1187-1). U of Pa Pr.
--Mapping Software & Cartographic Data Bases, Vol. 2. (The Harvard Library of Computer Graphics, Mapping Collection). (Illus.). 240p. 1979. pap. 12.50 (ISBN 0-8122-1182-0). U of Pa Pr.
--Thematic Map Design, Vol. 6. (The Harvard Library of Computer Graphics, Mapping Collection). (Illus.). 134p. 1979. pap. 12.50 (ISBN 0-8122-1186-3). U of Pa Pr.
--Urban, Regional, & State Applications: Plus a Special Section on Cadastral Systems, Vol. 3. (The Harvard Library of Computer Graphics, Mapping Collection). (Illus.). 195p. 1979. pap. 12.50 (ISBN 0-8122-1183-9). U of Pa Pr.
--Urban, Regional, & State Government Applications of Computer Mapping: Plus Computer Mapping in Education, Vol. 11. (The Harvard Library of Computer Graphics, Mapping Collection). (Illus.). 232p. 1980. pap. 12.50 (ISBN 0-8122-1191-X). U of Pa Pr.
Lambert, Steve. Presentation Graphics on the Apple Macintosh: How to Use Microsoft Chart to Create Dazzling Graphics for Professional & Corporate Applications. 288p. 1984. pap. 18.95 (ISBN 0-914845-11-X). Microsoft.
--Presentation Graphics on the IBM PC: How to use Microsoft Chart to Create Dazzling Graphics for Corporate & Professional Applications. (Illus.). 320p. (Orig.). 1986. pap. 19.95 (ISBN 0-914845-12-8). Microsoft.
Lane, J. E. Graphics on the Microcomputer. 44p. 1981. pap. 13.15 (ISBN 0-471-89454-0). Wiley.
Lane, John E. Graphics on Microcomputers. 57p. (Orig.). 1981. pap. 10.00x (ISBN 0-85012-333-X). Intl Pubns Serv.
Lane, John M. Programming Commodore Graphics with Your 64 or 128. 1985. pap. 14.95 (ISBN 0-673-18084-0). Scott F.
Lange. Design Dimensioning with Computer Graphics. (Mechanical Engineerign Ser.). 304p. 1984. 35.00 (ISBN 0-8247-7119-2). Dekker.
Lange, Jerome C. & Shanahan, Dennis P. Interactive Computer Graphics Applied to Mechanical Drafting & Design. LC 83-6999. 345p. 1984. pap. text ed. 29.95x (ISBN 0-471-86916-3). Wiley.
Lansdown. Business Graphics. (Illus.). 328p. 1982. 445.00 (ISBN 0-08-028566-X). Pergamon.
Larsen, Elmer. Icons & Images. Compute!, ed. (Orig.). 1985. pap. 14.95 (ISBN 0-942386-84-1). Compute Pubns.
Larsen, Sally G. Sprite Graphics for the Commodore 64. 184p. 1983. 21.95 (ISBN 0-13-838144-5); pap. 15.95 (ISBN 0-13-838136-4). P-H.
Lee, Kaiman. Interactive Computer Graphics in Architecture. LC 76-366950. 100p. 1976. 30.00x (ISBN 0-915250-21-7). Environ Design.
Liming, Roy A. Mathematics for Computer Graphics. LC 79-65814. 1979. 38.00 (ISBN 0-8168-6751-8). Aero.
Lord, Kenniston W., Jr. Graphics with the IBM-PC. 1985. pap. 19.95 (ISBN 0-673-15971-X). Scott F.
Lourie, Janice. Textile Graphics: Computer Aided. new ed. LC 73-188789. (Illus.). 300p. 1973. 15.00 (ISBN 0-87005-108-3). Fairchild.
Lund, Charles & Andersen, Edwin D. Computer Graphing Experiments, 4 vols. 1982. write for info, vol. 1 (ISBN 0-201-23465-3); write for info, vol. 2 (ISBN 0-201-23470-X); write for info, vol. 3 (ISBN 0-201-23475-0); write for info, vols. 1-3 (ISBN 0-201-23480-7). Addison-Wesley.
Luzadder, Warren J. Fundamentals of Engineering Drawing: With an Intro to Interactive Computer Graphics for Design & Production. 9th ed. (Illus.). 656p. 1986. text ed. 34.95 (ISBN 0-13-338427-6). P-H.
McGee, Kate & Matthews, Catherine, eds. Design of Interactive Computer Displays: A Guide to the Select Literature. LC 85-60627. (Orig.). 1985. pap. 125.00 (ISBN 0-916313-08-5). Report.
McMahan, Mike. Graphics & Sound for Your IBM-PC. Berliner, Thomas H., ed. LC 85-719. (Illus.). 240p. 1984. pap. 19.95 (ISBN 0-915381-66-4). WordWare Pub.
Mallgren, William R. Formal Specification of Interactive Graphics Programming Languages. (Association for Computing Machinery Distinguished Dissertation Ser.). (Illus.). 269p. 1983. text ed. 40.00x (ISBN 0-262-13191-9). MIT Pr.
Mar, Jerry. MacGraphics for Business. 1985. pap. 17.95 (ISBN 0-673-18158-8). Scott F.
Maran, Richard. The Graphic Macintosh Book. 1985. FPT 11.95 (ISBN 0-03-928875-7). CBS Ed.
Marcus, Aaron. Graphic Design for Computer Graphics. 300p. 1984. write for info. (ISBN 0-201-15856-6). Benjamin-Cummings.
Marquis Who's Who Directory of Computer Graphics, 1984. 549p. 1984. 125.00 (ISBN 0-8379-5901-2, 031121). Marquis.
Marshall, Garry. Programming with Graphics. (Illus.). 120p. 1983. 19.95 (ISBN 0-13-729616-9); pap. 12.95 (ISBN 0-13-729608-8). P-H.
Masalski, William J. Programming Animation & Graphics Task Cards for the Apple. Fanning, Tom, ed. 1982. 9.95 (ISBN 0-88049-063-2, 7889). Milton Bradley Co.
Meilach, Dona Z. The Dynamics of Presentation Graphics. (Illus.). 350p. 1985. pap. 24.95 (ISBN 0-87094-656-0). Dow Jones-Irwin.
Micrographics & Its Relationship with Word Processing, CAR & Optical Disk. (Special Interest Packages Ser.). pap. 23.00 (ISBN 0-317-06205-0, PO19). Assn Inform & Image Mgmt.
Miller, Craig G. Smart Programming Guide for Sprites. 74p. (Orig.). 1983. pap. 6.95 (ISBN 0-931831-00-8). Millers Graphics.
Milton, Marcus. Moving Graphics: Invaders. (Write Your Own Program Ser.). (Illus.). 48p. 1985. lib. bdg. 10.90 (ISBN 0-531-03491-7). Watts.
Money, Steve. Commodore 64 Graphics & Sound. 1985. 12.95 (ISBN 0-13-152034-2). P H.
Moore, Herb. Sound & Graphics for the Commodore 64. 240p. 1985. pap. 14.95 (ISBN 0-471-80556-4, Pub by Wiley Pr). Wiley.
Moore, Herb, et al. Atari Sound & Graphics. LC 81-23111. (Self-Teaching Guides Ser.: No. 1-581). 234p. 1982. pap. text ed. 10.95 (ISBN 0-471-09593-1, Pub. by Wiley Pr). Wiley.
Mufti. Elementary Computer Graphics. 22.95 (ISBN 0-8359-1654-5). Reston.
Murphy, James L. Understanding Computer Graphics. (Handy Guide Ser.). 64p. (Orig.). 1984. pap. 3.50 (ISBN 0-88284-294-3). Alfred Pub.
Murvin, H. L. Computer Aided Drafting on the Bausch & Lomb Producer Drafting System (Beginning Level) (Illus.). 84p. 1983. pap. 11.95 (ISBN 0-9608498-1-5). H L Murvin.
Myers, Roy E. Microcomputer Graphics. (Illus.). 304p. 1984. pap. text ed. 12.95 (ISBN 0-201-05096-X). Addison-Wesley.
--Microcomputer Graphics for the IBM PC. 1438p. 1984. pap. 14.95 (ISBN 0-201-05158-3); apple disk package 29.95 (ISBN 0-201-05312-8). Addison-Wesley.
Network Editors, ed. Computer Graphic Display Devices & Systems, 2 Vols. 1982. Vol. 1. 55.00 ea. (ISBN 0-904999-70-X, Pub. by Network). Vol. 2 (ISBN 0-904999-69-6). State Mutual Bk.
--Computer Graphics & Interactive Devices. 1982. 90.00x (ISBN 0-904999-54-8, Pub. by Network). State Mutual Bk.
--Graphics & Interactive Display. 1982. 50.00x (ISBN 0-904999-65-3, Pub. by Network). State Mutual Bk.
--Software for Computer Display Systems, Vol. 3. 1982. 79.00x (ISBN 0-904999-71-8, Pub. by Network). State Mutual Bk.
Neundorf, Norman. Computer Aided Drawing Using the Tektronix Graphic System. (Illus.). 320p. 1983. 23.95 (ISBN 0-13-164723-7). P-H.
Newman, William M. & Sproull, Robert F. Principles of Interactive Computer Graphics. 2nd ed. (Illus.). 1979. text ed. 41.95 (ISBN 0-07-046338-7). McGraw.
Nievergelt, Jurg & Faiman, Michael, eds. Pertinent Concepts in Computer Graphics. LC 74-83553. (Illus.). 1969. 37.50 (ISBN 0-252-00032-3). U of Ill Pr.
Nitz, Lawrence H. Business Analysis & Graphics with Lotus 1-2-3. (Illus.). 176p. 1985. pap. 17.95 (ISBN 0-13-091604-8). P-H.
O'Malley, Timothy J. Twenty-Five Graphics Programs in Microsoft BASIC. (Illus.). 160p. 1983. 17.95 (ISBN 0-8306-0133-3, 1533); pap. 11.95 (ISBN 0-8306-0533-9). TAB Bks.
Pare, Eugene G. & Shook, Micheal. Computer Graphics Project for Design & Descriptive Geometry. 149p. 1985. pap. write for info. (ISBN 0-02-390980-3). MacMillan.
Parslow, R. D. & Green, R. Elliot, eds. Advanced Computer Graphics: Economics, Techniques & Applications. LC 77-137740. 1230p. 1971. 145.00x (ISBN 0-306-30517-8, Plenum Pr). Plenum Pub.
--Computer Graphics in Medical Research & Hospital Administration. LC 77-137741. 100p. 1971. 25.00x (ISBN 0-306-30518-6, Plenum Pr). Plenum Pub.
Parslow, R. D., et al. Computer Graphics: Techniques & Applications. LC 68-58992. 233p. 1969. 35.00x (ISBN 0-306-30393-0, Plenum Pr); pap. 9.95 (ISBN 0-306-20016-3). Plenum Pub.
Pavlidis, Theo. Algorithms for Graphics & Image Processing. LC 81-9832. (Illus.). 416p. 1982. text ed. 37.95 (ISBN 0-914894-65-X). Computer Sci.
Peddicord, Richard G. Creating Graphics & Music on the Commodore 64. 128p. 1985. incl. disk 19.95 (ISBN 0-88284-305-2). Alfred Pub.
--Understanding Apple Graphics. (Handy Guide Ser.). 64p. (Orig.). 1983. pap. 3.50 (ISBN 0-88284-250-1). Alfred Pub.
--Understanding Commodore 64 Graphics. (Handy Guide Ser.). 64p. (Orig.). 1984. pap. 3.50 (ISBN 0-88284-282-X). Alfred Pub.
Pelczarski, Mark & Tate, Joe, eds. The Creative Apple. (The Creative Ser.). (Illus.). 448p. 1983. 16.95 (ISBN 0-916688-25-9, 18R). Creative Comp.
Penna, Michael A. & Patterson, Richard R. Projective Geometry & Its Applications to Computer Graphics. (Illus.). 592p. 1986. text ed. 37.50 (ISBN 0-13-730649-0). P-H.
Perry, Gregory. Graphics & Sound on the Commodore 64. (Illus.). 304p. 1985. pap. text ed. 29.95 incl. disk (ISBN 0-13-363151-6); pap. text ed. 15.95 (ISBN 0-13-363144-3); disk 14.85 (ISBN 0-13-363169-9). P-H.
Person, Ron. Animation Magic with Your Apple IIe & IIc. 224p. (Orig.). 1985. pap. 15.95 (ISBN 0-07-881161-9, 161-9). Osborne McGraw.
Pfaff, G. E., ed. User Interface Management Systems. (Eurographic Seminars Ser.). (Illus.). 240p. 1985. 34.50 (ISBN 0-387-13803-X). Springer-Verlag.
Plenge, Axel. The Graphics Book for the Commodore. Dykema, Greg, tr. from Ger. 350p. (Orig.). 1984. pap. text ed. 19.95 (ISBN 0-916439-05-4). Abacus Soft.
Posdamer, Jeffrey. Using the IBM Personal Computer: Graphics. 1984. 18.45 (ISBN 0-03-063167-X). HR&W.
Prague, Cary N. Micro Business Graphics. (Illus.). 192p. (Orig.). 1985. 25.95 (ISBN 0-8306-0876-1); pap. 17.95 (ISBN 0-8306-1876-7). TAB Bks.
Prueitt, Melvin L. Computer Graphics: 118 Computer-Generated Designs. LC 74-18611. (Pictorial Archive Ser.). (Illus.). 80p. 1975. pap. 3.95 (ISBN 0-486-23178-X). Dover.
Rogers, D. F., ed. Computer Graphics in Engineering Education. 136p. 1982. 36.00 (ISBN 0-08-028949-5). Pergamon.
Rogers, David F. & Adams, J. Alan. Mathematical Elements for Computer Graphics. 1976. 24.00 (ISBN 0-07-053527-2). McGraw.
Rudman, Jack. Micrographics Operator. (Career Examination Ser.: C-2157). (Cloth bdg. avail. on request). 1976. pap. 10.00 (ISBN 0-8373-2157-3). Natl Learning.
--Senior Micrographics Operator. (Career Examination Ser.: C-2760). (Cloth bdg. avail. on request). 1980. pap. 12.00 (ISBN 0-8373-2760-1). Natl Learning.
Ryan, D. Computer Aided Graphics & Design. (Mechanical Engineering Ser.: Vol. 2). 1979. 32.75 (ISBN 0-8247-6912-0). Dekker.
Ryan, Daniel L. Computer-Aided Graphics & Design. 2nd, rev. ed. (Mechanical Engineering Ser.). 400p. 1985. 34.75 (ISBN 0-8247-7305-5). Dekker.
--Modern Graphic Communications: A CAD Approach. (Illus.). 304p. 1986. text ed. 34.95 (ISBN 0-13-594839-8). P-H.
Sandler, Corey. Desktop Graphics for the IBM PC. (Illus.). 240p. (Orig.). 1984. pap. 14.95 (ISBN 0-916688-60-7, 60-7). Creative Comp.
SAS Institute Inc. SAS Color Graphics 100-Series Video Training Instructional Guide, 1983 Edition. 308p. (Orig.). 1983. pap. 14.95 (ISBN 0-917382-46-3). SAS Inst.
--SAS Color Graphics 100-Series Video Training Workbook, 1983 Edition. 301p. (Orig.). 1983. pap. 9.95 (ISBN 0-917382-41-2). SAS Inst.
--SAS Views: SAS Color Graphics, 1983 Edition. (Orig.). 1983. pap. 40.00 (ISBN 0-917382-47-1). SAS Inst.
Savic, Dusko. BASIC Interactive Graphics. (Illus.). 176p. 1985. pap. text ed. 15.95 (ISBN 0-408-01522-5). Butterworth.
Schachter, Bruce J., ed. Computer Image Generation. LC 82-17366. 236p. 1983. 32.50 (ISBN 0-471-87287-3). Wiley.
Schaffer & Schaffer. Commodore 64 Color Graphics: An Advanced Guide. (Illus.). 220p. 1984. pap. 14.95 (ISBN 0-8359-0787-2). Reston.
Schnapp, Russell L. Macintosh Graphics in Modula: Two. (Illus.). 176p. 1986. text ed. 19.95 (ISBN 0-13-542309-0). P-H.
Schnapp, Russell L. & Stafford, Irvin G. Commodore 64 Computer Graphics Toolbox. (Personal Computing Ser.). (Illus.). 192p. 1985. pap. text ed. 15.95 (ISBN 0-13-152075-X); cassette 14.95 (ISBN 0-13-152083-0); incl. disk 29.95 (ISBN 0-13-152091-1). P-H.
--Computer Graphics for the Timex-Sinclair 1000, ZX-81. (Personal Computing Ser.). (Illus.). 128p. 1984. pap. text ed. 13.95 (ISBN 0-13-164278-2); cassette 14.95 (ISBN 0-13-164286-3). P-H.
--VIC-20 Computer Graphics Toolbox. (Prentice-Hall Personal Computing Ser.). (Illus.). 176p. 1984. pap. text ed. 14.95 (ISBN 0-13-941998-5); incl. cassette 29.95 (ISBN 0-13-942012-6); cassette 14.95 (ISBN 0-13-942004-5). P-H.
Schneider, Jerry B., ed. Applications of Computer Graphics in the Transportation-Land Use Field: A Review & Forecast for the Eighties. (CPL Bibliographies Ser: 126). 35p. 1983. 8.00 (ISBN 0-86602-126-4). Coun Plan Librarians.
Schreiber, Linda M. Advanced Programming Techniques for Your Atari, Including Graphics & Voice Programs. (Illus.). 224p. 19.95 (ISBN 0-8306-0145-7, 1545); pap. 14.50 (ISBN 0-8306-1545-8). TAB Bks.
Schwartz, Roberta & Callery, Michael. Apple Graphics: Tools & Techniques. (Illus.). 288p. 1986. pap. 17.95 (ISBN 0-13-039512-9). P-H.
Scott, Joan. COMPUTERGRAPHIA. LC 84-8950. (Illus.). 192p. 1984. 24.95x (ISBN 0-87201-328-6). Gulf Pub.
Scott, Joan E. Introduction to Interactive Computer Graphics. LC 81-7621. 255p. 1982. 29.95 (ISBN 0-471-05773-8, Pub. by Wiley-Interscience); pap. 18.95x (ISBN 0-471-86623-7). Wiley.
Semrau, Penny. MacArt: Using MacPaint & MacWrite. McCroskey, Mia, ed. (Illus.). 256p. (Orig.). 1985. pap. 19.95 (ISBN 0-912003-46-4). Bk Co.
Shaffer & Shaffer. Commodore 64 Color Graphics: A Beginner's Guide. (Illus.). 1984. pap. 14.95 (ISBN 0-8359-0786-4). Reston.
Shaffer & Shaffer Applied Research & Development. Apple IIc-IIe Advanced Graphics. 270p. Date not set. pap. 16.95 (ISBN 0-912003-50-2). Bk Co.
--Apple IIc-IIe Beginning Graphics. Ritz, Roberta, ed. 270p. (Orig.). 1985. pap. 16.95 (ISBN 0-912003-49-9). Bk Co.
--Commodore 64 Color Graphics: A Beginner's Guide. 1983. pap. 14.95 (ISBN 0-912003-06-5). Bk Co.
--Commodore 64 Color Graphics: An Advanced Guide. 300p. (Orig.). 1983. pap. 14.95 (ISBN 0-912003-07-3). Bk Co.
--IBM PCjr Color Graphics: A Beginner's Guide. Date not set. cancelled. Bk Co.
--IBM PCjr Color Graphics: An Advanced Guide. Date not set. cancelled. Bk Co.
Sikonowiz, Walter. Complete Book of Word Processing & Business Graphics. 256p. (Orig.). 1982. pap. 14.95 (ISBN 0-942412-03-6). Micro Text Pubs.
--The Complete Book of Word Processing & Business Graphics. 212p. 1983. 21.95 (ISBN 0-13-158667-X); pap. 14.95 (ISBN 0-13-158659-9). P-H.
Simon. IBM Graphics from the Ground Up. 352p. 1984. 15.95 (ISBN 0-317-05883-5). Hayden.
Singer, Barbara. Exploring Careers in Computer Graphics. (Exploring Careers Ser.). 144p. 1985. lib. bdg. 8.97 (ISBN 0-8239-0624-8). Rosen Group.
Small, David, et al, eds. The Creative Atari. LC 82-71997. (The Creative Ser.). (Illus.). 244p. 1983. pap. 15.95 (ISBN 0-916688-34-8, 18B). Creative Comp.
Smith, Leslie & Cummings, Brian. Macintosh Graphics. Date not set. price not set. NAL.
Softsync Inc. Staff & Aker, Sharon. MacPack: Creative Activities with MacPaint & MacWhite. 350p. 1985. pap. 15.95 (ISBN 0-912677-42-2). Ashton-Tate Bks.
Solid Modeling in Computer Graphics: The Technology, Its Applications, & Supply Sources. (Illus.). 85p. 1984. 129.00 (ISBN 0-914849-02-6). TBC Inc.
Stanton, Jeffrey. Apple Graphics & Arcade Game Design. 288p. 1982. pap. 19.95 (ISBN 0-912003-01-4). Bk Co.
Stanton, Jeffrey & Pinal, Dan. Atari Graphics & Arcade Game Design. 1983. pap. 16.95 (ISBN 0-912003-05-7). Bk Co.

Abrams, Marshall D. & Stein, Philip G. Computer Hardware & Software: An Interdisciplinary Introduction. LC 72-3455. 1973. text ed. 31.95 (ISBN 0-201-00019-9). Addison-Wesley.

Allen, R. I. & Stewart, Ian, eds. Estimating & Projecting Input-Output Coefficients. 1975p. 1975. PLB 27.50x (ISBN 0-678-08071-2). Kelley.

Bates. Input-Output. (Infotech Computer State of the Art Reports). 524p. 1975. 85.00 (ISBN 0-08-028499-X). Pergamon.

Blum, J. & Blum, E. Keypunch, Keytape & Keydisc. 210p. 1975. 33.75 (ISBN 0-677-03950-6). Gordon.

Bridges, David & Naylor, Helen. The Commodore Disk & Printer Handbook. (Illus.). 192p. 1984. pap. 14.95 (ISBN 0-946576-23-8, Pub. by Phoenix Pub). David & Charles.

Briscall, C. M. & Farrell, Gordon H. Canadian Hardware Supplied Ltd: Four Parts. (Illus.). 1982. pap. text ed. 15.95 (ISBN 0-8403-2613-0). Kendall-Hunt.

Brown, Charles & Kreta, Eleanor. Introduction to Data Entry Devices with a Subset of BASIC. 1979. pap. text ed. 6.95 (ISBN 0-8403-1952-5, 40195201). Kendall-Hunt.

Business Communications Staff. Computer Printers. 1985. pap. 1500.00 (ISBN 0-89336-428-2, G-091). BCC.

Chorafas, Dimitris N. Interactive Workstation: Software & Hardware. (Illus.). 272p. 1985. text ed. 27.95 (ISBN 0-89433-258-9). Petrocelli.

Christie, Linda G. The Simon & Schuster Guide to Peripherals. 288p. 1985. pap. 12.95 (ISBN 0-671-50628-5, Pub. by Computer Bks). S&S.

Computer & Business Equipment Manufacturers Association Staff (CBEMA) Computer & Business Equipment Marketing & Forecast Data Book, 1984. 2nd ed. (Illus.). 1984. pap. write for info. (ISBN 0-912797-03-7). CBEMA.

Cortada, James W. Managing DP Hardware: Capacity Planning, Cost Justification, Availability & Energy Management. (Data Processing Management Ser.). (Illus.). 416p. 1983. text ed. 36.95 (ISBN 0-13-550392-2). P-H.

Cripps, Martin. An Introduction to Computer Hardware. 1978. text ed. 24.95 (ISBN 0-316-16114-4). Little.

Csepinszky, A., ed. Input-Output Techniques. 1976. 29.00 (ISBN 0-9960004-7-X, Pub. by Akademiai Kaido Hungary). Heyden.

Data Entry Equipment in the 1980's. (Reports Ser.: No. 153). 181p. 1980. 985.00x (ISBN 0-88694-153-9). Intl Res Dev.

Electronic Computer Data Processing Equipment. (Seventy Ser). 1972. pap. 2.00 (ISBN 0-685-58148-9, 75). Natl Fire Prot.

Data, Text & Voice Encryption Equipment. (Reports Ser.: No. 183). 151p. 1981. 985.00x (ISBN 0-88694-183-0). Intl Res Dev.

Davies, Owen, ed. Omni Complete Catalog of Hardware & Peripherals. 352p. 1984. 19.95 (ISBN 0-02-529830-5); pap. 12.95 (ISBN 0-02-008300-9). Macmillan.

Davis, Frederic E. & PC World Editors. Hardware for the IBM PC & XT. 256p. 1985. pap. 16.95 (ISBN 0-671-49278-0, Pub. by Computer Bks). S&S.

Electronics Magazine. Personal Computing: Hardware & Software Basics. 1979. 32.50 (ISBN 0-07-019151-4). McGraw.

Enright, Thomas E., et al. Compute's Guide to Telecomputing on the Apple. Compute Editors, ed. (Orig.). 1985. pap. 9.95 (ISBN 0-942386-98-1). Compute Pubns.

Flores, Ivan. Data Structure & Management. 2nd ed. 1977. 32.95 (ISBN 0-13-197335-5). P-H.

Fraade, David J., ed. The Aster Guide to Computer Applications in the Pharmaceutical Industry: An Overview of System Manufacturers' Hardware & Software. (Illus.). 250p. (Orig.). 1984. pap. 45.00x (ISBN 0-943330-05-X). Aster Pub Corp.

Hanson, Peggy. Operating Data Entry Systems. (Illus.). 1977. pap. text ed. 19.95 (ISBN 0-13-637819-6). P-H.

Harper, Steve, et al. The HP-IL System: An Introductory Guide to the Hewlett-Packard Interface Loop. 106p. (Orig.). 1982. pap. 17.95 (ISBN 0-07-931077-X, 77-X). Osborne-McGraw.

Hill, Frederick J. & Peterson, Gerald R. Digital Systems: Hardware Organization & Design. 2nd ed. LC 78-7209. 701p. 1978. text ed. 46.75 (ISBN 0-471-39608-7); write for info. tchrs. ed. (ISBN 0-471-03694-3). Wiley.

Hogan, Thom. All about Computer Printers. cancelled 19.95 (ISBN 0-89303-305-7). Brady Comm.

Hohenstein, C. Louis. Computer Peripherals for Minicomputers, Microprocessors & Personal Computers. LC 80-10907. (Illus.). 320p. 1980. 32.95 (ISBN 0-07-029451-8). McGraw.

Holt, Charles A. Microcomputer Systems: Hardware, Assembly Langauge, & Pascal. 547p. 1986. text ed. price not set write for info. (ISBN 0-02-356370-2). Macmillan.

Hutchinson, Betty & Hutchinson, Warner. Computer Typing Made Simple. LC 84-8143. (Made Simple Ser.). 112p. 1985. pap. 4.95 (ISBN 0-385-19429-3). Doubleday.

Inside Personal Computer Disk Storage Systems. (Illus.). 32p. 1984. 5.00 (ISBN 0-318-01707-5). Percom Data.

International Resource Development Inc. Integrated Voice-Data Terminals. 215p. 1984. 1850.00x (ISBN 0-88694-585-2). Intl Res Dev.

Kaplus. Peripheral Array Processors, Vol. 14. (SCS Series: No. 2). 1984. 30.00 (ISBN 0-317-17125-9). Soc Computer Sim.

Kelly, Brian W. & Grimes, Dennis J. IBM PC Compatible Computer Directory: Hardware, Software & Peripherals. (Kelly-Grimes Buyers Guide Ser.: No. 1702). 581p. 1985. pap. 26.95 (ISBN 0-471-87819-7, Pub. by Wiley Pr). Wiley.

--IBM Personal Computer Directory: Hardware, Software, & Peripherals. (Kelly-Grimes Buyers Guide Ser.: No. 1-702). 581p. 1985. pap. 26.95 (ISBN 0-471-87821-9, Pub. by Wiley Pr). Wiley.

Knott, Julie & Prochnow, David. Commodore Peripherals: A User's Guide. (Orig.). 1984. pap. 9.95 (ISBN 0-942386-56-6). Compute Pubns.

Kotov, V. E. & Miklosko, J., eds. Algorithms, Software & Hardware of Parallel Computers. (Illus.). 380p. 1984. 32.00 (ISBN 0-387-13657-6). Springer-Verlag.

Larson, James A. End User Facilities in the Nineteen Eighties. (Tutorial Texts Ser.). 503p. 1982. 30.00 (ISBN 0-8186-0449-2, Q449). IEEE Comp Soc.

Ledin, Victor. How to Buy & Use a Printer. 1984. pap. 3.50 (ISBN 0-88284-315-X). Alfred Pub.

Lee, Kaiman. Evaluation of Computer Graphic Terminals. 2nd ed. LC 74-184824. 92p. 1975. 12.00x (ISBN 0-915250-11-X). Environ Design.

Levitan, Arlan R. & Leemon, Sheldon. Compute's Telecomputing on the IBM. Compute Editors, ed. (Orig.). 1985. pap. 14.95 (ISBN 0-942386-96-5). Compute Pubns.

McKay, Charles W. Experimenting with MSI, LSI, IO & Modular Memory Systems. (Illus.). 304p. 1981. 29.95 (ISBN 0-13-295477-X). P-H.

Moschytz, G. S. & Horn, Paul. Active Filter Design Handbook: For Use with Programmable Pocket Calculators & Minicomputers. LC 80-40845. 316p. 1981. 53.95x (ISBN 0-471-27850-5, Pub. by Wiley-Interscience). Wiley.

Nichols, E. & Jocelyn, S. Selection of Data Communications Equipment. (Illus.). 239p. (Orig.). 1979. pap. 37.50x (ISBN 0-85012-217-1). Intl Pubns Serv.

Peripherals Guide. 463p. 1984. 19.95 (ISBN 0-317-04402-8). Micro Info.

Personal Workstations: The Impact of Throwaway Memory. (Reports Ser.: No. 507). 163p. 1982. 985.00x (ISBN 0-88694-507-0). Intl Res Dev.

Pirisino, Jim. Minute Manual for the Dot Matrix Printer. 1985. pap. 12.95 (ISBN 0-913131-04-0). Minuteware.

Pirisino, Jim, ed. Minute Manual for the Letter Quality Printer. 150p. Date not set. pap. 12.95 (ISBN 0-913131-09-1). Minuteware.

Portable Terminals. (Reports Ser.: No. 149). 168p. 1980. 895.00x (ISBN 0-88694-149-0). Intl Res Dev.

Pritchard, J. A. Selection & Use of Terminals in On-Line Systems. LC 74-76261. 120p. 1974. 30.00x (ISBN 0-85012-117-5). Intl Pubns Serv.

Reymann, Joseph. How to Buy & Use a Modem. 1984. pap. 3.50 (ISBN 0-88284-319-2). Alfred Pub.

Salkind, Neil. A Guide to Commodore 64 Software & Hardware. cancelled (ISBN 0-317-07075-4). Datamost.

Seyer, Martin. RS-232C Made Easy: Connecting Computers, Printers, Terminals & Modems. LC 83-13939. 214p. 1983. text ed. 26.95 (ISBN 0-13-783480-2); pap. text ed. 21.95 (ISBN 0-13-783472-1). P-H.

Silveria, Terry C., et al. Buyer's Guide to Modems & Communications Software. (Illus.). 192p. (Orig.). 1985. 19.95 (ISBN 0-8306-0882-6, 1882); pap. 12.95 (ISBN 0-8306-1882-1). TAB Bks.

Sloan, M. E. Computer Hardware & Organization. 2nd ed. 514p. 1983. text ed. 33.95 (ISBN 0-574-21425-9, 13-4425); instr's. guide avail. (ISBN 0-574-21426-7, 13-4426). SRA.

Tedeschi, Frank P. The Active Filter Handbook. (Illus.). 1979. pap. 11.50 (ISBN 0-8306-1133-9, 1133). TAB Bks.

Teja, Edward R. Designer Guide to Disk Drivers. 1984. text ed. 29.95 (ISBN 0-8359-1268-X). Reston.

Tsukui, J. & Murakami, Y. Turnpike Optimality in Input-Output Systems: Theory & Application for Planning. (Contributions to Economic Analysis Ser.: Vol. 122). 260p. 1979. 51.00 (ISBN 0-444-85221-2, North Holland). Elsevier.

Uehara, T. & Barbacci, M., eds. Computer Hardware Description Languages & Their Applications. 244p. 1984. 38.50 (ISBN 0-444-86633-7, North Holland). Elsevier.

Umbers, I. G. A Review of Human Factors Data on Input Devices Used for Process Computer Communication, 1977. 1981. 40.00x (ISBN 0-686-97156-6, Pub. by W Spring England). State Mutual Bk.

Vendor Strategies for Personal Computers-Workstations. (Reports Ser.: No.524). 163p. 1982. 985.00x (ISBN 0-88694-524-0). Intl Res Dev.

Weber Systems, Inc. Epson Printer User's Handbook. 280p. 1985. pap. 9.95 (ISBN 0-345-31842-0). Ballantine.

Weber Systems Inc. Staff. Juki 6100 Printer User's Handbook. 270p. (Orig.). pap. cancelled. Weber Systems.

Weber Systems, Inc. Staff. Okidata Printer User's Handbook. LC 84-29172. (WSI's User's Handbooks to Personal Computers Ser.). 300p. (Orig.). 1985. pap. 15.95 (ISBN 0-938862-19-7). Weber Systems.

--Sourcebook of IBM Compatible Hardware, Software & Peripherals. 608p. (Orig.). 1985. pap. 18.95 (ISBN 0-345-31843-9). Ballantine.

Weiss, Eberhard. Input-Output Modellgenerator. (European University Studies Ser.: No. 5, Vol. 373). 284p. 1982. 34.20 (ISBN 3-8204-5808-5). P Lang Pubs.

Wells, M. Computing Systems Hardware. LC 75-27263. (Cambridge Computer Science Texts Ser.: No. 6). (Illus.). 225p. 1976. 18.95x (ISBN 0-521-29034-1). Cambridge U Pr.

Williams, Martha & Hogan, Thomas H., eds. National Online Meeting, Fourth, New York, April 12-14, 1983: Proceedings. (Illus.). 622p. 1983. pap. 50.00 (ISBN 0-938734-05-9). Learned Info.

Wolfe, Gordon W. Computer Peripherals That You Can Build. (Illus.). 272p. (Orig.). 1982. 19.95 (ISBN 0-8306-2449-X); pap. 15.95 (ISBN 0-8306-1449-4, 1449). TAB Bks.

COMPUTER INTERFACES

The Adaptation of Virtual Man-Computer Interfaces to User Requirements in Dialogs. Dehning, W. (Lecture Notes in Computer Sciences Ser.: Vol. 110). 142p. 1981. pap. 12.00 (ISBN 0-387-10826-2). Springer-Verlag.

Andrews, Michael. Programming Microprocessor Interface for Control & Instrumentation. (Illus.). 368p. 1982. 39.95 (ISBN 0-13-729996-6). P-H.

Artwick, B. Microcomputer Interfacing. 1980. 37.95 (ISBN 0-13-580902-9). P-H.

Bauer, F. L. & Samelson, K., eds. Language Hierarchies & Interfaces. (Lectures in Computer Science Ser.: Vol. 46). 1976. pap. 23.00 (ISBN 0-387-07994-7). Springer-Verlag.

Beer, Martin D. Microcomputer Interfacing & Associated Programming Techniques. (Illus.). 300p. (Orig.). 1985. pap. text ed. 19.95x (ISBN 0-00-383034-9, Pub. by Collins England). Sheridan.

Bibbero, Robert J. & Stern, David. Microprocessor Systems: Interfacing & Applications. 195p. 1982. 25.50x (ISBN 0-471-05306-6, Pub. by Wiley-Interscience). Wiley.

Bishop, Owen. Simple Interfacing Projects. (Illus.). 168p. 1983. 17.95 (ISBN 0-13-811091-3); pap. 10.95 (ISBN 0-13-811083-2). P-H.

Bohl, Marilyn. Introduction to IBM Direct Access Storage Devices. 224p. 1981. text ed. 20.95 (ISBN 0-574-21140-3, 13-4140). SRA.

Bolt, Richard A. The Human Interface: Where People & Computers Meet. (Computer Science Ser.). (Illus.). 192p. 1984. 28.00 (ISBN 0-534-03380-6); pap. 16.95 (ISBN 0-534-03387-3). Lifetime Learn.

Brey, Barry B. Microprocessor-Hardware Interfacing & Applications. 448p. 1984. Additional supplements may be obtained from publisher. text ed. 29.95 (ISBN 0-675-20158-6). Merrill.

Buchsbaum, Walter H. Interface IC. (Vestpocket Handbook). (Illus.). 1984. pap. 8.95 (ISBN 0-13-469205-5, Busn). P-H.

Carr, Joseph J. Interfacing Your Microcomputer to Virtually Anything. LC 84-8709. (Illus.). 336p. (Orig.). 1984. 21.95 (ISBN 0-8306-0890-7); pap. 13.95 (ISBN 0-8306-1890-2, 1890). TAB Bks.

--Microprocessor Interfacing. (Illus.). 252p. 1982. 14.95 (ISBN 0-8306-0064-7); pap. 7.95 o.p (ISBN 0-8306-1396-X, 1396). TAB Bks.

CES Industries, Inc. Ed-Lab Eighty Experiment Manual: Printer Interfacing. (Illus., Orig.). 1983. write for info. (ISBN 0-86711-033-3). CES Industries.

CES Industries, Inc. Staff. Ed-Lab Eighty Exercise Manual: Interfaces, Unit 2. (Illus.). 1982. write for info. (ISBN 0-86711-057-0). CES Industries.

--Ed-Lab Nine Hundred & Eighty Experiment: Projects & Interfacing. (Illus.). 1982. 9.50 (ISBN 0-86711-025-2). CES Industries.

Cluley, J. C. Interfacing to Microprocessors. 160p. 1983. 26.50 (ISBN 0-07-011409-9). McGraw.

--Minicomputer & Microprocessor Interfacing. 2nd ed. LC 82-8003. (Computer Systems Engineering Ser.). 272p. 1982. 27.50x (ISBN 0-8448-1400-8). Crane-Russak Co.

--Minicomputer & Microprocessor Interfacing. 280p. 1982. 95.00x (ISBN 0-7131-3474-7, Pub. by E Arnold). State Mutual Bk.

Cluley, John C. Computer Interfacing & On-Line Operation. LC 74-16952. (Computer Systems Engineering Ser.). (Illus.). 181p. 1975. 19.50x (ISBN 0-8448-0567-X). Crane-Russak Co.

Coffron, James & Harmon, Bill. Microprocessor Interfacing Techniques, Vol. II. 300p. pap. cancelled (ISBN 0-89588-196-9). SYBEX.

Coffron, James W. & Long, William E. Practical Interfacing Techniques for Microprocessor Systems. (Illus.). 432p. 1983. 31.95 (ISBN 0-13-691394-6). P-H.

Data Communications Magazine Staff, ed. Interface Proceedings '84. 1984. softcover 40.00 (ISBN 0-317-04545-8). McGraw.

DeRossi, Claude & Hopper, David. Software Interfacing: A User & Supplier Guide. (Illus.). 208p. 1984. 29.95 (ISBN 0-13-822353-X). P-H.

Disney, R. & Ott, T., eds. Applied Probability--Computer Science: The Interface, 2 Vols. (Progress in Computer Science Ser.). 1982. text ed. 39.95x ea. Vol. 2, 532pp (ISBN 0-8176-3067-8). Vol. 3, 514pp (ISBN 0-8176-3093-7). Birkhauser.

Downey, James & Rindsberg, Don. Timex-Sinclair Interfacing: Tested Interfacing Projects for the ZX-80, ZX-81 & the Timex-Sinclair 1000. (Illus.). 176p. 1983. 17.95 (ISBN 0-13-921759-2); pap. 10.95 (ISBN 0-13-921742-8). P-H.

Downey, James M. & Rogers, Steven M. PET Interfacing. LC 81-50568. 264p. 1981. pap. 16.95 (ISBN 0-672-21795-3). Sams.

Eggebrecht, Lewis C. Interfacing to the IBM Personal Computer. LC 83-61065. 272p. 1983. pap. 15.95 (ISBN 0-672-22027-X, 22027). Sams.

Field, Paul E. & Davies, John A. Computer Interfacing Techniques in Science. LC 84-26714. 224p. 1985. pap. 12.95 (ISBN 0-673-18112-X). Scott F.

Freeman, Jeff. How to Attach An Interface Card to An Apple IIe Computer. (Illus.). 36p. 1984. pap. 8.95 (ISBN 0-915509-05-9). Argos Pub Co.

Georgiou, V. J. Commodore 64 Interfacing Blue Book. (Illus.). 186p. 1984. pap. 16.95 (ISBN 0-912911-01-8). Microsignal.

Goldman, Joshua & Zolotow, Nina. System 1032 Host Language Interface User's Guide. rev. ed. (Illus.). 126p. 1985. looseleaf 21.50x (ISBN 0-912055-11-1). Software Hse.

Goldsbrough, et al. Analog Electronics for Microcomputer Systems. LC 83-61062. 440p. 1983. pap. 19.95 (ISBN 0-672-21821-6, 21821). Sams.

Hallgren, Richard. Interface Projects for the Apple II. (Illus.). 192p. 1982. 18.95 (ISBN 0-13-469395-7); pap. 12.95 (ISBN 0-13-469387-6). P-H.

--Interface Projects for the PET-CBM. (Illus.). 200p. Date not set. cancelled (ISBN 0-13-469494-5); pap. cancelled (ISBN 0-13-469486-4). P-H.

--Interface Projects for the TRS-80. (Illus.). 152p. 1982. 18.95 (ISBN 0-13-469437-6); pap. 12.95 (ISBN 0-13-469429-5). P-H.

Harper, Steve, et al. The HP-IL System: An Introductory Guide to the Hewlett-Packard Interface Loop. 106p. (Orig.). 1982. pap. 17.95 (ISBN 0-07-931077-X, 77-X). Osborne-McGraw.

Holland, John M. Advanced Sixty-Five Two Interfacing. LC 81-86551. 192p. 1982. pap. 13.95 (ISBN 0-672-21836-4, 21836). Sams.

Holland, R. C. Microcomputers & Their Interfacing. (Illus.). 191p. 1984. 26.00 (ISBN 0-08-031124-5); pap. 11.00 (ISBN 0-08-031125-3). Pergamon.

IEEE Standard 488-1978: IEEE Standard Digital Interface for Programmable Instrumentation. 1978. 10.00 (ISBN 0-317-03948-2, SHO7260). IEEE.

IEEE Standard 696-1983: IEEE Standard 696 Interface Devices. 1983. 7.50 (ISBN 0-317-03955-5, SHO8995). IEEE.

Institue of Electrical & Electronics Engineers. CAMAC Instrumentation & Interface Standards, 1982. 225p. 1982. 34.95 (ISBN 0-471-89737-X). Wiley.

Jackson, Ken, et al. System 1022 Host Language Interface: User's Reference Manual. 3rd ed. 153p. 1983. loose leaf 21.50x (ISBN 0-912055-05-7). Software Hse.

Kane, Gerry. The CRT Controller Handbook. 224p. (Orig.). 1980. pap. 9.95 (ISBN 0-07-931045-1, 45-1). Osborne-McGraw.

Labuz, Ronald A. How to Typeset from a Wordprocessor: An Interfacing Guide. 218p. 1984. pap. 29.95 (ISBN 0-8352-1899-6). Bowker.

Jefimenko, Oleg D. Thirty Music Programs for Timex-Sinclair 2068. 139p. 1984. pap. 8.00 (ISBN 0-917406-20-6). Electret Sci.
Kostka, Stefan M. A Bibliography of Computer Applications in Music. (Music Indexes & Bibliographies: No. 7). 1974. pap. 5.00 (ISBN 0-913574-07-4). Eur-Am Music.
Lefkoff, Gerald, ed. Papers from the West Virginia University Conference on Computer Applications in Music. (Illus.). 1967. 5.00 (ISBN 0-685-30820-0). McClain.
Manning, Peter. Electronic & Computer Music. (Illus.). 250p. 1985. 29.95x (ISBN 0-19-311918-8). Oxford U Pr.
Mathews, M. V., et al. Technology of Computer Music. 1969. 22.50x (ISBN 0-262-13050-5). MIT Pr.
Parker, Charlie. Music Major: Atari. (Illus.). 48p. 1984. pap. 24.95 canceled (ISBN 0-88056-208-0). Dilithium Pr.
Roads, Curtis & Strawn, John. Foundations of Computer Music. (Illus.). 736p. 1985. text ed. 50.00x (ISBN 0-262-18114-2). MIT Pr.
Strawn, John, ed. Digital Audio Signal Processing: An Anthology. (The Computer Music & Digital Audio Ser.). (Illus.). 283p. 1985. 34.95 (ISBN 0-86576-082-9). W Kaufmann.
Tjepkema, Sandra L. A Bibliography of Computer Music: A Reference for Composers. LC 81-2967. 294p. 1981. text ed. 24.00x (ISBN 0-87745-110-9). U of Iowa Pr.
Traister, Robert J. Music & Speech Programs for the IBM PC. (Illus.). 192p. 1983. 16.95 (ISBN 0-8306-0196-1); pap. 11.50 (ISBN 0-8306-0596-7, 1596). TAB Bks.
Von Foerster, H. & Beauchamp, James W., eds. Music by Computers. LC 69-19244. 139p. 1969. 15.00 (ISBN 0-471-91030-9, Pub. by Wiley). Krieger.
Whitney, John. Digital Harmony: On the Complementarity of Music & Visual Art. (Illus.). 200p. 1981. 24.95 (ISBN 0-07-070015-X, BYTE Bks). McGraw.
Winsor, Phil. Computer-Assisted Music Composition. 330p. 1986. pap. 29.95 (ISBN 0-89433-262-7). Petrocelli.

COMPUTER NETWORKS

see also Electronic Data Processing–Distributed Processing

Ahuja, V. Design & Analysis of Computer Communication Networks. 1982. 41.95x (ISBN 0-07-000697-0). McGraw.
All about One Hundred Forty-Eight Communications Software Packages. 58p. 25.00 (ISBN 0-318-03645-2). Datapro Res.
Amukotuwa, Sarath, et al. Radio Database International. Magne, Lawrence & Jensen, Don, eds. (Illus.). 200p. (Orig.). 1983. pap. 9.95 (ISBN 0-914941-00-3). Intl Broadcasting Serv.
Barrett, Judy. Joys of Computer Networking: The Personal Connection Handbook. 219p. 1984. pap. 9.95 (ISBN 0-07-003768-X, BYTE Bks). McGraw.
Bartee, Tom. Data Communications, Networks & Systems. Date not set. 39.95 (ISBN 0-672-22235-3, 22235). Sams.
Bates. Network Systems & Software. (Infotech Computer State of the Art Reports). 692p. 1975. 85.00 (ISBN 0-08-028507-4). Pergamon.
Beauchamp, K. G., ed. Information Technology & the Computer Network. (NATO ASI Series, Computer & Systems Sciences: Ser. F, No. 6). x, 281p. 1984. 34.50 (ISBN 0-387-12883-2). Springer-Verlag.
Bellamy, John C. Digital Telephony. 526p. 1982. 37.50 (ISBN 0-686-98112-X). Telecom Lib.
Bhargava, V. K. & Haccoun, D. Digital Communications by Satellite: Modulation, Multiple Access & Coding. 569p. 1981. 45.00 (ISBN 0-686-98094-8). Telecom Lib.
BIS Applied Systems & MacKintosh International. The Local Area Network Reference Guide. Brooks, Tom, ed. (Illus.). 288p. 1985. text ed. 70.00 (ISBN 0-13-539586-0). P-H.
Brooner, E. G. The Local Area Network Book. LC 83-51227. 128p. 1984. pap. 7.95 (ISBN 0-672-22254-X, 22254). Sams.
Bux, W. & Rudin, H., eds. Performance of Computer Communication Systems: Proceedings of the IFIP WG 7.3 TC 6 International Symposium on the Performance of Computer Communication Systems, Zurich, Switzerland, 21-23 March, 1984. 500p. 1985. 50.00 (ISBN 0-444-86883-6). Elsevier.
Chandler, David. Dialing for Data: A Consumer's How-To Handbook on Computer Communications. LC 84-42659. (Illus.). 256p. 1984. pap. 9.95 (ISBN 0-394-72774-6). Random.
Cheong, V. E. & Hirschheim, R. A. Local Area Networks: Issues, Products & Developments. LC 82-23778. (Wiley Series in Computing). 190p. 1983. 29.95x (ISBN 0-471-90134-2, 1-320, Wiley-Interscience). Wiley.
Chorafas, Dimitris. Computer Networks for Distributed Information Systems. 1980. 24.00 (ISBN 0-89433-105-1). Petrocelli.
--Data Communications for Distributed Information Systems. (Illus.). 300p. text ed. 24.00 (ISBN 0-89433-108-6). Petrocelli.
Chorafas, Dimitris N. Databases for Networks & Minicomputers. (Illus.). 250p. 1982. 25.00 (ISBN 0-89433-136-1). Petrocelli.
--Handbook of Data Communication & Computer Networks. (Illus.). 600p. 1985. text ed. 59.95 (ISBN 0-89433-244-9). Petrocelli.
Chu, Wesley W., ed. Advances in Computer Communications & Networking. LC 79-55305. (Illus.). 1979. pap. 49.00x (ISBN 0-89006-049-5). Artech Hse.
Cole, Robert. Computer Communications. 200p. 1982. pap. 17.95 (ISBN 0-387-91204-5). Springer-Verlag.
Computer Clubs, 1973. 7.50x (ISBN 0-85012-087-X). Intl Pubns Serv.
Computer Networking in the University: Success & Potential: Proceedings. 332p. 12.00 (ISBN 0-318-14012-8); members 6.00 (ISBN 0-318-14013-6). Educom.
Computer Telecommunications. Date not set. price not set (C101392). HarBraceJ.
Computers in Communication & Control: EUROCON 84. (PPL Conference Publication Ser.: No. 22). 424p. 1984. 80.00 (ISBN 0-86341-029-4, PC022). Inst Elect Eng.
Connell, Stephen & Galbraith, Ian A. Electronic Mail: A Revolution in Business Communications. LC 82-44. (Information & Communications Management Guides Ser.). 141p. 1982. text ed. 32.95 (ISBN 0-86729-015-3, 702-BW); pap. text ed. 22.95 (ISBN 0-86729-016-1). Knowledge Indus.
Cooper, Edward & Poda, Christopher L., eds. Broadband Network Technology: An Overview for the Data & Telecommunications Industries. LC 83-51319. (Illus.). 163p. (Orig.). 1984. pap. 19.95 (ISBN 0-9613248-0-5). Sytek Pr.
Crop, Sheldon. Local Area Networks for the IBM PC XT. 225p. 1984. pap. 14.95 (ISBN 0-89588-243-4). SYBEX.
Cypser, R. J. Communications Architecture for Distributed Systems. LC 76-52673. (Illus.). 1978. text ed. 38.95 (ISBN 0-201-14458-1). Addison-Wesley.
--Communications Architecture for Distributed Systems. 711p. 1978. 21.95 (ISBN 0-686-98122-7). Telecom Lib.
Davies, D. W. & Price, W. L. Security for Computer Networks: An Introduction to Data Security in Teleprocessing & Electronic Funds Transfer. (Computing Ser.). 300p. 1984. 34.95 (ISBN 0-471-90063-X). Wiley.
--Security in Teleprocessing & EPT Encryptian & Authentication in Computer Networks. LC 84-3662. (Computing Ser. 1-320). 300p. 1984. 34.95. Wiley.
Davies, D. W., et al. Computer Networks & Their Protocols. LC 78-21973. (Wiley Series in Computing). 487p. 1979. 71.95 (ISBN 0-471-99750-1, Pub. by Wiley Interscience). Wiley.
Davies, Donald W. The Security of Data in Networks. (Tutorial Texts Ser.). 241p. 1981. 20.00 (ISBN 0-8186-0366-6, Q366). IEEE Comp Soc.
Deasington, R. X.25 Explained: Protocols for Packet Switching Networks. (Computer Communications Ser.). 1985. 21.95 (ISBN 0-470-20183-5). Halsted Pr.
Deasington, R. J. A Practical Guide to Computer Communications & Networking. LC 84-4617. (Computers & Their Applications Ser.: 1-403). 126p. 1984. pap. text ed. 24.95x (ISBN 0-470-20078-2). Halsted Pr.
Doll, Dixon R. Data Communications: Facilities, Networks & System Design. 493p. 1978. 34.50 (ISBN 0-686-98099-9). Telecom Lib.
Durr, Michael. Networking IBM PCs: A Practical Guide. 320p. 1984. pap. 18.95 (ISBN 0-88022-106-2, 125). Que Corp.
Ellis, Robert L. Designing Data Networks. (Illus.). 224p. 1986. text ed. 32.95 (ISBN 0-13-201864-0). P-H.
Erickson, Jonathan & Cramer, William D. MacTelecommunications. 180p. (Orig.). 1984. pap. 17.95 (ISBN 0-07-881155-4, 155-4). Osborne-McGraw.
Feher, K. Digital Communications: Microwave Applications. 1981. 41.95 (ISBN 0-13-214080-2). P-H.
First Local Area Networks Exposition, 1982. Date not set. 125.00. Info Gatekeepers.
Fitzgerald, Jerry. Business Data Communications: Basic Concepts, Security & Design. LC 83-14798. (Wiley Series in Computers & Information Processing Systems for Business: 1-661). 502p. 1984. 33.45x (ISBN 0-471-89549-0); tchr's. ed. avail. (ISBN 0-471-88327-1). Wiley.
Flint, David C. The Data Ring Main: An Introduction to Local Area Networks. LC 82-23738. (Computing Science Ser.: I-652). 375p. 1983. 39.95x (ISBN 0-471-26251-X, Pub. by Wiley Heyden). Wiley.
Freeman, Harvey A. & Thurber, Kenneth J. Microcomputer Networks. (Tutorial Texts Ser.). 268p. 1981. 27.00 (ISBN 0-8186-0395-X, Q395). IEEE Comp Soc.
Gee, K. C. Introduction to Local Area Computer Networks. 150p. 1984. pap. 18.50 (ISBN 0-471-80036-8). Wiley.
--Local Area Network Gateways. 150p. 1984. pap. text ed. 12.95x (ISBN 0-471-81054-1). Wiley.
--Local Area Networks. 150p. 1982. 27.50x (ISBN 0-85012-365-8). Taylor & Francis.
--Proprietary Network Architectures. 250p. 1981. pap. 109.25 (ISBN 0-471-89423-0). Wiley.
Gengle, Dean. The Netweaver's Sourcebook: A Guide to Micro Networking & Communications. LC 84-6212. 1438p. 1984. pap. 14.95 (ISBN 0-201-05208-3). Addison-Wesley.
Grange, Jean-Louis & Gein, M., eds. Flow Control in Computer Networks: Proceedings of International Symposium Held in France, Feb. 1979. 430p. 1979. 64.00 (ISBN 0-444-85297-2, North Holland). Elsevier.
Green, James H. Local Area Networks: A User's Guide for Business Professionals. 1985. pap. 17.95 (ISBN 0-673-18065-4). Scott F.
Green, Paul E., Jr., ed. Computer Network Architectures & Protocols. LC 82-5227. (Applications of Communications Theory Ser.). 735p. 1982. 65.00x (ISBN 0-306-40788-4, Plenum Pr). Plenum Pub.
Hamelink, Cees J. Finance & Information: A Study of Converging Interests. Voigt, Melvin J., ed. LC 81-17587. (Communication & Information Science Ser.). 192p. 1982. text ed. 29.50 (ISBN 0-89391-091-0). Ablex Pub.
--Transnational Data Flows in the Information Age. 115p. 1984. pap. text ed. 19.95x (ISBN 0-86238-042-1, Pub. by Chartwell-Bratt England). Brookfield Pub Co.
Hammond, Joseph L. & O'Reilly, Peter J. Performance Analysis of Local Computer Networks. LC 85-13526. 1986. text ed. 35.95x (ISBN 0-201-11530-1). Addison-Wesley.
Hayes, Jeremiah F. Modeling & Analysis of Computer Communications Networks. (Applications of Communications Theory Ser.). 414p. 1984. 35.00x (ISBN 0-306-41782-0, Plenum Pr). Plenum Pub.
Held, Gilbert. Data Communication Components: Characteristics, Operation, Applications. LC 79-2041. 280p. 1979. 23.50 (ISBN 0-8104-5126-3, 5126). Hayden.
Helfrick, Albert D. Practical Repair & Maintenance of Communications Equipment. 320p. pap. 16.95 (ISBN 0-13-693516-8). P-H.
Holtz, Herman. Computer Work Stations: The Manager's Guide to Office Automation & Multi-Users Systems. 280p. 1985. 24.50 (ISBN 0-412-00711-8, NO. 9004, Pub. by Chapman & Hall). Methuen Inc.
House, William C. Electronic Communication Systems. 1980. 25.00 (ISBN 0-89433-098-5). Petrocelli.
Housley, Trevor. Data Communications & Teleprocessing Systems. (P-H Data Processing Management Ser.). (Illus.). 1979. text ed. 34.95 (ISBN 0-13-197368-1). P-H.
Hufault, J. R. OP AMP Network Design Manual. 448p. 1985. 37.00 (ISBN 0-471-81327-3). Wiley.
Hutchison, D., et al, eds. Local Area Networks: An Advanced Course. (Lecture Notes in Computer Science: Vol. 184). viii, 497p. 1985. pap. 31.00 (ISBN 0-387-15191-5). Springer-Verlag.
International Resource Development Inc. Terminals & Network Products for the 3270 Environment. 199p. 1983. write for info (ISBN 0-88694-580-1). Intl Res Dev.
Jefferson, George. Communications Getting It All Together: The British Computer Society Lecture, No. 4. (British Computer Society). 14p. 1983. 11.95x (ISBN 0-471-26269-2, Wiley Heyden). Wiley.
Karp, H. R. Practical Applications of Data Communications: A Users Guide. (Illus.). 424p. 1980. 39.50 (ISBN 0-07-033423-4). Mcgraw.
Kasperek, Gabriel. Troubleshooting the Data Comm Network. 292p. 1984. looseleaf 59.95 (ISBN 0-935506-27-6). Carnegie Pr.
Knight, Timothy O. The World Connection. LC 82-61969. 144p. 1983. pap. 9.95 (ISBN 0-672-22042-3, 22042). Sams.
Kreager, Paul S. Practical Aspects of Data Communications. (Illus.). 256p. 1983. 34.95 (ISBN 0-07-035429-4). McGraw.
Kruglinski, David. The Osborne-McGraw-Hill Guide to Your IBM PC Communications. 250p. (Orig.). 15.95 (ISBN 0-07-881126-0, 126-0). Osborne-McGraw.
Kuo, Benjamin C. Linear Networks & Systems. LC 78-27007. 426p. 1979. Repr. of 1967 ed. lib. bdg. 26.00 (ISBN 0-88275-835-7). Krieger.
Kuo, F. Protocols & Techniques for Data Communication Networks. 1981. 45.95 (ISBN 0-13-731729-8). P-H.
Lambert, Steve. Online: A Guide to America's Leading Information Services. LC 84-27159. 319p. 1985. pap. 19.95 (ISBN 0-914845-35-7). Microsoft.
Lenk, John D. Handbook of Data Communications. (Illus.). 352p. 1984. 27.95 (ISBN 0-13-377317-5). P-H.
Local Networks: Strategy & Systems. 536p. 1983. 112.00x (ISBN 0-903796-93-7, Pub. by Online). Taylor & Francis.
Local Networks: Strategy & Systems: Proceedings of Localnet 83 (Europe) 536p. (Orig.). 1983. pap. text ed. 134.00x (ISBN 0-903796-93-7, Pub. by Online Conferences England). Brookfield Pub Co.
Longley, D. & Shain, M. Expanding & Networking Computers. 1985. 39.95 (ISBN 0-444-00956-6). Elsevier.
--Expanding & Networking Microcomputers: The Complete & Up-to-Date Guide to over 600 Boards for Apple & IBM-PCs. 200p. 1985. 39.95 (ISBN 0-444-00957-4, North-Holland). Elsevier.
McGlynn, Daniel R. Distributed Processing & Data Communications. LC 78-1117. 305p. 1978. 35.95x (ISBN 0-471-01886-4, Pub. by Wiley-Interscience). Wiley.
McQuillan, John M. & Cerf, Vinton G. A Practical View of Computer Communications Protocols. (Tutorial Texts Ser.). 258p. 1978. 16.00 (ISBN 0-8186-0201-5, Q201); members 12.00. IEEE Comp Soc.
Maronski, J. & Rupinska, M. Computer Networks Terminology. 73p. 1980. pap. 7.50 (ISBN 83-01-01179-3, M-9061). French & Eur.
Meditch, J. S., ed. Computer-Communication Networks. 140p. 1983. 52.25 (ISBN 0-08-031132-6). Pergamon.
Milenkovic, Milan. Update Synchronization in Multiaccess Systems. Stone, Harold S., ed. LC 81-16034. (Computer Science Ser.: Distributed Database Systems: No. 8). 94p. 1981. 34.95 (ISBN 0-8357-1223-0). UMI Res Pr.
National Computing Centre. Handbook of Data Communications. 250p. 1982. pap. 27.35 (ISBN 0-471-89456-7, DP00, Pub. by Wiley-Interscience). Wiley.
Network Editors, ed. New Techniques in Telecontrol Using Microprocessors, Computer Based Communication Networks. 1982. 60.00x (ISBN 0-904999-32-7, Pub. by Network). State Mutual Bk.
The Networking Software. 1985. price not set (ISBN 0-912603-63-1). Micro Info.
The Networking Software Guide. 283p. 49.95 (ISBN 0-912603-63-1). Micro Info.
Networks. (Infotech Computer State of the Art Reports). 422p. 1981. 405.00 (ISBN 0-08-028539-2). Pergamon.
North American Perspective: Computing & Networks in Canada & the United States: Proceedings. 222p. 12.00 (ISBN 0-318-14026-8); members 6.00 (ISBN 0-318-14027-6). Educom.
Online Publications Ltd. Data Networks: Development & Use. 720p. 199.00x (ISBN 0-903796-59-7, Pub by. Online England). State Mutual Bk.
Owen, Jan. Understanding Computer Information Networks. (Handy Guide Ser.). 64p. (Orig.). 1984. pap. 3.50 (ISBN 0-88284-267-6). Alfred Pub.
Ozkarahan, Esen. Database Machines & Database Management. (Illus.). 576p. 1986. text ed. 39.95 (ISBN 0-13-196031-8). P-H.
Padlipsky, Michael A. Elements of Networking Style: Essays & Animadversions on the Art of Intercomputer Networking. (Illus.). 236p. 1985. pap. text ed. 24.95 (ISBN 0-13-268111-0). P-H.
Pouzin. The Cyclades Computer Network: Toward Layered Network Architectures. (International Council for Computer Communications Ser.: Vol. 2). 388p. 1982. 40.00 (ISBN 0-444-86482-2, North-Holland). Elsevier.
A Practical Guide to Data Communications Management. 1985. pap. write for info (ISBN 0-442-20918-5). Van Nos Reinhold.
QED Information Sciences, Inc. Multi-Vendor Data Communications Networks. 480p. 1982. 3-ring binder 95.00 (ISBN 0-89435-057-9). QED Info Sci.
St. Amand, Joseph V. A Guide to Packet-Switched Value-Added Networks. 150p. 1985. pap. text ed. 19.95 (ISBN 0-02-949020-0). Macmillan.
Sauer, Charles H. & MacNair, Edward A. Simulation of Computer Communication Systems. (Illus.). 176p. 1983. text ed. 35.00 (ISBN 0-13-811125-1). P-H.
Schoemaker, S. Computer Network & Simulations. 256p. 1978. 47.00 (ISBN 0-444-85208-5, North-Holland). Elsevier.
Schwartz, M. Computer Communications Network Design & Analysis. 1977. sol. manual 4.00 (ISBN 0-13-165159-5). P-H.
Scott, P. R. Reviewing Your Data Transmission Network. 160p. 1982. pap. 54.65 (ISBN 0-471-89424-9). Wiley.

Beizer, Boris. Software Testing Techniques. (Electrical-Computer Science & Engineering Ser.). 300p. 1982. 29.95 (ISBN 0-442-24592-0). Van Nos Reinhold.
Berenbon, Howard. TRS-80 Sharp Pocket Computer Programs. LC 83-50938. 224p. 1984. pap. 15.95 (ISBN 0-672-22078-4, 22078). Sams.
Berg, H. K. & Giloi, W. K., eds. The Use of Formal Specification of Software. (Informatik-Fachberichte Ser.: Vol. 36). 388p. 1980. pap. 22.10 (ISBN 0-387-10442-9). Springer-Verlag.
Bergland, Glen D. & Gordon, Ronald D. Software Design Strategies. 2nd ed. (Tutorial Texts Ser.). 479p. 1981. 30.00 (ISBN 0-8186-0389-5, Q389). IEEE Comp Soc.
Berliner, Thomas H. & Kathman, Clemens A. The Illustrated TK! Solver Book. LC 84-25692. (Illus.). 240p. 1984. pap. 17.95 (ISBN 0-915381-63-X). WordWare Pub.
Bersoff, Edward, et al. Software Configuration Management: An Investment in Product Integrity. 1980. 36.95 (ISBN 0-13-821769-6). P-H.
Biermann, Alan W. & Guiho, Gerard. Automatic Program Construction. 1982. write for info. Elsevier.
--Computer Program Synthesis Methodologies. 1982. lib. bdg. 52.50 (ISBN 90-277-1504-1, Pub. by Reidel Holland). Kluwer Academic.
Biliography on Available Computer Programs in the General Area of HVAC&R. 260p. 1981. 32.00 (ISBN 0-318-12756-3, SP153); members 16.00 (ISBN 0-318-12757-1). Am Heat Ref & Air Eng.
Bingham, Julie. One-Two-Three Go. (Illus.). 256p. 1984. pap. 14.38 (ISBN 0-201-13047-5). Addison-Wesley.
Birrell, N. D. & Ould, M. A. A Practical Handbook for Software Development. (Illus.). 275p. 1985. 34.50 (ISBN 0-521-25462-0). Cambridge U Pr.
BIS-PEDDER Associates Ltd. Computing Marketplace: A Directory of Computing Services & Software Supplies for Word Processors, Micros, Minis, & Mainframes. 2nd ed. (Computing Services for the Eighties). 472p. (Orig.). 1983. pap. text ed. 69.50x (ISBN 0-566-03476-X). Gower Pub Co.
Bishop, Bob, et al. Apple Visions. 256p. (Orig.). 1985. pap. 39.95 315 bk. disk package (ISBN 0-201-15324-6). Addison-Wesley.
Bitter, Gary G. & Gore, Kay. The Best of Educational Software for Apple II Computers. 375p. 1984. pap. 12.95 (ISBN 0-89588-206-X). SYBEX.
Bjorner, D., ed. Abstract Software Specifications. (Lecture Notes in Computer Sciences Ser.: Vol. 86). 567p. 1980. pap. 35.00 (ISBN 0-387-10007-5). Springer-Verlag.
Blackadar, Thomas. The Best of Commodore 64 Software. LC 84-50352. (Illus.). 181p. 1984. pap. 12.95 (ISBN 0-89588-194-2). SYBEX.
Blanking-Clark, T. & Cross, T. B. The Soft Side of Software: A Management Approach to Producing Documentation. 1985. write for info. (ISBN 0-471-81527-6). Wiley.
Blasewitz, Robert M. & Stern, Frank. Microcomputer Systems: Hardware-Software Design. 560p. 29.95 (5123). Hayden.
Bleazard, G. B. Teleprocessing Monitor Packages for ICL 2903-04. 1978. pap. 34.50x (ISBN 0-85012-197-3). Intl Pubns Serv.
Boehm, B. W., et al. Characteristics of Software Quality. (TRW Series on Software Technology: Vol. 1). 166p. 1978. 53.25 (ISBN 0-444-85105-4, North-Holland). Elsevier.
The Book of Apple Software 1983. 491p. 1983. 19.95 (ISBN 0-317-05196-2). Bk Co.
Borking, John J. Third Party Protection of Software & Firmware: Direct Protection of Zeros & Ones. LC 84-24752. 522p. 1985. 74.00 (ISBN 0-444-87677-4, North-Holland). Elsevier.
Boyce, David E., et al. A Computer Program for Optimal Regression Analysis. (Discussion Paper Ser.: No. 28). 1969. pap. 5.75 (ISBN 0-686-32197-9). Regional Sci Res Inst.
Boyer, Robert S. & Moore, J. Strother. The Correctness Problem in Computer Science. LC 81-67887. (International Lecture in Computer Science Ser.). 1982. 39.50 (ISBN 0-12-122920-3). Acad Pr.
Brand, Stewart. Whole Earth Software Catalog. LC 84-15096. 208p. 1984. pap. 17.50 (ISBN 0-385-19166-9, Quantum Pr). Doubleday.
Brandon, Peter S., et al. Computer Programs for Building Cost Appraisal. 200p. (Orig.). 1985. pap. text ed. 25.00x (ISBN 0-00-383043-8, Pub. by Collins England). Sheridan.
Brebbia, C. A., et al, eds. Hydrosoft '84; Hydraulic Engineering Software: Proceedings of the International Conference, Protoroz, Yugoslavia, Sept. 10-14, 1984. 1984. 129.75 (ISBN 0-444-99607-9). Elsevier.
Brelsford, William M. & Relles, Daniel A. Statlib: A Statistical Computing Library. 448p. 1981. pap. text ed. 33.95 (ISBN 0-13-846220-8). P-H.
Bretz, Jeff & Craig, John C. One Hundred Ready-to-Run Programs & Subroutines for the IBM PC. (Illus.). 320p. (Orig.). 1983. 22.95 (ISBN 0-8306-0540-1); pap. 16.50 (ISBN 0-8306-1540-7, 1540). TAB Bks.
Bridges, George. IBM PCjr Charts & Graphs. 96p. 1984. 7.95 (ISBN 0-86668-042-X). ARCsoft.
--IBM PCjr Personal Finance Programs. 96p. 1984. 7.95 (ISBN 0-86668-043-8). ARCsoft.
--The IBM PCjr Songbook. 96p. 1984. 7.95 (ISBN 0-86668-041-1). ARCsoft.
Briefs, U., et al, eds. Systems Design for, with, & by the Users. 424p. 1983. 55.50 (ISBN 0-444-86613-2, I-174-83, North Holland). Elsevier.
British Computer Society. Buying Financial Accounting Software. (Software Package Buyer's Guides Ser.). 48p. 1985. pap. 8.95 (ISBN 0-521-31781-9). Cambridge U Pr.
Brockmann, J. R. Writing Better Software Computer Documentation. 500p. 1985. 30.00 (ISBN 0-471-88472-3). Wiley.
Brooner, E. G. BASIC Business Software. LC 80-52232. 144p. 1981. pap. 11.95 (ISBN 0-672-21751-1, 21751). Sams.
Brown, Gary D. & Sefton, Donald. Surviving with Financial Application Packages for the Computer. 233p. 1983. 24.50 (ISBN 0-471-87065-X, Pub. by Wiley-Interscience). Wiley.
Brown, P. J. Macroprocessors & Techniques for Portable Software. LC 3-17597. (Computing Ser.). 244p. 1974. 53.95 (ISBN 0-471-11005-1, Pub. by Wiley-Interscience). Wiley.
--Writing Interactive Compilers & Interpreters. LC 79-40513. (Computing Ser.). 265p. 1981. pap. 17.95x (ISBN 0-471-10072-2, Pub. by Wiley-Interscience). Wiley.
--Writing Interactive Compilers & Interpreters. LC 79-40513. (Wiley Series in Computing). 265p. 1979. 44.95 (ISBN 0-471-27609-X, Pub. by Wiley-Interscience). Wiley.
Brownstein, Irv & Lerner, Nancy. Guidelines for Evaluating Software Packages. 200p. 1982. 110.00 (ISBN 0-444-00767-9). Elsevier.
Bryan, William B, et al. Software Configuration Management. (Tutorial Texts Ser.). 452p. 1980. 25.00 (ISBN 0-8186-0309-7, Q309). IEEE Comp Soc.
Buckle, J. K. Managing Software Projects. LC 84-796. 124p. 1984. Repr. of 1977 ed. lib. bdg. 29.75 (ISBN 0-89874-743-0). Krieger.
--Software Configuration Management. (Computer Science Ser.). (Illus.). 168p. 1983. 35.00x (ISBN 0-333-30719-4); pap. 19.95x (ISBN 0-333-33228-8). Scholium Intl.
Buckleitner, Warren. Survey of Early Childhood Software. 100p. 1985. 19.95 (ISBN 0-931114-32-2). High-Scope.
--Survey of Early Childhood Software. 100p. (Orig.). 1985. pap. 19.95 (ISBN 0-931114-32-2). High-Scope.
Budin, Howard. Speed Walker: Fun to Program Your IBM-PC. 89p. (Orig.). 1984. pap. 2.95 (ISBN 0-523-42246-6). Pinnacle Bks.
Burkhard, R. E. & Derigs, U. Assignment & Matching Problems: Solution Methods with FORTRAN-Programs. (Lecture Notes in Economics & Mathematical Systems Ser.: Vol. 184). 148p. 1980. pap. 18.00 (ISBN 0-387-10267-1). Springer-Verlag.
Burnham, Don, intro. by. Manufacturing Productivity Solutions II. LC 80-54415. (Illus.). 161p. 1980. pap. text ed. 20.00 (ISBN 0-87263-106-0). SME.
Burns, Edward. TRS-80 Teaching Aid: Ready-to-Run Programs for the Classroom & Home. (Illus.). 1984. pap. 15.95 (ISBN 0-8359-7875-3). Reston.
Burton, Kevin R. Advanced Applications for PFS & the IBM Assistant Series. (Illus.). 224p. (Orig.). 1985. 22.95 (ISBN 0-8306-0989-X, 1989); pap. 16.95 (ISBN 0-8306-1989-5). Tab Bks.
Busch, David. Commodore 64 Subroutine Cookbook. LC 84-2775. (Illus.). 208p. 1984. pap. 12.95 (ISBN 0-89303-383-9). Brady Comm.
--IBM PCjr Subroutine Cookbook. cancelled 12.95 (ISBN 0-89303-541-6). Brady Comm.
--Keyboard Challenge with Commodore 64. (Illus.). 208p. 1984. 12.95 (ISBN 0-89303-601-3). Brady Comm.
Busch, David D. Apple Soft Subroutine Cookbook. (Illus.). 208p. 1985. pap. 12.95 (ISBN 0-89303-322-7). Brady Comm.
Business Mini-Micro Software Directory. 809p. 1984. 75.00 (ISBN 0-8352-1970-4). Bowker.
Business Mini-Micro Software Directory Supplement. 200p. 1985. 45.00 (ISBN 0-8352-1976-3). Bowker.
Business Programs Applications. 282p. 4.95 (ISBN 0-317-05257-8, 62-2074). Radio Shack.
Calingaert, Peter. Assemblers, Compilers, & Program Translation. LC 78-21905. 270p. 1979. 28.95 (ISBN 0-914894-23-4). Computer Sci.
Cameron, John. JSP & JSD: The Jackson Approach to Software Development. 257p. 1983. 30.00 (ISBN 0-8186-8516-6). IEEE Comp Soc.
Carr, Joseph J. Sixty-Eight Scientific & Engineering Programs for the Apple II & IIe. 1984. 19.95 (ISBN 0-8359-6920-7). Reston.
Carr, Joseph L. Sixty-Eight Scientific & Engineering Programs for the IBM PC & PC XT. 1984. 19.95 (ISBN 0-8359-6921-5). Reston.
Carroll, Charles J. Eighty Practical Time-Saving Programs for the TRS-80. (Illus.). 252p. o.p 15.95 (ISBN 0-8306-0010-8, 1293); pap. 11.50 (ISBN 0-8306-1293-9, 1293). TAB Bks.
Carter, Lee. Fifty Programs for the Timex-Sinclair 1000. 72p. 1983. pap. 6.95 (ISBN 0-916688-23-2, 15T). Creative Comp.
Carter, Lynn R. An Analysis of Pascal Programs. Stone, Harold, ed. LC 82-4925. (Computer Science: Systems Programming: No. 6). 202p. 1982. 44.95 (ISBN 0-8357-1331-8). UMI Res Pr.
Cartin, Roger J. & Osborne, Wilma M. Guidance on Software Maintenance. (National Bureau of Standards Special Publications 500-105. Computer Science & Technology Ser.). 72p. (Orig.). 1983. pap. 2.50 (ISBN 0-318-11727-4). Gov Printing Office.
Casciato & Horsfall. TI 99-4A: Twenty-Four BASIC Programs. LC 83-50831. 224p. 1983. pap. 12.95 (ISBN 0-672-22247-7, 22247); incl. tape 19.95 (ISBN 0-672-26172-3, 26172). Sams.
Castlewitz, David M. The VisiCalc Program Made Easy. 160p. (Orig.). 1983. pap. 12.95 (ISBN 0-07-931089-3, 89-3). Osborne-McGraw.
Catalog of Computer Programs. 95p. 1977. 4.50 (ISBN 0-318-14973-7). NARUC.
Catalog of Computer Programs & Data Bases. 416p. 1984. 30.00 (ISBN 0-318-14974-5). NARUC.
Catalogue of Computer Programs in Meteorology. (Publications Ser.: No. 409). 1976. pap. 60.00 (ISBN 92-63-10409-3, W175, WMO). Unipub.
CDS-ISIS & MINISIS: A Functional Analysis & Comparison. 88p. 1981. pap. 9.00 (ISBN 0-88936-296-3, IDRCTS37, IDRC). Unipub.
Chalksoft Educational Software. (Ward Lock Educational Ser.). 29.00x (ISBN 0-317-28560-2, Pub. by Ward Lock Educational England). State Mutual Bk.
Chan, Julie M. & Korostoff, Marilyn. Teachers' Guide to Designing Classroom Software. LC 84-6962. 95p. (Orig.). 1984. pap. 9.95 (ISBN 0-8039-2313-9). Sage.
Chance, David. Thirty Computer Programs for the Homeowner, in BASIC. (Illus.). 364p. 1982. 16.95 (ISBN 0-8306-0050-7); pap. 10.25 (ISBN 0-8306-1380-3, 1380). TAB Bks.
Chandy, K. & Yeh, Raymond T., eds. Current Trends in Programming Methodology: Software Modeling, Vol. 3. (Illus.). 1978. ref. 34.95 (ISBN 0-13-195727-9). P-H.
Chang, Huan-Yang & Over, Ira Earl. Selected Numerical Methods & Computer Programs for Chemical Engineers. 235p. (Orig.). 1980. pap. text ed. 11.95 (ISBN 0-88408-131-1). Sterling Swift.
Chantico-QED. Management Evaluation of Software Packages. LC 85-60181. (The Chantico Technical Management Ser.). (Illus.). 150p. (Orig.). 1985. pap. 29.50 (ISBN 0-89435-155-9, CP 1559). QED Info Sci.
Charles, Thomas W. & Stiner, Frederic M., Jr. Your Name Company: Accounting Practice Set for the Computer. 144p. 1985. pap. write for info. (ISBN 0-534-04506-5). Kent Pub Co.
Chartrand, Marilyn J. & Williams, Constance D., eds. Educational Software Directory: A Subject Guide to Microcomputer Software. 1982. pap. text ed. 27.50 (ISBN 0-87287-352-8). Libs Unl.
Chaudier, Louann. Leading Consultants in Computer Software. 2nd ed. 290p. (Orig.). 1984. pap. 67.00 (ISBN 0-943692-08-3). Res Pubns VA.
Chenevert, Martin & Roye, J. PIPECALC (TM) 1: Practical Pipeline Hydraulics. LC 84-9007. (Microcomputer Software for Pipeline Engineers Ser.). 1984. incl. disk 295.00x (ISBN 0-87201-741-9). Gulf Pub.
Cho, Chin-Kuei. An Introduction to Software Quality Control. LC 80-15244. (Business Data Processing Ser.). 445p. 1980. 48.50 (ISBN 0-471-04704-X, Pub. by Wiley-Interscience). Wiley.
Chorafas, Dimitris N. Interactive Workstation: Software & Hardware. (Illus.). 272p. 1985. text ed. 27.95 (ISBN 0-89433-258-9). Petrocelli.
Chorafas, Dirmitris N. The Software Handbook. (Illus.). 500p. 1984. reference 49.95 (ISBN 0-89433-248-1). Petrocelli.
Chorafas, Dmitris N. Interactive Workstations: Software & Hardware. (Illus.). 272p. 1985. 27.95 (ISBN 0-89433-258-9). Van Nos Reinhold.
Cibbarelli, Pamela & Kazlauskas, Edward, eds. Directory of Information Management Software for Libraries, Information Centers, Record Centers, 1985-1986. 239p. 1985. pap. 49.00 (ISBN 0-913203-14-9). Pacific Info.
Clapp, Doug. Doug Clapp's Jazz Book. 1985. pap. 17.95 (ISBN 0-673-18266-5). Scott F.
Clarke, E. & Kozen, D., eds. Logics of Program: Workshop, Carnegie-Mellon University, Pittsburgh, Pa., June 6-8, 1983. (Lecture Notes in Computer Science: Vol. 164). vi, 528p. 1984. pap. 25.50 (ISBN 0-387-12896-4). Springer-Verlag.
Clarke, R. M. American Motors Muscle Cars 1966-1970. (Illus.). 100p. 1982. pap. 11.95 (ISBN 0-907073-58-1, Pub. by Brooklands Bks England). Motorbooks Intl.
Clay, Susan & Brooks, JoeAnn. Software Primer: Computer Accounting. Harper, Larry D., ed. LC 83-82214. (Software Primer Ser.). 180p. 1984. binder cancelled (ISBN 0-913871-04-4). JNZ.
Cobb, Douglas F. & LeBlond, Geoffrey. Using 1-2-3. (Illus.). 420p. 1983. pap. 17.95 (ISBN 0-88022-045-7, 39). Que Corp.
Cody, William J., Jr. & White, William. Software Manual for the Elementary Functions. (Illus.). 288p. 1980. text ed. 29.95 (ISBN 0-13-822064-6). P-H.
Cole, Jim. Fifty More Programs in BASIC for the Home, School & Office. 96p. (Orig.). 1981. pap. 9.95 (ISBN 0-86668-003-9). ARCsoft.
--Fifty Programs in BASIC for the Home, School & Office. 2nd ed. (Illus.). 96p. 1981. pap. 9.95 (ISBN 0-86668-502-2). ARCsoft.
--Thirty-Five Practical Programs for the Casio Pocket Computer. (Illus.). 96p. Date not set. 8.95 (ISBN 0-86668-014-4). ARCsoft.
Collins, Rob. Software by Design. (Illus.). 352p. 1984. pap. 19.95 (ISBN 0-88056-310-9). Dilithium Pr.
Colonias, John S. Particle Accelerator Design Computer Programs. 1974. 70.50 (ISBN 0-12-181550-1). Acad Pr.
Color Computer Programs. 334p. 9.95 (ISBN 0-317-05263-2, 62-2313). Radio Shack.
Comer, Douglas. Operating System Design: The Xinu Approach. (P-H Software Ser.). (Illus.). 496p. 1984. text ed. 34.95 (ISBN 0-13-637539-1). P-H.
Commodore Computer Staff. Commodore Software Encyclopedia. 3rd ed. 896p. 1983. pap. text ed. 19.95 (ISBN 0-672-22091-1, 22091). Sams.
Computer Software. Date not set. price not set (C01422). HarbraceJ.
Computer Software. (Scientific American Ser.). 124p. Date not set. pap. 13.95 (ISBN 0-7167-1712-3). W H Freeman.
Computer Software Programs for Demographic Analysis: Aspects of Technological Co-operation. 29p. 1983. pap. text ed. 4.00 (ISBN 0-686-46318-8, UN83/2A5, UN). Unipub.
Compute's Atari Collection, Vol. I. 1985. pap. 12.95 (ISBN 0-942386-79-5). Compute Pubns.
Consumer Guide Editors. Atari Software: Rating the Best. LC 83-737274. 154p. 1984. spiral bd. 1.98 (ISBN 0-517-42474-6). Outlet Bk Co.
Consumer Guide Editors & Adams, Roe R., III. Apple Software: Rating the Best. LC 83-73275. 154p. 1984. pap. 4.98 spiral bdg. (ISBN 0-517-42475-4). Outlet Bk Co.
Consumer Guide Editors & Goodman, Danny. A Parent's Guide to Personal Computers & Software. 80p. 1983. pap. 6.95 (ISBN 0-671-49173-3, 22083, Touchstone). S&S.
Consumer Software: Protection & Marketing, 1984, 2 vols. 1984. write for info. (G4-3751). PLI.
Continental Software. write for info. Bk Co.
Continental Software. The Home Accountant - IBM PC. 1985. manual 9.95 (ISBN 0-538-01012-6, A013). SW Pub.
Controls Over Using & Changing Computer Programs. (Computer Services Guidelines Ser.). 27p. 1979. pap. 7.50 (ISBN 0-686-70228-X). Am Inst CPA.
Cooper. Software Quality Management. 1979. 25.00 (ISBN 0-89433-093-4). Petrocelli.
Corchado, Veronica & McHugh, Kathleen. Selecting the Right Word Processing Software for the IBM PC. LC 84-50991. 96p. 1984. pap. 11.95 (ISBN 0-89588-177-2). SYBEX.
Cowell, Wayne R., ed. Sources & Development of Mathematical Software. (Illus.). 416p. 1984. text ed. 35.00 (ISBN 0-13-823501-5). P-H.
Cratch, Stephen C. & Johansson, Anders B. The Hindu Vedic Master Operations Guide: Astrological Software for the IBM PC. Johansson, Lilian M., ed. (Illus.). 200p. (Orig.). 1985. 30.00 (ISBN 0-914725-12-2); pap. 18.00 (ISBN 0-914725-10-6); spiral 24.00 (ISBN 0-914725-11-4). Astro Dynasty Pub Hse.
Creative Programming Inc., Staff. Creative Programming: All Stars Level III. (All Stars Ser.). (Illus.). 40p. 1983. pap. 9.95 (ISBN 0-912079-07-X, 1003). Creat Prog Inc.
Crider, Janet. Word for Word: A Comparative Guide to Word Processing Software. 250p. (Orig.). 1984. pap. 16.95 (ISBN 0-88134-154-1, 154-1). Osborne-McGraw.

Halamka, John D. The Best of CP-M Software. LC 84-50361. 252p. 1984. pap. 14.95 (ISBN 0-89588-100-4). SYBEX.

Halligan, Joseph. Accounting-SOFTWHERE. Halligan, Joseph & Winther, Richard P., eds. (SOFTWHERE Software Directories Ser.: Vol. 1). (Orig.). 1984. pap. 49.95 (ISBN 0-918451-00-0). Moore Data.

--Agri-Business-SOFTWHERE. Winther, Richard P., ed. (SOFTWHERE Software Directories Ser.: Vol. 1). (Orig.). 1984. pap. 49.95 (ISBN 0-918451-10-8). Moore Data.

--Banking & Finance-SOFTWHERE. Winther, Richard, ed. (SOFTWHERE Software Directories Ser.: Vol. 1). (Orig.). 1984. pap. 39.95 (ISBN 0-918451-20-5). Moore Data.

Halstead, Maurice H. Elements of Software Science. LC 77-1321. (Operating & Programming Systems Ser.: Vol. 3). 128p. 1977. 31.75 (ISBN 0-444-00205-7, North Holland). Elsevier.

Hamilton, Catherine D., et al, eds. Text Retrieval: A Directory of Software. LC 84-22284. 180p. 1985. text ed. 34.50 (ISBN 0-566-03527-8). Gower Pub Co.

Hamilton, S. S. Accounting Applications for the Microcomputer. (Microcomputer Software Program Ser.). 1983. 9.65 (ISBN 0-07-025736-1). McGraw.

Hamilton, S. S., et al. Microcomputer Accounting Applications. (Microcomputer Software Program Ser.). 128p. 1982. text ed. 6.84 (ISBN 0-07-025818-X). McGraw.

Hammel, E. A. & Deuel, R. Z. Five Classy Programs: Computer Procedures for the Classification of Households. (Research Ser: No. 33). 1977. pap. 3.75x (ISBN 0-87725-133-9). U of Cal Intl St.

Hammel, E. A., et al. The SOCSIM Demographic-Sociological Microsimulation Program: Operating Manual. LC 76-620046. (Research Ser: No. 27). 225p. 1976. pap. 4.50x (ISBN 0-87725-127-4). U of Cal Intl St.

Hannah, John. Using Dollars & Sense. 250p. 1985. pap. 14.95 (ISBN 0-88022-164-X, 182). Que Corp.

Hansen, B. Brinch Hansen on Pascal Compilers. (Illus.). 256p. Date not set. text ed. 27.95 (ISBN 0-13-083098-4). P-H.

Harper, Larry D. The Software Primer: R Base-Level 1. (Software Primer Ser.). 180p. 1984. binder cancelled (ISBN 0-913871-10-9). JNZ.

Harris, Thorne D., III. The Legal Guide to Computer Software Protection: A Practical Handbook on Copyrights, Trademarks, Publishing & Trade Secrets. (Illus.). 320p. 1984. 24.95 (ISBN 0-13-528373-6, Busn); pap. 19.95 (ISBN 0-13-528365-5). P-H.

Hausen, H. L. Software Validation: Inspection - Testing - Verification - Alternatives. 1984. 55.75 (ISBN 0-444-87593-X). Elsevier.

Heiney, Mildred A. Software Author's Guide. 208p. (Orig.). 1983. pap. text ed. 19.95 (ISBN 0-88190-235-7, BO235). Datamost.

Heiserman, David L. Microprocessor Instruction Sets & Software Principles. (Illus.). 464p. 1983. 31.95 (ISBN 0-13-581090-6). P-H.

Heller, Dave & Heller, Dorothy. Free Software for Your Apple. (Free Software Ser.). (Illus.). 224p. 1984. pap. 8.95 (ISBN 0-86582-123-2, EN79213). Enrich.

--Free Software for Your Atari. (Free Software Ser.). (Illus.). 208p. 1983. pap. 8.95 (ISBN 0-86582-117-8, EN79211). Enrich.

--Free Software for Your Commodore. (Free Software Ser.). (Illus.). 224p. 1984. pap. text ed. 8.95 (ISBN 0-86582-122-4, EN79212). Enrich.

--Free Software for Your TI 99-4A. (Free Software Ser.). (Illus.). 208p. 1984. pap. 8.95 (ISBN 0-86582-124-0, EN79214). Enrich.

Helm, Virginia. Software Quality & Copyright: Issues in Computer-Assisted Instruction. 152p. 1984. 16.00 (ISBN 0-89240-047-1). Assn Ed Comm Tech.

Hennell, M. A. & Delves, L. M. Production & Assessment of Numerical Software. LC 80-40073. 1980. 55.00 (ISBN 0-12-340940-3). Acad Pr.

Hession, W. & Rubel, M. Performance Guide to Word Processing Software. 1985. write for info. (ISBN 0-07-028451-2). McGraw.

Hetzel, William. The Complete Guide to Software Testing. LC 83-83116. (Illus.). 247p. 1984. pap. 29.50 (ISBN 0-89435-110-9, HG1109). QED Info Sci.

Hewlett Packard Company Staff. Series Eighty Software Catalog. 4th ed. 1984. pap. 15.95 (ISBN 0-8359-6980-0). Reston.

Hibbard, P. G. & Schuman, S. A., eds. Constructing Quality Software: Proceedings of the IFIP Working Conference on Constructing Quality Software, Novosibirsk, U.S.S.R., May, 1977. 520p. 1978. 64.00 (ISBN 0-444-85106-2, North-Holland). Elsevier.

Hildebrand. Business Programs for the IBM PC. 1983. 15.95 (ISBN 0-317-02367-5, 6351). Hayden.

Hill, MaryAnn, ed. BMDP User's Digest: BMDP Statistical Software, Inc. rev. ed. 157p. 1982. text ed. 6.00 (ISBN 0-935386-02-5). BMDP Stat.

Hindelang, Thomas J., et al. The IBM PC Guide to Accounting for the Manager: The Latest Accounting Principles on Disk. (Business Applications Library). 320p. 1984. pap. cancelled (ISBN 0-88693-159-2). Banbury Bks.

Hively, Wells, et al, eds. Hively's Choice: A Curriculum Guide to Outstanding Educational Microcomputer Programs for Preschool Through Grade 9 - School Year 1983-84. LC 83-73030. 1983. pap. 19.95 (ISBN 0-8454-8100-2). Continental Pr.

Hixson, Amanda C. A Buyer's Guide to Microcomputer Business Software: Accounting & Spreadsheets. 1918p. 1984. pap. 19.95 (ISBN 0-201-11065-2). Addison-Wesley.

Hodges, William S. & Novak, Neal. Practical Programs for Home Computers. (Microcomputer Bookshelf Ser.). 200p. 1984. pap. text ed. 14.95 (ISBN 0-316-61151-4). Little.

Hoffman, Paul S. The Software Legal Book. 309p. 1982. looseleaf 85.00 (ISBN 0-935506-01-2). Carnegie Pr.

Hoffmann, Roger. The Complete Software Marketplace, 1984-85. 256p. (Orig.). 1984. pap. 17.50 (ISBN 0-446-38024-5). Warner Bks.

Holtz, Frederick. Using & Programming the Macintosh, with 32 Ready-to-Run Programs. (Illus.). 256p. (Orig.). 16.95 (ISBN 0-8306-0840-0, 1840); pap. 12.50 (ISBN 0-8306-1840-6). TAB Bks.

Holzberlein, Deanne. Computer Software Cataloging: Techniques & Examples. (Cataloging & Classification Quarterly: Vol. 6, No. 2). 96p. text ed. 19.95 (ISBN 0-86656-477-2). Haworth Pr.

Home Computer Programs. 330p. 7.95 (62-2069). Radio Shack.

Hordeski, Michael F. Microprocessor Cookbook. (Illus.). 1979. 13.95 (ISBN 0-8306-9778-0); pap. 9.25 (ISBN 0-8306-1053-7, 1053). TAB Bks.

How to Profitably Sell Your Own Software. 20.00 (ISBN 0-318-02639-2). ACS Sftwre.

Howland, James & Roizen, Ron. T-Maker III Applications Book. 17.95 (ISBN 0-8359-7730-7). Reston.

Hudson, Keith. Introducing CAL: A Practical Guide to Writing Computer Assisted Learning Programs. 200p. 1984. 39.95 (ISBN 0-412-26230-4, NO. 9315, Pub. by Chapman & Hall); pap. 19.95 (ISBN 0-412-26240-1, NO. 9190, Pub. by Chapman & Hall). Methuen Inc.

Hunke, H., ed. Software Engineering Environments: Proceedings of the Symposium Held in Lahnstein, West Germany, June 1980. 410p. 1981. 57.50 (ISBN 0-444-86133-5, North-Holland). Elsevier.

Hunter, James & Guntle, Gregory. Commodore 64 Trivia Data Base. LC 84-51504. 112p. 1984. 8.95 (ISBN 0-672-22396-1, 22396). Sams.

Hurley, Richard B. Decision Tables in Software Engineering. (VNR Data Processing Ser.). 184p. 1982. text ed. 22.95 (ISBN 0-442-23599-2); disks for Apple II & IBM-PC 59.50 ea. (ISBN 0-442-23666-2). Van Nos Reinhold.

IBM Software Directory 1985. Date not set. pap. text ed. 29.95 (ISBN 0-8352-1972-0). Bowker.

IEEE Standard 729-1983: IEEE Standard Glassary of Software Engineering Terminology. 1983. 7.50 (ISBN 0-317-03952-0, SHO8920). IEEE Comp Soc.

IEEE Standard 730-1981: IEEE Standard for Software Quality Assurance Plans. 1981. 5.00 (ISBN 0-317-03939-3, SHO9555). IEEE Comp Soc.

IEEE Standard 829-1983: IEEE Standard for Software Test Documentation. 1983. 8.00 (ISBN 0-317-03954-7, SHO8672). IEEE.

Improving EDP Software Production. 1979. pap. 5.00 (ISBN 0-918734-04-5). Reymont.

Infotech. Microcomputer Software, 2 vols. Set. 145.00x (ISBN 0-08-028506-6). Pergamon.

INIS: Description of Computer Programs. (INIS Reference Ser.: No. 14). pap. 5.75 (ISBN 92-0-178675-1, IN14/R1, IAEA). Unipub.

Institute of Electrical & Electronics Engineers, Inc. IEEE Transaction on Communications: Communication Software. (Illus.). 192p. 1984. text ed. 35.00 (ISBN 0-13-450271-X). P-H.

Institution of Electrical Engineers (UK) & Peter Peregrinus, Ltd. Software Engineering for Telecommunication Switching Systems. (IEE Conference Publication Series). 234p. 1983. pap. 74.00 (ISBN 0-85296-276-2, IC223). Inst Elect Eng.

Insurance-SOFTWHERE. Halligan, Joseph. (SOFTWHERE Software Directories Ser.: Vol. 1). (Orig.). 1984. pap. 29.95 (ISBN 0-918451-50-7). Moore Data.

Intel Staff. Reference Software Products Handbook. 352p. (Orig.). 1985. pap. 10.00 (ISBN 0-917017-24-2, 231195-001). Intel Corp.

--Software Handbook. rev. ed. 512p. 1985. text ed. 12.00 (ISBN 0-917017-20-X, 230786-002). Intel Corp.

International Computer Program Inc. ICP Software Directory, Vol. 1: Syatems Software. Hamilton, Dennis L., ed. 1984. pap. 150.00 (ISBN 0-88094-025-5). Intl Computer.

International Computer Programs Inc. ICP Software Directory, 7 Vols. Hamilton, Dennis L., ed. 1984. Set. pap. 550.00 (ISBN 0-88094-024-7). Intl Computer.

International Computer Programs, Inc. ICP Software Directory: Cross Industry Applications. Spangler, Richard J., ed. 1983. 150.00 (ISBN 0-88094-020-4). D L Hamilton.

--ICP Software Directory: System Software. Spangler, Richard J., ed. 1983. 150.00 (ISBN 0-686-39679-0). D L Hamilton.

International Computer Programs, Inc & Spangler, Richard J. ICP Software Directory-United Kingdom: Software Products, Services & Suppliers. 1983. 125.00 (ISBN 0-88094-018-2). D L Hamilton.

International Computer Programs Inc. ICP Software Directory, Vol. 2: General Accounting Systems. Hamilton, Dennis L., ed. 1984. pap. 95.00 (ISBN 0-88094-026-3). Intl Computer.

--ICP Software Directory, Vol. 3: Management & Administration Systems. Hamilton, Dennis L., ed. 1984. pap. 95.00 (ISBN 0-88094-027-1). Intl Computer.

--ICP Software Directory, Vol. 4: Banking Insurance & Finance Systems. Hamilton, Dennis L., ed. 1984. pap. 95.00 (ISBN 0-88094-028-X). Intl Computer.

--ICP Software Directory, Vol. 5: Manufacturing & Engineering Systems. Hamilton, Dennis L., ed. 1984. pap. 95.00 (ISBN 0-88094-029-8). Intl Computer.

--ICP Software Directory, Vol. 6: Specialized Industry Systems. Hamilton, Dennis L., ed. 1984. pap. 95.00 (ISBN 0-88094-030-1). Intl Computer.

International Computer Programs Staff. ICP Software Directory, 7 vols. Hamilton, Dennis L., ed. 1985. Set. softcover 550.00 (ISBN 0-88094-041-7). Intl Computer.

--ICP Software Directory, Vol. 1: Systems Software. Hamilton, Dennis L., ed. 1985. softcover 150.00 (ISBN 0-88094-042-5). Intl Computer.

International Resource Development Inc. Courseware & Software for Micros in Education. 174p. 1984. 1650.00x (ISBN 0-88694-602-6). Intl Res Dev.

--Videocassette & Videodisc Hardware & Software Markets. 167p. 1983. 1285.00x (ISBN 0-88694-579-8). Intl Res Dev.

International Resource Development Staff. Software Publishing & Distribution. 215p. 1983. 1850.00x (ISBN 0-88694-574-7). Intl Res Dev.

International Software Database. The Software Catalog: Business Software. 1984. 35.00 (ISBN 0-444-00934-5). Elsevier.

--The Software Catalog: Microcomputers, Summer 1984, Update. 1984. 15.00 (ISBN 0-444-00916-7). Elsevier.

--The Software Catalog: Microcomputers, Winter 1984-85 Update. 1984. 15.00 (ISBN 0-444-00885-3). Elsevier.

Irvine, Thomas F., Jr. Steam & Gas Tables with Computer Equations. 1984. 29.50 (ISBN 0-12-374080-0). Acad Pr.

Jacobs, D., ed. Numerical Software: Needs & Availability. (Institute of Mathematics & Its Applications Conference Ser.). 1978. 45.00 (ISBN 0-12-378660-6). Acad Pr.

Johansson, Anders B. Data Entry on Vedic Master Astrology Software for Apple Computers. Johansson, Lilian M., ed. (Illus.). 170p. 1984. 23.45 (ISBN 0-914725-09-2); pap. 19.75 (ISBN 0-914725-07-6). Astro Dynasty Pub Hse.

Johnson, Scott D. A Computer System for Checking Proofs. Stone, Harold, ed. LC 82-6990. (Computer Science: Artificial Intelligence Ser.: No. 12). 280p. 1983. 44.95 (ISBN 0-8357-1343-1). UMI Res Pr.

Johnston, Randolph P. BASIC Using Micros: With an Overview of Popular Software Packages. LC 83-60976. 168p. (Orig.). 1983. pap. text ed. 10.95 (ISBN 0-938188-06-2). Mitchell Pub.

Johnston, Robert L. Numerical Methods: A Software Approach. LC 81-12974. 276p. 1981. text ed. 32.50x (ISBN 0-471-09397-1). Wiley.

Jones, Jesse A. Software: Royalties for Life. 140p. 1984. pap. 28.95 (ISBN 0-916791-00-9). Concho Corp.

Joseph, M. & Shyamasundar, R., eds. Foundations of Software Technology & Theoretical Computer Science. (Lecture Notes in Computer Science Ser.: Vol. 181). viii, 468p. 1984. pap. 22.50 (ISBN 0-387-13883-8). Springer-Verlag.

Joslin, Edward O. Software for Computer Systems. 400p. 1970. pap. 6.95 (ISBN 0-916580-08-3). College Readings.

Kahn, G., ed. Semantics of Concurrent Computation. (Lecture Notes in Computer Science Ser.: Vol. 70). 1979. pap. 22.00 (ISBN 0-387-09511-X). Springer-Verlag.

Kamin, Jonathan. The ThinkTank Book. 259p. 1984. pap. 14.95 (ISBN 0-89588-224-8). SYBEX.

Kelley, James E., Jr. The IBM PC & Business Software: VisiCalc, dBASE II & WordStar Explained. 320p. 1983. pap. 39.95 incl. 2 floppy disks (ISBN 0-38693-000-6). Banbury Bks.

--The IBM PC & 1-2-3: Real World Applications of the IBM-PC's Most Popular Software Package. 320p. 1983. pap. 39.95 incl. disk (ISBN 0-88693-032-4). Banbury Bks.

Kelly, Brian W. & Grimes, Dennis J. IBM PC Compatible Computer Directory: Hardware, Software & Peripherals. (Kelly-Grimes Buyers Guide Ser.: No. 1702). 581p. 1985. pap. 26.95 (ISBN 0-471-87819-7, Pub. by Wiley Pr). Wiley.

--IBM Personal Computer Directory: Hardware, Software, & Peripherals. (Kelly-Grimes Buyers Guide Ser.: No. 1-702). 581p. 1985. pap. 26.95 (ISBN 0-471-87821-9, Pub. by Wiley Pr). Wiley.

Kelly, Derek A. Documenting Computer Application Systems. (Illus.). 192p. 1983. 19.95 (ISBN 0-89433-206-6). Petrocelli.

Kernighan, Brian W. & Plauger, P. J. Software Tools. 286p. 1976. pap. text ed. 21.95 (ISBN 0-201-03669-X); tape 75.00 (ISBN 0-201-03668-1). Addison-Wesley.

--Software Tools in Pascal. LC 81-3629. 1981. pap. 21.95 (ISBN 0-201-10342-7); tape 75.00 (ISBN 0-201-10343-5). Addison-Wesley.

Kerr, Elaine B. & Hiltz, Starr R. Computer-Mediated Communication Systems: Status & Evaluation. (Human Communication Research Ser.). 1982. 29.50 (ISBN 0-12-404980-X). Acad Pr.

King, David. Current Practices in Software Development: A Guide to Successful Systems. LC 83-27401. (Illus.). 232p. 1984. pap. 28.00 (ISBN 0-917072-29-4); pap. text ed. 28.00. Yourdon.

Kingsley, Henry E. CHEMCALC (TM) 1: Separations Calculations. LC 84-6562. (CHEMCALC (TM) Software for Process Engineers Ser.). 128p. 1984. ring binder incl. disk 295.00x (ISBN 0-87201-085-6). Gulf Pub.

Kinney, Martha. Software & Bookstores, 1984-85: The Market Develops. 85p. 1985. looseleaf binder 295.00x (ISBN 0-88709-001-X). Comm Trends Inc.

Kirkpatrick, Michael. Essential Programs for Small Business for the Apple II-IIe. LC 84-2303. 1984. 16.95 (Pub. by Wiley Pr); bk. & software set 46.90 (ISBN 0-471-80602-1, Wiley Professional Software); disk 29.95 (ISBN 0-471-80547-5). Wiley.

Klein, Fred. Pocket Computer Programs for Astronomers. 100p. (Orig.). 1983. pap. 12.95 (ISBN 0-913051-01-2). F Klein Pubns.

Klotz, Jerome H. & Meyer, R. Daniel. Biostatistical Microcomputing in Pascal. LC 84-27546. (Probability & Statistics). 150p. 1985. 19.95x (ISBN 0-8476-7357-X). Rowman & Allanheld.

Knight, Timothy & LaBatt, Darren. Commodore 64 BASIC Programs. 2nd ed. LC 83-50832. 9.95 (ISBN 0-672-22402-X). Sams.

Knight, Timothy O. Basic BASIC Programs for the Adam. (Illus.). 144p. 1984. 12.95 (ISBN 0-8306-0116-3, 01008897X); pap. 8.25 (ISBN 0-8306-0716-1). TAB Bks.

Knuth, E & Neuhold, E. J., eds. Specification & Design of Software Systems: Proceedings, Visegrad, Hungary, 1982. (Lecture Notes in Computer Science: Vol. 152). v, 152p. 1985. pap. 12.00 (ISBN 0-387-12284-2). Springer-Verlag.

Koberg, Don & Bagnall, Jim. Universal Traveler: A Soft-Systems Guide to Creativity, Problem-Solving & the Process of Reaching Goals. rev. ed. LC 81-17123. (Illus.). 130p. (Orig.). 1981. pap. 9.95 (ISBN 0-86576-017-9). W Kaufmann.

Kompass, Edward J. & Williams, Theodore J., eds. Computer Software for Industrial Control: Proceedings of the 7th Annual Advanced Control Conference. 180p. 1983. Repr. of 1981 ed. Conference Papers 20.50 (ISBN 0-914331-06-X). Control Eng.

Konopasek, Milos & Jayaraman, Sundaresan. The TK! Solver Book: A Guide to Problem-Solving in Science, Engineering, Business & Education. 360p. (Orig.). 1984. pap. 19.95 (ISBN 0-07-881115-5, 115-5). Osborne-McGraw.

Kopetz, H. Software Reliability. 118p. 1980. pap. 15.50 (ISBN 0-387-91169-3). Springer-Verlag.

Kotov, V. E. & Miklosko, J., eds. Algorithms, Software & Hardware of Parallel Computers. (Illus.). 380p. 1984. 32.00 (ISBN 0-387-13657-6). Springer-Verlag.

Pepper, P., ed. Program Transformation & Programming Environments. (NATO ASI Ser. Series F Computer & Systems Sciences: No. 8). 400p. 1984. 39.50 (ISBN 0-387-12932-4). Springer-Verlag.
Perlis, Alan, et al, eds. Software Metrics. (Computer Science Ser.). (Illus.). 350p. 1981. 37.50x (ISBN 0-262-16083-8). MIT Pr.
Perrone, Nicholas & Pilkey, Walter D., eds. Structural Mechanics Software Series, Vol. IV. (Illus.). 467p. 1982. 30.00x (ISBN 0-8139-0918-X). U Pr of Va.
Perry, William E. How to Buy Software for Personal Computers. LC 83-60388. (Minicomputer Software Selection Guide Ser.). 150p. 1984. 14.95 (ISBN 0-89435-106-0). QED Info Sci.
--A Structured Approach to Systems Testing. (Q.E.D. Information Services Inc. Ser.). (Illus.). 464p. 1984. text ed. 40.00 (ISBN 0-13-854373-9). P-H.
Perry, William E. & Kuong, Javier F. Generalized Computer Audit Software-Selection & Application. 1980. 40.00 (ISBN 0-940706-15-6, MAP-14). Management Advisory Pubns.
Petersen, J. L. Computer Programs for Spelling Correction. (Lecture Notes in Computer Science Ser.: Vol. 96). 213p. 1980. pap. 17.00 (ISBN 0-387-10259-0). Springer-Verlag.
Phillips, Gary. Apple II Free Software. 250p. pap. cancelled (ISBN 0-89588-200-0). SYBEX.
--Commodore 64 Free Software. 300p. pap. cancelled (ISBN 0-89588-201-9). SYBEX.
--Commodore 64 Software Buyers Guide. (Illus.). 496p. 1984. pap. 16.95 (ISBN 0-89303-382-0). Brady Comm.
--IBM PC Public Domain Software, Vol. 1. Thomson, Monet, ed. 547p. 1983. pap. 24.95 (ISBN 0-912677-06-6). Ashton-Tate Bks.
--IBM Public Domain Software, Vol. 1. 1984. 24.95 (ISBN 0-8359-3042-4). Reston.
Phillips, Gary, et al. Apple IIe & IIc Software Encyclopedia. 320p. Date not set. pap. cancelled (ISBN 0-89303-213-1). Brady Comm.
Pilkey, Walter D. & Perrone, Nicholas, eds. Structural Mechanics Software Series, Vol. III. (Illus.). 344p. 1980. 30.00x (ISBN 0-8139-0857-4). U Pr of Va.
--The Structural Mechanics Software Series, 2 vols. (Software Ser.). 1977. 30.00x ea.; Vol. 1. (ISBN 0-8139-0735-7); Vol. 2. (ISBN 0-8139-0781-0). U Pr of Va.
Pirisino, Jim. Minute Manual for Appleworks. 150p. 1985. 12.95 (ISBN 0-913131-07-5). Minuteware.
Poage, James & Landis, Carolyn P. Contracting for Computing: A Checklist of Terms & Clauses for Use in Contracting with Vendors for Software Packages & Custom Software, Vol. II. 148p. 1975. 16.00 (ISBN 0-318-14014-4); members 9.00 (ISBN 0-318-14015-2). Educom.
Polak, W. Compiler Specification & Verification. (Lecture Notes in Computer Science Ser.: Vol. 124). 269p. 1981. pap. 19.00 (ISBN 0-387-10886-6). Springer-Verlag.
Porter, Kent. Porter's Programs for the Apple II Family: For the Apple II, II Plus, IIe & IIc. 167p. 1985. pap. 6.95 (ISBN 0-451-82107-6, Sig). NAL.
--Porter's Programs for the Commodore 64. 1984. pap. 6.95 (ISBN 0-451-82090-8, Sig). NAL.
--Porter's Programs for the IBM PCjr. 1984. pap. 6.95 (ISBN 0-451-82088-6, Sig). NAL.
Practical Engineering Applications Software. Continuous Span. 1985. IBM-PC Version. incl. disk 125.00 (ISBN 0-471-80299-9); Apple Version. incl. disk 125.00 (ISBN 0-471-88423-5). Wiley.
Price, Jonathan. How to Write a Computer Manual: A Handbook of Software Documentation. 224p. 1985. pap. text ed. 22.95 (ISBN 0-8053-6870-1); write for info. instr's manual (ISBN 0-8053-6871-X). Benjamin-Cummings.
Proceedings: Conferende on Software Maintenance 1985. 300p. 1985. 44.00 (ISBN 0-8186-0648-7); prepub. 39.60 (ISBN 0-317-31776-8). IEEE Comp Soc.
Program Optimization. (Infotech Computer State of the Art Reports). 448p. 1976. 85.00 (ISBN 0-08-028508-2). Pergamon.
Public Domain Exchange, ed. The Best of Apple Public Domain Software. 160p. (Orig.). 1985. write for info. (ISBN 0-9614731-0-X). Pub Domain.
Putnam, Lawrence H. Software Cost Estimating & Life-Cycle Control: Getting the Software Numbers. (Tutorial Texts Ser.). 349p. 1980. 25.00 (ISBN 0-8186-0314-3, Q314). IEEE Comp Soc.
Que Corporation. DEC Personal Computers Expansion & Software Guide. LC 84-60000146. 432p. 1984. pap. 19.95 (ISBN 0-88022-111-9, 128). Que Corp.
Que Staff. IBM PC Expansion & Software Guide. 5th ed. LC 84-62134. 1000p. 1985. pap. 21.95 (ISBN 0-88022-096-1, 169). Que Corp.
Que Staff & Digital Research Staff. CP-M Software Finder. (Illus.). 354p. 1983. pap. 14.95 (ISBN 0-88022-021-X, 13). Que Corp.
Que Staff, compiled by. IBM PC Expansion & Software Guide. 6th ed. LC 85-60687. 1000p. 1985. pap. 21.95 (ISBN 0-88022-156-9, 189). Que Corp.
Quinn, Elizabeth. Manager's Guide to Visi-On. (Illus.). 200p. 1984. 18.95 (ISBN 0-912213-07-8). Paladin.
Rabbat, Guy. Hardware & Software Concepts in VLSI. Rabbat, Guy, ed. (Van Nostrand Electrical-Computer Science & Engineering Ser.). (Illus.). 512p. 1983. 42.50 (ISBN 0-442-22538-5). Van Nos Reinhold.
Rader, Robert J. Advanced Software Design Techniques. (Illus.). 172p. 1979. text ed. 17.50 (ISBN 0-89433-046-2). Petrocelli.
Radio Shack TRS-80 Educational Software Sourcebook. 6.95 (ISBN 0-317-11010-1). Radio Shack.
Regena, C. Compute's BASIC Programs for Small Computers: Things to Do in 4k or Less. 267p. (Orig.). 1984. pap. 12.95 (ISBN 0-942386-38-8). Compute Pubns.
Reifer, D. J. Software Management. 2nd rev. ed. (Tutorial Texts Ser.). 502p. 1981. 30.00 (ISBN 0-8186-0396-8, Q396). IEEE Comp Soc.
Rice, John G. Build Program Technique: A Practical Approach for the Development of Automatic Software Generation Systems. LC 80-20742. (Business Data Processing Ser.). 372p. 1981. 39.95x (ISBN 0-471-05278-7, Pub. by Wiley-Interscience). Wiley.
Rice, John R. Matrix Computation & Mathematical Software. Stewart, Charles E., ed. (Computer Science Ser.). (Illus.). 288p. 1981. text ed. 39.95 (ISBN 0-07-052145-X). McGraw.
Rice, John R., ed. Mathematical Software III. (Mathematics Research Center: No. 39). 1977. 22.50 (ISBN 0-12-587260-7). Acad Pr.
Richardson, Robert M. Synchronous Packet Radio Using the Software Approach: AX.25 Protocal, Vol. 2. Belvins, T. F., ed. 280p. 1984. 22.00x (ISBN 0-940972-08-5). Richcraft Eng.
Riddle, W. E. & Fairley, R. E. Software Development Tools. (Illus.). 280p. 1980. pap. 22.00 (ISBN 0-387-10326-0). Springer-Verlag.
Rinder, Robert. Cookbook of Creative Programs for the Commodore 64. 1984. pap. 12.95 (ISBN 0-452-25571-6, Plume). NAL.
--Cookbook of Creative Programs for the IBM PC, PCjr: Projects for Music, Animation, & Telecommunications. (Illus.). 1985. 14.95 (ISBN 0-452-25572-4, Plume). NAL.
Roberts, Don. Two Hundred Twenty-two BASIC Computer Programs for Home, School & Office. 256p. 1984. 9.95 (ISBN 0-86668-039-X). ARCsoft.
Rogers, Charles E. Model Rocket Computer Programs: Malewicki Closed-Form Altitude, Coefficient of Drag & Center of Pressure. 1983. 29.00 (ISBN 0-912468-12-2). CA Rocketry.
--Sub & Supersonic Experimental Rocket Computer Programs: Fourth Order Range-Kutta, Altitude Prediction, Drag, Center of Pressure. 1983. 49.00 (ISBN 0-912468-13-0). CA Rocketry.
Rohl, J. S. Writing Pascal Programs. LC 82-14591. (Cambridge Computer Science Texts Ser.: No. 16). (Illus.). 250p. 1983. 27.95 (ISBN 0-521-25077-3); pap. 12.95 (ISBN 0-521-27196-7). Cambridge U Pr.
Rose, Richard. PFS: User's Handbook. 300p. (Orig.). 1985. pap. cancelled (ISBN 0-317-19099-7). Weber Systems.
Rugg, Tom & Feldman, Phil. More Than Thirty-Two BASIC Programs for the Commodore 64. (Illus.). 350p. 1983. pap. 19.95 (ISBN 0-88056-112-2); incl. disk 39.95 (ISBN 0-88056-180-7); incl. cassette 39.95 (ISBN 0-88056-183-1). Dilithium Pr.
--Thirty-Two BASIC Programs for the Apple Computer. LC 80-68533. (Illus.). 280p. 1983. pap. 19.95 (ISBN 0-918398-34-7); incl. disk 39.95 (ISBN 0-88056-151-3). Dilithium Pr.
--Thirty-Two BASIC Programs for the Atari Computer. (Illus.). 288p. 1983. pap. 19.95 (ISBN 0-88056-084-3); incl. disk 39.95 (ISBN 0-88056-172-6). Dilithium Pr.
--Thirty-Two BASIC Programs for the Coleco Adam. 288p. 1984. pap. 19.95 (ISBN 0-88056-141-6); incl. disk 39.95 (ISBN 0-88056-201-3). Dilithium Pr.
Salkind, Neil. A Guide to Commodore 64 Software & Hardware. cancelled (ISBN 0-317-07075-4). Datamost.
Sami, M., et al, eds. Microprocessor Systems Software: Firmware & Hardware. 372p. 1981. 64.00 (ISBN 0-444-86098-3, North-Holland). Elsevier.
Sandford, D. M. Using Sophisticated Models in Resolution Theorem Proving. (Lecture Notes in Computer Science Ser.: Vol. 90). (Illus.). 239p. 1980. pap. 17.00 (ISBN 0-387-10231-0). Springer Verlag.
SAS Institute Inc. SUGI Supplemental Library User's Guide, 1983 Edition. 402p. (Orig.). 1983. pap. 11.95 (ISBN 0-917382-48-X). SAS Inst.
Scanlon, Leo J. Sixty-Five Two Software Design. LC 79-67131. 272p. 1980. pap. 13.95 (ISBN 0-672-21656-6, 21656). Sams.
Schechter, Gil M. TI 99-4A: Fifty-One Fun & Educational Programs. LC 83-50373. 96p. 1983. pap. 4.95 (ISBN 0-672-22192-6, 22192); incl. tape 11.95 (ISBN 0-672-26168-5, 26168). Sams.
Schindler, Max. Microprocessor Software Design. 304p. 1980. pap. 14.50 (ISBN 0-8104-5190-5). Hayden.
Schlaifer, Robert. Computer Programs for Elementary Decision Analysis. LC 75-151633. (Illus.). 247p. 1971. 24.95x (ISBN 0-87584-091-4). Harvard Busn.
Schmucker, Kurt J. Fuzzy Sets, Natural Language Computations & Risk Analysis. LC 82-23648. 193p. 1984. text ed. 37.95 (ISBN 0-914894-83-8). Computer Sci.
Schreiber, Linda M. Atari Programming... with Fifty-five Programs. (Illus.). 256p. (Orig.). 1982. 21.95 (ISBN 0-8306-1385-4); pap. 14.50 (ISBN 0-8306-1485-0, 1485). TAB Bks.
Schultz, Owen C., ed. Microcomputer Programs in Print. (Illus.). 208p. (Orig.). 1983. pap. 19.95 (ISBN 0-912691-01-8). Postroad Pr Inc.
Schwartz, Ron & Basso, David. Statistical Programs in BASIC. 1984. cancelled (ISBN 0-8359-7107-4); pap. text ed. 16.95 (ISBN 0-8359-7106-6). Reston.
Schwarz, Jerald. Description of Computer Programs for the Analysis & Presentation of Trade Winds Data. LC 76-135092. 152p. 1969. 19.00 (ISBN 0-403-04537-1). Scholarly.
Scientific & Engineering Software Guide. 287p. 1984. 19.95 (ISBN 0-317-04403-6). Micro Info.
Seiden, Eric A. DARAD Plus: A Self Teaching Manual. rev. ed. 50p. 1984. spiral bd. 21.95 (ISBN 0-916163-00-8). Dar Syst.
Seybold, P. B. & Marshak, R. T. Word Processing Software for the IBM PC. (Illus.). 201p. 1984. pap. 15.95 (ISBN 0-07-056322-5, Byte Bks). McGraw.
Shamlin, Carolyn. A User's Guide for Defining Software Requirements. LC 83-72640. (Illus.). 129p. (Orig.). 1985. pap. 19.50 (ISBN 0-89435-071-4, DC 0714). QED Info Sci.
Sherman, Ed. Up & Running: Adventures of a Software Entrepreneurs. 300p. 1984. pap. 15.95 (ISBN 0-912677-14-7). Ashton-Tate Bks.
Sherman, J. M., et al. Wind Systems Life Cycle Cost Analysis: A Description & Users Manual. 88p. (Orig.). 1984. pap. 19.95 (ISBN 0-88016-019-5). Windbks.
Shneiderman, Ben. Software Psychology: Human Factors in Computer & Information Systems. 319p. 1980. text ed. 29.95 (ISBN 0-316-78727-2). Little.
Shooman, M. L. Software Engineering: Reliability, Development & Management. (Computer Science Ser.). 1983. text ed. 42.95 (ISBN 0-07-057021-3). McGraw.
Shumaker, Terence M. & Aronson, Mike. GRID: Computer-Aided Drafting Program. 2nd ed. (Illus.). 119p. 1985. pap. text ed. 9.75x (ISBN 0-928459-00-4). Respons Logic.
Sigel, Efrem. Guide to Software Publishing. 195.00 (ISBN 0-86729-108-7). Comm Trends Inc.
Silveria, Terry C., et al. Buyer's Guide to Modems & Communications Software. (Illus.). 192p. (Orig.). 1985. 19.95 (ISBN 0-8306-0882-6, 1882); pap. 12.95 (ISBN 0-8306-1882-1). TAB Bks.
Simon, Gary. Choosing Accounting Software for Your Micro. (Illus.). 160p. 1985. pap. 17.95 (ISBN 0-00-383006-3, Pub. by Collins England). Sheridan.
Simon, Sheridan A. The Astronomy Disk. 48p. 1984. pap. text ed. 34.95 incl. disk (ISBN 0-13-049834-3). P-H.
Simpson, Henry. Design of User-Friendly Programs for Small Computers. 256p. 1984. pap. 18.95 (ISBN 0-07-057300-X). McGraw.
Skarbet Software Directory. 14.95 (ISBN 0-318-01612-5). Vogeler Pub.
Skees, William D. Computer Software for Data Communications. LC 80-24266. 163p. 1981. 21.00 (ISBN 0-534-97979-3). Lifetime Learn.
Small Business Accounting Software Guide. 340p. 1984. 19.95 (ISBN 0-317-04404-4). Micro Info.
Smit, Rudolf. Commodore 64 Software Projects. (Illus.). 88p. (Orig.). 1984. pap. 12.95 (ISBN 0-86161-146-2). Melbourne Hse.
Smith, David J. Reliability & Maintainability in Perspective: Practical, Contractual, Commercial & Software Aspects. 29.95 (ISBN 0-470-20175-4). Halsted Pr.
Smith, Gary D. & Smith, Scott N. Agricultural Software Directory for IBM Computers & Computers with CPIM Operating Systems. 378p. 1983. pap. 19.95 (ISBN 0-912859-02-4). Agriware Pubns.
--Agricultural Software Directory for the Apple Computer. 197p. 1983. pap. 19.95 (ISBN 0-912859-00-8). Agriware Pubns.
Smith, Truck. Secrets of Software Debugging. LC 84-8792. (Illus.). 288p. (Orig.). 1984. 21.95 (ISBN 0-8306-0811-7, 1811); pap. 13.95 (ISBN 0-8306-1811-2). TAB Bks.
Smithy-Willis, Deborrah, et al. TeloFacts IBM PC Software. TeloFacts 1. 49.95 (ISBN 0-317-00073-X); TeloFacts 2. 199.95 (ISBN 0-88056-177-7). Dilithium Pr.
Softindex, 1982: Periodical Guide for Computerists Annual. 19.95 (ISBN 0-686-40865-9). Applegate Comp Ent.
Softky, Sheldon D. ABC's of Developing Software. LC 83-7051. 136p. (Orig.). 1983. pap. 13.95 (ISBN 0-912957-00-X). ABC Pr Silicon.
The Software Catalog: Microcomputers, Complete Catalog. 1984. 75.00 (ISBN 0-444-00914-0). Elsevier.
The Software Catalog of Microcomputers. 1983. write for info. Elsevier.
The Software Catalog: Science & Engineering International Software Database. 450p. 1984. pap. 29.00 (ISBN 0-444-00925-6). Elsevier.
Software Contracts. 50p. 1980. 15.00x (ISBN 0-85012-221-X). Intl Pubns Serv.
Software Digest. The Ratings Book: IBM-PC Word Processing Programs. 1984. pap. 14.95 (ISBN 0-916543-00-5). Software Inc.
The Software Encyclopedia 1985-86, 2 vols. 2300p. 1985. Set. 95.00 (ISBN 0-8352-1944-5). Bowker.
Software Gourmet Guide & Cookbook: 6800. pap. 12.95 (ISBN 0-8104-6281-8, 6281). Hayden.
Software-Intensive Portable Products. (Reports Ser.: No. 186). 189p. 1981. 1285.00x (ISBN 0-88694-186-5). Intl Res Dev.
Software Protection (1982) 35.00 (ISBN 0-317-29502-0, #CO1422, Law & Business). HarBraceJ.
Software Protection (1984) 35.00 (ISBN 0-317-29504-7, #CO2615, Law & Business). HarBraceJ.
Software Publisher's Catalogs Annual. 1984. 165.00x (ISBN 0-88736-013-0). Meckler Pub.
Software Reliability, 2 vols. (Infotech Computer State of the Art Reports). 700p. 1977. Set. pap. 105.00 (ISBN 0-08-028514-7). Pergamon.
Software Reports. 180.00 (ISBN 0-317-13100-1). Trade Srv Pubns.
Soltzberg, Leonard J. Sing a Song of Software: Verse & Images for the Computer-Literate. (Illus.). 88p. pap. 9.95 (ISBN 0-86576-073-X). W Kaufmann.
Sorger, T. J. The Computer Buyer's Attorney. (Illus., Orig.). pap. 39.95 (ISBN 0-9604072-0-0). Sorger Assocs.
--Managements Guide to Software Development. (Illus., Orig.). pap. 12.95 (ISBN 0-9604072-2-7). Sorger Assocs.
Spangenburg & Moser. Educational Software. 1984. write for info. (ISBN 0-534-03329-6). Wadsworth Pub.
Spath. Cluster Dissection & Analysis Theory FORTRAN Programs Examples. 226p. 1985. 49.95 (ISBN 0-470-20129-0). Wiley.
Spear, Barbara. How to Document Your Software. (Illus.). 208p. (Orig.). 1984. 19.95 (ISBN 0-8306-0724-2); pap. 13.50 (ISBN 0-8306-1724-8, 1724). TAB Bks.
Speitel, Tom, et al. Science Computer Programs for Kids... & Other People: Apple Version. (Illus.). 1984. pap. 12.95 (ISBN 0-8359-6901-0). Reston.
--Science Computer Programs for Kids & Other People: Commodore Version. 1984. pap. 12.95. Reston.
--Science Computer Programs for Kids... & Other People: TI Version. (Illus.). 1984. pap. 12.95 (ISBN 0-8359-6902-9). Reston.
Spezzano, Charles. Using Enable. 300p. 1985. pap. 17.95 (ISBN 0-88022-165-8, 186). Que Corp.
Spirn, Jeffrey R. Program Behavior: Models & Measurements. (Operating & Programming Systems Ser.: Vol. 2). 1977. text ed. 31.50 (ISBN 0-444-00219-7, North Holland); pap. 19.00 (ISBN 0-444-00220-0). Elsevier.
Stagewise Computations. (Computer Programs for Chemical Engineering Education Ser.). 1972. pap. 15.95 (ISBN 0-88408-034-X). Sterling Swift.
Standage, Blaine D., et al. Compute's Data File Handler for the Commodore 64. Compute!, ed. (Orig.). 1985. pap. 12.95 (ISBN 0-942386-86-8). Compute Pubns.
Stanton, Jeffrey, et al, eds. Book of Atari Software 1985. (Software Reference Guides Ser.). 468p. 1984. pap. 19.95 (ISBN 0-912003-04-9). Bk Co.
Staunstrup, J., ed. Program Specification, Aarhus, Denmark, 1981: Proceedings. (Lecture Notes in Computer Science Ser.: Vol. 134). 426p. 1982. pap. 24.00 (ISBN 0-387-11490-4). Springer-Verlag.
Steely, Donald G. A Writer's Guide to Software Documentation. 1983. 3-ring notebk 34.50 (ISBN 0-9612620-0-1). Goode Steely Assocs.

Steingart, David & Zaks, Rodnay. Bit Slice. LC 79-64867. (Illus.). 270p. 1979. incl. 4 cassettes 69.95 (ISBN 0-89588-027-X). SYBEX.

Sternberg. IBM Programs for the Home: For the PC & PCjr. 208p. 1984. 15.95 (ISBN 0-317-05881-9, 6376). Hayden.

Sternberg, Charles D. BASIC Computer Programs for Business. 1982. Vol. 1. 14.95 (ISBN 0-8104-5162-X, 5162); Vol. 2. pap. 15.95 (ISBN 0-8104-5178-6, 5178). Hayden.

Stewart, George. The Apple Program Factory. 150p. (Orig.). 1984. 12.95 (ISBN 0-07-881132-5, 132-5). Osborne-McGraw.

Subbarao, Wunnava. Microprocessors: Hardware, Software, & Design Applications. 1984. text ed. 29.95 (ISBN 0-8359-4394-1); solutions manual avail. (ISBN 0-8359-4395-X). Reston.

Sueltz, Daniel & Kinder, Bruce. Templus Financial Planning Models for 1-2-3. 1984. pap. 14.95 cancelled (ISBN 0-13-903063-8). P-H.

Swan. Pascal Programs for Business. 1983. 18.95 (ISBN 0-317-02343-8, 6270); disks & documentation 59.95 (7270). Hayden.

Swift's Directory of Educational Software for the IBM PC, 1984-85. 19.95 (ISBN 0-88408-274-1). Sterling Swift.

Swift's Educational Software Directory for Corvus Networks 1984: Apple II Edition. 16.95 (ISBN 0-317-03120-1). Sterling Swift.

Swift's 1984-1985 Educational Software Directory: Apple II Edition. 480p. soft spiral bdg. 24.95 (ISBN 0-88408-270-9). Sterling Swift.

Syposium on Engineering Computer Software (1971: San Francisco, CA). Engineering Computer Software: Verification, Qualification, Certification; Symposium. Presentations from ASME First National Congress on Pressure Vessels & Piping, San Francisco, CA, May 1971. Berman, Irwin, ed. LC 73-173859. pap. 32.50 (ISBN 0-317-08079-2, 2016828). Bks Demand UMI.

Tagg, W. & Templeton, R. Computer Software: Supplying It & Finding It. (LIR Report: No. 10). 59p. (Orig.). 1983. pap. 10.50 (ISBN 0-7123-3014-3, Pub. by British Lib). Longwood Pub Group.

Takamura, S., et al. Software Design for Electronic Switching Systems. (Illus.). 256p. 1979. 48.00 (ISBN 0-906048-18-4). Inst Elect Eng.

Tausworthe, Robert C. Standardized Development of Computer Software: Part 1, Methods. 1977. Pt. 2, Standards. 32.95 (ISBN 0-13-842195-1); 32.95 (ISBN 0-13-842203-6); comb. set (pts 1&2) 54.00 (ISBN 0-13-842211-7). P-H.

Taylor, F. E. Teleprocessing Monitor Packages. 1979. 27.50x (ISBN 0-85012-195-7). Intl Pubns Serv.

Thompson, Andrew V. Micro-Cap Analog Circuit Design Software: Package Apple II Version. 1983. 475.00 (ISBN 0-07-060016-3). Mcgraw.

--Micro-Cap Analog Circuit Design Software: Package IBM-PC Version. 1983. 475.00 (ISBN 0-07-060018-X). Mcgraw.

Throop, Thomas. Computer Bridge. 160p. 1983. pap. 10.95 (ISBN 0-317-00356-9). Hayden.

Titus, Christopher A., et al. Eighty-Eighty Eighty-Eighty-Five Software Design, Bk. 2. LC 78-57207. 352p. 1979. pap. 12.95 (ISBN 0-672-21615-9, 21615). Sams.

Townsend, Carl. PFS: Software Made Easy: Write, File, Report, Access, Graph. 250p. (Orig.). 1984. pap. 17.95 (ISBN 0-07-881147-3, 147-3). Osborne-McGraw.

Townsend, Kevin, ed. Choosing & Using Business Micro Software. 227p. 1984. text ed. 32.95x (ISBN 0-566-02496-9). Gower Pub Co.

Triebel, Walter & Singh, Avtar. The Ninety-Nine Hundred Microprocessor: Architecture, Software, & Interface Techniques. (Illus.). 224p. 1984. text ed. 27.95 (ISBN 0-13-622853-4); pap. text ed. 14.95 (ISBN 0-13-622846-1). P-H.

Trost, Stanley R. Apple II BASIC Programs in Minutes. LC 83-61385. (Illus.). 176p. 1983. pap. 12.95 (ISBN 0-89588-121-7). SYBEX.

--The Best of IBM PC Software. LC 84-50362. 351p. 1984. pap. 16.95 (ISBN 0-89588-104-7). SYBEX.

--IBM PCjr BASIC Programs in Minutes. 160p. 1984. pap. 14.95 (ISBN 0-89588-205-1). SYBEX.

--Useful BASIC Programs for the IBM PC. LC 83-60487. (Illus.). 174p. 1983. pap. 12.95 (ISBN 0-89588-111-X). SYBEX.

Trost, Stanley R. & Lima, Anthony K. Introducing Visi-On: The System, Its Concepts & Applications. (Illus.). 159p. (Orig.). 1983. pap. 18.95 (ISBN 0-912213-03-5). Paladin.

--Introducing Visi-On: The System, Its Concepts & Applications. 1984. 18.95 (ISBN 0-912213-03-5). Random.

TRS-80 Educational Software Sourcebook. 1983. pap. 6.95 (ISBN 0-318-01175-1). Radio Shack.

Truett, Carol & Gillespie, Lori. Choosing Educational Software: A Buyer's Guide. LC 83-24906. 202p. 1983. lib. bdg. 18.50 (ISBN 0-87287-388-9). Libs Unl.

Turner, Ray. Software Engineering Methodology. 1984. text ed. 21.95 (ISBN 0-8359-7022-1). Reston.

Tymes, Elna. Mastering AppleWorks. 201p. 1984. pap. 15.95 (ISBN 0-89588-240-X). SYBEX.

Urschel, William. Ready to Run Accounting with Lotus 1-2-3 & Symphony. 225p. 1984. incl. disk 44.95 (ISBN 0-88284-330-3). Alfred Pub.

--Urschel's Guide to IBM Software. (Urschel's Guide Ser.). 200p. 1984. 6.95 (ISBN 0-88284-328-1). Alfred Pub.

Valentine, Roger. What Can I Do with My Timex-Sinclair 1000? Lots! 56 Programs for the Timex-Sinclair 1000 & ZX-81. LC 83-1339. (Wiley Professional Software Ser.). (Illus.). 164p. 1983. pap. 9.95 (ISBN 0-471-88730-7, Pub. by Wiley Pr); program cassette 19.95 (ISBN 0-471-88729-3, Wiley Professional Software). Wiley.

Vallabhaneni, S. Rao. Auditing Purchased Software: Aquisition, Adaptation, & Installation. Holman, Richard, ed. (IIA Monographs). (Illus.). 55p. 1985. pap. text ed. 12.00 (ISBN 0-89413-129-X). Inst Inter Aud.

Van Loves Apple Software Directory, 1985. 965p. Date not set. pap. text ed. 29.95 (ISBN 0-8352-1971-2). Bowker.

VanDiver, Gerald. The IBM PC & XT Business Software Guide. 231p. 1984. 19.95 (ISBN 0-912603-12-7). Micro-Info.

--The IBM PC & XT Educational Software Guide. 124p. 1984. 5.95 (ISBN 0-912603-03-8). Micro Info.

--The IBM PC & XT Software Guide. 1036p. (Orig.). 1983. pap. 24.95 (ISBN 0-912603-00-3). Micro Info.

--The IBM PC & XT Word Processing Software Guide. 187p. 1984. 9.95 (ISBN 0-912603-11-9). Micro Info.

--The IBM PCjr Software Guide & Handbook. 500p. 1984. pap. 19.95 (ISBN 0-912603-13-5). Micro Info.

Van Meter, Blake H. & Hatcher, Patricia L. The Free Software Handbook: 1984-85 CP-M Edition. (PeopleTalk Ser.). 1984. pap. 17.95 (ISBN 0-915907-07-0). Peopletalk.

Van Tassel, Dennis. Program Style, Design, Efficiency, Debugging & Testing. 2nd ed. (Illus.). 1978. ref. ed. 32.95 (ISBN 0-13-729947-8). P-H.

Vertical Markets for Microcomputer Software. (Reports Ser: No. 528). 158p. 1982. 985.00x (ISBN 0-88694-528-3). Intl Res Dev.

Videodisc Hardware & Software Market. 1983. 1375.00 (ISBN 0-86621-158-6). Frost & Sullivan.

Vockell, E. Prototype Programs for Instruction. cancelled (ISBN 0-317-05657-3). Reston.

Vocknell, Edward. Model Programs for Instruction. 1984. 21.95 (ISBN 0-8359-4511-1); pap. 16.95 (ISBN 0-8359-4510-3). Reston.

Wadsworth, Nat. Z80 Software Gourmet Guide & Cookbook. pap. 17.50 (ISBN 0-8104-6276-1, 6276). Hayden.

Waldron, Joseph A. Automated Social History (ASH) Software. 1984. write for info. (ISBN 0-87084-049-5). Anderson Pub Co.

Walker, Decker F. & Hess, Robert D., eds. Instructional Software: Principles & Perspectives for Design & Use. LC 83-12531. (Illus.). 308p. 1984. pap. write for info. (ISBN 0-534-01459-3). Wadsworth Pub.

Wallace, Jonathan D. Software Law. (Handy Guide Ser.). 64p. (Orig.). 1984. pap. 2.95 (ISBN 0-88284-268-4). Alfred Pub.

--Understanding Software Law. pap. 3.50 (ISBN 0-88284-268-4). Alfred Pub.

Wallis, P. J., ed. Software Engineering Developments, Series 11. (Computer State of the Arts Reports: No. 3). 400p. 1983. 445.00 (ISBN 0-08-028574-0). Pergamon.

Wanner, Craig. Managerial Decision Making: Microcomputer Programs & Applications. 125p. 1983. pap. text ed. 9.95x (ISBN 0-8290-1433-0). Irvington.

Warren, Carl D. The MC6809 Cookbook. (Illus.). 176p. 11.95 (ISBN 0-8306-9683-0); pap. 7.95 (ISBN 0-8306-1209-2). TAB Bks.

Wasserman, Anthony I. Software Development Environments. (Tutorial Texts Ser.). 476p. 1981. 30.00 (ISBN 0-8186-0385-2, Q385). IEEE Comp Soc.

Watson, W. Scott. Fifty-Five Advanced Computer Programs in BASIC. (Illus.). 252p. 16.95 (ISBN 0-8306-0012-4); pap. 10.25 (ISBN 0-8306-1295-5, 1295). TAB Bks.

Weber Systems Inc. Staff. Apple IIe BASIC Programs for Business. (Applications Software Ser.). 300p. pap. cancelled. Weber Systems.

Weber Systems, Inc. Staff. IBM PCjr Business Software in BASIC. (Applications Software Ser.). 300p. (Orig.). pap. cancelled; diskette 49.95. Weber Systems.

Weber Systems Inc. Staff. Sanyo MBC Business Software in BASIC. LC 85-5386. (Application Software Ser.). 330p. (Orig.). 1985. pap. 17.95 (ISBN 0-938862-37-5); incl. diskette 20.00 (ISBN 0-938862-38-3). Weber Systems.

Weber Systems, Inc. Staff. Sourcebook of IBM Compatible Hardware, Software & Peripherals. 608p. (Orig.). 1985. pap. 18.95 (ISBN 0-345-31843-9). Ballantine.

Weber Systems Inc. Staff. TK Solver Business Models. (Application Software Models Ser.). 300p. 1984. pap. cancelled. Weber Systems.

Weber Systems Staff. BASIC Business Package for TRS-80 Computers. LC 82-70599. (Applications Software Ser.). 210p. (Orig.). 1984. pap. 14.95 (ISBN 0-938862-27-8). Weber Systems.

--IBM PC Business Software in BASIC. LC 84-51354. (Applications Software Ser.). 300p. 1985. pap. 17.95 (ISBN 0-938862-35-9); incl. disk 20.00 (ISBN 0-938862-36-7). Weber Systems.

Webster, Tony. Software Buyer's Guide. (A BYTE Book). (Illus.). 1984. pap. 19.95 (ISBN 0-07-068967-9). McGraw.

Wegner, Peter, ed. Research Directions in Software Technology. (MIT Computer Science & Artificial Intelligence Ser.: No. 2). (Illus.). 1979. text ed. 47.50x (ISBN 0-262-23090-9). MIT Pr.

Weldon, Roger J. & Humphrey, Alan B. ANOVA 45: A Flexible Computer Program for the Analysis of Variance-Instructions for Use. LC 70-163009. pap. 20.00 (ISBN 0-317-11040-3, 2022751). Bks Demand UMI.

Wells, Robert P. The Quick & Easy Guide to Educational Software on the Apple. 128p. pap. 4.95 (ISBN 0-912003-27-8). Bk Co.

Wenzel, Robert J. Computer Programs for Machine Design. LC 82-50657. 272p. 1982. pap. 21.95 (ISBN 0-672-21960-3, 21960). Sams.

Werum, W. & Windauer, H. Introduction to PEARL. 2nd ed. 1984. pap. 20.00 (ISBN 0-9904000-2-6, Pub. by Vieweg & Sohn Germany). Heyden.

Westerberg, A., ed. Control. (Computer Programs for Chemical Engineering Education Ser.). 1972. pap. 13.95 (ISBN 0-88408-030-7). Sterling Swift.

Westlaw-West Publishing Company. Westlaw Reference Manual. 60p. 1981. pap. text ed. write for info. (ISBN 0-314-62801-0). West Pub.

Westley. Software Testing, 2 vols. (Infotech Computer State of the Art Reports). 600p. 1979. Set. 145.00 (ISBN 0-08-028503-1). Pergamon.

White, Fred. Apple Computer Programs for Beginners. 96p. 1984. 8.95 (ISBN 0-86668-035-7). ARCsoft.

--Easy Apple Computer Programs. 96p. 1984. 8.95 (ISBN 0-86668-047-0). ARCsoft.

--Thirty-Three New Apple Computer Programs for Home, School & Office. (Illus.). 96p. (Orig.). 1982. pap. 8.95 (ISBN 0-86668-016-0). ARCsoft.

Whitebread, Martin. Microprocessor Software. (Topics in Microprocessing Bk No.2). (Illus.). 150p. 1980. pap. text ed. 21.00 (ISBN 0-7194-0013-9, Pub. by Castle Hse England). J. K. Burgess.

Whitehead, Martin. Microprocessor Software. (Topics in Microprocessing Ser.: Bk. 2). 160p. 1980. 50.00x (Pub. by Castle Hse England). State Mutual Bk.

Whitehous, Gary, ed. Microsoftware: Statistical Analysis. 1984. 175.00 (ISBN 0-89806-084-2). Inst Indus Eng.

Whitehouse, Gary. Microsoftware: Forecasting. 1984. 175.00 (ISBN 0-89806-079-6). Inst Indus Eng.

Whitehouse, Gary, ed. Microsoftware: Operations Research. 1984. 175.00 (ISBN 0-89806-080-X). Inst Indus Eng.

Whitehouse, Gary, et al. IIE Microsoftware: Economic Analysis. 1981. 175.00 (ISBN 0-89806-013-3). Inst Indus Eng.

--IIE Microsoftware: Production Control. 1981. 175.00 (ISBN 0-89806-012-5). Inst Indus Eng.

--IIE Microsoftware: Project Management. 1981. 175.00 (ISBN 0-89806-030-3). Inst Indus Eng.

--IIE Microsoftware: Work Measurement. 1982. 175.00 (ISBN 0-89806-035-4). Inst Indus Eng.

Whitehouse, Gary E., ed. Softcover Software: Twenty-Eight Microcomputer Programs for IE's & Managers. 1985. write for info. (ISBN 0-89806-094-X). Inst Indus Eng.

Wichmann, Brian A. & Ciechanowicz, Z. J., eds. Pascal Compiler Validation. LC 82-23882. 176p. 1983. 26.95 (ISBN 0-471-90133-4, Pub. by Wiley-Interscience). Wiley.

Wilkes, Maurice, et al. The Preparation of Programs for An Electronic Digital Computer. (The Charles Babbage Institute Reprint Series for the History of Computing: Vol. 1). (Illus.). 1983. 30.00x (ISBN 0-938228-03-X). Tomash Pubs.

Wilkins, Maurice, et al. The Preparation of Programs for an Electronic Digital Computer. (Charles Babbage Institute Reprint Ser. for the History of Computing Ser.: Vol. 1). (Illus.). 165p. 1984. Repr. of 1951 ed. text ed. 30.00x (ISBN 0-262-23118-2). MIT Pr.

Williams, Esther A. & Gottman, John M. A User's Guide to the "Gottman-Williams Time Series Analysis Computer Programs for Social Scientists". 86p. 1982. pap. 11.95 (ISBN 0-521-28059-1). Cambridge U Pr.

Williams, Frederick & Williams, Victoria. Success with Educational Software. LC 85-5679. 192p. 1985. 32.95 (ISBN 0-03-003687-9). Praeger.

Williams, Robert. Power of CalcResult For the Commodore 64. (Power Ser.). 1983. pap. 14.95. P-H.

Wingrove, S. Getting the Most from Wordperfect. 1984. 12.95 (ISBN 0-07-071018-X). McGraw.

Witham, Joan, ed. The Softside Sampler: TRS-80 Entertainment Programs. 128p. 1983. pap. 10.95 (ISBN 0-317-00366-6). Hayden.

Wolberg, John R. Conversion of Computer Software. (Illus.). 240p. 1983. text ed. 28.95 (ISBN 0-13-172148-8). P-H.

Wolfe, Philip & Koelling, C. Patrick. BASIC Engineering Science & Business Programs for the Apple II & IIe. 352p. 1984. pap. 19.95 (ISBN 0-89303-284-0); bk. & diskette 44.95 (ISBN 0-89303-290-5); diskette 25.00 (ISBN 0-89303-288-3). Brady Comm.

Wolff, Terris B. Microcomputer Applications: Using Small Systems Software. rev. ed. 1985. pap. text ed. 21.00 (ISBN 0-87835-813-7); instr's. manual 8.00 (ISBN 0-87835-811-0); test bank avail. (ISBN 0-87835-812-9). Boyd & Fraser.

Woods, John L. Path Selection for Symbolic Execution Systems. Stone, Harold, ed. LC 82-6957. (Computer Science: Systems Programming Ser.: No. 12). 118p. 1982. 34.95 (ISBN 0-8357-1344-X). UMI Res Pr.

Word Processing Software Guide. 221p. 1984. 19.95 (ISBN 0-317-04407-9). Micro Info.

Wortman, Leon A. & Sidebottom, Thomas O. Business Programs in C. 200p. (Orig.). 1984. pap. cancelled (ISBN 0-89588-153-5). SYBEX.

Yau, Stephen S., ed. Advances in Software Engineering, Vol. 1. 1983. 45.00 (ISBN 0-89232-422-8). Jai Pr.

Yourdon, Edward. Managing the System Life Cycle: A Software Development Methodology Overview. LC 81-72107. (Illus.). 160p. (Orig.). 1982. pap. 29.50 (ISBN 0-917072-26-X). Yourdon.

Zaks, Rodnay. Your First Apple II Program. LC 83-50717. (Illus.). 182p. 1983. pap. 12.95 (ISBN 0-89588-136-5). SYBEX.

--Your First Atari Program. LC 83-51191. (Illus.). 182p. 1984. pap. 12.95 (ISBN 0-89588-130-6). SYBEX.

--Your First VIC-20 Program. LC 83-50670. (Illus.). 182p. 1983. pap. 12.95 (ISBN 0-89588-129-2). SYBEX.

Zarrella, John. Language Translators. LC 82-48049. (Microprocessor Software Engineering Concepts Ser.). 200p. (Orig.). 1982. pap. 16.95 (ISBN 0-935230-06-8). Microcomputer Appns.

Zboray, R. & Sachs, D. Programs for Profit: How to Really Make Money with a Personal Computer. LC 83-17542. (VTX Ser.). (Illus.). 256p. 1984. pap. 9.95 (ISBN 0-07-072785-6, Byte Bks). McGraw.

COMPUTER PROGRAMS–DESIGN

Aron, Joel D. The Program Development Process: Pt. II: The Programming Team. LC 74-2847. (Illus.). 704p. 1983. text ed. 32.95 (ISBN 0-201-14463-8). Addison-Wesley.

Ayer, Steve J. & Patrinostro, Frank S. Software Configuration Management Documentation. LC 85-51305. (Software Development Documentation Ser.: Vol. 6). (Illus., Orig.). 1985. pap. 49.50 (ISBN 0-9611694-7-8). Tech Comm Assoc.

--Software Development Analysis Documentation. LC 85-51301. (Software Development Documentation Ser.: Vol. 2). (Orig.). 1985. pap. 55.00 (ISBN 0-9611694-4-3). Tech Comm Assoc.

--Software Development Design Documentation. LC 85-51302. (Software Development Documentation Ser.: Vol. 3). (Illus., Orig.). 1985. pap. 60.00 (ISBN 0-317-19586-7). Tech Comm Assoc.

--Software Development Documentation, 6 vols. (Software Development Documentation Ser.). (Illus., Orig.). Date not set. Set. pap. 314.00 (ISBN 0-9611694-8-6). Tech Comm Assoc.

--Software Implementation Documentation. LC 85-51304. (Software Development Documentation Ser.: Vol. 5). (Illus., Orig.). 1985. pap. 65.00 (ISBN 0-9611694-6-X). Tech Comm Assoc.

--Software Program & Test Documentation. LC 85-51303. (Software Development Documentation Ser.: Vol. 4). (Illus., Orig.). 1985. pap. 35.00 (ISBN 0-9611694-5-1). Tech Comm Assoc.

Bailey, T. E. & Lundgaard, Kris. Program Design with Pseudocode. 2nd ed. LC 85-15170. 200p. 1985. pap. text ed. 10.00 (ISBN 0-534-05574-5). Brooks-Cole.

Benton, Stan & Weekes, Len. Program It Right: Structured Methods in BASIC. (Orig.). 1985. pap. text ed. write for info. Yourdon.

Bergland, Glen D. & Gordon, Ronald D. Software Design Strategies. 2nd ed. (Tutorial Texts Ser.). 479p. 1981. 30.00 (ISBN 0-8186-0389-5, Q389). IEEE Comp Soc.

Bersoff, Edward, et al. Software Configuration Management: An Investment in Product Integrity. 1980. 36.95 (ISBN 0-13-821769-6). P-H.

Blank, J., et al. Software Engineering: Methods & Techniques. 241p. 1983. 26.95 (ISBN 0-471-88503-7). Wiley.

Bleazard, G. B. Program Design Methods: Results of an NCC Study. LC 78-314354. 1976. pap. 15.50x (ISBN 0-85012-164-7). Intl Pubns Serv.

Boehm, Barry W. Software Engineering Economics. (Illus.). 768p. 1981. text ed. 45.00 (ISBN 0-13-822122-7). P-H.

Brinch-Hanson, P. Architecture of Concurrent Programs. 1977. 36.95 (ISBN 0-13-044628-9). P-H.

Brooks, Frederick P., Jr. The Mythical Man-Month: Essays on Software Engineering. (Illus.). 200p. 1974. pap. text ed. 15.95 (ISBN 0-201-00650-2). Addison-Wesley.

Bruno, James E. Designing Education Information Systems Using 2BaseII & the Apple II: A Systems Guide to the Apple & dBase II. 250p. 1985. pap. text ed. 29.95 (ISBN 0-86542-314-8). Blackwell Pubns.

Budde, R., et al. Approaches to Prototyping: Proceedings of the Working Conference on Prototyping, Namur, October 1983. Kuhlenkamp, K. & Mathiassen, L., eds. (Illus.). xii, 458p. 1984. pap. 23.00 (ISBN 0-387-13490-5). Springer-Verlag.

Bugnolo, Dimitri. Computer Programs for Electronic Analysis & Design. 1983. pap. text ed. 17.95 (ISBN 0-8359-0874-7). Reston.

Chow, T. S. Software Quality Assurance: A Practical Approach. 1984. write for info. IEEE Comp Soc.

Chu, Yaohan. Software Blueprint & Examples. LC 81-48268. (Computer Science Ser.). (Illus.). 544p. 1982. 40.00x (ISBN 0-669-05329-5). Lexington Bks.

Clarke, E. & Kozen, D., eds. Logics of Program: Workshop, Carnegie-Mellon University, Pittsburgh, Pa., June 6-8, 1983. (Lecture Notes in Computer Science: Vol. 164). vi, 528p. 1984. pap. 25.50 (ISBN 0-387-12896-4). Springer-Verlag.

Cohen, Alan. Structure, Logic & Program Design. LC 83-10207. 287p. 1983. 37.95x (ISBN 0-471-16400-3, Pub. by Wiley-Interscience). Wiley.

Curtis, Bill. Human Factors in Software Development. (Tutorial Texts Ser.). 641p. 1981. 36.00 (ISBN 0-8186-0390-9, Q390). IEEE Comp Soc.

DeMarco, Tom. Concise Notes on Software Engineering. LC 79-66408. (Illus.). 104p. (Orig.). 1979. pap. 9.50 (ISBN 0-917072-16-2). Yourdon.

Dershowitz. Evolution of Programs. (Progress in Computer Science Ser.: Vol. 5). 1983. 24.95 (ISBN 3-7643-3156-9); pap. 16.95 (ISBN 0-8176-3171-2). Birkhauser.

Ejiogu, Lem O. Software Engineering: Design & Discipline. (Illus.). 300p. 1985. text ed. 32.95 (ISBN 0-89433-276-7). Petrocelli.

--Software Engineering Design & Discipline. (Illus.). 300p. 1985. 32.95 (ISBN 0-89433-276-7). Van Nos Reinhold.

Emmerichs, Jack. How to Build a Program. (Illus.). 352p. (Orig.). 1983. pap. 19.95 (ISBN 0-88056-068-1). Dilithium Pr.

--How to Build a Program. (Illus.). 400p. 1983. 21.95 (ISBN 0-8306-0622-X, 1622). TAB Bks.

Flanders, Robert & Flanders, Dennis. Systems Made Simple on the IBM PC: How to Design & Develop Applications Programs. 1984. cancelled (ISBN 0-89303-242-5). Brady Comm.

Freedman, Roy S. Programming with APSE Software Tools. (Illus.). 276p. 1985. text ed. 27.50 (ISBN 0-89433-220-1). Petrocelli.

Freeman, Herbert & Lewis, P. M., II, eds. Software Engineering. 1980. 31.50 (ISBN 0-12-267160-0). Acad Pr.

Freeman, Peter & Wasserman, Anthony I. Software Design Techniques. 4th ed. (Tutorial Texts Ser.). 719p. 1983. 36.00 (ISBN 0-8186-0514-6). IEEE Comp Soc.

Gilbert, Philip. Software Design & Development. 608p. 1983. text ed. 33.95 (ISBN 0-574-21430-5, 13-4430); instr's. guide avail. (ISBN 0-574-21431-3, 13-4431). SRA.

Glass, Robert. Real-Time Software. (Illus.). 464p. 1984. text ed. 26.95 (ISBN 0-13-767103-2). P-H.

Greenberg, H. J., ed. Design & Implementation of Optimization of Software, No. 28. (Nato Advanced Study Institute, Applied Science Ser.). 566p. 1978. 45.00x (ISBN 90-286-0728-5). Sijthoff & Noordhoff.

Hansen, Kirk. Data Structured Program Design. LC 83-62177. (Illus.). 414p. (Orig.). 1984. casebound 22.95 (ISBN 0-9605884-2-6). Orr & Assocs.

Heckel, Paul. Elements of Friendly Software Design. 155p. 1984. pap. 8.95 (ISBN 0-446-38040-7). Warner Bks.

Hibbard, P. G. & Schuman, S. A., eds. Constructing Quality Software: Proceedings of the IFIP Working Conference on Constructing Quality Software, Novosibirsk, U.S.S.R., May, 1977. 520p. 1978. 64.00 (ISBN 0-444-85106-2, North-Holland). Elsevier.

Higgins, David. Program Design & Construction. LC 78-31097. (Personal Computing Ser.). (Illus.). 1979. pap. text ed. 21.95 (ISBN 0-13-729525-1). P-H.

IEEE Standard 729-1983: IEEE Standard Glassary of Software Engineering Terminology. 1983. 7.50 (ISBN 0-317-03952-0, SHO8920). IEEE Comp Soc.

Ingevaldsson, Leif. JSP Practical Method of Program Design. 194p. 1979. pap. text ed. 19.95x (ISBN 91-44-15751-7, Chartwell). Brookfield Pub Co.

Jackson, M. A. Principles of Program Design. (Automatic Programming Information Centre Studies in Data Processing Ser.). 310p. 1975. 35.00 (ISBN 0-12-379050-6). Acad Pr.

Janossy, James. Software Engineering Techniques for Designing Business Data Processing Programs. 472p. 1985. 24.95 (ISBN 0-471-81576-4). Wiley.

Jelinek, R., ed. Design. (Computer Programs for Chemical Engineering Education Ser.). 1972. pap. 15.95 (ISBN 0-88408-033-1). Sterling Swift.

Jensen, R. & Tonies, C. Software Engineering. 1979. 43.95 (ISBN 0-13-822130-8). P-H.

Lane, Malcolm G. Data Communications Software Design. (Computer Science Ser.). (Illus.). 304p. 1985. text ed. 30.00 (ISBN 0-87835-145-0); write for info. tchr's. manual (ISBN 0-87835-148-5). Boyd & Fraser.

Larson, David, et al. Eighty-Eighty, Eighty-Eighty-Five, Software Design, Bk. 1. LC 78-57207. 336p. 1978. pap. 13.95 (ISBN 0-672-21541-1, 21697). Sams.

Law, Victor J. ANSI FORTRAN 77: An Introduction to Software Design. 400p. 1983. pap. write for info. (ISBN 0-697-08167-2); instr's manual avail. (ISBN 0-697-08175-3); wkbk. avail. (ISBN 0-697-08176-1). Wm C Brown.

Leathrum, J. F. Foundations of Software Design. LC 82-20540. (Illus.). 182p. 1983. 27.95 (ISBN 0-8359-2094-1). Reston.

Ledgard, Henry. ANSI-IEEE Pascal Standard: The American Pascal Standard. 1984. write for info. Springer-Verlag.

Lewin, Morton H. Logic Design & Computer Organization. LC 81-20636. 478p. 1983. 36.95 (ISBN 0-201-04144-8). Addison-Wesley.

Liffick, Blaise, ed. Program Design. LC 78-8649. 1978. pap. 9.95 (ISBN 0-07-037825-8, BYTE Bks). McGraw.

McKeag, R. M. & MacNaghten, A. M., eds. On the Construction of Programs. 432p. 1980. 32.50 (ISBN 0-521-23090-X). Cambridge U Pr.

Martin, James & McClure, Carma. Action Diagrams: Clearly Structural Program Design. (Illus.). 176p. 1985. text ed. 35.00 (ISBN 0-13-003302-2). P-H.

Merchant. WATFIV S: Language & Style. 464p. 1985. write for info. (ISBN 0-534-04728-9). Wadsworth Pub.

Neel, D., ed. Tools & Notions for Program Construction: An Advanced Course. LC 82-4141. 350p. 1982. 34.50 (ISBN 0-521-24801-9). Cambridge U Pr.

Pepper, P., ed. Program Transformation & Programming Environments. (NATO ASI Ser. Series F Computer & Systems Sciences: No. 8). 400p. 1984. 39.50 (ISBN 0-387-12932-4). Springer-Verlag.

Perrott, R. H., ed. Software Engineering. 1978. 39.00 (ISBN 0-12-551450-6). Acad Pr.

Pizzarello, Anthony. Development & Maintenance of Large Software Systems. (Illus.). 288p. 1985. 39.95 (ISBN 0-534-02785-7). Van Nos Reinhold.

Proceedings: Eights International Congerence on Software Engineering. 420p. 1985. 50.00 (ISBN 0-8186-0620-7); prepub. 45.00 (ISBN 0-317-31660-5). IEEE Comp Soc.

Proceedings: Third International Workshop on Software Specification & Design. 270p. 1985. 44.00 (ISBN 0-8186-0638-X); prepub. 39.60 (ISBN 0-317-31659-1). IEEE Comp Soc.

Reynolds. Program Design & Data Structures in PASCAL. 1986. text ed. write for info. Wadsworth Pub.

Sampath, G. An Introduction to Text Processing. (Illus.). xii, 273p. (Orig.). 1985. pap. 20.00 (ISBN 0-9615070-0-4). River Valley Pub.

Schank, Roger C. & Riesbeck, Christopher K. Inside Computer Understanding: Five Programs Plus Miniatures. LC 80-18314. (Artificial Intelligence Ser.). 400p. 1981. text ed. 29.95x (ISBN 0-89859-071-X). L Erlbaum Assocs.

Schindler, Max. Microprocessor Software Design. 304p. 1980. pap. 14.50 (ISBN 0-8104-5190-5). Hayden.

Simondi, Thomas. What If...? A Guide to Computer Modelling. (Illus.). 251p. 1983. pap. 19.95 (ISBN 0-912003-00-6). Bk Co.

Softky, Sheldon D. The ABC's of Developing Software: A Primer on Essentials of Software Development. (Illus.). 130p. 1985. pap. 13.95 (ISBN 0-912957-00-X). W Kaufmann.

Softsyn Staff & Goldstein, Lou. How to Build Programs on Your Commodore 64. 256p. 1984. 13.95 (ISBN 0-89303-522-X). Brady Comm.

Sommerville, I. Software Engineering. 1982. pap. text ed. 16.95 (ISBN 0-201-13795-X). Addison-Wesley.

Tou, Julius. Software Engineering, Vols. 1-2. 1971. Vol. 1. 61.00 (ISBN 0-12-696201-4); Vol. 2. 61.00 (ISBN 0-12-696202-2). Acad Pr.

Wallis. Life-Cycle Management, 2 vols. (Infotech State of the Art Reports). 504p. 1980. Set. 310.00s (ISBN 0-08-028501-5). Pergamon.

Wasserman, Anthony I. Software Development Environments. (Tutorial Texts Ser.). 476p. 1981. 30.00 (ISBN 0-8186-0385-2, Q385). IEEE Comp Soc.

Wells, Timothy. A Structured Approach to Building Programs: BASIC, Vol. 1. (Orig.). 1985. pap. text ed. write for info. (ISBN 0-917072-45-6). Yourdon.

--A Structured Approach to Building Programs: COBOL, Vol. 2. (Orig.). 1985. pap. text ed. write for info. (ISBN 0-917072-44-8). Yourdon.

--A Structured Approach to Building Programs: Pascal, Vol. 3. (Orig.). 1985. pap. text ed. write for info. (ISBN 0-917072-46-4). Yourdon.

Wiener, Richard S. & Ford, Gary A. Software Development with Modula-2. 672p. 1985. pap. 23.95 (ISBN 0-471-87834-0). Wiley.

Wiener, Richard S. & Sincovec, Richard F. Software Engineering with Modula-2 & Ada. LC 83-21827. 451p. 1984. text ed. 28.95 (ISBN 0-471-89014-6). Wiley.

Yourdon, Edward N., ed. Classics in Software Engineering. LC 79-63449. (Illus.). 440p. (Orig.). 1979. pap. 33.50 (ISBN 0-917072-14-6). Yourdon.

COMPUTER PROGRAMS–DIRECTORIES

AT&T Information Systems Inc. Staff. AT&T Computer Software Guide PC 6300. 1985. pap. 19.95 (ISBN 0-8359-9279-9). Reston.

--AT&T Computer Software Guide 3B2. 1985. pap. 19.95 (ISBN 0-8359-9279-9). Reston.

--AT&T Computer Software Guide 3B5-3B20. 1985. pap. 19.95 (ISBN 0-8359-9277-2). Reston.

British Computer Society. Buying Financial Accounting Software. (Software Package Buyer's Guides Ser.). 48p. 1985. pap. 8.95 (ISBN 0-521-31781-9). Cambridge U Pr.

--Buying Payroll Software. (Software Package Buyer's Guides Ser.). 48p. 1985. pap. 8.95 (ISBN 0-521-31783-5). Cambridge U Pr.

--Buying Purchases Software. (Software Package Buyer's Guides Ser.). 48p. Date not set. pap. 8.95 (ISBN 0-521-31782-7). Cambridge U Pr.

--Buying Sales Software. (Software Package Buyer's Guides Ser.). 48p. Date not set. pap. 8.95 (ISBN 0-521-31784-3). Cambridge U Pr.

Chain Store Guide Staff. Directory of Computer & Software Retailers, 1985. (Chain Store Guide Ser.). 1985. 389.00 (ISBN 0-86730-010-8, Pub. by Bus Guides Inc). Lebhar Friedman.

Ching, Hih Chen. MicroUse Directory: Software. 440p. (Orig.). 1984. pap. 99.50 (ISBN 0-931555-01-9). MicroUse Info.

Flora, Philip C. International CAD-CAM Software Directory. (Illus.). 140p. (Orig.). Date not set. pap. text ed. 35.00 (ISBN 0-910747-06-7). Tech Data TX.

--International Computer Aided Design Directory. (Illus.). 240p. (Orig.). pap. text ed. 35.00 (ISBN 0-910747-01-6). Tech Data TX.

--International Engineering-Scientific Software Directory. (Illus., Orig.). Date not set. pap. text ed. 35.00 (ISBN 0-910747-05-9). Tech Data TX.

Freed, Paul. The General Ledger Software Consultant. 80p. 1985. spiral bdg. 24.95 (ISBN 0-931281-06-7). Mykro.

Halligan, Joseph. Education Administration Software. Winther, Richard, ed. (Software Directories Ser.: Vol. 1). (Orig.). 1985. pap. 29.95 (ISBN 0-918451-81-7). Moore Data.

--Education Courseware: Software. Winther, Richard, ed. (Software Directories Ser.: Vol. 2). (Orig.). 1985. pap. 49.95 (ISBN 0-918451-80-9). Moore Data.

The Hewlett-Packard Software Catalog: Summer 1985. 378p. 1984. pap. 9.95 (ISBN 0-471-81912-3). Wiley.

Hunt, Alfred J. & Nielsen, Lynne C. Hunt's Directory of Microcomputer Software & Services for Civil Engineering& Construction. 384p. (Orig.). 1984. pap. text ed. 50.00 (ISBN 0-934617-00-7). Hunt Assocs Consult.

International Computer Programs, Inc. Staff & Hamilton, Dennis L. ICP Software Directory, 7 vols. (ICP Software Directory Ser.). 1985. software trade 550.00 (ISBN 0-88094-050-6). Intl Computer.

International Computer Programs, Inc. Staff. ICP Software Directory, Vol. 1: Systems Software. Hamilton, Dennis L., ed. 1985. pap. 150.00 (ISBN 0-88094-051-4). Intl Computer.

--ICP Software Directory, Vol. 2: General Accounting Systems. Hamilton, Dennis L., ed. 1985. pap. 95.00 (ISBN 0-88094-052-2). Intl Computer.

--ICP Software Directory, Vol. 3: Management & Administration Systems. Hamilton, Dennis L., ed. 1985. pap. 95.00 (ISBN 0-88094-053-0). Intl Computer.

--ICP Software Directory, Vol. 4: Banking, Insurance & Finance Systems. Hamilton, Dennis L., ed. 1985. pap. 95.00 (ISBN 0-88094-054-9). Intl Computer.

--ICP Software Directory, Vol. 5: Manufacturing & Engineering Systems. Hamilton, Dennis L., ed. 1985. pap. 95.00 (ISBN 0-88094-055-7). Intl Computer.

--ICP Software Directory, Vol. 6: Specialized Industry Systems. Hamilton, Dennis L., ed. 1985. pap. 95.00 (ISBN 0-88094-056-5). Intl Computer.

International Computer Programs, Inc. ICP Software Directory, Vol. 7: Microcomputer Systems Pt. I-Systems Software & General Business Applications. 1984. pap. 95.00 (ISBN 0-88094-039-5). Intl Computer.

--ICP Software Directory, Vol. 7: Microcomputer Systems, Pt. II-Specialized Business Applications. Hamilton, Dennis L., ed. 1984. pap. 95.00 (ISBN 0-88094-040-9). Intl Computer.

International Computer Programs, Inc. Staff. ICP Software Directory, Vol. 7: Microcomputer Systems, Pt. I-Systems Software & General Business Applications. Hamilton, Dennis L., ed. 1985. pap. 95.00 (ISBN 0-88094-057-3). Intl Computer.

--ICP Software Directory, Vol. 7: Microcomputer Systems, Pt. II-Specialized Business Applications. Hamilton, Dennis L., ed. 1985. pap. 95.00 (ISBN 0-88094-058-1). Intl Computer.

International Directory of Software. 250.00 (ISBN 0-318-03639-8). Computing Pubns.

Lathrop, Ann, ed. Educational Software Preview Guide, 1985. 10.00 (ISBN 0-318-03643-6). CA Lib Media.

Phillips, Gary, et al. Apple IIe & IIc Software Encyclopedia. 320p. Date not set. pap. cancelled (ISBN 0-89303-213-1). Brady Comm.

The Software Catalog: Business Software. 2nd ed. 1985. pap. 45.00 (ISBN 0-444-00986-8). Elsevier.

Templeton, Ray & Witten, Anita. Study of Cataloguing Computer Software: Applying AACR2 to Microcomputer Programs. (LIR Report 28). 85p. (Orig.). 1984. pap. 16.50 (ISBN 0-7123-3041-0, Pub. by British Lib). Longwood Pub Group.

COMPUTER PROGRAMS–PATENTS

Brickman, Bruce. Legal Aspects of Acquiring & Protecting Software. 343p. 1984. looseleaf 59.95 (ISBN 0-935506-26-8). Carnegie Pr.

Goldberg, Morton David. Computer Software: Protection & Marketing 1984, 2 vols. 1470p. 1984. Set. pap. 35.00 (ISBN 0-317-27383-3, #G4-3751). PLI.

COMPUTER PROSE

Clarke, Thursten. Evaluating Written Copy-Techniques for High-Tech Managers. 82p. Date not set. 19.95 (ISBN 0-935506-29-2). Carnegie Pr.

COMPUTER RELIABILITY

Iazeolla, G., et al, eds. Mathematical Computer Performance & Reliability: Proceedings of the International Workshop held in Pisa, Italy, 26-30, 1983. 430p. 1984. 50.00 (ISBN 0-444-86892-5). Elsevier.

Longbottom, Roy. Computer System Reliability. LC 79-40649. (Wiley Computing Ser.). 321p. 1980. 57.95x (ISBN 0-471-27634-0, Pub. by Wiley-Interscience). Wiley.

Shrivastava, S. K. Reliable Computer Systems. (Texts & Monographs in Computer Science). (Illus.). 620p. 1985. 39.50 (ISBN 0-387-15256-3). Springer-Verlag.

Software Reliability, 2 vols. (Infotech Computer State of the Art Reports). 700p. 1977. Set. pap. 105.00 (ISBN 0-08-028514-7). Pergamon.

White. System Reliability & Integrity, 2 vols. (Infotech Computer State of the Art Reports). 636p. 1978. Set. 125.00 (ISBN 0-08-028540-6). Pergamon.

COMPUTER SCIENCE LITERATURE

Ausiello, G. & Protasi, M., eds. CAAP 1983. (Lecture Notes in Computer Science: Vol. 159). (Eng. & Fr.). 416p. 1983. pap. 20.00 (ISBN 0-387-12727-5). Springer-Verlag.

COMPUTERIZED TYPE-SETTING

Caird, Kenneth A. Cameraready. (Illus.). 400p. 1973. looseleaf 40.00x (ISBN 0-87703-066-9). Univelt Inc.

McSherry, James E. Computer Typesetting: A Guide for Authors, Editors & Publishers. LC 82-22936. 1984. pap. 12.50x (ISBN 0-912162-05-8). Open-Door.

Phillips. Handbook of Computer Aided Composition. (Books in Library & Information Science: Vol. 31). 344p. 1980. 69.75 (ISBN 0-8247-6963-5). Dekker.

COMPUTERS

Here are entered works on modern electronic computers first developed after 1945. works on present-day calculators, as well as on calculators and all mechanical computers of pre-1945 vintage, are entered under calculators.

see also Computation Laboratories; Computer Art; Computer Literacy; Electronic Analog Computers; Electronic Data Processing; Electronic Digital Computers; Hybrid Computers; Information Storage and Retrieval Systems; Minicomputers;

also headings beginning with the word Computer

Acquisition Guidelines for Small Computer Systems. 288p. 1982. 60.00 (ISBN 0-317-36410-3, 264); members 40.00 (ISBN 0-317-36411-1). Bank Admin Inst.

Advances in Computers, Vol. 21. 452p. 1982. 70.00 (ISBN 0-12-012121-2). Acad Pr.

Ahl, David H. & Green, Burchenal, eds. Best of Creative Computing, Vol. 3. LC 76-438. (Illus.). 323p. 1980. pap. 12.95 (ISBN 0-916688-12-7, 12C). Creative Comp.

Albrecht, Karl & Churchill, Winton. Computers & Productivity. 300p. 1983. cancelled (ISBN 0-201-10148-3). Benjamin-Cummings.

Alt, Franz L. Advances in Computers, Vol. 23. LC 59-15761. 1984. 52.00 (ISBN 0-12-012123-9). Acad Pr.

Alt, Franz L., et al, eds. Advances in Computers. Incl. Vol. 1. 1960. 80.00 (ISBN 0-12-012101-8); Vol. 2. 1961. 80.00 (ISBN 0-12-012102-6); Vol. 3. Alt, Franz L. & Rubinoff, M., eds. 1962. 80.00 (ISBN 0-12-012103-4); Vol. 4. 1964. 80.00 (ISBN 0-12-012104-2); Vol. 5. 1964. 80.00 (ISBN 0-12-012105-0); Vol. 6. 1966. 80.00 (ISBN 0-12-012106-9); Vol. 7. 1966. 80.00 (ISBN 0-12-012107-7); Vol. 8. 1967. 80.00 (ISBN 0-12-012108-5); Vol. 9. 1969. 80.00 (ISBN 0-12-012109-3); Vol. 10. Freiberger, Walter, ed. 1970. 80.00 (ISBN 0-12-012110-7); Vol. 11. Yovits, Marshall C., ed. 1971. 80.00 (ISBN 0-12-012111-5); Vol. 12. Rubinoff, M. & Finerman, A., eds. 1972. 80.00 (ISBN 0-12-012112-3); Vol. 13. Yovits, Marshall C. & Rubinoff, Morris, eds. 1975. 80.00 (ISBN 0-12-012113-1); Vol. 14. 1976. 75.00 (ISBN 0-12-012114-X); Vol. 15. 1976. 75.00 (ISBN 0-12-012115-8); Vol. 16. 1978. 75.00 (ISBN 0-12-012116-6); Vol. 17. 1978. 70.00 (ISBN 0-12-012117-4). LC 59-15761. Acad Pr.

American Production & Inventory Control Society, ed. Readings in Computers & Software. LC 84-72234. 64p. 1984. pap. 9.00 (ISBN 0-935406-56-5, 40656). Am Prod & Inventory.

Andriole, Stephen J. Interactive Computer Based Systems. (Illus.). 198p. 1983. 16.95 (ISBN 0-89433-191-4). Petrocelli.

Angus, Anne D. Computer People. (Illus.). 1970. 9.50 (ISBN 0-571-08288-2). Transatlantic.

Application of Computer Technology for Development. pap. 3.00 (ISBN 0-686-94704-5, UN71/2A/1, UN). Unipub.

Arabian Computer Guide. 284p. 1984. 65.00x (ISBN 0-906358-35-3, Pub. by Beacon). Taylor & Francis.

Arato, M., et al, eds. Performance of Computer Systems. 566p. 1979. 81.00 (ISBN 0-444-85332-4). Elsevier.

Armstrong, R. D., et al. Robust Estimation Procedures & Visual Display Techniques in a Two-Way Classification Model. (Research Report Ser.: 1978-2). (Illus.). 1978. pap. 4.00 (ISBN 0-87755-229-0). Bureau Busn UT.

Ashida, T. & Hall, Sydney, eds. Methods & Applications in Crystallographic Computing. (Illus.). 500p. 1984. 32.50x (ISBN 0-19-855190-8). Oxford U Pr.

Athey, Thomas H. & Zmud, Robert W. Introduction to Computers & Information Systems. 1986. text ed. 24.95x (ISBN 0-673-15961-2). Scott F.

--Introduction to Computers & Information Systems with BASIC. 1986. text ed. 26.95x (ISBN 0-673-18185-5). Scott F.

Atkinson, William & DeSanctis, Paul. Introduction to VSAM. 168p. 14.50 (5159). Hayden.

Auerbach, ed. Best Computer Papers, 1979. (Annual Computer Papers). 334p. 1980. 60.00 (ISBN 0-444-00350-9). Elsevier.

--Best Computer Papers, 1980. (Annual Computer Papers). 412p. 1980. 71.75 (ISBN 0-444-00447-5). Elsevier.

Augarten, Stan. Bit by Bit: An Illustrated History of Computers & Their Inventors. LC 84-2508. 304p. 1984. 29.95 (ISBN 0-89919-268-8); pap. 17.95 (ISBN 0-89919-302-1). Ticknor & Fields.

Awad, Elias M. Introduction to Computers. 2nd ed. (Illus.). 496p. 1983. text ed. 25.95 (ISBN 0-13-479444-3). P-H.

Babbage, Henry P., ed. Babbage's Calculating Engines. (The Charles Babbage Institute Reprint Series for the History of Computing: Vol. 2). (Illus.). 1983. Repr. of 1889 ed. 55.00x (ISBN 0-938228-04-8). Tomash Pubs.

Bach, C. Microeconomics: Analysis & Applications. 2nd ed. 1980. pap. 20.95 (ISBN 0-13-581298-4). P-H.

Baczynsky, Mark. How I Make a Comfortable Living with My Computer. 1983. pap. 9.95 (ISBN 0-89816-010-3). Embee Pr.

Balser, A. & Zoeppritz, M., eds. Enduser Systems & Their Human Factors: Proceedings, Heidelberg, FRG, 1983. (Lecture Notes in Computer Science Ser.: Vol. 150). 138p. 1983. pap. 10.50 (ISBN 0-387-12273-7). Springer-Verlag.

Baron, Robert J. & Shapiro, Linda G. Data Structures & Their Implementation. (University Computer Science Ser.). 416p. 1980. 23.95 (ISBN 0-442-20586-4). Van Nos Reinhold.

Barron, D. W. Computer Operating Systems: For Micros, Minis & Mainframes. 2nd ed. 184p. 1984. 35.00 (ISBN 0-412-15620-2, NO. 6708, Pub. by Chapman & Hall); pap. 15.95 (ISBN 0-412-15630-X, NO. 6588). Methuen Inc.

Bartee, Thomas C. Introduction to Computer Science. 1974. 38.95 (ISBN 0-07-003880-5). McGraw.

Bassler, Richard A. & Joslin, Edward O. Applications of Computer Systems. 1974. pap. 5.95 (ISBN 0-916580-06-7). College Readings.

--Introduction to Computer Systems. 3rd rev. ed. 1974. pap. 6.95 (ISBN 0-916580-04-0). College Readings.

BBC Publications, ed. The Computer Book. 208p. 1982. pap. 30.00x (ISBN 0-563-16484-0, Pub. by BBC Pubns). State Mutual Bk.

Beakley, George C. & Lovell, Robert E. Computation, Calculators & Computers: Tools of Engineering Problem Solving-Including FORTRAN. 368p. 1983. pap. text ed. write for info. (ISBN 0-02-307150-8). Macmillan.

Bellman, Richard. An Introduction to Artificial Intelligence: Can Computers Think? LC 78-9474. 160p. 1978. text ed. 20.00x (ISBN 0-87835-066-7). Boyd & Fraser.

Bellman, Richard E., et al. Algorithms, Graphs & Computers. (Mathematics in Science & Engineering Ser.: Vol. 62). 1970. 35.00 (ISBN 0-12-084840-6). Acad Pr.

Benice, Daniel D. Introduction to Computers & Data Processing. (Applied Mathematics Ser). 1970. ref. ed. 21.95 (ISBN 0-13-479543-1). P-H.

Bennett, J. M. & Kalman, R. E., eds. Computers in Developing Nations. 272p. 1981. 47.00 (ISBN 0-444-86270-6, North-Holland). Elsevier.

Bennett, Wilma E. Checklist-Guide to Selecting a Small Computer. LC 80-13996. 32p. 1980. pap. 5.00 (ISBN 0-87576-091-0). Pilot Bks.

Bentley, Colin. Computer Project Management. (Computing Science Ser.). 107p. 1983. 34.95 (ISBN 0-471-26208-0, Pub. by Wiley Heyden). Wiley.

Berrick, Ronald P. & Berrick, Stephen W. How Much is that Computer in the Window? (Illus.). 67p. (Orig.). 1982. spiral bdg. 9.95 (ISBN 0-910045-00-3). R Berrick.

Bertrand, Armand L., Jr. How to Start Understanding the Computer. (Illus.). 250p. (Orig.). 1984. pap. 12.95 suppl. avail. (ISBN 0-912447-02-8). Eclectical.

Billard, E., ed. Computer Science & Statistics: Proceedings of the Symposium on the Interface, 16th, Atlanta, Georgia, March 1984. 296p. 1985. 43.00 (ISBN 0-444-87725-8, North-Holland). Elsevier.

Bird, E. A. Electronic Data Processing & Computers for Commercial Students. 1979. pap. 9.50 (ISBN 0-434-90142-3, Pub. by W Heinemann Ltd). David & Charles.

Bitter, Gary G. Computers in Today's World. LC 83-10588. 306p. 1984. 21.95x (ISBN 0-471-87552-X); tchr's. edition avail. (ISBN 0-471-87206-7); avail. student wkbk. 10.95x (ISBN 0-471-87205-9); BASIC supplement 10.45 (ISBN 0-471-87551-1); Pascal supplement 10.45 (ISBN 0-471-87553-8). Wiley.

Blotnick, S. Computers Made (Ridiculously) Easy. (Illus.). 198p. 1984. pap. 12.95 (ISBN 0-07-006123-8). McGraw.

Bohl, Marilyn. Computer Concepts. LC 75-101499. (Illus.). 1970. text ed. 24.95 (ISBN 0-574-16080-9, 13-0751); instr's guide avail. (ISBN 0-574-16082-5, 13-0753); problems & exercises 10.95 (ISBN 0-574-16081-7, 13-0752). SRA.

Bolt, Richard A. The Human Interface: Where People & Computers Meet. (Illus.). 114p. 1984. 22.95 (ISBN 0-534-03380-6); pap. 16.95 (ISBN 0-534-03387-3). Van Nos Reinhold.

Borovits, Israel. Management of Computer Operations. (Illus.). 288p. 1984. 35.95 (ISBN 0-13-549493-1). P-H.

Bosworth, Bruce. Codes, Ciphers, & Computers: An Introduction to Information Security. 1982. pap. 16.50 (5149). Hayden.

Brady, M., ed. Computer Vision. (Journal: Artifical Intelligence Ser.: Vol. 17). 1984. pap. 30.00 (ISBN 0-444-87511-5). Elsevier.

Brenan, Kathleen M. & Mandell, Steven L. Introduction to Computers & BASIC Programming. (Illus.). 409p. 1983. text ed. 20.95 (ISBN 0-314-78551-5); tchrs.' manual avail. (ISBN 0-314-81042-0). West Pub.

Brophy, P. Computers Can Read. 1985. text ed. write for info. (ISBN 0-566-00805-X). Gower Pub Co.

Brown, John A. Computers & Automation. rev. ed. LC 73-76928. (Illus.). 248p. 1974. 7.50 (ISBN 0-668-01623-X); pap. 5.95 (ISBN 0-668-01745-7). Arco.

Brown, Mike. Computers from First Principles. (Hatfield Polytechnic Computer Science Series). 126p. (Orig.). 1982. pap. text ed. 11.95x (ISBN 0-86238-027-8, Pub. by Chartwell-Bratt England). Brookfield Pub Co.

Buchanan, David A. & Boddy, David. Organizations in the Computer Age. 279p. 1983. text ed. 45.00 (ISBN 0-566-00488-7). Gower Pub Co.

Bundesverband der Pharmzeutischen Industrie, ed. Rote Liste 1982. (Ger.). 1167p. 1982. 45.00 (ISBN 3-87193-063-6). Intl Pubns Serv.

Bunyan. Computer Systems Measurement. (Infotech Computer State of the Art Reports). 701p. 1974. 310.00 (ISBN 0-08-028551-1). Pergamon.

Burch, John L., ed. Computers: The Non-Technological (Human) Factors: A Recommended Reading List on Computer Ergonomics & User Friendly Design. LC 84-60013. 101p. 1984. pap. 34.95 (ISBN 0-916313-00-X). Report.

Burke, Anna M. Computer Discovery Workbook, College Version. 144p. 1984. pap. 9.95 wkbk. (ISBN 0-574-21460-7, 13-4460); tchr's ed. 5.95 (ISBN 0-574-21461-5, 13-4461). SRA.

Burnham, David. The Rise of the Computer State. Date not set. pap. 6.95 (ISBN 0-394-72375-9, Vin). Random.

Burns, Alan. Microchip Appropriate or Inappropriate Technology. (Computers & Their Applications Ser.). 180p. 1981. 48.95x (ISBN 0-470-27206-6). Halsted Pr.

--New Information Technology. LC 83-22766. (Computers & Their Applications Ser.: 1-403). 245p. 1984. pap. 26.95x (ISBN 0-470-27494-8, Pub by Halsted Pr). Wiley.

Busald, Gerald. An Introduction to Computer Terminals. 64p. 1982. pap. text ed. 4.50 (ISBN 0-8403-3058-8, 40305802). Kendall-Hunt.

Bytheway, A., ed. Structured Methods. (Computer State of the Art Report, Series 12: No. 1). (Illus.). 250p. 1984. 460.00 (ISBN 0-08-028585-6). Pergamon.

Campbell-Kelley, M. An Introduction to Macros. (Computer Monograph Ser.: Vol. 21). 114p. 1973. 24.75 (ISBN 0-444-19563-7). Elsevier.

Campbell-Kelly, Martin. The Charles Babbage Institute Reprint Series for the History of Computing. 1983. write for info. limited edition (ISBN 0-938228-01-3). Tomash Pubs.

Capron, H. & Williams, B. Computers & Data Processing. 1982. text ed. 28.95 (ISBN 0-8053-2201-9); instr's. guide 4.95; trans. 40.00; study guide 9.95. Benjamin-Cummings.

Carter, Ciel. Guide to Reference Sources in the Computer Sciences. LC 72-82745. 1974. 25.00 (ISBN 0-02-468300-0). Macmillan Info.

Cayot, Billie J., et al. How to Select a Business Computer. LC 81-85927. (Successful Business Library). 150p. 1982. 29.95 (ISBN 0-916378-17-9, Oasis). PSI Res.

Chambers, Andrew D. Computer Auditing. 256p. 1981. 24.50 (ISBN 0-317-04274-2, 5047). Commerce.

Chartrand, Robert L. Computers & Political Campaigning. LC 72-75713. 1972. 5.00 (ISBN 0-87671-178-6). Chartrand.

Chou, Wushow. Computer Communications: Systems & Applications, Vol. II. (Illus.). 496p. 1983. text ed. 41.95 (ISBN 0-13-165050-5). P-H.

Chou, Wushow, ed. Computer Communications, Vol. I: Principles. (Illus.). 496p. 1982. text ed. 41.95 (ISBN 0-13-165043-2). P-H.

Christensen, R. Computer Implementation of Entropy Minimax. (Entropy Minimax Sourcebook Ser.: Vol. III). x, 254p. 1980. 32.95 (ISBN 0-938876-05-8). Entropy Ltd.

Chubb, Bruce. Computers in Model Railroading. Hayden, Bob, ed. (Illus., Orig.). 1985. pap. price not set (ISBN 0-89024-077-9). Kalmbach.

CINDA: An Index to the Literature on Microscopic Neutron Data. Incl. CINDA-A (1935-1976, 2 Vols. 1929p. 1980. Set. pap. 95.50 (ISBN 0-686-60074-6, ICIN35/76); Vol. 1 Z-50. pap. (ISBN 92-0-039079-X); Vol. 2 Z-51. pap. (ISBN 92-0-039179-6); CINDA 79 (1977-1979) 376p. 1980. pap. 33.00 (ISBN 92-0-039279-2, ICIN77/79); free supplement (ISBN 92-0-039379-9); 1977-1981. 542p. 1981. pap. 52.00 (ISBN 92-0-039081-1, ICIN81); Supplement to CINDA 81. pap. 8.25 (ISBN 92-0-039181-8, ICIN81SUPP); An Index to the Literature on Microscopic Neutron Data. IAEA). Unipub.

Clark, Jon D. & Reisman, Arnold. Computer System Selection: An Intergrated Approach. LC 80-21496. 236p. 1981. 37.95x (ISBN 0-03-057888-4). Praeger.

Cluff, E. F., ed. The Computer User, No. 6. (Computer State of the Art Report Ser.: 11-6). 400p. 1983. 445.00 (ISBN 0-08-028577-5). Pergamon.

Cohen, Daniel. Introduction to Computer Theory. 1985. text ed. write for info. (ISBN 0-471-80271-9); tchr's ed. avail. (ISBN 0-471-80766-4). Wiley.

Collin, W. G. Computers in Distribution. LC 75-326180. (Illus.). 1975. pap. 26.50x (ISBN 0-85012-127-2). Intl Pubns Serv.

Computer-Aided Hull Surface Definition. 234p. 6.00 (ISBN 0-317-35868-5, S-5); members 4.00 (ISBN 0-317-35869-3). Soc Naval Arch.

Computer-Aided Studies of Fishing Boat Hull Resistance. (Fisheries Technical Papers: No. 87). 127p. 1969. pap. 7.50 (ISBN 0-686-93179-3, F1741, FAO). Unipub.

Computer BookBase: Annual Edition 1985-86. 1985. 4.95 (ISBN 0-86672-002-2). DemoNet.

Computer Science & Statistics: Proceedings. Eddy, W., ed. (Illus.). 378p. 1981. pap. 29.50 (ISBN 0-387-90633-9). Springer-Verlag.

Computer Technology & Employment. (Illus.). 1979. pap. 14.50x (ISBN 0-85012-212-0). Intl Pubns Serv.

Computer Technology for Development: 2nd Report. pap. 3.50 (ISBN 0-686-95000-3, UN73/2A/12, UN). Unipub.

The Computer User's Yearbook, 1982. LC 78-617411. 1448p. 1982. 135.00x (ISBN 0-902908-15-4). Intl Pubns Serv.

Computer White Paper: 1983-84. (Illus.). 60p. 1985. pap. 45.00 (FPC102, FUJI). Unipub.

Computers & Related Equipment: Korea. 75.00 (ISBN 0-686-32989-9). Info Gatekeepers.

Computers & Related Equipment: Thailand. 75.00 (ISBN 0-686-38463-6). Info Gatekeepers.

Computers & Related Equipment: The Netherlands. 75.00 (ISBN 0-686-32990-2). Info Gatekeepers.

Computers in the City. 400p. 1983. pap. 105.00x (ISBN 0-903796-94-5, Pub. by Online). Taylor & Francis.

Computers in the City: Proceedings of the International Conference London 1983. 400p. (Orig.). 1983. pap. text ed. 123.00x (ISBN 0-903796-94-5, Pub. by Online Conferences England). Brookfield Pub Co.

Computing Systems Fundamentals: A Programmed Instruction Course. 1969. overview 10.95 (ISBN 0-574-16077-9, 15-0060); techniques 13.95 (ISBN 0-574-16078-7, 15-0061); wkbk. 3.95 (ISBN 0-574-16079-5, 15-0062). SRA.

Conference on Systems & Computer Science, 1965: University of Western Ontario. Systems & Computer Science. Hart, John F. & Takasu, Satoru, eds. LC 68-114245. pap. 65.30 (ISBN 0-317-10999-5, 2014240). Bks Demand UMI.

Conley, William C. Computer Optimization Techniques. rev. ed. (Illus.). 350p. 1984. text ed. 29.95 (ISBN 0-89433-213-9). Petrocelli.

Cook, William J. The Joy of Computer Communications. 192p. (Orig.). 1984. pap. 5.95 (ISBN 0-440-54412-2, Dell Trade Pbks). Dell.

Cooke, D., et al. BASIC Statistical Computing. 176p. 1982. pap. text ed. 14.95 (ISBN 0-7131-3441-0). E Arnold.

Couger, Daniel. Computer & the School of Business. 98p. 1967. 4.00 (ISBN 0-89478-006-9). U CO Busn Res Div.

Covvey, H. Dominic & McAlister, Neil H. Computer Choices: Beware of Conspicuous Computing. (Illus.). 192p. pap. 8.95 (ISBN 0-201-10113-0). Addison-Wesley.

--Computer Consciousness: Surviving the Automated Eighties. LC 79-27144. 1980. pap. text ed. 7.95 (ISBN 0-201-01939-6). Addison-Wesley.

--Conspicuous Computing - or Informed Choices for the Computer Age. LC 81-3646. 192p. 1981. pap. 8.95 (ISBN 0-201-10113-0). Addison-Wesley.

Crawford, T. Basic Computing: A Complete Course. 393p. 16.25 (ISBN 0-07-548076-X). McGraw.

Kuong, Javier F. Computer Security, Auditing & Controls, Text & Readings. Incl. EDP Security, Auditing & Controls Text; Selected Readings. 400p. 1974. 35.00 (ISBN 0-940706-05-9, MAP-3). Management Advisory Pubns.

Lamb, G. M. Computers in the Public Service. 258p. 1973. 15.95x (ISBN 0-8464-1250-0). Beekman Pubs.

--Computers in the Public Service. 260p. 1973. 40.00x (ISBN 0-04-363003-0, Pub by Royal Inst Pub Anmin England). State Mutual Bk.

Laurie, Edward J. Computers, Automation, & Society. 1979. 19.95x (ISBN 0-256-02140-6). Irwin.

Laurie, Peter. The Joy of Computers. (Illus.). 192p. 1983. 19.45i (ISBN 0-316-51636-8). Little.

Laver, Murray. An Introduction to the Uses of Computers. LC 75-23535. (Cambridge Computer Science Texts Ser.: No. 5). (Illus.). 187p. 1976. 14.95x (ISBN 0-521-29035-X). Cambridge U Pr.

Lavington, Simon. Early British Computers: The Story of Vintage Computers & The People Who Built Them. (Illus.). 140p. 1980. pap. 9.00 (ISBN 0-932376-08-8, EY-AX012-DP). Digital Pr.

Lechner, H. D. Computer Chronicles. (Illus.). 260p. 1984. pap. write for info. (ISBN 0-317-18567-5). Wadsworth Pub.

Ledgard, Henry, et al. From Baker Street to Binary: An Introduction to Computers & Computer Programming with Sherlock Holmes. 288p. 1983. pap. 10.95 (ISBN 0-07-036983-6, BYTE Bks). McGraw.

Lee, Fred. The Computer Book. LC 78-17450. pap. 95.30 (ISBN 0-317-27667-0, 2025058). Bks Demand UMI.

Leeson, Marjorie M. Computer Operations. 2nd ed. 512p. 1982. pap. text ed. 22.95 (ISBN 0-574-21345-7, 13-4345); instrs'. guide avail. (ISBN 0-574-21346-5, 13-4346). SRA.

Leilich, H. O. & Missikoff, M., eds. Database Machines. (Illus.). 344p. 1983. pap. 25.00 (ISBN 0-387-12959-6). Springer Verlag.

Lewin, Morton H. Logic Design & Computer Organization. LC 81-20636. 478p. 1983. 36.95 (ISBN 0-201-04144-8). Addison-Wesley.

Lindelof, E. T. Cobra: The Computer-Designed Bidding System. (Master Bridge Ser.). 320p. 1983. 32.00 (ISBN 0-575-02987-0, Pub. by Gollancz England). David & Charles.

Logica Ltd. Introducing Communications Protocols. (Illus.). 83p. (Orig.). 1978. pap. 16.75x (ISBN 0-85012-208-2). Intl Pubns Serv.

Logsdon. How to Cope with Computers. 1983. pap. 10.95 (ISBN 0-686-82003-7, 5193). Hayden.

London, Keith. Introduction to Computers. 4th ed. 270p. 1979. pap. 8.95 (ISBN 0-571-04975-3). Faber & Faber.

Long, Larry. Introduction to Computers & Information Processing. 512p. 1984. text ed. 26.95 (ISBN 0-13-480534-8). P-H.

Long, Larry & Kreutzer, N. Introduction to Computers & Information Processing: Study Guide. 256p. 1984. pap. text ed. 9.95 (ISBN 0-13-480427-9); pap. text ed. instructor's manual incl. P-H.

Lord, Norman W. & Giragosian, Paul A. Advanced Computers: Parallel & Biochip Processors. (Illus.). 170p. 1983. 39.95 (ISBN 0-250-40626-8). Butterworth.

Lynch, Thomas J. Data Compression Techniques & Applications. (Engineering Ser.). (Illus.). 350p. 1984. text ed. 38.00 (ISBN 0-534-03418-7). Lifetime Learn.

Macchi, C. & Guilbert, J. F. Teleinformatics: Data & Computer Communications. St. Quinton, J. M., tr. (Studies in Telecommunications: Vol. 3). 452p. 1985. 89.00 (ISBN 0-444-87507-7, North-Holland). Elsevier.

McCorduck, Pamela. The Universal Machine: Confessions of a Technological Optimist. 304p. 1985. 16.95 (ISBN 0-07-044882-5). McGraw.

Mace, P. W. Visible Record Computers. 216p. 1974. 22.00x (ISBN 0-8464-0957-7). Beekman Pubs.

McEntire, P. L., et al, eds. Distributed Computing: Concepts & Implementations. LC 84-6648. 1984. 61.95 (ISBN 0-87942-175-4, PC01693). Inst Electrical.

Mack, J. & Haden, Douglas H. Computers, Appreciation, Applications, Implications: An Introduction. LC 73-1688. pap. 150.00 (ISBN 0-317-19893-9, 2012504). Bks Demand UMI.

Maddux, Cleborne D., ed. LOGO in the Schools. (Computers in the Schools: Vol. 2. Nos. 2-3). 312p. 1985. text ed. 22.95 (ISBN 0-86656-424-1, B424); pap. text ed. 16.95 (ISBN 0-86656-425-X, B425). Haworth Pr.

Mair, William C., et al. Computer Control & Audit. 2nd rev. ed. 512p. 1976. 24.50 (ISBN 0-686-78426-X). QED Info Sci.

Mandell, Steven L. Computers & Data Processing: Concepts & Applications. 3rd ed. (Illus.). 550p. 1984. text ed. 25.95 (ISBN 0-314-85262-X). West Pub.

--Computers & Data Processing: Concepts & Applications with BASIC. 3rd ed. (Illus.). 736p. 1984. text ed. 27.95 (ISBN 0-314-87560-3). West Pub.

--Computers & Data Processing Today. 2nd ed. (Illus.). 500p. 1985. pap. text ed. 25.00 (ISBN 0-314-93200-3). West Pub.

--Computers & Data Processing Today with BASIC. 2nd ed. (Illus.). 600p. 1985. pap. text ed. 27.95 (ISBN 0-314-96079-1). West Pub.

--Computers & Data Processing Today with Pascal. 2nd ed. (Illus.). 550p. 1985. pap. text ed. 27.95 (ISBN 0-314-96080-5). West Pub.

--Computers & Data Processing Without BASIC. 2nd ed. (Illus.). 528p. 1982. text ed. 23.95 (ISBN 0-314-63268-9). West Pub.

Martin, Edley W. & Perkins, William C. Computers & Information Systems: An Introduction. LC 72-95392. (Irwin-Dorsey Information Processing Ser.). pap. 160.00 (ISBN 0-317-29612-4, 2021665). Bks Demand UMI.

Martinson, S. A. Managing Computer Applications Development. 1983. write for info. looseleaf bound (ISBN 0-935506-14-4). Carnegie Pr.

Massam, Thomas, ed. Computer Frontiers. (Illus.). 1977. 32.25x (ISBN 2-604-00024-5). Brookfield Pub Co.

Mathias, Jim & Kennedy, Thomas L., eds. Computers, Language Reform, & Lexicography in China. vii, 76p. (Orig.). 1980. pap. 10.95 (ISBN 0-87422-015-7). Wash St U Pr.

Mehlhorn, K., ed. STACS 85. (Lecture Notes in Computer Science Ser.: Vol. 182). vii, 374p. 1985. pap. 16.00 (ISBN 0-387-13912-5). Springer-Verlag.

Merrill, H. W. Merrill's Guide to Computer Performance Evaluation: Analysis of SMF-RMF Data with SAS. (Illus.). 352p. 1980. 395.00 (ISBN 0-917382-09-9). SAS Inst.

Metropolis, N., et al, eds. A History of Computing in the Twentieth Century. LC 79-51683. 1980. 35.00 (ISBN 0-12-491650-3). Acad Pr.

Michie, Donald & Johnston, Rory. The Knowledge Machine: Artificial Intelligence & the Future of Man. LC 84-29582. (Illus.). 192p. 1985. 16.95 (ISBN 0-688-03267-2). Morrow.

Miller, Boulton B. Computers & Data Processing. Woltering, Denise M. & Oberthaler, James V., eds. (Illus.). 335p. 1982. 12.95 (ISBN 0-915234-06-8); pap. text ed. 7.95 (ISBN 0-915234-05-X). Bainbridge.

Monteleone. R. A. M. Random Access Messages of the Computer Age. 256p. 1984. pap. 6.95 (ISBN 0-317-05885-1, 6333). Hayden.

Moshell, Michael. Computer Power. 224p. 1981. 14.20 (ISBN 0-07-065773-4). McGraw.

Mumford, Enid & Ward, T. B. Computers: Planning for People. (Modern Management Ser.). (Illus.). 176p. 1968. text ed. 19.50x (ISBN 0-8464-1177-6). Beekman Pubs.

Murray, Jerome T. & Murray, Marilyn J. Computers in Crisis. (Illus.). 240p. 1984. 32.95. Van Nos Reinhold.

Myers, Charles A. Computers in Knowledge-Based Fields. 1970. pap. 5.95x (ISBN 0-262-63053-2). MIT Pr.

Nagel, H. T., et al. An Introduction to Computer Logic. (Illus.). 544p. 1975. ref. ed. 40.95 (ISBN 0-13-480012-5). P-H.

National Computer Conference: Proceedings, Chicago, May 1981. Evens, Martha, ed. LC 81-65717. (AFIPS Conference Proceedings Ser.: Vol. 50). (Illus.). xv, 719p. 1981. 75.00 (ISBN 0-88283-032-5). AFIPS Pr.

National Computer Conference, 1979. AFIPS Proceedings, Vol. 48. Merwin, Richard E., ed. LC 55-44701. (Illus.). xi, 1114p. 1979. 69.00 (ISBN 0-88283-005-8). AFIPS Pr.

National Computing Centre. Working with Computers. 86p. 1982. pap. 7.65 (ISBN 0-471-89433-8, DP00, Pub. by Wiley-Interscience). Wiley.

National Computing Centre Ltd, ed. Computer Appreciation for the Majority. LC 72-97128. 220p. 1973. pap. 2750.00x (ISBN 0-85012-153-1). Intl Pubns Serv.

National Database & Fourth Generation Language Symposium Workbook & Proceedings. 500p. 1984. pap. 250.00 (ISBN 0-318-01070-4). Software Inst Am.

Naur, Peter. Concise Survey of Computer Methods. 397p. (Orig.). 1974. pap. text ed. 35.50x (ISBN 0-317-02800-6, Pub. by Chartwell-Bratt England). Brookfield Pub Co.

Negoita, Constantin. Expert Systems & Fuzzy Systems. 1985. 39.95 (ISBN 0-8053-6840-X). Benjamin-Cummings.

Neill, Graham. Introduction to Computer Science. 3rd ed. (Illus.). 1985. 32.95 (ISBN 0-314-85240-9). West Pub.

Nelson, Theodor H. Computer Lib. (Illus.). 1974. pap. 7.00 with 1975 supplement (ISBN 0-89347-002-3). T Nelson.

Neumann, John Von. Computer & the Brain. LC 58-6542. (Silliman Lectures Ser.). 1958. pap. 4.95x (ISBN 0-300-02415-0). Yale U Pr.

New Concepts in Business Information. 1979. pap. text ed. 46.50x (ISBN 0-903796-39-2, Pub. by Online Conferences England). Brookfield Pub Co.

Norback, Craig T. The Computer Invasion. LC 80-23902. 288p. 1981. 23.95 (ISBN 0-442-26121-7). Van Nos Reinhold.

Norman, Adrian. Computer Insecurity. 1985. pap. 15.95 (ISBN 0-412-00861-0, Pub. by Chapman & Hall England). Methuen Inc.

Norusis, Marija J. SPSS-X Introducing Statistics Guide. 1983. 15.95 (ISBN 0-07-046549-5). McGraw.

O'Donnell, M. J. Computing in Systems Described by Equations. LC 77-25999. (Lecture Notes in Computer Science: Vol. 58). 1977. pap. text ed. 14.00 (ISBN 0-387-08531-9). Springer-Verlag.

OECD Staff. Computer Technologies & Consumer Information Interactive Videtex Systems. 36p. (Orig.). 1983. pap. 6.50x (ISBN 92-64-12389-X). OECD.

Organick, Elliot I. Computer System Organization: The B-Fifty-Seven Hundred-B Sixty-Seven Hundred Series. (ACM Monograph Ser.). 1973. text ed. 37.00 (ISBN 0-12-528250-8). Acad Pr.

Orilia, L. Schaum's Outline of Computers & Business. 304p. 1984. pap. 8.95 (ISBN 0-07-047834-1). McGraw.

Paker, Yacup, ed. Distributed Computing Systems. Verjus, J. P. 1983. 29.50 (ISBN 0-12-543970-9). Acad Pr.

Parker, Charles S. Understanding Computers & Data Processing: Today & Tomorrow. 1984. text ed. 27.95x (ISBN 0-03-063424-5); study guide 10.95 (ISBN 0-03-063428-8). HR&W.

Patterson, Diane A. The Computer Documentation Kit. 176p. 24.95 (ISBN 0-317-13748-4). P-H.

Paul, J. K., ed. High Technology International Trade & Competition: Robotics, Computers, Telecommunications, Semiconductors. LC 84-5916. (Illus.). 394p. 1984. 42.00 (ISBN 0-8155-0988-X). Noyes.

Pelton, Dan & Pelton, Jeanette. The Microheart. 75p. pap. cancelled (ISBN 0-88056-073-8). Dilithium Pr.

Peltu, Malcolm. Introducing Computers. (Illus.). 326p. (Orig.). 1983. pap. text ed. 20.00x (ISBN 0-85012-321-6). Intl Pubns Serv.

Pergamon-Infotech. Computer State of the Art Reports. write for info. Pergamon.

Perry, William E. Managing Systems Maintenance. (Q. E. D. Information Sciences Ser.). (Illus.). 384p. 1984. text ed. 39.95 (ISBN 0-13-550450-3). P-H.

--Survival Guide to Computer Systems: A Primer for Executives. 249p. 1982. 17.95 (ISBN 0-8436-0880-3). Van Nos Reinhold.

Petit, Jean-Pierre. Informagic: Computers & How They Work. Stewart, Ian, tr. (The Adventures of Archibald Higgins Ser.). pap. 7.95 (ISBN 0-317-19305-8). W Kaufmann.

Petrocelli Books Editorial Staff. The Future of the Semiconductors Computer, Robotics & Telecommunication: A Source Book. (Illus.). 300p. 1984. text ed. 49.95 (ISBN 0-89433-259-7). Petrocelli.

Petty. Computers. (First Library). (Illus.). 32p. 1984. lib. bdg. 8.60 (ISBN 0-531-04810-1). Watts.

Planning & Executing Computer Applications Development. 1984. write for info. loose-leaf (ISBN 0-935506-23-3). Carnegie Pr.

Poirot, Jim, et al. Practice in Computers & Data Processing. pap. 7.95. Sterling Swift.

Polya, et al. Notes on Introductory Combinatorics. (Progress in Computer Science Ser.: Vol. 4). 1983. 14.95 (ISBN 3-7643-3123-2); pap. 9.95 (ISBN 0-8176-3170-4). Birkhauser.

Privacy & Computers: A Bibliography. 96p. 1978. soft cover 29.00 (ISBN 0-85296-451-X). Inst Elect Eng.

Racter. The Policeman's Beard Is Half-Constructed: Computer Prose & Poetry. (Illus.). 128p. (Orig.). 1984. pap. 9.95 (ISBN 0-446-38051-2). Warner Bks.

Rademacher, Robert & Gibson, Harry. An Introduction to Computers & Information Systems. 1983. text ed. 21.95 (ISBN 0-538-10250-0, J25). SW Pub.

Radlow, J. Computers & the Information Society. 544p. 1986. pap. price not set (ISBN 0-07-003901-1). McGraw.

Raff, Ellison S., ed. Computers & Operations Research: Environmental Applications. 1977. pap. text ed. 38.00 (ISBN 0-08-021348-0). Pergamon.

Raphael, Bertram. The Thinking Computer: Mind Inside Matter. LC 75-30839. (Psychology Ser.). (Illus.). 322p. 1976. pap. text ed. 13.95x (ISBN 0-7167-0723-3). W H Freeman.

Rattenbury, Judith, et al. Computer Processing of Social Science Data Using OSIRIS IV. 200p. (Orig.). 1984. pap. text ed. 20.00x (ISBN 0-87944-295-6). Inst Soc Res.

REA Staff. Computer Science Problem Solver. rev. ed. LC 81-50900. (Illus.). 896p. (Orig.). 1984. pap. text ed. 23.85x (ISBN 0-87891-525-7). Res & Educ.

Reichman, Rachel. Getting Computers to Talk Like You & Me: Discourse, Context, Focus & Semantics; an ATN Model. (Comput'l Models Ser.). (Illus.). 144p. 1985. text ed. 25.00x (ISBN 0-262-18118-5, Pub. by Bradford). MIT Pr.

Research & Education Association Staff. Handbook of Computers & Data Processing. LC 83-61837. (Illus.). 480p. 1983. 19.85 (ISBN 0-87891-546-X). Res & Educ.

Rheingold, Howard. Tools for Thought: The People & Ideas Behind the Next Computer Revolution. LC 85-1986. (Illus.). 335p. 1985. 17.95 (ISBN 0-671-49292-6). S&S.

Ribler, Ronald I. Training Applications Using Microcomputers. 1985. 24.95 (ISBN 0-8359-7789-7); pap. 16.95 (ISBN 0-8359-7790-0). Reston.

Rine, D. C., ed. Computer Science & Multiple Valued Logic: Theory & Applications. rev. ed. 642p. 1984. 65.00 (ISBN 0-444-86882-8, North Holland). Elsevier.

Rogowski, Stephen J. Computers for Sea & Sky. 108p. 9.95 (ISBN 0-916688-38-0, 14F). Creative Comp.

Rossi, Lee D., et al. Computer Notions. (Illus.). 176p. 1985. pap. text ed. 10.95 (ISBN 0-13-163932-3). P-H.

Rossman, Parker. Computers: Bridges to the Future. 144p. 1985. pap. 9.95 (ISBN 0-8170-1058-0). Judson.

Rota, Gian-Carlo & Reynolds, Mark, eds. Science, Computers, & People: From the Tree of Mathematics, Stanislaw Ulam. (Illus.). 1985. 14.95 (ISBN 0-8176-3276-X). Birkhauser.

Rothfeder, Jeffrey. Mind over Matter. 320p. 1985. 17.95 (ISBN 0-671-53206-5, Pub. by Computer Bks). S&S.

Rowan, T. G. Managing with Computers. (Illus.). 312p. 1984. pap. 19.95 (ISBN 0-434-91760-5, Pub. by W Heinemann Ltd). David & Charles.

Rudall, B. Computers & Cybernetics. 1981. 27.00 (ISBN 0-9961004-1-5, Pub. by Abacus England). Heyden.

Rudman, Jack. Computer Science. (Graduate Record Examination Ser.). 21.95 (ISBN 0-8373-5271-1); pap. 13.95 (ISBN 0-8373-5221-5). Natl Learning.

--Computer Specialist. (Career Examination Ser.: C-161). (Cloth bdg. avail. on request). pap. 14.00 (ISBN 0-8373-0161-0). Natl Learning.

--Computer Specialist (Applications Programming) (Career Examination Ser.: C-2871). (Cloth bdg. avail. on request). pap. 14.00 (ISBN 0-8373-2874-8). Natl Learning.

--Computer Specialist (Data Base Administration) (Career Examination Ser.: C-2876). (Cloth bdg. avail. on request). pap. 14.00 (ISBN 0-8373-2876-4). Natl Learning.

--Computers & Data Processing. (College Level Examination Ser.: CLEP-8). (Cloth bdg. avail. on request). pap. 9.95 (ISBN 0-8373-5308-4). Natl Learning.

Rushforth, J. M. & Morris, J. L. Computers & Computing. LC 72-8616. (Introductory Mathematics for Scientists & Engineers Ser.). pap. 67.30 (ISBN 0-317-08336-8, 2022104). Bks Demand UMI.

Rustin, Randall, ed. Courant Computer Science, Symposium 7: Computational Complexity. (Illus.). 268p. 1973. 25.00x (ISBN 0-917448-01-4). Algorithmics.

--Courant Computer Science, Symposium 8: Natural Language Processing. (Illus.). 350p. 1973. 30.00x (ISBN 0-917448-02-2). Algorithmics.

Salton, Gerard. The Computer Science CumIndex, Vol. 12. 1979. 60.00 (ISBN 0-88274-011-3). R & D Pr.

Salvendy, G., ed. Human-Computer Interaction: Proceedings of the U. S. A.-Japan Conference on Human-Computer Interaction, 1st Honolulu, Hawaii, Aug. 18-20, 1984. (Advances in Human Factors-Ergonomics Ser.: Vol. 1). 1984. 74.50 (ISBN 0-444-42395-8). Elsevier.

Sambridge, Edward R. Purchasing Computers. 156p. 1979. text ed. 37.25x (ISBN 0-566-02193-5). Gower Pub Co.

Sanders, B. D. Computer Confidence: A Human Approch to Computers. (Professional Computing Bks.). (Illus.). 130p. 1984. pap. 13.00 (ISBN 0-387-90917-6). Springer-Verlag.

Sanders, D. H. Computers Today. 2nd ed. 672p. 1985. write for info. (ISBN 0-07-054701-7); write for info. slides (ISBN 0-07-054714-9). McGraw.

Sanders, Donald H. Computers Today. Vastyan, James E., ed. LC 82-4626. (Illus.). 1982. text ed. 26.95 (ISBN 0-07-054681-9). McGraw.

Sanders, Norman. A Manager's Guide to Profitable Computers. LC 78-23624. 224p. 1979. 14.95 (ISBN 0-8144-5495-X). Am Mgmt Assns.

Leiss, Ernst L. Principles of Data Security. LC 82-22272. (Foundations of Computer Science Ser.). 238p. 1982. 27.50 (ISBN 0-306-41098-2, Plenum Pr). Plenum Pub.
Marchand, Donald A. The Politics of Privacy, Computers, & Criminal Justice Records: Controlling the Social Costs of Technological Change. LC 80-80675. xvi, 433p. 1980. text ed. 34.95 (ISBN 0-87815-030-7). Info Resources.
Norman, Adrian R. Computer Insecurity. (Illus.). 250p. 1983. 29.95 (ISBN 0-412-22310-4, NO. 6640). Methuen Inc.
Parker, Donn. Computer Security Management. 304p. 1981. text ed. 26.95 (ISBN 0-8359-0905-0). Reston.
Perry, William E. Management Strategies for Computer Security. 240p. 1985. text ed. 24.95 (ISBN 0-409-95135-8). Butterworth.
Schweitzer, James. Protecting Information in the Electronic Workplace: A Guide for Managers. 1983. text ed. 22.95 (ISBN 0-8359-5702-0). Reston.
Simons, Geoffrey L. Privacy in the Computer Age. 147p. (Orig.). 1982. pap. 22.50x (ISBN 0-85012-348-8). Intl Pubns Serv.
Smith, Leighton F. An Executive Briefing on the Control of Computers. 160p. 1979. pap. 11.95 (ISBN 0-318-13881-6, D2); pap. 9.95 members (ISBN 0-318-13882-4). Data Process Mgmt.
Talbot, J. R. Management Guide to Computer Security. 180p. 1981. text ed. 36.95x (ISBN 0-566-02190-0). Gower Pub Co.
Turn, Rein. Advances in Computer System Security, Vol. 2. 350p. 1984. pap. text ed. 50.00 (ISBN 0-89006-156-4). Artech Hse.
Turn, Rein, intro. by. Advances in Computer System Security. LC 81-65989. (Illus.). 403p. (Orig.). 1981. pap. text ed. 44.00 (ISBN 0-89006-096-7). Artech Hse.
Westin, Alan F. Computers, Health Records & Citizen Rights. 1977. text ed. 17.50 (ISBN 0-89433-014-4). Petrocelli.
Yankee Group. The Electronic Vault: Computer Piracy & Privacy. LC 84-210486. (Industry Research Report Ser.). (Illus.). 122p. 1984. write for info. Yankee Group.

COMPUTERS–ANECDOTES, FACETIAE, SATIRE, ETC.

Amann, Dick & Smith, Dick. Forgotten Women of Computer History. Whitson, Dick, ed. (Illus.). 1978. pap. 9.95 (ISBN 0-917194-09-8). Prog Studies.
Arneson, D. J. The Official Computer Hater's Handbook. (Orig.). 1983. pap. 3.95 (ISBN 0-440-56619-3, Dell Trade Pbks). Dell.
Baker, Mark. I Hate Videots. 1983. write for info. S&S.
Bass, Thomas A. The Eudaemonic Pie: Or Why Would Anyone Play Roulette Without a Computer in His Shoe? 324p. 1985. 15.95 (ISBN 0-395-35335-1); pap. write for info. HM.
Bell, Patty & Myrland, Doug. The Official Silicon Valley Guy Handbook. 128p. 1983. pap. 3.95 (ISBN 0-380-84392-7, 84392-7). Avon.
Berkeley, Edmund C. The Computer Book of Lists & the First Computer Almanac. (Illus.). 176p. 1984. pap. 14.95 (ISBN 0-8359-0864-X). Reston.
Brown, Eugene & Tarratt, Sara L. Small Bytes: An Irreverent Computer Dictionary. 96p. 1983. pap. 4.95 (ISBN 0-02-003920-4). Macmillan.
Busch, David D. Sorry about the Explosion: A Humorous Guide to Computers. (P-H Personal Computing Ser.). (Illus.). 128p. 1985. pap. text ed. 7.95 (ISBN 0-13-822834-5). P-H.
Byte, Maurice K., et al. How to Make Love to a Computer. 96p. (Orig.). 1984. pap. 3.95 (ISBN 0-671-50370-7). PB.
Clark, Ron, ed. My Buttons Are Blue & Other Love Poems from the Digital Heart of an Electronic Computer. (Illus.). 96p. 1983. 4.95 (ISBN 0-86668-013-6). ARCsoft.
Dedini. A Much Much Better World. (Illus.). 128p. 1985. pap. 6.95 (ISBN 0-914845-50-0). Microsoft.
Ferrarini, Elizabeth M. Confessions of an Infomaniac. LC 84-50357. 202p. 1984. 12.95 (ISBN 0-89588-221-3); pap. 6.95 (ISBN 0-89588-186-1). SYBEX.
Glass, Robert L. The Power of Peonage. 1979. 9.00 (ISBN 0-686-23742-0). Computing Trends.
Gonick, Larry. The Cartoon Guide to Computer Science. 1983. pap. 5.05 (ISBN 0-06-460417-9). Har-Row.
Gonick, Larry & Hosler, Jay. Cartoon Guide to Computer Science. (Illus.). 224p. (Orig.). 1983. pap. 4.76i (ISBN 0-06-460417-9, COS CO 417). B&N NY.
Harris, Sidney. What's So Funny about Computers? LC 82-21227. (Illus.). 128p. 1983. pap. 6.95 (ISBN 0-86576-049-7). W Kaufmann.
Le Noury, Daniel. Computer Crazy. LC 84-50034. (Illus.). 96p. (Orig.). 1984. pap. 5.95 (ISBN 0-89588-173-X). SYBEX.
Ley, James M. Computers Are Useless: One Hundred Uses for a Dead Computer. LC 83-51250. (Illus.). 96p. (Orig.). 1984. pap. 4.95 (ISBN 0-9612538-9-4). Thunderbolt Pubns.
Panish, Paul & Panish, Anna B. Mother Goose Your Computer: A Grownup's Garden of Silicon Satire. LC 84-51239. (Illus.). 96p. 1984. 8.95 (ISBN 0-89588-198-5). SYBEX.
Rattiner, Dan. The Computer Raiders News. LC 83-63249. (Illus.). 32p. (Orig.). 1984. pap. 4.95 (ISBN 0-932966-54-3). Permanent Pr.
Simons, Geoff. Computer Bits & Pieces: A Compendium of Curiosities. (Penguin Nonfiction Ser.). 190p. 1985. pap. 4.95 (ISBN 0-14-007028-1). Penguin.
Van Tassel, Dennie & Van Tassel, Cynthia L. The Compleat Computer. 2nd ed. 280p. 1983. pap. text ed. 17.95 (ISBN 0-574-21415-1, 13-4415). SRA.
Williamson, John McKim. Software Sayings of Jack Mack: Wit & Humor with Word Processing. LC 82-60964. (Jack Mack Paperbacks). 134p. 1982. pap. 8.95 (ISBN 0-910391-00-9). Jack Mack.

COMPUTERS–BIBLIOGRAPHY

Agajanian, A. H. Computer Technology: Logic, Memory, & Microprocessors; A Bibliography. 360p. 1978. 95.00x (ISBN 0-306-65174-2, IFI Plenum). Plenum Pub.
Bell, D. H., et al. Parallel Programming: A Bibliography. Willis, N., ed. (Mongraphs in Informatics (British Computer Society)). 64p. 1983. 19.95x (ISBN 0-471-26277-3, 1601). Wiley.
Bessant, J. & Dickson, K. Computers & Employment: An Annotated Bibliography. (British Computer Society Ser.). 1981. 21.95 (ISBN 0-471-26205-6). Wiley.
The Blue Book Family of Computer Directories. 1977. 17.95 (ISBN 0-317-04667-5). Visual Materials.
Computer Books & Serials in Print, 1985-1986. 630p. 1985. 59.95x (ISBN 0-8352-2044-3). Bowker.
Deighton, Suzan, et al, eds. Computers & Information Processing World Index. 626p. 1984. lib. bdg. 85.00 (ISBN 0-89774-116-1, Co-Pub. with Gower Pub. Co). Oryx Pr.
Gaber, Walter A. PC Abstracts: Abstracts & Index of Periodical Literature for the IBM-PC & PC Compatible User. (Reference Library of the Humanities). 400p. 1985. lib. bdg. 60.00 (ISBN 0-8240-8720-8). Garland Pub.
Hsiao, T. C., ed. Computer Dissertations 1950-1975. LC 78-59418. 500p. 1984. 60.00x (ISBN 0-912291-03-6). Sci & Tech Pr.
Kylstra, F. J., ed. Performance, 1981: Proceedings of International Symposium on Computer Performance Modelling, Measurement. 545p. 1982. 74.50 (ISBN 0-444-86330-3, North-Holland). Elsevier.
Management Contents Staff. Computer Publications Index & Abstracts 1985: Subject-Product Citations, No. 1. pap. cancelled (ISBN 0-8103-2108-4). Gale.
Management Contents Staff, ed. Computer Publications Index & Abstracts 1985: Abstracts, 12 vols. Set. pap. text ed. cancelled (ISBN 0-8103-2110-6). Gale.
Morrill, Chester, Jr. Computers & Data Processing Information Sources. LC 70-85486. (Management Information Guide Ser.: No. 15). 1969. 60.00x (ISBN 0-8103-0815-0). Gale.
Polin, Glenn, ed. Will Someone Please Tell Me What an Apple Can Do. (Orig.). 1983. pap. text ed. 12.95 (ISBN 0-88408-152-4). Sterling Swift.
Solomon, Martin B., Jr. & Lovan, Nora G. Annotated Bibliography of Films in Automation, Data Processing, & Computer Science. LC 67-23778. 44p. 1967. pap. 5.00x (ISBN 0-8131-1145-5). U Pr of Ky.
Vaillancourt, Pauline M. International Directory of Acronyms in Library, Information & Computer Sciences. LC 80-18352. xi, 518p. 1980. 50.00 (ISBN 0-8352-1152-5). Bowker.
Youden, W. W., ed. Computer Literature Bibliography, 1946-1967, 2 Vols. in 1. LC 70-194009. 1970. Repr. of 1967 ed. 55.00 (ISBN 0-405-00068-5). Ayer Co Pubs.

COMPUTERS–CIRCUITS

Adams, Charles K. Master Handbook of Microprocessor Chips. (Illus.). 378p. 1981. 18.95 (ISBN 0-8306-9633-4); pap. 11.50 (ISBN 0-8306-1299-8, 1299). TAB Bks.
Berlin, Howard M. Circuit Design Programs for the TRS-80. LC 80-52227. 144p. 1980. pap. 14.50 (ISBN 0-672-21741-4, 21741). Sams.
--Design of Op-Amp Circuits, with Experiments. LC 78-56606. 224p. 1978. pap. 11.95 (ISBN 0-672-21537-3). Sams.
Byers, T. J. Microprocessor Support Chips: Theory, Design & Applications. 302p. (Orig.). 1982. 38.00 (ISBN 0-942412-05-2). Micro Text Pubs.
--Microprocessor Support Chips: Theory, Design, & Applications. (Illus.). 300p. 1983. 39.50 (ISBN 0-07-009518-3). McGraw.
Chirlian, Paul M. Digital Circuits with Microprocessor Applications. 432p. 1981. text ed. 26.95 (ISBN 0-916460-32-0). Matrix Pub.
Howe, Harlan, Jr. Stripline Circuit Design. LC 73-81242. 1975. 51.00 (ISBN 0-89006-020-7). Artech Hse.
Ilardi, Frank A. Computer Circuit Analysis: Theory & Application. (Illus.). 416p. 1976. 31.95 (ISBN 0-13-165357-1). P-H.
Lenk, John D. Logic Designer's Manual. (Illus.). 512p. 1977. text ed. 28.95 (ISBN 0-87909-450-8). Reston.
McKay, Charles W. Digital Circuits: A Preparation for Microprocessors. LC 77-13058. (Illus.). 1978. ref. 32.95 (ISBN 0-13-212175-1). P-H.
Noll, Edward M. Microprocessor Circuits, Vol. 2. LC 83-60193. 128p. 1983. pap. 9.95 (ISBN 0-672-21977-8). Sams.
--Microprocessor Circuits: Fundamentals & Microcontrollers, Vol. 1. LC 82-50010. 109p. 1982. pap. 9.95 (ISBN 0-672-21877-1, 21877). Sams.
Ritterman, S. Computer Circuit Concepts. (Electrical Engineering Ser.). 480p. 1985. text ed. price not set (ISBN 0-07-052952-3); price not set lab. manual (ISBN 0-07-052965-5). McGraw.
Teng, Albert Y. & Malmgren, William A. Experiments in Logic & Computer Design. (Illus.). 144p. 1984. text ed. 16.95 (ISBN 0-13-295833-3). P-H.
Tokheim, L. Electronic & Microcomputer Circuits. 1985. 9.95 (ISBN 0-07-064984-7, BYTE Bks). McGraw.
Turino, Jon. Microprocessors Board Testability. 100p. 175.00x (ISBN 0-686-87079-4, Pub. by Network). State Mutual Bk.
Turino, Jon & Mei, David. Microprocessor Board Testability. (Illus.). 110p. 1980. text ed. 95.00 (ISBN 0-912253-00-2). Logical Solns Tech.
Uhr, Leonard, ed. Algorithm-Structured Computer Arrays & Networks: Architectures & Processes for Images, Precepts, Models, Information. 1984. 37.50 (ISBN 0-12-706960-7). Acad Pr.
Veronis, Andrew. The Complete Microprocessor Circuits Reference Manual. 1985. text ed. 39.95 (ISBN 0-8359-0806-2). Reston.
Zarrella, John. Designing with the 8088 Microprocessor. LC 82-21694. 304p. (Orig.). 1984. pap. 23.95 (ISBN 0-935230-07-6). Microcomputer Appns.

COMPUTERS–CONGRESSES

AFIPS. National Computer Conference 1984: AFIPS Proceedings, Vol. 53. (Illus.). 1984. 80.00 (ISBN 0-88283-043-0). AFIPS Pr.
Allen, R. F., ed. Computers & the Humanities: Proceedings of the Symposium, Raleigh, NC. June 6-8, 1983. 300p. 1984. write for info. (North-Holland). Elsevier.
Ames, W. F., et al, eds. Scientific Computing: Proceedings of the IMACS World Congress on Systems, Simulation, & Scientific Computation, Tenth, Montreal, Canada, 8-13 Aug., 1982. (IMACS Transactions on Scientific Computation Ser.: Vol. 1). 364p. 1983. 51.00 (ISBN 0-444-86607-8, North Holland). Elsevier.
Barnes, J. G. & Fisher, G., eds. Ada in Use: Proceedings of the ADA International Conference, Paris. (Ada Companion Ser.). 350p. 1985. 49.50 (ISBN 0-521-30968-9). Cambridge U Pr.
Barnhill, Robert E. & Boehm, Wolfgang, eds. Surfaces in Computer Aided Geometric Design: Proceedings of a Conference, Mathematisches Forschungsinstitut, Oberwolfach, F.R.G., April 25-30, 1982. xvi, 216p. 1983. 47.00 (ISBN 0-444-86550-0, I-32-83, North-Holland). Elsevier.
Carnegie Symposium on Cognition, Eighth Annual. Visual Information Processing: Proceedings. Chase, William G., ed. 1973. 49.50 (ISBN 0-12-170150-6). Acad Pr.
Cause RFP Committee. Computer-Related Acquisitions. (Cause Monographs). 16.00 (ISBN 0-933783-02-7). CAUSE.
Clinic on Library Applications of Data Processing, 1968. Proceedings. Carroll, Dewey E., ed. LC 65-1841. 235p. 1969. 7.00x (ISBN 0-87845-017-3). U of Ill Lib Info Sci.
Clinic on Library Applications of Data Processing, 1969. Proceedings. Carroll, Dewey E., ed. LC 65-1841. 149p. 1970. 7.00x (ISBN 0-87845-018-1). U of Ill Lib Info Sci.
Conference on Computer Simulation Staff. UKSC '84: Proceedings. Murray-Smith, D. J., ed. (Illus.). 560p. 1984. text ed. 89.00 (ISBN 0-408-01504-7). Butterworth.
Cote, R. A., et al, eds. Role of Informatics in Health Data Coding & Classification Systems: Proceedings of the IFIP-IMIA International Working Conference on the Role of Informatics in Health Data Decoding & Classification Systems, Ottawa, Canada, 26-28 September, 1984. 394p. 1985. 59.25 (ISBN 0-444-87682-0, North-Holland). Elsevier.
Courcelle, B., et al, eds. Trees in Algebra & Programming: Proceedings of the Ninth Colloquium, Bordeaux, France, March 1984. 350p. 1984. 39.50 (ISBN 0-521-26750-1). Cambridge U Pr.
The Data Comms Market in Western Europe 1981-87. (Online Seminar 1981). 179p. (Orig.). 1981. pap. text ed. 75.95 (ISBN 0-903796-72-4, Pub. by Online Conferences England). Brookfield Pub Co.
Digest of Papers from the SPIE International Optical Computing Conference, Italy, 1976. 158p. 16.00 (ISBN 0-317-34624-5); members 12.00 (ISBN 0-317-34625-3). SPIE.
Digest of Papers from the SPIE International Optical Computing Conference, Washington, D.C., 1975. 180p. 16.00 (ISBN 0-317-34626-1); members 12.00 (ISBN 0-317-34627-X). SPIE.
Emmen, A. H., ed. Supercomputer Applications: Proceedings of the Supercomputer Applications Symposium Amsterdam, the Netherlands, Nov. 7-9, 1984. 262p. 1985. 44.50 (ISBN 0-444-87752-5, North Holland). Elsevier.
Engquist, B. & Smedsaas, T., eds. PDE Software-Modules, Interfaces & Systems: Proceedings of the IFIP TC 2 Working Conference Held in Soderkoping, Sweden, 22-26 August 1983. 454p. 1984. 50.00 (ISBN 0-444-87620-0, North-Holland). Elsevier.
European Fiber Optics & Communications Exposition, Cologne, Federal Republic of Germany, 1981: Conference Program EFOC '81, Vols. 1 & 2. Date not set. Set. 125.00. Info Gatekeepers.
Gelenbe, E., ed. Performance Eighty-Four: Models of Computer System Performance: Proceedings of the Anniversary Symposium of IFIP WG 7.3. on Computer Performance, 10th, Paris, France, 19-21 December, 1984. 560p. 1985. 68.00 (ISBN 0-444-87680-4, North-Holland). Elsevier.
Gero, J. S., ed. Optimization in Computer-Aided Design: Proceedings of the IFIP WG 5.2. Working Conference on Optimization of Computer-Aided Design, Lyon, France, 24-26 October, 1983. 382p. 1985. 50.00 (ISBN 0-444-87690-1, North-Holland). Elsevier.
Harvard Computation Laboratory. Proceedings of a Symposium on Large Scale Digital Calculating Machinery 1948. (Charles Babbage Institute Reprint Ser.: No. 8). 340p. 1985. Repr. of 1948 ed. text ed. 35.00x (ISBN 0-262-08152-0). MIT Pr.
Heiner, K. W., et al, eds. Computer Science & Statistics: Proceedings of the 14th Symposium on the Interface. (Illus.). 313p. 1983. pap. 25.00 (ISBN 0-387-90835-8). Springer-Verlag.
Horizon House, Inc. Intelcom '80 Conference Proceedings: Competition in the Information Economy. 464p. 1980. pap. text ed. 10.00 (ISBN 0-89006-105-X). Artech Hse.
IFAC-IFIP Conference, 6th, Dusseldorf, BRD, Oct. 1980. Digital Computer Applications to Process Control: Proceedings. Isermann, R. & Kaltenecker, H., eds. LC 80-41343. (IFAC Proceedings). 550p. 1981. 110.00 (ISBN 0-08-026749-1). Pergamon.
International Conference on Information Sciences & Systems, 1st, Patras, Greece, Aug. 1976. Applications & Research in Information Systems & Sciences: Proceedings, 3 vols. new ed. Lainiotis, Demetrios G. & Tzannes, Nicolaos, eds. LC 77-15000. (Illus.). 920p. 1977. Set. pap. text ed. 169.00 (ISBN 0-89116-078-7). Hemisphere Pub.
International Conference, 3rd, U. K. 1978: Proceedings. 348p. 1978. pap. 56.00 (ISBN 0-317-05232-2). SME.
International Online Information Meeting, First: Proceedings, Dec. 13-15, 1977. 240p. 1983. 30.00 (ISBN 0-317-01058-1). Learned Info.
International Online Information Meeting, 2nd: Proceedings, Dec. 5-7. 286p. 1983. 35.00 (ISBN 0-317-01059-X). Learned Info.
International Online Information Meeting, 3rd: Proceedings, Dec. 4-6, 1979. 436p. 1983. 50.00 (ISBN 0-317-01060-3). Learned Info.
International Online Information Meeting, 4th: Proceedings, Dec. 9-11. 527p. 1983. 50.00 (ISBN 0-317-01061-1). Learned Info.
International Online Information Meeting, 5th: Proceedings, Dec. 8-10, 1981. 502p. 1983. 70.00 (ISBN 0-317-01062-X). Learned Info.
International Online Information Meeting, 6th: Proceedings, Dec. 7-9, 1982. 1983. 70.00 (ISBN 0-317-01063-8). Learned Info.
International Optical Computing Conference I, 1980: Proceedings of the SPIE Technical Symposium East, Washington, D.C., 1980. (SPIE Seminar Proceedings: Vol. 231). 326p. 30.00 (ISBN 0-89252-260-7); members 23.00 (ISBN 0-317-34699-7). SPIE.
International Optical Computing Conference II, 1980: Proceedings of the SPIE Technical Symposium East, Washington, D.C., 1980. (SPIE Seminar Proceedings: Vol. 232). 240p. 30.00 (ISBN 0-89252-261-5); members 23.00 (ISBN 0-317-34700-4). SPIE.

Karpinski, M., ed. Fundamentals of Computation Theory: Proceedings of the 1977 International FCT-Conference,Poznan-Kornik, Poland, Sept. 19-23, 1977. (Lecture Notes in Computer Science: Vol. 56). 1977. pap. text ed. 29.00 (ISBN 0-387-08442-8). Springer-Verlag.

Kraus, Harry, ed. The Software User: Education & Qualification. Papers Presented at a Panel Discussion, Winter Annual Meeting of ASME, New York, NY, November 16, 1972. Sponsored by ASME Pressure Vessels & Piping Division. LC 72-93670. pap. 20.00 (ISBN 0-317-08070-9, 2016826). Bks Demand UMI.

Longstaff, J., ed. Third British National Conference on Databases (BNCOD 3) held July 11-12, 1984. (British Computer Society Workshop Ser.). 250p. 1984. 44.50 (ISBN 0-521-26841-9). Cambridge U Pr.

Martin, Thea, ed. Rochester FORTH Conference on Data Bases & Process Control, 1982: Proceedings. 321p. 1982. pap. 25.00 (ISBN 0-914593-03-X). Inst Appl Forth.

--Rochester FORTH Standards Conference, 1981: Proceedings. 374p. 1981. pap. 25.00 (ISBN 0-914593-04-8). Inst Appl Forth.

Morgan, Howard L., ed. AFIPS Proceedings: National Computer Conference, 1982, Vol. 51. LC 80-649583. (Illus.). xi, 843p. 1982. 80.00 (ISBN 0-88283-039-2). AFIPS Pr.

National Computer Conference, 1977. AFIPS Proceedings, Vol. 46. Korfhage, Robert R., ed. LC 55-44701. (Illus.). xiv, 1026p. 1977. 69.00 (ISBN 0-88283-007-4). AFIPS Pr.

National Computer Conference, 1978. AFIPS Proceedings, Vol. 47. Ghosh, Sakti P. & Liu, Leonard Y., eds. LC 55-44701. (Illus.). xxxiv, 1300p. 1978. 69.00 (ISBN 0-88283-006-6). AFIPS Pr.

National Computer Conference, 1980. AFIPS Proceedings, Vol. 49. Medley, Donald B., ed. LC 80-66206. (Illus.). 1980. 69.00 (ISBN 0-88283-003-1). AFIPS Pr.

National Online Meeting, 2nd, 1981: Proceedings. 1983. 40.00 (ISBN 0-317-01056-5). Learned Info.

National Online Meeting, 3rd, New York, March 30-April 1, 1982. Proceedings. Williams, Martha & Hogan, Thomas H., eds. (Illus.). 602p. 1982. pap. text ed. 50.00x (ISBN 0-938734-04-0). Learned Info.

National Online Meeting, 3rd: Proceedings 1982. 1983. 50.00 (ISBN 0-317-01057-3). Learned Info.

O'Neil, Thomas J., ed. Application of Computers & Operations Research in the Mineral Industry: 16th International Symposium. LC 79-52273. (Illus.). 651p. 1979. text ed. 33.00x (ISBN 0-89520-261-1). Soc Mining Eng.

Online Information: Abstracts of the First National Meeting. 1983. 5.00 (ISBN 0-317-01055-7). Learned Info.

Pagels, Heinz R., pref. by. Computer Culture: The Scientific, Intellectual, & Social Impact of the Computer. (Annals of the New York Academy of Sciences Ser.: Vol. 426). 228p. 1984. lib. bdg. 66.00x (ISBN 0-89766-244-X); pap. 66.00x (ISBN 0-89766-245-8). NY Acad Sci.

Paul, M. & Robinet, B., eds. International Symposium on Programming: Sixth Colloquium, Toulouse, April 17-19, 1984 Proceedings. (Lecture Notes in Computer Science Ser.: Vol. 167). vi, 262p. 1984. pap. 16.50 (ISBN 0-387-12925-1). Springer-Verlag.

Proceedings: First International Conference on Supercomputing Systems. 600p. 1985. 66.00 (ISBN 0-8186-0654-1); prepub. 59.40 (ISBN 0-317-31781-4). IEEE Comp Soc.

Proceedings: International Test Conference 1985. 900p. 1985. 80.00 (ISBN 0-8186-0641-X); prepub. 72.00 (ISBN 0-317-31778-4). IEEE Comp Soc.

Proceedings: Second Conference on Artificial Intelligence Applications. 700p. 1985. 75.00 (ISBN 0-8186-0624-X); prepub. 67.50 (ISBN 0-317-31780-6). IEEE Comp Soc.

Proceedings: The Fourth International Conference on Entity-Relationship Approach. 350p. 1985. 44.00 (ISBN 0-8186-0645-2); prepub. 39.60 (ISBN 0-317-31761-X). IEEE Comp Soc.

Proceedings: The Ninth Annual Symposium on Computer Applications in Medical Care. 1300p. 1985. 88.00 (ISBN 0-8186-0647-9); prepub. 79.20 (ISBN 0-317-31762-8). IEEE Comp Soc.

Rustin, Randall, ed. Courant Computer Science Symposia, Vols. 7-9. Incl. Vol. 7. Computational Complexity. 25.00 (ISBN 0-686-46259-9); Vol. 8. Natural Language Processing. 30.00 (ISBN 0-686-46260-2); Vol. 9. Combinatorial Algorithms. 20.00 (ISBN 0-686-46261-0). Date not set. (sum) 75.00 (ISBN 0-686-46258-0). Algorithmics.

Second International Conference on Software Engineering for Telecommunication Switching Systems, 2nd, 1976, Salzburg. International Conference on Software Engineering for Telecommunication Switching Systems, Second, 18-20 February 1976, Salzburg. LC 76-373462. (Institution of Electrical Engineers Conference Publications Ser.: 135). pap. 34.00 (ISBN 0-317-10188-9, 2010357). Bks Demand UMI.

Teller, Joachim, ed. Proceedings of the Third Joint Ada Europe & Ada Tec Conference. (Ada Companion Ser.). 350p. 1985. 39.50. Cambridge U Pr.

Warnecke, H. J., ed. Automated Guided Vehicle Systems: Proceedings of the 2nd International Conference on AGVS & 16th IPA Conference, Stuttgart, F. R. G. June 7-9, 1983. iv, 346p. 1984. 75.00 (ISBN 0-444-86686-8, I-507-83). Elsevier.

Williams, Martha & Hogan, Thomas H., eds. National Online Meeting, Fourth, New York, April 12-14, 1983: Proceedings. (Illus.). 622p. 1983. pap. 50.00 (ISBN 0-938734-05-9). Learned Info.

Williams, Martha E. & Hogan, Thomas H., eds. National Online Meeting Proceedings, 1981. (Illus.). 554p. 1981. pap. text ed. 40.00x (ISBN 0-938734-02-4). Learned Info.

Wojcik, Anthony S. AFIPS Conference: Proceedings of the National Computer Conference 1985, Vol. 54. 800p. 1985. 80.00 (ISBN 0-88283-046-5). AFIPS Pr.

COMPUTERS–DEBUGGING

see Debugging (Electronic Computers)

COMPUTERS–DESIGN AND CONSTRUCTION

see Computer Engineering

COMPUTERS–DICTIONARIES

Agnew, Irene, ed. Glossary of English & Russian Computer & Automated Control Systems Terminology. (Eng. & Rus.). 1978. soft covers 15.00 (ISBN 0-686-31723-8). Agnew Tech-Tran.

American National Standards Committee, X3, Information Processing System. American National Dictionary for Information Systems. LC 83-73087. 350p. 1984. 32.50 (ISBN 0-87094-503-3). Dow Jones-Irwin.

Anderson, R. G. Concise Dictionary of Data Processing & Computer Terms. 2nd ed. 149p. 1984. 23.50x (ISBN 0-7121-0435-6). Trans-Atlantic.

--Dictionary of Data Processing & Computer Terms. 112p. 1982. 23.50x (ISBN 0-7121-0429-1). Trans-Atlantic.

AOG Systems Corp. Draft Proposed American National Standard Information Resource Dictionary System. 1985. write for info. QED Info Sci.

Attiyate, Y. H. & Shah, R. Dictionary of Microelectronics & Microcomputed Technology: German-English, English-German. 460p. 1984. 31.00 (ISBN 0-9907001-0-0, Pub. by VDI Verlag Gmbh Dusseldorf). Heyden.

Belzer. Encyclopedia of Computer Science & Technology, Vol. 13. 1979. 115.00 (ISBN 0-8247-2263-9). Dekker.

--Index to Encyclopedia of Computer Science & Technology, Vol. 16. 464p. 1981. 115.00 (ISBN 0-8247-2266-3). Dekker.

Belzer, J., ed. Encyclopedia of Computer Science & Technology, Vol. 15. 1980. 115.00 (ISBN 0-8247-2265-5). Dekker.

Belzer, Jack. Encyclopedia of Computer Science & Technology, Vol. 9. 1978. 115.00 (ISBN 0-8247-2259-0). Dekker.

Belzer, Jack, ed. Encyclopedia of Computer Science & Technology, Vol. 1. 1975. 115.00 (ISBN 0-8247-2251-5). Dekker.

--Encyclopedia of Computer Science & Technology, Vol. 2. 1975. 115.00 (ISBN 0-8247-2252-3). Dekker.

--Encyclopedia of Computer Science & Technology, Vol. 3. 1976. 115.00 (ISBN 0-8247-2253-1). Dekker.

--Encyclopedia of Computer Science & Technology, Vol. 5. 1976. 115.00 (ISBN 0-8247-2255-8). Dekker.

--Encyclopedia of Computer Science & Technology, Vol. 10. 1978. 115.00 (ISBN 0-8247-2260-4). Dekker.

--Encyclopedia of Computer Science & Technology, Vol. 12. 1979. 115.00 (ISBN 0-8247-2262-0). Dekker.

--Encyclopedia of Computer Science & Technology, Vol. 14. 1980. 115.00 (ISBN 0-8247-2264-7). Dekker.

Belzer, Jack & Holzman, Albert G., eds. Encyclopedia of Computer Science & Technology, Vol. 4. 1976. 115.00 (ISBN 0-8247-2254-X). Dekker.

Belzer, Jack, et al, eds. Encyclopedia of Computer Science, Vol. 7. 1977. 115.00 (ISBN 0-8247-2257-4). Dekker.

--Encyclopedia of Computer Science & Technology, Vol. 8. 1977. 115.00 (ISBN 0-8247-2258-2). Dekker.

--Encyclopedia of Computer Science & Technology, Vol. 6. 1977. 115.00 (ISBN 0-8247-2256-6). Dekker.

Berkeley, Edmund C. The Computer Book of Lists & the First Computer Almanac. (Illus.). 176p. 1984. pap. 14.95 (ISBN 0-8359-0864-X). Reston.

Bola Glossary of Electronic Data Processing & Computer Terms English-Spanish & Spanish-English. LC 82-71113. (Bola Glossary Ser.: Vol. 1). (Span. & Eng.). 206p. (Orig.). 1982. pap. 29.95 (ISBN 0-943118-00-X). Bola Pubns.

Brinkman & Schmidt, eds. Datasystems Dictionary. 733p. 1984. 41.00 (ISBN 0-9913001-2-2, Pub. by O Brandstetter WG). Heyden.

Brinkman, Karl-Heinz & Schmidt, Rudolf. Data Systems Dictionary: English-German & German-English. 1974. pap. 40.00x (ISBN 3-87097-095-2). Intl Learn Syst.

Brinkmann, Karl H. Dictionary of Dataprocessing. (Ger. & Eng.). 1974. 59.95 (ISBN 3-87097-059-6, M-7117). French & Eur.

British Computer Society. A Glossary of Computing Terms: An Introduction. 4th ed. LC 84-45366. 64p. 1985. pap. 3.95 (ISBN 0-521-31777-0). Cambridge U Pr.

Brown, Gary D. FORTRAN to PL-I Dictionary: PL-I to FORTRAN Dictionary. LC 82-21283. 218p. 1984. Repr. of 1975 ed. lib. bdg. 19.50 (ISBN 0-89874-587-X). Krieger.

Brown, P. R. Dictionary of Electrical, Electronic & Computer Abbreviations. 232p. 1985. text ed. 34.95 (ISBN 0-408-01210-2). Butterworth.

Burger, E. Technical Dictionary of Data Processing, Computers & Office Machines, English, German, French, Russian. (Eng., Ger., Fr & Rus.). 1970. 145.00 (ISBN 0-08-006425-6). Pergamon.

Burger, E., ed. Technical Dictionary of Automatization & Programming: English, French, German, Russian, Slovene. (Eng., Fr., Ger., Rus. & Slovene.). 479p. 1976. 95.00 (ISBN 0-686-92330-8, M-9889). French & Eur.

Burger, Ing H. Dictionary of Automatic Data Processing. (Eng., Ger., Fr., Rus. & Slovak.). 480p. 1976. 80.00x (ISBN 0-569-08521-7, Pub. by Collets). State Mutual Bk.

Burton, Philip E. A Dictionary of Minicomputing & Microcomputing. 368p. 1985. pap. 20.00 (ISBN 0-8240-7286-3). Garland Pub.

--Dictionary of Minicomputing & Microcomputing. 1984. lib. bdg. 42.50 (ISBN 0-8240-7263-4). Garland Pub.

--A Dictionary of Word Processing. 256p. 1984. pap. 15.95 (ISBN 0-8240-7289-8). Garland Pub.

--A Dictionary of Word Processing & Printers. LC 84-10348. 264p. 1985. 22.95 (ISBN 0-8240-7289-8); pap. 15.95 (ISBN 0-8240-7291-X). Garland Pub.

Burton, Phillip E. The Dictionary of Robotics. 1984. write for info. Garland Pub.

CAD-CAM Glossary. 19.25 (ISBN 0-686-40545-5). C I M Systems.

Chandor, Anthony. Diccionario de Computadores. (Span.). 402p. 1975. leather 28.50 (ISBN 84-335-6411-0, S-31859). French & Eur.

--The Facts on File Dictionary of Micro Computers. 1981. 14.95 (ISBN 0-87196-597-6). Facts on File.

--The Penguin Dictionary of Microprocessors. 192p. 1981. pap. 5.95 (ISBN 0-14-051100-8). Penguin.

Chandor, Anthony, ed. Dictionary of Computers. (Reference Ser.). (Orig.). 1970. pap. 5.95 (ISBN 0-14-051039-7). Penguin.

Clason, W. E. Elsevier's Dictionary of Computers, Automatic Control & Data Processing. 2nd ed. (Eng., Fr., Span., & Ital.). 474p. (Polyglot). 1971. 98.00 (ISBN 0-444-40928-9). Elsevier.

The Computer Dictionary. 1984. pap. 5.95 (ISBN 0-671-50498-3, Wallaby). PB.

Computer Dictionary. (The Pocket Professor Ser.). 1984. pap. 2.95 (ISBN 0-946913-15-3, Pub. by Coll Lane Pubs). Kampmann.

Congressional Information Service, Inc. Staff. CIS Online User Guide & Thesaurus. 400p. 1982. loose-leaf guide 75.00 (ISBN 0-912380-98-5). Thesaurus (ISBN 0-912380-99-3). Cong Info.

Conniffe, Patricia. Computer Dictionary. pap. 4.95 (ISBN 0-317-33054-3); tchr's guide 1.50 (ISBN 0-317-06582-3). Scholastic Inc.

Cowan, Les. The Illustrated Computer Dictionary & Handbook. (Illus.). 224p. 1983. pap. 9.95 (ISBN 0-86582-116-X, EN79101). Enrich.

Dasenbrock, David H. User's Guide to Microcomputer Buzzwords. LC 83-60161. 110p. 1983. pap. text ed. 9.95 (ISBN 0-672-22049-0, 22049). Sams.

The DEC DICTIONARY: A Guide to Digital's Technical Terminology. LC 84-7806. (DECbooks). 376p. 1984. 21.00 (ISBN 0-932376-70-3, EY-00040-DP). Digital Pr.

DeLegall, Walter & Johnston, Percy. Computer Dictionary. (Desein Literary Society Ser.). 400p. 1984. lib. bdg. 32.95 (ISBN 0-915833-18-2); pap. text ed. 17.50 (ISBN 0-915833-20-4). Drama Jazz Hse Inc.

Dictionary of Abbreviations in Information Science. 406p. 1976. 50.00x (ISBN 0-686-44776-X, Pub. by Collets). State Mutual Bk.

Dictionary of Measurement Technology for Computers. (Eng. & Chinese.). 161p. 1977. pap. 3.95 (ISBN 0-686-92302-2, M-9565). French & Eur.

Downing, Douglas. Encyclopedia of Computer Terms. LC 82-11350. 160p. 1983. pap. 6.95 (ISBN 0-8120-2519-9). Barron.

Drieux, Jean P. & Jarlaud, Alain. Let's Talk D. P. Computer Lexicon. (Eng., Amer. & Fr.). 116p. 1977. pap. 11.95 (ISBN 0-686-57123-1, M-6171). French & Eur.

Durbin, Harold C. Printing & Computer Terminology. LC 80-65655. 206p. (Orig.). 1980. pap. 9.50 (ISBN 0-936786-00-0); pap. text ed. 8.50 (ISBN 0-936786-01-9). Durbin Assoc.

Edmunds, Robert A. The Prentice-Hall Standard Glossary of Computer Terminology. LC 84-4765. 1984. 34.95 (ISBN 0-13-698234-4); pap. 26.95 (ISBN 0-13-698226-3). P-H.

Encyclopedia of Computers & Data Processing, Vol. 1. 39.00 (ISBN 0-403-04498-7). Scholarly.

Fisher, R. & Kruchten, P. French-English, English-French Dictionary of Computer Science, 2 vols. (Eng. & Fr.). Set. 50.00 (ISBN 0-686-46529-6). Heinman.

Freedman, Alan. The Computer Glossary: It's Not Just a Glossary. 3rd ed. (Illus.). 324p. 1983. 14.95 (ISBN 0-941878-02-3). Computer Lang.

Freedman, Alan & Morrison, Irma L. The Computer Glossary: It's Not Just a Glossary! 320p. 1983. pap. 15.95 (ISBN 0-13-164483-1). P-H.

Freeman, A. Glosario de Computation. 396p. 1985. 19.95 (ISBN 0-07-021920-6). McGraw.

Galland, Frank J., ed. Dictionary of Computing: Data Communications, Hardware & Software Basics, Digital Electronics. 330p. 1982. 37.95x (ISBN 0-471-10468-X, Pub. by Wiley-Interscience); pap. 21.95x (ISBN 0-471-10469-8). Wiley.

Gerberg, Mort. The Computer Dictionary. (Illus.). 96p. (Orig.). 1984. pap. 5.95 (ISBN 0-671-50498-3, Wallaby). S&S.

Godman, Arthur. Barnes & Noble Thesaurus of Computer Science: The Principles of Computer Science Explained & Illustrated. LC 83-48348. (Illus.). 256p. 1984. 13.41i (ISBN 0-06-015270-2); pap. 6.68i (ISBN 0-06-463594-5). Har-Row.

Goodstein, David & Newhouse, Rosalyn, eds. Glossary of Typesetting, Computer, & Communications Terms. 65p. 20.00 (ISBN 0-318-17397-2); members 10.00 (ISBN 0-318-17398-0). Print Indus Am.

Harris, Donald E. EDP Manager's Glossary of Computer & Data Communications Terminology. LC 83-81247. 172p. (Orig.). 1984. pap. 24.95 (ISBN 0-914145-00-2). Info Syst Con.

Helms, Harry L., Jr. Computer Language Reference Guide - With Keyword Dictionary. 2nd ed. LC 83-51705. 192p. 1984. pap. 9.95 (ISBN 0-672-21786-4); pap. 9.95 (ISBN 0-672-21823-2). Sams.

Hofmann, Egon. Dictionary of Dataprocessing. 4th ed. (Eng. & Ger.). 1976. 15.95 (ISBN 3-19-006288-9, M-7115). French & Eur.

Hordeski, Michael. Illustrated Dictionary of Microcomputer Terminology. (Illus.). 1978. pap. 10.25 (ISBN 0-8306-1088-X, 1088). TAB Bks.

Isaacs, Alan, ed. The Multilingual Computer Dictionary. 336p. 1981. 22.50 (ISBN 0-87196-431-7); pap. 12.95 (ISBN 0-87196-822-3). Facts on File.

Kelly-Bootle, Stan. The Devil's DP Dictionary. (Illus.). 160p. 1981. pap. 9.95 (ISBN 0-07-034022-6). McGraw.

Kotz, Samuel. Russian-English Dictionary & Reader in the Cybernetical Sciences. 1966. 49.00 (ISBN 0-12-422450-4). Acad Pr.

Ledin, George. The Personal Computer Glossary. 1982. 3.50 (ISBN 0-88284-233-1). Alfred Pub.

Lefkovits, Henry C., et al. Information Resource-Data Dictionary Systems. LC 83-60770. 600p. 1983. 95.00 (ISBN 0-89435-068-4). QED Info Sci.

Leong, Carol. Dictionary of Library & Information Sciences, English-Chinese, Chinese-English. 328p. 1984. lib. bdg. 41.00 (ISBN 3-598-10532-0). K G Saur.

Leong-Hong, Belkis W. & Plagman, Bernard K. Data Dictionary-Directory Systems: Administration Implementation & Usage. LC 81-21875. 328p. 1982. 36.50x (ISBN 0-471-05164-0, Pub. by Wiley-Interscience). Wiley.

LINC Associates Inc. Staff. The SpecialWare Directory: A Guide to Software Sources for Special Education. 108p. 1983. pap. 16.95 (ISBN 0-89774-200-1). Oryx Pr.
Lomax, J. D. Data Dictionary Systems. (Illus.). 1977. pap. 45.00x (ISBN 0-85012-191-4). Intl Pubns Serv.
Lukers, Tom. The Illustrated Datastar Book. (Illus.). 224p. 1984. cancelled (ISBN 0-13-450289-2); pap. 16.95 (ISBN 0-13-450263-9). P-H.
McGraw-Hill Editors. Dictionary of Electronics & Computer Science. 480p. 1984. 32.50 (ISBN 0-07-045416-7). McGraw.
--McGraw-Hill Encyclopedia of Electronics & Computers. (Illus.). 976p. 1983. 67.50 (ISBN 0-07-045487-6). McGraw.
Makower, Joel. Personal Computers A-Z: The Three Hundred Fifty Key Terms You Need to Understand Personal Computers. LC 83-45193. (Illus.). 224p. 1983. 15.95 (ISBN 0-385-19053-0, Quantum Pr); pap. 8.95 (ISBN 0-385-19054-9, Quantum Pr). Doubleday.
Malstrom, Robert C. SRA Data Processing Glossary. 281p. 1979. pap. 12.95 (ISBN 0-574-21250-7, 13-4250). SRA.
Mayer, JoAnne C. & Sippl, Charles J. Essential Computer Dictionary & Speller for Secretaries, Managers, & Office Personnel. (Illus.). 256p. 1980. text ed. 14.95 (ISBN 0-13-284364-1, Spec); pap. 6.95 (ISBN 0-13-284356-0). P-H.
Maynard. Dictionary of Data Processing. 2nd ed. 1982. text ed. 34.95 (ISBN 0-408-00591-2). Butterworth.
Mazloum, N. & Breskin, M. Your Personal Computer Dictionary. 160p. 1984. pap. 9.95 (ISBN 0-07-041196-4, BYTE Bks). McGraw.
Meadows, A. J. & Gordon, M., eds. The Random House Dictionary of New Information Technology. LC 82-40026. 200p. 1982. pap. 7.95 (ISBN 0-394-71202-1, Vin). Random.
Meadows, A. J., et al, eds. Dictionary of Computing & New Information Technology. rev. ed. LC 84-4874. 260p. 1984. 27.50 (ISBN 0-89397-197-9). Nichols Pub.
Mullen, Norma D. & Brown, P. Charles. English for Computer Science. 1983. pap. 8.95x (ISBN 0-19-437650-8); ans. bk. 1.75x (ISBN 0-19-437651-6). Oxford U Pr.
Multilingual Dictionary of Computer Science & Data Processing Terms. (Eng., Fr., Ital., Span. & Portugese.). 1000p. 1983. 75.00 (ISBN 0-8442-9108-0, 9108-0, Passport Bks.). Natl Textbk.
Naiman, Arthur, ed. Computer Dictionary for Beginners. 1983. pap. 6.95 (ISBN 0-345-31223-6). Ballantine.
National Computing Centre, ed. Thesaurus of Computing Terms. 8th ed. 1977. pap. 82.50x (ISBN 0-85012-169-8). Intl Pubns Serv.
Noonan, Larry. The Basic BASIC-English Dictionary: For the Apple, IBM-PC, Commodore 64, VIC-20, Atari, TRS-80, TRS-80 Color Computer, TI 99-4A, PET & Timex-Sinclair. (Illus.). 288p. 1985. pap. 19.95 (ISBN 0-88056-354-0). Dilithium Pr.
--Basic BASIC-English Dictionary for the Apple, PET & TRS-80. (Illus.). 154p. 1983. 17.95 (ISBN 0-8306-1521-0, 1521). TAB Bks.
Oppermann, Alfred. Dictionary of Dataprocessing. 2nd ed. (Ger. & Eng.). 1973. pap. 30.00 (ISBN 3-7940-3099-0, M-7116). French & Eur.
Poage, James & Landis, Carolyn P. Contracting for Computing: A Checklist of Terms & Clauses for Use in Contracting with Vendors for Software Packages & Custom Software, Vol. II. 148p. 1975. 16.00 (ISBN 0-318-14014-4); members 9.00 (ISBN 0-318-14015-2). Educom.
Porter, Kent. The New American Computer Dictionary. 320p. 1983. pap. 4.50 (ISBN 0-451-13794-9, Sig). NAL.
Prenis, John. Computer Terms. LC 77-343. (Orig.). 1977. lib. bdg. 12.90 (ISBN 0-914294-75-X); pap. 4.95 (ISBN 0-914294-76-8). Running Pr.
Prenis, John, ed. The Computer Dictionary: A User-Friendly Guide to Language, Terms, & Jargon. LC 83-13668. (Illus.). 128p. 1983. lib. bdg. 12.90 (ISBN 0-89471-232-2); pap. 4.95 (ISBN 0-89471-231-4). Running Pr.
Purdue Workshop on Standardization of Industrial-Computer Languages, Glossary Committee. Dictionary of Industrial Digital Computer Terminology. LC 72-81778. pap. 24.00 (ISBN 0-317-08566-2, 2051117). Bks Demand UMI.
Pyle, Ian & Glazer, Edward, eds. Dictionary of Computing. 1983. 24.95 (ISBN 0-19-853905-3). Oxford U Pr.
Ralston, Anthony & Reilly, Edwin D., Jr. Encyclopedia of Computer Science & Engineering. 2nd ed. (Illus.). 1678p. 1982. 87.50 (ISBN 0-442-24496-7). Van Nos Reinhold.
Raymond, Jacques. Informatique I: Introductory Computer Text for French Speaking Students. (Fr.). 134p. 1983. pap. text ed. 11.95 (ISBN 0-8403-3106-1). Kendall-Hunt.
Redlin, Paul. The Personal Computer Dictionary. 256p. 1984. pap. 10.95 (ISBN 0-471-88714-5, Pub. by Wiley Pr). Wiley.
Rosenberg, Jerry M. Dictionary of Computers, Data Processing, & Telecommunications. LC 83-12359. 614p. 1984. 32.50x (ISBN 0-471-87638-0); pap. 14.95 (ISBN 0-471-88582-7). Assn Inform & Image Mgmt.
Rosenthal, Steven. Rosenthal's Computer Glossary. 350p. 1984. 17.95 (ISBN 0-13-783192-7); pap. 10.95 cancelled (ISBN 0-13-783184-6). P-H.
--Rosenthal's Dictionary of the Automated Office. 350p. 1984. 19.95 (ISBN 0-13-783218-4); pap. 12.95 cancelled (ISBN 0-13-783200-1). P-H.
Ross, Ronald G. Data Dictionaries & Data Administration: Concepts & Practices for Data Resource Management. 384p. 1981. 29.95 (ISBN 0-8144-5596-4). AMACOM.
Rowell, Harry & Landis, Carolyn P. Contracting for Computing: A Checklist of Terms & Clauses for Use in Contracting with Vendors for Computing Resources, Vol. I. 156p. 1973. 16.00 (ISBN 0-318-14016-0); members 9.00 (ISBN 0-318-14017-9). Educom.
Russian-English Dictionary of Data Processing Terminology. (Rus. & Eng.). 359p. 1971. text ed. 6.95 (ISBN 0-686-92123-2, M-9127). French & Eur.
Schulz, Joachim. Data Systems Dictionary: English-Russian-German. (Eng., Rus. & Ger.). 1978. pap. 39.95 (ISBN 3-87097-075-8, M-7325, Pub. by Brandstetter Verlag). French & Eur.
Shishmarev, A. I. & Zamorin, A. P. Explanatory Dictionary of Computing Machinery & Data Processing. 416p. 1978. 60.00x (ISBN 0-686-44717-4, Pub. by Collets). State Mutual Bk.
Shismarev, A. I. & Zamorin, A. P. Explanatory Dictionary of Computing Machinery & Data Processing. 416p. 1978. Leatherette 7.95 (ISBN 0-686-92229-8, M-9080). French & Eur.
Shopay-Kolatis, Maria. Mathematics for Data Processing & Computing. 1985. text ed. 26.95 (ISBN 0-201-14955-9). Addison-Wesley.
Sippl, C. J. Data Communications Dictionary. 2nd ed. 34.95 (ISBN 0-470-20182-7). Halsted Pr.
Sippl, Charles. Data Communications Dictionary. 545p. 1984. pap. 12.95. Van Nos Reinhold.
--Microcomputer Dictionary. 2nd ed. LC 81-50565. 608p. 1981. pap. 16.95 (ISBN 0-672-21696-5, 21696). Sams.
Sippl, Charles J. Data Communications Dictionary. 544p. 1980. pap. text ed. 13.95 (ISBN 0-442-21931-8). Van Nos Reinhold.
Sippl, Charles J. & Carter, George. Computer Dictionary. 4th ed. LC 84-51436. 1985. 17.95 (ISBN 0-672-22205-1). Sams.
Sippl, Charles J. & Sippl, Roger J. Computer Dictionary. 3rd ed. LC 79-91696. 624p. 1980. pap. 16.95 (ISBN 0-672-21652-3, 21652). Sams.
Spencer, Donald D. Computer Dictionary. 2nd ed. LC 78-31738. 1979. pap. 6.95 (ISBN 0-89218-038-2). Camelot Pub.
--The Illustrated Computer Dictionary. Rev. ed. 187p. 1983. pap. 9.95 (ISBN 0-675-20075-X). Merrill.
--Illustrated Computer Dictionary for Young People. LC 81-21795. (Illus.). 1982. 8.95x (ISBN 0-89218-052-8). Camelot Pub.
--The Pocket Guide of Computer Terminology. 1982. pap. 1.25x (ISBN 0-317-04657-8). Camelot Pub.
--Spencer's Computer Dictionary for Everyone. 3rd ed. (Illus.). 288p. 1985. 17.95 (ISBN 0-684-18250-5, ScribT); pap. 8.95 (ISBN 0-684-18251-3). Scribner.
Steele, Guy L. The Hacker's Dictionary: A Guide to the Computer Underworld. LC 83-47573. 96p. (Orig.). 1983. pap. 5.72i (ISBN 0-06-091082-8, CN 1082, CN). Har-Row.
Steiner, John P. The Standard BASIC Dictionary for Programming. LC 84-11436. 256p. 1983. 23.95 (ISBN 0-13-841560-9, Busn); pap. 19.95 (ISBN 0-13-841552-8). P-H.
Stokes, Adrian V. Concise Encyclopedia of Computer Terminology. 300p. 1980. text ed. 37.00x (ISBN 0-905897-32-3). Gower Pub Co.
Stultz, Russell A. The Illustrated CP-M WordStar Dictionary with MailMerge & SpellStar Operations. LC 82-21559. (Illus.). 272p. 1983. pap. text ed. 14.95 (ISBN 0-13-450528-X). P-H.
--The Illustrated Word Processing Dictionary. (Illus.). 176p. 1983. 23.95 (ISBN 0-13-450726-6); pap. 14.95 (ISBN 0-13-450718-5). P-H.
Sybex Staff & Zaks, Rodnay. The SYBEX Personal Computer Dictionary. LC 83-51824. (Eng., Ger., Span., Ital., Fr. & Pol.). 121p. 1984. pap. 3.95 (ISBN 0-89588-199-3). SYBEX.
Sydow, A. Cibernetical Dictionary: E-G-F-R-Slovene. (Eng., Ger., Fr., Rus. & Slovene.). 171p. 1974. 75.00 (ISBN 0-686-92219-0, M-9895). French & Eur.
--Dictionary of Cybernetics. 172p. 1980. 50.00x (ISBN 0-569-08527-6, Pub. by Collet's). State Mutual Bk.
Sykora, Jiri. Dictionary of Automation Techniques. 1024p. 1980. 80.00x (Pub. by Collet's). State Mutual Bk.
Technical Committee on Computer Controlled Environmental Testing of the Institute of Environmental Sciences. Glossary of Computer Controlled Environmental Testing Terminology. LC 62-38584. 27p. 1977. pap. text ed. 3.00 (ISBN 0-915414-53-8). Inst Environ Sci.
Tver, David F. & Bolz, Roger W. Robotics Sourcebook & Dictionary. 304p. 1983. 30.95 (ISBN 0-8311-1152-6). Indus Pr.
Van Duyn, Julia. Developing a Data Dictionary System. (Illus.). 208p. 1982. text ed. 34.95 (ISBN 0-13-204289-4). P-H.
Vince, John. Dictionary of Computer Graphics. LC 84-17178. (Video Bookshelf Ser.). 200p. 1984. 34.95 (ISBN 0-86729-134-6, 533-BW). Knowledge Indus.
Vollnhals, O. Elsevier's Dictionary of Personal & Office Computing-In English, German, French, Italian & Portuguese. 1984. 120.50 (ISBN 0-444-42390-7). Elsevier.
Wayne Green Books Editors. Encyclopedia for the TRS-80, No. 10. (Illus.). 250p. (Orig.). 1981-82. 19.50 (ISBN 0-88006-056-5, EN8100); pap. 10.50 (ISBN 0-88006-057-3, EN8080). Green Pub Inc.
Webster's New World Compact Dictionary of Computer Terms. 416p. 1984. pap. 4.95 vinyl (ISBN 0-671-49692-1). S&S.
Webster's New World Dictionary of Computer Terms. 1983. 5.95 (ISBN 0-671-46866-9). S&S.
Weik, Martin H. Standard Dictionary of Computers & Information Processing. rev., 2nd ed. 1977. 23.95 (ISBN 0-8104-5099-2). Hayden.
--Standard Dictionary of Computers & Information Processing. 2nd ed. 400p. 1983. 26.50 (ISBN 0-317-00361-5). Hayden.
Welk, Martin H. Standard Dictionary of Computers & Information Processing. 2nd, rev. ed. 390p. 1977. 23.95 (ISBN 0-686-98126-X). Telecom Lib.
Wilhelm, Carl & Amkreutz, Johann, eds. Dictionary of Data Processing, 2 Vols. 2nd ed. 1349p. 1981. Set. cancelled (ISBN 3-921899-25-7). Intl Pubns Serv.
Windsor, A. T., ed. Using the ICL Data Dictionary: Proceedings of the ICL DDS User Group. 160p. 1980. text ed. 29.95 (ISBN 0-906812-06-2). Birkhauser.
Wittman, A. & Klos, J. Dictionary of Data Processing, Including Applications in Industry, Administration & Business. 4th, rev., enlg. ed. 1984. 106.00 (ISBN 0-444-99628-1, I-121-84). Elsevier.
Wold, Allen L. & Hunter, C. Bruce. New Webster's Computer Dictionary. 368p. pap. 1.95 vest pocket ed. (ISBN 0-8326-0068-7, 6455); deluxe ed. 2.50 (ISBN 0-8326-0069-5, 6532). Delair.
Yakubaitis, E. A. English-Russian Glossary of Computer Systems & Networks Terminology. (Eng. & Rus.). 270p. 1981. 40.00x (ISBN 0-686-44705-0, Pub. by Collets). State Mutual Bk.
Yourwith, William J., Jr. Computer Jargon & Terms Made Non-Technical. (Illus.). 1986. 15.00 (ISBN 0-917818-03-2). Exec Stand.
Zejdenberg, V. K., et al. English-Russian Dictionary of Computer Science. 3rd ed. 300p. 1985. 50.00 (ISBN 0-08-031157-1). Pergamon.

COMPUTERS–DIRECTORIES

ACEC Computer User Listing. 176p. 1983. pap. 30.00 (ISBN 0-686-48373-1); pap. 30.00 members (ISBN 0-686-48374-X). Am Consul Eng.
Bates, Williams S. The Computer Cookbook, 1984: Computers & the Computer Industry from A to Z. LC 83-40142. 416p. 1984. pap. 14.95 (ISBN 0-385-19291-6, Quantum Pr). Doubleday.
Cane, Mike. The Computer Phone Book. 1983. pap. 14.95 (ISBN 0-452-25446-9, Plume). NAL.
Computer Blue Book, 1985. 250p. 1985. 49.50. Orion Res.
Computer Management Research, Inc. Staff, ed. Mid-Atlantic Directory of Computer Installations. 320p. 1985. 370.00 (ISBN 0-930411-05-6). Computer Res.
Computer Strategies. The Association Computer Handbook. 150p. 1984. 45.00x. Computer Strat.
Consumer Guide Staff. Computer Buying Guide 1985. 380p. pap. cancelled (ISBN 0-451-13244-0, Sig). NAL.
Cowan, Les. The Illustrated Computer Dictionary & Handbook. (Illus.). 224p. 1983. pap. 9.95 (ISBN 0-86582-116-X, EN79101). Enrich.
Davis, Robert E., Jr. Selling Your Software. (General Trade Books). 224p. 1985. pap. 16.95 (ISBN 0-471-80737-0). Wiley.
Edelhart, Mike & Davies, Owen. Omni: Online Database Directory. 384p. 1983. 19.95 (ISBN 0-02-535000-5); pap. 10.95 (ISBN 0-02-079910-1). Macmillan.
Evan, Frederica, ed. Computer Publishers & Publications: An International Directory & Yearbook. 1984 ed. 400p. 1983. pap. 85.00x (ISBN 0-88709-000-1). Comm Trends Inc.
Flora, Philip C. International Computer Aided Manufacturing Directory. (Illus., Orig.). Date not set. pap. text ed. 35.00 (ISBN 0-910747-00-8). Tech Data TX.
--International Computer Vision Directory. (Illus.). 160p. (Orig.). Date not set. pap. text ed. 35.00 (ISBN 0-910747-08-3). Tech Data TX.
--International Programmable Controllers Directory. (Illus.). 136p. (Orig.). Date not set. pap. text ed. 35.00 (ISBN 0-910747-07-5). Tech Data TX.
Forrest, E. & Johnson, R. H. CAE, CAD, CAD-CAM Service Bureaus: Directory, Review, & Outlook, 1983. (Illus.). 130p. 1983. cancelled (ISBN 0-938484-09-5). Daratech.
Guide to Free Computer Materials. 3rd ed. 1985. 30.25 (ISBN 0-87708-153-0). Ed Prog.
Hamilton, Catherine D., et al, eds. Text Retrieval: A Directory of Software. LC 84-22284. 180p. 1985. text ed. 34.50 (ISBN 0-566-03527-8). Gower Pub Co.
Hsiao, T. C., ed. Computer Faculty Directory (U. S. Edition) LC 81-51817. 450p. 1985. 50.00x (ISBN 0-912291-07-9). Sci & Tech Pr.
Index of Computer Hardware & Software in Use in North Carolina Local Governments. 209p. 1984. 8.00 (ISBN 0-686-39424-0). U of NC Inst Gov.
Instructor Magazine Staff, ed. Computer Directory for Schools. 19.95 (ISBN 0-318-02634-1). Instructor Bks.
Jones, Michael P. Computer Technology Resource Guide. (Illus.). 40p. (Orig.). 1985. pap. text ed. 9.00 (ISBN 0-89904-133-7); pap. 6.50 (ISBN 0-89904-134-5). Crumb Elbow Pub.
The Kaypro Software Directory. 25.00 (ISBN 0-318-03641-X). Kaypro.
Levine, Ellen. Periodical Guide for Computerists, 1982: Annual Since 1975-76. 70p. (Orig.). 1982. pap. 15.95 (ISBN 0-686-40864-0). Applegate Comp Ent.
Marquis Who's Who Directory of Online Professionals, 1984. 852p. 1984. 85.00 (ISBN 0-8379-6001-0, 031132). Marquis.
Mayo, Jack, ed. Campus Computers of California. 300p. cancelled. Bernardo Press.
Merrill, Martha, ed. New England Directory for Computer Professionals, 1984. LC 83-72594. 280p. 1983. pap. 28.50 (ISBN 0-318-00096-2). Bradford Co.
Microcomputer Market Place, 1986. 516p. 1986. pap. text ed. 95.00 (ISBN 0-8352-2096-6). Bowker.
The PC Telemart-VanLoves CP-M Software Directory. 700p. 1984. pap. 24.95 (ISBN 0-8352-1973-9). Bowker.
The PC Telemart-VanLoves IBM Software Directory. 964p. 1984. pap. 24.95 (ISBN 0-8352-1969-0). Bowker.
Real Estate Institute of Canada. Computer Product & Service Directory. 1983. 29.95 (ISBN 0-317-12272-X). Inst Real Estate.
Retailers' Microcomputer Market Place, Spring 1985. 1783p. 1985. pap. 49.95 (ISBN 0-8352-1977-1). Bowker.
Schwartz, Narda L. The Whole Computer Catalog. 1984. pap. 35.00 (ISBN 0-9609254-0-6). Designs Three.
Software Catalog. Vol. 1. 69.00 (ISBN 0-318-03637-1). ISD.
Software Publishers' Catalogs Annual. 1983. 97.50 (ISBN 0-317-12959-7). Meckler Pub.
Stevens, Mary, ed. The Equipment Directory of Audio-Visual Computer & Video Products, 1985-1986. 31st ed. LC 53-35264. (Illus.). 564p. 1985. 25.00 (ISBN 0-939718-04-9). Internatl Comms.
Verniero, Joan, ed. Computers & Electronics Market Research Reports, Studies & Surveys. De Gange, Susan. 185p. (Orig.). 1984. pap. 95.00 (ISBN 0-931634-06-7). FIND-SVP.
Weiner, Roberta, ed. Computers, Productivity & Management in Construction. 3rd ed. 117.00 (ISBN 0-686-42716-5). Constr Ind Pr.
Williams, Martha E. & Hogan, Thomas H., eds. Online Review: The International Journal of Online Information Systems. 1984. per year 70.00 (ISBN 0-317-00228-7). Learned Info.

COMPUTERS–HANDBOOKS, MANUALS, ETC.

Arnold, Bob. Discount America Guide's Directory of Discount Computer Supplies. 1983. pap. text ed. 3.50 (ISBN 0-942528-05-0). Discount America.
Atkin, J. K. Computer Science. 2nd ed. (Illus.). 224p. (Orig.). 1980. pap. 14.95x (ISBN 0-7121-0396-1). Trans-Atlantic.

Bagai, Eric & Bagai, Judith. System FORE Handbook. (System FORE Ser.: Vol. 1). 96p. (Orig.). 1979. pap. text ed. 7.00x (ISBN 0-943292-01-8). Foreworks.

Bakry, S. H. & Bakry, F. H. Introduction to Computers. (Arabic.). 1985. pap. 7.50 (ISBN 0-471-81337-0). Wiley.

Bender, Jack. A Layman's Guide to Installing A Small Business Computer. (Illus.). 128p. 1979. 15.00 (ISBN 0-89433-097-7). Petrocelli.

Bonelli, Robert A. The Executive Handbook to Minicomputers. (Illus.). text ed. 16.00 (ISBN 0-89433-090-X). Petrocelli.

Borgerson, Mark J. A BASIC Programmer's Guide to Pascal. LC 81-16281. 118p. 1982. pap. text ed. 11.95 (ISBN 0-471-09293-2, Pub. by Wiley Pr). Wiley.

Bosworth, Bruce. A User's Guide to Statistics Programs: The Rapidata Timesharing System. 1977. pap. text ed. 6.95 (ISBN 0-89529-018-9). Avery Pub.

Brown, Carol W. The Minicomputer Simplified: An Executive's Guide to the Basics. LC 80-1031. (Illus.). 1980. 14.95 (ISBN 0-02-905130-4). Free Pr.

Buchsbaum, Walter H. Digital IC. (Vestpocket Handbook). (Illus.). 1984. pap. 8.95 (ISBN 0-13-212316-9, Busn). P-H.

Burke, Anna M. The Plain Brown Wrapper Book of Computers. 184p. (Orig.). 1983. pap. 9.95 (ISBN 0-936602-59-7). Kampmann.

Buschsbaum, Walter H. Analog IC. (Vestpocket Handbook). (Illus.). 1984. pap. 8.95 (ISBN 0-13-032748-4, Busn). P-H.

CAD-CAM Glossary. 19.25 (ISBN 0-686-40545-5). C I M Systems.

Carr, Joseph J. CMOS-TTL-A: User's Guide with Projects. (Illus.). 336p. 1984. 19.95 (ISBN 0-8306-0650-5); pap. 13.50 (ISBN 0-8306-1650-0, 1650). TAB Bks.

Cassel, Don. Computers Made Easy. 1984. text ed. 25.95 (ISBN 0-8359-0859-3); pap. text ed. 18.95 (ISBN 0-8359-0858-5). Reston.

Cassel, Don & Jackson, Martin. Introduction to Computers & Information Processing: Language Edition. 1981. pap. text ed. 23.95 (ISBN 0-8359-3150-1). Reston.

Clark, Dana. Classroom Notes for Fundamentals of Computer Science. 256p. 1981. pap. text ed. 8.95 (ISBN 0-8403-2395-6). Kendall-Hunt.

Cohen, G. Creating Technical Manuals: A Step-by-Step Approach to Writing User-Freindly Instructions. 1984. 16.95 (ISBN 0-07-011584-2). McGraw.

Computer Blue Book, 1985. 250p. 1985. 49.50. Orion Res.

Computer Strategies. The Agriculture Computer Handbook. 150p. 1983. looseleaf 45.00x. Computer Strat.

The Computer User's Handbook, 1983. 1552p. 1983. 135.00 (ISBN 0-902908-17-0). Intl Pubns Serv.

Computers & Data Processing Examinations: CDP-CCP-CLEP. pap. 10.00 (ISBN 0-668-04670-8). Arco.

Congressional Information Service, Inc. Staff. CIS Online User Guide & Thesaurus. 400p. 1982. loose-leaf guide 75.00 (ISBN 0-912380-98-5). Thesaurus (ISBN 0-912380-99-3). Cong Info.

Conway, Richard, et al. A Primer on Pascal. 2nd ed. 430p. 1981. pap. text ed. 16.95 (ISBN 0-316-15416-4). Little.

Cooper, Doug. Standard Pascal User Reference Manual. 1983. pap. 12.95 (ISBN 0-393-30121-4). Norton.

Crondahl, Judy R. IBM Displaywriter User's Guide. 2nd ed. (Illus.). 252p. 1985. pap. 16.95 (ISBN 0-89303-608-0). Brady Comm.

Degano, P. & Sandewall, E., eds. Integrated Interactive Computing Systems. 374p. 1983. 51.00 (ISBN 0-444-86595-0, I-176-83, North Holland). Elsevier.

Documentation Standards Manual for Computer Systems. (Bookshelf Ser.). 1974. 5.00 (ISBN 0-934356-03-3); member 4.00 (ISBN 0-686-00269-5). Assn Syst Mgmt.

East, Mary Lou & East, Fred B., eds. Programmers' Handbook of Computer Printer Commands. 1985. pap. 39.95 (ISBN 0-932065-00-7). Cardinal Pt.

Economics Abstracts International Online User Manual. 1983. 30.00 (ISBN 0-317-01044-1). Learned Info.

Farrow, H. F. Computerisation Guidelines. 100p. 1979. pap. 24.05 (ISBN 0-471-89437-0). Wiley.

Friedberg, Ardy. Computer Freelancer's Handbook. 1984. pap. 10.95 (ISBN 0-452-25562-7, Plume). NAL.

Gelb, Neil G. Using COBOL in an MP-M System. LC 82-61965. 112p. 1983. pap. 12.95 (ISBN 0-672-21936-0, 21936). Sams.

Gilmour, R. Business Systems Handbook: Analysis, Designs & Documentation Standards. 1979. 33.95 (ISBN 0-13-107755-4). P-H.

Glossbrenner, Alfred. The Complete Handbook of Personal Computer Communications: Everything You Need to Know to Go Online with the World. 352p. 1983. pap. 14.95 (ISBN 0-312-15718-5). St Martin.

Goldstein, Larry J. Computers & Their Applications. (Illus.). 672p. 1986. text ed. 26.95 (ISBN 0-13-163544-1). P-H.

Graham, L. J. & Field, T. Your IBM PC. 400p. 1983. 17.95 (ISBN 0-88134-120-7, 112-6, Osborne-McGraw). Mcgraw.

Grebnikov, E. A. & Ryabov, Yu A. Constructive Methods in the Analysis of Nonlinear Systems. 328p. 1983. 9.95 (ISBN 0-8285-2406-8, Pub. by Mir Pubs USSR). Imported Pubns.

Grimm, Susan. How to Write Computer Manuals for Users. 211p. 1982. 21.00 (ISBN 0-534-97941-6). Van Nos Reinhold.

Handbook of Industrial Instruments, Microprocessors & Computers. (Illus.). 500p. 1984. text ed. 122.50x (ISBN 0-85461-092-8). Brookfield Pub Co.

Horsburgh, E. M., ed. Handbook of the Napier Tercentary Celebration or Modern Instruments & Methods of Calculation. (The Charles Babbage Institute Reprint Series for the History of Computing: Vol. 3). (Illus.). 1983. Repr. of 1914 ed. 45.00x (ISBN 0-938228-10-2). Tomash Pubs.

Hoyt, Douglas B., ed. Computer Handbook for Senior Management. LC 77-74855. (Illus.). 1978. 18.95 (ISBN 0-02-468030-3). Macmillan Info.

Hull, C. Hadlai & Nie, Norman. SPSS Update: New Procedures & Facilities for Releases 7-9. 2nd ed. 1981. text ed. 16.95 (ISBN 0-07-046542-8). McGraw.

Huskins, D. J. General Handbook of On-Line Process Analysers. (Analytical Chemsitry Ser.). 310p. 1982. 89.95 (ISBN 0-470-27292-9). Halsted Pr.

Hutchinson, Sandra, ed. The Rest of Eighty. 232p. 1983. spiral 9.97 (ISBN 0-88006-062-X, BK7392). Green Pub Inc.

IEEE Standard 716-1982: IEEE Standard C-Atlas Test Language. 1982. 25.00 (ISBN 0-317-03946-6, SHO8656). IEEE.

IEEE Standard 717-1982: IEEE Standard C-Atlas Syntax. 1982. 12.50 (ISBN 0-471-87406-X, SHO8664). IEEE.

IEEE Standard 728-1982: IEEE Standard Recommended Practice for Code & Format Conventions for Use with ANSI-IEEE Standard 488-1978, IEEE Standard Digital Interface for Programmable Instrumentation. 1982. 8.00 (ISBN 0-317-03940-7, SHO8854). IEEE.

IEEE Standard 771-1984: IEEE Guide to the Use of Atlas (Abbreviated Test Language for All Systems) 1984. 27.95 (ISBN 0-471-82746-0, SHO9191). IEEE.

Industrial Bar Code Systems. 1984. 83.00. C I M Systems.

Inman, Don, et al. Beginner's BASIC. LC 79-65510. (Texas Instruments Home Computer User Software Ser.). 144p. 1979. pap. 9.95 (ISBN 0-89512-028-3). Tex Instr Inc.

Intel Staff. CHMOS Components Handbook. 352p. 1985. pap. 12.00 (ISBN 0-917017-35-8, 290005-001). Intel Corp.

Jackson, Ken. System 1022 Primer. (Illus.). 149p. (Orig.). 1982. pap. text ed. 17.00x (ISBN 0-912055-00-6). Software Hse.

Jamison, Steven. Signs for Computing Terminology. (Illus.). 182p. (Orig.). 1983. pap. text ed. 10.95x (ISBN 0-913072-63-X). Natl Assn Deaf.

Kane, Gerry. The CRT Controller Handbook. 224p. (Orig.). 1980. pap. 9.95 (ISBN 0-07-931045-1, 45-1). Osborne-McGraw.

Katzin, Emanuel. How to Write a Really Good User's Manual. (Illus.). 256p. 1985. 29.95 (ISBN 0-442-24758-3). Van Nos Reinhold.

Knight, P. A. Installing a Small Business Computer. 111p. 1981. pap. 12.05 (ISBN 0-471-89459-1). Wiley.

Koehn, Bruce W. Digital Hardware Laboratory. 96p. 1983. pap. 8.95 (ISBN 0-8403-3142-8). Kendall-Hunt.

Kowalik, S., ed. Parallel MIMD Computation: HEP Supercomputer & Its Applications. 1985. 35.00x (ISBN 0-262-11101-2). MIT Pr.

Libes, Sol. Small Computer Systems Handbook. 1978. pap. 12.95 (ISBN 0-8104-5678-8). Hayden.

Lipman, Matthew & Sharp, Ann M. Wondering at the World: Instructional Manual to Accompany KIO & GUS. (Philosophy for Children Ser.). 400p. 1986. 30.00x (ISBN 0-916834-20-4). First Mntn Foun.

Long, Larry E. Managers Guide to Computers & Information Systems. (Illus.). 400p. 1983. text ed. 35.00 (ISBN 0-13-549394-3). P-H.

Longworth, G. Management Handbook of Computer Operations. 300p. 1982. pap. 109.25 (ISBN 0-471-89408-7). Wiley.

Longworth, Gordon. Management Handbook of Computer Operations. (Illus.). 364p. 1983. 110.00x (ISBN 0-85012-360-7). Intl Pubns Serv.

Lord, Kenniston W., Jr. Using the Osborne Personal Computer. (Illus.). 336p. 1983. 19.95 (ISBN 0-442-26010-5); pap. 12.95 (ISBN 0-442-26054-7). Van Nos Reinhold.

McQuaker, R. J. Computer Choice: A Manual for the Practitioner. 178p. 1979. 49.00 (ISBN 0-444-85250-6, North Holland). Elsevier.

Makower, Joel & Murray, Edward. Everybody's Computer Fix-It Book. LC 84-24885. (Illus.). 216p. 1985. pap. 10.95 (ISBN 0-385-19661-X, Quantum Pr). Doubleday.

Malewicki, Douglas J. How to Build the One Hundred Fifty-Five MPG at 55 MPH California Commuter. 2nd ed. 50p. 1982. pap. 15.00 (ISBN 0-941730-00-X); pap. text ed. 15.00 (ISBN 0-941730-01-8). Aero Vis.

Mandell, Steven L. A Pascal Supplement for Computers & Data Processing Today. 150p. 1983. write for info (ISBN 0-314-77494-7). West Pub.

Maynard, Jeff. Computer & Telecommunications Handbook. (Illus.). 1984. text ed. 25.00x (ISBN 0-246-12253-6, Pub. by Granada England). Sheridan.

Milkes, Julian. Keyboarding Capers. 1985. spiral bound 9.92 (ISBN 0-87350-347-3); teacher's manual 9.59 (ISBN 0-87350-601-4); pad form 5.64. Milady.

Mims, Forrest M., III. Forrest Mims's Computer Projects. 200p. (Orig.). 1985. pap. 14.95 (ISBN 0-07-881193-7). Osborne-McGraw.

Morrill, Chester, Jr. Computers & Data Processing Information Sources. LC 70-85486. (Management Information Guide Ser.: No. 15). 1969. 60.00x (ISBN 0-8103-0815-0). Gale.

NACCS. Computing Practice: Security Aspects. 49p. 1979. pap. 22.95 (ISBN 0-471-89436-2). Wiley.

National Computing Centre, Ltd. Guidelines for Computer Managers. 265p. (Orig.). 1981. pap. 40.00x (ISBN 0-85012-248-1). Intl Pubns Serv.

National Computing Centre (Manchester, England) Systems Documentation Manual. 3rd ed. LC 72-97127. (Illus.). 160p. 1973. 40.00x (ISBN 0-85012-101-9). Intl Pubns Serv.

Newchurch, Karen, et al, eds. Programmable Controllers: Concepts & Applications. rev. ed. (Illus.). 342p. (Orig.). 1983. pap. text ed. 27.50 (ISBN 0-915425-00-9). Intl Prog Controls.

Norusis, M. J. SPSS Introductory Guide: Basic Statistics & Operations. 1982. 15.95x (ISBN 0-07-047528-8). McGraw.

Osborne, D. J. Computers at Work: A Behavioural Approach (Controlled Drug Bioavailability) 1985. 29.95 (ISBN 0-471-90410-4). Wiley.

Owen, Jan. Guidebook to Adventure, Vol. II. 2nd ed. (Illus.). 112p. 1985. pap. 12.95 (ISBN 0-13-368846-1). P-H.

Parikh, G. Handbook of Software Maintenance. 1985. 35.00 (ISBN 0-471-82813-0). Wiley.

Peltu, M. Introducing Computers. 180p. 1982. pap. 12.05 (ISBN 0-471-89461-3). Wiley.

--Using Computers: A Manager's Guide. 200p. 1980. pap. 18.60 (ISBN 0-471-89429-X). Wiley.

Perry, William E. Survival Guide to Computer Systems: A Primer for Executives. 249p. 1982. 17.95 (ISBN 0-8436-0880-3). Van Nos Reinhold.

Philipp & Day. A Pathfinders Guide to Understanding Computers. 176p. 1984. pap. text ed. 11.95 (ISBN 0-8403-3297-1). Kendall Hunt.

Pollack, Seymour V. & Sterling, Theodore. Guide to PL-One & Structured Programming. 3rd ed. 672p. 1980. text ed. 26.95 (ISBN 0-03-055821-2, HoltC). HR&W.

Pradhan, Dhiraj K. Fault-Tolerant Computing: Theory & Techniques, Vol. II. (Illus.). 432p. 1986. text ed. 39.95 (ISBN 0-13-308222-9). P-H.

--Fault-Tolerant Computing: Theory & Technique. (Illus.). 432p. 1986. text ed. 39.95 (ISBN 0-13-308230-X). P-H.

Pray, Thomas & Strang, Daniel. Decide: A Computer-Based Decision Game Student Manual. (Random House Business Division Ser.). 120p. 1981. pap. text ed. 10.00 (ISBN 0-394-32698-9, RanC). Random.

Reithmaier, Larry. Computer Guide for Pilots. LC 78-94966. (Pilot Guides). pap. 2.95 (ISBN 0-8168-7200-7). Aero.

Rodwell, Peter, ed. Personal Computer Handbook: An Illustrated Guide to Choosing & Using Your Micro. LC 83-12270. (Illus.). 208p. 1983. pap. 15.95 (ISBN 0-8120-2704-3). Barron.

Rosenau, Milton D. & Lewin, Marsha D. Successful Software Project Management. (Computers Ser.). 300p. 1984. 30.00 (ISBN 0-534-03379-2). Lifetime Learn.

Rowntree, Derek. Do You Really Need a Home Computer? The Book to Read Before You Byte. (Illus.). 120p. 1985. pap. 6.95 (ISBN 0-684-18182-7). Scribner.

Rubin, Charles & McCarthy, Michael. Thinking Small: The Buyer's Guide to Portable Computers. LC 84-6237. 1245p. 1984. pap. 12.95 (ISBN 0-201-05793-X). Addison-Wesley.

Sachs, Jonathan. Your IBM PC Made Easy. (Made Easy Ser.). 250p. (Orig.). 1983. pap. 12.95 (ISBN 0-07-881112-0, 112-0). Osborne-McGraw.

SAS Institute Inc. SAS User's Guide: Basics, 1982 Edition. 923p. (Orig.). 1982. pap. 14.95 (ISBN 0-917382-36-6). SAS Inst.

SAS Institute, Inc. SAS User's Guide: Statistics, 1982 Edition. 584p. (Orig.). 1982. pap. 14.95 (ISBN 0-917382-37-4). SAS Inst.

SAS Institute Inc., ed. SAS Programmer's Guide, 1981 Edition. (SAS Programmer's Guide). 208p. (Orig.). 1980. pap. 9.95 (ISBN 0-917382-17-X). SAS Inst.

Scheid, Francis. Schaum's Outline of Computers & Programming. (Schaum's Outline Ser.). 320p. 1982. pap. 9.95 (ISBN 0-07-055196-0). McGraw.

Segal, Hillel & Burst, Jess. How to Select Your Small Computer Without Frustration. (Illus.). 208p. 1983. 22.95 (ISBN 0-13-431320-8); pap. 14.95. P-H.

Seiden, Eric A. DARAD II: A Self-Teaching Manual. DAR Systems International Staff, ed. 60p. 1985. spiral bd. with software 119.95 (ISBN 0-916163-49-0); spiral bd. 21.95 (ISBN 0-916163-48-2). DAR Syst.

Seiden, Eric A., et al. DARAD II Technical Manual. DAR Systems International Staff, ed. 25p. 1985. pap. 12.00 3 ring (ISBN 0-916163-50-4). DAR Syst.

Seidman, Arthur & Flores, Ivan. Handbook of Computers & Computing. (Illus.). 874p. 1984. 77.50 (ISBN 0-442-23121-0). Van Nos Reinhold.

Shaffer & Shaffer Applied Research & Development. Commodore 64 Color Graphics: An Advanced Guide. 300p. (Orig.). 1983. pap. 14.95 (ISBN 0-912003-07-3). Bk Co.

Skees, William D. Writing Handbook for Computer Professionals. (Computer Technology Ser.). (Illus.). 296p. 1982. 27.50 (ISBN 0-534-97946-7). Lifetime Learn.

--Writing Handbook for Computer Professionals. 296p. 1982. 27.50 (ISBN 0-534-97946-7). Van Nos Reinhold.

Smith, Ronald. The Kiss Principle: Approaches to a Reliable System. (Illus.). 176p. 1983. text ed. 19.95 (ISBN 0-89433-198-1). Petrocelli.

SOS Reference Manual, 2 Vols. Date not set. 50.00 (ISBN 0-317-04441-9, A3L0027). Apple Comp.

Storage Systems Handbook. (DECbooks). 350p. 1984. pap. 10.00 (ISBN 0-932376-71-1, EY-24466-DP). Digital Pr.

Stuart, Ann. Writing Good Computer System Documentation: How to Write It & Know It's Good. 1985. text ed. 20.95 (ISBN 0-03-063892-5). HR&W.

Sundgren, Bo. Data Bases & Data Models. 134p. 1985. pap. text ed. 21.50x (ISBN 0-86238-031-6, Pub. by Chartwell-Bratt England). Brookfield Pub Co.

Tartaglia, Gary. Computers in Plain English: Everything You Need to Know about Computers in Language Anyone Can Understand. David, Bruce, ed. (In Plain English Ser.: No. 1). (Illus.). 155p. 1985. pap. 14.95 (ISBN 0-933117-00-0). Targeted Comm.

Van Trees, James & Wolenik, Robert. A Buyer's Guide to Home Computers. 288p. (Orig.). 1983. pap. 3.75 (ISBN 0-523-41992-9). Pinnacle Bks.

Vick, Charles R., ed. Handbook of Software Engineering. Ramamoorthy, C. V. 768p. 1983. 62.50 (ISBN 0-442-26251-5). Van Nos Reinhold.

Vision Systems. 87.00 (ISBN 0-686-40543-9). C I M Systems.

Wasserman, Harry, et al. Killing Our Own: The Disaster of America's Experience with Atomic Radiation. 384p. (Orig.). 1982. pap. 12.95 (ISBN 0-385-28536-1, Delta). Dell.

Weber Systems, Inc. Staff. User's Handbook to the Atari 400-800. LC 82-51088. (How to Use Your Personal Computer Ser.). 320p. 1983. pap. 13.95 (ISBN 0-938862-15-4). Weber Systems.

Weiss, Edmond H. How to Write a Usable User Manual. (Professional Writing Ser.). 167p. 1985. 21.95 (ISBN 0-89495-051-7); pap. 14.95 (ISBN 0-89495-052-5). ISI Pr.

What the Manager Should Know about the Computer. pap. 2.95x (ISBN 0-686-02556-3). Dun.

Williams, Frederick & Williams, Victoria. Growing Up with Computers: A Parent's Survival Guide. LC 83-62846. 280p. 1983. 15.95 (ISBN 0-688-02607-9). Morrow.

Windsor, A. T., ed. Using the ICL Data Dictionary: Proceedings of the ICL DDS User Group. 160p. 1980. text ed. 29.95 (ISBN 0-906812-06-2). Birkhauser.

Winger, Martin. Electronic Calculator Handbook for Pilots. (Illus.). 1978. spiral bdg. 3.95 (ISBN 0-911721-77-0, Pub. by Winger). Aviation.

Wold, Allen L. & Hunter, C. Bruce. New Webster's Computer Dictionary. 368p. pap. 1.95 vest pocket ed. (ISBN 0-8326-0068-7, 6455); deluxe ed. 2.50 (ISBN 0-8326-0069-5, 6532). Delair.

Wooldridge, Susan & London, Keith. The Computer Survival Handbook. rev. ed. LC 78-72933. (Illus.). 1980. pap. 8.95 (ISBN 0-87645-103-2, Pub. by Gambit). Harvard Common Pr.

COMPUTERS–HISTORY

Bashe, Charles, et al. IBM's Early Computers: A Technical History. (History of Computing Ser.). (Illus.). 650p. 1985. text ed. 27.50x (ISBN 0-262-02225-7). MIT Pr.

Campbell-Kelly, Martin & Williams, M. R., eds. The Moore School Lectures. (Charles Babbage Institute Reprint Series for the History of Computing). (Illus.). 736p. 1985. text ed. 50.00x (ISBN 0-262-03109-4). MIT Pr.

Stein, Dorothy. Ada Lovelace & the Thinking Machine. (Series in the History of Computing). (Illus.). 368p. 1985. 25.00 (ISBN 0-262-19242-X). MIT Pr.

Williams, Michael R. A History of Computing Technology. (Illus.). 480p. 1985. text ed. 34.00 (ISBN 0-13-389917-9). P-H.

COMPUTERS–LAW AND LEGISLATION

American Institute of Certified Public Accountants Staff. EDP Engagement: Assisting Clients in Software Contract Negotiations. LC 84-188421. (Management Advisory Services Practice Aids Ser.). Date not set. price not set. Am Inst CPA.

American Law Institute-American Bar Association Committee on Continuing Professional Education Staff. Computer Law: ALI-ABA Course of Study Materials. LC 84-223486. 578p. 1984. write for info. Am Law Inst.

Auer, Joseph & Harris, Charles E. Computer Contract Negotiations. 423p. 1981. 39.50 (ISBN 0-442-20369-1). Van Nos Reinhold.

Bing, Jon & Harvold, Trygve. Legal Decisions & Information Systems. 1977. 25.00x (ISBN 82-00-05031-9, Dist. by Columbia U Pr). Universitet.

Bing, Jon & Selmer, Knut S. A Decade of Computers & Law. 480p. 1980. pap. 35.00x (ISBN 82-0005-376-8). Universitet.

A Boon to Legal Research-Computers. 5p. pap. 2.00 (ISBN 0-317-30763-0). Amer Bar Assn.

Borking, John J. Third Party Protection of Software & Firmware: Direct Protection of Zeros & Ones. LC 84-24752. 522p. 1985. 74.00 (ISBN 0-444-87677-4, North-Holland). Elsevier.

Brandon, Dick H., et al. Data Processing Contracts: Structure, Contents, & Negotiations. 2nd ed. LC 83-5842. 1983. 44.50 (ISBN 0-442-21034-5). Van Nos Reinhold.

Brickman, Bruce. Legal Aspects of Acquiring & Protecting Software. 343p. 1984. looseleaf 59.95 (ISBN 0-935506-26-8). Carnegie Pr.

Brooks, Daniel T. Computer Law Institute. rev. ed. (Commercial Law & Practices Course Handbook 1983-84). 775p. 1983. pap. text ed. 35.00 (ISBN 0-317-02424-8, G4-3736). PLI.

Computer Crime. 35.00 (ISBN 0-317-29483-0, #CO1775, Law & Business). HarBraceJ.

Computer Law Institute & Mass. Acquiring & Serving Computer Clients. LC 84-60195. 1984. 25.00. Mass CLE.

Computer Law Institute: Fifth Annual Institute. 35.00 (ISBN 0-317-29490-3, #CO3042, Law & Business). HarBraceJ.

Computer Law Institute Staff & Johnston, Ronald L. Fourth Annual Computer Law Institute. LC 83-234269. Date not set. price not set (Law & Business). HarBraceJ.

Computer Law Reporter Editors, ed. Computer Law Developments: 1984. 120.00x (ISBN 0-318-04463-3). Comp Law Rep.

--The Semiconductor Chip Protection Act of 1984: Analysis, History & Practical Applications, 2 vols. 140.00x (ISBN 0-318-04464-1). Comp Law Rep.

Computer Litigation 1985: Trial Tactics & Techniques, Vol. 280. 617p. 1985. pap. 40.00 (ISBN 0-317-27593-3, #H4-4966). PLI.

Computers & the Law: An Introductory Handbook, 1981. 3rd ed. 368p. 1981. pap. 22.50 (ISBN 0-317-04275-0, 5124). Commerce.

Council of Europe. Harmonisation of Laws Relating to the Requirement of Written Proof & the Admissibility of Reproductions of Documents & Recordings on Computers. 21p. 1982. 6.00 (ISBN 92-871-0044-6, Council of Europe). Unipub.

Dammann, Ulrich, et al, eds. Data Protection Legislation: An International Documentation, Bd. 5. (Kybernetik, Datenverarbeitung, Recht). 203p. 1977. pap. text ed. 21.00x (ISBN 3-7875-3005-3, Pub. by Alfred Metzner Verlag). Rothman.

Danziger, James N. & Dutton, William H. Computers & Politics. 320p. 1983. 32.00x (ISBN 0-231-04888-2); pap. 16.00x (ISBN 0-231-04889-0). Columbia U Pr.

Davis, G. Gervaise, III. Software Protection: Practical & Legal Steps to Protect Computer Programs. 400p. 1985. 35.00 (ISBN 0-534-02703-2). Lifetime Learn.

Davis, Lanny J. A User's Guide to Computer Contracting: Forms, Techniques, Strategies. LC 84-9667. 1984. 75.00 (ISBN 0-15-004368-6, Law & Business). HarBraceJ.

Davis, Lanny J. & Ortner, Charles B. Negotiating Computer Contracts. LC 84-198741. (Illus.). write for info. Amer Bar Assn.

Deutsch, Dennis S. Protect Yourself: The Guide to Understanding & Negotiating Contracts for Business Computers & Software. LC 83-6524. 248p. 1983. 21.95 (ISBN 0-471-89217-3). Wiley.

Electronic & Software Publishing. 35.00 (ISBN 0-317-29488-1, #CO2712, Law & Business). HarBraceJ.

Fenwick, William A. & Practising Law Institute. Computer Litigation 1984, Resolving Computer Related Disputes & Protecting Proprietary Rights. LC 82-63160. (Litigation & Administrative Practice Ser.: No. 216). (Illus.). 1002p. 1984. 35.00 (H4-4933). PLI.

Frantzich, Stephen E. Computers in Congress: The Politics of Information. (Managing Information Ser.: Vol. 4). (Illus.). 288p. 1982. 25.00 (ISBN 0-686-97289-9). Sage.

Fuchigami, Harry H. & Ruttinger, George. Government Procurement of Computers & Telecommunications Equipment. LC 83-186015. (Illus.). v, 442p. Date not set. 35.00 (Law & Business). HarBraceJ.

Galin, Joseph J. Computers & the Law: A Selected Bibliography. (Public Administration Ser.: Bibliography P 1627). 1985. pap. 2.00 (ISBN 0-89028-297-8). Vance Biblios.

Gemignani, Michael. Law & the Computer. 244p. 1981. 19.95 (ISBN 0-8436-1604-0). Van Nos Reinhold.

Gemignani, Michael C. Computer Law. LC 84-82460. 1985. 67.50 (ISBN 0-318-04386-6). Lawyers Co-Op.

Gilburne, Miles R. & Johnson, Ronald L., eds. The Computer Law Annual 1985. 1985. 60.00 (ISBN 0-317-29409-1, #H44038). HarBraceJ.

Goldberg, Morton D. & Practicing Law Institute. Software Proctection & Marketing: Computer Programs & Data Bases, Video Games & Motion Pictures 1983, 2 vols. (Patents, Copyrights, Trademarks, & Literacy Course Handbook Ser.). 1983. vols. 159, 160 35.00 (G6-3723). PLI.

Goldberg, Morton David. Computer Software: Protection & Marketing 1984, 2 vols. 1470p. 1984. Set. pap. 35.00 (ISBN 0-317-27383-3, #G4-3751). PLI.

Greguras, Fred M. Summary of Coopers & Lybrand Study of Computer-Assisted Legal Research for the Department of Justice. (Computer Law Monograph Ser). 19p. (Orig.). 1980. 5.00 (ISBN 0-935200-02-9). Ctr Comp Law.

Greguras, Fred M. & Kawashima, Kiyoshi. Legal Protection of Computer Software in Japan. 32p. 1982. pap. 15.00 (ISBN 0-910215-02-2). Law & Tech Pr.

Hagelshaw, R. Lee. The Computer User's Legal Guide. LC 84-45690. 240p. (Orig.). 1985. pap. 17.95 (ISBN 0-8019-7550-6). Chilton.

Hamline University. Advanced Legal Education. Computers, Privacy, & the Law. LC 84-107995. (Illus.). 290p. 1983. write for info. Hamline Law.

Harris, Thorne D., III. The Legal Guide to Computer Software Protection: A Practical Handbook on Copyrights, Trademarks, Publishing & Trade Secrets. (Illus.). 320p. 1984. 24.95 (ISBN 0-13-528373-6, Busn); pap. 19.95 (ISBN 0-13-528365-5). P-H.

Haynes, Stephen L. Computers & Litigation Support. 791p. 1981. 75.00 (ISBN 0-15-100014-X, H39980). HarBraceJ.

Hewitt, Patricia, ed. Computers, Records & the Right to Privacy. 1979 ed. 210p. (Orig.). pap. text ed. 29.50x (ISBN 0-905897-27-7). Gower Pub Co.

Hoffman, Paul S. The Software Legal Book. rev ed. 363p. 1985. looseleaf binder 90.00 (ISBN 0-931687-00-4). Shafer Bks.

Hondius, F. Emerging Data Protection in Europe. LC 75-20210. 282p. 1975. 40.50 (ISBN 0-444-10942-0, North-Holland). Elsevier.

Huband, Frank & Shelton, Duane, eds. Protecting Computer Systems & Software. 1985. 50.00 (ISBN 0-317-29415-6, #H43937). HarBraceJ.

Kuong, Javier F. Computer Security, Auditing & Controls: A Bibliography. 31p. 1973. 7.50 (ISBN 0-940706-04-0, MAP-1). Management Advisory Pubns.

--Computer Security, Auditing & Controls, Text & Readings. Incl. EDP Security, Auditing & Controls Text; Selected Readings. 400p. 1974. 35.00 (ISBN 0-940706-05-9, MAP-3). Management Advisory Pubns.

Lautsch, John C. American Standard Handbook of Software Business Law. write for info. Amer Bar Assn.

Law & Business Inc. & Legal Times Seminars, eds. Contesting Computer Disputes. (Seminar Course Handbooks). 1983. pap. 30.00 (ISBN 0-686-89333-6, C00957, Law & Business). HarBraceJ.

Legal Problems Associated with Ocean Data Acquisition Systems (ODAS) (Intergovernmental Oceanographic Commission Technical Ser.: No. 5). 1970. pap. 5.00 (ISBN 92-3-100762-9, U350, UNESCO). Unipub.

Legal Responsibilities. LC 83-142775. Date not set. price not set. Control Patents.

Leininger, Joseph E. & Gilchrist, Bruce, eds. Computers, Society & Law: The Role of Legal Education. LC 73-93427. (Illus.). 264p. 1973. pap. 12.00 (ISBN 0-88283-001-5). AFIPS Pr.

Luedtke, Peter & Luedtke, Rainer. Computers for Law Offices. LC 84-4488. (Computer Selection Books for Professionals Ser.). 1984. 19.95 (ISBN 0-15-600288-4, BFP). HarBraceJ.

Mandell, Steven L. Computers, Data Processing & the Law: Text & Cases. (Illus.). 1175p. 1984. text ed. 15.95 (ISBN 0-314-70624-0). West Pub.

--Computers, Data Processing & the Law. 275p. 1984. pap. 16.95 (ISBN 0-314-69664-4). West Pub.

Matthew Bender Editorial Staff. Computer Law: Evidence & Procedure. 70.00 (#068); 1981 27.50; 1982 47.50. Bender.

Model Provisions on the Protection of Computer Software. 27p. 1981. pap. 7.50 (ISBN 0-686-71856-9, WIPO64, WIPO). Unipub.

Murphy, Maureen & Gasaway, Laura N. Legal Protection for Computer Programs. (CAUSE Monographs). 117p. 1980. 10.00 (ISBN 0-317-33896-X); members 6.00 (ISBN 0-317-33897-8). Cause.

Negotiating Computer Contracts. 35.00 (ISBN 0-317-29492-X, #CO3670, Law & Business). HarBraceJ.

Neitzke, Frederic W. A Software Law Primer. LC 83-23508. 176p. 1984. 24.95 (ISBN 0-442-26866-1). Van Nos Reinhold.

Niblett, Brian, ed. Computer Science & Law. LC 80-40071. 256p. 1980. 42.50 (ISBN 0-521-23451-4). Cambridge U Pr.

Nimmer. Law of Computer Technology. 1985. 78.00 (ISBN 0-88712-355-4). Warren.

Norback, Craig T. The Computer Invasion. LC 80-23902. 288p. 1981. 23.95 (ISBN 0-442-26121-7). Van Nos Reinhold.

Pacific Rim Computer Law Institute. 1984. 45.00 (ISBN 0-88129-116-1). Wash Bar CLE.

Pearson, Hilary E. Computer Contracts: An International Guide to Agreements & Software Protection. 312p. 1984. 29.95 (ISBN 0-412-00801-7, NO. 9243, Pub. by Chapman & Hall England). Methuen Inc.

Pennsylvania Bar Institute. Computer Law: Buying & Selling Computer Hardware & Software. 221p. 1983. 40.00 (ISBN 0-318-02159-5, 239). PA Bar Inst.

Perry, Lawrence & Brett, Hugh, eds. The Legal Protection of Computer Software. 1981. 60.00 (ISBN 0-906214-06-8, Pub. by ESC Pub England). State Mutual Bk.

Poage, James & Landis, Carolyn P. Contracting for Computing: A Checklist of Terms & Clauses for Use in Contracting with Vendors for Software Packages & Custom Software, Vol. II. 148p. 1975. 16.00 (ISBN 0-318-14014-4); members 9.00 (ISBN 0-318-14015-2). Educom.

Practising Law Institute. Introduction to Computer Law, Vol. 195. 681p. 1985. pap. 40.00 (ISBN 0-317-27499-6, #G4-3763). PLI.

Raysman, Richard & Brown, Peter. Computer Law: Drafting & Negotiating Forms & Agreements. 1984. 70.00 (ISBN 0-318-12028-3). NY Law Pub.

Remer, Daniel. Legal Care for Your Software. 2nd ed. LC 82-1822. 247p. 1984. pap. 24.95 (ISBN 0-917316-85-1). Nolo Pr.

Rostoker, Michael D. & Rines, Robert H. Computer Jurisprudence: Legal Responses to the Computer Revolution. 1985. lib. bdg. 60.00 (ISBN 0-379-20790-7). Oceana.

Rowell, Harry & Landis, Carolyn P. Contracting for Computing: A Checklist of Terms & Clauses for Use in Contracting with Vendors for Computing Resources, Vol. I. 156p. 1973. 16.00 (ISBN 0-318-14016-0); members 9.00 (ISBN 0-318-14017-9). Educom.

Salone, M. J. How to Copyright Software. LC 84-61587. (Illus.). 238p. 1984. 21.95 (ISBN 0-917316-79-7). Nolo Pr.

Scott, Michael D. Computer Law. LC 84-11892. (Business Practice Library). 632p. 1984. 75.00 (ISBN 0-471-89096-0, Pub by Wiley-Law Pubns). Wiley.

--Computer Law Reading List. 2nd ed. 39p. 1982. pap. 25.00 (ISBN 0-910215-01-4). Law & Tech Pr.

--Pretrial Proceedings in Litigating Computer Contract Disputes. (Computer Law Monograph Ser.). 44p. 1980. 10.00 (ISBN 0-935200-03-7). Ctr Comp Law.

Scott, Michael D. & Yen, David. Computer Law Bibliography Nineteen Seventy-Nine. 172p. (Orig.). 1980. 18.50 (ISBN 0-935200-01-0). Ctr Comp Law.

Semiconductor Chip Protection Act of 1984. 35.00 (ISBN 0-317-29500-4, #CO3298, Law & Business). HarBraceJ.

Shepard's Citations, Inc. & Soma, John T. Computer Technology & the Legal Environment. 1984. 75.00 (ISBN 0-07-059642-5). McGraw.

Sizer, Richard & Newman, Philip. Data Protection Act: A Practical Guide. LC 84-18702. 256p. 1985. text ed. 32.50 (ISBN 0-566-02445-4). Gower Pub Co.

Sizer, T. R. & Kelman, A. Computer Generated Output as Admissible Evidence in Civil & Criminal Cases. (Monographs in Informatics: 1-601). 1982. pap. text ed. 21.95x (ISBN 0-471-26204-8). Wiley.

Sloan, Irving J. The Computer & the Law. LC 84-18889. (Legal Almanac Ser.: No. 83). 160p. 1984. pap. 7.50 (ISBN 0-379-11149-7). Oceana.

--Laws Governing Computer Related Crime & Abuse. 1984. 7.50 (ISBN 0-317-30265-5). Oceana.

Software Protection (1982) 35.00 (ISBN 0-317-29502-0, #CO1422, Law & Business). HarBraceJ.

Software Protection (1984) 35.00 (ISBN 0-317-29504-7, #CO2615, Law & Business). HarBraceJ.

Soma, John T. Computer Technology & the Law. (Commercial Law Publications). 500p. 1983. write for info. (Pub. By Shepards-McGraw). McGraw.

Tapper, Colin. Computer Law. 3rd ed. LC 83-783. (Business Data Processing Ser.). 1983. 19.95 (ISBN 0-582-49717-5). Longman.

Turi, Leonard F. OEM & Turnkey Contracts. 202p. 1982. 59.95 (ISBN 0-935506-09-8). Carnegie Pr.

--Preventative Computer Law: How to Properly Buy Hardware & Software. 222p. pap. text ed. 39.95 (ISBN 0-317-18390-7). Carnegie Pr.

UCLA Law Review & Douglas, William O. Computerization of Government Files: What Impact on the Individual? 128p. (Reprinted from 15 UCLA Law Review 1371 (1968)). 1969. pap. 3.00 (ISBN 0-317-33324-0). Am Bar Foun.

U. S. Dept. of Health, Education & Welfare, Advisory Committee on Automated Personal Data Systems. Records, Computers & the Rights of Citizens. 344p. 1973. pap. 6.95x (ISBN 0-262-58025-X). MIT Pr.

Wallace, Jonathan D. Understanding Software Law. pap. 3.50 (ISBN 0-88284-268-4). Alfred Pub.

Westermeir, Jr T. J. DP & the Law. Data Processing Management Association. (MR.3) PAP. Data Process Mgmt. CDP. 56p. MR-3 7.50 (ISBN 0-318-17042-6); data processing mgmt specify issue 10.50 (ISBN 0-318-17043-4). Data Process Mgmt.

Yates, John C. The Business Legal Guide for Computer Entrepreneurs. 288p. 1985. 24.95 (ISBN 0-13-104175-4); pap. 14.95 (ISBN 0-13-104167-3). P H.

COMPUTERS–MAINTENANCE AND REPAIR

Beechhold, Henry F. The Plain English Maintenance & Repair Guide for the IBM PC & PCjr. 288p. 1985. pap. 14.95 (ISBN 0-671-52864-5, Pub. by Computer Bks). S&S.

--The Plain English Repair & Maintenance Guide for Home Computers. (Illus.). 224p. 1984. pap. 14.95 (ISBN 0-671-49293-4, Pub. by Computer Bks). S&S.

Helfrick, Albert D. Practical Repair & Maintenance of Communications Equipment. 320p. pap. 16.95 (ISBN 0-13-693516-8). P-H.

Hildebrand, James K. Maintenance Turns to the Computer. LC 75-109095. 176p. 1972. 13.95 (ISBN 0-8436-0808-0). Van Nos Reinhold.

How to Repair & Maintain Your Own PC XT. 19.95 (ISBN 0-317-05234-9). Personal Sys Pubns.

Margolis, Art. Computer Technician's Handbook. 2nd ed. (Illus.). 490p. 24.95 (ISBN 0-8306-0939-3, 1939); pap. 16.45 (ISBN 0-8306-1939-9). TAB Bks.

Parikh, G. Handbook of Software Maintenance. 1985. 35.00 (ISBN 0-471-82813-0). Wiley.

Parikh, Girish. Techniques of Program & System Maintenance. 300p. 1982. text ed. 27.95 (ISBN 0-316-69064-3). Little.

Perry, William E. Installing Personal Computer. LC 84-61515. (QED Personal Computing Ser.). (Illus.). 164p. 1984. pap. 14.95 (ISBN 0-89435-115-X). QED Info Sci.

Schwieder, Pete H. How to Repair & Maintain Your Own Apple IIe plus. (Illus.). 154p. 1985. pap. 19.95 (ISBN 0-915097-06-0). Personal Sys Pubns.

--How to Repair & Maintain Your Own Apple IIe. (Illus.). 154p. 1985. pap. 19.95 (ISBN 0-915097-07-9). Personal Sys Pubns.

--How to Repair & Maintain Your Own IBM PC XT to the Component Level Using an Oscilloscope. (Illus.). 120p. 1985. pap. 29.95 (ISBN 0-915097-01-X). Personal Sys Pubns.
--How to Repair Your Own Adapter Boards for the IBM PC. (Illus.). 80p. 1985. pap. 19.95 (ISBN 0-915097-03-6). Personal Sys Pubns.
--How to Repair Your Own Compaq Portable PC. (Illus.). 186p. 1985. pap. 24.95 (ISBN 0-915097-05-2). Personal Sys Pubns.
--How to Repair Your Own IBM PC Related Monitors. (Illus.). 80p. 1985. pap. 19.95 (ISBN 0-915097-04-4). Personal Sys Pubns.
--How to Repair Your Own Multifunction Boards for the IBM PC. (Illus.). 100p. 1985. pap. 24.95 (ISBN 0-915097-02-8). Personal Sys Pubns.
Third Party Computer & Communications Equipment Maintenance. 1983. 1350.00 (ISBN 0-86621-149-7). Frost & Sullivan.
Third Party Computer Maintenance (Europe) 1985. write for info. (ISBN 0-86621-677-4, E749). Frost & Sullivan.
U. S. Third-Party Maintenance Market for Computer Datacom Equipment. (Reports Ser.: No. 512). 145p. 1982. 985.00x (ISBN 0-88694-512-7). Intl Res Dev.
Williams, Gene B. Repair & Maintenance for the IBM PC. LC 84-45156. 220p. (Orig.). 1984. pap. 12.95 (ISBN 0-8019-7537-9). Chilton.
Zaks, Rodnay. Don't (or How to Care for Your Computer) 1984. write for info. SYBEX.

COMPUTERS–MEMORY SYSTEMS
see Computer Storage Devices

COMPUTERS–MORAL AND RELIGIOUS ASPECTS
Abshire, Gary M. The Impact of Computers on Society & Ethics: A Bibliography. LC 80-65696. 120p. 1980. 17.95 (ISBN 0-916688-17-8, 12E). Creative Comp.
Baber, Robert L. Software Reflected: The Socially Responsible Programming of Computers. 192p. 1982. 29.95 (ISBN 0-444-86372-9). Elsevier.
Davis, Dennis M. & Clapp, Steve. The Third Wave & the Local Church. 175p. (Orig.). 1983. pap. 8.00 (ISBN 0-914527-54-1). C-Four Res.
Green, Thomas, et al, eds. The Psychology of Computer Use. (Computers & People Ser.). 1983. 23.00 (ISBN 0-12-297420-4). Acad Pr.
Hoffman, Lance J., ed. Computers & Privacy in the Next Decade. LC 80-11388. 1980. 24.00 (ISBN 0-12-352060-6). Acad Pr.
Johnson, Deborah C. Computer Ethics. 128p. 1985. pap. text ed. 12.95 (ISBN 0-13-164005-4). P-H.
Johnson, Deborah G. & Snapper, John W. Ethical Issues in the Use of Computers. 363p. 1984. write for info. (ISBN 0-534-04257-0). Wadsworth Pub.
Johnson, Douglas W. Computer Ethics: A Guide for the New Age. 128p. (Orig.). 1984. pap. 6.95 (ISBN 0-87178-155-7). Brethren.
Kropp, Paul. Micro Man. (Encounters Ser.). 96p. 1985. pap. 3.95 (ISBN 0-8219-0162-1, 35354); wkbk. 1.20 (ISBN 0-8219-0163-X, 35713). EMC.
Parkhill, D. F. & Emslow, P. H., Jr., eds. So This Is Nineteen Eighty-Four: Some Personal Views by Governors of the International Council for Computer Communication. 76p. 1984. 25.00 (ISBN 0-444-87638-3, North-Holland). Elsevier.

COMPUTERS–OPTICAL EQUIPMENT
see also Information Display Systems; Optical Data Processing
Barrett, R. Developments in Optical Disc Technology & the Implications for Information Storage & Retrieval. 80p. 1981. 129.00x (ISBN 0-905984-71-4, Pub. by Brit Lib England). State Mutual Bk.
Biotechnology Equipment & Supplies. (Reports Ser.: No. 513). 179p. 1982. 985.00x (ISBN 0-88694-513-5). Intl Res Dev.
Condon, M. A. Office Workstations. (Office Technology in the 80's Ser.: Vol. 6). 197p. (Orig.). 1982. pap. 15.00x (ISBN 0-85012-387-9). Taylor & Francis.
Francon, M. Optical Image Formation & Processing. 1979. 29.50 (ISBN 0-12-264850-1). Acad Pr.
Gaskill, Jack D. Linear Systems, Fourier Transforms & Optics. LC 78-1118. (Pure & Applied Optics Ser.). 554p. 1978. 44.50x (ISBN 0-471-29288-5, Pub. by Wiley-Interscience). Wiley.
Hanson, Allen R. & Riseman, Edward M., eds. Computer Vision Systems. 1978. 65.00 (ISBN 0-12-323550-2). Acad Pr.
Minicomputers & Microprocessors in Optical Systems: Proceedings of the SPIE Technical Symposium East, Washington, D.C., 1980. (SPIE Seminar Proceedings: Vol. 230). 216p. 37.00 (ISBN 0-89252-259-3); members 30.00 (ISBN 0-317-34690-3). SPIE.
Optical Character Recognition Markets. (Reports Ser.: No. 521). 188p. 1982. 985.00x (ISBN 0-88694-521-6). Intl Res Dev.
Optical Signaling Processing for C3I: Proceedings of the SPIE Seminar, Newton, 1979. (SPIE Seminar Proceedings: Vol. 209). 186p. 38.00 (ISBN 0-89252-237-2); members 30.00 (ISBN 0-317-34715-2). SPIE.
Optical Storage Materials & Methods: Proceedings of the SPIE Annual Technical Symposium, 21st, San Diego, 1977. (SPIE Seminar Proceedings: Vol. 123). 144p. 35.00 (ISBN 0-89252-150-3); members 24.00 (ISBN 0-317-34716-0). SPIE.
Optical Storage Materials: Proceedings of the SPIE Seminar, Yorktown Heights, 1980. (SPIE Seminar Proceedings: Vol. 263). 50p. 10.00 (ISBN 0-317-34717-9); members 8.00 (ISBN 0-317-34718-7). SPIE.
Optical Systems Engineering: Proceedings of the SPIE Annual Technical Symposium, 23rd, San Diego, 1979. (SPIE Seminar Proceedings: Vol. 193). 302p. 38.00 (ISBN 0-89252-221-6); members 30.00 (ISBN 0-317-34719-5). SPIE.
Reichardt, W., ed. Processing of Optical Data by Organisms & by Machines. (Italian Physical Society: Course No. 43). 1970. 95.00 (ISBN 0-12-368843-4). Acad Pr.
Utility Industry Process Control Computer Equipment & Services Market. 240p. 1984. 1500.00 (ISBN 0-86621-215-9, A1282). Frost & Sullivan.

COMPUTERS–PERIODICALS
Amato, Francis. Guide to Computer Magazines, 1985 Edition. LC 84-91752. 144p. 1985. pap. 9.95 (ISBN 0-911061-11-8). S Davis Pub.
Computer Consultants Ltd. British Commercial Computer Digest. 11th ed. 1970. 94.00 (ISBN 0-08-016279-7). Pergamon.
Evan, Frederica. Computer Publishers & Publications: An International Directory & Yearbook, 1985. 2nd. ed. 500p. 1985. 95.00 (ISBN 0-88709-009-5); pap. 90.00 (ISBN 0-88709-008-7). Comm Trends Inc.
Gerdes, James R., ed. Personal Computing Digest, NNC 1981. LC 81-67132. (Illus.). ix, 298p. 1981. 15.00 (ISBN 0-88283-033-3). AFIPS Pr.
Press, Larry & Whittaker, Lou, eds. Personal Computing Digest. (Illus.). vi, 211p. 1980. pap. 14.00 (ISBN 0-88283-012-0). AFIPS Pr.
Robertin, Hector & Bratton, Joseph C. Computers, Video Games & Your Child's Development. LC 83-62878. (Illus.). 120p. 1984. pap. 9.95 (ISBN 0-912921-02-1). Pau Hana Pr.

COMPUTERS–PHYSIOLOGICAL AFFECT
Hutchinson, R. Anthony. Computer Eye Stress: How to Avoid It, How to Alleviate It. Heffernen, Maureen, ed. (Illus.). 96p. (Orig.). 1985. pap. text ed. 4.95 (ISBN 0-87131-457-6). M Evans.
Whitson, Dick. Your Computer Can Kill You: Startling Report. 1984. 9.95 (ISBN 0-917194-17-9). Prog Studies.

COMPUTERS–PROGRAMMING
see Programming (Electronic Computers)

COMPUTERS–PSYCHOLOGICAL ASPECTS
Coombs, M. J. & Alty, J. L. Computing Skills & the User Interface. LC 80-2768. (Computers & People Ser.). 1981. 49.50 (ISBN 0-12-186520-7). Acad Pr.
Dreyfus, Hubert & Dreyfus, Stuart. Mind Over Machine: The Power of Human Intuition & Expertise in the Era of the Computer. 250p. 1985. 16.95 (ISBN 0-02-908060-6). Free Pr.
Hart, Lois B. The Computer Quest, No. 1: Preparing for Your Journey. LC 84-91466. (Illus.). 112p. 1985. pap. 7.00x (ISBN 0-911777-03-2). Leadership Dyn.
--The Computer Quest, No. 3: Living With Your Computer. LC 84-91468. (Illus.). 100p. 1985. pap. 7.00x (ISBN 0-911777-05-9). Leadership Dyn.
Monk. Fundamentals of Human-Computer Interaction. 1984. 26.50 (ISBN 0-12-504580-8). Acad Pr.
Simons, Geoff. Silicon Shock: The Menace of the Computer Invasion. 192p. 1985. 19.95 (ISBN 0-631-13835-8). Basil Blackwell.
Smith, Brian R. Soft Words for a Hard Technology: Humane Computerization. 192p. 1984. 16.95 (ISBN 0-13-822438-2); pap. 18.95 (ISBN 0-13-822420-X). P-H.
Turkle, Sherry. The Second Self: Computers & the Human Spirit. 1985. pap. 8.95 (ISBN 0-671-60602-6, Touchstone). S&S.

COMPUTERS–SOCIETIES AND CLUBS
Deighton, Suzan, et al, eds. Computers & Information Processing World Index. 626p. 1984. lib. bdg. 85.00 (ISBN 0-89774-116-1, Co-Pub. with Gower Pub. Co). Oryx Pr.
Parent-Teacher's Microcomputing Sourcebook for Children, 1985. 846p. 1985. pap. 19.95 (ISBN 0-8352-1959-3). Bowker.

COMPUTERS–SOCIOLOGICAL ASPECTS
Adams, J. Mack & Haden, Douglas H. Social Effects of Computer Use & Misuse. LC 76-10698. 326p. 1976. 28.00 (ISBN 0-471-00463-4). Wiley.
Amara, Roy. Toward Understanding the Social Impact of Computers. 136p. 1974. 10.50 (ISBN 0-318-14427-1, R29). Inst Future.
Baber, Robert L. Software Reflected: The Socially Responsible Programming of Computers. 192p. 1982. 29.95 (ISBN 0-444-86372-9). Elsevier.
British Computer Society. Britain & the Information Society. (British Computer Society Ser.). 1985. pap. write for info. (ISBN 0-471-26235-8). Wiley.
Bucci, G. & Valle, G., eds. Computing '85: A Broad Perspective of Current Developments: Proceedings of the Computing Symposium, 8th, Florence, Italy, 27-29 March, 1985. 263p. 1985. 74.00 (ISBN 0-444-87738-X, North-Holland). Elsevier.
Cheney, Robert S. & Cheney, Jean E. Coping: Survival in a Computerized Society. (Illus.). 250p. 1984. pap. 19.95. Van Nos Reinhold.
Computers in the City: Opportunities in the New Financial Era. 290p. 1984. pap. text ed. 170.00x (ISBN 0-86353-019-2, Pub. by Online). Brookfield Pub Co.
Cornish, Edward, ed. The Computerized Society: Living & Working in an Electronic Age. 160p. 1985. pap. 6.95 (ISBN 0-930242-27-0). Transaction Bks.
Donnelly, Denis, ed. The Computer Culture: A Symposium to Explore the Computer's Impact on Society. LC 83-49215. (Illus.). 176p. 1985. 24.50 (ISBN 0-8386-3220-3). Fairleigh Dickinson.
Dreyfus, Hubert & Dreyfus, Stuart. Mind Over Machine: The Power of Human Intuition & Expertise in the Era of the Computer. 250p. 1985. 16.95 (ISBN 0-02-908060-6). Free Pr.
Dubreuil, Hyacinth. Robots or Men: French Workman's Experience in American Industry. Stein, Leon, ed. LC 77-70491. (Work Ser.). 1977. Repr. of 1930 ed. lib. bdg. 24.50x (ISBN 0-405-10163-5). Ayer Co Pubs.
Evans, Susan H. & Clarke, Peter, eds. The Computer Culture. LC 84-52255. (ITT Key Issues Lecture Ser.). 112p. (Orig.). 1984. pap. write for info. (ISBN 0-932431-01-1). White River.
Flaherty, Doug. Computers & Culture: A Cure for the Deadly Embrace. 300p. 1985. pap. text ed. write for info. (ISBN 0-534-05436-6). Wadsworth Pub.
Frates, Jeffrey E. & Moldrup, William. Computers & Life: An Integrative Approach. (Illus.). 448p. 1983. pap. 25.95 (ISBN 0-13-165084-X). P-H.
Gallo, Michael A. & Nenno, Robert B. Computers in Society with BASIC & Pascal. 1985. pap. text ed. write for info. (ISBN 0-87150-852-4, 37L8700). PWS Pubs.
Graham, Neill. The Mind Tool: Computers & Their Impact on Society. 3rd ed. (Illus.). 410p. 1983. pap. text ed. 21.95 (ISBN 0-314-69650-4); study manual avail. (ISBN 0-314-71093-0); instrs.' manual avail. (ISBN 0-314-71094-9). West Pub.
Hamelink, Cees J. Finance & Information: A Study of Converging Interests. Voigt, Melvin J., ed. LC 81-17587. (Communication & Information Science Ser.). 192p. 1982. text ed. 29.50 (ISBN 0-89391-091-0). Ablex Pub.
Ho, Y. C. & Mitter, S., eds. Directions in Large-Scale Systems: Many-Person Optimization & Decentralized Control. LC 76-10279. 434p. 1976. 65.00x (ISBN 0-306-30937-8, Plenum Pr). Plenum Pub.
IFIP 2nd, Conference, Baden, Austria, June 1979. Human Choice & Computers, 2. Mowshowitz, A., ed. 306p. 1980. 44.75 (ISBN 0-444-85456-8, North-Holland). Elsevier.
Laver, Murray. Computers & Social Change. (Cambridge Computer Science Texts Ser.: No. 10). 128p. 1980. 24.95 (ISBN 0-521-23027-6); pap. 10.95x (ISBN 0-521-29771-0). Cambridge U Pr.
McQuillan, John M. & Cerf, Vinton G. A Practical View of Computer Communications Protocols. (Tutorial Texts Ser.). 258p. 1978. 16.00 (ISBN 0-8186-0201-5, Q201); members 12.00. IEEE Comp Soc.
Mims, Forrest M., III. Siliconnections: Coming of Age in the Electronic Era. 216p. 1985. 16.95 (ISBN 0-07-042411-X). McGraw.
Myers, Charles A., ed. Impact of Computers on Management. 1967. pap. 6.95x (ISBN 0-262-63016-8). MIT Pr.
National Computing Centre. Impact of Microprocessors on British Business. LC 80-478324. 72p. (Orig.). 1979. pap. 15.00x (ISBN 0-85012-232-5). Intl Pubns Serv.
Nestman, Chadwick H. & Feinstein, David L. Computers in Society (by Stern & Stern) Instructor's Resource Manual. 288p. 1983. avail. (ISBN 0-13-164715-6). P-H.
Nikolaieff, George A. Computers & Society. (Reference Shelf Ser: Vol. 41, No. 6). 1970. 8.00 (ISBN 0-8242-0111-6). Wilson.
Peitchinis, Stephen G. Computer Technology & Employment. LC 83-3401. 260p. 1984. 35.00 (ISBN 0-312-15875-0). St Martin.
Peopleware in Systems. (Management Ser.). 1977. 6.50 (ISBN 0-934356-13-0); member 5.00 (ISBN 0-686-00285-7). Assn Syst Mgmt.
Remmes, Harold. Computers: New Opportunities for the Disabled. LC 84-1058. 32p. (Orig.). 1984. pap. 3.50 (ISBN 0-87576-114-3). Pilot Bks.
Rosenberg. Computers & the Information Society. 1986. price not set (ISBN 0-471-82639-1). Wiley.
Shallis, Michael. The Silicon Idol: The Micro Revolution & Its Social Implications. LC 84-5296. 198p. 1984. 15.95 (ISBN 0-8052-3927-8). Schocken.
Sherman, B. The New Revolution: The Impact of Computers on Society. 1985. pap. 14.95 (ISBN 0-471-90485-6). Wiley.
Simons, Geoff. Silicon Shock: The Menace of the Computer Invasion. 192p. 1985. 19.95 (ISBN 0-631-13835-8). Basil Blackwell.
Thomas, John & Shneider, Michael. Human Factors in Computer Systems. Shneiderman, Ben, ed. LC 84-6371. (Human-Computer Interaction Ser.: Vol. 3). 340p. 1984. text ed. 34.50 (ISBN 0-89391-146-1). Ablex Pub.
Weinberg, Sanford B. & Fuerst, Mark L. Computer Phobia: How to Slay the Dragon of Computer Fear. 152p. 1984. pap. 7.95 (ISBN 0-88693-063-4). Banbury Bks.
Witten, Ian. Communicating with Microcomputers: An Introduction to the Technology of Man-Computer Communication. LC 80-40650. (Computers & People Ser.). 1980. 27.00 (ISBN 0-12-760750-1); pap. 17.00 (ISBN 0-12-760752-8). Acad Pr.

COMPUTERS–STORAGE DEVICES
see Computer Storage Devices

COMPUTERS–STUDY AND TEACHING
American University Programs in Computer Science: Their Facilities, Resources & Course Offering. 2nd ed. LC 85-70986. 22.00x (ISBN 0-317-19427-5). GGL Educ Press.
Austing, Richard H., et al. Advanced Placement Test in Computer Science (Pascal) 160p. 1985. pap. 8.95 (ISBN 0-668-06095-6). Arco.
Berkeley, Peter E. Computer Training Operations: A Strategy for Change. 336p. 1984. 29.95 (ISBN 0-442-20993-2). Van Nos Reinhold.
Computer Courses, 1972. 17.50x (ISBN 0-317-11966-4). Intl Pubns Serv.
Dale, Evelyn. The Complete LOGO Handbook for Teachers. (Illus.). 352p. 1985. pap. text ed. 21.95 (ISBN 0-89303-477-0). Brady Comm.
D'Ignazio, Fred. Computing Together: A Parents & Teachers Guide to Computing with Young Children. 320p. (Orig.). 1984. pap. 12.95 (ISBN 0-942386-51-5). Compute Pubns.
The Elements of Computer Education: A Complete Program. 1983. 7.00 (ISBN 0-318-01751-2). Office Pub Instruct.
Flake, Janice L., et al. Fundamentals of Computer Education. 416p. 1985. write for info. (ISBN 0-534-04764-5). Wadsworth Pub.
Harper, Dennis O. & Stewart, James H. Run: Computer Education. 245p. 1983. pap. write for info. Wadsworth Pub.
Kansky, Robert, et al. Guidelines for Evaluating Computerized Instructional Materials. 2nd, rev. ed. 32p. 1984. pap. 3.00 (ISBN 0-87353-219-8). NCTM.
Kewitz, Dale. Understanding Computers: A Self Instructional Guide. (Illus.). 120p. (Orig.). 1984. pap. 12.95 (ISBN 0-930529-00-6, Pub. by Five-K Hearthstone). Five-K Press.
Lau, William W., ed. American University Programs in Computer Science: Their Resources, Facilities & Course Offerings. 2nd ed. LC 85-70986. 220p. 1985. 22.00x (ISBN 0-317-30950-1). GGL Educ Press.
Niman, John. A Teachers' Companion to Microcomputers. LC 83-49527. (Illus.). 208p. 1984. pap. 13.95x (ISBN 0-669-08267-8). Lexington Bks.
Peters, G. David & Eddins, John M. A Planning Guide to Successful Computer Instruction. 1981. 19.95 (ISBN 0-942132-00-9). Electron Course.
Roper, Paul M. & Loertscher, David V. Modular Computer Lesson Design. 2nd ed. 1985. pap. 10.00x (ISBN 0-931510-12-0). Hi Willow.
Shaw, M., ed. The Carnegie Mellon Curriclum for Undergraduate Computer. (Illus.). xiii, 198p. 1984. pap. 18.50 (ISBN 0-387-96099-6). Springer-Verlag.
Sleeman, D. & Brown, J. S., eds. Intelligent Tutoring Systems. (Computers & People Ser.). 1982. 39.50 (ISBN 0-12-648680-8). Acad Pr.
Thompson, Ann. Personal Applications in Computer Education. 168p. 1984. pap. text ed. 21.95 (ISBN 0-8403-3345-5). Kendall-Hunt.
Vocknell, Edward. Model Programs for Instruction. 1984. 21.95 (ISBN 0-8359-4511-1); pap. 16.95 (ISBN 0-8359-4510-3). Reston.

COMPUTERS–STUDY AND TEACHING (ELEMENTARY)
Culp, George & Nickles, Herbert. An Apple for the Teacher: Fundamentals of Instructional Computing. 225p. 1983. pap. write for info. Wadsworth Pub.

Datnow, Claire L. Computerventures-1: Instructor's Guide & Reference Manual-A BASIC Computer Curriculum for Beginners. (Illus.). 123p. (Orig.). 1984. tchr's. ed. 20.00 (ISBN 0-913956-14-7). EBSCO Ind.

Savas, Stephen D. & Savas, E. S. Teaching Children to Use Computers: A Friendly Guide. (Computers & Education Ser.). 112p. 1985. pap. text ed. 7.95x (ISBN 0-8077-2791-1). Tchrs Coll.

Scharf, Peter. A Guide to Computer-Age Parenting: Learning Together with Your Family Personal Computer. 256p. 1984. pap. 9.95 (ISBN 0-07-055168-5, BYTE Bks). McGraw.

Stedman, Robert & Cosgrove, Ron. Kids BASIC for the TI 99-4A. cancelled 9.95 (ISBN 0-89303-603-X). Brady Comm.

Stephenson, John W. Brain Games for Kids & Adults Using the Commodore 64. (Illus.). 224p. 1984. pap. 12.95 (ISBN 0-89303-349-9); bk. & diskette 27.95 (ISBN 0-89303-350-2); bk. diskette 15.00 (ISBN 0-89303-353-7). Brady Comm.

COMPUTERS–TIME-SHARING SYSTEMS

Schoenberg, Isaac J. Mathematical Time Exposures. LC 82-62766. 270p. 1983. 34.50 (ISBN 0-88385-438-4); pap. 18.00. Math Assn.

COMPUTERS–VALUATION

Anderson, T. & Randell, B., eds. Computing Systems Reliability. LC 78-75253. (Illus.). 1979. 52.50 (ISBN 0-521-22767-4). Cambridge U Pr.

Barnes, Michael F. Measurement & Modelling Methods for Computer Systems Performance Studies. 177p. 1979. pap. 44.50x (ISBN 0-905897-18-8). Gower Pub Co.

Beilner, H. & Gelenbe, E., eds. Measuring, Modelling & Evaluating Computer Systems: Proceedings of the Third International Workshop on Modelling & Performance Evaluation of Computer Systems, Bonn, October, 1977. 470p. 1978. 76.75 (ISBN 0-444-85058-9, North-Holland). Elsevier.

--Modelling & Performance Evaluation of Computer Systems: Proceedings of the International Workshop Organized by the Commission of the European Communities, Italy, 1976. LC 77-1179. 516p. 1977. 72.50 (ISBN 0-7204-0554-8, North-Holland). Elsevier.

Chantico-QED. Reviewing the Operation of Small Computer Systems. LC 85-60180. (The Chantico Technical Management Ser.). (Illus.). 166p. (Orig.). 1985. pap. 29.50 (ISBN 0-89435-153-2, CP 1532). QED Info Sci.

Clifton, H. D. Choosing & Using Computers: Assessing Data Processing Requirements for Smaller Companies. 1975. 22.00x (ISBN 0-8464-0247-5). Beekman Pubs.

Cruz, Jose B., Jr., ed. Advances in Large Scale Systems: Theory & Applications, Vol. 1. 1984. 45.00 (ISBN 0-89232-252-7). Jai Pr.

Durbin, Harold. Text Processing Computer System Comparison Charts: 1985 Edition. 1985. pap. 25.00 (ISBN 0-936786-04-3). Durbin Assoc.

Ferrari, Domenico. Computer Systems Performance Evaluation. LC 77-15096. (Illus.). 1978. ed. 425.00ref. (ISBN 0-13-165126-9). P-H.

Gabriel, Richard P. Performance & Evaluation of LISP Systems. (Series in Computer Systems, Research Reports & Notes). 350p. 1985. pap. text ed. 22.50x (ISBN 0-262-07093-6). MIT Pr.

Howard, Ethel M. & Cappell, Ralph. Reading & Writing about Computer Careers. (Career Ser.). 81p. 1985. wkbk. 3.95 (ISBN 0-910307-03-2). Comp Pr.

Kleinjnen, Jack P. Computers & Profits: Quantifying Financial Benefits of Information. LC 79-14097. 1980. text ed. 27.95 (ISBN 0-201-03813-7). Addison-Wesley.

Kobayashi, Hisashi. Modeling & Analysis: An Introduction to System Performance Evaluation Methodology. LC 77-73946. (IBM Ser.). (Illus.). 1978. text ed. 36.95 (ISBN 0-201-14457-3). Addison-Wesley.

Landa, Ruth K. Creating Courseware: A Beginner's Guide. 380p. 1984. pap. text ed. 17.50 scp (ISBN 0-06-043837-1, HarpC). Har-Row.

Lavenberg, Stephen, ed. Computer Performance Modeling Handbook. (Notes & Reports in Computer Science & Applied Mathematics Ser.: No. 3). 1983. 47.50 (ISBN 0-12-438720-9). Acad Pr.

Osaki, S. & Nishio, T. Reliability Evaluation of Some Fault-Tolerant Computer Architectures. (Lecture Notes in Computer Science Ser.: Vol. 97). 129p. 1980. pap. 13.00 (ISBN 0-387-10274-4). Springer-Verlag.

Rosen, Saul. Lectures on the Measurement & Evaluation of the Performance of Computing Systems. (CBMS-NSF Regional Conference Ser.: No. 23). vii, 138p. (Orig.). 1976. pap. text ed. 13.00 (ISBN 0-89871-020-0). Soc Indus-Appl Math.

Sauer, Charles & Chandy, Mani K. Computer Systems Performance Modeling. (Illus.). 384p. 1981. text ed. 41.95 (ISBN 0-13-165175-7). P-H.

Stuck, B. W. & Arthurs, E. A Computer & Communications Network Performance Analysis Primer. (Illus.). 608p. 1985. text ed. 39.95 (ISBN 0-13-163981-1). P-H.

Suobodova, L. Computer Performance Measurement & Evaluation Methods: Analysis & Applications. (Computer Design & Architecture Ser.: Vol. 2). 146p. 1976. text ed. 35.75 (ISBN 0-444-00192-1, North-Holland). Elsevier.

Thompson, Mark S. Decision Analysis for Program Evaluation. 424p. 1982. prof ref 35.00x (ISBN 0-88410-865-1). Ballinger Pub.

Tozer, ed. Integrity & Recovery in Complex Systems. (Computer State of the Art Report, Series 12: No. 4). (Illus.). 300p. 1984. 460.00 (ISBN 0-08-028588-0). Pergamon.

Webster, Tony. Portable Computer Buyer's Guide. (Illus.). 151p. 1985. pap. 9.95 (ISBN 0-07-068969-5). McGraw.

Wooldridge, Ronald J., ed. Evaluation of Complex Systems. LC 80-84297. (Program Evaluation Ser.: No. 10). 1981. pap. text ed. 8.95x (ISBN 0-686-78534-7). Jossey-Bass.

COMPUTERS–VOCATIONAL GUIDANCE

Bailey, David & Castoro, Laura. Careers in Computers. (Illus.). 192p. 1985. 9.79 (ISBN 0-671-49849-5). Messner.

Ball, Les, ed. New England Directory for Computer Professionals, 1985. 128p. 1985. pap. 49.95 (ISBN 0-318-04766-7). Bradford Co.

Billy, Christopher, ed. Engineering, Science, & Computer Jobs 1985. 6th ed. (Peterson's Annual Guides-Careers Ser.). 686p. (Orig.). 1984. pap. 14.95 (ISBN 0-87866-248-0). Petersons Guides.

Birkenbihl, Michael. Train the Trainer: In Effective Course Design & Presentation. 201p. 1977. pap. text ed. 19.95x (ISBN 0-86238-045-6, Pub. by Chartwell-Bratt England). Brookfield Pub Co.

Brechner, Irv. Getting into Computers: A Career Guide to Today's Hottest New Field. 224p. (Orig.). 1983. pap. 4.95 (ISBN 0-345-30172-2). Ballantine.

Briefs, U., et al, eds. Computerization & Work. viii, 180p. 1985. pap. 22.00 (ISBN 0-387-15367-5). Springer-Verlag.

Burke, Anna M. So You Want a Job in Computers. 150p. 1985. 9.95 (ISBN 0-912603-21-6). Micro Info.

Career Choices: Computer Science. LC 83-40445. 144p. 1985. cancelled (ISBN 0-8027-0791-2); pap. 5.95 (ISBN 0-8027-7242-0). Walker & Co.

Carron, L P. How to Break into the Computer Field. LC 81-69763. (Illus.). 140p. 1981. pap. 7.95 (ISBN 0-9607242-0-6). Carron Pubs.

Consumer Guide Editors. Computer Careers: Where the Jobs Are & How to Get Them. 256p. 1981. 6.95 (ISBN 0-449-90064-9, Columbine). Fawcett.

Consumer Guide Publications International Ltd. Computer Careers: Where the Jobs Are & How to Get Them. 256p. 1984. pap. 6.95. Ballantine.

Cornelius, Hal & Lewis, William. A Career Blazer Guide to Word Processing. (Career Blazers Guides Ser.). 192p. 1983. pap. 7.95 (ISBN 0-671-45869-8). Monarch Pr.

Educational Research Council of America. Computer Operator. rev. ed. Ferris, Theodore N., et al, eds. (Real People at Work Ser: I). (Illus.). 36p. 1980. pap. text ed. 2.70 (ISBN 0-89247-062-3, 9412). Changing Times.

Engineering, Science & Computer Jobs 1986. 7th ed. 900p. 1985. pap. 15.95 (ISBN 0-87866-348-7). Petersons Guides.

Herrup, Steven. Exploring Careers in Research & Information Retrieval. 1986. text ed. 8.97 (ISBN 0-8239-0650-7). Rosen Group.

Howard, Ethel M. & Cappell, Ralph. Reading & Writing about Computer Careers. (Career Ser.). 81p. 1985. wkbk. 3.95 (ISBN 0-910307-03-2). Comp Pr.

Hsiao, T. C., ed. Directory of Computer Education & Research: (U. S. Edition) LC 81-51816. 1100p. 1985. 120.00x (ISBN 0-912291-06-0). Sci & Tech Pr.

Jones, Marilyn. Exploring Computer Careers for the Handicapped. 1985. 8.97 (ISBN 0-8239-0647-7). Rosen Group.

Katz, et al. The Computer Entrepeneurs. 1984. 19.95 (ISBN 0-453-00477-6). NAL.

Kennedy, Joyce L. & Winkler, Connie. Computer Careers: The Complete Pocket Guide to America's Fastest-Growing Job Market. 28p. 1983. pap. 3.50 (ISBN 0-937238-02-3). Sun Features.

Kling, Judy Lepick. Opportunities in Computer Science. 150p. 1984. 5.95 (ISBN 0-317-37008-1). ALA.

Lewis, Adele & Hartman, Berl. Resumes for Computer Personnel. 224p. 1984. pap. 6.95 (ISBN 0-8120-2860-0). Barron.

McDaniel, Herman. Careers in Computers & Data Processing. LC 77-25076. 1978. 12.50 (ISBN 0-89433-029-2). Petrocelli.

Marrs, Texe W. Careers in Computers. 160p. 1984. pap. 8.95 (ISBN 0-671-50221-2). Monarch Pr.

Muller, Peter. The Fast Track to the Top Jobs in Computer Careers. (Fast Track Guides to Successful Careers). 128p. (Orig.). 1983. pap. 4.95 (ISBN 0-399-50753-1, G&D). Putnam Pub Group.

Parnell, John E. Computer Science Advanced Placement Guidebook. (Illus.). 224p. 1985. 24.95 (ISBN 0-13-163874-2); pap. 12.95 (ISBN 0-13-163866-1). P-H.

Pell, Arthur R. & Sadek, George. Resumes for Computer Professionals. 128p. 1985. pap. 7.95 (ISBN 0-671-50338-3, Pub. by Monarch Pr). S&S.

Rudman, Jack. Computer Operator Trainee. (Career Examination Ser.: C-878). (Cloth bdg. avail. on request). pap. 10.00 (ISBN 0-8373-0878-X). Natl Learning.

--Multi-Keyboard Operator. (Career Examination Ser.: C-455). (Cloth bdg. avail. on request). pap. 10.00 (ISBN 0-8373-0455-5). Natl Learning.

Shanahan, William F. Resumes for Computer Professionals: A Complete Resume Preparation & Job-Getting Guide. LC 83-3914. 144p. (Orig.). 1983. lib. bdg. 12.95 (ISBN 0-668-05785-8); pap. 6.95 (ISBN 0-668-05789-0). Arco.

Singer, Barbara. Exploring Careers in Computer Graphics. (Exploring Careers Ser.). 144p. 1985. lib. bdg. 8.97 (ISBN 0-8239-0624-8). Rosen Group.

Southworth, Scott. Exploring Computer Careers at Home. 1985. pap. 8.97 (ISBN 0-8239-0651-5). Rosen Group.

Spencer, Donald D. A Guide to Computer Careers. (Illus.). 154p. pap. 8.95 (ISBN 0-02-930450-4). Free Pr.

Stair, Lila B. Careers in Computers. LC 83-72624. 175p. 1984. 12.25 (ISBN 0-87094-441-X); pap. 9.95 (ISBN 0-87094-549-1). Dow Jones-Irwin.

Stone, Jack L. & Roberts, Stephen S. You Don't Have to Be a Computer Genius to Land a Computer Job: How to Find a Career in the World's Fastest Growing Field. LC 83-17910. 252p. 1984. pap. 9.95 (ISBN 0-672-52790-1). Bobbs.

Weinberg, Gerald M. Understanding the Professional Programmer. 240p. 1982. text ed. 22.95 (ISBN 0-316-92845-3). Little.

Weintraub, Joseph S. Exploring Careers in the Computer Field. (Careers in Depth Ser.). 140p. 1983. lib. bdg. 8.97 (ISBN 0-8239-0567-5). Rosen Group.

COMPUTERS, ELECTRONIC

see Computers; Electronic Digital Computers

COMPUTERS, ELECTRONIC ANALOG

see Electronic Analog Computers

COMPUTERS, HYBRID

see Hybrid Computers

COMPUTERS AND CHILDREN

Anstis, Stuart. Write Your Own Apple Games. (Illus.). 174p. 1983. 12.95 (ISBN 0-916688-49-6, 2W). Creative Comp.

Baker, Justine. Microcomputers in the Classroom. LC 82-60799. (Fastback Ser.: No. 179). 50p. 1982. pap. 1.50 (ISBN 0-87367-179-1). Phi Delta Kappa.

Bennett, Randy E. & Maher, Charles A., eds. Microcomputers & Exceptional Children. LC 84-10784. (Special Services in the Schools Ser.: Vol. 1, No. 1). 113p. 1984. text ed. 22.95 (ISBN 0-86656-297-4, B297); pap. text ed. 13.95 (ISBN 0-86656-440-3). Haworth Pr.

Chandler, Daniel. Young Learners & the Microcomputer. 128p. 1984. 34.00x (ISBN 0-335-10579-3, Pub. by Open Univ Pr); pap. 13.00x (ISBN 0-335-10578-5, Pub. by Open Univ Pr). Taylor & Francis.

Chen, Milton & Paisley, William, eds. Children & Microcomputers. 1985. 29.00 (ISBN 0-8039-2446-1); pap. 14.95 (ISBN 0-8039-2447-X). Sage.

Christie, Linda G. & Bullard, Gary J. Almost Free Computer Stuff for Kids. 1984. 9.95 (ISBN 0-452-25561-9, PLume). NAL.

Clark, Gary. Computers & Young Minds. (Illus.). 1984. pap. 9.95 (ISBN 0-88190-372-8, BO372). Datamost.

Frank, Mary, ed. Young Children in a Computerized Environment. LC 81-20028. (Journal of Children in Contemporary Society Ser.: Vol. 14, No. 1). 96p. 1981. text ed. 20.00 (ISBN 0-86656-108-0, B108). Haworth Pr.

Gebhardt-Seele, Peter A. The Computer & the Child: A Montessori Approach. LC 84-19921. 1985. 19.95 (ISBN 0-88175-013-1). Computer Sci.

Geoffrion, Leo D. & Geoffrion, Olga P. Computers & Reading Instruction. LC 83-8727. (Computers in Education). (Illus.). 224p. 1983. pap. 14.95 (ISBN 0-201-10566-7). Addison-Wesley.

Gerber, Carole H. Turn Your Kid into a Computer Genius. (Illus.). 250p. 1984. pap. 10.95 (ISBN 0-525-48119-2, 01063-320). Dutton.

Hammond, Ray. Computers & Your Child. LC 83-9205. (Illus.). 264p. 1984. 15.95 (ISBN 0-89919-210-6); pap. 6.95 (ISBN 0-89919-211-4). Ticknor & Fields.

Holton, Felicia A. Compukids: A Parent's Guide to Computers & Learning. 1985. 9.95 (ISBN 0-452-25560-0, Plume). NAL.

Kidd, Kathy H. & Kidd, Clark. Commodore 64 Games for Kids. 267p. (Orig.). 1984. 12.95 (ISBN 0-942386-37-X). Compute Pubns.

Klein, Elisa L., ed. Children & Computers. LC 84-82365. (Child Development Ser.: No. 28). (Orig.). 1985. pap. text ed. 9.95x (ISBN 0-87589-795-9). Jossey-Bass.

Lawler, Robert W. Computer Experience & Cognitive Development: A Child's Learning. (Cognitive Sciences Ser.). Date not set. 59.95 (ISBN 0-470-20193-2); pap. 29.95 (ISBN 0-470-20194-0). Halsted Pr.

Riley, John T. & Hurtz, Judie L. Organizing a Computer Club for Elementary School Children. 43p. (Orig.). 1983. pap. 7.95 (ISBN 0-912007-00-1). Computer Direct.

Robertin, Hector & Bratton, Joseph C. Computers, Video Games & Your Child's Development. LC 83-62878. (Illus.). 120p. 1984. pap. 9.95 (ISBN 0-912921-02-1). Pau Hana Pr.

Savas, Stephen D. & Savas, E. S. Teaching Children to Use Computers: A Friendly Guide. (Computers & Education Ser.). 112p. 1985. pap. text ed. 7.95x (ISBN 0-8077-2791-1). Tchrs Coll.

Tashner, John, ed. Improving Instruction with Microcomputers: Readings & Resources for Elementary & Secondary Schools. LC 83-42502. 272p. 1984. pap. 28.50x (ISBN 0-89774-095-5). Oryx Pr.

Thornburg, David D. Picture This Too! An Introduction to Computer Graphics for Kids of All Ages. 1982. text ed. 14.95 spiral bdg. (ISBN 0-201-07767-1). Addison-Wesley.

Weinstein, Cheryl & Harris, Carol. Computer Programming for Young Children: A Step-by-Step Guide for Teachers & Parents. 1983. pap. 12.95 (ISBN 0-936386-21-5). Creative Learning.

Yourdon, Edward. Coming of Age in the Land of Computers: A Parent's Guide to Computers for Children. (Illus.). 160p. 1985. pap. text ed. 16.95 (ISBN 0-13-152125-X). P-H.

COMPUTERS AND CIVILIZATION

see also Computer Literacy

Abshire, Gary M. The Impact of Computers on Society & Ethics: A Bibliography. LC 80-65696. 120p. 1980. 17.95 (ISBN 0-916688-17-8, 12E). Creative Comp.

Adams, J. Mack & Haden, Douglas H. Social Effects of Computer Use & Misuse. LC 76-10698. 326p. 1976. 28.00 (ISBN 0-471-00463-4). Wiley.

Barron, Iann & Curnow, R. C. The Future with Microelectronics: Forecasting the Effects of Information Technology. 243p. 1979. write for info (ISBN 0-89397-055-7). Nichols Pub.

Bennett, J. M. & Kalman, R. E., eds. Computers in Developing Nations. 272p. 1981. 47.00 (ISBN 0-444-86270-6, North-Holland). Elsevier.

Bolter, J. David. Turing's Man: Western Culture in the Computer Age. LC 83-6942. (Illus.). xii, 264p. 1984. 19.95 (ISBN 0-8078-1564-0); pap. 8.95 (ISBN 0-8078-4108-0). U of NC Pr.

Burton, Sarah K. & Short, Douglas D. Sixth International Conference on Computers & the Humanities. LC 83-7479. 781p. 1983. 40.00 (ISBN 0-914894-96-X). Computer Sci.

Cheney, Robert S. & Cheney, Jean E. Coping: Survival in a Computerized Society. 1984. 19.95 (ISBN 0-89433-232-5). Petrocelli.

De Lorely, Augustus. The Civilization of the Computer & the Brutalization of American Culture. (Illus.). 119p. 1983. 77.85x (ISBN 0-86654-088-1). Inst Econ Finan.

Dertouzos, Michael L. & Moses, Joel, eds. The Computer Age: A Twenty-Year View. 1979. pap. text ed. 10.95 (ISBN 0-262-54036-3). MIT Pr.

Dorf, Richard C. Computers & Man. 3rd ed. LC 82-70804. 560p. 1982. pap. text ed. 17.50x (ISBN 0-87835-121-3). Boyd & Fraser.

Evans, Christopher. The Micro Millenium. 320p. 1981. pap. 3.95 (ISBN 0-671-46212-1). WSP.

--The Micro Millennium. 1980. 10.95 (ISBN 0-670-47400-2). Viking.

Forester, Tom, ed. The Microelectronics Revolution: The Complete Guide to the New Technology & Its Impact on Society. (Illus.). 589p. 1981. 37.50x (ISBN 0-262-06075-2); pap. 13.50 (ISBN 0-262-56021-6). MIT Pr.

Frates, Jeffrey E. & Moldrup, William. Computers & Life: An Integrative Approach. (Illus.). 448p. 1983. pap. 25.95 (ISBN 0-13-165084-X). P-H.

Frederiksen, Lee W. & Riley, Anne W., eds. Computers, People & Productivity. LC 84-25281. (Journal of Organizational Behavior Management: Vol. 6, Nos. 3 & 4). 205p. 1985. text ed. 19.95 (ISBN 0-86656-339-3). Haworth Pr.

George, F. H. Machine Takeover: The Growing Threat to Human Freedom in a Computer-Controlled Society. LC 76-27722. 208p. 1977. text ed. 24.00 (ISBN 0-08-021229-8). Pergamon.

Graham, Neill. The Mind Tool: Computers & Their Impact on Society. 3rd ed. (Illus.). 410p. 1983. pap. text ed. 21.95 (ISBN 0-314-69650-4); study manual avail. (ISBN 0-314-71093-0); instrs.' manual avail. (ISBN 0-314-71094-9). West Pub.

Holoien, Martin O. Computers & Their Societal Impact. 264p. 1977. pap. 26.00 (ISBN 0-471-02197-0). Wiley.

Kochenburger, Ralph J. & Turcio, Carolyn J. Computers in Modern Society. LC 73-21685. Repr. of 1974 ed. 70.50 (ISBN 0-8357-9862-3, 2015187). Bks Demand UMI.

Laurie, Edward J. Computers, Automation, & Society. 1979. 19.95x (ISBN 0-256-02140-6). Irwin.

Laver, Murray. Computers & Social Change. (Cambridge Computer Science Texts Ser.: No. 10). 128p. 1980. 24.95 (ISBN 0-521-23027-6); pap. 10.95x (ISBN 0-521-29771-0). Cambridge U Pr.

--Computers, Communications, & Society. (Science & Engineering Policy Ser.). (Illus.). 1975. 21.95x (ISBN 0-19-858323-0). Oxford U Pr.

Levy, Steven. Hackers: Heros of the Computer Revolution. LC 84-6188. (Illus.). 480p. 1984. 17.95 (ISBN 0-385-19195-2, Anchor Pr). Doubleday.

Logsdon, Thomas. Computers & Social Controversy. LC 79-24611. (Illus.). 400p. 1980. text ed. 27.95 (ISBN 0-914894-14-5); wkbk. 9.95 (ISBN 0-914894-68-4). Computer Sci.

Martin, James & Norman, Adrian. The Computerized Society. 560p. 1970. 18.95 (ISBN 0-686-98121-9). Telecom Lib.

Masuda, Yoneji. The Information Society: As Post-Industrial Society. (Illus.). 178p. 1980. pap. text ed. 12.50x (ISBN 0-930242-15-7). Transaction Bks.

Mathews, Walter M., ed. Monster or Messiah? The Computer's Impact on Society. LC 79-16737. 1980. text ed. 9.95x (ISBN 0-87805-108-2). U Pr of Miss.

Nora, Simon & Minc, Alain. The Computerization of Society: A Report to the President of France. 1980. pap. 6.95 (ISBN 0-262-64020-1). MIT Pr.

Raviv, J., ed. Uses of Computers in Aiding the Disabled: Proceedings of the IFIP-IMIA Working Conference, Haifa, Israel, November 3-5, 1981. 446p. 1982. 55.50 (ISBN 0-444-86436-9, North Holland). Elsevier.

Rogers, Everett M. & Larsen, Judith K. Silicon Valley Fever: The Growth of High-Technology Culture. LC 83-45257. 302p. 1984. 19.95 (ISBN 0-465-07821-4). Basic.

Rothman, Stanley & Mosmann, Charles. Computers & Society. 2nd ed. LC 75-31622. (Illus.). 416p. 1976. text ed. 20.95 (ISBN 0-574-21055-5, 13-4055); instr's guide avail. (ISBN 0-574-21056-3, 13-4056). SRA.

Sanders, Donald H. Computers in Society. 3rd ed. 536p. 1981. text ed. 27.95 (ISBN 0-07-054672-X). McGraw.

Shaw, M. L., ed. Recent Advances in Personal Construct Technology. (Computers & People Ser.). 1981. 39.00 (ISBN 0-12-639260-9). Acad Pr.

Sherman, B. The New Revolution: The Impact of Computers on Society. 1985. pap. 14.95 (ISBN 0-471-90485-6). Wiley.

Silver, Gerald A. The Social Impact of Computers. 342p. 1979. pap. text ed. 14.95 (ISBN 0-15-581427-3, HC). HarBraceJ.

Simons, Geoff. Silicon Shock: The Menace of the Computer Invasion. 192p. 1985. 19.95 (ISBN 0-631-13835-8). Basil Blackwell.

Stern, Nancy B. & Stern, Robert A. Computers in Society. (Illus.). 624p. 1983. pap. text ed. 24.95 (ISBN 0-13-165282-6). P-H.

Turkle, Sherry. Second Self: Computers & the Human Spirit. 352p. 1984. 17.95 (ISBN 0-671-46848-0). S&S.

Vassiliou, Yannis. Human Factors & Interactive Computer Systems. Shneiderman, Ben, ed. LC 84-14511. (Human-Computer Interaction Ser.: Vol. 4). 320p. 1984. text ed. 35.00 (ISBN 0-89391-182-8). Ablex Pub.

COMPUTING MACHINES
see Calculating-Machines
COMPUTING MACHINES (COMPUTERS)
see Computers
COMPUTING TABLES
see Ready-Reckoners
COMPUTUS
see Calendar
CONCEPTION OF GEOMETRY
see Geometry Concept
CONCHIFERA
see Lamellibranchiata
CONCHOLOGY
see Mollusks; Shells
CONCORDE (JET TRANSPORTS)

Calvert, Brian. Flying Concorde. 272p. 1982. 39.00x (ISBN 0-906393-14-0, Pub. by Airlife England). State Mutual Bk.

Larson, Ken. To Fly the Concorde. (Illus.). 144p. 1982. pap. 9.95 (ISBN 0-8306-2342-6, 2342). TAB Bks.

Owen, Ken. Concorde. (Illus.). 240p. 1982. 24.95 (ISBN 0-86720-630-6). Jane's Pub Inc.

CONCRETE
see also Asphalt; Asphalt Concrete; Cement; Gunite; Heat Resistant Concrete; Pavements; Prestressed Concrete; Reinforced Concrete

ACI Committee 116. Cement & Concrete Terminology. 1978. pap. 17.75 (ISBN 0-685-85102-8, 116R-78). ACI.

ACI Committee 209. Shrinkage & Creep in Concrete. (Bibliography: No. 10). 1972. pap. 36.25 (ISBN 0-685-85150-8, B-10) (ISBN 0-685-85151-6). ACI.

ACI Committee 311. ACI Manual of Concrete Inspection. 7th ed. 1981. 33.95 (ISBN 0-685-85096-X, SP-2) (ISBN 0-685-85097-8). ACI.

ACI Manual of Concrete Practice, 5 pts. Incl. Pt. 1. 60.00 (ISBN 0-686-70198-4); Pt. 2. 60.00 (ISBN 0-686-70199-2); Pt. 3. 60.00 (ISBN 0-686-70200-X); Pt. 4. 60.00 (ISBN 0-686-70201-8); Pt. 5. 47.50 (ISBN 0-686-70202-6). 1983. ACI.

Ahrens, Donald L., et al. Concrete & Concrete Masonry. (Illus.). 1976. pap. text ed. 5.65x (ISBN 0-913163-09-0, 176). Hobar Pubns.

American Concrete Institute. Abeles Symposium: Fatigue of Concrete. LC 73-92588. (American Concrete Institute Ser.: SP-41). (Illus.). pap. 89.50 (ISBN 0-317-10268-0, 2013340). Bks Demand UMI.

--Behavior of Concrete under Temperature Extremes. LC 73-85854. (American Concrete Institute. Publication: No. SP-39). (Illus.). pap. 53.50 (ISBN 0-317-10013-0, 2004296). Bks Demand UMI.

--Concrete for Nuclear Reactors, 3 vols. LC 72-81007. (American Concrete Institute Publication Ser.: No. SP-34). (Illus.). Vol. 1. pap. 160.00 (ISBN 0-317-10390-3, 2012301); Vol. 2. pap. 135.30 (ISBN 0-317-10391-1); Vol. 3. pap. 142.30 (ISBN 0-317-10392-X). Bks Demand UMI.

--Polymers in Concrete. LC 73-86176. (American Concrete Institute Publication Ser.: No. SP-40). (Illus.). pap. 92.00 (ISBN 0-317-10006-8, 2004294). Bks Demand UMI.

--Polymers in Concrete: International Symposium. LC 78-73077. (American Concrete Institute, Publication: SP-58). pap. 106.50 (ISBN 0-317-27232-2, 2025082). Bks Demand UMI.

Austin, Cyril K. Formwork to Concrete. 3rd ed. LC 78-315629. pap. 81.80 (ISBN 0-317-27850-9, 2025255). Bks Demand UMI.

Avram, C., et al. Concrete Strength & Strains. (Developments in Civil Engineering Ser.: Vol. 3). 558p. 1982. 100.00 (ISBN 0-444-99733-4). Elsevier.

Barker. Dictionary of Concrete. LC 82-19825. 1984. text ed. 34.95 (ISBN 0-86095-042-5). Longman.

Bennett, E. W. Structural Concrete Elements. (Illus.). 1973. 21.95x (ISBN 0-412-09020-1, 6034, Pub. by Chapman & Hall). Methuen Inc.

Better Homes & Gardens Books Editor, ed. Step-by-Step Masonry & Concrete. (Step-by-Step Home Repair Ser.). (Illus.). 96p. 1982. pap. 6.95 (ISBN 0-696-00685-5). BH&G.

Biczok, I. Concrete Corrosion & Concrete Protection. 3rd ed. 1972. 38.50x (ISBN 0-685-27529-9). Adlers Foreign Bks.

Bungey, John H. Testing of Concrete in Structures. 1983. 41.00X (ISBN 0-412-00231-0, NO. 5017, Pub. by Chapman & Hall England). Methuen Inc.

Carpinteri, A., ed. Fracture Mechanics of Concrete: Material Characterization & Testing. 1984. lib. bdg. 49.50 (ISBN 90-247-2959-9, Pub. by Martinus Nijhoff Netherlands). Kluwer Academic.

Cement & Concrete Industry. (UNIDO Guides to Information Sources: No. 2). pap. 4.00 (ISBN 0-686-94964-1, UN185, UN). Unipub.

Cement & Concrete Thesaurus. 1969. pap. 19.95 (ISBN 0-685-85158-3, CCT). ACI.

Clark, John E. Structural Concrete Cost Estimating. 256p. 1983. 34.50 (ISBN 0-07-011163-4). McGraw.

Concrete Masonry Units. 38p. 1979. 5.75 (ISBN 0-8031-0310-7, 03-315079-07). ASTM.

Conseil International de la Langue Francaise. Vocabulaire du Beton. (Fr.). 192p. 1976. pap. 39.95 (ISBN 0-686-56961-X, M-6084). French & Eur.

Cordon, William A. Freezing & Thawing of Concrete: Mechanisms & Control. LC 66-14390. (American Concrete Institute Monograph: No. 3). pap. 27.80 (ISBN 0-317-08526-3, 2012299). Bks Demand UMI.

Corrosion of Reinforcing Steel in Concrete, STP 713. 224p. 1980. 22.50x (ISBN 0-8031-0316-6, 713, 04-713000-27). ASTM.

Dartsch, B., ed. Concrete According to German Standards: Production, Testing & Quality Control. 1977. 10.00 (ISBN 0-9960095-7-4, Pub. by Beton Bks W Germany). Heyden.

DeCristoforo, R. J. Concrete & Masonry: Techniques & Design. (Illus.). 384p. 1975. 23.95 (ISBN 0-87909-149-5). Reston.

--Handyman's Guide to Concrete & Masonry. (Illus.). 1978. pap. 10.95 (ISBN 0-8359-2752-0). Reston.

Design of Structural Concrete. 164p. 1983. 33.95 (ISBN 0-317-37036-7); members 24.95 (ISBN 0-317-37037-5). ACI.

Everard & Tanner, J. L. Reinforced Concrete Design. (Schaum Outline Ser.). 1966. text ed. 9.95 (ISBN 0-07-019770-9). McGraw.

Federation Internationale de la Precontrainte (FIP), ed. FIP Manual of Lightweight Aggregate Concrete. LC 83-12739. 259p. 1983. 39.95x (ISBN 0-470-27484-0). Halsted Pr.

Federation Internationale de la Precontrainte. Multi-Lingual Dictionary of Concrete. (Eng., Fr., Ger., Span., Rus. & Dutch.). 202p. 1976. 53.25 (ISBN 0-444-41237-9). Elsevier.

Fly Ash, Silica Fume, Slag & Other Mineral By-Products in Concrete. 1196p. 1983. 119.00 (ISBN 0-317-37048-0); members 80.00 (ISBN 0-317-37049-9). ACI.

Fookes, P. J. & Collis, L. Concrete in the Middle East, Pt. I. 1982. pap. 5.00x (ISBN 0-86310-001-5). Scholium Intl.

Fookes, P. J. & Pollock, D. J. Concrete in the Middle East, Pt. II. 1982. pap. 19.75x (ISBN 0-86310-007-4). Scholium Intl.

Gage, Michael & Vandenberg, M. Hard Landscape in Concrete. LC 75-31700. 167p. 1975. 34.95x (ISBN 0-470-28913-9). Halsted Pr.

Gilson, George. Concrete Flatwork Manual. 160p. (Orig.). 1982. pap. 7.75 (ISBN 0-910460-93-0). Craftsman.

Graduck, I. I. Prestressed Concrete. 150p. 1970. 42.95 (ISBN 0-677-61730-5). Gordon.

Hill, A. W., et al. Handbook on BS 5337, 1976: Incorporating Amendment No. 1 & No. 2. 2nd ed. (Viewpoint Publication Ser.). (Illus.). 64p. 1983. text ed. 30.00x (ISBN 0-86310-009-0, Pub. by C&CA London). Scholium Intl.

Hoerner, Thomas A. & Bear, W. Forrest. Quality Concrete. rev. ed. (Illus.). 36p. 1971. pap. text ed. 2.65x (ISBN 0-913163-00-7, 164). Hobar Pubns.

Iegel, Leonard S. & Limbrunner, George. Reinforced Concrete Design. 2nd ed. (Illus.). 1986. text ed. 31.95 (ISBN 0-13-771684-2). P-H.

Institution of Civil Engineers Staff, ed. Concrete Afloat. 208p. 1977. 34.25x (ISBN 0-7277-0048-0). Am Soc Civil Eng.

Konglomerati Concrete II. 1977. cloth 50.00 (ISBN 0-916906-76-0). Konglomerati.

Kreijger, Pieter C., ed. Adhesion Problems in the Recycling of Concrete. LC 81-15411. (Nato Conference Series, Ser. VI Materials: Vol. 4). 430p. 1981. 65.00x (ISBN 0-306-40817-1, Plenum Pr). Plenum Pub.

Kukacka, Lawrence E., ed. Applications of Polymer Concrete. LC 81-67492. (SP-69). 228p. (Orig.). 1981. pap. 41.95 (ISBN 0-686-95240-5). ACI.

Lea, F. M. Chemistry of Cement & Concrete. 1971. 58.75 (ISBN 0-8206-0212-4). Chem Pub.

Levitt, M., ed. Precast Concrete: Materials, Manufacture, Properties & Usage. (Illus.). ix, 233p. 1982. 48.00 (ISBN 0-85334-994-0, Pub. by Elsevier Applied Sci England). Elsevier.

Lydon, F. D. Concrete Mix Design. (Illus.). 1972. text ed. 26.00x (ISBN 0-85334-552-X, Pub. by Applied Science). Burgess-Intl Ideas.

--Concrete Mix Design. 2nd ed. (Illus.). xii, 196p. 1983. 44.50 (ISBN 0-85334-162-1, I-358-82, Pub. by Elsevier Applied Sci England). Elsevier.

Lydon, F. D., ed. Developments in Concrete Technology, Vol. 1. (Illus.). 325p. 1979. 52.00 (ISBN 0-85334-855-3, Pub. by Elsevier Applied Sci England). Elsevier.

McIntosh, J. D. Concrete & Statistics. (Illus.). 139p. 1963. 20.50 (ISBN 0-85334-038-2, Pub. by Elsevier Applied Sci England). Elsevier.

McMillan, F. R. & Tuthill, Lewis H. Concrete Primer. 3rd ed. 1973. 9.50 (ISBN 0-685-85094-3, SP-1) (ISBN 0-685-85095-1). ACI.

Maguire, Byron W. Masonry & Concrete. (Illus.). 1978. ref. ed. 24.95 (ISBN 0-87909-521-0). Reston.

Malhotra, V. M. Testing Hardened Concrete: Nondestructive Methods. (Monograph: No. 9). 1976. 29.95 (ISBN 0-685-85144-3, M-9) (ISBN 0-685-85145-1). ACI.

Mehta, P. Kumar. Concrete: Structure, Properties, & Materials. (Illus.). 416p. 1986. text ed. 43.95 (ISBN 0-317-29663-9). P-H.

Mindess, Sidney & Young, J. Francis. Concrete. (Civil Engineering & Engineering Mechanics Ser.). 4488p. 1981. text ed. 45.95 (ISBN 0-13-167106-5). P-H.

Murdock, L. J. & Brook, K. M. Concrete Materials & Practices. 5th ed. LC 78-27476. 434p. 1979. 84.95x (ISBN 0-470-26639-2). Halsted Pr.

Neville, Adam M. Properties of Concrete. 3rd ed. LC 80-25198. (Civil Engineering Ser.). 779p. 1981. text ed. 34.95 (ISBN 0-273-01641-5). Pitman Pub MA.

Neville, Adam M. & Wainwright, P. High Alumina Cement Concrete. LC 76-354854. pap. 50.30 (ISBN 0-317-08024-5, 2016302). Bks Demand UMI.

Newlon, Howard, Jr., ed. A Selection of Historic American Papers on Concrete. 1st ed. LC 76-47294. (American Concrete Institute, Publication: SP-52). pap. 85.50 (ISBN 0-317-27231-4, 2025081). Bks Demand UMI.

Orchard, D. F. Concrete Technology, 2 vols. 4th ed. 1979. Vol 1: Properties of Materials. 44.50 (ISBN 0-85334-794-8, Pub. by Elsevier Applied Sci England); Vol. 2: Practice. 46.25 (ISBN 0-85334-837-5). Elsevier.

--Concrete Technology: Properties & Testing of Aggregates. 3rd ed. (Concrete Technology Ser.: Vol. 3). 1976. 40.75 (ISBN 0-85334-654-2, Pub. by Elsevier Applied Sci England). Elsevier.

--Concrete Techology: Vol. 2, Practice. 4th ed. 1979. 67.40 (ISBN 0-85334-837-5, Pub. by Applied Science). Burgess-Intl Ideas.

Popov, Egor P. & Medwadowski, Stefan J., eds. Concrete Shell Buckling. LC 80-69968. (SP-67). 240p. (Orig.). 1981. pap. 39.95 (ISBN 0-686-95244-8). ACI.

Popovics, Sandor. Concrete Making Materials. LC 78-1111. (Illus.). 1979. text ed. 45.00 (ISBN 0-07-050505-5). McGraw.

Ramachandran, V. S. Calcium Chloride in Concrete: Science & Technology. (Illus.). 216p. 1976. 55.50 (ISBN 0-85334-682-8, Pub. by Elsevier Applied Sci England). Elsevier.

Ramachandran, V. S., et al. Concrete Science: A Treatise on Current Research. 1981. text ed. 69.95 (ISBN 0-471-26187-4). Wiley.

Ready-Mixed Concrete. 1983. 450.00 (ISBN 0-318-00504-2). Busn Trend.

Realism in the Application of ACI Standard 214-65. 1973. pap. 25.90 (ISBN 0-685-85114-1, SP-37). ACI.

Research & Education Association. Handbook of Concrete Technology & Masonry Construction. LC 81-50761. (Illus.). 832p. (Orig.). 1981. 26.75x (ISBN 0-87891-528-1). Res & Educ.

Residential Concrete. (Illus.). 79p. 1983. pap. 12.00 (ISBN 0-86718-158-3). Natl Assn Home.

Richardson, J. G. Precast Concrete Production. 1977. pap. 35.00 (ISBN 0-7210-0912-3). Scholium Intl.

Ritter, P. Concrete Fit for People. 1981. 40.00 (ISBN 0-08-024671-0). Pergamon.

Rose, T. & Rider, R. Corrosion of Metals in Concrete. (Technical Report Ser.: No. 58). 142p. 1977. 2.00 (ISBN 0-938412-28-0, P629). URI MAS.

Sharp, D. R. Concrete in Highway Engineering. LC 77-118319. 1970. 23.00 (ISBN 0-08-015845-5). Pergamon.

Short, Andrew & Kinniburgh, William. Lightweight Concrete. 3rd ed. (Illus.). 464p. 1978. text ed. 68.50 (ISBN 0-85334-734-4, Pub. by Elsevier Applied Sci England). Elsevier.

Significance of Tests & Properties of Concrete & Concrete-Making Materials- STP 169B. 882p. 1978. 65.00x (ISBN 0-8031-0612-2, 04-169020-07). ASTM.

Sih, G. C. & DiTomasso, A., eds. Fracture Mechanics of Concrete: Structural Application & Numerical Calculation. 1984. lib. bdg. 57.50 (ISBN 90-247-2960-2, Pub. by Martinus Nijhoff Netherlands). Kluwer Academic.

Survey of Concrete Research in Australia: A Report on Information Subjects Allied to Concrete. 86p. (Orig.). 1979. pap. text ed. 18.00x (ISBN 0-85825-108-6, Pub. by Inst Engineering Australia). Brookfield Pub Co.

Swany, R N., ed. New Concrete Material. (Concrete Technology & Design Ser.: Vol. 1). 180p. 1983. pap. 30.00 (ISBN 0-903384-34-5, Pub. by Blackie & Son UK). Heyden.

Swany, R. N., ed. New Reinforced Concretes. (Concrete Technology & Design Ser.: Vol. 2). 200p. 1984. pap. 39.00 (ISBN 0-903384-47-7, Pub. by Blackie & Son UK). Heyden.

Symposium on Concrete 1983: The Material for Tomorrow's Demands. 136p. (Orig.). 1984. pap. text ed. 28.00x (ISBN 0-85825-201-5, Pub. by Inst. Engineering Australia). Brookfield Pub Co.

Tattersall, G. H. & Banfill, P. F. The Rheology of Fresh Concrete. 368p. 1983. text ed. 65.00 (ISBN 0-273-08558-1). Pitman Pub MA.

Troxell, George E., et al. Composition & Properties of Concrete. 2nd ed. LC 68-13104. (Series in Civil Engineering). 1968. text ed. 44.00 (ISBN 0-07-065286-4). McGraw.

Troy, J. F. Concrete Materials Technology. 31p. 1982. pap. 4.75x (ISBN 0-7277-0139-8). Am Soc Civil Eng.

USDI. Concrete Manual. 8th ed. (1698). 627p. 1983. 37.50x (ISBN 0-471-80012-0, Pub. by Wiley-Interscience). Wiley.

White, George R. Concrete Technology. 3rd ed. LC 76-5304. 1977. pap. text ed. 10.40 (ISBN 0-8273-1095-1); instructor's guide 3.60 (ISBN 0-8273-1092-7). Delmar.

Whitehurst, Eldridge A. Evaluation of Concrete Properties from Sonic Tests. LC 65-27929. (American Concrete Institute Monograph Ser.: No. 2). (Illus.). pap. 26.50 (ISBN 0-317-11011-X, 2004713). Bks Demand UMI.

Wiedyke, Robert G. & Hurd, Mary K., eds. American Concrete Institute Fifty-Five Year Index, 1905-1959: Index of Proceedings & Journal of the American Concrete Institute. LC 7-6419. pap. 92.50 (ISBN 0-317-10746-1, 2022759). Bks Demand UMI.

Wilby, C. B. Structural Concrete. 264p. (Orig.). 1983. pap. text ed. 34.95 (ISBN 0-408-01170-X). Butterworth.

Wittman, F. H., ed. Autoclaved Aerated Concrete: Moisture & Properties. (Developments in Civil Engineering Ser.: No. 6). 380p. 1983. 81.00 (ISBN 0-444-42117-3, I-481-82). Elsevier.

Wittmann, F. H., ed. Fracture Mechanics of Concrete. (Developments in Civil Engineering Ser.: No. 7). 680p. 1983. 138.50 (ISBN 0-444-42199-8, I-303-83). Elsevier.

Wynne, George. Reinforced Concrete. 1981. text ed. 27.95 (ISBN 0-8359-6638-0); instrs'. manual avail. (ISBN 0-8359-6639-9). Reston.

CONCRETE–CREEP

ACI Committee 209. Shrinkage & Creep in Concrete. (Bibliography: No. 10). 1972. pap. 36.25 (ISBN 0-685-85150-8, B-10) (ISBN 0-685-85151-6). ACI.

Bazant, Z. P. & Wittmann, F. H. Creep & Shrinkage in Concrete Structures. LC 82-4766. (Numerical Methods in Engineering Ser.: I-405). 363p. 1983. 58.95x (ISBN 0-471-10409-4, Pub. by Wiley Interscience). Wiley.

Prediction of Creep, Shrinkage, & Temperature Effects in Concrete Structures. 108p. 1982. 54.50 (ISBN 0-317-37032-4); members 42.25 (ISBN 0-317-37033-2). ACI.

Wittmann, F. H. Fundamental Research on Creep & Shrinkage of Concrete. 550p. 1981. 55.00 (ISBN 90-286-2491-0). Sijthoff & Noordhoff.

CONCRETE, HEAT RESISTANT

see Heat Resistant Concrete

CONCRETE, PRESTRESSED

see Prestressed Concrete

CONCRETE, REINFORCED

see Reinforced Concrete

CONCRETE BEAMS

Beckett, Derrick. Ultimate Load Design of Continuous Concrete Beam. LC 67-31269. 116p. 1968. 25.00x (ISBN 0-306-30656-5, Plenum Pr). Plenum Pub.

--The Ultimate Load Design of Continuous Concrete Beams. LC 67-31269. pap. 31.50 (ISBN 0-317-08608-1, 2020707). Bks Demand UMI.

Design Data for Singly Supported Prestressed Beams in One-Story Buildings. 72p. 1965. 10.50 (ISBN 0-89312-053-7, EB036D). Portland Cement.

Fatigue Tests of Pretensioned Girders with Blanketed & Draped Strands. (PCI Journal Reprints Ser.). 16p. pap. 6.00 (ISBN 0-686-40122-0, JR214). Prestressed Concrete.

Serviceability-Based Design of Partially Prestressed Beams. (PCI Journal Reprints Ser.). 47p. pap. 8.00 (JR209). Prestressed Concrete.

Staggered Transverse Wall Beams for Multi-Story Concrete Buildings: A Detailed Study. 114p. 1968. 12.00 (ISBN 0-89312-118-5, EB019D). Portland Cement.

Thurlimann, Bruno. Torsional Strength of Reinforced & Prestressed Concrete Beams: CEB Approach. (IBA Ser.: No. 92). 27p. 1979. pap. text ed. 13.95x (ISBN 0-8176-1125-8). Birkhauser.

Thverlimann, Bruno. Plastic Analysis of Reinforced Concrete Beams. (IBA Ser.: No. 86). 20p. 1979. pap. text ed. 9.95x (ISBN 0-8176-1064-2). Birkhauser.

--Shear Strength of Reinforced & Prestressed Concrete Beams: CEB Approach. (IBA Ser.: No. 93). 23p. 1979. pap. text ed. 12.95x (ISBN 0-8176-1131-2). Birkhauser.

Wilby, C. B. Prestressed Concrete Beams: Design & Logical Analysis. (Illus.). 97p. 1969. 20.50 (ISBN 0-444-20037-1, Pub. by Elsevier Applied Sci England). Elsevier.

CONCRETE BLOCKS

see also Concrete Slabs

Putnam, Robert E. & Burnett, John. Concrete Block Construction. 3rd ed. LC 73-75302. (Illus.). pap. 58.00 (ISBN 0-317-10862-X, 2011567). Bks Demand UMI.

CONCRETE BOATS

Cairncross, Chris. Ferrocement Boat Construction. LC 72-76553. (Illus.). pap. 48.00 (ISBN 0-317-08220-5, 2010131). Bks Demand UMI.

Tucker, Robert. Fitting Out Ferrocement Hulls. (Illus.). 180p. 1977. 34.95x (ISBN 0-8464-1097-4). Beekman Pubs.

CONCRETE BRIDGES

see Bridges, Concrete

CONCRETE BUILDING

see Concrete Construction

CONCRETE CONSTRUCTION

see also Bridges, Concrete; Columns, Concrete; Floors, Concrete; Grouting; Precast Concrete Construction; Prestressed Concrete; Prestressed Concrete Construction; Reinforced Concrete; Reinforced Concrete Construction

ACI Committee 224. Causes, Mechanism, & Control of Cracking in Concrete. (Bibliography: No. 9). 1971. pap. 36.25 (ISBN 0-685-85148-6, B-9). ACI.

ACI Committee 311. ACI Manual of Concrete Inspection. 7th ed. 1981. 33.95 (ISBN 0-685-85096-X, SP-2) (ISBN 0-685-85097-8). ACI.

ACI Committee 349. Code Requirements for Nuclear Safety Related Concrete Structures: ACI 349-80. 1980. 59.75 (ISBN 0-685-85087-0, 349-80) (ISBN 0-685-85088-9). ACI.

ACI Detailing Manual. 1980. 59.95 (ISBN 0-686-70073-2, SP-66). ACI.

ACI Ten Year Index: 1959-1968. 256p. 1970. 24.50 (ISBN 0-685-85156-7, I-68) (ISBN 0-685-85157-5). ACI.

ACI Ten Year Index: 1969-1978. 256p. 1980. 26.50 (ISBN 0-317-17417-7). ACI.

Adams, J. T. The Complete Concrete Masonry & Brick Handbook. 1979. pap. 19.95 (ISBN 0-442-20830-8). Van Nos Reinhold.

American Concrete Institute. Concrete Design: United States & European Practices. LC 78-72044. (American Concrete Institute. Publication: No. SP-59). (Illus.). pap. 88.00 (ISBN 0-317-10026-2, 2022762). Bks Demand UMI.

--Designing for Effects of Creep, Shrinkage, Temperature in Concrete Structures. LC 78-156591. (American Concrete Institute. Publication: No. SP-27). (Illus.). pap. 107.00 (ISBN 0-317-10018-1, 2004492). Bks Demand UMI.

--Impact of Computers on the Practice of Structural Engineering in Concrete. LC 72-78494. (American Concrete Institute Publication Ser.: SP-33). (Illus.). pap. 80.00 (ISBN 0-317-10253-2, 2012300). Bks Demand UMI.

--Response of Multistory Concrete Structures to Lateral Forces. LC 72-93775. (American Concrete Institute Publications Ser.: SP-36). (Illus.). pap. 80.00 (ISBN 0-317-10936-7, 2002352). Bks Demand UMI.

American Society of Civil Engineers, compiled By. Composite or Mixed Steel: Concrete Construction for Buildings. 160p. 1977. pap. 11.50x (ISBN 0-87262-079-4). Am Soc Civil Eng.

--Design of Cylindrical Concrete Shell Roofs. (Manual & Report on Engineering Practice Ser.: No. 31). 185p. 1952. pap. 6.75x (ISBN 0-87262-209-6). Am Soc Civil Eng.

--Economical Construction of Concrete Dams. 566p. 1972. pap. 19.75x (ISBN 0-87262-043-3). Am Soc Civil Eng.

--Finite Element Analysis of Reinforced Concrete. LC 82-71691. 553p. 1982. pap. 39.00x (ISBN 0-87262-307-6). Am Soc Civil Eng.

Anchor, R. D. Design of Liquid-Retaining Concrete Structures. LC 80-29093. 153p. 1981. 59.95x (ISBN 0-470-27123-X). Halsted Pr.

Austin, C. K. Formwork to Concrete: Basic Design Principles & Construction Methods. 3rd ed. (Illus.). 1978. text ed. 43.50x (ISBN 0-7114-3602-9). Intl Ideas.

Bachmann, Hugo. Partial Prestressing of Concrete Structures. (IBA Ser.: No. 95). 20p. 1979. pap. text ed. 9.95x (ISBN 0-8176-1150-9). Birkhauser.

Bazant, Z. P. & Wittmann, F. H. Creep & Shrinkage in Concrete Structures. LC 82-4766. (Numerical Methods in Engineering Ser.: I-405). 363p. 1983. 58.95x (ISBN 0-471-10409-4, Pub. by Wiley Interscience). Wiley.

Billington, David P. Thin-Shell Concrete Structures. 2nd ed. (Illus.). 432p. 1981. 48.50 (ISBN 0-07-005279-4). McGraw.

Brann, Donald R. Concrete Work Simplified. rev. ed. LC 66-24876. 1974. lib. bdg. 5.95 (ISBN 0-87733-017-4). Easi-Bild.

--Concrete Work Simplified. LC 66-24876. 1980. pap. 7.95 (ISBN 0-87733-617-2). Easi-Bild.

Building Research Advisory Board For The Federal Construction Council. Dimensional Tolerances for Cast-In-Place Concrete. 1964. pap. 3.00 (ISBN 0-309-01227-9). Natl Acad Pr.

Childe, Henry L. Everyman's Guide to Concrete Work. LC 71-487900. pap. 42.50 (ISBN 0-317-27787-1, 2025238). Bks Demand UMI.

Circular Concrete Tanks Without Prestressing. 32p. 1942. pap. 2.00 (ISBN 0-89312-008-1, IS072D). Portland Cement.

Concrete Crafstman Series: Cast-in-Place Walls. 74p. 1984. 1-9 copies 7.95 ea.; 10-49 copies 6.35 ea.; 50 or more copies 4.00 ea.; member bulk prices avail. ALA.

Concrete Manual. 29.90 (ISBN 0-318-00061-X). Intl Conf Bldg Off.

Concrete Materials. (Civil-Structural Inspection Ser.: Module 29-3). (Illus.). 50p. 1979. spiral bdg. 7.00x (ISBN 0-87683-118-8). G P Courseware.

Concrete Pipe & the Soil Structure System, STP 630. 148p. 1977. pap. 14.00 (ISBN 0-8031-0311-5, 04-630000-07). ASTM.

Concrete Preparation, Production, Placement, & Finishing. (Civil-Structural Inspection Ser.: Module 29-4). (Illus.). 44p. 1979. spiral bdg. 7.00x (ISBN 0-87683-119-6). G P Courseware.

Concrete Testing & Inspection. (Civil-Structural Inspection Ser.: Module 29-5). (Illus.). 42p. 1979. spiral bdg. 7.00x (ISBN 0-87683-120-X). G P Courseware.

Continuity in Concrete Building Frames. 56p. 1959. pap. 5.00 (ISBN 0-89312-020-0, EB033D). Portland Cement.

Council on Tall Buildings & Urban Habitats of Fritz Engineering Lab., Lehigh Univ. Structural Design of Tall Concrete & Masonry Buildings. LC 78-60643. 960p. 1978. 62.50x (ISBN 0-87262-152-9). Am Soc Civil Eng.

Dalzell, J. Ralph. Simplified Concrete Masonry Planning & Building. 2nd, rev. ed. Merritt, Frederick S., rev. by. LC 81-385. 398p. 1981. Repr. of 1972 ed. lib. bdg. 19.50 (ISBN 0-89874-278-1). Krieger.

Design & Construction of Large-Panel Concrete Structures: Methodology. 116p. 1980. pap. 10.00 (ISBN 0-89312-036-7, EBO96D). Portland Cement.

Design & Construction of Large-Panel Concrete Structures, Report 1: Loading Conditions. 65p. 1976. pap. 5.00 (ISBN 0-89312-029-4, EB091D). Portland Cement.

Design & Construction of Large-Panel Concrete Structures, Report 2: Structural Response to Normal & Abnormal Loads. 133p. 1976. pap. 8.00 (ISBN 0-89312-030-8, EB092D). Portland Cement.

Design & Construction of Large-Panel Concrete Structures, Report 3: Wall Elements. 78p. 1976. pap. 5.00 (ISBN 0-89312-031-6, EB093D). Portland Cement.

Design & Construction of Large-Panel Concrete Structures, Report 4: A Design Approach to General Structural Integrity. (Illus.). 174p. 1978. pap. text ed. 11.00 (ISBN 0-89312-032-4, EB094D). Portland Cement.

Design & Construction of Large-Panel Concrete Structures: Special Topics. 196p. 1980. pap. 13.50 (ISBN 0-89312-037-5, EBO95D). Portland Cement.

Design, Fabrication & Erection of Uni Dome Stadium. (PCI Journal Reprints Ser.). 16p. pap. 5.00 (ISBN 0-686-40100-X, JR181). Prestressed Concrete.

Design of Multistory Reinforced Concrete Buildings for Earthquake Motions. 330p. 1961. text ed. 20.00 (ISBN 0-89312-057-X, EB032D). Portland Cement.

Design Proposals for Shear & Torsion. (PCI Journal Reprints Ser.). 72p. pap. 12.00 (ISBN 0-686-40133-6, JR228). Prestressed Concrete.

Designing for Creep & Shrinkage in Concrete Structures. 496p. 1982. 48.25 (ISBN 0-317-37030-8); members 36.25 (ISBN 0-317-37031-6). ACI.

Developing Structural Integrity in Bearing Wall Buildings. (PCI Journal Reprints Ser.). 33p. pap. 7.00 (ISBN 0-686-40151-4, JR248). Prestressed Concrete.

Douglas McHenry International Symposium on Concrete & Concrete Structures. 1978. 44.75 (ISBN 0-686-70304-9, SP-55). ACI.

Durability of Concrete. 1975. pap. 36.25 (ISBN 0-685-85126-5, SP-47) (ISBN 0-685-85127-3). ACI.

Engineering Foundation Conference on Use of Shotcrete for Underground Structural Support. Use of Shotcrete for Underground Structural Support: Proceedings of the Engineering Foundation Conference, Berwick Academy, South Berwick, Maine, July 16-20, 1973 - with the Cooperation of ASCE & ACI. (American Concrete Institute Ser.: SP-45). (Illus.). pap. 118.80 (ISBN 0-317-10278-8, 2019550). Bks Demand UMI.

Federal Construction Council - Building Research Advisory Board. Crack Control in Concrete Masonry Unit Construction. 1964. pap. 3.00. Natl Acad Pr.

Ferguson, Phil M. Reinforced Concrete Fundamentals: SI Version. 4th ed. LC 80-24409. 694p. 1981. text ed. 45.45x (ISBN 0-471-05897-1). Wiley.

Fintel, Mark. Handbook of Concrete Engineering. 2nd ed. (Illus.). 780p. 1985. 89.50 (ISBN 0-442-22623-3). Van Nos Reinhold.

Fire Resistance: Fire Safety of Concrete Structures. 308p. 1983. 42.50 (ISBN 0-317-37046-4); members 32.25 (ISBN 0-317-37047-2). ACI.

Gerwick, Ben C., Jr. & Peters, V. P., eds. Russian-English Dictionary of Prestressed Concrete & Concrete Construction. (Rus. & Eng.). 120p. 1966. 38.50 (ISBN 0-677-00260-2). Gordon.

Giant Precast Silo for Storing Fertilizers Built in Mexican Port. (PCI Journal Reprints Ser.). 13p. pap. 5.00 (ISBN 0-686-40160-3, JR260). Prestressed Concrete.

Gilbreth, Frank B. Concrete System. (Management History Ser.: No. 70). (Illus.). 182p. 1974. Repr. of 1908 ed. 24.00 (ISBN 0-87960-106-X). Hive Pub.

Green, J. Keith & Perkins, Philip H. Concrete Liquid Retaining Structures. (Illus.). 355p. 1979. 52.00 (ISBN 0-85334-856-1, Pub. by Elsevier Applied Sci England). Elsevier.

Guide to the Use of Waterproofing, Dampproofing, Protective & Decorative Barrier Systems for Concrete. 1979. 22.50 (ISBN 0-686-71036-3, 515.1R-79) (ISBN 0-686-71037-1). ACI.

Harris, Harry G., ed. Dynamic Modelling of Concrete Structures. LC 82-70083. (SP-73). 248p. (Orig.). 1982. pap. 40.75 (ISBN 0-686-95252-9). ACI.

Hurd, M. K. Formwork for Concrete. 1981. 59.75 (ISBN 0-685-85098-6, SP-4) (ISBN 0-685-85099-4). ACI.

Industrialization in Concrete Building Construction. 1975. pap. 32.75 (ISBN 0-685-85128-1, SP-48) (ISBN 0-685-85129-X). ACI.

International Symposium on Fiber Reinforced Concrete 1973, Ottawa. Fiber Reinforced Concrete: An International Symposium Papers. LC 74-77433. (American Concrete Institute Publication Ser.: No. SP-44). pap. 141.00 (ISBN 0-317-27877-0, 2025080). Bks Demand UMI.

Jacobs, David H., Jr. The Homeowner's Illustrated Guide to Concrete. (Illus.). 352p. (Orig.). 1984. 24.95 (ISBN 0-8306-0626-2); pap. 15.50 (ISBN 0-8306-1626-8, 1626). TAB Bks.

Johnson, R. P. Composite Structures of Steel & Concrete: Beams, Columns, Frames & Applications in Buildings, Vol. 1. 224p. 1982. pap. 18.00x (ISBN 0-246-11919-5, Pub. by Granada England). Sheridan.

Johnson, R. P. & Buckby, R. J. Composite Structures of Steel & Concrete, Vol. 11: Bridges with a Commentary on BS 5400, Pt. 5. 524p. 1979. text ed. 76.00x (ISBN 0-258-97104-5, Pub. by Granada England). Brookfield Pub Co.

Jones, Peter. Concrete & Masonry: A Complete Handbook of Materials & Methods. (Illus.). 416p. 1984. 24.95 (ISBN 0-13-167197-9); pap. 14.95 (ISBN 0-13-167189-8). P-H.

Kong, F. & Cohen, Edward. Handbook of Structural Concrete. 1936p. 1983. 90.00 (ISBN 0-07-011573-7). McGraw.

LaGuardia Airport Runway Extension Program. (PCI Journal Reprints). 6p. pap. 4.00 (ISBN 0-686-39987-0, JR40). Prestressed Concrete.

The Large Panel Building System. (PCI Journal Reprints Ser.). 16p. pap. 5.00 (ISBN 0-686-40018-6, JR75). Prestressed Concrete.

Lee County Library, Sanford, North Carolina. (PCI Journal Reprints Ser.). 7p. pap. 4.00 (ISBN 0-686-40147-6, JR243). Prestressed Concrete.

Load-Bearing Wall Panels: Design & Application. (PCI Journal Reprints Ser.). 16p. pap. 5.00 (ISBN 0-686-40039-9, JR106). Prestressed Concrete.

Long, Leslie, et al. Design Mix Manual for Concrete Construction. Allen-Brown, Patricia, ed. LC 81-2363. 384p. 1982. 56.50x (ISBN 0-07-038683-8). McGraw.

Love, T. W. Construction Manual: Concrete & Formwork. (Illus.). 178p. 1973. pap. 8.00 (ISBN 0-910460-03-5). Craftsman.

McCormac, Jack C. Design of Reinforced Concrete. 1978. text ed. 35.50 scp (ISBN 0-7002-2523-4, HarpC); solutions man. avail. (ISBN 0-06-364300-6). Har-Row.

Mason, Robin, ed. Shotcrete for Underground Support, Vol. III. 346p. (Orig.). 1980. pap. 20.00x (ISBN 0-939204-04-5, 78-14). Eng Found.

Menzel Symposium on High Pressure Steam Curing. 1972. pap. 31.65 (ISBN 0-685-85106-0, SP-32) (ISBN 0-685-85107-9). ACI.

Moore, Cairl E. Concrete Form Construction. 1977. pap. text ed. 12.80 (ISBN 0-8273-1094-3); instructor's guide 3.00 (ISBN 0-8273-1093-5). Delmar.

Ouden, P. & Boom, B. K. Manual of Cultivated Conifers: Hardy in the Cold & Warm Temperature Zone. 1982. text ed. 59.00 (ISBN 90-247-2148-2, Pub. by Martinus Nijhoff); pap. text ed. 37.00 (ISBN 90-247-2644-1). Kluwer Academic.

Stein, Norbert. Coniferen Im Westlichen: Malayischen Archipel. (Biogeographica Ser.: No. 11). 1978. lib. bdg. 31.50 (ISBN 90-6193-212-2, Pub. by Junk Pubs Netherlands). Kluwer Academic.

Veitch, James. A Manual of Coniferae, Containing a General Review of the Order. (Illus.). 350p. 1980. Repr. of 1881 ed. text ed. 56.25x (ISBN 0-934454-96-5). Lubrecht & Cramer.

Welch, Humphrey J. Manual of Dwarf Conifers. LC 79-675. 504p. 1979. lib. bdg. 51.00 (ISBN 0-8240-7400-9). Garland Pub.

CONIFERAE, FOSSIL

Harris, Thomas M. Yorkshire Jurassic Flora: Vol. V, Coniferales. (Illus.). 1979. 52.00x (ISBN 0-565-00803-X, Pub. by Brit Mus Nat Hist). Sabbot-Natural Hist Bks.

CONNECTIVE TISSUES

see also Adipose Tissues; Collagen

Ebner, Maria. Connective Tissue Manipulations. LC 84-9636. 230p. 1985. lib. bdg. 17.50 (ISBN 0-89874-763-5). Krieger.

Hall, David & Jackson, D. S., eds. International Review of Connective Tissue Research, Vol. 10. (Serial Publication). 1983. 65.00 (ISBN 0-12-363710-4). Acad Pr.

Hukins, W. L., ed. Connective Tissue Matrix. (Topics in Molecular & Structural Biology Ser.: Vol. 5). 245p. 1984. 69.50x (ISBN 0-89573-209-2). VCH Pubs.

Piez, K. A. & Reddi, A. H., eds. Extracellular Matrix Biochemistry. 528p. 1984. 60.00 (ISBN 0-444-00799-7). Elsevier.

Ruggeri, A. & Motta, P. M., eds. Ultrastructure of the Connective Tissue Matrix. 228p. 1984. text ed. 59.00 (ISBN 0-89838-600-4, Pub. by Martinus Nijhoff Netherlands). Kluwer Academic.

Schubert, Maxwell & Hamerman, David. A Primer on Connective Tissue Biochemistry. LC 68-25209. pap. 82.50 (ISBN 0-317-29249-8, 2055443). Bks Demand UMI.

Veis. Chemistry & Biology of Mineralized Connective Tissue. (Developments in Biochemistry Ser.: Vol. 22). 630p. 1981. 124.00 (ISBN 0-444-00678-8, Biomedical Pr). Elsevier.

Woolley, David E. & Evanson, John M. Collagenase in Normal & Pathological Connective Tissues. LC 79-40821. 292p. 1980. 69.95x (ISBN 0-471-27668-5, Pub. by Wiley-Interscience). Wiley.

CONODONTS

Ellison, S. P., Jr. Annotated Bibliography, & Index, of Conodonts. (Pub. Ser: 6210). (Illus.). 128p. 1962. incl. supplements 2.25 (ISBN 0-318-03316-X). Bur Econ Geology.

Lofgren, Anita. Arenigian & Llanvirnian Conodonts from Jamtland, Northern Sweden. 1979. 39.00x (ISBN 82-00-09476-6). Universitet.

Martinsson, Anders, ed. Taxonomy, Ecology & Identity of Conodonts: Fossils & Strata No. 15. 192p. (Orig.). 1984. pap. 35.00x (ISBN 82-00-06737-8). Universitet.

Seddon, G. Pre-Chappel Conodonts of the Llano Region, Texas. (Report of Investigations Ser.: RI 68). (Illus.). 130p. 1970. 7.50 (ISBN 0-318-03170-1). Bur Econ Geology.

Symposium on Conodont Biostratigraphy 1969:(Ohio State University) Symposium on Conodont Biostratigraphy. Sweet, Walter C. & Bergstrom, Stig M., eds. (Geological Society of America Ser.: No. 127). pap. 128.00 (ISBN 0-317-28379-0, 2025461). Bks Demand UMI.

Ziegler, W., et al, eds. Catalogue of Conodonts, Vol. 1. (Illus.). 504p. 1973. looseleaf 39.20 (ISBN 3-510-65049-2). Lubrecht & Cramer.

--Catalogue of Conodonts, Vol. 2. (Illus.). 404p. 1975. looseleaf 37.50 (ISBN 3-510-65050-6). Lubrecht & Cramer.

--Catalogue of Conodonts, Vol. 3. (Illus.). 574p. 1977. looseleaf 50.00 (ISBN 3-510-65051-4). Lubrecht & Cramer.

--Catalogue of Conodonts, Vol. 4. (Illus.). 445p. 1981. looseleaf 49.00 (ISBN 3-510-65052-2). Lubrecht & Cramer.

CONSCIOUS AUTOMATA

Anderson, Alan R., ed. Minds & Machines. (Orig.). 1964. pap. 12.95 ref. ed. (ISBN 0-13-583393-0). P-H.

Bond. Machine Intelligence. (Infotech Computer State of the Art Reports). 407p. 1981. 405.00 (ISBN 0-08-028556-2). Pergamon.

Hayes, J. E., et al. Machine Intelligence: Machine Expertise & the Human Interface. LC 79-40785. (Machine Intelligence Ser.: Vol. 9). 492p. 1979. 114.95 (ISBN 0-470-26714-3). Halsted Pr.

McCorduck, Pamela. Machines Who Think. LC 79-13809. (Illus.). 375p. 1981. pap. text ed. 12.95 (ISBN 0-7167-1135-4). W H Freeman.

CONSERVATION LAWS (PHYSICS)

Blecher, M. & Gotow, K., eds. Low Energy Tests of Conservation Laws in Particle Physics: Conference Proceedings, Blacksburg, Virginia, 1983. LC 84-71157. (AIP Conference Proceedings: No. 114, Subseries on Particles & Fields No. 33). 322p. 1984. lib. bdg. 40.50 (ISBN 0-88318-313-7). Am Inst Physics.

Elkana, Yehuda. Discovery of the Conservation of Energy. LC 73-88897. (Monographs in the History of Science). 277p. 1974. text ed. 15.00x (ISBN 0-674-21240-1). Harvard U Pr.

Lax, P. D. Hyperbolic Systems of Conservation Laws & the Mathematical Theory of Shock Waves. (CBMS-NSF Regional Conference Ser.: No. 11). v, 48p. 1973. pap. text ed. 8.00 (ISBN 0-89871-177-0). Soc Indus-Appl Math.

Liu, Tai-Ping. Admissible Solutions of Hyperbolic Conservation Laws: Memoirs of the Arms. LC 80-28506. (Memoirs Ser.: No. 240). 78p. 1981. pap. 9.00 (ISBN 0-8218-2240-3). Am Math.

Majda, A. Compressible Fluid Flow & Systems of Conservation Laws in Several Space Variables. (Applied Mathematical Sciences Ser.: Vol. 53). 160p. 1984. pap. 16.80 (ISBN 0-387-96037-6). Springer-Verlag.

CONSERVATION OF BOOKS

see Books–Conservation and Restoration

CONSERVATION OF ENERGY RESOURCES

see Energy Conservation

CONSERVATION OF FORESTS

see Forest Conservation

CONSERVATION OF MANUSCRIPTS

see Manuscripts–Conservation and Restoration

CONSERVATION OF NATURAL RESOURCES

see also Energy Conservation; Forest Conservation; Human Ecology; Marine Resources Conservation; Nature Conservation; Reclamation of Land; Recycling (Waste, etc.); Soil Conservation; Water; Wildlife Conservation

Aldridge, Don. The Master Book of Environmental Education. 1981. pap. 25.00x (ISBN 0-686-81322-7, Pub. by GEO Abstracts England). State Mutual Bk.

Allen, Robert. How to Save the World. (Illus.). 150p. 1980. cloth 14.95 (ISBN 0-389-20011-5, IUCN79, IUCN); 7.50 (IUCN120). Unipub.

--How to Save the World: Strategy for World Conservation. (Illus.). 150p. 1980. 18.95x (ISBN 0-389-20011-5, 06786). B&N Imports.

--How to Save the World: Strategy for World Conservation. (Illus.). 144p. 1981. pap. 1.95 (ISBN 0-8226-0366-7). Littlefield.

Allman, S. Audean, et al. Environmental Education: A Promise for the Future. 196p. 1982. pap. text ed. 8.95x (ISBN 0-89641-085-4). American Pr.

Anglemyer, Mary, et al, eds. A Search for Environmental Ethics: An Initial Bibliography. LC 80-15026. 119p. 1982. Repr. text ed. 12.50x (ISBN 0-87474-212-9). Smithsonian.

ASCE National Convention, Environmental Analysis Research Council, Atlanta, 1979. Appropriate Technology in Resource Conservation & Recovery. Gunnerson, Charles G. & Kalbermatten, John M., eds. LC 80-65304. 218p. 1979. pap. 19.50x (ISBN 0-87262-035-2). Am Soc Civil Eng.

Avriel, Mordecai & Amit, Raphael, eds. Perspectives on Resource Policy Modeling: Theory & Applications. LC 81-12697. 456p. 1982. prof ref 42.00x (ISBN 0-88410-837-6). Ballinger Pub.

Ayensu, Edward S., et al. Our Green & Living World: The Wisdom to Save It. (Illus.). 256p. 1984. 24.95 (ISBN 0-521-26842-7). Cambridge U Pr.

--Our Green & Living World: The Wisdom to Save It. Goodwin, Joseph, ed. LC 84-600181. (Illus.). 256p. 1984. 25.00 (ISBN 0-89599-016-4, Dist. by Cambridge). Smithsonian Bks.

Baker, Mark & Bassett, Libby. The World Environment Handbook: A Directory of Global Natural Resource Management Agencies & Non-Governmental Environment Organizations in 145 Countries. 2nd ed. 290p. 1984. pap. 29.50. Wiley.

Beck, Paul, et al. Individual Energy Conservation Behaviors. LC 80-12699. 240p. 1980. text ed. 35.00 (ISBN 0-89946-018-6). Oelgeschlager.

Bender, P. Phyiscal Resources Management. 32.50 (ISBN 0-471-80026-0). Wiley.

Bender, Paul S. Resource Management: An Alternative View of the Management Process. LC 82-13471. (Systems Engineering & Analysis Ser.). 227p. 1983. 42.25x (ISBN 0-471-08179-5, Pub. by Wiley-Interscience); 41.95. Assn Inform & Image Mgmt.

Berndt, Ernst R. & Field, Barry C., eds. Modeling & Measuring Natural Resource Substitution. 384p. 1982. text ed. 50.00x (ISBN 0-262-02174-9). MIT Pr.

Berry, D., et al. The Preservation of Open Space in the New Jersey Pinelands. (Discussion Paper Ser.: No. 73). 1974. pap. 4.50 (ISBN 0-686-32239-8). Regional Sci Res Inst.

Biology Colloquium, 40th, Oregon State University, 1979. Forests: Fresh Perspectives from Ecosystem Analysis: Proceedings. Waring, Richard H., ed. LC 80-14883. (Illus.). 210p. 1979. pap. 15.95x (ISBN 0-87071-179-2). Oreg St U Pr.

Blacksell, Mark & Gilg, Andrew. The Countryside: Planning & Change. (Resource Management Ser.: No. 2). (Illus.). 288p. (Orig.). 1981. text ed. 35.00x (ISBN 0-04-711008-2); pap. text ed. 17.95x (ISBN 0-04-711009-0). Allen Unwin.

Blustain, Harvey. Resource Management & Agricultural Development in Jamaica: Lessons for a Participatory Approach. (Special Series on Resource Management: No. 2). 151p. (Orig.). 1982. pap. text ed. 9.00 (ISBN 0-86731-083-9). RDC Ctr Intl Stud.

Boardman, Robert. International Organization & the Conservation of Nature. LC 80-8638. 232p. 1981. 25.00x (ISBN 0-253-16474-5). Ind U Pr.

Bothe, Michael. Trends in Environmental Policy & Law. (Environmental Policy & Law Papers: No. 15). 404p. 1980. pap. 27.50 (ISBN 2-88032-085-2, IUCN94, IUCN). Unipub.

Brookfield, H. Population Environment Relations in Tropical Islands: The Case of Eastern Fiji. (MAB Technical Notes: No. 13). (Illus.). 233p. (Based on the Findings of the UNESCO-UNFPA Pilot Project "Studies on Population-Environment, relationships in the Eastern Islands of Fiji"). 1981. pap. 18.00 (ISBN 92-3-101821-3, U1054, UNESCO). Unipub.

Brookins, Douglas G. Earth Resources, Energy & the Environment. (Illus.). 160p. (Orig.). 1981. pap. text ed. 13.50 (ISBN 0-675-08113-0). Merrill.

Brown, Lester. The Twenty-Ninth Day. 1978. 11.95 (ISBN 0-393-05664-3); pap. 7.95 (ISBN 0-393-05673-2). Norton.

Brown, Lester R., et al. State of the World, 1985: A Worldwatch Institute Report on Progress Toward a Sustainable Society. (Illus.). 301p. 1985. 18.95 (ISBN 0-393-01930-6); pap. 8.95 (ISBN 0-393-30218-0). Norton.

Brubaker, Sterling. To Live on Earth: Man & His Environment in Perspective. LC 75-185514. (Resources for the Future Ser.). 218p. 1972. 16.50x (ISBN 0-8018-1378-6). Johns Hopkins.

Bruchey, Stuart & Bruchey, Eleanor, eds. Use & Abuse of America's Natural Resources, 41 bks. 1972. Set. 1500.50 (ISBN 0-405-04500-X). Ayer Co Pubs.

Bruyns, M. F. & Wolff, W. J., eds. Nature Conservation, Management & Physical Planning in the Wadden Sea Area: Final Report of the Section "Physical Planning & Nature Management" of the Wadden Sea Working Group, Report 11. 164p. 1983. lib. bdg. 8.00 (ISBN 90-6191-061-7, Pub. by Balkema RSA). IPS.

Buck, Wolfgang. Lenkungsstrategien fuer die Optimale Allokation von Umweltgutern. (European University Studies: No. 5, Vol. 454). (Ger.). 346p. 1983. 38.95 (ISBN 3-8204-7879-5). P Lang Pubs.

Butterworth Staff, ed. Land Conservation & Development Commission Decisions (LCDC) Selected Decisions, 1974-1979, 3 vols. 1984. Set. write for info.; Individual vols. 40.00 (ISBN 0-317-12918-X). Butterworth Legal Pubs.

Canter, Larry W. Environmental Impact Statements on Municipal Wastewater Programs. LC 79-53112. vi, 95p. (Orig.). 1979. pap. 15.00 (ISBN 0-87815-026-9). Info Resources.

Canter, Larry W., et al. Environmental Impact of Growth. LC 84-26187. (Illus.). 600p. 1985. 44.80 (ISBN 0-87371-013-4). Lewis Pubs Inc.

Categories, Objectives & Criteria for Protected Areas. 26p. 1978. pap. 5.00 (ISBN 2-88032-403-3, IUCN88, IUCN). Unipub.

Chadwick, M. J. & Goodman, G. T. The Ecology of Resource Degradation & Renewal. LC 75-5776. (British Ecological Society Symposia Ser.). 480p. 1975. 64.95x (ISBN 0-470-14295-2). Halsted Pr.

Clapham, Arthur R., ed. The IBP Survey of Conservation Sites: An Experimental Study. LC 79-50233. (International Biological Programme Ser.: No. 24). (Illus.). 500p. 1980. 62.50 (ISBN 0-521-22697-X). Cambridge U Pr.

Clepper, Henry, ed. Leaders of American Conservation. LC 75-155206. Repr. of 1971 ed. 69.40 (ISBN 0-8357-9921-2, 2012429). Bks Demand UMI.

Committee on Natural Resources. Working Group Meeting on Energy Planning: Proceedings, 5th Session. (Energy Resources Development Ser.: No. 20). 151p. 1980. pap. 12.00 (ISBN 0-686-70131-3, UN792F11, UN). Unipub.

Conservation & Development in Northern Thailand. 114p. 1980. pap. 15.00 (ISBN 92-808-0077-9, TUNU083, UNU). Unipub.

Conservation & Values: The Conservation Foundation's Thirtieth Anniversary Symposium. new ed. LC 79-88093. (Illus.). 1979. pap. 5.00 (ISBN 0-89164-053-3). Conservation Foun.

Conservation Education Association. Critical Index of Films on Man & His Environment. LC 65-23951. 32p. 1972. pap. text ed. 1.25x (ISBN 0-8134-1374-5, 1374). Interstate.

Conservation for Development. (Illus.). 383p. 1973. pap. 30.00 (ISBN 2-88032-003-8, IUCN48, IUCN). Unipub.

Conservation in Malaysia: A Manual on the Conservation of Malaysia's Renewable Natural Resources. (Illus.). 1969. pap. 12.00 (ISBN 2-88032-047-X, IUCN33, IUCN). Unipub.

Conservation Measures in China. (Illus.). 38p. 1977. pap. 5.00 (ISBN 0-686-93488-1, UNEP026, UNEP). Unipub.

Coughlin, Robert E. & Plaut, Thomas. The Use of Less-Than-Fee Acquisition for the Preservation of Open Space. (Discussion Paper Ser.: No. 101). 1977. pap. 3.25 (ISBN 0-686-32267-3). Regional Sci Res Inst.

Council Envir. Quality. The Global Two Thousand Report to the President: Entering the Twenty-First Century, Vol. I. (Illus.). 766p. 1982. pap. 10.00 (ISBN 0-14-022441-6). Penguin.

Council on Economic Priorities & Buchsbaum, Steven. Jobs & Energy: The Employment & Economic Impacts of Nuclear Power, Conservation, & Other Energy Options. Schwartz, Wendy C., ed. LC 79-91065. 1979. 35.00 (ISBN 0-87871-011-6). CEP.

Courrier, Kathleen & Munson, Richard, eds. Life after Eighty: Environmental Choices We Can Live With. LC 80-11783. 304p. 1980. pap. 8.95x (ISBN 0-931790-13-1). Brick Hse Pub.

Cousteau, Jacques-Yves. A Bill of Rights for Future Generations. 33p. (Orig.). 1980. pap. 1.50 (ISBN 0-913098-29-9). Myrin Institute.

Curry-Lindahl, Kai. Report to the Government of Liberia on Conservation Management & Utilization of Wildlife Resources. (Illus.). 31p. 1969. pap. 8.00 (ISBN 2-88032-044-5, IUCN61, IUCN). Unipub.

Dahlberg, Kenneth & Bennett, John, eds. Improving Natural Resource Management: Approaches to Multidisciplinary Research. (WVST in Natural Resource & Energy Management Ser.). 360p. 1985. pap. text ed. 28.50x (ISBN 0-8133-7079-5). Westview.

Davidson, J. A., intro. by. Resource Developments in the Eighties. (Chemeca Ser.). 338p. (Orig.). 1982. pap. text ed. 54.00x (ISBN 0-85825-169-8, Pub. by Inst Engineering Australia). Brookfield Pub Co.

Davidson, John & Lloyd, Richard, eds. Conservation & Agriculture. LC 77-697. 252p. 1978. 58.95x (ISBN 0-471-99502-9, Pub. by Wiley-Interscience). Wiley.

Davis, Ray J. Ecology & Conservation of Natural Resources. 1978. lib. bdg. 7.70 (ISBN 0-931054-02-8). Clark Pub.

De Boer, Leobert E., ed. Workshop on the Conservation of the Orangutan. LC 82-7722. (Illus.). 353p. 1982. 76.00 (ISBN 90-6193-702-7, Pub. by Junk Pubs Netherlands). Kluwer Academic.

Denver Public Library. Catalog of the Conservation Library, 6 vols. 1974. Set. lib. bdg. 575.00 (ISBN 0-8161-1113-8, Hall Library). G K Hall.

Dietrich, Irvine T. & Hove, John. Conservation of Natural Resources: North Dakota. LC 62-63204. (Illus.). 1962. 3.00 (ISBN 0-911042-06-7). N Dak Inst.

Dryzek, John. Conflict & Choice in Resource Management: The case of Alaska. (Replica Edition Ser.). 175p. 1983. softcover 18.50x (ISBN 0-86531-978-2). Westview.

Dyballa, Cynthia D., et al. The Tug Hill Program: A Regional Planning Option for Rural Areas. LC 81-8999. (Illus.). 208p. 1981. pap. text ed. 11.95x (ISBN 0-8156-2241-4). Syracuse U Pr.

Dykstra, Dennis P. Mathematical Programming for Natural Resource Management. (Illus.). 384p. 1983. text ed. 36.95 (ISBN 0-07-018552-2). McGraw.

Eagles, Paul. The Planning & Management of Environmentally Sensitive Areas. pap. text ed. 13.95 (ISBN 0-582-30074-6). Longman.

Ehrlich, Paul R., et al. Ecoscience: Population, Resources, Environment. LC 77-6824. (Illus.). 1051p. 1977. pap. text ed. 28.95 (ISBN 0-7167-0029-8). W H Freeman.

Elkind-Savatsky, Pamela & Kaufman, Judith, eds. Differential Social Impacts of Rural Resource Development. (Social Impact Assessment Ser.). 175p. 1985. pap. text ed. 17.50x (ISBN 0-8133-0077-0). Westview.

English, H. E. & Scott, Anthony, eds. Renewable Resources in the Pacific: Proceedings of the Twelfth Pacific Trade & Development Conference, Held in Vancouver, Canada, September 7-11, 1981. 293p. 1982. pap. 20.00 (ISBN 0-88936-312-9, IDRC181, IDRC). Unipub.

Spofford, Walter O., Jr., et al, eds. Energy Development in the Southwest: Problems of Water, Fish & Wildlife in the Upper Colorado River Basin. LC 80-8020. (Resources for the Future Research Ser.: Paper R-18). 1126p. 1980. Set Of 2 Vols. pap. text ed. 25.00x (ISBN 0-8018-2495-8). Johns Hopkins.
Stoltenberg, Carl, et al. Planning Research for Resource Decisions. facsimile ed. LC 76-103839. (Illus.). 1970. pap. 10.25x (ISBN 0-8138-2260-2). Iowa St U Pr.
Stroud, Richard H., ed. National Leaders of American Conservation. rev. ed. LC 84-600245. 432p. 1985. pap. 24.95 (ISBN 0-87474-867-4, STLAP). Smithsonian.
Suri, R. Resource Management Concepts for Large Systems. (I S Modern Applied Mathematics & Computer Science Ser.: Vol. 3). (Illus.). 94p. 1981. 16.00 (ISBN 0-08-026473-5). Pergamon.
Swift, Ernest F. Conservation Saga. (Illus.). 1967. 1.50 (ISBN 0-912186-01-1). Natl Wildlife.
Tjallingii, S. P. & De Veer, A. A., eds. Perspectives in Landscape Ecology: Contributions to Research, Planning & Management of our Environment: Proceedings of the International Congress Organized by The Netherlands Society for Landscape Ecology, Veldhoven, the Netherlands, April 6-11, 1981. 352p. (22 lectures, 48 posters & 19 workshops). 1982. 30.25 (ISBN 90-220-0790-1, PDC237, Pudoc). Unipub.
Todd, John & Todd, Nancy J. Tomorrow Is Our Permanent Address. LC 78-2171. (Lindisfarne Bk.). (Illus.). 1980. 16.30i (ISBN 0-06-014319-3, HarpT). Har-Row.
Todd, Nancy, ed. The Journal of the New Alchemists, No. 6. LC 78-945501. (Illus.). 1980. 15.95 (ISBN 0-8289-0366-2). Greene.
Trzyna, Thaddeus C., pref. by. The United States & the Global Environment: A Guide to American Organizations Concerned with International Environment Issues. LC 79-53313. (Who's Doing What Ser.: No. 9). 72p. (Orig.). 1983. pap. 25.00x (ISBN 0-912102-45-4). Cal Inst Public.
The Use of Ecological Guidelines for Development in the American Humid Tropics. (Illus.). 249p. 1975. pap. 20.00 (ISBN 2-88032-004-6, IUCN62, IUCN). Unipub.
The Use of Ecological Guidelines for Development in Tropical Forest Areas of South East Asia. (Illus.). 185p. 1975. pap. 15.00 (ISBN 2-88032-005-4, IUCN64, IUCN). Unipub.
El Uso De Normas Ecologicas Para el Desarrollo En el Tropico Huedo Americano. (Illus.). 1976. pap. 25.00x (ISBN 2-88032-007-0, IUCN15, IUCN). Unipub.
Van Dyne, George, ed. Ecosystem Concept in Natural Resource Management. LC 72-86367. 1969. 45.00 (ISBN 0-12-713450-6). Acad Pr.
Van Hise, C. R. Conservation of Our Natural Resources. LC 30-12356. 1930. 29.00 (ISBN 0-527-92750-3). Kraus Repr.
Vicent, T. L. & Skowronski, J. M., eds. Renewable Resource Management: Proceedings. (Lecture Notes in Biomathematics Ser.: Vol. 40). 236p. 1981. pap. 15.00 (ISBN 0-387-10566-2). Springer-Verlag.
Vogt, Frederick, ed. Energy Conservation & Use of Renewable Energies in the Bio-Industries: Proceedings of the International Seminar on Energy Conservation & the Use of Solar & Other Renewable Energies in Agriculture, Horticulture & Fishculture, 15-19 September, 1980, Polytechnic of Central London. LC 80-49739. (Illus.). 580p. 1981. 110.00 (ISBN 0-08-026866-8). Pergamon.
Ward, Barbara. Progress for a Small Planet. (Illus.). 1979. 14.95 (ISBN 0-393-01277-8). Norton.
Ward, Barbara & Dubos, Rene. Only One Earth: The Care & Maintenance of a Small Planet. 256p. 1983. pap. 5.95 (ISBN 0-393-30129-X). Norton.
Wardhaugh, Ronald. How Conversation Works. 240p. 1985. 34.95x (ISBN 0-631-13921-4); pap. 14.95x (ISBN 0-631-13939-7). Basil Blackwell.
Warren, A. & Goldsmith, B. Conservation in Practice. LC 73-9281. pap. 133.00 (ISBN 0-8357-9865-8, 2013984). Bks Demand UMI.
Watterson, Gerald G. Conservation of Nature & Natural Resources in Modern African States. (Illus.). 367p. 1963. pap. 18.00 (ISBN 2-88032-042-9, IUCN47, IUCN). Unipub.
Wenner, Lettie M. The Environmental Decade in Court. LC 81-47778. 224p. 1982. 25.00x (ISBN 0-253-31957-9). Ind U Pr.
Whitaker, J. Russell & Ackerman, Edward A. American Resources: Their Management & Conservation. LC 72-2874. (Use & Abuse of America's Natural Resources Ser). 514p. 1972. Repr. of 1951 ed. 30.00 (ISBN 0-405-04542-5). Ayer Co Pubs.
Wilbur, Ray L. & DuPuy, William. Conservation in the Department of the Interior. LC 72-1341. (Select Bibliographies Reprint Ser.). 1972. Repr. of 1932 ed. 54.00 (ISBN 0-8369-6840-9). Ayer Co Pubs.
World Conservation Strategy. (Eng., Fr. & Span., Illus.). 70p. 1980. pap. 5.00 (ISBN 2-88032-101-8, IUCN95, IUCN). Unipub.
Wyant, William K. Westward in Eden: The Public Lands & the Conservation Movement. LC 81-7519. (Illus.). 500p. 1982. 24.50 (ISBN 0-520-04377-4). U of Cal Pr.
Yen, Teh Fu & Walsh, Don, eds. Energy & Resource Development of Continental Margins. LC 80-14813. (Illus.). 238p. 1980. 39.00 (ISBN 0-08-025127-7). Pergamon.
Young, Oran R. Natural Resources & the State: The Political Economy of Resource Management. 1981. 21.00x (ISBN 0-520-04285-9). U of Cal Pr.
--Resource Regimes: Natural Resources & Social Institutions. Krasner, Stephen, ed. LC 81-21979. (Studies in the International Political Economy Ser.). 284p. 1982. 26.00x (ISBN 0-520-04573-4). U of Cal Pr.

CONSERVATION OF NATURAL RESOURCES–STUDY AND TEACHING

Aldridge, Don. The Monster Book of Environmental Education. 29.50x (ISBN 0-686-78647-5, Pub. by GEO Abstracts England). State Mutual Bk.
Black, Peter E. & Herrington, Lee P., eds. Working with NEPA: Environmental Impact Analysis for the Resource Manager. LC 74-23639. 145p. 1974. pap. text ed. 4.75x (ISBN 0-8422-0483-0). Irvington.
Chemerinsky, Erwin, et al. The Complete Handbook of Issues on World Resources. 1975. pap. text ed. 4.00 (ISBN 0-8442-5216-6). Natl Textbk.
Christenson, Toni & Feia, Marian R. The Tree Book: Teaching Responsible Enviromental Education, Vol. 1. (Illus.). 78p. (Orig.). 1981. tchr's ed. 6.95 (ISBN 0-686-36286-1). Creative Curriculum.
Clepper, Henry, ed. Careers in Conservation: Opportunities in Natural Resource Management. 2nd ed. LC 78-21917. 1979. 42.00x (ISBN 0-471-05163-2, Pub. by Ronald Pr). Wiley.
Conservation Education Association. Education, Key to Conservation: Critical Index of Films on Man & His Environment, Bk. 8. 32p. 1972. pap. text ed. 1.25 (ISBN 0-8134-1374-5). Interstate.
--Education, Key to Conservation: Environmental Conservation Education, a Selected Annotated Bibliography. LC 73-92152. 70p. 1974. pap. text ed. 2.50x (ISBN 0-8134-1633-7, 1633). Interstate.
--Environmental Conservation Education: A Selected Annotated Bibliography-1976 Supplement. LC 73-92152. 44p. 1977. pap. text ed. 1.50x (ISBN 0-8134-1899-2, 1899). Interstate.
--Environmental Conservation Education: A Selected Annotated Bibliography, 1975 Supplement. LC 73-92152. 32p. 1975. pap. text ed. 1.00 (ISBN 0-8134-1763-5, 1763). Interstate.
Environmental Education in the Light of the Tbilisi Conference. (Education on the Move Ser.). 100p. 1980. pap. 7.00 (ISBN 92-3-101787-X, U1035, UNESCO). Unipub.
Franklin Institute. ENGUIDE: A Guide to Bibliographic Data for Users of Environmental Information. 100p. 1980. pap. text ed. 8.95 (ISBN 0-686-70970-5). L Erlbaum Assocs.
Harrah, David F. & Harrah, Barbara K. Conservation-Ecology: Resources for Environmental Education. LC 74-23055. 323p. 1975. 18.50 (ISBN 0-8108-0780-7). Scarecrow.
Intergovernmental Conference on Environmental Education: Final Report. (Unipub Reprint Ser.). 101p. 1980. pap. 7.50 (ISBN 0-686-68812-0, U1021, UNESCO). Unipub.
Knapp, Cliff & Goodman, Joel. Humanizing Environmental Education. 252p. 1981. pap. 15.95 (ISBN 0-87603-065-7). Am Camping.
Mason, William H. & Folkerts, George W. Environmental Problems: Principles, Readings & Comments. 2nd ed. 440p. 1979. pap. text ed. write for info. (ISBN 0-697-04703-2). Wm C Brown.
Meeker, Joseph W. The Comedy of Survival: In Search of an Environmental Ethic. (Illus.). 174p. 1980. pap. 7.95 (ISBN 0-917270-03-7). Finn Hill.
PADC Environmental Impact Assessment & Planning Unit. Environmental Impact Assessment: University of Aberdeen, Dept. of Geography, Old Aberdeen, U. K. 1983. lib. bdg. 59.00 (ISBN 90-247-2765-0, Pub. by Martinus Nijhoff Netherlands). Kluwer Academic.
Pitts, J. N. & Metcalf, R. L., eds. Advances in Environmental Science & Technology, Vol. 6. LC 75-33225. 540p. 1976. 31.50 (ISBN 0-471-59860-7). Krieger.
Robinson, Barbara & Wolfson, Evelyn. Environmental Education Manual. LC 82-741. 1982. pap. text ed. 15.95x (ISBN 0-8077-2715-6). Tchrs Coll.
Trends in Environmental Education. (Illus.). 244p. 1977. pap. 13.75 (ISBN 92-3-101401-3, U780, UNESCO). Unipub.
Turk, Amos & Turk, Jonathan. Physical Science with Environmental & Practical Applications. 2nd ed. 1981. text ed. 35.95 (ISBN 0-03-057782-9, HoltC); instr's manual 9.95 (ISBN 0-03-058242-3). HR&W.

CONSERVATION OF NATURE
see Nature Conservation
CONSERVATION OF PETROLEUM
see Petroleum Conservation
CONSERVATION OF POWER RESOURCES
see Energy Conservation
CONSERVATION OF RESOURCES
see Conservation of Natural Resources
CONSERVATION OF THE SOIL
see Soil Conservation
CONSERVATION OF WATER
see Water-Conservation
CONSERVATION OF WILDLIFE
see Wildlife Conservation
CONSERVATIONISTS
see also Ecologists

De Sormo, Maitland C. John Bird Burnham: Klondiker, Adirondacker & Eminent Conservationist. LC 78-50570. (Illus.). 1978. 12.50 (ISBN 0-9601158-5-4). Adirondack Yes.
Wild, Peter. Pioneer Conservationists of Early America. (Pioneer Conservation Ser.). (Illus.). 288p. 1985. 15.95 (ISBN 0-87842-187-4); pap. 9.95 (ISBN 0-87842-188-2). Mountain Pr.
--Pioneer Conservationists of Eastern America. 1985. 15.95 (ISBN 0-87842-126-2); pap. 9.95 (ISBN 0-87842-124-6). Mountain Pr.
--Pioneer Conservationists of Western America. LC 78-15042. (Illus.). 246p. 1979. 12.95 (ISBN 0-87842-107-6). Mountain Pr.

CONSERVATORIES
see Greenhouses
CONSTANTS
see Units
CONSTELLATION (FRIGATE)

Sternlicht, Sanford & Jameson, Edwin M. The U. S. F. Constellation: Yankee Racehorse. LC 81-84998. (Illus.). 192p. 1981. pap. 4.95 (ISBN 0-89709-030-6). Liberty Pub.

CONSTELLATION (SHIP)

Ferguson, Eugene S. Truxtun of the Constellation. LC 81-18734. 340p. 1982. 12.95 (ISBN 0-87021-712-7). Naval Inst Pr.

CONSTELLATIONS
see also Stars;
also names of constellations

Berger, Paul & Searle, Leroy. Radical Rational-Space Time: Idea Networks in Photography. LC 83-80314. (Illus.). 72p. (Orig.). 1983. pap. 22.50 (ISBN 0-935558-10-1). Henry Art.
Bullinger, Ethelbert W. Witness of the Stars. LC 68-16762. 1972. 12.95 (ISBN 0-8254-2209-4). Kregel.
Chapelle, Howard I. & Polland, Leon D. The Constellation Question. LC 77-609565. (Smithsonian Studies in History & Technology Ser.: No. 5). (Illus.). pap. 42.30 (ISBN 0-317-09469-6, 2004204). Bks Demand UMI.
Martin, Martha E. The Friendly Stars. rev. ed. Menzel, Donald H., ed. (Illus.). 147p. 1964. pap. 3.50 (ISBN 0-486-21099-5). Dover.
--Friendly Stars. rev. ed. (Illus.). 13.25 (ISBN 0-8446-2538-8). Peter Smith.
Merrill, Arthur A. Circumpolar Constellations. (Illus.). 1962. pap. 3.00 (ISBN 0-911894-37-3). Analysis.
Moxon, Joseph. Tutor to Astronomy & Geography. 3rd rev., enl. ed. LC 68-56778. (Research & Source Works Ser.: No. 264). (Illus.). 1968. Repr. of 1674 ed. 24.50 (ISBN 0-8337-2478-9). B Franklin.
Sanborn, Laura. Bright Star Guide to the Heavens of the Northern Laatitudes. (Illus.). 46p. (Orig.). 1985. pap. 3.50x (ISBN 0-910715-03-3). Search Public.
Vautier, Ghislaine. The Way of the Stars: Greek Legends of the Constellations. (Illus.). 32p. 1983. 10.95 (ISBN 0-521-25061-7). Cambridge U Pr.
Zigel, F. Wonders of the Night Sky. Yankovsky, George, tr. from Rus. (Illus.). 208p. 1968. 12.00x (ISBN 0-8464-0975-5). Beekman Pubs.

CONSTITUTION OF MATTER
see Matter–Constitution
CONSTRUCTION
see Architecture; Building; Engineering
CONSTRUCTION, CONCRETE
see Concrete Construction
CONSTRUCTION, HOUSE
see House Construction
CONSTRUCTION BLOCK PRINCIPLE
see Unit Construction
CONSTRUCTION EQUIPMENT
see also Earthmoving Machinery; Excavating Machinery; Hoisting Machinery; Pumping Machinery

Bucksch, Herbert. Dictionary of Civil Engineering & Construction Machinery & Equipment, Vol. 1. 5th ed. (Fr. & Eng.). 420p. 1976. 30.00 (ISBN 3-7625-0533-0, M-7120). French & Eur.
--Dictionary of Civil Engineering & Construction Machinery & Equipment, Vol. 1. 7th ed. (Eng. & Ger.). 1978. leatherette 135.00 (ISBN 3-7625-0950-6, M-7122). French & Eur.
--Dictionary of Civil Engineering & Construction Machinery & Equipment, Vol. 2. 5th ed. (Fr. & Eng.). 548p. 1976. 40.00 (ISBN 3-7625-0534-9, M-7119). French & Eur.
--Dictionary of Civil Engineering & Construction Machinery & Equipment, Vol. 2. 7th ed. (Eng. & Ger.). 1978. leatherette 135.00 (ISBN 3-7625-0951-4, M-7121). French & Eur.
Burgess, Roger A., et al, eds. Progress in Construction Science & Technology, 2 vols. Vol. 1. pap. 82.50 (ISBN 0-317-10675-9, 2015502); Vol. 2. pap. 62.80 (ISBN 0-317-10676-7). Bks Demand UMI.
Dagostino, Frank. Mechanical & Electrical Systems in Construction & Architecture. (Illus.). 1978. ref. ed. 29.95 (ISBN 0-87909-511-3); solutions manual avail. (ISBN 0-87909-510-5). Reston.
Fuchs, Sheldon J., ed. Complete Building Equipment Maintenance Desk Book. 450p. 1981. 49.95 (ISBN 0-13-158808-7). P-H.
Fullerton, R. L. Construction Technology: Level 1. (Illus.). 188p. 1980. pap. text ed. 19.95x (ISBN 0-19-859520-4). Intl Ideas.
Grundy, J. T. Construction Technology, Vol. 3. (Illus.). 208p. 1981. pap. 19.95x (ISBN 0-7131-3419-4). Intl Ideas.
Higgins, Lindley R. Handbook of Construction Equipment Maintenance. (Illus.). 1979. 56.50 (ISBN 0-07-028764-3). McGraw.
International Committee for Lift Regulations. Code of Practice for the Safe Construction & Installation of Electric Passenger Goods & Service Lifts. 108p. 1972. 4.55 (ISBN 92-2-100159-8). Intl Labour Office.
McGuinness, William, et al. Mechanical & Electrical Equipment for Buildings. 6th ed. LC 79-12979. 1336p. 1980. 41.95 (ISBN 0-471-58432-0). Wiley.
Marshall, R. T. The French Building Industry. 1981. 40.00x (ISBN 0-686-75648-7, Pub. by Surveyors Tech Serv). State Mutual Bk.
Morgan-Grampian Books, ed. Construction Plant & Equipment International Annual, 1984. 486p. 1985. 130.00x (ISBN 0-686-75510-3, Pub. by Morgan-Grampian Bk). State Mutual Bk.
Rosen, H. J. Construction Materials for Architecture. (Practical Construction Guides Ser.). 248p. 1985. 42.95 (ISBN 0-471-86421-8). Wiley.
Rudman, Jack. Pile Driving Engineer. (Career Examination Ser.: C-2558). (Cloth bdg. avail. on request). pap. 12.00 (ISBN 0-8373-2558-7). Natl Learning.
Russell, James E. Construction Equipment. 1985. text ed. 28.95 (ISBN 0-8359-0954-9). Reston.
Schexnayder, C. J. Construction Equipment & Techniques for the Eighties. LC 81-71797. 404p. 1982. pap. 29.50x (ISBN 0-87262-293-2). Am Soc Civil Eng.
Shuttleworth, Riley & Verma, Kiran. Mechanical & Electrical Systems for Construction. (Construction Ser.). (Illus.). 736p. 1983. text ed. 42.00 (ISBN 0-07-057215-1). McGraw.
Specification for Welding Earthmoving & Construction Equipment: D14.3-82. (Illus.). 80p. 1982. pap. 26.00; member 19.50. Am Welding.
Vance, Mary. Mechanical Equipment for Buildings: A Bibliography. (Architecture Ser.: Bibliography A 1331). 1985. pap. 3.00 (ISBN 0-89028-281-1). Vance Biblios.

CONSTRUCTION INDUSTRY
Here are entered works dealing comprehensively with the construction business, including finance, planning, management, and skills.
see also Building; Building Trades

ASCE Committee on Engineering Management, Aug. 1976. Civil Engineer's Role in Productivity in the Construction Industry, 2 vols. 402p. 1976. Set. pap. 17.75x (ISBN 0-87262-075-1). Am Soc Civil Eng.
Ball, John E. Carpenters & Builders Library, 4 vols. 5th ed. 1982. 35.95 (ISBN 0-672-23244-8). G K Hall.
--Carpenters & Builders Library, Vol. 1. 5th ed. LC 82-1340. 1982. 10.95 (ISBN 0-672-23365-7). G K Hall.
--Carpenters & Builders Library, Vol. 2. 5th ed. LC 82-1341. 1982. 10.95 (ISBN 0-672-23366-5). G K Hall.
--Carpenters & Builders Library, Vol. 3. 5th ed. LC 82-1339. 1982. 10.95 (ISBN 0-672-23367-3). G K Hall.
--Carpenters & Builders Library, Vol. 4. 5th ed. LC 82-1332. 1982. 10.95 (ISBN 0-672-23368-1). G K Hall.
Banz, Hans. Building Construction Details: Practical Drawings. 272p. pap. 14.95 (ISBN 0-442-21325-5). Van Nos Reinhold.

Management of Small Construction Firms: A Case Study of Sri Lanka, Singapore, Hong Kong, Thailand, the Philippines, & Japan: A Report Prepared Under APO Oshikawa Fellowship, 1979-80. 240p. 1982. pap. 16.25 (ISBN 92-833-1474-3, APO126, APO). Unipub.

O'Brien, J. J. CP-M in Construction Management. 3rd ed. 416p. 1984. 39.95 (ISBN 0-07-047663-2). McGraw.

O'Brien, James J. & Zilly, R. G. Contractor's Management Handbook. 1971. 53.50 (ISBN 0-07-047565-2). McGraw.

Oxley, R. & Poskitt, J. Management Techniques Applied to the Construction Industry. 2nd ed. 1971. pap. 17.95x (ISBN 0-8464-0593-8). Beekman Pubs.

--Management Techniques Applied to the Construction Industry. 3rd ed. 298p. 1980. text ed. 17.00x (ISBN 0-246-11341-3, Pub. by Granada England). Brookfield Pub Co.

--Management Techniques Applied to the Construction Industry. 304p. 1981. pap. 20.00x (ISBN 0-246-11434-7, Pub. by Granada England). Sheridan.

Parker, Henry & Oglesby, C. H. Methods Improvement for Construction Managers. (Illus.). 320p. 1972. text ed. 45.00 (ISBN 0-07-048503-8). McGraw.

Paterson, John. Information Methods: For Design & Construction. LC 76-29649. 200p. 1977. 45.95x (ISBN 0-471-99449-9, Pub. by Wiley-Interscience). Wiley.

Pilcher, Roy. Project Cost Control in Construction. (Illus.). 404p. 1985. 50.00x (ISBN 0-00-383017-9, Pub. by Collins England). Sheridan.

Royer, King. The Construction Manager in the Eighties. (Illus.). 496p. 1981. text ed. 37.95 (ISBN 0-13-168690-9). P-H.

Rudman, Jack. Construction Manager. (Career Examination Ser.: C-1789). (Cloth bdg. avail on request). 14.00 (ISBN 0-8373-1789-4). Natl Learning.

Stallworthy, E. A. & Kharbanda, O. P. International Construction: The Challenge for Project Management. LC 84-24657. 250p. 1985. 47.50 (ISBN 0-566-02546-9). Gower Pub Co.

Stark, Robert M. & Mayer, Robert H. Quantitative Construction Management: Uses of Linear Optimization. LC 83-6907. (Construction Management & Engineering Ser.). 162p. 1983. 37.50x (ISBN 0-471-86959-7, 1-102, Pub. by Wiley-Interscience). Wiley.

Stillman, W. J. Construction Practices for Project Managers & Superintendents. (Illus.). 1978. text ed. 24.95 (ISBN 0-87909-164-9). Reston.

Stone, P. A. Building Economy: Design, Production & Organization. 3rd ed. 280p. text ed. 50.00 (ISBN 0-08-028677-1); pap. text ed. 17.00 (ISBN 0-08-028678-X). Pergamon.

Tanah, Kwaku A. The Construction Management Process. 1985. text ed. 27.95 (ISBN 0-8359-0955-7); instrs' manual avail. (ISBN 0-8359-0956-5). Reston.

Tenah, Kwaku A. & Guevera, Jose M. Fundamentals of Construction Management & Organization. 1985. text ed. 29.95 (ISBN 0-8359-2132-8). Reston.

Thomsen, Charles B. CM: Developing, Marketing & Delivering Construction Management Services. (Illus.). 192p. 1982. 36.50x (ISBN 0-07-064490-X). McGraw.

Upson, Alan. Financial Management in the Construction Industry. 224p. 1986. 35.00x (ISBN 0-246-12132-7, Pub by Granada England). Sheridan.

Vance, Mary. Management in the Construction Industry: A Bibliography. (Architecture Ser.: Bibliography A-1314). 30p. 1985. pap. 4.50 (ISBN 0-89028-244-7). Vance Biblios.

Walker, Anthony. Project Management in Construction. 224p. 1984. 35.00x (ISBN 0-246-12199-8, Pub. by Granada England). Sheridan.

Wass, A. Construction Management & Contracting. 1972. 29.95 (ISBN 0-13-168708-5). P-H.

Willis, E. C. Scheduling Construction Projects. 29.95 (ISBN 0-471-80869-5). Wiley.

Wohl, Martin & Hendrickson, Chris. Transportation Investment & Pricing Principles: An Introduction for Engineers Planners & Economists. LC 84-7347. (Construction Management & Engineering Ser.: No. 1-102). 380p. 1984. 49.95 (ISBN 0-471-87989-4, Pub. by Wiley-Interscience). Wiley.

Woodward, J. F. Quantitative Methods in Construction Management & Design. (Illus.). 1976. pap. text ed. 19.95x (ISBN 0-333-18602-8). Scholium Intl.

CONSTRUCTION INDUSTRY–VOCATIONAL GUIDANCE

see Building Trades–Vocational Guidance

CONSTRUCTION MACHINERY

see Construction Equipment

CONSTRUCTION OF ROADS

see Road Construction

CONSTRUCTIVE MATHEMATICS

see also Logic, Symbolic and Mathematical

Beeson, M. Foundations of Constructive Mathematics. (Ergebnisse der Mathematik Ser.: Vol. 6). 480p. 1985. 49.00 (ISBN 0-387-12173-0). Springer-Verlag.

Bishop, Errett & Cheng, Henry. Constructive Measure Theory. LC 52-42839. (Memoirs: No. 116). 85p. 1972. pap. 9.00 (ISBN 0-8218-1816-3, MEMO-116). Am Math.

Bridges, Douglas S. Constructive Functional Analysis. (Research Notes in Mathematics Ser.: No. 28). 203p. (Orig.). 1979. pap. text ed. 23.95 (ISBN 0-273-08418-6). Pitman Pub MA.

Ceitin, G. S., et al. Five Papers on Logic & Foundations. new ed. LC 51-5559. (Translations Ser.: No. 2, Vol. 99). 280p. 1972. 33.00 (ISBN 0-8218-1799-X, TRANS 2-99). Am Math.

Devlin, K. J. The Axiom of Constructibility: A Guide for the Mathematician. LC 77-17119. (Lecture Notes in Mathematics Ser.: Vol. 617). 1977. pap. 14.00 (ISBN 0-387-08520-3). Springer-Verlag.

Richman, F., ed. Constructive Mathematics: Proceedings. (Lecture Notes in Mathematics Ser.: Vol. 873). 347p. 1981. pap. 22.00 (ISBN 0-387-10850-5). Springer-Verlag.

Slisenko, A. O., ed. Studies in Constructive Mathematics & Mathematical Logic. LC 69-12507. (Seminars in Mathematics Ser.: Vol. 4, Pt. 1). pap. 24.00 (ISBN 0-317-08580-8, 2020696). Bks Demand UMI.

--Studies in Constructive Mathematics & Mathematical Logic, Pt. 3. LC 69-12507. (Seminars in Mathematics Ser.: Vol. 16). 1971. 25.00x (ISBN 0-306-18816-3, Consultants). Plenum Pub.

Steklov Institute of Mathematics, Academy of Sciences, U. S. S. R. Problems in the Constructive Trend in Mathematics: Pt. V Proceedings. Orevkov, V. P. & Sanin, N. A., eds. (Proceedings of the Steklov Institute of Mathematics: No. 113). 296p. 1972. 47.00 (ISBN 0-8218-3013-9, STEKLO-113). Am Math.

CONSULTING ENGINEERS

American Consulting Engineers Council. ACEC Membership Directory, 1984-85. 413p. 1983. 50.00 (ISBN 0-686-60620-5). Am Consul Eng.

Automotive Consultants Directory. 1984. 16.00 (ISBN 0-89883-750-2). Soc Auto Engineers.

Coe, Charles K. Consulting Engineer. (Getting the Most from Professional Services Ser.). 38p. (Orig.). 1979. pap. 4.00 (ISBN 0-89854-046-1). U of GA Inst Govt.

Consulting Engineers Who's Who & Year Book. 1985. 250.00 (Pub. by A J Grice Group England). State Mutual Bk.

Guide for Drawing up International Contracts on Consulting Engineering, Including Some Related Aspects of Technical Assistance. 36p. 1983. pap. text ed. 5.00 (ISBN 0-317-01253-3, UN83/2E3, UN). Unipub.

Kelley, Robert E. Consulting: The Complete Guide to a Profitable Career. 272p. 1981. 19.95 (ISBN 0-684-17148-1, ScribT). Scribner.

Public Relations Guide for Consulting Engineers. 61p. 1982. member 10.00 (ISBN 0-686-48365-0); non-member 20.00 (ISBN 0-686-48366-9). Am Consul Eng.

Wasserman, Paul, ed. Who's Who in Consulting Supplement, 3 pts. 2nd ed. LC 73-16373. 1982. Set. pap. 160.00x (ISBN 0-8103-0361-2). Gale.

CONTACT LENSES

Bennett, A. G. Optics of Contact Lenses. 1981. 30.00x (ISBN 0-686-45409-X, Pub. by Assn Disp Opt England). State Mutual Bk.

Critser, James R., Jr. Prostheses & Contact Lens. (Ser. 10PC-79). 1981. refer. 70.00 (ISBN 0-914428-67-5). Lexington Data.

--Prostheses & Contact Lenses. (Ser. 10PC-81). 126p. 1982. 80.00 (ISBN 0-914428-96-9). Lexington Data.

--Prostheses & Contact Lenses. (Ser. 10PC-83). 101p. 1984. 80.00 (ISBN 0-88178-020-0). Lexington Data.

Dabezies, Oliver H., Jr., et al, eds. Contact Lenses: The CLAO Guide to Basic Science & Clinical Practice. 848p. 1984. 199.00 (ISBN 0-8089-1642-4, 790957). Grune.

Hill, Richard M. Curiosities of the Contact Lens. LC 81-80236. 1981. 22.50 (ISBN 0-87873-026-5). Prof Press.

IPC Business Press, ed. International Contact Lens Year Book. 40.00x (ISBN 0-617-00343-2, Pub. by IPC Busn England). State Mutual Bk.

Jones, Jenkins & Jones, Tyler. Theory & Practice of Contact Lens Fitting. 1981. 60.00x (ISBN 0-686-45412-X, Pub. by Assn Disp Opt England). State Mutual Bk.

Lowther. Contact Lenses: Procedures & Techniques. 1982. 39.95 (ISBN 0-409-95012-2). Butterworth.

McGregor, Ian P. & Gardner, Alvin F. Contact Lens Fitting. (Allied Health Professions Monograph Ser.). 144p. 1985. 21.25 (ISBN 0-87527-321-1). Green.

Ruben, Montague. Soft Contact Lenses: Clinical & Applied Technology. LC 77-26918. (Clinical Ophthalmology Ser.). 496p. 1978. 70.00 (ISBN 0-471-74430-1, Pub. by Wiley Medical). Wiley.

CONTACT PRINTS

see Blue-Prints

CONTACTORS, ELECTRIC

see Electric Contactors

CONTAINER INDUSTRY

Bell, Clint C. Preventive Maintenance in a Corrugated Container Plant. (Reports Ser.). (Illus.). 50p. 1981. pap. 43.95 (ISBN 0-89852-388-5, 01-01-R088). TAPPI.

Containerisation International Yearbook 1982. 13th ed. LC 70-617164. (Illus.). 634p. 1982. 75.00x (ISBN 0-85223-231-4). Intl Pubns Serv.

Corrugated Containers Conference Proceedings. 80p. 1981. 34.95 (ISBN 0-686-98479-X, 01-05-0981). TAPPI.

Diernisse, Villy. Retort Pouch: New Growth Industry. (Illus.). 191p. 1981. 950.00x (ISBN 0-910211-00-0). Laal Co.

CONTAINER TRANSPORTATION

see Containerization

CONTAINERIZATION

Containerisation International Yearbook, 1981. LC 70-617164. (Illus.). 608p. 1981. 70.00x (ISBN 0-85223-195-4). Intl Pubns Serv.

Ebury Press, ed. Containerisation International Yearbook, 1984. 522p. 1981. 175.00x (ISBN 0-85223-195-4, Pub. by Ebury Pr England). State Mutual Bk.

Ernst, Edgar. Fahrplanerstellung und Umlaufdisposition Im Containerschiffsverkehr. (European University Studies Ser.: No. 5, Vol. 377). (Ger.). 136p. 1982. 16.30 (ISBN 3-8204-5822-0). P Lang Pubs.

Finlay, Patrick, ed. Jane's Freight Containers 1983. 15th ed. (Jane's Yearbooks). (Illus.). 640p. 1983. 140.00x (ISBN 0-86720-642-X). Jane's Pub Inc.

--Jane's Freight Containers, 1984. 16th ed. (Jane's Yearbooks). (Illus.). 600p. 1984. 125.00x (ISBN 0-7106-0790-3). Jane's Pub Inc.

Lidgren, K. & Butlin, J. Container Costs. 1983. 69.50 (ISBN 0-442-30534-6). Van Nos Reinhold.

Physical Requirements of Transport Systems for Large Freight Containers. pap. 6.00 (ISBN 0-686-94662-6, UN73/8/1, UN). Unipub.

Society of Plastics Engineers. High Performance Container Technology: Technical Conference, Supplement. pap. 20.00 (ISBN 0-317-28096-1, 2022518). Bks Demand UMI.

--High Performance Container Technology: Technical Conerence, Nov. 14, 15, & 16, 1983, Sheraton Naperville Hotel, Naperville, Illinois. pap. 31.30 (ISBN 0-317-28093-7, 2022519). Bks Demand UMI.

Van Den Burg, G. Containerisation & Other Unit Transportation. rev. ed. (Illus.). 336p. 1975. 18.50x (ISBN 0-8476-1370-4). Rowman.

CONTAINERS

see also Packaging; Sealing (Technology)

Allard, G. F., et al, eds. High Speed Can Manufacture, 2 vols. (Engineering Craftsmen Ser.: No. H301). (Illus.). 1972. Set. spiral bdg. 69.95x (ISBN 0-85083-159-8). Intl Ideas.

Edmonds, John. Container Plant Manual. 172p. 1981. 40.00x (ISBN 0-686-75410-7, Pub. by Grower Bks). State Mutual Bk.

Franklin, M. J. British Biscuit Tins, 1868-1939: An Aspect of Decorative Packaging. 1980. 99.95 (ISBN 0-904568-11-3, NO.0224, Pub. by New Cavendish). Methuen Inc.

Gaylord, Edwin H., Jr. & Gaylord, Charles N. Design of Steel Bins for Storage of Bulk Solids. (Illus.). 400p. 1984. professional 70.00 (ISBN 0-13-201368-1). P-H.

High Speed Can Manufacture, 2 vols. 1982. 50.00x (ISBN 0-85083-159-8, Pub. by Engineering Ind). State Mutual Bk.

CONTAINERS, PRESSURIZED

see Pressure Vessels

CONTAMINATED FOOD

see Food Contamination

CONTAMINATION (TECHNOLOGY)

see also Cleaning; Cleaning Machinery and Appliances; Fume Control

Constance. Controlling In-Plant Airborne Contaminants. (Mechanical Engineering Ser.). 352p. 1983. 45.00 (ISBN 0-8247-1900-X). Dekker.

International Symposium on Contamination Control. Contamination Control: Proceedings of the Third International Symposium: Copenhagen, 1976, Vol. 2: Sectional Meetings. pap. 58.50 (ISBN 0-317-20111-5). Bks Demand UMI.

International Symposium on Contamination Control, Fourth: Proceedings. LC 62-38584. (Illus.). 1978. pap. text ed. 25.00 (ISBN 0-915414-58-9). Inst Environ Sci.

CONTAMINATION OF ENVIRONMENT

see Pollution

CONTENT ANALYSIS (COMMUNICATION)

Rosengren, Karl E. Advances in Content Analysis. (Sage Annual Reviews of Communication Research: Vol. 9). 282p. 1981. pap. 12.50 (ISBN 0-8039-1556-X); 25.00 (ISBN 0-8039-1555-1). Sage.

Stavroulakis, P., ed. Interference Analysis of Communication Systems. LC 80-18464. 1980. 44.65 (ISBN 0-87942-135-5, PC01321). Inst Electrical.

Weber, Robert P. Basic Content Analysis. 1985. 5.00 (ISBN 0-8039-2448-8). Sage.

CONTINENTAL DISPLACEMENT

see Continental Drift

CONTINENTAL DRIFT

see also Paleomagnetism; Plate Tectonics; Submarine Geology

Andel, Tjeerd H. van. New Views on an Old Planet: Continental Drift & the History of the Earth. (Illus.). 272p. 1985. 19.95 (ISBN 0-521-30084-3). Cambridge U Pr.

Ciochon, Russell L. & Chiarelli, A. B., eds. Evolutionary Biology of the New World Monkeys & Continental Drift. LC 80-16063. (Advances in Primatology Ser.). 560p. 1981. 59.50x (ISBN 0-306-40487-7, Plenum Pr). Plenum Pub.

Colbert, Edwin H. Wandering Lands & Animals: The Story of Continental Drift & Animal Populations. 352p. 1985. pap. 7.95 (ISBN 0-486-24918-2). Dover.

Coulomb, J. Sea Floor Spreading & Continental Drift. Tanner, R. W., tr. from Fr. LC 79-179891. (Geophysics & Astrophysics Monographs: No. 2). 184p. 1972. lib. bdg. 31.50 (ISBN 90-277-0232-2, Pub. by Reidel Holland); pap. 18.50 (ISBN 90-277-0238-1). Kluwer Academic.

Davies, P. A. & Runcorn, S. K., eds. Mechanisms of Continental Drift & Plate Tectonics. 1981. 72.00 (ISBN 0-12-206160-8). Acad Pr.

DuToit, Alexander L. Our Wandering Continents: An Hypothesis of Continental Drifting. LC 76-147217. 366p. 1972. Repr. of 1957 ed. lib. bdg. 24.75x (ISBN 0-8371-5982-2, DUWC). Greenwood.

Glen, William. Continental Drift & Plate Tectonics. (Physics & Physical Science Ser.). 192p. 1975. pap. text ed. 12.95 (ISBN 0-675-08799-6). Merrill.

I.A.U. Symposium, 32nd, Stresa, Italy, 1967. Continental Drift: Secular Motion of the Pole & Rotation of the Earth. Markowitz, William & Guinot, B., eds. (Proceedings: I.A.U. Symposia). 107p. 1968. lib. bdg. 18.50 (ISBN 90-277-0129-6, Pub. by Reidel Holland). Kluwer Academic.

King, Lester C. Wandering Continents & Spreading Sea Floors of an Expanding Earth. LC 81-1345. 232p. 1984. 32.95x (ISBN 0-471-90156-3, Wiley-Interscience). Wiley.

Miller, Russell. Continents in Collision. LC 82-16778. (Planet Earth Ser.). 1983. lib. bdg. 19.94 (ISBN 0-8094-4325-2, Pub. by Time-Life). Silver.

Munyan, Arthur C., ed. Polar Wandering & Continental Drift. LC 64-6318. (Society of Economic Paleontologists & Mineralogists, Special Publication: No. 10). pap. 43.80 (ISBN 0-317-27161-X, 2024736). Bks Demand UMI.

Ocean Sciences Board, National Research Council. Continental Margins: Geological & Geophysical Research Needs. 1979. pap. 17.75 (ISBN 0-309-02793-4). Natl Acad Pr.

Owen, H. G. Atlas of Continental Displacement: 200 Million Years to the Present: A Test of Conventional & Expanding Earth Models. LC 83-675083. (Cambridge Earth Sciences Ser.). 159p. 1984. 32.50 (ISBN 0-521-25817-0). Cambridge U Pr.

Runcorn, S. K., ed. Continental Drift. (International Geophysics Ser: Vol. 3). 1962. 70.00 (ISBN 0-12-602450-2). Acad Pr.

Shea, James H., ed. Continental Drift. (Benchmark Papers in Geology: Vol. 88). (Illus.). 368p. 1985. 49.50 (ISBN 0-442-28240-0). Van Nos Reinhold.

Takeuchi, H., et al. Debate about the Earth: An Approach to Geophysics Through Analysis of Continental Drift. rev. ed. Kanamori, K., tr. from Japanese. LC 67-21261. (Illus.). 281p. 1970. text ed. 9.00 (ISBN 0-87735-303-4). Freeman Cooper.

Tarling, D. H. Continental Drift & Biological Evolution. Head, J. J., ed. LC 78-53329. (Carolina Biology Readers Ser.). (Illus.). 32p. 1980. pap. 2.00 (ISBN 0-89278-313-3, 45-9713). Carolina Biological.

Tarling, D. H. & Runcorn, S. K., eds. Implications of Continental Drift to the Earth Sciences, Vol. 2. 1973. 90.00 (ISBN 0-12-683702-3). Acad Pr.

CONTINENTAL SHELF

Andrassy, Juraj. International Law & the Resources of the Sea. LC 76-130960. (International Legal Studies). (Illus.). 191p. 1970. 26.00x (ISBN 0-231-03409-1). Columbia U Pr.

Burghes, D. N. & Graham, M. A. Introduction to Control Theory, Including Optimal Control. LC 80-40386. (Mathematics & Its Applications Ser.: I-176). 400p. 1980. 89.95x (ISBN 0-470-26998-7). Halsted Pr.

Control & Dynamic Systems: Advances Theory & Application, Vol. 16. LC 64-8027. (Serial Publications Ser.). 1980. 45.00 (ISBN 0-12-012716-4). Acad Pr.

Coppel, W. A., ed. Mathematical Control Theory: Proceedings, Canberra, Australia, Aug. 23 - Sep. 2, 1977. LC 78-11960. (Lecture Notes in Mathematics: Vol. 680). 1978. pap. 20.00 (ISBN 0-387-08941-1). Springer-Verlag.

Corduneanu, Constantin. Integral Equations & Stability of Feedback Systems. (Mathematics in Science & Engineering Ser.). 1973. 60.00 (ISBN 0-12-188350-7). Acad Pr.

Craven, B. D. Mathematical Programming & Control Theory. (Mathematics Ser.). 1978. pap. 15.95 (ISBN 0-412-15500-1, NO. 6070, Pub. by Chapman & Hall). Methuen Inc.

Csaki. State-Space Methods for Control Systems. 1976. 46.00 (ISBN 0-9960005-1-8, Pub. by Akademiai Kaido Hungary). Heyden.

Davis, M. H. Linear Estimation & Stochastic Control. LC 77-23389. 1977. pap. text ed. 16.95x (ISBN 0-412-15130-8). Halsted Pr.

Doebelin, Ernest O. Control System Principles & Design. 624p. Date not set. price not set (ISBN 0-471-08815-3). Wiley.

Dolezal, V. J. Monotone Operators & Applications in Control & Network Theory. (Studies in Automation & Control: Vol. 2). 174p. 1979. 42.75 (ISBN 0-444-41791-5). Elsevier.

Dontchev, A. L. Perturbations, Approximations, & Sensitivity Analysis of Optimal Control Systems. (Lecture Notes in Control & Information Sciences Ser.: Vol. 52). 162p. 1983. pap. 13.00 (ISBN 0-387-12463-2). Springer-Verlag.

Dyer, P. & McReynolds, S. R. Computation & Theory of Optimal Control. (Mathematics in Science & Engineering Ser., Vol. 65). 1970. 70.00 (ISBN 0-12-226250-6). Acad Pr.

El-Fattah, Y. M. & Foulard, C. Learning Systems: Decision, Simulation, & Control. (Lecture Notes in Control & Information Sciences: Vol. 9). (Illus.). 1978. pap. 14.00 (ISBN 0-387-09003-7). Springer-Verlag.

Elliott, Robert J. & Kalton, Nigel J. The Existence of Value in Differential Games. LC 72-4562. (Memoirs: No. 126). 67p. 1972. pap. 9.00 (ISBN 0-8218-1826-0, MEMO-126). Am Math.

Emanuel, Pericles & Leff, Edward. Introduction to Feedback Control Systems. (Electrical Engineering). (Illus.). 1979. text ed. 42.00 (ISBN 0-07-019310-X). McGraw.

Fallside, F., ed. Control System Design by Pole-Zero Assignment. 1978. 44.00 (ISBN 0-12-248250-6). Acad Pr.

Faurre, Pierre & Depeyrot, Michel. Elements of System Theory. LC 76-3056. 1976. 47.00 (ISBN 0-7204-0440-1, North-Holland). Elsevier.

Feichtinger, G., ed. Optimal Control Theory & Economic Analysis: Workshop on Economic Applications of Control Theory, 2nd, Held in Vienna, 16-18 May, 1984, No. 2. 662p. 1985. 60.00 (ISBN 0-444-87688-X, North-Holland). Elsevier.

Findeisen, W., et al. Control & Coordination in Hierarchical Systems. (IIASA International Ser. on Applied Systems Analysis: No. 9). 467p. 1980. 82.95x (ISBN 0-471-27742-8). Wiley.

Fitzgerald, Jerry. Designing Controls into Computerized Systems. LC 81-67870. (Illus.). 157p. 1981. pap. 16.95 (ISBN 0-932410-36-7). FitzGerald & Assocs.

Fleming, W. H. & Rishel, R. W. Deterministic & Stochastic Optimal Control. LC 75-28391. (Applications of Mathematics Ser.: Vol. 1). (Illus.). xi, 222p. 1975. 44.00 (ISBN 0-387-90155-8). Springer-Verlag.

Frank, P. M. Introduction to System Sensitivity Theory. 1978. 47.50 (ISBN 0-12-265650-4). Acad Pr.

Franklin, Gene F. & Powell, J. David. Digital Control of Dynamic Systems. LC 79-16377. 1980. text ed. 34.95 (ISBN 0-201-02891-3); solution manual 2.00 (ISBN 0-201-02892-1). Addison-Wesley.

Friedland, B. Control System Design: An Introduction to State-Space Methods. (Electrical Engineering Ser.). 512p. 1985. text ed. price not set (ISBN 0-07-022441-2). McGraw.

Gabasov, R. & Kirillova, F. M., eds. Singular Optimal Controls. (Mathematical Concepts & Methods in Science & Engineering Ser.: Vol. 10). (Illus.). 262p. 1978. 29.50x (ISBN 0-306-39250-X, Plenum Pr). Plenum Pub.

Gopal, M. Modern Control System Theory. 644p. 1984. 27.95 (ISBN 0-470-27424-7). Halsted Pr.

Gruver, W. A. & Sachs, E. Algorithmic Methods in Optimal Control. (Research Notes in Mathematics Ser.: No. 47). 256p. 1981. pap. text ed. 27.50 (ISBN 0-273-08473-9). Pitman Pub MA.

Gumowski, Igor & Mira, C. Optimization in Control Theory & Practice. LC 68-12059. pap. 63.00 (ISBN 0-317-26399-4, 2024456). Bks Demand UMI.

Gunn, Thomas G., Jr. Computer Applications in Manufacturing. LC 81-6544. (Illus.). 224p. 1981. 28.95 (ISBN 0-8311-1087-2). Indus Pr.

Gupta, Someshwar C. & Hasdorff, Lawrence. Fundamentals of Automatic Control. LC 82-20338. 602p. 1983. Repr. of 1970 ed. lib. bdg. 39.50 (ISBN 0-89874-578-0). Krieger.

Hale, Francis J. Introduction to Control System Analysis & Design. (Illus.). 400p. 1973. ref. ed. 35.95 (ISBN 0-13-479824-4). P-H.

Halmos, F. & Somogyi, J. Optimization of Design & Computation of Control Networks. 1981. 129.00x (ISBN 0-569-08552-7, Pub. by Collet's). State Mutual Bk.

Hammer, Preston, ed. Advances in Mathematical Systems Theory. LC 67-27111. (Illus.). 1967. 20.00x (ISBN 0-271-73132-X). Pa St U Pr.

Hermann, R. Cartanian Geometry, Nonlinear Waves & Control Theory, Pt. A. (Interdisciplinary Mathematics Ser.: Vol. XX). 501p. 1970. pap. 60.00 (ISBN 0-915692-27-9, 991600290). Math Sci Pr.

--Geometric Structure of Systems-Control Theory & Physics, Pt. A. (Interdisciplinary Mathematics: Vol. IX). 450p. 1974. pap. 35.00 (ISBN 0-915692-08-2, 99160038X). Math Sci Pr.

Hermes, Henry & La Salle, Joseph. Functional Analysis & Time Optimal Control. (Mathematics in Science & Engineering Ser.: Vol. 56). 1969. 41.50 (ISBN 0-12-342650-2). Acad Pr.

Hettich, R., ed. Semi-Infinite Programming: Proceedings. (Lecture Notes in Control & Information Science: Vol. 15). (Illus.). 1979. pap. 14.00 (ISBN 0-387-09479-2). Springer-Verlag.

IFAC Workshop, 4th, DCCS-82, Tallin, USSR, May 1982 & Gellie, R. W. Distributed Computer Control Systems 1982: Proceedings. Tavast, R. R., ed. (IFAC Proceedings Ser.). 215p. 1983. 60.00 (ISBN 0-08-028675-5). Pergamon.

International Centre for Theoretical Physics. Control Theory & Topics in Functional Analysis, 3 vols. (Illus.). 432p. Vol. 1. pap. 45.50 (ISP415-1, IAEA); Vol. 2. pap. 32.50 (ISBN 92-0-130176-6, ISP415-2); Vol. 3. pap. 40.75 (ISBN 9-2013-0276-2, ISP415-3). Unipub.

International Federation of Automatic Control & Akashi, H. Design & Reliability Systems: Proceedings. (Control Science & Technology Ser.: Vol. 3). 258p. 99.00 (ISBN 0-08-028715-8). Pergamon.

Isermann, R. Digital Control Systems. (Illus.). 566p. 1981. pap. 48.50 (ISBN 0-387-10728-2). Springer-Verlag.

Jackson, Barbara B. Multivariate Data Analysis: An Introduction. 1983. pap. 15.95x (ISBN 0-256-02848-6). Irwin.

Jacobs, O. L. Introduction to Control Theory. (Illus.). 1974. pap. 19.95x (ISBN 0-19-856148-2). Oxford U Pr.

Jacobson, D. H., et al. Extensions of Linear-Quadratic Control Theory. (Lecture Notes in Control & Information Sciences: Vol. 27). 288p. 1980. text ed. 23.00 (ISBN 0-387-10069-5). Springer-Verlag.

Kaczorek, T. Two-Dimensional Linear Systems. (Lecture Notes in Control & Information Sciences Ser.: Vol. 68). x, 398p. 1985. pap. 28.00 (ISBN 0-387-15086-2). Springer-Verlag.

Kappel, F., et al, eds. Control Theory for Distributed Parameter System & Applications. (Lecture Notes in Control & Information Sciences: Vol. 54). 246p. 1983. pap. 19.00 (ISBN 0-387-12554-X). Springer-Verlag.

Kirk, D. Optimal Control Theory: An Introduction. 1970. ref. ed. 42.95 (ISBN 0-13-638098-0). P-H.

Knobloch, H. W. Higher Order Necessary Conditions in Optimal Control Theory. (Lecture Notes in Control & Information Sciences Ser.: Vol. 34). 173p. 1981. pap. 12.00 (ISBN 0-387-10985-4). Springer Verlag.

Komkov, V., ed. Sensitivity of Functionals with Applications to Engineering Sciences. (Lecture Notes in Mathematics Ser.: Vol. 1086). v, 130p. 1984. pap. 10.00 (ISBN 0-387-13871-4). Springer-Verlag.

Kushner, H. Probability Methods for Approximations in Stochastic Control & for Elliptic Equations. (Math in Science & Engineering Ser.). 1977. 55.00 (ISBN 0-12-430140-1). Acad Pr.

Kushner, Harold J. Stochastic Stability & Control. (Mathematics in Science & Engineering Ser.: Vol. 33). 1967. 39.50 (ISBN 0-12-430150-9). Acad Pr.

Kwakernaak, Huibert & Sivan, Raphael. Linear Optimal Control Systems. LC 72-3576. 575p. 1972. 59.95x (ISBN 0-471-51110-2, Pub. by Wiley-Interscience). Wiley.

Landau. Adaptive Control: The Model Reference Approach. (Control & Systems Theory Ser.: Vol. 8). 1979. 64.25 (ISBN 0-8247-6548-6). Dekker.

Lathi, B. P. Signals, Systems & Controls. LC 73-464. 640p. 1974. text ed. 36.95 scp (ISBN 0-7002-2431-9, HarpC). Har-Row.

Lee, E. B. & Markus, L. Foundations of Optimal Control Theory. LC 84-21772. 588p. 1985. Repr. of 1967 ed. lib. bdg. write for info. (ISBN 0-89874-807-0). Krieger.

Lefcourt, Herbert M. Locus of Control: Current Trends in Theory & Research. 2nd ed. 288p. 1982. text ed. 29.95x (ISBN 0-89859-222-4). L Erlbaum Assocs.

Lefschetz, Solomon. Stability of Nonlinear Control Systems. (Mathematics in Science & Engineering Ser.: Vol. 13). 1965. 42.50 (ISBN 0-12-440350-6). Acad Pr.

Leigh, J. R. Applied Control Theory. (IEE Control Engineering Ser.: No. 18). 192p. 1982. 68.00 (ISBN 0-906048-72-9, CE018). Inst Elect Eng.

Leondes, C. T., ed. Advances in Control Systems, Vols. 1-8. Incl. Vol. 1. 1964 (ISBN 0-12-012701-6); Vol. 2. 1965 (ISBN 0-12-012702-4); Vol. 3. 1966 (ISBN 0-12-012703-2); Vol. 4. 1966 (ISBN 0-12-012704-0); Vol. 5. 1967 (ISBN 0-12-012705-9); Vol. 6. 1968 (ISBN 0-12-012706-7); Vol. 7. 1969 (ISBN 0-12-012707-5); Vol. 8. 1971 (ISBN 0-12-012708-3). 70.00 ea. Acad Pr.

--Control of Dynamic Systems: Advances in Theory & Application, Vols. 9, 10, 13 & 15. Incl. Vol. 9. 1973. 65.00 (ISBN 0-12-012709-1); Vol. 10. 1973. 65.00 (ISBN 0-12-012710-5); Vol. 13. 1977. 65.00 (ISBN 0-12-012713-X); Vol. 15. 1979. 44.00 (ISBN 0-12-012715-6). 1973. Acad Pr.

Lions, J. L. Optimal Control of Systems Governed by Partial Differential Equations. Mitter, S. K., tr. LC 78-113638. (Grundlehren der Mathematischen Wissenschaften: Vol. 170). (Illus.). 1971. 48.00 (ISBN 0-387-05115-5). Springer-Verlag.

Liu & Roxin. Differential Games & Control Theory III: Proceedings of the Third Kingston Conference, Pt. A. (Lecture Notes in Pure & Applied Mathematics Ser.: Vol. 44). 1979. 45.00 (ISBN 0-8247-6845-0). Dekker.

Luenberger, David G. Introduction to Dynamic Systems: Theory, Models & Applications. LC 78-12366. 446p. 1979. 46.00 (ISBN 0-471-02594-1); solutions manual avail. (ISBN 0-471-06081-X). Wiley.

MacFarlane, A. G., ed. Frequency: Response Methods in Control Systems. LC 79-90572. 1979. 56.10 (ISBN 0-87942-125-8, PC01206). Inst Electrical.

Maciejowski, J. M. The Modelling of Systems with Small Observation Sets. (Lecture Notes in Control & Information Sciences: Vol. 10). (Illus.). 1978. pap. 18.00 (ISBN 0-387-09004-5). Springer-Verlag.

Martin, C & Hermann, R. The Nineteen Seventy-Six Ames Research Center NASA Conference on Geometric Control Theory, Vol. VII. 354p. 1977. pap. 44.00 (ISBN 0-915692-21-X, 991600088). Math Sci Pr.

Martin, Clyde & Hermann, Robert, eds. Ames Research Center (NASA) Conference on Geometric Control Theory, 1976. (Lie Groups: History, Frontiers & Applications Ser.: Vol. 7). 1977. 44.00 (ISBN 0-915692-21-X). Math Sci Pr.

Mathematics of the Decision Sciences Part I. Dantzig, G. B. & Veinott, A. F., Jr., eds. LC 62-21481. 429p. 1970. Repr. of 1968 ed. with corrections 41.00 (ISBN 0-8218-1111-8, LAM-11). Am Math.

Meetham, A. R. Encyclopedia of Linguistics, Information & Control. 1969. 140.00 (ISBN 0-08-012337-6). Pergamon.

Melsa, James L. & Schultz, Donald. Computer Programs for Computational Assistance in the Study of Linear Control Theory. 2nd ed. 1973. text ed. 30.00 (ISBN 0-07-041498-X). McGraw.

--Linear Control Systems. LC 68-8664. (Electronic Systems Ser.). (Illus.). 1969. text ed. 48.00 (ISBN 0-07-041481-5). McGraw.

Mendel, Jerry M. Discrete Techniques of Parameter Estimation: The Equation Error Formulation. (Control & Systems Theory Ser.: Vol. 1). 408p. 1973. 65.00 (ISBN 0-8247-1455-5). Dekker.

Mohler, R. R. & Ruberti, A. Theory & Applications of Variable Structure Systems with Emphasis on Modeling & Identification. 1972. 46.50 (ISBN 0-12-504160-8). Acad Pr.

Mohler, Ronald R. Bilinear Control Processes: With Applications to Engineering, Ecology & Medicine. (Mathematics in Science & Engineering Ser.). 1973. 60.00 (ISBN 0-12-504140-3). Acad Pr.

Morris, D. J. Communication for Command & Control Systems. (International Series on Systems & Control: Vol. 5). 470p. 1983. 77.00 (ISBN 0-08-027597-4); 25.00 (ISBN 0-08-027596-6). Pergamon.

Murata, Yasuo. Optimal Control Methods for Linear Discrete-Time Economic Systems. (Illus.). 175p. 1982. 41.00 (ISBN 0-387-90709-2). Springer-Verlag.

Nagrath, I. J. & Gopal, M. Control Systems Engineering. 2nd ed. LC 81-17470. 525p. 1982. 26.95x (ISBN 0-470-27148-5). Halsted Pr.

NATO Advanced Study Institute, 1973. Geometric Methods in System Theory: Proceedings. Mayne, D. Q. & Brockett, R. W., eds. LC 73-91206. (NATO Advanced Study Institutes: No. C-3). 1973. lib. bdg. 39.50 (ISBN 90-277-0415-5, Pub. by Reidel Holland). Kluwer Academic.

Newman, William H. Constructive Control: Design & Use of Control Systems. (Illus.). 176p. 1975. pap. text ed. 15.95 (ISBN 0-13-169359-X). P-H.

Noton, M. Modern Control Engineering. LC 72-181056. 288p. 1973. text ed. 33.00 (ISBN 0-08-016820-5). Pergamon.

Ogata, Katsuhiko. Modern Control Engineering. LC 72-84843. (Electrical Engineering Ser). 1970. ref. ed. 40.95 (ISBN 0-13-590232-0). P-H.

--State Space Analysis of Control Systems. 1966. ref. ed. 37.00 (ISBN 0-13-844530-3). P-H.

Owens, David. Multivariable & Optimal Systems. LC 81-67886. 1981. 55.00 (ISBN 0-12-531720-4); pap. 21.00 (ISBN 0-12-531722-0). Acad Pr.

Petrov, I. P. Variational Methods in Optimum Control Theory. Friedman, Morris D., tr. LC 68-18678. (Mathematics in Science & Engineering Ser.: Vol. 45). 1968. 60.00 (ISBN 0-12-552850-7). Acad Pr.

Postlethwaite, I. & Macfarlane, A. G. A Complex Variable Approach to the Analysis of Linear Multivariable Feedback Systems. (Lecture Notes in Control & Information Sciences: Vol. 12). (Illus.). 1979. pap. 14.00 (ISBN 0-387-09340-0). Springer-Verlag.

Rajbman, N. S., ed. Identification & System Parameter Estimation: Proceedings of the 4th IFAC Symposium, Tbilisi, USSR, September, 1976, 3 vols. 2178p. 1978. Set. 191.50 (ISBN 0-444-85096-1, North-Holland). Elsevier.

Rao, G. P. Piecewise Constant Orthogonal Functions & Their Application to Systems & Control. (Lecture Notes in Control & Information Sciences: Vol. 55). 254p. 1983. pap. 19.00 (ISBN 0-387-12556-6). Springer-Verlag.

Rao, Guthikonda V. Complex Digital Control Systems. 300p. 1979. 46.50 (ISBN 0-442-20110-9). Van Nos Reinhold.

Ray, W. Harmon & Lainiotis, Demetrious, eds. Distributed Parameter Systems: Identification, Estimation & Control. (Control & System Theory Ser.: Vol. 6). 1978. 95.00 (ISBN 0-8247-6601-6). Dekker.

Roxin, E. O., et al, eds. Differential Games & Control Theory. (Lecture Notes in Pure & Applied Mathematics Ser.: Vol. 10). 432p. 1975. 65.00 (ISBN 0-8247-6257-6). Dekker.

Roxin, Emilio, et al, eds. Differential Games in Control Theory II. (Lecture Notes in Pure & Applied Math: Vol. 30). 75.00 (ISBN 0-8247-6549-4). Dekker.

Ruberti, A., ed. Modelling & Identification of Distributed Parameter Systems: IFIP Working Conference, Rome Italy, June 21-24,1976. (Lecture Notes in Control & Information Sciences: Vol. 1). 1978. pap. text ed. 25.00 (ISBN 0-387-08405-3). Springer-Verlag.

Russell. Mathematics of Finite Dimensional Control Systems. LC 79-9847. (Lecture Notes in Pure & Applied Mathematics Ser.: Vol. 43). 1979. pap. 49.75 (ISBN 0-8247-7211-3). Dekker.

Sage, Andrew P. & White, Chelsea C. Optimum Systems Control. 2nd ed. (Illus.). 1977. ref. ed. 42.95 (ISBN 0-13-638296-7). P-H.

Salamon, D. Control & Observation of Neutral Systems. (Research Notes in Mathematics: No. 91). 220p. 1984. pap. text ed. 19.95 (ISBN 0-273-08618-9). Pitman Pub MA.

Salukvadze, M. Vector-Valued Optimization Problems in Control Theory. Casti, John, tr. LC 79-23364. (Mathematics in Science & Engineering Ser.). 1979. 49.50 (ISBN 0-12-616750-8). Acad Pr.

Shinners, Stanley M. Modern Control, System Theory & Application. 2nd ed. LC 78-52497. (Electrical Engineering Ser.). 1978. text ed. 34.95 (ISBN 0-201-07494-X); instr's man. 3.00 (ISBN 0-201-07495-8). Addison-Wesley.

Strejc, Vladimir. State Space Theory of Discrete Linear Control. LC 79-991. 426p. 1981. 59.95x (ISBN 0-471-27594-8, Pub. by Wiley-Interscience). Wiley.

Swan. Applications of Optical Control Theory. 320p. 1984. 55.00 (ISBN 0-8247-7192-3). Dekker.

Symposium on Optimization, Nice, 1969. Proceedings. Balakrishna, A. V., et al, eds. LC 70-120380. (Lecture Notes in Mathematics: Vol. 132). (Illus.). 1970. pap. 18.30 (ISBN 0-387-04921-5). Springer-Verlag.
Takahashi, Y., et al. Control & Dynamic Systems. 1970. 39.95 (ISBN 0-201-07440-0). Addison-Wesley.
Tan, K. C. & Bennett, R. J. Optimal Control of Spatial Systems. LC 83-25701. (London Research Series in Geography: No. 6). (Illus.). 172p. 1984. text ed. 29.95x (ISBN 0-04-519018-6). Allen Unwin.
Toates, F. M. Control Theory in Biology & Experimental Psychology. 1980. text ed. 21.50x (ISBN 0-09-119660-4, Hutchinson U Lib). Humanities.
Tzafestas, S. G., ed. Distributed Parameter Control Systems: Theory & Application. (International Series on Systems & Control: Vol. 6). 525p. 1982. 66.00 (ISBN 0-08-027624-5). Pergamon.
Vernon, J. B. Linear Vibration & Control System Theory with Computer Applications. LC 67-13530. 281p. 1967. text ed. 19.50 (ISBN 0-471-90651-4, Pub. by Wiley). Krieger.
Vidyasagar, M. Control System Synthesis: A Factorization Approach. LC 84-14411. (Series in Signal Processing, Optimization & Control). (Illus.). 300p. 1984. text ed. 35.00x. MIT Pr.
Warga, J. Optimal Control of Differential & Functional Equations. 1972. 77.00 (ISBN 0-12-735150-7). Acad Pr.
Watts, Don. A Catalog of Operational Transfer Functions. LC 76-25745. (Reference Library of Science & Technology: Vol. 9). (Illus.). 1977. lib. bdg. 32.00 (ISBN 0-8240-9901-X). Garland Pub.
Yavin, Y. Numerical Studies in Nonlinear Filtering. (Lecture Notes in Control & Information Sciences Ser.: Vol. 65). vi, 273p. 1985. pap. 13.00 (ISBN 0-387-13958-3). Springer-Verlag.
Young, Laurence C. Lectures on the Calculus of Variations & Optimal Control Theory. 2nd ed. LC 79-57387. 1980. 16.95 (ISBN 0-8284-0304-X). Chelsea Pub.

CONTROLLED ACCESS HIGHWAYS
see Express Highways

CONTROLLED FUSION
Artsimovich, L. A., et al, eds. Controlled Thermonuclear Reactions. (Illus.). 422p. 1964. 112.25 (ISBN 0-677-20020-X). Gordon.
Atomic Industrial Forum Staff. Industry's Role in Development of Fusion Power: Set of Papers. (Technical & Economic Reports: Fusion). 1984. 375.00 (ISBN 0-318-02241-9). Atomic Indus Forum.
Brunelli, B. Driven Magnetic Fusion Reactors: Proceedings. (Commission of the European Communities Ser.: EUR 6146). (Illus.). 1979. pap. 97.00 (ISBN 0-08-024459-9). Pergamon.
Casini, G., ed. Engineering Aspects of Thermonuclear Fusion Reactors. (Ispra Courses on Nuclear Engineering & Technology Ser.). 642p. 1982. 97.00 (ISBN 3-7186-0090-0). Harwood Academic.
Commission of the European Communities, Luxembourg, ed. Fusion Technology: Proceedings of the 12th Symposium (SOFT), Julich Laboratory, Federal Republic of Germany, 13-17 Setember 1982, 2 Vols. (International School of Fusion Reactor Technology (CEC) Ser.). 1564p. 1983. Set. pap. 250.00 (ISBN 0-08-029977-6). Pergamon.
Commission of the European Communities. Fusion Technology 1984: Proceedings of the 13th Symposium (SOFT), Varese, Italy, 24-28 Sept. 1984, 2 vols. (International School of Fusion Reactor Tecnology (CEC) Ser.). (Illus.). 1749p. 1985. Set. pap. 250.00 (ISBN 0-08-032559-9, Pub. by PPI). Pergamon.
Dean, Stephen O., ed. Prospects for Fusion Power. (Illus.). 112p. 1981. 21.00 (ISBN 0-08-028046-3). Pergamon.
Draper, E. Linn, Jr., ed. Technology of Controlled Thermonuclear Fusion Experiments & the Engineering Aspects of Fusion Reactors: Proceedings. LC 74-600044. (AEC Symposium Ser.). 1052p. 1974. pap. 34.25 (ISBN 0-87079-221-0, CONF-721111); microfiche 4.50 (ISBN 0-87079-222-9, CONF-721111). DOE.
Fusion Reactor Design Concepts. (Panel Proceedings Ser.). (Illus.). 784p. 1979. pap. 45.75 (ISBN 92-0-131178-8, ISP487, IAEA). Unipub.
Gibson, A., ed. Controlled Fusion & Plasma Physics: Invited Papers from the Eleventh European Conference of the European Physical Society Plasma Physics Division, 5-9 September 1983, Aachen, Federal Republic of Germany. 276p. 1984. pap. 24.00 (ISBN 0-08-030286-6). Pergamon.
Glasstone, Samuel & Lovberg, Ralph H. Controlled Thermonuclear Reactions: An Introduction to Theory & Experiment. LC 75-11911. 540p. 1975. Repr. of 1960 ed. 32.50 (ISBN 0-88275-326-6). Krieger.
Gruen, D. M., ed. Chemistry of Fusion Technology. LC 72-89488. 394p. 1972. 55.00x (ISBN 0-306-30714-6, Plenum Pr). Plenum Pub.
Joachain, Charles J. & Post, Douglas E., eds. Atomic & Molecular Physics of Controlled Thermonuclear Fusion. (NATO ASI Series B, Physics: Vol. 101). 575p. 1983. 79.50x (ISBN 0-306-41398-1, Plenum Pr). Plenum Pub.
McDowell, M. R. & Ferendeci, A. M., eds. Atomic & Molecular Processes in Controlled Thermonuclear Fusion. LC 80-238. (NATO ASI Series B, Physics: Vol. 53). 500p. 1980. 75.00x (ISBN 0-306-40424-9, Plenum Pr). Plenum Pub.
Miyamoto, Kenro. Plasma Physics for Nuclear Fusion. (Illus.). 623p. 1980. text ed. 60.00x (ISBN 0-262-13145-5). MIT Pr.
Plasma Physics & Controlled Nuclear Fusion Research: Supplement, 1972, 1971. (Illus.). 357p. (Orig.). 1973. pap. 24.25 (ISBN 92-0-139072-6, ISP 23-72, IAEA). Unipub.
Plasma Physics & Controlled Nuclear Fusion Research: 1968, 2 vols. (Proceedings Ser.). (Illus.). 1834p. (Vol. 1). 1968. Vol. 1. pap. 68.00 (ISBN 92-0-530168-X, ISP192-1, IAEA); Vol. 2. pap. 57.25 (ISBN 92-0-530268-6, ISP 192-2). Unipub.
World Survey of Major Activities in Controlled Fusion Research, 1982 Edition, Special Supplement 1982. 432p. 1983. pap. 56.00 (ISBN 92-0-139082-3, ISP23/82, IAEA). Unipub.

CONTROLLERS, ELECTRIC
see Electric Controllers

CONVECTION OF HEAT
see Heat–Convection

CONVERGENCE
see also Asymptotic Expansions; Law of Large Numbers
Attouch, H. & Universite de Paris-Sud. Variational Convergence for Functions & Operators. (Applicable Math Ser.). 304p. 1984. pap. text ed. 29.95 (ISBN 0-273-08583-2). Pitman Pub MA.
Billingsley, P. Convergence of Probability Measures. (Probability & Mathematical Statistics Tracts: Probability & Statistics Section). 253p. 1968. 41.95x (ISBN 0-471-07242-7, Pub. by Wiley-Interscience). Wiley.
--Weak Convergence of Measures: Applications in Probability. (CBMS-NSF Regional Conference Ser.: No. 5). v, 31p. 1971. pap. text ed. 6.50 (ISBN 0-89871-176-2). Soc Indus-Appl Math.
Ferrar, W. L. A Textbook of Convergence. (Illus.). 1980. Repr. of 1938 ed. 19.95x (ISBN 0-19-853176-1). Oxford U Pr.
Fuller, Jack. Convergence. LC 81-43483. 384p. 1982. 16.95 (ISBN 0-385-18023-3). Doubleday.
Kushner, H. J. & Clark, D. S. Stochastic Approximation Methods for Constrained & Unconstrained Systems. LC 78-16855. (Applied Mathematical Sciences Ser.: Vol. 26). (Illus.). 1978. text ed. 18.50 (ISBN 0-387-90341-0). Springer-Verlag.
Kushner, Harold. Approximation & Weak Convergence Methods for Random Processes with Application to Stochastic Systems Theory. (Signal Processing, Optimization & Control Ser.). (Illus.). 361p. 1984. text ed. 40.00x (ISBN 0-262-11090-3). MIT Pr.
Malik, S. C. Introduction to Convergence. 210p. 1984. text ed. 24.95x (ISBN 0-470-20070-7). Halsted Pr.
Steklov Institute of Mathematics, Academy of Sciences, U S S R & Steckin, S. B. Sequences of Convergence for Series: Proceedings. (Proceedings of the Steklov Institute of Mathematics: No. 86). 1967. 25.00 (ISBN 0-8218-1886-4, STEKLO-86). Am Math.

CONVERSION OF SALINE WATERS
see Saline Water Conversion

CONVERSION OF WASTE PRODUCTS
see Recycling (Waste, etc.); Salvage (Waste, etc.)

CONVERTER REACTORS
see Breeder Reactors

CONVERTERS, ELECTRIC
see Electric Current Converters; Rotary Converters

CONVERTERS, SYNCHRONOUS
see Rotary Converters

CONVEX BODIES
Bourgin, R. D. Geometric Aspects of Convex Sets with the Radon-Nikodym Property. (Lecture Notes in Mathematics: Vol. 993). 474p. 1983. pap. 24.00 (ISBN 0-387-12296-6). Springer-Verlag.
Eggleston, H. G. Convexity. (Cambridge Tracts in Mathematics & Mathematical Physics: No. 47). 1958. 24.95 (ISBN 0-521-07734-6). Cambridge U Pr.
Ekeland, I. & Temam, R. Convex Analysis & Variational Problems. (Applied Mathematics & Its Applications Ser.: Vol. 1). 402p. 1976. 72.50 (ISBN 0-444-10898-X, North Holland). Elsevier.
Gruber, Peter & Wills, Jorg. Convexity & Its Applications. 420p. 1983. text ed. 59.95 (ISBN 0-8176-1384-6). Birkhauser.
Pogorelov, A. V. Extrinsic Geometry of Convex Surfaces. LC 72-11851. (Translations of Mathematical Monographs: Vol. 35). 1972. 80.00 (ISBN 0-8218-1585-7, MMONO-35). Am Math.
Roberts, A. Wayne & Varberg, Dale E. Convex Function. (Pure & Applied Mathematics Ser.). 1973. 59.00 (ISBN 0-12-589740-5). Acad Pr.
Smith, P. Convexity Methods in Variational Calculus. (Applied Engineering & Mathematical Sciences Ser.). 222p. 1985. 41.95 (ISBN 0-471-90679-4). Wiley.
Steklov Institute of Mathematics, Academy of Sciences, USSR & Stogrin, M. I. Regular Dirichlet-Voronoi Partitions for the Second Triclinic Group: Proceedings. LC 75-23284. (Proceedings of the Steklov Institute of Mathematics: No.123). 116p. 1975. 39.00 (ISBN 0-8218-3023-6, STEKLO-123). Am Math.
Zalgaller, Viktor A. Convex Polyhedra with Regular Faces. LC 69-12505. (Seminars in Mathematics Ser.: Vol. 2). 130p. 1969. 29.50x (ISBN 0-306-18802-3, Consultants). Plenum Pub.

CONVEX DOMAINS
see also Convex Bodies
Alfsen, E. M. Compact Convex Sets & Boundary Integrals. LC 72-136352. (Ergebnisse der Mathematik und Ihrer Grenzgebiete: Vol. 57). (Illus.). 1971. 31.00 (ISBN 0-387-05090-6). Springer-Verlag.
Convexity: Proceedings, Symposia in Pure Mathematics, Seattle, 1961. Klee, V., ed. LC 63-10760. (Proceedings of Symposia in Pure Mathematics: Vol. 7). 516p. 1979. pap. 45.00 (ISBN 0-8218-1407-9, PSPUM-7). Am Math.
Dineen, S. Complex Analysis in Locally Convex Spaces. (Mathematical Studies Ser.: Vol. 57). 492p. 1982. 59.75 (ISBN 0-444-86319-2, North Holland). Elsevier.
Fuchssteiner, B. & Lusky, W. Convex Cones. (Mathematics Studies: Vol. 56). 430p. 1981. 57.50 (ISBN 0-444-86290-0, North-Holland). Elsevier.
Gol'Stein, E. G. Theory of Convex Programming. LC 72-3180. (Translations of Mathematical Monographs: Vol. 36). 57p. 1972. 24.00 (ISBN 0-8218-1586-5, MMONO-36). Am Math.
Granirer, Edmond E. Exposed Points of Convex Sets & Weak Sequential Convergence. LC 72-2682. (Memoirs: No. 123). 80p. 1972. pap. 10.00 (ISBN 0-8218-1823-6, MEMO-123). Am Math.
Israel, Robert B. Convexity in the Theory of Lattice Gasses. LC 78-51171. (Physic Ser). 1979. 27.00 (ISBN 0-691-08209-X); pap. 13.50 (ISBN 0-691-08216-2). Princeton U Pr.
Istrautescu. Strict Convexity & Complex Strick Convexity. (Lecture Notes in Pure & Applied Mathematics Ser.). 208p. 1984. 49.75 (ISBN 0-8247-1796-1). Dekker.
Krasnosel'Ski, M. A. & Rutickii, Y. B. Convex Functions & Orlicz Spaces. (Russian Monographs & Texts on the Physical Sciences). 256p. 1962. 64.95. Gordon.
Lay, Steven R. Convex Sets & Their Applications. LC 81-19738. (Pure & Applied Mathematics Ser.). 244p. 1982. 34.95x (ISBN 0-471-09584-2, Pub. by Wiley-Interscience). Wiley.
Rockafellar, R. T. Monotone Processes of Convex & Concave Type. LC 52-42839. (Memoirs Ser.: No. 77). 74p. 1967. pap. 9.00 (ISBN 0-8218-1277-7, MEMO-77). Am Math.
Rockafellar, R. Tyrrell. Convex Analysis. LC 68-56318. (Mathematical Ser.: No. 28). 1969. 40.00 (ISBN 0-691-08069-0). Princeton U Pr.
Stoer, J. & Witzgall, C. Convexity & Optimization in Finite Dimensions One. LC 75-92789. (Die Grundlehren der Mathematischen Wissenschaften: Vol. 163). 1970. 39.00 (ISBN 0-387-04835-9). Springer-Verlag.
Yamamuro, S. A Theory of Differentiation in Locally Convex Spaces. LC 78-22099. (Memoirs: No. 212). 82p. 1981. pap. 13.00 (ISBN 0-8218-2212-8). Am Math.

CONVEYING MACHINERY
see also Bulk Solids Handling; Hoisting Machinery; Hydraulic Conveying; Pneumatic-Tube Transportation
American Chain Association, compiled by. Chains for Power Transmission & Materials Handling: Design & Applications Handbook. (Mechanical Engineering Ser.: Vol. 18). (Illus.). 368p. 1982. 35.00 (ISBN 0-8247-1701-5). Dekker.
Bhatia, M. V. & Cheremisinoff, Paul N., eds. Solids & Liquids Conveying Systems. (Process Equipment Ser.: Vol. 4). 254p. 1982. 35.00 (ISBN 0-87762-311-2). Technomic.
Conveyor Equipment Manufacturers Association. Belt Conveyors for Bulk Materials. 2nd ed. LC 78-31987. 384p. 1979. 34.95 (ISBN 0-8436-1008-5). Van Nos Reinhold.
Jones, R. J. & Laws, K. G. Speed Sensing in Belt Weighing, 1979. 1981. 95.00x (ISBN 0-686-97162-0, Pub. by W Spring England). State Mutual Bk.
Keller, Henry C. Unit-Load & Package Conveyors: Application & Design. LC 66-21856. (Illus.). pap. 62.30 (ISBN 0-317-11121-3, 2012434). Bks Demand UMI.
Smith, D. K. Package Conveyors: Design & Estimating. 136p. 1972. 25.00x (ISBN 0-85264-213-X, Pub. by Griffin England). State Mutual Bk.
Stoess, H. A., Jr. Pneumatic Conveying. 2nd ed. LC 83-6915. 277p. 1983. 41.95x (ISBN 0-471-86935-X, Pub. by Wiley-Interscience). Wiley.

COOK, JAMES, 1728-1779
Stamp, Tom & Stamp, Cordelia. James Cook, Maritime Scientist. 1981. 25.00x (ISBN 0-686-98237-1, Pub. by Caedmon of Whitby). State Mutual Bk.

COOKE, WILLIAM FOTHERGILL, SIR, 1806-1879
Hubbard, Geoffrey. Cooke & Wheatstone & the Invention of the Electric Telegraph. LC 66-38233. (Illus.). 1965. 22.50x (ISBN 0-678-06529-2). Kelley.

COOKERY–VOCATIONAL GUIDANCE
Culinary Institute of America. The Professional Chef. 5th ed. Folsom, Le Roi A., ed. 608p. 1986. text ed. cancelled (ISBN 0-8436-2201-6). Van Nos Reinhold.

COOKIES
Matz, Samuel A. & Matz, Theresa D. Cookie & Cracker Technology. 2nd ed. (Illus.). 1978. lib. bdg. 49.50 (ISBN 0-87055-235-X). AVI.

COOLIDGE, WILLIAM DAVID, 1873-
Miller, J. A. William David Coolidge: Yankee Scientist. 224p. 1963. 37.25x (ISBN 0-677-65150-3). Gordon.

COOLING APPLIANCES
see Refrigeration and Refrigerating Machinery

COOLING STRESSES
see Residual Stresses

COOLING-TOWERS
Baker, Donald R. Cooling Tower Performance. (Illus.). 1984. 40.00 (ISBN 0-8206-0300-7). Chem Pub.
Cheremisinoff, Nicholas P. & Cheremisinoff, Paul N. Cooling Towers: Selection, Design, Practice. LC 81-65711. 1981. text ed. 59.95 (ISBN 0-250-40407-9). Butterworth.
Environmental Effects of Cooling Systems. (Technical Reports Ser.: No. 202). (Illus.). 196p. 1981. pap. 30.75 (ISBN 92-0-125380-X, IDC202, IAEA). Unipub.
Environmental Systems Corporation Staff. Environmental Effects of Cooling Towers: AIF-NESP-026. (National Environmental Studies Project: NESP Reports). 1983. 50.00 (ISBN 0-318-02234-6). Atomic Indus Forum.
Gould, P. L., et al, eds. Natural Draught Cooling Towers: Proceedings of the Second International Symposium, Ruhr University Bochum, Germany, September 5-7, 1984. (Illus.). xv, 548p. 1984. 34.40 (ISBN 0-387-13703-3). Springer-Verlag.

COORDINATES
see also Complexes
Gelfand, I. M., ed. Method of Coordinates, Vol. 1. (Library of School Mathematics). 1967. text ed. 10.00x (ISBN 0-262-07028-6). MIT Pr.
Gelfand, I. M., et al. Coordinate Method. (Pocket Mathematical Library). 80p. 1968. 24.50 (ISBN 0-677-20640-2). Gordon.
Hirschel. Shear Flow in Surface Oriented Co-Ordinates. 1981. 40.00 (ISBN 0-9940017-3-8, Pub. by Vieweg & Sohn Germany). Heyden.
Laurent, J. P., ed. Coordination Chemistry-Twenty One: Twenty-First International Conference on Coordination Chemistry, Toulouse, France, 1980. (IUPAC Symposium Ser.). 200p. 1981. 55.00 (ISBN 0-08-025300-8). Pergamon.
Moon, P. & Spencer, D. E. Field Theory Handbook: Including Coordinate Systems, Differential Equations & Their Solutions. 2nd ed. LC 77-178288. (Illus.). viii, 236p. 1971. 57.90 (ISBN 0-387-02732-7). Springer-Verlag.
Smogorzhevsky, A. Method of Coordinates. 47p. 1980. pap. 2.95 (ISBN 0-8285-1645-6, Pub. by Mir Pubs USSR). Imported Pubns.

COORDINATION COMPOUNDS
see also Ligand Field Theory
Berezin, B. D. Coordination Compounds of Porphyrins & Phthalocyanine. LC 80-40958. 286p. 1981. 69.95 (ISBN 0-471-27857-2, Pub. by Wiley-Interscience). Wiley.
Cais, Michael, ed. Progress in Coordination Chemistry. 1969. 59.75 (ISBN 0-444-40746-4). Elsevier.
Coordination Polymerization-a Memorial to Karl Ziegler: Proceedings, American Chemical Symposium, UCLA, Los Angeles, California, April 1974. 1975. 49.50 (ISBN 0-12-172450-6). Acad Pr.
Gutmann, Viktor. Coordination Chemistry in Non-Aqueous Solutions. LC 68-13490. (Illus.). 1968. 29.50 (ISBN 0-387-80867-1). Springer-Verlag.
Hargittai, M. & Hargittai, I. The Molecular Geometries of Coordination Compounds in the Vapour Phase. 276p. 1977. 53.25 (ISBN 0-444-99832-2). Elsevier.

International Union of Pure & Applied Chemistry. Stability of Constants: Second Supplement. Incl. Inorganic Ligands. Hogfeldt, E., ed. LC 80-471237. 324p. 195.00 (ISBN 0-08-020959-9, E120, E125); 85.00 (ISBN 0-686-86592-8); Organic Ligands. Perrin, D. D., ed. 1200p. 150.00 (ISBN 0-08-020958-0). 1976. Pergamon.

Kauffmann, George B. Alfred Werner: Founder of Coordination Chemistry. (Illus.). 1966. pap. 27.20 (ISBN 0-387-03577-X). Springer-Verlag.

Kirschner, Stanley, ed. Coordination Chemistry. LC 77-81522. 331p. 1969. 32.50x (ISBN 0-306-30402-3, Plenum Pr). Plenum Pub.

Kragten, J. Atlas of Metal-Ligand Equilibria in Aqueous Solution. LC 77-12168. 781p. 1978. 174.95x (ISBN 0-470-99309-X). Halsted Pr.

Nakamoto, Kazuo. Infrared & Raman Spectra of Inorganic & Coordination Compounds. 3rd ed. LC 77-15107. 1978. 45.50x (ISBN 0-471-62979-0, Pub. by Wiley-Interscience). Wiley.

Structural Problems. (Structure & Bonding Ser.: Vol. 37). (Illus.). 1979. 57.00 (ISBN 0-387-09455-5). Springer-Verlag.

COPEPODA

Brady, G. S. Monograph of the Free & Semi-Parasitic Copepoda of the British Islands, 3 Vols. Repr. of 1880 ed. Set. 46.00 (ISBN 0-384-05470-6). Johnson Repr.

Damkaer, Carl & Damkaer, David. Henrik Kroeyer's Publications on Pelagic Marine Copepoda (1838-1849) LC 79-51538. (Transactions Ser.: Vol. 69, Pt. 6). 1979. 8.00 (ISBN 0-87169-696-7). Am Philos.

Dudley, Patricia L. Development & Systematics of Some Pacific Marine Symbiotic Copepods: A Study of the Biology of the Notodelphyidae, Associates of Ascidians. LC 66-29836. (University of Washington Publications in Biology Ser.: No. 21). (Illus.). 282p. 1966. 20.00x (ISBN 0-295-73765-4). U of Wash Pr.

Harding, J. P. & Smith, W. A. A Key to the British Freshwater Cyclopid & Calanoid Copepods. 2nd ed. 1974. 20.00x (ISBN 0-900386-20-7, Pub. by Freshwater Bio). State Mutual Bk.

Lang, K. Monographie der Harpacticiden. (Ger., Illus.). 1682p. 1975. Repr. of 1948 ed. lib. bdg. 168.00 (ISBN 3-87429-089-1). Lubrecht & Cramer.

Marshall, S. M. & Orr, A. P. The Biology of a Marine Copepod: Calanus Finmarchicus (Gunnerus) (Illus.). vii, 195p. 1972. Repr. of 1955 ed. 21.00 (ISBN 0-387-05677-7). Springer-Verlag.

Owre, H. B. & Foyo, Maria. Copepods of the Florida Current. (Fauna Caribaea Ser: No. 1). 1967. 7.95x (ISBN 0-87024-081-1); pap. 6.00x (ISBN 0-87024-080-3). U Miami Marine.

Scott, T. & Scott, A. British Parasitic Copepoda, 2 Vols in 1. Repr. of 1913 ed. 28.00 (ISBN 0-384-54470-3). Johnson Repr.

COPERNICUS, NICOLAUS, 1473-1543

Armitage, Angus. The World of Copernicus. 1972. pap. 7.95x (ISBN 0-8464-0979-8). Beekman Pubs.

Baranowski, Henry K. Bibliografia Kopernikowska 1509-1955. 1969. Repr. of 1958 ed. 32.00 (ISBN 0-8337-0161-4). B Franklin.

Bienkowska, B., ed. The Scientific World of Copernicus. Cekalska, K., tr. from Pol. LC 73-85712. 1973. lib. bdg. 29.00 (ISBN 90-277-0353-1, Pub. by Reidel Holland). Kluwer Academic.

Kuhn, Thomas S. Copernican Revolution: Planetary Astronomy in the Development of Western Thought. LC 57-76121. (Illus.). 1957. 18.50x (ISBN 0-674-17100-4); pap. 7.95 (ISBN 0-674-17103-9). Harvard U Pr.

Markowski, Benedict. Kopernik the Great Humanist. (Illus.). 1973. 1.00 (ISBN 0-685-37750-4). Endurance.

Mizwa, Stephen P. Nicholas Copernicus: Fifteen Forty-Three To Nineteen Forty-Three. LC 68-8205. (Illus.). 1969. Repr. of 1943 ed. 16.00x (ISBN 0-8046-0316-2, Pub. by Kennikat). Assoc Faculty Pr.

Rosen, Edward. Copernicus & the Scientific Revolution. LC 83-9380. (Anvil Ser.). 224p. (Orig.). 1984. pap. text ed. 6.95 (ISBN 0-89874-573-X). Krieger.

Rusinek, Michal. Land of Nicholas Copernicus. Jordan, A. T., tr. (Library of Polish Studies: Vol. 2). (Illus.). 1973. text ed. 12.50 (ISBN 0-917004-03-5). Kosciuszko.

Smithsonian Institute. Nicolaus Copernicus Fourteen Seventy-Three to Fifteen Forty-Three, 500th Anniversary Celebration. 0.25 (ISBN 0-940962-14-4). Polish Inst Art & Sci.

Stachiewicz, Wanda. Copernicus & the Changing World. 64p. 1973. 2.00 (ISBN 0-940962-04-7). Polish Inst Art & Sci.

Swerdlow, N. M. & Neugebauer, O. Mathematical Astronomy in Copernicus' "De revolutionibus", 2 pts. (Studies in the History of Mathematics & Physical Sciences: Vol. 10). (Illus.). 736p. 1984. Set. 78.00 (ISBN 0-387-90939-7). Springer Verlag.

Symposium of 'Nicolas Copernicus Committee of International Union of History & Philosophy of Science, Torum, Poland, 1973. The Reception of Copernicus' Heliocentric Theory: Proceedings. Dobrzycki, Jerzy, ed. LC 72-95980. 368p. 1973. lib. bdg. 39.50 (ISBN 90-277-0311-6, Pub. by Reidel Holland). Kluwer Academic.

Westman, Robert S., ed. The Copernican Achievement. 1976. 41.00x (ISBN 0-520-02877-5). U of Cal Pr.

COPIERS

see Copying Machines

COPPER

see also Copperwork

Bowen, Robert & Gunatilaka, Ananda. Copper: Its Geology & Economics. LC 77-5877. 366p. 1977. 124.95x (ISBN 0-470-99156-9). Halsted Pr.

Ciba Foundation. Biological Roles of Copper. LC 80-23396. (Ciba Foundation Symposium, New Ser.: 79). pap. 87.80 (ISBN 0-317-29742-2, 2022198). Bks Demand UMI.

Division of Medical Sciences, National Research Council. Copper. LC 76-57888. (Medical & Biologic Effects of Environmental Pollutants Ser.). 115p. 1977. pap. 8.50 (ISBN 0-309-02536-2). Natl Acad Pr.

Ehrlich, Reinhart P., ed. Copper Metallurgy. LC 70-633878. pap. 94.80 (ISBN 0-317-10290-7, 2012652). Bks Demand UMI.

Extractive Metallurgy of Copper. 2nd ed. (International Ser. on Materials Science & Technology: Vol. 32). (Illus.). 1980. 56.00 (ISBN 0-08-024736-9); pap. 23.00 (ISBN 0-685-97184-8). Pergamon.

Haas, Larry A. & Weir, D. Robert, eds. Hydrometallurgy of Copper, Its Byproducts & Rarer Metals. LC 83-71424. (Illus.). 113p. 1983. pap. text ed. 20.00x (ISBN 0-89520-412-6). Soc Mining Eng.

Habashi, Fathi. Chalcopyrite: Its Chemistry & Metallurgy. (Illus.). 1978. text ed. 45.00x (ISBN 0-07-025383-8). McGraw.

Jones, R. Copper Book. 1986. cancelled (ISBN 0-442-23165-2). Van Nos Reinhold.

Karlin, Kenneth D. & Zubieta, Jon, eds. Copper & Coordination Chemistry: Biochemical & Inorganic Perspectives. (Illus.). 500p. 1983. text ed. 65.00 (ISBN 0-940030-03-9). Adenine Pr.

L'Hermite, P. & Handtschutter, J., eds. Copper in Animal Wastes & Sewage Sludge. xiv, 378p. 1981. 42.00 (ISBN 90-277-1293-X, Pub. by Reidel Holland). Kluwer Academic.

Loneragan, J. F. Copper in Soils & Plants. 1981. 47.50 (ISBN 0-12-455520-9). Acad Pr.

Lontie, Rene, ed. Copper Proteins & Copper Enzymes, Vol. I. 256p. 1984. 70.00 (ISBN 0-8493-6470-1). CRC Pr.

--Copper Proteins & Copper Enzymes, Vol. II. 304p. 1984. 72.50 (ISBN 0-8493-6471-X). CRC Pr.

--Copper Proteins & Copper Enzymes, Vol. III. 272p. 1984. 70.00 (ISBN 0-8493-6472-8). CRC Pr.

Mendenhall, J. Howard, ed. Understanding Copper Alloys: The Manufacture & Use of Copper & Copper Alloy Sheet & Strip. LC 79-24502. pap. 84.50 (ISBN 0-317-28055-4, 2055774). Bks Demand UMI.

Nriagu, Jerome O. Copper in the Environment, 2 pts. Incl. Pt. 1. Ecological Cycling. LC 79-10875. 522p. 94.00x (ISBN 0-471-04778-3); Pt. 2. Health Effects. LC 79-15062. 489p. 1980. 90.00x (ISBN 0-471-04777-5). (Environmental Science & Technology: Texts & Monographs). 1980 (Pub. by Wiley-Interscience). Wiley.

Owen, Charles A., Jr. Biochemical Aspects of Copper: Copper Proteins, Ceruloplasmin, & Copper Protein Binding. LC 81-18988. (Copper in Biology & Medicine Ser.). 205p. 1982. 28.00 (ISBN 0-8155-0891-3). Noyes.

--Biological Aspects of Copper: Occurrence, Assay & Interrelationships. LC 82-7931. (Copper in Biology & Medicine Ser.). 156p. 1983. 28.00 (ISBN 0-8155-0918-9). Noyes.

Specification for Copper & Copper Alloy Bare Arc-Welding Electrodes: A5.70. 11p. 10.00 (ISBN 0-87171-242-3); member 7.50. Am Welding.

Specification for Copper & Copper Alloy Gas Welding Rods: A5.27. 11p. 1978. 10.00 (ISBN 0-87171-154-0); member 7.50. Am Welding.

Tatsch, J. H. Copper Deposits: Origin, Evolution, & Present Characteristics. LC 74-78916. (Illus.). 339p. 1975. 72.00 (ISBN 0-912890-08-8). Tatsch.

Titley, Spencer & Hicks, Carol, eds. Geology of the Porphyry Copper Deposits: Southwestern North America. LC 66-14229. (Illus.). 287p. 1966. 24.50x (ISBN 0-8165-0037-1). U of Ariz Pr.

Welcher, Frank J. & Boschmann, Erwin. Organic Reagents for Copper. LC 76-18141. 632p. (Orig.). 1979. 41.50 (ISBN 0-88275-440-8). Krieger.

West, E. G. Copper & Its Alloys. (Industrial Metals Ser.). 241p. 1982. 69.95X (ISBN 0-470-27533-2). Halsted Pr.

West, George A. Copper: Its Mining & Use by the Aborigines of the Lake Superior Region. Repr. of 1929 ed. lib. bdg. 18.75 (ISBN 0-8371-4634-8, WECO). Greenwood.

COPPER ALLOYS

see also Bronze

LeMay, Iain & Schetky, L. McDonald. Copper in Iron & Steel. LC 82-17615. 512p. 1983. 59.50X (ISBN 0-471-05913-7, Pub. by Wiley-Interscience). Wiley.

Ling, E. & Taubenblat, P. W., eds. High Conductivity Cooper & Aluminum Alloys. LC 84-61484. (Illus.). 189p. 1984. 55.00 (ISBN 0-89520-479-7). Metal Soc.

--High Conductivity Copper & Aluminum Alloys. 190p. 1984. 55.00 (ISBN 0-317-37221-1); members 34.00 (ISBN 0-317-37222-X). Metal Soc.

Mendenhall, J. Howard, ed. Understanding Copper Alloys. LC 85-5173. 342p. 1986. Repr. of 1977 ed. lib. bdg. price not set (ISBN 0-89874-855-0). Krieger.

--Understanding Copper Alloys: The Manufacture & Use of Copper & Copper Alloy Sheet & Strip. LC 79-24502. pap. 84.50 (ISBN 0-317-28055-4, 2055774). Bks Demand UMI.

Specification for Copper & Copper Alloy Bare Arc-Welding Electrodes: A5.70. 11p. 10.00 (ISBN 0-87171-242-3); member 7.50. Am Welding.

Specification for Copper & Copper Alloy Gas Welding Rods: A5.27. 11p. 1978. 10.00 (ISBN 0-87171-154-0); member 7.50. Am Welding.

TMS-AIME 113th Annual Meeting, Los Angeles, Feb. 26 - March 1, 1984. High Conductivity Copper & Aluminum Alloys. Taubenblat, P. W. & Ling, E., eds. (Proceedings). 190p. 55.00 (ISBN 0-89520-479-7, 249); members 34.00 (ISBN 0-317-37163-0); student members 18.00 (ISBN 0-317-37164-9). Metal Soc.

COPPER IN THE BODY

CIBA Foundation Symposium. Biological Roles of Copper. (Ciba Symposium Ser.: No. 79). 1981. 61.50 (ISBN 0-444-90177-9). Elsevier.

Owen, Charles A., Jr. Biological Aspects of Copper: Occurrence, Assay & Interrelationships. LC 82-7931. (Copper in Biology & Medicine Ser.). 156p. 1983. 28.00 (ISBN 0-8155-0918-9). Noyes.

--Copper Deficiency & Toxicity: Acquired & Inherited, in Plants, Animals, & Man. LC 81-11061. (Noyes Publications-Copper in Biology & Medicine Ser.). 189p. 1982. 28.00 (ISBN 0-8155-0868-9). Noyes.

--Physiological Aspects of Copper: Copper in Organs & Systems. LC 82-3421. (Copper in Biology & Medicine Ser.). 286p. 1982. 28.00 (ISBN 0-8155-0904-9). Noyes.

Spiro, Thomas G. Copper Proteins, Vol. 3. LC 81-7465. (Metal Ions in Biology Ser.). 363p. 1981. 78.50 (ISBN 0-471-04400-8, Pub. by Wiley-Interscience). Wiley.

COPPER INDUSTRY AND TRADE

Bernstein, Jacob. An Investor's Guide to Using Cycles in the Precious Metals & Copper. LC 84-19561. 224p. 1985. 34.95x (ISBN 0-471-88746-3, Pub. by Wiley-Interscience). Wiley.

Bowen, Robert & Gunatilaka, Ananda. Copper: Its Geology & Economics. LC 77-5877. 366p. 1977. 124.95x (ISBN 0-470-99156-9). Halsted Pr.

Gomez, Manuel, et al. At Work in Copper: Occupational Health & Safety in Copper Smelting, 3 vols. LC 79-63375. (Illus.). 1979. Set. pap. 70.00x (ISBN 0-918780-11-X); Vol. I. 40.00x; Vols. II & III. 20.00x ea. INFORM.

Hamilton, Henry. English Brass & Copper Industries to 1800. 2nd ed. LC 67-3032. (Illus.). Repr. of 1926 ed. 35.00x (ISBN 0-678-05171-2). Kelley.

Lasaga, Manuel. The Copper Industry in the Chilean Economy: An Econometric Analysis. LC 81-47025. (The Wharton Econometric Studies). (Illus.). 224p. 1981. 28.00x (ISBN 0-669-04543-8). Lexington Bks.

Malhotra, Subhash C. Bibliography on Copper Smelting Nineteen-Forty to Nineteen Seventy-Three. LC 73-87447. 300p. 1973. 31.45 (ISBN 0-686-05581-0). Malhotra.

Mezger, Dorothea. Copper in the World Economy. LC 79-3883. 282p. 1980. 16.00 (ISBN 0-85345-544-9); pap. 8.00 (ISBN 0-85345-545-7). Monthly Rev.

Mikesell, Raymond. World Copper Industry: Structure & Economic Analysis. LC 79-4581. (Resources for the Future Ser.). 1979. pap. 10.95x (ISBN 0-8018-2270-X). Johns Hopkins.

Obidegwu, Chukwuma F. & Nziramasanga, Mudziviri. Copper & Zambia: An Econometric Analysis. (The Wharton Econometric Studies). 240p. 1981. 32.00x (ISBN 0-669-04659-0). Lexington Bks.

Przeworski, Joanne F. The Decline of the Copper Industry in Chile & the Entrance of North American Capital, 1870 to 1916. Bruchey, Stuart, ed. LC 80-609. (Multinational Corporations Ser.). 1980. lib. bdg. 33.50x (ISBN 0-405-13379-0). Ayer Co Pubs.

Weber, Sophie. How OSHA Enforces the Law. 82p. (Orig.). 1981. pap. 15.00 (ISBN 0-918780-21-7). INFORM.

Whiteman, Maxwell. Copper for America: The Hendricks Family & a National Industry, 1755-1939. LC 79-153446. 1971. 30.00x (ISBN 0-8135-0687-5). Rutgers U Pr.

COPPER MINES AND MINING

Arrington, Leonard J. & Hansen, Gary B. The Richest Hole on Earth: A History of the Bingham Copper Mine. 103p. (Orig.). 1963. pap. 4.50 (ISBN 0-87421-028-3). Utah St U Pr.

Emerson, C. & Warr, P. G. Economic Evaluation of Mineral Processing Projects. (Development Studies Centre: Occ. pap. 32). 29p. 1983. pap. text ed. 5.95 (ISBN 0-909150-91-5, Pub. by ANUP Australia). Australia N U P.

Gluschke, Wolfgang, et al. Copper, the Next Fifteen Years: A United Nations Study. 1978. lib. bdg. 21.00 (ISBN 90-277-0898-3, Pub. by Reidel Holland); pap. 8.95 (ISBN 90-277-0899-1, Pub. by Reidel Holland). Kluwer Academic.

Hamilton, Henry. English Brass & Copper Industries to 1800. 2nd ed. LC 67-3032. (Illus.). Repr. of 1926 ed. 35.00x (ISBN 0-678-05171-2). Kelley.

Hollister, Victor F. Geology of the Porphyry Copper Deposits of the Western Hemisphere. LC 77-71575. (Illus.). 1978. text ed. 20.00x (ISBN 0-89520-048-1). Soc Mining Eng.

Hoshino, Yoshiro. History of Technological & Administrative Development in the Ashio Copper Mine. (Project on Technology Transfer, Transformation & Development: The Japanese Experience). 20p. 1983. pap. text ed. 5.00 (ISBN 92-808-0417-0, TUNU216, UNU). Unipub.

Leifchild, J. R. Cornwall: Its Mines & Miners. 2nd ed. LC 68-58855. Repr. of 1857 ed. 29.50x (ISBN 0-678-05064-3). Kelley.

Muhly, James D. Copper & Tin: The Distribution of Mineral Resources & the Nature of the Metals Trade in the Bronze Age, Including Supplement. new ed. (Connecticut Academy of Arts & Sciences Transaction Ser.: Vol. 43 & 46). 380p. 1976. 29.50 (ISBN 0-208-01573-6, Archon). Shoe String.

Navin, Thomas R. Copper Mining & Management. LC 78-2669. pap. 112.50 (ISBN 0-317-28914-4, 2020438). Bks Demand UMI.

Schlitt, W. J., ed. Leaching & Recovering Copper from As-Mined Materials. LC 79-57347. (Illus.). 124p. 1980. pap. 20.00x (ISBN 0-89520-272-7). Soc Mining Eng.

Sir Ronald Prain Mining Journal Books Ltd. Copper: The Anatomy of an Industry. 300p. 1980. 20.25x (ISBN 0-900117-07-9, Pub. by Mining Journal England). State Mutual Bk.

Sutulov, Alexander. Copper Porphyries. LC 73-93695. (A World Mining Book). (Illus.). 206p. 1974. 20.00 (ISBN 0-87930-028-0). Miller Freeman.

Titley, Spencer R., ed. Advances in Geology of the Porphyry Copper Deposits: Southwestern North America. LC 81-16461. 560p. 1982. 39.50x (ISBN 0-8165-0730-9). U of Ariz Pr.

Whiteley, Robert J. Geophysical Case Study of the Woodlawn Orebody, New South Wales,Australia. LC 79-42637. (Illus.). xviii, 592p. 1981. 110.00 (ISBN 0-08-023996-X). Pergamon.

COPPER WORK

see Copperwork

COPPERSMITHING

see Copperwork

COPPERWORK

Kramer, Karl & Kramer, Nora. Coppercraft & Silver Made at Home. 1971. pap. 5.95 (ISBN 0-486-22790-1). Dover.

Rose, Wendy. Lost Copper. 1980. 8.95 (ISBN 0-939046-20-2). Malki Mus Pr.

Tuddenham, W. M. & Hibbeln, R. J., eds. Sampling & Analysis of Copper Cathodes - STP 831. LC 83-72052. 179p. 1984. text ed. 29.00 (ISBN 0-8031-0217-8, 04-831000-03). ASTM.

COPYING MACHINES

Bedini, Silvio A. Thomas Jefferson & His Copying Machines. LC 81-7288. (Monticello Monograph Ser.). (Illus.). 233p. 1984. text ed. 20.00x (ISBN 0-8139-1025-0). U Pr of Va.

Craver, John. Graph Paper from Your Copier. LC 80-80170. (Illus.). 232p. 1980. pap. 12.95 (ISBN 0-89586-045-7). H P Bks.

Tract, Sam. A Planned Approach for Penetrating the High Speed Copying Market for Instant & Small Commercial Printers. (Illus.). 100p. 1984. 3-ring binder 79.95 (ISBN 0-930579-01-1). S Tract Advert.

COPYING PROCESSES

see also Copying Machines; Photocopying Processes; Thermography (Copying Process)

BOOKS - SUBJECT INDEX CORRELATION (STATISTICS)

Chambers, Harry T. Copying, Duplication & Microfilm. 192p. 1972. 17.95x (ISBN 0-8464-0291-2). Beekman Pubs.
Deutsches Komittee fuer Reprographie. Woerterbuch der Reprographie: Begriffe und Definitionen. 3rd rev. ed. (Ger., Eng. & Fr.). 273p. (Dictionary of Reprography: Terms & Definitions). 1976. pap. 44.00 (ISBN 0-686-56614-9, M-6961). French & Eur.
Hanson, Richard E. The Manager's Guide to Copying & Duplicating. (Illus.). 1980. 23.50 (ISBN 0-07-026080-X). McGraw.
Hewson, John E. Process Instrumentation Manifolds: Their Selection & Use, a Handbook. LC 80-82115. 320p. 1981. text ed. 44.95x (ISBN 0-87664-447-7). Instru Soc.
Rudman, Jack. Duplicating Equipment Operator. (Career Examination Ser.: C-208). (Cloth bdg. avail. on request). pap. 10.00 (ISBN 0-8373-0208-0). Natl Learning.
--Senior Duplicating Machine Operator. (Career Examination Ser.: C-1899). (Cloth bdg. avail. on request). pap. 12.00 (ISBN 0-8373-1899-8). Natl Learning.

COPYRIGHT–COMPUTER PROGRAMS

Davis, G. Gervaise, et al. Software Protection: Practical & Legal Steps to Protect & Market Computer Programs. 400p. 1985. 42.95 (ISBN 0-442-21903-2). Van Nos Reinhold.
Goldberg, Morton David. Computer Software: Protection & Marketing 1984, 2 vols. 1470p. 1984. Set. pap. 35.00 (ISBN 0-317-27383-3, #G4-3751). PLI.

COPYRIGHT AND ELECTRONIC DATA PROCESSING

Borking, John J. Third Party Protection of Software & Firmware: Direct Protection of Zeros & Ones. LC 84-24752. 522p. 1985. 74.00 (ISBN 0-444-87677-4, North-Holland). Elsevier.
Breslow, Marc. An Analysis of Computer & Photocopying Copyright Issues from the Point of View of the General Public & the Ultimate Consumer. 115p. 10.00 (ISBN 0-318-16242-3, A-15). Public Int Econ.
Bush, George P., ed. Technology & Copyright: Annotated Bibliography & Source Materials. LC 72-87129. 454p. 1972. 28.50 (ISBN 0-912338-03-2); microfiche 9.50 (ISBN 0-912338-04-0); pap. 14.50. Lomond.
Harris, Thorne D., III. The Legal Guide to Computer Software Protection: A Practical Handbook on Copyrights, Trademarks, Publishing & Trade Secrets. (Illus.). 320p. 1984. 24.95 (ISBN 0-13-528373-6, Busn); pap. 19.95 (ISBN 0-13-528365-5). P-H.
Henry, Nicholas L., ed. Copyright, Congress & Technology: The Public Record, 5 vols. Incl. The Formative Years, 1958-1966. (Vol. I). 1979. 45.00x (ISBN 0-912700-29-7); The Political Years, 1967-1973. (Vol. II). 1979. 45.00x (ISBN 0-912700-30-0); The Future of Copyright, 1973-1977. (Vol. III). 1980. 45.00x (ISBN 0-912700-31-9); Contu: The Future of Information Technology. (Vol. IV). 1980. 45.00x (ISBN 0-912700-32-7); Vol. V. Contu's Final Report & Recommendations. 1980. 45.00x (ISBN 0-912700-74-2). LC 78-2347. Set. 225.00 (ISBN 0-912700-13-0). Oryx Pr.
Hoffman, Paul S. The Software Legal Book. 309p. 1982. looseleaf 85.00 (ISBN 0-935506-01-2). Carnegie Pr.
Neitzke, Frederic W. A Software Law Primer. LC 83-23508. 176p. 1984. 24.95 (ISBN 0-442-26866-1). Van Nos Reinhold.
Wallace, Jonathan D. Understanding Software Law. pap. 3.50 (ISBN 0-88284-268-4). Alfred Pub.

CORAL REEFS AND ISLANDS

Adey, Walter H., et al. Field Guidebook to the Reefs & Reef Communities of St. Croix, Virgin Islands. (Third International Symposium on Coral Reefs Ser.). (Illus.). 52p. 1977. pap. 5.00 (ISBN 0-932981-40-2). Univ Miami A R C.
Alkire, William. Coral Islanders. Goldschmidt, Walter, ed. LC 77-90673. (World of Man Ser.). (Illus.). 1978. text ed. 18.95x (ISBN 0-88295-618-3); pap. text ed. 9.95x (ISBN 0-88295-619-1). Harlan Davidson.
Bemert, Gunnar & Ormond, Rupert. Red Sea Coral Reefs. (Illus.). 192p. 1981. 45.00 (ISBN 0-7103-0007-7). Routledge & Kegan.
Chaplin, Charles C. Fishwatcher's Guide to West Atlantic Coral Reefs. rev. ed. LC 72-9309. (Illus.). 64p. 1979. plastic bdg. 8.95 (ISBN 0-915180-08-1); pap. 4.95 (ISBN 0-915180-09-X). Harrowood Bks.
Darwin, Charles. The Structure & Distribution of Coral Reefs. LC 84-79. (Illus.). 239p. 1984. pap. 7.95 (ISBN 0-8165-0844-5). U of Ariz Pr.
Darwin, Charles R. The Structure & Distribution of Coral Reefs. 3rd ed. LC 73-147085. (Illus.). xx, 344p. 1972. 42.50 (ISBN 0-404-08402-8). AMS Pr.
Davis, W. M. The Coral Reef Problem. LC 75-45469. 612p. 1976. Repr. of 1928 ed. 39.50 (ISBN 0-88275-383-5). Krieger.
Davis, William M. Coral Reef Problem. Repr. of 1928 ed. 37.50 (ISBN 0-404-01998-6). AMS Pr.
Edmondson, C. H. Ecology of an Hawaiian Coral Reef. (BMB Ser.). Repr. of 1928 ed. 11.00 (ISBN 0-527-02148-2). Kraus Repr.
Endean, Robert. Australia's Great Barrier Reef. LC 82-2063. (Illus.). 348p. 1983. text ed. 29.95x (ISBN 0-7022-1678-X). U of Queensland Pr.
Greenberg, Jerry. The Coral Reef. (Orig.). saddlestiched 4.95x (ISBN 0-913008-06-0). Seahawk Pr.
Greenberg, Jerry & Greenberg, Idaz. The Living Reef. LC 70-187354. (Illus.). 126p. perfect bound 9.95x (ISBN 0-913008-01-X). Seahawk Pr.
Heatwolfe, H., et al. Community Ecology of Coral Cay: A Study of One-Tree Island, Great Barrier Reef, Australia. (Monographiae Biologicae: No. 43). 400p. 1981. 74.00 (ISBN 90-6193-096-0, Pub. by Junk Pubs Netherlands). Kluwer Academic.
James, Noel P., et al. Field Guidebook to Modern & Pleistocene Reef Carbonates, Barbados, W. I. (Third International Symposium on Coral Reefs Ser.). (Illus.). 30p. 1977. pap. 4.00 (ISBN 0-932981-37-2). Univ Miami A R C.
Jones, O. A. & Endean, R., eds. Biology & Geology of Coral Reefs, 4 vols. Incl. Vol. 1. Geology. 1973. 71.50 (ISBN 0-12-389601-0); Vol. 2. Biology - One. 1974. 83.50 (ISBN 0-12-389602-9); Vol. 3. Biology - Two. 1976. 95.50 (ISBN 0-12-389603-7); Vol. 4. 1977. 75.00 (ISBN 0-12-389604-5). Set. Acad Pr.
Kaplan, Eugene H. A Field Guide to Coral Reefs of the Caribbean & Florida. (Peterson Field Guide Ser.). (Illus.). 384p. 1984. 17.95 (ISBN 0-395-31321-X). HM.
Kensley, Brian. The Atlantic Barrier Reef Ecosystem at Carrie Bow Cay, Belize, III-New Marine Isopods. LC 84-600999. (Smithsonian Contributions to the Marine Sciences: No. 24). pap. 21.30 (ISBN 0-317-26741-8, 2024355). Bks Demand UMI.
Kuhlmann, Dietrich. Living Coral Reefs of the World. (Illus.). 186p. 1985. 24.95 (ISBN 0-668-06327-0). Arco.
Miller, James A. & Macintyre, Ian G. Field Guidebook to the Reefs of Belize. (Third International Symposium on Coral Reefs Ser.). (Illus.). 36p. 1977. pap. 4.00 (ISBN 0-932981-41-0). Univ Miami A R C.
Muller, K., ed. Coastal Research in the Gulf of Bothnia. (Monographiae Biologicae: No. 45). 480p. 1982. 87.00 (ISBN 90-6193-098-7, Pub. by Junk Pubs Netherlands). Kluwer Academic.
Riefenstahl, Leni. Coral Gardens. LC 78-2163. (Illus.). 1978. 29.95i (ISBN 0-06-013591-3, HarpT). Har-Row.
Roberts, Harry H. Field Guidebook to the Reefs & Geology of Grand Cayman Island, B.W.I. (Third International Symposium on Coral Reefs Ser.). (Illus.). 44p. 1977. pap. 4.00 (ISBN 0-932981-39-9). Univ Miami A R C.
Robertson, D. Ross & Glynn, Peter W. Field Guidebook to the Reefs of San Blas Island, Panama. (Third International Symposium on Coral Reefs Ser.). (Illus.). 16p. 1977. pap. 2.00 (ISBN 0-932981-42-9). Univ Miami A R C.
Romashko, Sandra. Living Coral. 3rd ed. LC 76-12930. 1985. pap. 3.95 (ISBN 0-317-19733-9). Windward Pub.
Romashko, Sandra D. Living Coral & Other Inhabitants of the Reef. 3rd ed. LC 76-12930. (Illus.). 64p. 1985. pap. 3.95 (ISBN 0-89317-011-9). Windward Pub.
Wilson, Roberta & Wilson, James Q. Watching Fishes: Life & Behavior on Coral Reefs. LC 84-48205. (Illus.). 224p. 1985. 24.04i (ISBN 0-06-015371-7, HarpT). Har-Row.
Wood, Elizabeth M. Corals of the World. (Illus.). 256p. 1983. 29.95 (ISBN 0-87666-809-0, H-1049). TFH Pubns.
Woodley, Jeremy D. & Robinson, Ted. Field Guidebook to the Modern & Ancient Reefs of Jamaica. (Third International Symposium on Coral Reefs Ser.). (Illus.). 33p. 1977. pap. 4.00 (ISBN 0-932981-38-0). Univ Miami A R C.
Zoological Society of London - 28th Symposium. Regional Variation in Indian Ocean Coral Reefs. Stoddart, D. R. & Yonge, Maurice, eds. 1972. 78.00 (ISBN 0-12-613328-X). Acad Pr.

CORALS

see also Coelenterata; Marine Fauna

Bauer, Max. Precious Stones: A Popular Account of Their Characters, Occurence & Applications. Spencer, L. J., tr. LC 69-12082. (Illus.). 1969. 52.50 (ISBN 0-8048-0489-3). C E Tuttle.
--Precious Stones: A Popular Account of Their Characters, Occurrence & Applications with an Introduction to Their Determination with an Appendix on Pearls & Coral, 2 Vols. Spencer, L. J., tr. (Illus.). 1968. Vol. 1. pap. 6.95 (ISBN 0-486-21910-0); Vol. 2. pap. 7.95 (ISBN 0-486-21911-9). Dover.
Burgess, Warren E. Corals. (Illus.). 1979. 4.95 (ISBN 0-87666-521-0, KW-053). TFH Pubns.
Corals of Pennekamp. (Illus.). 48p. 18.00 (ISBN 0-88014-009-7). Mosaic Pr OH.
Edmondson, C. H. Growth of Hawaiian Corals. (BMB Ser.). pap. 8.00 (ISBN 0-527-02164-4). Kraus Repr.
Edwards, Milne & Haime, Jules. The Fossil Corals, 5 Pts. 1849-1854. Set. 89.00 (ISBN 0-384-13870-5). Johnson Repr.
Glynn, Peter W. & Wellington, Gerard M. Corals & Coral Reefs of the Galapagos Islands. LC 82-25161. (Illus.). 1984. lib. bdg. 45.00x (ISBN 0-520-04713-3). U of Cal Pr.
Greenberg, Idaz. Guide to Corals & Fishes. (Illus.). 1977. saddlestitched 4.95x (ISBN 0-913008-08-7). Seahawk Pr.
--Waterproof Guide to Corals & Fishes. (Illus.). 1977. soft plastic pages, rust-proof bdg. 9.95x (ISBN 0-913008-07-9). Seahawk Pr.
Hill, D. The Carboniferous Rugose Corals of Scotland, Pts. 1-4. 1938-41. Set. 47.00 (ISBN 0-384-23240-X). Johnson Repr.
Romashko, Sandra. Living Coral. 3rd ed. LC 76-12930. 1985. pap. 3.95 (ISBN 0-317-19733-9). Windward Pub.
Romashko, Sandra D. The Coral Book: A Guide to Collecting & Identifying the Corals of the World. LC 76-360436. (Illus.). 64p. (Orig.). 1975. pap. 2.95 (ISBN 0-89317-005-4). Windward Pub.
Smith, F. G. Atlantic Reef Corals: A Handbook of the Common Reef & Shallow-Water Corals of Bermuda, the Bahamas, Florida, the West Indies & Brazil. rev. ed. LC 75-125663. (Illus.). 1971. 9.95x (ISBN 0-87024-179-6). U of Miami Pr.

CORD (AUTOMOBILE)

see Automobiles–Types–Cord

CORDAGE

see also Fibers; Knots and Splices; Rope

Snyder, Paul & Snyder, Arthur. Knots & Lines Illustrated. LC 73-107462. 1970. 9.95 (ISBN 0-8286-0046-5). J De Graff.
Stopford, P. J. Cordage & Cables: Their Uses at Sea. 109p. 1968. pap. 8.50x (ISBN 0-85174-163-0). Sheridan.

CORE DRILLING

Anderson, Gene. Coring & Core Analysis Handbook. LC 74-33713. 200p. 1975. 39.95 (ISBN 0-87814-058-1). Pennwell Bks.
EXLOG Staff. Coring Operations: Procedures for Sampling & Analysis of Bottomhole & Sidewall Cores. Whittaker, Alun, ed. (The EXLOG Series of Petroleum Geology & Engineering Handbooks). (Illus.). 191p. 1985. text ed. 29.00 (ISBN 0-88746-053-4). Intl Human Res.
Gumenskii, B. M. & Komarov, N. S. Soil Drilling by Vibration. LC 61-12724. 80p. 1961. 29.50x (ISBN 0-306-10604-3, Consultants). Plenum Pub.
Kull, Tamara. Coring & Core Analysis. (Illus.). 80p. (Orig.). pap. text ed. 5.00 (ISBN 0-88698-041-0, 83-61932). PETEX.
Leecraft, Jodie, ed. Power & Power Transmission. 2nd ed. (Rotary Drilling Ser.: Unit I). (Illus.). 1983. pap. text ed. 5.00 (ISBN 0-88698-011-9, 2.10720). PETEX.
--Power & Power Transmission: Canadian Metric Edition. 2nd ed. (Rotary Drilling Ser.: Unit I). (Illus.). 1983. pap. text ed. 5.00 (ISBN 0-88698-023-2). PETEX.
Splettstoesser, John F., ed. Ice-Core Drilling. LC 76-3219. (Illus.). x, 189p. 1976. pap. 11.95x (ISBN 0-8032-5843-7). U of Nebr Pr.

CORN

Agrometeorology of the Maize (Corn) Crop. (Illus.). 1978. pap. 55.00 (ISBN 92-63-10481-6, W381, WMO). Unipub.
Bottrell, Dale G. Guidelines for Integrated Control of Maize Pests. (Plant Production & Protection Papers: No. 18). (Eng. & Fr., Illus.). 98p. 1978. pap. 14.50 (ISBN 92-5-100875-2, F1942, FAO). Unipub.
Bunting, E. S. Forage Maize. 346p. 1978. 89.00x (ISBN 0-7084-0082-5, Pub. by CAB Bks England). State Mutual Bk.
Carboxylates & the Uptake of Ammonium by Excised Maize Roots. (Agricultural Research Reports: No. 837). 1975. pap. 13.00 (ISBN 90-220-0570-4, PDC198, PUDOC). Unipub.
Cooperative Hybrid Maize Tests in Europe & Mediterranean Countries: 1952. (Agricultural Development Papers: No. 42). pap. 7.50 (F105, FAO). Unipub.
Dudley, J. W., ed. Seventy Generations of Selection for Oil & Protein in Maize. 1974. 10.00 (ISBN 0-89118-502-X). Crop Sci Soc Am.
Hallauer, Arnel R. & Miranda, J. B., Jr. Quantitative Genetics in Maize Breeding. (Illus.). 468p. 1981. pap. 33.95 (ISBN 0-8138-1519-3). Iowa St U Pr.
Hardeman, Nicholas P. Shucks, Shocks, & Hominy Blocks: Corn As a Way of Life in Pioneer America. LC 80-26534. (Illus.). xiv, 270p. 1981. 25.00x (ISBN 0-8071-0793-X). La State U Pr.
Holm, Seto & Travaglini. The Chemistry of Corn into Alcohol. 134p. 7.95 (ISBN 0-686-92653-6). Rutan Pub.
Improvement & Production of Maize, Sorghum & Millet, 2 vols. (Plant Production & Protection Papers: Nos. 24-1 & 24-2). 703p. 1980. Set. pap. 51.75 (ISBN 0-686-74540-X, F2129, FAO). Vol. 1, General Principles, 226p (ISBN 92-5-101012-9). Vol. 2, Breeding, Agronomy & Seed Production, 500p (ISBN 92-5-101011-0). Unipub.
Inglett, George E., ed. Maize: Recent Progress in Chemistry & Technology. LC 82-20711. 1982. 27.50 (ISBN 0-12-370940-7). Acad Pr.
Jugenheimer, Robert W. Corn: Improvement, Seed Production & Uses. LC 83-17491. 688p. 1985. Repr. of 1976 ed. write for info. (ISBN 0-89874-662-0). Krieger.
Kiesselbach, T. A. The Structure & Reproduction of Corn. LC 79-19648. viii, 96p. 1980. 9.50x (ISBN 0-8032-2703-5); pap. 2.95x (ISBN 0-8032-7751-2, BB 724, Bison). U of Nebr Pr.
Klippart, John H. The Wheat Plant: Its Origin, Culture, Growth, Development, Composition, Varieties Together with Information on Corn & Its Culture, 2 vols. 1980. Set. lib. bdg. 200.00 (ISBN 0-8490-3119-2). Gordon Pr.
Mangelsdorf, Paul C. Corn: Its Origin, Evolution, & Development. LC 72-95454. 288p. 1974. 20.00x (ISBN 0-674-17175-6). Harvard U Pr.
Miracle, Marvin P. Maize in Tropical Africa. (Illus.). 346p. 1966. 25.00x (ISBN 0-299-03850-5). U of Wis Pr.
Neuffer, M. G., et al, eds. The Mutants of Maize. (Illus.). 1968. 5.00 (ISBN 0-89118-501-1). Crop Sci Soc Am.
On-Farm Maize Drying & Storage in the Humid Tropics. (Agricultural Services Bulletins: No. 40). 69p. 1980. pap. 7.50 (ISBN 92-5-100944-9, F2077, FAO). Unipub.
Pollmer, W. G. & Phipps, R. H., eds. Improvement of Quality Traits of Maize for Grain & Silage Use. (World Crops: Production, Utilization & Description: No. 2). 505p. 1980. lib. bdg. 63.20 (ISBN 90-247-2289-6). Kluwer Academic.
Shurtleff, M. C. Compendium of Corn Diseases. 2nd ed. LC 80-67517. (Illus.). 105p. 1980. 17.00 (ISBN 0-89054-029-2); members 14.00. Am Phytopathol Soc.
Small-Scale Maize Milling. (Technology Series: Technical Memorandums: No. 7). 143p. 1985. pap. 10.00 (ISBN 92-2-103640-5, ILO359, ILO). Unipub.
Smil, Vaclav & Nachman, Paul. Energy Analysis & Agriculture: An Application to U. S. Corn Production. (Special Studies in Agricultural Science & Policy). 175p. 1982. 27.00x (ISBN 0-86531-167-6). Westview.
Sprague, George F., ed. Corn & Corn Improvement. 1977. 20.00 (ISBN 0-89118-043-5). Am Soc Agron.
Technical Guideline for Maize Seed Technology. (AGP-SIDP Ser.: No. 82-1). 211p. 1982. pap. 15.00 (ISBN 92-5-101190-7, F2323, FAO). Unipub.
Uhlig, Stephen & Bhat, B. A. Choice of Technique in Maize Milling. 135p. 1980. pap. 11.50x (ISBN 0-7073-0240-4, Pub by Scottish Academic Pr Scotland). Columbia U Pr.
U.S. Dept. of Agriculture Library. Corn in the Development of the Civilization of the Americas. LC 70-170182. (American Classics in History & Social Science Ser.: No. 201). 1971. Repr. of 1940 ed. lib. bdg. 23.50 (ISBN 0-8337-0240-8). B Franklin.
Walden, David B., ed. Maize Breeding & Genetics. LC 78-6779. 794p. 1978. 82.95x (ISBN 0-471-91805-9, Pub. by Wiley-Interscience). Wiley.
Will, George F. & Hyde, George E. Corn among the Indians of the upper Missouri. LC 64-63592. 323p. 1964. 23.95x (ISBN 0-8032-0892-8); pap. 5.95x (ISBN 0-8032-5846-1, BB 195, Bison). U of Nebr Pr.
Willis, Harold L. How to Grow Top Quality Corn. (Illus.). 58p. (Orig.). 1984. pap. 5.25 (ISBN 0-912311-02-9). H L Willis.

CORN–BIBLIOGRAPHY

International Maize & Wheat Improvement Center. Bibliography of Corn, 3 vols. LC 78-154562. 1971. Set. 85.00 (ISBN 0-8108-0378-X). Scarecrow.

CORONA (ELECTRICITY)

see also Kirlian Photography

Engineering Dielectrics: Volume 1: Corona Measurement & Interpretation, STP 669. 520p. 1979. 49.00x (ISBN 0-8031-0332-8, 04-669000-21). ASTM.

CORONA, SOLAR

see Sun

CORONA DISCHARGE PHOTOGRAPHY

see Kirlian Photography

CORPUSCULAR THEORY OF MATTER

see Electrons; Matter–Constitution

CORRELATION (STATISTICS)

see also Cluster Analysis; Factor Analysis; Frequency Curves; Latent Structure Analysis; Regression Analysis; Spatial Analysis (Statistics)

Bean, Louis H., compiled by. Graphic Method of Curvilinear Correlation. LC 66-21654. 1968. 22.50x (ISBN 0-678-00282-7). Kelley.

Chayes, Felix. Ratio Correlation: A Manual for Students of Petrology & Geochemistry. LC 71-146110. 1971. text ed. 7.00x (ISBN 0-226-10218-1); pap. text ed. 3.00x (ISBN 0-226-10220-3). U of Chicago Pr.
Dudewicz, Edward J. Solutions in Statistics & Probability. LC 80-68285. (The American Sciences Press Ser. in Mathematical & Management Sciences: Vol. 3). 1980. pap. text ed. 24.95 (ISBN 0-935950-00-1). Am Sciences Pr.
Ezekiel, Mordecai & Fox, Karl A. Methods of Correlation & Regression Analysis: Linear & Curvilinear. 3rd ed. LC 59-11993. (Illus.). 548p. 1959. 55.95 (ISBN 0-471-25014-7, Pub. by Wiley-Interscience). Wiley.
Gradstein, F. M., et al. Quantitative Stratigraphy. 1985. lib. bdg. 77.00 (Pub. by Reidel Holland). Kluwer Academic.
Kendall, Maurice G. Rank Correlation Methods. 4th ed. 1962. 34.95x (ISBN 0-02-847750-2). Hafner.
Kenny, David A. Correlation & Causality. LC 79-4855. 277p. 1979. 35.00x (ISBN 0-471-02439-2, Pub. by Wiley-Interscience). Wiley.
Martin, Paul C. Measurements & Correlation Functions. 108p. 1968. 37.25x (ISBN 0-677-02440-1). Gordon.
Mitropol'skii, Aristarkh K. Correlation Equations for Statistical Computations. LC 65-25246. 103p. 1966. 25.00x (ISBN 0-306-10744-9, Consultants). Plenum Pub.
Tinbergen, Jan. Statistical Testing of Business-Cycle Theories. LC 68-16357. 1968. Repr. of 1939 ed. 15.00x (ISBN 0-87586-009-5). Agathon.

CORRELATION ANALYSIS (CHEMISTRY)
see Linear Free Energy Relationship

CORRELATION EQUATION (CHEMISTRY)
see Linear Free Energy Relationship

CORRELATION OF FORCES
see Force and Energy

CORROSION AND ANTI-CORROSIVES
see also Cathodic Protection; Electrolytic Corrosion; Metals–Pickling; Paint; Protective Coatings; Soil Corrosion; Stress Corrosion; Waterproofing

Accelerated Test Procedures for Screening Atmospheric Surface Coating Systems for Offshore Platforms & Equipment. 5.00 (ISBN 0-317-06634-X). Natl Corrosion Eng.
Acker, Robert F., et al, eds. Proceedings of the Third International Congress on Marine Corrosion & Fouling. 1974. 36.00x (ISBN 0-8101-0445-8). Northwestern U Pr.
Ailor, William H., ed. Atmospheric Corrosion. LC 82-2059. (Corrosion Monograph). 1056p. 1982. 172.50 (ISBN 0-471-86558-3, Pub. by Wiley-Interscience). Wiley.
Ailor, William H., Jr. Handbook on Corrosion Testing & Evaluation. LC 74-162423. (Corrosion Monograph). 873p. 1971. 99.50x (ISBN 0-471-00985-7, Pub. by Wiley-Interscience). Wiley.
American Society for Materials & Testing. Corrosion & Degradation of Implant Materials, STP 684. 369p. 1979. 37.75x (ISBN 0-8031-0313-1, 04-684000-27). ASTM.
American Water Works Association. Corrosion Control. (AWWA Handbooks-Proceedings Ser.). (Illus.). 70p. 1982. pap. 10.20 (ISBN 0-89867-283-X). Am Water Wks Assn.
Ash Deposit & Corrosion from Impurities in Combustion Gases Symposium, June 26-July 1, 1977, New England College, Henniker, New Hampshire. Ash Deposits & Corrosion Due to Impurities in Combustion Gases: Proceedings. Bryers, R. W., ed. LC 78-7001. (Illus.). 691p. 1978. text ed. 89.95 (ISBN 0-89116-074-4). Hemisphere Pub.
Ashworth, V., ed. Corrosion-Industrial Problems, Treatment & Control Techniques: Proceedings of the 1st Arabian Conference on Corrosion, Kuwait, 1984. (Kuwait Foundation for the Advancement of Science Ser.: Vol. 2). (Illus.). 450p. 1986. 75.00 (ISBN 0-08-032576-9, Pub. by Aberdeen Scotland). Pergamon.
Atmospheric Corrosion Investigation of Aluminum-Coated, Zinc-Coated & Copper-Bearing Steel Wire & Wire Products- STP 585. 90p. 1975. pap. 5.50 (ISBN 0-8031-0285-2, 04-585000-02). ASTM.
Atmospheric Factors Affecting the Corrosion of Engineering Metals - STP 646. 238p. 1978. 24.50 (ISBN 0-8031-0286-0, 04-646000-27). ASTM.
Barer, R. D. & Peters, B. F. Why Metals Fail-Selected Case Histories. 350p. 1970. 70.50x (ISBN 0-677-02630-7). Gordon.
Brubaker, George R. & Phipps, P. Beverley, eds. Corrosion Chemistry. LC 78-25554. (ACS Symposium Ser.: No. 89). 1979. 29.95 (ISBN 0-8412-0471-3). Am Chemical.
Business Communications Staff. Corrosion Inhibitors: Market, Material, Trends. 1984. 1750.00 (ISBN 0-89336-366-9, C-020A). BCC.
Butler, G. & Ison, H. C. Corrosion & Its Prevention in Waters. LC 76-30515. 310p. 1978. Repr. of 1966 ed. 21.00 (ISBN 0-88275-515-3). Krieger.
Carter. Corrosion Testing for Metal Finishing. 1982. text ed. 29.95 (ISBN 0-408-01194-7). Butterworth.
Cathodic Protection of Production Platforms in Cold Seawaters. 192p. 60.00 (ISBN 0-317-06640-4, 52122). Natl Corrosion Eng.
Cathodic Protection of Pulp & Paper Mill Effluent Clarifiers. 5.00 (ISBN 0-317-06637-4, 53043). Natl Corrosion Eng.
Cichy, F. C. & Schenck, H. V. Corrosion of Steel & Aluminum Scuba Tanks. (Technical Report Ser.: No. 62). 20p. 1978. 2.00 (ISBN 0-938412-05-1, P769). URI MAS.
Clark, David E., et al. Corrosion of Glass. LC 79-50921. 75p. 1979. 24.95 (ISBN 0-911993-18-5). Ashlee Pub Co.
Clayton, R. R. & Preece, C. M., eds. Corrosion of Metals Processed by Directed Energy Beams. 163p. 1981. 36.00 (ISBN 0-89520-393-6); members 24.00 (ISBN 0-317-37204-1); student members 12.00 (ISBN 0-317-37205-X). Metal Soc.
Coburn, Seymour K., ed. Corrosion: Source Book. 1984. 49.00 (ISBN 0-87170-177-4). Am Soc Pub Admin.
Collection & Identification of Corrosion Products. 5.00 (ISBN 0-317-06636-6, 53014). Natl Corrosion Eng.
Collie, M. J., ed. Corrosion Inhibitors: Developments since 1980. LC 83-13055. (Chemical Technology Review No. 223). 379p. 1984. 48.00 (ISBN 0-8155-0957-X). Noyes.
Congress on Metallic Corrosion. Metallic Corrosion: Proceedings of the 8th International Congress on Metallic Corrosion, Mainz, Germany, Sept. 1981 (111th Event, 8th ICMC, 7th CEFC, 3 Vols. (Dechema Proceedings Ser.). 2300p. 1982. Set. pap. text ed. 150.00x (ISBN 3-921567-36-X, Pub. by Dechema Germany). Scholium Intl.
Corrosion. (Illus.). 250p. 1981. looseleaf 40.00x (ISBN 0-87683-343-1); lessons plans 850.00x (ISBN 0-87683-344-X); transparencies 250.00x (ISBN 0-87683-345-8); question bank 165.00x (ISBN 0-87683-346-6); training package 1175.00x (ISBN 0-87683-342-3). G P Courseware.
Corrosion Fatigue. 182p. (Orig.). 1983. pap. text ed. 50.00x (ISBN 0-904357-51-1, Pub. by the Metals Society). Brookfield Pub Co.
Corrosion Fatigue Technology, STP 642. 1978. 32.00 (ISBN 0-8031-0314-X, 04-642000-27). ASTM.
Corrosion in Natural Environments, STP 558. 352p. 1974. 29.75 (ISBN 0-8031-0315-8, 04-558000-27). ASTM.
Corrosion in the Marine Environment: A Joint Conference Held on 8-9 Nov. 1973. (Illus.). 104p. 1975. pap. 21.00x (ISBN 0-900976-34-9, Pub. by Inst Marine Eng). Intl Spec Bk.
Corrosion Inhibitors. 1984. 1750.00 (ISBN 0-89336-261-1, C-020A). BCC.
Corrosion of Reinforcing Steel in Concrete, STP 713. 224p. 1980. 22.50x (ISBN 0-8031-0316-6, 713, 04-713000-27). ASTM.
Corrosion Prevention in Solar Heating Systems. (NRC Solar Information Ser.: No. 2). 42p. 1980. pap. 5.75 (ISBN 0-660-10188-2, SSC140, SSC). Unipub.
Crooker, T. W. & Leis, B. N., eds. Corrosion Fatigue: Mechanics, Metallurgy, Electrochemistry, & Engineering. LC 82-83519. (Special Technical Publications Ser.: No. 801). 522p. 1983. text ed. 62.00 (ISBN 0-8031-0245-3, 04-801000-30). ASTM.
Davis, D. R. Food Container Corrosion. 350p. 1985. lib. bdg. 64.00 (ISBN 0-89573-408-7, Pub. By Ellis Horwood Ltd UK). VCH Pubs.
Dean, Jr. & Rhea, eds. Atmospheric Corrosion of Metals- STP 767. 413p. 1982. 42.50 (ISBN 0-8031-0702-1, 04-767000-27). ASTM.
De Brasunas, Anton & Stansbury, E. E., eds. Symposium on Corrosion Fundamentals: A Series of Lectures Presented at the University of Tennessee Corrosion Conference at Knoxville on March 1-3, 1955. LC 56-13073. pap. 65.30 (ISBN 0-317-10658-9, 2022212). Bks Demand UMI.
Draley, J. E. & Weeks, J. R. Corrosion by Liquid Metals. LC 75-119057. 615p. 1970. 49.50x (ISBN 0-306-30482-1, Plenum Pr). Plenum Pub.
Effects of Environment & Complex Load History on Fatigue Life, STP 462. 332p. 1970. 22.00 (ISBN 0-8031-0032-9, 04-462000-30). ASTM.
Electrochemical Corrosion Testing - STP 727. 411p. 1981. 36.00 (ISBN 0-8031-0704-8, 04-727000-27). ASTM.
Erosion, Wear & Interfaces with Corrosion, STP 567. 343p. 1974. 35.00 (ISBN 0-8031-0335-2, 04-567000-29). ASTM.
Escalante, E., ed. Underground Corrosion - STP 741. 210p. 1981. 26.00 (ISBN 0-8031-0703-X, 04-741000-27). ASTM.
Evans, U. R. An Introduction to Metallic Corrosion. 3rd ed. 320p. 1981. pap. text ed. 24.50 (ISBN 0-7131-2758-9). E Arnold.
Evans, Ulick R. The Corrosion & Oxidation of Metals. 1094p. 1971. Repr. 110.00x (ISBN 0-8448-1067-3). Crane-Russak Co.
--The Corrosion & Oxidation of Metals: Supplementary Volume, No. One. 488p. 1968. 59.50x (ISBN 0-8448-1066-5). Crane-Russak Co.
--The Corrosion & Oxidation of Metals: Supplementary Volume, No. Two. 432p. 1976. 97.50x (ISBN 0-8448-1065-7). Crane-Russak Co.
Fontana, M. G. & Staehle, R. W., eds. Advances in Corrosion Science & Technology. Incl. Vol. 1. 384p. 1970 (ISBN 0-306-39501-0); Vol. 2. 354p. 1972 (ISBN 0-306-39502-9); Vol. 3. 431p. 1973 (ISBN 0-306-39503-7); Vol. 4. 340p. 1974 (ISBN 0-306-39504-5); Vol. 5. 407p. 1976 (ISBN 0-306-39505-3); Vol. 6. 277p. 1976 (ISBN 0-306-39506-1); Vol. 7. 375p. 1980 (ISBN 0-306-39507-X). LC 76-107531. (Illus.). each 59.50 (Plenum Pr). Plenum Pub.
Fontana, Mars G. & Greene, Norbert D. Corrosion Engineering. 2nd ed. (Materials Sciences & Engineering). (Illus.). 1978. text ed. 48.00 (ISBN 0-07-021461-1). McGraw.
Fraker, Anna C. & Griffin, Charles D., eds. Corrosion & Degradation of Implant Materials-STP 859: Second Symposium. LC 84-70337. (Illus.). 470p. 1985. text ed. 62.00 (ISBN 0-8031-0427-8, 04-859000-27). ASTM.
Galvanic & Pitting Corrosion - Field & Laboratory Studies, STP 576. 300p. 1976. 29.75 (ISBN 0-8031-0369-7, 04-576000-27). ASTM.
Gatty, Oliver & Spooner, E. C. The Electrode Potential Behaviour of Corroding Metals in Aqueous Solutions. (Illus.). Repr. of 1938 ed. 40.00 (ISBN 0-384-17730-1). Johnson Repr.
Graver, D. L., ed. Corrosion Data Survey--Metals Section. 6th ed. LC 84-62018. 200p. 160.00 (ISBN 0-915567-06-7); member 130.00 (ISBN 0-317-18660-4). Natl Corrosion Eng.
Guttman, V. & Merz, M., eds. Corrosion & Mechanical Stress at High Temperatures. (Illus.). 477p. 1981. 52.00 (ISBN 0-85334-956-8, Pub. by Elsevier Applied Sci England). Elsevier.
Holmes, D. R. & Rahmel, A., eds. Materials & Coatings to Resist High Temperature Corrosion. (Illus.). 410p. 1978. 89.00 (ISBN 0-85334-784-0, Pub. by Elsevier Applied Sci England). Elsevier.
Institution of Civil Engineers Staff, ed. Corrosion in Civil Engineering. 186p. 1979. 26.50x (ISBN 0-7277-0079-0). Am Soc Civil Eng.
Intergranular Corrosion of Stainless Alloys- STP 656. 268p. 1978. 24.00 (ISBN 0-8031-0378-6, 04-656000-27). ASTM.
International Symposium on Solving Corrosion & Scaling Problems in Geothermal Systems: Proceedings. LC 84-61388. (Illus.). 332p. 50.00 (ISBN 0-915567-03-2); member 40.00 (ISBN 0-317-18668-X). Natl Corrosion Eng.
Jaffee, R. I., ed. Corrosion Fatigue of Steam Turbine Blade Materials: Workshop Proceedings, Palo Alto, CA, U. S. A., 21-24 September 1981. (Illus.). 732p. 1983. 65.00 (ISBN 0-08-030163-0). Pergamon.
Jaromir Tousek Institute of Physical Metallurgy Czechoslovakian Academy of Sciences, Brno, CSSR. Theoretical Aspects of the Localized Corrosion of Metals. (Materials Science Surveys Ser.: Vol. 3). 180p. 1985. 32.00 (ISBN 0-87849-526-6). Trans Tech.
Jaske, Carl E., et al. Corrosion Fatigue of Metals in Marine Environments. (Metals & Ceramics Information Center Ser.). (Illus.). 245p. 1981. 49.95 (ISBN 0-935470-07-7). Battelle.
Kirkley, Charles, ed. Corrosion Control. (Oil & Gas Production Ser.). (Illus.). 76p. (Orig.). 1982. pap. text ed. 5.00 (ISBN 0-88698-110-7, 3.30110). Petex.
Klinov, I. Ya. Corrosion & Protection of Materials Used in Industrial Equipment. LC 61-15171. 228p. 1962. 37.50x (ISBN 0-306-10521-7, Consultants). Plenum Pub.
Koch, G. H. & Thompson, N. G., eds. Corrosion in Flue Gas Desulfurization Systems. LC 84-61873. 479p. 35.00 (ISBN 0-915567-05-9); 28.00. Natl Corrosion Eng.
LaQue, Francis L. Marine Corrosion: Causes & Prevention. LC 75-16307. (Corrosion Monograph Ser). 332p. 1975. 48.95x (ISBN 0-471-51745-3, Pub. by Wiley-Interscience). Wiley.
Leidheiser, Henry, Jr., ed. Corrosion Control by Coatings. LC 79-3990. (Illus.). 1979. lib. bdg. 48.00 (ISBN 0-89500-018-0). Sci Pr.
Localized Corrosion-Cause of Metal Failure, STP 516. 322p. 1972. 22.50 (ISBN 0-8031-0110-4, 04 516000 07). ASTM.
Manual of Industrial Corrosion Standards & Control, STP 534. 311p. 1974. 16.75 (ISBN 0-8031-0395-6, 04-534000-27). ASTM.
Meadowcroft, D. B. & Manning, M. I., eds. Corrosion Resistant Materials for Coal Conversion Systems. 612p. 1983. 100.00 (ISBN 0-85334-198-2, I-208-83, Pub. by Elsevier Applied Sci England). Elsevier.
Melnikova, M. M. & Smirnov, I. P. English-Russian Dictionary of Electrochemistry & Corrosion. (Eng. & Rus.). 496p. 1976. 9.95 (ISBN 0-686-92367-7, M-9121). French & Eur.
Mittal, K. L., ed. Surface Contamination: Genesis, Detection & Control, 2 vols. LC 79-15433. 1979. Set. 120.00x (ISBN 0-685-97229-1, Plenum Pr); Vol. 1, 554p. 69.50x (ISBN 0-306-40176-2); Vol. 2, 547p. 69.50x (ISBN 0-306-40177-0). Plenum Pub.
Modern Anticorrosion Pigment. (Bibliographies in Paint Technology Ser.: No. 38). 62p. 1982. 70.00x (ISBN 0-686-44680-1, Pub. by Chandler England). State Mutual Bk.
Munger, C. G. Corrosion Prevention by Protective Coatings. LC 84-61872. (Illus.). 511p. 75.00 (ISBN 0-915567-04-0); member 60.00 (ISBN 0-317-18666-3). Natl Corrosion Eng.
National Association of Corrosion Engineers. Compilation of Papers on Rebar Corrosion. (Illus.). 333p. 60.00 (ISBN 0-317-06683-8, 52166). Natl Corrosion Eng.
--Corrosion Inhibitors. Nathan, C. C., ed. (Illus.). 260p. 1983. 35.00 (ISBN 0-317-06686-2, 51073). Natl Corrosion Eng.
--Co2 Corrosion in Oil & Gas Production: Selected Papers, Abstracts, & References. 687p. 1984. 100.00 (ISBN 0-317-06639-0, 51120). Natl Corrosion Eng.
--Evaluation of Pipeline Steels for Resistance to Stepwise Cracking. 5.00 (ISBN 0-317-06635-8). Natl Corrosion Eng.
--A Handbook of Protective Coatings for Military & Equipment (TPC-10) 109p. 20.00 (ISBN 0-317-06631-5). Natl Corrosion Eng.
--The International Symposium on Environmental Degradation of Materials in Nuclear Power Systems-Water Reactors: Proceedings. (Illus.). 996p. 75.00 (ISBN 0-317-06633-1). Natl Corrosion Eng.
Neufeld, P. Elementary Aspects of Corrosion. 74p. 1981. 50.00x (ISBN 0-901994-56-1, Pub. by Portcullio Pr). State Mutual Bk.
North Sea Corrosion - What Have We Learnt? 1981. 110.00x (ISBN 0-686-97105-1, Pub. by Marine Mgmt England). State Mutual Bk.
Occasione, John F., et al. Atmospheric Corrosion Investigations of Aluminum-Coated, Zinc-Coated. & Copper-Bearing Steel Wire & Wire Products: A Twenty-Year Report. LC 83-73647. (Special Technical Publications Ser.: No. 585A). (Illus.). 53p. 1984. pap. text ed. 14.00 (ISBN 0-8031-0205-4, 04-585010-02). ASTM.
Parkins, R. N., ed. Corrosion Processes. (Illus.). 317p. 1982. 61.00 (ISBN 0-85334-147-8, I-356-82, Pub. by Elsevier Applied Sci England). Elsevier.
Perservatives, Biocides & Antifouling Agents: Preventing Organic Growth in Paints & Paint Films. 88p. 1977. 40.00x (ISBN 0-686-44695-X, Pub. by Chandler England). State Mutual Bk.
Pollock, Vera & Weiner, Jack. Corrosion of Pulp & Paper Mill Equipment. LC 76-21187. (Bibliographic Ser.: No. 269). 1976. pap. 40.00 (ISBN 0-87010-054-8). Inst Paper Chem.
Rabald, Erich. Corrosion Guide. 2nd rev. ed. 900p. 1968. 159.75 (ISBN 0-444-40465-1). Elsevier.
Riggs, Olen L., Jr. & Locke, Carl E. Anodic Protection: Theory & Practice in the Prevention of Corrosion. LC 80-20412. 297p. 1981. 52.50x (ISBN 0-306-40597-0, Plenum Pr). Plenum Pub.
Rose, T. & Rider, R. Corrosion of Metals in Concrete. (Technical Report Ser.: No. 58). 142p. 1977. 2.00 (ISBN 0-938412-28-0, P629). URI MAS.
Roth, Lillian, et al. Corrosion of Pulp & Paper Mill Equipment, Suppl. 1. LC 76-21187. (Bibliographic Ser.: No. 269, Suppl. 1). 1979. pap. 45.00 (ISBN 0-87010-056-4). Inst Paper Chem.
Rothman, Michael F., ed. High Temperature Corrosion in Energy Systems. 832p. 1985. 60.00 (ISBN 0-89520-490-8). Metal Soc.
Savic, Dimitrije & Opik, Ilmar, eds. Fouling & Corrosion in Steam Generators. (Illus.). 154p. 1980. 39.95 (ISBN 0-89116-249-6). Hemisphere Pub.
Schweitzer, Philip A. Corrosion Resistance Tables: Metals, Plastics, Nonmetallics & Rubber. 1976. 145.00 (ISBN 0-8247-6488-9). Dekker.
--Handbook of Corrosion Resistant Piping. 2nd ed. LC 81-19291. 434p. 1985. lib. bdg. 44.00 (ISBN 0-89874-457-1). Krieger.
Scully, J. C. Corrosion: Aqueous Processes & Pasive Films. 1983. 72.00 (ISBN 0-12-633670-9). Acad Pr.
--The Fundamentals of Corrosion. 2nd ed. 252p. 1975. pap. text ed. 12.50 (ISBN 0-08-018080-9). Pergamon.

Scully, J. C., ed. Ion Implementation & Ion Beam Analysis Techniques in Corrosion: Selected Papers Presented at the Conference at the Corrosion & Protection Centre, UMIST, Manchester, 28-30 June 1978. 148p. 1981. 17.50 (ISBN 0-08-026135-3). Pergamon.

Scully, J. S. Electrochemical Techniques in Corrosion Testing & Research. pap. 20.00 (ISBN 0-08-030540-7). Pergamon.

Sedriks, A. John. Corrosion of Stainless Steels. LC 79-11985. (Corrosion Monographs). 282p. 1979. 48.95x (ISBN 0-471-05011-3, Pub. by Wiley-Interscience). Wiley.

Seymour, R. B. Plastics vs. Corrosives. LC 81-21996. (Society of Plastics Engineers Monographs). 285p. 1982. text ed. 54.95x (ISBN 0-471-08182-5, Pub. by Wiley-Interscience). Wiley.

Seymour, Raymond B. Plastics vs. Corrosives. 285p. 55.00 (ISBN 0-686-48130-5, 0807). T-C Pubns CA.

Shreir, L. L. Corrosion, Vol. I & II. 2nd ed. 1976. 275.00 (ISBN 0-408-00267-0). Butterworth.

Shvartz, Galina L. & Kristal, M. M. Corrosion of Chemical Apparatus: Corrosion, Cracking & Methods of Protection Against It. LC 59-9233. pap. 64.00 (ISBN 0-317-10621-X, 2020646). Bks Demand UMI.

Singley, J. E., et al. Corrosion Prevention & Control in Water Treatment & Supply Systems. LC 85-4915. (Pollution Technology Review Ser.: No. 122). (Illus.). 313p. 1985. 42.00 (ISBN 0-8155-1031-4). Noyes.

Slater, John E., ed. Corrosion of Metals in Association with Concrete. LC 83-70430. (Special Technical Publications Ser.: No. 818). 90p. 1984. pap. 16.00 (ISBN 0-8031-0210-0, 04-818000-27). ASTM.

Solving Corrosion Problems in Air Pollution Control Equipment. LC 84-62370. 479p. 35.00 (ISBN 0-915567-07-5); member 28.00 (ISBN 0-317-18669-8). Natl Corrosion Eng.

Solving Rebar Corrosion Problems in Concrete: Proceedings. (Illus.). 147p. 1983. pap. 25.00 (ISBN 0-915567-99-7, 52165). Natl Corrosion Eng.

Speidel, Markus O. & Atrens, Andrejs, eds. Corrosion in Power Generating Equipment. (Brown Boveri Symposium Ser.). 574p. 1984. 79.50x (ISBN 0-306-41706-5, Plenum Pr). Plenum Pub.

Strafford, K. N., et al, eds. Coatings & Surface Treatment for Corrosion & Wear Resistance. (Applied Science & Industrial Technology Ser.). 362p. 1984. text ed. 79.95x (ISBN 0-470-20090-1). Halsted Pr.

The Study & Prevention of Corrosion. 1983. 33.00 (ISBN 0-89883-309-4, SP538). Soc Auto Engineers.

Tedmon, Craig S., Jr., ed. Corrosion Problems in Energy Conversion & Generation: Papers. LC 74-84701. pap. 120.50 (ISBN 0-317-11080-2, 2050864). Bks Demand UMI.

Tomashov, N. D. & Chernova, G. P. Passivity & Protection of Metals Against Corrosion. LC 66-19933. 208p. 1967. 45.00 (ISBN 0-306-30276-4, Plenum Pr). Plenum Pub.

Uhlig, Herbert H. Corrosion Handbook. (Electrochemical Society Ser.). 1188p. 1948. 79.95x (ISBN 0-471-89562-8, Pub. by Wiley-Interscience). Wiley.

Uhlig, Herbert H. & Revie, R. Winston. Corrosion & Corrosion Control. 3rd ed. 464p. 1984. text ed. 42.50 (ISBN 0-471-07818-2, Pub. by Wiley-Interscience). Wiley.

VanDelinder, L. S., ed. Corrosion Basics: An Introduction. LC 84-61042. (Illus.). 364p. 40.00 (ISBN 0-915567-02-4); member 32.00 (ISBN 0-317-18658-2). Natl Corrosion Eng.

Vesely, E. J., Jr., et al. Erosion-Corrosion of Structual Materials in a Simulated Coal Gasification Environment. write for info. Metal Prop Coun.

Von Fraunhofer, J. A. Concise Corrosion Science. 1981. 60.00x (ISBN 0-901994-54-5, Pub. by Portcullio Pr). State Mutual Bk.

Warren, Nigel. Metal Corrosion in Boats. 224p. 39.00x (ISBN 0-540-07397-0, Pub. by Stanford Maritime England). State Mutual Bk.

--Metal Corrosion in Boats. LC 80-82546. pap. 60.00 (ISBN 0-317-27595-X, 2025074). Bks Demand UMI.

Water Chemistry & Corrosion Problems in Nuclear Power Plants: Proceedings of a Symposium, Vienna, 22-26 November 1982. (Proceedings Ser.). (Eng., Fr. & Rus.). 516p. 1984. pap. 80.00 (ISBN 92-0-050783-2, ISP630, IAEA). Unipub.

Waterhouse, R. B. Fretting Corrosion. 1973. text ed. 44.00 (ISBN 0-08-016902-3). Pergamon.

West, J. M. Basic Corrosion & Oxidation. LC 80-41158. 247p. 1980. 74.95x (ISBN 0-470-27080-2); pap. 32.95 (ISBN 0-470-20081-2). Halsted Pr.

Wranglen, Gosta. An Introduction to Corrosion & Protection of Metals. 2nd ed. 300p. 1985. text ed. 55.00 (ISBN 0-412-26040-9, NO. 9304, Pub. by Chapman & Hall England); pap. text ed. 25.00 (ISBN 0-412-26050-6, NO. 9305). Methuen Inc.

CORROSION AND ANTI-CORROSIVES–RESEARCH

Chemical Engineering Magazine. Selecting Materials for Process Equipment. (Chemical Engineering Ser.). 280p. 1980. 35.00 (ISBN 0-07-010692-4). McGraw.

Scully, J. C., ed. Ion Implantation & Ion Beam Analysis Techniques in Corrosion Studies. 1977. pap. text ed. 17.50 (ISBN 0-08-021420-7). Pergamon.

CORSAIR (FIGHTER PLANES)

Maloney, Edward T. & Feist, Uwe. Chance Vought F4U Corsair. Rev. ed. LC 67-16731. (Aero Ser: Vol. 11). (Illus.). 100p. 1984. pap. 6.95 (ISBN 0-8168-0541-5). Aero.

Musciano, Walter A. Corsair Aces: The Bent-Wing Bird over the Pacific. LC 78-2452. (Illus.). 1978. lib. bdg. 6.95 (ISBN 0-668-04597-3); pap. 6.95 (ISBN 0-668-04600-7). Arco.

Rice, Michael S. Pilot's Manual for F4U Corsair. (Illus.). 80p. 1974. pap. 7.95 (ISBN 0-87994-026-3, Pub. by AvPubns). Aviation.

CORT, HENRY, 1740-1800

Mott, R. A. Henry Cort: The Great Finer: Creator of Puddled Iron. Singer, Peter, ed. 132p. (Orig.). 1983. pap. text ed. 24.00x (ISBN 0-904357-55-4, Pub. by the Metals Society). Brookfield Pub Co.

CORTICAL EVOKED POTENTIALS

see Evoked Potentials (Electrophysiology)

CORVAIR (AUTOMOBILE)

see Automobiles–Types–Corvair

CORVETTE (AUTOMOBILE)

see Automobiles–Types–Corvette

CORVIDAE

Angell, Tony. Ravens, Crows, Magpies, & Jays. LC 77-15185. (Illus.). 112p. 1978. 25.00 (ISBN 0-295-95589-9). U of Wash Pr.

COSMETICS

see also Perfumes

Ash, M. & Ash, I. Formulary of Cosmetic Preparations. 1977. text ed. 35.00 (ISBN 0-8206-0218-3). Chem Pub.

Balsam, M. S. & Sagarin, Edward, eds. Cosmetics: Science & Technology, 3 vols. 2nd ed. LC 75-177888. Set, 2083p. 268.00 (ISBN 0-471-04650-7); Vol. 1, 1972, 605 Pgs. 86.00 (ISBN 0-471-04646-9); Vol. 2, 1972, 691 Pgs. 86.00 (ISBN 0-471-04647-7); Vol. 3, 1974, 787 Pgs. 97.00 (ISBN 0-471-04649-3, Pub. by Wiley-Interscience). Wiley.

Breuer, M., ed. Cosmetic Science. Vol. 1, 1978. 61.50 (ISBN 0-12-133001-X); Vol. 2, 1981. 56.00 (ISBN 0-12-133002-8). Acad Pr.

Cooley, Arnold J. The Toilet & Cosmetic Arts in Ancient & Modern Times: With a Review of All the Different Theories of Beauty, & Copious Allied Information Social, Hygienic, & Medical. LC 78-80248. (Research & Source Ser.: No. 511). 1970. Repr. of 1866 ed. 43.00 (ISBN 0-8337-0653-5). B Franklin.

Directory of Cosmetic & Toiletry Ingredients. 2d ed. Rich, Susan, ed. 365p. 1982. pap. 985.00 (ISBN 0-686-84482-3). Kline.

The Directory of Toiletry & Cosmetic Manufacturers in Western Europe. 1985. 150.00x (ISBN 0-686-75445-X, Pub. by European Directories England). State Mutual Bk.

Estrin, Norman. The Cosmetic Industry: Scientific & Regulatory Foundations. Jungermann, Eric, ed. (Cosmetic Science & Technology Ser.: Vol. 2). (Illus.). 720p. 1984. 95.00 (ISBN 0-8247-7105-2). Dekker.

Evans, Joyce. Practical Problems in Mathematics for Cosmetology. LC 81-71649. (Illus.). 128p. 1983. pap. text ed. 7.40 (ISBN 0-8273-1380-2); instr's. guide 3.30 (ISBN 0-8273-1381-0). Delmar.

Feinberg, H. Cosmetics-Perfumery Thesaurus. 1972. 17.95 (ISBN 0-02-469030-9). Macmillan Info.

Flick, Ernest W. Cosmetic & Toiletry Formulations. LC 84-14771. (Illus.). 596p. 1985. 64.00 (ISBN 0-8155-0995-2). Noyes.

Food & Drug Administration. FDA Inspections Operations Manual for Drugs, Devices, & Cosmetics. Hadley, Richard D., ed. 162p. 1983. pap. text ed. 39.00 (ISBN 0-914176-22-6). Wash Busn Info.

Jellinek, S. Formulation & Function of Cosmetics. Fenton, G. L., tr. from Ger. LC 74-110170. 586p. 1970. 91.00 (ISBN 0-471-44150-3, Pub. by Wiley-Interscience). Wiley.

Kabara. Cosmetic Preservation: Principles & Practice. (Cosmetic Science & Technology Ser.). 680p. 1984. 99.75 (ISBN 0-8247-7104-4). Dekker.

Kabara, Jon J. & Jungermann, Eric, eds. Cosmetic & Drug Preservation: Principles & Practice. (Cosmetic Science & Technology Ser.: Vol. 1). (Illus.). 792p. 1984. 99.75 (ISBN 0-8247-7104-4). Dekker.

Kallet, Arthur & Schlink, F. J. One Hundred Million Guinea Pigs: Dangers in Everyday Foods, Drugs, & Cosmetics. LC 75-39252. (Getting & Spending: the Consumer's Dilemma). 1976. Repr. of 1933 ed. 24.50x (ISBN 0-405-08025-5). Ayer Co Pubs.

Moskowitz. Cosmetic Product Testing. (Cosmetic Science & Technology Ser.). 432p. 1985. 89.75 (ISBN 0-8247-7090-0). Dekker.

Rieger. Surfactants in Cosmetics. (Surfactant Science Ser.). 576p. 1985. 89.00 (ISBN 0-8247-7262-8). Dekker.

Rose, Jeanne. Kitchen Cosmetics: Using Plants & Herbs in Cosmetics. LC 77-17077. 128p. 1978. 10.95 (ISBN 0-915572-25-7); pap. 5.95 (ISBN 0-915572-24-9). Panjandrum.

Thompson, C. J. Mystery & Lure of Perfume. LC 74-75789. 1969. Repr. of 1927 ed. 30.00x (ISBN 0-8103-3842-4). Gale.

Toiletries & Cosmetics. (BTA Studies). 200p. 1984. 595.00 (ISBN 0-686-31555-3). Busn Trend.

Torrey, S., ed. Health Care Products: Recent Developments. LC 81-11083. (Chemical Technical Review Ser.: No. 196). (Illus.). 354p. 1982. 45.00 (ISBN 0-8155-0862-X). Noyes.

COSMIC CHEMISTRY

see Cosmochemistry

COSMIC ELECTRODYNAMICS

see also Magnetohydrodynamics

Coroniti, Samuel C. & Hughes, J., eds. Planetary Electrodynamics, 2 Vols. (Illus.). 1132p. 1969. Set. 216.25 (ISBN 0-677-13600-5). Gordon.

Piddington, J. H. Cosmic Electrodynamics. 2nd ed. LC 77-22303. 376p. 1981. lib. bdg. 29.50 (ISBN 0-88275-587-0). Krieger.

Sturrock, P. A., ed. Plasma Astrophysics. (Italian Physical Society: Course 39). 1967. 70.00 (ISBN 0-12-368839-6). Acad Pr.

COSMIC PHYSICS

see also Astrophysics; Auroras; Cosmic Electrodynamics; Magnetic Fields (Cosmic Physics); Magnetism, Terrestrial; Magnetohydrodynamics; Van Allen Radiation Belts

Apparao, K. M. Composition of Cosmic Radiation. (Topics in Astrophysics & Space Physics Ser.). 96p. 1975. 37.25 (ISBN 0-677-03770-8). Gordon.

Carrington, A. & Ramsay, D. A., eds. Molecules in Interstellar Space: Proceedings. (Royal Society of London Ser.). (Illus.). 167p. 1982. text ed. 51.00x (ISBN 0-85403-180-4, Pub. by Royal Soc London). Scholium Intl.

Dorman, L. I., ed. Cosmic Rays. 675p. 1974. 91.50 (ISBN 0-444-10480-1, North-Holland). Elsevier.

Heller, Michael. Questions to the Universe: Ten Lectures on Foundations of Physics & Cosmology. (Astronomy & Astrophysics Ser.: Vol. 14). (Illus.). 160p. Date not set. 24.00 (ISBN 0-912918-01-2). Pachart Pub Hse.

Kruger, Albrecht, ed. Introduction to Solar Radio Astronomy & Radio Physics. (Geophysics & Astrophysics Monographs: No. 16). 1979. lib. bdg. 50.00 (ISBN 90-277-0957-2, Pub. by Reidel Holland); pap. 23.50 (ISBN 90-277-0997-1, Pub. by Reidel Holland). Kluwer Academic.

Martin, P. G. Cosmic Dust. (Studies in Physics). (Illus.). 1978. 34.50x (ISBN 0-19-851458-1). Oxford U Pr.

NATO Advanced Study Institute, Urbino, 1975. The Physics of Non-Thermal Radio Sources: Proceedings. new ed. Setti, Giancarlo, ed. (Mathematical & Physical Sciences Ser: No. 28). 1976. lib. bdg. 34.00 (ISBN 90-277-0753-7, Pub. by Reidel Holland). Kluwer Academic.

Ortner, J. & Maseland, H., eds. Introduction to Solar-Terrestial Relations. 514p. 1965. 132.95 (ISBN 0-677-00650-0). Gordon.

La Radiacion Cosmica. (Serie De Fisica: No. 9). (Span.). 1973. pap. 3.50 (ISBN 0-8270-6185-4). OAS.

White, R. S. Space Physics. 332p. 1970. 80.95 (ISBN 0-677-02020-1). Gordon.

COSMIC RAYS

see also Mesons; Positrons; Van Allen Radiation Belts

Apparao, K. M. Composition of Cosmic Radiation. (Topics in Astrophysics & Space Physics Ser.). 96p. 1975. 37.25 (ISBN 0-677-03770-8). Gordon.

Basov, N. G., ed. Cosmic Rays in the Stratosphere & in Near Space. LC 78-2007. (P. N. Lebedev Physics Institute Ser.: Vol. 88). (Illus.). 186p. 1978. 59.50x (ISBN 0-306-10946-8, Consultants). Plenum Pub.

Dorman, L. I., ed. Cosmic Rays. 675p. 1974. 91.50 (ISBN 0-444-10480-1, North-Holland). Elsevier.

ESLAB Symposium, 7th, Saulgau, Germany, May 22-25, 1973. Correlated Interplanetary & Magnetospheric Observations: Proceedings. Page, D. E., ed. LC 73-91433. (Astrophysics & Space Science Library: No. 42). 676p. 1974. lib. bdg. 103.00 (ISBN 90-277-0429-5, Pub. by Reidel Holland). Kluwer Academic.

Gaisser, T. K., ed. Cosmic Rays & Particle Physics - Nineteen Seventy-Eight: Bartol Conference. LC 79-50489. (AIP Conference Proceedings Ser.: No. 49). (Illus.). 1979. lib. bdg. 23.50 (ISBN 0-88318-148-7). Am Inst Physics.

Ginzburg, Vitalii L. The Astrophysics of Cosmic Rays. 2nd., Rev. & Supplemented ed. Hardin, Ron, ed. LC 73-606893. (U. S. National Aeronautics & Space Administration. NASA Technical Translation Ser.: TT F-561). pap. 20.00 (ISBN 0-317-09306-1, 2003731). Bks Demand UMI.

Ginzburg, Vitaly L. Elementary Processes for Cosmic Ray Astrophysics. (Topics in Astrophysics & Space Physics Ser.). 140p. 1969. 45.25 (ISBN 0-677-01980-7). Gordon.

--Origin of Cosmic Rays. (Topics in Astrophyscis & Space Physics Ser.). 70p. 1969. 23.25 (ISBN 0-677-01970-X). Gordon.

Greisen, Kenneth. The Physics of Cosmic X-Ray, Gamma-Ray & Particle Sources. 2nd ed. Cameron, A. G. W. & Field, G. B., eds. LC 78-135063. (Topics in Astrophysics & Space Physics Ser.). (Illus.). 124p. 1971. 28.95 (ISBN 0-677-03380-X). Gordon.

Hillas, A. M. Cosmic Rays. 306p. 1972. text ed. 28.00 (ISBN 0-08-016724-1). Pergamon.

International Conference on Cosmic Rays, 11th, Budapest, August 25-September 4, 1969. Proceedings. Somogyi, A., ed. Incl. Vol. 1. (Illus.). 571p. pap. 36.90x (ISBN 0-685-42280-1); Vol. 2. (Illus.). 767p. pap. 52.00x (ISBN 0-685-42281-X); Vol. 3. (Illus.). 767p. pap. 52.00x (ISBN 0-685-42282-8); Vol. 4. (Illus.). 607p. pap. 41.00x (ISBN 0-685-42283-6). Adlers Foreign Bks.

Johnson, Thomas H. Review of Cosmic Rays (Sesquicentennial Celebration) Proceedings, Part 3. (Connecticut Academy of Arts & Sciences Transaction: Vol. 38). 1950. pap. 9.50 (ISBN 0-208-01098-X). Shoe String.

NATO Advanced Study Institute, Urbino, 1975. The Physics of Non-Thermal Radio Sources: Proceedings. new ed. Setti, Giancarlo, ed. (Mathematical & Physical Sciences Ser: No. 28). 1976. lib. bdg. 34.00 (ISBN 90-277-0753-7, Pub. by Reidel Holland). Kluwer Academic.

Nieto, Michael M. & Haxton, W. C., eds. Science Underground. LC 83-70377. (AIP Conference Proceedings No. 96). 446p. 1983. lib. bdg. 38.75 (ISBN 0-88318-195-9). Am Inst Physics.

Osborne, J. L. & Wolfendale, A. W., eds. Origin of Cosmic Rays. LC 75-2436. (NATO Advanced Study Institutes Ser: No. C14). x, 466p. 1975. lib. bdg. 55.00 (ISBN 90-277-0585-2, Pub. by Reidel Holland). Kluwer Academic.

Peters, B., ed. Cosmic Rays, Solar Particles & Space Research. (Italian Physical Society: Vol. 19). 1964. 70.00 (ISBN 0-12-368819-1). Acad Pr.

Randall, Charles A., Jr., ed. Extra-Terrestrial Matter. LC 69-15447. (Illus.). 331p. 1969. 15.00 (ISBN 0-87580-009-2). N Ill U Pr.

Sekido, Yataro & Elliot, Harry. Early History of Cosmic Ray Studies: Personal Reminiscences with Old Photographs. 1985. lib. bdg. 89.00 (ISBN 90-277-2083-5, Reidel Holland). Kluwer Academic.

Setti, G. & Spada, G., eds. Origin of Cosmic Rays. 1981. 52.50 (ISBN 90-277-1271-9, Pub. by Reidel Holland); pap. 23.50 (ISBN 90-277-1272-7, Pub. by Reidel Holland). Kluwer Academic.

Skobel'tsyn, D. V., ed. Cosmic Rays. LC 65-13582. (P. N. Lebedev Physics Institute Ser.: Vol. 26). 254p. 1965. 32.50x (ISBN 0-306-10720-1, Consultants). Plenum Pub.

--Cosmic Rays & Nuclear Interactions at High Energies. LC 75-157933. (P. N. Lebedev Physics Institute Ser.: Vol. 46). 229p. 1971. 35.00x (ISBN 0-306-10862-3, Consultants). Plenum Pub.

--Primary Cosmic Radiation. LC 75-22281. (P. N. Lebedev Physics Institute Ser.: Vol. 64). (Illus.). 109p. 1975. 49.50 (ISBN 0-306-10914-X, Consultants). Plenum Pub.

Somogyi, A. J., ed. Cosmic Rays in the Heliosphere. (Advances in Space Research: Vol. 1, No. 3). (Illus.). 177p. 1981. pap. 23.00 (ISBN 0-08-027159-6). Pergamon.

Wilson, J. G. Cosmic Rays. (Wykeham Science Ser.: No. 40). 150p. 1976. pap. cancelled (ISBN 0-85109-500-3). Taylor & Francis.

Wilson, J. G. & Perry, G. E. Cosmic Rays. LC 75-38743. (Wykeham Science Ser.: No. 40). 150p. 1976. 8.60x (ISBN 0-8448-1167-X). Crane Russak Co.

Wolfendale, A. W., ed. Cosmic Rays at Ground Level. (Illus.). 1973. 49.50 (ISBN 0-9960018-0-8, Pub. by A Hilger England). Heyden.

COSMOBIOLOGY

see Space Biology

COSMOCHEMISTRY

Boschke, F., ed. Cosmochemistry. LC 51-5479. (Topics in Current Chemistry: Vol. 44). (Illus.). 200p. 1974. 31.00 (ISBN 0-387-06457-5). Springer-Verlag.

Raymond, K. N., ed. Cosmo & Geochemistry. (Topics in Current Chemistry Ser.: Vol. 99). (Illus.). 140p. 1981. 35.00 (ISBN 0-387-10920-X). Springer-Verlag.

Ringwood, A. E. Origin of the Earth & Moon. (Illus.). 1979. 35.00 (ISBN 0-387-90369-0). Springer-Verlag.

COSMOGONY

see also Creation; Interstellar Matter; Nebulae

Alfven, Hannes. Worlds-Antiworlds: Antimatter in Cosmology. Feichtner, Rudy, tr. LC 66-27947. (Illus.). 103p. 1966. 13.95 (ISBN 0-7167-0317-3). W H Freeman.

Asimov, Isaac. Universe. 1980. 15.95 (ISBN 0-8027-0655-X). Walker & Co.

Audouze, Jean & Tran Thanh Van, Jean. Formation & Evolution of Galaxies & Large Structures in the Universe. 1984. lib. bdg. 58.00 (ISBN 90-277-1685-4, Pub. by Reidel Holland). Kluwer Academic.

Benko, F. Geological & Cosmogonie Cycles as Reflected by the New Law of Universal Cyclicity. 400p. 1984. text ed. 45.00 (991000382). Heyden.

Blum, Harold F. Time's Arrow & Evolution. 3rd ed. LC 68-31676. (Illus.). 1968. pap. 8.95x (ISBN 0-691-02354-9). Princeton U Pr.

Brandt, John C. Our Changing Universe. (Physical Science Ser.). 1976. pap. text ed. 9.95 (ISBN 0-675-08574-8). Additional supplements may be obtained from publisher. Merrill.

Burnet, Thomas. Sacred Theory of the Earth. LC 65-10027. (Centaur Classics Ser.). (Illus.). 414p. 1965. 22.50x (ISBN 0-8093-0186-5). S Ill U Pr.

Chaisson, Eric. Cosmic Dawn: The Origins of Matter & Life. (Illus.). 320p. 1981. 18.45i (ISBN 0-316-13590-9, Pub. by Atlantic Monthly Pr). Little.

Collier, Katherine B. Cosmogonies of Our Fathers. 1968. lib. bdg. 29.00x (ISBN 0-374-91862-7). Octagon.

Davies, Paul. The Edge of Infinity. 1983. pap. 7.95 (ISBN 0-671-46062-5, Touchstone Bks). S&S.

Eliade, Mircea. Cosmos & History: The Myth of the Eternal Return. Winks, Robin W., ed. LC 83-49168. (History & Historiography Ser.). 182p. 1985. lib. bdg. 20.00 (ISBN 0-8240-6360-0). Garland Pub.

Gibbons, G. W., et al, eds. The Very Early Universe. 480p. 1985. 24.95 (ISBN 0-521-31677-4). Cambridge U Pr.

Hawkins, Gerald S. Mindsteps to the Cosmos. LC 82-48655. (Illus.). 384p. 1983. 19.18 (ISBN 0-06-015156-0, HarpT). Har-Row.

Heidel, Alexander. Babylonian Genesis. 2nd ed. LC 51-822. 1963. 6.00x (ISBN 0-226-32399-4, P133, Phoen). U of Chicago Pr.

Hinman, Frank. Impact of the New Physics. LC 60-15956. 1961. 5.00 (ISBN 0-8022-0725-1). Philos Lib.

Hoyle, Fred. The Cosmogony of the Solar System. LC 78-21286. (Illus.). 168p. 1979. 17.95x (ISBN 0-89490-023-4). Enslow Pubs.

Irwin, John. Ancient Indian Cosmogony. Kuiper, F. B., ed. 257p. 1983. text ed. 32.50x (ISBN 0-7069-1370-1, Pub. by Vikas India). Advent NY.

Jastrow, R. & Cameron, A. G., eds. Origin of the Solar System: Proceedings. 1963. 49.00 (ISBN 0-12-381150-3). Acad Pr.

Jeans, J. H. Eos or the Wider Aspects of Cosmogony. 1929. 17.50 (ISBN 0-686-17425-9). Ridgeway Bks.

--The Universe Around Us. 1929. 30.00 (ISBN 0-686-17428-3). Ridgeway Bks.

Jeans, James H. Eos: Or the Wider Aspects of Cosmogony. (Select Bibliographies Reprint Ser.). 1928. 17.00 (ISBN 0-8369-5091-7). Ayer Co Pubs.

--The Mysterious Universe. 1939. 22.50 (ISBN 0-686-17426-7). Ridgeway Bks.

Jehan, L. F. Dictionnaire de Cosmogonie et de Paleontologie. Migne, J. P., ed. (Nouvelle Encyclopedie Theologique Ser.: Vol. 48). (Fr.). 732p. Repr. of 1854 ed. lib. bdg. 93.00x (ISBN 0-89241-286-0). Caratzas.

Mayr, Otto, ed. The Clockwork Universe. 1980. lib. bdg. 55.00 (ISBN 0-88202-188-5) (ISBN 0-686-77549-X). Watson Pub Intl.

Munitz, Milton K., ed. Theories of the Universe: From Babylonian Myth to Modern Science. LC 57-6746. 438p. 1965. pap. 10.95 (ISBN 0-02-922270-2). Free Pr.

Norman, Ernest L. Cosmic Continuum. 2nd ed. (Illus.). 1960. 7.95 (ISBN 0-932642-17-9). Unarius.

Smith, William F. The Shaping of the Earth. (Illus.). 128p. 1981. 7.00 (ISBN 0-682-49715-0). Exposition Pr FL.

Swann, W. F. The Architecture of the Universe. 1934. 20.00 (ISBN 0-686-17432-1). Ridgeway Bks.

L' Univers. (Illus.). 1978. text ed. 25.00x (ISBN 2-03-019111-6). Larousse.

Van Woerden, Hugo, et al, eds. Oort & the Universe. 210p. 1980. PLB 29.00 (ISBN 9-0277-1180-1, Pub. by D. Reidel); pap. 12.95 (ISBN 90-277-1209-3, Pub. by Reidel Holland). Kluwer Academic.

Zee, A. Unity of Forces in the Universe, 2 vols. 1104p. 1982. Set. 97.00x (ISBN 9971-950-38-3, Pub. by World Sci Singapore); Set. pap. 43.00x (ISBN 9971-950-14-6, Pub. by World Sci Singapore). Taylor & Francis.

COSMOGRAPHY

see also Geography

Cuningham, William. The Cosmographical Glasse, Conteinyng the Principles of Cosmographie, Etc. LC 68-54632. (English Experience Ser.: No. 44). 1968. Repr. of 1559 ed. 49.00 (ISBN 90-221-0044-8). Walter J Johnson.

McCann, Franklin T. English Discovery of America to 1585. LC 73-86280. 1969. Repr. of 1952 ed. lib. bdg. 19.00x (ISBN 0-374-95434-8). Octagon.

Waldseemuller, Martin. Cosmographiae Introductio of Martin Waldseemuller in Facsimile. facsimile ed. LC 77-102258. (Select Bibliographies Reprint Ser). 1907. 29.00 (ISBN 0-8369-5143-3). Ayer Co Pubs.

COSMOLOGY

see also Astronomy; Creation; Earth; Life on Other Planets; Space Sciences

Abell, George & Peebles, P. J., eds. Objects of High Redshift: I. A. U. Symposium Los Angeles, Aug. 28 to 31, 1979. (International Astronomical Union Symposium Ser.: No. 92). 328p. 1980. lib. bdg. 42.00 (ISBN 90-277-1118-6, Pub. by Reidel Holland); pap. 21.00 (ISBN 90-277-1119-4). Kluwer Academic.

Allen, Phil, et al. Energy, Matter, & Form. 2nd ed. Hills, Christopher, ed. LC 77-84873. (Illus.). 311p. 1977. pap. 11.95 (ISBN 0-916438-07-4). Univ of Trees.

Aragone, C., ed. Relativity, Cosmology, Topological Mass & Supergravity: Proceedings of the Silarg Symposium on Gravity, Gauge Theories & Supergravity, USB Campus, Caracas, Dec. 5-11, 1982. 400p. 1984. 44.00x (ISBN 9971-950-95-2, Pub. by World Sci Singapore). Taylor & Francis.

Asimov, Isaac. Universe. 1980. 15.95 (ISBN 0-8027-0655-X). Walker & Co.

Balian, R. & Adouse, J. Physical Cosmology. (Les Houches Summer School Ser.: Vol. 32). 668p. 1980. 115.00 (ISBN 0-444-85433-9). Elsevier.

Beckett, L. C. Movement & Emptiness. 1969. pap. 1.45 (ISBN 0-8356-0414-4, Quest). Theos Pub Hse.

Benjamin, Elsie. The Stanzas of Dzyan: Notes for Study on Cosmogenesis & Anthropogenesis. (Study Ser.: No. 5). 45p. 1981. pap. 3.00 (ISBN 0-913004-40-5). Point Loma Pub.

Bergmann, Peter G. & De Sabbath, Venzo, eds. Cosmology & Gravitation: Spin, Torsion, Rotation, & Supergravity. LC 80-23742. (NATO ASI Series B, Physics: Vol. 58). 519p. 1980. 75.00x (ISBN 0-306-40478-8, Plenum Pr). Plenum Pub.

Berry, M. Principles of Cosmology & Gravitation. LC 75-22559. (Illus.). 200p. 1976. 44.50 (ISBN 0-521-21061-5); pap. 14.95 (ISBN 0-521-29028-7). Cambridge U Pr.

Boodin, J. E. Cosmic Evolution: Outlines of Cosmic Idealism. Repr. of 1925 ed. 21.00 (ISBN 0-527-09800-0). Kraus Repr.

Borchardt, Glenn. The Scientific Worldview. (Illus.). xiii, 343p. (Orig.). 1984. 49.95 (ISBN 0-917929-01-2); pap. 29.95 (ISBN 0-917929-00-4). Progressive Sci Inst.

Bos, A. P. On the Elements: Aristotle's Early Cosmology. 168p. 1972. text ed. 21.75x (ISBN 90-232-1027-1). Humanities.

Boslough, John. Stephen Hawking's Universe. LC 84-4673. (Illus.). 160p. 1984. 12.95 (ISBN 0-688-03530-2). Morrow.

Bucher, Hubert. Spirits & Power: An Analysis of Shona Cosmology. (Illus.). 1980. 19.95x (ISBN 0-19-570176-3). Oxford U Pr.

Burke, William L. Spacetime, Geometry, Cosmology. LC 79-57226. 1980. text ed. 26.00x (ISBN 0-935702-01-6). Univ Sci Bks.

Cadogan, Peter H. From Quark to Quasar. (Illus.). 192p. Date not set. price not set (ISBN 0-521-30135-1). Cambridge U Pr.

Calder, Nigel. The Key to the Universe. (Large Format Ser.). 1978. pap. 8.95 (ISBN 0-14-005065-5). Penguin.

Calvino, Italo. Cosmicomics. Weaver, William, tr. LC 76-14795. 1976. pap. 2.95 (ISBN 0-15-622600-6, Harv). HarBraceJ.

Chaisson, Eric. Cosmic Dawn: The Origins of Matter & Life. (Illus.). 320p. 1981. 18.45i (ISBN 0-316-13590-9, Pub. by Atlantic Monthly Pr). Little.

Chelvam, Reginald T. Einstein Was Wrong: Or the Scroll Theory of Cosmology & of Matter. LC 82-71689. (Illus.). 268p. (Orig.). 1982. pap. 19.95 (ISBN 0-943796-00-8). Penso Pubns.

Choate, Albert G. The Core of Creation: An Investigation into the Fundamentals of Reality & the Foundation of Existence. LC 82-80727. (Illus.). 128p. 1982. pap. 7.50 (ISBN 0-943108-00-4). Syzygy.

Cloud, Preston. Cosmos, Earth & Man: A Short History of the Universe. LC 78-2666. (Illus.). 1978. 31.00x (ISBN 0-300-02146-1); pap. 10.95 (ISBN 0-300-02594-7). Yale U Pr.

Collin, Rodney. The Theory of Celestial Influence: Man, The Universe, & Cosmic Mystery. LC 83-20286. (Illus.). 392p. (Orig.). 1984. pap. 10.95 (ISBN 0-87773-267-1, 72391-0). Shambhala Pubns.

Collins, M. Fred. Space Shots. LC 78-68713. (Illus.). 1979. pap. 7.95 (ISBN 0-8129-0823-6). Times Bks.

Conference of the Summer School, Banff Centre, Banff, Alberta, Canada, August 14-26, 1972. Relativity, Astrophysics & Cosmology: Proceedings. Israel, Werner, ed. LC 72-97957. (Astrophysics & Space Science Library: Vol. 38). 340p. 1973. lib. bdg. 52.65 (ISBN 90-277-0369-8, Pub. by Reidel Holland). Kluwer Academic.

Cosmos Nine-Five-Four: The Occurrence & Nature of Recovered Debris. 60p. 1980. pap. 9.25 (ISBN 0-660-10589-6, SSC155, SSC). Unipub.

Craig, William L. The Cosmological Argument from Plato to Leibniz. LC 79-10394. (Library of Philosophy & Religion Ser.). 305p. 1980. text ed. 26.50x (ISBN 0-06-491311-2). B&N Imports.

Cronin, Vincent. The View from Planet Earth: Man Looks at the Cosmos. LC 82-16654. (Illus.). 384p. 1983. pap. 6.70 (ISBN 0-688-01479-8, Quill NY). Morrow.

Davies, P. C. The Accidental Universe. LC 81-21592. (Illus.). 160p. 1982. 22.95 (ISBN 0-521-24212-6); pap. 10.95 (ISBN 0-521-28692-1). Cambridge U Pr.

Davies, Paul. Superforce: The Search for a Grand Unified Theory of Nature. LC 84-5473. 288p. 1984. 16.95 (ISBN 0-671-47685-8). S&S.

Demianski, M., ed. Physics of the Expanding Universe. (Lecture Notes in Physics: Vol. 109). 1979. pap. 17.00 (ISBN 0-387-09562-4). Springer-Verlag.

Denbigh, K. G. An Inventive Universe. LC 75-13561. 220p. 1975. 8.95 (ISBN 0-8076-0802-5). Braziller.

Dodson, E. O. The Phenomenon of Man Revisited: A Biological Viewpoint on Teilhard de Chardin. (Illus.). 288p. 1984. 25.00x (ISBN 0-231-05850-0). Columbia U Pr.

Douglas, Mary. Natural Symbols: Explorations in Cosmology. 1972. pap. 5.95 (ISBN 0-394-71105-X, VG42, Vin). Random.

--Natural Symbols: Explorations in Cosmology. 1982. pap. 5.95 (ISBN 0-394-71105-X). Pantheon.

Edelen, D. G. & Wilson, A. G. Relativity & the Question of Discretization in Astronomy. LC 79-108675. (Springer Tracts in Natural Philosophy: Vol. 20). (Illus.). 1970. 32.00 (ISBN 0-387-05254-2). Springer-Verlag.

Eigen, Manfred & Winkler, Ruthild. Laws of the Game. LC 81-47550. (Illus.). 368p. 1982. pap. 8.61i (ISBN 0-06-090971-4, CN-971, CN). Har-Row.

Einasto, Jaan & Longair, Malcolm S., eds. The Large Scale Structure of the Universe. 1978. lib. bdg. 58.00 (ISBN 90-277-0895-9, Pub. by Reidel Holland); pap. 37.00 (ISBN 90-277-0896-7, Pub. by Reidel Holland). Kluwer Academic.

Eiseley, Loren. The Unexpected Universe. LC 67-20308. 239p. 1972. pap. 4.95 (ISBN 0-15-692850-7, Harv). HarBraceJ.

Finlay-Freundlich, E. Cosmology. LC 51-4594. (Foundations of the Unity of Science Ser: Vol. 1, No. 8). 1951. pap. 1.50x (ISBN 0-226-57583-7, P407, Phoen). U of Chicago Pr.

Fustero, X. & Verdaguer, E. Relativistic Astrophysics & Cosmology: Proceedings of the XIV Gift International Seminar Sant Feliu de Guixols, Spain, June 27-July 1, 1983. 320p. 1984. 37.00x (ISBN 9971-966-60-3, Pub. by World Sci Singapore). Taylor & Francis.

Gal-Or, B. Cosmology, Physics & Philosophy. (Illus.). 522p. 1981. 34.00 (ISBN 0-387-90581-2). Springer-Verlag.

Gibbons, G. W., et al, eds. The Very Early Universe. LC 83-7330. (Illus.). 500p. 1983. 52.50 (ISBN 0-521-25349-7). Cambridge U Pr.

--The Very Early Universe. 480p. 1985. 24.95 (ISBN 0-521-31677-4). Cambridge U Pr.

Godwin, Joscelyn. Cosmic Music: Keys for the Musical Interpretation of Reality. 260p. 1985. pap. 9.95 (ISBN 0-89281-070-X). Inner Tradit.

Goldberg, Howard S. & Scadron, Michael D. Physics of Stellar Evolution & Cosmology. 405p. 1982. 59.50 (ISBN 0-677-05540-4). Gordon.

Gribbin, John. Genesis: The Origins of Man & the Universe. 352p. 1981. 35.00x (ISBN 0-460-04505-9, Pub. by Dent Australia). State Mutual Bk.

Hahm, David E. The Origins of Stoic Cosmology. LC 76-20712. 312p. 1977. 17.50x (ISBN 0-8142-0253-5). Ohio St U Pr.

Halpern, Leopold. On the Measurement of Cosmological Variations of the Gravitational Constant: Proceedings of the Workshop Meetings Held Nov. 12-14, 1975, at the Dept. of Physics, Florida State University, Tallahassee. LC 78-8350. (Monograph Publishing on Demand: Imprint Ser.). pap. 31.50 (ISBN 0-317-29818-6, 2016494). Bks Demand UMI.

Harrison, Edward R. Cosmology: The Science of the Universe. LC 80-18703. (Illus.). 480p. 1981. 32.50 (ISBN 0-521-22981-2). Cambridge U Pr.

Heidegger, Martin. Essence of Reasons. bilingual ed. Malick, Terrence, tr. (Studies in Phenomenology & Existential Philosophy Ser). (Ger. & Eng.). 1969. 9.95 (ISBN 0-8101-0004-5). Northwestern U Pr.

Heidmann, J. Relativistic Cosmology: An Introduction. (Illus.). 168p. 1980. pap. 28.00 (ISBN 0-387-10138-1). Springer-Verlag.

Heller, Michael. Questions to the Universe: Ten Lectures on Foundations of Physics & Cosmology. (Astronomy & Astrophysics Ser.: Vol. 14). (Illus.). 160p. Date not set. 24.00 (ISBN 0-912918-01-2). Pachart Pub Hse.

Henbest, Nigel, ed. Observing the Universe. (New Scientist Guides Ser.). (Illus.). 340p. 1984. 24.95x (ISBN 0-85520-727-2); pap. 8.95 (ISBN 0-85520-726-4). Basil Blackwell.

Holdridge, L. R. A Complete Cosmology. 1985. 11.95 (ISBN 0-533-06498-8). Vantage.

Hoyle, Fred. Astronomy & Cosmology: A Modern Course. LC 74-28441. (Illus.). 711p. 1975. text ed. 33.95 (ISBN 0-7167-0351-3). W H Freeman.

--The Intelligent Universe: A New View of Creation & Evolution. 1984. 18.95 (ISBN 0-03-070083-3). HR&W.

I.A.U. Symposium No. 63 Cracow, Poland, 10-12 September 1973. Confrontation of Cosmological Theories & Observation Data: Proceedings. Longair, M. S., ed. LC 74-76474. (Symposium of the International Astronomical Union: No. 63). 400p. 1974. lib. bdg. 60.50 (ISBN 90-277-0456-2, Pub. by Reidel Holland); pap. text ed. 45.00 (ISBN 90-277-0457-0, Pub. by Reidel Holland). Kluwer Academic.

Islam, Jumal N. The Ultimate Fate of the Universe. LC 82-14558. 150p. 1983. 14.95 (ISBN 0-521-24814-0). Cambridge U Pr.

Jakubowsky, Frank. Creation. (Illus.). 106p. (Orig.). 1978. pap. 3.95 (ISBN 0-932588-00-X). Jakubowsky.

Jauncey, D. L., ed. Radio Astronomy & Cosmology. (Symposium of the International Astronomical Union: No. 74). 1977. lib. bdg. 50.00 (ISBN 90-277-0838-X, Pub. by Reidel Holland); pap. 26.00 (ISBN 90-277-0839-8, Pub. by Reidel Holland). Kluwer Academic.

Kahn, F. D., ed. Investigating the Universe. 448p. 1981. 54.50 (ISBN 90-277-1325-1, Pub. by Reidel Holland). Kluwer Academic.

Kaufman, William J. Universe. LC 84-13830. (Illus.). 640p. 1984. write for info. (ISBN 0-7167-1673-9); 32.95; slides avail. (ISBN 0-7167-1744-1). W H Freeman.

Kaufmann, William J., 3rd. Relativity & Cosmology. 2nd ed. (Illus.). 1977. pap. text ed. 12.20 scp (ISBN 0-06-043572-0, HarpC). Har-Row.

Kleczek, Josip. The Universe. (Geophysics & Astrophysics Ser.: Monograph 11). 1976. lib. bdg. 37.00 (ISBN 90-277-0684-0, Pub. by Reidel Holland); pap. 21.000 (ISBN 90-277-0685-9). Kluwer Academic.

Kolb, Edward W., et al, eds. Inner Space-Outer Space: The Interface Between Cosmology & Particle Physics. (Theoretical Astrophysics Ser.). 576p. 1985. lib. bdg. 52.00x (ISBN 0-226-45032-5); pap. 24.00x (ISBN 0-226-45033-3). U of Chicago Pr.

Koyre, Alexandre. From the Closed World to the Infinite Universe. LC 57-7080. 313p. 1968. pap. 6.95x (ISBN 0-8018-0347-0). Johns Hopkins.

Kranich, Ernst M. Planetary Influences Upon Plants: Cosmological Botany. 184p. (Orig.). 1984. pap. 12.50 (ISBN 0-938250-20-5). Anthroposophic.

Krogdahl, Wasley S. Tensor Analysis: Fundamentals & Applications. LC 78-62755. 1978. 21.75 (ISBN 0-8191-0594-5). U Pr of Amer.

Kuhn, Thomas S. Copernican Revolution: Planetary Astronomy in the Development of Western Thought. LC 57-76121. (Illus.). 1957. 18.50x (ISBN 0-674-17100-4); pap. 7.95 (ISBN 0-674-17103-9). Harvard U Pr.

Kundakunda Acharya. Building of the Cosmos; or, Panchastikayasara (the Five Cosmic Constituents) Chakravartinayanan, A., ed. LC 73-3837. (No. 3). Repr. of 1920 ed. 25.00 (ISBN 0-404-57703-2). AMS Pr.

Laird, John. Theism & Cosmology. facs. ed. LC 74-84317. (Essay Index Reprint Ser). 1942. 21.50 (ISBN 0-8369-1147-4). Ayer Co Pubs.

Lawden, D. F. An Introduction to Tensor Calculus: Relativity & Cosmology. 3rd ed. LC 81-14801. 1982. 205p. 44.95x, (ISBN 0-471-10082-X, Pub. by Wiley-Interscience); pap. 19.95, 235p. (ISBN 0-471-10096-X). Wiley.

Layzer, David. Constructing the Universe. LC 84-5351. (Scientific American Library Ser.). (Illus.). 313p. 1984. smyth sewn case 27.95 (ISBN 0-7167-5003-1). W H Freeman.

Street, James H. New Revolution in the Cotton Economy: Mechanization & Its Consequences. LC 57-2545. Repr. of 1957 ed. 29.00 (ISBN 0-384-58640-6). Johnson Repr.

Thompson, Holland. From the Cotton Field to the Cotton Mill. facsimile ed. LC 71-148900. (Select Bibliographies Reprint Ser). Repr. of 1906 ed. 20.00 (ISBN 0-8369-5663-X). Ayer Co Pubs.

Toscano, N. C., et al. Pest Management Guide for Insects & Nematodes of Cotton in California. LC 78-73066. 1979. pap. 5.00 (ISBN 0-931876-30-3, 4089). Ag & Nat Res.

Tunstall, J. P. & King, W. J. The Gumbia Cotton Handbook. 1979. 40.00x (ISBN 0-85135-100-X, Pub. by Centre Overseas Research). State Mutual Bk.

Turner, J. A. Cotton Planter's Manual. LC 74-90138. Repr. of 1857 ed. 22.50x (ISBN 0-8371-1996-0, TUC/, Pub. by Negro U Pr). Greenwood.

Woofter, T. J., Jr. Landlord & Tenant on the Cotton Plantation. LC 77-165691. (FDR & the Era of the New Deal Ser.). 1971. Repr. of 1936 ed. lib. bdg. 29.50 (ISBN 0-306-70337-8). Da Capo.

Woofter, Thomas J. Landlord & Tenant on the Cotton Plantation. LC 74-75537. (Illus.). Repr. of 1936 ed. 19.75x (ISBN 0-8371-1035-1, WOL&, Pub. by Negro U Pr). Greenwood.

COTTON MANUFACTURE

see also Cotton Combing; Cotton Spinning; Textile Industry

Batchelder, Samuel. Introduction & Early Progress of the Cotton Manufacture in the U.S. 59.95 (ISBN 0-8490-0414-4). Gordon Pr.

--Introduction & Early Progress of the Cotton Manufacture in the United States. LC 68-55476. Repr. of 1863 ed. 22.50x (ISBN 0-678-00903-1). Kelley.

Chapman, Stanley D. The Cotton Industry in the Industrial Revolution. (Studies in Economic & Social History). 1972. pap. text ed. 6.00x (ISBN 0-333-13584-9). Humanities.

Chin, Rockwood. Management, Industry & Trade in Cotton Textiles. 1965. 10.95x (ISBN 0-8084-0207-2). New Coll U Pr.

Guest, R. Compendious History of the Cotton Manufacture. (Illus.). 74p. 1968. Repr. of 1823 ed. 28.50x (ISBN 0-7146-1396-7, BHA-01396, F Cass Co). Biblio Dist.

Hamby, D. S. American Cotton Handbook, 2 vols. 3rd ed. LC 65-21455. 518p. 1965-66. Vol. 1. 69.50x (ISBN 0-470-34640-X); Vol. 2. 723p. 86.50x (ISBN 0-470-34644-2, Pub by Wiley-Interscience). Wiley.

Harper, R. J. Durable Press Cotton Goods. 60p. 1971. 39.00x (ISBN 0-900541-40-7, Pub. by Meadowfield Pr England). State Mutual Bk.

Harrison, P. W. Cotton in a Competitive World. 311p. 1979. 90.00x (ISBN 0-686-63757-7). State Mutual Bk.

Kraus, Richard. A Cotton & Cotton Goods in China. LC 78-22779. (The Modern Chinese Economy Ser.). 500p. 1980. lib. bdg. 61.00 (ISBN 0-8240-4276-X). Garland Pub.

McKelvey, J. B. Cotton Modification with Oxiranes (Epoxides) 58p. 1971. 39.00x (ISBN 0-900541-10-5, Pub. by Meadowfield Pr England). State Mutual Bk.

Mazzaoui, Maureen F. The Italian Cotton Industry in the Later Middle Ages: 1100 to 1600. LC 80-41023. (Illus.). 272p. 1981. 62.50 (ISBN 0-521-23095-0). Cambridge U Pr.

Miller, Randall M. The Cotton Mill Movement in Antebellum Alabama. LC 77-14771. (Dissertations in American Economic History Ser.). 1978. 27.50 (ISBN 0-405-11049-9). Ayer Co Pubs.

Mitchell, Broadus. The Rise of Cotton Mills in the South. LC 78-63974. (Johns Hopkins University. Studies in the Social Sciences. Thirty-Ninth Ser. 1921: 2). Repr. of 1921 ed. 24.50 (ISBN 0-404-61219-9). AMS Pr.

--Rise of Cotton Mills in the South. 2nd ed. LC 68-8128. (American Scene Ser). 1968. Repr. of 1921 ed. lib. bdg. 37.50 (ISBN 0-306-71141-9). Da Capo.

Montalvo, Joseph G., Jr., ed. Cotton Dust: Controlling an Occupational Health Hazard. LC 82-6857. (ACS Symposium Ser.: No. 189). 1982. 44.95 (ISBN 0-8412-0716-X). Am Chemical.

Montgomery, James. Cotton Manufacture of the U. S. A. Contrasted & Compared with That of Great Britain. (History of American Economy Ser). Repr. of 1840 ed. 14.00 (ISBN 0-384-39900-2). Johnson Repr.

--A Practical Detail of the Cotton Manufacture of the U. S. LC 70-127191. (Research & Source Work Ser: No. 491). 1970. Repr. of 1840 ed. 18.50 (ISBN 0-8337-2442-8). B Franklin.

--Practical Detail of the Cotton Manufacture of the United States of America. LC 68-56266. Repr. of 1840 ed. 25.00x (ISBN 0-678-00572-9). Kelley.

New Techniques in Web-Processing of Textiles with Emphasis on Cotton. pap. 2.50 (ISBN 0-686-94694-4, UN76/2B1, UN). Unipub.

Onikov, E. Handbook of Cotton Weaving, 2 Vols. 501p. 1981. 15.00 set (ISBN 0-8285-2079-8, Pub. by Mir Pubs USSR). Imported Pubns.

Reeves, Wilson A. Flame Resistant Cotton. 64p. 1971. 39.00x (ISBN 0-900541-42-3, Pub. by Meadowfield Pr England). State Mutual Bk.

Segal, Leon. Decrystallized Cotton. 62p. 1971. 39.00x (ISBN 0-900541-02-4, Pub. by Meadowfield Pr England). State Mutual Bk.

Smith, Elliot D. & Nyman, Richmond C. Technology & Labor: Study of the Human Problems of Labor Saving. Stein, Leon, ed. LC 77-70533. (Work Ser.). 1977. Repr. of 1939 ed. lib. bdg. 24.50x (ISBN 0-405-10201-1). Ayer Co Pubs.

Synnott, Thomas W., III. Investment Policies, Growth & Profitability in the New England Cotton Textile Industry, 1830-1914. LC 77-14801. (Dissertations in American Economic History Ser.). 1978. 22.00 (ISBN 0-405-11061-8). Ayer Co Pubs.

Transformation & Development of Technology in the Japanese Cotton Industry. 86p. 1980. pap. 5.00 (ISBN 92-808-0091-4, TUNU093, UNU). Unipub.

Ware, Caroline F. The Early New England Cotton Manufacture: A Study in Industrial Beginnings. 16.00 (ISBN 0-384-65800-8). Johnson Repr.

Watts, Martin. Corn Milling. (Album Ser.: No. 98). (Illus.). 32p. (Orig.). 1983. pap. 2.95 (ISBN 0-85263-623-7, Pub. by Shire Pubns England). Seven Hills Bks.

White, George S. Memoir of Samuel Slater. LC 66-18322. (Illus.). Repr. of 1836 ed. 37.50x (ISBN 0-678-00218-5). Kelley.

Woodbury, Charles J. Bibliography of the Cotton Manufacture. 1910. 22.50 (ISBN 0-8337-3869-0). B Franklin.

COTTON MANUFACTURE–GREAT BRITAIN

Baines, Edward. History of the Cotton Manufacture in Great Britain. 2nd ed. (Illus.). 544p. 1966. 36.00x (ISBN 0-7146-1386-X, F Cass Co). Biblio Dist.

Chapman, Sydney J. Lancaster Cotton Industry. LC 68-55503. Repr. of 1904 ed. 29.50x (ISBN 0-678-00896-5). Kelley.

Fitton, R. S. & Wadsworth, A. P. Strutts & the Arkwrights, 1758-1830. LC 72-375. Repr. of 1958 ed. 35.00x (ISBN 0-678-06758-9). Kelley.

Howe, Anthony. The Cotton Masters, 1830-1860. 1984. 39.95x (ISBN 0-19-821894-X). Oxford U Pr.

Lee, C. H. Cotton Enterprise Seventeen Ninety-Five to Eighteen Forty: A History of M'connel & Kennedy Fine Cotton Spinners. 188p. 1972. 16.50x (ISBN 0-87471-353-6). Rowman.

Montgomery, James. Cotton Manufacture of the U. S. A. Contrasted & Compared with That of Great Britain. (History of American Economy Ser). Repr. of 1840 ed. 14.00 (ISBN 0-384-39900-2). Johnson Repr.

Sandberg, Lars G. Lancashire in Decline: A Study in Entrepreneurship, Technology, and International Trade. LC 73-18435. (Illus.). 290p. 1974. 15.00 (ISBN 0-8142-0199-7). Ohio St U Pr.

Unwin, George. Samuel Oldknow & the Arkwrights. LC 68-5554. (Illus.). Repr. of 1924 ed. 27.50x (ISBN 0-678-06767-8). Kelley.

Ure, Andrew. Cotton Manufacture of Great Britain Systematically Investigated, 2 Vols. LC 73-136749. Repr. of 1836 ed. Set. 80.00 (ISBN 0-384-63350-1). Johnson Repr.

Wadsworth, Alfred P. & Mann, Julia. Cotton Trade & Industrial Lancashire 1600-1780. LC 68-6121. (Illus.). Repr. of 1931 ed. 37.50x (ISBN 0-678-06768-6). Kelley.

COTTON SPINNING

Lee, C. H. Cotton Enterprise Seventeen Ninety-Five to Eighteen Forty: A History of M'connel & Kennedy Fine Cotton Spinners. 188p. 1972. 16.50x (ISBN 0-87471-353-6). Rowman.

Shrigley, C. Manual of Cotton Spinning: Opening & Cleaning, Vol. 2, Pt. 2. 229p. 1973. 45.00x (ISBN 0-686-63773-9). State Mutual Bk.

COTTON TRADE

Chin, Rockwood. Management, Industry & Trade in Cotton Textiles. 1965. 10.95x (ISBN 0-8084-0207-2). New Coll U Pr.

Copeland, Melvin T. Cotton Manufacturing Industry of the United States. LC 66-23981. Repr. of 1917 ed. lib. bdg. 37.50x (ISBN 0-678-00196-0). Kelley.

Edwards, Michael M. Growth of the British Cotton Trade, 1780-1815. LC 67-31864. (Illus.). 1967. 29.50x (ISBN 0-678-06775-9). Kelley.

Hammond, Matthew B. Cotton Industry, Pt. 1. Cotton Culture & The Cotton Trade. 1897. 24.00 (ISBN 0-384-21270-0). Johnson Repr.

Ishii, Osamu. Cotton-Textile Diplomacy: Japan, Great Britain & the United States, 1930-1936. Bruchey, Stuart, ed. LC 80-2813. (Dissertations in European Economic History II). 1981. lib. bdg. 49.50x (ISBN 0-405-13996-9). Ayer Co Pubs.

Moore, Henry L. Forecasting the Yield & Price of Cotton. LC 67-16343. Repr. of 1917 ed. 22.50x (ISBN 0-678-00230-4). Kelley.

Sandberg, Lars G. Lancashire in Decline: A Study in Entrepreneurship, Technology, and International Trade. LC 73-18435. (Illus.). 290p. 1974. 15.00 (ISBN 0-8142-0199-7). Ohio St U Pr.

Stigum, Marcia L. The Impact of the European Economic Community on the French Cotton & Electrical Engineering Industries. Bruchey, Stuart, ed. LC 80-2830. (Dissertations in European Economic History II). (Illus.). 1981. lib. bdg. 26.50x (ISBN 0-405-14012-6). Ayer Co Pubs.

Thompson, Holland. From the Cotton Field to the Cotton Mill. facsimile ed. LC 71-148900. (Select Bibliographies Reprint Ser). Repr. of 1906 ed. 20.00 (ISBN 0-8369-5663-X). Ayer Co Pubs.

Tolley, Brian H. Liverpool & the American Cotton Trade. Reeves, Marjorie, ed. (Then & There Ser.). (Illus.). 96p. (Orig.). 1978. pap. text ed. 3.75 (ISBN 0-582-21722-9). Longman.

Ure, Andrew. Cotton Manufacture of Great Britain Systematically Investigated, 2 Vols. LC 73-136749. Repr. of 1836 ed. Set. 80.00 (ISBN 0-384-63350-1). Johnson Repr.

Wadsworth, Alfred P. & Mann, Julia. Cotton Trade & Industrial Lancashire 1600-1780. LC 68-6121. (Illus.). Repr. of 1931 ed. 37.50x (ISBN 0-678-06768-6). Kelley.

Watkins, James L. King Cotton: A Historical & Statistical Review. LC 72-89062. Repr. of 1908 ed. 22.50x (ISBN 0-8371-1944-8, WAK&, Pub. by Negro U Pr). Greenwood.

Woodbury, Charles J. Bibliography of the Cotton Manufacture. 1910. 22.50 (ISBN 0-8337-3869-0). B Franklin.

COTTONSEED OIL

Okura, Nagatsune. Seiyu Roku: On Oil Manufacturing. Ariga, Eiko, tr. LC 74-6761. (Illus.). 79p. 1974. 20.00 (ISBN 0-917526-01-5). Olearius Edns.

COTYLEDON (ANATOMY)

see Placenta

COUGARS

see Pumas

COULOMB FUNCTIONS

Alder, Kurt & Winther, Aage, eds. Coulomb Excitation: A Collection of Reprints. (Perspectives in Physics Ser). 1966. 49.50 (ISBN 0-12-049250-4). Acad Pr.

March, Norman H. & Tosi, Mario P. Coulomb Liquids: Monograph. 1984. 65.00 (ISBN 0-12-470520-0). Acad Pr.

COUNTERS, DIGITAL

see Digital Counters

COUNTING

see Numeration

COUNTING DEVICES, DIGITAL

see Digital Counters

COUPLING CONSTANTS

Lucken, E. A. Nuclear Quadrupole Coupling Constants. 1969. 57.50 (ISBN 0-12-458450-0). Acad Pr.

COUPLINGS

Broersma, G. Couplings & Bearings. 122p. 1968. 50.00x (ISBN 0-85950-050-0, Pub. by Stam Pr England). State Mutual Bk.

CISM (International Center for Mechanical Sciences), Dept. for Mechanics of Deformable Bodies, 1970. Theory of Couple-Stresses in Bodies with Constrained Rotations. Sokolowski, M., ed. (CISM International Centre for Mechanical Sciences Ser.: No. 26). (Illus.). 143p. 1974. pap. 14.90 (ISBN 0-387-81143-5). Springer-Verlag.

Vance, Edward F. Coupling to Shielded Cables. LC 78-16186. 183p. 1978. 32.50x (ISBN 0-471-04107-6, Pub. by Wiley-Interscience). Wiley.

Young, Leo. Parallel Coupled Lines & Directional Couplers. LC 76-168946. (Illus.). pap. 71.80 (ISBN 0-317-08875-0, 2012103). Bks Demand UMI.

COVER CROPS

see also Legumes; Soil Conservation

Leatherbarrow, Margaret. Gold in the Grass. Bargyla & Rateaver, Gylver, eds. LC 75-23179. (Conservation Gardening & Farming Ser: Ser. C). 1975. pap. 10.00 (ISBN 0-9600698-8-7). Rateavers.

Turner, F. Newman. Fertility Pastures & Cover Crops. Bargyla & Rateaver, Gylver, eds. LC 74-33123. (Conservation Gardening & Farming Ser: Ser. C). pap. 10.00 (ISBN 0-9600698-6-0). Rateavers.

COVERED BRIDGES

Adams, Kramer. Covered Bridges of the West. LC 63-19906. (Illus.). 1963. 14.95 (ISBN 0-8310-7037-4). Howell-North.

Congdon, Herbert W. Covered Bridge. (Illus.). 1970. pap. 4.95 (ISBN 0-911570-05-5). Vermont Bks.

Kenyon, Thedia C. New Hampshire's Covered Bridges. rev. ed. (Illus.). 1966. 5.00 (ISBN 0-87482-023-5). Wake-Brook.

Sangster, Tom & Sangster, Dess L. Alabama's Covered Bridges. LC 80-68408. (Illus.). 162p. (Orig.). 1980. pap. 25.00 (ISBN 0-938252-00-3); includes 13 lithographs 29.50, 1st 500 numbered & signed by artist Tom Sangster (ISBN 0-686-69146-6). Coffeetable.

Sloane, Eric. Americana, 3 vols. Incl. Vol. 1. American Barns & Covered Bridges. LC 54-12510. 112p; Vol. 2. American Yesterday. LC 56-10710. 123p. 10.95i (ISBN 0-308-70042-2); Vol. 3. Our Vanishing Landscape. LC 55-12078. 107p. 10.95i (ISBN 0-308-70047-3). (Funk & W Bk.). (Illus.). T Y Crowell.

Swanson, Leslie C. Covered Bridges in Illinois, Iowa, & Wisconsin. rev. ed. (Illus., Orig.). 1970. pap. 3.00 (ISBN 0-911466-14-2). Swanson.

COW

see Cows

COWS

see also Cattle; Dairying; also particular breeds of cattle

Gallant, Marc. The Cow Book. LC 82-47816. 1983. 17.95 (ISBN 0-394-52034-3). Knopf.

Karg, H. & Schallenberger, E. Factors Influencing Fertility in the Post-Partum Cow. 1982. 76.00 (ISBN 90-247-2715-4, Pub. by Martinus Nijhoff Netherlands). Kluwer Academic.

King, Una. So Fine Bovine: Understanding Cattle. Moon, Delia, ed. 350p. (Orig.). 1981. pap. text ed. 8.95 (ISBN 0-937770-01-9). Family Pub CA.

Lodrick, Deryck O. Sacred Cows, Sacred Places: Origins & Survivals of Animal Homes in India. (Illus.). 350p. 1981. 32.50x (ISBN 0-520-04109-7). U of Cal Pr.

Mansfield, Richard H. Progress of the Breed: A History of U. S. Holsteins. Hastings, Robert H., ed. 350p. 1985. 34.95 (ISBN 0-9614711-0-7). Holstein-Friesian.

Meijs, J. A. Herbage Intake by Grazing Dairy Cows. (Agricultural Research Reports: No. 909). 280p. 1981. pap. 22.00 (ISBN 90-220-0764-2, PDC229, PUDOC). Unipub.

Olsen, S. J. Post-Cranial Skeletal Characters of Bison & Bos. (Harvard University Peabody Museum of Archaeology & Ethnology Papers). Repr. of 1960 ed. 15.00 (ISBN 0-527-01291-2). Kraus Repr.

Van Loon, Dirk. The Family Cow. LC 75-26148. (Illus.). 272p. 1975. pap. 8.95 (ISBN 0-88266-066-7). Garden Way Pub.

COYOTES

Anderson, Peter. In Search of the New England Coyote. LC 81-86602. (Illus.). 228p. (Orig.). 1983. pap. 9.95 (ISBN 0-87106-966-0). Globe Pequot.

Bekoff, Marc, ed. Cayotes: Biology, Behavior & Management. 1978. 55.00 (ISBN 0-12-086050-3). Acad Pr.

Cadieux, Charles L. Coyotes: Predators & Survivors. LC 82-62895. (Illus.). 240p. 1983. 16.95 (ISBN 0-913276-42-1). Stone Wall Pr.

Dobie, J. Frank. The Voice of the Coyote. LC 49-8879. (Illus.). xx, 386p. 1961. pap. 6.95 (ISBN 0-8032-5050-9, BB 109, Bison). U of Nebr Pr.

Leydet, Francois. The Coyote: Defiant Songdog of the West. LC 79-4744. (Illus.). 236p. 1979. pap. 7.95 (ISBN 0-8061-1547-5). U of Okla Pr.

Ryden, Hope. God's Dog. (Illus.). 1979. 14.95 (ISBN 0-670-34297-1). Viking.

CP-M (COMPUTER OPERATING SYSTEM)

Arnow, Murray. The Apple CP-M Book. LC 85-2393. 164p. 1985. pap. 12.95 (ISBN 0-673-18068-9). Scott F.

Barbier, Ken. CP-M Assembly Language Programming: A Guide to Integrated Learning of the CP-M Operating & Assembly Language Programming. (Illus.). 226p. 1982. 19.95 (ISBN 0-13-188268-6, Spec); pap. 12.95 (ISBN 0-13-188250-3). P-H.

--CP-M Solutions. (Illus.). 144p. 1985. 22.95 (ISBN 0-13-188186-8); pap. 14.95 (ISBN 0-13-188178-7). P H.

--CP M Techniques. (Illus.). 224p. 1984. 27.95 (ISBN 0-13-187865-4); pap. 19.95 (ISBN 0-13-187857-3). P-H.

Blackburn, Laurie & Taylor, Marcus. Pocket Guide: CP-M. (Pitman Programming Pocket Guides Ser.). 64p. (Orig.). 1984. pap. 6.95 (ISBN 0-273-02136-2). Pitman Pub MA.

Bove, Tony & Rhodes, Cheryl. InfoWorld's Essential Guide to CP-M Systems. (InfoWorld's Essential Guides Ser.). 250p. (Orig.). 1984. pap. 16.95 (ISBN 0-06-669003-X). Har Row.

--The User's Guide to CP-M Systems. (Orig.). 1984. pap. 8.95 (ISBN 0-671-55921-4, Pub. by Baen Books). PB.

Brigham, Bruce. CP-M Programmer's Encyclopedia. 225p. 1984. pap. 19.95 (ISBN 0-88022-043-0, 31). Que Corp.

Heidel, Alexander. Babylonian Genesis. 2nd ed. LC 51-822. 1963. 6.00x (ISBN 0-226-32399-4, P133, Phoen). U of Chicago Pr.

Katter, Reuben L. History of Creation & Origin of the Species: A Scientific Theological Viewpoint. 3rd ed. 480p. 1984. 16.95 (ISBN 0-911806-01-6, C13374); durable softcover 11.95 (ISBN 0-911806-00-8). Theotes.

Kitcher, Philip. Abusing Science: The Case Against Creationism. (Illus.). 224p. 1982. 20.00x (ISBN 0-262-11085-7); pap. 7.95 (ISBN 0-262-61037-X). MIT Pr.

Larson, Edward J. Trial & Error: The American Controversy over Creation & Evolution. LC 85-7144. 224p. 1985. 17.95 (ISBN 0-19-503666-2). Oxford U Pr.

Morris, Henry. Biblical Cosmology & Modern Science. 1970. pap. 4.50 (ISBN 0-87552-349-8). Presby & Reformed.

National Research Council. Science & Creationism: A View from the National Academy of Sciences. 28p. 1984. pap. 4.00 (ISBN 0-309-03440-X). Natl Acad Pr.

Nelkin, Dorothy. The Creation Controversy: Science or Scripture in the Schools. 256p. 1982. 16.95 (ISBN 0-393-01635-8). Norton.

--The Creation Controversy: Science or Scripture in the Schools? LC 83-45954. 242p. 1984. pap. 9.95x (ISBN 0-8070-3155-0, BP 675). Beacon Pr.

Newell, Norman D. Creation & Evolution: Myth or Reality? (Convergence Ser.). 232p. 1982. 22.00x (ISBN 0-231-05348-7). Columbia U Pr.

Peacocke, Arthur R. Creation & the World of Science. LC 79-40267. 408p. 1985. Repr. text ed. 9.95 (ISBN 0-268-00755-1, 85-07550, Dist. by Har-Row). U of Notre Dame Pr.

Rusch, Wilbert H., Sr. The Argument: Creationism vs. Evolutionism. Mulfinger, George, Jr., ed. (Creation Research Society Monograph Ser.: No. 3). (Illus.). 86p. (Orig.). 1984. pap. 6.95 (ISBN 0-940384-04-3). Creation Res.

Salisbury, Frank B. The Creation. LC 76-47071. (Illus.). 1976. 9.95 (ISBN 0-87747-627-6). Deseret Bk.

Tarneja, Sukh R. Nature, Spirituality & Science. 240p. 1980. text ed. 27.50x (ISBN 0-7069-1203-9, Pub by Vikas India). Advent NY.

Teilhard De Chardin, Pierre. Hymn of the Universe. LC 65-10375. 1969. pap. 5.95xi (ISBN 0-06-131910-4, TB1910, Torch). Har-Row.

--Hymne De L'univers. 1966. 13.95 (ISBN 0-685-11240-3). French & Eur.

Trefil, James. The Moment of Creation: Big Bang Physics from Before the First Millisecond to the Present Universe. (Illus.). 240p. 1984. pap. 6.95 (ISBN 0-02-096770-5, Collier). Macmillan.

Wesner, R. The Wesner Conjectures. LC 82-21421. 128p. 1985. pap. 4.95 (ISBN 0-88437-070-4). Psych Dimensions.

Whitcomb, John C. Origin of the Solar System. (Biblical & Theological Studies). pap. 1.75 (ISBN 0-8010-9590-5). Baker Bk.

CREDIT MANAGEMENT–DATA PROCESSING

Bryan, William H. The Computer Book for Managing Credit. Andover, James J., ed. LC 85-4808. 136p. 1985. pap. 17.95 (ISBN 0-934914-61-3). NACM.

Richardson, Dennis W. Electric Money: Evolution of an Electronic Funds-Transfer System. 1970. pap. 6.95x (ISBN 0-262-68025-4). MIT Pr.

Whiteside, Conon D. EDP Systems for Credit Management. LC 74-156330. (Illus.). pap. 39.00 (ISBN 0-317-09900-0, 2019525). Bks Demand UMI.

CREEP OF MATERIALS

see Materials–Creep; also subdivision Creep under names of specific materials, e.g. Concrete–Creep

CREPIDOTUS

Hesler, L. R. & Smith, A. H. North American Species of Crepidotus. (Illus.). 1965. 22.95x (ISBN 0-02-845980-6). Hafner.

Singer, R. The Genera Marasmiellus, Crepidotus & Simocybe in the Neotropics. 1973. 70.00 (ISBN 3-7682-5444-5). Lubrecht & Cramer.

CREPUSCULE

see Twilight

CRETACEOUS PERIOD

see Geology, Stratigraphic–Cretaceous

CRICKETS

Otte, Daniel & Alexander, Richard D. The Australian Crickets (Orthoptera: Gryllidae) (Monograph: No. 22). (Illus.). 477p. 1983. pap. 45.00 (ISBN 0-910006-30-X). Acad Nat Sci Phila.

CRIMINAL JUSTICE, ADMINISTRATION OF–DATA PROCESSING

Archambeault, William G. & Archambeault, Betty J. Computers for Criminal Justice Administration & Management. 186p. 1984. pap. 12.95 (ISBN 0-932930-65-4). Pilgrimage Inc.

Boxerman, Lawerence A., intro. by. Computer Applications in Juvenile Court. 78p. 1974. 3.00 (ISBN 0-318-15763-2, T900). Natl Juv & Family Ct Judges.

Greenwood, Michael & Tollar, Jerry R., eds. Evaluation Guidebook to Computer-Aided Transcription. 124p. 1975. 3.84 (ISBN 0-89656-001-5, R0019). Natl Ctr St Courts.

Kelman, Alistair & Sizer, Richard. The Computer in Court. 112p. 1982. text ed. 35.50x (ISBN 0-566-03419-0). Gower Pub Co.

CRINOIDEA

Moore, C. Raymond & Laudon, Lowell R. Evolution & Classification of Paleozoic Crinoids: Geological Society of America Special Papers, No. 46. Gould, Stephen J., ed. LC 79-8352. (The History of Paleontology Ser.). (Illus.). 1980. Repr. of 1943 ed. lib. bdg. 14.00x (ISBN 0-405-12721-9). Ayer Co Pubs.

Webster, G. D. Bibliography & Index of Paleozoic Crinoids, Nineteen Sixty-Nine to Nineteen Seventy-Three. LC 77-76475. (Microform Publication: No. 8). 1977. 4.50 (ISBN 0-8137-6008-9). Geol Soc.

Wright, James. The British Carboniferous Crinoidea, Vol. 1, Pts. 1-5, Vol. 2, Pts. 1-3. Set. 109.00 (ISBN 0-384-69455-1). Johnson Repr.

CRINOTHENE

see Polyethylene

CRITICAL PATH ANALYSIS

Antill, James M. & Woodhead, Ronald. Critical Path Methods in Construction Practice. 2nd ed. LC 79-121902. pap. 81.40 (ISBN 0-8357-9870-4, 2019295). Bks Demand UMI.

Antill, James M. & Woodhead, Ronald W. Critical Path Methods in Construction Practice. 3rd. ed. LC 81-19713. 425p. 1982. 42.95x (ISBN 0-471-86612-1, Pub. by Wiley-Interscience). Wiley.

Benson. Construction with Critical Path Methods. (Practical Construction Guides Ser.). Date not set. price not set (ISBN 0-471-82506-9). Wiley.

Grant, Donald P. PERT & CPM: Network Methods for Project Planning, Scheduling & Control. LC 83-60947. (Illus.). vi, 58p. (Orig.). 1983. pap. 6.00x (ISBN 0-911215-01-8). Small Master.

Grantham, Emily. PERT-CPM for Population Program Management. LC 75-29488. (PopCase Series B). (Illus.). 119p. 1975. pap. 3.00 (ISBN 0-89055-302-5). U of NC Dept Health.

Kaufman, A. & Desbazielle, G. Critical Path Method. 178p. 1970. 57.75 (ISBN 0-677-01880-0). Gordon.

Lockyer, K. G. Introduction to Critical Path Analysis. 1969. 15.00x (ISBN 0-8464-0522-9). Beekman Pubs.

Martino, R. L. Critical Path Networks. 176p. 1968. 74.25x (ISBN 0-677-61040-8). Gordon.

--Dynamic Costing. 162p. 1968. 74.25x (ISBN 0-677-61060-2). Gordon.

--Resources Management. 168p. 1968. 74.25 (ISBN 0-677-61050-5). Gordon.

Moder, J., et al. Project Management with CPM, PERT & PRECEDENCE Diagramming. 3rd ed. 464p. 1983. 27.50 (ISBN 0-442-25415-6). Van Nos Reinhold.

Morris, L. W. Critical Path: Construction & Analysis. 1967. pap. text ed. 14.00 (ISBN 0-08-012471-2). Pergamon.

Waldron, A. James. Applied Principles of Project Planning & Control: 70 Practical Problems & Solutions. 2nd ed. LC 68-22562. (Illus.). 1968. 25.00 (ISBN 0-911590-02-1). Waldron.

Wiest, Jerome D. & Levy, Ferdinand K. A Management Guide to PERT-CPM: With Gert-PDM, DCPM & Other Networks. 2nd ed. (Illus.). 1977. ref. ed. o.p. 22.00x (ISBN 0-13-549113-4); pap. text ed. 18.95 (ISBN 0-13-549105-3). P-H.

CRITICAL PATH ANALYSIS–PROGRAMMED INSTRUCTION

Lang. Teach Yourself Critical Path Analysis. (Teach Yourself Ser.). 1977. 6.95 (ISBN 0-679-10504-2). McKay.

CRITICAL PHENOMENA (PHYSICS)

see also Critical Point; Phase Rule and Equilibrium

Ceausescu, V., et al, eds. Critical Phenomena: 1983 Brasov School Conference. (Progress in Physics Ser.: Vol. 11). 436p. 1985. text ed. write for info. (ISBN 0-8176-3289-1). Birkhauser.

Hahne, F. J. Critical Phenomena. (Lecture Notes in Physics: Vol. 186). 353p. 1983. pap. 21.00 (ISBN 0-387-12675-9). Springer-Verlag.

Pekalski, A., et al, eds. Static Critical Phenomena in Inhomogeneous Systems: Proceedings of the XX Karpacz Winter School of Theoretical Physics, February 20-March 3, 1984, Karpacz, Poland. (Lectures Notes in Physics Ser.: Vol. 206). viii, 376p. 1984. pap. 21.00 (ISBN 0-387-13369-0). Springer-Verlag.

Pfeuty, Pierre & Toulouse, Gerard. Introduction to the Renormalization Group & to Critical Phenomena. LC 76-26111. pap. 50.50 (ISBN 0-317-29389-3, 2024283). Bks Demand UMI.

CRITICAL POINT

see also Phase Rule and Equilibrium

Domb, C. & Green, M., eds. Phase Transitions & Critical Phenomena. Vol. 1. 1973. 83.00 (ISBN 0-12-220301-1); Vol. 2. 1972. 84.50 (ISBN 0-12-220302-X); Vol. 5a. 1976. 69.50 (ISBN 0-12-220305-4); Vol. 5B. 1976. 69.50 (ISBN 0-12-220351-8); Vol. 6. 1977. 99.50 (ISBN 0-12-220306-2). Acad Pr.

--Phase Transitions & Critical Phenomena: Series Expansion for Lattice Models, Vol. 3. 1974. 99.00 (ISBN 0-12-220303-8). Acad Pr.

Stanley, H. Eugene. Introduction to Phase Transitions & Critical Phenomena. (International Series of Monographs on Physics). (Illus.). 1971. text ed. 24.95x (ISBN 0-19-501458-8). Oxford U Pr.

CROCODILES

For the American species of this group see Alligators.

Boulenger, G. A. Catalogue of the Chelonians, Rhynchocephalians, & Crocodiles in the British Museum. new ed. (Illus.). 1966. 26.60 (ISBN 3-7682-0443-X). Lubrecht & Cramer.

British Museum. Dinosaurs & Their Living Relatives. LC 79-14504. (Natural History Ser.). 1980. 24.95 (ISBN 0-521-22887-5); pap. 8.95 (ISBN 0-521-29698-6). Cambridge U Pr.

Crocodiles: Proceedings of the First Working Meeting of Crocodile Specialists. (Illus.). 191p. 1971. pap. 12.50 (ISBN 2-88032-008-9, IUCN5, IUCN). Unipub.

Hirschhorn, Howard H. Complete Guide to Alligators & Crocodilians of Florida & the Caribbean. 60p. 1984. pap. write for info. (ISBN 0-940810-04-2). Phoenix FL.

Messel, H., ed. Surveys of Tidal River Systems in the Northern Territory & Their Crocodile Populations, 7 vols. Incl. Tidal Waterways of Castlereagh Bay & Hutchinson & Cadell Straits: Bennett, Darbitla, Djigaglia Djabura, Ngandadauda Creeks & the Glyde & Woolen Rivers. (Monograph: No. 9). 23.25 (ISBN 0-08-024801-2); Tidal Waterways of Buckingham & Ulundurwi Bays: Buckingham, Kalarwoi, Warawuruwoi & Kurala Rivers & Slippery Creek. (Monograph: No. 10). 18.00 (ISBN 0-08-024802-0); Tidal Waterways of Arnhem Bay: Darwarunga, Habgood, Baralminer, Gobalpa, Coromuro, Cato, Peter John & Burungbirinung Rivers. (Monograph: No. 11). 21.50 (ISBN 0-08-024803-9); Tidal Waterways on the South-Western Coast of the Gulf of Carpentaria: Limmen Bight Towns, Roper, Phelp & Wilson Rivers; Nayarnpi, Wungguliyanga, Painnyilatya, Mangkurdurrungku & Yiwapa Creeks. (Monograph: No. 12). 17.00 (ISBN 0-08-024804-7); Tidal Waterways on the Southern Coast of the Gulf of Carpentaria: Calvert, Robinson, Wearyan & McArthur Rivers & Some Intervening Creeks. (Monograph: No. 13). 19.00 (ISBN 0-08-024805-5); Tidal Waterways of the Van Diemen Gulf: Ilamary; River, Iwalg, Saltwater & Minimini: Creeks & Coastal Arms on Cobourg Peninsula. Resurveys of the Alligator Region Rivers. (Monograph: No. 14). 20.00 (ISBN 0-08-024806-3); Some River & Creek Systems on the West Coast of Cape York Peninsula in the Gulf of Carpentaria: Nassau, Staaten & Gilbert Rivers & Duck Creek. (Monograph: No. 16). write for info. (ISBN 0-08-024807-1). (Illus.). 1980. write for info. Pergamon.

Messel, H., et al. Survey of Tidal River Systems in the Northern Territory & Their Crocodile Populations: Monographs, Nos. 2-8. Incl. No. 2. The Victoria & Fitzmaurice River Systems. 52p (ISBN 0-08-023098-9); No. 3. The Adelaide, Daly & Moyle Rivers. 58p (ISBN 0-08-023099-7); No. 4. The Alligator Region River System: Murgenella & Cooper's Creeks; East, South & West Alligator Rivers & Wildman River. 70p (ISBN 0-08-024789-X); No. 5. The Goodmadeer & King River Systems: Majarie, Wurugoij & All Night Creeks. 62p (ISBN 0-08-024790-3); No. 6. Some River & Creek Systems on Melville & Grant Islands: North & South Creeks on Grant Island. 64p (ISBN 0-08-024784-9); No. 7. The Liverpool-Tomkinson River Systems & Nungbulgarri Creek. 84p (ISBN 0-08-024785-7); No. 8. Some Rivers & Creeks on the Western Shore of the Gulf of Carpentaria: Rose River, Muntak Creek; Hart, Walker & Koolatong Rivers. 40p (ISBN 0-08-024786-5). (Illus.). 1979. pap. write for info. Pergamon.

--Surveys of Tidal River Systems in the Northern Territory & Their Crocodile Populations. (Monograph: No. 17). (Illus.). 92p. 1981. pap. 22.00 (ISBN 0-08-024818-7). Pergamon.

--Surveys of Tidal River Systems in the Northern Territory & Their Crocodile Population. (Monograph: No. 1). (Illus.). 464p. 1982. 125.00 (ISBN 0-08-024819-5, G135). Pergamon.

Messel, M. Surveys of Tidal River Systems in the Northern Territory & Their Crocodile Populations. (Monograph: No. 15). (Illus.). 368p. 1982. 112.00 (ISBN 0-08-024831-4). Pergamon.

Scott, H. B. & Pooley, A. C. The Status of Crocodiles in Africa. 98p. 1972. pap. 10.00 (ISBN 2-88032-010-0, IUCN43, IUCN). Unipub.

Smith, Malcolm. The Fauna of British India, Including Ceylon & Burma: Reptilia & Amphibia, 2 vols. Incl. Vol. 1. Loricata, Testudines. 189p. Repr. of 1931 ed. Vol. 1. 15.00 (ISBN 0-88359-005-0); Vol. 2. Sauria. Repr. of 1935 ed. Vol. 2. 22.50 (ISBN 0-88359-006-9). (Illus.). 1973. Set. 35.00 (ISBN 0-88359-007-7). R Curtis Bks.

CROP REPORTS

see Agriculture–Statistics

CROP STATISTICS

see Agriculture–Statistics

CROP YIELDS

see also Agriculture–Statistics; Crops and Climate

Bishop, D. & Carter, L. P. Crop Science & Food Production. 416p. 1983. text ed. 19.60 (ISBN 0-07-005431-2); activity guide 6.76 (ISBN 0-07-005432-0). McGraw.

Brickbauer, Elwood A. & Mortenson, William P. Approved Practices in Crop Production. 2nd ed. LC 77-89853. (Illus.). 396p. 1978. 18.60 (ISBN 0-8134-1975-1, 1975); text ed. 13.95x. Interstate.

Brown, Lester R. Increasing World Food Output. LC 75-26298. (World Food Supply Ser). (Illus.). 1976. Repr. of 1965 ed. 14.00x (ISBN 0-405-07770-X). Ayer Co Pubs.

CAB Books, ed. Crop Loss Assessment Methods: FAO Manual on the Evaluation & Prevention of Losses by Pests, Disease & Weeds. 276p. 1971. 59.00x (ISBN 0-85198-185-2, Pub. by CAB Bks England). State Mutual Bk.

Carlson, Peter S. The Biology of Crop Productivity. LC 79-28261. 1980. 52.50 (ISBN 0-12-159850-0). Acad Pr.

Crop Loss Assessment Methods: FAO Manual on the Evaluation & Prevention of Losses by Pests, Diseases, & Weeds. (Illus.). 1976. looseleaf bdg. 16.80 (ISBN 0-685-67374-X, FAO); suppl. 1 4.80 (ISBN 0-685-67375-8). Unipub.

Crop Production Levels & Fertilizer Use. (Fertilizer Bulletins: No. 2). (Eng. & Fr.). 78p. 1981. pap. 8.25 (ISBN 92-5-101099-4, F2216, FAO). Unipub.

Crosson, Pierre R. & Stout, Anthony T. Productivity Effects of Cropland Erosion in the United States. LC 83-19094. 152p. 1984. pap. text ed. 11.00x (ISBN 0-8018-3207-1). Johns Hopkins.

De Wit, C. T. Simulation of Assimilation, Respiration & Transpiration of Crops. 148p. 1978. pap. 11.50 (ISBN 90-220-0601-8, PDC141, PUDOC). Unipub.

The Effect of Meteorological Factors on Crop Yields & Methods of Forecasting the Yield. (Technical Note Ser.: No. 174). 54p. 1982. pap. 7.00 (ISBN 92-63-10566-9, W540, WMO). Unipub.

Feddes, R. A., et al. Simulation of Field Water Use & Crop Yield. LC 78-10697. (Simulation Monographs Ser.). 188p. 1979. pap. 34.95x (ISBN 0-470-26463-2). Halsted Pr.

Hall, Carl W. Drying & Storage of Agricultural Crops. (Illus.). 1980. pap. text ed. 29.50 (ISBN 0-87055-364-X). AVI.

Hurd, R. G., et al, eds. Opportunities for Increasing Crop Yields. LC 79-25924. (Pitman International Ser. in Bioscience). 320p. 1980. text ed. 71.50 (ISBN 0-273-08481-X). Pitman Pub MA.

Improving Agricultural Yields Using Biotechnologies. 1983. 1250.00 (ISBN 0-89336-340-5, GA-051). BCC.

Metcalf, Darrel S. & Elkins, Donald M. Crop Production: Principles & Practices. 4th ed. (Illus.). 1980. text ed. write for info. (ISBN 0-02-380710-5). Macmillan.

Morachan, Y. B. Crop Production & Management. 267p. 1981. 50.00x (ISBN 0-686-76633-4, Pub. by Oxford & IBH India). State Mutual Bk.

Pest Resistance to Pesticides & Crop Loss Assessment: Report of the 2nd Session of the FAO Panel of Experts Held in Rome, Aug.-Sept. 1978, Vol. 2. (Plant Production & Protection Papers: No. 6). (Eng., Fr & Span.). 47p. 1979. pap. 7.50 (ISBN 92-5-100762-4, F1838, FAO). Unipub.

Rubenstein, Irwin, et al, eds. Genetic Improvement of Crops: Emergent Techniques. 232p. 1980. 22.50x (ISBN 0-8166-0966-7). U of Minn Pr.

Simulation of Field Water Use & Crop Yield. 1979. pap. 27.95 (PDC142, PUDOC). Unipub.

Stoskopf, Neal C. Understanding Crop Production. 420p. 1981. text ed. 24.95 (ISBN 0-8359-8027-8); instructor's manual O.P. (ISBN 0-8359-8028-6). Reston.

Hofmeister, W. Vergleichende Untersuchungen der Keimung Entfaltung, und Fruchtbildung Hoeherer Kryptogamen (Moose, Farne, Equisetaceen, Rhizocarpeen und Lycopodiaceen) und der Samenbildung der Coniferen. (Historia Naturalis Classica Ser.: No. 105). (Ger., Illus.). 1979. Repr. of 1851 ed. lib. bdg. 21.00 (ISBN 3-7682-1250-5). Lubrecht & Cramer.

Hofmeister, W. F. On the Germination, Development, & the Fructification of the Higher Cryptogamia & on the Fructification of the Coniferoe. Repr. of 1862 ed. 35.00 (ISBN 0-527-41600-2). Kraus Repr.

Pritchard, Hayden N. & Bradt, Patricia T. Biology of Nonvascular Plants. LC 83-1018. (Illus.). 550p. 1983. text ed. 28.95 (ISBN 0-8016-4043-1). Mosby.

Rabenhorst, G. Ludwig. Kryptogamenflora Von Deutschland Osterreich und der Schweiz. (Illus.). Set. 2375.00 (ISBN 0-384-49385-8); Set. pap. 2200.00 (ISBN 0-685-13484-9). Johnson Repr.

Scagel, Robert F., et al. Non-Vascular Plants. 592p. 1982. text ed. write for info. (ISBN 0-534-01029-6). Wadsworth Pub.

CRYPTOGAMS, VASCULAR

see Pteridophyta

CRYPTOGRAPHY

see also Ciphers

Applied Cryptology, Cryptographic Protocols, & Computer Security Models. Davida, George I., et al, eds. LC 83-15548. (Proceedings of Symposia in Applied Mathematics: Vol. 29). 204p. 1983. pap. 23.00 (ISBN 0-8218-0041-8). Am Math.

Barker, Wayne G. Cryptanalysis of Shift-Register Generated Stream Cipher Systems. (Orig.). 1984. pap. text ed. 48.80 (ISBN 0-89412-062-X). Aegean Park Pr.

--Cryptanalysis of the Hagelin Cryptograph. (Cryptographic Ser.). 1977. 24.80 (ISBN 0-89412-022-0). Aegean Park Pr.

--Cryptanalysis of the Simple Substitution Cipher with Word Divisions: Using Non-Pattern Word Lists. LC 75-18083. (Cryptographic Ser.). 1975. pap. 16.00 (ISBN 0-89412-000-X). Aegean Park Pr.

Barker, Wayne G., ed. The History of Codes & Ciphers in the United States During World War I. (Cryptographic Ser.). (Illus.). 1979. 20.80 (ISBN 0-89412-031-X). Aegean Park Pr.

--History of Codes & Ciphers in the United States Prior to World War I. (Cryptographic Ser.). 1978. 16.80 (ISBN 0-89412-026-3). Aegean Park Pr.

--Manual of Cryptography. 1981. pap. text ed. 14.80 (ISBN 0-89412-042-5). Aegean Park Pr.

Beth, T., ed. Cryptography: Burg Feuerstein, FRG 1982. (Lecture Notes in Computer Science: Vol. 149). 402p. 1983. pap. 20.50 (ISBN 0-387-11993-0). Springer-Verlag.

Bosworth, Bruce. Codes, Ciphers, & Computers: An Introduction to Information Security. 1982. pap. 16.50 (5149). Hayden.

Course in Cryptanalysis. S I Course, 2 vols. 1981. pap. 18.80 ea.; Vol. I, 72p. pap. (ISBN 0-89412-052-2); Vol. II, 69p. pap. (ISBN 0-89412-053-0). Aegean Park Pr.

Deavours, Cipher & Kruh, Louis. Machine Cryptography & Modern Cryptanalysis. 1985. text ed. 56.00 (ISBN 0-89006-161-0). Artech Hse.

Denning, Dorothy E. Cryptography & Data Security. LC 81-15012. (Computer Science Ser.). (Illus.). 500p. 1982. text ed. 36.95 (ISBN 0-201-10150-5). Addison-Wesley.

Flicke, Wilhelm F. War Secrets in the Ether, 2 vols. LC 77-88801. (Cryptographic Ser.). 1977. Vol. 1. 17.80 (ISBN 0-89412-021-2); Vol. 2. 18.80 (ISBN 0-89412-023-9). Aegean Park Pr.

Friedman, William F. Advanced Military Cryptography. rev. ed. (Cryptographic Ser.). 1976. Repr. of 1941 ed. 14.80 (ISBN 0-89412-011-5). Aegean Park Pr.

--Elementary Military Cryptography. rev. ed. LC 76-53119. (Cryptographic Ser.). 1976. Repr. of 1941 ed. 14.00 (ISBN 0-89412-010-7). Aegean Park Pr.

--Elements of Cryptanalysis. LC 76-19947. (Cryptographic Ser.). 1976. pap. 16.80 (ISBN 0-89412-002-6). Aegean Park Pr.

--History of the Use of Codes. (Cryptographic Ser.). 1977. Repr. of 1928 ed. 13.80 (ISBN 0-89412-018-2). Aegean Park Pr.

--Military Cryptanalysis, 4 vols. 1980. lib. bdg. 500.00 (ISBN 0-87700-271-1). Revisionist Pr.

--Military Cryptanalysis, Pt. II. rev ed. Barker, Wayne G., ed. (Cryptographic Ser.). 161p. 1984. pap. 22.80 (ISBN 0-89412-064-6). Aegean Park Pr.

--Military Cryptanalysis, Pt. 1. 1981. pap. 20.80 (ISBN 0-89412-044-1). Aegean Park Pr.

--The Riverbank Publications, 3 vols. (Cryptographic Ser.). 1979. 18.00 ea. Vol. 1 (ISBN 0-89412-032-8). Vol. 2 (ISBN 0-89412-033-6). Vol. 3 (ISBN 0-89412-034-4). Aegean Park Pr.

--Solving German Codes in World War I. (Cryptographic Ser.). 1977. 16.80 (ISBN 0-89412-019-0). Aegean Park Pr.

Friedman, William F. & Mendelsohn, Charles J. The Zimmermann Telegram of January 16, 1917 & Its Cryptographic Background. LC 76-53121. (Cryptographic Ser.). 1976. pap. 8.20 (ISBN 0-89412-009-3). Aegean Park Pr.

Friedman, William F., ed. Cryptography & Cryptanalysis Articles, 2 vols. rev. ed. (Cryptographic Ser.). 1976. Repr. of 1941 ed. Vol. 1. 16.80 (ISBN 0-89412-003-4); Vol. 2. 16.80 (ISBN 0-89412-004-2). Aegean Park Pr.

Gaines, Helen F. Cryptanalysis: A Study of Ciphers & Their Solutions. (Illus.). 1939. pap. text ed. 4.50 (ISBN 0-486-20097-3). Dover.

Galland, Joseph S. Historical & Analytical Bibliography of the Literature of Cryptology. LC 75-128996. (Northwestern University. Humanities Ser.: No. 10). Repr. of 1945 ed. 29.00 (ISBN 0-404-50710-7). AMS Pr.

Gardner, Martin. Codes, Ciphers & Secret Writing. 96p. 1984. pap. 2.95 (ISBN 0-486-24761-9). Dover.

Givierge, Marcel. Course in Cryptography. (Cryptographic Ser.). 1978. 20.80 (ISBN 0-89412-028-X). Aegean Park Pr.

Gleason, Andrew M. Elementary Course in Probability for the Cryptanalyst. (Orig.). pap. 24.80 (ISBN 0-89412-072-7). Aegean Park Pr.

Gleason, Norma. Cryptograms & Spygrams. 128p. (Orig.). 1981. pap. 3.50 (ISBN 0-486-24036-3). Dover.

Gylden, Yves. Contribution of the Cryptographic Bureaus in the World War. Friedman, William F., ed. (Cryptographic Ser). 1978. 14.80 (ISBN 0-89412-027-1). Aegean Park Pr.

Jarvis, William R. The Journey Beyond. (Orig.). 1983. pap. 3.95 (ISBN 0-89412-060-3). Aegean Park Pr.

Kahn, David. The Codebreakers. 1967. 39.95 (ISBN 0-02-560460-0). Macmillan.

Konheim, Alan G. Cryptography: A Primer. LC 80-24978. 432p. 1981. 43.95x (ISBN 0-471-08132-9, Pub. by Wiley-Interscience). Wiley.

Kullback, Solomon. Statistical Methods in Cryptanalysis. rev. ed. LC 76-42183. (Cryptographic Ser.). 1976. Repr. of 1941 ed. 18.80 (ISBN 0-89412-006-9). Aegean Park Pr.

Lange, Andre & Soudart, E. A. Treatise on Cryptography: An English Translation of the Original "Traite de Cryptographie". 181p. 1982. pap. text ed. 22.80 (ISBN 0-89412-055-7). Aegean Park Pr.

Langie, Andre. Cryptography. rev. ed. 1984. pap. text ed. 19.80 (ISBN 0-89412-061-1). Aegean Park Pr.

Lauer, Rudolph F. Computer Simulation of Classical Substitution: Cryptographics Systems. 1981. pap. 24.80 (ISBN 0-89412-050-6). Aegean Park Pr.

Lawrence, V. B. & LoCicero, J. L., eds. IEEE Communications Society's Tutorials in Modern Communication. LC 82-10599. 348p. 1982. text ed. 36.95 (ISBN 0-914894-48-X). Computer Sci.

Longo, G., ed. Secure Digital Communications. (CISM International Centre for Mechanical Sciences, Courses & Lectures Ser.: No. 279). (Illus.). v, 332p. 1983. pap. 25.00 (ISBN 0-387-81784-0). Springer-Verlag.

Lynch, Frederick D. Pattern-Word List, Vol. 1. (Cryptographic Ser.). 1977. pap. 14.80 (ISBN 0-89412-017-4). Aegean Park Pr.

Lysing, Henry, pseud. Secret Writing: An Introduction to Cryptograms, Ciphers, & Codes. LC 74-75261. 128p. 1974. pap. 2.50 (ISBN 0-486-23062-7). Dover.

Meyer, Carl & Matyas, Stephen. Cryptography: A New Dimension in Computer Data Security: A Guide for the Design & Implementation of Secure Systems. LC 82-2831. 755p. 1982. 49.95x (ISBN 0-471-04892-5, Pub. by Wiley-Interscience). Wiley.

Migne, J. P., ed. Dictionnaire de Paleographie, de Cryptographie, de Dactylologie. (Nouvelle Encyclopedie Theologique Ser.: Vol. 47). (Fr.). 668p. Repr. of 1854 ed. lib. bdg. 85.00x (ISBN 0-89241-285-2). Caratzas.

Sacco, Luigi. Manual of Cryptography. (Cryptographic Ser.). 1977. Repr. of 1935 ed. 20.80 (ISBN 0-89412-016-6). Aegean Park Pr.

Simmons, Gustavus J., ed. Secure Communications & Asymetric Crypto-Systems. (Selected Symposium Ser. 69). 225p. 1982. lib. bdg. 34.00x (ISBN 0-86531-338-5). Westview.

Sinkov, Abraham. Elementary Cryptanalysis: A Mathematical Approach. LC 72-89953. (New Mathematical Library: No. 22). 189p. 1980. pap. 10.00 (ISBN 0-88385-622-0). Math Assn.

Smith, Laurence D. Cryptography: The Science of Secret Writing. 1955. pap. 2.95 (ISBN 0-486-20247-X). Dover.

U. S. Army. Security Agency. Historical Section. Origin & Development of the Army Security Agency, 1917-1947. (Cryptographic Ser.). 1978. 8.80 (ISBN 0-89412-025-5). Aegean Park Pr.

Yardley, Herbert O. The American Black Chamber. 375p. 1981. Repr. of 1931 ed. lib. bdg. 25.00 (ISBN 0-8495-6102-7). Arden Lib.

CRYSTAL DIODES

see Diodes, Semiconductor

CRYSTAL FIELD THEORY

see also Ligand Field Theory

Furrer, A., ed. Crystal Field Effects in Metals & Alloys. LC 76-55802. 379p. 1977. 59.50x (ISBN 0-306-31008-2, Plenum Pr). Plenum Pub.

CRYSTAL GROWTH

see Crystals–Growth

CRYSTAL LATTICES

see also Color Centers

Beran, Ladislav. Orthomodular Lattices. 1985. lib. bdg. 69.00 (ISBN 90-277-1715-X, Pub. by Reidel Holland). Kluwer Academic.

Birman, J. L. Theory of Crystal Space Groups & Lattice Dynamics: Infra-Red & Raman Optical Processes of Insulating Crystals. (Illus.). 570p. 1984. pap. 35.00 (ISBN 0-387-13395-X). Springer Verlag.

Bollmann, W. Crystal Lattices, Interfaces, Matrices: An Extension of Crystallography. (Illus.). 360p. 1982. 45.00 (ISBN 2-88105-000-X). Polycrystal Bk Serv.

Born, Max & Huang, Kun. Dynamical Theories of Crystal Lattics. (The International Series of Monographs on Physics). pap. cancelled (ISBN 0-317-08962-5, 2051181). Bks Demand UMI.

Hardy, J. R. & Karo, A. M. The Lattice Dynamics & Statistics of Alkali Halide Crystals. LC 79-339. 324p. 1979. 49.50x (ISBN 0-306-40221-1, Plenum Pr). Plenum Pub.

Kitaigorodsky, A. I. Molecular Crystals & Molecules. (Physical Chemistry Ser.). 1973. 95.00 (ISBN 0-12-410550-5). Acad Pr.

Maradudin, A. A., et al, eds. Theory of Latice Dynamics in the Harmonic Approximation. 2nd ed. (Solid State Physics: Suppl. 3). 1971. 91.50 (ISBN 0-12-607783-5). Acad Pr.

Poulet, H. & Mathieu, J. P. Vibration Spectra & Symmetry of Crystals. 586p. 1976. 120.25 (ISBN 0-677-30180-4). Gordon.

CRYSTAL OPTICS

Agranovich, V. M. & Ginzburg, V. Crystal Optics with Spatial Dispersion, & Excitons. 2nd ed. (Springer Series in Solid-State Sciences: Vol. 42). (Illus.). 455p. 1984. 49.00 (ISBN 0-387-11520-X). Springer-Verlag.

Bloss, Donald F. The Spindle Stage: Principles & Practice. LC 80-21488. (Illus.). 416p. 1981. 79.50 (ISBN 0-521-23292-9). Cambridge U Pr.

Bloss, F. D. Introduction to the Methods of Optical Crystallography. LC 61-6759. 1961. text ed. 38.95 (ISBN 0-03-010220-0, HoltC). HR&W.

Hellwege, K. H. Elastic, Piezoelectric, Pyroelectric, Piezooptic Electrooptic Constants & Nonlinear Dielectric Susceptibilities of Crystals. Hellwege, A. M., ed. LC 62-53136. (Landolt-Boernstein New Ser. Group III: Vol. 11). (Illus.). 1978. 344.40 (ISBN 0-387-08506-8). Springer-Verlag.

Kaminow, Ivan P. An Introduction to Electrooptic Devices. 1974. 49.50 (ISBN 0-12-395050-3). Acad Pr.

Pekar, S. I. Crystal Optics & Additional Light Waves. 1983. text ed. 78.95x (ISBN 0-8053-6945-7). Benjamin-Cummings.

Personick, Stewart D. Optical Fiber Transmission Systems. LC 80-20684. (Applications of Communications Theory Ser.). 192p. 1981. 27.50x (ISBN 0-306-40580-6, Plenum Pr). Plenum Pub.

Shubnikov, A. V. Principles of Optical Crystallography. LC 59-14222. 186p. 1960. 27.50x (ISBN 0-306-10582-9, Consultants). Plenum Pub.

Wood, Elizabeth A. Crystals & Light: An Introduction to Optical Crystallography. LC 76-27458. (Illus.). 156p. 1977. pap. text ed. 4.00 (ISBN 0-486-23431-2). Dover.

Yariv, Amnon & Yeh, Pochi. Optical Waves in Crystals: Propagation & Control of Laser Radiation. LC 83-6892. (Pure & Applied Optics Ser.). 589p. 1983. 53.50 (ISBN 0-471-09142-1, 1-349, Pub. by Wiley-Interscience). Wiley.

CRYSTALLINE LENS

Bloemendal, Hans. Molecular & Cellular Biology of the Eye Lens. LC 80-26815. 469p. 1981. 109.95 (ISBN 0-471-05171-3, Pub. by Wiley-Interscience). Wiley.

Hockwin, O. Bonn, ed. Growth Control, Differentiation, & Aging of the Eye Lens. (Journal: Ophthalmic Research, Vol. 11, No. 5-6, 1979). (Illus.). 242p. 1979. softcover 21.00 (ISBN 3-8055-0862-X). S Karger.

CRYSTALLINE SEMICONDUCTORS

see Semiconductors

CRYSTALLIZATION

see also Crystals–Growth; Solidification; Solutions, Solid; Zone Melting

Bockris, J. O'M. & Razumney, G. A. Fundamental Aspects of Electrocrystallization. LC 66-22123. 155p. 1967. 29.50x (ISBN 0-306-30254-3, Plenum Pr). Plenum Pub.

Chalmers, Bruce. Principles of Solidification. LC 76-18772. 336p. 1977. Repr. of 1964 ed. 22.50 (ISBN 0-88275-446-7). Krieger.

De Jong, E. J. & Jancic, S. J., eds. Industrial Crystallization, '78. 588p. 1979. 106.50 (ISBN 0-686-63101-3, North Holland). Elsevier.

Elwell, D. & Scheel, H. J. Crystal Growth from High Temperature Solutions. 1975. 98.50 (ISBN 0-12-237550-5). Acad Pr.

Epstein, Mary Anne, ed. Nucleation, Growth, & Impurity Effects in Crystallization Process Engineering. LC 82-11460. (AICHE Symposium Ser.: Vol. 78). 90p. 1982. pap. 22.00 (ISBN 0-8169-0226-7, S-215); pap. 12.00 members (ISBN 0-686-47547-X). Am Inst Chem Eng.

Gittus, J. Irradiation Effects in Crystalline Solids. (Illus.). 523p. 1978. 81.50 (ISBN 0-85334-778-6, Pub. by Elsevier Applied Sci England). Elsevier.

Hagenmuller, Paul, ed. Preparative Methods in Solid State Chemistry. 1972. 95.00 (ISBN 0-12-313350-5). Acad Pr.

Hargittai, I. & Orville-Thomas, W. J. Diffraction Studies in Non-Crystalline Substances. (Studies in Physical & Theoretical Chemistry: Vol. 13). 894p. 1982. 117.00 (ISBN 0-444-99752-0). Elsevier.

Industrial Crystallisation: Proceedings, No. 36, London, April 1969. 248p. 1981. 40.00x (ISBN 0-85295-079-9, Pub. by Inst Chem Eng England). State Mutual Bk.

Jancic, S. J. & Grootscholten, P. A. Industrial Crystallization. 1984. lib. bdg. 64.00 (ISBN 90-277-1771-0, Pub. by Reidel Holland). Kluwer Academic.

Kapustin, Alexander P. Effects of Ultrasound on the Kinetics of Crystallization. LC 63-17640. 65p. 1963. 20.00x (ISBN 0-306-10661-2, Consultants). Plenum Pub.

Kelly, F. H. & Mark, F. The Sucrose Crystal & Its Solutions. 272p. 1975. pap. 17.50x (ISBN 0-8214-0497-0, 82-93334, Pub. by Singapore U Pr). Ohio U Pr.

Lobachev, A. N., ed. Crystallization Processes Under Hydrothermal Conditions. LC 73-79420. (Studies in Soviet Science - Physical Sciences Ser.). (Illus.). 225p. 1973. 35.00x (ISBN 0-306-10892-5, Consultants). Plenum Pub.

Miller, Robert L., ed. Flow-Induced Crystallization in Polymer Systems. (Midland Macromolecular Monographs: Vol. 6). 380p. 1979. 63.25 (ISBN 0-677-12540-2). Gordon.

Mullin, J. W., ed. Industrial Crystallization. LC 76-10859. 473p. 1976. 75.00x (ISBN 0-306-30945-9, Plenum Pr). Plenum Pub.

Myuller, R. L. Solid State Chemistry. LC 65-26631. 256p. 1966. 42.50x (ISBN 0-306-10743-0, Consultants). Plenum Pub.

Nyvlt, J. & Sohnel, O. The Kinetics of Industrial Crystallization. (Chemical Engineering Monographs: Vol. 19). 1985. 65.00 (ISBN 0-444-99610-9). Elsevier.

Nyvlt, Jaroslav. Industrial Crystallization: The Present State of the Art. 2nd ed. (Illus.). 180p. 1982. pap. 31.00x (ISBN 0-89573-069-3). VCH Pubs.

Pfeiffer. Sensitive Crystallization Processes. LC 68-31125. 1975. pap. 16.00 (ISBN 0-910142-66-1). Anthroposophic.

Randolph, Alan D. & Larson, Maurice A. Theory of Particulate Processes. 1971. 57.00 (ISBN 0-12-579650-1). Acad Pr.

Rudman, Reuben, ed. Diffraction Aspects of Orientationally Disordered (Plastic) Crystals. (Transactions of the American Crystallographic Association Ser.: Vol. 17). 114p. 1981. pap. 15.00 (ISBN 0-937140-26-0). Polycrystal Bk Serv.

Sirota, N. N., et al. Crystallization Processes. LC 66-18734. 169p. 1966. 27.50x (ISBN 0-306-10755-4, Consultants). Plenum Pub.

Youngquist, Gordon R., ed. Advances in Crystallization from Solutions, Vol. 80. (AIChE Symposium Ser.). 126p. pap. 30.00 (ISBN 0-317-36923-7); pap. 15.00 members (ISBN 0-317-36924-5). Am Inst Chem Eng.

CRYSTALLOGRAPHY

see also Anisotropy; Crystal Optics; Crystals; Dislocations in Crystals; Geology; Mineralogy; Oscillators, Crystal; Phonons; Pyro- and Piezo-Electricity; X-Ray Crystallography; also names of minerals

Adams, D. M. Inorganic Solids: An Introduction to Concepts in Solid State Structural Chemistry. LC 73-16863. 336p. 1974. pap. 29.95x (ISBN 0-471-00471-5, Pub. by Wiley-Interscience). Wiley.

American Crystallographic Association, ed. Workshop on Calculation of Crystal Packing & Non-Bonded Forces. 1984. 15.00 (ISBN 0-317-12233-9). Polycrystal Bk Serv.

Arndt, Ulrich W. & Willis, B. T. Single Crystal Diffractometry. LC 66-13637. (Cambridge Monographs on Physics). pap. 88.80 (ISBN 0-317-26117-7, 2024404). Bks Demand UMI.

Ashida, T. & Hall, Sydney, eds. Methods & Applications in Crystallographic Computing. (Illus.). 500p. 1984. 32.50x (ISBN 0-19-855190-8). Oxford U Pr.

Bacon, G. E. X-Ray & Neutron Diffraction. 1966. pap. text ed. 21.00 (ISBN 0-08-011998-0). Pergamon.

Bednowitz, A. L., ed. World Directory of Crystallographers: & of Other Scientists Employing Crystallographic Methods. 6th ed. 1981. pap. 10.00 (ISBN 90-277-1310-3, Pub. by Reidel Holland). Kluwer Academic.

Belk, J. A., ed. Electron Microscopy & Microanalysis of Crystalline Materials. (Illus.). 240p. 1979. 40.75 (ISBN 0-85334-816-2, Pub. by Elsevier Applied Sci England). Elsevier.

Bell, James F. Physics of Large Deformation of Crystalline Solids. (Springer Tracts in Natural Philosophy: Vol. 14). (Illus.). 1968. 35.00 (ISBN 0-387-04343-8). Springer-Verlag.

Bernal, Ivan, et al. Symmetry: A Stereoscopic Guide for Chemists. LC 75-178258. (Illus.). 180p. 1972. text ed. 35.95 (ISBN 0-7167-0168-5). W H Freeman.

Bethe, Hans A. Splitting of Terms in Crystals. 73p. 1962. 20.00x (ISBN 0-306-10639-6, Consultants). Plenum Pub.

--Splitting of Terms in Crystals. LC 58-2296. (Translated from Annals of Physics Ser.: Vol. 3). (Illus.). pap. 20.00 (ISBN 0-317-09920-5, 2003370). Bks Demand UMI.

Bishop, Arthur C. Outline of Crystal Morphology. 1970. pap. text ed. 10.00x (ISBN 0-09-079423-0). Humanities.

Bloss, F. D. Crystallography & Crystal Chemistry. LC 77-136774. 1971. text ed. 40.95 (ISBN 0-03-085155-6, HoltC). HR&W.

Blundell, T. L. & Johnson, Louise. Protein Crystallography. (Molecular Biology Ser.). 1976. 87.50 (ISBN 0-12-108350-0). Acad Pr.

Brown, F. C. & Noriaki Itoh, eds. Recombination-Induced Defect Formation in Crystals. (Special Topics Issue of Semiconductors & Insulators Ser.). 484p. 1983. 88.75 (ISBN 0-677-40365-8). Gordon.

Burke, John. Origins of the Science of Crystals. LC 66-13584. 1966. 38.00x (ISBN 0-520-00198-2). U of Cal Pr.

Chang, S. L. Multiple Diffraction of X-Rays in Crystals. (Springer Series in Solid State Sciences: Vol. 50). (Illus.). 320p. 1984. 49.50 (ISBN 0-387-12955-3). Springer-Verlag.

Chernov, A. A. Modern Crystallography III. (Series in Solid State Sciences: Vol. 36). (Illus.). 530p. 1984. 59.50 (ISBN 0-387-11516-1). Springer-Verlag.

Clark, L. J. Surface Crystallography: An Introduction to Low Energy Electron Diffraction. 1985. 49.95 (ISBN 0-471-90513-5). Wiley.

Cole, Henderson, ed. Instrumentation for Tomorrow's Crystallography. (Transactions of the American Crystallographic Association Ser.: Vol. 12). 146p. 1976. pap. 15.00 (ISBN 0-686-60382-6). Polycrystal Bk Serv.

Cracknell, A. P., et al, eds. Kronecker Product Tables, Vols. 1-4. LC 79-14566. 2600p. 1979. Set. 395.00 (ISBN 0-306-65175-0, IFI Plenum). Plenum Pub.

Cullen, G. W. & Wang, C. C., eds. Heteroepitaxial Semiconductors for Electronic Devices. LC 77-21749. (Illus.). 1978. 98.00 (ISBN 0-387-90285-6). Springer-Verlag.

Dana, E. S. & Ford, W. E. Textbook of Mineralogy. 4th ed. 851p. 1932. 51.95x (ISBN 0-471-19305-4). Wiley.

Dana, E. S. & Hurlbut, C. S. Minerals & How to Study Them. 3rd ed. 323p. 1963. pap. 16.50 (ISBN 0-471-19195-7). Wiley.

Dieke, Gerhard H. Spectra & Energy Levels of Rare Earth Ions in Crystals. Crosswhite, H. M. & Crosswhite, Hannah, eds. LC 67-29453. pap. 103.30 (ISBN 0-317-09061-5, 2011960). Bks Demand UMI.

Dienes, G. J., et al, eds. Molecular Crystals & Liquid Crystals: Proceedings of the International Conference on Low-Dimensional Conductors, Boulder, Colorado, August 1981. (Molecular Crystals & Liquid Crystals Ser.: Vols. 77, 79, 81, 83, 85, & 86). 2078p. 1982. Set. 620.00 (ISBN 0-677-16405-X). Gordon.

Diffractometry Tutorial. (Lecture Notes of the American Crystallographic Association Ser.). 1978. pap. 12.00 (ISBN 0-686-47204-7). Polycrystal Bk Serv.

Evans, Robert C. Introduction to Crystal Chemistry. 2nd ed. (Illus.). 1964. pap. text ed. 29.95 (ISBN 0-521-09367-8). Cambridge U Pr.

Fedorov, Fedor I. Theory of Elastic Waves in Crystals. LC 65-27349. 375p. 1968. 49.50x (ISBN 0-306-30309-4, Plenum Pr). Plenum Pub.

Flint, E. Essentials of Crystallography. 2nd ed. MIR Publishers, tr. from Rus. (Illus.). 231p. 1974. text ed. 15.00x (ISBN 0-8464-0389-7). Beekman Pubs.

Gay, Peter. The Crystalline State. (Illus.). 1972. 20.95x (ISBN 0-02-845220-8). Hafner.

Giacovazzo, Carmelo. Direct Methods in Crystallography. 1980. 70.00 (ISBN 0-12-282450-4). Acad Pr.

Hahn, Theo. International Tables for Crystallograpy. 1985. lib. bdg. 8.50 (ISBN 90-277-1964-0, Pub. by Reidel Holland). Kluwer Academic.

Hamlin, R. C., ed. New Crystallographic Detectors & the Workshop on Crystallographic Detectors at the Nat. Bureau of Standards, Wash. D. C. (Transactions of the American Crystallographic Association Ser.: Vol. 18). 179p. 1982. pap. 15.00 (ISBN 0-686-45036-1). Polycrystal Bk Serv.

Hauptman, H. A., ed. Direct Methods in Crystallography: Proceedings of the 1976 Intercongress Symposium. 297p. 1978. pap. text ed. 13.50 (ISBN 0-9602470-0-9, Pub by Med Found Buffalo). Polycrystal Bk Serv.

Hellwege, K. H. Elastic, Piezoelectric, Pyroelectric, Piezooptic Electrooptic Constants & Nonlinear Dielectric Susceptibilities of Crystals. Hellwege, A. M., ed. LC 62-53136. (Landolt-Boernstein New Ser. Group III: Vol. 11). (Illus.). 1978. 344.40 (ISBN 0-387-08506-8). Springer-Verlag.

Jaswon, M. A. & Rose, M. A. Crystal Symmetry: The Theory of Colour Crystallography. LC 82-21380. (Mathematics & Its Applications Ser.). 190p. 1983. 48.95x (ISBN 0-470-27353-4). Halsted Pr.

Khamskii, Eugenii. Crystallization from Solutions. LC 72-76425. (Illus.). 106p. 1969. 34.50x (ISBN 0-306-10826-7, Consultants). Plenum Pub.

Kitaigorodsky, A. I. Mixed Chrystals. (Springer Series in Solid-State Sciences: Vol. 33). (Illus.). 400p. 1984. 45.00 (ISBN 0-387-10922-6). Springer-Verlag.

--Molecular Crystals & Molecules. (Physical Chemistry Ser.). 1973. 95.00 (ISBN 0-12-410550-5). Acad Pr.

Kleber, Will. An Introduction to Crystallography. 10th, rev. ed. (Illus.). 366p. 1970. 18.00 (ISBN 0-686-45044-2). Polycrystal Bk Serv.

Klemen, M. Points, Lines & Walls: In Liquid Crystals, Magnetic Systems & Various Ordered Media. LC 81-21976. 322p. 1982. 64.95 (ISBN 0-471-10194-X, Pub. by Wiley-Interscience). Wiley.

Koetzle, T. F., ed. Structure & Bonding: Relationships Between Quantum Chemistry & Crystallography. (Transactions of the ACA: Vol. 16). 95p. 1980. pap. 15.00 (ISBN 0-937140-25-2). Polycrystal Bk Serv.

Krivoglaz, M. A. Theory of X-Ray & Thermal Neutron Scattering by Real Crystals. LC 68-26771. (Illus.). 405p. 1969. 55.00x (ISBN 0-306-30347-7, Plenum Pr). Plenum Pub.

Ladd, M. F. & Palmer, R. A., eds. Theory & Practice of Direct Methods in Crystallography. LC 79-10566. (Illus.). 436p. 1980. 45.00x (ISBN 0-306-40223-8, Plenum Pr). Plenum Pub.

Least Squares Tutorial. (Lecture Notes of the American Crystallographic Association Ser.). 1974. pap. 13.50 (ISBN 0-686-47221-7). Polycrystal Bk Serv.

Levy, F., ed. Crystallography & Crystal Chemistry of Materials with a Layered Structure. (Physics & Chemistry of Materials Ser: No. 2). 380p. 1975. lib. bdg. 55.00 (ISBN 90-277-0586-0, Pub. by Reidel Holland). Kluwer Academic.

Lieth, Ronald M., ed. Preparation & Crystal Growth of Materials with Layered Structures. (Physics & Chemistry of Materials with Layered Structures: Vol. I). 200p. 1978. lib. bdg. 50.00 (ISBN 90-277-0638-7, Pub. by Reidel Holland). Kluwer Academic.

Lipson, H. Crystals & X-rays. (The Wykeham Science Ser.: No. 13). 198p. 1970. pap. cancelled (ISBN 0-85109-150-4). Taylor & Francis.

Love, Warner & Lattman, Eaton, eds. Biophysical Applications of Crystallographic Techniques. (Transactions of the American Crystallographic Association Ser.: Vol. 9). 140p. 1973. pap. 15.00 (ISBN 0-686-60380-X). Polycrystal Bk Serv.

Low Temperature X-ray Diffraction Tutorial (LTXRD-Tutorial) (Lecture Notes of the American Crystallographic Association Ser.). 48p. 1977. pap. 3.50 (ISBN 0-686-47226-8). Polycrystal Bk Serv.

MacGillavry & Rieck. International Tables for X-Ray Crystallography. 1983. lib. bdg. 67.50 (ISBN 90-277-1532-7, Pub. by Reidel Holland). Kluwer Academic.

McLachlan, Dan & Glusker, Jenny, eds. Crystallography in North America. LC 81-71539. 479p. 1985. Repr. of 1983 ed. 50.00 (ISBN 0-937140-07-4). Polycrystal Bk Serv.

Manning, John R. Diffusion Kinetics for Atoms in Crystals. LC 68-20921. pap. 68.50 (ISBN 0-317-09190-5, 2005790). Bks Demand UMI.

Mason, Warren P., ed. Crystal Physics of Interaction Processes. (Pure & Applied Physics Ser.: Vol. 23). 1966. 60.00 (ISBN 0-12-477950-6). Acad Pr.

Mathematical Tools in Crystallography Tutorial. (Lecture Notes of the American Crystallography Association). 98p. 1980. pap. 12.00 (ISBN 0-686-47113-X). Polycrystal Bk Serv.

Meier, W. M. & Olson, D. H. Atlas of Zeolite Structure Types. (Illus.). 99p. pap. text ed. 5.00 (ISBN 0-9601830-0-0, Pub by Structure Comm of Intl Zeolite). Polycrystal Bk Serv.

Morkike, B. L., ed. Phase Transformations in Crystalline & Amorphous Alloys: Proceedings. 266p. 1983. 70.00 (ISBN 0-9911000-6-9, Pub. by Aluminium W Germany). Heyden.

Muller, O. & Roy, R. The Major Ternary Structure Families. LC 73-11536. (Crystal Chemistry Ser.: Vol. 4). (Illus.). 487p. 1974. 47.00 (ISBN 0-387-06430-3). Springer-Verlag.

Narasimhamurty, T. S. Photoelastic & Electro-Optic Properties of Crystals. LC 79-409. (Illus.). 543p. 1981. 59.50 (ISBN 0-306-31101-1, Plenum Pr). Plenum Pub.

New Crystallographic Detectors: Detectors in Crystallographic Applications. (American Crystallographic Association Program & Abstracts Ser. 2: Vol. 10, 1). 1982. pap. 5.00 (ISBN 0-317-02526-0). Polycrystal Bk Serv.

Newnham, Robert E., ed. Applied Crystal Chemistry & Physics. (Transactions of the American Crystallography Association: Vol. 11). 117p. 1975. pap. 15.00 (ISBN 0-686-47114-8). Polycrystal Bk Serv.

Nicholas, J. F. An Atlas of Models of Crystal Surfaces. 238p. 1965. 92.50x (ISBN 0-677-00580-6). Gordon.

Nishiyama, Zenji. Martensitic Transformation. Fine, M. & Meshii, M., trs. (Materials Science & Technology Ser.). 1978. 82.50 (ISBN 0-12-519850-7). Acad Pr.

Pamplin, B., ed. Inorganic Biological Crystal Growth. (Illus.). 284p. 1981. 66.00 (ISBN 0-08-028420-5, C999, H210, H999). Pergamon.

Pamplin, B. R., et al, eds. Progress in Crystal Growth & Characterization, Vol. 10: Proceedings of the 6th International Conference on Ternary & Multinary Compounds, Car acas, Venezuela, 15-17 August 1984. (Illus.). 430p. 1985. 162.00 (ISBN 0-08-032344-8). Pergamon.

Parsonage, N. G. & Staveley, L. A., eds. Disorder in Crystals. (International Monographs on Chemistry). (Illus.). 1979. 79.00x (ISBN 0-19-855604-7). Oxford U Pr.

Parthe, Erwin. Crystal Chemistry of Tetrahedral Structures. 186p. 1964. 57.75x (ISBN 0-677-00700-0). Gordon.

Pauling, Linus. The Nature of the Chemical Bond & the Structure of Molecules & Crystals: An Introduction to Modern Structural Chemistry. 3rd ed. (Baker Non-Resident Lectureship in Chemistry Ser.). (Illus.). 644p. 1960. 39.95x (ISBN 0-8014-0333-2). Cornell U Pr.

Peterson, Serenity. Crystal Visioning: A Crystal Workbook. 96p. (Orig.). 1984. pap. 8.95 (ISBN 0-932389-00-7). Inter Pub.

Phillips, F. C. An Introduction to Crystallography. 4th ed. LC 77-127036. 351p. 1979. pap. text ed. 32.95x (ISBN 0-470-26347-4). Halsted Pr.

Pies, W. & Weiss, A. Crystal Structure Data of Inorganic Compounds: Part B: Key Elements O, S, Se, Te. Part B2: Substance Numbers B1818...2804. (Landolt-Boernstein: Group III, Vol. 7). 1980. 117.60 (ISBN 0-387-09593-4). Springer-Verlag.

--Landolt-Boernstein Numerical Data & Functional Relationships in Science & Technology, New Series, Group 3: Crystal & Solid State Physics, Vol. 7, Key Elements O, S, Se, Te, Bl. Substance Numbers B1 - B1817. (Illus.). xxiii, 674p. 1974. 281.40 (ISBN 0-387-06919-4). Springer-Verlag.

Pockels, Friedrich C. Lehrbuch der Kristalloptik. (Bibliotheca Mathematica Teubneriana Ser: No. 39). (Ger). 1969. Repr. of 1906 ed. 53.00 (ISBN 0-384-47000-9). Johnson Repr.

Povarennykh, A. S. Crystal Chemical Classification of Minerals, 2 vols. LC 68-26769. (Monographs in Geoscience Ser.). 1972. Set. 75.00x (ISBN 0-306-30348-5, Plenum Pr). Plenum Pub.

Protein-Ligand Interactions: Precise Molecular Dimensions & Thermal Motion. (American Crystallographic Association Program & Abstracts Ser. 2: Vol. 10, 2). 1982. pap. 5.00 (ISBN 0-317-02525-2). Polycrystal Bk Serv.

Sanborn, William B. Handbook of Crystal & Mineral Collecting. 1966. pap. 2.50 (ISBN 0-910652-05-8). Gembooks.

Sayre, David. Computational Crystalaography. 1982. 47.50x (ISBN 0-19-851954-0). Oxford U Pr.

Schmidt, Paul W., ed. Proceedings of the Symposium on the Small-Angle Scattering: University of Missouri, Columbia, March, 1983. (Transactions of the American Crystallographic Association Ser.: Vol. 19). 92p. 1984. pap. 15.00 (ISBN 0-937140-27-9). Polycrystal Bk Serv.

Schneer, C. J., ed. Crystal Form & Structure. (Benchmark Papers in Geology: Vol. 34). 1977. 66.00 (ISBN 0-12-787425-9). Acad Pr.

Shubnikov, Aleksei V. & Sheftal, N. N., eds. Growth of Crystals: Interim Reports Between the First (1956) & Second Conference on Crystal Growth, Institute of Crystallography, Academy of Sciences, USSR, Vol. 2. LC 58-1212. pap. 46.50 (ISBN 0-317-28733-8, 2020690). Bks Demand UMI.

Smith, J. V. Geometrical & Structural Crystallography. LC 82-2058. (Smith-Wylie Intermediate Geology Ser.). 450p. 1982. text ed. 40.95 (ISBN 0-471-86168-5). Wiley.

Stezowski, John J., ed. Proceedings of the Symposium on "Molecules in Motion", University of Kentucky, Lexington, May 20-21, 1984: Transactions of the American Crystallographic Association, 1984, Vol. 20. 166p. 1985. pap. 15.00 (ISBN 0-937140-28-7). Polycrystal Bk Serv.

Swalin, Richard A. Thermodynamics of Solids. 2nd ed. LC 72-6334. (Wiley Series on the Science & Technology of Materials). 387p. 1972. 52.50 (ISBN 0-471-83854-3, Pub. by Wiley-Interscience). Wiley.

Technical Dictionary of Crystallography. 132p. 1980. 40.00x (ISBN 0-686-72093-8, Pub. by Collet's). State Mutual Bk.

Tunell, George & Murdoch, Joseph. Introduction to Crystallography: A Laboratory Manual for Students of Mineralogy & Geology. 2nd ed. pap. 20.00 (ISBN 0-317-09901-9, 2055545). Bks Demand UMI.

Tutton, A. E. Crystallography & Practical Crystal Measurement, 2 vols. 2nd ed. Incl. Vol. 1. Form & Structure; Vol. 2. Physical & Chemical. 1964. Set. 25.00 (ISBN 0-934454-27-2). Lubrecht & Cramer.

Vainshtein, B. K. Modern Crystallography I. (Springer Series in Solid-State Sciences: Vol. 15). (Illus.). 420p. 1981. 51.00 (ISBN 0-387-10052-0). Springer-Verlag.

Vainshtein, B. K., et al. Modern Crystallography II: Structure of Crystals. (Springer Series in Solid State Sciences: Vol. 21). (Illus.). 460p. 1982. 52.00 (ISBN 0-387-10517-4). Springer-Verlag.

Van Hove, M. A. & Tong, S. Y. Surface Crystallography by LEED: Theory, Computation & Structural Results. (Springer Ser. in Chemical Physics: Vol. 2). (Illus.). 1979. 39.00 (ISBN 0-387-09194-7). Springer-Verlag.

Verma, A. R., et al. Crystallography for Solid State Physics. 1982. 26.95 (ISBN 0-470-27214-7). Halsted Pr.

Wahlstrom, Ernest E. Optical Crystallography. 5th ed. LC 78-13695. 488p. 1979. text ed. 40.50 (ISBN 0-471-04791-0). Wiley.

Wells, A. F. Further Studies of Three Dimensional Nets. (American Crystallographic Association Monographs: Vol. 8). 73p. 1979. pap. 12.95 (ISBN 0-88318-259-9). Polycrystal Bk Serv.

Whittaker, E. J. Crystallography: An Introduction for Earth Science (and Other Solid State) Students. LC 80-41188. (Illus.). 240p. 1981. 36.00 (ISBN 0-08-023805-X); pap. 19.95 (ISBN 0-08-023804-1). Pergamon.

Willis, B. T. & Pryor, A. W. Thermal Vibrations in Crystallography. LC 73-94357. (Illus.). 280p. 1975. 57.50 (ISBN 0-521-20447-X). Cambridge U Pr.

Wyckoff, Ralph W. Crystal Structures, Vol. 1. LC 78-23589. (Crystal Structures Ser.). 474p. 1982. Repr. of 1963 ed. 34.50 (ISBN 0-89874-387-7). Krieger.

--Crystal Structures, Vol. 3. LC 78-23589. 989p. 1981. Repr. of 1965 ed. lib. bdg. 59.50 (ISBN 0-88275-800-4). Krieger.

Zhdanov, G. S. Crystal Physics. 1966. 76.00 (ISBN 0-12-779650-9). Acad Pr.

Zoltai, Tibor. Systematics of Simple Sulfide Structures. rev. ed. 93p. 1974. pap. 3.50 (ISBN 0-686-47229-2). Polycrystal Bk Serv.

Zvyagin, B. B. Electron-Diffraction Analysis of Clay Mineral Structures. LC 65-17783. (Monographs in Geoscience Ser.). 264p. 1967. 42.50x (ISBN 0-306-30273-X, Plenum Pr). Plenum Pub.

CRYSTALLOGRAPHY, MATHEMATICAL

see also Crystal Lattices; Energy-Band Theory of Solids; Lattice Theory

Bernal, J. D. The Analytic Theory of Point Systems, 1923. 1981. pap. 5.00 (ISBN 0-686-45041-8). Polycrystal Bk Serv.

Bollmann, W. Crystal Lattices, Interfaces, Matrices: An Extension of Crystallography. (Illus.). 360p. 1982. 45.00 (ISBN 2-88105-000-X). Polycrystal Bk Serv.

Campillo, A. Algebroid Curves in Positive Characteristic. (Lecture Notes in Mathematics Ser.: Vol. 813). 168p. 1980. pap. text ed. 15.00 (ISBN 0-387-10022-9). Springer-Verlag.

Clemens, C. Herbert. A Scrapbook of Complex Curve Theory. LC 80-20214. (The University Series in Mathematics). 200p. 1980. 29.50x (ISBN 0-306-40536-9, Plenum Pr). Plenum Pub.

Fulton, William. Algebraic Curves: An Introduction to Algebraic Geometry. (Math Lecture Notes Ser.: No. 30). 1974. (Adv Bk Prog); pap. 27.95 (ISBN 0-8053-3082-8, Adv Bk Prog). Benjamin-Cummings.

Gerritzen, L. & Van Der Put, M. Schottky Groups & Mumford Curves. (Lecture Notes in Mathematics: Vol. 817). 317p. 1980. pap. 23.00 (ISBN 0-387-10229-9). Springer-Verlag.

Griffiths, Phillip A. An Introduction to the Theory of Special Divisors on Algebraic Curves. LC 80-16415. (Conference Board of Mathematical Sciences Ser.: Vol. 44). 1980. 9.00 (ISBN 0-8218-1694-2, CBMS 44). Am Math.

Hoffman, Jerome W. The Hodge Theory of Stable Curves. LC 84-14608. (Memoirs of the American Mathematical Society: No. 308). 91p. 1984. pap. 11.00 (ISBN 0-8218-2310-8). Am Math.

Iversen, B. Linear Determinants with Applications to Picard Scheme of a Family of Algebraic Groups. (Lecture Notes in Mathematics: Vol. 174). 1970. pap. 11.00 (ISBN 0-387-05301-8). Springer-Verlag.

Koblitz, N. Introduction to Elliptic Curves & Modular Forms. (Graduate Texts in Mathematics: Vol. 97). (Illus.). 250p. 1984. 35.00 (ISBN 0-387-96029-5). Springer-Verlag.

Namba. Geometry of Projective Algebraic Curves. (Pure & Applied Mathematics Ser.). 232p. 1984. 69.75 (ISBN 0-8247-7222-9); text ed. 39.75. Dekker.

Orzech. Plane Algebraic Curves. (Pure & Applied Mathematics Ser.: Vol. 67). 240p. 1981. 45.00 (ISBN 0-8247-1159-9). Dekker.

Steklov Institute of Mathematics & Kuz'mina, G. V. Moduli of Families of Curves & Quadratic Differentials. LC 82-8902. (Proceedings of the Steklov Institute of Mathematics Ser.: No. 139). 88.00 (ISBN 0-8218-3040-6, STEKLO-139). Am Math.

Tu, Loring W. Hodge Theory & the Local Torelli Problem. LC 83-3781. (Memoirs of the American Mathematical Society Ser.: No. 279). 66p. 1983. pap. 10.00 (ISBN 0-8218-2279-9). Am Math.

Walker, R. J. Algebraic Curves. LC 78-11956. 1978. pap. 19.50 (ISBN 0-387-90361-5). Springer-Verlag.

CURVES, PLANE

see also Asymptotes; Circle; Conic Sections

Eisenbud, David & Neumann, Walter D. Three-Dimensional Link Theory & Invariants of Plane Curve Singularities. (Annals of Mathematics Studies: No. 110). 185p. 1985. text ed. 37.50x (ISBN 0-691-08380-0); pap. text ed. 13.95x (ISBN 0-691-08381-9). Princeton U Pr.

Lawrence, J. Dennis. Catalog of Special Plane Curves. LC 72-80280. (Illus.). 218p. 1972. pap. text ed. 6.95 (ISBN 0-486-60288-5). Dover.

Lockwood, Edward H. & Prag, A. Book of Curves. 1961. 42.50 (ISBN 0-521-05585-7). Cambridge U Pr.

CURVES IN ENGINEERING

see also Railroads–Construction

Hickerson, Thomas F. Route Location & Design. 5th ed. (Illus.). 1967. text ed. 44.00 (ISBN 0-07-028680-9). McGraw.

Ives, Howard C. Highway Curves. 4th ed. Kissam, Philip, ed. LC 52-9033. 389p. 1952. 42.95x (ISBN 0-471-43032-3, Pub. by Wiley-Interscience). Wiley.

CURVES ON SURFACES

Buseman, Herbert. Geometry of Geodesics. (Pure and Applied Mathematics: Vol. 6). 1955. 69.50 (ISBN 0-12-148350-9). Acad Pr.

Klingenberg, Wilhelm. Closed Geodesics on Riemannian Manifolds. LC 83-5979. (CBMS Regional Conference Series in Mathematics, Vol. 53). 79p. 1983. pap. 13.00 (ISBN 0-8218-0703-X). Am Math.

Miyanishi, M. Lectures on Curves on Rational & Unirational Surfaces. (Tata Institute Lecture Notes). 1979. pap. 15.00 (ISBN 0-387-08943-8). Springer-Verlag.

CUTLERY

see also Knives

Barney, Richard & Loveless, Bob. How to Make Knives. 5th ed. (Illus.). 182p. Repr. of 1977 ed. 16.95 (ISBN 0-911881-00-X). Am Blade Bk Serv.

Kelley, Ben, Jr. Complete Book of Pocketknife Repair: A Cutlers Manual. Voyles, J. Bruce, ed. (Illus.). 129p. (Orig.). 1982. pap. 9.95 (ISBN 0-911881-01-8). Am Blade Bk Serv.

Lloyd, Godfrey I. Cutlery Trades. LC 68-102951. (Illus.). Repr. of 1913 ed. 35.00x (ISBN 0-678-05183-6). Kelley.

Simmons E. C. Hardware Co. 1930 Keen Kutter & Winchester Pocket Knives. 1974. pap. 3.50 (ISBN 0-915706-07-5). Am Reprints.

Smyth, R. L. & Weightman, R. S. The International Ceramic Tableware Industry. 160p. 1984. 40.00 (ISBN 0-7099-2352-X, Pub. by Croom Helm Ltd). Longwood Pub Group.

CUTTING

see also Garment Cutting; Gem Cutting; Metal-Cutting; Saws; Turning

The Effect of Cutting Treatments on Dry Matter Production of Lolium Perenne & Dactylis. 1963. pap. 5.00 (ISBN 90-220-0099-0, PDC162, PUDOC). Unipub.

CUTTING FLUIDS

see Metal-Working Lubricants

CUTTING MACHINES

see also Metal-Cutting Tools

Modern Trends in Cutting Tools. LC 82-61010. 265p. 1982. 32.00 (ISBN 0-87263-109-5). SME.

Swinehart, Haldon J., ed. Cutting Tool Material Selection. LC 68-27332. (American Society of Tool & Manufacturing Engineers Manufacturing Data Ser.). pap. 41.80 (ISBN 0-317-10924-3, 2016003). Bks Demand UMI.

CUTTING OF GEMS

see Gem Cutting

CUTTING OF METALS

see Metal-Cutting

CUVIER, GEORGES, BARON, 1769-1832

Outram, Dorinda. Georges Cuvier: Vocation, Science & Authority in Post-Revolutionary France. LC 84-861. 288p. 1984. 32.50 (ISBN 0-7190-1077-2, Pub. by Manchester Univ Pr). Longwood Pub Group.

CYANIDES

Doudoroff, Peter. A Critical Review of Recent Literature on Toxicity of Cyanides to Fish. LC 80-68588. 71p. (Orig.). 1980. pap. 3.60 (ISBN 0-89364-039-5, API 847-87000). Am Petroleum.

Van Zyl, Dirk, ed. Cyanide & the Environment: Proceedings, 2 vols. 580p. (Orig.). 1985. pap. 40.00 (ISBN 0-910069-14-X). Geotech Engineer Prog.

Vennesland, B., et al, eds. Cyanide in Biology. LC 81-67912. 1982. 59.50 (ISBN 0-12-716980-6). Acad Pr.

CYANIDING

see Case Hardening

CYANINES

Patai, Saul. Chemistry of Cyanates & Their Derivatives. (Interscience Publication, Chemistry of Functional Groups Ser.). Part I. pap. 158.00 (ISBN 0-317-26341-2); Part 2. pap. 160.00 (ISBN 0-317-26342-0). Bks Demand UMI.

CYANOCOBALAMINE

Pratt, J. M. Inorganic Chemistry of Vitamin B1120. 1972. 60.00 (ISBN 0-12-564050-1). Acad Pr.

CYANOPHYCEAE

Fremy, Pierre. Cyanophycees des Cotes d'Europe. (Memoires of the National Society of Natural Sciences & Mathematics of Cherborg Ser.). (Illus.). 1972. 30.40 (ISBN 90-6123-274-0). Lubrecht & Cramer.

Rodriguez-Lopez, M., et al. Blue-Green Algae: Current Research, 4 vols, Vol. 1. 213p. 1974. text ed. 23.50x (ISBN 0-8422-7187-2). Irvington.

CYBERNETICS

see also Biological Control Systems; Bionics; Computers; Conscious Automata; Information Theory; Perceptrons; Self-Organizing Systems; System Analysis; Systems Engineering

Aleksander, Igor. The Human Machine: A View of Intelligent Mechanisms. (Illus.). 1978. pap. text ed. 9.95x (ISBN 2-604-00023-7). Brookfield Pub Co.

Alger, Philip L., ed. The Human Side of Engineering. 170p. 1972. 46.25 (ISBN 0-677-65180-5). Gordon.

Altschuller, G. S. Creativity as An Exact Science. (Studies in Cybernetics: Vol. 5). 332p. 1984. 54.00 (ISBN 0-677-21230-5). Gordon.

Andrew. Computational Methods in Operations Research. (Cybernetics & Systems Ser.). 1984. 25.00 (ISBN 0-9901002-9-4, Pub. by Abacus England). Heyden.

Arbib, Michael. Computers & the Cybernetic Society. 2nd ed. 1984. 17.00i (ISBN 0-12-059046-8); instr's. manual 10.00i (ISBN 0-12-059047-6). Acad Pr.

--The Metaphorical Brain: An Introduction to Cybernetics As Artificial Intelligence & Brains Theory. LC 72-2490. (Illus.). 243p. 1972. 36.95x (ISBN 0-471-03249-2, Pub. by Wiley-Interscience). Wiley.

Ashby, W. Ross. Introduction to Cybernetics. 1964. pap. 12.95 (ISBN 0-416-68300-2, NO. 2064). Methuen Inc.

--Mechanisms of Intelligence: Ashby's Writings on Cybernetics. Conant, Roger, ed. (Systems Inquiry Ser.). 394p. (Orig.). 1981. pap. text ed. 16.95x (ISBN 0-914105-04-3). Intersystems Pubns.

Aulin-Ahmavaara, Arvid. Cybernetic Laws of Social Progress: Towards a Critical Social Philosophy & a Criticism of Marxism. (Systems Science & World Order Library). (Illus.). 224p. 1981. 50.00 (ISBN 0-08-025782-8). Pergamon.

Baumgartmer, Thomas, et al. The Shaping of the Socio-Economic Systems. (Studies In Cybernetics). 369p. 1985. text ed. 56.00 (ISBN 2-88124-003-8); pap. text ed. 24.00 (ISBN 2-88124-027-5). Gordon.

Beer, Stafford. Decision & Control: The Meaning of Operational Research & Management Cybernetics. LC 66-25668. 556p. 1966. 52.95x (ISBN 0-471-06210-3, Pub. by Wiley-Interscience). Wiley.

Bernard, E. E. & Kare, M. R. Biological Prototypes & Synthetic Systems. LC 62-9964. 397p. 1962. 39.50x (ISBN 0-306-30114-8, Plenum Pr). Plenum Pub.

Braitenbach, E. H., tr. from Ger. On the Texture of Brains: An Introduction to Neuroanatomy for the Cybernetically Minded. LC 77-21851. (Illus.). 1977. pap. 14.00 (ISBN 0-387-08391-X). Springer-Verlag.

Burns, Tom R., et al. Mans, Decision, Society. (Studies in Cybernetics: Vol. 10). 288p. 1985. text ed. 52.00 (ISBN 2-88124-004-6); pap. 22.00 (ISBN 2-88124-026-7). Gordon.

Busnel, R. G. & Classe, A. Whistled Languages. (Communication & Cybernetics Ser.: Vol. 13). (Illus.). 1976. 32.00 (ISBN 0-387-07713-8). Springer-Verlag.

Caianiello, E. & Musso, G. Cybernetic Systems: Recognition, Learning, Self-Organization. (Pattern Recognition & Image Processing Research Studies Press Ser.: 1208). 248p. 1984. 59.95x (ISBN 0-471-90219-5, Pub by Res Stud Pr). Wiley.

Calow, P. Biological Machines: A Cybernetic Approach to Life. LC 76-27603. 133p. 1976. pap. 14.95x (ISBN 0-8448-1005-3). Crane-Russak Co.

Chandler, William J. The Science of History: A Cybernetic Approach. (Studies in Cybernetics: Vol. 7). 160p. 1984. text ed. 37.00 (ISBN 2-88124-012-7). Gordon.

Clemson, D. Organizational Cybernetics. 1984. 25.00 (ISBN 0-9961005-9-8, Pub. by Abacus England). Heyden.

Daellenbach, Hans G. & George, John A. Introduction to Ope ations Research Techniques. 2nd ed. 1983. text ed. 41.43 (ISBN 0-205-07718-8, EDP 107718); answer book (ISBN 0-205-05756-X). Allyn.

Darrow, Frank M. Cybernetics versus Homeostasis. (Illus.). 42p. 1977. pap. 4.00 (ISBN 0-686-82893-3). Darrow.

European Meeting on Cybernetics & Systems Research, Linz, Austria, Mar. 1978. General Systems Methodology, Organization & Management, Cognition & Learning: Symposia. Pichler, Franz R. & Hanika, Francis de P., eds. LC 75-6641. (Progress in Cybernetics & Systems Research: Vol. 7). (Illus.). 393p. 1980. text ed. 110.00 (ISBN 0-89116-195-3). Hemisphere Pub.

European Meeting on Cybernetics & Systems Research, 5th, Vienna, Austria, April 1980. Progress in Cybernetics & Systems Research, Vol. 9. Trappl, Robert, et al, eds. LC 75-6641. (Illus.). 532p. 1982. text ed. 110.00 (ISBN 0-89116-238-0). Hemisphere Pub.

--Progress in Cybernetics & Systems Research: Proceedings, Vol. 11. Trappl, Robert, et al, eds. LC 75-6641. (Illus.). 601p. 1982. text ed. 110.00 (ISBN 0-89116-240-2). Hemisphere Pub.

European Meeting on Cybernetics & Systems Research, Linz, Austria, Mar. 1978. Progress in Cybernetics & Systems Research: Symposia, Vol. 6. Pichler, Franz R. & Trappl, Robert, eds. LC 75-6641. (Progress in Cybernetics & Systems Research: Vol. 6). (Illus.). 398p. 1982. text ed. 110.00 (ISBN 0-89116-194-5). Hemisphere Pub.

European Meeting on Cybernetics & Systems Research, 5th, Vienna, Austria, April 1980. Structure & Dynamics of Socioeconomic Systems, Cybernetics in Organization & Management, Engineering Systems Methodology, Systems Research on Science & Technology: Proceedings. Trappl, Robert, et al, eds. LC 75-6641. (Progress in Cybernetics & Systems Research: Vol. 10). (Illus.). 562p. 1982. text ed. 110.00 (ISBN 0-89116-239-9). Hemisphere Pub.

Felsen, Jerry. Cybernetic Approach to Stock Market Analysis vs. Efficient Market Theory. LC 74-34512. 1975. 20.00 (ISBN 0-916376-01-X). CDS Pub.

--Cybernetic Approach to Stock Market Analysis: Versus Efficient Market Theory. LC 74-34512. 1975. 20.00 (ISBN 0-682-48224-2, University). Exposition Pr FL.

--Cybernetic Decision Systems. 350p. 25.00 (ISBN 0-916376-07-9). CDS Pub.

George, F. H. The Foundations of Cybernetics. 300p. 1977. text ed. 46.25x (ISBN 0-677-05340-1). Gordon.

--Philosophical Foundations of Cybernetics. 1979. 28.00 (ISBN 0-9961002-6-1, Pub. by Abacus England). Heyden.

George, Frank & Johnson, Les, eds. Purposive Behaviour & Teleological Explanations. (Studies in Cybernetics: Vol. 8). 334p. 1985. text ed. 64.00 (ISBN 2-88124-110-7). Gordon.

Geyer, R. F. & Zouwen, J. van der, eds. Sociocybernetics, Vols. 1 & 2. 1978. Vol. 1. pap. 17.00 (ISBN 90-207-0854-6, Pub. by Martinus Nijhoff Netherlands); Vol. 2. pap. 17.00 (ISBN 90-207-0855-4). Kluwer Academic.

Glorioso, Robert M. & Colon-Osorio, Fernando C. Engineering Intelligent Systems: Concepts, Theory, & Application. 2nd ed. (Illus.). 472p. 1980. 29.00 (ISBN 0-932376-06-1, EY-AX011-DP). Digital Pr.

Hanken, A. F. Cybernetics & Society. (Cybernetics & Systems Ser.). 1981. 25.00 (ISBN 0-9961004-0-7, Pub. by Abacus England). Heyden.

Helvey, T. C. Age of Information: An Interdisciplinary Survey of Cybernetics. LC 78-125870. 224p. 1971. 27.95 (ISBN 0-87778-008-0). Educ Tech Pubns.

Hillier, Frederick S. & Lieberman, Gerald J. Introduction to Operations Research. 3rd ed. LC 78-54193. 848p. 1980. text ed. 39.00x (ISBN 0-8162-3867-7); solutions manual 10.00x (ISBN 0-8162-4518-5); Study guide 10.00x. Holden-Day.

Holzman. Mathematical Programming for Operations Researchers. (Industrial Engineering Ser.: Vol. 6). 392p. 1981. 55.00 (ISBN 0-8247-1499-7). Dekker.

Hook, Sidney, ed. Dimensions of Mind: A Symposium. 1961. pap. 1.50 (ISBN 0-02-065670-X, Collier). Macmillan.

Jumarie, Guy M. Subjectivity, Information, Systems: Introduction to a Theory of Relativistic Cybernetics. (Studies in Cybernetics: Vol. 13). 357p. 1985. text ed. 59.00 (ISBN 2-88124-011-9). Gordon.

Keys, Paul & Jackson, Michael C., eds. Managing Transport Systems: A Cybernetic Analysis. LC 84-21242. 202p. 1985. text ed. 35.50 (ISBN 0-566-00791-6). Gower Pub Co.

Kirschenmann, P. K. Information & Reflections on Some Problems of Cybernetics & How Contemporary Dialectical Materialsim Copes with Them. Blakely, T. J., tr. from Ger. (Sovietica Ser.: No. 31). 225p. 1970. lib. bdg. 31.50 (ISBN 90-277-0055-9, Pub. by Reidel Holland). Kluwer Academic.

Korshunov, Y. M. Fundamentos Matematicos de la Cibernetica. (Span.). 326p. 1979. 7.45 (ISBN 0-8285-1453-4, Pub. by Mir Pubs USSR). Imported Pubns.

Kotz, Samuel. Russian-English Dictionary & Reader in the Cybernetical Sciences. 1966. 49.00 (ISBN 0-12-422450-4). Acad Pr.

Lange, Oskar. Introduction to Economic Cybernetics. Banasinski, Antoni, ed. Stadler, Jozef, tr. LC 73-106449. (Illus.). 200p. 1970. 23.00 (ISBN 0-08-006652-6). Pergamon.

Lasker, George E., ed. Applied Systems & Cybernetics: Proceedings of the International Congress on Applied Systems Research & Cybernetics, Acapulco, Mexico, Dec. 12-16, 1980, 6 Vols. Incl. Vol. 1. The Quality of Life: Systems Approaches. 600p. 1981. 80.00 (ISBN 0-08-027198-7); Vol. 2. Systems Concepts, Models & Methodology. 540p. 1981. 77.00 (ISBN 0-08-027199-5); Vol. 3. Human Systems, Sociocybernetics, Management & Organizations. 580p. 1981. 88.00 (ISBN 0-08-027200-2); Vol. 4. Systems Research in Health Care, Biocybernetics & Ecology. 425p. 1981. 66.00 (ISBN 0-08-027201-0); Vol. 5. Systems Approaches to Computer Science & Mathematics. 670p. 1981. 99.00 (ISBN 0-08-027202-9); Vol. 6. Fuzzy Sets & Systems, Possibility Theory, & Special Topics in Systems Research. 670p. 1981. 88.00 (ISBN 0-08-027203-7). 1981. Set. 400.00 (ISBN 0-08-027196-0). Pergamon.

Lerner, A. Ya. Fundamentals of Cybernetics. LC 75-30901. 306p. 1975. 10.95x (ISBN 0-306-20018-X, Rosetta). Plenum Pub.

Lexikon der Kybernetik, 4 vols. (Ger.). 590p. 1980. Set. 395.00x (ISBN 0-686-44730-1, Pub. by Collets). State Mutual Bk.

Lissak. Results in Neurochemistry, Neuroendocrinology, Neurophysiology & Behavior, Neuropharmacology, Neuropathology, Cybernetics, Vol. 5. 1978. 19.50 (ISBN 0-9960007-2-0, Pub. by Akademiai Kaido Hungary). Heyden.

Manescu, M. Economic Cybernetics. (Cybernetics & Systems Ser.). 1980. 32.00 (ISBN 0-9961003-9-3, Pub. by Abacus England). Heyden.

Masturzo, Aldo. Cybernetic Medicine. (Illus.). 160p. 1965. 14.75x (ISBN 0-398-01234-2). C C Thomas.

Michie, Donald, ed. Introductory Readings in Expert Systems. (Studies in Cybernetics: Vol. 1). 252p. 1982. 25.00 (ISBN 0-677-16350-9). Gordon.

Goldstein, L. & Prescott, David, eds. Cell Biology: A Comprehensive Treatise, 4 vols. Incl. Vol. 1. 1978. 65.00 (ISBN 0-12-289501-0); Vol. 2. The Structure & Replication of Genetic Material. 1979. 65.00 (ISBN 0-12-289502-9). LC 78-10457. Acad Pr.

Grun, Paul. Cytoplasmic Genetics & Evolution. LC 75-43987. (Illus.). 435p. 1976. 50.00x (ISBN 0-231-03975-1). Columbia U Pr.

Hamerton, John L. Human Cytogenetics, 2 V00863403x. 1970-71. Vol. 1, 1971. 67.50 (ISBN 0-12-321001-1); Vol. 2, 1971. 73.00 (ISBN 0-12-321002-X). Acad Pr.

Hamkalo, Barbara A. & Papaconstantinou, John, eds. Molecular Cytogenetics. LC 73-18008. 378p. 1973. 47.50x (ISBN 0-306-30765-0, Plenum Pr). Plenum Pub.

Hare, W. C. & Singh, E. L. Cytogenetics in Animal Reproduction. 150p. 1979. cloth 59.00x (ISBN 0-85198-444-4, Pub. by CAB Bks England). State Mutual Bk.

Hooper, Martin L. Mammalian Cell Genetics. (Cell Biology: A Series of Monographs 1-507). 225p. 1985. 49.95 (ISBN 0-471-89201-7, Pub. by Wiley-Interscience). Wiley.

ICN-UCLA Symposia on Molecular & Cellular Biology. Human Cytogenetics, Vol. 7. Sparkes, Robert S., et al, eds. (ICN-UCLA Symposia on Molecular & Cellular Biology Ser.). 1977. 49.50 (ISBN 0-12-656350-0). Acad Pr.

International Conference on Comparative Mammalian Cytogenetics, Dartmouth Medical School, 1968. Proceedings. Benirschke, K., ed. (Illus.). 1969. 66.00 (ISBN 0-387-04442-6). Springer-Verlag.

International Society For Cell Biology. Cytogenetics of Cells in Culture. Harris, R. J., ed. (Proceedings: Vol. 3). 1964. 67.50 (ISBN 0-12-611903-1). Acad Pr.

Jauhar, Prem P., ed. Cytogenetics & Breeding of Pearl Millet & Related Species. LC 81-3744. (Progress & Topics in Cytogenetics Ser.: Vol. 1). 310p. 1981. 48.00x (ISBN 0-8451-2400-5). A R Liss.

Jotterand-Bellomo, Martine & Klinger, H. P., eds. The Robert Malthey Dedication. (Cytogenetics & Cell Genetics: Vol. 34, Nos. 1-2). (Illus.). vi, 192p. 1982. pap. 68.25 (ISBN 3-8055-3650-X). S Karger.

Khush, Gurdev S. Cytogenetics of Aneuploids. 1973. 59.50 (ISBN 0-12-406250-4). Acad Pr.

McDermott, A. Cytogenetics of Man & Other Animals. (Outline Studies in Biology). 1975. pap. 6.95 (ISBN 0-412-13910-3, NO.6197, Pub. by Chapman & Hall). Methuen Inc.

Mitelman, Felix. Catalog of Chromosome Aberrations in Cancer. 2nd ed. LC 85-7022. (Progress & Topics in Cytogenetics Ser.: Vol. 5). 722p. 1985. 96.00 (ISBN 0-8451-2405-6). A R Liss.

Monroy, Alberto & Moscona, A. A., eds. Current Topics in Developmental Biology, Vols. 1-12. Incl. Vol. 1. 1966. 65.00 (ISBN 0-12-153101-5); Vol. 2. 1967. 65.00 (ISBN 0-12-153102-3); Vol. 3. 1968. 65.00 (ISBN 0-12-153103-1); Vol. 4. 1969. 65.00 (ISBN 0-12-153104-X); Vol. 5. 1970. 65.50 (ISBN 0-12-153105-8); Vol. 6. 1971. 65.00 (ISBN 0-12-153106-6); Vol. 7. 1972. 65.00 (ISBN 0-12-153107-4); Vol. 8. 1974. 65.00 (ISBN 0-12-153108-2); Vol. 9. 1975. 55.00 (ISBN 0-12-153109-0); Vol. 10. 1975. 55.00 (ISBN 0-12-153110-4); Vol. 11. 1977. 55.00 (ISBN 0-12-153111-2); Vol. 12. 1978. 55.00 (ISBN 0-12-153112-0). Acad Pr.

Pal, R., et al, eds. Cytogenetics & Genetics of Vectors. Kanda. 266p. 1982. 64.25 (ISBN 0-444-80382-3, Biomedical Pr). Elsevier.

Phillips, Ronald L. & Burnham, Charles R. Cytogenetics. (Benchmark Papers in Genetics: Vol. 6). 1977. 71.00 (ISBN 0-12-787225-6). Acad Pr.

Sandberg, Avery A. Cytogenetics of the Mammalian X Chromosome, Pt. A: Basic Mechanisms of X Chromosome BEH. LC 83-19992. (Progress & Topics in Cytogenetics Ser.: Vol 3A). 522p. 1983. 98.00 (ISBN 0-8451-2402-1). A R Liss.

--Cytogenetics of the Mammalian X Chromosome, PT. B: X Chromosome Anomalies & Their Clinical Manifestations. LC 83-19992. (Progress & Topics in Cytogenetics: Vol. 3B). 532p. 1983. 98.00 (ISBN 0-8451-2403-X). A R Liss.

--Sister Chromatid Exchange. LC 82-157. (Progress & Topics in Cytogenetics Ser.: Vol. 2). 724p. 1982. 98.00 (ISBN 0-8451-2401-3). A R Liss.

Schulz-Schaeffer, J. Cytogenetics: Plants, Animals, Humans. (Illus.). 460p. 1980. 39.00 (ISBN 0-387-90467-0). Springer-Verlag.

Schwarzacher, H. G. & Wolf, U., eds. Methods in Human Cytogenetics. Passarge, E., tr. from Ger. (Illus.). 295p. 1974. 45.00 (ISBN 0-387-06610-1). Springer-Verlag.

Shay, Jerry W., ed. Techniques in Somatic Cell Genetics. (Illus.). 568p. 1982. 49.50x (ISBN 0-306-41040-0, Plenum Pr). Plenum Pub.

Sinha, U. & Sinha, S. Cytogenetics, Plant Breeding & Evolution. 1976. 13.50 (ISBN 0-7069-0469-9). Intl Bk Dist.

Sinha, U. & Sinha, Sunita. Cytogenetics: Plant Breeding & Evolution. 1980. text ed. 30.00x (ISBN 0-7069-0469-9, Pub. by Vikas Indig). Advent NY.

Sparkes. Research Perspectives in Cytogenetics. (Illus.). 176p. 1983. text ed. 32.00 (ISBN 0-8391-1834-1, 19992). Univ Park.

Starlinger, P. & Schell, J., eds. The Impact of Gene Transfer Techniques in Eucaryotic Cell Biology. (Colloquium der Gesellschaft fur Biologische Chemie Ser.: Vol. 35). (Illus.). 230p. 1985. 33.50 (ISBN 0-387-13836-6). Springer-Verlag.

Swanson, Carl B., et al. Cytogenetics: The Chromosome in Division, Inheritance, & Evolution. 2nd ed. (Biology Ser.). (Illus.). 1980. text ed. 39.95 (ISBN 0-13-196618-9). P-H.

Taylor, J. Herbert, ed. Selected Papers on Molecular Genetics. (Perspectives in Modern Biology). (Illus., Orig.). 1965. pap. 44.00 (ISBN 0-12-684456-9). Acad Pr.

Uebele-Kallhardt, B. M. Human Oocytes & Their Chromosomes: An Atlas. (Illus.). 1978. 35.00 (ISBN 0-387-08879-2). Springer-Verlag.

Yunis, G. J. New Chromosomal Syndromes. 1977. 70.00 (ISBN 0-12-775165-3). Acad Pr.

CYTOGENETICS–DICTIONARIES

Harnden, D. G. & Klinger, H. P., eds. An International System for Human Cytogenetic Nomenclature (1985) ISCN (1985) (Illus.). vi, 118p. 1985. pap. 29.50 (ISBN 3-8055-3870-7). S Karger.

Rieger, R., et al. Glossary of Genetics & Cytogenetics. 4th rev. ed. LC 76-16183. (Illus.). 1976. pap. 20.00 (ISBN 3-540-07668-9). Springer-Verlag.

CYTOLOGY

see also Cell Differentiation; Cells; Cytogenetics; Exfoliative Cytology; Plant Cells and Tissues

Acosta, Enrique V. & Fedoroff, Sergey, eds. Eleventh International Congress of Anatomy, Part A: Glial & Neuronal Cell Biology. LC 81-2778. (Progress in Clinical & Biological Research Ser.: Vol. 59A). 352p. 1981. 38.00 (ISBN 0-8451-0153-6). A R Liss.

Aidley, D. J. The Physiology of Excitable Cells. 2nd ed. LC 77-87375. (Illus.). 1979. 79.50 (ISBN 0-521-21913-2); pap. 24.95 (ISBN 0-521-29308-1). Cambridge U Pr.

Alberts, Bruce, et al. Molecular Biology of the Cell. LC 82-15692. 1250p. 1983. lib. bdg. 37.95 (ISBN 0-8240-7282-0). Garland Pub.

Aldrich, Henry & Daniel, John W., eds. Cell Biology of Physarum & Didymium: Vol. I, Organisms, Nucleus & Cell Cycle. LC 81-20483. (Cell Biology Ser.). 1982. 60.00 (ISBN 0-12-049601-1). Acad Pr.

Aloia, Roland C. & Boggs, Joan M., eds. Membrane Fluidity in Biology: Cellular Activities, Vol. 4. Date not set. price not set (ISBN 0-12-053004-X). Acad Pr.

Althaus, F., et al, eds. ADP-Ribosylation of Proteins. (Proceedings in Life Sciences Ser.). (Illus.). 585p. 1985. 89.50 (ISBN 0-387-15598-8). Springer Verlag.

Altman, Philip L. & Katz, Dorothy D., eds. Cell Biology. LC 75-42787. (Biological Handbks: Vol. 1). (Illus.). 1976. 55.00 (ISBN 0-913822-10-8). Pergamon.

Ambrose, E. J. Cell Biology. 2nd ed. (Illus.). 576p. 1978. pap. text ed. 19.95 (ISBN 0-8391-1236-X). Univ Park.

Ansari, Aftab A. & De Serres, Frederick, eds. Single-Cell Mutation Monitoring Systems: Methodologies & Applications. (Topics in Chemical Mutagenesis Ser.: Vol. 2). 308p. 39.50x (ISBN 0-306-41537-2, Plenum Pr). Plenum Pub.

Ashley, C. C. & Campbell, A. K. Measurement of Free Calcium in Cells. 1980. 81.00 (ISBN 0-444-80185-5). Elsevier.

Axel, Richard, et al, eds. Eucaryotic Gene Regulation: Icn-Ucla Symposia on Molecular & Cellular Biology, Vol. XIV. LC 79-23151. 1979. 50.00 (ISBN 0-12-068350-4). Acad Pr.

Baker, J. R. Cytological Technique. 1966. pap. 7.95x (ISBN 0-412-20300-6, NO.6580, Pub. by Chapman & Hall). Methuen Inc.

Bardin, C. Wayne, ed. The Cell Biology of the Testis, Vol. 383. 450p. 1982. 118.00x (ISBN 0-89766-156-7); pap. 118.00. NY Acad Sci.

Barnes, David W., et al. Methods for Preparation of Media Supplements, & Substrata for Serum-Free Animal Cell Culture. LC 84-7203. (Cell Culture Methods for Molecular & Cell Biology Ser.: Vol. 1). 378p. 1984. 49.50 (ISBN 0-8451-3800-6). A R Liss.

--Methods for Serum-Free Culture of Cells of the Endocrine System. LC 84-7202. (Cell Culture Methods for Molecular & Cell Biology Ser.: Vol. 2). 272p. 1984. 39.00 (ISBN 0-8451-3801-4). A R Liss.

--Methods for Serum-Free Culture of Neuronal & Lymphoid Cells. LC 84-7204. (Cell Culture Methods for Molecular & Cell Biology Ser.: Vol. 4). 280p. 1984. 39.50 (ISBN 0-8451-3803-0). A R Liss.

Baserga, Renato. The Biology of Cell Reproduction. (Illus.). 256p. 1985. text ed. 25.00x (ISBN 0-674-07406-8). Harvard U Pr.

Becker, Robert P. & Johari, Om. Cell Surface Labeling. (Illus.). 100p. 1979. pap. text ed. 10.00 (ISBN 0-931288-07-X). Scanning Electron.

Bell, Carol, ed. A Seminar on Immune Mediated Cell Destruction. (Illus.). 208p. 1981. 20.00 (ISBN 0-914400-70-9). Am Assn Blood.

Bell, Paul B., Jr., ed. Scanning Electron Microscopy of Cells in Culture. (Illus.). vi, 314p. 1984. pap. 29.00 (ISBN 0-931288-31-2). Scanning Electron.

Bellairs, Ruth, et al, eds. Cell Behaviour: A Tribute to Michael Abercrombie. Ruth & Curtis, Dunn. LC 81-6119. (Illus.). 500p. 1982. 110.00 (ISBN 0-521-24107-3). Cambridge U Pr.

Billinghurst, Mervyn W., ed. Studies of Cellular Function Using Radiotracers. 272p. 1981. 74.50 (ISBN 0-8493-6025-0). CRC Pr.

Biology Colloquium, 30th, Oregon State University, 1969. Biological Ultrastructure: The Origin of Cell Organelles: Proceedings. Harris, Patricia J., ed. LC 52-19235. (Illus.). 1971. 9.95x (ISBN 0-87071-169-5). Oreg St U Pr.

Bittar, E. Edward, ed. Cell Biology in Medicine. LC 75-19060. Repr. of 1973 ed. 120.00 (ISBN 0-8357-9853-4, 2012595). Bks Demand UMI.

Blecher, Melvin, ed. Methods in Receptor Research, Pt. 2. (Methods in Molecular Biology Ser.: Vol. 9). 1976. 69.75 (ISBN 0-8247-6415-3). Dekker.

Blerkom, Jonathan Van & Motta, Pietro. The Cellular Basis of Mammalian Reproduction. LC 78-10230. (Illus.). 263p. 1979. text ed. 42.00 (ISBN 0-8067-2041-7). Urban & S.

Bloch, Konrad, et al, eds. Membranes, Molecules, Toxins, & Cells. LC 80-16595. 350p. 1981. 37.00 (ISBN 0-88416-309-1). PSG Pub Co.

Boeck, P., et al. Peroxisomes & Related Particles in Animal Tissues. (Cell Biology Monographs: Vol. 7). (Illus.). 250p. 1980. 86.00 (ISBN 0-387-81582-1). Springer-Verlag.

Bonnley, Brian H. Cell Biology Level II. (Illus.). 256p. 1982. pap. text ed. 18.50x (ISBN 0-7121-0389-9). Trans-Atlantic.

Boon, Mathilde E. Gynaecological Cytology. (Illus.). 278p. 1980. pap. 37.50 (ISBN 0-8391-4105-X). Univ Park.

Borisy, Gary G., et al, eds. Molecular Biology of the Cytoskeleton. LC 84-17566. 576p. 1984. 58.00 (ISBN 0-87969-174-3). Cold Spring Harbor.

Bourne, G. H. & Danielli, J. F. International Review of Cytology. Incl. Vol. 1. 1952. 85.00 (ISBN 0-12-364301-5); Vol. 2. 1953. 85.00 (ISBN 0-12-364302-3); Vol. 3. 1954. 85.00 (ISBN 0-12-364303-1); Vol. 4. 1955. 85.00 (ISBN 0-12-364304-X); Vol. 5. 1956. 85.00 (ISBN 0-12-364305-8); Vol. 6. 1957. 85.00 (ISBN 0-12-364306-6); Vol. 7. 1958. 85.00 (ISBN 0-12-364307-4); Vol. 8. 1959. 85.00 (ISBN 0-12-364308-2); Vol. 9. 1960. 85.00 (ISBN 0-12-364309-0); Vol. 10. 1961. 85.00 (ISBN 0-12-364310-4); Vol. 11. 1961. 85.00 (ISBN 0-12-364311-2); Vol. 12. 1962. 85.00 (ISBN 0-12-364312-0); Vol. 13. 1962. 85.00 (ISBN 0-12-364313-9); Vol. 14. 1963. 85.00 (ISBN 0-12-364314-7); Vol. 15. 1963. 85.00 (ISBN 0-12-364315-5); Vol. 16. 1964. 85.00 (ISBN 0-12-364316-3); Vol. 17. 85.00 (ISBN 0-12-364317-1); Vol. 18. 1965. 85.00 (ISBN 0-12-364318-X); Vol. 19. 1966. 85.00 (ISBN 0-12-364319-8); Vol. 20. 1966. 85.00 (ISBN 0-12-364320-1); Vol. 21. 1967. 85.00 (ISBN 0-12-364321-X); Vol. 22. Jeon, K., ed. 1967. 85.00 (ISBN 0-12-364322-8); Vol. 23. 1968. 85.00 (ISBN 0-12-364323-6); Vol. 24. 1968. 85.00 (ISBN 0-12-364324-4); Vol. 25. 1969. 85.00 (ISBN 0-12-364325-2); Vol. 26. 1969. 85.00 (ISBN 0-12-364326-0); Vol. 27. 1970. 85.00 (ISBN 0-12-364327-9); Vol. 28. 1970. 85.00 (ISBN 0-12-364328-7); Vol. 29. 1970. 85.00 (ISBN 0-12-364329-5). Acad Pr.

--International Review of Cytology. Incl. Vol. 30. 1971. 85.00 (ISBN 0-12-364330-9); Vol. 31. 1971. 85.00 (ISBN 0-12-364331-7); Vol. 32. 1972. 85.00 (ISBN 0-12-364332-5); Vol. 33. 1972. 85.00 (ISBN 0-12-364333-3); Vol. 34. 1973. 85.00 (ISBN 0-12-364334-1); Vol. 35. 1973. 85.00 (ISBN 0-12-364335-X); Vol. 36. 1973. 85.00 (ISBN 0-12-364336-8); Vol. 37. 1974. 85.00 (ISBN 0-12-364337-6); Vol. 38. 1974. 85.00 (ISBN 0-12-364338-4); Vol. 39. 1974. 85.00 (ISBN 0-12-364339-2); Vol. 40. Jones, R. N., ed. 1975. 85.00 (ISBN 0-12-364340-6); Vol. 41. Leibowitz, Paul J. & Schaechter, Moselio, eds. 1975. 85.00 (ISBN 0-12-364341-4); Vol. 42. Lozzio, Bismarck B. & Lozzio, Carmen, eds. 1975. 85.00 (ISBN 0-12-364342-2); Vol. 43. Mahler, Henry R. & Raff, Rudolf A., eds. 1976. 85.00 (ISBN 0-12-364343-0); Vol. 44. 1976. 85.00 (ISBN 0-12-364344-9); Vol. 45. 85.00 (ISBN 0-12-364345-7); Vol. 46. 1976. 85.00 (ISBN 0-12-364346-5); Vol. 47. 1976. 85.00 (ISBN 0-12-364347-3); Vol. 48. 1977. 85.00 (ISBN 0-12-364348-1); Vol. 49. 1977. 85.00 (ISBN 0-12-364349-X); Vol. 50. 1977. 85.00 (ISBN 0-12-364350-3). Acad Pr.

--International Review of Cytology, Vol. 69. (Serial Publications Ser.). 1981. 65.00 (ISBN 0-12-364469-0). Acad Pr.

--International Review of Cytology, Vol. 86. (Serial Publication). 1984. 49.50 (ISBN 0-12-364486-0). Acad Pr.

--International Review of Cytology, Vol. 87. (Serial Publication). 1984. 49.50 (ISBN 0-12-364487-9). Acad Pr.

--International Review of Cytology, Vol. 88. (Serial Publication). 1984. 60.00 (ISBN 0-12-364488-7). Acad Pr.

--International Review of Cytology, Vol. 89. (Serial Publication). 1984. 49.50 (ISBN 0-12-364489-5). Acad Pr.

Bourne, G. H. & Danielli, J. F., eds. International Review of Cytology, Vol. 71. 1981. 65.00 (ISBN 0-12-364471-2). Acad Pr.

--International Review of Cytology, Vol. 78. 360p. 1982. 55.00 (ISBN 0-12-364478-X). Acad Pr.

--International Review of Cytology, Vol. 79. 315p. 1982. 49.50 (ISBN 0-12-364479-8). Acad Pr.

--International Review of Cytology, Vol. 80. 322p. 1982. 49.50 (ISBN 0-12-364480-1). Acad Pr.

--International Review of Cytology, Vol. 84. (Serial Publication). 1983. 55.00 (ISBN 0-12-364484-4). Acad pr.

--International Review of Cytology, Vol. 85. (Serial Publication). 1983. 46.00 (ISBN 0-12-364485-2). Acad Pr.

--International Review of Cytology, Vol. 90. (Serial Publication). 1984. 52.50 (ISBN 0-12-364490-9). Acad Pr.

--International Review of Cytology, Vol. 91: Membranes. (Serial Publications). 1984. 36.50 (ISBN 0-12-364491-7). Acad Pr.

--International Review of Cytology, Vol. 92. (Serial Publications). 1984. 36.50 (ISBN 0-12-364492-5). Acad Pr.

Bourne, G. H. & Muggleton-Harris, Audrey L., eds. International Review of Cytology: Supplement 12. (Serial Publication). 1981. 65.00 (ISBN 0-12-364373-2). Acad Pr.

Bourne, Geoffrey & Danielli, J. F., eds. International Review of Cytology, Vol. 83. (Serial Publication). 1983. 47.50 (ISBN 0-12-364483-6). Acad Pr.

Bourne, Geoffrey & Danielli, James, eds. International Review of Cytology. LC 52-5203. (Serial Publication). 1982. 55.00 ea. Vol. 74 (ISBN 0-12-364474-7). Vol. 75 (ISBN 0-12-364475-5). Acad Pr.

--International Review of Cytology, Vol. 72. (Serial Publication). 1981. 65.00 (ISBN 0-12-364472-0). Acad Pr.

--International Review of Cytology Supplement, No. 14. (Serial Publication). 1983. 46.50 (ISBN 0-12-364375-9). Acad Pr.

Bourne, Geoffrey & Giles, Kenneth, eds. International Review of Cytology: Supplement 13, Biology of Rhizobiaceae. (Serial Publication). 1981. 52.50 (ISBN 0-12-364374-0). Acad Pr.

Bourne, Geoffrey H. & Danielli, James F., eds. International Review of Cytology, Vol. 58. 1979. 70.00 (ISBN 0-12-364358-9). Acad Pr.

--International Review of Cytology, Vol. 59. LC 52-5203. 1979. 65.00 (ISBN 0-12-364359-7). Acad Pr.

--International Review of Cytology, Vol. 60. 1979. 65.00 (ISBN 0-12-364360-0). Acad Pr.

--International Review of Cytology, Vol. 61. LC 52-5203. 1979. 75.00 (ISBN 0-12-364461-5). Acad Pr.

--International Review of Cytology, Vol. 62. LC 52-5203. (Serial Publication). 1980. 75.00 (ISBN 0-12-364462-3). Acad Pr.

--International Review of Cytology, Vol. 63. LC 52-5203. (Serial Publication). 1980. 75.00 (ISBN 0-12-364463-1). Acad Pr.

Hilfer, S. R. & Sheffield, J. B., eds. Ocular Size & Shape: Regulation During Development. (Illus.). 211p. 1981. 32.00 (ISBN 0-387-90619-3). Springer Verlag.

Hood, Leroy E., et al. Molecular Biology of Eucaryotic Cells. 1975. 26.95 (ISBN 0-8053-9851-1, 39851). Benjamin-Cummings.

Hooper, Martin L. Mammalian Cell Genetics. (Cell Biology: A Series of Monographs 1-507). 225p. 1985. 49.95 (ISBN 0-471-89201-7, Pub. by Wiley-Interscience). Wiley.

Hopkins, Colin A. Structure & Function of Cells. (Illus.). 266p. 1978. 5.00 (ISBN 0-7216-4775-8). Saunders.

Horecker, Bernard L. & Stadtman, Earl R. Current Topics in Cellular Regulation. (Serial Publication: Vol. 19). 1981. 55.00 (ISBN 0-12-152819-7). Acad Pr.

--Current Topics in Cellular Regulation, Vol. 23. (Serial Publication). 1984. 45.00 (ISBN 0-12-152823-5). Acad Pr.

Horecker, Bernard L. & Stadtman, Earl R., eds. Current Topics in Cellular Regulation, 17 vols. Incl. Vol. 1. 1969. 65.00 (ISBN 0-12-152801-4); Vol. 2. 1970. 65.00 (ISBN 0-12-152802-2); Vol. 3. 1971. 60.00 (ISBN 0-12-152803-0); Vol. 4. 1971. 60.00 (ISBN 0-12-152804-9); Vol. 5. 1972. 65.00 (ISBN 0-12-152805-7); Vol. 6. 1972. 65.00 (ISBN 0-12-152806-5); Vol. 7. 1973. 55.00 (ISBN 0-12-152807-3); Vol. 8. 1974. 65.00 (ISBN 0-12-152808-1); Vol. 9. 1975. 60.00 (ISBN 0-12-152809-X); Vol. 10. 1974. 65.00 (ISBN 0-12-152810-3); Vol. 11. 1976. 60.00 (ISBN 0-12-152811-1); Vol. 12. 1977. 70.00 (ISBN 0-12-152812-X); Vol. 13. 1978. 60.00 (ISBN 0-12-152813-8); Vol. 14. 1978. 65.00 (ISBN 0-12-152814-6); Vol. 15. 1979. 49.50 (ISBN 0-12-152815-4); Vol. 16. 1980. 49.50 (ISBN 0-12-152816-2); Vol. 17. 1980. 49.50 (ISBN 0-12-152817-0). Acad Pr.

Horeker, B. L. & Stadtman, E. R., eds. Current Topics in Cellular Regulation Vol. 24: Enzyme Catalysis & Control. (Serial Publication). 1984. 89.00 (ISBN 0-12-152824-3). Acad Pr.

ICN-UCLA Conference, Squaw Valley, Calif., March 2-7, 1975. Cell Surface Receptors: Proceedings. Nicolson, Garth L., et al, eds. LC 76-8160. (Progress in Clinical & Biological Research: Vol. 8). 532p. 1976. 65.00x (ISBN 0-8451-0008-4). A R Liss.

Ingraham, John L. & Maaloe, Ole. Growth of the Bacterial Cell. LC 83-496. (Illus.). 375p. 1983. text ed. 28.75x (ISBN 0-87893-352-2). Sinauer Assoc.

International Review of Cytology, Vol. 76. 337p. 1982. 57.50 (ISBN 0-12-364476-3). Acad Pr.

International Society for Cell Biology. Control Mechanisms in the Expression of Cellular Phenotypes. Padyluka, Helen A., ed. (Proceedings: Vol. 9). 1970. 67.50 (ISBN 0-12-611909-0). Acad Pr.

--Formation & Fate of Cell Organelles. Warren, Katherine B., ed. (Proceedings: Vol. 6). 1968. 67.50 (ISBN 0-12-611906-6). Acad Pr.

--Intracellular Transport. Warren, Katherine B., ed. (Proceedings: Vol. 5). 1967. 67.50 (ISBN 0-12-611905-8). Acad Pr.

Jimenez de Asua, L., et al, eds. Control Mechanisms in Animal Cells: Specific Growth Factors. 406p. 1980. text ed. 52.50 (ISBN 0-89004-509-7). Raven.

John, P. C., ed. The Cell Cycle. (Society for Experimental Biology Seminar Ser.: No. 10). (Illus.). 200p. 1981. 54.50 (ISBN 0-521-23912-5); pap. 21.95 (ISBN 0-521-28342-6). Cambridge U Pr.

Jope, Charlene A. Cellular & Molecular Laboratory Manual. 64p. 1981. pap. text ed. 5.95 (ISBN 0-8403-2353-0). Kendall-Hunt.

Kahan, B. D. & Reisfeld, R. A., eds. The Cell Surface. LC 74-20983. (Advances in Experimental Medicine & Biology Ser.: Vol. 51). 287p. 1974. 42.50x (ISBN 0-306-39051-5, Plenum Pr). Plenum Pub.

Kandel, Eric R. Behavioral Biology of Aplysia: A Contribution to the Comparative Study of Opisthobranch Molluces. LC 78-18226. (Psychology Ser.). (Illus.). 463p. 1979. text ed. 59.95 (ISBN 0-7167-0021-2); pap. text ed. 33.95 (ISBN 0-7167-1070-6). W H Freeman.

Karp, Gerald C. Cell Biology. 2nd ed. (Illus.). 912p. 1984. text ed. 40.95 (ISBN 0-07-033365-3). McGraw.

Kass, Lawrence. Leukemia: Cytology & Cytochemistry. (Illus.). 272p. 1982. text ed. 59.95 (ISBN 0-397-50463-2, 65-06034, Lippincott Medical). Lippincott.

Key, Joe L. & Kosuge, Tsune. Cellular & Molecular Biology of Plant Stress. LC 84-28849. (UCLA Ser.: Vol. 22). 514p. 1985. 66.00 (ISBN 0-8451-2621-0). A R Liss.

Kimball, John W. Cell Biology. 2nd ed. LC 77-77742. (Life Sciences Ser.). (Illus.). 1978. pap. text ed. 19.95 (ISBN 0-201-03628-2). Addison-Wesley.

Kline, Tilde S. Handbook of Fine Needle Aspiration Biopsy Cytology. LC 81-38371. (Illus.). 319p. 1981. text ed. 49.50 (ISBN 0-8016-2701-X). Mosby.

Knox, Peter, ed. The Cell Surface, Vol. IV. (Biochemistry of Cellular Regulation). 336p. 1981. 94.50 (ISBN 0-8493-5457-9). CRC Pr.

Koelmel, H. W. Atlas of Cerebrospinal Fluid Cells. 2nd enl. ed. (Illus.). 1977. 64.00 (ISBN 0-387-08186-0). Springer-Verlag.

Koss, Leopold G. Diagnostic Cytology: And Its Histopathologic Bases, 2 vols. 3rd ed. (Illus.). 1226p. 1979. Set. text ed. 149.00 (ISBN 0-397-50402-0, 65-02645, Lippincott Medical). Lippincott.

Krstic, R. V. Ultrastructure of the Mammalian Cell: An Atlas. Hochstetter, A. R., tr. from Ger. 1979. 32.00 (ISBN 0-387-09583-7). Springer-Verlag.

Kuehn, K., et al, eds. New Trends in Basement Membrane Research. (Tenth Workshop-Conference Hoechst Ser.). 310p. 1982. text ed. 82.00 (ISBN 0-89004-774-X). Raven.

Kuhnel. Pocket Atlas of Cytology & Microscopic Anatomy. 1981. 18.95 (ISBN 0-8151-5208-6). Year Bk Med.

Labella, Frank S., et al. Pinocytosis. (Illus.). 220p. 1973. text ed. 28.50x (ISBN 0-8422-7084-1). Irvington.

Laerum, O. D., ed. Flow Cytometry, Four. 550p. 1981. 72.00x (ISBN 8-20005-399-7, Dist. by Columbia U Pr). Universitet.

Lamberg, Stanley L. & Rothstein, Robert. Histology & Cytology: Functional Medical Laboratory Manual. (Illus.). 1978. 12.00 (ISBN 0-87055-272-4). AVI.

Lambert, P. P., et al, eds. The Pathogenicity of Cationic Proteins. 396p. 1983. pap. text ed. 39.50 (ISBN 0-89004-689-1). Raven.

Le Douarin, N. & Monroy, A., eds. Cell Lineage, Stem Cells & Cell Determination. (INSERM Symposium Ser.: Vol. 10). 378p. 1979. 66.00 (ISBN 0-7204-0673-0, North Holland). Elsevier.

Le-Douarin, Nicole. The Neural Crest. LC 82-1183. (Developmental & Cell Biology Ser.: No. 12). (Illus.). 200p. 1983. 67.50 (ISBN 0-521-24770-5). Cambridge U Pr.

Leistenschneider, R. N., et al. Atlas of Prostatic Cytology. Mills, R. & Walther, M., trs. from Ger. (Illus.). 240p. 1985. 75.00 (ISBN 0-387-13954-0). Springer-Verlag.

Lembi, Carole A., et al. Green Algae, II: Cytology. LC 73-10108. 216p. 1973. 26.00x (ISBN 0-8422-7161-9). Irvington.

McIntosh, J. Richard & Satir, Birgit H., eds. Modern Cell Biology: Spatial Organization of Eukaryotic Cells. LC 83-909. (Modern Cell Biology Ser.: Vol. 2). 600p. 1983. 50.00 (ISBN 0-8451-3301-2). A R Liss.

McKinnell, Robert C. Cloning: A Biologist Reports. LC 79-10569. (Illus.). 1979. 8.95 (ISBN 0-8166-0883-0). U of Minn Pr.

Mak, Tak W. & Tannock, Ian. Cellular & Molecular Biology of Neoplasia. LC 84-14349. 228p. 1984. 58.00 (ISBN 0-8451-0236-2). A R Liss.

Marme, D., ed. Calcium & Cell Physiology. (Illus.). 415p. 1985. 45.00 (ISBN 0-387-13841-2). Springer-Verlag.

Mathe, G. & Rappaport, H. Histological & Cytological Typing of Neoplastic Diseases of Haematopoietic & Lymphoid Tissues. (World Health Organization: International Histological Classification of Tumours Ser.: No. 14). (Illus.). 45p. 1976. 52.00 (ISBN 92-4-176014-1, 70-1-014-20); incl. slides 139.00 (ISBN 0-89189-126-9, 70-1-014-00). Am Soc Clinical.

Methods for Serum-Free Culture of Epithelial & Fibroblastic Cells. LC 84-7910. (Cell Culture Methods for Molecular & Cell Biology Ser.: Vol. 3). 306p. 1984. 49.50 (ISBN 0-8451-3802-2). A R Liss.

Mihich, Enrico, ed. Regulation of Cell Metabolism: Organizational & Pharmacological Aspects on the Molecular Level. 382p. 1971. 76.00 (ISBN 0-12-495760-9). Acad Pr.

Miyake, T., et al, eds. Cytoprotection & Biology: Proceedings of the Symposium on Cytoprotection & Biology, 1st, Kyoto, Japan, February 26, 1983. (Current Clinical Practice Ser.: Vol. 24). 200p. 1985. 59.25 (ISBN 0-444-90388-7). Elsevier.

Morgan, H. E., ed. Cellular Biology of the Heart: Supplement to Journal of Molecular & Cellular Cardiology. 1982. 19.00 (ISBN 0-12-506960-X). Acad Pr.

Moscona, Aron A. & Monroy, Alberto, eds. Current Topics in Developmental Biology: Vol. 18: Genome Function, Cell Interactions, & Differentiation. (Serial Publication). 1983. 37.50 (ISBN 0-12-153118-X). Acad Pr.

Mullins, L. J., compiled by. Annual Reviews Reprints. Incl. Cell Membranes, 1975-1977. Mullins, L. J., compiled by. LC 78-55105. (Illus.). 1978. pap. text ed. 12.00 (ISBN 0-8243-2501-X); Cell Membranes, 1978-1980. Mullins, L. J., compiled by. LC 81-65983. (Illus.). pap. text ed. 28.00 (ISBN 0-8243-2503-6). (Illus.). Annual Reviews.

Naib, Zuther M. & Willis, Dean, eds. Cytology Examination Review Book, Vol. 1. 2nd ed. 1978. 12.75 (ISBN 0-87488-454-3). Med Exam.

Najjar, Victor A. & Lorand, Laszlo, eds. Transglutaminase. (Developments in Molecular & Cellular Biochemistry). 1984. lib. bdg. 52.50 (ISBN 0-89838-593-8, Pub. by Martinus Nijhoff Netherlands). Kluwer Academic.

Nanninga, N., ed. Molecular Cytology of the Escherichia Coli. 1985. 69.00 (ISBN 0-12-513950-0). Acad Pr.

NATO Advanced Study Institution, et al. Cytopharmacology of Secretion: Proceedings. Ceccarelli, B., et al, eds. LC 74-76090. (Advances in Cytopharmacology Ser: Vol. 2). 400p. 1974. 84.50 (ISBN 0-911216-58-8). Raven.

New York Academy of Sciences, March 10-12, 1980. Modulation of Cellular Interactions by Vitamin A & Derivatives: Retinoids, Vol. 359. De Luca, Luigi M. & Shapiro, Stanley S., eds. 431p. 1981. 85.00x (ISBN 0-89766-107-9). NY Acad Sci.

Nicholls, J. G., ed. The Role of Intercellular Signals: Navigation, Encounter, Outcome, LSRR 14. (Dahlem Workshop Reports Ser.). 309p. 1979. pap. 27.50x (ISBN 0-89573-096-0). VCH Pubs.

Nicholls, Peter. Cytochromes & Cell Respiration. 2nd ed. Head, J. J., ed. LC 78-55322. (Carolina Biology Readers Ser.). (Illus.). 16p. 1984. pap. 1.60 (ISBN 0-89278-266-8, 45-9666). Carolina Biological.

Nichols, Warren, ed. International Review of Cytology: Differentiated Cells in Aging Research, Suppl. 10. 1979. 37.50 (ISBN 0-12-364370-8). Acad Pr.

Nieuwkoop, P. D. & Sutasurya, L. A. Primordial Germ Cells in the Invertebrates. (Developmemt & Cell Biology Ser.: No. 10). (Illus.). 256p. 1982. 65.00 (ISBN 0-521-22189-7). Cambridge U Pr.

Nieuwkoop, P. D., et al. The Epigenetic Nature of Early Chordate Development. (Developmental & Cell Biology Ser.: No. 16). 368p. 1985. 69.50 (ISBN 0-521-25107-9). Cambridge U Pr.

Nover, L., ed. Heat Shock Response of Eukaryotic Cells. (Illus.). 130p. 1984. pap. 12.50 (ISBN 0-387-13640-1). Springer-Verlag.

O'Malley, Bert W., ed. Gene Regulation: UCLA Symposium Molecular Cellular Biology. LC 82-20709. (Vol. 26). 1982. 42.50 (ISBN 0-12-525960-3). Acad Pr.

Opitz, John M. X-Linked Mental Retardation. LC 84-3858. 392p. 1984. 39.00 (ISBN 0-8451-0234-6). A R Liss.

Oppenheim, J. J. & Rosenstreich, D. L., eds. Cellular Functions in Immunity & Inflammation. 480p. 1981. 48.00 (ISBN 0-444-00554-4). Elsevier.

Oppenheim, J. J., et al. Cellular Functions in Immunity & Inflammation. 1984. pap. 35.00 (ISBN 0-444-00951-5). Elsevier.

Ord, Margery G. & Stocken, Lloyd A. Cell & Tissue Regeneration: A Biochemical Approach. LC 84-3536. (Cell Biology; a Series of Monographs: 1570). 221p. 1984. 42.50x (ISBN 0-471-86248-7, Pub. by Wiley-Interscience). Wiley.

Pain, R. H. & Smith, B. J., eds. New Techniques in Biophysics & Cell Biology, Vol. 1. LC 72-8611. pap. 64.80 (ISBN 0-317-29873-9, 2016156). Bks Demand UMI.

Palade, George L., et al, eds. Annual Review of Cell Biology, Vol. 1. (Illus.). 600p. 1985. text ed. 27.00 (ISBN 0-8243-3101-X). Annual Reviews.

Perelson. Cell Surface Dynamics. 552p. 1984. 85.00 (ISBN 0-8247-7115-X). Dekker.

Pernis, Benvenuto & Vogel, Henry J., eds. Cell Biology of the Major Histocompatibility Complex. Edited Treatise ed. (P & S Biomedical Sciences Symposia Ser.). Date not set. 75.00; pap. 39.95 (ISBN 0-12-550871-9). Acad Pr.

Pfaller, W. Structure Function Correlation on Rat Kidney. (Advances in Anatomy, Embriology, & Cell Biology Ser.: Vol 70). (Illus.). 106p. 1982. pap. 30.00 (ISBN 0-387-11074-7). Springer-Verlag.

Pfeffer, Wilhelm. Osmotic Investigations. (Illus.). 304p. 1985. 32.50 (ISBN 0-442-27583-8). Van Nos Reinhold.

Pines, Maya. Inside the Cell: The New Frontier of Medical Science. LC 79-22746. (Illus.). 96p. 1980. 11.95x (ISBN 0-89490-031-5). Enslow Pubs.

Polak, Julia M. & Van Noorden, Susan. An Introduction to Immunocytochemistry: Current Techniques & Problems. (Royal Microscopical Society Microscopy Handbooks Ser.). (Illus.). 1984. pap. 7.95x (ISBN 0-19-856411-2). Oxford U Pr.

Porter, Keith R. & Bonneville, Mary A. Fine Structure of Cells & Tissues. 4th ed. LC 73-11314. (Illus.). 204p. 1973. text ed. 18.50 (ISBN 0-8121-0430-7). Lea & Febiger.

Poste & Nicholson. Cytoskeletal Elements. (Cell Surface Reviews Ser.: Vol. 7). 350p. 1982. 99.75 (ISBN 0-444-80335-1, Biomedical Pr). Elsevier.

--Membrane Reconstitution. (Cell Surface Reviews Ser.: Vol. 8). 274p. 1983. 76.75 (ISBN 0-444-80391-2, Biomedical Pr). Elsevier.

Poste, G. & Nicholson, G., eds. The Cell Surface in Animal Embryogenesis & Development. (Cell Surface Reviews: Vol. 1). 766p. 1977. 142.75 (ISBN 0-7204-0597-1, Biomedical Pr). Elsevier.

Prescott, D. M. Reproduction of Eukaryotic Cells. Head, J. J., ed. LC 76-62968. (Carolina Biology Readers Ser.). (Illus.). 16p. 1978. pap. 1.60 (ISBN 0-89278-296-X, 45-9696). Carolina Biological.

Prescott, David & Hand, Arthur, eds. Methods in Cell Biology: Basic Mechanisms of Cellular Secretion, Vol. 23. LC 64-14220. (Serial Publication). 1981. 69.00 (ISBN 0-12-564123-0). Acad Pr.

Prescott, David M., ed. Methods in Cell Physiology. Incl. Vol. 1. 1964. 75.00 (ISBN 0-12-564101-X); Vol. 2. 1966. 75.00 (ISBN 0-12-564102-8); Vol. 3. 1969. 75.00 (ISBN 0-12-564103-6); Vol. 4. 1970. 75.00 (ISBN 0-12-564104-4); Vol. 5. 1972. 75.00 (ISBN 0-12-564105-2); Vol. 6. 1973. 75.00 (ISBN 0-12-564106-0); Vol. 7. 1974. 75.00 (ISBN 0-12-564107-9); Vol. 8. 1974. 75.00 (ISBN 0-12-564108-7); Vol. 9. 1975. 75.00 (ISBN 0-12-564109-5); Vol. 10. 1975. 75.00 (ISBN 0-12-564110-9); Vol. 11. Yeast Cells. 1975. 75.00 (ISBN 0-12-564111-7); Vol. 12. 1975. 75.00 (ISBN 0-12-564112-5); Vol. 13. 1976. 75.00 (ISBN 0-12-564113-3); Vol. 14. 1976. 75.00 (ISBN 0-12-564114-1); Vol. 15. 1977. 75.00 (ISBN 0-12-564115-X); Vol. 16. Chromatin & Chromosomal Protein Research I. Stein, Gary & Stein, Janet, eds. 1977. 75.00 (ISBN 0-12-564116-8). Acad Pr.

Prescott, David M & Harris, Curtis, eds. Methods in Cell Biology: Methods to Culture Normal Human Tissues & Cells: Respiratory, Cardiovascular, & Intgumentary Systems, Vol. 21. (Serial Publication Ser.: Pt. A). 1980. 59.50 (ISBN 0-12-564121-4). Acad Pr.

--Methods in Cell Biology: Methods to Culture Normal Human Tissues & Cells: Endocrine, Urogenital, & Gastro-Intestinal Systems, Vol. 21. (Serial Publication Ser.: Pt. B). 1980. 65.00 (ISBN 0-12-564140-0). Acad Pr.

Prescott, David M., et al, eds. Advances in Cell Biology, 2 vols. LC 70-85896. 27.50x ea. (Plenum Pr). Plenum Pub.

--Methods in Cell Biology, Vols. 17-20. 1978. Vol. 17. 75.00 (ISBN 0-12-564117-6); Vol. 18. 70.00 (ISBN 0-12-564118-4); Vol. 19. 70.00 (ISBN 0-12-564119-2); Vol. 20. 85.00 (ISBN 0-12-564120-6). Acad Pr.

Preston, Kendall, Jr. & Duff, Michael J. Modern Cellular Automata: Theory & Applications. (Advanced Applications of Pattern Recognition Ser.). 340p. 1984. 49.50x (ISBN 0-306-41737-5, Plenum Pr). Plenum Pub.

Prunieras, M., ed. Epidermal Keratinocyte Differentiation & Fibrillogenesis. (Frontiers of Matrix Biology: Vol. 9). (Illus.). viii, 192p. 1981. 52.25 (ISBN 3-8055-0893-X). S Karger.

Prydz, H., ed. The Cell Biology of Triggers in Coagulation. (Journal: Haemostasis: Vol. 14 No. 5). (Illus.). 68p. 1985. pap. 24.00 (ISBN 3-8055-4046-9). S Karger.

Rasmussen, Howard. Calcium & Camp As Synarchic Messengers. LC 81-10482. 370p. 1981. 51.50 (ISBN 0-471-08396-8, Pub. by Wiley-Interscience). Wiley.

Reanney. International Review of Cytology, Vol. 93. 1985. 49.50 (ISBN 0-317-26973-9). Acad Pr.

Reeves, G. W., ed. Recent Developments in Clinical Immunology. (Research Monographs in Immunology: Vol. 6). 216p. 1984. 59.25 (ISBN 0-444-80554-0, I-273-84). Elsevier.

Reich, J. G. & Selkov, E. Energy Metabolism of the Cell: A Theoretical Treatise. LC 81-66389. 352p. 1982. 74.00 (ISBN 0-12-585920-1). Acad Pr.

Riethmuller, Gert, et al, eds. Natural & Induced Cell-Mediated Cytotoxicity: Effector & Regulatory Mechanisms. LC 79-14162. (Perspectives in Immunology Ser.). 1979. 35.00 (ISBN 0-12-584650-9). Acad Pr.

Riotton, C. & Christopherson, William. Cytology of the Female Genital Tract Tumours. (World Health Organization: International Histological Classification of Tumours Ser.: No. 8). (Illus.). 1977. books & slides 168.50 (ISBN 0-89189-109-9, 70-1-008-00). Am Soc Clinical.

Riotton, G. & Christopherson, W. M. Cytology of Non-Gynaecological Sites. (World Health Organization: International Histological Classification of Tumours Ser.: No. 17). (Illus.). 1977. text ed. 69.50 (ISBN 92-4-176017-6, 70-1-017-20); with slides 205.00 (ISBN 0-89189-125-0, 70-1-017-00). Am Soc Clinical.

Roland, Jean-Claude, et al. Atlas of Cell Biology. 1977. 14.95 (ISBN 0-316-75450-1). Little.

Richardson, Gary H., ed. Standard Methods for the Examination of Dairy Products. 15th ed. 412p. 1985. 40.00x (ISBN 0-87553-118-0); pap. 30.00x (ISBN 0-87553-132-6). Am Pub Health.

Walstra, Pieter & Jenness, Robert. Dairy Chemistry & Physics. LC 83-16902. 467p. 1984. 59.95 (ISBN 0-471-09779-9, Pub. by Wiley-Interscience). Wiley.

Webb, Byron H., et al, eds. Fundamentals of Dairy Chemistry. 2nd ed. 1974. text ed. 69.50 (ISBN 0-87055-143-4). AVI.

WHO Food Standards Programme. Joint FAO-WHO Committee of Government Experts on the Code of Principles Concerning Milk & Milk Products: Report of the Twentieth Session, Rome, April 1982. (Joint FAO-WHO Food Standards Programme). (Eng., Fr. & Span.). 77p. 1982. pap. 7.50 (ISBN 92-5-101244-X, F2363, FAO). Unipub.

DAIRYING

see also Butter; Cheese; Cows; Dairy Bacteriology; Dairy Cattle; Dairy Products; Milk; Milk Plants; Radioisotopes in Dairying

Baker, Frank H., ed. Dairy Science Handbook: International Stockmen's School Handbooks, Vol. 15. 500p. Date not set. text ed. 36.50 (ISBN 0-86531-673-2). Westview.

Bundy, et al. Dairy Production. 4th ed. 1977. 31.52 (ISBN 0-13-197079-8). P-H.

Castle, Malcolm & Watkins, Paul. Modern Milk Production. (Illus.). 320p. 1979. 18.95 (ISBN 0-571-11312-5); pap. 13.50 (ISBN 0-571-11347-8). Faber & Faber.

The Changing Dairy Industry. 1985. cancelled (ISBN 0-89336-280-8, GA-048R). BCC.

Cullity, Maurice. The History of Dairying in Western Australia. 488p. 1980. 35.00x (ISBN 0-85564-177-0, Pub. by U of West Australia Pr Australia). Intl Spec Bk.

The Dairy Products Manufacturing Industry. (UNIDO Guides to Information Sources: No. 23). pap. 4.00 (ISBN 0-686-93189-0, UNID177, UN). Unipub.

Energy Management & Membrane Technology in Food & Dairy Processing. LC 83-72936. 128p. 1983. pap. 15.50 (ISBN 0-916150-57-7). Am Soc Ag Eng.

Ensminger, M. E. Dairy Cattle Science. 2nd ed. LC 78-78193. (Illus.). 630p. 1980. 35.95 (ISBN 0-8134-2079-2, 2079); text ed. 26.95x. Interstate.

Establishment of Dairy Training Centers. (Animal Production & Health Papers: No. 15). 64p. 1979. pap. 7.50 (ISBN 92-5-100738-1, F1629, FAO). Unipub.

Fagard, P. Guideline for Dairy Accounting. (Animal Production & Health Papers: No. 21). 39p. 1980. pap. 7.50 (ISBN 92-5-100998-8, F2127, FAO). Unipub.

Farrall, Arthur W. Engineering for Dairy & Food Products. 2nd ed. LC 79-1171. (Illus.). 1980. lib. bdg. 36.00 (ISBN 0-88275-859-4). Krieger.

Fontana, Marjorie A. & Larson, Jean L. Say Cheese & Milk Please. LC 78-67289. (Illus.). 62p. (Orig.). 1978. 7.95 (ISBN 0-9603596-0-5); pap. 5.95 (ISBN 0-9603596-1-3). Fontastic.

Fussell, G. E. English Dairy Farmer: 1500-1900. (Illus.). 357p. 1966. 27.50x (ISBN 0-7146-1309-6, F Cass Co). Biblio Dist.

Fussell, George E. English Dairy Farmer, 1500-1900. LC 67-16355. (Illus.). 1966. 29.50x (ISBN 0-678-05046-5). Kelley.

Hall, H. S. & Tuszynski, W. B. Maintenance Systems for the Dairy Plant. (Animal Production & Health Papers: No. 45). 73p. 1985. pap. 7.50 (ISBN 92-5-101448-5, F2702 5071, FAO). Unipub.

Juergenson, Elwood M. & Mortenson, William P. Approved Practices in Dairying. 4th ed. LC 77-74120. (Illus.). 356p. 1977. 18.60 (ISBN 0-8134-1954-9, 1954); text ed. 13.95x. Interstate.

Lowe, F. R. Milking Machines: A Comprehensive Guide for Farmers, Herdsmen & Students. (Illus.). 200p. 1981. 31.00 (ISBN 0-08-024381-9); pap. 13.00 (ISBN 0-08-024382-7). Pergamon.

Means of Adjustment of Dairy Supply & Demand. (Commodity Bulletins: No. 204). 107p. 1963. pap. 10.00 (ISBN 92-5-101650-X, F272, FAO). Unipub.

Mortenson, W. P. & Juergenson, E. M. Approved Practices in Dairying. 299p. 1981. 44.00x (ISBN 0-686-72941-2, Pub. by Oxford & IBH India). State Mutual Bk.

Oskam, A. J. Policy Models for the Dairy Sector of the European Community & The Netherlands. (Agricultural Research Reports: No. 915). 79p. 1981. pap. 11.25 (ISBN 90-220-0790-1, PDC238, PUDOC). Unipub.

Pirtle, Thomas R. History of the Dairy Industry. LC 72-89079. (Rural America Ser.). 1973. Repr. of 1926 ed. 39.00 (ISBN 0-8420-1494-2). Scholarly Res Inc.

Schmidt, Glen H. & Van Vleck, L. Dale. Principles of Dairy Science. LC 73-2860. (Animal Science Ser.). (Illus.). 558p. 1974. text ed. 32.95x (ISBN 0-7167-0830-2). W H Freeman.

Solar Energy in Small-Scale Milk Collection & Processing. (Animal Production & Health Papers: No. 39). 120p. 1984. pap. 8.75 (ISBN 92-5-101339-X, F2481, FAO). Unipub.

Velitok, I. G. Machine Milking & Its Effects on Cows. 136p. 1981. 50.00x (ISBN 0-686-72955-2, Pub. by Oxford & IBH India). State Mutual Bk.

--Physiology of Milk Secretion in Machine Milking. 109p. 1981. 50.00x (ISBN 0-686-72960-9, Pub. by Oxford & IBH India). State Mutual Bk.

The World Dairy Economy in Figures. (Commodity Reference Ser.: No. 5). 119p. (Orig.). 1969. pap. 7.25 (ISBN 92-5-001705-7, F507, FAO). Unipub.

DAIRYING–LABORATORY MANUALS

Harrigan, W. F. & McCance, M. E., eds. Laboratory Methods in Food & Dairy Microbiology. 1977. 62.00 (ISBN 0-12-326040-X). Acad Pr.

D'ALEMBERT EQUATION

see Lagrange Equations

DALMATIAN (DOG)

see Dogs–Breeds–Dalmatians

DALTON, JOHN, 1766-1844

Millington, John P. John Dalton. LC 73-14966. (English Men of Science: No. 6). Repr. of 1906 ed. 19.45 (ISBN 0-404-07896-6). AMS Pr.

Roscoe, Henry E. & Harden, Arthur. A New View of the Origin of Dalton's Atomic Theory. (Sources of Science Ser.: No. 100). Repr. of 1896 ed. 17.00 (ISBN 0-384-51970-9). Johnson Repr.

Thackray, Arnold. John Dalton: Critical Assessments of His Life & Science. LC 72-75403. (Monographs in the History of Science). (Illus.). 216p. 1972. 14.00x (ISBN 0-674-47525-9). Harvard U Pr.

DAMAGE CONTROL (WARSHIPS)

see also Ships–Fires and Fire Prevention

Livingston, David, et al. Shipboard Damage Control. LC 76-4674. 1976. text ed. 15.95x (ISBN 0-87021-627-9). Naval Inst Pr.

DAMPING (MECHANICS)

see also Internal Friction; Shock (Mechanics)

Nashif, Ahid & Jones, David I G. Vibration Damping. LC 84-17247. 416p. 1985. 51.50x (ISBN 0-471-86772-1, Pub. by Wiley-Interscience). Wiley.

Torvik, P. J., ed. Damping Applications for Vibration Control. (AMD: Vol. 38). 164p. 1980. 24.00 (ISBN 0-686-69848-7, G00171). ASME.

DAMPNESS IN BUILDINGS

see also Air Conditioning; Ventilation

Croome, D. J. & Sherratt, A. F., eds. Condensation in Buildings. (Illus.). 271p. 1972. 39.00 (ISBN 0-85334-548-1, Pub. by Elsevier Applied Sci England). Elsevier.

Duell, J. & Lawson, F. Damp Proof Course Detailing. (Illus.). 64p. 1983. 18.80x (ISBN 0-85139-150-8, Pub. by Architectural Pr England); pap. text ed. 12.50x (ISBN 0-85139-149-4). Humanities.

Lieff & Trechsel, eds. Moisture Migration in Buildings - STP 779. 291p. 1982. 29.00 (ISBN 0-8031-0605-X, 04-779000-10). ASTM.

Oxley, T. & Gobert, E. Dampness in Buildings: Diagnosis, Treatment, Instruments. (Illus.). 120p. 1983. text ed. 12.50 (ISBN 0-408-01463-6). Butterworth.

Seiffert, Karl, et al. Damp Diffusion & Buildings. (Illus.). 209p. 1970. 40.75 (ISBN 0-444-20073-8, Pub. by Elsevier Applied Sci England). Elsevier.

DAMS

see also Flood Dams and Reservoirs

also particular dams, e.g. Grand Coulee Dam

American Society of Civil Engineers, compiled By. Economical Construction of Concrete Dams. 566p. 1972. pap. 19.75x (ISBN 0-87262-043-3). Am Soc Civil Eng.

--Environmental Effects of Large Dams. 229p. 1978. pap. 9.00x (ISBN 0-87262-125-1). Am Soc Civil Eng.

--Inspection, Maintenance & Rehabilitation of Old Dams. 956p. 1974. pap. 34.00x (ISBN 0-87262-061-1). Am Soc Civil Eng.

Canadian Bulletin of Fisheries & Aquatic Sciences: Environmental Effects of Dams & Impoundments in Canada - Experience & Prospects. (Bulletin Ser.: No. 205). 34p. 1981. pap. 5.00 (ISBN 0-660-10485-7, SSC147, SSC). Unipub.

Creager, William P., et al. Engineering for Dams: Concrete Dams, Vol. II. pap. 104.00 (ISBN 0-317-10812-3, 2012625). Bks Demand UMI.

Engineering Foundation Conference, Mar. 1974. Foundations for Dams. 480p. 1974. pap. 27.50x (ISBN 0-87262-100-6). Am Soc Civil Eng.

Engineering Foundation Conference, Nov. 1976. Evaluation of Dam Safety. American Society of Civil Engineers, compiled By. 529p. 1977. pap. 16.00x (ISBN 0-87262-088-3). Am Soc Civil Eng.

Golze, Alfred R., ed. Handbook of Dam Engineering. 1977. 68.50 (ISBN 0-442-22752-3). Van Nos Reinhold.

Gupta, H. & Rastogi, B. Dams & Earthquakes. (Developments in Geotechnical Engineering Ser.: Vol. 11). 230p. 1976. 70.25 (ISBN 0-444-41330-8). Elsevier.

Hirschfeld, Ronald C. & Poulos, Steve J., eds. Embankment Dam Engineering: The Casagrande Volume. LC 72-8626. 454p. 1973. 71.50 (ISBN 0-471-40050-5, Pub by Wiley-Interscience). Wiley.

Institution of Civil Engineers Staff, ed. Dams & Earthquakes. 319p. 1981. 62.50x (ISBN 0-7277-0123-1). Am Soc Civil Eng.

International Science & Technology, Inc. Report on the Potential Use of Small Dams to Produce Power for Low-Income Communities. Allen, Mary M., ed. (Illus.). 1979. 15.00 (ISBN 0-936130-02-4). Intl Sci Tech.

Lessons from Dam Incidents: USA. 392p. 1975. pap. 18.00x (ISBN 0-87262-104-9). Am Soc Civil Eng.

National Research Council. Safety of Dams: Flood & Earthquake Criteria. 320p. 1985. pap. 16.50 (ISBN 0-309-03532-5). Natl Acad Pr.

Priscu, R. Earthquake Engineering for Large Dams. 1985. 41.95 (ISBN 0-471-90047-8). Wiley.

Responsibility & Liability of Public & Private Interests on Dams. 210p. 1976. pap. 12.00x (ISBN 0-87262-167-7). Am Soc Civil Eng.

Safety of Small Dams. 472p. 1974. pap. 23.00x (ISBN 0-87262-112-X). Am Soc Civil Eng.

Sherard, James L., et al. Earth & Earth-Rock Dams: Engineering Problems of Design & Construction. LC 63-14068. 725p. 1963. 76.95 (ISBN 0-471-78547-4, Pub. by Wiley-Interscience). Wiley.

Smith, Norman. A History of Dams. (Illus.). 280p. 1972. 10.00 (ISBN 0-8065-0291-6). Citadel Pr.

Soil-Cement for Water Control: Laboratory Tests. 27p. 1976. pap. 1.75 (ISBN 0-89312-117-7, IS166W). Portland Cement.

Thomas, Henry H. The Engineering of Large Dams. LC 75-15886. 777p. 1978. 2 vol. set 217.95x (ISBN 0-471-01528-8, Pub. by Wiley-Interscience). Wiley.

Vick, Steven G. Planning, Design, & Analysis of Tailings Dams. LC 83-7028. (Geotechnical Engineering Ser.). 384p. 1983. 49.50x (ISBN 0-471-89829-5, 1-256, Pub. by Wiley-Interscience). Wiley.

Wahlstrom, E. Dams: Dam Foundations & Reservoir Sites. 1974. 59.75 (ISBN 0-444-41236-0). Elsevier.

Walters, R. C. Dam Geology. 2nd ed. (Illus.). 470p. 1971. 27.75 (ISBN 0-8088-7019-X). Davey.

Warren, William M. & Neville, Rubin. Dams in Africa: Inter-Disciplinary Study of Manmade Lakes in Africa. (Illus.). 200p. 1968. 32.50x (ISBN 0-7146-1248-0, F Cass Co). Biblio Dist.

Wilson, David, ed. Design & Construction of Tailing Dams: First Seminar on Design & Construction of Tailing Dams, Nov. 6-7, 1980. LC 81-10273. (Illus.). 280p. 1981. Repr. of 1980 ed. text ed. 9.00 (ISBN 0-918062-45-4). Colo Sch Mines.

Wilson, Stanley D. & Marsal, Raul. Current Trends in Design & Construction of Embankment Dams. 133p. 1979. pap. 11.75x (ISBN 0-87262-197-9). Am Soc Civil Eng.

DANISH DOGS

see Dogs–Breeds–Dalmatians

DAPHNIA

Brooks, John L. The Systematics of North American Daphnia. (Memoirs of the Connecticut Academy of Arts & Sciences Ser.: Vol. 13). 180p. 1963. 22.50 (ISBN 0-317-03797-8). Shoe String.

DARK ROOMS

see Photography–Studios and Dark Rooms

DARKROOM TECHNIQUE IN PHOTOGRAPHY

see Photography–Processing

DARTERS (FISHES)

Braasch, Marvin E. & Page, Lawrence M. Systematic Studies of Darters of the Subgenus Catonotus (Percidae), with the Description of a New Species from Caney Fork, Tennessee. (Occasional Papers: No. 78). 10p. 1979. 1.25 (ISBN 0-317-04822-8). U of KS Mus Nat Hist.

Kuehne, Robert A. & Barbour, Roger W. The American Darters. LC 83-5934. (Illus.). 208p. 1984. 45.00x (ISBN 0-8131-1452-7). U Pr of Ky.

Lingquist, David G. & Page, Lawrence M., eds. Environmental Biology of Darters. (Developments in Environmental Biology of Fishes Ser.). 1984. lib. bdg. 44.00 (ISBN 90-6193-506-7, Pub. by Junk Pubs Netherlands). Kluwer Academic.

Page, Lawrence M. The Genera & Subgenera of Darters: (Percidae, Etheostomatini) (Occassional Papers: No. 90). 69p. 1981. 3.75 (ISBN 0-317-04830-9). U of KS Mus Nat Hist.

--Redescription of Etheostoma Australe & a Key for the Identification of Mexican Etheostoma Percidae. (Occasional Papers: No. 89). 10p. 1981. 1.25 (ISBN 0-317-04828-7). U of KS Mus Nat Hist.

Page, Lawrence M. & Burr, Brooks M. Three New Species of Darters (Percidae, Etheostoma) of the Subgenus Nanostoma from Kentucky & Tennessee. (Occasional Papers: No. 101). (Illus.). 20p. 1982. 4.00 (ISBN 0-317-04835-X). U of KS Mus Nat Hist.

DARWIN, CHARLES ROBERT, 1809-1882

Allen, Grant. Charles Darwin. 1973. Repr. of 1888 ed. 15.00 (ISBN 0-8274-1805-1). R West.

Angell, J. R., et al. Darwinism. Bd. with Natural Inheritance. Galton, Francis. (Contributions to the History of Psychology Ser., Vol. IV, Pt. D: Comparative Psychology). 1978. 30.00 (ISBN 0-89093-173-9). U Pubns Amer.

Appleman, Philip, ed. Darwin. 2nd ed. (Norton Critical Edition). (Illus.). 1979. 24.95x (ISBN 0-393-01192-5); pap. 8.95x (ISBN 0-393-95009-3). Norton.

Ashley Montagu. Darwin: Competition & Cooperation. LC 72-11332. 148p. 1973. Repr. of 1952 ed. lib. bdg. 24.75 (ISBN 0-8371-6657-8, MODC). Greenwood.

Barnett, Samuel, ed. Century of Darwin. facs. ed. LC 71-76891. (Essay Index Reprint Ser). 1958. 21.25 (ISBN 0-8369-1019-2). Ayer Co Pubs.

Baum, R. F. Doctors of Modernity: Darwin, Marx, & Freud. 148p. (Orig.). Date not set. pap. 6.95 (ISBN 0-317-30088-1). Sugden.

Berry, R. J. Charles Darwin: A Commemoration 1882-1982. 140p. 1982. 19.00 (ISBN 0-12-093180-X). Acad Pr.

Bettany, G. T. Life of Charles Darwin. 1977. Repr. of 1887 ed. lib. bdg. 20.00 (ISBN 0-8495-0327-2). Arden Lib.

--Life of Charles Darwin. 1973. Repr. of 1887 ed. 15.00 (ISBN 0-8274-1801-9). R West.

Brent, Peter. Charles Darwin: A Man of Enlarged Curiosity. (Illus.). 560p. 1983. pap. 9.50 (ISBN 0-393-30109-5). Norton.

--Darwin. LC 80-7889. 512p. 1981. 23.99i (ISBN 0-06-014880-2, HarpT). Har-Row.

Burkardt, Frederick. A Calendar of the Correspondence of Charles Darwin, 1821-1882. LC 82-14565. (Humanities Ser.). 700p. 1984. lib. bdg. 100.00 (ISBN 0-8240-9224-4). Garland Pub.

Burkhardt, Frederick & Smith, Sydney, eds. The Correspondence of Charles Darwin, 1821-1836, Vol. 1. 672p. 1985. 37.50 (ISBN 0-521-25587-2). Cambridge U Pr.

Carroll, P. Thomas, ed. Annotated Calendar of the Letters of Charles Darwin in the Library of the American Philosophical Society. LC 75-29739. 1976. Repr. 31.00 (ISBN 0-8420-2077-2). Scholarly Res Inc.

Clark, Ronald W. The Survival of Charles Darwin: A Biography of a Man & an Idea. LC 84-42507. (Illus.). 544p. 1985. 19.45 (ISBN 0-394-52134-X). Random.

Darwin. (A Clarendon Biography Ser.). (Illus.). 1975. pap. 3.50 (ISBN 0-912728-91-4). Newbury Bks.

Darwin, Charles. Autobiography & Selected Letters. Darwin, Francis, ed. 1892. pap. 5.95 (ISBN 0-486-20479-0). Dover.

--Autobiography & Selected Letters. Darwin, Francis, ed. 14.00 (ISBN 0-8446-1947-7). Peter Smith.

--Book of Darwin. Simpson, George G., intro. by. 224p. (Orig.). 1983. pap. 6.95 (ISBN 0-671-43126-9). WSP.

--The Collected Papers of Charles Darwin, Vols. I & II. Barrett, Paul H., ed. LC 76-606. (Illus.). 1977. lib. bdg. 40.00x set (ISBN 0-226-13657-4); pap. 12.50 (ISBN 0-226-13658-2, P886, Phoen). U of Chicago Pr.

--The Origin of Species. Irvine, Charlotte & Irvine, William, eds. LC 56-7502. pap. 3.95 (ISBN 0-8044-6105-8). Ungar.

--The Origins of Species. 1982. pap. 8.00 (ISBN 0-318-04039-5, DEL-05136, Evman). Biblio Dist.

--The Voyage of Charles Darwin. Ralling, Christopher, ed. LC 79-916. (Illus.). 1980. 12.50 (ISBN 0-8317-9212-4, Mayflower Bks). Smith Pubs.

Darwin, Charles R. Life & Letters of Charles Darwin, 3 Vols. Darwin, Francis, ed. (Sources of Science Ser: No. 102). 1969. Repr. of 1888 ed. Set. 110.00 (ISBN 0-384-10900-4). Johnson Repr.

--The Life & Letters of Charles Darwin, 2 Vols. Darwin, Francis, ed. LC 72-3904. (Illus.). 1972. Vol. I. (ISBN 0-404-08417-6). Vol. II (ISBN 0-404-08418-4). 85.00 set. AMS Pr.

Darwin, Francis. The Life & Letters of Charles Darwin, 2 vols. 1973. Repr. of 1893 ed. 75.00 (ISBN 0-8274-1406-4). R West.

Darwin, Francis, ed. The Life & Letters of Charles Darwin, 2 vols. 1981. Repr. of 1891 ed. lib. bdg. 125.00 set (ISBN 0-8495-1133-X). Arden Lib.

Distributed Database. 155p. 1981. text ed. 60.75x (ISBN 0-903796-73-2, Pub. by Online Conferences England). Brookfield Pub Co.

Distributed Database. 154p. 1981. pap. 48.00x (ISBN 0-903796-73-2, Pub. by Online). Taylor & Francis.

Draffan, I. W. & Poole, F., eds. Distributed Data Bases. LC 80-40399. 400p. 1981. 37.50 (ISBN 0-521-23091-8). Cambridge U Pr.

Durell, W. R. Data Administration: A Practical Guide to Successful Data Management. 192p. 1984. 32.95 (ISBN 0-07-018391-0). McGraw.

Einhorn, David. Minute Manual for DB Master. Pirisino, Jim, ed. 137p. 1983. pap. 12.95 (ISBN 0-913131-02-4). Minuteware.

Elbra, R. A. Database for the Small Computer User. 150p. 1982. pap. 20.75 (ISBN 0-471-89443-5). Wiley.

Epstein, Robert S. Query Processing Techniques for Distributed, Relational Data Base Systems. Stone, Harold, ed. LC 82-6949. (Computer Science: Distributed Database Systems Ser.: No. 13). 106p. 1982. 34.95 (ISBN 0-8357-1341-5). UMI Res Pr.

Erickson, Steve. Management Tools for Everyone. 1986. pap. 12.95. Petrocelli.

Establishment of an Automated Data Base on Disarmament (UNIDIR) pap. 10.00 (UNEP203, UN). Unipub.

Everest, G. Database Management. 1986. write for info. (ISBN 0-07-019781-4). McGraw.

Feastr, Thelma J., et al. Databases & Clearinghouses: Information Resources for Education. 156p. 1979. 9.75 (ISBN 0-318-15440-4, IN 167). Natl Ctr Res Voc Ed.

Federal Communications Commission Planning Conference November 8 & 9, 1976 & Hopewell, Lynn. Computers & Communications: Proceedings. (Illus.). 197p. 1976. pap. 11.50 (ISBN 0-88283-022-8). AFIPS Pr.

Fernandez, Eduardo B., et al. Database Security & Integrity. LC 80-15153. (IBM Systems Programming Ser.). (Illus.). 288p. 1981. text ed. 31.95 (ISBN 0-201-14467-0). Addison-Wesley.

Flavin, Matt. Fundamental Concepts of Information Modeling. (Illus.). 136p. (Orig.). 1981. pap. 17.50 (ISBN 0-917072-22-7). Yourdon.

Florence, Alan. Information Management with dBASE II. cancelled (ISBN 0-89303-550-5). Brady Comm.

Flores, Ivan. Data Base Architecture. 480p. 1981. 28.50 (ISBN 0-442-22729-9). Van Nos Reinhold.

Freedman, Daniel P. & Weinberg, Gerald M. Handbook of Walkthroughs, Inspections, & Technical Reviews. 3rd ed. 448p. 1982. text ed. 38.00 (ISBN 0-316-29282-6). Little.

Freiling, Michael J. Understanding Data Base Management. (An Alfred Handy Guide Ser.). 63p. 1982. 3.50 (ISBN 0-88284-221-8). Alfred Pub.

Frost, R. A. Database Management Systems. 288p. 1984. 36.95 (ISBN 0-07-022564-8). McGraw.

Gallaire, Herve, et al, eds. Advances in Data Base Theory, Vol. 1. 440p. 1981. 59.50x (ISBN 0-306-40629-2, Plenum Pr). Plenum Pub.

Galliare, Herve, et al, eds. Advances in Data Base Theory, Vol. 2. 442p. 1984. 59.50x (ISBN 0-306-41636-0, Plenum Pr). Plenum Pub.

Garcia-Molina, Hector. Performance of Update Algorithms for Replicated Data. Stone, Harold S., ed. LC 81-10454. (Computer Science Ser.: Distributed Database Systems: No. 5). 338p. 1981. 49.95 (ISBN 0-8357-1219-2). UMI Res Pr.

Gardarin, Georges & Gelenbe, Erol, eds. New Applications of Data Bases. 1984. 25.00 (ISBN 0-12-275550-2). Acad Pr.

Garland, Andrew, et al. System 1022 User's Reference Manual. rev. ed. 500p. 1984. looseleaf 28.50X (ISBN 0-912055-09-X). Software Hse.

Gaydasch, Alex. Effective Database Management. 1985. text ed. 24.95 (ISBN 0-8359-1574-3). Reston.

Gaydasch, Alexander. Principles of Electronic Data Processing Management. 300p. 1982. text ed. 26.95 (ISBN 0-8359-5604-0); instr's. manual free (ISBN 0-8359-5605-9). Reston.

Ghosh, Sakti P., et al, eds. Data Base File Organization: Theory & Applications of Consecutive Retrieval Property (Symposium) Kambayashi, Y. & Lipski, W. (Notes & Reports in Computer & Science Applied Mathematics Ser.). 1983. 21.50 (ISBN 0-12-281860-1). Acad Pr.

Gillenson, M. L. Database: The Fundamentals. 1985. 34.95 (ISBN 0-471-80702-8). Wiley.

Goldberg, Robert & Lorin, Harold. The Economics of Information Processing: Vol. 1, Management Perspectives. LC 81-11429. 238p. 1982. 34.95 (ISBN 0-471-09206-1, Pub. by Wiley Interscience); member 28.75. Assn Inform & Image Mgmt.

Goldstein, Robert C. Database: Technology & Management. 352p. 1985. 28.95 (ISBN 0-471-88737-4). Wiley.

Gorman, Michael M. Managing Database: Four Critical Factors. LC 83-83114. 216p. pap. 32.50 (ISBN 0-89435-103-6). QED Info Sci.

Gorney, Leonard. Invitation to Database Processing. (Illus.). 276p. 1985. text ed. 27.95 (ISBN 0-89433-217-1). Petrocelli.

Greenberg, Gary. C-BIMS: Cassette-Based Information Management System for the PET. (Illus.). 224p. (Orig.). 1983. 16.95 (ISBN 0-8306-0489-8); pap. 10.95 (ISBN 0-8306-1489-3, 1489). TAB Bks.

Greene, Greg. Database Manager in Microsoft BASIC. (Illus.). 176p. 1983. 18.95 (ISBN 0-8306-0167-8, 1567); pap. 12.50 (ISBN 0-8306-0567-3). TAB Bks.

Gustavson, Frances G. The Automatic Revision of Storage Structures. Stone, Harold, ed. LC 82-6974. (Computer Science: Systems Programming Ser.: No. 11). 154p. 1982. 39.95 (ISBN 0-8357-1345-8). UMI Res Pr.

Hardgrave & Deutsch, eds. Data Base Concepts. 1986. text ed. price not set (ISBN 0-538-10960-2, J96). SW Pub.

Haueisen, William D. & Camp, James L. Business Systems for Microcomputers: Concept, Design & Implications. (Series in Data Processing Management). (Illus.). 480p. 1982. text ed. 31.95 (ISBN 0-13-107805-4). P-H.

Hawryszkiewycz, Igor. Database Analysis & Design. 416p. 1984. pap. text ed. 33.95 (ISBN 0-574-21485-2, 13-4485); avail. (ISBN 0-574-21486-0, 13-4486). SRA.

Head, Robert V. Planning Techniques for Systems Management. LC 83-63210. (Illus.). 160p. 1984. pap. 27.50 (ISBN 0-89435-108-7). QED Info Sci.

Hlava, Marjorie M., ed. Private File Creation Data Base Construction: A Proceeding with Five Case Studies. 120p. 1985. 15.00 (ISBN 0-87111-312-0). SLA.

Hoffer, Jeffrey A. Methods for Primary & Secondary Key Selection. LC 79-93023. (Data Base Monograph: No. 9). 143p. (Orig.). 1980. pap. 15.00 (ISBN 0-89435-040-4). QED Info Sci.

Hogan, Rex. Diagnostic Techniques for IMS Data Bases. 1985. pap. write for info. (ISBN 0-89435-174-5). Qed Info Sci.

Holsapple, Clyde W. & Whinston, Andrew B. Data Base Management: Theory & Applications. 1982. lib. bdg. 54.50 (ISBN 90-277-1516-5, Pub. by Reidel Holland). Kluwer Academic.

Hsiao, David K., ed. Advanced Database Machine Architecture. (Illus.). 464p. 1983. text ed. 43.95 (ISBN 0-13-011262-3). P-H.

Hubbard, George V. Computer-Assisted Data Base Design. 248p. 1984. pap. 16.95 (ISBN 0-442-23330-2). Van Nos Reinhold.

Humphrey, Susanne M. & Milloni, John B. Databases: A Primer for Retrieving Information by Computer. 1985. text ed. 25.95 (ISBN 0-8359-1319-8). Reston.

Hutt, A. T. A Relational Data Base Management System. LC 79-40516. (Wiley Computing Ser.). 226p. 1979. 39.95 (ISBN 0-471-27612-X, Pub. by Wiley-Interscience). Wiley.

Hyde, William F. Improving Productivity by Classification Coding & Data Standardization: The Key to Maximizing CAD-CAM & Group Technology. (Industrial Engineering Ser.: Vol. 5). (Illus.). 352p. 1981. 45.00 (ISBN 0-8247-1404-0). Dekker.

Infotech, ed. Database: The Second Generation. (Computer State of the Art Report, Series 10: No. 7). (Illus.). 662p. 1982. 445.00 (ISBN 0-08-028570-8). Pergamon.

Inmon, William. Effective Data Base Design. (P-H Series in Data Processing Management). (Illus.). 240p. 1981. text ed. 36.95 (ISBN 0-13-241489-9). P-H.

Inmon, William H. & Friedman, L. Jeanne. Design Review Methodology for a Data Base Environment. (Prentice-Hall Ser. in Data Processing Management). (Illus.). 288p. 1982. 34.95 (ISBN 0-13-201392-4). P-H.

Jacobs, Barry E. Applied Database Logic: Fundamental Database Issues, Vol. I. (Advances in Computing Series & Technology). (Illus.). 272p. 1985. text ed. 37.95 (ISBN 0-13-040205-2). P-H.

Janning, et al. An Introduction to Associative Databases & the CS4 System. 255p. (Orig.). 1981. pap. text ed. 21.95x (ISBN 0-86238-012-X, Pub. by Chartwell-Bratt England). Brookfield Pub Co.

Jefferson, David. Data Base Design. 1982. text ed. 22.95 (ISBN 0-8359-1221-3). Reston.

Johnson, Leroy F. & Cooper, Rodney H. File Techniques for Data Base Organization in COBOL. (P-H Software Ser.). (Illus.). 384p. 1981. text ed. 28.95 (ISBN 0-13-314039-3). P-H.

Kambayashi, Yahiko. Database: A Bibliography, Vol. 1. LC 80-26672. 499p. 1981. text ed. 45.00x (ISBN 0-914894-64-1). Computer Sci.

Katzan, Harry, Jr. Computer Data Management & Data Base Technology. (Illus.). 347p. 1975. pap. 12.95 (ISBN 0-442-23896-7). Van Nos Reinhold.

Kent, W. Data & Reality: Basic Assumptions in Data Processing Reconsidered. 212p. 1978. 34.00 (ISBN 0-444-85187-9, North-Holland). Elsevier.

Kieran, Michael. Friday! Electronic Filing Made Easy. 15.95 (ISBN 0-8359-2107-7). Reston.

Kim, W., et al. Database Engineering, Vol. 1. 303p. 1983. 25.00 (ISBN 0-8186-0488-3, Q488). IEEE Comp Soc.

Kinderlehrer, Robert. Handbook for Data Center Management. LC 79-67203. (Illus.). 139p. (Orig.). 1980. pap. 19.50 (ISBN 0-89435-036-6). QED Info Sci.

King, Judy. Evaluation of Database Management Systems. 416p. 1981. 24.50 (ISBN 0-442-23994-7). Van Nos Reinhold.

Knowledge Industry Publications & American Society for Information Science, eds. Data Base Directory, 1984-1985. (American Society for Information Science Ser.). 607p. 1984. pap. 120.00 (ISBN 0-86729-081-1, 349-BW). Knowledge Indus.

Korfhage, Robert R., ed. Computer Networks & Communication. (The Information Technology Ser.: Vol. IV). 150p. 1977. pap. 23.00 (ISBN 0-88283-017-1). AFIPS Pr.

Kroenke, David M. Database Processing: Fundamentals, Design, Implementation. 2nd ed. 448p. 1983. text ed. 34.95 (ISBN 0-574-21320-1, 13-4320); instr's guide avail. (ISBN 0-574-21321-X, 13-4321). SRA.

Kruglinski, David. Data Base Management Systems - MS-DOS: Evaluating MS-DOS Database Software. 400p. (Orig.). 1985. pap. 18.95 (ISBN 0-07-881180-5). Osborne-McGraw.

--Data Base Management Systems: A Guide to Microcomputer Software. 260p. (Orig.). 1982. pap. 16.95 (ISBN 0-07-931084-2, 84-2). Osborne-McGraw.

Landis, Dick & Schmisseur, Edward. Agricultural Database Management. 1985. text ed. 23.95 (ISBN 0-8359-9130-X); pap. 19.95 (ISBN 0-8359-9129-6). Reston.

Larson, J. A. & Rahimi, S. Distributed Database Management. 1984. write for info. IEEE Comp Soc.

Larson, James A. & Freeman, Harvey A. Data Base Management in the Eighties. (Tutorial Texts Ser.). 497p. 1981. 27.00 (ISBN 0-8186-0369-0, Q369). IEEE Comp Soc.

Larson, James A. & Rahimi, Saeed, eds. Tutorial: Distributed Database Management. LC 84-48797. (Tutorial Text Ser.). 669p. (Orig.). 1985. pap. text ed. 36.00 (ISBN 0-8186-0575-8, 575); microfiche 36.00 (ISBN 0-8186-4575-X). IEEE Comp Soc.

Laurie, Peter. Databases: How to Manage Information on Your Micro. (Illus.). 200p. (Orig.). 1985. pap. 16.95 (ISBN 0-412-26380-7, NO. 9317, Pub. by Chapman & Hall England). Methuen Inc.

Lefkovits, Henry C., et al. Information Resource-Data Dictionary Systems. LC 83-60770. 600p. 1983. 95.00 (ISBN 0-89435-068-4). QED Info Sci.

Leong-Hong, Belkis W. & Plagman, Bernard K. Data Dictionary-Directory Systems: Administration Implementation & Usage. LC 81-21875. 328p. 1982. 36.50x (ISBN 0-471-05164-0, Pub. by Wiley-Interscience). Wiley.

Lewis, Bryan. Data Management for Professionals. 153p. 1983. pap. 15.95 (ISBN 0-912677-04-X). Ashton-Tate Bks.

Lewis, Ted. Microbook: Database Management for the Apple II Computer. (Illus.). 322p. (Orig.). 1982. pap. 19.95 (ISBN 0-88056-072-X); incl. disk 39.95 (ISBN 0-88056-156-4). Dilithium Pr.

--Microbook-Database Management for the IBM PC. 310p. 1983. pap. 19.95 (ISBN 0-88056-114-9); pap. 39.95 incl. disk (ISBN 0-88056-165-3). Dilithium Pr.

Lientz, Bennet P. An Introduction to Distributed Systems: Contract Title: Network Services--Managerial Evaluation. (Computer-Business Interface Ser.). 1981. pap. text ed. 21.95 (ISBN 0-201-04297-5). Addison-Wesley.

Lomax, J. D. Evaluating the Database Approach. 155p. 1979. pap. 28.40 (ISBN 0-471-89451-6). Wiley.

Loomis, Mary E. Data Management & File Processing. (Software Ser.). (Illus.). 544p. 1983. 32.95 (ISBN 0-13-196477-1). P-H.

Lyon, John K. The Database Administrator. LC 75-42442. (Business Data Processing, a Wiley Ser.). pap. 43.80 (ISBN 0-317-28106-2, 2055733). Bks Demand UMI.

--An Introduction to Data Base Design. LC 75-155904. (The Wiley Communigraph Series on Business Data Processing). (Illus.). pap. 22.50 (ISBN 0-317-10969-3, 2055124). Bks Demand UMI.

McClelland, Trish. Creating the Perfect Database Using DB MASTER. 1985. pap. 17.95 (ISBN 0-673-18039-5). Scott F.

McCracken, Daiel D. A Guide to NOMAD for Applications Development. (Computer Science Ser.). (10/1981). pap. text ed. 21.95 (ISBN 0-201-04624-5). Addison-Wesley.

McFadden, Fred R. & Hoffer, Jeff. An Introduction to Database Management. 600p. 1985. 37.95 (ISBN 0-8053-6780-2); Casebook. text ed. 10.95 (ISBN 0-8053-6782-9); instr's guide 11.95 (ISBN 0-8053-6781-0). Benjamin Cummings.

McMahon, Marilyn, et al. Report Writing in dBASE II. 1985. pap. 15.95 (ISBN 0-912677-19-8). Ashton-Tate Bks.

McNichols, Charles. Data Base Management System Design Using dBASE II. 1984. text ed. 29.95 (ISBN 0-8359-1222-1). Reston.

McNichols, Charles W. Using dBASE II to Design a Data Base Management System. 1984. pap. 19.95 (ISBN 0-8359-8149-5). Reston.

Management of Compu Base. 10.00 (ISBN 0-85012-028-4). Intl Pubns Serv.

Martin, James. Managing the Data Base Environment. (Illus.). 752p. 1983. text ed. 49.95 (ISBN 0-13-550582-8). P-H.

--Principles of Data Base Management. (Illus.). 320p. 1976. Ref. Ed. 37.50 (ISBN 0-13-708917-1). P-H.

--Strategic Data Planning Methodologies. (Illus.). 240p. 1982. text ed. 37.50 (ISBN 0-13-851113-6). P-H.

Mayne, A. Database Management Systems: A Technical Review. 220p. 1982. pap. 35.00x (ISBN 0-85012-323-2). Intl Pubns Serv.

--Database Management Systems: A Technical Review. 275p. 1981. pap. 32.80 (ISBN 0-471-89441-9). Wiley.

Meldman, Monte, et al. RISS: A Relational Data Base Management System for Minicomputers. LC 81-8256. 120p. 1981. Repr. of 1978 ed. lib. bdg. 14.95 (ISBN 0-89874-373-7). Krieger.

Mellin, Michael. The Quick & Easy Guide to Database Management on the Apple. 200p. Date not set. pap. cancelled (ISBN 0-912003-26-X). Bk Co.

Milenkovic, Milan. Update Synchronization in Multiaccess Systems. Stone, Harold S., ed. LC 81-16034. (Computer Science Ser.: Distributed Database Systems: No. 8). 94p. 1981. 34.95 (ISBN 0-8357-1223-0). UMI Res Pr.

Mohan, C. Recent Advances in Distributed Data Base Management. 1984. write for info. IEEE Comp Soc.

National Computer Centre. Audit & Control of Systems Software. 150p. 1983. pap. 18.10x (ISBN 0-471-87895-2). Wiley.

National Computing Centre. Control of DP Production. Walker, G. S., ed. LC 80-483613. (Illus.). 121p. 1980. 27.50x (ISBN 0-85012-227-9). Intl Pubns Serv.

--Data Base in Perspective. Davis, Brian, ed. 110p. (Orig.). 1980. 27.50x (ISBN 0-85012-219-8). Intl Pubns Serv.

--Database Application Design: A Case Study. 90p. 1980. pap. 21.85 (ISBN 0-471-89440-0, DP00, Pub. by Wiley Interscience). Wiley.

--Distributed Database Technology. (Illus.). 149p. (Orig.). 1980. pap. 20.00x (ISBN 0-85012-226-0). Intl Pubns Serv.

Neimat, Marie-Anne K. Search Mechanisms for Large Files. Stone, Harold S., ed. LC 81-13036. (Computer Science: Distributed Database Systems Ser.: No. 11). 114p. 1981. 34.95 (ISBN 0-8357-1231-1). UMI Res Pr.

Neufeld, M. Lynne & Cornog, Martha. A Study of Data Base Access Alternatives: Final Report. 1981. 25.00 (ISBN 0-942308-14-X). NFAIS.

Newlin, Barbara. Answers Online: Your Guide to Informational Data Bases. 250p. (Orig.). 1984. pap. 16.95 (ISBN 0-07-881136-8, 136-8). Osborne-Mcgraw.

Nilson, Donald E. & Kroenke, David M. Managing Information with Microcomputers: Featuring R BASE Series, Database Management Systems. Craig, Dorothy P., ed. (Illus., Orig.). 1984. 19.95 (ISBN 0-916937-00-3). MicroRim.

Nolan, Richard L. Managing the Data Resource Function. 2nd ed. (Illus.). 465p. 1982. text ed. 31.95 (ISBN 0-314-63285-9). West Pub.

Norusis, M. J. SPSS-X Advanced Statistical Guide. 820p. 1983. 15.95 (ISBN 0-07-046548-7). McGraw.

Olle, T. William. The CODASYL Approach to Data Base Management. LC 77-12375. (Wiley Computing Ser.). 287p. 1978. 49.95x (ISBN 0-471-99579-7, 1-320). Wiley.

Oppenheim, R. Controlling Computerized Information. 1986. cancelled (ISBN 0-442-21207-0). Van Nos Reinhold.

Osterbind, Carter C. & Bell, William G., eds. Data Based Planning in the Field of Aging. x, 159p. (Orig.). 1983. pap. 8.50 (ISBN 0-8130-0765-8). U Presses Fla.

Ozkarahan, Esen. Database Machines & Database Management. (Illus.). 576p. 1986. text ed. 39.95 (ISBN 0-13-196031-8). P-H.

DATA COMPRESSION (COMPUTER SCIENCE)

DATA DISPLAY SYSTEMS
see Information Display Systems

DATA FILES, MACHINE-READABLE
see Machine-Readable Data Files

DATA NETWORKS, COMPUTER
see Computer Networks

DATA PROCESSING
see Electronic Data Processing; Information Storage and Retrieval Systems; Punched Card Systems

DATA SMOOTHING FILTERS
see Digital Filters (Mathematics)

DATA STRUCTURES (COMPUTER SCIENCE)

DATA TAPES

DATA TERMINALS (COMPUTERS)
see Computer Input-Output Equipment

DATA TRANSMISSION SYSTEMS
see also Computer Networks; Library Information Networks; Telemeter; Teletype

DEC SYSTEM 20 (COMPUTER)

DECSYSTEM 20 Macro. 1978. pap. 23.00 (ISBN 0-317-17260-3). Digital Pr.

DECSYSTEM-20 Macro Assembler Reference Manual. (DECbooks). 202p. 1978. 23.00 (ISBN 0-932376-47-9, AA-4159C-DP). Digital Pr.

Gorin, Ralph E. Introduction to DECsystem 20: Assembly Language Programming. 545p. 1981. pap. 39.00 (ISBN 0-932376-12-6, EY-AX017-DP). Digital Pr.

Longo, Stephen A. Introduction to DECsystem 20 Assembly Programming. LC 83-7414. (Computer Science Ser.). 224p. 1983. pap. text ed. 14.50 pub net (ISBN 0-534-02942-6). Brooks-Cole.

--Introduction to DECsystem 20 Assembly Programming. 200p. 1984. pap. write for info. Wadsworth Pub.

Skvarcius, Romualdas. Using DEC Personal Computers: A Self-Teaching Guide. 1985. pap. 14.95 (ISBN 0-471-81150-5). Wiley.

DECAY, BETA

see Beta Decay

DECELERATION

see Acceleration (Mechanics)

DECIMAL SYSTEM

The Arithmetic Classroom: Decimals. (Courses by Computers Ser.). Apple. 49.95 (ISBN 0-88408-203-2); IBM-PC, PCjr. 49.95 (ISBN 0-88408-291-1); 49.95 (ISBN 0-88408-348-9). Sterling Swift.

Fineberg, Marjorie & Shaw, John. Decimals. LC 79-730043. (Illus.). 1978. pap. text ed. 135.00 (ISBN 0-89290-095-4, A511-SATC). Soc for Visual.

Howett, J. Basic Skills with Decimals & Percents. 128p. 1980. pap. text ed. 3.67 (ISBN 0-8428-2118-X). Cambridge Bk.

Rasmusen & Rosekrans. Key to Decimals Reproducible Tests. 32p. 1985. pap. 9.95 (ISBN 0-913684-26-0). Key Curr Proj.

Resource Systems International. Applied Math: II. 1982. pap. text ed. 15.00 (ISBN 0-8359-0141-6). Reston.

Stevin, Simon. Dezimalbruchrechnung. 12.00 (ISBN 0-384-58150-1). Johnson Repr.

Wright, Patricia. Compute a Design: Decimals. Jacobs, Russell, ed. 50p. (Orig.). 1985. pap. text ed. 11.95 (ISBN 0-918272-13-0). Jacobs.

DECIMAL SYSTEM–PROGRAMMED INSTRUCTION

Loose, Frances F. Decimals & Percentages. reusable ed. (Illus.). 96p. 1977. 7.50 (ISBN 0-89039-200-5); answer key incl. Ann Arbor FL.

DECISION LOGIC TABLES

Bell, Peter M. Programming in Decision Tables. (Illus.). 176p. (Orig.). 1984. pap. 24.50 (ISBN 0-930953-01-0). Albion PA.

McDaniel, Herman. An Introduction to Decision Logic Tables. rev. ed. 1978. text ed. 14.00 (ISBN 0-89433-092-6). Petrocelli.

Metzner, John R. & Barnes, B. H., eds. Generalized Decision Table Programming. 1977. 35.00 (ISBN 0-12-492050-0). Acad Pr.

Schwartz, Thomas. The Logic of Collective Choice. 288p. 1985. 30.00x (ISBN 0-231-05896-9). Columbia U Pr.

DECISION-MAKING

see also Decision Logic Tables; Statistical Decision

Allais, Maurice & Hagen, Ole, eds. Expected Utility Hypotheses & the Allais Paradox. (Theory & Decision Library: No. 21). 1979. lib. bdg. 87.00 (ISBN 90-277-0960-2, Pub. by Reidel Holland). Kluwer Academic.

Anderson, Barry F., et al. Concepts in Judgement & Decision Research: Definitions, Sources, Interrelations, Comments. LC 81-7345. 320p. 1981. 39.95x (ISBN 0-03-059337-9). Praeger.

Bates, Donald L. Cases for Strategy & Policy Analysis. 272p. 1981. pap. text ed. write for info. (ISBN 0-697-08066-8). Wm C Brown.

Bell, David E. Conflicting Objectives in Decisions. LC 77-5064. (Wiley International Ser. on Applied Systems Analysis). 442p. 1977. 54.95x (ISBN 0-471-99506-1, Pub. by Wiley-Interscience). Wiley.

Blumberg, Donald F. & Dooley, Brian J. The IBM PC Guide to Risk & Decision Making: Acting Wisely in An Uncertain World. 320p. 1985. pap. 49.95 incl. disk (ISBN 0-88693-064-2). Banbury Bks.

Bodily, S. Modern Decision Making: A Guide to Modeling with Decision Support Systems. 448p. 1984. 26.95 (ISBN 0-07-006360-5). McGraw.

Bommer, Michael R. & Chorba, Ronald W. Decision Making for Library Management. LC 81-17160. (Professional Librarian Ser.). 178p. 1982. pap. text ed. 27.50 professional (ISBN 0-86729-000-5, 208-BW). Knowledge Indus.

Brinkers, Henry S., ed. Decision-Making: Creativity, Judgment, & Systems. LC 71-188740. (Illus.). 286p. 1972. 10.00 (ISBN 0-8142-0165-2). Ohio St U Pr.

Brown, Rex V., et al. Decision Analysis: An Overview. LC 74-1212. 1974. pap. text ed. 14.95 (ISBN 0-03-088408-X, HoltC). HR&W.

Bunn, Derek W. Analysis for Optimal Decisions. LC 81-19698. 275p. 1982. 44.95 (ISBN 0-471-10132-X, Pub. by Wiley-Interscience); pap. 24.95 (ISBN 0-471-10133-8, Pub. by Wiley-Interscience). Wiley.

Bursk, Edward C. & Chapman, John F., eds. New Decision-Making Tools for Managers: Mathematical Programing As an Aid in the Solving of Business Problems. LC 63-11416. (Illus.). Repr. of 1963 ed. 107.80 (ISBN 0-8357-9168-8, 2017752). Bks Demand UMI.

Carisson, C. & Kochetkov, Y., eds. Theory & Practice of Multiple Criteria Decision Making: Collection of Papers Presented at a Workshop, Moscow, May 1981. x, 170p. 1983. 42.75 (ISBN 0-444-86579-9, I-004-83, North-Holland). Elsevier.

Cetron, Marvin J., et al, eds. Quantitative Decision Aiding Techniques for Research & Development Management. LC 70-129677. (Illus.). 214p. 1972. 46.25 (ISBN 0-677-14250-1). Gordon.

Dillon, Robert J. Reality & Value Judgment in Policymaking: A Study of Expert Judgments about Alternative Energy Technologies. Bruchey, Stuart, ed. LC 78-22674. (Energy in the American Economy Ser.). (Illus.). 1979. lib. bdg. 16.00x (ISBN 0-405-11977-1). Ayer Co Pubs.

Easton, Allan. Decision Making: A Short Course for Professionals. (Professional Development Programs Ser.). 352p. 1976. Set. 64.95x (ISBN 0-471-01700-0). Wiley.

Egan, James P. Signal Detection & ROC-Analysis. (Academic Press Ser. in Cognition & Perception). 1975. 49.00 (ISBN 0-12-232850-7). Acad Pr.

English, J. M. Cost Effectiveness: Economic Evaluation of Engineered Systems. LC 68-28500. Repr. of 1968 ed. 59.90 (ISBN 0-8357-9868-2, 2013052). Bks Demand UMI.

Enrick, Norbert L. Management Handbook of Decision-Oriented Statistics. LC 79-13206. 250p. 1980. lib. bdg. 15.40 (ISBN 0-88275-984-1). Krieger.

Fandel, G. & Spronk, J., eds. Multiple Criteria Decision Methods & Applications. (Illus.). xiv, 404p. 1985. 42.00 (ISBN 0-387-15596-1). Springer-Verlag.

Felsen, Jerry. Decision Making Under Uncertainty: An Artificial Intelligence Approach. LC 75-32712. (Illus.). 150p. 1976. pap. 20.00 (ISBN 0-916376-00-1). CDS Pub.

Festinger, Leon. Conflict, Decision & Dissonance. 1964. 12.50x (ISBN 0-8047-0205-5). Stanford U Pr.

Gallagher, C. A. & Watson, H. J. Quantitative Methods for Business Decisions. 1980. text ed. 35.95 (ISBN 0-07-022751-9). McGraw.

Gatza, Jim, et al. Decision Making in Administration: Text, Critical Incidents & Cases. 1979. pap. text ed. 13.95 (ISBN 0-7216-4056-7). SCP.

Ginter, Peter M. & Rucks, Andrew C. Basic Decision Making on the Microcomputer. 475p. 1985. pap. text ed. 23.95 (ISBN 0-394-33928-2, RanC). Random.

Goehle, Donna G. Decision Making in Multinational Corporations. Dufey, Gunter, ed. LC 80-23596. (Research for Business Decisions: No. 18). 242p. 1980. 39.95 (ISBN 0-8357-1102-1). UMI Res Pr.

Grauer, M. & Wierzbicki, A. P., eds. Interactive Decision Analysis: Proceedings of an International Workshop on Interactive Decision Analysis & Interpretative Computer Intellegence Held at the International Institute for Applied System Analysis (IIASA), Laxenberg, Austria, Sept. 20-23, 1983. (Lecture Notes in Economics & Mathematical Systems Ser.: Vol. 229). viii, 269p. 1984. pap. 18.00 (ISBN 0-387-13354-2). Springer-Verlag.

Grayson, C. Jackson, Jr. Decisions Under Uncertainty: Drilling Decisions by Oil & Gas Operators. Bruchey, Stuart, ed. LC 78-22686. (Energy in the American Economy Ser.). (Illus.). 1979. Repr. of 1960 ed. lib. bdg. 32.50x (ISBN 0-405-11989-5). Ayer Co Pubs.

Gulezian, Ronald C. Statistics for Decision Making. LC 78-52729. (Illus.). 1979. text ed. 31.95x (ISBN 0-7216-4350-7). Dryden Pr.

Gulezian, Ronald C. & Weiland, Jerome. Statistics for Decision Making: Workbook. 1979. pap. 11.95 (ISBN 0-7216-4353-1). HR&W.

Gupta, M. M. & Saridis, G. N. Fuzzy Automata & Decision Processes. 496p. 1977. 62.50 (ISBN 0-444-00231-6, North-Holland). Elsevier.

Gupta, M. M. & Sanchez, E., eds. Approximate Reasoning in Decision Analysis. 480p. 1983. 68.00 (ISBN 0-444-86492-X, North Holland). Elsevier.

Hansen, P., ed. Essays & Surveys on Multiple Criteria Decision Making: Proceedings, Mons, Belgium, 1982. (Lecture Notes in Economics & Mathematical Systems: Vol. 209). (Illus.). 441p. 1983. pap. 30.00 (ISBN 0-387-11991-4). Springer-Verlag.

Harvey, C. M. Operations Research: An Introduction to Linear Optimization & Decision Analysis. 454p. 1979. 33.00 (ISBN 0-444-00300-2). Elsevier.

Hastings, N. A. & Mello, J. M. Decision Networks. 196p. 1978. 62.95 (ISBN 0-471-99531-2, Pub. by Wiley-Interscience). Wiley.

Hesse, Rick. Decision Making: A Management Science Guide for the IBM-PC. (IBM-PC Ser.: 1-646). 224p. 1984. pap. 16.95 (ISBN 0-471-89206-8, Wiley Professional Software); disk 29.95 (ISBN 0-471-89026-X); bk. & disk 46.90 (ISBN 0-471-89003-0). Wiley.

House, William C. Decision Support Systems. 250p. pap. 17.50 (ISBN 0-89433-208-2). Petrocelli.

House, William C., Jr. Interactive Decision Oriented Data Base Systems. 1977. 29.95 (ISBN 0-442-80339-7). Van Nos Reinhold.

Houston, Samuel R., ed. Judgement Analysis: Tools for Decision Makers. LC 73-17374. 1975. 29.50x (ISBN 0-8422-5145-6); pap. text ed. 12.50x (ISBN 0-8422-0365-6). Irvington.

Howell, William C. & Fleishman, Edwin A., eds. Information Processing & Decision Making. (Human Performance & Productivity Ser.: Vol. 2). 192p. 1982. text ed. 24.95x (ISBN 0-89859-090-6). L Erlbaum Assocs.

Kaufman, Roger. Identifying & Solving Problems: A System Approach. 3rd ed. LC 76-5702. (Illus.). 163p. 1982. pap. 12.50 (ISBN 0-88390-050-5). Univ Assocs.

Keen, Peter F. & Scott-Morton, Michael S. Decision Support Systems: An Organizational Perspective. 1978. text ed. 28.95 (ISBN 0-201-03667-3). Addison-Wesley.

Keeney, Ralph L. & Raiffa, Howard. Decisions with Multiple Objectives: Preferences, & Value Tradeoffs. LC 76-7895. (Probability & Mathematical Statistics Ser.). 569p. 1976. 44.50x (ISBN 0-471-46510-0). Wiley.

Kickert, Walter J. Fuzzy Theories on Decision-Making. (Frontiers in Systems Research Ser.: Vol. 3). 1979. lib. bdg. 29.00 (ISBN 90-207-0760-4, Pub. by Martinus Nijhoff Netherlands). Kluwer Academic.

Leitmann, George, ed. Multicriteria Decision Making & Differential Games. LC 76-22775. (Mathematical Concepts & Methods in Science & Engineering Ser.: Vol. 3). 461p. 1976. 49.50x (ISBN 0-306-30920-3, Plenum Pr). Plenum Pub.

Lim, R. Y. What You Should Know about Scientific Management for Small Business. LC 73-1806. (Business Almanac Ser: No. 22). 128p. 1973. lib. bdg. 5.95 (ISBN 0-379-11222-1). Oceana.

Loasby, B. J. Choice, Complexity & Ignorance. LC 75-22558. 1976. 44.50 (ISBN 0-521-21065-8). Cambridge U Pr.

Lyles, Richard I. Practical Management Problem Solving & Decision Making. 224p. 1982. 21.95 (ISBN 0-442-25889-5). Van Nos Reinhold.

McKenna, Christopher K. Quantitative Methods for Business Decisions. (Quantitative Methods for Management Ser.). (Illus.). 1980. text ed. 36.50 (ISBN 0-07-045351-9). McGraw.

Martin, Edley W. Mathematics for Decision Making: A Programmed Basic Text, Vol. 1: Linear Mathematics. LC 69-17157. pap. 160.00 (ISBN 0-317-08612-X, 2021671). Bks Demand UMI.

Mathematics of the Decision Sciences Part I. Dantzig, G. B. & Veinott, A. F., Jr., eds. LC 62-21481. 429p. 1970. Repr. of 1968 ed. with corrections 41.00 (ISBN 0-8218-1111-8, LAM-11). Am Math.

Nelkin, Dorothy. Controversy: Politics of Technical Decisions. 2nd ed. LC 78-21339. (Focus Editions Ser.: Vol. 8). 256p. 1984. 28.00 (ISBN 0-8039-2250-7); pap. 14.00 (ISBN 0-8039-2251-5). Sage.

Newton, Grant W., ed. Decision Analysis Including Modeling & Information Systems CMA Review, Vol. V. (CMA Review Ser.). 1983. pap. 27.95x (ISBN 0-911238-41-7, Malibu Pubns); pap. text ed. 23.95 (ISBN 0-686-87518-4). B of A.

Park, W. R. & Maillie, J. B. Strategic Analysis for Venture Evaluation: The Safe Approach to Business Decisions. 224p. 1981. 22.95 (ISBN 0-442-24507-6). Van Nos Reinhold.

Problem Solving & Decision Making. 1982. 50.00x (ISBN 0-904951-31-6, Pub. by Bristol Poly). State Mutual Bk.

Rapoport, Amnon, et al. Response Models for Detection of Change. (Theory & Decision Library: No. 18). 1979. lib. bdg. 30.00 (ISBN 90-277-0934-3, Pub. by Reidel Holland). Kluwer Academic.

Roberts, Fred S. Encyclopedia of Mathematics & Its Applications: Measurement Theory with Applications to Decision Utility & Making the Social Sciences, Vol. 7. 1984. 34.50 (ISBN 0-521-30227-7). Cambridge U Pr.

Rosen, George. Decision-Making Chicago-Style: The Genesis of a University of Illinois Campus. LC 79-25643. (Illus.). 224p. 1980. 17.50x (ISBN 0-252-00803-0). U of Ill Pr.

Saaty, Thomas L. The Analytic Hierarchy Process. (Illus.). 296p. 1980. text ed. 49.00 (ISBN 0-07-054371-2). McGraw.

Sage, Andrew P. & Melsa, James L. Estimation Theory with Applications to Communications & Control. LC 79-4648. 542p. 1979. Repr. of 1971 ed. lib. bdg. 30.50 (ISBN 0-88275-920-5). Krieger.

Schaller, Lyle E. The Decision-Makers. LC 73-16411. 224p. 1974. 9.95 (ISBN 0-687-10402-5). Abingdon.

Schwartz, Thomas. The Logic of Collective Choice. 288p. 1985. 30.00x (ISBN 0-231-05896-9). Columbia U Pr.

Scott Morton, Michael. Management Decision Systems: Computer-Based Support for Decision Making. LC 72-132152. (Illus.). 216p. 1971. 14.95x (ISBN 0-87584-090-6). Harvard Busn.

Sprague, Ralph H., Jr. & Carlson, Eric D. Building Effective Decision Support Systems. 304p. 1982. 29.95 (ISBN 0-13-086215-0). P-H.

Tainiter, Melvin. The Art & Science of Decision Making. (Commuter Series in Management Science). 80p. (Orig.). 1971. pap. 3.25 (ISBN 0-87974-001-9). Timetable Pr.

Taylor, Marcia W. A Computer Simulation of Innovative Decision-Making in Organizations. LC 78-56051. 1978. pap. text ed. 9.25 (ISBN 0-8191-0517-1). U Pr of Amer.

Thiriez, H. & Zionts, S., eds. Multiple Criteria Decision Making. (Lecture Notes in Economics & Mathematical Systems: Vol. 130). 1976. pap. 23.00 (ISBN 0-387-07794-4). Springer-Verlag.

Thompson, Gerald E. Management Science: An Introduction to Modern Quantitative Analysis & Decision Making. LC 82-13071. 466p. 1982. Repr. of 1976 ed. lib. bdg. 26.50 (ISBN 0-89874-547-0). Krieger.

Trueman, Richard E. Quantitative Methods for Decision Making in Business. LC 80-65810. 736p. 1981. text ed. 38.95x (ISBN 0-03-051356-1). Dryden Pr.

Tummala, V. M. & Henshaw, Richard C. Concepts & Applications of Modern Decision Models. LC 75-620052. 486p. 1976. pap. 7.50 (ISBN 0-87744-131-6). Mich St U Pr.

Unny, T. E. & McBean, Edward A., eds. Decision Making for Hydrosystems: Forecasting & Operation. LC 82-50384. 1982. 37.00 (ISBN 0-918334-50-0). WRP.

Vonderembse, Mark A. Decision Making in Continuous Steel Casting. Dufey, Gunter, ed. LC 80-17297. (Research for Business Decisions: No. 23). 124p. 1980. 39.95 (ISBN 0-8357-1107-2). UMI Res Pr.

Wagner, Thomas A. Kognitive Problemlosungsbarrieren Bei Entscheidungsprozessen In der Unternehmung. (European University Studies ser.: No. 5, Vol. 363). (Ger.). vi, 250p. 1982. 30.55 (ISBN 3-8204-5774-7). P Lang Pubs.

Welland, R. Decision Tables & Computer Programming. 1982. 34.95 (ISBN 0-471-26193-9). Wiley.

White, D. J. Finite Dynamic Programming: An Approach to Finite Markov Decision Processes. LC 77-26333. 220p. 1978. 69.95x (ISBN 0-471-99629-7, Pub. by Wiley-Interscience). Wiley.

Williams, Donald R. Modern Mathematics for Business Decision-Making. 2nd ed. 1978. text ed. write for info. (ISBN 0-534-00558-6). Wadsworth Pub.

Williams, M. R. Decision-Making in Forest Management. (Forestry Research Press Ser.). 143p. 1981. 48.95x (ISBN 0-471-10097-8, Pub. by Res Stud Pr). Wiley.

Witte & Zimmerman. Empirical Research on Organizational Decision Making. Date not set. write for info. (ISBN 0-444-86888-7). Elsevier.

Worms, G. Modern Methods of Applied Economics. 242p. 1970. 55.75x (ISBN 0-677-01990-4). Gordon.

Xerox Learning Systems. Defender-Challenger: Advanced Financial Decision Making System. Levine, Barbara, ed. (Illus.). 278p. 1983. 165.00 (ISBN 0-935268-03-0). Xerox Learning.

DECISION-MAKING–DATA PROCESSING

Cave, Martin. Computers & Economic Planning. LC 79-7659. (Soviet & East European Studies). 1980. 37.50 (ISBN 0-521-22617-1). Cambridge U Pr.

Cohon, Jared L. Multiobjective Programming & Planning. (Mathematics in Science & Engineering Ser.). 1978. 49.50 (ISBN 0-12-178350-2). Acad Pr.

Kallman, Ernest A. & Reinharth, Leon. Information Systems for Planning & Decision Making. 360p. 1984. 36.95 (ISBN 0-442-25628-0). Van Nos Reinhold.

Nijkamp, Peter. Multidimensional Spatial Data & Decision Analysis. LC 79-40518. 322p. 1979. 73.95x (ISBN 0-471-27603-0, Pub. by Wiley-Interscience). Wiley.

DECISION-MAKING–MATHEMATICAL MODELS

see also Critical Path Analysis

Frost, H. J. & Ashby, M. F. Deformation-Mechanism Maps: The Plasticity & Creep of Metals & Ceramics. (Illus.). 184p. 1982. 50.00 (ISBN 0-08-029338-7); pap. 25.00 (ISBN 0-08-029337-9). Pergamon.

Gupta, N. K., ed. Large Deformations: Proceedings of the Symposium in the Memory of Professor B. Karunes, Organized by the Department of Applied Mechanics, Indian Institute of Technology, New Delhi. LC 83-900047. 491p. 1982. 59.00 (ISBN 0-9605004-6-4, Pub. by South Asian Pubs India). Eng Pubns.

International Union of Theoretical & Applied Mechanics Colloquium, Madrid, 1955. Deformation & Flow of Solids: Proceedings. Grammel, Richard, ed. Tr. of Verformung & Fliessen Des Festokoerpors. (Eng, Ger, Fr. & Span., Illus.). 1956. 34.30 (ISBN 0-387-02095-0). Springer-Verlag.

Juo & Detrekoei. Deformation Measurements. 1984. 83.00 (ISBN 0-9910000-8-0, Pub. by Akademiai Kaido Hungary). Heyden.

Kausch, H. Henning, et al, eds. Deformation & Fracture of High Polymers. LC 73-19857. 644p. 1973. 69.50x (ISBN 0-306-30772-3, Plenum Pr). Plenum Pub.

Koistinen, D. P. & Wang, N. M., eds. Mechanics of Sheet Metal Forming: Material Behavior & Deformation Forming. LC 78-21587. (General Motors Research Symposia Ser.). 426p. 1978. 59.50x (ISBN 0-306-40068-5, Plenum Pr). Plenum Pub.

McLellan, A. G. The Classical Thermodynamics of Deformable Materials. LC 76-2277. (Cambridge Monographs on Physics). (Illus.). 1980. 85.00 (ISBN 0-521-21237-5). Cambridge U Pr.

Ogden, R. W. Non-Linear Elastic Deformations. (1-176). 532p. 1984. 95.00 (ISBN 0-470-27508-1, Pub. by Wiley Interscience). Wiley.

Rhode & Swearengen, eds. Mechanical Testing for Deformation Model Development- STP 765. 478p. 1982. 51.50 (ISBN 0-8031-0581-9, 04-765000-23) (ISBN 0-317-17767-2). ASTM.

DEFORMATIONS, CONTINUOUS

see Homotopy Theory

DEGENERATE GASES, CONDENSED

see Superfluidity

DEGRADATION, BIOLOGICAL

see Biodegradation

DEGREES OF LATITUDE AND LONGITUDE

see Geodesy; Longitude

DE HAVILLAND COMPANY

Boyne, Walter J. De Havilland DH-4: From Flaming Coffin to Living Legend. LC 84-1391. (Famous Aircraft of the National Air & Space Museum Ser.). (Illus.). 160p. 1984. pap. 8.95 (ISBN 0-87474-277-3, BODHP). Smithsonian.

Jackson, A. J. DeHavilland Aircraft Since 1909. 2nd ed. LC 78-310065. (Putnam Aeronautical Books). (Illus.). 490p. 1979. 31.95 (ISBN 0-370-30022-X, Pub. by the Bodley Head). Merrimack Pub Cir.

DEHYDRATED MILK

see Milk, Dried

DEHYDRATION OF FOOD

see Food–Drying

DEHYDROFROZEN FOOD

see Food, Frozen

DEHYDROGENASE

Jonathan, Jeffrey, ed. Dehydrogenases Requiring Nicotinamide Coenzymes. (Experientia-Supplementa: No. 36). 276p. 1980. 41.95x (ISBN 0-8176-1104-5). Birkhauser.

Schwert, George W. & Winer, Alfred D., eds. The Mechanism of Action of Dehydrogenases: A Symposium in Honor of Hugo Theorell. LC 73-80094. (Illus.). 272p. 1970. 12.00x (ISBN 0-8131-1188-9). U Pr of Ky.

Sund, Horst, ed. Pyridine Nucleotide: Dependent Dehydrogenases. 513p. 1977. text ed. 66.00x (ISBN 3-11007-091-X). De Gruyter.

DELAY CIRCUITS

see Delay Lines

DELAY LINES

Millman, Jacob & Taub, H. Pulse, Digital & Switching Waveforms. 1965. text ed. 49.95 (ISBN 0-07-042386-5). McGraw.

DELAYED-ACTION PREPARATIONS

Cardarelli, Nate F. Controlled Release Pesticides Formulations. LC 75-46632. (Uniscience Ser.). 224p. 1976. 66.00 (ISBN 0-8493-5114-6). CRC Pr.

Das, K. G. Controlled-Release Technology: Bioengineering Aspects. LC 82-11052. 225p. 1983. 57.95 (ISBN 0-471-08680-0, Pub. by Wiley-Interscience). Wiley.

Gebelein, Charles G. & Carraher, Charles E., Jr., eds. Bioactive Polymeric Systems: An Overview. 675p. 1985. 95.00x (ISBN 0-306-41855-X, Plenum Pr). Plenum Pub.

Kydonieus, Agis F. Controlled Release Technologies: Methods, Theory, & Applications, 2 vols. 1980. Vol. 1, 272p. 84.00 (ISBN 0-8493-5641-5); Vol. 2, 288p. 84.00 (ISBN 0-8493-5642-3). CRC Pr.

Langer, Robert S. & Wise, Donald L. Medical Applications of Controlled Release, 2 vols, Vols. I-II. 1984. 272p 88.00 (ISBN 0-8493-5405-6); 248p 80.00 (ISBN 0-8493-5406-4). CRC Pr.

Lewis, D. H., ed. Controlled Release of Pesticides & Pharmaceuticals. LC 81-7336. 350p. 1981. 55.00x (ISBN 0-306-40743-4, Plenum Pr). Plenum Pub.

Roseman, Mansdorf. Controlled Released Delivery Systems. 400p. 1983. 57.50 (ISBN 0-8247-1728-7). Dekker.

Scher, Herbert B., ed. Controlled Release Pesticides. LC 77-22339. (ACS Symposium Ser.: No. 53). 1977. 29.95 (ISBN 0-8412-0382-2). Am Chemical.

DELPHINIDAE

see Dolphins

DELPHINIUM

Edwards, Colin. Delphiniums. (Illus.). 192p. 1981. 22.95x (ISBN 0-460-04423-0, Pub. by J. M. Dent England). Biblio Dist.

DELTAS

see also Alluvial Plains

Russell, Richard J. River & Delta Morphology. LC 67-29343. (Louisiana State University Studies, Coastal Studies Ser.: No. 20). pap. 20.00 (ISBN 0-317-29938-7, 2051688). Bks Demand UMI.

DEMINERALIZATION OF SALINE WATERS

see Saline Waters–Demineralization

DEMOGRAPHY–MATHEMATICAL MODELS

Flieger, Wilhelm, et al. One the Road to Longevity: 1970 National, Regional & Provincial Mortality for the Philippines. 333p. 1981. pap. 15.75x (ISBN 0-686-34625-4, Pub. by San Carlos Philippines). Cellar.

Land, Kenneth C. & Rogers, Andrei, eds. Multidimensional Mathematical Demography. LC 82-6821. (Studies in Population). 602p. 1982. 35.00 (ISBN 0-12-435640-0). Acad Pr.

DEMOGRAPHY–METHODOLOGY

Jaffe, A. J. Handbook of Statistical Methods for Demographers. 288p. 1977. 47.75 (ISBN 0-677-02740-0). Gordon.

Manual X: Indirect Techniques for Demographic Estimation. (Population Studies: No. 81). 304p. 1983. pap. text ed. 32.00 (UN83/13/2, UN). Unipub.

Mode, C. J. Stochastic Processes in Demography & Their Computer Implementation. (Biomathematics: Vol. 14). (Illus.). 430p. 1985. 70.00 (ISBN 0-387-13622-3). Springer-Verlag.

Weiss, K. M. & Ballonoff, P. A., eds. Demographic Genetics. LC 75-31580. (Benchmark Papers in Genetics: Vol. 3). 414p. 1975. 61.50 (ISBN 0-12-787745-2). Acad Pr.

DEMOUNTABLE BUILDINGS

see Buildings, Prefabricated

DENDROCHRONOLOGY

see also Rain and Rainfall

Hughes, M. K., et al, eds. Climate from Tree Rings. LC 81-17056. (Illus.). 400p. 1982. 42.50 (ISBN 0-521-24291-6). Cambridge U Pr.

Libby, Leona M. Past Climates: Tree Thermometers, Commodities, & People. (Illus.). 157p. 1983. text ed. 25.00x (ISBN 0-292-73019-5). U of Tex Pr.

Scott, Stuart. Dendrochronology in Mexico. LC 66-63675. (Papers of the Laboratory of Tree-Ring Research: No. 2). 80p. 1966. pap. 4.50x (ISBN 0-8165-0025-8). U of Ariz Pr.

Webb, George E. Tree Rings & Telescopes: The Scientific Career of A. E. Douglass. LC 83-1152. 242p. 1983. 19.50x (ISBN 0-8165-0798-8). U of Ariz Pr.

DENDROLOGY

see Trees

DENSITY

see Specific Gravity

DENTISTRY–PRACTICE–DATA PROCESSING

Computer Strategies. The Dental Office Computer Handbook. 150p. 1983. looseleaf 45.00x (ISBN 0-913505-07-2). Computer Strat.

Computers in Dental Practice. 9.00 (ISBN 0-934510-12-1, J006). Am Dental.

Erlich, Ann. The Role of Computers in Dental Practice Management. LC 81-67044. (Illus.). 8.95 (ISBN 0-940012-00-6). Colwell Syst.

Health Care Microcomputing Sourcebook 1985: A Guide to Information for the Physician, Dentist & Health Care Professional. 500p. Date not set. pap. cancelled (ISBN 0-8352-1920-8). Bowker.

Snyder, Thomas L. & Felmeister, Charles J., eds. Personalized Guide to Computers & Your Dental Practice. (Mosby's Dental Practice Management Ser.). (Illus.). 176p. 1983. pap. text ed. 19.95 (ISBN 0-8016-4721-5). Mosby.

DEODORIZATION

Carleton, A. J. Absorption of Odours: Summary Report, 1979. 1981. 65.00x (ISBN 0-686-97007-1, Pub. by W Spring England). State Mutual Bk.

--Odour Control by Thermal Incineration, 1978. 1981. 75.00x (ISBN 0-686-97130-2, Pub. by W Spring England). State Mutual Bk.

Dorling, T. A. Activated Carbon Adsorption in Odour Control: The Adsorption of Styrene Vapour, 1979. 1981. 65.00x (ISBN 0-686-97008-X, Pub. by W Spring England). State Mutual Bk.

Irwin, J. G. Odour Removal by Catalytic Oxidation Nineteen Seventy Eight. 1982. 75.00x (ISBN 0-686-97132-9, Pub. by W Spring England). State Mutual Bk.

Pope, D. & Moss, R. L. Current Odour Problems & Control Techniques in the UK, 1980. 1981. 35.00x (ISBN 0-686-97053-5, Pub. by W Spring England). State Mutual Bk.

Warren Spring Laboratory, ed. Odours Control: A Concise Guide, Nineteen Eighty. 1981. 85.00x (ISBN 0-686-97135-3, Pub. by W Spring England). State Mutual Bk.

DEOXYRIBONUCLEIC ACID

Academy Forum. Research with Recombinant DNA. 1977. pap. text ed. 9.95 (ISBN 0-309-02641-5). Natl Acad Pr.

Alberts, Bruce & Fox, C. Fred, eds. Mechanistic Studies of DNA Replication & Genetic Recombination. (ICN-UCLA Symposia on Molecular & Cellular Biology Ser.: Vol. XIX). 1980. 66.00 (ISBN 0-12-048850-7). Acad Pr.

Banerjee, P. K. Biophysical Chemistry Metal Ions DNA: Interactions. (International Bioscience Monographs: No. 8). 1979. 10.00 (ISBN 0-88065-022-2, Pub. by Messers Today & Tomorrows Printers & Publishers India). Scholarly Pubns.

Becker, Yechiel, ed. Recombinant DNA Research & Viruses. (Developments in Molecular Virology Ser.). 1984. lib. bdg. 59.95 (ISBN 0-89838-683-7, Pub. by Martinus Nijhoff Netherlands). Kluwer Academic.

Beers, Roland F., Jr., et al, eds. Molecular & Cellular Repair Processes Johns Hopkins Medical Journal Supplement, No. 1. LC 78-184199. (Miles International Symposia on Molecular Biology Ser). Repr. of 1972 ed. 54.60 (ISBN 0-8357-9278-1, 2015685). Bks Demand UMI.

Beljanski, M. The Regulation of DNA Replication & Transcription. (Experimental Biology & Medicine Series: Vol. 8). (Illus.). x, 190p. 1983. pap. 53.25 (ISBN 3-8055-3631-3). S Karger.

Bertinchamps, A. J., et al, eds. Effects of Ionizing Radiation on DNA: Physical, Chemical & Biological Aspects. LC 77-25857. (Molecular, Biology, Biochemistry & Biophysics: Vol 27). (Illus.). 1978. 56.00 (ISBN 0-387-08542-4). Springer-Verlag.

Bollon, Arthur P. Recombinant DNA Products: Insulin-Interferon-Growth Hormone. 208p. 1984. 70.00 (ISBN 0-8493-5542-7). CRC Pr.

Busch, Harris & Rothblum, Lawrence. The Cell Nucleus: DNA, Vol. 12. 248p. 1982. 50.00 (ISBN 0-12-147612-X). Acad Pr.

Busch, Harris, ed. The Cell Nucleus: DNA, Vol. 10. 408p. 1982. 70.00 (ISBN 0-12-147610-3). Acad Pr.

Caskey, C. Thomas & White, Raymond, eds. Banbury Report 14: Recombinant DNA Applications to Human Disease. LC 82-19712. (Banbury Report Ser.: Vol. 14). 371p. 1983. 55.00x (ISBN 0-87969-214-6). Cold Spring Harbor.

Cold Spring Harbor Symposia on Quantitative Biology: Dna: Replication & Recombination, 2 bks, Vol. 43. LC 34-8174. (Illus.). 1387p. 1979. Set. 164.50x (ISBN 0-87969-042-9). Cold Spring Harbor.

Cold Spring Harbor Symposia on Quantitative Biology: Replication of Dna in Micro-Organisms, Vol. 33. LC 34-8174. 884p. 1969. 38.00x (ISBN 0-87969-032-1). Cold Spring Harbor.

Cold Spring Harbor Symposia on Quantitative Biology: Structures of DNA, Vol. 47. LC 34-8174. 1250p. 1983. 165.50x (ISBN 0-87969-046-1). Cold Spring Harbor.

Colowick, Sidney P. & Kaplan, Nathan O., eds. Methods in Enzymology: Recombinant DNA. LC 79-26584. 1983. Vol. 100: Pt. B. 65.00 (ISBN 0-12-182000-9); Vol. 101: Pt. C. 70.00 (ISBN 0-12-182001-7). Acad Pr.

Conference on Recombinant DNA, Committee on Genetic Experimentation (COGENE) & the Royal Society of London, Wye College, Kent, UK, April, 1979. Recombinant DNA & Genetic Experimentation: Proceedings. Morgan, Joan & Whelan, W. J., eds. LC 79-40962. (Illus.). 334p. 1979. 73.00 (ISBN 0-08-024427-0). Pergamon.

Cozzarelli, Nicholas R. Mechanisms of DNA Replication & Recombination. LC 83-18710. (UCLA Symposia on Molecular & Cellular Biology, New Ser.: Vol. 10). 902p. 1983. 136.00 (ISBN 0-8451-2609-1). A R Liss.

Cummings, Donald J., et al, eds. Extra Chromosomal DNA: Icn-Ucla Symposia on Molecular & Cellular Biology, Vol. XV. LC 79-26592. 1979. 49.50 (ISBN 0-12-198780-9). Acad Pr.

Denhardt, David T. Replication of DNA. Head, John J., ed. LC 83-71256. (Carolina Biology Readers Ser.). 16p. 1983. pap. 1.60 (ISBN 0-89278-320-6, 45-9720). Carolina Biological.

Denniston, K. J. & Enquist, L. W., eds. Recombinant DNA. LC 80-14100. (Benchmark Papers in Microbiology Ser.: Vol. 15). 391p. 1981. 56.95 (ISBN 0-87933-378-2). Van Nos Reinhold.

De Recondo, A. M., ed. New Approaches in Eukaryotic DNA Replication. 374p. 1983. 47.50x (ISBN 0-306-41182-2, Plenum Pr). Plenum Pub.

De Serres, Frederick J., ed. Genetic Consequences of Nucleotide Pool Imbalance. (Basic Life Sciences Ser.: Vol. 31). 504p. 1985. 69.50x (ISBN 0-306-41902-5, Plenum Pr). Plenum Pub.

Drlica, Karl. Understanding DNA & Gene Cloning: A Guide for the Curious. LC 84-3518. 205p. 1984. pap. text ed. 12.50 (ISBN 0-471-87942-8). Wiley.

Esposito, Michael S., ed. Yeast Molecular Biology-Recombinant DNA: Recent Advances. LC 84-4096. (Illus.). 349p. 1984. 35.00 (ISBN 0-8155-0987-1). Noyes.

FEBS Symposium on DNA, Liblice, 24-29 September, 1979. DNA: Recombination, Interactions & Repair. Zadrazil, S. & Sponar, J., eds. (Vol. 63). (Illus.). 600p. 1980. 110.00 (ISBN 0-08-025494-2). Pergamon.

Freidberg & Hanawalt. DNA Repair, Pt. 1A. 312p. 1981. pap. 49.75 (ISBN 0-8247-7248-2). Dekker.

Freifelder, David. The DNA Molecule: Structure & Properties. LC 77-2768. (Illus.). 1978. text ed. 36.95 (ISBN 0-7167-0287-8); pap. text ed. 23.95 (ISBN 0-7167-0286-X). W H Freeman.

Freifelder, David, intro. by. Recombinant DNA: Readings from Scientific American. LC 77-29159. (Illus.). 1978. pap. text ed. 10.95 (ISBN 0-7167-0092-1). W H Freeman.

Friedberg & Hanawalt. DNA Repair, Vol. 2. 296p. 1983. 59.75 (ISBN 0-8247-1805-4). Dekker.

--DNA Repair: A Laboratory Manual of Research Procedures, Vol. 1, Pts. A & B. 424p. 1981. Pt. A. pap. 49.75 (ISBN 0-8247-7248-2); Pt. B. pap. 59.75 (ISBN 0-8247-1184-X). Dekker.

Friedberg, Errol C. DNA Repair. LC 84-18688. (Illus.). 614p. 1984. text ed. 39.95 (ISBN 0-7167-1674-7). W H Freeman.

Friedberg, Errol G. & Bridges, Bryn A. Cellular Responses to DNA Damage. LC 83-19955. (UCLA Symposia on Molecular & Cellular Biology, New Ser.: Vol. 11). 768p. 1983. 98.00 (ISBN 0-8451-2610-5). A R Liss.

Generoso, W. M., et al, eds. DNA Repair & Mutagenesis in Eukaryotes. LC 80-18743. (Basic Life Sciences Ser.: Vol. 15). 470p. 1980. 55.00x (ISBN 0-306-40552-0, Plenum Pr). Plenum Pub.

Giannelli, F. Human Chromosomes DNA Synthesis. Beckman, L. & Hauge, M., eds. (Monographs in Human Genetics: Vol. 5). 1970. 20.00 (ISBN 3-8055-0448-9). S Karger.

Glover, D. M., ed. DNA Cloning, 2 vols, Vols. 1 & 2. (Practical Approach Ser.). (Illus.). 250p. (Orig.). 1985. Vol. 1. pap. text ed. 25.00 ea. (ISBN 0-947946-18-7). Vol. 2 (ISBN 0-947946-19-5). IRL Pr.

Glover, David M. Gene Cloning: The Mechanics of DNA Manipulation. 1985. 29.95 (ISBN 0-412-26600-8, NO. 9338, Pub. by Chapman & Hall); pap. 11.95 (ISBN 0-412-25430-1, NO. 9161, Pub. by Chapman & Hall). Methuen Inc.

Grobstein, Clifford. A Double Image of the Double Helix: The Recombinant-DNA Debate. LC 78-26093. (Biology Ser.). (Illus.). 177p. 1979. text ed. 20.95 (ISBN 0-7167-1056-0); pap. text ed. 11.95 (ISBN 0-7167-1057-9). W H Freeman.

Grover, Philip L. Chemical Carcinogens & DNA, 2 vols. 1979. Vol. 1, 256p. 79.50 (ISBN 0-8493-5303-3); Vol. 2, 224p. 74.50 (ISBN 0-8493-5304-1). CRC Pr.

Gueriguian, J. L., et al, eds. Insulins, Growth Hormone, & Recombinant DNA Technology. 248p. 1981. 42.50 (ISBN 0-89004-544-5). Raven.

Hanawalt, Philip C. & Setlow, Richard B., eds. Molecular Mechanisms for Repair of DNA. LC 75-17731. (Basic Life Sciences Ser.: Vol. 5A). (Illus.). 462p. 1975. 42.50 (ISBN 0-306-36593-6, Plenum Pr). Plenum Pub.

--Molecular Mechanisms for Repair of DNA. LC 75-17731. (Basic Life Sciences: Vol. 5B). (Illus.). 442p. 1975. 42.50x (ISBN 0-306-36594-4, Plenum Pr). Plenum Pub.

Hanawalt, Philip C., et al, eds. DNA Repair Mechanisms. (ICN-UCLA Symposia on Molecular & Cellular Biology Ser.: Vol. IX, 1978). 1978. 67.50 (ISBN 0-12-322650-3). Acad Pr.

Hanson, Earl D., ed. Recombinant DNA Research & the Human Prospect. (Other Technical Bks.). 129p. 1983. text ed. 19.95 (ISBN 0-8412-0750-X); pap. text ed. 14.95 (ISBN 0-8412-0754-2). Am Chemical.

Hoagland, Mahlon B. Discovery: The Search for the DNA's Secrets. (Illus.). 224p. 1981. 10.95 (ISBN 0-395-30510-1). HM.
Hubbard, Earl. Man As DNA. 96p. 1982. 9.95 (ISBN 0-8022-2408-3). Philos Lib.
Huebscher, Ulrich & Spardari, Silvio, eds. Proteins Involved in DNA Replication. 584p. 1984. 85.00x (ISBN 0-306-41804-5, Plenum Pr). Plenum Pub.
ICN-UCLA Symposia on Molecular & Cellular Biology March, 1981, Salt Lake City, Utah. The Initiation of DNA Replication: Proceedings. Ray, Dan S., ed. LC 81-17541. 1981. 60.00 (ISBN 0-12-583580-9). Acad Pr.
Jackson, David A. & Stitch, Stephen P. Recombinant DNA Debate. LC 78-26385. 1979. text ed. 35.95 (ISBN 0-13-767442-2). P-H.
Kahn, Carol. Beyond the Helix: DNA & the Quest for Longevity. LC 85-40343. 288p. 1985. 16.95 (ISBN 0-8129-1153-9). Times Bks.
Kaplan, Albert S. Organization & Replication of Viral DNA. 208p. 1982. 67.00 (ISBN 0-8493-6405-1). CRC Pr.
Kirchner, H. & Schellekens, H., eds. The Biology of the Interferon System, 1984: Proceedings of the 1984 TNO-ISIR Meeting on the Biology of the Interferon System, Held in Heidelberg, FRG, 21-25 October, 1984. 654p. 1985. 111.00 (ISBN 0-444-80661-X). Elsevier.
Kohiyama, M. & Molineux, I., eds. DNA Synthesis: Present & Future. LC 78-2832. (NATO ASI Series A, Life Sciences: Vol. 17). 1175p. 1978. 110.00x (ISBN 0-306-35617-1, Plenum Pr). Plenum Pub.
Kolber, Alan & Kohiyama, Masamichi, eds. Mechanism & Regulation of DNA Replication. LC 74-14571. 469p. 1974. 49.50 (ISBN 0-306-30818-5, Plenum Pr). Plenum Pub.
Kornberg, Arthur. DNA Replication. LC 79-19543. (Illus.). 724p. 1980. text ed. 47.75 (ISBN 0-7167-1102-8). W H Freeman.
--DNA Replication, 1982 Supplement. LC 82-5117. (Illus.). 273p. 1982. pap. text ed. 11.95 (ISBN 0-7167-1410-8). W H Freeman.
Krimsky, Sheldon. Genetic Alchemy: The Social History of the Recombinant DNA Controversy. (Illus.). 440p. 1982. 35.00x (ISBN 0-262-11083-0); pap. 9.95x (ISBN 0-262-61038-8). MIT Pr.
Kueck, H. U. Struktur und Funktionen Mitochondrialer dna Bei Pilzen. (No. 84, Bibliotheca Mycologica Ser.). (Ger., Illus.). 148p. pap. text ed. 14.70x (ISBN 3-7682-1323-4). Lubrecht & Cramer.
Lampton, Christopher. DNA & the Creation of New Life. LC 82-6874. (How It Works Ser.). (Illus.). 224p. 1982. 12.95 (ISBN 0-668-05396-8, 5396). Arco.
Lark, Karl G. The Mystery of DNA Replication. (The University of Utah Frederick William Reynolds Lecture Ser.: No. 43). 1980. 4.95 (ISBN 0-87480-179-6). U of Utah Pr.
Lo. Fundamentals of DNA Engineering. Date not set. write for info. (ISBN 0-444-00845-4). Elsevier.
Menditto, Joseph & Kirsch, Debbie. Genetic Engineering, DNA & Cloning: A Bibliography in the Future of Genetics. LC 82-50417. 790p. 1982. 50.00 (ISBN 0-87875-241-2). Whitston Pub.
Natarajan. DNA Repair: Chromosome Alterations & Chromatin Structure. (Progress in Mutation Research Ser.: Vol. 4). 390p. 1982. 89.50 (ISBN 0-444-80367-X, Biomedical Pr). Elsevier.
National Science Foundation. DNA: The Master Molecule. Kornberg, Warren, ed. (Mosaic Reader Ser.). 64p. (Orig.). 1982. pap. text ed. 5.00 (ISBN 0-89529-172-X). Avery Pub.
Parker, Gary, et al. DNA: The Key to Life. (EMI Programed Biology Ser.). 1975. text ed. 6.95 (ISBN 0-88462-003-4, Ed Methods). Longman USA.
Perkins, F. T. & Hennessen, W., eds. Standardization & Control of Biologicals Produced by Recombinant DNA Technology. (Developments in Biological Standardization Ser.: Vol. 59). (Illus.). viii, 216p. 1985. pap. 30.00 (ISBN 3-8055-4027-2). S Karger.
Portugal, Franklin H. & Cohen, Jack S. A Century of DNA. (Illus.). 400p. 1977. 35.00x (ISBN 0-262-16067-6); pap. 7.95 (ISBN 0-262-66046-6). MIT Pr.
Razin, A., et al, eds. DNA Methylation. (Springer Series in Molecular Biology). (Illus.). xiii, 392p. 1984. 59.50 (ISBN 0-387-96038-4). Springer-Verlag.
Recombination at the DNA Level. LC 34-8174. (Symposia on Quantitative Biology Ser.: Vol. 49). 854p. 1985. 130.00 (ISBN 0-87969-049-6). Cold Spring Harbor.
Replication of DNA & RNA. (The Landmark Ser.). 1979. 22.50x (ISBN 0-8422-4124-8). Irvington.
Rogers, Michael. Biohazard. 1979. pap. 2.25 (ISBN 0-380-41731-6, 41731). Avon.
Rosenfield, Israel, et al. DNA for Beginners. 1983. 14.95 (ISBN 0-86316-022-0); pap. 6.95 (ISBN 0-86316-023-9). Writers & Readers.
Sarin, Prem S. & Gallo, Robert C., eds. Inhibitors of DNA & RNA Polymerases. (International Encyclopedia of Pharmacology & Therapeutics Ser.: Section 103). (Illus.). 1980. 81.00 (ISBN 0-08-024932-9). Pergamon.
Sarma, R. H. & Sarma, M. H. DNA Double Helix & the Chemistry of Cancer. (Illus.). 450p. 1983. text ed. 24.50 (ISBN 0-940030-06-3); pap. text ed. 15.95 (ISBN 0-940030-08-X). Adenine Pr.
Schiminovich, Samuel, ed. Biology of the DNA Tumor Viruses. LC 76-25874. 273p. 1976. 35.00x (ISBN 0-306-32201-3, Plenum Pr). Plenum Pub.
Scott, W. A. & Werner, R., eds. Molecular Cloning of Recombinant DNA. 1977. 39.00 (ISBN 0-12-634250-4). Acad Pr.
Sluyser, Mels. Interaction of Steroid Hormone Receptors with DNA. 200p. 1985. lib. bdg. 46.50 (ISBN 0-89573-366-8, Pub. by Ellis Horwood Ltd UK). VCH Pubs.
Stebbins, G. Ledyard. Darwin to DNA, Molecules to Humanity. LC 81-15152. (Illus.). 491p. 1982. pap. text ed. 17.95 (ISBN 0-7167-1332-2). W H Freeman.
Superhelical DNA. (Landmark Ser.). 1979. 22.50x (ISBN 0-8422-4125-6). Irvington.
Szekely, Maria. From DNA to Protein: The Transfer of Genetic Information. LC 79-11894. 284p. 1981. pap. 21.95x (ISBN 0-470-27155-8). Halsted Pr.
--From DNA to Protein: The Transfer of Genetic Information. LC 79-11894. 284p. 1980. 54.95x (ISBN 0-470-26687-2). Halsted Pr.
Taylor, J. H. DNA Methylation & Cellular Differentiation. (Cell Biology Monographs: Vol. 11). (Illus.). 150p. 1984. 39.50 (ISBN 0-387-81761-1). Springer Verlag.
Tiley, Nancy A. Discovering DNA. LC 82-4771. 304p. 1983. 18.95 (ISBN 0-442-26260-4). Van Nos Reinhold.
Travers, A. A. Transcription of DNA. rev. ed. Head, J. J., ed. LC 76-29378. (Carolina Biology Readers Ser.). (Illus.). 16p. 1978. pap. 1.60 (ISBN 0-89278-275-7, 45-9675). Carolina Biological.
Walton, A. G., ed. Recombinant DNA: Proceedings 3rd Cleveland Symposium on Macromolecules, Cleveland, June 1981. 310p. 1982. 78.75 (ISBN 0-444-42039-8). Elsevier.
Watson, James D. Double Helix. (Illus.). 1969. pap. 3.50 (ISBN 0-451-62387-8, Ment). NAL.
--The Double Helix: A Norton Critical Edition. Stent, Gunther S., ed. (Illus.). 1980. pap. text ed. 7.95x (ISBN 0-393-95075-1). Norton.
--Double Helix: Being a Personal Account of the Discovery of the Structure of DNA. LC 68-11211. (Illus.). 1968. 7.95 (ISBN 0-689-10285-2); pap. 5.95 (ISBN 0-689-70602-2, 261). Atheneum.
Watson, James D. & Tooze, John. The DNA Story: A Documentary History of Gene Cloning. (Illus.). 605p. 1983. text ed. 29.95 (ISBN 0-7167-1292-X); pap. text ed. 15.95 (ISBN 0-7167-1590-2). W H Freeman.
--Recombinant DNA: A Short Course. LC 83-9069. (Illus.). 256p. 1983. text ed. 27.95 (ISBN 0-7167-1483-3); pap. text ed. 17.95 (ISBN 0-7167-1484-1). W H Freeman.
Weir. Statistical Analysis of DNA Sequence Data. (Statistics, Textbooks & Monographs Ser.). 264p. 1983. 45.00 (ISBN 0-8247-7032-3). Dekker.
Weissmann, Sherman M., ed. Methods for DNA & RNA Sequencing. LC 82-22261. 480p. 1983. 46.95 (ISBN 0-03-059174-0). Praeger.
Whelan, W. J., et al. From Genetic Experimentation to Biotechnology: The Critical Transition. LC 81-19838. 266p. 1982. 44.95x (ISBN 0-471-10148-6, Pub. by Wiley-Interscience). Wiley.
Wickner, Reed B., ed. DNA Replication & Biosynthesis. LC 74-77107. (Methods in Molecular Biology Ser.: Vol. 7). 320p. 1974. 65.00 (ISBN 0-8247-6202-9). Dekker.
Zilinskas, Raymond A. & Zimmerman, Burke K., eds. The Gene Splicing Wars, Nineteen Seventy-Four to Nineteen Seventy-Eight: Reflections on the Recombinant DNA Controversy. 320p. 1985. 24.95x (ISBN 0-02-948560-6). Macmillan.

DEPILATION
see Hair, Removal Of

DEPOSITION AND SEDIMENTATION
see Sedimentation and Deposition

DEPOSITS, DEEP-SEA
see Marine Sediments; Sedimentation and Deposition

DERRICKS
see Cranes, Derricks, etc.

DESALINIZATION OF WATER
see Saline Waters–Demineralization

DESCARTES, RENE, 1596-1650

Balz, Albert G. Descartes & the Modern Mind. xiv, 492p. 1967. Repr. of 1952 ed. 32.50 (ISBN 0-208-00023-2, Archon). Shoe String.
Beck, Leslie J. The Metaphysics of Descartes: A Study of the Meditations. LC 79-14519. 1979. Repr. of 1965 ed. lib. bdg. 25.00x (ISBN 0-313-21480-8, BEMD). Greenwood.
Clarke, Desmond M. Descartes' Philosophy of Science. LC 82-82082. 224p. 1982. text ed. 22.50x (ISBN 0-271-00325-1). Pa St U Pr.
Cottingham, John, ed. & tr. Descartes' Conversation with Burman. 1974. 10.95x (ISBN 0-19-824671-4). Oxford U Pr.
Descartes, Rene. Lettres. 2nd ed. 248p. 1964. 12.95 (ISBN 0-686-55672-0). French & Eur.
--Oeuvres et Lettres: Avec: Discours de la Methode. 1424p. 1937. 42.95 (ISBN 0-686-55676-3). French & Eur.
De Spinoza, Benedictus. The Principles of Descartes' Philosophy. Britan, Halbert H., tr. from Lat. LC 74-3096. 1978. pap. 6.75 (ISBN 0-87548-053-5). Open Court.
Federico, P. J. Descartes on Polyhedra: A Study of the "De Solidorum Elementis". (Sources in the History of Mathematics & Physical Sciences: Vol. 4). (Illus.). 144p. 1982. 39.50 (ISBN 0-387-90760-2). Springer-Verlag.
Gaukroger, Stephen, ed. Descartes: Philosophy, Mathematics & Physics. (Harvester Readings in the History of Science & Philosophy Ser.: No. 1). 329p. 1980. 30.00x (ISBN 0-389-20084-0). B&N Imports.
Gysi, Lydia. Platonism & Cartesianism in the Philosophy of Ralph Cudworth. 163p. 1962. 14.35 (ISBN 3-261-00648-X). P Lang Pubs.
Hooker, Michael, ed. Descartes: Critical & Interpretive Essays. 1978. text ed. 25.00x (ISBN 0-8018-2111-8); pap. text ed. 8.95x (ISBN 0-8018-2122-3). Johns Hopkins.
Joachim, Harold H. Descartes's Rules for the Direction of the Mind. Harris, Errol E., ed. LC 79-9958. 1979. Repr. of 1957 ed. lib. bdg. 19.75x (ISBN 0-313-21263-5, JODE). Greenwood.
Lindeboom, G. A. Descartes & Medicine. (Nieuwe Nederlandse Bijdragen Tot De Geschiedenis der Geneekundem: No. 1). (Illus.). 1978. pap. text ed. 17.75x (ISBN 90-6203-882-4). Humanities.
Mahaffy, John P. Descartes. facs. ed. LC 71-94277. (Select Bibliographies Reprint Ser). 1902. 19.00 (ISBN 0-8369-5051-8). Ayer Co Pubs.
Pfaff, Rudolph F. Die Unterschiede Zwischen der Naturphilosophie Descartes und Derjenigen Gassendis und der Gegensatz Beider Philosophen Ueberhaupt. 1964. 18.00 (ISBN 0-8337-2732-X). B Franklin.
Popkin, Richard H. History of Scepticism from Erasmus to Descartes. rev. ed. (Philosophical Texts & Studies). 1964. text ed. 26.75x (ISBN 9-0232-0438-7). Humanities.
Schouls, Peter A. The Imposition of Method: A Study of Descartes & Locke. 1980. text ed. 45.00x (ISBN 0-19-824613-7). Oxford U Pr.
Scott, J. F. The Scientific Work of Rene Descartes (1596-1650) (Illus.). 211p. 1952. 18.50x (ISBN 0-8464-0821-X). Beekman Pubs.
Talmor, Ezra. Descartes & Hume. LC 79-41748. 188p. 1980. 23.00 (ISBN 0-08-024274-X). Pergamon.
Valery, Paul. Descartes. 133p. 1980. Repr. lib. bdg. 15.00 (ISBN 0-89984-477-4). Century Bookbindery.
Versfeld, Marthinus. An Essays on the Metaphysics of Descartes. LC 68-26210. 1968. Repr. of 1940 ed. 20.00 (ISBN 0-8046-0481-9, Pub. by Kennikat). Assoc Faculty Pr.

DESCENT
see Heredity

DESCRIPTIVE GEOMETRY
see Geometry, Descriptive

DESERT BIOLOGY
see also Desert Ecology; Desert Fauna; Desert Flora

Bhandari, M. M. Flora of the Indian Desert. 472p. 1978. 89.00x (ISBN 0-686-45804-4, Pub. by United Bk Traders India). State Mutual bk.
Brown, G. W. Desert Biology, 2 vols. Set. 152.50; Vol. 1, 1968. 92.50 (ISBN 0-12-135901-8); Vol. 2. 92.50 (ISBN 0-12-135902-6). Acad Pr.
Cowles, Raymond B. & Bakker, Elna S. Desert Journal: Reflections of a Naturalist. 1977. 14.95 (ISBN 0-520-02879-1); pap. 4.95 (ISBN 0-520-03636-0). U of Cal Pr.
Hadley, Neil F. Environmental Physiology of Desert Organisms. LC 75-14408. 283p. 1975. 53.00 (ISBN 0-12-786620-5). Acad Pr.
Jaeger, Edmund C. The North American Deserts. (Illus.). 1957. 14.95 (ISBN 0-8047-0498-8). Stanford U Pr.
Kirk, Ruth. Desert: The American Southwest. (Naturalist's America Ser.: Vol. 3). (Illus.). 1973. 10.00 (ISBN 0-395-17209-8). HM.
Louw, G. N. & Seely, M. K. Ecology of Desert Organisims. LC 81-6027. (Tropical Ecology Ser.). (Illus.). 240p. 1982. pap. text ed. 17.50x (ISBN 0-582-44393-8). Longman.
O'Kane, Walter C. The Intimate Desert. 160p. 1985. pap. 8.50 (ISBN 0-8165-0938-7). U of Ariz Pr.
Orians, Gordon H. & Solbrig, Otto T., eds. Convergent Evolution in Warm Deserts. (US-IBP Synthesis Ser.: No. 3). 1977. 55.50 (ISBN 0-12-787165-9). Acad Pr.
Perry, Richard. Life in Desert & Plain. LC 75-34733. (The Many Worlds of Wildlife Ser.). (Illus.). 256p. 1976. 10.95 (ISBN 0-8008-4798-9). Taplinger.
Schmidt-Nielsen, Knut. Desert Animals. LC 79-52528. (Illus.). 1980. pap. 6.95 (ISBN 0-486-23850-4). Dover.
Singh, Alam, ed. Desret Resources & Technology, Vol. 1. 500p. 1982. 90.00x (ISBN 0-686-45801-X, Pub. by United Bk Traders India). State Mutual Bk.
Stebbins, Robert C., et al. Teaching & Research in the California Desert. LC 77-29266. (Research Report Ser.: No. 78-1). 26p. 1978. pap. 3.00x (ISBN 0-87772-253-6). Inst Gov Stud Berk.
Waggin, Chuck. A Light-Hearted Look at the Desert. LC 74-101697. (Illus.). 95p. 1969. pap. 4.95 (ISBN 0-8165-0208-0). U of Ariz Pr.

DESERT ECOLOGY

Krutch, Joseph W. The Desert Year. LC 84-24127. 270p. 1985. pap. 9.95 (ISBN 0-8165-0923-9). U of Ariz Pr.
O'Kane, Walter C. The Intimate Desert. 160p. 1985. pap. 8.50 (ISBN 0-8165-0938-7). U of Ariz Pr.

DESERT FAUNA

Alcock, John. Sonoran Desert Spring. LC 84-16468. (Illus.). 196p. 1985. 19.95 (ISBN 0-226-01258-1). U of Chicago Pr.
Bank, Stanley. Strange Creatures of the Desert. LC 83-60112. (Strange but True Ser.). 1983. 10.00 (ISBN 0-382-06692-8). Silver.
Crawford, Clifford C. Biology of Desert Invertebrates. (Illus.). 314p. 1981. 42.00 (ISBN 0-387-10807-6). Springer Verlag.
Goodall, David W., ed. Evolution of Desert Biota. (Illus.). 250p. 1976. 20.00x (ISBN 0-292-72015-7). U of Tex Pr.
Jaeger, Edmund C. Desert Wildlife. (Illus.). 1961. 11.95 (ISBN 0-8047-0123-7); pap. 6.95 (ISBN 0-8047-0124-5, SP68). Stanford U Pr.
Kirmiz, John P. Adaptation to Desert Environment: A Study of the Jerboa, Rat & Man. 168p. 1962. 24.50x (ISBN 0-306-30658-1, Plenum Pr). Plenum Pub.
Krutch, Joseph W. The Voice of the Desert: A Naturalist's Interpretation. (Illus.). 1971. pap. 7.95 (ISBN 0-688-07715-3). Morrow.
Miller, Alden H. & Stebbins, Robert C. The Lives of Desert Animals in Joshua Tree National Monument. 1964. 32.50 (ISBN 0-520-00866-9). U of Cal Pr.
Schmidt-Nielsen, Knut. Desert Animals: Physiological Problems of Heat & Water. 11.75 (ISBN 0-8446-5811-1). Peter Smith.
Wallwork, John A. Desert Soil Fauna. LC 81-12030. 304p. 1982. 42.95x (ISBN 0-03-055306-7). Praeger.
Zoological Society of London - 31st Symposium. Comparative Physiology of Desert Animals. Maloiy, C. M. O. & MacFarlane, W. V., eds. 1973. 63.50 (ISBN 0-12-613331-X). Acad Pr.

DESERT FLORA
see also Cactus; Succulent Plants

Alcock, John. Sonoran Desert Spring. LC 84-16468. (Illus.). 196p. 1985. 19.95 (ISBN 0-226-01258-1). U of Chicago Pr.
Dodge, Natt N. & Janish, Jeanne R. Flowers of the Southwest Deserts. 10th ed. LC 72-92509. (Popular Ser.: No. 4). (Illus.). 1976. pap. 2.50 (ISBN 0-911408-45-2). SW Pks Mnmts.
Goodall, David W., ed. Evolution of Desert Biota. (Illus.). 250p. 1976. 20.00x (ISBN 0-292-72015-7). U of Tex Pr.
Hastings, James R. & Turner, Raymond. The Changing Mile. LC 65-25019. (Illus.). 317p. 1965. 25.00x (ISBN 0-8165-0014-2). U of Ariz Pr.
Humphrey, Robert R. The Boojum & Its Home. LC 73-87548. 214p. 1974. pap. 8.95 (ISBN 0-8165-0436-9). U of Ariz Pr.
Jaeger, Edmund C. Desert Wild Flowers. rev. ed. LC 41-22485. (Illus.). 1941. 11.95 (ISBN 0-8047-0364-7); pap. 6.95 (ISBN 0-8047-0365-5, SP81). Stanford U Pr.
Krutch, Joseph W. The Voice of the Desert: A Naturalist's Interpretation. (Illus.). 1971. pap. 7.95 (ISBN 0-688-07715-3). Morrow.
Mabry, T. J., et al, eds. Creosote Bush. LC 76-58381. (US-IBP Synthesis Ser.). 1977. 55.50 (ISBN 0-12-787010-5). Acad Pr.
MacDougal, Daniel T. Botanical Features of North American Deserts. Repr. of 1908 ed. 19.00 (ISBN 0-384-34782-7). Johnson Repr.
Munz, Philip A. California Desert Wildflowers. (Illus., Orig.). 1962. pap. 5.95 (ISBN 0-520-00899-5). U of Cal Pr.
Pate, J. S. & Beard, J. S., eds. Kwongan: Plant Life of the Sandplain. (Illus.). 284p. 1984. 40.00x (ISBN 0-85564-228-9, Pub. by U of W Austral Pr); pap. 28.00 (ISBN 0-85564-230-0). Intl Spec Bk.
Shreve, Forrest & Wiggins, Ira L. Vegetation & Flora of the Sonoran Desert, 2 Vols. (Illus.). 1964. Set. 100.00x (ISBN 0-8047-0163-6). Stanford U Pr.

Simpson, B. B., ed. Mesquite: Its Biology in Two Desert Scrub Ecosystems. (US-IBP Synthesis Ser.: Vol. 4). 1977. 49.00 (ISBN 0-12-787460-7). Acad Pr.

Watts, May T. & Watts, Tom. Desert Tree Finder: A Manual for Identifying Desert Trees of Ariz., Calif., N. Mex. 1974. pap. 1.50 (ISBN 0-912550-07-4). Nature Study.

Weinberg, Julie B. Growing Food in the High Desert Country. LC 85-2682. 96p. (Orig.). 1985. pap. 10.95 (ISBN 0-86534-066-8). Sunstone Pr.

DESERTS

see also names of deserts e.g.; Kalahari Desert, Sahara Desert; also headings beginning with the word Desert

Adams, Robert, et al. Dry Lands: Man & Plants. LC 78-65219. 1979. 35.00x (ISBN 0-312-22042-1). St Martin.

Alcock, John. Sonoran Desert Spring. LC 84-16468. (Illus.). 196p. 1985. 19.95 (ISBN 0-226-01258-1). U of Chicago Pr.

Amiran, David H. K. & Wilson, Andrew H., eds. Coastal Deserts: Their Natural & Human Environments. LC 73-76305. 207p. 1973. 22.50x (ISBN 0-8165-0312-5). U of Ariz Pr.

Bender, Gordon L., ed. Reference Handbook on the Deserts of North America. LC 80-24791. (Illus.). xiii, 594p. 1982. lib. bdg. 75.00 (ISBN 0-313-21307-0, BRD/). Greenwood.

Benson, Lyman & Darrow, Robert A. Trees & Shrubs of the Southwestern Deserts. rev. ed. LC 81-7617. 416p. 1981. text ed. 49.50 (ISBN 0-8165-0591-8). U of Ariz Pr.

Bishay, A. & McGinnies, W. G., eds. Applications of Science & Technology for Desert Development. (Advances in Desert & Arid Land Technology & Development: Vol. 1). 630p. 1979. lib. bdg. 102.95 (ISBN 3-7186-0002-1). Harwood Academic.

Biswas, Margaret R. & Biswas, Asit K. Desertification: Associated Case Studies Prepared for the United Nations Conference on Desertification. LC 80-40024. (Environmental Sciences & Applications: Vol. 12). (Illus.). 532p. 1980. 105.00 (ISBN 0-08-023581-6). Pergamon.

Chapman, V. J. Salt Marshes & Salt Deserts of the World. 2nd ed. 1974. 52.50 (ISBN 3-7682-0927-X). Lubrecht & Cramer.

Cloudsley-Thompson, J. L. The Ecology of Oases. 49p. 1974. 39.00x (ISBN 0-900541-71-7, Pub. by Meadowfield Pr England). State Mutual Bk.

Combating Desertification in China. (Reports & Proceedings Ser.: No. 3). 70p. 1983. pap. 8.50 (ISBN 92-807-1035-4, UNEP079, UNEP). Unipub.

Cooke, Ronald U. & Warren, Andrew. Geomorphology in Deserts. 1974. 40.00x (ISBN 0-520-02280-7). U of Cal Pr.

Davey, Keith. Australian Desert Life. 8.50x (ISBN 0-392-07552-0, SpS). Sportshelf.

The Desert Realm: Lands of Majesty & Mystery. LC 80-7568. (Illus.). 304p. 1982. 19.95 (ISBN 0-87044-331-3); lib. bdg. 21.95. Natl Geog.

Eckholm, Erik & Brown, Lester R. Spreading Deserts: The Hand of Man. LC 77-81479. (Institute Papers). 1977. pap. 2.00 (ISBN 0-916468-12-7). Worldwatch Inst.

Evenari, M., et al. Hot Deserts & Arid Shrublands, Vols. 12A & B. (Ecosystems of the World Ser.). Date not set. Set. price not set (ISBN 0-444-42297-8). Vol. 12A (ISBN 0-444-42282-X). Vol. 12B (ISBN 0-444-42296-X). Elsevier.

Findley, Rowe. Great American Deserts. LC 72-75382. (Special Publications Ser.). (Illus.). 1972. 6.95 (ISBN 0-87044-107-8). Natl Geog.

Golany, Gideon, ed. Desert Planning. 192p. 1982. 110.00 (ISBN 0-89397-119-7). Nichols Pub.

Goudie, A. & Wilkinson, J. The Warm Desert Environment. LC 76-9731. (Topics in Geography Ser). (Illus.). 1977. 16.95 (ISBN 0-521-21330-4); pap. 8.95 o. p. (ISBN 0-521-29105-4); slides 27.95x (ISBN 0-521-21912-4). Cambridge U Pr.

Helms, Christopher L. The Sonoran Desert. LC 80-82918. (Illus.). 1980. 8.95 (ISBN 0-916122-72-7); pap. 3.75 (ISBN 0-916122-71-9). KC Pubns.

Jaeger, Edmund C. The North American Deserts. (Illus.). 1957. 14.95 (ISBN 0-8047-0498-8). Stanford U Pr.

Kraus, Joseph. Alive in the Desert: The Complete Guide for Desert Recreation & Survival. new ed. (Illus.). 130p. 1978. pap. 8.00 (ISBN 0-87364-127-2). Paladin Pr.

Krutch, Joseph W. The Voice of the Desert: A Naturalist's Interpretation. (Illus.). 1971. pap. 7.95 (ISBN 0-688-07715-3). Morrow.

Lawson, Merlin P. The Climate of the Great American Desert: Reconstruction of the Climate of Western Interior United States, 1800-1850. LC 74-78480. (Landmark Ed. Ser.). (Illus.). viii, 135p. 1976. 11.95x (ISBN 0-8032-0226-1). U of Nebr Pr.

Lindsay, Diana E. Our Historic Desert. Pourade, Richard F., ed. LC 73-11878. (Illus.). 160p. 1973. 14.50 (ISBN 0-913938-15-7). Copley Bks.

Lopez, Barry H. Desert Notes: Reflections in the Eye of the Raven. 96p. 1981. pap. 2.95 (ISBN 0-380-53819-9, 65805-4, Bard). Avon.

Mabbutt, J. A. Desert Landforms. 1977. 25.00x (ISBN 0-262-13131-5). MIT Pr.

Mabbutt, J. A. & Floret, C., eds. Case Studies on Desertification: Prepared by UNESCO-UNEP-UNDP. (Natural Resources Research Ser.: No. 18). (Illus.). 280p. 1981. pap. 44.75 (ISBN 92-3-101820-5, U1103, UNESCO). Unipub.

McGinnies, William G. Discovering the Desert: The Legacy of the Carnegie Desert Botanical Laboratory. LC 81-1554. 276p. 1981. pap. 10.95 (ISBN 0-8165-0728-7). U of Ariz Pr.

McGinnies, William G., et al, eds. Deserts of the World: An Appraisal of Research into Their Physical & Biological Environments. LC 68-9338. 788p. 1968. 29.50x (ISBN 0-8165-0181-5). U of Ariz Pr.

Matlock, W. G. Realistic Planning for Arid Lands: Natural Resource Limitations to Agricultural Development, Vol. 2. (Advances in Desert & Arid Land Development Ser.). 284p. 1981. 49.50 (ISBN 3-7186-0051-X). Harwood Academic.

Nechaeva, Nina T., ed. Improvement in Desert Ranges in Soviet Central Asia. (Advances in Desert & Arid Land Technology & Developmental Ser.). 342p. 1985. text ed. 130.00 (ISBN 3-7186-0222-9). Harwood Academic.

Petrov, M. P. Deserts of the World. LC 75-12921. 447p. 1977. 114.95 (ISBN 0-470-68447-X). Halsted Pr.

Pewe, Troy L., ed. Desert Dust: Origin, Characteristics, & Effects on Man. (Special Paper: No. 186). (Illus.). 186p. 1981. 30.00 (ISBN 0-8137-2186-5). Geol Soc.

Pond, Alonzo W. The Desert World. LC 75-9899. (Illus.). 342p. 1975. Repr. of 1962 ed. lib. bdg. 22.50x (ISBN 0-8371-8120-8, PODW). Greenwood.

Shantz, Homer L. & Marbut, Curtis F. Vegetation & Soils of Africa. LC 70-170848. Repr. of 1923 ed. 19.00 (ISBN 0-404-05953-8). AMS Pr.

Smiley, Terah L. & Zumberge, James H., eds. Polar Deserts & Modern Man. LC 73-85722. 173p. 1974. 22.50x (ISBN 0-8165-0383-4). U of Ariz Pr.

Social & Environmental Aspects of Desertification. 40p. 1980. pap. 6.75 (ISBN 92-808-0127-9, TUNU085, UNU). Unipub.

Spooner, B. & Mann, H. S. Desertification & Development: Dryland Ecology in Social Perspective. 1983. 59.00 (ISBN 0-12-658050-2). Acad Pr.

Spreading Deserts: The Hand of Man. (Worldwatch Institute Papers: No. 13). 40p. 1977. pap. 2.95 (ISBN 0-686-94927-7, WW13, WW). Unipub.

United Nations Institute for Training & Research. Alternative Strategies for Desert Development & Management: Proceedings of an International Conference, Sacramento California, June 1977, 4 pts. Incl. Vol. I. Energy & Minerals. 320p. 45.00 (ISBN 0-08-022402-4); Vol. II. Agriculture. 264p. 40.00 (ISBN 0-08-022403-2); Vol. III. Water. 504p. 70.00 (ISBN 0-08-022404-0); Vol. IV. Desert Management. 488p. 65.00 (ISBN 0-08-022405-9). LC 81-23433. (Environmental Sciences & Application Ser.: Vol. 3). 1576p. 1979. Set. 220.00 (ISBN 0-08-022401-6, G135). Pergamon.

United Nations, Secretariat. Conference on Desertification, Nairobi 1977. Desertification: Its Causes & Consequences. LC 77-81423. 1977. text ed. 97.00 (ISBN 0-08-022023-1). Pergamon.

Van Dyke, John C. The Desert. LC 80-10892. (Literature of the American Wilderness Ser.). 272p. 1980. pap. 3.45 (ISBN 0-87905-073-X, Peregrine Smith). Gibbs M Smith.

Wagner, Frederic H. Wildlife of the Deserts. (Wildlife Habitat Ser.). (Illus.). 232p. 1980. 19.95 (ISBN 0-8109-1764-5, 1764-5). Abrams.

Walls, James. Land, Man & Sand: Desertification & Its Solution. LC 79-7852. (Illus.). 1980. 19.95 (ISBN 0-02-699810-6). Macmillan Info.

Waloff, Z. Field Studies on Solitary & Transient Desert Locusts in the Red Sea Area. 1963. 40.00 (ISBN 0-85135-040-2, Pub. by Centre Overseas Research). State Mutual Bk.

Wells, Stephen G. & Haragan, Donald R., eds. Origin & Evolution of Deserts. (Publications of the Committee on Desert & Arid Zones). (Illus.). 240p. 22.50x (ISBN 0-8263-0605-5, O-11); pap. 11.95x (ISBN 0-8263-0606-3, O-12). U of NM Pr.

West, N. E., ed. Temperate Deserts & Semi-Deserts. (Ecosystems of the World Ser.: Vol. 5). 522p. 1983. 170.25 (ISBN 0-444-41931-4, I-483-82). Elsevier.

West, N. E. & Skujins, J., eds. Nitrogen in Desert Ecosystems. LC 78-17672. (US-IBP Synthesis Ser.: Vol. 9). 307p. 1978. 31.50 (ISBN 0-87933-333-2). Van Nos Reinhold.

Wheeler, Sessions S. Nevada Desert. LC 72-123581. (Illus., Orig.). 1970. pap. 4.95 (ISBN 0-87004-205-X). Caxton.

DESIGN, BOOK

see Book Design

DESIGN, ENGINEERING

see Engineering Design

DESIGN, INDUSTRIAL

see also Engineering Design; Engineering Models; Environmental Engineering; Human Engineering; Mechanical Drawing; Unit Construction

American National Standard Practice for Industrial Lighting. rev. ed. (Illus.). 52p. 1984. 14.00 (ISBN 0-87995-001-3, RP7); member 5.00. Illum Eng.

Arends, Mark. Product Rendering with Markers. (Illus.). 180p. 1985. 35.00 (ISBN 0-442-20952-5). Van Nos Reinhold.

Becker, Franklin D. Workspace: Creating Environments in Organizations. LC 81-10671. 238p. 1981. 31.95 (ISBN 0-03-059137-6); pap. 15.95 (ISBN 0-03-062184-4). Praeger.

Burklin, Ray. Process Plant Designer's Pocket Handbook of Codes & Standards. LC 79-17599. 172p. (Orig.). 1979. pap. 9.95x (ISBN 0-87201-115-1). Gulf Pub.

Chen, Carson. Active Filter Design. 144p. pap. 11.95 (0959). Hayden.

Cocomas Committee & Nakanishi, Motoo. Corporate Design Systems. (Illus.). 125p. 32.50 (ISBN 0-686-61692-8). Art Dir.

Design Engineering Conference, 7th: Proceedings. 1984. lib. bdg. 94.00x (ISBN 0-903608-74-X, Pub. by IFS Pubns UK). Air Sci Co.

Design for the Eighties. (Illus.). 1981. text ed. 40.00 (ISBN 0-937976-05-9). Enviro Pr.

Design Laws & Treaties of the World. 2 binder set 540.00 (ISBN 0-686-88608-9). BNA.

Design of Industrial Floors. 178p. 1983. 24.00 (ISBN 0-317-37034-0); members 18.00 (ISBN 0-317-37035-9). ACI.

Design of Structural Concrete. 164p. 1983. 33.95 (ISBN 0-317-37036-7); members 24.95 (ISBN 0-317-37037-5). ACI.

Evans, Helen M. & Dumesil, Carla D. Invitation to Design. 2nd ed. 1982. text ed. write for info. (ISBN 0-02-334540-3). Macmillan.

Garner, Philippe. Twentieth Century Style & Design: Nineteen Hundred to the Present. LC 84-3706. 320p. 1985. 39.95 (ISBN 0-442-23008-7). Van Nos Reinhold.

Goodrich, Kristina, ed. Industrial Design Excellence U. S. A. (Illus.). 96p. (Orig.). 1985. pap. 15.00 (ISBN 0-9614683-0-0). Indus Design.

Haddon, Randolph J. The Basic Guidebook for Industrial Designers. (Illus.). 129p. 1981. 67.45 (ISBN 0-930582-92-6). Gloucester Art.

The Hague Agreement Concerning the International Deposit of Industrial Designs. 1975. pap. 7.50 (ISBN 0-686-53004-7, WIPO13, WIPO). Unipub.

Hamilton, N. Design & Industry. 88p. (Orig.). 1981. pap. 39.95x (ISBN 0-85072-114-8, Pub. by Design Council England). Intl Spec Bk.

Hearn, Patrick. The Business of Industrial Licensing: A Practical Guide to Patents, Know-How Trademarks & Industrial Designs. 272p. 1981. text ed. 45.00x (ISBN 0-566-02212-5). Gower Pub Co.

Heskett, John. Industrial Design. (World of Art Ser.). (Illus.). 214p. 1985. pap. 9.95 (ISBN 0-500-20181-1). Thames Hudson.

Hubka, V., et al. Practical Studies in Systematic Design. 216p. 1985. text ed. 37.95 (ISBN 0-408-01420-2). Butterworth.

Hughes, D. R. & Piper, F. C. Design Theory. (Illus.). 250p. Date not set. 39.50 (ISBN 0-521-25754-9). Cambridge U Pr.

International Classification for Industrial Designs. 1972. pap. 44.00 (ISBN 0-686-53006-3, WIPO40, WIPO). Unipub.

International Conference on Current Advances in Mechanical Design & Production, 1st, Cairo University, Dec. 1979. Current Advances in Mechanical Design & Production: Proceedings. Shawki, G. S. & Metwalli, S. M., eds. LC 80-41666. (Illus.). 496p. 1981. 83.00 (ISBN 0-08-027294-0); pap. 25.00 (ISBN 0-08-027306-8). Pergamon.

Locarno Agreement Establishing an International Classification for Industrial Designs. 24p. 1977. pap. 7.50 (ISBN 0-686-53010-1, WIPO19, WIPO). Unipub.

Loewy, Raymond. Industrial Design. LC 79-15104. (Illus.). 250p. 1979. 85.00 (ISBN 0-87951-098-6); deluxe ed. 275.00 signed, ltd. ed. (ISBN 0-87951-102-8). Overlook Pr.

Lucie-Smith, Edward. A History of Industrial Design. 1983. 44.50 (ISBN 0-442-25804-6). Van Nos Reinhold.

Meikle, Jeffrey. Twentieth Century Limited: Industrial Design in America, 1925-1939. (American Civilization Ser.). (Illus.). 264p. 1979. 34.95 (ISBN 0-87722-158-8). Temple U Pr.

Meikle, Jeffrey L. Twentieth Century Limited: Industrial Design in America, 1925-1939. 249p. 1981. pap. 12.95 (ISBN 0-87722-246-0). Temple U Pr.

Model Law for Developing Countries on Industrial Designs. 1970. pap. 7.50 (ISBN 0-686-53016-0, WIPO48, WIPO). Unipub.

Molian, S. Mechanism Design: An Introductory Text. LC 81-15552. 200p. 1982. 34.50 (ISBN 0-521-23193-0); pap. 12.95 (ISBN 0-521-29863-6). Cambridge U Pr.

Moss, Arthur. Successful Industrial Design. 76p. 1970. 14.00x (ISBN 0-8464-0897-X); pap. 7.00x (ISBN 0-8464-0898-8). Beekman Pubs.

Noyes, Eliot F. Organic Design in Home Furnishings. LC 70-86424. (Museum of Modern Art Publications in Reprint Ser). (Illus.). 1970. Repr. of 1941 ed. 16.00 (ISBN 0-405-01540-2). Ayer Co Pubs.

Pao, Y. C. Elements of Computer-Aided Design & Manufacturing. LC 84-5256. 498p. 1985. 33.95 (ISBN 0-471-88194-5); solution manual avail. (ISBN 0-471-80146-1). Wiley.

Pulos, Arthur J. American Design Ethic: A History of Industrial Design. (Illus.). 453p. 1983. 50.00 (ISBN 0-262-16085-4). MIT Pr.

Pye, David. Nature & Art of Workmanship. LC 68-12062. (Illus.). 1968. 34.50 (ISBN 0-521-06016-8); pap. 12.95 (ISBN 0-521-29356-1). Cambridge U Pr.

Ramirez-Vazquez, P. Industrial Design & Human Development: Proceedings Mexico, Oct. '79. Lazo-Margain, A., ed. (Vol, 51). 354p. 1981. 79.75 (ISBN 0-444-90170-1, Excerpta Medica). Elsevier.

Records of the Locarno Conference: 1968, for the Purpose of Setting Up an International Classification for Industrial Designs. 1972. 19.25 (ISBN 0-686-53025-X, WIPO31, WIPO). Unipub.

Ruskin, John. The Application of the Idea of Art to Decorative & Manufacturing Processes, 2 vols. (Illus.). 277p. 1984. Repr. of 1865 ed. 197.75 set (ISBN 0-89901-177-2). Found Class Reprints.

Smith, Robert J. Physical Design Automation: System Study & Implementation Plans. LC 76-52066. 1977. 100.00 (ISBN 0-686-18276-6). V-R Information.

Sparke, Penny. Consultant Design: The History & Practice of the Designer in Industry. (Pembridge History of Design Ser.). 98p. 1983. 17.50 (ISBN 0-86206-007-9, Pub. by Pembridge Pr UK). Shoe String.

Trucks, H. E. Designing for Economical Production. new ed. LC 74-18555. (Manufacturing Data Ser.). 221p. 1974. 15.00 (ISBN 0-87263-030-7). SME.

Westbury House, ed. Design: Science, Method. 350p. 1980. pap. 59.00x (ISBN 0-86103-047-8, Pub. by Westbury House). State Mutual Bk.

Wilson, Forrest. Building Diagnostics: New Opportunities for the Design Professions. 35.95 (ISBN 0-471-80441-X). Wiley.

Woodham, Jonathan. The Industrial Designer & the Public. (Pembridge History of Design Ser.). 144p. 1983. 17.50 (ISBN 0-86206-006-0, Pub. by Pembridge Pr UK). Shoe String.

Woodson, Wesley E. & Conover, Donald W. Human Engineering Guide for Equipment Designers. 2nd rev ed. (Illus.). 1965. 42.00x (ISBN 0-520-01363-8). U of Cal Pr.

DESIGN OF EXPERIMENTS

see Experimental Design

DESIGN PERCEPTION

see Pattern Perception

DESIGNED GENETIC CHANGE

see Genetic Engineering

DESMIDIEAE

Bicudo, Carlos M. Contribution to the Knowledge of the Desmids of the State of Sao Paulo. (Illus.). 1969. 10.00 (ISBN 3-7682-0653-X). Lubrecht & Cramer.

Croasdale, Hannah & Bicudo, Carlos E. A Synopsis of North American Desmids Part II: Desmidiaceae: Placodermae Section 5. The Filamentous Genera. LC 70-183418. (Illus.). vi, 117p. 1983. 26.50x (ISBN 0-8032-3661-1). U of Nebr Pr.

Lind, Edna M. & Brook, Alan J. Desmids of the English Lake District. 1980. 25.00x (ISBN 0-686-75592-8, Pub. by Freshwater Bio). State Mutual Bk.

Nordstedt, C. F. Index Desmidiacearum citationibus locupletissimus atque bibliographia & Suppl. 1978. lib. bdg. 70.00 (ISBN 3-7682-1171-1). Lubrecht & Cramer.

Prescott, G. W., et al. A Synopsis of North American Desmids, Part II: Desmidiaceae, Placodermae, Section 1. LC 70-183418. (Illus.). x, 275p. 1975. 31.50x (ISBN 0-8032-0854-5). U of Nebr Pr.

Prescott, Gerald W. Bibliographia Desmidiacearum Universalis: A Contribution to a Bibliography of Desmid Systematics, Biology & Ecology from 1744 to 1982. 600p. 1985. lib. bdg. 70.00 (ISBN 3-87429-215-0). Lubrecht & Cramer.

Ralfs, J. British Desmidieae. (Illus.). 1962. 28.00 (ISBN 3-7682-0144-9). Lubrecht & Cramer.

Moore, D., et al, eds. Developmental Biology of Higher Fungi. (British Mycological Society Symposium Ser.: No. 10). (Illus.). 500p. Date not set. price not set (ISBN 0-521-30161-0). Cambridge U Pr.

Moore, Keith L. The Developing Human. 3rd ed. (Illus.). 496p. 1982. 26.95 (ISBN 0-7216-6472-5). Saunders.

Newth, D. R. & Balls, M., eds. Maternal Effects in Development. LC 78-73812. (British Society for Developmental Biology Symposium Ser.: No. 4). (Illus.). 1980. 99.00 (ISBN 0-521-22685-6). Cambridge U Pr.

Nieuwkoop, P. D., et al. The Epigenetic Nature of Early Chordate Development. (Developmental & Cell Biology Ser.: No. 16). 368p. 1985. 69.50 (ISBN 0-521-25107-9). Cambridge U Pr.

O'Connor, Raymond. The Growth & Development of Birds. 315p. 1984. 39.95 (ISBN 0-471-90345-0). Wiley.

Parvez, S. & Parvez, H. Biogenic Amines in Development. 1980. 101.50 (ISBN 0-444-80215-0). Elsevier.

Poglazov, B. F. Morphogenesis of T-Even Bacteriophages. (Monographs in Developmental Biology: Vol. 7). 1973. 23.00 (ISBN 3-8055-1645-2). S Karger.

Pomerai, David De. From Gene to Animal: An Introduction to the Molecular Biology of Animal Development. (Illus.). 250p. 1985. 44.50 (ISBN 0-521-26084-1); pap. 14.95 (ISBN 0-521-27829-5). Cambridge U Pr.

Ralovich, B. Usteriosis Research: Present Situation & Perspective. 1984. text ed. 29.00 (ISBN 0-9910001-8-8, Pub. by Akademiai Kaido Hungary). Heyden.

Ransom, R. J. Computers & Embryos: Models in Developmental Biology. 224p. 1981. 42.95 (ISBN 0-471-09972-4, Pub. by Wiley-Interscience). Wiley.

Rockstein, Morris & Baker, George T., eds. Molecular Genetic Mechanisms in Aging & Development. 1972. 38.50 (ISBN 0-12-591550-0). Acad Pr.

Sauer, H. W., ed. Cellular Ageing. (Monographs in Developmental Biology: Vol. 17). (Illus.). x, 278p. 1984. 63.00 (ISBN 3-8055-3860-X). S Karger.

Sauer, Helmut. Developmental Biology of Physarum. LC 81-21682. (Developmental & Cell Biology Ser.: No. 11). 250p. 1982. 64.50 (ISBN 0-521-22703-8). Cambridge U Pr.

Scott, J. P., ed. Critical Periods. LC 78-632. (Benchmark Papers in Animal Behavior: Vol. 12). 381p. 1978. 52.95 (ISBN 0-87933-119-4). Van Nos Reinhold.

Sinclair, David. Human Growth after Birth. 4th ed. (Illus.). 245p. 1985. pap. 13.95x (ISBN 0-19-261494-0). Oxford U Pr.

Slack, J. From Egg to Embryo. (Developmental & Cell Biology Monographs: No. 13). 241p. 1984. pap. 24.95 (ISBN 0-521-27329-3). Cambridge U Pr.

Society For The Study Of Developmental Biology - 25th Symposium. Current Status of Some Major Problems in Developmental Biology: Proceedings. Locke, Michael, ed. 1967. 64.50 (ISBN 0-12-454162-3). Acad Pr.

Society For The Study Of Developmental Biology - 27th Symposium. Emergence of Order in Developing Systems: Proceedings. Locke, N., ed. 1969. 58.00 (ISBN 0-12-612960-6); pap. 44.50 (ISBN 0-12-612966-5). Acad Pr.

Society for the Study of Experimental Biology - 28th Symposium, 1969. Communication in Development. Lang, Anton, ed. (Journal of Developmental Biology: Suppl. 3). 1970. 54.00 (ISBN 0-12-612968-1); pap. 39.00 (ISBN 0-12-612969-X). Acad Pr.

Subtelny, Stephen & Green, Paul B. Development Order, Its Origin & Regulation: Fortieth Symposium for Developmental Biology. LC 81-20939. 582p. 1982. 68.00 (ISBN 0-8451-1501-4). A R Liss.

Subtelny, Stephen & Sussex, Ian M., eds. The Clonal Basis of Development. (Thirty Sixth Symposia of the Society for Developmental Biology Ser.). 1979. 41.00 (ISBN 0-12-612982-7). Acad Pr.

Tanner, J. M. Fetus into Man: Physical Growth from Conception to Maturity. (Illus.). 1978. 15.00x (ISBN 0-674-30703-8); pap. 7.95x (ISBN 0-674-30704-6). Harvard U Pr.

--A History of the Study of Human Growth. (Illus.). 500p. 1981. 77.50 (ISBN 0-521-22488-8). Cambridge U Pr.

Thorbecke, Gertruida J., ed. Biology of Aging & Development. LC 75-34295. (Illus.). 350p. 1976. 39.50x (ISBN 0-306-34503-X, Plenum Pr). Plenum Pub.

Vogel, M. Postnatal Development of the Cat's Retina. (Advances in Anatomy, Embryology, & Cell Biology: Vol. 54, Pt. 4). (Illus.). 1978. pap. 23.00 (ISBN 0-387-08799-0). Springer-Verlag.

Wachs, Theodore D. & Gruen, Gerald E. Early Experience & Human Development. LC 82-5273. 308p. 1982. 24.50x (ISBN 0-306-40685-3, Plenum Pr). Plenum Pub.

Watts, Elizabeth S. Nonhuman Primate Models for Human Growth & Development. (MP Ser.: Vol. 6). 328p. 1985. 46.00 (ISBN 0-8451-3405-1). A R Liss.

Weiss, Paul A. Dynamics of Development: Experiments & Inferences. LC 68-23476. (Illus.). 1968. 49.50 (ISBN 0-12-742850-X). Acad Pr.

Yamada, T. Control Mechanisms in Cell - Type Conversion in Newt Lens Regeneration. Walsky, A., ed. (Monographs in Developmental Biology: Vol. 13). (Illus.). 1977. 32.00 (ISBN 3-8055-2642-3). S Karger.

DEVELOPMENTAL GENETICS

American Society of Zoologists. Molecular Aspects of Early Development. Malacinski, George M. & Klein, William H., eds. 316p. 1984. 47.50x (ISBN 0-306-41496-1, Plenum Pr). Plenum Pub.

Davidson, Eric H. Gene Activity in Early Development. 1977. 35.50 (ISBN 0-12-205160-2). Acad Pr.

Rendel, James M. Canalisation & Gene Control. LC 67-28421. (Illus.). 1968. 41.50 (ISBN 0-12-586950-9). Acad Pr.

Stewart, Alistair D. & Hunt, David M. Genetic Basis of Development. LC 81-11591. (Tertiary Level Biology Ser.). 200p. 1982. 27.95x (ISBN 0-470-27234-1); pap. 29.95. Halsted Pr.

Waddington, Conrad H. New Patterns in Genetics & Development. LC 62-12875. (Illus.). 1962. 37.00x (ISBN 0-231-02509-2); pap. 15.00x (ISBN 0-231-08570-2). Columbia U Pr.

Wilkins, A. S. Genetic Analysis of Animal Development. 688p. 1985. 50.00 (ISBN 0-471-87662-3); pap. 30.00 (ISBN 0-471-87664-X). Wiley.

DEVELOPMENTAL NEUROLOGY

Duprat, A. M., et al, eds. The Role of Cell Interactions in Early Neurogenesis. (NATO ASI Life Sciences Series: Series A: Vol. 77). 344p. 1984. 55.00x (ISBN 0-306-41716-2, Plenum Pr). Plenum Pub.

Gribnau, A. A. & Geijsberts, L. G. Morphogenesis of the Brain in Staged Rhesus Monkey Embryos. (Advances in Anatomy, Embryology & Cell Biology Ser.: Vol. 91). (Illus.). 70p. 1985. pap. 19.50 (ISBN 0-387-13709-2). Springer-Verlag.

Lash, James W. & Saxen, Lauri. Developmental Mechanisms: Normal & Abnormal. LC 84-21863. (Progress in Clinical & Biological Research Ser.: Vol. 171). 352p. 1984. 56.00 (ISBN 0-8451-5021-9). A R Liss.

Rickmann, M. & Wolff, J. R. Prenatal Gliogenesis in the Neopallium of the Rat. (Advances in Anatomy, Embryology & Cell Biology Ser.: Vol. 93). (Illus.). 100p. 1985. pap. 25.00 (ISBN 0-387-13849-8). Springer-Verlag.

DEVILFISH

see Octopus

DEVONIAN PERIOD

see Geology, Stratigraphic–Devonian

DEXTRAN

Gronwall, Anders. Dextran & Its Use in Colloidal Infusion Solutions. (Illus.). 1957. 39.00 (ISBN 0-12-304050-7). Acad Pr.

Steinbereithner, K. & List, W. F., eds. Infusionstherapie mit Dextranen. (Beitraege zu Infusiostherapie und klinische Ernaehrung: Vol. 8). viii, 114p. 1981. 9.00 (ISBN 3-8055-2840-X). S Karger.

DIACETYLENE

see Acetylene

DIAGNOSIS, CYTOLOGIC

see also Exfoliative Cytology

LiVolsi, Virginia A. Practical Clinical Cytology. (Illus.). 352p. 1980. photocopy ed. 38.50x (ISBN 0-398-03927-5). C C Thomas.

Priest, Jean H. Human Cell Culture in Diagnosis of Disease. (Illus.). 300p. 1971. photocopy ed. 29.50x (ISBN 0-398-02384-0). C C Thomas.

DIAGRAMS, STATISTICAL

see Statistics–Charts, Tables, etc.; Statistics–Graphic Methods

DIALOG (INFORMATION RETRIEVAL SYSTEM)

The Adaptation of Virtual Man-Computer Interfaces to User Requirements in Dialogs. Dehning, W. (Lecture Notes in Computer Sciences Ser.: Vol. 110). 142p. 1981. pap. 12.00 (ISBN 0-387-10826-2). Springer-Verlag.

Dunster, Mark. Dialogue. 15p. (Orig.). 1985. pap. 4.00 (ISBN 0-89642-120-1). Linden Pubs.

Palmer, Roger C. Online Reference & Information Retrieval. (Library Science Text). 140p. (Orig.). 1982. pap. text ed. 18.50 (ISBN 0-87287-347-1). Libs Unl.

DIAMOND DRILLING

see Boring

DIAMOND MINES AND MINING

Burton, Richard F. Explorations of the Highlands of Brazil, with a Full Account of the Gold & Diamond Mines. Incl. Canoeing Down Fifteen Hundred Miles of the Great River Sao Francisco, from Sabara to the Sea. LC 68-55181. (Illus.). 1968. Repr. of 1869 ed. Set. 2 Vols. lib. bdg. 32.75x (ISBN 0-8371-3793-4, BUHB). Greenwood.

LaVarre, William J., Jr. Up the Mazaruni for Diamonds. (Illus.). 1.50 (ISBN 0-8338-0039-6). M Jones.

Reunert, Theodore. Diamonds & Gold in South Africa. LC 72-3916. (Black Heritage Library Collection Ser.). Repr. of 1893 ed. 29.50 (ISBN 0-8369-9106-0). Ayer Co Pubs.

Terry, Thomas P. Arkansas Diamonds. (Illus.). 40p. (Orig.). 1977. pap. 3.95 (ISBN 0-939850-04-4). Spec Pub.

DIAMONDS

see also Diamond Mines and Mining

Boyd, F. R. & Meyer, H. O., eds. Kimberlites, Diatremes, & Diamonds: Their Geology, Petrology & Geochemistry. LC 78-72025. (Illus.). 408p. 1979. 25.00 (ISBN 0-87590-212-X, SP0024). Am Geophysical.

Burton, Eric. Diamonds. 2nd ed. LC 78-66362. (Illus.). 1979. 35.00 (ISBN 0-8019-6789-9). Chilton.

Emmanuel, Harry. Diamonds & Precious Stones. 1977. 79.95 (ISBN 0-8490-1716-5). Gordon Pr.

Gaal, Robert A. The Diamond Dictionary. 2nd ed. (Illus.). 1977. 16.95 (ISBN 0-87311-008-0). Gemological.

Koskoff, David. The Diamond World. LC 81-47357. (Illus.). 352p. 1981. 15.34i (ISBN 0-06-038005-5, HarpT). Har-Row.

Lenzen. Diamonds & Diamond Grading. 1983. text ed. 59.95 (ISBN 0-408-00547-5). Butterworth.

Orlov, Yu L. Minerology of the Diamond. LC 77-12633. 1977. 62.00x (ISBN 0-471-01869-4, Pub. by Wiley-Interscience). Wiley.

Patch, Susanne S. Blue Mystery: The Story of the Hope Diamond. LC 75-619404. (Illus.). 64p. 1975. 9.95 (ISBN 0-87474-740-6); pap. 4.50 (ISBN 0-87474-165-3). Smithsonian.

Streeter, E. W. The Great Diamonds of the World. 75.00 (ISBN 0-8490-0257-5). Gordon Pr.

Wilson, Arthur N. Diamonds: From Birth to Eternity. Ross, Michael & Eash, Dianne, eds. 1982. 29.95 (ISBN 0-87311-010-2). Gemological.

DIAPHRAGMS (MECHANICAL DEVICES)

see also Pressure-Gages; Pressure–Measurement

Boyes, R. G. Structural & Cut-off Diaphragm Walls. (Illus.). 181p. 1975. 40.75 (ISBN 0-85334-607-0, Pub. by Elsevier Applied Sci England). Elsevier.

DiGiovanni. Flat & Corrugated Diapharm Design Handbook. (Mechanical Engineering Ser.: Vol. 9). 424p. 1982. 65.00 (ISBN 0-8247-1281-1). Dekker.

Hajnal, I., et al. Construction of Diaphragm Walls. 399p. 1984. 49.95 (ISBN 0-471-10002-1). Wiley.

Institution of Civil Engineers Staff, ed. Diaphragm Walls & Anchorages. 231p. 1975. 55.50x (ISBN 0-7277-0005-7). Am Soc Civil Eng.

DIASPINAE

see Scale-Insects

DIATOMACEAE

Bicudo, C. E. & Azevedo, M. T. Desmidioflorula Paulista I: Genero Arthordesmus Ehr. ex Ralfs Emend. Arch. (Bibliotheca Phycologica Ser.: No. 36). (Port., Illus.). 1978. text ed. 14.00 (ISBN 3-7682-1156-8). Lubrecht & Cramer.

Brun, J. Diatomees des Alpes et du Jura et de la region suisse et francaise de Environs de Geneve. (Illus.). 1965. 12.40 (ISBN 90-6123-028-4). Lubrecht & Cramer.

Camburn, K. E., et al. The Haptobenthic Diatom Flora of Long Branch Creek, South Carolina. (Offprint from Nova Hedwigia Ser.: No. 30). (Illus.). 1979. 21.00x (ISBN 3-7682-1197-5). Lubrecht & Cramer.

Castracane Degli Antelminelli, F. Report on the Diatoms Collected During the Voyage of H.M.S. Challenger. (Illus.). 1966. Repr. of 1886 ed. 33.60 (ISBN 3-7682-0293-3). Lubrecht & Cramer.

Cholnoky, B. J. Die Oekologie der Diatomeen in Binnengewaessern. (Illus.). 1968. 52.50 (ISBN 3-7682-5421-6). Lubrecht & Cramer.

Cholnoky, B. J., ed. Diatomaceae I. 1966. 42.00 (ISBN 3-7682-5421-6). Lubrecht & Cramer.

Clark, R. L. & Rushforth, S. R. Diatom Studies of the Headwaters of Henrys Fork of the Snake River, Island Park, Idaho, USA. (Bibliotheca Phycologica Ser.: No. 33). 1977. pap. text ed. 17.50x (ISBN 3-7682-1149-5). Lubrecht & Cramer.

Cleve, P. T. Synopsis of the Naviculoid Diatoms. (Illus.). 1965. Repr. of 1895 ed. 41.85 (ISBN 90-6123-034-9). Lubrecht & Cramer.

Cleve, P. T. & Grunow, A. Beitraege zur Kenntnis der arctischen Diatomeen. 1976. pap. text ed. 17.15 (ISBN 3-87429-101-4). Lubrecht & Cramer.

Cleve-Euler, A. Die Diatomeen von Schweden und Finnland, 5 pts. (Kungl. Sv. Vetenskapsak Handl Ser.). (Illus.). 1968. pap. 122.50 (ISBN 3-7682-0550-9). Lubrecht & Cramer.

Collins, Gary B. & Kalinsky, Robert G. Studies on Ohio Diatoms: Diatoms of the Scioto River Basin & Referenced Checklist from Ohio Exclusive of Lake Erie & the Ohio River. 1977. 7.00 (ISBN 0-86727-080-2). Ohio Bio Survey.

Cupp, Easter E. Marine Plankton Diatoms of the West Coast of North America. 1977. pap. text ed. 33.60x (ISBN 3-87429-125-1). Lubrecht & Cramer.

Czarnecki, D. B. & Blinn, D. W. Diatoms of Southwestern U. S. A. Diatoms of Lower Lake Powell & Vicinity, Vol. 1. (Bibliotheca Phycologica: No. 28). 1977. pap. text ed. 12.40 (ISBN 3-7682-1102-9). Lubrecht & Cramer.

--Diatoms of Southwestern USA: Diatoms of the Colorado River in Grand Canyon National Park and Vicinity, Vol. 2. (Illus.). 1978. pap. text ed. 17.50 (ISBN 3-7682-1182-7). Lubrecht & Cramer.

Feldmann-Mazoyer, Genevieve. Recherches sur les Ceramiaceae de la Mediterranee. 1977. pap. text ed. 61.60x (ISBN 3-87429-120-0). Lubrecht & Cramer.

Foged, N. Diatom Fora in Springs in Jutland Denmark. (Illus.). 344p. 1984. lib. bdg. 35.00x (ISBN 3-7682-1378-1). Lubrecht & Cramer.

--Diatoms Found in a Bottom Sediment Sample from a Small Deep Lake in the Northern Slope, Alaska. 1971. pap. text ed. 10.50 (ISBN 3-7682-0824-9). Lubrecht & Cramer.

--Diatoms in Eastern Australia. (Bibliotheca Phycologica Ser.: No. 41). (Illus.). 1979. 21.00 (ISBN 3-7682-1203-3). Lubrecht & Cramer.

--Diatoms in New Zealand, the North Island. (Bibliotheca Phycologica: No. 47). (Illus.). 1979. pap. text ed. 21.00x (ISBN 3-7682-1253-X). Lubrecht & Cramer.

--Freshwater Diatoms in Ireland. (Bibliotheca Phycologica Ser.: No. 34). (Illus.). 1977. lib. bdg. 17.50x (ISBN 3-7682-1155-X). Lubrecht & Cramer.

Foged, Niels. Diatoms in Alaska. (Bibliotheca Phycologica). (Illus.). 318p. 1981. text ed. 28.00x (ISBN 3-7682-1303-X). Lubrecht & Cramer.

--Diatoms in Oland, Sweden. (Bibliotheca Phycologica Ser.: No. 49). (Illus.). 194p. 1980. pap. 17.50 (ISBN 3-7682-1269-6). Lubrecht & Cramer.

--Diatoms in Samos, a Greek Island in the Aegean: Diatoms in Kos & Kalymnos, Two Greek Islands. (Bibliotheca Diatomologica Ser.: No. 10). (Illus.). 226p. 1985. lib. bdg. 28.00 (ISBN 3-7682-1443-5). Lubrecht & Cramer.

--Freshwater & Littoral Diatoms from Cuba. (Bibliotheca Diatomologica Ser.: Vol. 5). (Illus.). 248p. 1984. lib. bdg. 35.00x (ISBN 3-7682-1407-9). Lubrecht & Cramer.

Gerloff, J. & Cholnoky, B. J., eds. Friedrich-Hustedt-Gedenkband: Diatomaceae 2. 1970. 87.500 (ISBN 3-7682-5431-3). Lubrecht & Cramer.

Gleser, S. I., et al. The Diatoms of the USSR, Fossil & Recent, Vol. 1. (Illus.). 403p. 1979. Repr. of 1974 ed. lib. bdg. 79.20 (ISBN 3-87429-168-5). Lubrecht & Cramer.

Greville, R. K. Descriptions of New & Rare Diatoms. (Trans. Microscop. Soc. Ser.). (Illus.). 1968. 28.00 (ISBN 3-7682-0570-3). Lubrecht & Cramer.

Grimes, Judith A. & Rushforth, S. R. Diatoms of Recent Bottom Sediments of Utah Lake, Utah, USA. (Bibliotheca Phycologica Ser.: No. 55). (Illus.). 180p. 1982. text ed. 21.00x (ISBN 3-7682-1310-2). Lubrecht & Cramer.

Hanna, G. Dallas. Species-Index to Schmidt-Hustedt: Atlas Zur Diatomaceen Kunde. (Illus.). 1969. pap. 14.00 (ISBN 3-7682-0611-4). Lubrecht & Cramer.

Helmcke, J. G. & Krieger, W. Diatomeenschalen Im Elektronenmikroskopischen Bild. Incl. Part 6. 1966 (ISBN 3-7682-0174-0); Part 7. Marine Diatoms. Okumo, H., ed. 1969 (ISBN 3-7682-0175-9). (Illus.). 52.50. Lubrecht & Cramer.

Hohn, Matthew H. Qualitative & Quantitative Analyses of Plankton Diatoms. 1969. 6.00 (ISBN 0-86727-057-8). Ohio Bio Survey.

Hustedt, F. Die Diatomeenflora des Fluss-Systems der Weser im Gebiet der Hansestadt Bremen. 1976. pap. text ed. 40.00x (ISBN 3-87429-102-2). Lubrecht & Cramer.

--The Pennate Diatoms: A Translation of Hustedt's Die Kieselagen, Vol. 2. Jensen, Norman G., tr. from Ger. Tr. of Die Kieselalgen. (Illus.). 918p. 1985. Repr. of 1959 ed. lib. bdg. 87.50x (ISBN 3-7682-1416-8). Lubrecht & Cramer.

Hustedt, Friedrich. Bacillariophyta: Diatomeae. (Suesswasserflora Mitteleuropas Ser.: Vol. 10). (Ger., Illus.). 466p. 1976. 48.30x (ISBN 3-87429-111-1). Lubrecht & Cramer.

--Suesswasser-Diatomeen des indo-Malayischen Archipels und der Hawaii-Inseln. (Ger.). 1979. Repr. of 1942 ed. lib. bdg. 56.00x (ISBN 3-87429-162-6). Lubrecht & Cramer.

--Systematische und Oekologische Untersuchungen ueber die Diatomeenflora von Java, Bali und Sumatra. (Illus.). 709p. 1980. Repr. lib. bdg. 161.00x (ISBN 3-87429-170-7). Lubrecht & Cramer.

Inte. Table Constants Tables of V17. 1971. 170.00 (ISBN 0-08-016546-X). Pergamon.

John, Jacob. Diatom Flora of the Swan River Esturary Western Australia. (Bibliotheca Phycologia Ser.: No. 64). (Illus.). 360p. 1983. lib. bdg. 35.00x (ISBN 3-7682-1360-9). Lubrecht & Cramer.

Lawson, L. L. & Rushforth, S. R. The Diatom Flora of the Provo River, Utah (USA) 1975. 17.50 (ISBN 3-7682-0955-5). Lubrecht & Cramer.

Mann, Albert. Report on the Diatoms of the Albatross Voyage in the Pacific Ocena, 1888-1904. 1978. pap. text ed. 21.00x (ISBN 3-87429-132-4). Lubrecht & Cramer.

Mann, D. G., ed. International Diatom Symposium, 7th, Philadelphia, Aug. 1982: Proceedings. (Illus.). 541p. 1984. lib. bdg. 26.25x (ISBN 3-87429-217-7). Lubrecht & Cramer.

Patrick, Ruth & Reimer, Charles W. The Diatoms of the United States Exclusive of Alaska & Hawaii, Vol. 1. LC 65-29113. (Monograph: No. 13). (Illus.). 688p. 1966. lib. bdg. 41.00 (ISBN 0-910006-20-2); Set. write for info. (ISBN 0-910006-19-9). Acad Nat Sci Phila.

--The Diatoms of the United States Exclusive of Alaska & Hawaii, Vol. 2, Pt. 1. (Monograph: No. 13). (Illus.). 213p. 1975. lib. bdg. 30.00 (ISBN 0-910006-21-0). Acad Nat Sci Phila.

Peragallo, H & Peragallo, M. Les Diatomees Marines de France et des Districts Maririmes Voisins. (Gr., Illus.). 539p. 1984. Repr. of 1908 ed. lib. bdg. 133.00X (ISBN 3-87429-219-3). Lubrecht & Cramer.

Peragallo, H. & Peragallo, M. Les Diatomees Marines De la France, 2 vols. (Illus.). 1965. 100.00 (ISBN 90-6123-212-0). Lubrecht & Cramer.

Podzorski, A. C. An Illustrated & Annotated Check-list of Diatoms from the Black River Waterways, St. Elizabeth, Jamaica. (Bibliotheca Diatomologica Ser.: No. 7). (Illus.). 178p. 1985. lib. bdg. 21.00x (ISBN 3-7682-1422-2). Lubrecht & Cramer.

Recent & Fossil Marine Diatoms, 3rd Symposium, 1975. Proceedings. Simonsen, R., ed. 1975. 87.50 (ISBN 3-7682-5453-4). Lubrecht & Cramer.

Reichardt, E. Die Diatomeen der Altmuehl. (Bibliotheca Diatomologica Ser.: Vol. 6). (Illus.). 170p. 1985. lib. bdg. 21.00 (ISBN 3-7682-1411-7). Lubrecht & Cramer.

Ross, R., ed. Symposium on Recent & Fossil Diatoms Proceedings Budapest Sept. 1980, Taxonomy, Morphology, Ecology, Biology, 6th. (Illus.). 500p. 1982. text ed. 87.50x (ISBN 3-87429-192-8). Lubrecht & Cramer.

Schrader, H. J. Die Pennaten Diatomeen Aus Dem Obereozaen Von Oamaru, Neuseeland. (Illus.). 1969. 14.00 (ISBN 3-7682-5428-3). Lubrecht & Cramer.

Simonsen, R. Bacillaria: International Journal for Diatom Research, Vol. 6. (Illus.). 292p. 1983. lib. bdg. 28.00x (ISBN 0-686-40539-0). Lubrecht & Cramer.

--Bacillaria: International Journal for Diatom Research, Vol. 7. (Illus.). 200p. 1984. lib. bdg. 28.00x (ISBN 0-318-04382-3). Lubrecht & Cramer.

Simonsen, R., ed. Bacillaria: International Journal for Diatom Research, Vol. 2. (Illus.). lib. bdg. 28.00x (ISBN 0-17-001891-1). Lubrecht & Cramer.

--Fifth Symposium on Recent & Fossil Diatoms, Antwerp, 1978: Proceedings. (Illus.). 1979. lib. bdg. 70.00 (ISBN 3-7682-5464-X). Lubrecht & Cramer.

--Fourth Symposium on Recent & Fossil Marine Diatoms, Oslo 1976: Proceedings. (Beiheft zur Nova Hedwigia Ser.: No. 54). (Illus.). 1977. lib. bdg. 70.00x (ISBN 3-7682-5454-2). Lubrecht & Cramer.

--Symposium on Recent & Fossil Marine Diatoms, 3rd, Oslo, 1976: Proceedings. (Illus.). 1977. text ed. 70.00x (ISBN 3-7682-5453-4). Lubrecht & Cramer.

Symposium on Recent & Fossil Marine Diatoms, First, 1972. Proceedings. Simonsen, R., ed. 1972. 52.50 (ISBN 3-7682-5439-9). Lubrecht & Cramer.

Symposium on Recent & Fossil Marine Diatoms, Second, 1974. Proceedings. Simonsen, R., ed. 1974. 87.50 (ISBN 3-7682-5445-3). Lubrecht & Cramer.

Van Der Werff, A. & Huls, H. Diatomeenflora van Nederland, 10 fasc. in one vol. 1976. Repr. looseleaf binder 98.00x (ISBN 3-87429-113-8). Lubrecht & Cramer.

Van Heurck, H. A. A Treatise on the Diatomacea. 1962. Repr. of 1896 ed. 42.00 (ISBN 3-7682-0116-3). Lubrecht & Cramer.

Van Landingham, S. Catalogue of the Fossil & Recent Genera & Species of Diatoms & Their Synonyms: Suppl. Taxa, Additions & Corrections, Pt. 8. 1979. lib. bdg. 35.00 (ISBN 3-7682-0478-2). Lubrecht & Cramer.

Van Landingham, S. L. Catalogue of the Fossil & Recent Genera & Species of Diatoms & Their Synonyms-Part 7: Rhoicosphenia Through Zygoceros. 1979. lib. bdg. 35.00x (ISBN 3-7682-0477-4). Lubrecht & Cramer.

--Miocene Non-Marine Diatoms from the Yakima Region in South Central Washington. (Illus.). 1965. pap. 16.00 (ISBN 3-7682-5414-3). Lubrecht & Cramer.

--Paleoecology & Microfloristics of Miocene Diatomites from the Otis Basin-Juntura Region of Harney & Malheur Counties, Oregon. (Illus.). 1967. pap. 14.00 (ISBN 3-7682-5426-7). Lubrecht & Cramer.

Vinyard, William C. Diatoms of North America. 2nd ed. (Illus.). 120p. 1979. pap. 8.95x (ISBN 0-916422-15-1). Mad River.

Werner, Dietrich, ed. The Biology of Diatoms. LC 76-55574. (Botanical Monographs: Vol. 13). 1977. 68.50x (ISBN 0-520-03400-7). U of Cal Pr.

West, W. & West, G. S. Monograph of the British Desmidiaceae, 5 Vols. Repr. of 1923 ed. Set. 185.00 (ISBN 0-384-66946-8). Johnson Repr.

Williams, D. M. Morphology, Taxonomy & Interrelationships of the Ribbed Araphid Diatoms from the Genera Diatoma & Meridion: Diatomaceae, Bacillariophyta. (Bibliotheca Diatomologica Ser.: No. 9). (Illus.). 256p. 1985. lib. bdg. 28.00x (ISBN 3-7682-1431-1). Lubrecht & Cramer.

Wujek, E. D. & Rupp, R. F. Diatoms of the Tittabawassee River, Michigan. (Bibliotheca Phycologica: No. 50). (Illus.). 160p. 1981. pap. text ed. 17.50x (ISBN 3-7682-1271-8). Lubrecht & Cramer.

DIAZO COMPOUNDS

Patai, Saul, ed. The Chemistry of Diazonium & Diazo Groups, 2 pts. LC 75-6913. (Chemistry of Functional Groups Ser.). Pt. 1. pap. 131.00 (ISBN 0-317-10696-1, 2022404); Pt. 2. pap. 143.00 (ISBN 0-317-10697-X). Bks Demand UMI.

Regitz, Manfred & Maas, Gerhard. Diazo Compounds: Properties & Synthesis. Date not set. price not set (ISBN 0-12-585840-X). Acad Pr.

Saunders, K. H. & Allen, R. L. Aromatic Diazo Compounds. 3rd ed. 850p. 1985. 175.00 (ISBN 0-7131-3499-2). E Arnold.

DICHROISM

Crabbe, Pierre. ORD & CD in Chemistry & Biochemistry: An Introduction. 1972. 41.50 (ISBN 0-12-194650-9). Acad Pr.

Mason, S. F. Molecular Optical Activity & the Chiral Discriminations. LC 82-1125. (Illus.). 250p. 1982. 44.50 (ISBN 0-521-24702-0). Cambridge U Pr.

OAS General Secretariat Dept. of Scientific & Technological Affairs. Actividad Optica, Dispersion Rotatoria Optica y Dicroismo Circular En Quimica Organica. 2nd ed. (Quimica Ser.: Monografia No. 11). (Span.). 70p. 1981. pap. 3.50 (ISBN 0-8270-1418-X). OAS.

Velluz, L., et al. Optical Circular Dichroism: Principles Measurements, & Applications. (Illus.). 1969. 34.20x (ISBN 3-527-25289-4). VCH Pubs.

DICOTYLEDONS

Chater, Hara H. & Williams, A. O. An Enumeration of the Flowering Plants of Nepal: Vol. 3, Dicotyledons. (Illus.). 226p. 1982. pap. text ed. 66.00x (ISBN 0-565-00854-4). Sabbot-Natural Hist Bks.

Corner, E. J. H. The Seeds of Dicotyledons, 2 vols. LC 74-14434. (Illus.). 860p. 1976. Vol. 1. 99.50 (ISBN 0-521-20688-X); Vol. 2. 145.00 (ISBN 0-521-20687-1). Cambridge U Pr.

Godfrey, Robert K. & Wooten, Jean W. Aquatic & Wetland Plants of Southeastern United States: Dicotyledons. LC 80-16452. (Illus.). 944p. 1981. lib. bdg. 45.00x (ISBN 0-8203-0532-4). U of Ga Pr.

Hara, H. & Williams, L. H. Enumeration of the Flowering Plants of Nepal: Vol. 2, Dicotyledons. 1979. pap. 56.00x (ISBN 0-565-00810-2, Pub. by Brit Mus Nat Hist). Sabbot-Natural Hist Bks.

Metcalfe, C. R. & Chalk, L., eds. Anatomy of the Dicotyledons, Vol. 1. 2nd ed. (Illus.). 1980. 68.00x (ISBN 0-19-854383-2). Oxford U Pr.

Metclfe, C. R. & Chalk, L. Anatomy of the Dicotyledons: Wood Structure & Conclusion of the General Introduction, Vol. 2. 2nd ed. (Illus.). 1983. 75.00x (ISBN 0-19-854559-2). Oxford U Pr.

Mohlenbrock, Robert H. Flowering Plants: Basswoods to Spurges. LC 81-8585. (Illustrated Flora of Illinois). (Illus.). 256p. 1982. 22.95x (ISBN 0-8093-1025-2). S Ill U Pr.

--Flowering Plants: Hollies to Loasas. LC 77-28934. (Illustrated Flora of Illinois Ser.). (Illus.). 320p. 1978. 22.95x (ISBN 0-8093-0845-2). S Ill U Pr.

Rendle, Alfred B. Classification of Flowering Plants, 2 bks. Incl. Bk. 1. Gymnosperms & Monocotyledons; Bk. 2. Dicotyledons. 90.00 (ISBN 0-521-06057-5). Cambridge U Pr.

Seedlings of Dicotyledons. 1980. pap. 88.00 (ISBN 90-220-0696-4, PDC167, Pudoc). Unipub.

Stone, B. C. The Genus Pelea A. Gray: Rutaceae: Evodiiae. (Taxonomic Monographs). 1969. pap. 35.00 (ISBN 3-7682-0635-1). Lubrecht & Cramer.

Willis, J. H. A Handbook to Plants in Victoria, Vol. 2: Dicotyledons. 1972. 40.00x (ISBN 0-522-84037-X, Pub by Melbourne U Pr Australia). Intl Spec Bk.

DIE CASTING

Brazier, L. R., et al, eds. Die & Mould Making. (Engineering Craftsmen: No. H22). (Illus.). 1970. spiral bdg. 42.50x (ISBN 0-85083-126-1). Trans-Atlantic.

Kaye & Street. Die Casting Metallurgy. 1982. text ed. 49.95 (ISBN 0-408-10717-0). Butterworth.

Plyatskii, V. M. Extrusion Casting. LC 65-29302. (Illus.). 316p. 1965. 22.50x (ISBN 0-911184-06-6). Primary.

Street, Arthur. The Diecasting Book. 796p. 1981. 150.00x (ISBN 0-901994-98-7, Pub. by Portcullio Pr). State Mutual Bk.

Upton, B. Pressure Diecasting: Metals-Machines-Furnaces, Pt. 1. (Materials Engineering Practice Ser.). (Illus.). 165p. 1982. 28.00 (ISBN 0-08-027621-0); pap. 13.25 (ISBN 0-08-027622-9). Pergamon.

DIELECTRICS

see also Dipole Moments; Electrets; Ferroelectricity

Akhadov, Ya Y. Dielectric Properties of Binary Solutions: A Data Handbook. 400p. 1981. 125.00 (ISBN 0-08-023600-6). Pergamon.

American Society for Testing & Materials. Measurement of Dielectric Properties under Space Conditions. LC 67-17472. (American Society for Testing & Materials. Special Technical Publication: No. 420). pap. 26.50 (ISBN 0-317-08047-4, 2001119). Bks Demand UMI.

Bottcher, C. J., et al. Theory of Electric Polarization, Vol. 1: Dielectrics in Static Fields. 2nd ed. Van Belle, O.. C. & Bordewijk, P., eds. LC 72-83198. 396p. 1973. 106.50 (ISBN 0-444-41019-8). Elsevier.

Bunget, I. & Popescu, M. Physics of Solid Dielectrics. (Materials Science Monographs: No. 19). 446p. 1984. 90.75 (ISBN 0-444-99632-X, I-039-84). Elsevier.

Christophorou, L. G., ed. Gaseous Dielectrics III: Proceedings of the Third International Symposium on Gaseous Dielectrics, Knoxville, Tennessee, USA, March 7-11, 1982. LC 82-9825. (Illus.). 600p. 1982. 105.00 (ISBN 0-08-029381-6, A110). Pergamon.

Christophorou, Loucas G., ed. Gaseous Dielectrics II: Proceedings of the Second International Symposium on Gaseous Dielectrics, Knoxville, Tenn., U.S.A., March 9-13, 1980. 506p. 1980. 30.00 (ISBN 0-08-025978-2). Pergamon.

CISM (International Center for Mechanical Sciences) Polorization Gradient in Elastic Dielectric. Mindlin, R. D., ed. (CISM Pubns. Ser.: No. 24). (Illus.). 55p. 1973. pap. 10.40 (ISBN 0-387-81087-0). Springer-Verlag.

Conference on Electrical Insulation & Dielectric Phenomena. Annual Report. Incl. 1952. 61p; 1957. 69p; 1958. 57p; 1963. 144p. 5.00 (ISBN 0-309-01141-8); 1964. 146p. 5.00 (ISBN 0-309-01238-4); 1965. 139p. 5.00 (ISBN 0-686-64609-6); 1966. 129p. 10.00 (ISBN 0-309-01484-0); 1967. 201p. 10.00 (ISBN 0-309-01578-2); 1968. 204p. 10.00 (ISBN 0-309-01705-X); 1969. 193p. 15.00 (ISBN 0-309-01764-5); 1970. 258p. 15.00 (ISBN 0-309-01870-6); 1971. 289p. 15.00 (ISBN 0-309-02032-8); 1972. 496p. 20.00 (ISBN 0-309-02112-X); 1973. 638p. 25.00 (ISBN 0-309-02229-0); 1974. 706p. 25.00 (ISBN 0-309-02416-1); 1975. 544p. 22.00 (ISBN 0-686-64610-X); 1976. 576p. 25.00 (ISBN 0-686-64611-8); 1977. 596p. 25.00 (ISBN 0-309-02866-3); 1978. 405p. 25.00 (ISBN 0-309-02861-2); 1979. 25.00 (ISBN 0-309-02933-3). Natl Acad Pr.

--Digest of Literature on Dielectrics, Vols. 11-13, 18-42. Incl. Vol. 11. 1947; Vol. 12. 1948; Vol. 13. 1949; Vol. 18. 1954; Vol. 19. 1955; Vol. 20. 1956; Vol. 21. 1957; Vol. 22. 1958; Vol. 24. 1960; Vol. 25. 1961. 15.00 (ISBN 0-309-01034-9); Vol. 26. 1962; Vol. 27. 1963. 15.00 (ISBN 0-309-01230-9); Vol. 28. 1964. 27.00 (ISBN 0-309-01342-9); Vol. 29. 1965. 27.00 (ISBN 0-309-01461-1); Vol. 30. 1966. 27.00 (ISBN 0-309-01496-4); Vol. 31. 1967. 27.00 (ISBN 0-309-01595-2); Vol. 32. 1968. 35.00 (ISBN 0-309-01732-7); Vol. 33. 1969. 35.00 (ISBN 0-309-01856-0); Vol. 34. 1970. 35.00 (ISBN 0-309-01920-6); Vol. 35. 1971. 40.00 (ISBN 0-309-02049-2); Vol. 36. 1972. 40.00 (ISBN 0-309-02316-5); Vol. 37. 1973. 40.00 (ISBN 0-309-02437-4); Vol. 38, 1977. 40.00 (ISBN 0-309-02643-1); Vol. 39, 1975. 45.00 (ISBN 0-309-02748-9); Vol. 40, 1976. 45.00 (ISBN 0-309-02787-X); Vol. 41, 1979. 45.00 (ISBN 0-309-02886-8); Vol. 42, 1979. 45.00 (ISBN 0-309-02934-1). Natl Acad Pr.

Croydon, W. F. & Parker, E. H. Dielectric Films on Gallium Arsenide, Vol.1. (Electrocomponent Science Monographs). 160p. 1981. 23.00 (ISBN 0-677-05710-5). Gordon.

Davies, Mansel, ed. Dielectric & Related Molecular Processes, Vols. 1-3. LC 72-83457. Vol. 1. 1966-71 literature 41.00 (ISBN 0-85186-505-4); Vol. 2. 1972-73 literature 43.00 (ISBN 0-85186-515-1); Vol. 3. 1974-76 literature 57.00 (ISBN 0-85186-525-9). Am Chemical.

Dielectric Materials Measurements & Applications. (IEE Conference Publications Ser.: No. 239). 313p. 1984. pap. 80.00 (ISBN 0-85296-296-7). Inst Elect Eng.

Engineering Dielectrics: Volume 1: Corona Measurement & Interpretation, STP 669. 520p. 1979. 49.00x (ISBN 0-8031-0332-8, 04-669000-21). ASTM.

Gallagher, T. J. Simple Dielectric Liquids: Mobility, Conduction, & Breakdown. (Oxford Science Research Papers Ser). (Illus.). 1975. pap. 34.95x (ISBN 0-19-851933-8). Oxford U Pr.

Grant, E. H., et al. Dielectric Behaviour of Biological Molecules in Solution. (Monographs on Physical Biochemistry). (Illus.). 1978. 55.00x (ISBN 0-19-854621-1). Oxford U Pr.

Heller, Wilfried, et al. Angular Scattering Functions for Spheroids. LC 77-156067. 144p. 1972. text ed. 12.00x (ISBN 0-8143-1454-6). Wayne St U Pr.

International Conference on Electrets, Charge Storage, & Transport in Dielectrics (2d: 1972 Miami Beach, FL) Electrets, Charge Storage, & Transport in Dielectrics. Perlman, Martin M., ed. LC 73-75172. pap. 160.00 (ISBN 0-317-08563-8, 2050863). Bks Demand UMI.

Jennings, B. R., ed. Electro-Optics & Dielectrics of a Macromolecules & Colloids. LC 79-10117. 423p. 1979. 65.00x (ISBN 0-306-40169-X, Plenum Pr). Plenum Pub.

Kaminow, Ivan P. An Introduction to Electrooptic Devices. 1974. 49.50 (ISBN 0-12-395050-3). Acad Pr.

Karasz, Frank E., ed. Dielectric Properties of Polymers. LC 74-185258. 375p. 1972. 59.50x (ISBN 0-306-30581-X, Plenum Pr). Plenum Pub.

Kirkwood, John G. Dielectrics-Intermolecular Forces-Optical Rotation. Cole, Robert H., ed. (Documents on Modern Physics Ser.). (Illus.). 282p. (Orig.). 1965. 44.25 (ISBN 0-677-00405-2). Gordon.

Kiselev, V. F. & Krylov, O. V. Adsorption Processes on Semiconductor & Dielectric Surfaces I. (Springer Series in Chemical Physics: Vol. 32). (Illus.). 295p. Date not set. 43.50 (ISBN 0-387-12416-0). Springer-Verlag.

McConnell, James. Rotational Brownian Motion & Dielectric Theory. 1980. 56.50 (ISBN 0-12-481850-1). Acad Pr.

Morgan, J. Derald & Abdullah, Mohammed. Dielectric Engineering Practice in Power Apparatus. 450p. 1984. pap. text ed. 49.95 (ISBN 0-317-05122-9). Macmillan.

Pethig, Ronald. Dielectric & Electronic Properties of Biological Materials. LC 78-13694. 376p. 1979. 71.95 (ISBN 0-471-99728-5, Pub. by Wiley-Interscience). Wiley.

Phillips, James C. Covalent Bonding in Crystals, Molecules & Polymers. LC 74-104037. (Chicago Lectures in Physics Ser). 1970. pap. 8.00x (ISBN 0-226-66770-7). U of Chicago Pr.

Physics of Dielectric Solids. (Reports on Progress in Physics Ser.: No. 58). 1981. 57.50 (ISBN 0-9960039-4-0, Pub. by Inst Physics England). Heyden.

Poole, Charles P., et al. Relaxation in Magnetic Resonance: Dielectric & Mossbauer Applications. 1971. 70.50 (ISBN 0-12-561450-0). Acad Pr.

Zhelduev, I. S. Physics of Crystalline Dielectrics, 2 vols. Incl. Vol. 1: Crystallography & Spontaneour Polarization. 336p. 34.50 (ISBN 0-306-37781-0); Vol. 2: Electrical Properites. 284p. 35.00 (ISBN 0-306-37782-9). 1977 (Plenum Pr). Plenum Pub.

DIES (METAL-WORKING)

see also Die Casting; Punching Machinery; Tool and Die Industry

American Society Of Tool & Manufacturing Engineers. ASTME Die Design Handbook. 2nd ed. Wilson, Frank W., ed. 1965. 74.50 (ISBN 0-07-001523-6). McGraw.

Dallas, Daniel B. Pressworking Aids for Designers & Diemakers. LC 77-90988. (Manufacturing Data Ser.). 1978. 26.50x (ISBN 0-87263-042-0). SME.

Keyes, Karl A., ed. Innovations in Die Design. LC 81-84032. (Manufacturing Update Ser.). (Illus.). 250p. 1982. text ed. 32.00 (ISBN 0-87263-073-0). SME.

Paquin, J. R. Die Design Fundamentals. LC 62-19251. (Illus.). 1962. 23.95 (ISBN 0-8311-1010-4); wkbk. o.p. 7.00 (ISBN 0-8311-1011-2). Indus Pr.

Pollack, Herman. Tool Design. (Illus.). 528p. 1976. 25.95 (ISBN 0-87909-840-6). Reston.

Society of Manufacturing Engineers. Die Design & Construction, Pts. 1 & 2 In One Vol. Vezzani, A. A., ed. LC 61-17931. 1971. pap. 9.75x (ISBN 0-911168-13-3). Prakken.

DIES (SCREW-CUTTING)

see Taps and Dies

DIESEL ENGINE

see Diesel Motor

DIESEL FUEL

American Society of Mechanical Engineers. Report on Diesel & Gas Engines Power Costs, 1974: Data for 1972 & Previous Years. pap. 20.00 (ISBN 0-317-08172-1, 2013318). Bks Demand UMI.

Matching Diesel Fuel Quality to Diesel Engine Requirements. 48p. 1984. 17.50 (ISBN 0-89883-348-5, SP577). Soc Auto Engineers.

DIESEL LOCOMOTIVE ENGINES

see Diesel Locomotives

DIESEL LOCOMOTIVES

Albert, Dave & Melvin, George F. New England Diesels. LC 75-27730. (Illus.). 1977. 28.95 (ISBN 0-916160-01-7). G R Cockle.

Allen, David. Diesels in the North East. 112p. 30.00x (ISBN 0-86093-262-1, Pub. by ORPC Ltd UK). State Mutual Bk.

--Diesels Nationwide, Vol. 3. 128p. 30.00x (ISBN 0-86093-113-7, Pub. by ORPC Ltd UK). State Mutual Bk.

Allen, Jan. Diesels in East Anglia. 80p. 30.00x (ISBN 0-86093-105-6, Pub. by ORPC Ltd UK). State Mutual Bk.

American Society of Mechanical Engineers. Report on Diesel & Gas Engines Power Costs, 1974: Data for 1972 & Previous Years. pap. 20.00 (ISBN 0-317-08172-1, 2013318). Bks Demand UMI.

Cortani, R. M. Diesels of the Espee: Alco PA's. LC 75-38238. (Illus.). 1975. 22.50 (ISBN 0-89685-034-X). Chatham Pub CA.

Diesel Years. 19.95 (ISBN 0-685-83333-X). Chatham Pub CA.

Dolzall, Gary & Dolzall, Stephen. Diesel From Eddystone: The Story of Baldwin Diesel Locomotives. Hayden, Bob, ed. (Illus.). 152p. (Orig.). 1984. pap. 18.95 (ISBN 0-89024-052-3). Kalmbach.

Harris, Ken. World Diesel Locomotives. (Illus.). 160p. Date not set. text ed. 16.95 (ISBN 0-7106-0126-3). Jane's Pub Inc.

Judge, Colin. Diesels Nationwide, Vol. 2. 128p. 30.00x (ISBN 0-86093-068-8, Pub. by ORPC Ltd UK). State Mutual Bk.

Judge, Colin W. Diesels Nationwide, Vol. 4. 128p. 30.00x (ISBN 0-86093-114-5, Pub. by ORPC Ltd UK). State Mutual Bk.

Kennedy, Rex. Diesels & Electrics on Shed: Eastern Region, Vol. 2. 96p. 30.00x (ISBN 0-86093-036-X, Pub. by ORPC Ltd UK). State Mutual Bk.

--Diesels & Electrics on Shed: London Midland Region, Vol. 1. 80p. 30.00x (ISBN 0-86093-035-1, Pub. by ORPC Ltd UK). State Mutual Bk.

--Diesels & Electrics on Shed: Scottish Region, Vol. 4. 112p. 30.00x (ISBN 0-86093-043-2, Pub. by ORPC Ltd UK). State Mutual Bk.

--Diesels & Electrics on Shed: Western Region, Vol. 3. 104p. 30.00x (ISBN 0-86093-042-4, Pub. by ORPC Ltd UK). State Mutual Bk.

Kirkland, John F. Dawn of the Diesel Age: A History of the Diesel Locomotive in America. Sebree, Mac, ed. (Special Ser.: No. 80). 204p. 1983. 29.95 (ISBN 0-916374-52-1). Interurban.

McMillan, Joe. Santa Fe's Diesel Fleet: The Systems Diesels from the Beginning in the 30's. LC 74-17816. (Illus.). 1975. 25.00 (ISBN 0-89685-033-1). Chatham Pub CA.

Marsden, C. J. The Power of the Electro-Diesels. 112p. 30.00x (ISBN 0-86093-065-3, Pub. by ORPC Ltd UK). State Mutual Bk.

Marsden, Colin. Thirty-Five Years of Main Line Diesel Traction. 176p. 35.00x (ISBN 0-86093-171-4, Pub. by ORPC Ltd UK). State Mutual Bk.

New England Diesels. 28.95 (ISBN 0-686-70727-3). Chatham Pub CA.

The Next Generation of Diesel Engines for Rail Traction. 150p. 1982. 110.00x (ISBN 0-85298-495-2, Pub. by Mechanical Eng Pubns). State Mutual Bk.

Nicolle, B. Spotters Guide to Diesel Recognition, No. 10. 32p. 20.00x (ISBN 0-86093-099-8, Pub. by ORPC Ltd UK). State Mutual Bk.

Olmsted, Robert. The Diesel Years. LC 75-17721. (Illus.). 170p. 1975. 20.95 (ISBN 0-87095-054-1). Golden West.

Our GM Scrap Book. 10.95 (ISBN 0-685-83364-X). Chatham Pub CA.

Schulz, Erich J. Diesel Mechanics. 2nd ed. 496p. 1983. 33.45 (ISBN 0-07-055639-3). McGraw.

Siviter, Roger. Diesels & Semaphores. 128p. 45.00x (ISBN 0-86093-345-8, Pub. by ORPC Ltd UK). State Mutual Bk.

Strapac, Joseph A. Southern Pacific Review 1977. (Illus.). 1977. pap. 10.00 (ISBN 0-930742-01-X). Shade Tree.

Thompson, Chris. Care & Repair of Small Marine Diesels. LC 81-85261. (Illus.). 130p. 1982. 17.50 (ISBN 0-87742-159-5). Intl Marine.

Vaughan, John. Double-Headed Diesels Nationwide. 112p. 30.00x (ISBN 0-86093-081-5, Pub. by ORPC Ltd UK). State Mutual Bk.

Walton, Peter. Diesels over the Settle to Carlisle Route. 120p. 30.00x (ISBN 0-86093-119-6, Pub. by ORPC Ltd UK). State Mutual Bk.

Western Pacific Diesel Years. softcover 18.95 (ISBN 0-686-75213-9). Chatham Pub CA.

Wright, Roy V., ed. Diesel Electric Locomotives, 1925-1938. (Train Shed Cyclopedia Ser., No. 20). (Illus.). 1974. pap. 5.95 (ISBN 0-912318-49-X). N K Gregg.

DIESEL MOTOR

see also Automobiles–Motors; Marine Diesel Motors

Adiabatic Diesel Engines. 88p. 1983. 18.00 (ISBN 0-89883-314-0, SP543). Soc Auto Engineers.

Alternate Fuels for S.I. & Diesel Engines. 128p. 1983. 25.00 (ISBN 0-89883-313-2, SP542). Soc Auto Engineers.

Babb, Kenneth R. Diesel Engine Service. 1984. text ed. 29.95 (ISBN 0-8359-1291-4). Reston.

Black, Perry O. & Scahill. Diesel Engine Manual. 3rd ed. LC 82-20635. (Audel Ser.). 1983. 12.95 (ISBN 0-672-23371-1). Bobbs.

Black, Perry O. & Schahill, William E. Diesel Engine Manual. 4th ed. LC 82-20635. (Illus.). 499p. 1983. 12.95 (ISBN 0-672-23371-1). Audel.

Brady, Robert N. Diesel Fuel Systems. (Illus.). 640p. 1981. text ed. 29.95 (ISBN 0-8359-1293-0). soln. manual avail. (ISBN 0-8359-1294-9). Reston.

--Servicing Diesel Engines. 1985. text ed. 29.95 (ISBN 0-8359-6996-7). Reston.

Burghardt, M. David. Know Your Diesel. (Illus.). 160p. 1984. pap. 15.95 (ISBN 0-13-516591-1). P-H.

Crape, James R. Steam & Diesel Power Plant Operators Examinations. 2nd ed. LC 82-2198. (Illus.). 252p. 1982. pap. 21.95x (ISBN 0-916367-00-2, CU47-SD2). J R C Pub.

Crouse, William H. & Anglin, Donald L. Automotive Tools, Fasteners, & Measurements: A Text-Workbook. (Automotive Technology Ser.). (Illus.). 1977. 14.15 (ISBN 0-07-014630-6). McGraw.

Dagel, John F. Diesel Engine Repair. LC 81-615. 586p. 1982. 31.95x (ISBN 0-471-03542-4); tchrs' manual avail. (ISBN 0-471-86373-4); student wkbk. 9.95 (ISBN 0-471-88449-9). Wiley.

Dempsey, Paul. How to Repair Diesel Engines. LC 75-20847. (Illus.). 308p. 1975. o.p 15.95 (ISBN 0-8306-5817-3); pap. 10.95 (ISBN 0-8306-4817-8, 817). TAB Bks.

Dempsy, Paul. How to Convert Your Car, Van or Pickup to Diesel. (Illus.). 1978. pap. 7.95 (ISBN 0-8306-7968-5, 968). TAB Bks.

Diesel Engine Thermal Loading. LC 79-66979. 1979. 25.00 (ISBN 0-89883-220-9, SP449). Soc Auto Engineers.

Diesel Engineering Handbook. 28.50 (ISBN 0-686-31370-4). Busn Journals.

Diesel Engines for Passenger Cars & Light Duty Vehicles. 1982. 200 pp 110.00x, (ISBN 0-85298-496-0, Pub. by Mechanical Eng Pubns). State Mutual Bk.

Diesel Engines Noise Conference: Proceedings. LC 79-83912. 370p. 1979. Thirty papers. 45.00 (ISBN 0-89883-050-8, P80). Soc Auto Engineers.

Diesel Particulate Control. 1985. 38.00 (ISBN 0-89883-719-7, P158). Soc Auto Engineers.

Diesel Particulate Emissions Controls. 1983. 30.00 (ISBN 0-89883-308-6, SP537). Soc Auto Engineers.

Fuel Alternatives for S. I. & Diesel Engines. 108p. 1983. 25.00 (ISBN 0-89883-319-1, SP548). Soc Auto Engineers.

Haddad, S. D. & Watson, N., eds. Design & Applications in Diesel Engineering. (Mechanical Engineering Ser.(Ellis Horwood)). 360p. 1984. 59.95x (ISBN 0-470-20074-X, 1-476). Wiley.

--Principles & Performance in Diesel Engineering. (Mechanical Engineering Ser.: 1-476). 360p. 1984. text ed. 59.95x (ISBN 0-470-20075-8). Halsted Pr.

Heavy Duty Diesel Lubrication. 1984. 25.00 (ISBN 0-89883-810-X, SP589). Soc Auto Engineers.

Hudson, F. K., ed. Diesel & Electric Locomotive Specifications. LC 81-50698. 1981. pap. 7.95 (ISBN 0-913556-13-0). Spec Pr NJ.

Leecraft, Jodie. Diesel Engines & Electric Power. (Rotary Drilling Ser.: Unit I, Lesson 11). (Illus.). 90p. (Orig.). 1982. pap. text ed. 5.00 (ISBN 0-88698-027-5, 2.11121). PETEX.

Leecraft, Jodie, ed. Diesel Engines & Electric Power. 2nd ed. (Rotary Drilling Ser.: Unit I, Lesson 11). (Illus.). 99p. (Orig.). 1981. pap. text ed. 5.00 (ISBN 0-88698-015-1, 2.11120). PETEX.

Lewtas. Toxicology Effects of Emissions from Diesel Engines. (Developments in Toxicology & Environmental Science: Vol. 10). 380p. 1982. 81.50 (ISBN 0-444-00687-7, Biomedical Pr). Elsevier.

Lilly, L. R. Diesel Engine Reference Book. LC 83-26240. (Illus.). 720p. 1984. text ed. 129.95 (ISBN 0-408-00443-6). Butterworth.

Little, Richard L. & Edmondson, Garry C. Diesel Mechanics: An Introduction. 1982. text ed. write for info. (ISBN 0-534-01054-7, Breton Pubs). Wadsworth Pub.

Maleev, Vladimir L. Diesel Engine Operation & Maintenance. 1954. text ed. 32.25 (ISBN 0-07-039770-8). McGraw.

Measurement & Control of Diesel Particulate Emissions. LC 79-67589. 388p. 1979. 45.00 (ISBN 0-89883-105-9, PT17). Soc Auto Engineers.

National Research Council Assembly of Engineering. Diesel Cars: Benefits, Risks & Public Policy. 1982. pap. text ed. 9.50 (ISBN 0-309-03237-7). Natl Acad Pr.

National Research Council, Diesel Impact Study Committee. Diesel Technology. 1982. pap. text ed. 18.95 (ISBN 0-309-03243-1). Natl Acad Pr.

New Diesel Engines. 1985. 17.00 (ISBN 0-89883-836-3, SP615). Soc Auto Engineers.

The Next Generation of Diesel Engines for Rail Traction. 150p. 1982. 110.00x (ISBN 0-85298-495-2, Pub. by Mechanical Eng Pubns). State Mutual Bk.

Oil Companies Materials Association (OCMA) Recommendations for the Protection of Diesel Engines Operating in Hazardous Areas. 1977. pap. 21.95x (ISBN 0-471-25940-3, Wiley Heyden). Wiley.

Ralbovsky, Edward. Automotive Diesels. LC 84-19956. 288p. 1985. pap. text ed. 16.80 (ISBN 0-8273-2217-8); instr's guide 3.00 (ISBN 0-8273-2218-6). Delmar.

Rudman, Jack. Diesel Engine Repair. (Occupational Competency Examination Ser.: OCE-16). (Cloth bdg. avail. on request). pap. 13.95 (ISBN 0-8373-5716-0). Natl Learning.

Schulz, Erich J. Diesel Equipment One: Lubrication, Hydraulics, Brakes, Wheels, Tires. Gilmore, D. E., ed. (Illus.). 56p. 1980. 28.20 (ISBN 0-07-055716-0). McGraw.

--Diesel Equipment Two: Design, Electronic Controls, Frames, Suspensions, Steering, Transmissions, Drive Lines, Air Conditioning. Gilmore, D. E., ed. (Illus.). 64p. 1981. 28.20 (ISBN 0-07-055708-X). McGraw.

Society of Automotive Engineers. Diesel Combustion & Emissions, Pt. I. LC 80-50154. 308p. 1980. Twenty-three papers. 45.00 (ISBN 0-89883-055-9, P86). Soc Auto Engineers.

--New Diesel Engines, Combustion & Emissions Research in Japan. LC 80-52981. 248p. 1980. Fourteen papers. 38.00 (ISBN 0-89883-239-X, SP 468). Soc Auto Engineers.

Springer, G. S. & Patterson, D. J., eds. Engine Emissions: Pollutant Formation & Measurement. LC 71-188716. 371p. 1973. 55.00x (ISBN 0-306-30585-2, Plenum Pr). Plenum Pub.

Staton-Bevan, William N. Diesel Fault Tracing Maintenance & Repair: Covering All Types of High-Speed Diesel Engines. LC 70-404820. pap. 71.50 (ISBN 0-317-11174-4, 2051549). Bks Demand UMI.

Theissen, Frank & Dales, Dave. Diesel Fundamentals: Principles & Service. 1982. text ed. 27.95 (ISBN 0-8359-1284-1); instrs' manual avail. (ISBN 0-8359-1285-X). Reston.

Toboldt, Bill. Diesel: Fundamentals, Service, Repair. Rev. ed. LC 82-14319. (Illus.). 1983. text ed. 16.00 (ISBN 0-87006-424-X). Goodheart.

Weathers, Tom & Hunter, Claud. Diesel Engines for Automobiles & Small Trucks. 300p. 1981. text ed. 24.95 (ISBN 0-8359-1288-4); instr's. manual free (ISBN 0-8359-1289-2). Reston.

Wharton, A. J. Diesel Engines: Questions & Answers. (Marine Engineering Ser.). 1975. pap. 9.95x (ISBN 0-540-07342-3). Sheridan.

DIET

see also Animal Food; Beverages; Dieticians; Food; Food, Raw; Nutrition

Airola, Paavo O. Health Secrets from Europe. LC 79-135618. 1971. pap. 2.50 (ISBN 0-668-02411-9). Arco.

Alcott, William A. Vegetable Diet. 2nd rev. & enl. ed. LC 74-29280. Repr. of 1851 ed. 17.50 (ISBN 0-404-13400-9). AMS Pr.

Arnow, E. Earle. Food Power: A Doctor's Guide to Common Sense Nutrition. LC 75-185419. (Illus.). 305p. 1972. 19.95x (ISBN 0-911012-37-0). Nelson-Hall.

Ballentine, R. Diet & Nutrition. LC 78-110274. 634p. 1978. text ed. 17.95 (ISBN 0-89389-022-7); pap. 12.95 (ISBN 0-89389-048-0). Himalayan Pubs.

Bassler, Thomas J. & Burger, Robert E. The Whole Life Diet: An Integrated Program of Nutrition & Exercise for a Lifestyle of Total Health. LC 79-19375. 204p. 1979. 9.95 (ISBN 0-87131-305-7). M Evans.

Bavly, Sarah. Family Food Consumption in Palestine. LC 76-176544. (Columbia University. Teachers College. Contributions to Education: No. 946). Repr. of 1949 ed. 22.50 (ISBN 0-404-55946-8). AMS Pr.

Bender, Arnold & Nash, Tony. Pocket Encyclopedia of Calories & Nutrition. 1979. pap. 4.95 (ISBN 0-671-24839-1). S&S.

Bourne, G. H., ed. Human & Animal Nutrition. (World Review of Nutrition & Dietetics: Vol. 32). (Illus.). 1978. 63.00 (ISBN 3-8055-2855-8). S Karger.

--World Review of Nutrition & Dietetics, Vol. 19. (Illus.). 319p. 1974. 70.25 (ISBN 3-8055-1589-8). S Karger.

--World Review of Nutrition & Dietetics, Vol. 22. (Illus.). 1975. 84.25 (ISBN 3-8055-2135-9). S Karger.

--World Review of Nutrition & Dietetics, Vol. 24. (Illus.). 250p. 1976. 64.75 (ISBN 3-8055-2344-0). S Karger.

--World Review of Nutrition & Dietetics, Vol. 25. (Illus.). 300p. 1976. 73.25 (ISBN 3-8055-2363-7). S Karger.

--World Review of Nutrition & Dietetics, Vol. 38: Physiology & Social Nutrition & Nutritional Education. (Illus.). x, 230p. 1981. 69.50 (ISBN 3-8055-3048-X). S Karger.

Bourne, Geoffrey H., ed. Some Special Aspects of Nutrition. (World Review of Nutrition & Dietetics: Vol. 33). (Illus.). 1979. 67.25 (ISBN 3-8055-2942-2). S Karger.

Bragg, Paul C. & Bragg, Patricia. Healthful Eating Without Confusion. 11th ed. LC 71-152392. pap. 4.95 (ISBN 0-87790-024-8). Health Sci.

--Natural Way to Reduce. 16th ed. LC 84-62770. pap. 4.95 (ISBN 0-87790-040-X). Health Sci.

Brennan, Richard O. Dr. Brennan's Treasury of Diet Menus. LC 78-74136. (Illus.). 1979. pap. 6.95 (ISBN 0-933092-01-6). Educ Editions.

Burt, Brian A., et al. A Study of Relationships Between Diet & Dental Health, United States, 1971-1974. Cox, Klaudia, ed. 60p. 1981. pap. text ed. 1.75 (ISBN 0-8406-0235-9). Natl Ctr Health Stats.

Carston, Rachel. Devil's Claw Root & Other. 1981. pap. 8.95x (ISBN 0-317-06967-5, Regent House). B of A.

Christensen, Raymond P. Efficient Use of Food Resources in the United States. LC 75-26300. (World Food Supply Ser). (Illus.). 1976. Repr. of 1948 ed. 12.00x (ISBN 0-405-07772-6). Ayer Co Pubs.

Cummings, Richard O. American & His Food: A History of Food Habits in the United States. LC 74-112536. (Rise of Urban America). (Illus.). 1970. Repr. of 1940 ed. 21.00 (ISBN 0-405-02445-2). Ayer Co Pubs.

Dachslager, Howard, et al. Learning BASIC Programming: A Systematic Approach. LC 83-2519. 280p. 1983. pap. text ed. 19.00 pub net (ISBN 0-534-01422-4). Brooks-Cole.

Darby, W. J., ed. Food: the Gift of Osiris. 1977. Vol. 1. 69.50 (ISBN 0-12-203401-5); Vol.2. 69.50 (ISBN 0-12-203402-3). Acad Pr.

Davidson, Stanley, et al. Human Nutrition & Dietetics. 7th ed. (Illus.). 1979. text ed. 37.00 (ISBN 0-443-01765-4); pap. text ed. 49.50 (ISBN 0-443-01764-6). Churchill.

Davis, Adelle. Let's Eat Right to Keep Fit. rev. ed. LC 75-134581. 1970. 8.95 (ISBN 0-15-150304-4). HarBraceJ.

Dusek, Dorothy E. Thin & Fit: Your Personal Lifestyle. 288p. 1982. pap. text ed. write for info. (ISBN 0-534-01077-6). Wadsworth Pub.

Ehret, Arnold. Instructions for Fasting & Dieting. 1983. pap. 3.95 (ISBN 0-87904-003-3). Lust.

Eisenman, Patricia & Johnson, Dennis. Coaches' Guide to Nutrition & Weight Control. LC 81-82452. (Illus.). 255p. 1982. pap. text ed. 10.95 (ISBN 0-931250-25-0, BE150025). Human Kinetics.

Gibbons, Barbara. Lean Cuisine. LC 79-1663. (Illus.). 1980. pap. 7.64i (ISBN 0-06-090737-1, CN). Har-Row.

Gibbons, Barbara & Consumer Guide Editors. Lean Cuisine. LC 79-1663. (Illus.). 1980. 13.41i (ISBN 0-06-011498-3, HarpT). Har-Row.

Gibbons, Emma & Jessup, George. Figure Control for Fun & Fitness. (Illus.). 1979. pap. text ed. 4.95 (ISBN 0-8403-1959-2, 40195902). Kendall-Hunt.

Goulart, Frances S. The Official Eating to Win Cookbook: Super Foods for Super Athletic Performance. LC 81-40806. 224p. 1983. 16.95 (ISBN 0-8128-2832-1). Stein & Day.

Haggard, Howard W. & Greenberg, Leon A. Diet & Physical Efficiency: Influence of Frequency of Meals Upon Physical Efficiency & Industrial Productivity. Stein, Leon, ed. LC 77-70500. (Work Ser.). (Illus.). 1977. lib. bdg. 20.00x (ISBN 0-405-10171-6). Ayer Co Pubs.

Hurdel, J. Frank. The Biofeedback Diet: A Doctor's Revolutionary Approach. 240p. 1977. (Reward); pap. 14.95 (ISBN 0-13-076422-1). P-H.

Kulvinskas, Viktoras. Sprout for the Love of Everybody: Nutritional Evaluation of Sprouts & Grasses. pap. 2.95 (ISBN 0-933278-03-9). Twen Fir Cent.

Langier, Jose D. Economical & Nutritional Diets Using Scarce Resources. LC 75-627749. 1969. 7.00 (ISBN 0-87744-093-X). Mich St U Pr.

Lanz, Sally J. An Introduction to the Profession of Dietetics. LC 82-18683. (Illus.). 169p. 1983. pap. 11.00 (ISBN 0-8121-0883-3). Lea & Febiger.

Lolli, Giorgio, et al. Alcohol in Italian Culture: Food & Wine in Relation to Sobriety Among Italians & Italian Americans. LC 58-9167. (Rutgers Center of Alcohol Studies: Monograph No. 3). 1958. 7.50 (ISBN 0-911290-27-3). Rutgers Ctr Alcohol.

Lovewisdom, Johnny. Spiritualizing Dietetics. lib. bdg. cancelled (ISBN 0-933278-09-8). Twen Fir Cent.

May, Jacques M. & McLellan, Donna L., eds. Studies in Medical Geography, 14 vols. Incl. Vol. 2. Studies in Disease Ecology. (Illus.). 1961. 27.95x (ISBN 0-02-848980-2); Vol. 3. The Ecology of Malnutrition in the Far & Near East. (Illus.). 1961. 24.95x (ISBN 0-02-849010-X); Vol. 4. The Ecology of Malnutrition in Five Countries of Eastern & Central Europe: East Germany,Poland, Yugoslavia, Albania, Greece. (Illus.). 1964. 18.95x (ISBN 0-02-848970-5); Vol. 5. The Ecology of Malnutrition in Middle Africa: Ghana, Nigeria, Republic of the Congo, Rwanda & Burundi & the Former French Equatorial Africa. (Illus.). 1965. 16.95x (ISBN 0-02-848990-X); Vol. 6. The Ecology of Malnutrition in Central & Southern Europe: Austria, Hungary, Romania, Bulgaria & Czechoslovakia. (Illus.). 1966. 18.95x (ISBN 0-02-849000-2); Vol. 7. The Ecology of Malnutrition in Northern Africa: Libya, Tunisia, Algeria, Morocco, Spanish Sahara & Ifni, Mauretania. (Illus.). 1967. 18.95x (ISBN 0-02-848950-0); Vol. 8. The Ecology of Malnutrition in the French-Speaking Countries of West Africa & Madagascar: Senegal, Guinea, Ivory Coast, Togo, Dahomey, Cameroon, Niger, Mali, Upper Volta, & Madagascar. (Illus.). 1968. 21.95x (ISBN 0-02-848960-8); Vol. 9. The Ecology of Malnutrition in Eastern Africa: Equatorial Guinea, the Gambia, Liberia, Sierra Leone, Malawi, Rhodesia, Zambia, Kenya, Tanzania, Uganda, Ethiopia, the French Territory of the Atars & Issas, the Somali Republic & Sudan. 1970. 32.95x (ISBN 0-02-849020-7); Vol. 10. The Ecology of Malnutrition in Seven Countries of Southern Africa and in Portuguese Guinea: The/Republic of South Africa, South West Africa (Namibia), Botswana, Lesotho, Swaziland, Mozambique, Angola, Portuguese Guinea. 1971. 27.95x (ISBN 0-02-848940-3); Vol. 11. The Ecology of Malnutrition in Mexico & Central America. 1972. 24.95x (ISBN 0-02-848930-6); Vol. 12. The Ecology of Malnutrition in the Caribbean. 1973. 21.95x (ISBN 0-02-848920-9); Vol. 13. The Ecology of Malnutrition in Eastern South America. 1975. 41.95x (ISBN 0-02-849060-6); Vol. 14. The Ecology of Malnutrition in Western South America. 1975. 32.95x (ISBN 0-02-849070-3). Hafner.

Null, Gary & Null, Steve. The Complete Handbook of Nutrition. 1973. pap. 3.95 (ISBN 0-440-11613-9). Dell.

--The Complete Handbook of Nutrition. LC 78-187994. (The Health Library: Vol. 1). 340p. 1972. 7.95 (ISBN 0-8315-0124-3). Speller.

Null, Gary, et al. The Complete Question & Answer Book of General Nutrition. LC 79-187997. (The Health Library: Vol. 5). 184p. 1972. 9.95 (ISBN 0-8315-0128-6). Speller.

Oddy, Derek T. & Miller, Derek S., eds. The Making of the Modern British Diet. 235p. 1976. 17.50x (ISBN 0-87471-803-1). Rowman.

Ornish, Dean. Stress, Diet, & Your Heart. LC 81-24003. (Illus.). 400p. 1982. 16.95 (ISBN 0-03-049011-1). HR&W.

Patwardhan, Vinayak N. & Darby, William J. State of Nutrition in the Arab Middle East. LC 73-123036. (Illus.). 1972. 15.00x (ISBN 0-8265-1162-7). Vanderbilt U Pr.

Pennington, Jean A. Dietary Nutrient Guide. (Illus.). 1976. pap. text ed. 24.50 (ISBN 0-87055-196-5). AVI.

Rodale, Robert. Our Next Frontier: A Personal Guide for Tomorrow's Lifestyle. Stoner, Carol, ed. (Illus.). 252p. 1981. 14.95 (ISBN 0-87857-365-8). Rodale Pr Inc.

Rorty, James & Norman, Philip. Tomorrow's Food. 9.95 (ISBN 0-8159-6906-6). Devin.

Smith, Victor E. Electronic Computation of Human Diets. LC 63-64038. 1964. 8.50 (ISBN 0-87744-024-7). Mich St U Pr.

Spiller, Gene A., ed. Topics in Dietary Fiber Research. LC 77-26883. 233p. 1978. 27.50x (ISBN 0-306-31126-7, Plenum Pr). Plenum Pub.

Spillman, Martha. Simplified Diet Manual Study Guide. 3rd ed. (Illus.). 80p. 1985. pap. 5.75x (ISBN 0-8138-1435-9). Iowa St U Pr.

Yudkin, John, ed. Diet of Man: Needs & Wants. (Illus.). 358p. 1978. text ed. 48.00 (ISBN 0-85334-750-6, Pub. by Elsevier Applied Sci England). Elsevier.

DIETICIANS

Clarke, Helen. The Professional Training of the Hospital Dietician. LC 70-176651. (Columbia University. Teachers College. Contributions to Education: No. 602). Repr. of 1934 ed. 22.50 (ISBN 0-404-55602-7). AMS Pr.

Lanz, Sally J. An Introduction to the Profession of Dietetics. LC 82-18683. (Illus.). 169p. 1983. pap. 11.00 (ISBN 0-8121-0883-3). Lea & Febiger.

Rudman, Jack. Chief Dietician. (Career Examination Ser.: C-1174). (Cloth bdg. avail. on request). pap. 12.00 (ISBN 0-8373-1174-8). Natl Learning.

--Dietician. (Career Examination Ser.: C-196). (Cloth bdg. avail. on request). pap. 12.00 (ISBN 0-8373-0196-3). Natl Learning.

--Head Dietician. (Career Examination Ser.: C-320). (Cloth bdg. avail. on request). pap. 10.00 (ISBN 0-8373-0320-6). Natl Learning.

--Registration Examination for Dieticians (RED) (Admission Test Ser.: ATS-41). (Cloth bdg. avail. on request). pap. 13.95 (ISBN 0-8373-5041-7). Natl Learning.

--Senior Dietician. (Career Examination Ser.: C-1985). (Cloth bdg. avail. on request). pap. 12.00 (ISBN 0-8373-1985-4). Natl Learning.

--Supervising Dietician. (Career Examination Ser.: C-1968). (Cloth bdg. avail. on request). pap. 10.00 (ISBN 0-8373-1968-4). Natl Learning.

DIFFERENCE ALGEBRA

see Algebra, Difference

DIFFERENCE-DIFFERENTIAL EQUATIONS

see Differential-Difference Equations

DIFFERENCE EQUATIONS

see also Algebra, Difference; Asymptotic Expansions; Differential-Difference Equations

Aizerman, M. A., et al. Sixteen Papers on Differential & Difference Equations, Functional Analysis, Games & Control. LC 51-5559. (Translations Ser.: No. 2, Vol. 87). 1970. 36.00 (ISBN 0-8218-1787-6, TRANS 2-87). Am Math.

Bender, Carl M. & Orszag, Steven A. Advanced Mathematical Methods for Scientists & Engineers. (International Series in Pure & Applied Mathematics). (Illus.). 1978. text ed. 49.95 (ISBN 0-07-004452-X). McGraw.

Berezanskii, Ju. M. Expansions in Eigenfunctions of Selfadjoint Operators. LC 67-22347. (Translations of Mathematical Monographs: Vol. 17). 1968. 67.00 (ISBN 0-8218-1567-9, MMONO-17). Am Math.

Cadzow, James A. Discrete Time Systems: An Introduction with Interdisciplinary Applications. (Computer Applications in Electrical Engineering Ser.). (Illus.). 448p. 1973. ref. ed. 39.95 (ISBN 0-13-215996-1). P-H.

Hejhal, D. A. The Selberg Trace Formula for PSL; 2, IR, Vol. 2. (Lecture Notes in Mathematics: Vol. 1001). 806p. 1983. pap. 38.00 (ISBN 0-387-12323-7). Springer-Verlag.

Henrici, Peter. Error Propagation for Difference Methods. LC 76-18838. 82p. 1977. Repr. of 1963 ed. 8.50 (ISBN 0-88275-448-3). Krieger.

Immink, G. K. Asymptotics of Analytic Difference Equations. (Lecture Notes in Mathematics Ser.: Vol. 1085). v, 134p. 1984. pap. 10.00 (ISBN 0-387-13867-6). Springer-Verlag.

Jordan, Charles. Calculus of Finite Differences. 3rd ed. LC 65-29977. 24.95 (ISBN 0-8284-0033-4). Chelsea Pub.

LaSalle, J. P. The Stability of Dynamical Systems. (CBMS-NSF Regional Conference Ser.: No. 25). v, 76p. (Orig.). 1976. pap. text ed. 14.00 (ISBN 0-89871-022-7). Soc Indus-Appl Math.

Marchuk, G. I. & Shaidurov, V. V. Difference Methods & their Extrapolations. (Applications of Mathematics: Vol. 19). (Illus.). 334p. 1983. 57.00 (ISBN 0-387-90794-7). Springer-Verlag.

Miranker, Willard L. Numerical Methods for Stiff Equations & Singular Perturbation Problems. (Mathematics & Its Applications Ser.: No. 5). 216p. 1980. lib. bdg. 30.00 (ISBN 90-277-1107-0, Pub. by Reidel Holland). Kluwer Academic.

Noerlund, Niels H. Differenzenrechung. LC 56-1592. (Ger). 25.00 (ISBN 0-8284-0100-4). Chelsea Pub.

Richtmyer, Robert D. & Morton, K. W. Difference Methods for Initial-Value Problems. 2nd ed. LC 67-13959. (Pure & Applied Mathematics Ser.). (Illus.). 405p. 1967. 53.50 (ISBN 0-470-72040-9, Pub. by Wiley-Interscience). Wiley.

Ross, Shepley L. Differential Equations, 3rd ed. LC 83-21643. 807p. 1984. text ed. 37.50 (ISBN 0-471-03294-8, Pub by Wiley). Wiley.

Steklov Institute of Mathematics, Academy of Sciences, USSR, No. 74. Difference Methods of Solution of Problems of Mathematical Physics I: Proceedings. Janenko, N. N., ed. (Proceedings of the Steklov Institute of Mathematics: No. 74). 1967. 43.00 (ISBN 0-8218-1874-0, STEKLO-74). Am Math.

Steklov Institute of Mathematics, No. 122. Difference Methods of Solving Problems of Mathematical Physics II: Proceedings. Janenko, N. N., ed. LC 75-20006. (Proceedings of the Steklov Institutue of Mathematics: No. 122). 99p. 1975. 39.00 (ISBN 0-8218-3022-8, STEKLO-122). Am Math.

Stetter, H. J. Analysis of Discretization Methods for Ordinary Differential Equations. LC 72-90188. (Springer Tracts in Natural Philosophy: Vol. 23). (Illus.). 390p. 1973. 69.00 (ISBN 0-387-06008-1). Springer-Verlag.

DIFFERENTIAL ALGEBRA

see Algebra, Differential

DIFFERENTIAL ANALYZERS, ELECTRONIC

see Electronic Differential Analyzers

DIFFERENTIAL CALCULUS

see Calculus, Differential

DIFFERENTIAL-DIFFERENCE EQUATIONS

Bellman, Richard E. & Cooke, Kenneth L. Differential-Difference Equations. (Mathematics in Science & Engineering Ser.: Vol. 6). 1963. 75.00 (ISBN 0-12-084850-3). Acad Pr.

Blaquiere, Austin, ed. Topics in Differential Games. LC 73-75528. 460p. 1973. 42.75 (ISBN 0-444-10467-4, North-Holland). Elsevier.

Collatz, L. & Meinardus, G., eds. Differential Difference Equations: Applications & Numerical Problems. (International Series of Numerical Mathematics: Vol. 62). (Eng. & Ger.). 196p. 1983. text ed. 24.95 (ISBN 0-8176-1499-0). Birkhauser.

Flett, T. M. Differential Analysis. Pym, J. S., ed. LC 78-67303. (Illus.). 1980. 59.50 (ISBN 0-521-22420-9). Cambridge U Pr.

Halanay, A. Differential Equations: Stability, Oscillations, Time Lags. (Mathematics in Science & Engineering Ser.: Vol. 23). 1966. 83.00 (ISBN 0-12-317950-5). Acad Pr.

Jaiswal, N. K. Priority Queues. (Mathematics in Science & Engineering Ser.: Vol. 50). 1968. 65.00 (ISBN 0-12-380050-1). Acad Pr.

DIFFERENTIAL EQUATIONS

see also Algebra, Differential; Boundary Value Problems; Calculus, Integral; Calculus, Operational; Differential-Difference Equations; Differential Operators; Electronic Differential Analyzers; Existence Theorems; Functions; Green's Functions; Groups, Continuous; Lagrange Equations; Laplace Transformation; Liapunov Functions; Potential, Theory of; Surfaces; Transformations, Infinitesimal; Weber Functions

Adamov, N. V., et al. Differential Equations. (Translations, Ser.: No. 1, Vol. 4). 1962. 24.00 (ISBN 0-8218-1604-7, TRANS 1-4). Am Math.

Advances in Differential & Integral Equations: Studies in Applied Mathematics 5. Nohel, John S., ed. xvi, 207p. 1969. text ed. 16.50 (ISBN 0-89871-037-5). Soc Indus-Appl Math.

Ahiezer, N. I., et al. Fifteen Papers on Real & Complex Functions, Series, Differential & Integral Equations. LC 51-5559. (Translations Ser.: No. 2, Vol. 86). 1970. 34.00 (ISBN 0-8218-1786-8, TRANS 2-86). Am Math.

Ahmad, Shair & Keener, Marvin, eds. Differential Equations. LC 80-16549. 1980. 33.00 (ISBN 0-12-045550-1). Acad Pr.

Aiken, Richard C. Stiff Computation. (Illus.). 400p. 1984. 75.00x (ISBN 0-19-503453-8). Oxford U Pr.

Aizerman, M. A., et al. Sixteen Papers on Differential & Difference Equations, Functional Analysis, Games & Control. LC 51-5559. (Translations Ser.: No. 2, Vol. 87). 1970. 36.00 (ISBN 0-8218-1787-6, TRANS 2-87). Am Math.

Aleksandrov, A. D., et al. Eleven Papers on Topology, Function Theory, & Differential Equations. LC 51-5559. (Translations Ser.: No. 2, Vol. 1). 1955. 26.00 (ISBN 0-8218-1701-9, TRANS 2-1). Am Math.

--Nine Papers on Topology, Lie Groups, & Differential Equations. LC 51-5559. (Translations Ser.: No. 2, Vol. 21). 1962. 33.00 (ISBN 0-8218-1721-3, TRANS 2-21). Am Math.

--Ten Papers on Differential Equations & Functional Analysis. LC 51-5559. (Translations Ser.: No. 2, Vol. 68). 1968. 35.00 (ISBN 0-8218-1768-X, TRANS 2-68). Am Math.

Alekseev, V. M., et al. Thirteen Papers on Differential Equations. LC 51-5559. (Translations Ser.: No. 2, Vol. 89). 1970. 35.00 (ISBN 0-8218-1789-2, TRANS 2-89). Am Math.

Amann, Herbert. Gewoehnliche Differentialgleichungen. 497p. 1983. 23.60 (ISBN 3-11-009573-4). De Gruyter.

Andreev, A. E., et al. Twelve Papers on Function Theory, Probability, & Differential Equations. LC 51-5559. (Translations Ser.: No. 2, Vol. 8). 1957. 43.00 (ISBN 0-8218-1708-6, TRANS 2-8). Am Math.

Andrews, Larry C. Ordinary Differential Equations. 1982. text ed. 27.75 (ISBN 0-673-15800-4). Scott F.

Andronov, A. A., et al. Eleven Papers on Differential Equations & Two in Information Theory. LC 51-5559. (Translations, Ser.: No. 2, Vol. 33). 1963. 35.00 (ISBN 0-8218-1733-7, TRANS 2-33). Am Math.

Ansorge, R. & Toernig, W., eds. Numerical Treatment of Differential Equations in Applications: Proceedings, Oberwolfach, Germany, Dec. 1977. LC 78-11883. (Lecture Notes in Mathematics: Vol. 679). 1978. pap. 15.00 (ISBN 0-387-08940-3). Springer-Verlag.

Antosiewicz, H. A., ed. International Conference on Differential Equation: Proceedings. 1975. 76.50 (ISBN 0-12-059650-4). Acad Pr.

Arnold, Ludwig. Stochastic Differential Equations: Theory & Applications. LC 73-22256. 228p. 1974. 48.50x (ISBN 0-471-03359-6, Pub. by Wiley-Interscience). Wiley.

Arnold, V. I. Geometrical Methods in the Theory of Ordinary Differential Equations. (Grundlehren der Mathematischen Wissenschaften: Vol. 250). (Illus.). 384p. 1983. 39.50 (ISBN 0-387-90681-9). Springer-Verlag.

--Ordinary Differential Equations. Silverman, Richard A., tr. from Rus. (Illus.). 270p. 1973. pap. 13.75x (ISBN 0-262-51018-9). MIT Pr.

Arnol'd, V. I., et al. Fourteen Papers on Functional Analysis & Differential Equations. LC 51-5559. (Translations Ser.: No. 2, Vol. 61). 1967. 38.00 (ISBN 0-8218-1761-2, TRANS 2-61). Am Math.

--Thirteen Papers on Functional Analysis & Differential Equations. LC 51-5559. (Translations Ser.: No. 2, Vol. 79). 1968. 35.00 (ISBN 0-8218-1779-5, TRANS 2-79). Am Math.

Arrowsmith, D. K. & Place, C. M. Ordinary Differential Equations. LC 81-14003. 1982. 43.00 (ISBN 0-412-22600-6, NO. 6618, Pub. by Chapman & Hall); pap. 19.95 (ISBN 0-412-22610-3, NO. 6617). Methuen Inc.

Aulbach, B. Continuous & Discrete Dynamics near Manifolds of Equilibria. (Lecture Notes in Mathematics Ser.: Vol. 1058). ix, 142p. 1984. pap. 11.00 (ISBN 0-387-13329-1). Springer-Verlag.

Ayres, Frank, Jr. Differential Equations. (Schaum's Outline Ser). (Orig.). 1952. pap. 8.95 (ISBN 0-07-002654-8). McGraw.

Azbelev, N. V., et al. Fifteen Papers on Differential Equations. LC 51-5559. (Translations Ser.: No. 2, Vol. 42). 1964. 25.00 (ISBN 0-8218-1742-6, TRANS 2-42). Am Math.

Bahtin, I. A., et al. Eleven Papers on Differential Equations, Functional Analysis & Measure Theory. LC 51-5559. (Translations Ser: No. 2, Vol. 51). 1966. 39.00 (ISBN 0-8218-1751-5, TRANS 2-51). Am Math.

Barbu. Optimal Control of Variational Inequalities. (Research Notes in Mathematics: No. 100). 312p. 1984. 23.95 (ISBN 0-273-08629-4). Pitman Pub MA.

Bateman, Harry. Differential Equations. LC 66-23754. 1967. 14.95 (ISBN 0-8284-0190-X). Chelsea Pub.

Bellman, Richard & Adomian, George. Partial Differential Equations. 312p. 1984. PLB 49.00 (ISBN 90-277-1681-1, Pub. by Reidel Holland). Kluwer Academic.

Bellman, Richard & Cooke, Kenneth L. Asymptotic Behavior of Solutions of Differential-Difference Equations. (Memoirs Ser.: No. 35). 95p. 1982. pap. 16.00 (ISBN 0-8218-1235-1). Am Math.

Benton, Stanley H., ed. The Hamilton-Jacobi Equation: A Global Approach. 1977. 37.50 (ISBN 0-12-089350-9). Acad Pr.

Berezin, F. A., et al. Eight Papers on Differential Equations & Functional Analysis. LC 51-5559. (Translations, Ser.: No. 2, Vol. 56). 1966. 37.00 (ISBN 0-8218-1756-6, TRANS 2-56). Am Math.

Betz. Ecuaciones Diferenciales. (Span.). 1977. pap. text ed. 11.40 (ISBN 0-06-310058-4, IntlDept). Har-Row.

Bibikov, Y. N. Local Theory of Nonlinear Analytic Ordinary Differential Equations. (Lecture Notes in Mathematics: Vol. 702). 1979. pap. 14.00 (ISBN 0-387-09114-9). Springer-Verlag.

Birkhoff, Garrett & Gian-Carlo Rota. Ordinary Differential Equations. 3rd ed. LC 78-8304. 350p. 1978. text ed. 42.50x (ISBN 0-471-07411-X). Wiley.

Bloom, C. O. & Kazarinoff, N. D. Short Wave Radiation Problems in Homogeneous Media: Asymptotic Solutions. (Lecture Notes in Mathematics: Vol. 522). 1976. 13.00 (ISBN 0-387-07698-0). Springer-Verlag.

Bloom, F. Ill-Posed Problems for Integrodifferential Equations in Mechanics & Electromagnetic Theory. LC 80-53713. (SIAM Studies in Applied Mathematics: No. 3). ix, 222p. 1981. 37.50 (ISBN 0-89871-171-1). Soc Indus-Appl Math.

Boltyanskii, V. G., et al. Twenty Papers on Analytic Functions & Ordinary Differential Equations. LC 51-5559. (Translations Ser.: No. 2, Vol. 18). 1961. 30.00 (ISBN 0-8218-1718-3, TRANS 2-18). Am Math.

Botha, J. F. & Pinder, G. F. Fundamental Concepts in the Numerical Solution of Differential Equations. LC 83-1213. 202p. 1983. 26.95 (ISBN 0-471-87546-5, Pub. by Wiley-Interscience). Wiley.

Boyce, W. E. & Diprima, R. C. Elementary Differential Equations. 3rd ed. (Arabic.). 391p. 1983. pap. 15.40 (ISBN 0-471-09414-5). Wiley.

--Elementary Differential Equations & Boundary Value Problems. 4th ed. 1985. pap. text ed. write for info. (ISBN 0-471-87096-X). Wiley.

Boyce, William E. & Di Prima, Richard C. Elementary Differential Equations. 3rd ed. LC 75-35565. 497p. 1977. text ed. 32.95 (ISBN 0-471-09339-4). Wiley.

Boyce, William E. & DiPrima, Richard C. Elementary Differential Equations & Boundary Value Problems. 3rd ed. LC 75-45093. 638p. 1977. 35.45 (ISBN 0-471-09334-3); student manual avail. (ISBN 0-471-04707-4). Wiley.

--Introduction to Differential Equations. 310p. 1970. text ed. 31.00x (ISBN 0-471-09338-6). Wiley.

Braun, M. Differential Equations & Their Applications: An Introduction to Applied Mathematics. 3rd ed. (Applied Mathematical Sciences: Vol. 15). (Illus.). 546p. 1983. pap. 28.00 (ISBN 0-387-90806-4). Springer-Verlag.

Brezis, H. & Lions, J. L., eds. Nonlinear Partial Differential Equations & Their Applications: College de France Seminar, Vol. 2. (Research Notes in Mathematics Ser.: No. 60). 250p. 1982. pap. text ed. 27.50 (ISBN 0-273-08541-7). Pitman Pub MA.

Brocker, T. H. Differentiable Germs & Catastrophes. Lander, L., tr. from Ger. LC 74-17000. (London Mathematical Society Lecture Note Ser.: No. 17). (Eng.). 160p. 1975. pap. text ed. 22.95 (ISBN 0-521-20681-2). Cambridge U Pr.

Bucy, R. S., et al. Stochastic Differential Equations. McKean, H. P. & Keller, J. B., eds. LC 72-13266. (SIAM-AMS Proceedings: No. 6). 1973. 39.00 (ISBN 0-8218-1325-0, SIAMS-6). Am Math.

Bugrov, Y. S. & Nikolsky, S. M. Differential Equations, Multiple Integrals. (Theory of Functions of a Complex Variable Ser.). 475p. 1983. 9.95 (ISBN 0-8285-2657-5, Pub. by Mir Pubs USSR). Imported Pubns.

Burghes, D. N. & Borrie, M. S. Modelling with Differential Equations. (Mathematics & Its Applications Ser.). 172p. 1981. pap. 31.95 (ISBN 0-470-27360-7). Halsted Pr.

Burkhill, John Charles. The Theory of Ordinary Differential Equations. LC 76-369325. (Longman Mathematical Ser.). pap. 32.50 (ISBN 0-317-08520-4, 2013563). Bks Demand UMI.

Burton. Modeling & Differential Equations in Biology. (Lecture Notes in Pure & Applied Mathematics Ser.: Vol. 58). 296p. 1980. 49.50 (ISBN 0-8247-1075-4). Dekker.

Burton, T. A. Stability & Periodic Solutions of Ordinary & Functional Differential Equations. Monograph ed. Date not set. price not set (ISBN 0-12-147360-0). Acad Pr.

Busenberg, Stavros & Cooke, Kenneth. Differential Equations & Applications in Ecology, Epidemics & Population Problems. LC 81-14897. 1981. 47.50 (ISBN 0-12-148360-6). Acad Pr.

Campbel, S. L. Singular Systems of Differential Equations. LC 79-20908. (Reserach Notes in Mathematics Ser.: No. 40). 176p. (Orig.). 1980. pap. text ed. 22.95 (ISBN 0-273-08438-0). Pitman Pub MA.

Campbell, S. L. Singular Systems of Differential Equations, Vol. 2. (Research Notes in Mathematics Ser.: No. 61). 200p. 1982. pap. text ed. 22.95 (ISBN 0-273-08516-6). Pitman Pub MA.

Carroll, R. W. Transmutation & Operator Differential Equations. (Mathematics Studies: Vol. 37). 246p. 1979. 47.00 (ISBN 0-444-85328-6, North Holland). Elsevier.

Cauchy, Augustin. Ordinary Differential Equations. 24.50 (ISBN 0-384-07950-4). Johnson Repr.

Cederberg, William E. On the Solution of the Differential Equations of Motion of a Double Pendulum. LC 24-3604. (Augustana College Library Publications: No. 9). 62p. 1923. pap. 0.75 (ISBN 0-910182-06-X). Augustana Coll.

Centro Internationale Mathematico Estivo. Bifurcation Theory & Applications: Lectures Given at the Second Session of the Centro Internationale Mathematico Estivo held at Montecatini, Italy, June 24-July 2, 1983. Salvadori, L., ed. (Lecture Notes in Mathematics Ser.: Vol. 1057). vii, 223p. 1984. pap. 12.50 (ISBN 0-387-12931-6). Springer-Verlag.

Chern, S. S. Differential Geometry & Differential Equations: Proceedings of the 1980 Conference in Beijing, The People's Republic of China. 652p. 1982. 341.25 (ISBN 0-677-31120-6). Gordon.

Coddington, Earl A. & Levinson, Norman. Theory of Ordinary Differential Equations. LC 84-4438. 444p. 1984. Repr. of 1955 ed. lib. bdg. 31.50 (ISBN 0-89874-755-4). Krieger.

Collet, Pierre & Eckman, Jean-Pierre. Iterated Maps on the Interval As Dynamical Systems. (Progress in Physics, Ser.: No. 1). 227p. 1980. text ed. 19.95x (ISBN 0-8176-3026-0). Birkhauser.

Conference on Analytical Theory of Differential Equations, Kalamazoo, Mich, 1970. Analytic Theory of Differential Equations: Proceedings. Hsieh, P. F. & Stoddart, A. W., eds. LC 77-153467. (Lecture Notes in Mathematics: Vol. 183). (Illus.). 1971. 13.00 (ISBN 0-387-05369-7). Springer-Verlag.

Conference on the Theory of Ordinary & Partial Differential Equations, Dundee, Scotland, 1972. Proceedings. Everitt, W. N. & Sleeman, B. D., eds. LC 72-87925. (Lecture Notes in Mathematics: Vol. 280). (Illus.). xv, 367p. 1972. pap. 13.00 (ISBN 0-387-05962-8). Springer-Verlag.

Conference on the Theory of Ordinary & Partial Differential Equations, Dundee, Scotland, 1974. Proceedings. Sleeman, B. D. & McRae, I. M., eds. LC 74-18467. (Lecture Notes in Mathematics Ser.: Vol. 415). xvii, 447p. 1974. pap. 24.00 (ISBN 0-387-06959-3). Springer-Verlag.

Conti, Roberto, ed. Recent Advances in Differential Equations. LC 81-15042. 1981. 47.50 (ISBN 0-12-186280-1). Acad Pr.

Control Theory Centre Symposium, University of Warwick, 1972. Stability of Stochastic Dynamical Systems: Proceedings. Curtain, R. F., ed. LC 72-91895. (Lecture Notes in Mathematics: Vol. 294). (Illus.). 332p. 1972. pap. 13.00 (ISBN 0-387-06050-2). Springer-Verlag.

Cooke, R. The Mathematics of Sonya Kovalevskaya. (Illus.). 275p. 1984. 29.80 (ISBN 0-387-96030-9). Springer-Verlag.

Coppel, W. A. Dichotomies in Stability Theory. (Lecture Notes in Mathematics: Vol. 629). 1978. pap. 14.00 (ISBN 0-387-08536-X). Springer-Verlag.

--Disconjugacy. (Lecture Notes in Mathematics: Vol. 220). v, 148p. 1971. pap. 11.00 (ISBN 0-387-05584-3). Springer-Verlag.

Corduneanu, Constantin. Principles of Differential & Integral Equations. 2nd ed. LC 77-2962. 1977. text ed. 14.95 (ISBN 0-8284-0295-7). Chelsea Pub.

Creese, Thomas M. & Haralick, Robert M. Differential Equations for Engineers. 1978. text ed. 37.95 (ISBN 0-07-013510-X). McGraw.

Cullen, Charles G. Linear Algebra & Differential Equations. 1979. write for info. (ISBN 0-87150-262-3, PWS 2131, Prindle). PWS Pubs.

Daleckii, Ju. L. & Krein, M. G. Stability of Solutions of Differential Equations in Banach Space. LC 74-8403. (Translations of Mathematical Monographs: Vol. 43). 1974. 72.00 (ISBN 0-8218-1593-8, MMONO-43). Am Math.

Danby, J. M. Computer Applications to Differential Equations. 1985. pap. text ed. 17.95 (ISBN 0-8359-0962-X). Reston.

Daniel, James W. & Moore, Ramon E. Computation & Theory in Ordinary Differential Equations. LC 71-117611. (Mathematics Ser.). (Illus.). 172p. 1970. text ed. 23.95 (ISBN 0-7167-0440-4). W H Freeman.

Davis, Harold T. Introduction to Nonlinear Differential & Integral Equations. 1960. pap. 8.95 (ISBN 0-486-60971-5). Dover.

--Studies in Differential Equations. Scott, Walter, ed. LC 56-14277. (Northwestern University Series in Mathematical & Physical Sciences: No. 3). pap. 30.00 (ISBN 0-317-08636-7, 2006876). Bks Demand UMI.

De Figueiredo, D. G., ed. Differential Equations, Sao Paulo, Brazil, 1981: Proceedings. (Lecture Notes in Mathematics: Vol. 957). 301p. 1982. pap. 18.00 (ISBN 0-387-11951-5). Springer-Verlag.

Deimling, K. Ordinary Differential Equations in Banach Spaces. (Lecture Notes in Mathematics: Vol. 596). 1977. 13.00 (ISBN 0-387-08260-3). Springer-Verlag.

Derrick, William R. & Grossman, Stanley I. Elementary Differential Equations with Applications. 2nd ed. (Mathematics Ser.). (Illus.). 576p. 1981. text ed. 31.95 (ISBN 0-201-03162-0); answer bk. 2.00 (ISBN 0-201-03166-3). Addison-Wesley.

--Elementary Differential Equations with Applications: A Short Course. 2nd ed. (Mathematics Ser.). (Illus.). 384p. 1981. text ed. 27.95 (ISBN 0-201-03164-7). Addison-Wesley.

Deuflhard, Peter & Hairer, Ernst. Workshop on Numerical Treatment of Inverse Problems in Differential & Integral Equations. (Progress in Scientific Computing: Vol. 2). 372p. 1983. 27.50x (ISBN 0-8176-3125-9). Birkhauser.

Dollard, John D. & Friedman, Charles N. Encyclopedia of Mathematics & Its Applications: Product Integration with Applications to Differential Equations, Vol. 10. 1984. 39.50 (ISBN 0-521-30230-7). Cambridge U Pr.

Donaldson, Thomas. A Laplace Transform Calculus for Partial Differential Operators. LC 74-7370. (Memoirs: No. 143). 166p. 1974. pap. 11.00 (ISBN 0-8218-1843-0, MEMO-143). Am Math.

Driver, R. Ordinary & Delay Differential Equations. LC 76-58452. (Applied Mathematical Sciences Ser.: Vol. 20). 1977. pap. 25.00 (ISBN 0-387-90231-7). Springer-Verlag.

Duff, George F. Partial Differential Equations. LC 56-4187. (Mathematical Expositions: No. 9). pap. 64.50 (ISBN 0-317-08885-8, 2014193). Bks Demand UMI.

Duff, George F. & Naylor, D. Differential Equations of Applied Mathematics. LC 65-26844. pap. 82.30 (ISBN 0-317-08714-2, 2012598). Bks Demand UMI.

Dwork, Bernard. Lectures on P-Adic Differential Equations. (Grundlehron der Mathematischen Wissenschaften Ser.: Vol. 253). (Illus.). 304p. 1982. 54.00 (ISBN 0-387-90714-9). Springer-Verlag.

Eckhaus, W. New Developments in Differential Equations: Proceedings of the Scheveningen Conference, 2nd, the Netherlands, 1975. (North Holland Mathematics Studies: Vol. 21). 348p. 1976. 47.00 (ISBN 0-444-11107-7, North-Holland). Elsevier.

Edwards, C. H., Jr. & Penney, David E. Elementary Differential Equations with Applications. (Illus.). 608p. 1985. text ed. 29.95 (ISBN 0-13-254129-7). P-H.

Egorov, V. G., et al. Eight Papers on Differential Equations. LC 51-5559. (Translations, Ser.: No. 2, Vol. 24). 1963. 26.00 (ISBN 0-8218-1724-8, TRANS 2-24). Am Math.

Elsgolts, L. Differential Equations & the Calculus of Variations. Yankovsky, George, tr. from Rus. (Illus.). 440p. 1970. 17.95x (ISBN 0-8464-0335-8). Beekman Pubs.

El'Sgol'Ts, L. E. Differential Equations. (Russian Monographs). (Illus.). 372p. 1961. 98.25 (ISBN 0-677-20060-9). Gordon.

Everett, W. N., ed. Ordinary & Partial Differential Equations. (Lecture Notes in Mathematics Ser.: Vol. 827). (Illus.). 271p. 1980. pap. 20.00 (ISBN 0-387-10252-3). Springer-Verlag.

Everitt, W. N. & Lewis, R. T., eds. Ordinary Differential Equations & Operators. (Lecture Notes in Mathematics: Vol. 1032). 521p. 1983. pap. 25.00 (ISBN 0-387-12702-X). Springer-Verlag.

Everitt, W. N. & Sleeman, B. D., eds. Ordinary & Partial Differential Equations: Proceedings. (Lecture Notes in Mathematics Ser.: Vol. 846). 384p. 1981. pap. 24.00 (ISBN 0-387-10569-7). Springer-Verlag.

Farkas. Qualitative Theory of Differential Equations, 2 vols. (Colloquia Mathematica Ser.: Vol. 30). 1090p. 1982. Set. 159.75 (ISBN 0-444-86173-4, North-Holland). Elsevier.

Farkas, M., ed. Differential Equations. (Colloquia Mathematica Societatis Janos Bolyai: Vol. 15). 418p. 1977. 85.00 (ISBN 0-7204-0496-7, North-Holland). Elsevier.

Farlow, S. J. Partial Differential Equations for Scientists & Engineers. (Japanese.). 300p. 1983. pap. 29.95 (ISBN 0-471-88698-X). Wiley.

Finizio, Norman & Ladas, Gerasimons. An Introduction to Differential Equations. 608p. 1981. text ed. write for info. (ISBN 0-534-00960-3). Wadsworth Pub.

--Ordinary Differential Equations with Modern Applications. 2nd ed. 432p. 1981. text ed. write for info. (ISBN 0-534-00898-4). Wadsworth Pub.

Fink, A. M. Almost Periodic Differential Equations. (Lecture Notes in Mathematics: Vol. 377). viii, 336p. 1974. pap. 18.00 (ISBN 0-387-06729-9). Springer-Verlag.

Finney, Ross L. & Ostberg, Donald E. Elementary Differential Equations with Linear Algebra. 2nd ed. LC 75-12096. (Mathematics Ser.). 704p. 1976. text ed. 31.95 (ISBN 0-201-05515-5). Addison-Wesley.

Fourth Conference Held at Dundee, Scotland, Mar 30-Apr 2, 1976. Ordinary & Partial Differential Equations, Dundee 1976: Proceedings. Everitt, W. N. & Sleeman, B. D., eds. (Lecture Notes in Mathematics Ser.: Vol. 564). 1976. soft cover 29.00 (ISBN 0-387-08058-9). Springer-Verlag.

Friedman, Avner. Differential Games. LC 73-15872. (CBMS Regional Conference Series in Mathematics: No. 18). 66p. 1974. pap. 16.00 (ISBN 0-8218-1668-3, CBMS-18). Am Math.

--Stochastic Differential Equations & Applications, 2 vols. (Probability & Mathematical Statistics Ser.). Vol. 1,1975. 49.50 (ISBN 0-12-268201-7); Vol. 2, 1976. 64.50 (ISBN 0-12-268202-5). Acad Pr.

Friedrichs, K. O. Advanced Ordinary Differential Equations. (Notes on Mathematics & Its Applications Ser.). 216p. 1965. 41.75 (ISBN 0-677-00960-7); pap. 26.00 (ISBN 0-677-00965-8). Gordon.

Gabasov, R. & Kirillova, F. The Qualitative Theory of Optimal Processes. Casti, John L., tr. (Control & Systems Theory: Vol. 3). 1976. 110.00 (ISBN 0-8247-6545-1). Dekker.

Galin, D. M., et al. Sixteen Papers on Differential Equations. LC 82-20595. (AMS Translations Ser.: No. 2 vol. 118). 74.00 (ISBN 0-8218-3073-2, TRANS/2/118). Am Math.

Gel'fand, M. S., et al. Twelve Papers on Logic & Differential Equations. LC 51-5559. (Translations Ser.: No. 2, Vol. 29). 1963. 30.00 (ISBN 0-8218-1729-9, TRANS 2-29). Am Math.

Gerard, R. & Ramis, J. P., eds. Equations Differentielles et Systemes de Pfaff Dans le Champs Complex-II. (Lecture Notes in Mathematics: Vol. 1015). 411p. 1983. pap. 20.00 (ISBN 0-387-12684-8). Springer-Verlag.

Gihman, I. I. & Skorohod, A. V. Stochastic Differential Equations. Wickwire, K., tr. from Rus. LC 72-86885. (Ergebnisse der Mathematik und Ihrer Grenzgebiete: Vol. 72). viii, 354p. 1972. 56.00 (ISBN 0-387-05946-6). Springer-Verlag.

Gilbarg, D. & Trudinger, N. S. Elliptic Partial Differential Equations of Second Order. 2nd ed. (Grundlehren der mathematischen Wissenschaften. A Series of Comprehensive Studies in Mathematics: Band 224). 530p. 1983. 48.00 (ISBN 0-387-13025-X). Springer Verlag.

Gilbert, R. & Weinacht, R. Function Theoretic Methods in Differential Equations. (Research Notes in Mathematics Ser.: No. 8). (Orig.). 1976. pap. text ed. 27.95 (ISBN 0-273-00306-2). Pitman Pub MA.

Gladwell, I. & Wait, R., eds. A Survey of Numerical Methods for Partial Differential Equations. (Illus.). 1979. 49.50x (ISBN 0-19-853351-9). Oxford U Pr.

Gladwell, R. & Sayers, D. K., eds. Computational Techniques for Ordinary Differential Equations. LC 79-42626. (IMA & ITS Applications Conference Ser.). 1980. 33.00 (ISBN 0-12-285780-1). Acad Pr.

Gould, Sydney H. Variational Methods for Eigenvalue Problems: An Introduction to the Weinstein Method of Intermediate Problems. 2nd ed. LC 66-76289. (Mathematical Expositions Ser.). 1966. 27.50x (ISBN 0-8020-1404-6). U of Toronto Pr.

Grabmuller, H. Singular Perturbation Techniques Applied to Integro-Differential Equations. (Research Notes in Mathematics: No. 20). 148p. (Orig.). 1978. pap. text ed. 22.95 (ISBN 0-273-08409-7). Pitman Pub MA.

Graef, John R. Stability of Dynamical Systems: Theory & Application. (Lecture Notes in Pure & Applied Mathematics: Vol. 28). 1977. 55.00 (ISBN 0-8247-6410-2). Dekker.

Gregory, John, ed. Quadratic Form Theory & Differential Equations. LC 80-520. (Mathematics in Science & Engineering Ser.). 1981. 39.50 (ISBN 0-12-301450-6). Acad Pr.

Guterman, Martin M. & Nitecki, Zbigniew H. Differential Equations. 1984. text ed. 35.95 (ISBN 0-03-062502-5, CBS C); study manual 11.95 (ISBN 0-03-062503-3). SCP.

Haberman, Richard. Elementary Applied Partial Differential Equations. (Illus.). 560p. 1983. text ed. 39.95 (ISBN 0-13-252833-9). P-H.

Hagedorn, P., et al, eds. Differential Games & Applications: Proceedings of a Workshop, Enschede, Netherlands, March 16-25,1977. (Lecture Notes in Control & Information Sciences: Vol. 3). 1977. pap. text ed. 19.00 (ISBN 0-387-08407-X). Springer-Verlag.

Hagin, F. G. A First Course in Differential Equations. (Illus.). 384p. 1975. text ed. 31.95 (ISBN 0-13-318394-7). P-H.

Hajek, O., et al, eds. Global Differentiable Dynamics, Proceedings. (Lecture Notes in Mathematics.: Vol. 235). (Illus.). x, 140p. 1971. pap. 9.00 (ISBN 0-387-05674-2). Springer-Verlag.

Halanay, A. Differential Equations: Stability, Oscillations, Time Lags. (Mathematics in Science & Engineering Ser.: Vol. 23). 1966. 83.00 (ISBN 0-12-317950-5). Acad Pr.

Hale, J. K. Theory of Functional Differential Equations. LC 76-26611. (Applied Mathematical Sciences: Vol. 3). 1977. 46.00 (ISBN 0-387-90203-1). Springer-Verlag.

Hale, Jack. Studies in Ordinary Differential Equations. LC 77-8289. (MAA Studies: No. 14). 278p. 1977. 21.00 (ISBN 0-88385-114-8). Math Assn.

Hale, Jack K. Ordinary Differential Equations. 2nd. ed. LC 79-17238. (Pure & Applied Mathematics Ser.: Vol. 21). 386p. 1980. lib. bdg. 27.50 (ISBN 0-89874-011-8). Krieger.

Hale, Jack K. & LaSalle, Joseph P., eds. Differential Equations & Dynamical Systems. 1967. 75.00 (ISBN 0-12-318450-9). Acad Pr.

Hannsgen, Kenneth B. & Herdman, Terry L., eds. Volterra & Functional Differential Equations. (Lecture Notes in Pure & Applied Mathematics Ser.: Vol. 81). (Illus.). 352p. 1982. 55.00 (ISBN 0-8247-1721-X). Dekker.

Hartman, P. Ordinary Differential Equations. 2nd ed. 1982. text ed. 29.95 (ISBN 0-8176-3068-6). Birkhauser.

Henrici, Peter. Discrete Variable Methods in Ordinary Differential Equations. LC 61-17359. 407p. 1962. 42.95x (ISBN 0-471-37224-2, Pub. by Wiley-Interscience). Wiley.

Hill, J. M. Solution of Differential Equations by Means of One-Parameter Groups. LC 82-621. (Research Notes in Mathematics Ser.: No. 63). 176p. 1982. pap. text ed. 21.95 (ISBN 0-273-08506-9). Pitman Pub MA.

Hille, Einar. Ordinary Differential Equations in the Complex Domain. LC 75-44231. (Pure & Applied Mathematics Ser.). 484p. 1976. 59.95x (ISBN 0-471-39964-7, Pub. by Wiley-Interscience). Wiley.

Hirsch, Morris & Smale, Stephen. Differential Equations, Dynamical Systems & Linear Algebra. 1974. text ed. 23.25i (ISBN 0-12-349550-4). Acad Pr.

Hirschowitz, A., ed. Vector Bundles & Differential Equations. (Progress in Math. Ser.: No. 7). 255p. 1980. pap. text ed. 20.00x (ISBN 0-8176-3022-8). Birkhauser.

Hochstadt, Harry. Differential Equations: A Modern Approach. LC 75-2569. (Illus.). 320p. 1975. pap. text ed. 6.50 (ISBN 0-486-61941-9). Dover.

Howes, F. A. Singular Perturbations & Differential Inequalities. LC 75-44235. (Memoirs: No. 168). 75p. 1976. pap. 13.00 (ISBN 0-8218-1868-6, MEMO-168). Am Math.

Hubbard, Bert. Numerical Solution of Partial Differential Equations-2. 1971. 76.00 (ISBN 0-12-358502-3). Acad Pr.

Ince, Edward L. Ordinary Differential Equations. (Illus.). 1953. pap. text ed. 8.95 (ISBN 0-486-60349-0). Dover.

Ito, Kiyosi. On Stochastic Differential Equations. LC 52-42839. (Memoirs: No. 4). 51p. 1969. pap. 10.00 (ISBN 0-8218-1204-1, MEMO-4). Am Math.

Ize, A. F., ed. Functional Differential Equations & Bifurcations: Proceedings. (Lecture Notes in Mathematics: Vol. 799). 409p. 1980. pap. 28.00 (ISBN 0-387-09986-7). Springer-Verlag.

Jain, M. K. Numerical Solution of Differential Equations. 2nd ed. 698p. 1979. 34.95 (ISBN 0-470-27389-5). Halsted Pr.

Japan - United States Seminar on Ordinary Differential & Functional Equations, Kyoto, 1971. Proceedings. Urabe, M., ed. (Lecture Notes in Mathematics: Vol. 243). viii, 332p. 1971. pap. 13.00 (ISBN 0-387-05708-0). Springer-Verlag.

John, F. Partial Differential Equations. 4th ed. (Applied Mathematical Sciences Ser.: Vol. 1). (Illus.). 249p. 1981. 21.95 (ISBN 0-387-90609-6). Springer-Verlag.

Johnson, R. M. Theory & Applications of Linear Differential & Difference Equations: A Systems Approach in Engineering. (Mathematics & Its Applications Ser.). 183p. 1984. 29.95 (ISBN 0-470-20106-1). Halsted Pr.

Johnstone, I. A Probabilistic Study of Linear Elliptic-Parabolic Equations of Second Order. (Notes on Pure Mathematics Ser.: No. 12). 217p. (Orig.). 1980. pap. text ed. 10.00 (ISBN 0-908160-32-1, 0564). Australia N U P.

Jones, D. S. & Sleeman, B. D. Differential Equations & Mathematical Biology. 320p. 1982. text ed. 35.00x (ISBN 0-04-515001-X). Allen Unwin.

Jones, L. B. Ordinary Differential Equations. (Mathematical Topics for Engineering & Science Students Ser.). (Illus.). 1976. pap. 11.00x (ISBN 0-8464-0689-6). Beekman Pubs.

Journe, J. L. Calderon-Zymund Operators, Pseudo-Differential & the Cauchy Integral of Calderon. (Lecture Notes in Mathematics: Vol. 994). 129p. 1983. pap. 10.00 (ISBN 0-387-12313-X). Springer-Verlag.

Kappel, F. & Schappacher, W. Abstract Cauchy Problems & Functional Differential Equations. LC 80-22557. (Research Notes in Mathematics Ser.: No. 48). 240p. (Orig.). 1981. pap. text ed. 28.95 (ISBN 0-273-08494-1). Pitman Pub MA.

--Infinite-Dimensional Systems: Proceedings of the Conference on Operator Semigroups & Applications, Held in Styria, Austria, June 5-11, 1983. (Lecture Notes in Mathematics Ser.: Vol. 1076). viii, 278p. 1984. pap. 16.00t (ISBN 0-387-13376-3). Springer-Verlag.

Kartsatos, Athanassios G. Advanced Ordinary Differential Equations. LC 80-10881. 185p. 1980. text ed. 32.50 (ISBN 0-936166-02-9). Mariner Pub.

Kashiwara, Masaki. Systems of Microdifferential Equations. Fernandes, Teresa M., tr. (Progress in Mathematics Ser.). 200p. 1983. text ed. 16.00 (ISBN 0-8176-3138-0). Birkhauser.

Kaufman, R. M., et al. The Deficency Index Problem for Powers of Ordinary Differential Expressions. LC 77-25921. (Lecture Notes in Mathematics: Vol. 621). 1977. text ed. 14.00 (ISBN 0-387-08523-8). Springer-Verlag.

Koonin, Steven E. Computational Physics. 1985. 31.95. Addison-Wesley.

Krasnoselsky, Mark A. Operator of Translation Along the Trajectories of Differential Equations. LC 67-22349. (Translations of Mathematical Monographs: Vol. 19). 1968. Repr. of 1950 ed. 37.00 (ISBN 0-8218-1569-5, MMONO-19). Am Math.

Krasnov, M. L., et al. Book of Problems in Ordinary Differential Equations. 332p. 1981. 6.80 (ISBN 0-8285-1925-0, Pub. by Mir Pubs USSR). Imported Pubns.

Krein, M. G. & Jakubovic, V. A. Four Papers on Ordinary Differential Equations. LC 83-2825. (Translations Series 2: Vol. 120). 1983. 35.00 (ISBN 0-8218-3075-9). Am Math.

Kumpel, P. G. & Thorpe, J. A. Linear Algebra, with Differential Equations. LC 82-60630. 353p. 1983. text ed. 32.95x (ISBN 0-03-060556-3, CBS C). SCP.

Kumpera, Antonio & Spenser, Donald. Lie Equations: General Theory. LC 77-39055. (Annals of Mathematics Studies: No. 73). 300p. 1972. 25.00 (ISBN 0-691-08111-5). Princeton U Pr.

Ladas, G. & Lakshmikantham, V. Differential Equations in Abstract Spaces. (Mathematics in Science & Engineering Ser.: Vol. 85). 1972. 60.00 (ISBN 0-12-432650-1). Acad Pr.

Ladde, G. S. & Laksmikantham, V. Random Differential Inequalities. LC 80-521. (Mathematics in Science & Engineering Ser.). 1980. 47.50 (ISBN 0-12-432750-8). Acad Pr.

Laken, William D. & Sanchez, David A. Topics in Ordinary Differential Equations. 160p. 1982. pap. 4.00 (ISBN 0-486-61606-1). Dover.

Lakshmikantham, V. & Leela, S. Differential & Integral Inequalities: Theory & Application, 2 vols. Incl. Vol. 1. Ordinary Differential Equations. 1969. 80.00 (ISBN 0-12-434101-2); Vol. 2. Functional, Partial, Abstract & Complex Differential Equations. 80.00 (ISBN 0-12-434102-0). LC 68-8425. (Mathematics in Science & Engineering Ser.: Vol. 55). 1969. Acad Pr.

Langer, Rudolph E., ed. Boundary Problems in Differential Equations: Proceedings of a Symposium Conducted by the Mathematics Research Center at the University of Wisconsin, Madison, April 20-22, 1959. LC 60-60003. (U.S. Army, Mathematics Research Center Publication Ser.: No. 2). pap. 83.50 (ISBN 0-317-08301-5, 2021137). Bks Demand UMI.

Lappo-Danilevskii, J. A. Systemes des Equations Differentielles, 3 Vols. in 1. LC 53-7110. (Fr). 27.50 (ISBN 0-8284-0094-6). Chelsea Pub.

Laurie, Dirk P. Numerical Solution of Partial Differential Equations. (International Series of Numerical Mathematics: Vol. 66). 334p. 1983. text ed. 29.95 (ISBN 3-7643-1561-X). Birkhauser.

Lax, P. D. Hyperbolic Systems of Conservation Laws & the Mathematical Theory of Shock Waves. (CBMS-NSF Regional Conference Ser.: No. 11). v, 48p. 1973. pap. text ed. 8.00 (ISBN 0-89871-177-0). Soc Indus-Appl Math.

Lefschetz, S. Lectures on Differential Equations. (Annals of Math Studies). 1946. 15.00 (ISBN 0-527-02730-8). Kraus Repr.

Lefschetz, Solomon. Differential Equations: Geometric Theory. 1977. pap. text ed. 7.95 (ISBN 0-486-63463-9). Dover.

Leighton, Walter. First Course in Ordinary Differential Equations. 5th ed. 304p. 1980. text ed. write for info. (ISBN 0-534-00837-2). Wadsworth Pub.

Levitan, B. M. & Zhikov, V. V. Almost Periodic Functions & Differential Equations. Longdon, L. V., tr. LC 82-4352. 150p. 1983. 37.50 (ISBN 0-521-24407-2). Cambridge U Pr.

Lie, Sophus. Differentialgleichungen. LC 66-12880. (Ger). 25.00 (ISBN 0-8284-0206-X). Chelsea Pub.

Littman, Walter, ed. Studies in Partial Differential Equations. LC 82-62782. (MAA Studies in Mathematics Ser.: No. 23). 268p. 1983. 24.00 (ISBN 0-88385-125-3). Math Assn.

Lomen, David & Mark, James. Ordinary Differential Equations with Linear Algebra. (Illus.). 416p. 1986. text ed. 28.95 (ISBN 0-13-639782-4). P-H.

Loud, Warren S. Periodic Solutions of Perturbed Second-Order Autonomous Equations. LC 52-42839. (Memoirs: No. 47). 133p. 1964. pap. 10.00 (ISBN 0-8218-1247-5, MEMO-47). Am Math.

--Periodic Solutions of X Double Prime Plus C Times X Plus G of (X) Equals F of T. LC 52-42839. (Memoirs: No. 31). 58p. 1966. pap. 9.00 (ISBN 0-8218-1231-9, MEMO-31). Am Math.

Lucas, W. F., ed. Modules in Applied Mathematics: Differential Equation Models, Vol. 1. (Illus.). 400p. 1982. 29.50 (ISBN 0-387-90695-9). Springer-Verlag.

Lukes, Dahlard L. Differential Equation: Classical to Controlled. (Mathematics in Science and Engineering Ser.). 1982. 48.50 (ISBN 0-12-459980-X). Acad Pr.

McCann, Roger C. Introduction to Ordinary Differential Equations. 451p. 1982. text ed. 27.95 (ISBN 0-15-543485-3, HC); answer bk. avail. (ISBN 0-15-543486-1). HarBraceJ.

MacDonald, N. Time Lags in Biological Models. (Lecture Notes in Biomathematics: Vol. 27). (Illus.). 1978. pap. 14.00 (ISBN 0-387-09092-4). Springer-Verlag.

McKelvey, Robert, ed. Lectures on Ordinary Differential Equations: A Symposium Vol. 1970. 59.50 (ISBN 0-12-485150-9). Acad Pr.

Maddox, I. J. Infinite Matrices of Operators. (Lecture Notes in Mathematics: Vol. 786). 122p. 1980. pap. 13.00 (ISBN 0-387-09764-3). Springer-Verlag.

Majima, H. Asymptotic Analysis for Integrable Connections with Irregular Singular Points. (Lecture Notes in Mathematics Ser.: Vol. 1075). ix, 159p. 1984. pap. 12.00 (ISBN 0-387-13375-5). Springer-Verlag.

Marchuk, G. I. Differential Equations & Numerical Mathematics: Proceedings of a U. S. S. R. Council of Ministers for Science & Technology, Moscow. LC 81-81912. (Illus.). 176p. 1982. 55.00 (ISBN 0-08-026491-3, D120). Pergamon.

Markley, N. G., et al, eds. The Structure of Attractors in Dynamical Systems: Proceedings, North Dakota, June 20-24, 1977. LC 78-13670. (Lecture Notes in Mathematics: Vol. 668). 1978. pap. 20.00 (ISBN 0-387-08925-X). Springer-Verlag.

Markus, L. & Meyer, K. R. Generic Hamiltonian Dynamical Systems Are Neither Integrable Nor Ergodic. LC 74-8095. (Memoirs: No. 144). 52p. 1974. pap. 10.00 (ISBN 0-8218-1844-9, MEMO-144). Am Math.

Martin, R. H. Elementary Differential Equations with Boundary Value Problems. 1984. 39.95 (ISBN 0-07-040689-8). McGraw.

Martin, Robert E., Jr. Ordinary Differential Equations. (Illus.). 496p. 1983. text ed. 34.95 (ISBN 0-07-040687-1). McGraw.

Martin, William T., et al. Elementary Differential Equations. 3rd ed. text ed. I (ISBN 0-8162-5435-4). Holden-Day.

Martini, R., ed. Geometrical Approaches to Differential Equations: Proceedings. (Lecture Notes in Mathematics: Vol. 810). (Illus.). 339p. 1980. pap. 23.00 (ISBN 0-387-10018-0). Springer-Verlag.

Matsuda, M. First-Order Algebraic Differential Equations: A Differential Algebraic Approach. (Lectures Notes in Mathematics: Vol. 804). 111p. 1980. pap. 13.00 (ISBN 0-387-09997-2). Springer-Verlag.

Mikhailov, V. Partial Differential Equations. 395p. 1978. 7.95 (ISBN 0-8285-0734-1, Pub. by Mir Pubs USSR). Imported Pubns.

Miller, Richard & Michel, A. Ordinary Differential Equations. 1981. 34.50 (ISBN 0-12-497280-2). Acad Pr.

Mingarelli, A. B. Volterra-Stieltjes Integral Equations & Generalized Ordinary Differential Expressions. (Lecture Notes in Mathematics: Vol. 989). 318p. 1983. pap. 18.00 (ISBN 0-387-12294-X). Springer-Verlag.

Mishchenko, E. F. & Rozov, B. Kh. Differential Equations with Small Parameters & Relaxation Oscillations. LC 78-4517. (Mathematical Concepts & Methods in Science & Engineering Ser.: Vol. 13). (Illus.). 238p. 1980. 37.50x (ISBN 0-306-39253-4, Plenum Pr). Plenum Pub.

Mohammed, A. E. Retarded Functional Differential Equations: A Global Point of View. (Research Notes in Mathematics Ser.: No. 21). 147p. (Orig.). 1978. pap. text ed. 20.95 (ISBN 0-273-08401-1). Pitman Pub MA.

Muller-Pfeiffer, Erich. Spectral Theory of Ordinary Differential Operators. LC 80-42097. (Mathematics & Its Application Ser.). 246p. 1981. 69.95 (ISBN 0-470-27103-5). Halsted Pr.

Murray, Francis J. & Miller, Kenneth S. Existence Theorems for Ordinary Differential Equations. LC 54-10566. pap. 41.00 (ISBN 0-317-08535-2, 2050206). Bks Demand UMI.

NATO Advanced Study Institute, University of Warwick, Coventry England, August 27-September 6, 1974. The Theory & Application of Differential Games: Proceedings. Grote, J. D., ed. LC 74-34041. (NATO Advanced Study Institutes: No. C13). 310p. 1975. lib. bdg. 39.50 (ISBN 90-277-0581-X, Pub. by Reidel Holland). Kluwer Academic.

Nemytsky, V. V. & Stepanov, V. V. Qualitative Theory of Differential Equations. (Mathematical Ser.: Vol. 22). 1960. 50.00 (ISBN 0-691-08020-8). Princeton U Pr.

Nielsen, Kaj L. Differential Equations. 2nd ed. (Orig.). 1969. pap. 5.50 (ISBN 0-06-460072-6, CO 72, COS). B&N NY.

Nikol'ski, S. M., ed. Theory & Applications of Differentiable Functions of Several Variables, 4. LC 68-1677. (Proceedings of the Steklov Institute: No. 117). 1974. 79.00 (ISBN 0-8218-3017-1, STEKLO-117). Am Math.

Norkin, S. B. Differential Equations of the Second Order with Retarded Argument: Some Problems of the Theory of Vibrations of Systems with Retardation. LC 70-37627. (Translations of Mathematical Monographs,: Vol. 31). 1972. 39.00 (ISBN 0-8218-1581-4, MMONO-31). Am Math.

Nussbaum, Roger D. Differential-Delay Equations with Two Time Lags. LC 78-16320. (Memoirs: No. 205). 62p. 1978. pap. 12.00 (ISBN 0-8218-2205-5, MEMO-205). Am Math.

O'Malley, Robert E., ed. Asymptotic Methods & Singular Perturbations: Proceedings of a Symposium, New York, April 1976. LC 76-27872. (SIAM-AMS Proceedings: Vol. 10). 1976. 30.00 (ISBN 0-8218-1330-7, SIAMS10). Am Math.

Ordinary & Partial Differential Equations: Proceedings, Dundee, Scotland, 1982. (Lecture Notes in Mathematics: Vol. 964). 726p. 1982. pap. 34.00 (ISBN 0-387-11968-X). Springer-Verlag.

Ovsiannikov, L. V. Group Analysis by Differential Equations. Ames, William, tr. 1982. 59.50 (ISBN 0-12-531680-1). Acad Pr.

Pavel, A. H. Differential Equations, Flow Invariance & Applications. (Research Notes in Mathematics Ser.: No.113). 256p. 1984. pap. text ed. 18.95 (ISBN 0-317-08651-0). Pitman Pub Ma.

Peitgen, H. O. & Walther, H. O., eds. Functional Differential Equations & Approximations of Fixed Points. (Lecture Notes in Mathematics: Vol. 730). 1979. pap. 28.00 (ISBN 0-387-09518-7). Springer-Verlag.

Petrovski, I. G. Ordinary Differential Equations. 232p. 1984. pap. 5.50 (ISBN 0-486-64683-1). Dover.

Piccinini, Livio C., et al. Ordinary Differential Equations in R to the Nth Power. (Applied Mathematical Sciences Ser.: Vol. 39). 386p. 1984. pap. 32.00 (ISBN 0-387-90723-8). Springer-Verlag.

Plaat, Otto. Ordinary Differential Equations. LC 70-156869. 350p. 1971. 32.50x (ISBN 0-8162-6844-4). Holden-Day.

Powers, David L. Elementary Differential Equations with Boundary Value Problems. 1985. text ed. write for info. (ISBN 0-87150-431-6, 33L2810, Prindle). PWS Pubs.

Protter, M. & Weinberger, H. Maximum Principles in Differential Equations. (Illus.). 1984. 28.00 (ISBN 0-387-96068-6). Springer-Verlag.

Rabenstein, Albert. Introduction to Ordinary Differential Equations. 2nd ed. 538p. 1972. 22.50i (ISBN 0-12-573957-5). Acad Pr.

Rainville, E. D. & Bedient, P. E. Elementary Differential Equations. 6th ed. 1981. write for info. (ISBN 0-02-397770-1). Macmillan.

--Short Course in Differential Equations. 6th ed. 1981. write for info. (ISBN 0-02-397760-4). Macmillan.

Ramis, Jean-Pierre. Theoremes d'indices Gevrey pour les equations differentielles ordinaires. LC 83-27157. (Memoirs: No. 296). 96p. 1984. pap. 10.00 (ISBN 0-8218-2296-9, MEMO 296). Am Math.

Ranquan, Wu. Stochastic Differential Equations. (Research Notes in Mathematics Ser.). 160p. 1985. pap. text ed. 15.95 (ISBN 0-273-08685-5). Pitman Pub MA.

Reid, W. T. Riccati Differential Equations. (Mathematics in Science & Engineering Ser.: Vol. 86). 1972. 60.00 (ISBN 0-12-586250-4). Acad Pr.

Reid, William T. Ordinary Differential Equations. LC 74-123745. 553p. 1971. 31.00 (ISBN 0-471-71499-2, Pub. by Wiley). Krieger.

--Sturmian Theory for Ordinary Differential Equations. (Applied Mathematical Sciences: Vol. 31). 559p. 1980. pap. 33.50 (ISBN 0-387-90542-1). Springer-Verlag.

Ritger, Paul D. & Rose, Nicholas J. Differential Equations with Applications. (International Ser. in Pure & Applied Physics). 1968. text ed. 42.95 (ISBN 0-07-052945-0). McGraw.

Roberts, Charles E., Jr. Ordinary Differential Equations: A Computational Approach. LC 78-13023. 1979. 32.95 (ISBN 0-13-639757-3). P-H.

Romanov, V. G. Integral Geometry & Inverse Problems for Hyperbolic Equations. (Springer Tracts in Natural Philosophy: Vol. 26). (Illus.). 152p. 1974. 39.00 (ISBN 0-387-06429-X). Springer-Verlag.

Rosinger, E. E. Distributions & Nonlinear Partial Differential Equations. (Lecture Notes in Mathematics Ser.: Vol. 684). 1978. pap. 15.00 (ISBN 0-387-08951-9). Springer-Verlag.

Ross, S. An Introduction to Ordinary Differential Equations. 3rd ed. LC 79-12800. 1980. text ed. 32.00, 503p. (ISBN 0-471-03295-6); 392p. 14.45, (ISBN 0-471-05775-4). Wiley.

Rouche, N. & Mawhin, J. Ordinary Differential Equations: Stability & Periodic Solutions. LC 80-13039. (Surveys & References Ser.: No. 5). 208p. 1980. text ed. 62.95 (ISBN 0-273-08419-4). Pitman Pub MA.

Roxin, E. O., et al, eds. Differential Games & Control Theory. (Lecture Notes in Pure & Applied Mathematics Ser.: Vol. 10). 432p. 1975. 65.00 (ISBN 0-8247-6257-6). Dekker.

Roxin, Emilio, et al, eds. Differential Games in Control Theory II. (Lecture Notes in Pure & Applied Math: Vol. 30). 75.00 (ISBN 0-8247-6549-4). Dekker.

Sacker, R. J. Lifting Properties in Skew-Product Flows with Applications to Differential Equations. LC 77-8941. (Memoirs: No. 190). 67p. 1977. pap. 13.00 (ISBN 0-8218-2190-3, MEMO 190). Am Math.

Sakamoto, Reiko. Hyperbolic Boundary-Value Problems. LC 81-3865. 230p. 1982. 39.50 (ISBN 0-521-23568-5). Cambridge U Pr.

Salamon, D. Control & Observation of Neutral Systems. (Research Notes in Mathematics: No. 91). 220p. 1984. pap. text ed. 19.95 (ISBN 0-273-08618-9). Pitman Pub MA.

Sanchez, David A. & Allen, Richard C., Jr. Differential Equations: An Introduction. LC 82-16326. (Illus.). 512p. 1983. text ed. 32.95 (ISBN 0-201-07760-4). Addison-Wesley.

Santilli, R. M. Foundations of Theoretical Mechanics Part I: The Inverse Problem in Newtonian Mechanics. LC 78-9735. (Texts & Monographs in Physics). 1978. 45.00 (ISBN 0-387-08874-1). Springer-Verlag.

Schuss, Zeev. Theory & Applications of Stochastic Differential Equations. LC 80-14767. (Wiley Ser. in Probability & Mathematical Statistics: Applied Probability & Statistics). 321p. 1980. 39.95 (ISBN 0-471-04394-X). Wiley.

Schwabik, Stefan, et al. Differential & Integral Equations: Boundry Value Problems & Adjoints. 1979. 39.50 (ISBN 90-277-0802-9, Pub. by Reidel Holland). Kluwer Academic.

Schwarzenberger, R. L. Elementary Differential Equations. 1969. pap. 6.95x (ISBN 0-412-09580-7, NO.6247, Pub. by Chapman & Hall). Methuen Inc.

Schwarzkopf, A. B., et al, eds. Optimal Control & Differential Equation. 1978. 41.00 (ISBN 0-12-632250-3). Acad Pr.

Seminar on Differential Equations & Dynamical Systems, University of Maryland, 1968. Proceedings. Jones, G. S., ed. (Lecture Notes in Mathematics: Vol. 60). 1968. pap. 10.70 (ISBN 0-387-04230-X). Springer-Verlag.

Shokin, Yu. I. The Method of Differential Approximation. Roesner, K. G., tr. from Rus. (Springer Series in Computational Physics). (Illus.). 296p. 1983. 44.00 (ISBN 0-387-12225-7). Springer-Verlag.

Simmons, George F. Differential Equations with Applications & Historical Notes. (Pure & Applied Mathematics Ser.). (Illus.). 480p. 1972. text ed. 38.95 (ISBN 0-07-057375-1). McGraw.

Soong, T. T. Random Differential Equations in Science & Engineering. (Mathematics in Science & Engineering Ser.). 1973. 70.00 (ISBN 0-12-654850-1). Acad Pr.

Sperline, Meredith E. Ordinary Differential Equations: Solutions & Applications. LC 80-6101. 584p. 1981. pap. text ed. 21.25 (ISBN 0-8191-1358-1). U Pr of Amer.

Spiegal, Murray R. Applied Differential Equations. 3rd ed. 1980. text ed. 35.95 (ISBN 0-13-040097-1). P-H.

Stability Theory by Liapunov's Direct Method. LC 77-7285. (Applied Mathematical Sciences: Vol. 22). (Illus.). 1977. 25.00 (ISBN 0-387-90258-9). Springer-Verlag.

Stech, H. W. Integral & Functional Differential Equations. (Lecture Notes in Pure & Applied Mathematics Ser.: Vol. 67). 296p. 1981. 45.00 (ISBN 0-8247-1354-0). Dekker.

Steklov Institute of Mathematics, Academy of Sciences, U S S R. Theory & Applications of Differentiable Functions of Several Variables: Proceedings. Nikol'skii, S. M., ed. (Proceedings of the Steklov Institute of Mathematics: No. 77). 1967. 46.00 (ISBN 0-8218-1877-5, STEKLO-77). Am Math.

--Theory & Applications of Differentiable Functions of Several Variables, 2: Proceedings. Nikol'skii, S. M., ed. (Proceedings of the Steklov Institute of Mathematics: No. 89). 1968. 67.00 (ISBN 0-8218-1889-9, STEKLO-89). Am Math.

--Theory & Applications of Differentiable Functions of Several Variables, 3: Proceedings. Nikol'skii, S. M., ed. (Proceedings of the Steklov Institute of Mathematics: No. 105). 1971. 46.00 (ISBN 0-8218-3005-8, STEKLO-105). Am Math.

Strodt, Walter. Contributions to the Asymptotic Theory of Ordinary Differential Equations in the Complex Domain. LC 52-42839. (Memoirs: No. 13). 81p. pap. 9.00 (ISBN 0-8218-1213-0, MEMO-13). Am Math.

--Principal Solutions of Ordinary Differential Equations in the Complex Domain. LC 52-42839. (Memoirs: No. 26). 107p. 1972. pap. 12.00 (ISBN 0-8218-1226-2, MEMO-26). Am Math.

Stroock, D. W. Topics in Stochastic Differential Equations. (Tata Institute Lectures on Mathematics). 91p. 1982. pap. 9.00 (ISBN 0-387-11549-8). Springer-Verlag.

Stroock, D. W. & Varadhan, S. S. Multi-Dimensional Diffusion Processes. (Grundlehren der Mathematischen Wissenschaften: Vol. 233). 1979. 48.50 (ISBN 0-387-90353-4). Springer-Verlag.

Sychev, V. V. Differential Equations of Thermodynamics. 240p. 1983. 7.95 (ISBN 0-8285-2593-5, Pub. by Mir Pubs USSR). Imported Pubns.

Symposium on Differential Equations & Dynamical Systems, Warwickshire, 1968. Proceedings. Chillingworth, D., ed. LC 79-164961. (Lecture Notes in Mathematics: Vol. 206). 1971. pap. 11.00 (ISBN 0-387-05495-2). Springer-Verlag.

Symposium on Ordinary Differential Equations, Minneapolis, May, 1972. Proceedings. Harris, W. A., Jr. & Sibuya, Y., eds. LC 72-97022. (Lecture Notes in Mathematics: Vol. 312). (Illus.). 204p. 1973. pap. 14.00 (ISBN 0-387-06146-0). Springer-Verlag.

Symposium on the Numerical Treatment of O.D.E. Integral & Integro-Differential Equations. Rome 1960. 680p. 1961. 36.95x (ISBN 0-8176-0378-6). Birkhauser.

Tenenbaum, Morris & Pollard, Harry. Ordinary Differential Equations. 818p. 1985. pap. 16.95 (ISBN 0-486-64940-7). Dover.

Tierney. Differential Equations. 2nd ed. 1985. 34.30 (ISBN 0-205-08315-3, 568315). Allyn.

Tikhonov, A. N., et al. Differential Equations. Sossinskij, A. B., tr. from Rus. (Illus.). 250p. 1985. pap. 38.00 (ISBN 0-387-13002-0). Springer-Verlag.

Titchmarsh, Edward C. Eigenfunctional Expansions Associated with Second-Order Differential Equations. Pt. 1. pap. 52.80 (ISBN 0-317-28449-5); Pt. 2. pap. 104.00 (ISBN 0-317-28450-9). Bks Demand UMI.

Valiron, George. The Geometric Theory of Ordinary Differential Equations. Glazebrook, James, tr. Hermann, Robert, ed. (LIE Groups Ser.: Vol. 14; Pt. A). 1985. 75.00 (ISBN 0-915692-38-4, 991600134). Math Sci Pr.

Van Iwaarden, John L. Elementary Numerical Techniques for Ordinary Differential Equations. 207p. 1980. pap. 7.95 (ISBN 0-933694-14-8). COMPress.

Villadsen, John & Michelson, Michael. Solution of Differential Equation Models for Polynomial Approximation. LC 77-4331. (Illus.). 1977. 50.00 (ISBN 0-13-822205-3). P-H.

Walter, Wolfgang. Differential & Integral Inequalities. rev. ed. Rosenblatt, L. & Shampine, L., trs. from Ger. LC 72-103330. (Ergebnisse der Mathematik und Ihrer Grenzgebiete: Vol. 55). (Illus.). 1970. 48.00 (ISBN 0-387-05088-4). Springer-Verlag.

Waltman, Paul. A Second Course in Elementary Differential Equations. Date not set. text ed. price not set (ISBN 0-12-733910-8). Acad Pr.

Warga, J. Optimal Control of Differential & Functional Equations. 1972. 77.00 (ISBN 0-12-735150-7). Acad Pr.

Wasow, W. Linear Turning Point Theory. (Applied Mathematical Sciences Ser.: Vol. 54). (Illus.). 280p. 1985. 38.00 (ISBN 0-387-96046-5). Springer-Verlag.

Watanabe, S. Lectures on Stochastic Differential Equations & Malliavin Calculus. (Tata Institute Lectures on Mathematics Ser.). viii, 118p. 1984. pap. 9.50 (ISBN 0-387-12897-2). Springer-Verlag.

Weiss, Leonard, ed. Ordinary Differential Equations: The 1971 NRL-MRC Conference. 1972. 71.50 (ISBN 0-12-743650-2). Acad Pr.

Williamson, Richard E. Introduction to Differential Equations. (Illus.). 416p. 1986. text ed. 29.95 (ISBN 0-13-480989-0). P-H.

Witten, M., ed. Hyperbolic Partial Differential Equations: Populations, Reactors, Tides & Waves: Theory & Applications. (International Series of Modern Applied Mathematics & Computer Science: Vol. 6). 250p. 1983. 37.50 (ISBN 0-08-030254-8, 1803, 1805, 0299). Pergamon.

Wood, A. D. & Paris, R. B. Asymptotics of High Order Differential Equations. (Research Notes in Mathematics Ser.). 200p. 1985. pap. text ed. write for info. (ISBN 0-273-08585-9). Pitman Pub MA.

Wylie, C. Ray. Differential Equations. (Illus.). 1979. text ed. 37.95 (ISBN 0-07-072197-1). McGraw.

Yoshida, Kosaku. Lectures in Differential & Integral Equations. LC 60-53007. (Pure & Applied Mathematics Ser.: Vol. 10). pap. 57.50 (ISBN 0-317-08522-0, 2007077). Bks Demand UMI.

Zaidman, Samuel D. Abstract Differential Equations. LC 79-9061. (Research Notes in Mathematics Ser.: No. 36). 130p. (Orig.). 1979. pap. text ed. 20.50. Pitman Pub MA.

Zill, Dennis G. Differential Equations with Boundary Value Problems. 1986. text ed. write for info. (ISBN 0-87150-933-4, 33L3090, Prindle). PWS Pubs.

--A First Course in Differential Equations with Applications. 2nd ed. 540p. 1982. text ed. write for info. (ISBN 0-87150-319-0, 33L-2514, Prindle). PWS Pubs.

--First Course in Differential Equations with Applications. 3rd ed. 1985. text ed. write for info. (ISBN 0-87150-928-8, 33L3080, Prindle). PWS Pubs.

Zuev, V. E. & Naats, I. E. Inverse Problems of Lidar Sensing of the Atmosphere. (Springer Ser. in Optical Sciences: Vol. 29). (Illus.). 260p. 1983. 44.00 (ISBN 0-387-10913-7). Springer-Verlag.

DIFFERENTIAL EQUATIONS–NUMERICAL SOLUTIONS

see also Error Functions

Bender, Carl M. & Orszag, Steven A. Advanced Mathematical Methods for Scientists & Engineers. (International Series in Pure & Applied Mathematics). (Illus.). 1978. text ed. 49.95 (ISBN 0-07-004452-X). McGraw.

Colton, D. L. & Gilbert, R. P., eds. Constructive & Computational Methods for Differential & Integral Equations. (Lecture Notes in Mathematics Ser.: Vol. 430). vii, 476p. 1974. pap. 23.00 (ISBN 0-387-07021-4). Springer-Verlag.

Conference, Oberwolfach, Germany, July 4-10, 1976. Numerical Treatment of Differential Equations: Proceedings. Bulirsch, R., et al, eds. (Lecture Notes in Mathematics Ser.: Vol. 631). (Eng. & Ger.). 1978. pap. 18.00 (ISBN 0-387-08539-4). Springer-Verlag.

Conference on Numerical Solution of Ordinary Differential Equations. Proceedings. Bettis, D. G., ed. LC 73-20914. (Lecture Notes in Mathematics Ser.: Vol. 362). viii, 490p. 1974. pap. 22.00 (ISBN 0-387-06602-0). Springer-Verlag.

Conference on the Numerical Solution of Differential Equations. Proceedings. Watson, G. A., ed. (Lecture Notes in Mathematics Ser.: Vol. 363). ix, 221p. 1974. pap. 14.00 (ISBN 0-387-06617-9). Springer-Verlag.

Cronin, J. Differential Equations: Pure & Applied Math, Vol. 54. 392p. 1980. 39.75 (ISBN 0-8247-6819-1). Dekker.

Daniel, James W. & Moore, Ramon E. Computation & Theory in Ordinary Differential Equations. LC 71-117611. (Mathematics Ser.). (Illus.). 172p. 1970. text ed. 23.95 (ISBN 0-7167-0440-4). W H Freeman.

Fabera, J., ed. Equadiff IV: Proceedings, Prague, August 22 - 26, 1977. LC 79-11103. (Lecture Notes in Mathematics: Vol. 703). 1979. pap. 26.00 (ISBN 0-387-09116-5). Springer-Verlag.

Finlayson, Bruce A. The Method of Weighted Residuals & Variational Principles. (Mathematics in Science & Engineering Ser.). 1972. 85.00 (ISBN 0-12-257050-2). Acad Pr.

Fletcher, C. A. Computational Galerkin Methods. (Computational Physics Ser.). (Illus.). 335p. 1984. 39.00 (ISBN 0-387-12633-3). Springer-Verlag.

Fried, Isaac. Numerical Solution of Differential Equations. (Computer Science & Applied Math Ser.). 1979. 47.50 (ISBN 0-12-267780-3). Acad Pr.

Gottlieb, David & Orszag, Steven A. Numerical Analysis of Spectral Methods: Theory & Applications. (CBMS-NSF Regional Conference Ser.: No. 26). v, 170p. (Orig.). 1977. pap. text ed. 17.50 (ISBN 0-89871-023-5). Soc Indus-Appl Math.

Greenspan, Donald, ed. Numerical Solutions of Nonlinear Differential Equations. LC 66-29278. pap. 88.80 (ISBN 0-317-08570-0, 2006351). Bks Demand UMI.

Hall, G. & Watt, J. M., eds. Modern Numerical Methods for Ordinary Differential Equations. 1976. 42.50x (ISBN 0-19-853348-9). Oxford U Pr.

Has'Minskii, R. Z. Stochastic Stability of Differential Equations. 2nd ed. 360p. 50.00x (ISBN 90-286-0100-7). Sijthoff & Noordhoff.

Lambert, J. D. Computational Methods in Ordinary Differential Equations. LC 72-5718. (Introductory Mathematics for Scientists & Engineers Ser.). 278p. 1973. text ed. 48.95x (ISBN 0-471-51194-3, Pub. by Wiley-Interscience). Wiley.

Lapidus, Leon & Seinfeld, John H. Numerical Solution of Ordinary Differential Equations. (Mathematics in Science & Engineering Ser.: Vol. 74). 1971. 70.00 (ISBN 0-12-436650-3). Acad Pr.

Liu, Tai-Ping. Admissible Solutions of Hyperbolic Conservation Laws: Memoirs of the Arms. LC 80-28506. (Memoirs Ser.: No. 240). 78p. 1981. pap. 9.00 (ISBN 0-8218-2240-3). Am Math.

Lloyd, N. G. Degree Theory. LC 77-3205. (Tracts in Mathematics Ser.: No. 73). (Illus.). 1978. 44.50 (ISBN 0-521-21614-1). Cambridge U Pr.

Milne, William E. Numerical Solution of Differential Equations. 1970. pap. text ed. 7.00 (ISBN 0-486-62437-4). Dover.

Nakamura, Shoichiro. Computational Methods in Engineering & Science: With Applications to Fluid Dynamics & Nuclear Systems. LC 77-5471. 457p. 1977. 48.95x (ISBN 0-471-01800-7, Pub. by Wiley-Interscience). Wiley.

Noye, J. Numerical Solutions of Partial Differential Questions. 648p. 1982. 85.00 (ISBN 0-444-86356-7, North-Holland). Elsevier.

Ortega, James M. & Poole, William G., Jr. An Introduction to Numerical Methods for Differential Equations. LC 81-817. 320p. 1981. text ed. 34.95 (ISBN 0-273-01637-7). Pitman Pub MA.

Rektorys, Karel. Variational Methods in Mathematics, Sciences & Engineering. new ed. SNTL, ed. LC 74-80530. 1976. lib. bdg. 71.00 (ISBN 90-277-0488-0, Pub. by Reidel Holland). Kluwer Academic.

Research & Education Association Staff, ed. Advanced Methods for Solving Differential Equations. LC 82-80750. (Illus.). 352p. (Orig.). 1982. pap. text ed. 13.30x (ISBN 0-87891-541-9). Res & Educ.

Stetter, H. J. Analysis of Discretization Methods for Ordinary Differential Equations. LC 72-90188. (Springer Tracts in Natural Philosophy: Vol. 23). (Illus.). 390p. 1973. 69.00 (ISBN 0-387-06008-1). Springer-Verlag.

Willoughby, Ralph A., ed. Stiff Differential Systems. LC 74-6300. (IBM Research Symposia Ser). 323p. 1974. 49.50x (ISBN 0-306-30797-9, Plenum Pr). Plenum Pub.

Yoshizawa, T. Stability Theory & Existence of Periodic Solutions & Almost Periodic Solutions. LC 74-28140. (Applied Mathematical Sciences Ser.: Vol. 14). vii, 233p. 1975. pap. 19.50 (ISBN 0-387-90112-4). Springer-Verlag.

DIFFERENTIAL EQUATIONS–PROBLEMS, EXERCISES, ETC.

The Differential Equations Problem Solver. rev. ed. LC 78-63609. 1408p. 1984. pap. text ed. 24.85 (ISBN 0-87891-513-3). Res & Educ.

Lavrentiev, M. M., et al. Multidimensional Inverse Problems for Differential Equations. LC 70-140559. (Lecture Notes in Mathematics: Vol. 167). 1970. pap. 11.00 (ISBN 0-387-05282-8). Springer-Verlag.

DIFFERENTIAL EQUATIONS–PROGRAMMED INSTRUCTION

Hale, Jack K. Topics in Dynamic Bifurcation Theory. LC 81-3445. (Conference Board of the Mathematical Sciences Ser.: No. 47). 84p. 1983. pap. 8.00 (ISBN 0-8218-1698-5). Am Math.

DIFFERENTIAL EQUATIONS, ELLIPTIC

Agmon, Samuel. Lectures on Exponential Decay of Solutions of Second-Order Elliptic Equations. LC 82-14978. (Mathematical Notes Ser.: No. 29). 118p. 1983. 11.50 (ISBN 0-691-08318-5). Princeton U Pr.

Almgren, F. J., Jr. Existence & Regularity Almost Everywhere of Solutions to Ellipic Variational Problems with Constraints. LC 75-41603. (Memoirs: No. 165). 199p. 1976. pap. 15.00 (ISBN 0-8218-1865-1, MEMO-165). Am Math.

Aubin, Jean-Pierre. Approximation of Elliptic Boundary-Value Problems. LC 79-26276. 386p. 1980. Repr. of 1972 ed. lib. bdg. 26.00 (ISBN 0-89874-077-0). Krieger.

Birkhoff, Garrett. The Numerical Solution of Elliptic Equations. (CBMS-NSF Regional Conference Ser.: No. 1). xi, 82p. (Orig.). 1972. pap. text ed. 8.00 (ISBN 0-89871-001-4). Soc Indus-Appl Math.

Gilbert, R. P. Constructive Methods for Elliptic Equations. LC 73-21280. (Lectures Notes in Mathematics: Vol. 365). vii, 397p. 1974. pap. 18.00 (ISBN 0-387-06690-X). Springer-Verlag.

Kudrjavcev, L. D. Direct & Inverse Imbedding Theorem. LC 73-22139. (Translations of Mathematical Monographs: Vol. 42). 1974. 47.00 (ISBN 0-8218-1592-X, MMONO-42). Am Math.

Kushner, H. Probability Methods for Approximations in Stochastic Control & for Elliptic Equations. (Math in Science & Engineering Ser.). 1977. 55.00 (ISBN 0-12-430140-1). Acad Pr.

Oden, J. T. & Reddy, J. N. An Introduction to the Mathematical Theory of Finite Elements. LC 76-6953. (Pure & Applied Mathematics Ser.). 429p. 1976. 50.95x (ISBN 0-471-65261-X, Pub. by Wiley-Interscience). Wiley.

Rempel, S. & Schulze, B. W. Index Theory of Elliptic Boundary Problems. 394p. 1982. text ed. 48.95. Birkhauser.

Stredulinsky, E. W. Weighted Inequalities & Degenerate Elliptic Partial Differential Equations. (Lecture Notes in Mathematics Ser.: Vol. 1074). iii, 143p. 1984. pap. 10.00 (ISBN 0-387-13370-4). Springer-Verlag.

Temam, R. Numerical Analysis: Approximation of Some Partial Differential Equations. Neinhuys, J. W., tr. from Fr. LC 73-75643. 163p. 1973. lib. bdg. 26.00 (ISBN 90-277-0308-6, Pub. by Reidel Holland). Kluwer Academic.

DIFFERENTIAL EQUATIONS, LINEAR

see also Differential Equations, Elliptic

Bertrand, D. & Waldschmidt, M., eds. Approximations Diophantiennes et Nombres Transcendants: Proceedings. (Progress in Mathematics Ser.: Vol. 31). 336p. 1983. write for info (ISBN 0-8176-3120-8). Birkhauser.

Cheng, D. G. Analysis of Linear Systems. 1959. 29.95 (ISBN 0-201-01020-8). Addison-Wesley.

Conti, R. Institutiones Mathematicae: Linear Differential Equations & Control, Vol. 1. 1977. 34.50 (ISBN 0-12-363601-9). Acad Pr.

Coppel, W. A. Disconjugacy. (Lecture Notes in Mathematics: Vol. 220). v, 148p. 1971. pap. 11.00 (ISBN 0-387-05584-3). Springer-Verlag.

Dickson, D. G. Expansions in Series of Solutions of Linear Difference-Differential & Infinite Order Differential Equations with Constant Coefficients. LC 52-42839. (Memoirs: No. 23). 72p. 1982. pap. 12.00 (ISBN 0-8218-1223-8, MEMO-23). Am Math.

Erugin, Nikolai P. Linear Systems of Ordinary Differential Equations. (Mathematics in Science & Engineering: Vol. 28). 1966. 71.00 (ISBN 0-12-241850-6). Acad Pr.

Fattorini, H. O. Second Order Linear Differential Equations in Banach Spaces. (Mathematical Studies: Vol. 108). 1985. 40.75 (ISBN 0-444-87698-7, North-Holland). Elsevier.

Fenyo, S. & Stolle, H. Theorie und Praxis der Linearen Integralgleichungen: Vol. I. (LMW - MA Ser.: 74). (Ger.). 250p. 1982. text ed. 50.95x (ISBN 0-8176-1164-9). Birkhauser.

--Theorie und Praxis der Linearen Integralgleichungen: Vol. 2. (Ger.). 304p. 1982. text ed. 44.95x (ISBN 0-8176-1165-7). Birkhauser.

Friedland, Shmuel. Nonoscillation, Disconjugacy & Integral Inequalities. LC 76-25246. 1976. 13.00 (ISBN 0-8218-2176-8, MEMO-176). Am Math.

Gelman, I. W. & Mazja, W. G. Abschatzung fur Differentialoperationen. (Ger.). 192p. 1981. text ed. 36.95x (ISBN 0-8176-1275-0). Birkhauser.

Greer, R. Trees & Hills: Methodology for Maximising Functions of Systems of Linear Relations. (Mathematical Studies, No. 96; Annals of Discrete Mathematics). 1984. 44.50 (ISBN 0-444-87578-6). Elsevier.

Henry, D. Geometric Theory of Semilinear Parabolic Equations. (Lecture Notes in Mathematics Ser.: Vol. 840). 348p. 1981. pap. 24.00 (ISBN 0-387-10557-3). Springer-Verlag.

Hinze, J., ed. Numerical Integration of Differential Equations & Large Linear Systems: Proceedings, Bielefeld, FRG, 1980. (Lecture Notes in Mathematics: Vol. 968). 412p. 1982. pap. 22.00 (ISBN 0-387-11970-1). Springer-Verlag.

Hocking, Ronald R. The Analysis of Linear Models. LC 84-14606. (Statistics Ser.). 400p. 1984. text ed. 44.95 (ISBN 0-534-03618-X). Brooks-Cole.

Huntley, Ian D. & Johnson, Mike R. Linear & Nonlinear Differential Equations. (Mathematics & Its Applications Ser.). 190p. 1983. 53.95x (ISBN 0-470-27413-1); pap. 24.95x (ISBN 0-470-27420-4). Halsted Pr.

Krall, A. M. Stability Techniques for Continuous Linear Systems. (Notes on Mathematics & Its Applications Ser.). 160p. (Orig.). 1967. 33.75 (ISBN 0-677-01420-1). Gordon.

Krein, M. G. Topics in Differential & Integral Equations & Operator Theory. (Operator Theory, Advances & Applications Ser.: Vol. 7). 312p. 1983. text ed. 39.95 (ISBN 0-8176-1517-2). Birkhauser.

Krein, S. G. Linear Differential Equations in Banach Space. LC 71-37141. (Translations of Mathematical Monographs Ser.: Vol. 29). 1972. 50.00 (ISBN 0-8218-1579-2, MMONO-29). Am Math.

--Linear Equations in Banach Spaces. 128p. 1982. text ed. 14.95 (ISBN 3-7643-3101-1). Birkhauser.

Ladyzhenskaya, O. A. & Uraltseva, N. N. Linear & Quasilinear Elliptic Equations. LC 67-23164. (Mathematics in Science & Engineering). 1968. 86.50 (ISBN 0-12-432850-4). Acad Pr.

Massera, Jose L. & Schaffer, Juan J. Linear Differential Equations & Function Spaces. (Pure & Applied Mathematics Ser.: Vol. 2). 1966. 82.50 (ISBN 0-12-478650-2). Acad Pr.

Naimark, M. A. Linear Differential Operators, 2 pts. Everitt, W. N., ed. Dawson, E. R., tr. Incl. Pt. 1. Elementary Theory of Linear Differential Operators. LC 66-19469. xi, 144p. 12.00 (ISBN 0-8044-4682-2); Pt. 2. Linear Differential Operators in Hilbert Space. LC 66-19469. xv, 352p. 18.50 (ISBN 0-8044-4683-0). Ungar.

Rabenstein, Albert. Elementary Differential Equations with Linear Algebra. 3rd ed. 518p. 1982. text ed. 22.50i (ISBN 0-12-573945-1); instr's manual 2.50i (ISBN 0-12-573946-X). Acad Pr.

Schlesinger, Ludwig. Handbuch der Theorie der Linearen Differentialgleichungen, 2 Vols. (Bibliotheca Mathematica Teubneriana, 30-31). (Ger.). Repr. Set. 88.00 (ISBN 0-384-53978-5). Johnson Repr.

Shtokalo, I. Z. Linear Differential Equations with Variable Coefficients. (Illus.). 106p. 1961. 27.95x (ISBN 0-677-20460-4). Gordon.

Stanley, Richard. Commutative Algebra & Combinatorics. (Progress in Mathematics Ser.: Vol. 41). 102p. 1983. text ed. 12.95 (ISBN 0-8176-3112-7). Birkhauser.

Szmydt, Zofia. Fourier Transformation & Linear Differential Equations. new ed. PWN, Polish Scientific Pb., ed. (Symposia of the Intl. Astronomical Union: No. 71). 1976. lib. bdg. 47.50 (ISBN 90-277-0622-0, Pub. by Reidel Holland). Kluwer Academic.

Tiersten, H. F. Linear Piezoelectric Plate Vibrations: Elements of the Linear Theory of Piezoelectricity & the Vibrations of Piezoelectric Plates. LC 69-14562. (Illus.). 212p. 1969. 39.50x (ISBN 0-306-30376-0, Plenum Pr). Plenum Pub.

Treves, Francois. Basic Linear Partial Differential Equations. 1975. 68.50 (ISBN 0-12-699440-4). Acad Pr.

--Linear Partial Differential Equations. (Notes on Mathematics & Its Applications Ser.). 130p. 1970. 42.95x (ISBN 0-677-02520-3). Gordon.

Treves, Franxois. Locally Convex Spaces & Linear Partial Differential Equations. LC 67-25286. (Grundlehren der Mathematischen Wissenschaften: Vol. 146). 1967. 28.00 (ISBN 0-387-03833-7). Springer-Verlag.

Yakubovich, V. A. & Starzhinskii, V. M. Linear Differential Equations with Periodic Coefficients, 2 vols. 775p. 1975. text ed. 56.75 (ISBN 0-470-96953-9). Krieger.

DIFFERENTIAL EQUATIONS, LINEAR–NUMERICAL SOLUTIONS

Conference on the Numerical Solution of Differential Equations. Proceedings. Morris, J. L., ed. LC 77-101372. (Lecture Notes in Mathematics: Vol. 109). 1969. pap. 14.70 (ISBN 0-387-04628-3). Springer-Verlag.

Hormander, Lars, ed. Seminar on Singularities of Solutions of Linear Partial Differential Equations. LC 78-70300. (Annals of Mathematics Studies: No. 91). 1979. 31.00x (ISBN 0-691-08221-9). Princeton U Pr.

Sibuya, Yasataka. Uniform Simplification in a Full Neighborhood of a Transition Point. LC 74-11246. (Memoirs: No. 149). 106p. 1974. pap. 10.00 (ISBN 0-8218-1849-X, MEMO-149). Am Math.

DIFFERENTIAL EQUATIONS, LINEAR–PROGRAMMED INSTRUCTION

Strum, Robert D. & Ward, John R. Laplace Transform Solution of Differential Equations. (Orig., Prog. Bk.). 1968. pap. 25.95 ref. ed. (ISBN 0-13-522805-0). P-H.

DIFFERENTIAL EQUATIONS, NONLINEAR

Ames, W. F., ed. Nonlinear Partial Differential Equations: A Symposium on Methods of Solution. 1967. 72.00 (ISBN 0-12-056754-7). Acad Pr.

--Nonlinear Partial Differential Equations in Engineering, 2 vols. (Mathematics in Science & Engineering Ser). Vol. 1, 1965. 75.00 (ISBN 0-12-056756-3); Vol. 2, 1972. 75.00 (ISBN 0-12-056755-5). Acad Pr.

Ames, William F., ed. Nonlinear Ordinary Differential Equations in Transport Processes. (Mathematics in Science & Engineering: Vol. 42). 1968. 55.00 (ISBN 0-12-056753-9). Acad Pr.

Bank, B. & Guddat, J., eds. Non-Linear Parametric Optimization. 224p. 1983. 29.95 (ISBN 0-8176-1375-7). Birkhauser.

Bardos, C., ed. Bifurcation & Nonlinear Eigenvalue Problems: Proceedings. (Lecture Notes in Mathematics: Vol. 782). 296p. 1980. pap. 23.00 (ISBN 0-387-09758-9). Springer-Verlag.

Bellman, Richard E. Methods of Nonlinear Analysis. (Mathematics in Science & Engineering Ser.: Vol. 61). Vol. 1 1970. 45.00 (ISBN 0-12-084901-1); Vol. 2. 1973. 35.00 (ISBN 0-12-084902-X). Acad Pr.

Berestycki, H. & Brezis, H. Recent Contributions to Nonlinear Partial Differential Equations. LC 81-700. (Research Notes in Mathematics Ser.: No. 50). 288p. 1981. pap. text ed. 28.95 (ISBN 0-273-08492-5). Pitman Pub MA.

Bierens, H. J. Robust Methods & Asymptotic Theory in Nonlinear Econometrics. (Lecture Notes in Economics & Mathematical Systems Ser.: Vol. 192). (Illus.). 198p. 1981. pap. 20.00 (ISBN 0-387-10838-6). Springer-Verlag.

Boiti, M., et al, eds. Nonlinear Evolution Equations & Dynamical Systems. (Lecture Notes in Physics: Vol. 120). 368p. 1980. pap. 29.00 (ISBN 0-387-09971-9). Springer-Verlag.

Brezis, H. & Lions, J. L. Nonlinear Partial Differential Equations & Their Applications: College de France Seminar Vol. 1. (Research Notes in Mathematics Ser.: No. 53). 350p. 1981. pap. text ed. 27.50 (ISBN 0-273-08491-7). Pitman Pub MA.

--Nonlinear Partial Differential Equations & Their Applications: College de France Seminar, Vol. 6. (Research Notes in Mathematics Ser.: No. 109). 336p. 1984. pap. text ed. 27.50 (ISBN 0-273-08646-4). Pitman Pub MA.

Brezis, H. & Lions, J. L., eds. Nonlinear Partial Differential Equations & Their Applications, Vol. 7. (Research Notes in Mathematics Ser.: No. 122). 300p. 1985. pap. text ed. 21.50 (ISBN 0-273-08679-0). Pitman Pub MA.

Bucy, Richard S. & Moura, Jose M., eds. Nonlinear Stochastic Problems. 1983. PLB 79.50 (ISBN 90-277-1590-4, Pub. by Reidel Holland). Kluwer Academic.

Calogero, F., ed. Nonlinear Evolution Equations Solvable by the Spectral Transform. (Research Notes in Mathematics Ser.: No. 26). 257p. (Orig.). 1978. pap. text ed. 27.00 (ISBN 0-273-08402-X). Pitman Pub MA.

Cesari, Lamberto, et al, eds. Nonlinear Functional Analysis & Differential Equations: Proceedings of the Michigan State University Conference. (Lecture Notes in Pure and Applied Math Ser.: Vol. 19). 1976. 65.00 (ISBN 0-8247-6452-8). Dekker.

Chadam, J. M., ed. Nonlinear Partial Differential Equations & Applications: Proceedings of a Special Seminar Held at Indiana University, 1976-1977. (Lecture Notes in Mathematics: Vol. 648). 1978. pap. 16.00 (ISBN 0-387-08759-1). Springer-Verlag.

Cherm, S. S., ed. Seminar on Nonlinear Partial, & Differential Equations. (Mathematical Sciences Research Institute Publications: Vol. 2). (Illus.). 373p. 1984. 24.00 (ISBN 0-387-96079-1). Springer-Verlag.

Crandall, Michael G., ed. Nonlinear Evolution Equations. (MEC Seminars & Symposia: No. 40). 1978. 15.50 (ISBN 0-12-195250-9). Acad Pr.

Dekker, K. & Verwer, J. G. Stability of Runge-Kutta Methods for Stiff Nonlinear Differential Equations. (CWI Monographs: No. 2). 308p. 1984. 35.25 (ISBN 0-444-87634-0, North-Holland). Elsevier.

Diaz, J I. Nonlinear Partial Differential Equations & Free Boundaries Vol. 1: Elliptic Equations. (Research Notes in Mathematics Ser.: No. 106). 250p. 1985. pap. text ed. write for info. (ISBN 0-273-08572-7). Pitman Pub MA.

Forster, Walter. Numerical Solution of Highly Nonlinear Problems. 440p. 1980. 68.00 (ISBN 0-444-85427-4, North-Holland). Elsevier.

Fucik, S. & Kufner, A. Nonlinear Differential Equations. (Studies in Applied Mechanics: Vol. 2). 360p. 1980. 81.00 (ISBN 0-444-99771-7). Elsevier.

Fucik, Svatopluk. Solvability of Nonlinear Equations & Boundry Value Problems. (Mathematics & Its Applications Ser.: No. 4). 400p. 1980. 29.95 (ISBN 90-277-1077-5, Pub. by Reidel Holland). Kluwer Academic.

Fujita, H., et al, eds. Nonlinear Partial Differential Equations in Applied Science: Proceedings of the U.S.- Japan Seminar, Held in Tokyo, 1982. (Mathematics Studies: No. 81). 474p. 1984. 60.00 (ISBN 0-444-86681-7, I-128-84, North-Holland). Elsevier.

Gaines, R. E. & Mawhin, J. L. Coincidence Degree, & Non-Linear Differential Equations. LC 76-58453. (Lecture Notes in Mathematics Ser: Vol. 568). 1977. pap. 18.00 (ISBN 0-387-08067-8). Springer-Verlag.

Graffi, D. Nonlinear Partial Differential Equations in Physical Problems. (Research Notes in Mathematics Ser.: No. 42). 105p. (Orig.). 1980. pap. text ed. 21.95 (ISBN 0-273-08474-7). Pitman Pub MA.

Greenspan, Donald, ed. Numerical Solutions of Nonlinear Differential Equations. LC 66-29278. pap. 88.80 (ISBN 0-317-08570-0, 2006351). Bks Demand UMI.

Hagedorn, Peter. Non-Linear Oscillations. (Engineering Science Ser.). (Illus.). 1981. pap. 19.95x (ISBN 0-19-856156-3). Oxford U Pr.

Hale, Jack K. Topics in Dynamic Bifurcation Theory. LC 81-3445. (Conference Board of the Mathematical Sciences Ser.: No. 47). 84p. 1983. pap. 8.00 (ISBN 0-8218-1698-5). Am Math.

Holmes, P. J., ed. New Approaches to Nonlinear Problems in Dynamics. LC 80-52593. xii, 529p. 1980. text ed. 48.00 (ISBN 0-89871-167-3). Soc Indus-Appl Math.

Huntley, Ian D. & Johnson, Mike R. Linear & Nonlinear Differential Equations. (Mathematics & Its Applications Ser.). 190p. 1983. 53.95x (ISBN 0-470-27413-1); pap. 24.95x (ISBN 0-470-27420-4). Halsted Pr.

Ize, Jorge. Bifurcation Theory for Fredholm Operators. LC 76-25186. (Memoirs of the American Mathematical Society: 174). 128p. 1976. pap. 14.00 (ISBN 0-8218-2174-1). Am Math.

Jordan, D. W. & Smith, P. Nonlinear Ordinary Differential Equations. (Oxford Applied Mathematics & Computing Science Ser.). (Illus.). 1977. pap. 19.95x (ISBN 0-19-859621-9). Oxford U Pr.

Kral, J., ed. Nonlinear Evolution Equations & Potential Theory. LC 74-20000. 145p. 1975. 35.00x (ISBN 0-306-30835-5, Plenum Pr). Plenum Pub.

Lakshmikantham. Trends in Theory & Practice of Non-Linear Differential Equations. (Lecture Notes in Pure & Applied Mathematics). 576p. 1983. 59.75 (ISBN 0-8247-7130-3). Dekker.

Lakshmikantham, V. Nonlinear Differential Equations in Abstract Spaces. LC 80-41838. (I.S. Nonlinear Mathematics Series; Theory, Methods and Applications: Vol. 2). 272p. 1981. 50.00 (ISBN 0-08-025038-6). Pergamon.

Lakshmikantham, V., ed. Nonlinear Equations in Abstract Spaces. 1978. 55.00 (ISBN 0-12-434160-8). Acad Pr.

--Nonlinear Systems & Applications: An International Conference. 1977. 65.00 (ISBN 0-12-434150-0). Acad Pr.

Langer, Rudolph E., ed. Nonlinear Problems: Proceedings of a Symposium Conducted by the Mathematics Research Center, United States Army, at the University of Wisconsin, Madison, April 30-May 2, 1962. LC 63-8971. (U. S. Army. Mathematics Research Center Ser.: No. 8). pap. 84.00 (ISBN 0-317-09187-5, 2021138). Bks Demand UMI.

Marino, A., et al, eds. Nonlinear Variational Problems. (Research Notes in Mathematics Ser.: No. 127). 248p. 1985. pap. text ed. 14.95 (ISBN 0-273-08670-7). Pitman Pub MA.

Mimura, M. & Nishida, T., eds. Recent Topics in Non-Linear Partial Differential Equations. (Mathematics Studies: Vol. 98). 1985. 46.50 (ISBN 0-444-87544-1, North-Holland). Elsevier.

Rankin & Lightbourne. Physical Mathematics & Nonlinear Partial Differential Equations. (Lecture Notes in Pure & Applied Mathematics Ser.). 296p. 1985. 59.75 (ISBN 0-8247-7343-8). Dekker.

Rheinboldt, Werner C. Methods for Solving Systems of Nonlinear Equations. (CBMS-NSF Regional Conference Ser.: No. 14). ix, 104p. (Orig.). 1974. pap. text ed. 12.00 (ISBN 0-89871-011-1). Soc Indus-Appl Math.

Rheinbolt, W. C. Numerical Analysis of Parameterized Nonlinear Equations. (Lecture Notes in the Mathematical Sciences Ser.). 256p. 1985. pap. 29.50 (ISBN 0-471-88814-1). Wiley.

Rosinger. Nonlinear Partial Differential Equations: Sequential & Weak Solutions. (Mathematical Studies: Vol. 44). 318p. 1980. 51.00 (ISBN 0-444-86055-X, North Holland). Elsevier.

Saaty, Thomas L. Modern Nonlinear Equations. xvii, 473p. 1982. pap. 8.95 (ISBN 0-486-64232-1). Dover.

Saaty, Thomas L. & Bram, Joseph. Nonlinear Mathematics. xv, 381p. 1982. pap. text ed. 7.00 (ISBN 0-486-64233-X). Dover.

Smoller, Joel A., ed. Nonlinear Partial Differential Equations. LC 83-2844. (Contemporary Mathematics Ser.: Vol. 17). 446p. 1983. pap. 29.00 (ISBN 0-8218-5017-2). Am Math.

Sparrow, C. The Lorenz Equations: Bifurcations, Chaos & Strange Attractors. (Applied Mathematical Sciences Ser.: Vol. 41). (Illus.). 288p. 1982. 23.50 (ISBN 0-387-90775-0). Springer-Verlag.

Sternberg, Robert L., et al, eds. Nonlinear Partial Differential Equations in Engineering & Applied Science. (Lecture Notes in Pure & Applied Mathematics Ser.: Vol. 54). (Illus.). 504p. 1980. 63.75 (ISBN 0-8247-6996-1). Dekker.

Strodt, Walter & Wright, Robert K. Asymptotic Behavior of Solutions & Adjunction Fields for Nonlinear First Order Differential Equations. LC 52-42839. (Memoirs: No. 109). 284p. 1971. pap. 10.00 (ISBN 0-8218-1809-0, MEMO-109). Am Math.

Struble, Raimond A. Nonlinear Differential Equations. LC 79-23165. 1983. Repr. of 1962 ed. lib. bdg. 19.50 (ISBN 0-89874-056-8). Krieger.

Symposium in Applied Mathematics - 17th - New York - 1964. Applications of Nonlinear Partial Differential Equations in the Mathematical Physics: Proceedings. Finn, R., ed. LC 65-18255. (Proceedings of Symposia in Applied Mathematics: Vol. 17). 234p. 1965. 25.00 (ISBN 0-8218-1317-X, PSAPM-17). Am Math.

Temam, R. Navier-Stokes Equations & Nonlinear Functional Analysis. LC 82-62216. (CBMS-NSF Regional Conference Ser.: No. 41). xii, 122p. 1983. pap. text ed. 15.50 (ISBN 0-89871-183-5). Soc Indus-Appl Math.

Todd, R. K., et al. Solitons & Nonlinear Equations. 1983. 49.50 (ISBN 0-12-219120-X). Acad Pr.

Venkatesh, Y. V. Energy Methods in Time-Varying System Stability & Instability Analyses. (Lecture Notes in Physics: Vol. 68). 1977. pap. 18.00 (ISBN 0-387-08430-4). Springer-Verlag.

Von Wahl, W. Nonlinear Evolution Equations with Applications to the Navier-Stokes Equation. Date not set. price not set (ISBN 0-9940018-1-9, Pub. By Vieweg & Sohn Germany). Heyden.

DIFFERENTIAL EQUATIONS, PARTIAL

see also Differential Equations, Elliptic; Harmonic Functions; Maxwell Equations; Scattering (Mathematics)

Aleksandrjan, R. A., et al. Partial Differential Equations: Proceedings. LC 76-8428. (Translations Ser.: No. 2, Vol. 105). 1976. 62.00 (ISBN 0-8218-3055-4, TRANS 2-105). Am Math.

Ames, W. F. Numerical Solution of Partial Differential Equations. 2nd ed. 1977. 47.00 (ISBN 0-12-056760-1). Acad Pr.

Ames, W. F., ed. Nonlinear Partial Differential Equations: A Symposium on Methods of Solution. 1967. 72.00 (ISBN 0-12-056754-7). Acad Pr.

--Nonlinear Partial Differential Equations in Engineering, 2 vols. (Mathematics in Science & Engineering Ser). Vol. 1, 1965. 75.00 (ISBN 0-12-056756-3); Vol. 2, 1972. 75.00 (ISBN 0-12-056755-5). Acad Pr.

Aziz, A. K., ed. The Mathematical Foundations of the Finite Element Method with Applications to Partial Differentail Equations. 1972. 84.00 (ISBN 0-12-068650-3). Acad Pr.

Aziz, A. K., et al, eds. Control Theory of Systems Governed by Partial Differential Equations. 1977. 41.50 (ISBN 0-12-068640-6). Acad Pr.

Babuska, I., et al, eds. Adaptive Computational Methods for Partial Differential Equations. LC 83-51382. xii, 251p. 1984. text ed. 25.50 (ISBN 0-89871-191-6). Soc Indus-Appl Math.

Bardos, C., ed. Bifurcation & Nonlinear Eigenvalue Problems: Proceedings. (Lecture Notes in Mathematics: Vol. 782). 296p. 1980. pap. 23.00 (ISBN 0-387-09758-9). Springer-Verlag.

Bardos, C. & Damlamian, A., eds. Contributions to Nonlinear Partial Differential Equations. (Research Notes in Mathematics: No. 89). 360p. 1983. pap. text ed. 24.95 (ISBN 0-273-08595-6). Pitman Pub MA.

Bauer, K. W. & Ruscheweyh, S. Differential Operators for Partial Differential Equations & Function-Theoretic Applications. (Lecture Notes in Mathematics: Vol. 791). 258p. 1980. pap. 20.00 (ISBN 0-387-09975-1). Springer-Verlag.

Bensoussan, A. & Lions, J. L. Applications of Variational Inequalities in Stochastic Control. (Studies in Mathematics & Its Applications: Vol. 12). Orig. Title: Applications des Inequations Variationnelles en Controle Stochastique. 564p. 1982. 74.50 (ISBN 0-444-86358-3, North-Holland). Elsevier.

Berenstein, C. A. & Dostal, M. A. Analytically Uniform Spaces & Their Applications to Convolution Equations. LC 70-189386. (Lecture Notes in Mathematics: Vol. 256). 137p. 1972. pap. 9.00 (ISBN 0-387-05746-3). Springer-Verlag.

Berestyci, H. & Brezis, H. Recent Contributions to Nonlinear Partial Differential Equations. LC 81-700. (Research Notes in Mathematics Ser.: No. 50). 288p. 1981. pap. text ed. 28.95 (ISBN 0-273-08492-5). Pitman Pub MA.

Berezanskii, Ju. M. Expansions in Eigenfunctions of Selfadjoint Operators. LC 67-22347. (Translations of Mathematical Monographs: Vol. 17). 1968. 67.00 (ISBN 0-8218-1567-9, MMONO-17). Am Math.

Berg, Paul W. & McGregor, James L. Elementary Partial Differential Equations. LC 66-28845. (Illus.). 1966. 37.00x (ISBN 0-8162-0584-1). Holden-Day.

Bers, L., et al. Contributions to the Theory of Partial Differential Equations. (Annals of Math Studies). Repr. of 1954 ed. 21.00 (ISBN 0-527-02749-9). Kraus Repr.

Borok, V. M., et al. Eight Papers on Functional Analysis & Partial Differential Equations. LC 51-5559. (Translations, Ser.: No. 2, Vol. 5). 1957. 29.00 (ISBN 0-8218-1705-1, TRANS 2-5). Am Math.

Brackbill, Jeremiah U. & Cohen, Bruce I., eds. Multiple Time Scales. (Computational Techniques Ser.). Date not set. 75.00 (ISBN 0-12-123420-7). Acad Pr.

Brenner, P., et al. Besov Spaces & Applications to Difference Methods for Initial Value Problems. (Lecture Notes in Mathematics Ser.: Vol. 434). ii, 154p. 1975. pap. 13.00 (ISBN 0-387-07130-X). Springer-Verlag.

Brezis, H. & Lions, J. L. Nonlinear Partial Differential Equations & Their Applications: College de France Seminar, Vol. 6. (Research Notes in Mathematics Ser.: No. 109). 336p. 1984. pap. text ed. 27.50 (ISBN 0-273-08646-4). Pitman Pub MA.

Brezis, H. & Lions, J., eds. Nonlinear Partial Differential Equations & Their Applications: College de France Seminar, Vol. 4. (Research Notes in Mathematics: No. 84). 312p. 1983. pap. text ed. 27.50 (ISBN 0-273-08592-1). Pitman Pub MA.

Brezis, H. & Lions, J. L., eds. Nonlinear Partial Differential Equations & Their Applications, Vol. 3. (Research Notes in Mathematics: No. 70). 350p. 1982. pap. text ed. 27.50 (ISBN 0-273-08568-9). Pitman Pub MA.

--Nonlinear Partial Differential Equations & their Applications: College de France Seminar, Vol. 5. (Research Notes in Mathematics: No. 93). 384p. 1983. pap. text ed. 27.50 (ISBN 0-273-08620-0). Pitman Pub MA.

Brodskii, M. S., et al. Nine Papers on Partial Differential Equations & Functional Analysis. LC 51-5559. (Translations Ser.: No. 2, Vol. 65). 1967. 37.00 (ISBN 0-8218-1765-5, TRANS 2-65). Am Math.

--Thirteen Papers on Functional Analysis & Partial Differential Equations. LC 51-5559. (Translations Ser.: No. 2, Vol. 47). 1965. 25.00 (ISBN 0-8218-1747-7, TRANS 2-47). Am Math.

Byrnes. Partial Differential Equations & Geometry. (Lecture Notes in Pure & Applied Math Ser.: Vol. 48). 1979. 55.00 (ISBN 0-8247-6775-6). Dekker.

Carroll, R. W. & Showalter, R. E. Singular & Degenerate Cauchy Problems. 1976. 47.50 (ISBN 0-12-161450-6). Acad Pr.

Chazarain, J. Fourier Integral Operators & Partial Differential Equations. (Lecture Notes in Mmathematics: Vol. 459). 372p. 1975. pap. 21.00 (ISBN 0-387-07180-6). Springer-Verlag.

Chazarain, J. & Piriou, A. Introduction to the Theory of Linear Partial Differential Equations. (Studies in Mathematics & Its Applications: Vol. 14). 560p. 1982. 74.50 (ISBN 0-444-86452-0, North Holland). Elsevier.

Cherm, S. S., ed. Seminar on Nonlinear Partial, & Differential Equations. (Mathematical Sciences Research Institute Publications: Vol. 2). (Illus.). 373p. 1984. 24.00 (ISBN 0-387-96079-1). Springer-Verlag.

Colton, D. L. Analytic Theory of Partial Differential Equations. LC 80-14112. (Monographs & Studies in Mathematics Ser.: No. 8). 240p. 1980. text ed. 72.50 (ISBN 0-273-08462-3). Pitman Pub MA.

Conference on Hyperfunctions & Pseudo-Differential Equations, Katata 1971. Proceedings. Komatsu, H., ed. LC 72-88782. (Lecture Notes in Mathematics: Vol. 287). vii, 529p. 1973. pap. 23.00 (ISBN 0-387-06218-1). Springer-Verlag.

Conference on the Theory of Ordinary & Partial Differential Equations, Dundee, Scotland, 1972. Proceedings. Everitt, W. N. & Sleeman, B. D., eds. LC 72-87925. (Lecture Notes in Mathematics: Vol. 280). (Illus.). xv, 367p. 1972. pap. 13.00 (ISBN 0-387-05962-8). Springer-Verlag.

Copson, Edward T. Partial Differential Equations. LC 74-12965. (Illus.). 316p. 1975. 54.50 (ISBN 0-521-20583-2); pap. 21.95 (ISBN 0-521-09893-9). Cambridge U Pr.

Czou Jui-Lin, et al. Four Papers on Partial Differential Equations. LC 51-5559. (Translations Ser.: No. 2, Vol. 41). 1964. 26.00 (ISBN 0-8218-1741-8, TRANS 2-41). Am Math.

De Boor, Carl, ed. Mathematical Aspects of Finite Elements in Partial Differential Equations. 1974. 23.00 (ISBN 0-12-208350-4). Acad Pr.

Diaz, J I. Nonlinear Partial Differential Equations & Free Boundaries Vol. 1: Elliptic Equations. (Research Notes in Mathematics Ser.: No. 106). 250p. 1985. pap. text ed. write for info. (ISBN 0-273-08572-7). Pitman Pub MA.

Dou, Alberto. Lectures on Partial Differential Equations of First Order. LC 74-186519. 248p. 1972. pap. 9.95x (ISBN 0-268-00468-4). U of Notre Dame Pr.

Dresner, L. Similarity Solutions of Nonlinear Partial Differential Equations. (Research Notes in Mathematics: No. 88). 136p. 1983. pap. text ed. 18.95 (ISBN 0-273-08621-9). Pitman Pub MA.

DuChateau, Paul. The Cauchy-Goursat Problem. LC 52-42839. (Memoirs: No. 118). 60p. 1972. pap. 9.00 (ISBN 0-8218-1818-X, MEMO-118). Am Math.

Elschner, J. Singular Ordinary Differential Operators & Pseudodifferential Equations. (Lecture Notes in Mathematics: Vol. 1128). 200p. 1985. pap. 14.40 (ISBN 0-387-15194-X). Springer-Verlag.

Engelsman, S. B., ed. Families of Curves & the Origins of Partial Differentiation. (North-Holland Mathematics Studies: No. 93). 238p. 1984. 29.00 (ISBN 0-444-86897-6, I-126-84). Elsevier.

Epstein, Bernard. Partial Differential Equations: An Introduction. LC 75-11905. 284p. 1975. Repr. of 1962 ed. 16.50 (ISBN 0-88275-330-4). Krieger.

Everett, W. N., ed. Ordinary & Partial Differential Equations. (Lecture Notes in Mathematics Ser.: Vol. 827). (Illus.). 271p. 1980. pap. 20.00 (ISBN 0-387-10252-3). Springer-Verlag.

Everitt, W. N. & Sleeman, B. D., eds. Ordinary & Partial Differential Equations: Proceedings. (Lecture Notes in Mathematics Ser.: Vol. 846). 384p. 1981. pap. 24.00 (ISBN 0-387-10569-7). Springer-Verlag.

Farlow, Stanley J. Partial Differential Equations for Scientists & Engineers. LC 81-12993. 402p. 1982. text ed. 38.00x (ISBN 0-471-08639-8); solutions manual avail. (ISBN 0-471-09582-6). Wiley.

Fasano, A. & Primcerio, M., eds. Free Boundary Problems: Theory & Applications, Vol. 1. (Research Notes in Mathematics Ser.: No. 78). 272p. 1983. pap. text ed. 28.50 (ISBN 0-273-08589-1). Pitman Pub MA.

--Free Boundary Problems: Theory & Applications, Vol. 2. (Research Notes in Mathematics: No. 79). 448p. 1983. pap. text ed. 28.50 (ISBN 0-273-08590-5). Pitman Pub MA.

Fife, P. C. Mathematical Aspects of Reacting & Diffusing Systems. LC 79-10216. (Lecture Notes in Biomathematics Ser.: Vol. 28). 1979. pap. text ed. 14.00 (ISBN 0-387-09117-3). Springer-Verlag.

Fitzgibbon, W. E., ed. Partial Differential Equations & Dynamical Systems. (Research Notes in Mathematics Ser.: No. 101). 384p. (Orig.). 1984. pap. 24.95 (ISBN 0-273-08644-8). Pitman Pub MA.

Folland, G. B. Partial Differential Equations. (Tata Institute Lectures on Mathematics). 160p. 1983. pap. 10.00 (ISBN 0-387-12280-X). Springer-Verlag.

Folland, Gerald B. Introduction to Partial Differential Equations. LC 76-3029. (Mathematical Notes Ser.: No. 17). 349p. (Orig.). 1976. pap. 20.00 (ISBN 0-691-08177-8). Princeton U Pr.

Ford Foundation Program Tulane University, Jan. to May, 1947. Partial Differential Equations & Related Topics. Goldstein, J. A., ed. LC 75-6604. (Lecture Notes in Mathematics Ser: Vol. 446). iv, 389p. 1975. pap. 21.00 (ISBN 0-387-07148-2). Springer-Verlag.

Friedman, Avner. Partial Differential Equations. LC 76-3513. 272p. 1976. Repr. of 1969 ed. 18.50 (ISBN 0-88275-405-X). Krieger.

--Partial Differential Equations of Parabolic Type. LC 83-12005. 364p. 1983. Repr. of 1964 ed. text ed. 21.50 (ISBN 0-89874-660-4). Krieger.

Fujita, H., et al, eds. Nonlinear Partial Differential Equations in Applied Science: Proceedings of the U.S.- Japan Seminar, Held in Tokyo, 1982. (Mathematics Studies: No. 81). 474p. 1984. 60.00 (ISBN 0-444-86681-7, I-128-84, North-Holland). Elsevier.

Gilbert, R. P. Function Theoretic Methods in Partial Differential Equations. (Mathematics in Science & Engineering Ser: Vol. 54). 1969. 75.00 (ISBN 0-12-283050-4). Acad Pr.

Gladwell, I. & Wait, R., eds. A Survey of Numerical Methods for Partial Differential Equations. (Illus.). 1979. 49.50x (ISBN 0-19-853351-9). Oxford U Pr.

Gustafson, Karl E. Introduction to Partial Differential Equations & Hilbert Space Methods. LC 80-331. 270p. 1980. text ed. 38.50 (ISBN 0-471-04089-4). Wiley.

Hoffmann, K. H., et al. Optimal Control of Partial Differential Equations. (International Series of Numerical Mathematics: Vol. 68). (Eng. & Ger.). 264p. 1984. 39.95 (ISBN 3-7643-1598-9). Birkhauser.

Hogbe-Nlend, H. Bornologies & Functional Analysis. (Mathematics Studies: Vol. 26). 144p. 1977. 42.75 (ISBN 0-7204-0712-5, North-Holland). Elsevier.

International Conference on Computational Methods in Nonlinear Mechanics, 2nd, Univ. of Texas at Austin. Computational Methods in Nonlinear Mechanics: Selected Papers. Oden, J. T., ed. 160p. 1980. pap. 45.00 (ISBN 0-08-025068-8). Pergamon.

International Symposium Held at Darmstadt, Germany, April 12-15, 1976. Function Theoretic Methods for Partial Differential Equations: Proceedings. Meister, V. E., et al, eds. (Lecture Notes in Mathematics Ser.: Vol. 561). 1976. soft cover 26.00 (ISBN 0-387-08054-6). Springer-Verlag.

John, F. Plane Waves & Spherical Means Applied to Partial Differential Equations. (Illus.). 172p. 1981. pap. 23.00 (ISBN 0-387-90565-0). Springer-Verlag.

Knops, R. J. & Payne, L. E. Uniqueness Theorems in Linear Elasticity. LC 70-138813. (Springer Tracts in Natural Philosophy: Vol. 19). 1971. 28.00 (ISBN 0-387-05253-4). Springer-Verlag.

Koselev, A. I., et al. Six Papers on Partial Differential Equations. LC 51-5559. (Translations Ser.: No. 2, Vol. 20). 1962. 30.00 (ISBN 0-8218-1720-5, TRANS 2-20). Am Math.

Kreith, K. Oscillation Theory. LC 73-79366. (Lecture Notes in Mathematics: Vol. 324). 109p. 1973. pap. 12.00 (ISBN 0-387-06258-0). Springer-Verlag.

Ladyzenskaja, O. A., et al. Linear & Quasilinear Equations of Parabolic Type. LC 68-19440. (Translations of Mathematical Monographs: Vol. 23). 1968. 71.00 (ISBN 0-8218-1573-3, MMONO-23). Am Math.

Langer, Rudolph E., ed. Partial Differential Equations & Continuum Mechanics. (Mathematics Research Center Pubns., No. 5). (Illus.). 414p. 1961. 17.00x (ISBN 0-299-02350-8). U of Wis Pr.

--Partial Differential Equations & Continuum Mechanics. LC 61-600003. (U. S. Army. Mathematics Research Center: No. 5). pap. 103.30 (ISBN 0-317-09147-6, 2015364). Bks Demand UMI.

Lieberstein, H. Melvin. Theory of Partial Differential Equations. (Mathematics in Science & Engineering Ser.: Vol. 93). 1972. 70.00 (ISBN 0-12-449550-8). Acad Pr.

Lions, J. L. Optimal Control of Systems Governed by Partial Differential Equations. Mitter, S. K., tr. LC 78-113638. (Grundlehren der Mathematischen Wissenschaften: Vol. 170). (Illus.). 1971. 48.00 (ISBN 0-387-05115-5). Springer-Verlag.

Miller, Kenneth S. Partial Differential Equations in Engineering Problems. 1953. ref. ed. 33.95 (ISBN 0-13-650408-6). P-H.

Miranda, C. Partial Differential Equations of Elliptic Type. 2nd rev ed. LC 71-75930. (Ergebnisse der Mathematik und Ihrer Grenzgebiete: Vol. 2). 1970. 40.00 (ISBN 0-387-04804-9). Springer-Verlag.

Mitchell, A. R. & Griffiths, D. F. The Finite Difference Method in Partial Differential Equations. LC 79-40646. 272p. 1980. 44.95x (ISBN 0-471-27641-3, Pub. by Wiley-Interscience). Wiley.

Mitchell, A. R. & Wait, R. A. The Finite Element Method in Partial Differential Equations. LC 76-13533. 1977. 44.95x (ISBN 0-471-99405-7, Pub. by Wiley-Interscience). Wiley.

Mizohata, Sigeru. The Theory of Partial Differential Equations. LC 72-83593. 350p. 1973. 79.95 (ISBN 0-521-08727-9). Cambridge U Pr.

Morozov, V. A. Methods for Solving Incorrectly Posed Problems. Nashed, Z., ed. Aries, A. B., tr. from Rus. (Illus.). 270p. 1984. pap. 36.00 (ISBN 0-387-96059-7). Springer-Verlag.

Myint-U, Tyn. Partial Differential Equations of Mathematical Physics. 2nd ed. 1980. 33.50 (ISBN 0-444-00383-5). Elsevier.

Nirenberg, Louis. Lectures on Linear Partial Differential Equations. LC 74-4400. (CBMS Regional Conference Series in Mathematics: No. 17). 58p. 1983. pap. 9.00 (ISBN 0-8218-1667-5, CBMS-17). Am Math.

Noye, J. & Fletcher, C., eds. Computational Techniques & Applications CTAC-83: Proceedings of International Conference, University of Sidney, Australia, 1983. 982p. 1984. 92.75 (ISBN 0-444-87527-1, I-188-84, North Holland). Elsevier.

Parter, Seymour V., ed. Numerical Methods for Partial Differential Equations. (Mathematic Research Center Symposium & Advanced Seminars Ser.). 1979. 17.00 (ISBN 0-12-546050-3). Acad Pr.

Payne, L. E. Improperly Posed Problems in Partial Differential Equations. (CBMS-NSF Regional Conference Ser.: No. 22). v, 76p. (Orig.). 1975. pap. text ed. 10.50 (ISBN 0-89871-019-7). Soc Indus-Appl Math.

Pazy, A. Semigroups of Linear Operators & Applications to Partial Differential Equations. (Applied Mathematical Sciences Ser.: Vol. 44). 288p. 1983. 31.50 (ISBN 0-387-90845-5). Springer-Verlag.

Pinsky, Mark A. Introduction to Partial Differential Equations with Applications. (Illus.). 336p. 1984. text ed. 37.95 (ISBN 0-07-050117-3). McGraw.

Pommaret, J. Systems of Partial Differential Equations & Lie Pseudogroups. (Mathematics & Its Applications Ser.). 426p. 1978. 65.95 (ISBN 0-677-00270-X). Gordon.

Price, P. F. & Simon, L. M., eds. Miniconference on Partial Differential Equations. new ed. 133p. (Orig.). pap. text ed. 8.50 (ISBN 0-86784-123-0, 1246, Pub. by ANUP Australia). Australia N U P.

Rautmenn, R., ed. Approximation Methods for Navier-Stokes Problems: Proceedings. (Lecture Notes in Mathematics Ser.: Vol. 771). 581p. 1980. pap. 39.00 (ISBN 0-387-09734-1). Springer-Verlag.

Rockland, C. Hypoellipticity & Eigenvalue Asymptotics. (Lecture Notes in Mathematics Ser.: Vol. 464). 171p. 1975. pap. 14.00 (ISBN 0-387-07175-X). Springer-Verlag.

Rogers, C. & Shadwick, W. F. Backlund Transformations & Their Applications. LC 81-22783. (Mathematics in Science & Engineering Ser.). 1982. 49.50 (ISBN 0-12-592850-5). Acad Pr.

Rothe, F. Global Solutions of Reaction-Diffusion Systems. (Lecture Notes in Mathematics Ser.: Vol. 1072). v, 216p. 1984. pap. 13.50 (ISBN 0-387-13365-8). Springer-Verlag.

Schapira, P. Microdifferential Systems in the Complex Domain. (Grundlehren der Mathematischen Wissenschaften Ser.: Band 269). 240p. 1985. 34.50 (ISBN 0-387-13672-X). Springer-Verlag.

Schneider, Hans, ed. Recent Advances in Matrix Theory. LC 64-20843. (U. S. Army Mathematics Research Center Publication: No. 12). pap. 38.50 (ISBN 0-317-09153-0, 2015372). Bks Demand UMI.

Shilov, George E., ed. Generalized Functions & Partial Differential Equations. rev. ed. Seckler, B., tr. LC 67-28235. (Mathematics & Its Applications Ser.). 358p. 1968. 68.25x (ISBN 0-677-20660-7). Gordon.

Showalter, R. E. Hilbert Space Methods for Partial Differential Equations. (Monographs & Studies: No. 1). 196p. 1977. pap. 49.50 (ISBN 0-273-08440-2). Pitman Pub MA.

Smoller, Joel A., ed. Nonlinear Partial Differential Equations. LC 83-2844. (Contemporary Mathematics Ser.: Vol. 17). 446p. 1983. pap. 29.00 (ISBN 0-8218-5017-2). Am Math.

Stephenson, G. Partial Differential Equations for Scientists & Engineers. 3rd ed. (Illus.). 164p. 1985. pap. 9.95 (ISBN 0-582-44696-1). Longman.

Stredulinsky, E. W. Weighted Inequalities & Degenerate Elliptic Partial Differential Equations. (Lecture Notes in Mathematics Ser.: Vol. 1074). iii, 143p. 1984. pap. 10.00 (ISBN 0-387-13370-4). Springer-Verlag.

Swaminathan, S., ed. Fixed Point Theory & Its Applications. 1976. 34.00 (ISBN 0-12-678650-X). Acad Pr.

Symposium on Non-Well-Posed Problems & Logarithmic Convexity, Edinburgh, 1972. Proceedings. Knops, R. J., ed. LC 72-98023. (Lecture Notes in Mathematics: Vol. 316). v, 176p. 1973. pap. 13.00 (ISBN 0-387-06159-2). Springer-Verlag.

Treves, Francois. Basic Linear Partial Differential Equations. 1975. 68.50 (ISBN 0-12-699440-4). Acad Pr.

--Linear Partial Differential Equations. (Notes on Mathematics & Its Applications Ser.). 130p. 1970. 42.95x (ISBN 0-677-02520-3). Gordon.

--Linear Partial Differential Equations with Constant Coefficients. (Mathematics & Its Applications Ser.). 544p. 1966. 132.95x (ISBN 0-677-01190-3). Gordon.

Treves, Franxois. Locally Convex Spaces & Linear Partial Differential Equations. LC 67-25286. (Grundlehren der Mathematischen Wissenschaften: Vol. 146). 1967. 28.00 (ISBN 0-387-03833-7). Springer-Verlag.

Varadhan, S. R. Diffusion Problems & Partial Differential Equations. (Tata Institute Lectures on Mathematics Ser.). 315p. 1980. pap. 13.00 (ISBN 0-387-08773-7). Springer-Verlag.

Vejvoda, O. Partial Differential Equations. 380p. 1981. 50.00 (ISBN 0-686-30667-8). Sijthoff & Noordhoff.

Vichenevetsky, Robert. Computer Methods for Partial Differential Equations: Elliptical Equations & the Finite Element Method, Vol. 1. (Illus.). 400p. 1981. text ed. 45.00 (ISBN 0-13-165233-8). P-H.

Voigt, Robert G., et al, eds. Spectral Methods for Partial Differential Equations. LC 84-50634. (Illus.). vii, 267p. 1984. text ed. 26.50 (ISBN 0-89871-195-9). Soc Indus-Appl Math.

Weinberger, Hans F. First Course in Partial Differential Equations with Complex Variables & Transform Methods. 446p. 1965. 45.45x (ISBN 0-471-00623-8). Wiley.

Williams, W. E. Partial Differential Equations. (Oxford Applied Mathematics & Computing Science Ser.). (Illus.). 1980. text ed. 38.00x (ISBN 0-19-859633-2); pap. text ed. 22.50x (ISBN 0-19-859632-4). Oxford U Pr.

Zuily, Claude. Uniqueness & Non-Uniqueness in the Cauchy Problem. (Progress in Mathematics Ser.). 250p. 1983. text ed. 14.00 (ISBN 0-8176-3121-6). Birkhauser.

DIFFERENTIAL EQUATIONS, PARTIAL–NUMERICAL SOLUTIONS

Angel, Edward & Bellman, Richard. Dynamic Programming & Partial Differential Equations. (Mathematics in Science & Engineering Ser: Vol. 88). 1972. 60.00 (ISBN 0-12-057950-2). Acad Pr.

Bensoussan, A., et al. Asymptotic Analysis for Periodic Structures. (Studies in Mathematics & Its Applications Ser.: Vol. 5). 700p. 1978. 70.25 (ISBN 0-444-85172-0, North-Holland). Elsevier.

Colton, D. L. & Gilbert, R. P., eds. Constructive & Computational Methods for Differential & Integral Equations. (Lecture Notes in Mathematics Ser.: Vol. 430). vii, 476p. 1974. pap. 23.00 (ISBN 0-387-07021-4). Springer-Verlag.

Fabera, J., ed. Equadiff IV: Proceedings, Prague, August 22 - 26, 1977. LC 79-11103. (Lecture Notes in Mathematics: Vol. 703). 1979. pap. 26.00 (ISBN 0-387-09116-5). Springer-Verlag.

Fairweather, Graeme. Finite Element Galerkin Methods for Differential Equations. (Lecture Notes in Pure & Applied Mathematics Ser.: Vol. 34). 1978. 45.00 (ISBN 0-8247-6673-3). Dekker.

Fletcher, C. A. Computational Galerkin Methods. (Computational Physics Ser.). (Illus.). 335p. 1984. 39.00 (ISBN 0-387-12633-3). Springer-Verlag.

Gekeler, E. Discretization Methods for Stable Initial Value Problems. (Lecture Notes in Mathematics: Vol. 1044). viii, 201p. pap. 13.00 (ISBN 0-387-12880-8). Springer-Verlag.

Hormander, Lars, ed. Seminar on Singularities of Solutions of Linear Partial Differential Equations. LC 78-70300. (Annals of Mathematics Studies: No. 91). 1979. 31.00x (ISBN 0-691-08221-9). Princeton U Pr.

Ize, Jorge. Bifurcation Theory for Fredholm Operators. LC 76-25186. (Memoirs of the American Mathematical Society: 174). 128p. 1976. pap. 14.00 (ISBN 0-8218-2174-1). Am Math.

Lapidus, Leon & Pinder, George F. Numerical Solution of Partial Differential Equations in Science & Engineering. LC 81-16491. 677p. 1982. 51.95x (ISBN 0-471-09866-3, Pub. by Wiley-Interscience). Wiley.

Lions, J. L. & Magenes, E. Non-Homogeneous Boundary Value Problems & Applications, Vol. 1. Kenneth, P., tr. LC 71-151407. (Die Grundlehren der Mathematischen Wissenschaften: Vol. 181). 355p. 1972. 38.00 (ISBN 0-387-05363-8). Springer-Verlag.

--Non-Homogeneous Boundary Value Problems & Applications, Vol. 2. Kenneth, P., tr. LC 71-151407. (Die Grundlehren der Mathematischen Wissenschaften: Vol. 182). 242p. 1972. 28.00 (ISBN 0-387-05444-8). Springer-Verlag.

--Non-Homogeneous Boundary Value Problems & Applications, Vol. 3. Kenneth, P., tr. from Fr. LC 71-151407. (Die Grundlehren der Mathematischen Wissenschaften: Vol. 183). 330p. 1973. 55.00 (ISBN 0-387-05832-X). Springer-Verlag.

Meis, T. & Marcowitz, U. Numerical Solution of Partial Differential Equations. (Applied Mathematical Sciences Ser.: Vol. 32). 541p. 1981. pap. 28.00 (ISBN 0-387-90550-2). Springer-Verlag.

NATO Advanced Study Institute, Kjeller, Norway, Aug., 1973. Numerical Solution of Partial Differential Equations: Proceedings. Gram, J., ed. LC 73-91204. (NATO Advanced Study Institutes: No. C-2). 1973. lib. bdg. 33.00 (ISBN 90-277-0413-9, Pub. by Reidel Holland). Kluwer Academic.

Noye, B. J. Computational Techniques for Differential Equations. (Mathematical Studies: Vol. 83). 1984. 67.50 (ISBN 0-444-86783-X, I-446-83, North-Holland). Elsevier.

Smith, Gordon D. Numerical Solution of Partial Differential Equations. 2nd ed. (Oxford Mathematical Handbooks Ser.). (Illus.). 1978. pap. text ed. 15.95x (ISBN 0-19-859626-X). Oxford U Pr.

Yanenko, N. N. Method of Fractional Steps: The Solution of Problems of Mathematical Physics in Several Variables. Holt, M., ed. LC 78-139953. (Illus.). 1971. 36.00 (ISBN 0-387-05272-0). Springer-Verlag.

DIFFERENTIAL FIELDS

see Algebra, Differential

DIFFERENTIAL FORMS

Bott, R. & Tu, L. W. Differential Forms in Algebraic Topology. (Graduate Texts in Mathematics Ser.: Vol. 82). (Illus.). 288p. 1982. 33.00 (ISBN 0-387-90613-4). Springer-Verlag.

Griffiths, P. A. & Morgan, J. Rational Homotopy Theory & Differential Forms. 256p. 1981. text ed. 19.95x (ISBN 0-8176-3041-4). Birkhauser.

Schreiber, M. Differential Forms-A Heuristic Introduction (Universitext) LC 77-14392. (Illus.). 1977. pap. text ed. 19.80 (ISBN 0-387-90287-2). Springer-Verlag.

DIFFERENTIAL GEOMETRY

see Geometry, Differential

DIFFERENTIAL INVARIANTS

see also Transformations (Mathematics)

Gilkey, Peter B. Invariance Theory, the Heat Equation, & the Atiyah-Singer Index Theorem. LC 84-61166. (Mathematics Lecture Ser.: No. 11). viii, 349p. 1985. text ed. 40.00 (ISBN 0-914098-20-9). Publish or Perish.

Segre, Beniamino. Some Properties of Differentiable Varieties & Transformations: With Special Reference to the Analytic & Algebraic Cases. 2nd ed. LC 72-137498. (Ergebnisse der Mathematik und Ihrer Grenzgebiete: Vol. 13). 1971. pap. 34.00 (ISBN 0-387-05085-X). Springer-Verlag.

Tannenbaum, A. Invariance & System Theory: Algebraic & Geometric Aspects. (Lecture Notes in Mathematics Ser.: Vol. 845). 161p. 1981. pap. 13.00 (ISBN 0-387-10565-4). Springer-Verlag.

DIFFERENTIAL OPERATORS

see also Differential Equations

Aliprantis, Charalambous D. & Burkinshaw, Owen. Positive Operators. (Pure & Applied Mathematics Ser.). Date not set. price not set (ISBN 0-12-050260-7). Acad Pr.

Andreotti, Aldo. Complexes of Partial Differential Operators. LC 75-8440. (Yale Mathematical Monographs: No. 6). pap. 15.00 (ISBN 0-8357-9106-8, 2016793). Bks Demand UMI.

Apostol, ed. Topics in Modern Operator Theory. (Operator Theory, Advances & Applications Ser.: 2). 335p. 1981. text ed. 32.95x (ISBN 0-8176-1244-0). Birkhauser.

Arsene, Gr., ed. Invariant Subspaces & Other Topics. (Operator Theory: Advances & Applications Ser.: No. 6). 229p. 1983. 28.95x (ISBN 0-8176-1360-9). Birkhauser.

Bauer, K. W. & Ruscheweyh, S. Differential Operators for Partial Differential Equations & Function-Theoretic Applications. (Lecture Notes in Mathematics: Vol. 174). 258p. 1980. pap. 20.00 (ISBN 0-387-09975-1). Springer-Verlag.

Bjork, J. E. Rings of Differential Operators. (Mathematical Library: Vol. 21). 360p. 1979. 66.00 (ISBN 0-444-85292-1, North Holland). Elsevier.

Browder, F., ed. Nonlinear Functional Analysis, Pts. 1 & 2. LC 73-91392. (Proceedings of Symposia in Pure Mathematics Ser.: Vol. 18). 1970. Set. 81.00 (ISBN 0-8218-0243-7); Pt. 1 36.00 (ISBN 0-8218-0244-5); Pt. 2 55.00. Am Math.

Carroll, R. Transmutation Theory & Applications. (Mathematics Studies: Vol. 117). 352p. 1985. 35.00 (ISBN 0-444-87805-X, North-Holland). Elsevier.

Coddington, Earl A. Extension Theory of Formally Normal & Symmetric Subspaces. LC 73-7870. (Memoirs: No. 134). 80p. 1973. pap. 10.00 (ISBN 0-8218-1834-1, MEMO-134). Am Math.

Elschner, J. Singular Ordinary Differential Operators & Pseudodifferential Equations. (Lecture Notes in Mathematics: Vol. 1128). 200p. 1985. pap. 14.40 (ISBN 0-387-15194-X). Springer-Verlag.

Erdelyi, I., ed. Operator Theory & Functional Analysis. LC 79-18548. (Research Notes in Mathematics Ser.: No. 38). 176p. (Orig.). 1979. pap. text ed. 22.95 (ISBN 0-273-08450-X). Pitman Pub MA.

Folland, G. B. & Kohn, J. J. The Neumann Problem for the Cauchy-Riemann Complex. LC 72-1984. (Annals of Mathematics Studies: No. 75). 180p. 1972. lib. bdg. 22.00 (ISBN 0-691-08120-4). Princeton U Pr.

Hoermander, L. The Analysis of Linear Partial Differential Operators II: Differential Operators with Constant Coefficients. (Grundlehren der Mathematischen Wissenschaften: Vol. 257). (Illus.). 380p. 1983. 49.50 (ISBN 0-387-12139-0). Springer-Verlag.

--The Analysis of Linear Partial Differential Operators I: Distribution Theory & Fourier Analysis. (Grundlehren der Mathematischen Wissenschaften: Vol. 256). (Illus.). 380p. 1983. 39.00 (ISBN 0-387-12104-8). Springer-Verlag.

Hormander, L. The Analysis of Linear Partial Differential Operators IV. (Grundlehren der Mathematishchen Wissenschaften Ser.: Vol. 275). 360p. 1985. 45.00 (ISBN 0-387-13829-3). Springer-Verlag.

Jackson, R. J. Canonical Differential Operators & Lower-Order Symbols. LC 73-8760. (Memoirs: No. 135). 235p. 1973. pap. 12.00 (ISBN 0-8218-1835-X, MEMO-135). Am Math.

Kamber, Franz W. & Tondeur, Philippe. Invariant Differential Operators & Cohomology of Lie Algebra Sheaves. LC 52-42839. (Memoirs: No. 113). 1971. pap. 9.00 (ISBN 0-8218-1813-9, MEMO-113). Am Math.

Kappel, F. & Schappacher, W. Infinite-Dimensional Systems: Proceedings of the Conference on Operator Semigroups & Applications, Held in Styria, Austria, June 5-11, 1983. (Lecture Notes in Mathematics Ser.: Vol. 1076). viii, 278p. 1984. pap. 16.00t (ISBN 0-387-13376-3). Springer-Verlag.

Knowles, E. W. & Lewis, R. T., eds. Spectral Theory of Differential Operators. (Mathematics Studies: Vol. 55). 384p. 1981. 53.25 (ISBN 0-444-86277-3, North-Holland). Elsevier.

Lepowsky, J., et al, eds. Vertex Operators in Mathematics & Physics. (Mathematical Sciences Research Institute Publications Ser.: Vol. 3). (Illus.). xiv, 482p. 1985. 29.80 (ISBN 0-387-96121-6). Springer-Verlag.

Przeworska-Rolewicz, D. Shifts & Periodicity for Right Invertible Operators. LC 80-467. (Research Notes in Mathematics Ser.: No. 43). 191p. (Orig.). 1980. pap. text ed. 22.95 (ISBN 0-273-08478-X). Pitman Pub MA.

Schapira, P. Microdifferential Systems in the Complex Domain. (Grundlehren der Mathematischen Wissenschaften Ser.: Band 269). 240p. 1985. 34.50 (ISBN 0-387-13672-X). Springer-Verlag.

Taylor, Michael E. Pseudodifferential Operators. LC 80-8580. (Princeton Mathematical Ser.: No. 34). 468p. 1981. 45.00 (ISBN 0-691-08282-0). Princeton U Pr.

DIFFERENTIAL THERMAL ANALYSIS

see Thermal Analysis

DIFFERENTIAL TOPOLOGY

see also Global Analysis (Mathematics)

Anderson, R. D., ed. Symposium on Infinite Dimensional Topology. LC 69-17445. (Annals of Mathematic Studies, 69). 230p. 1972. text ed. 29.00x (ISBN 0-691-08087-9). Princeton U Pr.

Armentrout, Steve. Cellular Decompositions of Three-Manifolds that Yield Three-Manifolds. LC 52-42839. (Memoirs). 72p. 1971. pap. 9.00 (ISBN 0-8218-1807-4, MEMO-107). Am Math.

Arnold, V. I. Singularity Theory. LC 81-6091. (London Mathematical Society Lecture Notes Ser.: No. 53). (Illus.). 280p. 1981. pap. 34.50 (ISBN 0-521-28511-9). Cambridge U Pr.

Auslander, Louis & Mackenzie, Robert E. Introduction to Differentiable Manifolds. 1977. pap. 4.50 (ISBN 0-486-63455-8). Dover.

Boothby, William M. An Introduction to Differentiable Manifolds & Riemannian Geometry. (Pure & Applied Mathematics Ser.). 424p. 1975. Acad Pr.

--An Introduction to Differentiable Manifolds & Riemannian Geometry. (Pure & Applied Mathematics Ser.). 1986. price not set (ISBN 0-12-116052-1). Acad Pr.

Bott, R. & Tu, L. W. Differential Forms in Algebraic Topology. (Graduate Texts in Mathematics Ser.: Vol. 82). (Illus.). 288p. 1982. 33.00 (ISBN 0-387-90613-4). Springer-Verlag.

Brocker, Theodor & Janich, Klaus. Introduction to Differential Topology. LC 81-21591. (Illus.). 150p. 1982. 32.50 (ISBN 0-521-24135-9); pap. 13.95 (ISBN 0-521-28470-8). Cambridge U Pr.

Colloquium Held at Dijon, June 17-22, 1974, et al. Differential Topology & Geometry: Proceedings. Joubert, G. P. & Moussu, R. P., eds. LC 75-25927. (Lecture Notes in Mathematics: Vol. 484). ix, 287p. 1975. pap. 14.70 (ISBN 0-387-07405-8). Springer-Verlag.

Conner, P. E. Differentiable Periodic Maps. 2nd ed. (Lecture Notes in Mathematics: Vol. 738). 1979. pap. 14.00 (ISBN 0-387-09535-7). Springer-Verlag.

De Rham, G. Differentiable Manifolds. Smith, F. R., tr. from Fr. (Grundlehren der mathematischen Wissenschaften. A Series of Comprehensive Studies in Mathematics: Vol. 266). (Illus.). 180p. 1984. 28.50 (ISBN 0-387-13463-8). Springer-Verlag.

Eisenman, D. A. Intrinsic Measures on Complex Manifolds & Holomorphic Mappings. LC 52-42839. (Memoirs: No. 96). 80p. 1970. pap. 9.00 (ISBN 0-8218-1296-3, MEMO-96). Am Math.

Gauld. Differential Topology: An Introduction. (Texts & Monographs in Pure & Applied Mathematics). 312p. 1982. 39.75 (ISBN 0-8247-1709-0). Dekker.

Guillemin, Victor & Pollack, Alan. Differential Topology. (Math. Ser). (Illus.). 324p. 1974. 36.95x (ISBN 0-13-212605-2). P-H.

Hano, Jun-Ichi, ed. Manifolds & Lie Groups: Papers in Honor of Yozo Matsushima. (Progress in Mathematics Ser.: 14). 608p. 1981. text ed. 35.00x (ISBN 0-8176-3053-8). Birkhauser.

Jaworski, John & Stewart, Ian, eds. Seven Years of Manifold: 1968-1980. 96p. (Orig.). 1981. pap. 9.95 (ISBN 0-906812-07-0). Birkhauser.

Lang, S. Differential Manifolds. 2nd ed. (Illus.). ix, 230p. 1985. pap. 19.80 (ISBN 0-387-96113-5). Springer-Verlag.

Michor, P. W. Manifolds of Differentiable Mappings. (Shiva Mathematics Ser.: 3). 160p. (Orig.). 1981. pap. text ed. 16.95x (ISBN 0-906812-03-8). Birkhauser.

Milnor, John W. Topology from the Differentiable Viewpoint. LC 65-26874. (Illus.). 64p. 1965. pap. 4.95x (ISBN 0-8139-0181-2). U Pr of Va.

Morse, Martson & Cairns, Stewart S. Critical Point Theory in Global Analysis & Differential Topology. (Pure & Applied Mathematics Ser: Vol. 33). 1969. 76.00 (ISBN 0-12-508150-2). Acad Pr.

Poston, T. & Woodcock, A. E. A Geometrical Study of the Elementary Catastrophes. LC 73-22575. (Lectures Notes in Mathematics: Vol. 373). (Illus.). v, 257p. 1974. pap. 18.00 (ISBN 0-387-06681-0). Springer-Verlag.

Seminar on Periodic Maps. Proceedings. (Lecture Notes in Mathematics: Vol. 46). 1967. pap. 10.70 (ISBN 0-387-03917-1). Springer-Verlag.

Shanahan, P. The Atiyah-Singer Index Theorem: An Introduction. (Lecture Notes in Mathematics: Vol. 638). (Illus.). 1978. pap. 18.00 (ISBN 0-387-08660-9). Springer-Verlag.

Spivak, Michael. Calculus on Manifolds: A Modern Approach to Classical Theorems of Advanced Calculus. (Orig.). 1965. pap. 20.95 (ISBN 0-8053-9021-9). Benjamin-Cummings.

Wallace, Andrew. Differential Topology: First Steps. 1968. pap. 27.95 (ISBN 0-8053-9485-0). Benjamin-Cummings.

Warner, F. W. Foundations of Differentiable Manifolds & Lie Groups. (Graduate Texts in Mathematics Ser.: Vol. 94). (Illus.). 270p. 1983. 22.00 (ISBN 0-387-90894-3). Springer Verlag.

DIFFERENTIATION OF CELLS
see Cell Differentiation

DIFFRACTION

Beeston, B. E., et al, eds. Electron Diffraction & Optical Diffraction Techniques. (Practical Methods in Electron Microscopy Ser.: Vol. 1, Pt. 2). 260p. 1973. 24.00 (ISBN 0-444-10411-9, Biomedical Pr). Elsevier.

Cowley, J. M. Diffraction Physics. 2nd, rev. ed. 1981. 68.00 (ISBN 0-444-86121-1). Elsevier.

Hansen, Robert C. Geometric Theory of Diffraction. 406p. 1981. 44.95x (ISBN 0-471-09842-6, Pub. by Wiley-Interscience); pap. 29.50x (ISBN 0-471-09841-8, Pub. by Wiley-Interscience). Wiley.

Jull, E. V. Aperture Antennas & Diffraction Theory. (IEE Electromagnetic Waves Ser.: No. 10). 192p. 1981. 76.00 (ISBN 0-906048-52-4, EW010, Pub. by Peregrinus England). Inst Elect Eng.

DIFFRACTION HOLOGRAPHY
see also subdivision diffraction under subjects, e.g. X-rays–Diffraction

French, Alfred D. & Gardner, KennCorwin H., eds. Fiber Diffraction Methods. LC 80-21566. (ACS Symposium Ser.: No. 141). 1980. 49.95 (ISBN 0-8412-0589-2). Am Chemical.

Schultz, Jerold M. Diffraction for Materials Scientists. (Illus.). 336p. 1982. 41.95 (ISBN 0-13-211920-X). P-H.

DIFFRACTION GRATINGS
see also Moire Method

Hutley, M. C. Diffraction Gratings. LC 81-67893. (Techniques of Physics Ser.: No. 6). 1982. 57.50 (ISBN 0-12-362980-2). Acad Pr.

Wilcox, C. H. Scattering Theory for Diffraction Gratings. (Applied Mathematical Sciences: Vol. 46). (Illus.). 170p. 1984. pap. 19.00 (ISBN 0-387-90924-9). Springer-Verlag.

DIFFUSERS

Japikse, David. Turbomachinery Diffuser Design Technology. LC 85-90311. (Design Technology Ser.: DTS 1). (Illus.). 400p. 1984. text ed. 1450.00 (ISBN 0-933283-00-8). Concepts ETI.

DIFFUSION
see also Biological Transport; Colloids; Extraction (Chemistry); Gases; Light–Scattering; Mass Transfer; Matter–Properties

Abelson, Philip H., et al, eds. Liquid Thermal Diffusion. AEC Technical Information Center. (National Nuclear Energy Ser.: Div. IX, Vol. 1). 258p. 1958. 22.00 (ISBN 0-87079-259-8, TID-5229); microfilm 10.00 (ISBN 0-87079-260-1, TID-5229). DOE.

American Society for Metals Staff. Diffusion: Papers Presented at a Seminar of the American Society for Metals, October 14 & 15, 1972. LC 73-88315. pap. 95.80 (2019479). Bks Demand UMI.

Aris, R. & Strieder, W. C. Variational Methods Applied to Problems of Diffusion & Reaction. (Springer Tracts in Natural Philosophy: Vol. 24). (Illus.). 120p. 1973. 25.00 (ISBN 0-387-06311-0). Springer-Verlag.

Askill, John. Tracer Diffusion Data for Metals, Alloys, & Simple Oxides. LC 73-95202. 107p. 1970. 37.50x (ISBN 0-306-65147-5, IFI Plenum). Plenum Pub.

Bamford, C. H., et al, eds. Comprehensive Chemical Kinetics, Vol. 25: Diffusion-Limited Reactions. 404p. 1985. 135.25 (ISBN 0-444-42354-0). Elsevier.

Brown, Lawrence. Diffusion Processes & Location. (Bibliography Ser.: No. 4). 177p. 1968. 4.00 (ISBN 0-686-32163-4). Regional Sci Res Inst.

Brutsaert, Wilfried & Jirka, Gerhard H., eds. Gas Transfer at Water Surfaces. 1984. lib. bdg. 78.00 (ISBN 0-318-00439-9, Pub. by Reidel Holland). Kluwer Academic.

Crank, J. The Mathematics of Diffusion. 2nd ed. (Illus.). 1975. pap. 26.95x (ISBN 0-19-853411-6). Oxford U Pr.

Crank, John & Park, Geoffrey S., eds. Diffusion in Polymers. 1968. 86.00 (ISBN 0-12-197050-7). Acad Pr.

Csanady, G. T. Turbulent Diffusion in the Environment. LC 72-92527. (Geophysics & Astrophysics Monographs: No. 3). (Illus.). 248p. 1973. lib. bdg. 37.00 (ISBN 90-277-0260-3); pap. text ed. 21.00 (ISBN 90-277-0261-6). Kluwer Academic.

Cunningham, Roberto E. & Williams, R. J. Diffusion in Gases & Porous Media. LC 79-12120. 298p. 1980. 45.00x (ISBN 0-306-40537-7, Plenum Pr). Plenum Pub.

Cussler, E. L. Diffusion: Mass Transfer in Fluid Systems. LC 83-1905. (Illus.). 400p. 1984. 49.50 (ISBN 0-521-23171-X). Cambridge U Pr.

--Multicomponent Diffusion. (Chemical Engineering Monographs: Vol. 3). 176p. 1976. 51.00 (ISBN 0-444-41326-X). Elsevier.

Doyama, Masa & Yoshida, Sho, eds. Progress in the Study of Point Defects. 440p. 1977. 64.50x (ISBN 0-86008-185-0, Pub. by U of Tokyo Japan). Columbia U Pr.

Emelus, K. G. & Woolsey, G. A., eds. Discharges in Electronegative Gases. 162p. 1970. cancelled (ISBN 0-85066-035-1). Taylor & Francis.

Fedorov, G. B. & Smirnov, E. A. Diffusion in Reactor Materials. (Diffusion & Defect Monogr Ser.: Vol. 8). 182p. 1984. 36.00 (ISBN 0-87849-531-2). Trans Tech.

Fleming, W. H. & Rishel, R. W. Deterministic & Stochastic Optimal Control. LC 75-28391. (Applications of Mathematics Ser.: Vol. 1). (Illus.). xi, 222p. 1975. 44.00 (ISBN 0-387-90155-8). Springer-Verlag.

Frank-Kamenetskii, D. A. Diffusion & Heat Transfer in Chemical Kinetics. LC 68-26770. 574p. 1969. 45.00x (ISBN 0-306-30349-3, Plenum Pr). Plenum Pub.

Geguzin, Y. E. & Krivoglaz, M. A. Migration of Macroscopic Inclusions in Solids. LC 73-83894. (Studies in Soviet Science - Physical Sciences Ser.). (Illus.). 342p. 1973. 37.50x (ISBN 0-306-10889-5, Consultants). Plenum Pub.

Girifalco, L. A. & Welch, D. O. Point Defects & Diffusion in Strained Metals. 180p. (Orig.). 1967. 57.75 (ISBN 0-677-01400-7). Gordon.

Hofmann, A. W., et al. Geochemical Transport & Kinetics. 1974. 27.00 (ISBN 0-87279-644-2, 634). Carnegie Inst.

Ikeda, N. & Watanabe, S. Stochastic Differential Equations & Diffusion Processes. (North-Holland Mathematical Library: Vol. 24). 464p. 1981. 85.00 (ISBN 0-444-86172-6, North-Holland). Elsevier.

Ito, K. & McKean, H. P., Jr. Diffusion Processes & Their Sample Paths. (Grundlehren der Mathematischen Wissenschaften: Vol. 125). 1965. 39.00 (ISBN 0-387-03302-5). Springer-Verlag.

Jacobs, M. H. Diffusion Processes. 1967. Repr. of 1935 ed. 22.00 (ISBN 0-387-03882-5). Springer-Verlag.

Kedves, F. J. & Beke, D. L., eds. Diffusion in Metals & Alloys: Proceedings of an International Conference Held at Tihany, Hungary. (Diffusion & Defect Monograph Ser.: Vol. 7). 685p. 1983. 84.00 (ISBN 0-87849-527-4). Trans Tech.

Knibbe, D. E. Diffusion-Controlled Stress Relaxation of Swollen Rubber-Like Networks. 60p. 1968. 24.25 (ISBN 0-677-61185-4). Gordon.

Krylov, N. V. Controlled Diffusion Processes. (Applications of Mathematics Ser.: Vol. 14). 448p. 1980. 49.50 (ISBN 0-387-90461-1). Springer-Verlag.

Manning, John R. Diffusion Kinetics for Atoms in Crystals. LC 68-20921. pap. 68.50 (ISBN 0-317-09190-5, 2005790). Bks Demand UMI.

Marder, William. The History & Technique of a New Diffusion Process. 1980. pap. 10.00 (ISBN 0-9607480-5-9). Pine Ridge.

Mikhailov, M. D. & Ozisik, M. N. Unified Analysis & Solutions of Heat & Mass Diffusion. LC 83-14562. 524p. 1984. 62.50x (ISBN 0-471-89830-9, Pub. by Wiley-Interscience). Wiley.

Mrowec, S. Defects & Diffusion in Solids: An Introduction. (Materials Science Monographs: Vol. 5). 466p. 1980. 72.50 (ISBN 0-444-99776-8). Elsevier.

Murch, G. E., et al, eds. Nontraditional Methods in Diffusion. LC 84-60064. (Illus.). 311p. 1984. 42.00 (ISBN 0-89520-473-8); members 26.00; student members 13.00. Metal Soc.

Murch, Graeme E. & Nowick, Arthur S., eds. Diffusion in Solids II. (Materials Science & Technology Ser.). 1984. 73.00 (ISBN 0-12-522662-4). Acad Pr.

Nowick, A. S. & Burton, J. J. Diffusion in Solids: Recent Developments. 1975. 75.00 (ISBN 0-12-522660-8). Acad Pr.

Pasquill, F. Atmospheric Diffusion: Study of the Dispersion of Windbourne Material from Industrial & other Sources. 3rd ed. LC 83-219. (Environmental Sciences Ser.). 437p. 1983. 64.95x (ISBN 0-470-27404-2). Halsted Pr.

Ricciardi, L. M. Diffusion Processes & Related Topics in Biology. LC 77-7464. (Lecture Notes in Biomathematics Ser: Vol. 14). 1977. pap. 18.00 (ISBN 0-387-08146-1). Springer-Verlag.

Satterfield, Charles N. & Sherwood, Thomas K. The Role of Diffusion in Catalysis. LC 63-16570. (Addison Wesley Series in Chemical Engineering). pap. 31.30 (ISBN 0-317-10680-5, 2055595). Bks Demand UMI.

Sherwood, J. N., ed. Diffusion Processes. 1971. Set. 202.25 (ISBN 0-677-14260-9); Vol. 1. 106.50 (ISBN 0-677-14820-8); Vol. 2, 444p. 119.25 (ISBN 0-677-14830-5). Gordon.

Springer, T. Quasielastic Neutron Scattering for the Investigation of Diffusive Motions in Solids & Liquids. (Springer Tracts in Modern Physics: Vol. 64). (Illus.). 102p. 1972. 24.80 (ISBN 0-387-05808-7). Springer-Verlag.

Stark, J. P. Solid State Diffusion. LC 80-11750. 252p. 1983. Repr. of 1976 ed. lib. bdg. 23.00 (ISBN 0-89874-145-9). Krieger.

Tuwiner, Sidney B. Diffusion & Membrane Technology. LC 62-20783. (ACS Monograph: No. 156). 1962. 35.50 (ISBN 0-8412-0284-2). Am Chemical.

Walker, H. F. & Fitzgibbon, W. E., eds. Nonlinear Diffusion. LC 77-8501. (Research Notes in Mathematics Ser: No. 14). (Illus.). pap. 22.95 (ISBN 0-273-01066-2, 1066). Pitman Pub MA.

Watts, Richard J. Elementary Principles of Diffusion Theory & the Chain Reaction. (Illus.). 307p. (Orig.). 1982. pap. 25.00x (ISBN 0-9609112-0-0). Desperation Pr.

DIFFUSION COATINGS

Hausner, H. H. Coatings of High-Temperature Materials. LC 65-12156. 296p. 1966. 32.50x (ISBN 0-306-30210-1, Plenum Pr). Plenum Pub.

Jilek, J. H. Powder Coatings Buyer's Guide. 36p. 1983. pap. text ed. 20.00 (ISBN 0-318-01977-9). Tech Marketing.

Kedves, F. J. & Beke, D. L., eds. Diffusion in Metals & Alloys: Proceedings of an International Conference Held at Tihany, Hungary. (Diffusion & Defect Monograph Ser.: Vol. 7). 685p. 1983. 84.00 (ISBN 0-87849-527-4). Trans Tech.

Samsonov, G. V. Diffusion Cladding of Metals. LC 66-17190. 89p. 1967. 25.00x (ISBN 0-306-10776-7, Consultants). Plenum Pub.

Technology Marketing Staff Editors. High Solids Coatings Buyer's Guide. 32p. 1984. pap. text ed. 21.00 (ISBN 0-318-01976-0). Tech Marketing.

--Powder Coatings Buyer's Guide. 16p. 1984. pap. text ed. 20.00 (ISBN 0-318-01978-7). Tech Marketing.

DIFFUSION OF INNOVATIONS
see also Technology Transfer

Davies, S. The Diffusion of Process Innovations. LC 78-15143. 1979. 42.50 (ISBN 0-521-22193-5). Cambridge U Pr.

Gould, Peter. Spatial Diffusion: The Spread of Ideas & Innovations in Geographic Space. (CISE Learning Package Ser.: No. 11). (Illus.). 55p. (Orig.). 1975. pap. text ed. 3.00x (ISBN 0-936876-26-3). Learn Res Intl Stud.

Rogers, E. & Shoemaker, F. Communication of Innovations. 2nd ed. LC 78-122276. 1971. text ed. 16.95 (ISBN 0-02-926680-7). Free Pr.

Rogers, Everett M. Diffusion of Innovations. 3rd ed. (Illus.). 512p. 1982. text ed. 18.95 (ISBN 0-02-926650-5). Free Pr.

Rosenberg, Nathan. Perspectives on Technology. LC 75-14623. 336p. 1976. 52.50 (ISBN 0-521-20957-9). Cambridge U Pr.

Zaltman, Gerald & Duncan, Robert. Strategies for Planned Change. LC 76-39946. 404p. 1977. 39.95x (ISBN 0-471-98131-1, Pub. by Wiley-Interscience). Wiley.

DIGESTIVE ORGANS
see also Biliary Tract;
also names of individual organs, e.g. Intestines; Stomach

Bolt, Robert J., et al. The Digestive System. LC 82-10906. 429p. 1983. pap. 27.50x (ISBN 0-471-92207-2, Pub. by Wiley Med). Wiley.

Case, Maynard, et al, eds. Electrolyte & Water Transport Across Gastrointestinal Epithelia. 335p. 1982. text ed. 53.50 (ISBN 0-89004-765-0). Raven.

Davenport, Horace W. Physiology of the Digestive Tract. 5th ed. (Illus.). 1982. 28.50 (ISBN 0-8151-2330-2); pap. 23.50 (ISBN 0-8151-2329-9). Year Bk Med.

Demling, L., et al. Atlas of Enteroscopy. Soergel, K. H. & Pease, H., trs. from Ger. LC 75-11709. (Illus.). 270p. 1975. 140.00 (ISBN 0-387-07292-6). Springer-Verlag.

Drake, M. Gastro-Esophageal Cytology. (Monographs in Clinical Cytology: Vol. 10). (Illus.). xii, 268p. 1985. 52.50 (ISBN 3-8055-3931-2). S Karger.

Grossman, Morton, et al, eds. Gastrointestinal Hormones & Pathology of the Digestive System. LC 78-17547. (Advances in Experimental Medicine & Biology Ser.: Vol.106). 336p. 1978. 45.00x (ISBN 0-306-40023-5, Plenum Pr). Plenum Pub.

Grossman, Morton I., et al, eds. Cellular Basis of Chemical Messengers in the Digestive System. LC 81-2318. (UCLA Forum in Medical Sciences Ser.: No. 23). 1981. 30.00 (ISBN 0-12-304420-0). Acad Pr.

McMinn, R. M. & Hobdell, M. H. Functional Anatomy of the Digestive System. (Illus.). 282p. 1974. pap. text ed. 16.95x (ISBN 0-8464-0434-6). Beekman Pubs.

Nahum, Henri & Fekete, Francois. Radiology of the Postoperative Digestive Tract. Oestreich, Alan E., tr. from Fr. LC 79-83738. (Illus.). 160p. 1979. 39.50x (ISBN 0-89352-027-6). Masson Pub.

Sanford. Digestive System Physiology. (Physical Principles in Medicine Ser.). (Illus.). 160p. 1982. pap. text ed. 17.00 (ISBN 0-8391-1751-5). Univ Park.

Sanford, Paul A. Digestive System Physiology. (Physiological Principles in Medicine Ser.: No. 2). 180p. 1982. 30.00x (ISBN 0-7131-4380-0, Pub. by E Arnold). State Mutual Bk.

Sawyer, Kenneth C. Management of Foreign Bodies in the Food & Air Passages. (Illus.). 208p. 1967. photocopy ed. 19.75x (ISBN 0-398-01653-4). C C Thomas.

Wienbeck, Martin, ed. Motility of the Digestive Tract. 638p. 1982. text ed. 98.50 (ISBN 0-89004-806-1). Raven.

Wise, Robert E. & O'Keeffe, Austin P. Accessory Digestive Organs. (Atlas of Tumor Radiology Ser.). (Illus.). 1975. 58.50 (ISBN 0-8151-9333-5). Year Bk Med.

DIGGING MACHINES
see Excavating Machinery

DIGITAL COMMUNICATION

Computer-Based Conference Systems for Developing Countries: Report of a Workshop Held in Ottawa, Canada, 26-30 October 1981. 43p. 1982. pap. 7.00 (ISBN 0-88936-325-0, IDRC190, IDRC). Unipub.

Design Curves for Optical Waveguide Digital Communications Systems. (User Manual & Handbook Ser.: Vol. III). 168p. 50.00 (ISBN 0-686-32957-0). Info Gatekeepers.

Inose, Hiroshi, ed. An Introduction to Digital Integrated Communications Systems. 342p. 1979. 38.00 (ISBN 0-86008-250-4, Pub. by U of Tokyo Japan). Columbia U Pr.

Kanefsky, Morton. Communication Techniques for Digital & Analog Signals. 344p. 1985. text ed. 43.20 scp (ISBN 0-06-043475-9, HarpC); solutions manual avail. (ISBN 0-06-363485-6). Har-Row.

Lawrence, V. B. & LoCicero, J. L., eds. IEEE Communications Society's Tutorials in Modern Communication. LC 82-10599. 348p. 1982. text ed. 36.95 (ISBN 0-914894-48-X). Computer Sci.

Schwaderer, David A. Digital Communications Programming on the IBM PC. (Wiley IBM PC Ser.: 1-598). 332p. 1984. book & software set 47.90 (ISBN 0-471-88390-5, Wiley Professional Software); pap. 17.95 (ISBN 0-471-89016-2). Wiley.

DIGITAL COMPUTER CIRCUITS
see Electronic Digital Computers–Circuits

DIGITAL COMPUTER SIMULATION
see also Artificial Intelligence; SIMSCRIPT (Computer Program Language)

Englesher, Charles J. Interfacing & Digital Experiments with Your APPLE. (Illus.). 320p. (Orig.). 1984. 21.95 (ISBN 0-8306-0717-X, 1717); pap. 15.50 (ISBN 0-8306-1717-5). TAB Bks.
Ercegovac, Milos D. & Lang, Tomas. Digital Systems & Hardware: Firmware Algorithms. LC 84-21983. 832p. 1985. 37.00 (ISBN 0-471-88393-X). Wiley.
Fleischer, D. Digital Logic Elements. 228p. 1979. pap. 35.95 (ISBN 0-471-25675-7, Pub. by Wiley Heyden). Wiley.
Fletcher, William I. An Engineering Approach to Digital Design. (Illus.). 1980. text ed. 40.95 (ISBN 0-13-277699-5). P-H.
Floyd, Thomas L. Digital Fundamentals. 2nd ed. Orig. Title: Digital Logic Fundamentals. 624p. 1982. text ed. 29.95 (ISBN 0-675-09876-9). Additional Supplements May Be Obtained From Publisher. Merrill.
Forbes, Mark M. & Brey, Barry B. Digital Electronics. 520p. 1985. text ed. 27.68 scp (ISBN 0-672-98490-3); scp instr's. guide 3.67 (ISBN 0-672-98491-1); scp lab manual 12.95 (ISBN 0-672-98492-X). Bobbs.
Friedman, Arthur & Menon, Premachandran R. Theory & Design of Switching Circuits. LC 75-15888. (Illus.). 581p. 1975. 36.95 (ISBN 0-914894-52-8). Computer Sci.
Gasperini, Richard E. Digital Experiments. (Illus.). 1976. pap. 9.95 (ISBN 0-8104-5713-X). Hayden.
--Digital Troubleshooting: Practical Digital Theory & Troubleshooting Tips. 1976. pap. 11.95 (ISBN 0-8104-5708-3). Hayden.
Genn, Robert C., Jr. Digital Electronics: A Workbench Guide to Circuits, Experiments & Applications. LC 81-16837. 256p. 1982. 18.95 (ISBN 0-13-214163-9); pap. 12.95 (ISBN 0-13-212530-7). P-H.
Gold, Bernard & Rader, Charles M. Digital Processing of Signals. LC 82-14072. 282p. 1983. Repr. of 1969 ed. lib. bdg. 19.50 (ISBN 0-89874-548-9). Krieger.
Goodman, Robert L. Troubleshooting Microprocessors & Digital Logic. (Illus., Orig.). 1980. 16.95 (ISBN 0-8306-9950-3); pap. 10.95 (ISBN 0-8306-1183-5, 1183). TAB Bks.
Gothmann, William H. Digital Electronics. 2nd ed. (Illus.). 400p. 1982. 31.95 (ISBN 0-13-212159-X). P-H.
Hall, D. V. Microprocessors & Digital Systems. 1980. text ed. 33.00 (ISBN 0-07-025571-7). McGraw.
Hall, Douglas V. Microprocessors & Digital Systems. 2nd ed. (Illus.). 480p. 1983. 33.00 (ISBN 0-07-025552-0). McGraw.
Hawkins, Harry M. Concepts of Digital Electronics. (Illus.). 196p. 1983. 17.95 (ISBN 0-8306-0431-6, 1531); pap. 11.95 (ISBN 0-8306-1431-1). TAB Bks.
--Digital Electronics Projects. (Illus.). 240p. 1983. 17.95 (ISBN 0-8306-0431-6, 1431); pap. 11.95 (ISBN 0-8306-1431-1). TAB Bks.
Heap, N. W. & Martin, G. S. Introductory Digital Electronics. 192p. 1983. pap. 19.00x (ISBN 0-335-10184-4, Pub. by Open Univ Pr). Taylor & Francis.
Heiserman, D. Handbook of Digital IC Applications. 1980. 27.95 (ISBN 0-13-372698-3). P-H.
Helms, Howard D., et al, eds. Literature in Digital Signal Processing: Authors & Permitted Title Index. rev & expanded ed. LC 75-61351. 1975. 13.50 (ISBN 0-87942-052-9, PC00455). Inst Electrical.
Higgins, Richard J. Electronics with Digital & Analog Integrated Circuits. (Illus.). 784p. 1982. 35.95 (ISBN 0-13-250704-8). P-H.
Hodges, David A. & Jackson, Horace G. Analysis & Design of Digital Integrated Circuits. (Series in Electrical Engineering). (Illus.). 448p. 1983. 40.00 (ISBN 0-07-029153-5). McGraw.
Holdsworth. Digital Logic Design. 1981. pap. text ed. 24.95 (ISBN 0-408-00566-1). Butterworth.
Hope, Gordon S. Integrated Devices in Digital Circuit Design. LC 80-17172. 368p. 1981. 43.95x (ISBN 0-471-07920-0, Pub. by Wiley-Interscience). Wiley.
Horn, Delton T. Using Integrated Circuit Logic Devices. (Illus.). 434p. (Orig.). 1984. 21.95 (ISBN 0-8306-0645-9, 1645); pap. 15.50 (ISBN 0-8306-1645-4). TAB Bks.
Hurst, Stanley L., et al. Spectral Techniques in Digital Logic. (Microelectric Signal Processing Techniques Ser.). 1985. 79.50 (ISBN 0-12-362680-3). Acad Pr.
Hyltin, Tom M. It's About Time: The Digital Electronic Watch. (Illus.). 224p. 1984. 21.95 (ISBN 0-317-17088-0). Am Watchmakers.
Institute of Electrical & Electronics Engineers. IEEE Standard Digital Interface for Programmable Instrumentation: IEEE Recommended Practice for Code & Format Conventions for Use with ANSI. 136p. 1983. 18.95 (ISBN 0-471-80786-9). Wiley.
Institute of Electrical & Electronics Engineers, Inc. Digital Signal Processing Committee. Programs in Digital Signal Processing. 576p. 1979. 46.95x (ISBN 0-471-05962-5, Pub. by Wiley-Interscience); pap. 30.50x (ISBN 0-471-05961-7, Pub. by Wiley-Interscience). Wiley.
Joel, J. F., ed. Electronic Switching: Digital Control Office Systems of the World. LC 81-20041. 1981. 35.30 (ISBN 0-87942-159-2, PC01545). Inst Electrical.
Johnson, David E., et al. Digital Circuits & Microcomputers. LC 78-13244. (Illus.). 1979. ref. ed. 33.95 (ISBN 0-13-214015-2). P-H.
Jones, Larry D. Principles & Applications of Digital Electronics. 576p. 1985. text ed. write for info. (ISBN 0-02-361320-3). Macmillan.
Jones, N. B. Digital Signal Processing. (IEE Control Engineering Ser.: No. 5). 490p. 1982. pap. 72.00 (ISBN 0-906048-91-5, CE022). Inst Elect Eng.
Joynson, R. H. Introduction to Digital Electronics & Logic. 192p. 1981. pap. text ed. 13.95 (ISBN 0-7131-3440-2). E Arnold.
Kale, Clyde O. Introduction to Passive, Linear & Digital Electronics. 1984. text ed. 38.95 (ISBN 0-8359-3263-X). Reston.
Kasper, Joseph & Feller, Steven. Digital Integrated Circuits. 197p. 1982. 19.95 (ISBN 0-13-213587-6); pap. 12.95 (ISBN 0-13-213579-5). P-H.
Kershaw, John K. Digital Electronics: Logic & Systems. 2nd ed. 1983. text ed. write for info. (ISBN 0-534-01471-2, Breton Pubs). Wadsworth Pub.
Klousky, D. A. Sequential Transmission of Digital Information. 215p. 1978. 4.95 (ISBN 0-8285-0694-9, Pub. by Mir Pubs USSR). Imported Pubns.
Kostopoulos, George K. Digital Engineering. LC 74-13427. 524p. 1975. 47.50 (ISBN 0-471-50460-2). Krieger.
Kybett, Harry & Martin, Vaughan D. Digital Electronics. LC 83-21589. (Self-Teaching Guide Ser.: 1-581). 248p. (Orig.). 1984. pap. 10.95 (ISBN 0-471-88035-3, Pub. by Wiley Pr). Wiley.
Leach, Donald P. Experiments in Digital Principles. 2nd ed. (Illus.). 176p. 1980. 25.65 (ISBN 0-07-036916-X). McGraw.
Lee, Samuel C. Modern Switching Theory & Digital Design. 1978. ref. 36.95 (ISBN 0-13-598680-X). P-H.
Leigh, J. R. Applied Digital Control: Theory, Design & Implementation. (Illus.). 448p. 1985. text ed. 36.95 (ISBN 0-13-040189-7). P-H.
Lenk, John D. Handbook of Digital Electronics. (Illus.). 384p. 1981. text ed. 27.95 (ISBN 0-13-377184-9). P-H.
Lindquist, Claude S. Adaptive Digital Signal Processing with Signal Filtering Applications. 1986. 34.95 (ISBN 0-317-03339-5). Steward & Sons.
McCurdy, Lyle B. & McHenry, Albert L. Digital Logic Design & Applications: An Experimental Approach. (Illus.). 144p. 1981. pap. text ed. 14.95 (ISBN 0-13-212381-9). P-H.
McDonald, John C., ed. Fundamentals of Digital Switching. (Applications of Communications Theory Ser.). 432p. 1983. 55.00x (ISBN 0-306-41224-1, Plenum Press). Plenum Pub.
McKay, Charles W. Digital Circuits: A Preparation for Microprocessors. LC 77-13058. (Illus.). 1978. ref. 32.95 (ISBN 0-13-212175-1). P-H.
McWhorter, E. W. Understanding Digital Electronics. 2nd ed. LC 84-51467. (The Understanding Ser.). 264p. 1984. pap. 14.95 (ISBN 0-89512-163-8, LCB8471). Tex Instr Inc.
Malvino, A. P. & Leach, D. Digital Principles & Applications. 560p. 1985. price not set (ISBN 0-07-039883-6). McGraw.
Malvino, Albert P. & Leach, Donald P. Digital Principles & Applications. 3rd ed. LC 80-19631. (Illus.). 496p. 1980. text ed. 35.30x (ISBN 0-07-039875-5). McGraw.
--Digital Principles & Applications. 2nd ed. (Illus.). 608p. 1975. text ed. 34.00 (ISBN 0-07-039837-2). McGraw.
Mandl, Matthew. Introduction to Digital Logic Techniques & Systems. LC 82-13337. (Illus.). 201p. 1983. 31.95 (ISBN 0-8359-3175-7). Reston.
Markus, John. Digital Circuits Ready-Reference. (Illus.). 160p. 1982. pap. 12.50 (ISBN 0-07-040457-7). McGraw.
Marston, R. M. One Hundred & Ten CMOS Digital IC Projects. 1976. pap. 7.95 (ISBN 0-8104-0856-2). Hayden.
Middleton, Robert G. Digital Logic Circuits: Tests & Analysis. LC 81-86555. 224p. 1983. pap. 16.95 (ISBN 0-672-21799-6). Sams.
--Understanding Digital Logic Circuits. LC 81-51558. 392p. 1982. pap. 18.95 (ISBN 0-672-21867-4). Sams.
Motil, John. Digital Systems Fundamentals. xx, 490p. 1983. pap. text ed. 20.00x (ISBN 0-917930-65-7). Ridgeview.
Mowle, Frederic J. Systematic Approach to Digital Logic Design. LC 75-18156. (A-W Series in Electrical Engineering). 500p. 1976. text ed. 31.95 (ISBN 0-201-04920-1); solution manual 6.95 (ISBN 0-201-04921-X). Addison-Wesley.
Namgostar, M. Digital Equipment Troubleshooting. (Illus.). 288p. 1977. text ed. 24.95 (ISBN 0-87909-201-7). Reston.
O'Connor, Patrick J. Understanding Digital Electronics: How Microcomputers & Microprocessors Work. LC 83-21206. (Illus.). 266p. 1984. pap. text ed. 14.95 (ISBN 0-13-936964-3). P-H.
Pasahow, Edward J. Learning Digital Electronics Through Experiments. LC 81-2688. (Electro-Skills Ser.). (Illus.). 256p. 1982. pap. 10.15 (ISBN 0-07-048722-7). McGraw.
Porat, Dan I. & Barna, Arpad. Introduction to Digital Techniques. LC 78-17696. (Electronic Technology Ser.). 527p. 1979. 31.95 (ISBN 0-471-02924-6); solutions manual 3.00 (ISBN 0-471-04351-6). Wiley.
Primer on Integrated Services Digital Networks (ISDN) Implications for Future Global Communications. 1983. 75.00 (ISBN 0-317-11976-1). Info Gatekeepers.
Putman, Byron W. Digital Electronics: Theory, Applications & Troubleshooting. (Illus.). 320p. 1986. text ed. 31.95 (ISBN 0-13-212481-5). P-H.
Rabiner, Lawrence R. & Gold, Bernard. Theory & Application of Digital Signal Processing. (Illus.). 720p. 1975. ref. ed. 38.95 (ISBN 0-13-914101-4). P-H.
Rabiner, Lawrence R. & Schafer, Ronald W. Digital Processing of Speech Signals. (P-H Signal Processing Ser.). 1978. ref. ed. 41.95 (ISBN 0-13-213603-1). P-H.
Robinson, Enders A. & Silvia, Manuel T. Digital Signal Processing & Time Series Analysis. 1978. 34.00x (ISBN 0-8162-7264-6). Holden-Day.
Rohde, Ulrich L. Digital PLL Frequency Synthesizers: Theory & Design. (Illus.). 608p. 1983. text ed. 51.95 (ISBN 0-13-214239-2). P-H.
Rutkowski, George B. & Oleksy, Jerome. Fundamentals of Digital Electronics: A Text Laboratory Manual. 2nd ed. (Illus.). 288p. 1985. text ed. 27.95 (ISBN 0-13-336132-2). P-H.
Ryan, Ray. Basic Digital Electronics: Understanding Number Systems, Boolean Algebra & Logical Circuits. LC 74-14326. (Illus.). 1975. pap. 8.95 (ISBN 0-8306-3728-1, 728). TAB Bks.
Sacks, Richard D., et al. Simplified Circuit Analysis: Digital-Analog Logic. LC 79-179386. (Illus.). pap. 43.50 (ISBN 0-317-08020-2, 2017857). Bks Demand UMI.
Sifferlen, Thomas P. & Vartanian, Vartan. Digital Electronics with Engineering Applications. (Electrical Engineering Ser). 1970. ref. ed. 36.95 (ISBN 0-13-214304-6). P-H.
Smith, David R. Digital Transmission Systems. (Engineering). (Illus.). 560p. 1984. 48.00 (ISBN 0-534-03382-2). Lifetime Learn.
Smith, Dean L. Advanced Digital Electronics. 2nd, rev. ed. (Illus.). 260p. (Orig.). 1984. pap. text ed. 30.00x (ISBN 0-918699-00-2). D L Smith.
Stearns, Sam D. Digital Signal Analysis. 288p. 1975. text ed. 31.95 (ISBN 0-8104-5828-4). Hayden.
Stein, David H. Introduction to Digital Data Communications. LC 84-20072. 320p. 1985. pap. text ed. 30.00 (ISBN 0-8273-2436-7); instr's. guide 6.80 (ISBN 0-8273-2437-5). Delmar.
Storr, Eric D. Measurement, Instrumentation & Digital Technology. 250p. 1984. pap. text ed. 30.00x (ISBN 0-85825-216-3, Pub. by Inst Engineers Australia). Brookfield Pub Co.
Strangio, Christopher E. Digital Electronics: Fundamental Concepts & Applications. (Illus.). 1980. text ed. 34.95 (ISBN 0-13-212100-X). P-H.
Taub, Herbert. Digital Circuits & Microprocessors. (Electrical Engineering Ser.). (Illus.). 608p. 1981. text ed. 41.95 (ISBN 0-07-062945-5). McGraw.
Taub, Herbert & Schilling, Donald. Digital Integrated Electronics. (E & EE). (Illus.). 1976. text ed. 42.00 (ISBN 0-07-062921-8). McGraw.
Tocci, Ronald J. Digital Systems: Principles & Applications. 3rd ed. (Illus.). 496p. 1985. text ed. 34.95 (ISBN 0-13-212374-6). P-H.
--Fundamentals of Pulse & Digital Circuits. 3rd ed. 1983. text ed. 27.95 (ISBN 0-675-20033-4). Additional supplements may be obtained from publisher. Merrill.
Tokheim, R. L. Digital Electronics. 2nd ed. 256p. 1984. 18.08 (ISBN 0-07-064980-4). McGraw.
Tokheim, Roger. Digital Electronics. Schuler, Charles A., ed. (Basic Skills in Electricity & Electronics Ser). (Illus.). 1979. pap. text ed. 18.06 (ISBN 0-07-064954-5). McGraw.
Tokheim, Roger L. Schaum's Outline of Digital Principles. (Illus., Orig.). 1980. pap. 8.95 (ISBN 0-07-064928-6). McGraw.
Triebel, Walter A. Integrated Digital Electronics. 2nd ed. (Illus.). 448p. 1985. pap. text ed. 31.95 (ISBN 0-13-469172-5). P-H.
Uzunoglu, Vasil. Analysis & Design of Digital Systems. 520p. 1975. 106.50x (ISBN 0-677-04100-4). Gordon.
Vassos, B. H. & Ewing, C. W. Analog & Digital Electronics for Scientists. 3rd ed. 448p. 1985. 35.00 (ISBN 0-471-81138-6). Wiley.
Wakerly, John. Logic Design Projects Using Standard Integrated Circuits. LC 76-5471. 203p. 1976. pap. 21.95 (ISBN 0-471-91705-2). Wiley.
Ward, Dennis M. Applied Digital Electronics. 408p. 1981. text ed. 26.95 (ISBN 0-675-09925-0). Additional supplements may be obtained from publisher. Merrill.
Warring, R. H. Understanding Digital Electronics. 128p. 1982. 39.00x (ISBN 0-7188-2521-7, Pub. by Lutterworth Pr England). State Mutual Bk.
--Understanding Digital Electronics. (Illus.). 154p. (Orig.). 1984. 13.95 (ISBN 0-8306-0193-7); pap. 7.95 (ISBN 0-8306-0593-2, 1593). TAB Bks.
Williams, Gerald E. Digital Technology. 2nd ed. 512p. 1981. text ed. 26.95 (ISBN 0-574-21555-7, 13-4555); instr. guide avail. (ISBN 0-574-21556-5, 13-4556); lab manual 15.95 (ISBN 0-574-21557-3, 13-4557). SRA.
Woolvet, G. A. Transducers in Digital Systems. rev. ed. (IEE Control Engineering Ser.: No. 3). (Illus.). 201p. 1979. pap. 26.00 (ISBN 0-906048-13-3, CE003). Inst Elect Eng.
Young, George. Digital Electronics: A Hands-on Learning Approach. 1980. pap. 9.95 (ISBN 0-8104-5668-0). Hayden.
Young, George & Stark, Peter. Kilobaud Klassroom: A Course in Digital Electronics. Crocker, Chris, et al, eds. 419p. (Orig.). 1982. pap. text ed. 14.95 (ISBN 0-88006-027-1, BK 7386). Green Pub Inc.

DIGITAL FILTERS (MATHEMATICS)

Antoniou, Andreas. Digital Filters: Analysis & Design. (Electrical Engineering Ser.). (Illus.). 1979. text ed. 46.00 (ISBN 0-07-002117-1). McGraw.
Bierman, Gerald J. Factorization Methods for Discrete Sequential Estimation. 1977. 42.50 (ISBN 0-12-097350-2). Acad Pr.
Bogner, R. E. & Constantinides, A. G., eds. Introduction to Digital Filtering. LC 74-4924. 198p. 1975. 45.95 (ISBN 0-471-08590-1, Pub. by Wiley-Interscience). Wiley.
Bose, Nirmal. Digital Filters: Theory & Applications. price not set. Elsevier.
Bozic, S. M. Digital & Kalman Filtering: An Introduction to Discrete - Time Filtering & Optimum Linear Estimation. 157p. 1980. pap. 26.95x (ISBN 0-470-26924-3). Halsted Pr.
Cappallini, V., et al. Digital Filters & Their Applications. (Techniques of Physics Ser.). 1979. 69.50 (ISBN 0-12-159250-2). Acad Pr.
Childers, Donald G. & Durling, Allen E. Digital Filtering & Signal Processing. LC 75-8776. (Illus.). 539p. 1975. text ed. 38.95 (ISBN 0-8299-0056-X). West Pub.
DeVore, Ronald A. & Sharpley, Robert C. Maximal Functions Measuring Smoothness. LC 83-21494. (Memoirs Ser.: No. 293). 116p. 1984. pap. 11.00 (ISBN 0-8218-2293-4). Am Math.
Hamming, Richard W. Digital Filters. (Illus.). 304p. 1983. 35.95 (ISBN 0-13-212506-4). P-H.
Hralick, R. M. & Simon, J. C., eds. Issues in Digital Image Processing. LC 80-50682. (NATO Advanced Study Institute Ser.: No. 34). 356p. 1980. 40.75x (ISBN 90-286-0460-X). Sijthoff & Noordhoff.
Huang, T. S. Picture Processing & Digital Filtering. LC 75-5770. (Illus.). 270p. 1979. 26.00 (ISBN 0-387-09339-7). Springer-Verlag.
Huang, T. S., ed. Two-Dimensional Digital Signal Processing I: Linear Filters. (Topics in Applied Physics Ser.: Vol. 42). (Illus.). 1981. 50.00 (ISBN 0-387-10359-7). Springer-Verlag.
Liddell, Heather. Computer-Aided Techniques for the Design of Multilayer Filters. 1981. 49.00 (ISBN 0-9960020-2-2, Pub. by A Hilger England). Heyden.
Mesko, A. Fundamentals of Digital Filtering with Applications in Geophysical Prospecting for Oil. LC 83-5835. 512p. 1984. 69.95x (ISBN 0-470-27444-1). Halsted Pr.
Nussbaumer, H. Fast Fourier Transform & Convolution Algorithms. 2nd ed. (Springer Series in Information Sciences). (Illus.). 280p. 1982. pap. 31.00 (ISBN 0-387-11825-X). Springer-Verlag.
Robinson, Enders A. Digital Seismic Inverse Methods. 431p. 1984. 55.00 (ISBN 0-934634-69-6). Intl Human Res.
Sedra, Adel & Brackett, Peter. Filter Theory & Design: Active & Passive. (Illus.). 800p. 1978. 34.95 (ISBN 0-916460-14-2). Matrix Pub.

Crosskey, R. W., ed. Catalogue of the Diptera of the Afrotropical Region. 1437p. 1980. 124.00x (ISBN 0-565-00821-8, Pub. by Brit Mus Nat Hist England). Sabbot-Natural Hist Bks.
Davies, Lewis. A Key to the British Species of Simulidae (Diptera) in the Larval, Pupal & Adult Stages. 1968. 20.00x (ISBN 0-900386-12-6, Pub. by Freshwater Bio). State Mutual Bk.
Delfinado, Mercedes D. & Hardy, D. Elmo. A Catalog of the Diptera of the Oriental Region, Vol. 3. LC 74-174544. 1977. text ed. 40.00x (ISBN 0-8248-0346-9). UH Pr.
--Catalog of the Diptera of the Oriental Region, Vol. 1: Suborder Nematocera. LC 74-174544. 350p. 1973. text ed. 30.00x (ISBN 0-8248-0205-5). UH Pr.
--A Catalog of the Diptera of the Oriental Region, Vol. 2: Suborder Brachycera, Suborder Cyclorrhapha Through Division Aschiza. LC 74-174544. 480p. 1975. text ed. 30.00x (ISBN 0-8248-0274-8). UH Pr.
Disney, R. H. A Key to the Larvae, Pupae & Adults of the British Dixidae (Diptera) 1975. 20.00x (ISBN 0-900386-23-1, Pub. by Freshwater Bio). State Mutual Bk.
Fabricius, J. C. Systema Antialorum, Secundum Ordines, Genera, Species. 1970. Repr. of 1805 ed. 26.75 (ISBN 90-6123-060-8). Lubrecht & Cramer.
Greene, Joseph. Pupa Digging. 1984. 25.00x (ISBN 0-317-07171-8, Pub. by FW Classey UK). State Mutual Bk.
Hall, Jack C. A Review of the North & Central American Species of Paravilla Painter (Diptera--Bombyliidae) (U. C. Publications in Entomology Ser.: Vol. 92). 192p. 1981. 15.00x (ISBN 0-520-09625-8). U of Cal Pr.
Holland, D. G. A Key to the Larvae, Pupae & Adults of the British Species of Elminthidae. 1972. 20.00x (ISBN 0-900386-16-9, Pub. by Freshwater Bio). State Mutual Bk.
Johannsen, Oskar A. Aquatic Diptera. LC 78-7782. (Illus.). 370p. 1969. 17.50 (ISBN 0-911836-01-2). Entomological Repr.
Manual of Nearctic Diptera, Vol. 1. (Monograph Ser.: No. 27). 674p. 1981. 74.25 (ISBN 0-660-10731-7, SSC166, SSC). Unipub.
Middlekauff, Woodrow W. & Lane, Robert S. Adult & Immature Tabanidae (Diptera) of California. (Bulletin of the California Insect Survey Ser.: Vol. 22). 1980. pap. 17.00x (ISBN 0-520-09604-5). U of Cal Pr.
Nearctic & Palaearctic Heterotrissocladius (Diptera: Chironomidae) 1975. pap. 6.50 (SSC64, SSC). Unipub.
Peterson, Alvah. The Head-Capsule & Mouth-Parts of Diptera. (Illus.). Repr. of 1916 ed. 12.00 (ISBN 0-384-45920-X). Johnson Repr.
Pinder, L. C. A Key to the Adult Males of the British Chironomidae (Diptera) 1978. 25.00x (ISBN 0-900386-32-0, Pub. by Freshwater Bio). State Mutual Bk.
Roback, Selwyn S. The Adults of the Subfamily Tanypodinae (Pelopiinae) in North America: Diptera: Chironomidae. (Monograph: No. 17). (Illus.). 410p. (Orig.). 1970. pap. 27.00 (ISBN 0-910006-25-3). Acad Nat Sci Phila.
Rozkosny, R. A Biosystematic Study of the European Stratiomyidae (Diptera) 1982. lib. bdg. 79.50 (ISBN 90-6193-132-0, Pub. by Junk Pubs Netherlands). Kluwer Academic.
Soos, A. & Papp, L. Clusiidae-Chloropidae. (Catalogue of Palaearctic Diptera Ser.: Vol. 10). 1984. 102.00 (ISBN 0-444-99601-X). Elsevier.
--Micropezidae-Agromyzidae. (Catalogue of Palaearctic Diptera Ser.: Vol. 9). 1984. 102.00 (ISBN 0-444-99602-8). Elsevier.
Soos, A. & Papp, L., eds. Catalogue of Palaearctic Diptera, Vols. 9 & 10. 1984. 106.00 ea. Vol. 9, Micropezidae-Agromyzidae. Vol. 10, Clusiidae-Chloropidae. Elsevier.
Stone, Alan, et al, eds. A Catalog of the Diptera of America North of Mexico. 2nd printing ed. 1700p. 1983. Repr. of 1965 ed. text ed. 37.50x (ISBN 0-87474-890-9). Smithsonian.
Stubbs, A. E. & Chandler, P. J. A Dipterist's Handbook. 260p. 60.00 (ISBN 0-686-75582-0, Pub. by Amateur Entomol Soc). State Mutual Bk.
Theodor, Oskar. Diptera: Asilidae Insecta II. (Fauna Palaestina Ser.: No. 2). (Illus.). 448p. 1981. text ed. 40.00x (ISBN 0-87474-910-7, Pub. by the Israel Academy of Sciences & Humanities). Smithsonian.
--Diptera: Pupipara. (Insecta I Fauna Palaestina Ser.: No. 1). (Illus.). 169p. 1975. 30.00x (ISBN 0-87474-912-3, Pub. by the Israel Academy of Sciences & Humanities). Smithsonian.
--An Illustrated Catalogue of the Rothschild Collection of Nycteribiidae (Diptera) in the British Museum (Natural History) (Illus.). viii, 506p. 1967. 76.00x (ISBN 0-565-00655-X, Pub. by British Mus Nat Hist England). Sabbot-Natural Hist Bks.
White, R. S., et al. Diptera: Family Calliphoridae, Vol. 6. (Fauna of British India Ser.). (Illus.). xiv, 294p. 1977. Repr. of 1940 ed. 30.00 (ISBN 0-88065-210-1, Pub. by Messers Today & Tomorrows Printers & Publishers India). Scholarly Pubns.
Williams, C. B. & Nijveldt, W., eds. Gall Midges of Economic Importance: Miscellaneous, Vol. 8. 221p. 1969. 40.00x (ISBN 0-317-07067-3, Pub. by EW Classey UK). State Mutual Bk.
Wirth, Willis W. & Atchley, William R. A Review of the North American Leptoconops (Diptera: Ceratopogonidae) (Graduate Studies: No. 5). (Illus.). 57p. (Orig.). 1973. pap. 3.00 (ISBN 0-89672-012-8). Tex Tech Pr.

DIRECT CURRENT MACHINERY
see Electric Machinery–Direct Current

DIRECT CURRENTS
see Electric Currents, Direct

DIRECT ENERGY CONVERSION
see also Controlled Fusion; Fuel Cells; Ion Rockets; Nuclear Rockets; Photoelectric Cells; Plasma Rockets; Solar Batteries; Thermionic Emission; Thermoelectric Apparatus and Appliances

AGARD-NATO. Combustion & Propulsion: Colloquium on Energy Sources & Energy Conversion. (Agardographs Ser.: No. 81). 936p. 1967. 236.95 (ISBN 0-677-10560-6). Gordon.
Bailie, Richard C. Energy Conversion Engineering. LC 78-11969. (Series of Graduate Textbooks, Monographs & Research Papers). (Illus.). 1978. text ed. 45.95 (ISBN 0-201-00840-8). Addison-Wesley.
Brown, David. Electromechanical Energy Conversion. (Illus.). 624p. 1984. text ed. write for info. (ISBN 0-02-315590-6). Macmillan.
Buckmaster, J. D., ed. Fluid Mechanics in Energy Conversion. LC 80-65817. (SIAM-SIMS Conference Ser.: No. 7). ix, 315p. 1980. pap. 31.00 (ISBN 0-89871-165-7). Soc Indus-Appl Math.
Energy for the Marketplace, Intersociety Energy Conversion Engineering Conference, 18th, August 21-26, 1983, Orlando, Florida, 5 vols. 1983. text ed. 165.00 set (ISBN 0-317-03771-4); text ed. 140.00 set members (ISBN 0-317-03772-2). AM Inst Chem Eng.
Environmental Engineering: 1979. 840p. 1979. pap. 48.00x (ISBN 0-317-03698-X). Am Soc Civil Eng.
Grabiel, Federico. Theory of Energy Transfers & Conversions. LC 67-23440. (Illus.). pap. 57.80 (ISBN 0-317-07883-6, 2006350). Bks Demand UMI.
Hanley, Wayne & Mitchell, John, eds. The Energy Book: A Non-Technical Approach to the Issues. LC 79-26295. (Illus.). 192p. 1980. 11.95 (ISBN 0-8289-0379-4). Greene.
Hoffman, E. J. Coal Conversion. LC 77-93533. (Illus.). 464p. 1978. 65.00x (ISBN 0-9601552-1-X). Energon Co.
International Conference on Energetics (1965: University of Rochester) Engineering Developments in Energy Conversion. LC 66-1330. pap. 82.80 (ISBN 0-317-10000-9, 2016820). Bks Demand UMI.
International Solvent Extraction Conference, Denver, Colorado, August 26th to September 2, 1983: Proceedings. 559p. 1983. pap. 80.00 (ISBN 0-8169-0254-2, P-37); pap. 60.00 members (ISBN 0-317-03770-6). Am Inst Chem Eng.
Intersociety Energy Conversion Engineering Conference Proceedings, 16th, 3 vols. 2608p. 1981. Set. 165.00 (H00179). ASME.
Levine, Sumner N., ed. Selected Papers on New Techniques for Energy Conversion. 11.25 (ISBN 0-8446-2460-8). Peter Smith.
Miley, George H. Direct Conversion of Nuclear Radiation Energy. LC 70-155742. (ANS Monographs). 532p. 1970. 34.90 (ISBN 0-89448-004-9, 300003). Am Nuclear Soc.
Sorensen, Harry A. Energy Conversion Systems. LC 82-20076. 563p. 1983. text ed. 45.00 (ISBN 0-471-08872-2); solution manual (ISBN 0-471-87156-7). Wiley.
Spring, Kenneth H., ed. Direct Generation of Electricity. 1966. 69.00 (ISBN 0-12-659550-X). Acad Pr.
Symposium on Electrode Materials & Processes for Energy Conversion & Storage (1977: Philadelphia) Electrode Materials & Processess for Energy Conversion & Storage: Nineteen Seventy-Seven Proceedings of the Symposium. Srinivasan, S., et al, eds. LC 77-79769. (Illus.). pap. 160.00 (ISBN 0-317-09184-0, 2050186). Bks Demand UMI.

DIRECTION, SENSE OF
see Orientation

DIRICHLET'S SERIES
see Series, Dirichlet's

DIRIGIBLE BALLOONS
see Air-Ships

DISCOMYCETES

Le Gal, M. Recherches Sur les Ornementations Sporales Des Discomycetes Opercules. 1970. Repr. of 1947 ed. 14.00 (ISBN 3-7682-0694-7). Lubrecht & Cramer.
Seaver, F. J. North American Cup Fungi: Inoperculates, Vol. 2. 1978. Repr. of 1951 ed. lib. bdg. 28.00x (ISBN 3-7682-1175-4). Lubrecht & Cramer.
--North American Cup Fungi: Operculates, Vol. 1. 1978. Repr. of 1942 ed. lib. bdg. 28.00x (ISBN 3-7682-1174-6). Lubrecht & Cramer.
Tylutki, Edmund E. Mushrooms of Idaho & the Pacific Northwest (Discomycetes) LC 79-64127. (GEM Books-Natural History). (Illus.). 166p. (Orig.). 1979. pap. 6.95 (ISBN 0-89301-062-6). U Pr of Idaho.

DISCOVERIES (IN SCIENCE)
see Industrial Arts; Inventions; Patents; Science

DISCOVERY (SHIP)

Scott, Robert F. Voyage of the Discovery, 2 Vols. LC 68-55218. (Illus.). 1969. Repr. of 1905 ed. Set. lib. bdg. 57.00x (ISBN 0-8371-1334-2, SCDI). Greenwood.

DISCRETE GROUPS

Grimaldi, Ralph P. & Rose-Hulman. Discrete & Combinatorial Mathematics. LC 84-9359. 1985. text ed. 32.95 (ISBN 0-201-12590-0). Addison-Wesley.
Howe, ed. Discrete Groups: Papers Honoring G. D. Moston on the Occassion of his 60th Birthday. (Progress in Mathematics Ser.). 1985. text ed. write for info. (ISBN 0-8176-3301-4). Birkhauser.
Polimeni, Albert D. & Straight, H. Joseph. Foundations of Discrete Mathematics. LC 84-23309. (Mathematics Ser.). 400p. 1985. text ed. 24.00 pub net (ISBN 0-534-03612-0). Brooks-Cole.
Pouzet, M. & Richard, D. Orders: Descriptions & Roles. (Mathematical Studies, No. 99; Annals of Discrete Mathematics: No. 23). 1984. 69.00 (ISBN 0-444-87601-4, North-Holland). Elsevier.
Ross, Kenneth & Wright, Charles. Discrete Mathematics. (Illus.). 672p. 1985. text ed. 32.95 (ISBN 0-13-215286-X). P-H.
Trombi, Peter C., ed. Representation Theory of Reductive Groups. (Progress in Mathematics). 1983. text ed. 24.95 (ISBN 0-8176-3135-6). Birkhauser.

DISCRETE MATHEMATICS
see Electronic Data Processing–Mathematics

DISCRETE TIME SYSTEMS
see also Feedback Control Systems

Ahmed, Nasir & Natarajan, T. Discrete Time Systems & Signals. 1983. text ed. 33.95 (ISBN 0-8359-1375-9); solutions manual incl. (ISBN 0-8359-1376-7). Reston.
Banks, Jerry & Carson, John. Discrete Event System Simulation. (Illus.). 560p. 1984. professional 24.95 (ISBN 0-13-215582-6). P-H.
Bishop, Albert B. Introduction to Discrete-Linear Controls: Theory & Applications. (Operations Research & Industrial Engineering Ser.). 1975. 70.00 (ISBN 0-12-101650-1). Acad Pr.
Boltianskii, Vladimir G. Optimal Control of Discrete Systems. LC 78-67814. 392p. 1978. 89.95x (ISBN 0-470-26530-2). Halsted Pr.
Brulin, O. & Hsieh, R. K., eds. Continuum Models of Discrete Systems. 520p. 1981. 72.50 (ISBN 0-444-86309-5, North-Holland). Elsevier.
Cadzow, James A. Discrete Time Systems: An Introduction with Interdisciplinary Applications. (Computer Applications in Electrical Engineering Ser.). (Illus.). 448p. 1973. ref. ed. 39.95 (ISBN 0-13-215996-1). P-H.
Cadzow, James A. & Martens, Hinrich R. Discrete Time & Computer Control Systems. (Electrical Engineering Ser.). 1970. ref. ed. 39.95 (ISBN 0-13-216036-6). P-H.
Cuenod, M. & Durling, A. Discrete-Time Approach for System Analysis. (Electrical Science Ser.). 1969. 60.00 (ISBN 0-12-198550-4). Acad Pr.
Freeman, Herbert. Discrete-Time Systems. LC 80-15357. 256p. 1980. Repr. of 1965 ed. lib. bdg. 19.25 (ISBN 0-89874-228-5). Krieger.
Goessel, M. Nonlinear Time-Discrete Systems: A General Approach by Nonlinear Superposition. (Lecture Notes in Control & Information Science: Vol. 41). 112p. 1982. pap. 10.00 (ISBN 0-387-11914-0). Springer-Verlag.
Hinderer, Karl. Foundations of Non-Stationary Dynamic Programming with Discrete Time Parameter. (Lecture Notes in Operations Research & Mathematical Systems: Vol. 33). 1970. pap. 10.70 (ISBN 0-387-04956-8). Springer-Verlag.
Jong, M. T. Methods of Discrete Signal & System Analysis. 1982. 42.00 (ISBN 0-07-033025-5). McGraw.
Lucas, W. F., et al, eds. Modules in Applied Mathematics, Vol. 3: Discrete & System Models. (Illus.). 353p. 1983. 29.50 (ISBN 0-387-90724-6). Springer-Verlag.
Mahmoud, M. S., et al. Discrete Systems: Analysis, Control & Optimization. (Communications & Control Engineering Ser.). (Illus.). 690p. 1984. 49.50 (ISBN 0-387-13645-2). Springer-Verlag.
Mayhan, Robert J. Discrete-Time & Continuous-Time Linear Systems. LC 83-5999. (Electrical Engineering Ser.). (Illus.). 640p. 1983. 38.95 (ISBN 0-201-05596-1); solutions manual 7.50 (ISBN 0-201-05597-X). Addison-Wesley.
Moroney, Paul. Issues in the Implementation of Digital Feedback Compensators. (Signal Processing, Optimization & Control Ser.). (Illus.). 224p. 1983. 35.00x (ISBN 0-262-13185-4). MIT Pr.
Nahorski, Z., et al. Optimization of Discrete Time Systems: The Upper Boundary Approach. (Lecture Notes in Control & Information Sciences Ser.: Vol. 51). 137p. 1983. pap. 11.00 (ISBN 0-387-12258-3). Springer-Verlag.
Sontag, E. D. Polynomial Response Maps. (Lecture Notes in Control & Information Sciences: Vol. 13). 1979. pap. 14.00 (ISBN 0-387-09393-1). Springer-Verlag.
Steiglitz, Kenneth. An Introduction to Discrete Systems. LC 73-6820. 318p. 1974. 40.00 (ISBN 0-471-82097-0); 8.00 (ISBN 0-471-82103-9). Wiley.
Tretter, Steven A. Introduction to Discrete-Time Signal Processing. LC 76-25943. 460p. 1976. text ed. 46.50x (ISBN 0-471-88760-9). Wiley.
Vidal, P. Non-Linear Sampled Data Systems - Exercises & Problems. (Information & Systems Theory Ser.). 112p. 1972. 37.25x (ISBN 0-677-30500-1). Gordon.
--Nonlinear Sampled-Data Systems. (Information & Systems Theory Ser). 362p. 1969. 93.75x (ISBN 0-677-30230-4). Gordon.
--Systemes Echantillonnes Nonlineaires. (Theorie des Systemes Ser.). (Fr.). 378p. 1968. 93.75x (ISBN 0-677-50230-3). Gordon.
--Systems Echantillonnes Nonlineaires-Exercises et Problemes: Exercises et Problemes. (Theorie des Systemes Ser.). (Fr.). 124p. 1970. 40.50 (ISBN 0-677-50500-0). Gordon.

DISEASE RESISTANCE OF PLANTS
see Plants–Disease and Pest Resistance

DISEASES OF PLANTS
see Plant Diseases

DISINFECTION AND DISINFECTANTS
see also Air–Purification; Formaldehyde; Hydrazene; Sterilization

Benarde, Melvin A., ed. Disinfection. 1970. 85.00 (ISBN 0-8247-1040-1). Dekker.
Block, Seymor S., ed. Disinfection, Sterilization & Preservation. 3rd ed. LC 82-24002. (Illus.). 1053p. 1983. text ed. 87.50 (ISBN 0-8121-0863-9). Lea & Febiger.
Collins, C. H., et al, eds. Disinfectants: Their Use & Evaluation of Effectiveness. (Society for Applied Bacteriology Technical Ser.: No. 16). 1981. 45.00 (ISBN 0-12-181380-0). Acad Pr.
Fochtman, Edward G., et al, eds. Forum on Ozone Disinfection. LC 76-51563. 1977. text ed. 18.00 (ISBN 0-918650-01-1); text ed. 25.00 non-members (ISBN 0-918650-00-3). Intl Ozone.
Russell, A. D., et al. Principles & Practice of Disinfection: Preservation & Sterilization. (Illus.). 653p. 1982. text ed. 65.00 (ISBN 0-632-00547-5, B 4228-0). Mosby.

DISK RECORDING
see Sound–Recording and Reproducing

DISKS (MECHANICS)
see Plates (Engineering)

DISKS, MAGNETIC
see Magnetic Disks

DISLOCATIONS IN CRYSTALS
see also Color Centers; Dislocations in Metals; Strengthening Mechanisms in Solids

Amelinckx, S. The Direct Observation of Dislocations. (Solid State Physics Ser.: Suppl. 6). 1964. 75.00 (ISBN 0-12-607766-5). Acad Pr.
Bollmann, W. Crystal Defects & Crystalline Interfaces. LC 77-124069. (Illus.). 1970. 69.00 (ISBN 0-387-05057-4). Springer-Verlag.
Cottrell, A. H. Theory of Crystal Dislocations. (Documents on Modern Physics Ser.). 104p. 1964. pap. 27.95 (ISBN 0-677-00175-4). Gordon.
Hull, Derek. Introduction to Dislocations. 3rd ed. text ed. 36.00 (ISBN 0-08-028721-2). Pergamon.
Klassen-Neklyudova, M. V. Mechanical Twinning of Crystals. LC 63-17638. 213p. 1964. 30.00x (ISBN 0-306-10551-9, Consultants). Plenum Pub.
Klassen-Neklyudova, M. V., ed. Plasticity of Crystals. LC 62-12853. 196p. 1962. 30.00x (ISBN 0-306-10580-2, Consultants). Plenum Pub.
Kovacs, T. & Zsoldos, L. Dislocations & Plastic Deformations. LC 73-6995. 364p. 1974. 28.00 (ISBN 0-08-017062-5). Pergamon.
Lardner, R. W. Mathematical Theory of Dislocations & Fracture. LC 75-190346. (Mathematical Expositions Ser.: No. 17). pap. 93.80 (ISBN 0-317-09423-8, 2020498). Bks Demand UMI.
Mura, Toshio, ed. Mathematical Theory of Dislocations. LC 70-88019. pap. 53.80 (ISBN 0-317-08725-8, 2004722). Bks Demand UMI.

Patel & Read. Handbook of the Normal Distribution. (Statistics - Textbooks & Monographs: Vol. 40). 352p. 1982. 45.00 (ISBN 0-8247-1541-1). Dekker.
Patel, J. K., et al. Handbook of Statistical Distributions. (Statistics: Textbooks & Monographs: Vol. 20). 1976. pap. 49.75 (ISBN 0-8247-7202-4). Dekker.
Reichenbach, Hans. The Theory of Probability: An Inquiry into the Logical & Mathematical Foundations of the Calculus of Probability. (California Library Reprint Series: No. 23). 1971. 42.50x (ISBN 0-520-01929-6). U of Cal Pr.
Scheaffer, R. L. & Mendenhall, Wm. Introduction to Probability: Theory & Applications. LC 75-3562. 1975. text ed. 14.95x (ISBN 0-87872-084-7, Duxbury Pr). PWS Pubs.
Steklov Institute of Mathematics, Academy of Sciences, U S S R, No. 108, 1968. Infinite-Dimensional Gaussian Distributions: Proceedings. Rozanov, J. A., ed. (Proceedings of the Steklov Institute of Mathematics: No. 108). 1971. 27.00 (ISBN 0-8218-3008-2, STEKLO-108). Am Math.
Tapia, Richard A. & Thompson, James R. Nonparametric Probability Density Estimation. LC 77-17249. (Illus.). 1978. text ed. 22.00x (ISBN 0-8018-2031-6). Johns Hopkins.

DISTRIBUTION OF GOODS, PHYSICAL
see Physical Distribution of Goods

DISTRIBUTION OF VALUES THEORY
see Value Distribution Theory

DISTRIBUTIONS, THEORY OF (FUNCTIONAL ANALYSIS)
The Applications of Generalized Functions: Studies in Applied Mathematics 2. v, 183p. 1967. text ed. 15.50 (ISBN 0-89871-046-4). Soc Indus-Appl Math.
Baer, Donald M. How to Plan for Generalization. 36p. 1981. 5.00 (ISBN 0-89079-061-2). Pro Ed.
Barros-Neto, Jose. An Introduction to the Theory of Distributions. LC 80-11323. 234p. 1981. Repr. of 1973 ed. lib. bdg. 16.50 (ISBN 0-89874-128-9). Krieger.
Beltrami, E. J. & Wohlers, M. R. Distributions & the Boundary Values of Analytic Functions. 1966. 29.00 (ISBN 0-12-085550-X). Acad Pr.
Challifour, John L. Generalized Functions & Fourier Analysis: An Introduction. (Math Lecture Notes Ser.: No. 49). 188p. 1972. 16.95 (ISBN 0-8053-1875-5, Adv Bk Prog). Benjamin-Cummings.
Colombeau, J. F. Elementary Introduction to New Generalized Functions. (Mathematics Studies: Vol. 113). 290p. 1985. 44.50 (ISBN 0-444-87756-8, North Holland). Elsevier.
--New Generalized Functions & Multiplication of Distributions. (Mathematics Studies: No. 84). 376p. 1984. 38.50 (ISBN 0-444-86830-5, North-Holland). Elsevier.
Durbin, J. Distribution Theory for Tests Based on the Sample Distribution Function. (CBMS-NSF Regional Conference Ser.: No. 9). (Orig.). 1973. pap. text ed. 8.00 (ISBN 0-89871-007-3). Soc Indus-Appl Math.
Ehrenpreis, Leon. Theory of Distributions for Locally Compact Spaces. LC 52-42839. (Memoirs: No. 21). 80p. 1982. pap. 14.00 (ISBN 0-8218-1221-1, MEMO-21). Am Math.
Friedlander, F. G. Introduction to the Theory of Distributions. LC 82-4504. 150p. 1983. 37.50 (ISBN 0-521-24300-9); pap. 15.95 (ISBN 0-521-28591-7). Cambridge U Pr.
Halperin, Israel. Introduction to the Theory of Distributions. LC 53-6659. (Canadian Mathematical Congress Lecture Ser.: No. 1). pap. 20.00 (ISBN 0-317-08548-4, 214232). Bks Demand UMI.
Hoermander, L. The Analysis of Linear Partial Differential Operators I: Distribution Theory & Fourier Analysis. (Grundlehren der Mathematischen Wissenschaften: Vol. 256). (Illus.). 380p. 1983. 39.00 (ISBN 0-387-12104-8). Springer-Verlag.
Hoskins, R. F. Generalised Functions. LC 79-40995. (Mathematics & Its Applications Ser.). 192p. 1980. 58.95x (ISBN 0-470-26608-2). Halsted Pr.
Kolmogorov, A. N. & Fomin, S. V. Elements of the Theory of Functions & Functional Analysis, 2 vols. Incl. Vol. 1. Metric & Normed Spaces. LC 57-14021. 1957 (ISBN 0-910670-06-4); Vol. 2. Measure, the Lebesue Integral, Hilbert Space. 1961 (ISBN 0-910670-07-2). LC 57-14021. 10.50x ea. Graylock.
Lieberman, Gerald J. & Owen, Donald B. Tables of the Hypergeometric Probability Distribution. 1961. 45.00x (ISBN 0-8047-0057-5). Stanford U Pr.
Luetzen, J. The Prehistory of the Theory of Distributions. (Studies in the History of Mathematics & Physical Sciences: Vol. 7). (Illus.). 232p. 1982. 48.00 (ISBN 0-387-90647-9). Springer-Verlag.
Medgyessy, Pal. Decomposition of Superpositions of Distribution Functions. 227p. 1961. 27.50x (ISBN 0-306-30119-9, Plenum Pr). Plenum Pub.
Shilov, George E., ed. Generalized Functions & Partial Differential Equations. rev. ed. Seckler, B., tr. LC 67-28235. (Mathematics & Its Applications Ser.). 358p. 1968. 68.25x (ISBN 0-677-20660-7). Gordon.
Treves, Francois. Topological Vector Spaces, Distributions & Kernels. 1967. 79.50 (ISBN 0-12-699450-1). Acad Pr.

DISTRICT HEATING
see Heating From Central Stations

DIURNAL RHYTHMS
see Circadian Rhythms

DIVERSIFICATION IN INDUSTRY
Biggadike, E. Ralph. Corporate Diversification: Entry, Strategy, & Performance. (Harvard Business School Publications, Division of Research Ser.). (Illus.). 1979. 16.00x (ISBN 0-87584-118-X). Harvard U Pr.
Das, Ranjan. Managing Diversification: The General Management Process. 1981. 14.00x (ISBN 0-8364-0710-5, Pub. by Macmillan India). South Asia Bks.
OECD Staff. Product Durability & Product Life Extension: Their Contribution to Solid Waste Management. 129p. (Orig.). 1982. pap. 10.00x (ISBN 92-64-12293-1). OECD.
Prance, Ghillean T., ed. The Biological Model of Diversification in the Tropics. 752p. 1982. 75.00x (ISBN 0-231-04876-9). Columbia U Pr.
Salter, Malcolm S. & Weinhold, Wolf A. Diversification Through Acquisition: Strategies for Maximizing Economic Value. LC 79-7370. (Illus.). 1979. 29.95 (ISBN 0-02-928020-6). Free Pr.
Taylor, Bernard & Wills, Gordon. Long Range Planning for Marketing & Diversification. 464p. 1971. 22.00x (ISBN 0-8464-1112-1). Beekman Pubs.
Utton, M. A. Diversification & Competition. LC 79-11664. (NIESR, Occasional Papers: No. 31). 1979. 22.95 (ISBN 0-521-22725-9). Cambridge U Pr.

DIVING, SUBMARINE
see also Manned Undersea Research Stations; Underwater Exploration
Anderson, Frank J. Submarines, Diving, & the Underwater World: A Bibliography. ix, 238p. 1975. 25.00 (ISBN 0-208-01508-6, Archon). Shoe String.
Cayford, John E. Underwater Work: A Manual of Scuba Commercial Salvage & Construction Operations. 2nd ed. LC 66-28081. (Illus.). 271p. 1966. 13.50x (ISBN 0-87033-129-9). Cornell Maritime.
Miller, James W. & Koblick, Ian G. Living & Working in the Sea. (Illus.). 496p. 1984. 32.95 (ISBN 0-317-16231-4). Van Nos Reinhold.
Paasche, Arvid & Tonjum, Stein. Applied Medicine in Saturation Diving. 150p. (Orig.). 1984. pap. 14.00x (ISBN 82-00-06369-0). Universitet.
Paton, William, et al, eds. Diving & Life at High Pressures. (Philosophical Transactions of the Royal Society: Series B Vol. 304). (Illus.). 197p. 1984. Repr. write for info. (Pub. by Royal Soc London). Scholium Intl.
Sanderson, Jeppesen. Sport Diver Manual. 3rd ed. (Illus.). 300p. 1978. pap. text ed. 9.25 (ISBN 0-88487-051-0, RE314761); wkbk., 48pgs 2.00 (ISBN 0-88487-052-9, RE325700). Jeppesen Sanderson.
Thompson, Frank E., Jr. Diving, Cutting & Welding in Underwater Salvage Operations. LC 70-92687. (Illus.). 1944. pap. 4.00x (ISBN 0-87033-139-6). Cornell Maritime.

DIVINING-ROD
Naylor, Peter. Discovering Dowsing & Divining. (Discovering Ser.: No. 251). (Illus.). 40p. (Orig.). 1983. pap. 3.50 (ISBN 0-85263-516-8, Pub. by Shire Pubns England). Seven Hills Bks.

DIVISION
The Arithmetic Classroom: Division, 3 pts. (Courses by Computers Ser.). Apple. 49.95 (ISBN 0-88408-199-0); IBM-PC, PCjr. 49.95; Acom. 49.95 (ISBN 0-88408-344-6). Sterling Swift.
Fuller, Kenneth G. An Experimental Study of Two Methods of Long Division. LC 78-176791. (Columbia University. Teachers College. Contributions to Education: No. 951). Repr. of 1949 ed. 22.50 (ISBN 0-404-55951-4). AMS Pr.
Hunt, R. Multiplication & Division. LC 78-730962. 1978. pap. text ed. 135.00 (ISBN 0-89290-093-8, A509-SATC). Soc for Visual.
Laycock, Mary & McLean, Peggy. Skateboard Practice: Multiplication & Division. (Illus.). 1979. pap. text ed. 6.50 (ISBN 0-918932-65-3). Activity Resources.

DNA
see Deoxyribonucleic Acid

DO-IT-YOURSELF WORK
see specific fields of activity for do-it-yourself manuals in such fields, e.g. House Painting; Interior Decoration

DO THREE-THIRTY-FIVE (FIGHTER PLANES)
see Pfeil (Fighter Planes)

DOBERMAN PINCHERS
see Dogs–Breeds–Doberman Pinschers

DOCKS
see also Harbors; Wharves
Cornick, H. F. Dock & Harbour Engineering: The Design of Docks, Vol. 1. 338p. 200.00x (ISBN 0-85264-037-4, Pub. by Griffin England). State Mutual Bk.
Dock & Harbour Engineering: The Design of Harbours, Vol. 2. 352p. 1969. 200.00x (ISBN 0-85264-041-2, Pub. by Griffin England). State Mutual Bk.
Marine Publications Intl. Ltd., ed. Dry Dock Planning Manual. 1981. 300.00x (ISBN 0-906314-11-9, Pub. by Marine Pubns Intl England). State Mutual Bk.
Mazurkiewicz, B. K. Design & Consruction of Dry Docks. (Illus.). 500p. 68.00x (ISBN 0-87849-028-0); pap. 38.00x (ISBN 0-87849-036-1). Trans Tech.
--Design & Construction of Dry Docks. LC 81-80936. 382p. 1981. 54.95x (ISBN 0-87201-209-3). Gulf Pub.
Source Book on Environmental & Safety Considerations for Planning & Design of LNG Marine Terminals. 46p. 1976. pap. 7.00x (ISBN 0-87262-158-8). Am Soc Civil Eng.

DOCUMENT COPYING
see Photocopying Processes

DOCUMENT FILES
Arthur D. Little. Electronic Document Delivery. 233p. 1983. 45.00 (ISBN 0-317-00234-1). Learned Info.
Commission of the European Communities. Electronic Document Delivery II. 1980. 45.00 (ISBN 0-317-00235-X). Learned Info.
Document Retrieval: Sources & Services, (the Only Directory of Public & Private Document Retrieval Suppliers) 1983. 50.00 (ISBN 0-317-00239-2). Learned Info.
Information Management Associates. Electronic Document III: Trends in Electronic Publishing in Europe & the U. S. 1983. 25.00 (ISBN 0-317-00236-8). Learned Info.
James, G. Document Databases. 184p. 1984. 26.95 (ISBN 0-442-28185-4). Van Nos Reinhold.

DOCUMENTATION IN ELECTRONIC DATA PROCESSING
see Electronic Data Processing Documentation

DOCUMENTS, CONSERVATION OF
see Manuscripts–Conservation and Restoration

DOCUPOWER (COMPUTER PROGRAM)
Steiner, Shari. Docupower: CP-M Version. 1984. pap. write for info. (ISBN 0-913733-04-0). Computing.
--Docupower: IBM-PC Version. 1984. pap. write for info. (ISBN 0-913733-05-9). Computing.

DOG
see Dogs

DOG BREEDING
Fletcher, Walter R. My Times with Dogs. LC 79-24575. (Illus.). 320p. 1980. 14.95 (ISBN 0-87605-664-8). Howell Bk.
Ford, Lee E. Animal Welfare Encyclopedia: Breeder's Journal for 1958, Vols. 7, 7A, 7B, 7C. 100p. 1975. Set. pap. 40.00 (ISBN 0-88017-068-9); Vol. 7. pap. (ISBN 0-88017-069-7); Vol. 7A. pap. (ISBN 0-88017-070-0); Vol. 7B. pap. (ISBN 0-88017-071-9); Vol. 7C. pap. (ISBN 0-88017-072-7). Ford Assocs.
--Animal Welfare Encyclopedia: Breeder's Journal for 1959, Vols. 8, 8A, 8B, 8C. 100p. 1975. Set. pap. 40.00 (ISBN 0-88017-114-6); Vol. 8. pap. (ISBN 0-88017-073-5); Vol. 8A. pap. (ISBN 0-88017-074-3); Vol. 8B. pap. (ISBN 0-88017-075-1); Vol. 8C. pap. (ISBN 0-88017-076-X). Ford Assocs.
--Animal Welfare Encyclopedia: Breeder's Journal for 1960, Vols. 9, 9A-9E. 100p. 1975. Set. pap. 60.00 (ISBN 0-88017-115-4); Vol. 9. pap. (ISBN 0-88017-077-8); Vol. 9A. pap. (ISBN 0-88017-078-6); Vol. 9B. pap. (ISBN 0-88017-079-4); Vol. 9C. pap. (ISBN 0-88017-080-8); Vol. 9D. pap. (ISBN 0-88017-081-6); Vol. 9E. pap. (ISBN 0-88017-082-4). Ford Assocs.
--Animal Welfare Encyclopedia: Breeder's Journal for 1961, Vols. 10, 10A, 10B, 10C. 100p. 1975. Set. pap. 40.00 (ISBN 0-88017-116-2); Vol. 10. pap. (ISBN 0-88017-083-2); Vol. 10A. pap. (ISBN 0-88017-084-0); Vol. 10B. pap. (ISBN 0-88017-085-9); Vol. 10C. pap. (ISBN 0-88017-086-7). Ford Assocs.
Ford, Lee E., ed. Animal Welfare Encyclopedia, Vol. 11: Anthology of Dog Genetics & Breeding. 100p. 1975. pap. 7.00 (ISBN 0-88017-087-5). Ford Assocs.
Ford, Lee Ellen, ed. Canine Genetics & Breeding, 5 Vols. (Animal Welfare Encyclopedia Ser.: 19). 100p. (Orig.). 1984. Set. pap. text ed. 60.00 (ISBN 0-318-01272-3). Ford Assocs.
Grossman, Alvin. Breeding Better Cocker Spaniels. LC 76-56011. (Other Dog Bks.). (Illus.). 1977. 24.95 (ISBN 0-87714-044-8). Denlingers.
--The Standard Book of Dog Breeding. LC 74-29654. (Other Dog Bks.). (Illus.). 1983. 16.95 (ISBN 0-87714-054-5). Denlingers.
Holst, Phyllis A. Canine Reproduction: A Breeder's Guide. (Illus.). 256p. 1985. 17.98 (ISBN 0-931866-21-9). Alpine Pubns.
Hutt, Frederick B. Genetics for Dog Breeders. LC 79-15169. (Illus.). 245p. 1979. text ed. 23.95 (ISBN 0-7167-1069-2). W H Freeman.
Meisenzahl, Hilda. Meisen Breeding Manual. LC 73-84517. (Other Dog Books). (Illus.). 128p. 1975. 7.95 (ISBN 0-87714-017-0). Denlingers.
Onstott, Kyle. The New Art of Breeding Better Dogs. 2nd ed. LC 62-15387. (Illus.). 264p. 1983. 14.95 (ISBN 0-87605-400-9). Howell Bk.
Richards, Herbert. Dog Breeding for Professionals. (Illus.). 1978. 12.95 (ISBN 0-87666-659-4, H969). TFH Pubns.
Robinson, Roy. Genetics for Dog Breeders. LC 81-15891. (Illus.). 272p. 1982. 22.00 (ISBN 0-08-025917-0, H235). Pergamon.
Seranne, Anne. The Joy of Breeding Your Own Show Dog. LC 80-16081. (Illus.). 272p. 1984. 14.95 (ISBN 0-87605-413-0). Howell Bk.
Sutton, Catherine G. Dogs: Breeding & Showing. LC 82-22830. (Illus.). 176p. 1983. 16.95 (ISBN 0-668-05799-8, 5799). Arco.
Walkowicz, Chris & Wilcox, Bonnie. Successful Dog Breeding: The Complete Handbook of Canine Midwifery. (Illus.). 224p. 1985. 19.95 (ISBN 0-668-06134-0). Arco.
Whitney, Leon F. How to Breed Dogs. 3rd ed. LC 70-130972. (Illus.). 384p. 1984. 15.95 (ISBN 0-87605-411-4). Howell Bk.

DOG FOOD
see Dogs–Food

DOGS
Here are entered works on dogs in general. For works on specific breeds of dogs see subdivision breeds, further subdivided by specific names, e.g. Dogs–Breeds–Dalmatians.
see also Bird Dogs; Dog Breeding
Abbey, Staten. Book of the Rover. pap. 6.00x (ISBN 0-392-05798-0, SpS). Sportshelf.
Adam, William S., et al. Microscopic Anatomy of the Dog: A Photographic Atlas. 304p. 1970. photocopy ed. 33.50x (ISBN 0-398-00006-9). C C Thomas.
Adams, Donald R. Canine Anatomy: A Systematic Study. (Illus.). 512p. 1985. text ed. 39.75x (ISBN 0-8138-0281-4). Iowa St U Pr.
American Kennel Club. The Complete Dog Book. 17th ed. LC 85-4296. (Illus.). 768p. 1985. 16.95 (ISBN 0-87605-463-7). Howell Bk.
Andersen, A. C., ed. Beagle As an Experimental Dog. LC 79-83321. (Illus.). 616p. 1970. 20.50x (ISBN 0-8138-0169-9). Iowa St U Pr.
Andersen, A. C., et al. Dogs & Other Large Mammals in Aging Research, Vol. 1. LC 74-8039. 168p. 1974. text ed. 21.50x (ISBN 0-8422-7226-7). Irvington.
Ash, Edward C. Dogs: Their History & Development, 2 vols. LC 72-79945. Set. 50.00x (ISBN 0-405-08218-5, Pub. by Blom); 27.50 ea.; Vol. 1. 25.00 (ISBN 0-405-08219-3). Vol. 2 (ISBN 0-405-08220-7). Ayer Co Pubs.
Belfield, Wendel & Zulker, Martin. How to Have a Healthier Dog: The Benefits of Vitamins & Minerals for Your Dog's Life Cycles. LC 80-1081. 288p. 1981. 13.50 (ISBN 0-385-15992-7). Doubleday.
Bergman, Goran. Why Does Your Dog Do That. LC 73-165560. (Illus.). 160p. 1985. 11.95 (ISBN 0-87605-808-X). Howell Bk.
Brearly, Joan McD. & Nicholas, Anna K. This Is the Bichon Frise. (Illus.). 1973. 14.95 (ISBN 0-87666-247-5, PS-700). TFH Pubns.
Bueler, Lois E. Wild Dogs of the World. LC 72-96435. (Illus.). 274p. (Orig.). 1980. pap. 6.95 (ISBN 0-8128-6075-6). Stein & Day.
Caras, Roger. The Roger Caras Dog Book. LC 79-17757. (Illus.). 304p. 1980. 16.95 (ISBN 0-275-23540-8). HR&W.
Caras, Roger A., ed. Dog Owner's Bible. (Illus.). 480p. pap. 7.95 (ISBN 0-88317-089-2). Stoeger Pub Co.
Christiansen, J. Reproduction in the Dog & Cat. (Illus.). 225p. Date not set. pap. price not set (Pub. by Bailliere-Tindall). Saunders.
Coffey, David. A Veterinary Surgeon's Guide to Dogs. (Illus.). 199p. 1980. 12.50 (ISBN 0-437-02500-4, Pub. by Worlds Work). David & Charles.
Damroth, Marion. Country Dogs & City Cousins: The Care & Loving of All Puppies. LC 80-81371. (Illus.). 125p. write for info. (ISBN 0-937118-01-X). Home Frosted.
Dapper, Gertrude. Canine Genetics. (Other Dogs Bks). (Illus.). 1986. 16.95 (ISBN 0-87714-112-6). Denlingers.
--German Names for German Dogs. LC 78-52184. (Other Dog Bks.). (Illus.). 1980. 11.95 (ISBN 0-87714-066-9). Denlingers.
Dog-Access. (Access Guides Ser.). pap. 2.50 (ISBN 0-671-60378-7). S&S.
Donovan, John A. Gaelic Names for Celtic Dogs. LC 78-56243. (Other Dog Bks.). (Illus.). 1980. 11.95 (ISBN 0-87714-067-7). Denlingers.
Ensminger, M. E. The Complete Book of Dogs. LC 74-13. (Illus.). 960p. 1977. 25.00 (ISBN 0-498-01457-6). A S Barnes.

Ettinger, Stephen J. & Suter, Peter F. Canine Cardiology. LC 77-97547. (Illus.). 1970. 42.00 (ISBN 0-7216-3437-0). Saunders.
Evans, Howard E. & Christensen, George C. Miller's Anatomy of the Dog. 2nd ed. (Illus.). 1181p. 1979. 47.50 (ISBN 0-7216-3438-9). Saunders.
Evans, Howard E. & De Lahunta, Alexander. Miller's Guide to the Dissection of the Dog. 2nd ed. (Illus.). 318p. 1980. 19.50 (ISBN 0-7216-3444-3). Saunders.
Evans, Job M. The Evans Guide for Counseling Dog Owners. LC 84-1092. (Illus.). 160p. 1985. 12.95 (ISBN 0-87605-660-5). Howell Bk.
Fletcher, Walter. Dogs of the World. (All Color Guides). 1977. pap. 3.95 (ISBN 0-553-23525-7). Bantam.
Fletcher, Walter R. My Times with Dogs. LC 79-24575. (Illus.). 320p. 1980. 14.95 (ISBN 0-87605-664-8). Howell Bk.
Ford, Lee E., ed. Animal Welfare Encyclopedia: Dog Genetics & Legislation, 28 vols. 100p. (Orig.). 1975. Set. pap. 280.00. Ford Assocs.
Fox, M. W. Canine Behavior. (Illus.). 152p. 1978. photocopy ed. 15.75x (ISBN 0-398-00599-0). C C Thomas.
Fox, Michael W. Behavior of Wolves, Dogs & Related Canids. LC 83-18706. 220p. 1984. Repr. of 1971 ed. lib. bdg. 15.75 (ISBN 0-89874-686-8). Krieger.
--The Dog: Its Domestication & Behavior. LC 76-57852. 1978. 40.00 (ISBN 0-8240-9858-7). Garland Pub.
--The Whistling Hunters: Field Studies of the Asiatic Wild Dog (Cuon Alpinus) (Animal Behavior Ser.). 224p. 1984. 29.50x (ISBN 0-87395-842-X); pap. 9.95x (ISBN 0-87395-843-8). State U NY Pr.
Gerstenfeld, Sheldon L. Taking Care of Your Dog. LC 79-2339. (Illus.). 1979. o. p. 11.95 (ISBN 0-201-03060-8); pap. 7.95 (ISBN 0-201-03061-6). Addison-Wesley.
Haycroft, W. C. Book of the Royal Enfield. pap. 6.00x (ISBN 0-392-02349-0, SpS). Sportshelf.
Hollenbeck, Leon. Dynamics of Canine Gait. 2nd, rev. ed. (Other Dog Bk.). (Illus.). 240p. 1981. 19.95 (ISBN 0-87714-081-2). Denlingers.
Johnson, Glen R. Tracking Dog: Theory & Methods. LC 75-14693. (Illus.). 240p. 1975. 13.95 (ISBN 0-914124-04-8). Arner Pubns.
Johnson, Norman. The Complete Puppy & Dog Book. rev. ed. LC 77-5685. (Illus.). 1977. 16.95 (ISBN 0-689-10808-7). Atheneum.
Le Roi, David. Town Dogs. 6.50x (ISBN 0-392-05025-0, SpS). Sportshelf.
Liebers, Arthur. How to Raise & Train a Pedigreed or a mixed breed Puppy. pap. 2.95 (ISBN 0-87666-370-6, DS-1027). TFH Pubns.
Lim, Robert K., et al. A Stereotaxic Atlas of the Dog's Brain. (Illus.). 102p. 1960. photocopy ed. 11.75x (ISBN 0-398-01129-X). C C Thomas.
Lorenz, Konrad Z. Man Meets Dog. (Illus.). 1965. pap. 3.95 (ISBN 0-14-002214-7). Penguin.
Lyon, McDowell. Dog in Action. (Illus.). 304p. 1985. 14.95 (ISBN 0-87605-468-8). Howell Bk.
McGinnis, Terri. Well Dog Book. LC 74-7496. (Illus.). 1974. 14.95 (ISBN 0-394-48948-9, Co-Pub by Bookworks). Random.
Margolis, Matthew & Swan, Catherine. The Dog in Your Life. LC 79-14100. 1979. 12.95 (ISBN 0-394-50759-2). Random.
Messent, Peter. Understanding Your Dog: The Intelligent Person's Guide to a Lifelong Relationship with Another Species. LC 80-51643. (Illus.). 160p. 1982. 18.95 (ISBN 0-8128-2746-5). Stein & Day.
Metcalf, Tom, et al. My Dog's First Five Years. (Illus.). 1977. 6.95 (ISBN 0-916054-46-2, Dist. by Kampmann). Green Hill.
Mondadori, ed. Simon & Schuster's Guide to Dogs. pap. 9.95 (ISBN 0-671-25527-4). S&S.
Novotny, Josef & Najman, Josef. Field Guide in Color to Dogs. (Octopus Book). (Illus.). 1978. 5.95 (ISBN 0-7064-0611-7, Mayflower Bks). Smith Pubs.
O'Connor, Richard F. Ident-A-Dog: A Complete Identification Record of Your Dog. (Ident-A Ser.). (Illus.). 32p. (Orig.). 1985. pap. 2.95 (ISBN 0-913243-98-1). O'Connor Hse-Pubs.
Olsen, Stanley J. Origins of the Domestic Dog: The Fossil Record. LC 85-1024. (Monographs). 1985. 19.95x (ISBN 0-8165-0909-3). U of Ariz Pr.
Our Puppy's Baby Book: Blue for Boy Dogs. (Illus.). 32p. 1983. 6.95 (ISBN 0-87605-772-5). Howell Bk.
Our Puppy's Baby Book: Pink for Girl Dogs. (Illus.). 32p. 1983. 6.95 (ISBN 0-87605-773-3). Howell Bk.
Padwee, Howard. Live-Longer Diet for Dogs & Cats. (Illus.). 128p. 1980. 8.95 (ISBN 0-312-48885-8). St Martin.
Palmer, Joan. A Illustrated Guide to Dogs. LC 81-68053. (Illus.). 240p. 1981. 9.95 (ISBN 0-668-05362-3). Arco.
Patient Care Publications Staff. Your Dog: An Owner's Manual. (Illus.). 128p. 1984. pap. 6.95 (ISBN 0-668-06121-9). Arco.
Prine, Virginia B. How Puppies Are Born. LC 75-182240. (Illus.). 80p. 1983. 8.95 (ISBN 0-87605-553-6). Howell Bk.
Riddle, Maxwell. Puppies. (Illus.). 80p. 1984. pap. text ed. 3.95 (ISBN 0-86622-245-6, PB-123). TFH Pubns.
--Wild Dogs: In Life & Legend. LC 79-18689. (Illus.). 299p. 1979. 14.95 (ISBN 0-87605-809-8). Howell Bk.
Rousselet-Blanc. Chien. (La Vie active). (Fr.). 1959. 34.95x (ISBN 0-685-13828-3). Larousse.
Rousselet-Blanc, Pierre & Rousselet-Blanc, Josette. Dictionnaire du Chien. (Fr.). 267p. 1976. 27.50 (ISBN 0-686-56869-9, M-6647). French & Eur.
Schwartz, Charlotte. Friend to Friend: Dogs That Help Mankind. 192p. 1984. pap. 12.95 (ISBN 0-87605-545-5). Howell Bk.
Scott, John P. & Fuller, John L., eds. Dog Behavior: The Genetic Basis. LC 64-23429. 1974. pap. 12.50x (ISBN 0-226-74338-1). U of Chicago Pr.
Shattuck, Louise F. From Riches to Bitches (And a Cadillac for Your Vet) Being a Mirthful Recounting of the Carry-on Kennel Chronicles. LC 78-31874. (Illus.). 144p. 1985. 11.95 (ISBN 0-87605-548-X). Howell Bk.
Shields, G. O. The American Book of the Dog. 1977. lib. bdg. 150.00 (ISBN 0-8490-1413-1). Gordon Pr.
Smith, A. Broxton. About Our Dogs. 17.50x (ISBN 0-392-06336-0, SpS). Sportshelf.
Stranger, Joyce. All about Your Pet Puppy. 2nd ed. (All About Ser.). (Illus.). 144p. 1980. 12.95 (ISBN 0-7207-1216-5, Pub. by Michael Joseph). Merrimack Pub Cir.
Trumbler, Eberhard. Understanding Your Dog. (Illus.). 264p. 1973. 9.95 (ISBN 0-571-10373-1). Faber & Faber.
Vine, Louis D. Your Dog, His Health & Happiness: The Breeder's & Pet Owners Guide to Better Dog Care. LC 72-88607. 446p. 1973. pap. 6.95 (ISBN 0-668-02876-9). Arco.
Vine, Louis L. Behavior & Training of Dogs & Puppies. LC 77-1387. 1977. pap. 2.50 (ISBN 0-668-04162-5). Arco.
--Your Neurotic Dog. 272p. pap. 3.95 (ISBN 0-523-42314-4). Pinnacle Bks.
Way, Robert F. Dog Anatomy. LC 74-75114. (Illus.). 1974. pap. 3.95 (ISBN 0-88376-054-1). Dreenan Pr.
Well, Judy. All about All Dogs. 15.00 (ISBN 0-685-48898-5). Judy.
Woodhouse, Barbara. Encyclopedia of Dogs & Puppies. 224p. 1985. pap. 3.50 (ISBN 0-425-08469-8). Berkley Pub.
Zahn, Siegfried. First Aid Manual: General First Aid for Dogs. 106p. (Orig.). 1984. pap. 7.00x (ISBN 0-317-13690-9, Pub. by J & J Enter). Univelt Inc.

DOGS–BREEDING
see Dog Breeding

DOGS–BREEDS
Barnes, Duncan & American Kennel Club Staff. The AKC'S World of the Pure-Bred Dog. LC 83-6117. (Illus.). 352p. 1983. 15.00 (ISBN 0-87605-406-8). Howell Bk.
Gordon, John F. The Spaniel Owner's Encyclopedia. 183p. 1967. 7.95 (ISBN 0-7207-0098-1, Pub. by Michael Joseph). Merrimack Pub Cir.
Hart, E. Encyclopedia of Dog Breeds. (Illus.). 782p. 14.95 (ISBN 0-87666-285-8, H-927). TFH Pubns.
Leen, Nina. What Kind of a Dog Is That? (Illus.). 1979. pap. 4.95 (ISBN 0-393-00934-3). Norton.
Little, Clarence C. Inheritance of Coat Color in Dogs. LC 67-8658. (Illus.). 208p. 1984. 15.95 (ISBN 0-87605-621-4). Howell Bk.
Margolis, Matthew & Siegal, Mordecai. Good Dog, Bad Dog. LC 72-78139. 1973. 8.95 (ISBN 0-03-001421-2). HR&W.
Meisenzahl, Hilda. Meisen Breeding Manual. LC 73-84517. (Other Dog Books). (Illus.). 128p. 1975. 7.95 (ISBN 0-87714-017-0). Denlingers.

DOGS–BREEDS–AFGHAN HOUNDS
Brearley, Joan M. Book of the Afghan Hound. (Illus.). 1978. 29.95 (ISBN 0-87666-665-9, H-991). TFH Pubns.
--This Is the Afghan Hound. (Illus.). 1965. 12.95 (ISBN 0-87666-231-9, PS-639). TFH Pubns.
Kauffman, Sue A. Your Afghan Hound. LC 69-19735. (Your Dog Bk.). (Illus.). 1969. 12.95 (ISBN 0-87714-018-9). Denlingers.
Miller, Constance O. & Gilbert, Edward M., Jr. Complete Afghan Hound. 3rd ed. LC 74-81138. (Complete Breed Book). (Illus.). 304p. 1982. 15.95 (ISBN 0-87605-000-3). Howell Bk.
Pisano, Beverly. Afghan Hounds. (Illus.). 125p. 1980. 4.95 (ISBN 0-87666-682-9, KW-077). TFH Pubns.
Shay, Sunny & Barbaresi, Sara M. How to Raise & Train an Afghan. (Orig.). pap. 2.95 (ISBN 0-87666-232-7, DS-1001). TFH Pubns.

DOGS–BREEDS–AIREDALE TERRIERS
Edwards, Gladys B. The New Complete Airedale Terrier. 3rd ed. LC 78-7051. (Complete Breed Book Ser.). (Illus.). 304p. 1978. 15.95 (ISBN 0-87605-005-4). Howell Bk.
Strebeigh, Barbara & McCready, Pauline I. Your Airedale Terrier. LC 76-45234. (Your Dog Bk.). (Illus.). 1977. 12.95 (ISBN 0-87714-040-5). Denlingers.

DOGS–BREEDS–AKITA
Van Der Lyn, Edita. Akitas. (Illus.). 128p. 1981. 4.95 (ISBN 0-87666-710-8, KW-107). TFH Pubns.

DOGS–BREEDS–ALASKAN MALAMUTE
Berger, Charles J. How to Raise & Train an Alaskan Malamute. (Orig.). pap. 2.95 (ISBN 0-87666-235-1, DS-1042). TFH Pubns.
Brearley, Joan M. This Is the Alaskan Malamute. (Illus.). 415p. 1975. 19.95 (ISBN 0-87666-650-0, PS-737). TFH Pubns.
Le Kernec, Bill. Alaskan Malamutes. (Illus.). 128p. 1983. 4.95 (ISBN 0-87666-711-6, KW-094). TFH Pubns.
Riddle, Maxwell & Seeley, Eva B. The Complete Alaskan Malamute. LC 75-43221. (Complete Breed Book). (Illus.). 288p. 1983. 15.95 (ISBN 0-87605-009-7). Howell Bk.
Ross, Dianne. Your Alaskan Malamute. LC 76-45235. (Your Dog Bk.). (Illus.). 1977. 12.95 (ISBN 0-87714-047-2). Denlingers.

DOGS–BREEDS–ALSATIANS
Cree, John. Training the Alsatian. (Illus.). 160p. 1978. 13.95 (ISBN 0-7207-0993-8, Pub. by Michael Joseph). Merrimack Pub Cir.
Pickup, Madeleine. The Alsatian Owner's Encyclopaedia. 104p. 1964. 8.95 (ISBN 0-7207-0001-9, Pub. by Michael Joseph). Merrimack Pub Cir.

DOGS–BREEDS–BASENJI
Green, Evelyn M. Your Basenji. LC 76-20959. (Your Dog Bk.). (Illus.). 1976. 12.95 (ISBN 0-87714-041-3). Denlingers.

DOGS–BREEDS–BASSET HOUNDS
Braun, Mercedes. The New Complete Basset Hound. 4th ed. LC 79-4465. (Complete Breed Book Ser.). (Illus.). 352p. 1982. 15.95 (ISBN 0-87605-021-6). Howell Bk.
McCarty, Diane & Look, Mrs. Travis. Basset Hounds. (Illus.). 125p. 1979. 4.95 (ISBN 0-87666-679-9, KW-069). TFH Pubns.

DOGS–BREEDS–BEAGLES
Andersen, A. C., ed. Beagle As an Experimental Dog. LC 79-83321. (Illus.). 616p. 1970. 20.50x (ISBN 0-8138-0169-9). Iowa St U Pr.
Berndt, Robert J. Your Beagle. LC 75-41979. (Your Dog Book Ser.). (Illus.). 1976. 12.95 (ISBN 0-87714-034-0). Denlingers.
Colombo, Henry J., et al. The New Complete Beagle. 3rd ed. Madden, et al, eds. LC 70-161397. (Complete Breed Book Ser.). (Illus.). 1971. 12.95 (ISBN 0-87605-024-0). Howell Bk.
Pisano, Beverly & Holcombe, A. D. Beagles. (Illus.). 125p. 1979. 4.95 (ISBN 0-87666-686-1, KW-080). TFH Pubns.
Priestley, Heather. All about the Beagle. 140p. 1973. 9.95 (ISBN 0-7207-0613-0, Pub. by Michael Joseph). Merrimack Pub Cir.
Ward, Mary A. & Barbaresi, Sara M. How to Raise & Train a Beagle. 1966. pap. 2.95 (ISBN 0-87666-242-4, DS-1004). TFH Pubns.

DOGS–BREEDS–BLOODHOUNDS
Brey, Catherine F., et al. The Complete Bloodhound. LC 77-81706. (The Complete Breed Bk.). (Illus.). 304p. 1984. 15.95 (ISBN 0-87605-052-6). Howell Bk.

DOGS–BREEDS–BORZOI
Edlin, Alfred W. Your Borzoi. LC 75-41983. (Your Dog Bk.). 1976. 12.95 (ISBN 0-87714-042-1). Denlingers.
Thomas, Joseph B. Observations on Borzoi, Called in America Russian Wolfhounds. LC 75-42030. 1976. Repr. of 1912 ed. 15.00x (ISBN 0-686-17807-6). Dehack.

DOGS–BREEDS–BOUVIER D'FLANDRES
McLean, Claire. The Bouvier des Flandres. 2nd, rev. ed. LC 80-66115. (Other Dog Bks.). (Illus.). 1981. 24.95 (ISBN 0-87714-077-4). Denlingers.

DOGS–BREEDS–BOXERS
Barbaresi, Sara M. How to Raise & Train a Boxer. pap. 2.95 (ISBN 0-87666-253-X, DS-1006). TFH Pubns.
Denlinger, Milo G. Complete Boxer. 3rd ed. LC 69-19392. (Complete Breed Book Ser.). (Illus.). 304p. 1982. 15.95 (ISBN 0-87605-060-7). Howell Bk.
Gordon, John F. All about the Boxer. 164p. 1970. 9.95 (ISBN 0-7207-0317-4, Pub. by Michael Joseph). Merrimack Pub Cir.
Meyer, Lorraine C. Your Boxer. LC 78-187777. (Your Dog Bk.). (Illus.). 128p. 1973. 12.95 (ISBN 0-87714-004-9). Denlingers.
Pisano, Beverly. Boxers. (Illus.). 1979. 4.95 (ISBN 0-87666-688-8, KW-041). TFH Pubns.

DOGS–BREEDS–BRITTANY SPANIEL
Hammond, Ralph B. & Hammond, Robert D. Training & Hunting the Brittany Spaniel. LC 76-160475. (Illus.). 166p. 1972. 12.95 (ISBN 0-498-07900-7). A S Barnes.
Pisano, Beverly & Monte, Evelyn, eds. Brittany Spaniels. (Illus.). 128p. 1980. lib. bdg. 4.95 (ISBN 0-87666-708-6, KW-092). TFH Pubns.
Riddle, Maxwell. The Complete Brittany Spaniel. LC 72-88976. (Complete Breed Book Ser.). (Illus.). 288p. 1984. 15.95 (ISBN 0-87605-065-8). Howell Bk.
Rosenblum, Edwin E. How to Raise & Train a Brittany Spaniel. (Orig.). pap. 2.95 (ISBN 0-87666-257-2, DS-1063). TFH Pubns.

DOGS–BREEDS–BULL TERRIERS
Drewes, Marilyn. Your Bull Terrier. LC 77-92121. (Your Dog Bk.). (Illus.). 1978. 12.95 (ISBN 0-87714-043-X). Denlingers.
Eberhard, Ernest. The New Complete Bull Terrier. 2nd ed. LC 69-19207. (Complete Breed Book Ser.). (Illus.). 256p. 1985. 15.95 (ISBN 0-87605-071-2). Howell Bk.
Gordon, John F. The Staffordshire Bull Terrier Owner's Encyclopedia. 2nd ed. (Illus.). 240p. 1977. 12.95 (ISBN 0-7207-0944-X, Pub. by Michael Joseph). Merrimack Pub Cir.
Horner, Tom. All about the Bull Terrier. (All About Ser.). (Illus.). 150p. 1983. 12.95 (ISBN 0-7207-1086-3, Pub by Michael Joseph). Merrimack Pub Cir.
Rosenblum, Edwin E. How to Raise & Train a Bull Terrier. (Orig.). pap. 2.95 (ISBN 0-87666-261-0, DS-1066). TFH Pubns.
Stratton, Richard F. The Book of the American Pit Bull Terrier. (Illus.). 352p. 29.95 (ISBN 0-87666-734-5, H-1024). TFH Pubns.
--This Is the American Pit Bull Terrier. (Illus.). 1976. 14.95 (ISBN 0-87666-660-8, PS-613). TFH Pubns.
--World of the American Pit Bull Terrier. LC 83-215316. (Illus.). 288p. 1983. 29.95 (ISBN 0-87666-851-1, H-1063). TFH Pubns.

DOGS–BREEDS–BULLDOGS
Berndt, Robert J. Your Bulldog. LC 75-41980. (Your Dog Book Ser.). (Illus.). 1976. 12.95 (ISBN 0-87714-036-7). Denlingers.
Brearley, Joan. The Book of the Bulldog. (Illus.). 320p. 1984. 29.95 (ISBN 0-86622-027-5, H-1071). TFH Pubns.
Hanes, Bailey C. The New Complete Bulldog. 4th, rev. ed. LC 73-78984. (Illus.). 288p. 1984. 15.95 (ISBN 0-87605-068-2). Howell Bk.
TFH Publications Staff. Bulldogs. (Illus.). 125p. 1980. 4.95 (ISBN 0-87666-714-0, KW-101). TFH Pubns.

DOGS–BREEDS–CAIRN TERRIERS
McCormack, Erliss. How to Raise & Train a Cairn Terrier. pap. 2.95 (ISBN 0-87666-262-9, DS-1068). TFH Pubns.
Marvin, John T. The Complete Cairn Terrier. LC 74-84760. (Complete Breed Book Ser.). (Illus.). 256p. 1982. 15.95 (ISBN 0-87605-072-0). Howell Bk.

DOGS–BREEDS–CHESAPEAKE BAY RETRIEVER
Beaman, Arthur S. The Chesapeake Bay Retriever. LC 80-69084. (Other Dog Bk.). (Illus.). 96p. 1981. 24.95 (ISBN 0-87714-075-8). Denlingers.
Cherry, Eloise H. The Complete Chesapeake Bay Retriever. LC 80-25037. (Complete Breed Book). (Illus.). 288p. 1985. 15.95 (ISBN 0-87605-074-7). Howell Bk.

DOGS–BREEDS–CHIHUAHUA
Denlinger, William, et al. Complete Chihuahua. 4th ed. LC 63-21874. (Complete Breed Book Ser.). (Illus.). 256p. 1983. 15.95 (ISBN 0-87605-100-X). Howell Bk.
Ferguson, Estelle & Barbaresi, Sara M. How to Raise & Train a Chihuahua. pap. 2.95 (ISBN 0-87666-266-1, DS-1008). TFH Pubns.
Murray, Ruth L. Your Chihuahua. LC 66-22308. (Your Dog Books). (Illus.). 1966. 7.95 (ISBN 0-87714-019-7); pap. 4.95 (ISBN 0-87714-020-0). Denlingers.
Pisano, Beverly & Thurmer, Tressa E. Chihuahuas. (Illus.). 128p. 1980. 4.95 (ISBN 0-87666-701-9, KW-087). TFH Pubns.
Riddle, Maxwell. This Is the Chihuahua. (Illus.). 1959. 12.95 (ISBN 0-87666-267-X, PS-611). TFH Pubns.

DOGS–BREEDS–CHOW CHOWS
Nicholas, Anna K. The Chow Chow. (Illus.). 320p. 1984. text ed. 14.95 (ISBN 0-86622-029-1, PS-812). TFH Pubns.
Pisano, Beverly. Chow Chows. (Illus.). 125p. 4.95 (ISBN 0-87666-702-7, KW-089). TFH Pubns.
Shryock, Clifford. How to Raise & Train a Chow Chow. (Orig.). pap. 2.95 (ISBN 0-87666-268-8, DS-1070). TFH Pubns.

DOGS–BREEDS–COCKER SPANIEL
Brearley, Joan McD. The Book of the Cocker Spaniel. (Illus.). 300p. 1982. 29.95 (ISBN 0-87666-737-X, H-1034). TFH Pubns.
Gannon, Robert. How to Raise & Train an English Cocker Spaniel. pap. 2.95 (ISBN 0-87666-291-2, DS-1014). TFH Pubns.
Gordon, John F. All about the Cocker Spaniel. 147p. 1971. 8.95 (ISBN 0-7207-0424-3, Pub. by Michael Joseph). Merrimack Pub Cir.
Grossman, Alvin. Breeding Better Cocker Spaniels. LC 76-56011. (Other Dog Bks.). (Illus.). 1977. 24.95 (ISBN 0-87714-044-8). Denlingers.

Hart, Ernest H. Cocker Spaniel Handbook. text ed. 12.95 (ISBN 0-87666-270-X, H-923). TFH Pubns.

King, Bert. Cocker Spaniels. (Illus.). 1979. 4.95 (ISBN 0-87666-692-6, KW-043). TFH Pubns.

Kraeuchi, Ruth M. The New Cocker Spaniel. LC 78-12698. (The Complete Breed Bk.). (Illus.). 288p. 1985. 15.95 (ISBN 0-87605-104-2). Howell Bk.

McKinney, et al, eds. The English Cocker Spaniel Handbook. 2nd ed. (Illus.). 208p. 1974. pap. 7.50 (ISBN 0-9613761-0-4). Eng Cocker Spaniel.

Miller, Evelyn. How to Raise & Train a Cocker Spaniel. pap. 2.95 (ISBN 0-87666-269-6, DS-1009). TFH Pubns.

T.F.H. Publications Staff & King, Bart. Cocker Spaniels. (Illus.). 80p. 1984. pap. text ed. 3.95 (ISBN 0-86622-242-1, PB-105). TFH Pubns.

Whitney, Leon F. This Is the Cocker Spaniel. (Illus.). 12.95 (ISBN 0-87666-271-8, PS-612). TFH Pubns.

DOGS–BREEDS–COLLIES

Barbaresi, Sara M. How to Raise & Train a Collie. pap. 2.95 (ISBN 0-87666-272-6, DS-1010). TFH Pubns.

Bishop, Ada L. All about the Collie. 2nd ed. (All About Ser.). (Illus.). 144p. 1980. 12.95 (ISBN 0-7207-1215-7, Pub. by Michael Joseph). Merrimack Pub Cir.

Collie Club of America. The New Collie. LC 82-19049. (Complete Breed Book Ser.). 304p. 1985. 15.95 (ISBN 0-87605-130-1). Howell Bk.

Collis, Joyce. All about the Bearded Collie. (Illus.). 144p. 1981. 12.95 (ISBN 0-7207-1128-2, Pub. by Michael Joseph). Merrimack Pub Cir.

Combe, Iris. Border Collies. (Illus.). 198p. 1978. 15.95 (ISBN 0-571-11173-4). Faber & Faber.

McCarty, Diane & Kattell, Ted. Collies. (Illus.). 128p. 1980. 4.95 (ISBN 0-87666-684-5, KW-078). TFH Pubns.

McCloskey, Esther. This Is the Collie. 1963. 12.95 (ISBN 0-87666-273-4, PS-619). TFH Pubns.

Osborne, Margaret. Collie. rev. ed. LC 62-14988. Orig. Title: Popular Collie. (Illus.). 1974. 8.95 (ISBN 0-668-00943-8). Arco.

Rieseberg, Freedo V. & McKinney, B. J. Beardie Basics. rev. ed. (Illus.). 1984. 19.98 (ISBN 0-931866-16-2). Alpine Pubns.

Roos, Mrs. George. Collie Concept. (Illus.). 232p. 1982. 19.98 (ISBN 0-931866-10-3). Alpine Pubns.

DOGS–BREEDS–DACHSHUND

Adler, Lenore L. This Is the Dachshund. 3rd ed. 1966. 12.95 (ISBN 0-87666-278-5, PS-637). TFH Pubns.

Cox, Herman G. Your Dachshund. LC 66-22305. (Your Dog Book Ser). (Illus.). 1966. 7.95 (ISBN 0-87714-021-9); pap. 4.95 (ISBN 0-87714-022-7). Denlingers.

Horswell, Dorthy A. & Horswell, Laurence A. Dachshunds. (Illus.). 80p. 1984. pap. 3.95 (ISBN 0-86622-201-4, PB-106). TFH Pubns.

Meistrell, Lois. The New Dachshund. LC 75-30419. (Complete Breed Book Ser). (Illus.). 288p. 1982. 15.95 (ISBN 0-87605-107-7). Howell Bk.

Meistrell, Lois & Barbaresi, Sara M. How to Raise & Train a Dachshund. pap. 2.95 (ISBN 0-87666-276-9, DS-1011). TFH Pubns.

Raine, Katharine. All about the Dachshund. (All About Ser.). (Illus.). 160p. 1980. 12.95 (ISBN 0-7207-1178-9, Pub. by Michael Joseph). Merrimack Pub Cir.

Van Der Lyn, Edita. Dachshunds. (Illus.). 128p. 1980. 4.95 (ISBN 0-87666-704-3, KW-085). TFH Pubns.

DOGS–BREEDS–DALMATIANS

Liebers, Arthur. How to Raise & Train a Dalmatian. (Illus.). pap. 2.95 (ISBN 0-87666-279-3, DS-1012). TFH Pubns.

Pisano, Beverly, ed. Dalmatians. (Illus.). 128p. 1980. 4.95 (ISBN 0-87666-705-1, KW-090). TFH Pubns.

Treen, Alfred & Treen, Esmeralda. The Dalmatian: Coach Dog-Firehouse Dog. LC 80-10650. (Complete Breed Bk.). (Illus.). 281p. 1984. 15.95 (ISBN 0-87605-109-3). Howell Bk.

DOGS–BREEDS–DOBERMAN PINSCHERS

Brearley, Joan McD. The Book of the Doberman Pinscher. (Illus.). 1976. 17.95 (ISBN 0-87666-658-6, H-968). TFH Pubns.

Carey, Len. Doberman Pinschers. (Illus.). 80p. 1984. pap. 3.95 (ISBN 0-86622-249-9, PB-107). TFH Pubns.

Donnelly, Kerry. Doberman Pinschers. (Illus.). 1979. 4.95 (ISBN 0-87666-698-5, KW-009). TFH Pubns.

Migliorini, Mario. The Doberman Book. (Illus.). 256p. 16.95 (ISBN 0-668-05430-1). Arco.

Spirer, Louise Z. & Miller, E. This Is the Doberman Pinscher. 1963. 12.95 (ISBN 0-87666-283-1, PS-622). TFH Pubns.

Stebbins, Natalie & Barbaresi, Sara M. How to Raise & Train a Doberman Pinscher. (Illus.). pap. 2.95 (ISBN 0-87666-282-3, DS-1013). TFH Pubns.

DOGS–BREEDS–ENGLISH SETTERS

Pisano, Beverly, ed. English Setters. (Illus.). 128p. 1980. 4.95 (ISBN 0-87666-716-7, KW-102). TFH Pubns.

Tuck, Davis H., et al. The New Complete English Setter. 4th ed. LC 81-20267. Orig. Title: The Complete English Setter. (Illus.). 376p. 1983. 18.95 (ISBN 0-87605-116-6). Howell Bk.

DOGS–BREEDS–ENGLISH SHEEP DOGS

Boyer, Alice J. Your Old English Sheepdog. LC 75-41985. (Your Dog Bk.). (Illus.). 1978. 12.95 (ISBN 0-87714-048-0). Denlingers.

Gould, Jean. All about the Old English Sheepdog. 2nd ed. 136p. 1973. 8.95 (ISBN 0-7207-0619-X, Pub. by Michael Joseph). Merrimack Pub Cir.

Mandeville, John. The Complete Old English Sheepdog. LC 75-30418. (Complete Breed Book Ser.). (Illus.). 288p. 1982. 15.95 (ISBN 0-87605-219-7). Howell Bk.

Woods, Sylvia & Owen, Ray. Old English Sheepdogs. LC 81-670122. (Illus.). 224p. 1981. 17.95 (ISBN 0-571-11620-5). Faber & Faber.

DOGS–BREEDS–ENGLISH SPRINGER SPANIEL

Goodall, Charles S. & Gasow, Julia. The New Complete English Springer Spaniel. 3rd ed. LC 84-9048. (Illus.). 288p. 1985. 16.95 (ISBN 0-87605-118-2). Howell Bk.

Hampton, Olga M. All about the English Springer Spaniel. 2nd ed. (All About Ser.). (Illus.). 144p. 1980. 12.95 (ISBN 0-7207-1274-2, Pub. by Michael Joseph). Merrimack Pub Cir.

Hankwitz, Reed. F. Your English Springer Spaniel. LC 72-80629. (Your Dog Bk.). (Illus.). 160p. 1973. 12.95 (ISBN 0-87714-007-3). Denlingers.

McCarty, Diane & Henneberry, Mrs. Janet. English Springer Spaniels. (Illus.). 1980. 4.95 (ISBN 0-87666-687-X, KW-081). TFH Pubns.

Nicholas, Anna K. The Book of the English Springer Spaniel. (Illus.). 414p. 1983. 29.95 (ISBN 0-87666-744-2, H 1060). TFH Pubns.

DOGS–BREEDS–GERMAN SHEPHERD DOGS

Barbaresi, Sara M. How to Raise & Train a German Shepherd. pap. 2.95 (ISBN 0-87666-296-3, DS-1017). TFH Pubns.

Bennett, Jane G. The New Complete German Shepherd Dog. rev. ed. LC 82-1031. (Illus.). 256p. 1984. 14.95 (ISBN 0-87605-151-4). Howell Bk.

Cleveland, Reginald M. Your German Shepherd. LC 66-22306. (Your Dog Book Ser). (Illus.). 1966. pap. 4.95 (ISBN 0-87714-009-X). Denlingers.

Elliot, Nem & Elliot, Percy. The Complete German Shepherd Dog. 304p. 1982. 40.00x (ISBN 0-7182-2350-0, Pub. by Windmill Pr). State Mutual Bk.

--The Complete German Shepherd Dog. (Illus.). 304p. 1983. 22.50 (ISBN 0-7182-2350-0, Pub. by Kaye & Ward). David & Charles.

Goldbecker, William & Hart, Ernest H. This Is the German Shepherd. (Illus.). 296p. 12.95 (ISBN 0-87666-298-X, PS-614). TFH Pubns.

Hart, Ernest H. The German Shepherd Dog. (Illus.). 320p. 1984. 14.95 (ISBN 0-86622-031-3, PS-810). TFH Pubns.

Humphrey, Elliott & Warner, Lucien. Working Dogs: An Attempt to Produce a Strain of German Shepherds Which Combines Working Ability & Beauty of Conformation. 1973. Repr. of 1934 ed. 15.00x (ISBN 0-686-14938-6). Dehack.

Kern, Francis G. German Shepherd Dogs. (Illus.). 1979. 4.95 (ISBN 0-87666-697-7, KW-008). TFH Pubns.

Nicholas, Anna K. Book of the German Shepherd Dog. (Illus.). 480p. 1983. 29.95 (ISBN 0-87666-562-8, H-1062). TFH Pubns.

Pickup, Madeleine. All about the German Shepherd Dog. 2nd ed. (All About Ser.). (Illus.). 168p. 1980. 12.95 (ISBN 0-7207-1219-X, Pub. by Michael Joseph). Merrimack Pub Cir.

Schalk, Mansfield E. C. German Shepherds. (Illus.). 80p. 1984. pap. 3.95 (ISBN 0-86622-241-3, PB-111). TFH Pubns.

Strickland, Winifred G. & Moses, James A. The German Shepherd Today. LC 73-19044. (Illus.). 512p. 1974. 21.95 (ISBN 0-02-615030-1). Macmillan.

DOGS–BREEDS–GERMAN SHORT-HAIRED POINTERS

Dapper, Gertrude. Your German Shorthaired Pointer. LC 74-29657. (Your Dog Book Ser.). (Illus.). 1975. 12.95 (ISBN 0-87714-030-8). Denlingers.

Liebers, Arthur. How to Raise & Train a German Short-Haired Pointer. pap. 2.95 (ISBN 0-87666-301-3, DS-1016). TFH Pubns.

McCarty, Diane, ed. German Shorthaired Pointers. (Illus.). 128p. 1980. 4.95 (ISBN 0-87666-700-0, KW-086). TFH Pubns.

DOGS–BREEDS–GOLDEN RETRIEVERS

Fischer, Gertrude. The New Complete Golden Retriever. 2nd ed. LC 84-700. (Complete Breed Book Ser.). (Illus.). 304p. 1984. 16.95 (ISBN 0-87605-185-9). Howell Bk.

Miller, Evelyn. How to Raise & Train a Golden Retriever. (Illus.). pap. 2.95 (ISBN 0-87666-306-4, DS-1018). TFH Pubns.

Nicholas, Anna K. Book of the Golden Retriever. (Illus.). 480p. 1983. 29.95 (ISBN 0-87666-738-8, H-1058). TFH Pubns.

Pepper, Jeffrey. The Golden Retriever. (The Dog Breed Ser.: No. 3). (Illus.). 320p. 1984. 14.95 (ISBN 0-87666-668-3, PS-786). TFH Pubns.

Sawtell, Lucille. All about the Golden Retriever. 3rd ed. (All About Ser.). (Illus.). 144p. 1980. 12.95 (ISBN 0-7207-1217-3, Pub. by Michael Joseph). Merrimack Pub Cir.

TFH Publications Staff, ed. Golden Retrievers. (Illus.). 80p. 1984. pap. 3.95 (ISBN 0-86622-204-9, PB-130). TFH Pubns.

Walsh, James & Walsh, Phyllis A. Golden Retrievers. (Illus.). 128p. 1980. 4.95 (ISBN 0-87666-678-0, KW 067). TFH Pubns.

DOGS–BREEDS–GORDON SETTER

Look, Jean S. & Lustenberger, Anita. The Complete Gordon Setter. LC 84-9049. (Illus.). 408p. 1985. lib. bdg. 19.95 (ISBN 0-87605-158-1). Howell Bk.

DOGS–BREEDS–GREAT DANE

Basquette, Lina. Your Great Dane. LC 70-187772. (Your Dog Bk.). (Illus.). 128p. 1972. 12.95 (ISBN 0-87714-000-6). Denlingers.

Denlinger, Milo G., et al. New Complete Great Dane. 3rd ed. LC 62-20219. (Complete Breed Book Ser.). (Illus.). 352p. 1983. 14.95 (ISBN 0-87605-161-1). Howell Bk.

Draper, Nancy-Carroll. The Great Dane: Dogdom's Apollo. LC 81-6404. (Illus.). 203p. 1982. 15.95 (ISBN 0-87605-162-X). Howell Bk.

Hart, Ernest H. This Is the Great Dane. 1966. 12.95 (ISBN 0-87666-310-2, PS-620). TFH Pubns.

McCarty, Diane. Great Danes. (Illus.). 125p. 1980. 4.95 (ISBN 0-87666-693-4, KW-082). TFH Pubns.

Ostovar. Great Danes in Canada. (Other Dog Bk.). (Illus.). 96p. 1982. 24.95 (ISBN 0-87714-080-4). Denlingers.

DOGS–BREEDS–GREAT PYRENEES

Strang, Paul D. & Giffin, James M. The Complete Great Pyrenees. LC 76-51095. (The Complete Breed Book Ser.). (Illus.). 288p. 1983. 15.95 (ISBN 0-87605-163-8). Howell Bk.

DOGS–BREEDS–GREYHOUNDS

Clarke, H. Edwards. The Greyhound. rev., 7th ed. 222p. 1980. text ed. 24.95x (ISBN 0-09-141410-5, SpS). Sportshelf.

Genders, Roy. Encyclopaedia of Greyhound Racing. 416p. 24.95 (ISBN 0-7207-1106-1, Pub. by Michael Joseph). Merrimack Pub Cir.

Regan, Ivy M. The Greyhound Owner's Encyclopaedia. 2nd ed. 144p. 1981. 16.95 (ISBN 0-7207-1348-X, Pub. by Michael Joseph). Merrimack Pub Cir.

DOGS–BREEDS–IRISH SETTERS

Brearley, Joan McD. This Is the Irish Setter. (Illus.). 480p. 1975. 19.95 (ISBN 0-87666-655-1, H-952). TFH Pubns.

Gannon, Robert. How to Raise & Train an Irish Setter. (Illus.). pap. 2.95 (ISBN 0-87666-319-6, DS-1024). TFH Pubns.

Hulvenstot, Luz. Irish Setters. (Illus.). 1979. 4.95 (ISBN 0-87666-691-8, KW-044). TFH Pubns.

DOGS–BREEDS–IRISH WOLF HOUNDS

Brearley, Joan McD. Ibizan Hounds. (Illus.). 128p. 1980. 4.95 (ISBN 0-87666-694-2, KW-060). TFH Pubns.

Donovan, John A. You & Your Irish Wolfhound. LC 76-20960. (Other Dog Bks.). (Illus.). 1977. 24.95 (ISBN 0-87714-053-7). Denlingers.

Gordon, John. Irish Wolfhound. LC 73-91146. 1974. 7.50 (ISBN 0-668-03435-1). Arco.

Pasano, Beverly, ed. Irish Wolfhounds. (Illus.). 128p. 1983. 4.95 (ISBN 0-87666-718-3, KW-108). TFH Pubns.

Starbuck, Alma J. Complete Irish Wolfhound. 3rd ed. LC 79-76834. (Complete Breed Book Ser.). (Illus.). 1969. 15.95 (ISBN 0-87605-170-0). Howell Bk.

DOGS–BREEDS–JACK RUSSELL TERRIER

Huxham, Mona. All about the Jack Russell Terrier. 2nd ed. (All About Ser.). (Illus.). 150p. 1983. 12.95 (ISBN 0-7207-1201-7, Pub. by Michael Joseph). Merrimack Pub Cir.

Tottenham, Katherine & Nicholas, Anna K. This Is the Jack Russell Terrier. (Illus.). 192p. 1982. 19.95 (ISBN 0-87666-746-9, H-1053). TFH Pubns.

DOGS–BREEDS–KEESHOND

Nicholas, Anna K. The Keeshond. (Illus.). 287p. 1984. 14.95 (ISBN 0-86622-032-1, PS-807). TFH Pubns.

Peterson, Clementine. The Complete Keeshond. LC 77-130971. (Complete Breed Book Ser.). (Illus.). 256p. 1983. 15.95 (ISBN 0-87605-174-3). Howell Bk.

Westcott, William D. How to Raise & Train a Keeshond. (Orig.). pap. 2.95 (ISBN 0-87666-326-9, DS-1091). TFH Pubns.

DOGS–BREEDS–KERRY BLUE TERRIERS

Izant, Edith. The Kerry Blue Terrier. LC 77-87764. (Other Dog Books). (Illus.). 1982. 24.95 (ISBN 0-87714-060-X). Denlingers.

DOGS–BREEDS–LABRADOR DOGS

Farrington, S. Kip, Jr. Labrador Retriever: Friend & Worker. (Illus.). 176p. 1976. 13.95 (ISBN 0-8038-4295-3). Hastings.

Henschel, Stan. How to Raise & Train a Labrador Retriever. (Illus.). pap. 2.95 (ISBN 0-87666-330-7, DS-1095). TFH Pubns.

Nicholas, Anna K. The Book of the Labrador Retriever. (Illus.). 480p. 1983. 29.95 (ISBN 0-87666-748-5, H 1059). TFH Pubns.

Roslin-Williams, Mary. All about the Labrador. 2nd ed. (All About Ser.). (Illus.). 144p. 1980. 12.95 (ISBN 0-7207-0842-7, Pub. by Michael Joseph). Merrimack Pub Cir.

TFH Publications, ed. Labrador Retrievers. (Illus.). 80p. 1984. pap. 3.95 (ISBN 0-86622-248-0, PB-115). TFH Pubns.

Warwick, Helen. Complete Labrador Retriever. 2nd ed. LC 65-24487. (Complete Breed Book Ser.). (Illus.). 304p. 1983. 15.95 (ISBN 0-87605-205-7). Howell Bk.

Williams, Mary R. The Dual Purpose Labrador. 192p. 1969. 8.95 (ISBN 0-7207-0242-9, Pub. by Michael Joseph). Merrimack Pub Cir.

Wolters, Richard. The Labrador Retriever: The History & the People. (Illus.). 200p. 1981. 37.50 (ISBN 0-8227-8037-2). Petersen Pub.

DOGS–BREEDS–LAKELAND TERRIER

Plummer, D. Brian. The Fell Terrier. (Illus.). 244p. 1983. 16.40 (ISBN 0-85115-181-7, Pub. by Boydell & Brewer). Longwood Pub Group.

DOGS–BREEDS–LHASA APSO

Berndt, Robert J. Your Lhasa Aspo. LC 74-77246. (Your Dog Book Ser.). (Illus.). 1982. rev. 12.95 (ISBN 0-87714-078-2). Denlingers.

Brearley, Joan McD. This Is the Lhasa Apso. (Illus.). 1977. text ed. 14.95 (ISBN 0-87666-663-2, PS-744). TFH Pubns.

Chenoweth, Patricia & Chenoweth, Thomas. How to Raise & Train a Lhasa Apso. (Orig.). pap. 2.95 (ISBN 0-87666-334-X, DS-1097). TFH Pubns.

Herbel, Norman & Herbel, Carolyn. The Complete Lhasa Apso. LC 78-21601. (Complete Breed Book). 304p. 1984. 15.95 (ISBN 0-87605-208-1). Howell Bk.

McCarty, Diane. Lhasa Apsos. (Illus.). 125p. 1979. 4.95 (ISBN 0-87666-681-0, KW-076). TFH Pubns.

Vervaeke-Helf, Sally A. Lhasa Lore. (Illus.). 300p. 1983. 22.98 (ISBN 0-931866-12-X). Alpine Pubns.

DOGS–BREEDS–MALTESE DOGS

Berndt, Robert J. Your Maltese. LC 75-20787. (Your Dog Book Ser.). (Illus.). 1975. 12.95 (ISBN 0-87714-033-2). Denlingers.

DiGiacomo, Kathy & Bergquist, Barbara J. Maltese. (Illus.). 128p. 1983. 4.95 (ISBN 0-87666-720-5, KW-111). TFH Pubns.

Liebers, Arthur. How to Raise & Train a Maltese. pap. 2.95 (ISBN 0-87666-335-8, DS-1025). TFH Pubns.

DOGS–BREEDS–MASTIFF

Hahn, Joan & Powers, Judy. Champions: A View of the Mastiff in America. LC 82-21714. 408p. 1984. 35.00 (ISBN 0-317-13758-1). Mastiff Club Am.

Moore, Marie A. The Mastiff. LC 77-87765. (Other Dog Bk.). (Illus.). 112p. 1978. 24.95 (ISBN 0-87714-059-6). Denlingers.

DOGS–BREEDS–MINIATURE PINSCHERS

Boshell, Buris R. Your Miniature Pinscher. LC 69-19733. (Your Dog Book Ser). (Illus.). 1969. 12.95 (ISBN 0-87714-024-3). Denlingers.

DOGS–BREEDS–NEWFOUNDLAND

Chern, Margaret B. New Complete Newfoundland. 2nd ed. LC 75-18266. (Complete Breed Book Ser.). (Illus.). 288p. 1985. 15.95 (ISBN 0-87605-217-0). Howell Bk.

McDonnell, Betty & Riley, Jo ann. The Newfoundland Handbook. LC 84-13524. (Other Dog Bks.). (Illus.). 1985. 5.95 (ISBN 0-87714-108-8). Denlingers.

DOGS–BREEDS–NORWEGIAN ELKHOUND

Crafts, Glenna C. How to Raise & Train a Norwegian Elkhound. (Orig.). pap. 2.95 (ISBN 0-87666-342-0, DS-1101). TFH Pubns.

Franciose, Helen E. & Swanson, Nancy C. Your Norwegian Elkhound. LC 73-84513. (Your Dog Bk.). (Illus.). 160p. 1974. 12.95 (ISBN 0-87714-014-6). Denlingers.

Nicholas, Anna K. Norwegian Elkhounds. (Illus.). 128p. 1983. 4.95 (ISBN 0-87666-722-1, KW-110). TFH Pubns.

DOGS–BREEDS–OLD ENGLISH SHEEPDOG

Berkowitz, Mona. How to Raise & Train an Old English Sheepdog. pap. 2.95 (ISBN 0-87666-344-7, DS-1103). TFH Pubns.

Longton, Tim & Hart, Edward. The Sheep Dog: Its Work & Training. (Illus.). 124p. 1976. 12.95 (ISBN 0-7153-7149-5). David & Charles.

Griffen, Jeff. How to Raise & Train Your Puppy. pap. 5.00 (ISBN 0-87980-330-4). Wilshire.
Haggerty, Arthur J. & Benjamin, Carol L. Dog Tricks. LC 77-16919. (Illus.). 160p. 1985. Repr. 10.95 (ISBN 0-87605-517-X). Howell Bk.
Hillmann, Bill. Training Retrievers: Methods & Concepts of 20 Top Professionals. LC 79-63126. 19.50 (ISBN 0-686-24829-5). Seattle Pub Co.
Holmes, John & Holmes, Mary. Looking after Your Dog: Training & Care. LC 81-4894. 128p. 1982. pap. 5.95 (ISBN 0-668-05271-6). Arco.
Irving, Joe. Training Spaniels. (Illus.). 230p. 1980. 16.95 (ISBN 0-7153-8008-7). David & Charles.
Kalsone, Shirlee. Dogs: Breeds, Care & Taining. (Orig.). 1982. pap. 4.95 (ISBN 0-440-32626-5, LE). Dell.
Kellogg, John W. Dog Training Made Easy & Fun. pap. 4.00 (ISBN 0-87980-028-3). Wilshire.
Kerr, David. Training Your Dog. 1978. 7.50 (ISBN 0-7153-7541-5). David & Charles.
Kersley, J. A. Training the Retriever: A Manual. LC 77-165561. (Illus.). 208p. 1985. 13.95 (ISBN 0-87605-774-1). Howell Bk.
Kessopulos, Gust. Dog Obedience Training. 1975. pap. 5.00 (ISBN 0-87980-301-0). Wilshire.
Koehler, William R. Guard Dog Training: The Koehler Method. 2nd ed. LC 67-26609. (Illus.). 1967. Repr. 14.95 (ISBN 0-87605-552-8). Howell Bk.
--Koehler Method of Dog Training. LC 62-14225. (Illus.). 208p. 1984. 10.95 (ISBN 0-87605-657-5). Howell Bk.
--Koehler Method of Open Obedience for Ring, Home, & Field. LC 70-114681. (Illus.). 160p. 1971. 10.95 (ISBN 0-87605-753-9). Howell Bk.
Liebers, Arthur. Housebreak & Train Your Dog. (Orig.). 1958. pap. 2.95 (ISBN 0-87666-318-8, DS-1020). TFH Pubns.
--How to Raise & Train a Pedigreed or a mixed breed Puppy. pap. 2.95 (ISBN 0-87666-370-6, DS-1027). TFH Pubns.
Loeb, Jo & Loeb, Paul. Supertraining Your Dog. LC 80-10623. (Illus.). 1980. 9.95 (ISBN 0-13-876730-0). P-H.
Loeb, Paul. Paul Loeb's Complete Book of Dog Training. 1983. pap. 3.50 (ISBN 0-671-47297-6). PB.
Lucky, Mr. Mr. Lucky's Trick Dog Training Book. LC 80-23215. (Illus.). 64p. 1981. pap. 4.95 (ISBN 0-87714-086-3). Denlingers.
Maller, Dick & Feinman, Jeffrey. Twenty-One Days to a Trained Dog. 1979. pap. 5.95 (ISBN 0-671-25193-7, Fireside). S&S.
Margolis, Matthew & Siegal, Mordecai. Good Dog, Bad Dog. LC 72-78139. 1973. 8.95 (ISBN 0-03-001421-2). HR&W.
Meisterfeld, C. W. Hows & Whys of Psychological Dog Training. rev ed. LC 79-66550. (Illus.). 1979. 5.90 (ISBN 0-9601292-3-5). M R K.
--Hows & Whys of Psychological Dog Training. LC 77-79620. (Illus.). 1977. pap. 4.95 (ISBN 0-9601292-1-9). M R K.
Miller, Harry. Common Sense Book of Puppy & Dog Care. (Orig.). pap. 3.95 (ISBN 0-553-24657-7). Bantam.
Monks of New Skete. How to Be Your Dog's Best Friend: A Training Manual for Dog Owners. LC 78-8553. (Illus.). 1978. 14.45 (ISBN 0-316-60491-7). Little.
Morsell, Curt. Training Your Dog to Win Obedience Titles. LC 76-21586. (Illus.). 160p. 1985. 11.95 (ISBN 0-87605-674-5). Howell Bk.
Mulvany, Mollie. All about Obedience Training for Dogs. 2nd ed. (All About Ser.). 150p. 1983. 12.95 (ISBN 0-7207-1089-8, Pub. by Michael Joseph). Merrimack Pub Cir.
Neil, David H. & Rutherford, Clarice. How to Raise a Puppy You Can Live With. (Illus.). 122p. 1982. pap. 6.98x (ISBN 0-931866-09-X). Alpine Pubns.
Pearsall, Margaret. The Pearsall Guide to Successful Dog Training. 3rd ed. LC 80-16840. (Illus.). 352p. 1984. 14.95 (ISBN 0-87605-759-8). Howell Bk.
Pearsall, Mile D. & Verbruggen, Hugo. Scent: Training to Track, Search, & Rescue. (Illus.). 224p. 1982. 14.98 (ISBN 0-931866-11-1). Alpine Pubns.
Pearsall, Milo & Leedham, Charles G. Dog Obedience Training. rev. ed. (Illus.). 1978. 17.95 (ISBN 0-684-16158-3, ScribT). Scribner.
Pearsall, Milo D. & Pearsall, Margaret E. Your Dog: Companion & Helper. LC 80-14115. (Illus.). 160p. 1980. 11.98 (ISBN 0-931866-07-3). Alpine Pubns.
Pfaffenberger, Clarence J. New Knowledge of Dog Behavior. LC 63-13674. (Illus.). 208p. 1985. 12.95 (ISBN 0-87605-704-0). Howell Bk.
Radcliffe, Talbot. Spaniels for Sport. 136p. 1983. text ed. 9.95 (ISBN 0-571-08772-8). Faber & Faber.
Rapp, Jay. Rappid Obedience & Watchdog Training. LC 77-87766. 1978. 7.95 (ISBN 0-87714-070-7); pap. 4.95 (ISBN 0-87714-055-3). Denlingers.
Reel, Rita & Reel, Val. TLC (Two Thousand Tips on Dog Care) Rev. ed. LC 82-99845. (Illus.). 240p. 1982. 12.95 (ISBN 0-9607100-2-7); pap. 9.95 (ISBN 0-9607100-1-9). Rival Pubs.
Richards, Herbert. The T.F.H. Book of Puppies. (Illus.). 96p. 6.95 (ISBN 0-87666-816-3, HP-013). TFH Pubns.
Roebuck, Kenneth C. Gun-Dog Training Spaniels & Retrievers. LC 82-5667. (Illus.). 192p. 1982. 12.95 (ISBN 0-8117-0778-4). Stackpole.
Saunders, Blanche. The Complete Book of Dog Obedience. 4th ed. LC 77-91206. (Illus.). 288p. 1984. 14.95 (ISBN 0-87605-459-9). Howell Bk.
Scales, Susan. Retriever Training. LC 76-40806. (Illus.). 1977. 15.95 (ISBN 0-7153-7246-7). David & Charles.
Schellenberg, Dietmar. Top Working Dogs: A Training Manual. 2nd, rev. & exp. ed. LC 82-90110. (Illus.). 192p. (Orig.). 1985. pap. 24.90 (ISBN 0-9608798-0-3). DBC.
Sessions, Bruce. How to Train a Watchdog. LC 74-33626. (Illus.). 224p. 1975. pap. 9.25 (ISBN 0-8306-4753-8, 753). TAB Bks.
Sierra Nevada Dog Drivers, Inc. Mush: A Beginners Manual of Sled Dog Training. new ed. Levorsen, Bella, ed. LC 75-23913. (Illus.). 250p. 1984. 13.95 (ISBN 0-914124-06-4, Top). Arner Pubns.
Spencer, James. Retriever Training Tests. LC 83-3709. (Arco Outdoor Ser.). (Illus.). 192p. 1983. 14.95 (ISBN 0-668-05681-9, 5681). Arco.
Strickland, Winifred G. Expert Obedience Training for Dogs. 2nd rev. ed. LC 76-1875. (Illus.). 1976. 17.95 (ISBN 0-02-615020-4). Macmillan.
--Obedience Class Instruction for Dogs: The Trainer's Manual. rev. ed. 1978. 15.95 (ISBN 0-02-615010-7). Macmillan.
Taylor-Moore, Suzanne. Puppies Need Love Too. 48p. 1980. pap. 3.50x (ISBN 0-938758-08-X). MTM Pub Co.
Teitler, Risa. Taming & Training Conures. (Illus.). 96p. 1981. 4.95 (ISBN 0-87666-842-2, KW-139). TFH Pubns.
Vine, Louis L. Behavior & Training of Dogs & Puppies. LC 77-1387. 1977. pap. 2.50 (ISBN 0-668-04162-5). Arco.
Volhard, Joachim J. & Fisher, Gail T. Training Your Dog: The Step-by-Step Manual. LC 82-21327. (Illus.). 240p. 1985. 12.95 (ISBN 0-87605-775-X). Howell Bk.
Weiss, John D. Training a Dog to Live in Your Home: Housebreaking, Chewing, Book ONe. LC 80-67749. (Bk. One). (Illus.). 84p. (Orig., Prog. Bk.). 1980. pap. 6.95x (ISBN 0-9604576-0-7). Animal Owners.
Whitney, Leon F. Dog Psychology: The Basis of Dog Training. 2nd ed. LC 73-161395. (Illus.). 352p. 1971. 14.95 (ISBN 0-87605-520-X). Howell Bk.
--The Natural Method of Dog Training. LC 63-9770. 128p. 1963. 6.95 (ISBN 0-87131-079-1); pap. 3.95 (ISBN 0-87131-246-8). M Evans.
Widmer, Patricia P. Pat Widmer's Dog Training Book. 1980. pap. 3.50 (ISBN 0-451-13250-5, AE3250, Sig). NAL.
Wimhurst, Cecil. Obedience Training for Your Dog. (Illus.). 70p. 1955. pap. 2.50 (ISBN 0-486-20938-5). Dover.
Wolters, Richard A. City Dog. 1975. 8.95 (ISBN 0-87690-148-8). Dutton.
--Family Dog. rev. ed. 1975. 12.50 (ISBN 0-87690-173-9, 01214-360). Dutton.
--Game Dog: The Hunter's Retriever. (Illus.). 1983. 15.95 (ISBN 0-525-93299-2, 01549-460). Dutton.
--Gun Dog. Revolutionary Rapid Training Method. (Illus.). 1961. 12.50 (ISBN 0-525-12005-X, 01214-360). Dutton.
--Water Dog. 1964. 12.50 (ISBN 0-525-23021-1, 01214-360). Dutton.
Woodhouse, Barbara. Dog Training My Way. LC 72-82833. (Illus.). 128p. 1981. pap. 6.95 (ISBN 0-8128-6082-9). Stein & Day.
--Dog Training My Way. 192p. 1985. pap. 3.50 (ISBN 0-425-08108-7). Berkley Pub.
--No Bad Dogs: The Woodhouse Way. Silberman, J. & Tsukahira, P., eds. 160p. 1982. 12.95 (ISBN 0-671-44962-1). Summit Bks.

DOLERITE
see Basalt

DOLPHINS
see also Porpoises

Doak, Wade. Dolphin Dolphin. (Illus.). 298p. 1982. 19.95 (ISBN 0-911378-43-X). Sheridan.
Dobbs, Horace. Follow the Wild Dolphins. LC 82-5712. (Illus.). 292p. 1982. 15.95 (ISBN 0-312-29752-1). St Martin.
Ellis, Richard. Dolphins & Porpoises. LC 82-47823. 1982. 25.00 (ISBN 0-394-51800-4). Knopf.
Gaskin, D. E. The Ecology of Whales & Dolphins. LC 82-11703. (Illus.). 434p. 1982. 25.00x (ISBN 0-435-62287-0). Heinemann Ed.
Gawain, Elizabeth. The Dolphins' Gift. Clemens, Paul, ed. LC 81-3039. (Illus.). 256p. (Orig.). 1981. pap. 7.95 (ISBN 0-931432-10-3). Whatever Pub.
Heintzelman, Donald. A World Guide to Whales, Dolphins & Porpoises. LC 80-20823. 176p. 1981. pap. 9.95 (ISBN 0-8329-3230-2, Pub. by Winchester Pr). New Century.
McIntyre, Joan. Mind in the Waters: A Book to Celebrate the Consciousness of Whales & Dolphins. LC 74-13000. (Illus.). 224p. 1984. pap. 16.95 (ISBN 0-684-14443-3, ScribT). Scribner.
Norris, Kenneth S., ed. Whales, Dolphins, & Porpoises. (Library Reprint Ser.). 1978. 64.00x (ISBN 0-520-03283-7). U of Cal Pr.
Purves, P. E. & Pilleri, G., eds. Echolocation in Whales & Dolphins. 1983. 47.00 (ISBN 0-12-567960-2). Acad Pr.
Shea, George. Dolphins. LC 80-18259. (Creatures Wild & Free Ser.). 1981. 6.95 (ISBN 0-88436-770-3, 35457). EMC.
Slijper, Everhard J. Whales & Dolphins. Drury, John, tr. from Ger. LC 73-90889. (Ann Arbor Science Library). (Illus.). 1976. 9.95x (ISBN 0-472-00122-1). U of Mich Pr.
--Whales & Dolphins. Drury, John, tr. from Ger. LC 73-90889. (Ann Arbor Science Library). (Illus.). 1975. pap. 6.50 (ISBN 0-472-05022-2, AA). U of Mich Pr.
Truitt, Deborah, ed. Dolphins & Porpoises: A Comprehensive, Annotated Bibliography of the Smaller Cetacea. LC 73-19803. 584p. 1974. 90.00x (ISBN 0-8103-0966-1). Gale.

DOMAIN CONFIGURATION
see Domain Structure

DOMAIN STRUCTURE

Carey, Roy & Isaac, E. D. Magnetic Domains & Techniques for Their Observation. 1966. 52.50 (ISBN 0-12-159550-1). Acad Pr.
Cohn, Leslie. Dimension of Spaces of Automorphic Forms on a Certain Two-Dimensional Complex Domain. (Memoirs: No. 158). 97p. 1975. pap. 11.00 (ISBN 0-8218-1858-9, MEMO-158). Am Math.
Kalinowski, A. J., ed. Computational Methods for Infinite Domain Media-Structure Interaction. (AMD Ser.: Vol. 46). 236p. 1981. 40.00 (ISBN 0-686-34478-2, H00195). ASME.
Malozemoff, A. P. & Slonczewski, J. C. Applied Solid State Science, Supplement I: Magnetic Domain Walls in Bubble Materials. (Serial Publication). 1979. 65.00 (ISBN 0-12-002951-0). Acad Pr.
O'Dell, T. H. Ferromagnetodynamics: The Dynamics of Magnetic Bubbles Domains & Domain Walls. LC 80-25331. 230p. 1981. 64.95x (ISBN 0-470-27084-5). Halsted Pr.
Wohlfarth, E. P., ed. Handbook on Ferromagnetic Materials: A Notebook on the Properties of Magnetically Ordered Substances, Vols. 1-3. 1980-83. Vol. 1. 119.25 (ISBN 0-444-85311-1); Vol. 2. 119.25 (ISBN 0-444-85312-X); Vol. 3. 159.75 (ISBN 0-444-86378-8). Elsevier.

DOMES
see also Roofs; Roofs, Shell

Geodesic Services, Inc. The Dome Scrap Book. 176p. 1981. pap. text ed. 9.95 (ISBN 0-8403-2394-8). Kendall-Hunt.
Hopster, Gene. How to Design & Build Your Dome Home. LC 81-80940. (Illus.). 96p. 1981. pap. 9.95 (ISBN 0-89586-100-3). H P Bks.
Parkin, John H. Bell & Baldwin, Their Development of Aerodomes & Hydrodomes at Baddeck, Nova Scotia. LC 65-1207. pap. 154.80 (ISBN 0-317-10252-4, 2014333). Bks Demand UMI.
Prenis, John, ed. The Dome Builder's Handbook. LC 74-19509. (Illus.). 144p. (Orig.). 1973. lib. bdg. 15.90 (ISBN 0-914294-35-0); pap. 6.00 (ISBN 0-914294-03-2). Running Pr.

DOMES (GEOLOGY)
see also Salt Domes

Morgan, George W. Geodesic & Geolatic Domes & Space Structures. LC 85-50009. (Illus.). 315p. (Orig.). 1985. pap. text ed. 65.00 (ISBN 0-914469-01-0). Sci-Tech Pubns.
Relation of Ore Deposition to Doming in the North American Cordillera. LC 60-2730. (Geological Society of America, Memoir Ser.: No. 77). pap. 32.80 (ISBN 0-317-10779-8, 2007960). Bks Demand UMI.

DOMESTIC ANIMALS
see also Animals, Treatment of; Cats; Cattle; Cows; Dogs; Goats; Horses; Livestock; Pets; Reindeer; Sheep; Swine

Animal Breeding: Selected Articles from the World Animal Review. (Animal Production & Health Papers: No. 1). (Eng., Fr., & Span.). 137p. 1977. pap. 7.50 (ISBN 92-5-100288-6, F1315, FAO). Unipub.
Arnold, G. W. & Dudzinski, M. L. Ethology of Free Ranging Domestic Animals. (Developments in Animal & Veterinary Sciences Ser.: Vol. 2). 198p. 1979. 57.50 (ISBN 0-444-41700-1). Elsevier.
Baldwin, B. A., et al. Report on Research & Development in Relation to Farm Animal Welfare. (Animal Management Ser.). 92p. 1981. pap. 17.95x (ISBN 0-8176-1241-6). Birkhauser.
Belanger, Jerome D. The Homesteader's Handbook to Raising Small Livestock. LC 73-88254. 1976. pap. 9.95 (ISBN 0-87857-122-1). Rodale Pr Inc.
Berry, W. T., Jr., et al. Basic Animal Science. 6th ed. (Illus.). 187p. 1980. Repr. wire coil lab. manual 6.95x (ISBN 0-89641-052-8). American Pr.
Blakely, James & Bade, David. The Science of Animal Husbandry. 4th ed. 1985. text ed. 24.95 (ISBN 0-8359-6897-9); instr's manual avail. (ISBN 0-8359-6898-7). Reston.
Clutton-Brock, Juliet. Domesticated Animals from Early Times. (Illus.). 210p. 1981. 24.95 (ISBN 0-292-71532-3). U of Tex Pr.
Cockrill, W. The Buffaloes of China. (Illus.). 96p. 1976. pap. 18.50 (ISBN 92-5-101578-3, F85, FAO). Unipub.
Cole, H. H. & Cupps, P. T., eds. Reproduction in Domestic Animals. 3rd ed. 1977. 53.00 (ISBN 0-12-179252-8). Acad Pr.
Courot, M., ed. The Male in Farm Animal Reproduction. (Current Topics in Veterinary Medicine Ser.). 1985. lib. bdg. 69.50 (ISBN 0-89838-682-9, Pub. by Martinus Nijhoff Netherlands). Kluwer Academic.
Craig, James V. Domestic Animal Behavior: Causes & Implications for Animal Care & Management. (Illus.). 400p. 1981. text ed. 28.95 (ISBN 0-13-218339-0). P-H.
Epstein, H. Domestic Animals of China. LC 73-152339. (Illus.). 166p. 1971. 39.50x (ISBN 0-8419-0073-6). Holmes & Meier.
--Domestic Animals of China. 164p. 1969. cloth 45.00x (ISBN 0-686-45812-5, Pub. by CAB Bks England). State Mutual Bk.
--Domestic Animals of Nepal. LC 75-6685. (Illus.). 160p. 1977. 39.50x (ISBN 0-8419-0202-X). Holmes & Meier.
Ewer, T. K. Practical Animal Husbandry. (Illus.). 272p. 1982. text ed. 26.00 (ISBN 0-7236-0635-8). PSG Pub Co.
Farming with Animal Power. (Better Farming Ser.: No. 14). 57p. 1977. pap. 7.50 (ISBN 92-5-100157-X, F71, FAO). Unipub.
Fogle, Bruce. Interrelations Between People & Pets. (Illus.). 370p. 1981. 32.75x (ISBN 0-398-04169-5). C C Thomas.
Folsch, D. W., ed. The Ethology & Ethics of Farm Animal Production. (Animal Management Ser.: No. 6). (Ger. & Eng.). 144p. 1978. pap. 22.95x (ISBN 0-8176-1004-9). Birkhauser.
Fowler, Murray E. Restraint & Handling of Wild & Domestic Animals. (Illus.). 332p. 1978. text ed. 28.95x (ISBN 0-8138-1890-7). Iowa St U Pr.
Fox, Michael W. Farm Animals: Husbandry, Behavior, & Veterinary Practice. (Illus.). 288p. 1983. pap. 25.00 (ISBN 0-8391-1769-8). Univ Park.
Hammond, J., Jr. & Robinson, T. Hammond's Farm Animals. 5th ed. 350p. 1983. pap. text ed. 24.50 (ISBN 0-7131-2848-8). E Arnold.
Hart, Benjamin L. The Behavior of Domestic Animals. LC 84-25893. (Illus.). 390p. 1985. text ed. 29.95 (ISBN 0-7167-1595-3). W H Freeman.
Herrtage, S. J., ed. Palladius on Husbondrie, English, Part. II. (EETS OS Ser.: Vol. 72). pap. 18.00 (ISBN 0-317-17879-2). Kraus Repr.
International Histological Classification of Tumors of Domestic Animals, Vol. 50, No. 1-2. (WHO Bulletin). (Illus.). 1974. pap. 7.20 (ISBN 0-686-16786-4). World Health.
Jochle, Wolfgang & Lamond, Ross. Control of Reproductive Functions in Domestic Animals. (Current Topics in Veterinary Medicine & Animal Science Ser.: No. 7). (Illus.). 1981. PLB 39.50 (ISBN 90-247-2400-7, Pub. by Martinus Nijhoff Netherlands). Kluwer Academic.
Juergenson, Elwood M. Handbook of Livestock Equipment. 2nd ed. LC 78-51667. (Illus.). 374p. 1979. 17.65 (ISBN 0-8134-2030-X, 2030); text ed. 13.25x. Interstate.
Kaneko, Jiro J., ed. Clinical Biochemistry of Domestic Animals. 3rd ed. LC 79-8873. 1980. 65.00 (ISBN 0-12-396350-8). Acad Pr.
Lockwood, Guy. Raising & Caring for Animals, a Handbook of Animal Husbandry & Veterinary Care. LC 79-14025. (Encore Edition). 1979. pap. 3.50 (ISBN 0-684-17742-0). Scribner.
Mourant, A. E., ed. Man & Cattle: Proceedings of a Symposium on Domestication. 1963. 50.00x (ISBN 0-686-98310-6, Pub. by Royal Anthro Ireland). State Mutual Bk.
National Research Council Committee on Natural Resources. Effect of Environment on Nutrient Requirements of Domestic Animals. 152p. 1981. pap. text ed. 8.95 (ISBN 0-309-03181-8). Natl Acad Pr.
Nelson, R. H. An Introduction to Feeding Farm Livestock. 2nd ed. 1979. pap. text ed. 9.75 (ISBN 0-08-023756-8). Pergamon.

Untermann, Richard. Principles & Practices of Grading, Drainage & Road Alignment: An Ecological Approach. (Illus.). 1978. ref. & text ed. 25.95 (ISBN 0-87909-641-1). Reston.

Urban Runoff-Quantity & Quality. 278p. 1975. pap. 14.00x (ISBN 0-87262-103-0). Am Soc Civil Eng.

Van Schilfgaarde, J., ed. Drainage for Agriculture. (Illus.). 1974. 16.00 (ISBN 0-89118-018-4). Am Soc Agron.

Vermairan, I. & Jobling, G. A. Localized Irrigation: Design, Installation, Operation, Evaluation. (Irrigation & Drainage Papers: No. 36). (Eng. & Fr.). 221p. 1980. pap. 15.75 (ISBN 92-5-100986-4, F2130, FAO). Unipub.

Water Management for Irrigation & Drainage: Proceedings of the ASCE Irrigation & Drainage Division Specialty Conference on July 20-22, (1977: Reno, Nevada) LC 78-101244. (Illus.). Vol. 1. pap. 111.50 (ISBN 0-317-10797-6, 2019557); Vol. 2. pap. 48.00 (ISBN 0-317-10798-4, X1977). Bks Demand UMI.

Zavoianu, I. Morphometry of Drainage Basins. (Developments in Water Science Ser.: No. 20). 238p. 1985. 61.00 (ISBN 0-444-99587-0). Elsevier.

DRAINAGE, HOUSE

see also Plumbing; Sanitary Engineering; Sewerage

Briggs Amasco Ltd. Flat Roofing: A Guide to Good Practice. (Illus.). 216p. 1982. pap. 33.95x (ISBN 0-9507919-0-3, Pub. by RIBA). Intl Spec Bk.

National Association of Home Builders, et al. Residential Storm Water Management: Objectives, Principles & Design Considerations. LC 75-34759. 64p. 1975. pap. 6.00 (ISBN 0-87420-564-6, R04); pap. 4.50 members. Natl Assn Home.

Winneberger. Septic Tank Systems: A Consultant's Toolkit, 2 Vol. set. 1983. text ed. 45.00 set (ISBN 0-250-40635-7); Vol. 1. text ed. 29.95 (ISBN 0-250-40586-5); Vol. 2. text ed. 19.95 (ISBN 0-250-40634-9). Butterworth.

DRAPER, JOHN WILLIAM

Fleming, Donald. John William Draper & the Religion of Science. LC 74-120254. 1970. Repr. lib. bdg. 16.50x (ISBN 0-374-92750-2). Octagon.

DRAWING (METAL WORK)

Developments in the Drawing of Metals. 644p. (Orig.). 1983. pap. text ed. 50.00x (ISBN 0-904357-56-2, Pub. by the Metals Society). Brookfield Pub Co.

Severdenko, V. P., et al, eds. Ultrasonic Rolling & Drawing of Metals. LC 73-188920. 206p. 1972. 35.00x (ISBN 0-306-10872-0, Consultants). Plenum Pub.

DRAWING, STRUCTURAL

see Structural Drawing

DRAWING-ROOM PRACTICE

see also Engineering Drawings

Amiss, John M. & Jones, Franklin D. The Use of Handbook Tables & Formulas. 22nd ed. Ryffel, Henry H., ed. LC 75-10949. (Illus.). 224p. 1984. 9.95 (ISBN 0-8311-1156-9). Indus Pr.

Fryklund, Verne C. & Kepler, Frank R. General Drafting. 4th ed. LC 78-81375. (Illus.). 1969. text ed. 14.63 (ISBN 0-87345-095-7). McKnight.

Rudman, Jack. Principal Draftsman. (Career Examination Ser.: C-1576). (Cloth bdg. avail. on request). pap. 12.00 (ISBN 0-8373-1576-X). Natl Learning.

DREDGING

see also Manganese Mines and Mining, Submarine

Bouma, Arnold H., ed. Shell Dredging & Its Influence on Gulf Coast Environments. LC 75-39416. 464p. 1976. 38.95x (ISBN 0-87201-805-9). Gulf Pub.

Cooper, H. R. Practical Dredging. 1981. 60.00x (ISBN 0-85174-079-0, Pub. by Nautical England). State Mutual Bk.

Dredging & Its Environmental Effects. 1045p. 1976. pap. 30.00x (ISBN 0-87262-165-0). Am Soc Civil Eng.

Dredging Technology, 2nd International Conference. Proceedings, 2 vols. Stephens, H. S., ed. 1979. Set. pap. 62.00x (ISBN 0-900983-76-0, Dist. by Air Science Co). BHRA Fluid.

Huston, John. Hydraulic Dredging: Theoretical & Applied. LC 71-100659. (Illus.). 350p. 1970. 17.50x (ISBN 0-87033-142-6). Cornell Maritime.

Institution of Civil Engineers Staff, ed. Dredging. 126p. 1968. 32.25x (ISBN 0-901948-40-3). Am Soc Civil Eng.

International Symposium on Dredging Technology, 1st. Proceedings. 1976. text ed. 58.00x (ISBN 0-900983-47-7, Dist. by Air Science Co.). BHRA Fluid.

International Symposium on Dredging Technology, 3rd. Proceedings. Stephens, H. S., ed. (Illus.). 446p. (Orig.). 1980. pap. 91.00x (ISBN 0-906085-09-8). BHRA Fluid.

The Real Beneficiaries of Federal Dredging: A Legal, Political & Economic Assessment of the Fifty-Foot Channel for the Port of Baltimore. pap. 4.00 (ISBN 0-943676-00-2). MD Sea Grant Col.

Turner, Thomas M. Fundamentals of Hydraulic Dredging. LC 83-46038. (Illus.). 256p. 1984. 16.00 (ISBN 0-87033-319-4). Cornell Maritime.

DREDGING (BIOLOGY)

see also Marine Biology

Herbich, John B. Coastal & Deep Ocean Dredging. LC 74-4828. 622p. 1975. 39.95x (ISBN 0-87201-194-1). Gulf Pub.

DRESS

see Clothing and Dress

DRESSING OF ORES

see Ore-Dressing

DRESSMAKING

see also Sewing

Bishop & Burns. Lining, Underlining, Interfacing. (Illus.). 72p. (Orig.). 1976. pap. 4.12 (ISBN 0-397-40245-7). Har-Row.

Cotten, Emmi. Clothes Make Magic. 2nd, rev. ed. Rateaver, Bargyla & Rateaver, Gylver, eds. LC 79-55932. (Conservation Gardening & Farming Ser. The Home). (Illus.). 223p. 1980. pap. 10.00 (ISBN 0-915966-00-X). Rateavers.

Gioello, Debbie A. & Berke, Beverly. Figure Types & Size Ranges. LC 78-20736. (Language of Fashion Ser.). (Illus.). 1979. 12.50 (ISBN 0-87005-291-8). Fairchild.

Heafield, Margaret. Young Dressmaker. (Illus.). 120p. 1984. 14.95 (ISBN 0-7134-0584-8, Pub. by Batsford England). David & Charles.

Iowa Home Economics Association. Unit Method of Clothing Construction. 6th ed. Brackelsberg, Phyllis & Shaw, Bertha, eds. (Illus.). 172p. 1977. text ed. 8.95x (ISBN 0-8138-1710-2). Iowa St U Pr.

Jones, Frances. Modern Sewing: A Text & Handbook. LC 71-155248. (Illus.). 498p. 1972. text ed. 7.50x (ISBN 0-8134-1300-1, 1300). Interstate.

Ladbury, Ann. The Dressmaker's Dictionary. LC 82-8725. (Illus.). 360p. 1983. 19.95 (ISBN 0-668-05653-3, 5653). Arco.

Martensson, Kerstin. Kwik-Sew Method for Easy Sewing. (Illus.). pap. 8.50 (ISBN 0-913212-09-1). Kwik Sew.

Minott, Jan. Fitting Commercial Patterns: The Minott Method. LC 77-87335. 1978. spiral bdg. 12.95x (ISBN 0-8087-3907-7). Burgess.

Oblander, Ruth. Dresses Cut-to-Fit. Leppert, Mary, ed. LC 76-53237. 1976. 4.00x (ISBN 0-933956-02-9). Sew-Fit.

Redmile, Brenda. Machine Dressmaking. (Illus.). 96p. 1984. 18.95 (ISBN 0-7134-3860-6, Pub. by Batsford England); pap. 9.95 (ISBN 0-7134-3861-4). David & Charles.

Rhea, Mini & Leighton, Frances. Sew Simply, Sew Right. LC 72-76031. (Illus.). 1969. 9.95 (ISBN 0-8303-0069-4). Fleet.

DRESSMAKING–PATTERN DESIGN

see also Garment Cutting

Bray, Natalie. Dress Pattern Designing: Basic Principles of Cut & Fit, Metric System. (Illus.). 160p. 1974. 17.95x (ISBN 0-8464-0343-9). Beekman Pubs.

--Dress Pattern Designing: The Basic Principles of the Cut & Fit. 4th ed. (Illus.). 144p. 1982. pap. text ed. 14.50 (ISBN 0-246-11716-8, Granada England). Brookfield Pub Co.

--More Dress Pattern Designing: Metric System. (Illus.). 184p. 1974. 17.95x (ISBN 0-8464-0643-8). Beekman Pubs.

Hillhouse, Marion S. & Mansfield, E. A. Dress Design: Draping & Flat Pattern Making. LC 48-7554. 1948. text ed. 29.95 (ISBN 0-395-04627-0). HM.

Kopp, Ernestine, et al. How to Draft Basic Patterns. 2nd ed. LC 74-18758. 1975. 12.50 (ISBN 0-87005-147-4); designer's neckline curve incl. Fairchild.

Redmile, Brenda. Make Your Own Dress Patterns. 1978. pap. 9.95 (ISBN 0-7134-0389-6, Pub. by Batsford England). David & Charles.

Saoben, Marten & Ward, Janet. Pattern Cutting & Making Up: Vol. 2, Cutting & Making Skirts & Sleeves. 192p. 1980. 32.00 (ISBN 0-7134-3559-3, Pub. by Batsford England); pap. 17.95 (ISBN 0-7134-3560-7). David & Charles.

Tanous, Helen N. Designing Dress Patterns. rev. ed. (Illus.). 1971. text ed. 19.96 (ISBN 0-02-663210-1). Bennett IL.

DRIED MILK

see Milk, Dried

DRIFT, CONTINENTAL

see Continental Drift

DRIFTING OF CONTINENTS

see Continental Drift

DRILLING, OIL WELL

see Oil Well Drilling

DRILLING, UNDERWATER

see Underwater Drilling

DRILLING AND BORING

Here are entered works relating to the drilling and boring of holes in metal, wood, other materials, as carried on in workshops, etc., for building and constructive purposes.

Adams, Neal J. Drilling Engineering: A Complete Well Planning Approach. LC 84-1110. 1985. 84.95 (ISBN 0-87814-265-7). Pennwell Bks.

American Society for Metals. Influence of Metallurgy on Hole Making Operations: Drilling, Reaming, Tapping & Others. Tipnis, Vijay A., compiled by. LC 77-13357. (Materials-Metalworking Technology Ser.). (Illus.). pap. 54.00 (ISBN 0-317-09756-3, 2019491). Bks Demand UMI.

Byrum, Douglas. Practical Drilling & Production Design. 528p. 1982. 49.95x (ISBN 0-87814-180-4). Pennwell Bks.

Chater. The Oil Industry & Microbial Ecosystems. 260p. 1978. 65.95 (ISBN 0-471-25627-7, Pub. by John Wiley & Sons England). Heyden.

Davenport, Byron. Handbook of Drilling Practices. LC 84-662. (Illus.). 192p. 1984. 32.95x (ISBN 0-87201-120-8). Gulf Pub.

Drilling Fluid Materials: Barytes. (OCMA). 1978. pap. 21.95 (ISBN 0-471-25923-3, Pub. by Wiley Heyden). Wiley.

Drilling Fluid Materials: Bentonite. (OCMA). 1973. 16.95 (ISBN 0-471-25927-6, Pub. by Wiley Heyden). Wiley.

Editions Technip. Drilling Data Handbook. 448p. 1980. 43.00x (ISBN 0-86010-195-9, Pub. by Graham & Trotman England). State Mutual Bk.

Gingery, David J. The Drill Press. LC 80-66142. (Build Your Own Metal Working Shop from Scrap Ser.: Bk. 5). (Illus.). 128p. (Orig.). 1982. pap. 7.95 (ISBN 0-9604330-4-X). D J Gingery.

Kelsay, R. E. An Insider's View of the Drilling Funds. xvii, 76p. 1982. 14.95 (ISBN 0-943424-00-3); pap. 12.00 (ISBN 0-943424-01-1). RPI Pubns.

Kennedy, John L. Fundamentals of Drilling. 216p. 1982. 43.50x (ISBN 0-87814-200-2). Pennwell Bks.

Krar, S. F. & Oswald, J. W. Drilling Technology. LC 73-13486. 1977. pap. text ed. 10.20 (ISBN 0-8273-0210-X). Delmar.

Oil Companies Materials Association (OCMA) Drilling Fluid Materials: High Viscosity Carboxymethyl Cellulose. 1973. pap. 21.95 (ISBN 0-471-25929-2, Pub by Wiley Heyden). Wiley.

Robert A. Stanger & Co., ed. Stanger's Drilling Fund Yearbook, 1983-84. 2nd ed. LC 83-644748. 290p. 1984. 75.00 (ISBN 0-943570-04-2). R A Stanger.

Society of Manufacturing Engineers. Turning & Boring. 1985. 35.00 (ISBN 0-87263-169-9). SME.

Tiraspolski, W. Hydraulic Downhole Drilling Motors. LC 85-70853. (Illus.). 576p. 1985. 89.95x (ISBN 0-87201-766-4). Gulf Pub.

World Petroleum Congress. Proceedings of Eighth World Petroleum Congress: Geographical Exploration, Vol. 3. 427p. 1971. 105.50 (ISBN 0-85334-518-X, Pub. by Elsevier Applied Sci England). Elsevier.

DRILLING AND BORING MACHINERY

see also Broaching Machines

Albornoz, Fernando, ed. The Auxiliaries. Quiroga, Roberto, tr. (Rotary Drilling Ser.: Unit I, Lesson 9). (Span., Illus.). 60p. (Orig.). 1983. pap. text ed. 5.00 (ISBN 0-88698-037-2, 2.10922). PETEX.

--The Drill Stem. 2nd ed. Quiroga, Roberto, tr. (Rotary Drilling Ser.: Unit I, Lesson 3). (Span., Illus.). 51p. (Orig.). 1983. pap. text ed. 5.00 (ISBN 0-88698-031-3, 2.10322). PETEX.

--The Rotary, Kelly, & Swivel. Quiroga, Roberto, tr. (Rotary Drilling Ser.: Unit I, Lesson 4). (Span., Illus.). 69p. (Orig.). 1982. pap. text ed. 5.00 (ISBN 0-88698-032-1, 2.10422). PETEX.

--The Rotary Rig & its Components. Carmona-Agosto, Vivian, tr. (Rotary Drilling Ser.: Unit I, Lesson 1). (Span., Illus.). 47p. (Orig.). 1980. pap. text ed. 5.00 (ISBN 0-88698-029-1, 2.10132). PETEX.

Bradley, Ian. Screw Threads & Twist Drills. (Illus.). 112p. 1985. pap. 6.95 (ISBN 0-317-14788-9, Pub. by Argus). Aztex.

Carmona-Agosto, Vivian, ed. Safety on the Rig. rev. ed. Albornoz, Fernando, tr. from Eng. (Rotary Drilling Ser.: Unit I, Lesson6). (Span., Illus.). 77p. 1981. pap. text ed. 5.00 (ISBN 0-88698-038-0, 2.11032). PETEX.

Engineering Industry Training Board, ed. Training for Drilling Machine Operators, 17 vols. (Illus.). 1978. Set. 69.95x (ISBN 0-89563-024-9). Intl Ideas.

Gerding, Mildred. The Rotary Rig & Its Components: Canadian Metric Edition. 3rd ed. (Rotary Drilling Ser.: Unit I, Lesson 1). (Illus.). 1979. pap. text ed. 5.00 (ISBN 0-88698-017-8). PETEX.

Gerding, Mildred, ed. The Rotary Rig & Its Components. 3rd ed. (Rotary Drilling Ser.: Unit I, Lesson 1). (Illus.). Date not set. pap. text ed. 5.00 (ISBN 0-88698-005-4, 2.10130). PETEX.

Gingery, David J. The Dividing Head & Deluxe Accessories. LC 80-66142. (Build Your Own Metal Working Shop from Scrap Ser.: Bk. 6). (Illus.). 160p. (Orig.). 1982. pap. 8.95 (ISBN 0-9604330-5-8). D J Gingery.

Handbook 1: Introduction to Drilling Mud Systems. LC 83-161604. (Mud Equipment Manual Ser.). (Illus.). 150p. (Orig.). 1985. pap. 24.95x (ISBN 0-87201-613-7). Gulf Pub.

Leecraft, Jodie, ed. The Auxiliaries. 2nd ed. (Rotary Drilling Ser.: Unit I, Lesson 9). (Illus.). 48p. 1981. pap. text ed. 5.00 (ISBN 0-88698-013-5, 2.10920). PETEX.

--The Auxiliaries: Canadian Metric Edition. rev. ed. (Rotary Drilling Ser.: Unit I, Lesson 9). (Illus.). Date not set. pap. text ed. 5.00 (ISBN 0-88698-025-9, 2.10921). PETEX.

--The Drill Stem. 2nd ed. (Rotary Drilling Ser.: Unit I, Lesson 3). (Illus.). 52p. (Orig.). 1981. pap. text ed. 5.00 (ISBN 0-88698-007-0, 2.10320). PETEX.

--The Drill Stem: Metric Version. 2nd, rev. ed. (Rotary Drilling Ser.: Unit I, Lesson 3). (Illus.). 40p. (Orig.). 1981. pap. text ed. 5.00 (ISBN 0-88698-019-4, 2.10321). PETEX.

--The Hoist. 2nd ed. (Rotary Drilling Ser.: Unit I, Lesson 6). (Illus.). 40p. (Orig.). 1982. pap. text ed. 5.00 (ISBN 0-88698-010-0, 2.10620). PETEX.

--The Hoist: Metric Edition. 3rd, rev. ed. (Rotary Drilling Ser.: Unit I, Lesson 6). (Illus.). 32p. (Orig.). 1982. pap. text ed. 5.00 (ISBN 0-88698-022-4, 2.10621). PETEX.

--Mud Pumps & Conditioning Equipment. 2nd, rev. ed. (Rotary Drilling Ser.: Unit I, Lesson 12). (Illus.). 67p. (Orig.). 1982. pap. text ed. 5.00 (ISBN 0-88698-016-X, 2.11220). PETEX.

--Mud Pumps & Conditioning Equipment: Metric Version. 2nd, rev. ed. (Rotary Drilling Ser.: Unit I, Lesson 12). (Illus.). 63p. (Orig.). 1982. pap. text ed. 5.00 (ISBN 0-88698-028-3, 2.11221). PETEX.

--Rotary, Kelly, & Swivel. 2nd ed. (Rotary Drilling Ser.: Unit I, Lesson 4). (Illus.). 57p. (Orig.). pap. text ed. 5.00 (ISBN 0-88698-008-9, 2.10420). PETEX.

--Rotary, Kelly & Swivel: Canadian Metric Edition. 2nd ed. (Rotary Drilling Ser.: Unit I, Lesson 4). (Illus.). 1981. pap. text ed. 5.00 (ISBN 0-88698-020-8, 2.10421). PETEX.

--Safety on the Rig. (Rotary Drilling Ser.: Unit I, Lesson 10). (Illus.). 72p. 1981. pap. text ed. 5.00 (ISBN 0-88698-014-3, 2.11030). PETEX.

Leecraft, Jodie & Greenlaw, Martha, eds. Safety on the Rig: Canadian Metric Version. 3rd, rev. ed. (Rotary Drilling Ser.: Unit I, Lesson 10). (Illus.). 63p. 1981. pap. text ed. 5.00 (ISBN 0-88698-026-7, 2.11031). PETEX.

Production Rig Equipment. (Well Servicing & Workover Ser.: Lesson 6). (Illus.). 39p. (Orig.). 1971. pap. text ed. 4.50 (ISBN 0-88698-062-3, 3.70610). PETEX.

Vessel Inspection & Maintenance. (Rotary Drilling Ser., Unit V,: Lesson 6). (Illus.). 37p. 1977. pap. text ed. 4.50 (ISBN 0-88698-074-7). PETEX.

DRILLING MUDS

Boyd, William. Principles of Drilling Fluid Control. (Illus.). 215p. 1978. pap. text ed. 8.00 (ISBN 0-88698-096-8). Petex.

Chemicals for Enhanced Oil Recovery: C-014R. 1983. 1500.00 (ISBN 0-89336-210-7). BCC.

Chilingarian, G. V. & Vorabutr, P. Drilling & Drilling Fluids. (Developments in Petroleum Science Ser.: Vol. 11). xx, 802p. 1983. pap. 49.50 (ISBN 0-444-42177-7). Elsevier.

Drilling Mud. rev. ed. (Rotary Drilling Ser.: Unit II, Lesson 2). (Illus., Orig.). 1975. pap. text ed. 5.00 (ISBN 0-88698-054-2, 2.20220). PETEX.

Drilling Mud & Cement Slurry Rheology Manual. 152p. 1982. 80.00x (ISBN 2-7108-0373-9, Pub. by Order Dept Graham Trotman England). State Mutual Bk.

Leecraft, Jodie, ed. Circulating Systems. 3rd, rev. ed. (Rotary Drilling Ser.: Unit I, Lesson 8). (Illus.). 47p. (Orig.). 1981. pap. text ed. 5.00 (ISBN 0-88698-024-0, 2.10831). PETEX.

--Mud Pumps & Conditioning Equipment. 2nd, rev. ed. (Rotary Drilling Ser.: Unit I, Lesson 12). (Illus.). 67p. (Orig.). 1982. pap. text ed. 5.00 (ISBN 0-88698-016-X, 2.11220). PETEX.

--Mud Pumps & Conditioning Equipment: Metric Version. 2nd, rev. ed. (Rotary Drilling Ser.: Unit I, Lesson 12). (Illus.). 63p. (Orig.). 1982. pap. text ed. 5.00 (ISBN 0-88698-028-3, 2.11221). PETEX.

Love, W. W. Disposal Systems. LC 83-161604. (Mud Equipment Manual Ser.: No. 11). 58p. (Orig.). 1982. pap. 15.95x (ISBN 0-87201-623-4). Gulf Pub.

Love, W. W. & Brandt, Louis. Shale Shakers. (Mud Equipment Manual Ser.: No. 3). 14p. (Orig.). 1982. pap. 10.75x (ISBN 0-87201-615-3). Gulf Pub.

Oil Companies Materials Association (OCMA) The Use of Iron-Based Weighting Agents in Drilling Fluids. 1977. pap. 18.95 (ISBN 0-471-25931-4, Wiley Heyden). Wiley.

Ormsby, George. Hydrocyclones. (Mud Equipment Manual Ser.: No. 6). 44p. (Orig.). 1982. pap. 10.75x (ISBN 0-87201-618-8). Gulf Pub.

Ormsby, George S. & Young, Grant. Mud System Arrangements. (Mud Equipment Manual Ser.: No. 2). 44p. (Orig.). 1982. pap. 15.95x (ISBN 0-87201-614-5). Gulf Pub.

Robinson, L. H. Mud Cleaners & Combination Separators. (Mud Equipment Manual Ser.: No. 7). 24p. (Orig.). 1982. pap. 10.75x (ISBN 0-87201-619-6). Gulf Pub.

White, Doug. Agitation & Addition. LC 83-161604. (Mud Equipment Manual Ser.: No. 9). 42p. (Orig.). 1982. 10.75x (ISBN 0-87201-621-8). Gulf Pub.

DRINK INDUSTRY

see Beverage Industry

DRINKING WATER

Amavis, R., et al, eds. Hardness of Drinking Water & Public Health: Proceedings. 1976. 89.00 (ISBN 0-08-020898-3). Pergamon.

International Standards for Drinking Water. 3rd ed. (Also avail. in French, Russian & Spanish). 1971. 4.80 (ISBN 92-4-154024-9). World Health.

Rice, Rip G., ed. Safe Drinking Water: The Impact of Chemicals on a Limited Resource. LC 84-25105. (Illus.). 280p. 1985. 34.95 (ISBN 0-9614032-0-9). Lewis Pubs Inc.

Safe Drinking Water Committee National Research Council. Drinking Water & Health, Vol. 5. 1983. pap. text ed. 15.95 (ISBN 0-309-03381-0). Natl Acad Pr.

DROMEDARIES

see Camels

DROP-FORGING

see Forging

DROP TESTS (CHEMISTRY)

see Spot Tests (Chemistry)

DROPS

see also Atomization

Clift, Roland, et al. Bubbles, Drops & Particles. LC 77-6592. 1978. 58.50 (ISBN 0-12-176950-X). Acad Pr.

Hartland, S. & Hartley, R. W. Axisymmetric Fluid-Liquid Interfaces. 782p. 1976. 127.75 (ISBN 0-444-41396-0). Elsevier.

DROUGHTS

see also Dust Storms; Rain and Rainfall

Berk, Richard A., et al. Water Shortage: Lessons in Conservation from the Great California Drought, 1976-77. (Illus.). 232p. 1981. text ed. 20.00 (ISBN 0-89011-560-5). Abt Bks.

Food & Agriculture Organization. Drought in the Sahel: International Relief Operations, 1973-1975. 48p. 1976. pap. 7.50 (ISBN 0-685-66344-2, F751, FAO). Unipub.

Ganzel, Bill. Dust Bowl Descent. LC 83-3521. (Illus.). vi, 130p. 1984. 29.95 (ISBN 0-8032-2107-X). U of Nebr Pr.

Garcia, R. V. & Escudero, J. Drought & Man: The Nineteen Seventy-Two Case History. (Drought & Man Case Studies: Vol. 3). 1985. 40.00 (ISBN 0-08-025825-5). Pergamon.

Garcia, Rolando V. & Escudero, Jose. Drought of Man the Nineteen Seventy-Two Case History: Vol. 2, The Constant Catastrophe-Malnutrition, Famines & Drought. (IFIAS Publications Ser.: Vol. 2). (Illus.). 304p. 1981. 50.00 (ISBN 0-08-025824-7). Pergamon.

Hall, A. Drought & Irrigation in North-East Brazil. LC 77-82497. (Latin American Studies: No. 29). (Illus.). 1978. 34.50 (ISBN 0-521-21811-X). Cambridge U Pr.

Hurt, R. Douglas. The Dust Bowl: An Agricultural & Social History. LC 81-4031. 240p. 1981. text ed. 22.95x (ISBN 0-88229-541-1); pap. 11.95x (ISBN 0-88229-789-9). Nelson-Hall.

Paleg, L. G. & Aspinall, D., eds. Physiology & Biochemistry of Drought Resistance in Plants. LC 80-70894. 1982. 70.00 (ISBN 0-12-544380-3). Acad Pr.

Pereira, Charles, et al, eds. Scientific Aspects of the Nineteen Seventy-Five-Nineteen Seventy-Six Drought in England & Wales. (Proceedings of the Royal Society). (Illus.). 1979. text ed. 19.50x (ISBN 0-85403-103-0, Pub. by Royal Soc London). Scholium Intl.

Powers of Nature. LC 76-57002. (Special Publication Ser.: No. XII). (Illus.). 1978. 6.95 (ISBN 0-87044-234-1); lib. bdg. 8.50 (ISBN 0-87044-239-2). Natl Geog.

Rosenberg, Norman J., ed. Drought in the Great Plains: Research on Impacts & Strategies. LC 80-51532. 1980. 18.00 (ISBN 0-918334-34-9). WRP.

Saarinen, Thomas F. Perception of the Drought Hazard on the Great Plains. LC 66-22754. (University of Chicago, Department of Geography Research Paper Ser.: No. 106). pap. 49.80 (ISBN 0-317-28820-2, 2017805). Bks Demand UMI.

Schultz, E. F., et al, eds. Floods & Droughts: Proceedings. LC 73-80676. 1973. 21.00 (ISBN 0-918334-03-9). WRP.

Stone, J. F. & Willis, W. O., eds. Plant Production & Management under Drought Conditions: Papers Presented at the Symposium, 4-6 Oct., 1982, Held at Tulsa, OK. (Developments in Agricultural & Managed-Forest Ecology Ser.: Vol. 12). 398p. 1983. Repr. 74.50 (ISBN 0-444-42214-5). Elsevier.

Tannehill, Ivan R. Drought, Its Causes & Effects. LC 47-2193. pap. 69.30 (ISBN 0-317-07873-9, 2000594). Bks Demand UMI.

Weinberg, Michael A. Plants Are Waters' Factories: A Book About Drouth. LC 75-4850. 110p. 1976. pap. 1.95 (ISBN 0-9601014-1-1). Weinberg.

WMO Executive Committee, 26th Session. Drought: Lectures presented at the 25th Session of the WMO Executive Committee. (Special Environmental Reports: No. 5). (Eng. & Fr., Illus.). 113p. 1975. pap. 18.00 (ISBN 92-63-00403-X, W251, WMO). Unipub.

Yevjevich, V., et al, eds. Drought Research Needs. LC 78-64652. 1978. 21.00 (ISBN 0-918334-26-8). WRP.

Yevjevich, Vujica, ed. Coping with Droughts. Da Cunha, L. V., et al. LC 83-50242. 450p. 1984. 39.00 (ISBN 0-918334-52-7). WRP.

DROWNING

Lanoue, F. Drownproofing: A New Technique for Water Safety. 1978. pap. 3.95 (ISBN 0-13-220780-X). P-H.

DRUG METABOLISM

Albert, Kenneth S., ed. Drug Absorption & Disposition: Statistical Considerations. 152p. 1980. 18.00 (ISBN 0-917330-28-5). Am Pharm Assn.

Bertaccini, G., ed. Meditators & Drugs in Gastrointestinal Motility I: Morphological Basis & Neurophysiological Control. (Handbook of Experimental Pharmacology Ser.: Vol. 59, I). (Illus.). 468p. 1982. 160.00 (ISBN 0-387-11296-0). Springer-Verlag.

Bridges, J. W. & Chasseaud, L. F. Progress in Drug Metabolism, Vol. 5. LC 80-40128. (Progress in Drug Metabolism Ser.). 362p. 1980. 104.00 (ISBN 0-471-27776-2, Pub. by Wiley-Interscience). Wiley.

--Progress in Drug Metabolism, Vol. 6. LC 80-42314. (Progress in Drug Metabolism Ser.). 320p. 1981. 79.95x (ISBN 0-471-28023-2, Pub. by Wiley Interscience). Wiley.

Bridges, J. W. & Chasseaud, L. F., eds. Progress in Drug Metabolism, Vols. 1-4. Incl. Vol. 1. 286p. 1976. 68.95x (ISBN 0-471-10370-5); Vol. 2. 350p. 1977. 79.95 (ISBN 0-471-99442-1); Vol. 3. LC 75-19446. 372p. 1979. 84.95x (ISBN 0-471-99711-0); Vol. 4. LC 79-42723. 335p. 1980. 89.95x (ISBN 0-471-27702-9). Pub. by Wiley-Interscience). Wiley.

--Progress in Drug Metabolism, Vol. 8. 407p. 1984. 77.00x (ISBN 0-85066-269-9). Taylor & Francis.

Colowick, Sidney & Jakoby, William, eds. Methods in Enzymology: Detoxication & Drug Metabolism: Conjugation & Related Systems, Vol. 77. (Methods in Enzymology Ser.). 1981. 55.00 (ISBN 0-12-181977-9). Acad Pr.

Frigerio, Alberto & Ghisalberti, Emilio L., eds. Mass Spectrometry in Drug Metabolism. LC 76-53013. 544p. 1977. 65.00x (ISBN 0-306-31018-X, Plenum Pr). Plenum Pub.

Garrett & Hirtz. Drug Fate & Metabolism, Vol. 5. 320p. 1985. 79.50 (ISBN 0-8247-7423-X). Dekker.

Gillette, James R., et al, eds. Microsomes & Drug Oxidations: Proceedings. 1969. 65.00 (ISBN 0-12-283650-2). Acad Pr.

Gudzinowicz, B. J. Analysis of Drugs & Metabolites by Gas Chromatography - Mass Spectometry: Antipsychotic, Antiemetic & Antidepressant Drugs, Vol. 3. 1977. 49.75 (ISBN 0-8247-6586-9). Dekker.

Gudzinowicz, B. J. & Gudzinowicz, M. J. Analysis of Drugs & Meta-Bolites by Gas Chromotography-Mass Spectometry: Analgesics, Local Anesthetics, & Antibiotics, Vol. 5. 1978. 89.75 (ISBN 0-8247-6651-2). Dekker.

Gudzinowicz, Michael J. & Gudzinowicz, Benjamin J. The Analysis of Drugs & Related Compounds by Gas Chromatography-Mass Spectometry: Respiratory Gases, Volatile Anesthetics, Ethyl Alcohol, & Related Toxicological Materials, Vol. 1. 1977. 89.75 (ISBN 0-8247-6576-1). Dekker.

Higuchi, T. & Stella, V., eds. Pro-Drugs as Novel Drug Delivery Systems. LC 75-11721. (ACS Symposium Ser.: No. 14). 1975. 29.95 (ISBN 0-8412-0291-5). Am Chemical.

Hirtz, Jean L. Fate of Drugs in the Organism: A Bibliographic Survey, Vol. 4. 1979. 125.00 (ISBN 0-8247-6587-7). Dekker.

Hirtz, Jean L. & Garrett, E. R., eds. Drug Fate & Metabolism, Vol. 2. 1978. 75.00 (ISBN 0-8247-6603-2). Dekker.

Jenner & Testa. Concepts in Drug Metabolism, Part B. (Drug & the Pharmaceutical Sciences Ser.: Vol. 10). 648p. 1981. 85.00 (ISBN 0-8247-1323-0). Dekker.

Jenner, P. A. & Testa, B. Concepts in Drug Metabolism, Pt. A-1. (Drugs & the Pharmaceutical Sciences: Vol. 10). 424p. 1980. 65.00 (ISBN 0-8247-6906-6). Dekker.

Knoll. Symposium on Recent Trends in Development of Drug Metabolism, Vol. 4. 1979. 6.00 (ISBN 0-9960007-7-1, Pub. by Akademiai Kaido Hungary). Heyden.

Leigh, D. A. & Robinson, O. P. Augmentin: Clavulanate-Potentiated Amoxycillin. (International Congress Ser.: Vol. 590). 246p. 1982. 47.00 (ISBN 0-444-90271-6, Excerpta Medica). Elsevier.

Mitchell, Jerry R. & Horning, Marjorie G., eds. Drug Metabolism & Drug Toxicity. (Illus.). 448p. 1984. text ed. 86.00 (ISBN 0-89004-997-1). Raven.

Paoletti, R. Drugs Affecting Lipid Metabolism. Date not set. 55.50 (ISBN 0-686-94149-7). Elsevier.

Paoletti, Rodolfo, ed. Lipid Pharmacology. (Medicinal Chemistry: Vol. 2). 1964. 75.00 (ISBN 0-12-544950-X). Acad Pr.

Pirola, R. C. Drug Metabolism & Alcohol. LC 77-18759. 1978. 29.50 (ISBN 0-8391-1228-9). Univ Park.

Reidenberg, Marcus. Renal Function & Drug Action. LC 74-135334. 1971. 10.95 (ISBN 0-7216-7538-7). Saunders.

Rolinson, G. N. & Watson, A. Augmentin: Clavulanate Potentiated Amoxycillin. (International Congress Ser.: Vol. 544). 310p. 1981. 61.00 (ISBN 0-444-90188-4, Excerpta Medica). Elsevier.

Singer, T. P. & Ondarza, P. N., eds. Molecular Basis of Drug Action. (Developments in Biochemistry Ser.: Vol. 19). 408p. 1981. 75.75 (ISBN 0-444-00632-X, Biomedical Pr). Elsevier.

Soda, ed. Drug Induced Sufferings: Medical, Pharmaceutical & Legal Aspects. (International Congress Ser.: Vol. 513). 516p. 1980. 105.75 (ISBN 0-444-90140-X, Excerpta Medica). Elsevier.

Sodium & Potassium in Foods & Drugs. pap. 6.00 (ISBN 0-89970-007-1, OP-080). AMA.

Testa, Bernard & Jenner, Peter. Drug Metabolism: Chemical & Biochemical Aspects. (Drugs & the Pharmaceutical Sciences: Vol. 4). 1976. 79.75 (ISBN 0-8247-6371-8). Dekker.

Weizman Institute of Science, Rehovot, Israel, Feb. 1980 & Littauer, U. Z. Neurotransmitters-Receptor Interactions: Proceedings. LC 80-41130. 570p. 1980. 57.95x (ISBN 0-471-27893-9, Pub. by Wiley-Interscience). Wiley.

DRUGS

see also Botany, Medical; Drug Metabolism; Pharmacy; Poisons

also names of particular drugs and groups of drugs, e.g. Narcotics, Stimulants

Albanese, Joseph. The Nurses' Drug Reference: Nineteen Eighty-Two Drug Update. 128p. 1983. pap. 3.00 (ISBN 0-07-000769-1). McGraw.

American Society of Hospital Pharmacists. Consumer Drug Digest. 496p. 1982. 19.95 (ISBN 0-87196-554-2); pap. 9.95 (ISBN 0-87196-686-7). Facts on File.

Anthraquinone Symposium, Buergenstock-Luzern, September, 1978. Natural Anthraquinone Drugs. Fairbairn, J. W., ed. (Pharmacology Journal: Vol. 20, Suppl. 1). (Illus.). 140p. 1980. pap. 17.25 (ISBN 3-8055-0683-X). S Karger.

Ariens, E. J. Drug Design. (Medicinal Chemistry Ser.: Vol. 11). Vol. 1 1971. 88.00 (ISBN 0-12-060301-2); Vol. 2 1972. 88.00 (ISBN 0-12-060302-0); Vol.3 1972. 85.50 (ISBN 0-12-060303-9); Vol 4. 1973. 85.50 (ISBN 0-12-060304-7); Vol. 5 1975. 82.50 (ISBN 0-12-060305-5); Vol. 6 1975. 82.50 (ISBN 0-12-060306-3); Vol. 7 1976. 80.00 (ISBN 0-12-060307-1); Vol. 8, 1978. 74.50 (ISBN 0-12-060308-X). Acad Pr.

Ariens, E J., ed. Drug Design, Vol. 9. LC 72-127678. (Medicinal Chemistry Ser.). 1980. 55.00 (ISBN 0-12-060309-8). Acad Pr.

Ariens, E. J., ed. Drug Design, Vol. 10. (Medicinal Chemistry Ser.). 1980. 66.00 (ISBN 0-12-060310-1). Acad Pr.

August, J. Thomas, ed. Biological Response Mediators & Modulators (Symposium) (John Jacob Abel Symposium on Drug Development). 1983. 33.00 (ISBN 0-12-068050-5). Acad Pr.

Basu, T. K. Clinical Implications of Drug Use, 2 vols. 1980. Vol. 1, 160p. 59.00 (ISBN 0-8493-5391-2); Vol. 2, 144p. 59.00 (ISBN 0-8493-5392-0). CRC Pr.

Bindra, Jasjit S. & Lednicer, Daniel. Chronicles of Drug Discovery, Vol. 1. LC 81-11471. 283p. 1982. cloth 37.50x (ISBN 0-471-06516-1, Pub. by Wiley-Interscience). Wiley.

--Chronicles of Drug Discovery, Vol. 2. LC 81-11471. 272p. 1983. cloth 48.50 (ISBN 0-471-89135-5, Pub. by Wiley-Interscience). Wiley.

Blum, Kenneth. Handbook of Abusable Drugs. 1984. 79.95 (ISBN 0-89876-036-4). Gardner Pr.

Brain, Paul F., ed. Hormones, Drugs & Aggression. (Hormone Research Review Ser.: Vol. 3). 173p. 1980. Repr. of 1979 ed. 24.95 (ISBN 0-87705-959-4). Human Sci Pr.

Breuning, Stephen E. & Poling, Alan D. Drugs & Mental Retardation. (Illus.). 450p. 1982. 44.75x (ISBN 0-398-04599-2). C C Thomas.

Brewer, George J. Orphan Drugs & Orphan Diseases: Clinical Realities & Public Policy. LC 83-9865. (Progress in Clinical & Biological Research Ser.: Vol. 127). 298p. 1983. 38.00 (ISBN 0-8451-0127-7). A R Liss.

Brown, G. R. Drug Consultant: 1984-85 A Current Guide to Clinical Drug Treatments & Their Usefulness. Michaels, Rhoda M., ed. 383p. 1984. pap. text ed. 18.95 (ISBN 0-471-80894-6, Pub. by Wiley Med). Wiley.

Bundgaard, Hans, et al. Drug Design & Adverse Reactions. 1977. 75.00 (ISBN 0-12-141150-8). Acad Pr.

Byrn, Stephen. Solid State Chemistry of Drugs. LC 82-13950. 349p. 1982. 60.00 (ISBN 0-12-148620-6). Acad Pr.

Cohen, Sidney, et al. Frequently Prescribed & Abused Drugs: Their Indications, Efficacy & Rational Prescribing. LC 81-20222. 80p. 1982. Repr. of 1980 ed. text ed. 22.95 (ISBN 0-86656-115-3, B115). Haworth Pr.

Coleman, Richard. Is Your Prescription Killing You? Richards, Carolyn, ed. LC 79-28294. 1981. 12.95 (ISBN 0-87949-164-7). Ashley Bks.

Colowick, Sidney P. & Kaplan, Nathan O., eds. Methods in Enzymology: Drug & Enzyme Targeting, Vol. 112. 1985. 69.00 (ISBN 0-12-182012-2). Acad Pr.

Conference Held at Silver Spring, Maryland, Mar. 1978. Membrane Mechanisms of Drugs of Abuse: Proceedings. Abood, Leo G. & Sharp, Charles W., eds. LC 78-19682. (Progress in Clinical & Biological Research: Vol. 27). 280p. 1979. 29.00 (ISBN 0-8451-0027-0). A R Liss.

Cooley, Donald G. Science Book of Wonder Drugs. facsimile ed. LC 72-99627. (Essay Index Reprint Ser.). 1954. 20.00 (ISBN 0-8369-1562-3). Ayer Co Pubs.

Corrigan, L. Luan, ed. APHA Drug Names. Shoff, Janet. LC 78-78275. 1979. softcover 18.00 (ISBN 0-917330-24-2). Am Pharm Assn.

Curry, Stephen H. Drug Disposition & Pharmacokinetics. 3rd ed. (Illus.). 344p. 1981. pap. text ed. 37.00 (ISBN 0-632-00639-0, B-1126-1). Mosby.

Dearden, J. C., ed. Quantitative Approaches to Drug Design: Proceedings of the Fourth European Symposium on Chemical Structure Biological Activity: Bath, U.K., Sept. 6-9, 1982. (Pharmacochemistry Library: Vol. 6). 296p. 1983. 64.00 (ISBN 0-444-42200-5). Elsevier.

Domino, E. F., ed. PCP (Phencyclidine) Historical & Current Perspectives. LC 80-81498. (Illus.). 537p. 1981. 40.00x (ISBN 0-916182-03-7). NPP Bks.

Donaruma, L. Guy & Vogl, Otto, eds. Polymeric Drugs. 1978. 49.50 (ISBN 0-12-220750-5). Acad Pr.

Donaruma, L. Guy, et al. Anionic Polymeric Drugs. LC 80-11364. (Polymers in Biology & Medicine Ser. of Monographs: Vol. 1). 356p. 1980. 64.50x (ISBN 0-471-05530-1, Pub. by Wiley-Interscience). Wiley.

Doyle, A. E., ed. Clinical Pharmacology of Antihypertensive Drugs. (Handbook of Hypertension Ser.: Vol. 5). 428p. 1984. 96.50 (ISBN 0-444-90354-2). Elsevier.

Dreyfus, Jack. A Remarkable Medicine Has Been Overlooked. rev. ed. 1983. pap. 4.95 (ISBN 0-671-47673-4). PB.

Dusek-Girdano, Dorothy. Drugs: A Factual Account. 3rd ed. 352p. 1980. text ed. 13.95 (ISBN 0-394-34875-3, RanC). Random.

Dusted: Facts about PCP. 1983. pap. 0.25 (ISBN 0-89230-165-1). Do it Now.

Einstein, Stanley. Beyond Drugs. LC 73-7940. 1974. pap. text ed. 12.00 (ISBN 0-08-017768-9). Pergamon.

Enna, S. J., et al, eds. Antidepressants: Neurochemical, Behavioral, & Clinical Perspectives. (Central Nervous System Pharmacology Ser.). 275p. 1981. Set. 46.00 (ISBN 0-89004-534-8). Raven.

Faber, Stuart J., et al. Angel Dust: What Everyone Should Know about PCP. 1982. pap. 7.95 (ISBN 0-89074-066-6). Lega Bks.

Fann, William E. & Maddox, George L. Drug Issues in Geropsychiatry. LC 74-1491. 122p. 1974. pap. 9.50 (ISBN 0-683-03002-7). Krieger.

Florey, Klaus, et al, eds. Analytical Profiles of Drug Substances, Vols. 1-6. Vol. 1, 1972. 70.00 (ISBN 0-12-260801-1); Vol. 2, 1973. 70.00 (ISBN 0-12-260802-X); Vol. 3, 1974. 70.00 (ISBN 0-12-260803-8); Vol. 4, 1975. 75.00 (ISBN 0-12-260804-6); Vol. 5, 1976. 70.00 (ISBN 0-12-260805-4); Vol. 6, 1977. 70.00 (ISBN 0-12-260806-2). Acad Pr.

Forney, Robert & Hughes, Francis. Combined Effects of Alcohol & Other Drugs. 132p. 1968. 12.75x (ISBN 0-398-00597-4). C C Thomas.

Gannon, Frank. Drugs, What They Are- How They Look- What They Do. LC 70-148361. 1971. 8.95 (ISBN 0-89388-005-1). Okpaku Communications.

Garratt & Hirtz. Drug Fate & Metabolism, Vol. 3. 1979. 75.00 (ISBN 0-8247-6841-8). Dekker.

Goldberg, Eugene P. Targeted Drugs. (Polymers in Biology & Medicine Ser.). 288p. 1983. 63.50 (ISBN 0-471-04884-4, Pub. by Wiley-Interscience). Wiley.

Goldstein, Eleanor C., ed. Drugs, Vol. 1 (incl. 1973 & 1974 Supplements) (Social Issues Resources Ser.). 1975. 70.00 (ISBN 0-89777-002-1). Soc Issues.

--Drugs, Vol. 2 (incl. 1975-1979 Supplements) (Social Issues Resources Ser.). 1980. 70.00 (ISBN 0-89777-034-X). Soc Issues.

--Drugs, Vol. 3 (incl. 1980-1984 Supplements) (Social Issues Resources Ser.). 1984. 70.00 (ISBN 0-89777-066-8). Soc Issues.

Goldstein, Paul J. Prostitution & Drugs. LC 78-24766. 208p. 1979. 26.00x (ISBN 0-669-02833-9). Lexington Bks.

Gregoriadis, G., et al, eds. Receptor-Mediated Targeting of Drugs. (NATO ASI Series A, Life Sciences). 492p. 1985. 79.50x (ISBN 0-306-41831-2, Plenum Press). Plenum Pub.

Gregoriadis, Gregory, ed. Drug Carriers in Biology & Medicine. 1979. 67.50 (ISBN 0-12-301050-0). Acad Pr.

Gregoriadis, Gregory, et al, eds. Targeting of Drugs. (NATO ASI Series A, Life Sciences: Vol. 47). 440p. 1982. 55.00x (ISBN 0-306-41001-X, Plenum Pr). Plenum Pub.

Gudzinowicz. Analysis of Drugs, Vol. 6: Cardiovascular, Antihypertensive, Hypoglycemic & Thyroid-Related Agents. 1979. 89.75 (ISBN 0-8247-6757-8). Dekker.

--Drug Dynamics for Analytical, Clinical & Biological Chemists. (Drugs & the Pharmaceutical Sciences Ser.). 176p. 1984. 39.75 (ISBN 0-8247-7239-3). Dekker.

Gudzinowicz, Michael J. & Gudzinowicz, Benjamin J. The Analysis of Drugs & Related Compounds by Gas Chromotography-Mass Spectometry: Respiratory Gases, Volatile Anesthetics, Ethyl Alcohol, & Related Toxicological Materials, Vol. 1. 1977. 89.75 (ISBN 0-8247-6576-1). Dekker.

Hafen, Brent Q. & Frandsen, Kathryn J. PCP, Phencyclidine, "Angel Dust". 20p. 1.25 (ISBN 0-89486-074-7, 1942B). Hazelden.

Hawkins, D. F., ed. Drugs & Pregnancy: Human Teratogenesis & Related Problems. LC 82-17813. (Illus.). 243p. 1983. text ed. 20.00 (ISBN 0-443-02466-9). Churchill.

Hopkins, s. J. Principal Drugs: An Alphabetical Guide to Therapeutic Agents. 8th ed. 186p. 1985. pap. 4.95 (ISBN 0-571-13423-8). Faber & Faber.

Hutchison, James. That Drug Danger. 1980. 25.00x (ISBN 0-900871-31-8, Pub. by Standard Scotland). State Mutual Bk.

International Colloquium on Prospective Biology, 4th, Pont-A-Mousson, October 1978. Drug Measurement & Drug Effect in Laboratory Health Science. Siest, G. & Young, D. S., eds. (Illus.). 1979. 56.75 (ISBN 3-8055-3045-5). S Karger.

Jolles, Georges & Woolridge, Ken R. Drug Design: Fact or Fantasy. 1984. 30.00 (ISBN 0-12-388180-3). Acad Pr.

Jones, Kenneth L., et al. Drugs & Alcohol. 3rd ed. 1978. pap. text ed. 10.95 scp (ISBN 0-06-043436-8, HarpC). Har-Row.

Juliano, R. L., ed. Drug Delivery Systems: Characteristics & Biomedical Applications. (Illus.). 1980. text ed. 39.95x (ISBN 0-19-502700-0). Oxford U Pr.

Julien, Robert M. A Primer of Drug Action. 3rd ed. LC 81-4957. (Psychology Ser.). (Illus.). 306p. 1981. text ed. 21.95 (ISBN 0-7167-1287-3); pap. text ed. 13.95 (ISBN 0-7167-1288-1). W H Freeman.

Kakis, Frederic J. Drugs: Facts & Fictions. 384p. 1982. pap. text ed. 12.95 (ISBN 0-531-05638-4). Watts.

Karch. Orphan Drugs. (Drugs & the Pharmaceutical Sciences Ser.: Vol. 13). 288p. 1982. 49.50 (ISBN 0-8247-1681-7). Dekker.

Kastrup & Boyd. Drug Facts & Comparisons, 1985. LC 65-96035. 1984. 59.50 (ISBN 0-397-50693-7, Lippincott Medical). Lippincott.

Krantz, John C., Jr. Historical Medical Classics Involving New Drugs. LC 73-21982. 129p. 1974. 10.50 (ISBN 0-683-04779-5, Pub. by W & W). Krieger.

Kritchevky, David, et al, eds. Lipids, Lipoproteins, & Drugs. LC 75-31790. (Advances in Experimental Medicine & Biology Ser.: Vol. 63). 527p. 1975. 49.50x (ISBN 0-306-39063-9, Plenum Pr). Plenum Pub.

Ladewig, D. & Hobi, V. Drogen unter uns. 4th ed. Dubacher, H. & Faust, V., eds. (Illus.). viii, 100p. 1983. pap. 5.25 (ISBN 3-8055-3608-9). S Karger.

Ladewig, D., ed. Drogen & Alkohol. (Illus.). xii, 220p. 1980. pap. 14.25 (ISBN 3-8055-1624-X). S Karger.

Langstron, Kathleen U. Drugs in All Phases of Life & Medicine: Subject Analysis Index With Research Bibliography. LC 85-47581. 150p. 1985. 29.95 (ISBN 0-88164-336-X); pap. 21.95 (ISBN 0-88164-337-8). ABBE Pubs Assn.

Liska, Ken. Drugs & the Human Body: With Implications for Society. 2nd ed. 573p. 1986. pap. price not set write for info. (ISBN 0-02-371070-5). Macmillan.

Li Wan Po, A. Non-Prescription Drugs. (Illus.). 477p. 1982. pap. text ed. 49.95 (ISBN 0-632-00857-1, B2969-1). Mosby.

Loebl, Suzanne, et al. The Nurse's Drug Handbook. 3rd ed. LC 80-15274. 1115p. 1983. 25.95 (ISBN 0-471-09661-X, Pub. by Wiley Med); pap. 22.50 (ISBN 0-471-09660-1, Pub. by Wiley-Med). Wiley.

Lomax, P. & Schoenbaum, E. Environment, Drugs & Thermoregulation: International Symposium on the Pharmacology of Thermoregulation, 5th, Saint-Paul-de-Vence, November 1982. (Illus.). xvi, 224p. 1983. 33.75 (ISBN 3-8055-3654-2). S Karger.

McGrady, Pat. Persecuted Drug: Story of DMSO. 2.95x (ISBN 0-441-15101-9). Cancer Control Soc.

Manell, P. & Johansson, S. G., eds. The Impact of Computer Technology on Drug Information: Proceedings of the IFIP-IMIA Working Conference, Uppsala, Sweden, October 26-28, 1981. 262p. 1982. 34.00 (ISBN 0-444-86451-2, North Holland). Elsevier.

Medicinal Chemistry Symposium, 20th, New York, May 1979. Drug Action & Design Mechanism Based on Enzyme Inhibitors: Proceedings. Kalman, Thomas, ed. LC 79-17370. (Developments in Biochemistry: Vol. 6). 310p. 1979. 68.50 (ISBN 0-444-00345-2, Biomedical Pr). Elsevier.

Mitchell, Jerry R. & Horning, Marjorie G., eds. Drug Metabolism & Drug Toxicity. (Illus.). 448p. 1984. text ed. 86.00 (ISBN 0-89004-997-1). Raven.

Modell, Walter. Drugs in Current Use & New Drugs 1982. 27th ed. (Annual Publication). 1981. pap. text ed. 9.95 (ISBN 0-8261-0160-7). Springer Pub.

--Drugs in Current Use & New Drugs 1983. 29th ed. 192p. 1983. pap. text ed. 10.95 (ISBN 0-8261-0162-3). Springer Pub.

Morgan, H. Wayne. Drugs in America: A Social History, 1800-1980. LC 81-14531. (Illus.). 248p. 1981. pap. 9.95x (ISBN 0-8156-2282-1). Syracuse U Pr.

Najean, Y., et al, eds. Safety Problems Related to Chloramphenicol & Thiamphenicol Therapy. (Monographs of the Mario Negri Institute of Pharmacological Research). 128p. 1981. text ed. 20.50 (ISBN 0-89004-547-X). Raven.

Petersen, David M., et al. Drugs & the Elderly: Social & Pharmacological Issues. (Illus.). 280p. 1979. 26.25x (ISBN 0-398-03758-2). C C Thomas.

Pfleger, K., et al, eds. Mass Spectral & GC Data of Drugs, Poisons & Their Metabolites, 2 vols. 1985. Vol. 1, 208p. lib. bdg. 195.00 set (ISBN 0-317-30652-9). Vol. 2, 744p. VCH Pubs.

Phillips, I. & Collier, J., eds. Metronidazole. (Royal Society of Medicine International Congress & Symposium Ser.: No. 18). 262p. 1980. pap. 39.50 (ISBN 0-8089-1236-4, 793288). Grune.

Reilly, Mary J. & Kepler, Judith A., eds. American Hospital Formulary Service, 2 vols. LC 59-7620. 1982. looseleaf set 50.00 (ISBN 0-930530-03-9); vol. 1 (ISBN 0-930530-01-2); vol. 2 (ISBN 0-930530-02-0). Am Soc Hosp Pharm.

Richardson, L. I. & Richardson, J. K. The Mathematics of Drugs & Solutions with Clinical Applications. 3rd ed. 192p. 1984. 16.95 (ISBN 0-07-052314-2). McGraw.

Richardson, R. G., ed. Round Table Discussion on Gentamicin & Tobramycin. (Royal Society of Medicine International Congress & Symposium Ser.: No. 4). 72p. 1978. pap. 18.50 (ISBN 0-8089-1149-X, 793530). Grune.

Rodman, Morton J. & Smith, Dorothy W. Pharmacology & Drug Therapy in Nursing. 2nd ed. LC 79-11342. 1979. text ed. 37.50x (ISBN 0-397-54230-5, 64-01822, Lippincott Nursing). Lippincott.

Roe, Campbell. Drugs & Nutrients. (Drugs & the Pharmaceutical Science Ser.). 568p. 1984. 99.75 (ISBN 0-8247-7054-4). Dekker.

Sager, Diane P. & Bomar, Suzanne K. Quick Reference to Intravenous Drugs. (Quick References for Nurses Ser.). 375p. 1982. pap. text ed. 14.00 (ISBN 0-397-54411-1, 00712897, Lippincott Nursing). Lippincott.

Sanberg, Paul. Over-the-Counter Drugs: Harmless or Hazardous? (Encyclopedia of Psychoactive Drugs Ser.). (Illus.). 1985. PLB 15.95x (ISBN 0-87754-764-5). Chelsea Hse.

Schlaadt, Richard G. & Shannon, Peter T. Drugs of Choice: Current Perspectives on Drug Use. (Illus.). 464p. 1982. pap. 22.95 (ISBN 0-13-220772-9). P-H.

Schuetz, Harald. Benzodiazepines: A Handbook. (Illus.). 460p. 1982. 88.00 (ISBN 0-387-11270-7). Springer-Verlag.

Schwartz, M., ed. Prescription Drugs in Short Supply: Case Histories. (Drugs & the Pharmaceutical Science Ser.: Vol. 8). 1980. 35.00 (ISBN 0-8247-6910-4). Dekker.

Sewell, Winifred. Guide to Drug Information. LC 75-17156. 218p. (Orig.). 1976. 16.00 (ISBN 0-914768-21-2). Drug Intl Pubns.

Siest, G., ed. Drug Effects on Laboratory Test Results. (Developments in Clinical Biochemistry: No. 2). (Illus.). 338p. 1981. PLB 49.50 (ISBN 9-0247-2419-8, Pub. by Martinus Nijhoff). Kluwer Academic.

Silverstone, T., ed. Drugs & Appetite. 1982. 33.00 (ISBN 0-12-643780-7). Acad Pr.

Skoutakis, Vasilios A., ed. Clinical Toxicology of Drugs: Principles & Practice. LC 81-20930. (Illus.). 293p. 1982. text ed. 25.50 (ISBN 0-8121-0807-8). Lea & Febiger.

Solomon, Joel & Keeley, Kim. Perspective in Alcohol & Drug Abuse: Similarities & Differences. 270p. 1982. 26.00 (ISBN 0-88416-306-7). PSG Pub Co.

Statistics on Psychotropic Substances. Incl. 1977. 88p. 1979. 9.00 (ISBN 0-686-61480-1, UN79/11/4); 1978. pap. 10.00 (ISBN 0-686-94219-1, UN80/11/3); 1979. 97p. 1980. pap. 10.00 (UN80/11/6); 1980. 72p. 1981. pap. 10.00 (UN81/11/4); 1981. 86p. 1983. pap. 10.00 (ISBN 0-686-46334-X, UN82/11/5); 1982. 86p. 1984. pap. 11.00 (UN83/11/8); 1983. 89p. 1985. pap. text ed. 12.50 (UN84/11/7). (Eng., Fr. & Span., Orig., UN). Unipub.

Stein, Benjamin. Ludes. 256p. 1982. 12.95 (ISBN 0-312-50012-2). St Martin.

Stockley, Ivan H. Drug Interaction. (Illus.). 512p. 1981. pap. text ed. 34.00 (ISBN 0-632-00843-1, B 4658-8). Mosby.

Sunshine, Irving, ed. CRC Handbook of Spectrophotometric Data of Drugs. 496p. 1981. 78.00 (ISBN 0-8493-3571-X). CRC Pr.

Swartz, H. Prescriber's Handbook of Therapeutic Drugs. 1981. pap. 19.95 (ISBN 0-87489-190-6). Med Economics.

Turner, Paul & Volans, Glyn. The Drugs Handbook. 1978. text ed. 21.25x (ISBN 0-333-21612-1). Humanities.

United States Pharmacopeial Convention, Inc. Drug Information for the Health Care Provider, Vol. 1. LC 81-640842. 1985. 41.95 (ISBN 0-913595-15-2). USPC.

United States Pharmacopoeial Convention. The Physicians' & Pharmacists' Guide to Your Medicines. 500p. (Orig.). 1981. 20.00 (ISBN 0-345-29724-5); pap. 9.95 (ISBN 0-345-29635-4). Ballantine.

Usdin, E. & Eckert, H., eds. Phenothiazines & Structurally Related Drugs: Basic & Clinical Studies. (Developments in Neuroscience Ser.: Vol. 7). 376p. 1980. 62.25 (ISBN 0-444-00401-7). Elsevier.

Vida, Julius A. & Gordon, Maxwell, eds. Conformationally Directed Drug Design: Peptides & Nucleic Acids as Templates or Targets. LC 84-2921. (ACS Symposium Ser.: No. 251). 271p. 1984. lib. bdg. 45.95x (ISBN 0-8412-0836-0). Am Chemical.

Vohora, S. B. & Khan, S. Y. Animal Origin Drugs Used in Unani Medicine. LC 79-903036. 1980. text ed. 25.00x (ISBN 0-7069-0768-X, Pub. by Vikas India). Advent NY.

White, D. J., ed. Cyclosporin A: Proceedings of the International Symposium, Cambridge, U. K., September 1981. 350p. 1982. 36.75 (ISBN 0-444-80410-2, I-296-82, Biomedical Bks). Elsevier.

Witters-Jones, Patricia & Witters, Weldon. Drugs & Society: A Biological Perspective. LC 82-21738. 400p. 1983. pap. text ed. 15.25 pub net (ISBN 0-534-01412-7). Brooks-Cole.

Wolfe, Sidney M. & Coley, Christopher M. Pills That Don't Work: A Consumer's & Doctor's Guide to Prescription Drugs that Lack Evidence of Effectiveness. 221p. 1980. 6.95. Pub Citizen Inc.

Wood, Margaret & Wood, Alastair J. Drugs & Anesthesia: Pharmacology for Anesthesiologists. (Illus.). 736p. 1982. lib. bdg. 62.00 (ISBN 0-683-09251-0). Williams & Wilkins.

Worick, W. & Schaller, W. Alcohol, Tobacco & Drugs: Their Use & Abuse. 1977. pap. 16.95 (ISBN 0-13-021436-1). P-H.

DRUGS–ADULTERATION AND ANALYSIS

Baer, Daniel M. & Dito, William R., eds. Interpretations in Therapeutic Drug Monitoring. LC 81-826. (Illus.). 388p. 1981. text ed. 35.00 (ISBN 0-89189-080-7, 45-9-009-00). Am Soc Clinical.

Bozarth, M. A., ed. Methods of Assessing the Reinforcing Properties of Abused Drugs. (Illus.). 470p. 1984. 40.00 (ISBN 0-940090-04-X). Haer Inst.

Bryant, Rhys. The Pharmaceutical Quality Control Handbook. (Illus.). 220p. 1984. 45.00 (ISBN 0-943330-04-1); pap. 38.00. Aster Pub Corp.

Cosofret, V. V. Membrane Electrodes in Drug-Substances Analysis. Thomas, J. D., ed. (Illus.). 376p. 1981. 66.00 (ISBN 0-08-026264-3). Pergamon.

Darvas, F. & Knoll, J., eds. Chemical Structure - Biological Activity Relationships, Quantitative Approaches: Proceedings of the Third Congress of the Hungarian Pharmacological Society, Budapest, 1979. LC 80-41281. (Advances in Pharmacological Research & Practice Ser.: Vol. III). 355p. 1981. 74.00 (ISBN 0-08-026388-7). Pergamon.

DeWolff, Frederick A., et al, eds. Therapeutic Relevance of Drug Assays. (Boehaave Series for Postgraduate Medical Education: No. 14). 1979. lib. bdg. 35.00 (ISBN 90-6021-443-9, Pub. by Leiden Univ Holland). Kluwer Academic.

Educational Research Council of America. FDA Investigator. rev. ed. Kunze, Linda J. & Marchak, John P., eds. (Real People at Work Ser: E). (Illus.). 36p. 1976. pap. text ed. 2.45 (ISBN 0-89247-038-0, 9318). Changing Times.

Estabrook, R., et al, eds. Microsomes & Drug Oxidations. LC 73-6403. 486p. 1973. 30.00 (ISBN 0-683-02918-5, Pub. by W & W). Krieger.

Fell, A. F., ed. Drug Analysis: Keynote & Plenary Papers from the First International Symposium, June 1983, Brussels, Belgium. 200p. 1984. pap. 20.00 (ISBN 0-08-031441-4). Pergamon.

Fishbein, L. Chromatography of Environmental Hazards, Vol. 4: Drugs of Abuse. 496p. 1982. 106.50 (ISBN 0-444-42024-X). Elsevier.

Florey, Klaus, ed. Analytical Profiles of Drug Substances, Vol. 11. LC 70-187259. 1982. 55.00 (ISBN 0-12-260811-9). Acad Pr.

Food & Drug Administration. FDA Inspections Operations Manual for Drugs, Devices, & Cosmetics. Hadley, Richard D., ed. 162p. 1983. pap. text ed. 39.00 (ISBN 0-914176-22-6). Wash Busn Info.

Goldberg, Morton E., ed. Pharmacological & Biochemical Properties of Drug Substances, Vol. 1. LC 77-88184. 413p. 1979. 30.00 (ISBN 0-917330-17-X). Am Pharm Assn.

Gudzinowicz, B. J. Analysis of Drugs & Metabolites by Gas Chromatography - Mass Spectrometry: Antipsychotic, Antiemetic & Antidepressant Drugs, Vol. 3. 1977. 49.75 (ISBN 0-8247-6586-9). Dekker.

Jack, David B. Drug Analysis by Gas Chromatography. 1984. 49.50 (ISBN 0-12-378250-3). Acad Pr.

Kallet, Arthur & Schlink, F. J. One Hundred Million Guinea Pigs: Dangers in Everyday Foods, Drugs, & Cosmetics. LC 75-39252. (Getting & Spending: the Consumer's Dilemma). 1976. Repr. of 1933 ed. 24.50x (ISBN 0-405-08025-5). Ayer Co Pubs.

Kuhnert-Brandstatter, M. Thermomicroscopy in the Analysis of Pharmaceuticals. 424p. 1971. 85.00 (ISBN 0-08-006990-8). Pergamon.

Lamb, Ruth D. American Chamber of Horrors: The Truth About Food & Drugs. LC 75-39255. (Getting & Spending: the Consumer's Dilemma). (Illus.). 1976. Repr. of 1936 ed. 32.00x (ISBN 0-405-08028-X). Ayer Co Pubs.

Matteis, F. De & Aldridge, W. N., eds. Heme & Hemoproteins. LC 77-13134. (Handbook of Experimental Pharmacology Ser.: Vol. 44). (Illus.). 1977. 113.00 (ISBN 0-387-08460-6). Springer-Verlag.

Mills, K., et al, eds. Instrumental Data for Drug Analysis, Vol. 1. 648p. 1982. 102.50 (ISBN 0-444-00718-0). Elsevier.

Mills, T., et al, eds. Instrumental Data for Drug Analysis, Vol. 2. (Elsevier Series in Forensic & Police Science). 650p. 1983. 95.00 (ISBN 0-444-00769-5). Elsevier.

Reid, Eric & Wilson, Ian D., eds. Drug Determination in Therapeutic & Forensic Contexts. (Methodological Surveys in Biochemistry & Analysis Ser.: Vol. 14). 406p. 1984. 62.50x (ISBN 0-306-41809-6, Plenum Pr). Plenum Pub.

Singer, Thomas P., et al, eds. Mechanism of Drug Action: Symposium. LC 83-22362. 1984. 44.00 (ISBN 0-12-646680-7). Acad Pr.

Smith, Robert V. & Stewart, James T. Textbook of Biopharmaceutic Analysis: A Description of Methods for the Determination of Drugs in Biologic Fluids. LC 80-39872. (Illus.). 308p. 1981. text ed. 25.00 (ISBN 0-8121-0770-5). Lea & Febiger.

Sunshine, Irving & Gerber, S. R. Spectrophotometric Analysis of Drugs: Including Atlas of Spectra. (Illus.). 256p. 1963. 25.75x (ISBN 0-398-04420-1). C C Thomas.
Sunshine, Irving, ed. Handbook of Mass Spectra of Drugs. 472p. 1981. 76.00 (ISBN 0-8493-3572-8). CRC Pr.
Wagner, H., et al. Plant Drug Analysis: A Thin Layer Chromatography Photo-Atlas. Scott, T. A., tr. (Ger., Illus.). 350p. 1984. 58.00 (ISBN 0-387-13195-7). Springer-Verlag.
Wolfe, Margaret R. Lucius Polk Brown & Progressive Food & Drug Control: Tennessee & New York City,1908-1920. LC 77-6637. 1978. 22.50x (ISBN 0-7006-0163-5). U Pr of KS.

DRUGS–PHYSIOLOGICAL EFFECT
Albert, Adrien. Selective Toxicity: The Physico-Chemical Basis of Theory. 6th ed. LC 78-15491. 1979. pap. text ed. 19.95x (ISBN 0-412-23650-8). Halsted Pr.
Atkinson, Arthur J., Jr. & Ambre, John J. Kalman & Clark's Drug Assay: The Strategy of Therapeutic Drug Monitoring. 2nd ed. (Illus.). 200p. 1984. text ed. 29.50 (ISBN 0-89352-216-3). Masson Pub.
Bartone, John C., II. Drug Effects on Memory: Medical Subject Analysis with Research Bibliography. LC 84-45656. 150p. 1985. 29.95 (ISBN 0-88164-218-5); pap. 21.95 (ISBN 0-88164-219-3). ABBE Pubs Assn.
--Muscles & Drug Effects: Medical Subject Analysis with Research Bibliography. LC 84-45657. 150p. 1985. 29.95 (ISBN 0-88164-216-9); pap. 21.95 (ISBN 0-88164-217-7). ABBE Pubs Assn.
Black, Perry, ed. Drugs & The Brain: Papers on the Action, Use, & Abuse of Psychotropic Agents. LC 68-31642. pap. 104.00 (ISBN 0-317-07918-2, 2001191). Bks Demand UMI.
Brackbill, Yvonne, et al. Medication in Maternity: Infant Exposure & Maternal Information. (International Academy for Research in Learning Disabilities Monographs). 160p. 1985. pap. text ed. 8.95x (ISBN 0-472-08059-8). U of Mich Pr.
Caird, F. I. & Scott, P. J. Drug Induced Disorders: Geriatrics One. (Drug Induced Disorders Ser.: No. C1). 1984. write for info. (ISBN 0-444-90362-3, Excerpta Medica). Elsevier.
Campbell, F. & Singer, G. Stress, Drugs & Health - Recent Brain-Behavior Research. (Illus.). 136p. 1983. pap. 13.70 (ISBN 0-08-024838-1). Pergamon.
Debry, G., ed. Nutrition, Food & Drug Interactions in Man. (World Review of Nutrition & Dietetics: Vol. 43). (Illus.). x, 210p. 1984. 70.75 (ISBN 3-8055-3800-6). S Karger.
Dimitriv, Nikolay V. & Nodine, John H., eds. Drugs & Hematologic Reactions: The Twenty-Ninth Hahnemann Symposium. 416p. 1974. 87.50 (ISBN 0-8089-0812-X, 791048). Grune.
Dukes, M. N. Encyclopedia of Adverse Reactions & Interactions, Vol. 10. (Side Effects of Drugs Ser.). 1984. 107.50 (ISBN 0-444-90323-2). Elsevier.
Goldberg, Leonard, ed. Alcohol, Drugs & Traffic Safety: Proceedings of the 8th International Conference on Alcohol, Drugs and Traffic Safety, 3 vols. 1489p. 1981. Set. text ed. 115.50x (Pub. by Almquist & Wiksell Sweden). Vol. 1 (ISBN 91-22-00425-4). Vol. 2 (ISBN 91-22-00427-0). Vol. 3 (ISBN 91-22-00429-7). Humanities.
Goldberg, Morton E., ed. Pharmacological & Biochemical Properties of Drug Substances, Vol. 2. 257p. 1977. 36.00 (ISBN 0-917330-25-0). Am Pharm Assn.
Goldstein, Avram, et al. Principles of Drug Action: The Basis of Pharmacology. 2nd ed. LC 73-15871. 834p. 1974. 52.00x (ISBN 0-471-31260-6, Pub. by Wiley-Medical). Wiley.
Gorrod, J. W., ed. Drug Toxicity. 340p. 1979. 27.50x (ISBN 0-85066-179-X). Taylor & Francis.
Hathcock, John N. & Coon, Julius, eds. Nutrition & Drug Interrelations. 1978. 65.00 (ISBN 0-12-332550-1). Acad Pr.
Lomax & Schonbaum. Body Temperature: Regulation, Drug Effects, & Theraputic Implications. (Modern Pharmacology-Toxicology Ser.: Vol. 16). 1979. 99.75 (ISBN 0-8247-6655-5). Dekker.
Miller, Russell R. & Greenblatt, David J., eds. Drug Effects in Hospitalized Patients: Experiences of the Boston Collaborative Drug Surveillance Program 1966-1975. LC 75-28124. 364p. 1976. 35.95 (ISBN 0-471-60372-4). Krieger.
Nahas, G. G., ed. Marihuana: Chemistry, Biochemistry, & Cellular Efffects. 400p. 1976. 35.00 (ISBN 0-387-07554-2). Springer-Verlag.
Nater, J. P., et al, eds. Unwanted Effects of Cosmetics & Drugs Used in Dermatology. 2nd, rev. ed. 650p. 1985. 129.00 (ISBN 0-444-90358-5). Elsevier.
Purcell, William P., et al. Strategy of Drug Design: A Guide to Biological Activity. LC 72-13240. 38.00 (ISBN 0-8357-9983-2, 2055156). Bks Demand UMI.
Robinson, R G. Therapeutic & Unwanted Effects: Drug Related or Not. 55p. 1978. 30.00 (ISBN 3-456-80580-2, Pub. by Holdan Bk Ltd UK). State Mutual Bk.
Rockford, Doris E. Drug Effects on the Fetus: Medical Research Subject Analysis with Bibliography. LC 84-45735. 150p. 1985. 29.95 (ISBN 0-88164-248-7); pap. 21.95 (ISBN 0-88164-249-5). ABBE Pubs Assn.
Societe Francaise Des Sciences et Techniques Pharmaceutiques Working Group & Hirtz, J. L., eds. The Fate of Drugs in the Organism: A Bibliographic Survey, Vol. 1. 600p. 1974. 125.00 (ISBN 0-8247-6133-2). Dekker.
Stafford, Peter. Psychedelics Encyclopedia. LC 82-10482. (Illus.). 416p. 1982. pap. 12.95 (ISBN 0-87477-231-1). J P Tarcher.
Topliss, John G., ed. Quantitative Structure-Activity Relationships of Drugs. 1983. 69.00 (ISBN 0-12-695150-0). Acad Pr.
Towse, G., ed. Progress with Domperidone: A Gastrokinetic & Anti-Emetic Agent. (Royal Society of Medicine International Congress & Symposium Ser.: No. 36). 110p. 1981. 20.00 (ISBN 0-8089-1350-6, 794643); pap. 10.50. Grune.
Weiss, G. B., ed. Calcium in Drug Action. LC 78-8517. 376p. 1978. 45.00 (ISBN 0-306-40015-4, Plenum Pr). Plenum Pub.
Young, Donald, et al. Effects of Drugs on Clinical Laboratory Tests, Vol. 21, No. 5. LC 81-65486. 432p. 1975. 25.00 (ISBN 0-915274-00-0); members 20.00. Am Assn Clinical Chem.

DRUGS–TESTING
Crouthamel, William & Sarupu, Allen, eds. Animal Models for Oral Drug Delivery in Man: In Situ & In Vivo Approaches. 192p. 1983. text ed. 54.00 (ISBN 0-917330-49-8). Am Pharm Assn.
Florey, Klaus, ed. Analytical Profiles of Drug Substances, Vol. 9. 1980. 50.00 (ISBN 0-12-260809-7). Acad Pr.
Fulton, Charles C. Modern Microcrystal Tests for Drugs: The Identification of Organic Compounds by Microcrystalloscopic Chemistry. LC 68-54599. (Illus.). pap. 121.50 (ISBN 0-317-07900-X, 2012486). Bks Demand UMI.
Gearien, James E. Methods of Drug Analysis. LC 68-25207. pap. 72.80 (20255999). Bks Demand UMI.
Hanson, William A. Handbook of Dissolution Testing. LC 82-81536. (Illus.). 176p. 1982. 26.50 (ISBN 0-943330-00-9). Aster Pub Corp.
Kuhnert-Brandstatter, M. Thermomicroscopy in the Analysis of Pharmaceuticals. 424p. 1971. 85.00 (ISBN 0-08-006990-8). Pergamon.
Moyer, T. & Boeckx, R. Applied Therapeutic Drug Monitoring, Vol. 2. 1984. 22.00 (ISBN 0-915274-23-X); members 19.50 (ISBN 0-317-13770-0). Am Assn Clinical Chem.
Testing Drugs for the Ageing Brain. (Journal: Gerontology: Vol. 28, Suppl. 2). (Illus.). xiv, 58p. 1983. pap. 23.50 (ISBN 3-8055-3659-3). S Karger.
Turner, Robert A. & Hebborn, Peter. Screening Methods in Pharmacology, Vol. 2. 1971. 68.00 (ISBN 0-12-704252-0). Acad Pr.
WHO Scientific Group. Geneva, 1967. Principles for the Clinical Evaluation of Drugs: Report. (Technical Report Ser.: No. 403). (Also avail. in French, Russian & Spanish). 1968. pap. 2.00 (ISBN 92-4-120403-6). World Health.
WHO Scientific Group. Geneva, 1968. Principles for the Testing & Evaluation of Drugs for Carcinogenicity: Report. (Technical Report Ser.: No. 426). (Also avail. in French & Spanish). 1969. pap. 1.20 (ISBN 92-4-120426-5). World Health.

DRY CLEANING
Dry Cleaning Plants. (Thirty Ser). 1974. pap. 2.50 (ISBN 0-685-58112-8, 32). Natl Fire Prot.
Johnson, Albert E. Drycleaning. 54p. 1971. 39.00x (ISBN 0-900541-22-9, Pub. by Meadowfield Pr England). State Mutual Bk.
Lyle, Dorothy S. Performance of Textiles. LC 76-54110. 592p. 1977. 48.50x (ISBN 0-471-01418-4). Wiley.

DRYING
Hall. Dictionary of Drying. 1979. 59.75 (ISBN 0-8247-6652-0). Dekker.
Masters, K. Spray Drying Handbook. 3rd ed. 687p. 1979. 113.95x (ISBN 0-470-26549-3). Halsted Pr.
Mujumdar, A. S. Advances in Drying, Vol. 2. 1980. text ed. 58.00x (ISBN 0-07-043977-X). McGraw.
--Drying Eighty-Two. 1982. text ed. 95.00x (ISBN 0-07-043982-6). McGraw.
Mujumdar, A. S., ed. Developments in Drying. LC 79-7623. (Illus.). 1979. lib. bdg. 62.00 (ISBN 0-89500-021-0). Sci Pr.
--Drying 'Eighty-Four. (Illus.). 500p. 1984. 72.40 (ISBN 0-387-13429-8). Springer Verlag.
--Drying: First International Symposium. LC 78-19938. (Illus.). 1978. lib. bdg. 35.00 (ISBN 0-89500-015-6). Sci Pr.
Mujumdar, Arun S., ed. Advances in Drying, Vol. 2. LC 80-10432. (Advances in Drying Ser.). (Illus.). 301p. 1983. text ed. 74.50 (ISBN 0-89116-255-0). Hemisphere Pub.
--Drying Eighty-Two. LC 81-13394. (Illus.). 254p. 1982. text ed. 89.95 (ISBN 0-89116-236-4). Hemisphere Pub.
Weiner, Jack. Drying of Paper & Board. LC 61-66525. (Bibliographic Series: No. 196). 1976. pap. 18.00 (ISBN 0-87010-038-6). Inst Paper Chem.
Williams-Gardner, A. Industrial Drying. LC 77-77814. 328p. 1977. 29.95x (ISBN 0-87201-197-6). Gulf Pub.

DRYING APPARATUS
see also Freeze-Drying; Kilns
Keey, R. B. Introduction to Industrial Drying Operations. LC 77-30467. 396p. 1978. 72.00 (ISBN 0-08-020594-1); pap. 23.00 (ISBN 0-08-020593-3). Pergamon.
Mujumdar, Arun S., ed. Advances in Drying, Vol. 1. LC 80-10432. (Advances in Drying Ser.). (Illus.). 301p. 1980. text ed. 76.50 (ISBN 0-89116-185-6). Hemisphere Pub.

DRYING APPARATUS–FOOD
see also Canning and Preserving
Kline, Jeff, ed. How to Sun Dry Your Food. (Illus.). 114p. (Orig.). 1983. pap. 6.95x (ISBN 0-941580-00-8). Self Reliance.

DUCK-HAWK
see Peregrine Falcon

DUCKS
Dethier, Vincent G. Fairweather Duck. LC 77-101628. 1970. 4.95 (ISBN 0-8027-0102-7). Walker & Co.
Embryonic Development in the Eggs of the Peking Duck. (Eng. & Dutch., Illus.). 1971. pap. 9.25 (ISBN 90-220-0353-1, PDC32, PUDOC). Unipub.
Holderread, Dave. Raising the Home Duck Flock. rev. ed. LC 80-10992. (Illus.). 192p. 1980. pap. 7.95 (ISBN 0-88266-169-8). Garden Way Pub.
Humphrey, Philip S. & Livezey, Bradley C. Molts & Plumages of Flying Steamer-Ducks: Tachyeres Patachonicus. (Occasional Papers: No. 103). 30p. 1982. pap. 4.25 (ISBN 0-317-04597-0). U of KS Mus Nat Hist.
Humphrey, Phillip S. & Thompson, Max C. A New Species of Steamer-Duck (Tachyeres) from Argentina. (Occasional Papers: No. 95). 12p. 1981. pap. 2.25 (ISBN 0-317-04596-2). U of KS Mus Nat Hist.
Kortright, E. H. Ducks, Geese & Swans of North America. rev. ed. Bellrose, Frank C., rev. by. LC 75-33962. (Illus.). 568p. 1981. 29.95 (ISBN 0-8117-0535-8). Stackpole.
McKane, John G. Ducks of the Mississippi Flyway. LC 79-105937. (Illus.). 1969. pap. 5.00 (ISBN 0-87839-003-0). North Star.
Romashko, Sandra D. Wild Ducks & Geese of North America. LC 77-81167. (Illus.). 1978. pap. 2.95 (ISBN 0-89317-018-6). Windward Pub.
Sowls, Lyle K. Prairie Ducks: A Study of Their Behavior, Ecology & Management. LC 77-14153. (Illus.). xiv, 194p. 1978. pap. 3.50 (ISBN 0-8032-5895-X, BB 665, Bison). U of Nebr Pr.
Trautman, Milton B. Autumn Migrations of Selected Species of Ducks at Buckeye Lake, Ohio. 1978. 1.00 (ISBN 0-86727-085-3). Ohio Bio Survey.
Walters, John & Parker, Michael. Keeping Ducks, Geese, & Turkeys. (The Garden Farming Ser.). (Illus.). 125p. 1983. pap. 5.95 (ISBN 0-7207-1437-0, Pub. by Michael Joseph). Merrimack Pub Cir.
Wildlife Education Staff. Ducks, Geese & Swans: Waterfowl. (Illus., Orig.). 1984. pap. 1.95 (ISBN 0-937934-21-6). Wildlife Educ.

DUCTLESS GLANDS
see Endocrine Glands

DUCTS, AIR
see Air Ducts

DUCTS, BILE
see Biliary Tract

DUEHRING, EUGEN KARL, 1833-1921
Engels, Frederick. Anti-Duhring: Herr Eugen Duhring's Revolution in Science. 402p. 1984. 29.95x (ISBN 0-88286-082-8). C H Kerr.

DUESENBERG (AUTOMOBILE)
see Automobiles–Types–Duesenberg

DUHEM, PIERRE MAURICE MARIE, 1861-1916
Jaki, Stanley. Uneasy Genius: The Life & Work of Pierre Duham. 1984. lib. bdg. 65.50 (ISBN 90-247-2897-5, Pub. by Martinus Nijhoff Netherlands). Kluwer Academic.
Lowinger, Armand. Methodology of Pierre Duhem. Repr. of 1941 ed. 10.00 (ISBN 0-404-04058-6). AMS Pr.

DUNES
see Sand Dunes

DUPLICATING MACHINES
see Copying Machines

DUPLICATING PROCESSES
see Copying Processes

DURUM WHEAT
see Wheat

DUST
see also Cleaning Machinery and Appliances
Cross, Jean & Farrer, Donald. Dust Explosions. LC 82-7499. 259p. 1982. text ed. 37.50 (ISBN 0-306-40871-6, Plenum Pr). Plenum Pub.
Dust Explosion Prevention in Feed Mills. (Sixty Ser). 1973. pap. 2.00 (ISBN 0-685-58078-4, 61C). Natl Fire Prot.
Fibrous Dusts: Measurement, Effects, Prevention. 1983. pap. 142.00 (ISBN 0-9907000-3-8, Pub. by VDI W Germany). Heyden.
Fundamental Principles for the Prevention of Dust Explosions in Industrial Plants. (Sixty Ser.). 1971. pap. 2.00 (ISBN 0-685-58075-X, 63). Natl Fire Prot.
Hesketh, Howard E. & El-Shobokshy, Mohammad S. Predicting & Measuring Fugitive Dust. LC 84-51877. 131p. 1985. pap. 45.00 (ISBN 0-87762-375-9). Technomic.
Malissa, Hanns, ed. Analysis of Airborne Particles by Physical Methods. (Uniscience Ser.). 320p. 1978. 85.00 (ISBN 0-8493-5275-4). CRC Pr.
Milling of Agricultural Commodities for Human Consumption. (Sixty Ser). 1973. pap. 2.00 (ISBN 0-685-58077-6, 61D). Natl Fire Prot.
Morales, C., ed. Saharan Dust: Mobilization Transport Deposition. LC 78-8687. (SCOPE Ser. (Scientific Committee on Problems of the Environment): SCOPE Report 14). 297p. 1979. 58.95x (ISBN 0-471-99680-7, Pub. by Wiley-Interscience). Wiley.
Nagy & Verakis. Development & Control of Dust Explosions. (Occupational Safety & Health Ser.). 352p. 1983. 55.00 (ISBN 0-8247-7004-8). Dekker.
Pneumatic Conveying Systems for Handling Feed, Flour, Grain & Other Agricultural Dusts. (Sixty Ser). 1973. pap. 2.00 (ISBN 0-685-58068-7, 66). Natl Fire Prot.
Prevention of Dust Explosions in Coal Preparation Plants. (Sixty Ser.). 1971. pap. 2.00 (ISBN 0-685-58072-5, 653). Natl Fire Prot.
Prevention of Dust Explosions in Confectionery Manufacturing Plants. (Sixty Ser.). 1967. pap. 2.00 (ISBN 0-685-58070-9, 657). Natl Fire Prot.
Prevention of Dust Explosions in Woodworking & Wood Flour Manufacturing Plants. (Sixty Ser.). 1971. pap. 2.00 (ISBN 0-685-58069-5, 664). Natl Fire Prot.
Prevention of Dust Explosions, Pulverized Sugar & Cocoa. (Sixty Ser.). 1967. pap. 2.00 (ISBN 0-685-58076-8, 62). Natl Fire Prot.
Prevention of Dust Ignitions in Spice Grinding Plants. (Sixty Ser.). 1971. pap. 2.00 (ISBN 0-685-58045-8, 656). Natl Fire Prot.
Prevention of Fire & Dust Explosions in Grain Elevators & Bulk Grain Handling Facilities. (Sixty Ser.). 1973. pap. 2.00 (ISBN 0-685-58080-6, 61B). Natl Fire Prot.
Starch Manufacturing & Handling. 1973. pap. 2.00 (ISBN 0-685-58081-4, 61A). Natl Fire Prot.
Zimon, A. D. Adhesion of Dust & Powder. LC 69-12547. 424p. 1969. 47.50x (ISBN 0-306-30391-4, Plenum Pr). Plenum Pub.

DUST–REMOVAL
see also Clean Rooms; Cleaning Machinery and Appliances; Electrostatic Precipitation
Mednikov, Evgenii P. Acoustic Coagulation & Precipitation of Aerosols. LC 64-23251. 180p. 1965. 32.50x (ISBN 0-306-10718-X, Consultants). Plenum Pub.
Sittig, M. Particulates & Fine Dust Removal: Processes & Equipment. LC 77-77018. (Pollution Technology Review Ser.: No. 34). (Illus.). 1977. 48.00 (ISBN 0-8155-0664-3). Noyes.
Storch, O. Industrial Separators for Gas Cleaning. LC 78-10916. (Chemical Engineering Monographs: Vol. 6). 388p. 1979. 66.00 (ISBN 0-444-99808-X). Elsevier.
Theodore, Louis & Buonicore, Anthony. Industrial Air Pollution Control Equipment for Particulates. LC 76-25095. (Uniscience Ser.). 288p. 1976. 62.00 (ISBN 0-8493-5132-4). CRC Pr.
User Guide to Dust & Fume Control. 130p. 1981. 75.00x (ISBN 0-85295-125-6, Pub. by IChemE). State Mutual Bk.

DUST, RADIOACTIVE
see Radioactive Fallout

DUST EXTRACTION
see Dust–Removal

DUST STORMS
Hurt, R. Douglas. The Dust Bowl: An Agricultural & Social History. LC 81-4031. 240p. 1981. text ed. 22.95x (ISBN 0-88229-541-1); pap. 11.95x (ISBN 0-88229-789-9). Nelson-Hall.

DWARF FRUIT TREES
Tukey, Harold B. Dwarfed Fruit Trees. LC 77-12289. (Illus.). 576p. 1978. 45.00x (ISBN 0-8014-1126-2). Comstock.

Welch, Humphrey J. Manual of Dwarf Conifers. rev. ed. (Illus.). 1976. 20.00 (ISBN 0-913728-07-1). Theophrastus.

DWARF TREES

see Bonsai; Dwarf Fruit Trees

DWELLINGS

see also Apartment Houses; Basements; Bathrooms; Domestic Engineering; House Construction; Kitchens; Solar Houses

Architectural Digest Editors. Celebrity Homes I. Rense, Paige, ed. (Large Format Ser.). (Illus.). 1979. pap. 14.95 (ISBN 0-14-005229-1). Penguin.

Architectural Record Magazine Staff. More Houses Architects Design for Themselves. (Illus.). 1983. 38.50 (ISBN 0-07-002365-4). McGraw.

Better Homes & Gardens Editors. Better Homes & Gardens All About Your House: Your Kitchen. (All About your House Ser.). 160p. 1983. 9.95 (ISBN 0-696-02161-7). BH&G.

--Better Homes & Gardens All About Your House: Your Walls & Ceilings. LC 81-70036. (All About Your House Ser.). (Illus.). 160p. 1983. 9.95 (ISBN 0-696-02163-3). BH&G.

--Better Homes & Gardens Step-by-Step Cabinets & Shelves. (Illus.). 1983. pap. 6.95 (ISBN 0-696-01065-8). BH&G.

Flaccus, Edward. North Country Cabin. LC 78-21638. (Illus.). 122p. 1979. pap. 5.95 (ISBN 0-87842-111-4). Mountain Pr.

Gnuva, Paul. Vox--Enciclopedia Cultural, Tomo 6: Pueblos. (Espn.). 210p. 1977. leatherette 29.95 (ISBN 84-7153-493-2, S-50503). French & Eur.

Homes & Homebuilding 1983. 16th ed. 234p. 1983. 15.00 (ISBN 0-86718-161-3). Natl Assn Home.

Keller, Suzanne, ed. Building for Women. LC 80-8783. 240p. 1981. 29.50x (ISBN 0-669-04368-0). Lexington Bks.

Koenigsberger, O. H., et al. Manual of Tropical Housing & Building Design: Climatic Design, Pt. 1. (Illus.). 344p. 1974. pap. text ed. 17.95x (ISBN 0-582-44546-9). Longman.

McClain, Harry W. Beat the Building Cost Boom: How to Build Your Own Home for 1/10th the Cost of Conventional Construction. (Illus.). 1978. pap. text ed. 12.95 (ISBN 0-933608-00-4). Mountain View.

Miller, Rex. Residential Electrical Wiring. (Illus.). 300p. 1981. text ed. 14.24 (ISBN 0-02-665620-5); student guide 5.32 (ISBN 0-02-665640-X); tchr's. ed. 5.32 (ISBN 0-02-665630-2). Bennett IL.

Nolte, Robert C. & Ruel, Oliver J. Residential Construction Wiring: Updated for 1981 Code. LC 78-16245. 1979. 23.95 (ISBN 0-574-21520-4, 13-4545). SRA.

Rapoport, Amos. House Form & Culture. LC 69-14550. (Geography Ser). 1969. pap. 18.95 ref. ed. (ISBN 0-13-395673-3). P-H.

Reynolds, Mack & Ing, Dean. Home Sweet Home Two Thousand Ten A. D. 256p. (Orig.). 1984. pap. 2.95 (ISBN 0-440-03658-5). Dell.

Roberts, Rex. Your Engineered House. LC 64-20782. (Illus.). 240p. 1964. 8.95 (ISBN 0-87131-110-0); pap. 5.95 (ISBN 0-87131-154-2). M Evans.

Rogers, Marc & Griffith, Roger. Getting a Roof over Your Head: Affordable Housing Alternatives. LC 82-20941. (Illus.). 167p. 1982. pap. 9.95 (ISBN 0-88266-317-8). Garden Way Pub.

Shelters of Other Lands. (Learning Shelf Kits Ser.). 1977. incl. cassette & tchrs. guide 14.95 (ISBN 0-686-74397-0, 04988). Natl Geog.

Sherwood, Ruth & Sherwood, George. Homes, Today & Tomorrow. 8th. ed. 1981. text ed. 18.88 (ISBN 0-02-664530-0); trans. master 20.00 (ISBN 0-02-664570-X); student guide 7.48 (ISBN 0-02-664550-5); tchrs.' guide 8.16 (ISBN 0-02-664540-8). Bennett IL.

Southwick, Marcia. Build with Adobe. 3rd rev. & enl. ed. LC 73-1504. (Illus.). 230p. 1974. pap. 7.95 (ISBN 0-8040-0634-2, 82-73443, Pub. by Swallow). Ohio U Pr.

Stickley, Gustav. More Craftsman Homes: Floor Plans & Illustrations for 78 Mission Style Dwellings. (Illus.). 210p. 1982. pap. 6.95 (ISBN 0-486-24252-8). Dover.

U. S. Housing & Home Finance Agency. Application of Climatic Data to House Design. LC 77-10240. 1977. Repr. of 1954 ed. 22.50 (ISBN 0-404-16218-5). AMS Pr.

U. S. Navy Bureau of Naval Personnel. Basic Construction Techniques for Houses & Small Buildings. (Illus.). 568p. 1972. pap. 8.95 (ISBN 0-486-20242-9). Dover.

Van Dresser, Peter. Homegrown Sundwellings. LC 77-73461. 1977. 15.00 (ISBN 0-89016-034-1); pap. 7.95 (ISBN 0-89016-033-3). Lightning Tree.

Vaux, Calvert. Villas & Cottages: The Great Architectural Style-Book of the Hudson School. (Illus.). 12.00 (ISBN 0-8446-0951-X). Peter Smith.

DWELLINGS–AIR CONDITIONING

Barton, George S. How to Really Save Money & Energy in Cooling Your Home. rev. ed. LC 78-54385. (Illus.). 1980. pap. 9.95 (ISBN 0-931624-01-0). Chester-Leeds.

Daniels, George. Home Guide to Plumbing, Heating, & Air Conditioning. 2nd ed. LC 67-10841. (Popular Science Skill Bk). (Illus.). 1976. pap. 3.95i (ISBN 0-06-010957-2, TD-271, HarpT). Har-Row.

Morrison, James W. The Complete Energy-Saving Home Improvement Guide. 4th ed. LC 80-23996. (Illus.). 1981. pap. 2.50 (ISBN 0-668-05085-3, 5085-3). Arco.

DWELLINGS–ENERGY CONSERVATION

Ackerman, Allan D., et al. In the Bank...or up the Chimney? A Dollars & Cents Guide to Energy-Saving Home Improvements. (Illus.). 1975. pap. 1.25x (ISBN 0-89011-477-3, ECR-107). Abt Bks.

AIA Research Corporation. Passive Solar Design: A Short Bibliography for Practitioners. 1979. pap. 6.50x (ISBN 0-89934-040-7, A-007). Solar Energy Info.

Blandy, Thomas & Lamoureux, Denis. All Through the House: A Guide to Home Weatherization. (Illus., Orig.). 1980. pap. 7.95 (ISBN 0-07-005871-7). McGraw.

Burby, Raymond J. & Marsden, Mary E., eds. Energy & Housing: Consumer & Builder Perspectives. LC 79-26662. 288p. 1980. text ed. 35.00 (ISBN 0-89946-030-5). Oelgeschlager.

Chapman, C. Keeler & Traister, John E. Homes for the Nineteen-Eighties: An Energy & Construction Design Aid. LC 82-5929. (Illus.). 256p. (Orig.). 1982. pap. 17.95 (ISBN 0-8306-1425-7, 1425). TAB Bks.

Clayton, Michael. Cutting the Cost of Energy: A Practical Guide for the Householder. LC 80-67579. (Illus.). 160p. 1981. 14.95 (ISBN 0-7153-7927-5). David & Charles.

Coe, Gigi, et al. The Home Energy Decision Book: Remodeling Your Home for Low-Cost Energy Efficiency. LC 83-19574. (Tools for Today Bks.). (Illus.). 180p. (Orig.). 1984. pap. 9.95 (ISBN 0-87156-811-X). Sierra.

Coffee, Frank. The Self-Sufficient House. LC 80-13434. (Illus.). 1981. 17.95 (ISBN 0-03-053611-1); pap. 9.95 (ISBN 0-03-059171-6). HR&W.

Davis, Joseph C. & Walker, Claxton. Wage the Energy War at Home. LC 78-51121. (Illus.). 1978. 10.95 (ISBN 0-87523-191-8). Emerson.

Environmental Science Deptartment of the Massachusetts Audubon Society. The Home Tune-Up Manual. (Illus.). 156p. (Orig.). 1985. pap. 9.95 (ISBN 0-931790-62-X). Brick Hse Pub.

Field, Paul E. Computer-Assisted Home Energy Management. LC 82-50649. 182p. 1982. pap. 15.95 (ISBN 0-672-21817-8, 21817). Sams.

Fossel, Peter V. Keeping Warm: A Sensible Guide to Heat Conservation. (Illus.). 196p. (Orig.). 1983. pap. 7.95 (ISBN 0-399-50845-7, GD Perigee). Putnam Pub Group.

Hardenbrook, Harry. Walker's Insulation Techniques & Estimating Handbook. (Illus.). 128p. pap. 12.95 (ISBN 0-911592-51-2, ScribT). Scribner.

Heat Saving Home Insulation. (Illus.). 1982. pap. 9.95 (ISBN 0-918984-03-3). Solarvision.

Kliewer, Tim. A Home for All Seasons. (Illus.). 50p. (Orig.). 1982. pap. 3.95 (ISBN 0-9608402-0-6). Energy Self Suff.

Kokette, Stephen. Money Saving Conservation Products & Projects for the Homeowner. LC 78-55883. 1978. pap. 6.95 (ISBN 0-932314-07-4). Aylmer Pr.

Leckie, Jim, et al. More Other Homes & Garbage: Designs for Self-Sufficient Living. rev. ed. LC 79-22175. (Illus.). 416p. (Orig.). 1981. pap. 14.95 (ISBN 0-87156-274-X). Sierra.

Lindahl, Judy. Energy Saving Decorating. new ed. LC 81-90134. (Illus.). 128p. (Orig.). 1981. pap. 5.95 (ISBN 0-9603032-3-5). Lindahl.

Mecca, Stephen J. & Robertshaw, Joseph E. Home Energy Management: Principles & Practices. (Illus.). 160p. 1981. 12.95 (ISBN 0-89433-146-9). Petrocelli.

Morris, David. Be Your Own Power Company. (Illus.). 336p. 1983. 15.95 (ISBN 0-87857-477-8); pap. 9.95 (ISBN 0-87857-478-6). Rodale Pr Inc.

Morrison, James. The Complete Energy Savings Handbook for Home Owners. (P-BN 5108 Ser.). 288p. (Orig.). 1979. pap. 2.25i (ISBN 0-06-465108-8). Har-Row.

Palz, W & Steemers, Tc, eds. Solar Houses in Europe: How They Have Worked. LC 80-49715. (Illus.). 320p. 1981. 44.00 (ISBN 0-08-026743-2); pap. 22.00 (ISBN 0-08-026744-0). Pergamon.

Pearson, James, et al. Hawaii Home Energy Book. LC 77-79935. 1978. pap. 8.95 (ISBN 0-8248-0596-8). UH Pr.

Schipper, Lee, et al. Coming in from the Cold: Energy-Wise Housing in Sweden. (Illus.). 104p. (Orig.). 1985. pap. 19.95 (ISBN 0-932020-37-2). Seven Locks Pr.

Socolow, Robert H., ed. Saving Energy in the Home: Princeton's Experiments at Twin Rivers. LC 78-2598. 368p. 1978. prof ref 29.95 (ISBN 0-88410-080-4). Ballinger Pub.

Solar Dwelling Designs. LC 80-52592. (Illus.). 144p. 1980. pap. 6.95 (ISBN 0-8069-8674-3). Sterling.

Time-Life Books, ed. Weatherproofing. (The Home Repair Ser.). (Illus.). 1977. 11.95 (ISBN 0-8094-2370-7). Time-Life.

Twenty Ways to Conserve Energy in Office Buildings, Shopping Centers, & Other Commercial Properties. 50 copies 11.00 (ISBN 0-686-46419-2). Inst Real Estate.

U. S. Department of Housing & Urban Development. How to Insulate Your Home & Save Fuel. LC 77-74565. (Illus.). 1977. pap. 3.50 (ISBN 0-486-23521-1). Dover.

Wade, Alex & Ewenstein, Neal. Thirty Energy-Efficient Houses You Can Build. 1977. pap. 12.95 (ISBN 0-87857-191-4). Rodale Pr Inc.

Wahlfeldt, B. G. The Energy Efficient Home: One Hundred & One Money Saving Ideas. (Illus.). 228p. (Orig.). 1982. 19.95 (ISBN 0-8306-2415-5, 1415); pap. 12.95 (ISBN 0-8306-1415-X). TAB Bks.

DWELLINGS–HEATING AND VENTILATION

see Heating

DWELLINGS–MAINTENANCE AND REPAIR

see also Buildings–Repair and Reconstruction

Adams, J. T. The Complete Home Electrical Wiring Handbook. LC 78-21969. (Illus.). 1979. pap. 12.95 (ISBN 0-668-04525-6). Arco.

Albright, Roger. Old Houses, New Homes. LC 80-21288. (Illus.). 256p. 1981. pap. 9.95 (ISBN 0-8289-0396-4). Greene.

Augustin, Ann S. Help! I Want to Remodel My Home: The New Woman's Guide to Home Improvement. LC 74-28307. (Illus.). 221p. 1975. 17.95 (ISBN 0-88229-214-5). Nelson-Hall.

Barry, Dave. Taming of the Screw: Several Million Homeowner's Problems. (Illus.). 96p. (Orig.). 1983. pap. 4.95 (ISBN 0-87857-484-0). Rodale Pr Inc.

Baum, Herman. House Doctor's Book of Simple Home Repairs. 192p. 1982. pap. 2.95 (ISBN 0-523-41270-3). Pinnacle Bks.

Becker, Norman. The Complete Book of Home Inspection. (McGraw Hill Paperbacks). (Illus., Orig.). 1980. pap. 8.95 (ISBN 0-07-004180-6). McGraw.

Better Homes & Gardens Books Editor, ed. Step-by-Step Household Repairs. (Step-by-Step Home Repair Ser.). (Illus.). 96p. 1982. pap. 6.95 (ISBN 0-696-00775-4). BH&G.

Better Homes & Gardens Editors. Better Homes & Gardens Complete Guide to Home Repair, Maintenance & Improvement. (Illus.). 1980. 22.95 (ISBN 0-696-00545-X). BH&G.

Bingham, John. The Handbook for Apartment Living. LC 80-70350. 288p. 1981. 13.95 (ISBN 0-8019-6987-5); pap. 8.95 (ISBN 0-8019-6988-3). Chilton.

Bragdon, Allen D., ed. The Homeowner's Complete Manual of Repair & Improvement. LC 82-18184. (Illus.). 576p. 1983. 19.95 (ISBN 0-668-05737-8, 5737). Arco.

Brann, Donald R. How to Build Outdoor Projects. LC 81-65039. 210p. 1981. pap. 7.95 (ISBN 0-87733-807-8). Easi-Bild.

Branson, Gary D. Home Maintenance & Repair: Walls, Ceilings, & Floors. (Illus.). 1979. pap. 6.95 (ISBN 0-672-23281-2, 23281). Audel.

Briggs Amasco Ltd. Flat Roofing: A Guide to Good Practice. (Illus.). 216p. 1982. pap. 33.95x (ISBN 0-9507919-0-3, Pub. by RIBA). Intl Spec Bk.

Brightman, Robert. Bernzomatic Torch Tips. LC 77-71478. (Illus.). 1977. 6.95 (ISBN 0-916752-16-X). Dorison Hse.

Built-Ins. LC 79-18674. (Home Repair & Improvement Ser.). (Illus.). 1979. lib. bdg. 15.94 (ISBN 0-8094-2431-2, Pub. by Time-Life); 13.27 (ISBN 0-8094-2432-0). Silver.

Cabins & Cottages. LC 78-24577. (Home Repair & Improvement Ser.). (Illus.). 1978. lib. bdg. 15.94 (ISBN 0-8094-2411-8, Pub. by Time-Life). Silver.

Carrell, Al. A Super Handyman's Do-It-Quick but Do-It Right Home Repair Hints. LC 80-24659. 1981. 9.95 (ISBN 0-13-875906-5). P-H.

Cleaning. LC 82-5717. (Home Repair & Improvement Ser.). lib. bdg. 15.94 (ISBN 0-8094-3491-1, Pub. by Time-Life). Silver.

Cobb, Hubbard H. Improvements That Increase the Value of Your House. (McGraw-Hill Paperback Ser.). 1976. pap. 6.95 (ISBN 0-07-011488-9). McGraw.

Complete Handyman Do-It-Yourself Encyclopedia, 26 vols. LC 74-21375. 1983. 155.48 (ISBN 0-87475-725-8). Stuttman.

Consumer Guide Editors. Home Repair Money Saver. 1981. pap. 2.50 (ISBN 0-449-90027-4, Columbine). Fawcett.

Davis, Jerry C. Rehabbing for Profit. (Illus.). 224p. 1981. 31.50 (ISBN 0-07-015695-6). McGraw.

De Marne, Henri. Entering the Remodeling Field: A Manual for Small-Volume Builders. 96p. 1977. pap. 12.00 (ISBN 0-86718-050-1); pap. 9.00 members. Natl Assn Home.

Demske, Dick. Electrical Installations & Repairs. Wolf, Donald D. & Wolf, Margot L., eds. LC 76-8372. (Adventures in Home Repair Ser.). (Illus.). 1977. pap. 3.95 (ISBN 0-8326-2211-7, 7701). Delair.

--Exterior Home Repairs. Wolf, Donald D. & Wolf, Margot L., eds. LC 76-52268. (Adventures in Home Repair Ser.). (Illus.). 1979. pap. 3.95 (ISBN 0-8326-2216-8, 7704). Delair.

--Home Comfort. Wolf, Donald D. & Wolf, Margot L., eds. LC 76-52269. (Adventures in Home Repair Ser.). (Illus.). 1979. pap. 3.95 (ISBN 0-8326-2217-6, 7703). Delair.

--Home Repair Book. Wolf, Margot L. & Wolf, Donald D., eds. LC 78-13807. (Illus.). 1979. 19.95 (ISBN 0-8326-2238-9, 7720); deluxe ed. 19.95 (ISBN 0-8326-2239-7, 7721). Delair.

--Home Repairs Made Easy. Wolf, Donald D., ed. LC 79-84283. (Illus.). 1979. pap. 9.95 (ISBN 0-8326-2240-0, 7725). Delair.

--Interior Home Repairs. Wolf, Donald D. & Wolf, Margot L., eds. LC 76-52267. (Adventures in Home Repair Ser.). (Illus.). 1979. pap. 3.95 (ISBN 0-8326-2215-X, 7705). Delair.

--Painting, Paneling, & Wallpapering. Wolf, Donald D. & Wolf, Margot L., eds. LC 76-8373. (Adventures in Home Repair Ser.). (Illus.). 1977. pap. 3.95 (ISBN 0-8326-2212-5, 7702). Delair.

--Plumbing. Wolf, Donald D. & Wolf, Margot L., eds. LC 76-8370. (Adventures in Home Repair Ser.). (Illus.). 1976. pap. 3.95 (ISBN 0-8326-2210-9, 7700). Delair.

Demske, R. J. Instant Home Repair. LC 72-91408. (Illus.). 320p. 1973. 4.95 (ISBN 0-911744-13-4). Career Pub IL.

Do-It-Yourself & Home Improvement Markets. 1985. 250.00x (ISBN 0-686-71951-4, Pub. by Euromonitor). State Mutual Bk.

Edgerton, William H. How to Renovate Townhouses & Brownstones. 2nd ed. 156p. 1980. 16.95 (ISBN 0-442-24841-5). Van Nos Reinhold.

Falcone, J. D. How to Design, Build, Remodel, & Maintain Your Home. 2nd ed. 1984. 32.95 (ISBN 0-471-81843-7). Halsted Pr.

Falcone, Joseph D. How to Design, Build, Remodel & Maintain Your Home. 1980. pap. write for info. (Fireside). S&S.

Family Handyman Magazine. Family Handyman Answer Book Number 2. 1983. pap. 12.95 (ISBN 0-8359-1839-4). Reston.

Family Handyman Magazine Staff. America's Handyman Book. rev. ed. (Illus.). 1983. 16.95 (ISBN 0-684-16296-2). Scribner.

Floors & Stairways. LC 77-89982. (Home Repair & Improvement Ser.). (Illus.). 1978. lib. bdg. 15.94 (ISBN 0-8094-2395-2, Pub. by Time-Life). Silver.

Geary. The Complete Handbook of Home Exterior Repair & Maintenance. (Illus.). 352p. 1982. pap. 9.95 (ISBN 0-8306-1382-X, 1382). TAB Bks.

Gladstone, Bernard. The New York Times Complete Manual of Home Repair. LC 75-13756. 1980. 15.95 (ISBN 0-8129-0873-2). Times Bks.

Hand, Jackson. How to Repair, Renovate, & Decorate Your Walls, Floors, & Ceilings. LC 80-50595. (Illus.). 212p. (Orig.). 1980. pap. 4.95i (ISBN 0-06-090825-4, CN 825, HarpT). Har-Row.

Hedden, Jay. Plumbing for Old & New Houses. 2nd ed. Horowitz, Shirley M., ed. LC 81-67297. (Illus.). 160p. (Orig.). 1980. 19.95 (ISBN 0-932944-45-0); pap. 6.95 (ISBN 0-932944-46-9). Creative Homeowner.

Hinde, Thomas. Cottage Book: Manual of Maintenance, Repair, Construction. 1979. 18.95 (ISBN 0-432-06770-1, Pub. by W Heinemann Ltd). David & Charles.

Home Security. LC 78-27634. (Home Repair & Improvement Ser.). (Illus.). 1979. lib. bdg. 15.94 (ISBN 0-8094-2419-3, Pub. by Time-Life). Silver.

Hotton, Peter. So You Want to Fix up an Old House. LC 79-14961. (Illus.). 1979. pap. 11.00 (ISBN 0-316-37387-7). Little.

How to Fix a Leak. (Home Care Guides Ser.). (Illus.). 1981. pap. 2.50 (ISBN 0-686-71123-8). S&S.

How to Wire Electrical Outlets, Switches & Lights. (Home Care Guides Ser.). (Illus.). 1981. pap. 2.50 (ISBN 0-686-71125-4). S&S.

Hutchins, Nigel. Restoring Houses of Brick & Stone. 192p. 1983. 29.95 (ISBN 0-7706-0029-8). Van Nos Reinhold.

Johnson, Alan. How to Restore & Improve Your Victorian House. (Illus.). 160p. 1983. 26.00 (ISBN 0-7153-8334-5). David & Charles.

Lamb, Curt. Homestyles. LC 78-21201. (Illus.). 1979. 14.95 (ISBN 0-312-38899-3). St Martin.

Lee, Reginald. Building Maintenance Management. 1976. 17.95x (ISBN 0-8464-0222-X). Beekman Pubs.
--Building Maintenance Management. 194p. 1976. pap. text ed. 17.50x (ISBN 0-258-96947-4, Pub. by Granada England). Brookfield Pub Co.
McClintock, Mike. Popular Science Do-It-Yourself Yearbook 1985. (Illus.). 248p. 1985. 19.95 (ISBN 0-943822-38-6). Rodale Pr Inc.
McGrath, Ed. The Superinsulated House: A Working Guide for Owner-Builders & Architects. (Illus.). 128p. 1982. pap. 11.95 (ISBN 0-918270-12-X). That New Pub.
Matthews, Roberta Ritz. Our Home Memory & Maintenance Album. LC 81-14991. (Illus.). 127p. 1982. 12.95 (ISBN 0-87491-464-7); pap. 6.95 (ISBN 0-87491-467-1). Acropolis.
Miller, Michael C. The Guide to Home Renovation: For Those Without the Time or Inclination to Do It Themselves. LC 80-70390. (Illus.). 136p. (Orig.). 1981. pap. 7.95 (ISBN 0-8019-7095-4). Chilton.
Mills, Richard G. Jackie's Home Repair & Maintenance Charts. Hostage, Jacqueline, ed. LC 82-25290. (Illus.). 128p. 1983. pap. 5.95 plastic comb bdg. (ISBN 0-932620-18-3). Betterway Pubns.
Mitchell, Harris. The Basement Book. (Illus.). 96p. 1984. pap. 8.95 (ISBN 0-88639-010-9, Pub. by New Trend). Dodd.
--The New Encyclopedia of Home Repair. pap. 8.95 (ISBN 0-88639-005-2, Pub. by New Trend). Dodd.
Morrison, James W. The Complete Energy-Saving Home Improvement Guide. 4th ed. LC 80-23996. (Illus.). 1981. pap. 2.50 (ISBN 0-668-05085-3, 5085-3). Arco.
National Association of Home Builders. Basement Water Leakage: Causes, Prevention, & Correction. 30p. 1978. pap. 7.00 (ISBN 0-86718-005-6); pap. 5.00. Natl Assn Home.
Newton, Mark. Home Repairs: A Guide for the Amateur Handyman. 9.50x (ISBN 0-392-08202-0, SpS). Sportshelf.
Nunn, Richard E. Popular Mechanics Complete Manual of Home Repair & Improvement. (Illus.). 1975. pap. 5.95 (ISBN 0-380-00431-3, 46607-4). Avon.
Our Home Memory & Maintenance Album. (Illus.). 127p. 1982. 12.95 (ISBN 0-686-96540-X). Natl Assn Home.
Outdoor Recreational Areas. (Home Repair and Improvement). 128p. (Orig.). 1980. 11.95 (ISBN 0-8094-2434-7). Time-Life.
Outdoor Structures. LC 78-1110. (Home Repair & Improvement Ser.). (Illus.). 1978. lib. bdg. 15.94 (ISBN 0-8094-2403-7). Silver.
Pegg, Brian F. & Stagg, William D. Plastering: A Craftsman's Encyclopedia. 276p. 1976. text ed. 14.75 (ISBN 0-258-97007-3, Pub. by Granada England). Brookfield Pub Co.
Philbin, Tom. Home Repairs Any Woman Can Do. LC 72-8625. (Illus.). 160p. 1973. 5.95 (ISBN 0-13-395038-7). P-H.
Philbin, Tom & Koelbel, Fritz. The Nothing Left Out Home Improvement Book. (Illus.). 272p. 1982. pap. 5.95 (ISBN 0-13-624346-0). P-H.
Popular Mechanics Complete Manual of Home Repair & Improvement. 480p. 1972. 8.95 (ISBN 0-910990-50-6). Hearst Bks.
Proulx, E. Annie. Plan & Make Your Own Fences & Gates, Walkways, Walls & Drives. Halpin, Anne, ed. (Illus.). 224p. 1983. pap. 11.95 (ISBN 0-87857-453-0, 14-048-1). Rodale Pr Inc.
Proulx, Earl. Yankee Magazine's Home Fix-It Book. Walz, Lila, ed. LC 81-52931. (Illus.). 64p. (Orig.). 1982. pap. 3.95 (ISBN 0-911658-33-5). Yankee Bks.
Reader's Digest Editors. Complete Do-It-Yourself Manual. LC 72-87867. (Illus.). 600p. 1973. 20.95 (ISBN 0-89577-010-5, Pub. by RD Assn). Random.
Rockis, G. Residential Wiring. (Illus.). 1977. pap. 14.95 (ISBN 0-8269-1650-3). Am Technical.
Roofs & Siding. LC 77-90094. (Home Repair & Improvement Ser.). (Illus.). 1978. lib. bdg. 15.94 (ISBN 0-8094-2391-X, Pub. by Time-Life). Silver.
Roybal, T. J. & Edmondson, G. C. The Basic Book of Home Maintenance & Repair. (Basic Industrial Arts Ser.). (Illus.). 122p. 1984. 7.50 (ISBN 0-8269-4410-8). Am Technical.
Rudman, Jack. Building Maintenance Foreman. (Career Examination Ser.: C-1147). (Cloth bdg. avail. on request). pap. 12.00 (ISBN 0-8373-1147-0). Natl Learning.
--Building Maintenance Supervisor. (Career Examination Ser.: C-1148). (Cloth bdg. avail. on request). pap. 12.00 (ISBN 0-8373-1148-9). Natl Learning.
--Gang Foreman (Structures-Group F) (Painting) (Career Examination Ser.: C-295). (Cloth bdg. avail. on request). pap. 12.00 (ISBN 0-8373-0295-1). Natl Learning.
Rusk, Katherine. Renovating the Victorian House: A Guide for Aficionados of Old Houses. LC 82-12397. (Illus.). 200p. (Orig.). 1983. 24.95 (ISBN 0-89286-217-3); pap. 12.95 (ISBN 0-89286-187-8). One Hund One Prods.
Schwartz, Robert. Home Owner's Legal Guide. 1969. pap. 2.95 (ISBN 0-02-081980-3, Collier). Macmillan.
Seaquist, Edgar O. Diagnosing & Repairing House Structure Problems. (Illus.). 1980. 27.50 (ISBN 0-07-056013-7). McGraw.
Sikking, Robert P. Do It Yourself. 44p. 1981. pap. 1.50 (ISBN 0-87516-436-6). De Vorss.
Sinnott, Ralph. Safety & Security in Building Design. (Illus.). 258p. 1985. 29.50 (ISBN 0-442-28212-5). Van Nos Reinhold.
Sunset Editors. Basic Home Repairs Illustrated. LC 73-115166. (Illus.). 96p. 1980. pap. 4.95 (ISBN 0-376-01025-8, Sunset Bks). Sunset-Lane.
--Roofing & Siding. LC 80-53487. (Illus.). 120p. 1981. pap. 5.95 (ISBN 0-376-01491-1, Sunset Bks). Sunset-Lane.
Symons, Arthur. Fix-It Book. pap. 2.00 (ISBN 0-87980-289-8). Borden.
Time-Life Bks, ed. Walls & Ceilings. (Home Repair & Improvement Ser.). (Illus.). 128p. 1980. 11.95 (ISBN 0-8094-3450-4). Time-Life.
Time-Life Books. Kitchens & Bathrooms. LC 77-83171. (Home Repair & Improvement Ser.). (Illus.). 1977. lib. bdg. 15.94 (ISBN 0-8094-2387-1, Pub. by Time-Life). Silver.
Time-Life Books, ed. Heating & Cooling. (Home Repair & Improvement Ser.). 1977. 11.95 (ISBN 0-8094-2378-2). Time-Life.
--Home Security. (Home Repair & Improvement Ser.). (Illus.). 1979. 11.95 (ISBN 0-8094-2418-5). Time-Life.
--Kitchens & Bathrooms. (Home Repair Ser.). (Illus.). 1977. 11.95 (ISBN 0-8094-2386-3). Time-Life.
Time Life Books Editors. Floors & Stairways. (Home Repair Ser.). (Illus.). 1978. 11.95 (ISBN 0-8094-2394-4). Time-Life.
Time-Life Books Editors. The Old House. (Home Repair & Improvement Ser.). (Illus.). 1980. 11.95 (ISBN 0-8094-2422-3). Time-Life.
--Special Purpose Rooms. (Home Repair & Improvement Ser.). (Illus.). 128p. 1981. 11.95 (ISBN 0-8094-3458-X). Time-Life.
--Working with Wood. (Home Repair & Improvement Ser.). (Illus.). 1979. 11.95 (ISBN 0-8094-2426-6). Time-Life.
Time-Life Books Editors, ed. Built-Ins. (Home Repairs & Improvement Ser.). (Illus.). 1980. 11.95 (ISBN 0-8094-2430-4). Time-Life.
Time-Life Editors. Outdoor Structures. (Home Repair Ser.). (Illus.). 1978. 11.95 (ISBN 0-8094-2402-9). Time-Life.
--Roofs & Siding. (Home Repair & Improvement Ser.). 1977. 11.95 (ISBN 0-8094-2390-1). Time-Life.
Watkins, A. M. New Complete Book of Home Remodeling, Improvements & Repairs. (Illus.). 363p. 1979. 15.95 (ISBN 0-911749-04-7). Building Inst.
Weiss. Home Maintenance. 1978. text ed. 15.20; student guide 3.96 (ISBN 0-02-664400-2); tchr's. guide 2.00 (ISBN 0-02-664390-1). Bennett IL.
--Home Maintenance. rev. ed. 1983. text ed. 15.20 (ISBN 0-02-664380-4). Bennett IL.
Williams, Guy. Instructions for Home Handyman. (Illus.). 14.50x (ISBN 0-392-03419-0, SpS). Sportshelf.
Williams, T. Jeff. All about Basic Home Repairs. Ortho Books Editorial Staff, ed. LC 79-52989. (Illus.). 112p. (Orig.). 1980. pap. 5.95 (ISBN 0-917102-82-7). Ortho.
Woodin, J. C. & Hayes, Louis. Home & Building Maintenance. 18.64 (ISBN 0-87345-466-9). McKnight.

DWELLINGS–REMODELING

see also Buildings–Repair and Reconstruction

Abrams, Lawrence & Abrams, Kathleen. Salvaging Old Barns & Houses: Tear it Down & Save Their Places. LC 82-19330. (Illus.). 128p. (Orig.). 1983. pap. 7.95 (ISBN 0-8069-7666-7). Sterling.
Adding on. LC 79-9759. (Home Repair & Improvement Ser.). (Illus.). 1979. lib. bdg. 15.94 (ISBN 0-8094-2415-0, Pub. by Time-Life). Silver.
Augustin, Ann S. Help! I Want to Remodel My Home: The New Woman's Guide to Home Improvement. LC 74-28307. (Illus.). 221p. 1975. 17.95 (ISBN 0-88229-214-5). Nelson-Hall.
Brann, Donald R. Brann's Guide to Home Improvement. LC 63-9605. (Illus.). 1963. 10.95 (ISBN 0-8303-0053-8). Fleet.
--How to Add an Extra Bathroom. rev. ed. LC 68-18108. 1976. lib. bdg. 5.95 (ISBN 0-87733-082-4); pap. 6.95 (ISBN 0-87733-682-2). Easi-Bild.
--How to Build a Patio, Porch, & Sundeck. LC 78-55238. 1979. pap. 6.95 (ISBN 0-87733-781-0). Easi-Bild.
--How to Create Room at the Top. LC 77-15691. 1978. pap. 6.95 (ISBN 0-87733-773-X). Easi-Bild.
--How to Install Paneling, Make Valances, Cornices. LC 65-25756. 1979. pap. 6.95 (ISBN 0-87733-605-9). Easi-Bild.
--How to Rehabilitate an Abandoned Building, Bk. L85. LC 73-87513. 258p. 1974. lib. bdg. 6.95 (ISBN 0-87733-085-9). Easi-Bild.
Burch, Monte. Brick, Concrete, Stonework. Kummings, Gail, ed. LC 81-66575. (Illus.). 144p. (Orig.). 1981. 17.95 (ISBN 0-932944-29-9); pap. 6.95 (ISBN 0-932944-30-2). Creative Homeowner.
Cabinets, Bookcases & Closets. 1981. pap. 6.95 (ISBN 0-932944-22-1). Creative Homeowner.
Coe, Gigi, et al. The Home Energy Decision Book: Remodeling Your Home for Low-Cost Energy Efficiency. LC 83-19574. (Tools for Today Bks.). (Illus.). 180p. (Orig.). 1984. pap. 9.95 (ISBN 0-87156-811-X). Sierra.
Cohen, M. K. Old Houses into New: Successful Real Estate Renovation for Profit. (Illus.). 134p. 1982. 11.95 (ISBN 0-13-633966-2); pap. 5.95 (ISBN 0-13-633958-1). P-H.
Curran, June. Profile Your Lifestyle: Questions to Ask Yourself Before Building, Buying or Remodeling a Home. Wilbur, Shay & Weine, Ruth, eds. LC 78-72187. 1979. pap. 7.95 (ISBN 0-932370-00-4). Brooks Pub Co.
Falcone, J. D. How to Design, Build, Remodel, & Maintain Your Home. 2nd ed. 1984. 32.95 (ISBN 0-471-81843-7). Halsted Pr.
Falcone, Joseph D. How to Design, Build, Remodel & Maintain Your Home. 1980. pap. write for info. (Fireside). S&S.
Fine Homebuilding Magazine Editors. Fine Homebuilding Construction Techniques. LC 84-50164. (Illus.). 240p. 1984. 24.95 (ISBN 0-918804-23-X, Dist. by W W Norton). Taunton.
Galvin, Patrick. Remodeling Your Bathroom. LC 79-91444. (Popular Science Skill Bks.). (Orig.). 1980. pap. 4.95i (ISBN 0-06-090780-0, CN 780, CN). Har-Row.
Garages & Carports. pap. 6.95 (ISBN 0-686-73200-6). Creative Homeowner.
Hardenbrook, Harry. Walker's Remodeling Estimator's Reference Book. (Illus.). 325p. 1982. 25.00 (ISBN 0-911592-60-1, ScribT). Scribner.
Henkin, William. How to Design & Remodel Bathrooms. Ortho Bks Editorial Staff, ed. LC 81-86180. (Illus.). 96p. (Orig.). 1982. pap. 5.95 (ISBN 0-917102-99-1). Ortho.
Jones, Markley L., et al. Restore Your Future. (Illus.). 115p. 1982. pap. 5.95 (ISBN 0-13-774927-9). P-H.
Kangas, Robert. The Old House Rescue Book: Buying & Renovating on a Budget. 330p. 1982. 19.95 (ISBN 0-8359-5213-4). Reston.
Kinney, Cle & Roberts, Barry. Don't Move--Improve! Hundreds of Ways to Make a Good House Better. LC 78-3305. (Funk & W Bk.). (Illus.). 1979. 14.95i (ISBN 0-308-10314-9). T Y Crowell.
Labine, Clem & Flaherty, Carolyn, eds. The Old-House Journal Compendium. LC 78-4360. (Illus.). 400p. 1980. 27.95 (ISBN 0-87951-080-3); pap. 15.95 (ISBN 0-87951-186-9). Overlook Pr.
Lang, Andy. Andy Lang's Remodeling Handbook. LC 78-17860. (Home Construction Ser.). (Illus.). 96p. 1979. pap. 4.95 (ISBN 0-8437-3413-2). Hammond Inc.
Leckie, Jim, et al. More Other Homes & Garbage: Designs for Self-Sufficient Living. rev. ed. LC 79-22175. (Illus.). 416p. (Orig.). 1981. pap. 14.95 (ISBN 0-87156-274-X). Sierra.
Midwest Plan Service Personnel. Home & Yard Improvements Handbook. LC 78-4505. (Illus.). 100p. 1978. pap. 6.00 (ISBN 0-89373-034-3, MWPS-21). Midwest Plan Serv.
Myers, Stanley & Figiel, Richard. Creative Home Remodeling. (Illus.). 240p. 1981. text ed. 16.95 (ISBN 0-13-189613-X, Spec); pap. text ed. 8.95 (ISBN 0-13-189605-9, Spec). P-H.
Nash, George. Old Houses: A Rebuilder's Manual. (Illus.). 1979. (Spec); pap. 12.95 (ISBN 0-686-96841-7). P-H.
Nunn, Richard V. Home Improvement, Home Repair. Horowitz, Shirley M., ed. LC 80-66637. (Illus.). 256p. 1980. 17.95 (ISBN 0-932944-17-5). Creative Homeowner.
--Home Improvement-Home Repair. Horowitz, Shirley M., ed. LC 80-66637. (Illus.). 256p. (Orig.). 1980. pap. 7.95 (ISBN 0-932944-18-3). Creative Homeowner.
One-Hundred Seventy-Five Home Plans. 1981. pap. 6.95 (ISBN 0-932944-04-3). Creative Homeowner.
Philbin, Tom & Koelbel, Fritz. The Nothing Left Out Home Improvement Book. (Illus.). 272p. 1982. pap. 5.95 (ISBN 0-13-624346-0). P-H.
Reader's Digest Editors. Home Improvements Manual. LC 81-84488. (Illus.). 384p. 1982. 23.95 (ISBN 0-89577-132-2, Pub. by RD Assn). Random.
Reed, Mortimer. Complete Guide to Residential Remodeling. (Illus.). 320p. 1983. 30.95 (ISBN 0-13-160663-8); pap. 15.95 (ISBN 0-13-160671-9). P-H.
Rural Home Modifications for Survival (Retreat Security) (Economic & Survival Ser.). (Illus.). 65p. (Orig.). 1981. pap. 15.00 (ISBN 0-939856-22-0). Tech Group.
Scharff, Robert. The Complete Book of Home Remodeling. 1975. 37.95 (ISBN 0-07-055167-7). McGraw.
Sherwood, Gerald E. How to Select & Renovate an Older House. (Illus.). 1976. pap. 3.50 (ISBN 0-486-23374-X). Dover.
--How to Select & Renovate an Older House. 13.50 (ISBN 0-8446-5523-6). Peter Smith.
Stephen, George. Remodeling Old Houses: Without Destroying Their Character. (Illus.). 1972. pap. 6.95 (ISBN 0-394-70756-7). Knopf.
Sunset Editors. Children's Rooms & Play Yards. 3rd ed. LC 79-90336. (Illus.). 96p. 1980. pap. 4.95 (ISBN 0-376-01055-X, Sunset Bks). Sunset-Lane.
--Home Lighting. LC 82-81371. (Illus.). 96p. (Orig.). 1982. pap. 4.95 (ISBN 0-376-01312-5, Sunset Bks). Sunset-Lane.
--Remodeling Your Home. 3rd ed. LC 78-53674. (Illus.). 96p. 1978. pap. 4.95 (ISBN 0-376-01506-3, Sunset Bks.). Sunset-Lane.
--Wallcoverings. LC 82-81370. (Illus.). 96p. (Orig.). 1982. pap. 5.95 (ISBN 0-376-01719-8, Sunset Bks). Sunset-Lane.
--Windows & Skylights. LC 81-82871. (Illus.). 112p. (Orig.). 1982. pap. 5.95 (ISBN 0-376-01751-1, Sunset Bks). Sunset-Lane.
Sunset Editors, ed. Bedroom & Bath Storage. LC 81-82870. (Illus.). 80p. (Orig.). 1982. pap. 4.95 (ISBN 0-376-01121-1, Sunset Bks). Sunset-Lane.
--Flooring: Do it Yourself. LC 81-82872. (Illus.). 112p. (Orig.). 1982. pap. 4.95 (ISBN 0-376-01141-6). Sunset-Lane.
--Solar Remodeling. LC 82-81372. (Illus.). 96p. (Orig.). 1982. pap. 5.95 (ISBN 0-376-01535-7, Sunset Bks). Sunset-Lane.
Time-Life Books Editors. Adding on. (Home Repair & Improvement). (Illus.). 1979. 11.95 (ISBN 0-8094-2414-2). Time-Life.
Time-Life Books Editors, ed. Built-Ins. (Home Repairs & Improvement Ser.). (Illus.). 1980. 11.95 (ISBN 0-8094-2430-4). Time-Life.
Vila, Bob & Davison, Jane. This Old House: Restoring, Rehabilitating & Renovating. (Illus.). 336p. 1980. 22.50 (ISBN 0-316-17704-0); pap. 17.45 (ISBN 0-316-17702-4). Little.
Wahlfeldt, Bette G. Home Remodeling: A How-To, Money-Saving Handbook. (Illus.). 400p. (Orig.). 1984. 24.95 (ISBN 0-8306-0215-1); pap. 16.95 (ISBN 0-8306-1515-6, 1515). TAB Bks.
Walker, Jenepher. How to Design & Remodel Kitchens. ORTHO Books Editorial Staff, ed. LC 81-86179. (Illus.). 96p. 1982. pap. 5.95 (ISBN 0-917102-98-3). Ortho.
Watkins, A. M. New Complete Book of Home Remodeling, Improvements & Repairs. (Illus.). 363p. 1979. 15.95 (ISBN 0-911749-04-7). Building Inst.
Werner, Frank R. New Living in Old Houses. (Illus.). 160p. 1982. 35.00 (ISBN 0-8109-1366-6). Abrams.
Williams, Benjamin, ed. Remodelers Handbook: A Manual of Professional Practice for Home Improvement Contractors. LC 76-53565. (Illus.). 416p. 1977. pap. 18.50 (ISBN 0-910460-21-3); pap. 13.50 members. Natl Assn Home.
Wing, Charles. From the Walls In. LC 78-26354. (Illus.). 1979. pap. 12.95 (ISBN 0-316-94740-7, Pub. by Atlantic Monthly Pr). Little.

DYE PLANTS

see also Lichens

Bliss, Anne. North American Dye Plants. (Illus.). 1980. pap. 5.95 (ISBN 0-684-16393-4). Scribner.
--Weeds: A Guide for Dyers & Herbalists. LC 78-59236. (Illus.). 1978. pap. 5.00x (ISBN 0-931870-01-1). Juniper Hse.
Casselman, Karen L. The Craft of the Dyer: Color from Plants & Lichens of the North East. 1980. 30.00 (ISBN 0-8020-2362-2). U of Toronto Pr.
Conner, Berenice G. Dyes from Your Garden. LC 75-33970. (Illus.). 128p. 1976. spiral bdg. 7.95 (ISBN 0-912458-61-5). E A Seemann.
Davidson, Mary F. The Dye Pot. 3rd rev. ed. 1981. pap. text ed. 3.00 (ISBN 0-686-10137-5). M F Davidson.
Donkin, R. A. Spanish Red: An Ethnogeographical Study of Cochineal & the Opuntia Cactus. LC 77-76426. (Transactions Ser.: Vol. 67, Pt. 5). (Illus.). 1977. pap. 7.00 (ISBN 0-87169-675-4). Am Philos.
Dye Plants & Dyeing. 2.25 (ISBN 0-686-21141-3). Bklyn Botanic.
Kramer, Jack. Natural Dyes: Plants & Processes. LC 76-179554. (Illus.). 128p. 1972. 9.95 (ISBN 0-684-12828-4, ScribT). Scribner.
Natural Plant Dyeing. 2.25 (ISBN 0-686-21164-2). Bklyn Botanic.

Ouzinkie Botanical Society Staff & Graham, Frances K. Plant Lore of an Alaskan Island. (Illus.). 210p. 1985. 9.95 (ISBN 0-88240-266-8). Alaska Northwest.
Weigle, Palmy. Ancient Dyes for Modern Weavers. (Illus.). 128p. 1974. 12.95 (ISBN 0-8230-0223-3). Watson-Guptill.

DYEING
see Dyes and Dyeing

DYES AND DYEING
see also Bleaching; Coloring Matter; Dye Plants; Textile Chemistry

Adrosko, Rita J. Natural Dyes & Home Dyeing. (Illus.). 1971. pap. 2.95 (ISBN 0-486-22688-3). Dover.
--Natural Dyes & Home Dyeing. Orig. Title: Natural Dyes in the United States. (Illus.). 11.25 (ISBN 0-8446-4500-1). Peter Smith.
Advances in Preparation, Coloration & Finishing. 1982. 60.00x (ISBN 0-686-81693-5, Pub. by Soc Dyers & Colour). State Mutual Bk.
Allen, R. L. Colour Chemistry. (Studies in Modern Chemistry Ser.). 336p. 1971. 34.50x (ISBN 0-306-50002-7, Plenum Pr). Plenum Pub.
Beer, John. The Emergence of the German Dye Industry. Cohen, I. Bernard, ed. LC 80-2115. (Development of Science Ser.). (Illus.). 1981. lib. bdg. 15.00x (ISBN 0-405-13835-0). Ayer Co Pubs.
Bemiss, Elijah. The Dyer's Companion. LC 73-77377. 307p. 1973. pap. 4.50 (ISBN 0-486-20601-7). Dover.
--The Dyer's Companion. 3rd enl ed. 11.25 (ISBN 0-8446-5003-X). Peter Smith.
Berry, C. & Ferguson, J. G. Chapter Six - Discharge, Resist & Special Styles. 75.00x (ISBN 0-686-98198-7, Pub. by Soc Dyers & Colour); pap. 50.00x (ISBN 0-686-98199-5). State Mutual Bk.
Bird, C. L. The Theory & Practice of Wool Dyeing. 4th ed. 249p. 1972. 39.00x (ISBN 0-686-91778-2, Pub. by Soc Dyers & Colour). State Mutual Bk.
Bird, C. L. & Boston, W. S. The Theory of Coloration of Textiles. 432p. 1975. 80.00x (ISBN 0-686-98192-8, Pub. by Soc Dyers & Colour). State Mutual Bk.
Bliss, Anne. A Handbook of Dyes from Natural Materials. (Illus.). 192p. 1983. pap. 9.95 (ISBN 0-684-17893-1, ScribT). Scribner.
--Weeds: A Guide for Dyers & Herbalists. LC 78-59236. (Illus.). 1978. pap. 5.00x (ISBN 0-931870-01-1). Juniper Hse.
Bloomfield, Dennis A., ed. Dye Curves: The Theory & Practice of Indicator Dilution. LC 77-356568. pap. 116.50 (ISBN 0-317-26199-1, 2052067). Bks Demand UMI.
Bogle, Michael. Textile Dyes, Finishes & Auxiliaries. LC 76-25746. (Reference Library of Science & Technology Ser.: Vol. 8). (Illus.). 1977. lib. bdg. 24.00 (ISBN 0-8240-9902-8). Garland Pub.
Brewster, Mela S. A Practical Study of the Use of the Natural Vegetable Dyes in New Mexico. LC 38-28365. 1982. lib. bdg. 19.95x (ISBN 0-89370-726-0). Borgo Pr.
Bronson, J. & Bronson, R. Early American Weaving & Dyeing: The Domestic Manufacturer's Assistant, & Family Directory in the Arts of Weaving & Dyeing. (Illus.). 224p. 1977. pap. 4.50 (ISBN 0-486-23440-1). Dover.
Brown, Rachel. The Weaving, Spinning, & Dyeing Book. LC 77-1653. (Illus.). 1978. 25.00 (ISBN 0-394-49801-1). Knopf.
Colour Index. 3rd, Rev. ed. 1982. 900.00x (ISBN 0-686-81698-6, Pub. by Soc Dyers & Colour). State Mutual Bk.
Colour Index: Supplement, Vol. 5. Rev. ed. 1982. 210.00x (ISBN 0-686-81697-8, Pub. by Soc Dyers & Colour). State Mutual Bk.
Conner, Berenice G. Dyes from Your Garden. LC 75-33970. (Illus.). 128p. 1976. spiral bdg. 7.95 (ISBN 0-912458-61-5). E A Seemann.
Davidson, Mary F. The Dye Pot. 3rd rev. ed. 1981. pap. text ed. 3.00 (ISBN 0-686-10137-5). M F Davidson.
Dawson, T. L. Chapter Four - Carpet & Yarn Printing. 75.00x (ISBN 0-686-98203-7, Pub. by Soc Dyers & Colour); pap. 50.00x (ISBN 0-686-98204-5). State Mutual Bk.
Donkin, R. A. Spanish Red: An Ethnogeographical Study of Cochineal & the Opuntia Cactus. LC 77-76426. (Transactions Ser.: Vol. 67, Pt. 5). (Illus.). 1977. pap. 7.00 (ISBN 0-87169-675-4). Am Philos.
Dye Plants & Dyeing. 2.25 (ISBN 0-686-21141-3). Bklyn Botanic.
Dyer, Anne. Dyes from Natural Sources. 88p. 1976. pap. 7.25 (ISBN 0-8231-5049-6). Branford.
Efficiency & Control of Coloration Process. 1982. 35.00x (ISBN 0-686-81695-1, Pub. by Soc Dyers & Colour). State Mutual Bk.
Fabian, J. & Hartmann, H. Light Absorption of Organic Colorants: Theoretical Treatment & Empirical Rules. (Reactivity & Structure Ser.: Vol. 12). (Illus.). 280p. 1980. 86.00 (ISBN 0-387-09914-X). Springer-Verlag.
Gittinger, Mattiebelle. Master Dyers to the World: Technique & Trade in Early Indian Dyed Cotton Textiles. McEuen, Caroline K., ed. (Illus.). 208p. 1982. pap. 20.00 (ISBN 0-87405-020-0). Textile Mus.
Golden Jubilee of Colour in the CJE. 185p. 1981. 110.00x (ISBN 0-901956-34-1, Pub. by Soc Dyers & Colour). State Mutual Bk.
Goodwin, Jill. A Dyer's Manual. (Illus.). 128p. 1983. 17.95 (ISBN 0-7207-1327-7, Pub by Michael Joseph). Merrimack Pub Cir.
Gore, T. S., et al, eds. Recent Progress in the Chemistry of Natural & Synthetic Colouring Matters & Related Fields. 1962. 81.00 (ISBN 0-12-291650-6). Acad Pr.
Grae, Ida. Nature's Colors: Dyes from Plants. LC 73-11836. (Illus.). 230p. 1979. pap. 10.95 (ISBN 0-02-012390-6, Collier). Macmillan.
Green, Judy. Natural Dyes from Northwest Plants. pap. 5.95 (ISBN 0-686-19929-4). Robin & Russ.
Griffiths, J., ed. Developments in the Chemistry & Technology of Organic Dyes. (Illus.). 138p. (Orig.). 1984. text ed. 39.00x (ISBN 0-632-01304-4). Blackwell Pubns.
Gutjahr, H. Chapter Five - Direct Print Coloration. 75.00x (ISBN 0-686-98200-2, Pub. by Soc Dyers & Colour); pap. 50.00x (ISBN 0-686-98201-0). State Mutual Bk.
Hurry, Jamieson B. Woad Plant & Its Dye. LC 70-132019. (Illus.). Repr. of 1930 ed. 35.00x (ISBN 0-678-00779-9). Kelley.
Johnston, Ruth M. & Saltzman, Max, eds. Industrial Color Technology. LC 73-184207. (Advances in Chemistry Ser: No. 107). 1972. 19.95 (ISBN 0-8412-0134-X). Am Chemical.
Kierstead, Sallie P. Natural Dyes. 4.95 (ISBN 0-8283-1394-6). Branden Pub Co.
Knutson, Linda. Synthetic Dyes for Natural Fibers. LC 81-12418. (Connecting Threads Ser.). (Illus.). 228p. 1982. 18.95 (ISBN 0-914842-65-X). Madrona Pubs.
Kramer, Jack. Natural Dyes: Plants & Processes. LC 76-179554. (Illus.). 128p. 1972. 9.95 (ISBN 0-684-12828-4, ScribT). Scribner.
Krohn, Val F. Hawaii Dye Plants & Dye Recipes. LC 79-27162. (Illus.). 136p. 1980. pap. 8.95 (ISBN 0-8248-0698-0). UH Pr.
Lesch, Alma. Vegetable Dyeing. (Illus.). 144p. 1971. 12.95 (ISBN 0-8230-5600-7). Watson-Guptill.
Lubs, H. A., ed. Chemistry of Synthetic Dyes & Pigments. LC 64-7905. (A C S Ser: No. 127). 750p. 1971. Repr. of 1955 ed. 47.50 (ISBN 0-88275-039-9). Krieger.
McGregor, R. Diffusion & Sorption in the Fibers & Films: An Introduction with Particular Reference to Dyes, Vol. 1. 1974. 45.00 (ISBN 0-12-484101-5). Acad Pr.
Metzger, Jacques. Thiazole & Its Derivatives, 3 pts. LC 78-17740. (Chemistry of Heterocyclic Compounds Ser.: Vol. 34). 1979. Pt. 1, 612p. 190.95 ea (ISBN 0-471-03993-4, Pub. by Wiley-Interscience). Pt. 2, 590p (ISBN 0-471-04126-2). Pt. 3, 406p (ISBN 0-471-04127-0). Wiley.
Nunn, D. M. The Dyeing of Synthetic-Polymer & Acetate Fibres. 1979p. 1979. 100.00x (ISBN 0-686-98190-1, XPub. by Soc Dyers & Colour); pap. 55.00x (ISBN 0-686-98191-X). State Mutual Bk.
Park, J. A Practical Introduction to Yarn Dyeing. 120p. 1981. 59.00x (ISBN 0-901956-28-7, Pub. by Soc Dyers & Colour). State Mutual Bk.
Pettit, Florence H. America's Indigo Blues: Resist - Printed & Dyed Textiles of the Eighteenth Century. (Illus.). 1975. 24.95 (ISBN 0-8038-0376-1). Hastings.
Physical & Chemical Applications of Dyestuffs. (Topics in Current Chemistry Ser.: Vol. 61). (Illus.). 180p. 1976. 42.00 (ISBN 0-387-07559-3). Springer-Verlag.
Ponting, Ken. A Dictionary of Dyes & Dyeing. 216p. 1982. 35.00x (ISBN 0-7135-1311-X, Pub. by Bell & Hyman England). State Mutual Bk.
Progress & Productivity in Coloration. 1982. 60.00x (ISBN 0-686-81692-7, Pub. by Soc Dyers & Colour). State Mutual Bk.
Purple Dyeing: Ancient & Modern. (Shorey Historical Ser.). 220p. pap. 3.95 (ISBN 0-8466-4077-5, 177). Shorey.
Rice, Miriam C. How to Use Mushrooms for Color. rev. ed. (Illus.). 145p. 1980. pap. 8.95x (ISBN 0-916422-19-4). Mad River.
Rys, Paul & Zollinger, H. Fundamentals of the Chemistry & Application of Dyes. LC 78-37108. (Illus.). pap. 39.20 (ISBN 0-317-10909-X, 2051228). Bks Demand UMI.
Schultz, Kathleen. Create Your Own Natural Dyes. LC 74-31708. (Illus.). 96p. 1982. pap. 6.95 (ISBN 0-8069-7576-8). Sterling.
Sinclair, R. S. Numerical Problems in Colour Physics. 1982. 27.00 (ISBN 0-686-81691-9, Pub. by Soc Dyers & Colour). State Mutual Bk.
Standard Methods for the Determination of the Colour Fastness of Textiles & Leather. 1982. 75.00x (ISBN 0-686-81696-X, Pub. by Soc Dyers & Colour). State Mutual Bk.
Thurstan, Violetta. The Use of Vegetable Dyes. 3.00 (ISBN 0-913714-64-X). Legacy Bks.
Tidball, Harriet. Color & Dyeing. LC 76-24007. (Shuttle Craft Guild Monograph: No. 16). (Illus.). 53p. 1965. pap. 8.75 (ISBN 0-916658-16-3). HTH Pubs.
Trotman, E. R. Dyeing & Chemical Technology of Textile Fibres. 6th ed. 592p. 1984. text ed. 65.00 (ISBN 0-471-80910-1, Pub. by Wiley-Interscience). Wiley.
Valcl, O., et al, eds. Handbook Triarylmethane & Xanthene Dyes: Spectphoto Deter of Mtls. 400p. 1985. 122.50 (ISBN 0-8493-2941-8). CRC Pr.
Venkataraman, K. The Analytical Chemistry of Synthetic Dyes. LC 76-39881. 591p. 1977. 115.00x (ISBN 0-471-90575-5, Pub. by Wiley-Interscience). Wiley.
Venkataraman, Krishnasami, ed. The Chemistry of Synthethic Dyes, 8 vols. Incl. Vol. 1. 1952. 98.50 (ISBN 0-12-717001-4); Vol. 2. 1952. 98.50 (ISBN 0-12-717002-2); Vol. 3. 1970. 98.50 (ISBN 0-12-717003-0); Vol. 4. 1971. 98.50 (ISBN 0-12-717004-9); Vol. 5. 1971. 99.00 (ISBN 0-12-717005-7); Vol. 6. 1972. 98.50 (ISBN 0-12-717006-5); Vol. 7. 1974. 98.50 (ISBN 0-12-717007-3); Vol. 8. 1978. 98.50 (ISBN 0-12-717008-1). (Organic & Biological Chemistry Ser.). Set. 649.50. Acad Pr.
Vinroot, Sally & Crowder, Jennie. The New Dyer. LC 81-80904. (Illus.). 118p. 1981. 18.00 (ISBN 0-934026-05-X). Interweave.
Wada, Yoshiko. Shibori: Japanese Shaped Resist Dyeing. LC 82-48789. (Illus.). 296p. 1983. 65.00 (ISBN 0-87011-559-6). Kodansha.
Weigle, Palmy. Ancient Dyes for Modern Weavers. (Illus.). 128p. 1974. 12.95 (ISBN 0-8230-0223-3). Watson-Guptill.

DYNAMIC DISPLAY SYSTEMS
see Information Display Systems

DYNAMIC MODELS (COMPUTER PROGRAM LANGUAGE)
see DYNAMO (Computer Program Language)

DYNAMIC PROGRAMMING

Angel, Edward & Bellman, Richard. Dynamic Programming & Partial Differential Equations. (Mathematics in Science & Engineering Ser: Vol. 88). 1972. 60.00 (ISBN 0-12-057950-2). Acad Pr.
Avant-Garde Creations. The Creativity Life Dynamic Book. (Illus.). 84p. 1980. pap. 9.95 (ISBN 0-930182-07-3); pkg. including book, 2 drawing cards & program disk 24.95 (ISBN 0-930182-08-1). Avant Garde Pub.
Beckmann, Martin J. Dynamic Programming of Economic Decisions. LC 68-21990. (Econometrics & Operations Research: Vol. 9). 1968. 24.00 (ISBN 0-387-04292-X). Springer-Verlag.
Bellman, R. E. & Kalaba, Robert. Dynamic Programming & Modern Control. 1966. 31.50 (ISBN 0-12-084856-2). Acad Pr.
Bellman, Richard E. Some Vistas of Modern Mathematics: Dynamic Programming, Invariant Imbedding, & the Mathematical Biosciences. LC 68-12974. pap. 37.80 (ISBN 0-317-08655-3, 2004315). Bks Demand UMI.
Bellman, Richard E. & Dreyfus, S. Applied Dynamic Programming. (Rand Corporation Research Studies). 1962. 38.00x (ISBN 0-691-07913-7). Princeton U Pr.
Bertele, Umberto & Brioschi, Francesco. Nonserial Dynamic Programming. (Mathematics in Science & Engineering Ser.: Vol. 91). 1972. 60.00 (ISBN 0-12-093450-7). Acad Pr.
Bertsekas, Dimitri P. Dynamic Programming & Stochastic Control. (Math in Science & Engineering Ser.). 1976. 45.00 (ISBN 0-12-093250-4). Acad Pr.
Boudarel, R., et al. Dynamic Programming & Its Applications to Optimal Control. (Mathematics in Science & Engineering Ser.: Vol. 81). 1971. 70.00 (ISBN 0-12-118950-3). Acad Pr.
Cherene, L. J., Jr. Set Valued Dynamical Systems & Economic Flow. (Lecture Notes in Economics & Mathematical Systems: Vol. 158). 1978. pap. 12.00 (ISBN 0-387-08847-4). Springer-Verlag.
Control & Dynamic Systems: Advances Theory & Application, Vol. 16. LC 64-8027. (Serial Publications Ser.). 1980. 45.00 (ISBN 0-12-012716-4). Acad Pr.
Cooper, L. & Cooper, Mary W. Introduction to Dynamic Programming. LC 79-42640. (International Ser. in Modern Applied Mathematics & Computer Science: Vol. 1). (Illus.). 256p. 1981. 36.00 (ISBN 0-08-025065-3); pap. 21.00 (ISBN 0-08-025064-5). Pergamon.
Dan, S. Nonlinear & Dynamic Programming: An Introduction. LC 75-6503. (Illus.). vii, 164p. (Orig.). 1975. pap. text ed. 20.00 (ISBN 0-387-81289-X). Springer-Verlag.
Davisson, William I. & Uhran, John J., Jr. NDTRAN: A Primer for a Systems Dynamics Interpreter. (Illus.). pap. text ed. write for info. (ISBN 0-89651-504-4). Icarus.
Denardo, Eric V. Dynamic Programming: Models & Applications. (Illus.). 240p. 1982. 34.95 (ISBN 0-13-221507-1). P-H.
Derman, Cyrus. Finite State Markovian Decision Processes. (Mathematics in Science & Engineering Ser.: Vol. 67). 1970. 49.50 (ISBN 0-12-209250-3). Acad Pr.
Dolcetta, I. C., et al, eds. Recent Mathematical Methods in Dynamic Programming. (Lecture Notes in Mathematics: Vol. 1119). vi, 202p. 1985. pap. 14.40 (ISBN 0-387-15217-2). Springer-Verlag.
Dreyfus, Stuart E. The Art & Theory of Dynamic Programming. (Mathematics in Science & Engineering Ser.). 1977. 19.25i (ISBN 0-12-221860-4). Acad Pr.
--Dynamic Programming & the Calculus of Variations. (Mathematics in Science & Engineering Ser.: Vol. 21). 1965. 55.00 (ISBN 0-12-221850-7). Acad Pr.
Franklin, Gene F. & Powell, J. David. Digital Control of Dynamic Systems. LC 79-16377. 1980. text ed. 34.95 (ISBN 0-201-02891-3); solution manual 2.00 (ISBN 0-201-02892-1). Addison-Wesley.
Gresser, Ion, ed. Interferon Eighty-Two. (Serial Publication). 1983. 22.00 (ISBN 0-12-302253-3). Acad Pr.
Guckenheimer, John & Holmes, Philip. Nonlinear Oscillations, Dynamical Systems, & Bifurcations of Vector Fields. (Applied Mathematical Sciences Ser.: Vol. 42). (Illus.). 400p. 1983. 34.00 (ISBN 0-387-90819-6). Springer-Verlag.
Kaufmann, A. Graphs, Dynamic Programming & Finite Games. (Mathematics in Science & Engineering Ser.: Vol. 36). 1967. 70.00 (ISBN 0-12-402356-8). Acad Pr.
Larson & Casti. Principles of Dynamic Programming, Pt. 1. (Control & Systems Theory Ser.: Vol. 7). 1978. 34.50 (ISBN 0-8247-6589-3). Dekker.
Larson, Robert E. & Casti, John L. Principles of Dynamic Programming, Part Two. (Control & Systems Theory Ser.: Vol. 7). 1982. 39.75 (ISBN 0-8247-6590-7). Dekker.
Lindsay, James F. & Katz, Silas. Dynamics of Physical Circuits & Systems. (Illus.). 480p. 1978. 29.95 (ISBN 0-916460-21-5). Matrix Pub.
Magnus, K., ed. Dynamics of Multibody Systems: Symposium Munich, Germany, August 29 - September 3,1977. (International Union of Theoretical & Applied Mechanics). (Illus.). 1978. 43.70 (ISBN 0-387-08623-4). Springer-Verlag.
Nemhauser, George L. Introduction to Dynamic Programming. LC 66-21046. (Series in Decision & Control). pap. 67.50 (ISBN 0-317-08720-7, 2013053). Bks Demand UMI.
O'Leary, Michael K. Forecasting with Dynamic Systems. (Learning Packages in the Policy Sciences Ser.: No. 8). (Illus.). 40p. 1975. 2.50x (ISBN 0-936876-02-6). Pol Stud Assocs.
Puterman, Martin L., ed. Dynamic Programming & Its Application. LC 78-21621. 1979. 44.00 (ISBN 0-12-568150-X). Acad Pr.
Ross, Sheldon, ed. Introduction to Stochastic Dynamic Programming: Probability & Mathematical. LC 82-18163. 1983. 26.50 (ISBN 0-12-598420-0). Acad Pr.
Szlenk, W. Introduction to the Theory of Smooth Dynamical Systems. LC 82-23771. 416p. 1984. 54.95 (ISBN 0-471-90117-2, Pub. by Wiley-Interscience). Wiley.
Tou, Julius, ed. Optimum Design of Digital Control Systems Via Dynamic Programming. (Mathematics in Science & Engineering: Vol. 10). 1963. 55.00 (ISBN 0-12-696250-2). Acad Pr.
Vick, Charles R. Dynamic Resource Allocation in Distributed Computing Systems. Stone, Harold S., ed. LC 81-7613. (Computer Science Ser.: Distributed Database Systems: No. 2). 170p. 1981. 39.95 (ISBN 0-8357-1210-9). UMI Res Pr.
White, D. J. Finite Dynamic Programming: An Approach to Finite Markov Decision Processes. LC 77-26333. 220p. 1978. 69.95x (ISBN 0-471-99629-7, Pub. by Wiley-Interscience). Wiley.

DYNAMICS
see also Aerodynamics; Astrodynamics; Control Theory; Electrodynamics; Force and Energy; Hydrodynamics; Irreversible Processes; Kinematics; Matter; Mechanics; Motion; Perturbation (Mathematics); Physics; Plasma Dynamics; Quantum Theory; Rotational Motion; Stability; Statics; Thermodynamics; Transients (Dynamics)

Abbot, David. An Introduction to Reaction Kinetics. LC 67-7380. (Longman Concepts in Chemistry Ser.). pap. 40.00 (ISBN 0-317-09056-9, 2016336). Bks Demand UMI.

DYNAMICS OF A PARTICLE

Gibbs, Terry R. & Popolato, Alphonse, eds. LASL Explosive Property Data. (Los Alamos Scientific Laboratory Series on Dynamic Material Properties). 1980. 42.50x (ISBN 0-520-04012-0). U of Cal Pr.

Harkness, H. W. Elementary Dynamics of Particles. (Orig.). 1964. 39.50 (ISBN 0-12-325362-4); pap. 21.50 (ISBN 0-12-325368-3). Acad Pr.

Kerner, Edward H. Theory of Action-at-a-Distance in Relativistic Particle Dynamics. (International Science Review Ser.). 232p. 1972. 64.95 (ISBN 0-677-13990-X). Gordon.

Mader, Charles L. & Neal, Timothy R., eds. LASL Phermex Data, Vol. 1. (Los Alamos Scientific Laboratory Series on Dynamic Material Properties). 1980. 65.00x (ISBN 0-520-04009-0). U of Cal Pr.

Mann, Ronald A. The Classical Dynamics of Particles: Galilean & Lorentz Relativity. 1974. 38.00 (ISBN 0-12-469250-8). Acad Pr.

Marsh, Stanley P. LASL Shock Hugoniot Data. (Los Alamos Scientific Laboratory Series on Dynamic Material Properties). 1980. 55.00x (ISBN 0-520-04008-2). U of Cal Pr.

Watson, K. M. & Nuttall, J. Topics in Several Particle Dynamics. LC 67-13836. 1967. 22.00x (ISBN 0-8162-9362-7). Holden-Day.

DYNAMO (COMPUTER PROGRAM LANGUAGE)

Pugh, Alexander, III. Dynamo Users Manual. 6th ed. LC 83-43024. (Illus.). 200p. (Orig.). 1983. pap. text ed. 19.95x (ISBN 0-262-66052-0). MIT Pr.

Richardson, George P. & Pugh, Alexander L., III. Introduction to System Dynamics Modeling with DYNAMO. (Wright-Allen Ser. in System Dynamics). 400p. 1981. 32.50x (ISBN 0-262-18102-9). MIT Pr.

DYNAMOMETER

Slonneger, J. C. Dynagraph Analysis of Sucker Rod Pumping. LC 60-53496. 216p. 1961. 32.50x (ISBN 0-87201-216-6). Gulf Pub.

DYNAMOS

see also Armatures; Turbogenerators

Direct Current Dynamo Design. 1982. pap. 8.95 (ISBN 0-917914-05-8). Lindsay Pubns.

Electric Generating Stations: Outdoor Locations. (IES Committee Reports Ser.). 1975. member 2.75 (ISBN 0-686-96171-4, CP-8); non-member 5.50 (ISBN 0-686-99718-2). Illum Eng.

Glebov, I. A. & Komarsky, E. G. Synchronous Generators in Electrophysical Installations. Skrebtsov, G. P., tr. from Rus. LC 81-48563. (Illus.). 208p. 1982. 31.00x (ISBN 0-669-05434-8). Lexington Bks.

Grundy, R. F. Magnetohydrodynamic Energy for Electric Power Generation. LC 77-15220. (Energy Technology Review Ser.: No. 20). (Illus.). 1978. 36.00 (ISBN 0-8155-0689-9). Noyes.

Kuecken, John A. How to Make Home Electricity from Wind, Water & Sunshine. (Illus.). 1979. 14.95 (ISBN 0-8306-9785-3); pap. 9.95 (ISBN 0-8306-1128-2, 1128). TAB Bks.

Motors & Generators. 1983. 495.00 (ISBN 0-318-00533-6). Busn Trend.

Seifert, Walter. Generators - Motors: Physical Fundamentals & Basic Mechanical Forms. (Siemens Programmed Instruction Ser.: 7). pap. 23.00 (ISBN 0-317-26172-X, 2052084). Bks Demand UMI.

Stockman, Harry E. The Equivalent Generator Theorem. 1977. pap. 3.00 (ISBN 0-918332-06-0). Sercolab.

E

EAGLES

see also Bald Eagle; Golden Eagle

Steyn, Peter. Eagle Days: A Study of African Eagles at the Nest. 2nd ed. (Illus.). 163p. 1985. 24.95 (ISBN 0-88072-065-4, Pub. by Tanager). Longwood Pub Group.

True, Dan. A Family of Eagles. LC 79-92193. (Illus.). 224p. 1980. 12.95 (ISBN 0-89696-078-1, An Everest House Book). Dodd.

EAR

see also Hearing; Labyrinth (Ear)

Fleischer, G. Evolutionary Principles of the Mammalian Middle Ear. (Advances in Anatomy, Embriology & Cell Biology: Vol. 55, Pt. 5). (Illus.). 1978. pap. 29.00 (ISBN 0-387-09140-8). Springer-Verlag.

Grote, J. J., ed. Biomaterials in Otology. 324p. 1984. text ed. 52.00 (ISBN 0-89838-610-1, Pub. by Martinus Nijhoff Netherlands). Kluwer Academic.

Harada, Yasuo. An Atlas of the Ear: By Scanning Electron Microscopy. (Illus.). 220p. 1983. text ed. 53.00 (ISBN 0-8391-1922-4, 20362). Univ Park.

Hughes, Gordon H. Textbook of Clinical Otology. (Illus.). 448p. 1985. text ed. 88.00 (ISBN 0-86577-183-9). Thieme Stratton.

Katsuki, Yasuji. Receptive Mechanisms of Sound in the Ear. LC 81-12241. 135p. 1982. 44.50 (ISBN 0-521-24346-7). Cambridge U Pr.

Keidel, Wolfgang D. The Physiological Basis of Hearing. (Illus.). 262p. 1983. 25.00 (ISBN 0-86577-072-7). Thieme-Stratton.

Lewis, E. R., et al, eds. The Vertebrate Inner Ear. 256p. 1985. price not set (ISBN 0-8493-6465-5). CRC Pr.

Monro, Alexander. Three Treatises: On the Brain, the Eye, & the Ear. Bd. with Croonian Lectures on Cerebrqal Localization. Ferrier, D. (Contributions to the History of Psychology Ser., Vol. VII, Pt. E: Psysiological Psychology). 1980. Repr. of 1797 ed. 30.00 (ISBN 0-89093-326-X). U Pubns Amer.

Offutt, George. The Electromodel of the Auditory System. 196p. (Orig.). 1984. pap. 15.00 (ISBN 0-9614983-0-7). GoLo Press.

Oosterveld, W. J. Otoneurology. 274p. 1984. 52.00 (ISBN 0-471-90441-4, Pub. by Wiley Med). Wiley.

Politzer, Adam. History of Otology. Milstein, Stanley, et al, trs. (Illus.). 324p. 1981. write for info. Columella Pr.

Rasmussen, Grant L. & Windle, William F. Neural Mechanisms of the Auditory & Vestibular Systems. (Illus.). 436p. 1965. photocopy ed. 43.50x (ISBN 0-398-01554-6). C C Thomas.

Regenbogen, Lucian S. & Coscas, Gabriel J., eds. Oculo-Auditory Syndromes. (Illus.). 400p. 1985. text ed. write for info. (ISBN 0-89352-225-2). Masson Pub.

Wever, Ernest G. The Reptile Ear: Its Structure & Function. LC 78-51204. (Illus.). 1978. 90.00 (ISBN 0-691-08196-4). Princeton U Pr.

EARLY MAN

see Fossil Man

EARTH

see also Antarctic Regions; Arctic Regions; Atmosphere; Biosphere; Climatology; Cosmogony; Cosmology; Creation; Earthquakes; Geodesy; Geography; Geology; Geophysics; Glacial Epoch; Longitude; Magnetism, Terrestrial; Meteorology; Ocean; Oceanography; Physical Geography

Albritton, Claude C., Jr. Abyss of Time: Changing Conceptions of the Earth's Antiquity after the 16th Century. LC 79-57131. (Illus.). 252p. 1980. text ed. 14.95x (ISBN 0-87735-341-7); pap. text ed. 8.95x. Freeman Cooper.

Allen, Oliver. Atmosphere. LC 82-16768. (Planet Earth Ser.). 1983. lib. bdg. 19.94 (ISBN 0-8094-4337-6, Pub. by Time-Life). Silver.

Andel, Tjeerd H. van. New Views on an Old Planet: Continental Drift & the History of the Earth. (Illus.). 272p. 1985. 19.95 (ISBN 0-521-30084-3). Cambridge U Pr.

Baden, John. Earth Day Reconsidered. LC 80-81670. 1980. 4.00 (ISBN 0-89195-028-1). Heritage Found.

Bott, M. H. Interior of the Earth: Its Structure, Constitution & Evolution. 2nd ed. 404p. 1982. 37.00 (ISBN 0-444-00723-7). Elsevier.

Brown, G. C. & Mussett, A. E. The Inaccessible Earth. (Illus.). 272p. 1981. pap. text ed. 22.50x (ISBN 0-04-550028-2). Allen Unwin.

Brown, Walter R. & Anderson, Norman D. Earth Science: A Search for Understanding. rev. ed. 1977. text ed. 18.60i (ISBN 0-397-43747-1); tchr's. ed. 20.80i (ISBN 0-397-43748-X). Har-Row.

Bullen, K. E. The Earth's Density. 1975. 49.95 (ISBN 0-412-10860-7, NO.6045, Pub. by Chapman & Hall). Methuen Inc.

Calder, Nigel. Restless Earth: A Report on the New Geology. 1978. pap. 9.95 (ISBN 0-14-004902-9). Penguin.

Caldwell, Erskine. This Very Earth. 10.95 (ISBN 0-89190-164-7, Pub. by Am Repr). Amereon Ltd.

Carey, W. S. The Expanding Earth. (Developments in Geotectonics Ser.: Vol. 10). 488p. 1976. 61.75 (ISBN 0-444-41485-1). Elsevier.

Cattermole, Peter & Moore, Patrick. The Story of the Earth. (Illus.). 224p. 1985. 24.95 (ISBN 0-521-26292-5). Cambridge U Pr.

Cottrell, Ron. The Remarkable Spaceship Earth. LC 82-70775. (Accent Imperials Ser.). (Illus.). 64p. (Orig.). 1982. gift book 9.95 (ISBN 0-89636-088-1). Accent Bks.

Daly, Reginald A. Igneous Rocks & the Depths of the Earth. (Illus.). 1968. Repr. of 1933 ed. 28.50x (ISBN 0-02-843510-9). Hafner.

Delobeau, F. The Environment of the Earth. LC 71-170338. (Astrophysics & Space Science Library: No. 28). 113p. 1972. 21.00 (ISBN 90-277-0208-X, Pub. by Reidel Holland). Kluwer Academic.

Eicher, Don & McAlester, Lee. History of the Earth. (Illus.). 1980. text ed. 34.95 (ISBN 0-13-390047-9). P-H.

Elder, John. The Bowels of the Earth. (Illus.). 1976. 21.95x (ISBN 0-19-854412-X); pap. 8.95x (ISBN 0-19-854413-8). Oxford U Pr.

Ernst, W. G. Earth Materials. 1969. pap. text ed. 15.95 (ISBN 0-13-222604-9). P-H.

Fifield, Richard, ed. The Making of the Earth. (New Scientist Guides Ser.). 240p. 1985. 24.95x (ISBN 0-85520-733-7); pap. 8.95 (ISBN 0-85520-732-9). Basil Blackwell.

Flint, Richard F. Earth & Its History. (Illus.). 500p. 1973. text ed. 13.95x (ISBN 0-393-09377-8). Norton.

Forbes, George. The Earth, the Sun, & the Moon. 1928. 15.00 (ISBN 0-686-17422-4). Ridgeway Bks.

Foth, Henry D. Fundamentals of Soil Science. 1977. pap. text ed. 9.50 study guide (ISBN 0-8403-2790-0, 40279001). Kendall-Hunt.

Francis, Peter. Images of Earth. (Illus.). 160p. 1984. 24.95 (ISBN 0-13-451394-0). P-H.

Friedman, Herbert. Sun & Earth. LC 85-14295. (Scientific American Library). (Illus.). 256p. 1985. write for info. (ISBN 0-7167-5012-0). W H Freeman.

Gass, J. G., et al, eds. Understanding the Earth: A Reader in the Earth Sciences. 384p. 1981. 35.00x (ISBN 0-686-79153-3, Pub. by Artemis England). State Mutual Bk.

Geophysics Research Board & Division Of Earth Sciences. Solid-Earth Geophysics: Survey & Outlook. 1964. pap. 5.00 (ISBN 0-309-01231-7). Natl Acad Pr.

Goldman, Emma & Berkman, Alexander. Mother Earth Anthology. 1000.00 (ISBN 0-87968-420-8). Gordon Pr.

Grant, Edward. In Defense Of The Earth's Centrality & Immobility: Scholastic Reaction To Copernicanism In The Seventeenth Century. 67p. 10.00 (ISBN 0-87169-744-0). Am Philos.

Habberjam, G. M. Apparent Resistivity Observations & the Use of Square Array Techniques. (Geoexploration Monographs: No. 9). (Illus.). 1979. 55.00xcancelled (ISBN 3-443-13013-5). Intl Pubns Serv.

Haber, Heinz. Our Blue Planet: The Story of the Earth's Evolution. LC 77-85276. 1969. 6.95 (ISBN 0-684-31048-1, ScribT); (ScribT). Scribner.

Hobbs, William. The Earth Generated & Anatomized. Porter, Roy, ed. (Illus.). 168p. 1981. 37.50x (ISBN 0-8014-1366-4, Pub. by British Museum (Natural History)). Cornell U Pr.

Huang, Yang. Stability Analysis of Earth Slopes. 1983. 31.95 (ISBN 0-442-23689-1). Van Nos Reinhold.

Hurlbut, Cornelius S., Jr., ed. The Planet We Live on: An Illustrated Encyclopedia of the Earth Sciences. LC 75-29977. (Illus.). 544p. 1976. 40.00 (ISBN 0-8109-0415-2). Abrams.

Hutton, James. System of the Earth, 1785. White, George W., ed. & frwd. by. Bd. with Theory of the Earth, 1788; Observations on Granite, 1795; Biography of Hutton. Playfair, John. (Contributions to the History of Geology Ser.: Vol. 5). 1970. Repr. 20.95x (ISBN 0-02-846220-3). Hafner.

--Theory of the Earth, 2 vols. 1960. Repr. of 1795 ed. 50.75 (ISBN 3-7682-0025-6). Lubrecht & Cramer.

Jackson, Donald. Underground Worlds. (Planet Earth Ser.). 1982. lib. bdg. 19.94 (ISBN 0-8094-4321-X, Pub. by Time-Life). Silver.

Jacobs, J. A. The Earth's Core. (International Geophysics Ser.). 1976. 49.00 (ISBN 0-12-378950-8). Acad Pr.

Jeffreys, Harold. The Earth. 6th ed. LC 74-19527. (Illus.). 600p. 1976. 99.50 (ISBN 0-521-20648-0). Cambridge U Pr.

Kuiper, Gerard P., ed. Earth As a Planet. LC 54-7183. (Solar System Ser: Vol. 2). 1954. 45.00x (ISBN 0-226-45926-8). U of Chicago Pr.

Kummel, Bernhard. History of the Earth: An Introduction to Historical Geology. 2nd ed. LC 73-114579. (Geology Books Ser.). pap. 160.00 (ISBN 0-317-29244-7, 2055551). Bks Demand UMI.

Lanham, Url. The Sapphire Planet. LC 77-13160. 138p. 1978. 26.50x (ISBN 0-231-03956-5). Columbia U Pr.

Leliwa-Kopystynski, J. & Teisseyre, R. Constitution of the Earth's Interior. (Physics & Evolution of the Earth's Interior Ser.: Vol. 1). 1984. 75.00 (ISBN 0-444-99646-X, I-344-83). Elsevier.

Lovelock, J. E. Gaia: A New Look at Life on Earth. (Illus.). 1979. pap. 6.95 (ISBN 0-19-520358-5, GB 667, GB). Oxford U Pr.

Lye, Keith. The Earth. LC 83-50390. (Silver Burdett Color Library). 48p. 1983. lib. bdg. 14.00 (ISBN 0-382-06727-4). Silver.

McElhinny, M. W., ed. The Earth: Its Origin, Structure & Evolution. 1979. 70.00 (ISBN 0-12-482750-0). Acad Pr.

Malakhov, A. Mystery of the Earth's Mantle. (Illus.). 204p. 1975. 7.95x (ISBN 0-8464-0664-0). Beekman Pubs.

Mantell, C. L. & Mantell, A. M. Our Fragile Water Planet: An Introduction to the Earth Sciences. LC 76-20730. 221p. 1976. 29.50 (ISBN 0-306-30877-0, Plenum Pr). Plenum Pub.

Mehlin, Theodore G. & Schweighauser, Charles A. Astronomy & the Origin of the Earth. 3rd ed. 150p. 1979. pap. text ed. write for info. (ISBN 0-697-05018-1). Wm C Brown.

Miller, Russell. Continents in Collision. LC 82-16778. (Planet Earth Ser.). 1983. lib. bdg. 19.94 (ISBN 0-8094-4325-2, Pub. by Time-Life). Silver.

Morris, Henry M. The Remarkable Birth of Planet Earth. LC 73-166083. 112p. 1972. pap. 2.95 (ISBN 0-87123-485-8, 200485). Bethany Hse.

Murphey, Rhoads. Patterns on the Earth. 4th ed. 1978. 29.95 (ISBN 0-395-30827-5); Tchrs. Manual 1.50 (ISBN 0-395-30828-3). HM.

Navarra, John G. Earth, Space, & Time: An Introduction to Earth Science. LC 79-14000. 438p. 1980. 34.00x (ISBN 0-471-63061-6). Wiley.

Osborn, Fairfield. Limits of the Earth. LC 76-148640. 1971. Repr. of 1953 ed. lib. bdg. 15.00 (ISBN 0-8371-6005-7, OSLE). Greenwood.

Ozima, Minoru. The Earth: Its Birth & Growth. Wakabayashi, J. F., tr. (Illus.). 180p. 1981. 29.95 (ISBN 0-521-23500-6); pap. 11.95 (ISBN 0-521-28005-2). Cambridge U Pr.

Parratt, Mark W. A Spaceship Called Earth: Our Living Environment. 384p. 1982. PLB 24.95 (ISBN 0-8403-2741-2). Kendall-Hunt.

Pember, G. H. Earth's Earliest Ages. LC 75-13928. 1975. 10.95 (ISBN 0-8254-3508-0). Kregel.

Petersen, Morris S. & Rigby, J. Keith. Interpreting Earth History: A Manual in Historical Geology. 3rd ed. 188p. 1982. write for info. wire coil (ISBN 0-697-05063-7); instr's. manual avail. (ISBN 0-697-05064-5). Wm C Brown.

Phillips, Owen M. Heart of the Earth. LC 68-14223. (Illus.). 236p. 1968. text ed. 7.50x (ISBN 0-87735-327-1). Freeman Cooper.

Phinney, Robert A., ed. The History of the Earth's Crust: A Symposium. LC 68-20875. (Illus.). 244p. 1968. 37.50 (ISBN 0-691-08063-1); pap. text ed. 11.50x (ISBN 0-691-02379-4). Princeton U Pr.

Press, Frank & Siever, Raymond. Earth. 3rd ed. LC 81-17451. (Illus.). 613p. 1982. text ed. 29.95x (ISBN 0-7167-1362-4); pap. text ed. 12.50 (ISBN 0-7167-1382-9). W H Freeman.

--Earth. 4th ed. (Illus.). 832p. 1986. text ed. price not set. W H Freeman.

Raymo, Chet. Biography of a Planet: Geology, Astronomy, & the Evolution of Life on Earth. LC 84-4810. (Illus.). 176p. 1984. 22.95 (ISBN 0-13-078221-1); pap. 12.95 (ISBN 0-13-078213-0). P-H.

Reim, Terry, ed. Daily Planet Almanac, 1983. 1982. pap. 3.95 (ISBN 0-380-80838-2, 80838-2). Avon.

Royal Society Discussion Meeting, January 27-28, 1982, Proceedings. The Earth's Core: Its Structure, Evolution & Magnetic Field. Runcorn, S. K. & Creer, K. M., eds. (Illus.). 289p. 1982. text ed. 87.00x (ISBN 0-85403-192-8, Pub. by Royal Soc London). Scholium Intl.

Scientific American. Volcanoes & the Earth's Interior: Readings from Scientific American. LC 81-15092. (Illus.). 141p. 1982. text ed. 21.95 (ISBN 0-7167-1383-7); pap. text ed. 10.95 (ISBN 0-7167-1384-5). W H Freeman.

Scientific American Reader Staff. The Dynamic Earth. (Scientific American Reader Series: September '83 Issue). 128p. 1983. pap. text ed. 13.95 (ISBN 0-7167-1611-9). W H Freeman.

Smith, William F. The Shaping of the Earth. (Illus.). 128p. 1981. 7.00 (ISBN 0-682-49715-0). Exposition Pr FL.

Sobolev, N. V. Deep-Seated Inclusions in Kimberlites & the Problem Composition of the Upper Mantle. Brown, David A., tr. from Rus. LC 76-62627. (Eng., Illus.). 279p. 1977. 28.00 (ISBN 0-87590-202-2). Am Geophysical.

Spectorsky, Auguste C., ed. Book of the Earth. facs. ed. LC 72-142697. (Essay Index Reprint Ser). 1957. 40.00 (ISBN 0-8369-2135-6). Ayer Co Pubs.

Steele, Robert D. The Sun Rises: A True Account of Events Which Occured Over 78,000 Years Ago. pap. 6.95 (ISBN 0-87505-093-X). Borden.

Stokes, William L. Essentials of Earth History. 4th ed. (Illus.). 640p. 1982. text ed. 33.95 (ISBN 0-13-285890-8). P-H.

Stumpff, Karl. Planet Earth. Wayne, Philip, tr. LC 59-5266. (Ann Arbor Science Library Ser.). pap. 47.80 (ISBN 0-317-09526-9, 2055653). Bks Demand UMI.

Sunagawa, I., ed. Materials Science of the Earth's Interior. 1983. lib. bdg. 120.00 (ISBN 90-277-1649-8, Pub. by Reidel Holland). Kluwer Academic.

Teisseyre, R., ed. Continuum Theories in Solid Earth Physics: Physics & Evolution of the Earth's Interior, No. 3. 587p. 1985. 107.50 (ISBN 0-444-99569-2). Elsevier.

--Proceedings of the Geoscience Information Society, Meeting, Minneapolis, 1972, Vol. 3. Phinney, H. K., ed. (Proceedings Ser.). 1973. 6.00 (ISBN 0-318-02260-5). Geosci Info.

Glen, William. The Road to Jaramillo: Critical Years of the Revolution in Earth Science. LC 80-51647. (Illus.). xvi, 459p. 1982. 40.00x (ISBN 0-8047-1119-4). Stanford U Pr.

Gould, Joseph C. & Mott, Charles J. Earth Science: An Individualized Approach. 3rd ed. (Illus.). 250p. 1982. pap. text ed. 13.95x (ISBN 0-89459-185-1). Hunter Textbks.

Gould, Joseph C., et al. Earth Science: An Individualized Approach. 4th ed. 250p. 1985. pap. 14.95 (ISBN 0-88725-031-9). Hunter Textbks.

Grossinger, Richard & Hough, Lindy, eds. Imago Mundi. (Earth Geography Booklet Ser.: No. 3). (Illus.). 1972. 6.50 (ISBN 0-913028-14-2). North Atlantic.

Grossmann, Walter & Kahmen, Heribert. Vermessungskunde I: Fehlerlehre, Vermessungen und Berechnungen fur Grossmassstabige Karten und Plane, Nivellieren. (Sammlung Goeschen: No. 2160). (Ger.). 252p. 1985. pap. 9.90x (ISBN 3-11-010262-5). De Gruyter.

Grunbaum, B. & Shephard, G. C. Tillings & Patterns. 1985. write for info (ISBN 0-7167-1193-1); pap. write for info (ISBN 0-7167-1194-X). W H Freeman.

Hake, Guenter. Kartographie II: Thematische Karten, Atlanten, Kartenverwandte Darstellungen, Kartenredaktion und Kartentechnik, Rechnergestuetzte Kartenherstellung, Kartenauswertung, Kartengeschichte. 3rd ed. (Sammlung Goeschen Ser.: No. 2166). (Ger., Illus.). 382p. 1984. pap. 11.90x (ISBN 3-11-010286-2). De Gruyter.

Hallam, A. A Revolution in the Earth Sciences: From Continental Drift to Plate Tectonics. (Illus.). 1973. pap. text ed. 7.95x (ISBN 0-19-858145-9). Oxford U Pr.

Hamblin, Kenneth W. Earth's Dynamic Systems. 4th. ed. (Illus.). 544p. 1985. text ed. write for info. (ISBN 0-8087-4742-8). Burgess.

Henderson, B., et al. Defects in the Alkaline Earth Oxides. 276p. 1977. cancelled (ISBN 0-686-44435-3). Taylor & Francis.

Horowitz, Irving L. Contemporary Earth Science. (Orig.). 1976. pap. text ed. 7.75 (ISBN 0-87720-150-1). AMSCO Sch.

Howell, Benjamin F., Jr. Earth & Universe. LC 71-167500. 480p. 1972. 19.95x (ISBN 0-675-09183-7). Merrill.

Huggett, R. Earth Surface Systems. (Physical Environment Ser.: Vol. 1). (Illus.). 280p. 1985. 52.00 (ISBN 0-387-15421-3). Springer Verlag.

Jagoda, Susan. Changing Earth. (Science in Action Ser.). (Illus.). 48p. 1984. pap. text ed. 2.85 (ISBN 0-88102-024-9). Janus Bks.

Kilburn, Robert E. & Howell, Peter S. Exploring Earth Science. (Junior High Science Program Ser.). 1981. text ed. 19.96 (ISBN 0-205-06733-6, 6967337); tchrs'. guide & tests 14.00 (ISBN 0-205-06734-4, 696734); record bk 9.23 (ISBN 0-205-06735-2, 6967353). Allyn.

Krinitzsky, E. L. Radiography in the Earth Sciences & Soil Mechanics. LC 75-207539. (Monographs in Geoscience Ser.). 157p. 1970. 29.50x (ISBN 0-306-30448-1, Plenum Pr). Plenum Pub.

Kveton, Edward J. Earth Science One Hundred: Lab Manual. 1981. spiral bdg. 7.95 (ISBN 0-88252-059-8). Paladin Hse.

Lounsbury, John F. & Ogden, Lawrence. Earth Science. 3rd ed. LC 78-21130. pap. 130.80 (ISBN 0-317-28121-6, 2022505). Bks Demand UMI.

Lyon, Edward, et al. Earth Science Manual. 4th ed. 224p. 1976. write for info. wire coil (ISBN 0-697-05079-3); tchr's. manual avail. (ISBN 0-697-05059-9). Wm C Brown.

McElhinny, M. W., ed. The Earth: Its Origin, Structure & Evolution. 1979. 70.00 (ISBN 0-12-482750-0). Acad Pr.

McGraw-Hill Editors & Parker, Sybil P., eds. McGraw Hill Dictionary of Earth Sciences. 3rd ed. 856p. 1984. 36.00 (ISBN 0-07-045252-0). McGraw.

Malone, T. F. & Roederer, J. G., eds. Global Change. (Symposium Ser.: No. 5). 1984. write for info. (ISBN 0-930357-02-7). ICSU Pr.

Marsal, D. Statistics for Geoscientists. 1985. 43.20 (ISBN 0-08-026268-6); flexi-cover 21.50 (ISBN 0-08-026260-0). Pergamon.

Michel, Jean-Pierre & Fairbridge, Rhodes W. Dictionary of Earth Science: French-English & English-French. LC 80-80095. (Fr. & Eng.). 340p. 1980. 17.50x (ISBN 0-89352-076-4). Masson Pub.

Middlemiss, F. A., et al. Faunal Provinces in Space & the Time: Geological Journal Special Issue, Vol. 4. (Liverpool Geological Society & the Manchester Geological Association Ser.). 246p. 1971. 57.95x (ISBN 0-471-27751-7, Pub. by Wiley-Interscience). Wiley.

Mitchell, A. H. & Garson, M. S. Mineral Deposits & Global Tectonic Settings. (Earth Science Ser.). 1982. 50.00 (ISBN 0-12-499050-9). Acad Pr.

Morner, Nils-Axel, ed. Earth Rheology, Isostasy & Eustasy. LC 79-1473. 599p. 1980. 143.95x (ISBN 0-471-27593-X). Wiley.

Mulfinger, George, Jr. & Snyder, Donald E. Earth Science for Christian Schools. (Science for Christian Schools Ser.). (Illus.). 479p. 1979. text ed. 21.25 (ISBN 0-89084-092-X); tchr's. ed. 31.50 (ISBN 0-89084-093-8). Bob Jones Univ Pr.

Murty, T. V. Studies in Earth Sciences. 614p. 1971. 25.00 (ISBN 0-88065-164-4, Pub. by Messers Today & Tomorrows Printers & Publishers India). Scholarly Pubns.

National Referral Center in the Library of Congress. A Directory of Information Resources in the United States: Geosciences & Oceanography. LC 81-607045. xx, 375p. 1981. pap. 8.50 (ISBN 0-8444-0372-5). Lib Congress.

Ojakangas, Richard & Darby, David. The Earth: Past & Present. new ed. (Earth Science Paperback Ser.). (Illus., Orig.). 1976. pap. text ed. 21.95 (ISBN 0-07-047676-4). McGraw.

Parker, Ronald B. Inscrutable Earth: Explorations into the Science of Earth. 240p. 1984. 14.95 (ISBN 0-684-18173-8, ScribT). Scribner.

Porter, Roy. The Making of Geology: Earth Science in Britain, 1660-1815. LC 76-56220. pap. 75.00 (ISBN 0-317-27575-5, 2024515). Bks Demand UMI.

Pouquet, J. Earth's Science in the Age of the Satellite. LC 73-94454. Orig. Title: Les Sciences De la Terre a L'heure Des Satellites. 190p. 1974. lib. bdg. 34.25 (ISBN 90-277-0437-6). Kluwer Academic.

Rachocki, Andrzej. Alluvial Fans: An Attempt at an Empirical Approach. LC 80-42061. 161p. 1981. 44.95 (ISBN 0-471-27999-4, Pub. by Wiley-Interscience). Wiley.

Rikitake, T., et al. Applied Mathematics for Earth Scientists. 1984. lib. bdg. 89.00 (ISBN 90-277-1796-6, Pub. by Reidel Holland). Kluwer Academic.

Rudman, Jack. Earth Science. (ACT Proficiency Examination Program: PEP-5). (Cloth bdg. avail. on request). pap. 9.95 (ISBN 0-8373-5505-2). Natl Learning.

Runcorn, S. K., ed. Earth Science, 3 vols. (Royal Institution Library of Science). (Illus.). 1564p. 1971. Set. 107.50 (ISBN 0-85334-505-8, Pub by Elsevier Applied Sci England). Elsevier.

Sasaki, A., et al. World Resources & the Development of the Earth's Surface. (Texts in Earth Sciences). 1985. 41.95 (ISBN 0-471-10536-8). Wiley.

Sawkins, F. J., et al. Evolving Earth. 2nd ed. 1978. write for info. (ISBN 0-02-406510-2, 40651). Macmillan.

Seeley, H. G. The Story of the Earth in Past Ages. 1979. Repr. of 1904 ed. lib. bdg. 25.00 (ISBN 0-8495-4912-4). Arden Lib.

Shagam, R., et al, eds. Studies in Earth & Space Sciences: A Memoir in Honor of Harry Hammond Hess. LC 76-190172. (Geological Society of America Memoir Ser.: No. 132). pap. 160.00 (ISBN 0-317-29124-6, 2025026). Bks Demand UMI.

Sinha, Shyama, ed. Systematics & the Properties of the Lanthanides. 1983. lib. bdg. 85.00 (ISBN 90-2771-613-7, Pub. by Reidel Holland). Kluwer Academic.

Sladd, Robin. The Earth's Atmosphere: Syllabus. 1978. pap. text ed. 5.85 (ISBN 0-89420-045-3, 235011); cassette recordings 41.25 (ISBN 0-89420-141-7, 235000). Natl Book.

Smith, David G., ed. Cambridge Encyclopedia of Earth Sciences. (Illus.). 496p. 1982. 37.50 (ISBN 0-521-23900-1). Cambridge U Pr.

Stiegeler, Stella E., ed. A Dictionary of Earth Sciences. (A Helix Bks.: No. 377). (Illus.). 308p. 1983. pap. text ed. 9.95 (ISBN 0-8226-0377-2). Rowman & Allanheld.

Tarbuck, Edward J. & Lutgens, Frederick K. Earth Science. 3rd ed. 544p. 1982. text ed. 26.95 (ISBN 0-675-09921-8). Merrill.

--Earth Science. 4th, rev. ed. 576p. 1984. Additional supplements may be obtained from the publisher. text ed. 27.95 (ISBN 0-675-20336-8). Merrill.

Tevesz, Michael J. & McCall, Peter L., eds. Biotic Interactions in Recent & Fossil Benthic Communities. (Topics in Geobiology: Vol. 3). 812p. 1983. 95.00x (ISBN 0-306-41292-6, Plenum Pr). Plenum Pub.

Till, Roger. Statistical Methods for the Earth Scientist: An Introduction. LC 73-22704. 154p. 1978. pap. 26.95x (ISBN 0-470-26340-7). Halsted Pr.

Todd, A. H. Earth Sciences & Energy. 1982. 110.00x (ISBN 0-86010-403-6, Pub. by Order Dept Graham Trotman England). State Mutual Bk.

Tomikel, John. Basic Earth Science. LC 80-66211. (Illus.). 166p. (Orig.). 1981. pap. 6.00x (ISBN 0-910042-38-1). Allegheny.

Trudgill, Stephen A. Soil & Vegetation Systems. (Contemporary Problems in Geography Ser.). (Illus.). 1977. 33.00x (ISBN 0-19-874058-1); pap. 11.95x (ISBN 0-19-874059-X). Oxford U Pr.

Tufty, Barbara. One Thousand & One Questions Answered about Earthquakes, Avalanches, Floods & Other Natural Disasters. (The One Thousand & One Question Ser.). (Illus.). 350p. 1978. pap. 5.95 (ISBN 0-486-23646-3). Dover.

Van Balen, John, compiled by. Index to Maps in Earth Science Publications, 1963-1983. LC 85-7978. v, 400p. 1985. lib. bdg. 49.95 (ISBN 0-313-24963-6, VBI/). Greenwood.

Watznauer, A. Dictionary of Geosciences, 2 vols. (Eng. & Ger.). 1982. English-German. 57.50 (ISBN 0-444-99702-4); German-English. 57.50 (ISBN 0-444-99701-6). Elsevier.

--Woerterbuch Geowissenschaften, Vol. 1. (Eng. & Ger., English-German Dictionary of Geo-Sciences). 1973. 38.00 (ISBN 3-87144-139-2, M-6917). French & Eur.

Williams, Peter J. The Surface of the Earth: An Introduction to Geotechnical Science. LC 81-3683. (Illus.). 228p. (Orig.). 1982. pap. text ed. 14.95 (ISBN 0-582-30043-6). Longman.

Wood, Robert M. The Dark Side of the Earth: The Battle for the Earth Sciences, 1800-1980. (Illus.). 320p. 1985. 19.95 (ISBN 0-04-550033-9). Allen Unwin.

Young, Louise B. The Blue Planet. 304p. 1984. pap. 8.95 (ISBN 0-452-00708-9, Mer). NAL.

Yoxall, William H. Dynamic Models in Earth-Science Instruction. LC 82-4385. (Illus.). 200p. 1983. 52.50 (ISBN 0-521-24262-2). Cambridge U Pr.

EARTH SCIENCES–BIBLIOGRAPHY

Porter, Roy S. The History of the Earth Sciences: An Annotated Bibliography. LC 81-43367. 250p. 1983. lib. bdg. 33.00 (ISBN 0-8240-9267-8). Garland Pub.

Van Balen, John. Geography & Earth Science Publications, 2 vols. Incl. 1968-1972 (ISBN 0-87650-090-4); 1973-1975 (ISBN 0-87650-091-2). LC 78-52361. 39.50 ea. (ISBN 0-685-38823-9); Vol. 1, 1968-1972. 39.50 ea. (ISBN 0-87650-090-4). Vol. 2, 1973-1975 (ISBN 0-87650-091-2). Set. 62.50 (ISBN 0-685-38823-9). Pierian.

EARTH SCIENCES–DATA PROCESSING

Huggett, R. Earth Surface Systems. (Physical Environment Ser.: Vol. 1). (Illus.). 280p. 1985. 52.00 (ISBN 0-387-15421-3). Springer Verlag.

Merriam, D. F., ed. Computer Applications in the Earth Sciences: An International Symposium. LC 76-102212. 281p. 1969. 45.00x (ISBN 0-306-30445-7, Plenum Pr). Plenum Pub.

--Computer Applications in the Earth Sciences: An Update of the Seventies. LC 81-10707. (Computer Applications in the Earth Sciences Ser.). 400p. 1981. 59.50x (ISBN 0-306-40809-0, Plenum Pr). Plenum Pub.

Schwarz, Jerald. Description of Computer Programs for the Analysis & Presentation of Trade Winds Data. LC 76-135092. 152p. 1969. 19.00 (ISBN 0-403-04537-1). Scholarly.

EARTH SCIENCES–RESEARCH

see Earth Science Research

EARTH SCIENCES–STUDY AND TEACHING

Horowitz, Irving L. Earth Science Investigations: A Laboratory Manual, ESCP Oriented. 1973. pap. text ed. 9.00 (ISBN 0-87720-155-2). AMSCO Sch.

Rudman, Jack. Earth Science. (College Proficiency Examination Ser.: CPEP-7). (Cloth bdg. avail. on request). pap. 9.95 (ISBN 0-8373-5407-2). Natl Learning.

Tomikel, John. Exercises for & Introduction to Earth Science. 1978. pap. 4.95 (ISBN 0-910042-40-3). Allegheny.

--Teaching-Earth Science in the Secondary School. LC 72-78361. 1972. 6.00 (ISBN 0-910042-09-8); pap. 3.00 (ISBN 0-910042-12-8). Allegheny.

EARTH TEMPERATURE

see also Geothermal Resources

Frivik, P. E., et al. Ground Freezing 1980: Selected Papers on the International Symposium on Ground Freezing, 2nd, Trondheim, June 24-26, 1980. Janbu, N. & Saetersdal, R., eds. (Developments in Geotechnical Engineering: Vol. 28). 420p. 1982. 85.00 (ISBN 0-444-42010-X). Elsevier.

Geophysics Research Board, National Research Council. Climate in Earth History. 1982. pap. text ed. 16.25 (ISBN 0-309-03329-2). Natl Acad Pr.

Kappelmeyer, O. & Haenel, R. Geothermics with Special Reference to Application. (Geoexploartion Monographs: Ser. 1, No. 4). (Illus.). 238p. 1974. lib. bdg. 37.10x (ISBN 3-4431-3006-2). Lubrecht & Cramer.

EARTH TIDES

Kuo, John T., ed. Earth Tides Symposium, Ninth International Proceedings: New York City, August, 1981. (Illus.). 747p. 1983. lib. bdg. 32.80x (ISBN 0-318-01311-8). Lubrecht & Cramer.

EARTHMOVING MACHINERY

see also Construction Equipment; Excavating Machinery

Areskoug, S., et al, eds. Off-Road Transportation & Soil-Working: Means to Promote Development & Operations. 120p. 1985. pap. 30.00 (ISBN 0-08-031652-2). Pergamon.

Dwyer, M. J., ed. The Performance of Off-Road Vehicles & Machines: Proceedings of the 8th International ISTVS Conference, Cambridge, August 1984. 120p. 1984. pap. 30.00 (ISBN 0-08-031655-7). Pergamon.

Grimshaw, Peter. Excavators. (Illus.). 160p. 1985. 14.95 (ISBN 0-7137-1335-6, Pub. by Blandford Pr England). Sterling.

Specification for Welding Earthmoving & Construction Equipment: D14.3-82. (Illus.). 80p. 1982. pap. 26.00; member 19.50. Am Welding.

EARTHQUAKE SEA WAVES

see Tsunamis

EARTHQUAKES

see also Seismic Waves; Seismology; Seismometry

Advisory Notes on Lifeline Earthquake Engineering. 242p. 1983. pap. 24.00x (ISBN 0-87262-377-7). Am Soc Civil Eng.

Ambraseys, N. N. & Melville, C. P. A History of Persian Earthquakes. LC 81-15540. (Cambridge Earth Science Ser.). (Illus.). 400p. 1982. 64.50 (ISBN 0-521-24112-X). Cambridge U Pr.

American Society of Civil Engineers & Smith, D. J., Jr., eds. Lifeline Earthquake Engineering: The Current State of Knowledge. LC 81-67748. 360p. 1981. pap. 28.00x (ISBN 0-87262-274-6). Am Soc Civil Eng.

Annotated Bibliography on Lifeline Earthquake Engineering. 247p. 1980. pap. 25.00x (ISBN 0-87262-326-2). Am Soc Civil Eng.

Assessment & Mitigation of Earthquake Risk. (Natural Hazards Ser.). 341p. 1978. pap. 26.25 (ISBN 92-3-101451-X, U843, UNESCO). Unipub.

Berlin, G. Lennis. Earthquakes & the Urban Environment, 3 Vols. 1980. Vol. 1, 224 Pgs. 74.00 (ISBN 0-8493-5173-1); Vol. 2, 192 Pgs. 66.00 (ISBN 0-8493-5174-X); Vol. 3, 288 Pgs. 88.00 (ISBN 0-8493-5175-8). CRC Pr.

Bolt, Bruce A. Earthquakes: A Primer. LC 77-12908. (Geology Ser.). (Illus.). 241p. 1978. pap. text ed. 12.95 (ISBN 0-7167-0057-3). W H Freeman.

--Inside the Earth: Evidence From Earthquakes. LC 81-17431. (Illus.). 191p. 1982. text ed. 24.95 (ISBN 0-7167-1359-4); pap. text ed. 13.95 (ISBN 0-7167-1360-8). W H Freeman.

--Nuclear Explosions & Earthquakes: The Parted Veil. LC 75-28295. (Illus.). 309p. 1976. text ed. 26.95 (ISBN 0-7167-0276-2). W H Freeman.

Bolt, Bruce A., intro. by. Earthquakes & Volcanoes: Readings from Scientific American. LC 79-21684. (Illus.). 154p. 1980. text ed. 20.95 (ISBN 0-7167-1163-X); pap. text ed. 10.95 (ISBN 0-7167-1164-8). W H Freeman.

Byerlee, J. D. & Wyss, M. Rock Friction & Earthquake Prediction. (Contributions to Current Research in Geophysics: No. 6). (Illus.). 413p. 1978. 70.95x (ISBN 0-8176-1018-9). Birkhauser.

Commission on Sociotechnical Systems, National Research Council. A Program of Studies on Socioeconomic Effects of Earthquake Predictions. 1978. pap. text ed. 9.95 (ISBN 0-309-02789-6). Natl Acad Pr.

Committee on Seismology, National Research Council. Predicting Earthquakes: A Scientific & Technical Evaluation--with Implications for Society. LC 76-40493. 1976. pap. 6.75 (ISBN 0-309-02527-3). Natl Acad Pr.

--U. S. Earthquake Observatories: Recommendations for a New National Network. 122p. (Orig.). 1980. pap. 7.00x (ISBN 0-309-03131-1). Natl Acad Pr.

Committee on the Alaska Earthquake. The Great Alaska Earthquake of 1964: Biology. (Illus.). 320p. 1972. text ed. 23.50 (ISBN 0-309-01604-5). Natl Acad Pr.

--The Great Alaska Earthquake of 1964: Geology. (Illus.). 848p. 1972. text ed. 36.50 (ISBN 0-309-01601-0). Natl Acad Pr.

--Great Alaska Earthquake of 1964: Hydrology. (Great Alaskan Earthquake Ser.). (Illus.). 1968. 26.50 (ISBN 0-309-01603-7). Natl Acad Pr.

--The Great Alaska Earthquake of 1964: Oceanography & Coastal Engineering. LC 68-60037. (Illus.). 624p. 1972. 34.00 (ISBN 0-309-01605-3). Natl Acad Pr.

--The Great Alaska Earthquake of 1964: Seismology & Geodesy. LC 68-60037. (Illus.). 592p. 1972. 25.50 (ISBN 0-309-01602-9). Natl Acad Pr.

--The Great Alaska Earthquake of 1964: Summary & Recommendations Including Index to Series. (Illus.). 288p. 1973. 17.50 (ISBN 0-309-01608-8). Natl Acad Pr.

Committee on the Great Alaska Earthquake of 1964. The Great Alaska Earthquake of 1964: Engineering. (The Great Alaska Earthquake of 1964 Ser.). (Illus.). 1210p. 1973. 39.00 (ISBN 0-309-01606-1). Natl Acad Pr.

Conference Sponsored by ASCE Construction Division, May 1980, San Francisco, CA. Social & Economic Impact of Earthquakes on Utility Lifelines: Seismic Considerations in Lifelines Planning, Siting and Design. Isenberg, J., ed. LC 80-69153. 250p. 1981. pap. 21.00x (ISBN 0-87262-254-1). Am Soc Civil Eng.

Corliss, William R. Earthquakes, Tides, Unidentified Sounds & Related Phenomena. LC 83-50781. (Catalog of Geophysical Anomalies Ser.). (Illus.). 214p. 1983. 12.95 (ISBN 0-915554-11-9). Sourcebook.

Crosson, Robert S. Compilation of Earthquake Hypo-Centers in Western Washington: July 1970-Dec. 1972. (Information Circular Ser.: No. 53). (Illus.). 26p. 1974. 0.75 (ISBN 0-686-34716-1). Geologic Pubns.

--Compilation of Earthquake Hypo-Centers in Western Washington: 1973. (Information Circular Ser.: No. 55). (Illus.). 14p. 1975. 0.50 (ISBN 0-686-34722-6). Geologic Pubns.

Crosson, Robert S. & Noson, Linda. Compilation of Earthquake Hypo-Centers in Western Washington: 1975. (Information Circular Ser.: No. 64). (Illus.). 12p. 1978. 0.50 (ISBN 0-686-34738-2). Geologic Pubns.

--Compilation of Earthquake Hypo-Centers in Western Washington: 1976. (Information Circular Ser.: No. 65). (Illus.). 13p. 1978. 0.50 (ISBN 0-686-34739-0). Geologic Pubns.

Earthquake Engineering & Hazards Reduction in China. 1980. 12.95 (ISBN 0-309-02937-6). Natl Acad Pr.

Earthquake Engineering & Soil Dynamics, 3 vols. 1641p. 1979. pap. 68.00x (ISBN 0-87262-177-4). Am Soc Civil Eng.

Earthquake Engineering Research Institute. Eighth World Conference on Earthquake Engineering, Vol. I. 896p. 1984. text ed. 20.00 (ISBN 0-13-246364-4). P-H.

--Eighth World Conference on Earthquake Engineering, Vol. II. 928p. 1984. text ed. 20.00 (ISBN 0-13-246372-5). P-H.

--Eighth World Conference on Earthquake Engineering, Vol. III. 1120p. 1984. text ed. 20.00 (ISBN 0-13-246380-6). P-H.

--Eighth World Conference on Earthquake Engineering, Vol. IV. 928p. 1984. text ed. 20.00 (ISBN 0-13-246398-9). P-H.

--Eighth World Conference on Earthquake Engineering, Vol. V. 1264p. 1984. text ed. 20.00 (ISBN 0-13-246406-3). P-H.

--Eighth World Conference on Earthquake Engineering, Vol. VI. 1024p. 1984. text ed. 20.00 (ISBN 0-13-246414-4). P-H.

--Eighth World Conference on Earthquake Engineering, Vol. VII. 976p. 1984. text ed. 20.00 (ISBN 0-13-246422-5). P-H.

The Estimation of Seismic Risk in Canada: A Review. pap. 4.65 (SSC37, SSC). Unipub.

Foraker, Joseph W. What You Should Know about Earthquakes: It Could Save Your Life. (Illus.). 64p. (Orig.). 1983. pap. 5.95 (ISBN 0-912287-00-4). SJB Pub Co.

Garland, William S. Earthquake New England: Learning to Live in a Seismic Zone. (Illus.). 64p. (Orig.). 1982. write for info. (ISBN 0-943440-00-9); pap. 6.95 (ISBN 0-686-99300-4). Home-Science.

Garny, Patricia M. Alaskan Earthquake, Nineteen Sixty-Four. (Events of Our Times Ser.: No. 11). 32p. (Orig.). 1973. lib. bdg. 3.50 incl. catalog cards (ISBN 0-87157-712-7); pap. 1.95 vinyl laminated covers (ISBN 0-87157-212-5). SamHar Pr.

Gere, James M. & Shah, Haresh C. Terra Non Firma: Understanding & Preparing for Earthquakes. 278p. 1984. pap. 11.95 (ISBN 0-7167-1497-3). W H Freeman.

Gouin, Pierre. Earthquake History of Ethiopia & the Horn of Africa. 258p. 1979. pap. 25.00 casebound (ISBN 0-88936-194-0, IDRC118, IDRC). Unipub.

Gribbin, John R. & Plagemann, Stephen H. The Jupiter Effect: The Planets As Triggers of Devastating Earthquakes. 144p. 1976. pap. 3.95 (ISBN 0-394-70827-X, 72221, Vin). Random.

Gupta, H. & Rastogi, B. Dams & Earthquakes. (Developments in Geotechnical Engineering Ser.: Vol. 11). 230p. 1976. 70.25 (ISBN 0-444-41330-8). Elsevier.

Hooke, Robert. Lectures & Discourses of Earthquakes & Subterraneous Eruptions. Albritton, Claude C., Jr., ed. LC 77-6521. (History of Geology Ser.). 1978. Repr. of 1705 ed. lib. bdg. 21.00x (ISBN 0-405-10443-X). Ayer Co Pubs.

Iacopi, Robert, ed. Earthquake Country: California. LC 78-163736. (Illus.). 160p. 1971. pap. 5.95 (ISBN 0-376-06144-8, Sunset Bks.). Sunset-Lane.

Institution of Civil Engineers Staff, ed. Dams & Earthquakes. 319p. 1981. 62.50x (ISBN 0-7277-0123-1). Am Soc Civil Eng.

Kasahara, K. Earthquake Mechanics. LC 79-50624. (Cambridge Earth Science Ser.). (Illus.). 256p. 1980. 67.50 (ISBN 0-521-22736-4). Cambridge U Pr.

Kisslinger, C. & Suzuki, Z., eds. Earthquake Precursors. 1979. 32.50x (ISBN 0-89955-129-7, Pub. by Japan Sci Soc Japan). Intl Spec Bk.

Lawson, A. California Earthquake of April 18, 1906: Report of the State Earthquake Commission. new ed. (Illus.). 721p. 1970. Repr. 29.00 (ISBN 0-87279-086-X, 87). Carnegie Inst.

Lee, W. H. & Steward, S. W. Advances in Geophysics, Supplement 2: Principles & Applications of Microearthquake Networks. LC 80-70588. 1981. 32.00 (ISBN 0-12-018862-7). Acad Pr.

Lomnitz, C. Global Tectonics & Earthquake Risk. LC 72-87960. (Developments in Geotectonics Ser.: Vol. 5). 330p. 1974. 85.00 (ISBN 0-444-41076-7). Elsevier.

Mack, Gerstle. Nineteen Hundred Six: Surviving the Great Earthquake & Fire. LC 81-1660. 128p. (Orig.). 1981. pap. 5.95 (ISBN 0-87701-176-1). Chronicle Bks.

Mackenzie Valley Earthquake Hazard. 1979. pap. 2.00 (ISBN 0-685-96909-6, SSC127, SSC). Unipub.

Mallin, Jay. The Great Managua Earthquake. Rahmas, D. Steve, ed. (Events of Our Times Ser.: No. 14). 32p. (Orig.). 1974. lib. bdg. 3.50 incl. catalog cards (ISBN 0-87157-715-1); pap. 1.95 vinyl laminated covers (ISBN 0-87157-215-X). SamHar Pr.

Meehan, Richard L. The Atom & the Fault: Experts, Earthquakes, & Nuclear Power. (Illus.). 208p. 1984. 13.95 (ISBN 0-262-13199-4). MIT Pr.

Melchior, Paul, ed. Seismic Activity in Western Europe: With Particular Consideration to the Liege Earthquake of November 8, 1983. 1984. lib. bdg. 59.00 (ISBN 90-277-1889-X, Pub. by Reidel Holland). Kluwer Academic.

Mueller, Myrl R. Lost in the Annals: The Story of the New Madrid Earthquake, Eighteen Eleven to Eighteen Twelve. (Orig.). 1980. pap. 4.95 (ISBN 0-917200-29-2). ESPress.

National Research Council. Safety of Dams: Flood & Earthquake Criteria. 320p. 1985. pap. 16.50 (ISBN 0-309-03532-5). Natl Acad Pr.

NATO Advanced Study Institute Conference, Department of Geophysics, University of Western Ontario, London, Canada, June 22-28, 1969. Earthquake Displacement Fields & the Rotation of the Earth: Proceedings. Mansinha, L., et al, eds. LC 72-118130. (Astrophysics & Space Science Library: No.20). 308p. 1970. 39.50 (ISBN 90-277-0159-8, Pub. by Reidel Holland). Kluwer Academic.

Noson, Linda L. & Crosson, Robert S. Compilation of Earthquake Hypo-Centers in Western Washington: 1978. (Information Circular Ser.: No. 72). (Illus.). 18p. 1980. 0.50 (ISBN 0-686-36908-4). Geologic Pubns.

Penick, James L., Jr. The New Madrid Earthquakes. rev. ed. LC 81-50531. 192p. 1981. pap. 8.95 (ISBN 0-8262-0344-2). U of Mo Pr.

Powers of Nature. LC 76-57002. (Special Publication Ser.: No. XII). (Illus.). 1978. 6.95 (ISBN 0-87044-234-1); lib. bdg. 8.50 (ISBN 0-87044-239-2). Natl Geog.

Rikitake, T. Earthquake Prediction. (Developments in Solid Earth Geophysics: Vol. 9). 358p. 1976. 70.25 (ISBN 0-444-41373-1). Elsevier.

Rikitake, Tsuneji. Earthquake Forecasting. 1982. lib. bdg. 45.00 (ISBN 90-277-1218-2, Pub. by Reidel Holland). Kluwer Academic.

Rikitake, Tsuneji, ed. Current Research in Earthquake Prediction, Vol. 1. (Developments in Earth & Planetary Sciences Ser.: No. 2). 400p. 1981. PLB 37.00 (ISBN 9-0277-1133-X, Pub. by Reidel Holland). Kluwer Academic.

Rinehart, C. Dean & Smith, Ward C. Earthquakes & Young Volcanoes Along the Eastern Sierra Nevada: At Mammoth Lakes 1980, Lone Pine 1872, & Inyo & Mono Craters. Smith, Genny, ed. LC 81-51293. (Illus.). 64p. (Orig.). 1982. pap. 5.95 (ISBN 0-931378-02-8, Dist. by W. Kaufmann Inc.). Genny Smith Bks.

Shibata, H. & Ariman, T., eds. Recent Advances in Lifeline Earthquake Engineering in Japan. (PVP: No. 43). 158p. 1980. 24.00 (ISBN 0-686-69859-2, H00170). ASME.

Simpson, David W. & Richards, Paul, eds. Earthquake Prediction: An International Review. (Maurice Ewing Series 4). (Illus.). 680p. 1981. 38.00 (ISBN 0-87590-403-3). Am Geophysical.

Steinbrugge, Karl V. Earthquakes, Volcanoes, & Tsunamis: An Anatomy of Hazards. (Illus.). 1982. 35.00 (ISBN 0-9609050-0-6). Skandia.

Svenson, Arthur G. Earthquakes, Earth Scientists & Seismic-Safety Planning in California. 146p. (Orig.). 1984. lib. bdg. 19.75 (ISBN 0-8191-3735-9); pap. text ed. 9.00 (ISBN 0-8191-3736-7). U Pr of Amer.

Tatsch, J. H. Earthquakes: Cause, Prediction, & Control. LC 75-9305. (Illus.). 451p. 1977. 108.00 (ISBN 0-912890-02-9). Tatsch.

The Southern California Earthquake Preparedness Project. Earthquake Public Information Materials: An Annotated Bibliography. (CPL Bibliographies Ser.: No.105). 51p. 1983. 9.00 (ISBN 0-86602-105-1). Coun Plan Librarians.

Thomas, Gordon & Witts, Max M. The San Francisco Earthquake. pap. 2.95 (ISBN 0-8128-7028-X). Stein & Day.

Tributsch, Helmut. When the Snakes Awake: Animals & Earthquake Prediction. Langner, Paul, tr. from Ger. (Illus.). 264p. 1982. 25.00x (ISBN 0-262-20044-9); pap. 8.95 (ISBN 0-262-70025-5). MIT Pr.

Tufty, Barbara. One Thousand & One Questions Answered about Earthquakes, Avalanches, Floods, & Other Natural Disasters. LC 78-51736. 1978. lib. bdg. 12.50x (ISBN 0-88307-612-8). Gannon.

--One Thousand & One Questions Answered about Earthquakes, Avalanches, Floods & Other Natural Disasters. 14.25 (ISBN 0-8446-5826-X). Peter Smith.

Vogel, A., ed. Terrestrial & Space Techniques in Earthquake Prediction Research. (Progress in Earthquake Prediction Research Ser.: Vol. 1). 1979. 75.00 (ISBN 0-9940012-4-X, Pub. by Vieweg & Sohn Germany). Heyden.

Vogel, A. & Isikara, A. M., eds. Multidisciplinary Approach to Earthquake Prediction Research: Vol. 2, Progress in Earthquake Prediction Research, Vol. 2. 1982. 70.00 (ISBN 0-9940013-4-7, Pub. by Vieweg & Sohn Germany). Heyden.

Walker, Bryce. Earthquake. (Planet Earth Ser.). 1982. 14.95 (ISBN 0-8094-4300-7). Time-Life.

--Earthquake. LC 81-16662. (Planet Earth Ser.). lib. bdg. 19.94 (ISBN 0-8094-4301-5, Pub. by Time-Life). Silver.

Wiegel, Robert L., et al. Earthquake Engineering. (Civil Engineering Ser). 1969. ref. ed. 50.00 (ISBN 0-13-222646-4). P-H.

Wyss, M., ed. Earthquake Prediction & Seismicity Patterns. (Contributions to Current Research in Geophysics Ser.: No. 8). 240p. 1980. 47.95x (ISBN 0-8176-1122-3). Birkhauser.

Yanev, Peter. Peace of Mind in Earthquake Country: How to Save Your Home & Life. LC 74-7406. (Illus.). 320p. 1974. 9.95 (ISBN 0-87701-050-1); pap. 8.95 (ISBN 0-87701-216-4). Chronicle Bks.

EARTHQUAKES AND BUILDING

American Society of Civil Engineers, compiled by. The Current State of Knowledge of Lifeline Earthquake Engineering. 486p. 1977. pap. 23.00x (ISBN 0-87262-086-7). Am Soc Civil Eng.

Arnold, Christopher & Reitherman, Robert. Building Configuration & Seismic Design: The Architecture of Earthquake Resistance. 296p. 1982. 45.95 (ISBN 0-471-86138-3). Wiley.

Berlin, G. Lennis. Earthquakes & the Urban Environment, 3 Vols. 1980. Vol. 1, 224 Pgs. 74.00 (ISBN 0-8493-5173-1); Vol. 2, 192 Pgs. 66.00 (ISBN 0-8493-5174-X); Vol. 3, 288 Pgs. 88.00 (ISBN 0-8493-5175-8). CRC Pr.

Borg, S. F. Earthquake Engineering: Damage Assessment & Structural Design. (Methods & Applications in Civil Engineering Ser.). 110p. 1983. 24.95 (ISBN 0-471-26261-7). Wiley.

Chopra, Anil K. Dynamics of Structures: A Primer. 120p. 1982. 10.00 (ISBN 0-9605004-4-8). Earthquake Eng.

Earthquake Guidelines for Reactor Siting. (Proceedings Ser.: No. 139). (Illus.). 26p. (Orig.). 1973. pap. 6.25 (ISBN 92-0-125272-2, IDC139, IAEA). Unipub.

Earthquake Problems Related to the Siting of Critical Facilities, Committee on Seismology. Earthquake Research for the Safer Siting of Critical Facilities. LC 80-82030. 1980. pap. text ed. 5.95 (ISBN 0-309-03082-X). Natl Acad Pr.

Englekirk, Robert & Hart, Gary. Earthquake Design of Concrete & Masonry Buildings: Response Spectrual Analysis & General Earthquake Modeling Considerations, Vol. I. (Illus.). 160p. 1982. 30.00 (ISBN 0-13-223065-8). P-H.

Englekirk, Robert E. & Hart, Gary C. Earthquake Design of Concrete Masonry Buildings: Strength Design of One to Four Buildings. (Illus.). 224p. 1984. text ed. 33.95 (ISBN 0-13-223156-5). P-H.

Green, Norman E. Earthquake Resistant Building Design & Construction. 2nd ed. 216p. 1981. 21.95 (ISBN 0-442-28799-2). Van Nos Reinhold.

International Seminar on Earthquake Engineering: Proceedings, Held at Skopje, 1964. (Eng. & Fr.). 1968. pap. 6.25 (ISBN 92-3-000705-6, U486, UNESCO). Unipub.

Lindeburg, Michael R. Seismic Design for the Professional Engineering Examination. 3rd ed. LC 80-81796. (Engineering Review Manual Ser.). (Illus.). 104p. 1980. 13.95 (ISBN 0-932276-32-6). Prof Engine.

Lomnitz, C. & Rosenblueth, E. Seismic Risk & Engineering Decisions. (Developments in Geotechnical Engineering Ser.: Vol. 15). 426p. 1976. 78.75 (ISBN 0-444-41494-0). Elsevier.

McGavin, Gary L. Earthquake Protection of Essential Building Equipment: Design, Engineering, Installation. LC 80-23067. 464p. 1981. 58.95x (ISBN 0-471-06270-7, Pub. by Wiley-Interscience). Wiley.

Medvedev, Sergei V. Problems of Engineering Seismology. LC 63-17635. 112p. 1963. 32.50x (ISBN 0-306-10576-4, Consultants). Plenum Pub.

Newmark, N. M. & Rosenblueth, E. Fundamentals of Earthquake Engineering. (Civil Engineering & Engineering Mechanics Ser.). (Illus.). 1972. ref. ed. 50.00 (ISBN 0-13-336206-X). P-H.

Okamoto, Shunzo. Introduction to Earthquake Engineering. 629p. 1985. Repr. of 1973 ed. 74.50x (ISBN 0-86008-361-6, Pub. by U of Tokyo Japan). Columbia U Pr.

Parkus, H., ed. Random Excitation of Structures by Earthquakes & Atmospheric Turbulence. (CISM-International Center for Mechanical Sciences: Vol. 225). (Illus.). 1977. pap. 33.00 (ISBN 0-387-81444-2). Springer-Verlag.

Priscu, R. Earthquake Engineering for Large Dams. 1985. 41.95 (ISBN 0-471-90047-8). Wiley.

Repair of Buildings Damaged by Earthquakes. pap. 9.50 (ISBN 0-686-94378-3, UN77/4/8, UN). Unipub.

Wakabayashi, M. Design of Earthquake Resistant Buildings. 320p. 1985. 44.50 (ISBN 0-07-067764-6). McGraw.

Wiegel, Robert L., et al. Earthquake Engineering. (Civil Engineering Ser). 1969. ref. ed. 50.00 (ISBN 0-13-222646-4). P-H.

EARTHS, RARE

see also kinds of rare earths, e.g. Cerium

Elliott, R. J., ed. Magnetic Properties of Rare Earth Metals. LC 72-161302. 384p. 1972. 59.50x (ISBN 0-306-30565-8, Plenum Pr). Plenum Pub.

Eyring, L. Progress in the Science & Technology of the Rare Earths. write for info. Pergamon.

Eyring, L., ed. Rare Earth Research, Vol. 3. (Rare Earth Research Ser.). 770p. 1965. 180.50 (ISBN 0-677-10130-9). Gordon.

Fields, Paul R. & Moeller, Therald, eds. Lanthanide-Actinide Chemistry. LC 67-31656. (Advances in Chemistry Ser: No. 71). 1967. 29.95 (ISBN 0-8412-0072-6). Am Chemical.

Gschneider, K. A. & Eyring, L., eds. Handbook of Physics & Chemistry of Rare Earths, 4 Vols. 1979. Vol. 1: Metals. 176.50 (ISBN 0-444-85020-1); Vol. 2: Alloys & Intermetallics. 130.00 (ISBN 0-444-85021-X); Vol. 3: Non-Metallic Compounds I. 134.00 (ISBN 0-444-85215-8); Vol. 4: Non Metallic Compounds II. 123.50 (ISBN 0-444-85216-6). Elsevier.

Gschneidner, K. A. & Eyring, L., eds. Handbook on the Physics & Chemistry of Rare Earths, Vol. 5. 700p. 1983. 153.25 (ISBN 0-444-86375-3, I-002-83, North Holland). Elsevier.

Gschneidner, K. A., Jr. & Eyring, L., eds. Handbook on the Physics & the Chemistry of Rare Earths, Vol. 6. 604p. 1984. 124.00 (ISBN 0-444-86592-6, North Holland). Elsevier.

Gschneidner, Karl, Jr., ed. Industrial Applications of Rare Earth Elements. LC 81-10875. (ACS Symposium Ser.: No. 164). 1981. 36.95 (ISBN 0-8412-0641-4). Am Chemical.

Henderson, P., ed. Rare Earth Element Geochemistry. (Developments in Geochemistry: Vol. 2). 510p. 1984. 84.75 (ISBN 0-444-42148-3). Elsevier.

Hufner, S. Optical Spectra of Transparent Rare Earth Compounds. 1978. 49.00 (ISBN 0-12-360450-8). Acad Pr.

Jorgenson, C. K., et al. Rare Earths. (Structure & Bonding Ser.: Vol. 25). (Illus.). iv, 152p. 1976. 46.00 (ISBN 0-387-07508-9). Springer-Verlag.

McCarthy, G. J. & Rhyne, J. J., eds. The Rare Earths in Modern Science & Technology, Vol. 1. LC 78-5365. 645p. 1978. 95.00 (ISBN 0-306-31149-6, Plenum Pr). Plenum Pub.

McCarthy, G. J., et al, eds. The Rare Earths in Modern Science & Technology, Vol. 2. 670p. 1980. 95.00 (ISBN 0-306-40347-1, Plenum Pr). Plenum Pub.

McCarthy, Gregory J. & Silber, Herbert B., eds. The Rare Earths in Modern Science & Technology, Vol. 3. LC 78-5365. 610p. 1982. 69.50 (ISBN 0-306-40919-4, Plenum Pr). Plenum Pub.

Michelsen, Odd B. Analysis & Application of Rare Earth Materials. 374p. 1973. 57.00x (ISBN 8-200-04780-6, Dist. by Columbia U Pr). Universitet.

Nachman, Joseph F. & Lundin, C. E., eds. Rare Earth Research, Vol. 1. (Rare Earth Research Ser.). 370p. 1962. 99.50x (ISBN 0-677-10490-1). Gordon.

Nesbitt, E. A. & Wernick, J. A. Rare Earth Permanent Magnets. (Materials Science Ser). 1973. 30.00 (ISBN 0-12-515450-X). Acad Pr.

Nieboehr, E., et al. Rare Earths. LC 67-11280. (Structure & Bonding Ser.: Vol. 22). iv, 1p. 1975. 43.00 (ISBN 0-387-07268-3). Springer-Verlag.
Parker. Rare Earth Permanent Magnets. Date not set. price not set (ISBN 0-471-82293-0). Wiley.
Rare Earths & Actinides Nineteen Seventy-Seven: Durham. (Institute of Physics Conference Ser.: No. 37). 1978. 67.50 (ISBN 0-9960031-7-7, Pub. by Inst Physics England). Heyden.
Reisfeld, R. & Jorgensen, C. K. Lasers & Excited States of Rare Earths. LC 77-24052. (Inorganic Chemistry Concepts: Vol. 1). (Illus.). 1977. 41.00 (ISBN 0-387-08324-3). Springer-Verlag.
Sinha, S. P., et al, eds. Rare Earths. LC 67-11280. (Structure & Bonding Ser: Vol. 30). 1976. 42.00 (ISBN 0-387-07887-8). Springer-Verlag.
Spedding, E. H. & Danne, A. H., eds. Rare Earths. LC 61-15413. 654p. 1971. Repr. of 1961 ed. 35.00 (ISBN 0-88275-052-6). Krieger.
Subbarao, E. C. & Wallace, W. E., eds. Science & Technology of Rare Earth Materials. 1980. 44.00 (ISBN 0-12-675640-6). Acad Pr.
Villani, F., ed. Rare Earth Technology & Applications. LC 80-42. (Chemical Technology Review: No. 154). (Illus.). 367p. 1980. 48.00 (ISBN 0-8155-0795-X). Noyes.
Vorres, Karl S., ed. Rare Earth Research, Vol. 2. (Rare Earth Research Ser.). 638p. 1964. 144.50 (ISBN 0-677-10620-3). Gordon.

EARTHWORK

see also Dams; Earthmoving Machinery; Excavation; Fortification; Foundations; Soil Mechanics; Tunnels and Tunneling; Underground Construction

Atcheson, Daniel B. Estimating Earthwork Quantities. 2nd ed. LC 84-62802. (Illus.). 216p. 1985. pap. 25.95 (ISBN 0-9613202-3-0). Norseman Pub.
Building Research Advisory Board - Federal Housing Administration. Criteria for Compacted Fills. 1965. pap. 3.00 (ISBN 0-309-01281-3). Natl Acad Pr.
Performance of Earth & Earth-Supported Structures: Proceedings of the Specialty Conference on June 11-14, 1972, Purdue University, Lafayette, Indiana, 3 vols. Vol. 1, Pt. 1. pap. 160.00 (ISBN 0-317-10643-0, 2019546); Vol. 1, Pt. 2. pap. 160.00 (ISBN 0-317-10644-9); Vol. 2. pap. 40.00 (ISBN 0-317-10645-7); Vol. 3. pap. 105.80 (ISBN 0-317-10646-5). Bks Demand UMI.
Platt, Hugh. A New, Cheape & Delicate Fire of Cole-Balles. LC 72-7838. (English Experience Ser.: No. 550). 32p. 1972. Repr. of 1603 ed. 7.00 (ISBN 90-221-0550-4). Walter J Johnson.

EARTHWORMS

Appelhof, Mary. Workshop on the Role of Earthworms in the Stabilization of Organic Residues: Proceedings, Vol. I. LC 81-65289. 340p. 1981. pap. 25.00x (ISBN 0-939294-07-9). Flower Pr.
--Workshop on the Role of Earthworms in the Stabilization of Organic Residues, Vol. 1. (Orig.). pap. 25.00 (TD-772-W6). Beech Leaf.
Barrett, Thomas J. Harnessing the Earthworm. (Illus.). 192p. 1976. 7.95 (ISBN 0-916302-14-8); pap. 5.95 (ISBN 0-916302-09-1). Bookworm Pub.
Darwin, Charles. Darwin on Earthworms: The Formation of Vegetable Mould Through the Action of Worms. (Illus.). 160p. 1976. 7.95 (ISBN 0-916302-10-5); pap. 5.95 (ISBN 0-916302-06-7). Bookworm Pub.
Earthworms for Ecology & Profit: Successful Earthworm Marketing. (Fun & Profit Ser.: Vol. III). (Illus.). 1985. 9.95 (ISBN 0-916302-22-9); pap. 6.95. Bookworm Pub.
Edwards, C. A. & Lofty, J. F. Biology of Earthworms. 2nd ed. 1977. 29.95 (ISBN 0-412-14950-8, NO.6096, Pub. by Chapman & Hall). Methuen Inc.
Edwards, C. A. & Lofty, J. R. Biology of Earthworms. (Illus.). pap. 7.95 (ISBN 0-916302-20-2). Bookworm Pub.
Gaddie, Ronald E. & Douglas, Donald. Earthworms for Ecology & Profit: Earthworms & the Ecology, Vol. II. (Illus.). 1977. pap. 6.95 (ISBN 0-916302-01-6). Bookworm Pub.
--Earthworms for Ecology & Profit: Scientific Earthworm Farming, Vol. 1. (Illus.). 192p. 1975. 9.95 (ISBN 0-916302-11-3); pap. 6.95 (ISBN 0-916302-05-9). Bookworm Pub.
Handreck, K. A. Earthworms for Gardeners & Fishermen. (Discovering Soils Ser.: No. 5). 15p. 1978. pap. 6.00 (ISBN 0-686-71830-5, C037, CSIRO). Unipub.
Holwager, George. Larger Red Worms. (Illus.). 1952. pap. 3.00 (ISBN 0-9600102-3-8). Shields.
Home, Farm & Garden Research Association. Let an Earthworm Be Your Garbage Man. (Illus.). 1954. pap. 3.00 (ISBN 0-9600102-6-2). Shields.
Mays, Howard L. Raising Fishworms with Rabbits. rev. ed. 1981. pap. 4.00 (ISBN 0-914116-10-X). Shields.
Morgan, Charlie. Earthworm Feeds & Feeding. 1978. pap. 4.00 (ISBN 0-914116-02-9). Shields.
--How to Raise, Store & Sell Nightcrawlers. 1975. pap. 2.50 (ISBN 0-686-65538-9). Shields.
--Manual of Therapeutic Medications & Pesticides for Worm Growers. (Illus.). 1979. pap. 7.50 (ISBN 0-914116-17-7). Shields.
--Raising the African Nightcrawler. 1978. pap. 3.00 (ISBN 0-9600102-9-7). Shields.
Olson, H. W. The Earthworms of Ohio. 1928. 1.00 (ISBN 0-86727-016-0). Ohio Bio Survey.
Satchell, J. E. Earthworm Ecology. 1983. 75.00 (ISBN 0-412-24310-5, NO. 6805, Pub. by Chapman & Hall). Methuen Inc.
Smith, Frank. The Calciferous Glands of Lumbricidae & Diplocardia. 1923. pap. 8.00 (ISBN 0-384-56130-6). Johnson Repr.
Worden, Diane, compiled by. Workshop on the Role of Earthworms in the Stabilization of Organic Residues: Volume 2, Bibliography. LC 81-65289. 490p. (Orig.). 1981. pap. 50.00 (ISBN 0-939294-08-7, TD-772-W6). Beech Leaf.
Workshop on the Role of Earthworms in the Stabilization of Organic Residues, 2 vols. 1981. 70.00 set (ISBN 0-686-84201-4, TD-772-W6). Beech Leaf.

EASYWRITER II (COMPUTER PROGRAM)

Cassel, Don. EasyWriter Simplified for the IBM Personal Computer. 208p. 1984. text ed. 21.95 (ISBN 0-13-222449-6); pap. text ed. 12.95 (ISBN 0-13-222431-3). P-H.
Scanlon, Leo J. EasyWriter II System Made Easy-er. 128p. 1984. text ed. 23.95 (ISBN 0-13-223587-0); pap. text ed. 15.95 (ISBN 0-13-223579-X). P-H.
Stultz, Russell. The Illustrated EasyWriter II Book. (Illus.). 1984. pap. 16.95 (ISBN 0-13-450297-3). P-H.
Stultz, Russell A. The Illustrated EasyWriter II Book. LC 84-2306. (Illus.). 240p. 1984. pap. 16.95 (ISBN 0-915381-58-3). WordWare Pub.
Topham, Douglas W. Writing with the Easywriter II System. LC 84-50355. (Illus.). 300p. 1984. pap. cancelled (ISBN 0-89588-141-1). SYBEX.
Williams, Linda, et al. Using Easywriter II. 256p. 1984. pap. 16.95 (ISBN 0-471-80029-5, Pub by Wiley Pr). Wiley.

EAVESDROPPING

see also Wire-Tapping

Brown, Robert M. The Electronic Invasion. rev. 2nd ed. (Illus.). 192p. 1975. pap. 7.15 (ISBN 0-8104-0825-2). Hayden.
Carr, James G. The Law of Electronic Surveillance. LC 76-56748. 1977. 65.00 (ISBN 0-87632-108-2). Boardman.
Dash, Samuel, et al. Eavesdroppers. LC 71-136498. (Civil Liberties in American History Ser). (Illus.). 1971. Repr. of 1959 ed. lib. bdg. 35.00 (ISBN 0-306-70074-3). Da Capo.
Moran, William B., ed. Covert Surveillance & Electronic Penetration. (Illus.). 1983. pap. 9.95 (ISBN 0-317-03311-5). Loompanics.
Paulsen, Monrad G. The Problems of Electric Eavesdropping. 136p. 1977. pap. 10.00 (ISBN 0-317-30880-7, B175). Am Law Inst.
Pollock, David A. Methods of Electronic Audio Surveillance. (Illus.). 406p. 1979. 28.00x (ISBN 0-398-02382-4). C C Thomas.

EBONITE

see Rubber

EBULLITION

American Society of Mechanical Engineers. The Role of Nucleation in Boiling & Cavitation: Symposium Presented at Joint Fluids Engineering, Heat Transfer & Lubrication Conference, Detroit, Michigan, May 26-27, 1970. pap. 20.00 (ISBN 0-317-09023-2, 2016877). Bks Demand UMI.
Collier, J. G. Convective Boiling & Condensation. 2nd ed. (Illus.). 460p. 1981. text ed. 85.00 (ISBN 0-07-011798-5). McGraw.
Dwyer, O. E. Boiling Liquid-Metal Heat Transfer. LC 75-11012. (Nuclear Science Technology Ser.). (Illus.). 1976. text ed. 37.95 (ISBN 0-89448-000-6, 300008). Am Nuclear Soc.
Tong, L. S. Boiling Heat Transfer & Two-Phase Flow. LC 74-26607. 256p. 1975. Repr. of 1965 ed. 18.50 (ISBN 0-88275-251-0). Krieger.
Winter, E. R., et al. Recent Developments in Boiling & Condensation: Reprotext. (Illus.). 117p. 1977. 21.20x (ISBN 0-89573-000-6). VCH Pubs.

ECHINOCOCCOSIS

Echinococcosis (Hydatidosis) (Bulletin of WHO: Vol. 39, No. 1). (Eng, Fr, Rus.). 136p. 1968. pap. 3.60 (ISBN 0-686-09223-6). World Health.
Eckert, J., et al, eds. Echinococcosis-Hydatidosis Surveillance, Prevention & Control: FAO-UNEP-WHO Guidelines. Gemmell, M. & Soulsby, E. (Animal Production & Health Papers: No. 29). 157p. 1982. pap. 11.50 (ISBN 92-5-101205-9, F2343, FAO). Unipub.
Thompson, R. C., ed. The Biology of Echinococcus & Hydatid Disease. (Illus.). 336p. 1985. text ed. 35.00x (ISBN 0-04-591020-0). Allen Unwin.

ECHINODERMATA

see also Crinoidea; Sea-Urchins; Starfishes

Broadhead, T. W. & Waters, J. A., eds. Echinoderms: Notes for a Short Course. (University of Tennessee Studies in Geology). (Illus.). iv, 235p. 1980. pap. 6.00 (ISBN 0-910249-01-6). U of Tenn Geo.
Clark, A. M. & Courtman-Stock, J. The Echinoderms of Southern Africa. (Illus.). 1976. 55.00x (ISBN 0-565-00776-9, Pub. by Brit Mus Nat Hist). Sabbot-Natural Hist Bks.
Forbes, E. The Echinoderms of the Crag, London Clay, Etc. pap. 10.00 (ISBN 0-384-16390-4). Johnson Repr.
Jangoux, Michel & Lawrence, John M., eds. Echinoderm Studies, Vol. 1. 204p. 1983. lib. bdg. 25.00 (ISBN 90-6191-290-3, Pub. by Balkema RSA). IPS.
Kolisko, Eugen. Zoology for Everybody: Coelentrates & Echinoderms, Vol. 5. (Illus.). 1982. pap. 4.50 (ISBN 0-906492-42-4, Pub. by Kolisko Archives). St George Bk Serv.
Moore, Raymond C. Treatise on Invertebrate Paleontology, Pt. U: Echinodermata 3, 2 vols. LC 53-12913. (Illus.). 1966. 27.50 (ISBN 0-8137-3022-8). Geol Soc.
Moore, Raymond C., ed. Treatise on Invertebrate Paleontology, Pt. S: Echinodermata 1, 2 vols. LC 53-12913. (Illus.). 1968. 26.00 (ISBN 0-8137-3020-1). Geol Soc.
Pawson, David L. Molpadiid Sea Cucumbers (Echinodermata: Holothuroidea) of the Antarctic Seas: Paper 3 in Biology of the Antarctic Seas VI. LC 77-2320. (Antarctic Research Ser.: Vol. 26). (Illus.). 28p. 1977. pap. 10.70 (ISBN 0-87590-131-X). Am Geophysical.
Wright, T. The Fossil Echinodermata, Oolitic, 1 vol in 2 pts. 38.00 (ISBN 0-384-69500-0). Johnson Repr.
Zoological Society Of London - 20th Symposium. Echinoderm Biology. Millot, N., ed. 1968. 44.00 (ISBN 0-12-613320-4). Acad Pr.

ECHINOIDEA

see Sea-Urchins

ECHO

Hollander, John. The Figure of Echo: A Mode of Allusion in Milton & After. LC 80-26227. (A Quantum Book). 192p. 1981. 19.50x (ISBN 0-520-04187-9). U of Cal Pr.
Needham, Joseph & Gwei-Djen, Lu. Trans-Pacific Echoes & Resonances: Listening Once Again. 120p. 1985. 18.00x (ISBN 9971-950-86-3, Pub. by World Sci Singapore). Taylor & Francis.

ECHO RANGING

see Sonar

ECLIPSES

see also Transits

Anastassiades, M. A., ed. Solar Eclipses & the Ionosphere. LC 71-119056. 309p. 1970. 34.50x (ISBN 0-306-30480-5, Plenum Pr). Plenum Pub.
Brewer, Bryan. Eclipse. LC 78-73047. (Illus., Orig.). 1978. pap. 5.95 (ISBN 0-932898-26-2). Earth View.
Chambers, George F. The Story of Eclipses. 1904. 15.00 (ISBN 0-686-17419-4). Ridgeway Bks.
Jansky, Robert. Interpreting the Eclipses. 128p. (Orig.). 1977. pap. 7.95 (ISBN 0-917086-08-2). A C S Pubns Inc.
Kolisko, Lily, et al. The Sun Eclipse. 1979. pap. 5.50 (ISBN 0-906492-09-2, Pub. by Kolisko Archives). St George Bk Serv.
Lowenthal, James. The Hidden Sun: Solar Eclipses & Astrophotography. (Illus.). 128p. 1984. pap. 5.95 (ISBN 0-380-86959-4, 86959). Avon.
Newton, Robert R. Ancient Astronomical Observations & the Accelerations of the Earth & Moon. LC 70-122011. (Illus.). Repr. of 1970 ed. 62.60 (ISBN 0-8357-9264-1, 2013730). Bks Demand UMI.
Schove, D. J. Chronology of Eclipses & Comets AD1-1000. (Illus.). 356p. 1985. 29.50 (ISBN 0-85115-406-9, Pub. by Boydell & Brewer). Longwood Pub Group.

ECOLOGISTS

Bakker, Elna. An Island Called California: An Ecological Introduction to Its Natural Communities. 2nd. rev. ed. (Illus.). 400p. pap. 10.95 (ISBN 0-520-04948-9, CAL 641). U of Cal Pr.
Cooper, David J. Brooks Range Passage. (Illus.). 208p. 1982. 14.95 (ISBN 0-89886-061-X). Mountaineers.
Hutchinson, G. Evelyn. The Kindly Fruits of the Earth: An Environmental Study of an Embryo Ecologist. LC 78-21689. (Illus.). 1979. 27.00x (ISBN 0-300-02272-7). Yale U Pr.

ECOLOGY

see also Animal Ecology; Animal Populations; Aquatic Ecology; Bioclimatology; Botany–Ecology; Conservation of Natural Resources; Desert Ecology; Food Chains (Ecology); Forest Ecology; Fresh-Water Ecology; Geographical Distribution of Animals and Plants; Grassland Ecology; Human Ecology; Marine Ecology; Mountain Ecology; Paleoecology; Predation (Biology); Radioecology

Abbott, R. Tucker, ed. Indexes to the Nautilus: Geographical, Vols. 1-90, & Scientific Names, Vols. 61-90. 1979. Set. 24.00x (ISBN 0-915826-06-2). Am Malacologists.
Adams, Charles C., 3rd. Guide to the Study of Animal Ecology. Edgerton, Frank N., ed. LC 77-74201. (History of Ecology Ser.). (Illus.). 1978. Repr. of 1913 ed. lib. bdg. 16.00x (ISBN 0-405-10371-9). Ayer Co Pubs.
Adler, Irving. The Environment. LC 75-35526. (Reason Why Ser.). (Illus.). 1976. PLB 10.89 (ISBN 0-381-99617-4, JD-J). Har-Row.
Adriano, Domy C. & Brisbin, I. Lehr, eds. Environmental Chemistry & Cycling Processes: Proceedings. LC 78-6603. (DOE Symposium Ser.). 943p. 1978. pap. 31.50 (ISBN 0-87079-302-0, CONF-760429); microfiche 4.50 (ISBN 0-87079-199-0, CONF-760429). DOE.
Alexander, M., ed. Advances in Microbial Ecology, Vol. 4. 262p. 1980. 39.50x (ISBN 0-306-40493-1, Plenum Pr). Plenum Pub.
--Advances in Microbial Ecology, Vol. 5. 262p. 1981. 39.50x (ISBN 0-306-40767-1, Plenum Pr). Plenum Pub.
Ali, M. A., ed. Sensory Ecology: Review & Perspectives. LC 78-17597. (NATO ASI Series A, Life Sciences: Vol. 18). 607p. 1978. 69.50x (ISBN 0-306-40024-3, Plenum Pr). Plenum Pub.
All India Symposium, Muzaffarnagar, Dec. 1976. Advancement of Ecology: Proceedings. Agarwal, V. P. & Sharma, V. K., eds. (Current Trends in Life Sciences: Vol. 4). xxii, 218p. 1978. 22.50 (ISBN 0-88065-005-2, Pub. by Messers Today & Tomorrows Printers & Publishers India). Scholarly Pubns.
Allaby, Michael. Dictionary of the Environment. 2nd, rev. ed. (Illus.). 608p. 1984. 55.00x (ISBN 0-8147-0582-0). NYU Pr.
Allen, T. F. & Starr, Thomas B. Hierarchy: Perspectives for Ecological Complexity. LC 81-22010. (Illus.). 1982. lib. bdg. 27.50x (ISBN 0-226-01431-2). U of Chicago Pr.
Allin, Craig W. The Politics of Wilderness Preservation. LC 81-6234. (Contributions in Political Science Ser.: No. 64). 344p. 1982. lib. bdg. 29.95 (ISBN 0-313-21458-1, ALP/). Greenwood.
Altman, Irwin. The Environment & Social Behavior. 256p. 1981. pap. text ed. 14.95x (ISBN 0-8290-0639-7). Irvington.
Anderson, D. J. & Kikkawa, J. Community Ecology: Pattern & Process. (Illus.). 400p. 1985. text ed. 50.00x (ISBN 0-632-01062-2); pap. text ed. 28.00x (ISBN 0-632-01063-0). Blackwell Sci.
Anderson, J. M. Ecology for Environmental Sciences: Biosphere Ecosystems & Man. LC 81-3349. (Resources & Environmental Science Ser.). 208p. 1981. 19.95x (ISBN 0-470-27216-3); pap. 24.95. Halsted Pr.
Anderson, R. A. Abandon Earth: Last Call. Douglas, Herb & Torkelson, T. R., eds. (RWD Ser.). 64p. 1982. pap. 3.95 (ISBN 0-8163-0476-9). Pacific Pr Pub Assn.
Armstrong, Patrick. Changing Landscape. (Illus.). 1979. 20.00 (ISBN 0-900963-53-0, Pub. by Terence Dalton England). State Mutual Bk.
Ayensu, Edward S., et al. Our Green & Living World: The Wisdom to Save It. (Illus.). 256p. 1984. 24.95 (ISBN 0-521-26842-7). Cambridge U Pr.
--Our Green & Living World: The Wisdom to Save It. Goodwin, Joseph, ed. LC 84-600181. (Illus.). 256p. 1984. 25.00 (ISBN 0-89599-016-4, Dist. by Cambridge). Smithsonian Bks.
Bailey, R. A., et al. Introduction to the Chemistry of the Environment. 1979. 59.50 (ISBN 0-12-073050-2). Acad Pr.
Bakker, Elna. An Island Called California: An Ecological Introduction to Its Natural Communities. 2nd, rev. & exp. ed. LC 82-17453. (Illus.). 400p. 1985. 29.95 (ISBN 0-520-04947-0). U of Cal Pr.
Barbour, Ian G. Technology, Environment & Human Values. LC 80-12330. 344p. 1980. 16.95 (ISBN 0-03-055886-7); pap. 16.95 (ISBN 0-03-055881-6). Praeger.
Barkley, Paul W. & Seckler, David. Economic Growth & Environmental Decay: The Solution Becomes the Problem. 193p. 1972. pap. text ed. 11.95 (ISBN 0-15-518795-3, HC). HarBraceJ.
Barrett, Thomas S. & Livermore, Putnam. The Conservation Easement in California. 256p. 1983. 44.95 (ISBN 0-933280-20-3); pap. 24.95 (ISBN 0-933280-19-X). Island CA.

Engel, F., ed. Chilca. (Prehistoric Andean Ecology, Man, Settlement & the Environment Ser.: Vol. 4). 186p. 1984. pap. text ed. 45.50x (ISBN 0-391-02773-5). Humanities.

Enger, Eldon D., et al. Environmental Science: The Study of Interrelationships. 544p. 1982. pap. text ed. write for info. (ISBN 0-697-04729-6); instr's manual avail. (ISBN 0-697-04745-8); transparencies avail. (ISBN 0-697-04749-0). Wm C Brown.

The Environment, Water, & the Coast, 1977-1982. LC 83-26398. 108p. (Orig.). 1984. pap. 4.00 (ISBN 0-87772-296-X). Inst Gov Stud Berk.

An Environmental Bibliography: Publications Issued by UNEP or Under Its Auspices 1973-80. (Reference Ser.: Vol. 2). 67p. 1981. pap. 12.00 (ISBN 92-807-1008-7, UNEP052, UNEP). Unipub.

Environmental Ethics: Values & Obligations in the Landscape. (CELA Forum Ser.: Vol. 1, No. 4). pap. 20.00 (ISBN 0-317-26818-X, 2023483). Bks Demand UMI.

Environmental Resources Ltd. Environmental Impact of Energy Strategies within the EEC. flexi-cover 32.00 (ISBN 0-08-025681-3). Pergamon.

Erickson, Paul A. Environmental Impact Assessment: Principles & Applications. 1979. 49.50 (ISBN 0-12-241550-7). Acad Pr.

Ewusie, J. Yanney. Elements of Tropical Ecology. (Orig.). 1980. pap. text ed. 16.50x (ISBN 0-435-93700-6). Heinemann Ed.

Exline, Christopher H., et al. The City: Patterns & Processes in the Urban Ecosystem. (Illus.). 300p. (Orig.). 1981. lib. bdg. 34.00x (ISBN 0-89158-904-X); pap. 15.00 (ISBN 0-89158-905-8). Westview.

Fairbridge, R. W., ed. The Encyclopedia of Geochemistry & Environmental Sciences. LC 75-152326. (Encyclopedia of Earth Sciences Ser.: Vol. IVA). 1321p. 1972. 98.00 (ISBN 0-87933-180-1). Van Nos Reinhold.

Farnworth, E. G. & Golley, F. B., eds. Fragile Ecosystems: Evaluation of Research & Applications in the Neotropics. LC 74-8290. (Illus.). 280p. 1974. pap. 20.00 (ISBN 0-387-06695-0). Springer-Verlag.

Felins, Yehuda. Nature & Man in the Bible: Chapters in Biblical Ecology. 1982. 25.00x (ISBN 0-900689-19-6). Bloch.

Fernando, C. H. Ecology & Biogeography of Sri Lanka. (Monographiae Biologicae: No. 57). 520p. 1984. 110.00 (ISBN 90-6193-109-6, Pub. by Junk Pubs Netherlands). Kluwer Academic.

Florman, Samuel. Blaming Technology: The Irrational Search for Scapegoats. 224p. 1982. pap. 6.95 (ISBN 0-312-08363-7). St Martin.

Foin, Theodore C. Ecological Energetics. Head, J. J., ed. LC 83-70605. (Carolina Biology Readers Ser.). (Illus.). 16p. 1984. pap. 1.60 (ISBN 0-89278-291-9, 45-9691). Carolina Biological.

Fontaine, Thomas D., III & Bartell, Steven M., eds. Dynamics of Lotic Ecosystems. LC 82-48641. (Illus.). 450p. 1983. 34.95 (ISBN 0-250-40612-8). Butterworth.

Frenkiel, Francois N. & Goodall, David W., eds. Simulation Modeling of Environmental Problems. LC 77-92369. (SCOPE Ser. (Scientific Committee on Problems of the Environment): Scope Report 9). 112p. 1978. 24.95x (ISBN 0-471-99580-0, Pub. by Wiley-Interscience). Wiley.

Friedman, G. M. & Krumbein, W., eds. Hypersaline Ecosystems. (Ecological Studies: Vol. 53). (Illus.). 500p. 1985. 98.00 (ISBN 0-387-15245-8). Springer-Verlag.

Gauch, Hugh G., Jr. Multivariate Analysis in Community Ecology. LC 81-9974. (Cambridge Studies in Ecology: No. 1). (Illus.). 300p. 1982. 44.50 (ISBN 0-521-23820-X); pap. 16.95 (ISBN 0-521-28240-3). Cambridge U Pr.

Gehu, J. M., ed. La Vegetation des Pelouses Seches a Therophytes. (Colloques Phytosociologiques Ser.: No. 6). 1979. lib. bdg. 42.00 (ISBN 3-7682-1207-6). Lubrecht & Cramer.

Geological & Ecological Studies of the Qinghai-Xizang (Tibet) Plateau: Vol. 1, Geology, Geological History & the Origin of the Qinghai-Xizang (Tibet) Plateau. 182p. 1981. 157.50 (ISBN 0-677-60210-3). Gordon.

Gerasimov, I. P. Geography & Ecology. 167p. 1983. 5.95 (ISBN 0-8285-2394-0, 095, Pub. by Progress Pubs USSR). Imported Pubns.

Gerrick, David J. Job Hunting in Conservation: A Guide to Job Sources in Conservation, Park Management & Ecology. 1975. pap. 11.95 (ISBN 0-916750-67-1). Dayton Labs.

Gibbons, J. Whitfield & Sharitz, Rebecca R., eds. Thermal Ecology: Proceedings. LC 74-600136. (AEC Symposium Ser.). 687p. 1974. 25.25 (CONF-730505); microfiche 4.50 (ISBN 0-87079-225-3, CONF-730505). DOE.

Gilbertson, David, et al. Practical Ecology for Geography & Biology: Survey, Mapping & Data Analysis. (Illus.). 350p. (Orig.). 1985. pap. 11.95 (ISBN 0-09-162651-X, Pub. by Hutchinson Educ). Longwood Pub Group.

Gill, Don & Bonnett, Penelope. Nature in the Urban Landscape: A Study of City Ecosystems. LC 73-76409. (Illus.). 209p. 1973. 12.00x (ISBN 0-912752-03-3). York Pr.

Giller, P. S. Community Structure & the Niche. (Outline Studies in Ecology). 186p. 1984. pap. text ed. 11.95 (ISBN 0-412-25110-8, NO. 9033, Pub. by Chapman & Hall). Methuen Inc.

Gilpin, Alan. Dictionary of Environmental Terms. 191p. 1976. 14.95x (ISBN 0-7022-1010-2); pap. 8.95x (ISBN 0-7022-1011-0). U of Queensland Pr.

Glaeser, B., ed. Ecodevelopment: Concepts, Projects, Strategies. (Illus.). 300p. 1984. 49.50 (ISBN 0-08-028936-3, 2300/3). Pergamon.

Gold, John. Valued Environments. Burgess, Jacquelin, ed. (Illus.). 1982. text ed. 35.00x (ISBN 0-04-710001-X). Allen Unwin.

Golley, F. B. & Medina, E., eds. Tropical Ecological Systems: Trends in Terrestrial & Aquatic Research. LC 74-8828. (Illus.). xvi, 398p. 1975. 43.00 (ISBN 0-387-06706-X). Springer-Verlag.

Golley, Frank B., ed. Ecological Succession. LC 76-52930. (Benchmark Papers in Ecology Ser.: Vol. 5). 1977. 46.50 (ISBN 0-87933-256-5). Van Nos Reinhold.

Goodman, G. T. & Bray, S. An Annotated Bibliography of Ecological Aspects of the Reclamation of Derelict & Disturbed Land. (Bibliography Ser.). 351p. 1980. 14.95x (ISBN 0-902246-52-6, Pub. by GEO Abstracts England). State Mutual Bk.

Gopal, Brij & Bhardwaj, N. Elements of Ecology. (Illus.). 200p. 1979. text ed. 15.00x (ISBN 0-7069-0754-X, Pub. by Vikas India). Advent NY.

Gordon, G & Gordon, L. Sky Will Be Blue. 160p. 1984. 5.95 (ISBN 0-8285-2819-5, Pub. by Mir Pubs USSR). Imported Pubns.

Gore, A. J., ed. Mires: Swamp, Fog, Fen & Moor. (Ecosystems of the World Ser.: Vol. 4). 1983. Set. (ISBN 0-444-42005-3); Pt. A: Analytical Studies. 161.75 (ISBN 0-444-42003-7); Pt. B: Descriptive Studies. 161.75 (ISBN 0-444-42004-5, I-493-82). Elsevier.

Gorman, M. L. Island Ecology. 1979. pap. 6.95 (ISBN 0-412-15540-0, NO.6131, Pub. by Chapman & Hall). Methuen Inc.

Gorz, Andre. Ecology As Politics. Vigderman, Patsy & Cloud, Jonathan, trs. LC 79-64086. Tr. of Ecologie et Politique. 215p. 1980. 15.00 (ISBN 0-89608-089-7); pap. 6.50 (ISBN 0-89608-088-9). South End Pr.

Goudie, Andrew. Environmental Change. 2nd ed. (Contemporary Problems in Geography Ser.). (Illus.). 1983. 34.95x (ISBN 0-19-874132-4); pap. 12.50x (ISBN 0-19-874135-9). Oxford U Pr.

Grace, J., et al. Plants & Their Atmospheric Environment. (British Ecological Society Symposia Ser.). 419p. 1981. 89.95x (ISBN 0-470-27125-6). Halsted Pr.

Graham, Alistair. The Gardeners of Eden. (Illus.). 246p. 1973. 14.50x (ISBN 0-87471-633-0). Rowman.

Graham, Edward H. Natural Principles of Land Use. Repr. of 1944 ed. lib. bdg. 17.00x (ISBN 0-8371-2394-1, GRLU). Greenwood.

Graham, Michael. A Natural Ecology. (Illus.). 251p. 1973. 17.50x (ISBN 0-87471-024-3). Rowman.

Grassle, J. F., et al, eds. Ecological Diversity in Theory & Practice. (Statistical Ecology Ser.: Vol. 6). 1979. 45.00 (ISBN 0-89974-003-0). Intl Co-Op.

Green, Roger H. Sampling Design & Statistical Methods for Environmental Biologists. LC 78-24422. 257p. 1979. 32.50x (ISBN 0-471-03901-2). Wiley.

Greenberg, Michael, et al. Environmental Impact Statements. Natoli, Salvatore J., ed. LC 78-59102. (Resource Papers for College Geography). (Illus.). 1978. pap. text ed. 4.00 (ISBN 0-89291-131-X). Assn Am Geographers.

Gressitt, J. L. Biogeography & Ecology of New Guinea, 2 vols. 1982. lib. bdg. 195.00 (ISBN 90-6193-094-4, Pub. by Junk Pubs Netherlands). Kluwer Academic.

Hair, Jay D. Ecological Perspectives of Wildlife Management. 390p. 1977. pap. text ed. 16.95x (ISBN 0-8290-1394-6). Irvington.

Hall, Charles A. & Day, John W., Jr., eds. Ecosystem Modeling in Theory & Practice: An Introduction with Case Histories. LC 76-57204. 684p. 1977. 71.00 (ISBN 0-471-34165-7, Pub. by Wiley-Interscience). Wiley.

Hancock, William K. Discovering Monaro: A Study of Man's Impact on His Environment. LC 78-178280. (Illus.). 256p. 1972. 37.50 (ISBN 0-521-08439-3). Cambridge U Pr.

Harborne, J. B., ed. Phytochemical Ecology. 1972. 49.00 (ISBN 0-12-324663-6). Acad Pr.

Hardin, Veralee B. & Pettit, Neila T. A Guide to Ecological Screening & Assessment. 150p. 1978. write for info. wire coil (ISBN 0-697-06159-0). Wm C Brown.

Hay, Robert K. Chemistry for Agriculture & Ecology. (Illus.). 240p. 1981. pap. text ed. 13.95 (ISBN 0-632-00699-4, B 2114-3). Mosby.

Haynes, R., ed. Environmental Science Methods. (Illus.). 400p. 1982. 45.00x (ISBN 0-412-23280-4, NO. 6604, Pub. by Chapman & Hall England); pap. 19.95x (ISBN 0-412-23290-1, NO. 6603). Methuen Inc.

Henderson, Lawrence J. Fitness of the Environment: An Inquiry into the Biological Significance of the Properties of Matter. 11.50 (ISBN 0-8446-0691-X). Peter Smith.

Henion, Karl E. Ecological Marketing. LC 76-8799. (Grid Series in Marketing). pap. 64.50 (ISBN 0-317-29927-1, 2021728). Bks Demand UMI.

Hepburn, H. R. & Mitchell, G. Milk & Honey. 1981. 23.00 (ISBN 0-444-80272-X). Elsevier.

Herman, Herbert, ed. Treatise on Materials Science & Technology: Vol. 20, Ultrarapid Quenching of Liquid Alloys. LC 81-22860. 1981. 74.00 (ISBN 0-12-341820-8). Acad Pr.

Hetzel, B. S. & Frith, H. J. Nutrition of Aborigines in Relations to the Ecosystem of Central Australia. 150p. 1981. 37.00x (ISBN 0-643-00306-1, Pub. by CSIRO Australia). State Mutual Bk.

Hill, Stuart & Ott, Pierre. Basic Techniques in Ecological Farming. 365p. 1983. 19.95x (ISBN 0-8176-1374-9). Birkhauser.

Hinckley, Alden D. Applied Ecology: A Nontechnical Approach. (Illus.). 384p. 1976. pap. text ed. write for info. (ISBN 0-02-354550-X). Macmillan.

Hogetsu, K., et al, eds. Productivity of Biocenoses in Coastal Regions of Japan, Vol. 14. (Japan International Biological Program Synthesis Ser.). 345p. 1977. 45.00 (ISBN 0-86008-224-5, Pub. by U of Tokyo Japan). Columbia U Pr.

Holdgate, M. W. A Perspective of Environmental Pollution. LC 78-8394. (Illus.). 1979. 54.50 (ISBN 0-521-22197-8). Cambridge U Pr.

Holdgate, M. W. & Woodman, M. J., eds. The Breakdown & Restoration of Ecosystems. LC 77-18922. (NATO Conference Ser. I-Ecology: Vol. 3). 508p. 1978. 59.50x (ISBN 0-306-32803-8, Plenum Pr). Plenum Pub.

Holism & Ecology. 16p. 1981. pap. 5.00 (ISBN 92-808-0326-3, TUNU141, UNU). Unipub.

Holland, Marjorie & Burk, C. John. Stone Walls & Sugar Maples: An Ecology for Northeasterners. (Illus.). 188p. (Orig.). 1979. pap. text ed. 3.50 (ISBN 0-910146-22-5). Appalach Mtn.

Holldobler, Bert & Lindauer, Martin, eds. Experimental Behavioral Ecology & Sociobiology. LC 84-29807. (Illus.). 500p. 1985. text ed. 55.00x (ISBN 0-87893-460-X); pap. text ed. 30.00x (ISBN 0-87893-461-8). Sinauer Assoc.

Holling, C. S., ed. Adaptive Environmental Assessment & Management. LC 78-8523. (IIASA International Series on Applied Systems Analysis). 377p. 1978. 32.95 (ISBN 0-471-99632-7, Pub. by Wiley-Interscience). Wiley.

Howes, Paul G. Mini-Wood Community. LC 74-84425. 1975. 20.00 (ISBN 0-682-48069-X). Exposition Pr FL.

Hungerford, Harold R., et al. Investigation & Action Skills for Environmental Problem Solving. (Illus.). 1978. pap. text ed. 5.20x (ISBN 0-87563-150-9); tchrs. ed. 6.20x (ISBN 0-87563-189-4). Stipes.

Hunt, Charles B. Death Valley: Geology, Ecology, Archaeology. LC 74-2460. 256p. 1975. 19.95 (ISBN 0-520-02460-5); pap. 9.95 (ISBN 0-520-03013-3, CAL 315). U of Cal Pr.

Hurdle, William R. Ecology Experienced. 265p. 1973. text ed. 15.45 (ISBN 0-943956-00-5). Trippensee Pub.

Hutziger, O., ed. The Natural Environment & the Biogeochemical Cycles B. (Handbook of Environmental Chemistry Ser.: Vol. I, B). (Illus.). 340p. 1982. 80.00 (ISBN 0-387-11106-9). Springer-Verlag.

Innis, G. S. & O'Neill, R. V., eds. Systems Analysis of Ecosystems. (Statistical Ecology Ser.: Vol. 9). 1979. 45.00 (ISBN 0-89974-006-5). Intl Co-Op.

Institute of Environmental Sciences, 13th Annual Meeting, Washington D.C., 1967. Environmental Evolution: Proceedings. (Illus.). 1967. pap. text ed. 8.00 (ISBN 0-915414-07-4). Inst Environ Sci.

International Biological Program, National Research Council. Productivity of World Ecosystems. 1975. pap. 17.50 (ISBN 0-309-02317-3). Natl Acad Pr.

International Congress of Ecology, First, The Hague, Netherlands, September 8-14, 1974: Structure, Functioning & Management of Ecosystems. 1974. pap. 40.00 (ISBN 90-220-0525-9, PDC70, PUDOC). Unipub.

Irby, Bobby N., et al. Diversity of Marine Animals. LC 83-19721. (Man & the Gulf Ser.: Vol. 3). 120p. 1984. pap. text ed. 6.00 (ISBN 0-87805-203-8). U Pr of Miss.

--Diversity of Marine Plants. LC 83-16994. (Man & the Gulf Ser.: Vol. 4). (Illus.). 120p. 1984. pap. text ed. 6.00 (ISBN 0-87805-204-6). U Pr of Miss.

--Marine & Estuarine Ecology. LC 83-19654. (Man & the Gulf Ser.: Vol. 1). (Illus.). 88p. 1984. pap. text ed. 5.00 (ISBN 0-87805-201-1). U Pr of Miss.

--Marine Habitats. LC 83-19726. (Man & the Gulf Ser.: Vol. 2). 96p. 1984. pap. text ed. 5.00x (ISBN 0-87805-202-X). U Pr of Miss.

Ito, Y. Comparative Ecology. 2nd ed. Kikkawa, J., ed. LC 79-41581. (Illus.). 350p. 1981. text ed. 67.50 (ISBN 0-521-22977-4); pap. text ed. 27.95 (ISBN 0-521-29845-8). Cambridge U Pr.

Jenkins, S. H. Environmental Impact of Man's Use of Water, 2 pts. Part 1. flexi-cover 33.00x (ISBN 0-08-028406-X); Part 2. flexi-cover 33.00x (ISBN 0-08-028412-4). Pergamon.

Jorgensen, S. E. State of the Art of Ecological Modelling: Proceedings of the Conference on Ecological Modelling, Copenhagen, 28 August 2, September 1978. LC 78-41208. (Environmental Sciences & Applications Ser.: Vol. 7). 1979. 150.00 (ISBN 0-08-023443-7). Pergamon.

Jorgensen, S. E. & Johnson, I. Principles of Environmental Science & Technology. (Studies in Environmental Science: Vol. 14). 516p. 1981. 53.25 (ISBN 0-444-99721-0). Elsevier.

Jorgensen, S. E., ed. Handbook of Environmental Data & Ecological Parameters. rev. ed. LC 78-41207. (Enviromental Sciences & Applications Ser.: Vol. 6). (Illus.). 1100p. 1979. 265.00 (ISBN 0-08-023436-4). Pergamon.

Kalk, M., et al, eds. Lake Chilwa. (Monographiase Bilogicae: No. 35). 1979. lib. bdg. 79.00 (ISBN 90-6193-087-1, Pub. by Junk Pubs Netherlands). Kluwer Academic.

Karasek, F. W., et al, eds. Mass Spectrometry in Environmental Sciences. 598p. 1985. 75.00x (ISBN 0-306-41552-6, Plenum Pr). Plenum Pub.

Kitchen, Clarrissa. The Ecology Hymnal. 1978. 1.75 (ISBN 0-941500-09-8). Sharing Co.

Kixmiller-Smith. The Global Environment. 96p. 1983. pap. text ed. 5.95 (ISBN 0-8403-3107-X). Kendall-Hunt.

Klein, Donald A. Environmental Impacts of Artificial Ice Nucleating Agents. LC 78-7985. 256p. 1978. 36.00 (ISBN 0-87933-334-0). Van Nos Reinhold.

Klekowski, Edward J., Jr., ed. Environmental Mutagenesis, Carcinogenesis, & Plant Biology, 2. 208p. 1982. 59.95 (ISBN 0-03-061601-8); Vol. 1. 32.95 set (ISBN 0-03-057953-8); Vol. 2. 32.95 (ISBN 0-03-061602-6). Praeger.

Kline, A. Burt, Jr., ed. The Environmental & Ecological Forum, 1970-1971. AEC Technical Information Center. LC 72-600120. 194p. 1972. pap. 12.75 (ISBN 0-87079-197-4, TID-25857); microfiche 4.50 (ISBN 0-87079-198-2, TID-25857). DOE.

Klingmuller, W., ed. Azospirillum II: Genetics, Physiology, Ecology, Vol. 48. (Experimentia Supplementa Ser.). 196p. 1984. 27.95 (ISBN 3-7643-1576-8). Birkhauser.

Klug, M. J. & Reddy, C. A., eds. Current Perspectives in Microbial Ecology. 710p. 1984. 47.00 (ISBN 0-914826-60-3). Am Soc Microbio.

Knight, C. Gregory. Ecology & Change: Rural Modernization in an American Community. 1974. 47.50 (ISBN 0-12-785435-5). Acad Pr.

Kormondy, Edward J. Concepts of Ecology. 3rd ed. (Illus.). 288p. 1984. text ed. 22.95 (ISBN 0-13-166710-6); pap. text ed. 17.95 (ISBN 0-13-166702-5). P-H.

Kormondy, Edward J. & McCormick, J. Frank, eds. Handbook of Contemporary Developments in World Ecology. LC 80-1797. (Illus.). 704p. 1981. lib. bdg. 75.00 (ISBN 0-313-21381-X, KHC/). Greenwood.

Kozlovsky, Daniel G., ed. An Ecological & Evolutionary Ethic. (Illus.). 128p. 1974. pap. 17.95 (ISBN 0-13-222935-8). P-H.

Kozlowski, T. T. & Ahlgren, C. E., eds. Fire & Ecosystems. 1974. 75.00 (ISBN 0-12-424255-3). Acad Pr.

Krebs, Charles J. Ecology: The Experimental Analysis of Distribution & Abundance. 3rd ed. 704p. 1985. text ed. 33.50 scp (ISBN 0-06-043778-2, HarpC). Har-Row.

Kruger, F. J., et al, eds. Mediterranean-Type Ecosystems: The Role of Nutrients. (Ecological Studies: Vol. 43). (Illus.). 530p. 1983. 43.00 (ISBN 0-387-12158-7). Springer-Verlag.

Kumar, H. D. Modern Concepts of Ecology. 2nd ed. (Illus.). xii, 293p. 1982. text ed. 22.50x (ISBN 0-7069-1245-4, Pub by Vikas India). Advent NY.

Saarinen, Esa. Conceptual Issues in Ecology. 1982. pap. 15.95 (ISBN 90-277-1391-X, Pub. by Reidel Holland). Kluwer Academic.

Salt, George W., ed. Ecology & Evolutionary Biology: A Round Table on Research. LC 83-24088. (Illus.). vi, 130p. 1984. pap. 7.95 (ISBN 0-226-73443-9). U of Chicago Pr.

Sandler, Shiphrah. Discovering Ecology. (The Discovering Ser.). (Illus.). 76p. (Orig.). 1982. tchr's manual 5.95 (ISBN 0-914634-99-2, 8202). DOK Pubs.

Sarmiento, Guillermo. The Ecology of Neotropical Savannas. Solbrig, Otto, tr. from Span. (Illus.). 240p. 1984. text ed. 22.50x (ISBN 0-674-22460-4). Harvard U Pr.

Schnitzer, M. & Khan, S. U. Humic Substances in the Environment. LC 72-76064. (Books in Soils & the Environment). pap. 63.50 (ISBN 0-317-28553-X, 2055014). Bks Demand UMI.

Schoenbaum, Thomas J. The New River Controversy. LC 79-24108. (Illus.). 1979. 14.95 (ISBN 0-89587-008-8). Blair.

Schultz, V., et al. A Bibliography of Quantitative Ecology. 1976. 49.00 (ISBN 0-12-787430-5). Acad Pr.

Scudo, F. M. & Ziegler, J. R. The Golden Age of Theoretical Ecology: 1925-1940. A Collection of Works by Volterra, Kostitzin, Lotka & Kolmogoroff. (Lecture Notes in Biomathematics: Vol. 22). 1978. pap. 28.00 (ISBN 0-387-08769-9). Springer-Verlag.

Seielstad, George A. Cosmic Ecology: The View from the Outside In. LC 82-15944. (Illus.). 180p. 1983. 24.95 (ISBN 0-520-04753-2). U of Cal Pr.

Sheehan, Patrick J., et al. Effects of Pollutants at the Ecosystem Level Scope 22 (SAC1) (Scientific Committee on Problems of the Environment Scope). 459p. 1984. 59.95 (ISBN 0-471-90204-7, Pub. by Wiley-Interscience). Wiley.

Shorrocks, B. A., ed. Evolutionary Ecology. 424p. 1984. text ed. 62.00x (ISBN 0-632-01189-0). Blackwell Pubns.

Shuval, Hillel I. Environmental Quality & Ecology: Proceedings of the 2nd International Conference Ecology & Environmental Quality, Vol. II. 620p. 1983. pap. 44.00 (ISBN 0-86689-020-3, 992200156). Balaban Intl Sci Serv.

Simmons, T. G. The Ecology of Natural Resources. 448p. 1981. 40.00x (ISBN 0-7131-6328-3, Pub. by E Arnold England). State Mutual Bk.

Sims, Harold W. Ecology Selected Readings. 3rd ed. 1983. pap. text ed. 14.95 (ISBN 0-8403-3040-5, 40304001). Kendall-Hunt.

Sinclair, A. R. & Norton-Griffiths, M. Serengeti: Dynamics of an Ecosystem. LC 79-10146. (Illus.). 384p. 1979. lib. bdg. 35.00x (ISBN 0-226-76028-6). U of Chicago Pr.

Sloan, Irving J. Environment & the Law. 2nd ed. LC 79-156377. (Legal Almanac Ser: No. 65). 120p. 1978. 5.95 (ISBN 0-379-11114-4). Oceana.

Smeins, Fred E. & Slack, Douglas R. Fundamentals of Ecology Laboratory Manual. 1978. pap. text ed. 11.95 (ISBN 0-8403-2628-9, 40262802). Kendall-Hunt.

Smith, C. J. Ecology of the English Chalk. LC 79-41168. 1980. 63.00 (ISBN 0-12-651850-5). Acad Pr.

Smith, Gary M. Windsinger. (Illus.). 176p. 1976. 7.95 (ISBN 0-87156-192-1). Windsinger.

Smith, Robert L. Ecology & Field Biology. 3rd ed. 800p. 1980. text ed. 32.50 scp (ISBN 0-06-046329-5, HarpC). Har-Row.

--Elements of Ecology & Field Biology. 1977. text ed. 24.50 scp (ISBN 0-06-046328-7, HarpC); instructor's manual avail. (ISBN 0-06-366306-6). Har-Row.

Solberg, Delores. We All Live on Earth: A Sketchbook. (Illus.). 80p. 1982. 6.95 (ISBN 0-8138-1902-4). Iowa St U Pr.

Southwood, T. R. Ecological Methods: With Particular Reference to the Study of Insect Population. 2nd ed. 1978. 30.00 (ISBN 0-412-15760-8, NO.6268, Pub. by Chapman & Hall). Methuen Inc.

Steward, Julian. Evolution & Ecology: Essays on Social Transformation. Steward, Jane C. & Murphy, Robert F., eds. LC 76-46341. 410p. 1977. 29.50x (ISBN 0-252-00612-7); pap. 9.95x (ISBN 0-252-00709-3). U of Ill Pr.

Stockholm International Peace Research Institute. Ecological Consequences of the Second Indochina War. 1976. text ed. 22.25x (ISBN 91-22000-62-3). Humanities.

Storer, John. The Web of Life. 1972. pap. 1.95 (ISBN 0-451-61952-8, MJ1952, Ment). NAL.

Stucki, Margaret E. Eco-Elegia: Elegies in Ecology. 110p. 1981. 10.00 (ISBN 0-686-30605-8). Birds' Meadow Pub.

--Eco-Elegia or Elegies in Ecology. 1981. 7.50 (ISBN 0-686-31135-3). Freedom Univ-FSP.

Studies on Tropical Andean Ecosystems: La Cordillera Central Colombiano Transacto parque los Nevados, Vol. 1. (Illus.). 346p. 1984. lib. bdg. 54.00 (ISBN 3-7682-1371-4). Lubrecht & Cramer.

Sturm, H. Zur Okologie der Andinen Paramoregion. (Biogeographica: No. 14). 1978. lib. bdg. 24.00 (ISBN 90-6193-215-7, Pub. by Junk Pubs Netherlands). Kluwer Academic.

Subramanyam, K. & O'Pecko, Mary M. Directory of Environment Periodicals. (Public Administration Ser.: P-345). 60p. 1979. pap. 6.00 (ISBN 0-88066-035-X). Vance Biblios.

Sumner, William G. Earth Hunger & Other Essays. 1913. 6.50x (ISBN 0-686-83530-1). Elliots Bks.

Svirezhev, Y. Stability of Biological Communities. 319p. 1983. 9.95 (ISBN 0-8285-2371-1, Pub. by Mir Pubs USSR). Imported Pubns.

Swift, M. J., et al. Decomposition in Terrestrial Ecosystems. (Studies in Ecology: Vol. 5). 1980. 65.00x (ISBN 0-520-04001-5). U of Cal Pr.

Symposium on Energy, the Environment, & Education. Energy Needs & the Environment. Seale, Robert L. & Sierka, Raymond A., eds. LC 72-83559. pap. 90.80 (ISBN 0-317-26798-1, 2024321). Bks Demand UMI.

Tamarin, R. H., ed. Population Regulation. LC 77-16178. (Benchmark Papers in Ecology Ser.: Vol. 7). 389p. 1978. 46.00 (ISBN 0-87933-324-3). Van Nos Reinhold.

Tanaka, Jiro. The San, Hunter-Gatherers of the Kalahari: A Study in Ecological Anthropology. 199p. 1980. 20.00x (ISBN 0-86008-276-8, Pub. by U of Tokyo Japan). Columbia U Pr.

Thomas, Keith. Man & the Natural World: A History of Modern Sensibility. LC 82-14384. (Illus.). 432p. 1983. 19.45 (ISBN 0-394-49945-X). Pantheon.

Tjallingii, S. P. & De Veer, A. A., eds. Perspectives in Landscape Ecology: Contributions to Research, Planning & Management of our Environment: Proceedings of the International Congress Organized by The Netherlands Society for Landscape Ecology, Veldhoven, the Netherlands, April 6-11, 1981. 352p. (22 lectures, 48 posters & 19 workshops). 1982. 30.25 (ISBN 90-220-0790-1, PDC237, Pudoc). Unipub.

Townsend, Colin R. & Calow, Peter, eds. Physiological Ecology: An Evolutionary Approach to Resource Use. LC 81-13559. (Illus.). 480p. 1981. text ed. 45.00x (ISBN 0-87893-827-3); pap. text ed. 27.95x (ISBN 0-87893-828-1). Sinauer Assoc.

Trojan, P. Ecosystem Homeostasis. 1984. pap. text ed. 32.50 (ISBN 90-6193-622-5, Pub. by Junk Pubs Netherlands). Kluwer Academic.

Turk, Amos, et al. Ecology, Pollution & Environment. 1972. pap. text ed. 16.95 (ISBN 0-7216-8925-6, CBS C). SCP.

Turk, Jonathan & Turk, Amos. Environmental Science. 3rd ed. 1984. text ed. 32.95 (ISBN 0-03-058467-1, CBS C); instr's manual 10.95 (ISBN 0-03-058468-X). SCP.

Unifying Concept in Ecology: Proceedings of the 1st International Congress of Ecology, Plenary Sessions, Sept. 1974 The Hague. 250p. 1975. 60.00 (ISBN 90-220-0524-0, PDC7, PUDOC). Unipub.

U. S. Army Natick Laboratories. Glossary of Environmental Terms (Terrestrial) LC 73-2851. 149p. 1973. Repr. of 1968 ed. 40.00x (ISBN 0-8103-3277-9). Gale.

Vade-Mecum Pour le Releve Methodique de la Vegetation et du Milieu. (Fr.). 170p. 1970. pap. 12.50 (ISBN 0-686-57240-8, M-6541). French & Eur.

Valaskakis, Kimon, et al. The Conserver Society: A Blueprint for the Future. LC 77-90868. 1979. 19.18i (ISBN 0-06-014489-0, HarpT). Har-Row.

Van Dyne, George, ed. Ecosystem Concept in Natural Resource Management. LC 72-86367. 1969. 45.00 (ISBN 0-12-713450-6). Acad Pr.

Van Leeuwenhoek, Antony. The Select Works of Antony Van Leeuwenhoek: His Microscopical Discoveries in Many Works of Nature, 2 vols in 1. Egerton, Frank N., ed. Hoole, Samuel, tr. LC 77-74236. (History of Ecology Ser.). (Illus.). 1978. Repr. of 1807 ed. lib. bdg. 54.00x (ISBN 0-405-10405-7). Ayer Co Pubs.

Vowles, P. D. & Connell, D. W. Experiments in Environmental Chemistry: A Laboratory Manual. LC 80-40270. (Pergamon Ser. on Environmental Science: Vol. 4). (Illus.). 108p. 1980. pap. 9.95 (ISBN 0-08-024009-7). Pergamon.

Wallace, Bruce & Srb, Adrian M. Adaption. LC 77-18812. (Foundations of Modern Biology Ser.). 1978. Repr. of 1964 ed. lib. bdg. 19.75x (ISBN 0-313-20212-5, WAAD). Greenwood.

Wallace, Bruce, ed. People, Their Needs, Environment, Ecology: Vol. 1, Essays in Social Biology. LC 79-167789. 1972. pap. 11.95 (ISBN 0-13-656827-0). P-H.

Walter, H. Vegetation of the Earth & Ecological Systems of the Geobiosphere. 3rd, rev. ed. Muise, O., tr. from Ger. (Heidelberg Science Library). (Illus.). 340p. 1985. pap. 17.00 (ISBN 0-387-13748-3). Springer-Verlag.

Walter, H. & Breckle, S. W. Ecological Systems of the Geobiosphere. Gruber, S., tr. from Ger. (Illus.). 260p. 1985. 34.50 (ISBN 0-387-13792-0). Springer-Verlag.

Ward, Diana V. Biological Environmental Impact Studies: Theory & Methods. LC 78-10595. 1978. 31.00 (ISBN 0-12-735350-X). Acad Pr.

Wein, Ross W. & MacLean, David A. The Role of Fire in Northern Circumpolar Ecosystems. LC 82-2036. (Scope Series Scientific Committee on Problems of the Enviroment: No. 18). 322p. 1982. 64.95x (ISBN 0-471-10222-9, Pub. by Wiley-Interscience). Wiley.

Wenig, Jeffrey. An Introduction to Environmental Science: The Ecology of Long Island. 1976. pap. 5.75x. Environ Pubns.

West, N. E. & Skujins, J., eds. Nitrogen in Desert Ecosystems. LC 78-17672. (US-IBP Synthesis Ser.: Vol. 9). 307p. 1978. 31.50 (ISBN 0-87933-333-2). Van Nos Reinhold.

Westman, Walter E. Ecology, Impact, Assessment & Environmental Planning. LC 84-11867. (Environmental Science & Technology: A wiley-Interscience Series of Texts & Monographs: 1-121). 532p. 1985. text ed. 65.00x (ISBN 0-471-89621-7, Wiley-Interscience); pap. text ed. 34.95x (ISBN 0-471-80895-4). Wiley.

Wetherbee, David K., et al. Time-Lapse Ecology, Muskegat Island, Nantucket, Massachusetts. 1972. pap. text ed. 14.50x (ISBN 0-8422-0185-8). Irvington.

Whitaker, C. R. A Bibliography of Pediments. (Bibliography Ser.). 95p. 1980. pap. 3.50x (ISBN 0-686-27380-X, Pub. by GEO Abstracts England). State Mutual Bk.

Whittaker, Robert H. Communities & Ecosystems. 2nd ed. (Illus.). 352p. 1975. pap. text ed. write for info. (ISBN 0-02-427390-2). Macmillan.

Wiegert, Richard G., ed. Ecological Energetics. LC 75-30762. (Benchmark Papers in Ecology: Vol. 4). 448p. 1976. 63.00 (ISBN 0-12-787763-0). Acad Pr.

Williams, J., ed. Carbon Dioxide, Climate & Society: Proceedings of an IIASA Workshop, Feb. 1978. 1978. text ed. 53.00 (ISBN 0-08-023252-3). Pergamon.

Wilson, A. G. Geography & the Environment: Systems' Analytical Methods. LC 80-41696. 297p. 1981. 48.95x (ISBN 0-471-27956-0, Pub. by Wiley-Interscience); pap. 23.95x (ISBN 0-471-27957-9, Pub. by Wiley-Interscience). Wiley.

Wilson, Edward O. & Bossert, William H. Primer of Population Biology. LC 73-155365. (Illus.). 192p. (Orig.). 1971. pap. text ed. 7.95x (ISBN 0-87893-926-1). Sinauer Assoc.

Worster, Donald. Nature's Economy: A History of Ecological Ideas. (Studies in Environment & History). 404p. 1985. 34.50 (ISBN 0-521-26792-7); pap. 9.95 (ISBN 0-521-31870-X). Cambridge U Pr.

Worthington, E. Barton. The Ecological Century: A Personal Appraisal. (Illus.). 206p. 1983. 27.50x (ISBN 0-19-854556-8). Oxford U Pr.

Wratten, S. D. & Fry, G. L. Field & Lab Exercises in Ecology. 216p. 1980. pap. text ed. 18.95 (ISBN 0-7131-2725-2). E Arnold.

Yapp, W. B. & Smith, M. I. Production, Pollution, Protection. (Wykeham Science Ser.: No. 19). 196p. 1972. 9.95x (ISBN 0-8448-1121-1). Crane-Russak Co.

ECOLOGY–MATHEMATICAL MODELS

Bartlett, M. S. Stochastic Population Models in Ecology & Epidemology. (Monographs in Applied Probability & Statistics). 1960. 10.95x (ISBN 0-416-52330-7, NO.6429). Methuen Inc.

Busenberg, Stavros & Cooke, Kenneth. Differential Equations & Applications in Ecology, Epidemics & Population Problems. LC 81-14897. 1981. 47.50 (ISBN 0-12-148360-6). Acad Pr.

Cohen, Joel E. A Model of Simple Competition. LC 66-23470. (Annals of the Computation Laboratory). (Illus.). 138p. 1966. 10.00x (ISBN 0-674-57800-7). Harvard U Pr.

Felsenstein, J., ed. Numerical Taxonomy. (NATO ASI Ser.: Series G, Ecological Sciences, No. 1). (Illus.). 655p. 1983. 66.00 (ISBN 0-387-12293-1). Springer-Verlag.

Gates, D. M. & Schmere, R. B., eds. Perspectives of Biophysical Ecology. LC 74-17493. (Illus.). 1975. 55.00 (ISBN 0-387-06743-4). Springer-Verlag.

Getz, W. M., ed. Mathematical Modelling in Biology & Ecology: Proceedings of a Symposium Held at the CSIR, Pretoria, July 1979. (Lecture Notes in Biomathematics Ser.: Vol. 33). viii, 355p. 1980. pap. 28.00 (ISBN 3-540-09735-X). Springer-Verlag.

Hall, Charles A. A. & Day, John W., Jr., eds. Ecosystem Modeling in Theory & Practice: An Introduction with Case Histories. LC 76-57204. 684p. 1977. 71.00 (ISBN 0-471-34165-7, Pub. by Wiley-Interscience). Wiley.

Jorgensen, S. E., ed. Modelling the Fate & Effect of Toxic Substances in the Environment: Proceedings of a Symposium 6-10 June, 1983, Copenhagen, Denmark. (Developments in Enviornmental Modelling Ser.: Vol. 6). 350p. 1984. 72.25 (ISBN 0-444-42386-9). Elsevier.

Kitching, R. L. Systems Ecology: An Introduction to Ecological Modelling. LC 82-20032. (Illus.). 280p. 1984. text ed. 29.95 (ISBN 0-7022-1813-8). U of Queensland Pr.

Levin, S. A. & Hallam, T., eds. Mathematical Ecology: Proceedings of the Autumn Research Seminar, Held at the International Centre for Theoretical Physics, Miramare-Trieste, Italy, November 29-December 10, 1982. (Lecture Notes in Biomathematics Ser.: Vol. 54). xii, 513p. 1984. 27.00 (ISBN 0-387-12919-7). Springer-Verlag.

May, Robert M. Stability & Complexity in Model Ecosystems. (Population Biology Monographs: No. 6). 150p. 1973. 26.00x (ISBN 0-691-08125-5); pap. 9.95x (ISBN 0-691-08130-1). Princeton U Pr.

NATO Conference, Instanbul, Turkey, July 1973. Mathematical Analysis of Decision Problems in Ecology: Proceedings. Charnes, A. & Lynn, W. R., eds. LC 75-19493. (Lecture Notes in Biomathematics Ser.: Vol. 5). viii, 421p. (Orig.). 1975. pap. 23.00 (ISBN 0-387-07188-1). Springer-Verlag.

Patten, Bernard C., ed. Systems Analysis & Simulation in Ecology, 3 vols. 78.00 ea. Vol. 1, 1971 (ISBN 0-12-547201-3). Vol. 2, 1972 (ISBN 0-12-547202-1). Vol. 3, 1975 (ISBN 0-12-547203-X). Acad Pr.

Pielou, E. C. Mathematical Ecology. LC 76-49441. 385p. 1977. 37.50x (ISBN 0-471-01993-3, Pub. by Wiley-Interscience). Wiley.

--Population & Community Ecology: Principles & Methods. new ed. LC 72-86334. (Illus.). 432p. 1974. 67.25x (ISBN 0-677-03580-2). Gordon.

Pielou, Evelyn C. Ecological Diversity. LC 75-9663. 165p. 1975. 29.95 (ISBN 0-471-68925-4, Pub. by Wiley-Interscience). Wiley.

Podolsky, Alexander S. New Phenology: Elements of Mathematical Forecasting in Ecology. LC 83-16723. 480p. 1984. 64.95 (ISBN 0-471-86451-X, Pub. by Wiley-Interscience). Wiley.

Shugart, H. H., Jr., ed. Time Series & Ecological Processes. LC 78-5410. (SIAM-SIMS Conference Ser.: No. 5). (Illus.). xxi, 303p. (Orig.). 1978. pap. text ed. 26.00 (ISBN 0-89871-032-4). Soc Indus-Appl Math.

Smith, J. Maynard. Models in Ecology. (Illus.). 200p. 1974. 29.95 (ISBN 0-521-20262-0). Cambridge U Pr.

Vandermeer, John. Elementary Mathematical Ecology. LC 80-18664. 294p. 1981. 39.95x (ISBN 0-471-08131-0, Pub. by Wiley-Interscience). Wiley.

ECOLOGY–STUDY AND TEACHING

Amidei, Rosemary E., compiled by. Environment: The Human Impact, Selections from the Science Teacher. 1973. pap. 7.50 (ISBN 0-87355-001-3). Natl Sci Tchrs.

Andrews, W., et al. Guide to the Study of Terrestrial Ecology. 1974. lib. bdg. 12.40 (ISBN 0-13-370940-X); pap. text ed. 10.84 (ISBN 0-13-370932-9). P-H.

Bakshi, Trilochan S. & Naveh, Zev, eds. Environmental Education: Principles, Methods & Applications. LC 80-11837. (Environmental Science Research Ser.: Vol. 18). 300p. 1980. 42.50x (ISBN 0-306-40433-8, Plenum Pr). Plenum Pub.

Carson, S. McB, ed. Environmental Education-Principles & Practice. (Illus.). 1978. pap. 24.95x (ISBN 0-7131-0133-4). Intl Ideas.

Conservation Education Association. Environmental Conservation Education: A Selected Annotated Bibliography-1977 Supplement. 32p. 1978. pap. text ed. 1.50x (ISBN 0-8134-2027-X, 2027). Interstate.

Fanning, Odom. Opportunities in Environmental Careers. LC 74-25902. (VGM Career Bks.). (Illus.). 1975. 7.95 (ISBN 0-8442-6381-8, 6381-8); pap. text ed. 5.95 (ISBN 0-8442-6382-6, 6382-6). Natl Textbk.

Ford, Phyllis. Eco-Acts. rev. 2nd ed. 259p. 1983. 10.00 (ISBN 0-943272-04-1). Inst Recreation Res.

Gray, David B., et al. Ecological Beliefs & Behaviors: Assessment & Change. LC 84-12833. (Contributions in Psychology Ser.: No. 4). (Illus.). 256p. 1985. lib. bdg. 35.00 (ISBN 0-313-24319-0, GRB/). Greenwood.

Harrah, David F. & Harrah, Barbara K. Conservation-Ecology: Resources for Environmental Education. LC 74-23055. 323p. 1975. 18.50 (ISBN 0-8108-0780-7). Scarecrow.

Institute of Environmental Sciences, 18th Annual Meeting, New York, 1972. Environmental Progress in Science & Education: Proceedings. LC 62-38584. 1972. pap. text ed. 20.00 (ISBN 0-915414-12-0). Inst Environ Sci.

Johnston, Timothy D. & Pietrewicz, Alexandra T., eds. Issues in the Ecological Study of Learning. 464p. 1985. text ed. 49.95 (ISBN 0-89859-521-5). L Erlbaum Assocs.

Basar, T. Dynamic Modelling & Control of National Economies, 1983: Proceedings of the IFAC-IFORS Symposium, 4th, Washington, DC, June 1983. Pau, F. L., ed. 550p. 116.00 (ISBN 0-08-030557-1). Pergamon.
Bornstein, Morris, ed. Comparative Economic Systems: Models & Cases. 4th ed. 1979. 25.50x (ISBN 0-256-02152-X). Irwin.
Buehlmann, Hans. Mathematical Methods in Risk Theory. LC 79-126042. (Grundlehren der Mathematischen Wissenschaften: Vol. 17). (Illus.). 1970. 36.00 (ISBN 0-387-05117-1). Springer-Verlag.
Cahiers de l'Institut de Science Economique Appliquee: Modeles Operationnels Regionaux. (Economies et Societes Series L: No. 9). 1962. pap. 11.00 (ISBN 0-317-16167-9). Kraus Repr.
Cassels, J. W. Economics for Mathematicians. LC 81-15461. (London Mathematical Society Lecture Note Ser.: No. 62). 150p. 1982. pap. 16.95 (ISBN 0-521-28614-X). Cambridge U Pr.
Cherene, L. J., Jr. Set Valued Dynamical Systems & Economic Flow. (Lecture Notes in Economics & Mathematical Systems: Vol. 158). 1978. pap. 12.00 (ISBN 0-387-08847-4). Springer-Verlag.
Clements, David L. An Introduction to Mathematical Models in Economic Dynamics. LC 83-23078. 175p. 1984. 18.95x (ISBN 0-936428-07-4). Polygonal Pub.
Cole, Sam, ed. Models, Planning & Basic Needs: Conference on the Applicability of Global Modelling to Integrated Planning & Developing Countries. (Illus.). 1979. text ed. 33.00 (ISBN 0-08-023732-0). Pergamon.
Day, R. H. & Cigno, A. Modelling Economic Change: The Recursive Programming Approach. (Contributions to Economic Analysis Ser.: Vol. 117). 448p. 1978. 70.25 (ISBN 0-444-85056-2, North Holland). Elsevier.
First Stanford Symposium. Mathematical Methods in the Social Sciences, 1959: Proceedings. Arrow, Kenneth J., et al, eds. 1960. 27.50x (ISBN 0-8047-0021-4). Stanford U Pr.
Ford, Lester R., Jr. & Fulkerson, D. R. Flows in Networks. (Rand Corp. Research Studies Ser.). 1962. 20.00 (ISBN 0-691-07962-5). Princeton U Pr.
Gale, David. Theory of Linear Economic Models. 1960. 39.95 (ISBN 0-07-022728-4). McGraw.
Gandolfo, G. & Padoan, P. C. A Disequilibrium Model of Real & Financial Accumulation in an Open Economy. (Lecture Notes in Economics & Mathematical Systems Ser.: Vol. 236). vi, 172p. 1984. pap. 14.00 (ISBN 0-387-13889-7). Springer-Verlag.
Glass, J. Colin. Introduction to Mathematical Methods in Economics. 352p. 1980. text ed. 38.95 (ISBN 0-07-084116-0). McGraw.
Goodwin, R. Essays in Linear Economic Structures. 190p. 1983. text ed. 37.50x (ISBN 0-333-29102-6, Pub. by Macmillan England). Humanities.
Goodwin, R. M., et al, eds. Nonlinear Models of Fluctuating Growth: An International Symposium, Siena, Italy, March 24-27, 1983. (Lecture Notes in Economics & Mathematical Systems Ser.: Vol. 228). xvii, 277p. 1984. pap. 20.00 (ISBN 0-387-13349-6). Springer-Verlag.
Hildenbrand, W. Core & Equilibria of a Large Economy. (Studies in Mathematical Economies: No. 5). 1974. 32.00 (ISBN 0-691-04189-X). Princeton U Pr.
Katzner, Donald W. Analysis Without Measurement. LC 82-4469. 366p. 1983. 39.50 (ISBN 0-521-24847-7). Cambridge U Pr.
Kendall, M. G., et al, eds. Mathematical Model Building in Economics & Industry: Series II. (Illus.). 1970. 13.00x (ISBN 0-02-847760-X). Hafner.
Kenkel, J. L. Dynamic Linear Economic Models. LC 73-85833. 400p. 1974. 56.75 (ISBN 0-677-04950-1). Gordon.
Khoury, S. J. & Parsons, T. D. Mathematical Methods in Finance & Economics. 296p. 1981. 49.00 (ISBN 0-444-00425-4, North-Holland). Elsevier.
Kindleberger, Charles P. & De Tella, G., eds. Economics in the Long View: Models & Methodology, 3 vols. 288p. 1982. Vol. 1; Models & Methodology. per vol. 35.00x (ISBN 0-8147-4582-2); Vol. 2: Application & Cases (1) write for info. (ISBN 0-8147-4580-6); Vol. 3: Application & Cases (2) NYU Pr.
Klein, Lawrence. Economic Theory & Econometrics. Marquez, Jaime, ed. LC 84-13142. 580p. Date not set. text ed. 40.00 (ISBN 0-8122-7937-9). U of Pa Pr.
Kuh, E., et al. Structural Sensitivity in Econometric Models. (Probability & Mathematical Statistics Ser.). 288p. 1985. 32.95 (ISBN 0-471-81930-1). Wiley.
Liu, Pon-Tai, ed. Dynamic Optimization & Mathematical Economics. LC 79-9088. (Mathematical Concepts & Methods in Science & Engineering Ser.: Vol. 19). (Illus.). 280p. 1979. 39.50x (ISBN 0-306-40245-9, Plenum Pr). Plenum Pub.
Malgrange, Pierre & Muet, Pierre-Alain, eds. Contemporary Macroeconomic Modelling. 300p. 1984. 45.00 (ISBN 0-631-13471-9). Basil Blackwell.
Malliaris, T. G. Stochastic Methods in Economics & Finance. (Advanced Textbooks in Economics: Vol. 17). 304p. 1982. 37.50 (ISBN 0-444-86201-3, North-Holland). Elsevier.
Manski, Charles F. & McFadden, Daniel, eds. Structural Analysis of Discrete Data with Econometric Applications. 588p. 1981. text ed. 37.50x (ISBN 0-262-13159-5). MIT Pr.
Moeschlin, O. & Pallaschke, D., eds. Game Theory & Mathematical Economics: Proceedings of the Seminar in Bonn/Hagen, Oct. 1980. 464p. 1981. 68.00 (ISBN 0-444-86296-X, North-Holland). Elsevier.
Morishima, M., et al. The Working of Econometric Models. LC 79-184901. (Illus.). 300p. 1972. 49.50 (ISBN 0-521-08502-0). Cambridge U Pr.
Onimode, B. & Osayimwese, Iz. Basic Mathematics for Economists. (Illus.). 192p. (Orig.). 1980. pap. text ed. 12.50x (ISBN 0-04-330304-8). Allen Unwin.
Ormerod, Paul. Economic Modelling. 1980. text ed. 74.00x (ISBN 0-435-84585-3). Gower Pub Co.
Patterson, K. D. & Ryding, J. Deriving & Testing Rate of Growth & Higher Order Growth Effects in Dynamic Economic Models. (Bank of England, Discussion paper: No. 21). pap. 20.00 (ISBN 0-317-26765-5, 2024345). Bks Demand UMI.
Qayaum, A. Numerical Models of Economic Development. 106p. 1969. 37.25x (ISBN 0-677-61600-7). Gordon.
Roehrig, Charles S. Estimation of M-Equation Linear Models Subject to a Constraint on the Endogenous Variables. LC 79-53644. (Outstanding Dissertations in Economics Ser.). 144p. 1984. lib. bdg. 24.00 (ISBN 0-8240-4167-4). Garland Pub.
Salant, Stephen W. Imperfect Competition in the World Oil Market: A Computerized Nash-Cournot Model. LC 80-8737. 192p. 1981. 27.50x (ISBN 0-669-04344-3). Lexington Bks.
Sato, R. & Beckmann, M. J, eds. Technology, Organization, & Economic Structure: Essays in Honor of Prof. Isamu Yamada. (Lecture Notes in Economics & Mathematical Systems: Vol. 210). (Illus.). 195p. 1983. pap. 18.00 (ISBN 0-387-11998-1). Springer-Verlag.
Satp, R. & Nono, T. Invariance Principles & the Structure of Technology. (Lecture Notes in Economics & Mathematical Systems: Vol. 212). (Illus.). 94p. 1983. pap. 13.00 (ISBN 0-387-12008-4). Springer-Verlag.
Schaible, Siegfried & Ziemba, William, eds. Generalized Concavity in Optimization & Economics. LC 81-17644. 1981. 55.00 (ISBN 0-12-621120-5). Acad Pr.
Schofield, Norman. Mathematical Methods in Economics. 296p. 1985. 39.50x (ISBN 0-8147-7842-9). NYU Pr.
Shvyrkov, V. V. Statistical Science in Economics, Vol. II. 4th ed. LC 83-50656. (Illus.). 187p. (Orig.). 1983. 19.20 (ISBN 0-942004-08-6). G Throwkoff.
Smith, Alasdair. A Mathematical Introduction to Economics. LC 82-11560. (Illus.). 270p. 1982. text ed. 29.95x (ISBN 0-389-20325-4). B&N Imports.
Streissler, E. W. The Failure of Econometrics, 2 vols. (Illus.). 1985. Set. 195.45 (ISBN 0-86654-160-8). Inst Econ Finan.
Sydsaeter, Knut. Topics in Mathematical Analysis for Economists. LC 81-66692. 1981. 44.00 (ISBN 0-12-679980-6). Acad Pr.
Telser, Lester G. & Graves, Robert L. Functional Analysis in Mathematical Economics: Optimization Over Infinite Horizons. LC 70-163718. 1972. 15.00x (ISBN 0-226-79190-4). U of Chicago Pr.
Van Duyne, Carl. Modsim: A Computer Program for Simulating Macroeconomic Models. Hepler, Molly L., ed. (Orig., User's man., 92 p.; instr's. man., 74 p.). 1980. User's Manual. pap. text ed. 5.00 (ISBN 0-686-27411-3); Instructor's Manual. 5.50 (ISBN 0-686-27412-1). Conduit.
Weintraub, E. Roy. Mathematics for Economists: An Integrated Approach. 208p. Date not set. pap. price not set (ISBN 0-521-28769-3). Cambridge U Pr.
--Microfoundations. LC 78-16551. (Cambridge Surveys of Economic Literature Ser.). 1979. pap. 12.95 (ISBN 0-521-29445-2). Cambridge U Pr.
Whiteman, Charles H. Linear Rational Expectations Models: A User's Guide. 130p. 1983. 19.50 (ISBN 0-8166-1181-5); pap. 9.95 (ISBN 0-8166-1179-3). U of Minn Pr.
Yohe, Gary W. A Comparison of Price Controls & Quantity Controls Under Uncertainty. LC 78-75060. (Outstanding Dissertations in Economics Ser.). 1979. lib. bdg. 34.00 (ISBN 0-8240-4137-2). Garland Pub.
Zambell, Richard G. Condensed Weekley, Monthly, Quarterly: Economic Models of the U. S. Economy, Vol. 2. LC 84-3727. (Illus.). 160p. 1984. 24.95 (ISBN 0-9613048-4-7). M D Weiss Pub.
Zameeruddin, Qazi & Khanna, V. K. Mathematics in Commerce & Economics. 253p. 1983. text ed. 22.50x (ISBN 0-7069-2188-7, Pub. by Vikas India). Advent NY.

ECONOMICS, MATHEMATICAL

see also Economics–Mathematical Models

Allen, Roy G. Mathematical Analysis for Economists. rev. ed. 1969. pap. 13.95 (ISBN 0-312-52185-5). St Martin.
Aumann, R. J. & Harsanyi, J. C., eds. Essays in Game Theory & Mathematical Economics. 196p. 1981. pap. text ed. 21.95x (ISBN 3-411-01609-4). Birkhauser.
Baumol, W. Economic Theory & Operations Analysis. 4th ed. 1977. 32.95 (ISBN 0-13-227132-X). P-H.
Beckmann, Martin J. Dynamic Programming of Economic Decisions. LC 68-21990. (Econometrics & Operations Research: Vol. 9). 1968. 24.00 (ISBN 0-387-04292-X). Springer-Verlag.
Birchenhall, Chris & Grout, Paul. Mathematics for Modern Economics. 424p. 1984. 32.50x (ISBN 0-389-20521-4, BNB-08083); pap. 20.00x (ISBN 0-389-20522-2, BNB-08084). B&N Imports.
Blackorby, C. & Primont, D. Duality, Separability & Functional Structure: Theory & Economic Applications. (Dynamic Economics Ser.: Vol. 2). 396p. 1978. 59.00 (ISBN 0-444-00235-9, North-Holland). Elsevier.
Border, Kim C. Fixed Point Theorems with Applications to Economics & Game Theory. (Illus.). 128p. 1985. 29.95 (ISBN 0-521-26564-9). Cambridge U Pr.
Casson, M. Introduction to Mathematical Economics. 1973. pap. 19.95 (ISBN 0-442-30718-7). Van Nos Reinhold.
Davis, Harold T. Analysis of Economic Time Series. (Cowles Commission Monograph Ser., No. 6). 1941. 8.50 (ISBN 0-911536-18-3). Trinity U Pr.
Davis, Harold T. & Nelson, William F. Elements of Statistics with Application to Economic Data. rev. & enl. 2nd ed. LC 78-163681. Repr. of 1937 ed. 28.50 (ISBN 0-404-01994-3). AMS Pr.
Day, Richard H. & Robinson, Stephen M., eds. Mathematical Topics in Economic Theory & Computation. LC 72-96283. v, 149p. 1972. text ed. 12.50 (ISBN 0-89871-045-6). Soc Indus-Appl Math.
Debreu, Gerard. Mathematical Economics: Twenty Papers of Gerard Debreu. LC 82-12875. (Econometric Society Monographs in Pure Theory). 320p. 1983. 34.50 (ISBN 0-521-23736-X). Cambridge U Pr.
Dhrymes, P. J. Mathematics for Econometrics. 2nd ed. 150p. 1984. pap. 19.80 (ISBN 0-387-90988-5). Springer-Verlag.
Dowling, Seward T. Schaum's Outline of Mathematics for Economists. (Illus., Orig.). 1979. pap. 9.95 (ISBN 0-07-017760-0). McGraw.
Dutta, Manoranjan & Alonso, Irma T. Metodos Econometricos. (Span.). 1982. text ed. 11.30 (ISBN 0-538-22880-6, V88). SW Pub.
Erlander, S. Optimal Spatial Interaction & the Gravity Model. (Lecture Notes in Economics & Mathematical Systems Ser.: Vol. 173). (Illus.). 107p. 1980. pap. 15.00 (ISBN 0-387-09729-5). Springer-Verlag.
Fabrycky, Walter J. & Thuesen, G. J. Economic Decision Analysis. 2nd ed. 1980. text ed. 31.95 (ISBN 0-13-223248-0). P-H.
Faere, R. Laws of Diminishing Returns. (Lecture Notes in Economics & Mathematical Systems Ser.: Vol. 176). (Illus.). 97p. 1980. pap. 15.00 (ISBN 0-387-09744-9). Springer-Verlag.
Franklin, J. Methods of Mathematical Economics, Linear & Nonlinear Economics: Fixed-Point Theories. (Undergraduate Texts in Mathematics Ser.). (Illus.). 297p. 1980. 29.00 (ISBN 0-387-90481-6). Springer-Verlag.
Gandolfo, G. Qualitative Analysis & Econometric Estimation of Continuous Time Dynamic Models. (Contributions to Economic Analysis Ser.: Vol. 136). 254p. 1981. 34.00 (ISBN 0-444-86025-8, North-Holland). Elsevier.
Garcia, Ramon J., et al. Principios y Metodos Estadisticos para Comercio y Economia (I) (Span.). 1980. text ed. 12.40 (ISBN 0-538-22810-5, V81). SW Pub.
--Principios y Metodos Estadisticos para Comercio y Economia (II) 1982. text ed. 12.40 (ISBN 0-538-22820-2, V82). SW Pub.
Glaister, Stephen. Mathematical Models for Economists. 3rd ed. 216p. 1984. pap. 12.95x (ISBN 0-631-13712-2). Basil Blackwell.
Haga, H. A Disequilibrium-Equilibrium Model with Money & Bonds: A Keynesian-Walrasian Synthesis. (Lecturenotes in Economics & Mathematical Systems Ser.: Vol. 135). 1976. soft cover 13.00 (ISBN 0-387-07992-0). Springer-Verlag.
Hammer, G. & Pallaschke, D., eds. Selected Topics in Operations Research & Mathematical Economics: Proceedings of the Eighth Symposium on Operations Research Held at the University of Karlsruhe, West Germany, August 22-25, 1984. (Lecture Notes in Economics & Mathematical Systems). ix, 478p. 1984. pap. 30.00 (ISBN 0-387-12918-9). Springer-Verlag.
Hehn, R. & Moeschlin, O., eds. Mathematical Economics & Game Theory: Essays in Honor of Oskar Morgenstern. LC 76-30791. (Lecture Notes in Economics & Mathematical Systems Ser.: Vol. 141). 1977. pap. 33.00 (ISBN 0-387-08063-5). Springer-Verlag.
Intriligator, Michael D. Mathematical Optimization & Economic Theory. (Mathematical Economics Ser.). 1971. text ed. 32.95 (ISBN 0-13-561753-7). P-H.
Kemp, C. & Kimura, Y. Introduction to Mathematical Economics. LC 77-26117. (Illus.). 1978. 29.50 (ISBN 0-387-90304-6). Springer-Verlag.
Kennedy, Gavin. Mathematics for Innumerate Economists. 134p. 1982. text ed. 34.50x (ISBN 0-8419-0777-3); pap. 15.50 (ISBN 0-8419-0789-7). Holmes & Meier.
Khoury, S. J. & Parsons, T. D. Mathematical Methods in Finance & Economics. 296p. 1981. 49.00 (ISBN 0-444-00425-4, North-Holland). Elsevier.
Kothari, C. R. Quantitative Techniques. 1979. text ed. 20.00x (ISBN 0-7069-0642-X, Pub. by Vikas India). Advent NY.
Kriens, J., ed. Convex Analysis & Mathematical Economics. (Lecture Notes in Economics & Mathematical Systems: Vol. 168). 1979. pap. 13.00 (ISBN 0-387-09247-1). Springer-Verlag.
Liu & Sutinen. Control Theory & Mathematical Economics, Pt. B. (Lecture Notes in Pure & Applied Mathematics Ser.: Vol. 47). 1979. 45.00 (ISBN 0-8247-6852-3). Dekker.
Makarov, V. L. & Rubinov, A. M. Mathematical Theory of Economical Dynamics & Equilibria. El-Hodiri, M., tr. from Rus. LC 76-15219. 1977. 55.00 (ISBN 0-387-90191-4). Springer-Verlag.
Mills, Gordon. Optimization in Economic Analysis. (Illus.). 208p. 1984. text ed. 27.50x (ISBN 0-04-311001-0); pap. text ed. 10.95 (ISBN 0-04-311002-9). Allen Unwin.
Onimode, B. & Osayimwese, Iz. Mathematics for Economics & Business. 250p. 1980. pap. text ed. 11.95 (ISBN 0-04-330304-8). Allen Unwin.
Ostrosky, Anthony L., Jr. & Koch, James V. Introduction to Mathematical Economics. LC 78-69569. (Illus.). 1979. text ed. 35.95 (ISBN 0-395-27052-9); solutions manual 1.50 (ISBN 0-395-27053-7). HM.
Paelinck, J. H. Qualitative & Quantitative Mathematical Economics. 1982. lib. bdg. 34.50 (ISBN 90-247-2623-9, Pub. by Martinus Nijhoff Netherlands). Kluwer Academic.
Paelinick, J. H., et al. Formal Spatial Economic Analysis. LC 83-6722. (Illus.). 404p. 1983. 25.00x (ISBN 0-566-00477-1, Pub. by Gower Pub Co England). Lexington Bks.
Rapoport, A., et al. Coalition Formation by Sophisticated Players. (Lecture Notes in Economics & Mathematical Systems: Vol. 169). 1979. pap. 14.00 (ISBN 0-387-09249-8). Springer-Verlag.
Razumikhin, B. S. Physical Models & Equilibrium Methods in Programming & Economics. (Mathematics & Its Applications Soviet Ser.). 372p. 1984. lib. bdg. 64.00 (ISBN 90-277-1644-7, Pub. by Reidel Holland). Kluwer Academic.
Roberts, Blaine & Schulze, David L. Modern Mathematics & Economic Analysis. 1973. study guide 4.95x (ISBN 0-393-09374-3). Norton.
Scalzo, Frank. Mathematics for Business & Economics With Computing. 1980. 27.00 (ISBN 0-89433-039-X). Petrocelli.
Shvyrkov, V. V. Statistical Science in Economics. LC 84-90294. (Illus.). 188p. (Orig.). 1984. wkbk. 19.99 (ISBN 0-942004-11-6). G Throwkoff.
Skolka, J. V., ed. Compilation of Input-Output Tables, Gouvieux, France, 1981: Proceedings. (Lecture Notes in Economics & Mathematical Sciences: Vol. 203). 307p. 1982. pap. 23.00 (ISBN 0-387-11553-6). Springer-Verlag.
Stewart, Jon. Understanding Econometrics. 1980. text ed. 18.75x (ISBN 0-09-126230-5, Hutchinson U Pr); pap. text ed. 11.25x (ISBN 0-09-126231-3). Humanities.
Telser, Lester G. & Graves, Robert L. Functional Analysis in Mathematical Economics: Optimization Over Infinite Horizons. LC 70-163718. 1972. 15.00x (ISBN 0-226-79190-4). U of Chicago Pr.
Theochares, Reghinos D. Early Developments in Mathematical Economics. rev. ed. LC 80-16638. 1983. lib. bdg. 25.00x (ISBN 0-87991-808-X). Porcupine Pr.

Tozer, John. Mathematical Investigation of the Effect of Machinery on the Wealth of a Community & On the Effect Of the Non-Residence of Landlords On the Wealth of a Community. LC 66-21696. 1968. 15.00x (ISBN 0-678-00300-9). Kelley.

U. S. - Italy Seminar on Variable Structure Systems, 2nd. Variable Structure Systems with Application to Economics & Biology: Proceedings. Mobler, R. R. & Ruberti, A., eds. (Lecture Notes in Economics & Mathematical Systems: Vol. 111). (Illus.). vi, 321p. 1975. pap. 20.00 (ISBN 0-387-07390-6). Springer-Verlag.

Weintraub, E. Roy. Mathematics for Economists: An Integrated Approach. LC 82-4244. 250p. 1982. 18.95 (ISBN 0-521-24535-4). Cambridge U Pr.

Woods, J. E. Mathematical Economics. LC 77-1660. (Modern Economics Ser.). pap. 94.50 (ISBN 0-317-28359-6). Bks Demand UMI.

Wycech-Los, M., et al, eds. Warsaw Fall Seminars in Mathematical Economics 1975. (Lecture Notes in Economics & Mathematical Systems Ser.: Vol. 133). 1976. pap. 13.00 (ISBN 0-387-07871-1). Springer-Verlag.

ECTOCARPACEAE

Cardinal, Andre. Etude Sur les Ectocarpacees de la Manche. (Illus.). 1965. pap. 21.00 (ISBN 3-7682-5415-1). Lubrecht & Cramer.

EDDINGTON, ARTHUR STANLEY, SIR, 1882-1944

Chandrasekhar, S. Eddington: The Most Distinguished Astrophysicist of His Time. 64p. 1984. 12.50 (ISBN 0-521-25746-8). Cambridge U Pr.

EDENTATA

see also Armadillos

Packard, Earl L. Fossil Edentates of Oregon. (Studies in Geology Ser: No. 8). 16p. 1952. pap. 3.95x (ISBN 0-87071-066-4). Oreg St U Pr.

EDIBLE FUNGI

see Mushrooms, Edible; Truffles

EDIBLE MUSHROOMS

see Mushrooms, Edible

EDIBLE OILS AND FATS

see Oils and Fats, Edible

EDIBLE PLANTS

see Plants, Edible

EDISON, THOMAS ALVA, 1847-1931

Crowther, James G. Famous American Men of Science. facs. ed. LC 69-18925. (Essay Index Reprint Ser). 1937. 27.50 (ISBN 0-8369-0040-5). Ayer Co Pubs.

Dethlefson, Ronald, ed. Edison Blue Amberol Recordings: 1915-1929. (Illus.). 512p. 1981. 49.50 (ISBN 0-686-78147-3). A P M Pr.

Ellis, Keith. Thomas Edison: Genius of Electricity. 99p. 1976. 9.95x (ISBN 0-8448-1010-X). Crane-Russak Co.

Frost, Lawrence A. The Thomas A. Edison Album. 25.95 (ISBN 0-89190-406-9, Pub. by Am Repr). Amereon Ltd.

Hendricks, Gordon. Origins of the American Film. LC 74-169345. (Arno Press Cinema Program). (Illus.). 600p. 1972. Repr. of 1971 ed. 37.50 (ISBN 0-405-03919-0). Ayer Co Pubs.

Hubbard, Elbert. Thomas Edison: A Study. 1979. pap. 2.00 (ISBN 0-932282-45-8). Caledonia Pr.

Josephson, Matthew. Edison. (Illus.). 1959. pap. 7.95 (ISBN 0-07-033046-8). McGraw.

Kurland, Gerald. Thomas Edison: Father of Electricity & Master Inventor of Our Modern Age. Rahmas, D. Steve, ed. LC 72-89210. (Outstanding Personalities Ser.: No. 46). 32p. 1972. lib. bdg. 3.50 incl. catalog cards (ISBN 0-87157-542-6); pap. 1.95 vinyl laminated covers (ISBN 0-87157-042-4). SamHar Pr.

Runes, Dagobert D., ed. Diary & Observations of Thomas Alva Edison. 1983. pap. 6.95 (ISBN 0-8022-2434-2). Philos Lib.

Vanderbilt, Byron M. Thomas Edison, Chemist. LC 75-172526. 1971. 12.95 (ISBN 0-8412-0129-3); pap. 8.95 (ISBN 0-8412-0534-5). Am Chemical.

Wachorst, Wyn. Thomas Alva Edison: An American Myth. (Illus.). 256p. 1981. 25.00x (ISBN 0-262-23108-5). MIT Pr.

EDISON EFFECT

see Thermionic Emission

EDTA

see Ethylenediaminetetraacetic Acid

EDUCATION–DATA PROCESSING

see also Computer-Assisted Instruction

Abelson, Robert B., ed. Using Microcomputers in the Social Studies Classroom. LC 83-14925. (Orig.). 1983. pap. 9.95 (ISBN 0-89994-282-2). Soc Sci Ed.

Adams, Dennis M., ed. Computers & Teacher Training: A Practical Guide. (Monographic Supplement to Computers in the Schools Ser.: Vol. 2). 152p. 1985. text ed. 22.95 (ISBN 0-86656-312-1, B312); 16.95 (ISBN 0-86656-378-4). Haworth Pr.

Alessi, Stephen M. & Trollip, Stanley. Computer-Based Instruction: Methods & Development. (Illus.). 480p. 1985. pap. text ed. 21.95 (ISBN 0-13-164161-1). P-H.

Archer, Doug, ed. Microcomputer CAI-ASE: An In-Service Module Computer Assisted Instruction-Applications for Special Education. 20p. 1981. pap. 2.15 (ISBN 0-318-03750-5); microfiche 0.97 (ISBN 0-318-03751-3). ERIC Clear.

Association of Educational Data Systems. Capitol-izing on Computers in Education: Proceedings. Martin, C. Dianne, ed. LC 84-7084. 1984. 35.95 (ISBN 0-88175-019-0). Computer Sci.

Automated Education Center. Automated Data Processing for Education-Curricular Implications. LC 79-119433. 29.00 (ISBN 0-403-04453-7). Scholarly.

--Computerized Educational Technology, Vol. 1. LC 79-119433. 25.00 (ISBN 0-403-04459-6). Scholarly.

--Computers in Education: Their Use & Cost. LC 78-119891. 25.00 (ISBN 0-403-04460-X). Scholarly.

--Establishing an Educational Data Processing Center. 29.00 (ISBN 0-403-04467-7). Scholarly.

Baker, Justine. Microcomputers in the Classroom. LC 82-60799. (Fastback Ser.: No. 179). 50p. 1982. pap. 1.50 (ISBN 0-87367-179-1). Phi Delta Kappa.

Banathy, Bela. Developing a Systems View of Education. (Systems Inquiry Ser.). 92p. (Orig.). 1980. pap. text ed. 9.95x (ISBN 0-914105-01-9). Intersystems Pubns.

Barrette, Pierre, ed. Microcomputers in K-Twelve Education, First Annual Conference Proceedings. LC 82-2522. 123p. 1982. pap. text ed. 30.00 (ISBN 0-914894-32-3). Computer Sci.

Behrmann, Michael M. & Lahm, Liz, eds. National Conference on the Use of Microcomputers in Special Education, Proceedings, Hartford, CT, March 10-12, 1983. 217p. 1984. 20.00 (ISBN 0-86586-149-8). Coun Exc Child.

Bennett, Randy E. & Maher, Charles A., eds. Microcomputers & Exceptional Children. (Speical Services in the Schools Ser.: Vol. 1, No. 1). 1984. text ed. 22.95 (ISBN 0-86656-297-4, B297); pap. text ed. 13.95 (ISBN 0-86656-440-3, B440). Haworth Pr.

Bork, Alfred. Personal Computers for Education. 179p. 1985. pap. text ed. 24.95 scp (ISBN 0-06-040868-5, HarpC). Har-Row.

Bozeman, William C. Computers & Computing in Education: An Introduction. (Illus.). 180p. 1985. pap. text ed. 14.95 (ISBN 0-89787-407-2). Gorsuch Scarisbrick.

Bruno, James E. Designing Education Information Systems Using 2BaseII & the Apple II: A Systems Guide to the Apple & dBase II. 250p. 1985. pap. text ed. 29.95 (ISBN 0-86542-314-8). Blackwell Pubns.

Buckleitner, Warren. Survey of Early Childhood Software. 100p. 1985. 19.95 (ISBN 0-931114-32-2). High-Scope.

Burns, Edward. TRS-80 Teaching Aid: Ready-to-Run Programs for the Classroom & Home. (Illus.). 1984. pap. 15.95 (ISBN 0-8359-7875-3). Reston.

Bushnell, Donald D. The Role of the Computer in Future Instructional Systems. 1963. 12.00 (ISBN 0-384-06720-4). Johnson Repr.

Caffarella, Edward. Spreadsheets Go to School: Applications for Administrators. 1985. 19.95 (ISBN 0-8359-7060-4). Reston.

Camuse, Ruth, ed. Fourth Annual Microcomputers in Education Conference: Literacy Plus. LC 84-17597. 465p. 1984. text ed. 35.00 (ISBN 0-88175-077-8). Computer Sci.

Chartrand, Marilyn J. & Williams, Constance D., eds. Educational Software Directory: A Subject Guide to Microcomputer Software. 1982. pap. text ed. 27.50 (ISBN 0-87287-352-8). Libs Unl.

Clay, Katherine, ed. Microcomputers in Education: A Handbook of Resources. LC 82-12596. 80p. 1982. pap. 27.50 (ISBN 0-89774-064-5). Oryx Pr.

Clements, Douglas H. Computers in Early & Primary Education. (Illus.). 352p. 1985. text ed. 17.95 (ISBN 0-13-164013-5). P-H.

Coburn, Peter, et al. A Practical Guide to Computers in Education. LC 82-1718. (Computers in Education Ser.). (Illus.). 192p. 1982. pap. text ed. 12.95 (ISBN 0-201-10563-2). Addison-Wesley.

Conference of the British Educational Research Association 1980. Microcomputers in Secondary Education: Proceedings. Howe, Jim & Ross, Peter, eds. 162p. 1981. pap. 23.50 (ISBN 0-89397-108-1). Nichols Pub.

Crick, Joe E. & Stolurow, Lawrence M. The Use of Computers in High Schools. LC 74-121200. 172p. 1965. 25.00 (ISBN 0-403-04492-8). Scholarly.

Culp, George & Nickles, Herbert N. An Apple for the Teacher: Fundamentals of Instructional Computing. 256p. 1983. pap. text ed. 14.00 pub net (ISBN 0-534-01378-3, 82-24506). Brooks-Cole.

Dennis, J. Richard & Kansky, Robert. Instructional Computing: An Action Guide for Educators. 1984. pap. 15.50x (ISBN 0-673-16606-6). Scott F.

Duggan, Michael A., et al, eds. The Computer Utility: Implications for Higher Education. LC 75-12104. 1969. 28.00x (ISBN 0-89197-708-2); pap. text ed. 14.95x (ISBN 0-89197-709-0). Irvington.

Educational Management System. McGraw-Hill Interactive Authoring System. 1984. write for info. (ISBN 0-07-019554-4). McGraw.

Educational Software Guide. 327p. 1984. 19.95 (ISBN 0-317-04399-4). Micro Info.

Educational Source Disk. 79.95 (ISBN 0-318-03616-9). Educational Assocs.

The Educational Technology Cartoon Book. LC 78-116648. 128p. 1970. pap. 24.95 (ISBN 0-87778-000-5). Educ Tech Pubns.

Eerkes. Classroom Records Software System: Apple Version. 1986. user's manual & software 29.95 (ISBN 0-538-10221-7, J221). SW Pub.

Favaro, P. J. An Educator's Guide to Microcomputers & Learning. (Illus.). 192p. 1985. 19.95 (ISBN 0-13-240839-2); pap. 14.95 (ISBN 0-13-240821-X). P-H.

Godfrey, David & Sterling, Sharon. The Elements of CAL. 1983. text ed. 22.95 (ISBN 0-8359-1701-0); pap. text ed. 17.95 (ISBN 0-8359-1700-2). Reston.

Gueulette, David G., ed. Microcomputers for Adult Learning: Potentials & Perils. 228p. pap. 29.27 (ISBN 0-8428-2205-4). Cambridge Bk.

Guide to Personal Computers in Education. Date not set. 1.95 (ISBN 0-317-04445-1, A9G0200). Apple Comp.

Gustafson, Thomas J. Microcomputers & Educational Administration. (Illus.). 240p. 1985. pap. text ed. 18.95 (ISBN 0-13-580267-9). P-H.

Halligan, Joseph. Education Administration Software. Winther, Richard, ed. (Software Directories Ser.: Vol. 1). (Orig.). 1985. pap. 29.95 (ISBN 0-918451-81-7). Moore Data.

--Education Courseware: Software. Winther, Richard, ed. (Software Directories Ser.: Vol. 2). (Orig.). 1985. pap. 49.95 (ISBN 0-918451-80-9). Moore Data.

Hamblen, John W. & Baird, Thomas B. Fourth Inventory of Computing in Higher Education: Statistical Report. 400p. 1979. 25.00 (ISBN 0-318-14024-1); members 15.00 (ISBN 0-318-14025-X). Educom.

Hansen, Viggo P., ed. Computers in Mathematics Education: 1984 Yearbook. LC 84-2037. (Illus.). 256p. 1984. 14.50 (ISBN 0-87353-210-4). NCTM.

Harlow, Steven, ed. Humanistic Perspectives on Computers in the Schools. LC 84-27986. (Computers in the Schools Series: Vol. 1, No. 4). 104p. 1985. text ed. 19.95 (ISBN 0-86656-397-0); pap. text ed. 14.95 (ISBN 0-86656-444-6). Haworth Pr.

Hentrel, Bobbie K. & Harper, Linda. Computers in Education: A Guide for Educators. 104p. 1985. pap. text ed. 7.95x (ISBN 0-472-08058-X). U of Mich Pr.

Hernandez-Logan, Carmella, et al. Computer Support for Education. Reed, R., ed. LC 81-84976. 90p. (Orig.). 1982. 10.95 (ISBN 0-88247-645-9); pap. 6.95 (ISBN 0-88247-635-1). R & E Pubs.

Hively, Wells, et al, eds. Hively's Choice: A Curriculum Guide to Outstanding Educational Microcomputer Programs for Preschool Through Grade 9 - School Year 1983-84. LC 83-73030. 1983. pap. 19.95 (ISBN 0-8454-8100-2). Continental Pr.

Hsiao, T. C., ed. Computer Faculty Directory (International Edition) LC 81-51818. 450p. 1985. 50.00x (ISBN 0-912291-09-5). Sci & Tech Pr.

Human Resources Research Organization. Academic Computing Directory: A Search for Exemplary Institutions Using Computers for Learning & Teaching. (Orig.). 1977. pap. write for info (ISBN 0-686-26204-2). Human Resources.

Hunter, Beverly, et al. Learning Alternatives in U. S. Education: Where Student & Computer Meet. LC 74-31417. 424p. 1975. 29.95 (ISBN 0-87778-078-1). Educ Tech Pubns.

IFIP World Conference, 2nd. Computers in Education: Proceedings. Lecarme, O. & Lewis, R., eds. 1020p. 1976. 106.50 (ISBN 0-444-10987-0, North-Holland). Elsevier.

International Resource Development Inc. Courseware & Software for Micros in Education. 174p. 1984. 1650.00x (ISBN 0-88694-602-6). Intl Res Dev.

Johnson, Cynthia. Microcomputer & the School Counselor. 125p. 1982. pap. text ed. 13.95 (ISBN 0-911547-55-X, 72245W34). Am Assn Coun Dev.

Joiner. Microcomputers in Education. 1985. 26.95 (ISBN 0-205-08211-4, 238211). Allyn.

Joiner, Lee M., et al. Microcomputers in Education. LC 81-84658. 320p. 1982. 24.95 (ISBN 0-918452-31-7); pap. text ed. 14.95 (ISBN 0-918452-46-5). Learning Pubns.

Jones, Ron, ed. Micros in the Primary Classroom. 128p. 1984. pap. text ed. 11.95 (ISBN 0-7131-0934-3). E Arnold.

Judd, Dorothy H. & Judd, Robert. Mastering the Micro: Using the Microcomputer in the Elementary Classroom. (YA) 1984. pap. 9.95 (ISBN 0-673-15909-4). Scott F.

Kanter, Harold M. Computer Applications of Educational Measurement Concepts. 160p. 1985. text ed. write for info. (ISBN 0-02-362700-X). Macmillan.

Kelly, A. V. Microcomputers & the Curriculum. 1984. pap. text ed. 11.00i (ISBN 0-06-318273-4). Har-Row.

Kepner, Henry S., Jr. Computers in the Classroom. 160p. 1982. 7.95 (ISBN 0-317-35376-4). NEA.

Kleiman, Glenn. Brave New Schools: How Computers Can Change Education. 1984. text ed. 18.95 (ISBN 0-8359-0527-6); pap. text ed. 14.95 (ISBN 0-8359-0526-8). Reston.

Kuchinskas, Gloria A. Micros in Your School: A Principal's Handbook for Implementing Microcomputer Education. LC 83-82892. (Illus.). 240p. (Orig.). 1984. pap. text ed. 19.95 (ISBN 0-918452-61-9). Learning Pubns.

Lathrop, Ann & Goodson, Bobby. Courseware in the Classroom: Selecting, Organizing, & Using Educational Software. 1983. pap. 9.95 (ISBN 0-201-20007-4, Sch Div). Addison-Wesley.

Lewis, B. & Tagg, E. D., eds. Computers in Education. 876p. 1982. 95.75 (ISBN 0-444-86255-2, North-Holland). Elsevier.

Lewis, R., ed. Involving Micros in Education: Proceedings of the IFIP TC 3 & University of Lancaster Joint Working Conference, Lancaster, England, March 24-26, 1982. 240p. 1982. 36.25 (ISBN 0-444-86459-8, North-Holland). Elsevier.

Lindelow, John. Administrator's Guide to Computers in the Classroom. LC 83-80834. x, 54p. (Orig.). 1983. pap. 5.50 (ISBN 0-86552-084-4). U of Oreg ERIC.

--Microcomputers in the School Office: Primer for Administrators. LC 84-81811. x, 42p. (Orig.). 1984. pap. 4.95 (ISBN 0-86552-087-9). U of Oreg ERIC.

Lippey, Gerald, ed. Computer-Assisted Test Construction. LC 74-11416. 260p. 1974. 26.95 (ISBN 0-87778-073-0). Educ Tech Pubns.

Lipsitz, Lawrence, ed. Technology & Education: Articles from Educational Technology Magazine. LC 79-125873. 192p. 1971. 23.95 (ISBN 0-87778-011-0). Educ Tech Pubns.

Little, Joseph R., et al, eds. Micros for Managers: A Software Guide for School Administrators. rev. ed. LC 84-62050. xxi, 298p. (Orig.). 1984. pap. 25.00 (ISBN 0-912337-05-2). NJ Schl Bds.

McCredie, John, ed. Campus Computing Strategies. 316p. 1983. 25.00 (ISBN 0-932376-20-7, EY-00009-DP). Digital Pr.

McKay, Anne. Computers in the Schools: The New Frontier. LC 85-106180. 66p. (Orig.). 1984. pap. 4.50 (ISBN 0-88156-027-8). Comm Serv Soc Ny.

McKenzie, J., et al, eds. Interactive Computer Graphics in Science Teaching. LC 78-40598. (Computers & Their Applications Ser.). 247p. 1978. 42.95x (ISBN 0-470-26419-5). Halsted Pr.

Maddison, John. Education in the Microelectronics Era. LC 99-943832. 208p. 1983. pap. 13.00x (ISBN 0-335-10182-8, Pub. by Open Univ Pr). Taylor & Francis.

Maffi, Anthony C. Classroom Computers: A Practical Guide for Effective Teaching. (Illus.). 219p. 1985. 29.95 (ISBN 0-89885-251-X); pap. 16.95 (ISBN 0-89885-255-2). Human Sci Pr.

Masie, Elliott & Stein, Michele. Using Computers in High School Student Activities. (National Student Leadership Center Ser.). 104p. (Orig.). 1984. pap. 12.95 (ISBN 0-913393-15-0). Sagamore.

Mayo, Jack, ed. Campus Computers of California. 300p. cancelled. Bernardo Press.

Megarry, Jacquetta, et al, eds. World Yearbook of Education, 1982-83: Computers & Education. LC 82-12414. (Illus.). 350p. 1983. 36.00 (ISBN 0-89397-138-3). Nichols Pub.

Microcomputers Directory: Applications in Educational Settings. 1983. write for info. Harvard U Pr.

Microcomputers Go to School. LC 84-123. 180p. 1984. pap. text ed. 16.95 (ISBN 0-931028-53-1). Teach'em.

Microcomputers in Education. (Reports Ser.: No. 538). 191p. 1983. 985.00x (ISBN 0-88694-538-0). Intl Res Dev.

Miller, Inabeth. Microcomputers in School Library Media Centers. 165p. 1984. pap. 19.95x (ISBN 0-918212-51-0). Neal-Schuman.

Miller, Joan M. & Chaya, Ruth K. BASIC Programming for the Classroom & Home Teacher. 262p. 1982. pap. text ed. 17.95x (ISBN 0-8077-2728-8). Tchrs Coll.
Milner, Joseph O., ed. Micro to Main Frame Computers in English Education. 41p. 1982. pap. 3.00 (ISBN 0-8141-3156-5). NCTE.
Mosmann, Charles. Academic Computers in Service: Effective Uses for Higher Education. LC 72-13602. (Higher Education Ser.). 1973. 19.95x (ISBN 0-87589-161-6). Jossey-Bass.
Mowe, Richard & Ronald, Mummaw. The Academic Commodore 64. 1984. pap. text ed. 15.95 (ISBN 0-8359-0017-7). Reston.
Muscat, E. & Lorton, P. Microcomputer Applications for the Data Processing Work Kit TRS-80 Diskette. (Microcomputer Software Ser.). 1982. 99.00 (ISBN 0-07-044107-3); Apple II Plus Version. 99.00 (ISBN 0-07-044108-1); user's guide 4.80 (ISBN 0-07-044109-X). McGraw.
Nibeck, Richard G., intro. by. Learning with Microcomputers, Readings from Instructional Innovator-5. 80p. 1983. pap. 10.95 (ISBN 0-89240-042-0). Assn Ed Comm Tech.
Patterson, Jerry L. & Patterson, Janice H. Putting Computer Power in Schools: A Step-by-Step Approach. LC 83-8017. 227p. 1983. 17.95 (ISBN 0-13-744474-5, Busn); pap. 12.95 (ISBN 0-13-744467-2). P-H.
Piele, Philip K. Local Area Networks in Education: Overview, Applications, & Current Limitations. LC 85-70944. viii, 35p. (Orig.). 1985. pap. 4.00 (ISBN 0-86552-090-9). U of Oreg ERIC.
Pogrow, Stanley. Computer Decisions for Board Members: Getting the Most from What Your District Selects. LC 85-50953. 250p. (Orig.). 1985. pap. text ed. 18.95 (ISBN 0-931028-70-1). Teach'em.
Radin, Stephen & Lee, Fayvian. Computers in the Classroom: A Survival Guide for Teachers. 296p. 1984. pap. text ed. 16.95 (ISBN 0-574-23105-6, 13-6105). SRA.
Ragsdale, Ronald G. Computers in the Schools. 107p. 1982. 8.25 (ISBN 0-7744-5056-8, 1273). Ont ISE.
Ramsden, E. & Green, R. N. Microcomputers in Education: Commodore in the Classroom. (Computers & Their Applications Ser.). 206p. 1984. 29.95 (ISBN 0-470-20121-5). Halsted Pr.
Razik, Taher A., ed. Bibliography of Programmed Instruction & Computer Assisted Instruction. LC 76-125875. (Educational Technology Bibliography Ser.: Vol.1). 288p. 1971. 26.95 (ISBN 0-87778-013-7). Educ Tech Pubns.
Readings in Microcomputers & Special Education. 1984. 16.00 (ISBN 0-89568-445-4). Spec Learn Corp.
Rodenstein, Judith. Microcomputers in Vocational Education: Programs & Practices. (Illus.). 224p. 1986. pap. text ed. 16.95 (ISBN 0-13-580507-4). P-H.
Roman, Richard A. Teaching Problem Solving & Mathematics by Computer: An Interim Report. 63p. 1974. 1.50 (ISBN 0-318-14743-2, ED 101 690). Learn Res Dev.
Ross, Steven M. BASIC Programming for Educators. (Illus.). 400p. 1986. pap. text ed. 21.95 (ISBN 0-13-066127-9). P H.
Rushton, James & Reid, Ivan, eds. Teachers, Computers & the Classroom. LC 85-2896. 1985. pap. 11.00 (ISBN 0-7190-1774-2, Pub. by Manchester Univ Pr). Longwood Pub Group.
Russell, Terry. Computers in the Primary School. (Illus., Orig.). 1985. pap. 19.95 (ISBN 0-7121-0451-8). Trans Atlantic.
Sauve, Deborah. Guide to Microcomputer Courseware for Bilingual Education. rev. & expanded ed. LC 84-63153. 304p. 1985. pap. 11.00 (ISBN 0-317-20692-3). Natl Clearinghse Bilingual Ed.
Saville, Anthony. Instructional Programming: Issues & Innovations in School Scheduling. LC 72-84125. 1973. text ed. 12.50x (ISBN 0-675-09064-4). Merrill.
Sedlik, Jay M. Systems Engineering of Education: Systems Techniques for Pretesting Mediated Instructional Materials, No. 14. LC 79-162916. (Illus.). 1971. text ed. 18.00 (ISBN 0-87657-112-7). Ed & Training.
Silvern, Leonard C. Systems Engineering of Education: Application of Systems Thinking to the Administration of Instruction, 2 vols, No. 2. LC 75-27690. (Illus.). 178p. 1976. 25.00 (ISBN 0-87657-114-3). Ed & Training.
--Systems Engineering of Education: General Systems Model for Effective Curriculums, No. 7. (Illus.). 1971. incl. cassettes & charts 25.00 (ISBN 0-87657-120-8). Ed & Training.
--Systems Engineering of Education: Model for Producing a System, No. 11. 1970. Set. 20.00 (ISBN 0-87657-109-7); slides & cassette incl. Ed & Training.
--Systems Engineering of Education: Simulating a Real-Life Problem on the General System Model for Effective Curriculums, No. 15. (Illus.). 1972. incl. wrkbk. 2 cassettes & 1 chart 30.00 (ISBN 0-87657-121-6). Ed & Training.
--Systems Engineering of Education: Synthesis As a Process, No. 16. LC 73-76218. 1973. incl. slides & cassette 40.00 (ISBN 0-87657-122-4). Ed & Training.
--Systems Engineering of Education: Systems Analysis & Synthesis Applied to Occupational Instruction in Secondary Schools, No. 3. LC 67-31679. (Illus.). 99p. 1967. text ed. 10.00 (ISBN 0-87657-123-2). Ed & Training.
--Systems Engineering of Education: Systems Analysis & Synthesis Applied Quantitatively to Create an Instructional System, No. 4. LC 65-27696. (Illus.). 120p. 1969. text ed. 18.00 (ISBN 0-87657-124-0). Ed & Training.
--Systems Engineering of Education: System Conceptualizations, No. 17. 1973. 80.00, incl. cassette & slides (ISBN 0-87657-125-9). Ed & Training.
Smith, I. C. Microcomputers in Education. LC 81-20176. (Computers & Their Applications Ser.). 212p. 1982. 34.95x (ISBN 0-470-27362-3). Halsted Pr.
Sordillo, Donald A. The Personal Computer BASIC(s) Reference Manual. (Illus.). 320p. 1983. pap. text ed. 18.95 (ISBN 0-13-658047-5). P-H.
Spangenburg & Moser. Educational Software. 1984. write for info. (ISBN 0-534-03329-6). Wadsworth Pub.
Spencer, Richard E., et al, eds. MERMAC Manual: Test & Questionnaire Analysis Programs Written for the IBM System-360. LC 71-131006. 1971. pap. 10.00 (ISBN 0-252-00131-1); computer program 800.00 (ISBN 0-252-00227-X); non-profit institions 460.00 (ISBN 0-252-00205-9); supplement to manual 4.95 (ISBN 0-252-00651-8). U of Ill Pr.
Standiford, Sally N., et al. Computers in the English Classroom: A Primer for Teachers. 56p. 1983. pap. 5.50 (ISBN 0-8141-0818-0); pap. 4.75 members. NCTE.
Suppes, Patrick & Morningstar, Mona. Computer-Assisted Instruction at Stanford, 1966-68. 1972. 52.00 (ISBN 0-12-676856-0). Acad Pr.
Suppes, Patrick C., et al. Computer-Assisted Instruction: Stanford's 1965-66 Arithmetic Program. (Illus.). 1968. 52.00 (ISBN 0-12-676850-1). Acad Pr.
Swartz, Theodore F., et al. Educator's Complete Guide to Computers. LC 83-19335. 280p. 1984. 19.95 (ISBN 0-13-240813-9, Parker). P-H.
Tagg, D., ed. Microcomputers in Secondary Education: Proceedings of the IFIP TC3 Working Conference, Sevres, Paris, France, April 1980. 152p. 1980. 30.00 (ISBN 0-444-86047-9, North-Holland). Elsevier.
Tanner, C. Kenneth & Holmes, C. Thomas. Microcomputer Applications in Educational Planning & Decision Making. (Computers in Education Ser.). 1985. text ed. 25.95x (ISBN 0-8077-2766-0). Tchrs Coll.
Tashner, John, ed. Improving Instruction with Microcomputers: Readings & Resources for Elementary & Secondary Schools. LC 83-42502. 272p. 1984. pap. 28.50x (ISBN 0-89774-095-5). Oryx Pr.
Tashner, John H., ed. Educational Microcomputing Annual: Vol. 1, 1985. LC 84-42811. 200p. 1985. pap. 28.50 (ISBN 0-89774-169-2). Oryx Pr.
The Teacher's Pal: A Test Generator & Gradekeeper for the Microcomputer. 1985. incl. software 59.50 (ISBN 0-538-10091-5, J091-2). SW Pub.
Terry, Colin, ed. Using Microcomputers in Schools. 224p. 1984. 28.50 (ISBN 0-89397-172-3); pap. 14.50 (ISBN 0-89397-229-0). Nichols Pub.
Terry, Patricia J. How to Use Computers with Gifted Students: Creative Microcomputing in a Differentiated Curriculum. (Genesis Ser.). (Illus.). 47p. (Orig.). 1984. pap. 10.00 (ISBN 0-910609-06-3). Reading Tutor.
Tessier, Judith & Settel, Barbara. Education. Mignon, Edmond, ed. LC 81-67092. (Print Samples Ser.: Vol. 4). 180p. (Orig.). 1981. pap. 25.00 (ISBN 0-939920-04-2). Database Serv.
Thomas, James L., ed. Microcomputers in the Schools. 178p. 1981. lib. bdg. 32.50x (ISBN 0-89774-001-7); pap. 27.50x (ISBN 0-89774-017-3). Oryx Pr.
Thomason, Nevada. Circulation Systems for School Media Centers: A Manual to Microcomputers. (Illus.). 250p. 1985. lib. bdg. 23.50 (ISBN 0-87287-370-6). Libs Unl.
Thorson, Esther, ed. Simulation in Higher Education: Papers from the Denison Simulation Center, Denison University, Granville, Ohio. 1979. 15.00 (ISBN 0-682-49122-5, University). Exposition Pr FL.
TRS-80 Educational Software Sourcebook. 1983. pap. 6.95 (ISBN 0-318-01175-1). Radio Shack.
TRS-80 Microcomputer Information Handbook for Educators. 1981. pap. 2.50 (ISBN 0-318-01174-3). Radio Shack.
Valett, Robert E. Remediation of Learning Disabilities: A Handbook of Psychoeducational Resource Programs. 2nd ed. LC 67-26847. 1974. 3-ring bdg. o.p. 24.50; pap. 18.50 (ISBN 0-8224-5851-9). Pitman Learning.
VanDiver, Gerald. The IBM PC & XT Educational Software Guide. 124p. 1984. 5.95 (ISBN 0-912603-03-8). Micro Info.
Van Dusen, William D., et al. The CSS Guide to Implementing Financial Aid Data Processing Systems. 56p. (Orig.). 1980. pap. 8.95 (ISBN 0-87447-134-6). College Bd.
Watson, Paul G. Using the Computer in Education: A Briefing for School Decision Makers. LC 72-86779. 144p. 1972. pap. 13.95 (ISBN 0-87778-042-0). Educ Tech Pubns.
Wayth, Peter J. Using Microcomputers in the Primary School. 175p. 1983. text ed. 21.90x (ISBN 0-566-03480-8). Gower Pub Co.
Wells, Robert P. The Quick & Easy Guide to Educational Software on the Apple. 128p. pap. 4.95 (ISBN 0-912003-27-8). Bk Co.
Wildenberg, D., ed. Computer Simulation in University Teaching. 264p. 1981. 42.75 (ISBN 0-444-86142-4). Elsevier.
Wilkinson, Alex C., ed. Classroom Computers & Cognitive Science. (Educational Technology Ser.). 1983. 28.00 (ISBN 0-12-752070-8). Acad Pr.
Williams, Frederick & Williams, Victoria. Success with Educational Software. LC 85-5679. 192p. 1985. 32.95 (ISBN 0-03-003687-9). Praeger.
Willis, Jerry & Johnson, D. Lamont. Computers, Teaching & Learning: A Guide to Using Computers in Schools. (Illus.). 272p. 1983. pap. 12.95 (ISBN 0-88056-065-7). Dilithium Pr.
Wilson, D. R. & Van Spronsen, C. J., eds. Microcomputers: Developments in Industry, Business & Education. 426p. 1984. 61.75 (ISBN 0-444-86742-2, North-Holland). Elsevier.
Zender, Bryce F. Computers & Education in the Soviet Union. LC 75-19470. 184p. 1975. 26.95 (ISBN 0-87778-082-X). Educ Tech Pubns.

EDUCATION–MATHEMATICAL MODELS

Landa, L. N. Algorithmization in Learning & Instruction. Kopstein, Felix F., ed. Bennett, Virginia, tr. from Rus. LC 73-11044. 752p. 1974. Repr. of 1966 ed. 37.95 (ISBN 0-87778-063-3). Educ Tech Pubns.
Wholeben, Brent E. The Design, Implementation & Evaluation of Mathematical Modeling Procedures for Decisioning Among Educational Alternatives. LC 80-5437. 474p. 1980. lib. bdg. 31.00 (ISBN 0-8191-1093-0); pap. text ed. 19.00 (ISBN 0-8191-1094-9). U Pr of Amer.

EDUCATIONAL TECHNOLOGY

see also Computer-Assisted Instruction

American Association of School Admin. High Tech for Schools: Problems & Solutions. Neill, Shirley B., ed. 96p. (Orig.). 1984. pap. 12.95 (ISBN 0-87652-076-X). Am Assn Sch Admin.
Association for Educational Communications & Technology. Task Force on Definition & Terminology. Educational Technology: A Glossary of Terms. Silber, Kenneth, ed. LC 79-53125. 1979. pap. text ed. 21.00 (ISBN 0-89240-007-2); pap. text ed. 18.00 members. Assn Ed Comm Tech.
Association for Programmed Learning & Educational Technology Conference, 1979. Aspects of Educational Technology, Vol. XIII: Educational Technology Twenty Years On. Page, G. Terry & Whitlock, Quentin, eds. 1979. 36.00 (ISBN 0-85038-247-5). Nichols Pub.
Automated Education Center. Automated Data Processing for Education-Curricular Implications. LC 79-119433. 29.00 (ISBN 0-403-04453-7). Scholarly.
Bates, A. W., ed. The Role of Technology in Distance Education. LC 84-40035. 231p. 1984. 25.00 (ISBN 0-312-68942-X). St Martin.
Blackwell, Deborah J. Telecommunications & Education. 1974. pap. 4.00x (ISBN 0-89011-467-6, TEC-103). Abt Bks.
Cline, Hugh F., et al, eds. The Electronic Schoolhouse. 148p. 1985. text ed. 16.50 (ISBN 0-89859-649-1). L Erlbaum Assocs.
Computer Assisted Learning Symposium, 1981. Computer Assisted Learning: Selected Proceedings. Smith, P. R., ed. (Journal of Computers & Education Ser.: No. 6). 150p. 1981. 36.00 (ISBN 0-08-028111-7). Pergamon.
Cuban, Larry. Teachers & Machines: The Classroom Use of Technology. 112p. 1985. pap. text ed. 8.95x (ISBN 0-8077-2792-X). Tchrs Coll.
DeBloois, Michael L., ed. Videodisc-Microcomputer Courseware Design. LC 81-22161. 192p. 1982. 26.95 (ISBN 0-87778-183-4). Educ Tech Pubns.
The Definition of Educational Technology. LC 79-53125. 1979. pap. 10.95 (ISBN 0-89240-006-4); pap. 8.95 members. Assn Ed Comm Tech.
Directory of Resources for Technology in Education, 1984. 242p. (Orig.). 1984. 19.95 (ISBN 0-914409-02-6); pap. 12.95. Far West Lab.
Durnin, John. Toward Educational Engineering. LC 81-40101. (Illus.). 134p. (Orig.). 1982. PLB 21.75 (ISBN 0-8191-2435-4); pap. text ed. 9.50 (ISBN 0-8191-2436-2). U Pr of Amer.
Ellington, H. I., et al. Games & Simulations in Science Education. 180p. 1981. 27.50x (ISBN 0-89397-093-X). Nichols Pub.
Eraut, Michael, et al. Training in Curriculum Development & Educational Technology. 92p. 1981. 18.00 (ISBN 0-900868-77-5). Taylor & Francis.
Evans & Leedham, ed. Aspects of Educational Technology, Vol. IX. 308p. 1975. 35.00 (ISBN 0-85038-291-2). Nichols Pub.
Glossary of Educational Technology Terms. (IBEDATA Ser.). (Eng. & Fr.). 250p. 1985. pap. 14.50 (ISBN 92-3-002189-X, U1410, UNESCO). Unipub.
Green, Douglas A. An Index to Collected Essays on Educational Media & Technology. LC 81-18249. 197p. 1982. 15.00 (ISBN 0-8108-1490-0). Scarecrow.
Hawkridge, David G. New Information Technology in Education. 256p. 1983. 20.00x (ISBN 0-8018-2980-1). Johns Hopkins.
Hepburn, Mary A., ed. New Information Technology in Social Science Education: Viewpoints from Europe & the U. S. 227p. (Orig.). 1985. pap. 10.00 (ISBN 0-89994-301-2). Soc Sci Ed.
Hills, Philip, ed. Aspects of Educational Technology XI: The Spread of Educational Technology. Gilbert, John. 474p. 1977. 36.00x (ISBN 0-85038-093-6, Pub by Kogan Pg). Nichols Pub.
Hughes, Phillip. Social & Technological Interaction with Education. (APEID Occasional Papers: No. 13). 22p. 1985. pap. 5.00 (UB156, UB). Unipub.
Huntington, John F. Computer-Assisted Instruction Using BASIC. LC 79-539. (Illus.). 240p. 1979. 26.95 (ISBN 0-87778-135-4). Educ Tech Pubns.
Joyce, Bruce, et al. The Structure of School Improvement. (Illus.). 304p. 1983. text ed. 18.95 (ISBN 0-582-28092-3). Longman.
Knapper, Christopher K. Evaluating Instructional Technology. (New Pattern in Learning Ser.). 163p. 1980. 37.95x (ISBN 0-470-26994-4). Halsted Pr.
Liao, Thomas T. & Miller, David C., eds. Systems Approach to Instructional Design. LC 77-86497. (Technology of Learning Systems Ser.: Vol. 1). (Illus.). 1978. pap. 10.00x (ISBN 0-89503-004-7). Baywood Pub.
Lindelow, John. Administrator's Guide to Computers in the Classroom. LC 83-80834. x, 54p. (Orig.). 1983. pap. 5.50 (ISBN 0-86552-084-4). U of Oreg ERIC.
Miller, Elwood E., ed. Educational Media & Technology Yearbook: 1985. 400p. 1985. lib. bdg. 47.50 (ISBN 0-87287-446-X). Libs Unl.
National Academy of Engineering. Educational Technology in Engineering. 1981. pap. text ed. 6.50 (ISBN 0-309-03138-9). Natl Acad Pr.
National Conference on Technology & Education, January 26-28, 1981. Technology & Education: Policy, Implementation, Evaluation-Proceedings. 340p. 1981. lib. bdg. 20.00 (ISBN 0-318-03015-2). Inst Educ Lead.
New Trends in the Utilization of Educational Technology for Science Education. (Illus.). 248p. (Orig.). 1975. pap. 13.25 (ISBN 92-3-101143-X, U428, UNESCO). Unipub.
O'Neil, Harold F., ed. Procedures for Instructional Systems Development. LC 79-12002. (Educational Technology Ser.). 1979. 32.50 (ISBN 0-12-526660-X). Acad Pr.
O'Neil, Harold F., Jr., ed. Issues in Instructional Systems Development. 224p. 1979. 27.50 (ISBN 0-12-526640-5). Acad Pr.
Osborne, C. W., ed. International Yearbook of Educational & Instructional Technology 1984-1985. 450p. 1984. 38.50 (ISBN 0-89397-188-X). Nichols Pub.
--International Yearbook of Educational & Instructional Technology 1984-85. 450p. 1984. 37.50 (ISBN 0-89397-188-X). Taylor & Francis.
Poirot, James L. Computers & Education. (Illus.). 96p. (Orig.). 1980. pap. 6.95 (ISBN 0-88408-137-0). Sterling Swift.
Professional Development & Educational Technology. LC 80-81616. 1980. 15.00 (ISBN 0-89240-036-6); members 13.50. Assn Ed Comm Tech.
Rostron, Andrew & Sewell, David. Microtechnology in Special Education. LC 83-18723. 256p. 1984. text ed. 25.00x (ISBN 0-8018-3215-2). Johns Hopkins.

Panovko, Ya. G. & Gubanova, I. I. Stability & Oscillations of Elastic Systems: Paradoxes, Fallacies, & New Concepts. LC 65-11341. 291p. 1965. 40.00x (ISBN 0-306-10735-X, Consultants). Plenum Pub.
Rapoport, I. M. Dynamics of Elastic Containers Partially Filled with Liquid. Abramson, H. N., tr. LC 68-22689. (Applied Physics & Engineering: Vol. 5). 1968. 48.00 (ISBN 0-387-04051-X). Springer-Verlag.
Teodorescu, P. Dynamics of Linear Elastic Bodies. 1975. 30.00 (ISBN 0-9961000-2-4, Pub. by Abacus England). Heyden.
Truesdale, C., ed. Mechanics of Solids, Vol. 4: Waves in Elastic & Viscoelastic Solids (Theory & Experiment) (Illus.). 350p. 1984. pap. 28.50 (ISBN 0-387-13163-9). Springer-Verlag.
Truesdell, C., ed. Mechanics of Solids, Theory of Viscoelasticity, Plasticity, Elastic Waves, & Elastic Stability, Vol. 3. (Illus.). 600p. 1984. pap. 32.00 (ISBN 0-387-13162-0). Springer-Verlag.
--Mechanics of Solids, Vol. 2: Linear Theories of Elasticity & Thermoelasticity, Linear & Nonlinear Theories of Rods, Plates, & Shells. (Illus.). 760p. 1984. pap. 34.50 (ISBN 0-387-13161-2). Springer-Verlag.
Wempner, Gerald. Mechanics of Solids with Application to Thin Bodies, No. 2. (Mechanics of Elastics & Viscoelastic Solids Ser.). 620p. Date not set. 79.00x. Sijthoff & Noordhoff.

ELASTIC SOLIDS–THERMAL PROPERTIES
see Thermoelasticity

ELASTIC WAVES
see also Aeroelasticity; Elastic Plates and Shells; Elastic Solids; Internal Friction; Seismic Waves; Stress Waves; Underground Nuclear Explosions

Dieulesaint, E. & Royer, D. Elastic Waves in Solids: Applications to Signal Processing. LC 80-49980. 511p. 1981. 74.95x (ISBN 0-471-27836-X, Pub. by Wiley-Interscience). Wiley.
Fedorov, Fedor I. Theory of Elastic Waves in Crystals. LC 65-27349. 375p. 1968. 49.50x (ISBN 0-306-30309-4, Plenum Pr). Plenum Pub.
Haszpra, Otto. Modelling Hydroelastic Vibrations. (Water Resources Engineering Ser.). 136p. 1979. text ed. 29.95x (ISBN 0-273-08441-0). Pitman Pub MA.
Hudson, J. A. The Excitation & Propagation of Elastic Waves. LC 79-4505. (Monographs on Mechanics & Applied Mathematics Ser.). (Illus.). 1980. 49.50 (ISBN 0-521-22777-1). Cambridge U Pr.
--The Excitation & Propagation of Elastic Waves. (Illus.). 234p. pap. 19.95 (ISBN 0-521-31867-X). Cambridge U Pr.
Ivakin, B. N. The Microstructure & Macrostructure of Elastic Waves in One-Dimensional Continous Nonhomogeneous Media. LC 60-9253. (Soviet Research in Geophysics in English Translation Ser.: Vol. 3). pap. 30.30 (ISBN 0-317-08395-3, 2020661). Bks Demand UMI.
Konopinski, Emil J. Classical Descriptions of Motion: The Dynamics of Particle Trajectories, Rigid Rotations, & Elastic Waves. LC 71-75626. (A Series of Books in Physics). pap. 129.30 (ISBN 0-317-12988-0, 2055550). Bks Demand UMI.
Kunin, I. A. Elastic Media with Microstructure I: One-Dimensional Models. (Springer Series in Solid-State Sciences: Vol. 26). (Illus.). 291p. 1982. 48.00 (ISBN 0-387-11145-X). Springer-Verlag.
Miklowitz, J. The Theory of Elastic Waves & Waveguides. (Applied Mathematics & Mechanics Ser.: Vol. 22). 618p. 1978. 95.75 (ISBN 0-7204-0551-3, North-Holland). Elsevier.
Miklowitz Symposium at Northwestern Univ. Sept, & Miklowitz, Juluis. Modern Problems in Elastic Wave Propagation. 561p. 1978. 71.95x (ISBN 0-471-04696-5, Pub. by Wiley-Interscience). Wiley.
Santosa, Fadil, et al, eds. Inverse Problems of Acoustic & Elastic Waves. LC 84-52372. (Illus.). ix, 365p. 1984. text ed. 38.50 (ISBN 0-89871-050-2). Soc Indus Appl Math.
Steklov Institute of Mathematics, Academy of Sciences, U. S. S. R. No. 95. Asymptotic Methods & Stochastic Models in Problems of Wave Propagation: Proceedings. Petrasen, G. I. & Latysev, K. P., eds. (Proceedings of the Steklov Institute of Mathematics: No.95). 1971. 43.00 (ISBN 0-8218-1895-3, STEKLO-95). Am Math.
Vernon, James B. Linear Vibration Theory: Generalized Properties & Numerical Methods. pap. 95.30 (ISBN 0-317-09206-5, 2007405). Bks Demand UMI.
Wasley, Richard J. Stress Wave Propagation in Solids. (Monographs & Textbooks in Material Science: Vol. 7). 328p. 1973. 65.00 (ISBN 0-8247-6039-5). Dekker.
Wessel, E. T. & Loss, F. J., eds. Elastic-Plastic Fracture Test Methods - STP 856: The User's Experience. LC 84-70607. (Illus.). 430p. 1985. text ed. 49.00 (ISBN 0-8031-0419-7, 04-856000-30). ASTM.

ELASTICITY
see also Aeroelasticity; Continuum Mechanics; Elastic Plates and Shells; Elastic Waves; Photoelasticity; Plasticity; Plates (Engineering); Shells; Strains and Stresses; Strength of Materials; Thermoelasticity; Viscoelasticity

Achenbach, J. D. A Theory of Elasticity with Microstructure for Directionally Reinforced Composites. (International Centre for Mechanical Sciences Courses & Lectures: No. 167). (Illus.). 1976. pap. 24.00 (ISBN 0-387-81234-2). Springer-Verlag.
Amenzade, Y. W. The Theory of Elasticity. 284p. 1979. 8.45 (ISBN 0-8285-1522-0, Pub. by Mir Pubs USSR). Imported Pubns.
American Society of Mechanical Engineers, Applied Mechanics Division. Finite Elasticity: Presented at the Winter Annual Meeting of American Society of Mechanical Engineerings, Atlanta, Georgia, 1977. Rivlin, R. S., ed. LC 77-89014. (American Society of Mechanical Engineers: AMD; Vol. 27). pap. 39.50 (ISBN 0-317-13000-5, 2020934). Bks Demand UMI.
Blazynski, T. Z. Applied Elasto-Plasticity of Solids. (Illus.). 272p. 1984. text ed. 39.50x (ISBN 0-317-18202-1). Scholium Intl.
Brown, William F., Jr. Magnetoelastic Interactions. (Springer Tracts in Natural Philosophy: Vol. 9). (Illus.). 1966. 39.00 (ISBN 0-387-03674-1). Springer-Verlag.
Carlson, D. & Shield, R., eds. Finite Elasticity. 1982. lib. bdg. 79.00 (ISBN 90-247-2629-8, Pub. by Martinus Nijhoff Netherlands). Kluwer Academic.
Ciarlet, P. G. Lectures on Three-Dimensional Elasticity. (Tata Institute Lectures on Mathematics). 160p. 1983. pap. 7.90 (ISBN 0-387-12331-8). Springer-Verlag.
CISM (International Center for Mechanical Sciences), Dept. for Mechanics of Deformable Bodies, 1970. Theory of Popular Elasticity: Proceedings. Nowacki, W., ed. (CISM Pubns. Ser.: No. 25). (Illus.). 286p. 1974. pap. 27.20 (ISBN 0-387-81078-1). Springer-Verlag.
Clarkson, James. The Elastic Analysis of Flat Grillages: With Particular Reference to Ship Structures. LC 65-16200. (Cambridge Engineering Ser.). pap. 35.80 (ISBN 0-317-08721-5, 2050786). Bks Demand UMI.
Clebsch, Alfred. Theorie De L'elasticite Des Corps Solides. 1883. 60.00 (ISBN 0-384-09285-3). Johnson Repr.
Cyras, A. A. Mathematical Models for the Analysis & Optimization of Elastoplastic Structures. (Series in Civil & Mechanical Engineering: 1-622). 121p. 1983. text ed. 39.95x (ISBN 0-470-20020-0). Halsted Pr.
De Veubeke, B. M. A Course in Elasticity. (Applied Mathematical Sciences Ser.: Vol. 29). (Illus.). 1979. 22.95 (ISBN 0-387-90428-X). Springer-Verlag.
Dugdale, D. S. Elements of Elasticity. 1968. 25.00 (ISBN 0-08-012634-0); pap. 11.25 (ISBN 0-08-012633-2). Pergamon.
Dunn, A. S. Rubber & Rubber Elasticity, No. 48. (Journal of Polymer Science: Polymer Symposia). 232p. 1974. pap. 15.00 (ISBN 0-685-88107-5, Pub. by Wiley). Krieger.
Eringen, A. Cemal & Suhubi, Erdogan S. Elastodynamics. 1974. Vol. 1. 1974. 78.00 (ISBN 0-12-240601-X); Vol. 2. 1975. 119.50 (ISBN 0-12-240602-8). Acad Pr.
Fung, Y. C. Foundations of Solid Mechanics. 1965. ref. ed. 41.95 (ISBN 0-13-329912-0). P-H.
Gladwell, G. M. Contact Problems in the Classical Theory of Elasticity. (Mechanics of Elastic & Viscoelastic Solids Ser.). 716p. 1980. 60.00x (ISBN 9-0286-0440-5); pap. 35.00x (ISBN 9-0286-0760-9). Sijthoff & Noordhoff.
Gould, P. L. Introduction to Linear Elasticity. (Illus.). 195p. 1983. 24.00 (ISBN 0-387-90876-5). Springer Verlag.
Gurtin, M. E. On the Thermodynamics of Elastic Materials & of Reacting Fluid Mixtures. (CISM - International Centre for Mechanical Sciences, Courses & Lectures: Vol. 75). (Illus.). 47p. 1975. pap. 7.10 (ISBN 0-387-81178-8). Springer-Verlag.
--Topics in Finite Elasticity. LC 80-53711. (CBMS-NSF Regional Conference Ser.: No. 35). v, 58p. 1981. pap. text ed. 10.50 (ISBN 0-89871-168-1). Soc Indus-Appl Math.
Haichang, Hu. Variational Principles of the Theory of Elasticity with Applications. 491p. 1985. text ed. 97.50 (ISBN 0-677-31330-6). Gordon.
Hanyga, A. Mathematical Theory of Nonlinear Elasticity. (Mathematics & Its Applications Ser.). 400p. 1985. 95.00x (ISBN 0-470-27493-X, 1-176). Halsted Pr.
Hohenemser, Kurt. Elastokinetik. LC 50-2567. (Ger). 9.95 (ISBN 0-8284-0055-5). Chelsea Pub.
Houwink, Roelof. Elasticity, Plasticity & Structure of Matter. 3rd ed. LC 72-154515. (Illus.). 1971. 67.50 (ISBN 0-521-07875-X). Cambridge U Pr.
Huntington, Hillard B. Elastic Constants of Crystals. (Solid State Reprint Ser.). (Illus.). 1964. 21.50 (ISBN 0-12-608456-4). Acad Pr.
Jaeger, J. C. Elasticity, Fracture & Flow: With Engineering & Geological Applications. 3rd ed. 1971. pap. 10.95 (ISBN 0-412-20890-3, NO.6164, Pub. by Chapman & Hall). Methuen Inc.
Kalandiya, A. I. Mathematical Methods of Two Dimensional Elasticity. 351p. 1975. 8.95 (ISBN 0-8285-0792-9, Pub. by Mir Pubs USSR). Imported Pubns.
Kitahara, M. Boundary Integral Equation Methods in Eigenvalue Problems of Elastodynamics & Thin Plates. (Studies in Applied Mechanics: Vol. 10). 1985. 66.75 (ISBN 0-444-42447-4). Elsevier.
Knops, R. J. & Payne, L. E. Uniqueness Theorems in Linear Elasticity. LC 70-138813. (Springer Tracts in Natural Philosophy: Vol. 19). 1971. 28.00 (ISBN 0-387-05253-4). Springer-Verlag.
Kupradze, V. D., et al. Three-Dimensional Problems of Elasticity & Thermoelasticity. 930p. 1979. 149.00 (ISBN 0-444-85148-8, North-Holland). Elsevier.
Leipholz, H. Stability of Elastic Systems. (Mechanics of Elastic Stability Ser.: No. 7). 492p. 1980. 75.00x (ISBN 90-286-0050-7). Sijthoff & Noordhoff.
Lekhnitskii, S. G. Theory of Elasticity of an Anisotropic Body. 1981. 8.00 (ISBN 0-8285-1902-1, Pub. by Mir Pubs USSR). Imported Pubns.
Love, Augustus E. Treatise on the Mathematical Theory of Elasticity. 4th ed. (Illus.). 1927. pap. text ed. 10.95 (ISBN 0-486-60174-9). Dover.
Magrab, E. B. Vibrations of Elastic Structural Members, No. 3. (Mechanics of Structural Systems Ser.). 404p. 1979. 60.00x (ISBN 90-286-0207-0). Sijthoff & Noordhoff.
Mark, James E. & Lal, Joginder, eds. Elastomers & Rubber Elasticity. LC 82-11320. (ACS Symposium Ser.: No. 193). 576p. 1982. lib. bdg. 59.95x (ISBN 0-8412-0729-1). Am Chemical.
Marsden, Jerrold E. & Hughes, Thomas J. Mathematical Foundations of Elasticity. (Illus.). 496p. 1983. 75.00 (ISBN 0-13-561076-1). P-H.
Milne-Thomson, L. M. Plane Elastic Systems. 2nd ed. LC 68-56947. (Ergebnisse der Angewandten Mathematik: Vol. 6). 1965. pap. 19.00 (ISBN 0-387-03407-2). Springer-Verlag.
Necas, J. & Hlavacek, I. Mathematical Theory of Elastic & Elasto-Plastic Bodies: An Introduction. (Studies in Applied Mechanics: Vol. 3). 342p. 1981. 70.25 (ISBN 0-444-99754-7). Elsevier.
Novozhilov, V. V. Foundations of the Nonlinear Theory of Elasticity. LC 53-10160. (Illus.). 1953. 15.00x (ISBN 0-910670-08-0). Graylock.
Nowaki, W. Theory of Asymmetrical Elasticity. 2nd ed. 1985. 75.00 (ISBN 0-08-027584-2). Pergamon.
Parton, V. Integral Equations in Elasticity. 303p. 1982. 9.95 (ISBN 0-8285-2441-6, Pub. by Mir Pubs USSR). Imported Pubns.
Parton, V. Z. & Perlin, P. I. Mathematical Methods of the Theory of Elasticity, Vol. 1. 317p. 1984. 10.00 (ISBN 0-8285-2931-0, Mir Pubs USSR). Imported Pubns.
--Mathematical Methods of the Theory of Elasticity, Vol. 2. 356p. 1984. 10.00 (ISBN 0-8285-2932-9, Pub. by Mir Pubs USSR). Imported Pubns.
Pearson, Carl E. Theoretical Elasticity. LC 59-9283. pap. 57.50 (ISBN 0-317-08681-2, 2001586). Bks Demand UMI.
Penn, W. S. Injection Moulding of Elastomers. 220p. 1969. 80.95x (ISBN 0-677-61620-1). Gordon.
Reismann, Herbert & Pawlik, Peter S. Elasticity, Theory & Applications. LC 80-10145. 425p. 1980. 58.95 (ISBN 0-471-03165-8, Pub. by Wiley-Interscience). Wiley.
Rekach, V. G. Manual of the Theory of Elasticity. 317p. 1979. 6.95 (ISBN 0-8285-1527-1, Pub. by Mir Pubs USSR). Imported Pubns.
Saada, Adel S. Elasticity Theory & Applications. LC 82-17171. 660p. 1983. Repr. of 1974 ed. lib. bdg. 39.95 (ISBN 0-89874-559-4). Krieger.
Schimke, Joel, et al. Approximate Solution of Plane Orthotropic Elasticity Problems. LC 73-135086. 366p. 1970. 39.00 (ISBN 0-403-04535-5). Scholarly.
Simmons, Gene & Wang, Herbert. Single Crystal Elastic Constants & Calculated Aggregate Properties. 1971. 32.50x (ISBN 0-262-19092-3). MIT Pr.
Singer, Ferdinand L. & Pytel, Andrew. Strength of Materials. 3rd ed. (Illus.). 1980. text ed. 33.50 scp (ISBN 0-06-046229-9, HarpC); solutions manual avail. (ISBN 0-06-366232-9); 1.50, scp problem suppl. (ISBN 0-06-046234-5). Har-Row.
Sneddon, I. N. Applications of Integral Transforms in the Theory of Elasticity. (International Center for Mechanical Sciences: Vol. 220). (Illus.). 1975. pap. 44.90 (ISBN 0-387-81342-X). Springer-Verlag.
Sneddon, Ian & Lowengrub, M. Crack Problems in the Classical Theory of Elasticity. LC 75-84971. (The Siam Series in Applied Mathematics). pap. 57.80 (ISBN 0-317-08602-2, 2006312). Bks Demand UMI.
Sokolnikoff, I. S. Mathematical Theory of Elasticity. LC 82-14844. 488p. 1983. Repr. of 1956 ed. lib. bdg. 32.50 (ISBN 0-89874-555-1). Krieger.
Stoker, J. J. Nonlinear Elasticity. (Notes on Mathematics & Its Applications Ser.). (Illus.). 142p. (Orig.). 1968. 37.25x (ISBN 0-677-00660-8). Gordon.
Symposium in Applied Mathematics, Ann Arbor, 1949. Elasticity. Churchill, R. V., ed. LC 50-1183. (Proceedings of Symposia in Applied Mathematics: Vol. 3). 233p. 1950. pap. 36.00 (ISBN 0-8218-1303-X, PSAPM-3). Am Math.
Symposium in Applied Mathematics, Providence R.I., 1947. Nonlinear Problems in Mechanics of Continua: Proceedings, Vol. 1. Reissner, E., ed. LC 50-1183. (Proceedings of Symposia in Applied Mathematics). 219p. 1949. 21.00 (ISBN 0-8218-1301-3, PSAPM-1). Am Math.
Symposium on Nonlinear Elasticity, University of Wisconsin, April, 1973. Nonlinear Elasticity: Proceedings. Dickey, R. W., ed. 1973. 24.00 (ISBN 0-12-215150-X). Acad Pr.
Thompson, J. M. & Hunt, G. W. Elastic Instability Phenomena. LC 83-14514. 209p. 1984. 35.95x (ISBN 0-471-90279-9, Pub. by Wiley-Interscience). Wiley.
--A General Theory of Elastic Stability. LC 73-8199. pap. 84.00 (ISBN 0-317-08648-0, 2022105). Bks Demand UMI.
Timoshenko, Stephen P. History of Strength of Materials: With a Brief Account of the History of Theory of Elasticity & Theory of Structure. (Illus.). 452p. 1983. pap. 8.95 (ISBN 0-486-61187-6). Dover.
Timoshenko, Stephen P. & Gere, J. Theory of Elastic Stability. 2nd ed. (Engineering Societies Monographs). (Illus.). 1961. text ed. 52.00 (ISBN 0-07-064749-6). McGraw.
Timoshenko, Stephen P. & Goodier, J. N. Theory of Elasticity. 3rd ed. LC 69-13617. (Engineering Societies Monographs Ser). (Illus.). 1969. text ed. 52.00 (ISBN 0-07-064720-8). McGraw.
Truesdell, C., ed. Continuum Mechanics, 4 vols. Incl. Vol. 1. Mechanical Foundations of Elasticity. 324p. 1966. 46.25x (ISBN 0-677-00820-1); Vol. 2. Rational Mechanics of Materials. 446p. 1965. 54.50x (ISBN 0-677-00830-9); Vol. 3. Foundations of Elasticity Theory. 320p. 1965. 49.95x (ISBN 0-677-00840-6); Vol. 4. Problems of Nonlinear Elasticity. 276p. 1965. 46.25x (ISBN 0-677-00850-3). (International Science Review Ser.). (Illus.). 1965. Gordon.
Ugural, A. C. & Fenster, S. K. Advanced Strength & Applied Elasticity. LC 74-27388. 1975. text ed. 34.25 (ISBN 0-444-00160-3); instr's manual avail. Elsevier.
--Advanced Strength & Applied Elasticity: The SI Version. 424p. 1981. 34.25 (ISBN 0-444-00428-9); instr's. manual avail. Elsevier.
Washizu, K. Variational Methods in Elasticity & Plasticity. 3rd ed. (Illus.). 540p. 1982. 110.00 (ISBN 0-08-026723-8). Pergamon.
Wempner, Gerald. Mechanics of Solids with Application to Thin Bodies, No. 2. (Mechanics of Elastics & Viscoelastic Solids Ser.). 620p. Date not set. 79.00x. Sijthoff & Noordhoff.
Wesolowski, Z., ed. Nonlinear Dynamics of Elastic Bodies. (CISM Courses & Lectures: Vol. 227). (Illus.). 1978. pap. 23.10 (ISBN 0-387-81512-0). Springer-Verlag.
Zener, Clarence M. Elasticity & Anelasticity of Metals. pap. 45.00 (ISBN 0-317-26792-2, 2024328). Bks Demand UMI.

ELASTOMERS
see also Plastics; Rubber

Advances in Synthetic Rubbers & Elastomers Science & Technology. LC 79-64141. 334p. 1977. pap. 14.95 (ISBN 0-87762-237-X). Technomic.
Alliger, G. & Sjothun, I. J., eds. Vulcanization of Elastomers: Principles & Practice of Vulcanization of Commercial Rubbers. LC 78-8167. 1978. Repr. of 1964 ed. lib. bdg. 24.50 (ISBN 0-88275-686-9). Krieger.
Elastomeric Materials Desk-Top Data Bank. 85.00 (ISBN 0-686-48149-6, 0303). T-C Pubns CA.
Harper, Charles A. Handbook of Plastics & Elastomers. 950p. 1975. 74.50 (ISBN 0-07-026681-6). McGraw.
Hepburn, C. & Reynolds, R. J., eds. Elastomers: Criteria for Engineering Design. (Illus.). 372p. 1979. 55.50 (ISBN 0-85334-809-X, Pub. by Elsevier Applied Sci England). Elsevier.

Dictionary of Electrical Circuits. (Eng. & Chinese.). 203p. 1975. pap. 3.95 (ISBN 0-686-92288-3, M-9572). French & Eur.
Director, S. W. Circuit Theory: The Computational Approach. LC 75-2016. 679p. 1975. text ed. 48.50 (ISBN 0-471-21580-5); tchrs manual 10.00 (ISBN 0-471-21582-1). Wiley.
Draper, Alec. Electrical Circuits: Including Machines. 2nd ed. LC 73-173070. (Electrical Engineering Ser.). pap. 106.30 (ISBN 0-317-10117-X, 2006385). Bks Demand UMI.
Driscoll, Frederick, Jr. Analysis of Electric Circuits. LC 72-3691. (Illus.). 544p. 1973. text ed. 31.95 (ISBN 0-13-032912-6). P-H.
Durney, Carl H., et al. Electric Circuit Theory & Engineering Applications. 1982. pap. text ed. 40.95 (ISBN 0-03-057951-1). HR&W.
Edminister, J. Schaum's Outline of Electric Circuits. 2nd ed. (Schaum's Outline Ser.). 304p. 1983. pap. 8.95 (ISBN 0-07-018984-6). McGraw.
Floyd, Thomas L. Principles of Electric Circuits. (Illus.). 768p. 1981. text ed. 28.95 (ISBN 0-675-08081-9). Additional supplements may be obtained from publisher. Merrill.
--Principles of Electric Circuits. 2nd ed. 864p. 1985. text ed. 31.50 (ISBN 0-675-20402-X). Additional supplements may be obtained from publisher. Merrill.
Govinda Rao, C. Generalised Circuit Theory of Electrical Machines. 248p. 1981. 30.00x (ISBN 0-86131-028-4, Pub. by Orient Longman India). State Mutual Bk.
Grantham, Donald J. Fundamental Properties of AC Circuits. LC 75-18398. (Grantham Electronics-with-Mathematics Ser.: Vol. 2). (Illus.). 1976. pap. text ed. 15.95x (ISBN 0-915668-02-5). G S E Pubns.
--Mathematics for Basic Circuit Analysis. LC 76-40449. (Grantham Electronics-with-Mathematics Ser: Vol. 3). 1976. pap. text ed. 18.95x (ISBN 0-915668-03-3). G S E Pubns.
Grob, B. Direct & Alternating Current Circuits. 624p. 1985. price not set (ISBN 0-07-024959-8). McGraw.
Gurley. Flexible Circuit Application & Design Guide. (Electrical Engineering & Electronics Ser.). 136p. 1984. 39.75 (ISBN 0-8247-7215-6). Dekker.
Harter, Jim & Lin, Paul. Essentials of Electric Circuits. 1982. text ed. 29.95 (ISBN 0-8359-1767-3); instr's. manual avail. (ISBN 0-8359-1768-1). Reston.
Hayt, William & Kemmerly, Jack. Engineering Circuit Analysis. 3rd ed. (Illus.). 1978. text ed. 46.95 (ISBN 0-07-027393-6). McGraw.
Homes, P. J. & Loasby, R. C. Handbook of Thick Film Technology. 430p. 1980. 165.00x (ISBN 0-901150-05-3, Pub. by Electrochemical Scotland). State Mutual Bk.
Horn, Delton T. How to Design Op Amp Circuits, with Projects & Experiments. (Illus.). 432p. (Orig.). 1984. 21.95 (ISBN 0-8306-0765-X); pap. 15.50 (ISBN 0-8306-1765-5, 1765). TAB Bks.
Hubert, C. I. Electric Circuits AC-DC: An Integrated Approach. 576p. 1982. text ed. 40.00x (ISBN 0-07-030845-4). McGraw.
Huelsman, Lawrence P. Basic Circuit Theory. 2nd ed. (Illus.). 688p. 1984. text ed. 41.95 (ISBN 0-13-057711-1). P-H.
Hughes, Frederick W. Illustrated Guidebook to Electronic Devices & Circuits. (Illus.). 432p. 1983. 31.95 (ISBN 0-13-451328-2). P-H.
Jackson, Herbert. Introduction to Electric Circuits. 6th ed. (Illus.). 800p. 1986. text ed. 37.95 (ISBN 0-13-481425-8). P-H.
Javid, Mansour & Brenner, Egon. Analysis, Transmission, & Filtering of Signals. LC 77-23951. 476p. 1978. Repr. of 1963 ed. lib. bdg. 27.50 (ISBN 0-88275-599-4). Krieger.
Johnson, D. & Johnson, J. Introductory Electric Circuit Analysis. 1981. 32.95 (ISBN 0-13-500835-2). P-H.
Johnson, David E., et al. Basic Electric Circuit Analysis. 2nd ed. (Illus.). 592p. 1984. 41.95 (ISBN 0-13-060111-X). P-H.
Jones. Hybrid Circuit Design. (Electrical Engineering & Electronics Ser.: Vol. 12). 224p. 1982. 35.00 (ISBN 0-8247-1689-2). Dekker.
Kirwin, Gerald J. & Grodzinsky, Stephen. Basic Circuit Analysis. LC 79-88449. (Illus.). 1980. text ed. 39.95 (ISBN 0-395-28488-0); solutions manual 1.00 (ISBN 0-395-28489-9). HM.
Klir, J. & Seidl, L. Synthesis of Switching Circuits. 326p. 1966. 80.95 (ISBN 0-677-61830-1). Gordon.
Koller, Alois. The Electric Circuit. (Siemens Programmed Instruction Ser.: 10). pap. 20.00 (ISBN 0-317-27762-6, 2052087). Bks Demand UMI.
Lafferty, J. M., ed. Vacuum Arcs: Theory & Application. LC 79-15654. 372p. 1980. 52.50x (ISBN 0-471-06506-4). Wiley.
Lagasse, J. Linear Circuit Theory: Study of Electric Circuits. 294p. 1968. 80.95 (ISBN 0-677-61520-5). Gordon.
Lancaster, G. D.C. & A.C. Circuits. 2nd ed. (Oxford Physics Ser.). (Illus.). 1980. 59.00x (ISBN 0-19-851848-X); pap. 29.95x (ISBN 0-19-851849-8). Oxford U Pr.
Lang, Johannes G. The Magnetic Circuit. (Siemens Programmed Instruction Ser.: 3). pap. 20.00 (ISBN 0-317-26183-5, 2052080). Bks Demand UMI.
Leach, Donald P. Basic Electric Circuits. 3rd ed. 834p. 1984. text ed. 28.95 (ISBN 0-471-05421-6, Pub. by Wiley-Interscience); write for info. tchr's ed. (ISBN 0-471-88497-9); manual 12.95 (ISBN 0-471-88496-0). Wiley.
Lieblich, Jerome H., ed. Printed Wiring Circuit - Board, 2 vols. 1253p. loose-leaf 129.95 (ISBN 0-912702-13-3, PW C/B). Global Eng.
Lurch, Norman. Electric Circuit Fundamentals. (Illus.). 1979. text ed. 31.95 (ISBN 0-13-247189-2). P-H.
Maloney, Timothy J. Electric Circuits: Principles & Applications. (Illus.). 896p. 1984. 32.15; lab manual, 128p. 14.95 (ISBN 0-13-247396-8). P-H.
Malvino, Albert P. Resistive & Reactive Circuits. (Illus.). 640p. 1974. text ed. 29.95 (ISBN 0-07-039856-9). McGraw.
Markus, J. Popular Circuits Ready-Reference. 160p. 1982. pap. 12.50 (ISBN 0-07-040458-5). McGraw.
Markus, John. Manual De Circuitos Electronicos. 984p. 1974. 59.95 (ISBN 84-267-0282-1, S-30723). French & Eur.
Metzger, Daniel L. Electronic Circuit Behavior. 2nd ed. (Illus.). 400p. 1983. 32.95 (ISBN 0-13-250241-0); lab manual 14.95 (ISBN 0-13-250191-0). P-H.
Mix, D. F. & Schmitt, N. M. Circuit Analysis for Engineers: Continuous & Discrete Time Systems. 638p. 1985. 35.95 (ISBN 0-471-08432-8). Wiley.
Nashelsky, Louis & Boylestad, Robert L. BASIC Applied to Circuit Analysis. 1984. Additional supplements may be obtained from publisher. text ed. 18.95 (ISBN 0-675-20161-6). Merrill.
Nilsson, James W. Electric Circuits. LC 82-8719. 1983. pap. text ed. 41.95 (ISBN 0-201-06238-0). Addison-Wesley.
Okoshi, T. Planar Circuits. (Springer Series in Electrophysics: Vol. 18). (Illus.). 220p. 1985. 41.50 (ISBN 0-387-13853-6). Springer-Verlag.
O'Malley, John R. Circuit Analysis. 1980. text ed. 31.95 (ISBN 0-13-133827-7). P-H.
Oppenheimer, S. L. & Borchers. Direct & Alternating Currents. 2nd ed. 1973. text ed. 32.00 (ISBN 0-07-047665-9). McGraw.
Oppenheimer, Samuel. Fundamentals of Electric Circuits. (Illus.). 592p. 1984. text ed. 34.95 (ISBN 0-13-336974-9). P-H.
Pearson, S. Ivar & Maler, George J. Introductory Circuit Analysis. LC 74-10895. 566p. 1974. Repr. of 1965 ed. 29.50 (ISBN 0-88275-175-1). Krieger.
Reeves, Thomas C. The Life & Times of Joe McCarthy. LC 79-3730. 1981. 19.95 (ISBN 0-8128-2337-0). Stein & Day.
Research & Education Association Staff. The Electric Circuits Problem Solver. rev. ed. LC 79-92401. (Illus.). 1184p. 1984. pap. text ed. 23.85 (ISBN 0-87891-517-6). Res & Educ.
Reynolds, James A. Applied Transformed Circuit Theory for Technology. LC 84-7525. 335p. 1985. 34.95 (ISBN 0-471-09819-1). Wiley.
Ridsdale, R. E. Electric Circuits. 2nd ed. 736p. 1983. 28.20 (ISBN 0-07-052948-5). McGraw.
Rieger, Heinz. The Magnetic Circuit. (Siemens Programmed Instruction Ser.: 4). pap. 20.00 (ISBN 0-317-26181-9, 2052081). Bks Demand UMI.
Scott, Ronald E. Linear Circuits, Complete. Incl. Pt. 2. Frequency-Domain Analysis. 1961. Set. 34.95 (ISBN 0-201-06820-6). Addison-Wesley.
Seippel, Robert G. & Nelson, Roger L. Direct Current Circuit Analysis. LC 74-24889. (Illus.). pap. 28.30 (ISBN 0-317-08817-3, 2011569). Bks Demand UMI.
Siebert, W. M. Circuits, Signals & Systems. 472p. 1985. text ed. 37.95 (ISBN 0-07-057290-9). McGraw.
Smith, J. Modern Communication Circuits. (Electrical Engineering Ser.). 576p. 1986. 43.95 (ISBN 0-07-058730-2). McGraw.
Sonsky, Sidney N. Theory & Experiments in Basic Electric Circuits. (Illus.). 1978. lab manual 12.95 (ISBN 0-89529-050-2). Avery Pub.
Stanley, Brian H. Experiments in Electric Circuits. 256p. 1982. text ed. 15.95 (ISBN 0-675-09805-X). Additional supplements may be obtained from publisher. Merrill.
--Experiments in Electric Circuits. 2nd ed. 256p. 1985. lab manual 15.95 (ISBN 0-675-20403-8). Merrill.
Stanley, William D. Transform Circuit Analysis for Engineering & Technology. 1967. ref. ed. 29.95 (ISBN 0-13-928804-X). P-H.
Strum, R. D. & Ward, J. R. Electric Circuits & Networks. (Illus.). 448p. 1982. pap. 11.95 (ISBN 0-13-248153-7). P-H.
Strum, Robert D. & Ward, John R. Electric Circuits & Networks. 2nd ed. (Illus.). 672p. 1985. text ed. 34.95 (ISBN 0-13-248170-7). P-H.
Taber, Margaret R. & Silgalis, Eugene. Electric Circuit Analysis. LC 78-69525. (Illus.). 1980. text ed. 32.50 (ISBN 0-395-26706-4); instr's. manual 1.25 (ISBN 0-395-26707-2). HM.
Temes, Gabor & Lapatra, Jack. Introduction to Circuit Synthesis. 1977. text ed. 46.00 (ISBN 0-07-063489-0). McGraw.
Texas Instruments Inc. Designing with TTL Integrated Circuits. 1971. 49.90 (ISBN 0-07-063745-8). McGraw.
Tocci, Ronald J. Introduction to Electric Circuit Analysis. 2nd ed. 1983. text ed. 31.50 (ISBN 0-675-20002-4). Additional supplements may be obtained from publisher. Merrill.
Tontsch. Fundamental Circuit Analysis. rev. ed. 512p. 1978. text ed. 28.95 (ISBN 0-574-21570-0, 13-4570); write for info. solution manual (ISBN 0-574-21572-7, 13-4572). SRA.
Trejo, Paul E. AC Circuits Text & Handbook. 402p. pap. 15.00 (ISBN 0-8428-1374-8); pap. 5.41 instr's. guide (ISBN 0-8428-1400-0); pap. 8.34 progress tests (ISBN 0-8428-1384-5); pap. 4.00 student handbook (ISBN 0-8428-1385-3). Cambridge Bk.
--DC Circuits. 390p. pap. 15.00 (ISBN 0-8428-1373-X); instr's. guide 5.41 (ISBN 0-8428-1402-7); progress tests 8.34 (ISBN 0-8428-1397-7); student handbk. 4.16 (ISBN 0-8428-1398-5). Cambridge Bk.
Van Valkenburg, M. Linear Circuits. LC 81-17809. (Illus.). 448p. 1982. 36.95 (ISBN 0-13-536722-0). P-H.
Van Valkenburg, M. E., ed. Circuit Theory: Foundations & Classical Contributions. LC 74-2475. (Benchmark Papers in Electrical Engineering & Computer Science: Vol. 8). 464p. 1974. 57.00 (ISBN 0-87933-084-8). Van Nos Reinhold.
Veatch, Henry C., ed. Electrical Circuit Action. LC 77-22049. 1978. text ed. 26.95 (ISBN 0-574-21590-5, 13-4590); instr's guide avail. (ISBN 0-574-21591-3, 13-4591). SRA.
Weiner, Donald D. & Spina, John F. The Sinusoidal Analysis & Modeling of Weakly Nonlinear Circuits: With Application to Nonlinear Interference Effects. (Electrical-Computer Science & Engineering Ser.). 304p. 1980. 27.50 (ISBN 0-442-26093-8). Van Nos Reinhold.
Yorke, R. Electric Circuit Theory. LC 80-41323. (Applied Electricity & Electronics Ser.). (Illus.). 272p. 1981. 35.00 (ISBN 0-08-026133-7); pap. 19.25 (ISBN 0-08-026132-9). Pergamon.
Zeueke, G., et al, eds. Analysis of Electric Circuits. MIR Publishers, tr. from Rus. (Illus.). 690p. 1969. text ed. 20.00x (ISBN 0-8464-0129-0). Beekman Pubs.

ELECTRIC COILS

Zelazny, Roger & Saberhagen, Fred. Coils. LC 82-1993. (Illus.). 250p. 1982. pap. 7.95 (ISBN 0-671-44915-X, Wallaby). S&S.

ELECTRIC COMMUNICATION

see Telecommunication

ELECTRIC CONDENSERS

see Capacitors

ELECTRIC CONDUCTIVITY

see also Electrolytes; Photoconductivity; Photoelectricity; Semiconductors; Semimetals; Tunneling (Physics); Superconductivity; Tunneling (Physics)

Coutts, T. J. Electrical Conduction in Thin Metal Films. 244p. 1974. 61.75 (ISBN 0-444-41184-4). Elsevier.
Lipinski. Electrical Conduction & Mechanoelectrical Intransduction in Biological Materials. 376p. 1982. 65.00 (ISBN 0-8247-1865-8). Dekker.
Myuller, R. L. Solid State Chemistry. LC 65-26631. 256p. 1966. 42.50x (ISBN 0-306-10743-0, Consultants). Plenum Pub.
Tallan, N. M., ed. Electrical Conductivity in Ceramics & Glass, Pt. B. (Ceramics & Glass: Science & Technology Ser.: Vol. 4). 400p. 1974. 75.00 (ISBN 0-8247-6088-3). Dekker.
Uman, Myron F. Introduction to the Physics of Electronics. 1974. 41.95 (ISBN 0-13-492702-8). P-H.

ELECTRIC CONDUCTORS

see also Electric Cables; Microwave Wiring; Radio, Short Wave; Wave Guides

ASTM Standards on Metallic Electrical Conductors (B-1) 12th ed. 627p. 1980. pap. 36.00x (ISBN 0-8031-0283-6, 03-201080-03). ASTM.
Salamon, M. B., ed. Physics of Superionic Conductors. (Topics in Current Physics Ser.: Vol. 15). (Illus.). 1979. 37.00 (ISBN 0-387-09333-8). Springer-Verlag.
Tsalf, A. Combined Properties of Conductors: An Aid for Calculation of Thermal Processes in Electrical & Heat Engineering. (Physical Science Data Ser.: No. 9). 596p. 1981. 119.25 (ISBN 0-686-80759-6). Elsevier.

ELECTRIC CONTACTORS

Here are entered works on devices for repeatedly establishing and interrupting an electric circuit.

CES Industries, Inc. Staff. Ed-Lab Eighty Experiment Manual: Contactor Sensor Operation. (Illus.). 1982. write for info. (ISBN 0-86711-063-5). CES Industries.
Holm, Ragnar & Holm, Else. Electric Contacts: Theory & Application. 4th ed. (Illus.). 1967. 74.00 (ISBN 0-387-03875-2). Springer-Verlag.
Receiving Tube Characteristics & Socket Connection Guide. 1981. 3.00 (ISBN 0-938630-11-3). ARS Enterprises.

ELECTRIC CONTRACTING

see also Electricians

Cubit, Harry. Electrical Construction Cost Estimating. (Illus.). 320p. 1981. 39.95 (ISBN 0-07-014885-6). McGraw.
Dries, Bob. Manual of Electrical Contracting. 224p. (Orig.). 1983. pap. 17.00 (ISBN 0-910460-33-7). Craftsman.
Johnson, R. E. Electrical Contracting Business Handbook. 480p. 1985. 39.50 (ISBN 0-07-032335-6). McGraw.
Kolstad, C. Kenneth & Kohnert, Gerald V. Rapid Electrical Estimating & Pricing: A Handy, Quick Method of Directly Determining the Selling Prices of Electrical Construction Work. 3rd ed. (Illus.). 1979. 42.50 (ISBN 0-07-035129-5). McGraw.
Rudman, Jack. Electrical Installation. (Occupational Competency Examination Ser.: OCE-18). (Cloth bdg. avail. on request). pap. 13.95 (ISBN 0-8373-5718-7). Natl Learning.
Traister, John E. Construction Electrical Contracting. LC 78-13441. (Wiley Series on Practical Construction Guides). 299p. 1978. 44.50x (ISBN 0-471-02986-6). Wiley.
Tyler, Edward J. Electrical Construction Estimator 1985-1986. 400p. (Orig.). 1985. pap. 25.00 (ISBN 0-910460-48-5). Craftsman.

ELECTRIC CONTROLLERS

see also Magnetic Amplifiers; Remote Control; Voltage Regulators

Gould, J. K. Controllers & Control Elements. 1982. pap. text ed. 29.95x (ISBN 0-87664-622-4); instr's guide 10.00x (ISBN 0-87664-623-2). Instru Soc.
Heumann, Gerhart W. Magnetic Control of Industrial Motors: D-C Motors Controllers, Pt. 3. LC 61-11593. Repr. of 1961 ed. 59.50 (ISBN 0-8357-9925-5, 2012624). Bks Demand UMI.
Klaasen, K. B. Reliability of Analogue Electronic Systems. (Studies in Electrical & Electronic Engineering: Vol. 13). 278p. 1984. 61.00 (ISBN 0-444-42388-5). Elsevier.
Kosow, Irving L. Control of Electric Machines. LC 72-5631. (Electronic Technology Ser.). (Illus.). 368p. 1973. ref. ed. 31.95 (ISBN 0-13-171785-5). P-H.
Kusko, Alexander. Solid-State DC Motor Drives. 1969. 25.00x (ISBN 0-262-11031-8). MIT Pr.
Leonhard, W. Control of Electrical Drives. (Electric Energy Systems & Engineering Ser.). 315p. 1985. 49.00 (ISBN 0-387-13650-9). Springer-Verlag.
McIntyre, R. L. Electric Motor Control Fundamentals. 3rd ed. (Illus.). 448p. 1974. text ed. 30.95 (ISBN 0-07-045103-6). McGraw.
Millermaster, Ralph A. Harwood's Control of Electric Motors. 4th ed. 1970. 56.50x (ISBN 0-471-60620-0, Pub. by Wiley-Interscience). Wiley.
Rexford, Kenneth. Electrical Control for Machines. 2nd ed. 384p. 1983. pap. text ed. 22.80 (ISBN 0-8273-2175-9); lab manual 6.60 (ISBN 0-8273-2177-5); instr's guide 4.80 (ISBN 0-8273-2176-7). Delmar.
Siskind, Charles S. Electrical Control Systems in Industry. 1963. text ed. 31.00 (ISBN 0-07-057746-3). McGraw.
Smeaton, R. W. Switchgear & Control Handbook. 1976. 57.50 (ISBN 0-07-058439-7). McGraw.

ELECTRIC CONVERTERS

see Electric Current Converters; Rotary Converters

ELECTRIC CURRENT CONVERTERS

see also Frequency Changers; Klystrons; Rotary Converters

Bedford, Burnice D. & Hoft, R. G. Principles of Inverter Circuits. LC 64-20078. 413p. 1964. 42.95x (ISBN 0-471-06134-4, Pub. by Wiley-Interscience). Wiley.
Dewan, Shashi & Straughen, Alan. Power Semiconductor Circuits. LC 75-8911. 523p. 1975. 45.50 (ISBN 0-471-21180-X, Pub. by Wiley-Interscience). Wiley.
Ehsani, Mehrdad & Kustom, Robert L. Converter Circuits for Superconducting Inductive Energy Storage. LC 85-40055. (TEES Monograph Ser.: No. 4). 286p. 1986. lib. bdg. 42.50x (ISBN 0-89096-257-X). Tex A&M Univ Pr.
Gottlieb, Irving. Switching Regulators & Power Supplies with Practical Inverters & Converters. LC 75-41722. (Illus.). 252p. 1976. 13.95 (ISBN 0-8306-6828-4); pap. 6.95 (ISBN 0-8306-5828-9, 828). TAB Bks.

Zwicky, R., ed. Control in Power Electronics & Electrical Drives 1983: Proceedings of the 3rd IFAC Symposium, Lausanne, Switzerland, 12-14 Sept. 1983. (IFAC Proceedings Ser.). 828p. 1984. 175.00 (ISBN 0-08-030536-9). Pergamon.

ELECTRIC CURRENT RECTIFIERS

see also Junction Transistors

Scoles, G. Handbook of Rectifier Circuits. LC 79-41814. (Ellis Horwood Electrical & Electronic Engineering Ser.). 238p. 1980. 84.95x (ISBN 0-470-26950-2). Halsted Pr.

ELECTRIC CURRENTS

see also Electric Measurements; Electric Noise; Electric Transformers; Galvanomagnetic Effects; Hall Effect; Transients (Electricity)

Birnbaum & Free, eds. Eddy-Current Characterization of Materials & Structures - STP 722. 505p. 1981. 44.50 (ISBN 0-8031-0752-8, 04-722000-22). ASTM.

Cline, C. Terry, Jr. Cross Current. 1980. pap. 2.50 (ISBN 0-449-24289-7, Crest). Fawcett.

Garland, J. D. National Electrical Code Reference Book, 1984. 4th ed. (Illus.). 624p. 1984. text ed. 27.95 O.P. (ISBN 0-13-609546-1). P-H.

Kato, S. & Roper, R. G. Electric Current & Atmospheric Motion. (Advances in Earth & Planetary Sciences Ser.: No. 7). 294p. 1980. 24.50x (ISBN 0-89955-314-1, Pub. by Japan Sci Soc Japan). Intl Spec Bk.

Ohm, G. S. Galvanic Circuit Investigated Mathematically. Lockwood, Thomas D., ed. Francis, William, tr. 1891. 17.00 (ISBN 0-527-68260-8). Kraus Repr.

Oppenheimer, S. L. & Borchers. Direct & Alternating Currents. 2nd ed. 1973. text ed. 32.00 (ISBN 0-07-047665-9). McGraw.

Rieger, Heinz. Alternating Voltage & Current. (Siemens Programmed Instruction Ser.: No. 12). pap. 20.00 (ISBN 0-317-27756-1, 2052089). Bks Demand UMI.

Rosenblatt, Jack & Friedman, M. Harold. Direct & Alternating Current Machinery. 1984. Additional supplements may be obtained from publisher. text ed. 29.95 (ISBN 0-675-20160-8). Merrill.

Rudenberg, Reinhold. Electrical Shock Waves in Power Systems: Traveling Waves in Lumped & Distributed Circuit Elements. LC 68-14272. (Illus.). 1968. 20.00x (ISBN 0-674-24350-1). Harvard U Pr.

Woolman, M. & Valentine, C. G. From Electrons to Power: AC & DC. 1968. text ed. 11.95x (ISBN 0-02-479180-6, 479181). Glencoe.

ELECTRIC CURRENTS, ALTERNATING

Consumers Power Company. Fundamentals of Electricity, 2 vols. Incl. Vol. 1. Basic Principles. pap. 15.95 (ISBN 0-201-01185-9); Vol. 2. Alternating Current. pap. 15.95 (ISBN 0-201-01186-7). 1966. pap. Addison-Wesley.

Duff, John R. & Kaufman, Milton. Alternating Current Fundamentals. 2nd ed. (Electrical Trades Ser.). 1980. 22.00 (ISBN 0-8273-1133-8); pap. 18.00 (ISBN 0-8273-1142-7). Delmar.

Fiske, Kenneth A. & Harter, James H. Alternating Current Circuit Analysis through Experimentation. 3rd ed. 176p. 1982. pap. 8.50x (ISBN 0-911908-41-2). Tech Ed Pr.

Fulton, Stanley R. & Rawlins, John C. Practical Applications of AC Theory. LC 81-51518. (Illus.). 320p. (Orig.). 1981. pap. 12.00 (ISBN 0-89512-043-7, LCW8169). Tex Instr Inc.

Kittel, Joseph P. Understanding DC & AC Circuits Through Analogies. LC 79-65896. (Illus.). viii, 416p. (Orig.). 1983. pap. text ed. 14.95 (ISBN 0-9603198-0-8). B Royal Pr.

Kosow, Irving L. Study Guide in Alternating Current Circuits: A Personalized System of Instruction. LC 77-22152. (Electronic Technology Ser.). pap. 128.80 (ISBN 0-317-10110-2, 2015180). Bks Demand UMI.

Scroggie, Marcus G. Phasor Diagrams. 12.50x (ISBN 0-685-20612-2). Transatlantic.

Seippel, Robert G. & Nelson, Roger L. Alternating Current Analysis. LC 74-24890. (Illus.). pap. 33.80 (ISBN 0-317-08821-1, 2011570). Bks Demand UMI.

ELECTRIC CURRENTS, DIRECT

see also Electric Machinery–Direct Current

Dale, Charles W. & Oliva, Ralph A. Practical Applications of D. C. Theory. LC 77-84131. (Illus.). 402p. 1977. pap. text ed. 12.00 (ISBN 0-89512-010-0, LCW8162). Tex Instr Inc.

Fiske, Kenneth & Harter, James H. Direct Current Circuit Analysis through Experimentation. 4th ed. 240p. 1982. pap. 9.50x (ISBN 0-911908-17-X). Tech Ed Pr.

Kittel, Joseph P. Understanding DC & AC Circuits Through Analogies. LC 79-65896. (Illus.). viii, 416p. (Orig.). 1983. pap. text ed. 14.95 (ISBN 0-9603198-0-8). B Royal Pr.

Kosow, I. L. Study guide in Direct Current Circuits: A Personalized System of Instruction. LC 77-1739. (Ser. in Electronic Technology). Repr. of 1977 ed. 99.80 (ISBN 0-8357-9873-9, 2015181). Bks Demand UMI.

Loper. Direct Current Fundamentals. 2nd ed. LC 70-153729. 352p. 1978. 18.40 (ISBN 0-8273-1143-5); pap. 14.40 (ISBN 0-8273-1147-8); instructor's guide 4.20 (ISBN 0-8273-1145-1). Delmar.

Oliva, Ralph A. & Dale, Charles W. Basic Electricity & DC Circuits. 2nd ed. LC 79-92192. (Basic Electricity Ser.). (Illus.). 924p. 1980. text ed. 19.95 (ISBN 0-89512-034-8, LCW8161C); six cassette audio course 14.95 (LCB5922). Tex Instr Inc.

Rosen, Stanley L. Direct Current Circuits. (Avionics Technician Training Course Ser.). 158p. (Orig.). 1980. pap. text ed. 8.95 (ISBN 0-89100-121-2, EA-DCC). Aviation Maintenance.

Seippel, Robert G. & Nelson, Roger L. Direct Current Circuit Analysis. LC 74-24889. (Illus.). pap. 28.30 (ISBN 0-317-08817-3, 2011569). Bks Demand UMI.

ELECTRIC DIPOLE MOMENTS

see Dipole Moments

ELECTRIC DISCHARGE MACHINING

see Electric Metal-Cutting

ELECTRIC DISCHARGES

see also Exploding Wire Phenomena; Photoelectricity

Lacy, Edward A. Protecting Electronic Equipment from Electrostatic Discharge. LC 84-8902. (Illus.). 176p. (Orig.). 1984. 16.95 (ISBN 0-8306-0820-6); pap. 11.95 (ISBN 0-8306-1820-1, 1820). TAB Bks.

Pechuro, N. S., ed. Organic Reactions in Electrical Discharges. LC 68-28093. (Illus.). 135p. 1968. 25.00x (ISBN 0-306-10809-7, Consultants). Plenum Pub.

ELECTRIC DISCHARGES THROUGH GASES

see also Electron Tubes; Electrons–Emission; Ionization of Gases; Plasma (Ionized Gases); Vacuum; Vacuum-Tubes; X-Rays

Bekefi, George. Principles of Laser Plasmas. LC 76-28311. 736p. 1976. 76.95x (ISBN 0-471-06345-2, Pub. by Wiley-Interscience). Wiley.

Blaustein, Bernard D., ed. Chemical Reactions in Electrical Discharges. LC 70-76951. (Advances in Chemistry Ser: No. 80). 1969. 39.95 (ISBN 0-8412-0081-5). Am Chemical.

Cherrington, B. E. Gaseous Electronics & Gas Lasers. 1979. text ed. 57.00 (ISBN 0-08-020622-0). Pergamon.

Franklin, Raoul N. Plasma Phenomena in Gas Discharges. (Oxford Engineering Science Ser.). (Illus.). 1976. 59.00x (ISBN 0-19-856113-X). Oxford U Pr.

Hirsh, Merle N. & Oskam, H. J., eds. Gaseous Electronics: Electrical Discharge, Vol. 1. 1978. 74.50 (ISBN 0-12-349701-9). Acad Pr.

Huxley, L. G. & Crompton, R. W. The Diffusion & Drift of Electrons in Gases. LC 73-12313. 669p. (Orig.). 1974. 43.95 (ISBN 0-471-42590-7). Krieger.

Kesaev, I. G. Cathode Processes in the Mercury Arc. LC 63-17629. 345p. 1964. 42.50x (ISBN 0-306-10673-6, Consultants). Plenum Pub.

Kunhardt, Erich E. & Luessen, Lawrence H., eds. Electrical Breakdown & Discharges in Gases. Incl. Part A. Fundamental Processes & Breakdown. 474p. 1983. 75.00x (ISBN 0-306-41194-6); Part B. Macroscopic Processes & Discharges. 478p. 1983. 75.00x (ISBN 0-306-41195-4). (NATO ASI Series B, Physics: Vol. 89). price 135.00 set (ISBN 0-686-46277-7, Plenum). Plenum Pub.

McIntosh, Robert L. Dielectric Behavior of Physically Absorbed Gases. LC 67-82258. pap. 43.00 (ISBN 0-317-08353-8, 2055411). Bks Demand UMI.

Penning, F. M. Electrical Discharges in Gases. 84p. 1957. 23.25 (ISBN 0-677-61230-3). Gordon.

Raizer, Y. P., ed. Laser-Induced Discharge Phenomena. LC 77-21738. (Illus.). 380p. 1977. 55.00x (ISBN 0-306-10923-9, Consultants). Plenum Pub.

ELECTRIC DRAFTING

see also Electric Wiring–Diagrams; Electronic Drafting

Baer, C. J. & Ottaway, J. R. Electrical & Electronic Drawing. 5th ed. 560p. 1985. 31.50 (ISBN 0-07-003028-6). McGraw.

Baer, Charles J. & Ottaway, John R. Electrical & Electronics Drawing. 4th ed. LC 79-15837. (Illus.). 1980. text ed. 31.50 (ISBN 0-07-003010-3). McGraw.

Bethune, James D. Basic Electronic & Electrical Drafting. (Illus.). 1980. text ed. 24.95 (ISBN 0-13-060301-5). P-H.

General Electric Company. Modern Drafting Practices & Standards Manual. (Illus.). 940p. 1981. 140.00x (ISBN 0-931690-01-3). Genium Pub.

Miller, William C. Estimating & Cost Control in Electrical Construction Design. (Illus.). 1978. 26.50 (ISBN 0-442-12203-9). Van Nos Reinhold.

Richter, H. W. & Rubenstein, C. F. Electrical & Electronic Drafting. 2nd ed. 317p. 1985. 28.95 (ISBN 0-471-05784-3). Wiley.

Richter, Herbert W. Electrical & Electronic Drafting. LC 76-20506. (Electronic Technology Ser.). 272p. 1977. 29.95x (ISBN 0-471-72035-6); solutions manual 3.00 (ISBN 0-471-02541-0). Wiley.

Rudman, Jack. Electrical Engineering Draftsman. (Career Examination Ser.: C-222). (Cloth bdg. avail. on request). pap. 12.00 (ISBN 0-8373-0222-6). Natl Learning.

Schriever, Errol G. Electrical Drafting. (Illus.). 256p. 1984. pap. 27.95 (ISBN 0-13-247288-0). P-H.

Snow, Charles W. Electrical Drafting & Design. (Illus.). 416p. 1976. 27.95 (ISBN 0-13-247379-8). P-H.

ELECTRIC DRIVING

Kosow, Irving L. Control of Electric Machines. LC 72-5631. (Electronic Technology Ser.). (Illus.). 368p. 1973. ref. ed. 31.95 (ISBN 0-13-171785-5). P-H.

Leonhard, W. Control of Electrical Drives. (Electric Energy Systems & Engineering Ser.). 315p. 1985. 49.00 (ISBN 0-387-13650-9). Springer-Verlag.

Pillai, S. K. First Course on Electrical Drives. LC 82-224149. 208p. 1982. 15.95X (ISBN 0-470-27531-6). Halsted Pr.

Zwicky, R., ed. Control in Power Electronics & Electrical Drives 1983: Proceedings of the 3rd IFAC Symposium, Lausanne, Switzerland, 12-14 Sept. 1983. (IFAC Proceedings Ser.). 828p. 1984. 175.00 (ISBN 0-08-030536-9). Pergamon.

ELECTRIC ENGINEERING

see also Electric Apparatus and Appliances; Electric Lighting; Electric Machinery; Electric Network Analyzers; Electric Power Distribution; Electric Power Systems; Electricity in Mining; Electro-Acoustics; Electromechanical Devices; Radio; Telegraph; Telephone

Adams, James E. Electrical Principles & Practices. 2nd ed. 1973. text ed. 28.70 (ISBN 0-07-000281-9). McGraw.

Advances in Command Control & Communication Systems: Theory & Applications. 246p. 1985. 77.00 (ISBN 0-85296-308-4, IC247). Inst Elect Eng.

Advances in Command, Country & Communications. (IEE Conference Ser.: No. 247). 1985. 77.00 (ISBN 0-85296-308-4). Inst Electrical.

Aggarwal, J. K. & Vidyasagar, M., eds. Nonlinear Systems: Stability Analysis. (Benchmark Papers in Electrical Engineering & Computer Science: Vol. 16). 1977. 70.50 (ISBN 0-12-786035-5). Acad Pr.

Ahmed, H. & Spreadbury, P. J. Analogue & Digital Electronics for Engineers. (Illus.). 300p. 1984. 39.50 (ISBN 0-521-26463-4); pap. 18.95 (ISBN 0-521-31910-2). Cambridge U Pr.

American Electrican Magazine Staff. Electrical Designs. 1984. pap. 10.95 (ISBN 0-917914-22-8). Lindsay Pubns.

Anderson, R. T., et al, eds. Electrical Fitting, Vol. 1. (Engineering Craftsmen: No. G3). (Illus.). 1968. spiral bdg. 39.95x (ISBN 0-85083-015-X). Trans-Atlantic.

Application Guide for Ceramic Suspension Insulators. 1984. 6.50 (ISBN 0-318-18021-9, HV 2-1984). Natl Elec Mfrs.

Arps, Louisa W. Denver in Slices. LC 83-11058. (Illus.). 268p. 1983. 17.95 (ISBN 0-8040-0840-X, 82-76123, Swallow); pap. 9.95 (ISBN 0-8040-0841-8, 82-76131). Ohio U Pr.

Arrillaga, J. High Voltage Direct Current Transmission. (IEE Power Engineering Ser.: No. 6). 245p. 1983. casebound 66.00 (ISBN 0-906048-97-4, PO006, Pub. by Peregrinus England). Inst Elect Eng.

Arsenault, J. E. & Roberts, J. A., eds. Reliability & Maintainability of Electronic Systems. LC 79-10543. (Computer Software Engineering Ser.). (Illus.). 584p. 1980. text ed. 41.95 (ISBN 0-914894-24-2). Computer Sci.

Ayraud, Steve & Thumann, Albert. Introduction to Efficient Electrical System Design. LC 83-49500. 300p. 1985. text ed. 29.95 (ISBN 0-915586-98-3). Fairmont Pr.

Baitch. Electrical Technology. 2nd ed. 1984. pap. write for info. (ISBN 0-471-33394-8). Wiley.

Bartnikas, R. & Eichhorn, R. M., eds. Engineering Dielectrics, Volume IIA, Electrical Properties of Solid Insulating Materials: Molecular Structure & Electrical Behavior. LC 82-70637. (Special Technical Publications Ser.: No. 783). 695p. 1983. text ed. 60.00 (ISBN 0-8031-0228-3, 04-783000-21). ASTM.

Bell, E. C. & Whitehead, R. W. Basic Electrical Engineering & Instrumentation for Engineers. (Illus.). 1977. pap. 17.95x (ISBN 0-8464-0175-4). Beekman Pubs.

--Basic Electrical Engineering & Instrumentation for Engineers. 2nd ed. 487p. 1981. pap. text ed. 22.00x (ISBN 0-258-97051-0, Pub. by Granada England); pap. 14.75. Brookfield Pub Co.

--Basic Electrical Engineering & Instrumentation for Engineers. 2nd ed. 560p. 1981. pap. 18.00x (ISBN 0-246-11477-0, Pub. by Granada England). Sheridan.

Bensoussan, Alain & Lions, Jacques-Louis. Impulse Control & Quasi-Variational Inequalities. 640p. 1984. 76.00 (ISBN 0-9912000-1-2, Pub. by Gauthier-Villars FR). Heyden.

Berger & Associates Cost Consultants, Inc. The Berger Building & Design Cost File, 1983: Mechanical, Electrical Trades, Vol. 2. LC 83-70008. 207p. 1983. pap. 26.45 (ISBN 0-942564-04-9). Building Cost File.

Bethell, E., et al, eds. Electrical Assembly & Wiring. (Engineering Craftsmen: No. G4). (Illus.). 1969. spiral bdg. 39.95x (ISBN 0-85083-031-1). Trans-Atlantic.

Billings, S. A. & Gray, J. O., eds. Nonlinear Systems Design. (IEE Control Engineering Ser.: No. 25). 202p. 1984. 38.00 (ISBN 0-317-37229-7). Inst Elect Eng.

Bisby, J. R., et al, eds. Electrical Fitting, Vol. 2. (Engineering Craftsmen: No. G23). (Illus.). 1969. spiral bdg. 47.50x (ISBN 0-89563-002-8). Trans-Atlantic.

Boros, A. Electrical Measurements in Engineering: Studies in Electrical & Electronic Engineering Seventeen. 352p. 1985. 78.00 (ISBN 0-444-99582-X). Elsevier.

Boylestad, Robert & Nashelsky, Louis. Electricity, Electronics, & Electromagnetics: Principles & Applications. 2nd ed. (Illus.). 544p. 1983. 31.95 (ISBN 0-13-248146-4). P-H.

Brown, Howard J. & Strumolo, Tom R., eds. Decentralizing Electricity Production. LC 83-3677. 288p. 1983. 31.00x (ISBN 0-300-02569-6). Yale U Pr.

Bruton, Len T. RC-Active Networks: Theory & Design. (Series in Electrical & Computer Engineering). (Illus.). 1980. text ed. 45.95 (ISBN 0-13-753467-1). P-H.

Bumby, J. R. Superconducting Rotating Electrical Machines. (Monographs in Electrical & Electronic Engineering). (Illus.). 1983. 39.00x (ISBN 0-19-859327-9). Oxford U Pr.

Butchbaker, Allen F. Electricity & Electronics for Agriculture. (Illus.). 392p. 1977. text ed. 21.95x (ISBN 0-8138-0525-2). Iowa St U Pr.

Butcher, F., et al, eds. Electrical Maintenance & Installation: Part One. 2nd ed. (Engineering Craftsmen: No. J2). (Illus.). 1975. spiral bdg 42.50x (ISBN 0-89563-003-6). Trans-Atlantic.

Cadzow, James & Van Landingham, Hugh. Signals, Systems & Transforms. (Illus.). 384p. 1985. text ed. 34.95 (ISBN 0-13-809542-6). P-H.

Carlson, A. Bruce & Gisser, David G. Electrical Engineering: Concepts & Applications. LC 80-21519. (Electrical Engineering Ser.). 640p. 1981. text ed. 39.95 (ISBN 0-201-03940-0); solutions manual 4.00 (ISBN 0-201-03941-9). Addison-Wesley.

Cartridge Type Solid-State Pulse Recorders for Electricity Meters. 1983. 13.00 (ISBN 0-318-18026-X, EI 25-1983). Natl Elec Mfrs.

Chen Wai-Kai. Active Network Feedback Amplifier Theory. LC 79-16997. (Illus.). 550p. 1980. text ed. 48.00 (ISBN 0-07-010779-3). McGraw.

Chirlian, Paul. Fundamentals of Electrical Engineering Analysis. 750p. 1984. text ed. 34.95. Matrix Pub.

Chirlian, Paul M. Beginning FORTH. rev. ed. 220p. (Orig.). 1983. pap. 16.95 (ISBN 0-916460-36-3). Matrix Pub.

--Fundamentals of Electrical Engineering Analysis. 650p. 1984. 34.95. Dilithium Pr.

Clement, Preston R. & Johnson, Walter C. Electrical Engineering Science. LC 82-14796. 602p. 1982. Repr. of 1960 ed. lib. bdg. 35.50 (ISBN 0-89874-442-3). Krieger.

Clidero, Robert K. & Sharpe, Kenneth H. Applied Electrical Systems for Construction. 1982. 21.95 (ISBN 0-442-21660-2). Van Nos Reinhold.

Communications 1984. (IEE Conference Publications Ser.: No. 235). 179p. 1984. pap. 62.00 (ISBN 0-85296-292-4). Inst Elect Eng.

Control Eighty-five. (IEE Conference Publication Ser.). 1985. avail. Inst Elect Eng.

Cruz, J. B., Jr., ed. System Sensitivity Analysis. LC 72-93263. (Benchmark Papers in Electrical Engineering & Computer Science Ser: Vol. 1). 428p. 1973. 55.95 (ISBN 0-87933-020-1). Van Nos Reinhold.

Davey, R., et al, eds. Electrical Inspection. (Engineering Craftsmen: No. G24). (Illus.). 1969. spiral bdg. 47.50x (ISBN 0-85083-066-4). Trans-Atlantic.

Davis, Henry B. Electrical & Electronic Technologies: A Chronology of Events & Inventors to 1900. LC 81-9179. 221p. 1981. 16.00 (ISBN 0-8108-1464-1). Scarecrow.

--Electrical & Electronic Technologies: A Chronology of Events & Inventors from 1900 to 1940. LC 82-16739. 220p. 1983. 16.00 (ISBN 0-8108-1590-7). Scarecrow.

--Electrical & Electronic Technologies: A Chronology of Events & Inventors from 1940 to 1980. LC 84-13957. 321p. 1985. 25.00 (ISBN 0-8108-1726-8). Scarecrow.

Del Toro, Vincent. Electrical Engineering Fundamentals. (Illus.). 832p. 1972. ref. ed. 36.95 (ISBN 0-13-247056-X). P-H.
Dertouzos, Michael L., et al. Systems, Networks & Computation: Basic Concepts. LC 79-4556. 528p. 1979. Repr. of 1972 ed. lib. bdg. 29.50 (ISBN 0-88275-916-7). Krieger.
Developments in Power System Protection. (IEE Conference Ser.: No. 249). 1985. 74.00 (ISBN 0-85296-305-X). Inst Electrical.
Dictionary of Electronics Engineering. (Eng. & Chinese.). 785p. 1976. 12.95 (ISBN 0-686-92369-3). French & Eur.
Din Standards for Electrical Engineering: Graphical Symbols & Wiring Diagrams. 325.00 (ISBN 0-01-006120-7, 10061-5/07). Heyden.
Donnelly, E. L. Electrical Installation Theory & Practice. 2nd ed. (Illus.). 1972. pap. text ed. 23.50x (ISBN 0-245-51007-9). Intl Ideas.
Douglas-Young, John. Complete Guide to Reading Schematic Drawings. 2nd ed. 303p. 1972. pap. 8.95 (ISBN 0-13-160424-4, Reward). P-H.
Egan, William F. Frequency Synthesis by Phase-Lock. LC 80-16917. 279p. 1981. text ed. 42.95x (ISBN 0-471-08202-3, Pub. by Wiley-Interscience). Wiley.
Electric Utilities: New Directions. 1983. 975.00 (ISBN 0-89336-294-8, E-044). BCC.
Electrical Equipment Maintenance. 1974. pap. 4.00 (ISBN 0-685-58206-X, 70B-7). Natl Fire Prot.
Electrical Fitting One. 55.00x (ISBN 0-85083-015-X, Pub. by Engineering Ind). State Mutual Bk.
Electrical Fitting Two. 55.00x (ISBN 0-85083-054-0, Pub. by Engineering Ind). State Mutual Bk.
Electrical Inspection. 55.00x (ISBN 0-85083-066-4, Pub. by Engineering Ind). State Mutual Bk.
Electrical Installations in Buildings. (IEE Conference Publication Ser.: No. 211). 58p. 1982. pap. 36.00 (ISBN 0-85296-261-4, IC 211, Pub. by Peregrinus England). Inst Elect Eng.
Electrical Maintenance & Installation. 1982. 52.00x (ISBN 0-85083-061-3, Pub. by Engineering Ind). State Mutual Bk.
Electrical Maintenance One. 1983. 52.00x (ISBN 0-85083-029-X, Pub. by Engineering Ind). State Mutual Bk.
Elgerd, O. I. Electric Energy Systems Theory: An Introduction. 2nd ed. (Electrical Engineering Ser.). 576p. 1982. 45.00x (ISBN 0-07-019230-8). McGraw.
Elgerd, Olle I. Basic Electric Power Engineering. LC 76-1751. (Electrical Engineering Ser.). 1977. text ed. 36.95 (ISBN 0-201-01717-2); solution Manual 2.50 (ISBN 0-201-01918-3). Addison-Wesley.
Faber, Rodney B. Applied Electricity & Electronics for Technology. 2nd ed. LC 77-15037. (Electronics Technology Ser.). 477p. 1982. text ed. 29.95 (ISBN 0-471-05792-4); avail. solutions (ISBN 0-471-86322-X). Wiley.
Ferguson, R. Comparative Risks of Electricity Generating Fuel Systems in the UK. 216p. 1981. 80.00 (ISBN 0-906048-66-4). Inst Elect Eng.
Fink, Donald G. & Beaty, H. Wayne. Standard Handbook for Electrical Engineers. 11th ed. (Illus.). 1978. 79.95 (ISBN 0-07-020974-X). McGraw.
Fink, Donald G. & Christiansen, Donald. Electronics Engineer's Handbook. 2nd ed. 2496p. 1982. 83.50 (ISBN 0-07-020981-2). McGraw.
Fitzgerald, A. E., et al. Basic Electrical Engineering. 5th ed. 1981. text ed. 42.00 (ISBN 0-07-021154-X). McGraw.
Flach, George. Changes in the Nineteen Eighty-One National Electrical Code. 145p. 1981. 18.95 (ISBN 0-13-127860-6, Reward); pap. 9.95 (ISBN 0-13-127852-5). P-H.
Flurscheim, C. H., ed. Power Circuit Breaker Theory & Design. rev. ed. (IEE Power Engineering Ser.: No. 1). 602p. 1982. pap. 75.00 (ISBN 0-906048-70-2, P0001, Pub. by Peregrinus England). Inst Elect Eng.
Foster, Abram J. The Coming of the Electrical Age to the United States. Bruchey, Stuart, ed. LC 78-22680. (Energy in the American Economy Ser.). 1979. lib. bdg. 28.50x (ISBN 0-405-11983-6). Ayer Co Pubs.
Frankel, Sidney. Multiconductor Transmission Line Analysis. LC 77-28230. (Illus.). 1978. 36.00x (ISBN 0-89006-054-1). Artech Hse.
Future Energy Concepts. (Conference Publication Ser.: No. 192). 360p. 1981. 78.00 (ISBN 0-85296-229-0). Inst Elect Eng.
Gagliardi, Robert. Introduction to Communications Engineering. LC 77-18531. 508p. 1978. 49.95x (ISBN 0-471-03099-6, Pub. by Wiley-Interscience). Wiley.
Gallagher, T. J. & Pearmain, A. J. High Voltage: Measurement, Testing & Design. LC 82-20398. 245p. 1983. 39.95x (ISBN 0-471-90096-6, Pub. by Wiley-Interscience). Wiley.
Gandhi, Om P. Microwave Engineering & Applications. (Illus.). 543p. 1981. 66.00 (ISBN 0-08-025589-2); pap. 27.00 (ISBN 0-08-025588-4). Pergamon.
Gee, K. C. Introduction to Open Systems Interconnection. 61p. (Orig.). 1980. pap. 17.50x (ISBN 0-85012-250-3). Intl Pubns Serv.
--Proprietary Network Architectures. (Illus.). 258p. 1981. 110.00x (ISBN 0-85012-327-5). Intl Pubns Serv.
Gerbrands, Jan J., ed. EURASIP Directory 1983: Directory of European Signal Processing Research Institutions. LC 84-15892. 1984. lib. bdg. 59.00 (ISBN 90-277-1824-5, Pub. by Reidel Holland). Kluwer Academic.
Gilder, Jules H. & Barrus, J. Scott. Pascal Programs in Science & Engineering. 2nd ed. 384p. pap. 18.95 (6265). Hayden.
Gilli, Angelo C., Sr. Electrical Principles for Electronics. rev ed. LC 77-4676. (Illus.). 1977. text ed. 32.00 (ISBN 0-07-023293-8). McGraw.
Gonen, T. Electric Power Distribution System Engineering. (Electrical Engineering Ser.). 752p. 1986. 51.95 (ISBN 0-07-023707-7). McGraw.
Gregory, B. A. An Introduction to Electrical Instrumentation & Measurement Systems. 2nd ed. LC 80-22869. 446p. 1981. pap. 34.95x (ISBN 0-470-27092-6). Halsted Pr.
Haddad, Abraham H., ed. Nonlinear Systems: Processing of Random Signals-Classical Analysis. LC 75-1014. (Benchmark Papers in Electrical Engineering & Computer Science Ser: No. 10). 1975. 67.00 (ISBN 0-12-786612-4). Acad Pr.
Hall. The Language of Electrical & Electronic Engineering in English. (English for Careers Ser.). 1977. pap. text ed. 4.25 (ISBN 0-88345-301-0, 18517). Regents Pub.
Hamilton, R. Electrical Principles for Technicians. (Electrical & Telecommunications Technicians Ser.). (Illus.). 1980. 37.50x (ISBN 0-19-859360-0). Oxford U Pr.
Hammond, Seymour B. & Gehmlich, D. K. Electrical Engineering. 2nd ed. 1971. text ed. 45.00 (ISBN 0-07-025901-1). McGraw.
Hayashi, Chihiro. Nonlinear Oscillations in Physical Systems. LC 85-42664. 400p. 1985. pap. text ed. 19.95x (ISBN 0-691-08383-5). Princeton U Pr.
Heiserman, R. L. Diagnostic Testing of Static Electrical Equipment. 127p. 1983. pap. 15.95 (ISBN 0-471-86179-0). Wiley.
--Mechanical Skills for Industrial Electricians. 1983. pap. 16.95 ea. Vol. 1, 172 pp (ISBN 0-471-86180-4). Vol. 2, 195 pp (ISBN 0-471-87579-1). Wiley.
Hettema, Robert M. Mechanical & Electrical Building Construction. (Illus.). 400p. 1984. 35.95 (ISBN 0-13-569608-9). P-H.
HF Communications Systems & Techniques. (IEE Conference Ser.: No. 245). 1985. 69.00 (ISBN 0-85296-306-8). Inst Electrical.
Hine, Fumio. Electrode Processes & Electrochemical Engineering. 428p. 1985. 55.00x (ISBN 0-306-41656-5, Plenum Pr). Plenum Pub.
Holt, Charles A. Microcomputer Organization. 1985. text ed. write for info. (ISBN 0-02-356350-8). Macmillan.
IEEE Standard 446-1980: IEEE Orange Book: IEEE Recommended Practice for Emergency & Standby Power Systems for Industrial & Commercial Applications. 1980. 19.95 (ISBN 0-471-08031-4, SHO7799). IEEE.
Inose, H. Digital Integrated Communication Systems. 368p. (not avail. in U.S.). 1980. pap. write for info. (ISBN 0-906048-61-3, TE99). Inst Elect Eng.
Institute of Electrical & Electronics Engineers. IEEE Recommended Practice for Grounding of Industrial & Commercial Power Systems. LC 82-83209. (Illus.). 136p. 1982. 17.95 (ISBN 0-471-89573-3). Wiley.
--IEEE: Recommended Practice for Protection & Coordination of Industrial & Commercial Power Systems. LC 75-27282. 312p. 1976. 19.95x (ISBN 0-471-01802-3, Pub. by Wiley-Interscience). Wiley.
Institute of Electrical & Electronics Engineering, Inc. (IEEE) IEEE Standard C-Atlas - Common ATLAS, A Subset of the ATLAS Test Language. 371p. 1982. 25.00 (ISBN 0-471-87405-1). Wiley.
Institute of Electrical & Electronics Engineers, Inc. (IEEE) Recommended Practice for Electric Power Systems in Commercial Buildings. Rev. ed. 616p. 1983. 29.95 (ISBN 0-471-89357-9). Wiley.
Institution of Electrical Engineers (UK) & Peter Peregrinus, Ltd. Software Engineering for Telecommunication Switching Systems. (IEE Conference Publication Series). 234p. 1983. pap. 74.00 (ISBN 0-85296-276-2, IC223). Inst Elect Eng.
International Conference on Centralised Control Systems (1978) Staff. International Conference on Centralised Control Systems, Second, 20-23 March, 1978. LC 78-322202. (IEE Conference Publication Ser.: No. 16). (Illus.). pap. 58.00 (ISBN 0-317-09923-X, 2051592). Bks Demand UMI.
International Conference on Pressure Surges, 3rd. Proceedings, 2 vols. Hansan, J. A. & Stephens, H. S., eds. 600p. (Orig.). 1980. PLB 87.00x (ISBN 0-906085-24-1, Dist. by Air Science Co.). BHRA Fluid.
International Conference on the Design & Application of EHV Substations (1977: London) The Design & Application of EHV Substations. (Institution of Electrical Engineers Conference Publications: No. 157). pap. 42.00 (ISBN 0-317-10191-9, 2012125). Bks Demand UMI.
IPC Business Press, ed. Electrical & Electronic Trader Year Book. 1984. 90.00x (ISBN 0-617-00243-6, Pub. by IPC Busn England). State Mutual Bk.
Johnk, Carl T. Engineering Electromagnetic Fields & Waves. LC 74-13567. 655p. 1975. 41.45x (ISBN 0-471-44289-5, Pub. by Wiley-Interscience). Wiley.
Johnson, A. Process Dynamics Estimation & Control. (IEE Control Engineering Ser.: No. 27). 187p. 1985. 47.00 (ISBN 0-86341-032-4, CE027). Inst Elect Eng.
Jones, Lincoln D. & Lima, James A. Electrical Engineering License Review. 5th ed. LC 79-21987. 282p. (Orig.). 1980. pap. 21.95 (ISBN 0-910554-30-7). Engineering.
Jordan, Edward C. & Balmain, K. G. Electromagnetic Waves & Radiating Systems. 2nd ed. 1968. ref. ed. 42.95 (ISBN 0-13-249995-9). P-H.
Jowett, C. E. Application of Engineering in Microelectronic Industries. 184p. 1975. text ed. 22.00x (ISBN 0-220-66278-9, Pub. by Busn Bks England). Brookfield Pub Co.
Jowett, Charles E. Electronic Engineering Processes. 1973. 27.50x (ISBN 0-8464-0364-1). Beekman Pubs.
Kasatkin, A. & Perekalin, M. Basic Electrical Engineering. (Russian Monographs & Texts on the Physical Sciences). 386p. 1965. 88.00 (ISBN 0-677-20100-1). Gordon.
Kazakos, D. & Papantoni-Kazakos, P. Nonparametric Methods in Communications. (Electrical Engineering & Electronics Ser.: Vol. 2). 1977. 65.00 (ISBN 0-8247-6660-1). Dekker.
Key, Eugene. Principles of Electricity for Students of Physics & Engineering. (Orig.). 1967. pap. 5.95 (ISBN 0-06-460118-8, CO 118, COS). B&N NY.
Klaasen, K. B. Reliability of Analogue Electronic Systems. (Studies in Electrical & Electronic Engineering: Vol. 13). 278p. 1984. 61.00 (ISBN 0-444-42388-5). Elsevier.
Knable, Alvin H. Electrical Power Systems Engineering: Problems & Solutions. LC 82-14801. 256p. 1982. Repr. of 1967 ed. lib. bdg. 22.50 (ISBN 0-89874-549-7). Krieger.
Kolstad, C. K. & Kohnert, G. V. Rapid Electrical Estimating & Pricing. 4th, rev. ed. (Illus.). 352p. 1985. price not set (ISBN 0-07-035131-7). McGraw.
Kotrly, Stanislav & Sucha, Ladislav. Handbook of Chemical Equilibria in Analytical Chemistry. (Ellis Horwood Analytical Chemistry Ser.: I-118). 414p. 1985. 97.00x (ISBN 0-470-27479-4). Halsted Pr.
Kucera, Vladimir. Discrete Linear Control: The Polynomial Equation Approach. LC 78-12956. 206p. 1979. 59.95x (ISBN 0-471-99726-9, Pub. by Wiley-Interscience). Wiley.
Kuffel & Abdullah, M. High Voltage Engineering. 1970. text ed. 45.00 (ISBN 0-08-024213-8); pap. text ed. 17.50 (ISBN 0-08-024212-X). Pergamon.
Kuffel, E. A. & Zaengl, W. S. High Voltage Technology: Fundamentals. (Applied Electricity & Electronics Ser.). 45.00 (ISBN 0-08-024213-8); pap. 17.50 (ISBN 0-08-024212-X). Pergamon.
Kuo, Benjamin C. Linear Networks & Systems. LC 78-27007. 426p. 1979. Repr. of 1967 ed. lib. bdg. 26.00 (ISBN 0-88275-835-7). Krieger.
Kuznetsov, M. Fundamentals of Electrical Engineering. (Russian Monographs). 460p. 1969. 117.95 (ISBN 0-677-20870-7). Gordon.
Laithwaite, L. & Freris, T. Electrical Energy: Its Generation, Transmission & Use. 365p. 1980. 20.95 (ISBN 0-07-084109-8). McGraw.
Lazar, Irwin. Electrical Systems Analysis & Design for Industrial Plants. (Illus.). 1980. 34.95 (ISBN 0-07-036789-2). McGraw.
Lee, R. R. Pocket Guide to Electrical Equipment & Instrumentation. LC 84-25340. (Illus.). 320p. (Orig.). 1985. 17.95x (ISBN 0-87201-246-8). Gulf Pub.
Lewis, R., ed. Electrical Engineering Principles & Listing Methods. (Illus.). 289p. 1973. 24.00 (ISBN 0-85334-902-9, Pub. by Elsevier Applied Sci England). Elsevier.
Lewis, Rhys. Electrical & Electronic Principles: Level Two. 192p. 1982. pap. 10.00x (ISBN 0-246-11575-0, Pub. by Granada England). Sheridan.
--Electrical & Electronic Principles: Level Three. 176p. 1983. pap. 12.00x (ISBN 0-246-11814-8, Pub. by Granada England). Sheridan.
--Electrical Engineering Principles & Testing Methods. (Illus.). 1973. 22.30x (ISBN 0-85334-564-3, Pub. by Applied Science). Burgess-Intl Ideas.
Libby, Hugo L. Introduction to Electromagnetic Nondestructive Test Methods. LC 79-9758. 382p. 1979. Repr. of 1971 ed. lib. bdg. 29.50 (ISBN 0-88275-964-7). Krieger.
Liboff, Richard L. & Dalman, G. Conrad. Transmission Lines, Waveguides, & Smith Charts. (Illus.). 320p. 1985. 37.95x (ISBN 0-02-949540-7). Macmillan.
Lindeburg, Michael R. Solutions Manual for the Electrical Engineering Review Manual. (Engineering Review Manual Ser.). 81p. 1983. pap. 9.50 (ISBN 0-932276-41-5). Prof Engine.
Lovelace, T. A. Engineering Principles for Electrical Tehcnicians, 2 vols. 1975. pap. text ed. 36.50x (ISBN 0-89563-042-7). Vol. 1 (ISBN 0-17-741108-2). Vol. 2 (ISBN 0-17-741109-0). Intl Ideas.
Mablekos, Van E. Electric Machine Theory for Power Engineers. (Illus.). 698p. 1980. text ed. 36.50 scp (ISBN 0-06-044149-6, HarpC); solutions manual avail. (ISBN 0-06-364110-0). Har-Row.
McCarthy, Oliver J. MOS Design Guide. LC 81-14645. (Wiley Ser. in Computing). 261p. 1982. 49.95x (ISBN 0-471-10026-9, Pub. by Wiley-Interscience). Wiley.
McMahon, M. The Making of a Profession: A Century of Electrical Engineering in America. LC 83-22325. 1984. 39.95 (ISBN 0-87942-173-8, PC01677). Inst Electrical.
McPartland, Joseph F. & Novak, W. J. Practical Electricity. 1964. 35.95 (ISBN 0-07-045694-1). McGraw.
Mahmoud. Large-Scale Control Systems. (Electrical Engineering & Electronics Ser.). 440p. 1985. 69.75 (ISBN 0-8247-7289-X). Dekker.
Marcus, A. & Marcus, W. Basic Electricity. 4th ed. 1973. 30.00 (ISBN 0-13-060152-7). P-H.
Marston, R. M. One Hundred-Ten Thyristor Projects Using SCR's & TRIAC's. (Illus.). 1973. pap. 8.25 (ISBN 0-8104-5096-8). Hayden.
Matt, Stephen R. Electricity & Basic Electronics. LC 81-20008. (Illus.). 1982. text ed. 16.80 (ISBN 0-87006-401-0). Goodheart.
Mazda. Electronic Engineers Reference Book. 5th ed. 1983. text ed. 119.95 (ISBN 0-408-00589-0). Butterworth.
Meiksin, Z. H. & Thackray, Philip. Electronic Design with Off-the-Shelf Integrated Circuits. 220p. 1979. 27.95 (ISBN 0-13-250282-8, Parker); pap. 9.95 (ISBN 0-13-250274-7). P-H.
Meland, Sam. Electrical Project Management. (Illus.). 320p. 1983. 34.50 (ISBN 0-07-041338-X). McGraw.
Middleton, Robert & Meyers, L. Donald. Practical Electricity. 4th ed. LC 82-20642. (Illus.). 1983. 13.95 (ISBN 0-672-23375-4). Audel.
Middleton, Robert G. & Meyers. Practical Electricity. 3rd ed. LC 82-20642. (Audel Ser.). (Illus.). 512p. 1983. 13.95 (ISBN 0-672-23375-4). G K Hall.
Molchanov, A. & Zanadvorov, P. Electrical & Radio Engineering for Physicists. (Illus.). 480p. 1975. 22.00x (ISBN 0-8464-0360-9). Beekman Pubs.
Morrison, Ralph. Grounding & Shielding Techniques in Instrumentation. 2nd ed. LC 77-3265. 146p. 1977. 26.95x (ISBN 0-471-02992-0, Pub. by Wiley-Interscience). Wiley.
Morton, A. H. Advanced Electrical Engineering. pap. 33.50x (ISBN 0-392-02075-0, SpS). Sportshelf.
Muller-Schwarz. Basic Electrical Theory & Practice. 312p. 1981. 49.95x (ISBN 0-471-25912-8, Pub. by Wiley Heyden). Wiley.
Mylroi, M. G. & Calvert, G. Measurement & Instrumentation for Control. (IEE Control Engineering Ser.: No. 26). 296p. 1984. 40.00 (ISBN 0-86341-024-3, CE026). Inst Elect Eng.
Naidu, N. S. & Kamaraju, V. High Voltage Engineering. 384p. 1983. 4.00 (ISBN 0-07-451786-4). McGraw.
Nau, Robert H. Basic Electrical Engineering. LC 83-17581. 448p. 1983. Repr. of 1958 ed. 28.50 (ISBN 0-89874-650-7). Krieger.
Neidle, M. Electrical Installation Theory & Practice. 1983. 9.95 (ISBN 0-07-084668-5). McGraw.
Ng, K. C. Electrical Network Theory. (Illus.). 1977. pap. text ed. 16.95x (ISBN 0-8464-0362-5). Beekman Pubs.
Novosad, John P. Automatic Apparatus. 408p. 1983. pap. text ed. 19.95 (ISBN 0-8403-2940-7). Kendall-Hunt.
Nunz, Gregory J. Electronics in Our World: A Survey. LC 70-146682. (Illus.). 1972. ref. ed. 32.95 (ISBN 0-13-252288-8). P-H.

Palmquist, Roland. Electrical Course for Apprentices & Journeymen. 2nd ed. LC 73-85725. 1984. 13.95 (ISBN 0-672-23393-2). Audel.

Pascoe, K. J. Properties of Materials for Electrical Engineers. LC 72-8612. 324p. 1973. (Pub. by Wiley-Interscience); pap. 28.95x (ISBN 0-471-66911-3, Pub. by Wiley-Interscience). Wiley.

Pelly, Brian R. Thyristor Phase-Controlled Converters & Cycloconverters: Operation, Control, & Performance. LC 70-125276. 1971. 69.95x (ISBN 0-471-67790-6, Pub. by Wiley-Interscience). Wiley.

Piraux, H. Dizionario Inglese-Italiano dei Termini Relativi All'Elettronica: All'Elettrotecnica e Alle Applicazioni Connesse. (Eng. & Ital.). 534p. 1977. pap. 29.95 (ISBN 0-686-92527-0, M-9195). French & Eur.

Piraux, Henri. Dictionnaire Allemand-Francais des Termes Relatifs a l'Electrorechnique, l'Electronique, et aux Applications Connexes. 4th ed. (Fr. & Ger.). 254p. 1976. pap. 31.95 (ISBN 0-686-57080-4, M-6455). French & Eur.

Plonus, Martin. Applied Electromagnetics. (Illus.). 1978. text ed. 42.00 (ISBN 0-07-050345-1). McGraw.

Porges, F. The Design of Electrical Services for Buildings. 2nd ed. 320p. 1982. 33.00 (ISBN 0-419-12360-1, NO. 6682, Pub. by E & FN Spon). Methuen Inc.

Prakash, Braham & Christensen, H., eds. International Conference on Optimum Resources Utilizations through Tribo Terotechnology & Maintenance Management: Proceedings, TRIBO-MAINT '81, 2 vols. 1250p. 1982. Set. 199.00 (ISBN 0-9605004-5-6, Pub. by Sarita Prakashan India). Eng Pubns.

Pratley, J. B. Study Notes for Technicians: Electrical & Electronic Principles, Vol. 1. 96p. 1982. 7.00 (ISBN 0-07-084661-8). McGraw.

Ragaller, Klaus, ed. Current Interruption in High-Voltage Networks. LC 78-6057. (Brown Boveri Symposia Ser.). 380p. 1978. 59.50x (ISBN 0-306-40007-3, Plenum Pr). Plenum Pub.

Ramm, A. G. Iterative Methods of Calculating Static Fields & Wave Scattering by Small Bodies. (Illus.). 124p. 1982. 29.00 (ISBN 0-387-90682-7). Springer-Verlag.

Reagan, J., et al, eds. Electrical Maintenance & Installation: Supplementary Training Material. (Engineering Craftsmen: No. J22S). (Illus.). 1976. 37.95x (ISBN 0-85083-329-9). Trans-Atlantic.

Reeves, E. A., ed. Handbook of Electrical Installation Practice, 2 vols. 1983. Set. 95.00x (ISBN 0-246-11949-7, Pub. by Granada England); Vol. 1, 368pp. write for info.; Vol. 2, 384pp. write for info. Sheridan.

Reswick, James B. & Hambrecht, F. Terry, eds. Functional Electrical Stimulation: Applications in Neural Protheses. (Biochemical & Instrumentation Engineering Ser.: Vol. 3). 1977. 95.00 (ISBN 0-8247-6632-6). Dekker.

Rhodes, Donald R. Synthesis of Planar Antenna Sources. (Oxford Engineering Science Ser.). (Illus.). 1974. 54.00x (ISBN 0-19-856123-7). Oxford U Pr.

Robinson, Enders A. Times Series Analysis & Applications. LC 81-81825. (Illus.). 628p. 1981. 25.00 (ISBN 0-910835-00-4). Goose Pond Pr.

Roe, L. B. Practical Electrical Project Engineering. 1978. 38.50 (ISBN 0-07-053392-X). McGraw.

--Practices & Procedures of Industrial Electrical Design. LC 70-168754. (Illus.). 288p. 1972. 52.50 (ISBN 0-07-053390-3). McGraw.

Roos, Attilya J. Phasors. (Operations in Electrical Engineering Ser.: VII). 83p. 1984. pap. text ed. 10.00 (ISBN 0-9800162-2-3, 991700015). Heyden.

--Resultants. (Operations in Electrical Engineering Ser.). 65p. 1982. pap. text ed. 10.00 (ISBN 0-9800162-2-3, 991700007). Heyden.

Roth, Charles H. Fundamentals of Logic Design. 2nd ed. (Electrical Engineering Ser.). (Illus.). 1979. pap. 29.95 (ISBN 0-8299-0226-0); instrs. manual avail. (ISBN 0-8299-0572-3). West Pub.

Rural Electrification. (Working Paper). 80p. 1975. 5.00 (ISBN 0-686-36160-1, PP-7505). World Bank.

Safonov, Michael G. Stability & Robustness of Multivariable Feedback Systems. (Signal Processing, Optimization & Control Ser.). 171p. 1980. 40.00x (ISBN 0-262-19180-6). MIT Pr.

Schallenberg, Richard H. Bottled Energy: Electrical Engineering & the Evolution of Chemical Energy. LC 80-68493. (Memoirs Ser.: Vol. 148). 1982. 20.00 (ISBN 0-686-82855-0). Am Philos.

Schlicke. Electrical Compossibility. (Electrical Engineering & Electronics Ser.) 224p. 1982. 45.00 (ISBN 0-8247-1887-9). Dekker.

Schwartz, Steven E. & Oldham, William G. Electrical Engineering: An Introduction. 722p. 1984. text ed. 36.95 (ISBN 0-317-06988-8). HR&W.

Seely, Samuel & Poularikas, Alexander. Electrical Engineering: Introduction & Concepts. 832p. 1981. text ed. 29.95 (ISBN 0-916460-31-2). Matrix Pub.

Sharick, Gilbert. Grounding & Bonding, Vol. XIII. 1981. 18.00 (ISBN 0-686-98069-7). Telecom Lib.

Shepherd, J. & Morton, A. H. Higher Electrical Engineering. (Pitman Paperback Ser.). (Illus.). 877p. pap. text ed. 38.50x (ISBN 0-273-40063-0). Sportshelf.

Shrader, Robert L. Electrical Fundamentals for Technicians. 2nd ed. (Illus.). 1977. text ed. 30.95 (ISBN 0-07-057141-4). McGraw.

Sinclair, Ian R. Electronics for the Service Engineer, Bk. 1, Pt. 2. 160p. 1985. text ed. 15.50x (ISBN 0-566-02575-2). Gower Pub Co.

Smith, A. V. Electrical & Electronic Applications: Level Two. 192p. 1983. pap. 12.00x (ISBN 0-246-11609-9, Pub. by Granada England). Sheridan.

Smith, Ralph J. Circuits, Devices & Systems: A First Course in Electrical Engineering. 4th ed. 751p. 1984. text ed. 38.95 (ISBN 0-471-87496-5). Wiley.

Smyth, Michael P. Linear Engineering Systems: Tools & Techniques. 386p. 1972. text ed. 33.00 (ISBN 0-08-016324-6). Pergamon.

Snow, Charles W. Electrical Drafting & Design. (Illus.). 416p. 1976. 27.95 (ISBN 0-13-247379-8). P-H.

Solymar, L. & Walsh, D. Lectures on the Electrical Properties of Materials. 3rd ed. (Illus.). 1984. 39.95x (ISBN 0-19-851163-9); pap. 19.95x (ISBN 0-19-851162-0). Oxford U Pr.

Steinberg, Bernard D. Principles of Aperture & Array System Design: Including Random & Adaptive Arrays. LC 75-30847. 356p. 1976. 53.95x (ISBN 0-471-82102-0, Pub. by Wiley-Interscience). Wiley.

Storr, Eric D., ed. Electric Energy: Low Fault Level Systems. 250p. 1984. pap. text ed. 30.00x (ISBN 0-317-04035-9, Pub. by Inst Engineering Australia). Brookfield Pub Co.

Su, Kendall L. Fundamentals of Circuits, Electronics, & Signal Analysis. LC 77-74147. (Illus.). 1978. text ed. 39.95 (ISBN 0-395-25038-2); solutions manual 9.95 (ISBN 0-395-25039-0). HM.

Symposium on Incremental Motion & Control Systems & Devices, 7th Annual, Hyatt-Regency Hotel, O'hare, Ill., May 24-27, 1978. Proceedings. Kuo, B. C., ed. LC 78-53485. (Illus.). 1978. 40.00x (ISBN 0-931538-00-9). Incremental Motion.

Tegopoulos, J. A. & Kriezis, E. E. Eddy Currents in Linear Conducting Media. (Studies in Electrical & Electronic Engineering: No. 16). 304p. 1984. 68.75 (ISBN 0-444-42420-2). Elsevier.

Texas Instruments Engineering Staff. High Speed CMOS Logic Circuits Data Book. LC 82-74480. 288p. 1983. pap. 11.75 (ISBN 0-89512-114-X, SCLD001A). Tex Instr Inc.

--Linear & Interface Circuits-1984. LC 83-51811. 600p. (Orig.). 1984. pap. text ed. 13.50 (ISBN 0-89512-155-7, SLYA001). Tex Instr Inc.

--TTL Data Book, Vol. IV. LC 83-51810. 350p. (Orig.). 1984. pap. text ed. 4.95 (ISBN 0-89512-154-9, SDYD001). Tex Instr Inc.

Thomas, D. T. Engineering Electromagnetics. 416p. 1973. text ed. 36.00 (ISBN 0-08-016778-0). Pergamon.

Thompson, Donald O. & Chimenti, Dale E., eds. Review of Progress in Quantitative Nondestructive Evaluation, Vol. 3. 1516p. 1984. 225.00x (ISBN 0-306-41678-6, Plenum Pr). Plenum Pub.

Thumann, Albert. Electrical Design, Safety, & Energy Conservation. 29.95 (ISBN 0-915586-05-3). Fairmont Pr.

Tyler, D. W. Electrical Principles for Higher Tec. 448p. 1982. pap. 20.00x (ISBN 0-246-11622-6, Pub. by Granada England). Sheridan.

Tzafestas. Multidimensional Systems. (Electrical Engineering Ser.). 704p. 1985. price not set (ISBN 0-8247-7301-2). Dekker.

U. S. Navy Bureau of Naval Personnel. Basic Electricity. 1960. pap. 7.95 (ISBN 0-486-20973-3). Dover.

Veinott, Cyril G. Computer-Aided Design of Electric Machinery. (Monographs in Modern Electrical Technology). (Illus.). 168p. 1973. 30.00x (ISBN 0-262-22016-4). MIT Pr.

Wada, Y., et al, eds. Charge Storage, Charge Transport & Electrostatics & Their Applications. LC 79-20991. (Studies in Electrical & Electronic Engineering: Vol. 2). 460p. 1980. 81.00 (ISBN 0-444-99769-5). Elsevier.

Wadhwa, C. L. Electrical Power Systems. LC 83-8555. 666p. 1983. 26.95x (ISBN 0-470-27461-1). Halsted Pr.

Westlund, Donald A. Automotive Electrical Reference Manual. (Illus.). 256p. 1983. 25.95 (ISBN 0-13-054601-1). P-H.

Whitfield, I. C. Electrical Installations Technology. 1968. pap. text ed. 11.25 (ISBN 0-08-012703-7). Pergamon.

Wildes, Karl & Lindgren, Nilo. A History of Electrical Engineering & Computer Science at MIT, 1882-1982. (Illus.). 480p. 1985. 15.00x (ISBN 0-262-23119-0). MIT Pr.

Wright, A. & Newberry, P. G. Electric Fuses. (IEE Power Engineering Ser.: No. 2). 208p. 1982. pap. 26.00 (ISBN 0-906048-78-8, P0002, Pub. by Peregrinus England). Inst Elect Eng.

Yamamura, Sakae. Theory of Linear Induction Motors. 2nd ed. LC 78-21550. 235p. 1979. 45.95x (ISBN 0-470-26583-3). Halsted Pr.

Zbar, Paul B. & Electronic Industries Association. Electricity-Electronics Fundamentals: A Text-Lab Manual. 2nd ed. (Illus.). 1977. pap. 19.30x (ISBN 0-07-072748-1). McGraw.

Ziemer, Roger E. & Peterson, Roger L. Digital Communications & Spread Spectrum System. 896p. 1985. text ed. price not set (ISBN 0-02-431670-9). Macmillan.

ELECTRIC ENGINEERING-APPARATUS AND APPLIANCES
see Electric Apparatus and Appliances

ELECTRIC ENGINEERING-BIBLIOGRAPHY
Palyza, M. M. Useful Books of Reference for Designers (1926-1983) Held by the Science Reference Library: Pt. 2 Electrical & Electronic Engineering. 75p. (Orig.). 1984. pap. 7.50 (ISBN 0-7123-0713-3, Pub. by British Lib). Longwood Pub Group.

ELECTRIC ENGINEERING-DICTIONARIES
Bindmann. Festkoerperphysik und Elektronische Technik. (Eng. & Ger.). 1104p. (Dictionary of Solid State Physics and Electrical Engineering). 1972. 83.95 (ISBN 3-87097-055-3, M-7410, Pub. by Brandstetter). French & Eur.

Budig, P. K. Dictionary of Electrical Engineering & Electronics: English-German. 1985. 129.75 (ISBN 0-444-99595-1, I-422-84). Elsevier.

Budig, P. K., ed. Dictionary of Electrical Engineering & Electronics: German-English. 690p. 1985. 134.75 (ISBN 0-444-99594-3). Elsevier.

Budig, Peter K. Fachwoerterbuch Elektrotechnik, Elektronik. (Eng. & Ger., Dictionary of Electrical Engineering and Electronics). 1976. 86.50 (ISBN 3-7785-0357-X, M-7394, Pub. by Huethig). French & Eur.

Clason, W. E. Elsevier's Electrotechnical Dictionary. (Eng., Fr., Span., Ital., Dutch & Ger.). 731p. 1965. 125.75 (ISBN 0-444-40118-0). Elsevier.

Dunsheath, Percy. History of Electrical Power Engineering. 1969. pap. 8.95x (ISBN 0-262-54007-X). MIT Pr.

English-Chinese Glossary of Electronic & Electrical Engineering. (Eng. & Chinese.). 636p. 1980. 29.95 (ISBN 0-686-97364-X, M-9255). French & Eur.

Goedecke, W. Woerterbuch der Elektrotechnik, Fernmeldetechnik und Elektonik, Vol. 1. (Ger., Eng. & Fr., Dictionary of Electrical Engineering, Telecommunication Engineering & Electronics). 1966-68. 56.00 (ISBN 3-87097-013-8, M-7018). French & Eur.

--Woerterbuch der Elektrotechnik, Fernmeldetechnik und Elektonik, Vol. 2. (Fr., Eng. & Ger., Dictionary of Electrical Engineering, Telecommuunications Engineering & Electronics). 1966-68. 56.00 (ISBN 3-87097-014-6, M-7019). French & Eur.

McGraw-Hill Editors. Dictionary of Electrical & Electronic Engineering. 504p. 1985. 15.95 (ISBN 0-07-045413-2). McGraw.

Malinova, Libuse. ed. Czech-English-English-Czech Dictionary of Electrical Engineering & Electronics. 1982. 40.00 (ISBN 0-318-00245-0). Heinman.

Miladinovic, Tomislav. Woerterbuch der Elektrotechnik und Elektronik. (Ger. & Rus.). 1970. 92.00 (ISBN 3-7736-5285-2, M-7016). French & Eur.

Ministry of Education Science & Culture. Scientific Terms Electrical Engineering. (Eng. & Japanese.). 675p. 1979. 39.95 (ISBN 0-686-97433-6, M-9330). French & Eur.

Piraux, H. French-English, English-French Dictionary of Electrotechnic Electronics & Allied Fields, 2 vols. (Fr. & Eng.). Set. 90.00 (ISBN 0-685-12017-1). Heinman.

Schlomann, A. Illustrierte Technische Woerterbucher: Elektrotechnik und Elektrochemie, Vol. 2. (Ger., Eng., Fr., Rus., Span. & Ital., Illus., Illustrated Dictionary of Electrical Engineering & Electro-Ehemistry). 1963. 105.00 (ISBN 0-686-56483-9, M-7470, Pub. by R. Oldenbourg). French & Eur.

Schwenkhagen, H. Woerterbuch Elektrotechnik und Elektronik. 2nd ed. (Ger. & Eng., Dictionary of Electrical Engineering and Electronics). 1967. 128.00 (ISBN 0-686-56610-6, M-6927). French & Eur.

Schwenkhagen, H. F. & Meinhhold, H. Woerterbuch Elektrotechnik und Elektronik. (Ger. & Eng., Dictionary of Electrical Engineering and Electronics). 1978. 128.00 (ISBN 3-7736-5072-8, M-6928). French & Eur.

Sizaire, P. Dictionnaire Technique De la Construction Electrique. (Fr.). 172p. 1968. 29.95 (ISBN 0-686-57222-X, M-6520). French & Eur.

Wennrich, P. Anglo-Amerikanische Abkuerzungen und Kurzwoerter der Elektrotechnik. (Ger. & Eng.). 307p. (Anglo-American Abbreviations and Acronyms of Electrical Engineering). 1973. pap. 25.00 (ISBN 3-7940-3100-8, M-7296, Pub. by Vlg. Dokumentation). French & Eur.

Wernicke, H. Dictionary of Electronics, Communications & Electrical Engineering, 2 vols. 1300p. Vol. 1. 36.00x (ISBN 0-685-05199-4); Vol. 2. 36.00x (ISBN 0-685-05200-1). Adlers Foreign Bks.

ELECTRIC ENGINEERING-DRAFTING
see Electric Drafting

ELECTRIC ENGINEERING-ESTIMATES
Miller, William C. Estimating & Cost Control in Electrical Construction Design. (Illus.). 1978. 26.50 (ISBN 0-442-12203-9). Van Nos Reinhold.

Page, John S. Estimator's Electrical Man-Hour Manual. 2nd ed. LC 78-73000. (Estimator's Man-Hour Library). 428p. 1979. 39.95x (ISBN 0-87201-252-2). Gulf Pub.

R. S. Means Co. Staff. Means Electrical Cost Data, 1985. 8th annual ed. Sauerbier, A., ed. LC 84-645813. 325p. 1984. pap. 36.95 (ISBN 0-911950-92-3). R S Means.

Tyler, Edward J. Estimating Electrical Construction. 272p. 1983. pap. 19.00 (ISBN 0-910460-99-X). Craftsman.

ELECTRIC ENGINEERING-EXAMINATIONS, QUESTIONS, ETC.
Arco Editorial Board. Stationary Engineer & Fireman. 5th ed. LC 66-25664. (Orig.). 1967. pap. 9.00 (ISBN 0-668-00070-8). Arco.

Puri, J. K. Mulitple Choice Questions on Fundamentals of Electrical Engineering. 160p. 1982. 50.00x (ISBN 0-7069-1757-X, Pub. by Garlandfold England). pap. 30.00x (ISBN 0-7069-1758-8). State Mutual Bk.

Rudman, Jack. Armature Winder. (Career Examination Ser.: C-2481). (Cloth bdg. avail. on request). pap. 12.00 (ISBN 0-8373-2481-5). Natl Learning.

--Assistant Building Electrical Engineer. (Career Examination Ser.: C-1909). (Cloth bdg. avail. on request). 1977. pap. 12.00 (ISBN 0-8373-1909-9). Natl Learning.

--Assistant Electrical Engineer. (Career Examination Ser.: C-37). (Cloth bdg. avail. on request). pap. 12.00 (ISBN 0-8373-0037-1). Natl Learning.

--Assistant Supervisor of Electrical Installations. (Career Examination Ser.: C-1116). (Cloth bdg. avail. on request). pap. 12.00 (ISBN 0-8373-1116-0). Natl Learning.

--Electrical Engineer. (Career Examination Ser.: C-221). (Cloth bdg. avail. on request). pap. 12.00 (ISBN 0-8373-0221-8). Natl Learning.

--Electrical Engineering Trainee. (Career Examination Ser.: C-239). (Cloth bdg. avail. on request). pap. 10.00 (ISBN 0-8373-0239-0). Natl Learning.

--Electrical Inspector. (Career Examination Ser.: C-223). (Cloth bdg. avail. on request). pap. 12.00 (ISBN 0-8373-0223-4). Natl Learning.

--Electrical Service Supervisor. (Career Examination Ser.: C-1267). (Cloth bdg. avail. on request). pap. 12.00 (ISBN 0-8373-1267-1). Natl Learning.

--Electrician. (Career Examination Ser.: C-224). (Cloth bdg. avail. on request). pap. 12.00 (ISBN 0-8373-0224-2). Natl Learning.

--Electrician's Helper. (Career Examination Ser.: C-225). (Cloth bdg. avail. on request). pap. 12.00 (ISBN 0-8373-0225-0). Natl Learning.

--Electronic Engineer. (Career Examination Ser.: C-226). (Cloth bdg. avail. on request). pap. 12.00 (ISBN 0-8373-0226-9). Natl Learning.

--Electronic Technician. (Career Examination Ser.: C-229). (Cloth bdg. avail. on request). pap. 12.00 (ISBN 0-8373-0229-3). Natl Learning.

--Junior Electrical Engineer. (Career Examination Ser.: C-397). (Cloth bdg. avail. on request). pap. 12.00 (ISBN 0-8373-0397-4). Natl Learning.

--Maintenance Electrician. (Career Examination Ser.: C-1351). (Cloth bdg. avail. on request). pap. 10.00 (ISBN 0-685-18064-6). Natl Learning.

--Maintenance Electrician Foreman. (Career Examination Ser.: C-1352). (Cloth bdg. avail. on request). pap. 10.00 (ISBN 0-8373-1352-X). Natl Learning.

--Master Electrician. (Career Examination Ser.: C-475). (Cloth bdg. avail. on request). pap. 12.00 (ISBN 0-8373-0475-X). Natl Learning.

--Senior Building Electrical Engineer. (Career Examination Ser.: C-1916). (Cloth bdg. avail. on request). pap. 12.00 (ISBN 0-8373-1916-1). Natl Learning.
--Senior Stationary Engineer (Electric) (Career Examination Ser.: C-2433). (Cloth bdg. avail. on request). pap. 12.00 (ISBN 0-8373-2433-5). Natl Learning.
--Special Electrical License. (Career Examination Ser.: C-1492). (Cloth bdg. avail. on request). pap. 10.00 (ISBN 0-8373-1492-5). Natl Learning.
--Stationary Engineer (Electric) (Career Examination Ser.: C-759). (Cloth bdg. avail. on request). pap. 10.00 (ISBN 0-8373-0759-7). Natl Learning.
--Supervisor (Electrical Power) (Career Examination Ser.: C-2238). (Cloth bdg. avail. on request). pap. 10.00 (ISBN 0-8373-2238-3). Natl Learning.
--Supervisor of Electrical Installations. (Career Examination Ser.: C-1507). (Cloth bdg. avail. on request). pap. 10.00 (ISBN 0-8373-1507-7). Natl Learning.
--Supervisory Electric Engineer. (Career Examination Ser.: C-786). (Cloth bdg. avail. on request). pap. 10.00 (ISBN 0-8373-0786-4). Natl Learning.
Yarbrough, Raymond B. Electrical Engineering Review Manual. 4th ed. LC 80-81797. (Engineering Review Manual Ser.). (Illus.). 416p. 1983. pap. 35.45 (ISBN 0-932276-36-9); wkbk. o.p. 7.00 (ISBN 0-936754-03-6). Prof Engine.

ELECTRIC ENGINEERING–HANDBOOKS, MANUALS, ETC.

Belove, Charles. Handbook of Modern Electrical & Electronic Engineering. 2200p. 1985. text ed. 53.45 (ISBN 0-471-09754-3). Wiley.
Bovay, H. E., Jr., ed. Handbook of Mechanical & Electrical Systems for Buildings. (Illus.). 864p. 1981. 62.50 (ISBN 0-07-006718-X). McGraw.
Bow. Pattern Recognition & Picture Processing. (Electrical Engineering & Electronics Ser.). 304p. 1984. 37.50 (ISBN 0-8247-7176-1). Dekker.
Del Toro, Vincent. Electrical Engineering Fundamentals. 2nd ed. (Illus.). 896p. 1986. text ed. 39.95 (ISBN 0-13-247131-0). P-H.
General Electric Company. Components Technology & Standardization Manual, 3 vols. (Illus.). 2200p. 1981. 450.00x (ISBN 0-931690-03-X). Genium Pub.
Hansteen, H. Electricians Vest Pocket Reference Book. 190p. 1983. pap. 6.95 (ISBN 0-13-247973-7). P-H.
Larpenter, Carl. Electricians' Pocket Reference & Record. 1964. 1.50 (ISBN 0-87511-071-1). Claitors.
Laughton, M. A. & Say, M. G. Electrical Engineer's Reference Book. 14th ed. (Illus.). 1024p. 1985. text ed. 114.95 (ISBN 0-408-00432-0). Butterworth.
McPartland, Joseph F. McGraw-Hill's National Electrical Code Handbook. 17th ed. 928p. 1981. 29.95 (ISBN 0-07-045693-3). McGraw.
McPartland, Joseph F. & Novak, William J. Electrical Design Details. LC 82-94. 1983. Repr. of 1960 ed. 16.50 (ISBN 0-89874-412-1). Krieger.
Mazer, William M. Supplement to the Electrical Accident Investigation Handbook, 1985. LC 82-72167. (Illus.). 175p. 1985. loose leaf 55.00 (ISBN 0-317-18175-0). Electrodata.
Osborn, Richard W. & Flach, George W. Tapping in to the NEC. Osborn, Richard W., ed. LC 82-82124. (Illus.). 178p. 1982. pap. text ed. 8.50 (ISBN 0-87765-226-0, NEC-QUE). Natl Fire Prot.
Page, John S. Estimator's Electrical Man-Hour Manual. 2nd ed. LC 78-73000. (Estimator's Man-Hour Library). 428p. 1979. 39.95x (ISBN 0-87201-252-2). Gulf Pub.
Seevers, O. C. Unique Power Systems Solved. 1982. text ed. 32.00 (ISBN 0-915586-60-6). Fairmont Pr.
Seip, G. G. Electrical Installations Handbook, 2 vols. 1316p. 1979. Set. 158.95 (ISBN 0-471-26018-5, Pub. by Wiley Heyden). Wiley.
Siemens Teams of Authors. Electrical Engineering Handbook. 762p. 1976. 67.95 (ISBN 0-471-26020-7, Pub. by Wiley Heyden). Wiley.
Sinclair & Lewis. Electronics for the Service Engineer, Bk. 2, Pt. 2. 160p. 1985. text ed. price not set (ISBN 0-566-02576-0). Gower Pub Co.
Small, Lawrence F. A Century of Politics on the Yellowstone. LC 83-51275. 150p. 1983. pap. 4.95 (ISBN 0-934318-29-8). Falcon Pr Mt.
Stallcup. Journeyman Electrician Workbook. (Illus.). 160p. 1985. 12.95 (ISBN 0-8269-1700-3). Am Technical.
Van Valkenburg, M. Linear Circuits. LC 81-17809. (Illus.). 448p. 1982. 36.95 (ISBN 0-13-536722-0). P-H.
Watersworth, G. Electrical Principles for Technicians, Vol. 1. 264p. 1981. pap. text ed. 19.95x (ISBN 0-7131-3421-6). Intl Ideas.

ELECTRIC ENGINEERING–INSURANCE REQUIREMENTS

Flach, George W. Changes in the Nineteen Eighty-Four National Electrical Code. Revised ed. (Illus.). 176p. 1984. pap. text ed. 12.95 (ISBN 0-13-127762-6). P-H.
Garland, J. D. National Electrical Code Questions & Answers, 1984. 144p. 1985. text ed. 17.95 (ISBN 0-13-609561-5); pap. 12.95 (ISBN 0-13-609553-4). P-H.
McPartland, J. F. National Electrical Code Handbook. 18th ed. 1984. write for info. (ISBN 0-317-05867-3). McGraw.
National Electrical Code. (Seventy Ser). 1975. pap. 5.50 (ISBN 0-685-57560-8, 70). Natl Fire Prot.

ELECTRIC ENGINEERING–LABORATORY MANUALS

Zbar, Paul B. & Electronic Industries Association. Electricity-Electronics Fundamentals: A Text-Lab Manual. 2nd ed. (Illus.). 1977. pap. 19.30x (ISBN 0-07-072748-1). McGraw.

ELECTRIC ENGINEERING–LAWS AND LEGISLATION

Funigiello, Philip J. Toward a National Power Policy: The New Deal & the Electric Utility Industry, 1933-1941. LC 72-92695. pap. 78.50 (ISBN 0-317-28770-2, 2020622). Bks Demand UMI.
Garland, J. D. National Electrical Code Questions & Answers, 1984. 144p. 1985. text ed. 17.95 (ISBN 0-13-609561-5); pap. 12.95 (ISBN 0-13-609553-4). P-H.
--National Electrical Code Reference Book, 1981. 3rd ed. (Illus.). 640p. 1981. 31.95 (ISBN 0-13-609321-3). P-H.
Gerbert, Kenneth L. National Electrical Code Blueprint Reading: Based on 1981. 8th ed. LC 80-67345. pap. 50.00 (ISBN 0-317-19779-7, 2023203). Bks Demand UMI.
Harman, Thomas L. Guide to the National Electrical Code, 1984. rev., 3rd ed. (Illus.). 400p. 1984. text ed. 32.95 (ISBN 0-13-370420-3). P-H.
Harmon, T. & Allen, C. Guide to the National Electral Code R. 1981. 23.95 (ISBN 0-13-370478-5). P-H.
Honey, G. Appliance Switch Standards: Approvals & Safe Electrical Control. (Illus.). 112p. 1984. text ed. 30.00x (ISBN 0-246-12491-1, Pub. by Granada England). Sheridan.
National Electrical Code. 1984 ed. loose-leaf 15.00 (ISBN 0-318-03034-9). Intl Conf Bldg Off.
National Electrical Code Handbook: 1981. 1981. 25.00 (ISBN 0-317-07377-X, SPC-6C). Natl Fire Prot.
National Fire Protection Association. Model State Electrical Law: Inspection of Electrical Installations, 1973. 1973. 8.00 (ISBN 0-317-07381-8, NFPA 70L). Natl Fire Prot.
--National Electrical Code Handbook: 1984. 1074p. 1983. 27.50 (ISBN 0-317-07356-7, SPP-6D). Natl Fire Prot.
Palmquist, Roland E. Guide to the Nineteen Eighty-Four National Electrical Code. 1984. 18.95 (ISBN 0-672-23398-3). Audel.
Smith, K. Oldham. Electrical Safety & the Law. 320p. 1985. 30.00x (ISBN 0-00-383056-X, Pub. by Collins England). Sheridan.

ELECTRIC ENGINEERING–MATHEMATICS

Bailey, Frank A. Basic Mathematics for Electricity & Electronics. 1977. pap. 9.75x (ISBN 0-673-15067-4). Scott F.
Barker, Forrest. Problems in Technical Mathematics for Electricity-Electronics. LC 76-12728. 1976. pap. 12.95 (ISBN 0-8465-0403-0). Benjamin-Cummings.
Beiser, Arthur. Schaum's Outline of Basic Mathematics for Electricity & Electronics. (Schaum's Outline Ser.). (Illus.). 208p. 1980. pap. 7.95 (ISBN 0-07-004378-7). McGraw.
Bell, S. W., et al. Mathematics for Higher National Certificate: Volume II. 3rd ed. (Illus.). pap. 126.00 (ISBN 0-317-09177-8, 2050773). Bks Demand UMI.
Blake, Ian F., ed. Algebraic Coding Theory: History & Development. LC 73-9627. (Benchmark Papers in Electrical Engineering & Computer Science: Vol. 3). 413p. 1973. 52.50 (ISBN 0-87933-038-4). Van Nos Reinhold.
Cooke, Nelson M., et al. Basic Mathematics for Electronics. 5th ed. LC 82-226. (Illus.). 688p. 1982. 32.00x (ISBN 0-07-012514-7). McGraw.
Grob, B. Mathematics for Basic Electronics. 2nd ed. 128p. 1985. text ed. price not set (ISBN 0-07-024919-9). McGraw.
Harary, Frank & Wilf, Herbert S., eds. Mathematical Aspects of Electrical Network Analysis: Proceedings of the Society for Industrial & Applied Mathematics-American Mathematical Society Symposia-New York-April, 1969. LC 79-167683. (SIAM-AMS Proceedings Ser.: Vol. 3). 1971. 26.00 (ISBN 0-8218-1322-6, SIAMS-3). Am Math.
Malvino, Albert P. Calculus for Electronics. LC 76-56805. (Illus.). 316p. 1977. Repr. of 1969 ed. lib. bdg. 21.50 (ISBN 0-88275-497-1). Krieger.
Miller, Rex & Miller, Martin R. Mathematics for Electricians & Electronics Technicians. (AUDEL Ser.). 1985. lib. bdg. 14.95 (ISBN 0-8161-1700-4). G K Hall.
Saeks, Richard. Generalized Networks. LC 76-162146. 1972. 39.50x (ISBN 0-03-085195-5); pap. text ed. 16.50x (ISBN 0-89197-767-8). Irvington.
Silvester, Peter P. & Ferrari, Ronald L. Finite Elements for Electrical Engineers. LC 82-23550. 180p. 1983. 42.50 (ISBN 0-521-25321-7); pap. 15.95 (ISBN 0-521-27310-2). Cambridge U Pr.
Singer, Bertrand B. Basic Mathematics for Electricity & Electronics. 4th ed. (Illus.). 1978. text ed. 27.70 (ISBN 0-07-057472-3). McGraw.
Watkins, A. J. Electrical Installation Calculations, Vol. 1. 3rd ed. 112p. 1981. pap. text ed. 15.95x (ISBN 0-7131-3422-4). Intl Ideas.
Weiner, Donald D. & Spina, John F. The Sinusoidal Analysis & Modeling of Weakly Nonlinear Circuits: With Application to Nonlinear Interference Effects. (Electrical-Computer Science & Engineering Ser.). 304p. 1980. 27.50 (ISBN 0-442-26093-8). Van Nos Reinhold.
Wong, E. & Hajek, B. Stochastic Processes in Engineering Systems. 2nd ed. (Texts in Electrical Engineering Ser.). 240p. 1985. 29.80 (ISBN 0-387-96061-9). Springer-Verlag.

ELECTRIC ENGINEERING–PROBLEMS, EXERCISES, ETC.

Hafer, Charles R. Electronics Engineering for Professional Engineer's Examinations. (Illus.). 1980. 32.50 (ISBN 0-07-025430-3); pap. 16.95 (ISBN 0-07-025431-1). McGraw.
Heller, Samuel. Electric Motor Repair Shop: Problems & Solutions. LC 60-14903. 186p. 1960. 22.50 (ISBN 0-911740-02-3, T4). Datarule.

ELECTRIC ENGINEERING–PROGRAMMED INSTRUCTION

Bentley, James & Hess, Karen A. A Programmed Review for Electrical Engineers. 2nd ed. 1984. 28.50 (ISBN 0-442-21628-9). Van Nos Reinhold.
The Electrical Engineering Programmed Instruction Library. (Siemens Programmed Instructions "pi" Self Study Bks.: No. 01-16). 1981. 63.95x (ISBN 0-471-25986-1, Pub. by Wiley Heyden). Wiley.

ELECTRIC ENGINEERING–SAFETY MEASURES

ASTM Standards for Electrical Protective Equipment for Workers. 101p. 1981. pap. 9.00 (ISBN 0-8031-0823-0, 03-411001-20). ASTM.
Clapp, Allen L. NESC Handbook: Development & Application of the American National Standard National Electrical Safety Code. (Grounding Rules, General Rules, & Parts Ser.: No. 1-3). 430p. 1984. text ed. 22.00x (ISBN 0-471-80783-4, Pub. by Wiley-Interscience). Wiley.
Fire-Safe Electrical Installations. LC 75-15457. (Illus.). 56p. 1975. pap. 3.75 (ISBN 0-87765-045-4, SPP-29). Natl Fire Prot.
Horvath, T. Static Elimination. Berta, I., ed. LC 82-4791. (Electrostatics & Electrostatic Applications Ser.: 1-617). 118p. 1982. text ed. 29.95 (ISBN 0-471-10405-1, Pub. by Research Studies Pr). Wiley.
An Illustrated Guide to Electrical Safety. 1983. 12.00 (ISBN 0-939874-52-0). ASSE.
Institute of Electrical & Electronics Engineers Inc. National Electrical Safety Code, 1984 Edition. 384p. 1984. text ed. 20.00x (ISBN 0-471-80606-4); pap. text ed. 14.75x (ISBN 0-471-80604-8). Wiley.
Institute of Petroleum. Electrical Safety Code, Vol. 1. 1971. 22.25 (ISBN 0-444-39967-4, Pub. by Elsevier Applied Sci England). Elsevier.
Instrument Society of America. Electrical Safety Practices. LC 68-128186. (Instrument Society of America Monographs: No. 110). pap. 45.00 (ISBN 0-317-10021-1, 2051631). Bks Demand UMI.
International Conference on Electrical Safety in Hazardous Environments, 2nd, London, 1975. International Conference on Electrical Safety in Hazardous Environments, Second, 9-11 December 1975. LC 76-373514. (Institution of Electrical Engineers Conference Publication Ser.: No. 134). pap. 53.50 (ISBN 0-317-10144-7, 2012126). Bks Demand UMI.
ISA Electrical Safety Standards. LC 81-86097. 104p. 1982. pap. text ed. 25.00x (ISBN 0-87664-641-0). Instru Soc.
Levenson, Harold & Allocca, John A. Electrical & Electronic Safety. 1982. text ed. 28.95 (ISBN 0-8359-1617-0). Reston.
Magison, E. C. Electrical Instruments in Hazardous Locations. 3rd, rev. & enlg. ed. LC 79-104837. 420p. 1978. text ed. 44.95x (ISBN 0-87664-376-4). Instru Soc.
Magison, E. C. & Calder, W. Electrical Safety in Hazardous Locations. LC 83-169373. 200p. 1983. Instr. Guide: 72p. pap. text ed. 10.00x (ISBN 0-87664-705-0); Student Text: 200p. pap. text ed. 29.95x (ISBN 0-87664-704-2). Instru Soc.
Mazer, William M. Electrical Accident Investigation Handbook: 1983 Supplement. LC 82-72167. (Illus.). 100p. 1983. write for info. looseleaf (ISBN 0-943890-04-7). Electrodata.
Small, Lawrence F. A Century of Politics on the Yellowstone. LC 83-51275. 150p. 1983. pap. 4.95 (ISBN 0-934318-29-8). Falcon Pr Mt.
Smith, K. Oldham. Electrical Safety & the Law. 320p. 1985. 30.00x (ISBN 0-00-383056-X, Pub. by Collins England). Sheridan.
Spooner, Robert B., ed. Hospital Electrical Safety Simplified. (Illus.). 144p. 1983. pap. 20.95 paper (ISBN 0-13-394874-9). P-H.
Symposium on Flameproofing, Intrinsic Safety & Other Safeguards in Electrical Instrument Practice, 27th April, 1962. (Institution of Electrical Engineers Conference Report Ser.: No. 3). pap. 24.00 (ISBN 0-317-10109-9, 2007382). Bks Demand UMI.
Vainberg, M., ed. Electrical Shocks-Safety & Related Criteria: Symposium on Safety-Related Criteria for Electrical Shocks, Toronto, Canada, Sept. 7-9, 1983. (Illus.). 350p. 1984. 75.00 (ISBN 0-08-025399-7). Pergamon.

ELECTRIC ENGINEERING–STUDY AND TEACHING

Electrical Laboratories in Higher Technical Education. LC 73-75584. (Engineering Laboratories Ser.: No. 2). 126p. (Orig.). 1973. pap. 7.50 (ISBN 92-63-10515-4, U216, UNESCO). Unipub.
Self Study Books in Electrical & Semiconductor Engineering: P3 The Magnetic Field. 1978. pap. 3.95 (ISBN 0-471-25970-5). Wiley.

ELECTRIC ENGINEERING–TABLES, CALCULATIONS, ETC.

Fu, King & Yu, T. S. Statistical Pattern Classification Using Contextual Information. LC 80-40949. (Electronic & Electrical Engineering Research Studies, Pattern Recognition &Image Processing Ser.: Vol. 1). pap. 50.30 (ISBN 0-317-26335-8, 2025199). Bks Demand UMI.
Stallcup. Designing Electrical Systems Based on the 1984 National Electrical Code. (Illus.). 362p. 1984. pap. 17.95 spiral (ISBN 0-8269-1680-5). Am Technical.
Stallcup, J. Illustrated Changes of the 1984 National Electrical Code. 1983. 12.95 (ISBN 0-8269-1525-6). Am Technical.

ELECTRIC ENGINEERING–VOCATIONAL GUIDANCE

see Engineering–Vocational Guidance

ELECTRIC ENGINEERING MATHEMATICS

see Electric Engineering–Mathematics

ELECTRIC ENGINEERS

Goedecke. Dictionary of Electrical Engineering, Telecommunications & Electronics: English-German-French, Vol. 3. 1967. 39.00 (ISBN 0-9913001-1-4, Pub. by O Brandstetter WG). Heyden.
--Dictionary of Electrical Engineering, Telecommunications & Electronics: French-English-German, Vol. 2. 1966. 34.00 (ISBN 0-9913001-0-6, Pub. by O Brandstetter WG). Heyden.

ELECTRIC EQUIPMENT OF AUTOMOBILES

see Automobiles–Electric Equipment

ELECTRIC FIELDS

see also Electromagnetic Fields

Crow, Jack E., et al, eds. Crystalline Electric Field & Structural Effects in f-Electron Systems. LC 80-12454. 650p. 1980. 89.50x (ISBN 0-306-40443-5, Plenum Pr). Plenum Pub.
Lang, Johannes G. The Eletric Field. (Siemens Programmed Instruction Ser.: 2). pap. 20.00 (2052079). Bks Demand UMI.
Sulman, Felix G. The Effect of Air Ionization, Electric Fields, Atmospherics & Other Electric Phenomena on Man & Animal. (Illus.). 424p. 1980. photocopy ed. spiral 40.50x (ISBN 0-398-03930-5). C C Thomas.

ELECTRIC FILTERS

Blinchikoff, Herman J. & Zverev, Anatol I. Filtering in the Time & Frequency Domains. LC 76-120. 494p. 1976. 63.50x (ISBN 0-471-98679-8, Pub. by Wiley-Interscience). Wiley.
Bowron, P. & Stephenson, F. W. Active Filters for Communication & Instrumentation. (Illus.). 320p. 1979. text ed. 27.00 (ISBN 0-07-084086-5). McGraw.
Chen. Passive & Active Filters: Theory & Implementation. 1986. price not set (ISBN 0-471-82352-X). Wiley.
Chen, Carson. Active Filter Design. 144p. pap. 11.95 (0959). Hayden.
Craig, J. W. Design of Lossy Filters. 1970. 25.00x (ISBN 0-262-03038-1). MIT Pr.
Daryanani, Gobind. Principles of Active Network Synthesis & Design. LC 76-20659. 495p. 1976. 45.50 (ISBN 0-471-19545-6). Wiley.

BOOKS - SUBJECT INDEX

ELECTRIC MACHINERY

Huelsman, L. P., ed. Active RC Filters: Theory & Application. (Benchmark Papers in Electrical Engineering: Vol. 15). 1976. 66.00 (ISBN 0-12-786681-7). Acad Pr.
Huelsman, Lawrence P. & Allen, Philip. Introduction to the Theory & Design of Active Filters. (Electrical Engineering Ser.). (Illus.). 1980. text ed. 42.00x (ISBN 0-07-030854-3). McGraw.
Matthews, Herbert, ed. Surface Wave Filters: Design, Construction & Use. LC 77-3913. pap. 101.70 (ISBN 0-317-09163-8, 2019522). Bks Demand UMI.
Rhodes, John D. Theory of Electrical Filters. LC 75-30767. pap. 58.50 (ISBN 0-317-09071-2, 2022103). Bks Demand UMI.
Saleh, Adel A. Theory of Resistive Mixers. 1971. 27.50x (ISBN 0-262-19093-1). MIT Pr.
Stephenson, F. W. RC Active Filter Design Handbook. (Electrical & Electronics Technology Handbook Ser.). 480p. 1985. 39.95 (ISBN 0-471-86151-0). Wiley.
Temes, Gabor C. & Mitra, Sanjit K., eds. Modern Filter Theory & Design. 566p. 1973. 58.50x (ISBN 0-471-85130-2, Pub. by Wiley-Interscience). Wiley.
Williams, Arthur B. Active Filter Design. LC 75-4288. 1975. 20.00x (ISBN 0-89006-044-4). Artech Hse.
Zverev, Anatol I. Handbook of Filter Synthesis. 576p. 1967. 80.50x (ISBN 0-471-98680-1, Pub. by Wiley-Interscience). Wiley.

ELECTRIC FISHES
see Electric Organs in Fishes

ELECTRIC FURNACES
Electric Furnace Conference: Proceedings, 41st. LC 46-22879. 328p. 1984. 60.00 (ISBN 0-89520-161-5). Iron & Steel.
Electric Furnace Proceedings, Toronto 1984, Vol. 42. 407p. 1985. 60.00 (ISBN 0-89520-168-2). Iron & Steel.
Gingery, David J. Lil Bertha-Compact Electric Furnace. 1984. pap. 7.95 (ISBN 0-917914-16-3). Lindsay Pubns.
Plockinger, Erwin & Etterich, Otto, eds. Electric Furnace Steel Production. Babler, E. B. & Babler, P. E., trs. 500p. 1985. text ed. 57.00 (ISBN 0-471-90254-3, Pub. by Wiley Heyden). Wiley.
Robiette, A. G. Electric Melting Practice. 412p. 1972. 74.95x (ISBN 0-470-72787-X). Halsted Pr.

ELECTRIC GENERATORS
see Dynamos

ELECTRIC HEATING
see also Electric Furnaces
Barber, H. Electroheat. (Illus.). 300p. 1983. pap. 26.50x (ISBN 0-246-11739-7, Pub. by Granad England). Sheridan.
Masters, Richard & Oman, R. M. How to Convert Your Present Heater to Low-Cost Electric. (Illus.). 21p. 1978. pap. 7.95 (ISBN 0-931660-00-9). R Oman Pub.

ELECTRIC INDUSTRIES
see also Electric Contracting; Electric Machinery Industry; Electrochemistry, Industrial; Electronic Industries
also individual electric articles and industries
British Electrical & Allied Manufacturers' Association. Combines & Trusts in the Electrical Industry: The Position in Europe in 1927. Wilkins, Mira, ed. LC 76-29775. (European Business Ser.). (Illus.). 1977. Repr. of 1927 ed. lib. bdg. 23.50x (ISBN 0-405-09787-5). Ayer Co Pubs.
Byatt, I. C. The British Electrical Industry Eighteen Seventy-Five to Nineteen Fourteen. 1979. 42.00x (ISBN 0-19-828270-2). Oxford U Pr.
Electrical-Electronics Insulation Conference, 16th, 1981: Proceedings. 1981. 30.00 (ISBN 0-318-18038-3). Natl Elec Mfrs.
Electronic & Electrical Companies. 1983. 200.00x (Pub. by Jordan & Sons UK). State Mutual Bk.
Facts & Figures, Electrical Manufacturing Industry. 10.00 (ISBN 0-318-18041-3). Natl Elec Mfrs.
Filament-Wound Reinforced Thermosetting Resin Conduit & Fittings. 1984. 11.50 (ISBN 0-318-18016-2, TC 13-1984). Natl Elec Mfrs.
Flourescent Luminaries. 1980. 5.00 (ISBN 0-318-18022-7, LE 1-1974). Natl Elec Mfrs.
Harris, D. J., et al. Coal, Gas & Electricity Industries. (Reviews of United Kingdom Statistical Sources Ser.: Vol. XI). 1979. 65.00 (ISBN 0-08-022461-X). Pergamon.
Instructions for the Handling, Installation, Operation, & Maintenance of Motor Control Centers. 1983. 7.00 (ISBN 0-318-18017-0, ICS 2.3-1983). Natl Elec Mfrs.
Jacobson, D. M. & Evans, D. S. Critical Materials in the Electrical & Electronics Industry. 59p. 1985. pap. text ed. 16.00x (ISBN 0-901462-26-8, Metals Soc). Brookfield Pub Co.
Okochi, Akio & Uchida, Hoshimi, eds. The International Conferences on Business History: Development & Diffusion of Technology, Electrical & Chemical Industries, No. 6. 236p. 1980. 29.50x (ISBN 0-86008-270-9, Pub. by U of Tokyo Japan). Columbia U Pr.
Pinner, Felix. Emil Rathenau & das Elektrische Zeitalter. Wilkins, Mira, ed. LC 76-29777. (European Business Ser.). Tr. of Emil Rothenau & the Electrical Age. 1977. Repr. of 1918 ed. lib. bdg. 32.00x (ISBN 0-405-09789-1). Ayer Co Pubs.
Plugs, Receptacles, & Cable Connectors of the Pin & Sleeve Type for Industrial Use. 1983. 10.00 (ISBN 0-318-18029-4, PR 4-1983). Natl Elec Mfrs.
Plugs, Receptacles, & Connectors of the Pin & Sleeve Type for Hazardous Locations. 1983. 15.00 (ISBN 0-318-18028-6, PB 2.2-1983). Natl Elec Mfrs.
Renewal Parts for Motors & Generators (Performance, Selection, & Maintenance) 1981. 5.50 (ISBN 0-318-18027-8, RP 1-1981). Natl Elec Mfrs.
Safety Labels for Padmounted Switchgear & Transformers Sited in Public Areas. 1982. 6.50 (ISBN 0-318-18031-6, 260-1982). Natl Elec Mfrs.
Siemens, Georg. History of the House of Siemens, 2 vols. Wilkins, Mira, ed. LC 76-29776. (European Business Ser.). 1977. Repr. of 1957 ed. Set. lib. bdg. 51.00x (ISBN 0-405-09793-X); lib. bdg. 25.50x ea. Vol. 1 (ISBN 0-405-09794-8). Vol. 2 (ISBN 0-405-09795-6). Ayer Co Pubs.
Society of Plastics Engineers. Plastics in the Electrical Industry: Technical Papers, Regional Technical Conference, March 3-4, 1980, Milwaukee, Wisconsin. (Illus.). pap. 57.30 (ISBN 0-317-08863-7, 2012018). Bks Demand UMI.
Vennard, Edwin. Management of the Electric Energy Business. LC 79-696. (Illus.). 1979. 42.50 (ISBN 0-07-067402-7). McGraw.

ELECTRIC INSULATORS AND INSULATION
see also Electronic Apparatus and Appliances–Plastic Embedment
Conference on Electrical Insulation & Dielectric Phenomena. Annual Report. Incl. 1952. 61p; 1957. 69p; 1958. 57p; 1963. 144p. 5.00 (ISBN 0-309-01141-8); 1964. 146p. 5.00 (ISBN 0-309-01238-4); 1965. 139p. 5.00 (ISBN 0-686-64609-6); 1966. 129p. 10.00 (ISBN 0-309-01484-0); 1967. 201p. 10.00 (ISBN 0-309-01578-2); 1968. 204p. 10.00 (ISBN 0-309-01705-X); 1969. 193p. 15.00 (ISBN 0-309-01764-5); 1970. 258p. 15.00 (ISBN 0-309-01870-6); 1971. 289p. 15.00 (ISBN 0-309-02032-8); 1972. 496p. 20.00 (ISBN 0-309-02112-X); 1973. 638p. 25.00 (ISBN 0-309-02229-0); 1974. 706p. 25.00 (ISBN 0-309-02416-1); 1975. 544p. 22.00 (ISBN 0-686-64610-X); 1976. 576p. 25.00 (ISBN 0-686-64611-8); 1977. 596p. 25.00 (ISBN 0-309-02866-3); 1978. 405p. 25.00 (ISBN 0-309-02861-2); 1979. 25.00 (ISBN 0-309-02933-3). Natl Acad Pr.
Hilado, Carlos J. Flammability Handbook for Electrical Insulation. 145p. 1982. 40.00 (ISBN 0-87762-316-3). Technomic.
Insulation Specifications, Vol. 2. (Research Report Ser.). 54p. 1981. pap. 5.50 (ISBN 0-86718-115-X); pap. 4.00 members. Natl Assn Home.
Kind, D. & Karner, H. High Voltage Insulation Tec. 200p. (Orig.). 1985. pap. 20.00 (ISBN 3-528-08599-1, Pub. by Vieweg & Sohn Germany). Heyden.
Lampert, M. A. & Mark, P. Current Injections in Solids. (Electrical Science Ser). 1970. 80.00 (ISBN 0-12-435350-9). Acad Pr.
Latham, R. V. High Voltage Vacuum Insulation: The Physical Basis. LC 80-41602. 1981. 47.00 (ISBN 0-12-437180-9). Acad Pr.
Lucovsky, et al. The Physics of MOS Insulators. 400p. 1980. 59.00 (ISBN 0-08-025969-3). Pergamon.
Naidu, Motukuru S. & Maller, Venktesh N. Advances in High Voltage Insulation & Arc Interruption in SF & Vacuum. 1981. 39.00 (ISBN 0-08-024726-1). Pergamon.
Sillars, Ronald W. Electrical Insulating Materials & Their Application. (Institution of Electrical Engineers Monograph Ser.: No. 14). (Illus.). pap. 77.30 (ISBN 0-317-08846-7, 2011894). Bks Demand UMI.
Symposium on Etching for Pattern Definition (1976: Washington, D.C.) Etching for Pattern Definition: Proceedings of the Symposium, 1976. Hughes, Henry G., et al, eds. LC 76-9231. (Illus.). pap. 52.30 (ISBN 0-317-09171-9, 2050976). Bks Demand UMI.
Townsend, P. D. & Kelly, J. C. Colour Centres & Imperfections in Insulators & Semiconductors. 39.00x (ISBN 0-686-96992-8, Pub. by Scottish Academic Pr Scotland). State Mutual Bk.
Watkins, A. J. Electrical Installation Calculations, Vol. 2. 3rd ed. (Illus.). 100p. 1983. pap. text ed. 15.95x (ISBN 0-7131-3488-7). Intl Ideas.

ELECTRIC INSULATORS AND INSULATION–COLLECTORS AND COLLECTING
Tibbitts, John C. Guide for Insulator Collectors, with Prices, Vol. 3. LC 67-28696. (Illus.). 1969. pap. 4.00 (ISBN 0-911508-06-6). Little Glass.

ELECTRIC LAMPS
see also Electric Lighting; Neon Lamps
Bright, Arthur A., Jr. The Electric-Lamp Industry: Technological Change & Economic Development from 1800 to 1947. LC 72-5037. (Technology & Society Ser.). 554p. 1972. Repr. of 1949 ed. 41.00 (ISBN 0-405-04690-1). Ayer Co Pubs.
Martens, Rachel. Repairing, Rewiring & Restoring Lamps & Lighting Fixtures. (Illus.). 190p. pap. Cancelled (ISBN 0-385-14747-3). Wallace-Homestead.
Method for Electrical & Photometric Measurements of General Service Incandescent Filament Lamps. (Measurement & Testing Guides Ser.). 1981. 5.50 (ISBN 0-686-96301-6, LM-45); members 3.00 (ISBN 0-686-99759-X). Illum Eng.
Method for Photometric Testing of Indoor Luminaires Using HID Lamps. (Measurement & Testing Guides Ser.). 1974. 4.50 (ISBN 0-686-96305-9, LM-46); members 2.20 (ISBN 0-686-99760-3). Illum Eng.
Method for the Electrical & Photometric Measurements of Fluorescent Lamps. (Measurement & Testing Guides Ser.). 1982. 6.50 (ISBN 0-686-96228-1, LM-9); members 3.75 (ISBN 0-686-99739-5). Illum Eng.
Photometric Measurements of HID Lamps. (Measurement & Testing Guides Ser.). 1975. 4.50 (ISBN 0-686-96322-9, LM-51); members 2.00 (ISBN 0-686-99765-4). Illum Eng.
Photometric Testing of Indoor Fluorescent Luminaires. (Measurement & Testing Guides Ser.). 1972. 4.00 (ISBN 0-686-96289-3, LM-41); members 2.00 (ISBN 0-686-99755-7). Illum Eng.

ELECTRIC LIGHT
see Electric Lighting; Photometry

ELECTRIC LIGHTING
see also Electric Lamps; Lighting; Neon Lamps; Lighting, Architectural and Decorative; Neon Lamps
Frier, John P. & Frier, Mary E. Industrial Lighting Systems. (Illus.). 336p. 1980. 32.50 (ISBN 0-07-022457-9). McGraw.
Lightning & Power Systems. (IEE Conference Publications Ser.: No. 236). 209p. 1984. pap. 68.00 (ISBN 0-85296-293-2). Inst Elect Eng.
Pagen, Dennis. Powered Ultralight Training Course. (Illus.). 48p. 1981. pap. 9.95 (ISBN 0-686-32602-4). D Pagen.
Pellegrino, Ronald. The Electronic Arts of Sound & Light. 256p. 1982. 28.50 (ISBN 0-442-26499-2). Van Nos Reinhold.
Sorcar, Prafulla C. Energy Saving Lighting Systems. 368p. 1982. 27.50 (ISBN 0-442-26430-5). Van Nos Reinhold.

ELECTRIC LIGHTING–HISTORY
Cox, James A. A Century of Light. LC 78-19204. (Illus.). 1979. Set. 17.50 (ISBN 0-87502-062-3). Benjamin Co.

ELECTRIC LIGHTING, FLUORESCENT
see Fluorescent Lighting

ELECTRIC LINES
Here are entered works on general transmission systems, their construction and properties.
see also Electric Cables; Electric Circuits; Electric Networks; Electric Power Transmission; Electric Wiring
Anderson, Leonard. Electric Transmission Line Fundamentals. 1984. text ed. 35.95 (ISBN 0-8359-1597-2). Reston.
Chipman, R. A. Transmission Lines. (Schaum Outline Ser.). 1968. pap. 9.95 (ISBN 0-07-010747-5). McGraw.
Dearholt, Donald & McSpadden, William. Electromagnetic Wave Propagation. (Illus.). 480p. 1973. text ed. 58.00 (ISBN 0-07-016205-0). McGraw.
Metzger, G. & Vabre, J. P. Transmission Lines with Pulse Excitation. (Electrical Science Ser). (Fr). 1969. 60.00 (ISBN 0-12-493050-6). Acad Pr.
Receiving Tube Characteristics & Socket Connection Guide. 1981. 3.00 (ISBN 0-938630-11-3). ARS Enterprises.
Rudman, Jack. Lineman (Electrical Power) (Career Examination Ser.: C-450). (Cloth bdg. avail. on request). pap. 8.00 (ISBN 0-8373-0450-4). Natl Learning.
Shevchenko, Viktor V. Continuous Transitions in Open Waveguides. Beckmann, Petr, tr. from Rus. LC 72-145593. (Electromagnetics Ser.: Vol. 5). (Illus.). 1971. 25.00x (ISBN 0-911762-08-6). Golem.
Weeks, Walter L. Transmission & Distribution of Electrical Energy. (Illus.). 302p. 1981. text ed. 28.95 scp (ISBN 0-06-046982-X, HarpC). Harrow.

ELECTRIC LOCOMOTIVES
Harris, Ken. World Electric Locomotives. (Illus.). 160p. 1981. 17.95 (ISBN 0-86720-569-5). Jane's Pub Inc.
Haut, F. J. A History of the Electric Locomotive. LC 76-103871. 208p. 1981. 20.00 (ISBN 0-498-02466-0). A S Barnes.
Kennedy, Rex. Diesels & Electrics on Shed: Eastern Region, Vol. 2. 96p. 30.00x (ISBN 0-86093-036-X, Pub. by ORPC Ltd UK). State Mutual Bk.
--Diesels & Electrics on Shed: London Midland Region, Vol. 1. 80p. 30.00x (ISBN 0-86093-035-1, Pub. by ORPC Ltd UK). State Mutual Bk.
--Diesels & Electrics on Shed: Scottish Region, Vol. 4. 112p. 30.00x (ISBN 0-86093-043-2, Pub. by ORPC Ltd UK). State Mutual Bk.
Marsden, C. J. SR Electric Multiple Units, No. 7. 32p. 20.00x (ISBN 0-86093-096-3, Pub. by ORPC Ltd UK). State Mutual Bk.
Nicolle, B. B. R. Electrics: Midland Region, No. 3. 32p. 20.00x (ISBN 0-86093-056-4, Pub. by ORPC Ltd UK). State Mutual Bk.
Wright, Roy V., ed. Diesel Electric Locomotives, 1925-1938. (Train Shed Cyclopedia Ser., No. 20). (Illus.). 1974. pap. 5.95 (ISBN 0-912318-49-X). N K Gregg.

ELECTRIC LOGGING (OIL WELLS)
see Oil Well Logging, Electric

ELECTRIC MACHINERY
see also Dynamos; Electric Controllers; Electric Current Converters; Electric Driving; Electric Motors; Electric Transformers; Electricity in Mining; Oscillators, Electric
Anderson, Edwin. Electric Machines & Transformers. 2nd ed. 1985. text ed. 28.95 (ISBN 0-8359-1618-9). Reston.
Anderson, Leonard. Electric Machines & Transformers. (Illus.). 336p. 1980. text ed. 28.95 (ISBN 0-8359-1615-4); instr's. manual free (ISBN 0-8359-1616-2). Reston.
Anderson, R. T., et al, eds. Rotating Electrical Equipment Winding & Building, 2 vols. (Engineering Craftsmen: No. G2). (Illus.). 1969. Set. spiral bdg. 79.95x (ISBN 0-85083-030-3). Intl Ideas.
Buyse, H. & Robert, J., eds. Electrical Machines & Converters: Modelling & Simulation. 1985. 40.75 (ISBN 0-444-87596-4). Elsevier.
--Simulation of Electrical Machines: Proceedings of the Conference, Liege, Belgium, May 17-18, 1983. 1984. write for info. (North-Holland). Elsevier.
Caton, R. L., et al, eds. Rotating Electrical Equipment Testing, 2 vols. (Engineering Craftsmen: No. G22). (Illus.). 1969. Set. spiral bdg. 69.95x (ISBN 0-85083-072-9). Intl Ideas.
Chapman, S. J. Electric Machinery Fundamentals. 672p. 1984. 32.50 (ISBN 0-07-010662-2). McGraw.
Chaston, A. Norton. Electrical Machinery. 1985. text ed. 32.95 (ISBN 0-8359-1580-8). Reston.
Del Toro, Vincent. Electric Machines & Power Systems. (Illus.). 720p. 1985. text ed. 41.95 (ISBN 0-13-248709-8). P-H.
Draper, Alec. Electrical Machines. 2nd ed. LC 67-98866. (Electrical Engineering Ser.). pap. 101.00 (ISBN 0-317-27852-5, 2025256). Bks Demand UMI.
Electrical Equipment: Principles of Steam Generation, Module 15. (Illus.). 100p. 1982. 10.00 (ISBN 0-87683-265-6); instr's. manual 15.00 (ISBN 0-87683-286-9). G P Courseware.
Electrical Machines: Design & Applications. (IEE Conference Publication Ser.: No. 213). 272p. 1982. pap. 66.00 (ISBN 0-85296-260-6, IC 213, Pub. by Peregrinus England). Inst Elect Eng.
Emanuel, Pericles J. Motors, Generators, Transformers & Energy. (Illus.). 560p. 1985. text ed. 32.95 (ISBN 0-13-604026-8). P-H.
Engineering Industry Training Board, London, ed. Static Electrical Equipment Winding & Building, 2 vols. (Engineering Craftsmen: No. G1). (Illus.). 1968. Set. spiral bdg. 69.95x (ISBN 0-89563-022-2). Vol. 2 (ISBN 0-85083-128-8). Intl Ideas.
Fardo, Stephen W. & Patrick, Dale R. Rotating Electrical Machinery & Power Systems. (Illus.). 304p. 1985. text ed. 29.95 (ISBN 0-13-783309-1). P-H.
Fitzgerald, A. E., et al. Electric Machinery. 4th ed. (McGraw-Hill Series in Electrical Engineering). (Illus.). 640p. 1983. text ed. 42.00 (ISBN 0-07-021145-0). McGraw.
Govinda Rao, C. Generalised Circuit Theory of Electrical Machines. 248p. 1981. 30.00x (ISBN 0-86131-028-4, Pub. by Orient Longman India). State Mutual Bk.
Hancock, Norman N. Matrix Analysis of Electrical Machinery. 2nd ed. LC 74-3286. 1974. pap. text ed. 13.25 (ISBN 0-08-017899-5). Pergamon.
Hindmarsh, J. Electrical Machines & Their Applications. 4th ed. (Illus.). 692p. 1984. 42.00 (ISBN 0-08-030572-5); pap. 16.00 (ISBN 0-08-030573-3). Pergamon.
--Worked Examples in Electrical Machines & Drives. (Applied Electricity & Electronics Ser.). (Illus.). 150p. 1981. 28.00 (ISBN 0-08-026131-0); pap. 19.25 (ISBN 0-08-026130-2). Pergamon.
Hubert, Charles. Preventive Maintenance of Electrical Equipment. 2nd ed. 1969. 32.00 (ISBN 0-07-030839-X). McGraw.

Jacobson, D. M. & Evans, D. S. Critical Materials in the Electrical & Electronics Industry. 59p. 1985. pap. text ed. 16.00x (ISBN 0-901462-26-8, Metals Soc). Brookfield Pub Co.

Jurek, Stefan F. Electrical Machines for Technicians & Technician Engineers. LC 73-163561. pap. 87.50 (ISBN 0-317-09077-1, 2020980). Bks Demand UMI.

Kosow, Irving L. Electric Machinery & Transformers. (Illus.). 1972. ref. ed. 34.95 (ISBN 0-13-247205-8). P-H.

Kovacs, P. K. Transient Phenomena in Electrical Machines. (Studies in Electrical & Electronic Engineering: Vol. 9). 1984. 90.50 (ISBN 0-444-99663-X, I-345-83). Elsevier.

Krause, P. C. Analysis of Electric Machinery. (Electrical Engineering Ser.). 688p. 1986. price not set (ISBN 0-07-035436-7). McGraw.

Lindsay, J. F. & Rashid, M. H. Electromechanics & Electrical Machinery. (Illus.). 240p. 1986. text ed. 34.95 (ISBN 0-13-250093-0). P-H.

Liwschitz-Garik, Michael & Gentilini, Celso. Winding Alternating Current Machines: A Book for Winders, Repairmen, & Designers of Electric Machines. 1950. 59.00 (ISBN 0-911740-03-1). Datarule.

McLaren, Peter G. Elementary Electrical Power & Machines. LC 83-266. (Series in Electrical & Electronic Engineering (Ellis Horwood)). 320p. 1984. text ed. 69.95x (ISBN 0-470-20054-5); pap. text ed. 24.95x (ISBN 0-470-20057-X). Halsted Pr.

McPherson, George. An Introduction to Electrical Machines & Transformers. LC 80-19632. 557p. 1981. text ed. 37.50 (ISBN 0-471-05586-7); teacher's manual avail. (ISBN 0-471-07954-5). Wiley.

Magureanu, R. & Fransu, A. Electrical Machines & Systems. 750p. 1983. 59.00x (ISBN 0-686-92057-0, Pub. by Tech Pr). State Mutual Bk.

Matsch, Leander. Electromagnetic & Electromechanical Machines. 2nd ed. 521p. 1977. text ed. 36.95 scp (ISBN 0-7002-2501-3, HarpC); scp solutions manual 5.50 (ISBN 0-7002-2502-1). Har-Row.

Metzger, D. Electronic Components, Instruments & Troubleshooting. 1981. 34.95 (ISBN 0-13-250266-6). P-H.

Moore, Arthur H. & Elonka, Stephen M. Electrical Systems & Equipment for Industry. LC 77-5640. (Illus.). 368p. 1977. Repr. of 1971 ed. lib. bdg. 23.50 (ISBN 0-88275-561-7). Krieger.

Nasar, S. A. & Unnewehr, L. E. Electromechanics & Electric Machines. 2nd ed. LC 78-8967. 1979. 37.50 (ISBN 0-471-08091-8); tchrs. manual avail. (ISBN 0-471-03651-X); solutions manual avail. (ISBN 0-471-87154-0). Wiley.

Nasar, Syed A. Electric Energy Conversion & Transmission. 1985. text ed. write for info. (ISBN 0-02-385960-1); solutions manual avail. (ISBN 0-02-385970-9). Macmillan.

--Electric Machines & Transformers. 400p. 1983. text ed. write for info. (ISBN 0-02-385950-4). Macmillan.

--Power System & Electric Machines. 425p. 1985. text ed. write for info. (ISBN 0-02-385960-1). Macmillan.

--Schaum's Outline of Electric Machines & Electromechanics. (Schaum's Outline Ser.). (Illus.). 208p. 1981. pap. 8.95 (ISBN 0-07-045886-3). McGraw.

Purged & Pressurized Enclosures for Electrical Equipment. (Forty Ser.). 1974. pap. 2.50 (ISBN 0-685-58096-2, 496). Natl Fire Prot.

Richardson. Laboratory Operations for Rotating Electric Machinery & Transformer Technology. 256p. 1980. pap. text ed. 9.95 (ISBN 0-8359-3925-1). Reston.

Richardson, Donald V., ed. Handbook of Rotating Electric Machinery. (Illus.). 652p. 1980. text ed. 31.95 (ISBN 0-8359-2759-8). Reston.

Sarma, Mulukutla S. Electric Machines: Steady-State Theory & Dynamic Performance. 656p. 1984. text ed. write for info. (ISBN 0-697-00061-3); instr's. manual avail. (ISBN 0-697-00194-6). Wm C Brown.

Sen Gupta, D. P. & Lynn, J. W. Electrical Machine Dynamics. (Science Technology Ser.). (Illus.). 300p. 1980. text ed. 57.50x (ISBN 0-333-13884-8). Scholium Intl England.

Singh, Balbir. Electric Machine Design. 464p. 1981. text ed. 30.00x (ISBN 0-7069-1111-3, Pub. by Vikas India). Advent NY.

Siskind, Charles S. Electrical Machines: Direct & Alternating Currents. 2nd ed. 1959. text ed. 32.00 (ISBN 0-07-057728-5). McGraw.

Slemon, G. R. & Straughen, A. Electric Machines. LC 79-16369. (Illus.). text ed. 39.95 (ISBN 0-201-07730-2); solutions manual 3.00 (ISBN 0-201-07731-0). Addison-Wesley.

Smith, Richard T. Analysis of Electrical Machines. LC 81-4541. (Illus.). 240p. 1982. 40.00 (ISBN 0-08-027174-X). Pergamon.

Thaler, George J. & Wilcox, Milton L. Electric Machines: Dynamics & Steady State. LC 66-17610. (Illus.). pap. 160.00 (ISBN 0-317-08854-8, 2011952). Bks Demand UMI.

ELECTRIC MACHINERY–ALTERNATING CURRENT

see also Electric Machinery, Synchronous

Bose, Bimal K., ed. Adjustable Speed AC Drive Systems. LC 80-27789. 460p. 1981. 41.55 (ISBN 0-87942-145-2, PC01404). Inst Electrical.

Say, M. G. Alternating Current Machines. 5th ed. LC 83-10719. 632p. 1984. pap. 21.95x (ISBN 0-470-27451-4). Halsted Pr.

ELECTRIC MACHINERY–DIRECT CURRENT

Kuo, B. C. & Tal, J., eds. Incremental Motion Control: DC Motors & Controls, Vol. 1. LC 78-53480. (Illus.). 1978. 39.50x (ISBN 0-918152-02-X). SRL Pub Co.

ELECTRIC MACHINERY, SYNCHRONOUS

see also Synchros

Sarma, Mulukutla S. Synchronous Machines: Their Theory, Stability, & Excitation Systems. 600p. 1979. 79.75 (ISBN 0-677-03930-1). Gordon.

ELECTRIC MACHINERY INDUSTRY

Cilingiroglu, Ayhan. Manufacture of Heavy Electrical Equipment in Developing Countries. LC 76-89962. (World Bank Staff Occasional Papers Ser: No. 9). (Illus.). 135p. 1969. pap. 5.50x (ISBN 0-8018-1097-3). Johns Hopkins.

ELECTRIC MACHINING

see Electric Metal-Cutting

ELECTRIC MEASUREMENTS

see also Bridge Circuits; Cathode Ray Oscilloscope; Electric Meters; Electronic Measurements; Oil Well Logging, Electric; Radio Measurements; Strain Gages

Cooper, W. D. & Helfrick, A. D. Electronic Instrumentation & Measurement Techniques. 3rd ed. (Illus.). 496p. 1985. text ed. 32.95 (ISBN 0-13-250721-8). P-H.

Frank, Ernest. Electrical Measurement Analysis. LC 77-3508. (Electrical & Electronic Engineering Ser.). (Illus.). 458p. 1977. Repr. of 1959 ed. lib. bdg. 30.50 (ISBN 0-88275-554-4). Krieger.

Geczy, Steven. Basic Electrical Measurements. (Illus.). 144p. 1984. pap. 19.95 (ISBN 0-13-060285-X). P-H.

Handscombe, E. Electrical Measuring Instruments. (Wykeham Science Ser.: No. 2). 126p. 1970. pap. cancelled (ISBN 0-85109-130-X). Taylor & Francis.

Kroupa, V. F. Frequency Stability Fundamentals & Measurements. LC 83-18336. 400p. 1983. 62.95 (ISBN 0-87942-171-1, PC01644). Inst Electrical.

Stout, Melville B. Basic Electrical Measurements. 2nd ed. (Illus.). 1960. ref. ed. 35.95 (ISBN 0-13-059808-9); answers 0.25 (ISBN 0-13-059790-2). P-H.

Thompson, Lawrence M. Basic Electrical Measurements & Calibration: Instructor's Resource Manual. LC 78-73423. 24p. (Orig.). 1980. pap. text ed. 4.50x (ISBN 0-87664-451-5). Instru Soc.

Van Der Ziel, Aldert. Noise in Measurements. LC 76-12108. 228p. 1976. 40.50x (ISBN 0-471-89895-3, Pub. by Wiley-Interscience). Wiley.

Wieder, H. H. Laboratory Notes on Electrical & Galvano-Magnetic Measurements. (Materials Science Monographs: Vol. 2). 278p. 1979. 59.75 (ISBN 0-444-41763-X). Elsevier.

ELECTRIC MECHANICAL DEVICES

see Electromechanical Devices

ELECTRIC METAL-CUTTING

ANSI Accredited. Safety in Welding & Cutting: Z49. 1-83. (Illus.). 30p. (Orig.). 1983. pap. text ed. 20.00 (ISBN 0-87171-236-9); member 15.00. Am Welding.

Krasyuk, B. A., ed. Electrospark Machining of Metals, Vol. 3. LC 64-20561. 184p. 1965. 29.50x (ISBN 0-306-18243-2, Consultants). Plenum Pub.

ELECTRIC METERS

Handscombe, E. Electrical Measuring Instruments. (Wykeham Technology Ser.: No. 2). 126p. 1970. 9.95x (ISBN 0-8448-1173-4). Crane Russak Co.

--Electrical Measuring Instruments. (Wykeham Science Ser.: No. 2). 126p. 1970. pap. cancelled (ISBN 0-85109-130-X). Taylor & Francis.

Rudman, Jack. Electric Meter Tester. (Career Examination Ser.: C-2249). (Cloth bdg. avail. on request). pap. 12.00 (ISBN 0-8373-2249-9). Natl Learning.

ELECTRIC MOTORS

see also Armatures; Automobiles, Electric; Electric Railway Motors; Electric Transformers; Electricity in Mining; Frequency Changers

Acarnley, P. P. Stepping Motors: A Guide to Modern Theory & Practice. (IEE Control Engineering Ser.: No. 19). 160p. 1982. 48.00 (ISBN 0-906048-83-4, CEH19); pap. 29.00 (ISBN 0-906048-75-3, CEP19). Inst Elect Eng.

Alerich, Walter. Electric Motor Control. 3rd, rev ed. 1983. 11.95 (ISBN 0-442-20862-6). Van Nos Reinhold.

Anderson, Edwin P. & Miller, Rex. Electric Motors. 4th ed. LC 82-17788. (Audel Ser.). 1983. 12.95 (ISBN 0-672-23376-2). G K Hall.

Andreas. Energy-Efficient Electric Motors. (Electrical Engineering & Electronic Ser.: Vol. 15). 200p. 1982. 35.00 (ISBN 0-8247-1786-4). Dekker.

Bottle, E. K. Fractional Horse-Power Electric Motors: A Guide to Types & Applications. 209p. 1948. 10.95x (ISBN 0-85264-051-X, Pub. by Griffin England). State Mutual Bk.

Drives-Motors-Controls Nineteen Eighty-Two: Proceedings of the First European Conference Held in Leeds, England, June 29-July 1, 1982. (PPL Conference Publications: No. 19). 160p. 1982. pap. 54.00 (ISBN 0-906048-85-0, Pub. by Pereginus England). Inst Elect Eng.

Electro-Craft Corp. DC Motors, Speed Controls, Servo Systems: An Engineering Handbook. 3rd exp. ed. LC 76-56647. 504p. 1977. text ed. 45.00 (ISBN 0-08-021714-1); pap. text ed. 19.50 (ISBN 0-08-021715-X). Pergamon.

Gottlieb, Irving M. Electric Motors & Control Techniques. (Illus.). 252p. 1982. 16.95 (ISBN 0-8306-2565-8, 1465); pap. 10.25 (ISBN 0-8306-1465-6). TAB Bks.

Heller, Samuel. Electric Motor Repair Shop: Problems & Solutions. LC 60-14903. 186p. 1960. 22.50 (ISBN 0-911740-02-3, T4). Datarule.

--The Growler-Design & Application. LC 73-93292. (Illus.). 114p. 1974. 22.50 (ISBN 0-911740-06-6). Datarule.

--Multispeed & Standard Squirrel Cage Motors. Vol. 1 Standard (Single Speed Only) Motors Only: Testing, Rewinding, Reconnecting, & Redesigning. LC 75-36709. (Illus.). 704p. 1976. 46.50 (ISBN 0-911740-07-4). Datarule.

--Three-Phase Motor Winding Data from Simple Measurements. 3rd ed. (Illus., Orig.). 1961. pap. 32.00 (ISBN 0-911740-00-7). Datarule.

Heumann, Gerhart W. Magnetic Control of Industrial Motors: D-C Motors Controllers, Pt. 3. LC 61-11593. Repr. of 1961 ed. 59.50 (ISBN 0-8357-9925-5, 2012624). Bks Demand UMI.

Hudson, F. K., ed. Diesel & Electric Locomotive Specifications. LC 81-50698. 1981. pap. 7.95 (ISBN 0-913556-13-0). Spec Pr NJ.

Jordan, Howard E. Energy Efficient Electric Motors & Their Applications. 176p. 1983. 27.95 (ISBN 0-442-24523-8). Van Nos Reinhold.

Kuo, B. C., ed. Incremental Motion Control: Step Motors & Controls, Vol. 2. LC 78-53480. (Illus.). 1979. 42.50x (ISBN 0-918152-03-8). SRL Pub Co.

Kuo, B. C. & Tal, J., eds. Incremental Motion Control: DC Motors & Controls, Vol. 1. LC 78-53480. (Illus.). 1978. 39.50x (ISBN 0-918152-02-X). SRL Pub Co.

Kusko, Alexander. Solid-State DC Motor Drives. 1969. 25.00x (ISBN 0-262-11031-8). MIT Pr.

Lloyd, Tom C. Electric Motors & Their Applications. LC 70-77834. 1969. 34.95x (ISBN 0-471-54235-0, Pub. by Wiley-Interscience). Wiley.

McIntyre, R. L. & Losee, R. Electrical Motor Control Fundamentals. 4th ed. 464p. 1986. price not set (ISBN 0-07-045110-9). McGraw.

Miller, Rex & Anderson, Edwin P. Electric Motors. 4th ed. LC 82-17788. 1977. 12.95 (ISBN 0-672-23376-2). Audel.

Millermaster, Ralph A. Harwood's Control of Electric Motors. 4th ed. 1970. 56.50x (ISBN 0-471-60620-0, Pub. by Wiley-Interscience). Wiley.

Molloy, Edward, ed. Small Motors & Transformers: Design & Construction. LC 54-32875. pap. 44.00 (ISBN 0-317-10064-5, 2051335). Bks Demand UMI.

Nailen, Richard L. The Plant Engineer's Guide to Industrial Electric Motors. (Illus.). 498p. 1985. text ed. 54.95 (ISBN 0-943876-01-X). Baldner J V.

Nasar, S. A. & Boldea, I. Linear Motion Electromagnetic Systems. 352p. Date not set. 49.50 (ISBN 0-471-87451-5). Wiley.

Rejda, L. J. & Neville, Kris. Industrial Motor Users' Handbook of Insulation for Rewinds. new ed. LC 76-26949. 408p. 1977. 51.00 (ISBN 0-444-00191-3). Elsevier.

Rudman, Jack. Motor Equipment Repairman. (Career Examination Ser.: C-524). (Cloth bdg. avail. on request). pap. 8.00 (ISBN 0-8373-0524-1). Natl Learning.

Smeaton, R. W. Motor Application & Maintenance Handbook. 1969. 57.50 (ISBN 0-07-058438-9). McGraw.

Traister, John E. Handbook of Electric Motors: Use & Repair. (Illus.). 272p. 1984. text ed. 25.95 (ISBN 0-13-377383-3). P-H.

--Handbook of Electric Motors: Use & Repair. 272p. 1985. pap. 14.95 (ISBN 0-13-377425-2). P-H.

Veinott, Cyril G. Fractional & Subfractional Horsepower Electric Motors: What Kinds Are Available, How They Work & What They Will Do, How to Select, Apply, Connect & Service Them. LC 79-85117. pap. 126.30 (ISBN 0-317-09057-7, 2051938). Bks Demand UMI.

Yang, S. J. Low-Noise Electrical Motors. (Monographs in Electrical & Electronic Engineering). (Illus.). 1981. 34.50x (ISBN 0-19-859332-5). Oxford U Pr.

ELECTRIC MOTORS, ALTERNATING CURRENT

see also Electric Motors, Induction

McIntyre, R. L. Electric Motor Control Fundamentals. 3rd ed. (Illus.). 448p. 1974. text ed. 30.95 (ISBN 0-07-045103-6). McGraw.

ELECTRIC MOTORS, INDUCTION

Alger, Philip L. Induction Machines: Behavior & Uses. 2nd ed. 526p. 1970. 93.75 (ISBN 0-677-02390-1). Gordon.

Heller, B. & Hamata, V. Harmonic Field Effects in Induction Machines. 330p. 1977. 72.50 (ISBN 0-444-99856-X). Elsevier.

Poloujadoff, Michel. The Theory of Linear Induction Machinery. (Monographs in Electrical & Electronic Engineering). (Illus.). 1980. text ed. 49.00x (ISBN 0-19-859322-8). Oxford U Pr.

ELECTRIC NETWORK ANALYZERS

Hayt, William & Kemmerly, Jack. Engineering Circuit Analysis. 3rd ed. (Illus.). 1978. text ed. 46.95 (ISBN 0-07-027393-6). McGraw.

Hostetter, Gene H. Engineering Network Analysis. 912p. 1984. text ed. 35.50 (ISBN 0-06-042907-0, HarpC); write for info. solutions manual (ISBN 0-06-362983-6). Har-Row.

--Fundamentals of Network Analysis. 1979. text ed. 29.75 scp (ISBN 0-06-042909-7, HarpC); solutions manual avail. (ISBN 0-06-362692-6). Har-Row.

Penfield, Paul, Jr. MARTHA User's Manual. 1971. pap. 9.95x (ISBN 0-262-66015-6). MIT Pr.

ELECTRIC NETWORKS

see also Switching Theory

Aatre, V. K. Network Theory & Filter Design. LC 80-84534. 432p. 1981. cloth 21.95x (ISBN 0-470-26934-0). Halsted Pr.

Baher, H. Synthesis of Electrical Networks. 285p. 1984. 41.95x (ISBN 0-471-90399-X, Pub. by Wiley-Interscience). Wiley.

Balabanian, Norman & Bickart, Theodore. Electrical Network Theory. LC 82-21224. 954p. 1983. Repr. of 1969 ed. lib. bdg. 59.50 (ISBN 0-89874-581-0). Krieger.

Balasubramanian, N. V., et al. Differential Forms on Electromagnetic Networks. (Illus.). 1971. 17.25 (ISBN 0-8088-0040-X). Davey.

Belove, Charles & Drossman, Melvyn. Systems & Circuits for Electrical Engineering Technology. new ed. (Illus.). 1976. text ed. 45.00 (ISBN 0-07-004430-9). McGraw.

Boite, R. Network Theory. 588p. 1972. 131.95 (ISBN 0-677-14170-X). Gordon.

Brayton, R. K., et al. Modern Network Theory: An Introduction. Moschytz, G. S. & Neirynck, J., eds. 1978. text ed. 42.00 (ISBN 2-604-00034-2). Brookfield Pub Co.

Brown, R. G., et al. Lines, Waves & Antennas: The Transmission of Electric Energy. 2nd ed. (Illus.). 471p. 1973. text ed. 41.50 (ISBN 0-471-06677-X). Wiley.

Budak, Aram. Circuit Theory Fundamentals & Applications. LC 77-22344. (Illus.). 1978. 40.95 (ISBN 0-13-133975-3). P-H.

--Passive & Active Network Analysis & Synthesis. 600p. 1974. text ed. 39.95 (ISBN 0-395-17203-9). HM.

Chirlian, Paul M. Basic Network Theory. LC 68-25648. (Electrical & Electronic Eng. Ser). (Illus.). 1968. 48.00 (ISBN 0-07-010788-2). McGraw.

Choma, John. Electrical Networks: Theory & Analysis. LC 84-15319. 752p. 1985. 52.50 (ISBN 0-471-08528-6, Pub. by Wiley-Interscience). Wiley.

Clay, Richard. Nonlinear Networks & Systems. LC 76-127660. (Illus.). pap. 74.00 (ISBN 0-317-09121-2, 2010179). Bks Demand UMI.

Close, Charles M. Analysis of Linear Circuits. 716p. 1966. text ed. 36.95 (ISBN 0-15-502610-0, HC); solutions manual avail. (ISBN 0-15-502611-9, HC). HarBraceJ.

Connor, F. R. Networks. (Introductory Topics in Electronics & Telecommunication Ser.). (Illus.). 1972. pap. text ed. 17.95x (ISBN 0-7131-3258-2). Intl Ideas.

Cruz, Jose B. & Van Valkenburg, M. E. Signals in Linear Circuits. 480p. 1974. text ed. 37.95 (ISBN 0-395-16971-2); instr's. manual 11.50 (ISBN 0-395-17838-X). HM.

Daryanani, Gobind. Principles of Active Network Synthesis & Design. LC 76-20659. 495p. 1976. 45.50 (ISBN 0-471-19545-6). Wiley.

Desoer, C. A. & Kuh, E. S. Basic Circuit Theory. LC 68-9551. 1969. text ed. 45.00 (ISBN 0-07-016575-0). McGraw.

Dixon, Alan C. Network Analysis. LC 72-90475. 1973. text ed. 28.95 (ISBN 0-675-09024-5). Merrill.

Fulton, Stanley R. & Rawlins, John C. Basic AC Circuits. Luecke, G. & Battle, C., eds. LC 80-54793. (Basic Electricity Ser.). (Illus.). 560p. 1981. 19.95 (ISBN 0-89512-041-0, LCW8168); six cassette audio course 14.95 (LCB6651). Tex Instr Inc.

Off-Line Electronic Data Processing for Electricity Distribution. 337p. 1981. 70.00 (ISBN 0-686-37421-5). Inst Elect Eng.

Pai, M. A. Power System Stability: Analysis by the Direct Method of Lyapunov. (North-Holland Systems & Control Ser.: Vol. 3). 252p. 1982. 47.00 (ISBN 0-444-86310-9, North-Holland). Elsevier.

ELECTRIC POWER DISTRIBUTION–NETWORK ANALYZERS
see Electric Network Analyzers

ELECTRIC POWER IN MINING
see Electricity in Mining

ELECTRIC POWER-PLANTS
see also Steam Power-Plants; Water-Power Electric Plants

ASME Standard Number TWDPS-1: Recommended Practices for the Prevention of Water Damage to Steam Turbines Used for Electric Power Generation, 2 pts. Incl. Pt. I. TDP-1 Fossil Fueled Plants. 1980. pap. text ed. 10.00 (ISBN 0-685-37539-0, K00066); Pt. II. Nuclear Fueled Plants. 1973. pap. text ed. 4.00 (ISBN 0-685-37540-4, K00072). ASME.

Brown, Howard J. & Strumolo, Tom R., eds. Decentralizing Electricity Production. LC 83-3677. 288p. 1983. 31.00x (ISBN 0-300-02569-6). Yale U Pr.

Bullard, C. & Wameldorff, P., eds. Trends in Electric Utility Research: Proceedings of the Electric Utility Research Conference, Chicago, April 1984. 500p. 1984. pap. 75.00 (ISBN 0-08-030982-8); pap. 55.00 (ISBN 0-08-030983-6). Pergamon.

Giles, Robert L. Layout of E. H. V. Substations. LC 73-132285. (Institution of Electrical Engineers, IEE Monograph Ser.: No. 5). pap. 59.30 (ISBN 0-317-08132-2, 2004345). Bks Demand UMI.

Gill, A. B. Power Plant Performance. 624p. 1984. text ed. 110.00 (ISBN 0-408-01427-X). Butterworth.

Johnson, Charles J. Coal Demand in the Electric Utility Industry, Nineteen Forty-Six to Nineteen Ninety. Bruchey, Stuart, ed. LC 78-22689. (Energy in the American Economy Ser.). (Illus.). 1979. lib. bdg. 23.00x (ISBN 0-405-11992-5). Ayer Co Pubs.

Kruger, Paul & Otte, Carel, eds. Geothermal Energy: Resources, Production, Stimulation. LC 72-85700. (Illus.). xii, 372p. 1973. 27.50x (ISBN 0-8047-0822-3). Stanford U Pr.

Li, Kam W. & Priddy, A. Paul. Power Plant System Design. 641p. 1985. 40.95 (ISBN 0-471-88847-8). Wiley.

Longland, T., et al. Power Capacitor Handbook. (Illus.). 824p. 1984. text ed. 59.95 (ISBN 0-408-00292-1). Butterworth.

Maffezzoni, C., ed. Modeling & Control of Electric Power Plants: Proceedings of the IFAC Workshop, Como, Italy, 22-23 September 1983. (An IFAC Publication Ser.). 176p. 1984. 46.00 (ISBN 0-08-031163-6). Pergamon.

Nowill, Paul H. Productivity & the Technological Change in Electric Power Generating Plants. Bruchey, Stuart, ed. LC 78-22703. (Energy in the American Economy Ser.). (Illus.). 1979. lib. bdg. 17.00x (ISBN 0-405-12005-2). Ayer Co Pubs.

Potter, Philip J. Power Plant Theory & Design. 2nd ed. (Illus.). 710p. 1959. 47.50 (ISBN 0-471-06689-3). Wiley.

Willenbrock, Jack H. & Thomas, H. Randolph, eds. Planning, Engineering & Construction of Electric Power Generation Facilities. LC 79-21427. (Construction Management & Engineering Ser.). 869p. 1980. 78.50x (ISBN 0-471-03808-3, Pub. by Wiley-Interscience). Wiley.

ELECTRIC POWER-PLANTS–ENVIRONMENTAL ASPECTS

Axelrod, Regina. Conflict Between Energy & Urban Environment: Consolidated Edison Versus the City of New York. LC 80-67179. 214p. (Orig.). 1982. lib. bdg. 26.00 (ISBN 0-8191-2376-5); pap. text ed. 12.25 (ISBN 0-8191-2377-3). U Pr of Amer.

Beckmann, Petr. The Health Hazards of NOT Going Nuclear. LC 76-12720. (Illus.). 188p. 1976. pap. 7.95x (ISBN 0-911762-17-5). Golem.

Commoner, Barry & Boksenbaum, Howard, eds. Energy & Human Welfare: The Social Costs of Power Production, Vol. 1. LC 75-8986. 1975. 14.95 (ISBN 0-02-468420-1). Macmillan Info.

Hill, Philip G. Power Generation: Resources, Hazards, Technology & Costs. LC 76-54739. 1977. 40.00x (ISBN 0-262-08091-5). MIT Pr.

International Advanced Course & Workshop on Thermal Effluent Disposal from Power Generation, Aug. 23-28, 1976, Dubrovnik, Yugoslavia. Thermal Effluent Disposal from Power Generation: Proceedings. Zaric, Z., ed. LC 77-28808. (Thermal & Fluids Engineering, International Centre for Heat & Mass Transfer Ser.). (Illus.). 375p. 1978. text ed. 74.50 (ISBN 0-89116-093-0). Hemisphere Pub.

Jenkins, S. H. & Hansen, P. Schjodtz, eds. Airborne Pollutants from Coal Fired Power Plants: Water Pollution: Part of an IAWPRC International Conference on Coal Fired Power Plants & the Aquatic Environment, 16-18 August 1982, Copenhagen, Vol. 15-12. LC 83-19445. (Illus.). 144p. 1983. pap. 40.00 (ISBN 0-08-031024-9). Pergamon.

--Cooling Water Discharges from Coal Fired Power Plants: Water Pollution Problems: Part of an IAWPRC International Conference on Coal Fired Power Plants & the Aquatic Environment, 16-18 August 1982, Copenhagen, Vol. 15-10. LC 83-19445. (Illus.). 276p. 1983. pap. 40.00 (ISBN 0-08-031025-7). Pergamon.

--Solid Wastes from Coal Fired Power Plants: Water Pollution Problems: Part of an IAWPRC International Conference on Coal Fired Power Plants & the Aquatic Environment, 16-18 August 1982, Copenhagen, Vol. 15/11. LC 83-19445. (Illus.). 258p. 1983. pap. 40.00 (ISBN 0-08-031026-5). Pergamon.

Young, Louise B. Power Over People. LC 72-91020. (Illus.). 1973. pap. 3.95 (ISBN 0-19-501830-3, GB413, GB). Oxford U Pr.

ELECTRIC POWER-PLANTS–LOAD

Load Frequency Control & Operation. (Principles of Steam Generation Ser.: Module 19). (Illus.). 60p. 1982. spiral bdg. 10.00x (ISBN 0-87683-269-9); instr's. manual 15.00x (ISBN 0-87683-290-7). G P Courseware.

Robinson, J. E., ed. Abnormal Load on Power Systems: Report on the Symposium on Transient, Fluctuating & Distorting Loads & Their Effects on Power Systems & Communications, 25th & 26th February. LC 65-63212. (Institution of Electrical Engineers Conference Report Ser.: No. 8). pap. 48.00 (ISBN 0-317-10178-1, 2050830). Bks Demand UMI.

Symposium on Load-Curve Coverage in Future Electrical Power Generating Systems, Rome, Oct. 1977. Electrical Load-Curve Coverage: Proceedings. United Nations Economic Commission for Europe, ed. LC 78-40342. (Illus.). 1979. text ed. 125.00 (ISBN 0-08-022422-9). Pergamon.

ELECTRIC POWER SYSTEMS
Here are entered works on the complex assemblage of equipment and circuits for generating, transmitting, transforming, and distributing electric energy.
see also Electric Power Distribution; Electric Power Transmission

Anderson, Paul M. Analysis of Faulted Power Systems. (Illus.). 846p. 1973. 33.50x (ISBN 0-8138-1270-4). Iowa St U Pr.

Arrillaga. Power System Harmonics. LC 84-22097. 1985. 39.95 (ISBN 0-471-90640-9). Wiley.

Arrillaga, J. & Arnold, C. P. Computer Modeling of Electrical Power Systems. LC 82-2664. 423p. 1983. 63.95 (ISBN 0-471-10406-X, Pub. by Wiley-Interscience). Wiley.

Barzan, A. Automation in Electrical Power Systems. 430p. 1977. 9.45 (ISBN 0-8285-0670-1, Pub. by Mir Pubs USSR). Imported Pubns.

Billinton, Roy, et al. Power-System Reliability Calculations. (Modern Electrical Technology Ser.: No. 6). 195p. 1973. 32.50x (ISBN 0-262-02098-X). MIT Pr.

Developments in Power System Protection, 11-13 March, 1975, Savory Place, London. International Conference on Developments in Power System Production (1975: London) (Institution of Electrical Engineers Conference Publications: No. 125). pap. 140.00 (ISBN 0-317-10101-3, 2003628). Bks Demand UMI.

Elgerd, O. I. Electric Energy Systems Theory: An Introduction. 2nd ed. (Electrical Engineering Ser.). 576p. 1982. 45.00x (ISBN 0-07-019230-8). McGraw.

Elgerd, Olle I. Basic Electric Power Engineering. LC 76-1751. (Electrical Engineering Ser.). 1977. text ed. 36.95 (ISBN 0-201-01717-2); solution Manual 2.50 (ISBN 0-201-01918-3). Addison-Wesley.

El-Hawary, M. E. & Christensen, G. S. Optimal Economic Operation of Electric Power Systems. (Mathematics in Science & Engineering Ser.). 1979. 60.00 (ISBN 0-12-236850-9). Acad Pr.

El-Hawary, Mohamed. Electric Power Systems: Design & Analysis. 1982. text ed. 39.95 (ISBN 0-8359-1627-8); instrs'. manual avail. (ISBN 0-8359-1628-6). Reston.

Endrenyi, J. Reliability Modeling in Electric Power Systems. LC 78-6222. 1978. 79.95x (ISBN 0-471-99664-5, Pub. by Wiley-Interscience). Wiley.

Expansion Planning for Electrical Generating Systems: A Guidebook. (Technical Reports Ser.: No. 241). 614p. 1985. pap. 99.25 (ISBN 92-0-155484-2, IDC241, IAEA). Unipub.

Fardo, Stephen W. & Patrick, Dale R. Electrical Power Systems Technology. (Illus.). 256p. 1985. text ed. 29.95 (ISBN 0-13-247404-2). P-H.

--Rotating Electrical Machinery & Power Systems. (Illus.). 304p. 1985. text ed. 29.95 (ISBN 0-13-783309-1). P-H.

Gonen, T. Electric Power Distribution System Engineering. (Electrical Engineering Ser.). 752p. 1986. 51.95 (ISBN 0-07-023707-7). McGraw.

Gross, Charles A. Power System Analysis. LC 78-8631. 478p. 1979. 40.95 (ISBN 0-471-01899-6). Wiley.

Guile, A. E. & Paterson, W. Electrical Power Systems, Vol. 1. 2nd ed. LC 77-1789. 1977. text ed. 62.00 (ISBN 0-08-021728-1); pap. text ed. 18.75 (ISBN 0-08-021729-X). Pergamon.

--Electrical Power Systems, Vol. 2: In SI-Metric Units. 53.00 (ISBN 0-08-021730-3); pap. 18.75 (ISBN 0-08-021731-1). Pergamon.

Harrison, J. A. An Introduction to Electric Power Systems. LC 79-41201. (Illus.). 88p. 1980. pap. text ed. 11.95x (ISBN 0-582-30503-9). Longman.

Horowitz, S. H. Protective Relaying for Power Systems. LC 80-21776. 1980. 53.00 (ISBN 0-87942-139-8, PC01362). Inst Electrical.

--Protective Relaying for Power Systems. LC 80-21776. 575p. 1981. 50.95 (ISBN 0-471-08968-0, Pub. by Wiley-Interscience); pap. 33.00 (ISBN 0-471-08967-2). Wiley.

Hughes, Thomas P. Networks of Power: Electrification in Western Society, 1880-1930. LC 82-14858. (History of Technology Ser.). (Illus.). 496p. 1983. text ed. 38.50x (ISBN 0-8018-2873-2). Johns Hopkins.

Husain, Ashfaq. Electral Power System. (Illus.). 564p. 1982. text ed. 35.00x (ISBN 0-7069-1765-0, Pub. by Vikas India). Advent NY.

--Electrical Power System. 688p. 1982. 50.00x (ISBN 0-7069-1765-0, Pub. by Garlandfold England); pap. 40.00x (ISBN 0-7069-1766-9). State Mutual Bk.

Institute of Electrical & Electronics Engineers, Inc. Recommended Practice for Emergency & Standby Power Systems for Industrial & Commercial Applications. 208p. 1980. 19.95x (ISBN 0-471-08031-4). Wiley.

--Recommended Practice for Power Systems Analysis. 224p. 1981. 24.95x (ISBN 0-471-09262-2). Wiley.

--Recommended Practice for the Design of Reliable Industrial & Commercial Power Systems. LC 80-83819. 224p. 1981. 19.95x (ISBN 0-471-09261-4). Wiley.

International Federation of Automatic Control & Akashi, H. Electrical Power Systems: Proceedings. (Control Science & Technology Ser.: Vol. 6). 393p. 1982. 99.00 (ISBN 0-08-028718-2). Pergamon.

Knable, Alvin H. Electrical Power Systems Engineering: Problems & Solutions. LC 82-14801. 256p. 1982. Repr. of 1967 ed. lib. bdg. 22.50 (ISBN 0-89874-549-7). Krieger.

Miller, T. J. Reactive Power Control in Electric Systems. LC 82-10838. 381p. 1982. 53.95x (ISBN 0-471-86933-3, Pub. by Wiley-Interscience). Wiley.

Moltgen, Gottfried. Converter Engineering: An Introduction to Operation & Theory. 1985. 27.95 (ISBN 0-471-90561-5). Wiley.

Nasar, Syed A. Electric Energy Conversion & Transmission. 1985. text ed. write for info. (ISBN 0-02-385960-1); solutions manual avail. (ISBN 0-02-385970-9). Macmillan.

National Power Grids & Extra-High-Voltage Systems in the ESCAP Region. (Energy Resources Development Ser.: No. 14). pap. 5.00 (ISBN 0-686-94781-9, UN75/2F/13, UN). Unipub.

Roeper, R. Short-Circuit Currents in Three-Phase Systems. 2nd ed. Date not set. price not set (ISBN 0-471-90707-3). Wiley.

Stein, Robert & Hunt, William T. Electrical Power System Components: Transformers & Rotating Machines. 1979. 26.50 (ISBN 0-442-17611-2). Van Nos Reinhold.

Stevenson, William D., Jr. Elements of Power System Analysis. 4th ed. (Electrical Power & Energy Ser.). 416p. 1982. text ed. 44.00x (ISBN 0-07-061278-1). McGraw.

Traister, John E. Handbook of Power Generation: Transformers & Generators. (Illus.). 272p. 1982. 24.95 (ISBN 0-13-380816-5). P-H.

United Nations Economic Commission for Europe. Combined Production of Electric Power & Heat: Proceedings of a Seminar Organized by the Committee on Electric Power of the United Nations Economic Commission for Europe, Hamburg, FR Germany, 6-9 November 1978. LC 80-755. (Illus.). 150p. 1980. 37.00 (ISBN 0-08-025677-5). Pergamon.

Vardi, Joseph & Avi-Itzhak, Benjamin. Electric Energy Generation: Economics, Reliability & Rates. 192p. 1980. text ed. 37.50x (ISBN 0-262-22024-5). MIT Pr.

Venikov, V., ed. Cybernetics in Electric Power Systems. 314p. 1978. 8.95 (ISBN 0-8285-0674-4, Pub. by Mir Pubs USSR). Imported Pubns.

Venikov, V. A. Transient Processes in Electrical Power Systems. 501p. 1977. 12.00 (ISBN 0-8285-0699-X, Pub. by Mir Pubs USSR). Imported Pubns.

Wadhwa, C. L. Electrical Power Systems. LC 83-8555. 666p. 1983. 26.95x (ISBN 0-470-27461-1). Halsted Pr.

Weedy, B. M. Electric Power Systems. 3rd ed. LC 79-40081. 524p. 1979. 39.95x (ISBN 0-471-27584-0, Pub. by Wiley-Interscience). Wiley.

Wood, Allen J. & Wollenberg, Bruce F. Power Generation, Operation, & Control. LC 83-1172. 444p. 1983. text ed. 40.95x (ISBN 0-471-09182-0). Wiley.

Yu, Yao-Nan. Electric Power System Dynamics (Monograph) LC 83-2540. 1983. 39.00 (ISBN 0-12-774820-2). Acad Pr.

ELECTRIC POWER TRANSMISSION
see also Electric Lines; Electric Power Distribution

Bose, N. K. Adjustable Speed AC Drive Systems. LC 80-27789. 449p. 1981. 39.95 (ISBN 0-471-09395-5, Pub. by Wiley-Interscience); pap. 25.95 (ISBN 0-471-09396-3, Pub. by Wiley-Interscience). Wiley.

Conference on Design Criteria & Equipment for Transmission at 400 KV & High Voltages(1965: London) Conference on Design Criteria & Equipment for Transmission at 400 KV & High Voltages: Contributions, Pt. 1. LC 66-1977. (Institution of Electrical Engineers Conference Publications: No. 15). pap. 58.50 (ISBN 0-317-10161-7, 2007389). Bks Demand UMI.

Dworsky, Lawrence N. Modern Transmission Line Theory & Applications. LC 79-9082. 236p. 1979. 34.95x (ISBN 0-471-04086-X, Pub. by Wiley-Interscience). Wiley.

Eaton, J. Robert & Cohen, Edwin. Electric Power Transmission Systems. 2nd ed. (Illus.). 432p. 1983. 29.95 (ISBN 0-13-247304-6). P-H.

Graneau, Peter. Underground Power Transmission: The Science, Technology, & Economics of High Voltage Cables. LC 79-15746. 515p. 1979. 57.95x (ISBN 0-471-05757-6, Pub. by Wiley-Interscience). Wiley.

Guile, A. E. & Paterson, W. Electrical Power Systems, Vol. 1. 2nd ed. LC 77-1789. 1977. text ed. 62.00 (ISBN 0-08-021728-1); pap. text ed. 18.75 (ISBN 0-08-021729-X). Pergamon.

Pansini, Anthony J. Basic Electrical Power Transmission. (Illus.). 128p. 1975. pap. 7.50 (ISBN 0-8104-5928-0); final exam 0.30 (ISBN 0-8104-0599-7). Hayden.

Shepherd, W. & Zand, P. Energy Flow & Power Factor in Nonsinusoidal Circuits. LC 78-51684. (Illus.). 1979. 72.50 (ISBN 0-521-21990-6). Cambridge U Pr.

Skilling, Hugh H. Electric Transmission Lines: Distributed Constants, Theory & Applications. LC 78-23249. 456p. 1979. Repr. of 1951 ed. lib. bdg. 26.00 (ISBN 0-88275-792-X). Krieger.

Skrotzki, Bernhardt G., ed. Electric Transmission & Distribution. LC 80-16027. 466p. 1980. Repr. of 1954 ed. 32.50 (ISBN 0-89874-196-3). Krieger.

Weedy, B. M. Underground Transmission of Electric Power. 294p. 1979. text ed. 64.95x (ISBN 0-471-27700-2, Pub. by Wiley-Interscience). Wiley.

Weeks, Walter L. Transmission & Distribution of Electrical Energy. (Illus.). 302p. 1981. text ed. 28.95 scp (ISBN 0-06-046982-X, HarpC). Har-Row.

ELECTRIC PRECIPITATION
see Electrostatic Precipitation

ELECTRIC PROSPECTING

Editor, Adam A. Geoelectric & Geothermal Studies. 1976. 55.00 (ISBN 0-9960004-2-9, Pub. by Akademiai Kaido Hungary). Heyden.

Keller, G. V. & Frischknecht, F. C. Electrical Methods in Geophysical Prospecting. 1966. 66.25 (ISBN 0-08-011525-X). Pergamon.

Rokityansky, J. J. Geoelectromagnetic Investigation of the Earth's Crust & Mantle. (Illus.). 420p. 1982. 73.00 (ISBN 0-387-10630-8). Springer-Verlag.

Vanyan, L. L., et al. Electromagnetic Depth Soundings. LC 67-19390. 312p. 1967. 35.00x (ISBN 0-306-10794-5, Consultants). Plenum Pub.

ELECTRIC RAILROADS

see also Electric Locomotives; Electric Railway Motors

Andrews, J. H. A Short History of the Development of Street Railway Transportation in Philadelphia. (Illus.). 43p. 1979. pap. 2.50 (ISBN 0-911940-30-8). Cox.

Condit, Carl W. The Pioneer Stage of Railroad Electrification. LC 77-76428. (Transactions Ser.: Vol. 67, Pt. 7). 1977. pap. 6.00 (ISBN 0-87169-677-0). Am Philos.

Cox, Harold E. Early Electric Cars of Baltimore. (Illus.). 92p. (Orig.). 1979. pap. 9.00 (ISBN 0-911940-31-6). Cox.

Electrification by G.E. Bulletin No. 116. LC 76-22385. (Illus.). 256p. 1976. 18.00 (ISBN 0-915348-16-0). Central Electric.

Henry Huntington & the Pacific Electric. 10.00 (ISBN 0-686-70717-6). Chatham Pub CA.

Myers, Johnnie J. Texas Electric Railway: Bulletin No. 121. King, LeRoy O., Jr., ed. LC 82-71474. (Illus.). 256p. 1982. 36.00 (ISBN 0-915348-21-7). Central Electric.

Route of the Electroliners: Bulletin No. 107. (Illus.). 188p. 1975. 15.00 (ISBN 0-915348-07-1). Central Electric.

Through the Thirties. (Cincinnati Streetcars Ser.: No. 8). 1979. pap. 9.50 (ISBN 0-914196-20-0). Trolley Talk.

Woods, Herb. Galveston - Houston Electric Railway. (Special Ser.: No. 22). (Illus.). 84p. 1982. pap. 8.00 (ISBN 0-916374-23-8). Interurban.

Wright, Roy V., ed. Electric Motor Cars 1888-1928. (Train Shed Cyclopedia Ser., No. 25). (Illus.). 1974. pap. 4.50 (ISBN 0-912318-55-4). N K Gregg.

ELECTRIC RAILROADS–CARS

Albert, Richard C. Trolleys from the Mines: Street Railways of Centre, Clearfield, Indiana & Jefferson Counties, Pennsylvania. (Illus.). 100p. (Orig.). 1980. pap. 9.00 (ISBN 0-911940-32-4). Cox.

Crump, Spencer. Rail Car, Locomotive & Trolley Builders: An All-Time Directory. Date not set. write for info. (ISBN 0-87046-032-3, Pub. by Trans-Anglo). Interurban.

Cummings, O. R. Street Cars of Boston: Closed Horse & Electric Cars to 1900, Vol. 1. (Illus.). 92p. (Orig.). 1973. pap. 6.00 (ISBN 0-911940-18-9). Cox.

--Street Cars of Boston, Vol. 6: Birneys, Type 5, Semiconvertibles, Parlor, Private, & Mail Cars. (Illus.). 84p. (Orig.). 1980. pap. 9.00 (ISBN 0-911940-34-0). Cox.

Farrell, Michael R. Who Made All Our Streetcars Go? LC 73-85194. (Illus.). 320p. 1973. 16.00 (ISBN 0-9601320-1-5). Baltimore NRHS.

Hennick, Louis G. & Charlton, E. Harper. Street Railways of Louisiana. LC 76-30481. (Illus.). 143p. 1979. 19.95 (ISBN 0-88289-065-4). Pelican.

Sachs, Bernard J. & Nixon, George F. Baltimore Streetcars Nineteen Hundred Five to Nineteen Sixty-Three: The Semi-Convertible Era. (Orig.). 1982. pap. 14.95 (ISBN 0-9609638-0-4). Baltimore Streetcar.

Swett, Ira L. Cars of Pacific Electric: Locomotives, Combination Cars, Etc, Vol. 3. Walker, Jim, ed. (Special Ser.: No. 37). (Illus.). 1978. pap. 12.00 (ISBN 0-916374-30-0). Interurban.

ELECTRIC RAILWAY MOTORS

Houser, B. C. Rail Vehicle Energy Design Considerations. 1984. 55.75 (ISBN 0-444-86864-X, I-071-84). Elsevier.

Nene, Vilas D. Advanced Propulsion Systems for Urban Rail Vehicles. (Illus.). 304p. 1985. text ed. 40.95 (ISBN 0-13-012931-3). P-H.

ELECTRIC RELAYS

see also Switching Theory

Allen, Phillip E. & Sinencio, Edgar S. Switched Capacitor Circuits. 608p. 1984. 56.50 (ISBN 0-442-20873-1). Van Nos Reinhold.

CES Industries, Inc. Staff. Ed-Lab Experiment Manual: CES 318 Relay Module. (Illus.). 1981. write for info. (ISBN 0-86711-024-4). CES Industries.

Evans, Martin. Caribou Canadian Switcher. 80p. 1977. pap. 7.95 (ISBN 0-85242-500-7). Aztex.

Hobbs, Marvin. Modern Communications Switching Systems. 2nd ed. 308p. 1981. 9.95 (ISBN 0-686-98114-6). Telecom Lib.

Mason, C. R. Art & Science of Protective Relaying. LC 56-8694. 410p. 1956. 50.00x (ISBN 0-471-57552-6, Pub. by Wiley-Interscience). Wiley.

Sum. Switch Mode Power Conversation. (Electrical Engineering & Electronics Ser.). 240p. 1984. 45.00 (ISBN 0-8247-7234-2). Dekker.

Warrington, A. R. Protective Relays: Their Theory & Practice, 2 vols. Incl. Vol. 1, 2nd ed. LC 70-385616. 484p. 1968. text ed. 44.95x (ISBN 0-412-09060-0, NO. 6310); Vol. 2, 3rd ed. 434p. 1978. 44.95x (ISBN 0-412-15380-7, NO. 6311). Pub. by Chapman & Hall England). Methuen Inc.

ELECTRIC RESISTORS

see also Electrodes; Potentiometer; Strain Gages; Thermistors

Morrison, S. Roy. Electrochemistry at Semiconductor & Oxidized Metal Electrodes. LC 80-20416. 415p. 1980. 59.50x (ISBN 0-306-40524-5, Plenum Pr). Plenum Pub.

ELECTRIC SIGNAL THEORY

see Signal Theory (Telecommunication)

ELECTRIC SPARK MACHINING

see Electric Metal-Cutting

ELECTRIC STANDARDS

Gebert, K. National Electrical Code Blueprint Reading. 9th ed. (Illus.). 1983. pap. 15.95 (ISBN 0-8269-1550-7). Am Technical.

Institue of Electrical & Electronics Engineers. CAMAC Instrumentation & Interface Standards, 1982. 225p. 1982. 34.95 (ISBN 0-471-89737-X). Wiley.

Institute of Electrical & Electronics Engineers. American National Standard Code for Electricity Metering. LC 82-83450. 207p. 1983. 17.95 (ISBN 0-471-89356-0). Wiley.

Ledgard, Henry. ANSI-IEEE Pascal Standard: The American Pascal Standard. 1984. write for info. Springer-Verlag.

Palmer, J. D. & Saeks, R. The World of Large Scale Systems. LC 82-6169. 1982. 34.25 (ISBN 0-87942-161-4, PC01560). Inst Electrical.

ELECTRIC SURGE

see Transients (Electricity)

ELECTRIC TELEGRAPH

see Telegraph

ELECTRIC TESTING

see also Electric Engineering–Laboratory Manuals; Electric Measurements; Electricity–Laboratory Manuals

Institute of Electrical & Electronics Engineers, Inc. (IEEE) IEEE Standard Techniques for High-Voltage Testing. 6th ed. 125p. 1978. 13.00 (ISBN 0-471-04991-3). Wiley.

Mhyre, Noel L. Testing for Electrical Safety in Hospitals. 27p. 1975. 2.00 ea. (ISBN 0-917054-03-2). Med Communications.

ELECTRIC THERMOMETRY

see Thermometers and Thermometry

ELECTRIC TOOLS, PORTABLE

see Power Tools

ELECTRIC TRANSFORMERS

see also Electric Current Rectifiers; Electronic Transformers

Anderson, Edwin. Electric Machines & Transformers. 2nd ed. 1985. text ed. 28.95 (ISBN 0-8359-1618-9). Reston.

Anderson, Leonard. Electric Machines & Transformers. (Illus.). 336p. 1980. text ed. 28.95 (ISBN 0-8359-1615-4); instr's. manual free (ISBN 0-8359-1616-2). Reston.

Flanagan, W. M. Handbook of Transformer Applications. 448p. 1985. price not set (ISBN 0-07-021290-2). McGraw.

Franklin, A. C. & Franklin, D. P. The J & P Transformer Book. 11th ed. Woth, C. A., ed. (Illus.). 320p. 1983. text ed. 99.95 (ISBN 0-408-00494-0). Butterworth.

Gebert, et al. Transformers. 2nd ed. (Illus.). 1974. 16.95 (ISBN 0-8269-1602-3). Am Technical.

Heller, Samuel. Medium Size Transformers: Practical Methods for Designing, Reconnecting & Testing. (Illus., Orig.). 1957. 35.00 (ISBN 0-911740-01-5). Datarule.

Instrument Transformers for Revenue Metering 125kV BIL through 350 kV BIL. 1983. 15.50 (ISBN 0-318-18025-1, EI 21.2 1983). Natl Elec Mfrs.

Instrument Transformers for Revenue Metering 110 kV BIL & Less. 1983. 18.00 (ISBN 0-318-18024-3, EI 21.1983). Natl Elec Mfrs.

Kosow, Irving L. Electric Machinery & Transformers. (Illus.). 1972. ref. ed. 34.95 (ISBN 0-13-247205-8). P-H.

Lowden. Transformer Design Manual. 1983. write for info. (ISBN 0-07-038841-5). McGraw.

Lowden, Eric. Practical Transformer Design Handbook. LC 80-50057. 240p. 1980. pap. 23.95 (ISBN 0-672-21657-4). Sams.

McLyman, C. Transformer & Inductor Design Handbook. (Electrical Eng. & Electronics Ser.: Vol. 7). 1978. 39.75 (ISBN 0-8247-6801-9). Dekker.

McPherson, George. An Introduction to Electrical Machines & Transformers. LC 80-19632. 557p. 1981. text ed. 37.50 (ISBN 0-471-05586-7); teacher's manual avail. (ISBN 0-471-07954-5). Wiley.

Molloy, Edward, ed. Small Motors & Transformers: Design & Construction. LC 54-32875. pap. 44.00 (ISBN 0-317-10064-5, 2051335). Bks Demand UMI.

Myers, S. D., et al. A Guide to Transformer Maintenance. LC 81-50169. (Illus.). 836p. 1981. 59.95 (ISBN 0-939320-00-2). Myers Inc.

Oil Companies Materials Association (OCMA) Power Transformers of the Oil Immersed Sealed Type. (OCMA Ser.). 1974. pap. 21.95 (ISBN 0-471-25934-9, Wiley Heyden). Wiley.

Pansini, Anthony J. Basic Electrical Power Transformers. 1976. pap. 7.50 (ISBN 0-8104-0020-0); final exam 0.30 (ISBN 0-8104-0600-4). Hayden.

Production of Distribution Transformers in Developing Countries. pap. 2.00 (ISBN 0-686-94421-6, UN70/2B/11, UN). Unipub.

Richardson. Laboratory Operations for Rotating Electric Machinery & Transformer Technology. 256p. 1980. pap. text ed. 9.95 (ISBN 0-8359-3925-1). Reston.

Richardson, Donald. Rotating Electric Machines & Transformers. 2nd ed. 1982. text ed. 32.95 (ISBN 0-8359-6750-6); instrs'. manual avail. (ISBN 0-8359-6751-4). Reston.

Say, M. G. Alternating Current Machines. 5th ed. LC 83-10719. 632p. 1984. pap. 21.95x (ISBN 0-470-27451-4). Halsted Pr.

Transformers. 1984. 595.00 (ISBN 0-318-00534-4). Busn Trend.

ELECTRIC TRANSIENT PHENOMENA

see Transients (Electricity)

ELECTRIC VALVES

see Electron Tubes

ELECTRIC VEHICLES

see also Automobiles, Electric

McNicol, B. D. & Rand, D. A., eds. Power Sources for Electric Vehicles. (Studies in Electrical & Electronic Engineering: No. 11). 1066p. 1984. 203.75 (ISBN 0-444-42315-X, I-134-84). Elsevier.

ELECTRIC WAVE FILTERS

see Electric Filters

ELECTRIC WAVES

see also Delay Lines; Electromagnetic Waves; Electrooptics; Microwaves; Radio, Short Wave; Radio Measurements; Radio Waves; Signal Theory (Telecommunication); Transients (Electricity); Wave Guides

Al'pert, Y. L. & Fligel', D. S. Propagation of ELF & VLF Waves Near the Earth. LC 69-12526. 171p. 1970. 32.50x (ISBN 0-306-10836-4, Consultants). Plenum Pub.

Brown, R. G., et al. Lines, Waves & Antennas: The Transmission of Electric Energy. 2nd ed. (Illus.). 471p. 1973. text ed. 41.50 (ISBN 0-471-06677-X). Wiley.

Langer, Rudolph E., ed. Electromagnetic Waves. (Mathematics Research Center Pubns., No. 6). (Illus.). 408p. 1962. 17.50x (ISBN 0-299-02500-4). U of Wis Pr.

Lodge, Oliver J. Signalling Through Space Without Wires: Being a Description of the Work of Hertz & His Successors. 3rd ed. LC 74-9688. (Telecommunications Ser.). (Illus.). 138p. 1974. 14.00x (ISBN 0-405-06051-3). Ayer Co Pubs.

Mueller, C. Foundations of the Mathematical Theory of Electromagnetic Waves. rev ed. Higgins, T. P., tr. LC 75-81586. (Grundlehren der Mathematischen Wissenschaften: Vol. 155). (Illus.). 1969. 41.00 (ISBN 0-387-04506-6). Springer-Verlag.

Schwinger, Julian & Saxon, D. Discontinuities in Wave Guides. (Documents on Modern Physics Ser.). 178p. 1968. 46.25x (ISBN 0-677-01840-1). Gordon.

Skilling, H. H. Fundamentals of Electric Waves. 2nd ed. LC 74-8930. 256p. 1974. Repr. of 1948 ed. 15.25 (ISBN 0-88275-180-8). Krieger.

ELECTRIC WELDING

American Welding Society. Specification for Carbon, Steel, Covered Arc Welding Electrodes: A5.1. 35p. 1981. 10.00 (ISBN 0-87171-169-9); member 7.50. Am Welding.

--Specification for Carbon Steel Electrodes for Flux Cored Arc Welding: A5.20. rev. ed. LC 78-74839. 24p. 1979. pap. 10.00 (ISBN 0-87171-171-0); pap. 7.50 member. Am Welding.

--Specification for Consumables Used for Electroslag Welding of Carbon & High Strength Low Alloy Steel: A5.25. 20p. 1978. 10.00 (ISBN 0-87171-150-8); member 7.50. Am Welding.

--Specification for Consumables Used for Electrogas Welding of Carbon & High Strength Low Alloy Steel: A5.26. 20p. 1978. 10.00 (ISBN 0-87171-147-8); member 7.50. Am Welding.

American Welding Society, Inc. Arc Welding & Cutting Noise, AWN. LC 79-51314. (Illus.). 40p. 1979. pap. 24.00 (ISBN 0-87171-176-1); pap. 18.00 members. Am Welding.

ANSI Accredited. Safety in Welding & Cutting: Z49. 1-83. (Illus.). 30p. (Orig.). 1983. pap. text ed. 20.00 (ISBN 0-87171-236-9); member 15.00. Am Welding.

AWS-SAE Joint Committee on Automotive Welding. Standard for Automotive Resistance Spot Welding Electrodes, D8.6-77. (Illus.). 67p. 1977. pap. 20.00 (ISBN 0-87171-136-2). Am Welding.

Balchin, N. C., ed. Manual Metal-Arc Welding. (Engineering Craftsmen: No. F24). (Illus.). 1977. 39.50x (ISBN 0-85083-395-7). Intl Ideas.

Balchin, N. C., et al, eds. Metal-Arc Gas Shielded Welding. (Engineering Craftsmen: No. F23). (Illus.). 1977. spiral bdg. 39.95x (ISBN 0-85083-385-X). Intl Ideas.

--Tungsten-Arc Gas Shielded Welding. (Engineering Craftsmen: No. F22). (Illus.). 1977. spiral bdg. 39.95x (ISBN 0-85083-394-9). Intl Ideas.

Cary, Howard B. Modern Welding Technology. LC 78-2966. (Illus.). 1979. 32.95 (ISBN 0-13-599290-7). P-H.

Cole, Jim. Pocket Computer Programming Made Easy. (Illus.). 128p. (Orig.). 1982. pap. 8.95 (ISBN 0-86668-009-8). ARCsoft.

Electric Arc-Welding Power Sources. 1983. 22.00 (ISBN 0-318-18033-2, EW 1-1983). Natl Elec Mfrs.

Engineering Industry Training Board, ed. Training for Manual Metal-Arc Welders, 14 vols. Incl. Vol. 1. Metal-Arc Welding; Vol. 2. Welding Electrodes; Vol. 3. Joints & Weld Symbols; Vol. 4. Limiting Distortion; Vol. 5. Basic Welding; Vol. 6. Plate Surfaces; Vol. 7. Fillet Joints; Vol. 8. Single Vee Butt Joints; Vol. 9. Pipe Welding; Vol. 10. Fault Diagnosis; Vol. 11. Branch Connections. 69.95. (Illus.). 1974. Set. 43.95x (ISBN 0-89563-026-5). Intl Ideas.

Giachino, J. W. Arc Welding. (Illus.). 1977. pap. text ed. 7.95 (ISBN 0-8269-3083-2). Am Technical.

Graphic Symbols for Arc Welding Apparatus. 1983. 7.50 (ISBN 0-318-18034-0, EW 4-1982). Natl Elec Mfrs.

Guidelines for the Preparation of the Material Safety Data Sheet for Welding Consumables & Related Products. 1982. 7.00 (ISBN 0-318-18035-9, EW 5-1982). Natl Elec Mfrs.

Guidlines for Precautionary Labeling for Arc Welding & Cutting Products. 1983. 5.00 (ISBN 0-318-18036-7, EW 6-1983). Natl Elec Mfrs.

Jefferson, T. B. Arc Electrode Manual. 4th ed. (Monticello Bks). 64p. 1978. softcover 7.50 (ISBN 0-686-12003-5). Jefferson Pubns.

Jennings, Royalston F. Gas & A.C. Arc Welding & Cutting. 3rd ed. 1956. pap. text ed. 6.64 (ISBN 0-87345-119-8). McKnight.

Mohler, Rudy. Practical Welding Technology. 216p. 1983. 27.50 (ISBN 0-8311-1143-7). Indus Pr.

O'Brien, R. L. Plasma Arc Metalworking Processes, PMP. 160p. 1967. 10.00 (ISBN 0-685-65957-7); member 7.50. Am Welding.

Paton, B. E., ed. Electroslag Welding, EW. 2nd ed. (Eng.). 468p. 1962. 12.00 (ISBN 0-685-65942-9); members 9.00. Am Welding.

Recommendations for Arc Welded Joints in Clad Steel Construction: IIW. 66p. 1969. 10.00 (ISBN 0-686-43359-9); member 7.50. Am Welding.

Recommended Practices for Resistance Welding: C1.1-66. 115p. 12.00 (ISBN 0-685-65992-5). Am Welding.

Recommended Practices for Welding Austenitic Chromium-Nickel Stainless Steel Piping & Tubing: AWS D10.4. LC 79-51316. (Illus.). 26p. 1979. pap. 10.00 (ISBN 0-87171-175-3); pap. 7.50 member. Am Welding.

Resource Systems International. Arc Welding: Equipment. 1982. pap. text ed. 15.00. Reston.

--Arc Welding: Gas Metal (Mig) 1982. pap. text ed. 15.00 (ISBN 0-8359-0304-4). Reston.

--Arc Welding: Gas Tungsten (Tig) 1982. 15.00 (ISBN 0-8359-0305-2). Reston.

--Arc Welding: Other Processes. 1982. pap. text ed. 15.00 (ISBN 0-8359-0306-0). Reston.

--Arc Welding: Shielded Metal I. 1982. pap. text ed. 15.00 (ISBN 0-8359-0307-9). Reston.

--Arc Welding: Shielded Metal II. 1982. pap. text ed. 15.00 (ISBN 0-8359-0309-5). Reston.

Specification for Aluminum & Aluminum Alloy Covered Arc Welding Electrodes: A5.3. 10p. 1980. 10.00 (ISBN 0-87171-204-0); member 7.50. Am Welding.

Specification for Composite Surfacing Welding Rods & Electrodes: A5.21. 16p. 1980. 10.00 (ISBN 0-87171-198-2); member 7.50. Am Welding.

Specification for Copper & Copper Alloy Bare Arc-Welding Electrodes: A5.70. 11p. 10.00 (ISBN 0-87171-242-3); member 7.50. Am Welding.

Specification for Copper & Copper Alloy Gas Welding Rods: A5.27. 11p. 1978. 10.00 (ISBN 0-87171-154-0); member 7.50. Am Welding.

Specification for Corrosion-Resisting Chromium & Chromium-Nickel Steel Covered Electrodes: A5.4. 21p. 1981. 10.00 (ISBN 0-87171-162-1); member 7.50. Am Welding.

Specification for Low-Alloy, Steel Electrodes & Fluxes for Submerged Arc Welding: A5.23. 20p. 1980. 10.00 (ISBN 0-87171-202-4); member 7.50. Am Welding.

Specification for Nickel & Nickel-Alloy Covered Welding Electrodes: A5.11. 32p. 1983. 10.00 (ISBN 0-87171-231-8); member 7.50. Am Welding.

Specification for Steel, Low-Alloy Flux Cored Arc Welding Electrodes: A5.29-80. 20p. 1980. 10.00 (ISBN 0-87171-208-3). Am Welding.

Specification for Tungsten Arc-Welding Electrodes: A5.12. 7p. 1980. 10.00 (ISBN 0-87171-197-4); member 7.50. Am Welding.

Specifications for Aluminum & Aluminum-Alloy Bare Welding Rods & Bare Electrodes: A5.10-80. 10.00 (ISBN 0-87171-203-2). Am Welding.

Tsegelsky, V. Electric Welder: A Manual. Kuznetsov, B., tr. (Rus.). 27.50 (ISBN 0-87559-118-3). Shalom.

ELECTRIC WELL LOGGING

see Oil Well Logging, Electric

ELECTRIC WIRING

see also Electric Cables

Adams, J. T. The Complete Home Electrical Wiring Handbook. LC 78-21969. (Illus.). 1979. pap. 12.95 (ISBN 0-668-04525-6). Arco.

Advanced Wiring. (Home Repair & Improvement Ser.). 1978. 11.95 (ISBN 0-8094-2398-7). Time-Life.

Alerich, W. N. Electrical Construction Wiring. (Illus.). 1971. 14.95 (ISBN 0-8269-1420-9). Am Technical.

Basic Wiring. (Home Repair & Improvement Ser.). (Illus.). 1976. 11.95 (ISBN 0-8094-2358-8). Time-Life.

Burch, Monte. Basic House Wiring. LC 75-13336. (Popular Science Bk.). (Illus.). 280p. 1976. 14.42i (ISBN 0-06-010587-9, HarpT). Har-Row.

Business Communications Staff. Markets & Materials for High Temp. Wire & Cable: G-070. 1983. 1250.00 (ISBN 0-89336-337-5). BCC.

Clidero, Robert & Sharpe, Kenneth. Construction Wiring. (Electrical Trades Ser.). (Illus.). 1982. Repr. text ed. 17.80 (ISBN 0-8273-2134-1). Delmar.

Demske, Dick. Electrical Installations & Repairs. Wolf, Donald D. & Wolf, Margot L., eds. LC 76-8372. (Adventures in Home Repair Ser.). (Illus.). 1977. pap. 3.95 (ISBN 0-8326-2211-7, 7701). Delair.

Diamond Dies. 15.00 (ISBN 0-318-03180-9, 7510). Wire Assn Intl.

Doyle, J. Introduction to Electrical Wiring. 2nd ed. (Illus.). 1980. text ed. 24.95 (ISBN 0-8359-3185-4). Reston.

Earl, John T. & Traister, John. Electrical Wiring: Design & Applications. (Illus.). 368p. 1985. text ed. 29.95 (ISBN 0-13-247685-1). P-H.

Edwards, Harry T. Residential Electrical Wiring. (Illus.). 240p. 1982. text ed. 22.95 (ISBN 0-8359-6652-6). Reston.

Electrical Assembling & Wiring. 55.00x (ISBN 0-85083-031-1, Pub. by Engineering Ind). State Mutual Bk.

Graf, R. & Whalen, G. Home Wiring. 1982. 24.95 (ISBN 0-13-392977-9). P-H.

Graham, Kennard C. Industrial & Commercial Wiring. 2nd ed. (Illus.). 1963. 12.00 (ISBN 0-8269-1500-0). Am Technical.

Harper, Charles A. Handbook of Wiring, Cabling, & Interconnecting for Electronics. LC 72-4069. 1152p. 1972. 55.00 (ISBN 0-07-026674-3). McGraw.

Hawkins, Harry. Residential Wiring: Concepts & Practices. 1983. text ed. 13.75 (ISBN 0-534-01356-2). Breton Pubs.

Herrick, C. Electrical Wiring: Principles & Practices. 1975. ref. ed. 29.95 (ISBN 0-13-247676-2). P-H.

Hoerner, Harry J., et al. Basic Electricity & Practical Wiring. (Illus.). 65p. 1977. pap. 4.50 (2377); tchrs. ed. 1.85 (ISBN 0-913163-13-9). Hobar Pubns.

How to Wire Electrical Outlets, Switches & Lights. (Home Care Guides Ser.). (Illus.). 1981. pap. 2.50 (ISBN 0-686-71125-4). S&S.

Johnson, R. & Cox, R. Electrical Wiring: Design & Construction. 1981. Repr. 29.95 (ISBN 0-13-247650-9). P-H.

Kittle, James L. Mastering Household Electrical Wiring. (Illus.). 304p. (Orig.). 1983. pap. 13.95 (ISBN 0-8306-1587-3, 1587). TAB Bks.

Lenk, John D. Handbook of Simplified Commercial & Industrial Wiring Design. (Illus.). 400p. 1984. text ed. 21.95 (ISBN 0-13-381666-4). P-H.

--Handbook of Simplified Electrical Wiring Design. (Illus.). 416p. 1975. ref. ed. 27.95 (ISBN 0-13-381723-7); pap. 8.95 (ISBN 0-13-381681-8). P-H.

Markall, Jeff. Residential Wiring. 1984. text ed. 24.95 (ISBN 0-8359-6661-5). Reston.

Martens, Rachel. Repairing, Rewiring & Restoring Lamps & Lighting Fixtures. (Illus.). 190p. pap. Cancelled (ISBN 0-385-14747-3). Wallace-Homestead.

Meyers, L. D. Chilton's Complete Home Wiring & Lighting Guide. LC 80-971. 1980. pap. 9.95 (ISBN 0-8019-6791-0). Chilton.

Miller, Henry A. Practical Wiring in SI Units, Vols. 1 & 2. rev. ed. LC 68-57882. (Pergamon International Library, Electrical Engineering Division). 108p. 1975. Vol. 1. 1975. pap. text ed. 6.25 (ISBN 0-08-019754-X); Vol. 2. 1976. pap. text ed. 5.75 (ISBN 0-08-020573-9). Pergamon.

Miller, Rex. Residential Electrical Wiring. (Illus.). 300p. 1981. text ed. 14.24 (ISBN 0-02-665620-5); student guide 5.32 (ISBN 0-02-665640-X); tchr's. ed. 5.32 (ISBN 0-02-665630-2). Bennett IL.

Mix, Floyd M. Housewiring Simplified. LC 80-21122. (Illus.). 176p. 1981. 8.80 (ISBN 0-87006-309-X). Goodheart.

Mullin, Ray C. Electrical Wiring-Residential. LC 80-75458. 1981. pap. 15.00 (ISBN 0-8273-1951-7); instr's. guide 4.10 (ISBN 0-8273-1952-5). Delmar.

--Electrical Wiring-Residential. 8th ed. LC 83-72062. 288p. 1984. pap. text ed. 16.20 (ISBN 0-8273-2260-7); instrs's guide 4.20 (ISBN 0-8273-2261-5). Delmar.

Mullin, Raymond & Smith, Robert. Electrical Wiring-Commercial. 5th ed. 240p. 1984. pap. text ed. 16.20 (ISBN 0-8273-2262-3); instrs' guide 4.80 (ISBN 0-8273-2263-1). Delmar.

National Fire Protection Association. Electrical Code for One & Two-Family Dwellings: 1981. 1981. 9.50 (ISBN 0-317-07379-6, NFPA 70A). Natl Fire Prot.

Nolte, Robert C. & Ruel, Oliver J. Residential Construction Wiring: Updated for 1981 Code. LC 78-16245. 1979. 23.95 (ISBN 0-574-21520-4, 13-4545). SRA.

Nonferrous-Electrical Conference, 1984. 30.00 (ISBN 0-318-04237-1). Wire Assn Intl.

Palmguist, Roland E. House Wiring. 6th ed. LC 81-21674. (Illus.). 1984. 12.95 (ISBN 0-672-23404-1). Audel.

Palmquist, Roland E. House Wiring. 5th ed. LC 78-50216. 9.95 (ISBN 0-672-23364-9). G K Hall.

Richter, H. P. & Schwan, W. C. Practical Electrical Wiring: Residential, Farm & Industrial. 13th ed. (Illus.). 685p. 1984. 29.95 (ISBN 0-07-052390-8). McGraw.

Richter, H. P. & Schwan, W. Creighton. Wiring Simplified. 34th ed. LC 33-7980. 160p. 1983. 4.45 (ISBN 0-9603294-2-0). Park Pub.

Rockis, G. Residential Wiring. (Illus.). 1977. pap. 14.95 (ISBN 0-8269-1650-3). Am Technical.

Rudman, Jack. Supervising Electrical Inspector. (Career Examination Ser.: C-778). (Cloth bdg. avail. on request). pap. 12.00 (ISBN 0-8373-0778-3). Natl Learning.

Safford, Edward L., Jr. Electrical Wiring Handbook. (Illus.). 434p. (Orig.). 1980. 17.95 (ISBN 0-8306-9932-5); pap. 16.95 (ISBN 0-8306-1245-9, 1245). TAB Bks.

Saleh, Adel A. Theory of Resistive Mixers. 1971. 27.50x (ISBN 0-262-19093-1). MIT Pr.

Schultz, Mort. Wiring: Basic Repairs & Advanced Projects. Kummings, Gail, ed. LC 81-67293. (Illus.). 160p. 1981. 19.95 (ISBN 0-932944-37-X); pap. 6.95 (ISBN 0-932944-38-8). Creative Homeowner.

Smith, Robert L. Electrical Wiring-Industrial. 4th ed. 135p. 1982. 15.95 (ISBN 0-442-28159-5). Van Nos Reinhold.

--Electrical Wiring-Industrial. 5th ed. LC 83-26307. 160p. 1984. pap. text ed. 14.80 (ISBN 0-8273-2265-8); instr's guide 2.85 (ISBN 0-8273-2266-6). Delmar.

Starr, William. Electrical Wiring & Design: A Practical Approach. LC 82-21936. (Electronic Technology Ser.). 412p. 1983. 27.95x (ISBN 0-471-05131-4); tchr's. ed. 10.00 (ISBN 0-471-89527-X). Wiley.

Step-by-Step Basic Wiring. (Step by Step Home Repair Ser.). 1980. pap. 6.95 (ISBN 0-696-01090-9). BH&G.

Sulphuric Acid Recovery. 15.00 (ISBN 0-318-03195-7, 7520). Wire Assn Intl.

Sunset Editors. Basic Home Wiring Illustrated. LC 76-46662. (Illus.). 88p. 1977. pap. 4.95 (ISBN 0-376-01094-0, Sunset Bks). Sunset-Lane.

Traister, John E. Handbook of Modern Electrical Wiring. 302p. 1985. pap. 14.75 (ISBN 0-934041-03-2). Craftsman.

U. L. & Wire-Cable Industry. 15.00 (ISBN 0-318-03189-2, 7518). Wire Assn Intl.

Volt Information Services, Inc. Electrical Wiring Fundamentals. (Contemporary Construction Ser.). 1981. text ed. 18.40 (ISBN 0-07-067561-9). McGraw.

Watkins, A. J. Electrical Installation Calculations, Vol. 1. 3rd ed. 100p. 1980. 25.00x (Pub. by Arnold Pubs England). State Mutual Bk.

--Electrical Installation Calculations, Vol. 3. (Illus.). 154p. 1982. pap. text ed. 15.95x (ISBN 0-7131-3224-8). Intl Ideas.

--Electrical Installation Calculations: SJ Units, Vol. 2. 2nd ed. 106p. 1980. 25.00x (ISBN 0-686-69894-0, Pub. by Arnold Pubs England). State Mutual Bk.

--Electrical Installation Calculations: S1 Units, Vol. 3. 154p. 1980. 25.00x (ISBN 0-7131-3224-8, Pub. by Arnold Pubs England). State Mutual Bk.

Whitney, W. J. Residential & Commercial Electrical Wiring. 461p. 1983. pap. 24.95 (ISBN 0-471-09319-X). Wiley.

Whitney, William J. Electrical Wiring: Residential. LC 78-12869. 190p. 1979. pap. text ed. 22.95 (ISBN 0-471-05643-X); solutions manual 4.00 (ISBN 0-471-05357-0). Wiley.

Williams, T. Jeff. Basic Wiring Techniques. LC 81-86181. (Illus.). 96p. (Orig.). 1982. pap. 5.95 (ISBN 0-89721-000-X). Ortho.

Wire Association International. Electrical Handbook. 40.00 (ISBN 0-318-03169-8, 8530). Wire Assn Intl.

--Electron Beam Crosslink Irradiation. 15.00 (ISBN 0-318-03181-7, 7512). Wire Assn Intl.

--European Conference, 3rd. 30.00 (ISBN 0-318-03214-7, 7804). Wire Assn Intl.

--European Conference, 4th. 30.00 (ISBN 0-318-03213-9, 7812). Wire Assn Intl.

--Ferrous Division Conference. Incl. 1980 ((7803)); 1981 ((7811)); 1982 ((7821)). 30.00 ea. (ISBN 0-318-03224-4). Wire Assn Intl.

--Nonferrous-Electrical Conference, 1978. 30.00 (ISBN 0-318-03227-9, 7781). Wire Assn Intl.

--Nonferrous-Electrical Conference, 1980. 30.00 (ISBN 0-318-03225-2, 7802). Wire Assn Intl.

--Nonferrous-Electrical Conference, 1982. 30.00 (ISBN 0-318-03218-X, 7822). Wire Assn Intl.

--Nonferrous-Electrical Conference, 1983. 30.00 (ISBN 0-318-03215-5, 7831). Wire Assn Intl.

--Nonferrous Wire Handbook, 2 vols. Vol. 1. 65.00 (ISBN 0-318-03176-0, 8529); Vol. 2. 40.00 (8520); 40.00 (8521). Wire Assn Intl.

--Scale Removal. 15.00 (ISBN 0-318-03183-3, 7514). Wire Assn Intl.

Wire Association International Proceedings. Incl. 50th Annual Meeting (7680); 51st Annual Meeting (7681); 52nd Annual Meeting (7682); 53rd Annual Meeting (7683). 50.00 ea. (ISBN 0-318-03210-4). Wire Assn Intl.

Wire Index. 150.00 (ISBN 0-318-03229-5, 8540). Wire Assn Intl.

ELECTRIC WIRING–DIAGRAMS

Aglow, Stanley H. Schematic Wiring Simplified. LC 83-2736. (Illus.). 180p. 14.95 (ISBN 0-912524-23-5). Busn news.

Garland, J. D. National Electrical Code Questions & Answers, 1981. 2nd ed. 144p. (Orig.). 1981. pap. 7.95 O.P. (ISBN 0-13-609339-6). P-H.

Gebert, Kenneth L. National Electrical Code Blueprint Reading: Based on the 1984 National Electrical Code. (Based on the Nineteen Eighty Four National Electrical Code Ser.). (Illus.). 192p. 1985. pap. 15.95 (ISBN 0-317-17095-3, Pub. by Am Technical). Sterling.

Segall, B. Z. Electrical Code Diagrams, 1981. 8th ed. (Illus.). 1273p. 97.00 (ISBN 0-686-35811-2). McGill Pubns.

Traister, John E. Electrical Blueprint Reading. 2nd ed. 128p. 1981. pap. 8.50 (ISBN 0-910460-86-8). Craftsman.

--Residential Electrical Design. 2nd ed. 192p. 1982. pap. 11.50 (ISBN 0-910460-90-6). Craftsman.

Watkins, A. J. Electrical Installation Calculations, Vol. 1. 3rd ed. 100p. 1980. 25.00x (Pub. by Arnold Pubs England). State Mutual Bk.

--Electrical Installation Calculations: SJ Units, Vol. 2. 2nd ed. 106p. 1980. 25.00x (ISBN 0-686-69894-0, Pub. by Arnold Pubs England). State Mutual Bk.

--Electrical Installation Calculations: S1 Units, Vol. 3. 154p. 1980. 25.00x (ISBN 0-7131-3224-8, Pub. by Arnold Pubs England). State Mutual Bk.

ELECTRIC WIRING–INSURANCE REQUIREMENTS

see also Electric Engineering–Insurance Requirements

Electrical Code for One & Two-Family Dwellings. (Seventy Ser.). 1972. pap. 2.00 (ISBN 0-685-46040-1, 70A). Natl Fire Prot.

Gebert, Kenneth L. National Electrical Code Blueprint Reading: Based on the 1984 National Electrical Code. (Based on the Nineteen Eighty Four National Electrical Code Ser.). (Illus.). 192p. 1985. pap. 15.95 (ISBN 0-317-17095-3, Pub. by Am Technical). Sterling.

ELECTRICAL ENGINEERING

see Electric Engineering

ELECTRICALLY EXPLODED WIRES

see Exploding Wire Phenomena

ELECTRICIANS

Hammer, Hy. Electrician-Electrician's Helper. LC 82-11405. 256p. 1982. pap. 8.00 (ISBN 0-668-05492-1, 5492). Arco.

Rudman, Jack. Foreman (Electrical Power) (Career Examination Ser.: C-267). (Cloth bdg. avail. on request). pap. 10.00 (ISBN 0-8373-0267-6). Natl Learning.

--Transit Electrical Helpers Series. (Career Examination Ser.: C-1963). (Cloth bdg. avail. on request). pap. 10.00 (ISBN 0-8373-1963-3). Natl Learning.

Stallcup. Journeyman Electrician Workbook. (Illus.). 160p. 1985. 12.95 (ISBN 0-8269-1700-3). Am Technical.

ELECTRICITY

see also Atmospheric Electricity; Electrons; Hall Effect; Lightning; Magnetism; Radioactivity; Telegraph; Telephone; Thermoelectricity; X-Rays also headings beginning with Electric and Electro

Adams, J. & Rockmaker, G. Industrial Electricity: Principles & Practices. 3rd ed. 1985. 26.90 (ISBN 0-07-000327-0). McGraw.

Alerich, Walter N. Electricity Four: AC Motors, Controls, Alternators. LC 79-93325. (Electrical Trades Ser.). 215p. 1981. pap. 9.60 (ISBN 0-8273-1363-2); instructor's guide 3.00 (ISBN 0-8273-1364-0). Delmar.

--Electricity Three: DC Motors & Generators, Controls, Transformers. LC 79-93324. (Electrical Trades Ser.). 224p. 1981. pap. 9.60 (ISBN 0-8273-1361-6); instructor's guide 3.00 (ISBN 0-8273-1362-4). Delmar.

Appleyard, Rollo. Pioneers of Electrical Communication. facs. ed. LC 68-54322. (Essay Index Reprint Ser). 1930. 24.50 (ISBN 0-8369-0156-8). Ayer Co Pubs.

Automatic Control in Electricity Supply Staff. Symposium on Automatic Control in Electricity Supply, 29-31 March, 1966 in Manchester, England. (IEE Conference Publication Ser.: No. 16, Pt. 1). (Illus.). pap. 98.00 (ISBN 0-317-09932-9, 2051588). Bks Demand UMI.

Bacharach, S. L., et al. Electricity & Electronic Fundamentals, 3 vols. (Illus.). 1971. Set. loseleaf 150.00x (ISBN 0-87683-316-4); Vol. 1. 60.00x (ISBN 0-87683-317-2); Vol. 2; lab. manual; 270p. looseleaf 50.00x (ISBN 0-87683-318-0); Vol. 3; solutions manual; 270p. losseleaf 45.00x (ISBN 0-87683-319-9); Lesson Plans; 320p. looseleaf 1500.00x (ISBN 0-87683-321-0); Transparencies. looseleaf 1500.00x (ISBN 0-87683-322-9). G P Courseware.

Basic Electricity. (Basic Academics Ser.: Module 8). (Illus.). 135p. 1982. spiral bdg. 10.00x (ISBN 0-87683-232-X); instr's. manual 15.00x (ISBN 0-87683-243-5). G P Courseware.

Basic Electricity. (NAVPERS 10086-B. Rate Training Manual Ser.). 490p. 1983. pap. 11.00 (ISBN 0-318-11758-4). Gov Printing Office.

Bennet, G. A. Electricity & Modern Physics. 2nd ed. 1974. pap. text ed. 28.50x (ISBN 0-7131-2459-8). Intl Ideas.

Bleaney, B. I. & Bleaney, B. Electricity & Magnetism. 3rd ed. (Illus.). 1976. pap. 29.95x (ISBN 0-19-851141-8). Oxford U Pr.

Blitz, J., et al. Electrical, Magnetic & Visual Methods of Testing Materials. (Illus.). 1970. 12.00 (ISBN 0-8088-8350-X). Davey.

Bodle, David W., et al. Characterization of the Electrical Environment. LC 76-22886. 1976. 30.00x (ISBN 0-8020-2194-8). U of Toronto Pr.

Buban, P., et al. Understanding Electricity & Electronics. 4th ed. 1981. text ed. 22.64 (ISBN 0-07-008678-8). McGraw.

Chapple, M. A-Level Physics: Electricity & Semiconductors, Vol.3. 2nd ed. (Illus.). 288p. (Orig.). 1980. pap. text ed. 14.95x (ISBN 0-7121-0158-6). Trans-Atlantic.

Cooper, Alan. Electricity. LC 83-50223. (Visual Science Ser.). 48p. 1983. 13.72 (ISBN 0-382-06715-0); pap. 6.75 (ISBN 0-382-09999-0). Silver.

Crane, Dale. Basic Electricity. (Aviation Techinican Training Ser.). (Illus.). 55p. 1975. pap. text ed. 5.95 (ISBN 0-89100-055-0, EA-BE-1). Aviation Maint.

Croft, Terrell, et al. American Electrician's Handbook. 10th ed. 1664p. 1980. 53.95 (ISBN 0-07-013931-8). McGraw.

D'Arcangelo, B. F., et al. Mathematics for Plumbers & Pipe Fitters. 3rd rev. ed. (Applied Mathematics Ser.). (Illus.). 244p. 1982. pap. text ed. 10.20 (ISBN 0-8273-1291-1); instr's. guide 4.20 (ISBN 0-8273-1292-X). Delmar.

Davis, Barry. Understanding DC Power Supplies. (Illus.). 240p. 1983. 22.95 (ISBN 0-13-936831-0); pap. 12.95 (ISBN 0-13-936823-X). P-H.

Davis, Henry B. Electrical & Electronic Technologies: A Chronology of Events & Inventors to 1900. LC 81-9179. 221p. 1981. 16.00 (ISBN 0-8108-1464-1). Scarecrow.

--Electrical & Electronic Technologies: A Chronology of Events & Inventors from 1900 to 1940. LC 82-16739. 220p. 1983. 16.00 (ISBN 0-8108-1590-7). Scarecrow.

--Electrical & Electronic Technologies: A Chronology of Events & Inventors from 1940 to 1980. LC 84-13957. 321p. 1985. 25.00 (ISBN 0-8108-1726-8). Scarecrow.

DeFrance, Joseph J. Electrical Fundamentals. 2nd ed. (Illus.). 672p. 1983. text ed. 37.95 (ISBN 0-13-247262-7). P-H.

DeGuilmo, Joseph M. Electricity-Electronics: Principles & Applications. LC 79-54909. (Electronics Technology Ser.). (Illus.). 706p. (Orig.). 1982. pap. 26.80 (ISBN 0-8273-1686-0); instr's. guide 5.25 (ISBN 0-8273-1687-9). Delmar.

EEE Meter & Service Committee, ed. Handbook for Electricity Metering. 523p. 1982. 25.00 (ISBN 0-931032-11-3). Edison Electric.

ELECTRICITY–APPARATUS AND APPLIANCES
see Electric Apparatus and Appliances

ELECTRICITY–BIBLIOGRAPHY

Mottelay, Paul F., ed. Bibliographical History of Electricity & Magnetism. LC 74-26277. (History, Philosophy & Sociology of Science Ser.). (Illus.). 1975. Repr. 48.00x (ISBN 0-405-06605-8). Ayer Co Pubs.

ELECTRICITY–DICTIONARIES

ANSI-IEEE Standard 100-1984: IEEE Standard Dictionary of Electrical & Electronic Terms. 3rd ed. 1173p. 1984. 49.95 (ISBN 0-471-80787-7, SH09332). IEEE.

Besse, B., et al. Lexique Anglais-Francais de L'Aciere Electrique. (Eng. & Fr.). 135p. 1975. pap. 8.95 (ISBN 0-686-92555-6, M-9239). French & Eur.

Breitsameter. Lexikon der Schulphysik: Elektrizitaet und Magnetismus A-K, Vol. 3A. (Ger.). 42.50 (ISBN 3-7614-0168-X, M-7224). French & Eur.

--Lexikon der Schulphysik: Elektrizitaet und Magnetismus L-Z, Vol. 3B. (Ger.). 42.50 (ISBN 3-7614-0169-8, M-7225). French & Eur.

Brown, P. R. Dictionary of Electrical, Electronic & Computer Abbreviations. 232p. 1985. text ed. 34.95 (ISBN 0-408-01210-2). Butterworth.

Colella, A. Nuovo Dizionario di Elettrotecnic e di Elettronica: Italiano-Inglese, Inglese-Italiano. (Ital. & Eng.). 541p. 1977. 95.00 (ISBN 0-686-92200-X, M-9296). French & Eur.

De Jussieu-Pontcarral, Pierre. Encyclopedie de l'electricite, 2 vols. (Illus.). 1970. 82.50x ea. Larousse.

Dejussieu-Pontcarral, Pierre. Encyclopedie De l'Electricite, 1: Production et Distribution. (Fr.). 1700p. 1969. 89.50 (ISBN 0-686-57135-5, M-6190). French & Eur.

--Encyclopedie de l'Electricite, 2: Application. (Fr.). 1024p. 1970. 89.50 (ISBN 0-686-56979-2, M-6106). French & Eur.

Mercier, Jean. Lexique Anglais-Francais Des Appareils De Mesures Electriques. (Eng. & Fr.). 44p. 1973. pap. 1.95 (ISBN 0-686-57044-8, M-6405). French & Eur.

--Lexique Anglais-Francais Du Compteur D'electricite: Principes et Pieces Composantes. (Eng. & Fr.). 42p. 1973. pap. 3.50 (ISBN 0-686-57046-4, M-6407). French & Eur.

Seevers, O. C. Efficient Electric Utility Operation. 1982. text ed. 32.00 (ISBN 0-915586-59-2). Fairmont Pr.

ELECTRICITY–DISCHARGES
see Electric Discharges

ELECTRICITY–DISCHARGES THROUGH GASES
see Electric Discharges through Gases

ELECTRICITY–DISTRIBUTION
see Electric Lines; Electric Power Distribution

ELECTRICITY–EARLY WORKS TO 1850

Home, R. W. Aepinus's Essay on the Theory of Electricity & Magnetism. Connor, P. J., tr. LC 78-10105. 1979. 53.00x (ISBN 0-691-08222-7). Princeton U Pr.

Priestley, Joseph. The History & Present State of Electricity, with Original Experiments, 2 vol. 3rd ed. Repr. of 1975 ed. 46.00 (ISBN 0-384-47790-9). Johnson Repr.

ELECTRICITY–EXPERIMENTS

CES Industries, Inc. Ed-Lab Six Hundred & Fifty Experiment Manual: Electricity-Electronics AC-DC, Bk. I. (Illus.). 288p. 1981. 12.50 (ISBN 0-86711-015-5). CES Industries.

CES Industries Inc. Ed-Lab Six Hundred & Fifty Experiment Manual: Electricity-Electronics Solid-State, Bk. II. (Illus.). 304p. 1981. 12.50 (ISBN 0-86711-014-7). CES Industries.

Electricity. (Tops Cards Ser.: No. 19). 1977. pap. 12.30 (ISBN 0-941008-19-3). Tops Learning.

Fuller, Nelson & Miller, Rex. Experiments for Electricity & Electronics. 2nd ed. LC 78-7708. 1978. pap. 10.83 scp (ISBN 0-672-97260-3); scp tchr's guide 3.67 (ISBN 0-672-97261-1). Bobbs.

Graf, Rudolf F. Safe & Simple Electrical Experiments. (Illus.). 14.00 (ISBN 0-8446-4747-0). Peter Smith.

Kind, Dieter. An Introduction to High-Voltage Experimental Technique. 1978. 19.50 (ISBN 0-9940011-8-5, Pub. by Vieweg & Sohn Germany). Heyden.

ELECTRICITY–HISTORY

Angevine, Erma. People -- Their Power: The Rural Electric Fact Book. rev. ed. (Illus.). 196p. 1981. pap. 3.75 (ISBN 0-686-31129-9). Natl Rural.

Benjamin, Park. A History of Electricity. LC 74-26249. (History, Philosophy & Sociology of Science Ser). 1975. Repr. 42.00x (ISBN 0-405-06579-5). Ayer Co Pubs.

Bordeau, Sanford P. Volts to Hertz: The Rise of Electricity. LC 82-17702. (Illus.). 308p. 1982. 18.95 (ISBN 0-8087-4908-0). Burgess.

Brittain, James E., ed. Turning Points in American Electrical History. LC 76-18433. (Illus.). 1977. 42.60 (ISBN 0-87942-081-2, PC00828). Inst Electrical.

DuBoff, Richard B. Electric Power in American Manufacturing, Eighteen Eighty-Nine to Nineteen Fifty-Eight. Bruchey, Stuart, ed. LC 78-22675. (Energy in the American Economy). (Illus.). 1979. lib. bdg. 23.00x (ISBN 0-405-11978-X). Ayer Co Pubs.

Hannah, Leslie. Electricity Before Nationalization: A Study of the Development of the Electricity Supply Industry in Britain to 1948. 488p. 1979. 38.00x (ISBN 0-8018-2145-2). Johns Hopkins.

Heilbron, J. L. Electricity in the Seventeenth & Eighteenth Centuries: A Study of Early Modern Physics. LC 77-76185. 1979. 60.00x (ISBN 0-520-03478-3). U of Cal Pr.

Hinton Of Bankside, Lord. Heavy Current Electricity in the United Kingdom. 1979. text ed. 18.00 (ISBN 0-08-023246-9); pap. text ed. 7.00 (ISBN 0-08-023247-7). Pergamon.

Lurkis, Alexander. The Power Brink: Con Edison, A Centennial of Electricity. (Illus.). 207p. (Orig.). 1982. 13.95x (ISBN 0-9609492-1-6); pap. 9.95x (ISBN 0-9609492-0-8). Icare Pr.

Palmquist, Roland E. Guide to the Nineteen Eighty-One National Electrical Code. LC 78-50211. 1982. 13.95 (ISBN 0-672-23362-2). G K Hall.

Passer, Harold C. The Electrical Manufacturers, 1875-1900: A Study in Competition, Entrepreneurship, Technical Change, & Economic Growth. LC 72-5066. (Technology & Society Ser.). (Illus.). 436p. 1972. Repr. of 1953 ed. 36.50 (ISBN 0-405-04717-7). Ayer Co Pubs.

Tesla, Nikola. Inventions, Researchs, & Writings. Repr. of 1894 ed. 14.00 (ISBN 0-913022-23-3). Angriff Pr.

Trowbridge, John. What Is Electricity. Cohen, I. Bernard, ed. LC 79-8000. (Three Centuries of Science in America Ser.). (Illus.). 1980. Repr. of 1899 ed. lib. bdg. 27.50x (ISBN 0-405-12588-7). Ayer Co Pubs.

ELECTRICITY–LABORATORY MANUALS
see also Electric Engineering–Laboratory Manuals; Electric Measurements

Fardo, Stephen W. & Prewitt, Roger W. Basic Electricity: A Lab Text. 2nd ed. (Illus.). 222p. 1983. pap. 14.95x (ISBN 0-89917-384-5). Tichenor Pub.

Henry, Dennis C., et al. Experiments in Light, Electricity, & Modern Physics, Laboratory Manual. 1978. pap. text ed. 7.95 (ISBN 0-8403-1889-8). Kendall-Hunt.

Patrick, Dale R. & Fardo, Stephen W. Industrial Electrical Experimentation. 2nd ed. (Illus.). 271p. 1983. pap. 14.95x (ISBN 0-89917-385-3). Tichenor Pub.

Power, Thomas C. DC-AC Laboratory Manual. Kosow, Irving L., ed. (Electronic Technology Ser.). 1969. pap. text ed. 17.95 (ISBN 0-13-197129-8). P-H.

Zbar, Paul. Basic Electricity: A Text-Lab Manual. 4th ed. (Illus.). 384p. 1974. pap. text ed. 18.55 (ISBN 0-07-072787-2). McGraw.

ELECTRICITY–MECHANICAL ANALOGIES
see Electromechanical Analogies

ELECTRICITY–PROBLEMS, EXERCISES, ETC.

Ash, Robert & Ash, Carol. The Calculus Tutoring Book. 1985. write for info. (ISBN 0-87942-183-5, PC01776). Inst Electrical.

Dagger, A. Multiple Choice Questions in Electrical Principles. (Illus.). 88p. 1981. pap. 16.50x (ISBN 0-7121-1274-X). Trans-Atlantic.

Kuehn, Martin H. Mathematics for Electricians. 3rd ed. 1949. text ed. 31.00 (ISBN 0-07-035599-1). McGraw.

Palmquist, Roland. Questions & Answers for Electricians Examinations. 8th ed. 1984. 12.95 (ISBN 0-672-23399-1). Audel.

--Questions & Answers for Electricians Examinations. 7th ed. LC 78-50280. 1982. 9.95 (ISBN 0-672-23363-0). G K Hall.

Waring, Gene. Mathematics for Electricity & Electronics. LC 83-70906. 608p. (Orig.). 1984. pap. text ed. 26.00 (ISBN 0-8273-1987-8); instr's. guide 5.25 (ISBN 0-8273-1988-6). Delmar.

ELECTRICITY–PROGRAMMED INSTRUCTION

Consumers Power Company. Fundamentals of Electricity, 2 vols. Incl. Vol. 1. Basic Principles. pap. 15.95 (ISBN 0-201-01185-9); Vol. 2. Alternating Current. pap. 15.95 (ISBN 0-201-01186-7). 1966. pap. Addison-Wesley.

Ryan, Charles W. Basic Electricity. LC 76-4031. (Self-Teaching Guides Ser.). 280p. 1976. pap. text ed. 9.95 (ISBN 0-471-74787-4, Pub. by Wiley Pr). Wiley.

ELECTRICITY–TRANSMISSION
see Electric Power Transmission

ELECTRICITY, ANIMAL
see Electrophysiology

ELECTRICITY, ATMOSPHERIC
see Atmospheric Electricity

ELECTRICITY, PIEZO-
see Pyro- and Piezo-Electricity

ELECTRICITY, PYRO-
see Pyro- and Piezo-Electricity

ELECTRICITY, STATIC
see Electrostatics

ELECTRICITY IN AGRICULTURE
see also Agricultural Engineering

Brown, Robert H. Farm Electrification. (Agricultural Engineering Ser). 1956. 39.95 (ISBN 0-07-008462-9). McGraw.

Butchbaker, Allen F. Electricity & Electronics for Agriculture. (Illus.). 392p. 1977. text ed. 21.95x (ISBN 0-8138-0525-2). Iowa St U Pr.

Childs, Marquis. The Farmer Takes a Hand: The Electric Power Revolution in Rural America. LC 73-19736. (Fdr & the Era of the New Deal Ser.). (Illus.). 256p. 1974. Repr. of 1952 ed. lib. bdg. 35.00 (ISBN 0-306-70478-1). Da Capo.

Gustafson. Fundamentals of Electricity for Agriculture. cancelled (ISBN 0-317-14342-5). AVI.

Pimentel, David. Handbook of Energy: Utilization in Agriculture. 496p. 1980. 76.50 (ISBN 0-8493-2661-3). CRC Pr.

Surbrook, Truman C. & Mullin, Ray C. Agricultural Electrification. Sprague, William W., ed. (Illus.). 442p. text ed. cancelled (ISBN 0-538-33550-5). SW Pub.

ELECTRICITY IN MINING
see also Mining Engineering

Mular, Andrew L. & Jergensen, Gerald V., III, eds. Design & Installation of Communication Circuits. LC 82-71992. (Illus.). 1022p. 1982. 40.00x (ISBN 0-89520-401-0). Soc Mining Eng.

Trotter, D. A. The Lighting of Underground Mines. 1982. 48.00x (ISBN 0-87849-041-8). Trans Tech.

ELECTRICITY IN TRANSPORTATION
see also Automobiles–Electric Equipment

Mueller, Siegfried. Elektrische und Dieselelektrische Triebfahrzeuge. (German., Illus.). 204p. 1979. 52.95x (ISBN 0-8176-1033-2). Birkhauser.

ELECTRICITY ON SHIPS

Bagshaw, Norman E. Batteries on Ships. LC 82-10954. (Battery Applications Bk.Ser.). 203p. 1983. 59.95x (ISBN 0-471-90021-4, Res Stud Pr). Wiley.

Beyn, Edgar J. The Twelve Volt Doctor's Practical Handbook: For the Boat's Electric System. rev. ed. (Illus.). 1983. write for info. (ISBN 0-911551-07-7). SPA Creek.

Laws, W. Electricity Applied to Marine Engineering. 4th ed. Tyrell, R., rev. by. 454p. 1966. pap. 12.00x (ISBN 0-900976-31-4, Pub. by Inst Marine Eng). Intl Spec Bk.

--Electricity Applied to Marine Engineering. 445p. 1981. 75.00x (ISBN 0-900976-31-4, Pub. by Marine Mgmt England). State Mutual Bk.

Watson. Marine Electrical Practice. 5th ed. 1981. text ed. 57.50 (ISBN 0-408-00498-3). Butterworth.

ELECTRIFICATION
see also Electric Industries; Electric Power; Electric Power Distribution

Foster, Abram J. The Coming of the Electrical Age to the United States. Bruchey, Stuart, ed. LC 78-22680. (Energy in the American Economy Ser.). 1979. lib. bdg. 28.50x (ISBN 0-405-11983-6). Ayer Co Pubs.

Urban Electrification Planning. (Energy Resources Development Ser.: No. 12). pap. 7.00 (ISBN 0-686-93078-9, UN75/2F6, UN). Unipub.

ELECTRO-ACOUSTICS
see also Magnetic Recorders and Recording; Phonograph

Anan'eva, A. A., et al. Ceramic Acoustic Detectors. LC 65-11334. 122p. 1965. 35.00x (ISBN 0-306-10702-3, Consultants). Plenum Pub.

Ando, Y. Concert Hall Acoustics. (Springer Series in Electrophysics: Vol. 17). (Illus.). 170p. 1985. 41.50 (ISBN 0-387-13505-7). Springer-Verlag.

Antsyferov, M. S., ed. Seismo-Acoustic Methods in Mining. LC 65-26634. 134p. 1966. 34.50x (ISBN 0-306-10752-X, Consultants). Plenum Pub.

Gayford, M. L. Electroacoustics. 289p. 1971. 37.75 (ISBN 0-444-19649-8). Elsevier.

Merhaut, Josef. Theory of Electroacoustics. (Illus.). 336p. 1981. 60.00 (ISBN 0-07-041478-5). McGraw.

Oringel, Robert S. Audio Control Handbook: For Radio & Television Broadcasting. 5th rev. & enl. ed. (Communication Arts Bks.). (Illus.). 380p. 1983. pap. text ed. 14.95 (ISBN 0-8038-0550-0). Hastings.

Schrader, Barry. Introduction to Electro-Acoustic Music. (Illus.). 224p. 1982. pap. 18.95 (ISBN 0-13-481515-7). P-H.

ELECTROBIOLOGY
see Electrophysiology

ELECTROCARDIOGRAPHY

Adamovich, David R. The Heart: Fundamentals of Electrocardiography, Exercise Physiology, & Exercise Stress Testing. LC 83-50971. (Illus.). 414p. (Orig.). 1984. pap. 29.95 (ISBN 0-914363-00-X). Sports Med Bks.

American National Standard ECG Connectors. 16p. 1983. pap. text ed. 35.00 (ISBN 0-910275-21-1). Assn Adv Med Instrn.

Armstrong, Michael L. Electrocardiograms. 5th ed. (Illus.). 336p. 1985. 20.00 (ISBN 0-7236-0793-1). PSG Pub Co.

Baker, Brian H. Performing the Electrocardiogram. (Illus.). 232p. 1982. spiral bdg. 26.75x (ISBN 0-398-04651-4). C C Thomas.

Blake, Thomas M. The Practice of Electrocardiography. 2nd ed. 1985. pap. text ed. price not set (ISBN 0-87488-897-2). Med Exam.

Bonner, Raymond E. & Pryor, T. Allan, eds. Computerized Interpretation of the Electrocardiogram VI. LC 82-82657. 224p. 1982. pap. write for info. (ISBN 0-939204-16-9, 81-12). Eng Found.

Chung. Fundamentals of Electrocardiography. (Illus.). 352p. 1984. 25.00 (ISBN 0-8391-1872-4, 19143). Univ Park.

--Office Electrocardiography. (Illus.). 384p. 1984. 30.00 (ISBN 0-8391-1878-3, 19178). Univ Park.

Chung, Edward K. Electrocardiography: Practical Applications with Vectorial Principles. 3rd ed. (Illus.). 784p. 1985. 75.00 (ISBN 0-8385-2167-3). ACC.

Conover, Mary B. Electrocardiography: A Home Study Course. (Illus.). 1984. pap. text ed. 12.95 (ISBN 0-8016-1179-2). Mosby.

The Electrocardiogram: A Self-Study Course in Clinical Electrocardiography. LC 75-8186. pap. 103.80 (ISBN 0-317-26146-0, 2025006). Bks Demand UMI.

Ervin. Memory Bank for Critical Care: EKG's & Cardiac Drugs. 2nd ed. (Illus.). 220p. 10.95 (ISBN 0-683-09530-7). Williams & Wilkins.

Friedan, Julian & Rubin, Ira. ECG Case Studies, Vol. 1. 3rd ed. LC 85-8966. 1985. pap. text ed. 24.50 (ISBN 0-87488-460-8). Med Exam.

Friedman, H. H. Diagnostic Electrocardiography & Vectorcardiography. 3rd ed. 688p. 1984. 45.00 (ISBN 0-07-022427-7). McGraw.

Garson, Arthur, Jr. The Electrocardiogram in Infants & Children: A Systematic Approach. LC 83-1039. (Illus.). 421p. 1983. text ed. 45.00 (ISBN 0-8121-0872-8). Lea & Febiger.

Goldschlager, Nora & Goldman, Mervin J. Electrocardiography: Essentials of Interpretation. LC 84-81105. (Illus.). 236p. 1984. lexotone cover 13.00 (ISBN 0-87041-290-6). Lange.

Horner, Susan L. Ambulatory Electrocardiography: Applications & Techniques. (Illus.). 400p. 1983. pap. text ed. 18.75 (ISBN 0-397-50586-8, 65-07487, Lippincott Medical). Lippincott.

IFPtC4 Working Conference, Amsterdam, 1976. Trends in Computer-Processed Electrocardiograms: Proceedings. Van Bemmel, J. H. & Willems, J. L., eds. LC 77-1801. 438p. 1977. 61.75 (ISBN 0-7204-0723-0, North-Holland). Elsevier.

Kapilian, Ralph H. A Statistical Computerized Electrocardiogram Norm for Males & Females 26 Yrs. Old to 65 Yrs. Old. 79p. (Orig.). 1984. wire spiral bdg. 114.99 (ISBN 0-916311-00-7). R H Kapilian.

Klinge, Rainer. The Electrocardiogram. (Flexibook Ser.). (Illus.). 292p. 1985. pap. text ed. 15.00 (ISBN 0-86577-186-3). Thieme Stratton.

Lipman, Bernard. Clinical Electrocardiography. 7th ed. 1984. 47.95 (ISBN 0-8151-5443-7). Year Bk Med.

Marriott, Henry J. Practical Electrocardiography. 7th ed. (Illus.). 496p. 1983. text ed. 19.95 (ISBN 0-683-05574-7). Williams & Wilkins.

Master, Arthur M., et al. The Electrocardiogram & Chest X-Ray in Diseases of the Heart. LC 63-16703. (Illus.). Repr. of 1963 ed. 107.40 (2014563). Bks Demand UMI.

Pilkington, T. C. & Plonsey, R. Engineering Contributions to Biophysical Electrocardiography. LC 82-9200. 1982. 41.55 (ISBN 0-87942-163-0, PC01586). Inst Electrical.

Pryor, T. Allan, et al. Computer Systems for the Processing of Diagnostic Electrocardiograms. (Tutorial Texts Ser.). 227p. 1980. 25.00 (ISBN 0-8186-0325-9, Q325). IEEE Comp Soc.

Rahr, Richard H., et al. Systematic Interpretation of the EKG: Basic Electrocardiography, Vol. I. (Illus.). 128p. (Orig.). 1984. pap. 12.00 (ISBN 0-668-05866-8). ACC.

Roelandt, J. & Hugenholtz, P. G. Long-Term Ambulatory Electrocardiography. 1982. text ed. 39.50 (ISBN 90-247-2664-6, Pub. by Martinus Nijhoff Netherlands). Kluwer Academic.

Ruttkay-Nedecky, I. & MacFarlane, P., eds. Electrocardiology, 1983: Proceedings of the International Congress on Electrocardiology, 10th, Bratislava, Czechoslovakia, 16-19 Aug., 1983. (International Congress Ser.: No. 653). 444p. 1985. 98.25 (ISBN 0-444-80585-0, Excerpta Medica). Elsevier.

Srinivasin, Supramanian, et al, eds. Comprehensive Treatise of Electrochemistry Vol. 10: Bioelectrochemistry. 560p. 1985. 75.00x (ISBN 0-306-41541-0, Plenum Pr). Plenum Pub.

Subbarao, E. C., ed. Solid Electrolytes & Their Applications. LC 80-14879. (Illus.). 315p. 1980. 45.00x (ISBN 0-306-40389-7, Plenum Pr). Plenum Pub.

Takamura, T. & Kozawa, A. Surface Electrochemistry. 1979. 35.00x (ISBN 0-89955-135-1, Pub. by Japan Sci Soc Japan). Intl Spec Bk.

Thirsk, H. R., ed. Electrochemistry, Vols. 1-6. Incl. Vol. 1. 1968-69 Literature. 1970. 34.00 (ISBN 0-85186-007-9); Vol. 2. 1970 Literature. 1971. 34.00 (ISBN 0-85186-017-6); Vol. 3. 1971 Literature. 1972. 34.00 (ISBN 0-85186-027-3); Vol. 4. 1972 Literature. 1974. 38.00 (ISBN 0-85186-037-0); Vol. 5. 1974 Literature. 1975. 49.00 (ISBN 0-85186-047-8); Vol. 6. 1976 Literature. 1977. 50.00 (ISBN 0-85186-057-5, Pub. by Royal Soc Chem London). LC 72-23822. Am Chemical.

Thomas, J. D., ed. Ion-Selective Electrode Reviews, Vol. 4. (Illus.). 286p. 1983. 84.00 (ISBN 0-08-030414-1). Pergamon.

Titkov, Nikolai I., et al. Electrochemical Induration of Weak Rocks. LC 60-13950. pap. 20.00 (ISBN 0-317-10409-8, 2020647). Bks Demand UMI.

Trasatti, S. Electrodes of Conductive Metallic Oxides, 2 Pts. (Studies in Physical & Theoretical Chemistry: VOl. 11). 1980-81. Pt. A. 83.00 (ISBN 0-444-41912-8); Pt. B. 83.00 (ISBN 0-444-41988-8). Elsevier.

Varma. Characterizing Electrodes & Electrochemical Processes. (Electrochemical Society Ser.). 1985. price not set (ISBN 0-471-82499-2). Wiley.

Venkatasetty, H. V., ed. Lithium Battery Technology. LC 83-27408. (Electrochemical Society Ser.: 1-117). 272p. 1984. text ed. 42.50 (ISBN 0-471-09609-1, Pub. by Wiley-Interscience). Wiley.

Vijh, Ashok K. Electrochemistry of Metals & Semiconductors: The Application of Solid State Science to Electrochemical Phenomena. (Monographs in Electroanalytical Chemistry & Electrochemistry: Vol. 3). 320p. 1973. 69.75 (ISBN 0-8247-6064-6). Dekker.

Vincent, G. A. Modern Batteries: An Introduction to Electrochemical Power Sources. 1984. pap. text ed. 29.95 (ISBN 0-7131-3469-0). E Arnold.

Warren, I. H., ed. Application of Polarization Measurements in the Control of Metal Deposition. (Process Metallurgy Ser.: Vol. 3). 314p. 1984. 72.25 (ISBN 0-444-42345-1, I-229-84). Elsevier.

Weissberger, A. & Rossiter, B. W. Physical Methods of Chemistry: Electrochemical Methods, Vol. 1, Pt. 2a. (Techniques of Chemistry Ser.). 723p. 1971. 107.50 (ISBN 0-471-92727-9). Wiley.

White, Ralph E., et al, eds. Modern Aspects of Electrochemistry, Vol. 15. 360p. 1983. 49.50x (ISBN 0-306-41287-X, Plenum Pr). Plenum Pub.

--Comprehensive Treatment of Electrochemistry: Vol. 8-Experimental Methods in Electrochemistry. 607p. 1984. 89.50x (ISBN 0-306-41448-1, Plenum Pr). Plenum Pub.

Whitfield, M. & Jagner, D. Marine Electrochemistry: A Practical Introduction. LC 80-42023. 529p. 1981. 84.95x (ISBN 0-471-27976-5, Pub. by Wiley-Interscience). Wiley.

Winter, D. G. The Application of the Rotating Disc Electrode to the Determination of Kinetic Parameters in Electrochemical Systems, 1980. 1981. 50.00x (ISBN 0-686-97033-0, Pub. by W Spring England). State Mutual Bk.

Workshop of the Electrocatalysis of Fuel Cell Reactions (1978: Brookhaven National Laboratory) The Electrocatalysis of Fuel Cell Reactions. O'Grady, W. E. & Srinivasan, S., eds. LC 79-51633. (Electrochemical Society Proceedings Ser.: Vol. 79-2). (Illus.). pap. 59.00 (ISBN 0-317-09592-7, 2051701). Bks Demand UMI.

Yeager, Ernest & Salkind, Alvin J., eds. Techniques of Electrochemistry, 3 vols. LC 73-37940. (Pub. by Wiley-Interscience); Vol. 3, 1978 - 495 Pgs. 68.50 (ISBN 0-471-02919-X). Wiley.

Yeager, Ernest, et al, eds. Comprehensive Treatise of Electrochemistry, Vol. 9. 470p. 1984. 65.00x (ISBN 0-306-41570-4, Plenum Pr). Plenum Pub.

Yoshida, Kunihisa. Electrooxidation in Organic Chemistry: The Role of Cation Radicals As Synthetic Intermediates. LC 83-10480. 323p. 1984. 52.50 (ISBN 0-471-88524-X, Pub. by Wiley-Interscience). Wiley.

Zuman, P. Elucidation of Organic Electrode Processes. (Current Chemical Concepts Ser.). 1969. 49.50 (ISBN 0-12-782750-1). Acad Pr.

ELECTROCHEMISTRY–BIBLIOGRAPHY

Nagy, Zoltan, ed. Electrochemical Synthesis of Inorganic Compounds: A Bibliography. 488p. 1985. 75.00x (ISBN 0-306-41938-6, Plenum Pr). Plenum Pub.

ELECTROCHEMISTRY, INDUSTRIAL

see also Electrostatic Precipitation

Alkire, Richard & Chin, Der-Tau, eds. Tutorial Lectures in Electrochemical Engineering & Technology II. (AIChE Symposium Ser.: Vol. 79, No. 229). 232p. 1983. pap. 45.00 (ISBN 0-317-05082-6). Am Inst Chem Eng.

Bockris, J. O'M. & Nagy, Zolton. Electrochemistry for Ecologists. LC 73-84003. 200p. 1974. 29.50x (ISBN 0-306-30749-9, Plenum Pr). Plenum Pub.

Bockris, J. O'M., ed. Electrochemistry of Cleaner Environments. LC 72-179762. 296p. 1972. 39.50x (ISBN 0-306-30560-7, Plenum Pr). Plenum Pub.

Feilden, G. B., et al, eds. Prospects for Industrial Electrochemistry. (Illus.). 165p. 1981. lib. bdg. 54.00x (ISBN 0-85403-174-X, Pub. by Royal Soc London). Scholium Intl.

Graham, Robert W., ed. Primary Electrochemical Cell Technology: Advances Since 1977. LC 81-38329. (Energy Tech. Rev. 66; Chem. Tech. Rev. 191). 388p. 1981. 48.00 (ISBN 0-8155-0853-0). Noyes.

Landau, Uziel & Yeager, Ernest, eds. Electrochemistry in Industry: New Directions. LC 82-5207. 400p. 1982. 59.50x (ISBN 0-306-40999-2, Plenum Pr). Plenum Pub.

Newman, John. Electrochemical Systems. (International Series in the Physical Chemical Engineering Sciences). (Illus.). 448p. 1973. ref. ed. 41.95 (ISBN 0-13-248922-8). P-H.

Pletcher, D. Industrial Electrochemistry. 340p. 1982. 110.00x (ISBN 0-412-16500-7, Pub. by Chapman & Hall England). State Mutual Bk.

Pletcher, Derek. Industrial Electrochemistry. (Illus.). 332p. 1984. 59.00 (ISBN 0-412-16500-7, NO. 6654, Pub. by Chapman & Hall); pap. 29.95 (ISBN 0-412-26530-3, NO. 9160, Pub. by Chapman & Hall). Methuen Inc.

Trescott, Martha M. The Rise of the American Electrochemicals Industry, 1880-1910: Studies in the American Technological Environment. LC 80-23469. (Contributions in Economics & Economic History Ser.: No. 38). (Illus.). 424p. 1981. lib. bdg. 45.00 (ISBN 0-313-20766-6, TRI/). Greenwood.

ELECTRODEPOSITION OF METALS

see Electroplating

ELECTRODES

see also Electric Resistors

Albery, John. Electrode Kinetics. (Oxford Chemistry Ser). (Illus.). 1975. 32.50x (ISBN 0-19-855433-8). Oxford U Pr.

Albery, W. J. & Hitchman, M. L. Ring-Disc Electrodes. (Oxford Science Research Papers Ser). (Illus.). 1971. pap. 42.50x (ISBN 0-19-855349-8). Oxford U Pr.

American Welding Society. Specification for Carbon, Steel, Covered Arc Welding Electrodes: A5.1. 35p. 1981. 10.00 (ISBN 0-87171-169-9); member 7.50. Am Welding.

--Specification for Welding Rods & Covered Electrodes for Welding Cast Iron: A5.15. 10p. 1982. 10.00 (ISBN 0-87171-220-2); member 7.50. Am Welding.

--Specification for Zirconium & Zirconium Alloy Bare Welding Rods & Electrodes: A5.24-79. 1979. 10.00 (ISBN 0-87171-184-2). Am Welding.

Antelman, Marvin S. & Harris, Franklin J., Jr. The Encyclopedia of Chemical Electrode Potentials. 286p. 1982. text ed. 42.50x (ISBN 0-306-40903-8, Plenum Pr). Plenum Pub.

Bailey, Peter. Analysis with Ion-Selective Electrodes. 2nd ed. (Heyden International Topics in Science Ser.). 264p. 1980. 34.95 (ISBN 0-471-25590-4, Pub. by Wiley Heyden). Wiley.

Camman, Karl. Working with Ion-Selective Electrodes. Schroeder, A. H., tr. from Ger. (Chemical Laboratory Practice Ser.). (Illus.). 1979. 49.00 (ISBN 0-387-09320-6). Springer-Verlag.

Conway, B. E. Theory & Principals of Electrode Processes. LC 65-17090. 302p. 1965. 20.50 (ISBN 0-686-74216-8). Krieger.

Cosofret, V. V. Membrane Electrodes in Drug-Substances Analysis. Thomas, J. D., ed. (Illus.). 376p. 1981. 66.00 (ISBN 0-08-026264-3). Pergamon.

Covington, A. Ion-Selective Electrodes. 1981. 29.50x (ISBN 0-85186-398-1). State Mutual Bk.

Covington, A. K., ed. Ion Selective Electrode Methodology, 2 vols. 1979. Vol. 1, 272 Pgs. 64.95 (ISBN 0-8493-5247-9); Vol. 2, 144 Pgs. 47.50 (ISBN 0-8493-5248-7). CRC Pr.

Damaskin, Boris B., et al. Adsorption of Organic Compounds on Electrodes. LC 69-17533. 500p. 1971. 69.50x (ISBN 0-306-30432-5, Plenum Pr). Plenum Pub.

Delahay, Paul. Double Layer & Electrode Kinetics. LC 65-16404. pap. 83.30 (ISBN 0-317-09078-X, 2009033). Bks Demand UMI.

Ferris, Clifford D. Introduction to Bioelectrodes. LC 74-19381. (Illus.). 255p. 1974. 32.50x (ISBN 0-306-30780-4, Plenum Pr). Plenum Pub.

Freiser, Henry, ed. Ion-Selective Electrodes in Analytical Chemistry, Vol. 2. LC 78-16722. (Modern Analytical Chemistry Ser.). (Illus.). 302p. 1980. 49.50x (ISBN 0-306-40500-8, Plenum Pr). Plenum Pub.

Fried, Ilana. The Chemistry of Electrode Processes. 1974. 39.50 (ISBN 0-12-267650-5). Acad Pr.

Gabow, Patricia A. Fluids & Electrolytes: Clinical Problems & Their Solutions. 1983. pap. 15.95 (ISBN 0-316-30114-0). Little.

Gileadi, Eliezer, ed. Electrosorption. LC 67-15143. 221p. 1967. 35.00x (ISBN 0-306-30283-7, Plenum Pr). Plenum Pub.

Havas, J. Ion & Molecule-Selective Electrodes in Biological Systems. (Illus.). 255p. 1985. 34.50 (ISBN 0-387-13725-4). Springer-Verlag.

Ives, David G. & Janz, George J., eds. Reference Electrodes: Theory & Practice. 1969. pap. 52.50 (ISBN 0-12-376856-X). Acad Pr.

Koryta, Jiri. Ions, Electrodes & Membranes. LC 81-14762. 197p. 1982. 44.95x (ISBN 0-471-10007-2, Pub. by Wiley-Interscience); pap. 22.95x (ISBN 0-471-10008-0, Pub. by Wiley-Interscience). Wiley.

Koryta, Jiri & Stulik, Karel. Ion-Selective Electrodes. 2nd ed. LC 82-25297. 200p. 1984. 49.50 (ISBN 0-521-23873-0). Cambridge U Pr.

Luebbers, D. W., et al, eds. Progress in Enzyme & Ion-Selective Electrodes. (Illus.). 240p. 1981. pap. 27.70 (ISBN 0-387-10499-2). Springer-Verlag.

Material Specifications: Welding Rods, Electrodes & Filler Metals, 3 pts, Pt. C. (Boiler & Pressure Vessel Code Ser.: Sec. II). 1980. loose leaf 70.00 (ISBN 0-686-70439-8, V0002C); pap. 55.00 bound (ISBN 0-686-70440-1, P0002C). ASME.

Miller, H. & Harrison, D. C. Biomedical Electrode Technology. 1974. 65.00 (ISBN 0-12-496850-3). Acad Pr.

Moody, G. J. & Thomas, J. D. Selective Ion Sensitive Electrodes. 148p. 1971. 39.00x (ISBN 0-900541-35-0, Pub. by Meadowfield Pr England). State Mutual Bk.

Pal'guev, S. F., ed. Mechanism & Kinetics of Electrode Processes. LC 61-15178. (Electrochemistry of Molten & Solid Electrolytes Ser.: Vol. 8, Trudy No. 11). 84p. 1970. 30.00x (ISBN 0-306-18008-1, Consultants). Plenum Pub.

Pleskov, Yu. V. & Filinovskii, V. Yu. The Rotating Disc Electrode. LC 76-22774. (Illus.). 402p. 1976. 75.00 (ISBN 0-306-10912-3, Consultants). Plenum Pub.

Pungor. Ion-Selective Electrodes. 1977. 18.50 (ISBN 0-9960003-5-6, Pub. by Akademiai Kaido Hungary). Heyden.

Pungor, E. & Buzas, I., eds. Non-Selective Electrodes. 1973. 18.50 (ISBN 0-9960003-5-6, Pub. by Akademiai Kaido Hungary). Heyden.

Specification for Low-Alloy, Steel Covered Arc Welding Electrodes: A5.5. 29p. 1981. 10.00; member 7.50. Am Welding.

Specification for Low-Alloy, Steel Electrodes & Fluxes for Submerged Arc Welding: A5.23. 20p. 1980. 10.00 (ISBN 0-87171-202-4); member 7.50. Am Welding.

Specification for Nickel & Nickel-Alloy Bare Welding Rods & Electrodes: A5.14. 1983. 10.00 (ISBN 0-87171-232-6); member 7.50. Am Welding.

Specification for Solid Surface Welding Rods & Electrodes: A5.21. 22p. 1980. 10.00; member 7.50 (ISBN 0-87171-196-6, A5.13-80). Am Welding.

Specification for Steel, Low-Alloy Flux Cored Arc Welding Electrodes: A5.29-80. 20p. 1980. 10.00 (ISBN 0-87171-208-3). Am Welding.

Specification for Titanium & Titanium-Alloy Bare Welding Rods & Electrodes: A5.16. 29p. 1970. 10.00 (ISBN 0-685-65978-X); member 7.50. Am Welding.

Symposium on Electrode Materials & Processes for Energy Conversion & Storage (1977: Philadelphia) Electrode Materials & Processess for Energy Conversion & Storage; Nineteen Seventy-Seven Proceedings of the Symposium. Srinivasan, S., et al, eds. LC 77-79769. (Illus.). pap. 160.00 (ISBN 0-317-09184-0, 2050186). Bks Demand UMI.

Thomas, J. D. Ion-Selective Electrode Reviews, Vol. 1. (Illus.). 280p. 1980. 47.00 (ISBN 0-08-026044-6). Pergamon.

Thomas, J. D., ed. Ion-Selective Electrode Reviews, Vol. 2, No. 2. (Illus.). 146p. 1981. pap. 31.00 (ISBN 0-08-027128-6). Pergamon.

--Ion-Selective Electrode Reviews, Vol. 3. (Illus.). 248p. 1982. 62.00 (ISBN 0-08-029692-0). Pergamon.

--Ion-Selective Electrode Reviews, Vol. 5. (Illus.). 298p. 1984. 84.00 (ISBN 0-08-031492-9). Pergamon.

Thomas, J. D. R. Ion-Selective Electrode Reviews, Vol. 2. 62.00 (ISBN 0-08-028434-5). Pergamon.

Thomas, R. C. Ion-Sensitive Intracellular Micro-Electrodes: How to Make & Use Them. (Biological Techniques Ser.). 1979. 29.50 (ISBN 0-12-688750-0). Acad Pr.

Tischer, R. P., ed. The Sulfur Electrode: Fused Salts & Solid Electrolytes. LC 82-22753. 1983. 68.00 (ISBN 0-12-691680-2). Acad Pr.

Varma. Characterizing Electrodes & Electrochemical Processes. (Electrochemical Society Ser.). 1985. price not set (ISBN 0-471-82499-2). Wiley.

Vesely, J., et al. Analysis with Ion-Selective Electrodes. 245p. 1978. 94.95x (ISBN 0-470-26296-6). Halsted Pr.

ELECTRODYNAMICS

see also Cosmic Electrodynamics; Ion Flow Dynamics; Magnetohydrodynamics; Wave Mechanics

Adey, W. Ross & Lawrence, A. F., eds. Nonlinear Electrodynamics in Biological Systems. 616p. 1984. 89.50x (ISBN 0-306-41736-7, Plenum Pr). Plenum Pub.

Barut, A. O. Electrodynamics & Classical Theory of Fields & Particles. (Illus.). 256p. 1980. pap. text ed. 4.50 (ISBN 0-486-64038-8). Dover.

Batygin, V. V. & Toptygin, I. N. Problems in Electrodynamics. 2nd ed. 1978. 44.00 (ISBN 0-12-082160-5). Acad Pr.

Bekefi, George. Electromagnetic Vibrations, Waves, & Radiation. Barrett, Alan H., ed. LC 77-10421. 1978. pap. text ed. 27.50x (ISBN 0-262-52047-8). MIT Pr.

Delahay, Paul. Double Layer & Electrode Kinetics. LC 65-16404. pap. 83.30 (ISBN 0-317-09078-X, 2009033). Bks Demand UMI.

Electrodynamics of Continuous Media. 2nd ed. Sykes, L. D., et al, trs. (Course of Theoretical Physics Ser.: Vol. 8). 600p. 1984. 60.00 (ISBN 0-08-030276-9); pap. 25.00 (ISBN 0-08-030275-0). Pergamon.

Grandy, Walter T., Jr. Introduction to Electrodynamics & Radiation. LC 78-117077. (Pure & Applied Physics Ser). 1970. 35.50 (ISBN 0-12-295250-2). Acad Pr.

Greiner, W., et al. Quantum Electrodynamics of Strong Fields. (Texts & Monographs in Physics). (Illus.). 610p. 1985. 43.00 (ISBN 0-387-13404-2). Springer-Verlag.

Griffiths, D. Introduction to Electrodynamics. 1981. 36.95 (ISBN 0-13-481374-X). P-H.

Ingarden, R. S. & Jamiolkowski, A. Classical Electrodynamics. (Studies in Electrical & Electronic Engineering: No. 12). 346p. 1985. 83.50 (ISBN 0-444-99604-4). Elsevier.

Jackson, J. D. Classical Electrodynamics. 2nd ed. LC 75-9962. 864p. 1975. text ed. 46.45x (ISBN 0-471-43132-X). Wiley.

Novozhilov, Y. V. & Yappa, Y. A. Electrodynamics. 352p. 1981. 10.00 (ISBN 0-8285-2061-5, Pub. by Mir Pubs USSR). Imported Pubns.

Oppenheimer, J. R. Lectures on Electrodynamics. (Documents on Modern Physics Ser.). 174p. 1970. 46.25 (ISBN 0-677-40130-2). Gordon.

Schwinger, Julian. Particles & Sources. (Documents on Modern Physics Ser.). 100p. 1969. 32.50x (ISBN 0-677-02060-0). Gordon.

Smyth, W. F. Electroanalysis in Hygiene, Environmental, Clinical & Pharmaceutical Chemistry. (Analytical Chemistry Symposia Ser.: Vol. 2). 474p. 1980. 68.00 (ISBN 0-444-41850-4). Elsevier.

Volland, H. Atmospheric Electrodynamics. (Physics & Chemistry in Space Ser.: Vol. 11). (Illus.). 210p. 1984. 35.50 (ISBN 0-387-13510-3). Springer-Verlag.

ELECTRODYNAMICS, QUANTUM

see Quantum Electrodynamics

ELECTROENCEPHALOGRAPHY

see also Evoked Potentials (Electrophysiology)

Buser, P. A. & Cobb, W. A., eds. Kyoto Symposia: Electroencephalography & Clinical Neurophysiology, Supp. No. 36. 770p. 1983. 204.25 (ISBN 0-444-80436-6, Biomedical Pr). Elsevier.

Duffy, Frank H. Topographic Mapping of Brain Electrical Activity. (Illus.). 336p. 1986. pap. text ed. 34.95 (ISBN 0-409-90008-7). Butterworth.

Kellaway, P. & Petersen, I., eds. Automation of Clinical Electroencephalography. LC 72-96334. (Illus.). 326p. 1973. 50.50 (ISBN 0-911216-45-6). Raven.

Laget, Paul & Salbreux, Roger. Atlas of Electroencephalography in the Child. (Illus.). 656p. 1982. 135.00 (ISBN 0-89352-189-2). Masson Pub.

Nunez, Paul L. Electric Fields of the Brain: The Neurophysics of EEG. (Illus.). 494p. 1984. text ed. 55.00x (ISBN 0-19-502796-5). Oxford U Pr.

Pfurtscheller, G., et al, eds. Rhythmic EEG Activities & Cortical Function. (Developments in Neuroscience Ser.: Vol. 10). 314p. 1980. 57.00 (ISBN 0-444-80028-X, Biomedical Pr). Elsevier.

--Brain Ischemia: Quantitative EEG & Imaging Techniques. (Progress in Brain Research Ser.: Vol. 62). 1985. 87.00 (ISBN 0-444-80582-6). Elsevier.

BOOKS - SUBJECT INDEX ELECTROMAGNETIC FIELDS

Pichlmayr, I., et al. The Electroencephalogram in Anesthesiology: Fundamentals, Practical Applications, Examples. Bonatz, E. & Masyk-Iverson, T., trs. from German. (Illus.). 225p. 1984. 38.50 (ISBN 0-387-13159-0). Springer-Verlag.
Redding, Richard W. & Knecht, Charles E. An Atlas of Electro-Encephalography in the Dog & Cat. LC 83-13693. (Illus.). 400p. 1984. 39.95x (ISBN 0-03-061929-7). Praeger.
Remond, A., ed. EEG Informatics: A Didactic Review of Methods & Applications of EEG Data Processing. 426p. 1977. 62.75 (ISBN 0-444-80005-0, Biomedical Pr). Elsevier.
Ruggiero, G., et al. Radiological Exploration of the Ventricles & Subarachnoid Space. LC 73-19548. (Illus.). 200p. 1974. 97.00 (ISBN 0-387-06572-5). Springer-Verlag.
Williams, Robert L., et al. Electroencephalography (EEG) of Human Sleep: Clincial Applications. LC 73-20032. (Wiley Biomedical-Health Publication). (Illus.). pap. 45.80 (ISBN 0-317-09238-3, 2055170). Bks Demand UMI.
Wilson, William P., ed. Applications of Electroencephalography in Psychiatry: A Symposium. LC 65-19449. pap. 70.00 (ISBN 0-317-26797-3, 2023471). Bks Demand UMI.
Yamaguchi, N. & Fujisawa, K., eds. Recent Advances in EEG & EMG Data Processing. 422p. 1981. 68.00 (ISBN 0-444-80356-4, Biomedical Pr). Elsevier.

ELECTROENDOSMOSIS
see Electro-Osmosis

ELECTROFORMING
see also Electroplating
Newman, Lee S. & Newman, Fay H. Electroplating & Electroforming: A Guide for the Craftsman. 1979. pap. 9.95 (ISBN 0-517-53059-7). Crown.
Spiro, Peter. Electroforming. 2nd rev. ed. 1971. 47.50x (ISBN 0-901994-34-0). Intl Pubns Serv.
--Electroforming. 335p. 1971. 70.00x (Pub. by Portcullio Pr). State Mutual Bk.

ELECTROGRAPHY
see Kirlian Photography

ELECTROLUMINESCENCE
Pankove, J. I., ed. Electroluminescence. LC 77-1911. (Topics in Applied Physics Ser: Vol. 17). 1977. 45.00 (ISBN 0-387-08127-5). Springer-Verlag.
Parkhomenko, E. I. Electrification Phenomena in Rocks. LC 73-107533. (Monographs in Geoscience Ser.). 285p. 1971. 29.50x (ISBN 0-306-30441-4, Plenum Pr). Plenum Pub.
Skobel'tsyn, D. V., ed. Electroluminescence. LC 71-157932. (P. N. Lebedev Physics Institute Ser.: Vol. 50). 137p. 1972. 20.00x (ISBN 0-306-10865-8, Consultants). Plenum Pub.

ELECTROLYSIS
see also Electrochemical Analysis; Electrolytes; Electrolytic Cells; Electrolytic Corrosion; Electrometallurgy; Electro-Osmosis; Ions
Miller, Joel S., ed. Chemically Modified Surfaces in Catalysis & Electrolysis. LC 82-8731. (ACS Symposium Ser.: No. 192). 301p. 1982. lib. bdg. 39.95 (ISBN 0-8412-0727-5). Am Chemical.
Molten Salt Electrolysis in Metal Production. 73p. (Orig.). 1977. pap. text ed. 49.00x (ISBN 0-900488-39-5). IMM North Am.
Noakes, G. R., et al, eds. Sources of Physics Teaching: Electrolysis, X-Ray Analysis. Electron Diffraction, Vol. 3. 1969. pap. 17.50x (ISBN 0-85066-031-9). Intl Ideas.
Rose, B. D. Clinical Physiology of Acid-Base & Electrolyte Disorders. 2nd ed. 720p. 1984. 26.95 (ISBN 0-07-053622-8). McGraw.
Shapiro, Julius. Electrolysis: Beauty & Confidence Through Permanent Hair Removal. LC 80-24691. (Illus.). 207p. 1981. 10.95 (ISBN 0-396-07903-2). Dodd.
Vallis, Charles P. Hair Transplantation for the Treatment of Male Pattern Baldness. (Illus.). 608p. 1982. 69.75x (ISBN 0-398-04165-2). C C Thomas.

ELECTROLYTE SOLUTIONS
Copeland, J. L. Transport Properties of Ionic Liquids. 84p. 1974. 28.95 (ISBN 0-677-02830-X). Gordon.
Gordon, John E. The Organic Chemistry of Electrolyte Solutions. LC 75-16139. 576p. 1975. 38.50 (ISBN 0-471-31620-2). Krieger.
Hladik, J., ed. Physics of Electrolytes, 2 vols. Incl. Vol. 1. Transport Processes in Solid Electrolytes. 89.50 (ISBN 0-12-349801-5); Vol. 2. Thermodynamics & Electrode Processes in Solid State Electronics. 97.00 (ISBN 0-12-349802-3). 1972. Acad Pr.
Inman, Douglas & Lovering, David G., eds. Ionic Liquids. LC 80-16402. 460p. 1981. 65.00x (ISBN 0-306-40412-5, Plenum Pr). Plenum Pub.
Janz, George J. & Tompkins, R. P. T. Non-Aqueous Electrolytes Handbook, 2 vols. Vol. 1, 1972. 130.00 (ISBN 0-12-380401-9); Vol. 2, 1974. 130.00 (ISBN 0-12-380402-7); Set. o. p. 216.00. Acad Pr.
Leyendekkers, J. V. Thermodynamics of Seawater As a Multicomponent Electrolyte Solution, Pt. 1. (Marine Science Ser: Vol. 3). 1976. 75.00 (ISBN 0-8247-6486-2). Dekker.
Martynov, G. A. & Salem, R. R. Electrical Double Layer at a Metal-dilute Electrolyte Solution Interface. (Lecture Notes in Chemistry: Vol. 33). 170p. 1983. pap. 15.60 (ISBN 0-387-11995-7). Springer-Verlag.
Masiak, Mary J. & Naylor, Mary D. Fluids & Electrolytes Through the Life Cycle. 1985. pap. 19.95 (ISBN 0-8385-2622-5). ACC.
NATO Advanced Study Institute, Forges-les-Eaux, June 18-28, 1972. Charged & Reactive Polymers, No. 1, Polyelectrolytes: Proceedings. Selegny, E., et al, eds. LC 73-91435. 300p. 1974. lib. bdg. 84.00 (ISBN 90-277-0434-1, Pub. by Reidel Holland). Kluwer Academic.
Polyelectrolytes: Aids to Better Water Quality. (AWWA Handbooks-Proceedings). (Illus.). 128p. 1972. pap. text ed. 6.00 (ISBN 0-89867-037-3). Am Water Wks Assn.
Pytkowicz, Ricardo M. Activity Coefficients in Electrolyte Solutions, 2 vols. 1979. Vol. 1, 304 Pgs. 86.00 (ISBN 0-8493-5411-0); Vol. 2, 336 Pgs. 89.00 (ISBN 0-8493-5412-9). CRC Pr.
Rice, Stuart A. Polyelectrolyte Solutions: A Theoretical Introduction. (Molecular Biology Ser.). 1961. 83.50 (ISBN 0-12-587350-6). Acad Pr.
Rooth, Gosta. Acid Base & Electrolyte Balance. (Illus.). 108p. 1975. pap. 17.95 (ISBN 0-8151-7427-6). Year Bk Med.
Schwoyer, William L., ed. Polyelectrolytes for Water & Wastewater Treatment. 288p. 1981. 86.50 (ISBN 0-8493-5439-0). CRC Pr.
Snipes, R. F. Statistical Mechanical Theory of the Electrolytic Transport of Non-Electrolytes. (Lecture Notes in Physics: Vol. 24). 210p. 1973. pap. 14.70 (ISBN 0-387-06566-0). Springer-Verlag.
Willatts, Sheila M. Lecture Notes on Fluid & Electrolyte Balance. (Illus.). 308p. 1982. pap. text ed. 15.95 (ISBN 0-632-00862-8, B5557-9). Mosby.

ELECTROLYTES
see also Activity Coefficients; Electrolyte Solutions
Alwitt, Robert S. Oxide-Electrolyte Interfaces: Proceedings of Symposium Papers Held at the 142nd Meeting of the Society. LC 73-75171. pap. 77.50 (ISBN 0-317-08905-6, 2051820). Bks Demand UMI.
Armstrong, R. D., ed. Solid Ionic & Ionic-Electronic Conductors. LC 77-747. 1977. text ed. 37.00 (ISBN 0-08-021592-0). Pergamon.
Baraboshkin, A. N., ed. Electrochemistry of Molten & Solid Electrolytes, 9 vols. Incl. Vol. 1. 106p. 1961. 29.50 (ISBN 0-306-18001-4); Vol. 2. 96p. 1964. 30.00 (ISBN 0-306-18002-2); Vol. 3. 133p. 1966. 29.50x (ISBN 0-306-18003-0); Vol. 4. 165p. 1967. 35.00 (ISBN 0-306-18004-9); Vol. 5. Physiochemical Properties of Electrolyte & Electrode Processes. 158p. 1967. 35.00x (ISBN 0-306-18005-7); Vol. 6. Structure & Properties of Electrolytes & Kinetics of Electrode Properties. 138p. 1968. 29.50x (ISBN 0-306-18006-5); Vol. 7. Physiochemical Properties of Electrolytes. 99p. 1969. 29.50x (ISBN 0-306-18007-3); Vol. 8. Mechanism & Kinetics of Electrode Processes. 84p. 1970. 30.00 (ISBN 0-306-18008-1); Vol. 9. Thermodynamics of Salt & Oxide Systems. 110p. 1972. 30.00 (ISBN 0-306-18009-X). LC 61-15178 (Consultants). Plenum Pub.
Collins, R. Douglas. Illustrated Manual of Fluid & Electrolyte Disorders. 2nd ed. (Illus.). 224p. 1983. text ed. 39.50 (ISBN 0-397-50516-7, 65-06604, Lippincott Medical). Lippincott.
Finberg, Laurence, et al. Water & Electrolytes in Pediatrics: Physiology, Pathophysiology & Treatment. (Illus.). 272p. 1982. 39.00 (ISBN 0-7216-3625-X). Saunders.
Frisch, Kurt C., et al. Polyelectrolytes. LC 76-177446. (Illus.). 1976. 14.95x (ISBN 0-87762-076-8). Technomic.
Geller, S., ed. Solid Electrolytes. LC 77-21873. (Topics in Applied Physics: Vol. 21). (Illus.). 1977. 49.00 (ISBN 0-387-08338-3). Springer-Verlag.
Hagenmuller, Paul & Van Gool, W., eds. Solid Electrolytes: General Principles, Characterization, Materials, Applications. (Materials Science & Technology Ser.). 1978. 81.00 (ISBN 0-12-313360-2). Acad Pr.
International Meeting on Solid Electrolytes, 2nd, University of St. Andrews, Sep. 20-22, 1978. Solid Electrolytes: Proceedings. Armstrong, R. D., ed. (Illus.). 68p. 1979. pap. 30.00 (ISBN 0-08-025267-2). Pergamon.
Li, A. K., et al. Fluid Electroytes, Acid Base & Nutrition. 1980. 12.00 (ISBN 0-12-448150-7). Acad Pr.
Masiak, Mary J. & Naylor, Mary D. Fluids & Electrolytes Through the Life Cycle. 1985. pap. 19.95 (ISBN 0-8385-2622-5). ACC.
Nicksic, Esther. The Plus & Minus of Fluids & Electrolytes. 1981. text ed. 21.00 (ISBN 0-8359-5561-3); pap. text ed. 15.95 (ISBN 0-8359-5560-5). Reston.
Nozik, Arthur J., ed. Photoeffects at Semiconductor-Electrolyte Interfaces. LC 80-27773. (Symposium Ser.: No. 146). 1981. 44.95 (ISBN 0-8412-0604-X). Am Chemical.
Oosawa, Fumio. Polyelectrolytes. LC 70-134786. (Illus.). pap. 31.80 (ISBN 0-317-07976-X, 2055010). Bks Demand UMI.
Pal'guev, S. F., ed. Thermodynamics of Salt & Oxide Systems. LC 61-15178. (Electrochemistry of Molten & Solid Electrolytes Ser.: Vol. 9, Trudy No. 12). (Illus.). 107p. 1972. 30.00x (ISBN 0-306-18009-X, Consultants). Plenum Pub.
Rembaum, Alan & Selegny, Eric, eds. Charged & Reactive Polymers, Vol. 2: Polyelectrolytes & Their Applications. LC 74-34151. 350p. 1975. lib. bdg. 68.50 (ISBN 90-277-0561-5, Pub. by Reidel Holland). Kluwer Academic.
Smedley, Stuart I. The Interpretation of Ionic Conductivity in Liquids. LC 80-17941. 211p. 1980. 35.00x (ISBN 0-306-40529-6, Plenum Pr). Plenum Pub.
Smith, E. Kinsey. Fluids & Electrolytes. Brain, Elizabeth, ed. (Illus.). 112p. 1980. pap. text ed. 10.50 (ISBN 0-443-08101-8). Churchill.
Strauss, Jose, ed. Neonatal Kidney & Fluid-Electrolytes. 1983. lib. bdg. 46.00 (ISBN 0-89838-575-X, Pub. by Martinus Nijhoff Netherlands). Kluwer Academic.
Subbarao, E. C., ed. Solid Electrolytes & Their Applications. LC 80-14879. (Illus.). 315p. 1980. 45.00x (ISBN 0-306-40389-7, Plenum Pr). Plenum Pub.
Vagramyan, A. T. & Petrova, Yu S. Mechanical Properties of Electrolytic Deposits. LC 62-8012. 120p. 1962. 25.00x (ISBN 0-306-10569-1, Consultants). Plenum Pub.
Weldy, Norma J. Body Fluids & Electrolytes: A Programmed Presentation. 3rd ed. (Illus.). 132p. 1980. pap. 10.95 (ISBN 0-8016-5383-5). Mosby.

ELECTROLYTIC ANALYSIS
see Electrochemical Analysis

ELECTROLYTIC CELLS
White, R., ed. Electrochemical Cell Design. 406p. 1984. 65.00x (ISBN 0-306-41805-3, Plenum Pr). Plenum Pub.

ELECTROLYTIC CORROSION
see also Cathodic Protection; Soil Corrosion
Galvanic & Pitting Corrosion - Field & Laboratory Studies, STP 576. 300p. 1976. 29.75 (ISBN 0-8031-0369-7, 04-576000-27). ASTM.
Gatty, Oliver & Spooner, E. C. The Electrode Potential Behaviour of Corroding Metals in Aqueous Solutions. (Illus.). Repr. of 1938 ed. 40.00 (ISBN 0-384-17730-1). Johnson Repr.
International Conference on Chemical Vapor Deposition. Chemical Vapor Deposition: Eigth International Conference Proceedings. Blocher, John M., Jr. & Vuillard, Guy E., eds. LC 81-68464. (Electrochemical Society, Proceedings: 81-7). pap. 160.00 (ISBN 0-317-26241-6, 2052141). Bks Demand UMI.
Pourbaix, Marcel. Lectures on Electrochemical Corrosion. LC 69-12537. (Illus.). 336p. 1973. 52.50x (ISBN 0-306-30449-X, Plenum Pr). Plenum Pub.

ELECTROLYTIC PICKLING OF METALS
see Metals–Pickling

ELECTROLYZERS
see Electrolytic Cells

ELECTROMAGNETIC FIELDS
see also Electromagnetic Waves; Plasma Instabilities
Anderson, N. The Electromagnetic Field. LC 68-16585. 124p. 1968. 24.50x (ISBN 0-306-30373-6, Plenum Pr). Plenum Pub.
Becker, Richard. Electromagnetic Fields & Interactions. (Illus.). 864p. 1982. pap. 12.50 (ISBN 0-486-64290-9). Dover.
Bekefi, George. Electromagnetic Vibrations, Waves, & Radiation. Barrett, Alan H., ed. LC 77-10421. 1978. pap. text ed. 27.50x (ISBN 0-262-52047-8). MIT Pr.
Capri, Anton Z. & Kamal, Abdul N., eds. Particles & Fields 2. 695p. 1983. 97.50x (ISBN 0-306-41162-8, Plenum Pr). Plenum Pub.
Carter, Geoffrey W. The Electromagnetic Field in Its Engineering Aspects. 2nd ed. LC 79-355853. (Electrical Engineering Ser.). pap. 97.00 (ISBN 0-317-09839-X, 2006978). Bks Demand UMI.
Cook, David M. The Theory of the Electromagnetic Field. (Illus.). 560p. 1975. ref. ed. 39.95 (ISBN 0-13-913293-7). P-H.
Della Torree, Edward, et al. The Electromagnetic Field. LC 79-23788. 1980. Repr. of 1979 ed. text ed. 44.50 (ISBN 0-89874-100-9). Krieger.
Eyges, Leonard. The Classical Electromagnetic Field. (Illus.). 432p. 1980. pap. text ed. 8.95 (ISBN 0-486-63947-9). Dover.
Felsen, L. B., contrib. by. Transient Electromagnetic Fields. (Tropics in Applied Physics Ser.: Vol. 10). (Illus.). 340p. 1976. 59.00 (ISBN 0-387-07553-4). Springer-Verlag.
Freeman, Ernest R. & Sechs, Michael. Electromagnetic Compatibility Design Guide for Avionics & Related Ground Support Equipment. LC 81-71923. pap. 69.80 (ISBN 0-317-30047-4, 2025049). Bks Demand UMI.
Gekker, I. R. Interaction of Strong Electromagnetic Fields with Plasmas. Sykes, J. B. & Franklin, R. N., trs. (Oxford Studies in Physics). (Illus.). 1982. 69.00x (ISBN 0-19-851467-0). Oxford U Pr.
Grandolfo, M. & Micaelson, S. M., Jr., eds. Biological Effects & Dosimetry of Static & Elf Electromagnetic Fields. (Ettore Majorana International Science Series Life Sciences: 19 vols.). 652p. 1985. 97.50x (ISBN 0-306-41923-8, Plenum Pr). Plenum Pub.
Harrington, Roger F. Time-Harmonic Electromagnetic Fields. (Electronic & Electrical Engineering Ser.). 1961. text ed. 58.00 (ISBN 0-07-026745-6). McGraw.
Johnk, Carl T. Engineering Electromagnetic Fields & Waves. LC 74-13567. 655p. 1975. 41.45x (ISBN 0-471-44289-5, Pub. by Wiley-Interscience). Wiley.
Kolm, Henry, et al, eds. High Magnetic Fields. 1961. 50.00x (ISBN 0-262-11008-3). MIT Pr.
Konopinski, Emil. Electromagnetic Fields & Relativistic Particles. (International Series in Pure & Applied Physics). (Illus.). 640p. 1981. text ed. 42.95x (ISBN 0-07-035264-X). McGraw.
Lorrain, Paul & Corson, Dale R. Electromagnetic Fields & Waves. 2nd ed. LC 72-94872. (Illus.). 706p. 1970. text ed. 32.95 (ISBN 0-7167-0331-9); solutions to problems avail. W H Freeman.
Magid, Leonard M. Electromagnetic Fields, Energy, & Waves. LC 80-16458. 808p. 1981. Repr. of 1972 ed. text ed. 45.00 (ISBN 0-89874-221-8). Krieger.
Maxwell, James C. A Dynamical Theory of the Electromagnetic Field. Torrance, Thomas F., ed. 128p. (Orig.). 1983. pap. 12.00x (ISBN 0-7073-0324-9, Pub. by Scottish Academic Pr Scotland). Columbia U Pr.
Neel, L., ed. Nonlinear Behaviour of Molecules, Atoms & Ions in Electric, Magnetic or Electromagnetic Fields. 516p. 1979. 100.00 (ISBN 0-444-41790-7). Elsevier.
Neff, Herbert P., Jr. Basic Electromagnetic Fields. (Illus.). 600p. 1981. text ed. 36.50 scp (ISBN 0-06-044785-0, HarpC); solutions manual avail. (ISBN 0-06-364714-1). Har-Row.
Paul, Clayton R. & Nasar, Syed A. Introduction to Electromagnetic Fields. (Electrical Engineering "Electromagnetics" Ser.). (Illus.). 544p. 1982. 44.00x (ISBN 0-07-045884-7). McGraw.
Persinger, Michael A. ELF & VLF Electromagnetic Field Effects. LC 74-23532. 316p. 1974. 42.50x (ISBN 0-306-30826-6, Plenum Pr). Plenum Pub.
Phillips, R. D. & Gillis, M. F., eds. Biological Effects of Extremely Low Frequency Electromagnetic Fields: Proceedings. LC 79-607778. (DOE Symposium Ser.). 577p. 1979. pap. 22.50 (ISBN 0-87079-118-4, CONF-781016); microfiche 4.50 (ISBN 0-87079-148-6, CONF-781016). DOE.
Polivanov, K. Theory of Electromagnetic Field. 271p. 1983. 8.95 (ISBN 0-8285-2747-4, Pub. by Mir Pubs USSR). Imported Pubns.
Radiofrequency Electromagnetic Fields: Properties, Quantities, & Units, Biophysical Interaction, & Measurements, No. 67. LC 80-82007. 1981. 10.00 (ISBN 0-913392-52-9). NCRP Pubns.
Read, F. H. Electromagnetic Radiation. LC 79-41484. (Manchester Physics Ser.). 331p. 1980. 69.95 (ISBN 0-471-27718-5); pap. 29.95 (ISBN 0-471-27714-2). Wiley.
Rojansky, Vladimir. Electromagnetic Fields & Waves. LC 79-52648. 1980. pap. text ed. 7.95 (ISBN 0-486-63834-0). Dover.
Rotkiewiez, W., ed. Electromagnetic Compatibility in Radio Engineering. (Studies in Electrical & Electronic Engineering: Vol. 6). 314p. 1982. 68.00 (ISBN 0-444-99722-9). Elsevier.
Seshadri, S. R. Fundamentals of Transmission Lines & Electromagnetic Fields. LC 77-128908. (Engineering Science Ser). 1971. text ed. 36.95 (ISBN 0-201-06722-6). Addison-Wesley.
Smith, Albert A. Coupling of External Electromagnetic Fields to Transmission Lines. LC 76-49504. pap. 36.00 (ISBN 0-317-09129-8, 2020597). Bks Demand UMI.
Tozoni, O. V. & Kaye, A. A. Mathematical Models for the Evaluation of Electric & Magnetic Fields. 338p. 1970. 90.25x (ISBN 0-677-61780-1). Gordon.
Van Bladel, J. Electromagnetic Fields. rev. ed. LC 84-25341. (SUMMA Bk.). (Illus.). 556p. 1985. 35.00 (ISBN 0-89116-420-0). Hemisphere Pub.
Von Engel, A. Electric Plasmas: Their Nature & Uses. LC 83-6166. 250p. 1983. 36.00x (ISBN 0-8002-3076-0). Taylor & Francis.
Wangsness, R. K. Electromagnetic Fields. 2nd ed. 1985. 35.50 (ISBN 0-471-81186-6). Wiley.

Wangsness, Ronald K. Electromagnetic Fields. LC 78-15027. 633p. 1979. text ed. 41.50x (ISBN 0-471-04103-3); solutions manual 7.75x (ISBN 0-471-05936-6). Wiley.

White, Carol. Energy Potential: Toward a New Electromagnetic Field Theory. Cleary, James, tr. 305p. 1978. pap. 7.95 (ISBN 0-918388-04-X, QC665.E4W45, Univ Edns). New Benjamin.

Zahn, Markus. Electromagnetic Field Theory: A Problem Solving Approach. LC 78-15928. 723p. 1979. text ed. 49.75 (ISBN 0-471-02198-9); tchr's manual 12.00x (ISBN 0-471-05415-1). Wiley.

ELECTROMAGNETIC INTERACTIONS

Balian, R. & Llewellyn-Smith, C. H. Weak & Electromagnetic Interactions at High Energy: Proceedings at the Summer School on Weak & Electromagnetic Interactions at High Energy, Session XXIX, les Houches, July 5 - August 14. 1976. 670p. 1978. 117.00 (ISBN 0-7204-0742-7, North-Holland). Elsevier.

Danos, M., et al. Methods in Relativistic Nuclear Physics. 308p. 1984. 74.00 (ISBN 0-444-86317-6, North-Holland). Elsevier.

Hobbs, B. A., ed. Surveying Electromagnetic Induction in the Earth & Moon. 185p. 1982. pap. 23.50 (ISBN 90-277-9041-8, Pub. by Reidel Holland). Kluwer Academic.

Keiser, B. J. Principles of Electromagnetic Compatibility. LC 79-12032. 1979. 54.00x (ISBN 0-89006-065-7). Artech Hse.

Levy, Maurice, et al, eds. Weak & Electromagnetic Interactions at High Energies, Pt. A. LC 76-3672. (NATO ASI Series B, Physics: Vol. 13A). 467p. 1976. 69.50 (ISBN 0-306-35795-X, Plenum Pr). Plenum Pub.

--Weak & Electromagnetic Interactions at High Energies, Pt. B. LC 76-3672. (NATO ASI Series B, Physics: Vol. 13B). 456p. 1976. 69.50x (ISBN 0-306-35796-8, Plenum Pr). Plenum Pub.

Parkus, H., ed. Electromagnetic Interactions in Elastic Solids. (CISM Courses & Lectures: Vol. 257). (Illus.). 425p. 1979. pap. 48.00 (ISBN 0-387-81509-0). Springer-Verlag.

Perry. Low Frequency Electromagnetic Design. (Electrical Engineering Ser.). 248p. 1985. 49.75 (ISBN 0-8247-7453-1). Dekker.

Schmucker, U., ed. Electromagnetics Induction in the Earth & Moon. (Advances in Earth & Planetary Sciences Ser.: No. 9). 200p. 1980. lib. bdg. 26.50 (ISBN 90-277-1131-3, Pub. by Reidel Holland). Kluwer Academic.

Stavroulakis, Peter, ed. Interference Analysis of Communication Systems. LC 80-18464. 424p. 1980. 38.95x (ISBN 0-471-08674-6, Pub. by Wiley-Interscience); pap. 27.95x (ISBN 0-471-08673-8, Pub. by Wiley-Interscience). Wiley.

University of Michigan, Ann Arbor, Department of Electrical & Computer Engineering. Electromagnetic Interference by Wind Turbine Generators. 163p. 1982. pap. 19.95x (ISBN 0-89934-171-3, W063). Solar Energy Info.

ELECTROMAGNETIC INTERFERENCE

Carstensen, Russell V. EMI Control in Boats & Ships. White, Donald R., ed. LC 80-51209. (Illus.). 280p. 1981. text ed. 37.00 (ISBN 0-932263-20-8). White Consult.

Don White Consultants Staff. EMC Technology: 1982 Anthology. (Illus.). 200p. 1984. text ed. 42.00 (ISBN 0-932263-24-0). White Consult.

Feher, Kamilo. Digital Modulation Techniques in an Interference Environment. White, Donald R., ed. LC 76-52508. (Illus.). 182p. 1977. text ed. 42.00 (ISBN 0-932263-18-6). White Consult.

Gard, Michael F. EMI Control in Medical Electronics. White, Donald R., ed. LC 78-66192. (Illus.). 175p. 1979. text ed. 32.00 (ISBN 0-932263-19-4). White Consult.

Georgopoulos, Chris J. Fiber Optics & Optical Isolators. Price, Edward R., ed. LC 81-52618. (Illus.). 271p. 1982. text ed. 37.00 (ISBN 0-932263-21-6). White Consult.

Herman, John R. Electromagnetic Ambients & Manmade Noise. White, Donald R., ed. LC 79-84817. (Illus.). 265p. 1979. text ed. 42.00 (ISBN 0-932263-13-5). White Consult.

Keiser, Bernhard E. EMI Control in Aerospace Systems. White, Donald R., ed. LC 79-54649. (Illus.). 282p. 1979. text ed. 37.00 (ISBN 0-932263-15-1). White Consult.

White, Donald R. Electrical Filters Synthesis, Design & Applications. 2nd ed. LC 63-23232. (Illus.). 295p. 1980. text ed. 37.00 (ISBN 0-932263-07-0). White Consult.

--Electrical Noise & EMI Specifications. LC 72-138444. (Electromagnetic Interference & Compatibility Ser.: Vol. 1). (Illus.). 482p. 1971. text ed. 58.00 (ISBN 0-932263-00-3). White Consult.

--Electromagnetic Shielding Materials & Performance. 2nd ed. LC 75-16592. 1980. text ed. 42.00 (ISBN 0-932263-08-9). White Consult.

--EMI Control in the Design of Printed Circuit Boards & Backplanes. 3rd ed. Price, Edward R., ed. LC 81-52618. 1982. text ed. 22.00 (ISBN 0-932263-12-7). White Consult.

--EMI Control Methods & Techniques. 3rd ed. LC 72-138444. (Electromagnetic Interference & Compatibility Ser.: Vol. 3). (Illus.). 668p. 1981. text ed. 111.00 (ISBN 0-932263-02-X). White Consult.

--EMI Specifications, Standards & Regulations. 2nd ed. LC 72-138444. (Electromagnetic Interference & Compatibility Ser.: Vol. 6). (Illus.). 1014p. 1981. text ed. 69.00 (ISBN 0-932263-05-4). White Consult.

--EMI Test Instrumentation & Systems. 2nd ed. LC 72-138444. (Electromagnetic Interference & Compatibility Ser.: Vol. 4). (Illus.). 353p. 1980. text ed. 80.00 (ISBN 0-932263-03-8). White Consult.

ELECTROMAGNETIC MEASUREMENTS

see also Electronic Measurements; Photometry; Radio Measurements

Bilenky, S. M. Introduction to the Physics of Electroweak Interactions. LC 81-15839. (Illus.). 250p. 1982. 66.00 (ISBN 0-08-026502-2). Pergamon.

Burnside, C. D. Electro-Magnetic Distance Measurement. (Illus.). 128p. 1971. pap. text ed. 12.95x (ISBN 0-8464-0363-3). Beekman Pubs.

--Electromagnetic Distance Measurement. 2nd ed. 224p. 1982. pap. 20.00x (ISBN 0-246-11624-2, Pub. by Granada England). Sheridan.

Libby, Hugo L. Introduction to Electromagnetic Nondestructive Test Methods. LC 79-9758. 382p. 1979. Repr. of 1971 ed. lib. bdg. 29.50 (ISBN 0-88275-964-7). Krieger.

Saastamoinen, J. J., ed. Surveyor's Guide to Electromagnetic Distance Measurement. LC 68-79061. pap. 50.80 (ISBN 0-317-08362-7, 2019159). Bks Demand UMI.

Shercliffe, John A. The Theory of Electromagnetic Flow-Measurement. (Cambridge Engineering Ser.). pap. 39.50 (ISBN 0-317-09192-1, 2050749). Bks Demand UMI.

Verma, Rajni K. Master Tables for Electromagnetic Depth Sounding Interpretation. LC 79-27044. (IFI Data Base Library Ser.). 480p. 1980. 125.00x (ISBN 0-306-65188-2, IFI Plenum). Plenum Pub.

ELECTROMAGNETIC SHIELDS

see Shielding (Electricity)

ELECTROMAGNETIC THEORY

see also Cosmic Electrodynamics; Electric Waves; Electromagnetic Fields; Electromagnetic Waves; Electrons; Field Theory (Physics); Light; Maxwell Equations; Nuclear Induction; Optics, Physical; Quantum Electrodynamics; Unified Field Theories

Berger, M. S., ed. J. C. Maxwell, the Sesquicentennial Symposium: Nonlinear Extensions of Maxwell's Electromagnetic Theory. 350p. 1984. 55.00 (ISBN 0-444-86707-4, I-549-83, North-Holland). Elsevier.

Bloom, F. Ill-Posed Problems for Integrodifferential Equations in Mechanics & Electromagnetic Theory. LC 80-53713. (SIAM Studies in Applied Mathematics: No. 3). ix, 222p. 1981. 37.50 (ISBN 0-89871-171-1). Soc Indus-Appl Math.

Buchwald, Jed Z. From Maxwell to Microphysics: Aspects of Electromagnetic Theory in the Last Quarter of the Nineteenth-Century. LC 85-1191. (Illus.). 384p. 1985. lib. bdg. 70.00x (ISBN 0-226-07882-5). U of Chicago Pr.

Button, Kenneth J., ed. Infrared & Millimeter Waves: Coherent Sources & Applications, Vol. 5 Pt. 1. LC 79-6949. 1982. 59.50 (ISBN 0-12-147705-3). Acad Pr.

Chirgwin, B., et al. Elementary Electromagnetic Theory, 3 vols. Incl. Vol. 1. Steady Electric Fields & Currents. 1971. pap. 9.00 (ISBN 0-08-016080-8); Vol. 2. Magnetic Fields, Special Relativity & Potential Theory. 1972. pap. 9.00 (ISBN 0-08-016600-8); Vol. 3. Maxwell's Equations & Their Consequences. 1973. pap. 10.00 (ISBN 0-08-017121-4). pap. write for info. Pergamon.

Clemmow, P. C. An Introduction to Electromagnetic Theory. LC 73-77174. (Illus.). 320p. 1973. pap. 18.95 (ISBN 0-521-09815-7). Cambridge U Pr.

Copson, David A. Informational Bioelectromagnetics. (Illus.). 766p. 1981. 24.95 (ISBN 0-916460-09-6). Matrix Pub.

Electromagnetic Lifetimes & Properties of Nuclear States. 1962. 5.00 (ISBN 0-309-00974-X). Natl Acad Pr.

Frankl, Daniel R. Electromagnetic Theory. (Illus.). 480p. 1986. text ed. 33.95 (ISBN 0-13-249095-1). P-H.

Hayt, William H., Jr. Engineering Electromagnetics. 4th ed. (Electrical Engineering Ser.). (Illus.). 512p. 1981. text ed. 47.95 (ISBN 0-07-027395-2). McGraw.

Heaviside, Oliver. Electromagnetic Theory: Including an Account of Heaviside's Unpublished Notes, 3 Vols. 3rd ed. LC 74-118633. 1971. Set. text ed. 79.50 (ISBN 0-8284-0237-X). Chelsea Pub.

Kerker, Milton. Scattering of Light & Other Electromagnetic Radiation. (Physical Chemistry Ser.: Vol. 16). 1969. 94.50 (ISBN 0-12-404550-2). Acad Pr.

King, Ronald W. & Hinchey, Sheila P. Fundamental Electromagnetic Theory & Applications. (Illus.). 560p. 1986. pap. 39.95 (ISBN 0-13-336959-5). P-H.

Klimontovich, Yu L. The Kinetic Theory of Electromagnetic Processes. (Springer Series in Synergetics: Vol. 10). 320p. 1983. 48.00 (ISBN 0-387-11458-0). Springer-Verlag.

Kline, Morris & Kay, Irvin W. Electromagnetic Theory & Geometrical Optics. LC 78-14351. (Pure & Applied Mathemetics Ser.: Vol. 12). 540p. 1979. Repr. of 1965 ed. lib. bdg. 30.50 (ISBN 0-88275-739-3). Krieger.

Kong, J. A. Research Topics in Electromagnetic Wave Theory. LC 80-28274. 355p. 1981. 45.50x (ISBN 0-471-08782-3, Pub. by Wiley-Interscience). Wiley.

Kraus, John D. Electromagnetics. 2nd ed. (Electrical & Electronic Engineering Ser.). (Illus.). 848p. 1973. text ed. 38.95 (ISBN 0-07-035396-4). McGraw.

Lerner, C. M. Problems & Solutions in Electromagnetic Theory. LC 83-6548. 800p. 1984. 30.00X (ISBN 0-471-88678-5, Pub. by Wiley-Interscience). Wiley.

Love, A. W. Electromagnetic Horn Antennas. 464p. 1976. pap. 20.75 (ISBN 0-317-05142-3, PP00752). Inst Electrical.

Panofsky, Wolfgang K. & Phillips, Melba. Classical Electricity & Magnetism. 2nd ed. 1962. 34.95 (ISBN 0-201-05702-6). Addison-Wesley.

Paris, D. T. & Hurd, F. K. Basic Electromagnetic Theory. LC 68-8775. (Physical & Quantum Electronic Ser.). (Illus.). 1969. text ed. 45.00 (ISBN 0-07-048470-8). McGraw.

Petit, R. Electromagnetic Theory of Gratings. (Topics in Current Physics Ser.: Vol. 22). (Illus.). 284p. 1980. 43.00 (ISBN 0-387-10193-4). Springer-Verlag.

Plonus, Martin. Applied Electromagnetics. (Illus.). 1978. text ed. 42.00 (ISBN 0-07-050345-1). McGraw.

Rowell, R. L. & Stein, R. S., eds. Electromagnetic Scattering. 862p. 1967. 163.25 (ISBN 0-677-11920-8). Gordon.

Schwarz, W. M. Intermediate Electromagnetic Theory. LC 74-163568. 454p. 1973. Repr. of 1964 ed. 26.50 (ISBN 0-88275-093-3). Krieger.

Skitok, J. & Marshall, R. Electromagnetic Concepts & Applications. 1981. 39.95 (ISBN 0-13-248963-5). P-H.

Solymar, L. Lectures on Electromagnetic Theory. (Illus.). 1984. pap. 18.95x (ISBN 0-19-856169-5). Oxford U Pr.

Stratton, Julius A. Electromagnetic Theory. (International Series in Pure & Applied Physics). (Illus.). 1941. text ed. 53.95 (ISBN 0-07-062150-0). McGraw.

Symposium in Applied Mathematics-Cambridge, Mass.-1948. Electromagnetic Theory. Taub, A. H., ed. LC 50-1183. (Proceedings of Symposia in Applied Mathematics: Vol. 2). 91p. 1950. 18.00 (ISBN 0-8218-1302-1, PSAPM-2). Am Math.

Takashima, Shiro & Postow, Elliot. Interaction of Acoustical & Electromagnetic Fields with Biological Systems. LC 82-7206. (Progress in Clinical & Biological Research Ser.: Vol. 86). 196p. 1982. 28.00 (ISBN 0-8451-0086-6). A R Liss.

Tonnelat, M. A. The Principles of Electromagnetic Theory & Relativity. Knodel, Arthur, tr. from Fr. 475p. 1966. lib. bdg. 47.50 (ISBN 90-277-0107-5, Pub. by Reidel Holland). Kluwer Academic.

Tyras, G. Radiation & Propagation of Electromagnetic Waves. (Electrical Science Ser). 1969. 80.00 (ISBN 0-12-705650-5). Acad Pr.

Zaky, A. A. & Hawley, R. Fundamentals of Electromagnetic Field Theory. (Illus.). 1974. 59.95x (ISBN 0-245-52023-6). Intl Ideas.

ELECTROMAGNETIC WAVES

Agranovich, V. M. & Mills, D. L., eds. Surface Polaritons: Electromagnetic Waves of Surfaces & Interfaces. (Modern Problems in Condensed Matter Sciences Ser.: Vol. 1). 704p. 1982. 147.00 (ISBN 0-444-86165-3). Elsevier.

Arams, Frank R., ed. Infrared-to-Millimeter Wavelength Detectors. LC 78-189396. (Modern Frontiers in Applied Science Ser.). (Illus.). 290p. 1973. pap. 12.00x (ISBN 0-89006-012-6). Artech Hse.

Basov, N. G., ed. The Dissipation of Electromagnetic Waves in Plasmas. McNeill, Donald H., tr. from Russian. (Lebedev Trudy Ser.: Vol. 92). 109p. 1982. 49.50 (ISBN 0-306-10969-7, Consultants). Plenum Pub.

Bass, F. G. & Fuchs, M. Wave Scattering from Statistically Rough Surfaces. LC 77-23113. 1979. text ed. 125.00 (ISBN 0-08-019896-1). Pergamon.

Bitter, Francis & Medicus, Heinrich A. Fields & Particles: An Introduction to Electromagnetic Wave Phenomena & Quantum Physics. LC 72-87209. pap. 160.00 (ISBN 0-317-08584-0, 2007763). Bks Demand UMI.

Bliokh, P. V., et al. Schumann Resonances in the Earth Ionosphere Cavity. Jones, D. Llanwyn, ed. Chomer, S., tr. (IEE Electromagnetic Waves Ser.). (Illus.). 176p. 1980. softcover casebound 78.00 (ISBN 0-906048-33-8, EW009, Pub. by Peregrinus London). Inst Elect Eng.

Boardman, A. D., ed. Electromagnetic Surface Modes. 776p. 1982. 94.95 (ISBN 0-471-10077-3, Pub. by Wiley-Interscience); pap. 89.95, 485p. (ISBN 0-471-27674-X). Wiley.

Boerner, Wolfgang M., et al, eds. Inverse Methods in Electromagnetic Imaging, 2 Vol. Set Only. 1984. Set. lib. bdg. 145.00 (ISBN 90-277-1890-3, Pub. by Reidel Holland). Kluwer Academic.

Button, Kenneth, ed. Infrared & Millimeter Waves: Millimeter Systems, Vol. 4. Wiltse, James. LC 79-6949. 1981. 64.00 (ISBN 0-12-147704-5). Acad Pr.

Button, Kenneth J., ed. Infrared & Millimeter Waves, Vol. 8: Electromagnetic Waves in Matter, Pt. I. LC 79-6949. 1983. 69.50 (ISBN 0-12-147708-8). Acad Pr.

--Reviews of Infrared & Millimeter Waves, Vol. 1. 365p. 1983. 55.00x (ISBN 0-306-41260-8, Plenum Pr). Plenum Pub.

Chen, Hollis C. Theory of Electromagnetic Waves: A Coordinate Free Approach. (McGraw-Hill Series in Electrical Engineering). (Illus.). 464p. 1983. text ed. 46.00 (ISBN 0-07-010688-6). McGraw.

Cheng, D. K. Field & Wave Electromagnetics. 640p. 1983. text ed. 39.95 (ISBN 0-201-01239-1). Addison-Wesley.

Dearholt, Donald & McSpadden, William. Electromagnetic Wave Propagation. (Illus.). 480p. 1973. text ed. 58.00 (ISBN 0-07-016205-0). McGraw.

Deirmendjian, D. Electromagnetic Scattering on Spherical Polydispersions. LC 68-28759. pap. 78.00 (ISBN 0-317-08591-3, 2007761). Bks Demand UMI.

Dobbs, Roland. Electromagnetic Waves. (Student Physics Ser.). (Illus.). 128p. (Orig.). 1985. pap. 9.95x (ISBN 0-7102-0506-6). Routledge & Kegan.

Electrodynamics of Continuous Media. 2nd ed. Sykes, L. D., et al, trs. (Course of Theoretical Physics Ser.: Vol. 8). 600p. 1984. 60.00 (ISBN 0-08-030276-9); pap. 25.00 (ISBN 0-08-030275-0). Pergamon.

Ginzburg, V. L. Propagation of Electromagnetic Waves in Plasma. (Russian Monographs & Texts on the Physical Science Ser.). 846p. 1962. 135.25 (ISBN 0-677-20080-3). Gordon.

--Propagation of Electromagnetic Waves in Plasmas. 2nd rev. ed. 1971. 72.00 (ISBN 0-08-015569-3). Pergamon.

Heller, Wilfried, et al. Angular Scattering Functions for Spheroids. LC 77-156067. 144p. 1972. text ed. 12.00x (ISBN 0-8143-1454-6). Wayne St U Pr.

Hudson, J. E. Adaptive Array Principles. (IEE Electromagnetic Waves Ser.). 288p. 1981. casebound 84.50 (ISBN 0-906048-55-9, EW011, Pub. by Peregrinus England). Inst Elect Eng.

James, G. J. Geometrical Theory of Diffraction for Electromagnetic Waves. rev. ed. (IEE Electromagnetic Waves Ser.: No. 1). (Illus.). 261p. 1980. pap. 38.00 (ISBN 0-906048-34-6, EW001, Pub. by Peregrinus England). Inst Elect Eng.

Jones, D. S. Methods in Electromagnetic Wave Propagation. (Engineering Science Ser.). (Illus.). 1979. 75.00x (ISBN 0-19-856131-8). Oxford U Pr.

Kong, J. A. Electromagnetic Wave Theory. 1985. 36.95 (ISBN 0-471-82823-8). Wiley.

--Research Topics in Electromagnetic Wave Theory. LC 80-28274. 355p. 1981. 45.50x (ISBN 0-471-08782-3, Pub. by Wiley-Interscience). Wiley.

Langer, Rudolph E., ed. Electromagnetic Waves. (Mathematics Research Center Pubns., No. 6). (Illus.). 408p. 1962. 17.50x (ISBN 0-299-02500-4). U of Wis Pr.

Lewin, L., et al. Electromagnetic Waves & Curved Structures. (IEE Electromagnetic Waves Ser.: No. 2). (Illus.). 206p. 1977. 46.00 (ISBN 0-901223-96-4, EW002, Pub. by Peregrinus England). Inst Elect Eng.

Lorrain, Paul & Corson, Dale R. Electromagnetic Fields & Waves. 2nd ed. LC 72-94872. (Illus.). 706p. 1970. text ed. 32.95 (ISBN 0-7167-0331-9); solutions to problems avail. W H Freeman.

Magid, Leonard M. Electromagnetic Fields, Energy, & Waves. LC 80-16458. 808p. 1981. Repr. of 1972 ed. text ed. 45.00 (ISBN 0-89874-221-8). Krieger.

Mohsenin, Nuri N. Electromagnetic Radiation Properties of Foods & Agricultural Products. 560p. 1984. 103.95. Gordon.

Rojansky, Vladimir. Electromagnetic Fields & Waves. LC 79-52648. 1980. pap. text ed. 7.95 (ISBN 0-486-63834-0). Dover.

Lenman, J. A. & Ritchie, A. E., eds. Clinical Electromyography. 3rd ed. LC 82-48997. 254p. 1983. text ed. 37.50 (ISBN 0-272-79708-1, Pub. by Pitman Bks Ltd UK). Urban & S.

Marinacci, Alberto A. Applied Electromyography. LC 68-25208. pap. 77.00 (ISBN 0-317-07922-0, 2003766). Bks Demand UMI.

Notermans, S. L., ed. Current Practice of Clinical Electromyography. 568p. 1984. 129.75 (ISBN 0-444-80567-2, I-482-84). Elsevier.

Shahani, Bhagwan T. Electromyography in CNS Disorders: Central EMG. 1984. text ed. 24.95 (ISBN 0-409-95144-7). Butterworth.

Thompson, Thomas T. The Electromyographer's Handbook. 1982. pap. text ed. 16.95 (ISBN 0-316-84185-4). Little.

ELECTRON BEAMS

Anderson, David L. & Cohen, I. Bernard, eds. The Discovery of the Electron. LC 80-2114. (Development of Science Ser.). (Illus.). 1981. lib. bdg. 15.00x (ISBN 0-405-13834-2). Ayer Co Pubs.

Bakish, Robert & White, S. S. Handbook of Electron Beam Welding. LC 64-7538. (Wiley Series on the Science & Technology of Materials). pap. 69.80 (ISBN 0-317-08643-X, 2007398). Bks Demand UMI.

Brewer, George R., ed. Electron Beam Technology in Microelectric Fabrication. LC 79-8856. 1980. 49.50 (ISBN 0-12-133550-X). Acad Pr.

Gibbons, J. F., et al, eds. Laser & Electron Beam Solid Interactions & Materials Processing. (Materials Research Society Proceedings: Vol. 1). 630p. 1981. 90.00 (ISBN 0-444-00595-1, North-Holland). Elsevier.

Klevenhagen, S. C. Physics of Electron Beam Therapy. (Medical Physics Handbook 13). 200p. 1985. 29.00 (ISBN 0-85274-781-0, Pub. by A Hilger Techo Hse UK). Heyden.

Loretto, M. H. Electron Beam Analysis of Materials. (Illus.). 208p. 1985. 49.95 (ISBN 0-412-23390-8, NO. 9154, Pub. by Chapman & Hall); pap. 19.95 (ISBN 0-412-23400-9, 9159). Methuen Inc.

Schiller, Siegfried, et al. Electron Beam Technology. LC 82-4774. 508p. 1983. 61.95 (ISBN 0-471-06056-9, Pub. by Wiley-Interscience). Wiley.

Schwartz, M. M. Source Book on Electron Beam & Laser Welding. 1981. 49.00 (ISBN 0-87170-104-9). ASM.

Tapley, Norah D. Clinical Applications of the Electron Beam. LC 81-19281. 288p. 1982. Repr. of 1976 ed. text ed. 29.50 (ISBN 0-89874-427-X). Krieger.

White, C. W. & Peercy, P. S., eds. Laser & Electron Beam Processing of Materials. 1980. 60.00 (ISBN 0-12-746850-1). Acad Pr.

ELECTRON CIRCUITS–DESIGN

see Electronic Circuit Design

ELECTRON COLLISIONS

see Collisions (Nuclear Physics)

ELECTRON DIFFRACTION

see Electrons–Diffraction

ELECTRON EMISSION

see Electrons–Emission

ELECTRON GAS

see also Free Electron Theory of Metals

Lundqvist, S. & March, N. H., eds. Theory of Inhomogeneous Electron Gas. (Physics of Solids & Liquids Ser.). 425p. 1983. 59.50x (ISBN 0-306-41207-1, Plenum Press). Plenum Pub.

ELECTRON-HOLE PAIR THEORY

see Exciton Theory

ELECTRON METALLOGRAPHY

Manual on Electron Metallography Techniques-STP 547. 78p. 1973. pap. 5.25 (ISBN 0-8031-0397-2, 04-547000-28). ASTM.

ELECTRON MICROSCOPE

Agar, A. W., et al. Principles & Practice of Electron Microscope Operation. (Practical Methods in Electron Microscopy: Vol. 2). 1974. 76.50 (ISBN 0-7204-4254-0, Biomedical Pr); pap. 27.75 (ISBN 0-7204-4255-9). Elsevier.

Alderson, R. H., ed. Design of the Electron Microscope Laboratory. (Practical Methods in Electron Microscopy Ser.: Vol. 4). 1975. pap. 13.75 (ISBN 0-444-10816-5, North-Holland). Elsevier.

American Society for Testing & Materials. Techniques of Electron Microscopy, Diffraction, & Microprobe Analysis. (American Society for Testing & Materials Special Technical Publication: No. 372). pap. 23.80 (ISBN 0-317-09550-1, 2000730). Bks Demand UMI.

Analytical Electron Microscopy: Conference Proceedings. (Illus.). 1984. 25.00 (ISBN 0-317-17155-0); 40.00 (ISBN 0-317-17156-9). San Francisco Pr.

Becker, R. P. & Johari, O. Scanning Electron Microscopy 1980, Pt. II. LC 72-626068. (Illus.). xiv, 658p. 50.00 (ISBN 0-931288-12-6). Scanning Electron.

Bell, Paul B., Jr., ed. Scanning Electron Microscopy of Cells in Culture. (Illus.). vi, 314p. 1984. pap. 29.00 (ISBN 0-931288-31-2). Scanning Electron.

Butler. Dynamic Experiments in the Electron Microscope. 458p. 1981. 83.00 (Biomedical Pr); pap. 42.25 (ISBN 0-444-80286-X). Elsevier.

Carr, K. E. & Toner, P. G. Cell Structure: An Introduction to Biomedical Electron Microscopy. LC 81-67939. (Illus.). 388p. 1983. text ed. 48.00 (ISBN 0-443-02324-7). Churchill.

Carter, H. W., et al. Clinical Applications of the Scanning Electron Microscope. Johari, Om & Becker, R. P., eds. (Illus.). 1980. pap. 10.00x (ISBN 0-931288-16-9). Scanning Electron.

Centre for Scientific Culture Ettore Majorana, International School of Electron Microscopy. Electron Microscopy in Material Science. Valdre, U., ed. 1972. 107.00 (ISBN 0-12-780584-2). Acad Pr.

Chescoe, Dawn & Goodhew, Peter. The Operation of the Transmission Electron Microscope. (Royal Microscopical Society Handbooks Ser.). (Illus.). 1984. pap. 7.95x (ISBN 0-19-856402-3). Oxford U Pr.

Cohen, A. Biomedical Scanning Electron Micro Handbook. 1986. cancelled (ISBN 0-442-25160-2). Van Nos Reinhold.

Cosslett, V. E. & Barer, R., eds. Advances in Optical & Electron Microscopy, Vol. 8. (Serial Publication Ser.). 281p. 1982. 65.00 (ISBN 0-12-029908-9). Acad Pr.

Daumeister, W., ed. Electron Microscopy at Molecular Dimensions. (Proceedings in Life Sciences). (Illus.). 300p. 1980. 66.00 (ISBN 0-387-10131-4). Springer-Verlag.

Developments in Electron Microscopy & Analysis, 1977. (Institute of Physics Conference Ser.: No. 36). 1977. 60.00 (ISBN 0-9960031-6-9, Pub. by Inst Physics England). Heyden.

Doig, P, ed. Electron Microscopy & Analysis 1983. (Institute of Physics Conference Ser.: No. 68). 1984. 60.00 (ISBN 0-9903800-0-9, Pub. by A Hilger England). Heyden.

Electron Microscopy & Analysis 1979: Sussex. (Institute of Physics Conference Ser.: No. 52). 1980. 65.00 (ISBN 0-9960033-2-0, Pub. by Inst Physics England). Heyden.

Electron Microscopy: Forty-One Exercises by Seventeen Scientists. 450p. 1985. 29.95 (ISBN 0-912526-40-8). Lib Res.

Electron Microscopy Society. Proceedings. Arcenaux, Claude, ed. (Annual). 1967-71 eds. 12.50x,; 1971-74 eds. 15.00x ea. Claitors.

Electron Microscopy Society of America: Conference Proceedings. (Illus.). 1984. 45.00 (ISBN 0-317-17158-5). San Francisco Pr.

Electron Microscopy Tutorial, Chalottesville 1975. (American Crystallographic Association Lecture Notes). pap. 15.00 (ISBN 0-317-02524-4). Polycrystal Bk Serv.

Electron Microscopy 1972: Manchester. (Institute of Physics Conference Ser.: No. 14). 1972. 62.50 (ISBN 0-9960029-3-6, Pub. by Inst Physics England). Heyden.

Felix, H., et al. Dynamic Morphology of Leukemia Cells: A Comparative Study by Scanning Electron Microscopy & Microcinematography. (Illus.). 1978. 63.00 (ISBN 0-387-08495-9). Springer-Verlag.

Fryer, J. R. The Chemical Applications of Transmission Electron Microscopy. 1979. 55.00 (ISBN 0-12-269350-7). Acad Pr.

Fuller, R., ed. Microbial Ultrastructure. 1977. 65.00 (ISBN 0-12-269450-3). Acad Pr.

Gabriel, Barbra L. Biological Electron Microscopy. 240p. 1982. 36.50 (ISBN 0-442-22923-2). Van Nos Reinhold.

--Biological Scanning Electron Microscopy. 192p. 1982. 28.50 (ISBN 0-442-22922-4). Van Nos Reinhold.

Ghadially, Feroze N. Diagnostic Electron Microscopy of Tumours. 2nd ed. 484p. 1985. text ed. 99.95 (ISBN 0-407-00299-5). Butterworth.

Glauert, A. Fixation, Dehydration & Embedding of Biological Specimens. (Practical Methods in Electron Microscopy Ser.: Vol. 3, No. 1). 1975. pap. 18.00 (ISBN 0-444-10666-9, Biomedical Pr). Elsevier.

Glauert, A. M. Practical Methods in Electron Microscopy, Vols. 1-8. Vol. 1, 1972. 87.25 (ISBN 0-444-10404-6, Biomedical Pr); Vol. 2, 1974. 76.75 (ISBN 0-444-10644-8); Vol. 3, 1975. 76.75 (ISBN 0-444-10665-0); Vol. 4, 1975. 38.50 (ISBN 0-444-10807-6); Vol. 5, 1977. 103.00 (ISBN 0-7204-0605-6); Vol. 6, 1978. 91.50 (ISBN 0-7204-0636-6); Vol. 7, 1979. 70.25 (ISBN 0-7204-0665-X); Vol. 8, 1980. 70.25 (ISBN 0-444-80166-9). Elsevier.

Goldstein, Joseph I. & Yakowitz, Harvey, eds. Practical Scanning Electron Microscopy: Electron & Ion Microprobe Analysis. LC 74-34162. (Illus.). 582p. 1975. 49.50 (ISBN 0-306-30820-7, Plenum Pr). Plenum Pub.

Goldstein, Joseph I., et al. Scanning Electron Microscopy & X-Ray Microanalysis: A Text for Biologists, Materials Scientists & Geologists. 688p. 1981. 32.50x (ISBN 0-306-40768-X, Plenum Pr). Plenum Pub.

Goodhew, P. J. Electron Microscopy & Analysis. (The Wykeham Science Ser.: No. 33). 200p. 1975. pap. cancelled. Taylor & Francis.

Goodhew, P. J. & Cartwright, L. E. Electron Microscopy & Analysis. LC 74-32449. (Wykeham Science Ser.: No. 33). 200p. 1975. 9.95x (ISBN 0-8448-1160-2). Crane Russak Co.

Goodhew, Peter. Specimen Preparation for Transmission Electron Microscopy of Materials. (Royal Microscopical Society Handbooks Ser.). (Illus.). 1984. pap. 9.95 (ISBN 0-19-856403-1). Oxford U Pr.

Goringe, M. J., ed. Electron Microscopy & Analysis, 1981. 570p. 1982. 90.00x (ISBN 0-85498-152-7, Pub. by A Hilger). State Mutual Bk.

Griffith, Jack D. Electron Microscopy in Biology, Vol. 1. (Electron Microscopy in Biology Ser.). 296p. 1981. 69.95x (ISBN 0-471-05525-5, Pub. by Wiley-Interscience). Wiley.

Griffith, Jack D., ed. Electron Microscopy in Biology, Vol. 2. (Electron Microscopy in Biology Ser.). 349p. 1982. text ed. 97.50x (ISBN 0-471-05526-3). Wiley.

Hafez, E. S. & Kenemans, P. An Atlas of Human Reproduction: By Scanning Electron Microscopy. 300p. 1982. text ed. 60.00 (ISBN 0-85200-411-7, Pub. by MTP Pr England). Kluwer Academic.

Hall, Cecil E. Introduction to Electron Microscopy. LC 80-39788. 410p. 1983. Repr. of 1966 ed. lib. bdg. 28.50 (ISBN 0-89874-302-8). Krieger.

Harada, Yasuo. An Atlas of the Ear: By Scanning Electron Microscopy. (Illus.). 220p. 1983. text ed. 53.00 (ISBN 0-8391-1922-4, 20362). Univ Park.

Hawkes, P. W. Electron Optics & Electron Microscopy. 264p. 1972. 33.00x (ISBN 0-85066-056-4). Taylor & Francis.

Hayat, M. A. Basic Techniques for Transmission Electron Microscopy. Date not set. price not set (ISBN 0-12-333925-1). Acad Pr.

--Fixation for Electron Microscopy. LC 81-12745. 1981. 52.50 (ISBN 0-12-333920-0). Acad Pr.

--Principles & Techniques of Electron Microscopy. 2nd ed. (Illus.). 544p. 1980. text ed. 37.00 (ISBN 0-8391-1602-0). Univ Park.

Hayat, M. Arif. Electron Microscopy of Enzymes: Principles & Methods, Vol. 4. 1975. 24.50 (ISBN 0-685-55048-6). Van Nos Reinhold.

--Electron Microscopy of Enzymes Principles & Methods, Vol. 5. 1977. 24.50 (ISBN 0-442-25690-6). Van Nos Reinhold.

--Positive Staining for Electron Microscopy. 1975. 27.50 (ISBN 0-442-25684-1). Van Nos Reinhold.

--Principles & Techniques of Electron Microscopy, Vol. 5: Biological Applications. 1975. 19.95 (ISBN 0-442-25681-7). Van Nos Reinhold.

--Principles & Techniques of Electron Microscopy, Vol. 4. 1974. 19.95 (ISBN 0-442-25680-9). Van Nos Reinhold.

--Principles & Techniques of Electron Microscopy, Vol. 6. 1976. 27.50 (ISBN 0-442-25688-4). Van Nos Reinhold.

--Principles & Techniques of Electron Microscopy, Vol. 7. 1977. 27.50 (ISBN 0-442-25691-4). Van Nos Reinhold.

--Principles & Techniques of Electron Microscopy, Vol. 9. 1978. 27.50 (ISBN 0-442-25694-9). Van Nos Reinhold.

--Principles & Techniques of Scanning Electron Microscopy, Vol. 3. 1975. 24.50 (ISBN 0-442-25682-5). Van Nos Reinhold.

--Principles & Techniques of Scanning Electron Microscopy, Vol. 4. 278p. 1975. 24.50 (ISBN 0-442-25686-8). Van Nos Reinhold.

--Principles & Techniques of Scanning Electron Microscopy, Vol. 5. 1976. 24.50 (ISBN 0-442-25692-2). Van Nos Reinhold.

--Principles & Techniques of Scanning Electron Microscopy, Vol. 6. 1978. 27.50 (ISBN 0-442-25687-6). Van Nos Reinhold.

--Principles & Techniques of Scanning Electron Microscopy, Vol. 2: Biological Applications. 186p. 1974. 24.50 (ISBN 0-442-25678-7). Van Nos Reinhold.

Hirsch, Peter B., et al. Electron Microscopy of Thin Crystals. LC 75-42162. 576p. 1977. 39.50 (ISBN 0-88275-376-2). Krieger.

Hodges, G. & Carr, K., eds. Biomedical Research Applications of Scanning Electron Microscopy, Vol. 3. 1984. 60.00 (ISBN 0-12-351003-1). Acad Pr.

Hodges, G. & Hallowes, R., eds. Biomedical Research Applications of Scanning Electron Microscopy, Vol. 2. LC 78-72550. 1980. 66.00 (ISBN 0-12-351002-3). Acad Pr.

Hodges, Gisele & Hallowes, Richard, eds. Biomedical Research Applications of Scanning Electron Microscopy, Vol. I. 1979. 86.50 (ISBN 0-12-351001-5). Acad Pr.

Holt, D. B., et al, eds. Quantitative Scanning Electron Microscopy. 1975. 91.00 (ISBN 0-12-353850-5). Acad Pr.

Hren, John J., et al, eds. Introduction to Analytical Electron Microscopy. LC 79-17009. 617p. 1979. 35.00x (ISBN 0-306-40280-7, Plenum Pr). Plenum Pub.

--Electron Optical Systems for Microscopy, Microanalysis & Microlithography. (Proceeding of the Third Pfefferkorn Conference). (Illus.). 272p. 1984. 44.00 (ISBN 0-931288-34-7). Scanning Electron.

Hunter, Elaine E. Practical Electron Microscopy: A Beginners Illustrated Guide. LC 83-17778. 112p. 1984. text ed. 24.95 (ISBN 0-03-069291-1). Praeger.

Institute of Physics. Electron Microscopy & Analysis. (Institute of Physics Conference Ser.: No. 10). 1972. 55.00 (ISBN 0-9960028-9-8, Pub. by Inst Physics England). Heyden.

International Conference on Electron Microscopy, 4th Berlin 1958. Proceedings, 2 vols. Mollenstedt, G., et al, eds. 1960. Vol. 1. 134.60 (ISBN 0-387-02562-6); Vol. 2. 115.70 (ISBN 0-387-02563-4). Springer-Verlag.

Johannessen, J. V. Electron Microscopy in Human Medicine: The Skin, Vol. 11a. 412p. 80.00 (ISBN 0-07-032510-3). McGraw.

--Electron Microscopy in Human Medicine, Vol. 7: Digestive System. (Electron Microscopy in Human Medicine Ser.). 250p. 1980. 69.00 (ISBN 0-07-032507-3). McGraw.

Johannessen, Jan V. Diagnostic Electron Microscopy. 210p. 1982. text ed. 38.00 (ISBN 0-07-032543-X). McGraw.

--Electron Microscopy in Human Medicine: Vol. I, Instrumentation & Techniques. (Electron Microscopy in Human Medicine). (Illus.). 1978. text ed. 60.00 (ISBN 0-07-032501-4). McGraw.

--Electron Microscopy in Human Medicine: Vol. 4, Soft Tissues, Bones & Joints. 325p. 1982. text ed. 78.00 (ISBN 0-07-032504-9). McGraw.

--Electron Microscopy in Human Medicine: Vol. 6, Nervous System, Sensory Organs, & Respiratory Tract. (Electron Microscopy in Human Medicine Ser.). (Illus.). 368p. 1980. text ed. 78.00 (ISBN 0-07-032506-5). McGraw.

--Electron Microscopy in Human Medicine: Vol. 8, the Liver, Gallbladder & Biliary Ducts. (Illus.). 1979. text ed. 65.00 (ISBN 0-07-032499-9). McGraw.

Johannessen, Jans V. Electron Microscopy in Human Medicine: Vol. 9, Urogenital System & Breast. (Illus.). 396p. 1980. text ed. 79.00 (ISBN 0-07-032508-1). McGraw.

Johannessen, Jans V., ed. Electron Microscopy in Human Medicine, Vol. 11: The Skin - Special Applications. (Electron Microscopy in Human Medicine). 250p. 1983. text ed. 65.00 (ISBN 0-07-032524-3). McGraw.

Johari, O., et al, eds. Scanning Electron Microscopy, 1981, Pt. III. (Illus.). xvi, 624p. 1981. 53.00 (ISBN 0-931288-19-3); of 4 pts. 109.00 set (ISBN 0-931288-21-5). Scanning Electron.

--Scanning Electron Microscopy 1981. LC 72-628068. (Illus.). xii, 516p. 1981. of 4 pts. 109.00 set (ISBN 0-931288-21-5); 52.00 (ISBN 0-931288-18-5). Scanning Electron.

Johari, Om. Scanning Electron Microscopy 1980, Pt. I. LC 72-626068. (Illus.). xvi, 608p. 1980. 50.00 (ISBN 0-931288-11-8). Scanning Electron.

Johari, Om, ed. Basic Methods in Biological X-Ray Microanalysis. (Illus.). iv, 284p. (Orig.). 1983. pap. text ed. 22.00 (ISBN 0-931288-28-2). Scanning Electron.

Johari, Om & Albrecht, R. M, eds. Scanning Electron Microscopy 1981, Pt. IV. LC 72-626068. viii, 312p. 1982. 53.00 (ISBN 0-931288-20-7). Scanning Electron.

Johari, Om & Albrecht, R. M., eds. Scanning Electron Microscopy, 1982, Pt. I. LC 72-626068. (Illus.). xvi, 464p. 1983. 53.00 (ISBN 0-931288-23-1); Set of 4 pts. 109.00 (ISBN 0-931288-27-4). Scanning Electron.

--Scanning Electron Microscopy 1982, Part II. LC 72-626068. (Illus.). xvi, 432p. 1983. 53.00 (ISBN 0-931288-24-X); Set of 4 parts. 109.00. Scanning Electron.

--Scanning Electron Microscopy 1982, Pt. IV. LC 72-626068. (Scanning Electron Microscopy Ser.). (Illus.). xxii, 458p. 1983. 53.00 (ISBN 0-931288-26-6); Set of 4 parts. 109.00. Scanning Electron.

Johari, Om & Becker, R. P., eds. Scanning Electron Microscopy 1980, Pt. III. LC 72-62608. (Illus.). xx, 670p. 50.00 (ISBN 0-931288-13-4). Scanning Electron.

--Scanning Electron Microscopy 1980, Pt. IV. (Scanning Electron Microscopy Ser.). (Illus.). iv, 220p. 1981. 50.00 (ISBN 0-931288-14-2). Scanning Electron.

Johari, Om & Becker, Robert P., eds. Scanning Electron Microscopy 1978: International Review of Advances in Techniques & Applications of the Scanning Electron Microscope, 1978, 2 pts. LC 72-626068. (Illus.). 1978. Set. text ed. 67.50 (ISBN 0-931288-00-2); Pt. I. text ed. 37.00 (ISBN 0-931288-01-0); Pt. II. text ed. 40.50 (ISBN 0-931288-02-9). Scanning Electron.

--Scanning Electron Microscopy 1979: International Review of Advances in Techniques & Applications of the Scanning Electron Microscope, 1979, 3 pts. LC 72-626068. (Illus.). 1979. Set. text ed. 84.00 (ISBN 0-931288-10-X); Pts. I & II. text ed. 65.50 (ISBN 0-931288-08-8); Pts. II & III. text ed. 67.00 (ISBN 0-931288-09-6). Pt. I (ISBN 0-931288-04-5). Pt. II (ISBN 0-931288-05-3). Pt. III (ISBN 0-931288-06-1). Scanning Electron.

Johari, Om & Sharma, R. A., eds. Scanning Electron Microscopy, 1982, Pt. III. LC 72-626068. (Scanning Electron Microscopy Ser.). (Illus.). xviii, 462p. 1983. 53.00 (ISBN 0-931288-25-8); of 4 parts 109.00 set. Scanning Electron.

Johari, Om & Zaluzec, N. J., eds. Scanning Electron Microscopy 1981, Vol. I. (Illus.). xiv, 666p. 1982. 53.00 (ISBN 0-931288-17-7); Set of 4 parts 109.00 (ISBN 0-931288-21-5). Scanning Electron.

Kessel, R. G. & Shih, C. Y. Scanning Electron Microscopy in Biology: A Students' Atlas of Biological Organization. (Illus.). x, 345p. 1974. 42.00 (ISBN 0-387-06724-8). Springer-Verlag.

Kisch, Bruno. Electron Microscopy of the Cardiovascular System: An Electron Microscopic Study with Applications to Physiology. Kisch, Arnold I., tr. (Illus.). 192p. 1960. photocopy ed. 19.50x (ISBN 0-398-01023-4). C C Thomas.

Koehler, J. K. Advanced Techniques in Biological Electron Microscopy 2. 1978. 36.00 (ISBN 0-387-08503-3). Springer-Verlag.

Kopp, Friedrich. Electron Microscopy. Head, J. J., ed. LC 78-58243. (Carolina Biology Reader Ser.). (Illus.). 32p. 1981. pap. 2.00 (ISBN 0-89278-305-2, 45-9705). Carolina Biological.

Krakow, W., et al. Electron Microscopy of Materials: Proceedings of the Symposium, Electron Microscopy of Materials, Boston, MA, 1983. (Materials Research Society Symposia Ser.: Vol. 31). 392p. 1984. 79.00 (ISBN 0-444-00897-7, North Holland). Elsevier.

Kyser, David F., et al, eds. Electron Beam Interactions with Solids for Microscopy, Microanalysis & Microlithography: Proceedings of the First Pfefferkorn Conference held April, 1982, at Asilomar. CA. (Illus.). 372p. 1984. text ed. 51.00 (ISBN 0-931288-30-4). Scanning Electron.

Lee, W. R., ed. Current Research in Ophthalmic Electron Microscopy, 3. (Illus.). 160p. 1981. 22.90. Springer-Verlag.

Liotet, Serge & Clergue, Gerard. Scanning Electron Microscopy of the Eye. (Illus.). 128p. 1985. text ed. 64.00 (ISBN 0-86577-185-5). Thieme Stratton.

Ludwig, H. & Metzger, H. The Human Female Reproductive Tract: A Scanning Electron Microscopic Atlas. (Illus.). 1976. 89.00 (ISBN 0-387-07675-1). Springer-Verlag.

Mackay, Bruce, ed. Introduction to Diagnostic Electron Microscopy. (Illus.). 262p. 1981. 35.00 (ISBN 0-8385-4315-4). ACC.

Mandal, Anil K. Electron Microscopy of the Kidney: A Clinicopathological Approach. LC 78-24409. (Illus.). 472p. 1978. 49.50x (ISBN 0-306-40110-X, Plenum Pr). Plenum Pub.

Marcus, R B. & Sheng, T T. Transmission Electron Microscopy of Silicon VLSI Circuits & Structure. LC 83-3469. 217p. 1983. 48.50x (ISBN 0-471-09251-7, Pub. by Wiley-Interscience). Wiley.

Meek, Geoffrey A. Practical Electron Microscopy for Biologists. 2nd. ed. LC 75-4955. 528p. 1976. text ed. 104.95 (ISBN 0-471-59031-2, Pub. by Wiley-Interscience); pap. 34.95x (ISBN 0-471-99592-4). Wiley.

Mercer, E. M. & Birbeck, M. S. Electron Microscopy: A Handbook for Biologists. 3rd ed. (Illus.). 152p. 1972. pap. 6.75 (ISBN 0-632-08330-1, B 3458-X, Blackwell). Mosby.

Mohanty, Sashi B. Electron Microscopy for Biologists. (Illus.). 376p. 1982. 39.75x (ISBN 0-398-04738-3). C C Thomas.

Mokotoff, Gertrude E. Electron Microscopy Laboratory Techniques. rev. ed. (Illus.). 1978. lab manual 8.95 (ISBN 0-912526-21-1). Lib Res.

Morgan, A. J. X-Ray Microanalysis in Electron Microscopy for Biologists. (Illus.). 1984. pap. 9.95 (ISBN 0-19-856406-6). Oxford U Pr.

Morgan, A. John. X-Ray Microanalysis in Electron Microscopy for Biologists. (Royal Microscopical Society Microscopy Handbooks Ser.). (Illus.). 72p. 1985. pap. 8.95 (ISBN 0-19-856409-0). Oxford U Pr.

Murr, Lawerence E. Electron & Ion Microscopy & Microanalysis: Principles & Applications. (Optical Engineering Ser.: Vol. 1). (Illus.). 816p. 1982. 65.00 (ISBN 0-8247-1553-5). Dekker.

Parsons, D. F., ed. Biological Techniques in Electron Microscopy. 1970. 37.50 (ISBN 0-12-545550-X). Acad Pr.

Pease, Daniel C. Histological Techniques for Electron Microscopy. 2nd ed. 1965. 45.00 (ISBN 0-12-548456-9). Acad Pr.

Polliack, A. Normal, Transformed & Leukemic Leukocytes: A Scanning Electron Microscopy Atlas. (Illus.). 1977. 56.00 (ISBN 0-387-08376-6). Springer-Verlag.

Racker, Darlene K. Transmission Electron Microscopy: Methods of Application. (Illus.). 142p. 1983. pap. 24.75x spiral (ISBN 0-398-04713-8). C C Thomas.

Rash, John & Hudson, C. S. Electron Microscopy Methods & Applications. 250p. 1986. 14.50tx (ISBN 0-03-056919-2). Praeger.

Reid, Norma, ed. Ultramicrotomy. (Practical Methods in Electron Microscopy Ser.: Vol. 3, Pt. 2). 353p. 1975. pap. text ed. 17.50 (ISBN 0-444-10667-7, North-Holland). Elsevier.

Reimer, L. Transmission Electron Microscopy. (Springer Series in Optical Sciences: Vol. 36). (Illus.). 530p. 1984. 49.00 (ISBN 0-387-11794-6). Springer Verlag.

Roomans, Godfried M., ed. Preparation of Biological Specimens for Scanning Electron Microscopy. Murphy, Judith A. (Illus.). 352p. (Orig.). 1984. pap. text ed. 32.00 (ISBN 0-931288-33-9). Scanning Electron.

Sandborn, E. B. Cells & Tissues by Light & Electron Microscopy. 1970. Vol. 1. 68.00 (ISBN 0-12-617901-8); Vol. 2. 68.00 (ISBN 0-12-617902-6). Acad Pr.

Scanning Electron Microscopy: Systems & Applications 1973. (Institute of Physics Conference Ser.: No. 18). 1973. 55.00 (ISBN 0-9960029-7-9, Pub. by Inst Physics England). Heyden.

Shih, Gene & Kessel, Richard. Living Images: Biological Microstructures Revealed by Scanning Electron Microscopy. 155p. 1982. write for info. (ISBN 0-86720-006-5); pap. write for info. (ISBN 0-86720-008-1). Jones & Bartlett.

Siegel, Benjamin M., ed. Modern Developments in Electron Microscopy. 1964. 69.50 (ISBN 0-12-641450-5). Acad Pr.

Spence, J. C. Experimental High-Resolution Electron Microscopy. (Monographs on the Physics & Chemistry of Materials). (Illus.). 1981. 69.00x (ISBN 0-19-851365-8). Oxford U Pr.

Stolinski, C. & Breathnach, A. S. Freeze-Fracture Replication of Biological Tissue: Techniques, Interpretation & Applications. 1976. 55.00 (ISBN 0-12-672050-9). Acad Pr.

Strum, Judy M. Electron Micrograph Study Atlas. LC 82-50722. (Illus.). 208p. 1982. text ed. 20.00 (ISBN 0-9608786-0-2). Univ Maryland.

Trump, B. F. Diagnostic Electron Microscopy, Vol. 3. LC 76-18952. (Diagnostic Electron Microscopy Ser.). 536p. 1980. 82.00x (ISBN 0-471-05150-0, Pub. by Wiley-Interscience). Wiley.

Trump, B. F. & Jones, R. T. Diagnostic Electron Microscopy. (Diagnostic Electron Microscopy Ser.). 346p. 1978. 70.00 (ISBN 0-471-89195-9). Wiley.

--Diagnostic Electron Microscopy, Vol. 2. LC 77-12817. (Diagnostic Electron Microscopy Ser.). 346p. 1979. text ed. 70.00 (ISBN 0-471-89196-7, Pub. by Wiley Med). Wiley.

Trump, Benjamin F. & Jones, Raymond T., eds. Diagnostic Electron Microscopy, Vol. 4. LC 77-12817. (Diagnostic Electron Microscopy Ser.). 544p. 1983. 70.00 (ISBN 0-471-05149-7, Pub. by Wiley Med). Wiley.

Venables, J. A. Developments in Electron Microscopy & Analysis. 1976. 79.50 (ISBN 0-12-716950-4). Acad Pr.

Von Heimendahl, Manfred & Wolff, U. Electron Microscopy of Materials: An Introduction. LC 79-6810. 1980. 29.00 (ISBN 0-12-725150-2). Acad Pr.

Watt, Ian M. The Principles & Practice of Electron Microscopy. (Illus.). 250p. 1985. 49.50 (ISBN 0-521-25557-0). Cambridge U Pr.

Weakley, Brenda. Beginner's Handbook in Biological Transmission Electron Microscopy. 2nd ed. 252p. 1981. 24.00 (ISBN 0-443-02091-4). Churchill.

Williams, David B. Practical Analytical Electron Microscopy in Materials Science. (Illus.). 180p. 1984. pap. 30.00 (ISBN 0-9612934-0-3). Electron Optics Pub Grp.

Willison, M. & Rowe, A. J. Replica Shadowing & Freeze-Etching Techniques. rev. ed. (Practical Methods in Electron Microscopy Ser.: Vol. 8). 302p. 1980. 70.25 (ISBN 0-444-80166-9, Biomedical Pr); pap. 24.00 (ISBN 0-444-80165-0). Elsevier.

Wischnitzer, Saul. Introduction to Electron Microscopy. 3rd ed. LC 80-15266. 320p. 1981. 43.00 (ISBN 0-08-026298-8). Pergamon.

Yoshii, Zensaku, et al. Atlas of Scanning Electron Microscopy in Microbiology. (Illus.). 1976. 52.00 (ISBN 0-89640-038-7). Igaku-Shoin.

ELECTRON OPTICS

see also Electron Beams; Electron Microscope; Electronics; Image Converters; Ion Flow Dynamics; Quantum Electronics

Albers, Walter A., Jr., ed. Physics of Opto-Electronic Materials. LC 73-173832. (General Motors Symposium Ser). 281p. 1971. 45.00 (ISBN 0-306-30558-5, Plenum Pr). Plenum Pub.

Applications of Electron Microfractography to Materials Research - STP 493. 96p. 1971. pap. 8.25 (ISBN 0-8031-0746-3, 04-493000-30). ASTM.

Dahl, Paul. Introduction to Electron & Ion Optics. 1973. 35.00 (ISBN 0-12-200650-X). Acad Pr.

Dietrich, I., ed. Superconducting Electron-Optic Devices. LC 76-20466. (International Cryogenics Monograph Ser.). (Illus.). 140p. 1976. 39.50x (ISBN 0-306-30882-7, Plenum Pr). Plenum Pub.

El-Kareh, A. B. & El-Kareh, J. C. Electron Beams, Lenses & Optics, Vols. 1 & 2. 1970. Vol. 1. 76.50 (ISBN 0-12-238001-0); Vol. 2. 76.00 (ISBN 0-12-238002-9). Acad Pr.

Fynn, G. W. & Powell, W. J. The Cutting & Polishing of Electro-Optic Materials. LC 78-21139. 215p. 1979. 94.95x (ISBN 0-470-26607-4). Halsted Pr.

Harting, E. & Read, F. H. Electrostatic Lenses. 322p. 1976. 76.75 (ISBN 0-444-41319-7). Elsevier.

Hawkes, P. W. Electron Optics & Electron Microscopy. 264p. 1972. 33.00x (ISBN 0-85066-056-4). Taylor & Francis.

--Properties of Magnetic Electron Lenses. (Topics in Current Physics Ser.: Vol. 18). (Illus.). 470p. 1982. 48.00 (ISBN 0-387-10296-5). Springer-Verlag.

Heath Company Staff. Operational Amplifiers. rev. ed. (Electronics Technology Ser.). (Illus.). 368p. 1979. looseleaf with experimental pts. 44.95 (ISBN 0-87119-034-6); pap. text ed. 18.95 (ISBN 0-87119-032-X); tchr's. manual 9.95 (ISBN 0-87119-033-8). Heathkit-Zenith Ed.

International Symposium Oln Electron & Photoninteractions at High Energies - Hamburg - 1965. Electron & Photon Interactions at High Energies: Invited Papers. (Springer Tracts in Modern Physics: Vol. 39). (Illus.). 1965. 34.30 (ISBN 0-387-03406-4). Springer-Verlag.

Klemperer, Otto & Barnett, M. E. Electron Optics. 3rd ed. LC 74-118065. (Cambridge Monographs on Physics). pap. 130.00 (ISBN 0-317-29381-8, 2024482). Bks Demand UMI.

Knight, P. L., ed. Quantum Electronics & Electro-Optics: Proceedings of the Fifth National Quantum Electronics Conference. 456p. 1983. 59.95 (ISBN 0-471-10278-4). Wiley.

Lee, Chi H., ed. Picosecond Optoelectronic Devices. LC 84-3016. 1984. 60.00 (ISBN 0-12-440880-X). Acad Pr.

Lexique Trilingue des Termes D'Usage Courant En Electrotechnique, Electronique, Acoustique, Optique et Controle Par Ultrasons. (Fr.). 340p. (Trilingual Lexicon of Currently Used Terms in Electrotechnics, Electronics, Acoustics, Optics and Control by Ultra-Sound). 1966. pap. 35.00 (ISBN 0-686-56793-5, M-6373). French & Eur.

Madey, J. M., et al, eds. Free Electron Generation of Extreme Ultraviolet Coherent Radiation (Brookhaven-OSA, 1983) AIP Conference Proceedings No. 118. LC 84-71539. (Optical Science & Engineering Ser.: No. 4). 319p. 1984. lib. bdg. 40.50 (ISBN 0-88318-317-X). Am Inst Physics.

Pinson, L. J. Electro-Optics. 352p. 34.95 (ISBN 0-471-88142-2). Wiley.

Seippel. Optoelectronics. 1981. text ed. 27.95 (ISBN 0-8359-5255-X). Reston.

Septier, A., ed. Focusing of Charged Particles, 2 Vols. 1967. Vol. 1. 79.50 (ISBN 0-12-636901-1); Vol. 2. 78.00 (ISBN 0-12-636902-X). Acad Pr.

Seyrafi, Khalil. Electro-Optical Systems Analysis. 3rd ed. LC 73-8681. 356p. 1985. 36.00 (ISBN 0-318-04675-X). Electro-Optical.

Texas Instruments Applications Laboratory, Deutschland GmbH, Staff. Optoelectronics: Theory & Practice. (Illus.). 434p. 1976. 42.50 (ISBN 0-317-27323-X, LCB4360). Tex Instr Inc.

Texas Instruments Engineering Staff. Optoelectronic Data Book. LC 83-70442. 480p. 1983. pap. 11.50 (ISBN 0-89512-115-8, SOYDOO1E). Tex Instr Inc.

Tischler, M. Optoelectronics: A Text-Lab Manual. 224p. 1985. write for info. (ISBN 0-07-064786-0). McGraw.

Waidelich, W., ed. Optoelectronics in Medicine: Proceedings of the Fifth International Congress LASER 81. (Illus.). 239p. 1982. pap. 25.80 (ISBN 0-387-10968-4). Springer-Verlag.

ELECTRON PARAMAGNETIC RESONANCE

see also Hyperfine Interactions

Alger, Raymond S. Electron Paramagnetic Resonance: Techniques & Applications. LC 67-20255. pap. 150.50 (ISBN 0-317-08506-9, 2010180). Bks Demand UMI.

Assenheim, Harry M. Introduction to Electron Spin Resonance. LC 67-21449. (Monographs of Electron Spin Resonance Ser.). 200p. 1967. 27.50x (ISBN 0-306-30306-X, Plenum Pr). Plenum Pub.

Ayscough, P. B., ed. Electron Spin Resonance, Vols. 1-5. Incl. Vol. 1. 1971-72 Literature. 1973. 36.00 (ISBN 0-85186-751-0); Vol. 2. 1972-73 Literature. 1974. 38.00 (ISBN 0-85186-761-8); Vol. 3. 1973-75 Literature. 1976. 45.00 (ISBN 0-85186-771-5); Vol. 4. 1975-76 Literature. 1977. 61.00 (ISBN 0-685-55713-8); Vol. 5. 1979. 77.00 (ISBN 0-85186-791-X, Pub. by Royal Soc Chem London). LC 72-95099. Am Chemical.

Bielski, Benon H. & Gebicki, Janusz M. Atlas of Electron Spin Resonance Spectra. 1967. 95.00 (ISBN 0-12-096650-6). Acad Pr.

Buchachenko, Anatoli L. Stable Radicals. LC 65-11336. 180p. 1965. 32.50x (ISBN 0-306-10729-5, Consultants). Plenum Pub.

Coogan, C. K., et al. Magnetic Resonance. LC 70-119613. 386p. 1970. 37.50x (ISBN 0-306-30487-2, Plenum Pr). Plenum Pub.

Cubitt, John M. & Burek, Cynthia V. A Bibliography of Electron Spin Resonance Applications in the Earth Sciences. (Bibliography Ser.). 1980. 10.00x (ISBN 0-686-27378-8, Pub. by GEO Abstracts England). State Mutual Bk.

Dixon, W. T. Theory & Interpretation of Magnetic Resonance Spectra. LC 73-180922. 168p. 1972. 29.50x (ISBN 0-306-30567-4, Plenum Pr). Plenum Pub.

Feher, G., ed. Electron Paramagnetic Resonance with Applications to Selected Problems in Biology. (Documents in Biology Ser.: Vol. 3). 152p. 1970. 45.25 (ISBN 0-677-02670-6). Gordon.

Freeman, Arthur J. & Frankel, Richard B. Hyperfine Interactions. 1967. 76.50 (ISBN 0-12-266750-6). Acad Pr.

Geschwind, S., ed. Electron Paramagnetic Resonance. LC 77-186261. 584p. 1972. 65.00x (ISBN 0-306-30580-1, Plenum Pr). Plenum Pub.

Harriman, John E., ed. Theoretical Foundations of Electron Spin Resonance. (Physical Chemistry Ser.). 1978. 70.00 (ISBN 0-12-326350-6). Acad Pr.

Hershenson, Herbert M. Nuclear Magnetic Resonance & Electron Spin Resonance: Index For 1958-1963. 1965. 41.50 (ISBN 0-12-343260-X). Acad Pr.

Ingram, D. J. Biological & Biochemical Applications of Electron Spin Resonance. LC 78-86923. 368p. 1969. 39.50x (ISBN 0-306-30437-6, Plenum Pr). Plenum Pub.

Kevan, Larry & Kispert, Lowell D. Electron Spin Double Resonance Spectroscopy. LC 75-44418. pap. 108.50 (ISBN 0-317-09907-8, 2055603). Bks Demand UMI.

Knowles, Peter F., et al. Magnetic Resonance of Biomolecules: An Introduction to the Theory & Practice of NMR & ESR in Biological Systems. LC 75-4872. 343p. 1976. o. p. 49.95 (ISBN 0-471-49575-1, Pub. by Wiley-Interscience); pap. 29.95x (ISBN 0-471-01672-1). Wiley.

Lancaster, Gordon. Electron Spin Resonance in Semiconductors. LC 67-21450. (Monographs on Electron Spin Resonance Ser.). 152p. 1967. 24.50x (ISBN 0-306-30307-8, Plenum Pr). Plenum Pub.

Lebedev, Y. S., et al. Atlas of Electron Spin Resonance Spectra: Theoretically Calculated Multicomponent Symmetrical Spectra. LC 63-21216. 195p. 1964. 35.00x (ISBN 0-306-65104-1, IFI Plenum). Plenum Pub.

Molin, Y. N., et al. Spin Exchange: Principles & Applications in Chemistry & Biology. (Springer Series in Chemical Physics: Vol. 8). (Illus.). 242p. 1980. 48.00 (ISBN 0-387-10095-4). Springer-Verlag.

Muus, L. T. & Atkins, P. W., eds. Electron Spin Relaxation in Liquids. LC 72-76022. 537p. 1972. 75.00x (ISBN 0-306-30588-7, Plenum Pr). Plenum Pub.

Orton, J. W. Electron Paramagnetic Resonance. 240p. 1970. 69.50 (ISBN 0-677-61900-6). Gordon.

Poole, Charles P. Electron Spin Resonance: A Comprehensive Treatise on Experimental Techniques. 2nd ed. LC 82-6911. 780p. 1983. 79.50 (ISBN 0-471-04678-7, Pub. by Wiley-Interscience). Wiley.

Skobel'tsyn, D. V., ed. Quantum Electronics & Paramagnetic Resonance. LC 73-120026. (P. N. Lebedev Physics Institute Ser.: Vol. 49). 148p. 1971. 30.00x (ISBN 0-306-10853-4, Consultants). Plenum Pub.

Sorin, L. A. & Vlasova, M. V. Electron Spin Resonance of Paramagnetic Crystals. LC 73-81407. (Illus.). 254p. 1973. 35.00x (ISBN 0-306-30746-4, Plenum Pr). Plenum Pub.

Wilmhurst, T. H. Electron Spin Resonance Spectrometers. LC 68-8257. (Monographs on Electron Spin Resonance Ser.). 280p. 1968. 29.50x (ISBN 0-306-30372-8, Plenum Pr). Plenum Pub.

Yen, Teh Fu, ed. Electron Spin Resonance of Metal Complexes. LC 69-19169. 204p. 1969. 32.50x (ISBN 0-306-30394-9, Plenum Pr). Plenum Pub.

ELECTRON PROBES

see Probes (Electronic Instruments)

ELECTRON RESONANCE

see Electron Paramagnetic Resonance

ELECTRON SCATTERING

see Electrons–Scattering

ELECTRON SPECTROSCOPY

Bonnelle, C. & Mande, C., eds. Advances in X-Ray Spectroscopy: A Reference Text in Honour of Professor Y. Cauchois. LC 82-12300. (Illus.). 400p. 1982. 88.00 (ISBN 0-08-025266-4). Pergamon.

Briggs, D. & Seah, M. P. Practical Surface Analysis by Auger & Photo-Electron Spectoscopy. 533p. 1983. 83.95x (ISBN 0-471-26279-X, Pub. by Wiley-Interscience). Wiley.

Brundle, C. R. & Baker, A. D., eds. Electron Spectroscopy: Theory, Techniques & Applications, Vol. 4. LC 76-1691. 1981. 77.00 (ISBN 0-12-137804-7). Acad Pr.

Cardona, M. & Ley, L., eds. Photoemission in Solids I: General Principles. LC 78-2503. (Topics in Applied Physics: Vol. 26). (Illus.). 1978. 52.00 (ISBN 0-387-08685-4). Springer-Verlag.

Carlson, T. A. X-Ray Photoelectron Spectroscopy. LC 77-28499. (Benchmark Papers in Physical Chemistry & Chemical Physics: Vol. 2). 341p. 1978. 51.00 (ISBN 0-87933-325-1). Van Nos Reinhold.

Carlson, Thomas A. Photoelectron & Auger Spectroscopy. LC 72-28025. (Modern Analytical Chemistry Ser.). (Illus.). 417p. 1975. 55.00 (ISBN 0-306-33901-3, Plenum Pr). Plenum Pub.

Dekeyser, W., et al, eds. Electron Emission Spectroscopy. LC 73-83559. 1973. lib. bdg. 79.00 (ISBN 90-277-0366-3, Pub. by Reidel Holland). Kluwer Academic.

Fiermans, L., et al, eds. Electron & Ion Spectroscopy of Solids. LC 78-6171. (NATO ASI Series B, Physics: Vol. 32). 487p. 1978. 75.00x (ISBN 0-306-35732-1, Plenum Pr). Plenum Pub.

Grove, E. L., ed. Analytical Emission Spectroscopy. LC 79-134783. (Analytical Spectroscopy Ser.: Vol.1, Pt.1). pap. 104.30 (ISBN 0-317-08368-6, 2055079). Bks Demand UMI.

Kaufmann, E. N. & Shenoy, G. K., eds. Nuclear & Electron Resonance Spectroscopies Applied to Materials Science. (Materials Research Society Proceedings Ser.: Vol. 3). 558p. 1981. 77.75 (ISBN 0-444-00597-8, North-Holland). Elsevier.

Nemoshkalenko, V. V. & Aleshin, V. G. Electron Spectroscopy of Crystals. LC 78-12954. (Physics of Solids & Liquids Ser.). (Illus.). 374p. 1978. 59.50x (ISBN 0-306-40109-6, Plenum Pr). Plenum Pub.

Phillips, J. P., et al, eds. Organic Electronic Spectral Data 1978, Vol. XX. (Organic Electronic Spectral Data Ser.: No. 2-197). 1040p. 1985. 120.00 (ISBN 0-471-81808-9). Wiley.

Thompson, Michael, et al. Auger Electron Spectroscopy. (Chemical Analysis: A Series of Monographs on Analytical Chemistry & Its Applications). 394p. 1985. text ed. 75.00 (ISBN 0-471-04377-X, Pub by Wiley-Interscience). Wiley.

Thyagarajan, B. S. Organic Electronic Spectral Data, Vol. XIX, 1977. Phillips, John P., et al, eds. LC 60-16428. (Organic Electronic Spectral Data Ser.). 1068p. 1983. 130.00 (ISBN 0-471-88637-8, 2197, Pub. by Wiley-Interscience). Wiley.

Windawi, H. & Ho, F. L. Applied Electron Spectroscopy for Chemical Analysis, Vol. 63. (Chemical Analysis Ser.). 213p. 1982. 51.50 (ISBN 0-471-09051-4). Wiley.

Wolf, E. L. Principles of Electron Tunneling Spectroscopy. (International Series of Monographs on Physics). (Illus.). 1985. 80.00x (ISBN 0-19-503417-1). Oxford U Pr.

Wolfram, T., ed. Inelastic Electron Tunneling Spectroscopy: Proceedings of the International Conference & Symposium on Electron Tunneling, Univ. of Missouri, Columbia, USA, May 25-27, 1977. (Springer Ser. in Solid-State Sciences: Vol. 4). (Illus.). 1978. 39.00 (ISBN 0-387-08691-9). Springer-Verlag.

ELECTRON SPIN RESONANCE

see Electron Paramagnetic Resonance

ELECTRON TUBES

see also Diodes; Electronic Circuits; Image Converters; Masers; Microwave Tubes; Oscillators, Crystal; Vacuum-Tubes

RCA Commercial Engineering Staff. Rca Receiving Tube Manual Rc-30. (Illus.). 752p. 1975. pap. 3.95 (ISBN 0-913970-17-4). RCA Dist Spec Prods.

ELECTRONIC ALARM SYSTEMS

see also Burglar-Alarms

Cunningham, John E. Building & Installing Electronic Intrusion Alarms. 3rd ed. LC 82-50021. 160p. 1982. pap. 10.95 (ISBN 0-672-21954-9). Sams.

Kinks & Hints for the Alarm Installer. LC 79-15921. (Illus.). 1979. pap. 9.95 (ISBN 0-913708-36-4). Butterworth.

ELECTRONIC ANALOG COMPUTERS

see also Electric Network Analyzers

Arbel, Arie F. Analog Signal Processing & Instrumentation. (Illus.). 246p. 1984. pap. 24.95 (ISBN 0-521-31866-1). Cambridge U Pr.

Belove, Charles, et al. Digital Analog System Circulation Development. Wade, Charles R., ed. (Illus.). 448p. 1973. text ed. 47.00 (ISBN 0-07-004420-1). McGraw.

Compatibility of Analog Signals for Electronic Industrial Process Instruments: ISA Standard S50.1, ANSI Standard MC12.1. 12p. 1975. pap. text ed. 10.00x (ISBN 0-87664-389-6). Instru Soc.

Goldsbrough, et al. Analog Electronics for Microcomputer Systems. LC 83-61062. 440p. 1983. pap. 19.95 (ISBN 0-672-21821-6, 21821). Sams.

Grebene, Alan B. Analog Integrated Circuit Design. LC 78-15389. 416p. 1978. Repr. of 1972 ed. lib. bdg. 24.50 (ISBN 0-88275-710-5). Krieger.

Haley & Scott. Analogue & Digital Computers. 15.00 (ISBN 0-685-28339-9). Philos Lib.

Hyndman, D. E. Analog & Hybrid Computing. LC 75-120691. 1970. pap. 14.50 (ISBN 0-08-015572-3). Pergamon.

Millman, Jacob & Halkias, Christos. Integrated Electronics: Analog Digital Circuits & Systems. Terman, F. E., ed. (Electrical & Electronic Engineering Ser.). (Illus.). 900p. 1972. text ed. 46.95 (ISBN 0-07-042315-6). McGraw.

Sinema, William & McGovern, Thomas. Digital, Analog & Data Communications. 1982. text ed. 34.95 (ISBN 0-8359-1301-5); solutions manual free (ISBN 0-8359-1302-3). Reston.

Wass, C. A. & Garner, K. C. Introduction to Electronic Analogue Computers. 2nd ed. 1965. pap. 11.75 (ISBN 0-08-013655-9). Pergamon.

Williams, Raymond W. Techniques & Components of Analogue Computation. 1962. 47.50 (ISBN 0-12-756250-8). Acad Pr.

ELECTRONIC ANALOG COMPUTERS–PROGRAMMING

Blum, Joseph J. Introduction to Analog Computation. 175p. (Orig.). 1969. pap. text ed. 18.95 (ISBN 0-15-541553-0, HC); solutions manual avail. (ISBN 0-15-541554-9, HC). HarBraceJ.

ELECTRONIC APPARATUS AND APPLIANCES

see also Airplanes–Electronic Equipment; Antennas (Electronics); Automobiles–Electronic Equipment; Computers; Electronic Control; Electronic Instruments; Electronic Office Machines; Electronic Toys; Industrial Electronics; Metal Detectors; Microwave Devices; Microwave Wiring; Miniature Electronic Equipment; Printed Circuits; Probes (Electronic Instruments); Storage Tubes; Transducers

Bezner, ed. Dictionary of Electrical Machines. 558p. 1978. 39.00 (ISBN 0-318-01455-6, Pub. by O Brandstetter WG). Heyden.

Bishop, Owen. Electronic Projects for Home Security. 96p. 1981. 9.95 (ISBN 0-408-00535-1). Butterworth.

Boylestad, Robert & Nashelsky, Louis. Electronic Devices & Circuit Theory. 3rd ed. (Illus.). 768p. 1982. 34.95 (ISBN 0-13-250324-7). P-H.

Buchsbaum, Frank & Freudenstein, Ferdinand. Design & Application of Small Standardized Components Data Book 757, Vol. 2. LC 83-60226. (Illus.). 784p. 1983. 12.95 (ISBN 0-9609878-1-9). Stock Drive.

Business Communications Staff. New Consumer Product Electronics: Growth Trends, G-040r. 1980. 875.00 (ISBN 0-89336-224-7). BCC.

CES Industries, Inc. Staff. Ed-Lab Experiment Manual: CES 349 Counter Timer Module; Troubleshooting System. (Illus.). 1982. write for info. (ISBN 0-86711-031-7). CES Industries.

Chryssis, George. High Frequency Switching Power Supplies: Theory & Design. 224p. 1984. 35.00 (ISBN 0-07-010949-4). McGraw.

Connor, F. R. Electronic Devices. 244p. 1982. scp 18.16 (ISBN 0-205-07780-3, 327780). Allyn.

Duarte, Salvador R. & Duarte, R. L. Electronics Assembly & Fabrication Methods. 2nd ed. LC 72-6495. 1973. text ed. 18.25 (ISBN 0-07-017880-1). McGraw.

Fairchild Market Research Division. Home Electronics. (Fairchild Fact File Ser.). 1979. pap. 15.00 (ISBN 0-87005-320-5). Fairchild.

Fleeman, Stephen. Electronic Principles. 1985. text ed. 28.95 (ISBN 0-8359-1587-5); solutions manual avail. (ISBN 0-8359-1588-3). Reston.

Floyd, Thomas L. Essentials of Electronic Devices. 1983. pap. text ed. 11.50 (ISBN 0-675-20062-8). Merrill.

Goldberg, Joel. Electronic Servicing of Robotic Equipment. LC 84-8198. (Illus.). 224p. 1985. text ed. 27.95 (ISBN 0-13-252131-8). P-H.

Haddad, George I., ed. Avalanche Transit-Time Devices. LC 72-77132. (Modern Frontiers in Applied Science Ser.). (Illus.). 580p. 1973. pap. 17.00x (ISBN 0-89006-016-9). Artech Hse.

Hannay, N. Bruce, ed. Electronic Materials. Colombo, Umberto. LC 73-13971. 646p. 1973. 79.50x (ISBN 0-306-30758-8, Plenum Pr). Plenum Pub.

Harper, Charles A. Handbook of Components for Electronics. 1977. 62.50 (ISBN 0-07-026682-4). McGraw.

Herrington, Donald. How to Read Schematic Diagrams. 3rd ed. LC 74-33834. (Illus.). 192p. 1975. pap. 8.95 (ISBN 0-672-21127-0). Sams.

Hnatek, Eugene R. Design of Solid-State Power Supplies. 2nd ed. 640p. 1980. 32.95 (ISBN 0-442-23429-5). Van Nos Reinhold.

Jeremiah, David. Computer Revolution. LC 83-60893. (Exploration & Discovery Ser.). 1983. 13.80 (ISBN 0-382-06700-2). Silver.

Lenk, John D. Handbook of Advanced Troubleshooting. (Illus.). 352p. 1983. text ed. 27.95 (ISBN 0-13-372391-7). P-H.

Marshak, Ronni T. A Seybold Study: Electronic Typewriters - Getting Started for Less than 2000.00. 1983. pap. 100.00 (ISBN 0-918514-04-5). Seybold.

Mottershead, Allen. Electronic Devices & Circuits: An Introduction. LC 72-93687. pap. 160.00 (ISBN 0-317-08651-0, 2007756). Bks Demand UMI.

Naegele, Carl J. Understanding Electronic Mail. (Handy Guide). 64p. (Orig.). 1984. pap. 3.50 (ISBN 0-88284-249-8). Alfred Pub.

Nashelsky, Louis & Boylestad, Robert. Devices: Discrete & Integrated. (Illus.). 448p. 1981. text ed. 27.95 (ISBN 0-13-208165-2). P-H.

National Electronic Packaging & Production Conference (1984: Anaheim, CA) National Electronic Packaging & Production Conference: Proceedings of the Technical Program. pap. 132.30 (ISBN 0-317-19835-1, 2023060). Bks Demand UMI.

National Materials Advisory Board. Yield of Electronic Materials & Devices. 96p. 1973. pap. 6.75 (ISBN 0-309-02108-1). Natl Acad Pr.

Neuberger, M. S., et al. Handbook of Electronic Materials. Incl. Vol. 2. III-V Semiconducting Compounds. 120p. 1971 (ISBN 0-306-67102-6); Vol. 4. Niobium Alloys & Compounds. 70p. 1972 (ISBN 0-306-67104-2); Vol. 5. Group IV Semiconducting Materials. 74p. 1971 (ISBN 0-306-67105-0); Vol. 7. III-V Ternary Semiconducting Compounds-Data Tables. 56p. 1972 (ISBN 0-306-67107-7). LC 76-147312. 55.00x ea. (IFI Plenum). Plenum Pub.

Price, S. G. Introducing the Electronic Office. (Illus.). 161p. 1979. pap. 27.50x (ISBN 0-85012-204-X). Intl Pubns Serv.

Ricketts, L. W. Fundamentals of Nuclear Hardening of Electronic Equipment. 548p. 1972. 72.50 (ISBN 0-471-72100-X). Wiley.

Rosenstein, Milton & Morris, Paul. Modern Electronic Devices: Circuit Design & Application. 1984. text ed. 34.95 (ISBN 0-8359-4548-0); solutions manual avail. (ISBN 0-8359-4549-9). Reston.

Ross, Douglas A. Optoelectronic Devices & Optical Imaging Techniques. (Electrical & Electronic Engineering Ser.). (Illus.). 137p. 1979. text ed. 27.50x (ISBN 0-333-24292-0); pap. text ed. 18.50x (ISBN 0-333-25335-3). Scholium Intl.

Rudman, Jack. Electronics Communication. (Occupational Competency Examination Ser.: OCE-19). (Cloth bdg. avail. on request). pap. 13.95 (ISBN 0-8373-5719-5). Natl Learning.

Scott, Allan W. Cooling of Electronic Equipment. LC 73-11154. 283p. 1974. 42.50x (ISBN 0-471-76780-8, Pub. by Wiley-Interscience). Wiley.

Seymour, J. Electronic Devices & Components. LC 80-28112. 504p. 1981. pap. 32.95x (ISBN 0-470-27108-6). Halsted Pr.

Siegman, Jean H. A Seybold Study: Electronic Mail Services. 1983. pap. 100.00 (ISBN 0-918514-05-3). Seybold.

Sinclair, Ian R. Understanding Electronic Components. 240p. 1980. 17.00x (ISBN 0-85242-104-4, Pub. by K Dickson). State Mutual Bk.

Steinberg, Dave S. Cooling Techniques for Electronic Equipment. LC 80-14141. 370p. 1980. 41.95 (ISBN 0-471-04403-2, Pub. by Wiley Interscience). Wiley.

--Vibration Analysis for Electronic Equipment. LC 72-13763. 467p. 1973. 57.50x (ISBN 0-471-82100-4, Pub. by Wiley-Interscience). Wiley.

Temes, Lloyd. Communication Electronics for Technicians. 400p. 1974. text ed. 29.95 (ISBN 0-07-063487-4). McGraw.

Tocci, Ronale J. Electronic Devices: Conventional Flow Version. 3rd ed. 1983. text ed. 27.95 (ISBN 0-675-20063-6). Merrill.

Webster, John G., et al. Electronic Devices for Rehabilitation. 446p. 1985. 45.00 (ISBN 0-471-80898-9, Pub by Wiley Med). Wiley.

Worden, Leslie E. Theory, Design & Application of Electronic Devices & Circuits. (Illus.). 700p. text ed. write for info. (ISBN 0-89894-014-1). Advocate Pub Group.

Zucker, Mitchell H. Electronic Circuits for the Behavioral & Biomedical Sciences: A Reference Book of Useful Solid-State Circuits. LC 76-81921. (Illus.). 241p. 1969. text ed. 25.50x (ISBN 0-7167-0918-X). W H Freeman.

ELECTRONIC APPARATUS AND APPLIANCES–BIBLIOGRAPHY

Koben, Shelly & Rose, Michael. Electronic Manufacturing Process. (Illus.). 320p. 1982. text ed. 27.95 (ISBN 0-8359-1642-1). Reston.

ELECTRONIC APPARATUS AND APPLIANCES–CATALOGS

German Electrical & Electronic Manufacturers Assoc., ed. Electro Buyers' Guide 1981. 1300p. (Orig.). 1981. pap. 27.50x (ISBN 0-686-79790-6). Intl Pubns Serv.

Macura, Paul. Supplement to Russian-English Dictionary of Electrotechnology & Applied Sciences. LC 85-8652. 240p. 1985. lib. bdg. price not set (ISBN 0-89874-873-9). Krieger.

Micro Automated Service Staff. Electronic Parts Suppliers: San Diego, California. 1st Ed. ed. Norton, Donna L., ed. LC 84-63079. 98p. 1985. pap. 49.99 incl. software database (ISBN 0-910733-02-3). ICTL Pubns.

ELECTRONIC APPARATUS AND APPLIANCES–DESIGN AND CONSTRUCTION

Becker, Peter W. & Jensen, Finn. Design of Systems & Circuits for Maximum Reliability or Maximum Production Yield. (Illus.). 1977. text ed. 44.00 (ISBN 0-07-004230-6). McGraw.

Berlin, Howard M. Design of Op-Amp Circuits, with Experiments. LC 78-56606. 224p. 1978. pap. 11.95 (ISBN 0-672-21537-3). Sams.

Carr, Joseph J. Designing & Building Electronic Gadgets, with Projects. (Illus.). 406p. (Orig.). 1984. 19.95 (ISBN 0-8306-0690-4); pap. 12.95 (ISBN 0-8306-1690-X, 1690). TAB Bks.

Doan, Cortland C. Design, Drafting, & Construction Practices for Electronics. LC 77-6064. 1985. pap. text ed. 18.00 (ISBN 0-534-04722-X). Breton Pubs.

Electronic Equipment Wiring & Assembling Two. 55.00x (ISBN 0-85083-059-1, Pub. by Engineering Ind). State Mutual Bk.

Electronic Equipment Wiring & Assembling One. 55.00x (ISBN 0-85083-014-1, Pub. by Engineering Ind). State Mutual Bk.

Hoffman, Edward G. Jig & Fixture Design. 2nd ed. LC 84-25976. 320p. 1985. pap. text ed. 15.80 (ISBN 0-8273-2439-1); instr's. guide avail. (ISBN 0-8273-2440-5). Delmar.

Malcolm, Douglas R., Jr. How to Build Electronic Projects. Goldberg, Joel, ed. LC 79-17829. (Electro-Skills Ser.). (Illus.). 1979. pap. 8.65 (ISBN 0-07-039760-0). McGraw.

Matisoff, Bernard S. Handbook of Electronics Packaging Design & Engineering. 400p. 1982. 37.50 (ISBN 0-442-20171-0). Van Nos Reinhold.

Sloan, J. Design & Packaging of Electronic Equipment. 1984. 47.50 (ISBN 0-442-28819-0). Van Nos Reinhold.

Williams, Arthur B. Electronic Filter Design Handbook. 1980. 47.50 (ISBN 0-07-070430-9). McGraw.

ELECTRONIC APPARATUS AND APPLIANCES–DRAWING

see Electronic Drafting

ELECTRONIC APPARATUS AND APPLIANCES–MAINTENANCE AND REPAIR

Adams, D., et al, eds. Electronic Equipment Wiring & Assembling: Part One. (Engineering Craftsmen: No. G5). 1968. spiral bdg. 38.50x (ISBN 0-85083-014-1). Trans-Atlantic.

--Electronic Inspection & Test, 2 vols. (Engineering Craftsmen: No. G26). (Illus.). 1969. Set. s 69.95x (ISBN 0-85083-035-4). Trans-Atlantic.

ARS Guide to Finding Servicing Information. 2.00 (ISBN 0-938630-03-2). ARS Enterprises.

Brann, Donald R. Electrical Repairs Simplified. LC 70-95701. 1979. pap. 5.95 (ISBN 0-87733-694-6). Easi-Bild.

Cameron, Derek. Advanced Electronic Troubleshooting. (Illus.). 1977. 24.95 (ISBN 0-87909-002-2). Reston.

Clark, N. F., et al, eds. Electronic Equipment Wiring & Assembling: Part Two. (Engineering Craftsmen: No. G25). (Illus.). 1969. spiral bdg. 47.50x (ISBN 0-89563-004-4). Trans-Atlantic.

Coates, S. D., et al, eds. Electronic Maintenance, Vol. 1. (Engineering Craftsmen: No. J4). (Illus.). 1969. spiral bdg. 45.00x (ISBN 0-85083-027-3). Trans-Atlantic.

Darr, Jack. How to Test Almost Everything Electronic. LC 66-30560. 1967. 10.95 (ISBN 0-8306-2422-8). TAB Bks.

Davidson, I., et al, eds. Electronic Maintenance, Vol. 2. (Engineering Craftsmen: No. J24). (Illus.). 1970. spiral bdg. 43.50x (ISBN 0-89563-005-2). Trans-Atlantic.

Electronic Maintenance. 1982. 52.00x (ISBN 0-85083-027-3, Pub. by Engineering Ind). State Mutual Bk.

Electronic Maintenance Two. 1982. 52.00x (ISBN 0-85083-082-6, Pub. by Engineering Ind). State Mutual Bk.

Grolle, Carl G. Electronic Workshop Manual & Guide. 240p. 1977. 16.95 (ISBN 0-13-252502-X, Parker). P-H.

Lacy, Edward A. Protecting Electronic Equipment from Electrostatic Discharge. LC 84-8902. (Illus.). 176p. (Orig.). 1984. 16.95 (ISBN 0-8306-0820-6); pap. 11.95 (ISBN 0-8306-1820-1, 1820). TAB Bks.

Lenk, John D. Handbook of Practical Solid State Troubleshooting. (Illus.). 1971. ref. ed. 27.95 (ISBN 0-13-380642-1); pap. 12.95 (ISBN 0-13-380725-8). P-H.

Middleton, Robert G. New Ways to Use Test Meters: A Modern Guide to Electronic Servicing. 256p. 1983. 21.95 (ISBN 0-13-616169-3, Busn). P-H.

Namgostar, M. Digital Equipment Troubleshooting. (Illus.). 288p. 1977. text ed. 24.95 (ISBN 0-87909-201-7). Reston.

Rudman, Jack. Electronic Equipment Maintainer. (Career Examination Ser.: C-227). (Cloth bdg. avail. on request). pap. 12.00 (ISBN 0-8373-0227-7). Natl Learning.

--Electronic Equipment Repairer. (Career Examination Ser.: C-243). (Cloth bdg. avail. on request). pap. 12.00 (ISBN 0-8373-0243-9). Natl Learning.

--Electronic Mechanic. (Career Examination Ser.: C-228). (Cloth bdg. avail. on request). pap. 12.00 (ISBN 0-8373-0228-5). Natl Learning.

ELECTRONIC APPARATUS AND APPLIANCES–PLASTIC EMBEDMENT

Business Communications Staff. Electrically Conductive Plastics, P-067. 1983. 1250.00 (ISBN 0-89336-325-1). BCC.

Licari, James J. Plastic Coating for Electronics. LC 79-26923. 398p. 1980. Repr. of 1970 ed. lib. bdg. 29.50 (ISBN 0-89874-107-6). Krieger.

ELECTRONIC APPARATUS AND APPLIANCES–RELIABILITY

Becker, Peter W. & Jensen, Finn. Design of Systems & Circuits for Maximum Reliability or Maximum Production Yield. (Illus.). 1977. text ed. 44.00 (ISBN 0-07-004230-6). McGraw.

Dummer, Geoffrey W. Electronic Reliability Electronics. Griffin, N. B., ed. 1966. 19.00 (ISBN 0-08-011448-2). Pergamon.

Saeks, Richard & Liberty, Stanley, eds. Rational Fault Analysis. (Electrical Engineering & Electronics Ser.: Vol. 1). 1977. 55.00 (ISBN 0-8247-6541-9). Dekker.

ELECTRONIC APPARATUS AND APPLIANCES–TESTING

Davis, B. P. The Economics of Automatic Testing: Electronics Components & Sub-Assemblies. 320p. 1982. 49.50 (ISBN 0-07-084584-0). McGraw.

Electronic Inspection & Test, 2 vols. 55.00x (ISBN 0-85083-034-6, Pub. by Engineering Ind). State Mutual Bk.

Environmental Stress Screening of Electronic Hardware: Proceedings of the 3rd National Conference-Workshop. LC 62-38584. 117p. 1984. pap. text ed. 25.00 (ISBN 0-915414-75-9). Inst Environ Sci.

Grevich, J. D. Testing Procedures for Automotive AC & DC Charging Systems. 1972. text ed. 26.90 (ISBN 0-07-024673-4). McGraw.

Heathkit-Zenith Educational Systems. Electronic Test Equipment. 512p. 1983. 21.95 (ISBN 0-13-252205-5); pap. 14.95 (ISBN 0-13-252197-0). P-H.

National Conference & Workshop, Mar. 1979. Environmental Stress Screening of Electronic Hardware: Proceedings. LC 62-38584. (Orig.). 1979. pap. text ed. 20.00 (ISBN 0-915414-59-7). Inst Environ Sci.

Saeks, Richard & Liberty, Stanley, eds. Rational Fault Analysis. (Electrical Engineering & Electronics Ser.: Vol. 1). 1977. 55.00 (ISBN 0-8247-6541-9). Dekker.

ELECTRONIC APPARATUS AND APPLIANCES, EFFECT OF RADIATION ON

Olesen, Henning L. Radiation Effects on Electronic Systems. LC 65-22183. 230p. 1966. 32.50x (ISBN 0-306-30228-4, Plenum Pr). Plenum Pub.

Srour, J. R., et al. Radiation Effects on & Dose Enhancement of Electronic Materials. LC 84-14770. (Illus.). 128p. 1985. 32.00 (ISBN 0-8155-1007-1). Noyes.

Van Lint, V. A., et al. Mechanisms of Radiation Effects in Electronic Materials. LC 79-9083. (A Wiley-Interscience Publication). pap. 93.30 (ISBN 0-317-26290-4, 2025181). Bks Demand UMI.

ELECTRONIC BATTLEFIELD

see Electronics in Military Engineering

ELECTRONIC BRAINS

see Artificial Intelligence; Computers; Conscious Automata

ELECTRONIC CALCULATING-MACHINES

see Computers

ELECTRONIC CAMERAS

see also Television Cameras

Abramson, Albert. Electronic Motion Pictures: A History of the Television Camera. LC 74-4663. (Telecommunications Ser). (Illus.). 228p. 1974. Repr. of 1955 ed. 24.50 (ISBN 0-405-06031-9). Ayer Co Pubs.

ELECTRONIC CERAMICS

Electrical & Magnetic Ceramics. 1982. 35.00x (ISBN 0-686-44607-0, Pub. by Brit Ceramic Soc England). State Mutual Bk.

Electrical Magnetic Ceramics, No. 2. 1982. 40.00x (ISBN 0-686-44593-7, Pub. by Brit Ceramic Soc England). State Mutual Bk.

Hench, L. & Dove, D., eds. Physics of Electronic Ceramics, Pt. B. (Ceramics & Glass, Science & Technology Ser: Vol. 2). 1971. 99.75 (ISBN 0-8247-1314-1). Dekker.

Norton, F. H. Fine Ceramics: Technology & Applications. LC 78-106. 524p. 1978. Repr. of 1970 ed. 34.50 (ISBN 0-88275-582-X). Krieger.

Scholes, Samuel R. Opportunities in Ceramic Engineering. LC 68-55528. 1968. pap. 1.25 (ISBN 0-8442-6494-6). Natl Textbk.

Yan, M. F. & Hever, A. H., eds. Advances in Ceramics: Additives & Interfaces in Electronic Ceramics. (Advances in Ceramics Ser.: Vol. 7). 1984. 45.00 (ISBN 0-916094-54-5). Am Ceramic.

ELECTRONIC CIRCUIT DESIGN

Bonebreak, Robert L. Practical Techniques of Electronic Circuit Design. LC 81-11394. 306p. 1982. 39.95 (ISBN 0-471-09612-1, Pub. by Wiley Interscience). Wiley.

Bowick, Christopher J. RF Circuit Design. LC 81-85517. 176p. 1982. pap. 22.95 (ISBN 0-672-21868-2). Sams.

Camenzind, Hans R. Electronic Integrated Systems Design. LC 78-12195. (Illus.). 342p. 1980. Repr. of 1972 ed. lib. bdg. 22.50 (ISBN 0-88275-763-6). Krieger.

Comer, David J. Electronic Design with Integrated Circuits. LC 80-23365. (Electrical Engineering Ser.). (Illus.). 416p. 1981. text ed. 27.95 (ISBN 0-201-03931-1); solutions manual 1.50 (ISBN 0-201-03932-X). Addison-Wesley.

--Modern Electronic Circuit Design. LC 75-9008. 704p. 1976. text ed. 36.95 (ISBN 0-201-01008-9). Addison-Wesley.

Daryanani, Gobind. Principles of Active Network Synthesis & Design. LC 76-20659. 495p. 1976. 45.50 (ISBN 0-471-19545-6). Wiley.

DeMaw, Doug. Practical RF Design Manual. (Illus.). 288p. 1982. 29.95 (ISBN 0-13-693754-3). P-H.

Electronics Magazine. Design Techniques for Electronics Engineers. 1978. 42.00 (ISBN 0-07-019158-1). McGraw.

Electronics Magazine & Weber, Samuel. Electronic Circuits Notebook: Proven Designs for Systems Applications. 344p. 1981. 37.50 (ISBN 0-07-019244-8). McGraw.

Glaser, Lance A. & Dobberpuhl, Daniel W. The Design & Analysis of VLSI Circuits. 556p. 1985. text ed. 39.95 (ISBN 0-201-12580-3); write for info. solution manual (ISBN 0-201-12581-1). Addison-Wesley.

Grinich, Victor. Introduction to Integrated Circuits. (Illus.). 672p. 1975. text ed. 48.00 (ISBN 0-07-024875-3). McGraw.

Hardy, Jim. High Frequency Circuit Design. (Illus.). 1979. ref. 28.95 (ISBN 0-8359-2824-1). Reston.

Hayt, William H. & Neudeck, Gerold W. Electronic Circuit Analysis & Design. 2nd ed. LC 83-80943. 416p. 1983. text ed. 38.95 (ISBN 0-395-32616-8); solution manual 3.00 (ISBN 0-395-32617-6). HM.

Hayward, W. H. Introduction to Radio Frequency Design. (Illus.). 384p. 1982. 34.95 (ISBN 0-13-494021-0). P-H.

Horowitz, Mannie. How to Design Circuits Using Semiconductors. LC 83-4920. (Illus.). 322p. (Orig.). 1983. 19.95 (ISBN 0-8306-0143-0); pap. 11.50 (ISBN 0-8306-1543-1, 1543). TAB Bks.

Johnson, David E. & Jayakumar, V. Operational Amplifier Circuits Design & Applications. (Illus.). 272p. 1982. 36.95 (ISBN 0-13-637447-6). P-H.

Leithauser, David. Programs for Electronic Circuit Design. (Illus.). 128p. (Orig.). 1984. Apple II, II. pap. 24.95 Spiral bound incl. disk (ISBN 0-88006-079-4, CC7409). Green Pub Inc.

Lenf, John D. Handbook of Simplified Solid State Circuit Design. 2nd ed. LC 77-23555. (Illus.). 1978. ref. 25.95 (ISBN 0-13-381715-6); pap. 12.95 (ISBN 0-13-381707-5). P-H.

Lenk, John D. Logic Designer's Manual. (Illus.). 512p. 1977. text ed. 28.95 (ISBN 0-87909-450-8). Reston.

Leonard, Vincent F., Jr. Passive Circuit Design. (Engineering Design Ser.). (Illus.). 583p. 1983. pap. text ed. 17.95 (ISBN 0-87119-020-6); 9.95 (ISBN 0-87119-022-2); lab manual 10.95 (ISBN 0-87119-021-4); looseleaf with experimental pts. 49.95 (ISBN 0-87119-019-2, EE-1001). Heathkit-Zenith Ed.

Lindsey, Darry. The Design & Drafting of Printed Circuits. 2nd ed. (Illus.). 400p. 1983. 48.95 (ISBN 0-07-037844-4). McGraw.

Lund, Preben. How to Design Printed Circuit Boards for UL Recognition. (Professional Printed Circuit Design Ser.). (Illus.). 32p. (Orig.). 1983. pap. 5.95 (ISBN 0-9601748-2-6, 10004). Bishop Graphics.

Mazda, F. F. Discrete Electronic Components. 200p. 1981. 44.50 (ISBN 0-521-23470-0). Cambridge U Pr.

Miller, Raymond E. Switching Theory, 2 vols. LC 78-11958. 618p. 1979. Repr. of 1965 ed. Set. lib. bdg. 35.00 (ISBN 0-88275-759-8). Vol. 1: Combinational Circuits. Vol. 2: Sequential Circuits & Machines. Krieger.

Motchenbacher, C. D. & Fitchen, F. C. Low-Noise Electronic Design. LC 72-8713. 1973. 52.50x (ISBN 0-471-61950-7, Pub. by Wiley-Interscience). Wiley.

Muroga, Saburo. VLSI Systems Design: When & How to Design Very Large Scale Integrated Circuits. LC 82-8598. 496p. 1982. 39.95x (ISBN 0-471-86090-5). Wiley.

O'Malley, John. Schaum's Outline of Basic Circuit Analysis. (Schaum's Outline Ser.). 400p. 1982. pap. 8.95 (ISBN 0-07-047820-1). McGraw.

Penfield, Paul, Jr. MARTHA User's Manual. 1971. pap. 9.95x (ISBN 0-262-66015-6). MIT Pr.

Rosenstein, Milton & Morris, Paul. Modern Electronic Devices: Circuit Design & Application. 1984. text ed. 34.95 (ISBN 0-8359-4548-0); solutions manual avail. (ISBN 0-8359-4549-9). Reston.

Seippel, Robert G. & Nelson, Roger L. Designing Circuits with IC Operational Amplifiers. LC 74-20344. (Illus.). pap. 27.30 (ISBN 0-317-08814-9, 2011568). Bks Demand UMI.

Sheingold, Daniel H., ed. Nonlinear Circuits Handbook. LC 75-42559. (Illus.). 1976. pap. text ed. 5.95 (ISBN 0-916550-01-X). Analog Devices.

Siliconix, Inc. Designing with Field Effect Transistors. (Illus.). 352p. 1981. 33.50 (ISBN 0-07-057449-9). McGraw.

Temes, Lloyd. Electronic Circuits for Technicians. 2nd ed. (Illus.). 1977. text ed. 29.95 (ISBN 0-07-063492-0). McGraw.

Warring, R. H. Electronic Components Handbook for Circuit Designers. (Illus.). 336p. 1983. o.p 21.95 (ISBN 0-8306-0493-6, 1493); pap. 13.95 (ISBN 0-8306-1493-1). TAB Bks.

Williams, Gerald E. Practical Transistor Circuit Design & Analysis. (Illus.). 420p. 1973. text ed. 31.00 (ISBN 0-07-070398-1). McGraw.

Wobschall, Darold. Circuit Design for Electronic Instrumentation: Analog & Digital Devices from Sensor to Display. LC 79-9084. (Illus.). 1979. 46.50 (ISBN 0-07-071230-1). McGraw.

ELECTRONIC CIRCUIT DESIGN–DATA PROCESSING

Becker, Peter W. & Jensen, Finn. Design of Systems & Circuits for Maximum Reliability or Maximum Production Yield. (Illus.). 1977. text ed. 44.00 (ISBN 0-07-004230-6). McGraw.

Brayton, R. & Spence, R. Sensitivity & Optimization. (Computer-aided Design of Electronic Circuits Ser.: No. 2). xii, 368p. 1980. 24.75 (ISBN 0-444-41929-2). Elsevier.

Bugnolo, Dimitri. Computer Programs for Electronic Analysis & Design. 1983. pap. text ed. 17.95 (ISBN 0-8359-0874-7). Reston.

Cuthbert, Thomas R., Jr. Circuit Design Using Personal Computers. LC 82-16015. 494p. 1983. 45.95x (ISBN 0-471-87700-X, Pub. by Wiley-Interscience). Wiley.

Grebene, Alan B. Bipolar & MOS Analog Integrated Circuit Design. 894p. 1983. 53.50x (ISBN 0-471-08529-4, Pub. by Wiley-Interscience). Wiley.

Sedra, Adel & Brackett, Peter. Filter Theory & Design: Active & Passive. (Illus.). 800p. 1978. 34.95 (ISBN 0-916460-14-2). Matrix Pub.

Texas Instruments Engineering Staff. High Speed CMOS Logic Circuits Data Book. LC 82-74480. 288p. 1983. pap. 11.75 (ISBN 0-89512-114-X, SCLD001A). Tex Instr Inc.

Vlach, Jiri & Singhal, Kishore. Computer Methods for Curcuit Analysis & Design. (Illus.). 624p. 1983. 42.50 (ISBN 0-442-28108-0). Van Nos Reinhold.

ELECTRONIC CIRCUITS

see also Bridge Circuits; Computers–Circuits; Electron Tubes; Electronic Digital Computers–Circuits; Integrated Circuits; Printed Circuits; Semiconductors; Transistor Circuits

Bateson, John T. In-Circuit Testing. (Illus.). 256p. 1985. 32.95 (ISBN 0-442-21284-4). Van Nos Reinhold.

Bedford, Burnice D. & Hoft, R. G. Principles of Inverter Circuits. LC 64-20078. pap. 107.30 (ISBN 0-317-09138-7, 2020596). Bks Demand UMI.

Boylestad, Robert & Nashelsky, Louis. Electronic Devices & Circuit Theory. 3rd ed. (Illus.). 768p. 1982. 34.95 (ISBN 0-13-250324-7). P-H.

Brown, Robert M. & Lawrence, Paul. How to Read Electronic Circuit Diagrams. LC 72-105970. 1970. 13.95 (ISBN 0-8306-0510-X); pap. 7.95 (ISBN 0-8306-9510-9, 510). TAB Bks.

Business Communications Staff. Rigid & Flexible Printed Circuit Boards. 1985. pap. 1750.00 (ISBN 0-89336-451-7, GO67R). BCC.

Bylander, E. G. Electronic Displays. LC 78-31849. (Illus.). 1979. 35.00 (ISBN 0-07-009510-8). McGraw.

Casasent, David. Electronic Circuits. (Illus.). 400p. 1982. pap. 13.95 (ISBN 0-13-250233-X). P-H.

Chirlian, Paul M. Analysis & Design of Integrated Electronic Circuits. (Illus.). 1072p. 1981. text ed. 38.75 scp (ISBN 0-06-041266-6, HarpC); solutions's manual avail. (ISBN 0-06-361176-7). Har-Row.

Chow, Woo F. Principles of Tunnel Diode Circuits. LC 64-20080. 387p. 1964. text ed. 24.50 (ISBN 0-471-15615-9, Pub. by Wiley). Krieger.

Chua, L. & Lin, P. Computer-Aided Analysis of Electronic Circuits: Algorithms & Computational Techniques. 1975. 41.95 (ISBN 0-13-165415-2). P-H.

Colclaser, Roy A., et al. Electronic Circuit Analysis: Basic Principles. LC 83-21743. 574p. 1984. text ed. 39.50 (ISBN 0-471-86626-1). Wiley.

Collins, Raymond A., ed. The Giant Handbook of Electronic Circuits. (Illus.). 882p. 1980. pap. 19.95 (ISBN -08306-9662-8, 1300). TAB Bks.

Davidse, J. Integration of Analogue Electronic Circuit. 1979. 55.00 (ISBN 0-12-204450-9). Acad Pr.

DeFrance, J. J. Communications Electronics Circuits. 2nd ed. LC 71-187116. 1972. text ed. 37.95 (ISBN 0-03-083139-3, HoltC). HR&W.

--General Electronic Circuits. 2nd ed. LC 75-25718. 1976. text ed. 28.95 (ISBN 0-03-015481-2, HoltC). HR&W.

Douglas-Young, John. Illustrated Encyclopedic Dictionary of Electronic Circuits. LC 82-23067. 444p. 1983. 29.95 (ISBN 0-13-450734-7). P-H.

Electronics: Circuits & Systems. 39.95 (ISBN 0-672-21984-0, 21984). Sams.

Fair, Michael L., ed. Master Handbook of One Thousand & One More Practical Electronic Circuits. (Illus.). 1979. pap. 19.95 (ISBN 0-8306-7804-2, 804). TAB Bks.

Fortino, Andre. Fundamentals of Computer Aided Analysis of Integrated Circuits Devices & Processes. 1983. pap. text ed. 18.95 (ISBN 0-8359-2120-4). Reston.

Genn, Robert C. Illustrated Guide to Practical Solid State Circuits...with Experiments & Projects. 335p. 1983. 21.95 (ISBN 0-13-450643-X). P-H.

Gibson, J. R. Electronic Logic Circuits. 2nd ed. 135p. 1983. pap. text ed. 13.95 (ISBN 0-7131-3407-0). E Arnold.

Goodman. How to Troubleshoot & Repair Electronic Circuits. 378p. 1981. 18.95 (ISBN 0-8306-9656-3); pap. 13.50 (ISBN 0-8306-1218-1, 1218). TAB Bks.

Goodman, Robert. Indexed Guide to Modern Electronic Circuits. LC 83-18752. 216p. 1984. pap. text ed. 14.95 (ISBN 0-89874-683-3). Krieger.

Graeme, Jerald G. Designing with Operational Amplifiers: Applications, Alternatives. (Illus.). 1977. 44.50 (ISBN 0-07-023891-X). McGraw.

Graf, Rudolf F. The Encyclopedia of Electronic Circuits. (Illus.). 768p. 1985. 50.00 (ISBN 0-8306-0938-5, 1938); pap. 29.95 (ISBN 0-8306-1938-0). TAB Bks.

Grantham, Donald J. Basic Electronic Devices & Circuits. LC 77-22488. (The Grantham Electronics-with-Mathematics Ser.: Vol. 4). (Illus.). 1977. pap. text ed. 18.95x (ISBN 0-915668-04-1). G S E Pubns.

Grob, Bernard. Electronic Circuits & Applications. LC 81-14298. (Illus.). 576p. 1982. text ed. 34.00 (ISBN 0-07-024931-8). McGraw.

Grossner, Nathan. Transformers for Electronic Circuits. 2nd ed. (Illus.). 400p. 1983. 46.95 (ISBN 0-07-024979-2). McGraw.

Hallmark, Clayton L. The Master IC Cookbook. (Illus.). 476p. (Orig.). 1980. 21.95 (ISBN 0-8306-9964-3); pap. 14.95 (ISBN 0-8306-1199-1, 1199). TAB Bks.

Harris, Frank. Electronic Circuit Devices. (Avionics Technician Training Course Ser.). 261p. (Orig.). 1983. pap. 7.95 (ISBN 0-89100-192-1, EA-192-1). Aviation Maintenance.

Hayt, William H. & Neudeck, Gerold W. Electronic Circuit Analysis & Design. 2nd ed. LC 83-80943. 416p. 1983. text ed. 38.95 (ISBN 0-395-32616-8); solution manual 3.00 (ISBN 0-395-32617-6). HM.

Hazeltine, Barrett. Introduction to Electronic Circuits & Applications: Preliminary Edition. 384p. (Orig.). 1980. pap. text ed. 15.95 (ISBN 0-8403-2182-1). Kendall-Hunt.

Heath Company Staff. Electronic Circuits. rev. ed. (Fundamental Electronics Ser.). (Illus.). 715p. 1982. looseleaf with experimental pts. 64.95 (ISBN 0-87119-010-9, EE-3104A). Heathkit-Zenith Ed.

--Electronic Circuits. (Fundamental Electronics Ser.). (Illus.). 448p. 1978. pap. text ed. 19.95 (ISBN 0-87119-007-9); tchr's ed. 9.95 (ISBN 0-87119-009-5); lab manual 10.95 (ISBN 0-87119-008-7). Heathkit-Zenith Ed.

--Linear Circuits. rev. ed. (Circuit Files Ser.). (Illus.). 89p. 1981. Repr. of 1980 ed. looseleaf with experimental pts. 49.95 (ISBN 0-87119-002-8, EH-801). Heathkit-Zenith Ed.

--TTL & CMOS Circuits. (Circuit Files Ser.). (Illus.). 124p. looseleaf with experimental pts. 59.95 (ISBN 0-87119-001-X, EH-702). Heathkit-Zenith Ed.

Heathkit-Zenith Educational Systems. Electronics Circuits. 352p. 1983. 19.95 (ISBN 0-13-250183-X); pap. 12.95 (ISBN 0-13-250175-9). P-H.

Helms, H. L. Contemporary Electronics Circuits Deskbook. 224p. 1986. price not set (ISBN 0-07-027980-2). McGraw.

Herrington, Donald. How to Read Schematic Diagrams. 3rd ed. LC 74-33834. (Illus.). 192p. 1975. pap. 8.95 (ISBN 0-672-21127-0). Sams.

Holt, C. A. Electronic Circuits, Vol. 2. 550p. 1985. pap. write for info. (ISBN 0-471-81072-X). Wiley.

--Electronic Circuits: Digital & Analog, Vol. 1. 450p. 1985. pap. price not set (ISBN 0-471-86544-3). Wiley.

Holt, Charles A. Electronic Circuits: Digital & Analog. LC 77-11654. 857p. 1978. 44.00 (ISBN 0-471-02313-2); tchr's manual avail. (ISBN 0-471-03044-9). Wiley.

Hughes, M. & Colwell, M. Printed Circuit Assembly. (Newnes Constructor's Guide Ser.). (Illus.). 1976. pap. 7.50 (ISBN 0-408-00203-4, 5446-7, Pub. by Newnes-Butterworth). Hayden.

Jackson, Herbert W. Introduction to Electric Circuits. 5th ed. (Illus.). 736p. 1981. text ed. 34.95 (ISBN 0-13-481432-0). P-H.

Jiles, Charles W. & Smith, Charles V., Jr. Introduction to Electric Circuits. 1985. text ed. 33.95 (ISBN 0-8359-3214-1); tchr's. manual avail. (ISBN 0-8359-3215-X). Reston.

Jones, M. H. A Practical Introduction to Electric Circuits. LC 76-11083. (Illus.). 1977. 49.50 (ISBN 0-521-21291-X); pap. 16.95x (ISBN 0-521-29087-2). Cambridge U Pr.

--A Practical Introduction to Electronic Circuits. 2nd ed. 275p. Date not set. price not set (ISBN 0-521-30785-6); pap. price not set (ISBN 0-521-31312-0). Cambridge U Pr.

King, Gordon J. Guide to Printed Circuits. 480p. 1980. 25.00x (ISBN 0-686-87304-1, Pub. by K Dickson). State Mutual Bk.

King, R. A. Electronic Circuits & System Solutions. 103p. 1976. pap. 6.95 (ISBN 0-470-01399-0). Halsted Pr.

Klein, Barry. Electronic Music Circuits. LC 81-84278. 16.95 (ISBN 0-672-21833-X). Sams.

Kosow, Irving L. Study Guide in Alternating Current Circuits: A Personalized System of Instruction. LC 77-22152. (Electronic Technology Ser.). pap. 128.80 (ISBN 0-317-10110-2, 2015180). Bks Demand UMI.

Lenk, John D. Handbook of Practical Electronic Circuits. (Illus.). 352p. 1982. 27.95 (ISBN 0-13-380741-X). P-H.

Long, W. E. & Evans, P. L. Electronic Principles & Circuits: An Introduction to Electronics for the Technicians. LC 73-11096. 432p. 1974. 32.95 (ISBN 0-471-54455-8); pap. text ed. 5.00x tchrs' manual o.s. (ISBN 0-471-54454-X). Wiley.

Loveday, George C. & Seidman, Arthur H. Troubleshooting Solid State Circuits. LC 80-21954. 110p. 1981. pap. text ed. 13.95 (ISBN 0-471-08371-2). Wiley.

Lowenberg, Edwin C. Electronic Circuits. (Schaum's Outline Ser). (Orig.). 1967. pap. 8.95 (ISBN 0-07-038835-0). McGraw.

McCray, James A. & Cahill, Thomas A. Electronic Circuit Analysis for Scientists. LC 72-8986. (Illus.). pap. 77.00 (ISBN 0-317-08897-1, 2012462). Bks Demand UMI.

MacDonald, Lorne. Basic Solid State Electronic Circuit Analysis Through Experimentation. 488p. 1981. pap. 16.00x (ISBN 0-911908-12-9). Tech Ed Pr.

--Basic Solid State Electronic Circuit Analysis Through Experimentation. 2nd ed. 488p. 1984. pap. 17.50 (ISBN 0-317-20395-9). Tech Ed Pr.

MacNeal, Richard H. Electric Circuit Analogies for Elastic Structures. LC 62-17465. (Airplane, Missile, & Spacecraft Structures Ser.: Vol. 2). pap. 69.50 (ISBN 0-317-09604-4, 2007401). Bks Demand UMI.

Malcolm, Douglas R., Jr. Fundamentals of Electronics. 1983. text ed. 24.00x (ISBN 0-534-01179-9). Breton Pubs.

Manera, Anthony S. Solid-State Electronic Circuits for Engineering Technology. (Illus.). 672p. 1973. text ed. 34.00 (ISBN 0-07-039871-2). McGraw.

Markus, John. Communications Circuits Ready-Reference. (Illus.). 160p. 1982. pap. 12.50 (ISBN 0-07-040460-7). McGraw.

--Electronic Circuits Manual. 1971. 68.50 (ISBN 0-07-040444-5). McGraw.

--Electronics Projects Ready-Reference. (Illus.). 180p. 1982. pap. 12.50 (ISBN 0-07-040459-3). McGraw.

--Guidebook of Electronic Circuits. (Illus.). 992p. 1974. 75.00 (ISBN 0-07-040445-3). McGraw.

--Modern Electronic Circuits Reference Manual. (Illus.). 1980. 74.95 (ISBN 0-07-040446-1). McGraw.

--Sourcebook of Electronic Circuits. 1967. 76.95 (ISBN 0-07-040443-7). McGraw.

--Special Circuits Ready-Reference. (Illus.). 230p. 1982. pap. 12.50 (ISBN 0-07-040461-5). McGraw.

Marrese, Michael A., ed. Advances in Electronic Circuit Packaging: Proceedings of the 4th International Electronic Circuit Packaging Symposium, Vol. 4. LC 72-187719. pap. 125.50 (ISBN 0-317-09084-4, 2020718). Bks Demand UMI.

Meindl, James D. Micropower Circuits. LC 68-28502. (Illus.). pap. 64.50 (ISBN 0-317-08756-8, 2010178). Bks Demand UMI.

Millman, Jacob & Taub, H. Pulse, Digital & Switching Waveforms. 1965. text ed. 49.95 (ISBN 0-07-042386-5). McGraw.

Mims. One Hundred & Three Projects for Electronics Experimenters. 308p. 1981. pap. 11.50 (ISBN 0-8306-1249-1, 1249). TAB Bks.

Mottershead, Allen. Electronic Devices & Circuits: An Introduction. LC 72-93687. pap. 160.00 (ISBN 0-317-08651-0, 2007756). Bks Demand UMI.

O'Malley, John. Schaum's Outline of Basic Circuit Analysis. (Schaum's Outline Ser.). 400p. 1982. pap. 8.95 (ISBN 0-07-047820-1). McGraw.

O'Malley, John R. Circuit Analysis. 1980. text ed. 31.95 (ISBN 0-13-133827-7). P-H.

Phelps, Roland S. Seven Hundred & Fifty Practical Electronic Circuits. (Illus.). 576p. (Orig.). 1983. 24.95 (ISBN 0-8306-2499-6, 1499); pap. 14.95 (ISBN 0-8306-1499-0). TAB Bks.

Prewitt, Roger W. & Fardo, Stephen W. Electronic Devices & Circuit Applications. 1985. text ed. 29.95 (ISBN 0-8359-1645-6). Reston.

Refioglu, H. I. Electronic Display. LC 83-16753. 1983. 54.50 (ISBN 0-87942-169-X, PC01628). Inst Electrical.

Rooney, Victor M. Analysis of Linear Circuits: Passive & Active Components. 608p. 1975. text ed. 28.95 (ISBN 0-675-08886-0). Merrill.

Rosine, Lawrence L., ed. Advances in Electronic Circuit Packaging: Proceedings of the 5th International Electronic Circuit Packaging Symposium Held at Boulder, Colorado, August 19-21, 1964, Vol. 5. LC 72-187718. pap. 75.80 (ISBN 0-317-09086-0, 2020719). Bks Demand UMI.

Ross, W. MacLeod. Modern Circuit Technology. 1981. 90.00x (ISBN 0-901994-59-6, Pub. by Portcullio Pr). State Mutual Bk.

Sabbagh, Elias M. Circuit Analysis. LC 61-6789. (Illus.). pap. 116.30 (ISBN 0-317-08887-4, 2012458). Bks Demand UMI.

Salvati, M. J. How to Custom Design Your Solid-State Equipment. (Illus.). 160p. 1974. pap. 7.75 (ISBN 0-8104-5585-4). Hayden.

Schilling, Donald & Belove, Charles. Electronic Circuits: Discrete & Integrated. 2nd ed. (Electical & Electronic Engineering). (Illus.). 1979. text ed. 44.00 (ISBN 0-07-055294-0). McGraw.

Seidman, Arthur H. & Waintraub, Jack L. Electronics: Devices, Discrete & Integrated Circuits. (Electronics Technology Ser.). 1977. text ed. 31.95 (ISBN 0-675-08494-6). Additional supplements may be obtained from publisher. Merrill.

Senturia, Stephen D. & Wedlock, Bruce D. Electronic Circuits & Applications. LC 74-7404. 623p. 1975. text ed. 41.45 (ISBN 0-471-77630-0); avail. tchr's manual (ISBN 0-471-77632-7). Wiley.

Sessions, Ken, ed. Master Handbook of One Thousand & One Practical Electronic Circuits. LC 75-31458. 602p. 1975. pap. 19.50 (ISBN 0-8306-4800-3, 800). TAB Bks.

Sheingold, Daniel H., ed. Nonlinear Circuits Handbook. LC 75-42559. (Illus.). 1976. pap. text ed. 5.95 (ISBN 0-916550-01-X). Analog Devices.

Sinclair, Ian R. Electronics Fault Diagnosis. 144p. 1980. 10.00x (ISBN 0-85242-530-9, Pub. by K Dickson). State Mutual Bk.

--Understanding Electronic Circuits. 1980. 17.00x (ISBN 0-85242-285-7, Pub. by K Dickson). State Mutual Bk.

Smith, R. J. Electronics Circuits & Devices, Vol. 1. 2nd ed. LC 80-13937. 494p. 1984. 40.50 (ISBN 0-471-05344-9). Wiley.

Soderstrand, Michael A. Electronic Circuits & Systems. 424p. 1981. pap. text ed. 28.00 (ISBN 0-8403-2581-9). Kendall-Hunt.

Stonham, T. J. Digital Logic Techniques. 1984. pap. 14.95 (ISBN 0-442-30595-8). Van Nos Reinhold.

Su, Kendall L. A Collection of Solved Problems in Circuits, Electronics, & Signal Analysis, Vol. 1. 96p. 1980. pap. text ed. 7.95 (ISBN 0-8403-2262-3). Kendall-Hunt.

--A Collection of Solved Problems in Circuits, Electronics & Signal Analysis, Vol. 2. 96p. 1981. pap. text ed. 7.50 (ISBN 0-8403-2486-3). Kendall-Hunt.

Sze, S. M. Physics of Semiconductor Devices. 2nd ed. LC 81-213. 868p. 1981. 54.95 (ISBN 0-471-05661-8, Pub. by Wiley-Interscience). Wiley.

Texas Instruments Engineering Staff. Linear Circuits Data Book, 1983. 920p. 1983. pap. text ed. 14.95 (ISBN 0-89512-089-5, SLYD001). Tex Instr Inc.

Tietze, U. & Schenk, C. Advanced Electronic Circuits. LC 78-13342. (Illus.). 1978. 58.00 (ISBN 0-387-08750-8). Springer-Verlag.

Traister, Robert J. Beginner's Guide to Reading Schematics. (Illus.). 140p. 1983. 14.95 (ISBN 0-8306-0136-8); pap. 9.25 (ISBN 0-8306-1536-9, 1536). TAB Bks.

Trick, Timothy N. An Introduction to Circuit Analysis. LC 77-10843. 510p. 1978. 45.00 (ISBN 0-471-88850-8); solutions manual avail. (ISBN 0-471-03041-4). Wiley.

Van Valkenburgh, Nooger & Neville Inc. Basic Electronic Circuits, British Edition, 2 pts. 1964. Set. pap. text ed. 9.60 (ISBN 0-685-07563-X); pap. text ed. 4.80 ea.; tests & foreign language eds. avail. (ISBN 0-685-07565-6). Brolet.

Veronis, Andrew. The Complete Microprocessor Circuits Reference Manual. 1985. text ed. 39.95 (ISBN 0-8359-0806-2). Reston.

Vlach, Jiri & Singhal, Kishore. Computer Methods for Curcuit Analysis & Design. (Illus.). 624p. 1983. 42.50 (ISBN 0-442-28108-0). Van Nos Reinhold.

Wait, John V., et al. Introduction to Operational & Amplifier Theory Applications. (Illus.). 480p. 1975. text ed. 48.00 (ISBN 0-07-067765-4). McGraw.

Walker, Gerald A., ed. Advances in Electronic Circuit Packaging: Proceedings of the First Electronic Circuit Packaging Symposium Held at Boulder, Colorado, Vol. 1. 2nd ed. LC 72-187721. pap. 97.30 (ISBN 0-317-09113-1, 2020717). Bks Demand UMI.

Watts, Don. A Catalog of Operational Transfer Functions. LC 76-25745. (Reference Library of Science & Technology: Vol. 9). (Illus.). 1977. lib. bdg. 32.00 (ISBN 0-8240-9901-X). Garland Pub.

Wickes, William E. Logic Design with Integrated Circuits. LC 68-21185. pap. 65.50 (ISBN 0-317-28030-9, 2055721). Bks Demand UMI.

Worden, Leslie E. Theory, Design & Application of Electronic Devices & Circuits. (Illus.). 700p. text ed. write for info. (ISBN 0-89894-014-1). Advocate Pub Group.

ELECTRONIC COMPUTER–DEBUGGING

see Debugging (Electronic Computers)

ELECTRONIC COMPUTER–PROGRAMMING

see Programming (Electronic Computers)

ELECTRONIC COMPUTERS

see Computers

ELECTRONIC CONTROL

see also Machine Tools–Numerical Control; Radio Control

Auslander, D. M., ed. Case Studies in Computer Control. 87p. 1978. 18.00 (ISBN 0-685-66791-X, H00117). ASME.

Chorafas, Dimitrius N. Control Systems Functions & Programming Approaches, 2 Vols. (Mathematics in Science & Engineering: Vol. 27A & B). 1966. Vol. A. 76.00 (ISBN 0-12-174061-7); Vol. B. 63.00 (ISBN 0-12-174062-5). Acad Pr.

D'Azzo, John & Houpis, Constantine. Linear Control System Analysis & Design. 2nd ed. (Electrical Engineering Ser.). (Illus.). 864p. 1981. text ed. 45.00 (ISBN 0-07-016183-6). McGraw.

Electronic Control & Monitoring of Off-Highway Equipment, 6 papers. 84p. 1982. pap. 18.00 (ISBN 0-89883-291-8, SP520). Soc Auto Engineers.

Eveleigh, Virgil. Introduction to Control Systems Design. (Electrical & Electronic Engineering Ser.). 1971. text ed. 48.00 (ISBN 0-07-019773-3). McGraw.

Froehr, Friedrich & Orttenburger, Fritz. Introduction to Electronic Control Engineering. 220p. 1981. 49.95 (ISBN 0-471-26200-5, Pub. by Wiley-Interscience). Wiley.

IFAC Symposium, New Delhi, India, Jan. 1981. Theory & Application of Digital Control: Proceedings. Mahalanabis, A. K., ed. (IFAC Proceedings Ser.). (Illus.). 670p. 1982. 165.00 (ISBN 0-08-027618-0). Pergamon.

IFAC Symposium, 2nd, Dusseldorf, BRD, Oct. 1977. Control in Power Electronics & Electrical Drives: Proceedings. Leonhard, W., ed. 1038p. 1978. 230.00 (ISBN 0-08-022014-2). Pergamon.

Isermann, R. Digital Control Systems. (Illus.). 566p. 1981. pap. 48.50 (ISBN 0-387-10728-2). Springer-Verlag.

Jacquot. Modern Digital Control Systems. (Electrical Engineering & Electronics Ser.: Vol. 11). 384p. 1981. 42.00 (ISBN 0-8247-1322-2). Dekker.

Leonhard, W. Control of Electrical Drives. (Electric Energy Systems & Engineering Ser.). 315p. 1985. 49.00 (ISBN 0-387-13650-9). Springer-Verlag.

Macfarlane, Alistair G. Frequency-Response Methods in Control Systems. LC 79-90572. 523p. 1979. 53.95 (ISBN 0-471-06486-6, Pub. by Wiley-Interscience). Wiley.

New Developments in Electronic Engine Management. (Illus.). 1984. pap. 35.00 (ISBN 0-89883-343-4, SP572). Soc Auto Engineers.

Phillips, Charles L. & Nagle, H. Troy, Jr. Digital Control System Analysis & Design. (Illus.). 608p. 1984. 39.95 (ISBN 0-13-212043-7). P-H.

Ryan, E. P. Optimal Relay & Saturating Control Systems Synthesis. (IEE Control Engineering Ser.: No. 14). 352p. 1982. 103.50 (ISBN 0-906048-56-7, CE014). Inst Elect Eng.

Schmitt, Neil M. & Farwell, Robert F. Understanding Electronic Control of Automation Systems. Luecke, G. & Battle, C., eds. LC 81-85603. (Understanding Ser.). (Illus.). 280p. 1983. pap. 6.95 (ISBN 0-89512-052-6, LCB6641). Tex Instr Inc.

Spencer, Donald D. Introduction to Information Processing. 3rd ed. 650p. 1981. text ed. 26.95 (ISBN 0-675-08073-8); basic supplement 4.95 (ISBN 0-675-09917-X). Additional supplements maybe obtained from publisher. Merrill.

Stern, Marc. Automotive Computers. 200p. 1984. 19.95 (ISBN 0-13-054651-8); pap. 12.95 (ISBN 0-13-054644-5). P-H.

Tedeschi, Frank P. How To Design, Build, & Use Electronic Control Systems. (Illus.). 308p. 1981. pap. 10.95 (ISBN 0-8306-1229-7). TAB Bks.

Texas Instruments Inc. Electronic Power Control & Digital Techniques. (Illus.). 1976. 42.50 (ISBN 0-07-063752-0). McGraw.

Weathers, Tom & Hunter, Claud. Automotive Computers & Control Systems. (Illus.). 256p. 1984. text ed. 24.95 (ISBN 0-13-054693-3). P-H.

Willsky, Alan S. Digital Signal Processing & Control & Estimation Theory: Points of Tangency, Areas of Intersection, & Parallel Directions. 1979. 37.50x (ISBN 0-262-23091-7). MIT Pr.

Wilson, J. A. Industrial Electronics & Control. LC 78-7424. 528p. 1978. text ed. 26.95 (ISBN 0-574-21515-8, 13-4515). SRA.

ELECTRONIC DATA PROCESSING

see also Analog-To-Digital Converters; Artificial Intelligence; Compiling (Electronic Computers); Computer Networks; Data Tapes; Data Transmission Systems; Debugging (Electronic Computers); Data Base Management; List Processing (Electronic Computers); Machine Accounting; Machine Tools–Numerical Control; Machine-Readable Data Files; Optical Data Processing; Programming (Electronic Computers); Programming Languages (Electronic Computers); Real-Time Data Processing

also subdivision Data Processing under subjects, e.g. Business–Data Processing

AASHTO Administrative Subcommittee on Computer Technology. Computer Systems Index. 1985. 15.00 (ISBN 0-686-20962-1, CSI). AASHTO.

Abraham, F. & Tiller, W. A., eds. An Introduction to Computer Simulation in Applied Science. LC 72-83047. 220p. 1972. 29.50 (ISBN 0-306-30579-8, Plenum Pr). Plenum Pub.

Adams, James M. Data Processing: An Introduction. LC 81-66793. (Data Processing Ser.). (Illus.). 253p. 1982. text ed. 14.60 (ISBN 0-8273-1616-X); tchr's. guide 5.25 (ISBN 0-8273-1617-8). Delmar.

Adler, Anne G. & Baber, Elizabeth A. Retrospective Conversion: From Cards to Computer. LC 84-81656. (Library Hi-Tech: No. 2). 324p. 1984. 39.50 (ISBN 0-87650-177-3). Pierian.

Foster, Caxton C. Content Addressable Parallel Processors. (Computer Science Ser.). 233p. 1976. 19.95 (ISBN 0-442-22433-8). Van Nos Reinhold.

Frank, Michael R. The Effective EDP Manager. LC 80-65876. pap. 51.80 (ISBN 0-317-20737-7, 2023895). Bks Demand UMI.

Friend, G. E., et al. Understanding Data Communications. LC 84-50867. (Understanding Ser.). (Illus.). 256p. 1984. pap. text ed. 14.95 (ISBN 0-89512-158-1, LCB8483). Tex Instr Inc.

Fuori, William M. & Tedesco, Dominick. Introduction to Information Processing. (Illus.). 352p. 1983. pap. text ed. 9.95 (ISBN 0-13-484634-6); text ed. 26.95 (ISBN -13-484601-X). P-H.

--Introduction to Information Processing: Study Guide. (Illus.). 80p. 1983. pap. 3.95 (ISBN 0-13-484659-1). P H.

Gane, C. & Sarson, T. Structured Systems Analysis: Tools & Techniques. 1979. 37.50 (ISBN 0-13-854547-2). P-H.

Gaydasch, Alexander. Principles of Electronic Data Processing Management. 300p. 1982. text ed. 26.95 (ISBN 0-8359-5604-0); instr's. manual free (ISBN 0-8359-5605-9). Reston.

Gear, C. W. Computer Organization & Programming. 4th ed. (Computer Science Ser.). 432p. 1985. 39.95 (ISBN 0-07-023049-8). McGraw.

General Electric Company. Data Processing Self-Study Kit. Incl. An Introduction to Electronic Data Processing. 256p. (ISBN 0-932078-38-9); An Introduction to Magnetic Discs. 98p. (ISBN 0-932078-39-7); An Introduction to Integrated Data Store. 97p. (ISBN 0-932078-40-0); Time-Sharing's BASIC Language. 250p. (ISBN 0-932078-41-9). 1970. pap. 8.50 ea. GE Tech Prom & Train.

Gesellschaft fuer Informatik: 3 Jahrestagung, Hamburg 1973. Lecture Notes in Computer Science, Vol. 1. Bauer, W., ed. xi, 508p. 1973. pap. 21.00 (ISBN 0-387-06473-7). Springer Verlag.

Gilb, Tom & Weinberg, Gerald M. Humanized Input: Techniques for Reliable Keyed Input. LC 83-62495. 283p. 1977. pap. 24.95 (ISBN 0-89435-073-0). QED Info Sci.

Glib, Tom. Critical-Factor Communication & Control. LC 84-61514. (Illus.). pap. cancelled (ISBN 0-89435-122-2, CF 1222). QED Info Sci.

Goldberg, Robert & Lorin, Harold, eds. The Economics of Information Processing. 1982. Vol. I. 27.50 (ISBN 0-686-98049-2); Vol. II. 25.00 (ISBN 0-686-98050-6). Telecom Lib.

Gore, Marvin R. & Stubbe, John W. Computers & Information Systems. 2nd ed. (Illus.). 512p. 1984. text ed. 32.95 (ISBN 0-07-023807-3). McGraw.

Gray, Paul. A Student Guide to IFPS. 384p. 1983. 19.95 (ISBN 0-07-024322-0). McGraw.

Greenbaum, Joan M. In the Name of Efficiency: Management Theory & Shopfloor Practice in Data Processing Work. 210p. 1979. 27.95 (ISBN 0-87722-151-0). Temple U Pr.

Gregory, Laura A. A Study of Data Base Processor Technology. LC 79-66678. (Data Base Monograph: No. 8). (Illus.). 77p. (Orig.). pap. 15.00 (ISBN 0-89435-035-8). QED Info Sci.

Groves, David N. & Poirot, James L. Computers & Data Processing. (Illus.). 1978. text ed. 12.95 (ISBN 0-88408-101-X). Sterling Swift.

Guide on the Global Data Processing System. 154p. 1983. pap. 21.00 (ISBN 92-63-12305-5, W546, WMO). Unipub.

Guide on the Global Data-Processing System, Vol. 1. (Illus.). 1976. pap. 32.00 (ISBN 0-685-68974-3, W108, WMO). Unipub.

Guide to Global Data-Processing System: Preparation of Synoptic Weather Charts & Diagrams, Supplement, Vol. 2. (Publications Ser.: 305). pap. 12.00 (W109, WMO). Unipub.

Gwartney, James D. & Stroup, Richard. Computer Test Bank for Economics: Private & Public Choice. 3rd ed. 1983. text ed. 125.00 (ISBN 0-12-311044-0). Acad Pr.

Handbook on Data Processing Methods, Pt. 2. 1962. pap. 6.75 (ISBN 0-685-36302-3, F221, FAO). Unipub.

Hardgrave, Terry, et al. Database Concepts. 1985. 19.50 (ISBN 0-538-10960-2, J96). SW Pub.

Harrison, William L. Computers & Information Processing: An Introduction. (Illus.). 650p. 1985. text ed. 26.95 (ISBN 0-314-85245-X). West Pub.

Hempel & Solem. Introduction to Data Processing for the New Age: Syllabus. 1977. pap. text ed. 8.95 (ISBN 0-89420-034-8, 223020); cassette recordings 140.65 (ISBN 0-89420-138-7, 223000). Natl Book.

Hestenes, Marshall & Hill, Richard. Algebra & Trigonometry with Calculators. (Illus.). 512p. 1981. text ed. 29.95 (ISBN 0-13-021857-X). P-H.

Hofeditz, Calvin A. Computers & Data Processing Made Simple. LC 78-22635. (Made Simple Ser.). (Illus.). 1979. pap. 4.95 (ISBN 0-385-14945-X). Doubleday.

Hopgood, F. R. Compiling Techniques. (Computer Monograph Ser: Vol. 8). 142p. 1969. 32.50 (ISBN 0-444-19769-9). Elsevier.

Huber, Norman F. Data Communications: The Business Aspects. 356p. 1983. looseleaf bound 59.95 (ISBN 0-935506-05-5). Carnegie Pr.

Huges, Patricia & Ochi, Kaz. The Power of VisiPlot-VisiCalc-VisiFile. 154p. 1982. pap. 14.95 (ISBN 0-13-687368-5). P-H.

Information Processing from the Manager's Viewpoint. (Special Interest Packages Ser.). pap. 23.00 (ISBN 0-317-06208-5, PO22); pap. 18.00 member. Assn Inform & Image Mgmt.

Infotech. Data Base Technology, 2 vols. (Infotech Computer State of the Art Reports). 820p. 1978. Set. 125.00 (ISBN 0-08-028541-4). Pergamon.

--Distributed Processing, 2 vols. (Infotech Computer State of the Art Reports). 600p. 1977. Set. pap. 105.00 (ISBN 0-08-028526-0). Pergamon.

Inmon, W. H. Integrating Data Processing Systems: In Theory & in Practice. (P-H Series in Data Processing Management). (Illus.). 288p. 1984. text ed. 36.95 (ISBN 0-13-468991-7). P-H.

Inmon, William H. Management Control of Data Processing: Preventing Management-By-Crisis. (Illus.). 384p. 1983. text ed. 36.95 (ISBN 0-13-549635-7). P-H.

Innes, A. E. Data Processing for Business Studies. (Illus.). 256p. 1983. pap. text ed. 17.50x (ISBN 0-7121-0421-6). Trans-Atlantic.

Instructions for the Submission of Input for OCR Processing. (INIS Reference Ser.: No. 19). 96p. 1981. pap. 13.00 (ISBN 92-0-178281-0, IN19/R0, IAEA). Unipub.

International Computation Centre. Symbolic Languages in Data Processing. 864p. 1962. 226.75 (ISBN 0-677-10200-3). Gordon.

International Conference on Information Sciences & Systems, 1st, Patras, Greece, Aug. 1976. Applications & Research in Information Systems & Sciences: Proceedings, 3 vols. new ed. Lainiotis, Demetrios G. & Tzannes, Nicolaos, eds. LC 77-15000. (Illus.). 920p. 1977. Set. pap. text ed. 169.00 (ISBN 0-89116-078-7). Hemisphere Pub.

Introduction to Computers & Data Processing. (Computer Literacy Ser.). pap. 9.95 (ISBN 0-318-02637-6). Sperry Comp Syst.

ISIS - A General Description of an Approach to Computerized Bibliographical Control. pap. 4.75 (ILO37, ILO). Unipub.

Jackson, Barbara B. Computer Models in Management. 1979. 27.95x (ISBN 0-256-02225-9). Irwin.

Jackson, H. L. & Wiechers, G., eds. Post-Secondary & Vocational Education in Data Processing. 186p. 1980. 38.50 (ISBN 0-444-85398-7, North Holland). Elsevier.

Jacobs, F. Robert, ed. Computer Applications. (Core Business Program Ser.). (Illus.). 128p. Date not set. pap. 7.95 (ISBN 0-87196-801-0). Facts on File.

Johnson, James R. Managing for Productivity in Data Processing. LC 80-65015. 1980. pap. text ed. 26.00 (ISBN 0-89435-041-2). QED Info Sci.

Jones, Paul E., Jr. Data Base Design Methodology. Curtice, Robert M., ed. (Data Base Monograph: No. 3). 1976. pap. 15.00 (ISBN 0-89435-019-6). QED Info Sci.

Jordain, Philip B. Enciclopedia Abreviada de Ordenadores. (Espn.). 672p. 1975. pap. 56.95 (ISBN 84-03-19058-1, S-50491). French & Eur.

Joslin, Edward & Bassler, Richard. Managing Data Processing. 1976. pap. 7.95 (ISBN 0-916580-00-8). College Readings.

Joslin, Edward O. Computer Readings for Making It Count. 2nd ed. 1976. pap. 8.00 (ISBN 0-916580-02-4). College Readings.

Joyce, M. Site Investigation Practice. (Illus.). 300p. 1982. 49.95 (ISBN 0-419-12260-5, NO. 6733, Pub. by E & FN Spon England). Methuen Inc.

Kan, A. H. & Rinnoy. Machine Scheduling Problems. 1976. pap. 29.00 (ISBN 90-247-1848-1, Pub. by Martinus Nijhoff Netherlands). Kluwer Academic.

Katzan, Harry, Jr. Introduction to Computer Science. LC 81-8255. 512p. 1982. Repr. of 1975 ed. 29.50 (ISBN -89874-371-0). Krieger.

Kay, Peg & Powell, Patricia, eds. Future Information Processing Technology. (National Bureau of Standards Special Pub. 500-103. Computer Science & Technology Ser.). 251p. 1983. pap. 6.50 (ISBN 0-318-11721-5). Gov Printing Office.

Kevolin, Nathan, et al. Keyboarding for Personal & Professional Use. 1985. pap. text ed. 19.95 (ISBN 0-8359-3648-1); tchr's. ed. avail. (ISBN 0-8359-3649-X). Reston.

Kieran, Michael. Friday! Electronic Filing Made Easy. 15.95 (ISBN 0-8359-2107-7). Reston.

Kimble, Gerald W. Information & Computer Science. LC 74-3316. (Illus.). 1975. text ed. 9.95x (ISBN 0-03-082833-3). Irvington.

Kuhn, Robert H. & Padua, David A. Parallel Processing. (Tutorial Texts Ser.). 498p. 1981. 36.00 (ISBN 0-8186-0367-4, Q367). IEEE Comp Soc.

Larson, Robert E., et al. Distributed Control. 2nd ed. (Tutorial Texts Ser.). 381p. 1982. 36.00 (ISBN 0-8186-0451-4, Q451); members 22.00. IEEE Comp Soc.

Laudon, Kenneth C. Computers & Bureaucratic Reform. LC 74-9750. 344p. 1974. 21.00 (ISBN 0-471-51840-9, Pub. by Wiley). Krieger.

Lavington, S. H., ed. Information Processing Eighty. 1070p. 1980. 95.75 (ISBN 0-444-86034-7, North-Holland). Elsevier.

Lawrence, John S. The Electronic Scholar. Voigt, Melvin J., ed. LC 84-16952. (Communication & Information Science Ser.). 200p. (Orig.). 1984. text ed. 26.50 (ISBN 0-89391-298-0); pap. text ed. 14.95 (ISBN 0-89391-299-9). Ablex Pub.

Lechner, H. D. Computer Chronicles. 391p. write for info. (ISBN 0-534-03396-2). Wadsworth Pub.

Leeson, Marjorie. Basic Concepts in Data Processing. 2nd ed. 550p. 1980. pap. text ed. write for info. (ISBN 0-697-08134-6); project manual avail. (ISBN 0-697-08135-4); instr's. manual avail. (ISBN 0-697-08163-X). Wm C Brown.

Leff, Lawrence. Data Processing the Easy Way. 240p. 1984. pap. 8.95 (ISBN 0-8120-2627-6). Barron.

Lewis, T. G. The Mind Appliance: Home Computer Applications. 1978. pap. 10.50 (ISBN 0-8104-5112-3). Hayden.

LIndsell, Sheryl L. Simplified Keyboarding for Data Entry. 96p. 1985. Reference Text 9.95 (ISBN 0-668-06087-5); pap. 5.95 (ISBN 0-668-06091-3). Arco.

Lipschutz, Martin & Lipschutz, Seymour. Schaum's Outline of Data Processing. (Schaum's Outline Ser.). (Illus.). 224p. (Orig.). 1981. pap. 8.95 (ISBN 0-07-037983-1). McGraw.

Long, Larry. Introduction to Computers & Information Processing. 512p. 1984. text ed. 26.95 (ISBN 0-13-480534-8). P-H.

Long, Larry & Kreutzer, N. Introduction to Computers & Information Processing: Study Guide. 256p. 1984. pap. text ed. 9.95 (ISBN 0-13-480427-9); pap. text ed. instructor's manual incl. P-H.

Lord, Kenniston W., Jr. & Steiner, James B. CDP Review Manual: A Data Processing Handbook. 3rd ed. (Illus.). 495p. 1984. pap. 32.95 (ISBN 0-442-26087-3). Van Nos Reinhold.

Lorin, Harold. Aspects of Distributed Computer Systems. LC 80-16689. 286p. 1980. 36.95x (ISBN 0-471-08114-0, Pub. by Wiley-Interscience). Wiley.

Lowe, Doug. MVS TSO. LC 84-61126. (Illus.). 454p. (Orig.). 1984. pap. 22.50 (ISBN 0-911625-19-4). M Murach & Assoc.

Lucas, H. C., et al, eds. Information Systems Environment. 346p. 1980. 47.00 (ISBN 0-444-86036-3, North-Holland). Elsevier.

Lucas, Henry C., Jr. Coping with Computers: A Manager's Guide to Controlling Information Processing. (Illus.). 192p. 1982. 14.95 (ISBN 0-02-919310-9). Free Pr.

--Introduction to Computers & Information Systems. 576p. 1985. text ed. price not set (ISBN 0-02-372210-X). Macmillan.

McElreath, T. Jack. IMS Design & Implementation Techniques. LC 83-83123. (Illus.). 256p. 1979. pap. 31.50 (ISBN 0-89435-023-4). QED Info Sci.

McWeeny, Mae & Loeper, Jennifer. Healthsource Computer Lifestyle Management Programs: Preventing Low Back Injury. 20p. 1983. Sis Kenny Inst.

Mader, Chris. Information Systems: Technology, Economics, Applications, Management. 2nd ed. LC 78-13048. 1979. text ed. 25.95 (ISBN 0-574-21150-0, 13-4150); instr's guide avail. (ISBN 0-574-21151-9, 13-4151). SRA.

Maly, Kurt & Hanson, Allen R. Fundamentals of the Computing Sciences. (Illus.). 1978. ref. ed. 32.95 (ISBN 0-13-335240-4); supplementary vol. 14.95 (ISBN 0-13-335257-9). P-H.

Mandell, Steve L. Principles of Data Processing. 3rd ed. (Illus.). 200p. 1984. pap. text ed. 15.50 (ISBN 0-314-77923-X); tchrs.' manual avail. (ISBN 0-314-77924-8). West Pub.

Mandell, Steven L. Computers & Data Processing: Concepts & Applications. 3rd ed. (Illus.). 550p. 1984. text ed. 25.95 (ISBN 0-314-85262-X). West Pub.

--Computers & Data Processing: Concepts & Applications, with BASIC. 2nd ed. (Illus.). 600p. 1982. text ed. 25.95 (ISBN 0-314-63263-8); instr's. manual avail. (ISBN 0-314-63264-6); study guide avail. (ISBN 0-314-63265-4). West Pub.

--Computers & Data Processing: Concepts & Applications with BASIC. 3rd ed. (Illus.). 736p. 1984. text ed. 27.95 (ISBN 0-314-87560-3). West Pub.

--Computers & Data Processing Today. (Illus.). 375p. 1983. pap. text ed. 22.95 (ISBN 0-314-69663-6); instrs.' manual avail. (ISBN 0-314-71105-8); study guide avail. (ISBN 0-314-71106-6). West Pub.

--Computers & Data Processing Today. 2nd ed. (Illus.). 500p. 1985. pap. text ed. 25.00 (ISBN 0-314-93200-3). West Pub.

--Computers & Data Processing Today with BASIC. (Illus.). 510p. pap. text ed. 24.95 (ISBN 0-314-70646-1). West Pub.

--Computers & Data Processing Today with Pascal. (Illus.). 450p. 1983. pap. text ed. 24.95 (ISBN 0-314-70647-X). West Pub.

--Computers & Data Processing Today with BASIC. 2nd ed. (Illus.). 600p. 1985. pap. text ed. 27.95 (ISBN 0-314-96079-1). West Pub.

--Computers & Data Processing Today with Pascal. 2nd ed. (Illus.). 550p. 1985. pap. text ed. 27.95 (ISBN 0-314-96080-5). West Pub.

--Computers & Data Processing Without BASIC. 2nd ed. (Illus.). 528p. 1982. text ed. 23.95 (ISBN 0-314-63268-9). West Pub.

--Principles of Data Processing. 2nd ed. (West Series in Data Processing & Information Systems). (Illus.). 160p. 1981. pap. text ed. 11.50 (ISBN 0-8299-0392-5). West Pub.

Manual on the Global Data-Processing System: Regional Aspects, Vol. 2. (Illus.). 72p. 1980. pap. 25.00 (ISBN 0-685-09233-X, W485, WMO). Unipub.

Mariani, M. P., ed. Distributed Data Processing: Technology & Critical Issues. (TRW Series of Software Technology: Vol. 4). 300p. 1984. 40.00 (ISBN 0-444-86796-1, I-028-84, North-Holland). Elsevier.

Martin, James. Application Development Without Programmers. 345p. 1982. 32.50 (ISBN 0-686-98081-6). Telecom Lib.

--Introduction to Teleprocessing. 267p. 1972. 22.95 (ISBN 0-686-98120-0). Telecom Lib.

Martin, James & McClure, Carma. Structured Techniques for Computing. (Illus.). 736p. 1985. text ed. 49.95 (ISBN 0-13-855180-4). P-H.

Mason, R. E. A., ed. Information Processing 83. (IFIP World Congress Ser.: Vol. 9). 1000p. 1984. 98.00 (ISBN 0-444-86729-5, I-407-83, North-Holland). Elsevier.

Meadow, Charles T. The Analysis of Information Systems. 2nd ed. LC 72-11518. (Information Sciences Ser.). 420p. 1973. 49.95x (ISBN 0-471-59002-9, Pub. by Wiley-Interscience). Wiley.

Milenkovic, Milan. Update Synchronization in Multiaccess Systems. Stone, Harold S., ed. LC 81-16034. (Computer Science Ser.: Distributed Database Systems: No. 8). 94p. 1981. 34.95 (ISBN 0-8357-1223-0). UMI Res Pr.

Miller, Boulton B. Computers & Data Processing. Woltering, Denise M. & Oberthaler, James V., eds. (Illus.). 335p. 1982. 12.95 (ISBN 0-915234-06-8); pap. text ed. 7.95 (ISBN 0-915234-05-X). Bainbridge.

Milton, J. S. & Arnold, J. C. Probability & Statistics in the Engineering & Computing Sciences. 672p. 1985. text ed. 38.95 (ISBN 0-07-042351-2). McGraw.

Mitchell, Ruth K. Information Science & Computer Basics: An Introduction. LC 70-142595. pap. 28.50 (ISBN 0-317-08826-2, 2021001). Bks Demand UMI.

Mitchell, William, et al. Keyboarding for Information Processors. 128p. 1982. pap. text ed. 13.95 (ISBN 0-574-20645-0, 13-3645); instr's guide avail. (13-3646); avail. keyboard tapes set of 12 cassette 175.00 (ISBN 0-686-86762-9, 13-3510). SRA.

Mixon, Shirley R. Handbook of Data Processing Administration, Operations & Procedures. LC 75-38914. pap. 101.30 (ISBN 0-317-20748-2, 2023901). Bks Demand UMI.

Molluzzo & Buckley. A First Course in Discrete Mathematics. 1985. text ed. write for info. (ISBN 0-534-05310-6). Wadsworth Pub.

Moss, John. Introduction to Data Processing. 1978. 25.00 (ISBN 0-905897-25-0). State Mutual Bk.

Mullins, Carolyn & West, Thomas. The Office Automation Primer: Harnessing Information Technologies for Greater Productivity. 158p. 1982. 18.95 (ISBN 0-13-631085-0); pap. 9.95 (ISBN 0-13-631077-X). P-H.

Murray Infotech. Data Communications, 2 vols. (Infotech Computer State of the Art Reports). 600p. 1980. Set. 310.00 (ISBN 0-08-028530-9). Pergamon.

Myers, Charles A. Computers in Knowledge-Based Fields. 1970. pap. 5.95x (ISBN 0-262-63053-2). MIT Pr.

Myerson, Kathleen & Fentress, Alvin K., Jr. Introduction to Data Processing. 1978. pap. text ed. 9.95 (ISBN 0-89433-035-7); text ed. 12.00 (ISBN 0-89433-036-5); visuals 15.00 (ISBN 0-89433-037-3). Petrocelli.

National Center for State Courts. Data Processing & the Courts: Guide for Court Managers. (Courts' Equipment Analysis Project Ser.). (Illus.). 1977. pap. 5.50 (ISBN 0-89656-021-X, R0033G). Natl Ctr St Courts.

National Computing Centre. Introducing Data Processing. 237p. 1980. pap. 16.40 (ISBN 0-471-89462-1, DP00, Pub. by Wiley Interscience). Wiley.

National Computing Centre Ltd. Introduction to On-Line Systems. Pritchard, J. A., ed. LC 72-97131. (Computers & the Professional Ser.). 120p. 1973. 21.00x (ISBN 0-85012-088-8). Intl Pubns Serv.

National Computing Centre Ltd., ed. Documenting Systems (the User's View) (Computers & the Professional Ser). 130p. 1972. pap. 23.00x (ISBN 0-85012-057-8). Intl Pubns Serv.

National Data Processing Institute, Inc. Computer Concepts, 2 vols. Incl. 1969. 3rd ed. Vol. 1. pap. text ed. (ISBN 0-672-96021-4) (ISBN 0-672-96023-0). pap. text ed. 20.51 scp ea. Bobbs.

Northwest Regional Educational Laboratory. Introduction to Data Processing. 1977. 14.40 (ISBN 0-02-831030-6); tchr's guide 5.20 (ISBN 0-02-831050-0); student guide 4.00 (ISBN 0-02-831040-3). Glencoe.

Norton, David P. & Rau, Kenneth G. Guide to EDP Performance Management. new ed. 1979. pap. 19.50 (ISBN 0-89435-022-6). QED Info Sci.

Nyborg, Philip S. & McCarter, Pender M., eds. Information Processing in the United States: A Quantitative Summary. (Illus.). vii, 55p. 1977. saddle-stitch 8.00 (ISBN 0-88283-019-8). AFIPS Pr.

Oliver & Chapman. Data Processing. 4th ed. 1980. 15.00x (ISBN 0-905435-08-7, Pub. by DP Pubns). State Mutual Bk.

Oliver, E. C. & Chapman, R. J. Data Processing: An Instructional Manual. 336p. 1981. 25.00x (ISBN 0-905435-15-X, Pub. by DP Pubns). State Mutual Bk.

Orlicky, Joseph A. Material Requirements Planning: The New Way of Life in Production & Inventory Management. (Illus.). 288p. 1975. 32.40 (ISBN 0-07-047708-6). McGraw.

Orr, Ken. The One Minute Methodology. LC 84-61222. (Illus.). 59p. 1984. 8.95 (ISBN 0-9605884-3-4). Orr & Assocs.

Ort, Harry H. Structured Data Processing Design. LC 84-14506. 224p. 1985. pap. 16.95 (ISBN 0-201-05425-6). Addison-Wesley.

Osley, Carol A. Computing to Success. (Orig.). 1985. price not set (ISBN 0-910119-14-7). S O C O Pubns.

Otnes, Robert K. & Enochson, Loren. Digital Time Series Analysis. LC 72-637. (Wiley Series in Probability & Mathematical Statistics: Applied Probability & Statistics Section). 467p. 1972. 48.50x (ISBN 0-471-65719-0, Pub. by Wiley-Interscience). Wiley.

Page, E. S. & Wilson, L. B. Information, Representation & Manipulation in a Computer. 2nd ed. (Cambridge Computer Science Texts Ser.: No. 2). (Illus.). 1978. 49.50 (ISBN 0-521-22088-2). Cambridge U Pr.

--Information Representation & Manipulation Using Pascal. LC 82-4505. (Cambridge Computer Science Texts: No. 15). (Illus.). 275p. 1983. 32.50 (ISBN 0-521-24954-6); pap. 13.95 (ISBN 0-521-27096-0). Cambridge U Pr.

Pall, Gabriel A. Introduction to Scientific Computing. LC 76-117055. 677p. 1971. 37.50x (ISBN 0-306-50060-4, Plenum Pr). Plenum Pub.

Pao, Yoh-Han & Ernst, George W. Context-Directed Pattern Recognition & Machine Intelligence Techniques for Information Processing, 41 papers. (Tutorial Texts Ser.). 559p. 1982. 36.00 (ISBN 0-8186-0423-9, Q423). IEEE Comp Soc.

Parker, Charles S. Understanding Computers & Data Processing: Today & Tomorrow. 1984. text ed. 27.95x (ISBN 0-03-063424-5); study guide 10.95 (ISBN 0-03-063428-8). HR&W.

Parker, Donn B. Ethical Conflicts in Computer Science & Technology. vi, 201p. 1979. 23.00 (ISBN 0-88283-009-0); 30.00 set; wkbk. 9.75 (ISBN 0-88283-010-4). AFIPS Pr.

Patrick, Robert L. Application Design Handbook for Distributed Systems: For Distributed Systems. LC 79-27205. (Illus.). 285p. 1980. 24.95 (ISBN 0-8436-1601-6). Van Nos Reinhold.

Peltu, Malcolm. A Guide to the Electronic Office. 200p. 1981. 34.95x (ISBN 0-470-27308-9). Halsted Pr.

Perriault, Jacques. Elements Pour un Dialogue Avec L'informaticien. (Textes De Sciences Sociales: No. 7). (Illus.). 1972. pap. 14.00x (ISBN 90-2796-963-9). Mouton.

Perry, William E. Effective Methods of EDP Quality Assurance. rev. ed. LC 81-5102. (Illus.). 378p. 1981. pap. 29.50 (ISBN 0-89435-048-X). QED Info Sci.

--Hatching the EDP Quality Assurance Function. 85p. 1981. pap. 14.95 (ISBN 0-89435-058-7). QED Info Sci.

--Structured Approach to Systems Testing. LC 83-60326. (Illus.). 451p. (Orig.). 1983. pap. 34.50 (ISBN 0-89435-061-7). QED Info Sci.

Perry, William E. & Kuong, Javier F. EDP Risk Analysis & Controls Justification. 1981. 55.00 (ISBN 0-940706-10-5). Management Advisory Pubns.

Personal Computer Data Communications. (Reports Ser.: No. 527). 112p. 1982. 985.00x (ISBN 0-88694-527-5). Intl Res Dev.

Pesaran, M. H. & Slater, L. J. Dynamic Regression: Theory & Algorithms. LC 79-41652. (Computers & Their Applications Ser.). 363p. 1980. 99.95x (ISBN 0-470-26939-1). Halsted Pr.

Peterson. File Programming & Processing. 1986. price not set (ISBN 0-471-82311-2). Wiley.

Pfaltz, John. Computer Data Structures. (Illus.). 1977. text ed. 44.95 (ISBN 0-07-049743-5). McGraw.

Philips, J. P. & Dacons, J. C. Organic Electronic Spectral Data, Vol. 11. 1072p. 1975. text ed. 54.00 (ISBN 0-471-68802-9). Krieger.

Phillips, William C. Data Processing on the HP-41C-CV. LC 83-81097. (EduCALC Technical Ser.). 1983. pap. 16.95 (ISBN 0-936356-02-2). EduCALC Pubns.

Phister, Montgomery, Jr. Data Processing Technology & Economics. 2nd ed. (Illus.). 720p. 1978. 45.00 (ISBN 0-932376-03-7, EY-BX004-DP, Co-Pub. with Santa Monica Pub); pap. 30.00 (ISBN 0-932376-04-5, EY-BX005-DP). Digital Pr.

--Data Processing Technology & Economics: 1975-1978 Supplement. LC 79-25052. (Illus.). 1979. pap. 10.00x (ISBN 0-917640-03-9). Santa Monica Pub.

Plauger, P. J. & Yourdon, Ed. Master File Update. cancelled (ISBN 0-917072-04-9). Yourdon.

Poirot, Jim, et al. Practice in Computers & Data Processing. pap. 7.95. Sterling Swift.

Pollack, Seymour, ed. Studies in Computer Science. LC 82-62390. (MAA Studies in Mathematics: No. 22). 408p. 1982. 29.00 (ISBN 0-88385-124-5). Math Assn.

Popkin, Gary S. & Pike, Arthur M. Introduction to Data Processing. 2nd ed. (Illus.). 1981. 25.95 (ISBN 0-395-29483-5); instr's manual 2.50 (ISBN 0-395-29484-3). HM.

--Introduction to Data Processing with BASIC. 2nd ed. (Illus.). 592p. 1981. text ed. 25.95 (ISBN 0-395-30091-6); study guide 10.50 (ISBN 0-395-29485-1). HM.

Potter, George B. Data Processing. 1984. 18.95 (ISBN 0-256-02373-5); study guide 5.95 (ISBN 0-256-02938-5). Business Pubns.

Prasad. Database-Datacommunication Systems. Date not set. price not set (ISBN 0-444-00888-8). Elsevier.

Price, Wilson T. Data Processing: The Fundamentals. 185p. 1982. pap. text ed. 13.95 (ISBN 0-03-059744-7); instr's manual 20.00 (ISBN 0-03-059824-9). HR&W.

--Introduction to Computer Data Processing. 3rd ed. 592p. 1981. text ed. 26.95 (ISBN 0-03-056728-9, HoltC); wkbk. 10.95 (ISBN 0-03-057697-0). HR&W.

Priel, V. Multi-Coordinate Data Presentation. 1977. 28.00x. Beekman Pubs.

Principles of Data Processing. pap. 7.50 (ISBN 0-668-04268-0). Arco.

Pritchard, J. A. Data Encryption. 110p. 1980. pap. 19.70 (ISBN 0-471-89444-3). Wiley.

Proceedings: International Symposium on New Directions in Computing. 406p. 1985. 45.00 (ISBN 0-8186-0639-8); prepub. 40.50 (ISBN 0-317-31653-2). IEEE Comp Soc.

Proceedings: Nineteen-Eighty Five International Conference of Parallel Processing. 888p. 1985. 80.00 (ISBN 0-8186-0637-1); prepub. 72.00 (ISBN 0-317-31657-5). IEEE Comp Soc.

Race, John. Effective Computer Applications. 1981. 90.00x (Pub. by MCB Pubns). State Mutual Bk.

--Managing the Smaller DP Facility. 1981. 90.00x (ISBN 0-86176-091-3, Pub. by MCB Pubns). State Mutual Bk.

Report of the Interregional Seminar on Electronic Data Processing in Government, 2 vols. Vol. 1: Report & Technical Papers. pap. 3.50 (ISBN 0-686-94277-9, UN72/2H/3, UN); Vol. 2: Papers Submitted by Participants. pap. 7.00 (ISBN 0-686-99327-6, UN72/2H4). Unipub.

Research & Education Association Staff. Electronic Communications Problem Solver. LC 84-61814. (Illus.). 1056p. 1984. pap. text ed. 23.85 (ISBN 0-87891-558-3). Res & Educ.

--Handbook of Computers & Data Processing. LC 83-61837. (Illus.). 480p. 1983. 19.85 (ISBN 0-87891-546-X). Res & Educ.

Robichaud, et al. Introduction to Data Processing. 3rd ed. 368p. 1983. text ed. 14.84 (ISBN 0-07-053194-3). McGraw.

Robichaud, Beryl & Muscat, Eugene. Data Processing Work Kit. 2nd ed. 96p. 1983. practice set 9.84 (ISBN 0-07-053207-9). McGraw.

Robichaud, Beryl, et al. Introduction to Data Processing. 2nd ed. Orig. Title: Understanding Modern Business Data Processing. (Illus.). 1976. text ed. 14.84 (ISBN 0-07-053190-0). McGraw.

Roden, Martin S. Digital & Data Communications Systems. (Illus.). 416p. 1982. 39.95 (ISBN 0-13-212142-5). P-H.

Roeske, Edward. The Data Factory: Data Center Operations & System Development. 1983. write for info. Yourdon.

Rudin, H. & West, C. H., eds. Protocol Specification, Testing & Verification: Proceedings of the IFIP WG 6.1 Third International Workshop on Protocol Specification, Testing & Verification, Organized by IBM Research, Ruschlikon, Switzerland, 31 May-2 June, 1983, Vol. 3. 532p. 1984. 65.00 (ISBN 0-444-86769-4, North Holland). Elsevier.

Rudman, Jack. Chief Data Processing Control Clerk. (Career Examination Ser.: C-2486). (Cloth bdg. avail. on request). pap. 14.00 (ISBN 0-8373-2486-6). Natl Learning.

--Computers & Data Processing. (College Level Examination Ser.: CLEP-8). (Cloth bdg. avail. on request). pap. 9.95 (ISBN 0-8373-5308-4). Natl Learning.

--Data Entry Machine Operator. (Career Examination Ser.: C-2409). (Cloth bdg. avail. on request). pap. 12.00 (ISBN 0-8373-2409-2). Natl Learning.

--Data Processing. (Occupational Competency Examination Ser.: OCE-14). (Cloth bdg. avail. on request). pap. 13.95 (ISBN 0-8373-5714-4). Natl Learning.

--Data Processing Control Clerk. (Career Examination Ser.: C-2483). (Cloth bdg. avail. on request). pap. 12.00 (ISBN 0-8373-2483-1). Natl Learning.

--Data Processing Operations Coordinator. (Career Examination Ser.: C-2759). (Cloth bdg. avail. on request). 1980. pap. 14.00 (ISBN 0-8373-2759-8). Natl Learning.

--Data Processing Specialist. (Career Examination Ser.: C-2242). (Cloth bdg. avail. on request). pap. 12.00 (ISBN 0-8373-2242-1). Natl Learning.

--Director of Data Processing. (Career Examination Ser.: C-2518). (Cloth bdg. avail. on request). pap. 14.00 (ISBN 0-8373-2518-8). Natl Learning.

--Principal Data Entry Machine Operator. (Career Examination Ser.: C-2866). (Cloth bdg. avail. on request). pap. 12.00 (ISBN 0-8373-2866-7). Natl Learning.

--Principal Data Processing Control Clerk. (Career Examination Ser.: C-2485). (Cloth bdg. avail. on request). pap. 12.00 (ISBN 0-8373-2485-8). Natl Learning.

--Programmer. (Career Examination Ser.: C-1430). (Cloth bdg. avail. on request). pap. 10.00 (ISBN 0-8373-1430-5). Natl Learning.

--Senior Data Processing Control Clerk. (Career Examination Ser.: C-2484). (Cloth bdg. avail. on request). pap. 12.00 (ISBN 0-686-53473-5). Natl Learning.

--Senior Programmer. (Career Examination Ser.: C-2580). (Cloth bdg. avail. on request). pap. 14.00 (ISBN 0-8373-2580-3). Natl Learning.

Sackman, Harold & Nie, Norman, eds. The Information Utility & Social Choice. LC 78-129364. (Illus.). 310p. 1970. 10.50 (ISBN 0-88283-019-8). AFIPS Pr.

Sanders, Donald H. Computers in Society. 3rd ed. 536p. 1981. text ed. 27.95 (ISBN 0-07-054672-X). McGraw.

--Computers Today. Vastyan, James E., ed. LC 82-4626. (Illus.). 1982. text ed. 26.95 (ISBN 0-07-054681-9). McGraw.

Sauvant, Karl P. Trade & Foreign Direct Investment in Data Services. (A Westview Special Study in International Economics & Business Ser.). 1985. pap. 23.50 (ISBN 0-317-28073-2). Westview.

Schaeffer, H. Data Center Operations: A Guide to Effective Planning, Processing & Performance. 1981. 42.50 (ISBN 0-13-196360-0). P-H.

Schleip, W. & Schleip, R. Planning & Control in Management: The German RPS System. 80p. 1971. 14.00 (ISBN 0-901223-12-3, NS003). Inst Elect Eng.

Scott, P. R. Introducing Data Communications Standards. (Illus.). 226p. 1979. pap. 30.00x (ISBN 0-85012-220-1). Intl Pubns Serv.

Seigneur, Fred. Distributed Data Processing. 1986. cancelled (ISBN 0-442-27930-2). Van Nos Reinhold.

Sessions, Laura S. How to Break into Data Processing. 130p. 1982. 12.95 (ISBN 0-13-402487-7); pap. 6.95 (ISBN 0-13-402479-6). P-H.

Sharp, J. A. Data Flow Computing. (Computers & Their Applications Ser.). 1985. 24.95 (ISBN 0-470-20167-3). Halsted Pr.

Sharratt, J. R. Data Control Guidelines. LC 73-92433. (Computerguide Ser.: No. 2). 100p. 1976. pap. 23.00x (ISBN 0-85012-099-3). Intl Pubns Serv.

Shelly, Gary B. & Cashman, Thomas J. Introduction to Computers & Data Processing. (Illus.). 512p. 1980. pap. text ed. 24.95 (ISBN 0-88236-115-5); pap. 10.95 wkbk. & study guide (ISBN 0-88236-116-3). Anaheim Pub Co.

Shelly, Gary B., et al. Computer Fundamentals for an Information Age: Workbook & Study Guide. 326p. 1984. pap. 10.95 wkbk (ISBN 0-88236-126-0). Anaheim Pub Co.

Sidman, Bernard. Educational Computer Technology: A Manual-Guide for Effective & Efficient Utilization by School Administrators. LC 78-68445. 1979. perfect bdg. 13.00 (ISBN 0-88247-574-6). R & E Pubs.

Silver, Gerald A. The Social Impact of Computers. 342p. 1979. pap. text ed. 14.95 (ISBN 0-15-581427-3, HC). HarBraceJ.

Simons, Geoffrey L. Privacy in the Computer Age. 147p. (Orig.). 1982. pap. 22.50x (ISBN 0-85012-348-8). Intl Pubns Serv.

Sklansky, J. & Wassel, G. N. Pattern Classifiers & Trainable Machines. (Illus.). 400p. 1981. 54.00 (ISBN 0-387-90435-2). Springer-Verlag.

Skok, W. Systems & Programming Exercises in Data Processing. 128p. 1982. 30.00x (ISBN 0-905435-30-3, Pub. by DP Pubns). State Mutual Bk.

Slaughter, Gary. Data Processing Training Handbook. 1979. 15.00 (ISBN 0-89433-118-3). Petrocelli.

Smalzer, William R., et al. The Computer Book: Programming & Language Skills for Students of ESL. (Illus.). 200p. 1985. pap. text ed. 14.95 (ISBN 0-13-164112-3). P-H.

Smith, Billy E. Managing the Information Systems Audit: A Case Study-Policies, Procedures, & Guidelines. (Illus.). 65p. 1980. Set. pap. text ed. 12.00 (ISBN 0-89413-086-2); avail. wkbk. (ISBN 0-89413-087-0). Inst Inter Aud.

Smith, H. T. & Green, T. Human Interaction with Computers. LC 79-42930. 1980. 42.00 (ISBN 0-12-652850-0); pap. 23.00 (ISBN 0-12-652852-7). Acad Pr.

Smith, J. E. Integrated Injection Logic. 421p. 1980. 42.95x (ISBN 0-471-08675-4, Pub. by Wiley-Interscience); pap. 22.00x (ISBN 0-471-08676-2). Wiley.

Smith, Reid G. A Framework for Distributed Problem Solving. Stone, Harold S., ed. LC 81-11496. (Computer Science: Artificial Intelligence Ser.: No. 10). 190p. 1981. 39.95 (ISBN 0-8357-1218-4). UMI Res Pr.

Snell, B., ed. Translating & the Computer: Proceedings of the Seminar in London, November, 1978. 190p. 1979. 38.50 (ISBN 0-444-85302-2, North Holland). Elsevier.

Sorin, Martin D. Data Entry Without Keypunching: Improved Preparation for Social-Data Analysis. LC 78-24637. 288p. 1982. 23.00x (ISBN 0-669-02803-7). Lexington Bks.

Speck, Pat K. Weslayan Computer Data Processing's General Ledger Operator's Manual. Lozano, Alva, ed. (Illus.). 354p. 1980. 100.00 (ISBN 0-912217-20-0); pap. 90.00 (ISBN 0-317-12066-2). Afton Oaks.

--Weslayan Computer Data Processing's General Ledger Package Programmer's Manual. Lozano, Alva, ed. (Illus.). 450p. 1980. text ed. 100.00 (ISBN 0-912217-22-7); pap. 90.00 (ISBN 0-912217-23-5). Afton Oaks.

--Weslayan Computer Data Processing's Inventory Package Operator's Manual. Lozano, Alva, ed. (Illus.). 350p. 1980. text ed. 100.00 (ISBN 0-912217-26-X); pap. 90.00 (ISBN 0-912217-27-8). Afton Oaks.

--Weslayan Computer Data Processing's Inventory Package Programmer's Manual. Lozano, Alva, ed. (Illus.). 450p. 1980. text ed. 100.00 (ISBN 0-912217-28-6); pap. 90.00 (ISBN 0-912217-29-4). Afton Oaks.

--Weslayan Computer Data Processing's Payroll Package Operator's Manual. Lozano, Alvin, ed. (Illus.). 350p. 1980. text ed. 100.00 (ISBN 0-912217-14-6); pap. 90.00 (ISBN 0-912217-15-4). Afton Oaks.

--Weslayan Computer Data Processing's Payroll Package Programmer's Manual. Lozano, Alva, ed. (Illus.). 450p. 1980. text ed. 100.00 (ISBN 0-912217-16-2); pap. 90.00 (ISBN 0-912217-17-0). Afton Oaks.

Spencer, Donald D. Computers & Information Processing. 608p. 1985. text ed. 25.95 (ISBN 0-675-20290-6); study guide 9.95 (ISBN 0-675-20367-8). Additional supplements maybe obtained from publisher. Merrill.

--Computers in Society: The Where's, Why's, & How's of Computer Use. 1974. pap. 8.95 (ISBN 0-8104-5915-9). Hayden.

--Data Processing: An Introduction with BASIC. 2nd ed. 576p. 1982. pap. text ed. 23.95 (ISBN 0-675-09854-8); study guide 9.95 (ISBN 0-675-09803-3). Additional supplements can be obtained from publisher. Merrill.

--Understanding Computers. (Illus.). 400p. 1983. pap. 13.95 (ISBN 0-684-18038-3, ScribT). Scribner.

--What Computers Can Do. 2nd ed. LC 81-21664. 1982. 12.95x (ISBN 0-89218-043-9). Camelot Pub.

Spirer, Herbert F. & Dueker, Marilynn. Vazsonyi's Introduction to Data Processing: Study Guide. 3rd ed. 1980. pap. 9.95x (ISBN 0-256-02381-6). Irwin.

Sproull, Lee S. & Larkey, Patrick D., eds. Advances in Information Processing in Organizations, Vol. 1. 1983. 40.00 (ISBN 0-89232-403-1). Jai Pr.

Squire, Enid. Introducing Systems Design. LC 78-18651. 1979. pap. text ed. 23.95 (ISBN 0-201-07421-4). Addison-Wesley.

Stair, Ralph M. Principles of Data Processing: Concepts, Cases & Applications. 2nd ed. 1984. 25.95x (ISBN 0-256-02991-1); study guide 9.95x (ISBN 0-256-02992-X). Irwin.

Stallings, William. Tutorial: Integrated Services Digital Networks. 400p. 1985. 48.40 (ISBN 0-8186-0625-8); prepub. 24.30 (ISBN 0-317-31810-1). IEEE Comp Soc.

Stallings, William, ed. Tutorial: Computer Communication: Architectures, Protocols, & Standards. LC 85-60383. (Tutorial Text Ser.). 485p. (Orig.). 1985. 36.00 (ISBN 0-8186-0604-5, 604); microfiche 36.00 (ISBN 0-8186-4604-7). IEEE Comp Soc.

Standish, Thomas A. Data Structure Techniques. LC 78-67454. 1979. text ed. 31.95 (ISBN 0-201-07256-4); instr's manual 4.95 (ISBN 0-201-07257-2). Addison-Wesley.

Stern, Nancy B. & Stern, Robert A. Computers in Society. (Illus.). 624p. 1983. pap. text ed. 24.95 (ISBN 0-13-165282-6). P-H.

Stern, Robert A. An Introduction to Computers & Information Processing. 2nd ed. Stern, Nancy, ed. LC 84-7422. 737p. 1985. 26.95x (ISBN 0-471-87687-9). Wiley.

Stern, Robert A. & Stern, Nancy. Concepts of Information Processing with BASIC. LC 82-17630. 216p. 1983. pap. text ed. 18.45x (ISBN 0-471-87617-8). Wiley.

--Study Guide to Accompany an Introduction to Computers & Information Processing. 2nd ed. 311p. 1985. pap. 13.95 (ISBN 0-471-88516-9). Wiley.

Stimler, Saul. Data Processing Systems: Their Performance Evaluation, Measurement & Improvement. LC 74-82616. (Illus.). 256p. 1974. 15.00 (ISBN 0-9600770-1-4). Stimler Assoc.

Stocker, P. M., et al. Databases-Role & Structure. 400p. 1984. 39.50 (ISBN 0-521-25430-2). Cambridge U Pr.

Stone, Harold. Introduction to Computer Organization & Data Structures. (Computer Science Ser.). 1971. text ed. 42.95 (ISBN 0-07-061726-0). McGraw.

Strackbein, Ray & Strackbein, Dorothy B. Computers & Data Processing Simplified & Self-Taught. LC 82-11664. (Simplified & Self-Taught Ser.). (Illus.). 128p. 1983. lib. bdg. 11.95 (ISBN 0-668-05553-7); pap. 5.95 (ISBN 0-668-05549-9). Arco.

Strock, O. J. Telemetry Computer Systems: An Introduction. LC 82-49001. 380p. 1983. text ed. 44.95x (ISBN 0-87664-711-5). Instru Soc.

Swan, A. J. Data Communications Protocols. (Illus.). 1978. pap. 32.50x (ISBN 0-85012-203-1). Intl Pubns Serv.

Symposium, 4th, Marianske Lazne, Sept. 1-5, 1975. Mathematical Foundations of Computer Science. Becvar, J., ed. (Lecture Notes in Computer Science Ser.: Vol. 32). x, 476p. 1975. pap. 25.00 (ISBN 0-387-07389-2). Springer-Verlag.

System-34 How & Why Book. 124p. 1983. pap. text ed. 39.95 (ISBN 0-915039-00-1). Profs Unltd.

Taube, Mortimer. Computers & Common Sense: The Myth of Thinking Machines. LC 61-17079. 1961. 25.00x (ISBN 0-231-02516-5). Columbia U Pr.

Teague, Robert & Erickson, Clint, eds. Computers & Society: A Reader. LC 74-4279. 350p. 1974. pap. text ed. 13.95 (ISBN 0-8299-0021-7). West Pub.

Terborgh, George. Automation Hysteria. 1966. pap. 1.45x (ISBN 0-393-00376-0, Norton Lib). Norton.

Thompson, T. The Basic Data Set Project. (GARP Publications Ser.: No. 9). (Illus.). 90p. (Orig.). 1972. pap. 20.00 (ISBN 0-685-34860-1, W298, WMO). Unipub.

Thompson, Treva L. The Comprehensive System Procedure Desk Book. LC 82-80832. 350p. 1982. 24.95 (ISBN 0-942898-01-X). Halpern & Simon.

--VSAM Performance & System Fine-Tuning Quick Reference Handbook. LC 82-83606. 150p. 1984. (list price) 17.50x (ISBN 0-942898-02-8); (net price) 10.25x. Halpern & Simon.

Tomeski, Edward A., et al. People-Oriented Computer Systems: The Computer in Transition. rev. ed. LC 81-14304. 368p. 1983. 24.50 (ISBN 0-89874-385-0). Krieger.

Turn, Rein, ed. Report of the AFIPS Panel on Transborder Data Flow: Proceedings. LC 79-93002. (Transborder Data Flow: Concerns in Privacy Protection & Free Flow of Information: Vol. 1). (Illus.). xviii, 186p. 1979. pap. 17.25 (ISBN 0-88283-004-X). AFIPS Pr.

Turn, Rein & Roth, Alexander D., eds. Supporting Documents: Transborder Data Flows: Concerns in Privacy Protection & Free Flow of Information, Vol. II. 300p. 1979. pap. 28.75 (ISBN 0-88283-024-4). AFIPS Pr.

Understanding Data Communications. 1983. 3.50 (ISBN 0-88284-236-6). Alfred Pub.

United Nations Centre on Transnational Corporations. Transnational Data Flow & Brazil. 418p. 1983. pap. 38.00 (ISBN 0-686-46338-2, UN83/2A3, UN). Unipub.

U. S. Library of Congress. Science Policy Reseach Division, 95th Congress, 1st Session 1977, et al. State Legislature Use of Information Technology. LC 78-18915. (House Document Ser.: No. 271). 1978. Repr. of 1977 ed. lib. bdg. 18.75x (ISBN 0-313-20519-1, CHSL). Greenwood.

Van de Riet, R. P. Distributed Data Sharing Systems. 314p. 1982. 42.75 (ISBN 0-444-86374-5, North-Holland). Elsevier.

Vazsonyi, Andrew. Introduction to Data Processing. 3rd ed. 1980. 25.95x (ISBN 0-256-02343-3). Irwin.

Verzello, J. R. & Reutter, J. This Is Data Processing: Systems & Concepts. 560p. 1982. 28.95x (ISBN 0-07-067325-X). McGraw.

Vickery. Computing Principles & Techniques. (Medical Physics Handbook: Vol. 2). 1979. 29.50 (ISBN 0-9960019-0-5, Pub. by A Hilger England). Heyden.

Viet, Jean. Thesaurus for Information Processing in Sociology. 1971. pap. text ed. 16.00x (ISBN 90-2796-941-8). Mouton.

Vinz, C. & Olzog, G. Dokumentation Deutschsprachiger Verlage. 6th ed. (Ger.). 700p. 1977. 43.50 (ISBN 3-7892-9814-X, M-7350, Pub. by Olzog). French & Eur.

Wagner, Michael J. Machine Language Disk I-O & Other Mysteries. (TRS-80 Information Ser.: Vol. 5). (Illus.). 288p. (Orig.). 1982. pap. 29.95 (ISBN 0-936200-06-5). Blue Cat.

Walsh, Robert J. Modern Guide to EDP Design & Analysis Techniques. LC 84-22322. 287p. 1985. 39.95 (ISBN 0-13-594920-3, Busn). P-H.

Wanous, S. J., et al. Introduccion al Procesamiento Automatico de Datos. (Span.). 1985. text ed. 13.75 (ISBN 0-538-22600-5, V60). SW Pub.

--Introduction to Automated Data Processing. 1979. text ed. 10.25 (ISBN 0-538-10600-X, J60). SW Pub.

Ward, Paul T. Systems Development Without Pain: A User's Guide to Modeling Organizational Patterns. LC 83-27368. (Illus.). 288p. 1984. pap. 27.50 (ISBN 0-917072-40-5). Yourdon.

Warnier, Jean-Dominique. Logical Construction of Systems. (Illus.). 186p. 1980. 24.95 (ISBN 0-442-22556-3). Van Nos Reinhold.

Weinberg, Gerald M. Computer Information Systems: An Introduction to Data Processing. Geller, Dennis P., ed. text ed. 20.95 (ISBN 0-316-92849-6); tchrs' ed. avail. (ISBN 0-316-92851-8). Little.

Weinbert, Gerald M. & Freedman, Daniel P. Handbook of Walkthroughs, Inspections & Technical Reviews. 3rd ed. 1978. 35.00 (ISBN 0-933950-39-X). Little.

Welke, H. J. Data Processing in Japan. (Information Research & Resource Reports Ser.: Vol. 1). 198p. 1982. 42.75 (ISBN 0-444-86379-6). Elsevier.

Wennrich, Peter. Anglo-American & German Abbreviations in Data Processing. 736p. 1984. lib. bdg. 95.00 (ISBN 3-598-20524-4). K G Saur.

Westermeir, Jr T. J. DP & the Law. Data Processing Management Association. (MR.3) PAP. Data Process Mgmt. CDP. 56p. MR-3 7.50 (ISBN 0-318-17042-6); data processing mgmt specify issue 10.50 (ISBN 0-318-17043-4). Data Process Mgmt.

Wilmott, G. M. The Fundamentals of Computing. (Illus.). 224p. 1985. pap. 15.95 (ISBN 0-434-92310-9, Pub. by W Heinemann Ltd). David & Charles.

Wolf, Jacob J. A Distributed Double-Loop Computer Network (DDLCN) Stone, Harold S., ed. LC 81-10319. (Computer Science: Distributed Database System Ser.: No. 4). 178p. 1981. 39.95 (ISBN 0-8357-1216-8). UMI Res Pr.

Wright, Becky A., ed. EDP Institute, Dec. 1-4, 1982, Miami, Florida: Proceedings. 136p. (Orig.). 1983. 14.00 (ISBN 0-89154-205-1). Intl Found Employ.

Wright, Tommy. Statistical Methods & the Improvement of Data Quality. 1983. 27.00 (ISBN 0-12-765480-1). Acad Pr.

Young, Paul. Electronic Communication Techniques. 736p. 1985. text ed. 31.95 (ISBN 0-675-20202-7). Additional supplements maybe obtained from publisher. Merrill.

Yourwith, William J. EDP Evaluation Questionnaire, Vol. 1. LC 76-45279. 1977. 30.00 (ISBN 0-917818-01-6). Exec Stand.

--Managements Evaluation of EDP, Vol. 2. LC 76-46263. 1977. 30.00 (ISBN 0-917818-00-8). Exec Stand.

Yourwith, William J., Jr. & Sullivan, Eugene J. Data Entry Control & Management Procedures, (C Entry) (Illus.). 1978. text ed. 35.00 (ISBN 0-917818-02-4). Exec Stand.

Zarrella, John. High-Tech Consulting: A Guide to Making Money as a Computer Consultant. LC 83-17340. 167p. (Orig.). 1983. pap. 19.95 (ISBN 0-935230-08-4). Microcomputer Appns.

Zeigler, Bernard P. Theory of Modelling & Simulation. LC 84-19443. 460p. 1984. Repr. of 1976 ed. lib. bdg. 32.50 (ISBN 0-89874-808-9). Krieger.

Zorkoczy, Peter. Information Technology. LC 82-23879. (Illus.). 152p. 1984. pap. 15.95 (ISBN 0-442-29391-7). Van Nos Reinhold.

ELECTRONIC DATA PROCESSING–AUDITING

Burch, John G., Jr. & Sardinas, Joseph L., Jr. Computer Control & Audit: A Total Systems Approach. LC 78-9093. 492p. 1978. 42.45 (ISBN 0-471-03491-6). Wiley.

Cornick, Delroy L. Auditing in the Electronic Environment: Theory, Practice & Literature. LC 80-81813. 316p. 1981. 19.75 (ISBN 0-912338-23-7); microfiche 14.75 (ISBN 0-912338-24-5). Lomond.

Davis, Keagle & Perry, William E. Auditing Computer Applications: A Basic Systematic Approach. 601p. 1982. 55.00x (ISBN 0-471-05482-8, Pub. by Ronald Pr). Wiley.

Douglas, I. J. Security & Audit of Database Systems. 23p. (Orig.). 1980. 15.00x (ISBN 0-85012-279-1). Intl Pubns Serv.

Duff, Larry J. Audit & Control of Distributed Data Processing Systems. 1983. 33.00 (ISBN 0-89413-104-4); nonmembers 33.00. Inst Inter Aud.

Eason, Tom S., et al, eds. Systems Auditability & Control Study, 3 Vols. Russell, Susan H. & Ruder, Brian. Incl. Data Processing Audit Practices Report. pap. text ed. 15.00 (ISBN 0-89413-052-8); Data Processing Control Practices Report. pap. text ed. 15.00 (ISBN 0-89413-051-X); Executive Report. pap. text ed. 15.00 (ISBN 0-89413-050-1). (Illus.). 1977. Set. pap. text ed. 37.50 (ISBN 0-686-86121-3). Inst Inter Aud.

Edwards, John. Accounting & Management Controls for Computer Systems. 236p. 1980. pap. 30.50 (ISBN 0-317-19246-9, 4569). Commerce.

IIA International Research Committee. Auditing Fast Response Systems. (Modern Concepts of Internal Auditing Ser.). (Illus.). 1974. pap. text ed. 13.50 (ISBN 0-89413-037-4). Inst Inter Aud.

IIA's International Research Committee. Auditing Computer Centers. (Modern Concepts of Internal Auditing Ser.). 1974. pap. text ed. 13.50 (ISBN 0-89413-038-2). Inst Inter Aud.

Kuong, Javier F. Audit & Control of Computerized Systems. 1983. manual 99.00 (ISBN 0-940706-01-6, MAP-6). Management Advisory Pubns.

--EDP System Auditability: Approaches & Techniques, MAP-17. 1983. 65.00 (ISBN 0-940706-11-3). Management Advisory Pubns.

Kuong, Javier F., ed. Audit & Control of Advanced On-Line Systems, Manual. 1983. 195.00 (ISBN 0-940706-00-8, MAP-7). Management Advisory Pubns.

Lott, Richard W. Auditing the Data Processing Function. (Illus.). 1980. 17.95 (ISBN 0-8144-5527-1). AMACOM.

Macchiaverna, Paul R. Auditing Corporate Data-Processing Activities. (Report Ser.: No. 776). (Illus.). 85p. (Orig.). 1980. pap. text ed. 30.00 (ISBN 0-8237-0212-X); pap. text ed. 10.00 member. Conference Bd.

Management Advisory Pubns. Computer Auditing & Security Manual: Operations & Systems Audits. 1976. 95.00 (ISBN 0-940706-03-2, MAP-5). Management Advisory Pubns.

Nolan, Richard L. Management Accounting & Control of Data Processing. 190p. pap. 16.95 (ISBN 0-86641-045-7, 7793). Natl Assn Accts.

Perry, William E. & Kuong, Javier F. Effective Computer Audit Practices Manual ECAP-Map-11: A Manual Containing Five Practice Books. 1980. 250.00 (ISBN 0-940706-12-1). Management Advisory Pubns.

Porter, W. Thomas & Perry, William E. EDP: Controls & Auditing. 4th ed. LC 83-25540. 592p. 1984. text ed. write for info. (ISBN 0-534-03062-9). Kent Pub Co.

A Practical Guide to EDP Auditing Management. 1985. pap. write for info (ISBN 0-442-20909-6). Van Nos Reinhold.

Pritchard, J. A. Risk Management in Action. 1978. 22.50x (ISBN 0-85012-180-9). Intl Pubns Serv.

Rothberg, Gabriel B. Structured EDP Auditing. (Data Processing Ser.). (Illus.). 302p. 1983. 31.50 (ISBN 0-534-97931-9). Lifetime Learn.

Sardinas, Joseph & Burch, John G. EDP Auditing: A Primer. LC 80-25981. 209p. 1981. pap. text ed. 23.00 (ISBN 0-471-12305-6); avail. tchr's manual (ISBN 0-471-09792-6). Wiley.

Thomas, A. J. & Douglas, I. J. Audit of Computer Systems. (Illus.). 202p. (Orig.). 1983. pap. 43.00x (ISBN 0-85012-299-6). Intl Pubns Serv.

Wagner, Charles R. The CPA & the Computer Fraud. LC 77-90861. (Illus.). 176p. 1979. 21.50x (ISBN 0-669-02079-6). Lexington Bks.

Watne, Donald A. & Turney, Peter B. Auditing EDP Systems. (Illus.). 640p. 1984. 34.95 (ISBN 0-13-051631-7). P-H.

Weber, R. EDP Auditing: Conceptual Foundation & Practice. (Management Information Systems Ser.). 672p. 1982. text ed. 40.95x (ISBN 0-07-068830-3). McGraw.

ELECTRONIC DATA PROCESSING–BIBLIOGRAPHY

Abshire, Gary M. The Impact of Computers on Society & Ethics: A Bibliography. LC 80-65696. 120p. 1980. 17.95 (ISBN 0-916688-17-8, 12E). Creative Comp.

Cortada, James W., compiled by. An Annotated Bibliography on the History of Data Processing. LC 83-8539. xlii, 216p. 1983. lib. bdg. 35.00 (ISBN 0-313-24001-9, CDP/). Greenwood.

Morrill, Chester, Jr., ed. Systems & Procedures Including Office Management Information Sources. LC 67-31261. (Management Information Ser.: No. 12). 1967. 60.00x (ISBN 0-8103-0812-6). Gale.

Solomon, Martin B., Jr. & Lovan, Nora G. Annotated Bibliography of Films in Automation, Data Processing, & Computer Science. LC 67-23778. 44p. 1967. pap. 5.00x (ISBN 0-8131-1145-5). U Pr of Ky.

ELECTRONIC DATA PROCESSING–DICTIONARIES

Aitchison, Jean, compiled by. UNESCO Thesaurus: A Structured List of Descriptors for Indexing & Retrieving Literature in the fields of Education, Science, Social Science, Culture & Communication, 2 Vols. 1977. Set. 93.00 (ISBN 92-3-101469-2, U816, UNESCO). Vol. 1: Introduction, Classified Thesaurus, Permuted Index, Hierarchical Display, 485 p. Vol. 2: Alphabetical Thesaurus, 530 p. Unipub.

American National Standards Committee, X3, Information Processing System. American National Dictionary for Information Systems. LC 83-73087. 350p. 1984. 32.50 (ISBN 0-87094-503-3). Dow Jones-Irwin.

Anderson, R. G. Dictionary of Data Processing & Computer Terms. 112p. 1982. 23.50x (ISBN 0-7121-0429-1). Trans-Atlantic.

Bola Glossary of Electronic Data Processing & Computer Terms English-Spanish & Spanish-English. LC 82-71113. (Bola Glossary Ser.: Vol. 1). (Span. & Eng.). 206p. (Orig.). 1982. pap. 29.95 (ISBN 0-943118-00-X). Bola Pubns.

Brinkman, Karl-Heinz & Schmidt, Rudolf. Data Systems Dictionary: English-German & German-English. 1974. pap. 40.00x (ISBN 3-87097-095-2). Intl Learn Syst.

Brinkmann, Karl H. Dictionary of Dataprocessing. (Ger. & Eng.). 1974. 59.95 (ISBN 3-87097-059-6, M-7117). French & Eur.

British Computer Society. A Glossary of Computing Terms: An Introduction. 4th ed. LC 84-45366. 64p. 1985. pap. 3.95 (ISBN 0-521-31777-0). Cambridge U Pr.

Buerger, E. Woerterbuch Datenerfassung-Programmierung. (Eng., Ger., Fr. & Rus., Dictionary of Data Processing & Programming). 1976. 56.00 (ISBN 3-87144-265-8, M-6967). French & Eur.

Burger, E. Technical Dictionary of Data Processing, Computers & Office Machines, English, German, French, Russian. (Eng., Ger., Fr. & Rus.). 1970. 145.00 (ISBN 0-08-006425-6). Pergamon.

Burger, Habil E. Dictionary of Automatic Data Processing. 480p. 1980. 75.00x (Pub. by Collet's). State Mutual Bk.

Burger, Ing H. Dictionary of Automatic Data Processing. (Eng., Ger., Fr., Rus. & Slovak.). 480p. 1976. 80.00x (ISBN 0-569-08521-7, Pub. by Collets). State Mutual Bk.

Clason, W. E. Elsevier's Dictionary of Computers, Automatic Control & Data Processing. 2nd ed. (Eng., Fr., Span., & Ital.). 474p. (Polyglot). 1971. 98.00 (ISBN 0-444-40928-9). Elsevier.

Diccionari d'Informatica. (Cata.). 214p. 1978. pap. 17.50 (ISBN 84-500-2780-2, S-50373). French & Eur.

Farkas, Daniel. Data Communications: Terms, Concepts & Definitions. 120p. 1983. 3 ring binder 39.95 (ISBN 0-935506-13-6). Carnegie Pr.

Freedman, Alan. The Computer Glossary: It's Not Just a Glossary. 3rd ed. (Illus.). 324p. 1983. 14.95 (ISBN 0-941878-02-3). Computer Lang.

Freedman, Alan & Morrison, Irma L. The Computer Glossary: It's Not Just a Glossary! 320p. 1983. pap. 15.95 (ISBN 0-13-164483-1). P-H.

Gould, I. IFIP-Sach Worterbuch der Datenverarbeitung. (Ger.). 170p. 1977. 19.95 (ISBN 3-87144-335-2, M-7467, Pub. by Verlag Harri Deutsch). French & Eur.

Guckler, G. Zweisprachiges Woerterbuch fuer Angenaeherte Operationelle Analyse Semantischer Entsprechungen Mittels EDV. (Ger. & It.). 300p. 1975. pap. 30.00 (ISBN 3-87808-053-0, M-7693, Pub. by G. Narr). French & Eur.

Harris, Donald E. EDP Manager's Glossary of Computer & Data Communications Terminology. LC 83-81247. 172p. (Orig.). 1984. pap. 24.95 (ISBN 0-914145-00-2). Info Syst Con.

Hofer, A. Fachbegriffe und Sinnbilder der Datenverarbeitung. (Ger.). 166p. 1976. 22.50 (ISBN 3-7940-4179-8, M-7375, Pub. by Vlg. Dokumentation). French & Eur.

Hofmann, Egon. Dictionary of Dataprocessing. 4th ed. (Eng. & Ger.). 1976. 15.95 (ISBN 3-19-006288-9, M-7115). French & Eur.

Isaacs, Alan, ed. The Multilingual Computer Dictionary. 336p. 1981. 22.50 (ISBN 0-87196-431-7); pap. 12.95 (ISBN 0-87196-822-3). Facts on File.

Kelly-Bootle, Stan. The Devil's DP Dictionary. (Illus.). 160p. 1981. pap. 9.95 (ISBN 0-07-034022-6). McGraw.

Loebel & Mueller. Lexikon der Datenverarbeitung. (Ger.). 704p. 1975. 62.00 (ISBN 3-478-33206-0, M-7264). French & Eur.

Lomax, J. D. Data Dictionary Systems. (Illus.). 1977. pap. 45.00x (ISBN 0-85012-191-4). Intl Pubns Serv.

Malstrom, Robert C. SRA Data Processing Glossary. 281p. 1979. pap. 12.95 (ISBN 0-574-21250-7, 13-4250). SRA.

Maynard. Dictionary of Data Processing. 2nd ed. 1982. text ed. 34.95 (ISBN 0-408-00591-2). Butterworth.

Meadows, A. J. & Gordon, M., eds. The Random House Dictionary of New Information Technology. LC 82-40026. 200p. 1982. pap. 7.95 (ISBN 0-394-71202-1, Vin). Random.

Mueller, Peter. Lexikon der Datenverarbeitung. (Ger.). 1968. 55.00 (ISBN 3-478-33205-2, M-7265). French & Eur.

Oppermann, A. Woerterbuch der Datenverarbeitung. 2nd ed. (Eng. & Ger.). 343p. (Dictionary of Dataprocessing). 1973. 28.00 (ISBN 3-7940-3099-0, M-7034). French & Eur.

Oppermann, Alfred. Dictionary of Dataprocessing. 2nd ed. (Ger. & Eng.). 1973. pap. 30.00 (ISBN 3-7940-3099-0, M-7116). French & Eur.

Prenis, John, ed. The Computer Dictionary: A User-Friendly Guide to Language, Terms, & Jargon. LC 83-13668. (Illus.). 128p. 1983. lib. bdg. 12.90 (ISBN 0-89471-232-2); pap. 4.95 (ISBN 0-89471-231-4). Running Pr.

Rosenberg, Jerry M. Dictionary of Computers, Data Processing, & Telecommunications. LC 83-12359. 614p. 1984. 32.50x (ISBN 0-471-87638-0); pap. 14.95 (ISBN 0-471-88582-7). Assn Inform & Image Mgmt.

Russian-English Dictionary of Data Processing Terminology. (Rus. & Eng.). 359p. 1971. text ed. 6.95 (ISBN 0-686-92123-2, M-9127). French & Eur.

Schmoll, G. Wortschatz der Information und Dokumentation. (Ger.). 160p. 15.95 (ISBN 3-7940-4037-6, M-7690, Pub. by Vlg. Dokumentation). French & Eur.

Schulz, Joachim. Data Systems Dictionary: English-Russian-German. (Eng., Rus. & Ger.). 1978. pap. 39.95 (ISBN 3-87097-075-8, M-7325, Pub. by Brandstetter Verlag). French & Eur.

Shishmarev, A. I. & Zamorin, A. P. Explanatory Dictionary of Computing Machinery & Data Processing. 416p. 1978. 60.00x (ISBN 0-686-44717-4, Pub. by Collets). State Mutual Bk.

Spencer, Donald D. The Illustrated Computer Dictionary. Rev. ed. 187p. 1983. pap. 9.95 (ISBN 0-675-20075-X). Merrill.

Stokes, Adrian. Concise Encyclopedia of Information Technology. 271p. 1983. 17.95 (ISBN 0-13-167213-4); pap. 9.95 (ISBN 0-13-167205-3). P-H.

Thesaurus. (INIS Reference Ser.: Rev. 20). 756p. 1981. pap. 46.50 (ISBN 92-0-178081-8, IN13/R20, IAEA). Unipub.

Welk, Martin H. Standard Dictionary of Computers & Information Processing. 2nd, rev. ed. 390p. 1977. 23.95 (ISBN 0-686-98126-X). Telecom Lib.

Wilhelm, Carl & Amkreutz, Johann, eds. Dictionary of Data Processing, 2 Vols. 2nd ed. 1349p. 1981. Set. cancelled (ISBN 3-921899-25-7). Intl Pubns Serv.

Wittman, A. & Klos, J. Dictionary of Data Processing, Including Applications in Industry, Administration & Business. 4th, rev., enlg. ed. 1984. 106.00 (ISBN 0-444-99628-1, I-121-84). Elsevier.

Wittmann, Alfred. Fachwoerterbuch der Datenverarbeitung. 3rd ed. (Eng., Ger. & Fr., Dictionary of Dataprocessing). 1977. 67.50 (ISBN 3-486-39063-5, M-7388, Pub. by Oldenbourg Verlag). French & Eur.

ELECTRONIC DATA PROCESSING–DIRECTORIES

Cane, Mike. The Computer Phone Book. 1983. pap. 14.95 (ISBN 0-452-25446-9, Plume). NAL.

Hsiao, T. C., ed. Directory of Computer Education and Research: (International Edition, 2 vols. LC 75-16507. 1800p. 1978. 150.00x (ISBN 0-912291-02-8). Sci & Tech Pr.

Lesko, Matthew. The Computer Data & Database Source Book. 768p. 1984. pap. 14.95 (ISBN 0-380-86942-X). Avon.

ELECTRONIC DATA PROCESSING–DISTRIBUTED PROCESSING

Akoka, J., ed. Management of Distributed Data Processing: Proceedings of the International Conference, Paris, France, June 23-26, 1982. 294p. 1982. 40.50 (ISBN 0-444-86458-X, I-299-82, North Holland). Elsevier.

Booth, Grayce M. The Distributed System Environment: Some Practical Approaches. (Illus.). 288p. 1980. 32.95 (ISBN 0-07-006507-1). McGraw.

Cary, John M. Data Security & Performance Overhead in a Distributed Architecture System. Stone, Harold S., ed. LC 81-11638. (Computer Science: Distributed Database Systems Ser.: No. 9). 188p. 1981. 39.95 (ISBN 0-8357-1225-7). UMI Res Pr.

Chu, Wesley W. & Chen, Peter P. Centralized & Distributed Data Base Systems. (Tutorial Texts Ser.). 662p. 1979. 32.00 (ISBN 0-8186-0261-9, Q261). IEEE Comp Soc.

Delobel, C. & Litwin, W., eds. Distributed Data Bases. 368p. 1980. 68.00 (ISBN 0-444-85471-1, North-Holland). Elsevier.

Expertise International, Ltd. Distributed Processing, 2 vols. Incl. Vol. 1. Management Report. pap. 18.00 (ISBN 0-89435-025-0); Vol. 2. Technical Report. 505p. pap. 35.00 (ISBN 0-89435-026-9). (Illus.). 1978. pap. QED Info Sci.

Filman, Robert E. & Friedman, Daniel P. Coordinated Computing: Tools & Techniques for Distributed Software. 320p. 1984. 38.95 (ISBN 0-07-022439-0). McGraw.

Germano, Frank, Jr. Automatic Transaction Decomposition in a CODASYL Prototype System. Stone, Harold S., ed. LC 81-12943. (Computer Science: Distributed Database Systems Ser.: No. 6). 150p. 1981. 34.95 (ISBN 0-8357-1221-4). UMI Res Pr.

Healey, Martin & Hebditch, David. The Minicomputer in On-Line Systems: Small Computers in Terminal-Based Systems & Distributed Processing Networks. 334p. 1981. text ed. 26.95 (ISBN 0-316-35394-9). Little.

Jones, Chambers D. Distributed Computing. 1984. 22.50 (ISBN 0-12-167350-2). Acad Pr.

Katzan, Harry, Jr. An Introduction to Distributed Data Processing. LC 78-27323. (Illus.). 242p. 1979. text ed. 20.00 (ISBN 0-89433-061-6). Petrocelli.

Liebowitz, Burt H. & Carson, John H. Distributed Processing. 3rd rev. ed. (Tutorial Texts Ser.). 640p. 1981. 25.00 (ISBN 0-8186-0363-1, Q363). IEEE Comp Soc.

Local Networks: Strategy & Systems. 536p. 1983. 112.00x (ISBN 0-903796-93-7, Pub. by Online). Taylor & Francis.

Lorin, Harold. Aspects of Distributed Computer Systems. LC 80-16689. 286p. 1980. 36.95x (ISBN 0-471-08114-0, Pub. by Wiley-Interscience). Wiley.

McGlynn, Daniel R. Distributed Processing & Data Communications. LC 78-1117. 305p. 1978. 35.95x (ISBN 0-471-01886-4, Pub. by Wiley-Interscience). Wiley.

--Distributed Processing & Data Communications. 2nd ed. 1986. write for info. (ISBN 0-471-88778-1). Wiley.

Management Strategy for Distributed Systems. 1978. pap. 23.00x (ISBN 0-85012-200-7). Intl Pubns Serv.

Martin, James. Design & Strategy for Distributed Data Processing. (Illus.). 672p. 1981. text ed. 45.00 (ISBN 0-13-201657-5). P-H.

NATO Advanced Study Institute, Bonas, France, June 15-26, 1981. New Advances in Distributed Computer Systems: Proceedings. Beauchamp, Kenneth G., ed. x, 417p. 1981. 48.00 (ISBN 90-277-1379-0, Pub. by Reidel Holland). Kluwer Academic.

A Practical Guide to Distributed Processing Management. 1985. pap. write for info (ISBN 0-442-20900-2). Van Nos Reinhold.

Tashenberg, C. Bradley. Design & Implementation of Distributed Processing Systems. LC 83-45205. 278p. 1984. 39.95x (ISBN 0-8144-5780-0). AMACOM.

Thierauf, Robert J. Distributed Processing Systems. (Illus.). 1978. 30.95 (ISBN 0-13-216507-4). P-H.

Thurber, Kenneth J. A Pragmatic View of Distributed Processing Systems. (Tutorial Texts Ser.). 626p. 1980. 32.00 (ISBN 0-8186-0299-6, Q299); members 24.00. IEEE Comp Soc.

ELECTRONIC DATA PROCESSING–EXAMINATIONS

Arco Editorial Board. CDP-CCP-CLEP Data Processing Examinations. LC 78-8753. 1979. pap. 10.00 (ISBN 0-668-04670-8). Arco.

Data Processing Management Association Staff & Washington Chapter Staff. CDP Examguide. (Computers & Information Processing Systems for Business Ser.). 126p. 1984. pap. 22.45 (ISBN 0-471-80444-4). Wiley.

Graybill, Donald, et al. Computer Aptitude Tests. LC 83-15628. 224p. (Orig.). 1984. 12.95 (ISBN 0-668-06012-3); pap. 7.95 (ISBN 0-668-05854-4). Arco.

Rudman, Jack. Computer Associate (Applications Programming) (Career Examination Ser.: C-2470). (Cloth bdg. avail. on request). pap. 14.00 (ISBN 0-8373-2470-X). Natl Learning.

--Computer Associate (Operations) (Career Examination Ser.: C-2471). (Cloth bdg. avail. on request). pap. 14.00 (ISBN 0-8373-2471-8). Natl Learning.

--Computer Associate (Systems Programming) (Career Examination Ser.). (Cloth bdg. avail. on request). pap. 14.00 (ISBN 0-8373-2472-6). Natl Learning.

--Computer Associate (Technical Support) (Career Examination Ser.: C-2473). (Cloth bdg. avail. on request). pap. 14.00 (ISBN 0-8373-2473-4). Natl Learning.

--Data Processing Clerk I. (Career Examination Ser.: C-536). (Cloth bdg. avail. on request). pap. 12.00 (ISBN 0-8373-0536-5). Natl Learning.

--Data Processing Clerk II. (Career Examination Ser.: C-537). (Cloth bdg. avail. on request). pap. 12.00 (ISBN 0-8373-0537-3). Natl Learning.

--Data Processing Clerk III. (Career Examination Ser.: C-538). (Cloth bdg. avail. on request). pap. 12.00 (ISBN 0-8373-0538-1). Natl Learning.

ELECTRONIC DATA PROCESSING–KEYBOARDING

Crawford, T. James, et al. Computer Keyboarding: An Elementary Course. 1985. 8.95 (ISBN 0-538-26300-8, Z30). SW Pub.

ELECTRONIC DATA PROCESSING–MANAGEMENT

Axelrod, C. Warren. Computer Productivity: A Planning Guide for Cost Effective Management. 254p. 1982. 29.95 (ISBN 0-471-07744-5). Wiley.

Gildersleeve, Thomas. Data Processing Project Management. 330p. 1974. 19.95 (ISBN 0-442-25309-5); pap. 18.95 (ISBN 0-442-22824-4). Van Nos Reinhold.

Gildersleeve, Thomas R. & Reynolds, Dean W. Data Processing Project Management. 2nd ed. (Illus.). 224p. 1985. 29.95 (ISBN 0-442-22851-1). Van Nos Reinhold.

A Practical Guide to Data Center Operations Management. 1985. pap. write for info (ISBN 0-442-20912-6). Van Nos Reinhold.

A Practical Guide to Data Processing Management. 1985. pap. write for info (ISBN 0-442-20922-3). Van Nos Reinhold.

A Practical Guide to Distributed Processing Management. 1985. pap. write for info (ISBN 0-442-20900-2). Van Nos Reinhold.

ELECTRONIC DATA PROCESSING–MATHEMATICS

Here are entered works on those mathematical topics essential to the study of electronic data processing and computer science. works on the use of electronic data processing and computers in mathematics are entered under mathematics–data processing.

Bachem, A., et al, eds. Mathematical Programming - Bonn 1982: The State of the Art. (Illus.). 660p. 1983. 57.00 (ISBN 0-387-12082-3). Springer-Verlag.

Barden, William. Microcomputer Math. LC 81-86554. 128p. 1982. pap. 12.95 (ISBN 0-672-21927-1, 21927). Sams.

Bavel, Zamir. A Math Companion for Computer Science. 1981. 23.95 (ISBN 0-8359-4300-3); pap. 18.95 (ISBN 0-8359-4299-6); solutions manual avail. (ISBN 0-8359-4301-1). Reston.

Bowyer, Adrian & Woodwark, John. A Programmer's Geometry. (Illus.). 160p. 1983. text ed. 39.95 (ISBN 0-408-01303-6); pap. text ed. 19.95 (ISBN 0-408-01242-0). Butterworth.

Bruell, S. C. & Balbo, G., eds. Computational Algorithms for Closed Queuing Networks. (Operating & Programming Systems Ser.: Vol. 7). 190p. 1980. 29.95 (ISBN 0-444-00421-1, North-Holland). Elsevier.

Butkovskiy, A. G. Structural Theory of Distributed Systems. LC 83-10727. (Mathematics & Its Applications Ser.). 314p. 1983. 89.95x (ISBN 0-470-27469-7). Halsted Pr.

Calmet, J., ed. Computer Algebra: EUROCAM 82, Marseille, France 1982. (Lecture Notes in Computer Science: Vol. 144). 301p. 1982. pap. 16.00 (ISBN 0-387-11607-9). Springer-Verlag.

Chytil, M. Mathematical Foundations of Computer Science 1981. Gruska, J., ed. (Lecture Notes in Computer Science Ser.: Vol. 118). 589p. 1981. pap. 31.50 (ISBN 0-387-10856-4). Springer-Verlag.

Clark, Frank. Mathematics for Data Processing. 2nd ed. 1982. text ed. 23.95 (ISBN 0-8359-4263-5); instr's. manual avail. (ISBN 0-8359-4264-3). Reston.

Computer-Based Electronic Mail. (Reports Ser.: No. 185). 141p. 1981. 985.00x (ISBN 0-88694-185-7). Intl Res Dev.

De Bakker, M. Mathematical Theory of Program Correctness. 1980. 44.95 (ISBN 0-13-562132-1). P-H.

Dembrinski, P., ed. Mathematical Foundation of Computer Science: Proceedings. (Lecture Notes in Computer Science Ser.: Vol. 88). 723p. 1980. pap. 42.00 (ISBN 0-387-10027-X). Springer-Verlag.

Dixon, W. J. & Nicholson, W. L. Exploring Data Analysis: The Computer Revolution in Statistics. LC 73-85786. 1974. 34.50x (ISBN 0-520-02470-2). U of Cal Pr.

Domolki, B. & Gergely, T., eds. Mathematical Logic in Computer Science. (Colloquia Mathematica Societatis Janos Bolyai Ser.: Vol. 26). 758p. 1982. 117.00 (ISBN 0-444-85440-1, North-Holland). Elsevier.

Ehrig, H., et al, eds. Mathematical Foundations of Software Development. (Lecture Notes in Computer Science: Vol. 185). xiv, 418p. 1985. pap. 22.80 (ISBN 0-387-15198-2). Springer-Verlag.

Evans, David J., ed. Preconditioning Methods: Analysis & Application. (Topics in Computer Mathematics Ser.: Vol. 1). 568p. 1983. 74.50 (ISBN 0-677-16320-7). Gordon.

Garey, Michael R. & Johnson, David S. Computers & Intractability: A Guide to the Theory of NP-Completeness. LC 78-12361. (Mathematical Sciences Ser.). (Illus.). 338p. 1979. pap. text ed. 17.95 (ISBN 0-7167-1045-5). W H Freeman.

Gohberg, I., et al. Matrix Polynomials. (Computer Science & Applied Mathematics Ser.). 1982. 55.00 (ISBN 0-12-287160-X). Acad Pr.

Gray, P. M. Logic, Algebra & Database. (Computers & Their Applications Ser.). 294p. 1984. 34.95 (ISBN 0-470-20103-7). Halsted Pr.

Graybill, Donald. Computer Mathematics: Essential Math for Computer Proficiency. LC 83-21539. 192p. (Orig.). 1984. lib. bdg. 14.95 (ISBN 0-668-06017-4); pap. 8.95 (ISBN 0-668-05845-5). Arco.

Gruska, J., ed. Mathematical Foundations of Computer Science 1977: Proceedings, 6th Symposium, Tatranska Lmnica, Sept. 5-9, 1977. LC 77-10135. (Lecture Notes in Computer Science: Vol. 53). 1977. pap. 28.00 (ISBN 0-387-08353-7). Springer-Verlag.

Hwang, Kai. Computer Arithmetic: Principles, Architecture & Design. LC 78-18922. 423p. 1979. text ed. 46.00 (ISBN 0-471-03496-7); solns. manual avail. (ISBN 0-471-05200-0). Wiley.

International Symposium, Karlsruhe, West Germany, May 20-24, 1975. Interval Mathematics: Proceedings. Nickel, K., ed. (Lecture Notes in Computer Science Ser.: Vol. 29). vi, 331p. 1975. pap. 20.00 (ISBN 0-387-07170-9). Springer-Verlag.

Karni, Shlomo & Byatt, William J. Mathematical Methods in Continuous & Discrete Systems. 1982. pap. text ed. 40.95 (ISBN 0-03-057038-7). HR&W.

Kay, Christine B. Mathematics for Computer Programmers. (Illus.). 304p. 1984. 27.95 (ISBN 0-13-562140-2). P-H.

Kolman, Bernard & Busby, Robert C. Discrete Mathematical Structures for Computer Science. (Illus.). 512p. 1984. text ed. 30.95 (ISBN 0-13-215418-8). P-H.

Korfhage, Robert. Discrete Computational Structures. 2nd ed. LC 83-2554. (Computer Science & Applied Mathematics Ser.). 1983. 35.00 (ISBN 0-12-420860-6). Acad Pr.

Kovach, Ladis D. Computer-Oriented Mathematics: An Introduction to Numerical Methods. LC 64-21711. pap. 26.30 (ISBN 0-317-09178-6, 2016291). Bks Demand UMI.

Kulisch, Ulrich W. & Miranker, Willard L. Computer Arithmetic in Theory & Practice. LC 80-765. (Computer Science & Applied Mathematics Ser.). 1981. 42.50 (ISBN 0-12-428650-X). Acad Pr.

Kuznetsov, O. P. & Adel'son-Vel'skii, G. M. Discrete Mathematics for Engineers. (Computer Mathematics Ser.). 420p. 1985. text ed. 195.00 (ISBN 2-88124-201-4). Gordon.

Lancaster, Peter & Tismenetsky, Miron. The Theory of Matrices. (Computer Science & Applied Mathematics Ser.). 1985. 59.00 (ISBN 0-12-435560-9). Acad Pr.

Lawler, E. L., et al. The Traveling Salesman Problem. (Discrete Mathematics Ser.). 1985. write for info. (ISBN 0-471-90413-9). Wiley.

Lucantoni, D. M. Algorithmic Analysis of a Communication Model with Retransmission of Fluid Messages. (Research Notes in Mathematics Ser. No. 81). 154p. 1983. pap. text ed. 20.95 (ISBN 0-273-08571-9). Pitman Pub MA.

Miller, R. E. & Thatcher, J. W., eds. Complexity of Computer Computations. LC 72-85736. (IBM Research Symposia Ser.). 225p. 1972. 39.50x (ISBN 0-306-30707-3, Plenum Pr). Plenum Pub.

Miller, Webb & Wrathall, Celia. Software for Roundoff Analysis of Matrix Algorithms. LC 80-12662. (Computer Science & Applied Mathematics Ser.). 1980. 28.50 (ISBN 0-12-497250-0). Acad Pr.

Norris, Fletcher R. Discrete Structures: An Introduction to Mathematics for Computer Scientists. (Illus.). 352p. 1985. text ed. 32.95 (ISBN 0-13-215260-6). P-H.

Number Systems. (Computer Literacy Ser.). pap. 4.95 (ISBN 0-318-04025-5). Sperry Comp Syst.

Poirot, James L., et al. Practice in Computer Mathematics. 227p 1980. pap. 7.95 (ISBN 0-317-05326-4). Sterling Swift.

Pollack, Seymour, ed. Studies in Computer Science. LC 82-62390. (MAA Studies in Mathematics: No. 22). 408p. 1982. 29.00 (ISBN 0-88385-124-5). Math Assn.

Prather, Ronald E. Discrete Mathematical Structures for Computer Science. LC 75-25014. (Illus.). 680p. 1976. text ed. 34.50 (ISBN 0-395-20622-7); solutions manual 3.50 (ISBN 0-395-20623-5). HM.

Ralston, Anthony & Wilf, H. S., eds. Mathematical Methods for Digital Computers, 2 Vols. LC 60-6509. 1960. Vol. 1, 293p. 49.95 (ISBN 0-471-70686-8); Vol. 2, 287p. 53.50 (ISBN 0-471-70689-2, Pub by Wiley-Interscience). Wiley.

Schmidt, R. Advances in Nonlinear Parameter Optimization. (Lecture Notes in Control & Information Sciences: Vol. 37). 159p. 1982. pap. 14.00 (ISBN 0-387-11396-7). Springer-Verlag.

Schwartz, J. T., ed. Mathematical Aspects of Computer Science: Proceedings of a Symposium, New York City, Apr. 1966. LC 67-16554. (Proceedings of Symposia in Applied Mathematics: Vol. 19). 1978. pap. 20.00 (ISBN 0-8218-1319-6, PSAPM-19). Am Math.

Sears, Joel L. Optimization Techniques in FORTRAN. (Illus.). 96p. (Orig.). 1979. pap. text ed. 10.00 (ISBN 0-89433-034-9). Petrocelli.

Sedlock. Mathematics for Computer Studies. 448p. 1984. write for info. (ISBN 0-534-04326-7). Wadsworth Pub.

Shanahan, William F. Essential Math, Science, & Computer Terms for College Freshmen. LC 79-3323. (Illus.). 1981. pap. 5.95 (ISBN 0-671-18435-0). Monarch Pr.

Spencer, Donald D. Computer Science Mathematics. (Mathematics Ser.). 320p. 1976. text ed. 23.95 (ISBN 0-675-08650-7). Merrill.

Sperry, Bryan. Programmed Algebra. 352p. 1981. pap. text ed. 16.95 (ISBN 0-8403-2516-9). Kendall-Hunt.

Stanat, Donald F. & McAllister, David F. Discrete Mathematics in Computer Science. LC 76-48915. (Illus.). 1977. 37.95 (ISBN 0-13-216150-8). P-H.

Stewart, G. W. Introduction to Matrix Computations. (Computer Science & Applied Mathematics Ser.). 1973. 23.25 (ISBN 0-12-670350-7). Acad Pr.

Tabler, D. N., et al. IBM OS Assembler Language-Arithmetic Operations. (Data Processing Training Ser.). 384p. 1985. pap. 49.95 (ISBN 0-471-80135-6). Wiley.

Talbot, Sandra, et al. Elements of Computer Mathematics. LC 84-21388. (Mathematics Ser.). 425p. 1985. text ed. 23.50 pub. net (ISBN 0-534-04392-5). Brooks-Cole.

Tremblay, J. P. & Manohar, R. Discrete Mathematical Structures with Applications to Computer Science. (Computer Science Ser.). (Illus.). 544p. 1975. text ed. 38.95 (ISBN 0-07-065142-6). McGraw.

Van Hulzen, J. A., ed. Computer Algebra. (Lecture Notes in Computer Science: Vol. 162). 305p. 1983. pap. 17.00 (ISBN 0-387-12868-9). Springer Verlag.

Wheaton, David. Mathematics for Data Processing. 392p. write for info. (ISBN 0-534-02771-7). Wadsworth Pub.

ELECTRONIC DATA PROCESSING–PROGRAMMED INSTRUCTION

Ahl, David H. Computers in Mathematics: A Sourcebook of Ideas. LC 79-57487. (Illus.). 214p. 1979. pap. 15.95 (ISBN 0-916688-16-X, 12D). Creative Comp.

George, F. H. Computer Arithmetic. 1966. pap. 8.50 (ISBN 0-08-011463-6). Pergamon.

Harris, Martin L. Introduction to Data Processing. 2nd ed. LC 78-21161. (Self-Teaching Guide Ser.). 304p. 1979. pap. text ed. 9.95 (ISBN 0-471-04657-4, Pub. by Wiley Pr). Wiley.

Mitchell, Ruth K. Information Science & Computer Basics: An Introduction. (Programmed Texts in Library & Information Science Ser.). 101p. 1971. 12.50 (ISBN 0-208-01118-8, Linnet). Shoe String.

National Computing Centre. Introducing Data Processing. 237p. (Orig.). 1980. pap. 18.50x (ISBN 0-85012-245-7). Intl Pubns Serv.

ELECTRONIC DATA PROCESSING–STUDY AND TEACHING

Clark & Lambrecht. Information Processing: Concepts, Principles & Procedures. 3rd ed. 1985. text ed. 14.95 (ISBN 0-538-10540-2, J54). SW Pub.

Culp, George & Nickles, Herbert N. An Apple for the Teacher: Fundamentals of Instructional Computing. 256p. 1983. pap. text ed. 14.00 pub net (ISBN 0-534-01378-3, 82-24506). Brooks-Cole.

Dawson, Peter P. & Gallegos, Frederick. Case Study II: MEDCO, Inc. (Illus.). 89p 1973. pap. text ed. 9.95 (ISBN 0-574-17920-8, 13-0920); instr's guide avail. (ISBN 0-574-17921-6, 13-0921). SRA.

Elson, Mark. Data Structures. LC 75-1451. 306p. 1975. text ed. 27.95 (ISBN 0-574-18020-6, 13-4020). SRA.

Forsythe, A. I., et al. Computer Science: A First Course. 2nd ed. LC 74-34244. 876p. 1975. 40.45 (ISBN 0-471-26681-7); tchrs.' manual avail. (ISBN 0-471-26682-5). Wiley.

Hsiao, T. C., ed. Directory of Computer Education and Research: (International Edition, 2 vols. LC 75-16507. 1800p. 1978. 150.00x (ISBN 0-912291-02-8). Sci & Tech Pr.

Lawler, E. L., et al. The Traveling Salesman Problem. (Discrete Mathematics Ser.). 1985. write for info. (ISBN 0-471-90413-9). Wiley.

Lord, Kenniston W., Jr. & Bloom, Allan M. One Thousand & One Questions & Answers to Help You Prepare for the CDP Exam. rev. ed. LC 83-63406. 294p. 1984. pap. 26.50 (ISBN 0-89435-113-3). QED Info Sci.

Scandura, Joseph M. Structural Learning, Vol. 1: Theory & Research. LC 73-76710. 382p. 1973. 53.50 (ISBN 0-677-04720-7). Gordon.

Sullivan, Roger. Handbook for Data Processing Educators. Kerr, Edwin F., ed. LC 79-67201. (Illus.). 191p. (Orig.). 1979. pap. 18.50 (ISBN 0-89435-038-2). QED Info Sci.

U Nu. U Nu: Saturday's Son. U Kyaw Win, ed. U Law Yone, tr. LC 74-79835. (Illus.). 372p. 1975. 33.00x (ISBN 0-300-01776-6). Yale U Pr.

Van Duyn, J. The DP Professional's Guide to Writing Effective Technical Communications. LC 81-15998. 218p. 1984. 29.95x (ISBN 0-471-05843-2, Pub. by Wiley-Interscience). Wiley.

ELECTRONIC DATA PROCESSING–VOCATIONAL GUIDANCE

see also Electronic Data Processing Personnel

Brechner, Irv. Getting into Computers: A Career Guide to Today's Hottest New Field. 224p. (Orig.). 1983. pap. 4.95 (ISBN 0-345-30172-2). Ballantine.

Consumer Guide Editors. Computer Careers: Where the Jobs Are & How to Get Them. 256p. 1984. pap. 6.95 (ISBN 0-449-90127-0, Columbine). Fawcett.

Hanse, P. Job Descriptions in Data Processing. (Illus.). 1977. plastic binder 35.00x (ISBN 0-85012-171-X). Intl Pubns Serv.

Hansen, P. & Penney, G. Job Trends in Data Processing. (Illus.). 1976. pap. 16.50x (ISBN 0-85012-167-1). Intl Pubns Serv.

McDaniel, Herman. Careers in Computers & Data Processing. LC 77-25076. 1978. 12.50 (ISBN 0-89433-029-2). Petrocelli.

Mainstream Access, Inc., Staff. The Data Processing-Information Technology Job Finder. 200p. 1981. 15.95 (ISBN 0-13-196394-5); pap. 5.95 (ISBN 0-13-196386-4). P-H.

Marrs, Texe W. Careers in Computers. 160p. 1984. pap. 8.95 (ISBN 0-671-50221-2). Monarch Pr.

Mitchell, Joyce S. Your Job in the Computer Age. LC 45-437. 192p. 1984. 14.95 (ISBN 0-684-18100-2, ScribT); pap. 8.95 (ISBN 0-684-18099-5). Scribner.

Morrison, Phyllis & Twing, J. W. The Business Office. (Illus.). 1977. text ed. 17.56 (ISBN 0-07-043231-7). McGraw.

Muller, Peter. The Fast Track to the Top Jobs in Computer Careers. (Fast Track Guides to Successful Careers). 128p. (Orig.). 1983. pap. 4.95 (ISBN 0-399-50753-1, G&D). Putnam Pub Group.

Noerper, Norman N. Opportunities in Data Processing. (VGM Career Bks.). (Illus.). 160p. 1983. 7.95 (ISBN 0-8442-6383-4, 6383-4, Passport Bks.); pap. 5.95 (ISBN 0-8442-6384-2, 6384-2). Natl Textbk.

Nussbaum, Martin. Opportunities in Electronic Data Processing. LC 73-184503. (Illus.). 1972. lib. bdg. 6.60 (ISBN 0-8442-6466-0). Natl Textbk.

Plevyak & Baggett. Exploring Accounting & Data Processing Careers. 1984. text ed. 6.95 wkbk. (ISBN 0-538-25420-3, Y42). SW Pub.

Spencer, Jean W. Exploring Careers in the Electronic Office. (Careers in Depth Ser.). (Illus.). 140p. 1985. lib. bdg. 8.97 (ISBN 0-8239-0657-4). Rosen Group.

Weintraub, Joseph S. Exploring Careers in the Computer Field. (Careers in Depth Ser.). 140p. 1983. lib. bdg. 8.97 (ISBN 0-8239-0567-5). Rosen Group.

Winkler, Connie. The Computer Careers Handbook. LC 82-18460. (Illus.). 160p. 1983. lib. bdg. 12.95 (ISBN 0-668-05528-6); pap. 7.95 (ISBN 0-668-05530-8). Arco.

ELECTRONIC DATA PROCESSING DEPARTMENTS

see also Computer Programming Management

Andersen, Anker. Budgeting for Data Processing. 49p. pap. 6.95 (ISBN 0-86641-089-9, 82141). Natl Assn Accts.

Brandon, Dick H. Data Processing Cost Reduction & Control. (Computer Science Ser.). (Illus.). 234p. 1978. text ed. 23.95 (ISBN 0-442-21032-9). Van Nos Reinhold.

Computer Center Construction: A Guide to Effective Planning, Construction, & Furnishing. LC 84-70742. 795p. 1984. 79.50 (ISBN 0-9613766-0-0). Bek Pr.

Data Processing Forms. (Easy-to-Make Photocopier Bks.). (Orig.). 1983. pap. 14.95 (ISBN 0-87280-047-4). Caddylak Pub.

Graef, Martin, et al. Organization & Operation of a Computer Center. Goldman, Abram F., tr. from Ger. 406p. 1985. text ed. 34.95x (ISBN 0-02-949990-9). Macmillan.

Schneiderman, Ben, ed. Data Bases: Improving Usability & Effectiveness. 1978. 47.50 (ISBN 0-12-642150-1). Acad Pr.

Sharpe, William F. Economics of Computers. LC 71-89567. 1969. 37.50x (ISBN 0-231-03266-8); pap. 18.50x (ISBN 0-231-08310-6). Columbia U Pr.

Smith, Rhandi S. Written Communication for Data Processing. LC 76-44292. pap. 51.80 (ISBN 0-317-09930-2, 2014904). Bks Demand UMI.

Wagner, Gerald E., et al. Computer Center Operations. 1984. text ed. 16.55 (ISBN 0-538-10300-0, J30). SW Pub.

ELECTRONIC DATA PROCESSING DEPARTMENTS–MANAGEMENT

Arthur, Lowell J. Programmer Productivity: Myths, Methods & Murphy's Law. 288p. 1984. pap. 17.95 (ISBN 0-471-81493-8, Pub. by Wiley-Interscience). Wiley.

Axelrod, C. Warren. Computer Effectiveness: Bridging the Management-Technology Gap. LC 79-53113. (Illus.). xi, 200p. 1979. text ed. 22.95 (ISBN 0-87815-028-5). Info Resources.

Axelrod, Warren C. Computer Productivity: A Planning Guide for Cost-Effective Management. 255p. 1982. members 22.95 (ISBN 0-318-17048-5); (W2) 24.95 (ISBN 0-318-17049-3). Data Process Mgmt.

Becker, Hal B. Information Integrity: A Structure for Its Definition & Management. (Illus.). 256p. 1983. 29.95 (ISBN 0-07-004191-1). McGraw.

Bonczek, Robert H., et al. Foundations of Decision Support Systems. LC 80-1779. (Operations Research & Industrial Engineering Ser.). 1981. 44.00 (ISBN 0-12-113050-9). Acad Pr.

Brandon, Dick H. Data Processing Cost Reduction & Control. (Computer Science Ser.). (Illus.). 234p. 1978. text ed. 23.95 (ISBN 0-442-21032-9). Van Nos Reinhold.

Brandon, Dick H. & Gray, Max. Project Control Standards. LC 79-23471. 214p. 1980. Repr. of 1970 ed. lib. bdg. 14.50 (ISBN 0-89874-039-8). Krieger.

Brandon, Dick H., et al. Data Processing Management: Methods & Standards. new ed. 1975. 34.50 (ISBN 0-02-468150-4). Macmillan Info.

Brill, Alan E., ed. Techniques of EDP Project Management: A Book of Readings. (Illus.). 296p. (Orig.). 1984. pap. 29.00 (ISBN 0-917072-42-1). Yourdon.

Burch, John G., Jr. & Sardinas, Joseph L., Jr. Computer Control & Audit: A Total Systems Approach. LC 78-9093. 492p. 1978. 42.45 (ISBN 0-471-03491-6). Wiley.

Burrill, Claude W. & Ellsworth, Leon W. Modern Project Management: Foundations for Quality & Productivity. LC 79-24457. (The Data Processing Handbook Ser.). (Illus.). 576p. 1980. text ed. 39.00x (ISBN 0-935310-00-2). Burrill-Ellsworth.

Cash, James I., Jr., et al. Corporate Information Systems Management: Text & Cases. 1983. text ed. 32.50x (ISBN 0-256-02912-1). Irwin.

Couger, J. Daniel & Zawacki, Robert A. Motivating & Managing Computer Personnel. 213p. 1980. 32.95 (ISBN 0-471-08485-9, Pub. by Wiley-Interscience). Wiley.

Donaldson, Hamish. A Guide to the Successful Management of Computer Projects. LC 78-16180. 266p. 1978. 44.95x (ISBN 0-470-26472-1). Halsted Pr.

Duffy, Neil & Assad, Mike. Information Management: An Executive Approach. (Illus.). 1980. 37.50x (ISBN 0-19-570190-9). Oxford U Pr.

Easley, Grady M. Primer for Small Systems Management. 164p. 1978. text ed. 24.95 (ISBN 0-316-20360-2). Little.

Edwards, John. Accounting & Management Controls for Computer Systems. 236p. 1980. pap. 30.50 (ISBN 0-317-19246-9, 4569). Commerce.

Eldin, H. K. & Beheshti, H. M. Management Science Applications: Computing & Systems Analysis. 316p. 1981. 31.50 (ISBN 0-444-00422-X, North-Holland). Elsevier.

Fisher, P. S., et al, eds. Advances in Distributed Processing Management, Vol. 2. LC 81-649059. (Advances in Library EDP Management: 1-604). 298p. 1983. 41.95x (ISBN 0-471-26232-3, Pub. by Wiley Heyden). Wiley.

FitzGerald, Jerry. Internal Controls for Computerized Systems. LC 78-69677. (Illus.). 93p. 1978. pap. text ed. 14.95 (ISBN 0-932410-04-9). FitzGerald & Assocs.

Frank, Michael R. The Effective EDP Manager. 288p. 1981. 17.95 (ISBN 0-8144-5635-9). AMACOM.

--The Effective EDP Manager. LC 80-65876. pap. 51.80 (ISBN 0-317-20737-7, 2023895). Bks Demand UMI.

Fried, Louis. Practical Data Processing Management. (Illus.). 1979. text ed. 25.95 (ISBN 0-8359-5589-3). Reston.

Froehlich, Allan F. Managing the Data Center. (Data Processing). (Illus.). 298p. 1982. 30.00 (ISBN 0-534-97942-4). Lifetime Learn.

--Managing the Data Center. 298p. 1982. 30.00 (ISBN 0-534-97942-4). Van Nos Reinhold.

Galley, J. N. The Board & Computer Management. 185p. 1978. text ed. 29.50x (ISBN 0-220-67000-5, Pub. by Busn Bks England). Brookfield Pub Co.

Greenbaum, Joan M. In the Name of Efficiency: Management Theory & Shopfloor Practice in Data Processing Work. 210p. 1979. 27.95 (ISBN 0-87722-151-0). Temple U Pr.

Head, Robert V. Federal Information Systems Management: Issues & New Directions. LC 81-70470. 67p. 1982. pap. 5.95 (ISBN 0-8157-3529-4). Brookings.

Hernandez, Ernie, Jr. Police Handbook for Applying the Systems Approach & Computer Technology. LC 82-17662. (Illus.). 231p. 1982. 26.95 (ISBN 0-910657-00-9); pap. 19.95 (ISBN 0-910657-01-7). Frontline.

Higgins, J. C. Information Systems for Planning & Control: Concepts & Cases. 1976. 37.50x (ISBN 0-7131-3375-9); pap. 23.95x (ISBN 0-7131-3376-7). Intl Ideas.

Hill, E., Jr. A Comparative Study of Very Large Data Bases. (Lecture Notes in Computer Sciences: Vol. 59). 1978. pap. 14.00 (ISBN 0-387-08653-6). Springer-Verlag.

Infotech. Management Report, 2 vols. (Infotech Structured Prog. Reports). 402p. 1978. 560.00 (ISBN 0-08-028546-5). Pergamon.

Johansen, Robert & Vallee, Jacques. Electronic Meetings: Technical Alternatives & Social Choices. 244p. 1979. 16.95 (ISBN 0-686-98116-2). Telecom Lib.

Kennevan, Walter & Joslin, Edward O. Management & Computer Systems. rev. 2nd ed. 354p. 1973. pap. 5.95 (ISBN 0-916580-07-5). College Readings.

Kraft, Philip. Programmers & Managers: The Routinization of Computer Programming in the United States. LC 77-1667. (Illus.). 1977. pap. 13.00 (ISBN 0-387-90248-1). Springer-Verlag.

Lucas, Henry C. Information Systems Concepts for Management. 2nd ed. 1982. 34.95 (ISBN 0-07-038924-1). McGraw.

McCarthy, M. Dianne. Project Management of Data Processing Application Development. (Professional Development Programs Ser.). 1984. 55.95x (ISBN 0-471-80712-5, Pub. by Wiley). Wiley.

McFarlan. Information Systems Administration. text ed. cancelled (ISBN 0-8290-0637-0). Irvington.

McFarlan, F. Warren & McKenney, James L. Corporate Information Systems Management: The Issues Facing Senior Executives. LC 82-73926. 180p. 1982. 25.00 (ISBN 0-87094-347-2). Dow Jones-Irwin.

McFarlan, F. Warren, et al. Information Systems Administration. LC 81-40920. (Illus.). 608p. 1982. pap. text ed. 23.25. U Pr of Amer.

Maddison, R. N., et al. Information System Methodologies: A Collective View. (Advances in Nuclear Quadruple Advances: 1-607). 128p. (Orig.). 1983. pap. 21.95x (ISBN 0-471-90332-9, Pub. by Wiley-Interscience). Wiley.

Management Strategy for Distributed Systems. 1978. pap. 23.00x (ISBN 0-85012-200-7). Intl Pubns Serv.

Martin, J. End User's Guide to Data Base. 1981. 35.00 (ISBN 0-13-277129-2). P-H.

Martin, James. An Information Systems Manifesto. (Illus.). 352p. 1984. text ed. 45.00 (ISBN 0-13-464769-6). P-H.

Mixon, S. R. Handbook of Data Processing Administration, Operations, & Procedures. new ed. LC 75-38914. (Illus.). 396p. 1976. 29.95 (ISBN 0-8144-5400-3). AMACOM.

Mixon, Shirley R. Handbook of Data Processing Administration, Operations & Procedures. LC 75-38914. pap. 101.30 (ISBN 0-317-20748-2, 2023901). Bks Demand UMI.

Morgan, Lyndon. Managing On-Line Data Communications Systems. (Illus.). 166p. (Orig.). 1979. pap. 35.00x (ISBN 0-85012-216-3). Intl Pubns Serv.

Morsley. Managing the Distribution of DP, 2 vols. (Infotech Computer State of the Art Reports). 450p. 1979. Set. 145.00s (ISBN 0-08-028518-X). Pergamon.

Perry, William E. Data Processing Budgets: How to Develop & Use Budgets Effectively. (Illus.). 256p. 1985. text ed. 41.95 (ISBN 0-13-196874-2). P-H.

--EDP Administration & Control. (Illus.). 416p. 1984. text ed. 39.95 (ISBN 0-13-235649-X). P-H.

--Effective Methods of EDP Quality Assurance. (Q. E. D. Information Sciences Ser.). (Illus.). 400p. 1983. text ed. 39.50 (ISBN 0-13-244336-8). P-H.

--Ensuring Data Base Integrity. LC 82-25922. 378p. 1983. 45.00x (ISBN 0-471-86526-5, Pub. by Ronald Pr). Wiley.

Pokempner, Stanley J. & O'Connor, Rochelle, eds. Senior Management & the Data Processing Function. (Report Ser: No. 636). 122p. 1974. pap. 25.00 (ISBN 0-8237-0051-8); pap. 5.00 member. Conference Bd.

A Practical Guide to Systems Development Management. 1985. pap. write for info (ISBN 0-442-20915-0). Van Nos Reinhold.

Roeske, Edward. The Data Factory: Data Center Operations & System Development. 1983. write for info. Yourdon.

Rudman, Jack. Director of Data Processing. (Career Examination Ser.: C-2518). (Cloth bdg. avail. on request). pap. 14.00 (ISBN 0-8373-2518-8). Natl Learning.

--Manager Computer Operations. (Career Examination Ser.: C-2241). (Cloth bdg. avail. on request). pap. 12.00 (ISBN 0-8373-2241-3). Natl Learning.

Rullo, Thomas A., ed. Advances in Data Communications Management, Vol. 1. (Wiley-Heyden Advances in Library in EDP Management Ser.). 210p. 1980. 35.95 (ISBN 0-471-25998-5, Pub. by Wiley Heyden). Wiley.

--Advances in Data Processing Management, Vol. 1. LC 81-640185. 207p. 1980. 35.95 (ISBN 0-471-25993-4). Wiley.

--Advances in Distributed Processing Management, Vol. 1. (Wiley-Heyden Advances Library in EDP Management Ser.). 225p. 1980. 35.95 (ISBN 0-471-25997-7, Pub. by Wiley Heyden). Wiley.

--The Heyden Advances Library in EDP Management in Six Volumes. 1980. 215.75 (ISBN 0-471-26002-9, Pub. by Wiley-Interscience). Wiley.

Schaeffer, H. Data Center Operations: A Guide to Effective Planning, Processing & Performance. 1981. 42.50 (ISBN 0-13-196360-0). P-H.

Share Working Conference on Data Base Management Systems, 2nd, Canada, 1977. The ANSI-SPARC DBMS Model: Proceedings. Jardine, D. A., ed. 226p. 1977. 59.75 (ISBN 0-7204-0719-2, North-Holland). Elsevier.

Shneiderman, Ben, ed. Database Management Systems. LC 76-41070. (Information Technology Ser.: Vol. I). (Illus.). 137p. 1976. pap. 17.25 (ISBN 0-88283-014-7). AFIPS Pr.

Singer, Larry M. The Data Processing Manager's Survival Manual: A Guide for Managing People & Resources. 240p. 1982. 28.95x (ISBN 0-471-86476-5, Pub by Ronald Pr). Wiley.

Slonin, Jacob & Unger, E. A. Advances in Data Communications Management, Vol. 2. (Advances Library in EDP Management: 1-604). 281p. 1984. 39.95x (ISBN 0-471-26233-1, Pub. by Wiley Heyden). Wiley.

Smith, Randi S. Written Communication for Data Processing. LC 81-6013. 208p. 1981. Repr. of 1976 ed. lib. bdg. 16.95 (ISBN 0-89874-361-3). Krieger.

Thompson, Treva L. Information Processing Job Description for Personnel Officers. LC 82-83717. 44p. 1983. 5.75 (ISBN 0-942898-00-1). Halpern & Simon.

Vichas, Robert P. New Encyclopedic Dictionary of Systems & Procedures. 700p. 1981. 39.95 (ISBN 0-13-612630-8). P-H.

Ward. Computer Audit & Control, 2 vols. (Infotech Computer State of the Art Reports). 570p. 1980. Set. 310.00 (ISBN 0-08-028502-3). Pergamon.

Weaver, Barbara N. & Bishop, Wiley L. The Corporate Memory: A Profitable & Practical Approach to Information Management & Retention Systems. LC 80-20187. 282p. 1981. Repr. of 1974 ed. text ed. 22.50 (ISBN 0-89874-245-5). Krieger.

Weber, H. & Wasserman, A. I., eds. Issues in Data Base Management. LC 79-10481. 264p. 1979. 47.00 (ISBN 0-444-85316-2, North Holland). Elsevier.

Wetherbe, James C. Cases in Systems Design. (Data Processing & Information Systems Ser.). 1979. pap. text ed. 11.95 (ISBN 0-8299-0229-5). West Pub.

Williams, Frederick & Dordick, Herbert. The Executive's Guide to Information Technology: How to Increase Your Competitive Edge. LC 83-12331. 314p. 1983. 24.95 (ISBN 0-471-86943-0); member 23.75. Assn Inform & Image Mgmt.

Zmud, Robert W. Information Systems in Organizations. 1983. text ed. 28.20x (ISBN 0-673-15438-6). Scott F.

ELECTRONIC DATA PROCESSING DEPARTMENTS–SECURITY MEASURES

Baker, Richard H. The Computer Security Handbook. (Illus.). 288p. 1985. 25.00 (ISBN 0-8306-0308-5, 2608). Tab Bks.

Becker, Hal B. Information Integrity: A Structure for Its Definition & Management. (Illus.). 256p. 1983. 29.95 (ISBN 0-07-004191-1). McGraw.

Becker, R. S. The Data Processing Security Game: Fundamentals of Data Processing Security. 1977. text ed. 8.75 (ISBN 0-08-021790-7). Pergamon.

Bequai, August. How to Prevent Computer Crime: A Guide for Managers. LC 83-6952. 308p. 1983. 29.95x (ISBN 0-471-09367-X, Pub. by Wiley-Interscience). Wiley.

Browne, Peter S. Security: Checklist for Computer Center Self-Audits. LC 79-56012. (Illus.). 189p. 1979. pap. 29.95. AFIPS Pr.

Buck, Edward R. Introduction to Data Security & Controls. LC 82-62128. (Illus.). 247p. (Orig.). 1982. pap. 19.50 (ISBN 0-89435-062-5). QED Info Sci.

Carroll, John M. Computer Security. LC 77-10615. (Illus.). 400p. 1977. 27.50 (ISBN 0-913708-28-3). Butterworth.

--Data Base & Computer Systems Security. Curtice, Robert M., ed. (Data Base Monograph: No. 4). 1976. pap. 15.00 (ISBN 0-89435-002-1). QED Info Sci.

Chantico-QED. Security Evaluation for Small Computer Systems. LC 85-60178. (The Chantico Technical Management Ser.). (Illus.). 159p. (Orig.). 1985. 29.50 (ISBN 0-89435-154-0, CP 1540). QED Info Sci.

Computer Security Techniques. 219p. 1982. pap. 7.50 (ISBN 0-318-11768-1). Gov Printing Office.

Cooper, James A. Computer-Security Technology. LC 82-49206. (Illus.). 192p. 1984. 26.50x (ISBN 0-669-06436-X). Lexington Bks.

Davies, D. W. & Price, W. L. Security for Computer Networks: An Introduction to Data Security in Teleprocessing & Electronic Funds Transfer. (Computing Ser.). 300p. 1984. 34.95 (ISBN 0-471-90063-X). Wiley.

--Security in Teleprocessing & EPT Encryptian & Authentication in Computer Networks. LC 84-3662. (Computing Ser. 1-320). 300p. 1984. 34.95. Wiley.

Davies, Donald W. The Security of Data in Networks. (Tutorial Texts Ser.). 241p. 1981. 20.00 (ISBN 0-8186-0366-6, Q366). IEEE Comp Soc.

Dinardo, C. T., ed. Computers & Security, Vol. III. (The Information Technology Ser.). (Illus.). 247p. 1977. pap. 23.00 (ISBN 0-88283-016-3). AFIPS Pr.

Doswell, R. Word Processing Security. 150p. 1982. pap. 20.75 (ISBN 0-471-89432-X). Wiley.

Douglas, I. J. Security & Audit of Database Systems. 23p. (Orig.). 1980. 15.00x (ISBN 0-85012-279-1). Intl Pubns Serv.

Eason, Thomas S. & Webb, Douglas A. Nine Steps to Effective EDP Loss Control. 177p. 1983. 25.00 (ISBN 0-932376-25-8, EY-00006-DP). Digital Pr.

EDP Physical Security Briefing & Checklist. 1977. pap. 5.00 (ISBN 0-918734-13-4). Reymont.

Elam, Phillip G. Checklist-Guide for Assessing Data Processing Safeguards. LC 82-22320. 64p. 1983. pap. 5.00 (ISBN 0-87576-101-1). Pilot Bks.

Ellison. Computer Systems Security. (Infotech Computer State of the Art Reports). 1981. 405.00 (ISBN 0-08-028558-9). Pergamon.

Enger, Norman L. & Howerton, Paul W. Computer Security: A Management Audit Approach. LC 80-65874. pap. 68.00 (ISBN 0-317-27070-2, 2023536). Bks Demand UMI.

Finch, J. H. & Dougall, E. G., eds. Computer Security: A Global Challenge. 1985. 50.00 (ISBN 0-444-87618-9, North-Holland). Elsevier.

Fine, Leonard H. Computer Security: Handbook for Management. 1984. 15.95 (ISBN 0-434-90578-X, Pub. by W Heinemann Ltd). David & Charles.

Fisher, Royal P. Information Systems Security. (Illus.). 208p. 1984. text ed. 34.95 (ISBN 0-13-464727-0). P-H.

Hemphill, Charles F., Jr. & Hemphill, Robert D. Security Safeguards in Computer Operations. 1979. pap. 7.50 (ISBN 0-8144-2232-2). AMACOM.

Hoffman, Lance J. Security & Privacy in Computer Systems. LC 73-6744. (Information Sciences Ser.). pap. 107.80 (ISBN 0-317-26258-0, 2055715). Bks Demand UMI.

Hsiao, David K., et al. Computer Security. LC 79-14503. (ACM Monograph Ser.). 1979. 45.00 (ISBN 0-12-357650-4). Acad Pr.

Kemmerer, Richard A. Formal Verification of an Operating Systems Security Kernel. Stone, Harold, ed. LC 82-4805. (Computer Science: Systems Programming Ser.: No. 2). 332p. 1982. 49.95 (ISBN 0-8357-1322-9). UMI Res Pr.

Krauss, Leonard I. SAFE: Security Audit & Field Evaluation for Computer Facilities & Information Systems. 336p. 1981. 29.95 (ISBN 0-8144-5526-3). AMACOM.

--SAFE: Security Audit & Field Evaluation for Computer Facilities & Information Systems. Rev. ed. LC 80-67963. pap. 80.00 (ISBN 0-317-27189-X, 2023923). Bks Demand UMI.

Krauss, Leonard I. & MacGahar, Aileen. Computer Fraud & Countermeasures. (Illus.). 1979. ref. ed. 45.00 (ISBN 0-13-164772-5). P-H.

Kuong, J. F., ed. Checklists & Guidelines for Reviewing Computer Security & Installations (Map-4) Updated & Complete Edition 1976. (Illus.). 1976. prepaid manual form, 3-ring binder 55.00 (ISBN 0-940706-02-4, MAP-4). Management Advisory Pubns.

Landreth, Bill. Out of the Inner Circle: A Hacker's Guide to Computer Security. 256p. 1985. 19.95 (ISBN 0-914845-45-4); pap. 9.95 (ISBN 0-914845-36-5). Microsoft.

Leiss, Ernst L. Principles of Data Security. LC 82-22272. (Foundations of Computer Science Ser.). 238p. 1982. 27.50 (ISBN 0-306-41098-2, Plenum Pr). Plenum Pub.

Lord, Kenniston W., Jr. The Data Center Disaster Consultant. rev. ed. 200p. 1981. 26.50 (ISBN 0-89435-000-5). QED Info Sci.

Management Handbook of Computer Security. 1978. 185.00x (ISBN 0-85012-185-X). Intl Pubns Serv.

Marting, James. Security, Accuracy, & Privacy in Computer Systems. new ed. (Illus.). 512p. 1973. 45.00 (ISBN 0-13-798991-1). P-H.

National Computing Centre. Planning for Standby. Waring, L. P., ed. LC 77-361948. 1976. pap. 16.50x (ISBN 0-85012-183-3). Intl Pubns Serv.

National Computing Centre (Manchester) Computing Practice: Security Aspects. 53p. (Orig.). 1979. pap. 25.00x (ISBN 0-85012-215-5). Intl Pubns Serv.

Norman, Adrian R. Computer Insecurity. (Illus.). 250p. 1983. 29.95 (ISBN 0-412-22310-4, NO. 6640). Methuen Inc.

Parker, Donn. Computer Security Management. 304p. 1981. text ed. 26.95 (ISBN 0-8359-0905-0). Reston.

Perry, William E. Computer Control & Security: A Guide for Managers & Systems Analysts. LC 80-39936. (Business Data Processing: a Wiley Ser.). 207p. 1981. 38.50x (ISBN 0-471-05235-3, Pub. by Wiley-Interscience). Wiley.

--Management Strategies for Computer Security. 240p. 1985. text ed. 24.95 (ISBN 0-409-95135-8). Butterworth.

Pritchard, J. A. Computer Security: Facts & Figures. LC 81-453659. (Illus.). 75p. (Orig.). 1979. pap. 15.00x (ISBN 0-85012-224-4). Intl Pubns Serv.

--Computer Security: Facts & Figures. 75p. 1979. pap. 15.30 (ISBN 0-471-89498-2). Wiley.

--Computer Security: Security Software. 123p. 1980. pap. 18.60 (ISBN 0-471-89434-6). Wiley.

--Risk Management in Action. 1978. 22.50x (ISBN 0-85012-180-9). Intl Pubns Serv.

--Security in On-Line Systems. (Illus., Orig.). 1979. pap. 35.00x (ISBN 0-85012-211-2). Intl Pubns Serv.

Protecting Personal Information in Computer Systems. 1978. pap. 3.00 (ISBN 0-918734-23-1). Reymont.

Rullo. Advances in Computer Security Management, Vol. 2. 1981. write for info. (ISBN 0-85501-612-4). Wiley.

Rullo, Thomas A., ed. Advances in Computer Security Management, Vol. 1. LC 81-641060. (Wiley-Heyden Advances in EDP Management Ser.). 210p. 1980. 35.95 (ISBN 0-471-25999-3, Pub. by Wiley Heyden). Wiley.

Sapse, Anne-Marie, et al. Computer Applications in the Private Security Business. LC 80-36754. 154p. 1980. 34.95x (ISBN 0-03-057031-X). Praeger.

Schweitzer, James. Protecting Information in the Electronic Workplace: A Guide for Managers. 1983. text ed. 22.95 (ISBN 0-8359-5702-0). Reston.

Squires, T. Computer Security: The Personal Aspect. 150p. 1980. pap. 29.50 (ISBN 0-471-89499-0). Wiley.

--People & Security: An Introduction. LC 80-148080. 61p. (Orig.). 1980. pap. 17.50x (ISBN 0-85012-237-6). Intl Pubns Serv.

--Security in Systems Design. 57p. 1981. pap. 14.20 (ISBN 0-471-89426-5). Wiley.

Systems Scurity: The Key to Computer Integrity. 201p. 1984. pap. text ed. 100.00x (ISBN 0-86353-018-4, Pub. by Online). Brookfield Pub Co.

Talbot, J. R. Management Guide to Computer Security. 180p. 1981. 34.95x (ISBN 0-470-27142-6). Halsted Pr.

--Management Guide to Computer Security. 180p. 1981. text ed. 36.95x (ISBN 0-566-02190-0). Gower Pub Co.

--Management Guide to Computer Security. 2nd ed. 200p. 1986. text ed. price not set (ISBN 0-566-02610-4). Gower Pub Co.

Turn, Rein, intro. by. Advances in Computer System Security. LC 81-65989. (Illus.). 403p. (Orig.). 1981. pap. text ed. 44.00 (ISBN 0-89006-096-7). Artech Hse.

User's Guide for Voice & Data Communications Security Equipment. 75.00 (ISBN 0-686-32978-3). Info Gatekeepers.

Walker, B. J. & Blake, Ian F. Computer Security & Protection Structures. 1977. 29.50 (ISBN 0-87933-247-6). Van Nos Reinhold.

Wofsey, Marvin M. Advances in Computer Security Management, Vol. 2. (Wiley-Heyden Advances in EDP Management Ser.). 268p. 1983. 39.95x (ISBN 0-471-26234-X, Pub. by Wiley Heyden). Wiley.

Wood, M. B. Introducing Computer Security. 160p. 1982. pap. 18.50x (ISBN 0-85012-340-2). Intl Pubns Serv.

--Introducing Computer Security. 160p. 1982. pap. 18.60 (ISBN 0-471-89460-5). Wiley.

Yankee Group. The Electronic Vault: Computer Piracy & Privacy. LC 84-210486. (Industry Research Report Ser.). (Illus.). 122p. 1984. write for info. Yankee Group.

ELECTRONIC DATA PROCESSING DOCUMENTATION

Aschner, Katherine, ed. Taking Control of Your Office Records: A Manager's Guide. LC 83-6133. (Information & Communications Management Guides Ser.). (Illus.). 264p. 1983. professional 32.95 (ISBN 0-86729-057-9, 704-BW); pap. 22.95 professional (ISBN 0-86729-058-7). Assn Inform & Image Mgmt.

Ayer, Steve J. & Patrinostro, Frank S. Systems Development Documentation: Forms Method. (Illus.). 430p. (Orig.). pap. 56.00 (ISBN 0-9611694-0-0). Tech Comm Assoc.

Bradley, James. File & Data Base Techniques. 480p. 1982. text ed. 35.95 (ISBN 0-03-058673-9, HoltC). HR&W.

Cook, Michael. Archives & the Computer. LC 80-41286. 152p. 1981. text ed. 49.95 (ISBN 0-408-10734-0). Butterworth.

Enger, Norman L. Documentation Standards for Computer Systems. 2nd ed. LC 79-5289. (Illus.). 1980. text ed. 25.00 (ISBN 0-89321-119-2). Tech Pr Inc.

Finkel, LeRoy & Brown, Jerald R. TRS-80 Data File Programming. (Self-Teaching Guides: No. 1-581). 320p. 1983. pap. text ed. 14.95 (ISBN 0-471-88486-3, Pub. by Wiley Press). Wiley.

Gildersleeve, Thomas R. Organizing & Documenting Data Processing Information. 1977. pap. text ed. 10.95x (ISBN 0-8104-5739-3). Hayden.

Harper, William L. Data Processing Documentation: Standards, Procedures & Applications. 2nd. ed. 288p. 1980. 60.00x (ISBN 0-13-196816-5). P-H.

Houghton-Alico, D. Creating Computer Software User Guides: From Manuals to Menus. 17.95 (ISBN 0-07-030471-8). McGraw.

Johnson, Leroy F. & Cooper, Rodney H. File Techniques for Data Base Organization in COBOL. (P-H Software Ser.). (Illus.). 384p. 1981. text ed. 28.95 (ISBN 0-13-314039-3). P-H.

Loomis, Mary E. Data Management & File Processing. (Software Ser.). (Illus.). 544p. 1983. 32.95 (ISBN 0-13-196477-1). P-H.

Mabbs, A. W. Organization of Intermediate Records Storage. (Documentation, Libraries & Archives: Bibliographies & Reference Works: No. 5). (Illus.). 74p. (Orig.). 1974. pap. 5.00 (ISBN 92-3-101152-9, U440, UNESCO). Unipub.

McKay, Lucia. Soft Words, Hard Words: A Common-Sense Guide to Creative Documentation. pap. 14.95 (ISBN 0-912677-13-9). Ashton-Tate Bks.

Mellor, Rickerby. Data Processing Documentation Standards. (Illus.). 1977. Ringbinder 168.50x (ISBN 0-85012-176-0). Intl Pubns Serv.

National Computing Centre Ltd. Technical Documentation Standards for Computer Programs & Computer-Based Systems Used in Engineering. (Illus.). 180p. 1980. 72.50x (ISBN 0-85012-247-3). Intl Pubns Serv.

Omlor, J. Dennis. Efficiency Analysis of File Organization & Information Retrieval. Stone, Harold S., ed. LC 81-11693. (Computer Science: Distributed Database Systems Ser.: No. 10). 124p. 1981. 29.95 (ISBN 0-8357-1226-5). UMI Res Pr.

Patterson, Diana. The Computer Documentation Kit. 1984. text ed. 34.95 (ISBN 0-8359-0841-0); pap. text ed. 24.95 (ISBN 0-8359-0845-3). Reston.

Poschmann, Andrew W. Standards & Procedures for Systems Documentation. LC 83-45207. 288p. 1984. pap. 55.00x comb bdg. (ISBN 0-8144-7015-7). AMACOM.

Whitehouse, Frank. Systems Documentation: Techniques of Persuasion in Large Organizations. 1973. 22.00x (ISBN 0-8464-0906-2). Beekman Pubs.

Zaneski, Richard. Software Manual Production Simplified. (Illus.). 224p. 1982. 20.00 (ISBN 0-89433-180-9). Petrocelli.

ELECTRONIC DATA PROCESSING IN RESEARCH

Afifi, Abdelmonem & Clark, Virginia. Computer-Aided Multivariate Analysis. (Illus.). 360p. 1984. 32.00 (ISBN 0-534-02786-5). Lifetime Learn.

Frieden, B. R., ed. The Computer in Optical Research: Methods & Applications. (Topics in Applied Physics: Vol. 41). (Illus.). 400p. 1980. 66.00 (ISBN 0-387-10119-5). Springer-Verlag.

Gilreath, Charles L. Computer Literature Searching: Research Strategies & Databases. 180p. 1984. softcover 22.00x (ISBN 0-86531-526-4). Westview.

Hopple, Gerald W. & Kuhlman, James A. Expert-Generated Data: Applications in International Affairs. (Westview Replica Edition Ser.). 225p. 1981. 32.00x (ISBN 0-89158-870-1). Westview.

Klopfenstein, Charles E. & Wilkins, Charles L., eds. Computers in Chemical & Biochemical Research, Vol. 1. 1972. 65.00 (ISBN 0-12-151301-7). Acad Pr.

Oakman, Robert L. Computer Methods for Literary Research. Rev. ed. LC 83-9237. 256p. 1984. pap. 8.95x (ISBN 0-8203-0686-X). U of Ga Pr.

Posey, Joanna W. Tracing Your Roots by Computer: An Overview & Introduction to Genealogical Computer Use. rev. ed. Woodbury, P., ed. (How To Ser.). (Illus.). 300p. 1984. pap. 24.95 (ISBN 0-940348-10-1). Posey Pubns.

Technical Insights, Inc. Managing Laboratory Information: The Computer Options. LC 85-52738. (Illus.). 1985. spiral bdg. 470.00 (ISBN 0-914993-11-9). Tech Insights.

--R&D Database Handbook: A Worldwide Guide to Key Scientific & Technical Databases. LC 85-51897. 203p. 1984. 292.00. Tech Insights.

Thesen, Arne, ed. Computer Methods in Operations Research. (Operations Research & Industrial Engineering Ser). 1978. 27.50 (ISBN 0-12-686150-1). Acad Pr.

World Weather Watch. International Global Data-Processing System Plan to Support the First GARP Global Experiment. (Illus.). iii, 75p. 1977. pap. 18.00 (ISBN 92-63-10469-7, W355, WMO). Unipub.

ELECTRONIC DATA PROCESSING PERSONNEL

Couger, Daniel J. & Zawacki, Robert A. Motivating & Managing Computer Personnel. 232p. 1980. members 25.95 (ISBN 0-318-17053-1); (W4) 27.95 (ISBN 0-318-17054-X). Data Process Mgmt.

Rudman, Jack. Associate Computer Programmer. (Career Examination Ser.: C-2206). (Cloth bdg. avail. on request). pap. 14.00 (ISBN 0-8373-2206-5). Natl Learning.

--Chief Data Processing Equipment Operator. (Career Examination Ser.: C-2305). (Cloth bdg. avail. on request). 1977. pap. 14.00 (ISBN 0-8373-2304-5). Natl Learning.

--Chief Electronic Computer Operator. (Career Examination Ser.: C-1550). (Cloth bdg. avail. on request). pap. 14.00 (ISBN 0-8373-1550-6). Natl Learning.

--Data Processing Equipment Operator. (Career Examination Ser.: C-2301). (Cloth bdg. avail. on request). 1977. pap. 12.00 (ISBN 0-8373-2301-0). Natl Learning.

--Data Processing Operations Supervisor. (Career Examination Ser.: C-2347). (Cloth bdg. avail. on request). pap. 12.00 (ISBN 0-8373-2347-9). Natl Learning.

--Key Punch Supervisor. (Career Examination Ser.: C-2102). (Cloth bdg. avail. on request). 1977. pap. 12.00 (ISBN 0-8373-2102-6). Natl Learning.

--Principal Data Processing Equipment Operator. (Career Examination Ser.: C-2303). (Cloth bdg. avail. on request). 1977. pap. 12.00 (ISBN 0-8373-2303-7). Natl Learning.

--Principal Key Punch Operator. (Career Examination Ser.: C-2103). (Cloth bdg. avail. on request). 1977. pap. 12.00 (ISBN 0-8373-2103-4). Natl Learning.

--Senior Data Processing Equipment Operator. (Career Examination Ser.: C-2302). (Cloth bdg. avail. on request). 1977. pap. 12.00 (ISBN 0-8373-2302-9). Natl Learning.

--Supervising Electronic Computer Operator. (Career Examination Ser.: C-1549). (Cloth bdg. avail. on request). pap. 10.00 (ISBN 0-8373-1549-2). Natl Learning.

Shanahan, William F. Resumes for Computer Professionals: A Complete Resume Preparation & Job-Getting Guide. LC 83-3914. 144p. (Orig.). 1983. lib. bdg. 12.95 (ISBN 0-668-05785-8); pap. 6.95 (ISBN 0-668-05789-0). Arco.

Weinberg, Gerald M. Understanding the Professional Programmer. 240p. 1982. text ed. 22.95 (ISBN 0-316-92845-3). Little.

ELECTRONIC DIFFERENTIAL ANALYZERS

Forbes, George F. Digital Differential Analyzers. 4th ed. LC 57-903. 1957. pap. text ed. 25.00 (ISBN 0-685-10947-X). G F Forbes.

--System Analyzer. 1961. pap. text ed. 2.25 (ISBN 0-685-10948-8). G F Forbes.

Luenberger, David G. Introduction to Dynamic Systems: Theory, Models & Applications. LC 78-12366. 446p. 1979. 46.00 (ISBN 0-471-02594-1); solutions manual avail. (ISBN 0-471-06081-X). Wiley.

Vichenevetsky, Robert. Computer Methods for Partial Differential Equations: Elliptical Equations & the Finite Element Method, Vol. 1. (Illus.). 400p. 1981. text ed. 45.00 (ISBN 0-13-165233-8). P-H.

ELECTRONIC DIGITAL COMPUTERS

see also Computer-Assisted Instruction; Computer Graphics; Digital Computer Simulation; Computer Sound Processing; Error-Correcting Codes (Information Theory); IBM 360 (Computer); IBM 1130 (Computer); Minicomputers; Sequential Machine Theory; Time-Sharing Computer Systems

A. Mathematische Auswahl-Funktionen und Gesellschaftliche Entscheidungen. (Interdisciplinary Systems Research Ser.: No. 14). (Ger., Illus.). 343p. 1976. 37.95x (ISBN 0-8176-0814-1). Birkhauser.

Aczel, J. Vorlesungen Uber Funktionalgleichungen und Ihre Anwendungen. (Mathematische Reihe Ser.: No. 25). (Ger., Illus.). 331p. 1961. 44.95x (ISBN 0-8176-0002-7). Birkhauser.

Aleksander, Igor, et al. Advanced Digital Information Systems. (Illus.). 576p. 1985. text ed. 39.95 (ISBN 0-13-011305-0). P-H.

Alt, Franz L. Electronic Digital Computers: Their Uses in Science & Engineering. (Applied Mathematics & Mechanics Ser: Vol. 4). 1958. 65.00 (ISBN 0-12-053650-1). Acad Pr.

Andrews, Harry C. & Hunt, B. R. Digital Image Restoration. (Signal Processing Ser.). (Illus.). 1977. 41.95 (ISBN 0-13-214213-9). P-H.

Atwood, Jerry W. The Systems Analyst: How to Design Computer-Based Systems. 1977. text ed. 14.50x (ISBN 0-8104-5102-6). Hayden.

Automated Education Center. Disc File Applications. LC 64-23108. 19.00 (ISBN 0-403-04466-9). Scholarly.

--Total Systems. LC 62-14778. 19.00 (ISBN 0-403-04483-9). Scholarly.

Ball, Marion J. What Is a Computer. (Illus.). 92p. 1972. pap. text ed. 8.88 (ISBN 0-395-13772-1). HM.

Bartee, Thomas. Digital Computer Fundamentals. 5th ed. (Illus.). 576p. 1980. text ed. 33.95 (ISBN 0-07-003894-5). McGraw.

Benson, Ian, ed. Intelligent Machinery: Theory & Practice. 250p. Date not set. price not set (ISBN 0-521-30836-4). Cambridge U Pr.

Bernstein, Jeremy. The Analytical Engine: Computers - Past, Present, & Future. rev. ed. LC 80-29413. 128p. 1981. pap. 8.95 (ISBN 0-688-00488-1). Morrow.

Blaauw, Gerritt A. Digital System Implementation. (Illus.). 1976. 36.95 (ISBN 0-13-212241-3). P-H.

Black, W. Wayne. An Introduction to On-Line Computers. LC 70-141580. (Illus.). 462p. 1971. 85.75 (ISBN 0-677-02930-6). Gordon.

Bohl, E., et al, eds. Numerik und Anwendungen von Eigenwertaufgaben und Verzweigungsproblemen. (International Series of Umerical Mathematics: No. 38). (Ger.). 218p. 1977. pap. 36.95x (ISBN 0-8176-0938-5). Birkhauser.

Borrmann, Axel, et al. The EC's Generalized System of Preferences. 276p. 1981. 56.00 (ISBN 90-286-2111-3). Sijthoff & Noordhoff.

Boyce, Jefferson C. Digital Computer Fundamentals. LC 76-11768. (Illus.). 1977. 32.95 (ISBN 0-13-214114-0). P-H.

Bray, Olin H. & Freeman, Harry A. Data-Base Computers. LC 78-24765. 192p. 1979. 27.00x (ISBN 0-669-02834-7). Lexington Bks.

Breuer, Melvin A. & Friedman, Arthur D. Diagnosis & Reliable Design of Digital Systems. LC 76-19081. 308p. 1976. 33.95 (ISBN 0-914894-57-9). Computer Sci.

Brookshear, Glenn. Computer Science: A Survey. 1985. 23.95 (ISBN 0-8053-0900-4); instr's. manual 5.95 (ISBN 0-8053-0901-2); Pascal Programming Supplement, by Mark A. Barnard. lab manual 7.95 (ISBN 0-8053-0902-0). Benjamin-Cummings.

Capron, H. L. & Williams, Brian K. Computers & Data Processing. 2nd ed. 1984. 28.95 (ISBN 0-8053-2214-0); instr's guide 5.95 (ISBN 0-8053-2215-9); study guide 8.95 (ISBN 0-8053-2216-7); guide to testing 5.95 (ISBN 0-8053-2217-5); transparency masters 40.00 (ISBN 0-8053-2218-3); instr's resource manual (3-ring binder) 150.00 (ISBN 0-8053-2219-1); guide to subscriptions, films & videos 5.95 (ISBN 0-8053-2222-1); transparencies 150.00 (ISBN 0-8053-2223-X). Benjamin-Cummings.

Carberry, M., et al. Foundations of Computer Science. LC 78-27891. 317p. 1979. text ed. 28.95 (ISBN 0-914894-18-8). Computer Sci.

Ceruzzi, Paul E. Reckoners: The Prehistory of the Digital Computer, From Relays to the Stored Program Concept, 1935-1945. LC 82-20980. (Contributions to the Study of Computer Science Ser.: No. 1). (Illus.). 240p. 1983. lib. bdg. 29.95 (ISBN 0-313-23382-9, CED/). Greenwood.

CES Industries, Inc. Ed-Lab Seven Hundred Experiment Manual: Digital Systems. (Illus.). 304p. 1979. 12.50 (ISBN 0-86711-001-5). CES Industries.

Clements, Alan. Principles of Computer Hardware. (Illus.). 450p. 1985. 32.50 (ISBN 0-19-853704-2); pap. 16.95 (ISBN 0-19-853703-4). Oxford U Pr.

Collatz, L. & Hadeler, K. P., eds. Numerische Behandlung von Eigenwertaufgaben. (International Series of Numerical Mathematics: No. 24). (Ger., Illus.). 142p. 1974. 30.25x (ISBN 0-8176-0739-0). Birkhauser.

Cook, John E. What You Should Know about Data Processing. LC 69-19799. (Business Almanac Ser.: No. 15). 90p. 1969. text ed. 5.95 (ISBN 0-379-11215-9). Oceana.

Couch, Leon W. Digital & Analog Communication Systems. 672p. 1983. text ed. write for info. (ISBN 0-02-325240-5). Macmillan.

Davis, Gordon B. Computers & Information Processing. (Illus.). 1977. text ed. 35.95 (ISBN 0-07-015564-X). McGraw.

--Introduction to Electronic Computers. 3rd ed. (Illus.). 1977. text ed. 41.95 (ISBN 0-07-015825-8). McGraw.

Decade of Digital Computing in the Mineral Industry. LC 72-91452. 1969. 23.00x (ISBN 0-89520-010-4). Soc Mining Eng.

Deussen, P., ed. Theoretical Computer Science Fifth Conference. (Lecture Notes in Computer Science Ser.: Vol. 104). 261p. 1981. pap. 19.00 (ISBN 0-387-10576-X). Springer-Verlag.

Diebold Group. Automatic Data Processing Handbook. (Illus.). 1977. 64.95 (ISBN 0-07-016807-5). McGraw.

Dorf, Richard C. Computers & Man. 3rd ed. LC 82-70804. 560p. 1982. pap. text ed. 17.50x (ISBN 0-87835-121-3). Boyd & Fraser.

--Introduction to Computers & Computer Science. 3rd ed. LC 81-66059. (Illus.). 632p. 1981. text ed. 25.00x (ISBN 0-87835-113-2); write for info. solutions manual. Boyd & Fraser.

Dunning, Kenneth A. Getting Started in General Purpose Simulation System. LC 80-28281. 117p. (Orig.). 1981. pap. 8.95x (ISBN 0-910554-34-X). Engineering.

Eames, Charles & Eames, Ray. A Computer Perspective. Fleck, Glen, ed. LC 72-88399. (Illus.). 1973. 15.00 (ISBN 0-674-15625-0). Harvard U Pr.

Edwards, Perry & Broadwell, Bruce. Data Processing: Computers in Action. 2nd ed. 608p. 1982. text ed. write for info (ISBN 0-534-01063-6); write for info. (ISBN 0-534-01064-4). Wadsworth Pub.

Ekstrom, Michael P., ed. Digital Image Processing Techniques. LC 83-22321. (Computer Techniques Ser.). 1984. 49.50 (ISBN 0-12-236760-X). Acad Pr.

Enslein, Kurt, et al, eds. Statistical Methods for Digital Computers. LC 60-6509. (Mathematical Methods for Digital Computers Ser.: Vol. 3). 454p. 1977. 59.95 (ISBN 0-471-70690-6, Pub. by Wiley-Interscience). Wiley.

Ercegovac, Milos D. & Lang, Tomas. Digital Systems & Hardware: Firmware Algorithms. LC 84-21983. 832p. 1985. 37.00 (ISBN 0-471-88393-X). Wiley.

Feingold, Carl. Introduction to Data Processing. 3rd ed. 752p. 1980. pap. text ed. write for info. (ISBN 0-697-08136-2); student wkbk avail. (ISBN 0-697-08140-0); instrs.' manual avail. (ISBN 0-697-08143-5). Wm C Brown.

Felsen, Jerry. How to Make Money with Computers: A Guide to Thirty High-Profit, Low Capital Computer Business & Investment Opportunities. LC 78-68050. (Illus.). 1979. 20.00 (ISBN 0-916376-05-2). CDS Pub.

Fenyo, S. & Frey, T. Moderne Mathematische Methoden in der Technik, 2 vols. Incl. Vol. 1. 409p. 1967. 66.95x (ISBN 0-8176-0192-9); Vol. 2. 336p. 1971. 64.95x (ISBN 0-8176-0529-0). (International Ser. of Numerical Mathematics: Nos. 8 & 11). (Illus.). Birkhauser.

Frenzel, Louis E., Jr. The Howard W. Sams Crash Course in Digital Technology. LC 82-50654. 208p. 1983. pap. 19.95 (ISBN 0-672-21845-3, 21845). Sams.

Fry, T. F. Computer Appreciation. 1972. 15.00 (ISBN 0-8022-2075-4). Philos Lib.

Fuori, W., et al. Introduction to Computer Operations. 2nd ed. 1981. 23.95 (ISBN 0-13-480392-2). P-H.

Gelenbe, E. & Mitrani, I. Analysis & Synthesis of Computer Systems. LC 80-49992. (Computer Science and Applied Mathematical Ser.). 1980. 45.00 (ISBN 0-12-279350-1). Acad Pr.

Greenblatt, Stanley. Understand Computers Through Common Sense. 1979. pap. 2.95 (ISBN 0-346-12374-7). Cornerstone.

Greenwood, Frank. Profitable Small Business Computing. 176p. 1982. text ed. 21.95 (ISBN 0-316-32711-5); pap. 9.95 (ISBN 0-316-32712-3). Little.

Grosch, Audrey N. Distributed Computing & the Electronic Library: Micros to Superminis. LC 85-7627. 250p. 1985. 36.50 (ISBN 0-86729-145-1, 246-BW); pap. 28.50 (ISBN 0-86729-144-3). Knowledge Indus.

Haley & Scott. Analogue & Digital Computers. 15.00 (ISBN 0-685-28339-9). Philos Lib.

Hall, D. V. Microprocessors & Digital Systems. 1980. text ed. 33.00 (ISBN 0-07-025571-7). McGraw.

Hall, Douglas V. Microprocessors & Digital Systems. 2nd ed. (Illus.). 480p. 1983. 33.00 (ISBN 0-07-025552-0). McGraw.

Hall, Douglas V. & Hall, Marybelle B. Experiments in Microprocessors & Digital Systems. (Illus.). 176p. 1981. 14.75 (ISBN 0-07-025576-8). McGraw.

Handler, W. & Unger, H., eds. Colloquium Uber Schaltkreis-und Schaltewerktheorie: 1965, Hannover. (International Ser. of Numerical Mathematics: No. 6). (Ger.). 324p. 1967. 42.95x (ISBN 0-8176-0190-2). Birkhauser.

Hartley, M. G., ed. Digital Simulation Methods, No. 5. (IEE Monograph Ser.). 229p. 1975. 38.00 (ISBN 0-901223-50-6, MO015). Inst Elect Eng.

Hastings, Cecil. Approximations for Digital Computers. (Rand Corporation Research Studies). 1955. 30.00x (ISBN 0-691-07914-5). Princeton U Pr.

Heath Company Staff. Digital Techniques. (Illus.). 587p. 1978. pap. text ed. 24.95 (ISBN 0-87119-012-5); tchr's. ed. 9.95 (ISBN 0-87119-014-1); lab manual 11.95 (ISBN 0-87119-013-3). Heathkit-Zenith Ed.

--Digital Techniques. rev. ed. (Illus.). 955p. 1983. looseleaf with experimental pts. 89.95 (ISBN 0-87119-011-7, EE-3201A). Heathkit-Zenith Ed.

Heller, Saul. Digital Computers Made Simple. LC 77-101399. 1978. pap. 2.50 (ISBN 0-912146-12-5). AMECO.

Hellwig, Jessica. Introduction to Computers & Programming. LC 71-85919. 1969. 23.00x (ISBN 0-231-03263-3). Columbia U Pr.

Hill, Frederick J. & Peterson, Gerald R. Introduction to Switching Theory & Logical Design. 3rd ed. LC 80-20333. 617p. 1981. text ed. 41.50 (ISBN 0-471-04273-0); solutions manual avail. (ISBN 0-471-09081-6). Wiley.

Hou, H. S. Introduction to Digital Document Processing. LC 82-17461. 336p. 1983. 40.50x (ISBN 0-471-86247-9, Pub. by Wiley Interscience). Wiley.

IEEE Standard 488-1978: IEEE Standard Digital Interface for Programmable Instrumentation. 1978. 10.00 (ISBN 0-317-03948-2, SHO7260). IEEE.

Inbody, Don. Principles & Practices of Digital ICs & LEDs. (Illus.). 288p. (Orig.). 1984. 19.95 (ISBN 0-8306-0277-1, 1577); pap. 13.50 (ISBN 0-8306-0177-5). TAB Bks.

Ivall, T. E. Electronic Computers. 20.00 (ISBN 0-685-28359-3). Philos Lib.

Joslin, Edward O. Computer Readings for Making It Count. 2nd ed. 1976. pap. 8.00 (ISBN 0-916580-02-4). College Readings.

Kanski, Stephen C. Principles of Computer Operations. LC 83-5087. 312p. 1984. pap. text ed. 20.95 (ISBN 0-471-86846-9); tchrs manual avail. (ISBN 0-471-87203-2). Wiley.

Heath Company Staff. CMOS Digital Techniques. rev. ed. (Illus.). 698p. 1983. looseleaf with experimental pts. 89.95 (ISBN 0-87119-035-4, EE-3203A). Heathkit-Zenith Ed.

Heiserman, D. Handbook of Digital IC Applications. 1980. 27.95 (ISBN 0-13-372698-3). P-H.

Holdsworth. Digital Logic Design. 1981. pap. text ed. 24.95 (ISBN 0-408-00566-1). Butterworth.

Hutchison, David. Fundamentals of Computer Logic. LC 80-42028. 214p. 1981. 69.95x (ISBN 0-470-27117-5). Halsted Pr.

Johnson, David E., et al. Digital Circuits & Microcomputers. LC 78-13244. (Illus.). 1979. ref. ed. 33.95 (ISBN 0-13-214015-2). P-H.

Johnson, Steven D. Synthesis of Digital Design from Recursive Equations. (ACM Distinguished Dissertation Ser.). (Illus.). 200p. 1984. text ed. 32.50x (ISBN 0-262-10029-0). MIT Pr.

Kunii, T. L., ed. VLSI Engineering: Beyond Software Engineering. (Lecture Notes in Computer Science Ser.: Vol. 163). viii, 308p. 1984. pap. 14.00 (ISBN 0-387-70002-1). Springer-Verlag.

Leiserson, Charles E. Area-Efficient VLSI Computation. (Association for Computing Machinery Doctoral Dissertation Award Ser.). (Illus.). 152p. 1983. 25.00x (ISBN 0-262-12102-6). MIT Pr.

Levine, Morris E. Digital Theory & Experimentation Using Integrated Circuits. rev. & enl. ed. (Illus.). 272p. 1982. 21.95 (ISBN 0-13-212688-5). P-H.

--Digital Theory & Practice Using Integrated Circuits. 1978. ref. 29.95 (ISBN 0-13-212613-3). P-H.

Malvino, Albert P. & Leach, Donald P. Digital Principles & Applications. 2nd ed. (Illus.). 608p. 1975. text ed. 34.00 (ISBN 0-07-039837-2). McGraw.

Mano, M. Digital Logic & Computer Design. 1979. 39.95 (ISBN 0-13-214510-3). P-H.

Mano, M. Morris. Computer Logic Design. (Automatic Computation Ser.). (Illus.). 464p. 1972. 38.95 (ISBN 0-13-165472-1). P-H.

Marcus, Abraham & Lenk, John D. Computers for Technicians. (Illus.). 400p. 1973. ref. ed. 25.95 (ISBN 0-13-166181-7). P-H.

Moore, William. Digital Logic Circuits: A Laboratory Manual. 1979. pap. text ed. 9.25x (ISBN 0-89917-020-X). TIS Inc.

Oberman, R. M. Digital Circuits for Binary Arithmetic. 340p. 1979. 59.95x (ISBN 0-470-26373-3). Halsted Pr.

Reeves, Colin. An Introduction to Logical Design of Digital Circuits. LC 77-182029. (Cambridge Computer Science Texts Ser.: No. 1). pap. 49.50 (ISBN 0-317-20798-9, 2024532). Bks Demand UMI.

Rose, Darrell D. Digital Circuit Logic & Design Through Experimentation. (Illus.). 256p. 1982. pap. text ed. 12.50x (ISBN 0-911908-13-7). Tech Ed Pr.

Sandige, Richard. Digital Concepts Using Standard Integrated Circuits. (Illus.). 1978. text ed. 42.95 (ISBN 0-07-054653-3). McGraw.

Scott, John. Basic Computer Logic. LC 80-5074. (The Lexington Books Series in Computer Science). 256p. 1981. 26.50x (ISBN 0-669-03706-0). Lexington Bks.

Stapleton, Gerald. Beginner's Guide to Computer Logic. LC 70-155978. (Illus.). 1971. pap. 7.95 (ISBN 0-8306-0548-7, 548). TAB Bks.

Tocci, Ronald J. Fundamentals of Pulse & Digital Circuits. 2nd ed. (Electronics Technology Ser.). 1977. text ed. 23.95 (ISBN 0-675-08492-X). Merrill.

ELECTRONIC DIGITAL COMPUTERS–DESIGN AND CONSTRUCTION

Abramson, N. & Kuo, F., eds. Computer-Communications Networks. 1973. 41.95 (ISBN 0-13-165431-4). P-H.

Baumgartner, William. Pulse Fundamentals & Small Scale Digital Design. LC 84-6888. 1983. text ed. 32.95 (ISBN 0-8359-5757-8); solutions manual avail. (ISBN 0-8359-5758-6). Reston.

Bell, C. G. & Newall, A. Computer Structures Readings & Examples. 1971. 51.95 (ISBN 0-07-004357-4). McGraw.

Bowen, B. A. & Brown, W. R. VLSI Systems Design for Digital Signal Processing, Vol. 1: Signal Processing & Signal Processors. (Illus.). 256p. 1982. text ed. 39.95 (ISBN 0-13-942706-6). P-H.

Braun, Edward L. Digital Computer Design: Its Logic, Circuitry, & Synthesis. 1963. 85.00 (ISBN 0-12-127250-8). Acad Pr.

Bywater, R. Hardware-Software Design of Digital Systems. 1981. 38.95 (ISBN 0-13-383950-8). P-H.

Chu, Yaohan. High-Level Language Computer Architecture. 1975. 74.50 (ISBN 0-12-174150-8). Acad Pr.

Davis, M. I. IBM Series One Design Decisions: Architecture. (Illus.). 48p. (Orig.). 1979. pap. text ed. 5.20 (ISBN 0-933186-01-0, G360-0060). IBM Armonk.

Dietmeyer. Logic Design of Digital Systems. 2nd ed. 1978. text ed. 42.89 (ISBN 0-205-05960-0, EDP 285960). Allyn.

Gear, C. William. Computer Organization & Programming. 2nd ed. (Computer Science Ser.). (Illus.). 448p. 1974. text ed. 37.95 (ISBN 0-07-023076-5). McGraw.

Greenfield, Joseph D. Practical Digital Design Using ICs. 2nd ed. LC 82-10931. (Electronic Technology Ser.). 717p. 1983. 31.95 (ISBN 0-471-05791-6). Wiley.

Harries, G. V. IBM Disk Storage Technology. (IBM Product Design & Development Ser.). (Illus.). 103p. 1980. pap. text ed. 3.80 (ISBN 0-933186-02-9, GA-26-1665-0). IBM Armonk.

Haviland, Robert P. How to Design, Build & Program Your Own Advanced Working Computer System. (Illus.). 322p. 1979. pap. 11.95 (ISBN 0-8306-1332-3, 1332). TAB Bks.

Langdon, Glen G., Jr. Computer Design. LC 81-71785. (Illus.). 575p. 1982. 36.00 (ISBN 0-9607864-0-6). Computeach.

Lewin. Theory & Design of Digital Computer Systems. 1980. pap. 29.95 (ISBN 0-442-30761-6). Van Nos Reinhold.

Lewin, Douglas. Theory & Design of Digital Computer Systems. 2nd ed. 472p. 1980. pap. text ed. 32.95 (ISBN 0-470-26959-6). Halsted Pr.

Llewellyn, J. A. & Gilbert, R. Basic Elements of Digital Systems 1982. (IRP-Digital Techniques Courses Ser.). 1983. Classroom Package: 10 student texts, 10 pencil boxes, 1 instr's guide, 10 wkbks., 10 components, 1 set of 49 slides. 1705.00x (ISBN 0-87664-676-3, I676-3); Student text. 19.95 (ISBN 0-87664-674-7); student wkbk. 19.95 (ISBN 0-87664-682-8, I682-8); instr's guide 10.00 (ISBN 0-87664-675-5, I675-5); of 49 slides 125.00 set (ISBN 0-686-47373-6, I676-35L). Instru Soc.

Mardiguian, Michel. Interference Control in Computers & Microprocessor-Based Equipment. (Illus.). 110p. 1984. text ed. 27.00 (ISBN 0-932263-23-2). White Consult.

Meltzer, A. C., et al. Principles of Digital Computer Design, Vol. 1. (Illus.). 624p. 1976. 41.95 (ISBN 0-13-701524-0). P-H.

Myers, Glenford J. Digital System Design with LSI Bit-Slice Logic. 338p. 1980. 44.95x (ISBN 0-471-05376-7, Pub. by Wiley-Interscience). Wiley.

Osaki, S. & Nishio, T. Reliability Evaluation of Some Fault-Tolerant Computer Architectures. (Lecture Notes in Computer Science Ser.: Vol. 97). 129p. 1980. pap. 13.00 (ISBN 0-387-10274-4). Springer-Verlag.

Passafiume, John & Douglas, Michael. Digital Logic Design: Tutorials & Laboratory Exercises. 113p. 1984. pap. text ed. 16.50 scp (ISBN 0-06-045028-2, HarpC). Har-Row.

Peatman, J. B. Digital Hardware Design. 1980. 42.00 (ISBN 0-07-049132-1). McGraw.

Pettit, F. R. Post-Digital Electronics. (Electrical & Electronic Engineering Ser.). 176p. 1982. 53.95x (ISBN 0-470-27334-8). Halsted Pr.

Phister, Montgomery. Logical Design of Digital Computers. LC 58-6082. pap. 106.00 (ISBN 0-317-09156-5, 2016482). Bks Demand UMI.

Rajaraman, V. & Radhakrishnan, T. An Introduction to Digital Computer Design. 2nd ed. (Illus.). 416p. 1983. pap. 32.95 (ISBN 0-13-480657-3). P-H.

Reeves, C. M. An Introduction to Logical Design of Digital Circuits. LC 77-182029. (Computer Science Texts Ser: No. 1). (Illus.). 200p. 1972. text ed. 13.95 (ISBN 0-521-09705-3). Cambridge U Pr.

Reeves, Colin. An Introduction to Logical Design of Digital Circuits. LC 77-182029. (Cambridge Computer Science Texts Ser.: No. 1). pap. 49.50 (ISBN 0-317-20798-9, 2024532). Bks Demand UMI.

Rubinstein, Richard & Hersh, Harry. The Human Factor: Designing Computer Systems for People. 256p. 1984. 25.00 (ISBN 0-932376-44-4, EY-00013-DP). Digital Pr.

Siewiorek, Daniel & Swarz, Robert. The Theory & Practice of Reliable System Design. 772p. 1982. pap. 45.00 (ISBN 0-932376-17-7, EY-AX016-DP). Digital Pr.

Steele, D. R. An Introduction to Elementary Computer & Compiler Design. 152p. 1978. 25.25 (ISBN 0-444-00243-X, North-Holland). Elsevier.

Symposium, Brussels, Nov. 1978. Computer-Aided Design of Digital Electronic Circuits & Systems: Proceedings. Musgrave, G., ed. 326p. 1979. 76.75 (ISBN 0-444-85374-X, North Holland). Elsevier.

Winkel, David E. & Prosser, Franklin P. The Art of Digital Design: An Introduction to Top-Down Design. (Illus.). 1980. text ed. 37.95 (ISBN 0-13-046607-7). P-H.

ELECTRONIC DIGITAL COMPUTERS–DICTIONARIES

Brinkman, Karl-Heinz & Schmidt, Rudolf. Data Systems Dictionary: English-German & German-English. 1974. pap. 40.00x (ISBN 3-87097-095-2). Intl Learn Syst.

Burger, E. Technical Dictionary of Data Processing, Computers & Office Machines, English, German, French, Russian. (Eng., Ger., Fr. & Rus.). 1970. 145.00 (ISBN 0-08-006425-6). Pergamon.

Chandor, Anthony, ed. Dictionary of Computers. (Reference Ser.). (Orig.). 1970. pap. 5.95 (ISBN 0-14-051039-7). Penguin.

Prenis, John. Computer Terms. LC 77-343. (Orig.). 1977. lib. bdg. 12.90 (ISBN 0-914294-75-X); pap. 4.95 (ISBN 0-914294-76-8). Running Pr.

Purdue Workshop on Standardization of Industrial-Computer Languages, Glossary Committee. Dictionary of Industrial Digital Computer Terminology. LC 72-81778. pap. 24.00 (ISBN 0-317-08566-2, 2051117). Bks Demand UMI.

Ross, Ronald G. Data Dictionaries & Data Administration: Concepts & Practices for Data Resource Management. 384p. 1981. 29.95 (ISBN 0-8144-5596-4). AMACOM.

Sippl, Charles J. & Sippl, Roger J. Computer Dictionary. 3rd ed. LC 79-91696. 624p. 1980. pap. 16.95 (ISBN 0-672-21652-3, 21652). Sams.

Spencer, Donald D. Computer Dictionary. 2nd ed. LC 78-31738. 1979. pap. 6.95 (ISBN 0-89218-038-2). Camelot Pub.

ELECTRONIC DIGITAL COMPUTERS–EVALUATION

Morris, Michael F. & Roth, Paul F. Computer Performance Evaluation: Tools & Techniques for Effective Analysis. 192p. 1981. 26.95 (ISBN 0-442-80325-7). Van Nos Reinhold.

ELECTRONIC DIGITAL COMPUTERS–INPUT-OUTPUT EQUIPMENT

see Computer Input-Output Equipment

ELECTRONIC DIGITAL COMPUTERS–MEMORY SYSTEMS

see Computer Storage Devices

ELECTRONIC DIGITAL COMPUTERS–PROGRAMMED INSTRUCTION

Harris, Martin L. Introduction to Data Processing. 2nd ed. LC 78-21161. (Self-Teaching Guide Ser.). 304p. 1979. pap. text ed. 9.95 (ISBN 0-471-04657-4, Pub. by Wiley Pr). Wiley.

ELECTRONIC DIGITAL COMPUTERS–PROGRAMMING

see also Compiling (Electronic Computers); Computer Programs; Data Base Management; List Processing (Electronic Computers)

also names of specific computers, with or without the subdivision programming

Adam, Nabil R. & Dogramaci, Ali, eds. Current Issues in Computer Simulation. LC 79-51696. 1979. 47.50 (ISBN 0-12-044120-9). Acad Pr.

Alagic, S. & Arbib, M. A. The Design of Well-Structured & Correct Programs. LC 77-27087. (Texts & Monographs in Computer Science). 1978. 23.00 (ISBN 0-387-90299-6). Springer-Verlag.

Andriole, Stephen J. Software Development Tools: A Source Book. (Illus.). 300p. 1985. 29.95 (ISBN 0-89433-272-4). Van Nos Reinhold.

Arsac, Jacques. Foundations of Programming. Duncan, Fraser, tr. (APIC Studies in Data Processing Monographs: No. 20). 1985. 29.50 (ISBN 0-12-064460-6). Acad Pr.

Baase, Sara. Computer Algorithms: Introduction to Design & Analysis. LC 77-81197. 1978. text ed. 31.95 (ISBN 0-201-00327-9). Addison-Wesley.

Bailey, T. E. & Lundgaard, Kris. Program Design with Pseudocode. LC 82-17802. (Computer Science Ser.). 160p. 1983. pap. text ed. 10.00 pub net (ISBN 0-534-01361-9). Brooks-Cole.

Barnaal, Dennis. Analog & Digital Electronics for Scientific Application. 1982. text ed. write for info. (ISBN 0-534-01044-X, Breton Pubs). Wadsworth Pub.

Barron, D. W. Pascal: The Language & Its Implementation. (Computing Ser.). 301p. 1981. 44.95x (ISBN 0-471-27835-1, Pub. by Wiley-Interscience). Wiley.

--Recursive Techniques in Programming. 2nd ed. (Computer Monograph Series: Vol. 3). 1974. text ed. 24.75 (ISBN 0-444-19524-6). Elsevier.

Barstow, D. R., et al. Interactive Programming Environments. 1983. 37.95 (ISBN 0-07-003885-6). McGraw.

Bauer, F. L. & Woessner, H. Algorithmic Language & Program Development. (Texts & Monographs in Computer Science). (Illus.). 520p. 1982. pap. 32.00 (ISBN 0-387-11148-4). Springer-Verlag.

Beaumont, et al. RT-11 Training Set, 4 Vols. 800p. 1984. Set. pap. 100.00 (EY-00036-DP). Digital Pr.

Beckman, Frank S. Mathematical Foundations of Programming. LC 79-1453. 1980. text ed. 31.95 (ISBN 0-201-14462-X). Addison-Wesley.

Bentley, Jon L. Writing Efficient Programs. 192p. 1982. lib. bdg. 24.95 (ISBN 0-13-970251-2); pap. text ed. 16.95 (ISBN 0-13-970244-X). P-H.

Bergman, Samuel & Bruckner, Steven. Introduction to Computers & Computer Programming. LC 72-140834. 1972. text ed. 28.95 (ISBN 0-201-00552-2). Addison-Wesley.

Bohl, Marilyn. Flowcharting Techniques. 208p. 1971. pap. text ed. 11.95 (ISBN 0-574-16096-5, 13-1440). SRA.

--A Guide for Programmers. LC 77-14982. (Illus.). 1978. ref. 17.95x (ISBN 0-13-370551-X); pap. text ed. 15.95 (ISBN 0-13-370544-7). P-H.

Boillot, Michel H., et al. Essentials of Flowcharting. 4th. ed. 176p. 1985. pap. text ed. write for info. (ISBN 0-697-00420-1). Wm C Brown.

Booch, Grady. Software Engineering with Ada. 1983. text ed. 25.95 (ISBN 0-8053-0600-5); transparency masters o.p. 50.95 (ISBN 0-8053-0601-3). Benjamin-Cummings.

Booth, Taylor L. & Chien, Yi-Tzuu. Computing: Fundamentals & Applications. LC 73-20157. 497p. 1974. 40.95x (ISBN 0-471-08847-1). Wiley.

Borgerson, Mark J. A BASIC Programmer's Guide to Pascal. LC 81-16281. 118p. 1982. pap. text ed. 11.95 (ISBN 0-471-09293-2, Pub. by Wiley Pr). Wiley.

Brainerd, Walter S., et al. Pascal Programming: A Spiral Approach. LC 82-70213. 597p. (Orig.). 1982. pap. text ed. 25.00x (ISBN 0-87835-122-1); solutions manual avail. Boyd & Fraser.

Calderbank, V. J. A Course on Programming in FORTRAN. 2nd ed. 1983. 25.00 (ISBN 0-412-24270-2, NO.6737); pap. 9.95 (ISBN 0-412-23790-3, NO.6738). Methuen Inc.

Carter, James R. Computer Mapping: Progress in the Eighties. LC 84-70007. (Resource Publications in Geography). 100p. 1984. pap. 5.00 (ISBN 0-89291-175-1). Assn Am Geographers.

Chantler, Alan. Programming Techniques & Practice. 250p. 1981. pap. 24.50x (ISBN 0-85012-338-0). Intl Pubns Serv.

Clinch, Simon & Peters, Stephen. Tailoring RT-11: System Management & Programming Facilities. (Illus.). 220p. 1984. pap. 36.00 (ISBN 0-932376-34-7, EY-00024-DP). Digital Pr.

Cohen, Doron J. & Brillinger, Peter C. Introduction to Data Structures & Non-Numeric Computation. (Illus.). 656p. 1972. ref. ed. 32.95 (ISBN 0-13-479899-6). P-H.

Dahlstrand, Ingemar. Software Portability & Standards. (Computers & Their Applications Ser.: No. 1403). 150p. 1984. 24.95x (ISBN 0-470-20083-9). Halsted Pr.

Daniels, Alan & Yeates, Don. Design & Analysis of Software Systems. 257p. 1983. pap. 14.95 (ISBN 0-89433-212-0). Petrocelli.

Davison, J. F. Programming for Digital Computers. (Illus.). 186p. 1962. 42.95 (ISBN 0-677-00210-6). Gordon.

Dickinson, Brian. Developing Structured Systems: A Methodology Using Structured Techniques. LC 80-54609. (Illus.). 360p. 1981. 49.00 (ISBN 0-917072-24-3); pap. 42.50 (ISBN 0-917072-23-5). Yourdon.

Dijkstra, Edward W. A Discipline of Programming. (Illus.). 240p. 1976. 35.00x (ISBN 0-13-215871-X). P-H.

Disney, R. & Ott, T., eds. Applied Probability--Computer Science: The Interface, 2 Vols. (Progress in Computer Science Ser.). 1982. text ed. 39.95x ea. Vol. 2, 532pp (ISBN 0-8176-3067-8). Vol. 3, 514pp (ISBN 0-8176-3093-7). Birkhauser.

Donovan, John. Systems Programming. LC 79-172263. (Computer Science Ser). (Illus.). 480p. 1972. text ed. 45.95 (ISBN 0-07-017603-5). McGraw.

Edwards, Perry. Flowcharting & FORTRAN IV. (Illus.). 132p. 1973. 14.15 (ISBN 0-07-019042-9, G). McGraw.

Farina, Mario V. Flowcharting. 1970. pap. 14.95 ref. ed. (ISBN 0-13-322750-2). P-H.

Feingold, Carl. Introduction to Data Processing. 3rd ed. 752p. 1980. pap. text ed. write for info. (ISBN 0-697-08136-2); student wkbk avail. (ISBN 0-697-08140-0); instrs.' manual avail. (ISBN 0-697-08143-5). Wm C Brown.

Ford, Donald H. & Rue, Joseph. Standard FORTRAN Programming. 4th ed. 1982. pap. 19.95x (ISBN 0-256-02608-4). Irwin.

Foster, C. C. Real Time Programming: Neglected Topics. 1981. 9.95 (ISBN 0-201-01937-X). Addison-Wesley.

Fowles, A. J. Complex Sequencing by Programmable Logic Controller, 1977. 1981. 35.00x (ISBN 0-686-97049-7, Pub. by W Spring England). State Mutual Bk.

Freedman, Roy S. Programming Concepts with the Ada Reference Manual. (Illus.). 128p. 1982. pap. text ed. 12.00 (ISBN 0-89433-190-6). Petrocelli.

Friedman, F. L. & Koffman, E. B. Problem Solving & Structured Programming in FORTRAN. 2nd ed. 1981. pap. 23.95 (ISBN 0-201-02461-6); wkbk. 7.95 (ISBN 0-201-02465-9). Addison-Wesley.

BOOKS - SUBJECT INDEX
ELECTRONIC DIGITAL COMPUTERS–PROGRAMMING

Gallo, Michael A. & Nenno, Robert B. Computers in Society with BASIC & Pascal. 1985. pap. text ed. write for info. (ISBN 0-87150-852-4, 37L8700). PWS Pubs.
Gear, C. William. Computer Organization & Programming. 2nd ed. (Computer Science Ser.). (Illus.). 448p. 1974. text ed. 37.95 (ISBN 0-07-023076-5). McGraw.
Glass, Robert L. Modern Programming Practices: A Report from Industry. (Illus.). 304p. 1982. text ed. 34.95 (ISBN 0-13-597294-9). P-H.
Goodman, S. E. & Hedetniemi, S. T. Introduction to the Design & Analysis of Algorithms. (Computer Science Ser.). (Illus.). 1977. text ed. 41.95 (ISBN 0-07-023753-0). McGraw.
Gordon, M., et al. Edinburgh LCF: A Mechanised Logic of Computation. (Lecture Notes in Computer Sciences: Vol. 78). 159p. 1979. pap. 15.00 (ISBN 0-387-09724-4). Springer-Verlag.
Graham, Robert M. Principles of Systems Programming. LC 74-19390. 422p. 1975. text ed. 40.00 (ISBN 0-471-32100-1). Wiley.
Gries, David. The Science of Programming. (Texts & Monographs in Computer Science). 366p. 1981. 22.00 (ISBN 0-387-90641-X). Springer-Verlag.
Gries, David, ed. Programming Methodology: A Collection of Articles by Members of IFIP WG 2.3. LC 78-16539. (Texts & Monographs in Computer Science). (Illus.). 1978. 36.00 (ISBN 0-387-90329-1). Springer-Verlag.
Grillo, John P. & Robertson, J. D. More Subroutine Sandwich. LC 82-13506. 260p. 1983. pap. text ed. 12.95 (ISBN 0-471-86921-X). Wiley.
--Subroutine Sandwich. LC 82-13516. 251p. 1983. pap. text ed. 12.95 (ISBN 0-471-86920-1). Wiley.
Groner, Gabriel F. PL-One Programming in Technological Applications. LC 70-136713. Repr. of 1971 ed. 60.50 (ISBN 0-8357-9955-7, 2012585). Bks Demand UMI.
Grout, Jarrell C. Fundamental Computer Programming Using FORTRAN 77. (Software Ser.). (Illus.). 432p. 1983. pap. text ed. 21.95 (ISBN 0-13-335141-6). P-H.
Halpern, M., et al, eds. Annual Review in Automatic Programming. Incl. Vol. 5, Pt. 1. Data Structures & Their Representation in Storage. D'Imperio, A. LC 60-12884. 1970; Vol. 5, Pt. 2. Generalized File Processing. McGee, W. C. 1970; Vol. 6, Pt. 1. Some Studies in Machine Learning Using the Game of Checkers 2. Samuel, A. L. 1969. pap. 15.50 (ISBN 0-08-006575-9); Vol. 6, Pt. 2. A Survey of Macro Processors: A Machine-Independent Assembly Language for Systems Programs. Brown, P. J. & Colouris, G. F. 1969. pap. 15.50 (ISBN 0-08-006586-4); Vol. 6, Pt. 3. On the Formal Description of PL-1. Lucas, P. & Walk, K. 1970. pap. 15.50 (ISBN 0-08-006689-5); Vol. 6, Pt. 4. Joss Two: Design Philosophy. Smith, J. W. 1970. pap. 15.50 (ISBN 0-08-006694-1); Vol. 6, Pt. 5. A New Approach to Optimization of Sequencing Decisions. Shapiro, R. M. & Saint, H. 1970. pap. 15.50 (ISBN 0-08-016336-X); Vol. 7, Pt. 1. Tutorial on Data-Base Organization. Smith, J. W. 1972. pap. 15.50 (ISBN 0-08-016947-3); Vol. 7, Pt. 2. Incremental Complication & Conversational Interpretation. Bertrand, M. & Griffiths, M. M. pap. 15.50 (ISBN 0-08-017049-8); Vol. 7, Pt. 3. Introduction to Algol 68: Automatic Theorem Proving Based on Resolution. Bekis, A. 1973. pap. 15.50 (ISBN 0-08-017128-1); Vol. 7, Pt. 4. Survey of Extensible Programming Language. Solnsteff, N. & Yezerski, A. 1973. pap. 15.50 (ISBN 0-08-017145-1); Vol. 7, Pt. 5. 1975. pap. 15.50 (ISBN 0-08-017881-2); Vol. 7 Complete. 1974. pap. text ed. 49.00 (ISBN 0-08-017806-5). LC 60-12884. pap. write for info. Pergamon.
Hanson, Peggy. Operating Data Entry Systems. (Illus.). 1977. pap. text ed. 19.95 (ISBN 0-13-637819-6). P-H.
Hare, Van Court, Jr. BASIC Programming. 2nd ed. 407p. 1982. pap. text ed. 19.95 (ISBN 0-15-505002-8, HC, HC). HarBraceJ.
Harel, D. First-Order Dynamic Logic. (Lecture Notes in Computer Science: Vol. 68). 1979. pap. 13.00 (ISBN 0-387-09237-4). Springer-Verlag.
Hartling, John. Introduction to Computer Programming: A Problem Solving Approach. 468p. 1983. 25.00 (ISBN 0-932376-21-5, EY-00010-DP). Digital Pr.
Hawksley, Chris. Pascal Programming: A Beginner's Guide to Computers & Programming. LC 82-19760. 200p. 1983. 27.95 (ISBN 0-521-25302-0); pap. 10.95 (ISBN 0-521-27292-0). Cambridge U Pr.
Hecht, Matthew S. Flow Analysis of Computer Programs. (Programming Languages Ser.: Vol. 5). 232p. 1977. 30.75 (ISBN 0-444-00210-3, North Holland). Elsevier.
Hellwig, Jessica. Introduction to Computers & Programming. LC 71-85919. 1969. 23.00x (ISBN 0-231-03263-3). Columbia U Pr.
Hoare, C. A. Communicating Sequential Processes. (International Book Ser.). (Illus.). 224p. 1985. text ed. 35.00 (ISBN 0-13-153271-5). P-H.
Hogger. Introduction to Logic Programming. 1984. pap. 46.00 (ISBN 0-12-352092-4). Acad Pr.
Holoien, Martin O. & Behforooz, Ali. Problem Solving & Structured Programming with FORTRAN 77. LC 82-24436. 560p. 1983. pap. text ed. 19.00 pub net (ISBN 0-534-01275-2). Brooks-Cole.
Horowitz, Ellis & Sahni, Sartaj. Fundamentals of Computer Algorithms. LC 78-14735. 1978. text ed. 34.95x (ISBN 0-914894-22-6). Computer Sci.
Houghton-Alico, D. Creating Computer Software User Guides: From Manuals to Menus. 17.95 (ISBN 0-07-030471-8). McGraw.
Hughes, J. & Michton, J. A Structured Approach to Programming. 1977. 30.00 (ISBN 0-13-854356-9). P-H.
Huyck, Peter & Kremenak, Nellie W. Design & Memory: Computer Programming in the 20th Century. (Illus.). 1980. 15.95 (ISBN 0-07-031554-X). McGraw.
James, M. L., et al. Applied Numerical Methods for Digital Computation. 3rd ed. 752p. 1985. text ed. 41.95 scp (ISBN 0-06-043281-0, HarpC). Har-Row.
Jones, Anita K., ed. Perspectives on Computer Science. (Acm Ser.). 1977. 55.00 (ISBN 0-12-389450-6). Acad Pr.
Jones, C. Software Development: A Rigorous Approach. 1980. 40.95 (ISBN 0-13-821884-6). P-H.
Kant, Elaine. Efficiency in Program Synthesis. Stone, Harold, ed. LC 81-7627. (Computer Science Ser.: Artificial Intelligence No. 8). 172p. 1981. 39.95 (ISBN 0-8357-1215-X). UMI Res Pr.
Katzan, Harry, Jr. Operating Systems: A Pragmatic Approach. (Computer Science Ser.). 392p. 1973. 24.50 (ISBN 0-442-24253-0). Van Nos Reinhold.
Kaufman, Roger. FORTRAN Coloring Book. LC 78-998. 1978. pap. 8.95 (ISBN 0-262-61026-4). MIT Pr.
Kemp, Rainer. Fundamentals of the Average Case Analysis of Particular Algorithms. (Teubner Series in Computer Science: 1-695). 200p. 1985. text ed. 34.95x (ISBN 0-471-90322-1). Wiley.
Kernighan, Brian W. & Plauger, P. J. The Elements of Programming Style. 2nd ed. 1978. pap. text ed. 17.95 (ISBN 0-07-034207-5, BYTE Bks). McGraw.
Kfoury, A. J., et al. A Programming Approach to Computability. (Texts & Monographs in Computer Science). (Illus.). 208p. 1982. 25.00 (ISBN 0-387-90743-2). Springer-Verlag.
Kimble, Gerald W. Information & Computer Science. LC 74-3316. (Illus.). 1975. text ed. 9.95x (ISBN 0-03-082833-3). Irvington.
Kindred, Alton R. Introduction to Computers. 2nd ed. (Illus.). 544p. 1982. pap. text ed. 25.95 (ISBN 0-13-480079-6). P-H.
King, James C. A Program Verifier. LC 76-127837. 262p. 1969. 19.00 (ISBN 0-403-04510-X). Scholarly.
Knuth, Donald E. Art of Computer Programming, Vol. 1: Fundamental Algorithms. 2nd ed. LC 73-1830. 640p. 1974. 36.95 (ISBN 0-201-03809-9). Addison-Wesley.
--MIX. LC 79-139160. (Computer Science Ser). 1971. pap. text ed. 6.95 (ISBN 0-201-03808-0). Addison-Wesley.
Korfhage, Robert. Discrete Computational Structures. 2nd ed. LC 83-2554. (Computer Science & Applied Mathematics Ser.). 1983. 35.00 (ISBN 0-12-420860-6). Acad Pr.
Korfhage, Robert R. Discrete Computational Structures. 1974. 35.00 (ISBN 0-12-420850-9). Acad Pr.
Kreitzberg, Charles B. & Shneiderman, Ben. Elements of FORTRAN Style: Techniques for Effective Programming. (Illus.). 121p. 1972. pap. text ed. 9.95 (ISBN 0-15-522156-6, HC). HarBraceJ.
Kuo, Franklin F. & Kaiser, J. F. System Analysis by Digital Computer. LC 66-25226. 438p. 1966. text ed. 28.00 (ISBN 0-471-51121-8, Pub. by Wiley). Krieger.
Ledgard, Henry F. Programming Proverbs. (Computer Programming Ser.). (Illus.). 144p. 1975. pap. text ed. 9.25x (ISBN 0-8104-5522-6). Hayden.
Ledgard, Henry F. & Chmura, Louis J. FORTRAN with Style: Programming Proverbs. (Computer Programming Ser.). 1978. pap. text ed. 10.95x (ISBN 0-8104-5682-6). Hayden.
Ledin, George, Jr. & Ledin, Victor. The Programmer's Book of Rules. LC 79-13746. 248p. 1979. pap. 12.95 (ISBN 0-534-97993-9). Lifetime Learn.
Lee, John A. Computer Semantics: Studies of Algorithms Processors & Languages. LC 77-7263. 416p. 1978. Repr. of 1972 ed. 24.00 (ISBN 0-88275-546-3). Krieger.
Leeson, Marjorie M. Programming Logic. 320p. 1983. pap. text ed. 19.95 (ISBN 0-574-21420-8, 13-4420); instr's. guide avail. (ISBN 0-574-21421-6, 13-4421). SRA.
Levy, Leon S. Discrete Structures of Computer Science. LC 79-11218. 310p. 1980. text ed. 33.95x (ISBN 0-471-03208-5). Wiley.
Lew, A. Computer Science: A Mathematical Introduction. (Illus.). 416p. 1985. text ed. 34.95 (ISBN 0-13-164252-9). P-H.
Lewis, William E. Problem-Solving Principles for BASIC Programmers: Applied Logic, Psychology & Grit. (Problem-Solving Principles Ser.). 166p. 1981. pap. 10.95 (ISBN 0-8104-5200-6). Hayden.
--Problem-Solving Principles for FORTRAN Programmers: Applied Logic, Psychology & Grit. (Problem-Solving Principles Ser.). 177p. pap. 10.95 (ISBN 0-8104-5430-0). Hayden.
--Problem-Solving Principles for Pascal Programmers: Applied Logic, Psychology & Grit. 179p. pap. 10.95 (ISBN 0-8104-5767-9). Hayden.
--Problem-Solving Principles for Programmers: Applied Logic, Psychology & Grit. 163p. (Orig.). 1981. pap. 11.95 (ISBN 0-8104-5138-7). Hayden.
Lindsey, William C. & Simon, Mark K., eds. Phase-Locked Loops & Their Application. LC 77-73101. 1978. 42.60 (ISBN 0-87942-101-0, PC00984). Inst Electrical.
Lucas, Henry C. The Analysis, Design & Implementation of Information Systems. rev. ed. (Management Information Systems Ser.). (Illus.). 416p. 1980. text ed. 36.95 (ISBN 0-07-038927-6). McGraw.
Lucas, John. Designing Applications for the Professional 300 Series: A Developer's Guide. 200p. 1984. pap. 35.00 (ISBN 0-932376-35-5, EY-00030-DP). Digital Pr.
Madison, Alan W. Characteristics of Program Localities. Stone, Harold, ed. LC 82-4847. (Computer Science: Systems Programming Ser.: No. 5). 138p. 1982. 34.95 (ISBN 0-8357-1328-8). UMI Res Pr.
Maly, Kurt & Hanson, Allen R. Fundamentals of the Computing Sciences. (Illus.). 1978. ref. ed. 32.95 (ISBN 0-13-335240-4); supplementary vol. 14.95 (ISBN 0-13-335257-9). P-H.
Manna, Z., et al. Studies in Automatic Programming Logic. (Artificial Intelligence Ser.: Vol. 4). 192p. 1977. 32.50 (ISBN 0-444-00224-3, North Holland); pap. text ed. 18.25 (ISBN 0-444-00225-1). Elsevier.
Martin, James. Application Development Without Programmers. 345p. 1982. 32.50 (ISBN 0-686-98081-6). Telecom Lib.
Maurer, Ward D. Programming: An Introduction to Computer Techniques. rev. 2nd ed. LC 70-188126. (Illus.). 1972. text ed. 32.00x (ISBN 0-8162-5453-2). Holden Day.
Meek, B. L. & Heath, P. M. Guide to Good Programming Practice. 2nd ed. (Computers & Their Applications Ser.). 192p. 1983. 47.95x (ISBN 0-470-27416-6); pap. 24.95x (ISBN 0-470-27417-4). Halsted Pr.
Miller, R. E. & Thatcher, J. W., eds. Complexity of Computer Computations. LC 72-85736. (IBM Research Symposia Ser.). 225p. 1972. 39.50x (ISBN 0-306-30707-3, Plenum Pr). Plenum Pub.
Mills, Harlan D. Software Productivity. 288p. 1982. text ed. 28.95 (ISBN 0-316-57388-4). Little.
Minkema, Douglas D. System Thirty-four Teacher's Guide. 48p. text ed. 110.00 (ISBN 0-9610582-7-7). Apollo Com.
Minkema, Douglas D. & Carter, Gerald L. RPG II Programming. 2nd ed. (RPG II Programming-Advanced Topics Ser.). 1977. pap. text ed. 17.50 (ISBN 0-9610582-2-6). Apollo Com.
--RPG II Programming Teacher's Guide. 175p. text ed. 55.00 (ISBN 0-9610582-5-0). Apollo Com.
Minkema, Douglas D. & Pasquini, Mark T. RPG II Programming Advanced Topics. (RPG II Programming-Advanced Topics Ser.). 187p. 1977. pap. text ed. 14.50 (ISBN 0-9610582-3-4). Apollo Com.
--RPG II Programming-Advanced Topics Teacher's Guide. 210p. text ed. 55.00 (ISBN 0-9610582-6-9). Apollo Com.
Mosteller, William S. Systems Programmer's Problem Solver. 223p. 1981. text ed. 24.95 (ISBN 0-316-58578-5). Little.
Mullish, Henry. Introduction to Computer Programming. (Notes on Mathematics & Its Applications Ser.). 256p. 1969. 40.50x (ISBN 0-677-01160-1); pap. 31.25x (ISBN 0-677-01165-2). Gordon.
Murrill, Paul W. & Smith, Cecil L. An Introduction to FORTRAN IV Programming: A General Approach. 2nd ed. 300p. 1975. pap. text ed. 20.50 scp (ISBN 0-7002-2469-6, HarpC); scp solutions manual 4.95 (ISBN 0-7002-2479-3). Har-Row.
Muxworthy, D. T. Programming for Software Sharing. 1983. lib. bdg. 39.50 (ISBN 90-2771-547-5, Pub. by Reidel Holland). Kluwer Academic.
Myers, Glenford J. Composite Structure Design. (Illus.). 174p. 1978. pap. 19.95 (ISBN 0-442-80584-5). Van Nos Reinhold.
Newey, M. C., ed. Programming Language Systems. new ed. Wolfendale, G. L. LC 78-60544. (Orig.). 1978. pap. text ed. 15.75 (ISBN 0-7081-0493-2, Pub. by ANUP Australia). Australia N U P.
Parikh, Girish. How to Measure Programmer Productivity. 95p. 1981. pap. 21.00 (ISBN 0-932888-02-X). Shetal Ent.
--How to Measure Programmer Productivity. (Illus.). 95p. 1981. pap. 21.00 (ISBN 0-89435-059-5). QED Info Sci.
--Techniques of Program & System Maintenance. 300p. 1982. text ed. 27.95 (ISBN 0-316-69064-3). Little.
Peatman, J. B. Design of Digital Systems. (Electronic Systems Ser.). 1972. text ed. 43.95 (ISBN 0-07-049136-4). McGraw.
Pollack, Seymour, ed. Studies in Computer Science. LC 82-62390. (MAA Studies in Mathematics: No. 22). 408p. 1982. 29.00 (ISBN 0-88385-124-5). Math Assn.
Popkin, Gary S. & Pike, Arthur M. Introduction to Data Processing. 2nd ed. (Illus.). 1981. 25.95 (ISBN 0-395-29483-5); instr's manual 2.50 (ISBN 0-395-29484-3). HM.
--Introduction to Data Processing with BASIC. 2nd ed. (Illus.). 592p. 1981. text ed. 25.95 (ISBN 0-395-30091-6); study guide 10.50 (ISBN 0-395-29485-1). HM.
Prather, Ronald E. Problem-Solving Principles: Programming with Pascal. (Illus.). 352p. 1982. text ed. 22.95 (ISBN 0-13-721316-6); pap. text ed. 20.95 (ISBN 0-13-721308-5). P-H.
Pressman, R. S. Software Engineering: A Practitioner's Approach. (Software Engineering & Technology Ser.). 1982. 41.95 (ISBN 0-07-050781-3). McGraw.
Price, Wilson T. Introduction to Computer Data Processing. 3rd ed. 592p. 1981. text ed. 26.95 (ISBN 0-03-056728-9, HoltC); wkbk. 10.95 (ISBN 0-03-057697-0). HR&W.
Price, Wilson T. & Miller, M. Elements of Data Processing Mathematics. 2nd ed. LC 71-140239. 1971. text ed. 29.95 (ISBN 0-03-084745-1, HoltC). HR&W.
Ralston, Anthony. Introduction to Programming & Computer Science. LC 77-13034. 538p. 1978. Repr. of 1971 ed. lib. bdg. 31.50 (ISBN 0-88275-619-2). Krieger.
Reid, Loretta G. Control & Communication in Programs. Stone, Harold, ed. LC 82-6893. (Computer Science: Systems Programming Ser.: No. 13). 176p. 1982. 39.95 (ISBN 0-8357-1349-0). UMI Res Pr.
Reps, Thomas. Generating Language-Based Environments. (ACM Doctoral Dissertation Awards Ser.: 1983). (Illus.). 150p. 1984. text ed. 30.00x (ISBN 0-262-18115-0). MIT Pr.
Reynolds, J. Craft of Programming. 1981. 31.95 (ISBN 0-13-188862-5). P-H.
Riddle, William E. & Wileden, Jack C. Tutorial on Software System Design: Description & Analysis. (Tutorial Texts Ser.). 242p. 1980. 25.00 (ISBN 0-8186-0311-9, Q311). IEEE Comp Soc.
Robinson, Enders A. & Silvia, Manual T. Digital Foundations of Time Series Analysis: Wave-Equation Space-Time Processing. 450p. 1981. Vol. I, 464. 1979. 46.00x (ISBN 0-8162-7270-0); Vol. II, 450. 1981. text ed. 46.00x (ISBN 0-8162-7271-9). Holden-Day.
Rood, Harold J. Logic & Structured Design for Computer Programmers. 1985. pap. text ed. write for info. (ISBN 0-87150-869-9, 37L8800, Prindle). PWS Pubs.
Rudman, Jack. Associate Computer Programmer. (Career Examination Ser.: C-2206). (Cloth bdg. avail. on request). pap. 14.00 (ISBN 0-8373-2206-5). Natl Learning.
--Digital Computer Programmer. (Career Examination Ser.: C-198). (Cloth bdg. avail. on request). pap. 14.00 (ISBN 0-8373-0198-X). Natl Learning.
--Digital Computer Systems Programmer. (Career Examination Ser.: C-1250). (Cloth bdg. avail. on request). pap. 14.00 (ISBN 0-8373-1250-7). Natl Learning.
--Digital Computer Systems Specialist. (Career Examination Ser.: C-1251). (Cloth bdg. avail. on request). pap. 14.00 (ISBN 0-8373-1251-5). Natl Learning.
Sanderson, J. G. A Relational Theory of Computing. (Lecture Notes in Computer Science: Vol. 82). 147p. 1980. pap. 15.00 (ISBN 0-387-09987-5). Springer-Verlag.
Saret, L. Data Processing Logic. 1984. 19.95 (ISBN 0-07-054723-8). McGraw.
Saxon, James A. COBOL: A Self-Instructional Manual. 2nd ed. 1971. pap. 18.95 ref. ed. (ISBN 0-13-139469-X). P-H.

Schneider, G. Michael & Weingart, Steven W. An Introduction to Programming & Problem Solving with Pascal. 2nd ed. LC 82-2809. 480p. 1982. 27.45 (ISBN 0-471-08216-3); pap. 23.00 (ISBN 0-471-80447-9). Wiley.
Singer, Bernard M. Programming in BASIC, with Applications. 1973. text ed. 26.90 (ISBN 0-07-057480-4). McGraw.
Skees, William D. Computer Software for Data Communications. 163p. 1981. 21.00 (ISBN 0-534-97979-3). Van Nos Reinhold.
Spencer, Donald D. BASIC Programming. LC 82-17689. (Illus.). 224p. 1983. pap. 8.95 (ISBN 0-684-18039-1, ScribT). Scribner.
--Introduction to Information Processing. 3rd ed. 650p. 1981. text ed. 26.95 (ISBN 0-675-08073-8); basic supplement 4.95 (ISBN 0-675-09917-X). Additional supplements maybe obtained from publisher. Merrill.
--Problem Solving with FORTRAN. LC 76-26040. (Illus.). 1977. pap. text ed. 21.95 (ISBN 0-13-720094-3). P-H.
Starkey, J. Denbigh & Ross, Rockford. Fundamental Programming. 256p. 1982. pap. text ed. write for info. (ISBN 0-314-71810-9). West Pub.
--Fundamental Programming: An Introduction to Computer Science. (Illus.). 450p. 1984. pap. text ed. 22.95 (ISBN 0-314-77801-2); Transparency masters; 90p. write for info. (ISBN 0-314-86346-X). West Pub.
Steele, D. R. An Introduction to Elementary Computer & Compiler Design. 152p. 1978. 25.25 (ISBN 0-444-00243-X, North-Holland). Elsevier.
Stern, Nancy, et al. RPG II & RPG III Programming. LC 83-12536. 680p. 1984. pap. text ed. 28.45x (ISBN 0-471-87625-9). Wiley.
Stevens, Wayne P. Using Structured Design: How to Make Programs Simple, Changeable, Flexible & Reusable. LC 80-23481. 213p. 1981. 35.95 (ISBN 0-471-08198-1, Pub. by Wiley-Interscience). Wiley.
Stuart, Frederic. FORTRAN Programming. LC 68-30922. 371p. 1970. Repr. 40.50 (ISBN 0-471-83466-1). Wiley.
Tanenbaum, Andrew S. Structured Computer Organization. 2nd ed. (Illus.). 480p. 1984. text ed. 38.95 (ISBN 0-13-854489-1); tchr's manual avail. (ISBN 0-13-854423-9). P-H.
Teng, Albert Y. & Malmgren, William A. Experiments in Logic & Computer Design. (Illus.). 144p. 1984. text ed. 16.95 (ISBN 0-13-295833-3). P-H.
Tou, Julius T., ed. Information Systems (COINS IV) LC 74-4403. (Illus.). 506p. 1974. 69.50x (ISBN 0-306-35134-X, Plenum Pr). Plenum Pub.
Traub, J. F., ed. Algorithms & Complexity: New Directions & Recent Results. 1976. 55.00 (ISBN 0-12-697540-X). Acad Pr.
--Complexity of Sequential & Parallel Numerical Algorithms. 1973. 47.50 (ISBN 0-12-697550-7). Acad Pr.
Tremblay, Jean-Paul & Bunt, Richard B. Introduction to Computer Science: An Algorithmic Approach. (Illus.). 1979. text ed. 37.95 (ISBN 0-07-065163-9). McGraw.
Turner, Lawrence E. & Howson, Rosemary J. Basic BASIC for Basic Beginners. x, 293p. 1982. pap. text ed. 9.95 (ISBN 0-943872-82-0). Andrews Univ Pr.
Van Tassel, Dennis. Program Style, Design, Efficiency, Debugging & Testing. 2nd ed. (Illus.). 1978. ref. ed. 32.95 (ISBN 0-13-729947-8). P-H.
Vazsonyi, Andrew. Introduction to Data Processing. 3rd ed. 1980. 25.95x (ISBN 0-256-02343-3). Irwin.
Vickers, Frank D. FORTRAN IV: A Modern Approach. 2nd ed. 1978. pap. text ed. 10.95 (ISBN 0-8403-1829-4). Kendall-Hunt.
Wand, M. Induction, Recursion & Programming. 202p. 1980. 33.50 (ISBN 0-444-00322-3, North-Holland). Elsevier.
Warnier, Jean-Dominique. Program Modification. 152p. 1978. 21.50 (ISBN 90-207-0777-9, Pub. by Martinus Nijhoff Netherlands). Kluwer Academic.
Watkins, R. P. Computer Problem Solving. LC 79-22235. 172p. 1980. Repr. of 1974 ed. lib. bdg. 10.50 (ISBN 0-89874-058-4). Krieger.
Weinberg, Gerald M. Psychology of Computer Programming. (Computer Science Ser.). (Illus.). 304p. 1971. 16.95 (ISBN 0-442-29264-3). Van Nos Reinhold.
Weinberg, Victor. Structured Analysis. (Illus.). 1980. text ed. 37.50 (ISBN 0-13-854414-X). P-H.
Wetherell, C. Etudes for Programmers. LC 77-13961. (Illus.). 1978. pap. 17.95 ref. (ISBN 0-13-291807-2). P-H.
Wirth, Niklaus. Systematic Programming: An Introduction. (Illus.). 208p. 1973. 32.95 (ISBN 0-13-880369-2). P-H.
Wos, Larry, et al. Automated Reasoning: Introduction & Applications. LC 83-22968. (Illus.). 482p. 1984. text ed. 28.95 (ISBN 0-13-054453-1); pap. text ed. 18.95 (ISBN 0-13-054446-9). P-H.
Young, S. J. An Introduction to Ada. LC 82-15547. (Computers & Their Applications Ser.: No.1403). 400p. 1983. 69.95x (ISBN 0-470-27551-0); pap. 29.95x (ISBN 0-470-27350-X). Halsted Pr.
Yourdan, Edward. Techniques of Program Structure & Design. (Illus.). 384p. 1976. 37.50 (ISBN 0-13-901702-X). P-H.
Yourdon, Edward. Design of On-Line Computer Systems. (Illus.). 576p. 1972. ref. ed. 37.50 (ISBN 0-13-201301-0). P-H.
--Structured Walkthroughs. 2nd ed. 152p. (Orig.). 1978. pap. 15.00 (ISBN 0-917072-09-X). Yourdon.
Yourdon, Edward & Constantine, Larry L. Structured Design: Fundamentals of a Discipline of Computer Program & System Design. 1979. text ed. 40.00 (ISBN 0-13-854471-9). P-H.
Yourdon, Edward, ed. Writings of the Revolution: Selected Readings on Software Engineering. (Illus.). 472p. (Orig.). 1982. pap. 33.00 (ISBN 0-917072-25-1). Yourdon.
Zelkowitz, Marvin V., et al. Principles of Software Engineering & Design. LC 78-27315. (Illus.). 1979. text ed. 36.95 (ISBN 0-13-710202-X). P-H.
Ziegler, Carol. Programming System Methodologies. (Illus.). 304p. 1983. text ed. 25.95 (ISBN 0-13-729905-2). P-H.
Zimmer, J. A. Abstraction for Programmers. 288p. 1985. 17.95 (ISBN 0-07-072832-1). McGraw.
Zwass, Vladimir. Programming in FORTRAN. 224p. 1980. pap. 5.95i (ISBN 0-06-460194-3, CO 194, COS). B&N NY.

ELECTRONIC DIGITAL COMPUTERS–PROGRAMMING–PROGRAMMED INSTRUCTION

George, F. H. An Introduction to Digital Computing. 1966. pap. 7.75 (ISBN 0-08-011280-3). Pergamon.

ELECTRONIC DIGITAL COMPUTERS–PROGRAMMING–STUDY AND TEACHING

Godfrey, David & Sterling, Sharon. The Elements of CAL. 1983. text ed. 22.95 (ISBN 0-8359-1701-0); pap. text ed. 17.95 (ISBN 0-8359-1700-2). Reston.
Spaniol, Otto. Computer Arithmetic: Logic & Design. LC 80-41867. (Computing Ser.). 280p. 1981. 53.95 (ISBN 0-471-27926-9, Pub. by Wiley-Interscience). Wiley.
Swartzlander, E. E., Jr., ed. Computer Arithmetic. LC 78-14397. (Benchmark Papers in Electrical Engineering & Computer Science: Vol. 21). 400p. 1979. 59.50 (ISBN 0-87933-350-2). Van Nos Reinhold.

ELECTRONIC DIGITAL COMPUTERS–TESTING

Perry, William E. & Kuong, Javier F. Developing & Implementing an Integrated Test Facility for Testing Computerized Systems. 1979. 50.00 (ISBN 0-940706-09-1, MAP-12). Management Advisory Pubns.
--How to Test Internal Control & Integrity in Computerized Systems. 1980. 50.00 (ISBN 0-940706-13-X, MAP-15). Management Advisory Pubns.

ELECTRONIC DRAFTING

Baer, C. J. & Ottaway, J. R. Electrical & Electronic Drawing. 5th ed. 560p. 1985. 31.50 (ISBN 0-07-003028-6). McGraw.
Baer, Charles J. & Ottaway, John R. Electrical & Electronics Drawing. 4th ed. LC 79-15837. (Illus.). 1980. text ed. 31.50 (ISBN 0-07-003010-3). McGraw.
Beakley, George C. Electronic Drafting. 1982. pap. text ed. write for info. (ISBN 0-02-307600-3). Macmillan.
Bethune, James. Basic Electronic & Electrical Drafting. 2nd ed. (Illus.). 304p. 1985. text ed. 27.95 (ISBN 0-13-060336-8); 21.95 (ISBN 0-13-060351-1). P-H.
Bethune, James D. Basic Electronic & Electrical Drafting. (Illus.). 1980. text ed. 24.95 (ISBN 0-13-060301-5). P-H.
Earle, J. H. Drafting Technology. 1982. 36.95 (ISBN 0-201-10233-1). Addison-Wesley.
Giachino, Joseph W. & Beukema, Henry J. Drafting Technology. 2nd ed. LC 64-12817. (Illus.). pap. 116.00 (ISBN 0-317-10628-7, 2011278). Bks Demand UMI.
Kirkpatrick, James M. Electronic Drafting & Printed Circuit Board Design. LC 84-14929. 288p. 1985. pap. text ed. 24.00 (ISBN 0-8273-2315-8); instr's. guide 4.00 (ISBN 0-8273-2316-6). Delmar.
Kirschner, E. & Stone, K. Electronics Drafting Workbook. 3rd ed. (Illus.). 1977. pap. text ed. 25.15 (ISBN 0-07-034890-1). McGraw.
Kirshner, C. & Stone, K. M. Electronics Drafting Workbook. 4th ed. 1985. 19.95 (ISBN 0-07-034907-X). McGraw.
Lamit, Louis G. & Lloyd, Sandra J. Drafting for Electronics. 480p. 1985. text ed. 27.95 (ISBN 0-675-20200-0). Additional supplements maybe obtained from publisher. Merrill.
Lamit, Louis G., et al. Workbook in Drafting for Electronics. 192p. 1985. 11.95 (ISBN 0-675-20417-8). Merrill.
Lindsey, Darry. The Design & Drafting of Printed Circuits. 2nd ed. (Illus.). 400p. 1983. 48.95 (ISBN 0-07-037844-4). McGraw.
Lopez, Ulises M. & Warrin, George E. Electronic Drawing & Technology. LC 77-16452. (Electronic Technology Ser.). 263p. 1978. text ed. 29.95 (ISBN 0-471-02377-9); solutions manual avail. (ISBN 0-471-03715-X). Wiley.
Madsen, David A. Drafting: Syllabus. 1974. pap. text ed. 8.35 (ISBN 0-89420-070-4, 107015); cassette recordings 104.95 (ISBN 0-89420-140-9, 107000). Natl Book.
Richter, H. W. & Rubenstein, C. F. Electrical & Electronic Drafting. 2nd ed. 317p. 1985. 28.95 (ISBN 0-471-05784-3). Wiley.
Richter, Herbert W. Electrical & Electronic Drafting. LC 76-20506. (Electronic Technology Ser.). 272p. 1977. 29.95x (ISBN 0-471-72035-6); solutions manual 3.00 (ISBN 0-471-02541-0). Wiley.
Ryan, Daniel L. Principles of Automated Drafting. (Mechanical Engineering Ser.: Vol. 28). (Illus.). 336p. 1984. 29.75 (ISBN 0-8247-7175-3). Dekker.
Shiers, George. Electronic Drafting Techniques & Exercises. (Illus.). 1963. pap. text ed. 16.95 (ISBN 0-13-250605-X). P-H.
Villanucci, Robert S. & Avtgis, Alexander W. Electronic Drafting. 512p. 1985. text ed. write for info. (ISBN 0-02-423050-2). Macmillan.
Zimmerman, L. & Clark, R. Drafting with Autocad 2.0. pap. 23.95 (ISBN 0-471-82974-9). Wiley.

ELECTRONIC EAVESDROPPING

see Eavesdropping

ELECTRONIC EQUIPMENT, MINIATURE

see Miniature Electronic Equipment

ELECTRONIC INDUSTRIES

see also names of individual industries and products, e.g. television industry; electron tubes

Brech, Michael & Sharp, Margaret. Inward Investment: Policy Options for the United Kingdom. (Chatham House Papers: No. 21). 128p. (Orig.). 1984. pap. 10.95x (ISBN 0-7102-0256-3). Routledge & Kegan.
Campbell, John & Goodman, Susan. High-Technology Employment in Texas: A Labor Market Analysis. 75p. (Orig.). 1985. pap. text ed. 6.00 (ISBN 0-87755-290-8). Bureau Busn UT.
Deloitte, Haskins & Sells & High Technology Industry Group. Tax Aspects of High Technology Operations. 500p. 1984. text ed. 65.00x (ISBN 0-471-88874-5, Pub. by Ronald Pr). Wiley.
Electronic & Electrical Companies. 1983. 200.00x (Pub. by Jordan & Sons UK). State Mutual Bk.
Electronics Industry. (UNIDO Guides to Information Sources: No. 32). pap. 4.00 (UN225, UN). Unipub.
Graeser, Kathi, ed. Who's Who in Electronics 1985 Annual. pap. 1029.00 (ISBN 0-916512-72-X). Harris Pub.
Hartmeyer, Fred C. Electronic Industry Cost Estimating Data. LC 64-16344. (Illus.). pap. 78.00 (ISBN 0-317-08841-6, 2011870). Bks Demand UMI.
Iacchia, Flora. A Manual for Exporting Electronic Products Overseas. 500p. 1985. prof. ref. 350.00x (ISBN 0-88730-031-6). Ballinger Pub.
International Resource Development Inc. Data & Voice Multiplexers. 164p. 1983. 985.00x (ISBN 0-88694-578-X). Intl Res Dev.
--EMP-Resistant Products & Systems. 144p. 1984. 1850.00x (ISBN 0-88694-608-5). Intl Res Dev.
--Evolving Keyboard Markets. 235p. 1984. 1850.00x (ISBN 0-88694-609-3). Intl Res Dev.
--Facsimile Markets in Europe. 201p. 1984. 1650.00x (ISBN 0-88694-599-2). Intl Res Dev.
--High Resolution Displays & HDTV. 178p. 1983. 1850.00x (ISBN 0-88694-553-4). Intl Res Dev.
--Personal Portable Consumer Electronics Market. 190p. 1984. 1285.00x (ISBN 0-88694-587-9). Intl Res Dev.
Jacobson, D. M. & Evans, D. S. Critical Materials in the Electrical & Electronics Industry. 59p. 1985. pap. text ed. 16.00x (ISBN 0-901462-26-8, Metals Soc). Brookfield Pub Co.
Kahn, Terry. MCC Impact Assessment. Farley, Josh, ed. (Illus.). 50p. (Orig.). 1985. pap. 6.00 (ISBN 0-87755-289-4). Bureau Busn UT.
Kelley, David & Donway, Roger. Laissez Parler: Freedom in the Electronic Media. (Studies in Social Philosophy & Policy: No. 1). 49p. 1982. pap. 4.00 (ISBN 0-935756-99-X). Soc Phil Pol.
McLean, Mick. The Japanese Electronics Challenge. LC 82-42710. 170p. 1982. 27.50x (ISBN 0-312-44066-9). St Martin.
McLean, Mick, ed. Mechatronics: Developments in Japan & Europe. LC 83-22925. vii, 129p. 1983. lib. bdg. 27.95 (ISBN 0-89930-087-1, MMT/, Quorum). Greenwood.
Matisoff, Bernard S. Handbook of Electronics Manufacturing Engineering. 1978. 42.50 (ISBN 0-442-25146-7). Van Nos Reinhold.
Morrison, Philip W. Environmental Control in Electronic Manufacturing. LC 73-9518. 488p. (Orig.). 1973. 29.50. Krieger.
Randle, Gretchen R., ed. Electronic Industries Information Sources. LC 67-31262. (Management Information Guide Ser.: No. 13). 1968. 60.00x (ISBN 0-8103-0813-4). Gale.
Steele, Kurt D. Electronic Information Publishing: Old Issues in a New Industry. 630p. 1984. pap. 35.00 (ISBN 0-317-27379-5, #G4-3753). PLI.
Varian, Dorothy. The Inventor & the Pilot: Russell & Sigurd Varian. LC 83-5329. (Illus.). 315p. 1983. 18.95 (ISBN 0-87015-237-8). Pacific Bks.
Washington Group. Major Markets in Electronics, Computers & Peripheral Equipment. 225p. 1985. 147.00 (ISBN 0-317-27288-8). Marketing Intl.
Welch, W. J. Electronic Mail Systems: A Practical Evaluation Guide. 130p. 1982. pap. 15.00 (ISBN 0-85012-350-X). Intl Pubns Serv.

ELECTRONIC INDUSTRIES–DIRECTORIES

Carlsen, Fran, ed. Harris Ohio Industrial Directory. (Illus.). 950p. 79.50 (ISBN 0-916512-61-4). Harris Pub.
--Ohio Buyers Industrial Directory. 720p. 25.00 (ISBN 0-916512-60-6). Harris Pub.
Goss, Ann, ed. Illinois Buyers Industrial Directory. 720p. 25.00 (ISBN 0-916512-40-1). Harris Pub.
Graeser, Kathie & Loesner, Bonnie, eds. Electronic Representative Directory 1985. 192p. 1985. 20.00 (ISBN 0-916512-73-8). Harris Pub.
Lace, Vivian, ed. Michigan Statewide Yellow Pages. 512p. 25.00 (ISBN 0-916512-20-7). Harris Pub.
Segulin, Fran, ed. Harris Pennsylvania Industrial Directory, 1984. (Illus.). 884p. 79.50 (ISBN 0-916512-45-2). Harris Pub.
Smith, Marellen & Mattern, Patricia, eds. Indiana State Wide Yellow Pages. 360p. 25.00 (ISBN 0-916512-31-2). Harris Pub.
Witt, Loretta & Brown, Sheri, eds. Electronic Industry Telephone Directory. 664p. 1984. 35.00 (ISBN 0-916512-10-X). Harris Pub.

ELECTRONIC INSTRUMENTS

see also Astronautical Instruments; Automatic Checkout Equipment; Electronic Apparatus and Appliances; Electronic Measurements; also specific electronic instruments, e.g. cathode ray oscillograph

Allocca, John & Stuart, Allen. Electronic Instrumentation. 1983. text ed. 29.95 (ISBN 0-8359-1633-2). Reston.
Analysis Instrumentation Division, et al. Productivity Through Control Technology: Proceedings of the Joint Symposium, Houston, Texas, 1983. LC 83-205565. 238p. 1983. pap. text ed. 36.00x (ISBN 0-87664-783-2). Instru Soc.
Arbel, Arie F. Analog Signal Processing & Instrumentation. LC 79-13461. (Illus.). 1980. 87.50 (ISBN 0-521-22469-1). Cambridge U Pr.
Bell, David. Electronic Instrumentation & Measurement. 1982. pap. text ed. 29.95 (ISBN 0-8359-1669-3); instrs'. manual avail. (ISBN 0-8359-1670-7). Reston.
Bellamy, John C. Digital Telephony. 526p. 1982. 37.50 (ISBN 0-686-98112-X). Telecom Lib.
Bibbero, Robert J. Microprocessors in Instruments & Control. LC 77-9929. 301p. 1977. 32.50x (ISBN 0-471-01595-4, Pub. by Wiley-Interscience). Wiley.
Brown, C. C. & Saucer, Rayford T. Electronic Instrumentation for the Behavioral Sciences. (Illus.). 176p. 1958. 18.75x (ISBN 0-398-04222-5). C C Thomas.
Carr, Joseph. Elements of Electronic Instrumentation & Measurement. (Illus.). 1979. text ed. 26.95 (ISBN 0-8359-1650-2). Reston.
Carter, Forrest L., ed. Molecular Electronic Devices. 424p. 1982. 65.00 (ISBN 0-8247-1676-0). Dekker.
Desa, A. Principles of Electronic Instrumentation. LC 80-28240. 280p. 1981. pap. 34.95x (ISBN 0-470-27135-3). Halsted Pr.
De Sa, A. Principles of Electronic Instrumentation. 280p. 1981. 50.00x (ISBN 0-7131-2799-6, Pub. by E Arnold England). State Mutual Bk.
Diefenderfer, James. Principles of Electronic Instrumentation. 2nd ed. 1979. text ed. 42.95 (ISBN 0-7216-3076-6, CBS C). SCP.
Discover the New World of Instrumentation: Proceedings of the Columbus Section Symposium, 1982. LC 82-164466. 330p. pap. text ed. 45.00x (ISBN 0-87664-671-2). Instru Soc.
Douglas-Young, John. Complete Guide to Electronic Test Equipment & Troubleshooting Techniques. 256p. cancelled 17.95 (ISBN 0-13-160085-0, Parker). P-H.
Eggert, Arthur A. Electronics & Instrumentation for the Clinical Laboratory. LC 83-10524. 432p. 1983. 26.95x (ISBN 0-471-86275-4, Pub. by Wiley Med). Wiley.
Floyd, Thomas L. Electronic Devices. 1984. Additional supplements may be obtained from publisher. text ed. 29.95 (ISBN 0-675-20157-8). Merrill.

Business Communications Staff. Dynamics of Cash in the Payments System. 1983. 1550.00 (ISBN 0-89336-316-2, G-066A). BCC.
Carlock, L. L. The Electronic Office & You: Managing Your Productivity. 192p. 1985. 7.04 (ISBN 0-07-027978-0). McGraw.
Donohue, Brian. How to Buy an Office Computer or Word Processor. (Illus.). 232p. 1983. 17.95 (ISBN 0-13-403113-X); pap. 8.95 (ISBN 0-13-403105-9). P-H.
Edwards, Nancy M., ed. Office Automation. 1983. 34.95 (ISBN 0-442-22202-5). Van Nos Reinhold.
Electronic Filing. (Reports Ser.: No. 187). 179p. 1981. 1285.00x (ISBN 0-88694-187-3). Intl Res Dev.
Ellis, Alec C. Educating Our Masters. 160p. 1985. text ed. write for info. (ISBN 0-566-00867-X). Gower Pub Co.
Future Office Systems Market, 2 vols. 493p. 1980. Set. 1000.00 (ISBN 0-86621-004-0, A778). Frost & Sullivan.
Green, James H. Automating Your Office: How to Do It, How to Justify It. 256p. 1984. 24.95 (ISBN 0-07-024318-2). McGraw.
Kamerschen, David R. Money & Banking. 1984. text ed. 21.35 (ISBN 0-538-08260-7, H26). SW Pub.
Kutie, Rita C. & Rhodes, Joan L. Secretarial Procedures for the Electronic Office. 2nd ed. 1985. pap. write for info. (ISBN 0-471-82156-X). Wiley.
--Secretarial Procedures for the Electronic Office. 371p. 1983. pap. 19.95 (ISBN 0-471-86156-1). Wiley.
McKenzie, Jimmy C. & Hughes, Robert J. Office Machines: A Practical Approach. 2nd ed. 352p. 1983. write for info. wire coil (ISBN 0-697-08088-9); instr's solutions manual avail. (ISBN 0-697-08194-X); practice set avail. (ISBN 0-697-08096-X). Wm C Brown.
Needles, Mark. Electronic Calculators in Business. 1982. pap. text ed. 21.70x (ISBN 0-673-16013-0). Scott F.
Office Automation Market in Banking. 1985. write for info. (ISBN 0-86621-193-4, A1255). Frost & Sullivan.
Office Automation Software Market. 336p. 1985. 1750.00 (ISBN 0-86621-291-4, A1368). Frost & Sullivan.
Office Automation Systems Market. 1983. 1275.00 (ISBN 0-86621-066-0). Frost & Sullivan.
Office Consumables & the Automated Office. (Reports Ser.: No. 199). 168p. 1982. 1285.00x (ISBN 0-88694-199-7). Intl Res Dev.
Office Machines Course. 1979. text ed. 5.75 wkbk. (ISBN 0-538-13800-9, M80). SW Pub.
Optical Discs for Office Automation & Electronic Publishing. (Reports Ser.: No. 191). 171p. 1982. 1285.00x (ISBN 0-88694-191-1). Intl Res Dev.
PABX, 2 vols. Incl. Vol. 1-Interconnect & the Future Office Controller. 196p. 1980. 985.00x (ISBN 0-88694-139-3); Vol. 2-Computer Model. 4500.00x. (Reports Ser.: No. 139). 1980. Intl Res Dev.
Pactor, Paul. Business Machines Projects. 1960. pap. 3.96 (ISBN 0-02-830970-7); answer key 1.60 (ISBN 0-02-830980-4). Glencoe.
Plastics in Business Machines. 1981. 1500.00 (ISBN 0-89336-304-9, P-064). BCC.
Pritchard, J. A. & Cole, I. Planning Office Automation: Information Management Systems. 180p. 1982. pap. 27.35 (ISBN 0-471-89419-2). Wiley.
Schneck & Giordano. Electronic Business Machines Calculation. (Illus.). 288p. 1986. pap. text ed. 21.95 (ISBN 0-13-250101-5). P-H.
A Survey of Commercial Turnkey CAD-CAM Systems. 2nd ed. 96.00 (ISBN 0-686-31441-7). C I M Systems.
Trudell, Libby, et al. Options for Electronic Mail. LC 84-15418. (Information & Communications Management Guides). 145p. 1984. 32.95 (ISBN 0-86729-105-2, 808-BW); pap. 24.95 (ISBN 0-86729-104-4). Knowledge Indus.
Wagoner, Kathleen P. & Ruprecht, Mary M. Office Automation: Technology & Concepts. 337p. 1984. pap. 20.95 (ISBN 0-471-88776-5); lab manual avail. (ISBN 0-471-09067-0). Wiley.
Wilson, P. A. & Pritchard, J. A. Planning Office Automation: Electronic Message Systems. 242p. 1982. pap. 27.35 (ISBN 0-471-89418-4). Wiley.

ELECTRONIC OPTICS
see Electron Optics
ELECTRONIC PROBES
see Probes (Electronic Instruments)
ELECTRONIC PUBLISHING
see also Teletex (Data Transmission System); Videotex (Data Transmission System)

Day, A. Colin. Text Processing. (Computer Science Text Ser.: No. 20). 150p. 1984. 29.95 (ISBN 0-521-24432-3); pap. 12.95 (ISBN 0-521-28683-2). Cambridge U Pr.
Electronic & Software Publishing. 35.00 (ISBN 0-317-29488-1, #CO2712, Law & Business). HarBraceJ.
Greenberger, Martin, ed. Electronic Publishing Plus: Media for a Technological Future. LC 85-12613. 330p. 1985. 45.00 (ISBN 0-86729-146-X, 432-BW). Knowledge Indus.
Information Management Associates. Electronic Document III: Trends in Electronic Publishing in Europe & the U. S. 1983. 25.00 (ISBN 0-317-00236-8). Learned Info.

ELECTRONIC PULSE TECHNIQUES
see Pulse Techniques (Electronics)
ELECTRONIC SPREADSHEETS

All about Seventy Electronic Spreadsheets. 32p. 19.00 (ISBN 0-318-03647-9). Datapro Res.
Anbarlian, H. An Introduction to Multiplan-86 Spreadsheeting on the DEC Rainbow 100: DEC Version. (Personnal Programming Ser.). 416p. 1984. 1.00 (ISBN 0-07-001735-2). McGraw.
Anbarlian, Harry. Spreadsheeting on the TRS-80 Color Computer. (Personal Computing Ser.). 320p. 1983. 22.95 (ISBN 0-07-001595-3, BYTE Bks); incl. cassettes 39.95 (ISBN 0-07-079110-4). McGraw.
Berry, Timothy. Working Smart with Electronic Spreadsheets. 1985. pap. 18.95 (ISBN 0-8104-6203-6). Hayden.
Berst, Jessie. Computhink Guide to Spreadsheet. LC 83-82557. 168p. 1983. pap. 11.95 (ISBN 0-672-22164-0, 22164). Sams.
Caffarella, Edward. Spreadsheets Go to School: Applications for Administrators. 1985. 19.95 (ISBN 0-8359-7060-4). Reston.
Clark, Philip M. Microcomputer Spreadsheet Models for Libraries: Preparing Documents, Budgets, & Statistical Reports. LC 84-20470. 134p. 1985. pap. text ed. 24.95x (ISBN 0-8389-0403-3). ALA.
Dobson, W. G. Engineering Problem Solving with Spreadsheet Programs. Wolff, A. K., ed. (Illus.). 125p. 1984. 79.95 (ISBN 0-932217-00-1). Binary Eng Assocs.
Hallam, Teresa A. Microcomputer Use: Word Processor, Spreadsheets, & Databases with Accompanying Concept 3 Software; Instructor's Manual. 1985. text ed. 5.00 (ISBN 0-12-319629-9). Acad Pr.
Hixson, Amanda C. A Buyer's Guide to Microcomputer Business Software: Accounting & Spreadsheets. 1918p. 1984. pap. 19.95 (ISBN 0-201-11065-2). Addison-Wesley.
Landis, Dick & Schmisseur, Ed. Spreadsheet Software for Farm Business Management. 1985. text ed. 24.95 (ISBN 0-8359-6956-8); pap. text ed. 19.95 (ISBN 0-8359-6955-X). Reston.
Landis, Dick & Schmisseur, Edward. The Farmer's Spreadsheet. LC 84-25150. 1985. text ed. 24.95 (ISBN 0-8359-1865-3); pap. 19.95 (ISBN 0-8359-1864-5). Reston.
Monroe, J. Spreadsheet Applications in Accounting Information Systems: Includes SuperCalc 3 Educational Version. 24.95 (ISBN 0-471-82255-8). Wiley.
O'Keeffe, Linda. Integrated Spreadsheet Software: Lotus 1-2-3 & Context MBA. Seybold, Patricia B., ed. (Seybold Series on Professional Computing). (Illus.). 183p. 1984. pap. 15.96 (ISBN 0-07-056321-7, BYTE Bks). McGraw.
Pentland, L. P. Salesbook Spreadsheets: Sales Management, Cash Management, General Management. 160p. 1984. 19.95 (ISBN 0-07-049701-X). McGraw.
Simondi, Tom. The Quick & Easy Guide to Spreadsheets on the Apple. 128p. 1984. pap. 4.95 (ISBN 0-912003-28-6). Bk Co.
--Spreadsheets on the IBM PC. 128p. 1984. pap. 4.95 (ISBN 0-912003-24-3). Bk Co.
Smith. Electronic Spreadsheet Applications for Financial Accounting. 1986. pap. text ed. price not set (ISBN 0-538-40182-6, O7A1). SW Pub.
--Electronic Spreadsheet Applications for Financial Management. 1986. pap. text ed. price not set (ISBN 0-538-40603-8, O1F1). SW Pub.
--Electronic Spreadsheet Applications for Managerial Accounting. 1986. pap. text ed. price not set (ISBN 0-538-40192-3, O8A1). SW Pub.
Software Digest. The Ratings Book: IBM-PC Spreadsheet Programs. 1984. pap. 14.95 (ISBN 0-916543-20-X). Software Inc.
Spreadsheet Software Guide & Handbook. 1985. Master Volume. 19.95 (ISBN 0-912603-34-8); 16.95 (ISBN 0-912603-23-2). Micro Info.
Williams, Andrew T. What If? A User's Guide to Spreadsheets on the IBM-PC. (IBM Personal Computer Ser.: Nos. 1-646). 281p. (Orig.). 1984. pap. text ed. 16.95 (ISBN 0-471-89218-1, Pub. by Wiley Pr). Wiley.

ELECTRONIC SWITCHING SYSTEMS (TELEPHONE)
see Telephone Switching Systems, Electronic
ELECTRONIC TOYS
see also Video Games

Ahl, David H., ed. More BASIC Computer Games: TRS-80. LC 78-50028. (Illus.). 196p. (Orig.). 1980. pap. 7.95 (ISBN 0-916688-19-4, 6C4). Creative Comp.
Buchsbaum, W. H. & Mauro, R. Microprocessor-Based Electronic Games. 350p. 1983. pap. 9.95 (ISBN 0-07-008722-9, BYTE Bks). McGraw.
Cohen, Henry B. The Home Video Book: How to Understand & Use Home Video, Home Computers & Electronic Games. (Illus.). 192p. 1983. pap. 9.95 (ISBN 0-8174-3993-5, Amphoto). Watson-Guptill.
Consumer Guide Editors. How to Win at Pac-Man. (Orig.). 1982. pap. 2.25 (ISBN 0-671-46072-2). PB.
Halpin, Daniel W. & Woodhead, Ronald W. Constructo: A Heuristic Game for Construction Management. LC 73-76342. 195p. 1973. pap. 10.00x (ISBN 0-252-00337-3); computer program, non-profit institutions 250.00 (ISBN 0-252-00400-0); computer program 500.00 (ISBN 0-252-00399-3). U of Ill Pr.
Hartnell, Tim. Seventy Games for the Timex-Sinclair 1000. 144p. 1983. pap. 9.95 (ISBN 0-201-11064-4). Addison-Wesley.
Heiserman, David L. How to Design & Build Your Own Custom TV Games. (Illus.). 1979. pap. 13.95 (ISBN 0-8306-9815-9, 1101). TAB Bks.
Renko, Hal & Edwards, Sam. Cosmic Games for the Commodore VIC-20. (Illus.). 192p. 1983. pap. 5.95 (ISBN 0-201-16476-0). Addison-Wesley.
--Tantalizing Games for the Timex-Sinclair 2000. (Illus.). 192p. 1983. pap. 5.95 (ISBN 0-201-16479-5). Addison-Wesley.
Sobie, Keith, et al. The Video Wizard Handbook. (Illus.). 196p. 1982. pap. 6.95 (ISBN 0-686-35866-X). Video Wizard.

ELECTRONIC TRAFFIC CONTROLS

Digital-Computer-Controlled Traffic Signal System for a Small City. (National Cooperative Highway Research Program Report). 82p. 1966. 4.00 (ISBN 0-317-36075-2, 1474). Transport Res Bd.
Research Directions in Computer Control of Urban Traffic Systems. 393p. 1979. pap. 20.00x (ISBN 0-87262-179-0). Am Soc Civil Eng.
Standard Specifications for Structural Supports for Highway Signs, Luminaires & Traffic Signals. 1975. pap. 3.00 (ISBN 0-686-20956-7, LTS-1). AASHTO.

ELECTRONIC TRANSFORMERS

Kiltie, Ordean. Design Shortcuts & Procedures for Electronics Power Transformers & Inductors. 2nd, rev. ed. LC 81-81620. (Illus.). 274p. (Orig.). 1981. 39.50 (ISBN 0-916512-27-4). Kiltie.

ELECTRONIC TRANSLATING
see Machine Translating
ELECTRONIC WARFARE
see Electronics in Military Engineering
ELECTRONIC WORK FUNCTION
see Electrons–Emission
ELECTRONICS
see also Astrionics; Cybernetics; Delay Lines; Electron Beams; Electron Tubes; Electronic Apparatus and Appliances; Electronic Circuits; Electronic Industries; Electronic Instruments; Electronic Transformers; Electronics in Aeronautics; Electronics in Biology; Electronics in Military Engineering; Electronics in Navigation; Feedback (Electronics); High-Fidelity Sound Systems; Industrial Electronics; Medical Electronics; Microelectronics; Microwave Circuits; Microwaves; Miniature Electronic Equipment; Modulation (Electronics); Oscillators, Crystal; Particle Accelerators; Pulse Techniques (Electronics); Quantum Electronics; Semiconductors; Shielding (Electricity); Thermoelectric Apparatus and Appliances; Transistors

Abelson, Philip H. & Hammond, Allen L., eds. Electronics: The Continuing Revolution. LC 77-77257. (Compendium Ser.: Vol. 5). 217p. casebound 10.00 (ISBN 0-87168-217-6); pap. 3.50 (ISBN 0-87168-230-3). AAAS.
Aden, et al. Electronic Countermeasures. Boyd, et al, eds. 1100p. 1978. Repr. of 1961 ed. 37.50 (ISBN 0-932146-00-7). Peninsula CA.
Advances in Electronics & Electron Physics, Vol. 59. 306p. 1982. 60.00 (ISBN 0-12-014659-2). Acad Pr.
Agranovitch, V. M. & Galanin, M. D. Electronic Excitation Energy Transfer in Condensed Matter. (Modern Problems in Condensed Matter Sciences Ser.: Vol. 3). xxiv, 372p. 1982. 95.75 (ISBN 0-444-86335-4). Elsevier.
Ahmad, M. F. & Katib, M. K. Principles of Electronics. (Arabic.). 300p. pap. 15.00 (ISBN 0-471-88556-8). Wiley.
Ainslie, Alan C. & Colwell, M. A. Practical Electronic Project Building. (Newnes Constructor's Guides Ser.). (Illus.). 1976. pap. 6.95 (ISBN 0-408-00231-X, 5448-3). Hayden.
Applications of Electronic Imaging Systems: Proceedings of the SPIE Technical Symposium East, Washington, D.C., 1978. (SPIE Seminar Proceedings: Vol. 143). 194p. 21.00 (ISBN 0-89252-170-8); members 14.00 (ISBN 0-317-34595-8). SPIE.
Auvray, J. & Fourrier, M. Problems in Electronics. LC 73-7617. 444p. 1974. text ed. 54.00 (ISBN 0-08-016982-1); pap. text ed. 17.50 (ISBN 0-08-017871-5). Pergamon.
Bacharach, S. L., et al. Electricity & Electronic Fundamentals, 3 vols. (Illus.). 1971. Set. looseleaf 150.00x (ISBN 0-87683-316-4); Vol. 1. 60.00x (ISBN 0-87683-317-2); Vol. 2; lab. manual; 270p. looseleaf 50.00x (ISBN 0-87683-318-0); Vol. 3; solutions manual; 270p. losseleaf 45.00x (ISBN 0-87683-319-9); Lesson Plans; 320p. looseleaf 1500.00x (ISBN 0-87683-321-0); Transparencies. looseleaf 1500.00x (ISBN 0-87683-322-9). G P Courseware.
Badrkhan & Larky. Electronic Principles & Applications. 1984. text ed. 21.00 (ISBN 0-538-33530-0, IE53). SW Pub.
Barnaal, Dennis. Analog Electronics for Scientific Application. 1982. pap. text ed. write for info. (ISBN 0-534-01015-6, Breton Pubs). Wadsworth Pub.
Bauer, R. S., ed. Surfaces & Interfaces: Physics & Electronics. 650p. 1984. 77.00 (ISBN 0-444-86784-8, I-200-84, North Holland). Elsevier.
Beards, Peter. Electronics: Level II. (Illus.). 192p. 1980. pap. text ed. 17.95x (ISBN 0-7121-0581-6). Trans-Atlantic.
Belove, Charles. Handbook of Modern Electrical & Electronic Engineering. 2200p. 1985. text ed. 53.45 (ISBN 0-471-09754-3). Wiley.
Benedict, R. Ralph. Electronics for Scientists & Engineers. 2nd ed. (Illus.). 1975. 39.95 (ISBN 0-13-252353-1). P-H.
Bird, B. M. & King, K. G. Power Electronics. 287p. 1983. cloth 49.95 (ISBN 0-471-10430-2, Pub. by Wiley-Interscience); pap. 21.95 (ISBN 0-471-90051-6, Pub. by Wiley-Interscience). Wiley.
Blitzer, Richard. Basic Electricity for Electronics. LC 73-20102. 727p. 1974. text ed. 31.95x (ISBN 0-471-08160-4). Wiley.
Boyce, Jefferson C. Modern Electronics: A Survey of the New Technology. Zuredjian, George Z., ed. (Illus.). 256p. 1982. 18.25x (ISBN 0-07-006915-8). McGraw.
Boylestad, Robert & Nashelsky, Louis. Electricity, Electronics, & Electromagnetics: Principles & Applications. 2nd ed. (Illus.). 544p. 1983. 31.95 (ISBN 0-13-248146-4). P-H.
Bramlett, George E. Electronics Fundamentals ET 110: A Hands-On Learning Approach. 200p. 1983. pap. text ed. 14.50 (ISBN 0-8403-3110-X). Kendall-Hunt.
Brant, Carroll A. Electronics for Communication. 800p. 1983. text ed. 31.95 (ISBN 0-574-21575-1, 13-4575); instr's. guide avail. (ISBN 0-574-21576-X, 13-4576). SRA.
Brophy, James J. Basic Electronics for Scientists. 4th ed. (Illus.). 464p. 1982. text ed. 43.95 (ISBN 0-07-008133-6). McGraw.
Brown, R. G. Electronics for the Modern Scientist. 496p. 1982. 33.50 (ISBN 0-444-00660-5, Biomedical Pr). Elsevier.
Bruce, David. Electronics: Basics, Device & Applications. 1984. text ed. 49.95 (ISBN 0-8359-1585-9); solutions manual avail. (ISBN 0-8359-4547-2). Reston.
--Modern Electronics: Basics, Devices & Applications. 1984. text ed. 31.95 (ISBN 0-8359-4546-4). Reston.
Buban, P., et al. Understanding Electricity & Electronics. 4th ed. 1981. text ed. 22.64 (ISBN 0-07-008678-8). McGraw.
Buchsbaum, Walter H. Tested Electronic Troubleshooting Methods. 2nd ed. LC 82-13167. 272p. 1982. 19.95 (ISBN 0-13-906966-6). P-H.
Business Communications Staff. Electronic Display Materials & Design: G-072. 1983. 1250.00 (ISBN 0-89336-339-1). BCC.
--Markets for Computer Technology in the Home: G-063. 1982. 950.00 (ISBN 0-89336-300-6). BCC.
Butchbaker, Allen F. Electricity & Electronics for Agriculture. (Illus.). 392p. 1977. text ed. 21.95x (ISBN 0-8138-0525-2). Iowa St U Pr.
Calvert, J. M. & McCausland, M. A. Electronics. LC 78-4113. (Manchester Physics Ser.). 615p. 1978. pap. 39.95 (ISBN 0-471-99639-4, Pub. by Wiley-Interscience). Wiley.
CES Industries, Inc. Ed-Lab Six Hundred & Fifty Experiment Manual: Basic Electronics Concepts, Book O. (Illus.). 206p. 1980. 11.50 (ISBN 0-86711-002-3). CES Industries.
CES Industries, Inc. Staff. Ed-Lab Eighty Exercise Manual: DC-AC Electronics Programming. (Illus.). 1982. write for info. (ISBN 0-86711-062-7). CES Industries.
--Ed-Lab Instructor's Guide: I-O Module CES 342; A-D Converter Latch-Module CES 343. (Illus.). 1982. write for info. (ISBN 0-86711-060-0). CES Industries.

Kybett, Harry. Electronics. LC 78-16821. (Wiley Self-Teaching Guides Ser.). 260p. 1979. pap. 9.95 (ISBN 0-471-01748-5, Pub. by Wiley Pr). Wiley.

Kyriacou, Demetrios. Basics of Electro-Organic Synthesis. 153p. 1981. 37.95 (ISBN 0-471-07975-8, Pub. by Wiley-Interscience). Wiley.

Lackey, John E., et al. Fundamentals of Electricity & Electronics. LC 82-12007. 1983. text ed. 31.95 (ISBN 0-03-060312-9). HR&W.

Lapatine, Sol. Electronics in Communications. LC 77-17573. (Electronic Technology Ser.). 341p. 1978. text ed. 31.95x (ISBN 0-471-01842-2); solutions manual 3.00 (ISBN 0-471-03713-3). Wiley.

Larson, Boyd. Power Control Electronics. 2nd ed. (Illus.). 176p. 1982. text ed. 29.95 (ISBN 0-13-687186-0). P-H.

Lauger, E. & Moltoft, J., eds. Reliability in Electrical & Electronic Components & Systems. 1172p. 1982. 106.50 (ISBN 0-444-86419-9, North-Holland). Elsevier.

Lenk, John D. Understanding Electronic Schematics. (Illus.). 304p. 1981. text ed. 26.95 (ISBN 0-13-935908-7). P-H.

Lewis, Rhys. Electrical & Electronic Principles: Level Two. 192p. 1982. pap. 10.00x (ISBN 0-246-11575-0, Pub. by Granada England). Sheridan.

--Electrical & Electronic Principles: Level Three. 176p. 1983. pap. 12.00x (ISBN 0-246-11814-8, Pub. by Granada England). Sheridan.

Local Government Engineering. 384p. (Orig.). 1981. pap. text ed. 37.50x (ISBN 0-85825-153-1, Pub. by Inst Engineering Australia). Brookfield Pub Co.

Loecherer, K. H. & Brandt, C. D. Parametric Electronics: An Introduction. (Springer Series in Electrophysics: Vol. 6). (Illus.). 345p. 1982. 41.00 (ISBN 0-387-10514-X). Springer-Verlag.

Long, W. E. & Evans, P. L. Electronic Principles & Circuits: An Introduction to Electronics for the Technicians. LC 73-11096. 432p. 1974. 32.95 (ISBN 0-471-54455-8); pap. text ed. 5.00x tchrs' manual o.s. (ISBN 0-471-54454-X). Wiley.

Loveday, George C. Electronic Testing & Troubleshooting. LC 81-12948. 293p. 1982. 23.95 (ISBN 0-471-08718-1). Wiley.

Ludwig, Raymond H. Illustrated Handbook of Electronic Tables, Symbols, Measurements & Values. (Illus.). 352p. 1977. 22.95 (ISBN 0-686-92215-8, Parker). P-H.

Lurch, Norman E. Fundamentals of Electronics. 3rd ed. LC 79-18696. 601p. 1981. 32.95 (ISBN 0-471-03494-0); solution manual avail. (ISBN 0-471-03716-8). Wiley.

MacDonald, Lorne. Practical Analysis of Advanced Electronic Circuits Through Experimentation. 2nd ed. 384p. 1984. pap. 16.50x (ISBN 0-911908-18-8). Tech Ed Pr.

McWane. Introduction to Electronic Technology. 2nd ed. text ed. write for info (ISBN 0-534-06342-X, 77F6069). Breton Pubs.

McWane, John W. Introduction to Electronics & Instrumentation. 1981. text ed. write for info. (ISBN 0-534-00938-7, Breton Pubs). Wadsworth Pub.

Maddock, R. J. Intermediate Electronics, Bk. 1. LC 68-18297. 315p. 1969. 34.50x (ISBN 0-306-30659-X, Plenum Pr). Plenum Pub.

Mahmoud. Large-Scale Control Systems. (Electrical Engineering & Electronics Ser.). 440p. 1985. 69.75 (ISBN 0-8247-7289-X). Dekker.

Malvino, Albert P. Electronic Principles. 2nd ed. (Illus.). 1979. text ed. 35.30 (ISBN 0-07-039867-4). McGraw.

Mandl, M. Fundamentals of Electronics. 3rd ed. 1973. 34.95 (ISBN 0-13-338160-9). P-H.

Marcus, Abraham. Electronics for Technicians. LC 69-10789. 1969. ref. ed. 25.95 (ISBN 0-13-252387-6). P-H.

Markum, A. & Silva, P. Intermediate Electronic Fabrication. 2nd ed. 192p. 1984. pap. 8.50x (ISBN 0-911908-09-9). Tech Ed Pr.

Markum, J. A. & Silva, M. P. Beginning Electronic Fabrication. new ed. (Illus.). 166p. 1975. pap. text ed. 7.50x (ISBN 0-911908-07-2). Tech Ed Pr.

Markus, John. Electronics Style Manual. 1978. 5.95 (ISBN 0-07-040432-1). McGraw.

Marton, C. & Septier, A., eds. Advances in Electronics & Electron Physics Supplement, No. 13C. (Serial Publication). 544p. 1983. 74.50 (ISBN 0-12-014576-6). Acad Pr.

Marton, Claire, ed. Advances in Electronics & Electron Physics, Vol. 56. (Serial Publication Ser.). 1981. 75.00 (ISBN 0-12-014656-8). Acad Pr.

--Advances in Electronics & Electron Physics, Vol. 57. (Serial Publication Ser.). 1981. 85.00 (ISBN 0-12-014657-6). Acad Pr.

--Advances in Electronics & Electron Physics, Vol. 58. (Serial Publication Ser.). 1982. 75.00 (ISBN 0-12-014658-4). Acad Pr.

Marton, L. Advances in Electronics & Electron Physics, Vol. 62. (Serial Publication Ser.). 1984. 59.50 (ISBN 0-12-014662-2). Acad Pr.

Marton, L. & Septier, A. Advances in Electronics & Electron Physics, Supplement 13A: Applied Charged Particle Optics. 1980. 60.00 (ISBN 0-12-014573-1). Acad Pr.

Marton, L., ed. Advances in Electronics & Electron Physics. Incl. Vols. 1-5. 85.00 ea. Vol. 1, 1948 (ISBN 0-12-014501-4). Vol. 2, 1950 (ISBN 0-12-014502-2). Vol. 3, 1951 (ISBN 0-12-014503-0). Vol. 4, 1952 (ISBN 0-12-014504-9). Vol. 5, 1953 (ISBN 0-12-014505-7); Vols. 6-8. 85.00 ea. Vol. 6, 1954 (ISBN 0-12-014506-5). Vol. 7, 1955 (ISBN 0-12-014507-3). Vol. 8, 1956 (ISBN 0-12-014508-1); Vols. 9-10. 85.00 ea. Vol. 9, 1957 (ISBN 0-12-014509-X). Vol. 10, 1958 (ISBN 0-12-014510-3); Vol. 11. 1959. 85.00 (ISBN 0-12-014511-1); Vol. 12. Proceedings. Symposium on Photo-Electronic Image Devices - 1st. McGee, J. D. & Wilcock, W. L., eds. 1960. 60.00 (ISBN 0-12-014512-X); Vols. 13-15. 85.00 ea. Vol. 13, 1960 (ISBN 0-12-014513-8). Vol. 14, 1961 (ISBN 0-12-014514-6). Vol. 15, 1961 (ISBN 0-12-014515-4); Vol. 16. Proceedings. Symposium on Photo-Electronic Image Devices - 2nd. McGee, J. D., et al, eds. 1962. 90.00 (ISBN 0-12-014516-2); Vol. 17. 1963. 85.00 (ISBN 0-12-014517-0); Vol. 18. 1963. 85.00 (ISBN 0-12-014518-9); Vol. 19. 1964. 85.00 (ISBN 0-12-014519-7); Vols. 20-21. 1965-66. 85.00 ea. Vol. 20 (ISBN 0-12-014520-0). Vol. 21 (ISBN 0-12-014521-9); Vol. 22. Proceedings. Symposium on Photo-Electronic Image Devices - 3rd. McGee, J. D., et al, eds. 1966. Pt. A. 90.00 (ISBN 0-12-014522-7); Pt. B. 70.00 (ISBN 0-12-014542-1); Vol. 23. 1967. 85.00 (ISBN 0-12-014523-5); Vol. 24. 1968. 85.00 (ISBN 0-12-014524-3); Vol. 25. 1968. 85.00 (ISBN 0-12-014525-1); Vol. 26. 1969. 85.00 (ISBN 0-12-014526-X); Vol. 27. 1970. 85.00 (ISBN 0-12-014527-8); Vol. 28. Proceedings. Symposium on Photo-Electronic Image Devices - 4th. McGee, J. D., et al, eds. 1969. Pt. A. 95.50 (ISBN 0-12-014528-6); Pt. B, 1970. 97.50 (ISBN 0-12-014548-0); Vol. 29. 1970. 85.00 (ISBN 0-12-014529-4); Vol. 30. 1971. 85.00 (ISBN 0-12-014530-8); Vol. 31. 1972. 85.00 (ISBN 0-12-014531-6); Vol. 32. 1973. 85.00 (ISBN 0-12-014532-4); Vol. 33. Proceedings. Symposium on Photo-Electronic Image Devices - 5th. McGee, J. D., et al, eds. 1973. Pt. A, 1972. 85.00 (ISBN 0-12-014533-2); Pt. B. 95.00 (ISBN 0-12-014553-7). Pt. B, 1973. Acad Pr.

--Advances in Electronics & Electron Physics. Vol. 34, 1973. 85.00 (ISBN 0-12-014534-0); Vol. 35, 1974. 85.00 (ISBN 0-12-014535-9). Acad Pr.

--Advances in Electronics & Electron Physics. Incl. Vol. 36. 1974. 85.00 (ISBN 0-12-014536-7); Vol. 37. 1975. 85.00 (ISBN 0-12-014537-5); Vol. 38. 1975. 85.00 (ISBN 0-12-014538-3); Vol. 39. 1975. 85.00 (ISBN 0-12-014539-1); Vol. 40a. Photo-Electronics Image Devices: Proceedings. Imperial College, London, Sept. 9-13, 1974, 6th Symposium, et al. Morgan, B. L., ed. 1976. 98.50 (ISBN 0-12-014540-5); Vol. 40B. Photo-Electronic Image Devices. 1977. 98.50 (ISBN 0-12-014554-5); Vol. 42. 1976. 80.00 (ISBN 0-12-014642-8); Vol. 45. 1978. 85.00 (ISBN 0-12-014645-2). (Serial Publication). Acad Pr.

--Advances in Electronics & Electron Physics, Vol. 41. 1976. 80.00 (ISBN 0-12-014541-3). Acad Pr.

--Advances in Electronics & Electron Physics, Vol. 43. 1977. 75.00 (ISBN 0-12-014643-6). Acad Pr.

--Advances in Electronics & Electron Physics, Vol. 44. 1978. 85.00 (ISBN 0-12-014644-4). Acad Pr.

--Advances in Electronics & Electron Physics, Vol. 46. LC 49-7504. 1978. 85.00 (ISBN 0-12-014646-0). Acad Pr.

--Advances in Electronics & Electron Physics, Vol. 49. (Serial Publication Ser.). 1979. 80.00 (ISBN 0-12-014649-5). Acad Pr.

--Advances in Electronics & Electron Physics, Vol. 60. (Serial Publication Ser.). 424p. 1983. 69.50 (ISBN 0-12-014660-6). Acad Pr.

--Advances in Electronics & Electron Physics: Supplements. Incl. Suppl. 1. Electroluminescence & Related Effects. Ivey, Henry F. 1963. 80.00 (ISBN 0-12-014561-8); Suppl. 2. Optical Masers. Birnbaum, George. 1964. 75.00 (ISBN 0-12-014562-6); Suppl. 3. Narrow Angle Electron Guns & Cathode Ray Tubes. Moss, Hilary. 1968. 65.00 (ISBN 0-12-014563-4); Suppl. 5. Linear Ferrite Devices for Microwave Applications. Von Aulock, W. H. & Fay, C. E. 1969. 65.00 (ISBN 0-12-014565-0); Suppl. 6. Electron Probe Microanalysis. Tousimis, A. J. & Marton, L. 1969. 85.00 (ISBN 0-12-014566-9); Suppl. 7. Quadruples in Electron Lens Design. Hawkes, P. W. 1970. 75.00 (ISBN 0-12-014567-7); Suppl. 9. Sequency Theory Foundations & Applications. Harmuth, Henning F., ed. 1977. 75.00 (ISBN 0-12-014569-3); Suppl. 11. Acoustic Imaging with Electronic Circuits. Harmuth, Henning F., ed. 1979. 80.00 (ISBN 0-12-014571-5). Acad Pr.

--Advances in Electrotronics & Electron Physics, Vol. 63. 1985. 75.00 (ISBN 0-12-014663-0). Acad Pr.

Marton, L. & Marton, C., eds. Advances in Electronics & Electron Physics, Vol. 51. LC 49-7504. (Serial Publication Ser.). 1980. 70.00 (ISBN 0-12-014651-7). Acad Pr.

--Advances in Electronics and Electron Physics, Vol. 52. 1980. 94.50 (ISBN 0-12-014652-5). Acad Pr.

Marton, L. & Marton, Claire, eds. Advances in Electronic & Electron Physics, Vol. 55. (Serial Publication Ser.). 1981. 79.00 (ISBN 0-12-014655-X) (ISBN 0-12-014701-7). Acad Pr.

--Advances in Electronics & Electron Physics, Vol. 50. LC 49-7504. 1980. 80.00 (ISBN 0-12-014650-9). Acad Pr.

--Advances in Electronics & Electron Physics, Vol. 53. (Serial Publication Ser.). 1980. 60.00 (ISBN 0-12-014653-3). Acad Pr.

--Advances in Electronics & Electron Physics, Vol. 54. (Serial Publication Ser.). 1980. 60.00 (ISBN 0-12-014654-1). Acad Pr.

Matt, Stephen R. Electricity & Basic Electronics. LC 81-20008. (Illus.). 1982. text ed. 16.80 (ISBN 0-87006-401-0). Goodheart.

Meikson, Z. H. & Thackray, Philip C. Electronic Design with Off-the-Shelf Integrated Circuits. 2nd ed. LC 83-26905. (Illus.). 448p. 1984. 31.95 (ISBN 0-13-250291-7, Busn). P-H.

Mileaf, Harry. Electronics Four. 2nd rev. ed. 1977. pap. 7.95 (ISBN 0-8104-5957-4). Hayden.

--Electronics Seven. rev., 2nd ed. 1978. pap. 7.20 (ISBN 0-8104-5960-4). Hayden.

Miller, Gary. Handbook of Electronic Communications. LC 78-11347. (Illus.). 1979. 27.95 (ISBN 0-13-377374-4). P-H.

Miller, Gary M. Modern Electricity-Electronics. (Illus.). 448p. 1981. text ed. 29.95 (ISBN 0-13-593160-6). P-H.

--Modern Electronic Communications. 2nd ed. (Illus.). 592p. 1983. text ed. 34.95 (ISBN 0-13-593152-5). P-H.

Miller, R. Communication: Electricity & Electronics. 1976. 7.69 (ISBN 0-13-153098-4); pap. text ed. 8.84 (ISBN 0-13-153072-0). P-H.

Miller, Rex & Culpepper, Fred W., Jr. Energy: Electricity - Electronics. 1982. text ed. 12.95 (ISBN 0-538-33500-9, IE50). SW Pub.

Milnes, A. G. Semiconductor Devices & Integrated Electronics. 1008p. 1983. pap. 19.95 (ISBN 0-442-26217-5). Van Nos Reinhold.

Mirsky, G. Radio Electronic Measurements. 503p. 1978. 10.20 (ISBN 0-8285-0692-2, Pub. by Mir Pubs USSR). Imported Pubns.

Morgan, B. L., ed. Advances in Electronics & Electron Physics, Vol. 64. 1985. 65.00 (ISBN 0-12-014664-9). Acad Pr.

Morgan-Grampian Book, ed. The Directory of Instruments, Electronics, Automation, 1984. 320p. 1985. 150.00x (ISBN 0-686-75507-3, Pub. by Morgan-Grampian Bk). State Mutual Bk.

Mottershead, Allen. Introduction to Electricity & Electronics: Conventional Current Version. LC 81-10472. 674p. 1982. 31.95 (ISBN 0-471-05751-7); avail. solutions manual (ISBN 0-471-86320-3); lab 13.95 (ISBN 0-471-86321-1). Wiley.

--Introduction to Electricity & Electronics. (Electron Flow Ser.). 674p. 1982. 31.95x (ISBN 0-471-09851-5). Wiley.

National Research Council. The Competitive Status of the U. S. Electronics Industry. 127p. 1984. pap. 10.95 (ISBN 0-317-06271-9). Natl Acad Pr.

NCR Corporation. NCR Basic Electronics Course, with Experiments. LC 78-56596. 432p. 1978. pap. 13.95 (ISBN 0-672-21549-7). Sams.

New Developments in Electronic Banking: G-069. 1982. 1250.00 (ISBN 0-89336-335-9). BCC.

Nichols, Kenneth G. Physical Electronics: A Guide to the Study of Paper 344 of the CEI Examinations. (PPL Study Guide Ser.: No. 4). pap. 20.00 (ISBN 0-317-08575-1, 2011488). Bks Demand UMI.

Novak, M. Integrated Functional Blocks. (Studies in Electrical & Electronic Engineering: Vol. 3). 388p. 1980. 74.50 (ISBN 0-444-99759-8). Elsevier.

Nunz, Gregory J. Electronics in Our World: A Survey. LC 70-146682. (Illus.). 1972. ref. ed. 32.95 (ISBN 0-13-252288-8). P-H.

Oda, N. & Takayanagi, K., eds. Electronic & Atomic Collisions: Invited Papers-11th International Conference on Physics of Electricity & Atomic Collisions, Kyoto, Japan, August 1979. 1980. 136.25 (ISBN 0-444-85434-7). Elsevier.

Oldham, William G. & Schwartz, Steven E. An Introduction to Electronics. LC 70-179870. 629p. 1972. text ed. 32.95 (ISBN 0-03-086075-X, HoltC). HR&W.

Patrick, Dale R. & Fardo, Stephen W. Electricity & Electronics. (Illus.). 528p. 1984. 27.95 (ISBN 0-13-248344-0). P-H.

Phang. Trends in Electronics: TENCON '84. 1984. 65.00 (ISBN 0-444-87582-4). Elsevier.

Power Electronics & Variable Speed Drives. (IEE Conference Publications Ser.: No. 234). 431p. 1984. pap. 102.00 (ISBN 0-85296-291-6). Inst Elect Eng.

Pratley, J. B. Study Notes for Technicians: Electrical & Electronic Principles, Vol. 1. 96p. 1982. 7.00 (ISBN 0-07-084661-8). McGraw.

Pratt, William K. & Marton, L. L., eds. Advances in Electronics & Electron Physics: Supplement No. 12 Image Transmission Techniques. LC 63-12814. 1979. 57.50 (ISBN 0-12-014572-3). Acad Pr.

Ramshaw, R. S. Power Electronics: Thyristor Controlled Power For Electric Motors. (Modern Electrical Studies). 1975. pap. 16.95 (ISBN 0-412-14160-4, NO. 6230, Pub. by Chapman & Hall). Methuen Inc.

Research & Education Association Staff. Electronics Problem Solver. rev. ed. LC 82-61484. (Illus.). 1312p. 1984. pap. text ed. 24.85 (ISBN 0-87891-543-5). Res & Educ.

Ritchie, George. Electronics Construction & Assembly. (Illus.). 1980. lib. bdg. 27.95 (ISBN 0-13-250472-3). P-H.

Roddy, Dennis & Coolen, John. Electronics: Theory, Devices & Circuits. 1982. text ed. 31.95 (ISBN 0-8359-1643-X); instrs'. manual avail. (ISBN 0-8359-1644-8). Reston.

Rudman, Jack. Certified Electronic Technician. (Admission Test Ser.: ATS-38). (Cloth bdg. avail. on request). 1977. pap. 11.95 (ISBN 0-8373-5038-7). Natl Learning.

--Electro-Mechanical Examination (U.S.P.S.) (Career Examination Ser.: C-1607). (Cloth bdg. avail. on request). pap. 12.00 (ISBN 0-8373-1607-3). Natl Learning.

Ruthkowski, George B. Solid-State Electronics. 2nd ed. 512p. 1980. text ed. write for info (ISBN 0-02-404500-4). Macmillan.

Rutkowski, George B. Basic Electricity for Electronics: A Text Laboratory Manual. 323p. (Orig.). 1984. pap. text ed. 11.51scp (ISBN 0-672-98488-1); solutions manual 3.67scp (ISBN 0-672-98489-X). Bobbs.

Ryan, Jeremy. Electronic Assembly. 2nd ed. 1985. text ed. 18.95 (ISBN 0-8359-1581-6). Reston.

Ryder, John D. Electronic Fundamentals & Applications: Integrated & Discrete Systems. 5th ed. (Illus.). 640p. 1975. 39.95 (ISBN 0-13-251371-4). P-H.

Sakura, Y. Recent Magnetics of Electronics, 1983. 1984. 95.00 (ISBN 0-444-86656-6, I-164-83). Elsevier.

Sams Editorial Staff. Basic Electricity & an Introduction to Electronics. 3rd ed. LC 73-75082. 1973. pap. 10.95 (ISBN 0-672-20932-2). Sams.

Schmitz, Norbert L. & Novotny, Donald. Introductory Electromechanics. LC 65-21815. (Illus.). pap. 82.30 (ISBN 0-317-08893-9, 2012459). Bks Demand UMI.

Schwartz, Leland. Survey of Electronics. 2nd ed. (Electronics Technology Ser.). 1977. pap. text ed. 15.95 (ISBN 0-675-08554-3). Merrill.

Schwartz, Leland P. Survey of Electronics. 224p. 1985. text ed. 15.95 (ISBN 0-675-20162-4). Additional supplements may be obtained from publisher. Merrill.

Schweitzer, James A. Managing Information Security: A Program for the Electronic Information Age. 113p. 1982. 23.50 (ISBN 0-409-95055-6). Butterworth.

Sedov, E. Entertaining Electronics. 351p. 1984. 7.95 (ISBN 0-8285-2787-3, Pub. by Mir Pubns). Imported Pubns.

Shaw, Dennis F. An Introduction to Electronics. 2nd ed. LC 76-524211. pap. 101.80 (ISBN 0-317-10122-6, 2004942). Bks Demand UMI.

Shrader, Robert L. Electronic Communication. 4th rev. ed. LC 79-13336. (Illus.). 1980. text ed. 31.95x (ISBN 0-07-057150-3). McGraw.

Simpson. Introductory Electronics for Scientists & Engineers. 2nd ed. 1985. write for info. (ISBN 0-205-08377-3, 738377). Allyn.
Sinclair, Ian R. Electronics for the Service Engineer, Vol. 1. 200p. 1980. 69.00x (ISBN 0-291-39638-0, Pub. by Tech Pr). State Mutual Bk.
--Electronics for the Service Engineer, Vol. 2. 280p. 1980. 72.00x (ISBN 0-291-39619-4, Pub. by Tech Pr). State Mutual Bk.
Sinclair, Lewis. Electronics for the Service Engineer, Pt. 2, Bk. 2. 160p. 1985. text ed. write for info. (ISBN 0-291-39700-X). Gower Pub Co.
Sinnema, William. Electronic Transmission Technology: Lines, Waves & Antennas. (Illus.). 1979. text ed. 31.95 (ISBN 0-13-252221-7). P-H.
Skobel'tsyn, D. V., ed. Electronics in Experimental Physics. LC 70-104715. (P. N. Lebedev Physics Institute Ser.: Vol. 42). 101p. 1970. 25.00x (ISBN 0-306-10834-8, Consultants). Plenum Pub.
Slurzberg, Morris & Osterheld, William. Essentials of Communication Electronics. 3rd ed. (Illus.). 784p. 1973. text ed. 32.00 (ISBN 0-07-058309-9). McGraw.
Smith, A. V. Electrical & Electronic Applications: Level Two. 192p. 1983. pap. 12.00x (ISBN 0-246-11609-9, Pub. by Granada England). Sheridan.
--Electronics for Technicians: Level Three. 120p. 1982. pap. 8.00x (ISBN 0-246-11488-6, Pub. by Granada England). Sheridan.
Soderstrand, Michael A. Electronic Circuits & Systems. 424p. 1981. pap. text ed. 28.00 (ISBN 0-8403-2581-9). Kendall-Hunt.
Soete, Luc & Dosi, Giovanni. Technology & Employment in the Electronics Industry. LC 83-43165. 90p. 1984. pap. 52.50 large format (ISBN 0-86187-378-5, Pub. by Frances Pinter). Longwood Pub Group.
Sprott, Julien C. Introduction to Modern Electronics. LC 80-25366. 349p. 1981. 34.50 (ISBN 0-471-05840-8); 10.50 (ISBN 0-471-86375-0). Wiley.
Stanley, J. A. Electronics for the Beginner. 3rd ed. LC 80-51718. 160p. 1980. pap. 9.95 (ISBN 0-672-21737-6). Sams.
Stanley, William D. Operational Amplifiers with Linear Circuits. 1984. Additional supplements may be obtained from publisher. text ed. 28.95 (ISBN 0-675-20090-3). Merrill.
Steinberg, W. F. & Ford, W. B. Electricity & Electronics, Basic. 4th ed. (Illus.). 1972. text ed. 18.25 (ISBN 0-8269-1402-0). Am Technical.
Steiner, John P. Illustrated Guide to Basic Electronics: With Useful Projects & Experiments. LC 83-3422. 322p. 1983. 19.95 (ISBN 0-13-450510-7, Busn); pap. 14.95 (ISBN 0-13-450502-6). P-H.
Stockman, Harry E. Scientific Models for Experimenters. 1976. pap. 19.00 (ISBN 0-918332-04-4). Sercolab.
Stubbins. Electronics Using Integrated Circuits. 608p. 1985. 32.95 (ISBN 0-471-88604-1). Wiley.
Sturridge, Helen, et al. The Arco Book of Electronics. LC 84-2868. (Illus.). 140p. 1984. 11.95 (ISBN 0-668-06154-5, 6154-5). Arco.
Su, Kendall L. A Collection of Solved Problems in Circuits, Electronics, & Signal Analysis, Vol. 3. 80p. 1981. pap. text ed. 5.50 (ISBN 0-8403-2629-7). Kendall-Hunt.
Supreme Publications Master Index. 49p. pap. 9.00 (ISBN 0-938630-21-0). Ars Enterprises.
Symposium on Materials Overview for 1982 - Including Electronics: Meeting Held May 4-6, 1982, San Diego, California. (The Science of Advanced Materials & Processes Engineering Ser.: Vol. 27). 1062p. 1983. 60.00 (ISBN 0-938994-20-4). Soc Adv Material.
Temes, Lloyd. Communication Electronics for Technicians. 400p. 1974. text ed. 29.95 (ISBN 0-07-063487-4). McGraw.
Tester, Jerry & Baker, Glenn. Electronics Today. 1983. perfect bdg. 23.95 (ISBN 0-88252-125-X). Paladin Hse.
--Electronics Today Laboratory Manual. 1982. Paladin Hse.
Uffenbeck, John E. Introduction to Electronics: Devices & Circuits. (Illus.). 432p. 1982. 31.95 (ISBN 0-13-481507-6). P-H.
U. S. Navy. Basic Electronics. (Illus.). 1962. pap. 8.95 (ISBN 0-486-21076-6). Dover.
U. S. Navy (Bureau of Naval Personnel) Second-Level Basic Electronics. Orig. Title: Basic Electronics Vol. 2. (Illus.). 352p. 1971. pap. text ed. 6.50 (ISBN 0-486-22841-X). Dover.
Van Valkenburgh, Nooger & Neville Inc. Basic Electronics, 6 Vols. (Prog. Bk.). 1959. Set. 23.70 (ISBN 0-685-07566-4); pap. text ed. 31.80 set (ISBN 0-685-07567-2); Vols. 1-6. pap. text ed. 5.30 ea.; tests & foreign language eds. avail. (ISBN 0-685-07570-2). Brolet.
Van Valkenburgh, et al. Basic Electronics, 6 Vols. (Illus.). 1959. combined cloth 25.95 (ISBN 0-8104-0049-9); Set. pap. 31.80 (ISBN 0-8104-0048-0); Vol. 1. pap. 5.30 (ISBN 0-8104-0041-3); Vols. 2-6. pap. 5.30 ea.; Vol. 2. pap. (ISBN 0-8104-0042-1); Vol. 3. pap. (ISBN 0-8104-0043-X); Vol. 4. pap. (ISBN 0-8104-0044-8); Vol. 5. pap. (ISBN 0-8104-0045-6); Vol. 6. pap. (ISBN 0-8104-0046-4). Hayden.
Veley. Semiconductors & Electronic Communications Made Easy. (Illus.). 322p. 1982. o.p 15.95 (ISBN 0-8306-0052-3); pap. 8.95 (ISBN 0-8306-1435-4). TAB Bks.
Veley, Victor F. & Dulin, John J. Modern Electronics: A First Course. (Illus.). 640p. 1983. 32.95 (ISBN 0-13-481663-3). P-H.
Vergara, William C. Electronics in Everyday Life. (Popular Science Ser.). 235p. 1984. pap. 4.95 (ISBN 0-486-24576-4). Dover.
Videoscope, 2 Vols. 64p. pap. 10.50xea. Vol. 1, No. 1. 1976 (ISBN 0-677-47015-0). Vol. 1, No. 2. 1977, 80p (ISBN 0-677-47025-8). Vol. 1, No. 3. 1977, 68p (ISBN 0-677-47035-5). Vol. 1, No. 4. 1977, 64p (ISBN 0-677-47045-2). Vol. 2, No. 1. 1978, 64p (ISBN 0-677-47055-X). Vol. 2, No. 2. 1978 (ISBN 0-677-47065-7). Gordon.
Vincent, Thomas L. & Grantham, Walter J. Optimality in Parametric Systems. LC 81-1870. (A Wiley-Interscience Publication). pap. 90.30 (ISBN 0-317-26087-1, 2025178). Bks Demand UMI.
Washington Group. Major Markets in Electronics. Rosenzweig, Benjamin Z., ed. (New Technologies Market Reviews Ser.). 250p. (Orig.). 1985. pap. text ed. 147.00 (ISBN 0-912257-06-7). Marketing Intl.
Waters, Farl J. ABC's of Electronics. 3rd ed. LC 77-93167. 1984. pap. 7.95 (ISBN 0-672-21507-1). Sams.
Weick, Carl. Applied Electronics. 1976. text ed. 29.70 (ISBN 0-07-069012-X). McGraw.
Williams, Gerald E. The Basic Book of Electricity & Electronics. (Basic Industrial Arts Ser.). (Illus.). 122p. 1984. 7.50 (ISBN 0-8269-1485-3). Am Technical.
--Electronics for Everyone. 1979. text ed. 23.95 (ISBN 0-574-21525-5, 13-4525); instr's guide avail. (ISBN 0-574-21526-3, 13-4526). SRA.
Williams, J. High Voltage Power Electronics. 1986. price not set (ISBN 0-442-29246-5). Van Nos Reinhold.
Wilson, J. A. Basic Electronics: Theory & Practice. (Illus.). 1977. pap. text ed. 31.00 (ISBN 0-07-070670-0). McGraw.
Wilson, J. A. & Kaufman, Milton. Learning Electricity & Electronics Through Experiments. LC 78-17723. (Illus.). 1979. pap. text ed. 9.10 (ISBN 0-07-070675-1). McGraw.
Winkler, G. & Hansen, P., eds. Intermag 84: Digest of the International Magnetics Conference, Hamburg, April 10-13, 1984. 546p. 1984. 70.00 (ISBN 0-444-87510-7). Elsevier.
Wojslaw, Charles F. Electronic Concepts: Principles & Circuits. (Illus.). 416p. 1980. text ed. 24.95 (ISBN 0-8359-1660-X); instrs.' manual avail. (ISBN 0-8359-1661-8). Reston.
Worden, Leslie E. Introduction to Electronics & Electronic Shop Practices. (Illus., Orig.). 1979. 18.95x (ISBN 0-89894-016-8). Advocate Pub Group.
Zbar, Paul B. & Electronic Industries Association. Electricity-Electronics Fundamentals: A Text-Lab Manual. 2nd ed. (Illus.). 1977. pap. 19.30x (ISBN 0-07-072748-1). McGraw.
Zbar, Paul B. & Malvino, Albert P. Basic Electronics: A Text-Lab Manual. 5th ed. (EIA Basic Electricity-Electronics Ser.). (Illus.). 352p. 1983. pap. text ed. 16.25 (ISBN 0-07-072803-8). McGraw.
Zbar, Paul B. & Orne, P. Industrial Electronics: A Text-Lab Manual. 2nd ed. 1951. text ed. 13.70 (ISBN 0-07-072740-6). McGraw.
Zherebstov, I. P. Fundamentos de la Electronica. (Span.). 543p. 1976. 7.95 (ISBN 0-8285-1685-5, Pub. by Mir Pubs USSR). Imported Pubns.

ELECTRONICS–AMATEURS' MANUALS

Colwell, Morris A. Project Planning & Building. (Newnes Constructor's Guides Ser.). (Illus.). 1976. pap. 6.95 (ISBN 0-408-00229-8, 5449-1). Hayden.
Elementary Electronics Editors. Second Book of Easy-to-Build Electronic Projects. 192p. (Orig.). 1984. 17.95 (ISBN 0-8306-0679-3, 1679); pap. 13.50 (ISBN 0-8306-1679-9). TAB Bks.
Florman, Monte & Consumer Reports Books Editors. Consumer Reports Guide to Electronics in the Home. LC 84-80383. (Illus.). 256p. 1984. pap. 12.95 (ISBN 0-316-15339-7). Little.
Iannini, Robert F. Build Your Own Laser, Phaser, Ion Ray Gun & Other Working Space-Age Projects. (Illus.). 308p. 1983. 24.95 (ISBN 0-8306-0204-6); pap. 15.95 (ISBN 0-8306-0604-1, 1604). TAB Bks.
Laurie, Peter. Electronics Explained: A Handbook for the Layman. LC 81-670089. (Illus.). 144p. 1980. pap. 14.95 (ISBN 0-571-11593-4). Faber & Faber.
Margolis, Art. Electronics for Computer Users. (Illus.). 320p. (Orig.). 1985. 24.95 (ISBN 0-8306-0899-0, 1899); pap. 15.95 (ISBN 0-8306-1899-6). TAB Bks.
Marks, Myles H. Twenty-Nine Electronic Projects for Your Home, Car & Workshop. (Illus.). 272p. (Orig.). 1984. pap. 18.95 (ISBN 0-8306-0719-6, 1719). TAB Bks.
Mims, Forrest. The Forrest Mims Circuit Scrapbook. (Illus.). 170p. 1982. pap. 15.95 (ISBN 0-07-042389-X). McGraw.
Traister, John E. The First Book of Electronic Projects. (Illus.). 1979. pap. 3.50 (ISBN 0-8306-1137-1, 1137). TAB Bks.
--Third Book of Electronic Projects. (Illus.). 80p. (Orig.). 1982. pap. 5.25 (ISBN 0-8306-1446-X, 1446). TAB Bks.
Traister, Robert J. The Five, Five, Five IC Project Book. (Illus.). 224p. (Orig.). 1985. 18.95 (ISBN 0-8306-0996-2, 1996); pap. 11.95 (ISBN 0-8306-1996-8). TAB Bks.
--Thirty-Nine One-Evening Electronic Projects. (Illus.). 182p. (Orig.). 1984. 14.95 (ISBN 0-8306-0492-8); pap. 9.95 (ISBN 0-8306-1492-3, 1492). TAB Bks.
--Thirty-Two Electronic Power Supply Projects. (Illus.). 300p. (Orig.). 1982. o.p 17.95 (ISBN 0-8306-2486-4, 1486); pap. 10.95 (ISBN 0-8306-1486-9). TAB Bks.
Warring, R. H. A Beginner's Guide to Making Electronic Gadgets. 2nd ed. 182p. (Orig.). 1984. 14.95 (ISBN 0-8306-0793-5, 1793); pap. 8.95 (ISBN 0-8306-1793-0). TAB Bks.
--Eighty-Four Practical IC Projects You Can Build. (Illus.). 1979. 8.95 (ISBN 0-8306-1142-8, 1142). TAB Bks.
--Understanding Electronics. 2nd ed. (Illus.). 210p. 1984. 15.95 (ISBN 0-8306-0253-4); pap. 9.95 (ISBN 0-8306-0153-8, 1553). TAB Bks.

ELECTRONICS–APPARATUS AND APPLIANCES

see Electronic Apparatus and Appliances

ELECTRONICS–BIBLIOGRAPHY

Marton, Claire, ed. Advances in Electronics & Electron Physics, Vol. 58. (Serial Publication Ser.). 1982. 75.00 (ISBN 0-12-014658-4). Acad Pr.
Moore, C. K. & Spencer, K. J. Electronics: A Bibliographical Guide, Vol. 2. 369p. 1965. 32.50x (ISBN 0-306-68242-7, IFI Plenum). Plenum Pub.
Palyza, M. M. Useful Books of Reference for Designers (1926-1983) Held by the Science Reference Library: Pt. 2 Electrical & Electronic Engineering. 75p. (Orig.). 1984. pap. 7.50 (ISBN 0-7123-0713-3, Pub. by British Lib). Longwood Pub Group.
Seventy-Three Magazine Editors. The Giant Book of Electronics Projects. (Illus.). 504p. 1982. 21.95 (ISBN 0-8306-0078-7); pap. 14.95 (ISBN 0-8306-1367-6). TAB Bks.
Shiers, George. Bibliography of the History of Electronics. LC 72-3740. 336p. 1972. 16.00 (ISBN 0-8108-0499-9). Scarecrow.

ELECTRONICS–DICTIONARIES

Amos, S. W. Dictionary of Electronics. 336p. 1981. 39.95 (ISBN 0-408-00331-6). Butterworth.
ANSI-IEEE Standard 100-1984: IEEE Standard Dictionary of Electrical & Electronic Terms. 3rd ed. 1173p. 1984. 49.95 (ISBN 0-471-80787-7, SH09332). IEEE.
Arnaud, Jean F. Diccionario de la Electronica. 3rd ed. (Span.). 368p. 1976. pap. 5.25 (ISBN 84-01-90304-1, S-14211). French & Eur.
Birdmann, G. English-German, German, English Solid State Physics & Electronics Dictionary. (Eng. & Ger.). 1103p. 1980. 100.00x (ISBN 0-569-07204-2, Pub. by Collet's). State Mutual Bk.
Brand, John R. Handbook of Electronic Formulas, Symbols, & Definitions. 1979. 22.95 (ISBN 0-442-20999-1). Van Nos Reinhold.
Brosset, Raymond & Fondaneche, Pierre. Dictionnaire Memento D'electronique. 3rd ed. (Fr.). 512p. 1969. 39.95 (ISBN 0-686-56929-6, M-6047). French & Eur.
Brown, P. R. Dictionary of Electrical, Electronic & Computer Abbreviations. 232p. 1985. text ed. 34.95 (ISBN 0-408-01210-2). Butterworth.
Budig, P. K. Dictionary of Electrical Engineering & Electronics: English-German. 1985. 129.75 (ISBN 0-444-99595-1, I-422-84). Elsevier.
Budig, P. K., ed. Dictionary of Electrical Engineering & Electronics: German-English. 690p. 1985. 134.75 (ISBN 0-444-99594-3). Elsevier.
Budig, Peter K. Fachwoerterbuch Elektrotechnik, Elektronik. (Eng. & Ger., Dictionary of Electrical Engineering and Electronics). 1976. 86.50 (ISBN 3-7785-0357-X, M-7394, Pub. by Huethig). French & Eur.
Carter, Harley. Diccionario de Electronica. (Span.). 416p. 1962. 19.95 (ISBN 0-686-56716-1, S-33049). French & Eur.
Clason, W. E. Elsevier's Dictionary of Electronics & Waveguides. 2nd ed. (Eng., Fr., Span., Ital., Dutch & Ger.). 833p. (Polyglot). 1965. 119.25 (ISBN 0-444-40119-9). Elsevier.
Diccionario Electromecanico Ingles-Espanol. (Eng. & Span.). 298p. 1969. pap. 18.95 (ISBN 84-7087-002-5, S-12420). French & Eur.
Douglas-Young, John. Illustrated Encyclopedic Dictionary of Electronics. LC 80-23639. 512p. 1981. 39.95 (ISBN 0-13-450791-6, Parker). P-H.
Electronics Dictionary. (Pol., Eng. & Rus.). 254p. 59.00x (ISBN 0-686-44676-3, Pub. by Collets). State Mutual Bk.
Goedecke. Dictionary of Electrical Engineering, Telecommunications & Electronics: English-German-French, Vol. 3. 1967. 39.00 (ISBN 0-9913001-1-4, Pub. by O Brandstetter WG). Heyden.
--Dictionary of Electrical Engineering, Telecommunications & Electronics: French-English-German, Vol. 2. 1966. 34.00 (ISBN 0-9913001-0-6, Pub. by O Brandstetter WG). Heyden.
Goedecke, W. Woerterbuch der Elektrotechnik, Fernmeldetechnik und Elektonik, Vol. 1. (Ger., Eng. & Fr., Dictionary of Electrical Engineering, Telecommunication Engineering & Electronics). 1966-68. 56.00 (ISBN 3-87097-013-8, M-7018). French & Eur.
--Woerterbuch der Elektrotechnik, Fernmeldetechnik und Elektronik, Vol. 2. (Fr., Eng. & Ger., Dictionary of Electrical Engineering, Telecommuunications Engineering & Electronics). 1966-68. 56.00 (ISBN 3-87097-014-6, M-7019). French & Eur.
Graf, Rudolf F. Modern Dictionary of Electronics. 6th ed. LC 83-51223. (Illus.). 1152p. 1984. 39.95 (ISBN 0-672-22041-5). Sams.
Handel, S. Diccionario De Electronica. (Span.). 470p. 1976. 39.75 (ISBN 84-335-6408-0, S-50070). French & Eur.
Hyman, Charles J. German-English, English-German Electronics Dictionary. LC 64-7757. (Ger. & Eng.). 182p. 1965. 35.00x (ISBN 0-306-10710-4, Consultants). Plenum Pub.
Institute Electrical & Electronics Engineers. IEC Multilingual Dictionary of Electricity. 461p. 1983. 49.95 (ISBN 0-471-80784-2). Wiley.
International Electrotechnical Com. Vocabulario Electronico Internacional. (Span.). 318p. 1975. 14.95 (ISBN 84-237-0148-4, S-50247). French & Eur.
International Electrotechnical Vocabulary: Electronics. (Eng., Fr. & Rus.). 335p. 1956. leatherette 9.95 (ISBN 0-686-92485-1, M-9071). French & Eur.
International Electrotechnical Vocabulary, Machines & Transformers. (Eng., Fr. & Rus.). 212p. 1958. leatherette 4.95 (ISBN 0-686-92488-6, M-9072). French & Eur.
Knaeps, E. & Zacharias, D. Woerterbuch der Elektronik. (Ger. & Fr.). 104p. 1976. pap. 9.95 (ISBN 3-7723-6231-1, M-7020). French & Eur.
McGraw-Hill Editors. McGraw-Hill Encyclopedia of Electronics & Computers. (Illus.). 976p. 1983. 67.50 (ISBN 0-07-045487-6). McGraw.
Markus, J. Electronics Dictionary. 4th ed. 1978. 41.30 (ISBN 0-07-040431-3). McGraw.
Markus, John. Diccionario de Electronica y Tecnica Nuclear. (Span. & Eng.). 1052p. 75.95 (ISBN 84-267-0003-9, S-14264). French & Eur.
--Enciclopedia De Circuitos Electronicos. (Espn.). 888p. 1977. 59.95 (ISBN 84-267-0002-0, S-14349). French & Eur.
--Vocabulario Ingles-Espanol De Electronica y Tecnica Nuclear. 2nd ed. (Span. & Eng.). 196p. pap. 16.75 (ISBN 84-267-0247-3, S-30684). French & Eur.
Marquet, Luis. Diccionari d'Electronica. (Catalan.). 208p. 1977. pap. 4.50 (ISBN 84-7306-116-0, S-50184). French & Eur.
Mataix Lord, Mariano. Diccionario De Electronica, Informatica y Centrales Nucleares. (Fr. & Eng.). 660p. 1978. leather 59.95 (ISBN 84-267-0350-X, S-30687). French & Eur.
Miladinovic, Tomislav. Woerterbuch der Elektrotechnik und Elektronik. (Ger. & Rus.). 1970. 92.00 (ISBN 3-7736-5285-2, M-7016). French & Eur.
Oppermann, Alfred, ed. Dictionary of Electronics: English-German. 692p. 1980. lib. bdg. 75.00 (ISBN 3-598-10312-3). K G Saur.
Piraux. Dictionaire Francais-Anglais d'electrotechnique et d'electronique. (Fr.). 32.50 (ISBN 0-685-36687-1). French & Eur.
Piraux, H. French-English, English-French Dictionary of Electrotechnic Electronics & Allied Fields, 2 vols. (Fr. & Eng.). Set. 90.00 (ISBN 0-685-12017-1). Heinman.

Piraux, Henri. Dictionnaire Allemand-Francais des Termes Relatifs a l'Electrorechnique, l'Electronique, et aux Applications Connexes. 4th ed. (Fr. & Ger.). 254p. 1976. pap. 31.95 (ISBN 0-686-57080-4, M-6455). French & Eur.

Proulx, G. J. Dictionnaire d'Electronique et Tele-Communication: Anglais-Francais. (Fr. & Eng.). 582p. 1979. 15.95 (ISBN 0-686-57089-8, M-6469). French & Eur.

Ramirez Villareal, Humberto. Diccionario Ilustrado de Electronica. (Span.). 192p. 12.95 (ISBN 0-686-56678-5, S-25248). French & Eur.

Rodgers, Harold R., et al, eds. Arlington Dictionary of Electronics. (Illus.). 1971. text ed. 16.95x (ISBN 0-8464-0146-0). Beekman Pubs.

Schneider, Leonhard. Woerterbuch der Elektronik. (Ger. & Pol.). 1977. pap. 13.50 (ISBN 3-7723-6431-4, M-7021). French & Eur.

Schwenkhagen, H. Woerterbuch Elektrotechnik und Elektronik. 2nd ed. (Ger. & Eng., Dictionary of Electrical Engineering and Electronics). 1967. 128.00 (ISBN 0-686-56610-6, M-6927). French & Eur.

Schwenkhagen, H. F. & Meinhhold, H. Woerterbuch Elektrotechnik und Elektronik. (Ger. & Eng., Dictionary of Electrical Engineering and Electronics). 1978. 128.00 (ISBN 3-7736-5072-8, M-6928). French & Eur.

Standards Council, Society for Technical Communication. Abbreviations & Symbols for Terms Used in Electronics. 1975. pap. 8.00 (ISBN 0-914548-19-0). Soc Tech Comm.

Susskind, Charles. Encyclopedia of Electronics. 2nd ed. 1984. write for info. (ISBN 0-442-28078-5). Van Nos Reinhold.

Technik-Worterbuch: Elektronik, Elektrotechnik. 1980. 120.00x (ISBN 0-686-72091-1, Pub. by Collet's). State Mutual Bk.

Traister, John E. & Traister, Robert J., Sr. Encyclopedic Dictionary of Electronic Terms. (Illus.). 608p. 1984. text ed. 30.95 (ISBN 0-13-276998-0). P-H.

Traister, John E. & Traister, Robert J. Encyclopedic Dictionary of Electronic Terms. 608p. 1985. pap. 17.95 (ISBN 0-13-276981-6). P-H.

Turner, Rufus P. & Gibilisco, Stan. The Illustrated Dictionary of Electronics. 3rd ed. (Illus.). 720p. 1985. 34.95 (ISBN 0-8306-0866-4, 1866); pap. 21.95 (ISBN 0-8306-1866-X). TAB Bks.

Wernicke, H. Dictionary of Electronics, Communications & Electrical Engineering, 2 vols. 1300p. Vol. 1. 36.00x (ISBN 0-685-05199-4); Vol. 2. 36.00x (ISBN 0-685-05200-1). Adlers Foreign Bks.

Young, E. C. Dictionary of Electronics. (Reference Ser.). 1979. pap. 5.95 (ISBN 0-14-051074-5). Penguin.

ELECTRONICS–DRAFTING

see Electronic Drafting

ELECTRONICS–EXAMINATIONS, QUESTIONS, ETC.

Benson, F. A. Problems in Electronics with Solutions. 5th ed. 1976. pap. 14.95x (ISBN 0-412-14770-X, NO. 6036, Pub. by Chapman & Hall). Methuen Inc.

Glass, Dick & Crow, Ron. The CET Exam Book. (Illus.). 210p. (Orig.). 1984. 14.95 (ISBN 0-8306-0670-X); pap. 9.95 (ISBN 0-8306-1670-5, 1670). TAB Bks.

Rudman, Jack. Assistant Electronic Technician. (Career Examination Ser.: C-1982). (Cloth bdg. avail. on request). pap. 12.00 (ISBN 0-8373-1982-X). Natl Learning.

--Electronic Technician. (Career Examination Ser.: C-229). (Cloth bdg. avail. on request). pap. 12.00 (ISBN 0-8373-0229-3). Natl Learning.

--Foreman (Electronic Equipment) (Career Examination Ser.: C-2032). (Cloth bdg. avail. on request). pap. 10.00 (ISBN 0-8373-2032-1). Natl Learning.

--Supervisor (Electronic Equipment) (Career Examination Ser.: C-2193). (Cloth bdg. avail. on request). pap. 10.00 (ISBN 0-8373-2193-X). Natl Learning.

Wilson, Sam. The CET Study Guide. LC 84-8517. (Illus.). 308p. (Orig.). 1984. 16.95 (ISBN 0-8306-0791-9); pap. 11.95 (ISBN 0-8306-1791-4, 1791). TAB Bks.

ELECTRONICS–HANDBOOKS, MANUALS, ETC.

Bruce, David. Vest Pocket Electronics Handbook. 1984. pap. 9.95 (ISBN 0-8359-8311-0). Reston.

Buchsbaum, Walter H. Buchsbaum's Complete Handbook of Practical Electronics Reference Data. 2nd ed. 672p. 1978. 29.95 (ISBN 0-13-084624-4, Busn). P-H.

Coombs, Clyde F., Jr. Basic Electronic Instrument Handbook. LC 72-1394. (Handbook Ser.). (Illus.). 832p. 1972. 56.50 (ISBN 0-07-012615-1). McGraw.

Edwards, John. Exploring Electricity & Electronics With Projects. (Illus.). 208p. (Orig.). 1983. 15.95 (ISBN 0-8306-0497-9, 1497); pap. 9.95 (ISBN 0-8306-1497-4). TAB Bks.

Fredericksen, Thomas M. Intuitive IC Electronics: A Sophisticated Primer for Engineers & Technicians. (Illus.). 208p. 1981. 27.95 (ISBN 0-07-021923-0). McGraw.

Freeman, Roger L. English-Spanish, Spanish-English Dictionary of Communications & Electronic Terms. LC 78-152639. Tr. of Diccionario de Terminologia Electronica y de Telecomunicaciones Ingles-Espanol, Espanol-Ingles. pap. 54.00 (ISBN 0-317-26395-1, 2024452). Bks Demand UMI.

General Electric Company. SCR Manual. 6th ed. (Illus.). 656p. 1982. pap. 14.95 (ISBN 0-13-796763-2); 23.95 (ISBN 0-13-796771-3). P-H.

Genn, Robert C. Manual of Electronic Servicing Tests & Measurements. 240p. 1979. 19.95 (ISBN 0-13-553388-0, Parker). P-H.

Genn, Robert, Jr. Electronic Troubleshooting Handbook. 215p. 1981. pap. 8.95 (ISBN 0-13-252585-2, Reward). P-H.

Giant Handbook of Two Hundred & Twenty-Two Weekend Electronics Projects. 496p. 1981. pap. 14.95 (ISBN 0-8306-1265-3, 1265). TAB Bks.

Greene, Bob. Twenty Five Quick-N-Easy Electronics Projects. 96p. (Orig.). 1982. pap. 4.95 (ISBN 0-86668-023-3). ARCsoft.

Grolle, Carl G. & Girosky, Michael B. Workbench Guide to Electronic Projects You Can Build in Your Spare Time. LC 81-2169. 256p. 1981. 17.95 (ISBN 0-13-965269-8, Parker). P-H.

A Handbook for Electrical & Electronics Translators. (Eng. & Japanese.). 490p. 1972. 75.00 (ISBN 0-686-92550-5, M-9331). French & Eur.

Hoenig, Stuart A. How to Build & Use Electronic Devices Without Frustration, Panic, Mountains of Money, or an Engineering Degree. 2nd ed. 1980. pap. 16.95 (ISBN 0-316-36808-3). Little.

Howard W. Sams Editorial Staff. Handbook of Electronic Tables & Formulas. 5th ed. LC 78-71889. 288p. 1979. 12.95 (ISBN 0-672-21532-2). Sams.

Howells, E. R., ed. Technology of Chemicals & Materials for Electronics. (Chemical Industry Ser.). 363p. 1984. 57.00 (ISBN 0-470-20118-5). Halsted Pr.

Hughes, Frederick W. Digital Electronics: Theory & Experimention. (Illus.). 352p. 1986. pap. text ed. 21.95 (ISBN 0-13-212556-0). P-H.

--Workbench Guide to Practical Solid State Electronics. 224p. 1979. cancelled (ISBN 0-686-92095-3, Parker). P-H.

Johnson. Handbook of Electric & Electronic Technology. Date not set. price not set (ISBN 0-471-82486-0). Wiley.

Jones, Thomas. Electronic Components Handbook. 1978. 25.95 (ISBN 0-87909-222-X). Reston.

Lenk, John D. Handbook of Electronic Test Procedures. (Illus.). 320p. 1982. 26.95 (ISBN 0-13-377457-0). P-H.

Loper, Orla, et al. Introduction to Electricity & Electronics. LC 77-78174. 1979. text ed. 21.40 (ISBN 0-8273-1160-5); teacher's manual 5.25 (ISBN 0-8273-1162-1). Delmar.

Ludwig, Raymond H. Illustrated Handbook of Electronic Tables, Symbols, Measurements & Values. 2nd ed. LC 83-17620. 415p. 1983. 32.95 (ISBN 0-13-450494-1, Busn); 22.95. P-H.

Mandl, Matthew. Basics of Electricity & Electronics. (Illus.). 448p. 1975. ref. ed. 27.95 (ISBN 0-13-060228-0). P-H.

--Electronics Handbook. 1983. text ed. 36.95 (ISBN 0-8359-1603-0). Reston.

Metzger, Daniel L. Electronics Pocket Handbook. (Illus.). 272p. 1982. 9.95 (ISBN 0-13-251835-X). P-H.

Olsen, George H. The Beginner's Handbook of Electronics. 1980. text ed. 17.95 (ISBN 0-13-074211-2, Spec); pap. text ed. 7.95 (ISBN 0-13-074203-1). P-H.

Pasahow, E. J. Electronics Ready Reference Manual. LC 84-11280. 592p. 1984. 24.50 (ISBN 0-07-048723-5). McGraw.

Pender, Harold & McIlwain, Knox - Electrical Engineers Handbook: Electric Communication & Electronics. 4th ed. (Wiley Engineers Handbook Ser.). 1618p. 1950. 64.95x (ISBN 0-471-67848-1, Pub. by Wiley-Interscience). Wiley.

Perozzo, James. Practical Electronics Troubleshooting. LC 84-28626. 256p. 1985. pap. text ed. 16.00 (ISBN 0-8273-2433-2). Delmar.

Putman, Byron. Digital & Microprogram Electronics: Theory Application Troubleshooting. (Illus.). 416p. 1986. text ed. 32.95 (ISBN 0-13-214354-2). P-H.

Rips, Ervine M. Discrete & Integrated Electronics. (Illus.). 512p. 1986. text ed. 36.95 (ISBN 0-13-215153-7). P-H.

Schoen, S. & Gutaj, R. Equipment Planning Guides. (Equipment Planning Guides: No. 10). v, 276p. 1981. pap. 23.00 (ISBN 92-2-102588-8, ILO196, ILO). Unipub.

Sinclair, Ian R. Electronics for the Service Engineer, 2 vols, Parts 1 & 2. (Illus.). 460p. 1981. Set. pap. text ed. 45.00x (ISBN 0-89563-041-9). Vol. 1 (ISBN 0-291-39638-0). Vol. 2 (ISBN 0-291-39619-4). Intl Ideas.

--Electronics for the Service Engineer, Vol. 1. 200p. 1980. 69.00x (ISBN 0-291-39638-0, Pub. by Tech Pr). State Mutual Bk.

--Electronics for the Service Engineer, Vol. 2. 280p. 1980. 72.00x (ISBN 0-291-39619-4, Pub. by Tech Pr). State Mutual Bk.

Su, Kendall L. A Collection of Solved Problems in Circuits, Electronics & Signal Electronics, Vol. 4. 80p. 1981. pap. text ed. 5.50 (ISBN 0-8403-2404-9). Kendall-Hunt.

Sullivan, Richard. Practical Problems in Mathematics for Electronics Technicians. LC 80-70484. (Practical Problems in Mathematics Ser.). (Illus.). 212p. (Orig.). 1982. pap. text ed. 7.80 (ISBN 0-8273-2086-8); instr.'s guide 4.20 (ISBN 0-8273-2087-6). Delmar.

Taylor, T. Handbook of Electronics Industry Cost Estimating Data. 464p. 1985. 59.50 (ISBN 0-471-82264-7). Wiley.

Thomas, H. The Electronics Vest Pocket Reference Book. 1982. pap. 5.95 (ISBN 0-13-252379-5). P-H.

Thomas, Harry. Electronics Vest Pocket Reference Book. 211p. 1983. pap. 5.95 (ISBN 0-13-252403-1). P-H.

Turner, Rufus. Electronic Conversions, Symbols, & Formulas. LC 75-31464. (Illus.). 224p. 1975. pap. 9.95 (ISBN 0-8306-4750-3, 750). TAB Bks.

Villanucci, Robert, et al. Electronic Techniques: Shop Practices & Construction. 3rd ed. (Illus.). 672p. 1986. text ed. 34.95 (ISBN 0-13-252529-1). P-H.

West, Gordon & Pittman, Freeman. The Straightshooter's Guide to Marine Electronics. (Illus.). 112p. 1985. pap. 9.95 (ISBN 0-87742-202-8). Intl Marine.

Wilson, J. A. & Kaufman, M. Schaum's Outline of Electronics Technology, Including 240 Solved Problems. (Schaum's Outline Ser.). 1982. pap. 9.95 (ISBN 0-07-070690-5). McGraw.

Young, Stephen D. Basic Electronic Technology: A Guide for the Beginning Technician. LC 82-84005. (Illus.). 103p. 1983. pap. 12.95 (ISBN 0-912633-01-8). Progressive Elect Pubs.

Zbar, Paul B. Basic Electronics: A Text-Lab Manual. 4th ed. 1976. text ed. 19.25 (ISBN 0-07-072761-9). McGraw.

ELECTRONICS–HISTORY

AT&T Bell Laboratories Staff. A History of Engineering & Science in the Bell System: Electronics Technology (1925-1975) Smits, F. M., ed. LC 84-73157. (Illus.). 400p. 1985. write for info (ISBN 0-932764-07-X, 500-472). Bell Telephone.

Atherton, W. A. From Compass to Computer: A History of Electrical & Electronics Engineering. (Illus.). 1983. 30.00 (ISBN 0-911302-48-4); pap. 12.50 (ISBN 0-911302-49-2). San Francisco Pr.

Dummer, G. W. Electronic Inventions & Discoveries: Electronics from Its Earliest Beginnings to the Present Day. 3rd, rev. ed. 220p. 1983. 40.00 (ISBN 0-08-029354-9); pap. 18.00 (ISBN 0-08-029353-0). Pergamon.

Finn. History of Electric Technology. 1985. lib. bdg. 52.00 (ISBN 0-8240-9120-5). Garland Pub.

Goetschalckx, J. & Rolling, L. Lexicography in the Electronic Age. 276p. 1982. 38.50 (ISBN 0-444-86404-0, North-Holland). Elsevier.

ELECTRONICS–LABORATORY MANUALS

Berlin, Howard M. Experiments in Electronic Devices. 1984. lab manual 16.95 (ISBN 0-675-20234-5). Merrill.

CES Industries. Ed-Lab Eight Hundred Exercise Manual: Programming for Ohm's Law, Unit 1. (Illus., Orig.). 1982. write for info. (ISBN 0-86711-029-5). CES Industries.

--Ed-Lab Eight Hundred Series Reference Manual: Operations & BASIC. (Illus., Orig.). 1983. write for info. (ISBN 0-86711-067-8). CES Industries.

--Ed-Lab Experiment Manual: Student Guide to Test Points; TV Trainer. (Illus., Orig.). 1983. write for info. (ISBN 0-86711-044-9). CES Industries.

CES Industries, Inc. Ed-Lab Eight Hundred Exercise Manual: Interfaces, Unit 2. (Illus., Orig.). 1982. write for info. (ISBN 0-86711-030-9). CES Industries.

--Ed-Lab Eight Hundred Experiment & Exercise Manual: Programming in BASIC. Rev. ed. (Illus.). 1983. write for info. (ISBN 0-86711-029-5). CES Industries.

--Ed-Lab Eight Hundred Experiment Manual: Contactor Sensor Operation. (Illus., Orig.). 1983. write for info. (ISBN 0-86711-048-1). CES Industries.

--Ed-Lab Eight Hundred Experiment Manual: Infra-Red Sensor. (Illus., Orig.). 1983. write for info. (ISBN 0-86711-047-3). CES Industries.

--Ed-Lab Eight Hundred Experiment Manual: Photocell Sensor. (Illus., Orig.). 1983. write for info. (ISBN 0-86711-049-X). CES Industries.

--Ed-Lab Eight Hundred Experiment Manual: Robotics Interfacing. (Illus., Orig.). 1983. write for info. (ISBN 0-86711-046-5). CES Industries.

--Ed-Lab Eight Hundred Experiment Manual: Talker Interfacing. (Illus., Orig.). 1983. write for info. (ISBN 0-86711-069-4). CES Industries.

--Ed-Lab Eight Hundred Experiment Manual: Touch Sensor. (Illus., Orig.). 1983. write for info. (ISBN 0-86711-068-6). CES Industries.

--Ed-Lab Eighty Experiment Manual: Photocell Sensor. (Illus., Orig.). 1983. write for info. (ISBN 0-86711-036-8). CES Industries.

--Ed-Lab Experiment Manual: Instructor Guide to Troubles: TV Trainer. (Illus., Orig.). 1983. write for info. (ISBN 0-86711-045-7). CES Industries.

--Ed-Lab Six Hundred & Fifty Experiment Manual: Electricity-Electronics AC-DC, Bk. I. (Illus.). 288p. 1981. 12.50 (ISBN 0-86711-015-5). CES Industries.

CES Industries Inc. Ed-Lab Six Hundred & Fifty Experiment Manual: Electricity-Electronics Solid-State, Bk. II. (Illus.). 304p. 1981. 12.50 (ISBN 0-86711-014-7). CES Industries.

CES Industries, Inc. Staff. Ed-Lab Eight Hundred Experiment Manual: Printer Interfacing. (Illus., Orig.). 1984. write for info. (ISBN 0-86711-070-8). CES Industries.

Veley, Victory & Dulin, John. Lab Experiments for Modern Electronics: A First Course. (Illus.). 256p. 1983. pap. text ed. 13.95 (ISBN 0-13-593103-7). P-H.

Villanucci, R., et al. Electronic Techniques: Shop Practices & Construction. 2nd ed. 1981. 32.95 (ISBN 0-13-252486-4). P-H.

Zbar, Paul B. & Orne, R. Electronics Instruments & Measurement. (Illus.). 1965. text ed. 19.25 (ISBN 0-07-072754-6). McGraw.

ELECTRONICS–MATERIALS

see also Electronic Apparatus and Appliances–Plastic Embedment; Electronic Ceramics; Semiconductors; Superconductors

Chang, R. P. & Abeles, B., eds. Plasma Synthesis & Etching of Electronic Materials, Vol. 38. LC 85-3085. 1985. text ed. 43.00 (ISBN 0-931837-03-0). Materials Res.

Colclaser, R. A. & Nagle, S. D. Materials & Devices for Electrical Engineers & Physicists. 304p. 1984. 36.50 (ISBN 0-07-011693-8). McGraw.

Electronic Properties of Materials: A Guide to the Literature, 3 vols. Incl. Vol. 1, Two Pts. Johnson, H. T. 1965 (ISBN 0-306-68221-4); Vol. 2 Pts. 1 & 2. Grigsby, D. L., et al. 1967 (ISBN 0-306-68222-2); Vol 3, Pts. 1 & 2. Grigsby, D. L. 1971 (ISBN 0-306-68223-0). LC 65-12176. 195.00x ea. (IFI Plenum); 495.00x set (ISBN 0-685-27217-6). Plenum Pub.

Harper, Charles A. Handbook of Materials & Processes for Electronics. 1970. 59.50 (ISBN 0-07-026673-5). McGraw.

Jakowlew, B., et al, eds. Synthetic Materials for Electronics: Proceedings of the 2nd International Summer School, Jachranka, October, '79. (Materials Science Monograph: Vol. 8). 350p. 1982. 74.50 (ISBN 0-444-99741-5). Elsevier.

Kaldis, E., ed. Crystal Growth of Electronic Materials: Proceedings of the International Summer School on Crystal Growth & Materials Research, 5th, Davos, Switzerland, Sept. 3-10, 1983. 396p. 1985. 87.00 (ISBN 0-444-86919-0, North-Holland). Elsevier.

Matthews, J. L. Solid State Electronics Concepts. 1971. text ed. 32.00 (ISBN 0-07-040960-9). McGraw.

Milek, J. T. & Neuberger, M. Handbook of Electronic Materials, Vol. 8: Linear Electrooptic Modular Materials. LC 76-147312. 258p. 1972. 55.00x (ISBN 0-306-67108-5, IFI Plenum). Plenum Pub.

Milek, John T. Silicon Nitride for Microelectronic Applications: Handbook of Electronic Materials. LC 76-147312. 126p. 1971. Part 1, Preparation & Properties. 55.00x (ISBN 0-306-67103-4, IFI Plenum). Plenum Pub.

Moses, A. J. Optical Materials Properties: Handbook of Electronic Materials. LC 76-147312. 110p. 1971. 55.00x (ISBN 0-306-67101-8, IFI Plenum). Plenum Pub.

National Materials Advisory Board. Materials & Processes for Electron Devices. LC 72-84753. (Illus.). 240p. 1972. pap. 11.25 (ISBN 0-309-02040-9). Natl Acad Pr.

Seymour, J. Electronic Devices & Components. LC 80-28112. 504p. 1981. pap. 32.95x (ISBN 0-470-27108-6). Halsted Pr.

Devreese, Jozef T. & Brosens, Fons, eds. Electron Correlations in Solids, Molecules, & Atoms. (NATO ASI Series B, Physics: Vol. 81). 448p. 1983. 55.00x (ISBN 0-306-41027-3, Plenum Pr). Plenum Pub.

Di Bartolo, Baldassare, ed. Radiationless Processes. LC 80-21961. (NATO ASI Series B, Physical Sciences: Vol. 62). 565p. 1981. 85.00 (ISBN 0-306-40577-6, Plenum Pr). Plenum Pub.

Drickamer, H. G. Electronic Transitions & the High Pressure Chemistry & Physics of Solids. (Studies in Chemical Physics). 1973. 35.00x (ISBN 0-412-11650-2, NO.6090, Pub. by Chapman & Hall). Methuen Inc.

Duntiz, J. D., et al, eds. Electrons & Transitions. (Structure & Bonding: Vol. 39). (Illus.). 1980. 42.00 (ISBN 0-387-09787-2). Springer-Verlag.

Elion & Elion. Electro-Optics Handbook. (Electro-Optics Ser.: Vol. 3). 1979. 65.00 (ISBN 0-8247-6879-5). Dekker.

Ertl, G. & Kuppers, J. Low Energy Electrons & Surface Chemistry. LC 74-82758. (Monographs in Modern Chemistry: Vol. 4). (Illus.). 261p. 1974. 57.70x (ISBN 3-527-25562-1). VCH Pubs.

Grubin, H. L., et al, eds. The Physics of Submicron Structures. 370p. 1984. 57.50x (ISBN 0-306-41715-4, Plenum Pr). Plenum Pub.

Harcourt, Richard D. Qualitative Valence-Bond Description of Electron-Rich Molecules: Pauling "Three Electron Bonds" & "Increased-Valence" Theory. (Lecture Notes in Chemistry: Vol. 30). 260p. 1982. pap. 21.40 (ISBN 0-387-11555-2). Springer-Verlag.

Hurley, A. C. Introduction to the Electron Theory of Small Molecules. 1977. 60.00 (ISBN 0-12-362460-6). Acad Pr.

Ibach, H. & Mills, L. Electron Energy Loss Spectroscopy & Surface Vibrations. LC 81-22938. 384p. 1982. 58.00 (ISBN 0-12-369350-0). Acad Pr.

International Commission on Radiation Units & Measurements. Stopping Powers for Electrons & Positrons. LC 84-12780. (Report Ser.: No. 37). 268p. 1984. pap. text ed. 24.00 (ISBN 0-913394-31-9). Intl Comm Rad Meas.

International Conference on Electron & Ion Beam Science & Technology (7th: 1976: San Francisco) Electron & Ion Beam Science & Technology: 7th International Conference, Proceedings of the Symposium. Bakish, Robert, ed. LC 71-120300. pap. 158.00 (ISBN 0-317-09048-8, 2051977). Bks Demand UMI.

International Symposium Oln Electron & Photoninteractions at High Energies - Hamburg - 1965. Electron & Photon Interactions at High Energies: Invited Papers. (Springer Tracts in Modern Physics: Vol. 39). (Illus.). 1965. 34.30 (ISBN 0-387-03406-4). Springer-Verlag.

Kaganov, M. I. Electrons, Phonons, Magnons. 260p. 1981. pap. 4.00 (ISBN 0-8285-2011-9, Pub. by Mir Pubs USSR). Imported Pubns.

Kaplan, I. G. Symmetry of Many Electron Systems. 1975. 77.50 (ISBN 0-12-397150-0). Acad Pr.

Kirschner, J. M. Polarized Electrons at Surfaces. (Tracts in Modern Physics Ser.: Vol. 106). (Illus.). 175p. 1985. 24.00 (ISBN 0-387-15003-X). Springer-Verlag.

Kitaigorodsky, A. I. Physics for Everyone: Electrons. 1981. 6.60 (ISBN 0-8285-1904-8, Pub. by Mir Pubs USSR). Imported Pubns.

Kleinpoppen, H. & MacDowell, M. R., eds. Electron & Photon Interactions with Atoms. LC 75-37555. (Illus.). 682p. 1976. 79.50x (ISBN 0-306-30846-0, Plenum Pr). Plenum Pub.

Kramer, G. Theory of Jets in Electron: Position Annihilation. (Springer Tracts in Modern Physics: Vol. 102). (Illus.). 106p. 1984. 29.00 (ISBN 0-387-13068-3). Springer-Verlag.

Marton, L. & Septier, A. Advances in Electronics & Electron Physics, Supplement 13A: Applied Charged Particle Optics. 1980. 60.00 (ISBN 0-12-014573-1). Acad Pr.

Marton, L., ed. Advances in Electronics & Electron Physics. Incl. Vol. 36. 1974. 85.00 (ISBN 0-12-014536-7); Vol. 37. 1975. 85.00 (ISBN 0-12-014537-5); Vol. 38. 1975. 85.00 (ISBN 0-12-014538-3); Vol. 39. 1975. 85.00 (ISBN 0-12-014539-1); Vol. 40a. Photo-Electronics Image Devices: Proceedings. Imperial College, London, Sept. 9-13, 1974, 6th Symposium, et al. Morgan, B. L., ed. 1976. 98.50 (ISBN 0-12-014540-5); Vol. 40B. Photo-Electronic Image Devices. 1977. 98.50 (ISBN 0-12-014554-5); Vol. 42. 1976. 80.00 (ISBN 0-12-014642-8); Vol. 45. 1978. 85.00 (ISBN 0-12-014645-2). (Serial Publication). Acad Pr.

--Advances in Electronics & Electron Physics, Vol. 41. 1976. 80.00 (ISBN 0-12-014541-3). Acad Pr.

--Advances in Electronics & Electron Physics, Vol. 46. LC 49-7504. 1978. 85.00 (ISBN 0-12-014646-0). Acad Pr.

--Advances in Electronics & Electron Physics, Vol. 49. (Serial Publication Ser.). 1979. 80.00 (ISBN 0-12-014649-5). Acad Pr.

--Advances in Electronics & Electron Physics, Vol. 60. (Serial Publication Ser.). 424p. 1983. 69.50 (ISBN 0-12-014660-6). Acad Pr.

Marton, L. & Marton, C., eds. Advances in Electronics & Electron Physics, Vol. 51. LC 49-7504. (Serial Publication Ser.). 1980. 70.00 (ISBN 0-12-014651-7). Acad Pr.

--Advances in Electronics and Electron Physics, Vol. 52. 1980. 94.50 (ISBN 0-12-014652-5). Acad Pr.

Marton, L. & Marton, Claire, eds. Advances in Electronic & Electron Physics, Vol. 55. (Serial Publication Ser.). 1981. 79.00 (ISBN 0-12-014655-X) (ISBN 0-12-014701-7). Acad Pr.

--Advances in Electronics & Electron Physics, Vol. 50. LC 49-7504. 1980. 80.00 (ISBN 0-12-014650-9). Acad Pr.

--Advances in Electronics & Electron Physics, Vol. 53. (Serial Publication Ser.). 1980. 60.00 (ISBN 0-12-014653-3). Acad Pr.

--Advances in Electronics & Electron Physics, Vol. 54. (Serial Publication Ser.). 1980. 60.00 (ISBN 0-12-014654-1). Acad Pr.

Massey, H. S. Electronic & Ionic Impact Phenomena, 2 vols. Incl. Vol. 1. Collision of Electrons with Atoms. 2nd ed. Massey, H. S. & Burhop, E. H. 85.00x (ISBN 0-19-851247-3); Vol. 2. Electron Collisions with Molecules & Photoionization. Massey, H. S. 85.00x (ISBN 0-19-851249-X). 1969. Oxford U Pr.

Miller & Culpepper. Experiences with Electrons. 1983. text ed. 10.75 (ISBN 0-538-33520-3, IE52). SW Pub.

Millikan, Robert A. Electron: Its Isolation & Measurement & the Determination of Some of Its Properties. DuMond, Jesse W., ed. (Illus., Orig.). 1963. pap. 3.95x (ISBN 0-226-52883-9, P523, Phoen). U of Chicago Pr.

--The Electron: Its Isolation & Measurement & the Determination of some of it Properties. DuMond, Jesse W., ed. LC 63-20910. pap. 82.50 (ISBN 0-317-08089-X, 2019980). Bks Demand UMI.

Mott, Nevill F. & Jones, H. Theory of the Properties of Metals & Alloys. 1936. pap. 7.95 (ISBN 0-486-60456-X). Dover.

Nag, B. R. Electron Transport in Compound Semiconductors. (Springer Ser. in Solid-State Sciences: Vol. 11). (Illus.). 470p. 1980. 56.00 (ISBN 3-540-09845-3). Springer-Verlag.

Palmieri, F., et al, eds. Vectoral Reactions in Electron & Ion Transport in Michondria & Bacteria. (Developments in Bioenergetics & Biomembranes Ser.: Vol. 5). 430p. 1981. 73.75 (ISBN 0-444-80372-6, Biomedical Pr). Elsevier.

Phariseau, P. & Scheire, L., eds. Electrons in Finite & Infinite Structures. LC 77-5020. (NATO ASI Series B, Physics: Vol. 24). 433p. 1977. 69.50x (ISBN 0-306-35724-0, Plenum Pr). Plenum Pub.

Pippard, A. B. The Dynamics of Conduction Electrons. (Documents on Modern Physics Ser). 158p. 1965. 36.00x (ISBN 0-677-00720-5). Gordon.

Piret, John A. The Almighty Electron: A New Philosophy. 1983. 10.00 (ISBN 0-533-05754-X). Vantage.

Polarized Electrons. (Texts & Monographs in Physics). (Illus.). 1976. 39.00 (ISBN 0-387-07678-6). Springer-Verlag.

Pratt, William K. & Marton, L. L., eds. Advances in Electronics & Electron Physics: Supplement No. 12 Image Transmission Techniques. LC 63-12814. 1979. 57.50 (ISBN 0-12-014572-3). Acad Pr.

Ryder, J. D. & Fink, D. G. Engineers & Electrons. LC 83-22681. 251p. 1983. 29.95 (ISBN 0-87942-172-X, PC01669). Inst Electrical.

Salem, Lionel. Electrons in Chemical Reactions: First Priciples. LC 81-19833. 260p. 1982. 37.50 (ISBN 0-471-08474-3, Pub. by Wiley-Interscience). Wiley.

Schweiger, A. Electron Nuclear Double Resonance of Transition Metal Complexes with Organic Ligands. (Structure & Bonding Ser.: Vol. 51). (Illus.). 150p. 1982. 36.00 (ISBN 0-387-11072-0). Springer-Verlag.

Scott, Peter. Odd Electron Species: The Chemistry of Free Radicals. LC 81-3888. (Illus.). 128p. 1985. pap. text ed. 6.95 (ISBN 0-521-28177-6). Cambridge U Pr.

Segal, Gerald A., ed. Semiempirical Methods of Electronic Structure Calculation, 2 pts. Incl. Pt. A: Techniques. 274p (ISBN 0-306-33507-7); Pt. B: Applications. 308p (ISBN 0-306-33508-5). LC 76-48060. (Modern Theoretical Chemistry Ser.: Vols. 7 & 8). (Illus.). 1977. 49.50x ea. (Plenum Pr). Plenum Pub.

Sinanogly, Oktay & Brueckner, Keith A. Three Approaches to Electron Correlation in Atoms. LC 76-89666. (Yale Series in the Sciences). (Illus.). pap. 99.50 (ISBN 0-317-09328-2, 2022039). Bks Demand UMI.

Springford, Michael, ed. Electrons at the Fermi Surface. LC 79-50509. (Illus.). 496p. 1980. 99.50 (ISBN 0-521-22337-7). Cambridge U Pr.

Van Wazer, John R. & Absar, Ilyas. Electron Densities in Molecules & Molecular Orbitals. (Physical Chemistry Ser.). 1975. 40.00 (ISBN 0-12-714550-8). Acad Pr.

Very, Frank W. Luminiferous Ether. (Orig.). 1919. pap. 25.00 (ISBN 0-8283-1189-7). Branden Pub Co.

Weeks, Daniel P. Electron-Movement: A Guide for Students of Organic Chemistry. LC 75-8188. (Illus.). 150p. 1976. pap. text ed. 17.95 (ISBN 0-7216-9143-9, CBS C). SCP.

Weiss, R. J. X-Ray Determination of Electron Distribution. Wohlforth, E. P., ed. (Selected Topics in Solid State Physics: Vol. 6). 1966. 21.50 (ISBN 0-444-10305-8, North-Holland). Elsevier.

Woodward, R. B. & Hoffmann, R. The Conservation of Orbital Symmetry. LC 79-103636. (Illus.). 178p. 1970. pap. 14.95x (ISBN 0-89573-109-6). VCH Pubs.

Zlatkis, A. & Poole, C. F., eds. Electron Capture: Theory & Practice in Chromatography. (Journal of Chromatography Library: Vol. 20). 438p. 1981. 85.00 (ISBN 0-444-41954-3). Elsevier.

ELECTRONS–DIFFRACTION

American Society for Testing & Materials. Techniques of Electron Microscopy, Diffraction, & Microprobe Analysis. (American Society for Testing & Materials Special Technical Publication: No. 372). pap. 23.80 (ISBN 0-317-09550-1, 2000730). Bks Demand UMI.

Andrews, K. W., et al, eds. Interpretation of Electron Diffraction Patterns. 2nd ed. 239p. 1971. 42.50x (ISBN 0-306-30534-8, Plenum Pr). Plenum Pub.

Beeston, B. E., et al, eds. Electron Diffraction & Optical Diffraction Techniques. (Practical Methods in Electron Microscopy Ser.: Vol. 1, Pt. 2). 260p. 1973. 24.00 (ISBN 0-444-10411-9, Biomedical Pr). Elsevier.

Brockway, L. O., ed. Fifty Years of Electron Diffraction. (Transactions of the American Crystallographic Association Ser.: Vol. 13). 126p. 1977. pap. 15.00 (ISBN 0-686-60383-4). Polycrystal Bk Serv.

Cowley, John M. Diffraction Physics. 2nd, rev. ed. (Personal Library: Vol. 1). 430p. 1985. pap. 27.95 (ISBN 0-444-86925-5, North-Holland). Elsevier.

Electron Diffraction, 1927-1977: London. (Institute of Physics Conference Ser.: No. 41). 1978. 75.00 (ISBN 0-9960032-1-5, Pub. by Inst Physics England). Heyden.

Goodman, Peter, ed. Fifty Years of Electron Diffraction. xiv, 432p. 1981. 79.00 (ISBN 90-277-1246-8, Pub. by Reidel Holland). Kluwer Academic.

Haaland, A., et al. Gas-Phase Electron Diffraction. (Topics in Current Chemistry: Vol. 53). (Illus.). iv, 119p. 1975. 29.00 (ISBN 0-387-07051-6). Springer-Verlag.

Noakes, G. R., et al, eds. Sources of Physics Teaching: Electrolysis, X-Ray Analysis. Electron Diffraction, Vol. 3. 1969. pap. 17.50x (ISBN 0-85066-031-9). Intl Ideas.

Pendry, J. B. Low Energy Electron Diffraction. 1974. 47.50 (ISBN 0-12-550550-7). Acad Pr.

Zvyagin, B. B. Electron-Diffraction Analysis of Clay Mineral Structures. LC 65-17783. (Monographs in Geoscience Ser.). 264p. 1967. 42.50x (ISBN 0-306-30273-X, Plenum Pr). Plenum Pub.

ELECTRONS–EMISSION

see also Electron Spectroscopy; Field Emission; Photoelectricity; Thermionic Emission

Dobretsov, L. N. & Gomoyunova, M. V. Emission Electronics. 433p. 69.95x (ISBN 0-470-21680-8). Halsted Pr.

Fomenko, Vadim S. Handbook of Thermionic Properties: Electronic Work Functions & Richardson Constants of Elements & Compounds. LC 65-23385. 151p. 1966. 42.50x (ISBN 0-306-65117-3, IFI Plenum). Plenum Pub.

Lindinger, W., et al, eds. Swarms of Ions & Electrons in Gases. (Illus.). 320p. 1984. 35.00 (ISBN 0-387-81823-5). Springer-Verlag.

Zuppinger, A., et al, eds. High Energy Electrons in Radiation Therapy. (Illus.). 130p. 1980. pap. 28.40 (ISBN 0-387-10188-8). Springer-Verlag.

ELECTRONS–SCATTERING

Brown, S. C. Electron-Molecule Scattering. 196p. 1979. 34.95 (ISBN 0-471-05205-1). Krieger.

Gianturco, F. A. & Stefani, G., eds. Wavefunctions & Mechanisms from Electron Scattering Processes. (Lecture Notes in Chemistry Ser.: Vol. 35). ix, 279p. 1984. 19.70 (ISBN 0-387-13347-X). Springer-Verlag.

Herman, Robert C. & Hofstadter, Robert. High-Energy Electron Scattering Tables. 1960. 22.50x (ISBN 0-8047-0588-7). Stanford U Pr.

Huxley, L. G. & Crompton, R. W. The Diffusion & Drift of Electrons in Gases. LC 73-12313. 669p. (Orig.). 1974. 43.95 (ISBN 0-471-42590-7). Krieger.

Nesbet, Robert K. Variational Methods in Electron-Atom Scattering Theory. (Physics of Atoms & Molecules Ser.). (Illus.). 235p. 1980. 37.50x (ISBN 0-306-40413-3, Plenum Pr). Plenum Pub.

Olsen, Jorgen L. Electron Transport in Metals. LC 61-17893. (Interscience Tracts on Physics & Astronomy Ser.: No. 12). pap. 32.30 (ISBN 0-317-08470-4, 2011962). Bks Demand UMI.

Uberall, Herbert. Electron Scattering from Complex Nuclei Pts. A & B. (Pure & Applied Physics Ser: Vol. 25). 1971. Pt. A. 72.00 (ISBN 0-12-705701-3); Pt. B. 70.00 (ISBN 0-12-705702-1). Acad Pr.

Uslenghi, Piergiorgio L., ed. Electromagnetic Scattering. 1978. 69.50 (ISBN 0-12-709650-7). Acad Pr.

ELECTROOPTICAL PHOTOGRAPHY

Biberman, L. M. & Nudelman, S., eds. Photoelectronic Imaging Devices, 2 vols. Incl. Vol. 1, Physical Processes & Methods of Analysis. 430p. 59.50x (ISBN 0-306-37081-6); Vol. 2, Devices & Their Evaluation. 584p. 75.00x (ISBN 0-306-37082-4). LC 74-120029. (Optical Physics & Engineering Ser.). 1971 (Plenum Pr). Plenum Pub.

Camatini, Ezio, ed. Progress in Electro-Optics: Reviews of Recent Developments. LC 75-16350. (NATO ASI Series B, Physics: Vol. 10). (Illus.). 213p. 1975. 42.50x (ISBN 0-306-35710-0, Plenum Pr.). Plenum Pub.

Elion & Elion. Electro-Optics Handbook. (Electro-Optics Ser.: Vol. 3). 1979. 65.00 (ISBN 0-8247-6879-5). Dekker.

ELECTROOPTICS

see also Electrooptical Photography

Baker, L. R., ed. British Electro-Optics. 148p. 1977. cancelled (ISBN 0-85066-101-3). Taylor & Francis.

Danly. Emerging Opportunities for Electroorganic Processes. (Special Report Ser.). 216p. 1984. 435.00 (ISBN 0-8247-7148-6). Dekker.

Elion & Morozov. Optoelectronic Switching Systems in Telecommunications & Computers. (Electro-Optics Ser.). 264p. 1984. 37.50 (ISBN 0-8247-7163-X). Dekker.

Haus, Herman A. Waves & Fields in Optoelectronics. (Illus.). 464p. 1984. text ed. 32.95 (ISBN 0-13-946053-5). P-H.

Heath Company Staff. Optoelectronics. (Electronic Technology Ser.). (Illus.). 495p. 1981. pap. text ed. 14.95 (ISBN 0-87119-071-0, EB-605); tchr's. ed. 9.95 (ISBN 0-87119-073-7); lab manual 9.95 (ISBN 0-87119-072-9); looseleaf with experimental pts. 59.95 (ISBN 0-87119-070-2, EE-105). Heathkit-Zenith Ed.

Krause, Sonja, ed. Molecular Electro-Optics: Electro-Optic Properties of Macromolecules & Colloids in Solution. LC 81-1314. (NATO ASI Series B, Physics: Vol. 64). 528p. 1981. 75.00x (ISBN 0-306-40659-4, Plenum Pr). Plenum Pub.

O'Konski, Chester, ed. Molecular Electro-Optics, Pt. 2. (Electro-Optics Ser.: Vol. 1). 1978. 85.00 (ISBN 0-8247-6402-1). Dekker.

--Molecular Electro-Optics: Theory & Method, Pt. 1. (Electro-Optics Ser.: Vol. 1). 1976. 95.00 (ISBN 0-8247-6395-5). Dekker.

RCA Staff. RCA Electro-Optics Handbook. (Illus.). 1974. 4.95 (ISBN 0-913970-11-5, EOH-11). RCA Solid State.

ELECTRO-OSMOSIS

Nikolaev, B. A. Pile Driving by Electroosmosis. LC 61-18759. 62p. 1962. 25.00x (ISBN 0-306-10578-0, Consultants). Plenum Pub.

ELECTROPHORESIS

see also Immunoelectrophoresis

Advances in Electrophoretic Paint Deposition. 62p. 1969. 40.00x (ISBN 0-686-44643-7, Pub. by Chandler England). State Mutual Bk.

Advances in Electrophoretic Paint Deposition: 1969. 62p. 1970. 40.00x (ISBN 0-686-44645-3, Pub. by Chandler England). State Mutual Bk.

Advances in Electrophoretic Paint Deposition: 1970. 58p. 1971. 40.00x (ISBN 0-686-44646-1, Pub. by Chandler England). State Mutual Bk.

Advances in Electrophoretic Paint Deposition: 1971-72. 80p. 1973. 40.00x (ISBN 0-686-44652-6, Pub. by Chandler England). State Mutual Bk.

Advances in Electrophoretic Paint Deposition: 1975-77. 71p. 1978. 40.00x (ISBN 0-686-44655-0, Pub. by Chandler England). State Mutual Bk.

Advances in Electrophoretic Paint Deposition: 1973-74 (With Special Section on Cathodic Eletropainting) 63p. 1975. 40.00x (ISBN 0-686-44654-2, Pub. by Chandler England). State Mutual Bk.

Advances in Electrophoretic Painting: 1978-80. (Bibliographies in Paint Technology Ser.: No. 36). 85p. 1982. 45.00x (ISBN 0-686-44657-7, Pub. by Chandler England). State Mutual Bk.

Allen, Robert & Maurer, H. Rainer, eds. Electrophoresis & Isoelectric Focusing in Polyacrylamide Gel: Advances of Methods & Theories, Biochemical & Clinical Applications. LC 73-94225. (Illus.). 1974. 44.00x (ISBN 3-11-004344-0). De Gruyter.

ELECTROSMOSIS
see Electro-Osmosis
ELECTROSTATIC PRECIPITATION
Bohm, J. Electrostatic Precipitators. (Chemical Engineering Monographs: Vol. 14). 366p. 1982. 78.75 (ISBN 0-444-99764-4). Elsevier.
Katz, Jacob. The Art of Electrostatic Precipitation. (Illus.). 350p. 1980. text ed. 52.50x (ISBN 0-9603986-1-9, Pub. by Precipitator). Scholium Intl.
Oglesby, Sabert, et al. Electrostatic Precipitation. (Pollution Engineering & Technology Ser.: Vol. 8). 1978. 75.00 (ISBN 0-8247-6649-0). Dekker.
ELECTROSTATIC PROPULSION SYSTEMS
see Ion Rockets; Plasma Rockets
ELECTROSTATIC STORAGE TUBES
see Storage Tubes
ELECTROSTATICS
see also Electric Discharges; Electrostatic Precipitation; Induction (Electricity); Potential, Theory Of
Electrostatics 1979 (Oxford) (Reports on Progress in Physics: No. 48). 80.00 (ISBN 0-9960032-8-2, Pub. by Inst Physics England). Heyden.
Haase, Heinz. Electrostatic Hazards: Their Evaluation & Control. (Illus.). 125p. 1977. 21.30x (ISBN 3-527-25684-9). VCH Pubs.
Horvath, T. Static Elimination. Berta, I., ed. LC 82-4791. (Electrostatics & Electrostatic Applications Ser.: 1-617). 118p. 1982. text ed. 29.95 (ISBN 0-471-10405-1, Pub. by Research Studies Pr). Wiley.
Huges, J. F. Electrostatic Powder Coating. (Electrical & Electronic Engineering Ser.). 1984. 34.95 (ISBN 0-471-90569-0). Wiley.
Institute of Physics. Static Electrification London (1967) (Institute of Physics Conference Ser.: No. 4). 1968. 55.00 (ISBN 0-9960028-3-9, Pub. by Inst Physics England). Heyden.
Jefimenko, Oleg D. Electrostatic Motors. LC 73-180890. (Illus.). 124p. 1973. 11.00 (ISBN 0-917406-01-X); pap. 8.00 (ISBN 0-917406-02-8). Electret Sci.
Lacy, Edward A. Protecting Electronic Equipment from Electrostatic Discharge. LC 84-8902. (Illus.). 176p. (Orig.). 1984. 16.95 (ISBN 0-8306-0820-6); pap. 11.95 (ISBN 0-8306-1820-1, 1820). TAB Bks.
Langmuir, D. B. & Stuhlinger, E., eds. Electrostatic Propulsion. LC 60-16913. (Illus.). 579p. 1961. 29.00 (ISBN 0-317-36832-X); members 14.50 (ISBN 0-317-36833-8). AIAA.
McDonald, Jack R. & Dean, Alan H. Electrostatic Precipitator Manual. LC 82-3449. (Pollution Tech. Rev.: No. 91). (Illus.). 484p. 1982. 48.00 (ISBN 0-8155-0895-6). Noyes.
Moore, A. D., ed. Electrostatics & Its Applications. LC 12-13945. 592p. 1973. 64.50x (ISBN 0-471-61450-5, Pub. by Wiley-Interscience). Wiley.
Noakes, G. R., ed. Sources of Physics Teaching: Atomic Energy. Holography. Electrostatics, Vol. 4. 1970. pap. text ed. 18.50x (ISBN 0-85066-038-6). Intl Ideas.
Politzer, Peter & Truhlar, Donald G., eds. Chemical Applications of Atomic & Molecular Electrostatic Potentials: Reactivity, Structure, Scattering, & Energetics of Organic, Inorganic, & Biological Systems. LC 81-1329. 482p. 1981. 65.00x (ISBN 0-306-40657-8, Plenum Pr). Plenum Pub.
Recommended Practice on Static Electricity. (Seventy Ser.). 64p. 1972. pap. 2.00 (ISBN 0-685-46075-4, 77). Natl Fire Prot.
Singh, ed. Electrostatics 1983. 1983. 34.00 (ISBN 0-9960040-2-5, Pub. by A Hilger England). Heyden.
Static Electrical Equipment Testing. 55.00x (ISBN 0-85083-068-0, Pub. by Engineering Ind). State Mutual Bk.
Static Electrical Equipment Winding & Building One, 2 vols. 55.00x set (Pub. by Engineering Ind). State Mutual Bk.
Static Electrification: London 1971. (Institute of Physics Conference Ser.: No. 11). 1971. 55.00 (ISBN 0-9960029-0-1, Pub. by Inst Physics England). Heyden.
Static Electrification: London 1975. (Institute of Physics Conference Ser.: No. 27). 1975. 67.50 (ISBN 0-9960030-6-1, Pub. by Inst Physics England). Heyden.
Wada, Y., et al, eds. Charge Storage, Charge Transport & Electrostatics & Their Applications. LC 79-20991. (Studies in Electrical & Electronic Engineering: Vol. 2). 460p. 1980. 81.00 (ISBN 0-444-99769-5). Elsevier.
ELEMENTARY PARTICLES (PHYSICS)
see Particles (Nuclear Physics)
ELEMENTS, CHEMICAL
see Chemical Elements
ELEMENTS, INERT
see Gases, Rare
ELEPHANTS
Adams, Jack. Wild Elephants in Captivity. LC 81-69851. (Illus.). 206p. 1981. pap. 20.00x (ISBN 0-942074-00-9). Ctr Study Elephants.
Blunt, David. Elephant. (Illus.). 260p. 1972. Repr. of 1933 ed. 17.50x (ISBN 0-87556-535-2). Saifer.
Cuvier, Georges. Memoirs on Fossil Elephants & on Reconstruction of the Genera Palaeotherium & Anoplotherium. Gould, Stephen J., ed. LC 79-8327. (Fr., Illus.). 1980. Repr. of 1812 ed. lib. bdg. 80.00x (ISBN 0-405-12709-X). Ayer Co Pubs.
Elephants & Rhinos in Africa: A Time for Decision. (Illus.). 36p. 1982. pap. 10.00 (ISBN 2-88032-208-1, IUCN113, IUCN). Unipub.
Eltringham, S. K. Elephants. (Blandford Mammal Ser.). (Illus.). 264p. 1982. 19.95 (ISBN 0-7137-1041-1, Pub. by Blandford Pr England). Sterling.
Hanks, John. Struggle for Survival: The Elephant Problem. (Illus.). 1979. 14.95 (ISBN 0-8317-2756-X, Mayflower Bks). Smith Pubs.
Holder, Charles. The Ivory King: A Popular History of the Elephant & Its Allies. LC 72-5495. (Black Heritage Library Collection Ser). 1972. Repr. of 1886 ed. 30.50 (ISBN 0-8369-9141-9). Ayer Co Pubs.
Seidensticker, John. Managing Elephant Depredation in Agricultural & Forestry Projects. 50p. 3.00 (ISBN 0-318-02824-7, BK0297). World Bank.
ELEUTHERODACTYLUS
Lynch, John D. & Duellman, William E. The Eleutherodactylus of the Amazonian Slopes of the Ecuadorian Andes: (Anura: Lepodactylidae) (Miscellaneous Papers: No. 69). 86p. 1980. 4.75 (ISBN 0-317-04879-1). U of KS Mus Nat Hist.
ELEVATED TEMPERATURES
see High Temperatures
ELEVATORS
Adler, Rodney R. Vertical Transportation for Buildings. LC 73-104976. (Elsevier Architectural Science Ser.). pap. 59.50 (ISBN 0-317-11060-8, 2007760). Bks Demand UMI.
Chiles, L. B., et al, eds. Lift (Elevator) Erection. (Engineering Craftsmen: No. J26). (Illus.). 1978. spiral bdg. 39.95x (ISBN 0-85083-414-7). Intl Ideas.
--Lift (Elevator) Practice. (Engineering Craftsmen Ser.: No. J5). (Illus.). 203p. 1979. spiral bdg. 49.95x (ISBN 0-85083-458-9). Intl Ideas.
--Lift (Elevator) Servicing & Maintenance. (Engineering Craftsmen: No. J25). (Illus.). 1974. spiral bdg. 39.95x (ISBN 0-85083-236-5). Intl Ideas.
Donoghue, E. A., ed. Safety Code for Elevators & Escalators: Handbook on A17.1. 372p. 1981. 50.00 (A00112). ASME.
Lear, John. The Powerlifters Manual. (Illus.). 64p. (Orig.). 1982. pap. 4.95 (ISBN 0-7158-0796-X, Pub. by EP Publishing England). Sterling.
Lift Erection. 1982. 52.00x (ISBN 0-85083-414-7, Pub. by Engineering Ind). State Mutual Bk.
Lift Practice. 1982. 52.00x (ISBN 0-85083-154-7, Pub. by Engineering Ind). State Mutual Bk.
Lift Servicing & Maintenance. 1982. 52.00x (ISBN 0-85083-236-5, Pub. by Engineering Ind). State Mutual Bk.
Rudman, Jack. Chief Elevator Starter. (Career Examination Ser.: C-1175). (Cloth bdg. avail. on request). pap. 12.00 (ISBN 0-8373-1175-6). Natl Learning.
--Elevator Inspector. (Career Examination Ser.: C-244). (Cloth bdg. avail. on request). pap. 12.00 (ISBN 0-8373-0244-7). Natl Learning.
--Elevator Mechanic. (Career Examination Ser.: C-1056). (Cloth bdg. avail. on request). pap. 12.00 (ISBN 0-8373-1056-3). Natl Learning.
--Elevator Mechanics Helper. (Career Examination Ser.: C-237). (Cloth bdg. avail. on request). pap. 12.00 (ISBN 0-8373-0237-4). Natl Learning.
--Foreman Elevator Mechanic. (Career Examination Ser.: C-2165). (Cloth bdg. avail. on request). 1976. pap. 10.00 (ISBN 0-8373-2165-4). Natl Learning.
--Foreman (Elevators & Escalators) (Career Examination Ser.: C-1413). (Cloth bdg. avail. on request). pap. 10.00 (ISBN 0-8373-1413-5). Natl Learning.
Safety Code for Elevators & Escalators: ANS u c17.1-1981. (Bk. No. A9681B). 1981. 40.00 (ISBN 0-685-37579-X). ASME.
Strakosch, George R. Vertical Transportation: Elevators & Escalators. 2nd ed. 495p. 1983. 57.50 (ISBN 0-471-86733-0). Wiley.
ELEVATORS, GRAIN
see Grain Elevators
ELIMINATION REACTIONS
Crynes, Billy L. Chemical Reactions As a Means of Separation. (Chemical Processing & Engineering Ser.: Vol. 11). 1977. 65.00 (ISBN 0-8247-6374-2). Dekker.
ELIOT, JARED
Thoms, Herbert. Jared Eliot: Minister, Doctor, Scientist & His Connecticut. xii, 156p. 1967. 16.00 (ISBN 0-208-00433-5). Shoe String.
ELK
Houston, Douglas. The Northern Yellowstone Elk: Ecology & Management. LC 82-70079. 1982. 52.00x (ISBN 0-02-949450-8). Macmillan.
Krakel, Dean, II. Season of the Elk. LC 75-42982. (Illus.). 128p. 1980. 22.95 (ISBN 0-913504-28-9). Lowell Pr.
McCullough, D. R. The Tule Elk: Its History, Behavior & Ecology. (California Library Reprint Series: No. 16). 1971. 34.00x (ISBN 0-520-01921-0). U of Cal Pr.
Murie, Olaus J. Elk of North America. LC 79-83649. (Illus.). 376p. 1979. 15.98 (ISBN 0-933160-02-X); pap. 9.95 (ISBN 0-933160-03-8). Teton Bkshop.
Wildlife Management Institute & US Department of Agriculture, Forest Service. Elk of North America: Ecology & Management. Thomas, Jack W. & Toweill, Dale E., eds. LC 81-13572. (Illus.). 720p. 1982. 39.95 (ISBN 0-8117-0571-4). Stackpole.
ELLET, CHARLES, JR., 1810-1862
Sayenga, Donald. Ellet & Roebling: Their Friendship & Rivalry. 1983. 4.00 (ISBN 0-933788-42-8). Am Canal & Transport.
ELLIPSE
see also Conic Sections
Birkhoff, Garrett & Lynch, Robert E. Numerical Solution of Elliptic Problems. LC 84-51823. (SIAM Studies in Applied Mathematics: No. 6). (Illus.). xi, 319p. 1984. text ed. 31.50 (ISBN 0-89871-197-5). Soc Indus Appl Math.
Cordes, H. O. Elliptic Pseudo-Differential Operators: An Abstract Theory. (Lecture Notes in Mathematics: Vol. 756). 1979. pap. 23.00 (ISBN 0-387-09704-X). Springer-Verlag.
Sinisgalli, L. The Ellipse. 1982. 26.00 (ISBN 0-691-06529-2); pap. 8.95 (ISBN 0-691-01397-7). Princeton U Pr.
Stiller, P. F. Automorphic Forms & the Picard Number of an Elliptic Surface, Vol. 5. (Aspects of Mathematics Ser.). Date not set. pap. 15.00 (ISBN 0-9904001-1-5, Pub. by Vieweg & Sohn Germany). Heyden.
ELLIPSOIDAL HARMONICS
see Lame's Functions
ELLIPTIC DIFFERENTIAL EQUATIONS
see Differential Equations, Elliptic
ELLIPTIC FUNCTIONS
see Functions, Elliptic; Functions, Modular
EMBANKMENTS
see also Earthwork; Sea-Walls; Shore Protection
Soil-Cement Slope Protection for Embankments: Field Inspection & Control. 1976. pap. 2.10 (ISBN 0-89312-155-X, IS168W). Portland Cement.
EMBEDDINGS, TOPOLOGICAL
see Topological Imbeddings
EMBRYOLOGY
see also Cells; Chemical Embryology; Developmental Biology; Developmental Genetics; Developmental Neurology; Embryology, Experimental; Epigenesis; Fertilization (Biology); Fetus; Genetics; Morphogenesis; Neural Tube; Ovum; Placenta; Protoplasm; Reproduction
Adelmann, Howard B. Marcello Malpighi & the Evolution of Embryology, 5 Vols. (History of Science Ser.). 2548p. 1966. Set. boxed 200.00x (ISBN 0-8014-0004-X). Cornell U Pr.
Adelmann, Howard B., ed. & tr. from Lat. The Embryological Treatises of Hieronymus Fabricius of Aquapendente, 2 vols. Incl. Vol. 1. The Formation of the Egg & of the Chick. Tr. of De Formatione Ovi et Pulli; Vol. 2. The Formed Fetus. Tr. of De Formato Foetu. (History of Science Ser.). (Illus.). xxiv, 907p. (A facsimile reprint of the latin text). 1967. 69.50x (ISBN 0-8014-0122-4). Cornell U Pr.
Austin, C. R. & Short, R. V., eds. Embryonic & Fetal Development. 2nd ed. LC 81-18060. (Reproduction in Mammals Ser.: Bk. 2). (Illus.). 200p. 1983. 32.50 (ISBN 0-521-24786-1); pap. 12.95 (ISBN 0-521-28962-9). Cambridge U Pr.
Balinsky, B. I. An Introduction to Embryology. 5th ed. 1981. text ed. 36.95 (ISBN 0-03-057712-8, CBS C). SCP.
Bhaskar, S. N. Orban's Oral Histology & Embryology. 9th ed. LC 80-11972. (Illus.). 486p. 1980. pap. text ed. 39.95 (ISBN 0-8016-4609-X). Mosby.
Billett, F. S. EGG Structure & Animal Development. (Contemporary Biology Ser.). 180p. 1984. pap. text ed. write for info. (ISBN 0-7131-2809-7). E Arnold.
Budai, Joan. What's in an Egg? LC 80-80559. 1980. pap. 4.95 (ISBN 0-89051-061-X). Master Bks.
Carlson, Bruce M. Patten's Foundations of Embryology. 4th, rev. ed. (Organismal Biology Ser.). (Illus.). 608p. 1981. text ed. 38.95 (ISBN 0-07-009875-1). McGraw.
Cohen, J. Living Embryos. 3rd ed. 1967. 21.00 (ISBN 0-08-025926-X); pap. 7.95 (ISBN 0-08-025925-1). Pergamon.
Congress of International Society of Development Biologists, Basel, Switzerland, Aug. 28-Sept. 1, 1981 & Burger, Max M. Embryonic Development. LC 82-15351. (Progress in Clinical & Biological Research Ser.: Vols. 85 A & B). 1982. Pt. A: Genetic Aspects 520 pgs. 50.00 (ISBN 0-8451-0163-3); Pt. B: Cellular Aspects, 698 pgs. 68.00 (ISBN 0-8451-0164-1). Set (ISBN 0-8451-0085-8). A R Liss.
Craigmyle, M. B. & Presley, R. Embryology: (Concise Medical Textbook) 2nd ed. (Illus.). 1975. pap. text ed. 13.50 (ISBN 0-7216-0716-0, Pub. by Bailliere-Tindall). Saunders.
Crump, Martha L. Reproductive Strategies in a Tropical Anuran Community. (Miscellaneous Publications Ser.: No. 61). 68p. 1974. pap. 3.75 (ISBN 0-686-79838-4). U of KS Mus Nat Hist.
Disease Control in Semen & Embryos: Report of the Expert Consultation on Animal Disease Control in International Movement of Semen & Embryos, Held at FAO Headquarters, Rome, 23-27 February 1981. (Animal Production & Health Papers: No. 23). (Eng., Fr. & Span.). 103p. 1981. pap. 7.50 (ISBN 92-5-101123-0, F2255, FAO). Unipub.
Dnyansagar, V. R., et al, eds. Recent Trends & Contacts Between Cytogenetics Embryology & Morphology, 1976. (Current Trends in Life Sciences Ser.: Vol. 5). xiv, 592p. 1977. 50.00 (ISBN 0-88065-081-8, Pub. by Messers Today & Tomorrows Printers & Publishers India). Scholarly Pubns.
Dryden, Richard. Before Birth. 1978. text ed. 19.00x (ISBN 0-435-60225-X). Heinemann Ed.
Duckett, J. G. & Racey, P. A., eds. The Biology of the Male Gamete: Linnean Society Supplement No. 1 to the Biological Journal, Vol. 7. 1975. 73.00 (ISBN 0-12-223050-7). Acad Pr.
DuShane, Graham P. Supplement Drawings for Embryology. LC 55-5121. pap. 20.00 (ISBN 0-317-28105-4, 2024091). Bks Demand UMI.
Ebert, James D. & Sussex, Ian M. Interacting Systems in Development. 2nd ed. LC 78-100552. (Modern Biology Ser.). 338p. 1970. pap. text ed. 18.95x (ISBN 0-03-081306-9, HoltC). HR&W.
Embo Workshop on Patelets: Cellular Response Mechanisms & Their Biological Significance. Platelets, Cellular Response Mechanisms & Their Biological Significance: Proceedings. Rotman, A. & Meyer, F. A., eds. LC 80-41257. (A Wiley-Interscience Publication). pap. 87.30 (ISBN 0-317-27728-6, 2052095). Bks Demand UMI.
Fitzgerald, Maurice. Embriologia. (Span.). 1981. pap. text ed. 14.20 (ISBN 0-06-313120-X, Pub. by HarLA Mexico). Har-Row.
Fonts, Alfredo R. Histology & Embryology Notes for Dental Assistants & Dental Hygienists. 1980. pap. text ed. 8.50 (ISBN 0-89669-029-6). Collegium Bk Pubs.
Gaze, R. M., et al, eds. Growth & the Development of Pattern: Special Issue of Journal of Embryology & Experimental Morphology, Supplement to Vol. 65. LC 81-15452. (Illus.). 324p. 1982. Cambridge U Pr.
Gilchrist, Francis G. Survey of Embryology. 1968. text ed. 51.95 (ISBN 0-07-023208-3). McGraw.
Grey, R., et al. Readings in Embryology. 1969. pap. text ed. 4.95x (ISBN 0-8290-1182-X). Irvington.
Gropp, A., ed. Developmental Biology & Pathology. LC 56-49162. (Current Topics in Pathology: Vol. 62). (Illus.). 1976. 59.00 (ISBN 0-387-07881-9). Springer-Verlag.
Hajos, F. & Basco, E. Surface-Contact Glia. (Advances in Anatomy, Embryology & Cell Biology: Vol. 84). (Illus.). 100p. 1984. pap. 22.00 (ISBN 0-387-13243-0). Springer-Verlag.
Hall, B. K. Chondrogenesis of the Somitic Mesoderm. LC 77-21183. (Advances in Anatomy, Embryology & Cell Biology: Vol. 53, Pt. 4). (Illus.). 1977. pap. 19.00 (ISBN 0-387-08464-9). Springer-Verlag.
Hamburgh, Max. Theories of Differentiation. LC 72-181848. (Contemporary Biology Ser). 181p. 1972. pap. text ed. 16.50 (ISBN 0-7131-2321-4). Univ Park.
Hughes, Arthur F. Aspects of Neural Ontogeny. 1968. 52.50 (ISBN 0-12-360550-4). Acad Pr.
Jeffery, William R. & Raff, Rudolf A. Time, Space & Pattern in Embryonic Development. LC 83-5393. (MBL Lectures in Biology: Vol. 2). 408p. 1983. 58.00 (ISBN 0-8451-2201-0). A R Liss.
Jirasek, Jan E. Atlas of Human Prenatal Morphogenesis. 1983. lib. bdg. 65.00 (ISBN 0-89838-558-X, Pub. by Martinus Nijhoff Netherlands). Kluwer Academic.
Laane, Henk-Maarten. The Arterial Pole of the Embryonic Heart. 160p. 1978. pap. text ed. 26.50 (ISBN 90-265-0297-4, Pub. by Swets Pub Serv Holland). Swets North Am.

Blackley, D. C. Emulsion Polymerisation: Theory & Practice. (Illus.). 566p. 1975. 48.00 (ISBN 0-85334-627-5, Pub. by Elsevier Applied Sci England). Elsevier.
Colbert, J. C., ed. Foam & Emulsion Control Agents & Processes: Recent Developments. LC 81-2364. (Chemical Technology Review: No. 188). (Illus.). 419p. 1981. 48.00 (ISBN 0-8155-0846-8). Noyes.
Eliseeva, V. I., et al. Emulsion Polymerization & Its Applications in Industry. Teague, Sylvia J., tr. from Rus. LC 81-17477. Orig. Title: Emul'Sionnaya Polimerizatsiya I EE Primenenie V Promyshlenosti. 300p. 1981. 59.50 (ISBN 0-306-10961-1, Consultants). Plenum Pub.
Influence of Fat Crystals in the Oil Phase of Stability of Oil-in-Water Emulsions. (Agricultural Research Reports: No. 901). 1981. pap. 18.75 (ISBN 9-0220-0739-1, PDC216, PUDOC). Unipub.
Lissant. Emulsions & Emulsion Technology, Pt. III. (Surfactant Science Ser.). 272p. 1984. 49.75 (ISBN 0-8247-7083-8). Dekker.
Lissant, Kenneth J., ed. Emulsions & Emulsion Technology, Pt. I. (Surfactant Science Ser.: Vol. 6). 456p. 1974. soft cover 99.75 (ISBN 0-8247-1891-7). Dekker.
--Emulsions & Emulsion Technology, Pt. II. (Surfactant Science Ser.: Vol. 6). 544p. 1974. soft cover 99.75 (ISBN 0-8247-1892-5). Dekker.
Martens, Charles R. Emulsion & Water-Soluble Paints & Coatings. LC 64-22873. 168p. 1964. 13.95 (ISBN 0-442-15558-1). Krieger.
Prince, L., ed. Microemulsions: Theory & Practice. 1977. 37.00 (ISBN 0-12-565750-1). Acad Pr.
Robb, I. D., ed. Microemulsions. LC 81-17766. 275p. 1982. 42.50x (ISBN 0-306-40834-1, Plenum Pr). Plenum Pub.
Torrey, S., ed. Emulsions & Emulsifier Applications: Recent Developments. LC 84-6003. (Chemical Technology Review Ser.: No. 229). (Illus.). 319p. 1984. 48.00 (ISBN 0-8155-0985-5). Noyes.

ENAMEL AND ENAMELING

see also Metals–Finishing

American Craft Council. Enamel: A Bibliography. rev. ed. 1978. 2.70 (ISBN 0-88321-029-0). Am Craft.
Bates, Kenneth F. Enameling: Principles & Practices. (Funk & W Bk.). (Illus.). 272p. 1974. pap. 3.95i (ISBN 0-308-10137-5, F103). T Y Crowell.
--The Enamelist. LC 75-7618. (Funk & W Bk.). (Illus.). 256p. 1975. pap. 3.50i (ISBN 0-308-10196-0, F-127). T Y Crowell.
Kuehnemann, Ursula. Cold Enamelling. LC 72-2181. (Illus.). 65p. 1973. 4.95 (ISBN 0-8008-1684-6). Taplinger.
Liban, Felicia & Mitchell, Louise K. Cloisonne Enameling & Jewelry. 256p. 1980. 25.00 (ISBN 0-8019-6900-X). Chilton.
Maryon, Herbert. Metalwork & Enamelling. 4th ed. (Illus.). 1971. pap. 5.95 (ISBN 0-486-22702-2). Dover.
Matthews, Glenice L. Enamels, Enameling, Enamelists. LC 83-70776. (Illus.). 224p. 1984. 24.00 (ISBN 0-8019-7285-X). Chilton.
Robert, Jo & O'Hara, Jean. Copper Enameling. 2.95 (ISBN 0-934706-00-X). Prof Pubns Ohio.
Rothenberg, Polly. Metal Enameling. (Illus.). 1969. 8.95 (ISBN 0-517-02560-4). Crown.
Strolsahl, J. Patrick, et al. A Manual of Cloisonne & Champleve Enameling. (Illus.). 264p. 1981. 35.00 (ISBN 0-684-16822-7, ScribT). Scribner.
Taubes. Basic Enameling. (The Grosset Art Instruction Ser.: No. 68). (Illus.). 48p. 1970. pap. 2.95 (ISBN 0-448-00577-8, G&D). Putnam Pub Group.
Taylor, Louis S. Innovative Enameling. 1985. 20.00 (ISBN 0-533-06591-7). Vantage.

ENAMEL PAINTS

see Paint; Painting, Industrial; Varnish and Varnishing

ENCAPSULATION (ELECTRONICS)

see Electronic Apparatus and Appliances–Plastic Embedment

ENDANGERED SPECIES

see Rare Animals

ENDOCRINE GLANDS

see also Hormones; Hypothalamus; Parathyroid Glands; Pineal Body

Benagiano, Giuseppe & Diczfalusy, Egon, eds. Endocrine Mechanisms in Fertility Regulation. (Comprehensive Endocrinology Ser.). 368p. 1983. text ed. 65.50 (ISBN 0-89004-464-3). Raven.
Bhatnagar, Ajay S., ed. The Anterior Pituitary Gland. 472p. 1983. text ed. 59.50 (ISBN 0-89004-759-6). Raven.
Bloodworth, J. M., Jr. Endocrine Pathology: General & Surgical. 2nd ed. (Illus.). 894p. 1982. 99.00 (ISBN 0-683-00854-4). Williams & Wilkins.
Carson, E. R., et al. The Mathematical Modeling of Metabolic & Endocrine Systems: Model Formulation, Identification & Validation. (Biomedical Engineering & Health Systems Ser.). 394p. 1983. 57.50 (ISBN 0-471-08660-6). Wiley.
Cohen, Sidney. Clinical Gastroenterology: A Problem Oriented Approach. LC 82-10926. 464p. 1983. 35.00 (ISBN 0-471-08071-3, Pub. by Wiley Med). Wiley.
Cohn, D. V., et al. Endocrine Control of Bone & Calcium Metabolism, Vol. 8A. (International Congress Ser.: Vol. 619). 1984. 107.50 (ISBN 0-444-80589-3). Elsevier.
--Endocrine Control of Bone & Calcium Metabolism, Vol. 8B. (International Congress Ser.: Vol. 635). 1984. 102.00 (ISBN 0-444-80590-7). Elsevier.
Davies, Terry F. Autoimmune Endocrine Disease. LC 82-17318. 279p. 1983. 64.50 (ISBN 0-471-09778-0, Pub. by Wiley-Interscience). Wiley.
Endocrine System. Jones, T. C., et al, eds. (Monographs on Pathology of Laboratory Animals). (Illus.). 320p. 1983. 85.00 (ISBN 0-387-11677-X). Springer-Verlag.
Farid, Nadir R., ed. HLA in Endocrine & Metabolic Disorders. LC 80-70600. 1981. 55.00 (ISBN 0-12-247780-4). Acad Pr.
Geelhoed. Problem Management in Endocrine Surgery: Problem Oriented Approach. 1982. 30.95 (ISBN 0-8151-3412-6). Year Bk Med.
Gitman, Leo. Endocrines & Aging. (Illus.). 320p. 1967. photocopy ed. 27.50x (ISBN 0-398-00685-7). C C Thomas.
Gupta, Derek & Voelter, Wolfgang. Hypothalamic Hormones: Chemistry, Physiology & Clinical Applications. (Illus.). 766p. 1978. 75.30x (ISBN 3-527-25712-8). VCH Pubs.
--Hypothalamic Hormones: Structure, Synthesis, & Biological Activity. (Illus.). 328p. 1975. 34.20x (ISBN 3-527-25589-3). VCH Pubs.
Hardy. Endocrine Physiology. (Physical Principles in Medicine Ser.). (Illus.). 192p. 1982. pap. text ed. 16.50 (ISBN 0-8391-1753-1). Univ Park.
Hedlund, Laurence W., et al. Biological Rhythms & Endocrine Function. LC 74-23448. (Advances in Experimental Medicine & Biology Ser.: Vol. 54). 204p. 1975. 35.00x (ISBN 0-306-39054-X, Plenum Pr). Plenum Pub.
International Symposium on Brain-Endocrine Interaction, Munich, 1971. Brain-Endocrine Interaction I: Median Eminence-Structure & Function: Proceedings. Knigge, K. M., et al, eds. (Illus.). xii, 368p. 1972. 51.25 (ISBN 3-8055-1257-0). S Karger.
Jung, T. & Sikora, K. Endocrine Problems in Cancer. 300p. 1984. 32.00 (ISBN 0-433-30277-1, Pub. by W Heinemann Med Bks). Sheridan Med Bks.
Korenman, S. G., ed. Endocrine Aspects of Aging. (Current Endocrinology Ser.: Vol. 6). 276p. 1982. 47.25 (ISBN 0-444-00681-8, Biomedical Pr). Elsevier.
Kramer, Marc B., ed. Forensic Audiology. (Perspectives in Audiology Ser.). (Illus.). 376p. 1982. text ed. 46.50 (ISBN 0-8391-1613-6). Univ Park.
Labrie, Fernand, et al, eds. Hypothalamus & Endocrine Functions. LC 76-13912. (Current Topics in Molecular Endocrinology Ser.: Vol. 3). 519p. 1976. 59.50x (ISBN 0-306-34003-8, Plenum Pr). Plenum Pub.
Langer, Maria. The Endocrine & the Liver: Proceedings of the Serono Symposia, No. 51. 1983. 70.00 (ISBN 0-12-436580-9). Acad Pr.
Martin, Constance R. Endocrine Physiology. (Illus.). 1984. 47.50x (ISBN 0-19-503359-0). Oxford U Pr.
Morgan, Howard E. Endrocrine Control Systems. LC 72-85159. 193p. (Orig.). 1973. pap. 11.00. Krieger.
Ochiai, K., et al, eds. Endocrine Correlates of Reproduction. (Illus.). xii, 320p. 1984. 37.50 (ISBN 0-387-13514-6). Springer-Verlag.
Soto, Robert J., et al. Physiopathology of Endocrine Diseases & Mechanisms of Hormone Action. LC 81-17158. (Progress in Clinical & Biological Research Ser.: Vol. 74). 526p. 1981. 78.00 (ISBN 0-8451-0074-2). A R Liss.
Toft, A. D., et al. The Diagnosis & Management of Endocrine Disorders. (Illus.). 404p. 1982. pap. text ed. 24.95 (ISBN 0-632-00553-X, B 4998-6). Mosby.
Valenta, Lubomir & Afrasiabe, A. Ali. Handbook of Endocrine & Metabolic Emergencies. 1981. pap. text ed. 21.95 (ISBN 0-87488-597-3). Med Exam.
Volpe, R. Auto-Immunity in the Endocrine System. (Endocrinology Monographs: Vol. 20). (Illus.). 210p. 1981. 52.00 (ISBN 0-387-10677-4). Springer-Verlag.
Williams, E. D. & Siebenmann, R. E. Histological Typing of Endocrine Tumours. (World Health Organization: No. 23). 33.50 (ISBN 0-686-95504-8, 70-1-023-20); 118.00 (ISBN 0-686-99516-3). Am Soc Clinical.
Williams, E. D., ed. Current Endocrine Concepts. 252p. 1982. 49.95x (ISBN 0-03-062119-4). Praeger.
Zoppi, G., ed. Metabolic-Endocrine Responses to Food Intake in Infancy. (Monographs in Paediatrics: Vol. 16). (Illus.). viii, 116p. 1982. pap. 27.75 (ISBN 3-8055-3477-9). S Karger.

ENDOCRINOLOGY

see also Endocrine Glands; Gonadotropin; Hormones; Hormones, Sex; Ovaries; Parathyroid Glands; Pineal Body; Testicle

Albrecht, E. & Pepe, G., eds. Perinatal Endocrinology. (Research in Perinatal Medicine Ser.). 1985. 40.00 (ISBN 0-916859-11-8). Perinatology.
Angelini, Licino & Usadel, Klaus-Henning, eds. Therapeutic Effects of Somatostatin. (Serono Symposia Publications Ser.: Vol. 15). 325p. text ed. cancelled (ISBN 0-88167-003-0). Raven.
Asimov, Isaac. Human Brain: Its Capacities & Functions. pap. 4.95 (ISBN 0-451-62363-0, Ment). NAL.
Assenmacherm, I. & Farner, D. S., eds. Environmental Endocrinology: Proceedings of an International Symposium Held in Montpellier (France), July 11-15, 1977. (Proceedings in Life Sciences). (Illus.). 1978. 45.00 (ISBN 0-387-08809-1). Springer-Verlag.
Auer, L. M., et al, eds. Prolactinomas: An Interdisiplinary Approach. (Illus.). x, 439p. 1985. 59.20x (ISBN 3-11-010153-X). De Gruyter.
Baxter, J. D. & Rousseau, G. G., eds. Glucocorticoid Hormone Action. (Monographs on Endocrinology: Vol. 12). (Illus.). 1979. 75.00 (ISBN 0-387-08973-X). Springer-Verlag.
Bentley, P. J. Comparative Vertebrate Endocrinology. 2nd ed. LC 82-1205. (Illus.). 500p. 1982. 57.50 (ISBN 0-521-24653-9); pap. 22.95 (ISBN 0-521-28878-9). Cambridge U Pr.
--Endocrine Pharmacology: Physiological Basis & Therapeutic Applications. LC 79-19487. (Illus.). 700p. 1981. 32.50 (ISBN 0-521-22673-2). Cambridge U Pr.
Bentley, Peter J. Endocrines & Osmoregulation: A Comparative Account of the Regulation of Water & Salt in Vertebrates. LC 72-131549. (Zoophysiology & Ecology Ser.: Vol. 1). (Illus.). 1971. 36.00 (ISBN 0-387-05273-9). Springer-Verlag.
Beumont, P. J. & Burrows, G. D., eds. Handbook of Psychiatry & Endocrinology. 448p. 1982. 109.00 (ISBN 0-444-80355-6, Biomedical Pr). Elsevier.
Botella-Llusia, Jose. Obstetrical Endocrinology. (Illus.). 140p. 1961. 14.50x (ISBN 0-398-00199-5). C C Thomas.
Breipohl, W., ed. Olfaction & Endocrine Regulation: Proceedings of the Fourth European Chemoreception Research Organization Mini-Symposium & the Second International Laboratory Workshop on Olfaction, Essen FRG, 1981. 426p. 1982. pap. 35.00 (ISBN 0-904147-35-5). IRL Pr.
Briggs, Michael & Corbin, Alan, eds. Progress in Hormone Biochemistry & Pharmachology, Vol. 1. (Endocrinology Ser.). (Illus.). 300p. 1980. 34.95 (ISBN 0-88831-076-5). Eden Pr.
Burdette, W. J., ed. Invertebrate Endocrinology & Hormonal Heterophylly. (Illus.). 438p. 1974. 39.00 (ISBN 0-387-06594-6). Springer-Verlag.
Catt, K. J. An ABC of Endocrinology. 154p. 1972. 12.95 (ISBN 0-316-13190-3). Little.
Cohen, Margo P. & Foa, Piero P. Special Topics in Endocrinology & Metabolism, Vol. 6. 274p. 1984. 58.00 (ISBN 0-8451-0705-4). A R Liss.
Cohen, Margo P. & Foa, Piero P., eds. Special Topics in Endocrinology & Metabolism, Vol. 1. 154p. 1979. 22.00x (ISBN 0-8451-0700-3). A R Liss.
Cohen, Margo P & Foa, Piero P., eds. Special Topics in Endocrinology & Metabolism, Vol. 3. (Special Topics in Endocrinology & Metabolism Ser.). 142p. 1982. 28.00 (ISBN 0-8451-0702-X). A R Liss.
Cohen, Margo P. & Foa, Piero P., eds. Special Topics in Endocrinology & Metabolism, Vol. 4. (Special Topics in Endocrinology & Metabolism). 270p. 1982. 38.00 (ISBN 0-8451-0703-8). A R Liss.
Coupland, R. E. & Forssmann, W. G., eds. Peripheral Neuroendocrine Interaction. (Illus.). 1978. pap. 51.00 (ISBN 0-387-08779-6). Springer-Verlag.
Crosignani, P. G. & Rubin, Betty, eds. Endocrinology of Human Infertility: New Aspects. (Serono Clinical Colloquia on Reproduction Ser.: No. 2). 456p. 1981. 73.00 (ISBN 0-8089-1393-X, 790949). Grune.
Daughaday, W. H., ed. Endocrine Control of Growth. (Current Endocrinology Ser.: Vol. 1). 276p. 1981. 45.50 (ISBN 0-444-00434-3, Biomedical Pr). Elsevier.
Downer, Roger G. & Laufer, Hans. Endocrinology of Insects. LC 82-24987. (Invertebrate Endocrinology Ser.: Vol. 1). 724p. 1983. 146.00 (ISBN 0-8451-2900-7). A R Liss.
Endocytobiology II: Intracelluar Space Oligogenetic Ecosystem. LC 83-20973. (Illus.). xxv, 1071p. 1983. 118.00x (ISBN 3-11-008660-3). De Gruyter.
Endroczi, E., et al, eds. Neuropeptides, Neurotransmitters & Regulation of Endocrine Processes: Proceedings of the International Conference on Intergrative Neurohumoral Mechanisms. 1984. 56.00 (ISBN 0-9910000-5-6, Pub. by Akademiai Kaido Hungary). Heyden.
--Neuropeptides, Neurotransmitters, & Regulation of Endocrine: Processes-Neuropeptides & Psychosomatic, 2 Vols. 1984. 113.00 (ISBN 0-9910000-7-2, Pub. by Akademiai Kaido Hungary). Heyden.
Ensor, D. M. The Comparative Endocrinology of Prolactin. 1978. 53.00 (ISBN 0-412-12720-2, NO.6103, Pub. by Chapman & Hall). Methuen Inc.
Epple, August & Stetson, Milton. Avian Endocrinology. 1980. 55.00 (ISBN 0-12-240250-2). Acad Pr.
Essman, Walter B., ed. Hormonal Actions in Non-Endocrine Systems. 213p. 1983. text ed. 38.50 (ISBN 0-89335-170-9). SP Med & Sci Bks.
--Perspectives in Clinical Endocrinology. (Illus.). 390p. 1980. text ed. 45.00 (ISBN 0-89335-077-X). SP Med & Sci Bks.
Fellows, Robert & Eisenbarth, George, eds. Monoclonal Antibodies in Endocrine Research. 212p. 1981. text ed. 34.00 (ISBN 0-89004-687-5). Raven.
Fotherby, K. & Pal, S. B., eds. The Role of Drugs & Electrolytes in Hormonogenesis. LC 84-7611. (Illus.). xii, 360p. 1984. 72.00x (ISBN 3-11-008463-5). De Gruyter.
Frajese, G., et al, eds. Oligozoospermia: Recent Progress in Andrology. 496p. 1981. text ed. 70.50 (ISBN 0-89004-589-5). Raven.
Fregly, M. J. & Luttge, W. G. Human Endocrinology: An Interactive Text. 366p. 1982. 27.50 (ISBN 0-444-00662-1, Biomedical Pr). Elsevier.
Freinkel, Norbert, ed. Contemporary Metabolism, Vol. 1. LC 79-643531. (Illus.). 523p. 1979. 45.00x (ISBN 0-306-40127-4, Plenum Pr). Plenum Pub.
Fuchs, Fritz & Klopper, Arnold, eds. Endocrinology of Pregnancy. 3rd ed. (Illus.). 306p. 1983. text ed. 44.75 (ISBN 0-06-140845-X, 14-08459, Harper Medical). Lippincott.
Fuxe, K., et al, eds. Central Regulation of the Endocrine System. LC 78-27000. (Nobel Foundation Symposia Ser.). 569p. 1979. 69.50x (ISBN 0-306-40078-2, Plenum Pr). Plenum Pub.
Goldsworthy, Graham J. Endocrinology. LC 80-18704. (Tertiarty Level Biology Ser.). 184p. 1980. 42.95x (ISBN 0-470-27034-9). Halsted Pr.
Gorbman, Aubrey, et al. Comparative Endocrinology. LC 82-13455. 572p. 1983. 34.95 (ISBN 0-471-06266-9, Pub. by Wiley-Interscience). Wiley.
Hadley, Mac E. Endocrinology. (Illus.). 592p. 1984. 36.95 (ISBN 0-13-277137-3). P-H.
Hall, R., et al. Fundamentals of Clinical Endocrinology. 500p. 1980. pap. text ed. 59.95x (ISBN 0-8464-1246-2). Beekman Pubs.
Hall, Reginald. Fundamentals of Clinical Endocrinology. 550p. 1981. 125.00x (ISBN 0-272-79559-3, Pub. by Pitman Bks England). State Mutual Bk.
Hershman, J. M. Practical Endocrinology: Family Practice Today: A Comprehensive Post Graduate Library. 284p. 1981. pap. 36.00 (ISBN 0-471-09502-8, Pub. by Wiley Med). Wiley.
Hershman, Jerome M., ed. Endrocrine Pathophysiology: A Patient-Oriented Approach. 2nd ed. LC 82-7183. (Illus.). 316p. 1982. text ed. 15.75 (ISBN 0-8121-0840-X). Lea & Febiger.
Hutzinger, O., et al. Prolactin: Physiology, Pharmacology & Clinical Findings. (Monographs on Endocrinology: Vol. 23). (Illus.). 224p. 1982. 47.00 (ISBN 0-387-11071-2). Springer-Verlag.
Ingbar, S. H., ed. Contemporary Endocrinology, Vol. 1. (Illus.). 415p. 1979. 45.00x (ISBN 0-306-40133-9, Plenum Pr). Plenum Pub.
--The Year in Endocrinology, 1975 to 1976. 345p. 1977. 42.50x (ISBN 0-306-32101-7, Plenum Med Bk). Plenum Pub.
--The Year in Endocrinology, 1977. (Illus.). 417p. (Annual). 1978. 42.50x (ISBN 0-306-32102-5, Plenum Med Bk). Plenum Pub.
Institute of Endocrinology, Gunma Univ., ed. Progress & Prospects in Endocrinology. (Gunma Symposia on Endocrinology Ser.: Vol. 20). (Illus.). 152p. 1983. 28.00x (ISBN 4-905648-03-3, Pub by Sci Soc Japan). Intl Spec Bk.

International Foundation for Biochemical Endocrinology. Regulation of Target Cell Responsiveness, Vol. 1. McKerns, Kenneth W., et al, eds. (Biochemical Endocrinology Ser.). 520p. 1984. 75.00 (ISBN 0-306-41500-3, Plenum Pr). Plenum Pub.

Ismail, Adel A. Biochemical Investigations in Endocrinology. 258p. 1981. 37.00 (ISBN 0-12-374850-X). Acad Pr.

Jeffcoate, S. L. Efficiency & Effectiveness in the Endocrine Laboratory. LC 81-66369. 1981. 51.00 (ISBN 0-12-382160-6). Acad Pr.

Jubiz, W. Endocrinology. 2nd ed. 560p. 22.00 (ISBN 0-07-033069-7). McGraw.

Kleinsasser, O. Microlaryngoscopy & Endolaryngeal Microsurgery. 192p. 1979. text ed. 42.00 (ISBN 0-8391-1350-1). Univ Park.

Korenman, Stanley G., et al. Practical Diagnosis: Endocrine Diseases. (Illus.). 276p. 1978. pap. 30.00 (ISBN 0-471-09486-2, Pub. by Wiley Med). Wiley.

Krieger, D. T. Cushing's Syndrone. (Monographs on Endocinology: Vol. 22). (Illus.). 170p. 1982. 42.00 (ISBN 0-387-10811-4). Springer-Verlag.

Krieger, Dorothy T., ed. Endocrine Rhythms. LC 77-75655. (Comprehensive Endocrinology Ser.). 344p. 1979. 50.50 (ISBN 0-89004-234-9). Raven.

Kroger, William S. Psychosomatic Obstetrics, Gynecology & Endocrinology: Including Diseases of Metabolism. (Illus.). 848p. 1962. photocopy ed. 79.50x (ISBN 0-398-01052-8). C C Thomas.

Labhart, A. Clinical Endocrinology: Theory & Practice. LC 75-11535. 1976. 49.50 (ISBN 0-387-90175-2). Springer-Verlag.

Labrie, F., ed. Seventh International Congress of Endocrinology Abstracts: Proceedings of Congress Held 1-7 July, 1984, in Quebec City, Canada. (International Congress Ser.: No. 652). 1708p. 1984. 96.50 (ISBN 0-444-80587-7, Excerpta Medica). Elsevier.

Lee, J. B., ed. Prostaglandins: Basic & Clinical Aspects. (Current Endocrinology Ser.: Vol. 4). 378p. 1982. 59.95 (ISBN 0-444-00645-1, Biomedical Pr). Elsevier.

Lissak, K., ed. Hormones & Brain Function. LC 72-87943. 529p. 1974. 59.50x (ISBN 0-306-30712-X, Plenum Pr). Plenum Pub.

Lloyd, Charles W., ed. Recent Progress in the Endocrinology of Reproduction: Proceedings. 1959. 71.50 (ISBN 0-12-453450-3). Acad Pr.

McCann, S. M. Endocrine Physiology Three. (International Review of Physiology Ser.: Vol. 24). 296p. 1981. text ed. 48.00 (ISBN 0-8391-1071-5). Univ Park.

McIntosh, J. A. & McIntosh, R. P. Mathematical Modelling & Computers in Endocrinology. (Monographs on Endocrinology: Vol. 16). (Illus.). 370p. 1980. 54.00 (ISBN 0-387-09693-0). Springer-Verlag.

MacIntyre, I. & Szelke, M., eds. Molecular Endocrinology. 366p. (Proceedings). 1978. 80.00 (ISBN 0-444-80035-2, Biomedical Pr). Elsevier.

MacLeod, Robert & Scapagnini, Umberto, eds. Central & Peripheral Regulation of Prolactin Function. 418p. 1980. text ed. 57.00 (ISBN 0-89004-489-9). Raven.

Martin, Constance R. Textbook of Endocrine Physiology. (Illus.). 1976. 25.95x (ISBN 0-19-502295-5). Oxford U Pr.

Martini, L. & James, V. H., eds. Current Topics in Experimental Endocrinology, Vol. 4. (Serial Publication). 1983. 49.50 (ISBN 0-12-153204-6). Acad Pr.

Martini, Luciano & James, V. H., eds. Current Topics in Experimental Endocrinology. Vol. 1, 1972. 70.00 (ISBN 0-12-153201-1); Vol. 2, 1974. 70.00 (ISBN 0-12-153202-X); Vol. 3, 1978. 55.00 (ISBN 0-12-153203-8). Acad Pr.

--Current Topics in Experimental Endocrinology: Vol. 5: Fetal Endocrinology & Metabolism. (Serial Publication). 1983. 55.00 (ISBN 0-12-153205-4). Acad Pr.

Mazzaferri, Ernest L. Textbook of Endocrinology. 208p. 1984. pap. text ed. 24.95 (ISBN 0-87488-514-0). Med Exam.

Medvei, V. C. A History of Endocrinology. (Illus.). 900p. 1982. text ed. 95.00 (ISBN 0-85200-245-9, Pub. by MTP Pr England). Kluwer Academic.

Messiha, F. S. & Tyner, G. S., eds. Endocrinological Aspects of Alcoholism. (Progress in Biochemical Pharmacology: Vol. 18). (Illus.). xii, 232p. 1981. 66.00 (ISBN 3-8055-2689-X). S Karger.

Metz, Robert & Larson, Eric B. Blue Book of Endocrinology. (Saunders Blue Book Ser.). 250p. 1984. write for info. (ISBN 0-7216-5638-2). Saunders.

Mikami, S., et al, eds. Avian Endocrinology: Environmental & Ecological Perspectives. 380p. 1983. 55.00 (ISBN 0-387-11871-3). Springer-Verlag.

Montague, William. Diabetes & the Endocrine Pancreas: A Biochemical Approach. 1983. 28.95x (ISBN 0-19-520426-3); pap. 17.95x (ISBN 0-19-520427-1). Oxford U Pr.

Morgan, Howard E. Endrocrine Control Systems. LC 72-85159. 193p. (Orig.). 1973. pap. 11.00. Krieger.

Motta, Marcella, ed. Endocrine Functions of the Brain. (Comprehensive Endocrinology Ser.). 493p. 1980. text ed. 78.00 (ISBN 0-89004-343-4). Raven.

Motta, P. M., ed. Ultrastructure of Endocrene Cells & Tissues: Electron Microscopy in Biology & Medicine. 1983. lib. bdg. 90.00 (ISBN 0-89838-568-7, Pub. by Martinus Nijhoff Netherlands). Kluwer Academic.

Muthe, Norma C. Endocrinology: A Nursing Approach. 1981. pap. text ed. 11.95 (ISBN 0-316-59160-2). Little.

Norman, A. W. & Schaefer, K., eds. Vitamin D: Chemical, Biochemical & Clinical Endocrinology of Calcium Metabolism. (Illus.). 1288p. 1982. text ed. 114.00 (ISBN 3-11-008864-9). De Gruyter.

Norris, David O. Vertebrate Endocrinology. 2nd ed. LC 84-19425. (Illus.). 505p. 1985. text ed. 39.75 (ISBN 0-8121-0967-8). Lea & Febiger.

Novy, Miles J. & Resko, John A. Fetal Endocrinology. LC 81-19038. (ORPRC Symposium on Primate Reproductive Biology Ser.: Vol. 1). 1981. 49.50 (ISBN 0-12-522601-2). Acad Pr.

Pang, P. K., ed. Evolution of Vertebrate Endocrine Systems. Epple, A. (Texas Tech Univ. Graduate Studies: No. 21). 404p. (Orig.). 1980. 35.00 (ISBN 0-89672-077-2); pap. 25.00 (ISBN 0-89672-076-4). Tex Tech Pr.

Paxton, Mary J. Endocrinology: Biological & Medical Perspectives. 416p. 1986. text ed. price not set (ISBN 0-697-00779-0). Wm C Brown.

Portonovo Conferences on Endocrine Pharmacology, Compartmental Models & Control Systems, 1st & 2nd. Biomathematics: Proceedings. De Martinis, Carlo & Rossini, Luigi, eds. 320p. 1980. pap. 27.50 (ISBN 88-212-0838-9, Pub. by Piccin Italy). J K Burgess.

Potemkin, V. V. Endocrinology. 331p. 1981. 10.00 (ISBN 0-8285-2104-2, Pub. by Mir Pubs USSR). Imported Pubns.

Rabin, David & McKenna, Terence, eds. Clinical Endocrinology & Metabolism. (The Science & Practice of Clinical Medicine Ser.). 672p. 1982. 78.50 (ISBN 0-8089-1394-8, 793453). Grune.

Ramsay. Synopsis of Endocrinology & Metabolism. 2nd ed. 224p. 1980. pap. 17.50 (ISBN 0-7236-0485-1). PSG Pub Co.

Rodbard, David & Forti, Gianni, eds. Computers in Endocrinology. (Serono Symposia Publications: Vol. 14). 362p. 1984. text ed. 49.50 (ISBN 0-89004-368-X). Raven.

Rose, D. P. Endocrinology of Cancer, Vol. III. 208p. 1982. 62.00 (ISBN 0-8493-5339-4). CRC Pr.

Scanes, C. G., ed. Aspects of Avian Endocrinology: Practical & Theoretical Implications. (Graduate Studies: No. 26). 411p. 1982. 59.95 (ISBN 0-89672-103-5); pap. 29.95 (ISBN 0-89672-102-7). Tex Tech Pr.

Scaramuzzi, R. J. & Lincoln, D. W., eds. Reproductive Endocrinology of Domestic Ruminants. 270p. 95.00x (ISBN 0-906545-06-4, Pub. by Journals Repro England). State Mutual Bk.

Serio, M. & Pazzagli, M., eds. Luminescent Assays: Perspectives in Endocrinology & Clinical Chemistry. (Serono Symposia Publications from Raven Press Ser.: Vol. I). 304p. 1982. text ed. 51.00 (ISBN 0-89004-740-5). Raven.

Stanbury, John B. Endemic Goiter & Endemic Cretinism: Iodine Nutrition in Health & Disease. LC 79-22459. Repr. of 1980 ed. 155.00 (ISBN 0-8357-9883-6, 2019297). Bks Demand UMI.

Stark, E., et al, eds. Endocrinology, Neuroendocrinology, Neuropeptides-Part II: Proceedings of the 28th International Congress of Physiological Sciences, Budapest, 1980. LC 80-42046. (Advances in Physiological Sciences Ser.: Vol. 14). (Illus.). 350p. 1981. 44.00 (ISBN 0-08-026871-4). Pergamon.

--Endocrinology, Neuroendocrinology, Neuropeptides-Part 1: Proceedings of the 28th International Congress of Physiological Sciences, Budapest, 1980. LC 80-42047. (Advances in Physiological Sciences: Vol. 13). (Illus.). 350p. 1981. 44.00 (ISBN 0-08-026827-7). Pergamon.

Tepperman, Jay. Metabolic & Endocrine Physiology. 4th ed. (Illus.). 1980. 24.95 (ISBN 0-8151-8755-6); pap. 24.95 (ISBN 0-8151-8756-4). Year Bk Med.

Thrall, James H. Endocrinological Imaging. 280p. 1985. 25.00 (ISBN 0-87527-235-5). Green.

Tolis, George, et al, eds. Prolactin & Prolactinomas. (Illus.). 504p. 1983. text ed. 79.00 (ISBN 0-89004-804-5). Raven.

Tulchinsky, Dan & Ryan, Kenneth J. Maternal-Fetal Endocrinology. LC 79-66046. (Illus.). 418p. 1980. text ed. 49.95x (ISBN 0-7216-8911-6). Saunders.

Vokaer, R. & De Bock, G., eds. Sexual Endocrinology: Proceedings of the Fondation pour la recherche en endocrinologie sexuelle et la reproduction humaine. 252p. 1975. text ed. 52.00 (ISBN 0-08-018170-8). Pergamon.

Watts, Nelson B. & Keffer, Joseph H. Practical Endocrine Diagnosis. 3rd ed. LC 81-15607. (Illus.). 166p. 1982. pap. 18.75 (ISBN 0-8121-0818-3). Lea & Febiger.

Yen, Samuel S. & Jaffe, Robert B. Reproductive Endocrinology: Physiology, Pathophysiology & Clinical Management. new ed. LC 77-84682. (Illus.). 579p. 1978. text ed. 50.00x (ISBN 0-7216-9625-2). Saunders.

--Reproductive Endocrinology: Physiology, Pathophysiology & Clinical Management. 2nd ed. (Illus.). Date not set. price not set (ISBN 0-7216-9630-9). Saunders.

ENDOGENOUS RHYTHMS

see Biological Rhythms

ENDOTHELIUM

Cryer, A. Biochemical Interactions at the Endothelium. 1983. 106.50 (ISBN 0-444-80478-1, I-007-83). Elsevier.

Endothelium, Vol. 401. 52.00x (ISBN 0-89766-192-3); pap. 52.00x (ISBN 0-89766-195-8). NY Acad Sci.

Messmer, K., ed. Structure & Function of Endothelial Cells. Hammersen, F. (Mikrozirkulation in Forschung und Klinik, Progress in Applied Microcirculation: Vol. 1). (Illus.). x, 138p. 1983. pap. 19.75 (ISBN 3-8055-3635-6). S Karger.

ENDOTOXIN

Agarwal, M. K., ed. Bacterial Endotoxins & Host Response. x, 436p. 1981. 78.50 (ISBN 0-444-80301-7). Elsevier.

Berry, L. G. & Proctor, R. A., eds. Cellular Biology of Endotoxin: Handbook of Endotoxin, Vol. 3. 450p. 1985. 103.75 (ISBN 0-444-90389-5). Elsevier.

Hinshaw, L. B., ed. Pathophysiology of Endotoxin: Handbook of Endotoxin, Vol. 2. 400p. 1985. 96.50 (ISBN 0-444-90385-2). Elsevier.

Homma, J. Y., et al, eds. Bacterial Endotoxin: Chemical, Biological & Clinical Aspects. 420p. 1984. text ed. 52.50x (ISBN 0-89573-228-9). VCH Pubs.

Kass, Edward H. & Woolf, Sheldon M. Bacterial Lipopolysaccharides. 312p. 1973. text ed. 10.95x (ISBN 0-226-42564-9). U of Chicago Pr.

Majde, Jeannine A. & Person, Robert J. Pathophysiological Effects of Endotoxins at the Cellular Level. LC 81-6066. (Progress in Clinical & Biological Research Ser.: Vol. 62). 204p. 1981. 36.00 (ISBN 0-8451-0062-9). A R Liss.

Nowotny, Alois, ed. Beneficial Effects of Endotoxins. 570p. 1983. 69.50x (ISBN 0-306-41147-4, Plenum Press). Plenum Pub.

Pearson. Pyrogens, Endotoxins, LAL Testing & Depyrogenation. 272p. 1985. 59.75 (ISBN 0-8247-7436-1). Dekker.

Rietschel, E. T., ed. Chemistry of Endotoxin. (Handbook of Endotoxin Ser.: Vol. 1). 420p. 1985. 89.00 (ISBN 0-444-90384-4). Elsevier.

Watson, Stanley W. & Levin, Jack, eds. Endotoxins & Their Detection with the Limulus Amebocyte Lysate Test. LC 82-8967. (Progress in Clinical & Biological Research Ser.: Vol. 93). 438p. 1982. 44.00 (ISBN 0-8451-0093-9). A R Liss.

ENERGY

see Force and Energy; Power Resources

ENERGY AND STATE

see Energy Policy

ENERGY-BAND THEORY OF SOLIDS

see also Fermi Surfaces; Free Electron Theory of Metals

AIP Conference, Univ. of Rochester, 1971. Superconductivity in D- & F- Band Metals: AIP Conference Proceedings, No. 4. Douglass, D. H., ed. LC 74-188879. 375p. 1972. 14.00 (ISBN 0-88318-103-7). Am Inst Physics.

Bauer, G., et al. Solid-State Physics. (Tracts in Modern Physics Ser.: Vol. 74). (Illus.). v, 153p. 1974. 46.10 (ISBN 0-387-06946-1). Springer-Verlag.

Bube, Richard H. Electronic Properties of Crystalline Solids: An Introduction to Fundamentals. 1974. 59.00 (ISBN 0-12-138550-7). Acad Pr.

Callaway, Joseph. Energy Band Theory. (Pure and Applied Physics: Vol. 16). 1964. 59.50 (ISBN 0-12-155250-0). Acad Pr.

Electrons in Crystalline Solids: Trieste Lectures, 1972. (Proceedings Ser.). (Illus.). 753p. (Orig.). 1974. pap. 59.25 (ISBN 92-0-130073-5, ISP335, IAEA). Unipub.

Fabian, Derek J., ed. Soft X-Ray Band Spectra & the Electronic Structures of Metals & Materials. 1969. 65.00 (ISBN 0-12-247450-3). Acad Pr.

Platzman, P. M. & Wolff, P. A. Waves & Interactions in Solid State Plasmas. (Solid State Physics Ser.: Suppl. 13). 1973. 35.00 (ISBN 0-12-607773-8). Acad Pr.

Slater, John C. Solid State & Molecular Theory: A Scientific Biography. LC 74-22367. 357p. 1975. text ed. 36.95x (ISBN 0-471-79681-6, Pub. by Wiley-Interscience). Wiley.

Timmerhaus, K. D., et al, eds. Low Temperature Physics - LT-13, 4 vols. Incl. Vol. 1. Quantum Fluids. 669p. 95.00x (ISBN 0-306-35121-8); Vol. 2. Quantum Crystals & Magnetism. 668p. 95.00x (ISBN 0-306-35122-6); Vol. 3. Superconductivity. 834p. 105.00x (ISBN 0-306-35123-4); Vol. 4. Electronic Properties, Instrumentation, & Measurement. 684p. 95.00x (ISBN 0-306-35124-2). LC 73-81092. (Illus.). 1974 (Plenum Pr). Plenum Pub.

ENERGY BUDGET (GEOPHYSICS)

see also Bioenergetics; Hydrologic Cycle; Ocean-Atmosphere Interaction

Daly, Herman E. & Umana, Alvaro F., eds. Energy, Economics, & Environment: Conflicting Views of an Essential Interrelationship. (AAAS Selected Symposium Ser.: No. 64). 200p. 1981. 25.00x (ISBN 0-86531-282-6). Westview.

ENERGY CONSERVATION

Here are entered general works on the conservation of all forms of energy. Works on the conservation of a specific form of energy are entered under that form, e.g. Petroleum Conservation. Works on the conservation of energy as a physical concept are entered under Force and Energy.

see also Architecture and Energy Conservation; Energy Policy; Petroleum Conservation; Recycling (Waste, etc.); Waste Heat

A E E World Energy Engineering Congress, 1st. Energy Engineering Technology: Proceedings. pap. 45.00 (ISBN 0-915586-15-0). Fairmont Pr.

Abelson, Philip H. & Hammond, Allen L., eds. Energy Two: Use, Conservation & Supply. LC 78-59190. (Science Compendia Ser.: Vol. 6). 1978. 12.00 (ISBN 0-87168-300-8); pap. 5.00 (ISBN 0-87168-237-0). AAAS.

Academy for Educational Development. Energy Conservation Idea Handbook. 1981. 17.00 (ISBN 0-02-900950-2). ACE.

Aird, Catherine. The Religious Body. 176p. 1980. pap. 2.95 (ISBN 0-553-24602-X). Bantam.

Aluminium Association. Aluminium Industry Energy Conservation Workshop, 7: Proceedings. 357p. 1983. 102.00 (ISBN 0-9911000-8-5, Pub. by Aluminium W Germany). Heyden.

Aluminium Industry Energy Conservation Workshop: Proceedings, No. VI. 260p. 1981. 96.00 (ISBN 0-9911002-4-7, Pub. by Aluminium W Germany). Heyden.

American Management Association. Managing Industrial Energy Conservation. LC 77-22251. (An American Management Associations' Management Briefing Ser.). (Illus.). pap. 20.00 (ISBN 0-317-11154-X, 2050200). Bks Demand UMI.

American Society of Civil Engineers, compiled By. Conservation & Utilization of Water & Energy Resources. 541p. 1979. pap. 34.75x (ISBN 0-87262-189-8). Am Soc Civil Eng.

American Society of Mechanical Engineers. Energy Conservation in Building Heating & Air Conditioning Systems. Gopal, R., et al, eds. LC 78-60047. pap. 27.30 (ISBN 0-317-19849-1, 2023146). Bks Demand UMI.

Analysis Instrumentation Symposium, 26th, Baton Rouge, 1980. Analysis Instrumentation, Vol. 18: Proceedings. Bd. with Vol. 14. Instrument Maintenance Management. 156p. 1980. pap. text ed. 24.00x (ISBN 0-87664-471-X). Instru Soc.

Anderson, Russell E. Biological Paths to Energy Self-Reliance. 400p. 1979. pap. 14.95 (ISBN 0-442-20872-3). Van Nos Reinhold.

Attkisson, Franklin. How to Cut Your Energy Bill Thirty per-Cent to Fifty per-Cent. rev. ed. 56p. (Orig.). 1977. pap. 3.00x (ISBN 0-686-30559-0). Energy Pub.

Axel, Helen. Organizing & Managing for Energy Efficiency. (Report: No. 837). (Illus.). 54p. (Orig.). 1983. pap. 100.00 (ISBN 0-8237-0277-4); pap. 20.00 member. Conference Bd.

Baehr, H. D., et al, eds. Power Engineering & Technology: Energy Efficient Use of Working Fluids, Alternative Processes, Heat Pumps& Organic Rankine Cycle. 1984. 179.50 (ISBN 0-89116-448-0). Hemisphere Pub.

Bailey, James. Energy Systems: An Analysis for Engineers & Policy Makers. (Energy Power & Environment: Vol. 2). 1978. 34.50 (ISBN 0-8247-6713-6). Dekker.

Bajaj & Singh. Cost-Effective Energy Management. LC 82-4243. (Illus.). 200p. 1982. 24.95x (ISBN 0-912524-22-7). Busn News.

Barnett, A. & Bell, R. M. Rural Energy & the Third World: A Review of Social Science Research & Technology Policy Problems. LC 82-373. (Illus.). 302p. 1982. 40.00 (ISBN 0-08-028953-3); 18.00 (ISBN 0-08-028954-1). Pergamon.

Baron, Stephen L. Manual of Energy Saving in Existing Buildings & Plants, Vol. I. (Illus.). 1978. 39.95 (ISBN 0-13-553578-6, Busn). P-H.

--Manual of Energy Saving in Existing Buildings & Plants: Vol. 2, Facility Modification. (Illus.). 1978. 49.95 (ISBN 0-13-553586-7, Busn). P-H.
Baum, Andrew & Singer, Jerome E., eds. Energy Conservation: Psychological Perspectives. LC 81-2820. (Advances in Environmental Psychology Ser.: Vol. 3). 224p. 1981. text ed. 29.95x (ISBN 0-89859-063-9). L Erlbaum Assocs.
Beck, Paul, et al. Individual Energy Conservation Behaviors. LC 80-12699. 240p. 1980. text ed. 35.00 (ISBN 0-89946-018-6). Oelgeschlager.
Beghi, G. Energy Storage & Transportation: Prospects for New Technologies. 1981. 39.50 (ISBN 90-277-1166-6, Pub. by Reidel Holland). Kluwer Academic.
Beierle, Herbert L. Making Energy Work. 1980. 5.00 (ISBN 0-940480-08-5). U of Healing.
Belgrave, Robert & Cornell, Margaret. Energy Self-Sufficiency for the U. K. 200p. 1985. text ed. write for info. (ISBN 0-566-00992-7). Gower Pub Co.
Bergman, M., ed. Subsurface Space--Environment Protection, Low Cost Storage, Energy Savings: Proceedings of the International Symposium, Stockholm, Sweden, June 23-27, 1980, 3 vols. (Illus.). 1500p. 1981. 275.00 (ISBN 0-08-026136-1). Pergamon.
Biological Sciences Curriculum Study. Energy & Society: Investigations in Decision Making. (Illus.). 1977. pap. text ed. 3.95 (ISBN 0-8331-1502-2); tchr's manual 7.95 (ISBN 0-8331-1503-0). Hubbard Sci.
Bogenschutz, ed. Technical Dictionary for Batteries & Direct Energy Conservation. 200p. 1968. 11.00 (ISBN 0-9913000-3-3, Pub. by O Brandstetter WG). Heyden.
Bohm, Robert A., et al, eds. Toward an Efficient Energy Future: Proceedings of the III International Energy Symposium III-May 23-27, 1982. Energy, Environment, & Resources Center,the University of Tennessee. (International Energy Symposia Ser.). 352p. 1983. prof. ref. 39.95 (ISBN 0-88410-878-3). Ballinger Pub.
--World Energy Production & Productivity: Proceedings of the International Energy Symposium I-October 14, 1980. Energy, Environment, & Resource Center, the University of Tennessee. (International Energy Symposia Ser.). 448p. 1981. prof ref 28.50x (ISBN 0-88410-649-7). Ballinger Pub.
Boyle, Godfrey. Living on the Sun: Harnessing Renewable Energy for an Equitable Society. (Ideas in Progress Ser.). (Illus.). 128p. 1978. (Dist by Scribner); pap. 6.95 (ISBN 0-7145-0862-4). M Boyars.
Brown, Robert J. & Yanuck, Rudolph R. Life Cycle Costing. 299p. 32.00 (ISBN 0-915586-17-7). Fairmont Pr.
Brunner, Ronald D. & Sandenburgh, Robin. Community Energy Options: Getting Started in Ann Arbor. (Illus.). 296p. 1982. text ed. 14.50x (ISBN 0-472-08025-3). U of Mich Pr.
Buck, L. E. & Goodwin, L. M. Alternative Energy: The Federal Role. 700p. 1982. 80.00 (ISBN 0-07-008730-X). Mcgraw.
Buggey, J. The Energy Crisis: What Are Our Choices? 1976. pap. text ed. 9.24 (ISBN 0-13-277301-5). P-H.
Bungay, Henry R. Energy, the Biomass Options. LC 80-19645. 347p. 1981. 46.50x (ISBN 0-471-04386-9, Pub. by Wiley-Interscience). Wiley.
Burberry, Peter. Building for Energy Conservation. LC 77-17943. 60p. 1978. 24.95x (ISBN 0-470-99350-2). Halsted Pr.
Business Communications Staff. Industrial Energy Conservation E-033R. 1982. text ed. 950.00 (ISBN 0-89336-167-4). BCC.
--New Residential, Commercial Hvac & Monitoring Systems E-034. 1981. text ed. 850.00 (ISBN 0-89336-168-2). BCC.
Cambridge Information & Research Services, Ltd. World Directory of Energy Information: Middle East, Africa & Asia Pacific, Vol. II. 336p. 1982. 85.00x (ISBN 0-87196-602-6). Facts on File.
CEP & White, Ronald. The Price of Power Update: Electric Utilities & the Environment. LC 77-92111. 1977. pap. 25.00 (ISBN 0-87871-007-8). CEP.
Chatterji, Manas, ed. Energy & Environment in the Developing Countries. LC 80-42143. 357p. 1981. 58.95x (ISBN 0-471-27993-5, Pub. by Wiley-Interscience). Wiley.
Chemical Engineering Magazine. Process Energy Conservation: Methods & Technology. (Illus.). 300p. 1982. 39.95 (ISBN 0-07-010697-5). McGraw.
Chigier, N. A., ed. Progress in Energy & Combustion Science, Vol. 6, Pt. 2. 102p. 1980. pap. 27.00 (ISBN 0-08-026059-4). Pergamon.
Chiogioji. Industrial Energy Conservation. (Energy, Power & Environment Ser.: Vol. 4). 1979. 89.75 (ISBN 0-8247-6809-4). Dekker.
Chiogioji, Oura. Energy Conservation in Commercial & Residential Buildings. (Clinical & Biochemical Analysis Ser.). 536p. 1982. 69.75 (ISBN 0-8247-1874-7). Dekker.
Clark, Jan R. Reservoir of Power. 1981. 25.00x (ISBN 0-686-78923-7, Pub. by Pickering & Inglis Scotland). State Mutual Bk.
Claxton, John D., et al, eds. Consumers & Energy Conservation: International Perspectives on Research & Policy Options. LC 81-10626. 318p. 1981. 42.95x (ISBN 0-03-059659-9). Praeger.
Cohen, I. Bernard, ed. The Conservation of Energy & the Principle of Least Action. LC 80-2097. (Development of Science Ser.). (Illus.). 1981. lib. bdg. 45.00x (ISBN 0-405-13862-8). Ayer Co Pubs.
Committee for Economic Development & the Conservation Foundation. Energy Prices & Public Policy. LC 82-7428. (CED Statement on National Policy Ser.). 88p. 1982. lib. bdg. 9.50 (ISBN 0-87186-775-3); pap. 7.50 (ISBN 0-87186-075-9). Comm Econ Dev.
Commoner, Barry & Boksenbaum, Howard, eds. Energy & Human Welfare: Human Welfare: the End Use for Power, Vol. 3. LC 75-8992. 1975. 14.95 (ISBN 0-02-468440-6). Macmillan Info.
Conta, Lewis D. Energy Conservation in Space Conditioning. Gyftopoulos, Elias P. & Cohen, Karen C., eds. (Industrial Energy-Conservation Manuals Ser.: No. 7). (Illus.). 120p. 1982. loose-leaf 20.00x (ISBN 0-262-03084-5). MIT Pr.
Cooper, Mark N. & Sullivan, Theodore L. Equity & Energy: Rising Energy Prices & the Living Standards of Lower Income Americans. LC 83-14642. 302p. 1983. softcover 30.00 (ISBN 0-86531-999-5). Westview.
Corporate Energy Management Manual. pap. 24.50 (ISBN 0-915586-21-5). Fairmont Pr.
Council on Economic Priorities & Buchsbaum, Steven. Jobs & Energy: The Employment & Economic Impacts of Nuclear Power, Conservation, & Other Energy Options. Schwartz, Wendy C., ed. LC 79-91065. 1979. 35.00 (ISBN 0-87871-011-6). CEP.
Cowan, H. J. Predictive Methods for the Energy Conserving Design of Buildings. (Illus.). 128p. 1983. pap. 33.50 (ISBN 0-08-029838-9). Pergamon.
Cox, Wesley. Energy Smarts: Low-Cost, No-Cost Ways to Shrink Your Energy Bills. (Illus.). 1984. pap. 4.95 (ISBN 0-517-55325-2). Crown.
Culp, Archie W. Principles of Energy Conversion. (Illus.). 1979. text ed. 42.00 (ISBN 0-07-014892-9). McGraw.
Cunningham, Chet. Two Hundred & Twenty-Two Ways to Save Gas: And Get the Best Possible Mileage. LC 80-26423. (Illus.). 96p. 1981. 10.95 (ISBN 0-13-935221-X); pap. 3.95 (ISBN 0-13-935213-9). P-H.
Cussler, Clive. Raise the Titanic! 384p. 1980. pap. 3.95 (ISBN 0-553-22889-7). Bantam.
Daly, Herman E. & Umana, Alvaro F., eds. Energy, Economics, & Environment: Conflicting Views of an Essential Interrelationship. (AAAS Selected Symposium Ser.: No. 64). 200p. 1981. 25.00x (ISBN 0-86531-282-6). Westview.
Daneke, Gregory A., ed. Energy, Economics & the Environment: Toward a Comprehensive Perspective. LC 81-47690. 304p. 1981. 31.00x (ISBN 0-669-04717-1). Lexington Bks.
Darmstadter & Landsberg. Energy Today & Tomorrow: Living with Uncertainty. (Illus.). 240p. 1983. 25.95 (ISBN 0-13-277640-5). P-H.
Darmstadter, Joel. Conserving Energy: Prospects & Opportunities in the New York Region. LC 75-15414. pap. 30.00 (ISBN 0-317-26459-1, 2023795). Bks Demand UMI.
Darmstadter, Joel, et al. How Industrial Societies Use Energy: A Comparative Analysis. LC 77-83780. (Resources for the Future Ser.). (Illus.). 300p. 1978. text ed. 22.50x (ISBN 0-8018-2041-3). Johns Hopkins.
--Energy Today & Tomorrow: Living with Uncertainty, A Book From Resources For The Future. 1983. pap. 13.95 (ISBN 0-13-277632-4). P-H.
De Oliveira, Fernandes E., et al. Building Energy Management--Conventional & Solar Approaches: Proceedings of the International Congress, 12-16 May 1980, Povoa de Varzim, Portugal. LC 80-40415. 800p. 1981. 175.00 (ISBN 0-08-026144-2). Pergamon.
Derricott, Robert & Chissick, Seymour. Energy Conservation & Thermal Insulation: Properties of Materials. LC 80-41587. (Safety & Environmental Factors Ser.). 785p. 1981. 100.00x (ISBN 0-471-27930-7, Pub. by Wiley-Interscience). Wiley.
Deudney, Daniel & Flavin, Christopher. Renewable Energy: The Power to Choose. 448p. 1984. 22.95 (ISBN 0-393-01999-3); pap. 8.95 (ISBN 0-393-30201-6). Norton.
Devito, Alfred & Krockover, Gerald. Activities Handbook for Energy Education. (Illus.). 192p. 1981. pap. 12.95 (ISBN 0-673-16464-0). Scott F.
Diamant, R. M. Energy Conservation Equipment. 156p. 1984. 29.50 (ISBN 0-89397-190-1). Nichols Pub.
Diamant, R. M. & Kut, David. District Heating & Cooling for Energy Conservation. LC 81-4110. 464p. 1981. 63.95x (ISBN 0-470-27182-5). Halsted Pr.
Dick-Larkham, Richard. Cutting Energy Costs. 1977. 24.95x (ISBN 0-8464-0309-9). Beekman Pubs.
Dorf, Richard C. The Energy Factbook. Dembofsky, Thomas J., ed. (Illus.). 256p. 1981. pap. 7.95 (ISBN 0-07-017629-9). McGraw.
Dorgan, C. Energy Management Manual. 1986. cancelled (ISBN 0-442-23877-0). Van Nos Reinhold.
Dukert, Joseph M. A Short Energy History of the United States & Some Thoughts About the Future. (Decisionmakers Bookshelf Ser.: Vol. 7). (Illus.). 88p. (Orig.). 1980. pap. 2.50 (ISBN 0-931032-07-5). Edison Electric.
Dunkerley, Joy & Alterman, Jack. Trends in Energy Use in Industrial Countries. LC 80-8022. (Resources for the Future Research Ser.: Paper R-19). (Illus., Orig.). 1980. pap. text ed. 8.00x (ISBN 0-8018-2487-7). Johns Hopkins.
Eckerlin, H. & Boyers, A. Energy-Conservation Opportunities in the Small Industrial Plant. Gyftopoulos, Elias P. & Cohen, Karen C., eds. (Industrial Energy-Conservation Manuals Ser.: No. 5). 96p. 1982. loose-leaf 20.00x (ISBN 0-262-05025-0). MIT Pr.
The Economic Commission for Europe & Energy Conservation. 76p. 1980. pap. 7.00 (ISBN 0-686-70498-3, UN80 2E4, UN). Unipub.
The Economy of Energy Conservation in Education Facilities. rev. ed. LC 73-83011. 91p. (Orig.). 1978. pap. 4.00 (ISBN 0-88481-206-5). Ed Facilities.
Ehringer, H. & Hoyaux, G. Energy Conservation in Industry Applications & Techiques. 1983. lib. bdg. 52.00 (ISBN 90-2771-580-7, Pub. by Reidel Holland). Kluwer Academic.
--Energy Conservation in Industry: Combustion Heat & Ranking Cycle Machines. 1983. lib. bdg. 32.50 (ISBN 90-2771-581-5, Pub. by Reidel Holland). Kluwer Academic.
Eklund, Ken & Baylon, David. Design Tools for Energy Efficient Homes. 3rd ed. Beckerman, Richard & Stewart, Annie, eds. (Illus.). 126p. 1984. pap. 14.95 (ISBN 0-934478-25-2). Ecotope.
El Mallakh, Ragaei & El Mallakh, Dorothea H., eds. Energy Options & Conservation. LC 78-70437. (Illus.). 1978. pap. 14.50x (ISBN 0-918714-04-4). Intl Res Ctr Energy.
Energy & the Environment, 1981 Proceedings, Vol. II. LC 62-38584. 158p. 1981. pap. text ed. 12.00 (ISBN 0-915414-63-5); pap. text ed. 9.60 members (ISBN 0-686-96257-5). Inst Environ Sci.
Energy Auditing. 45.00 (ISBN 0-915586-31-2). Fairmont Pr.
Energy Conservation. (Background Studies: No. 33). pap. 3.25 (SSC32, SSC). Unipub.
Energy Conservation Equipment for Residential & Commercial Sectors E-037R. 1981. 850.00 (ISBN 0-89336-252-2). BCC.
The Energy Conservation Idea Handbook. 171p. (Orig.). 1980. pap. 12.00 (ISBN 0-89492-047-2). Acad Educ Dev.
Energy Conservation in the International Energy Agency: 1978. 52p. 1979. 7.00x (ISBN 92-64-11969-8). OECD.
Energy Conservation Self-Evaluation Manual. 16.95 (ISBN 0-915586-39-8). Fairmont Pr.
Energy Conservation Sourcebook. LC 77-99086. (Business Publications). 507p. 29.50 (ISBN 0-89443-089-0). Aspen Systems.
Energy Information Resources: An Inventory of Energy Research & Development Information Resources in the Continental United States, Hawaii & Alaska, 1975. 1975. 18.50 (ISBN 0-317-13873-1, 336-BW). Knowledge Indus.
Energy Management & Conservation: Special Session on Energy Management at the 66th ASBO Annual Meeting & Exhibits. 1981. 7.50. Assn Sch Busn.
Energy Management in Municipal Operations: A Framework for Action. 80p. 1981. pap. 15.00 (ISBN 0-686-46562-8, 29084). Intl City Mgt.
Energy Management Systems. (Reports Ser.: No. 523). 186p. 1982. 985.00x (ISBN 0-88694-523-2). Intl Res Dev.
Energy Management Workbook. pap. 9.25 (ISBN 0-87102-027-0, 50-7848); pap. 6.25 members. Natl Ret Merch.
Energy Resources Center. Illustrated Guide to Home Retrofitting for Energy Savings. Knight, et al, eds. LC 80-23568. (Illus.). 384p. 1981. 19.95 (ISBN 0-07-019490-4). McGraw.
Energy Task Force. Controlling Energy Through Microprocessor Utilization. 77p. 21.00 (ISBN 0-913359-13-0). Assn Phys Plant Admin.
Energy: The Case for Conservation. (Worldwatch Institute Papers: No. 4). 77p. 1976. pap. 2.95 (ISBN 0-686-94953-6, WW4, WW). Unipub.
Energy Utilization: A Sourcebook of Current Technology. 388p. 45.00 (ISBN 0-915586-30-4). Fairmont Pr.
Europool. Secondary Materials in Domestic Refuse As Energy Sources. 80p. 1977. 16.50x (ISBN 0-86010-064-2, Pub. by Graham & Trotman England). State Mutual Bk.
Exploring Alternate Energy. instr's. guide 4.00 (ISBN 0-87006-478-9). Goodheart.
Farhar-Pilgrim, Barbara & Unseld, Charles T. America's Solar Potential: A National Consumer Study. Shama, Avraham, ed. LC 82-5231. (Studies in Energy Conservation & Solar Energy). 464p. 1982. 41.95x (ISBN 0-03-061696-4). Praeger.
Farmer, Penny. Energy Conservation in Buildings 1973-1983: A Bibliography of European & American Literature on Government, Commercial & Domestic Buildings. 107p. (Orig.). 1983. pap. text ed. 39.50 (ISBN 0-946655-00-6). Scholium Intl.
Faulkner, Edward A., Jr. Guide to Efficient Burner Operation: Gas, Oil, & Dual-Fuel. 32.00 (ISBN 0-915586-35-5). Fairmont Pr.
Fazzolare, R. A. & Smith, C. B. Changing Energy Use, Vol. 1. 165.00 (ISBN 0-08-025559-0). Pergamon.
--Changing Energy Use Futures, Vol. 2. 165.00 (ISBN 0-08-025560-4). Pergamon.
--Changing Energy Use Futures, Vol. 3. 165.00 (ISBN 0-08-025561-2). Pergamon.
--Changing Energy Use Futures, Vol. 4. 165.00 (ISBN 0-08-025562-0). Pergamon.
Fazzolare, Rocco A. & Smith, Craig B. Changing Energy Use Futures: Second International Conference on Energy Use Management, October 1979, L. A., Ca, 4 vols. (Illus.). 1979. 525.00 (ISBN 0-08-025099-8). Pergamon.
Felton, Vi B. One Hundred and Fifty Ways to Save Energy and Money. LC 77-13287. 39p. 1977. pap. 2.50 (ISBN 0-87576-062-7). Pilot Bks.
Field-Proven Programs to Conserve Energy in Schools: ASBO's 65th Annual Meeting Mini-workshops on Energy & Energy Management. 1980. 5.95. Assn Sch Busn.
Foell, W. K. National Perspectives on Management of Energy-Environment Systems. LC 82-7025. (International Series on Applied Systems Analysis). 343p. 1983. 64.95x (ISBN 0-471-10022-6, Pub. by Wiley-Interscience). Wiley.
Foley, D. Creating an Energy Empire. 1986. cancelled (ISBN 0-442-22766-3). Van Nos Reinhold.
Ford, K. W., et al. Efficient Use of Energy. LC 75-18227. (AIP Conference Proceedings Ser.: No. 25). 304p. 1975. 20.00 (ISBN 0-88318-124-X). Am Inst Physics.
Fowler, John M. Energy-Environment Source Book: Energy, Society, & the Environment; Energy, Its Extraction, Conversion, & Use, 2 vols. rev. ed. (Illus.). 1980. Set. pap. 9.00 (ISBN 0-87355-022-6). Natl Sci Tchrs.
Fox, William F. Federal Regulation of Energy. LC 83-20027. 920p. 1983. 75.00 (ISBN 0-07-021757-2). McGraw.
Freeman, S. David. Energy: The New Era. LC 74-77980. 1974. 14.50 (ISBN 0-8027-0460-3). Walker & Co.
Fuel Efficiency in Industrial Practice. (Illus.). 288p. 1979. 23.25 (ISBN 92-833-1051-9, APO81, APO). Unipub.
Fuelwood & Rural Energy Production & Supply in Humid Tropics: Report for the UNU with Special Reference to Tropical Africa & South East Asia, Vol. 4. (Natural Resources & the Environment Ser.). (Illus.). 224p. 1982. 19.50 (ISBN 0-907567-08-8, TYP104, TYP). Unipub.
Furbush, S. A. Energy-Conservation Opportunities in the Chemical Industry. Gyftopoulos, Elias P. & Cohen, Karen C., eds. (Industrial Energy-Conservation Manuals Ser.: No. 14). (Illus.). 136p. 1982. loose-leaf 20.00x (ISBN 0-262-06081-7). MIT Pr.
Garg, Prem C. Optimal Economic Growth with Exhaustible Resources. LC 78-75019. (Outstanding Dissertations on Energy Ser.). 1979. lib. bdg. 22.00 (ISBN 0-8240-4054-6). Garland Pub.
Gates, David M. Energy & Ecology. LC 84-27471. (Illus.). 300p. 1985. text ed. 40.00x (ISBN 0-87893-230-5); pap. text ed. 25.00x (ISBN 0-87893-231-3). Sinauer Assoc.
Georgescu-Roegen, Nicholas. Energy & Economic Myths. LC 76-10265. 1977. pap. text ed. 14.50 (ISBN 0-08-021056-2). Pergamon.
Gibbons, John H. & Chandler, W. U. Energy: The Conservation Revolution. LC 80-28431. 275p. 1981. 25.00x (ISBN 0-306-40670-5, Plenum Pr). Plenum Pub.
Gifford, Roger M. Energetics of Agriculture & Food Production. (Illus.). 29p. 1977. pap. 2.25x (ISBN 0-643-00147-6, Pub. by CSIRO). Intl Spec Bk.
Godel. Cost Estimating of Energy Conservation Systems. 1986. cancelled (ISBN 0-442-26362-7). Van Nos Reinhold.
Goran, Morris. Ten Lessons of the Energy Crisis. LC 80-130511. 1980. 19.80x (ISBN 0-915250-35-7). Environ Design.

BOOKS - SUBJECT INDEX ENERGY CONSERVATION

Gordon, Richard L. An Economic Analysis of World Energy Problems. (Illus.). 320p. 1981. text ed. 42.50x (ISBN 0-262-07080-4). MIT Pr.
Gore, Patrick D. & Masoncup, John E. Teaching Energy Awareness. rev. ed. (Illus.). 309p. pap. 16.95 (ISBN 0-943804-00-0). U of Denver Teach.
Gramm, R. J. The Energy Boom. (Illus.). 1976. pap. 10.00 (ISBN 0-918826-02-0). Time-Wise.
Grant, C. D. Energy Conservation in the Chemical & Process Industries. 112p. 1981. 2.00x (ISBN 0-85295-118-3, Pub. by Inst Chem Eng England). State Mutual Bk.
Grant, Colin D. Energy Consevation in the Chemical & Process Industries. 1979. 32.50x (ISBN 0-7114-5525-2). Intl Ideas.
Greenberger, Martin. Caught Unawares: The Energy Decade in Retrospect. 456p. 1983. prof ref. 29.95 (ISBN 0-88410-916-X). Ballinger Pub.
Guzman, Oscar, ed. Energy Use in Mexico: Perspectives on Efficiency & Conservation Policies. Yunez-Naude, Antonia. 330p. 1985. pap. 28.00 (ISBN 0-8133-0248-X). Westview.
Haimes, Yacov Y., ed. Energy Auditing & Conservation: Methods, Measurement, Management, & Case Studies. LC 79-23048. 261p. 1980. pap. text ed. 32.00 (ISBN 0-89116-175-9). Hemisphere Pub.
Hammerstrom, Gary. Energy Consumption & Conservation. (Learning Packages in Policy Issues Ser.: No. 2). (Illus.). 58p. (Orig.). 1977. pap. text ed. 2.50x (ISBN 0-936826-11-8). Pol Stud Assocs.
Harding, Jim & International Project for Soft Energy Paths. Tools for the Soft Path. 1982. pap. 11.95 (ISBN 0-913890-53-7); 25.00 (ISBN 0-913890-52-9). Friends of Earth.
Harsany, Peter. Energy Tomorrow. (Illus.). 1980. 17.50 (ISBN 0-686-64249-X). Heinman.
Hawkins, Paul, et al. Seven Tomorrows: Toward a Voluntary History. 1982. pap. 7.95 (ISBN 0-553-01475-7). Bantam.
Hayes, Denis. Energy: The Case for Conservation. LC 76-456. (Worldwatch Papers). 1976. pap. 2.00 (ISBN 0-916468-03-8). Worldwatch Inst.
Helcke, G. The Energy Saving Guide: Tables for Assessing the Profitability of Energy Saving Measures with Explanatory Notes and Worked Examples. Published for the Commission of the European Communities. LC 80-41528. 230p. 1981. 53.00 (ISBN 0-08-026738-6); pap. 18.00 (ISBN 0-08-026739-4). Pergamon.
Hiebert, Erwin N. Historical Roots of the Principles of Conservation of Energy. Cohen, I. Bernard, ed. LC 80-2131. (Development of Science Ser.). (Illus.). 1981. lib. bdg. 12.00x (ISBN 0-405-13880-6). Ayer Co Pubs.
Hill, Richard F., ed. Energy Technology IX: Energy Efficiency for the Eighties. LC 80-66431. (Energy Technology Ser.). (Illus.). 1562p. 1982. pap. text ed. 52.00 (ISBN 0-86587-009-8). Gov Insts.
Hollander, Rene & Percy, Bernard. Everyone's Guide to Saving Gas. (Illus., Orig.). 1979. pap. 2.95 (ISBN 0-9603194-0-9). Old Oaktree.
Household Energy Saving Guide. 96p. 1981. pap. 2.95 (ISBN 0-8249-4010-5). Ideals.
Howes, K. M. & Rummery, R. A. Energy & Agriculture: The Impact of Changes in Energy Costs on the Rural Sector of the Australian Economy. 308p. 1980. pap. 18.00 (ISBN 0-643-02654-1, C056, CSIRO). Unipub.
Hu, S. Handbook of Industrial Energy Conservation. 1982. 44.95 (ISBN 0-442-24426-6). Van Nos Reinhold.
Hunt, Daniel. Energy Conservation in Health Care Facilities. (Illus.). 300p. 1983. text ed. 36.00 (ISBN 0-915586-66-5). Fairmont Pr.
Hunter, Robert E. The Energy "Crisis" & U. S. Foreign Policy. LC 73-80017. (Headline Ser.: No. 216). (Illus., Orig.). 1973. pap. 3.00 (ISBN 0-87124-022-X). Foreign Policy.
Inhaber, Herbert. Energy Risk Assessment. 420p. 1982. 49.50 (ISBN 0-677-05980-9). Gordon.
International Deep Drawing Research Group. Sheet Metal Forming & Energy Conservation: Proceedings of the Biennial Congress of the International Deep Drawing Research Group, 9th, Ann Arbor, Michigan, U. S. A., October 13-14, 1976. LC 76-27547. (Illus.). pap. 73.00 (ISBN 0-317-10787-9, 2050982). Bks Demand UMI.
International Seminar on Energy Conservation & Use of Renewable Energies in the Bio-Industries, Trinity College, Oxford, UK, 2nd 6-10 Sept. 1982 & Vogt, F. Energy Conservation & Use of Renewable Energies in the Bio-Industries: Proceedings. (Illus.). 750p. 1982. 100.00 (ISBN 0-08-029781-1). Pergamon.
Jack Dale & Associates, Staff. Energy Audits Manual. (Illus.). 332p. 1984. pap. 48.00 (ISBN 0-86587-031-4). Gov Insts.
Jaffa, Harry V. American Conservatism & the American Founding. LC 83-70311. xiv, 278p. 1984. lib. bdg. 27.75 (ISBN 0-89089-264-4); pap. text ed. 12.75 (ISBN 0-89089-265-2). Carolina Acad Pr.
Jarmul, Seymour. The Architect's Guide to Energy Conservation. (Illus.). 1980. 29.95 (ISBN 0-07-032296-1). McGraw.
Kenney, W. F. Energy Conservation in the Process Industries (Monograph) (Energy Science & Technology Ser.). 1984. 46.00 (ISBN 0-12-404220-1). Acad Pr.
Knittel, Patricia, ed. A Selected Bibliography: Energy Conservation in the Graphic Arts, Vol. 1. 41p. (Orig.). 1981. pap. 20.00 (ISBN 0-89938-006-9). Tech & Ed Ctr Graph Arts RIT.
Knowles, Ruth S. America's Energy Famine: Its Cause & Cure. LC 80-8040. 352p. 1980. 17.95 (ISBN 0-8061-1669-2). U of Okla Pr.
Koral, Richard, ed. Industrial Energy Managers' Sourcebook. 1982. text ed. 32.00 (ISBN 0-915586-36-3). Fairmont Pr.
Kovach, E. G., ed. Thermal Energy Storage. LC 77-71233. 1977. pap. text ed. 11.25 (ISBN 0-08-021724-9). Pergamon.
Kreith, Frank & West, R. E. Economics of Solar Energy & Conservation Systems, 3 vols. 1980. 84.00 ea. Vol. 1, 320p (ISBN 0-8493-5229-0). Vol. 2. 320p (ISBN 0-8493-5230-4). Vol. 3, 288p (ISBN 0-8493-5231-2). CRC Pr.
Krenz, Jerrold H. Energy: From Opulence to Sufficiency. LC 79-15059. 272p. 1980. 35.95x (ISBN 0-03-057001-8). Praeger.
Kut, David. Dictionary of Applied Energy Conservation: An Illustrated Dictionary of Terms. (Illus.). 300p. 1982. 36.50 (ISBN 0-89397-131-6). Nichols Pub.
Laird, Jean. The Homemaker's Book of Energy Savers. LC 82-1295. 1982. pap. 8.95 (ISBN 0-672-52712-X). Bobbs.
Lakshmanan, T. R. & Nijkamp, Peter, eds. Systems & Models for Energy & Environmental Analysis. 240p. 1983. text ed. 35.50x (ISBN 0-566-00558-1). Gower Pub Co.
Landsberg, Hans, ed. Energy: The Next Twenty Years. LC 79-5226. 656p. 1979. prof ref 32.50x (ISBN 0-88410-092-8); pap. 15.00 (ISBN 0-88410-094-4). Ballinger Pub.
Lavine, Lance. Five Degrees of Conservation: A Graphic Analysis of Energy Alternatives for a Northern Climate. (Illus.). 65p. 1982. 19.50 (ISBN 0-943352-00-2); pap. 10.95 (ISBN 0-943352-01-0). Univ Minn Sch.
Lee, Kaiman & Rehr, Stuart. Energy Conservation & Building Codes: The Legislative & Planning Processes. LC 77-362518. 1977. 30.00x (ISBN 0-915250-23-3). Environ Design.
Leone, Bruno & Smith, Judy, eds. The Energy Crisis: Opposing Viewpoints. (Opposing Viewpoints Ser.). 160p. 1981. 11.95 (ISBN 0-89908-328-5); pap. 6.95 (ISBN 0-89908-303-X). Greenhaven.
Locke, H. B., ed. Energy Users Databook. 150p. 1981. 21.00x (ISBN 0-86010-302-1, Pub. by Graham & Trotman England). State Mutual Bk.
Lovins, Amory, et al. The Energy Controversy: Soft Path Questions & Answers. Nash, Hugh, ed. LC 78-67907. 1979. pap. 6.95 (ISBN 0-913890-22-7). Brick Hse Pub.
Luetzelschwab, John. Household Energy Use & Conservation: How to Prepare an Energy Budget. LC 79-16895. 1980. 23.95x (ISBN 0-88229-476-8); pap. 12.95x (ISBN 0-88229-733-3). Nelson-Hall.
Lund, Leonard, ed. Energy: Update & Outlook - November 1974. (Report Ser.: No. 663). 54p. (Orig.). 1975. pap. 15.00 (ISBN 0-8237-0101-8); pap. 5.00 member. Conference Bd.
McAvin, Margaret. Site Planning for Energy Conservation. (Architecture Ser.: Bibliography A-634). 1981. pap. 7.50 (ISBN 0-88066-128-3). Vance Biblios.
McClintock, Michael. Homeowners Energy Investment Handbook: A Guide to Energy-Efficient Home Improvement That Pay off. 128p. (Orig.). 1981. pap. 8.95 (ISBN 0-931790-30-1). Brick Hse Pub.
Mahon, Harold P., et al. Efficient Energy Management. (Illus.). 496p. 1983. 29.95 (ISBN 0-13-791434-2). P-H.
March, Frederick, et al. Wind Power for the Electric-Utility Industry: Policy Incentives for Fuel Conservation. LC 81-48267. (An Arthur D. Little Bk.). 176p. 1982. 23.00x (ISBN 0-669-05321-X). Lexington Bks.
Marion, Jerry B. & Roush, Marvin L. Energy in Perspective. 2nd ed. 1982. pap. 9.75i (ISBN 0-12-472276-8). Acad Pr.
Mauss, Evelyn A. & Ullmann, John E., eds. Conservation of Energy Resources. (Annals of the New York Academy of Sciences: Vol. 324). 83p. (Orig.). 1979. pap. 12.00x (ISBN 0-89766-015-3). NY Acad Sci.
Mazzoni, Steve. Safety Considerations of Energy Saving Materials & Devices. 3.25 (ISBN 0-686-12080-9, TR 78-6). Society Fire Protect.
Meckler, Milton. Energy Conservation in Buildings & Industrial Plants. (Illus.). 1980. 29.95 (ISBN 0-07-041195-6). McGraw.
Meier, Peter M. Energy Planning in Developing Countries. (Energy Management Training Program Monograph). 175p. 1985. softcover 18.00x (ISBN 0-86531-649-X). Westview.
Melott, Ronald K. Is Energy Conservation Firesafe? 2.50 (ISBN 0-686-12081-7, TR 78-8). Society Fire Protect.
Miller Freeman Publications, Inc., Staff. Energy Management & Conservation in Pulp & Paper Mills. Coleman, Matthew, ed. LC 81-81000. (A Pulp & Paper Focus Bk.). (Illus.). 206p. 1981. pap. 32.50 (ISBN 0-87930-099-X). Miller Freeman.
Miller, Richard K., compiled by. Energy Conservation & Utilization in Foundries. 45.00 (ISBN 0-915586-44-4). Fairmont Pr.
--Energy Conservation & Utilization in the Glass Industry. 45.00 (ISBN 0-915586-48-7). Fairmont Pr.
Mintz, Stephan L. & Widmayer, Susan M., eds. Topics in Energy & Resources. LC 74-14644. (Studies in the Natural Sciences: Vol. 7). 168p. 1974. 39.50x (ISBN 0-306-36907-9, Plenum Pr). Plenum Pub.
Mitchell, J. W. Energy Engineering. LC 82-19977. 236p. 1983. 41.95x (ISBN 0-471-08772-6, Pub. by Wiley-Interscience). Wiley.
Money, Lloyd J. Transportation Energy & the Future. (Illus.). 144p. 1984. text ed. 29.95 (ISBN 0-13-930230-1). P-H.
Montgomery, Richard H. The Home Energy Audit: Your Guide to Understanding & Reducing Your Energy Costs. LC 82-15992. 191p. 1982. pap. text ed. 10.95 (ISBN 0-471-86466-8, Pub. by wiley Pr). Wiley.
Moran, Michael. Availability Analysis: A Guide to Efficient Energy Use. (Illus.). 304p. 1982. 55.00 (ISBN 0-13-054874-X). P-H.
Morrison, James W. The Complete Energy-Saving Home Improvement Guide. 4th ed. LC 80-23996. (Illus.). 1981. pap. 2.50 (ISBN 0-668-05085-3, 5085-3). Arco.
Mother Earth News, ed. Mother's Energy Efficiency Book. 1983. pap. 14.95 (ISBN 0-938432-05-2). Brick Hse Pub.
Mulligan, Joseph F. Practical Physics: The Production & Conservation of Energy. (Illus.). 1980. text ed. 28.95 (ISBN 0-07-044032-8). McGraw.
Munasinghe, Mohan & Schramm, Gunther. Energy Policy & Demand Management Policy. 464p. 1983. 32.50 (ISBN 0-442-25838-0). Van Nos Reinhold.
Murphy, Earl F. Energy & Environmental Balance. (Pergamon Policy Studies). 1980. 43.00 (ISBN 0-08-025082-3). Pergamon.
Murphy, W. R. & McKay, G. Energy Management. 288p. (Orig.). 1982. pap. text ed. 59.95 (ISBN 0-408-00508-4). Butterworth.
National Research Council. Energy in Transition, Nineteen Eighty-Five to Two Thousand & Ten. 677p. 1982. pap. 22.50 (ISBN 0-309-03331-4). Natl Acad Pr.
National Trust for Historic Preservation. New Energy from Old Buildings. LC 81-8516. (Illus.). 208p. (Orig.). 1981. pap. 9.95 (ISBN 0-89133-095-X). Preservation Pr.
Nelson, Robert V., et al. E Equals M C Squared: Energy - Management, Conservation & Communication, 17 vols. Ide, Arthur F., ed. (Illus., Orig.). 1981. write for info. (ISBN 0-86663-800-8); pap. write for info. (ISBN 0-86663-801-6). Ide Hse.
Nemetz, Peter N. & Hankey, Marilyn. Economic Incentives for Energy Conservation. LC 83-17064. 324p. 1984. 45.95x (ISBN 0-471-88768-4, Pub. by Wiley-Interscience). Wiley.
Nemetz, Peter N., ed. Energy Crisis: Policy Response. 304p. 1981. pap. text ed. 10.95x (ISBN 0-920380-49-2, Pub. by Inst Res Pub Canada). Brookfield Pub Co.
Neufeld, Ronald D. & Goodwin, Richard W., eds. Emerging Energy: Environmental Trends & the Engineer. 59p. 1983. pap. 13.00x (ISBN 0-87262-380-7). Am Soc Civil Eng.
Nordlund, Willis J. & Robson, R. Thayne. Energy & Employment. LC 79-22133. 142p. 1980. 33.95x (ISBN 0-03-055291-5). Praeger.
O'Brien, Kevin & Corn, David. Energy Conservation: A Campus Guide. 33p. 1981. 5.00 (ISBN 0-936758-04-X). Ctr Responsive Law.
O'Callaghan, P. W. Design & Management for Energy Conservation. 41.00 (ISBN 0-08-027287-8). Pergamon.
Odum, Howard T. Environment Power & Society. LC 78-129660. (Environmental Science & Technology Ser). 331p. 1971. pap. text ed. 19.95x (ISBN 0-471-65275-X, Pub. by Wiley-Interscience). Wiley.
OECD Staff. Environmental Effects of Energy Systems: The OECD Compass Project. 138p. 1983. pap. 12.00 (ISBN 92-64-12470-5). OECD.
OECD Staff & IEA Staff. Energy Conservation: The Role of Demand Management in the Nineteen-Eighties. 68p. 1981. pap. 6.00x (ISBN 92-64-12190-0). OECD.
--Energy Policies & Programs of IEA Countries: 1982 Review. (Eng. & Fr.). 416p. 1983. pap. 22.00x (ISBN 92-64-12460-8). OECD.
Office of Technology Assessment, Congress of the United States. Residential Energy Conservation. LC 79-55053. 342p. 1980. text ed. 18.95x (ISBN 0-916672-38-7). Allanheld.
Oppenheimer, Ernest J. Solving the U. S. Energy Problem. 50p. (Orig.). 1984. pap. 5.00 (ISBN 0-9603982-4-4). Pen & Podium.
Oviatt, Mark D. & Miller, Richard K. Industrial Pneumatic Systems: Noise Control & Energy Conservation. 27.95 (ISBN 0-915586-19-3). Fairmont Pr.
Pachauri, Rajendra K., ed. Energy Policy for India. 1980. 22.50x (ISBN 0-8364-0620-6, Pub by Macmillan India). South Asia Bks.
Paparian, Michael, ed. California Energy Directory: A Guide to Organizations & Information Resources. LC 78-78313. (California Information Guides Ser.). (Illus.). 88p. (Orig.). 1980. pap. 16.50x (ISBN 0-912102-51-9). Cal Inst Public.
Parker, J. D., ed. Energy Conservation Measures: Proceedings of the International Symposium, Kuwait, 6-8 February 1983. LC 83-25137. 332p. 1984. 65.00 (ISBN 0-08-031141-5). Pergamon.
Parks, Alexis. People Heaters: A People's Guide to Keeping Warm in Winter. LC 80-21930. (Illus.). 128p. (Orig.). 1980. pap. 6.50 (ISBN 0-931790-16-6). Brick Hse Pub.
Patrick, Dale R. & Fardo, Stephen W. Energy Management & Conservation. (Illus.). 304p. 1982. 30.95 (ISBN 0-13-277657-X). P-H.
Pauker, G. Y., ed. Energy Efficiency & Conservation in the Asia-Pacific Region: Proceedings of the Fouth Workshop, Honolulu, Hawaii, June 2-5, 1981. 200p. 1983. pap. 25.00 (ISBN 0-08-030532-6). Pergamon.
Payne, F. William, ed. Compressed Air Systems: A Guidebook on Energy & Cost Savings. LC 84-48571. 185p. 1985. 36.00 (ISBN 0-88173-007-6). Fairmont Pr.
Pearson, Jon. Energy Conservation in Small Business: Promoting the Use of New Testament. LC 83-21739. (Illus.). 212p. (Orig.). 1984. lib. bdg. 25.00 (ISBN 0-8191-3659-X); pap. text ed. 13.50 (ISBN 0-8191-3660-3). U Pr of Amer.
Petrick, Alfred, Jr. Energy Resource Assessment. (Energy Management Training Program Monograph). 200p. 1985. hardcover 20.00x (ISBN 0-86531-764-X). Westview.
The Petroleum Refining Industry-Energy Saving & Environmental Control. (Energy Technology Review 24; Pollution Technology Review: 39). (Illus.). 374p. 1978. 39.00 (ISBN 0-8155-0694-5). Noyes.
Pindyck, Robert S. The Structure of World Energy Demand. (Illus.). 1979. 27.50x (ISBN 0-262-16074-9). MIT Pr.
Pinkus, O. & Wilcock, D. F., eds. Strategy for Energy Conservation Through Tribology. 2nd ed. (Bk. No. H00109). 1982. 20.00 (ISBN 0-685-37585-4). ASME.
Pollack, Kenneth & Gergen, Michael J. Energy Storage: Four Major Alternatives - Heat Storage, Cool Storage, Compressed Air Energy Storage & Underground Pumped Hydro Storage. Stryker, Perrin, ed. LC 83-80664. 275p. (Orig.). 1983. pap. 29.50 (ISBN 0-918780-23-3). INFORM.
Promoting Small Power Production: Implementing Section 210 of PURPA, Center for Renewable Resources, Solar Lobby & Others. 49p. 1981. 3.00 (ISBN 0-937446-04-1, 200). Ctr Renew Resources.
Rapolla, A., et al, eds. Geophysical Aspects of the Energy Problem. (Developments in Energy Research Ser.: Vol. 1). 326p. 1980. 68.00 (ISBN 0-444-41845-8). Elsevier.
Reay, David A. Industrial Energy Conservation: A Handbook for Engineers & Managers. 2nd ed. (Illus.). 1979. 72.00 (ISBN 0-08-023273-6); pap. 28.00 (ISBN 0-08-023274-4). Pergamon.
Reische, Diana, ed. Energy Demand vs. Supply. (Reference Shelf Ser: Vol. 47, No. 5). 1975. 8.00 (ISBN 0-8242-0573-1). Wilson.
Research Needs Report: Energy Conversion Research. 129p. 1976. pap. 10.00 (ISBN 0-685-99210-1, H00090). ASME.
Ritchie, Ralph W. How to Get the Most Heat from Your Fuel, No. 1. LC 81-90069. (Energy Conservation in the Crafts - a Craft Monograph). (Illus.). 39p. (Orig.). 1979. pap. 4.50 (ISBN 0-939656-00-0). Studios West.
--How to Lift & Move Almost Anything. LC 81-90071. (Energy Conservation in the Crafts Ser. - a Craft Monograph: No. 3). (Illus.). 52p. (Orig.). 1980. pap. 4.50 (ISBN 0-939656-02-7). Studios West.
--How to Recover & Re-Use Heat from Kilns & Furnaces. LC 81-90073. (Energy Conservation in the Crafts - a Craft Monograph: No. 5). (Illus.). 52p. (Orig.). 1981. pap. 4.50 (ISBN 0-939656-04-3). Studios West.

--Kiln & Furnace Stacks, No. 2. LC 81-90070. (Energy Conservation in the Crafts - a Craft Monograph). (Illus.). 46p. (Orig.). 1980. pap. 4.00 (ISBN 0-939656-01-9). Studios West.

--Understanding & Using Burners. LC 81-90072. (Energy Conservation in the Crafts - a Craft Monograph: No. 4). (Illus.). 60p. (Orig.). 1981. pap. 4.50 (ISBN 0-939656-03-5). Studios West.

--User's Fuel Handbook. LC 81-90075. (Energy Conservation in the Crafts - a Craft Monograph: No. 7). (Illus., Orig.). 1981. pap. 4.50 (ISBN 0-939656-06-X). Studios West.

Robinette, Gary O. & McClennon, Charles, eds. Landscape Planning for Energy Conservation. 224p. 1983. 24.95 (ISBN 0-442-22339-0). Van Nos Reinhold.

Russell, Joe W., Jr. Economic Disincentives for Energy Conservation. LC 79-13170. (Environmental Law Institute State & Local Energy Conservation Project Ser.). 176p. 1979. prof ref 29.95x (ISBN 0-88410-060-X). Ballinger Pub.

Saving Energy. 1981. 24.95 (ISBN 0-686-73893-4, 04917). Natl Geog.

Schwarz, Stephen C. & Brunner, Calvin R. Energy & Resource Recovery from Waste. LC 83-13110. (Energy Tech. Rev. No. 86; Pollution Tech. Rev. No. 102). 272p. 1984. 32.00 (ISBN 0-8155-0959-6). Noyes.

Scott, C. D. Fourth Symposium on Biotechnology in Energy Production & Conservation. 495p. 1983. text ed. 74.95x (ISBN 0-471-89122-3, Pub. by Wiley-Interscience). Wiley.

SERI. A New Prosperity: Building a Sustainable Energy Future the SERI (Solar Conservation Study) LC 81-6089. 454p. (Orig.). 1981. 39.95x (ISBN 0-471-88652-1, Brick Hse Pub.). Wiley.

Settlemire, Mary Ann. Energy Education Programs: Perspectives for Community, Junior, & Technical Colleges. 1981. pap. 4.00 (ISBN 0-87117-104-X). Am Assn Comm Jr Coll.

Sheahan, Richard T., ed. Evaluating the FBC Option: 1984. (Illus.). 286p. 3-ring binder 69.00 (ISBN 0-86587-068-3). Gov Insts.

Sherratt, A. F., ed. Air Conditioning & Energy Conservation. (Illus.). 287p. 1980. 69.50 (ISBN 0-89397-071-9, Pub. by Architectural Pr). Nichols Pub.

--Energy Conservation & Energy Management in Buildings. (Illus.). 330p. 1976. 55.50 (ISBN 0-85334-684-4, Pub. by Elsevier Applied Sci England). Elsevier.

Shinskey, F. G. Control Systems That Save Energy. Gyftopoulos, Elias P. & Cohen, Karen C., eds. (Industrial Energy-Conservation Manuals: No. 2). (Illus.). 64p. 1982. loose-leaf 20.00x (ISBN 0-262-19202-0). MIT Pr.

Silverman, J., ed. Energy Storage: Transactions of the First International Assembly on Energy Storage, Held in Dubrovnik, Yugoslavia, 1979. LC 80-40771. (Illus.). 512p. 1980. 120.00 (ISBN 0-08-025471-3). Pergamon.

Skinner, Brian J., ed. Earth's Energy & Mineral Resources. LC 80-23495. (The Earth & Its Inhabitants: Selected Readings from American Scientist Ser.). (Illus.). 200p. 1980. pap. 9.95x (ISBN 0-913232-90-4). W Kaufmann.

Smith, Craig B. Energy Management Principles: Applications, Benefits, Savings. (Illus.). 400p. 1981. 54.00 (ISBN 0-08-028036-6); pap. 29.50 (ISBN 0-08-028811-1). Pergamon.

Smith, John E. Conserve Energy & Save Money. (McGraw-Hill Paperbacks). (Illus.). 224p. (Orig.). 1980. pap. 8.95 (ISBN 0-07-058940-2). McGraw.

Snyder, Nathan W., ed. Energy Conservation for Space Power. LC 60-16913. 779p. 1961. 39.00 (ISBN 0-317-36834-6); members 19.50 (ISBN 0-317-36835-4). AIAA.

Sobel, Lester A., ed. Energy Crisis: 1977-1979, Vol. 4. 1980. lib. bdg. 19.95 (ISBN 0-87196-284-5). Facts on File.

Sorcar, Prafulla C. Energy Saving Lighting Systems. 368p. 1982. 27.50 (ISBN 0-442-26430-5). Van Nos Reinhold.

The Spec Guide: Energy Products Specifications for Conservation, Solar Wind & Photovoltaics. 7th ed. (Illus.). 1985. 49.00 (ISBN 0-317-17142-9). SolarVision.

Stanilad Hall. The European Energy Outlook to Nineteen Eighty-Five. 123p. 1978. 132.00x (ISBN 0-86010-142-8, Pub. by Graham & Trotman England). State Mutual Bk.

Steinhart, John, et al. Pathway to Energy Sufficiency: The 2050 Study. Hollister, Sidney, ed. LC 78-74807. (Illus.). 1979. pap. 4.95 (ISBN 0-913890-31-6). Friends of Earth.

Stephens, H. S. & Jarvis, B., eds. Proceedings of the International Conference on Energy Storage, 2 vols. 700p. 1981. pap. 98.00x (ISBN 0-906085-50-0). BHRA Fluid.

Strub, A. S. & Ehringer, H., eds. Energy Conservation in Industry, 3 Vols. 1089p. 1984. 247.50 (ISBN 0-89116-447-2). Hemisphere Pub.

--New Ways to Save Energy. 1238p. 1980. lib. bdg. 71.00 (ISBN 90-277-1078-3, Pub. by Reidel Holland). Kluwer Academic.

Stunkel, Kenneth R. National Energy Profiles. LC 80-25046. 430p. 1981. 45.95 (ISBN 0-03-050646-8). Praeger.

Summer Seminar, Heat & Mass Transfer in Buildings, Dubrovnik, Yugoslavia, Aug. 29-Sept. 3,1977. Energy Conservation in Heating, Cooling & Ventilating Buildings: Heat & Mass Transfer Techniques & Alternatives, Proceedings, 2 vols. Hoogendoorn, C. J. & Afgan, N., eds. LC 78-1108. (Thermal & Fluids Engineering Ser.). 901p. 1978. Set. text ed. 169.00 (ISBN 0-89116-095-7). Hemisphere Pub.

Sunset Editors. Energy-Saving Projects. LC 80-53485. (Illus.). 96p. (Orig.). 1981. pap. 3.95 (ISBN 0-376-01230-7, Sunset Bks.). Sunset-Lane.

Technical Association of the Pulp & Paper Industry. Energy Conservation-Technology & Methods Seminar, 1985: Notes of TAPPI, Holiday Inn, Pittsburg, PA, June 3-5. pap. 27.30 (ISBN 0-317-28027-9, 2025567). Bks Demand UMI.

Technology for Energy Conservation: Proceedings of First Annual Conference. 1977. pap. 12.00x (ISBN 0-686-26012-0); lib. bdg. 15.00x (ISBN 0-686-26013-9). Info Transfer.

Tempest, Paul, ed. International Energy Options: An Agenda for the Nineteen Eighties. LC 81-80575. 320p. 1981. text ed. 35.00 (ISBN 0-89946-089-5). Oelgeschlager.

Tether, Ivan J. Government Procurement & Operations. LC 77-333. (Environmental Law Institute State & Local Energy Conservation Project Ser.). 1977. prof ref 17.50 (ISBN 0-88410-057-X). Ballinger Pub.

Texas A & M University Library. Energy Bibliography & Index, Vol. 1. LC 77-93150. 1384p. 1978. 375.00x (ISBN 0-87201-965-9). Gulf Pub.

--Energy Bibliography & Index, Vol. 2. LC 77-93150. 1280p. 1979. 375.00x (ISBN 0-87201-970-5). Gulf Pub.

Thompson, William F. & Karaganis, Jerome J. Choice Over Chance: Options for Economic & Energy Options for the Future. LC 81-15851. 304p. 1981. 34.95x (ISBN 0-03-059554-1); pap. 15.95x (ISBN 0-03-059556-8). Praeger.

Thorp, James H. & Gibbons, J. Whitfield, eds. Energy & Environmental Stress in Aquatic Systems: Proceedings. LC 78-27913. (DOE Symposium Ser.). 876p. 1978. pap. 30.00 (ISBN 0-87079-115-X, CONF-771114); microfiche 4.50 (ISBN 0-87079-191-5, CONF-771114). DOE.

Thumann, Albert. Electrical Design, Safety, & Energy Conservation. 29.95 (ISBN 0-915586-05-3). Fairmont Pr.

--Handbook of Energy Audits. 440p. 32.00 (ISBN 0-915586-18-5). Fairmont Pr.

--Plant Engineers & Managers Guide to Energy Conservation: The Role of the Energy Manager. 2nd ed. 272p. 1982. 28.95 (ISBN 0-442-28414-4). Van Nos Reinhold.

Trumpower, Bernard L., ed. Function of Quinones in Energy Conserving Systems. 1982. 74.50 (ISBN 0-12-701280-X). Acad Pr.

Turner, Wayne C., ed. Energy Management Handbook. LC 81-10351. 714p. 1982. 69.95x (ISBN 0-471-08252-X, Pub. by Wiley-Interscience). Wiley.

United Nations Economic Commission for Europe, Geneva, Switzerland. Energy Modelling Studies & Conservation: Proceedings of a Seminar of the United Nations Economic Commission for Europe, Washington, D. C. 24-28 March 1980. (Illus.). 600p. 1982. 105.00 (ISBN 0-08-027416-1). Pergamon.

United Nations Economic Commission for Europe, Geneva, Switzerland, ed. Environment & Energy: Environmental Aspects of Energy Production & Use with Particular Reference to New Technologies. LC 79-40550. 1979. 25.00 (ISBN 0-08-024468-8). Pergamon.

United Nations Educational Scientific & Cultural Organization. International Directory of New & Renewable Energy Information Sources & 467p. 1982. pap. text ed. 35.00x (ISBN 0-89553-142-9). Am Solar Energy.

United States Department of Housing & Urban Development. How to Insulate Your Home & Save Fuel. 11.75 (ISBN 0-8446-5619-4). Peter Smith.

United States Energy Study Group. Energy R & D & National Progress. Cambel, Ali B., ed. LC 78-11792. (Illus.). 1978. Repr. of 1965 ed. lib. bdg. 37.50x (ISBN 0-313-20689-9, USEN). Greenwood.

Vesiland, P., et al. Unit Operations in Resource Recovery Engineering. (Illus.). 1980. text ed. 45.00 (ISBN 0-13-937953-3). P-H.

Veziroglu, T. Nejat, ed. Energy Conservation: Proceedings of the Energy Research & Development Administration Conference Held at the University of Miami, Dec. 1975. 1977. pap. text ed. 130.00 (ISBN 0-08-022134-3). Pergamon.

--Renewable Energy Sources: International Progress, Vols. 4 A & B. (Energy Research Ser.). 1984. Set. 222.25 (ISBN 0-444-42363-X); Vol. A, 456 pgs. 129.75 (ISBN 0-444-42361-3, I-313-84); Vol. B, 498 pgs. 129.75 (ISBN 0-444-42362-1). Elsevier.

Walker, G. & Senft, J. R. Free Piston Stirling Engines. (Lecture Notes in Engineering Ser.: Vol. 12). 290p. 1985. pap. 21.00 (ISBN 0-387-15495-7). Springer-Verlag.

Wasserman, Harvey. Energy War: Reports from the Front. 270p. 1979. 12.95 (ISBN 0-88208-105-5); pap. 5.95 (ISBN 0-88208-106-3). Lawrence Hill.

The Waste Watchers: A Citizen's Handbook for Conserving Energy & Resources. 1980. 5.50 (ISBN 0-686-27465-2). Tech Info Proj.

Webb, Michael G. & Ricketts, Martin J. The Economics of Energy. LC 79-18708. 315p. 1981. pap. 21.95x (ISBN 0-470-27312-7). Halsted Pr.

William, Lindsey & Wilson, Clifford. Energy Non-Crisis. 2nd, rev., enl. ed. 240p. pap. 3.95 (ISBN 0-89051-068-7). Master Bks.

Williams, Tyler E., Jr., ed. Energy Efficiency in Buildings & Industry. 744p. 1984. pap. 58.00 (ISBN 0-86587-063-2). Gov Insts.

Wilson, Richard, ed. Energy for the Year Two-Thousand. LC 80-18623. (Ettore Majorana International Science Series; Physical Sciences: Vol. 6). 410p. 1980. 65.00x (ISBN 0-306-40540-7, Plenum Pr). Plenum Pub.

Winning Low Energy Building Designs. 651p. 1980. 37.00 (ISBN 0-660-50675-0, SSC156, SSC). Unipub.

Woodburn, John H. Opportunities in Energy Careers. (VGM Career Bks.). (Illus.). 160p. 1983. 7.95 (ISBN 0-317-03474-X, 6584-6, Passport Bks.); pap. 5.95 (ISBN 0-317-03475-8, 6584-8). Natl Textbk.

Yannas, S., ed. Passive & Low Energy Architecture: Proceedings of the International Conference, 28 June - 3 July 1983, Crete, Greece. 835p. 1983. 160.00 (ISBN 0-08-030581-4). Pergamon.

Yaverbaum, L. H., ed. Energy Saving by Increasing Boiler Efficiency. LC 79-83772. (Energy Technology Review: No. 40). (Illus.). 226p. 1979. 32.00 (ISBN 0-8155-0745-3). Noyes.

Zackrison, Harry B., Jr. Energy Conservation Techniques for Engineers. 352p. 1984. 34.50 (ISBN 0-442-29392-5). Van Nos Reinhold.

Zichichi, Antonio, ed. The High-Energy Limit. (The Subnuclear Ser.: Vol. 18). 1116p. 1982. 135.00x (ISBN 0-306-41036-2, Plenum Pr). Plenum Pub.

ENERGY CONVERSION, DIRECT

see Direct Energy Conversion

ENERGY LEVELS (QUANTUM MECHANICS)

see also Nuclear Excitation; Triplet State

Bashkin, S. & Stoner, J. O., Jr. Atomic Energy Levels & Grotrian Diagrams, Vol. 2: Sulphur I to Titanium XXII. 1978. 115.00 (ISBN 0-444-85149-6, North-Holland). Elsevier.

Duncan, A. B. Rydberg Series in Atoms & Molecules. (Physical Chemistry Ser, Vol. 23). 1971. 45.00 (ISBN 0-12-223950-4). Acad Pr.

Fogler, H. S., ed. Energy Balances. LC 80-25594. (ALCHEMI Modular Instruction F-Ser.: Vol. 3). 74p. 1982. pap. 30.00 (ISBN 0-8169-0213-5, J-18); pap. 15.00 members. Am Inst Chem Eng.

Herman, F., et al, eds. Computational Methods for Large Molecules & Localized States in Solids. LC 72-92442. (IBM Research Symposia Ser.). 392p. 1973. 59.50x (ISBN 0-306-30716-2, Plenum Pr). Plenum Pub.

Horen, D. J., ed. Nuclear Level Schemes a-45 Through a-257. 1973. 40.00 (ISBN 0-12-355650-3). Acad Pr.

ENERGY METABOLISM

Catlett, Robert H. Readings in Animal Energetics. LC 73-11003. 237p. 1973. text ed. 29.50x (ISBN 0-8422-7119-8); pap. text ed. 9.75x (ISBN 0-8290-0668-0). Irvington.

Chance, Britton, et al, eds. Control of Energy Metabolism. 1966. 70.00 (ISBN 0-12-167850-4). Acad Pr.

Gessaman, James A. Ecological Energetics of Homeotherms. LC 72-80316. 155p. 1973. pap. 7.50 (ISBN 0-87421-053-4). Utah St U Pr.

Girardier, Lucien & Stock, Michael J., eds. Mammalian Thermogenesis. LC 83-1929. (Illus.). 359p. 1983. 80.00 (ISBN 0-412-23550-1, NO. 6822, Pub. by Chapman & Hall). Methuen Inc.

Goldsby, Richard A. Cells & Energy. 2nd ed. 1977. pap. text ed. write for info. (ISBN 0-02-344300-6, 34430). Macmillan.

Hommes, E. A. & Van Den Berg, C. J., eds. Normal & Pathological Development of Energy Metabolism. 1976. 44.00 (ISBN 0-12-354560-9). Acad Pr.

Klachko, D. M., et al, eds. Hormones & Energy Metabolism. LC 78-23943. (Advances in Experimental Medicine & Biology Ser.: Vol. 111). 212p. 1979. 35.00x (ISBN 0-306-40070-7, Plenum Pr). Plenum Pub.

McCandless, D. W., ed. Cerebral Energy Metabolism & Metabolic Encephalopathy. 478p. 1985. 65.00x (ISBN 0-306-41797-9, Plenum Pr). Plenum Pub.

Margaria, R. Biomechanics & Energetics of Muscular Exercise. (Illus.). 1976. text ed. 29.50x (ISBN 0-19-857397-9). Oxford U Pr.

Mehlman, Myron A. & Hanson, Richard W., eds. Energy Metabolism & the Regulation of Metabolic Processes in Mitochondria. 1972. 49.50 (ISBN 0-12-487850-4). Acad Pr.

Packer, Lester. Biomembranes, Architecture, Biogenesis, Bioenergetics & Differentiation. 1974. 55.00 (ISBN 0-12-543440-5). Acad Pr.

Sinclair, John C., ed. Temperature Regulation & Energy Metabolism in the Newborn. (Monographs in Neonatology). 272p. 1978. 42.00 (ISBN 0-8089-1090-6, 794085). Grune.

Stanier, M. W., et al. Energy Balance & Temperature Regulation. LC 83-18950. (Cambridge Texts in the Physiological Sciences Ser.: No. 4). (Illus.). 200p. 1984. 29.95 (ISBN 0-521-25827-8); pap. 12.95 (ISBN 0-521-27727-2). Cambridge U Pr.

Teilhard De Chardin, Pierre. Activation of Energy. Hague, Rene, tr. LC 75-142104. (Helen & Kurt Wolff Bk.). 416p. 1972. pap. 6.95 (ISBN 0-15-602860-3, Harv). HarBraceJ.

ENERGY POLICY

see also Energy Conservation

Abelson, Philip H. Energy for Tomorrow. LC 75-1368. (Jessie & John Danz Lecture Ser). (Illus.). 64p. 1975. 10.00x (ISBN 0-295-95413-2); pap. 3.95x (ISBN 0-295-95414-0). U of Wash Pr.

Abelson, Philip H., ed. Energy: Use, Conservation & Supply. LC 74-29004. (Science Compendium Ser.: Vol. 1). 154p. 1974. casebound 10.00 (ISBN 0-87168-213-3); pap. 3.50 (ISBN 0-87168-223-0). AAAS.

Abelson, Philip H. & Hammond, Allen L., eds. Energy Two: Use, Conservation & Supply. LC 78-59190. (Science Compendia Ser.: Vol. 6). 1978. 12.00 (ISBN 0-87168-300-8); pap. 5.00 (ISBN 0-87168-237-0). AAAS.

Academy Forum National Academy of Sciences. Energy: Future Alternatives & Risks. LC 74-13084. 202p. 1974. prof ref 18.50x (ISBN 0-88410-025-1). Ballinger Pub.

Ahuja, D., et al, eds. National Energy Data Systems. 511p. 1984. text ed. 30.50x (ISBN 0-391-03209-7, Pub. by Concept India). Humanities.

AIA Research Corporation. Energy Conservation in Building Design. 1974. pap. 3.50 (ISBN 0-913962-17-1). Am Inst Arch.

American Association for the Advancement of Science, et al. National Energy Policy Conference: Proceedings. (AAAS Report: No. 77-R-5). 1977. pap. 6.00 (ISBN 0-87168-247-8). AAAS.

American Gas Association. Policy Evaluation & Analysis Group. New Technologies for Gas Energy Supply & Efficient Use: 1983 Update. LC 83-174168. (Illus.). 43p. Date not set. price not set. Am Gas Assn.

American Petroleum Institute Staff. Two Energy Futures: A National Choice for the Eighty's. rev. ed. LC 81-7926. (Illus.). 187p. 1981. pap. text ed. write for info. (ISBN 0-89364-041-7). Am Petroleum.

Aronofsky, J. S., et al, eds. Energy Policy. (TIMS Studies in the Management Sciences: Vol. 10). 260p. 1979. 32.50 (ISBN 0-444-85238-7, North Holland). Elsevier.

Ashley, Holt, et al, eds. Energy & the Environment, a Risk-Benefit Approach. 1976. text ed. 31.00 (ISBN 0-08-020873-8). Pergamon.

Baehr, H. D., et al, eds. Power Engineering & Technology: Energy Efficient Use of Working Fluids, Alternative Processes, Heat Pumps& Organic Rankine Cycle. 1984. 179.50 (ISBN 0-89116-448-0). Hemisphere Pub.

Baldwin, Malcolm F. The Southwest Energy Complex: A Policy Evaluation. LC 73-79429. pap. 20.00 (ISBN 0-317-11229-5, 2015787). Bks Demand UMI.

Barbour, Ian. Energy & American Values. Brooks, Harvey, et al, eds. LC 82-13174. 256p. 1982. 32.95x (ISBN 0-03-062468-1); pap. 14.95x (ISBN 0-03-062469-X). Praeger.

Barzelay, Michael. The Politicized Market Economy: Alcohol in the Brazilian Energy Strategy. 1986. 28.50x (ISBN 0-520-05382-6). U of Cal Pr.

Baumgartner, Thomas, ed. Transitions to Alternative Energy Systems. (Replica Edition Ser.). 270p. 1984. softcover 23.50x (ISBN 0-86531-907-3). Westview.

Bayraktar, B. A., et al, eds. Energy Policy Planning. LC 80-26897. (NATO Conference Series II-Systems Science: Vol. 9). 478p. 1981. 69.50x (ISBN 0-306-40631-4, Plenum Pr). Plenum Pub.

Beaumont, John R. & Keys, Paul. Future Cities: Spatial Analysis of Energy Issues. (Geography & Public Policy Research Studies). 198p. 1982. 44.95x (ISBN 0-471-10451-5, Pub. by Res Stud Pr). Wiley.

Karam, R. A. & Morgan, Karl J., eds. Energy & the Environment-Cost Benefit Analysis. LC 75-42470. 1976. text ed. 92.00 (ISBN 0-08-020644-1). Pergamon.

Kash, Don E. & Rycroft, Robert W. U. S. Energy Policy: Crisis & Complacency. LC 83-17093. (Illus.). 334p. 1984. 19.95 (ISBN 0-8061-1869-5). U of Okla Pr.

Kavass, Igor I. & Bieber, Doris M., eds. Energy & Congress (1974-1978) LC 80-82112. 801p. 1982. lib. bdg. 40.00 (ISBN 0-89941-060-X). W S Hein.

Kelly, William J., et al. Energy Research & Development in the U. S. S. R. Preparations for the 21st Century. (Policy Studies). (Illus.). 514p. 1986. 60.00x (ISBN 0-8223-0604-2). Duke.

Kendall, Henry W., ed. Energy Strategies: Toward a Solar Future. Nadis, Steven J. LC 79-23757. 352p. 1979. prof ref 26.50 (ISBN 0-88410-622-5). Ballinger Pub.

Kneese & Sweeney. Handbook of Natural Resource & Energy Economics, 2 vols. Date not set. Set. write for info. (ISBN 0-444-87646-4). Vol. 1 (ISBN 0-444-87644-8). Vol. 2 (ISBN 0-444-87645-6). Elsevier.

Kursunoglu, Behram & Perlmutter, Arnold, eds. Directions in Energy Policy: A Comprehensive Approach to Energy Resource Decision-Making. LC 79-21524. 544p. 1980. prof ref 40.00 (ISBN 0-88410-089-8). Ballinger Pub.

Ladman, Jerry R., et al, eds. U. S.-Mexican Energy Relationships: Realities & Prospects. 256p. 1981. 28.50x (ISBN 0-669-04398-2); pap. 10.50x (ISBN 0-669-04399-0). Lexington Bks.

Laird, Melvin, et al. Energy Policy: A New War Between the States? 1976. pap. 3.75 (ISBN 0-8447-2074-7). Am Enterprise.

Landsberg, Hans, ed. Selected Studies on Energy: Background Papers for Energy, The Next Twenty Years. LC 79-24800. 464p. 1980. prof ref 39.50x (ISBN 0-88410-093-6). Ballinger Pub.

Lawrence, Robert, ed. Energy Policy Issues. 1978. pap. 8.00 (ISBN 0-918592-28-3). Policy Studies.

Lawrence, Robert M. & Heisler, Martin O., eds. International Energy Policy. LC 79-4748. (A Policy Studies Organization Book). 240p. 1980. 29.00x (ISBN 0-669-02929-7). Lexington Bks.

Leathers, Park & Ritts, Blaine. A Guide for Evaluating Energy Management. (Illus.). 177p. 1983. pap. text ed. 47.00 (ISBN 0-89413-100-1, 516). Inst Inter Aud.

LeBel, Phillip. Energy Economics & Technology. LC 82-15183. 576p. 1982. text ed. 37.50x (ISBN 0-8018-2772-8); pap. text ed. 14.95x (ISBN 0-8018-2773-6). Johns Hopkins.

Lev, B., et al, eds. Analytic Techniques for Energy Planning: Proceedings of the First Symposium Organized by the Operations Research Society of America Special Interest Group on Energy, Natural Resources & the Environment. 372p. 1984. 52.00 (ISBN 0-444-86884-4, I-291-84). Elsevier.

Lev, Benjamin, ed. Energy Models & Studies. (Studies in Management Science & Systems: Vol. 9). 600p. 1983. 89.50 (ISBN 0-444-86601-9, North Holland). Elsevier.

Littlechild, S. C. & Vaidya, K. G. Energy Strategies for the UK. 256p. 1982. text ed. 29.95x (ISBN 0-04-339029-3). Allen Unwin.

Lonnroth, Mans & Steen, Peter. Energy in Transition: A Report on Energy Policy & Future Options. LC 78-68827. 1980. 10.95 (ISBN 0-520-03881-9). U of Cal Pr.

Lovins, Amory & Lovins, Hunter. Brittle Power: Energy Strategy for National Security. 512p. 1983. pap. 8.95 (ISBN 0-931790-49-2). Brick Hse Pub.

Lovins, Amory & Lovins, L. Hunter. Brittle Power. 500p. 1982. 17.95 (ISBN 0-931790-28-X). Brick Hse Pub.

Lovins, Amory B. Soft Energy Paths: Toward a Durable Peace. LC 77-4349. 1979. pap. 4.95i (ISBN 0-06-090653-7, CN 653, CN). Har-Row.

Lowinger, Thomas C. Energy Policy in an Era of Limits. 238p. 1983. 27.95 (ISBN 0-03-060423-0). Praeger.

Lucas, Nigel. Energy & the European Communities. 1977. 15.00x (ISBN 0-905118-14-6). Intl Pubns Serv.

--Western European Energy Policies: A Comparative Study. 1984. 34.50x (ISBN 0-19-828488-8). Oxford U Pr.

McAfee, Gage, ed. Energy Laws of Asia. 350p. 1985. 59.95x (ISBN 0-87201-261-1). Gulf Pub.

McCarl, Henry N., et al. Bibliography on Energy Economics. (Public Administration Ser.: Bibliography P-903). 93p. 1982. pap. 14.25 (ISBN 0-88066-141-0). Vance Biblios.

MacLean, Douglas & Brown, Peter G., eds. Energy & the Future. LC 82-18609. (Illus.). 218p. 1983. text ed. 37.50x (ISBN 0-8476-7149-6); pap. text ed. 18.50x (ISBN 0-8476-7225-5). Rowman.

Mangone, G. J., ed. Energy Policies of the World. 1976-79. Vol. 1. 39.25 (ISBN 0-444-00196-4); Vol. 2. 39.25 (ISBN 0-444-00206-5); Vol. 3. 39.25 (ISBN 0-444-00351-7). Elsevier.

Manners, Ian. Coastal Energy Impact Program in Texas. (Research Monograph: 1980-1). 1980. pap. 6.00 (ISBN 0-87755-241-X). Bureau Busn UT.

Marshall, Eileen & Robinson, Colin. The Economics of Energy Self-Sufficiency: British Institute's Joint Energy Policy Programme; Energy Papers, No. 14. 149p. 1984. text ed. 31.50.x (ISBN 0-435-84518-7). Gower Pub Co.

Materials Aspects of World Energy Needs. 1980. 15.50 (ISBN 0-309-03042-0). Natl Acad Pr.

Maull, H. Europe & World Energy. LC 80-40488. (Illus.). 1980. text ed. 45.00 (ISBN 0-408-10629-8). Butterworth.

Maull, Hanns. Energy, Minerals, & Western Security. LC 84-15410. 432p. 1985. text ed. 35.00x (ISBN 0-8018-2500-8). Johns Hopkins.

Meier, Peter M. Energy Planning in Developing Countries. (Energy Management Training Program Monograph). 175p. 1985. softcover 18.00x (ISBN 0-86531-649-X). Westview.

Melby, Eric D. Oil & the International System: The Case of France, 1918-1969. Bruchey, Stuart, ed. LC 80-2816. (Dissertations in European Economic History II). (Illus.). 1981. lib. bdg. 38.50x (ISBN 0-405-14000-2). Ayer Co Pubs.

Melnicove, Mark, ed. Vote Yes on September 23rd. (Illus.). 56p. (Orig.). 1980. pap. 5.00 (ISBN 0-937966-02-9). Dog Ear.

Miller, G. Tyler, Jr. Energy & Environment: The Four Energy Crises. 2nd ed. 208p. 1980. pap. text ed. write for info. (ISBN 0-534-00836-4). Wadsworth Pub.

Mitchell, Edward J. U. S. Energy Policy: A Primer. 103p. 1974. pap. 5.25 (ISBN 0-8447-3131-5). Am Enterprise.

Mogilanski, Roy, ed. Energy Index, 1983. LC 73-89098. 600p. 1982. 175.00 (ISBN 0-89947-017-3). EIC Intell.

Morell, David & Singer, Grace, eds. Refining the Waterfront: Alternative Energy Facility Siting Policies for Urban Coastal Areas. LC 80-12839. (Illus.). 368p. 1980. text ed. 35.00 (ISBN 0-89946-035-6). Oelgeschlager.

Morgan, M. G., ed. Energy & Man: Technical & Social Aspects of Energy. LC 74-27680. 1975. 37.40 (ISBN 0-87942-043-X, PC00505). Inst Electrical.

Mudahar, M. S. & Hignett, T. P. Energy & Fertilizer: Policy Implications & Options for Developing Countries (Executive Brief) (Technical Bulletin Ser.: No. T-19). (Illus.). 25p. (Orig.). 1981. pap. 4.00 (ISBN 0-88090-018-0). Intl Fertilizer.

--Energy & Fertilizer: Policy Implications & Options for Developing Countries. LC 82-6084. (Technical Bulletin Ser.: No. T-20). (Illus.). 241p. (Orig.). 1982. pap. 15.00 (ISBN 0-88090-019-9). Intl Fertilizer.

Naill, Roger F. Managing the Energy Transition: A System Dynamics Search for Alternatives to Oil & Gas. LC 76-52752. prof ref 27.50 (ISBN 0-88410-608-X). Ballinger Pub.

Nordhaus, W. D. & Goldstein, R., eds. International Studies of the Demand for Energy: Selected Papers Presented at a Conference Held by the Institute for Applied Systems Analysis, Schloss Laxenburg, Austria. (Contributions to Economic Analysis: Vol. 120). 340p. 1978. 51.00 (ISBN 0-444-85079-1, North-Holland). Elsevier.

Novick, David. A World of Scarcities: Critical Issues in Public Policy. LC 75-42278. 194p. 1976. 45.95x (ISBN 0-470-15002-5). Halsted Pr.

O'Callaghan, P. W., ed. Energy for Industry. LC 78-41102. (Illus.). 1979. text ed. 89.00 (ISBN 0-08-022704-X). Pergamon.

OECD. Energy Technology Policy. 124p. (Orig.). 1985. pap. 15.00x (ISBN 92-64-12688-0). OECD.

OECD Staff. Annual Oil & Gas Statistics, 1980-1981. (Fr. & Eng.). 524p. (Orig.). 1983. pap. 36.00x (ISBN 92-64-02417-4). OECD.

--Energy Balances of Dev Countries Nineteen Seventy One-Nineteen Eighty Two. 346p. (Orig.). 1984. pap. 30.00x (ISBN 92-64-02543-X). OECD.

--Energy Policies & Programmes of IEA Countries, 1983 Review. 482p. (Orig.). 1984. pap. 36.00x (ISBN 92-64-12591-4). OECD.

OECD Staff & IEA Staff. Energy Conservation: The Role of Demand Management in the Nineteen-Eighties. 68p. 1981. pap. 6.00x (ISBN 92-64-12190-0). OECD.

Okagaki, Alan & Benson, Jim. County Energy Plan Guidebook. 2nd ed. (Illus.). 200p. (Orig.). 1979. pap. text ed. 10.00x (ISBN 0-937786-01-2). Inst Ecologica.

Oppenheimer, Ernest J. Solving the U. S. Energy Problem. 50p. (Orig.). 1984. pap. 5.00 (ISBN 0-9603982-4-4). Pen & Podium.

Pachauri, Rajendra K. Political Economy of Global Energy. LC 84-21825. 224p. 1985. text ed. 25.00x (ISBN 0-8018-2469-9); pap. text ed. 8.95x (ISBN 0-8018-2501-6). Johns Hopkins.

Pathak, K. K. Nuclear Policy of India. 1983. 18.50x (ISBN 0-8364-1024-6, Pub. by Gitanjali Prakashan). South Asia Bks.

Perelman, Lewis J., et al, eds. Energy Transitions: Long-Term Perspectives. (AAAS Selected Symposium: No. 48). 250p. 1981. 24.50x (ISBN 0-89158-862-0). Westview.

Perrot, M. de. Energie et Societe. pap. 36.00 (ISBN 0-08-027078-6). Pergamon.

Pluta, Joseph E., ed. The Energy Picture: Problems & Prospects. LC 80-68659. 185p. 1980. pap. 6.00 (ISBN 0-87755-243-6). Bureau Busn UT.

Purcell, Edward L. The States & Energy Siting, Vols. 1 & 2. 1982. Vol. 1, 70p. pap. 8.00 pap. (ISBN 0-87292-026-7). Vol. 2, 150p (ISBN 0-87292-027-5). Coun State Govts.

Purcell, L. E., ed. The States & Energy Siting, Vol. II. 150p. 1982. pap. 8.00 (ISBN 0-87292-027-5). Coun State Govts.

Ramsey, James B. The Economics of Exploration for Energy Resources. Altman, Edward I. & Walter, Ingo, eds. LC 80-82477. (Contemporary Studies in Economic & Financial Analysis: Vol. 26). 400p. 1981. 45.00 (ISBN 0-89232-159-8). Jai Pr.

--The Oil Muddle: Control vs. Competition. 144p. 1985. pap. text ed. 7.25 (ISBN 0-8191-4483-5). U Pr of Amer.

Ridgeway, James & Conner, Bettina. New Energy: Understanding the Crisis & a Guide to An Alternative Energy System. LC 74-16669. (Institute for Policy Studies Ser.). 228p. 1975. 9.95x (ISBN 0-8070-0504-5). Beacon Pr.

Robinson, Colin & Morgan, Jon. North Sea Oil in the Future. 1978. text ed. 26.00x (ISBN 0-8419-5043-1). Holmes & Meier.

Rodgers, William H., Jr. Energy & Natural Resources Law Cases & Materials. 2nd ed. LC 83-10505. (American Casebook Ser.). 877p. 1983. text ed. 24.95 (ISBN 0-314-74441-X). West Pub.

Rosenbaum, Walter A. Energy, Politics & Public Policy. LC 80-29273. 229p. 1981. 9.95 (ISBN 0-87187-166-1). Congr Quarterly.

Rycroft, Robert W., et al. Energy Policy-Making: A Selected Biography. LC 77-9118. 1978. pap. 8.95x (ISBN 0-8061-1448-7). U of Okla Pr.

Sachs, Robert G., ed. National Energy Issues: How Do We Decide? Plutonium As a Test Case. LC 79-18341. (American Academy of Arts & Sciences Ser.). 360p. 1980. prof ref 30.00 (ISBN 0-88410-620-9). Ballinger Pub.

SADCC Country Studies, Part 1: Energy & Development in Southern Africa. (Energy, Environment, & Development in Africa Ser.: Vol. 3). 200p. Date not set. 27.50 (ISBN 0-8419-9771-3, Africana). Holmes & Meier.

SADCC Country Studies, Part 2: Energy & Development in Southern Africa. (Energy, Environment & Development in Africa Ser.: Vol. 4). 238p. Date not set. text ed. 27.50 (ISBN 0-8419-9772-1, Africana). Holmes & Meier.

Sahr, Robert C. The Politics of Energy Policy Change in Sweden. 229p. 1985. text ed. 19.95x (ISBN 0-472-10058-0). U of Mich Pr.

Samouilidis, J. E. Management Science for Energy Policy. pap. 32.00 (ISBN 0-08-028172-9). Pergamon.

Sargent, Thomas J. Energy, Foresight, & Strategy. LC 84-42691. 220p. (Orig.). 1985. pap. text ed. 18.00 (ISBN 0-915707-10-1). Resources Future.

Sawyer, Stephen W. & Armstrong, John R., eds. State Energy Policy: Current Issues, Future Directions. (Special Studies in Natural Resources & Energy Management). 250p. 1985. pap. 22.50x (ISBN 0-8133-7027-2). Westview.

Scales, John K. & Popkin, James M. Energy & Jobs: Employment Implications of Alternate Energy & Conservation Stratgies in the Northeast. LC 83-164276. 97p. 1983. pap. 7.50 (ISBN 0-914193-00-7). Coalition NE Govn.

Schelling, Thomas C. Thinking Through the Energy Problem. LC 79-4583. (CED Supplementary Paper). 1979. pap. 5.00 (ISBN 0-87186-242-5). Comm Econ Dev.

Schmitz, Kurt. Langfristplanung in der Energiewirtschaft. (Interdisciplinary Systems Research Ser.: No. 65). (Ger.). 274p. 1979. pap. 27.95x (ISBN 0-8176-1068-5). Birkhauser.

Shaw, T. L., et al. Policy & Development of Energy Resources. LC 83-10197. (World Energy Options Ser.). 247p. 1984. 39.95x (ISBN 0-471-10537-6, 1-685, Pub. by Wiley-Interscience). Wiley.

Shepard's & McGraw-Hill & Fox, William. Federal Regulation of Energy. 1983. 75.00 (ISBN 0-07-021751-3, Shepards-McGraw). McGraw.

Siddigi, Toufig A. Environmental Standards & Energy Policies: Workshop Report Based on the Papers Presented & Discussed at a Workshop at East-West Center, Honolulu, Hawaii, 9-21 March, 1980. pap. 20.00 (ISBN 0-317-10686-4, 2021546). Bks Demand UMI.

Siever, Raymond, commentary by. Energy & Environment: Readings from Scientific American. LC 79-21980. (Illus.). 231p. 1980. text ed. 23.95x (ISBN 0-7167-1052-8); pap. text ed. 11.95x (ISBN 0-7167-1053-6). W H Freeman.

Sobel, Lester, ed. Energy Crisis: 1969-79, Vol. 4. 232p. 19.95x. Facts on File.

Sobel, Lester A., ed. Energy Crisis, Vol. 2: 1974-75. LC 74-75154. 213p. 1975. lib. bdg. 19.95 (ISBN 0-87196-279-9). Facts on File.

--Energy Crisis, Vol. 3: 1975-77. LC 74-75154. 1977. lib. bdg. 19.95 (ISBN 0-87196-280-2); 59.95 set (ISBN 0-686-85940-5). Facts on File.

Solar Energy Research Institute. A New Prosperity: Building a Sustainable Energy Future, 2 vols. in 1. (Illus.). 500p. lib. bdg. 125.00 cancelled (ISBN 0-686-73400-9). Revisionist Pr.

Sporn, Philip. Energy in an Age of Limited Availability & Delimited Applicability. 1976. pap. text ed. 11.75 (ISBN 0-08-020857-6). Pergamon.

Spurr, Stephen H., ed. Energy Policy in Perspective-Solutions, Problems & Prospects. (Symposia Ser.). 74p. 1982. 5.95 (ISBN 0-89940-410-3). LBJ Sch Pub Aff.

Stanford Environmental Law Annual 1983: Energy Development & the Environment. 225p. (Orig.). 1983. pap. 10.00 (ISBN 0-318-11833-5). Stanford Enviro.

Starr, C. Current Issues in Energy. 1979. text ed. 33.00 (ISBN 0-08-023243-4); pap. text ed. 12.75 (ISBN 0-08-023244-2). Pergamon.

Stern, Jonathan P. Gas's Contribution to U. K. Self-Sufficiency. (British Institute's Joint Energy Policy Programme - Energy Papers: No. 10). xi, 84p. 1984. pap. text ed. 11.50x (ISBN 0-435-84343-5). Gower Pub Co.

Stewart, Hugh B. Transitional Energy Policy 1980-2030: Alternative Nuclear Technologies. (Pergamon Policy Studies on Science & Technology). 266p. 1981. 33.00 (ISBN 0-08-027183-9); pap. 13.75 (ISBN 0-08-027182-0). Pergamon.

Strout, Alan M. Technological Change & United States Energy Consumption, 1939-1954. Bruchey, Stuart, ed. LC 78-22753. (Energy in the American Economy Ser.). (Illus.). 1979. lib. bdg. 25.50x (ISBN 0-405-12017-6). Ayer Co Pubs.

Tanzer, Michael. The Energy Crisis: World Struggle for Power & Wealth. LC 74-7787. 176p. 1976. pap. 4.50 (ISBN 0-85345-369-1). Monthly Rev.

Texas Energy Issues: 1978, No. 25. (Policy Research Project Reports). 123p. 1978. 4.00 (ISBN 0-89940-618-1). LBJ Sch Pub Aff.

Texas Energy Issues: 1979, No. 36. (Policy Research Project Reports). 135p. 1979. 5.95 (ISBN 0-89940-636-X). LBJ Sch Pub Aff.

Texas Energy Issues: 1980, No. 40. (Policy Research Project Reports). 95p. 1980. 4.95 (ISBN 0-89940-640-8). LBJ Sch Pub Aff.

Theodore, Louis, et al. Energy & the Environment: Interactions, Vol. I, Perspectives on Energy & the Environment, Pts. A & B. 1980. pt. a, 224 pgs. 68.50 (ISBN 0-8493-5562-1); pt. b, 224 pgs. 66.50 (ISBN 0-8493-5563-X). CRC Pr.

Thrall, Robert M. & Thompson, Russell G., eds. Large-Scale Energy Models: Prospects & Potential. (AAAS Selected Synposium 73). 350p. 1982. 26.50x (ISBN 0-86531-408-X). Westview.

Tomain, Joseph P. Energy Law in a Nutshell. LC 81-11636. (Nutshell Ser.). 338p. 1981. pap. text ed. 8.95 (ISBN 0-314-60134-1). West Pub.

Tosato, G., et al. Energy after the Eighties: Cooperative Study by Countries of the International Energy Agency. (Energy Research Ser.: No. 6). 298p. 1984. 72.25 (ISBN 0-444-42404-0). Elsevier.

Totten, Michael, intro. by. The Road to Trillion Dollar Energy Savings: A Safe Energy Platform. (Illus.). 84p. 1984. 25.00 (ISBN 0-937188-15-8); pap. 5.00 saddle stitched (ISBN 0-317-11381-X). Pub Citizen Inc.

Turner, Louis. Coal's Contribution to UK Self-Sufficiency. (British Institutes Joint Energy Policy Programme - Energy Papers: No. 9). viii, 60p. (Orig.). 1984. pap. text ed. 11.50x (ISBN 0-435-84340-0). Gower Pub Co.

Tuve, George L. Energy, Environment, Populations & Food: Our Four Interdependant Crises. LC 76-40351. 278p. 1976. 16.50 (ISBN 0-471-02090-7). Krieger.

Udall, Stewart, et al. The Energy Balloon. LC 74-14903. 288p. 1974. 7.95 (ISBN 0-07-065732-7). McGraw.

Engineering Manpower Commission. Demand for Engineers, 1982. 1983. pap. 100.00x (ISBN 0-87615-113-6, 231-83). AAES.
--Engineers' Salaries: Special Industry Report, 1982. (Illus.). 1982. pap. 225.00x (ISBN 0-87615-123-3, 301-82). AAES.
--Engineers' Salaries: Special Industry Report, 1983. (Illus.). 250p. pap. 226.00x (ISBN 0-87615-124-1, 301-83). AAES.
Engineering Technicians: Some Problems of Nomenclature & Classification. (Studies in Engineering Education: No. 7). 144p. 1981. pap. 11.50 (ISBN 92-3-101831-0, U1095, UNESCO). Unipub.
Engineering Towards the Twenty-First Century: Newcastle, Australia, April 18-22, 1983. 292p. (Orig.). 1983. pap. text ed. 45.00x (ISBN 0-85825-182-5, Pub. by Inst Engineering Australia). Brookfield Pub Co.
English, Morley J., ed. Economics of Engineering & Social Systems. LC 73-37644. 332p. 1972. 24.95 (ISBN 0-471-24180-6, Pub. by Wiley). Krieger.
The Environment in Engineering Education. (Studies in Engineering Education: No. 9). 120p. 1980. pap. 9.25 (ISBN 92-3-101793-4, U1028, UNESCO). Unipub.
Eringen, A. C., ed. Recent Advances in Engineering Science, 5 Vols. (Orig.). 1967-69. Vol. 1, 878p. 166.50 (ISBN 0-677-10790-0); Vol. 2, 456p. 119.25 (ISBN 0-677-10800-1); Vol. 3, 568p. 131.95 (ISBN 0-677-11880-5); Vol. 4, 362p. 93.75 (ISBN 0-677-13100-3); Vol. 5, 862p., 2 pt. set. 198.75 (ISBN 0-677-13780-X). Gordon.
Farag, M. M. Materials & Process Selection in Engineering. (Illus.). 320p. 1979. 64.00 (ISBN 0-686-48182-8, 0704). T-C Pubns CA.
Felbeck, David K. & Atkins, Anthony C. Strength & Fracture of Engineering Solids. (Illus.). 608p. 1984. 41.95 (ISBN 0-13-851709-6). P-H.
Ferris, Elvira B., et al. Body Structures & Functions. 6th ed. LC 83-71712. (Illus.). 356p. 1984. text ed. 13.80 (ISBN 0-8273-2185-6); instrs' guide 5.10 (ISBN 0-8273-2186-4). Delmar.
Fisk, Edward R. Construction Engineer's Form Book. LC 80-22395. 624p. 1981. text ed. 59.95 (ISBN 0-471-06307-X). Wiley.
Fletcher, L. S. & Shoup, T. E. Introduction to Engineering Including FORTRAN Programming. (Illus.). 1978. pap. 26.95 ref. ed. (ISBN 0-13-501858-7). P-H.
Florman, Samuel. The Existential Pleasures of Engineering. LC 75-9480. 1977. pap. 4.95 (ISBN 0-312-27546-3). St Martin.
Florman, Samuel C. Engineering & the Liberal Arts: A Technologist's Guide to History, Literature, Philosophy, Art & Music. LC 81-23607. 288p. 1982. Repr. of 1968 ed. 24.50 (ISBN 0-89874-402-4). Krieger.
Fundamentals of Power Plant Performance for Utility Engineers. 1984. looseleaf 150.00x (ISBN 0-87683-371-7). G P Courseware.
Global Engineering Documents. Qualified Products List & Sources. 64th ed. 344p. 1985. lib. bdg. 57.50 (ISBN 0-912702-28-1). Global Eng.
Glorioso, Robert M. & Hill, F. S., Jr. Introduction to Engineering. (Illus.). 448p. 1975. ref. ed. 27.95x. P-H.
Gogan, Robert. Engineering Triumphs: L3. McConochie, Jean, ed. (Regents Readers Ser.). pap. text ed. 2.25 (ISBN 0-88345-496-3, 20913). Regents Pub.
Goldstein, Amy J. & Granade, Charles, eds. Graduate Programs in Engineering & Applied Sciences 1986. 20th ed. (Peterson's Annual Guides to Graduate Study Ser.). 900p. (Orig.). pap. 24.95 (ISBN 0-87866-346-0). Petersons Guides.
Gottfried, Byron S. Introduction to Engineering Calculations. (Schaum's Outline Ser.). (Illus.). 1979. pap. 7.95 (ISBN 0-07-023837-5). McGraw.
Gray, Irwin. The Engineer in Transition to Management. LC 78-61533. 127p. 1979. 24.95x (ISBN 0-471-05212-4). Wiley.
Hahn, Thomas H., ed. Thermal Expansion Eight. 294p. 1984. 85.00x (ISBN 0-306-41825-8, Plenum Pr). Plenum Pub.
Harrison, H. R. & Nettleton, T. Principles of Engineering Mechanics. (Illus.). 255p. 1984. pap. text ed. 22.50x (ISBN 0-7131-3378-3). Trans-Atlantic.
Helander, Martin. Human Factors-Ergonomics for Building & Construction. LC 80-26717. (Construction Management & Engineering Ser.). 361p. 1981. 45.95x (ISBN 0-471-05075-X, Pub. by Wiley-Interscience). Wiley.
Hemond, Conrad J., Jr. Engineering Acoustics & Noise Control. (Illus.). 208p. 1983. 33.95 (ISBN 0-13-278911-6). P-H.
Hibbeler, R. C. Engineering Mechanics: Statics. 3rd ed. 448p. 1983. text ed. write for info. (ISBN 0-02-354310-8). Macmillan.
Hibbeler, Russell C. Mechanics for Engineers Dynamics. 528p. 1985. text ed. write for info. (ISBN 0-02-354260-8). Macmillan.
Hicks, Tyler G. & Edwards, T. Pump Application Engineering. 1970. 45.50 (ISBN 0-07-028741-4). McGraw.
Higginson, G. R. Foundations of Engineering Mechanics. LC 93-88375. (Introductory Engineering Ser.). pap. 47.30 (ISBN 0-317-08546-8, 2011909). Bks Demand UMI.
Hobart: Changing Society: A Challenge for Engineering. 261p. (Orig.). 1982. pap. text ed. 37.50x (Pub. by Inst Engineering Australia). Brookfield Pub Co.
Hobbs, F. D. & Doling, J. F. Planning for Engineers & Surveyors. LC 80-41553. (Illus.). 230p. 1981. 35.00 (ISBN 0-08-025459-4); pap. 17.25 (ISBN 0-08-025458-6). Pergamon.
Hsia, Han-Min, et al, eds. Proceedings of the International Symposium on Engineering Sciences & Mechanics. LC 57-43769. (Advances in the Astronautical Sciences Ser.: Vol. 50, Pts. I & II). (Illus.). 1574p. 1983. Pt. I. lib. bdg. 120.00x (ISBN 0-87703-166-5, Pub. by Am Astronaut). Pt. II (ISBN 0-87703-167-3). fiche suppl. 6.00. Univelt Inc.
Humphreys, K. K. & Novak, T., eds. Transactions of the American Association of Cost Engineers. (Illus.). 360p. 1983. 48.50x (ISBN 0-930284-18-6); pap. 38.50x (ISBN 0-930284-17-8). Am Assn Cost Engineers.
Institute of Environmental Sciences, 9th Annual Meeting, 1963. Bridging the Gap...Between an Understanding of the Physics & the Engineering Applications: Proceedings. (Illus.). 1963. pap. text ed. 1.00 (ISBN 0-915414-03-1). Inst Environ Sci.
Institution of Civil Engineers Staff, ed. Manual of Applied Geology for Engineers. 414p. 1976. pap. 30.25x (ISBN 0-7277-0038-3). Am Soc Civil Eng.
Instrument Society of America. Basic Instrumentation Lecture Notes & Study Guide: Measurement Fundamentals, Vol. I. rev. ed. Moore, Ralph L., ed. (Illus.). 320p. 1984. pap. 28.95 (ISBN 0-13-062471-3). P-H.
--Basic Instrumentation Lecture Notes & Study Guide: Process Analyzers & Recorders, Vol. II. rev. ed. Moore, Ralph, ed. (Illus.). 208p. 1984. pap. 28.95 (ISBN 0-13-062489-6). P-H.
Interdisciplinary Symposium on Flow, 2nd, 1981. Flow-Its Measurement & Control in Science & Industry: Proceedings, Vol. 2. LC 74-77995. 911p. 1981. Pt. 1. text ed. 95.00x (ISBN 0-87664-511-2). Instru Soc.
International Who's Who in Engineering. 600p. 1984. 115.00x (ISBN 0-900332-71-9, BMA 05083, Pub by Intl Biog Ctr). Biblio Dist.
Iowa State University Research Foundation. Fundamentals of Engineering Review. LC 80-83440. 224p. 1980. pap. text ed. 14.95 (ISBN 0-8403-2305-0). Kendall-Hunt.
Jenkins, Rhys. Links in the History of Engineering & Technology from Tudor Times. facs. ed. LC 72-121481. (Essay Index Reprint Ser). 1936. 18.00 (ISBN 0-8369-2167-4). Ayer Co Pubs.
Judd, A. M. Fast Breeder Reactors: An Engineering Introduction. LC 80-41929. (Illus.). 170p. 1981. 33.00 (ISBN 0-08-023220-5); pap. 13.75 (ISBN 0-08-023221-3). Pergamon.
Jumikis, Alfreds R. Foundation Engineering. 1986. lib. bdg. price not set. Krieger.
Kasner, Erick. Essentials of Engineering Economics. (Illus.). 1979. text ed. 33.45 (ISBN 0-07-033323-8). McGraw.
Kawata, K., ed. High Velocity Deformation of Solids: Symposium, Tokyo, Japan, Aug. 24-27, 1977. (International Union of Theoretical & Applied Mechanics Ser.). 1978. pap. 52.00 (ISBN 0-387-09208-0). Springer-Verlag.
Kitto, Michael & West, Richard. Engineering Information. 64p. 1984. pap. text ed. 7.75 (ISBN 0-7131-8154-0). E Arnold.
Kock, Winston E. The Creative Engineer: The Art of Inventing. new ed. LC 77-20220. (Illus.). 399p. 1978. 35.00x (ISBN 0-306-30987-4, Plenum Pr). Plenum Pub.
Kossowsky, Ram & Singhal, Subhash C., eds. Surface Engineering. 1984. lib. bdg. 89.50 (ISBN 90-247-3093-7, Pub. by Martinus Nijhoff Netherlands). Kluwer Academic.
Krick, Edward V. An Introduction to Engineering & Engineering Design. 2nd ed. LC 68-8106. (Illus.). 220p. 1969. pap. text ed. 24.50x (ISBN 0-471-50741-5). Wiley.
--An Introduction to Engineering: Methods, Concepts & Issues. LC 75-41432. 358p. 1976. text ed. 26.00x (ISBN 0-471-50750-4); instructor's manual avail. (ISBN 0-471-01912-7). Wiley.
Kyed, James M. & Matarazzo, James M. Scientific, Engineering, & Medical Societies Publications in Print, 1980-81. 4th ed. 626p. 1981. 65.00x (ISBN 0-8352-1403-6). Bowker.
Laithwaite, Eric. The Engineer Through the Looking Glass. 116p. 1980. 40.00x (ISBN 0-563-12979-4, Pub. by BBC Pubns). State Mutual Bk.
--Invitation to Engineering. (Invitation Ser.). 250p. 1985. 24.95x (ISBN 0-85520-661-6); pap. 7.95 (ISBN 0-85520-662-4). Basil Blackwell.
Larson, Harold J. & Shubert, Bruno O. Probabilistic Models in Engineering Sciences, 2 vols. Incl. Vol. 1. Random Variables & Stochastic Processes. 544p. 1979. text ed. 47.50x (ISBN 0-471-01751-5); solutions manual 8.95x (ISBN 0-471-05759-2); Vol. 2. Random Noise Signals & Dynamic Systems. 737p. 1979. text ed. 51.75x (ISBN 0-471-05179-9); solutions manual 10.95x (ISBN 0-471-05760-6). LC 79-755. 544p. 1979. Wiley.
Lewart, Cass. Science & Engineering Sourcebook. LC 82-80269. (Illus.). 96p. (Orig.). 1982. pap. 9.95 (ISBN 0-942412-02-8); Pre-recorded cass. 8.95 (ISBN 0-686-98227-4). Micro Text Pubs.
Lieblich, Jerome H. Source of Supply. 855p. (Orig.). 1984. lib. bdg. 79.95x (ISBN 0-912702-23-0). Global Eng.
Lindeburg, Michael R. Solutions Manual for the Engineer-In-Training Review Manual. (Engineering Review Manual Ser.). 130p. 1982. pap. text ed. 9.50 (ISBN 0-932276-49-0). Prof Engine.
Longland, F. Field Engineering: An Introduction to Development Work & Construction in Rural Areas. Stern, Peter, et al, eds. (Illus.). 251p. (Orig.). 1983. 17.50x (ISBN 0-903031-87-6, Pub. by Intermediate Tech England); pap. 11.50x (ISBN 0-903031-68-X, Pub. by Intermediate Tech England). Intermediate Tech.
Lusterman, Seymour. Minorities in Engineering: The Corporate Role. LC 79-51320. (Report Ser.: No. 756). (Illus.). 53p. 1979. pap. 15.00 (ISBN 0-8237-0192-1); pap. 5.00 member. Conference Bd.
Luxmoore, A. R., ed. Optical Transducers & Techniques in Engineering Measurement. (Illus.). 1983. 64.75 (ISBN 0-85334-203-2, Pub. by Elsevier Applied Sci England). Elsevier.
McDonagh, et al. Engineering Science for Technicians, Vol. 2. (Illus.). 1978. pap. 17.95x (ISBN 0-7131-3398-8). Intl Ideas.
McDonagh, I., et al. Engineering Science for Technicians, Vol. 1. 2nd ed. (Illus.). 256p. 1982. pap. text ed. 17.95x (ISBN 0-686-83107-1). Intl Ideas.
McGeorge, H. D. General Engineering Knowledge. 2nd ed. (Marine Engineering Ser.). (Illus.). 122p. 1984. pap. text ed. 9.95x (ISBN 0-540-07359-8, Pub. by Stanford Maritime England). Sheridan.
Malstrom. Manufacturing Cost Engineering Handbook. (Cost Engineering Ser.). 504p. 1984. 59.75 (ISBN 0-8247-7126-5). Dekker.
Maltbaek, J. C. Essential Engineering Dynamics. 359p. 1975. pap. text ed. 17.25x (ISBN 0-258-97070-7, Pub. by Granada England). Brookfield Pub Co.
--Further Engineering Dynamics. 177p. 1980. pap. 29.95x (ISBN 0-470-26943-X). Halsted Pr.
Manning, W. R. & Labrow, S. High Pressure Engineering. 1972. text ed. 62.50x (ISBN 0-7114-3804-8). Intl Ideas.
Marr, G. W. & Layton, R. C. General Engineering Science in SI Units, 2 vols. 2nd ed. 1971. Vol. 1. pap. 8.75 (ISBN 0-08-015804-8); Vol. 2. pap. 5.25 (ISBN 0-08-015806-4). Pergamon.
Marston, Anson, et al. Engineering Valuation & Depreciation. 2nd ed. (Illus.). 1953. 15.50x (ISBN 0-8138-0555-4). Iowa St U Pr.
Mathewson, Christopher C. Engineering Geology. (Illus.). 416p. 1981. text ed. 32.95 (ISBN 0-675-08032-0). Additional supplements may be obtained from publisher. Merrill.
Maunder, L., frwd. by. Engineering Challenges in the 1980's, Vol. 1. (Proceedings of the Engineering Section of the British Association for the Advancement of Science Ser.). (Illus.). 192p. 1982. text ed. 84.50 (ISBN 0-89116-348-4, Pub. by Cambridge Info & Res Serv England). Hemisphere Pub.
Mayne, R. & Margolis, S. Introduction to Engineering. 1982. 38.00 (ISBN 0-07-041137-9). McGraw.
Measuring & Forecasting Engineering Personnel Requirements. 1979. 50.00x (126-79). AAES.
Meriam, J. L. Engineering Mechanics, 2 vols. Incl. Vol. 1. Statics: SI Version. 397p. 1980. text ed. 36.00 (ISBN 0-471-05558-1); Arabic ed. 19.50 (ISBN 0-471-06312-6); Vol. 2. Dynamics: SI Version. 508p. text ed. 36.95 (ISBN 0-471-05559-X); Arabic ed. 19.50 (ISBN 0-471-06311-8). LC 79-11173. 1980. Wiley.
--Engineering Mechanics, 2 vols. Incl. Vol. 1. Statics. 398p. text ed. 35.45x (ISBN 0-471-59460-1); Vol. 2. Dynamics. 508p. text ed. 36.00 (ISBN 0-471-59461-X); Teacher's Manual. avail. (ISBN 0-471-02753-7). LC 77-24716. 1978. Wiley.
Meriman, J. L. ARA Engineering Mechanics, 2 vols. Incl. Vol. 1. SI Statics. 19.50 (ISBN 0-471-06312-6); Vol. 2. SI Dynamics. 1982. 21.50 (ISBN 0-471-06311-8). 1980. 0.00. Wiley.
Merkel, James A. Basic Engineering Principles. 2nd ed. (Illus.). 1983. text ed. 22.50 (ISBN 0-87055-421-2). AVI.
Middendorf. What Every Engineer Should Know about Inventing. (What Every Engineer Should Know Ser.: Vol. 7). 192p. 1981. 24.75 (ISBN 0-8247-1338-9). Dekker.
Moffat, Donald W. Plant Engineer's Handbook of Formulas, Charts & Tables. 2nd. ed. LC 81-15811. 397p. 1982. 57.95x (ISBN 0-13-680298-2, Busn). P-H.
Murphy, L. S., et al, eds. Moving up the Yield Curve: Advances & Obstacles. (Illus.). 1981. pap. 5.50 (ISBN 0-89118-064-8). Am Soc Agron.
Muth, Eginhard J. Transform Methods with Applications to Engineering & Operations Research. (Illus.). 1977. ref. ed. O.P. 29.95 (ISBN 0-13-928861-9). P-H.
National Academy of Engineering. Cutting Edge Technologies. 192p. 1984. pap. text ed. 18.95 (ISBN 0-309-03489-2). Natl Acad Pr.
--Educational Technology in Engineering. 1981. pap. text ed. 6.50 (ISBN 0-309-03138-9). Natl Acad Pr.
--Memorial Tributes. 318p. 1984. text ed. 14.75 (ISBN 0-309-03482-5). Natl Acad Pr.
National Conference on Local Government Engineering, 2nd. 416p. 1983. pap. text ed. 28.00x (ISBN 0-85825-193-0, Pub. by Inst Engineering Australia). Brookfield Pub Co.
NATO Advanced Study Institute, University of Waterloo, August, 2-12, 1977, Canada. Engineering Plasticity by Mathematical Programming: Proceedings. Cohn, M. Z. & Maier, G., eds. LC 78-8474. (Illus.). 1979. 65.00 (ISBN 0-08-022735-X); pap. 37.00 (ISBN 0-08-022736-8). Pergamon.
Newnan, Donald G. & Larock, Bruce E. Engineering Fundamentals: Examination Review. 2nd ed. LC 7-12592. 503p. 1978. 43.50 (ISBN 0-471-01900-3, Pub. by Wiley-Interscience). Wiley.
Novosad, John P. Automatic Apparatus. 408p. 1983. pap. text ed. 19.95 (ISBN 0-8403-2940-7). Kendall-Hunt.
OECD Staff. The Engineering Industries in OECD Member Countries, 1976-1979. 93p. 1982. pap. 10.00 (ISBN 92-64-02283-X). OECD.
Oppenheim, Alan V., et al. Signals & Systems. (Illus.). 464p. 1982. 38.95 (ISBN 0-13-809731-3). P-H.
Ovesen, Niels K. Advances in the Continuing Education of Engineers. (Studies in Engineering Education: No. 6). (Illus.). 199p. 1980. pap. 13.50 (ISBN 92-3-101832-9, U1069, UNESCO). Unipub.
Parker, Harry & Ambrose, James. Simplified Engineering for Architects & Builders. 447p. 1984. 30.95x (ISBN 0-471-86611-3, Pub. by Wiley-Interscience). Wiley.
Parsons, S. A. How to Find Out About Engineering. 285p. 1972. text ed. 25.00 (ISBN 0-08-016919-8). Pergamon.
Patton, Joseph D., Jr., ed. Preventive Maintenance. Instrument Society of America. (Illus.). 208p. 30.95 (ISBN 0-13-699215-3). P-H.
Pawlicki, T. How to Build a Flying Saucer: And Other Proposals in Speculative Engineering. 1980. pap. 5.95 (ISBN 0-13-402461-3). P-H.
Pennsylvania University Bicentennial Conference. Fluid Mechanics & Statistical Methods in Engineering. Dryden, Hugh & Von Karman, Theodore, eds. LC 68-26203. Repr. of 1941 ed. 21.50x (ISBN 0-8046-0359-6, Pub. by Kennikat). Assoc Faculty Pr.
Performance Monitoring for Geotechnical Construction - STP 584. 204p. 1975. 14.00 (ISBN 0-8031-0533-9, 04-584000-38). ASTM.
Phillips, Cushing, Jr. Plant Engineer's Desk Handbook. 232p. 1980. 57.95 (ISBN 0-13-680264-8). P-H.
Powell, P. C. Engineering with Polymers. LC 83-7180. 1983. 59.95 (ISBN 0-412-24160-9, NO. 6825, Pub. by Chapman & Hall); pap. 25.00 (ISBN 0-412-24170-6, NO. 6826). Methuen Inc.
Ragette, Friedrich, ed. Engineering & Architecture & the Future Environment of Man. 1968. pap. 14.95x (ISBN 0-8156-6013-8, Am U Beirut). Syracuse U Pr.
Rao, S. S., ed. The Finite Element Method in Engineering. LC 80-40817. 400p. 1981. 66.00 (ISBN 0-08-025467-5); pap. 24.95 (ISBN 0-08-025466-7). Pergamon.
Reddy, J. N. & Rasmussen, M. L. Advanced Engineering Analysis. LC 81-14730. 488p. 1982. 47.95 (ISBN 0-471-09349-1, Pub. by Wiley-Interscience). Wiley.
Reid, D. A. Construction Principles. 1973. text ed. 24.95x (ISBN 0-7114-3305-4). Intl Ideas.

BOOKS - SUBJECT INDEX ENGINEERING–DATA PROCESSING

Reklaitis, G. V., et al. Engineering Optimization: Methods & Application. LC 83-3545. 684p. 1983. 43.95 (ISBN 0-471-05579-4, Pub. by Wiley Interscience). Wiley.
Rektorys, Karel. Variational Methods in Mathematics, Science & Engineering. Basch, Michael, tr. from Czech. 572p. 1980. lib. bdg. 34.00 (ISBN 90-277-0561-5, Pub. by Reidel Holland). Kluwer Academic.
ReVelle, Jack B. Safety Training Methods. LC 80-16601. 248p. 1980. 37.95x (ISBN 0-471-07761-5, Pub. by Wiley-Interscience). Wiley.
Richards, R. J. An Introduction to Dynamics & Control. 1979. pap. text ed. 25.00x (ISBN 0-582-44183-8). Longman.
Rigby, G. R., intro. by. Expanding Horizons in Chemical Engineering. (Chemeca Ser.). 241p. (Orig.). 1979. pap. text ed. 54.00x (ISBN 0-85825-116-7, Pub. by Inst Engineering Australia). Brookfield Pub Co.
Ritterbush, Philip C. Built Environment: Ideas in Engineering for Human Adaptive Potential. (Illus.). 137p. 1983. 24.00x (ISBN 0-89062-153-5). Pub Ctr Cult Res.
Rogers, C. J. How to Read & Understand Engineering Prints. pap. 58.00 (ISBN 0-317-11046-2, 2005804). Bks Demand UMI.
Rudman, Jack. Director of Engineering, Building & Housing. (Career Examination Ser.: C-2391). (Cloth bdg. avail. on request). pap. 14.00 (ISBN 0-8373-2391-6). Natl Learning.
--Engineering. (Undergraduate Program Field Test Ser.: UPFT-8). (Cloth bdg. avail.). pap. 9.95 (ISBN 0-8373-6008-0). Natl Learning.
--Principal Engineering Inspector. (Career Examination Ser.: C-911). (Cloth bdg. avail. on request). pap. 14.00 (ISBN 0-8373-0911-5). Natl Learning.
Ryland's Directory of the Engineering Industry, 1982-83. 48th ed. 900p. 1982. pap. 60.00x (ISBN 0-86108-104-8). Intl Pubns Serv.
Sanders, Mark S. & McCormick, Ernest J. Workbook for Human Factors in Engineering & Design. 1982. pap. text ed. 9.95 (ISBN 0-8403-2716-1). Kendall-Hunt.
Savage, G. J. & Roe, P. H., eds. Large Engineering Systems, Two: Proceedings of the Second Symposium on Large Engineering Systems, University of Waterloo, Waterloo, Ontario, May 15, 1978. (Illus.). 1979. 105.00 (ISBN 0-08-025090-4). Pergamon.
Schaub, J. H. & Dickison, S. K. Engineering & the Humanities. LC 81-23153. 503p. 1982. pap. 22.95x (ISBN 0-471-08909-5, Pub. by Wiley-Interscience). Wiley.
Schofield, W. Engineering Surveying, Vol. 2. 2nd ed. 288p. (Orig.). 1984. pap. text ed. 34.95 (ISBN 0-408-01228-5). Butterworth.
Schuder, Charles B. Energy Engineering Fundamentals: With Residential & Commercial Applications. 176p. 1982. 22.95 (ISBN 0-442-28109-9). Van Nos Reinhold.
Seddiqui, Fred R. Engineering Functions: Concerns of the Industry. 1983. 20.00 (ISBN 0-533-05497-4). Vantage.
Sefi Guide: Engineering Education in Europe. 427p. 1978. pap. 55.00 (ISBN 2-87040-003-9, ORD9, ORDINA). Unipub.
Shames, I. Engineering Mechanics, 2 vols. 3rd ed. 1980. Vol. 1, Statics. 31.95 (ISBN 0-13-279141-2); Vol. 2, Dynamics. 31.95 (ISBN 0-13-279158-7); combined ed. 39.95 (ISBN 0-13-279166-8). P-H.
Shepherd, F. A. Advance Engineering Surveying. 288p. 1982. pap. text ed. 24.95 (ISBN 0-7131-3416-X). E Arnold.
Silvester, Richard, intro. by. Coastal & Ocean Engineering: Offshore Structures. (Australian Conference Ser.: No. 5). 471p. (Orig.). 1981. pap. text ed. 37.50x (ISBN 0-85825-159-0, Pub. by Inst Engineering Australia). Brookfield Pub Co.
Smith, W. Principles of Materials Science & Engineering. 896p. 1986. price not set (ISBN 0-07-058521-0). McGraw.
Sowers, George F. Introductory Soil Mechanics & Foundations: Geotechnic Engineering. 4th ed. (Illus.). 1979. text ed. write for info. (ISBN 0-02-413870-3). Macmillan.
Stern, Virginia W. & Redden, Martha R. Scientific & Engineering Societies: Resources for Career Planning. LC 80-66465. 196p. (Orig.). 1980. pap. text ed. 6.00x (ISBN 0-87168-246-X). AAAS.
Stock Drive Products Staff Engineers, et al. Handbook of Unique Components. 1978. pap. 2.95 (ISBN 0-686-23600-9). Stock Drive.
Storr, Eric D., ed. Engineering Australia. 300p. 1984. pap. text ed. 30.00x (ISBN 0-317-04036-7, Pub. by Inst Engineering Australia). Brookfield Pub Co.
Strom, Steven & Nathan, Kurt. Site Engineering for Landscape Architects. (Illus.). 1985. pap. text ed. 39.50 (ISBN 0-87055-471-9). AVI.
Suman, G. O., Jr., et al. Sand Control Handbook. 2nd ed. LC 83-12628. 96p. (Orig.). 1983. pap. 24.95x (ISBN 0-87201-793-1). Gulf Pub.
Sunar, D. G. The Expert Witness Handbook-A Guide for Engineers. 80p. (Orig.). 1985. pap. text ed. 6.95 (ISBN 0-932276-51-2). Prof Engine.
--How to Become a Professional Engineer. 96p. (Orig.). 1985. pap. text ed. 4.95 (ISBN 0-932276-52-0). Prof Engine.
Taylor, Edward S. Dimensional Analysis for Engineers. (Illus.). 1974. text ed. 47.50x (ISBN 0-19-856122-9). Oxford U Pr.
Telles, J. C. The Boundary Element Method Applied to Inelastic Problems. (Lecture Notes in Engineering: Vol. 1). 243p. 1983. pap. 18.00 (ISBN 0-387-12387-3). Springer-Verlag.
Thames Valley Group, ed. Student Project Work in Construction. 1971. pap. text ed. 19.95x (ISBN 0-7114-4903-1). Intl Ideas.
Thomson, James. Collected Papers in Physics & Engineering. LC 70-137300. Repr. of 1912 ed. 35.00 (ISBN 0-404-06422-1). AMS Pr.
Thumann, Albert & Fairmount Press, Inc. Fundamentals of Energy Engineering. (Illus.). 400p. 1984. 30.95 (ISBN 0-13-338327-X). P-H.
Van Brunt, Leroy B. Applied ECM, Vol. 1. EW Engineering Staff, ed. LC 78-50538. (Illus.). 45.95 (ISBN 0-931728-00-2). EW Eng.
Varju, D. & Schnitzler, H. U. Localization & Orientation in Biology & Engineering. (Proceedings in Life Sciences Ser.). (Illus.). 350p. 1984. 48.00 (ISBN 0-387-12741-0). Springer-Verlag.
Venning, Muriel & Frith, Owen. The Craftsman in Engineering. (Illus.). 107p. 1980. 44.95x (ISBN 0-85083-506-2). Trans-Atlantic.
Warner, Louis A. Stand Up but Don't Get Off. LC 72-85218. 306p. (Orig.). 1972. pap. 2.75 (ISBN 0-913502-08-1). NELF Pr.
Wearne, S. H. Principles of Engineering Organization. (Illus.). 1973. pap. text ed. 18.95x (ISBN 0-7131-3290-6). Intl Ideas.
Wearne, S. H., ed. Control of Engineering Projects. (Illus.). 1974. pap. 19.95x (ISBN 0-7131-3330-9). Intl Ideas.
Who's Who in Engineering, 1982. 5th ed. Incl. Who's Who in Engineering. 6th. ed. Davis, Gordon, ed. 1985. 200.00 (ISBN 0-87615-014-8). 1900p. 125.00x (ISBN 0-87615-013-X, 107-82). AAES.
Wilson, R. C. & Henry, Robert A. Introduction to Group Technology in Manufacturing & Engineering. (Illus.). 70p. 1977. 12.00 (ISBN 0-938654-19-5, GROUP). Indus Dev Inst Sci.
Winterkorn, Hans F. & Fang, F. Y., eds. Foundation Engineering Handbook. 736p. 1975. 54.50 (ISBN 0-442-29564-2). Van Nos Reinhold.
Workshop on Interactive Computing, CAD-CAM, Electrical Engineering Education, 2nd, George Washington Univ., Nov. 30 - Dec. 2, 1983: Proceedings. LC 83-82758. vi, 163p. 1984. 30.00 (ISBN 0-8186-8521-2); pap. write for info. (ISBN 0-8186-0521-9); write for info. microfiche (ISBN 0-8186-4521-0). IEEE Comp Soc.
Wynne, George, ed. Basic Engineering Design & Construction. 1983. text ed. 35.95 (ISBN 0-8359-0389-3). Reston.

ENGINEERING–ADDRESSES, ESSAYS, LECTURES

Johnson, Patricia, ed. Causes & Cure, CEPA 1985 Spring Conference, Caddmania: Proceedings. 1985. 30.00 (ISBN 0-933007-10-8). Soc Comp Eng.

ENGINEERING–AUTHORSHIP

see Technical Writing

ENGINEERING–BIBLIOGRAPHY

Engineering Societies Library Staff. Classed Subject Catalog of the Engineering Societies Library, New York City, 8th Supplement. 1972. lib. bdg. 110.00 (ISBN 0-8161-0982-6, Hall Library). G K Hall.
--Classed Subject Catalog of the Engineering Societies Library, New York City, 9th Supplement. 1973. lib. bdg. 110.00 (ISBN 0-8161-1050-6, Hall Library). G K Hall.
--Classed Subject Catalog of the Engineering Societies Library, New York City, 10th Supplement. 1974. 110.00 (ISBN 0-8161-1123-5, Hall Library). G K Hall.
--Classed Subject Catalog of the Engineering Societies Library, New York City, 6th Supplement. 1970. 110.00 (ISBN 0-8161-0883-8, Hall Library). G K Hall.
--Classed Subject Catalog of the Engineering Societies Library, New York City, 7th Supplement. 1971. lib. bdg. 110.00 (ISBN 0-8161-0913-3, Hall Library). G K Hall.
Godel, Jules B. Sources of Construction Information: An Annotated Guide to Reports, Books, Periodicals, Standards, and Codes. LC 77-4671. 673p. 1977. 40.00 (ISBN 0-8108-1030-1). Scarecrow.
John Crerar Library. List of Books on the History of Industry & the Industrial Arts. LC 67-14030. 1966. Repr. of 1915 ed. 46.00x (ISBN 0-8103-3104-7). Gale.
Krummes, Daniel & Kleiber, Michael. Recent Transportation Literature for Planning Engineering Librarians (January 1985) (Public Admnintration Ser.: Bibliography P-1598). 55p. 1985. pap. 8.25 (ISBN 0-89028-248-X). Vance Biblios.
Mildren, K. W., ed. Use of Engineering Literature. 608p. 1976. 99.95 (ISBN 0-408-70714-3). Butterworth.

ENGINEERING–COLD WEATHER CONDITIONS

Amaria, P. J, et al. Arctic Systems. LC 77-3871. (NATO Conference Series II, Systems Science: Vol. 2). 956p. 1977. 115.00x (ISBN 0-306-32842-9, Plenum Pr). Plenum Pub.
Andersland, Orlando B. & Anderson, Duwayne, eds. Geotechnical Engineering for Cold Regions. (Illus.). 1978. text ed. 52.00x (ISBN 0-07-001615-1). McGraw.
Phukan, Arvind. Frozen Ground Engineering. LC 84-6927. (International Series in Civil Engineering & Engineering Mechanics). (Illus.). 352p. 1985. text ed. 49.95 (ISBN 0-13-330705-0). P-H.

ENGINEERING–CONTRACTS AND SPECIFICATIONS

Abbett, R. W. Engineering Contracts & Specifications. 4th ed. LC 63-14072. 461p. 1963. 39.95x (ISBN 0-471-00035-3, Pub. by Wiley-Interscience). Wiley.
Barnes, Martin. Measurement in Contract Control. 304p. 1977. 23.75x (ISBN 0-7277-0040-5). Am Soc Civil Eng.
Bockrath, J. & Dunham, C. W. Contracts, Specifications & Law for Engineers. 4th ed. 544p. 1985. price not set (ISBN 0-07-018237-X). McGraw.
Burchess, D. Specifications & Quantities. 2nd ed. (Illus.). 136p. 1980. pap. text ed. 18.50x (ISBN 0-7114-5640-2). Intl Ideas.
Clark, John R. Commentary on Agreements for Engineering Services & Contract Documents. 62p. 1981. 10.00 (ISBN 0-686-48322-7). Am Consul Eng.
Consulting Engineering: Practice Manual. 195p. 1981. member 20.00 (ISBN 0-686-48380-4); non-member 24.95 (ISBN 0-686-48381-2). Am Consul Eng.
Cyriax, G. R., ed. Effective Use of the Fidic Contract & Standard Conditions: A Gower Executive Report. 154p. (Orig.). 1982. pap. text ed. 65.95x (ISBN 0-566-03036-5). Gower Pub Co.
Dunham, Clarence, et al. Contracts, Specifications & Law for Engineers. 3rd ed. (Illus.). 1979. text ed. 42.00 (ISBN 0-07-018236-1). McGraw.
Fischer, Martin. Engineering Specifications Writing Guide: An Authoritative Reference for Planning, Writing, & Administrating. 176p. 1983. 17.95 (ISBN 0-13-279208-7); pap. 8.95 (ISBN 0-13-279190-0). P-H.
Horgan, M. Competitive Tendering for Engineering Contracts. LC 83-14494. 250p. 1984. 35.00x (ISBN 0-419-11630-3, NO. 6841). Methuen Inc.
Johnston, K. F. Electrical & Mechanical Engineering Contracts in Great Britain. 1971. 27.50x (ISBN 0-8464-0359-5). Beekman Pubs.
Marks, R. J. & Jackson, R. Aspects of Civil Engineering Contract Procedure. 3rd ed. LC 84-25569. (International Library of Science, Technology, Engineering, & Social Studies). 1985. 30.00 (ISBN 0-08-031637-9). Pergamon.
Ohno, Y., ed. Requirements Engineering Environments: Proceedings of the International Symposium on Current Issues of Requirements Engineering Environments, Sept. 20-21, 1982, Kyoto, Japan. 174p. 1983. 51.00 (ISBN 0-444-86533-0, North Holland). Elsevier.
Patil, B. S. Civil Engineering Contracts & Estimates. (Illus.). 586p. 1981. pap. text ed. 20.00 (ISBN 0-86125-036-2, Pub. by Orient Longman Ltd India). Apt Bks.
Pike, Andrew. Engineering Tenders, Sales & Contracts: Standard Forms & Procedures. 462p. 1983. 70.00 (ISBN 0-419-12530-2, NO. 6764, E & FN Spon). Methuen Inc.
Sawyer, John G. & Gillott, C. A. FIDIC Conditions: Digest of Contractual Relationships & Responsibilities. 120p. 1981. pap. 20.50x (ISBN 0-7277-0127-4). Am Soc Civil Eng.
Shoup, T., et al. Introduction to Engineering Design with Graphics & Design Projects. 1981. pap. 29.95 (ISBN 0-13-482364-8); pap. 8.95 wkbk.o.p. P-H.

ENGINEERING–DATA PROCESSING

see also Structures, Theory of–Data Processing

Adey, R. A., ed. Engineering Software IV. 1200p. 1985. 118.00 (ISBN 0-318-11703-7). Springer Verlag.
Adey, Robert A., ed. Software for Engineering Problems. LC 83-81509. 130p. (Orig.). 1983. pap. 30.95x (ISBN 0-87201-832-6). Gulf Pub.
American Concrete Institute. Impact of Computers on the Practice of Structural Engineering in Concrete. LC 72-78494. (American Concrete Institute Publication Ser.: SP-33). (Illus.). pap. 80.00 (ISBN 0-317-10253-2, 2012300). Bks Demand UMI.
American Society of Mechanical Engineers. Interactive Computer Graphics in Engineering: Presented at the Winter Annual Meeting of the American Society of Mechanical Engineers, New York, N.Y. December 5-10-, 1976. Hulbert, L. E., ed. LC 77-77033. pap. 21.00 (ISBN 0-317-07994-8, 2051328). Bks Demand UMI.
Annino, R. & Driver, R. Personal Computers in Scientific & Engineering Applications. 1985. 39.95 (ISBN 0-471-79978-5). Wiley.
Beakley, George C. & Lovell, Robert E. Computation, Calculators & Computers: Tools of Engineering Problem Solving-Including FORTRAN. 368p. 1983. pap. text ed. write for info. (ISBN 0-02-307150-8). Macmillan.
Bernhardt, Ernest C., ed. Computer Aided Engineering for Injection Molding. 500p. 1984. text ed. 39.50 (ISBN 0-02-948590-8). Macmillan.
Boerstra, M. L., ed. Engineering Databases: Survey of Existing Engineering Database Management Systems, Criteria for Selecting a Database, & Some Practical Experiences in Applying a Database System. (Report of the CIAD Project Group on Engineering Databases). 178p. 1985. 111.00 (ISBN 0-444-42472-5). Elsevier.
Brebbia, C. A., ed. Boundary Element Techniques in Computer-Aided Engineering. LC 84-16710. 1984. lib. bdg. 58.50 (ISBN 90-247-3065-1, Pub. by Martinus Nijhoff Netherlands). Kluwer Academic.
Brebbia, C. A. & Keramidas, G. A., eds. Computational Methods & Experimental Measurements: Proceedings of the 2nd International Conference, on Board the Liner, the Queen Elizabeth 2, New York to Southhampton, June-July 1984. 800p. 76.60 (ISBN 0-387-13419-0). Springer-Verlag.
Brown, D. K. An Introduction to the Finite Element Method Using BASIC Programs. 196p. 1984. pap. 16.95 (ISBN 0-412-00581-6, NO. 9021, Pub. by Chapman & Hall); 34.00 (ISBN 0-412-00571-9, NO. 9020). Methuen Inc.
Bushnell, D. Computerized Buckling Analysis of Shells. (Mechanics of Elastic Stability Ser.). 1985. lib. bdg. 85.00 (ISBN 0-318-04125-1, Pub. by Martinus Nijhoff Netherlands). Kluwer Academic.
Calter, Paul. Problem Solving with Computers. 1972. pap. text ed. 27.65 (ISBN 0-07-009648-1). McGraw.
Carr, Joseph J. Sixty-Eight Scientific & Engineering Programs for the Apple II & IIe. 1984. 19.95 (ISBN 0-8359-6920-7). Reston.
Carr, Joseph L. Sixty-Eight Scientific & Engineering Programs for the IBM PC & PC XT. 1984. 19.95 (ISBN 0-8359-6921-5). Reston.
Chang, S. L. Fundamentals Handbook of Electrical & Computer Engineering, 3 Vols. 1983. 189.95 (ISBN 0-471-89690-X). Wiley.
Chang, Sheldon S. L. Fundamentals Handbook of Electrical & Computer Engineering: Communications, Control, Devices & Systems, Vol. 2. LC 82-4872. 737p. 1983. 74.95x (ISBN 0-471-86213-4). Wiley.
--Fundamentals Handbook of Electrical & Computer Engineering: Vol. 3: Computer Hardware, Software & Applications. LC 82-4872. 507p. 1982. 71.50 (ISBN 0-471-86214-2, Pub. by Wiley-Interscience). Wiley.
Chapra, S. C. & Canale, R. P. Numerical Methods for Engineering with Personal Computer Applications. 400p. 1985. 34.95 (ISBN 0-07-010664-9). McGraw.
Chasen, S. H. & Dow, J. W. The Guide for the Evaluation & Implementation of Cad-Cam Systems. 2nd ed. (Illus.). 461p. 1983. text ed. 250.00 (ISBN 0-938800-01-9). Cad Cam.
Chi, Joseph. CADSES: Computer Aided Design of Scientific & Engineering Systems. 268p. (Orig.). 1984. pap. text ed. 24.95 (ISBN 0-930945-01-8). HCP Systems.
Computer Engineering Div., ASME. Computer in Engineering Nineteen Eighty-Two: Vol. 3-Mesh Generation; Finite Elements; Computers in Structural Optimization; Computers in the Engineering Workplace; Computers in Energy Systems; Personal Computing, 4 Vol. Set. 1982. 60.00 ea. (G00217); 200.00 set (GX0219). ASME.
Computer in Engineering: Vol. 4-Process Control, State-of-the-Art Printing, Technology, Software Engineering & Management, Stastistical Modelling & Reliability Techniques. (Computers in Education Ser.). 1982. 60.00 (G00218). ASME.
Conference on Computers & Engineering 1983. 190p. 1983. pap. text ed. 28.00x (ISBN 0-85825-200-7, Pub. by Inst Engineering Australia). Brookfield Pub Co.

Dayasena, P. J. & Deighton, S., eds. Microprocessor Applications in Electrical Engineering, 1977-1978: Bibliography. 1980. 38.00 (ISBN 0-85296-453-6). Inst Elect Eng.
Deighton, S. & Mayne, K. D., eds. Microprocessor Applications in Engineering, 1977-1978: Bibliography. 1979. 23.00 (ISBN 0-85296-454-4). Inst Elect Eng.
Desk Top Computing for Engineers. 58p. 1982. pap. 19.00 (ISBN 0-85298-503-7, MEP157). Soc Auto Engineers.
Dietrich, D. E., ed. Pressure Vessels & Piping - Computer Program Evaluation & Qualification, Series PVP-PB-024. 1977. pap. text ed. 16.00 (ISBN 0-685-86875-3, G00124). ASME.
Director, S. W., ed. Computer-Aided Circuit Design: Simulation & Optimization. LC 73-16060. (Benchmark Papers in Electrical Engineering & Computer Science: Vol. 5). 380p. 1974. 51.95 (ISBN 0-87933-068-6). Van Nos Reinhold.
Dobson, W. G. Engineering Problem Solving with Spreadsheet Programs. Wolff, A. K., ed. (Illus.). 125p. 1984. 79.95 (ISBN 0-932217-00-1). Binary Eng Assocs.
Fielden, Christopher D. & Ede, Terence. Energy Management by Computer. 300p. 1981. 60.00x (ISBN 0-7198-2840-6, Pub. by Northwood Bks). State Mutual Bk.
Flora, Philip C. International Engineering-Scientific Software Directory. (Illus., Orig.). Date not set. pap. text ed. 35.00 (ISBN 0-910747-05-9). Tech Data TX.
FORTRAN 77 for Engineers. 1985. pap. text ed. write for info. (ISBN 0-534-04650-9, 22R2110). PWS Pubs.
Gibson, Glenn A. & Liu, Yu-Cheng. Microcomputers for Engineers & Scientists. (Illus.). 1980. text ed. 38.95 (ISBN 0-13-580886-3). P-H.
Gilder, Jules H. IBM Programs in Science & Engineering. 256p. pap. 16.95 (6356). Hayden.
Glowinski & Lions, eds. Computing Methods in Applied Sciences & Engineering. 724p. 1980. 70.25 (ISBN 0-444-86008-8, North-Holland). Elsevier.
Glowinski, R. & Lions, J. L. Computing Methods in Applied Sciences & Engineering, VI. 1984. 74.00 (ISBN 0-444-87597-2). Elsevier.
Gordon, R., ed. Transport. (Computer Programs for Chemical Engineering Education Ser.). 1972. pap. 15.95 (ISBN 0-88408-031-5). Sterling Swift.
Graham, J. A., ed. Use of Computers in Managing Material Property Data. (MPC: No. 14). 64p. 1980. 18.00 (ISBN 0-686-69865-7, G00192). ASME.
Halevi, Gideon. Role of Computers in Manufacturing Processes. LC 80-11378. 502p. 1980. 69.50x (ISBN 0-471-04383-4, Pub. by Wiley-Interscience). Wiley.
Halligan, Joseph. Engineering-SOFTWHERE. Winther, Richard P., ed. (SOFTWHERE-Software Directories Ser.: Vol. 1). (Orig.). 1984. pap. 49.95 (ISBN 0-918451-30-2). Moore Data.
Hovanessian, S. A. Computational Mathematics in Engineering. LC 76-14667. 272p. 1976. 38.00x (ISBN 0-669-00733-1). Lexington Bks.
Hubin, Wilbert N. BASIC Programming for Scientists & Engineers. LC 77-21343. (Illus.). 1978. pap. 21.95 ref. ed. (ISBN 0-13-066480-4). P-H.
Hyvaerinen, L. P. Information Theory for Systems Engineers. LC 79-124608. (Econometrics & Operations Research: Vol. 17). (Illus.). 1971. 34.00 (ISBN 0-387-05224-0). Springer-Verlag.
Inose, H. Digital Integrated Communication Systems. 368p. (not avail. in U.S.). 1980. pap. write for info. (ISBN 0-906048-61-3, TE99). Inst Elect Eng.
International Computer Programs Inc. ICP Software Directory, Vol. 5: Manufacturing & Engineering Systems. Hamilton, Dennis L., ed. 1984. pap. 95.00 (ISBN 0-88094-029-8). Intl Computer.
International Computer Programs Staff. ICP Software Directory, Vol. 5: Manufacturing & Engineering Systems. Hamilton, Dennis L., ed. 1985. pap. 95.00 (ISBN 0-88094-046-8). Intl Computer.
Korn, Granino A. Microprocessors & Small Digital Computer Systems: For Engineers & Scientists. LC 77-492. 1977. 49.95 (ISBN 0-07-035367-0). McGraw.
Kuo, Franklin F. & Kaiser, J. F. System Analysis by Digital Computer. LC 66-25226. 438p. 1966. text ed. 28.00 (ISBN 0-471-51121-8, Pub. by Wiley). Krieger.
Lewart, Cass. Science & Engineering Programs for the IBM PC. (Illus.). 150p. 1983. 18.95 (ISBN 0-13-794925-1). P-H.
--Science & Engineering Programs for the PCjr. 200p. 1985. pap. 14.95 (ISBN 0-13-794942-1); incl. disk 29.95 (ISBN 0-13-794975-8). P-H.
--Science & Engineering Programs for the Tandy 2000. 1984. pap. 14.95 cancelled (ISBN 0-13-795089-6). P-H.
--Science & Engineering Sourcebook. 96p. 1982. 17.95 (ISBN 0-13-795229-5); pap. 9.95 (ISBN 0-13-795211-2). P-H.
Lewart, Cass R. Science & Engineering Programs for the IBM PC. (Illus.). 240p. 1984. incl. diskette 39.95 (ISBN 0-13-794934-0). P-H.
--Scientific & Engineering Sourcebook: Professional Programs for the Timex Sinclair 1000. LC 82-62818. (Illus.). 120p. (Orig.). 1983. 14.95 (ISBN 0-07-037444-9, Byte Bks). McGraw.
Luzadder, Warren J. & Botkin, Kenneth E. Workbook, Problems in Engineering Drawing: With an Introduction to Interactive Computer. 9th ed. (Graphics for Design & Production Ser.: Vol. 1). (Illus.). xvi, 160p. 1986. pap. text ed. 13.95 (ISBN 0-13-716366-5). P-H.
Lykos, Peter. Personal Computers in Chemistry. LC 80-25445. 262p. 1981. 35.95x (ISBN 0-471-08508-1, Pub. by Wiley-Interscience). Wiley.
McCracken, Daniel D. Computing for Engineers & Scientists with FORTRAN 77. LC 83-23473. 361p. 1984. 23.45x (ISBN 0-471-09701-2); tchrs' manual avail. (ISBN 0-471-80090-2). Wiley.
--FORTRAN with Engineering Applications. LC 67-17343. (Illus.). 237p. 1967. pap. 26.50x (ISBN 0-471-58236-0, Pub. by Wiley-Interscience). Wiley.
Miller, Alan R. BASIC Programs for Scientists & Engineers. LC 81-84003. (Scientists & Engineers Ser.: No. 2). (Illus.). 318p. 1981. pap. 16.95 (ISBN 0-89588-073-3, B240). SYBEX.
--FORTRAN Programs for Scientists & Engineers. LC 82-80263. (Scientists & Engineers Ser.: No. 3). (Illus.). 280p. 1982. pap. 16.95 (ISBN 0-89588-082-2, F440). SYBEX.
--Pascal Programs for Scientists & Engineers. LC 81-51128. (Scientists & Engineers Ser.: No. 1). (Illus.). 374p. 1981. pap. 17.95 (ISBN 0-89588-058-X, P340). SYBEX.
Mortimore, Eugene. Macintosh MacDraw & MacWrite for Engineers, Vol. II. 1985. text ed. 21.95 (ISBN 0-8359-4150-7); pap. 17.95 (ISBN 0-8359-4149-3). Reston.
--Macintosh MacDraw & MacWrite for Engineers. 1985. text ed. 21.95 (ISBN 0-8359-4155-8); pap. 17.95 (ISBN 0-8359-4153-1). Reston.
Mosley, W. H. & Spencer, W. J. Microcomputer Applications in Structural Engineering. 250p. 1984. pap. 34.50 (ISBN 0-444-00919-1); diskette 25.00 (ISBN 0-444-00948-5). Elsevier.
Murrill, Paul W. & Smith, Cecil L. FORTRAN IV Programming for Engineers & Scientists. 2nd ed. LC 73-1689. (Illus.). 322p. 1973. pap. text ed. 6.50 scp (ISBN 0-352-03700-8, HarpC); scp solution manual 6.95 (ISBN 0-352-03700-8). Har-Row.
Nakamura, Shoichiro. Computational Methods in Engineering & Science. LC 85-9737. 472p. 1986. Repr. of 1977 ed. lib. bdg. price not set (ISBN 0-89874-867-4). Krieger.
Nelson, W. B. Applied Life Data Analysis. LC 81-14779. (Wiley Series Probability & Mathematical Statistics: Applied Probability & Statistics Section). 634p. 1982. 47.50x (ISBN 0-471-09458-7, Pub. by Wiley-Interscience). Wiley.
Noor, A. K. & McComb, H. G., eds. Computational Methods in Nonlinear Structural & Solid Mechanics: Papers Presented at the Symposium on Computational Methods in Nonlinear Structural & Solid Mechanics, 6-8 October 1980. LC 80-41608. 1980. 185.00 (ISBN 0-08-027299-1). Pergamon.
Ozan, Turgut M. Applied Mathematical Programming for Production & Engineering Management. 1985. text ed. 34.95 (ISBN 0-8359-0026-6); instrs.' manual avail. (ISBN 0-8359-0028-2). Reston.
Paker, Y. Minicomputers: A Reference Book for Engineers, Scientists & Managers. 1980. 59.00 (ISBN 0-9961005-0-4, 996100504, Pub. by Abacus England). Heyden.
Pipes, Louis A. & Hovanessian, Shahen A. Matrix-Computer Methods in Engineering. LC 77-23111. 346p. 1977. Repr. of 1969 ed. 19.50 (ISBN 0-88275-591-9). Krieger.
Pironneau, O. Optimal Shape Design for Elliptic Systems. (Springer Series in Computational Physics). (Illus.). 190p. 1984. 39.00 (ISBN 0-387-12069-6). Springer-Verlag.
Practical Engineering Applications Software. Beam Analysis. 1985. IBM-PC Version. incl. disk 125.00 (ISBN 0-471-80302-2); Apple Version. incl. disk 125.00 (ISBN 0-471-88420-0). Wiley.
--Continuous Span. 1985. IBM-PC Version. incl. disk 125.00 (ISBN 0-471-80299-9); Apple Version. incl. disk 125.00 (ISBN 0-471-88423-5). Wiley.
Scientific & Engineering Software Guide. 287p. 1984. 19.95 (ISBN 0-317-04403-6). Micro Info.
Severin, Ranier. Commodore 64 for Scientists & Engineers. Dykema, Greg, tr. from Ger. 250p. 1984. pap. text ed. 19.95 (ISBN 0-916439-09-7). Abacus Soft.
Simons, G. L. Computers in Engineering & Manufacture. 360p. 1982. pap. 32.80 (ISBN 0-471-89435-4). Wiley.
--Computers in Engineering & Manufacturing. 360p. 1982. 35.00x (ISBN 0-85012-347-X). Intl Pubns Serv.
Smardzewski, R. R. Microprocessor Programming & Applications for Scientists & Engineers. LC 84-13759. (Data Handling in Science & Technology Ser.: Vol. 1). 1984. 36.50 (ISBN 0-444-42407-5). Elsevier.
Smith, David R. Digital Transmission Systems. (Engineering). (Illus.). 560p. 1984. 48.00 (ISBN 0-534-03382-2). Lifetime Learn.
Southworth, R. & De Leeuw, S. Digital Computation & Numerical Methods. 1965. text ed. 45.00 (ISBN 0-07-059799-5). McGraw.
Spencer, Donald D. Computers & Programming Guide for Scientists & Engineers. 2nd ed. LC 80-50051. 464p. 1980. pap. 15.95 (ISBN 0-672-21693-0, 21693). Sams.
Spillers, W. R. Automated Structural Analysis: An Introduction. (Pergamon Unified Engineering Ser.: Vol. 7). 182p. 1972. 25.00 (ISBN 0-08-016782-9). Pergamon.
Stallings, William. Data & Computer Communications. 1985. text ed. write for info. (ISBN 0-02-415440-7). Macmillan.
Stanley, William. Network Analysis for Engineering & Technology. 1985. text ed. 36.95 (ISBN 0-8359-4880-3). Reston.
Suh, Chung Ha. Computer Aided Design of Mechanisms. 600p. Date not set. pap. text ed. 49.95 (ISBN 0-02-949720-5). Macmillan.
Syposium on Engineering Computer Software (1971: San Francisco, CA). Engineering Computer Software: Verification, Qualification, Certification; Symposium. Presentations from ASME First National Congress on Pressure Vessels & Piping, San Francisco, CA, May 1971. Berman, Irwin, ed. LC 73-173859. pap. 32.50 (ISBN 0-317-08079-2, 2016828). Bks Demand UMI.
Thompson, F. & Hayward, G. G. Structural Analysis Using Virtual Work. (Illus.). 320p. 1985. pap. 31.00 (ISBN 0-412-22290-6, NO. 9129, Pub. by Chapman & Hall); 59.95 (ISBN 0-412-22280-9, NO. 9128). Methuen Inc.
Valentino, James. FORTRAN for Engineers & Technologists. 1985. pap. text ed. 23.95x (ISBN 0-03-060569-5). HR&W.
Volk, William. Engineering Statistics with a Programmable Calculator. Davidson, Robert L., ed. (Illus.). 320p. 1981. 26.95x (ISBN 0-07-067552-X). McGraw.
Wang, Peter C. Advances in Engineering Data Handling. 1984. lib. bdg. 39.95 (ISBN 0-89838-154-1). Kluwer Academic.
Whitehouse, Gary E., ed. Software for Engineers & Managers: A Collection. 1984. pap. text ed. 24.95 (ISBN 0-89806-046-X). Inst Indus Eng.
Wolfe, Philip & Koelling, C. Patrick. Basic Engineering & Scientific Programs for the IBM PC. LC 83-7100. (Illus.). 356p. 1983. pap. text ed. 21.95 (ISBN 0-89303-330-8); bk. & diskette 46.95 (ISBN 0-89303-331-6); 25.00 (ISBN 0-89303-333-2). Brady Comm.
Wren, A. Computers in Transport Planning & Operation. 152p. 1971. 45.25 (ISBN 0-677-65370-0). Gordon.
Wright, Victor. TK! SOLVER for Engineers. 1984. pap. 19.95 (ISBN 0-8359-7711-0). Reston.
Yassinsky, George. Fifty-Two Programs for Engineers & Architects, Vol. 1. (Illus.). 352p. 1984. 18.95 (ISBN 0-931379-00-8). Polymus Pub.

ENGINEERING–DESIGN
see Engineering Design

ENGINEERING–DICTIONARIES

Barry, W. R., ed. Architectural, Construction, Manufacturing & Engineering Glossary of Terms. 519p. 1979. pap. 40.00 (ISBN 0-930284-05-4). Am Assn Cost Engineers.
Bosch, Ten. Dutch-English-French-German Engineering Dictionary. 11th ed. (Dutch, Eng., Fr. & Ger.). 45.00 (ISBN 90-2010-132-3). Heinman.
Brockhaus der Naturwissenschaften und der Technik. (Ger.). 832p. 35.00 (ISBN 3-7653-0019-5, M-7314, Pub. by Wiesbaden). French & Eur.
Burns, A. Concurrent Programming in Ada. 250p. Date not set. price not set. Cambridge U Pr.
Carcamo, L. Dictionnaire pour Ingenieurs et Techniciens: Francais-Espagnol, Espagnol-Francais. (Fr. & Span.). 1106p. 1981. 95.00 (ISBN 0-686-92423-1, M-7669). French & Eur.
Clauser, H. R. Diccionario De Materiales y Procesos De Ingenieria. (Span.). 820p. 1970. 98.00 (ISBN 84-335-6404-8, S-50067). French & Eur.
Considine, Douglas M. Van Nostrand's Scientific Encyclopedia. 6th ed. (Illus.). 3100p. 1984. 2 vol. ed. 139.50 (ISBN 0-442-25164-5); 1 vol. ed. 107.50 (ISBN 0-442-25161-0). Van Nos Reinhold.
DeVries, Louis. German-English Technical & Engineering Dictionary. 2nd ed. (Ger. & Eng.). 1966. 67.95 (ISBN 0-07-016631-5). McGraw.
Engineering Index, Inc. Engineering Index Thesaurus. LC 72-78325. 1972. 19.50 (ISBN 0-02-468550-X). Macmillan Info.
English-Chinese Dictionary of Construction Engineering. (Eng. & Chinese.). 251p. 1980. leatherette 14.95 (ISBN 0-686-97360-7, M-9279). French & Eur.
Ernst, Richard. Dictionary of Engineering & Technology: English-German, Vol. II. 5th ed. 1000p. 1985. 69.00 (ISBN 0-19-520485-9). Oxford U Pr.
--Dictionary of Engineering & Technology: With Extensive Treatment of the Most Modern Techniques & Processes, Vol. 2, English-German. 4th, rev. & enl. ed. (Eng. & Ger.). 1975. text ed. 69.00x (ISBN 0-19-520109-4). Oxford U Pr.
Ernst, Richard, compiled by. Comprehensive Dictionary of Engineering & Technology, 2 vols. 1085p. 1985. Vol. 1, French & English. 100.00 (ISBN 0-521-30377-X); Vol. 2, English & French. 110.00 (ISBN 0-521-30378-8). Cambridge U Pr.
Ernst, Richard, ed. Dictionary of Engineering & Technology, Vol. 1. 4th ed. 1980. 69.00x (ISBN 0-19-520269-4). Oxford U Pr.
Fachlexikon ABC Technik und Naturwissenschaft, Vols. 1 & 2. (Ger.). 1970. Set. leatherette 55.00 (ISBN 3-87144-004-3, M-7384). French & Eur.
Freeman, H. Taschenwoerterbuch Kraftfahrzeugtechnik. (Ger. & Eng.). 377p. (Dictionary of Automotive Engineering). 1968. 12.50 (ISBN 3-19-006270-6, M-7635, Pub. by M. Hueber). French & Eur.
Freeman, Henry G. Fachenglisch Fur Technik und Industrie. (Ger. & Eng.). 303p. (English for Engineering and Industry). 1974. 22.50 (ISBN 3-452-17766-1, M-7376, Pub. by Carl Heymanns Verlag KG). French & Eur.
Halbauer, S. Russisch-Deutsches Woerterbuch Fuer Naturwissenschaftler und Ingenieure. (Ger. & Rus.). 170p. 1971. 9.95 (ISBN 0-686-56466-9, M-7607, Pub. by M. Hueber). French & Eur.
Heck, Hans. Knaurs Lexikon der Technik. (Ger.). 55.00 (ISBN 3-426-04577-X, M-7520, Pub. by Druckenmueller). French & Eur.
Kovalenko, Y. G. English-Russian Dictionary of Reliability & Quality Control. LC 77-70279. (Eng. & Rus.). 1977. text ed. 79.00 (ISBN 0-08-021933-0). Pergamon.
McGraw-Hill, ed. McGraw-Hill Encyclopedia of Engineering. (Illus.). 1272p. 1983. 72.50 (ISBN 0-07-045486-8). McGraw.
McGraw-Hill Editors. Dictionary of Mechanical & Design Engineering. 400p. 1985. 15.95 (ISBN 0-07-045414-0). McGraw.
McGraw-Hill Editors & Parker, Sybil P., eds. Dictionary of Engineering. 530p. 1984. 32.50 (ISBN 0-07-045412-4). McGraw.
Mugica Urdangarin, Luis M. Diccionario General y Tecnico: Hiztegi Orokor-Teknikoa, 2 vols. (Span. & Vasco.). #1220p. 1977. Set. 80.00 (ISBN 84-85288-07-6, S-50100). French & Eur.
Naxerova, A. Technisches Woerterbuch, Vol. 2. (Czech. & Ger.). 1972. 40.00 (ISBN 3-87097-056-1, M-7650, Pub. by Brandstetter). French & Eur.
Neubert, Gunter, ed. Technical Dictionary of Hydraulics & Pneumatics. 1973. text ed. 44.00 (ISBN 0-08-016958-9). Pergamon.
O'Bannon, Loran S. Dictionary of Ceramic Science & Engineering. 350p. 1983. 45.00x (ISBN 0-306-41324-8, Plenum Pr). Plenum Pub.
Oppermann, A. Woerterbuch der Modernen Technik. (Ger. & Eng., Dictionary of Modern Engineering). 112.00 (ISBN 3-7940-6001-6, M-6982). French & Eur.
Oppermann, Alfred. Dictionary of Modern Engineering, Vol. 1. 3rd ed. (Eng. & Ger.). 1971. 113.00 (ISBN 3-7940-6001-6, M-7109). French & Eur.
--Dictionary of Modern Engineering, Vol. 2. 3rd ed. (Ger. & Eng.). 1974. 113.00 (ISBN 3-7940-6002-4, M-7108). French & Eur.
Oppermann, Alfred, ed. Dictionary of Modern Engineering: English-German-German-English, 2 Vols. 4th ed. 1864p. 1982. lib. bdg. 110.00 (ISBN 3-598-10471-5). K G Saur.
Orlando-Meyer, Salvatore. Technisches Woerterbuch, Vol. 1. 2nd ed. (Ital. & Ger.). 1977. 40.00 (ISBN 3-87097-079-0, M-7651, Pub. by Brandstetter). French & Eur.
--Technisches Woerterbuch, Vol. 2. 2nd ed. (Ital. & Ger.). 1977. 40.00 (ISBN 3-87097-080-4, M-7652, Pub. by Brandstetter). French & Eur.

Souders, Mott. Engineer's Companion: A Concise Handbook of Engineering Fundamentals. LC 65-26851. 426p. 1966. 37.50x (ISBN 0-471-81395-8, Pub. by Wiley-Interscience). Wiley.

Stanley, C. Maxwell. The Consulting Engineer. 2nd ed. LC 81-11593. 303p. 1982. 36.95x (ISBN 0-471-08920-6, Pub. by Wiley-Interscience). Wiley.

Stock Drive Products Staff Engineers & Freudenstein, Ferdinand. Stock Drive Products Handbook of Commercial Drive Components. 520p. 1971. pap. 1.75 (ISBN 0-686-01078-7). Stock Drive.

Thomas, Willard, et al. The Engineer's Vest Pocket Book. rev, 2nd ed. (Vest Pocket Library Ser.). pap. 48.00 (ISBN 0-317-26662-4, 2025105). Bks Demand UMI.

Towill, D. R. Transfer Function Techniques for Control Engineers. (Illus.). 1971. 22.50 (ISBN 0-8088-1911-9). Davey.

Transamerica Delaval Inc. Transamerica Delaval Engineering Handbook. 4th ed. Crawford, Harold B., ed. (Illus.). 640p. 1983. 47.50 (ISBN 0-07-016250-6). McGraw.

Yuen, Aubrey. Geometric & Positional Tolerancing Reference & Work Book. 2nd ed. 90p. 1973. perfect bdg. 18.95x (ISBN 0-912702-07-9). Global Eng.

ENGINEERING–HISTORY

Baynes, Ken & Pugh, Francis. The Art of the Engineer. LC 80-29190. (Illus.). 240p. 1981. 85.00 (ISBN 0-87951-128-1); deluxe ed. 175.00 (ISBN 0-87951-140-0). Overlook Pr.

Blake, Marion E. Ancient Roman Construction in Italy from the Prehistoric Period to Augustus. (Carnegie Institution Publication Ser.: No. 570). (Illus.). 1968. Repr. of 1947 ed. 44.00 (ISBN 0-527-08850-1). Kraus Repr.

Cooley, Mortimer E. Scientific Blacksmith. LC 72-5041. (Technology & Society Ser.). (Illus.). 290p. 1972. Repr. of 1947 ed. 18.00 (ISBN 0-405-04693-6). Ayer Co Pubs.

Corbett, Arthur. History of the Institution of Engineers: Australia 1919-1969. 288p. 1973. text ed. 19.50x (ISBN 0-207-12516-3, Pub. by Inst Engineering Australia). Brookfield Pub Co.

DeCamp, L. Sprague. The Ancient Engineers. 1980. pap. 2.95 (ISBN 0-345-29347-9). Ballantine.

Flaxman, Edward. Great Feats of Modern Engineering. facs. ed. rev. ed. LC 67-23219. (Essay Index Reprint Ser). 1938. 20.00 (ISBN 0-8369-0446-X). Ayer Co Pubs.

Foppl, August. Drang und Zwang: Eine Hoehere Festigkeitslehre Fuer Ingeneure, 3 Vols. LC 69-20268. (Ger). 1969. Repr. of 1941 ed. Set. 70.00 (ISBN 0-384-16275-4). Johnson Repr.

Gest, Alexander P. Engineering. LC 63-10287. (Our Debt to Greece & Rome Ser). Repr. of 1930 ed. 17.50 (ISBN 0-8154-0078-0). Cooper Sq.

Gillmor, C. Stewart. Coulomb & the Evolution of Physics & Engineering in Eighteenth Century France. LC 79-155006. (Illus.). 1971. 34.50x (ISBN 0-691-08095-X). Princeton U Pr.

Guest, G. Martin. Brief History of Engineering. (Illus.). 1974. pap. text ed. 17.50x (ISBN 0-245-52337-5). Intl Ideas.

Hart, Ivor B. Great Engineers. facs. ed. LC 67-23226. (Essay Index Reprint Ser). 1928. 12.00 (ISBN 0-8369-0515-6). Ayer Co Pubs.

Landels, John. Engineering in the Ancient World. LC 76-52030. 1978. pap. 5.95 (ISBN 0-520-04127-5). U of Cal Pr.

Malone, Patrick M. Canals & Industry: Engineering in Lowell, 1821-1880. (Illus.). 27p. (Orig.). 1983. pap. 2.50 (ISBN 0-942472-07-1). Lowell Museum.

Matschoss, Conrad. Great Engineers. Hatfield, H. S., tr. LC 70-128278. (Essay Index Reprint Ser). 1939. 27.50 (ISBN 0-8369-1837-1). Ayer Co Pubs.

Miller, John A. Master Builders of Sixty Centuries. facsimile ed. LC 70-37524. (Essay Index Reprint Ser). (Illus.). Repr. of 1938 ed. 20.00 (ISBN 0-8369-2566-1). Ayer Co Pubs.

Parsons, William B. Engineers & Engineering of the Renaissance. 1968. pap. 16.50x (ISBN 0-262-66026-1). MIT Pr.

The Principal Works of Simon Stevin, 5 vols. Incl. Vol. 1. General Introduction-Mechanism. Dijksterhuis, E. J., ed. 1955 (ISBN 90-265-0070-X); Vols. 2 A & B. Mathematics. Struik, D. J., ed. 973p. 1958 (ISBN 90-265-0071-8); Vol. 3. Astronomy & Navigation. Pannekoek, A. & Croone, E., eds. 632p. 1961 (ISBN 90-265-0073-4); Vol. 4. Art of War. Schukking, W. H., ed. 525p. 1964 (ISBN 90-265-0074-2); Vol. 5. Engineering-Music-Civic Life. Forbes, R. J., et al. 609p. 1967 (ISBN 90-265-0075-0). (Dutch & Eng.). text ed. 95.00 ea. (Pub. by Swets Pub Serv Holland). Swets North Am.

Reyes-Guerra, David R. & Fischer, Alan M. The Engineering High-Tech Student's Handbook. 122p. (Orig.). 1985. pap. 8.95 (ISBN 0-87866-270-7). Petersons Guides.

Turner, Roland & Goulden, Steven L., eds. Great Engineers: From Antiquity Through the Industrial Revolution, Vol. I. (Illus.). 630p. 1982. 69.50 (ISBN 0-312-34574-7). St Martin.

Weiss, John H. The Making of Technological Man: The Social Origins of French Engineering Education. 384p. 1982. 40.00x (ISBN 0-262-23112-3). MIT Pr.

ENGINEERING–INFORMATION SERVICES

see Technology–Information Services

ENGINEERING–LABORATORY MANUALS

Cowan, Henry J. & Dixon, John. Building Science Laboratory Manual. (Illus.). 156p. 1978. 24.00 (ISBN 0-85334-747-6, Pub. by Elsevier Applied Sci England). Elsevier.

Tuve, George L. & Domholdt, L. C. Engineering Experimentation. rev. ed. 1966. text ed. 48.00 (ISBN 0-07-065595-2). McGraw.

ENGINEERING–MANAGEMENT

American Society of Civil Engineers, compiled By. Effective Project Management Techniques. 83p. 1973. pap. 5.00x (ISBN 0-87262-058-1). Am Soc Civil Eng.

--Management of Engineering of Control Systems for Water Pipelines. 141p. 1978. pap. 16.25x (ISBN 0-87262-132-4). Am Soc Civil Eng.

Amos, John M. & Sarchet, Bernard R. Management for Engineers. (Series in Industrial Systems Engineering). (Illus.). 384p. 1981. text ed. 25.95 (ISBN 0-13-549402-8). P-H.

Antill, James M. & Woodhead, Ronald. Critical Path Methods in Construction Practice. 2nd ed. LC 79-121902. pap. 81.40 (ISBN 0-8357-9870-4, 2019295). Bks Demand UMI.

Antill, James M. & Woodhead, Ronald W. Critical Path Methods in Construction Practice. 3rd. ed. LC 81-19713. 425p. 1982. 42.95x (ISBN 0-471-86612-1, Pub. by Wiley-Interscience). Wiley.

ASGE Engineering Management Division Conference Held at Chicago, April 1981. Effective Management of Engineering Design. LC 81-65628. 175p. 1981. pap. 18.00x (ISBN 0-87262-268-1). Am Soc Civil Eng.

Baird, Bruce F. The Technical Manager: How to Manage People & Make Decisions. (Illus.). 168p. 1983. 22.50 (ISBN 0-534-97925-4). Lifetime Learn.

Blanchard, Benjamin S. Engineering Organization & Management. (P-H International Industrial & System Engineering Ser.). (Illus.). 544p. 1976. 30.95 (ISBN 0-13-279430-6). P-H.

Borsenik, Frank D. The Management of Maintenance & Engineering Systems in Hospitality Industries. LC 78-13677. (Service Management Ser.). 494p. 1979. text ed. 29.95 (ISBN 0-471-03213-1). Wiley.

Buchanan, C. R. & Eng, C. Control of Manufacture: An Introduction to Engineering Management. 160p. 1983. pap. text ed. 11.95 (ISBN 0-7131-3462-3). E Arnold.

Christian, Anthony J. Management, Machines & Methods in Civil Engineering. LC 81-2434. (Construction Management & Engineering Ser.). 360p. 1981. 45.95x (ISBN 0-471-06334-7, Pub. by Wiley-Interscience). Wiley.

Cohen, William A. Principles of Technical Management. LC 79-54829. pap. 58.50 (ISBN 0-317-26710-8, 2023515). Bks Demand UMI.

Engineering Management Conference, Melbourne, Australia, March 1979. Engineering Management Update. 78p. (Orig.). 1979. pap. text ed. 24.00x (ISBN 0-85825-105-1, Pub. by Inst Engineering Australia). Brookfield Pub Co.

Gangstad, E. O., ed. Rights of Way Management for Weeds Control Methods. 1981. 84.50 (ISBN 0-8493-5329-7). CRC Pr.

Gray, Irwin. The Engineer in Transition to Management. LC 78-61533. 1979. 25.95 (ISBN 0-87942-111-8, PC01164). Inst Electrical.

Joint Engineering Management Conference (23rd: 1975: Washington, D.C.) Effective Management of Engineering Resources. LC 75-329975. (Illus.). pap. 26.80 (ISBN 0-317-08475-5, 2016903). Bks Demand UMI.

Joint Engineering Management Conference (21st: 1973: St. Petersburg, Fla.) The Impact of Competitive Technology on Engineering Management: Presented at the Twenty-First Annual Joint Engineering Management Conference Held in St. Petersburg, Florida, October 25-26, 1973. LC 74-99882. (Illus.). pap. 34.80 (ISBN 0-317-08457-7, 2016896). Bks Demand UMI.

Joint Engineering Management Conference (22nd: 1974: Mexico City) International Patterns of Engineering Management: A Constructive Analysis. LC 74-99882. (Illus.). pap. 25.80 (ISBN 0-317-08464-X, 2016897). Bks Demand UMI.

Kern, Dale R., ed. Engineering & Construction Projects: The Emerging Management Roles. LC 82-70492. 335p. 1982. pap. 28.50x (ISBN 0-87262-299-1). Am Soc Civil Eng.

King, J. R., ed. Managing Liability. LC 82-70764. 95p. 1982. pap. 16.00x (ISBN 0-87262-304-1). Am Soc Civil Eng.

Lewis, Jack R. Architects & Engineers Office Practice Guide. (Illus.). 1978. ref. ed. 26.95 (ISBN 0-13-044669-6). P-H.

McCormick, E. J. & Sanders, M. S. Human Factors in Engineering & Design. 5th ed. 1982. 43.95 (ISBN 0-07-044902-3). McGraw.

Mackie, D. Engineering Management of Capital Projects: A Practical Guide. 208p. 1985. price not set (ISBN 0-07-548846-9). McGraw.

Managing the Engineering Function. (Didactic Simulation Game Ser). 1970. pap. 23.50 (ISBN 0-89401-063-8); pap. 24.90 german (ISBN 0-89401-099-9); pap. 21.50 for 2 or more (ISBN 0-685-77366-3); pap. 0.50 leader's gude (ISBN 0-686-57882-1). Didactic Syst.

Olsen, Shirley A., ed. Group Planning & Problem-Solving Methods in Engineering Management. LC 81-19675. (Construction Management & Engineering Ser.). 455p. 1982. 57.50x (ISBN 0-471-08311-9, Pub. by Wiley-Interscience). Wiley.

Ozan, Turgut M. Applied Mathematical Programming for Production & Engineering Management. 1985. text ed. 34.95 (ISBN 0-8359-0026-6); instrs.' manual avail. (ISBN 0-8359-0028-2). Reston.

Repic, Ed. Managing Engineers. (Illus., Orig.). 1981. pap. 25.00 (ISBN 0-939740-00-1). Effect Mgmt.

Rosenau, Milton D., Jr. Practical Engineering Project Management. (Illus.). 280p. 25.00 (ISBN 0-534-03383-0). Lifetime Learn.

--Projects Management for Engineers. (Illus.). 1984. 25.00 (ISBN 0-317-13780-8). Lifetime Learn.

Rowe, K. Management Techniques for Civil Engineering Construction. (Illus.). x, 268p. 1975. 39.00 (ISBN 0-85334-613-5, Pub. by Elsevier Applied Sci England). Elsevier.

Samaras, Thomas T. & Czerwinski, Frank L. Fundamentals of Configuration Management. LC 75-127668. Repr. of 1971 ed. 97.00 (ISBN 0-8357-9897-6, 2055259). Bks Demand UMI.

Shannon, R. E. Engineering Management. LC 79-14721. 400p. 1980. 40.50 (ISBN 0-471-03408-8). Wiley.

Silverman, Melvin. The Technical Manager's Survival Book. 300p. 1984. 29.95 (ISBN 0-07-057515-0). McGraw.

Sinha, A. K. & Sinha, Rama. Project Engineering & Management. 1983. text ed. 37.50x (ISBN 0-7069-2255-7, Pub. by Vikas India). Advent NY.

Thamhain, Hans J. Engineering Program Management. LC 83-21740. 351p. 1984. 37.50x (ISBN 0-471-05979-X, Pub. by Wiley-Interscience). Wiley.

Ullmann, J. E., et al. Handbook of Engineering Management. 1985. 49.95 (ISBN 0-471-87828-6). Wiley.

ENGINEERING–MATERIALS

see Materials

ENGINEERING–MODELS

see Engineering Models

ENGINEERING–NOTATION

Bradshaw, P. Engineering Calculation Methods for Turbulent Flow. 1981. 49.50 (ISBN 0-12-124550-0). Acad Pr.

Engineering Concepts Curriculum Project - State University of New York. Man & His Technology. (Illus.). 256p. 1973. text ed. 25.00 (ISBN 0-07-019510-2). McGraw.

Lapidus, Leon & Pinder, George F. Numerical Solution of Partial Differential Equations in Science & Engineering. LC 81-16491. 677p. 1982. 51.95x (ISBN 0-471-09866-3, Pub. by Wiley-Interscience). Wiley.

ENGINEERING–PROBLEMS, EXERCISES, ETC.

Albertson, Maurice L., et al. Fluid Mechanics for Engineers. 1960. text ed. 37.95 (ISBN 0-13-322578-X). P-H.

Anderson, W. J. MSC-Nastran: Interactive Training Program. 482p. 1983. pap. 31.50 (ISBN 0-471-89109-6). Wiley.

Brebbia, C., ed. Boundary Element Methods: Proceedings. (Illus.). 622p. 1981. 61.00 (ISBN 0-387-10816-5). Springer-Verlag.

Brebbia, C. A. & Ferrante, A. J. Computational Methods for the Solution of Engineering Problems. LC 76-53093. 354p. 1977. 34.50x (ISBN 0-8448-1079-7). Crane-Russak Co.

Dobrovolny, J. S., et al. Problems in Engineering Drawing & Geometry, Series 12, 13, 15, 16, 21. 1964. pap. 6.80x ea. Stipes.

Douthwaite, G. K. & Dunn, W. L. Introductory Engineering Problems by Computer Methods: Fortran Four. rev. ed. (Illus., Orig.). 1965. pap. text ed. 8.95x (ISBN 0-87015-135-5). Pacific Bks.

--Introductory Engineering Problems by Computer Methods: Fortran Two. (Illus.). 1964. pap. text ed. 6.95x (ISBN 0-87015-130-4). Pacific Bks.

Eide, A. R. & Jenison, R. D. Engineering Fundamentals & Problem Solving. 2nd ed. 416p. 1985. price not set (ISBN 0-07-019318-5). McGraw.

Ferziger, Joel H. Numerical Methods for Engineering Application. LC 81-1260. 288p. 1981. 34.95x (ISBN 0-471-06336-3, Pub. by Wiley-Interscience). Wiley.

Hartley, T. C. & O'Bryant, D. C. Problems in Engineering. (Graphics Ser.: No. 31). 1975. pap. 7.80 (ISBN 0-87563-109-6). Stipes.

Irvine. Engineering Technology Problem Solving: Techniques Using Electronic Calculators. (Engineering Technology Ser.: Vol. 2). 1981. 29.50 (ISBN 0-8247-1169-6). Dekker.

Johnson, David E. & Johnson, Johnny R. Mathematical Methods in Engineering & Physics. 208p. 1982. 38.95 (ISBN 0-13-561126-1). P-H.

Na, T. Y. Computational Methods in Engineering: Boundary Value Problems. LC 79-51682. (Mathematics in Science & Engineering Ser.). 1979. 60.00 (ISBN 0-12-512650-6). Acad Pr.

Polentz, Lloyd M. Engineering Fundamentals for Professional Engineers Exams. 2nd ed. LC 78-21927. (Illus.). 1980. 34.50 (ISBN 0-07-050380-X); pap. 17.95 (ISBN 0-07-050381-8). McGraw.

Yuen, Aubrey. Geometric & Positional Tolerancing Reference & Work Book. 2nd ed. 90p. 1973. perfect bdg. 18.95x (ISBN 0-912702-07-9). Global Eng.

ENGINEERING–STATISTICAL METHODS

Ang, A. H. & Tang, W. H. Probability Concepts in Engineering Planning & Design, Vol. 1. LC 75-5892. 409p. 1975. text ed. 44.50x (ISBN 0-471-03200-X). Wiley.

Beck, James V. & Arnold, Kenneth J. Parameter Estimation in Engineering & Science. LC 77-40293. (Probability & Statistics: Applied Probability & Statistics Section). 501p. 1976. 51.95x (ISBN 0-471-06118-2, Pub. by Wiley-Interscience). Wiley.

Bowker, Albert & Lieberman, Gerald. Engineering Statistics. 2nd ed. (Illus.). 608p. 1972. ref. ed. 31.95 (ISBN 0-13-279455-1). P-H.

Fu, King & Yu, T. S. Statistical Pattern Classification Using Contextual Information. LC 80-40949. (Electronic & Electrical Engineering Research Studies, Pattern Recognition &Image Processing Ser.: Vol. 1). pap. 50.30 (ISBN 0-317-26335-8, 2025199). Bks Demand UMI.

Hahn, Gerald J. & Shapiro, S. S. Statistical Models in Engineering. LC 67-12562. (Wiley Series on Systems Engineering & Analysis). 355p. 1967. 41.95 (ISBN 0-471-33915-6, Pub. by Wiley-Interscience). Wiley.

Lipson, Charles & Sheth, N. J. Statistical Design & Analysis of Engineering Experiments. (Illus.). 544p. 1972. text ed. 42.00 (ISBN 0-07-037991-2). McGraw.

Little, R. E. Probability & Statistics for Engineers. (Illus.). 552p. 1978. 29.95 (ISBN 0-916460-04-5). Matrix Pub.

McCuen, Richard H. Statistical Methods for Engineers. (Illus.). 400p. 1985. text ed. 35.95 (ISBN 0-13-844903-1). P-H.

Mann, Lawrence, Jr. Applied Engineering Statistics for Practicing Engineers. LC 76-129578. 184p. 1970. pap. 9.95 (ISBN 0-8436-0317-8). Van Nos Reinhold.

Map Uses, Scales & Accuracies for Engineering & Associated Purposes. 172p. 1983. pap. 16.00x (ISBN 0-87262-379-3). Am Soc Civil Eng.

Miller, Irwin & Freund, John. Probability & Statistics for Engineers. 3rd ed. (Illus.). 544p. 1985. text ed. 35.95 (ISBN 0-13-711938-0). P-H.

Stoodley, K. D. Basic Statistical Techniques for Engineering & Science Students. 120p. 1974. text ed. 17.95x (ISBN 0-8464-0182-7); pap. 12.95 (ISBN 0-686-77073-0). Beekman Pubs.

Uhl, Vincent W. & Lowthian, Walter E., eds. Uncertainty Analysis for Engineers. LC 82-24443. (AIChE Symposium: Vol. 78). 1982. pap. 20.00 (ISBN 0-8169-0244-5, S-220); pap. 10.00 members (ISBN 0-686-47552-6). Am Inst Chem Eng.

Volk, William. Applied Statistics for Engineers. 2nd ed. LC 79-24015. 1980. Repr. of 1969 ed. lib. bdg. 24.50 (ISBN 0-89874-071-1). Krieger.

ENGINEERING–STATISTICS

Guttman, Irwin, et al. Introductory Engineering Statistics. 3rd ed. 580p. 1982. text ed. 42.50 (ISBN 0-471-07859-X); solutions manual avail. (ISBN 0-471-08659-2). Wiley.

Hibbeler, R. C. Engineering Mechanics: Statics. 4th ed. 1211p. 1986. text ed. price not set (ISBN 0-02-354670-0). Macmillan.

Hines, William W. & Montgomery, Douglas C. Probability & Statistics in Engineering & Management Science. 2nd ed. LC 79-26257. 634p. 1980. text ed. 41.50 (ISBN 0-471-04759-7); solutions manual avail. (ISBN 0-471-05006-7). Wiley.

McGill, David J. & King, Milton W. Engineering Mechanics: Statics. 1985. text ed. write for info. (ISBN 0-534-02937-X, 23R3000, Pub. by PWS Engineering). PWS Pubs.

ENGINEERING, HYDRAULIC
see Hydraulic Engineering
ENGINEERING, INDUSTRIAL
see Industrial Engineering
ENGINEERING, MARINE
see Marine Engineering
ENGINEERING, MECHANICAL
see Mechanical Engineering; Mechanics, Applied
ENGINEERING, MINING
see Mining Engineering
ENGINEERING, MUNICIPAL
see Municipal Engineering
ENGINEERING, RAILROAD
see Railroad Engineering
ENGINEERING, SANITARY
see Sanitary Engineering
ENGINEERING, STEAM
see Steam Engineering
ENGINEERING, STRUCTURAL
see Structural Engineering
ENGINEERING, TRAFFIC
see Traffic Engineering
ENGINEERING, WATER-SUPPLY
see Water-Supply Engineering
ENGINEERING ANALYSIS
see Engineering Mathematics
ENGINEERING CYBERNETICS
see Automation
ENGINEERING DESIGN
see also Materials; Structural Design; Systems Engineering;
also subdivisions Design and Design and Construction under special subjects, e.g. Machinery–Design; Automobiles–Design and Construction

Ang, Alfredo H-S & Tang, Wilson H. Probability Concepts in Engineering Planning & Design, Vol. II. LC 75-5892. 562p. 1984. text ed. 42.50 (ISBN 0-471-03201-8). Wiley.
Araoz, A., ed. Consulting & Engineering Design in Developing Countries. 140p. 1981. pap. 10.00 (ISBN 0-88936-278-5, IDRC161, IDRC). Unipub.
Artobolevsky, I. Mechanism in Modern Engineering Design, Vol. V. (Illus.). 1101p. 1980. 15.00 (ISBN 0-8285-3012-2, Pub. by Mir Pubs USSR). Imported Pubns.
--Mechanisms in Modern Engineering Design, Vol. II. (Illus.). 1059p. 1979. 15.00 (ISBN 0-8285-0687-6, Pub. by Mir Pubs USSR). Imported Pubns.
--Mechanisms in Modern Engineering Design, Vol. III. (Illus.). 663p. 1977. 10.00 (ISBN 0-8285-0688-4, Pub. by Mir Pubs USSR). Imported Pubns.
--Mechanisms in Modern Engineering Design, Vol. IV. (Illus.). 663p. 1977. 9.45 (ISBN 0-8285-0689-2, Pub. by Mir Pubs USSR). Imported Pubns.
Automated Design & Engineering for Electronics. Automated Design & Engineering for Electronics: Proceedings of the Technical Sessions, February 26-28, 1985, Anaheim, CA. pap. 97.30 (ISBN 0-317-26163-0, 2025191). Bks Demand UMI.
Azadivar, Farhad. Design & Engineering of Production Systems. 630p. 1984. text ed. 28.95x (ISBN 0-910554-43-9). Engineering.
Beakley, George C., Jr. Graphics for Design & Visualization: Problem Series A. (Illus.). 120p. 1973. pap. text ed. write for info. (ISBN 0-02-307260-1, 30726). Macmillan.
Blake, Alexander. Practical Stress Analysis in Engineering Design. (Mechanical Engineering Ser.: Vol. 12). (Illus.). 680p. 1982. 49.50 (ISBN 0-8247-1370-2). Dekker.
Brichta, A. & Sharp, P. E. From Project to Production. LC 79-97830. 1970. pap. 14.50 (ISBN 0-08-006639-9). Pergamon.
Broersma, G. Design of Gears. 194p. 1967. 50.00x (ISBN 0-85950-055-1, Pub. by Stam Pr England). State Mutual Bk.
Bronikowski, R. J. Managing the Engineering Design Function. (Illus.). 416p. 1985. 42.95 (ISBN 0-442-21440-5). Van Nos Reinhold.
Brown, R. L. E. Design & Manufacture of Plastic Parts. 204p. 1980. 57.95 (ISBN 0-471-05324-4). Wiley.
Burgess. Design Assurance: A Guide for Engineers. (Mechanical Engineering Ser.). 352p. 1984. 49.75 (ISBN 0-8247-7258-X). Dekker.
Burgess, John. Designing for Humans: The Human Factor in Engineering. (Illus.). 450p. 1985. text ed. 39.95 (ISBN 0-89433-278-3). Petrocelli.
Cullum. Handbook of Engineering Design. Date not set. text ed. cancelled (ISBN 0-408-00558-0). Butterworth.
Davidson, Frank P., et al. Macroengineering & the Infra-Structure of Tomorrow. 1979. lib. bdg. 30.00x (ISBN 0-89158-294-0). Westview.
Davies, B. J. Design Engineering. 1984. 82.75 (ISBN 0-444-86817-8, I-509-83). Elsevier.
Davies, B. J., ed. Design Engineering, 1984: Proceedings of the 7th Annual Conference, Birmingham, UK, 25-27, September 1984. 530p. 1985. 92.75 (ISBN 0-444-87624-3, North-Holland). Elsevier.
Design Developments: Proceedings, No. 45, Birmingham, September 1976. 194p. 1981. 80.00x (ISBN 0-85295-104-3, Pub. by Inst Chem Eng England). State Mutual Bk.
Design Engineering Conference. New Design Standards for Flexible Couplings: Design Engineering Conference, Chicago, May 10, 1966. pap. 20.00 (ISBN 0-317-11086-1, 2011324). Bks Demand UMI.
Design Engineering Conference, 7th: Proceedings. 1984. lib. bdg. 94.00x (ISBN 0-903608-74-X, Pub. by IFS Pubns UK). Air Sci Co.
Design for the Eighties. (Illus.). 1981. text ed. 40.00 (ISBN 0-937976-05-9). Enviro Pr.
Designs of Electrical Devices, Engines & Motors of 1917. (Illus.). 250p. 1984. pap. text ed. 35.00 (ISBN 0-87556-394-5). Saifer.
The Development of Engineering Design Capabilities in Developing Countries. pap. 2.50 (ISBN 0-686-94786-X, UN72/2B2, UN). Unipub.
Dhillon. Quality Control, Reliability, & Engineering Design. (Industrial Engineering Ser.). 392p. 1985. 49.50 (ISBN 0-8247-7278-4). Dekker.
Dieter, George. Engineering Design: A Materials & Processing Approach. (Materials Science & Engineering Ser.). (Illus.). 608p. 1983. text ed. 44.00 (ISBN 0-07-016896-2). McGraw.
Doebelin, Ernest O. Control System Principles & Design. 624p. Date not set. price not set (ISBN 0-471-08815-3). Wiley.
Earle, James H. Engineering Design Graphics. 4th ed. LC 82-6709. 704p. 1983. text ed. 32.95 (ISBN 0-201-11318-X). Addison-Wesley.
Eastman Kodak Company. Ergonomic Design For People at Work, Vol. I. (Engineering Ser.). (Illus.). 406p. 1983. 45.00 (ISBN 0-534-97962-9). Lifetime Learn.
Ewins, D. J. Modal Testing: Theory & Practice. (Mechanical Engineering Research Studies Ser.: No. 1-535). 150p. 1984. text ed. 31.95x (ISBN 0-471-90472-4, Pub. by Wiley). Wiley.
Faupel, Joseph F. & Fisher, Franklin E. Engineering Design: A Synthesis of Stress Analysis & Materials Engineering. 2nd ed. LC 80-16727. 1056p. 1981. 58.95x (ISBN 0-471-03381-2, Pub. by Wiley-Interscience). Wiley.
Fiacco, A. V. & Kortanek, K. O., eds. Semi-Infinite Programming & Applications. (Lecture Notes in Economics & Mathematical Systems: Vol. 215). 322p. 1983. pap. 23.50 (ISBN 0-387-12304-0). Springer-Verlag.
Fox, Richard L. Optimization Methods for Engineering Design. LC 78-127891. (Engineering Ser). 1971. 31.95 (ISBN 0-201-02078-5). Addison-Wesley.
Fraser, D. J. Conceptual Design & Preliminary Analysis of Structures. LC 81-760. 320p. 1981. text ed. 34.95 (ISBN 0-273-01645-8). Pitman Pub MA.
French, M. Conceptual Design for Engineers. 2nd ed. (Illus.). 240p. 1985. 29.50 (ISBN 0-387-15175-3). Springer-Verlag.
Furman, T. T. Approximate Methods in Engineering Design. LC 80-40891. (Mathematics in Science & Engineering Ser.). 408p. 1981. 65.00 (ISBN 0-12-269960-2). Acad Pr.
Glegg, Gordon L. Design of Design. LC 69-12432. (Cambridge Engineering Pubns.). (Illus.). 1969. 19.95 (ISBN 0-521-07447-9). Cambridge U Pr.
--The Selection of Design. LC 72-80591. (Illus.). 96p. 1972. Cambridge U Pr.
Goodman, Louis J. & Karol, R. H. Theory & Practice of Foundation Engineering. LC 68-12070. (Macmillan Series in Civil Engineering). (Illus.). pap. 111.80 (ISBN 0-317-10610-4, 2010517). Bks Demand UMI.
Hilburn, John & Johnson, David E. Manual of Active Filter Design. 2nd ed. (Illus.). 256p. 1983. 41.50 (ISBN 0-07-028769-4). McGraw.
Hubka, V., et al. Practical Studies in Systematic Design. 216p. 1985. text ed. 37.95 (ISBN 0-408-01420-2). Butterworth.
Jackson, D. M. & Vanstone, S. A. Enumeration & Design. 1984. 39.50 (ISBN 0-12-379120-0). Acad Pr.
Jensen, C. & Helsel, J. Engineering Drawing & Design. 3rd ed. 800p. 1985. 32.95 (ISBN 0-07-032533-2). McGraw.
--Fundamentals of Engineering Drawing & Design. 2nd ed. 400p. 23.95 (ISBN 0-07-032534-0). McGraw.
Jensen, C. & Viosinet, D. Advanced Design Problems: To Accompany Engineering Drawing & Designs. 2nd ed. 1982. 10.65 (ISBN 0-07-032522-7). McGraw.
Jensen, Finn & Petersen, Niels E. Burn-In: An Engineering Approach to the Design & Analysis of Burn-In Procedures. LC 82-1952. 167p. 1982. 39.95x (ISBN 0-471-10215-6, Pub. by Wiley-Interscience). Wiley.
Jones, J. Christopher. Essays in Design. 335p. 1984. pap. 21.95x (ISBN 0-471-90297-7, Pub. by Wiley-Interscience). Wiley.
Kapur, K. C. & Lamberson, L. K. Reliability in Engineering Design. LC 76-1304. 586p. 1977. text ed. 48.50x (ISBN 0-471-51191-9). Wiley.
Krick, Edward V. An Introduction to Engineering & Engineering Design. 2nd ed. LC 68-8106. (Illus.). 220p. 1969. pap. text ed. 24.50x (ISBN 0-471-50741-5). Wiley.
--An Introduction to Engineering: Methods, Concepts & Issues. LC 75-41432. 358p. 1976. text ed. 26.00x (ISBN 0-471-50750-4); instructor's manual avail. (ISBN 0-471-01912-7). Wiley.
Lees, W. A. Adhesives in Engineering Design. 155p. 1985. 28.00 (ISBN 0-387-15024-2). Springer-Verlag.
Love, Sydney F. Planning & Creating Successful Engineered Designs. (Illus.). 260p. 1983. Repr. of 1980 ed. 16.95 (ISBN 0-912907-00-2). Adv Prof Dev.
Lucky, Luretha F. & Miller, Nancy O. Engineering Learning Through Creativity: Recycling Instructional Resources. 1979. pap. text ed. 12.00 (ISBN 0-8191-0779-4). U Pr of Amer.
Luzadder, Warren J. Innovative Design with an Introduction to Design Graphics. (Illus.). 496p. 1975. 33.95 (ISBN 0-13-465641-5). P-H.
Luzadder, Warren J. & Botkin, Kenneth E. Workbook, Problems in Engineering Drawing: With an Introduction to Interactive Computer. 9th ed. (Graphics for Design & Production Ser.: Vol. 1). (Illus.). xvi, 160p. 1986. pap. text ed. 13.95 (ISBN 0-13-716366-5). P-H.
McCormick, E. J. & Sanders, M. S. Human Factors in Engineering & Design. 5th ed. 1982. 43.95 (ISBN 0-07-044902-3). McGraw.
McKim, Robert H. Thinking Visually: A Strategy Manual for Problem-Solving. rev. ed. LC 80-16526. 210p. 1980. 27.95 (ISBN 0-534-97984-X); pap. 16.95 (ISBN 0-534-97978-5). Lifetime Learn.
Maxwell-Cook, John C. Structural Notes & Details. (C & CA Viewpoint Publication Ser.). (Illus.). 1976. text ed. 20.00x (ISBN 0-7210-1006-7). Scholium Intl.
Mechanical Engineering Publications Ltd. Staff, ed. Engineering Research & Design: Bridging the Gap. 78p. 1981. 75.95x (ISBN 0-85298-475-8, Pub. by Mechanical Eng Pubns). State Mutual Bk.
Nutt, Merle C. Functional Plant Planning, Layout & Materials Handling. LC 70-114266. 1970. text ed. 18.95 (ISBN 0-682-47092-9, University). Exposition Pr FL.
Pahl, G. & Beitz, W. Engineering Design. Wallace, K., ed. (Illus.). 460p. 1984. 66.00 (ISBN 0-387-13601-0). Springer-Verlag.
Parkinson, S. T. New Product Development in Engineering: A Comparison of the British & West German Machine Tool Industries. LC 83-20855. (Management & Industrial Relations Ser.: No. 6). 150p. 1984. 29.95 (ISBN 0-521-25796-4). Cambridge U Pr.
Parr, Robert E. Principles of Mechanical Design. (Illus.). 1969. text ed. 30.95 (ISBN 0-07-048512-7). McGraw.
Petroski, Henry. To Engineer Is Human: The Role of Failure in Successful Design. (Illus.). 288p. 1985. 16.95 (ISBN 0-312-80680-9). St Martin.
Rao, J. S. Rotor Dynamics. 244p. 1983. 29.95x (ISBN 0-470-27448-4). Halsted Pr.
Ratay, Robert T. Handbook of Temporary Structures in Construction: Engineering Standards, Designs, Practices & Procedures. 704p. 1984. 69.50 (ISBN 0-07-051211-6). McGraw.
Ray, Martyn S. Elements of Engineering Design: An Integrated Approach. 528p. 1985. text ed. 39.95 (ISBN 0-13-264185-2). P-H.
Research & Education Association Staff, ed. Technical Design Graphics Problem Solver. rev. ed. LC 81-86648. (Illus.). 960p. (Orig.). 1984. 19.85x (ISBN 0-87891-534-6). Res & Educ.
Richardson, John A. & Coleman, Floyd W. Basic Design: Systems, Elements, Applications. (Illus.). 320p. 1983. pap. 24.95 (ISBN 0-13-060186-1). P-H.
Sanders, Mark S. & McCormick, Ernest J. Workbook for Human Factors in Engineering & Design. 1982. pap. text ed. 9.95 (ISBN 0-8403-2716-1). Kendall-Hunt.
Sherwin, Keith. Engineering Design for Performance. LC 82-11779. (Ellis Horwood Series in Civil & Mechanical Engineering). 162p. 1982. 53.95X (ISBN 0-470-27534-0). Halsted Pr.
Siddall. Optimal Engineering Design: Principles & Applications. (Mechanical & Engineering Series: Vol. 14). 560p. 1982. 69.75 (ISBN 0-8247-1633-7). Dekker.
--Probabilistic Engineering Design. (Mechanical Engineering Ser.). 632p. 1983. 65.00 (ISBN 0-8247-7022-6). Dekker.
Simon, Harold A. A Student's Introduction to Engineering Design. LC 74-19010. 1975. text ed. 33.00 (ISBN 0-08-017103-6); pap. text ed. 21.00 (ISBN 0-08-018234-8). Pergamon.
Skaff, Andre M. Problems in Engineering Graphics & Design. 200p. 1983. pap. 13.95 (ISBN 0-8403-3166-5). Kendall-Hunt.
Smith, Brian J. Construction Science, Vol. 1. LC 72-178104. (Longman Technician Ser.). pap. 40.00 (ISBN 0-317-27854-1, 2025257). Bks Demand UMI.
Stephenson, John & Callander, R. A. Engineering Design. LC 73-5277. pap. 160.00 (ISBN 0-317-10690-2, 2055395). Bks Demand UMI.
Svensson, N. L. Introduction to Engineering Design. (Illus.). 1977. pap. text ed. 10.00x (ISBN 0-8464-0524-5). Beekman Pubs.
Texas Instruments Engineering Staff. The MOS Memory Data Book for Design Engineers, 1982. Rev. ed. 456p. pap. 8.35 (ISBN 0-89512-112-3, LCC7061). Tex Instr Inc.
--The TTL Data Book for Design Engineers. 2nd ed. 832p. 1981. text ed. 14.95 (ISBN 0-89512-111-5, LCC4112). Tex Instr Inc.
Tuttle, Stanley B. Mechanisms for Engineering Design. LC 67-19946. pap. 47.00 (ISBN 0-317-11055-1, 2007404). Bks Demand UMI.
Vajda, S. The Mathematics of Experimental Design: Incomplete Block Designs & Latin Squares. (Griffin's Statistical Monographs: No. 23). 110p. 1967. pap. text ed. 10.95x (ISBN 0-85264-036-6). Lubrecht & Cramer.
Vanderplaats, G. N. Numerical Optimization Techniques for Engineering Design. 352p. 1984. 42.00 (ISBN 0-07-066964-3). McGraw.
Vidosic, Joseph P. Elements of Design Engineering. LC 69-14675. (Illus.). 64.80 (ISBN 0-8357-9881-X, 2055112). Bks Demand UMI.
Woodson, T. T. Introduction to Engineering Design. 1966. text ed. 40.00 (ISBN 0-07-071760-5). McGraw.
Wynne, George, ed. Basic Engineering Design & Construction. 1983. text ed. 35.95 (ISBN 0-8359-0389-3). Reston.
Zamrik, S. Y., ed. Symposium on Design for Elevated Temperature Environment. LC 79-173043. pap. 20.00 (ISBN 0-317-10994-4, 2013307). Bks Demand UMI.

ENGINEERING DESIGN–DATA PROCESSING
see also Computer Graphics

Chasen, S. H. & Dow, J. W. The Guide for the Evaluation & Implementation of Cad-Cam Systems. 2nd ed. (Illus.). 461p. 1983. text ed. 250.00 (ISBN 0-938800-01-9). Cad Cam.
Cochin, Ira. Analysis & Design of Dynamic Systems. (Illus.). 796p. 1980. text ed. 36.95 scp (ISBN 0-7002-2531-5, HarpC); sol. manual avail. (ISBN 0-06-361222-4). Har-Row.
Desk Top Computing for Engineers. 58p. 1982. pap. 19.00 (ISBN 0-85298-503-7, MEP157). Soc Auto Engineers.
Engineering Staff of Texas Instruments Inc. T T L Data Book for Design Engineers: 1981 Supplement. 2nd. rev. ed. LC 81-50954. 380p. pap. 8.75 (ISBN 0-89512-108-5, LCC 5772). Tex Instr Inc.
European Symposium of the Working Party on Routine Computer Programs in Chemical Engineering, 5th, 1972. Decision, Design & the Computer: Proceedings, No. 35. 270p. 1981. 72.00x (ISBN 0-85295-076-4, Pub. by Inst Chem Eng England). State Mutual Bk.
Kaplinsky, Raphael. Computer-Aided Design: Electronics, Comparative Advantage, & Development. LC 82-14816. 144p. 1982. 22.95 (ISBN 0-02-949520-2). Macmillan.
Katz, R. H. Information Management for Engineering Design Applications. (Surveys in Computer Science). 105p. 1985. 22.50 (ISBN 0-387-15130-3). Springer-Verlag.
Lago, G. V. & Benningfield, L. M. Circuit & System Theory. LC 79-10878. 575p. 1979. text ed. 47.50x (ISBN 0-471-04927-1). Wiley.
Managing Computer Aided Design, 7 papers. 56p. 1980. pap. 30.00 (ISBN 0-85298-470-7, MEP133). Soc Auto Engineers.
Marter, Melvin L. Handheld Calculator Programs for Engineering Design. (Illus.). 448p. 1983. 37.95 (ISBN 0-07-040642-1). McGraw.
Proceeding of the Annual Conference on Design Engineering, 6th. iv, 388p. 1984. 85.00 (ISBN 0-903608-47-2, Pub. by IFSPUBS). Scholium Intl.
Shoup, T. Practical Guide to Computer Methods for Engineers. 1979. 28.95 (ISBN 0-13-690651-6). P-H.
Vallee, Jacques, et al. Design & Use of the Forum System. (Group Communication Through Computers: Vol. 1). 139p. 1974. 10.50 (ISBN 0-318-14412-3, R32). Inst Future.
Volk, William. Engineering Statistics with a Programmable Calculator. Davidson, Robert L., ed. (Illus.). 320p. 1981. 26.95x (ISBN 0-07-067552-X). McGraw.

ENGINEERING DRAWING
see Mechanical Drawing
ENGINEERING DRAWINGS

Abbott, W. Technical Drawing. 4th ed. (Illus.). 1976. pap. 23.50x (ISBN 0-216-90210-X). Intl Ideas.
Besterfield & O'Hagan. Technical Sketching for Engineers, Technologists & Technicians. 1983. text ed. 22.95 (ISBN 0-8359-7540-1). Reston.

Advances in Instrumentation: Proceedings of the 36th ISA Conference & Exhibit, 1981, Vol. 36, Pts. 1 & 2. LC 56-29277. 1981. Set. pap. text ed. 90.00x (ISBN 0-87664-526-0); Pt. 1; St. Louis, 504p. pap. text ed. 48.00x (ISBN 0-87664-514-7); Pt. 2; Anaheim, 728p. pap. text ed. 48.00x (ISBN 0-87664-525-2). Instru Soc.

Analysis Instrumentation Index to Technical Papers: A Cumulative Index of All Papers Sponsored by the Analysis Instrumentation Division of ISA from 1947 through 1981. LC 81-80529. 156p. 1982. pap. text ed. 30.00x (ISBN 0-87664-503-1). Instru Soc.

Anderson, Normaq A. Instrumentation for Process Measurement & Control. LC 78-14643. 384p. 1980. 22.50 (ISBN 0-8019-6766-X). Chilton.

Barney, George C. Intelligent Instrumentation: Microprocessor Applications in Measurement & Control. (Illus.). 528p. 1986. text ed. 39.95 (ISBN 0-13-468943-7). P-H.

Barr, J., et al, eds. Instrument Fitting. (Engineering Craftsmen: No. H24). (Illus.). 1969. spiral bdg 39.95x (ISBN 0-85083-069-9). Intl Ideas.

Bell, E. C. & Whitehead, R. W. Basic Electrical Engineering & Instrumentation for Engineers. (Illus.). 1977. pap. 17.95x (ISBN 0-8464-0175-4). Beekman Pubs.

--Basic Electrical Engineering & Instrumentation for Engineers. 2nd ed. 560p. 1981. pap. 18.00x (ISBN 0-246-11477-0, Pub. by Granada England). Sheridan.

Chemical & Allied Products Industry Training Board, ed. Instrument Manual: A Training Guide For Instrument Personnel. (Illus.). 650p. 1983. pap. 175.00x spiral bdg. (ISBN 0-89563-062-1). Intl Ideas.

Chemical & Petroleum Industries Instrumentation Symposium. Instrumentation in the Chemical & Petroleum Industries: Proceedings of the 20th Chemical & Petroleum Industries Instrumentation Symposium, Vol. 15. LC 64-7505. 124p. 1979. pap. text ed. 19.00x (ISBN 0-87664-432-9). Instru Soc.

Dally, James W. & Riley, William F. Instrumentation for Engineering Measurements. 576p. 1984. text ed. 40.45x (ISBN 0-471-04548-9). Wiley.

Elonka, Stephen M. & Parsons, Alonzo R. Standard Instrumentation Questions & Answers for Production-Processes Control, 2 vols. in 1. Incl. Vol. 1. Measuring Systems; Vol. 2. Control Systems. LC 79-1385. 1979. Repr. of 1962 ed. lib. bdg. 32.50 (ISBN 0-88275-896-9). Krieger.

Fribance, Austin E. Industrial Instrumentation Fundamentals. 1962. text ed. 30.95 (ISBN 0-07-022370-X). McGraw.

Graham, A. Richard. An Introduction to Engineering Measurements. (Illus.). 224p. 1975. ref. ed 29.95 (ISBN 0-13-482406-7). P-H.

Haslam, J. A. & Summers, G. R. Engineering Instrumentation & Control. 320p. 1981. pap. text ed. 13.95 (ISBN 0-7131-3431-3). E Arnold.

Hine, Charles R. Machine Tools & Processes for Engineers. LC 81-14246. 634p. 1982. Repr. of 1971 ed. lib. bdg. 36.50 (ISBN 0-89874-354-0). Krieger.

Institut Francais du Petrole Laboratoires des Ponts et Chaussees. The Pressuremeter & its Marine Applications. 430p. (Orig.). 1983. pap. 89.00x (ISBN 0-87201-735-4). Gulf pub.

Instrument Society of America. Dynamic Response Testing of Process Control Instrumentation Standard. (ISA Standard Ser.: No. S26). 1975. pap. text ed. 16.00x (ISBN 0-87664-349-7). Instru Soc.

Instrumentation in the Power Industry, Vol. 27: Proceedings of the Power Instrumentation Symposium, 27th. LC 62-52679. 192p. 1984. pap. text ed. 40.00x (ISBN 0-87664-837-5). Instru Soc.

Johnson, Curtis D. Process Control Instrumentation Technology. 2nd ed. LC 81-10488. (Electronic Technology Ser.). 497p. 1982. 31.95 (ISBN 0-471-05789-4); solutions manual avail. (ISBN 0-471-86317-3). Wiley.

Kirk, F. W. & Rimboi, N. R. Instrumentation. 3rd ed. (Illus.). 1974. 16.95 (ISBN 0-8269-3422-6). Am Technical.

O'Higgins, Patrick J. Basic Instrumentation, Industrial Measurement. 1966. text ed. 33.45 (ISBN 0-07-047649-7). McGraw.

Operation of Instruments in Adverse Environments 1976. (Institute of Physics Conference Ser.: No. 34). 1977. 49.00 (ISBN 0-9960031-4-2, Pub. by Inst Physics England). Heyden.

Patton, Joseph D., Jr., ed. Instrument Maintenance Manager's Sourcebook. 2nd ed. LC 80-83407. 332p. 1980. text ed. 39.95x (ISBN 0-87664-488-4). Instru Soc.

Pease, Burton F. Basic Instrumental Analysis. LC 79-92230. 448p. 1980. text ed. 24.95 (ISBN 0-442-24503-3). Krieger.

Pressure, Flow & Level Instrumentation Market. 260p. 1984. 1575.00 (ISBN 0-86621-260-4, A1332). Frost & Sullivan.

Process Analytical Instrumentation Market. 218p. 1984. 1575.00 (ISBN 0-86621-263-9, A1335). Frost & Sullivan.

Process Control Equipment (PCE) Market. 241p. 1983. 1475.00 (ISBN 0-86621-180-2, A1242). Frost & Sullivan.

Process Control Instrumentation Markets in S. Asia & the Far East. 273p. 1985. 1850.00 (ISBN 0-86621-656-1, W728). Frost & Sullivan.

Ramalingom, T. Dictionary of Instrument Science. LC 81-14724. 588p. 1982. 34.95x (ISBN 0-471-86396-3, Pub. by Wiley-Interscience). Wiley.

Schiller, Roger W., ed. Instrumentation Curriculum Guide for the Two-Year Post Secondary Institution. rev. ed. LC 77-210. 64p. 1977. pap. text ed. 6.25x (ISBN 0-87664-308-X). Instru Soc.

Soisson, Harold E. Instrumentation in Industry. LC 74-23222. 563p. 1975. 52.95x (ISBN 0-471-81049-5, Pub. by Wiley-Interscience). Wiley.

Thrift, Stanley W. TI-59 & HP-41CV Instrument Engineering Programs. LC 82-20920. 366p. 1983. 49.95x (ISBN 0-87201-387-1); 200p. Bar Code Supplement pap. (Orig.) 49.95x (ISBN 0-87201-389-8). Gulf Pub.

Trade & Technical Press Editors. Handbook of Instruments & Instrumentation. 650p. 1977. 108.00 (Pub by Trade & Tech England). Brookfield Pub Co.

ENGINEERING LAW

see also Engineering–Contracts and Specifications

Abrahamson, M. W. Engineering Law & the I.C.E. Contracts. 4th ed. 485p. 1979. 81.50 (ISBN 0-85334-826-X, Pub. by Elsevier Applied Sci England). Elsevier.

American Consulting Engineers Council. Guidelines for Ad Hoc Collaboration Agreements Between Consulting Firms. 54p. 1977. member 10.00 (ISBN 0-686-48325-1); non-member 15.00 (ISBN 0-686-48326-X). Am Consul Eng.

Dammann, Ulrich, et al, eds. Data Protection Legislation: An International Documentation, Bd. 5. (Kybernetik, Datenverarbeitung, Recht). 203p. 1977. pap. text ed. 21.00x (ISBN 3-7875-3005-3, Pub. by Alfred Metzner Verlag). Rothman.

Dunham, Clarence, et al. Contracts, Specifications & Law for Engineers. 3rd ed. (Illus.). 1979. text ed. 42.00 (ISBN 0-07-018236-1). McGraw.

A Guide to the Procurement of Architectural & Engineering Services. 77p. 1984. member 5.00 (ISBN 0-686-48347-2); non-member 5.00 (ISBN 0-686-48348-0). Am Consul Eng.

House, Peter W. & McLeod, John. Large-Scale Models for Policy Evaluation. LC 76-57255. (Wiley Series on Systems Engineering & Analysis). pap. 88.00 (ISBN 0-317-28124-0, 2022489). Bks Demand UMI.

Laidlaw, R. E., et al. Engineering Law. 5th rev. ed. (Illus.). 1981. 25.00 (ISBN 0-8020-2022-4). U of Toronto Pr.

Marston, D. L. Law for Professional Engineers. xi, 243p. Date not set. price not set (ISBN 0-07-548073-5). McGraw.

Meehan, Richard. Getting Sued & Other Tales of the Engineering Life. 264p. 1981. 22.50 (ISBN 0-262-13167-6); pap. 6.95 (ISBN 0-262-63089-3). MIT Pr.

Morton, Rebecca J. Engineering Law, Design Liability, & Professional Ethics. 88p. 1983. pap. 12.95 (ISBN 0-932276-37-7). Prof Engine.

Niederhauser, Warren D. & Meyer, E. Gerald, eds. Legal Rights of Chemists & Engineers. LC 77-9364. (Advances in Chemistry Ser.: No. 161). 1977. 24.95 (ISBN 0-8412-0357-1); pap. 14.95 (ISBN 0-8412-0537-X). Am Chemical.

Vaughn, Richard C. Legal Aspects of Engineering. 3rd ed. LC 73-93861. 1983. pap. text ed. 17.95 (ISBN 0-8403-3038-3, 40303801). Kendall-Hunt.

--Legal Aspects of Engineering. 4th ed. LC 84-118932. (Illus.). vii, 327p. 1983. write for info (ISBN 0-8403-3038-3). Kendall-Hunt.

Walker, N., et al. Legal Pitfalls in Architecture, Engineering & Building Construction. 1979. 8.85 (ISBN 0-07-067851-0). McGraw.

ENGINEERING LIBRARIES

see also Information Storage and Retrieval Systems–Engineering; Technical Libraries

Mount, Ellis. Ahead of Its Time: The Engineering Societies Library, 1913-1980. xvi, 214p. 1982. 25.00 (ISBN 0-208-01913-8, Linnet). Shoe String.

--University Science & Engineering Libraries. 2nd ed. LC 84-6530. (Contributions in Librarianship & Information Science Ser.: No. 49). (Illus.). x, 303p. 1985. lib. bdg. 35.00 (ISBN 0-313-23949-5, MOU/). Greenwood.

Mount, Ellis, ed. Training of Sci-Tech Librarians & Library Users. LC 81-6975. (Science & Technology Libraries: Vol. 1, No. 3). 72p. 1981. pap. text ed. 15.00 (ISBN 0-917724-75-5, B75). Haworth Pr.

ENGINEERING LITERATURE

see Technical Literature

ENGINEERING MATERIALS

see Materials

ENGINEERING MATHEMATICS

see also Dimensional Analysis; Electric Engineering–Mathematics; Engineering–Statistical Methods; Mechanics, Applied; Structures, Theory of

Adey, R. A. & Brebbia, C. A. Basic Computational Techniques for Engineers. LC 83-5739. 208p. 29.50 (ISBN 0-471-88970-9, Pub. by Wiley-Interscience). Wiley.

Albert, Arthur. Regression & the Moore-Penrose Pseudo-Inverse. (Mathematics in Science & Engineering Ser.: Vol. 94). 1972. 35.00 (ISBN 0-12-048450-1). Acad Pr.

Ames, W. F. & Vichnevetsky, R., eds. Modelling & Simulation in Engineering: Proceedings of the IMACS World Conference on Systems Simulation & Scientific Computation, Tenth, Montreal, Canada, 8-13 Aug., 1982. (IMACS Transactions on Scientific Computation Ser.: Vol. III). 340p. 1983. 49.00 (ISBN 0-444-86609-4, I-296-83, North Holland). Elsevier.

Arscott, et al. Remedial Mathematics for Science & Engineering. 152p. 1983. pap. text ed. 8.95 (ISBN 0-8403-3068-5). Kendall-Hunt.

Austin, Jacqueline & Isern, Margarita. Technical Mathematics. 3rd ed. LC 82-60533. 1983. pap. text ed. 25.95 (ISBN 0-03-061234-9); instr's manual 20.00 (ISBN 0-03-061236-5). HR&W.

Bailey, Frank A. Basic Mathematics for Automotive Technology. 1977. pap. 9.75x (ISBN 0-673-15065-8). Scott F.

Bajpai, A. C., et al. Numerical Methods for Engineers & Scientists. (Series of Programmes on Mathematics for Scientists & Technologists). 380p. 1977. 29.95x (ISBN 0-471-99542-8, Pub. by Wiley-Interscience). Wiley.

--Engineering Mathematics. LC 73-21230. 793p. 1974. pap. text ed. 29.95 (ISBN 0-471-04376-1, Pub. by Wiley-Interscience). Wiley.

--Specialist Techniques in Engineering Mathematics. LC 80-41274. 401p. 1980. 74.95 (ISBN 0-471-27907-2, Pub. by Wiley-Interscience); pap. 39.95 (ISBN 0-471-27908-0). Wiley.

Belding, W. G., ed. ASM Handbook of Engineering Mathematics. 1983. 83.00 (ISBN 0-87170-157-X). ASM.

Bender, Carl M. & Orszag, Steven A. Advanced Mathematical Methods for Scientists & Engineers. (International Series in Pure & Applied Mathematics). (Illus.). 1978. text ed. 49.95 (ISBN 0-07-004452-X). McGraw.

Blakeley, Walter R. Calculus for Engineering Technology. LC 67-29017. 441p. 1968. 31.95 (ISBN 0-471-07931-6). Wiley.

Blaquiere, A., et al. Quantitative & Qualitative Games. (Mathematics in Science & Engineering Ser.: Vol. 58). 1969. 49.50 (ISBN 0-12-104360-6). Acad Pr.

Boughton, Brian & Ballard, Peter. Construction Mathematics, Vol. 1. (Illus.). 160p. 1984. pap. 10.00x (ISBN 0-246-12125-4, Pub. by Granada England). Sheridan.

--Construction Mathematics, Vol. 2. (Illus.). 160p. 1985. pap. 10.00x (ISBN 0-00-383035-7, Pub. by Collins England). Sheridan.

Branan, Carl. FLEXCURV (TM) Curvefitting Utility. 40p. 1985. incl. floppy disk 95.00x (ISBN 0-87201-240-9). Gulf Pub.

Brebbia, C. Boundary Element Techniques in Engineering. new ed. (Illus.). 1980. text ed. 39.95 (ISBN 0-408-00340-5). Butterworth.

Brebbia, C. A., ed. Boundary Element Methods in Engineering, Southampton, England 1982: Proceedings. (Illus.). 649p. 1982. 66.00 (ISBN 0-387-11819-5). Springer-Verlag.

Brebbia, C. A. & Keramidas, G. A., eds. Computational Methods & Experimental Measurements: Proceedings of the 2nd International Conference, on Board the Liner, the Queen Elizabeth 2, New York to Southhampton, June-July 1984. 800p. 76.60 (ISBN 0-387-13419-0). Springer-Verlag.

Breipohl, Arthur M. Probabilistic System Analysis: An Introduction to Probabilistic Models, Decisions & Applications of Random Processes. LC 77-94920. 352p. 1970. 43.50 (ISBN 0-471-10181-8). Wiley.

Calter, Paul. Schaum's Outline of Technical Mathematics. (Schaum's Outline Ser). (Illus.). 1979. pap. 9.95 (ISBN 0-07-009651-1). McGraw.

Crandall, Stephen H. Engineering Analysis. LC 82-20335. 428p. 1983. Repr. of 1956 ed. lib. bdg. 28.50 (ISBN 0-89874-577-2). Krieger.

Creese, Thomas M. & Haralick, Robert M. Differential Equations for Engineers. 1978. text ed. 37.95 (ISBN 0-07-013510-X). McGraw.

Davies, Glyn A. Mathematical Methods in Engineering: Guidebook 5. (Handbook of Applicable Mathematics Ser.: Nos. 1-475). 458p. 1984. 31.95 (ISBN 0-471-10331-4, Pub. by Wiley Interscience). Wiley.

Desai, C. S. & Abel, John F. Introducing to the Finite Element Method: A Numerical Method for Engineering Analysis. (Illus.). 1972. 27.95 (ISBN 0-442-22083-9). Van Nos Reinhold.

Distefano, Nestor. Nonlinear Processes in Engineering: Dynamic Programming, Invariant Imbedding, Quasilinearization, Finite Element, System Identification & Optimization. 1974. 80.00 (ISBN 0-12-218050-X). Acad Pr.

Doraiswamy, L. K., ed. Recent Advances in the Engineering Analysis of Chemically Reacting Systems. 611p. 1984. 49.95 (ISBN 0-470-20026-X). Halsted Pr.

Ferziger, Joel H. Numerical Methods for Engineering Application. LC 81-1260. 288p. 1981. 34.95x (ISBN 0-471-06336-3, Pub. by Wiley-Interscience). Wiley.

Furman, T. T. Approximate Methods in Engineering Design. LC 80-40891. (Mathematics in Science & Engineering Ser.). 408p. 1981. 65.00 (ISBN 0-12-269960-2). Acad Pr.

Gilder, Jules H. & Barrus, J. Scott. Pascal Programs in Science & Engineering. 2nd ed. 384p. pap. 18.95 (6265). Hayden.

Glowinski, R. & Lions, J. L., eds. Computing Methods in Applied Sciences & Engineering: Proceedings of the Fifth International Symposium, Versailles, France, December 14-18, 1981, Vol. 5. 626p. 1982. 95.00 (ISBN 0-444-86450-4, I-321-82, North-Holland). Elsevier.

Goodson, C. E. & Miertschin, S. L. Technical Algebra with Applications. 592p. 1985. 26.95 (ISBN 0-471-08241-4). Wiley.

--Technical Mathematics with Calculus. 1152p. 1985. 33.95 (ISBN 0-471-86639-3). Wiley.

--Technical Trigonometry with Applications. 448p. 1985. 25.95 (ISBN 0-471-08240-6). Wiley.

Goodson, Carole E. & Miertschin, Susan L. Technical Mathematics with Applications. 1002p. 1983. 31.95x (ISBN 0-471-08244-9); tchr's. manual avail. (ISBN 0-471-89075-8); study guide avail. (ISBN 0-471-87578-3); student manual 21.95 (ISBN 0-471-88515-0); student solutions manual avail. (ISBN 0-471-89290-4). Wiley.

Greenberg, Michael D. Foundations of Applied Mathematics. LC 77-11125. (Illus.). 1978. ref. ed. 42.95 (ISBN 0-13-329623-7). P-H.

Haines, Charles W. Analysis for Engineers. LC 74-866. 280p. 1974. text ed. 27.95 (ISBN 0-8299-0011-X). West Pub.

Hancock, S. F. Mathematics for Engineers: Examination Subjects for Technical Students. 2nd ed. pap. 60.00 (ISBN 0-317-20817-9, 2025277). Bks Demand UMI.

Haug, Edward J., et al. Design Sensitivity Analysis of Structural Systems. (Mathematics in Science & Engineering Ser.). Date not set. price not set (ISBN 0-12-332920-5). Acad Pr.

Hughes, G. & Gaylord, E. W. Basic Equations of Engineering. (Orig.). 1964. pap. 7.95 (ISBN 0-07-031109-9). McGraw.

Jaeger, L. G. Cartesian Tensors in Engineering Science. 1966. 28.00 (ISBN 0-08-011222-6); pap. 12.50 (ISBN 0-08-011221-8). Pergamon.

Jain, M. K. Numerical Methods for Scientific & Engineering Computation. 1985. 24.95 (ISBN 0-470-20143-6). Wiley.

Jeffrey, Alan. Mathematics for Engineers & Scientists. 2nd. ed. 1979. 42.95 (ISBN 0-442-30729-2). Van Nos Reinhold.

Jones, M. K. Construction Mathematics, 2 vols. LC 76-9870. (Longman Technician Ser.). Vol. 1. pap. 59.80 (ISBN 0-317-27791-X, 2025241); Vol. 2. pap. 48.80 (ISBN 0-317-27792-8). Bks Demand UMI.

Kaplan, Wilfred. Advanced Mathematics for Engineers. LC 80-19492. (Mathematics Ser.). (Illus.). 960p. 1981. text ed. 39.95 (ISBN 0-201-03773-4). Addison-Wesley.

Ketter, Robert L. & Prawel, Sherwood, Jr. Modern Methods of Engineering Computation. LC 72-81608. (Illus.). 1969. text ed. 44.00 (ISBN 0-07-034423-X). McGraw.

Kreider, Donald L., et al. Introduction to Linear Analysis. 1966. 31.95 (ISBN 0-201-03949-4). Addison-Wesley.

Kreyszig, Erwin. Advanced Engineering Mathematics. 5th ed. 988p. 1983. 42.45 (ISBN 0-471-86251-7); tchrs.' manual avail. (ISBN 0-471-89855-4). Wiley.

Kuhfittig, Peter K. Basic Technical Mathematics. LC 83-20975. (Mathematics Ser.). 675p. 1984. text ed. 24.50 pub net (ISBN 0-534-03074-2); pub net solutions manual 8.00 (ISBN 0-534-03075-0). Brooks-Cole.

Lewis, R. Engineering Quantities & Systems of Units. (Illus.). 166p. 1972. 16.75 (ISBN 0-85334-530-9, Pub. by Elsevier Applied Sci England). Elsevier.

Donahue, Jack. Wildcatter: The Story of Michel T. Halbouty & the Search for Oil. LC 83-10781. 270p. 1983. Repr. of 1979 ed. 18.95x (ISBN 0-87201-915-2). Gulf Pub.

Durand, William F. Adventures in the Navy, in Education, Science, Engineering & the War: A Life Story. LC 53-2031. pap. 57.00 (ISBN 0-317-08712-6, 2013306). Bks Demand UMI.

International Who's Who in Engineering. 1st ed. 1983. 120.00x (ISBN 0-900332-71-9). Intl Pubns Serv.

Who's Who in Technology, 3 Vols. (International Red Ser.). 1984. Set. pap. 160.00 (WWIR102, WWIR). Unipub.

Who's Who of British Engineers 1980. 352p. 1981. 55.00x (ISBN 0-312-87413-8). St Martin.

ENGINES

see also Fire-Engines; Fuel; Gas and Oil Engines; Heat-Engines; Horsepower (Mechanics); Locomotives; Marine Engines; Pumping Machinery; Steam-Boilers; Steam-Engines; Traction Engines; Tractors; Turbines

ASTM Standards on Engine Coolants (D-15) 5th ed. 152p. 1980. pap. 12.75x (ISBN 0-8031-0282-8, 03-415080-12). ASTM.

Barkhouse, Bob. Engine Repair: Head Assembly & Valve Gear. LC 74-21562. 500p. 1974. text ed. 19.96 (ISBN 0-87345-101-5). McKnight.

Bracco. Stratified Charge Engines, Vol. 2. 112p. 1976. pap. 56.75 (ISBN 0-677-05355-X). Gordon.

British Motor Component Industry. 1985. 195.00x (ISBN 0-317-07212-9, Pub. by Jordan & Sons UK). State Mutual Bk.

Chatterjee, P. K. & Wetherall, P. J. Winding Engine Calculations for the Mining. 1982. 36.00 (ISBN 0-419-12650-3, NO. 6693, Pub. by E & FN Spon). Methuen Inc.

Chilton's Automotive Editorial Staff. Chilton's Small Engines: Repair & Tune-up Guide. 2nd ed. LC 78-21829. (Repair & Tune-up Guides Ser.). (Illus.). 1979. pap. 11.95 (ISBN 0-8019-6811-9). Chilton.

Church, Austin H. Centrifugal Pumps & Blowers. (Illus.). 320p. 1972. Repr. of 1944 ed. text ed. 20.50 (ISBN 0-88275-008-9). Krieger.

Conseil International Des Machines a Combustion. Lexique: Machines a Combustion. (Fr., Eng., Span., It., Ger. & Dutch.). 96p. pap. 23.95 (ISBN 84-600-0836-3, S-30858). French & Eur.

Crouse, William H. & Anglin, Donald L. Automotive Engines. 6th ed. (Illus.). 96p. 1980. 22.60 (ISBN 0-07-014825-2). McGraw.

Crowley, T. E. Beam Engines. 1982 ed. (Albums Ser.: No. 15). (Illus.). 32p. pap. 2.95 (ISBN 0-85263-595-8, Pub. by Shire Pubns England). Seven Hills Bks.

Deere & Company. Engines (Consumer Products) (Illus.). 100p. (Orig.). 1982. pap. text ed. 11.05 (ISBN 0-86691-004-2); wkbk. 4.60 (ISBN 0-86691-035-2). Deere & Co.

Dempsey, Paul. How to Repair Briggs & Stratton Engines. 2nd ed. 196p. 1985. pap. 8.95 (ISBN 0-8306-1687-X). Wallace-Homestead.

Edgington, David. Old Stationary Engines. (Shire Album Ser.: No. 49). 32p. 1985. pap. 2.95 (ISBN 0-85263-500-1, Pub. by Shire Pubns England). Seven Hills Bks.

Ellis, C. Hamilton. Engines That Passed. LC 72-364512. (Illus.). 1968. lib. bdg. 14.95x (ISBN 0-678-06005-3). Kelley.

Engine Coolant Testing: State of the Art, STP 705. 374p. 1980. 32.50x (ISBN 0-8031-0331-X, 04-705000-12). ASTM.

Engineering Applications: Vol. 1: Installation & Maintainance of Engines in Small Fishing Vessels. (Fisheries Technical Papers: No. 196). (Eng., Fr. & Span., Illus.). 138p. (2nd Printing 1982). 1979. pap. 9.75 (ISBN 92-5-100862-0, F1948, FAO). Unipub.

Fenn, John B. Engines, Energy, & Entropy: A Thermodynamics Primer. LC 81-17305. (Illus.). 293p. 1982. text ed. 19.95 (ISBN 0-7167-1281-4); pap. text ed. 12.95 (ISBN 0-7167-1282-2). W H Freeman.

Gilles, Tim. Engine Mechanics: Diagnosis & Repair. 350p. 1985. pap. text ed. write for info. (ISBN 0-534-04842-0, 77F6065). Breton Pubs.

Goering, Carroll E. Engine & Tractor Power. 1985. text ed. write for info. (ISBN 0-534-05814-0, 77F6068). Breton Pubs.

Huges, James G. Automotive Engine Diagnosis & Tune-Up. 1985. text ed. 29.95 (ISBN 0-8359-0285-4). Reston.

Hughes, James G. Automotive Engine Rebuilding. LC 83-23584. 590p. 1984. 31.95 (ISBN 0-471-03461-4); write for info. tchr's guide (ISBN 0-471-80379-0). Wiley.

Humphreys, B. J. & Malewicki, Douglas J. Rocket Powered Racing Vehicles Using Hydrogen Peroxide of Ninety Percent Strength. (Illus.). 100p. 1974. pap. 9.95 (ISBN 0-912468-11-4). CA Rocketry.

Jennings, Gordon. Two-Stroke Tuner's Handbook. (Illus.). 156p. 1974. pap. 5.95 (ISBN 0-912656-41-7). H P Bks.

Lewis, W. Engine Service. 256p. 1980. pap. 18.95 (ISBN 0-13-277236-1). P-H.

Lewis, William G. Engine Service. 2nd ed. (Illus.). 256p. 1986. text ed. 28.95 (ISBN 0-13-277864-5); pap. text ed. 21.95 (ISBN 0-13-277849-1). P-H.

Lynch, Philip F. The Powertrain. LC 80-16504. (A Primer in Drilling & Production Equipment Ser.: Vol. 1). (Illus.). 165p. (Orig.). 1980. pap. 16.95x (ISBN 0-87201-198-4). Gulf Pub.

Obert, Edward F. Internal Combustion Engines & Air Pollution. 736p. 1973. text ed. 40.00 scp (ISBN 0-7002-2183-2, HarpC); solution manual avail. Har-Row.

Piston Engine: Meeting the Challenge of the 1980's. 1980. Four papers. pap. 12.00 (ISBN 0-89883-238-1, SP467). Soc Auto Engineers.

Porter Manufacturing Co., Limited, Engines & Boilers. pap. 4.75 (ISBN 0-917914-29-5). Lindsay Pubns.

Reader, G. T. & Hooper, C. Stirling Engines. (Illus.). 400p. 1982. 57.50x (ISBN 0-419-12400-4, NO. 6577, Pub. by E & FN Spon England). Methuen Inc.

Robinson, Jeff, ed. Sachs Engine Service-Repair Handbook: 100 & 125cc, All Years. (Illus.). 144p. pap. text ed. 13.95 (ISBN 0-89287-025-7, M427). Clymer Pubns.

Roth, Alfred C. & Baird, Ronald J. Small Gas Engines. rev. ed. LC 81-6209. (Illus.). 232p. text ed. 14.64 (ISBN 0-87006-498-3). Goodheart.

Rudman, Jack. Engineman (U.S.P.S) (Career Examination Ser.: C-2371). (Cloth bdg. avail. on request). pap. 10.00 (ISBN 0-8373-2371-1). Natl Learning.

Russell, J. H. A Pictorial Record of Great Western Engines. 448p. 1982. 90.00x (ISBN 0-86093-024-6, Pub. by ORPC Ltd UK). State Mutual Bk.

Russell, James H. Painted Engines. LC 73-101572. (Illus.). 1965. 17.95x (ISBN 0-678-06012-6). Kelley.

Single Cylinder Engine Tests- STP 509-A: Caterpillar L38A Test Method, Pt. 4. 46p. 1980. pap. 7.25x (ISBN 0-8031-0575-4, 04-509040-12); looseleaf 9.50x (ISBN 0-8031-0576-2, 04-509041-12). ASTM.

Single Cylinder Engine Tests- STP 509-A: Caterpillar 1G2 Test Method, Pt. 1. 94p. 1979. pap. 9.75x (ISBN 0-8031-0569-X, 04-509010-12); looseleaf 12.75x (ISBN 0-8031-0570-3, 04-509011-12). ASTM.

Single Cylinder Engine Tests- STP 509A: Caterpillar 1D2 Test Method, Pt. 3. 86p. 1979. pap. 9.75x (ISBN 0-8031-0573-8, 04-509030-12); looseleaf 12.75x (ISBN 0-8031-0574-6, 04-509031-12). ASTM.

Small Engines. LC 82-10304. (Home Repair & Improvement). lib. bdg. 15.94 (ISBN 0-8094-3511-X, Pub. by Time-Life). Silver.

Small Engines. (Home Repair & Improvement). 1983. 11.95 (ISBN 0-8094-3510-1). Time Life.

Stationary Combustion Engines & Gas Turbines. (Thirty Ser). 1970. pap. 2.00 (ISBN 0-685-58106-3, 37). Natl Fire Prot.

Urieli, Israel & Berchowitz, David. Stirling Cycle Engine Analysis. (Modern Energy Studies). 250p. 1984. 45.00 (ISBN 0-9960021-9-7, Pub. by A Hilger England). Heyden.

Walker, G. & Senft, J. R. Free Piston Stirling Engines. (Lecture Notes in Engineering Ser.: Vol. 12). 290p. 1985. pap. 21.00 (ISBN 0-387-15495-7). Springer-Verlag.

Walker, Graham. Stirling Engines. (Illus.). 1980. text ed. 95.00x (ISBN 0-19-856209-8). Oxford U Pr.

Webster, J. Small Engines: Operation & Service. (Illus.). 278p. 1984. 14.95 (ISBN 0-8269-0004-6). Am Technical.

Wendel, Charles H. Stover Manufacturing & Engine Company. LC 82-80676. (Power in the Past: Vol. 3). (Illus.). 96p. 1982. pap. 12.50 (ISBN 0-942804-00-7). Old Iron Bk Co.

West, Colin D. Liquid Piston Stirling Engine. 144p. 1982. 22.50 (ISBN 0-442-29237-6). Van Nos Reinhold.

Wilson, Tom. How to Rebuild Your Honda Car Engine. 160p. 1985. pap. 9.95 (ISBN 0-89586-256-5). H P Bks.

World Engine Digest 1980-81. 400p. 1981. 325.00x (ISBN 0-312-89119-9). St Martin.

ENGLISH SETTERS

see Dogs–Breeds–English Setters

ENGLISH SPARROW

see Sparrows

ENGLISH SPRINGER SPANIEL

see Dogs–Breeds–English Springer Spaniel

ENHYDRINAE

see Sea-Otters

ENSEMBLES (MATHEMATICS)

see Set Theory

ENSILAGE

see also Silos

McDonald, P. The Biochemistry of Silage. LC 80-42018. 226p. 1981. 53.95 (ISBN 0-471-27965-X). Wiley.

ENTERPRISE (AIRCRAFT CARRIER, CVA N 65)

Ewing, Steve. U. S. S. Enterprise (CV-Six), the Most Decorated Ship of World War II: A Pictorial History. LC 82-61737. (Illus.). 132p. 1982. 7.95 (ISBN 0-933126-24-7). Pictorial Hist.

ENTIRE FUNCTIONS

see Functions, Entire

ENTOMOLOGICAL RESEARCH

Bhaskaran, Govindan, et al, eds. Current Topics in Insect Endocrinology & Nutrition. LC 80-24274. 368p. 1981. 49.50x (ISBN 0-306-40621-7, Plenum Pr). Plenum Pub.

Dirsh, V. A. Morphometrical Studies on Phases of the Desert Locust (Schistocerca Gregaria Forskal) 1953. 35.00x (ISBN 0-85135-066-6, Pub. by Centre Overseas Research). State Mutual Bk.

Neece, K. C. & Bartell, D. P. A Faunistic Survey of the Organisms Associated with Ants of Western Texas. (Graduate Studies: No. 25). (Illus.). 36p. (Orig.). 1982. pap. 6.00 (ISBN 0-89672-096-9). Tex Tech Pr.

Thomas Say Foundation Publications. Incl. Vol. 2. The Plecoptera or Stoneflies of America North of Mexico. Needham, J. G. & Claassen, P. W. (Illus.). 397p. 1925. 12.50 (ISBN 0-686-11692-5); Vol. 3. Plecoptera Nymphs of North America. Claassen, P. W. (Illus.). 199p. 1931. 10.90 (ISBN 0-686-11693-3); Vol. 4. The Blow Flies of North America. Hall, D. G. (Illus.). 477p. 1948. 15.00 (ISBN 0-686-11694-1); Vol. 5. Aphids of the Rocky Mountain Region. Palmer, Miriam A. (Illus.). 452p. 1952. 21.70 (ISBN 0-686-11695-X); Vol. 6. A Catalog of the Mosquitoes of the World. Stone, Alan, et al. 358p. 20.90 (ISBN 0-686-11696-8); suppl. o.p. 3.35 ea.; Vol. 7. Monograph of Cimicidae. Usinger, Robert L. (Illus.). 588p. 1966. 21.70 (ISBN 0-686-11698-4); Vol. 8. Anopheline Names: Their Derivations & Histories. Kitzmiller, James B. 26.50 (ISBN 0-938522-17-5). LC 66-22730. Entomol Soc.

Thomas Say Foundation Publications. Incl. Vol. 1. Sarcophaga & Allies of North America. Aldrich, J. M. (Illus.). 301p. 1916. pap. Entomol Soc.

ENTOMOLOGISTS

Callahan, Philip S. Soul of the Ghost Moth: Paths of a Naturalist. (Illus.). 1980. 10.00 (ISBN 0-8159-6840-X). Devin.

Canard, M., et al, eds. Biology of Chrysopidae. (Entomological Ser.). 1984. lib. bdg. 57.50 (ISBN 90-6193-137-1, Pub. by Junk Pubs Netherlands). Kluwer-Academic.

Gilbert, Pamela. Compendium of the Biographical Literature on Deceased Entomologists. (Illus.). 1977. 70.00x (ISBN 0-565-00786-6, Pub. by Brit Mus Nat Hist). Sabbot-Natural Hist Bks.

Heinrich, Bernd. In a Patch of Fireweed. (Illus.). 208p. 1984. 18.50 (ISBN 0-674-44548-1). Harvard U Pr.

Howard, Leland O. Fighting the Insects: The Story of an Entomologist, Telling the Life & Experience of the Writer. Cohen, I. Bernard, ed. LC 79-7968. (Three Centuries of Science in America Ser.). 1980. Repr. of 1933 ed. lib. bdg. 28.50x (ISBN 0-405-12550-X). Ayer Co Pubs.

Osten-Sacken, C. R. Record of My Life-Work in Entomology. 1978. 45.00x (ISBN 0-317-07172-6, Pub. by FW Classey UK). State Mutual Bk.

Parencia, Charles R. Incidents in the Careers of a Cotton Entomologist. 1985. 8.95 (ISBN 0-533-06082-6). Vantage.

ENTOMOLOGY

see also Entomological Research; Radioisotopes in Entomology

Adamson, A. M. Marquesan Insects: Environment. (BMB Ser.: No. 139). Repr. of 1936 ed. 14.00 (ISBN 0-527-02245-4). Kraus Repr.

Allen, Douglas G. & Coufal, James E. Introduction to Forest Entomology: A Training Manual for Forest Technicians. LC 84-8510. (Illus.). 168p. 1984. pap. 12.95x (ISBN 0-8156-2319-4). Syracuse U Pr.

Arnett, Ross H. & Jacques, Richard L. Insect Life: A Field Entomology Manual for the Amateur Naturalist. (Illus.). 384p. 1985. 25.95 (ISBN 0-13-467259-3); pap. 12.95 (ISBN 0-13-467242-9). P-H.

Arnett, Ross H., Jr. Entomological Information Storage & Retrieval. 210p. 1970. 4.95 (ISBN 0-916846-00-8). Flora & Fauna.

--Entomological Information Storage & Retrieval. LC 70-140434. 1970. 7.95 (ISBN 0-916846-00-8). World Natural Hist.

Atkins, Michael D. Insects in Perspectives. (Illus.). 1978. text ed. write for info. (ISBN 0-02-304500-0). Macmillan.

Australian Systematic Entomology: A Bicentary Perspective. 147p. 1983. pap. text ed. 9.00 (ISBN 0-643-03501-X, CO69, CSIRO). Unipub.

Balashov, Y. S. An Atlas of Ixodid Tick Ultrastructure. 289p. 1983. 18.00. Entomol Soc.

Balduf, W. V. The Bionomics of Entomophagous Insects. (The Bionomics of Entomophagous Insects other than Coleoptera Ser.: Vol. 2). 338p. Repr. of 1974 ed. 60.00x (ISBN 0-317-07033-9, Pub. by EW Classey UK). State Mutual Bk.

Barnard, J. L. Gammaridean Amphipoda in the Collections of Bishop Museum. (BMB). 1955. pap. 8.00 (ISBN 0-527-02323-X). Kraus Repr.

Belkin, John N. Fundamentals of Entomology. 220p. 1976. pap. 12.95x (ISBN 0-916846-10-5). Flora & Fauna.

--Fundamentals of Entomology. 1976. pap. 11.95 (ISBN 0-916846-10-5). World Natural Hist.

Bengtsson, Bengt A. The Scythrididae (Lepidoptera) of Northern Europe. (Fauna Entomologica Scandinavica Ser.: Vol. 13). (Illus.). 137p. 1984. write for info. (ISBN 90-04-07312-4). E J Brill.

Berrios-Ortiz, A. & Selandev, R. B. Skeletal Musculature in Larval Phases of the Beetle Epicauta Segmenta, (Coleoptera, Meloidae) (Entomologica Ser.: Vol. 16). (Illus.). 1979. lib. bdg. 26.00 (ISBN 90-6193-126-6, Pub. by Junk Pubs Netherlands). Kluwer Academic.

Bohart, R. M. & Kimsey, Lynn S. A Synopsis of the Chrysididae in America North of Mexico: Memoir 33. (Illus.). 266p. 1982. 26.00x (ISBN 0-686-40423-8). Am Entom Inst.

Bradley, T. J. & Miller, T. A., eds. Measurement of Ion Transport & Metabolic Rate in Insects. (Springer Series in Experimental Entomology). (Illus.). 290p. 1984. 41.00 (ISBN 0-387-90855-2). Springer-Verlag.

Breer, H., ed. Neurochemical Techniques in Insect Research. (Springer Series in Experimental Entomolgy). (Illus.). 310p. 1985. 59.50 (ISBN 0-387-13813-7). Springer-Verlag.

Bryce, D. & Hobart, A. The Biology & Identification of the Larvae of the Chironomidae. 43p. 1979. Repr. of 1972 ed. 25.00x (ISBN 0-317-07036-3, Pub. by EW Classey UK). State Mutual Bk.

Burton, John, et al. The Oxford Book of Insects. (Illus.). 1968. 19.95x (ISBN 0-19-910005-5). Oxford U Pr.

Chamberlin, Willard J. Entomological Nomenclature & Literature. 3rd rev. & enl. ed. LC 79-108387. vii, 141p. Repr. of 1952 ed. lib. bdg. 24.75x (ISBN 0-8371-3810-8, CHNO). Greenwood.

Collins, Michael M. Genetics & Ecology of a Hybrid Zone in Hyalophora. LC 83-18019. (Entomology Ser.: Vol. 104). 112p. 1984. lib. bdg. 11.50x (ISBN 0-520-09953-2). U of Cal Pr.

Comstock, John H. Introduction to Entomology. 9th ed. 1093p. 1940. 38.50x (ISBN 0-8014-0083-X). Comstock.

Daly, Howell V., et al. An Introduction to Insect Biology & Diversity. (Illus.). 1978. text ed. 39.95 (ISBN 0-07-015208-X). McGraw.

Dirsh, V. M. Classification of the Acridomorphoid Insects. 178p. 1975. 60.00x (ISBN 0-317-07056-8, Pub. by EW Classey UK). State Mutual Bk.

Ebeling, Walter. Urban Entomology. LC 78-72961. 1975. 27.50x (ISBN 0-931876-19-2, 4057). Ag & Nat Res.

Elzinga, Richard J. Fundamentals of Entomology. 2nd ed. (Illus.). 464p. 1981. text ed. 31.95 (ISBN 0-13-338194-3). P-H.

Evans, Howard E. The Bethylidae of America North of Mexico: Memoir Twenty-Seven. (Illus.). 332p. 1978. 28.00 (ISBN 0-686-40425-4). Am Entom Inst.

--The Pleasures of Entomology: Portraits of Insects & the People Who Study Them. LC 84-600318. (Smithsonian Nature Bks.). (Illus.). 238p. 1985. pap. 14.95 (ISBN 0-87474-421-0, EVPEP). Smithsonian.

Evans, Howard E., et al. Insect Biology: A Textbook of Entomology. (Illus.). 1984. 32.95 (ISBN 0-201-11981-1). Addison-Wesley.

Foote, ed. Thesaurus of Entomology. 1977. 15.00 (ISBN 0-686-22689-5); members 9.00. Entomol Soc.

Frankie, Gordon W. & Koehler, Carl S., eds. Urban Entomology: Interdisciplinary Perspectives. 512p. 1983. 45.00x (ISBN 0-03-057572-9). Praeger.

Freeman, Paul, ed. Common Insect Pests of Stored Food Products: A Guide to Their Identification. rev., 6th ed. (Illus.). 69p. 1980. pap. 4.50x (ISBN 0-565-00830-7, Pub. by Brit Mus Nat Hist England). Sabbot-Natural Hist Bks.

Frost, S. W. Insect Life & Insect Natural History. 2nd ed. Orig. Title: General Entomology. 1959. pap. 8.50 (ISBN 0-486-20517-7). Dover.

Garrison, Rosser W. Revision of the Genus Bnahagma of the U. S. West of the Rocky Mountains & Identification of Certain Larvae by Discriminand Analysis: Publications in Entomology. (Vol. 105). 1985. 11.00x (ISBN 0-520-09954-0). U of Cal Pr.

Gilbert, Pamela, ed. Entomology: A Guide to Information Services. 288p. 1983. 29.00x (ISBN 0-7201-1680-5). Mansell.

ENVIRONMENTAL ENGINEERING
see also Environmental Health; Environmental Policy; Environmental Protection; Environmental Testing; Human Engineering; Life Support Systems (Space Environment); Lighting; Noise Control; Pollution; Sanitary Engineering; Space Simulators

Adriano, Domy C. & Brisbin, I. Lehr, eds. Environmental Chemistry & Cycling Processes: Proceedings. LC 78-6603. (DOE Symposium Ser.). 943p. 1978. pap. 31.50 (ISBN 0-87079-302-0, CONF-760429); microfiche 4.50 (ISBN 0-87079-199-0, CONF-760429). DOE.

Ahmad, Yusuf J. & Muller, Frank G., eds. Integrated Physical, Socio-Economic & Environmental Planning, Vol. 10. (Natural Resources & the Environment Ser.). (Illus.). 196p. 1982. 30.00 (ISBN 0-907567-18-5, TYP115, TYP); pap. 21.00 (ISBN 0-907567-19-3, TYP111). Unipub.

Amy, Gary L. & Knocke, William R., eds. Register of Environmental Engineering Graduate Programs. 5th ed. LC 84-70854. 626p. 1984. pap. 30.00 (ISBN 0-917567-00-5). Assn Environ Eng.

Annual Meeting Education Sessions. Tutorial Lecture Series: Proceedings. 1969. pap. text ed. 10.00 (ISBN 0-915414-48-1). Inst Environ Sci.

Annual Meeting of I.E.S. Environmental Science-Challenge to E-E Education in the Seventies! 1972 Tutorial Proceedings. (Illus.). 1972. pap. text ed. 8.00 (ISBN 0-915414-46-5); pap. text ed. 6.40 members. Inst Environ Sci.

Annual Meeting of the Institute of Environmental Sciences, Boston, 1970. The Environmental Challenge of the 70's: Proceedings. LC 62-38584. (Illus.). 1970. pap. text ed. 20.00 (ISBN 0-915414-10-4). Inst Environ Sci.

Annual Meeting of the Institute of Environmental Sciences, 12th, 1966. The Environments & Man: Proceedings. LC 62-38584. (Illus.). 1966. pap. text ed. 8.00 (ISBN 0-915414-06-6). Inst Environ Sci.

Annual Meeting of the Institute of Environmental Sciences, 6th, 1960. Hyper-Environments...Space Frontier: Proceedings. (Illus.). 1960. pap. text ed. 8.00 (ISBN 0-915414-00-7). Inst Environ Sci.

Annual Meeting of the Institute of Environmental Sciences, 16th, 1970. Living Environments. (Nineteen-Seventy Tutorial Lecture Ser.). 1970. pap. text ed. 12.00 (ISBN 0-915414-47-3). Inst Environ Sci.

Annual Meeting of the Institute of Environmental Sciences, 8th, 1962. Product Improvement Through Environmental Science: Proceedings. LC 62-38584. (Illus.). 1962. pap. text ed. 8.00 (ISBN 0-915414-02-3). Inst Environ Sci.

Annual Meeting of the Institute of Environmental Sciences, 19th, Realism (Assessment) of Career Education in the Environmental Sciences. (Illus.). 1973. pap. text ed. 8.00 (ISBN 0-915414-45-7). Inst Environ Sci.

Annual Meeting of the Institute of Environmental Sciences, 10, 1964. Reliability vs. Reality: Proceedings. LC 62-38584. (Illus.). 1964. pap. text ed. 7.00 (ISBN 0-915414-04-X). Inst Environ Sci.

Annual Technical Meeting of Institute of Environmental Sciences April, 1977. Environmental Technology '77: Proceedings of the 23rd Annual Technical Meeting of the Institute of Environmental Sciences, Los Angeles. LC 62-38584. (Illus.). 1977. pap. text ed. 22.00 (ISBN 0-915414-17-1). Inst Environ Sci.

Annual Technical Meeting of the Institute of Environmental Sciences, 26th, Philadelphia, May 1980. Life Cycle Problems & Environmental Technology: Proceedings. LC 62-38584. (Illus.). 1980. pap. text ed. 25.00 (ISBN 0-915414-20-1). Inst Environ Sci.

Antoniades, Anthony C. Introduction to Environmental Design. LC 76-20696. (Illus.). 360p. 1976. pap. text ed. 8.95x (ISBN 0-8422-0543-8). Irvington.

An Approach to the Design of the Luminous Environment. 136p. (Orig.). 1976. pap. 8.00 (ISBN 0-88481-205-7). Ed Facilities.

ASCE Conference, Environment Engineering Division, 1980. Environmental Engineering. Saukin, Walter, ed. LC 80-66954. 719p. 1980. pap. 52.00x (ISBN 0-87262-249-5). Am Soc Civil Eng.

ASCE Geotechnical Engineering Division, New York, 1981. Recent Developments in Geotechnical Engineering for Hydro Projects: Embankment Dam Instrumentation Performance, Engineering Geology Aspects, Rock Mechanics Studies. Kulhavy, Fred, ed. LC 81-66345. 253p. 1981. pap. 17.00x (ISBN 0-87262-269-X). Am Soc Civil Eng.

ASCE Hydraulics Division, Univ. of Minnesota, June, 1980. Surface Water Impoundments, 2 vols. Stefan, H., ed. LC 81-67445. 1724p. 1981. Set. pap. 115.00x (ISBN 0-87262-271-1). Am Soc Civil Eng.

ASCE Technical Council on Cold Regions Engineering, Seattle, April 1981. The Northern Community: A Search for a Quality Environment. Vinson, Ted, ed. LC 81-65629. 794p. 1981. pap. 49.75x (ISBN 0-87262-267-3). Am Soc Civil Eng.

Attewell, P. B. & Taylor, A. K., eds. Ground Movements & Their Effects on Structures. 288p. 1984. 59.95 (ISBN 0-412-00391-0, 5048, Pub. by Chapman & Hall England). Methuen Inc.

Bailey, James & Ollis, David F. Biochemical Engineering Fundamentals. (McGraw-Hill Chemical Engineering Ser.). (Illus.). 1977. text ed. 47.00 (ISBN 0-07-003210-6). McGraw.

Banham, Reyner. Architecture of the Well-Tempered Environment. LC 69-13119. (Illus.). 1969. 8.95x (ISBN 0-226-03695-2). U of Chicago Pr.

--The Architecture of the Well-Tempered Environment. 2nd, rev. ed. LC 84-156. (Illus.). 296p. 1984. lib. bdg. 30.00x (ISBN 0-226-03697-9); pap. 12.50 (ISBN 0-226-03698-7). U of Chicago Pr.

Baram, Michael S. Alternatives to Regulation: Managing Risks to Health, Safety, & the Environment. LC 81-47560. 256p. 1981. 27.50x (ISBN 0-669-04666-3). Lexington Bks.

Barrekette, E. S., ed. Pollution: Engineering & Scientific Solutions. LC 72-91328. (Environmental Science Research Ser.: Vol. 2). 799p. 1973. 79.50 (ISBN 0-306-36302-X, Plenum Pr). Plenum Pub.

Barrett, Eric C. & Curtis, Leonard F., eds. Environmental Remote Sensing: Practices & Problems, Vol. 2. LC 73-91531. 309p. 1977. 40.00x (ISBN 0-8448-0967-5). Crane-Russak Co.

Barrett, Gary W. & Rosenberg, Rutger, eds. Stress Effects on Natural Ecosystems. LC 80-40851. (Environmental Monographs & Symposia, Environmental Science). 305p. 1981. 56.95x (ISBN 0-471-27834-3, Pub. by Wiley-Interscience). Wiley.

Bart, Polly, et al, eds. Design Through Knowledge. 500p. 1982. 33.00 (ISBN 0-939922-04-5). EDRA.

Bassett, Libby, ed. Conference Proceedings -- Environment & Development: The Future for Consulting Firms. LC 83-16903. (Illus.). 431p. 1983. pap. 85.00 (ISBN 0-317-17555-6). World Enviro.

Basta, Daniel J., et al. Analysis for Residuals-Environmental Quality Management: Case Study of the Ljubljana Area of Yugoslavia. LC 77-17250. (Resources for the Future). pap. 64.50 (ISBN 0-317-26216-5, 2052112). Bks Demand UMI.

Battelle Columbus Laboratories. Preliminary Environmental Assessment of Biomass Conversion to Synthetic Fuels. 346p. 1980. pap. 49.95x (ISBN 0-89934-049-0, B049-PP). Solar Energy Info.

Beeson, Richard D. & Crutcher, Ernest R. Hardware Cleaning & Sampling for Cleanliness Verification & Contamination Control Microscopy. LC 61-38584. 34p. 1983. pap. text ed. 25.00 (ISBN 0-915414-72-4). Inst Environ Sci.

Benefield, Larry, et al. Treatment Plant Hydraulics for Environmental Engineers. (Illus.). 240p. 1984. 45.00 (ISBN 0-13-930248-4). P-H.

Bergman, Harold L., et al, eds. Environmental Hazard Assessment of Effluents. (SETAC Special Publications Ser.). (Illus.). 390p. 1985. 40.00 (ISBN 0-08-030165-7). Pergamon.

Bethea, Robert M. Air Pollution Control Technology. (Environmental Engineering Ser). 1978. 39.95 (ISBN 0-442-20715-8). Van Nos Reinhold.

Billington, N. S. & Roberts, B. M. Building Services Engineering: A Review of Its Development. LC 80-42036. (International Ser. on Building Environmental Engineering: Vol. 1). 537p. 1981. 88.00 (ISBN 0-08-026741-6); pap. 24.00 (ISBN 0-08-026742-4). Pergamon.

Bockris, J. O'M., ed. Environmental Chemistry. LC 76-21081. (Illus.). 795p. 1977. 79.50x (ISBN 0-306-30869-X, Plenum Pr). Plenum Pub.

Boggess, W. R. & Wixson, B. G., eds. Lead in the Environment. (Illus.). 272p. 1979. text ed. 43.00 (ISBN 0-7194-0024-4, Pub. by Castle Hse England). J K Burgess.

Bolin, Bert, ed. Carbon Cycle Modelling-Scope Report 16. (SCOPE Ser. (Scientific Committe on Problems of the Environment): Vol. 16). 390p. 1981. 57.95 (ISBN 0-471-10051-X, Pub. by Wiley-Interscience). Wiley.

Bond, Richard G. & Straub, Conrad P., eds. Handbook of Environmental Control, CRC, 6 vols. Incl. Vol. 1. Air Pollution. 576p. 1973. 61.00 (ISBN 0-87819-271-9); Vol. 2. Solid Waste. 580p. 1973. 63.00 (ISBN 0-87819-272-7); Vol. 3. Water Supply & Treatment. 835p. 1973. 76.50 (ISBN 0-87819-273-5); Vol. 4. Waste Water Treatment & Disposal. 835p. 1974. 76.50 (ISBN 0-87819-274-3); Vol. 5, Hospital & Health Care Facilities, 440 Pgs. 1975. 54.00 (ISBN 0-87819-275-1); Series Index. 128p. 1978. 39.00 (ISBN 0-8493-0279-X). LC 72-92118. (Handbook Ser.). 1973. CRC Pr.

Bonn, George S., ed. Information Resources in the Environmental Sciences. LC 73-75784. (Allerton Park Institute Ser.: No. 18). 238p. 1973. 7.00x (ISBN 0-87845-037-8). U of Ill Lib Info Sci.

Bower, Blair T., ed. Regional Residuals Environmental Quality Management Modeling. LC 77-92413. (Resources for the Future, RFF Research Paper Ser.: NO. R-7). pap. 61.00 (ISBN 0-317-26044-8, 2023786). Bks Demand UMI.

Brebbia, C. A., et al, eds. Environmental Forces on Engineering Structures. LC 79-16733. 564p. 1979. 74.95x (ISBN 0-470-26820-4). Halsted Pr.

Burgess, John H. Human Factors in Built Environments. LC 81-184028. 137p. 1982. 30.00x (ISBN 0-915250-38-1). Environ Design.

Burk, Janet L. & Hayes, Stephen. Environmental Concerns: A Bibliography of U.S. Government Publications, 1971-1973. 1975. 4.00 (ISBN 0-932826-06-7). New Issues MI.

Butlin, J. A., ed. The Economics of Environmental & Natural Resources Policy. 200p. 1981. lib. bdg. 33.00x (ISBN 0-86531-190-0); pap. 14.50x (ISBN 0-86531-196-X). Westview.

Cairncross, S. & Feachem, R. G. Environmental Health Engineering in the Tropics: An Introductory Text. 283p. 1983. 42.95 (ISBN 0-471-90001-X). Wiley.

Camougis, G. Environmental Biology for Engineers: A Guide to Environmental Assessment. 1980. 28.50 (ISBN 0-07-009677-5). McGraw.

Canter, Larry. Environmental Impact Assessment. (McGraw-Hill Series in Environmental Engineering & Water Resources). (Illus.). 1977. text ed. 45.00 (ISBN 0-07-009764-X). McGraw.

Carleton, A. J. Odour Control by Thermal Incineration, 1978. 1981. 75.00x (ISBN 0-686-97130-2, Pub. by W Spring England). State Mutual Bk.

Chambers, B. & Chambers, E. J. Bulking of Activated Sludge: Preventative & Remedial Methods. 279p. 1982. 74.95x (ISBN 0-470-27299-6). Halsted Pr.

Chemistry, Man, Environment. (Eng. & Ger.). 406p. (Orig.). 1981. pap. text ed. 24.00 (ISBN 0-89192-324-1). Interbk Inc.

Cheremisinoff, Paul N. & Young, Richard A. Pollution Engineering Practice Handbook. LC 74-14427. 1975. 59.95 (ISBN 0-250-40075-8). Butterworth.

Chicorel, Marietta, ed. Chicorel Index to Urban Planning & Environmental Design, 2 vols. LC 75-30637. (Index Ser.). 1000p. 1975. Set. 250.00 (ISBN 0-934598-65-7). Vol. 17 (ISBN 0-934598-64-9). Vol. 17A. Am Lib Pub Co.

Chigier, Norman A. Energy, Combustion & Environment. (Illus.). 689p. 1981. text ed. 55.00 (ISBN 0-07-010766-1). McGraw.

Ciba Foundation. Environmental Chemicals, Enzyme Function & Human Disease. LC 80-18000. (Ciba Foundation Symposium, New Ser.: 76). pap. 97.50 (ISBN 0-317-29748-1, 2022195). Bks Demand UMI.

Cleaning Our Environment: A Chemical Perspective. LC 78-73104. 1978. 12.95 (ISBN 0-8412-0467-5). Am Chemical.

Cointreau, Sandra J. Environmental Management of Urban Solid Wastes in Developing Countries: A Project Guide. (Urban Development Technical Paper: No. 5). 214p. 1982. pap. 5.00 (ISBN 0-8213-0063-6). World Bank.

Compton, Paul & Pesci, Marton. Environmental Management. (Studies in Geography in Hungrary: 16). 264p. 1984. 32.00 (ISBN 963-05-3696-X, Pub. by Akademiai Kaido Hungary). Heyden.

Conant, Francis, et al, eds. Resource Inventory & Baseline Study Methods for Developing Countries. LC 83-15493. 539p. 1983. 22.95 (ISBN 0-87168-258-3). AAAS.

Coulston, F. & Korte, F., eds. Environmental Quality: Global Aspects of Chemistry, Toxicology & Technology As Applied to the Environment, 5 vols. Vol. 1, 1972. 29.50 (ISBN 0-12-227001-0); Vol. 2, 1973. 36.00 (ISBN 0-12-227002-9); Vol. 3, 1974. 32.00 (ISBN 0-12-227003-7); Vol.4, 1975. 29.00 (ISBN 0-12-227004-5); Vol. 5, 1976. 27.50 (ISBN 0-12-227005-3). Acad Pr.

Cowan, Henry J. & Smith, Peter R. Environmental Systems. 1983. 26.95 (ISBN 0-442-21490-1); pap. 18.95 (ISBN 0-442-21489-8). Van Nos Reinhold.

Croome-Gale, Derek J. Noise, Buildings, & People. LC 73-7982. 500p. 1977. pap. text ed. 50.00 (ISBN 0-08-019816-3). Pergamon.

Daetz, Pantell, ed. Environmental Modeling: Analysis & Management. LC 73-22191. (Benchmark Papers in Electric Engineering & Computer Science: Vol. 6). 407p. 1974. 57.00 (ISBN 0-87933-082-1); pap. 31.00 (ISBN 0-87933-138-0). Van Nos Reinhold.

Davis & Cornwell. Introduction to Environmental Engineering. 1985. text ed. write for info. (ISBN 0-534-04137-X, 21R4300, Pub. by PWS Engineering). PWS Pubs.

Davis, R. D. & Hucker, G., eds. Environmental Effects of Organic & Inorganic Contaminants in Sewage Sludge. 1983. lib. bdg. 36.95 (ISBN 90-277-1586-6, Pub. by Reidel Holland). Kluwer Academic.

Designing Electronic Equipment for Random Vibration Environments: Proceedings. LC 62-38584. 98p. (Orig.). 1982. pap. text ed. 22.00 (ISBN 0-915414-68-6). Inst Environ Sci.

Directory of Institutions & Individuals Active in Environmentally-Sound & Appropriate Technologies. (Reference Ser.: Vol. 1). 152p. 1979. pap. 20.00 (ISBN 0-08-025658-9, UNEP002, UNEP). Unipub.

Dober, Richard P. Environmental Design. LC 75-11961. 288p. 1975. Repr. of 1969 ed. 24.50 (ISBN 0-88275-331-2). Krieger.

Dolzer, Rudolf. Property & Environment: The Social Obligation Inherent in Ownership. (Environmental Policy & Law Papers: No. 12). 72p. 1976. pap. 10.00 (ISBN 2-88032-082-8, IUCN41, IUCN). Unipub.

Drucker, Harvey & Wildung, Raymond E., eds. Biological Implications of Metals in the Environment: Proceedings. LC 77-1039. (ERDA Symposium Ser.). 692p. 1977. pap. 25.25 (ISBN 0-87079-104-4, CONF-750929); microfiche 4.50 (ISBN 0-87079-149-4, CONF-750929). DOE.

Dury, G. H. Environmental Systems. LC 80-29151. (Orig.). 1981. 19.95x (ISBN 0-435-08001-6); instr's manual 6.00x (ISBN 0-435-08002-4). Heinemann Ed.

--Introduction to Environmental Systems. text ed. 19.95x (ISBN 0-435-08001-6); tchr's manual avail.; pap. text ed. 6.00x (ISBN 0-435-08002-4). Heinemann Ed.

Dyer, Jon C. & Mignone, Nicholas A. Handbook of Industrial Residues. LC 82-19082. (Environment Engineering Ser.). (Illus.). 453p. 1983. 54.00 (ISBN 0-8155-0924-3, Noyes Pubns). Noyes.

Dykstra, Dennis P. Mathematical Programming for Natural Resource Management. (Illus.). 384p. 1983. text ed. 36.95 (ISBN 0-07-018552-2). McGraw.

Ecology & Environment, Inc. Toxic Substance Storage Tank Containment. LC 84-22697. (Pollution Technology Review Ser.: No. 116). (Illus.). 274p. 1985. 36.00 (ISBN 0-8155-1018-7). Noyes.

El-Hinnawi, Essam & Biswas, Asit K., eds. Renewable Sources of Energy & the Environment. (Natural Resources & the Environment Ser.: Vol. 6). 219p. 1981. 32.50 (ISBN 0-907567-05-3, TYP101, TYP); pap. 17.50 (ISBN 0-907567-10-X, TYP120). Unipub.

Elkington, John. The Ecology of Tomorrow's World: Industry's Environments, Environments's Industry. 311p. 1980. 37.95 (ISBN 0-470-27120-5). Halsted Pr.

Enger, Eldon D., et al. Environmental Science: The Study of Interrelationships. 2nd ed. 568p. 1986. pap. text ed. price not set (ISBN 0-697-05103-X); price not set instr's. manual (ISBN 0-697-00642-5); price not set transparencies (ISBN 0-697-00641-7). Wm C Brown.

Enhancement of Quality Through Environmental Technology: Proceedings of the 28th Annual Technical Meeting of the Institute of Environmental Sciences, Atlanta, April 1982. LC 62-38584. (Illus.). 281p. 1982. pap. text ed. 30.00 (ISBN 0-915414-22-8). Inst Environ Sci.

Environmental Aspects of the Aluminum Industry. (Industry Overviews: Vol. 2). 32p. 1977. pap. 6.75 (ISBN 0-686-93504-7, UNEP027, UNEP). Unipub.

Environmental Aspects of the Iron & Steel Industry: A Workshop. (Industry Overviews: Vol. 8). pap. 5.00 (UNEP011, UNEP). Unipub.

Environmental Engineering. 472p. 1978. pap. 29.00x (ISBN 0-87262-128-6). Am Soc Civil Eng.

Environmental Engineering. LC 81-67747. 739p. 1981. pap. 49.00x (ISBN 0-87262-273-8). Am Soc Civil Eng.

Environmental Engineering. 838p. 1979. pap. text ed. 48.00 (ISBN 0-87262-185-5). Am Soc Civil Eng.

Odabasi, Halis & Ulug, S. Erol, eds. Environmental Problems & Their International Implications. LC 73-87538. (Illus.). 1973. 19.50x (ISBN 0-87081-052-9). Colo Assoc.
OECD. Siting Procedures for Major Energy Facilities: Some National Cases. (Illus.). 142p. (Orig.). 1980. pap. text ed. 8.00x (ISBN 92-64-11986-8). OECD.
--Urban Environmental Indicators. 274p. (Orig.). 1978. pap. 14.00x (ISBN 92-64-11754-7). OECD.
Ollerenshaw, R. J. Calibration of Cascadeimpactors Using Existing Theory, 1978. 1981. 69.00x (ISBN 0-686-97041-1, Pub. by W Spring England). State Mutual Bk.
Olwig, Kenneth R. Nature's Ideological Landscape. (London Research Series in Geography: No. 5). (Illus.). 144p. 1984. text ed. 24.95x (ISBN 0-04-710002-8). Allen Unwin.
O'Riordan, T. Environmentalism. 2nd ed. (Research in Planning & Design Ser.). 420p. 1981. pap. 12.95x (ISBN 0-85086-092-X, NO. 8004, Pub. by Pion England). Methuen Inc.
O'Riordan, T. & Turner, K., eds. An Annotated Reader in Environmental Planning & Management. LC 82-7569. (Urban & Regional Planning Ser.: Vol. 30). (Illus.). 484p. 1983. 45.00 (ISBN 0-08-024669-9); pap. 20.00 (ISBN 0-08-024668-0). Pergamon.
O'Riordan, Timothy & Sewell, W. R., eds. Project Appraisal & Policy Review. LC 80-40847. (Studies in Environmental Management & Resource Development). 304p. 1981. 44.95 (ISBN 0-471-27853-X, Pub. by Wiley-interscience). Wiley.
O'Riordan, Timothy & Turner, R. Kerry, eds. Progress in Resource Management & Environmental Planning, Vol. 4. 304p. 1984. 64.95x (ISBN 0-471-10534-1, 1469, Pub. by Wiley-Interscience). Wiley.
Osterberg, Arvid, et al, eds. Design Research Interactions. (EDRA Proceedings). 600p. 1981. pap. text ed. 30.00 (ISBN 0-939922-03-7). EDRA.
Pawlowski, L., ed. Physiochemical Methods for Water & Wastewater Treatment. (Studies in Environmental Science: Vol. 19). 394p. 1982. 89.50 (ISBN 0-444-42067-3). Elsevier.
Pawlowski, L., et al, eds. Chemistry for Protection of the Environment: Proceedings of an International Conference, Toulouse, France, 19-25, Sept., 1983. (Studies in Environmental Science: No. 23). 626p. 1984. 128.00 (ISBN 0-444-42347-8, I-227-84). Elsevier.
Perry, Allen H. Environmental Hazards in the British Isles. (Illus.). 192p. (Orig.). 1981. text ed. 27.50x (ISBN 0-04-910069-6); pap. text ed. 17.95x (ISBN 0-04-910070-X). Allen Unwin.
Pfafflin, James & Ziegler, Edward N. Advances in Environmental Science & Engineering, Vol. 1. 292p. 1979. 83.25x (ISBN 0-677-16070-4). Gordon.
--Advances in Environmental Science & Engineering, Vol. 2. 228p. 1979. 83.25x (ISBN 0-677-14810-0). Gordon.
--Advances in Environmental Science & Engineering, Vol. 3. 240p. 1979. 83.25 (ISBN 0-677-15760-6). Gordon.
--The Encyclopedia of Environmental Science & Engineering, 2 vol. set. 1124p. 1976. 361.75 set (ISBN 0-677-14670-1). Gordon.
Pfafflin, James & Ziegler, Edward, eds. Advances in Environmental Science & Engineering, Vol. 4. 188p. 1981. 78.75 (ISBN 0-677-16250-2). Gordon.
Pfafflin, James R. & Ziegler, Edward N., eds. Encyclopedia of Environmental Science & Engineering, 3 Vols. 1350p. 1983. Set. 500.00 (ISBN 0-677-06430-6). Gordon.
Pitts, James, Jr. & Metcalf, Robert L., eds. Advances in Environmental Science & Technology, Vol. 5. LC 74-644364. 382p. 1975. 37.50 (ISBN 0-471-69088-0). Krieger.
Pitts, James N., et al. Advances in Environmental Science & Technology, Vol. 10. LC 79-644364. 521p. 1980. 85.00x (ISBN 0-471-06480-7, Pub. by Wiley-Interscience). Wiley.
Pitts, James N., Jr. & Metcalf, Robert L., eds. Advances in Environmental Science & Technology, Vol. 3. 386p. 1974. 36.50 (ISBN 0-471-69086-4). Krieger.
Porteous, A., ed. Developments in Environmental Control & Public Health, Vol. 1. (Illus.). 311p. 1979. 53.75 (ISBN 0-85334-834-0, Pub. by Elsevier Applied Sci England). Elsevier.
Poulton, E. C. Environment & Human Efficiency. (Illus.). 336p. 1972. 21.75x (ISBN 0-398-01515-5). C C Thomas.
--The Environment at Work. (Illus.). 176p. 1979. 20.75x (ISBN 0-398-03848-1). C C Thomas.
Pratt, Joanne H., et al. Environmental Encounter: Experiences in Decision-Making for the Built & the Natural Environment. (Illus.). 1979. pap. 14.95 (ISBN 0-9601902-0-1). Reverchon Pr.
Purdom, P. Walton & Anderson, Stanley H. Environmental Science: Managing the Environment. (Physics & Physical Science Ser.). 536p. 1980. text ed. 24.95 (ISBN 0-675-08170-X). Additional supplements may be obtained from publisher. Merrill.
Quality Assurance of Environmental Measurements: Sampling, Validation, Quality Control. (Illus.). 1978. pap. 20.00 (QA8). Info Transfer.
Ridker, Ronald G. & Watson, William D., Jr. To Choose a Future. LC 79-3643. (Resources for the Future Ser.). 1980. 37.00x (ISBN 0-8018-2354-4). Johns Hopkins.
Rudman, Jack. Environmental Analyst. (Career Examination Ser.: C-2659). (Cloth bdg. avail. on request). pap. 12.00 (ISBN 0-8373-2659-1). Natl Learning.
--Environmental Assistant. (Career Examination Ser.: C-1583). (Cloth bdg. avail on request). pap. 12.00 (ISBN 0-8373-1583-2). Natl Learning.
--Environmental Conservation Officer Trainee. (Career Examination Ser.: C-1759). (Cloth bdg. avail. on request). 1976. 12.00 (ISBN 0-8373-1759-2). Natl Learning.
--Environmental Control Specialist. (Career Examination Ser.: C-2429). (Cloth bdg. avail. on request). pap. 12.00 (ISBN 0-8373-2429-7). Natl Learning.
--Environmental Control Specialist Trainee. (Career Examination Ser.: C-2067). (Cloth bdg. avail on request). 1977. pap. 12.00 (ISBN 0-8373-2067-4). Natl Learning.
--Environmental Planner. (Career Examination Ser.: C-2662). (Cloth bdg. avail. on request). pap. 14.00 (ISBN 0-8373-2662-1). Natl Learning.
--Environmentalist. (Career Examination Ser.: C-1584). (Cloth bdg. avail. on request). pap. 14.00 (ISBN 0-8373-1584-0). Natl Learning.
--Principal Environmental Analyst. (Career Examination Ser.: C-2661). (Cloth bdg. avail. on request). pap. 12.00 (ISBN 0-8373-2661-3). Natl Learning.
--Principal Environmental Planner. (Career Examination Ser.: C-2664). (Cloth bdg. avail. on request). pap. 12.00 (ISBN 0-8373-2664-8). Natl Learning.
--Senior Environmental Analyst. (Career Examination Ser.: C-2660). (Cloth bdg. avail. on request). pap. 14.00 (ISBN 0-8373-2660-5). Natl Learning.
--Senior Environmental Planner. (Career Examination Ser.: C-2663). (Cloth bdg. avail. on request). pap. 14.00 (ISBN 0-8373-2663-X). Natl Learning.
--Senior Environmentalist. (Career Examination Ser.: C-1585). (Cloth bdg. avail. on request). pap. 14.00 (ISBN 0-8373-1585-9). Natl Learning.
--Supervising Environmentalist. (Career Examination Ser.: C-1586). (Cloth bdg. avail. on request). pap. 10.00 (ISBN 0-8373-1586-7). Natl Learning.
Salvato, Joseph A. Environmental Engineering & Sanitation. 3rd ed. LC 81-11509. (Environmental Science & Technology Ser.). 1163p. 1982. 65.95x (ISBN 0-471-04942-5, Pub. by Wiley-Interscience). Wiley.
Second International Congress on Analytical Techniques in Environmental Chemistry & Albaiges, J. Analytical Techniques in Environmental Chemistry 2: Proceedings of the Second International Congress, Barcelona, Spain, November 1981. LC 82-15047. (Series on Environmental Science: Vol. 7). (Illus.). 482p. 1982. 83.00 (ISBN 0-08-028740-9). Pergamon.
Seidel, Andrew D. & Danford, Scott, eds. Environmental Design: Research, Theory & Application. (EDRA Proceedings). 444p. 1979. pap. text ed. 25.00 (ISBN 0-939922-01-0). EDRA.
Sharma, U. S. Current Practices in Environmental Engineering. Singh, Alam, ed. (International Overviews Ser.: No. 1). vii, 248p. 1984. text ed. 55.00x (ISBN 0-317-17274-3, Pub. by Geo-Environ Academia Jodhpur India). Apt Bks.
Shaw, A. M., ed. International Directory of Consulting Environmental & Civil Engineers. 2nd rev. ed. 1981. 10.00 (ISBN 0-934366-03-9). Intl Research Serv.
Siebert, Horst. Economics of the Environment. LC 80-7442. 1981. 29.50x (ISBN 0-669-03693-5). Lexington Bks.
Smellie, R. M. & Pennock, J. F., eds. Symposia No. Forty One: Biochemical Adaptation to Environmental Change. 240p. 1981. 29.00x (ISBN 0-904498-01-8, Pub. by Biochemical England). State Mutual Bk.
Spooner, Philip, et al. Slurry Trench Construction for Pollution Migration Control. LC 84-22747. (Pollution Technology Review Ser.: No. 118). (Illus.). 237p. 1985. 36.00 (ISBN 0-8155-1020-9). Noyes.
Stryker, Perrin, ed. How to Judge Environmental Planning for Subdivisions: A Citizen's Guide. (Orig.). 1981. pap. 3.95 (ISBN 0-918780-20-9). INFORM.
Technical Association of the Pulp & Paper Industry. Introduction to Environmental Control in the Pulp & Paper Industry: Short Cource. pap. 136.00 (ISBN 0-317-28020-1, 2025570). Bks Demand UMI.
Technical Meeting of the Institute of Environment Sciences, 25th Annual, Seattle, Washington, April 1979. Learning to Use Our Environment: Proceedings. (Illus.). 1979. pap. text ed. 25.00 (ISBN 0-915414-19-8). Inst Environ Sci.
Teich, Albert H., et al, eds. Biotechnology & the Environment: Risk & Regulation. 1985. pap. text ed. 12.95 (ISBN 0-87168-279-6). AAAS.
Thomas, D. H. & Davia, N. C. Komara Miniskimm ER: An Assessment of Performance, 1980. 1981. 30.00x (ISBN 0-686-97102-7, Pub. by W Spring England). State Mutual Bk.
United Nations Environment Programme. Directory of Institutions & Individuals Active in Environmentally-Sound & Appropriate Technologies. 28.00 (ISBN 0-08-025658-9). Pergamon.
Unruh, David R. Space & Environment: An Annotated Bibliography, No. 954. 5.00 (ISBN 0-686-20382-8). CPL Biblios.
Vesilind, P. Aarne. Environmental Engineering. LC 81-70872. 1982. 34.95 (ISBN 0-250-40422-2). Butterworth.
Villate, Jose T. Dictionary of Environmental Engineering & Related Sciences. LC 78-67002. (Coleccion Diccionrios). Orig. Title: Diccionario De Ingenieria Ambiental y Ciencias Afines. (Eng. & Span.). 445p. 1979. 25.00 (ISBN 0-89729-209-X). Ediciones.
Voight, Randall L. & Franklin, George, Jr. A Reference Guide to Environmental Management, Engineering & Pollution Control Resources. 305p. 1983. pap. 35.00 (ISBN 0-930318-12-9). Intl Res Eval.
Wang, Lawrence & Pereira, Norman, eds. Handbook of Environmental Engineering, Vol. 3. (Handbook of Environmental Engineering Ser.). 512p. 1985. 74.50 (ISBN 0-89603-058-X). Humana.
Wang, Lawrence K. & Pereira, Norman C., eds. Handbook of Environmental Engineering, Vol. 1. LC 78-78033. 484p. 1979. 69.50 (ISBN 0-89603-001-6). Humana.
--Handbook of Environmental Engineering, Vol. 2. LC 79-91087. 480p. 1980. 69.50 (ISBN 0-89603-008-3). Humana.
Warren Spring Laboratory, ed. Odours Control: A Concise Guide, Nineteen Eighty. 1981. 85.00x (ISBN 0-686-97135-3, Pub. by W Spring England). State Mutual Bk.
Watkins, George A., ed. A New Generation of Environmental Essays. LC 73-9938. 1973. Vol. 1. 21.00x (ISBN 0-8422-5126-X); pap. text ed. 6.95x (ISBN 0-8422-0318-4); Vol. 2. 24.00x (ISBN 0-8422-5127-8); pap. text ed. 8.95x (ISBN 0-8422-0348-6). Irvington.
Wenig, Jeffrey. An Introduction to Environmental Science: The Ecology of Long Island. 1976. pap. 5.75x. Environ Pubns.
Westman, Walter E. Ecology, Impact, Assessment & Environmental Planning. LC 84-11867. (Environmental Science & Technology: A wiley-Interscience Series of Texts & Monographs: 1-121). 532p. 1985. text ed. 65.00x (ISBN 0-471-89621-7, Wiley-Interscience); pap. text ed. 34.95x (ISBN 0-471-80895-4). Wiley.
Wheater, Delma J. Environmental Design: An Analysis of the Field, Its Implication for Libraries & a Guide to the Literature, Nos. 747-748. 1975. 8.50 (ISBN 0-686-20341-0). CPL Biblios.
White, Robert G. Applied Environmental Science. (Illus.). 73p. (Orig.). lab manual 73.00 (ISBN 0-318-03721-1). Lifecycle Inc.
White, T. D., et al. Environmental Systems: An Introductory Text. (Illus.). 480p. 1984. text ed. 50.00x (ISBN 0-04-551064-4); pap. text ed. 19.95x (ISBN 0-04-551065-2). Allen Unwin.
Yaron, B., et al, eds. Pollutants in Porous Media: The Unsaturated Zone Between Soil Surface & Groundwater. (Ecological Studies, Analysis & Synthesis: Vol. 47). (Illus.). 330p. 1984. 49.00 (ISBN 0-387-13179-5). Springer-Verlag.

ENVIRONMENTAL ENGINEERING–HANDBOOKS, MANUALS, ETC.

Moore, Gary T., et al. Environmental Design: Research Directions. LC 84-15975. 222p. 1985. 35.95 (ISBN 0-03-000522-1). Praeger.
Peavy, H. S. & Rowe, D. Environmental Engineering. 1985. 37.95 (ISBN 0-07-049134-8). McGraw.
Szokolay, Steven V. Environmental Science Handbook for Architects & Builders. LC 79-25004. 532p. 1980. 96.95x (ISBN 0-470-26904-9). Halsted Pr.
Truitt, Thomas H. Environmental Audit Handbook. 2nd ed. 1983. pap. 90.00 (ISBN 0-88057-023-7). Exec Ent Inc.
Zilly, Robert G., ed. Handbook of Environmental Civil Engineering. LC 74-26993. pap. 160.00 (ISBN 0-317-08181-0, 2014901). Bks Demand UMI.

ENVIRONMENTAL ENGINEERING (BUILDINGS)

see also Architectural Acoustics; Clean Rooms; Ventilation

Aho, Arnold J. Materials, Energies & Environmental Design. 1981. lib. bdg. 42.50 (ISBN 0-8240-7178-6). Garland Pub.
Aiello, J. R. & Baum, A., eds. Residential Crowding & Design. LC 79-357. (Illus.). 270p. 1979. 25.00x (ISBN 0-306-40205-X, Plenum Pr). Plenum Pub.
Ambrose, James & Vergun, Dimitry. Seismic Design of Buildings. 288p. 38.95 (ISBN 0-471-88979-2). Wiley.
Andrews, F. T. Building Mechanical Systems. 2nd ed. LC 75-11895. 412p. 1976. 24.50 (ISBN 0-88275-322-3). Krieger.
Canadian Government. Winning Low Energy Building Designs. 651p. 1980. text ed. 35.00x (ISBN 0-660-50675-0, Pub. by Inst Engeering Australia). Brookfield Pub Co.
Carpenter, Edward K. Thirty-Seven Design & Environment Projects: First Annual Review. (Illus.). 96p. 1976. 13.95 (ISBN 0-8230-7456-0, Whitney Lib). Watson-Guptill.
Close, Paul D. Sound Control & Thermal Insulation of Buildings. LC 65-28400. 510p. 1966. 31.50 (ISBN 0-442-35058-9). Krieger.
Coates, D. F. Rock Mechanics Principles. 442p. 1981. pap. text ed. 26.40 (ISBN 0-660-10933-6, Pub. by Inst Engineering Australia). Brookfield Pub Co.
Cross, Frank L., Jr. & Genetelli, Emil, eds. Environmental Planning. LC 75-26080. (Environmental Monograph). (Illus.). 49p. 1976. pap. 3.95 (ISBN 0-87762-181-0). Technomic.
Egan, M. David. Concepts in Thermal Comfort. (Illus.). 224p. 1975. 26.95 (ISBN 0-13-166447-6). P-H.
Esmay, Merle L. & Dixon, John E. Environmental Control for Agricultural Buildings. (Illus.). 1985. text ed. 45.00 pre-pub (ISBN 0-87055-469-7). AVI.
Fabrick, Martin N. & O'Rourke, Joseph J. Environmental Planning for Design & Construction. LC 81-23070. (Construction Management & Engineering Ser.). 304p. 1982. 48.50x (ISBN 0-471-05848-3, Pub. by Wiley-Interscience). Wiley.
Grant, Donald P. Design by Objectives: Multiple Objective Design Analysis & Evaluation in Architectural, Environmental & Product Design. LC 82-73290. 50p. (Orig.). 1982. pap. text ed. 6.00x (ISBN 0-910821-00-3). Design Meth.
Hutcheon, Neil B. & Handegord, Gustav O. Building Science for a Cold Climate. 440p. 1983. text ed. 58.95x (ISBN 0-471-79763-4, Pub. by Wiley-Interscience). Wiley.
Lee, Kaiman. Federal Environmental Impact Statements Related to Buildings. LC 75-323048. 102p. 1975. 30.00x (ISBN 0-915250-16-0). Environ Design.
Lee, Kaiman & Koumjian, Lauren. Environmental Court Cases Related to Buildings. LC 79-105955. 1979. 30.00x (ISBN 0-915250-28-4). Environ Design.
Macedo, Manuel C., Jr. Energy Management & Control Systems: Theory & Application, Vol. 1. LC 83-7043. (Construction Management & Engineering Ser.: Pt. 1-102). 293p. 1983. 45.95x (ISBN 0-471-08469-7, Pub. by Wiley-Interscience). Wiley.
McGuinness, William J. & Stein, Benjamin. Building Technology: Mechanical & Electrical Systems. LC 76-14961. 1977. 39.95 (ISBN 0-471-58433-9); teacher's manual avail. (ISBN 0-471-01601-2). Wiley.
Marans, Robert W. & Spreckelmeyer, Kent F. Evaluating Built Environments: A Behavioral Approach. (Illus.). 249p. 1981. 20.00x (ISBN 0-87944-272-7). Inst Soc Res.
Rapoport, Amos. The Meaning of the Built Environment: A Non-Verbal Communication Approach. 200p. 1982. 25.00 (ISBN 0-8039-1892-5); pap. 12.50 (ISBN 0-8039-1893-3). Sage.
Sheratt, A. F., ed. Integrated Environment in Building Design. (Illus.). x, 281p. 1974. 50.00 (ISBN 0-85334-609-7, Pub. by Elsevier Applied Sci England). Elsevier.
Sherratt, A. F., ed. Applications of Ambient Energy in Buildings. 200p. 1984. 55.00x (ISBN 0-419-12790-9, NO. 6809). Methuen Inc.

ENVIRONMENTAL HEALTH

see also Environmental Engineering; Man–Influence of Environment; Pollution

Baum, Andrew & Singer, Jerome E., eds. Environment & Health. (Advances in Environmental Psychology Ser.: Vol. 4). (Illus.). 352p. 1982. text ed. 39.95x (ISBN 0-89859-174-0). L Erlbaum Assocs.

Lee, Kaiman & Koumjian, Lauren. Environmental Court Cases Related to Buildings. LC 79-105955. 1979. 30.00x (ISBN 0-915250-28-4). Environ Design.

Mandelker, Daniel R. NEPA Law & Litigation: The National Environmental Policy Act. LC 84-23059. 1985. loose-leaf bdg. 75.00 (ISBN 0-317-14546-0). Callaghan.

Milbrath, Lester W., et al, eds. The Politics of Environmental Policy. LC 75-27013. (Sage Contemporary Social Science Issues Ser.: No. 18). pap. 34.00 (ISBN 0-317-09728-8, 2021932). Bks Demand UMI.

Morrisey, T. J., ed. Pollution Control Problems & Related Federal Legislation. 290p. 1974. text ed. 29.50x (ISBN 0-8422-5175-8); pap. text ed. 12.50x (ISBN 0-8422-0418-0). Irvington.

Resource Careers: Options & Opportunities in Environmental & Natural Resources Law. LC 79-55232. 107p. 1979. pap. 3.00 (ISBN 0-89707-012-7). Amer Bar Assn.

Rodgers, William H., Jr. Energy & Natural Resources Law Cases & Materials. 2nd ed. LC 83-10505. (American Casebook Ser.). 877p. 1983. text ed. 24.95 (ISBN 0-314-74441-X). West Pub.

Ryuen, Ekiji. The Model & Test of Environmental Politics: From Economic Externality to Political Externality. (Illus.). 1979. pap. text ed. 19.75x (ISBN 91-22-00192-1). Humanities.

Schoenbaum, Thomas J. Environmental Policy Law Cases, Readings, & Text, 1985 Edition. LC 84-21185. (University Casebook Ser.). 1011p. 1984. text ed. write for info. (ISBN 0-88277-196-5). Foundation Pr.

Stanford Environmental Law Annual 1983: Energy Development & the Environment. 225p. (Orig.). 1983. pap. 10.00 (ISBN 0-318-11833-5). Stanford Enviro.

Stewart, Richard B. & Krier, James E. Environmental Law & Policy. 2nd ed. (Contemporary Legal Education Ser.). 1000p. 1978. 26.00 (ISBN 0-672-82859-6, Bobbs-Merrill Law); Supplement 1982. 7.00 (ISBN 0-87215-547-1). Michie Co.

Taylor, Serge. Making Bureaucracies Think: The Environmental Impact Statement Strategy of Administrative Reform. LC 81-84456. 424p. 1984. 29.50x (ISBN 0-8047-1152-6). Stanford U Pr.

U. S. Environmental Protection Agency. Legislative History of Environmental Protection Agency: Legal Compilation, Forty Vols. & Index, January 1974. 1978. Repr. Set. lib. bdg. 1645.00 (ISBN 0-89941-282-3). W S Hein.

Vietor, Richard H. Environmental Politics & the Coal Coalition. LC 79-5277. (Environmental History Ser.: No. 2). 304p. 1980. 23.50x (ISBN 0-89096-094-1). Tex A&M Univ Pr.

Wenner, Lettie M. The Environmental Decade in Court. LC 81-47778. 224p. 1982. 25.00x (ISBN 0-253-31957-9). Ind U Pr.

Westing, Arthur. Environmental Warfare: A Technical, Legal & Policy Appraisal. 200p. 1984. 24.00 (ISBN 0-85066-278-8). Taylor & Francis.

ENVIRONMENTAL POLICY

see also Environmental Law

Ackerman, Bruce A., et al. The Uncertain Search for Environmental Quality. LC 73-21305. (Illus.). 1974. 16.95 (ISBN 0-02-900200-1). Free Pr.

Ahmad, Yusuf J. & Muller, Frank G., eds. Integrated Physical, Socio-Economic & Environmental Planning, Vol. 10. (Natural Resources & the Environment Ser.). (Illus.). 196p. 1982. 30.00 (ISBN 0-907567-18-5, TYP115, TYP); pap. 21.00 (ISBN 0-907567-19-3, TYP111). Unipub.

American Enterprise Institute for Public Policy Research. How Can Our Physical Environment Best be Controlled & Developed? (American Enterprise Institute for Public Policy Research. High School Debate Ser.). pap. 31.30 (ISBN 0-317-09965-5, 2017087). Bks Demand UMI.

Ananichev, K. Environment: International Aspects. 207p. 1976. pap. 2.45 (ISBN 0-8285-0430-X, Pub. by Progress Pubs USSR). Imported Pubns.

Anderson, Frederick R., et al. Environmental Improvement Through Economic Incentives. LC 76-47400. (Resources for the Future Ser.). 208p. 1978. text ed. 18.50x (ISBN 0-8018-2000-6); pap. text ed. 6.00x (ISBN 0-8018-2100-2). Johns Hopkins.

Antoniou, J. Environmental Management: Planning for Traffic. 1972. 39.95 (ISBN 0-07-094222-6). McGraw.

Ayres, Robert U. & McKenna, Richard P. Alternatives to the Internal Combustion Engine: Impacts on Environmental Quality. LC 74-181555. (Resources for the Future Ser). 340p. 1972. 27.50x (ISBN 0-8018-1369-7). Johns Hopkins.

Baden, John & Stroup, Richard L., eds. Bureaucracy vs. Environment: The Environmental Costs of Bureaucratic Governance. 248p. 1981. text ed. 15.00x (ISBN 0-472-10010-6). U of Mich Pr.

Baldwin, John H. Environmental Planning & Management. LC 84-2281. 1985. 42.50x (ISBN 0-86531-723-2); text ed. 19.95x (ISBN 0-8133-0063-0). Westview.

Barbaro, Ronald & Cross, Frank L., Jr. Primer on Environmental Impact Statements. LC 73-78925. 140p. 1973. pap. 4.95 (ISBN 0-87762-112-8). Technomic.

Barker, Michael J. Directory for the Environment: Organisations in Britain & Ireland, 1984-85. 296p. (Orig.). 1984. pap. 19.95x (ISBN 0-7102-0227-X). Routledge & Kegan.

Barney, Gerald O., ed. The Global Two Thousand Report to the President of the U. S.-Entering the 21st Century: The Summary Report--Special Edition with Environment Projections & the Government's Global Model, Vol. 1. (Pergamon Policy Studies Ser.). 200p. 1984. 33.00 (ISBN 0-08-024617-6); pap. 10.95 (ISBN 0-08-024616-8). Pergamon.

Barrett, Richard N. International Dimensions of the Environmental Crisis. (A Westview Replica Ser.). 300p. 1982. softcover 27.50x (ISBN 0-86531-343-1). Westview.

Basta, Daniel J., et al. Analysis for Residuals-Environmental Quality Management: Case Study of the Ljubljana Area of Yugoslavia. LC 77-17250. (Resources for the Future). pap. 64.50 (ISBN 0-317-26216-5, 2052112). Bks Demand UMI.

Baxter, William F. People or Penguins: The Case for Optimal Pollution. 110p. 1974. 17.00x (ISBN 0-231-03820-8); pap. 8.00x (ISBN 0-231-03821-6). Columbia U Pr.

Beale, Jack G. The Manager & the Environment: General Theory & Practice of Environmental Management. LC 79-40712. (Illus.). 192p. 1980. 39.00 (ISBN 0-08-024043-7); pap. 18.00 (ISBN 0-08-024044-5). Pergamon.

Bennett, R. J. & Chorley, R. J. Environmental Systems: Philosophy, Analysis, & Control. LC 78-55535. (Illus.). 1978. 100.00 (ISBN 0-691-08217-0). Princeton U Pr.

Berger, Jonathan & Sinton, John W. Water, Earth, & Fire: Land Use & Environmental Planning in the New Jersey Pine Barrens. LC 84-47963. (Illus.). 248p. 1985. text ed. 25.00x (ISBN 0-8018-2398-6). Johns Hopkins.

Bergman, M., ed. Subsurface Space--Environment Protection, Low Cost Storage, Energy Savings: Proceedings of the International Symposium, Stockholm, Sweden, June 23-27, 1980, 3 vols. (Illus.). 1500p. 1981. 275.00 (ISBN 0-08-026136-1). Pergamon.

BNA's Environmental & Safety Information Services. Environmental Reporter. write for info. BNA.

--International Environmental Reporter. write for info. BNA.

Bothe, Michael. Trends in Environmental Policy & Law. (Environmental Policy & Law Papers: No. 15). 404p. 1980. pap. 27.50 (ISBN 2-88032-085-2, IUCN94, IUCN). Unipub.

Boulding, Kenneth E. & Stahr, Elvis J. Economics of Pollution. LC 70-179973. (The Charles C. Moskowitz Lectures). 158p. 1971. 12.50x (ISBN 0-8147-0967-2). NYU Pr.

Brown, Richard D. National Environmental Policiea & Research Programs. LC 83-50572. 165p. 1983. pap. 25.00 (ISBN 0-87762-330-9). Technomic.

Bursnall, W., ed. Planning Challenges of the 70's in the Public Domain. (Science & Technology Ser.: Vol. 22). (Illus.). 1969. lib. bdg. 40.00x (ISBN 0-87703-050-2, Pub. by Am Astronaut); microfiche suppl 20.00x (ISBN 0-87703-131-2). Univelt Inc.

Buttel, Frederick H., et al, eds. Labor & the Environment: An Analysis of & Annotated Bibliography on Workplace Environmental Quality in the United States. LC 83-22575. viii, 148p. 1984. lib. bdg. 29.95 (ISBN 0-313-23935-5, BLE/). Greenwood.

Cahn, Robert. Footprints on the Planet: A Search for an Environmental Ethic. LC 78-56363. 1978. 12.50x (ISBN 0-87663-324-6). Universe.

--Footprints on the Planet: A Search for an Environmental Ethic. LC 78-56363. 1979. pap. 5.95x (ISBN 0-87663-988-0). Universe.

Cairns, J., Jr., et al, eds. Environmental Biomonitoring, Assessment, Prediction & Management-Certain Case Studies & Related Quantitative Issues. (Statistical Ecology Ser.: Vol. 11). 1979. 45.00 (ISBN 0-89974-008-1). Intl Co-Op.

Calabrese, E. J. The Environmental Gender Gap: Sex Differences in Response to Toxic Substances. (Environmental Science & Technology Ser.). 424p. 1985. 45.00 (ISBN 0-471-80903-9). Wiley.

Caldwell, Lynton K. Science & the National Environmental Policy Act: Redirecting Policy Through Procedural Reform. 1982. 18.50 (ISBN 0-8173-0111-9); pap. 8.75 (ISBN 0-8173-0112-7). U of Ala Pr.

Canter, L. W. Environmental Impact of Water Resources Projects. (Illus.). 400p. 1985. 39.95 (ISBN 0-87371-015-0). Lewis Pubs Inc.

Canter, Larry W. Environmental Impact Statements on Municipal Wastewater Programs. LC 79-53112. vi, 95p. (Orig.). 1979. pap. 15.00 (ISBN 0-87815-026-9). Info Resources.

Chemical Manufacturers Association. Risk Management of Existing Chemicals. LC 84-80974. (Illus.). 192p. 1984. pap. 28.00 (ISBN 0-86587-065-9). Gov Insts.

Compton, Paul & Pesci, Marton. Environmental Management. (Studies in Geography in Hungrary: 16). 264p. 1984. 32.00 (ISBN 963-05-3696-X, Pub. by Akademiai Kaido Hungary). Heyden.

Congressional Quarterly Inc. Environmental Issues: Prospects & Problems. LC 82-4975. (Editorial Research Reports Ser.). 161p. 1982. pap. 9.25 (ISBN 0-87187-238-2). Congr Quarterly.

Conservation for Development. (Illus.). 383p. 1973. pap. 30.00 (ISBN 2-88032-003-8, IUCN48, IUCN). Unipub.

Conservation Foundation Staff. Risk Assessment & Risk Control. LC 85-5743. 69p. 1985. pap. 7.50 (ISBN 0-89164-091-6). Conservation Foun.

Conyne, Robert K. & Clack, R. James. Environmental Assessment & Design: A New Tool for the Applied Behavioral Scientist. LC 80-24816. 204p. 1981. 32.95 (ISBN 0-03-057948-1). Praeger.

Cotgrove, Stephen. Catastrophe or Cornucopia: The Environment, Politics & the Future. LC 81-148827. 1982. 154p. 44.95x, (ISBN 0-471-10079-X, Pub. by Wiley-Interscience); pap. 24.95x, 232p. (ISBN 0-471-10166-4). Wiley.

Council Envir. Quality. The Global Two Thousand Report to the President: Entering the Twenty-First Century, Vol. I. (Illus.). 766p. 1982. pap. 10.00 (ISBN 0-14-022441-6). Penguin.

Cowan, Peter, ed. The Future of Planning. LC 73-80439. (Centre for Environmental Studies Ser.: Vol. 1). pap. 47.50 (ISBN 0-317-29598-5, 2021882). Bks Demand UMI.

Crawley, Gerald M. Energy. (Illus.). 320p. 1975. text ed. write for info. (ISBN 0-02-325580-3, 32558). Macmillan.

Culhane, Paul J. & Friesema, H. Paul. Forecasts & Environmental Decision Making: The Content & Accuracy of Environmental Impact Statements. (Social Impact Assessment Ser.: No. 11). 250p. 1985. pap. 21.50x (ISBN 0-8133-0154-8). Westview.

Cutter, Susan L., et al. Exploitation, Conservation, Preservation: A Geographic Perspective on Natural Resource Use. LC 84-18298. (Illus.). 468p. 1985. 25.00x (ISBN 0-86598-129-9). Rowman & Allanheld.

Dasgupta, Partha. The Control of Resources. (Illus.). 240p. 1983. text ed. 18.50x (ISBN 0-674-16980-8). Harvard U Pr.

Dewees, D. N., et al. Economic Analysis of Environmental Policies. LC 75-38798. (Ontario Economic Council Research Studies). 1975. pap. 8.50 (ISBN 0-8020-3335-0). U of Toronto Pr.

Directory of Environment Statistics. (Statistical Papers, Series M: No. 75). 305p. (Orig.). 1984. pap. 30.00 (UN83/17/12, UN). Unipub.

Disch, Robert, ed. Ecological Conscience: Values for Survival. LC 71-130009. 1970. pap. 2.45 (ISBN 0-13-222810-6, Spec). P-H.

Dobby, Alan. Conservation & Planning. (The Built Environment Ser.). 173p. 1978. pap. 10.00 (ISBN 0-09-132271-5, Pub. by Hutchinson Educ). Longwood Pub Group.

Dolan, Edwin G. TANSTAAFL: The Economic Strategy for Environmental Crisis. LC 73-147846. (Dryden Press). 1971. pap. text ed. 10.95 (ISBN 0-03-086315-5, HoltC). HR&W.

Dorfman, Nancy & Dorfman, Robert, eds. Economics of the Environment, Selected Readings. 2nd ed. LC 76-58542. (Illus.). 1977. pap. text ed. 13.95x (ISBN 0-393-09137-6). Norton.

Dover, Michael & Croft, Brian. Getting Tough: Public Policy & the Management of Pesticide Resistance. (Illus.). 77p. 1984. pap. text ed. 3.50 (ISBN 0-915825-03-1). World Resources Inst.

Eagles, Paul. The Planning & Management of Environmentally Sensitive Areas. pap. text ed. 13.95 (ISBN 0-582-30074-6). Longman.

Ehrlich, Paul R., et al. Human Ecology: Problems & Solutions. LC 72-12828. (Illus.). 304p. 1973. pap. 13.95 (ISBN 0-7167-0595-8). W H Freeman.

Eicher, George J. The Environmental Control Department in Industry & Government: It's Organization & Operation. 165p. 1982. 28.50x (ISBN 0-9607390-0-9). Words Pr.

Eisenbud, Merril. Environment, Technology & Health: Human Ecology in Historical Perspective. LC 78-55062. 1978. 32.50x (ISBN 0-8147-2154-0); pap. 17.50x (ISBN 0-8147-2160-5). NYU Pr.

Emonds, Gerhardt. Guidelines for National Implementation of the Convention on International Trade in Endangered Species of Wild Fauna & Flora. (Environmental Policy & Law Papers: No. 17). 148p. 1981. pap. 12.50 (ISBN 0-686-97536-7, IUCN104, IUCN). Unipub.

Energy & the Environment: Planning & Finance Service Report, No. 1. pap. 2.80 (SSC31, SSC). Unipub.

Environmental Aspects of the Sugar Industry. (Industry Overviews: Vol. 7). 27p. 1982. pap. 5.00 (ISBN 92-807-1046-X, UNEP013, UNEP). Unipub.

Environmental Impact Assessment. (Document Ser.). 1979. 4.00x (ISBN 92-64-11918-3). OECD.

Environmental Resources Ltd., ed. The Law & Practice Relating to Pollution Control in the Member States of the European Communities, 10 vols. 1982. Set. 850.00 (ISBN 0-686-82384-2, Pub. by Graham & Trotman England); 90.00x ea. State Mutual Bk.

Environmental Studies Board. Long-Range Environmental Outlook. x, 198p. 1980. pap. text ed. 11.95 (ISBN 0-309-03038-2). Natl Acad Pr.

Evans, Allan R. Energy & Environment. 265p. 1980. pap. text ed. 8.95x (ISBN 0-933694-15-6). COMPress.

Ewald, William R., ed. Environment & Policy: The Next Fifty Years. LC 68-27344. pap. 89.90 (ISBN 0-317-07768-6, 2017618). Bks Demand UMI.

Fallows, James M. The Water Lords: The Report on Industry & Environmental Crisis in Savannah, Georgia. LC 70-149318. (Ralph Nader Study Group Reports Ser.). 1971. 12.95 (ISBN 0-670-75160-X, Grossman). Viking.

Field, Barry C. & Willis, Cleve E., eds. Environmental Economics: A Guide to Information Sources. (Man & the Environment Information Guide Ser.: Vol. 8). 1979. 60.00x (ISBN 0-8103-1433-9). Gale.

Firestone, David B. & Reed, Frank C. Environmental Law for Non-Lawyers. LC 82-70697. (Illus.). 282p. 1983. 29.95 (ISBN 0-250-40529-6). Butterworth.

Foell, Wesley K. Management of Energy-Environment Systems: Methods & Case Studies. LC 78-13617. (International Institute Series on Applied Systems Analysis). 487p. 1979. 64.95x (ISBN 0-471-99721-8, Pub. by Wiley-Interscience). Wiley.

Ford Foundation Staff. Grass-Roots Environmentalists. LC 77-24992. 32p. 1977. pap. 3.00 (ISBN 0-916584-06-2). Ford Found.

Freeman, A. Myrick. Benefits of Environmental Improvement. LC 78-20532. (Resources for the Future Ser.). 1979. text ed. 23.00x (ISBN 0-8018-2163-0); pap. text ed. 7.95x (ISBN 0-8018-2195-9). Johns Hopkins.

Freeman, A. Myrick, et al. The Economics of Environmental Policy. LC 72-7249. 184p. 1973. pap. text ed. 15.50x (ISBN 0-471-27786-X). Wiley.

Freeman, A. Myrick, III, et al. The Economics of Environmental Policy. LC 84-4663. 198p. 1984. Repr. of 1973 ed. lib. bdg. 13.25 (ISBN 0-89874-741-4). Krieger.

Frick, G. William. Environmental Glossary. 2nd ed. LC 82-83908. 293p. 1982. text ed. 35.00 (ISBN 0-86587-096-9). Gov Insts.

Fullenbach. European Environmental Policy East & West. 1981. text ed. 59.95 (ISBN 0-408-10689-1). Butterworth.

Gaia Ltd. Staff & Myers, Norman. Gaia: An Atlas of Planet Management. LC 83-20837. (Illus.). 256p. 1984. 29.95 (ISBN 0-385-19071-9, Anchor Pr); pap. 17.95 (ISBN 0-385-19072-7, Anchor Pr). Doubleday.

Gilpin, Alan. Environmental Policy in Australia. (Australian Environment Ser.: No. 8). (Illus.). 380p. 1981. text ed. 36.25x (ISBN 0-7022-1366-7); pap. text ed. 21.75x (ISBN 0-7022-1367-5). U of Queensland Pr.

Goudie, Andrew. The Human Impact: Man's Role in Environmental Change. (Illus.). 328p. 1982. pap. text ed. 11.95x (ISBN 0-262-57058-0). MIT Pr.

Gould, Roy R. Going Sour: Science & Politics of Acid Rain. LC 84-21700. 200p. 1985. 11.95 (ISBN 0-8176-3251-4). Birkhauser.

Gov. Rockefeller Symposium Winrock, Arkansas, Oct. 1970. Technology Utilization Ideas for the 70's & Beyond. Forbes, Fred W. & Dergarabedian, Paul, eds. (Science & Technology Ser.: Vol. 26). 1971. lib. bdg. 30.00x (ISBN 0-87703-057-X, Pub. by Am Astronaut). Univelt Inc.

Greeney, William J., ed. Utilizing Scientific Information in Environmental Quality Planning: Proceedings of the Symposium Held in Las Vegas, Nevada, Sept. 26-27, 1979. LC 81-68086. (American Water Resources Association, Technical Publications Ser.: No. TPS81-2). (Illus.). pap. 54.00 (ISBN 0-317-09806-3, 2022208). Bks Demand UMI.

Tolley, George S. & Havlicek, Joseph, Jr. Environmental Policy Series Vol. V: Recreation & Aesthetics. 280p. 1985. prof ref 30.00 (ISBN 0-88410-628-4). Ballinger Pub.
Tolley, George S. & Havlicek, Joseph, Jr., eds. Environmental Policy Series Vol. IV: Solid Waste. 312p. 1985. prof. ref. 39.95 ea. (ISBN 0-88410-627-6). Ballinger Pub.
Tolley, George S., et al, eds. Environmental Policy Series Volume III: Water Quality. 232p. 1983. prof ref 28.00 (ISBN 0-88410-632-2). Ballinger Pub.
Tribe, Lawrence H., et al, eds. When Values Conflict: Essays on Environmental Analysis, Discourse & Decision. LC 75-45448. (American Academy of Arts & Sciences Ser.). 200p. 1976. text ed. 25.00 prof ref (ISBN 0-88410-431-1). Ballinger Pub.
Turner, R. Kerry, et al. Environmental Economics: Pollution. 1977. 90.00x (ISBN 0-905440-12-9, Pub. by MCB Pubns). State Mutual Bk.
Tuve, George L. Energy, Environment, Populations & Food: Our Four Interdependant Crises. LC 76-40351. 278p. 1976. 16.50 (ISBN 0-471-02090-7). Krieger.
United Nations Environment Programme Annual Review, 1978. 86p. 1981. pap. 10.00 (ISBN 92-807-1013-3, UNEP045, UNEP). Unipub.
United Nations Environment Programme Annual Review, 1980. 129p. 1982. pap. 12.00 (ISBN 92-807-1041-9, UNEP053, UNEP). Unipub.
United Nations Environment Programme Annual Review, 1979. pap. 11.00 (UNEP076, UNEP). Unipub.
U. S. Environmental Protection Agency, ed. Federal Insecticide, Fungicide, & Rodenticide Act: Compliance-Enforcement Guidance Manual. (Illus.). 512p. 1984. pap. 64.00 (ISBN 0-86587-032-2). Gov Insts.
U. S. Environmental Protection Agency Staff. Multi-Media Compliance Inspection Manual. (Illus.). 195p. 1984. pap. 35.00 (ISBN 0-86587-030-6). Gov Insts.
U. S. Environmental Protection Agency, ed. TSCA Compliance-Enforcement Guidance Manual. 500p. 1984. pap. 48.00 (ISBN 0-86587-072-1). Gov Insts.
The Use of Ecological Guidelines for Development in the American Humid Tropics. (Illus.). 249p. 1975. pap. 20.00 (ISBN 2-88032-004-6, IUCN62, IUCN). Unipub.
El Uso De Normas Ecologicas Para el Desarrollo En el Tropico Huedo American. (Illus.). 1976. pap. 25.00x (ISBN 2-88032-007-0, IUCN15, IUCN). Unipub.
Watts, N. & Knoepfel, P. Environment Policy & Politics. 1985. pap. text ed. 14.50 (ISBN 0-06-318280-7). Har-ROw.
Westing, Arthur. Environmental Warfare: A Technical, Legal & Policy Appraisal. 200p. 1984. 24.00 (ISBN 0-85066-278-8). Taylor & Francis.
Westing, Arthur, ed. The Environmental Modification Convention of 1977: A Technical, Legal & Policy Appraisal. 100p. 1984. pap. 21.00x (ISBN 0-85066-278-8). Taylor & Francis.
Willson, John S., et al. Comprehensive Planning & the Environment: A Manual for Planners. LC 78-66683. 1979. text ed. 25.00 (ISBN 0-89011-515-X). Abt Bks.
Wilson, Des, ed. The Environmental Crisis: A Handbook for All Friends of the Earth. xii, 196p. (Orig.). 1984. pap. text ed. 10.00x (ISBN 0-435-83944-6). Heinemann Ed.
Wilson, Richard & Jones, William. Energy, Ecology & the Environment. 353p. 1974. 17.75 (ISBN 0-12-757550-2). Acad Pr.
The World Environment, 1972-1982: A Report by UNEP, Vol. 8. (Natural Resources & the Environment Ser.). 637p. 1982. 95.00 (ISBN 0-907567-14-2, TYP106, TYP). Unipub.
Young, Oran R. Resource Regimes: Natural Resources & Social Institutions. Krasner, Stephen, ed. LC 81-21979. (Studies in the International Political Economy Ser.). 284p. 1982. 26.00x (ISBN 0-520-04573-4). U of Cal Pr.

ENVIRONMENTAL POLLUTION
see Pollution

ENVIRONMENTAL PROTECTION
see also Conservation of Natural Resources; Environmental Engineering; Environmental Law; Environmental Policy

Ahmad, Yusuf J. Evaluating the Environment: Application of Cost-Benefit Analysis in Environmental Protection Measures. (Studies Ser.: Vol. 6). pap. 12.50 (ISBN 92-807-1044-3, UNEP077, UNEP). Unipub.
Aizawa, Hirayasu. Metabolic Maps of Pesticides. (Ecotoxicology & Environmental Quality Ser.). 1982. 45.00 (ISBN 0-12-046480-2). Acad Pr.
Alheritiere, Dominique. Environmental Impact Assessment & Agricultural Development: A Comparative Law Study. (Environment Papers: No. 2). (Eng. & Fr.). 139p. 1982. pap. 10.00 (ISBN 92-5-101110-9, F2292, FAO). Unipub.
Annual Technical Meeting of the Institute of Environmental Sciences, Fort Worth, Texas, April 1978. Combined Environments Technology Interrelations: Proceedings. LC 62-38584. (Illus.). 1978. pap. text ed. 22.00 (ISBN 0-915414-18-X). Inst Environ Sci.
ASTM Committee D-19 on Water. Statistics in the Environmental Sciences - STP 845. Gertz, Steven M. & London, M. D., eds. LC 83-73439. 115p. 1984. pap. 24.00 (ISBN 0-8031-0206-2, 04-845000-16). ASTM.
Auerbach, Paul S. & Geehr, Edward C., eds. Management of Wilderness & Environmental Emergencies. 1983. write for info. (ISBN 0-02-304630-9). Macmillan.
Baldwin, John H. Environmental Planning & Management. LC 84-2281. 1985. 42.50x (ISBN 0-86531-723-2); text ed. 19.95x (ISBN 0-8133-0063-0). Westview.
Barbaro, Ronald & Cross, Frank L., Jr. Primer on Environmental Impact Statements. LC 73-78925. 140p. 1973. pap. 4.95 (ISBN 0-87762-112-8). Technomic.
Barrett, Gary W. & Rosenberg, Rutger, eds. Stress Effects on Natural Ecosystems. LC 80-40851. (Environmental Monographs & Symposia, Environmental Science). 305p. 1981. 56.95x (ISBN 0-471-27834-3, Pub. by Wiley-Interscience). Wiley.
Bauchum, Rosalind G. Needs Assessment Methodologies in the Development of Impact Statements. (Public Administration Ser.: Bibliography P 1640). 1985. pap. 2.00 (ISBN 0-89028-330-3). Vance Biblios.
Baxter, William F. People or Penguins: The Case for Optimal Pollution. 110p. 1974. 17.00x (ISBN 0-231-03820-8); pap. 8.00x (ISBN 0-231-03821-6). Columbia U Pr.
Beck, Theodore R., et al, eds. Electrochemical Contributions to Environmental Protection. LC 72-89668. (Illus.). pap. 45.00 (ISBN 0-317-10703-8, 2052001). Bks Demand UMI.
Bernard, Harold. The Greenhouse Effect. LC 80-8710. 256p. 1981. pap. 4.95i (ISBN 0-06-090855-6, CN 855, CN). Har-Row.
Berry, Brian J. & Horton, Frank E. Urban Environmental Management: Planning for Pollution Control. (Illus.). 448p. 1974. 34.95 (ISBN 0-13-939611-X). P-H.
Berthouex, P. Mac & Rudd, Dale F. Strategy of Pollution Control. LC 76-29008. 579p. 1977. text ed. 48.45 (ISBN 0-471-74449-2). Wiley.
Black, Peter E. & Herrington, Lee P., eds. Working with NEPA: Environmental Impact Analysis for the Resource Manager. LC 74-23639. 145p. 1974. pap. text ed. 4.75x (ISBN 0-8422-0483-0). Irvington.
BNA's Environmental & Safety Information Services. Chemical Substances Control. (Policy & Practice Ser.). write for info. BNA.
--International Environmental Reporter. write for info. BNA.
Bockris, J. O'M. & Nagy, Zolton. Electrochemistry for Ecologists. LC 73-84003. 200p. 1974. 29.50x (ISBN 0-306-30749-9, Plenum Pr). Plenum Pub.
Botkin, Daniel B. & Keller, Edward A. Environmental Studies. 480p. 1982. text ed. 27.95 (ISBN 0-675-09813-0). Additional supplements may be obtained from publisher. Merrill.
Bowen, A., ed. Passive & Low Energy Ecotechniques: Proceedings of the Third International PLEA Conference, Mexico City, Mexico, 6-11 August 1984. (Illus.). 1140p. 1985. 175.00 (ISBN 0-08-031644-1). Pergamon.
Brazee, Edward, ed. Index to the Sierra Club Bulletin, 1950-1976. (Bibliographic Ser.: No. 16). 60p. 1978. pap. 5.95x (ISBN 0-87071-136-9). Oreg St U Pr.
Brock, Neely W. & Gary, Blau, eds. Environmental Exposure From Chemicals, Vol. 2. 192p. 1985. 60.00 (ISBN 0-8493-6166-4). CRC Pr.
Brubaker, Sterling. In Commnand of Tomorrow: Resources & Environmental Strategies. LC 74-24401. (Resources for the Future Study Ser.). pap. 48.00 (ISBN 0-317-26027-8, 2023789). Bks Demand UMI.
Burchell, Robert & Hagevik, George. The Environmental Impact Handbook. 96p. 1974. pap. 8.95x (ISBN 0-87855-602-8). Transaction Bks.
Cairns, John, Jr. & Dickson, Kenneth L., eds. Recovery & Restoration of Damaged Ecosystems. LC 76-49453. (Illus.). 531p. 1977. 25.00x (ISBN 0-8139-0676-8). U Pr of Va.
Cargo, David N. & Mallory, Bob F. Man & His Geologic Environment. 2nd ed. LC 76-7655. 1977. text ed. 29.95 (ISBN 0-201-00894-7). Addison-Wesley.
Carter, Anne P., ed. Energy & the Environment: A Structural Analysis. LC 74-15447. (Illus.). 280p. 1976. 25.00x (ISBN 0-87451-112-7). U Pr of New Eng.
Chanlett, Emil T. Environmental Protection. 2nd ed. (Environmental Engineering Ser.). 1979. text ed. 45.00 (ISBN 0-07-010531-6). McGraw.
Chatterji, Manas, ed. Energy & Environment in the Developing Countries. LC 80-42143. 357p. 1981. 58.95x (ISBN 0-471-27993-5, Pub. by Wiley-Interscience). Wiley.
Christensen, John W. Energy, Resources & Environment. 224p. 1981. pap. text ed. 12.95 (ISBN 0-8403-2473-1); lab manual 6.95 (ISBN 0-8403-2575-4). Kendall-Hunt.
Cohn, Louis F. & McVoy, Gary R. Environmental Analysis of Transportation Systems. LC 81-14637. 374p. 1982. 53.50x (ISBN 0-471-08098-5, Pub. by Wiley-Interscience). Wiley.
Collins, M. B., et al, eds. Industrialised Embayments & Their Environmental Problems - a Case Study of Swansea Bay: Proceedings of an Interdisciplinary Symposium Held at University College, Swansea, 26-28 Sept. 1979. LC 80-40507. (Illus.). 608p. 1980. 88.00 (ISBN 0-08-023992-7). Pergamon.
Commission on Natural Resources. Environmental Monitoring. 1977. pap. 9.25 (ISBN 0-309-02639-3). Natl Acad Pr.
--Perspectives on Technical Information for Environmental Protection. 1977. pap. 7.75 (ISBN 0-309-02623-7). Natl Acad Pr.
Conservation Foundation Staff. Risk Assessment & Risk Control. LC 85-5743. 69p. 1985. pap. 7.50 (ISBN 0-89164-091-6). Conservation Foun.
Conway, Richard A. Environmental Risk Analysis of Chemicals. (Environmental Engineering Ser.). 640p. 1981. 42.50 (ISBN 0-442-21650-5). Van Nos Reinhold.
Coughlin, Robert E. & Goldstein, Karen A. The Extent of Agreement Among Observers on Environmental Attractiveness. (Discussion Paper Ser.: No. 37). 1970. pap. 5.75 (ISBN 0-686-32206-1). Regional Sci Res Inst.
Courrier, Kathleen. Life after Eighty: Environmental Choices We Can Live With. 280p. 1980. 6.95 (ISBN 0-931790-13-1, 209). Ctr Renew Resources.
Courrier, Kathleen & Munson, Richard, eds. Life after Eighty: Environmental Choices We Can Live With. LC 80-11783. 304p. 1980. pap. 8.95x (ISBN 0-931790-13-1). Brick Hse Pub.
Crawford, A. Berry & Peterson, Dean F. Environmental Management in the Colorado River Basin. LC 74-121364. 313p. 1974. pap. 8.00 (ISBN 0-87421-068-2). Utah St U Pr.
Cusine, Douglas J. & Grant, John P., eds. The Impact of Marine Pollution. LC 80-670. 324p. 1980. text ed. 32.50x (ISBN 0-916672-54-9). Allanheld.
Daly, Herman E. & Umana, Alvaro F., eds. Energy, Economics, & Environment: Conflicting Views of an Essential Interrelationship. (AAAS Selected Symposium Ser.: No. 64). 200p. 1981. 25.00x (ISBN 0-86531-282-6). Westview.
Dasmann, Raymond F., et al. Ecological Principles for Economic Development. LC 72-8597. 252p. 1973. pap. 28.95 (ISBN 0-471-19606-1, Pub. by Wiley-Interscience). Wiley.
Devos, Anthony. The Pollution Reader: Based on the National Conference on "Pollution & Our Environment". Pearson, Norman, et al, eds. LC 68-31597. (Harvest House Environment Ser.). (Illus.). pap. 66.00 (ISBN 0-317-09460-2, 2022293). Bks Demand UMI.
Directory of Canadian Environmental Experts. 482p. 1981. pap. 23.25 (ISBN 0-660-50634-3, SSC150, SSC). Unipub.
Directory of Environment Statistics. (Statistical Papers, Series M: No. 75). 305p. (Orig.). 1984. pap. 30.00 (UN83/17/12, UN). Unipub.
Dobby, Alan. Conservation & Planning. (The Built Environment Ser.). 173p. 1978. pap. 10.00 (ISBN 0-09-132271-5, Pub. by Hutchinson Educ). Longwood Pub Group.
Douglas, Mary & Wildavsky, Aaron. Risk & Culture: An Essay on the Selection of Technological & Environmental Dangers. LC 81-16318. 224p. 1982. 17.95 (ISBN 0-520-04491-6). U of Cal Pr.
Downing, Paul, ed. Cross-National Comparisons in Environmentals Protection. (Orig.). 1982. pap. 8.00 (ISBN 0-918592-57-7). Policy Studies.
Duffus, John H. Environmental Toxicology. LC 80-82387. (Resource & Environmental Science Ser.). 164p. 1980. pap. 19.95x (ISBN 0-470-27051-9). Halsted Pr.
Eastern Analytical Symposium, 1971. Chemical Analysis of the Environment & Other Modern Techniques. LC 73-82575. (Progress in Analytical Chemistry Ser.: No. 5). pap. 98.50 (ISBN 0-317-27112-1, 2024703). Bks Demand UMI.
Ebbin, Steven & Kasper, Raphael. Citizen Groups & the Nuclear Power Controversy: Uses of Scientific & Technological Information. (Environmental Studies). 318p. 1974. pap. 13.50x (ISBN 0-262-55003-2). MIT Pr.
Ehrlich, Paul R., et al. Ecoscience: Population, Resources, Environment. LC 77-6824. (Illus.). 1051p. 1977. pap. text ed. 28.95 (ISBN 0-7167-0029-8). W H Freeman.
Environment Resources Ltd. Cleaning & Conditioning Agents: Their Impact on the Environment in the EEC. 138p. 1978. 33.00x (ISBN 0-86010-108-8, Pub. by Graham & Trotman England). State Mutual Bk.
Environmental Aspects of Iron & Steel Industry: A Workshop. (Industry Overviews: Vol. 8). pap. 5.00 (UNEP011, UNEP). Unipub.
Environmental Aspects of the Aluminum Industry. (Industry Technical Review Ser.: Vol. 4). pap. 5.00 (UNEP016, UNEP). Unipub.
Environmental Aspects of the Cement Industry. (Industry Overviews: Vol. 6). pap. 6.75 (UNEP003, UNEP). Unipub.
Environmental Aspects of the Motor Vehicle & Its Use: A Technical Review. (Industry Technical Review Ser.: Vol. 2). 26p. 1977. pap. 6.75 (ISBN 0-686-93505-5, UNEP023, UNEP). Unipub.
Environmental Aspects of the Pulp & Paper Industry. (Industry Overviews: Vol. 1). 27p. 1977. pap. 6.75 (ISBN 0-686-93516-0, UNEP017, UNEP). Unipub.
Environmental Protection Within the Context of the Work of UNIDO. LC 82-175422. vii, 65p. Date not set. price not set. UN.
Environmental Resources Ltd. Product Planning: The Relationship Between Product Characteristics & Environmental Impact. 312p. 1978. 26.00x (ISBN 0-86010-126-6, Pub. by Graham & Trotman England). State Mutual Bk.
Fedorov, Evgenii K. Man & Nature: The Ecological Crisis & Social Progress. 280p. (Orig.). 1981. 8.00 (ISBN 0-7178-0573-5); pap. 2.75 (ISBN 0-7178-0567-0). Intl Pubs Co.
Ford Foundation Staff. Grass-Roots Environmentalists. LC 77-24992. 32p. 1977. pap. 3.00 (ISBN 0-916584-06-2). Ford Found.
A Framework for the Development of Environment Statistics. (Statistical Papers, Series M: No. 78). (Illus.). 28p. 1985. pap. 5.00 (UN84/17/12, UN). Unipub.
A Framework for the Development of Environment Statistics. (Statistical Papers, Series M: No. 78). 28p. 5.00 (ISBN 0-317-18808-9, E.84.XVII.12). UN.
Fresenius, W & Luderwald, I., eds. Environmental Research & Protection: Inorganic Analysis. 310p. 1984. pap. 15.30 (ISBN 0-387-13469-7). Springer Verlag.
Frieden, Bernard J. The Environmental Protection Hustle. (Joint Center for Urban Studies). (Illus.). 1979. 25.00x (ISBN 0-262-06068-X); pap. 6.95x (ISBN 0-262-56022-4). MIT Pr.
Geller, E. Scott, et al. Preserving the Environment: New Strategies for Behavior Change. (Pergamon General Psychology Ser.: No. 102). (Illus.). 300p. 1982. 39.00 (ISBN 0-08-024615-X); pap. 12.95 (ISBN 0-08-024614-1). Pergamon.
Goldstein, Joan. Environmental Decision Making in Rural Locales: The Pine Barrens. LC 81-5208. 186p. 1981. 29.95 (ISBN 0-03-059604-1). Praeger.
Goodavage, Joseph F. Our Threatened Planet. 1980. pap. 2.95 (ISBN 0-671-81640-3). PB.
Guidelines for Assessing Industrial Environmental Impact & Environmental Criteria for the Siting of Industry. (Industry & Environment Guidelines: Vol. 1). 105p. 1980. pap. 20.00 (ISBN 92-807-1015-X, UNEP048, UNEP). Unipub.
Haith, Douglas A. Environmental Systems Optimization. LC 81-3050. 306p. 1982. text ed. 44.50 (ISBN 0-471-08287-2) (ISBN 0-471-86673-3). avail. solutions manual. Wiley.
Hammond, Kenneth A., et al. Sourcebook on the Environment: A Guide to the Literature. LC 77-17407. 1978. lib. bdg. 27.50x (ISBN 0-226-31522-3). U of Chicago Pr.
Hellfach. Future of the Environment. (Future Studies Ser.). 1977. 9.24. P-H.
Holdgate, Martin W. & White, Gilbert F., eds. Environmental Issues-Scope Report 10. LC 77-2667. 224p. 1977. 39.95 (ISBN 0-471-99503-7, Pub. by Wiley-Interscience). Wiley.
Holling, C. S., ed. Adaptive Environmental Assessment & Management. LC 78-8523. (IIASA International Series on Applied Systems Analysis). 377p. 1978. 32.95 (ISBN 0-471-99632-7, Pub. by Wiley-Interscience). Wiley.
Howard, Arthur D. & Remson, Irwin. Geology in Environmental Planning. (Illus.). 1977. text ed. 47.95 (ISBN 0-07-030510-2). McGraw.
Huisingh, Donald & Bailey, Vicki, eds. Making Pollution Prevention Pay: Ecology with Economy As Policy. 168p. 1982. 28.00 (ISBN 0-08-029417-0). Pergamon.
Hutchins, G. B. Transportation & the Environment. 106p. 1977. 9.95x (ISBN 0-8464-1146-6). Beekman Pubs.
Hutnik, Russell & Davis, Grant, eds. Ecology & Reclamation of Devastated Land, 2 Vols. LC 76-122849. (Illus.). 1070p. 1973. Vol. 1, 552p. 98.25x (ISBN 0-677-15580-8); Vol. 2, 518p. 98.25x (ISBN 0-677-15590-5); Set. 175.75x (ISBN 0-677-15600-6). Gordon.

BOOKS - SUBJECT INDEX ENVIRONMENTAL TESTING

In Defence of the Earth: The Basic Texts on Environment. (Executive Ser.: Vol. 1). (Eng. & Fr.). pap. 8.50 (ISBN 92-807-1023-0, UNEP065, UNEP). Unipub.
Institute for Environmental Education & Association of New Jersey Environmental Commissions. Tuning the Green Machine, An Integrated View of Environmental Systems. LC 77-17902. (Illus.). 320p. 1978. lib. bdg. 12.50 (ISBN 0-379-00811-4). Oceana.
International Congress for Energy & the Ecosystem, University of North Dakota, 12-16 June 1978. Ecology & Coal Resource Development, 2 Vols. Wali, Mohan K., ed. LC 78-26238. 1980. 165.00 (ISBN 0-08-023863-7). Pergamon.
Kaplan, S. J. & Kivy-Rosenberg, E. Ecology & the Quality of Life. (Illus.). 308p. 1973. 31.00x (ISBN 0-398-02828-1). C C Thomas.
Kates, Robert W. Risk Assessment of Environmental Hazard: Scope Report 8. LC 77-12909. (Scientific Committee on Problems of the Environment). 112p. 1978. 21.95x (ISBN 0-471-99582-7, Pub. by Wiley-Interscience). Wiley.
Kay, David A. Environmental Protection: The International Dimension. Jacobson, Harold K., ed. LC 81-65020. (Illus.). 352p. 1983. text ed. 39.50x (ISBN 0-86598-034-9). Allanheld.
Kendall, Ronald J. Toxic Substances in the Environment. 80p. 1983. pap. text ed. 5.95 (ISBN 0-8403-2985-7). Kendall-Hunt.
King, Charles C. & Elfner, Lynn E. Organisms & Biological Communities As Indicators of Environmemtal Quality: A Symposium, the Ohio State University, March 25,1974. 1975. 3.00 (ISBN 0-86727-078-0). Ohio Bio Survey.
Klein, Jeffery A. & Ch'Uan-K'Ai Leung, Kenneth. Environmental Control Industry: An Analysis of Conditions & Prospects for the Pollution Control Equipment Industry. LC 76-1439. 157p. 1976. text ed. 14.50x (ISBN 0-916672-02-6). Allanheld.
Kneese, Allen V. Measuring the Benefits of Clean Air & Water. LC 84-42692. 174p. (Orig.). 1984. pap. text ed. 5.95 (ISBN 0-915707-09-8). Resources Future.
Komarov, Boris. The Destruction of Nature in the Soviet Union. Vale, Michel & Hollander, Joe, trs. from Rus. LC 80-5452. Orig. Title: Unichtozhenie Prioroda Obostrenie Ekologicheskogo Krizisa V SSSR. 132p. 1980. 25.00 (ISBN 0-87332-157-X). M E Sharpe.
Lack, T. J., ed. Environmental Protection: Standards & Compliance. (Water & Wastewater Technology Ser.). 329p. 1984. text ed. 59.95x (ISBN 0-470-20095-2). Halsted Pr.
Landy, Marc, ed. Environmental Impact Statement Directory: The National Network of EIS-Related Agencies & Organizations. LC 80-27909. 380p. 1981. text ed. 85.00x (ISBN 0-306-65195-5, IFI Plenum). Plenum Pub.
Likens, Gene E., ed. Some Perpectives of the Major Biochemical Cycles. LC 80-42017. (SCOPE Ser. (Scientific Committee on Problems of the Environment): Report 17). 175p. 1981. x 34.95 (ISBN 0-471-27989-7, Pub. by Wiley-Interscience). Wiley.
Lindeke, Wolfgang. Dictionary of Ventilation & Health. 186p. 1980. 25.00x (ISBN 0-569-08522-5, Pub. by Collet's). State Mutual Bk.
Lobell, John. The Little Green Book: A Guide to Self-Reliant Living in the '80s. LC 80-53445. (Illus.). 420p. (Orig.). 1981. pap. 5.95 (ISBN 0-87773-199-3). Shambhala Pubn.
Lowe, J. & Lewis, D. Total Environmental Control: The Economics of Cross-Media Pollution Transfers. LC 82-9827. (Illus.). 134p. 1982. 24.00 (ISBN 0-08-026276-7). Pergamon.
McAllister, Donald. Evaluation in Environmental Planning: Assessing Environmental, Social, Economic & Political Tradeoffs. 1980. pap. 10.95x (ISBN 0-262-63087-7). MIT Pr.
McCaffrey, Stephan C. Private Remedies for Transfrontier Environmental Disturbances. (Environmental Policy & Law Papers: No. 8). 156p. 1975. pap. 12.50 (ISBN 2-88032-078-X, IUCN8, IUCN). Unipub.
Milbrath, Lester W. Environmentalists: Vanguard for a New Society. (Environmental Public Policy Ser.). 158p. 1984. 29.50x (ISBN 0-87395-887-X); pap. 9.95x (ISBN 0-87395-888-8). State U NY Pr.
Moran, Joseph M., et al. Introduction to Environmental Science. LC 79-19007. (Illus.). 658p. 1980. text ed. 25.95x (ISBN 0-7167-1020-X); instr's manual & transparency masters avail. W H Freeman.
Munn, R. E. Environmental Impact Assessment: Principles & Procedures, SCOPE Report 5. 2nd ed. LC 78-10145. (SCOPE Ser. (Scientific Committee on Problems of the Environment)). 190p. 1979. pap. 34.95x (ISBN 0-471-99745-5, Pub. by Wiley-Interscience). Wiley.
Murch, Arvin W., ed. Environmental Concern: Personal Attitudes & Behavior Toward Environmental Problems. 378p. 1974. text ed. 29.50x (ISBN 0-8422-5169-3); pap. text ed. 11.00x (ISBN 0-8422-0410-5). Irvington.
National Research Council Commission on Natural Resources. Testing for Effects of Chemicals on Ecosystems. 128p. 1981. pap. 8.50 (ISBN 0-309-03142-7). Natl Acad Pr.
Neufeld, M. Lynne & Cornog, Martha. Energy & Environment Information Resource Guide. 1982. 12.50 (ISBN 0-942308-15-8). NFAIS.
OECD Staff. Coal & Environmental Protection: Costs & Costing Methods. 132p. (Orig.). 1983. pap. 12.00x (ISBN 92-64-12513-2). OECD.
Organization & Administration of Environmental Programmes. pap. 9.50 (ISBN 0-686-94691-X, UN74/2H5, UN). Unipub.
Organization for Economic Cooperation & Development Seminar, Paris, August 1972. Environmental Damage Costs: Proceedings. 332p. 1975. 11.25x (ISBN 92-64-11330-4). OECD.
O'Riordan, Timothy & Turner, R. Kerry, eds. Progress in Resource Management & Environmental Planning, Vol. 3. LC 80-42020. 324p. 1981. 79.95x (ISBN 0-471-27968-4, Pub. by Wiley-Interscience). Wiley.
Pantell, R. H. Techniques of Environmental Systems Analysis. LC 76-98. 202p. 1976. 27.00 (ISBN 0-471-65791-3). Krieger.
Papageorgiou, J. C. Management Science & Environmental Problems. (Illus.). 160p. 1980. 16.75x (ISBN 0-398-03995-X). C C Thomas.
People on Earth. pap. 14.95 (UNEP069, UNEP). Unipub.
Porter, Colin F. Environmental Impact Assessment: A Practical Guide. LC 84-3555. (Australian Environment Ser.: No. 9). (Illus.). 269p. 1985. text ed. 35.00x (ISBN 0-7022-1699-2). U of Queensland Pr.
Rajagopal, R., ed. Environmental Mediation & Conflict Management: A Selection of Papers Presented at the 5th Annual Conference of the NAEP, Washington Dc, April 21-23 1980. 120p. 1981. pap. 11.00 (ISBN 0-08-026261-9). Pergamon.
Reinig, William C. Environmental Surveillance in the Vicinity of Nuclear Facilities. (Illus.). 480p. 1970. 47.50x (ISBN 0-398-01568-6). C C Thomas.
Retrospective Programme Des Nations Unes Pour L'Environment. (Fr.). pap. 15.50 (ISBN 92-807-2002-3, UNEP072, UNEP). Unipub.
ReVelle, Charles & ReVelle, Penelope. The Environment: Issues & Choices for Society. 2nd ed. 650p. 1984. text ed. write for info (ISBN 0-87150-788-9, 4571, Pub. by Willard Grant Pr). PWS Pubs.
Reynolds, Josephine P. Conservation Planning in Town & Country. 136p. 1977. 35.00x (ISBN 0-85323-393-4, Pub. by Liverpool Univ England). State Mutual Bk.
Roberts, Alan. The Self-Managing Environment. 189p. 1980. 16.50x (ISBN 0-8476-6211-X). Rowman.
Rosen, Sherman J. Manual for Environmental Impact Evaluation. (Illus.). 1976. 25.95 (ISBN 0-13-553453-4). P-H.
Rudman, Jack. Environmental Conservation Officer. (Career Examination Ser.: C-2428). (Cloth bdg. avail on request). pap. 12.00 (ISBN 0-8373-2428-9). Natl Learning.
--Environmental Protection Director. (Career Examination Ser.: C-2849). (Cloth bdg. avail. on request). 1980. pap. 14.00 (ISBN 0-8373-2849-7). Natl Learning.
Ruster, Bernd & Simma, Bruno. International Protection of the Environment: Treaties & Related Documents, 30 vols. LC 75-24843. 1975. text ed. 50.00x ea. (ISBN 0-379-10086-X); 1575.00 set. Oceana.
Sandbach, Francis. Environment, Ideology & Policy. LC 80-65192. 270p. 1980. text ed. 32.50x (ISBN 0-916672-53-0). Allanheld.
Sauvegarde: Les Textes Fondamentaux sur l'Environnment. (Fr.). 150p. 1982. pap. 8.50 (UNEP075, UNEP). Unipub.
Schrepfer, Susan R. The Fight to Save the Redwoods: A History of Environmental Reform, 1917-1978. LC 81-69828. (Illus.). 296p. 1983. 25.00x (ISBN 0-299-08850-2). U of Wis Pr.
Schultz, Marilyn S. & Kasen, Vivian L. Encyclopedia of Community Planning & Environmental Protection. 400p. 1983. 45.00x (ISBN 0-87196-447-3). Facts on File.
Shackley, Myra. Environmental Archaeology. (Illus.). 256p. 1981. text ed. 40.00x (ISBN 0-04-913020-X); pap. text ed. 19.95x (ISBN 0-04-913021-8). Allen Unwin.
Shepard's Citation Staff. Environmental Protection: The Legal Framework. LC 81-1983. 1981. 75.00 (ISBN 0-07-057398-0). McGraw.
Sheridan, Diane B. Independent Observations on Ocean Incineration: Experiences on Vulcanus II Voyage, November 4-9, 1983. (Orig.). 1983. pap. text ed. 2.00 (ISBN 0-915757-08-7). League Women Voters TX.
Southwest Center for Urban Research. Principles for Local Environmental Management. LC 77-28081. 1978. 25.00 (ISBN 0-88410-077-4). Ballinger Pub.
Spiro, Thomas G. & Stigliani, William. Environmental Issues in Chemical Perspective. 1980. 24.50x (ISBN 0-87395-427-0). State U NY Pr.
The State of the Environment: Selected Topics, 1979. (S.O.T.E. Reports). 31p. 1979. pap. 5.00 (ISBN 0-686-93582-9, UNEP005, UNEP). Unipub.
Stewart, Alva W. Wilderness Protection: A Bibliographic Review. (Public Administration Ser.: Bibliography P 1642). 1985. pap. 2.00 (ISBN 0-89028-332-X). Vance Biblios.
Stringer, Peter & Wenzel, K., eds. Transportation Planning for a Better Environment. LC 76-46276. (NATO Conference Series II, Systems Science: Vol. 1). 439p. 1976. 59.50x (ISBN 0-306-32841-0, Plenum Pr). Plenum Pub.
Stumm, Werner, ed. Global Chemical Cycles & Their Alterations by Man, PCRR 2. (Physical & Chemical Sci. Rsch. Rept. Ser.: No. 2). (Illus.). 347p. 1977. 40.00x (ISBN 0-89573-084-7). VCH Pubs.
Survey of Environment Statistics: Frameworks, Approaches & Statistical Publications. pap. 10.00 (UN82/17/4, UN). Unipub.
Thibodeau, Francis R. & Field, Hermann H., eds. Sustaining Tomorrow: A Strategy for World Conservation & Development. LC 84-40297. (Illus.). 198p. 1984. 22.50x (ISBN 0-87451-305-7); pap. 12.50x (ISBN 0-87451-306-5). U Pr of New Eng.
Today Is Forever: Man, the Enviornment & the Problems, Reflections on the Maze. LC 75-4290. (Illus.). 5.95 (ISBN 0-932212-02-6). Avery Color.
Trzyna, Thaddeus C. California Environmental Directory: A Guide to Organizations & Resources. 3rd ed. LC 77-642158. (California Information Guides). (Illus.). 134p. (Orig.). 1980. pap. text ed. 18.50x (ISBN 0-912102-53-5). Cal Inst Public.
Trzyna, Thaddeus C. & Coan, Eugene V., eds. World Directory of Environmental Organizations. rev. 2nd ed. LC 75-38124. (Who's Doing What Ser.: No. 2). (Illus.). 290p. 1976. pap. 25.00x (ISBN 0-912102-20-9). Cal Inst Public.
Turk, Jonathan & Turk, Amos. Environmental Science. 3rd ed. 1984. text ed. 32.95 (ISBN 0-03-058467-1, CBS C); instr's manual 10.95 (ISBN 0-03-058468-X). SCP.
Tybout, Richard A., ed. Environmental Quality & Society. LC 75-2244. (Illus.). 327p. (Orig.). 1975. pap. 7.50x (ISBN 0-8142-0214-4). Ohio St U Pr.
United Nations Economic Commission for Europe. Environmental Impact Assessment: Proceedings of a Seminar of the United Nations Economic Commission for Europe, Villach, Austria. (ECE Seminars & Symposia). (Illus.). 368p. 1981. 61.00 (ISBN 0-08-024445-9). Pergamon.
United Nations Environment Programme: Annual Review 1976. 59p. 1977. pap. 6.00 (ISBN 0-686-93587-X, UNEP012, UNEP). Unipub.
United Nations Environment Programme: Annual Review 1977. (Eng., Fr. & Span., Illus.). 60p. 1978. pap. 6.00 (ISBN 0-686-93588-8, UNEP015, UNEP). Unipub.
United Nations Environment Programme Annual Review, 1979. pap. 11.00 (UNEP076, UNEP). Unipub.
The United Nations Programme: UNEP & its Activities. pap. 5.00 (UNEP029, UNEP). Unipub.
Urwick Technology Management Ltd. Environmental Impacts & Policies for the EEC Tanning Industry. 86p. 1977. 24.00x (ISBN 0-86010-065-0, Pub. by Graham & Trotman England). State Mutual Bk.
Uusitalo, Liisa. Consumer Behavior & Environmental Quality. LC 82-10686. 156p. 1983. 25.00x (ISBN 0-312-16606-0). St Martin.
Verner, S., ed. Sampling & Analysis of Toxic Organics in the Atmosphere -STP 721. 192p. 1981. 19.75 (ISBN 0-8031-0604-1, 04-721000-19). ASTM.
Voices in Defense of the Earth. pap. 0.00 write for info. (UNEP084, UNEP). Unipub.
Watt, Kenneth E. Understanding the Environment. 1982. pap. text ed. 35.00 (ISBN 0-205-07265-8, 677265-X); tchr's. ed. free (ISBN 0-205-07266-6). Allyn.
Westing, Arthur, ed. The Environmental Modification Convention of 1977: A Technical, Legal & Policy Appraisal. 100p. 1984. pap. 21.00x (ISBN 0-85066-278-8). Taylor & Francis.
Whyte, Ann V. & Burton, Ian. Environmental Risk Assessment. LC 79-42903. (SCOPE Ser. (Scientific Committee on Problems of the Environment): SCOPR Report 15). 157p. 1980. 37.95x (ISBN 0-471-27701-0, Pub. by Wiley-Interscience). Wiley.
Williams, J., ed. Carbon Dioxide, Climate & Society: Proceedings of an IIASA Workshop, Feb. 1978. 1978. text ed. 53.00 (ISBN 0-08-023252-3). Pergamon.
Wilson, John S., et al. Comprehensive Planning & the Environment: A Manual for Planners. 294p. 1984. Repr. of 1979 ed. lib. bdg. 25.00 (ISBN 0-8191-4085-6). U Pr of Amer.
Witschi, H. R., ed. Scientific Basis of Toxicity Assessment. (Developments in Toxicology & Environmental Science Ser.: Vol. 6). 330p. 1980. 61.00 (ISBN 0-444-80200-2). Elsevier.

ENVIRONMENTAL RADIOACTIVITY
see Radioecology

ENVIRONMENTAL TESTING
Annual Technical Meeting of the Institute of Environmental Sciences, 26th, Philadelphia, May 1980. Life Cycle Problems & Environmental Technology: Proceedings. LC 62-38584. (Illus.). 1980. pap. text ed. 25.00 (ISBN 0-915414-20-1). Inst Environ Sci.
Changing Role of Environmental Stress Screening: Seminar Notes. LC 62-38584. (Illus.). 135p. (Orig.). 1980. pap. text ed. 10.00 (ISBN 0-915414-61-9). Inst Environ Sci.
Clayton, P. & Wallin, S. C. An Environmental Study of an Activated Carbon Plant, 1978. 1981. 60.00x (ISBN 0-686-97068-3, Pub. by W Green England). State Mutual Bk.
Cornillon, Peter. A Guide to Environmental Satellite Data. (Technical Report Ser.: No. 79). 469p. 1982. 20.00 (ISBN 0-938412-21-3, P894). URI MAS.
Craik, Kenneth & Zube, Ervin H., eds. Perceiving Environmental Quality: Research & Applications. LC 76-13513. (Environmental Science Research Ser.: Vol. 9). (Illus.). 323p. 1976. 45.00x (ISBN 0-306-36309-7, Plenum Pr). Plenum Pub.
Eglington, G. Environmental Chemistry, Vol. 1. 1975. 30.00 (ISBN 0-85186-755-3, Pub. by Royal Soc Chem London). Am Chemical.
Environmental Stress Screening Guidelines. LC 62-38584. (Illus.). 122p. (Orig.). 1981. pap. text ed. 75.00 (ISBN 0-915414-66-X). Inst Environ Sci.
Environmental Stress Screening of Electronic Hardware: Proceedings, Second National Conference & Workshop, September 1981. LC 62-38584. (Illus.). 195p. (Orig.). 1982. pap. text ed. 25.00 (ISBN 0-915414-67-8). Inst Environ Sci.
Frei, R. W. & Hutzinger, Otto, eds. Analytical Aspects of Mercury & Other Heavy Metals in the Environment. LC 73-88229. (Current Topics in Environmental & Toxicological Chemistry Ser.). 204p. 1975. 48.75 (ISBN 0-677-15890-4). Gordon.
Hsu, T. C., ed. Cytogenetic Assays of Environmental Mutagens. LC 79-88262. 442p. 1982. text ed. 47.50x (ISBN 0-916672-56-5). Allanheld.
Inhaber, Herbert. Environmental Indices. LC 75-34290. 194p. 1976. 26.00 (ISBN 0-471-42796-9). Krieger.
Lawrence Berkeley Laboratory Environmental Instrumentation Survey. Instrumentation for Environmental Monitoring: Water, Vol. 2. 2nd ed. 1985. 160.00 (ISBN 0-471-88567-3). Wiley.
Marr, Ian & Cresser, Malcolm S. Environmental Chemical Analysis. 224p. 1983. 42.00 (ISBN 0-412-00201-9, NO. 5023, Pub. by Chapman & Hall England). Methuen Inc.
Mercer, Thomas T., et al. Assessment of Airborne Particles: Fundamentals, Applications, & Implications to Inhalation Toxicity. (Illus.). 560p. 1972. photocopy ed. 55.75x (ISBN 0-398-02360-3). C C Thomas.
MIL-STD-810C Seminar Proceedings. LC 62-38584. 68p. 1975. pap. text ed. 7.00 (ISBN 0-915414-49-X). Inst Environ Sci.
Milman, Harry A. & Sell, Stewart, eds. Application of Biological Markers to Carcinogen Testing. (Environmental Science Research: Vol. 29). 520p. 1983. 69.50x (ISBN 0-306-41490-2, Plenum Pr). Plenum Pub.
Richason, Benjamin F., Jr., ed. Laboratory Manual for Introduction to Remote Sensing of the Environment. (Pacesetter Ser). (Illus.). 1983. 10.95 (ISBN 0-8403-3186-X, 40318601). Kendall Hunt.
Robinson, J. P. The Effects of Weapons on Ecosystems. (Studies Ser.: Vol. 1). pap. 5.00 (UNEP009, UNEP). Unipub.
Schweitzer, Glenn E. & Santolucito, John A., eds. Environmental Sampling for Hazardous Wastes. LC 84-20480. (ACS Symposium Ser.: No. 267). 134p. 1984. lib. bdg. 34.95x (ISBN 0-8412-0884-0). Am Chemical.
Sheenan, P. J. Appraisal of Tests to Predict the Environmental Behavior of Chemicals: Scope 25. (Scope Ser.). 1984. 59.95 (ISBN 0-471-90545-3). Wiley.
Sixth Aerospace Testing Seminar: Proceedings. LC 62-38584. (Illus.). 221p. (Orig.). 1981. pap. text ed. 25.00 (ISBN 0-915414-65-1). Inst Environ Sci.
The State of the Environment: Selected Topics, 1981. (S.O.T.E. Reports). 26p. 1981. pap. 5.00 (ISBN 92-807-1045-1, UNEP062, UNEP). Unipub.

Taylor, John K. & Stanley, Thomas W., eds. Quality Assurance for Environmental Measurements: STP 867. LC 85-6074. (Illus.). 440p. 1985. text ed. 50.00 (ISBN 0-8031-0224-0, 04-867000-16). ASTM.

Tustin, Wayne. Environmental Virbration & Shock Testing, Measurement, Analysis & Calibration. rev. ed. 1962. text ed. write for info. Tustin Inst.

Tustin, Wayne & Hallstein, Frank W. Establishing & Maintaining the Quality of Environmental Testing. 1975. text ed. write for info. Tustin Inst.

Van Loon, J. C. Selected Methods of Trace Metal Analysis: Biological & Environmental Samples. (Chemical Analysis Ser.). 352p. 1985. 55.00 (ISBN 0-471-89634-9). Wiley.

Worf, Douglas L., ed. Biological Monitoring for Environmental Effects. LC 79-2977. 240p. 1980. 28.50x (ISBN 0-669-03306-5). Lexington Bks.

ENZYME INHIBITORS

see also Antimetabolites

Baker, B. R. Design of Active-Site Directed Irreversible Enzyme Inhibitors: The Organic Chemistry of the Enzymic Active-Site. LC 74-32255. 342p. 1975. Repr. of 1967 ed. 19.50 (ISBN 0-88275-259-6). Krieger.

Bergmeyer, H. U., ed. Methods of Enzymatic Analysis: Enzymes 3-Peptides, Protinases & Their Inhibitors, Vol. 5. 3rd ed. 558p. 1984. 120.00x (ISBN 0-89573-235-1). VCH Pubs.

Blomback, M. & Brakman, P., eds. Synthetic Substrates & Synthetic Inhibitors: The Use of Chromogenic Substrates in Studies of the Haemostatic Mechanism. (Haemostasis: Vol. 7, Nos. 2-3). (Illus.). 1978. pap. 16.25 (ISBN 3-8055-2907-4). S Karger.

Braude, M., et al, eds. Narcotic Antagonists. 1973. 38.00 (ISBN 0-7204-7507-4). Elsevier.

Brodbeck, U. Enzyme Inhibitors. (Illus.). 282p. (Orig.). 1980. pap. 42.50x (ISBN 0-89573-037-5). VCH Pubs.

Brown, J. C. Gastric Inhibitory Polypeptide. (Monographs on Endocrinology: Vol. 24). (Illus.). 200p. 1982. 34.00 (ISBN 0-387-11271-5). Springer-Verlag.

Collegium Internationale Neuro-Psychopharmacologicum; Congress. Monoamine Oxidase Inhibitors: The State of the Art. Youdim, M. B. & Paykel, E. S., eds. LC 80-41258. (A Wiley-Interscience Publication). pap. 58.00 (ISBN 0-317-27704-9, 2052101). Bks Demand UMI.

Corlin, Richard, et al. Converting Enzyme Inhibition in Heart Failure: Management Strategies for the Eighties. 54p. 1983. write for info. (ISBN 0-911741-03-8). Advanced Thera Comm.

Hochster, R. N. & Quastel, J. H., eds. Metabolic Inhibitors: A Comprehensive Treatise. Incl. Vol. 1. 1963. 92.50 (ISBN 0-12-350801-0); Vol. 2. 1963; Vol. 3. Hochster, R. M., et al, eds. 1972. 75.00 (ISBN 0-12-350803-7); Vol. 4. 1973. 76.00. Acad Pr.

Holzer, H., ed. Metabolic Interconversion of Enzymes 1980. (Proceedings in Life Science Ser.). (Illus.). 397p. 1981. 67.00 (ISBN 0-387-10979-X). Springer Verlag.

Hoyer, Leon W. Factor VII Inhibitors. LC 84-3947. (Progress in Clinical & Biological Research Ser.: Vol. 150). 422p. 1984. 48.00 (ISBN 0-8451-5000-6). A R Liss.

Jain, Mahendra K. Handbook of Enzyme Inhibitors (1965-1977) LC 82-2595. 447p. 1982. 115.50x (ISBN 0-471-86727-6, Pub. by Wiley-Interscience). Wiley.

Robinson, H. Prostaglandin Synthetase Inhibitors. Vane, J. E., ed. 1974. 31.00 (ISBN 0-7204-7529-5, North Holland). Elsevier.

Sandler, Merton, ed. Enzyme Inhibitors as Drugs. 296p. 1980. text ed. 53.50 (ISBN 0-8391-4130-0). Univ Park.

Scriabine, Alexander, et al. Nitrendipine. 566p. 1984. pap. 34.50 (ISBN 0-8067-1781-5). Urban & S.

Scrimgeour, K. G. Chemistry & Control of Enzyme Reactions. 1978. 86.50 (ISBN 0-12-634150-8). Acad Pr.

Sirotnak, F. M., et al, eds. Folate Antagonists As Therapeutics Agents: Biochemistry, Molecular Actions, & Synthetic Design, Vol. 1. LC 83-15774. 1984. 69.50 (ISBN 0-12-646901-6). Acad Pr.

Turk, V. & Vitale, L. J. Proteinases & Their Inhibitors: Structure, Function & Applied Aspects. LC 81-319. (Illus.). 500p. 1981. 88.00 (ISBN 0-08-027377-7). Pergamon.

Vogel, Rosemarie, et al. Natural Proteinase Inhibitors. 1969. 38.00 (ISBN 0-12-722850-0). Acad Pr.

Webb, J. L. Enzyme & Metabolic Inhibitors, 3 vols. Incl. Vol. 1. General Principles of Inhibition. 1963. 95.00 (ISBN 0-12-739201-7); Vol. 2. Malonate, Analogs, Dehydroacetate, Sulfhydryl Reagents, o-Iodosobenzoate, Mercurials. 1966. 95.00 (ISBN 0-12-739202-5); Vol. 3. Iodoacetate, Meleate, N-Ethylmaleimide, Alloxan, Quinones, Arsenicals. 1966. 95.00 (ISBN 0-12-739203-3). Acad Pr.

ENZYMES

see also Coenzymes; Enzyme Inhibitors; Fermentation; Fibrinolytic Agents; Malt
also names of enzymes, e.g. Diastase, Pepsin

Adelman, Richard C., et al. Enzyme Induction in Aging & Protein Synthesis. LC 74-6131. 172p. 1974. text ed. 21.50x (ISBN 0-8422-7222-4). Irvington.

Alfred Benzon Symposium - 1st. Role of Nucleotides for the Function & Conformation of Enzymes. Kalckar, H. M., et al, eds. 1970. 70.00 (ISBN 0-12-394550-X). Acad Pr.

Baker-Cohen, K. F. Comparative Enzyme Histochemical Observations on Submammalian Brains. Incl. Pt. 1: Striatal Structures in Reptiles & Birds; Pt. 2: Basal Structures of the Brainstem in Reptiles & Birds. (Advances in Anatomy: Vol. 40, Pt. 6). (Illus.). 70p. 1968. pap. 18.90 (ISBN 0-387-04090-0). Springer-Verlag.

Barman, T. E. Enzyme Handbook, 2 Vols. LC 69-19293. 1969. Set. 89.00 (ISBN 0-387-04423-X). Springer-Verlag.

--Enzyme Handbook: Suppl. 1. 517p. 1974. 47.00 (ISBN 0-387-06761-2). Springer-Verlag.

Barrett, Alan & McDonald, J. Ken. Mammalian Proteases: a Glossary & Bibliography: Vol. 1: Endopeptidases. 1980. 44.00 (ISBN 0-12-079501-9). Acad Pr.

Beauchene, Roy E., et al. Enzyme Activities & Aging. LC 74-5496. 208p. 1974. text ed. 34.50x (ISBN 0-8422-7217-8). Irvington.

Bender, Myron L. & Brubacher, Lewis J. Catalysis. (Illus.). 256p. 1973. text ed. 25.95 (ISBN 0-07-004450-3); pap. text ed. 21.95 (ISBN 0-07-004451-1). McGraw.

Bergmeyer, H. U. Principles of Enzymatic Analysis. (Illus.). 264p. 1978. pap. 30.70x (ISBN 0-89573-006-5). VCH Pubs.

Bergmeyer, H. U., ed. Metabolites One, Vol. 6. 3rd ed. (Methods of Enzymatic Analysis). 701p. 1984. 155.60 (ISBN 0-89573-236-X). VCH Pubs.

--Metabolites Two, Vol. 7. 3rd ed. (Methods of Enzymatic Analysis). 637p. 1985. 135.00 (ISBN 0-89573-237-8). VCH Pubs.

--Methods of Enzymatic Analysis: Enzymes 3-Peptides, Protinases & Their Inhibitors, Vol. 5. 3rd ed. 558p. 1984. 120.00x (ISBN 0-89573-235-1). VCH Pubs.

Bergmeyer, Hans U., ed. Methods of Enzymatic Analysis: Enzymes I, Vol. 3. 3rd, English ed. 603p. 1983. 129.00 (ISBN 0-89573-233-5). VCH Pubs.

--Methods of Enzymatic Analysis: Fundamentals, Vol. 1. 3rd, English ed. 574p. 1983. 116.00x (ISBN 0-89573-231-9). VCH Pubs.

--Methods of Enzymatic Analysis, Vol. 2: Samples, Reagents, Assessment of Results. 3rd, English ed. 539p. 1983. 122.50x (ISBN 0-89573-232-7). VCH Pubs.

Biochemical Societies of France, Great Britain, Italy, & the Netherlands. Joint Meeting, Venice, 1976. Phosphorylated Proteins & Related Enzymes: Proceedings. 128p. 1977. 10.00 (ISBN 0-904147-45-2). IRL Pr.

Birch, G. G. & Blakebrough. Enzymes & Food Processing: An Industry-University Co-Operation Symposium. Reading, England, April 1980. (Illus.). 295p. 1980. 48.00 (ISBN 0-85334-935-5, Pub. by Elsevier Applied Sci England). Elsevier.

Bishop, D. F. & Desnick, R. J., eds. Assays of the Heme Biosynthetic Enzymes. (Journal: Enzyme: Vol. 28, No. 2-3). (Illus.). vi, 144p. 1982. pap. 41.50 (ISBN 3-8055-3573-2). S Karger.

Bohak, Zvi & Sharon, Nathan, eds. Biotechnological Application of Proteins & Enzymes. 1977. 65.00 (ISBN 0-12-110950-X). Acad Pr.

Borgstrom, B. & Brockman, H. L. Lipases. 500p. 1984. 123.00 (ISBN 0-444-80526-5, I-208-84, Biomedical Pr). Elsevier.

Boyer, Paul D., ed. The Enzymes. Incl. Vol. 1. Enzyme Structure, Control. 3rd. ed. 1970. 80.00 (ISBN 0-12-122701-4); Vol. 2. Kinetics, Mechamisms. 3rd. ed. 1970. 75.00 (ISBN 0-12-122702-2); Vol. 3. Peptide Bond Hydrolysis. 3rd ed. 1971. 90.00 (ISBN 0-12-122703-0); Vol. 4. 1971. 90.00 (ISBN 0-12-122704-9); Vol. 5. 1971. 90.00 (ISBN 0-12-122705-7); Vol. 6. 1972. 88.00 (ISBN 0-12-122706-5); Vol. 7. 1972; Vol. 8. 1973. 83.50 (ISBN 0-12-122708-1); Vol. 9. 1973. 80.00 (ISBN 0-12-122709-X); Vol. 10. 1974. 90.00 (ISBN 0-12-122710-3); Vol. 11. 1975. 88.00 (ISBN 0-12-122711-1); Vol. 12. 1975. 88.00 (ISBN 0-12-122712-X); Vol. 13. 1976. 85.00 (ISBN 0-12-122713-8). student ed. 1973 24.00i (ISBN 0-12-122750-2). Acad Pr.

--The Enzymes, Vol. 14. 3rd ed. LC 75-117107. 1981. 82.50 (ISBN 0-12-122714-6). Acad Pr.

--The Enzymes: Lipid Enzymology: Fatty Acids, Glycerides, Phospholipids, Sphingolipids, Glycolipids, Cholesterol, Special Topics, Vol. 16. 3rd ed. 1983. 79.00 (ISBN 0-12-122716-2). Acad Pr.

--The Enzymes: Nucleic Acids, Vol. 15, Pt. B. 3rd ed. 1982. 79.50 (ISBN 0-12-122715-4). Acad Pr.

Brockerhoff, Hans & Jensen, Robert G. Lipolytic Enzymes. 1974. 70.00 (ISBN 0-12-134550-5). Acad Pr.

Broun, G. B., et al, eds. Enzyme Engineering, Vol. 4. LC 74-13768. 512p. 1978. 65.00x (ISBN 0-306-40021-9, Plenum Pr). Plenum Pub.

Burns, R. G., ed. Soil Enzymes. 1978. 69.50 (ISBN 0-12-145850-4). Acad Pr.

Carr, Peter & Bowers, Larry D. Immobilized Enzymes in Analytical & Clinical Chemistry: Fundamentals & Applications. LC 80-13694. (Chemical Analysis: A Series of Monographs on Analytical Chemistry & Its Applications). 460p. 1980. 75.95 (ISBN 0-471-04919-0, Pub. by Wiley-Interscience). Wiley.

Chang, T. M., ed. Biomedical Applications of Immobilized Enzymes & Proteins, 2 vols. Incl. Vol. 1. 448p. 1977. 49.50x (ISBN 0-306-34311-8); Vol. 2. LC 76-56231. 379p. 1977. 49.50x (ISBN 0-306-34312-6). (Illus., Plenum Pr). Plenum Pub.

Chibata, Ichiro, ed. Immobilized Enzymes: Research & Development. LC 78-13266. 284p. 1978. 53.95x (ISBN 0-470-26531-0). Halsted Pr.

Chibata, Ichiro & Fukui, Saburo, eds. Enzyme Engineering, Vol. 6. LC 74-13768. 560p. 1982. 69.50x (ISBN 0-306-41121-0, Plenum Pr). Plenum Pub.

Ciba Foundation. Environmental Chemicals, Enzyme Function & Human Disease. LC 80-18000. (Ciba Foundation Symposium, New Ser.: 76). pap. 97.50 (ISBN 0-317-29748-1, 2022195). Bks Demand UMI.

--Enzyme Defects & Immune Dysfunction. LC 79-17092. (Ciba Foundation Symposium, New Ser.: No. 68). pap. 74.80 (ISBN 0-317-29762-7, 2022188). Bks Demand UMI.

--Trends in Enzyme Histochemistry & Cytochemistry. (Ciba Symposium Ser.: No. 73). 1980. 58.50 (ISBN 0-444-90135-3). Elsevier.

--Trends in Enzyme Histochemistry & Cytochemistry. LC 80-11757. (Ciba Foundation Symposium, New Ser.: 73). pap. 80.50 (ISBN 0-317-29754-6, 2022192). Bks Demand UMI.

Cohen, Philip. Control of Enzyme Activity. 2nd ed. (Outlines Studies in Biology). 1983. pap. 7.50 (ISBN 0-412-25560-X, 6870, Pub. by Chapman & Hall). Methuen Inc.

A Collection of tRNA, 5S & 5.8S rRNA & Restriction Enzyme Recognition Site Sequences: A Supplement to the Journal Nucleic Acids Research. (Illus.). 200p. (Orig.). 1984. pap. 20.00 (ISBN 0-904147-69-X). IRL Pr.

Colowick & Kaplan, eds. Methods in Enzymology: Glutamate, Glutamine, Glutathione, & Related Compounds, Vol. 113. Date not set. 75.00 (ISBN 0-12-182013-0). Acad Pr.

Colowick, S. & Ginsburg, Victor, eds. Methods in Enzymology: Complex Carbohydrates, Vol. 83, Pt. D. 1982. 69.50 (ISBN 0-12-181983-3). Acad Pr.

Colowick, S. & Langone, John, eds. Methods in Enzymology: Immunological Techniques, Vol. 84, Pt. D. LC 82-1678. 736p. 1982. 70.00 (ISBN 0-12-181984-1). Acad Pr.

Colowick, S. & Lorand, L., eds. Methods in Enzymology: Proteolytic Enzymes, Vol. 80, Pt. C. 1982. 77.00 (ISBN 0-12-181980-9). Acad Pr.

Colowick, S. P., et al, eds. Methods in Enzymology: Lipids, Vol. 71, Pt. C. 1981. 76.50 (ISBN 0-12-181971-X). Acad Pr.

--Methods in Enzymology: Immunochemical Techniques, Vol. 70, Pt. A. (Serial Publications Ser.). 1980. 65.00 (ISBN 0-12-181970-1). Acad Pr.

Colowick, Sidney & Cunningham, Leon, eds. Methods in Enzymology: Structural & Contractile Proteins: Extracellular Matrix, Vol. 82, Pt. A. 1982. 75.00 (ISBN 0-12-181982-5). Acad Pr.

Colowick, Sidney P. & Kaplan, Nathan O. Methods in Enzymology: Enzyme Purification & Related Techniques, Vol. 104, Pt. C. 1984. 60.00 (ISBN 0-12-182004-1). Acad Pr.

--Methods in Enzymology: Oxygen Radicals in Biological Systems, Vol. 105. 1984. 70.00 (ISBN 0-12-182005-X). Acad Pr.

--Methods in Enzymology: Posttranslational Modification, Vol. 107, Pt. B. 1984. 69.50 (ISBN 0-12-182007-6). Acad Pr.

Colowick, Sidney P. & Kaplan, Nathan, eds. Methods in Enzymology: Postranslational Modifications, Vol. 106, Pt. A. 1984. 65.00 (ISBN 0-12-182006-8). Acad Pr.

Colowick, Sidney P. & Kaplan, Nathan O., eds. Methods in Enzymology, Vols. 1-15. Incl. Vol. 1. Preparation & Assay of Enzymes. 1955. 89.50 (ISBN 0-12-181801-2); Vol. 2. Preparation & Assay of Enzymes, Continued. 1955. 89.50 (ISBN 0-12-181802-0); Vol. 3. Preparation & Assay of Substrates. 1957. 94.00 (ISBN 0-12-181803-9); Vol. 4. Special Techniques for the Enzymologist. 1957. 94.00 (ISBN 0-12-181804-7); Vol. 5. Preparation & Assay of Enzymes, Supplement to Vols. 1 & 2. 1961. 94.00 (ISBN 0-12-181805-5); Vol. 6. Preparation & Assay of Enzymes, Continued & Preparation & Assay of Substrates, Special Techniques. 1963. 94.00 (ISBN 0-12-181806-3); Vol. 7. General Subject Index. 1964; Vol. 8. Complex Carbohydrates. Neufeld, Elizabeth F. & Ginsberg, Victor, eds. 1966. 90.00 (ISBN 0-12-181808-X); Vol. 9. Carbohydrate Metabolism. Wood, W. A., ed. 1967. 90.00 (ISBN 0-12-181809-8); Vol. 10. Oxidation & Phosphorylation. Estabrook, Ronald W. & Pullman, Maynard E., eds. 1967. 90.00 (ISBN 0-12-181850-0); Vol. 11. Enzyme Structure. Hirs, C. Werner, ed. 1967. 93.00 (ISBN 0-12-181860-8); Vol. 12. Nucleic Acids, Pts. A-B. Grossman, Lawrence & Moldave, Kivic, eds. Pt. A, 1967. 90.00 (ISBN 0-12-181854-3); Pt. B, 1968. 93.00 (ISBN 0-12-181856-X); Vol. 13. Citric Acid Cycle. Lowenstein, J. M., ed. 1969. 83.50 (ISBN 0-12-181870-5); Vol. 14. Lipids. Lowenstein, J. M. 1969. 83.50 (ISBN 0-12-181871-3); Vol. 15. Steroids & Terpenoids. Clayton, R. B., ed. 1969. 93.00 (ISBN 0-12-181872-1). Acad Pr.

--Methods in Enzymology, Vol. 87. 752p. 1982. 74.50 (ISBN 0-12-181987-6). Acad Pr.

--Methods in Enzymology: Diffraction Methods for Biological Macromolecules, Vol. 114, Pt. A. Edited Treatise ed. Date not set. 64.00 (ISBN 0-12-182014-9). Acad Pr.

--Methods in Enzymology: Drug & Enzyme Targeting, Vol. 112. 1985. 69.00 (ISBN 0-12-182012-2). Acad Pr.

--Methods in Enzymology: Enzyme Kinetics & Mechanism, Initial Rate & Inhibiter Methods, Vol. 63. LC 54-9110. (Serial Publication: Pt. A). 1979. 65.00 (ISBN 0-12-181963-9). Acad Pr.

--Methods in Enzymology: Enzyme Structure, Vol. 117, Pt. J. Date not set. 64.50 (ISBN 0-12-182017-3). Acad Pr.

--Methods in Enzymology: Enzyme Structure, Vol. 91, Pt. 1. 1983. 71.50 (ISBN 0-12-181991-4). Acad Pr.

--Methods in Enzymology: Recombinant DNA. LC 79-26584. 1983. Vol. 100: Pt. B. 65.00 (ISBN 0-12-182000-9); Vol. 101: Pt. C. 70.00 (ISBN 0-12-182001-7). Acad Pr.

--Methods in Enzymology: Steroids & Isoprenoids, Vol. 110, Pt. A. 1985. 55.00 (ISBN 0-12-182010-6). Acad Pr.

--Methods in Enzymology: Steroids & Isoprenoids, Vol. 111, Pt. B. 1985. 66.50 (ISBN 0-12-182011-4). Acad Pr.

Colowick, Sidney P., et al, eds. Methods in Enzymology: Enzyme Kinetics & Mechanism, Vol. 64. LC 54-9110. (150 tape probes & complex enzyme systems pt B). 1980. 55.00 (ISBN 0-12-181964-7). Acad Pr.

--Methods in Enzymology: Nucleic Acids, Vol. 65. LC 54-9110. (Methods in Enzymology Ser.: Pt. 1). 1980. 69.50 (ISBN 0-12-181965-5). Acad Pr.

--Methods in Enzymology: Recombinant Dna, Vol. 68. LC 54-9110. (Methods in Enzymology Ser.). 1980. 59.50 (ISBN 0-12-181968-X). Acad Pr.

Conn, Michael, ed. Methods in Enzymology: Hormone Action: Neuroendocrine Peptides, Vol. 103, Pt. H. 1983. 69.50 (ISBN 0-12-182003-3). Acad Pr.

Coodleyt, Eugene L., ed. Diagnostic Enzymology. LC 78-85839. pap. 84.00 (ISBN 0-317-07924-7, 2055417). Bks Demand UMI.

Cornish-Bowden, Athel. Fundamentals of Enzyme Kinetics. LC 79-40116. (Illus.). 1979. text ed. 24.95 (ISBN 0-408-10617-4). Butterworth.

Degen, H. & Cox, Raymond P., eds. Gas Enzymology. 1985. lib. bdg. 44.00 (ISBN 90-277-1900-4, Pub. by Reidel Holland). Kluwer Academic.

Desnick, Robert J., ed. Enzyme Therapy in Genetic Diseases: Part 2. LC 79-48026. (Alan R. Liss Ser.: Vol. 16, No. 1). 1980. 77.00 (ISBN 0-686-29474-2). March of Dimes.

Desnuelle, P., et al, eds. Structure-Function Relationships of Proteolytic Enzymes: Proceedings. 1970. 49.00 (ISBN 0-12-211850-2). Acad Pr.

Dickinson, W. J. & Sullivan, D. T. Gene-Enzyme Systems in Drosophila. LC 74-17430. (Results & Problems in Cell Differentiation: Vol. 6). (Illus.). xii, 163p. 1975. 37.00 (ISBN 0-387-06977-1). Springer-Verlag.

Dixon, Malcolm & Webb, Edwin. The Enzymes. 3rd ed. 1980. 64.95 (ISBN 0-12-218358-4). Acad Pr.

Dugas, H. & Penney, C. Bioorganic Chemistry: A Chemical Approach to Enzyme Action. (Springer Advanced Texts in Chemistry Ser.). (Illus.). 508p. 1981. 32.50 (ISBN 0-387-90491-3). Springer-Verlag.

Dunnill, Peter, et al, eds. Enzymic & Non-Enzymic Catalysis. LC 79-40784. 249p. 1980. 79.95x (ISBN 0-470-26773-9). Halsted Pr.

Ebner, K. E., ed. Subunit Enzymes: Biochemistry & Funtions. (Enzymology Ser.: Vol. 2). 352p. 1975. 59.75 (ISBN 0-8247-6280-0). Dekker.

Eggerer, H. & Hiber, R., eds. Structural & Functional Aspects of Enzyme Catalysis. (Colloquium Mosbach Ser.: Vol. 32). (Illus.). 280p. 1981. 33.00 (ISBN 0-387-11110-7). Springer-Verlag.

Emerson Enzyme Nomenclature. 1984. pap. 19.50 (ISBN 0-12-227163-7). Acad Pr.

Endrenyi, Laszlo, ed. Kinetic Data Analysis: Design & Analysis of Enzyme & Pharmacokinetic Experiments. LC 81-120. 438p. 1981. 69.50x (ISBN 0-306-40724-8, Plenum Pr). Plenum Pub.

Enzyme Activities of Human Tissue. (Enzymologia Biologica et Clinica: Vol. 11, Nos. 1-2). 1970. pap. 22.75 (ISBN 3-8055-0824-7). S Karger.

Erdoes, E. G., ed. Bradykinin, Kallidin, & Kallikrein-Supplement. (Handbook of Experimental Pharmacology: Vol. 25, Suppl.). (Illus.). 1979. 212.40 (ISBN 0-387-09356-7). Springer-Verlag.

Ferdinand, W. The Enzyme Molecule. LC 76-7530. 1976. 58.95x (ISBN 0-471-01822-8, Pub. by Wiley-Interscience); pap. 27.95x (ISBN 0-471-01821-X). Wiley.

Fersht, Alan. Enzyme Structure & Mechanism. LC 77-6441. (Illus.). 371p. 1977. pap. text ed. 18.95 (ISBN 0-7167-0188-X). W H Freeman.

--Enzyme Structure & Mechanism. 2nd ed. LC 84-4172. (Illus.). 496p. 1984. text ed. 24.95 (ISBN 0-7167-1614-3). W H Freeman.

Fleischer, Sidney & Fleicher, Becca, eds. Methods in Enzymology: Biomembranes: Membrane Biogenesis: Proceedings & Recycling, Vol. 98, Pt. L. 1983. 73.00 (ISBN 0-12-181998-1). Acad Pr.

Fleischer, Sidney & Fleischer, Becca, eds. Methods in Enzymology: Biomembranes: Membrane Biogenesis: Assembly & Targeting, Vol. 97. (Prokaryotes, Mitochondria & Chloroplasts Ser.: Pt. K). 1983. 69.50 (ISBN 0-12-181997-3). Acad Pr.

Fogarty, William M., ed. Microbial Enzymes & Biotechnology. (Illus.). 382p. 1983. 63.00 (ISBN 0-85334-185-0, Pub. by Elsevier Applied Sci England). Elsevier.

Freedman, Robert & Hawkins, H. G., eds. The Enzymology of Post-Translational Modification of Proteins, Vol. I. (Molecular Biology Ser.). 1981. 96.00 (ISBN 0-12-266501-5). Acad Pr.

Freidmann, H. Enzymes. 1981. 75.00 (ISBN 0-87933-367-7). Van Nos Reinhold.

Friedrich, P. Supramolecular Enzymes Organization: Quarternary Structure & Beyond. (Illus.). 294p. 1985. 36.00 (ISBN 0-08-026376-3). Pergamon.

Fromm, H. J. Initial Rate Enzyme Kinetics. LC 75-20206. (Molecular Biology, Biochemistry, & Biophysics: Vol. 22). (Illus.). 350p. 1975. 48.00 (ISBN 0-387-07375-2). Springer-Verlag.

Ghose, T. K., et al. Immobilized Enzymes I. (Advances in Biochemical Engineering Ser.: Vol. 10). (Illus.). 1978. 43.00 (ISBN 0-387-08975-6). Springer-Verlag.

Gillette, James R., et al, eds. Microsomes & Drug Oxidations: Proceedings. 1969. 65.00 (ISBN 0-12-283650-2). Acad Pr.

Glew, Robert H. & Peters, Stephen P., eds. Practical Enzymology of the Sphingolipidoses. LC 77-15819. (Laboratory & Research Methods in Biology & Medicine: Vol. 1). 322p. 1977. 47.00 (ISBN 0-8451-1650-9). A R Liss.

Goldberg, D. M. & Werner, M., eds. Selected Topics in Clinical Enzymology: Proceedings of the Third International Congress of Clinical Enzymology, Salzburg, Austria, September 6-9, 1981. 362p. 1983. 64.00 (ISBN 3-11-009688-9). De Gruyter.

Green, B. S. & Ashani, Y. Chemical Approaches to Understanding Enzyme Catalysis: Biomimetic Chemistry & Transition State Analogs. (Studies in Organic Chemistry: Vol. 10). 356p. 1982. 91.50 (ISBN 0-444-42063-0). Elsevier.

Gross, Franz, et al, eds. Enzymatic Release of Vasoactive Peptides: Eighth Workshop Conference HOECHST. (Illus.). 432p. 1980. text ed. 59.00 (ISBN 0-89004-458-9). Raven.

Guilbault. Analytical Uses of Immobilized Enzymes. (Modern Monographs in Analytical Chemistry). 528p. 1984. 75.00 (ISBN 0-8247-7125-7). Dekker.

Guilbault, George. Handbook of Enzymatic Methods of Analysis. (Clinical & Biochemical Analysis Ser.: Vol. 4). 1976. 99.75 (ISBN 0-8247-6425-0). Dekker.

Halpern, M. G., ed. Industrial Enzymes from Microbial Sources: Recent Advances. LC 81-1839. (Chemical Technology Review Ser.: No. 186). 1981. 45.00 (ISBN 0-8155-0843-3). Noyes.

Hammes, Gordon G. Enzyme Catalysis & Regulation. LC 82-1597. (Molecular Biology Ser.). 1982. 34.50 (ISBN 0-12-321960-4); pap. 14.95 (ISBN 0-12-321962-0). Acad Pr.

Harris, H. & Hopkinson, D. A. Handbook of Enzyme Electrophoresis in Human Genetics. 306p. (incl. 1977 & 1978 suppl.). 1976. 87.25 (ISBN 0-444-11203-0, Biomedical Pr). Elsevier.

Hasselberger, Francis. Uses of Enzymes & Immobilized Enzymes. LC 78-8498. (Illus.). 280p. 1978. text ed. 24.95x (ISBN 0-88229-345-1). Nelson-Hall.

Hayashi, K. & Sakamoto, N., eds. Dynamic Analysis of Enzyme Systems. 350p. 1985. 39.50 (ISBN 0-387-15485-X). Springer-Verlag.

Hayat, M. Arif. Electron Microscopy of Enzymes: Principles & Methods, Vol. 2. 200p. 1974. 19.95 (ISBN 0-442-25679-5). Van Nos Reinhold.

--Electron Microscopy of Enzymes: Principles & Methods, Vol. 3. 190p. 1974. 19.95 (ISBN 0-442-25683-3). Van Nos Reinhold.

--Electron Microscopy of Enzymes: Principles & Methods, Vol. 4. 1975. 24.50 (ISBN 0-685-55048-6). Van Nos Reinhold.

--Electron Microscopy of Enzymes Principles & Methods, Vol. 5. 1977. 24.50 (ISBN 0-442-25690-6). Van Nos Reinhold.

Hearse, David J., et al. Enzymes in Cardiology Diagnosis & Research. LC 78-13633. 586p. 1979. 133.95 (ISBN 0-471-99724-2, Pub. by Wiley-Interscience). Wiley.

Henley, Keith S., et al. Enzymes in Serum: Their Use in Diagnosis. (Illus.). 132p. 1966. 14.50x (ISBN 0-398-00825-6). C C Thomas.

Hiromi, Keitaro. Kinetics of Fast Enzyme Reactions: Theory & Practice. LC 79-19391. 346p. 1980. 86.00x (ISBN 0-470-26866-2). Halsted Pr.

Holcenberg, John C. & Roberts, Joseph. Enzymes As Drugs. LC 80-20641. 455p. 1981. 94.95 (ISBN 0-471-05061-X, Pub. by Wiley-Interscience). Wiley.

Holzer, H., ed. Metabolic Interconversion of Enzymes 1980. (Proceedings in Life Science Ser.). (Illus.). 397p. 1981. 67.00 (ISBN 0-387-10979-X). Springer Verlag.

Horl, Walter H. & Heidland, August, eds. Proteases Potential Role in Health & Disease. (Advances in Experimental Medicine & Biology Ser.: Vol. 167). 608p. 1984. 85.00x (ISBN 0-306-41488-0, Plenum Pr). Plenum Pub.

Howell, Edward. Enzyme Nutrition. 160p. 1985. pap. 9.95 (ISBN 0-89529-221-1). Avery Pub.

Immobilized Enzymes II. LC 72-152360. (Advances in Biochemical Engineering Ser. Vol. 12: Vol. 12). (Illus.). 1979. 63.00 (ISBN 0-387-09262-5). Springer-Verlag.

Industrial Enzymes. 170p. 1984. 1500.00 (ISBN 0-86621-128-4, A1185). Frost & Sullivan.

International Symposium on Metabolic Interconversion of Enzymes, 3rd, Seattle, 1973. Proceedings. Fischer, E. H., ed. (Illus.). 400p. 1974. 45.00 (ISBN 0-387-06650-0). Springer-Verlag.

Jacob, Samson T., ed. Enzymes of Nucleic Acid Synthesis & Modification: DNA Enzymes, Vol. I. 1982. 72.50 (ISBN 0-8493-5517-6). CRC Pr.

Kellerman, A. E. Guide to EC Court Decisions, 4 vols. T.M.C. Asser Institute of the Netherlands, ed. 646p. 1982. 276.00 (ISBN 0-444-86437-7, North-Holland). Elsevier.

Kernevez, J. P. Enzyme Mathematics. (Studies in Mathematics & Its Applications: Vol. 10). 262p. 1980. 53.25 (ISBN 0-444-86122-X, North-Holland). Elsevier.

Kirk, John E. Enzymes of the Arterial Wall. 1969. 76.50 (ISBN 0-12-409650-6). Acad Pr.

Knox, W. E. Enzyme Patterns in Fetal, Adult & Neo-Plastic Rat Tissues. 2nd ed. 1976. 29.50 (ISBN 3-8055-2357-2). S Karger.

Konferenz der Gesellschaft Deutscher Naturforscher und Aerzte, 2nd, Rottach-Egern, 1971. Metabolic Interconversion of Enzymes: Proceedings. Wieland, O., et al, eds. LC 72-85775. (Illus.). xi, 448p. 1972. pap. 43.00 (ISBN 0-387-05919-9). Springer-Verlag.

Kurganov, B. I. Allosteric Enzymes: Kinetic Behavior. LC 81-21861. 344p. 1983. 69.95x (ISBN 0-471-10195-8, Pub. by Wiley-Interscience). Wiley.

Lafferty, R. M. Enzyme Technology. (Illus.). 350p. 1983. pap. 48.50 (ISBN 0-387-12479-9). Springer-Verlag.

Lam, Cham F. Techniques for the Analysis & Modeling of Enzyme Kinetic Mechanisms. (Medical Computing Ser.). 396p. 1981. 79.95x (ISBN 0-471-09981-3, Pub. by Res Stud Pr). Wiley.

Laskin, A. I., et al, eds. Enzyme Engineering, Vol. 7. (Annals of The New York Academy of Science Ser.: Vol. 434). 596p. 1984. lib. bdg. 135.00x (ISBN 0-89766-262-8); text ed. 135.00x (ISBN 0-89766-263-6). NY Acad Sci.

Laskin, Allen I. Enzymes & Immobilized Cells in Biotechnology. 1985. 41.95 (ISBN 0-8053-6360-2). Benjamin-Cummings.

Lawrence, S. H. The Zymogram in Clinical Medicine. (Illus.). 124p. 1964. photocopy ed. 11.75x (ISBN 0-398-01087-0). C C Thomas.

London Chemical Engineering Congress, Second Session, 1977. Advance in Enzyme & Membrane Technology: Proceedings, No. 51. 100p. 1981. 70.00x (ISBN 0-85295-103-5, Pub. by Inst Chem Eng England). State Mutual Bk.

Lowry, Oliver H. & Passonneau, Janet V. Flexible System of Enzymatic Analysis. 1972. 49.00 (ISBN 0-12-457950-7). Acad Pr.

Luebbers, D. W., et al, eds. Progress in Enzyme & Ion-Selective Electrodes. (Illus.). 240p. 1981. pap. 27.70 (ISBN 0-387-10499-2). Springer-Verlag.

McComb, Robert B., et al. Alkaline Phosphatase. LC 79-436. 1004p. 1979. 115.00x (ISBN 0-306-40214-9, Plenum Pr). Plenum Pub.

Maggio, Edward T. Enzyme Immunoassay. 304p. 1980. 79.00 (ISBN 0-8493-5617-2). CRC Pr.

Manocha, S. L., et al. Macaca Mulatta Enzyme Histochemistry of the Nervous System. 1970. 60.00 (ISBN 0-12-469350-4). Acad Pr.

Marmasse, C. Enzyme Kinetics. 242p. 1977. 37.25x (ISBN 0-677-05420-3). Gordon.

Mehler, Alan H. Introduction to Enzymology. 1957. 59.50 (ISBN 0-12-487750-8). Acad Pr.

Meister, A. Advances in Enzymology & Related Areas of Molecular Biology, Vol. 57. 464p. 1985. 55.00 (ISBN 0-471-89011-1). Wiley.

Meister, Alton. Advances in Enzymology & Related Areas of Molecular Biology, Vol. 52. LC 42-9213. 408p. 1981. 52.50x (ISBN 0-471-08120-5, Pub. by Wiley-Interscience). Wiley.

--Advances in Enzymology & Related Areas of Molecular Biology, Vol. 56. (AERAMB Ser.: 2-011). 520p. 1984. 50.00 (ISBN 0-471-89012-X, Pub. by Wiley-Interscience). Wiley.

Meister, Alton, ed. Advances in Enzymology, Vol. 37. 726p. 1973. 42.50 (ISBN 0-471-59172-6). Krieger.

--Advances in Enzymology, Vol. 38. 506p. 1973. 39.50 (ISBN 0-471-59173-4). Krieger.

--Advances in Enzymology, Vol. 39. 487p. 1973. 39.50 (ISBN 0-471-59174-2). Krieger.

--Advances in Enzymology, Vol. 40. 399p. 1974. 39.50 (ISBN 0-471-59175-0). Krieger.

--Advances in Enzymology, Vol. 41. LC 41-9213. 364p. 1974. 39.50 (ISBN 0-471-59176-9). Krieger.

--Advances in Enzymology, Vol. 42. 393p. 1975. 39.50 (ISBN 0-471-59177-7). Krieger.

--Advances in Enzymology, Vol. 45. LC 41-9213. 552p. 42.50 (ISBN 0-471-02726-X). Krieger.

Messing, Ralph A., ed. Immobilized Enzymes for Industrial Reactors. 1975. 37.50 (ISBN 0-12-492350-X). Acad Pr.

Methods in Enzymology, Vols. 47-62. Incl. Vol. 47. Enzyme Structure, Pt. E. Hirs, C. H. & Timasheff, S. N., eds. 1977. 80.00 (ISBN 0-12-181947-7); Vol. 48. Enzyme Structures, Pt. F. Hirs, C. H., ed. 1978. 80.00 (ISBN 0-12-181948-5); Vol. 49. Enzyme Structure, Pt. G. Hirs, C. H. & Timasheff, S. N., eds. 1978. 80.00 (ISBN 0-12-181949-3); Vol. 50. Complex Carbohydrates, Pt. C. Colowick, Sidney P. & Kaplan, Nathan O., eds. 1978. 70.00 (ISBN 0-12-181950-7); Vol. 51. Purine & Pyrimidine Nucleotide Metabolism. Colowick, Sidney P., et al, eds. 1978. 75.00 (ISBN 0-12-181951-5); Vol. 52. Biomembranes, Pt. C, Biological Oxidations; Microsomal Electron Transport & Cytochrome P-450 Systems. Colowick, Sidney P. & Kaplan, Nathan O., eds. 1978. 67.50 (ISBN 0-12-181952-3); Vol. 53. Pt. D Biological Oxidations; Mitochondrial & Microbial Systems. Fleischer, Sidney & Packer, Lester, eds. 1978. 72.00 (ISBN 0-12-181953-1); Vol. 54. Pt. E Biological Oxidations; Specialized Techniques. Fleischer, Sidney & Packer, Lester, eds. 1978. 69.50 (ISBN 0-12-181954-X); Vol. 55. Pt. F, Bioenergetics Oxidative Phosphorylation. Colowick, Sidney P. & Fleischer, Sidney, eds. 1979. 75.00 (ISBN 0-12-181955-8); Vol. 56. Biomembranes, Pt. G; Bioenergetics, Biogenesis of Mitochondria, Organization & Transport. Colowick, Sidney P., et al, eds. 1979. 69.50 (ISBN 0-12-181956-6); Vol. 57. Bioluminescence & Chemiluminescence. Deluca, Marlene, ed. 1978. 69.50 (ISBN 0-12-181957-4); Vol. 58. Cell Culture. Colowick, Sidney & Jacoby, William, eds. 1979. 69.50 (ISBN 0-12-181958-2); Vol. 59. Nucleic Acids & Proteins Synthesis, Pt. G, Moldave. Colowick, Sidney, ed. 1979. 71.50 (ISBN 0-12-181959-0); Vol. 60. Pt. H, Moldave. Colowick, Sidney, ed. 1979. 71.50 (ISBN 0-12-181960-4); Vol. 61. Enzyme Structure, Pt. H. Colowick, Sidney & Hirs, C. H., eds. 1979. 67.50 (ISBN 0-12-181961-2); Vol. 62. Vitamins & Coenzymes, Pt. D. Colowick, Sidney, et al, eds. 1979. 67.50 (ISBN 0-12-181962-0). Acad Pr.

Mihalyi, Elemer. Application of Proteolytic Enzymes to Protein Structure Studies. LC 72-87570. (Uniscience Ser). 1978. Vol. 1. 83.00 (ISBN 0-8493-5189-8). CRC Pr.

--Application of Proteolytic Enzymes to Protein Structure Studies, Vol. 2. 2nd ed. 310p. 1978. 72.50 (ISBN 0-8493-5190-1). CRC Pr.

Mora, Jaime & Palacios, Rafael, eds. Glutamine: Metabolism, Enzymology & Regulation. 1980. 37.50 (ISBN 0-12-506040-8). Acad Pr.

Moss, D. W. Isoenzymes. (Illus.). 224p. 1982. 39.00 (ISBN 0-412-22200-0, NO. 6722, Pub. by Chapman & Hall England). Methuen Inc.

Najjar, Victor A., ed. Enzyme Induction & Modulation. 1983. lib. bdg. 78.00 (ISBN 0-89838-583-0, Pub. by Martinus Nijhoff Netherlands). Kluwer Academic.

Najjar, Victor A. & Fridkin, Mati, eds. Antineoplastic, Immunogenic & Other Effects of the Tetrapeptide Tuftsin, Vol. 419. 55.00 (ISBN 0-89766-232-6); pap. 55.00x (ISBN 0-89766-233-4). NY Acad Sci.

Nord, F. F, ed. Advances in Enzymology, Vol. 28. 547p. 1966. 36.50 (ISBN 0-470-64957-7). Krieger.

--Advances in Enzymology, Vol. 30. 371p. 1968. 36.50 (ISBN 0-470-64959-3). Krieger.

--Advances in Enzymology, Vol. 31. 261p. 1968. 36.50 (ISBN 0-470-64960-7). Krieger.

--Advances in Enzymology, Vol. 33. 595p. 1970. 36.50 (ISBN 0-471-64962-7). Krieger.

--Advances in Enzymology, Vol. 34. 619p. 1971. 36.50 (ISBN 0-471-64963-5). Krieger.

Olson, Alfred & Cooney, Charles L., eds. Immobilized Enzymes in Food & Microbial Processes. LC 74-9866. 278p. 1974. 39.50x (ISBN 0-306-30789-8, Plenum Pr). Plenum Pub.

Ory, Robert L. & St. Angelo, Allen J., eds. Enzymes in Food & Beverage Processing. LC 77-6645. (ACS Symposium Ser: No. 47). 1977. 34.95 (ISBN 0-8412-0375-X). Am Chemical.

Page, M. I., ed. The Chemistry of Enzyme Action. (New Comprehensive Biochemistry Ser.: Vol. 6). 568p. 1984. 69.00 (ISBN 0-444-80504-4, I-017-84). Elsevier.

Pal, S. B., ed. Enzyme Labelled Immunoassay of Hormones & Drugs. 1978. 64.00x (ISBN 3-11007-539-3). De Gruyter.

Palmer, T. Understanding Enzymes. 405p. 1981. 84.95x (ISBN 0-470-27186-8). Halsted Pr.

Parke, Dennis V., ed. Enzyme Induction. LC 74-32541. (Basic Life Sciences Ser.: Vol. 6). 340p. 1975. 37.50x (ISBN 0-306-36506-5, Plenum Pr). Plenum Pub.

Peterson, E. A. Cellulosic Ion Exchangers. (Laboratory Techniques in Biochemistry & Molecular Biology: Vol. 2, Pt. 2). 1970. pap. 15.00 (ISBN 0-444-10057-1, North-Holland). Elsevier.

Piper, Priscilla J. Leukotrienes & Other Lipoxygenase Products: Proceedings. LC 83-175919. 368p. 1983. 69.95x (ISBN 0-471-90142-3, Res Stud Pr). Wiley.

Piszkiewicz, Dennis. Kinetics of Chemical & Enzyme-Catalyzed Reactions. (Illus.). 1977. 23.95x (ISBN 0-19-502096-0); pap. text ed. 15.95 (ISBN 0-19-502095-2). Oxford U Pr.

Pitcher, Wayne H., Jr. Immobilized Enzymes for Food Processing. 232p. 1980. 69.50 (ISBN 0-8493-5345-9). CRC Pr.

Porcellati, Giuseppe & Di Jeso, Fernando, eds. Membrane-Bound Enzymes. LC 70-151767. (Advances in Experimental Medicine & Biology Ser.: Vol. 14). 292p. 1971. 42.50x (ISBN 0-306-39014-0, Plenum Pr). Plenum Pub.

Price, Christopher P. & Scawen, M., eds. Clinical Applications of Microbial Enzymes, Vol. 4. (Methods in Laboratory Medicine Ser.). 240p. 1983. 47.00x (ISBN 0-686-89427-8). Praeger.

Prusiner, Stanley & Stadtman, Earl R., eds. The Enzymes of Glutamine Metabolism. 1973. 59.50 (ISBN 0-12-566450-8). Acad Pr.

Purich, Daniel L., ed. Contemporary Enzyme Kinetics & Mechanisms. LC 82-16265. 1983. 34.50 (ISBN 0-12-568050-3). Acad Pr.

Pye, E. Kendall & Weetall, H. H., eds. Enzyme Engineering, Vol. 3. LC 74-13768. 594p. 1977. 75.00x (ISBN 0-306-35283-4, Plenum Pr). Plenum Pub.

Pye, E. Kendall & Wingard, Lemual B., eds. Enzyme Engineering, Vol. 2. LC 74-13768. 470p. 1974. 59.50x (ISBN 0-306-35282-6, Plenum Pr). Plenum Pub.

Reed, Gerald. Enzymes in Food Processing. 2nd ed. 1975. 80.00 (ISBN 0-12-584852-8). Acad Pr.

Retey, James & Robinson, John A. Stereospecificity in Organic Chemistry & Enzymology. (Monographs in Modern Chemistry: Vol. 13). (Illus.). 324p. 1982. 86.30x (ISBN 0-89573-038-3). VCH Pubs.

Roberts, D. V., ed. Enzyme Kinetics. LC 76-11091. (Cambridge Chemistry Texts Ser.). (Illus.). 1977. 62.50 (ISBN 0-521-21274-X); pap. 24.95x (ISBN 0-521-29080-5). Cambridge U Pr.

Roberts, R., tr. Nucleases. Linn, S., ed. LC 82-71651. (Cold Spring Harbor Monograph: Vol. 14). 378p. 1982. 57.00X (ISBN 0-87969-155-7). Cold Spring Harbor.

Rolih, Susan & Albietz, Carol, eds. Enzymes, Inhibitions & Absorptions. (Illus.). 72p. 1981. 10.40 (ISBN 0-914404-67-9). Am Assn Blood.

Roodyn, D. B. Automated Enzyme Assays, Vol. 2, Pt. 1. (Laboratory Techniques in Biochemistry & Molecular Biology). 1970. pap. 18 50 (ISBN 0-444-10056-3, North-Holland). Elsevier.

Rotilio, G. Oxidative Damage & Related Enzymes, Vol. 2. (Life Chemistry Reports Supplement Ser.). 448p. pap. text ed. 35.00 (ISBN 3-7186-0221-0). Harwood Academic.

Royal Society Discussion Meeting, June 16-17, 1982. Industrial & Diagnostic Enzymes: Proceedings. Hartley, B. S. & Atkinson, T., eds. (Phil. Trans. Report Society Series B: Vol. 300). (Illus.). 196p. 1983. Repr. text ed. 61.00 (ISBN 0-85403-207-X, Pub. by Royal Soc London). Scholium Intl.

Ruyssen, R. & Lauwers, A., eds. Pharmaceutical Enzymes: Properties & Assay Methods. 1979. text ed. 74.50x (ISBN 0-391-01629-6). Humanities.

Salmona, M., et al, eds. Insolubilized Enzymes. LC 74-80537. 236p. 1974. 40.00 (ISBN 0-911216-60-X). Raven.

Schwimmer, Sigmund. Source Book of Food Enzymology. (Illus.). 1981. lib. bdg. 89.50 (ISBN 0-87055-369-0). AVI.

Scott, R. P. Liquid Chromatography Detectors. Kucera, P., ed. (Journal of Chromatography Library: Vol. 11). 248p. 1977. 53.25 (ISBN 0-444-41580-7). Elsevier.

Segel, I. H. Enzyme Kinetics: Behavior & Analysis of Rapid Equilibrium & Steady State Enzyme Systems. LC 74-26546. 957p. 1975. 44.95x (ISBN 0-471-77425-1, Pub. by Wiley-Interscience). Wiley.

Singer, Thomas P., et al, eds. Monoamine Oxidase: Structure, Function & Altered Functions. LC 79-24107. 1980. 60.00 (ISBN 0-12-646880-X). Acad Pr.

Smith, H. Regulation of Enzyme Synthesis & Activity in Higher Plants. 1978. 68.00 (ISBN 0-12-650850-X). Acad Pr.

Smulson & Sugimura. Novel ADP-Ribosylations of Regulatory Enzymes & Proteins. (Developments in Cell Biology Ser.: Vol. 6). 452p. 1980. 76.00 (ISBN 0-444-00403-3, Biomedical Pr). Elsevier.

Specifications for the Identity & Purity of Some Enzymes & Certain Other Substances. (Nutrition Meetings Reports: No. 50B). pap. 11.50 (F1207, FAO). Unipub.

Spector, L. B. Covalent Catalysis by Enzymes. (Illus.). 250p. 1982. 38.50 (ISBN 0-387-90616-9). Springer-Verlag.

Spiro, T. G. Molybdenim Enzymes. (Metal Ions in Biology Ser.). 672p. 1985. 75.00 (ISBN 0-471-88542-8). Wiley.

Spiro, Thomas G. Zinc Enzymes, Vol. 5. LC 83-5918. (Metal Ions in Biology Ser.: No. 1-457). 376p. 1983. 89.95 (ISBN 0-471-89081-2, Pub. by Wiley-Interscience). Wiley.

Suckling, C. J., ed. Enzyme Chemistry: Impact & Applications. 256p. 1984. text ed. 36.00 (ISBN 0-412-25850-1, 9192, Pub by Chapman & Hall England). Methuen Inc.

Suelter, C. H. A Practical Guide to Enzymology. (Biochemistry Ser.). 1985. 35.00 (ISBN 0-471-86431-5). Wiley.

Technical Insights, Inc. Advances in Enzyme Technology: Artificial & Semisynthetic Designed Enzymes. LC 84-51898. (Emerging Technologies Ser.: No. 12). 181p. 1984. 580.00 (ISBN 0-914993-08-9). Tech Insights.

Tobe, John. Physical Power Thru Enzymes. 2.50x (ISBN 0-686-29980-9). Cancer Control Soc.

Torrey, S., ed. Enzyme Technology: Preparation, Purification, Stabilization, Immobilization-Recent Advances. LC 83-13157. (Biotechnology Review No. 2; Chemical Technology Review No. 222). 308p. 1984. 42.00 (ISBN 0-8155-0956-1). Noyes.

Trevan, Michael D. Immobilized Enzymes: An Introduction & Applications in Biotechnology. LC 80-40502. 138p. 1980. 34.95x (ISBN 0-471-27826-2, Pub. by Wiley-Interscience). Wiley.

Usdin, E. Structure & Function of Monoamine Enzymes. (Modern Pharmacology-Toxicology Ser.: Vol. 10). 1977. 125.00 (ISBN 0-8247-6689-X). Dekker.

Van Thoai, N. & Roche, J. Homologous Enzymes & Biochemical Evolution. LC 68-19934. (Illus.). 486p. 1968. 132.95 (ISBN 0-677-11930-5). Gordon.

Vonk, Hubertus J. & Western, Richard H., eds. Comparative Biochemistry & Physiology of Enzymatic Digestion. 1984. 29.50 (ISBN 0-12-374080-0). Acad Pr.

Wade, Carlson. Catalytic Hormones: Key to Extraordinary Weight Loss. 285p. 1982. 16.95 (ISBN 0-13-120857-8, Parker). P-H.

Walker, Roy. The Molecular Biology of Enzyme Synthesis: Regulatory Mechanisms of Enzyme Adaptation. LC 82-10950. 381p. 1983. 53.50x (ISBN 0-471-06051-8, Pub. by Wiley-Interscience). Wiley.

Wallace, J. C. & Keech, D. B. Pyruvate Carboxylase. 304p. 1985. 90.00 (ISBN 0-8493-6552-X). CRC Pr.

Walsh, Christopher. Enzymatic Reaction Mechanisms. LC 78-18266. (Illus.). 978p. 1979. text ed. 43.95x (ISBN 0-7167-0070-0). W H Freeman.

Walter, C. F., ed. Enzyme Reactions in Enzyme Systems. (Enzymology Ser.: Vol.4). 216p. 1975. 49.75 (ISBN 0-8247-6299-1). Dekker.

Wang, Daniel I., et al. Fermentation & Enzyme Technology. LC 78-7596. (Techniques in Pure & Applied Microbiology Ser.). 374p. 1979. 42.95x (ISBN 0-471-91945-4, Pub. by Wiley-Interscience). Wiley.

Weber, G. Advances in Enzyme Regulation: Proceedings of the 21st Symposium on Regulation of Activity & Synthesis in Normal & Neoplastic Tissues, held at Indiana University School of Medicine, Indianapolis, USA, 4-5 October 1982, Vol. 21. LC 63-19609. (Illus.). 448p. 1983. 150.00 (ISBN 0-08-030430-3). Pergamon.

Weber, G., ed. Advances in Enzyme Regulation: Proceedings of the Symposium Regulation of Enzyme Activity & Synthesis in Normal & Neoplastic Tissues, 22nd, Held at Indiana University School of Medicine, Indianapolis, U. S. A., 3-4 October 1983, Vol. 22. LC 63-19609. (Illus.). 600p. 1984. 150.00 (ISBN 0-08-031498-8). Pergamon.

--Advances in Enzyme Regulation: Proceedings of the 17th Symposium on Regulation of Enzyme Activity & Synthesis in Normal & Neoplastic Tissues, Indiana University School of Medicine, Indianapolis, 2-3 October 1978, Vol. 17. (Illus.). 1979. 140.00 (ISBN 0-08-024424-6). Pergamon.

--Advances in Enzyme Regulation, Vol. 20: Proceedings of the 20th Symposium on Regulation of Activity & Synthesis in Normal & Neoplastic Tissues Held at Indiana University School of Medicine, Indianapolis, USA, October 5-6, 1981. LC 63-19609. (Illus.). 420p. 1982. 130.00 (ISBN 0-08-028898-7). Pergamon.

Weetall, Howard H. & Royer, Garfield P., eds. Enzyme Engineering, Vol. 5. LC 74-13768. 503p. 1979. 65.00 (ISBN 0-306-40471-0, Plenum Pr). Plenum Pub.

Welch, G. Rickey. Organized Multienzyme Systems: Catalytic Properties. Date not set. 75.00 (ISBN 0-12-744040-2). Acad Pr.

Wharton, Christopher W. & Eisenthal, R. Molecular Enzymology. (Tertiary Level Biology Ser.). 335p. 1981. 53.95x (ISBN 0-470-27152-3). Halsted Pr.

Whitaker, J. R. Principles of Enzymology for the Food Sciences. (Food Science Ser: Vol. 2). 656p. 1972. 59.75 (ISBN 0-8247-1780-5). Dekker.

Whitaker, John R., ed. Food Related Enzymes. LC 74-20861. (Advances in Chemistry Ser: No. 136). 1974. 31.95 (ISBN 0-8412-0209-5). Am Chemical.

Wilkins, D. J., ed. Substrate-Induced Irreversible Inhibition of Enzymes. Date not set. price not set. Elsevier.

Wingard, L., et al, eds. Applied Biochemistry & Bioengineering: Vol. 3: Analytical Applications of Immobilized Enzymes & Cells. (Serial Publication). 1981. 55.00 (ISBN 0-12-041103-2); lib. ed. o.p. 59.50 (ISBN 0-12-041174-1). Acad Pr.

Wingard, Lemual B., et al, eds. Enzyme Engineering: Future Directions. LC 80-12061. 535p. 1980. 75.00x (ISBN 0-306-40442-7, Plenum Pr). Plenum Pub.

Wingard, Lemual B., Jr., et al. Applied Biochemistry & Bioengineering: Enzyme Technology, Vol. 2. (Serial Publication). 1979. 50.00 (ISBN 0-12-041102-4); lib ed 65.00 (ISBN 0-12-041172-5); microfiche 40.00 (ISBN 0-12-041173-3). Acad Pr.

Wingard, Lemuel B., Jr., ed. Applied Biochemistry & Bioengineering, Vol.1. 1976. 70.00 (ISBN 0-12-041101-6); lib. ed. o.p. 90.00 (ISBN 0-12-041170-9). Acad Pr.

Wiseman, A. Handbook of Enzyme Biotechnology. (Enzyme Biotechnology Ser.). 1985. 82.95 (ISBN 0-470-20153-3). Halsted Pr.

Wiseman, Alan. Handbook of Enzyme Biotechnology. LC 75-2466. 275p. 1975. 89.95x (ISBN 0-470-95617-8). Halsted Pr.

--Topics in Enzyme & Fermentation Biotechnology, Vol. 6. 232p. 1982. 74.95x (ISBN 0-470-27304-6). Halsted Pr.

--Topics in Enzyme & Fermentation Biotechnology, Vol. 7. LC 77-511. 345p. 1982. 84.95x (ISBN 0-470-27366-6). Halsted Pr.

Wiseman, Alan, ed. Topics in Enzyme & Fermentation Bio-Technology, Vol. 8. LC 78-643391. (Topics in Enzyme & Fermentation Bio-Technology Ser.: I-365). 179p. 1984. text ed. 54.95x (ISBN 0-470-20058-8). Halsted Pr.

--Topics in Enzyme & Fermentation Biotechnology, Vol. 4. (Topics in Enzyme & Fermentation Biotechnology Ser.). 242p. 1980. 89.95x (ISBN 0-470-26922-7). Halsted Pr.

Woodward, J., ed. Immobilized Cells & Enzymes: A Practical Approach. (Practical Approach Ser.). (Illus.). 250p. (Orig.). 1985. pap. 23.00 (ISBN 0-947946-21-7). IRL Pr.

Zikakis, John P., ed. Chitin, Chitosan, & Related Enzymes. 1984. 39.50 (ISBN 0-12-780950-3). Acad Pr.

ENZYMES–BIBLIOGRAPHY

Hoijer, D. J. A Bibliographic Guide to Neuroenzyme Literature. LC 72-102211. 306p. 1969. 75.00x (ISBN 0-306-65148-3, IFI Plenum). Plenum Pub.

EOCENE PERIOD

see Geology, Stratigraphic–Eocene

EPHEMERIDAE

see May-Flies

EPHEMERIDES

see also Nautical Almanacs

Benjamine, Elbert. How to Use Modern Ephemerides: Computed for Midnight & Noon & Eclipse Dates 1880-1990. rev. ed. 1983. pap. 1.50 (ISBN 0-933646-15-1). Aries Pr.

Michelsen, Neil. The American Sidereal Ephemeris, 1976-2000. 320p. (Orig.). 1981. pap. 19.50 (ISBN 0-917086-30-9). A C S Pubns Inc.

Michelsen, Neil F. The American Ephemeris: 1991 to 2000. (American Ephemeris Ser.). 128p. 1980. pap. 5.00 (ISBN 0-917086-21-X). A C S Pubns Inc.

Raphael. Raphael's Astro Ephemeris (Any Year) pap. 3.95x (ISBN 0-685-22085-0). Wehman.

EPHEMEROPTERA

Flannagan, John F. & Marshall, K. Eric, eds. Advances in Ephemeroptera Biology. LC 79-27713. 565p. 1980. 69.50x (ISBN 0-306-40357-9, Plenum Pr). Plenum Pub.

Kimmins, D. E. A Revised Key to the Adults of the British Species of Ephemeroptera. 2nd ed. 1972. 20.00x (ISBN 0-900386-17-7, Pub. by Freshwater Bio). State Mutual Bk.

Macan, T. T. A Key to the Nymphs of British Ephemeroptera. 3rd ed. 1979. 20.00x (ISBN 0-900386-35-5, Pub. by Freshwater Bio). State Mutual Bk.

EPICURUS

Asmis, Elizabeth. Epicurus' Scientific Method. LC 83-45133. 400p. 1983. 49.50x (ISBN 0-8014-1465-2). Cornell U Pr.

EPIGENESIS

Wauschkuhn, A., et al, eds. Syngenesis & Epigenesis in the Formation of Mineral Deposits. (Illus.). 660p. 1984. 61.50 (ISBN 0-387-13845-5). Springer-Verlag.

EPISOMES

Stuttard, Colins & Rozee, K. R., eds. Plasmids & Transposons: Environmental Efforts & Maintenance Mechanisms. LC 80-338. 1980. 38.50 (ISBN 0-12-675550-7). Acad Pr.

EPITHELIAL CELLS

see Exfoliative Cytology

EPITHELIUM

see also Cilia and Ciliary Motion; Exfoliative Cytology

Alfred Benzon Symposium 5th. Transport Mechanisms in Epithelia. Ussing, H. H., et al, eds. 1973. 65.00 (ISBN 0-12-709550-0). Acad Pr.

Al-Yassin, Ibrahim M. Growth Potential of Dental Epithelium in Tissue Culture. 180p. 1985. 55.00x (ISBN 0-7103-0073-5, Kegan Paul). Routledge & Kegan.

Berridge, Michael J. & Oschman, James L. Transporting Epithelia. (Monographs in the Ultrastructure of Cells & Organisms Ser.). 1972. 27.50 (ISBN 0-12-454135-6). Acad Pr.

Bronner, Felix & Peterlik, Meinrad. Epithelial Calcium & Phosphate Transport: Molecular & Cellular Aspects. LC 84-17149. (Progress in Clinical & Biological Research Ser.: Vol. 168). 416p. 1984. 68.00 (ISBN 0-8451-5018-9). A R Liss.

Case, Maynard, et al, eds. Electrolyte & Water Transport Across Gastrointestinal Epithelia. 335p. 1982. text ed. 53.50 (ISBN 0-89004-765-0). Raven.

Dinno, Mumtaz A., et al. Membrane Biophysics: Vol. II: Physical Methods in the Study of Epithelia. LC 83-9862. (Progress in Clinical & Biological Research Ser.: Vol. 126). 392p. 1983. 48.00 (ISBN 0-8451-0126-9). A R Liss.

Forte, John G., et al, eds. Hydrogen Ion Transport in Epithelia. LC 84-11935. 432p. 1984. text ed. 49.95 (ISBN 0-471-88262-3, Pub. by Wiley-Interscience). Wiley.

Kefalides, Nicholas A., ed. Biology & Chemistry of Basement Membranes. 1978. 59.50 (ISBN 0-12-403150-1). Acad Pr.

Lahlou, B., ed. Epithelial Transport in the Lower Vertebrates. LC 79-50884. (Illus.). 1980. 57.50 (ISBN 0-521-22748-8). Cambridge U Pr.

Macknight, Anthony D. & Leader, John P., eds. Epithelial Ion & Water Transport. 392p. 1981. 60.00 (ISBN 0-89004-537-2). Raven.

Parakkal, P. F. & Alexander, Nancy J. Keratinization - a Survey of Vertebrate Epithelia. (Monographs on the Ultrastructure of Cells & Organisms). 1972. 27.50 (ISBN 0-12-454140-2). Acad Pr.

Sawyer, Roger H. Epithelial-Mesenchymal Interactions in Development. Fallon, John F., ed. LC 82-13160. 270p. 1983. deluxe ed. 32.95 (ISBN 0-03-060326-9). Praeger.

Schultz, Stanley, ed. Ion Transport by Epithelia. (Society of General Physiologists Ser.: Vol. 36). 288p. 1981. text ed. 46.00 (ISBN 0-89004-610-7). Raven.

Scott, Walter N. & Goodman, David B., eds. Hormonal Regulation of Epithelial Transport of Ions & Water, Vol. 372. LC 81-14068. 660p. 1981. 142.00x (ISBN 0-89766-133-8). NY Acad Sci.

Ziegler, Thomas W. Transport in High Resistance Epithelia, Vol. 1. Horrobin, D., ed. 1978. 21.60 (ISBN 0-88831-012-9). Eden Pr.

Zinn, Keith M. & Marmor, Michael F., eds. The Retinal Pigment Epithelium. (Illus.). 531p. 1979. text ed. 45.00x (ISBN 0-674-76684-9). Harvard U Pr.

EPIZOA

see Parasites

EPOXIDES

see Epoxy Compounds

EPOXY COMPOUNDS

Carbon Reinforced Epoxy Systems, Part 2. (Materials Technology Ser.: Vol. 8). 243p. 1982. pap. 35.00 (ISBN 0-87762-318-X). Technomic.

Carbon Reinforced Epoxy Systems, Part 3. (Materials Technology Ser.: Vol. 9). 217p. 1982. pap. 35.00 (ISBN 0-686-89303-4). Technomic.

Glass Reinforced Epoxy Systems, Part 2. (Materials Technology Ser.: Vol. 10). 203p. 1982. pap. 35.00 (ISBN 0-87762-319-8). Technomic.

Hildo, Carlos, ed. Boron Reinforced Epoxy Systems, Vol. 3. LC 74-83231. (Materials Technology Ser.). 128p. 1974. pap. 17.00 (ISBN 0-87762-151-9). Technomic.

EPOXY RESINS

see also Epoxy Compounds

Bauer, Ronald S., ed. Epoxy Resin Chemistry. LC 79-21858. (ACS Symposium Ser.: No. 114). 1979. 34.95 (ISBN 0-8412-0525-6). Am Chemical.

--Epoxy Resin Chemistry II. LC 83-6385. (ACS Symposium Ser.: No. 221). 310p. 1983. lib. bdg. 39.95 (ISBN 0-8412-0777-1). Am Chemical.

BOOKS - SUBJECT INDEX

ERGODIC THEORY

DiStasio, J. I., ed. Epoxy Resin Technology: Developments Since 1979. LC 81-18926. (Chemical Technology Review Ser.: No. 204). (Illus.). 366p. (Orig.). 1982. 48.00 (ISBN 0-8155-0888-3). Noyes.
Foamed Plastics: Styrene, Epoxy & Other Polymeric Foams. 100p. 1984. 78.00 (ISBN 0-317-12677-6, LS114). T-C Pubns CA.
Hilado, Carlos J., ed. Carbon Reinforced Epoxy Systems, Pt. 4. LC 74-83231. (Materials Technology Ser.: Vol. 12). 266p. 1984. pap. 14.00 (ISBN 0-87762-342-2). Technomic.
--Carbon Reinforced Epoxy Systems, Pt. 5. LC 74-83231. (Materials Technology Ser.: Vol 13). 278p. 1984. pap. 35.00 (ISBN 0-87762-343-0). Technomic.
Lee, H. L. & Neville, K. O. Handbook of Epoxy Resins. 1966. 64.50 (ISBN 0-07-036997-6). McGraw.
Lee, Henry, ed. Epoxy Resins. LC 70-113408. (Advances in Chemistry Ser: No. 92). 1970. 22.95 (ISBN 0-8412-0093-9). Am Chemical.
May, C. & Tanaka, Y., eds. Epoxy Resins: Chemistry & Technology. 816p. 1973. 185.00 (ISBN 0-8247-1446-6). Dekker.
Potter, W. G. Uses of Epoxy Resins. 1976. 28.50 (ISBN 0-8206-0202-7). Chem Pub.

EPSON (COMPUTER)

see also Epson Hx-20 (Computer); Epson Qx-10 (Computer)

Curran, Susan. Get More from the Epson Printer. (Illus.). 160p. (Orig.). 1985. pap. 15.95 (ISBN 0-00-383001-2, Pub. by Collins England). Sheridan.
Darnall, William H. The Epson Connection: Apple. (Illus.). 1984. pap. text ed. 16.95 (ISBN 0-8359-1750-9). Reston.
Dodson, Susan. Medical Office Applications Using Your Epson. 1985. pap. 19.95 (ISBN 0-8359-4492-1). Reston.
Levine, Howard. Portable Calc & the Portable Schedules for the Portable Epson PX-8. 104p. (Orig.). 1984. pap. 16.95 (ISBN 0-553-34160-X). Bantam.
Smith, Marshall P. Portable Wordstar for the Portable Epson PX-8. 104p. (Orig.). 1984. pap. 16.95 (ISBN 0-553-34159-6). Bantam.
Weis, Rick. Epson Printers for Accountants. 1985. pap. 19.95 (ISBN 0-8359-1748-7). Reston.
--Epson Printers for CPA's. 1985. pap. 19.95 (ISBN 0-8359-1748-7). Reston.
Wood, Michael. Word Processing on the BBC Micro: Wordwise & Epson. 100p. 1982. pap. text ed. 9.05 (ISBN 0-471-81046-0). Wiley.

EPSON HX-20 (COMPUTER)

Ahl, David H. The Epson HX-20 Ideabook. (The Ideabook Ser.). 142p. 1983. pap. 8.95 (ISBN 0-916688-52-6, 3S). Creative Comp.
Corlett, Stan & Cain, John. Getting Started with the Epson HX-20 Portable Computer. 118p. 1984. pap. 12.95 (ISBN 0-946576-02-5, Pub. by Phoenix Pub). David & Charles.
Zimmerman, Steven & Conrad, Leo. User's Guide to Epson HX-20. 256p. pap. 14.95 (2200). Hayden.

EPSON QX-10 (COMPUTER)

Einhorn, Richard. Epson QX-10: Everything You Need to Know. LC 84-60790. (Illus.). 224p. 1984. pap. 12.95 (ISBN 0-688-02832-2, Quill NY). Morrow.
Hansen, Jim. The Epson QX-10 User's Guide. 159p. 1984. pap. 17.95 (ISBN 0-673-15973-6). Scott F.
Mills, David G. Using the Epson QX-10. 1984. pap. 15.95 (ISBN 0-943732-02-6). M & S Ent.

EQUATIONS

Burgers, J. M. The Non-Linear Diffusion Equation: Asymtotic Solutions & Statistical Problems. LC 74-81936. 192p. 1975. lib. bdg. 42.00 (ISBN 90-277-0494-5, Pub. by Reidel Holland). Kluwer Academic.
Douglas, J., Jr. & Dupont, T. Collocation Methods for Parabolic Equations in a Single Space Variable: Based on C to the First Power-Piecewise-Polynomial Spaces. (Lecture Notes in Mathematics: Vol. 385). v, 147p. 1974. pap. text ed. 12.00 (ISBN 0-387-06747-7). Springer-Verlag.
Elsgolts, L. E. & Norkin, S. B. Introduction to the Theory & Application of Differential Equations with Deviating Arguments. 1973. 61.50 (ISBN 0-12-237750-8). Acad Pr.
Fitts, Gary, ed. Module X: Functions & Word Problems. Ablon, Leon J. LC 76-1055. (Mathematics Modules Ser.). 1976. pap. 7.95 (ISBN 0-8465-0264-X). Benjamin-Cummings.
Froissart, Marcel, ed. Hyperbolic Equations & Waves: Battelle Seattle 1968 Recontres. LC 76-86498. (Illus.). 1970. 40.80 (ISBN 0-387-04883-9). Springer-Verlag.
Gelfond, A. O. Solving Equations in Integers. 56p. 1981. pap. 2.00 (ISBN 0-8285-2053-4, Pub. by Mir Pubs USSR). Imported Pubns.
Glimm, James & Lax, Peter D. Decay of Solutions of Systems of Nonlinear Hyperbolic Conservation Laws. LC 52-42839. (Memoirs Ser.: Vol. 101). 112p. 1970. pap. text ed. 9.00 (ISBN 0-8218-1801-5, MEMO-101). Am Math.
Gordon, R. J., ed. Equation of Motion, Boundry Layer Theory & Measurement. (AlCheEMI Modular Instruction C-Ser.: Vol. 3). 62p. 1982. pap. 30.00 (ISBN 0-8169-0210-0). Am Inst Chem Eng.
Haraux, A. Nonlinear Evolution Equations: Global Behavior of Solutions. (Lecture Notes in Mathematics Ser.: Vol. 841). 313p. 1981. pap. 20.00 (ISBN 0-387-10563-8). Springer-Verlag.
Institute of Mathematics, Oxford Conference, April 1970. Large Spare Sets of Linear Equations. Reid, R., ed. 1971. 39.50 (ISBN 0-12-586150-8). Acad Pr.
Johnson, Lee H. Nomography & Empirical Equations. LC 77-16063. 160p. 1978. Repr. of 1952 ed. lib. bdg. 14.00 (ISBN 0-88275-551-X). Krieger.
Keedy, Mervin & Bittinger, Marvin. Linear Equations & Systems of Equations. rev. ed. (Algebra, a Modern Introduction Ser.). 1981. pap. text ed. 4.32 (ISBN 0-201-03986-9). Addison-Wesley.
Kurosh, A. Algebraic Equations of Arbitrary Degrees. 1977. pap. 1.95 (ISBN 0-8285-0701-5, Pub. by Mir Pubs USSR). Imported Pubns.
Manwell, A. R. The Tricomi Equation with Applications to the Theory of Plane Transonic Flow. (Research Notes in Mathematics Ser.: No. 35). (Illus.). 176p. (Orig.). 1979. pap. text ed. 22.95 (ISBN 0-273-08428-3). Pitman Pub MA.
Nordgaard, M. A. An Historical Survey of Algebraic Methods of Approximating the Roots of Numerical Higher Equations up to the Year 1819. LC 76-177107. (Columbia University. Teachers College. Contributions to Education: No. 123). Repr. of 1922 ed. 22.50 (ISBN 0-404-55123-8). AMS Pr.
Oleinik, O. A. & Radkevic, E. V. Second-Order Equations with Non-Negative Characteristic Form. LC 73-16453. 259p. 1973. 39.50x (ISBN 0-306-30751-0, Plenum Pr). Plenum Pub.
Patterson, W. M. Iterative Methods for the Solution of a Linear Operator Equation in Hilbert Space: A Survey. (Lecture Notes in Mathematics: Vol. 394). 183p. 1974. pap. 14.00 (ISBN 0-387-06805-8). Springer-Verlag.
Reed, M. C. Abstract Non Linear Wave Equations. (Lecture Notes in Mathematics: Vol. 507). 128p. 1976. pap. 13.00 (ISBN 0-387-07617-4). Springer-Verlag.
Sakamoto, Reiko. Hyperbolic Boundary-Value Problems. LC 81-3865. 230p. 1982. 39.50 (ISBN 0-521-23568-5). Cambridge U Pr.
Smirnov, M. M. Equations of Mixed Type. LC 78-8260. (Translations of Mathematical Monographs: Vol. 51). 1978. 42.00 (ISBN 0-8218-4501-2, MMONO51). Am Math.
Solving Equations: Level Three Texts. rev. ed. (Math Components Ser.). 48p. 1983. 2.50 (ISBN 0-88336-831-5). New Readers.
Steindl, J. Random Processes & the Growth of Firms: A Study of the Pareto Law. 249p. 1965. text ed. 22.00x (ISBN 0-85264-063-3). Lubrecht & Cramer.
Struppa, Daniele C. The Fundamental Principle for Systems of Convolution Equations. LC 82-20614. (Memoirs of the American Mathematical Society Ser.: No. 273). 168p. 1982. pap. 12.00 (ISBN 0-8218-2273-X, MEMO/273). Am Math.
Teman, R. Navier-Stokes Equations. 2nd ed. LC 79-15106. (Studies Inmathematics & Its Applications: Vol. 2). 520p. 1979. 85.00 (ISBN 0-444-85307-3, North Holland); pap. 38.25 (ISBN 0-444-85308-1, North-Holland). Elsevier.
Thomasset, F. Implementation of Finite Element Methods for Navier-Stokes Equations. (Springer Series in Computational Phsyics). (Illus.). 160p. 1981. 36.00 (ISBN 0-387-10771-1). Springer Verlag.

EQUATIONS–NUMERICAL SOLUTIONS

Altman. Contractors & Contractor Direction Theory & Applications: A New Approach to Solving Equations. (Lecture Notes in Pure & Applied Math Ser.: Vol. 32). 1977. 55.00 (ISBN 0-8247-6672-5). Dekker.
Bharucha & Reid, eds. Approximate Solutions of Random Equations. (Series in Probability & Applied Mathematics: Vol. 3). 256p. 1979. 61.00 (ISBN 0-444-00344-4, North Holland). Elsevier.
Ortega, James M. & Rheinboldt, Werner C. Iterative Solution of Nonlinear Equations in Several Variables. (Computer Science & Applied Mathematics Ser). 1970. 70.00 (ISBN 0-12-528550-7). Acad Pr.
Rabinowitz, Philip, ed. Numerical Methods for Nonlinear Algebraic Equations. LC 78-115963. (Illus.). 212p. 1970. 42.95x (ISBN 0-677-14230-7). Gordon.
Wait, R. The Numerical Solution of Algebraic Equations. LC 78-21869. 158p. 1979. 38.95x (ISBN 0-471-99755-2, Pub. by Wiley-Interscience). Wiley.
Wilkinson, James H. Algebraic Eigenvalue Problem. (Monographs on Numerical Analysis). 1965. 77.00x (ISBN 0-19-853403-5). Oxford U Pr.

EQUATIONS, ABELIAN

see also Cyclotomy

Pusey, William A. The History & Epidemiology of Syphilis. (Illus.). 110p. 1933. photocopy ed. 10.75x (ISBN 0-398-04400-7). C C Thomas.

EQUATIONS, CHEMICAL

see Chemical Equations

EQUATIONS, CYCLOTOMIC

see Cyclotomy

EQUATIONS, DIFFERENCE

see Difference Equations

EQUATIONS, DIFFERENTIAL

see Differential Equations

EQUATIONS, EULER-LAGRANGE

see Lagrange Equations

EQUATIONS, FUNCTIONAL

see Functional Equations

EQUATIONS, INDETERMINATE

see Diophantine Analysis

EQUATIONS, INTEGRAL

see Integral Equations

EQUATIONS, LAGRANGE

see Lagrange Equations

EQUATIONS, QUADRATIC

Gregory, John, ed. Quadratic Form Theory & Differential Equations. LC 80-520. (Mathematics in Science & Engineering Ser.). 1981. 39.50 (ISBN 0-12-301450-6). Acad Pr.
Sakai, M. Quadrature Domains. (Lecture Notes in Mathematics: Vol. 934). 133p. 1982. pap. 11.00 (ISBN 0-387-11562-5). Springer-Verlag.
Steklov Institute of Mathematics & Kuz'mina, G. V. Moduli of Families of Curves & Quadratic Differentials. LC 82-8902. (Proceedings of the Steklov Institute of Mathematics Ser.: No. 139). 88.00 (ISBN 0-8218-3040-6, STEKLO-139). Am Math.
Strebel, K. Quadratic Differentials. (Ergebnisse der Mathematik und ihrer Grenzgebiete, 3. Folge A Series of Modern Surveys in Mathematics: Vol. 5). (Illus.). 200p. 1984. 38.00 (ISBN 0-387-13035-7). Springer Verlag.

EQUATIONS, QUARTIC

Jessop, Charles M. Quartic Surfaces with Singular Points. LC 17-11584. pap. 59.00 (ISBN 0-317-11078-0, 2051691). Bks Demand UMI.

EQUATIONS, SIMULTANEOUS

Bauwens, L. Bayesian Full Information Analysis of Simultaneous Equation Models Using Integration by Monte Carlo. (Lecture Notes in Economics & Mathematical Systems Ser.: Vol. 232). vi, 114p. 1984. pap. 11.00 (ISBN 0-387-13384-4). Springer-Verlag.
Dongarra, J. J., et al. LINPACK Users' Guide. LC 78-78206. viii, 367p. 1979. pap. text ed. 24.00 (ISBN 0-89871-172-X). Soc Indus-Appl Math.
Geraci, Vincent J. Simultaneous Equation Models with Measurement Error. LC 79-53208. (Outstanding Dissertations in Economics Ser.). 180p. 1984. lib. bdg. 29.00 (ISBN 0-8240-4158-5). Garland Pub.
Young, David M. Iterative Solution of Large Linear Systems. 1971. 75.00 (ISBN 0-12-773050-8). Acad Pr.

EQUATIONS, THEORY OF

see also Galois Theory; Groups, Theory Of; Symmetric Functions

Conkwright, Nelson B. Introduction to the Theory of Equations. LC 58-2094. pap. 56.30 (ISBN 0-317-08691-X, 2000509). Bks Demand UMI.
Dobbs, David & Hanks, Robert. A Modern Course on the Theory of Equations. LC 80-13487. 1980. 15.00x (ISBN 0-936428-03-1). Polygonal Pub.
Eaves, B. C. A Course in Triangulations for Solving Equations with Deformations. (Lecture Notes in Economics & Mathematical Systems Ser.: Vol. 234). 302p. 1984. pap. 19.50 (ISBN 0-387-13876-5). Springer-Verlag.
Netto, Eugen. Theory of Substitutions. 2nd ed. LC 64-10289. 1964. 13.95 (ISBN 0-8284-0165-9). Chelsea Pub.

EQUILIBRIUM

see also Irreversible Processes; Phase Rule and Equilibrium; Stability; Statics

Baldry, J. C. General Equilibrium Analysis: An Introduction to the Two Sector Model. LC 80-82652. 228p. 1980. 39.95 (ISBN 0-470-27024-1, Pub. by Halsted Pr). Wiley.
Bowers, T. S., et al. Equilibrium Activity Diagrams. xli, 398p. 1984. 35.50 (ISBN 0-387-13796-3). Springer-Verlag.
Ernst, George C., et al. Principles of Structural Equilibrium: A Study of Equilibrium Conditions by Graphic, Force-Moment & Virtual Displacement. LC 62-7876. pap. 42.50 (ISBN 0-317-10687-2, 2001977). Bks Demand UMI.
Garcia, C. B. & Zangwill, Willard I. Pathways to Solutions, Fixed Points, & Equilibria. (Computational Math Ser.). 336p. 1981. text ed. 42.95 (ISBN 0-13-653501-1). P-H.
Garrido, L., ed. Systems Far from Equilibrium: Sitges Conference. (Lecture Notes in Physics Ser.: Vol. 132). 403p. 1980. pap. 32.00 (ISBN 0-387-10251-5). Springer Verlag.
Hansen, B. Survey of General Equilibrium Systems. LC 81-20933. 254p. 1982. Repr. of 1970 ed. 18.95 (ISBN 0-89874-363-X). Krieger.
Liapounoff, M. A. Probleme General de la Stabilite du Mouvement. (Annals of Math Studies). 1947. 21.00 (ISBN 0-527-02733-2). Kraus Repr.
Pytkowicz, Ricardo M. Equilibria, Nonequilibria, & Natural Waters. 2nd ed. 1983. Set, 400p. 84.95x (ISBN 0-471-87831-6, Pub. by Wiley-Interscience); Vol. 1, 351p. 49.95x (ISBN 0-471-86192-8); Vol. 2, 353. 49.95x (ISBN 0-471-89111-8). Wiley.
Scarf, Hebert & Shoven, John, eds. Applied General Equilibrium Analysis. LC 83-7164. 576p. 1984. 59.50 (ISBN 0-521-25745-X). Cambridge U Pr.
Sterner, Wanda. Equilibrium Calculations: PH - Weak Acids. 1971. pap. 2.00x (ISBN 0-87881-004-8). Mojave Bks.
Valentinuzzi, M., ed. The Organs of Equilibrium & Orientation As a Control System. (Biomedical Engineering & Computation Ser.: Vol. 2). 208p. 1980. text ed. 63.75 (ISBN 3-7186-0014-5). Harwood Academic.
Van Damme, E. Refinements of the Nash Equilibrium Concept. (Lecture Notes in Economics & Mathematical Systems Ser.: Vol. 219). 151p. 1983. pap. 14.00 (ISBN 0-387-12690-2). Springer-Verlag.
West, D. R. Ternary Equilibrium Diagrams. 2nd ed. LC 81-14060. (Illus.). 1982. 27.00 (NO. 6615, Pub. by Chapman & Hall); pap. 13.95x (ISBN 0-412-22820-3, NO. 6614). Methuen Inc.

EQUILIBRIUM, CHEMICAL

see Chemical Equilibrium

EQUILIBRIUM, IONIC

see Ionic Equilibrium

EQUILIBRIUM, THERMAL

see Heat; Thermodynamics

EQUILIBRIUM, VAPOR-LIQUID

see Vapor-Liquid Equilibrium

EQUILIBRIUM THEORY OF TIDES

see Tides

EQUIPMENT, INDUSTRIAL

see Industrial Equipment

EQUIPMENT, POLLUTION CONTROL

see Pollution Control Equipment

ERGODIC THEORY

Billingsley, Patrick. Ergodic Theory & Information. LC 78-2442. 210p. 1978. Repr. of 1965 ed. lib. bdg. 15.00 (ISBN 0-88275-666-4). Krieger.
Brown, James R. Ergodic Theory & Topological Dynamics. (Pure & Applied Math Ser.). 1976. 42.50 (ISBN 0-12-137150-6). Acad Pr.
Caldirola, P., ed. Ergodic Theories. (Italian Physical Society: Course 14). 1962. 75.00 (ISBN 0-12-368814-0). Acad Pr.
Cornfeld, I. P., et al. Ergodic Theory. (Grundlehren der Mathematischen Wissenschafter Ser.: Vol. 245). (Illus.). 480p. 1982. 55.00 (ISBN 0-387-90580-4). Springer-Verlag.
Denker, M. & Jacobs, K., eds. Ergodic Theory: Proceedings, Oberwolfach, Germany, 11-17 June 1978. (Lecture Notes in Mathematics: Vol. 729). 1979. pap. 17.00 (ISBN 0-387-09517-9). Springer-Verlag.
Dudley, R. M., et al. Ecole d'Ete de Probabilities de Saint-Flour XII, 1982. (Lecture Notes in Mathematics Ser.: Vol. 1097). x, 396p. 1984. pap. 22.50 (ISBN 0-387-13897-8). Springer-Verlag.
Furstenberg, H. Recurrence in Ergodic Theory & Combinatorial Number Theory. LC 80-7518. (Rice University, Dept. of Mathematics, M. B. Porter Lectures). 228p. 1981. 27.50 (ISBN 0-691-08269-3). Princeton U Pr.
Halmos, P. R. Lectures on Ergodic Theory. LC 60-8964. 8.95 (ISBN 0-8284-0142-X). Chelsea Pub.
Katok, A. Ergodic Theory & Dynamical Systems. 338p. 1981. text ed. 24.95x (ISBN 0-8176-3036-8). Birkhauser.
Katok, A., ed. Ergodic Theory & Dynamical Systems Eleven. (Progress in Mathematics Ser.: Vol. 21). 210p. 1982. text ed. 17.50x (ISBN 0-8176-3096-1). Birkhauser.
Krengel, Ulrich. Ergodic Theorems: With a Supplement on Harris Processes Written by A. Brunel. (Studies in Mathematics: Vol. 9). viii, 357p. 1985. 49.95x (ISBN 3-11-008478-3). De Gruyter.
Markley, N. G., et al, eds. The Structure of Attractors in Dynamical Systems: Proceedings, North Dakota, June 20-24, 1977. LC 78-13670. (Lecture Notes in Mathematics: Vol. 668). 1978. pap. 20.00 (ISBN 0-387-08925-X). Springer-Verlag.
Ollagnier, J. Moulin. Ergodic Theory & Statistical Mechanics. (Lecture Notes in Mathematics: Vol. 1115). vi, 147p. 1985. pap. 12.00 (ISBN 0-387-15192-3). Springer Verlag.

Parry, William. Topics in Ergodic Theory. LC 79-7815. (Cambridge Tracts in Mathematics Ser.: No. 75). 1981. 29.95 (ISBN 0-521-22986-3). Cambridge U Pr.

Parry, William & Tuncel, Selim. Classification Problems in Ergodic Theory. (London Mathematical Society Lecture Note Ser.: No. 67). 150p. 1982. pap. 15.95 (ISBN 0-521-28794-4). Cambridge U Pr.

Petersen, Karl. Ergodic Theory. LC 82-4473. (Cambridge Studies in Advanced Mathematics: No. 2). (Illus.). 320p. 1983. 42.50 (ISBN 0-521-23632-0). Cambridge U Pr.

Rota, Gian-Carlo, ed. Studies in Probability & Ergodic Theory: Advances in Mathematics Supplementary Studies, Vol. 2. 1978. 75.00 (ISBN 0-12-599102-9). Acad Pr.

Sinai, Y. G. Introduction to Ergodic Theory. Scheffer, V., tr. from Russian. LC 76-3030. (Mathematical Notes Ser.: No. 18). 150p. 1976. pap. 19.50 (ISBN 0-691-08182-4). Princeton U Pr.

Steklov Institute of Mathematics, Academy of Sciences, U.S.S.R., No. 82 & Postinikov, A. G. Ergodic Problems in the Theory of Congruences & of Diophantine Approximations: Proceedings. (Proceedings of the Steklov Institute of Mathematics: No. 82). 1967. 33.00 (ISBN 0-8218-1882-1, STEKLO-82). Am Math.

Steklov Institute of Mathematics, Academy of Sciences, U.S.S.R. Geodesic Flows on Closed Riemann Manifolds with Negative Curvature: Proceedings. Anosov, D. V., ed. (Proceedings of the Steklov Institute of Mathematics: No. 90). 1969. 58.00 (ISBN 0-8218-1890-2, STEKLO-90). Am Math.

Symposium On Ergodic Theory - New Orleans - 1961. Ergodic Theory: Proceedings. Wright, Fred B., ed. 1963. 55.00 (ISBN 0-12-765450-X). Acad Pr.

Walters, P. An Introduction to Ergodic Theory. (Graduate Texts in Mathematics Ser.: Vol. 79). (Illus.). 272p. 1981. 34.00 (ISBN 0-387-90599-5). Springer Verlag.

ERGONOMETRICS
see Work Measurement

ERGONOMICS
see Human Engineering

ERGOT

Agnoli, A., et al, eds. Aging Brain & Ergot Alkaloids. (Aging Ser.: Vol. 23). 464p. 1983. text ed. 59.00 (ISBN 0-89004-853-3). Raven.

Fuxe, K., ed. Dopaminergic Ergot Derivatives & Motor Function: Proceedings of an International Symposium, Stockholm, 1978. (Wenner-Gren Center International Symposium Series: Vol. 31). (Illus.). 1979. 89.00 (ISBN 0-08-024408-4). Pergamon.

Goldstein, Menek, et al, eds. Ergot Compounds & Brain Function: Neuroendocrine & Neuropsychiatric Aspects. Calne, D. & Lieberman, A. (Advances in Biochemical Psychopharmacology Ser.: Vol. 23). 441p. 1980. text ed. 64.50 (ISBN 0-89004-450-3). Raven.

ERLANG TRAFFIC FORMULA
see Queuing Theory

ERMINES
see Weasels

EROSION
see also Beach Erosion; Coast Changes; Dust Storms; Geomorphology; Glaciers; Runoff; Sedimentation and Deposition; Soil Erosion; Solifluction; Weathering

American Society for Testing & Materials. Erosion by Cavitation or Impingement: A Symposium. LC 67-12411. (American Society for Testing & Materials Series, Special Technical Publication: No. 408). pap. 73.00 (ISBN 0-317-11247-3, 2000975). Bks Demand UMI.

Beasley, R. P., et al. Erosion & Sediment Pollution Control. 2nd ed. (Illus.). 304p. 1984. text ed. 27.95x (ISBN 0-8138-1530-4). Iowa St U Pr.

Finley, R. J. & Gustavson, T. C. Climatic Controls on Erosion in the Rolling Plains along the Caprock Escarpment of the Texas Panhandle: Geological Circular 80-11. (Illus.). 50p. 1980. 1.75 (ISBN 0-686-36578-X). Bur Econ Geology.

Herman, Herbert, ed. Treatise on Materials Science & Technology, Vol. 16: Erosion. (Treatise on Materials Science & Technology Ser.). 1979. 75.00 (ISBN 0-12-341816-X). Acad Pr.

Holy, M. Erosion & Environment. (Environmental Sciences & Applications: Vol. 9). (Illus.). 266p. 1980. 68.00 (ISBN 0-08-024466-1). Pergamon.

Komar, Paul D., ed. Handbook of Coastal Process & Erosion. 320p. 1983. 70.00 (ISBN 0-8493-0225-0). CRC Pr.

Laronne, Jonathan & Mosley, M. Paul, eds. Erosion & Sediment Yield. LC 81-6456. (Benchmark Papers in Geology: Vol. 63). 400p. 1982. 48.95 (ISBN 0-87933-409-6). Van Nos Reinhold.

Residential Erosion & Sediment Control: Objectives, Principles & Design Considerations. 64p. 1978. pap. 10.00x (ISBN 0-87262-133-2). Am Soc Civil Eng.

Sharma, H. S. Ravine Erosion in India. (Illus.). 100p. 1980. text ed. 12.25x (ISBN 0-391-02142-7). Humanities.

Soil Erosion by Water: Some Measures for Its Control on Cultivated Lands. (Agricultural Development Papers: No. 81). 284p. (2nd Printing 1978). 1965. pap. 21.50 (ISBN 92-5-100474-9, F1478, FAO). Unipub.

Soil Erosion by Wind & Measures for Its Control on Agriculture Lands. (Agricultural Development Papers: No. 71). 88p. 1960. pap. 5.25 (ISBN 92-5-100473-0, F424, FAO). Unipub.

Toy, Terrence J. Erosion: Research Techniques, Erodibility & Sediment Delivery. 86p. 1980. pap. 4.60x (ISBN 0-86094-000-4, Pub. by GEO Abstracts England). State Mutual Bk.

EROSION CONTROL
see Soil Conservation

EROSION OF METALS
see Metals–Erosion

ERROR-CORRECTING CODES (INFORMATION THEORY)

Blahut, Richard E. Theory & Practice of Error Control Codes. LC 82-11441. (Illus.). 512p. 1983. text ed. 35.95 (ISBN 0-201-10102-5). Addison-Wesley.

Clark, George C., Jr. & Cain, J. Bibb. Error-Correction Coding for Digital Communications. LC 81-1630. (Applications of Communications Theory Ser.). 436p. 1981. 45.00x (ISBN 0-306-40615-2, Plenum Pr). Plenum Pub.

Dion, Bernard A. Locally Least-Cost Error Correctors for Context-Free & Context-Sensitive Parsers. Stone, Harold, ed. LC 82-8397. (Computer Science: Systems Programming Ser.: No. 14). 102p. 1982. 34.95 (ISBN 0-8357-1358-X). UMI Res Pr.

Eckmann, J. P., et al. A Computer-Assisted Proof of Universality for Area-Preserving Maps. LC 83-22456. (Memoirs: No. 289). 126p. 1984. pap. 12.00 (ISBN 0-8218-2289-6, MEMO-289). Am Math.

Lin, Shu. Introduction to Error-Correcting Codes. LC 76-124417. 1970. ref. ed. 32.95. P-H.

MacWilliams, F. J. & Sloane, N. J. The Theory of Error Correcting Codes, 2 Pts. in 1 vol. (Mathematical Library: Vol. 16). 762p. 1978. 50.00 (ISBN 0-444-85193-3, North-Holland). Elsevier.

Peterson, W. Wesley & Weldon, E. J., Jr. Error-Correcting Codes. 2nd rev. ed. 1972. 34.95x (ISBN 0-262-16039-0). MIT Pr.

Pless, Vera. Introduction to the Theory of Error-Correcting Codes. LC 1-10417. (Wiley-Interscience Series in Discrete Mathematics). 169p. 1982. 26.50x (ISBN 0-471-08684-3, Pub. by Wiley-Interscience). Wiley.

Rao, T. R. Error Coding for Arithmetic Processors. 1974. 60.00 (ISBN 0-12-580750-3). Acad Pr.

Shu Lin & Costello, Daniel J., Jr. Error Control Coding: Fundamentals & Applications. (Illus.). 720p. 1983. 44.95 (ISBN 0-13-283796-X). P-H.

Sites, Michael J. Coded Frequency Shift Keyed Sequences with Applications to Low Data Rate Communication & Radar. LC 75-136728. 107p. 1969. 19.00 (ISBN 0-403-04540-1). Scholarly.

Sloane, N. J. A Short Course on Error Correcting Codes. (CISM International Centre for Mechanical Sciences Ser.: Vol. 188). (Illus.). 76p. 1982. pap. 11.20 (ISBN 0-387-81303-9). Springer-Verlag.

Wiggert, Djimitri. Error-Control Coding & Applications. LC 78-23237. (Illus.). 1978. 25.00x (ISBN 0-89006-066-5). Artech Hse.

ERROR FUNCTIONS

Nickel, Gerhard & Nehls, Dietrich, eds. Error Analysis, Contrastive Linguistics & Second Language Learning. Papers from the 6th International Congress of Applied Linguistics. Lund 1981. 186p. (Orig.). 1982. pap. 16.00x (ISBN 3-87276-288-5, Pub. by J Groos W Germany). Benjamins North Am.

ERRORS, SCIENTIFIC

Jastrow, Joseph, ed. Story of Human Error. facs. ed. LC 67-30219. (Essay Index Reprint Ser). 1936. 18.50 (ISBN 0-8369-0568-7). Ayer Co Pubs.

ERRORS, THEORY OF
see also Correlation (Statistics); Graphic Methods; Least Squares; Probabilities; Sampling (Statistics)

Beers, Yardley. Theory of Error. 2nd ed. LC 53-8616. (Physics Ser.). (Orig.). 1957. pap. 5.95 (ISBN 0-201-00470-4). Addison-Wesley.

Bevington, Philip R. Data Reduction & Error Analysis for the Physical Sciences. LC 69-16942. 1969. pap. text ed. 26.95 (ISBN 0-07-005135-6). McGraw.

Czuber, Eman. Wahrscheinlichkeitsrechnung & 'ihre Anwendung Auf Fehlerausgleichung, Statistik & Lebensversicherung, 2 Vols. (Bibliotheca Mathematica Teubneriana Ser.: Nos. 23 & 24). (Ger). 1969. Repr. of 1938 ed. Set. 60.00 (ISBN 0-384-10585-8). Johnson Repr.

Gadad, M. G. & Hiregoudar, H. R. Experimental Errors & Their Treatment. 220p. 1981. 20.00x (ISBN 0-86125-064-8, Pub. by Orient Longman India). State Mutual Bk.

Kirby, Robion C. & Siebenmann, Laurence C. Foundational Essays on Topological Manifolds, Smoothing & Triangulations. LC 76-45918. (Annals of Mathematical Studies: No. 88). 352p. 1977. 35.00 (ISBN 0-691-08190-5); pap. 15.50x (ISBN 0-691-08191-3). Princeton U Pr.

Muthu, S. K. Probability & Errors: For the Physical Sciences. 568p. 1982. text ed. 35.00x (ISBN 0-86131-137-X, Pub. by Orient Longman Ltd India). Apt Bks.

Taylor, John R. Error Analysis: The Study of Uncertainties in Physical Measurements. LC 81-51269. 270p. 1982. text ed. 16.00x (ISBN 0-935702-07-5); pap. text ed. 12.00x (ISBN 0-935702-10-5). Univ Sci Bks.

ERUPTIVE ROCKS
see Rocks, Igneous

ESAKI DIODES
see Tunnel Diodes

ESCALATORS

Adler, Rodney R. Vertical Transportation for Buildings. LC 73-104976. (Elsevier Architectural Science Ser.). pap. 59.50 (ISBN 0-317-11060-8, 2007760). Bks Demand UMI.

Donoghue, E. A., ed. Safety Code for Elevators & Escalators: Handbook on A17.1. 372p. 1981. 50.00 (A00112). ASME.

Safety Code for Elevators & Escalators: ANS u c17.1-1981. (Bk. No. A9681B). 1981. 40.00 (ISBN 0-685-37579-X). ASME.

Strakosch, George R. Vertical Transportation: Elevators & Escalators. 2nd ed. 495p. 1983. 57.50 (ISBN 0-471-86733-0). Wiley.

ESCHERICHIA

Kauffman, F. The Differentiation of Escherichia & Klebsiella Types. 56p. 1951. pap. 10.50x (ISBN 0-398-04304-3). C C Thomas.

Roberts, Richard B., et al. Studies of Biosynthesis in Escherichia Coli. (Illus.). 521p. 1958. pap. 21.50 (ISBN 0-87279-618-3, 607). Carnegie Inst.

Sojka, W. J. Escherichia Coli in Domestic Animals & Poultry. 232p. 1965. cloth 41.00x (ISBN 0-686-45819-2, Pub. by CAB Bks England). State Mutual Bk.

ESSENCES AND ESSENTIAL OILS
see also Flavoring Essences; Perfumes

Formacek & Kuboczka. Essential Oils Analysis by Carbon-13 NMR Spectroscopy. 1981. 112.00x (ISBN 0-471-26218-8). Wiley.

Guenther, Ernest, et al. The Essential Oils: Individual Essential Oils of the Plant Families, 6 vols. Vol. 1, 444p. 34.50 (ISBN 0-88275-073-9); Vol. 2, 866p. 66.50 (ISBN 0-88275-338-X); Vol. 3, 794p. 61.00 (ISBN 0-88275-163-8); Vol. 4, 766p. 59.00 (ISBN 0-88275-074-7); Vol. 5, 526p. 40.50 (ISBN 0-88275-354-1); Vol. 6, 498p. 40.50 (ISBN 0-88275-092-5); 257.00 set (ISBN 0-88275-953-1). Krieger.

Gurudas. Flower Essences. 314p. (Orig.). 1983. pap. cancelled (ISBN 0-914732-09-9). Bro Life Inc.

Information Sources on Essential Oils. (Guides to Information Sources: No. 38). 79p. 1981. pap. 4.00 (ISBN 0-686-79012-X, UNID267, UNIDO). Unipub.

Kapoor, L. D., ed. Advances in Essential Oil Industry. 284p. 1977. 10.00 (ISBN 0-88065-142-3, Pub. by Messers Today & Tomorrows Printers & Publishers India). Scholarly Pubns.

ESTERS
see also Polyesters

Ackman, R. G. & Metcalfe, L. D., eds. Analysis of Fatty Acids & Their Esters by Chromatographic Methods. 1976. 25.00 (ISBN 0-912474-07-6). Preston Pubns.

Bruins, Paul F. Unsaturated Polyester Technology. new ed. LC 74-12774. 448p. 1976. 69.50 (ISBN 0-677-21160-0). Gordon.

DeWolfe, R. H. Carboxylic Ortho Acid Derivatives: Preparation & Synthetic Applications. (Organic Chemistry Ser, Vol. 14). 1970. 90.00 (ISBN 0-12-214550-X). Acad Pr.

Patai, Saul. Chemistry of Carboxylic Acids & Esters. LC 70-82547. (Chemistry of Functional Groups Ser.). 1155p. 1970. 259.00 (ISBN 0-471-66919-9, Pub. by Wiley-Interscience). Wiley.

R. H. Chandler Ltd., ed. The Polymerisable Half Esters: Their Polymers & Applications. 95p. 1978. 100.00x (ISBN 0-686-78863-X, Pub. by Chandler England). State Mutual Bk.

Sadtler Spectra Handbook of Esters NMR. 1982. 195.00 (ISBN 0-8456-0079-6). Sadtler Res.

The Sadtler Spectra Handbooks of Esters: IR, NMR. 195.00 ea.; Set. 295.00 (ISBN 0-317-03729-3). Sadtler Res.

Sadtler's Spectra Handbook of Esters Ir. 1982. 195.00 (ISBN 0-8456-0078-8). Sadtler Res.

ESTIMATES
see subdivision Estimates and Estimates and Costs under technical subjects, e.g. Building–Estimates; Engineering–Estimates and Costs

ESTIMATION THEORY
see also Decision-Making

Balakrishnan, A. V. Kalman Filtering Theory. (University Series in Modern Engineering). xii, 222p. 1984. pap. 26.00 (ISBN 0-318-03102-7). Springer Verlag.

Bean, Judy A. Distribution & Properties of Variance Estimators for Complex Multistage Probability Samples. LC 74-16356. (Data Evaluation & Methods Research Ser. 2: No. 65). 70p. 1975. pap. 1.25 (ISBN 0-8406-0029-1). Natl Ctr Health Stats.

Beck, James V. & Arnold, Kenneth J. Parameter Estimation in Engineering & Science. LC 77-40293. (Probability & Statistics: Applied Probability & Statistics Section). 501p. 1976. 51.95x (ISBN 0-471-06118-2, Pub. by Wiley-Interscience). Wiley.

Bierman, Gerald J. Factorization Methods for Discrete Sequential Estimation. 1977. 42.50 (ISBN 0-12-097350-2). Acad Pr.

Cassel, Claes-Magnus, et al. Foundations of Inference in Survey Sampling. LC 77-5114. (Probability & Mathematical Statistics Ser., Probability & Statistics Section). 192p. 1977. 41.95 (ISBN 0-471-02563-1, Pub. by Wiley-Interscience). Wiley.

Davis, M. H. Linear Estimation & Stochastic Control. LC 77-23389. 1977. pap. text ed. 16.95x (ISBN 0-412-15130-8). Halsted Pr.

--Linear Estimation & Stochastic Control. 1977. (Pub. by Chapman & Hall); pap. 16.95x (ISBN 0-412-15130-8, NO. 6563). Methuen Inc.

Dubbelman, C. Disturbances in the Linear Model: Estimation & Hypothesis Testing. 1978. pap. 16.00 (ISBN 90-207-0772-8, Pub. by Martininus Nijhoff Netherlands). Kluwer Academic.

Farrell, James L., ed. Integrated Aircraft Navigation. 1976. 59.00 (ISBN 0-12-249750-3). Acad Pr.

Gerking, S. K. Estimation of Stochastic Input-Output Models. (Studies in Applied Regional Science: No. 3). 1976. pap. 16.00 (ISBN 90-207-0628-4, Pub. by Martinus Nijhoff Netherlands). Kluwer Academic.

Handbook on Estimating. 15.50 (ISBN 0-686-35911-9). Sound Pub.

Jazwinski, A. H. Stochastic Processes & Filtering Theory. (Mathematics in Science & Engineering: Vol. 64). 1970. 70.00 (ISBN 0-12-381550-9). Acad Pr.

Judge, G. G. & Bock, M. E. The Statistical Implications of Pre-Test & Stein-Rule Estimators in Econometrics. (Studies in Mathematical & Managerial Economics: Vol. 25). 340p. 1978. 61.75 (ISBN 0-7204-0729-X, North-Holland). Elsevier.

Kushner, H. J. & Clark, D. S. Stochastic Approximation Methods for Constrained & Unconstrained Systems. LC 78-16855. (Applied Mathematical Sciences Ser.: Vol. 26). (Illus.). 1978. text ed. 18.50 (ISBN 0-387-90341-0). Springer-Verlag.

Lehmann, Erich L. Theory of Point Estimation. LC 82-21881. (Wiley Series in Probability & Mathematical Statistics Ser.). 506p. 1983. 38.95x (ISBN 0-471-05849-1, Pub. by Wiley-Interscience). Wiley.

Lennik, J. V. Statistical Problems with Nuisance Parameters. LC 67-30101. (Translations of Mathematical Monographs: Vol. 20). 1968. 32.00 (ISBN 0-8218-1570-9, MMONO-20). Am Math.

Maybeck, Peter S. Stochastic Models, Estimation & Control, Vol. 2. (Mathematics in Science & Engineering Ser.). 289p. 1982. 42.00 (ISBN 0-12-480702-X). Acad Pr.

--Stochastic Models, Estimation & Control, Vol. 3. (Mathematics in Science & Engineering Ser.). 270p. 1982. 42.00 (ISBN 0-12-480703-8). Acad Pr.

Mehra, Raman K. & Lainiotis, Dmitri G., eds. System Identification: Advances & Case Studies. 1976. 58.50 (ISBN 0-12-487950-0). Acad Pr.

Melsa, James L. & Cohn, Davis L. Decision & Estimation Theory. (Illus.). 1978. text ed. 44.00 (ISBN 0-07-041468-8). McGraw.

Mendel, Jerry M. Discrete Techniques of Parameter Estimation: The Equation Error Formulation. (Control & Systems Theory Ser.: Vol. 1). 408p. 1973. 65.00 (ISBN 0-8247-1455-5). Dekker.

Nevelson, M. B. & Hasminsky, R. Z. Stochastic Approximation & Recursive Estimation. LC 76-48298. (Translations of Mathematical Monographs: Vol. 47). 1976. 55.00 (ISBN 0-8218-1597-0, MMONO47). Am Math.

Davenport, Charles B. Heredity in Relation to Eugenics. LC 73-180571. (Medicine & Society in America Ser.). (Illus.). 320p. 1972. Repr. of 1911 ed. 22.00 (ISBN 0-405-03946-8). Ayer Co Pubs.

First International Congress of Eugenics & Rosenberg, Charles. Problems in Eugenics: Papers Communicated to the First International Congress. LC 83-48620. (The History of Hereditarian Thought Ser.). 679p. 1985. lib. bdg. 80.00 (ISBN 0-8240-5806-2). Garland Pub.

Francis Galton Laboratory for National Eugenics Staff, et al. Eugenics Laboratory Lecture Series. Rosenberg, Charles, ed. LC 83-48563. (The History of Hereditarian Thought Ser.). 434p. 1985. lib. bdg. 52.00 (ISBN 0-8240-5815-1). Garland Pub.

Francis Galton Laboratory for National Eugenics Staff & Pearson, Karl. Questions of the Day & of the Fray. Rosenberg, Charles, ed. LC 83-48539. (The History of Hereditarian Thought Ser.). 350p. 1985. Repr. lib. bdg. 45.00 (ISBN 0-8240-5813-5). Garland Pub.

Francis Galton Laboratory for National Eugenics Staff, et al. Selected Eugenics Laboratory Memoirs. Rosenberg, Charles, ed. LC 83-48540. (The History of Hereditarian Thought Ser.). 330p. 1985. Repr. lib. bdg. 45.00 (ISBN 0-8240-5814-3). Garland Pub.

Galton, Francis. Essays in Eugenics. Rosenberg, Charles, ed. LC 83-48541. (The History of Hereditarian Thought Ser.). 109p. 1985. Repr. of 1909 ed. lib. bdg. 20.00 (ISBN 0-8240-5816-X). Garland Pub.

Haller, Mark H. Eugenics: Hereditarian Attitudes in American Thought. 271p. 1983. text ed. 30.00; pap. 10.95 (ISBN 0-8135-1023-6). Rutgers U Pr.

International Congress of Eugenics, Second Congress. Eugenics, Genetics & the Family: Eugenics in Race & State. Rosenberg, Charles, ed. LC 83-48622. (The History of Hereditarian Thought Ser.). 911p. 1985. Repr. of 1923 ed. lib. bdg. 55.00 (ISBN 0-8240-5807-0). Garland Pub.

International Congress of Eugenics, Third Congress. A Decade of Progress in Eugenics; Scientific Papers of the Third International Congress of Eugenics. LC 83-48621. (The History of Hereditarian Thought Ser.). 531p. 1984. Repr. of 1934 ed. lib. bdg. 63.00 (ISBN 0-8240-5809-7). Garland Pub.

McKim, W. D. Heredity & Human Progress. Rosenberg, Charles, ed. LC 83-48549. (The History of Hereditarian Thought Ser.). 279p. 1985. Repr. of 1900 ed. lib. bdg. 34.00 (ISBN 0-8240-5820-8). Garland Pub.

Newman, Horatio H., ed. Evolution, Genetics & Eugenics. LC 32-26475. (Illus.). 1969. Repr. of 1932 ed. lib. bdg. 27.50x (ISBN 0-8371-1880-8, NEEV). Greenwood.

Paul. Fabricated Man: The Ethics of Genetic Control. LC 78-123395. 1970. pap. 5.95x (ISBN 0-300-01374-4, YF6). Yale U Pr.

Popenoe, Paul. The Conservation of the Family. Rosenberg, Charles, ed. LC 83-48555. (The History of Hereditarian Thought Ser.). 266p. 1985. Repr. of 1926 ed. lib. bdg. 32.00 (ISBN 0-8240-5825-9). Garland Pub.

Rentoul, Robert R. Race Culture: Or Race Suicide? A Plea for the Unborn. Rosenberg, Charles, ed. LC 83-48556. (The History of Hereditarian Thought Ser.). 182p. 1985. lib. bdg. 25.00 (ISBN 0-8240-5826-7). Garland Pub.

Roper, Allen G. Ancient Eugenics. 1982. 16.00x (ISBN 0-317-19985-4). Cliveden Pr.

Schiller, Ferdinand C. Social Decay & Eugenical Reform. Rosenberg, Charles, ed. LC 83-48657. (The History of Hereditarian Thought Ser.). 164p. 1985. Repr. of 1932 ed. lib. bdg. 25.00 (ISBN 0-8240-5827-5). Garland Pub.

Stoddard, Lothrop. The Revolt Against Civilization, the Menace of the Under-Man. Rosenberg, Charles, ed. LC 83-48558. (The History of the Hereditarian Thought Ser.). 225p. 1985. Repr. of 1923 ed. lib. bdg. 32.00 (ISBN 0-8240-5828-3). Garland Pub.

Warshofsky, Fred, ed. Twenty-First Century: The New Age of Exploration, Vol. 1. (Twentyfirst Century Ser). (Illus.). 1969. 10.95 (ISBN 0-670-73582-5). Viking.

EUGLENA

Buetow, Dennis, ed. The Biology of Euglena: Vol. 3, Physiology. LC 68-14645. 1982. 60.00 (ISBN 0-12-139903-6). Acad Pr.

Buetow, Dennis E., ed. Biology of Euglena, 2 Vols. 1968. Set. 150.00; Vol. 1. 60.00 (ISBN 0-12-139901-X); Vol. 2. 70.00 (ISBN 0-12-139902-8). Acad Pr.

Walton, L. B. The Euglenoidina of Ohio. 1972. Repr. of 1915 ed. 3.50 (ISBN 0-86727-003-9). Ohio Bio Survey.

Wolken, Jerome J. Euglena: An Experimental Organism for Biochemical & Biophysical Studies. LC 67-13378. 204p. 1967. 19.50x (ISBN 0-306-50086-8, Plenum Pr). Plenum Pub.

EULER-LAGRANGE EQUATIONS

see Lagrange Equations

EUPHORBIACEAE

Deghan, Bijan & Webster, Grady L. Morphology & Infrageneric Relationships of the Genus "Jatropha" (Euphorbiaceae) LC 77-83116. (Publications in Botany Ser.: Vol. 74). 1979. 17.50x (ISBN 0-520-09585-5). U of Cal Pr.

EUTROPHICATION

see also Water–Pollution

Lewis, W. M., Jr., et al. Eutrophication & Land Use. (Ecological Studies. Analysis & Synthesis: Vol. 46). (Illus.). 275p. 1984. 39.80 (ISBN 0-387-90961-3). Springer Verlag.

EVAPORATION

Brutsaert, Wilfred H. Evaporation into the Atmosphere: Theory, History & Applications. 308p. 1982. 34.95 (ISBN 90-277-1247-6, Pub. by Reidel Holland). Kluwer Academic.

Hall, Vivian S. & Spencer, Mary R. Salt, Evaporites & Brines: An Annotated Bibliography. LC 83-42609. 224p. 1984. lib. bdg. 87.50x (ISBN 0-89774-042-4). Oryx Pr.

La Mer, Victor K., ed. Retardation of Evaporation by Monolayers. 1962. 59.50 (ISBN 0-12-435150-6). Acad Pr.

Stanhill, G. The CIMO International Evaporimeter Comparisons: Final Report. (Publications Ser.: No. 449). (Illus.). 38p. 1976. pap. 10.00 (ISBN 92-63-10449-2, W205, WMO). Unipub.

EVAPORATION OF FOOD

see Food–Drying

EVERGREENS

see also Coniferae

Beckett, Kenneth A. The Complete Book of Evergreens. 168p. 1981. 40.00x (ISBN 0-7063-5989-5, Pub. by Ward Lock Ed England). State Mutual Bk.

Bowmen, M. R. & Whitmore, T. C. A Second Look at Agathis. 1980. 30.00x (ISBN 0-85074-053-3, Pub. by For Lib Comm England). State Mutual Bk.

Broad-Leaved Evergreens. 2.25 (ISBN 0-686-21124-3). Bklyn Botanic.

Enviromental Design Press. Evergreen Form Studies. 1983. 25.95 (ISBN 0-442-22337-4). Van Nos Reinhold.

Huxley, Anthony. Evergreen Garden Trees & Shrubs. (Illus.). 181p. 1983. pap. 6.95 (ISBN 0-7137-1369-0, Pub. by Blandford Pr England). Sterling.

Loewer, H. Peter. Evergreens: A Guide for Landscape, Lawn & Garden. (Illus.). 144p. 1981. 14.95 (ISBN 0-8027-0662-2). Walker & Co.

Whitmore, T. C. A First Look at Agathis. 1977. 30.00x (ISBN 0-85074-018-5, Pub. by For Lib Comm England). State Mutual Bk.

EVOKED CORTICAL POTENTIALS

see Evoked Potentials (Electrophysiology)

EVOKED POTENTIALS (ELECTROPHYSIOLOGY)

Bodis-Wollner, Ivan, intro. by. Evoked Potentials. (Annals of The New York Academy of Sciences Ser.: Vol. 388). 738p. 1982. lib. bdg 157.00x (ISBN 0-89766-166-4); pap. 157.00x (ISBN 0-89766-167-2). NY Acad Sci.

Duffy, Frank H. Topographic Mapping of Brain Electrical Activity. (Illus.). 336p. 1986. pap. text ed. 34.95 (ISBN 0-409-90008-7). Butterworth.

Spehlmann, R. Evoked Potential Primer: Visual, Auditory & Somatosensory Evoked Potentials in Clinical Diagnosis. 416p. 1985. text ed. 45.00 (ISBN 0-409-95158-7); pap. text ed. 29.95 (ISBN 0-409-90005-2). Butterworth.

EVOLUTION

see also Adaptation (Biology); Anatomy, Comparative; Biology; Color of Animals; Creation; Embryology; Epigenesis; Genetic Psychology; Genetics; Heredity; Human Evolution; Island Flora and Fauna; Life–Origin; Living Fossils; Man–Influence of Environment; Man–Origin; Mendel'S Law; Mimicry (Biology); Natural Selection; Origin of Species; Phylogeny; Plants–Evolution; Variation (Biology)

Alcock, John. Animal Behavior: An Evolutionary Approach. 3rd, rev. ed. LC 83-14420. (Illus.). 380p. 1983. text ed. 27.50 (ISBN 0-87893-021-3). Sinauer Assoc.

Alexander, Richard D. Darwinism & Human Affairs. LC 78-65829. (Jessie & John Danz Lecture Ser.). (Illus.). 342p. 1980. 25.00x (ISBN 0-295-95641-0); pap. 10.95x (ISBN 0-295-95901-0). U of Wash Pr.

Andrews, S. Mahala, et al, eds. Problems in Vertebrate Evolution. (Linnean Society Symposium Ser.). 1977. 70.00 (ISBN 0-12-059950-3). Acad Pr.

Arthur, Wallace. Mechanisms of Morphological Evolution: A Combined Genetic, Developmental & Ecological Approach. LC 83-16993. 288p. 1984. 36.00x (ISBN 0-471-90347-7, Pub. by Wiley Interscience). Wiley.

Ayala, F. Evolutionary & Population Genetics: A Primer. 1982. text ed. 21.95. Addison-Wesley.

Ayala, Francisco J. & Valentine, James W. Evolving: The Theory & Processes of Organic Evolution. 1979. text ed. 30.95 (ISBN 0-8053-0310-3). Benjamin-Cummings.

Baldwin, James M. Development & Evolution: Including Psychophysical Evolution, Evolution by Orthoplasy & the Theory of Genetic Modes. LC 75-3022. (Philosophy in America Ser.). Repr. of 1902 ed. 42.50 (ISBN 0-404-59017-9). AMS Pr.

Banathy, B. H., ed. Evolutionary Visions of the Future. (Illus.). 96p. 1985. pap. 16.50 (ISBN 0-08-032563-7, Pub. by PPL). Pergamon.

Barber, Otto. H. G. Wells' Verhaltnis Zum Darwinismus. pap. 8.00 (ISBN 0-384-03380-6). Johnson Repr.

Barigozzi, Claudio, ed. Mechanisms of Speciation. LC 82-13014. (Progress in Clinical & Biological Research Ser.: Vol. 96). 560p. 1982. 88.00 (ISBN 0-8451-0096-3). A R Liss.

Barker, J. S. & Starmer, T., eds. Ecological Genetics & Evolutions: The Cactus-Yeast-Drosophila Model. LC 82-72224. 376p. 1982. 52.50 (ISBN 0-12-078820-9). Acad Pr.

Bateson. Problems of Genetics. LC 79-15467. 1979. text ed. 33.00x (ISBN 0-300-02435-5); pap. 9.95x (ISBN 0-300-02436-3, Y-350). Yale U Pr.

Beecher, Charles E. Studies in Evolution. Gould, Stephen J., ed. LC 79-8324. (History of Paleontology Ser.). (Illus.). 1980. Repr. of 1901 ed. lib. bdg. 55.50x (ISBN 0-405-12704-9). Ayer Co Pubs.

Bendall, D. S., ed. Evolution from Molecules to Men. LC 82-22020. (Illus.). 500p. 1983. 32.50 (ISBN 0-521-24753-5). Cambridge U Pr.

Bergman, Jerry. Teaching About the Creation-Evolution Controversy. LC 79-66529. (Fastback Ser.: No. 134). (Orig.). 1979. pap. 0.75 (ISBN 0-87367-134-1). Phi Delta Kappa.

Bergson, Henri. Creative Evolution. Mitxhell, Arthur, tr. LC 83-19859. 460p. 1984. pap. text ed. 13.50 (ISBN 0-8191-3553-4). U Pr of Amer.

Berry, R. J. Neo-Darwinism. (Studies in Biology: No. 144). 72p. 1982. pap. text ed. 8.95 (ISBN 0-7131-2849-6). E Arnold.

Birx, H. James. Pierre Teilhard De Chardin's Philosophy of Evolution. 192p. 1972. 18.50x (ISBN 0-398-02466-9). C C Thomas.

--Theories of Evolution. 432p. 1984. 39.50x (ISBN 0-398-04902-5). C C Thomas.

Blair, W. Frank, ed. Evolution in the Genus "Bufo". (Illus.). 467p. 1972. 35.00x (ISBN 0-292-72001-7). U of Tex Pr.

Bliss, Richard. Origins: Two Models. Gish, Duane T. & Moore, John N., eds. LC 76-20178. (Illus.). 1976. 4.95 (ISBN 0-89051-040-7); tchr's guide avail. Master Bks.

Blum, Harold F. Time's Arrow & Evolution. 3rd ed. LC 68-31676. (Illus.). 1968. pap. 8.95x (ISBN 0-691-02354-9). Princeton U Pr.

Boakes, Robert. From Darwin to Behaviourism: Psychology & the Minds of Animals. LC 83-10091. (Illus.). 300p. 1984. 69.50 (ISBN 0-521-23512-X); pap. 19.95 (ISBN 0-521-28012-5). Cambridge U Pr.

Bolsche, Wilhelm. The Evolution of Man. Untermann, Ernest, tr. from Ger. (Science for the Workers Ser.). (Illus.). 160p. 1984. lib. bdg. 7.95 (ISBN 0-88286-084-4). C H Kerr.

--The Triumph of Life. Simons, May W., tr. from Ger. (Science for the Workers Ser.). (Illus.). 157p. 1984. 7.95 (ISBN 0-88286-085-2). C H Kerr.

Bonner, J. T., ed. Evolution & Development. (Dahlem Workshop Reports Ser.: Vol. 22). (Illus.). 357p. 1982. 29.00 (ISBN 0-387-11331-2). Springer-Verlag.

Boodin, J. E. Cosmic Evolution: Outlines of Cosmic Idealism. Repr. of 1925 ed. 21.00 (ISBN 0-527-09800-0). Kraus Repr.

Bowden, Malcolm. Ape-Men. 1979. pap. 8.95 (ISBN 0-9506042-0-8). Master Bks.

--Rise of the Evolution Fraud. 1982. pap. 8.95 (ISBN 0-89051-085-7). Master Bks.

Bowman, Robert I., et al, eds. Patterns of Evolution in Galapagos Organisms. 568p. (Orig.). 1983. 32.50 (ISBN 0-934394-05-9). AAASPD.

Brace, C. L., et al. Atlas of Human Evolution. 2nd ed. LC 78-27723. 178p. 1979. pap. text ed. 17.95 (ISBN 0-03-045021-7, HoltC). HR&W.

Bradshaw, A. D. & McNeilly, D. T. Evolution & Pollution. (Studies in Biology: No. 130). 80p. 1981. pap. text ed. 8.95 (ISBN 0-7131-2818-6). E Arnold.

Bratchell, D. F. The Impact of Darwinism. (Orig.). 1981. pap. text ed. 19.50 (ISBN 0-86127-204-8, Pub. by Avebury England). Humanities.

British Museum. Man's Place in Evolution. (Natural History Ser.). (Illus.). 120p. 1981. 24.95 (ISBN 0-521-23177-9); pap. 9.95 (ISBN 0-521-29849-0). Cambridge U Pr.

--Origin of Species. LC 80-42170. (Natural History Ser.). 120p. 1981. 27.95 (ISBN 0-521-23878-1); pap. 9.95 (ISBN 0-521-28276-4). Cambridge U Pr.

Bryson, Vernon & Vogel, Henry J., eds. Evolving Genes & Proteins: A Symposium. 1965. 83.50 (ISBN 0-12-138250-8). Acad Pr.

Butler, Samuel. Essays on Life, Art & Science. Streatfeild, R. A., ed. LC 77-95333. 1970. Repr. of 1908 ed. 26.00 (ISBN 0-8046-1345-1, Pub. by Kennikat). Assoc Faculty Pr.

--Evolution, Old & New. 59.95 (ISBN 0-8490-0145-5). Gordon Pr.

Bylinsky, Gene. Life in Darwin's Universe: Evolution & the Cosmos. LC 80-2988. (Illus.). 256p. 1981. 17.95 (ISBN 0-385-17049-1). Doubleday.

Calogero, F. & Degasperis, A. Spectral Transform & Solutions: Tools to Solve & Investigate Evolution Equations. (Studies in Math & Its Applications: Vol. 13). 516p. 1982. 89.50 (ISBN 0-444-86368-0, North Holland). Elsevier.

Calow, Peter. Evolutionary Principles. LC 82-17834. (Tertiary Level Biology Ser.). (Illus.). 108p. 1983. 35.00 (ISBN 0-412-00321-X, NO. 5032, Pub. by Chapman & Hall); pap. 15.95 (ISBN 0-412-00331-7, NO. 5033). Methuen Inc.

Cannon, H. Graham. Lamarck & Modern Genetics. LC 75-10211. 152p. 1975. Repr. of 1959 ed. lib. bdg. 27.50x (ISBN 0-8371-8173-9, CALA). Greenwood.

Carney, Thomas P. Instant Evolution: We'd Better Get Good at It. LC 79-17835. 1981. pap. text ed. 6.95 (ISBN 0-268-01146-X, NDP-256). U of Notre Dame Pr.

Carter, G. S. Structure & Habit in Vertebrate Evolution. LC 67-25160. (Biology Ser.). (Illus.). 544p. 1967. 20.00x (ISBN 0-295-95121-4). U of Wash Pr.

Chiarelli, A. B. & Corruscini, R. S., eds. Primate Evolutionary Biology: Selected Papers - Proceedings, Pt. A. (Illus.). 150p. 1981. 29.00 (ISBN 0-387-11023-2). Springer-Verlag.

Ciochon, Russell L. & Fleagle, John G. Primate Evolution & Human Origins. (Illus.). 401p. 1985. pap. text ed. 34.95x (ISBN 0-8053-2240-X, 32240). Benjamin-Cummings.

Ciochon, Russell L. & Chiarelli, A. B., eds. Evolutionary Biology of the New World Monkeys & Continental Drift. LC 80-16063. (Advances in Primatology Ser.). 560p. 1981. 59.50x (ISBN 0-306-40487-7, Plenum Pr). Plenum Pub.

Clark, Robert B. Dynamics in Metazoan Evolution: The Origin of the Coelom & Segments. 1964. 45.00x (ISBN 0-19-854353-0). Oxford U Pr.

Clausen, Jens, et al. Plant Evolution Through Amphiploidy & Autoploidy, with Examples from the Madiinae. (Experimental Studies on the Nature of Species: Vol. 2). (Illus.). 564p. 1945. pap. 7.25 (ISBN 0-87279-575-6). Carnegie Inst.

Clayton, Donald D. Principles of Stellar Evolution & Nucleosynthesis. LC 83-5106. (Illus.). xii, 612p. 1984. 37.00x (ISBN 0-226-10952-6); pap. 17.00x (ISBN 0-226-10953-4). U of Chicago Pr.

Clodd, Edward. The Story of Creation: A Plain Account of Evolution. 1979. Repr. of 1894 ed. lib. bdg. 20.00 (ISBN 0-8492-4033-6). R West.

Colbert, Edwin H. An Outline of Vertebrate Evolution. Head, J. J., ed. LC 81-67987. (Carolina Biology Readers Ser.). (Illus.). 32p. 1983. pap. 2.00 (ISBN 0-89278-331-1, 45-9731). Carolina Biological.

Cold Spring Harbor Symposia on Quantitative Biology: Genetics & 20th Century Darwinism, Vol. 24. LC 34-8174. (Illus.). 334p. 1960. 38.00x (ISBN 0-87969-023-2). Cold Spring Harbor.

Cope, Edward D. The Origin of the Fittest: Essays on Evolution & the Primary Factors of Organic Evolution, 2 vols. in one. LC 73-17813. (Natural Sciencesin America Ser.). 1066p. 1974. Repr. 69.50x (ISBN 0-405-05729-6). Ayer Co Pubs.

The Creation-Evolution Controversy. 1976. 15.95 (ISBN 0-918112-01-X); pap. 8.95 kivar (ISBN 0-918112-02-8). Inquiry Pr.

Crook, D. P. Benjamin Kidd: Portrait of a Social Darwinist. LC 83-19009. 280p. 1984. 54.50 (ISBN 0-521-25804-9). Cambridge U Pr.

Csanyi. General Theory of Evolution. (Studia Biologica Academiae Scientiarum Hungaricae: Vol. 18). 1982. 16.00 (ISBN 0-9960072-7-X, Pub. by Akademiai Kaido Hungary). Heyden.

Custance, Arthur C. Evolution of Creation? (The Doorway Papers Ser.: Vol. 4). 340p. 1981. pap. 8.95 (ISBN 0-310-22981-2). Zondervan.

Dahlberg, Albert. Dental Morphology & Evolution. LC 73-158726. 1971. 20.00x (ISBN 0-226-13481-4). U of Chicago Pr.

Daly, Martin & Wilson, Margo. Sex, Evolution & Behavior. 2nd ed. 400p. 1983. pap. text ed. write for info. (ISBN 0-87150-767-6, 4511, Pub. by Willard Grant Pr). PWS Pubs.

Darlington, P. J. Evolution for Naturalists: The Simple Principles & Complex Reality. LC 79-22897. 262p. 1980. 32.50x (ISBN 0-471-04783-X, Pub. by Wiley-Interscience). Wiley.

Jones, C. & Sabater Pi, J. Comparative Ecology of Gorilla & Pan Troglodytes in Rio Muni, West Africa. (Bibliotheca Primatologica: No. 13). 1971. pap. 10.75 (ISBN 3-8055-0293-1). S Karger.
Kappel, F. & Schappacher, W., eds. Evolution Equations & Their Applications. (Research Notes In Mathematics: No. 68). 250p. 1982. pap. text ed. 27.95 (ISBN 0-273-08567-0). Pitman Pub MA.
Keith, Arthur. A New Theory of Human Evolution. x, 451p. 1968. 13.25 (ISBN 0-8446-1255-3). Peter Smith.
Kimura, M. Molecular Evolution, Protein Polymorphism, & Neutral Theory. 363p. 1982. 48.00 (ISBN 0-387-11466-1). Springer-Verlag.
Kimura, Motoo, ed. The Neutral Theory of Molecular Evolution. LC 82-22225. 400p. 1984. 69.50 (ISBN 0-521-23109-4). Cambridge U Pr.
Kitcher, Philip. Abusing Science: The Case Against Creationism. (Illus.). 224p. 1982. 20.00x (ISBN 0-262-11085-7); pap. 7.95 (ISBN 0-262-61037-X). MIT Pr.
Klotz, John W. Genes, Genesis & Evolution. rev. ed. 1970. pap. 17.95 (ISBN 0-570-03212-1, 12-2637). Concordia.
Kozlovsky, Daniel G., ed. An Ecological & Evolutionary Ethic. (Illus.). 128p. 1974. pap. 17.95 (ISBN 0-13-222935-8). P-H.
Krantz, Grover S. The Process of Human Evolution. LC 81-2745. 493p. 1981. pap. text ed. 15.95 (ISBN 0-87073-348-6). Schenkman Bks Inc.
Kueppers, B. O. Molecular Theory of Evolution: Outline of a Physico-Chemical Theory of the Origin of Life. (Illus.). 321p. 1983. 34.00 (ISBN 0-387-12080-7). Springer-Verlag.
Larson, Edward J. Trial & Error: The American Controversy over Creation & Evolution. LC 85-7144. 224p. 1985. 17.95 (ISBN 0-19-503666-2). Oxford U Pr.
Lau, Dicksen T. The New Religion & Relativity. LC 83-62038. 138p. (Orig.). 1983. pap. 5.95 (ISBN 0-9612000-0-6). Magnolia Bks.
Le Conte, Joseph. Evolution: Its Nature Its Evidences, - Its Relation to Religious Thought. 2nd ed. 1897. 29.00 (ISBN 0-527-55700-5). Kraus Repr.
Levins, Richard. Evolution in Changing Environments: Some Theoretical Explorations. LC 68-20871. (Monographs in Population Biology: No. 2). (Illus.). 1968. pap. 9.95 (ISBN 0-691-08062-3). Princeton U Pr.
Lewis, Arthur M. Evolution-Social & Organic: Linnaeus, Darwin, Kropotkin, Marx. (Science for the Workers Ser.). 186p. 1984. 7.95 (ISBN 0-88286-088-7). C H Kerr.
--Vital Problems in Social Evolution: An Introduction to the Materialist Conception of History. (Science for the Workers Ser.). 192p. 1984. 7.95 (ISBN 0-88286-089-5). C H Kerr.
Lewontin, R. C. The Genetic Basis of Evolutionary Change. LC 73-19786. (Biological Ser.: Vol. 25). 346p. 1974. pap. 16.00x (ISBN 0-231-08318-1). Columbia U Pr.
Lincoln, R. J. & Boxshall, G. A. A Dictionary of Ecology, Evolution & Systematics. LC 81-18013. 350p. 1982. 52.50 (ISBN 0-521-23957-5). Cambridge U Pr.
Little, Colin. The Colonisation of Land: Origins & Adaptations of Terrestrial Animals. LC 83-1787. (Illus.). 480p. 1984. 99.50 (ISBN 0-521-25218-0). Cambridge U Pr.
Litvak, Stuart & Senzee, A. Wayne. Toward a New Brain: Evolution & the Human Mind. 250p. 1985. 17.95 (ISBN 0-13-926056-0); pap. 8.95 (ISBN 0-13-926049-8). P-H.
Livesy, P. J. The Biology of Learning: Evolutionary Processes, Vol. I. 280p. 1985. pap. text ed. 24.95 (ISBN 0-89859-552-5). L Erlbaum Assocs.
Locker, A., ed. Biogenesis-Evolution-Homeostasis: A Symposium by Correspondence. LC 72-96743. (Illus.). 190p. 1973. pap. 33.00 (ISBN 0-387-06134-7). Springer-Verlag.
Luckett, W. Patrick, ed. Comparative Biology & Evolutionary Relationships of Tree Shrews. LC 80-19824. (Advances in Primatology Ser.). 330p. 1980. 49.50x (ISBN 0-306-40464-8, Plenum Pr). Plenum Pub.
Lumsden, Charles J. & Wilson, Edward O. Genes, Mind, Culture: The Coevolutionary Process. LC 80-26543. (Illus.). 512p. 1981. 25.00 (ISBN 0-674-34475-8). Harvard U Pr.
Macbeth, Norman. Darwin Retried: An Appeal to Reason. LC 73-160418. 1971. 9.95 (ISBN 0-87645-048-6, Pub. by Gambit). Harvard Common Pr.
--Darwin Retried: An Appeal to Reason. LC 73-160418. 1979. pap. 5.95 (ISBN 0-87645-105-9, Pub. by Gambit). Harvard Common Pr.
MacBride, E. W. Evolution. 1927. 15.00 (ISBN 0-8274-4230-0). R West.
Macedo, Jorge. Theoretical Basis of the Living System. LC 75-17399. (Illus.). 84p. 1979. 10.50 (ISBN 0-87527-158-8). Green.
Mader, Sylvia S. Biology: Evolution, Diversity & the Environment. 832p. 1985. text ed. write for info. (ISBN 0-697-04922-1); instr's. manual avail. (ISBN 0-697-00108-3); student study guide avail. (ISBN 0-697-00225-X); lab manual avail. (ISBN 0-697-00187-3); transparencies avail. (ISBN 0-697-00552-6). Wm C Brown.
March, Robert H. Physics for Poets. (Illus.). 304p. 1983. pap. 9.95 (ISBN 0-8092-5532-4). Contemp Bks.
Marchalonis, John J. Immunity in Evolution. (Illus.). 1977. 20.00x (ISBN 0-674-44445-0, MAIE). Harvard U Pr.
Marett, R. R. Head, Heart & Hands in Human Evolution. 1979. Repr. of 1933 ed. lib. bdg. 30.00 (ISBN 0-8495-3855-6). Arden Lib.
Mark-Age. Evolution of Man: Two Hundred & Six Million Years on Earth. LC 71-147256. 160p. 1971. 6.00 (ISBN 0-912322-02-0). Mark-Age.
Martin, Cecil P. Psychology, Evolution & Sex: A Study of the Mechanisms of Evolution Based on a Comprehensive View of Biology. 176p. 1956. 15.75x (ISBN 0-398-01224-5). C C Thomas.
Masterton, R. B. & Hodos, W., eds. Evolution, Brain, & Behavior: Persistent Problems. 276p. 1976. text ed. 29.95 (ISBN 0-89859-477-4). L Erlbaum Assocs.
Mauro, Philip. Evolution. pap. 2.25 (ISBN 0-685-88374-4). Reiner.
--The World & Its God. 95p. 1981. pap. 2.95 (ISBN 0-89084-151-9). Bob Jones Univ Pr.
Mayr, Ernest. Animal Species & Evolution. LC 63-9552. (Illus.). 1963. 35.00x (ISBN 0-674-03750-2, Belknap Pr). Harvard U Pr.
Mayr, Ernst. Populations, Species, & Evolution: An Abridgment of Animal Species & Evolution. abr. ed. LC 79-111486. 1970. 25.00x (ISBN 0-674-69010-9, Belknap Pr); pap. 8.95x (ISBN 0-674-69013-3). Harvard U Pr.
Mayr, Ernst & Provine, William B. The Evolutionary Synthesis: Perspectives on the Unification of Biology. LC 80-13973. 1980. text ed. 25.00x (ISBN 0-674-27225-0). Harvard U Pr.
Meyer, M. Wilhelm. The End of the World: The Destiny of Man & Our Planet. Wagner, Margaret, tr. from Ger. (Science for the Workers Ser.). (Illus.). 140p. 1984. 9.95 (ISBN 0-88286-087-9). C H Kerr.
Milkman, Roger, ed. Perspectives on Evolution. LC 81-21522. (Illus.). 250p. 1982. text ed. 36.00x (ISBN 0-87893-528-2); pap. text ed. 20.00x (ISBN 0-87893-529-0). Sinauer Assoc.
Miller, H. & Miller, C. Evolution: From Stellar Dust to Technological Society. 1975. pap. text ed. 8.80x (ISBN 0-87563-090-1). Stipes.
Millikan, Robert A. Evolution in Science & Religion. 1979. Repr. of 1929 ed. lib. bdg. 17.50 (ISBN 0-8495-3846-7). Arden Lib.
--Evolution in Science & Religion. 1935. 15.50x (ISBN 0-686-51381-9). Elliots Bks.
Minkoff, Eli C. Evolutionary Biology. (Biology Ser.). (Illus.). 640p. 1983. text ed. 34.95 (ISBN 0-201-15890-6); Instrs' Manual avail. (ISBN 0-201-15891-4). Addison-Wesley.
Moehn, Edwin. System und Phulogenie der Lebewesen. Physikalische, chemische und biologische Evolution, Vol. 1. (Illus.). 884p. 1984. lib. bdg. 132.00x (ISBN 3-51065-117-0). Lubrecht & Cramer.
Mooney, Harold A., ed. Convergent Evolution in Chile & California: Mediterranean Climate Ecosystems. (US-IBP Synthesis Ser.: Vol. 5). 1977. 45.00 (ISBN 0-12-787080-6). Acad Pr.
Moore, J. R. The Post Darwinian Controversies. LC 77-94372. 1979. 52.50 (ISBN 0-521-21989-2). Cambridge U Pr.
Morgan, Elaine. The Descent of Woman. LC 76-186494. 265p. (Orig.). 1980. pap. 8.95 (ISBN 0-8128-6078-0). Stein & Day.
Morris, H. Evolution in Turmoil. LC 82-73600. 200p. 1982. 6.95 (ISBN 0-89051-089-X). Master Bks.
Morris, Henry M. Evolution & the Modern Christian. pap. 3.50 (ISBN 0-8010-5881-3). Baker Bk.
--The Troubled Waters of Evolution. 2nd ed. LC 82-15254. (Illus.). 225p. 1975. pap. 5.95 (ISBN 0-89051-087-3). Master Bks.
--Twilight of Evolution. LC 76-2265. 1963. pap. 3.95 (ISBN 0-8010-5862-7). Baker Bk.
Mortlock, Robert P., ed. Microorganisms As Model Systems for Studying Evolution. (Monographs in Evolutionary Biology). 344p. 1984. 49.50x (ISBN 0-306-41788-X, Plenum Pr). Plenum Pub.
Mother & Satprem. Mother's Agenda, Vol. 2, 1961. LC 80-472990. Tr. of L' Agenda de Mere. 500p. (Orig.). 1981. pap. 12.50 (ISBN 0-938710-01-X). Inst Evolutionary.
Nagle, James J. Heredity & Human Affairs. 3rd ed. LC 82-25906. (Illus.). 420p. 1983. text ed. 21.95 (ISBN 0-8016-3626-4). Mosby.
National Research Council. Science & Creationism: A View from the National Academy of Sciences. 28p. 1984. pap. 4.00 (ISBN 0-309-03440-X). Natl Acad Pr.
Nelkin, Dorothy. The Creation Controversy: Science or Scripture in the Schools? LC 83-45954. 242p. 1984. pap. 9.95x (ISBN 0-8070-3155-0, BP 675). Beacon Pr.
Newell, Norman D. Creation & Evolution: Myth or Reality? (Convergence Ser.). 232p. 1982. 22.00x (ISBN 0-231-05348-7). Columbia U Pr.
Newman, Horatio H., ed. Evolution, Genetics & Eugenics. LC 32-26475. (Illus.). 1969. Repr. of 1932 ed. lib. bdg. 27.50x (ISBN 0-8371-1880-8, NEEV). Greenwood.
Niklas, Karl J., ed. Paleobotany, Paleoecology, & Evolution, 2 vols. LC 81-1838. 1981. Vol. 1. 50.00 (ISBN 0-03-059136-8); Vol. 2. 50.00 (ISBN 0-03-056656-8); Set. 90.00 (ISBN 0-03-060038-3). Praeger.
Ninio, Jacques. Molecular Approaches to Evolution. Lang, Robert, tr. from French. LC 83-4253. (Illus.). 144p. 1983. 25.00x (ISBN 0-691-08313-4); pap. 12.50x (ISBN 0-691-08314-2). Princeton U Pr.
Nitecki, Matthew H., ed. Biochemical Aspects of Evolutionary Biology. LC 82-70746. (Chicago Originals Ser.). 334p. 1982. lib. bdg. 17.00x (ISBN 0-226-58684-7). U of Chicago Pr.
--Coevolution. LC 83-47773. 382p. 1983. lib. bdg. 30.00x (ISBN 0-226-58686-3); pap. text ed. 17.00x (ISBN 0-226-58687-1). U of Chicago Pr.
Ohno, S. Evolution by Gene Duplication. LC 78-112882. (Illus.). 1970. 32.00 (ISBN 0-387-05225-9). Springer-Verlag.
Oldroyd, David R. & Langham, Ian G. The Wilder Domain of Evolutionary Thought. 1983. lib. bdg. 54.50 (ISBN 90-277-1477-0, Pub. by Reidel Holland). Kluwer Academic.
Omark, Donald, et al. Dominance Relations: An Ethological View of Human Conflict & Social Interactions. LC 79-14352. 528p. 1980. lib. bdg. 63.00 (ISBN 0-8240-7048-8). Garland Pub.
Oparin, A. I. The Origin of Life. Morgulis, Sergius, tr. & annotations by. LC 53-10161. lib. bdg. 12.50x (ISBN 0-88307-223-8). Gannon.
Osborn, Henry F. The Origin & Evolution of Life: On the Theory of Action, Reaction & Interaction of Energy. Gould, Stephen J., ed. LC 79-8340. (The History of Paleontology Ser.). (Illus.). 1980. Repr. of 1917 ed. lib. bdg. 33.50x (ISBN 0-405-12728-6). Ayer Co Pubs.
--The Origin & Evolution of Life: On the Theory of Action Reaction & Interaction of Energy. lib. bdg. 40.00. R West.
Ost, David H. Evolution. 2nd ed. (Programed Biology Studies). (Illus.). 1977. pap. text ed. 6.95 (ISBN 0-88462-012-3, Ed Methods). Longman USA.
Ouspensky, P. D. Psychology of Man's Possible Evolution. 1973. pap. 4.95 (ISBN 0-394-71943-3, Vin). Random.
Parsons, Peter A. The Evolutionary Biology of Colonizing Species. LC 82-19763. (Illus.). 304p. 1983. 32.50 (ISBN 0-521-25247-4). Cambridge U Pr.
Patterson, Colin. Evolution. LC 77-78656. (Illus.). 208p. 1978. pap. 8.95x (ISBN 0-8014-9173-8). Cornell U Pr.
Pearson, Roger, ed. Ecology & Evolution. (The Mankind Quarterly Monographs: No. 1). 92p. (Orig.). 1981. pap. 15.00x (ISBN 0-941694-00-3). Inst Study Man.
Pearson, Ronald. Climate & Evolution. 1979. 49.00 (ISBN 0-12-548250-7). Acad Pr.
Poirier, Frank E. Fossil Evidence: The Human Evolutionary Journey. 3rd ed. LC 80-24939. (Illus.). 428p. 1981. pap. text ed. 17.95 (ISBN 0-8016-3952-2). Mosby.
--An Introduction to Physical Anthropology & the Archeological Record. LC 81-70138. 480p. (Orig.). 1982. pap. text ed. 19.95x. Burgess.
Pollard, Jeffrey, ed. Evolutionary Theory: Paths into the Future. 336p. 1984. text ed. 37.95x (ISBN 0-471-90026-5, Pub by Wiley-Interscience). Wiley.
Poppelbaum, Hermann. New Light on Heredity & Evolution. Macbeth, Norman, tr. 1977. pap. 6.95 (ISBN 0-916786-15-3). St George Bk Serv.
Preston, Richard A., ed. Perspectives on Revolution & Evolution. LC 78-74448. 1979. 21.00 (ISBN 0-8223-0425-2). Duke.
Price, Peter W. Evolutionary Biology of Parasites. LC 79-3227. (Monographs in Population Biology: No. 15). 1980. 25.00 (ISBN 0-691-08256-1); pap. 10.95 (ISBN 0-691-08257-X). Princeton U Pr.
Racle, Fred. Introduction to Evolution. (P-H Biology Ser.). (Illus.). 1979. pap. 16.95 ref. (ISBN 0-13-482885-0). P-H.
Reid, Robert G. Evolutionary Theory: The Unfinished Synthesis. 416p. 1985. text ed. 34.50x (ISBN 0-8014-1831-3). Cornell U Pr.
Rensch, Bernard. Evolution Above the Species Level. Altevogt, tr. LC 58-13505. (Columbia Biological Ser.: No. 19). 1960. 47.50x (ISBN 0-231-02296-4). Columbia U Pr.
Ridley, Mark. The Problems of Evolution. LC 84-27300. (Illus.). 160p. 1985. 19.95x (ISBN 0-19-219194-2, OPUS); pap. 8.95x (ISBN 0-19-289175-8). Oxford U Pr.
Roe, Anne & Simpson, George G. Behavior & Evolution. LC 58-11260. pap. 141.80 (ISBN 0-317-10613-9, 2003070). Bks Demand UMI.
Roszak, Theodore. Unfinished Animal. 1977. pap. 5.95i (ISBN 0-06-090537-9, CN 537, CN). Har-Row.
Roughgarden, Jonathan. Theory of Population Genetics & Evolutionary Ecology: An Introduction. 1979. text ed. write for info. (ISBN 0-02-403180-1). Macmillan.
Ruffa, Anthony. Darwinism & Determinism: The Role of Direction in Evolution. 1983. 10.95 (ISBN 0-8283-1732-1); pap. 5.95 (ISBN 0-8283-1877-8). Branden Pub Co.
Rusch, Wilbert H., Sr. The Argument: Creationism vs. Evolutionism. Mulfinger, George, Jr., ed. (Creation Research Society Monograph Ser.: No. 3). (Illus.). 86p. (Orig.). 1984. pap. 6.95 (ISBN 0-940384-04-3). Creation Res.
Salisbury, Frank B. The Creation. LC 76-47071. (Illus.). 1976. 9.95 (ISBN 0-87747-627-6). Deseret Bk.
Sauvant, Karl P. The Group of Seventy-Seven: Evolution, Structure, Organization. LC 81-3998. 232p. 1981. 22.50 (ISBN 0-379-00964-1); pap. 10.00 (ISBN 0-686-84382-7). Oceana.
Savage, Jay M. Evolution. 3rd ed. LC 76-26696. 1977. pap. text ed. 17.95 (ISBN 0-03-089536-7, HoltC). HR&W.
Scheffer, Victor B. Spires of Form: Glimpses of Evolution. LC 83-47972. (Illus.). 152p. 13.95 (ISBN 0-295-96037-X). U of Wash Pr.
--Spires of Form: Glimpses of Evolution. (Illus.). 178p. 1985. pap. 7.95 (ISBN 0-15-684744-2, Harv). HarBraceJ.
Schindewolgf, Otto H. Grundfragen der Palontologie: Geologische Zeitmessung, Organische Stammesentwicklung, Biologische Systematick (Basic Question of Paleontology: Geologic Chronology, Organic Phylogeny, Biologic Systematics. Gould, Stephen J., ed. LC 79-8347. (Ger., Illus.). 1980. Repr. of 1950 ed. lib. bdg. 46.00x (ISBN 0-405-12741-3). Ayer Co Pubs.
Schopf, J. William, ed. Earth's Earliest Biosphere: Its Origin & Evolution. LC 82-61383. (Illus.). 632p. 1983. 95.00 (ISBN 0-691-08323-1); pap. 42.50 (ISBN 0-691-02375-1). Princeton U Pr.
Scientific American Editors. Evolution: A Scientific American Book. LC 78-10747. (Illus.). 135p. 1978. text ed. 20.95x (ISBN 0-7167-1065-X); pap. text ed. 10.95x (ISBN 0-7167-1066-8). W H Freeman.
Scopes, John. World's Most Famous Court Trial: State of Tennessee Vs. John T. Scopes. LC 78-121106. (Civil Liberties in American History Ser). 1971. Repr. of 1925 ed. lib. bdg. 35.00 (ISBN 0-306-71975-4). Da Capo.
Shahrokh, Bahman K. Inter-Relationships of the Evolutionary Systems. LC 76-51099. 1977. 16.50 (ISBN 0-8323-0293-7). Binford.
Sharma, Arun K. Chromosomes in Evolution of Eukaryotic Groups, Vol. I. 304p. 1983. 89.00 (ISBN 0-8493-6496-5). CRC Pr.
Sheldrake, Rupert. A New Science of Life. LC 81-1023. 240p. (Orig.). 1983. pap. 7.95 (ISBN 0-87477-281-8). J P Tarcher.
Shetler, St. G. Variation & Evolution of the Nearctic Harebells: Campanula Subsect. Heterophylla. (Phanerogamarum Monographiae: No. XI). (Illus.). 516p. 1982. lib. bdg. 70.00x (ISBN 3-7682-1241-6). Lubrecht & Cramer.
Shnol, S. E. The Physico-Chemical Factors of Biological Evolution. (Soviet Scientific Reviews, Biology Reviews Supplement Ser.: Vol. 1). 296p. 1981. 93.50 (ISBN 3-7186-0044-7). Harwood Academic.
Shuster, George N. & Thorson, Ralph E., eds. Evolution in Perspective: Commentaries in Honor of Pierre Lecomte Du Nouy. LC 78-105725. 1970. 18.95 (ISBN 0-268-00418-8). U of Notre Dame Pr.
Shvarts, S. S., ed. The Evolutionary Ecology of Animals. LC 76-50647. (Illus.). 300p. 1977. 45.00x (ISBN 0-306-10920-4, Consultants). Plenum Pub.
Sims, Reginald W. & Price, James H., eds. Evolution, Time & Space. 1983. 59.00 (ISBN 0-12-644550-8). Acad Pr.
Skinner, Brian J., ed. Paleontology & Paleoenvironments. (The Earth & Its Inhabitants: Selected Readings from American Scientist Ser.). (Illus.). 210p. (Orig.). 1981. pap. 10.95x (ISBN 0-913232-93-9). W Kaufmann.
Skutch, Alexander F. Life Ascending. LC 84-21879. (Corrie Herring Hooks Ser.: No. 7). 288p. 1985. 22.50x (ISBN 0-292-70374-0); pap. 10.95 (ISBN 0-292-74644-X). U of Tex Pr.

Church, Horace K. Excavation Handbook. 1981. 63.50 (ISBN 0-07-010840-4). McGraw.
Goodman, Richard & Gen-Hua Shi. Block Theory & Its Application to Block Engineering. LC 84-3348. (Illus.). 336p. 1985. text ed. 55.95 (ISBN 0-13-078189-4). P-H.
Grimshaw, Peter. Excavators. (Illus.). 160p. 1985. 14.95 (ISBN 0-7137-1335-6, Pub. by Blandford Pr England). Sterling.
Mann, C. David & Kelley, Martin N., eds. RETC Proceedings, 1985. LC 85-70960. (Rapid Excavation & Tunneling Ser.). (Illus.). 1278p. 1985. 75.00x (ISBN 0-89520-441-X, 441-X). Soc Mining Eng.
Roberts, A. Applied Geotechnology: A Text for Students & Engineers on Rock Excavation & Related Topics. (Illus.). 416p. 1982. 55.00 (ISBN 0-08-024015-1); pap. 25.00 (ISBN 0-08-024014-3). Pergamon.
Society of Mining Engineers of AIME-RETC Proceedings. LC 76-21404. 1976. 40.00x (ISBN 0-89520-037-6). Soc Mining Eng.
Sutcliffe, Harry & Wilson, John W., eds. Rapid Excavation & Tunneling Conference Proceedings, 1983, 2 vols. LC 83-70933. (Illus.). 1258p. 1983. Set. 70.00x (ISBN 0-89520-411-8, 411-8). Soc Mining Eng.
Tunnel & Shaft Conference, Minneapolis, 1968. Rapid Excavation: Problems & Progress Proceedings. Yardley, Donald H., ed. LC 78-98023. (Illus.). pap. 105.00 (ISBN 0-317-10974-X, 2002907). Bks Demand UMI.

EXCAVATIONS (ARCHAEOLOGY)

see also Archaeology
also subdivision Antiquities under names of countries, etc., names of sites of archeological excavations, e.g. Medinet-Abu

Bartlett, John. Jericho. 128p. 1982. 35.00x (ISBN 0-7188-2456-3, Pub. by Lutterworth Pr England). State Mutual Bk.
Bellwood, Peter S. Archaeological Research in the Cook Islands. LC 78-55064. (Pacific Anthropological Records: No. 27). 214p. 1978. pap. 10.00 (ISBN 0-910240-50-7). Bishop Mus.
Berrara, William M. & Hommon, Robert. Salvage Archaeology at Wailau, Ka'u, Island of Hawaii. (Departmental Report: No. 72-1). 60p. 1972. pap. 2.75 (ISBN 0-910240-79-5). Bishop Mus.
Bevacqua, Robert F. & Dye, Thomas S. Archaeological Reconnaissance of Proposed Kapoho-Kalapana Highway, District of Puna, Island of Hawaii. (Departmental Report: No. 72-3). 46p. 1972. pap. 2.00 (ISBN 0-686-47629-8). Bishop Mus.
Bevacqua, Robert F., ed. Archaeological Survey of Portions of Waikoloa, South Kohala District, Island of Hawaii. (Departmental Report: No. 72-4). 24p. 1972. pap. 2.00 (ISBN 0-910240-81-7). Bishop Mus.
Blakely, Jeffry A. & Toombs, Lawrence E. The Tell el-Hesi Field Manual: Joint Archaeological Expedition to Tell el-Hesi: Vol. 1. LC 80-21724. (Excavation Reports Ser.: No. 3). 134p. 1981. text ed. 15.00x (ISBN 0-89757-205-X, Am Sch Orient Res); pap. text ed. 12.00x (ISBN 0-89757-203-3). Eisenbrauns.
Carter, R. M. The Geology of Pitcairn Island, South Pacific Ocean. (Bulletin Ser.: No. 231). 44p. 1967. pap. 4.00 (ISBN 0-910240-52-3). Bishop Mus.
Chapman, Peter S. & Kirch, P. V. Archaeological Excavations at Seven Sites, Southeest Maui, Hawaiian Islands. (Departmental Report: 79-1). 40p. 1979. pap. 5.00 (ISBN 0-910240-86-8). Bishop Mus.
Cleghorn, Paul L. The Hilina Pali Petroglyph Cave, Hawai'i Island: A Report on Preliminary Archaeological Investigations. (Departmental Report: No. 80-1). 32p. 1980. pap. 4.00 (ISBN 0-910240-88-4). Bishop Mus.
Crozier, S. Neal. Archaeological Excavations at Kamehameha III Road, North Kona, Island of Hawaii-Phase II. (Departmental Report: No. 71-5). 30p. 1981. pap. 2.00 (ISBN 0-910240-78-7). Bishop Mus.
David, Nicholas & Bricker, Harvey, eds. Excavation of the Abri Pataud, les Eyzies (Dordogne) The Noaillian, Level 4. (American School of Prehistoric Research Bulletin: No. 37). (Illus.). 400p. 1985. pap. 35.00x (ISBN 0-87365-540-0). Peabody Harvard.
Denison, David O. & Forman, Arthur S. Archaeological Investigations in South Halawa Valley, Ewa District, Island of Oahu-Phase II. (Departmental Report: No. 71-9). 64p. 1971. pap. 3.00 (ISBN 0-910240-77-9). Bishop Mus.
Emory, Kenneth P. Material Culture of the Tuamotu Archipelago. (Pacific Anthropological Records: No. 22). 253p. 1975. 16.50 (ISBN 0-910240-53-1). Bishop Mus.
Fowler, Melvin L. Ferry Site, Hardin County, Illinois. facsimile ed. (Scientific Papers Ser.: Vol. VIII, No. 1). (Illus.). 36p. 1974. pap. 2.00 (ISBN 0-89792-016-3). Ill St Museum.
Gifford, Edward. Archaeological Excavations in Yap. LC 60-63050. (University of California, Anthropological Records: Vol. 18, No. 2). pap. 20.00 (ISBN 0-317-29122-X, 2021316). Bks Demand UMI.
Gifford, Edward W. & Shutler, Dick. Archaeological Excavations in New Caledonia. LC 56-4866. (University of California, Anthropological Records: Vol. 18, No. 1). pap. 38.00 (ISBN 0-317-29127-0, 2021315). Bks Demand UMI.
Hommon, Robert J. & Bevacqua, Robert F. Excavations in Kahana Valley, Oahu, 1972: Departmental Report. (No. 73-2). 48p. 1973. pap. 2.75 (ISBN 0-910240-83-3). Bishop Mus.
Jennings, Jesse D. & Holmer, Richard N. Excavations on Upolu, Western Samoa. LC 76-24248. (Pacific Anthropological Records: No. 25). 115p. 1976. pap. 6.00 (ISBN 0-910240-69-8). Bishop Mus.
Kelly, Marion. Pele & Hi'iaka Visit the Sites at Ke'e, Ha'ena, Island of Kaua'i. (Publication in Education Ser.: No. 1). 36p. 1984. 4.50 (ISBN 0-930897-01-3). Bishop Mus.
Kelly, Marion & Clark, Jeffrey T. Kawainui Marsh, O'ahu: Historical & Archaeological Studies. (Departmental Report: No. 80-3). 82p. 1980. pap. 7.00 (ISBN 0-910240-90-6). Bishop Mus.
Kelly, Marion & Crozier, S. Neal. Archaeological Survey & Excavations at Waiohinu Drainage Improvement Project, Ka'u Island of Hawaii. (Departmental Report: No. 72-6). 57p. 1972. pap. 2.75 (ISBN 0-910240-82-5). Bishop Mus.
Kelly, Marion, ed. Hawai'i in Eighteen Nineteen: A Narrative Account by Louis Claude de Saulses de Freycinet. Wiswell, Ella L., tr. LC 78-59286. (Pacific Anthropological Records: No. 26). 138p. 1978. pap. 6.00 (ISBN 0-910240-55-8). Bishop Mus.
Osborne, Douglas. The Archaeology of the Palau Islands: An Intensive Survey. 497p. 1966. pap. 4.00 (ISBN 0-910240-58-2). Bishop Mus.
Renger, Robert C. Archaeological Reconnaissance of Coastal Kaloko & Kukio 1, North Kona, Hawaii. (Departmental Report: No. 70-10). 56p. 1970. pap. 2.00 (ISBN 0-910240-74-4). Bishop Mus.
Satterthwaite, Linton. Description of the Site with Short Notes on the Excavations of 1931-32. (Piedras Negras Preliminary Papers: No. 1). pap. 20.00 (ISBN 0-317-26210-6, 2052122). Bks Demand UMI.
Schlit, Rose. Subsistence & Conflict in Kona, Hawai'i: An Archaeological Study of the Kuakini Highway Realignment Corridor. (Departmental Report Ser.: No. 84-1). (Illus.). 427p. 1984. 12.00 (ISBN 0-910240-96-5). Bishop Mus.
Sidrys, Raymond V. UCLA Excavations in Northern Belize, Central America. (Monograph: No. XVII). (Illus.). 434p. 1983. pap. 22.50x (ISBN 0-917956-21-4). UCLA Arch.
Sinoto, Yosihiko H. & Kelly, Marion. Archaeological & Historical Survey of Pakini-nui & Pakini-iki Coastal Sites; Waiahukini, Kailikii, & Hawea, Ka'u, Hawaii. (Departmental Report: No. 70-11). 166p. 1975. pap. 5.00 (ISBN 0-910240-85-X). Bishop Mus.
Skjolsvold, Arne & Bellwood, Peter S. Excavations of a Habitation Cave, Hanapete'o, Hiva Oa, Marquesas Islands, (16) A Settlement Pattern Survey, Hanatekua Valley, Hiva Oa, Marquesas Islands, (17, 2 titles in one vol. 41p. 1972. pap. 4.50 (ISBN 0-910240-63-9). Bishop Mus.
Sterling, Elspeth P. & Summers, Catherine C., eds. Sites of Oahu. LC 78-73981. (Special Publications-Anthropology). 372p. 1978. pap. 22.50 (ISBN 0-910240-73-6). Bishop Mus.
Ubelaker, Douglas H. Human Skeletal Remains: Excavation, Analysis, Interpretation. Rev. ed. LC 84-51025. (Manuals on Archeology: No. 2). (Illus.). xii, 119p. 1984. 18.00x (ISBN 0-9602822-4-6). Taraxacum.
White, Donald. The Extramural Sanctuary of Demeter & Persephone at Cyrene, Libya, Final Reports: Vol. 1-Background & Introduction to the Excavations. (University Museum Monographs: No. 52). (Illus.). xx, 144p. 1984. 50.00 (ISBN 0-934718-51-2). Univ Mus of U Pa.
Woolley, Leonard. Ur 'of the Chaldees' A Revised & Updated Edition of Sir Leonard Woolley's Excavations at Ur by P. R. S. Moorey. 1982. 24.95 (ISBN 0-8014-1518-7). Cornell U Pr.

EXCAVATIONS (ARCHAEOLOGY)–AFRICA

James, T. G. Excavating in Egypt: The Egypt Exploration Society 1882-1982. LC 81-21947. (Illus.). 192p. 1984. pap. 12.95 (ISBN 0-226-39192-2). U of Chicago Pr.
James, T. G., ed. Excavating in Egypt: The Egypt Exploration Society 1882-1982. 194p. 1982. 45.00x (ISBN 0-7141-0932-0, Pub. by Brit Mus Pubns England). State Mutual Bk.

EXCAVATIONS (ARCHAEOLOGY)–ASIA

Moorey, Roger. Excavation in Palestine. 1982. 35.00x (ISBN 0-7188-2432-6, Pub. by Lutterworth Pr England). State Mutual Bk.
Recent Archaeological Discoveries in the Republic of Korea. pap. 29.75 (ISBN 92-3-102001-3, U1334, UNESCO). Unipub.

EXCAVATIONS (ARCHAEOLOGY)–EUROPE

McDonald, William A. & Coulson, William D., eds. Excavations at Nichoria in Southwest Greece, Vol. III: The Dark Age & Byzantine Occupation. LC 78-3198. (Illus.). 544p. 1983. 49.50x (ISBN 0-8166-1144-0). U of Minn Pr.
Tomlinson, R. A. Epiduaros. (Illus.). 98p. 1983. 12.50 (ISBN 0-292-72044-0). U of Tex Pr.
Topal, Judit. The Southern Cemetery of Matricia. 106p. 1981. 90.00x (ISBN 0-569-08702-3, Pub. by Collets). State Mutual Bk.

EXCAVATIONS (ARCHAEOLOGY)–GREAT BRITAIN

Case, H. J. & Whittle, A. W. Settlement Patterns in the Oxford Region. 1982. 90.00x (ISBN 0-900090-85-5, Pub. by Ashmolean Mus UK). State Mutual Bk.
Hedges, John W. Isbister: A Chambered Tomb in Orkney. 313p. 75.00x (ISBN 0-86054-213-0, Pub. by Orkney Pr Uk). State Mutual Bk.
MacGregor, Arthur. Anglo-Scandinavian Finds from Lloyds Bank, Pavement & Other Sites. (Archaeology of York-Small Finds 17-3). 174p. 1982. pap. text ed. 15.50x (ISBN 0-906780-02-0, 40256, Pub. by Coun Brit Archaeology England). Humanities.
Pryor, Francis. Fengate. (Shire Archaeology Ser.: No. 20). (Illus.). 1982. pap. 5.95 (ISBN 0-85263-577-X, Pub. by Shire Pubns England). Seven Hills Bks.
Wilson, David. Moated Sites. (Shire Archaeology Ser.: No. 44). (Orig.). 1985. pap. 6.95 (ISBN 0-85263-756-X, Pub. by Shire Pubns England). Seven Hills Bks.

EXCAVATIONS (ARCHAEOLOGY)–NEAR EAST

Rast, Walter E., ed. Preliminary Reports of ASOR-Sponsored Excavations 1981-83. LC 85-12851. (Bulletin of the American Schools of Oriental Research, Supplement: No. 23). 135p. 1985. pap. 17.50x (ISBN 0-89757-323-4, Dist. by Eisenbrauns). Am Sch Orient Res.
Sarianidi, Victor. The Golden Hoard of Bacteria: From the Excavations of the Tillya-Tepe Necropolis in Northern Afghanistan. (Illus.). 260p. 1985. 49.50 (ISBN 0-8109-0987-1). Abrams.
Sussmann, Ayala & Pommerantz, Inna, eds. Excavations & Surveys in Israel, Vol. I. Tr. of Hadashot Arkheologiyst. (Hebrew., Illus.). viii, 114p. (Orig.). pap. text ed. 9.00x (ISBN 0-317-14669-6, Pub. by Israel Dep Anti Israel). Eisenbrauns.
Voigt, Mary M. Fijji Firuz Tepe, Iran, the Neolithic Settlement: Hasanlu Excavation Reports, Vol. 1. (University Museum Monographs: No. 50). (Illus.). 500p. 1984. text ed. 60.00 (ISBN 0-934718-49-0). Univ Mus of U Pa.
Woolley, Leonard, et al. Alalakh: An Account of the Excavations at Tell Atchana in the Hatav, 1937-1949. (Society of Antiquaries of London Research Committee Reports Ser.: No. 18). (Illus.). pap. 140.50 (ISBN 0-317-09269-3, 2013144). Bks Demand UMI.

EXCAVATIONS (ARCHAEOLOGY)–NORTH AMERICA

Andrews, Peter & Layhe, Robert. Excavations on Black Mesa, 1980: A Descriptive Report. LC 82-72189. (Research Paper: No. 24). (Illus.). xv, 360p. 1982. pap. 10.00 (ISBN 0-88104-003-7). Center Archaeo.
Autry, William O., Jr. Archaeological Investigations at the Tennessee Valley Authority Hartsville Nuclear Plants Off-Site Borrow Areas: The Taylor Tract. (T.A.R.A. Reports: No. 2). (Illus.). 125p. (Orig.). 1984. pap. 10.00x (ISBN 0-940148-03-X). Anthro Research.
Bareis, Charles J. & Porter, James W., eds. American Bottom Archaeology: A Summary of the FAI-270 Project Contribution to the Culture History of the Mississippi River Valley. LC 83-15366. (Illus.). 304p. 1984. 22.50x (ISBN 0-252-01111-2). U of Ill Pr.
Bender, Marilyn & Webb, Paul. Archaeological Investigations at the Roos Site, St. Clair County Illinois. new ed. Jeffries, Richard W., ed. (Research Paper Ser.: No. 43). (Illus.). 59p. 1984. pap. 1.25 (ISBN 0-88104-015-0). Center Archaeo.
Benthall, Joseph L. Archeological Investigation of the Shannon Site, Montgomery County, Virgini. (Virginia State Library Publications: No. 32). xi, 152p. 1969. pap. 5.00 (ISBN 0-88490-063-0). VA State Lib.
Blomberg, Belinda. Material Correlates of Increasing Sedentism: The Black Mesa Navajo. LC 82-72265. (Research Paper: No. 32). (Illus.). v, 65p. 1982. soft cover 5.00 (ISBN 0-88104-002-9). Center Archaeo.
Custer, Jay F. Delaware Prehistoric Archaeology: An Ecological Approach. (Illus.). 224p. 1984. 28.50 (ISBN 0-87413-233-9). U Delaware Pr.
Emerson, Thomas E. & Jackson, Douglas K. The BBB Motor Site. LC 83-18196. (American Bottom Archaeology: Selected Fai-270 Site Reports Ser.: Vol. 6). (Illus.). 454p. 1984. pap. 13.95 (ISBN 0-252-01068-X). U of Ill Pr.
Emerson, Thomas E., et al. The Florence Street Site. (American Bottom Archaeology: Selected FAI-270 Site Reports Ser.: Vol. 2). (Illus.). 366p. 1983. pap. 12.95x (ISBN 0-252-01064-7). U of Ill Pr.
Greber, N'omi. Recent Excavation at the Edwin Harness Mound Liberty Works, Ross County, Ohio. (MCJA Special Papers: No.5). (Illus.). 72p. 1984. pap. 9.95x (ISBN 0-87338-303-6). Kent St U Pr.
Kelley, Jane H. The Archaeology of the Sierra Blanca Region of Southeastern New Mexico. (Anthropological Papers: No. 74). (Illus.). 527p. 1984. pap. text ed. 15.00x (ISBN 0-932206-96-4). U Mich Mus Anthro.
McElrath, Dale L. & Fortier, Andrew C. The Missouri Pacific Number Two Site. Bareis, Charles J. & Porter, James W., eds. LC 83-8156. (American Bottom Archaeology: Selected FAI-270 Site Reports: Vol. 3). (Illus.). 272p. 1983. pap. 11.95x (ISBN 0-252-01065-5). U of Ill Pr.
Milner, George R. The East St. Louis Stone Quarry Site Cemetery. (American Bottom Archaeology: Selected FAI-270 Site Reports Ser.: Vol. 1). (Illus.). 192p. 1983. pap. 8.95x (ISBN 0-252-01060-4). U of Ill Pr.
--The Robinson's Lake Site: Emergent Mississippian Occupation. LC 84-24107. (American Bottom Archaeology: FAI-270 Site Reports Ser.: Vol. 10). (Illus.). 240p. 1985. pap. 12.50x (ISBN 0-252-01072-8). U of Ill Pr.
--The Turner & DeMange Sites, Vol. 4. (American Bottom Archaeology: Selected FAI-270 Site Reports Ser.). (Illus.). 256p. 1984. 10.95 (ISBN 0-252-01066-3). U of Ill Pr.
Nassaney, Michael S., et al. The Nineteen Eighty-Two Excavations at the Cahokia Interpretive Center Tract, St. Clair County, Illinois. (Southern Illinois University at Carbondale Center for Archaeological Investigations Research Paper Ser.: No. 37). (Illus.). 132p. 1983. pap. 7.50 (ISBN 0-88104-010-X). Center Archaeo.
Parry, William J. & Speth, John D. Contribution Ten in Research Reports in Archaeology: The Garnsey Spring Campsite: Late Prehistoric Occupation in Southeastern New Mexico. (Technical Reports Ser.: No. 15). (Illus.). 228p. (Orig.). 1984. pap. text ed. 8.00x (ISBN 0-932206-99-9). U Mich Mus Anthro.
Seeman, Mark. The Locust Site 33Mu160: The 1983 Test Excavation of a Multicomponent Workshop in East Central Ohio. (Kent State Research Papers in Archaeology: No. 7). 90p. 1985. pap. text ed. 7.00x (ISBN 0-87338-318-4). Kent St U Pr.
Tierney, John H. Acambaro-Archaeology's Astounding Scandal: The Conspiracy Against Julsrud's Incredible Discovery. LC 83-70806. (Illus.). 160p. (Orig.). 1983. pap. 9.95 (ISBN 0-912361-00-X). Trine Bks.

EXCAVATIONS (ARCHAEOLOGY)–SOUTH AMERICA

Bennett, Wendell C. Excavations at Tiahuanaco & Elsewhere in Bolivia. (Classics of Anthropology). 360p. 1985. lib. bdg. 62.00 (ISBN 0-8240-9633-9). Garland Pub.
Stafford, Barbara D. & Sant, Mark B., eds. Smiling Dan: Structure & Function at a Middle Woodland Settlement in the Illinois Valley. LC 85-7861. (Kampsville Archeological Center Research Ser.: No. 2). (Illus.). 513p. (Orig.). 1985. pap. 12.95 (ISBN 0-942118-19-7). Ctr Amer Arche.
Terada, Kazuo, ed. Excavations at Huacaloma in the North Highlands of Peru, 1979: Report No. 2 of the Japanese Scientific Expedition to Nuclear America. (Illus.). 485p. 1982. 105.00x (ISBN 0-86008-315-2, Pub. by U of Tokyo Japan). Columbia U Pr.

EXCHANGES, LITERARY AND SCIENTIFIC

see also Communication in Science; Information Networks

Balaban, Miriam, ed. Scientific Information Transfer: The Editor's Role. 1978. lib. bdg. 37.00 (ISBN 90-277-0917-3, Pub. by Reidel Holland). Kluwer Academic.
Uyehara, Cecil H., ed. United States-Japan Technological Exchange Symposium: Sponsored by the Japan-American Society of Washington, 1981. LC 82-40064. 142p. (Orig.). 1982. PLB 21.75 (ISBN 0-8191-2423-0); pap. text ed. 9.25 (ISBN 0-8191-2424-9). U Pr of Amer.
World Symposium on International Documentation, Second, Brussels, 1980. International Documents for the Eighties; Their Role & Use: Proceedings. Dimitrov, Th. & Marulli, L., eds. 650p. 1982. 85.00 (ISBN 0-89111-012-7). UNIFO Pubs.

World Weather Watch. International Global Data-Processing System Plan to Support the First GARP Global Experiment. (Illus.). iii, 75p. 1977. pap. 18.00 (ISBN 92-63-10469-7, W355, WMO). Unipub.

EXCITATION (PHYSIOLOGY)

Adam, Waldemar & Cilento, G., eds. Chemical & Biological Generation of Excited States. 1982. 59.50 (ISBN 0-12-044080-6). Acad Pr.

Caputto, R. & Marsan, C. Ajmone, eds. Neural Transmission, Learning, & Memory. (International Brain Research Organization Monographs: Vol. 10). (Illus.). 286p. 1983. text ed. 76.00 (ISBN 0-89004-860-6). Raven.

Chang, Donald C., et al, eds. Structure & Function of Excitable Cells. 516p. 1983. 65.00x (ISBN 0-306-41338-8, Plenum Pr). Plenum Pub.

Khodorov, B. I. The Problem of Excitability: Electrical Excitability & Ionic Permeability of the Nerve Membrane. LC 72-90339. (Illus.). 346p. 1974. 39.50x (ISBN 0-306-30593-3, Plenum Pr). Plenum Pub.

Sykova, Eva, et al, eds. Ion-Selective Microelectrodes & Their Use in Excitable Tissues. LC 81-1625. 380p. 1981. 39.50x (ISBN 0-306-40723-X, Plenum Pr). Plenum Pub.

EXCITATION, NUCLEAR

see Nuclear Excitation

EXCITON THEORY

see also Absorption Spectra; Dielectrics; Energy-Band Theory of Solids; Nuclear Excitation; Semiconductors

Broude, V. L., et al. Spectroscopy of Molecular Excitons. (Springer Series in Chemical Physics: Vol. 16). (Illus.). 290p. 1985. 48.00 (ISBN 0-387-12409-8). Springer-Verlag.

Cardona, M. Modulation Spectroscopy. (Solid State Physics: Suppl. 11). 1969. 76.00 (ISBN 0-12-607771-1). Acad Pr.

Cho, K., ed. Excitons. (Topics in Current Physics Ser.: Vol. 14). (Illus.). 1979. 43.00 (ISBN 0-387-09567-5). Springer-Verlag.

Davydov, A. S. Theory of Molecular Excitations. LC 72-75767. 313p. 1971. 45.00x (ISBN 0-306-30440-6, Plenum Pr). Plenum Pub.

Duckett, Steven W. Photoelectronic Processes & a Search for Exciton Mobility in Pure & Doped Alkali Halides. LC 79-135074. 145p. 1969. 25.00 (ISBN 0-403-04496-0). Scholarly.

Kenkre, V. M. & Reineker, P. Exciton Dynamics in Molecular Crystals & Aggregates. (Springer Tracts in Modern Physics Ser.: Vol. 94). (Illus.). 226p. 1982. 35.00 (ISBN 0-387-11318-5). Springer-Verlag.

Knox, Robert S. Theory of Excitons. (Solid State Physics: Advances in Research & Applications Suppl. 5). 1964. 50.00 (ISBN 0-12-607765-7). Acad Pr.

Oji Seminar, Tomakomai, Japan, Sept. 9-13, 1975. Physics of Highly Excited States in Solids: Proceedings. Ueta, M. & Nishina, Y., eds. (Lecture Notes in Physics: Vol. 57). 1976. soft cover 21.00 (ISBN 0-387-07991-2). Springer-Verlag.

Reynolds, Donald C. & Collins, Thomas C. Excitons: Their Properties & Uses. LC 80-1783. 1981. 38.00 (ISBN 0-12-586580-5). Acad Pr.

Ware, William R., ed. Creation & Detection of the Excited State, Vol. 3. 208p. 1974. 85.00 (ISBN 0-8247-6114-6). Dekker.

EXERCISE–PHYSIOLOGICAL EFFECT

Adamovich, David R. The Heart: Fundamentals of Electrocardiography, Exercise Physiology, & Exercise Stress Testing. LC 83-50971. (Illus.). 414p. (Orig.). 1984. pap. 29.95 (ISBN 0-914363-00-X). Sports Med Bks.

Andersen, K. Lange, et al. Fundamentals of Exercise Testing. 116p. 1970. pap. 9.60 (ISBN 92-4-156001-0, 241). World Health.

Berger, Richard A. Applied Exercise Physiology. LC 81-2322. (Illus.). 291p. 1982. text ed. 19.75 (ISBN 0-8121-0773-X). Lea & Febiger.

Clarke, David H. Exercise Physiology. LC 75-9735. 1975. 26.95 (ISBN 0-13-294967-9). P-H.

Cureton, Thomas K. Physiological Effects of Exercise Programs on Adults. (Illus.). 228p. 1971. photocopy ed. 23.00x (ISBN 0-398-00377-7). C C Thomas.

Dempsey, Jerome A. & Reed, Charles E., eds. Muscular Exercise & the Lung. (Illus.). 416p. 1977. 50.00x (ISBN 0-299-07220-7). U of Wis Pr.

Di Prampero, P. E. & Poortsmans, J., eds. Physiological Chemistry of Exercise & Training. (Medicine & Sport: Vol. 13). (Illus.). viii, 216p. 1981. 41.75 (ISBN 3-8055-2028-X). S Karger.

Falls, Harold B., ed. Exercise Physiology. 1968. 66.00 (ISBN 0-12-248050-3). Acad Pr.

Hietanen, Eino. Regulation of Serum Lipids by Physical Exercise. 192p. 1982. 64.00 (ISBN 0-8493-6330-6). CRC Pr.

Jokl, Ernst. Physiology of Exercise. (Illus.). 156p. 1971. photocopy ed. 15.75x (ISBN 0-398-02152-X). C C Thomas.

Jones, Norman L., et al. Clinical Exercise Testing: A Guide to the Use of Exercise Physiology in Clinical Investigation. LC 74-25477. Repr. of 1975 ed. 42.20 (ISBN 0-8357-9536-5, 2012287). Bks Demand UMI.

Katch, Frank I. & McArdle, William D. Nutrition, Weight Control, & Exercise. 2nd ed. LC 82-25873. (Illus.). 332p. 1983. 18.50 (ISBN 0-8121-0867-1). Lea & Febiger.

Lamb, David R. Physiology of Exercises: Responses & Adaptations. 2nd ed. 464p. 1984. text ed. write for info. (ISBN 0-02-367210-2); lab manual 9.95 (ISBN 0-02-367220-X). Macmillan.

McManus. Cardiovascular Complications of Exercise. 1985. 37.50 (ISBN 0-8151-5849-1). Year Bk Med.

Margaria, R. Biomechanics & Energetics of Muscular Exercise. (Illus.). 1976. text ed. 29.50x (ISBN 0-19-857397-9). Oxford U Pr.

Michael, Ernest D., et al. Laboratory Experiences in Exercise Physiology. 1979. lab manual 5.95 (ISBN 0-932392-05-9); text ed. 11.95. Mouvement Pubns.

Scherrer, M. Pulmonary Diffusing Capacity of Exercise. 214p. 1971. 70.00 (ISBN 3-456-00251-3, Pub. by Holdan Bk Ltd UK). State Mutual Bk.

Shephard, Roy J. Physical Activity & Growth. (Illus.). 340p. 1982. 26.50 (ISBN 0-8151-7643-0). Year Bk Med.

--Physiology & Biochemistry of Exercise. LC 81-1833. 682p. 1982. 78.50 (ISBN 0-03-059289-5). Praeger.

--Physiology & Biochemistry of Exercise. LC 81-1833. 682p. 1985. 35.00 (ISBN 0-03-003674-7). Praeger.

EXFOLIATIVE CYTOLOGY

Andrews, G. S. Exfoliative Cytology. (Illus.). 120p. 1971. 15.50x (ISBN 0-398-02188-0). C C Thomas.

Bronner, Felix & Peterlik, Meinrad. Epithelial Calcium & Phosphate Transport: Molecular & Cellular Aspects. LC 84-17149. (Progress in Clinical & Biological Research Ser.: Vol. 168). 416p. 1984. 68.00 (ISBN 0-8451-5018-9). A R Liss.

Franks, L. M. & Wigley, C. B., eds. Neoplastic Transformation in Differentiated Epithelial Cell Systems in Vitro. LC 79-41276. 1980. 48.50 (ISBN 0-12-266260-1). Acad Pr.

Kurth, Edmund A. Expolitation: Homo Homini Lupus. 320p. 1983. pap. text ed. 11.95 (ISBN 0-8403-3024-3). Kendall-Hunt.

LiVolsi, Virginia A. Practical Clinical Cytology. (Illus.). 352p. 1980. photocopy ed. 38.50x (ISBN 0-398-03927-5). C C Thomas.

Naib, Zuher M. Exfoliative Cytopathology. 2nd ed. 1976. 48.50 (ISBN 0-316-59672-8). Little.

Taub, Mary, ed. Tissue Culture of Epithelial Cells. 310p. 1984. 45.00x (ISBN 0-306-41740-5, Plenum Pr). Plenum Pub.

Wright, Nicholas & Alison, Malcolm. The Biology of Epithelial Cell Populations, Vol. 1. (Illus.). 1984. 49.95x (ISBN 0-19-857558-0). Oxford U Pr.

EXHAUST CONTROL DEVICES (MOTOR VEHICLES)

see Motor Vehicles–Pollution Control Devices

EXHAUST GAS, AUTOMOBILE

see Automobiles–Motors–Exhaust Gas

EXHAUSTERS

see Compressors; Fans (Machinery)

EXHIBITIONS

see also Fairs

also particular exhibitions, e.g. Chicago–World's Columbian Exposition, 1893; exhibitions under special subjects, e.g. Paintings–Exhibitions

Abbott, Carl. The Great Extravaganza: Portland & the Lewis & Clark Exposition. LC 80-83179. (Illus.). 96p. 1981. pap. 6.95 (ISBN 0-87595-088-4). Oreg Hist Soc.

Corn, Joseph J. & Horrigan, Brian, eds. Yesterday's Tomorrows: Past Visions of the American Future. (Illus.). 208p. (Orig.). 1984. 29.95 (ISBN 0-671-54276-1); pap. 17.95 (ISBN 0-671-54133-1). Summit Bks.

Harrison, Helen A., ed. Dawn of a New Day: The New York World's Fair, 1939-1940. (Illus.). 128p. 1980. 30.00x (ISBN 0-8147-3407-3); pap. 16.50x (ISBN 0-8147-3408-1). NYU Pr.

Maass, John. The Glorious Enterprise: The Centennial Exhibition of 1876 in Philadelphia, & H. J. Schwarzmann, Architect-in-Chief. LC 73-85943. (Illus.). 196p. 1973. 25.00 (ISBN 0-89257-004-0). Am Life Foun.

Moore, L. K. & Plung, D. L., eds. Marketing Technical Ideas & Products Successfully. LC 84-22414. (Reprint Ser.). 1985. 48.95 (ISBN 0-87942-185-1, PC01792). Inst Electrical.

Reff, Theodore, ed. World's Fair of Eighteen Eighty-Nine. (Modern Art in Paris 1855 to 1900). 330p. 1981. lib. bdg. 53.00 (ISBN 0-8240-4704-4). Garland Pub.

--World's Fair of Eighteen Fifty-Five: Modern Art in Paris 1855-1900. 694p. 1981. lib. bdg. 53.00 (ISBN 0-8240-4701-X). Garland Pub.

--World's Fair of Eighteen Sixty-Seven. (Modern Art in Paris 1855 to 1900). 224p. 1981. lib. bdg. 53.00 (ISBN 0-8240-4702-8). Garland Pub.

--World's Fair of Nineteen Hundred: General Catalogue. (Modern Art in Part in Paris 1855 to 1900). 582p. 1981. lib. bdg. 53.00 (ISBN 0-8240-4706-0). Garland Pub.

--World's Fair of Nineteen Hundred: Retrospective Exhibition of French Art, 1800 to 1889. (Modern Art in Paris 1855 to 1900). (Illus.). 442p. 1981. lib. bdg. 53.00 (ISBN 0-8240-4707-9). Garland Pub.

--World's Fair of Nineteen Hundred: Retrospective Exhibition of Fine Art, 1889 to 1900. (Modern Art in Paris 1855 to 1900). 581p. 1981. lib. bdg. 53.00 (ISBN 0-8240-4708-7). Garland Pub.

Rudman, Jack. Exhibits Technician. (Career Examination Ser.: C-1281). (Cloth bdg. avail. on request). pap. 10.00 (ISBN 0-8373-1281-7). Natl Learning.

Thirty-Eighth Western New York Exhibition. LC 80-50571. (Illus.). 43p. 1980. pap. 5.50 (ISBN 0-914782-33-9). Buffalo Acad.

EXHIBITIONS, LIVE STOCK

see Livestock Exhibitions

EXHIBITS

see Exhibitions

EXISTENCE THEOREMS

Barbu, V. & Da Prato, G. Hamilton-Jacobi Equations in Hilbert Space. (Research Notes in Mathematics Ser.: No. 86). 240p. 1983. pap. text ed. 18.95 (ISBN 0-273-08597-2). Pitman Pub MA.

Bernstein, D. L. Existence Theorems in Partial Differential Equations. (Annals of Mathematic Studies: No. 23). 1950. 18.00 (ISBN 0-527-02739-1). Kraus Repr.

Evans, Griffith C. Logarithmic Potential, 2 vols. in 1. 2nd ed. Incl. Fundamental Existence Theorems. Bliss, Gilbert A. Repr. of 1927 ed. 19.50 (ISBN 0-8284-0305-8). Chelsea Pub.

Murray, Francis J. & Miller, Kenneth S. Existence Theorems for Ordinary Differential Equations. LC 75-12685. 164p. 1976. Repr. of 1954 ed. 12.50 (ISBN 0-88275-320-7). Krieger.

--Existence Theorems for Ordinary Differential Equations. LC 54-10566. pap. 41.00 (ISBN 0-317-08535-2, 2050206). Bks Demand UMI.

Sprigge, Timothy L. Theories of Existence. 192p. 1985. pap. 5.95 (ISBN 0-14-022167-0). Penguin.

EXO-CONDENSATION

see Ring Formation (Chemistry)

EXOBIOLOGY

see Life on Other Planets; Space Biology

EXPANSION (HEAT)

see also Thermal Stresses

AIP Conference. Thermal Expansion: Proceedings, No. 17. Taylor, R. E. & Denman, G. L., eds. LC 73-94415. 1974. pap. 14.00 (ISBN 0-88318-116-9). Am Inst Physics.

Jetter, R. I., et al, eds. Metallic Bellows & Expansion Joints. (PVP Ser.: Vol. 51). 154p. 1981. 30.00 (ISBN 0-686-34510-X, H00187). ASME.

EXPANSION OF GASES

see Gases

EXPANSION OF SOLIDS

see also Thermal Stresses

Yates, B., ed. Thermal Expansion. LC 70-179759. 121p. 1972. 29.50x (ISBN 0-306-30550-X, Plenum Pr). Plenum Pub.

EXPEDITIONS, SCIENTIFIC

see Scientific Expeditions

EXPERIMENTAL ANIMALS

see Laboratory Animals

EXPERIMENTAL BIOLOGY

see Biology, Experimental

EXPERIMENTAL DESIGN

see also Factorial Experiment Designs

Anderson, Virgil L. & McLean, Robert A. Design of Experiments: A Realistic Approach. (Statistics, Textbks & Monographs: Vol. 5). 440p. 1974. 29.75 (ISBN 0-8247-6131-6). Dekker.

Brook. Applied Regression Analysis & Experimental Design. (Statistics: Monographs & Textbooks). 264p. 1985. 39.75 (ISBN 0-8247-7252-0). Dekker.

Burdette, Walter J. & Gehan, Edmund A. Planning & Analysis of Clinical Studies. (Illus.). 116p. 1970. 15.25x (ISBN 0-398-00257-6). C C Thomas.

Campbell, Donald T. & Stanley, Julian C. Experimental & Quasi-Experimental Designs for Research. LC 81-80806. 1966. pap. text ed. 12.50 (ISBN 0-395-30787-2). HM.

Caporaso, James A. & Roos, Leslie L., Jr., eds. Quasi-Experimental Approaches: Testing Theory & Evaluating Policy. LC 72-96703. Repr. of 1973 ed. 97.00 (ISBN 0-8357-9467-9, 2011468). Bks Demand UMI.

Cochran, William G. & Cox, Gertrude M. Experimental Designs. 2nd ed. LC 57-5908. (Wiley Series in Probability & Mathematics Statistics, Applied Problem & Statistics Section). 617p. 1957. 43.50 (ISBN 0-471-16203-5). Wiley.

Cox, David R. Planning of Experiments. LC 58-13457. (Probability & Statistics Ser.). (Illus.). 308p. 1958. 48.75x (ISBN 0-471-18183-8). Wiley.

Craig, James R. & Metze, Leroy P. Methods of Psychological Research. 2nd. ed. LC 85-9656. (Psychology Ser.). 350p. 1985. text ed. 25.00 (pub net) (ISBN 0-534-05358-0). Brooks-Cole.

Diamond, William J. Practical Experiment Designs for Engineers & Scientists. 348p. 1981. text ed. 33.50x (ISBN 0-534-97992-0). Lifetime Learn.

--Practical Experiment Designs for Engineers & Scientists. 348p. 1981. 33.50 (ISBN 0-534-97992-0). Van Nos Reinhold.

Fedorov, V. V. Theory of Optimal Experiments. (Probability & Mathematical Statistics Ser.). 1972. 67.00 (ISBN 0-12-250750-9). Acad Pr.

Finney, David J. Introduction to the Theory of Experimental Design. LC 60-8126. (Midway Reprint Ser.). 1975. pap. 9.00x (ISBN 0-226-25000-8). U of Chicago Pr.

Gardner, David M. & Belk, Russell W., eds. A Basic Bibliography on Experimental Design in Marketing. LC 80-19563. (Bibliography Ser.: No. 37). 59p. 1980. pap. 6.00 (ISBN 0-87757-142-2). Am Mktg.

Goodwin, G. C. & Payne, R. L., eds. Dynamic System Identification: Experimental Design & Data Analysis. 1977. 65.000007677p (ISBN 0-12-289750-1). Acad Pr.

Harrison, Nancy S. Understanding Behavioral Research. 1979. text ed. write for info. (ISBN 0-534-00597-7). Wadsworth Pub.

Hooke, Robert. Introduction to Scientific Inference. LC 75-28676. (Illus.). 101p. 1976. Repr. of 1963 ed. lib. bdg. 18.75 (ISBN 0-8371-8470-3, HOIS). Greenwood.

Johnson, Norman L. & Leone, Fred C. Statistics & Experimental Design in Engineering & the Physical Sciences, 2 vols. 2nd ed. LC 76-28337. (Wiley Series in Probability & Mathematical Statistics). 512p. 1977. Vol 1. 601 pgs. 56.95x, (ISBN 0-471-01756-6, Pub. by Wiley-Interscience); Vol 2. 512 pgs. 55.50x, (ISBN 0-471-01757-4). Wiley.

Kempthorne, Oscar. The Design & Analysis of Experiments. LC 51-13460. 652p. 1975. Repr. of 1952 ed. 36.50 (ISBN 0-88275-105-0). Krieger.

Kirk, Roger E. Experimental Design. 2nd ed. LC 82-9532. (Statistics Ser.). (Illus.). 850p. 1982. text ed. 36.00 pub net (ISBN 0-534-01173-X). Brooks-Cole.

Kleijnen, J. P. Statistical Techniques in Simulation, Pt. 2. (Statistics: Textbooks & Monographs: Vol. 9). 512p. 1975. 65.00 (ISBN 0-8247-6243-6). Dekker.

Lindman, Harold R. Analysis of Variance in Complex Experimental Designs. LC 74-11211. (Illus.). 352p. 1974. text ed. 30.95 (ISBN 0-7167-0774-8); answers to exercises avail. W H Freeman.

Lipson, Charles & Sheth, N. J. Statistical Design & Analysis of Engineering Experiments. (Illus.). 544p. 1972. text ed. 42.00 (ISBN 0-07-037991-2). McGraw.

Mendenhall, William. Introduction to Linear Models & the Design & Analysis of Experiments. 1968. write for info. (ISBN 0-685-21739-6). PWS Pubs.

Montgomery, Douglas C. Design & Analysis of Experiments. 2nd ed. 538p. 1984. 41.45 (ISBN 0-471-86812-4); solutions manual avail. (ISBN 0-471-86799-3). Wiley.

Myers, Jerome L. Fundamentals of Experimental Design. 3rd ed. 1979. text ed. 33.95 (ISBN 0-205-06615-1). Allyn.

Odeh, Robert E. & Fox, Martin. Sample Size Choice: Charts for Experiments with Linear Models. (Statistics: Textbooks & Monographs Ser.: Vol. 14). 208p. 1975. pap. 45.00 (ISBN 0-8247-7213-X). Dekker.

Ogawa, J. Statistical Theory of the Analysis of Experimental Design. (Statistics Textbooks & Monographs: Vol. 8). 352p. 1974. 59.75 (ISBN 0-8247-6116-2). Dekker.

Winer, B. J. Statistical Principles in Experimental Design. 2nd ed. (Psychology Ser.). text ed. 51.95 (ISBN 0-07-070981-5). McGraw.

Yates, Frank. Experimental Design: Selected Papers. (Illus.). 1970. 19.95x (ISBN 0-02-855490-6). Hafner.

Zarrop, M. B. Optimal Experiment Design for Dynamic System Identification. (Lecture Notes in Control & Information Sciences: Vol. 21). 197p. 1979. pap. 17.00 (ISBN 0-387-09841-0). Springer-Verlag.

EXPERIMENTAL EMBRYOLOGY

see Embryology, Experimental

EXPERIMENTAL PHYSIOLOGY

see Physiology, Experimental

EXPERIMENTAL ZOOLOGY

see Zoology, Experimental

EXPERT SYSTEMS (COMPUTER SCIENCE)

Gupta, M. M., et al, eds. Approximate Reasoning in Expert Systems. 840p. 1985. 92.75 (ISBN 0-444-87808-4, North-Holland). Elsevier.

EXPLODING WIRE PHENOMENA

see also Photography, High-Speed

Chace, W. G. & Moore, H. K., eds. Exploding Wires, 4 vols. Incl. Vol. 1. 373p. 1959. 32.50x (ISBN 0-306-37521-4); Vol. 2. 321p. 1962. 32.50x (ISBN 0-306-37522-2); Vol. 3. 410p. 1964. 37.50x (ISBN 0-306-37523-0); Vol. 4. 348p. 1968. 39.50x (ISBN 0-306-37524-9). LC 59-14822 (Plenum Pr). Plenum Pub.

EXPLORATION, SUBMARINE

see Underwater Exploration

EXPLORATION OF THE DEEP SEA

see Marine Biology; Marine Fauna; Marine Flora

EXPLOSION LOADS

see Blast Effect

EXPLOSIONS

see also Blast Effect; Shock Waves

Astbury, N. F., et al. Experimental Gas Explosions: Report of Further Tests at Potters Marston. 1972. 25.00x (ISBN 0-900910-17-8, Pub. by Brit Ceramic Soc England). State Mutual Bk.

--Gas Explosions in Load-Bearing Brick Structures. 1970. 10.00x (ISBN 0-900910-09-7, Pub. by Brit Ceramic Soc England). State Mutual Bk.

Baker. Explosion Hazards & Evaluation. (Fundamental Studies in Engineering: Vol. 5). 808p. 1983. 159.75 (ISBN 0-444-42094-0). Elsevier.

Bartknecht, W. Explosions: Course, Prevention, Protection. Burg, H. & Almond, T., trs. from Ger. (Illus.). 251p. 1981. 76.50 (ISBN 0-387-10216-7). Springer-Verlag.

CISM (International Center for Mechanical Sciences) Introduction to Gasdynamics of Explosions. Oppenheim, A. K., ed. (CISM Pubns. Ser.: No. 48). (Illus.). 220p. 1972. pap. 23.80 (ISBN 0-387-81083-8). Springer-Verlag.

Explosion Prevention Systems. (Sixty Ser). 60p. 1973. pap. 2.00 (ISBN 0-685-44174-1, 69). Natl Fire Prot.

Explosion Venting Guide. (Sixty Ser.). 60p. 1974. pap. 3.75 (ISBN 0-685-46074-6, 68). Natl Fire Prot.

Gould, Douglas W. Explosion: Some Sources, Causes & Effects in Man's Affairs. 1985. 6.95 (ISBN 0-533-06615-8). Vantage.

Gugan, Keith. Unconfined Vapour Cloud Explosions. 168p. 1981. 100.00x (ISBN 0-686-75389-5, Pub. by Inst Chem Eng England). State Mutual Bk.

Henrych, J. The Dynamics of Explosion & Its Use. LC 76-29648. (Developments in Civil Engineering: Vol. 1). 1979. 117.00 (ISBN 0-444-99819-5). Elsevier.

Hewison, C. H. Locomotive Boiler Explosions. (Illus.). 144p. 1983. 16.50 (ISBN 0-7153-8305-1). David & Charles.

Kennedy, John & Kennedy, Patrick. Fires & Explosions: Determining Cause & Origin. LC 84-62332. (Illus.). 1562p. 1985. text ed. 50.00 (ISBN 0-9607876-1-5). Investigations.

Kinney, G. F. & Graham, K. J. Explosive Shocks in Air. 2nd ed. (Illus.). 270p. 1985. 39.00 (ISBN 0-387-15147-8). Springer-Verlag.

Kirkwood, John G. Shock & Detonation Waves. Wood, W. W., ed. LC 68-7145. (Documents on Modern Physics Ser.). (Illus.). 142p. 1967. 40.50 (ISBN 0-677-00380-3). Gordon.

Lewis, Bernard & Von Elbe, Guenther. Combustion, Flames, & Explosions of Gases. 2nd ed. 1961. 91.50 (ISBN 0-12-446750-4). Acad Pr.

Mader, Charles S. Numerical Modeling of Detonations. (Los Alamos Ser. in Basic & Applied Sciences). 1979. 63.50x (ISBN 0-520-03655-7). U of Cal Pr.

Medvedev, Sergei V. Problems of Engineering Seismology. LC 63-17635. 112p. 1963. 32.50x (ISBN 0-306-10576-4, Consultants). Plenum Pub.

Prevention of Dust Explosions in the Plastic Industry. (Sixty Ser.). 51p. 1970. pap. 2.00 (ISBN 0-685-46073-8, 654). Natl Fire Prot.

Prevention of Furnace Explosions in Fuel-Oil & Natural Gas-Fired Watertube Boiler Furnaces with One Burner. (Eighty-Ninety Ser.). 68p. 1973. pap. 2.00 (ISBN 0-685-44149-0, 85). Natl Fire Prot.

Prevention of Furnace Explosions in Fuel Oil-Fired Multiple Burner Boiler-Furnaces. (Eighty-Ninety Ser.). 84p. 1974. pap. 3.50 (ISBN 0-685-44131-8, 85D). Natl Fire Prot.

Prevention of Furnace Explosions in Natural Gas-Fired Multiple Burner Boiler-Furnaces. (Eighty-Ninety Ser.). 68p. 1973. pap. 3.50 (ISBN 0-685-44130-X, 85B). Natl Fire Prot.

Prevention of Furnace Explosions in Pulverized Coal-Fired Multiple Burner Boiler-Furnaces. (Eighty-Ninety Ser.). 68p. 1974. pap. 3.50 (ISBN 0-685-44132-6, 85E). Natl Fire Prot.

Yallop, H. J. Explosion Investigation. 280p. 1980. 50.00x (ISBN 0-7073-0272-2, Pub. by Scottish Academic Pr Scotland). Columbia U Pr.

Zeldovich, Ya. B., et al. The Mathematical Theory of Combustion & Explosions. 620p. 1985. 95.00x (ISBN 0-306-10974-3, Plenum Pr). Plenum Pub.

EXPLOSIONS, UNDERGROUND NUCLEAR

see Underground Nuclear Explosions

EXPLOSIVE FORMING

see also Sheet-Metal Work

Ezra, A. A. Principles & Practice of Explosive Metalworking. 270p. 1981. 75.00x (ISBN 0-901994-05-7, Pub. by Portcullio Pr). State Mutual Bk.

Newby & Niemeier, eds. Formability of Metallic Materials, 2,000 A.D. - STP 753. 331p. 1981. 39.50 (ISBN 0-8031-0742-0, 04-753000-23). ASTM.

EXPLOSIVES

see also Ammunition; Blasting; Explosive Forming; Propellants

Berman, I. & Schroeder, J. W., eds. Explosive Welding, Forming, Plugging, & Compaction. (PVP: No. 44). 119p. 1980. 20.00 (ISBN 0-686-69850-9, H00171). ASME.

Brodie, Thomas G. Bombs & Bombings: A Handbook to Detection, Disposal & Investigation for Police & Fire Departments. (Illus.). 200p. 1980. photycopy ed. 24.75x (ISBN 0-398-02245-3). C C Thomas.

Brunswig, Heinrich. Explosives: A Synoptic & Critical Treatment of the Literature of the Subject As Gathered from Various Sources. Monroe, Charles E. & Kibler, Alton L., trs. 1980. lib. bdg. 69.95 (ISBN 0-8490-3153-2). Gordon Pr.

The Chemistry of Powder & Explosives. 1982. lib. bdg. 75.00 (ISBN 0-87700-430-7). Revisionist Pr.

Clark, George B. Basic Properties of Ammonium Nitrate Fuel Oil Explosives (ANFO) Raese, Jon W., ed. LC 81-38436. (Colorado School of Mines Quarterly Ser.: Vol. 76, No. 1). (Illus.). 32p. 1981. pap. text ed. 10.00 (ISBN 0-686-46975-5). Colo Sch Mines.

--Industrial High Explosives: Composition & Calculations for Engineers. Raese, Jon W., ed. LC 80-18063. (CSM Quarterly Ser.: Vol. 75, No. 1). (Illus.). 47p. (Orig.). 1980. pap. 8.00 (ISBN 0-686-63161-7). Colo Sch Mines.

Cook, Melvin A. The Science of High Explosives. LC 58-10260. (A C S Ser: No. 139). 456p. 1970. Repr. of 1958 ed. 37.50 (ISBN 0-88275-010-0). Krieger.

Davis, Tenny L. Chemistry of Powder & Explosives. 500p. 1972. Repr. of 1943 ed. 14.00 (ISBN 0-913022-00-4). Angriff Pr.

De Barry Barnett, Edward. Explosives. 1980. lib. bdg. 150.00 (ISBN 0-8490-3154-0). Gordon Pr.

Explosives & Demolitions. 1982. lib. bdg. 75.00 (ISBN 0-87700-418-8). Revisionist Pr.

Fordham, S. High Explosives & Propellants. 2nd ed. 1966. pap. 14.50 (ISBN 0-08-023833-5). Pergamon.

Gibbs, Terry R. & Popolato, Alphonse, eds. LASL Explosive Property Data. (Los Alamos Scientific Laboratory Series on Dynamic Material Properties). 1980. 42.50x (ISBN 0-520-04012-0). U of Cal Pr.

Gregory, C. E. Explosives for Australasian Engineers. 3rd ed. (Illus.). 1977. 25.00x (ISBN 0-7022-1391-8). U of Queensland Pr.

--Explosives for North American Engineers. 3rd ed. (Rock & Soil Mechanics Ser.). (Illus.). 1983p. 1979. 29.50x (ISBN 0-87849-025-6); 38.00x (ISBN 0-87849-051-5). Trans Tech.

--Explosives for North American Engineers. 3rd. ed. LC 83-80650. 316p. 1984. 37.95x (ISBN 0-87201-259-X). Gulf Pub.

Leet, Lewis D. Vibrations from Blasting Rock. LC 60-10037. Repr. of 1960 ed. 37.50 (ISBN 0-8357-9183-1, 2017747). Bks Demand UMI.

Lenz, Robert R. Explosives & Bomb Disposal Guide. (Illus.). 320p. 1976. photocopy ed. 34.50x (ISBN 0-398-01097-8). C C Thomas.

Mader, Charles L. & Neal, Timothy R., eds. LASL Phermex Data, Vol. 1. (Los Alamos Scientific Laboratory Series on Dynamic Material Properties). 1980. 65.00x (ISBN 0-520-04009-0). U of Cal Pr.

Marsh, Stanley P. LASL Shock Hugoniot Data. (Los Alamos Scientific Laboratory Series on Dynamic Material Properties). 1980. 55.00x (ISBN 0-520-04008-2). U of Cal Pr.

Marshall, Arthur. Explosives: Their History, Manufacture, Properties & Tests, 3 vols. 1980. lib. bdg. 600.00 (ISBN 0-8490-3151-6). Gordon Pr.

Meyer, Rudolph. Explosives. 2nd ed. (Illus.). 440p. 1981. 60.00x (ISBN 3-527-25933-3). VCH Pubs.

Rudman, Jack. Senior Demolition Inspector. (Career Examination Ser.: C-1475). (Cloth bdg. avail. on request). pap. 12.00 (ISBN 0-8373-1475-5). Natl Learning.

--Supervising Demolition Inspector. (Career Examination Ser.: C-777). (Cloth bdg. avail. on request). pap. 10.00 (ISBN 0-8373-0777-5). Natl Learning.

Separation Distances of Ammonium Nitrate & Blasting Agents from Explosives or Blasting Agents. (Forty Ser). 1968. pap. 2.00 (ISBN 0-685-58036-9, 492). Natl Fire Prot.

Socffern, J. Projectile Weapons of War & Explosive Compounds. 318p. 1984. Repr. of 1858 ed. 37.00x (ISBN 0-85546-164-0, Pub. by Richmond Pub England). State Mutual Bk.

Stoffel, Joseph. Explosives & Homemade Bombs. 2nd ed. (Illus.). 324p. 1977. photocopy ed. 33.50x (ISBN 0-398-02424-3). C C Thomas.

Toxic Chemical & Explosives Facilities: Safety & Engineering Design. LC 79-9760. (Symposium Ser.: No. 96). 1979. 39.95 (ISBN 0-8412-0481-0). Am Chemical.

Urbanski, T. Chemistry & Technology of Explosives, 4 vols. Vol. 1, 1964. 110.00 (ISBN 0-08-010238-7); Vol. 2, 1965. 110.00 (ISBN 0-08-010239-5); Vol. 3, 1967. 110.00 (ISBN 0-08-010401-0); Vol. 4, 1984. 120.01 (ISBN 0-08-026206-6); Set. 360.00 (ISBN 0-08-030252-1). Pergamon.

Van Gelder, et al. History of the Explosives Industry in America. LC 72-5051. (Technology & Society Ser.). (Illus.). 1170p. 1972. Repr. of 1927 ed. 67.00 (ISBN 0-405-04703-7). Ayer Co Pubs.

Wilkinson, Norman B. Explosives in History. (Industry in America Ser.). (Illus.). pap. 2.00 (ISBN 0-914650-12-2). Eleutherian Mills-Hagley.

--Lammont du pont & the American Explosives Industry 1850-1884. 332p. 1984. text ed. 16.95x (ISBN 0-8139-1012-9). U Pr of Va.

Yinon, Jehuda & Zitrin, Shmuel. The Analysis of Explosives. (Pergamon Ser. in Analytic Chemistry: Vol. 3). (Illus.). 300p. 1981. 66.00 (ISBN 0-08-023846-7); pap. 25.00 (ISBN 0-08-023845-9). Pergamon.

EXPLOSIVES, MILITARY

see also Chemical Warfare

Cowan, J. I. Manual of Grenades & New Grenade Chart. (War Documents Ser.: No. 23). (Illus.). 49p. pap. 4.95 (ISBN 0-86663-992-6). Ide Hse.

Glackin, James. Elements of Explosives Production. 60p. 1976. pap. 5.00 (ISBN 0-87364-083-7). Paladin Pr.

Lee, Chong. Advanced Explosive Kicks. LC 78-61152. (Ser. 133). (Illus.). 1978. pap. 6.95 (ISBN 0-89750-060-1). Ohara Pubns.

U. S. Army. Explosives & Demolitions. (Illus.). 188p. 1967. pap. 12.00 (ISBN 0-87364-077-2). Paladin Pr.

EXPONENTIAL FUNCTIONS

see Functions, Exponential

EXPOSITIONS

see Exhibitions

EXPRESS HIGHWAYS

Brodsly, David. L. A. Freeway: An Appreciative Essay. LC 80-29620. (Illus.). 224p. 1981. 19.95 (ISBN 0-520-04068-6). U of Cal Pr.

Design Standards: Interstate System. rev. & updated ed. 6p. pap. 1.00 (ISBN 0-686-32357-2, DS-2). AASHTO.

Inglesby, Edith. The Happy Highways. LC 81-84270. 1981. 12.00 (ISBN 0-937684-13-9). Tradd St Pr.

Oglesby, Clarkson H. & Hicks, Russell G. Highway Engineering. 4th ed. LC 81-12949. 844p. 1982. text ed. 46.00 (ISBN 0-471-02936-X). Wiley.

EXPRESSWAYS

see Express Highways

EXTENSION WORK, AGRICULTURAL

see Agricultural Extension Work

EXTERIOR BALLISTICS

see Ballistics

EXTERMINATION

see Insect Control; Pest Control; also names of specific pests, with or without the subdivision extermination

EXTINCT ANIMALS

see also Birds, Extinct; Paleontology; Rare Animals

Cuppy, Will. How to Become Extinct. LC 82-17649. (Illus.). 114p. 1941. pap. 5.95 (ISBN 0-226-12826-1). U of Chicago Pr.

Day, David. The Doomsday Book of Animals: A Natural History of Vanished Species. LC 81-43018. (Illus.). 288p. 1981. 40.00 (ISBN 0-670-27987-0, Studio); pap. 14.95 (ISBN 0-670-27988-9). Viking.

Gould, Charles. Mythical Monsters. LC 81-50199. (Secret Doctrine Reference Ser.). (Illus.). 412p. 1981. Repr. of 1886 ed. 20.00 (ISBN 0-913510-38-6). Wizards.

Greenberg, L. M., ed. Evolution, Extinction, & Catastrophism. 1982. pap. 5.00x (ISBN 0-917994-12-4). Kronos Pr.

Hoage, R. J., ed. Animal Extinctions: What Everyone Should Know. LC 85-8342. (National Zoological Park Symposia for the Public Ser.). (Illus.). 160p. (Orig.). 1985. pap. 9.95 (ISBN 0-87474-521-7, HOAEP). Smithsonian.

List of Mammals Which Have Become Extinct or Are Possibly Extinct Since Sixteen Hundred. 1973. pap. 7.50x (ISBN 0-686-53041-1, IUCN22, IUCN). Unipub.

Mowat, Farley. Sea of Slaughter. LC 84-72722. (Illus.). 438p. 1985. 24.95 (ISBN 0-87113-013-0). Atlantic Monthly.

Myers, Norman. The Sinking Ark: A New Look at the Problem of Disappearing Species. 1979. 12.50 (ISBN 0-08-024501-3). Pergamon.

Nitecki, Matthew H., ed. Extinctions. LC 84-40253. (Illus.). 340p. 1984. lib. bdg. 30.00x (ISBN 0-226-58689-8); pap. 16.00x (ISBN 0-226-58690-1). U of Chicago Pr.

Oliveros, Chuck. The Pterodactyl in the Wilderness. 56p. (Orig.). 1983. pap. 3.00 (ISBN 0-911757-00-7). Dead Angel.

Spotter's Guide to Dinosaurs & Other Prehistoric Animals. (Illus.). pap. 2.50 (ISBN 0-8317-7960-8). Smith Pubs.

Stewart, Darryl. From the Edge of Extinction. LC 78-61813. (Illus.). 1978. 12.95 (ISBN 0-458-93650-2, NO. 0058). Methuen Inc.

EXTRACTION (CHEMISTRY)

Braun, T. & Ghersini, G., eds. Extraction Chromatography. (Journal of Chromatography Library: Vol. 2). 592p. 1975. 76.75 (ISBN 0-444-99878-0). Elsevier.

Francis, Alfred W. Handbook of Components in Solvent Extraction. LC 72-78013. 544p. 1972. 132.95 (ISBN 0-677-03080-0). Gordon.

Keller, George E., II. Adsorption, Gas Absorption, & Liquid-Liquid Extraction: Selecting a Process & Conserving Energy. Gyftopoulos, Elias P. & Cohen, Karen C., eds. (Industrial Energy-Conservation Manuals Ser.: No. 9). (Illus.). 104p. 1982. loose-leaf 20.00x (ISBN 0-262-11082-2). MIT Pr.

Ritcey, G. M. & Ashbrook, A. W. Solvent Extraction: Principles & Applications to Process Metallurgy, Pt. 2. (Process Metallurgy Ser.: Vol. 1, Pt. 2). 738p. 1979. 117.00 (ISBN 0-444-41771-0). Elsevier.

Wisniak, J. & Tamir, A. Liquid-Liquid Equilibrium & Extraction: A Literature Source Book, 2 Pts. (Physical Science Data Ser.: Vol. 7). 1980-81. Pt. A, 1252p. 170.25 (ISBN 0-444-41909-8); Pt. B, 1438p. 202.25 (ISBN 0-444-42023-1). Elsevier.

Zief, M., ed. Purification of Inorganic & Organic Materials: Techniques of Fractional Solidification. 1969. 75.00 (ISBN 0-8247-1823-2). Dekker.

EXTRAGALACTIC NEBULAE

see Galaxies

EXTRATERRESTRIAL ENVIRONMENT

see Space Environment

EXTRATERRESTRIAL LIFE

see Life on Other Planets

EXTRATERRESTRIAL RADIATION

see also Cosmic Rays; Stars–Radiation; Solar Radiation; Van Allen Radiation Belts

ESRO Summer School in Space Physics, 3rd, Albach, Austria, July 19-August 13, 1965. Electromagnetic Radiation in Space: Proceedings. Emming, S. G., ed. (Astrophysics & Space Science Library: No. 9). 307p. 1968. 37.00 (ISBN 90-277-0116-4, Pub. by Reidel Holland). Kluwer Academic.

EXTRUSION (METALS)

see Metals–Extrusion

EXTRUSION (PLASTICS)

Bikales, Norbert M., ed. Extrusion & Other Plastics Operations. LC 78-172950. (Encyclopedia Reprints Ser). 281p. 1971. pap. 18.00 (ISBN 0-471-07232-X). Krieger.

Extrusion of Low Density Polyethylenes. 153p. 1982. 78.00 (ISBN 0-317-12672-5). T-C Pubns CA.

Extrusion of Polyprophylene. 105p. 1983. 78.00 (ISBN 0-317-12673-3). T-C Pubns CA.

Griff, Allan L. Plastics Extrusion Technology. 2nd ed. LC 75-45329. 364p. 1976. Repr. of 1968 ed. 23.50 (ISBN 0-88275-386-X). Krieger.

Levy, Sidney. Plastics Extrusion Technology Handbook. (Illus.). 316p. 1981. 34.00 (ISBN 0-686-48164-X, 1202). T-C Pubns CA.

Martelli, F. G. Twin-Screw Extruders: A Basic Understanding. (Illus.). 168p. 1983. 38.00 (ISBN 0-686-48173-9, 0216). T-C Pubns CA.

Michaeli, W. Extrusion Dies. LC 83-62288. 320p. 1984. text ed. 75.00 (ISBN 0-02-949550-4, Pub. by Hanser International). Macmillan.

Plastics Extrusion, June 1978-Feb. 1983. 282p. 1983. 78.00 (ISBN 0-686-48337-5, LS120). T-C Pubns CA.

Richardson, P. N. Introduction to Extrusion. Mendoza, Luis E., tr. (SPE Processing Ser.). (Span., Illus.). 90p. 26.50 (ISBN 0-686-48175-5, 1101). T-C Pubns CA.

Richardson, Paul N. Introduction to Extrusion. (SPE Processing Ser.). (Illus.). 96p. 9.50 (ISBN 0-686-48167-4, 1601). T-C Pubns CA.

Tadmor, Zehev & Klein, Imrich. Engineering Principles of Plasticating Extrusion. LC 78-9105. (Polymer Science & Engineering Ser.). 1978. Repr. of 1970 ed. lib. bdg. 34.50 (ISBN 0-88275-698-2). Krieger.

EYE

see also Crystalline Lens; Retina; Vision

Alexandridis, E. The Pupil. Telger, T., tr. from Ger. (Illus.). 115p. 1985. 29.90 (ISBN 0-387-96109-7). Springer-Verlag.

Allansmith, Mathea R. The Eye & Immunology. LC 81-14163. (Illus.). 209p. 1982. text ed. 37.95 (ISBN 0-8016-0117-7). Mosby.

Augusteyn, R. C. & Collin, H. B. The Eye, Vol. 2. Horrobin, David F., ed. LC 79-32253. (Annual Research Reviews). 344p. 1980. 36.00 (ISBN 0-88831-083-8). Eden Pr.

Augusteyn, R. C., et al. The Eye, Vol. 1. Horrobin, D. F., ed. (Annual Research Reviews Ser.). 1979. 22.00 (ISBN 0-88831-057-9). Eden Pr.
Bloemendal, Hans. Molecular & Cellular Biology of the Eye Lens. LC 80-26815. 469p. 1981. 109.95 (ISBN 0-471-05171-3, Pub. by Wiley-Interscience). Wiley.
Cassin, Barbara & Solomon, Sheila. Dictionary of Eye Terminology. (Illus., Orig.). 1984. 14.95x (ISBN 0-937404-07-1). Triad Pub FL.
Chalkley, Thomas. Your Eyes. 2nd ed. (Illus.). 144p. 1982. pap. 9.75x (ISBN 0-398-04629-8). C C Thomas.
Davson. The Eye. 1974. Vol. 5. 84.00 (ISBN 0-12-206755-X); Vol. 6. 78.00 (ISBN 0-12-206756-8). Acad Pr.
Davson, Hugh. The Eye: Vegetative Physiology & Biochemistry, 2 vols. 3rd ed. 1984. Vol. 1A. 80.00 (ISBN 0-12-206901-3); Vol. 1B. 70.00 (ISBN 0-12-206921-8). Acad Pr.
--The Eye: Visual Optics & Optical Space Sense. 2nd ed. Date not set. Vol. 4. price not set (ISBN 0-12-206754-1). Acad Pr.
Davson, Hugh, ed. Eye. 2nd ed. Vol. 1. 1969. 89.50 (ISBN 0-12-206751-7); Vol. 2A 1976. 90.00 (ISBN 0-12-206752-5); Vol. 2B 1977. 90.00 (ISBN 0-12-206762-2); Vol. 3. 1970. 64.50 (ISBN 0-12-206753-3). Acad Pr.
Drew, Ralph. Professional Ophthalmic Dispensing. LC 73-120180. 1970. leatherette 23.00 (ISBN 0-87873-007-9). Prof Press.
Duke-Elder, Stewart, ed. System of Ophthalmology Series. Incl. Vol. 1. The Eye in Evolution. (Illus.). 843p. 1958. 65.00 (ISBN 0-8016-8282-7); Vol. 2. The Anatomy of the Visual System. (Illus.). 901p. 1961. 67.50 (ISBN 0-8016-8283-5); Vol. 3, Pt. 1. Normal & Abnormal Development: Embryology. (Illus.). 330p. 1963. 51.50 (ISBN 0-8016-8285-1); Vol. 3, Pt. 2. Normal & Abnormal Development: Congenital Deformities. (Illus.). 1190p. 1964. 72.50 (ISBN 0-8016-8286-X); Vol. 4. The Physiology of the Eye & of Vision. (Illus.). xx, 734p. 1968. 79.50 (ISBN 0-8016-8296-7); Vol. 5. Ophthalmic Optics & Refraction. (Illus.). xix, 879p. 1970; Vol. 7. The Foundations of Ophthalmology: Heredity, Pathology, Diagnosis & Therapeutics. (Illus.). 829p. 1962. 69.50 (ISBN 0-8016-8284-3); Vol. 8. Diseases of the Outer Eye: Conjunctiva, Cornea & Sclera, 2 vols. (Illus.). 1242p. 1965. 100.00 (ISBN 0-8016-8287-8); Vol. 9. Diseases of Uveal Tract. (Illus.). xvi, 978p. 1966. 85.00 (ISBN 0-8016-8290-8); Vol. 10. Diseases of the Retina. (Illus.). xv, 878p. 1967. 85.00 (ISBN 0-8016-8295-9); Vol. 11. Diseases of the Lens & Vitreous: Glaucoma & Hypotony. (Illus.). xx, 779p. 1969. 85.00 (ISBN 0-8016-8297-5); Vol. 12. Neuro-Ophthalmology. (Illus.). xxi, 994p. 1971. 89.50 (ISBN 0-8016-8299-1); Vol. 14. Injuries, 2 vols. 1357p. 1972. Set. 125.00 (ISBN 0-8016-8300-9). Mosby.
Fein, Alan & Szuts, Ete Z. Photoreceptors: Their Role in Vision. LC 81-24209. (International Union of Pure & Applied Physics Biophysics Ser.: No. 5). (Illus.). 1982. 39.50 (ISBN 0-521-24433-1); pap. 15.95 (ISBN 0-521-28684-0). Cambridge U Pr.
Hilfer, S. R. & Sheffield, J. B., eds. Ocular Size & Shape: Regulation During Development. (Illus.). 211p. 1981. 32.00 (ISBN 0-387-90619-3). Springer Verlag.
Hockwin, O. Bonn, ed. Growth Control, Differentiation, & Aging of the Eye Lens. (Journal: Ophthalmic Research, Vol. 11, No. 5-6, 1979). (Illus.). 242p. 1979. softcover 21.00 (ISBN 3-8055-0862-X). S Karger.
Hollwich, F. The Influence of Ocular Light Perception on Metabolism in Man & Animal. LC 78-17076. (Topics in Environmental Physiology & Medicine Ser.). (Illus.). 1979. 52.00 (ISBN 0-387-90315-1). Springer-Verlag.
Hollyfield, J. G., ed. Structure of the Eye. 382p. 1982. 115.00 (ISBN 0-444-00613-3, Biomedical Pr). Elsevier.
Katsnelson, L. A. Rheography of the Eye. 125p. 1980. pap. 4.00 (ISBN 0-8285-2022-4, Pub. by Mir Pubs USSR). Imported Pubns.
Klintworth, Gordon K. & Landers, Maurice B. The Eye. LC 75-19061. 236p. 1976. 18.50 (ISBN 0-683-04628-4). Krieger.
Lerman, Sidney, ed. Radiant Energy & the Eye. (Illus.). 1980. text ed. write for info. (ISBN 0-02-369970-1). Macmillan.
Linksz, Arthur. Physiology of the Eye: Vol. I Optics. LC 50-5797. (Illus.). 366p. 1953. 71.50 (ISBN 0-8089-0267-9, 792561). Grune.
McDevitt, David, ed. Cell Biology of the Eye. (Cell Biology Ser.). 1982. 75.00 (ISBN 0-12-483180-X). Acad Pr.
Monro, Alexander. Three Treatises: On the Brain, the Eye, & the Ear. Bd. with Croonian Lectures on Cerebrqal Localization. Ferrier, D. (Contributions to the History of Psychology Ser., Vol. VII, Pt. E: Psysiological Psychology). 1980. Repr. of 1797 ed. 30.00 (ISBN 0-89093-326-X). U Pubns Amer.
O'Connor, G. Richard & Chandler, John W., eds. Advances in Immunology & Immunopathology of the Eye. (Illus.). 304p. 1985. text ed. write for info. (ISBN 0-89352-224-4). Masson Pub.
Polyak, Stephen. Vertebrate Visual System. Kluver, Heinrich, ed. LC 55-5153. (Illus.). 1957. 100.00x (ISBN 0-226-67494-0). U of Chicago Pr.
Prince, Jack H. The Rabbit in Eye Research. (Illus.). 672p. 1964. photocopy ed. 67.75x (ISBN 0-398-01525-2). C C Thomas.
Regenbogen, Lucian S. & Coscas, Gabriel J., eds. Oculo-Auditory Syndromes. (Illus.). 400p. 1985. text ed. write for info. (ISBN 0-89352-225-2). Masson Pub.
Ribi, W. A. The Neurons of the First Optic Ganglion on the Bee (Apis Mellifera) (Advances in Anatomy, Embryology & Cell Biology: Vol. 50, Pt. 4). (Illus.). 49p. 1975. pap. 16.60 (ISBN 0-387-07096-6). Springer-Verlag.
Roucoux, A. & Crommelinck, M. Physiological & Pathological Aspects of Eye Movements. 1983. 76.00 (ISBN 90-619-3730-2, Pub. by Junk Pubs Netherlands). Kluwer Academic.
Shapiro, Harvey. The Eye. LC 77-179810. (New Poetry Ser.). Repr. of 1953 ed. 16.00 (ISBN 0-404-56010-5). AMS Pr.
Sheffield, J. B. & Hilfer, S. R., eds. Cellular Communication During Ocular Development. (Cell & Developmental Biology of the Eye Ser.). (Illus.). 196p. 1982. 39.00 (ISBN 0-387-90773-4). Springer-Verlag.
Silverstein, Arthur M. & O'Connor, G. Richard. Immunology & Immunopathology of the Eye. LC 79-84781. 416p. 1979. 69.50x (ISBN 0-89352-042-X). Masson Pub.
Smelser, George K., ed. Structure of the Eye. 1961. 77.00 (ISBN 0-12-648950-5). Acad Pr.
Sooter, Wilburn L. Eye: A Light Receiver. LC 81-68313. 1981. pap. 3.95 (ISBN 0-89051-076-8); tchr's guide 2.95x (ISBN 0-686-33036-6). Master Bks.
Varma, S. D., et al, eds. International Symposium on Light & Oxygen Effects on the Eye, 1st: Proceedings. Lerman, S. & Hockwin, O. (Illus.). 278p. (Orig.). 1984. pap. 40.00 (ISBN 0-904147-62-2). IRL Pr.
Weale, R. A. The Vertebrate Eye. rev. ed. Head, J. J., ed. LC 76-29373. (Carolina Biology Readers Ser.). (Illus.). 16p. 1978. pap. 1.60 (ISBN 0-89278-271-4, 45-9671). Carolina Biological.
Wehner, R., ed. Information Processing in the Visual Systems of Arthropods. LC 72-91887. 340p. 1972. pap. 32.00 (ISBN 0-387-06020-0). Springer-Verlag.
Whitnall, Ernest S. The Anatomy of the Human Orbit & Accessory Organs of Vision. LC 78-27070. (Classics in Ophthalmology Ser.). (Illus.). 1979. Repr. of 1932 ed. Set. 175.00 (ISBN 0-88275-934-5); Set. lib. bdg. 28.50 (ISBN 0-88275-840-3). Krieger.
Zadunaisky, Jose & Davson, Hugh. Current Topics in Eye Research. (Serial Pulication: Vol. 4). 1984. 73.00 (ISBN 0-12-153004-3). Acad Pr.
Zadunaisky, Jose A. & Davson, Hugh, eds. Current Topics in Eye Research, Vol. 1. 1979. 45.00 (ISBN 0-12-153001-9). Acad Pr.
--Current Topics in Eye Research, Vol. 2. (Serial Publication). 1980. 47.50 (ISBN 0-12-153002-7). Acad Pr.
Zinn, Keith M. The Pupil. (Illus.). 152p. 1972. 14.95x (ISBN 0-398-02320-4). C C Thomas.

F

F CENTERS
see Color Centers
F-EIGHTY-SIX PLANES
see also sabre (jet fighter planes)
Davis, Larry. F-86 in Color. (Fighting Colors Ser.). (Illus.). 1984. pap. 5.95 (ISBN 0-89747-110-5, 6502). Squad Sig Pubns.
--F-86 Sabre in Action. (Aircraft in Action Ser.). (Illus.). 1984. pap. 4.95 (ISBN 0-89747-032-X, 1033). Squad Sig Pubns.
F-FIFTY-ONE (FIGHTER PLANES)
see Mustang (Fighter Planes)
F-ONE-ELEVEN (FIGHTER PLANES)
Coulam, Robert F. Illusions of Choice: Robert McNamara, the F-111 & the Problem of Weapons Acquisition Reform. LC 76-24292. 1977. 46.00 (ISBN 0-691-07583-2). Princeton U Pr.
F-111 in Action. (Aircraft in Action Ser.). (Illus.). 50p. 1984. pap. 4.95 (ISBN 0-89747-083-4, 1035). Squad Sig Pubns.
Kinzey, Bert. F-111 Aardvark in Detail & Scale. LC 82-6829. (Detail & Scale Ser.: Vol. 4). (Illus.). 72p. (Orig.). 1982. pap. 7.95 (ISBN 0-8168-5014-3). Aero.
Miller, Jay. General Dynamics F-111. LC 81-66062. (Aero Ser.: Vol. 29). (Illus.). 104p. (Orig.). 1981. pap. 7.95 (ISBN 0-8168-0606-3, 200). Aero.

FABRICS
see Textile Fabrics
FABRICS, CREASE-RESISTANT
see Crease-Resistant Fabrics
FABRICS, NONWOVEN
see Nonwoven Fabrics
FABRICS, SYNTHETIC
see Synthetic Fabrics
FACSIMILE TRANSMISSION
Costigan, Daniel M. Electronic Delivery of Documents & Graphics. 1978. text ed. 29.95 (ISBN 0-442-80036-3). Van Nos Reinhold.
--Electronic Delivery of Documents & Graphics. 344p. 1978. 24.25 (ISBN 0-686-98117-0). Telecom Lib.
Robinson, Lawrence. The Facts on FAX: An Executive's Guide to Facsimile Communications. LC 84-91757. 300p. 1985. pap. 19.95 (ISBN 0-911061-15-0). S Davis Pub.
FACTOR ANALYSIS
see also Factorial Experiment Designs
Anastasia, Salvatore & Willig, Paul M. Structure of Factors. new ed. LC 72-78469. 1974. 30.00x (ISBN 0-917448-04-9). Algorithmics.
Cattell, Raymond B. Factor Analysis. LC 72-10689. 462p. 1973. Repr. of 1952 ed. lib. bdg. 32.50x (ISBN 0-8371-6615-2, CAFA). Greenwood.
Cattell, Raymond B., ed. The Scientific Use of Factor Analysis in Behavioral & Life Sciences. LC 77-10695. (Illus.). 640p. 1978. 49.50x (ISBN 0-306-30939-4, Plenum Pr). Plenum Pub.
Cureton, E. E. & D'Agostino, R. B. Factor Analysis: An Applied Approach. (Illus.). 480p. 1983. text ed. 39.95x (ISBN 0-89859-048-5). L Erlbaum Assocs.
Factor Analysis & Related Methods. 272p. 1985. text ed. 29.95 (ISBN 0-89859-388-3). L Erlbaum Assocs.
Gorsuch, Richard L. Factor Analysis. 2nd ed. 448p. 1983. text ed. 36.00x (ISBN 0-89859-202-X). L Erlbaum Assocs.
Harman, Harry H. Modern Factor Analysis. 3rd, rev ed. LC 75-22267. (Illus.). 512p. 1976. 32.00x (ISBN 0-226-31652-1). U of Chicago Pr.
Hinman, Suki & Bolton, Brian. Factor Analytic Studies, 1971-1975. LC 78-69873. 1978. 27.50x (ISBN 0-87875-165-3). Whitston Pub.
Hinman, Sukit & Bolton, Brian. Factor Analytic Studies: 1941-1975, 5 vols. Set. 32.50x (ISBN 0-686-64136-1). Whitston Pub.
Joreskog, Karl G. & Sorbom, Dag. Advances in Factor Analysis & Structural Equation Models. Magidson, J., ed. 270p. 1984. lib. bdg. 33.50 (ISBN 0-8191-4095-3); pap. text ed. 17.75 (ISBN 0-8191-4137-2). U Pr of Amer.
--EFAP Two: Exploratory Factor Analysis Program. pap. 5.00 (ISBN 0-89498-007-6). Sci Ware.
Long, J. Scott. Confirmatory Factor Analysis. LC 83-50185. 88p. 1983. pap. text ed. 5.00 (ISBN 0-8039-2044-X). Sage.
--Covariance Structure Models. LC 83-50602. 95p. 1983. pap. text ed. 5.00 (ISBN 0-8039-2045-8). Sage.
Rummel, Rudolph J. Applied Factor Analysis. 1970. 25.95 (ISBN 0-8101-0254-4). Northwestern U Pr.
FACTORIAL EXPERIMENT DESIGNS
Box, George E. & Draper, Norman R. Evolutionary Operation: A Statistical Method for Process Improvement. LC 68-56159. (Applied Probability & Mathematical Statistics Ser). 237p. 1969. 42.50x (ISBN 0-471-09305-X, Pub. by Wiley-Interscience). Wiley.
McLean & Anderson. Applied Factorical & Fractional Designs. (Statistics - Textbooks & Monographs). 360p. 1984. 65.00 (ISBN 0-8247-7154-0). Dekker.
FACTORIES
see also Chemical Plants; Mills and Mill-Work; Workshops
also headings beginning with the word Factory
Adams, Carol, et al. Under Control: Life in a Nineteenth Century Silk Factory. LC 83-7500. (Women in History Ser.). 1984. pap. 3.95 (ISBN 0-521-27481-8). Cambridge U pr.
Balzer, Richard. Clockwork: Life in & Outside an American Factory. LC 75-21209. 352p. 1976. 10.00 (ISBN 0-385-11036-7). Doubleday.
Berg, Maxine, et al, eds. Manufacture in Town & Country Before the Factory. LC 83-1842. 244p. 1983. 42.50 (ISBN 0-521-24820-5). Cambridge U Pr.
Conta, Lewis D. Energy Conservation in Space Conditioning. Gyftopoulos, Elias P. & Cohen, Karen C., eds. (Industrial Energy-Conservation Manuals Ser.: No. 7). (Illus.). 120p. 1982. loose-leaf 20.00x (ISBN 0-262-03084-5). MIT Pr.
Eckerlin, H. & Boyers, A. Energy-Conservation Opportunities in the Small Industrial Plant. Gyftopoulos, Elias P. & Cohen, Karen C., eds. (Industrial Energy-Conservation Manuals Ser.: No. 5). 96p. 1982. loose-leaf 20.00x (ISBN 0-262-05025-0). MIT Pr.

Elonka, Stephen M. & Robinson, Joseph R. Standard Plant Operator's Questions & Answers, 2 vols. 2nd ed. 1981. Set. 49.50 (ISBN 0-07-079191-0); Vol. 1. 27.00 (ISBN 0-07-019315-0); Vol. 2. 27.00 (ISBN 0-07-019316-9). McGraw.
Fielden, John. Curse of the Factory System. 2nd rev. ed. 74p. 1969. 29.50x (ISBN 0-7146-1394-0, F Cass Co). Biblio Dist.
Hennessey, Robert. Factories. (Past into Present Ser.). (Illus.). 17.50x (ISBN 0-392-02822-0, LTB). Sportshelf.
Industrial Location in Ulsan: Results of Interview Survey of Plants in the Ulsan Industrial Complex. (Working Papers Ser.: No. 75-3). 43p. 1975. pap. 6.00 (ISBN 0-686-78497-9, CRD079, UNCRD). Unipub.
Kops, L., ed. Towards the Factory of the Future. (PED: Vol. 1). 115p. 1980. 18.00 (ISBN 0-317-06809-1, G00189). ASME.
Lee, Frank K. Outside Plant: Engineering & Practice, Vol. IV. 1977. 6.50 (ISBN 0-686-98060-3). Telecom Lib.
Magison, E. C. Electrical Instruments in Hazardous Locations. 3rd, rev. & enlg. ed. LC 79-104837. 420p. 1978. text ed. 44.95x (ISBN 0-87664-376-4). Instru Soc.
Marsh, Robert M. & Mannari, Hiroshi. Modernization & the Japanese Factory. LC 75-3466. 560p. 1976. 45.00x (ISBN 0-691-09365-2); pap. 16.00 LPE (ISBN 0-691-10037-3). Princeton U Pr.
Price, George M. Modern Factory: Safety, Sanitation & Welfare. LC 74-89758. (American Labor, from Conspiracy to Collective Bargaining, Ser. 1). 574p. 1969. Repr. of 1914 ed. 46.50 (ISBN 0-405-02144-5). Ayer Co Pubs.
Reed, Ruddell. Plant Layout: Factors, Principles & Techniques. LC 61-14497. (The Erwin Series in Management). pap. 118.30 (ISBN 0-317-10732-1, 2050147). Bks Demand UMI.
Rudman, Jack. Factory Inspector. (Career Examination Ser.: C-283). (Cloth bdg. avail. on request). pap. 12.00 (ISBN 0-8373-0283-8). Natl Learning.
FACTORIES–CLEAN ROOMS
see Clean Rooms
FACTORIES–DESIGN AND CONSTRUCTION
Apple, J. M. Plant Layout & Materials Handling. 3rd ed. LC 77-75127. (Illus.). 600p. 1977. 40.95x (ISBN 0-471-07171-4). Wiley.
Butt, L. T. & Wright, D. C. Use of Polymers in Chemical Plant Construction. (Illus.). 156p. 1981. text ed. 28.00 (ISBN 0-85334-914-2, Pub. by Applied Sci England). J K Burgess.
Coppa & Avery Consultants Staff. The Design of Sewage Disposal Plants: A Bibliography. (Architecture Ser.: Bibliography A 1320). 1985. pap. 2.00 (ISBN 0-89028-270-6). Vance Biblios.
Drury, Jolyon, ed. Factories: Planning & Design. (Illus.). 320p. 1981. 150.00 (ISBN 0-89397-113-8). Nichols Pub.
Kumar, Anil. Chemical Process Synthesis & Engineering Design. 556p. 1982. 29.95x (ISBN 0-07-096470-X). McGraw.
Layouts, Space Requirements & Facilities for Classrooms, Laboratories & Workshops: Equipment Planning Guides, Vol. 13. (Technical Training & Education Programme). pap. 22.80 (ILO246, ILO). Unipub.
Moore, James M. Plant Layout & Design. (Illus.). 1962. write for info. (ISBN 0-02-383180-4). Macmillan.
Muther, Richard. Practical Plant Layout. 1956. text ed. 45.95 (ISBN 0-07-044156-1). McGraw.
--Systematic Layout Planning. 2nd ed. LC 72-91983. 360p. 1973. 29.95 (ISBN 0-8436-0814-5). Van Nos Reinhold.
Peters, Max S. & Timmerhaus, Klaus. Plant Design & Economics for Chemical Engineers. 3rd ed. (Chemical Engineering Ser.). (Illus.). 1980. text ed. 45.00 (ISBN 0-07-049582-3). McGraw.
Tompkins, James A. & White, John A. Facilities Planning. LC 83-21715. 675p. 1984. text ed. 37.50 (ISBN 0-471-03299-9). Wiley.
FACTORIES–ELECTRIC EQUIPMENT
see also Industrial Electronics
Institute of Electrical & Electronics Engineers, Inc. Recommended Practice for Electric Power Distribution for Industrial Plants. 388p. 1976. 19.95x (ISBN 0-471-02686-7). Wiley.
Moore, Arthur H. & Elonka, Stephen M. Electrical Systems & Equipment for Industry. LC 77-5640. (Illus.). 368p. 1977. Repr. of 1971 ed. lib. bdg. 23.50 (ISBN 0-88275-561-7). Krieger.
FACTORIES–LOCATION
Halbritter, Gunter. Multidimensionale Optimierung bei der Standortwahl von Grosstechnischen Anlagen. (Interdisciplinary Systems Research: No. 62). (Ger., Illus.). 178p. 1979. pap. 26.95 (ISBN 0-8176-1055-3). Birkhauser.

Hunker, Henry L. & Wright, Alfred J. Factors of Industrial Location in Ohio. 1964. 5.00x (ISBN 0-87776-119-1, R-119); pap. 3.50x (ISBN 0-685-19028-5, R-119P). Ohio St U Admin Sci.

Rowe, James E. Industrial Plant Location. (Public Administation Ser.: Bibliography P-575). 52p. 1980. pap. 5.50 (ISBN 0-88066-083-X). Vance Biblios.

White, John A. & Francis, Richard L. Facility Layout & Location: An Analytical Approach. LC 73-18455. (Int'l. Series in Industrial & Systems Engineering). (Illus.). 448p. 1974. ref. ed. 33.95x (ISBN 0-13-299149-7). P-H.

FACTORIES–MAINTENANCE AND REPAIR

see Plant Maintenance

FACTORIES–MANAGEMENT

see Factory Management

FACTORIES–NOISE

see Industrial Noise

FACTORIES–SAFETY APPLIANCES

Hammer, Willie. Occupational Safety Management & Engineering. 3rd ed. (Illus.). 544p. 1985. text ed. 29.95 (ISBN 0-13-629437-5). P-H.

Heinrich, Herbert W. Industrial Accident Prevention. 4th ed. 1959. text ed. 29.00 (ISBN 0-07-028058-4). McGraw.

FACTORY AND TRADE WASTE

see also Agricultural Wastes; Petroleum Waste; Pollution; Refuse and Refuse Disposal

Alter & Dunn. Solid Waste Conversion to Energy. (Pollution Engineering & Technology Ser.: Vol. 11). 184p. 1980. 39.75 (ISBN 0-8247-6917-1). Dekker.

Arctic Waste Disposal - North. pap. 7.40 (SSC8, SSC). Unipub.

Azad, Hardam S. Industrial Wastewater Management Handbook. 1976. 57.00 (ISBN 0-07-002661-0). McGraw.

Barnes, D., et al, eds. Surveys in Industrial Wastewater Treatment, 2 vols. (Water Resources Engineering Ser.). 700p. 1984. Vol. 1. 64.95 (ISBN 0-273-08586-7); Vol. 2. 44.95 (ISBN 0-273-08588-3). Pitman Pub MA.

Bell, John B. Purdue Thirty-Ninth Industrial Waste Conference. 1008p. 1985. text ed. 79.95 (ISBN 0-250-40640-3). Butterworth.

Bell, John M., ed. Purdue Thirty-Eighth Industrial Waste Conference: Proceedings. 1000p. 1984. text ed. 75.00 (ISBN 0-250-40639-X). Butterworth.

--Purdue Thirty-Seventh University Industrial Waste Conference, 1982. LC 77-84415. (Illus.). 952p. 1983. 75.00 (ISBN 0-250-40592-X). Butterworth.

Beretka, J. Survey of Industrial Wastes & By-Products in Australia. 58p. 1978. pap. 6.00 (ISBN 0-643-02260-0, C041, CSIRO). Unipub.

Berkowitz, Joan B., et al, eds. Unit Operations for Treatment of Hazardous Industrial Wastes. LC 78-62520. (Pollution Technology Review: No. 47). (Illus.). 920p. 1979. 42.00 (ISBN 0-8155-0717-8). Noyes.

Brown, Michael. Laying Waste: The Poisoning of America by Toxic Chemicals. 384p. 1981. pap. 3.95 (ISBN 0-671-45359-9). WSP.

Brown, William H. How to Stop the Corporate Polluters. (Illus.). 1972. pap. 1.50 (ISBN 0-88388-020-2). Bellerophon Bks.

Callely, A., et al, eds. Treatment of Industrial Effluents. LC 76-54909. 378p. 1977. 42.95x (ISBN 0-470-98934-3). Halsted Pr.

Cannon, James S. A Clear View: Guide to Industrial Pollution Control. LC 75-15321. (Illus.). 1975. pap. 3.95 (ISBN 0-686-70491-6). INFORM.

CEP & Boothe, Norris. Cleaning up: The Cost of Refinery Pollution Control. Haley, Mary J., ed. LC 75-10535. 1975. pap. 25.00 (ISBN 0-87871-002-7). CEP.

Chapman, David W., et al. Hazardous Wastes & the Consumer Connection: A Guide for Educators & Citizens Concerned with the Role of Consumers in the Generation of Hazardous Wastes. (Hazardous Chemicals Education Project Ser.). 36p. (Orig.). 1984. pap. write for info.; pap. text ed. write for info. Sci Citizens.

Chemical Engineering Magazine. Industrial Waste Water & Solid Waste Engineering. LC 80-12608. 376p. 1980. pap. 37.50 (ISBN 0-07-010694-0). McGraw.

Commission on Natural Resources, National Research Council. The Shallow Land Burial of Low-Level Radioactively Contaminated Solid Waste. LC 76-56928. 1976. pap. 8.50 (ISBN 0-309-02535-4). Natl Acad Pr.

Conway, R. A. & Gulledge, W. P., eds. Hazardous & Industrial Solid Waste Testing: 2nd Symposium. LC 84-70420. (Special Technical Publications: No. 805). 332p. 1983. text ed. 44.00 (ISBN 0-8031-0246-1, 04-805000-16). ASTM.

Conway, Richard A. & Ross, Richard D. Handbook of Industrial Waste Disposal. 576p. 1980. text ed. 39.50 (ISBN 0-442-27053-4). Van Nos Reinhold.

Crandall, Robert W. Controlling Industrial Pollution: The Economics & Politics of Clean Air. LC 82-45982. 220p. 1983. 26.95 (ISBN 0-8157-1604-4); pap. 9.95 (ISBN 0-8157-1603-6). Brookings.

Cross, Frank L., Jr. Management Primer on Water Pollution Control. LC 74-76523. 150p. 1974. pap. 9.95 (ISBN 0-87762-136-5). Technomic.

Curi, K. Treatment & Disposal of Liquid & Solid Industrial Wastes: Proceedings of the Third Turkish-German Environmental Engineering Symposium, Istanbul, July 1979. LC 80-40993. (Illus.). 515p. 1980. 96.00 (ISBN 0-08-023999-4). Pergamon.

De Renzo, D. J., ed. Biodegradation Techniques for Industrial Organic Wastes. LC 80-12834. (Pollution Technology Review Ser. 65; Chemical Technology Review Ser. 158). (Illus.). 358p. 1980. 28.00 (ISBN 0-8155-0800-X). Noyes.

Disposal of Industrial Wastes by Combustion: Present State-of-the-Art. 62p. 1977. pap. text ed. 15.00 (ISBN 0-685-86859-1, H00092). ASME.

Duerksen, Christopher J. Environmental Regulation Of Industrial Plant Siting: How to Make it Work Better. LC 83-20901. 232p. 1983. pap. 15.00 (ISBN 0-89164-078-9). Conservation Foun.

Dyer, Jon C. Handbook of Industrial Wastes Pretreatment. LC 79-25702. 280p. 1980. lib. bdg. 36.00 (ISBN 0-8240-7066-6). Garland Pub.

Edwards, B. H., et al. Emerging Technologies for the Control of Hazardous Wastes. LC 83-4022. (Pollution Tech. Rev.: No. 99). (Illus.). 146p. (Orig.). 1983. 24.00 (ISBN 0-8155-0943-X). Noyes.

Ehrenfeld, John & Bass, Jeffrey. Evaluation of Remedial Action Unit Operations at Hazardous Waste Disposal Sites. LC 84-14834. (Pollution Technology Review Ser.: No. 110). (Illus.). 434p. 1985. 39.00 (ISBN 0-8155-0998-7). Noyes.

Eleventh Mid-Atlantic Industrial Waste Conference. (Illus.). 1979. pap. 10.00 (ISBN 0-318-01367-3). Hazardous Mat Control.

Epstein, Samuel S., et al. Hazardous Waste in America: Our Number One Environmental Crisis. LC 82-3304. (The Sierra Club Paperback Library). 640p. 1983. 27.50 (ISBN 0-87156-294-4); pap. 12.95 (ISBN 0-87156-807-1). Sierra.

Feder & Burrell. Impact of Seafood Cannery Waste on the Benthic Biota & Adjacent Waters at Dutch Harbor Alaska. (IMS Report Ser.: No. R82-1). 225p. 21.00. U of AK Inst Marine.

Forster, C. Oxidation Ditches. (Water Resources Engineering Ser.). 300p. 1983. text ed. 65.95 (ISBN 0-273-08527-1). Pitman Pub MA.

Fumes & Gases in Welding Environment, FGW. 244p. 1979. 56.00 (ISBN 0-87171-174-5); members 42.00. Am Welding.

Fung, R., ed. Surface Coal Mining Technology: Engineering & Environmental Aspects. LC 81-11036. (Energy Tech. Rev. 71; Pollution Tech Rev. 83). (Illus.). 380p. 1982. 45.00 (ISBN 0-8155-0866-2). Noyes.

Gehr, Marilyn. Solid Waste Management: A Selected & Annotated Bibliography, No. 1295. 1977. 7.00 (ISBN 0-686-19695-3). CPL Biblios.

Goodman, G. T. & Chadwick, M. H., eds. Environmental Management of Mineral Wastes. 382p. 1978. 42.50x (ISBN 9-0286-0054-X). Sijthoff & Noordhoff.

Green, John H. & Kramer, Amihud. Food Processing Waste Management. (Illus.). 1979. text ed. 49.50 (ISBN 0-87055-331-3). AVI.

Hadden, Susan G. Siting of Hazardous Waste Disposal Facilities in Texas, No. 53. LC 82-85620. 128p. 1982. 7.50 (ISBN 0-89940-655-6). LBJ Sch Pub Aff.

Hagerty, D. Joseph, et al. Solid Waste Management. LC 73-10281. (Van Nostrand Reinhold Environmental Engineering Ser.). pap. 79.00 (ISBN 0-317-11224-4, 2014903). Bks Demand UMI.

Handling of Tritium-Bearing Wastes. (Technical Reports Ser.: No. 203). (Illus.). 137p. 1981. pap. 21.25 (ISBN 92-0-125081-9, IDC203, IAEA). Unipub.

Harthill, Michalann, ed. Hazardous Waste Management: In Whose Backyard? (AAAS Selected Symposium, Ser.: 88). 212p. 1984. 24.00x (ISBN 0-86531-748-8). Westview.

Hazardous Waste Litigation 1984. (Litigation & Administrative Practice, Course Handbook Ser. 1983-1984). 708p. 1984. 30.00 (ISBN 0-686-80267-5, H4-4934). PLI.

Holmes, John R., ed. Managing Solid Wastes in Developing Countries. LC 83-10570. 320p. 1984. 48.95 (ISBN 0-471-90234-9, Pub. by Wiley-Interscience). Wiley.

Hooper, G. V., ed. Offshore Ship & Platform Incineration of Hazardous Wastes. LC 81-38372. (Pollution Tech. Rev. 79). (Illus.). 468p. 1981. 42.00 (ISBN 0-8155-0854-9). Noyes.

Industrial Waste Symposia Proceedings, 1980. 20.00 (ISBN 0-686-30995-2, T00053). Water Pollution.

Industrial Wastewater Control Program for Municipal Agencies. (Manual of Practice, Operations & Maintenance: No. 4). 166p. (Orig.). 1982. pap. text ed. 18.00 (ISBN 0-943244-37-4). Water Pollution.

J. J. Keller & Associates, Inc., ed. Hazardous Waste Audit Program. LC 81-86197. (10M). 400p. 1984. 3-ring binder 65.00 (ISBN 0-934674-41-8). J J Keller.

--Hazardous Waste Regulatory Guide. LC 81-86200. (26G). 500p. 1985. 3-ring binder 95.00 (ISBN 0-934674-44-2). J J Keller.

Jones, Jerry L. & Radding, Shirley B., eds. Thermal Conversion of Solid Waste & Biomass. LC 80-14754. (ACS Symposium Ser.: No. 130). 1980. 69.95 (ISBN 0-8412-0565-5, Pub. by Royal Soc Chem London). Am Chemical.

Jorgensen, S. E., ed. Industrial Waste Water Management. (Studies in Environmental Science: Vol. 5). 388p. 1979. 66.00 (ISBN 0-444-41795-8). Elsevier.

Ketchum, Bostwick H., et al, eds. Ocean Dumping of Industrial Wastes. (Marine Science Ser.: Vol. 12). 536p. 1981. 79.50x (ISBN 0-306-40653-5, Plenum Pr). Plenum Pub.

Khoury, D. L., ed. Flue Gas Cleaning Wastes Disposal & Utilization. LC 81-1631. (Pollution Technology, Review: No. 77, Energy Technology Review: No. 65). (Illus.). 1981. 45.00 (ISBN 0-8155-0847-6). Noyes.

Lagrega, ed. Toxic & Hazardous Waste. (Fifteenth Mid-Atlantic Conference on Industrial Waste). 1983. text ed. 49.95 (ISBN 0-250-40591-1). Butterworth.

LaGrega, Michael D. & Long, David A., eds. Toxic & Hazardous Wastes: Proceedings of the Sixteenth Mid-Atlantic Industrial Waste Conference. LC 84-51326. 587p. 1984. pap. 45.00 (ISBN 0-87762-363-5). Technomic.

Lof, George O. G. & Kneese, Allen V. The Economics of Water Utilization in the Beet Sugar Industry. LC 68-16166. (Resources for the Future Ser). (Illus.). Repr. of 1968 ed. 25.70 (ISBN 0-8357-9268-4, 2015741). Bks Demand UMI.

Lowe, J. & Lewis, D. Total Environmental Control: The Economics of Cross-Media Pollution Transfers. LC 82-9827. (Illus.). 134p. 1982. 24.00 (ISBN 0-08-026276-7). Pergamon.

Lund, H. F. Industrial Pollution Control Handbook. 1971. 83.50 (ISBN 0-07-039095-9). McGraw.

Majumdar, Shyamal K. & Miller, E. Willard, eds. Solid & Liquid Wastes: Management, Methods & Socioeconomic Considerations. (Illus.). xxii, 412p. 1984. 35.00 (ISBN 0-9606670-3-2). Penn Science.

Management & Disposal of Residues from the Treatment of Industrial Wastewaters. (Illus.). 1975. 5.00xsoftcover (ISBN 0-686-26014-7, 1WW5). Info Transfer.

Management of Alpha-Contaminated Wastes. (Proceedings Ser.). (Illus.). 714p. 1981. pap. 95.50 (ISBN 92-0-020081-8, ISP562, IAEA). Unipub.

Management of Uncontrolled Hazardous Waste Sites, 1983. 480p. 1983. 45.00 (ISBN 0-686-40173-5). Hazardous Mat Control.

Management of Uranium Mill Tailings, Low Level Waste & Hazardous Waste: Proceedings of the Seventh Symposium, 2 vols. (Orig.). 1985. pap. text ed. 38.00 (ISBN 0-910069-08-5). Geotech Engineer Prog.

Management of Uranium Mill Tailings, Low-Level Waste & Hazardous Waste: Proceedings of the Sixth Symposium, 1984. 670p. 1984. 35.00 (ISBN 0-910069-07-7). Geotech Engineer Prog.

Management of Uranium Mill Tailings, Low-Level Waste & Hazardous Waste: Proceedings of the Seventh Symposium, 1985, 2 vols. Set. write for info. (ISBN 0-910069-08-5); write for info. (ISBN 0-910069-09-3); write for info. (ISBN 0-910069-10-7). Geotech Engineer Prog.

Managing Industrial & Agricultural Wastes: Some Experiences. 137p. 1980. pap. 13.25 (ISBN 92-833-1460-3, APO89, APO). Unipub.

Mantell, Charles L. Solid Wastes: Origin, Collection, Processing & Disposal. LC 74-26930. 1152p. 1975. 106.95x (ISBN 0-471-56777-9, Pub by Wiley-Interscience). Wiley.

Mayer, Garry F., ed. Ecological Stress & the New York Blight: Science & Management. LC 82-71795. (Illus.). x, 717p. (Orig.). 1982. pap. text ed. 10.00 (ISBN 0-9608990-0-6). Estuarine Res.

Mid-Atlantic Industrial Waste Conference Proceedings, Ninth. (Illus.). 1977. softcover 10.00x (ISBN 0-686-25731-6, 91W7). Info Transfer.

Mid-Atlantic Industrial Waste Conference Proceedings, Tenth. (Illus.). 1978. softcover 5.00x (ISBN 0-686-25730-8, 101W8). Info Transfer.

Miller, E. Willard & Miller, Ruby M. Environmental Hazards-Industrial & Toxic Wastes: A Bibliography. (Public Administration Ser.: Bibliography P-1615). 99p. 1985. pap. 15.00 (ISBN 0-89028-265-X). Vance Biblios.

--Environmental Hazards-Liquid Wastes: A Bibliography. (Public Administration Ser.: Bibliography P-1614). 41p. 1985. pap. 6.00 (ISBN 0-89028-264-1). Vance Biblios.

Miller, Stanton S., ed. Solid Wastes, Vol. II. LC 73-87146. 1973. 8.50 (ISBN 0-8412-0184-6); pap. 6.95 (ISBN 0-8412-0238-9). Am Chemical.

Moore, Ralph L. Neutralization of Waste Water by pH Control. LC 77-94491. 160p. 1978. text ed. 29.95x (ISBN 0-87664-383-7). Instru Soc.

Municipal & Industrial Sludge Utilization & Disposal: Land Application, Compost, Sludge Utilization, Co-Disposal & Ocean Disposal, 1983. (Orig.). 1983. pap. 35.00 (ISBN 0-686-40170-0). Hazardous Mat Control.

Nemerow, Nelson L. Industrial Solid Waste. LC 82-13866. 384p. 1983. text ed. 45.00x prof. ref. (ISBN 0-88410-876-7). Ballinger Pub.

OECD Staff. Product Durability & Product Life Extension: Their Contribution to Solid Waste Management. 129p. (Orig.). 1982. pap. 10.00x (ISBN 92-64-12293-1). OECD.

--Used Tyres in Solid Waste Management. (Illus., Orig.). 1981. pap. text ed. 6.00x (ISBN 92-64-12131-5, 97-80-07-1). OECD.

Pratt, Alan, ed. Directory of Waste Disposal & Recovery. 232p. 1978. 60.00x (ISBN 0-686-99829-4, Pub. by Graham & Trotman England). State Mutual Bk.

Residue Utilization: Management of Agricultural & Agro-Industrial Wastes. 1978. pap. 7.50 (ISBN 92-5-100320-3, F1265, FAO). Unipub.

Shinskey, F. G. PH & pIon: Control in Process & Waste Streams. LC 73-7853. (Environmental Science & Technology Ser.). 259p. 1973. 47.95 (ISBN 0-471-78640-3, Pub. by Wiley-Interscience). Wiley.

Sittig, M. Pollution Control in the Plastics & Rubber Industry. LC 75-2940. (Pollution Technology Review Ser: No. 18). (Illus.). 306p. 1975. 36.00 (ISBN 0-8155-0572-8). Noyes.

Smith, M. A. Contaminated Land: Reclamation & Treatment. (NATO-Challenges of Modern Society Ser.). 456p. 1985. 65.00x (ISBN 0-306-41928-9, Plenum Pr). Plenum Pub.

State of California. Health Aspects of Wastewater Recharge: A State-of-the-Art Review. LC 78-69808. (Illus.). 1978. Repr. 26.00 (ISBN 0-912394-18-8). Water Info.

Steiker, Gene. Solid Waste Generation Coefficients: Manufacturing Sectors. (Discussion Paper Ser.: No. 70). 1973. pap. 4.50 (ISBN 0-686-32236-3). Regional Sci Res Inst.

Tearle, Keith, ed. Industrial Pollution Control. 1973. 22.00x (ISBN 0-8464-0510-5). Beekman Pubs.

Textile Wastes & Their Reclamation: A Survey of Recent Literature, 1980. 1981. 60.00x (ISBN 0-686-97148-5, Pub. by W Spring England). State Mutual Bk.

Theodore, Louis & Buonicore, Anthony. Industrial Air Pollution Control Equipment for Particulates. LC 76-25095. (Uniscience Ser.). 288p. 1976. 62.00 (ISBN 0-8493-5132-4). CRC Pr.

Treatment & Disposal of Hazardous Wastes from Industry: Some Experiences. 197p. 1983. pap. text ed. 14.75 (ISBN 92-833-2005-0, APO140, APO). Unipub.

Treatment & Disposal of Industrial Wastewaters & Residues. (Illus.). 1978. pap. 5.00x (ISBN 0-686-26017-1, 1WW8). Info Transfer.

Treatment & Disposal of Industrial Wastewaters & Residues. (Illus.). 1977. 10.00x (ISBN 0-686-26018-X, 1WW7); softcover 5.00x (ISBN 0-686-26019-8). Info Transfer.

Tripodi, Raymond A. & Cheremisinoff, Paul N. Coal Ash Disposal: Solid Waste Impacts. LC 80-54017. 52p. 1980. pap. 15.00 (ISBN 0-87762-289-2). Technomic.

Twelfth Mid-Atlantic Industrial Wastewater Conference. (Illus.). 1980. pap. 12.00 (ISBN 0-318-01366-5). Hazardous Mat Control.

Uranium Mill Tailings Management: Proceedings of the First Symposium, 1978, 2 vols. Set. 17.00 (ISBN 0-910069-11-5); Vol. 1; 172 pgs. write for info. (ISBN 0-910069-00-[illegible]); Vol. 2; 141 pgs. write for info. (ISBN 0-910069-01-8). Geotech Engineer Prog.

Vance, Mary. Industrial Waste Disposal: A Bibliography. (Public Administration Ser.: Bibliography: P-959). 1982. pap. 8.25 (ISBN 0-88066-153-4, P959). Vance Biblios.

Hunt, Donnell. Farm Power & Machinery Management. 8th ed. 1983. 15.75x (ISBN 0-8138-0580-5). Iowa St U Pr.
Mechanisation & Employment in Agriculture: Case Studies from Four Continents. 2nd ed. 1974. 8.55 (ISBN 92-2-101009-0). Intl Labour Office.
Stone, Archie & Gulvin, Harold E. Machines for Power Farming. 3rd ed. LC 76-42244. pap. 135.50 (ISBN 0-317-28619-6, 2055394). Bks Demand UMI.
Street, James H. New Revolution in the Cotton Economy: Mechanization & Its Consequences. LC 57-2545. Repr. of 1957 ed. 29.00 (ISBN 0-384-58640-6). Johnson Repr.

FARM PRODUCE
see also Field Crops; Food Industry and Trade
Agricultural Commodities: Projections for 1970. (Commodity Policy Studies). 1963. pap. 9.75 (ISBN 0-685-36268-X, F6, FAO). Unipub.
Benedict, M. R. The Agricultural Commodity Programs, Two Decades of Experience. (Twentieth Century Fund Ser.). Repr. of 1956 ed. 10.00 (ISBN 0-527-02815-0). Kraus Repr.
Nash, M. J. Crop Conservation & Storage. 2nd ed. LC 77-30345. 1985. text ed. 35.00 (ISBN 0-08-029809-5); 19.75 (ISBN 0-08-023762-2). Pergamon.
OECD. The Instability of Agricultural Commodity Markets. (Agricultural Products & Markets Ser.). (Illus.). 237p. 1980. pap. text ed. 9.50x (ISBN 92-64-12041-6, 51-80-03-1). OECD.
Peleg, Kaiman. Produce Handling, Packaging & Distribution. (Illus.). 1985. lib. bdg. 135.00 (ISBN 0-87055-466-2). AVI.
Post-Harvest Food Crop Conservation: Association of Consulting Scientists Symposium on Post-Harvest Food Crop Conservaion, Harrogate, 13-15 November, 1979. (Progress in Food & Nutrition Ser.: Vol. 4). (Illus.). 138p. 1980. 40.00 (ISBN 0-08-025907-3). Pergamon.
UN-ECE Standards for Fresh Fruit & Vegetables. 276p. 1981. pap. 18.00 (ISBN 0-686-78465-0, UN812E8, UN). Unipub.
Youtz, H. & Carlson, A. Judging Livestock, Dairy Cattle, Poultry & Crops. 2nd ed. 1970. text ed. 31.52 (ISBN 0-13-511717-8). P-H.

FARM PRODUCE–TRANSPORTATION
see also Plant Quarantine
Finney, Essex E., Jr., ed. Handbook of Transportation & Marketing in Agriculture: Food Commodities, Vol. 1. 464p. 1981. 69.50 (ISBN 0-8493-3851-4). CRC Pr.
--Handbook of Transportation & Marketing in Agriculture, Vol. II: Field Crops. (CRC Ser. in Agriculture). 520p. 1981. 74.50 (ISBN 0-8493-3852-2). CRC Pr.
Krzyminski, James. Agricultural Transportation: The National Policy Issues. (Agriculture Committee Ser.). 32p. (Orig.). 1978. pap. 2.00 (ISBN 0-89068-046-9). Natl Planning.

FARM SHOPS
see Agricultural Machinery

FARM SUPPLIES
see Farm Equipment

FARM TOOLS
see Agricultural Implements

FARMERS
see also Agriculture–Vocational Guidance; Farm Management
De Crevecoeur, J. Hector. Letters from an American Farmer. Repr. of 1782 ed. 11.25 (ISBN 0-8446-1139-5). Peter Smith.
Grant, H. Roger & Purcell, L. Edward, eds. Years of Struggle: The Farm Diary of Elmer G. Powers, 1931-1936. (Illus.). 158p. 1976. 8.50x (ISBN 0-8138-0600-3). Iowa St U Pr.
Hayter, Earl W. Troubled Farmer: Rural Adjustment to Industrialism, 1850-1900. LC 67-26267. 349p. pap. 6.00 (ISBN 0-87580-515-9). N Ill U Pr.
McMillen, Wheeler. Farmer. LC 66-14227. (U.S.A. Survey Ser.). (Illus.). 126p. 1966. 4.95 (ISBN 0-87107-004-9). Potomac.
Matlon, P. & Cantrell, R., eds. Coming Full Circle: Farmers' Participation in the Development of Technology. (Illus.). 176p. 1984. pap. 15.00 (ISBN 0-88936-324-2, IDRC189E, IDRC). Unipub.
Nichols, Mark. Young Farmers: Their Problems, Activities & Educational Program. (Illus.). 1952. text ed. 7.50x (ISBN 0-8134-0234-4, 234). Interstate.
Richards, Bartlett, Jr. & Van Ackeren, Ruth. Bartlett Richards: Nebraska Sandhills Cattleman. LC 79-92129. (Illus.). 289p. (Orig.). 1980. 12.00 (ISBN 0-686-31143-4). Nebraska Hist.
Thane, Elswyth. Strength of the Hills. (Illus.). lib. bdg. 14.95 (ISBN 0-88411-961-0, Pub. by Aeonian Pr). Amereon Ltd.

FARMING
see Agriculture

FARMS
see also Farm Management
Hamil, Harold. Farmland, U. S. A. LC 75-18756. (Illus.). 112p. 1975. 25.00 (ISBN 0-913504-24-6); deluxe ed. 100.00 (ISBN 0-913504-61-0). Lowell Pr.
McBride, George M. Chile: Land & Society. LC 71-154618. 1971. Repr. of 1936 ed. lib. bdg. 29.00x (ISBN 0-374-95429-1). Octagon.
Olson, Michael K. The Mini-Farm. LC 81-82263. Date not set. 8.95 (ISBN 0-916172-08-2). Janus Pr.
Schreiner, Olive. The Story of an African Farm. 12.00 (ISBN 0-8446-0247-7). Peter Smith.
Steiner, Frederick. Ecological Planning for Farmlands Preservation. LC 81-69863. 122p. 1981. pap. 15.95 (ISBN 0-918286-25-5). Planners Pr.
Trullinger, Robert W. & Warren, George M. Clean Water & Sewage Disposal on the Farm. facs. ed. (Shorey Lost Arts Ser.). 52p. pap. 3.95 (ISBN 0-8466-6036-9, U36). Shorey.
Trzyna, Thaddeus C., et al. Preserving Agricultural Land: An International Annotated Bibliography. LC 81-21629. (Environmental Studies: No. 7). 100p. (Orig.). 1984. pap. 25.00x (ISBN 0-912102-59-4). Cal Inst Public.
Woofter, T. J., Jr. Landlord & Tenant on the Cotton Plantation. LC 77-165691. (FDR & the Era of the New Deal Ser.). 1971. Repr. of 1936 ed. lib. bdg. 29.50 (ISBN 0-306-70337-8). Da Capo.
Woofter, Thomas J. Landlord & Tenant on the Cotton Plantation. LC 74-75537. (Illus.). Repr. of 1936 ed. 19.75x (ISBN 0-8371-1035-1, WOL&, Pub. by Negro U Pr). Greenwood.

FARMS–BIBLIOGRAPHY
Alabaster, John S. Report of the EIFAC Workshop on Fish-Farm Effluents: Silkeborg, Denmark, May 26-28, 1981. (European Inland Fisheries Advisory Commission (EIFAC): Technical Papers: No. 41). 174p. 1982. pap. 12.75 (ISBN 92-5-101162-1, F2285, FAO). Unipub.

FAST PULSE REACTORS
see Pulsed Reactors

FAST-RESPONSE DATA PROCESSING
see Real-Time Data Processing

FASTENERS
see also Locks and Keys; Sealing (Technology)
American Society for Testing & Materials, Committee F-16 on Fasteners. ASTM Standards on Fasteners. 1st ed. LC 78-108362. pap. 84.00 (ISBN 0-317-11195-7, 2015509). Bks Demand UMI.
Crouse, William H. & Anglin, Donald L. Automotive Tools, Fasteners, & Measurements: A Text-Workbook. (Automotive Technology Ser.). (Illus.). 1977. 14.15 (ISBN 0-07-014630-6). McGraw.
DIN Standards Fasteners: Bolts, Pins, Studs, Rivets, Keys, Adjusting Rings, Retaining Rings. 486.00 (ISBN 0-686-28182-9, 10407-6/43). Heyden.
Din Standards: Fasteners, Dimensional Standards for Screws, Nuts & Accessories. 1055.00 (ISBN 0-686-28165-9, 10049-7/10). Heyden.
Din Standards, Fasteners: Standards for Accessories for Screwed Connections. 299.00 (ISBN 0-686-28195-0, 11200-4/140). Heyden.
Din Standards for Clamping Devices, Pt. I. 449.00 (ISBN 0-686-28167-5, 10050-5/14). Heyden.
Dinstandards Fastners: Basic Standards, Quality Standards & Technical Conditions of Delivery for Bolts, Screws, Nuts & Accessories. 266.00 (ISBN 0-686-28190-X, 10794-6/55). Heyden.
Handbook of Industrial Fasteners. 700p. 1982. 165.00x (ISBN 0-85461-083-9, Trade & Tech). State Mutual Bk.
Industrial Fasteners Handbook. 2nd ed. (Illus.). 750p. 1980. text ed. 127.40x (ISBN 0-85461-083-9). Brookfield Pub Co.
Industrial Fasteners Market Including Adhesives. 375p. 1983. 1250.00 (ISBN 0-86621-121-7). Frost & Sullivan.
Jones, Peter. Fasteners, Joints & Adhesives: A Guide to Engineering Solid Constructions. 416p. 1983. 24.95 (ISBN 0-13-307694-6); pap. 14.95 (ISBN 0-13-307686-5). P-H.
Metric Mechanical Fasteners - STP 587. 122p. 1975. pap. 12.00 (ISBN 0-8031-0751-X, 04-587000-34). ASTM.
Morgan-Grampian Books, ed. Fastenings Locator, 1985. 114p. 1984. 90.00x (ISBN 0-686-75512-X, Pub. by Morgan-Grampian Bk). State Mutual Bk.
Self, Charles R. Fasten It! (Illus.). 304p. (Orig.). 1984. 23.95 (ISBN 0-8306-0744-7); pap. 14.95 (ISBN 0-8306-1744-2, 1744). TAB Bks.
Standards for Clamping Devices 2: Workpiece Holders, Clamping & Other Devices. (DIN Standards Ser.). 568.00 (ISBN 0-686-31853-6, 11354-2/151). Heyden.
Trade & Technical Press Editors. Handbook of Industrial Fasteners. 700p. 1975. 108.00 (ISBN 0-85461-062-6, Pub by Trade & Tech England). Brookfield Pub Co.
Transactions of Technical Conference on Metric Mechanical Fasteners. 122p. 1975. pap. text ed. 12.00 (ISBN 0-685-62576-1, E00092). ASME.

FAT
Here is entered material on fat in its relation to the animal organism. Works on the technological aspects of fats in general are entered under the heading Oils and Fats.
Holman, Ralph T., et al, eds. Progress in the Chemistry of Fats & Other Lipids, Vols. 5-14. Incl. Vol. 5. Advances in Technology. 1958. 50.00 (ISBN 0-08-009098-2); Vol. 6. 1963. 50.00 (ISBN 0-08-009863-0); Vol. 7. Pt. 1, 1964. pap. 15.50 (ISBN 0-08-010087-2); Vol. 8. 1965. Vol. 8, Pt. 2. pap. 15.50 (ISBN 0-686-57466-4); Vol. 9, Pt. 1. Polyunsaturated Acids. 1966. pap. 15.50 (ISBN 0-08-011797-X); Vol. 9, Pts. 2-5. pap. 20.00 ea.; Pt. 2, 1968. pap. (ISBN 0-08-012632-4); Pt. 3. 1967. pap. (ISBN 0-08-013239-1); Pt. 4. 1968. pap. (ISBN 0-08-015971-0); Pt. 5, 1970. pap. (ISBN 0-08-016111-1); Vol. 9, Complete, 1971 Cloth. 68.75 (ISBN 0-08-016041-7); Complete, 1970. Cloth. 50.00 (ISBN 0-08-016040-9); Vol. 10, 1-4. pap. 15.50 ea.; Pt. 1, 1967. pap. (ISBN 0-08-012292-2); Pt. 2, 1969. pap. (ISBN 0-08-012996-X); Pt. 3, 1969. pap. (ISBN 0-08-012997-8); Pt. 4, 1969. 68.75 (ISBN 0-08-013990-6); Complete, 1972. 50.00 (ISBN 0-08-016795-0); Vol. 11, Pts. 1-3. pap. 15.50 ea.; Pt. 1, 1970. pap. (ISBN 0-08-015847-1); Pt. 2, 1970. pap. (ISBN 0-08-016150-2); Pt. 3, 1971. pap. (ISBN 0-08-016571-0); Vol. 12. 1972. 50.00 (ISBN 0-08-016758-6); Complete. 50.00 (ISBN 0-08-017146-X); Vol. 13, Pts. 1-4. pap. 15.50 ea.; Pt. 1. pap. (ISBN 0-08-016942-2); Pt. 2. pap. (ISBN 0-08-017043-9); Pt. 3. pap. (ISBN 0-08-017176-1); Pt. 4. 62.50 (ISBN 0-08-017129-X); Vol. 14, Pt. 1. pap. 15.50 (ISBN 0-08-017130-3); Vol. 14, Pt. 2. Lipids of Fungi. pap. 15.50 (ISBN 0-08-017880-4); Vol. 14, Pt. 3. Infrared Absorption Spectroscopy of Normal & Substituted Long-Chain Fatty Acids & Esters in Solid State. Fischmeister. pap. 15.00 (ISBN 0-08-018073-6); Vol. 14, Pt. 4. Lipid Metabolism Membrane Functions of the Mammary Gland. Patton, S. & Jensen, R. G. pap. 15.50 (ISBN 0-08-018222-4); Vol. 14, Complete. 1975. 50.00 (ISBN 0-08-017808-1). LC 53-22998. pap. write for info. Pergamon.
Roche, A. F., et al. Serial Changes in Subcutaneous Fat Thicknesses of Children & Adults. (Monographs in Paediatrics: Vol. 17). (Illus.). x, 110p. 1982. pap. 33.75 (ISBN 3-8055-3496-5). S Karger.

FATIGUE OF MATERIALS
see Materials–Fatigue

FATIGUE OF METALS
see Metals–Fatigue

FATS
see Fat; Oils and Fats

FATTY ACIDS
see Acids, Fatty

FAULTS (GEOLOGY)
see also Rifts (Geology)
Himmelblau, D. M. Fault Detection & Diagnosis in Chemical & Petrochemical Processes. (Chemical Engineering Monographs: Vol. 8). 414p. 1978. 78.75 (ISBN 0-444-41747-8). Elsevier.
Jaroszewski, W. Fault & Fold Tectonics. (Geology Ser.: I-528). 550p. 1984. 97.00x (ISBN 0-470-27478-6). Halsted Pr.
Neumann, Else-Ragnhild & Ramberg, Ivar B., eds. Petrology & Geochemistry of Continental Rifts. (Nato Advanced Study Institute Ser. C: No. 36). 1978. lib. bdg. 42.00 (ISBN 90-277-0866-5, Pub. by Reidel Holland). Kluwer Academic.
Ramberg, Ivar B. & Neumann, Else-Ragnhild, eds. Tectonics & Geophysics of Continental Rifts. (NATO Advanced Study Institute Ser.: No. 37). 1978. lib. bdg. 42.00 (ISBN 90-277-0867-3, Pub. by Reidel Holland). Kluwer Academic.
Voight, Barry, ed. Mechanics of Thrust Faults & Decollement. LC 76-11741. (Benchmark Papers in Geology: Vol. 32). 1976. 72.00 (ISBN 0-12-787680-4). Acad Pr.

FAUNA
see Animals; Fresh-Water Biology; Zoology

FAUNA, PREHISTORIC
see Paleontology

FEATHERS
Doughty, Robin W. Feather Fashions & Bird Preservation: A Study in Nature Protection. LC 72-619678. 1975. 26.50x (ISBN 0-520-02588-1). U of Cal Pr.
Voitkevick, A. A. Feather & Plumage of Birds. 1966. 10.50 (ISBN 0-8079-0050-8). October.

FEED INDUSTRY AND TRADE
see Flour and Feed Trade

FEED-WATER
Flanagan, G. T. Feed Water Systems & Treatment. (Marine Engineering Ser.). 144p. 1978. pap. 9.95x (ISBN 0-540-07343-1). Sheridan.
McCoy, James W. Chemical Treatment of Boiler Water. (Illus.). 1981. 40.00 (ISBN 0-8206-0284-1). Chem Pub.
National Research Council, Committee on Animal Nutrition. Nutrients & Toxic Substances in Water for Livestock & Poultry. LC 74-2836. (Illus.). v, 93p. 1974. pap. 6.25 (ISBN 0-309-02312-2). Natl Acad Pr.
Pincus, Leo I. Practical Boiler Water Treatment: Including Air-Conditioning Systems. LC 80-29604. 284p. 1981. Repr. of 1962 ed. lib. bdg. 19.50 (ISBN 0-89874-255-2). Krieger.

FEEDBACK (ELECTRONICS)
Ashworth, M. J. Feedback Design of Systems with Significant Uncertainty. LC 82-1929. 246p. 1982. 44.95x (ISBN 0-471-10213-X, Pub. by Research Studies Pr). Wiley.
Desoer, C. A. & Vidyasagar, M. Feedback Systems: Input-Output Properties. (Electrical Science Ser.). 1975. 75.00 (ISBN 0-12-212050-7). Acad Pr.
Klapper, Jacob & Frankle, John T. Phase Lock & Frequency Feedback Systems: Principles & Techniques. (Electrical Science Ser.). 1972. 90.00 (ISBN 0-12-410850-4). Acad Pr.
Waldhauer, Fred D. Feedback. LC 81-13104. 651p. 1982. 64.50x (ISBN 0-471-05319-8, Pub. by Wiley Interscience). Wiley.

FEEDBACK CONTROL SYSTEMS
see also Adaptive Control Systems; Biological Control Systems; Feedback (Electronics); Servomechanisms
AIP Conference, Princeton, 1970. Feedback & Dynamic Control of Plasmas: Proceedings, No. 1. Chu, T. K. & Hendel, H. W., eds. LC 70-141596. 364p. 1970. 14.00 (ISBN 0-88318-100-2). Am Inst Physics.
Ashworth, M. J. Feedback Design of Systems with Significant Uncertainty. LC 82-1929. 246p. 1982. 44.95x (ISBN 0-471-10213-X, Pub. by Research Studies Pr). Wiley.
Atkinson, P. Feedback Control Systems for Engineers. LC 68-31674. 425p. 45.00x (ISBN 0-306-30363-9, Plenum Pr). Plenum Pub.
Aubin, J. P. & Cellina, A. Differential Inclusions: Set-Valued Maps & Viability Theory. LC 84-1327. (Grundlehren der Mathematischen Wissenschaften: Vol. 264). (Illus.). 350p. 1984. 44.00 (ISBN 0-387-13105-1). Springer-Verlag.
Automated Education Center. On the Feedback Complexity of Automata. LC 75-120080. 19.00 (ISBN 0-403-04476-6). Scholarly.
Bishop, Albert B. Introduction to Discrete-Linear Controls: Theory & Applications. (Operations Research & Industrial Engineering Ser). 1975. 70.00 (ISBN 0-12-101650-1). Acad Pr.
Callier, F. M. & Desoer, C. A. Multivariable Feedback Systems. (Springer Texts in Electrical Engineering). (Illus.). 275p. 1982. 42.00 (ISBN 0-387-90768-8); pap. 21.50 (ISBN 0-387-90759-9). Springer-Verlag.
Corduneanu, Constantin. Integral Equations & Stability of Feedback Systems. (Mathematics in Science & Engineering Ser.). 1973. 60.00 (ISBN 0-12-188350-7). Acad Pr.
D'Azzo, John J. & Houpis, Constantine. Feedback Control System Analysis & Synthesis. 2nd ed. (Electronic & Electrical Engineering Ser.). 1966. text ed. 45.00 (ISBN 0-07-016175-5). McGraw.
DeRusso, P. M., et al. State Variables for Engineers. LC 65-21443. 608p. 1965. 57.50 (ISBN 0-471-20380-7). Wiley.
DiStefano, J. J., et al. Feedback & Control Systems. (Schaum's Outline Ser.). (Orig.). 1967. pap. 9.95 (ISBN 0-07-017045-2). McGraw.
Dorf, Richard C. Modern Control Systems. LC 85-7532. 550p. 1985. text ed. price not set (ISBN 0-201-05326-8). Addison-Wesley.
Edgar, T. F., ed. Feedback Controller Synthesis. (Alchemi Modular Instruction A-Ser.: Vol. 2). 75p. 1981. pap. 30.00 (ISBN 0-8169-0176-7); pap. 15.00 (ISBN 0-317-03789-7). Am Inst Chem Eng.
Hostetter, Gene H., et al. Design of Feedback Control Systems. 1982. text ed. 41.95 (ISBN 0-03-057593-1). HR&W.
Hung, Y. S. & MacFarlane, A. G. Multivariable Feedback: A Quasi-Classical Approach. (Lecture Notes in Control & Information Sciences: Vol. 40). 182p. 1982. pap. 12.00 (ISBN 0-387-11902-7). Springer-Verlag.
Isidori, A. Nonlinear Control Systems: An Introduction. (Lecture Notes in Control & Information Sciences: Vol. 72). 300p. 1985. pap. 19.00 (ISBN 0-387-15595-3). Springer-Verlag.
Jones, Richard W. Principles of Biological Regulation: An Introduction to Feedback Systems. 1973. 51.00 (ISBN 0-12-389950-8). Acad Pr.
Kurman, K. J. Feedback Control: Theory & Design. (Studies in Automation & Control: Vol. 4). 1984. 90.75 (ISBN 0-444-99640-0, I-122-84). Elsevier.
McDonald, Anthony C. & Lowe, Harold. Feedback & Control Systems. 1981. text ed. 28.95 (ISBN 0-8359-1898-X); solutions manual avail. (ISBN 0-8359-1899-8). Reston.

MacLean, D. J. Broadband Feedback Amplifiers. LC 82-2066. (Electronic Circuits & Systems Ser.). 323p. 1982. 44.95 (ISBN 0-471-10214-8, Pub. by Res Stud Pr). Wiley.

Mayr, Otto. Origins of Feedback Control. 1970. pap. 4.95x (ISBN 0-262-63056-7). MIT Pr.

Mees, A. I. Dynamics of Feedback Systems. LC 80-40501. 214p. 1981. 49.95x (ISBN 0-471-27822-X, Pub. by Wiley-Interscience). Wiley.

Moroney, Paul. Issues in the Implementation of Digital Feedback Compensators. (Signal Processing, Optimization & Control Ser.). (Illus.). 224p. 1983. 35.00x (ISBN 0-262-13185-4). MIT Pr.

Nordholt, E. H. Design of High Performance Negative-Feedback Amplifiers. (Studies in Electric & Electronic Engineering: Vol. 7). 234p. 1983. 57.50 (ISBN 0-444-42140-8). Elsevier.

Owens, D. H. Feedback & Multivariable Systems. (IEE Control Engineering Ser.: No. 7). (Illus.). 320p. 1978. 56.00 (ISBN 0-906048-03-6, CE007). Inst Elect Eng.

Van de Vegte, John. Feedback Control Systems. (Illus.). 512p. 1986. text ed. 39.95 (ISBN 0-13-312950-0). P-H.

Yavin, Y. Feedback Strategies for Partially Observable Stochastic Systems. (Lecture Notes in Control & Information Sciences: Vol. 48). 233p. 1983. pap. 14.50 (ISBN 0-387-12208-7). Springer-Verlag.

FEEDBACK CONTROL SYSTEMS–MATHEMATICAL MODELS

Beachley, Norman H. & Harrison, Howard L. Introduction to Dynamic System Analysis. (Illus.). 1978. text ed. 31.95 scp (ISBN 0-06-040557-0, HarpC). Har-Row.

Bellman, Richard E. Adaptive Control Processes: A Guided Tour. (Rand Corporation Research Studies). 1961. 45.00 (ISBN 0-691-07901-3). Princeton U Pr.

Towill, Denis R. Coefficient Plane Models for Control System Analysis & Design. LC 80-41695. (Mechanical Engineering Research Studies: Vol. 1). 271p. 1981. 57.95x (ISBN 0-471-27955-2, Pub. by Wiley-Interscience). Wiley.

FEEDING BEHAVIOR

see Animals, Food Habits of

FEEDS

see also Animal Nutrition; Ensilage; Forage Plants;

also subdivision Feeding and Feeds under names of animals and groups of animals, e.g. Poultry–Feeding and Feeds

Aitken, F. c. & Hankin, R. G. Vitamins in Feeds for Livestock. 230p. 1970. cloth 40.00x (ISBN 0-686-45671-8, Pub. by CAB Bks England). State Mutual Bk.

CAN Task Force, National Research Council. Feeding Value of Ethanol Production by-Products. 79p. 1981. pap. text ed. 6.50 (ISBN 0-309-03136-2). Natl Acad Pr.

Committee to the Human Health Effects of Subtherapeutic Antibiotic Use in Animal Feeds. The Effects on Human Health of Subtherapeutic Use of Antimicrobials in Animal Feeds. LC 80-81486. 376p. 1980. pap. text ed. 10.75 (ISBN 0-309-03044-7). Natl Acad Pr.

Crampton, E. W. & Harris, L. E. Applied Animal Nutrition: The Use of Feedstuffs in the Formulation of Livestock Rations. 2nd ed. LC 68-10996. (Animal Science Ser.). (Illus.). 753p. 1969. text ed. 35.95 (ISBN 0-7167-0814-0). W H Freeman.

Cullison, Arthur E. Feeds & Feeding. 3rd ed. 600p. 1981. text ed. 24.95 (ISBN 0-8359-1905-6); instr's manual free (ISBN 0-8359-1906-4). Reston.

Culpin, Claude. Farm Machinery. 10th ed. (Illus.). 464p. 1981. pap. text ed. 24.50x (ISBN 0-246-11539-4, Pub. by Granada England). Brookfield Pub Co.

Decontamination of Animal Feeds by Irridation. (Panel Proceedings Ser.). (Illus.). 153p. 1979. pap. 22.75 (ISBN 92-0-111079-0, ISP508, IAEA). Unipub.

Ensminger, M. E. & Olentine, C. G., Jr. Feeds & Nutrition. (Illus.). 1978. Complete, 1417 Pgs. 49.50 (ISBN 0-941218-01-5); Abridged, 824 Pgs. 35.50 (ISBN 0-941218-02-3). Ensminger.

Gibbs, Dudley & Greenhalgh, Marilyn E. Biotechnology, Chemical Feedstocks & Energy Utilization. LC 83-62199. 184p. 1983. 22.50 (ISBN 0-86187-346-7). F Pinter Pubs.

Jackson, M. G. Treating Straw for Animal Feeding: An Assessment of Its Technical & Economic Feasibility. (Animal Production & Health Papers: No. 10). (Eng., Fr. & Span.). 84p. 1978. pap. 7.50 (ISBN 92-5-100584-2, F1480, FAO). Unipub.

Keith, T. B. & Baker, John P. Feed Formulation Manual. 3rd ed. xi, 93p. 1981. pap. text ed. 4.50x (ISBN 0-8134-2201-9); Answer Bk. pap. text ed. 0.50x (ISBN 0-8134-2202-7). Interstate.

Knobloch, E. & Cerna-Heyrovska, J. Fodder Biofactors: Their Methods of Determination. LC 78-25777. 318p. 1980. 68.00 (ISBN 0-444-99783-0). Elsevier.

Ledward, D., et al, eds. Upgrading Waste for Feeds & Food. (Illus.). 416p. 1983. text ed. 69.95 (ISBN 0-408-10837-1). Butterworth.

Matsushima, J. K. Feeding Beef Cattle. (Advanced Ser. in Agricultural Sciences: Vol. 7). (Illus.). 1979. 32.00 (ISBN 0-387-09198-X). Springer-Verlag.

Muller, Z. O. Feed from Animal Wastes: State of Knowledge. (Animal Production & Health Papers: No. 18). 201p. 1980. pap. 13.00 (ISBN 92-5-100946-5, F2100, FAO). Unipub.

New Feed Resources: Proceedings of a Technical Consultation Held at Rome, Nov. 22-24, 1976. (Animal Production & Health Papers: No. 4). (Trilingual.). 304p. 1977. pap. 20.25 (ISBN 92-5-000431-1, F1312, FAO). Unipub.

Perry, Tilden, ed. Feed Formulations. 3rd ed. 380p. 1981. 18.65 (ISBN 0-8134-2174-8); text ed. 14.00x. Interstate.

Pirie, N. W. Leaf Protein & Other Aspects of Fodder Fractionation. LC 77-87387. (Illus.). 1978. 37.50 (ISBN 0-521-21920-5). Cambridge U Pr.

Sauchelli, Vincent. Trace Elements in Agriculture. LC 74-81358. 228p. 1969. 16.50 (ISBN 0-442-15633-2, Pub. by Van Nos Reinhold). Krieger.

Sodano, C. S. Animal Feeds & Pet Foods: Recent Developments. LC 78-70746. (Food Technology Review Ser.: No. 50). 1979. 36.00 (ISBN 0-8155-0737-2). Noyes.

Tropical Feeds. (Animal Production & Health Papers: No. 12). 529p. 1981. 35.25 (ISBN 92-5-100463-3, F1209, FAO). Unipub.

U. S. - Canadian Tables of Feed Composition. 148p. 1982. 11.50 (ISBN 0-309-03245-8). Natl Acad Pr.

FELDSPAR

Brown, William L., ed. Feldspars & Feldspathoids: Structures, Properties & Occurances. lib. bdg. 74.00 (ISBN 90-277-1826-1, Pub. by Reidel Holland). Kluwer Academic.

Smith, J. V. Feldspar Minerals, Vol. 1: Physical Properties. LC 73-14236. (Illus.). 600p. 1974. 65.00 (ISBN 0-387-06490-7). Springer-Verlag.

--Feldspar Minerals, Vol. 2: Chemical & Textural Properties. LC 73-15294. (Illus.). 690p. 1974. 69.00 (ISBN 0-387-06516-4). Springer-Verlag.

Van Der Plas, Leendert. Identification of Detrital Feldspars. (Developments in Sedimentology: Vol. 6). 305p. 1966. 83.00 (ISBN 0-444-40597-6). Elsevier.

FELIDAE

Line, Les & Ricciuti, Edward R. The Audubon Society Book of Wild Cats. LC 84-18475. (Audubon Society Ser.). (Illus.). 240p. 1985. 50.00 (ISBN 0-8109-1828-5). Abrams.

FENS

see also Marshes; Moors and Heaths; Reclamation of Land

Davis, Hubert J. Great Dismal Swamp: Its Science, History & Folklore. (Illus.). 1971. 8.50 (ISBN 0-930230-11-6). Johnson NC.

Godwin, Harry. Fenland: Its Ancient Past & Uncertain Future. LC 77-8824. (Illus.). 1978. 37.50 (ISBN 0-521-21768-7). Cambridge U Pr.

Schueler, Don. Preserving the Pascagoula. LC 80-15931. (Illus.). 1980. 4.95 (ISBN 0-87805-123-6). U Pr of Miss.

FERMAT, PIERRE DE, 1601-1665

Mahoney, Michael S. The Mathematical Career of Pierre de Fermat (1601-1665) LC 72-733. pap. 109.80 (ISBN 0-317-08307-4, 2016017). Bks Demand UMI.

Renyi, Alfred. Letters on Probability. Vekerdi, Laslo, tr. from Hung. LC 74-179559. (Waynebooks Ser.: No. 33). (Eng.). 86p. 1973. pap. 3.95x (ISBN 0-8143-1465-1). Wayne St U Pr.

Scharlau, W. & Opolka, H. From Fermat to Minkowski: Lectures on the Theory of Numbers & Its Historical Development. Buhler, W. K. & Cornell, G., trs. from German. (Undergraduate Texts in Mathematics Ser.). (Illus.). 255p. 1985. 24.00 (ISBN 0-387-90942-7). Springer-Verlag.

FERMAT'S THEOREM

Klein, Felix. Famous Problems of Elementary Geometry & Other Monographs, 4 vols. in 1. Incl. From Determinant to Tensor. Sheppard, William F; Introduction to Combinatory Analysis. MacMahon, Percy A; Fermat's Last Theorem. Mordell, Louis J; Famous Problems of Elementary Geometry. Klein, Felix. 1956. 11.95 (ISBN 0-8284-0108-X). Chelsea Pub.

Ribenboim, P. Thirteen Lectures on Fermant's Last Theorem. 1979. 32.00 (ISBN 0-387-90432-8). Springer-Verlag.

FERMENTATION

see also Bacteriology; Brewing; Enzymes; Sugars; Wine and Wine Making;

also particular groups of organisms involved in fermentation, e.g. Bacteria, Molds (Botany)

Bushell, M. E., ed. Modern Applications of Traditional Biotechnologies. (Progress in Industrial Microbiology Ser.: No. 19). 462p. 1984. 85.25 (ISBN 0-444-42364-8, I-226-84). Elsevier.

Bushell, M. E & Slater, J. H., eds. Mixed Culture Fermentation. LC 81-68019. (Special Publications of the Society for General Microbiology Ser.: No. 5). 1982. 33.00 (ISBN 0-12-147480-1). Acad Pr.

Business Communications Staff. Fermentation Products & Processes, C-018R. 1984. 1500.00 (ISBN 0-89336-222-0). BCC.

Davies, F. L. & Law, B. A., eds. Advances in Microbiology & Biochemistry of Cheese & Fermented Milk. 268p. 1984. 42.00 (ISBN 0-85334-287-3, Pub. by Elsevier Applied Sci England). Elsevier.

Gastineau, Clifford F., et al, eds. Fermented Food Beverages in Nutrition. (Nutrition Foundation Ser.). 1979. 70.00 (ISBN 0-12-277050-1). Acad Pr.

Gray, William D. The Use of Fungi As Food & in Food Processing, Pt. 1. (Monotopic Reprint Ser.). 1971. 11.95 (ISBN 0-87819-104-6). CRC Pr.

Hollaender, A., et al, eds. Trends in the Biology of Fermentations for Fuels & Chemicals. LC 81-5928. (Basic Life Sciences Ser.). 604p. 1981. 85.00x (ISBN 0-306-40752-3, Plenum Pr). Plenum Pub.

Hunderfund, Richard. Wines, Spirits & Fermentations. (Illus.). 192p. (Orig.). 1983. pap. 10.95. Star Pub CA.

Jefferis, R. R. Workshop Computer Applications in Fermentation Technology, Nineteen Seventy-Six. (Illus.). 169p. 1977. pap. 38.30x (ISBN 3-527-25719-5). VCH Pubs.

LeRoith, Derek, et al, eds. Purification of Fermentation Products: Applications to Large-Scale Processes. LC 84-24316. (ACS Symposium Ser.: No. 271). 198p. 1985. lib. bdg. 44.95x (ISBN 0-8412-0890-5). Am Chemical.

Malek, Ivan & Fencl, Zdenek, eds. Continuous Cultivation of Microorganisms: Proceedings. 1970. 81.00 (ISBN 0-12-466260-9). Acad Pr.

Peppler, Henry J., ed. Microbial Technology. LC 77-796. (Illus.). 464p. 1977. Repr. of 1967 ed. lib. bdg. 27.00 (ISBN 0-88275-538-2). Krieger.

Peppler, Henry J. & Perlman, David, eds. Microbial Technology, Vol. 2: Fermentation Technology. 2nd ed. 1979. 60.50 (ISBN 0-12-551502-2). Acad Pr.

Perlman. Fermentation: 1977: Annual Reports. 1977. 55.00 (ISBN 0-12-040301-3). Acad Pr.

Perlman, D., ed. Annual Reports in Fermentation Processes, Vol. 6. (Serial Publication). 1983. 45.00 (ISBN 0-12-040306-4). Acad Pr.

--Annual Reports on Fermentation Processes, Vol. 5. (Serial Publication). 1982. 45.00 (ISBN 0-12-040305-6). Acad Pr.

--Fermentation Advances. 1969. 72.00 (ISBN 0-12-550850-6). Acad Pr.

Perlman, D. & Tsao, G. T., eds. Annual Reports on Fermentation Processes, Vol. 2. 1978. 55.00 (ISBN 0-12-040302-1). Acad Pr.

--Annual Reports on Fermentation Processes, Vol. 3. (Serial Publication). 1979. 50.00 (ISBN 0-12-040303-X). Acad Pr.

--Annual Reports on Fermentation Processes, Vol. 7. (Serial Publication Ser.). 1984. 42.50 (ISBN 0-12-040307-2). Acad Pr.

Solar Energy Research Institute. Fermentation Guide for Common Grains: A Step-by-Step Procedure for Small-Scale Ethanol Fuel Production. 1982. pap. 9.95 (ISBN 0-89934-157-8, B-026). Solar Energy Info.

Stanbury, P. F. & Whitaker, A. Principles of Fermentation Technology. (Illus.). 304p. 1984. 47.00 (ISBN 0-08-024400-9); pap. 17.50 (ISBN 0-08-024406-8). Pergamon.

Vogel, Henry C., ed. Fermentation & Biochemical Engineering Handbook: Principles, Process Design, & Equipment. LC 83-12164. (Illus.). 440p. 1984. 64.00 (ISBN 0-8155-0950-2). Noyes.

Wang, Daniel I., et al. Fermentation & Enzyme Technology. LC 78-7596. (Techniques in Pure & Applied Microbiology Ser.). 374p. 1979. 42.95x (ISBN 0-471-91945-4, Pub. by Wiley-Interscience). Wiley.

Whitaker, John R., ed. Food Related Enzymes. LC 74-20861. (Advances in Chemistry Ser: No. 136). 1974. 31.95 (ISBN 0-8412-0209-5). Am Chemical.

Whittow, Marion. Great Fermentations. (Illus.). 133p. Date not set. pap. 4.95 (ISBN 0-900841-69-9, Pub. by Aztex Corp). Argus Bks.

Wiseman, Alan. Topics in Enzyme & Fermentation Biotechnology, Vol. 6. 232p. 1982. 74.95x (ISBN 0-470-27304-6). Halsted Pr.

Wiseman, Alan, ed. Topics in Enzyme & Fermentation Bio-Technology, Vol. 8. LC 78-643391. (Topics in Enzyme & Fermentation Bio-Technology Ser.: I-365). 179p. 1984. text ed. 54.95x (ISBN 0-470-20058-8). Halsted Pr.

--Topics in Enzyme & Fermentation Biotechnology, Vol. 2. LC 76-25441. 1978. 54.95x (ISBN 0-470-99318-9). Vol. 2. Halsted Pr.

--Topics in Enzyme & Fermentation Biotechnology, Vol. 4. (Topics in Enzyme & Fermentation Biotechnology Ser.). 242p. 1980. 89.95x (ISBN 0-470-26922-7). Halsted Pr.

Wood, B. J., ed. Microbiology of Fermented Foods, 2 vols. 1985. Set. 120.00 (Pub. by Elsevier Applied Sci England); Vol. 1. 81.00 (ISBN 0-85334-332-2); Vol. 2. 63.00 (ISBN 0-85334-333-0). Elsevier.

Woolford. The Silage Fermentation. (Microbiology Ser.). 336p. 1984. 64.50 (ISBN 0-8247-7039-0). Dekker.

FERMENTATION GUM

see Dextran

FERMENTS

see Enzymes

FERMI, ENRICO, 1901-1954

Lichello, Robert. Enrico Fermi: Father of the Atomic Bomb. Rahmas, D. Steve, ed. LC 70-185667. (Outstanding Personalities Ser.: No. 11). 32p. (Orig.). 1972. lib. bdg. 3.50 incl. catalog cards (ISBN 0-87157-511-6); pap. 1.95 vinyl laminated covers (ISBN 0-87157-011-4). SamHar Pr.

Segre, Emilio. Enrico Fermi, Physicist. LC 71-107424. 288p. 1972. pap. 2.95X (ISBN 0-226-74473-6, P468, Phoen). U of Chicago Pr.

FERMI SURFACES

Cracknell, A. P. & Wong, K. C. Fermi Surface: Its Concept, Determination & Use in the Physics of Metals. (Monographs on the Physics & Chemistry of Materials). (Illus.). 1973. 69.00x (ISBN 0-19-851330-5). Oxford U Pr.

FERMIONS

Fries, D. E. C. & Wess, J., eds. New Phenomena in Lepton-Hadron Physics. LC 79-19005. (NATO ASI, Ser. B, Physics: Vol. 49). 444p. 1979. 65.00x (ISBN 0-306-40301-3, Plenum Pr). Plenum Pub.

Iachello, F., ed. Interacting Bose-Fermi Systems in Nuclei. LC 81-4319. (Ettore Majorana International Science Series; Physical Sciences: Vol. 10). 412p. 1981. 59.50x (ISBN 0-306-40733-7, Plenum Pr). Plenum Pub.

FERN ALLIES

see Pteridophyta

FERNS

see also Cryptogams

Abbe, Elfriede. The Fern Herbal: Including the Ferns, the Horsetails, & the Club Mosses. LC 84-45439. (Illus.). 120p. 1985. 35.00x (ISBN 0-8014-1718-X). Cornell U Pr.

Ayrey, Betty. Ferns: Facts & Fantasy. (Illus.). 1979. 6.95x (ISBN 0-85091-062-5, Pub. by Lothian). Intl Spec Bk.

Beddome, R. H. The Ferns of British India, Vols. I & II. 702p. 1978. 99.00x (ISBN 0-686-84451-3, Pub. by Oxford & I B H India). State Mutual Bk.

--Ferns of Southern India. 1969. Repr. of 1873 ed. 45.00 (ISBN 0-934454-31-0). Lubrecht & Cramer.

--Handbook to the Ferns of British India Ceylon & Malay Peninsula. 1969. Repr. of 1883 ed. 16.00 (ISBN 0-934454-47-7). Lubrecht & Cramer.

--Handbook to the Ferns of British India, Ceylon & Malaysia: Peninsula with Supplement. 502p. 1977. 20.00 (ISBN 0-88065-054-0, Pub. by Messers Today & Tomorrows Printers & Publishers India). Scholarly Pubns.

Benton, Allen H. Keys to Common Ferns of Western New York. (Marginal Media Bioguides Ser.: No. 1). (Illus.). 14p. 1975. pap. 1.00 (ISBN 0-942788-00-1). Marginal Med.

Birdseye, Clarence & Birdseye, Eleanor. Growing Woodland Plants. (Illus.). 1972. pap. 4.50 (ISBN 0-486-20661-0). Dover.

Blandford, H. F. A List of the Ferns of Simla & North Western Himalaya. (Illus.). 22p. 1978. Repr. of 1885 ed. 2.00 (ISBN 0-88065-065-6, Pub. by Messers Today & Tomorrows Printers & Publishers India). Scholarly Pubns.

Blatter, E. Ferns of Bombay. 1979. 15.00x (ISBN 0-89955-261-7, Pub. by Intl Bk Dist). Intl Spec Bk.

Brown, D. F. A Monographic Study of the Fern Genus Woodsia. (Illus.). 1964. 21.00 (ISBN 3-7682-5416-X). Lubrecht & Cramer.

Brownlie, G. The Pteridophyte Flora of Fiji. (Beihefte Zur Nova Hedwigia 55). 1977. lib. bdg. 70.00x (ISBN 3-7682-5455-0). Lubrecht & Cramer.

Clarke, Charles B. A Review of the Ferns of Northern India: With an Index of the Species & 36 Plates. (Illus.). 1978. Repr. of 1880 ed. 62.50x (ISBN 0-89955-303-6, Pub. by Intl Bk Dist). Intl Spec Bk.

Clifford, H. T. & Constantine, J. Ferns, Fern Allies & Conifers of Australia. (Illus.). 150p. 1980. text ed. 29.95x (ISBN 0-7022-1447-7). U of Queensland Pr.

Cobb, Boughton. A Field Guide to Ferns & Their Related Families. (Peterson Field Guide Ser.). 1977. 15.95 (ISBN 0-395-07560-2); pap. 10.95 (ISBN 0-395-19431-8). HM.

Dean, Blanche E. Ferns. (Southern Regional Nature Ser.). (Illus.). 1969. pap. 12.00 (ISBN 0-87651-019-5). Southern U Pr.
Dhir, K. K. Ferns of the Northwestern Himalayas. (Bibliotheca Pteridologica 1). (Illus.). 1979. pap. text ed. 14.00x (ISBN 3-7682-1222-X). Lubrecht & Cramer.
Dhir, K. K. & Sood, A. Fern Flora of Mussoorie Hills. (Bibliotheca Pteridologica 2). (Illus.). 1981. pap. text ed. 14.00x (ISBN 3-7682-1232-7). Lubrecht & Cramer.
Dyer, A. F., ed. The Experimental Biology of Ferns. (Experimental Biology Ser.). 1979. 99.50 (ISBN 0-12-226350-2). Acad Pr.
Fee, A. L. Memoires sur la Famille des Fougeres: 1844-66, 11parts in 1 vol. (Illus.). 1966. 245.00 (ISBN 3-7682-0447-2). Lubrecht & Cramer.
Ferns. 2.25 (ISBN 0-686-21153-7). Bklyn Botanic.
Foster, F. Gordon. Ferns to Know & Grow. (Illus.). 228p. 1984. Repr. of 1964 ed. 29.95 (ISBN 0-917304-98-5). Timber.
Frankel, Edward. Ferns: A Natural History. LC 81-6700. (Illus.). 256p. 1981. 17.50 (ISBN 0-8289-0429-4). Greene.
Hallowell, Anne E. & Hallowell, Barbara. Fern Finder. 1981. pap. 1.50 (ISBN 0-912550-11-2). Nature Study.
Hires, Clara S. Spores, Ferns, Microscopic Illusions Analyzed, Vol. 1. LC 65-19563. 1965. 22.50. Mistaire.
--Spores. Ferns. Microscopic Illusions Analyzed, Vol 2. LC 65-19563. (Illus.). 1978. 50.00 (ISBN 0-686-23109-0). Mistaire.
Hooker, W. J. Species Filicum, 5 vols. 1970. Repr. of 1864 ed. 175.00 (ISBN 3-7682-0690-4). Lubrecht & Cramer.
Hope, C. W. The Ferns of North Western India. (Illus.). 1978. Repr. 37.50x (ISBN 0-89955-262-5, Pub. by Intl Bk Dist). Intl Spec Bk.
Hoshizaki, Barbara J. Fern Growers Manual. LC 75-8220. (Illus.). 1979. pap. 11.95 (ISBN 0-394-73774-1). Knopf.
Jarrett, F. M. Index Filicum: Supplement Quintum: Pro Annis 1961-1975. 1985. 39.95x (ISBN 0-19-854579-7). Oxford U Pr.
Jermy, A. C., et al. The Phylogeny & Classification of the Ferns. (Illus.). 1984. Repr. of 1973 ed. lib. bdg. 52.50 (ISBN 3-87429-218-5). Lubrecht & Cramer.
Keator, Glenn & Atkinson, Ruth M. Pacific Coast Fern Finder. 1981. pap. 1.50 (ISBN 0-912550-13-9). Nature Study.
Kepler, Angela K. Common Ferns of Luquillo Forest. LC 72-91603. (Illus.). 125p. 1975. 15.00 (ISBN 0-913480-06-1); spanish ed. 15.00 (ISBN 0-913480-07-X); pap. 5.00 (ISBN 0-913480-08-8); pap. 5.00 Spanish ed. (ISBN 0-913480-09-6). Inter Am U Pr.
Lakela, Olga & Long, Robert W. Ferns of Florida. LC 76-18950. (Illus.). 1976. 12.50 (ISBN 0-916224-03-1). Banyan Bks.
Lellinger, David B. A Field Manual of the Ferns & Fern-Allies of the United States & Canada. LC 84-22216. (Illus.). 320p. 1985. 45.00 (ISBN 0-87474-602-7, LEFN); pap. 29.95 (ISBN 0-87474-603-5, LEFNP). Smithsonian.
McVaugh, Rogers & Pyron, Joseph H. Ferns of Georgia. LC 52-882. (Illus.). 208p. 1951. 17.00x (ISBN 0-8203-0209-0). U of Ga Pr.
Mickel, John T. How to Know the Ferns & Fern Allies. 250p. 1979. write for info. wire coil (ISBN 0-697-04771-7). Wm C Brown.
Mohlenbrock, Robert H. Ferns. LC 65-16533. (Illustrated Flora of Illinois Ser.). (Illus.). 207p. 1967. 15.00x (ISBN 0-8093-0251-9). S Ill U Pr.
Odgen, Edith B. The Ferns of Maine. 128p. pap. 3.50 (ISBN 0-89621-016-2). U Maine Orono.
Page, C. N. The Ferns of Britain & Ireland. LC 82-1126. (Illus.). 450p. 1983. 82.50 (ISBN 0-521-23213-9). Cambridge U Pr.
Parsons, Frances T. How to Know the Ferns. (Illus.). 12.75 (ISBN 0-8446-2707-0). Peter Smith.
--How to Know the Ferns: A Guide to the Names, Haunts, & Habits of Our Common Ferns. 2nd ed. (Illus.). 1899. pap. 3.50 (ISBN 0-486-20740-4). Dover.
Peck, James H. Ferns & Fern Allies of the Driftless Area of Illinois, Iowa, Minnesota & Wisconsin. 140p. 1982. 12.50 (ISBN 0-89326-083-5). Milwaukee Pub Mus.
Petrik-Ott, A. J. The Pteridophytes of Kansas, Nebraska, South Dakota & North Dakota, U. S. A. Nova Hedwigia Beiheft, No. 61. 1979. lib. bdg. 30.00 (ISBN 3-7682-5461-5). Lubrecht & Cramer.
Phillips, Roger. Grasses, Ferns, Mosses & Lichens of Great Britain & Ireland. (Illus.). 181p. (Orig.). 1980. pap. text ed. 14.95x (ISBN 0-916422-38-0, Pub. by Pan Bks England). Mad River.
Piggott, Audrey. Heinemann Guide to Common Epiphytic Ferns 0f Malaysia & Singapore. (Orig.). 1979. pap. text ed. 4.95x (ISBN 0-686-74446-2, 00140). Heinemann Ed.
Procter, G. R. Ferns of Jamaica: A Guide to The Pteridophytes. (Illus.). 610p. 1985. 82.50x (ISBN 0-565-00895-1, Pub. by Brit Mus of Nat Hist England). Sabbot Natural Hist Bks.
Roux, J. P. Cape Peninsula Ferns. (Illus.). 66p. 1982. (Pub. by H Timmons S Africa). Intl Spec Bk.
Santha Devi. Spores of Indian Ferns. (Illus.). 129p. 1973. 15.00 (ISBN 0-88065-190-3, Pub. by Messers Today & Tomorrows Printers & Publishers India). Scholarly Pubns.
Small, John K. Ferns of the Vicinity of New York. (Illus.). 288p. 1975. pap. 5.00 (ISBN 0-486-23118-6). Dover.
--Ferns of the Vicinity of New York. (Illus.). 9.00 (ISBN 0-8446-5244-X). Peter Smith.
Taylor, W. Carl. Arkansas Ferns & Fern Allies. Garity, Mary M., ed. (Illus.). 272p. 1984. pap. text ed. 29.95 (ISBN 0-89326-097-5). Milwaukee Pub Mus.
Tilton, George H. The Fern Lover's Companion: Guide for the Northeastern States & Canada. 1978. Repr. of 1923 ed. lib. bdg. 30.00 (ISBN 0-8495-5118-8). Arden Lib.
Tryon, Rolla & Tryon, Alice. Ferns & Allied Plants: With Special Reference to Tropical America. (Illus.). 896p. 1982. 155.00 (ISBN 0-387-90672-X). Springer-Verlag.
Tryon, Rolla M., Jr. The Ferns of Minnesota. rev. ed. LC 80-10368. (Illus.). 1980. 15.00x (ISBN 0-8166-0932-2); pap. 6.95 (ISBN 0-8166-0935-7). U of Minn Pr.
Wharton, Mary E. & Barbour, Roger W. A Guide to the Wildflowers & Ferns of Kentucky. LC 79-132833. (Illus.). 352p. 1971. 16.00 (ISBN 0-8131-1234-6). U Pr of Ky.
Wiley, Farida A. Ferns of Northeastern United States. (Illus.). 11.75 (ISBN 0-8446-4840-X). Peter Smith.
--Ferns of the Northeastern United States. (Illus.). 108p. 1973. pap. 2.50 (ISBN 0-486-22946-7). Dover.

FERRARI (AUTOMOBILE)
see Automobiles, Foreign–Types–Ferrari

FERRATES
see Ferrites (Magnetic Materials)

FERRETS
see also Weasels
Harding, A. R. Ferret Facts & Fancies. (Illus.). 214p. pap. 3.50 (ISBN 0-936622-04-0). A R Harding Pub.
Roberts, Mervin F. All about Ferrets. (Illus.). 1977. pap. 3.95 (ISBN 0-87666-914-3, PS-754). TFH Pubns.
Wellstead, Graham. Ferrets & Ferreting. LC 80-68900. (Illus.). 160p. 1981. 15.95 (ISBN 0-7153-8013-3). David & Charles.
--Ferrets & Ferreting. (Illus.). 192p. 1981. 12.95 (ISBN 0-87666-938-0, PS-792). TFH Pubns.
Winsted, Wendy. Ferrets. (Illus.). 96p. 1981. 4.95 (ISBN 0-87666-930-5, KW-074). TFH Pubns.

FERRIES
Downs, Art. Paddlewheels on the Frontier. (Illus.). 160p. 11.95 (ISBN 0-88826-033-4). Superior Pub.
Graves, Al, et al. Narrow-Gauge to the Redwoods: The Story of the North Pacific Coast Railroad & San Francisco Bay Paddle-Wheel Ferries. 2nd rev. ed. LC 81-52347. 18.95 (ISBN 0-87046-010-2, Pub. by Trans-Anglo). Interurban.
McNeill, Donald B. Irish Passenger Steamship Services Vol. 1: North of Ireland. LC 69-10861. (Illus.). 1969. 17.95x (ISBN 0-678-05610-2). Kelley.
McVicar, Don. Ferry Command. 210p. 1982. 42.00x (ISBN 0-906393-12-4, Pub. by Airlife England). State Mutual Bk.
Martin, Nancy. River Ferries. 144p. 1981. 30.00x (ISBN 0-900963-99-9, Pub. by Terence Dalton England). State Mutual Bk.
Phillps, G. A. Thames Crossings: Bridges, Tunnels & Ferries. LC 81-65954. (Illus.). 288p. 1981. 37.50 (ISBN 0-7153-8202-0). David & Charles.
Ruby, Robert H. & Brown, John A. Ferryboats on the Columbia River. LC 74-75658. (Illus.). 1974. 17.95 (ISBN 0-87564-616-6). Superior Pub.
Rudman, Jack. Ferry Terminal Supervisor. (Career Examination Ser.: C-2142). (Cloth bdg. avail. on request). 1977. pap. 12.00 (ISBN 0-8373-2142-5). Natl Learning.

FERRIMAGNETISM
Brown, William F., Jr. Micromagnetics. LC 78-2342. 152p. 1978. Repr. of 1963 ed. lib. bdg. 13.50 (ISBN 0-88275-665-6). Krieger.
International Conference on the Microwave Behavior of Ferrimagnetics & Plasmas, London, 1965. The Microwave Behaviour of Ferrimagnetics & Plasmas. LC 66-36909. (Institution of Electrical Engineers Conference Publications: No. 13). pap. 109.30 (ISBN 0-317-10123-4, 2007385). Bks Demand UMI.

FERRITES (MAGNETIC MATERIALS)
Davis, J. W. & Michel, D. J., eds. Topical Conference on Ferritic Alloys for Use in Nuclear Energy Technologies. LC 84-61008. (Illus.). 657p. 1984. 61.00 (ISBN 0-89520-458-4). Metal Soc.
Ferrites, Transition Elements, Luminescence. (Structure & Bonding Ser.: Vol. 47). (Illus.). 130p. 1981. 35.50 (ISBN 0-387-10788-6). Springer-Verlag.
Hellwege, K. H., ed. Magnetic & Other Properties of Oxides & Related Compounds: Hexagonal Ferrites. Special Lanthanide & Actinide Compounds. (Landolt-Boernstein Ser.: Group III, Vol. 12, Pt. C). (Illus.). 650p. 1983. 405.20 (ISBN 0-387-10137-3). Springer-Verlag.
Snelling, E. C. & Giles, A. D. Ferrites for Inductors & Transformers. LC 83-9595. (Magnetic Materials & Their Applications). 175p. 1983. 49.95x (ISBN 0-471-90208-X, Res Stud Pr). Wiley.
Toughness of Ferritic Stainless Steels-STP 706. 348p. 1978. 32.50x (ISBN 0-8031-0592-4, 04-706000-02). ASTM.
Von Aulock, Wilhelm H., ed. Handbook of Microwave Ferrite Materials. (Illus.). 1965. 70.50 (ISBN 0-12-723350-4). Acad Pr.
Watanabe, H., ed. Ferrites. 1982. 179.00 (ISBN 90-277-1413-4, Pub. by Reidel Holland). Kluwer Academic.

FERROCEMENT
see Reinforced Concrete

FERROCEMENT BOATS
see Concrete Boats

FERROELECTRIC CRYSTALS
Blinc, R., et al. Ferroelectric Liquid Crystals. 500p. 1984. text ed. 130.00 (ISBN 0-677-16595-1). Gordon.
Fridkin, V. M. Photoferroelectrics. (Ser. in Sold-State Sciences: Vol. 9). (Illus.). 1979. 40.00 (ISBN 0-387-09418-0). Springer-Verlag.
Hellwege, K. H., ed. Ferroelectrics & Related Substances: Non-Oxides. (Landolt-Boernstein Ser.: Group III, Vol. 16 Subvol. B). (Illus.). 820p. 1982. 612.80 (ISBN 0-387-10484-4). Springer-Verlag.
Smolenskii, G. A. Ferroelectrics & Related Materials. (Ferroelectricity & Related Phenomena Ser.: Vol. 3). 770p. 1984. text ed. 280.00 (ISBN 0-317-11706-8). Gordon.

FERROELECTRICITY
see also Domain Structure
Hellwege, K. H., ed. Landolt-Boernstein Numerical Data & Functional Relationships in Science & Technology, New Series, Group 3: Crystal & Solid State Physics, Vols. 1-6. Incl. Vol. 1. Elastic, Piezoelectric, Piezooptic & Electrooptic Constants of Crystals. Bechman, R. & Hearmon, R. F. x, 160p. 1966; Vol. 2. Elastic, Piezoelectric, Piezooptic, Electrooptic Constants, & Non-Linear Dielectric Susceptibilities of Crystals. Bechman, R., et al. (Illus.). ix, 232p. 1969; Vol. 3. Ferro- & Antiferroelectric Substances. Mitsui, T., et al. (Illus.). viii, 584p. 1969; Vol. 4, Pt. A. Magnetic & Other Properties of Oxides & Related Compounds. Goodenough, J. B., et al. (Illus.). xv, 367p. 1970. 130.20 (ISBN 0-387-04898-7); Vol. 4, Pt. B: Magnetic & Other Properties of Oxides & Related Compounds. Bonnenberg, F., et al. (Illus.). xvi, 666p. 1970. 235.20 (ISBN 0-387-05176-7); Vol. 5. Structure Data of Organic Crystals, 2 vols. Schudt, E. & Weitz, G. (Illus.). 1971. Set. 428.40 (ISBN 0-387-05177-5); Vol. 6. Structure Data of Elements & Intermetallic Phases. Eckerlin, P. & Kandler, H. 1971. 346.50 (ISBN 0-387-05500-2). LC 62-53136. Springer-Verlag.
Herbert, J. M. Ferroelectric Transducers & Sensors. (Electrocomponent Science Monographs). 464p. 1982. 49.50 (ISBN 0-677-05910-8). Gordon.
International Meeting on Ferroelectricity, Leningrad, U. S. S.R., Sept., 1977, et al. International Meeting on Ferroelectricity: Proceedings Leningrad, U. S. S. R., Sept., 1977, 3 vols. 850p. 1978. pap. 509.50x (ISBN 0-677-16215-4). Gordon.
Kanzig, Werner. Ferroelectrics & Antiferroelectrics. (Solid State Reprints Ser.). 1964. 27.50 (ISBN 0-12-608462-9). Acad Pr.
Lefkowitz, I. The Fourth European Meeting on Ferroelectricity: Proceedings, Portoroz, Yugoslavia, Sept. 1979, 3 vols. 864p. 1980. Set. pap. 642.50 (ISBN 0-677-16225-1). Gordon.
Lefkowitz, I. & Taylor, G., eds. Proceedings of the Nineteen Seventy-Five IEEE Symposium on Applications of Ferroelectrics (Albuquerque, 2 Vols. 428p. 1976. pap. 321.25x (ISBN 0-677-40195-7). Gordon.
--The Third European Meeting on Ferroelectricity (Zurich, 1975) Proceedings, 3 Vols. 762p. 1976. pap. 535.00x (ISBN 0-677-40205-8). Gordon.
--The Third International Meeting on Ferroelectricity, (Edingurgh, 1973) Proceedings, 2 Vols. 620p. 1974. 321.25 (ISBN 0-677-40215-5). Gordon.
Lefkowitz, I., et al. IEEE International Symposium on Applications of Ferroelectricity: Proceedings, Minnesota, 1979, 2 pt. 418p. 1980. pap. 454.25x (ISBN 0-677-40315-1). Gordon.
Lines, Malcom E. & Glass, Alastair M. Principles & Applications of Ferroelectrics & Related Materials. (International Series of Monographs on Physics). (Illus.). 1977. 89.00x (ISBN 0-19-851286-4); pap. 32.95x (ISBN 0-19-852003-4). Oxford U Pr.
Mitsui, T. An Introduction to the Physics of Ferroelectrics. (Ferroelectricity & Related Phenomena Ser.). 460p. 1976. 87.95 (ISBN 0-677-30600-8). Gordon.
Symposium on Semiconducting Ferroeletrics, Rostov-on-Don, U. S. S. R., 1976, et al. Proceedings. Lefkowitz, I., ed. 200p. 1978. 160.75x (ISBN 0-677-16205-7). Gordon.

FERROELECTRICS
see Ferroelectric Crystals
Lawless, W. N. International Symposium on Applications of Ferroelectrics (ISAF) Gaithersburg, Maryland, U. S. A., June 1-3, 1983. (Special Issue of the Journal Ferroelectrics & Related Materials). 892p. 1983. 200.00 (ISBN 0-677-16515-3). Gordon.

FERROMAGNETIC DOMAIN
see Domain Structure

FERROMAGNETISM
see also Domain Structure
DeMaw, M. Ferromagnetic-Core Design & Application Handbook. 1980. 28.95 (ISBN 0-13-314088-1). P-H.
McCoy, Barry & Wu, Tai T. The Two-Dimensional Ising Model. LC 72-188972. (Illus.). 1973. 27.50x (ISBN 0-674-91440-6). Harvard U Pr.
Moriya, T. Spin Fluctuations in Itinerant Electron Magnetism. (Solid-State Sciences Ser.: Vol. 56). (Illus.). 260p. 1985. 35.00 (ISBN 0-387-15422-1). Springer-Verlag.
O'Dell, T. H. Ferromagnetodynamics: The Dynamics of Magnetic Bubbles Domains & Domain Walls. LC 80-25331. 230p. 1981. 64.95x (ISBN 0-470-27084-5). Halsted Pr.
Sodha, M. S. & Srivastava, N. C. Microwave Propagation in Ferrimagnetics. LC 81-15364. 428p. 1981. 59.50x (ISBN 0-306-40716-7, Plenum Pr). Plenum Pub.

FERROUS METAL INDUSTRIES
see Iron Industry and Trade; Steel Industry and Trade

FERTILIZATION (BIOLOGY)
Dale, Brian. Fertilization in Animals. (Studies in Biology: No. 157). 64p. 1983. pap. text ed. 8.95 (ISBN 0-7131-2875-5). E Arnold.
Drayson, James E. Herd Bull Fertility. (Illus.). 160p. (Orig.). 1982. pap. 9.95 (ISBN 0-934318-08-5). Falcon Pr MT.
Edwards, Robert & Steptoe, Patrick. A Matter of Life. LC 80-17293. (Illus.). 208p. 1980. Repr. 9.95 (ISBN 0-688-03698-8). Morrow.
Fertilization & Cell Fusion. 1975. 32.00x (ISBN 0-686-45147-3, Pub. by Biochemical England). State Mutual Bk.
Forest Fertilization. LC 72-92357. (Bibliographic Ser.: No. 258, Supplement 1). 1975. pap. 25.00 (ISBN 0-87010-042-4). Inst Paper Chem.
Gwatkin, Ralph B. Fertilization Mechanisms in Man & Mammals. LC 77-1189. (Illus.). 171p. 1977. 29.50x (ISBN 0-306-31009-0, Plenum Pr). Plenum Pub.
Hadek, Robert. Mammalian Fertilization: An Atlas of Ultrastructure. 1969. 55.00 (ISBN 0-12-312950-8). Acad Pr.
Isotope Studies on Wheat Fertilization. (Technical Reports Ser.: No. 157). (Illus.). 99p. (Orig.). 1975. pap. 11.50 (ISBN 92-0-115074-1, IDC157, IAEA). Unipub.
Metz, Charles B. & Monroy, Alberto. Biology of Fertilization: The Fertilization Response of the Egg, Vol. 3. 1985. 75.00 (ISBN 0-12-492603-7). Acad Pr.
Metz, Charles B. & Monroy, Alberto, eds. Biology of Fertilization: General Principles, Sex Determination, Gonad & Germ Cell Growth & Differentiation, 2 vols. Treatise ed. 1985. Vol. 1. 65.00 (ISBN 0-12-492601-0); Vol. 2. 75.00 (ISBN 0-12-492602-9). Acad Pr.
--Fertilization: Comparative Morphology, Biochemistry & Immunology, 2 vols. Incl. Vol. 1. 1967. 76.50 (ISBN 0-12-492650-9); Vol. 2. 1969. 87.00 (ISBN 0-12-492651-7). Acad Pr.
Moghissi, Kamran S. & Hafez, E. S., eds. Biology of Mammalian Fertilization & Implantation. (Illus.). 520p. 1972. photocopy ed. 52.75x (ISBN 0-398-02362-X). C C Thomas.
Thompson, W., et al, eds. In Vitro Fertilisation & Donor Insemination. (Reproductive & Perinatal Medicine Ser.: No. II). 1985. 55.00 (ISBN 0-916859-06-1). Perinatology.

FERTILIZATION OF PLANTS
Darwin, Charles R. The Effects of Cross & Self Fertilisation in the Vegetable Kingdom. 1889. 40.00 (ISBN 0-8274-2230-X). R West.
Faegri, K. & Van Der Pijl, L. The Principles of Pollination Ecology. 2nd ed. 304p. 1972. 21.50 (ISBN 0-08-023160-8). Pergamon.
Frankel, R. & Galun, E. Pollination Mechanisms, Reproduction & Plant Breeding. (Monographs on Theoretical & Applied Genetics: Vol. 2). 1977. 39.00 (ISBN 0-387-07934-3). Springer-Verlag.

FERTILIZER INDUSTRY

FERTILIZERS AND MANURES

see also Agricultural Chemistry; Compost; Deficiency Diseases in Plants; Garden Fertilizers; Humus; Lime; Nitrogen Fertilizers; Nitrates; Peat; Phosphates; Potash; Salt; Soil Fertility.

--Energy & Fertilizer: Policy Implications & Options for Developing Countries. LC 82-6084. (Technical Bulletin Ser.: No. T-20). (Illus.). 241p. (Orig.). 1982. pap. 15.00 (ISBN 0-88090-019-9). Intl Fertilizer.
Munson, Robert D. Potassium, Calcium, & Magnesium in the Tropics & Subtropics. Brosheer, J. C., ed. LC 82-11944. (Technical Bulletins Ser.: T-23). (Illus.). 70p. (Orig.). pap. text ed. 8.00 (ISBN 0-88090-041-5). Intl Fertilizer.
Murray, T. P. & Horn, R. C. Organic Nitrogen Compounds for Use as Fertilizers. (Technical Bulletin Ser.: T-14). 64p. (Orig.). 1979. pap. 4.00 (ISBN 0-88090-013-X). Intl Fertilizer.
Nelson, L. B., ed. Changing Patterns in Fertilizer Use. (Illus.). 466p. 1968. 7.50 (ISBN 0-89118-751-0). Soil Sci Soc Am.
Organic Materials as Fertilizers: Report of an Expert Consultation Held in Rome, December 2-6, 1974. (Soils Bulletins: No. 27). (Illus.). 400p. (3rd Printing 1978). 1975. pap. 28.75 (ISBN 92-5-100395-5, F1170, FAO). Unipub.
Organic Recycling in Africa: Papers Presented at the FAO-SIDA Workshop on the Use of Organic Materials as Fertilizers in Africa, Buea, Cameroon, Dec. 5-14, 1977. (Soils Bulletins: No. 43). 308p. 1980. pap. 22.00 (ISBN 92-5-100945-7, F2096, FAO). Unipub.
Parish, D. H. Possibilities of the Improvement of Nitrogen Fertilizer Efficiency in Rice Production. (IFDC Paper Sers. P-1). 1980. 4.00 (ISBN 0-686-95954-X). Intl Fertilizer.
Parish, D. H., et al. Research on Modified Fertilizer Materials for Use in Developing-Country Agriculture. (IFDC Paper Sers. P-2). 1980. 4.00 (ISBN 0-686-95955-8). Intl Fertilizer.
Pronzini, Bill, et al, eds. The Arbor House Treasury of Horror & the Supernatural. LC 80-70220. 512p. (Orig.). 1981. 19.95 (ISBN 0-87795-309-0); pap. 8.95 (ISBN 0-87795-319-8). Arbor Hse.
Ranney, M. W. Fertilizer Additives & Soil Conditioners. LC 78-62524. (Chemical Technology Review: No. 116). (Illus.). 301p. 1979. 39.00 (ISBN 0-8155-0721-6). Noyes.
Recycling Organic Matter in Asia for Fertilizer Use. 232p. 1983. pap. text ed. 14.75 (ISBN 92-833-2012-3, APO143, APO). Unipub.
Report of the International Rice Commission, Working Party on Fertilizers: 3rd Meeting, Bangkok,1953. (Agricultural Development Papers: No. 39). 46p. 1953. pap. 4.50 (ISBN 0-686-92869-5, F1920, FAO). Unipub.
Report of 4th Meeting of the International Rice Commission's Working Party on Fertilizers. 1954. pap. 4.50 (F1921, FAO). Unipub.
Report on the FAO-NORAD Seminar on Fertilizer Use Development in Zambia: Held in Lusaka, Zambia, December 13-22, 1976. 1977. pap. 11.50 (ISBN 92-5-100378-5, F1255, FAO). Unipub.
Residue Utilization: Management of Agricultural & Agro-Industrial Residues: Seminar Papers & Documents: Presentations by Participants, 2 Vols. (Industry Sector Seminar Proceedings). 762p. 1977. Set. pap. 58.50 (UNEP004, UNEP). Unipub.
Residue Utilization: Management of Agricultural & Agro-Industrial Residues: An Overview. (Industry Overviews: Vol. 3). 24p. 1977. pap. 6.75 (UNEP014, UNEP). Unipub.
Response of Rice to Fertilizer. pap. 4.50 (F413, FAO). Unipub.
Rollett, R., et al. Fertilizers & Soil Amendments. 1981. 33.95 (ISBN 0-13-314336-8). P-H.
Ruffin, Edmund. Essay on Calcareous Manures. Sitterson, J. Carlyle, ed. LC 61-6352. (The John Harvard Library). (Illus.). 1961. 15.00x (ISBN 0-674-26201-8). Harvard U Pr.
Sauchelli, Vincent. Trace Elements in Agriculture. LC 74-81358. 228p. 1969. 16.50 (ISBN 0-442-15633-2, Pub. by Van Nos Reinhold). Krieger.
Silanpaa, Mikko. The Response of Wheat to Fertilizers. (Soils Bulletins: No. 12). 134p. 1971. pap. 9.00 (ISBN 92-5-100132-4, F1155, FAO). Unipub.
Sittig, M. Fertilizer Industry: Processes, Pollution Control & Energy Conservation. LC 78-70743. (Chem. Tech. Rev. 123; Pollution Tech. Rev. 55; Energy Tech. Rev, 36). (Illus.). 204p. 1979. 32.00 (ISBN 0-8155-0734-8). Noyes.
Stafford, D. A., et al. Methane Production from Waste Organic Matter. LC 78-31274. 304p. 1980. 86.50 (ISBN 0-8493-5223-1). CRC Pr.
Statistics of Crop Responses to Fertilizers. (Orig.). 1966. pap. 6.75 (ISBN 0-685-09408-1, F449, FAO). Unipub.
Thompson, M., ed. IFDC Annual Report 1980. (Circular Ser.: S-4). (Illus.). 64p. (Orig.). 1982. pap. 4.00 (ISBN 0-88090-030-X). Intl Fertilizer.
--Seminar on Phosphate Rock for Direct Application. (Special Publication Ser.: SP-1). (Illus.). 472p. (Orig.). 1979. pap. 10.00 (ISBN 0-88090-022-9). Intl Fertilizer.
Thompson, M. K., ed. IFDC Annual Report, 1981. (Circular Ser.: S-5). 58p. (Orig.). 1982. pap. text ed. 4.00. Intl Fertilizer.
Tiedjens, V. A. More Food from Soil Science: The Natural Chemistry of Lime in Agriculture. 1965. 15.00 (ISBN 0-682-43057-9, University). Exposition Pr FL.
Van Keulen, H. & Van Heemst, H. D. J. Crop Response to the Supply of Macronutrients. (Agricultural Research Reports: No. 916). 52p. 1982. pap. 6.75 (ISBN 90-220-0807-X, PDC247, PUDOC). Unipub.
Von Breman, L., et al. Economic Evaluation of Fertilizer Supply Strategies for the Asean Region: Linear Programming Approach. McCune, D. L., pref. by. (Technical Bulletins Ser.: T-21). (Illus.). 72p. (Orig.). 1981. pap. 4.00 (ISBN 0-88090-020-2). Intl Fertilizer.
Wines, Richard A. Fertilizer in America: From Waste Recycling to Resource Exploitation. LC 84-26855. 280p. 1985. 34.95 (ISBN 0-87722-374-2). Temple U Pr.
Wise, Donald L., ed. Fuel Gas Production from Biomass, 2 vols. 1981. Vol. I, 280 Pgs. 83.00 (ISBN 0-8493-5990-2); Vol. II, 296 Pgs. 91.50 (ISBN 0-8493-5991-0). CRC Pr.
Zalla, T. & Diamond, R. B. Economic & Technical Aspects of Fertilizer Production & Use in West Africa. (IFDC MSU Working Papers Ser.: No. 22). (IFDC Miscellaneous Publication A-1). 1977. 4.00 (ISBN 0-686-95956-6). Intl Fertilizer.

FERTILIZERS AND MANURES–MATHEMATICAL MODELS

Statistics of Crop Responses to Fertilizers. (Orig.). 1966. pap. 6.75 (ISBN 0-685-09408-1, F449, FAO). Unipub.

FETUS

Austin, C. R. & Short, R. V., eds. Embryonic & Fetal Development. 2nd ed. LC 81-18060. (Reproduction in Mammals Ser.: Bk. 2). (Illus.). 200p. 1983. 32.50 (ISBN 0-521-24786-1); pap. 12.95 (ISBN 0-521-28962-9). Cambridge U Pr.
Brambati, et al. Chorionic Villus Sampling: Fetal Diagnosis of Genetic Trimester. (Clinical & Biochemical Analysis Ser.). 344p. 1986. price not set (ISBN 0-8247-7360-8). Dekker.
Cold Spring Harbor Symposia on Quantitative Biology: The Mammalian Fetus, Volume 19. LC 34-8174. (Illus.). 237p. 1955. 38.00x (ISBN 0-87969-018-6). Cold Spring Harbor.
McClung, Jean. Effects of High Altitude on Human Birth: Observations on Mothers, Placentas, & the Newborn in Two Peruvian Populations. LC 72-91629. 1969. 11.00 (ISBN 0-674-24065-0). Harvard U Pr.
Martini, Luciano & James, V. H., eds. Current Topics in Experimental Endocrinology: Vol. 5: Fetal Endocrinology & Metabolism. (Serial Publication). 1983. 55.00 (ISBN 0-12-153205-4). Acad Pr.
Nitzan, Menachem, ed. The Influence of Maternal Hormones on the Fetus & Newborn. (Pediatric & Adolescent Endocrinology: Vol. 5). (Illus.). 1979. pap. 42.25 (ISBN 3-8055-2902-3). S Karger.
Novy, Miles J. & Resko, John A. Fetal Endocrinology. LC 81-19038. (ORPRC Symposium on Primate Reproductive Biology Ser.: Vol. 1). 1981. 49.50 (ISBN 0-12-522601-2). Acad Pr.
Scammon, Richard & Calkins, Leroy A. The Development & Growth of the External Dimensions of the Human Body in the Fetal Period. LC 29-23081. pap. 97.80 (ISBN 0-317-26311-0, 2155910). Bks Demand UMI.
Walsh, S. Zoe, et al. The Human Fetal & Neonatal Circulation: Function & Structure. (Illus.). 368p. 1974. photocopy ed. 36.75x (ISBN 0-398-02662-9). C C Thomas.

FIAT (AUTOMOBILE)

see Automobiles, Foreign–Types–Fiat

FIBER BUNDLES (MATHEMATICS)

Balachandran, A. P., et al. Gauge Symmetries & Fibre Bundles. (Lecture Notes in Physics: Vol. 188). 140p. 1983. pap. 9.00 (ISBN 0-387-12724-0). Springer Verlag.
Gunning, Robert C. Lectures on Vector Bundles Over Riemann Surfaces. (Mathematical Notes Ser.: No. 6). (Orig.). 1967. pap. 25.00 (ISBN 0-691-07998-6). Princeton U Pr.
Hirschowitz, A., ed. Vector Bundles & Differential Equations. (Progress in Math. Ser.: No. 7). 255p. 1980. pap. text ed. 20.00x (ISBN 0-8176-3022-8). Birkhauser.
Husemoller, D. Fibre Bundles. 2nd ed. LC 74-23157. (Graduate Texts in Mathematics: Vol. 20). (Illus.). 340p. 1975. Repr. of 1966 ed. 36.00 (ISBN 0-387-90103-5). Springer-Verlag.
Kamber, F. & Tondeur, P. Flat Manifolds. LC 68-55623. (Lecture Notes in Mathematics: Vol. 67). 1968. pap. 10.70 (ISBN 0-387-04237-7). Springer-Verlag.
Kamber, F. W. & Tondeur, P. Foliated Bundle & Characteristic Classes. (Lecture Notes in Mathematics: Vol. 493). xiii, 208p. 1975. pap. 16.00 (ISBN 0-387-07420-1). Springer-Verlag.
Koschorke, U. Vector Fields & Other Vector-Bundle Morphisms: A Singularity Approach. (Lecture Notes in Mathematics Ser.: Vol. 847). 304p. 1981. pap. 20.00 (ISBN 0-387-10572-7). Springer-Verlag.
Porter, Richard D. Introduction to Fibre Bundles. (Lecture Notes in Pure & Applied Math: Vol. 31). 1977. 35.00 (ISBN 0-8247-6626-1). Dekker.
Schwartz, Jacob T. Differential Geometry & Topology. (Notes on Mathematics & Its Applications Ser.). 180p. 1968. 47.75 (ISBN 0-677-01510-0). Gordon.
Stone, D. A. Stratified Polyhedra. LC 77-187427. (Lecture Notes in Mathematics: Vol. 252). 193p. 1972. pap. 10.00 (ISBN 0-387-05726-9). Springer-Verlag.
Yano, Kentaro & Ishihara, Shigeru. Tangent & Cotangent Bundles: Differential Geometry. LC 72-91438. (Pure & Applied Mathematics Ser.: 16). pap. 108.00 (ISBN 0-317-07841-0, 2055025). Bks Demand UMI.

FIBER OPTICS

Allan, W. B. Fibre Optics: Theory & Practice. LC 72-95066. (Optical Physics & Engineering Ser.). 247p. 1973. 42.50x (ISBN 0-306-30735-9, Plenum Pr). Plenum Pub.
Applications of Fiber Optics. 1984. 3 ring bdg. 250.00 (ISBN 0-317-20446-7). Optosonic Pr.
Arnaud, J. A. Beam & Fiber Optics. (Quantum Electronics Ser.). 1976. 76.50 (ISBN 0-12-063250-0). Acad Pr.
Baker, Donald. Fiber Optic Design & Application. 1985. text ed. 37.95 (ISBN 0-8359-1971-4). Reston.
Barnoski, Michael, ed. Fundamentals of Optical Fiber Communications. 2nd ed. LC 81-12883. 1981. 26.50 (ISBN 0-12-079151-X). Acad Pr.
Bendow, B. & Mitra, S. S., eds. Fiber Optics: Advances in Research & Development. 703p. 1979. 95.00x (ISBN 0-306-40167-3, Plenum Pr). Plenum Pub.
Bendow, Bernard & Mitra, Shashanka S., eds. Advances in Ceramics: Physics of Fiber Optics, Vol. 2. (Illus.). 1981. text ed. 50.00 (ISBN 0-916094-42-1); text ed. 30.00 student members. Am Ceramic.
Bodson, Dennis, ed. & frwd. by. Fiberoptics & Lightwave Communications Vocabulary. LC 80-26168. 156p. (Orig.). 1983. pap. text ed. 12.95 (ISBN 0-07-606706-8, R-030). McGraw.
Boyd, W. T. Fiber Optics Communications: Experiments & Projects. LC 82-50650. 224p. 1982. pap. 15.95 (ISBN 0-672-21834-8). Sams.
Business Communications Staff. Fiber Optics: G-044R. 1982. 975.00 (ISBN 0-89336-116-X). BCC.
--Material Requirements for Fiber Optics. 1985. 1750.00 (ISBN 0-89336-363-4, GB-073). BCC.
Centro Studi e Laboratori Telecomunicazioni. Optical Fiber Communication. (Illus.). 928p. 1981. 54.50 (ISBN 0-07-014882-1). McGraw.
Cheo, Peter K. Fiber Optics: Devices & Systems. (Illus.). 256p. 1985. text ed. 32.95 (ISBN 0-13-314204-3). P-H.
Cherin, Allen H. An Introduction to Optical Fibers. (McGraw-Hill Series in Electrical Engineering). (Illus.). 336p. 1982. text ed. 44.00 (ISBN 0-07-010703-3). McGraw.
Clarricoats, P. J., ed. Progress in Optical Communication, 1978-79. 1980. pap. 50.00 (ISBN 0-906048-32-X). Inst Elect Eng.
Design Handbook for Optical Fiber Systems. (User Manual & Handbook Ser.: Vol. II). 253p. 60.00 (ISBN 0-686-32956-2). Info Gatekeepers.
Elion, G. & Elion, H. Fiber Optics in Communications Systems. (Electro-Optics Ser.: Vol. 2). 1978. soft cover 65.00 (ISBN 0-8247-7132-X). Dekker.
European Conference on Optical Fibre Communication, 1st, London, 1975. Optical Fibre Communication: September 16-18, 1975. (Institution of Electrical Engineers Conference Publication Ser.: No. 132). pap. 56.00 (ISBN 0-317-10151-X, 2012127). Bks Demand UMI.
European Fiber Optics & Communications Exposition, Cologne, Federal Republic of Germany, 1981: Conference Program EFOC '81, Vols. 1 & 2. Date not set. Set. 125.00. Info Gatekeepers.
Ezekiel, S. & Arditty, H. J., eds. Fiber-Optic Rotation Sensors, Cambridge, MA: Proceedings, 1981. (Springer Ser. in Optical Sciences: Vol. 32). (Illus.). 440p. 1982. 37.00 (ISBN 0-387-11791-1). Springer-Verlag.
Fiber Optics & Communications Exposition, West, San Francisco, Calif., 1981: Conference Program. 1982. 125.00. Info Gatekeepers.
Fiber Optics Design Aid Package, 2 pts. (User Manual & Handbook Ser.: Vol. IV). 660p. Set. 150.00 (ISBN 0-686-32958-9). Info Gatekeepers.
Fiber Optics Directory. 1984. 50.00 (DIR 101). Market Res Co.
Fiber Optics Handbook & Buyers' Guide, 1979. 2nd ed. 20.00 (ISBN 0-686-32954-6). Info Gatekeepers.
Fiber Optics Handbook & Buyers Guide, 1980-1981. 3rd ed. 1982. pap. 45.00 (ISBN 0-686-32955-4). Info Gatekeepers.
Fiber Optics Handbook & Buyers Guide, 1983-84. 5th ed. 50.00. Info Gatekeepers.
Fiber Optics Handbook & Buyers' Guide, 1981-82. 4th ed. 45.00. Info Gatekeepers.
Fiber Optics Handbook & Market Guide 1978. 15.00 (ISBN 0-686-32953-8). Info Gatekeepers.
Fiber Optics in the Nuclear Environment. 25.00 (ISBN 0-686-32960-0). Info Gatekeepers.
Fiber Optics Markets in Germany. 1983. 75.00 (ISBN 0-317-11963-X). Info Gatekeepers.
Fiber Optics Operating Systems. 25.00 (ISBN 0-686-32963-5). Info Gatekeepers.
Fiber Optics Patent Directory, 1881-1979. LC 79-93150. 161p. 1980. 74.00x (ISBN 0-935714-01-4). Patent Data.
Fiber Optics System Components. 1984. 3 ring bdg. 225.00 (ISBN 0-317-20443-2). Optosonic Pr.
Fiber Optics Technology Transfer Book. 500.00 (ISBN 0-686-32965-1). Info Gatekeepers.
First European Fiber Optics & Communications Exposition: EFOC '80, Paris. 125.00 (ISBN 0-686-33024-2). Info Gatekeepers.
First Fiber Optics & Communications Exposition: FOC '78, Chicago, Ill. 125.00 (ISBN 0-686-33020-X). Info Gatekeepers.
Future Systems, Inc. Optical Fiber Communications: Current Systems & Future Developments. (Illus.). 135p. (Orig.). 1982. pap. 450.00x (ISBN 0-940520-47-8, F116). Monegon Ltd.
Future Trends in Fiber Optics Markets & Technology: Yearly Update. 225.00 (ISBN 0-686-33026-9). Info Gatekeepers.
Georgopoulos, Chris J. Fiber Optics & Optical Isolators. Price, Edward R., ed. LC 81-52618. (Illus.). 271p. 1982. text ed. 37.00 (ISBN 0-932263-21-6). White Consult.
Gloge, Detlef. Optical Fiber Technology. LC 75-23777. 1976. 36.35 (ISBN 0-87942-062-6, PC0588). Inst Electrical.
Glossary of Fiber Optics Terms. (Eng., Fr, Span. & Ger.). 35.00 (ISBN 0-686-32959-7). Info Gatekeepers.
Happey, F., ed. Fibre Science. 1978. Vol. 1. 75.00 (ISBN 0-12-323701-7). Acad Pr.
Heath Company Staff. Fiber Optics. (Illus.). 470p. 1983. looseleaf with experimental pts. 99.95 (ISBN 0-87119-069-9, EE-4201). Heathkit-Zenith Ed.
Hewlett-Packard. Optoelectronics-Fiber-Optics Applications Manual. 2nd ed. (Illus.). 448p. 1981. 39.50 (ISBN 0-07-028606-X). McGraw.
Hill, D. A. Fibre Optics. 176p. 1977. text ed. 29.50x (ISBN 0-220-66333-5, Pub. by Busn Bks England). Brookfield Pub Co.
Howes, M. J. & Morgan, D. V. Optical Fiber Communications: Devices, Circuits & Systems. LC 79-40512. (Wiley Series in Solid State Devices & Circuits). 304p. 1980. 64.95 (ISBN 0-471-27611-1, Pub. by Wiley-Interscience). Wiley.
Information Gatekeepers, Inc. The Sixth International Fiber Optics & Communications Exposition: FOC '82, Los Angeles, Calif. 1982. 125.00 (ISBN 0-686-38469-5). Info Gatekeepers.
The International Fiber Optics & Communications Exposition in Its Fourth Year: FOC '81 East, Cambridge, Mass. 125.00 (ISBN 0-686-33023-4). Info Gatekeepers.
International Resource Development Inc. Fiber Optic Markets. 184p. 1983. 985.00x (ISBN 0-88694-557-7). Intl Res Dev.
Jeunhomme, Luc B. Single-Mode Fiber Optics. 296p. 1983. 45.00 (ISBN 0-8247-7020-X). Dekker.
Kao, C. K. Optical Fiber Systems: Technology, Design & Applications. 1982. 33.50 (ISBN 0-07-033277-0). McGraw.
--Optical Fiber Technology II. LC 80-25665. 343p. 1981. 32.95x (ISBN 0-471-09169-3, Pub. by Wiley-Interscience); pap. 21.50x (ISBN 0-471-09171-5, Pub. by Wiley-Interscience). Wiley.
Kao, Charles K. Optical Fiber Technology, II. LC 80-25665. 352p. 1981. 34.25 (ISBN 0-87942-143-6, PC01388). Inst Electrical.
Keiser, Gerd. Optical Fiber Communications. (McGraw-Hill Ser. in Electrical Engineering). (Illus.). 336p. 1983. text ed. 44.00 (ISBN 0-07-033467-6). McGraw.
Keucken, John A. Fiberoptics. (Illus.). 363p. 1980. pap. 13.95 (ISBN 0-8306-1236-X, 1236). TAB Bks.
Lacy, Edward A. Fiber Optics. (Illus.). 256p. 1982. 28.95 (ISBN 0-13-314278-7). P-H.
Li, Tingye, ed. Advances in Optical-Fiber Communications, Vol. 1. 1985. 54.00 (ISBN 0-12-447301-6). Acad Pr.
Marcuse, Dietrich. Theory of Dielectric Optical Waveguides. (Quantum Electronics Ser.). 1974. 59.50 (ISBN 0-12-470950-8). Acad Pr.
Market Intelligence Research Company Staff. Fiber Optic Sensor Markets II: 1984-1994. 155p. pap. text ed. 695.00 (ISBN 0-317-19663-4). Market Res Co.
Military Fiber Optics Market (U.S.) 1985. write for info. (ISBN 0-86621-351-1, A1435). Frost & Sullivan.

Advanced Fibrous Reinforced Composites Symposium, San Diego, 9-11 November 1966: Proceedings. (Science of Advanced Materials & Process Engineering Ser., Vol. 10). 25.00 (ISBN 0-938994-10-7). Soc Adv Material.

American Society for Testing & Materials. Symposium on Standards for Filament-Wound Reinforced Plastics. LC 62-22246. (American Society for Testing & Materials Ser.: Special Technical Publication, No. 327). pap. 84.00 (ISBN 0-317-10780-1, 2000120). Bks Demand UMI.

Analysis of the Test Methods for High Modulus Fibers & Composites - STP 521. 416p. 1973. 30.75 (ISBN 0-8031-0701-3, 04-521000-33). ASTM.

Fatigue of Fibrous Composite Materials STP 723. 311p. 1981. 30.00 (ISBN 0-8031-0719-6, 04-723000-33). ASTM.

Fatigue of Filamentary Composite Materials- STP 636. 282p. 1977. 26.00 (ISBN 0-8031-0347-6, 04-636000-33). ASTM.

Fiber Reinforced Composites. 274p. 1982. 78.00 (ISBN 0-317-12674-1). T-C Pubns CA.

Fibro-Cement Composites: A Report of the Meeting. pap. 1.50 (ISBN 0-686-94611-1, UN71/2B1, UN). Unipub.

Galasso, F. S. High Modulus Fibers & Composites. 126p. 1970. 45.25 (ISBN 0-677-02550-5). Gordon.

Gill, R. M. Carbon Fibres in Composite Materials. (Illus.). 207p. 1972. 22.50x (ISBN 0-8448-0642-0). Crane-Russak Co.

Institution of Civil Engineers Staff, ed. Fibre Reinforced Materials: Design & Engineering Applications. 251p. 1977. 55.50x (ISBN 0-7277-0051-0). Am Soc Civil Eng.

Lenoe, Edward M., et al, eds. Fibrous Composites in Structural Design. LC 79-28668. 888p. 1980. 110.00x (ISBN 0-306-40354-4, Plenum Pr). Plenum Pub.

Nachmias, Vivianne T. Microfilaments. Head, J. J., ed. LC 82-73999. (Carolina Biology Readers Ser.). (Illus.). 16p. 1984. pap. 1.60 (ISBN 0-89278-330-3, 45-9730). Carolina Biological.

Rauch, H. W., et al. Ceramic Fibers & Fibrous Composite Materials. (Refractory Materials Ser: Vol. 3). 1968. 69.50 (ISBN 0-12-582850-0). Acad Pr.

Rosato, D. V. & Grove, C. S., Jr. Filament Winding: Its Development, Manufacture, Applications, & Design. LC 64-14998. (Polymer Engineering & Technology Ser.). pap. 92.80 (ISBN 0-317-28942-X, 2055989). Bks Demand UMI.

Society For Experimental Stress Analysis. Experimental Mechanics of Fiber Reinforced Composite Materials. (Illus.). 160p. 1982. 28.95 (ISBN 0-13-295196-7). P-H.

FIELD BIOLOGY

see Biology–Field Work

FIELD CAMERAS

see View Cameras

FIELD CROPS

see also Field Experiments; Forage Plants; Grain; Horticulture; Irrigation Farming; Tropical Crops; also names of specific crops, e.g. Cotton, Hay

Analysis of an FAO Survey of Post-Harvest Crop Losses in Developing Countries. (Illus.). 1978. pap. 13.00 (ISBN 0-685-86537-1, F719, FAO). Unipub.

Babakina, V. S., ed. Grain & Pulse Crops. 255p. 1981. 60.00x (ISBN 0-686-76641-5, Pub. by Oxford & IBH India). State Mutual Bk.

Balint, Andor. Physiological Genetics of Agricultural Crops. 167p. 15.00 (ISBN 9-63053-288-3, 991000439). Heyden.

Bishop, Douglas D. Working in Plant Science. Amberson, Max L. & Chapman, Stephen, eds. (Illus.). 1978. pap. text ed. 13.72 (ISBN 0-07-000835-3). McGraw.

Boone, L. V, et al. Producing Farm Crops. 3rd ed. 1981. 19.00 (ISBN 0-8134-2151-9); text ed. 14.25x (2151). Interstate.

Brickbauer, Elwood A. & Mortenson, William P. Approved Practices in Crop Production. 2nd ed. LC 77-89853. (Illus.). 396p. 1978. 18.60 (ISBN 0-8134-1975-1, 1975); text ed. 13.95x. Interstate.

Burger, A. W. Laboratory Exercises in Field Crop Science. 1977. spiral bdg. 8.60x (ISBN 0-87563-031-6). Stipes.

Carter, Jack, ed. Sunflower Science & Technology. 1978. 17.50 (ISBN 0-89118-054-0). Am Soc Agron.

Chapman, Stephen R. & Carter, Lark P. Crop Production: Principles & Practices. LC 75-40318. (Illus.). 566p. 1976. text ed. 31.95 (ISBN 0-7167-0581-8). W H Freeman.

China: Multiple Cropping & Related Crop Production Technology: Report of an FAO-UNDP Study Tour to the People's Republic of China, June 25 - July 22, 1979. (Plant Production & Protection Papers: No. 22). 66p. 1980. pap. 11.75 (ISBN 92-5-100977-5, F2108, FAO). Unipub.

Crop Calendars. (Plant Production & Protection Papers: No. 12). (Trilingual.). 131p. 1978. pap. 9.50 (ISBN 92-5-000684-5, F1579, FAO). Unipub.

Crop Farming. (Better Farming Ser.: No. 7). 29p. 1976. pap. 5.00 (ISBN 92-5-100146-4, F65, FAO). Unipub.

Delorit, Richard, et al. Crop Production. 4th ed. 1973. text ed. 31.52 (ISBN 0-13-194761-3). P-H.

Eastin, J. D., ed. Physiological Aspects of Crop Yield. (Illus.). 1969. 10.00 (ISBN 0-89118-004-4). Am Soc Agron.

Ennes, W. B., Jr., ed. Introduction to Crop Protection. (Foundation for Modern Crop Service Ser.: Vol. 2). (Illus.). 1979. 20.00 (ISBN 0-89118-033-8). Am Soc Agron.

Free, John B. Insect Pollination of Crops. 1971. 84.00 (ISBN 0-12-266650-X). Acad Pr.

Harlan, Jack R. Crops & Man. (Foundations for Modern Crop Science Ser.: Vol. 1). (Illus.). 1975. 11.25 (ISBN 0-89118-032-X). Am Soc Agron.

Harper, F. Principles of Arable Crop Production. 336p. (Orig.). 1983. pap. text ed. 21.95x (ISBN 0-246-11741-9, Pub. by Granada England). Brookfield Pub Co.

Hartley, W. Checklist of Economic Plants in Australia. 214p. 1979. pap. 9.00 (ISBN 0-643-02551-0, C004, CSIRO). Unipub.

Hoveland, C. S., ed. Crop Quality, Storage, & Utilization. (Foundations for Modern Crop Science Ser.: Vol. 3). (Illus.). 1980. 15.00 (ISBN 0-89118-035-4). Am Soc Agron.

Janick, Jules, et al. Plant Science: An Introduction to World Crops. 3rd ed. LC 81-4897. (Illus.). 868p. 1981. text ed. 30.95 (ISBN 0-7167-1261-X). W H Freeman.

Jones, F. G. & Jones, M. G. Pests of Field Crops. 3rd ed. 456p. 1984. pap. text ed. 64.50 (ISBN 0-7131-2881-X). E Arnold.

Jung, Gerald A., ed. Crop Tolerance to Suboptimal Land Conditions. 11.00 (ISBN 0-89118-051-6). Am Soc Agron.

Langer, R. H. & Hill, G. D. Agricultural Plants. LC 80-41536. (Illus.). 300p. 1982. 44.50 (ISBN 0-521-22450-0); pap. 17.95 (ISBN 0-521-29506-8). Cambridge U Pr.

Lieberman, Morris, ed. Post-Harvest Physiology & Crop Preservation. (NATO ASI Series A, Life Sciences: Vol. 46). 578p. 1983. 67.50x (ISBN 0-306-40984-4, Plenum Pr). Plenum Pub.

Lockhart, J. A. & Wiseman, A. J. Introduction to Crop Husbandry. 5th ed. (Illus.). 300p. 1983. 40.00 (ISBN 0-08-029793-5); pap. 16.00 (ISBN 0-08-029792-7). Pergamon.

Martin, John H., et al. Principles of Field Crop Production. 3rd ed. (Illus.). 1056p. 1976. text ed. write for info. (ISBN 0-02-376720-0). Macmillan.

Moncur, M. W. Floral Initiation in Field Crops: An Atlas of Scanning Electron Micrographs. 136p. 1981. pap. 18.00 (ISBN 0-643-02836-6, C062, CSIRO). Unipub.

Nash, M. J. Crop Conservation & Storage: In Cool Temperate Climates. 2nd ed. LC 84-9370. (Illus.). 260p. 1985. 35.00 (ISBN 0-08-029809-5). Pergamon.

Nyvall, Robert F. Field Crop Diseases Handbook. (Illus.). 1979. pap. text ed. 29.50 (ISBN 0-87055-344-5). AVI.

Oschwald, W. R., ed. Crop Residue Management Systems. 1978. pap. 9.00 (ISBN 0-89118-050-8). Am Soc Agron.

Papendick, R. I., et al, eds. Multiple Cropping. (Illus.). 378p. 1976. pap. 9.00 (ISBN 0-89118-045-1). Am Soc Agron.

Poehlam, J. M. & Borthakur, D. N. Breeding Asian Field Crops. 504p. 1981. 30.00x (ISBN 0-686-76626-1, Pub by Oxford & IBH India). State Mutual Bk.

Poehlman, John M. Breeding Field Crops. 2nd ed. (Illus.). 1979. text ed. 29.50 (ISBN 0-87055-328-3). AVI.

Prately, J. E. Principles of Field Crop Production. 1979. (Pub. by Sydney U Pr); pap. 28.00x (ISBN 0-424-00058-X, Pub. by Sydney U Pr). Intl Spec Bk.

Rae, Allan N. Crop Management Economics. 540p. 1981. pap. 24.00x (ISBN 0-246-11808-3, Pub. by Granada England). Sheridan.

Rechcigl, Miloslav, Jr. CRC Handbook of Agricultural Productivity, Vol. I: Plant Productivity. 464p. 1982. 81.00 (ISBN 0-8493-3961-8). CRC Pr.

Shaw, N. H. & Bryan, W. W. Tropical Pasture Research: Principles & Methods. 454p. 1976. 90.00x (ISBN 0-85198-358-8, Pub. by CAB Bks England). State Mutual Bk.

Simmonds, N. W. Principles of Crop Improvement. LC 78-40726. (Illus.). 1979. pap. text ed. 22.00x (ISBN 0-582-44630-9). Longman.

Simmonds, N. W., ed. Evolution of Crop Plants. LC 75-32563. (Illus.). 360p. 1976. pap. text ed. 20.95x (ISBN 0-582-44496-9). Longman.

Sinha. Field Crop Production in Tropical Africa. Date not set. price not set (ISBN 0-471-90102-4). Wiley.

Wang, Jaw-Kai, ed. Taro: A Review of "Colocasia Esculenta" & Its Potentials. LC 82-21903. (Illus.). 418p. 1983. text ed. 35.00x (ISBN 0-8248-0841-X). UH Pr.

Willis, Harold L. How to Grow Top Quality Corn. (Illus.). 58p. (Orig.). 1984. pap. 5.25 (ISBN 0-912311-02-9). H L Willis.

Wilson, Harold K. & Larson, Alvin H. Identification & Judging Crops, Weeds, Diseases. (Illus.). 65p. 1940. text ed. 3.25x spiral (ISBN 0-8134-0045-7, 45). Interstate.

Wilson, J. R., ed. Plant Relations in Pastures. 425p. 1978. 99.00x (ISBN 0-643-00264-2, Pub. by CAB Bks England). State Mutual Bk.

FIELD EFFECT TRANSISTORS

Craig, George B. & Sesnic, Steve S. Investigations of Field Effect Transistors at Cryogenic Temperatures. LC 75-139809. 85p. 1970. 19.00 (ISBN 0-403-04491-X). Scholarly.

Dascalu, D. Electronic Processes in Unipolar Solid State Devices. 1977. 33.00 (ISBN 0-9961000-3-2, Pub. by Abacus England). Heyden.

Lenk, John D. Handbook of Electronic Components & Circuits. LC 73-11038. (Illus.). 224p. 1973. ref. ed. 26.95 (ISBN 0-13-377283-7). P-H.

Oxner, Ed. Power FETs & Their Applications. (Illus.). 336p. 1982. 31.95 (ISBN 0-13-686923-8). P-H.

Richman, Paul. MOS Field-Effect Transistors & Integrated Circuits. LC 73-9892. 259p. 1973. 41.50 (ISBN 0-471-72030-5, Pub. by Wiley-Interscience). Wiley.

FIELD EMISSION

see also Field-Ion Microscope

Gomer, Robert. Field Emission & Field Ionization. LC 60-15237. (Harvard Monographs in Applied Science: No. 9). (Illus.). pap. 51.80 (ISBN 0-317-09155-7, 2002823). Bks Demand UMI.

Modinos, A. Field, Thermionic, & Secondary Electron Emission Spectroscopy. 388p. 1984. 55.00x (ISBN 0-306-41321-3, Plenum Pr). Plenum Pub.

FIELD EXPERIMENTS

Alberda, Th. Production & Water Use of Several Food & Fodder Crops Under Irrigation in the Desert Area of Southwestern Peru. (Agricultural Research Reports: No. 928). (Illus.). 50p. 1985. pap. 7.50 (ISBN 90-220-0869-X, PDC291, Pudoc). Unipub.

Bofinger, V. J. & Wheeler, J. L. Developments in Field Experiment Design & Analysis: Proceedings of Symposium held at the University of New England, Armidale, New South Wales, 3-7 September, 1973. 196p. 1975. 42.00x (ISBN 0-85198-333-2, Pub. by CAB Bks England). State Mutual Bk.

Boone, F. R., ed. Experiences with Three Tillage Systems on a Marine Loam Soil II: 1976-1979: A Joint Study of the Westmaas Research Group on New Tillage Systems, Carried Out on the Westmaas Experimental Husbandry Farm. (Agricultural Research Reports: No. 925). (Illus.). 263p. 1985. pap. 28.00 (ISBN 90-220-0855-X, PDC280, Pudoc). Unipub.

Pearce, S. C. Field Experiments with Fruit Tree & other Perennial Plants. 182p. 1976. 89.00x (ISBN 0-85198-354-5, Pub. by CAB Bks England). State Mutual Bk.

Seidensticker, John. Managing Elephant Depredation in Agricultural & Forestry Projects. 50p. 3.00 (ISBN 0-318-02824-7, BK0297). World Bank.

FIELD GEOLOGY

see also Geology–Field Work

Exlog. Field Geologist's Training Guide. (The Exlog Series of Petroleum Geology & Engineering Handbooks). (Illus.). 298p. 1985. text ed. 34.00 (ISBN 0-317-14155-4). Intl Human Res.

FIELD-ION MICROSCOPE

Hren, John J. & Ranganathan, S., eds. Field-Ion Microscopy. LC 68-14853. 244p. 1968. 32.50x (ISBN 0-306-30323-X, Plenum Pr). Plenum Pub.

Murr, Lawerence E. Electron & Ion Microscopy & Microanalysis: Principles & Applications. (Optical Engineering Ser.: Vol. 1). (Illus.). 816p. 1982. 65.00 (ISBN 0-8247-1553-5). Dekker.

Wagner, Richard. Field-Ion Microscopy in Materials Science. (Crystals Ser.: Vol. 6). (Illus.). 120p. 1982. 40.00 (ISBN 0-387-11712-1). Springer-Verlag.

FIELD PLOT TECHNIQUE

see Field Experiments

FIELD TESTS

see Field Experiments

FIELD THEORIES, UNIFIED

see Unified Field Theories

FIELD THEORY (PHYSICS)

see also Continuum Mechanics; Electromagnetic Fields; Electromagnetic Theory; Gravitation; Magnetic Fields; Quantum Field Theory; Unified Field Theories

Adamson, Iain T. An Introduction to Field Theory. 2nd ed. LC 82-1164. 192p. 1982. 22.95 (ISBN 0-521-24388-2); pap. 11.95 (ISBN 0-521-28658-1). Cambridge U Pr.

Aly, H. H. Lectures on Particles & Fields. 385p. 1970. 85.75 (ISBN 0-677-13740-0). Gordon.

Amit, D. J. Field Theory: The Renormalization Group & Critical Phenomena. 2nd ed. 400p. 1984. 56.00x (ISBN 9971-966-10-7, Pub. by World Sci Singapore); pap. 26.00x (ISBN 9971-966-11-5). Taylor & Francis.

Baden-Fuller, A. J. Engineering Field Theory. 272p. 1973. pap. text ed. 18.00 (ISBN 0-08-017034-X). Pergamon.

--Engineering Field Theory: Text & Examples, 2 vols. pap. 19.50 (ISBN 0-08-029320-4). Pergamon.

Balian, R. & Zinn-Justin, J., eds. Methods in Field Theory: Les Houches Session XXVIII. xx, 386p. 1981. pap. 21.00x (ISBN 9971-83-015-9, Pub. by World Sci Singapore). Taylor & Francis.

Budak, B. M. & Fomin, S. V. Multiple Integrals, Field Theory & Series. 640p. 1978. 18.00 (ISBN 0-8285-2096-8, Pub. by Mir Pubs USSR). Imported Pubns.

Caswell, W. E. & Snow, G. A. Particles & Fields, APS-DPF, University of Maryland, 1982: AIP Conference Proceedings No. 98, Particles & Fields Subseries, 29th. LC 83-70807. 413p. 1983. lib. bdg. 37.75 (ISBN 0-88318-197-5). Am Inst Physics.

Coulter, C. A. & Shatas, R. A., eds. Topics in Fields & Solids. 228p. 1968. 59.25 (ISBN 0-677-12740-5). Gordon.

De Leon, M. & Rodrigues, P. R. Generalized Classical Mechanics & Field Theory: A Geometrical Approach of Lagrangian & Hamiltonian Formalisms Involving Higher Order Derivatives. (Mathematics Studies: Vol. 112). 290p. 1985. 44.50 (ISBN 0-444-87753-3, North Holland). Elsevier.

Dittrich, W., ed. Recent Developments in Particle & Field Theory. 1979. casebound 47.50 (ISBN 0-9940012-0-7, Pub. by Vieweg & Sohn Germany). Heyden.

Garczynski, W., ed. Gauge Field Theories: Theoretical Studies & Computer Simulations. (Studies in High Energy Physics: Vol. 4). 800p. 1984. 67.50 (ISBN 3-7186-0121-4). Harwood Academic.

Garrido, L., ed. Applications of Field Theory to Statistical Mechanics. (Lecture Notes in Physics Ser.: Vol. 216). viii, 352p. 1985. pap. 23.70 (ISBN 0-387-13911-7). Springer-Verlag.

Hilbers, C. W. & MacLean, C. N M R of Molecules Oriented in Electric Fields. Bd. with N M R & Relaxation of Molecules Absorbed on Solids. Pfeifer, H. (N M R Basic Principles & Progress, Vol. 7). (Illus.). 1972. 38.00 (ISBN 0-387-05687-4). Springer-Verlag.

Iwasawa, Kenkichi. Local Classfield Theory. Miyahara, Katsumi, tr. (Oxford Mathematical Monographs). 1982. 35.00x (ISBN 0-19-853356-X). Oxford U Pr.

Kemmer, N. Vector Analysis. LC 75-36025. (Illus.). 230p. 1977. 59.50 (ISBN 0-521-21158-1); pap. 18.95x (ISBN 0-521-29064-3). Cambridge U Pr.

Kijowski, J. & Tulczyjew, W. M. A Symplectic Framework for Field Theories. (Lecture Notes in Physics: Vol. 107). 1979. pap. 19.00 (ISBN 0-387-09538-1). Springer-Verlag.

Klein, L. Dispersion Relations & the Abstract Approach to Field Theory. (International Science Review Ser.). 286p. 1961. pap. 55.75 (ISBN 0-677-00420-6). Gordon.

Lannutti, J. E. & Williams, P. K., eds. Current Trends in the Theory of Fields: Tallahassee, 1979. (AIP Conference Proceedings: No. 48). (Illus.). 1978. lib. bdg. 16.25 (ISBN 0-88318-147-9). Am Inst Physics.

Lee, T. D., ed. Particle Physics & Introduction to Field Theory. (Concepts in Contemporary Physics Ser.: Vol. 1). 886p. 1981. 66.00 (ISBN 3-7186-0032-3); pap. 22.00 (ISBN 3-7186-0033-1). Harwood Academic.

Lodge, Arthur S. Body Tensor Fields in Continuum Mechanics. 1975. 71.50 (ISBN 0-12-454950-0). Acad Pr.

Lopes, J. Leite. Gauge Field Theories: An Introduction. (Illus.). 450p. 1981. 39.00 (ISBN 0-08-026501-4). Pergamon.

Moon, P. & Spencer, D. E. Field Theory Handbook: Including Coordinate Systems, Differential Equations & Their Solutions. 2nd ed. LC 77-178288. (Illus.). viii, 236p. 1971. 57.90 (ISBN 0-387-02732-7). Springer-Verlag.

Nishijima, K. Fields & Particles: Field Theory & Dispersion Relations. 4th ed. 1981. 30.95 (ISBN 0-8053-7397-7). Benjamin-Cummings.

--Fields & Particles: Field Theory & Dispersion Relations. (Lecture Notes & Supplements in Physics: No. 11). 1969. pap. text ed. 30.95 (ISBN 0-8053-7397-7). Benjamin-Cummings.

Parisi, Giorgio. Modern Statistical Mechanics & Field Theory. 300p. 1986. text ed. 29.95x (ISBN 0-8053-6951-1). Benjamin-Cummings.

Perlmutter, Arnold, ed. Field Theory in Elementary Particles. (Studies in the Natural Sciences: Vol. 19). 479p. 1983. 72.50x (ISBN 0-306-41345-0, Plenum Pr). Plenum Pub.

Ramond, P. Field Theory: A Modern Primer. 1981. 45.95 (ISBN 0-8053-7892-8); pap. 23.95 (ISBN 0-8053-7893-6). Benjamin-Cummings.

Schroedinger. Collected Papers, 4 vols. Incl. Vol. 1. Contributions to Statistical Mechanics; Vol. 2. Contributions to Field Theory; Vol. 3. Contributions to Quantum Theory; Vol. 4. General Scientific & Popular Papers. 1984. Set. 175.00 (ISBN 0-9904001-7-4, Pub. by Vieweg & Sohn Germany). Heyden.

Sedov, L., ed. Macroscopic Theories of Matter & Fields: A Thermodynamic Approach. Yankovsky, Eusene, tr. 263p. 1983. pap. 7.95 (ISBN 0-8285-2742-3, Pub. by Mir Pubs USSR). Imported Pubns.

Society for Industrial & Applied Mathematics-American Mathematical Society Symposia-N.C.-April, 1968. Numerical Solution of Field Problems in Continuum Physics: Proceedings. Birkhoff, G. & Varga, R. S., eds. LC 75-92659. (SIAM-AMS Proceedings: Vol. 2). 1970. 27.00 (ISBN 0-8218-1321-8, SIAMS-2). Am Math.

Turchi, Peter J., ed. Megagauss Physics & Technology. LC 80-16385. 697p. 1980. 95.00x (ISBN 0-306-40461-3, Plenum Pr). Plenum Pub.

Urban, P., ed. Field Theory & Strong Interactions: Proceedings. (Acta Physica Austriaca Supplementum Ser.: No. 22). (Illus.). 815p. 1980. 98.00 (ISBN 0-387-81615-1). Springer-Verlag.

Ushenko, Andrew P. The Field Theory of Meaning. LC 58-5910. 1958. pap. 45.50 (ISBN 0-317-08174-8, 2055658). Bks Demand UMI.

Washington, L. C. Introduction to Cyclotomic Fields. (Graduate Texts in Mathematics Ser.: Vol. 83). 389p. 1982. 42.00 (ISBN 0-387-90622-3). Springer-Verlag.

White, Carol. Energy Potential: Toward a New Electromagnetic Field Theory. Cleary, James, tr. 305p. 1978. pap. 7.95 (ISBN 0-918388-04-X, QC665.E4W45, Univ Edns). New Benjamin.

Williams, L. Pearce. The Origins of Field Theory. LC 80-5710. 160p. 1980. lib. bdg. 20.00 (ISBN 0-8191-1175-9); pap. text ed. 8.75 (ISBN 0-8191-1176-7). U Pr of Amer.

Zuber, J & Stora, R. Recent Advances in Field Theory & Statistical Mechanics: Les Houches, Vol. 39. 1984. 166.75 (ISBN 0-444-86675-2). Elsevier.

FIELD THEORY, QUANTIZED
see Quantum Field Theory

FIELD WORK (BIOLOGY)
see Biology–Field Work

FIELD WORK (GEOLOGY)
see Geology–Field Work

FIELDS, ALGEBRAIC
see also Algebra, Differential; Algebraic Number Theory; Ideals (Algebra); Modular Fields; Numbers, Theory of; Quaternions; Rings (Algebra)

Abhyankar, S. Ramification Theoretic Methods in Algebraic Geometry. (Annals of Mathematics Studies: No. 43). (Orig.). 1959. 17.50 (ISBN 0-691-08023-2, AM43). Princeton U Pr.

Bhattacharya, P. B. & Jain, S. K. First Course in Rings, Fields & Vector Spaces. 238p. 1977. cloth 14.95x (ISBN 0-470-99047-3, 76-55303). Halsted Pr.

Cohn, P. M. Skew Field Constructions. LC 76-46854. (London Mathematical Society Lecture Note Series: No. 27). (Illus.). 1977. limp bdg. 32.50x (ISBN 0-521-21497-1). Cambridge U Pr.

Connor, P. E. & Perils, R. A Survey of Trace Forms of Algebraic Number Fields. (Lecture Notes on Pure Mathematics: Vol. 2). 325p. 1984. 35.00x (ISBN 9971-966-04-2, Pub. by World Sci Singapore); pap. 19.00x (ISBN 9971-966-05-0, Pub. by World Sci Singapore). Taylor & Francis.

Curtis, Charles W. & Reiner, Irving. Representation Theory of Finite Groups & Associative Algebras. LC 62-16994. (Pure & Applied Mathematics Ser.). 685p. 1962. 69.50 (ISBN 0-470-18975-4, Pub. by Wiley-Interscience). Wiley.

Deuring, M. Lectures on the Theory of Algebraic Functions of One Variable. LC 72-97679. (Lecture Notes in Mathematics: Vol. 314). 151p. 1973. pap. 12.00 (ISBN 0-387-06152-5). Springer-Verlag.

Endler, O. Valuation Theory. LC 72-92285. (Universitext). xii, 243p. 1972. pap. 18.50 (ISBN 0-387-06070-7). Springer-Verlag.

Fritz, J., et al. Random Fields, 2 vols. (Colloquia Mathematica Ser.: Vol. 27). 1112p. 1982. Set. 170.25 (ISBN 0-444-85441-X, North-Holland). Elsevier.

Frohlich, A. Central Extensions, Galois Groups, & Ideal Class Groups of Numbers Fields. LC 83-19685. (Contemporary Mathematics Ser.: Vol. 24). 86p. 1983. pap. 17.00 (ISBN 0-8218-5022-9). Am Math.

Frohlich, A., ed. Algebraic Number Field: L Functions & Galois Properties. 1977. 96.00 (ISBN 0-12-268960-7). Acad Pr.

Gerritzen, L. & Van Der Put, M. Schottky Groups & Mumford Curves. (Lecture Notes in Mathematics: Vol. 817). 317p. 1980. pap. 23.00 (ISBN 0-387-10229-9). Springer-Verlag.

Goldman, T. & Neito, M. M., eds. Proceedings of Nineteen Eighty-Four Meeting of the Division of Particles & Fields, American Physical Society. 600p. 1985. 67.00 (ISBN 0-317-27180-6). Taylor & Francis.

Hecke, E. Lectures on the Theory of Algebraic Numbers. (Graduate Texts in Mathematics Ser.: Vol. 77). 256p. 1981. 43.00 (ISBN 0-387-90595-2). Springer-Verlag.

Hecke, Erich. Algebraische Zahlen. 2nd ed. LC 50-3732. (Ger). 1970. 12.95 (ISBN 0-8284-0046-6). Chelsea Pub.

Hsu, D. F. Cyclic Neofields & Combinatorial Designs. (Lecture Notes in Mathematics Ser.: Vol. 824). (Illus.). 230p. 1980. pap. 17.00 (ISBN 0-387-10243-4). Springer-Verlag.

Kaplansky, Irving. Fields & Rings. rev. 2nd ed. LC 72-78251. (Chicago Lectures in Mathematics Ser). 224p. 1972. text ed. 12.50x (ISBN 0-226-42450-2); pap. text ed. 9.00x (ISBN 0-226-42451-0). U of Chicago Pr.

Landau, Edmund. Algebraische Zahlen. 2nd ed. (Ger). 9.95 (ISBN 0-8284-0062-8). Chelsea Pub.

Langlands, R. Base Change for GL (2) LC 79-28820. (Annals of Mathematics Studies: No. 96). 225p. 1980. 27.00x (ISBN 0-691-08263-4); pap. 12.00 (ISBN 0-691-08272-3). Princeton U Pr.

Laska, Michael. Elliptic Curves over Number Fields With Prescribed Reduction Type. 4th ed. (Aspects of Mathematics Ser.). 214p. (Orig.). 1983. pap. 15.00 (ISBN 0-9904000-0-X, Pub. by Vieweg & Sohn Germany). Heyden.

Linnik, Yu V. Ergodic Properties of Algebraic Fields. (Ergebnisse der Mathematik und Ihrer Grenzgebiete: Vol. 45). 1968. 33.00 (ISBN 0-387-04101-X). Springer-Verlag.

McCarthy, Paul J. Algebraic Extensions of Fields. 2nd ed. LC 75-41499. ix, 166p. 1976. 12.00 (ISBN 0-8284-1284-7). Chelsea Pub.

Marcus, D. A. Number Fields (Universitext) LC 77-21467. 1977. text ed. 23.00 (ISBN 0-387-90279-1). Springer-Verlag.

Meyer, R. M. Essential Mathematics for Applied Fields. (Universitets). (Illus.). 555p. 1979. pap. 23.00 (ISBN 0-387-90450-6). Springer-Verlag.

Nagata, Masayoshi. Field Theory. (Pure & Applied Mathematics Ser.: Vol. 40). 1977. 49.75 (ISBN 0-8247-6466-8). Dekker.

Reiner, I. Maximal Orders. (London Mathematical Society Monographs). 1975. 70.00 (ISBN 0-12-586650-X). Acad Pr.

Schilling, O. F. Theory of Valuations. LC 50-12178. (Mathematical Surveys Ser.: No. 4). 253p. 1982. pap. 35.00 (ISBN 0-8218-1504-0, SURV-4). Am Math.

Schofield, A. H. Representations of Rings over Skew Fields. (London Mathematical Society Lecture Note Ser.: No. 92). (Illus.). 240p. 1985. pap. 27.95 (ISBN 0-521-27853-8). Cambridge U Pr.

Secondary School Mathematics Curriculum Improvement Study. Algebraic Structures, Extensions, & Homomorphisms. LC 73-154476. (Unified Modern Mathematics Ser; Course 6, Bklet. C). pap. 22.00 (ISBN 0-317-29983-2, 2051821). Bks Demand UMI.

Stolarsky, Kenneth B. Algebraic Numbers & Diophantine Approximation. (Pure & Applied Mathematics Ser.: Vol. 26). 320p. 1974. 55.00 (ISBN 0-8247-6102-2). Dekker.

Taibleson, M. H. Fourier Analysis on Local Fields. LC 74-32047. (Mathematical Notes Ser.: No. 15). 308p. 1977. 27.00 (ISBN 0-691-08165-4). Princeton U Pr.

Weil, A. Dirichlet Series & Automorphic Forms. LC 72-151320. (Lecture Notes in Mathematics: Vol. 189). 1971. pap. 15.00 (ISBN 0-387-05382-4). Springer-Verlag.

Winter, D. J. The Structure of Fields. LC 73-21824. (Graduate Texts in Mathematics Ser.: Vol. 16). (Illus.). 320p. 1974. 28.00 (ISBN 0-387-90074-8). Springer-Verlag.

FIELDS, ELECTROMAGNETIC
see Electromagnetic Fields

FIGHTER-BOMBER SABRES
see Sabre (Jet Fighter Planes)

FIGHTER PLANES
see also Corsair (Fighter Planes); Heinkel (Fighter Planes); Mustang (Fighter Planes); P-Forty (Fighter Planes); Pfeil (Fighter Planes); Skyraider (Fighter Planes); Spitfire (Fighter Planes); Thunderbolt (Fighter Planes)

A-Seven Corsair II in Action. (Aircraft in Action Ser.). (Illus.). 1984. pap. 4.95 (ISBN 0-89747-021-4, 1022). Squad Sig Pubns.

A-Ten Warthog in Action. (Aircraft in Action Ser.). (Illus.). 50p. 1984. pap. 4.95 (ISBN 0-89747-122-9, 1049). Squad Sig Pubns.

A-26 Invader in Action. (Aircraft in Action Ser.). (Illus.). 1984. pap. 4.95 (ISBN 0-89747-093-1, 1037). Squad Sig Pubns.

Aeronautical Staff of Aero Publishers, et al. Boeing P12, F4B. LC 66-17554. (Aero Ser.: Vol. 5). 1966. pap. 3.95 (ISBN 0-8168-0516-4). Aero.

Aeronautical Staff of Aero Publishers. Nakajima KI-84. LC 65-24308. (Aero Ser: Vol. 2). (Illus.). 1965. pap. 3.95 (ISBN 0-8168-0504-0). Aero.

Albatros Fighters in Action. (Aircraft in Action Ser.). (Illus.). 50p. 1984. pap. 4.95 (ISBN 0-89747-115-6, 1046). Squad Sig Pubns.

Allied Fighters of World War II. (Illus.). 9.95 (ISBN 0-668-05228-7). Arco.

Anderton, David. Republic F-105 Thunderchief. (Illus.). 200p. 1983. 19.95 (ISBN 0-85045-530-8, Pub. by Osprey England). Motorbooks Intl.

Arnold, Rhodes. The Republic F-Eighty-Four: From "Lead Sled" to "Super Hawg". (Illus.). 128p. pap. 12.95 cancelled (ISBN 0-89404-054-5). Aztex.

B-26 Marauder in Action. (Illus.). 50p. 1984. pap. 4.95 (ISBN 0-89747-119-9, 1050). Squad Sig Pubns.

B-29 Superfortress in Action. (Aircraft in Action Ser.). (Illus.). 1984. pap. 4.95 (ISBN 0-89747-030-3, 1031). Squad Sig Pubns.

B-52 Two in Action. (Aircraft in Action Ser.). (Illus.). 1984. pap. 4.95 (ISBN 0-89747-022-2, 1023). Squad Sig Pubns.

Birdsall, Steve. B-24 in Action. (Aircraft in Action Ser.). (Illus.). 50p. 1984. pap. 4.95 (ISBN 0-89747-020-6, 1021). Squad Sig Pubns.

Bowers, Peter M. Forgotten Fighters & Experimental Aircraft of the U. S. Army, 1918-1941. LC 70-124505. (Illus.). 80p. (Orig.). 1971. pap. 3.95 (ISBN 0-668-02403-8). Arco.

Bramson, Alan & Birch, Neville. The Tiger Moth Story. 352p. 1982. 69.00x (ISBN 0-906393-19-1, Pub. by Airlife England). State Mutual Bk.

Bruce, J. M. The Bristol Fighter. (Vintage Warbirds Ser.). (Illus.). 64p. (Orig.). 1985. pap. 5.95 (ISBN 0-85368-704-8, Pub. by Arms & Armour). Sterling.

Burns, Michael. McDonnell Douglas F-4K & F-M Phantom II. (Illus.). 192p. 1984. 19.95 (ISBN 0-85045-564-2, Pub. by Osprey England). Motorbooks Intl.

C-130 Hercules in Action. (Aircraft in Action Ser.). (Illus.). 58p. 1984. pap. 4.95 (ISBN 0-89747-111-3, 1047). Squad Sig Pubns.

Caidin, Martin. Ragwings & Heavy Iron: The Agony & the Ecstasy of Flying History's Greatest Warbirds. (Illus.). 260p. 1984. 16.95 (ISBN 0-395-36141-9). HM.

Crocker, Mel. PBY-the Beloved Cat: The Navy's Astonishing Fighter Bomber of WWII. 1983. 35.00 (ISBN 0-917734-09-2). Monitor.

Curtiss P-40 in Action. (Aircraft in Action Ser.). (Illus.). 1984. pap. 4.95 (ISBN 0-89747-025-7, 1026). Squad Sig Pubns.

Davis, Jacquelyn K. & Pfaltzgraff, Robert L., Jr. Power Projection & the Long-Range Combat Aircraft: Missions, Capabilities & Alternative Designs. LC 81-82130. (Special Report Ser.). 37p. 1981. 6.50 (ISBN 0-89549-033-1). Inst Foreign Policy Anal.

Davis, Larry. F-4 Phantom II in Action. Campbell, Jerry, ed. (Aircraft in Action Ser.). (Illus.). 58p. 1984. pap. 4.95 (ISBN 0-89747-154-7). Squad Sig Pubns.

--F-84 Thunderjet. (Aircraft in Action Ser.: No. 1061). (Illus.). 50p. 1983. saddlestitch 4.95 (ISBN 0-89747-147-4). Squad Sig Pubns.

--F-86 Sabre in Action. (Aircraft in Action Ser.). (Illus.). 1984. pap. 4.95 (ISBN 0-89747-032-X, 1033). Squad Sig Pubns.

--P-50 Mustang in Color. (Fighting Colors Ser.). (Illus.). 32p. 1984. pap. 5.95 (ISBN 0-89747-135-0, 6505). Squad Sig Pubns.

--P-80 Shooting Star in Action. (Aircraft in Action Ser.). (Illus.). 1984. pap. 4.95 (ISBN 0-89747-099-0, 1040). Squad Sig Pubns.

Decock, Jean-Pierre. Mirage. (Illus.). 72p. (Orig.). 1985. pap. 5.95 (ISBN 0-85368-705-6, Pub. by Arms & Armour). Sterling.

Drendel, Lou. And Kill MIGs. pap. 6.95 (ISBN 0-89747-056-7). Squad Sig Pubns.

--Century Series. (Specials Ser.: No. 6039). (Illus.). 96p. 1983. pap. 8.95 (ISBN 0-89747-097-4). Squad Sig Pubns.

--F-Sixteeen Falcon in Action. (Aircraft in Action Ser.). (Illus.). 50p. 1982. saddlestitch 4.95 (ISBN 0-89747-133-4). Squad Sig Pubns.

--F-15 Eagle in Action. (Aircraft in Action Ser.). (Illus.). 1984. pap. 4.95 (ISBN 0-89747-023-0, 1024). Squad Sig Pubns.

Dunn, William R. Fighter Pilot: The First American Ace of World War II. LC 82-40172. (Illus.). 272p. 1982. 18.00 (ISBN 0-8131-1465-9). U Pr of Ky.

F-104 Starfighter in Action. (Aircraft in Action Ser.). (Illus.). 1984. pap. 4.95 (ISBN 0-89747-026-5, 1027). Squad Sig Pubns.

F-106 Delta Dart in Action. (Aircraft in Action Ser.). (Illus.). 50p. 1984. pap. 4.95 (ISBN 0-89747-014-1, 1015). Squad Sig Pubns.

F-111 in Action. (Aircraft in Action Ser.). (Illus.). 50p. 1984. pap. 4.95 (ISBN 0-89747-083-4, 1035). Squad Sig Pubns.

F-14 Tomcat in Action. (Aircraft in Action Ser.). (Illus.). 1984. pap. 4.95 (ISBN 0-89747-031-1, 1032). Squad Sig Pubns.

F-16 Falcon in Action. (Aircraft in Action Ser.). (Illus.). 50p. 1984. pap. 4.95 (ISBN 0-89747-133-4, 1053). Squad Sig Pubns.

F-4-U Corsair in Action. pap. 4.95 (ISBN 0-89747-028-1). Squad Sig Pubns.

F-4-U Corsair in Color. (Fighting Colors Ser.). (Illus.). 32p. 1984. pap. 5.95 (ISBN 0-89747-120-2, 6503). Squad Sig Pubns.

F-5 in Action. (Aircraft in Action Ser.). (Illus.). 1984. pap. 4.95 (ISBN 0-89747-095-8, 1038). Squad Sig Pubns.

F-9 F Panther-Cougar in Action. (Aircraft in Action Ser.). (Illus.). 50p. 1984. pap. 4.95 (ISBN 0-89747-127-X, 1051). Squad Sig Pubns.

Fighters of World War II, Vol. I. (Aerodata International Ser.). (Illus.). 120p. 1984. pap. 9.95 (ISBN 0-89747-109-1, 6201). Squad Sig Pubns.

German, Italian & Japanese Fighters of World War II. (Illus.). 9.95 (ISBN 0-668-05093-4). Arco.

Ginter, Steve. North American T-Twenty-Eight Trojan. (Naval Fighters Ser.: No. 5). (Illus.). 66p. 1981. pap. 8.95 (ISBN 0-942612-05-1). Aviation.

Ginter, Steve & Picciani, Ron. North American FJ-1 Fury. (Naval Fighter Ser.: No. 7). (Illus.). 1983. pap. 5.50 (ISBN 0-942612-07-8). Aviation.

Ginter, Steven J. Lockheed C-121 Constellation. (Naval Fighters Ser.). (Illus.). 78p. (Orig.). 1983. pap. 13.95 (ISBN 0-942612-08-6). Aviation.

--McDonnell FH-1 Phantom. (Naval Fighters Ser.: No. 3). (Illus.). 30p. (Orig.). 1981. pap. 4.25 (ISBN 0-942612-03-5). Aviation.

--McDonnell F2H Banshee. (Naval Fighters Ser.: No. 2). (Illus.). 78p. (Orig.). 1980. pap. 7.95 (ISBN 0-942612-02-7). Aviation.

Green, William & Swanborough, Gordon. Japanese Army Airforce Fighters. (World War II Aircraft Fact Files Ser.). (Illus.). 1977. pap. 4.95 (ISBN 0-668-04119-6). Arco.

Groh, Richard. The Dynamite Gang: The Three Hundred Sixty-Seventh Fighter Group in World War II. (Illus.). 192p. 1983. pap. write for info. Aero.

Gunslingers in Action. (Aircraft in Action Ser.). (Illus.). 50p. 1984. pap. 4.95 (ISBN 0-89747-013-3, 1014). Squad Sig Pubns.

Gunston, Bill. An Illustrated Guide to Allied Fighters of World War II. LC 80-70976. (Illustrated Military Guides Ser.). (Illus.). 160p. 1981. 9.95 (ISBN 0-668-05228-7, 5228). Arco.

--The Illustrated Guide to German, Italian & Japanese Fighters of World War II. LC 80-67627. (Illustrated Military Guides). (Illus.). 160p. 1981. 9.95 (ISBN 0-668-05093-4, 5093). Arco.

--The Illustrated Guide to Modern Fighters & Attack Aircraft. LC 80-65164. (Illustrated Military Guides Ser.). (Illus.). 160p. 1980. 9.95 (ISBN 0-668-04964-2, 4964-2). Arco.

--An Illustrated Guide to NATO Fighters & Attack Aircraft. LC 82-74479. (Illustrated Military Guides Ser.). (Illus.). 160p. 1983. 9.95 (ISBN 0-668-05823-4, 5823). Arco.

Hallion, Richard. Rise of the Fighter Aircraft: Nineteen Fourteen to Nineteen Eighteen. LC 83-26947. (Illus.). 196p. 1984. 18.95 (ISBN 0-933852-42-8). Nautical & Aviation.

Holder, William G. Convair F-106 Delta Dart. LC 75-15272. (Aero Ser.: Vol. 27). 104p. 1977. pap. 7.95 (ISBN 0-8168-0600-4). Aero.

Holder, William G. & Siuru, William D., Jr. General Dynamics F-16. 2nd ed. LC 82-70929. (Aero Ser.: No. 26). (Illus.). 104p. 1983. pap. 9.95 (ISBN 0-8168-0597-0). Aero.

Horikoshi, Jiro. Eagles of Mitsubishi: The Story of the Zero Fighter. Shindo, Shojiro & Wantiez, Harold N., trs. from Japanese. LC 80-29217. (Illus.). 176p. 1981. 19.95x (ISBN 0-295-95826-X). U of Wash Pr.

Jackson, Robert. Fighter Pilots of World War II. (Inflation Fighters Ser.). 176p. 1982. pap. 1.50 (ISBN 0-8439-1138-7, Leisure Bks). Dorchester Pub Co.

Jones, Lloyd. U. S. Fighters. LC 75-25246. (Illus.). 1975. 15.95 (ISBN 0-8168-9201-6). Aero.

--U. S. Naval Fighters. LC 77-20693. (Illus.). 1977. pap. 15.95 (ISBN 0-8168-9255-5). Aero.

Kinsey, Bert. F-9 F Panther in Detail & Scale, Vol. 15. Gentle, Ernest J., ed. (In Detail & Scale Ser.). (Illus.). 72p. 1983. pap. 7.95 (ISBN 0-8168-5025-9). Aero.

Kinzey, Bert. F-105 Thunderchief in Detail & Scale. LC 82-20715. (Detail & Scale Ser.: Vol. 8). 72p. 1982. pap. 7.95 (ISBN 0-8168-5020-8). Aero.

--F-14A Tomcat in Detail & Scale. (Detail & Scale Ser.: Vol. 9). 72p. 1982. pap. 7.95 (ISBN 0-8168-5018-6). Aero.

--F-16 A & B Fighting Falcon in Detail & Scale. (Detail & Scale Ser.: Vol. 3). (Illus.). 72p. 1982. pap. 7.95 (ISBN 0-8168-5013-5). Aero.

--F-4 Phantom II in Detail & Scale: Part 2. (Detail & Scale Ser.: Vol. 7). 72p. (Orig.). 1982. pap. 7.95 (ISBN 0-8168-5017-8). Aero.

--F-4 Phantom II in Detail & Scale: Part I: USAF F-4C, F-4D & RF-4C/B. LC 81-67593. (Detail & Scale Ser.: Vol. 1). (Illus.). 72p. 1981. pap. 7.95 (ISBN 0-8168-5011-9). Aero.

--F-5 E & F Tiger II in Detail & Scale: Aggressor Aircraft. (Detail & Scale Ser.: Vol. 5). 72p. 1982. pap. 7.95 (ISBN 0-8168-5015-1). Aero.

--F-9 F Cougar in Detail & Scale, Vol. 16. Gentle, Ernest J., ed. (In Detail & Scale Ser.). (Illus.). 72p. 1983. pap. 7.95 (ISBN 0-8168-5024-0). Aero.

Kinzey, Bertrum. Colors & Markings, F-106 Delta Dart, Vol. 1. Gentle, Ernest J., ed. (Colors & Markings Ser.). (Illus.). 64p. (Orig.). 1984. pap. 9.95 (ISBN 0-8168-4525-5). Aero.

--F-11F Tiger in Detail & Scale, Vol. 17. (Detail & Scale Ser.). (Illus.). 72p. 1984. pap. 7.95 (ISBN 0-8168-5026-7). Aero.

Koehnen, Richard. Chance Vought F6U Pirate. (Naval Fighter Ser.: No. 9). (Illus.). 34p. 1984. pap. 5.50 (ISBN 0-942612-09-4). Aviation.

Koku-Fan, ed. Kawasaki Ki-61, Tony Fighter. (Illus.). 1967. pap. 3.95 (ISBN 0-913076-08-2). Beachcomber Bks.

Krivinyi, Nikolaus. Warplanes of the World, 1983-84. (Illus.). 600p. 1983. 64.95x (ISBN 0-933852-37-1). Nautical & Aviation.

Lancaster in Action. (Aircraft in Action Ser.). (Illus.). 50p. 1984. pap. 4.95 (ISBN 0-89747-130-X, 1052). Squad Sig Pubns.

Linn, Don. F-18 Hornet in Detail & Scale. (Detail & Scale Ser.: Vol. 6). (Illus.). 72p. 1982. pap. 7.95 (ISBN 0-8168-5016-X). Aero.

Luukkanen, Eino. Fighter over Finland: The Memorirs of a Fighter Pilot. Gilbert, James & Green, William, eds. Salo, Mauno A., tr. LC 79-7282. (Flight: Its First Seventy-Five Years Ser.). (Illus.). 1979. Repr. of 1963 ed. lib. bdg. 23.00x (ISBN 0-405-12191-1). Ayer Co Pubs.

Macchi C.202 in Action. (Aircraft in Action Ser.). (Illus.). 1984. pap. 4.95 (ISBN 0-89747-100-8, 1041). Squad Sig Pubns.

McDowell, Ernie & Greer, Don. B-25 Mitchell in Action. (Aircraft in Action Ser.). (Illus.). 1984. pap. 4.95 (ISBN 0-89747-033-8, 1034). Squad Sig Pubns.

Maloney, Edward T. Zero Sen: Japanese Fighter. (Illus.). 1978. pap. 3.00 (ISBN 0-686-70936-5, Pub. by WW II). Aviation.

Mikesh, Robert C. B-57 Canberra at War: Nineteen Sixty-Four to Nineteen Seventy-Two. (Illus.). 160p. 1980. 17.95 (ISBN 0-684-16726-3, ScribT). Scribner.

Miller, Jay. Aerograph: General Dynamics F-16 Fighting Falcon, No.1. (Illus.). 116p. 1982. pap. 14.95 (ISBN 0-942548-01-9, Pub. by Aero Fax Inc.). Aviation.

--Aerograph 1: General Dynamics F-16 Fighting Falcon. (Aerograph Ser.). (Illus.). 124p. 1982. 25.00 (ISBN 0-942548-00-0); pap. 14.95 (ISBN 0-942548-01-9). Aerofax.

Moore, Carl H. WW II: Flying the B-26 Marauder over Europe. (Illus.). 176p. 1982. pap. 7.95 (ISBN 0-8306-2311-6, 2311). TAB Bks.

Moyes, Philip J. Modern U. S. Fighters. (Aerodata International Ser.). (Illus.). 120p. 1982. 9.95 (ISBN 0-89747-125-3, 6203). Squad Sig Pubns.

Myhra, David. Horten 229. LC 83-61694. (Monogram Close-up: No. 12). (Illus.). 1984. 6.95 (ISBN 0-914144-12-X). Monogram Aviation.

NATO Fighters & Attack Aircraft. (Illus.). 9.95 (ISBN 0-668-05823-4). Arco.

Nohara, Shigeru. A-Six-M Zero. (Aircraft in Action Ser.). (Illus.). 50p. 1983. saddlestitched 4.95 (ISBN 0-89747-141-5). Squad Sig Pubns.

P-39, P-63 in Action. 1980. pap. 4.95 (ISBN 0-89747-102-4). Squad Sig Pubns.

P-51 Mustang in Action. (Aircraft in Action Ser.). (Illus.). 58p. 1984. pap. 4.95 (ISBN 0-89747-114-8, 1045). Squad Sig Pubns.

PV-1 Ventura in Action. (Aircraft in Action Ser.). (Illus.). 50p. 1984. pap. 4.95 (ISBN 0-89747-118-0, 1048). Squad Sig Pubns.

RAF Fighters, Nineteen Eighteen to Nineteen Thirty-Seven. 96p. 1981. 25.00x (ISBN 0-85153-208-X, Pub. by D B Barton England). State Mutual Bk.

Rice, Michael S., ed. Pilot's Flight Operating Instructions for P-39 Airacobra. (Illus.). 48p. 1973. pap. 6.95 (ISBN 0-87994-024-7). Aviation.

--Pilots Manual for Northrop P-61 Black Widow Airplane. (Illus.). 72p. 1973. pap. 7.95 (ISBN 0-87994-025-5, Pub. by AvPubns). Aviation.

Smith, J. Richard & Creek, Eddie J. Arado 234B. LC 83-61698. (Monogram Close-up 23 Ser.). (Illus.). 1984. 6.95 (ISBN 0-914144-23-5). Monogram Aviation.

--Dornier 335. LC 83-61696. (Monogram Close-Up 21 Ser.). (Illus.). 32p. 1984. 6.95 (ISBN 0-914144-21-9). Monogram Aviation.

--Messerschmitt 262 A-1. LC 83-61695. (Monogram Close-up 17 Ser.). (Illus.). 32p. 1984. 6.95 (ISBN 0-914144-17-0). Monogram Aviation.

Spenser, Jay P. Moskito. LC 83-61697. (Monogram Close-up 22 Ser.). (Illus.). 1984. 6.95 (ISBN 0-914144-22-7). Monogram Aviation.

Spick, Mike. Fighter Pilot Tactics: The Techniques of Daylight Air Combat. LC 83-42829. (Illus.). 176p. 1983. 16.95 (ISBN 0-8128-2930-1). Stein & Day.

Stafford, Gene. P-38 Lightning in Action. (Aircraft in Action Ser.). (Illus.). 1984. pap. 4.95 (ISBN 0-89747-024-9, 1025). Squad Sig Pubns.

Stern, Rob. SB2C Helldiver in Action. (Aircraft in Action Ser.). (Illus.). 50p. 1982. saddlestitch 4.95 (ISBN 0-89747-128-8, 1054). Squad Sig Pubns.

Stern, Robert. SBD Dauntless in Action. Campbell, Jerry, ed. (Aircraft in Action Ser.). (Illus.). 50p. (Orig.). 1984. pap. 4.95 (ISBN 0-89747-153-9). Squad Sig Pubns.

Stern, Robert C. America's Fighters of the Nineteen Seventies: F14 & F15. (Warbirds Illustrated Ser.: No. 22). (Illus.). 68p. 1984. pap. 7.95 (ISBN 0-85368-608-4, Pub. by Arms & Armour). Sterling.

Sullivan, Jim. F-6 F Hellcat in Action. (Aircraft in Action Ser.). (Illus.). 1984. pap. 4.95 (ISBN 0-89747-088-5, 1036). Squad Sig Pubns.

Sweetman, Bill & Goulding, James. Jane's Aircraft Spectaculars: Phantom. (Jane's Aircraft Spectacular Ser.). (Illus.). 52p. 1984. 10.95 (ISBN 0-7106-0279-0). Jane's Pub Inc.

Tillman, Barrett. MIG Master: The Story of the F-8 Crusader. LC 80-83019. (Illus.). 220p. 1980. 19.95 (ISBN 0-933852-17-7). Nautical & Aviation.

U. S. A. F. Europe Eighteen Forty-Eight to Nineteen Sixty-Five in Color. (Fighting Colors Ser.). (Illus.). 36p. 1984. pap. 5.95 (ISBN 0-89747-132-6, 6504). Squad Sig Pubns.

U. S. Pursuit Aircraft: A Pictorial Survey. 96p. 1981. 25.00x (ISBN 0-85153-185-7, Pub. by D B Barton England). State Mutual Bk.

Walker, Bruce. Fighting Jets. (The Epic of Flight Ser.). (Illus.). 176p. 1983. 14.95 (ISBN 0-8094-3362-1). Time Life.

Wheeler, Barry C. Modern Fighters & Attack Aircraft. (Illus.). 9.95 (ISBN 0-668-04964-2). Arco.

Willmott, H. P. Zero: A6M. (Illus.). 64p. 1983. pap. 4.95 (ISBN 0-13-983965-8). P-H.

Winter, Denis. The First of the Few: Fighter Pilots of the First World War. LC 82-13478. (Illus.). 224p. 17.50 (ISBN 0-8203-0642-8). U of Ga Pr.

Wooldridge, E. T., Jr. The P-80 Shooting Star. Evolution of a Jet Fighter. LC 79-17648. (Famous Aircraft of the National Air & Space Museum Ser.: Bk. 3). (Illus.). 110p. 1979. pap. 6.95 (ISBN 0-87474-965-4). Smithsonian.

FILARIA AND FILARIASIS

WHO Expert Committee. Athens, 1973, 3rd. WHO Expert Committee on Filariasis: Report. (Technical Report Ser.: No. 542). (Also avail. in French & Spanish). 1974. pap. 2.00 (ISBN 92-4-120542-3). World Health.

WHO Expert Committee on Filariasis, Geneva, 1961. Report. (Technical Report Ser: No. 233). (Eng, Fr, Rus, & Span.). 49p. 1962. pap. 1.20 (ISBN 92-4-120233-5). World Health.

FILE ORGANIZATION (COMPUTER)

Finkel, LeRoy & Brown, Jerald R. TRS-80 Data File Programming. (Self-Teaching Guides: No. 1-581). 320p. 1983. pap. text ed. 14.95 (ISBN 0-471-88486-3, Pub. by Wiley Press). Wiley.

Gittleson, Stephen & Pirisino, Jim. Filing System for Apple Writer: Minute Manual for WPL. 200p. 1985. bk. & software disk 99.95 (ISBN 0-913131-11-3). Minuteware.

Grosshans, Daniel. File Systems. (Illus.). 496p. 1986. text ed. 32.95 (ISBN 0-13-314568-9). P-H.

Johnson, L. F. & Cooper, R. H. File Techniques for Data Base Organization in COBOL. 2nd ed. (Illus.). 416p. 1986. text ed. 28.95 (ISBN 0-13-314717-7). P-H.

Miller, David. Apple ProDOS Data Files: A Basic Tutorial. (Illus.). 232p. 18.95 (ISBN 0-8359-0134-3). Reston.

--IBM PCjr Data Files. 1984. 14.95 (ISBN 0-8359-3023-8). Reston.

--Macintosh Data Files. 1984. 16.95 (ISBN 0-8359-4173-6). Reston.

Omlor, J. Dennis. Efficiency Analysis of File Organization & Information Retrieval. Stone, Harold S., ed. LC 81-11693. (Computer Science: Distributed Database Systems Ser.: No. 10). 124p. 1981. 29.95 (ISBN 0-8357-1226-5). UMI Res Pr.

The Ratings Book: IBM-PC Database & File Management Programs. 1984. pap. 14.95 (ISBN 0-916543-10-2). Software Inc.

Thomas, Violet, et al. Filing Systems for Information Management. 103p. 1983. pap. 11.95 incl. pad of instructions & forms simulation (ISBN 0-471-89694-2). Wiley.

FILICINEAE

see Ferns

FILLERS (IN PAPER, PAINT, ETC.)

Business Communications Staff. Fillers & Extenders for Plastics. 1984. 1500.00 (ISBN 0-89336-407-X, P-031N). BCC.

FILLING STATIONS

see Automobiles–Service Stations

FILLS (EARTHWORK)

Sanitary Landfill. (ASCE Manual & Report on Engineering Practice Ser.: No. 39). 105p. 1976. 27.50x (ISBN 0-87262-215-0). Am Soc Civil Eng.

FILMS

see Photography–Films

FILMS, METALLIC

see Metallic Films

FILMS, THIN

see Thin Films

FILTERS, DIGITAL (MATHEMATICS)

see Digital Filters (Mathematics)

FILTERS, LIGHT

see Light Filters

FILTERS AND FILTRATION

see also Chemistry–Manipulation; Separators (Machines); Ultrafiltration

Anderson, Brian & Moore, John B. Optimal Filtering. 1979. 42.95 (ISBN 0-13-638122-7). P-H.

Biey, Mario & Premoli, Amedeo. Tables for Active Filter Design. 1985. pap. text ed. 55.00 (ISBN 0-89006-159-9). Artech Hse.

Business Communications Staff. High Tech Filtration. 1984. 1750.00 (ISBN 0-89336-359-6, C-046). BCC.

Cheremisinoff, Nicholas P. & Azbel, David S., eds. Liquid Filtration. LC 82-46063. (Illus.). 400p. 1983. 59.95 (ISBN 0-250-40600-4). Butterworth.

Comfort, W. W. & Negrepontis, S. The Theory of Ultra Filters. (Die Grundlehren der Mathematischen Wissenschaften Ser.: Vol. 211). 480p. 1974. 55.00 (ISBN 0-387-06604-7). Springer-Verlag.

Controlling Airborne Asbestos Contamination with Negative Air Filtration Systems: The U. S. Government's Technical Data Package. (Illus.). 120p. 1984. 14.95 (ISBN 0-917097-01-7). SourceFinders.

Driscoll, H. T. Filter Aids & Materials-Technology & Applications. LC 77-71926. (Chemical Technology Review Ser.: No. 86). (Illus.). 307p. 1977. 39.00 (ISBN 0-8155-0658-9). Noyes.

Dry Filtration. 1984. 25.00 (ISBN 0-318-01487-4, 11040). Indus Fabrics.

Fabric Filtration Seminar '81. 66p. 1981. 60.00 (ISBN 0-318-01529-3, 16015). Indus Fabrics.

Fabric Filtration Seminar '82. 130p. 1982. 60.00 (ISBN 0-318-01528-5, 16010). Indus Fabrics.

Fabric Filtration Seminar '83. 82p. 1983. 60.00 (ISBN 0-318-01527-7, 16005). Indus Fabrics.

Ghausi, M. & Laker, K. Modern Filter Design: Active RC & Switched Capacitor. 1981. 41.95 (ISBN 0-13-594663-8). P-H.

Goodwin, Graham C. & Sin, Kwai S. Adaptive Filtering, Prediction & Control. 688p. 1984. text ed. 47.95 (ISBN 0-13-004069-X). P-H.

Haykin, Simon. Adaptive Filter Theory. (Illus.). 480p. 1986. text ed. 45.95 (ISBN 0-13-004052-5). P-H.

--Introduction to Adaptive Filters. 256p. 1984. pap. text ed. 32.95 (ISBN 0-02-949460-5). Macmillan.

Heath Company Staff. Active Filters. rev. ed. (Electronics Technology Ser.). (Illus.). 304p. 1979. looseleaf with experimental pts. 39.95 (ISBN 0-87119-031-1); pap. text ed. 18.95 (ISBN 0-87119-029-X); tchr's. ed. 9.95 (ISBN 0-87119-030-3). Heathkit-Zenith Ed.

Helszajin, J. Y. I. G. Filters. 1985. 47.95 (ISBN 0-471-90050-X). Wiley.

Huisman, L. & Wood, W. E. Slow Sand Filtration. (Also avail. in French). 1974. 6.40 (ISBN 92-4-154037-0). World Health.

Ives, K. J., ed. The Scientific Basis of Filtration, No. 2. (NATO Advanced Study, Applied Science Ser.). 450p. 1975. 45.00x (ISBN 90-286-0523-1). Sijthoff & Noordhoff.

Johnson, D. E. & Hilburn, J. L. Rapid Practical Designs of Active Filters. LC 75-14074. 264p. 1975. 39.95x (ISBN 0-471-44304-2, Pub. by Wiley-Interscience). Wiley.

Johnson, David E. Introduction to Filter Theory. (Illus.). 336p. 1976. 41.95 (ISBN 0-13-483776-2). P-H.

Johnson, David E., et al. A Handbook of Active Filters. (Illus.). 1980. text ed. 28.95 (ISBN 0-13-372409-3). P-H.

Johnson, Robert A. Mechanical Filters in Electronics. LC 82-10922. (Series on Filters: Design, Manufacturing & Applications). 379p. 1983. 45.50x (ISBN 0-471-08919-2, Pub. by Wiley-Interscience). Wiley.

Kailath, T. Lectures on Wiener & Kalman Filtering. (CISM-International Centre for Mechanical Sciences Ser.: Vol. 140). 187p. 1981. pap. 19.00 (ISBN 0-387-81664-X). Springer-Verlag.

Madsen, R. F. Hyperfiltration & Ultrafiltration in Plate & Frame System. 368p. 1977. 74.50 (ISBN 0-444-41553-X). Elsevier.

Moschytz, G. M., ed. MOS Switched-Capacitor Filters: Analysis & Design. LC 84-9055. 1984. 66.95 (ISBN 0-87942-177-0, PC01701). Inst Electrical.

Orr, Clyde. Filtration, Pt. 2. (Chemical Processing & Engineering; an International Ser.: Vol. 10). 1979. 89.75 (ISBN 0-8247-6763-2). Dekker.

--Filtration: Principles & Practices, Pt. 1. (Chemical Processing & Engineering Ser.: Vol. 10). 1977. 89.75 (ISBN 0-8247-6283-5). Dekker.

Schaumann, R., et al, eds. Modern Active Filter Design. LC 81-2368. 1981. 35.30 (ISBN 0-87942-147-9, PC01420). Inst Electrical.

Sheahan, Desmond & Johnson, Robert, eds. Modern Crystal & Mechanical Filters. LC 76-57822. 1977. 43.65 (ISBN 0-87942-095-2, PC00927). Inst Electrical.

Tucker, Allen E., ed. Filtration & Contamination, Vol. D. rev. ed. (Fluid Power Standards 1984 Ser.). (Illus.). 300p. 1984. 83.00 (ISBN 0-942220-74-9); Set. write for info. Natl Fluid Power.

Van Valkenberg, M. E. Analog Filter Design. 604p. 1982. text ed. 41.95 (ISBN 0-03-059246-1). HR&W.

Wakeman, R. Filtration Post-Treatment Processes. LC 75-31613. (Chemical Engineering Monographs: Vol. 2). 149p. 1975. 40.50 (ISBN 0-444-41391-X). Elsevier.

Wakeman, R. J., ed. Progress in Filtration & Separation, Vol. 1. 346p. 1979. 72.50 (ISBN 0-444-41819-9). Elsevier.

--Progress in Filtration & Separation, Vol. 2. 306p. 1981. 72.50 (ISBN 0-444-42006-1). Elsevier.

Warring, R. H. Filters & Filtration. 250p. 1969. 33.00x (ISBN 0-85461-025-1, Pub by Trade & Tech England). Brookfield Pub Co.

--Filters & Filtration Handbook. LC 81-84307. 440p. 1981. 59.95x (ISBN 0-87201-283-2). Gulf Pub.

--Filters & Filtration Handbook. 450p. 1981. 125.00x (ISBN 0-686-81330-8, Pub. by Trade & Tech). State Mutual Bk.

FINANCE–DATA PROCESSING

Advanced Investment Strategies Inc. Investment Tax Analyst: IBM PC Visicalc. (Wiley Professional Software Ser.). 60p. 1983. incl. disc 150.00x (ISBN 0-471-88953-9). Wiley.

Berk, Joseph & Berk, Susan. Financial Analysis on the IBM PC. LC 84-12130. 222p. (Orig.). 1984. pap. 12.95 (ISBN 0-8019-7546-8). Chilton.

--Financial Analysis on TI Computers. LC 84-45158. 220p. (Orig.). 1984. pap. 12.95 (ISBN 0-8019-7518-2). Chilton.

Bookbinder, Albert I. Computer-Assisted Investment Handbook. LC 82-61048. (Illus.). 220p. 1983. pap. text ed. 19.95 (ISBN 0-916106-03-9). Prog Pr.

Brooks, Herb. Investing with a Computer: A Time-Series Analysis Approach. 1984. 19.95 (ISBN 0-89433-194-9). Petrocelli.

--Investing with a Computer: A Time-Series Analysis Approach. (A Petrocelli Bk.). 1984. 19.95. Van Nos Reinhold.

Business Communications Staff. Checks & the Future of the Retail Payments System. 1983. 1000.00 (ISBN 0-89336-378-2, G-066-B). BCC.

--Circuit Boards. 1982. 1250.00 (ISBN 0-89336-319-7, G-067). BCC.

--Credit Cards & the Future of the Retail Payment System. 1983. 1000.00 (ISBN 0-89336-379-0, G-066-C). BCC.

--Debit Cards & the Future of the Retail Payments System. 1984. 1250.00 (ISBN 0-89336-380-4, G-066-D). BCC.

Cohen, Neil & Graff, Lois. Financial Analysis with Lotus 1-2-3. (Illus.). 336p. 1984. pap. 19.95 (ISBN 0-89303-451-7); bk. diskette 44.95 (ISBN 0-89303-452-5); diskette 25.00 (ISBN 0-89303-453-3); kit 44.95 (ISBN 0-89303-452-5). Brady Comm.

Curtin, Dennis P., et al. Controlling Financial Performance for Higher Profits: A Multiplan Business User's Guide. (Illus.). 176p. 1984. pap. 19.50 (ISBN 0-930764-87-0); disk 29.95. Van Nos Reinhold.

Drew, Rodney. Microcomputers for Financial Planning. 116p. 1983. pap. 38.50x (ISBN 0-566-03443-3). Gower Pub Co.

Felsen, Jerry. Low-Cost, Personal-Computer-Based Investment Decision Systems. LC 77-83508. 1977. pap. 20.00 (ISBN 0-916376-03-6). CDS Pub.

Flast, Robert H. VisiCalc Models: Finance-Statistics-Mathematics. 240p. 1984. 15.95 (Osborne-Mcgraw). Mcgraw.

Kawai, T., ed. Finite Element Flow Analysis: Proceedings of the Fourth International Symposium on Finite Element Methods in Flow Problems, Held at Chuo University, Tokyo, July, 1982. 1096p. 1982. 95.00 (North Holland). Elsevier.
Kertz, George J. Applied Finite Mathematics. (Illus.). 530p. 1985. text ed. 27.95 (ISBN 0-314-85255-7). West Pub.
Kikuchi, Noboru. Finite Element Methods in Mechanics. (Illus.). 336p. Date not set. price not set (ISBN 0-521-30262-5). Cambridge U Pr.
--Laboratory Manual for Finite Element Methods in Mechanics. 150p. Date not set. pap. price not set (ISBN 0-521-30952-2). Cambridge U Pr.
Livesley, R. K. Finite Elements: An Introduction for Engineers. LC 82-22155. 199p. 1983. pap. 14.95 (ISBN 0-521-28597-6). Cambridge U Pr.
Logan. A First Course in the Finite Element Method. 1985. text ed. write for info. (ISBN 0-534-05394-7, 21R4000, Pub. by PWS Engineering). PWS Pubs.
Martin, Harold C. & Carey, G. F. Introduction to Finite Element Analysis. 1973. text ed. 42.00 (ISBN 0-07-040641-3). McGraw.
Mercier, B. Lectures on Topics in Finite Element Solution of Elliptic Problems. (Tata Institute Lectures on Mathematics). (Illus.). 191p. 1979. pap. 11.00 (ISBN 0-387-09543-8). Springer-Verlag.
Nath, B. Fundamentals of Finite Elements for Engineers. (Illus.). 256p. 1974. 54.00 (ISBN 0-485-11148-9, Pub. by Athlone Pr Ltd). Longwood Pub Group.
Norrie, D. H. & De Vries, G. An Introduction to Finite Element Analysis. 1978. 35.00 (ISBN 0-12-521660-2). Acad Pr.
Oden, J. T. & Reddy, J. N. An Introduction to the Mathematical Theory of Finite Elements. LC 76-6953. (Pure & Applied Mathematics Ser.). 429p. 1976. 50.95x (ISBN 0-471-65261-X, Pub. by Wiley-Interscience). Wiley.
Oden, J. Tinsley & Carey, Graham F. Finite Elements: Special Problems in Solid Mechanics, Vol. V. (Illus.). 288p. 1984. text ed. 36.95 (ISBN 0-13-317073-X). P-H.
Pinder, G. F. & Gray, W. G. Finite Element Simulation in Surface & Subsurface Hydrology. 1977. 43.00 (ISBN 0-12-556950-5). Acad Pr.
Ritt, Joseph F. Integration in Finite Terms: Liouville's Theory of Elementary. LC 48-2225. pap. 27.50 (ISBN 0-317-08490-9, 2050137). Bks Demand UMI.
Rockey, K. C., et al. The Finite Element Method. 2nd ed. LC 83-8487. 256p. 1983. pap. text ed. 19.95 (ISBN 0-470-27459-X). Halsted Pr.
Segerlind, Larry J. Applied Finite Element Analysis. 2nd ed. LC 84-7455. 1985. 39.95 (ISBN 0-471-80662-5). Wiley.
Shames, I. H. & Dym, C. L. Energy & Finite Element Methods in Structural Mechanics. 732p. 1985. 44.95 (ISBN 0-07-056392-6). McGraw.
Silvester, Peter P. & Ferrari, Ronald L. Finite Elements for Electrical Engineers. LC 82-23550. 180p. 1983. 42.50 (ISBN 0-521-25321-7); pap. 15.95 (ISBN 0-521-27310-2). Cambridge U Pr.
Smith, G. N. Introduction to Matrix & Finite Elements in Civil Engineering. (Illus.). 222p. 1971. 20.50 (ISBN 0-85334-502-3, Pub. by Elsevier Applied Sci England). Elsevier.
Strang, G. & Fix, George J. An Analysis of the Finite Element Method. LC 72-12642. (Illus.). 320p. 1973. ref. ed. 39.95 (ISBN 0-13-032946-0). P-H.
Thomasset, F. Implementation of Finite Element Methods for Navier-Stokes Equations. (Springer Series in Computational Phsyics). (Illus.). 160p. 1981. 36.00 (ISBN 0-387-10771-1). Springer Verlag.
Thomee, V. Galerkin Finite Element Methods for Parabolic Problems. (Lecture Notes in Mathematics Ser.: Vol. 1054). vii, 237p. 1984. pap. 13.50 (ISBN 0-387-12911-1). Springer-Verlag.
Tong, Pin & Rossettos, John N. Finite Element Method: Basic Technique & Implementation. LC 76-7453. 1976. text ed. 27.50x (ISBN 0-262-20032-5). MIT Pr.
Wachspress, Eugene L. A Rational Finite Element Basis. (Mathematics in Science & Engineering Ser.). 1975. 55.00 (ISBN 0-12-728950-X). Acad Pr.
Wait, R. & Mitchell, A. R. Finite Element Analysis & Applications. 1985. write for info. (ISBN 0-471-90677-8); pap. write for info. (ISBN 0-471-90678-6). Wiley.
Weaver, William, Jr. & Johnston, Paul R. Finite Elements for Structural Analysis. (Illus.). 448p. 1984. 40.95 (ISBN 0-13-317099-3). P-H.
White, R. E. An Introduction to the Finite Element Method with Applications to Nonlinear Problems. 320p. 1985. 34.95 (ISBN 0-471-80909-8). Wiley.
Whiteman, J. R., ed. The Mathematics of Finite Elements & Applications II: Mafelap 1977. 85.00 (ISBN 0-12-747252-5). Acad Pr.
--The Mathematics of Finite Elements & Application IV: Proceedings. 1982. 49.00 (ISBN 0-12-747254-1). Acad Pr.
Yamada, Yoshiaki & Gallagher, Richard H., eds. Theory & Practice in Finite Element Structural Analysis: Proceedings of the 1973 Tokyo Seminar on Finite Element Analysis. 733p. 1973. 60.00x (ISBN 0-86008-097-8, Pub. by U of Tokyo Japan). Columbia U Pr.
Yang, Henry T. Finite Element Structural Analysis. (Illus.). 464p. 1986. text ed. 41.95 (ISBN 0-13-317116-7). P-H.
Zienkiewicz, O. C. Finite Elements & Approximations. LC 82-16051. 328p. 1983. 39.95x (ISBN 0-471-98240-7, Pub. by Wiley-Interscience). Wiley.
--Introductory Lectures on the Finite Element Method. (CISM International Centre for Mechanical Sciences Courses & Lectures: Vol. 130). (Illus.). 1973. pap. 13.50 (ISBN 0-387-81202-4). Springer-Verlag.

FINITE FIELDS (ALGEBRA)
see Modular Fields

FINITE GEOMETRIES

Payne, S. E. & Thas, T. A. Finite Generalized Quandrangles. (Research Notes in Mathematics Ser.: No. 110). 328p. 1984. pap. text ed. 22.95 (ISBN 0-273-08655-3). Pitman Pub MA.

FINITE GROUPS
see also Modules (Algebra)

Adke, S. R. & Manjunath, Shri S. An Introduction to Finite Markov Processes: Continuous Time Finite Markow Processes. 310p. 1984. 24.95x (ISBN 0-470-27457-3). Halsted Pr.
Aschbacher, Michael, et al, eds. Future Directions in Finite Group Theory. 400p. 1984. 39.50 (ISBN 0-521-26493-6). Cambridge U Pr.
Blackburn, N. & Huppert, B. Finite Groups. (Grundlerhen der Mathematischen Wissenschaften Ser.: Vol. 242). 550p. 1982. lib. bdg. 72.00 (ISBN 0-387-10632-4). Springer-Verlag.
Carter, Roger W. Finite Groups of LIE Type Conjugacy Classes & Complex Characters. LC 84-13077. (Pure & Applied Mathematics Ser.: Vol. V). 1985. 69.95 (ISBN 0-471-90554-2, Pub. by Wiley-Interscience). Wiley.
Chesnut, D. B. Finite Groups & Quantum Theory. LC 81-19351. 270p. 1982. Repr. of 1974 ed. lib. bdg. 26.50 (ISBN 0-89874-468-7). Krieger.
Collins, Michael J., ed. Finite Simple Groups, II. LC 77-149703. 1981. 60.00 (ISBN 0-12-181480-7). Acad Pr.
Conference on Finite Elements Applied to Thin Shells & Curved Members (1974: University College, Cardiff, Wales) Finite Elements for Thin Shells & Curved Members. Ashwell, D. G. & Gallagher, R. H., eds. LC 75-37654. (Illus.). pap. 70.00 (ISBN 0-317-08377-5, 2016448). Bks Demand UMI.
Conner, P. E. Differentiable Periodic Maps. 2nd ed. (Lecture Notes in Mathematics: Vol. 738). 1979. pap. 14.00 (ISBN 0-387-09535-7). Springer-Verlag.
Conner, Pierre E. Lectures on the Action of a Finite Group. LC 68-57940. (Lecture Notes in Mathematics: Vol. 73). 1968. pap. 10.70 (ISBN 0-387-04243-1). Springer-Verlag.
Conway, John H., et al, eds. Atlas of Finite Groups: Maximal Subgroups & Ordinary Characters for Simple Groups. 250p. 1984. text ed. 45.00x (ISBN 0-19-853199-0). Oxford U Pr.
Curtis, Charles W. & Reiner, Irving. Methods of Representation Theory: With Applications to Finite Groups & Orders, Vol. I. LC 81-7416. (Pure & Applied Mathematics: Wiley-Interscience Series of Tests, Monographs & Tracts). 819p. 1981. 69.50x (ISBN 0-471-18994-4, Pub. by Wiley-Interscience). Wiley.
--Representation Theory of Finite Groups & Associative Algebras. LC 62-16994. (Pure & Applied Mathematics Ser.). 685p. 1962. 69.50 (ISBN 0-470-18975-4, Pub. by Wiley-Interscience). Wiley.
Curzio, M. Some Problems of Sylow Type in Locally Finite Groups. 1981. 23.00 (ISBN 0-12-363605-1). Acad Pr.
Feit, W. Representation Theory of Finite Groups. (Mathematical Library: Vol. 25). 502p. 1982. 55.00 (ISBN 0-444-86155-6, North Holland). Elsevier.
Gagen, T. M. Topics in Finite Groups. LC 75-17116. (London Mathematical Society Lecture Note Ser.: No. 16). 80p. 1976. 13.95 (ISBN 0-521-21002-X). Cambridge U Pr.
Gashutz, W. Lectures on Subgroups of Sylow Type in Finite Soluble Groups. Kuhn, U., tr. (Notes on Pure Mathematics Ser.: No. 11). 100p. (Orig.). 1980. pap. text ed. 5.00 (ISBN 0-908160-22-4, 0571). Australia N U P.
Glauberman, G. Factorization in Local Subgroups of Finite Groups. LC 77-13373. (Conference Board of the Mathematical Sciences Ser.: No. 33). 74p. 1977. pap. 13.00 (ISBN 0-8218-1683-7, CBMS33). Am Math.
Gorenstein, Daniel. Finite Groups. 2nd ed. xvii, 517p. 1980. 24.50 (ISBN 0-8284-0301-5). Chelsea Pub.
--Finite Simple Groups: An Introduction to Their Classification. LC 81-23414. (The University Series in Mathematics). 344p. 1982. 32.50x (ISBN 0-306-40779-5, Plenum Pr). Plenum Pub.
Gorenstein, Daniel & Harada, Kaichiro. Finite Groups Whose 2-Subgroups Are Generated by at Most 4 Elements. LC 74-11282. (Memoirs: No. 147). 464p. 1974. pap. 15.00 (ISBN 0-8218-1847-3, MEMO-147). Am Math.
Grossman. Applied Math for the Management Life & Social Sciences. 896p. 1985. write for info (ISBN 0-534-04239-2). Wadsworth Pub.
Grove, L. C. & Benson, C. T. Finite Reflection Groups. 2nd ed. (Graduate Texts in Mathematics Ser.: Vol. 99). (Illus.). 135p. 1985. 24.00 (ISBN 0-387-96082-1). Springer-Verlag.
Hajnal, A., et al, eds. Finite & Infinite Sets, 2 vols. (Colloquia Mathematica Societatis Janos Bolyai Ser.: No. 37). 902p. 1985. Set. 98.00 (ISBN 0-444-86763-5, North-Holland). Vol. 1 (ISBN 0-444-86893-3). Vol. 2 (ISBN 0-444-86894-1). Elsevier.
Hardy, Lane F. Finite Mathematics for the Managerial, Social, & Life Sciences. (Illus.). 450p. 1984. text ed. 28.95 (ISBN 0-314-77900-0). West Pub.
Huppert, B. & Blackburn, N. Finite Groups III. (Grundlehren der Mathematischen Wissenschaften Ser.: Vol. 243). 470p. 1982. 64.00 (ISBN 0-387-10633-2). Springer-Verlag.
Jones, Vaughan. Actions of Finite Groups on the Hyperfinite Type II (to the First Power) Factor. LC 80-22560. (Memoirs Ser.: No. 237). 70p. 1980. pap. 9.00 (ISBN 0-8218-2237-3, MEMO-237). Am Math.
Keown, R. An Introduction to Group Representation Theory. (Mathematics in Science & Engineering Ser.). 1975. 59.50 (ISBN 0-12-404250-3). Acad Pr.
Kletzing, D. Structure & Representations of Q-Groups. (Lecture Notes in Mathematics: Vol. 1984). vi, 290p. 1984. pap. 16.00 (ISBN 0-387-13865-X). Springer-Verlag.
Kosniowski, C. Actions of Finite Abelian Groups. (Research Notes in Mathematics Ser.: No. 18). 230p. (Orig.). 1978. pap. text ed. 23.95 (ISBN 0-273-08405-4). Pitman Pub MA.
Landrock, Peter. Finite Group Algebras & their Modules. LC 83-15049. 274p. 1984. pap. 27.50 (ISBN 0-521-27487-7). Cambridge U Pr.
Lomont, John S. Applications of Finite Groups. 1959. 57.50 (ISBN 0-12-455550-0). Acad Pr.
London Mathematical Society Instructional Conference. Finite Simple Groups: Proceedings. Powell, M. B. & Higman, G., eds. 1971. 55.00 (ISBN 0-12-563850-7). Acad Pr.
Morgan, John W. & Bass, Hyman. The Smith Conjecture. LC 83-15846. (Pure & Applied Mathematics Ser.). 1984. 55.00 (ISBN 0-12-506980-4). Acad Pr.
Norrie, Douglas H. & DeVries, Gerard, eds. The Finite Element Method: Fundamentals & Applications. 1973. 60.00 (ISBN 0-12-521650-5). Acad Pr.
Oden, J. Tinsley & Carey, Graham F. Finite Elements: Mathematical Aspects, Vol. IV. (Illus.). 208p. 1983. text ed. 37.95 (ISBN 0-13-317081-0). P-H.
Pleskin, W., ed. Group Rings of Finite Groups over p-adic Integers. (Lecture Notes in Mathematics: Vol. 1026). 151p. 1983. pap. 12.00 (ISBN 0-387-12728-3). Springer Verlag.
Rector, Robert E. & Zwick, Earl J. Finite Mathematics & Its Applications. LC 78-69547. (Illus.). 1979. text ed. 28.50 (ISBN 0-395-27206-8); instr's. manual 1.00 (ISBN 0-395-27207-6). HM.
Reiner, I., ed. Representation Theory of Finite Groups & Related Topics: Proceedings of the Symposia in Pure Mathematics-Madison, Wis.-1970. LC 79-165201. (Vol. 21). 1971. 29.00 (ISBN 0-8218-1421-4, PSPUM-21). Am Math.
Scott, William R. & Gross, Fletcher, eds. Proceedings of the Conference on Finite Groups. 1976. 70.50 (ISBN 0-12-633650-4). Acad Pr.
Serre, J. P. Linear Representations of Finite Groups. Scott, L. L., tr. LC 76-12585. (Graduate Texts in Mathematics: Vol. 42). 170p. (Corrected Second Printing). 1977. 29.50 (ISBN 0-387-90190-6). Springer-Verlag.
Shatz, Stephen S. Profinite Groups, Arithmetic, & Geometry. LC 77-126832. (Annals of Mathematics Studies: No. 67). 1972. 26.50 (ISBN 0-691-08017-8). Princeton U Pr.
Speiser, A. Die Theorie der Gruppen Von Endlicher Ordnung. (MA Ser.: No. 22). (Ger.). 272p. 1980. 38.95x (ISBN 0-8176-1151-7). Birkhauser.
Srinivasan, B. Representations of Finite Chevalley Groups. (Lecture Notes in Mathematics: Vol. 764). 177p. 1979. pap. text ed. 16.00 (ISBN 0-387-09716-3). Springer-Verlag.
Symposium in Pure Mathematics - Pasadena - 1960. Institute on Finite Groups, 1960: Proceedings. Hall, M., Jr., ed. LC 50-1183. (Proceedings of Symposia in Pure Mathematics: Vol. 6). 114p. 1979. pap. 21.00 (ISBN 0-8218-1406-0, PSPUM-6). Am Math.
Tsuzuku, Tosiro. Finite Groups & Finite Geometries. (Cambridge Tracts in Mathematics Ser.: No. 78). (Illus.). 250p. 1982. 47.50 (ISBN 0-521-22242-7). Cambridge U Pr.
Vazsonyi, Andrew. Finite Mathematics: Quantitative Analysis for Management. LC 76-7511. (Management, Accounting, & Information Systems). pap. 97.10 (ISBN 0-8357-9891-7, 2012400). Bks Demand UMI.
Whiteman, J. R., ed. The Mathematics of Finite Elements & Applications. 1973. 85.00 (ISBN 0-12-747250-9). Acad Pr.
Zelevinsky, A. V. Representations of Finite Classical Groups: A Hopf Algebra Approach. (Lecture Notes in Mathematics Ser.: Vol. 869). 184p. 1981. pap. 14.00 (ISBN 0-387-10824-6). Springer-Verlag.
Zieschang, H. Finite Groups of Mapping Classes of Surfaces. (Lecture Notes in Mathematics Ser.: Vol. 875). 340p. 1981. pap. 20.00 (ISBN 0-387-10857-2). Springer Verlag.

FINITE NUMBER SYSTEMS
see Modules (Algebra)

FINSLER SPACE
see Spaces, Generalized

FIORDS
see Fjords

FIRE
see also Combustion; Fires; Flame; Fuel; Heat; Heating; Smoke

Bachelard, Gaston. Psychoanalysis of Fire. Ross, A. C., tr. 1964. pap. 5.95x (ISBN 0-8070-6461-0, BP277). Beacon Pr.
Fire Stream Fundamentals. 32p. 1966. pap. 1.00 (ISBN 0-685-58181-0, FSD-4). Natl Fire Prot.
Karter, Michael J. Fire Facts. Carwile, Ruth H., ed. LC 81-85437. (Illus.). 86p. (Orig.). 1982. pap. text ed. 10.00 (ISBN 0-87765-211-2). Natl Fire Prot.
Kozlowski, T. T. & Ahlgren, C. E., eds. Fire & Ecosystems. 1974. 75.00 (ISBN 0-12-424255-3). Acad Pr.
Levine, Robert S. & Pagni, Patrick J. Fire Science for Fire Saftey. (Combustion Science & Technology Ser.). 510p. 1984. pap. text ed. 75.00 (ISBN 2-88124-115-8). Gordon.
Pyne, Stephen J. Fire in America: A Cultural History of Wildland & Rural Fire. LC 81-47945. (Illus.). 656p. 1982. 40.00 (ISBN 0-691-08300-2). Princeton U Pr.
Techniques of Fire Photography. (Illus.). 1978. 16.50 (ISBN 0-685-54503-2, SPP-39SP). Natl Fire Prot.
Turner & McCreery. Chemistry of Fire & Hazardous Materials. 1980. text ed. 29.29 (ISBN 0-205-06912-6, 826912-2); instrs' manual avail. (ISBN 0-205-06913-4). Allyn.
Wanstall, Thomas K. Fire in Focus: An Action Portfolio. (Illus.). 96p. 1984. 14.95 (ISBN 0-916290-21-2). Squarebooks.
Wein, Ross W. & MacLean, David A. The Role of Fire in Northern Circumpolar Ecosystems. LC 82-2036. (Scope Series Scientific Committee on Problems of the Enviroment: No. 18). 322p. 1982. 64.95x (ISBN 0-471-10222-9, Pub. by Wiley-Interscience). Wiley.
Wright, Henry A. & Bailey, Arthur W. Fire Ecology: United States & Southern Canada. LC 81-14770. 501p. 1982. 49.50x (ISBN 0-471-09033-6, Pub. by Wiley-Interscience). Wiley.

FIRE BALLS
see Meteors

FIRE-DEPARTMENT PUMPERS
see Fire-Engines

FIRE DOGS
see Dogs–Breeds–Dalmatians

FIRE-ENGINES

Automotive Fire Apparatus. (Ten Ser). 104p. 1973. pap. 2.00 (ISBN 0-685-44164-4, 19). Natl Fire Prot.
McCall, Walter P., ed. American Fire Engines Since Nineteen Hundred. LC 75-31498. (Automotive Ser.). (Illus.). 384p. 1976. 29.95 (ISBN 0-912612-08-8). Crestline.
Mallet, J. Fire Engines of the World. LC 81-70215. (Illus.). 224p. 1982. 25.95 (ISBN 0-86710-051-6). Edns Vilo.
National Fire Protection Assn. Features of Fire Department Pumpers. Lyons, Paul R., ed. LC 75-37324. (Slide Script Ser). (Illus.). 75p. 1976. 35.00 (ISBN 0-87765-067-5, SL-17). Natl Fire Prot.
Vanderveen, Bart H. Fire & Crash Vehicles from Nineteen Fifty. (Olyslager Auto Library). (Illus.). 72p. 1976. 10.95 (ISBN 0-7232-1845-5, Pub. by Warne Pubs England). Motorbooks Intl.
--Fire-Fighting Vechicles, Eighteen Forty to Nineteen Fifty. (Olyslager Auto Library). (Illus.). 80p. 1972. 10.95 (ISBN 0-7232-1464-6, Pub. by Warne Pubs England). Motorbooks Intl.

Whitehead, Trevor. Fire Engines. (Shire Album Ser.: No. 68). (Illus.). 32p. pap. 2.95 (ISBN 0-85263-555-9, 3380579, Pub. by Shire Pubns England). Seven Hills Bks.

FIRE EXTINCTION

see also Fire-Engines; Forest Fires

Air Operations for Forest, Brush & Grass Fires. 2nd ed. LC 75-12409. 68p. 1975. pap. 4.25 (ISBN 0-87765-035-7, FSP-9A). Natl Fire Prot.

Aircraft Hand Fire Extinguishers. (Four Hundred Ser.). 1973. pap. 2.00 (ISBN 0-685-58062-8, 408). Natl Fire Prot.

Aircraft Rescue & Fire Fighting Techniques for Fire Departments Using Conventional Fire Apparatus. (Four Hundred Ser.). 1968. pap. 2.00 (ISBN 0-685-58060-1, 406M). Natl Fire Prot.

Attacking & Extinguishing Interior Fires. 134p. 1960. 5.50 (ISBN 0-685-46059-2, FSP-12). Natl Fire Prot.

Averill, C. F. Sprinkler Systems Design: Past, Present & Future. 1979. 2.50 (TR 79-3). Society Fire Protect.

Bahme, Charles W. Fire Officer's Guide to Extinguishing Systems. (Get Ahead Ser.). 104p. 1970. 5.00 (ISBN 0-685-46047-9, FSP-30). Natl Fire Prot.

--Fire Officer's Guide to Extinguishing Systems. Lyons, Paul R., ed. LC 76-53155. (Fire Officer's Guide Ser.). 1977. text ed. 7.50 (ISBN 0-87765-091-8, FSP-30A). Natl Fire Prot.

Beatteay, Robert E. Fire Officer's Guide to Waterfront Fires. LC 75-18738. (Fire Officer's Guide Ser.). (Illus.). 150p. 1975. 8.50 (ISBN 0-87765-046-2, FSP-42). Natl Fire Prot.

Carbon Dioxide Extinguishing System. (Ten Ser.). 100p. 1973. pap. 2.25 (ISBN 0-685-44156-3, 12). Natl Fire Prot.

Care & Maintenance of Sprinkler Systems. (Ten Ser). 1971. pap. 2.00 (ISBN 0-685-58130-6, 13A). Natl Fire Prot.

Care of Fire Hose. (Ten Ser.). 52p. 1972. pap. 2.00 (ISBN 0-685-46062-2, 198). Natl Fire Prot.

Casey, James F. Fire Service Hydraulics. 2nd ed. (Illus.). 1970. 22.95 (ISBN 0-912212-05-5). Fire Eng.

Casey, James F., ed. The Fire Chief's Handbook. 4th ed. (Illus.). 1978. 24.95 (ISBN 0-912212-04-7). Fire Eng.

Clark, William E. Fire Fighting Principles & Practices. (Illus.). 1974. 22.95 (ISBN 0-686-12259-3). Fire Eng.

Cohen, Stan B. A Pictorial History of Smoke Jumping. LC 83-62751. (Illus.). 180p. 1983. pap. 10.95 (ISBN 0-933126-40-9). Pictorial Hist.

Colburn, Robert E. Fire Protection & Suppression. Williams, Carlton, ed. (Illus.). 352p. 1975. text ed. 29.95 (ISBN 0-07-011680-6, 11680-6). McGraw.

Committee on Fire Research & Committee on Toxicology Staff. An Appraisal of Halogenated Fire Extinguishing Agents. (Illus.). 360p. 1972. pap. 9.25 (ISBN 0-309-02111-1). Natl Acad Pr.

Committee on Fire Research, National Research Council. Directory of Fire Research. 8th ed. 1978. pap. text ed. 9.95 (ISBN 0-309-02799-3). Natl Acad Pr.

Cozad, Dale. Water Supply for Fire Protection. (Illus.). 304p. 1981. text ed. 26.95 (ISBN 0-13-945964-2). P-H.

Dean, Anabel. Fire! How Do They Fight It? LC 77-17635. (Illus.). 1978. text ed. 9.95 (ISBN 0-664-32626-9). Westminster.

Detecting Fires. (Illus.). 116p. 1975. pap. 5.50 (ISBN 0-87765-033-0, SPP-28). Natl Fire Prot.

Dry Chemical Extinguishing Systems. (Ten Ser). 1973. pap. 2.00 (ISBN 0-685-58126-8, 17). Natl Fire Prot.

Emergency Operations in High Rack Storage. 80p. pap. text ed. 10.00 (ISBN 0-317-06720-6). Intl Fire Serv.

Erven, Lawrence. Techniques of Fire Hydraulics. (Fire Science Ser). 1972. text ed. write for info. (ISBN 0-02-473000-9, 47300). Macmillan.

Evaluating Foam Fire Fighting Equipment on Aircraft Rescue & Fire Fighting Vehicles. (Four Hundred Ser). 1974. pap. 2.50 (ISBN 0-685-58233-7, 412). Natl Fire Prot.

Fighting Hazardous Material Fires. (Illus.). 1983. pap. 8.45 (ISBN 0-912212-00-4). Fire Eng.

Fighting Tank Fires with Water. LC 75-37306. (Slide Script Ser.). (Illus.). 60p. 1975. 25.00 (ISBN 0-87765-061-6, SL-2). Natl Fire Prot.

Fire Attack One. (Illus.). 28p. 1966. 7.00 (ISBN 0-685-46043-6, FSP-1). Natl Fire Prot.

Fire Attack Two. (Illus.). 234p. 1968. 7.50 (ISBN 0-685-46045-2, FSP-2). Natl Fire Prot.

Fire Department Ladders, Ground & Aerial. (Ten Ser.). 1972. pap. 2.00 (ISBN 0-685-58122-5, 193). Natl Fire Prot.

Fire Department Operations in Protected Properties. (Ten Ser.). 1973. pap. 2.00 (ISBN 0-685-58129-2, 13E). Natl Fire Prot.

Fire Fighting Tactics. 112p. 1953. 5.50 (ISBN 0-685-46060-6, FSP-13). Natl Fire Prot.

Fire Hose. (Ten Ser). 1974. pap. 2.00 (ISBN 0-685-58120-9, 196). Natl Fire Prot.

Fire Terminology. 4th ed. 67p. 1970. 4.00 (ISBN 0-685-46056-8, FSD-3A). Natl Fire Prot.

Foam Extinguishing Systems. (Ten Ser). 116p. 1974. pap. 3.75 (ISBN 0-685-44155-5, 11). Natl Fire Prot.

Foam Water Sprinkler & Spray Systems. (Ten Ser). 1974. pap. 2.50 (ISBN 0-685-58127-6, 16). Natl Fire Prot.

Gold, David T. Fire Brigade Training Manual: Emergency Forces Training for Work Environments. Carwile, Ruth, ed. LC 82-82125. (Illus.). 236p. 1982. pap. text ed. 17.00 (ISBN 0-87765-224-4, SPP-73); training manual 21.50 (SPP-73M). Natl Fire Prot.

Guides for Fighting Fires in & around Petroleum Tanks. 30p. 1975. pap. 2.50 (ISBN 0-87765-049-7). Natl Fire Prot.

Haessler, Walter M. The Extinguishment of Fire. rev. ed. 1974. pap. text ed. 3.75 (ISBN 0-87765-024-1, FSP-40). Natl Fire Prot.

Halogenated Extinguishing Agent Systems: Halcon 1301. (Ten Ser). 84p. 1973. pap. 2.00 (ISBN 0-685-44157-1, 12A). Natl Fire Prot.

Halogenated Fire Extinguishing Agent Systems: Halcon 1211. (Ten Ser). 84p. 1973. pap. 2.00 (ISBN 0-685-44161-X, 12B). Natl Fire Prot.

Handling Hose & Ladders. (Illus.). 144p. 6.50 (ISBN 0-685-44147-4, FSP-5). Natl Fire Prot.

Hazards of Vaporizing Liquid Extinguishing Agents. (Ten Ser). 1965. pap. 2.00 (ISBN 0-685-58124-1, 182M). Natl Fire Prot.

High Expansion Foam Systems. (Ten Ser). 1970. pap. 6.00 (ISBN 0-685-58133-0, 11A). Natl Fire Prot.

Hydraulics for Fire Protection. LC 79-91611. (Illus.). 340p. 1980. text ed. 16.50 (ISBN 0-87765-170-1, TXT-6). Natl Fire Prot.

Hydraulics for the Fire Service: Hydraulic Field Equations, Vol. VI. LC 78-50007. (Illus.). 72p. (Orig.). 1980. pap. text ed. 42.50 (ISBN 0-87765-171-X, SL-60). Natl Fire Prot.

IFSTA Committee. Essentials of Fire Fighting. 2nd ed. FPP, ed. LC 83-61105. (Illus.). 426p. 1983. pap. text ed. 20.00 (ISBN 0-87939-049-2). Intl Fire Serv.

--Fire Apparatus Practices. 6th ed. Carlson, Gene & Orton, Charles, eds. LC 80-82822. 217p. 1980. pap. text ed. 10.00 (ISBN 0-87939-040-9). Intl Fire Serv.

--Fire Service Rescue Practices. 5th ed. Carlson, Gene, ed. LC 81-82148. (Illus.). 272p. 1982. pap. 11.00 (ISBN 0-87939-044-1). Intl Fire Serv.

--Fire Stream Practices. 6th ed. Carlson, Gene & Orton, Charles, eds. LC 80-80447. (Illus.). 206p. 1980. pap. text ed. 10.00 (ISBN 0-87939-041-7). Intl Fire Serv.

--Fire Ventilation Practices. 6th ed. Carlson, Gene & Orton, Charles, eds. LC 80-84149. 144p. 1981. pap. text ed. 10.00 (ISBN 0-87939-039-5). Intl Fire Serv.

--Ground Cover Fire Fighting Practices. 2nd ed. Carlson, Gene, ed. LC 82-71898. (Illus.). 164p. 1982. pap. text ed. 10.00 (ISBN 0-87939-038-7). Intl Fire Serv.

--Water Supplies for Fire Protection. 3rd ed. Laughlin, Jerry & Williams, Connie E., eds. LC 78-58881. (Illus.). 147p. 1978. pap. text ed. 10.00 (ISBN 0-87939-029-8). Intl Fire Serv.

Incident Command System-Approved by the California State Board of Fire Services, 1983. LC 83-62493. 224p. 1983. pap. text ed. 12.00 (ISBN 0-87939-051-4). Intl Fire Serv.

International Symposium on Flammability & Fire Retardants. Fire Retardants: Proceedings. Bhatnagar, Vijay M., ed. LC 74-33842. (Illus.). 350p. 1975. pap. 9.95x (ISBN 0-87762-166-7). Technomic.

Kerlin, Donald J. A Marine View of Fire Protection. 1983. 4.65 (ISBN 0-318-00475-5, TR 82-10). Society Fire Protect.

Kimball, Warren Y. Effective Streams for Fighting Fires. 88p. 1961. 2.00 (ISBN 0-685-46054-1, FSD-1). Natl Fire Prot.

Klevan, Jacob B. Modeling of Available Egress Time from Assembly Spaces or Estimating the Advance of the Fire Threat. 1982. 4.65 (ISBN 0-686-37666-8, TR 82-2). Society Fire Protect.

Klote, John H. & Fothergill, John W. Design of Smoke Control Systems for Buildings. (Illus.). 192p. 1983. pap. text ed. 40.00 (ISBN 0-910110-03-4). Am Heat Ref & Air Eng.

Kravontka, Stanley J. Communications for Fire Fighting & Evaluation. 1976. 3.25 (ISBN 0-686-17607-3, TR 76-5). Society Fire Protect.

Kuvshinoff, B. W., et al, eds. Fire Sciences Dictionary. LC 77-3489. 439p. 1977. 26.95x (ISBN 0-471-51113-7, Pub. by Wiley-Interscience). Wiley.

Luke, R. H. & McArthur, A. G. Bushfires in Australia. (Illus.). 359p. 1982. text ed. 20.00x (ISBN 0-642-02341-7, Pub. by CSIRO Australia); pap. text ed. 15.50. Intl Spec Bk.

Lyons, Paul R. Testing Fire Apparatus: Acceptance & Service Tests for Aerial Ladders, Pt. II. LC 78-59790. (Illus.). 50p. (Orig.). 1979. pap. text ed. 65.00 (ISBN 0-87765-136-1, SL-31). Natl Fire Prot.

--Testing Fire Apparatus: Acceptance & Service Tests for Elevating Platforms, Pt. III. LC 78-59790. (Illus.). 54p. (Orig.). 1979. pap. text ed. 65.00 (ISBN 0-87765-137-X). Natl Fire Prot.

Lyons, Paul R., ed. Fire Attack! Horizontal Tanks & Loading Racks. LC 75-15296. (Slide Set Ser.). (Illus.). 65p. 1975. soft cover 35.00 (ISBN 0-87765-044-6); 40 slides incl. (ISBN 0-685-62582-6). Natl Fire Prot.

--Fire Attack Truck Terminals. LC 75-10887. (Slide Set Ser.). (Illus.). 58p. 1975. 35.00 (ISBN 0-87765-034-9); 41 slides incl. (ISBN 0-685-62583-4). Natl Fire Prot.

McAniff, Edward. Strategic Concepts in Fire Fighting. (Illus.). 1974. 22.95 (ISBN 0-912212-02-0). Fire Eng.

Manning for Fire Attack. 72p. 1969. pap. 2.50 (ISBN 0-685-46044-4, FSD-6). Natl Fire Prot.

Meidl, James. Hazardous Materials Handbook. (Fire Science Ser). 1972. pap. text ed. write for info. (ISBN 0-02-476370-5, 47637). Macmillan.

Meldrum, D. H. Fighting Fire with Foam: Basics of Effective Systems. 1979. 3.50 (ISBN 0-686-25956-4, TR 79-2). Society Fire Protect.

Mendes, Robert F. Fighting High-Rise Building Fires: Tactics & Logistics. Lyons, Paul R., ed. LC 75-13715. (Illus.). 160p. 1975. 12.50 (ISBN 0-87765-037-3). Natl Fire Prot.

Model Enabling Act for Portable Fire Extinguishers. (Ten Ser). 1969. pap. 2.00 (ISBN 0-685-58134-9, 10L). Natl Fire Prot.

Model Enabling Act for Portable Fire Extinguishers: 1980. 1980. 7.00 (ISBN 0-317-07370-2, NFPA 10L). Natl Fire Prot.

Nao, T. Van. Forest Fire Prevention & Control. 1982. text ed. 39.50 (ISBN 90-247-3050-3, Pub. by Martinus Nijhoff). Kluwer Academic.

National Fire Protection Association. The Fire Almanac, 1984. 2nd ed. Carwile, Ruth H. & Cole, Marion, eds. 805p. (Orig.). 1983. pap. 9.95 (ISBN 0-87765-263-5, FSP-62A). Natl Fire Prot.

--Hydraulics for the Fire Sevice: Operating the Pumper, Vol. V. Lyons, Paul R., ed. LC 78-50007. (Illus.). 88p. 1979. text ed. 42.50 (ISBN 0-87765-157-4, SL-51). Natl Fire Prot.

NFPA. The Fire Fighter & Plastics in a Changing Environment. 1977. 35.00 (ISBN 0-87765-093-4, SL-25). Natl Fire Prot.

--Thak Vehicle Fire Fighting. Lyons, Paul R., ed. LC 75-24677. (Slide Script Ser.: No. SL-1). 52p. 1975. pap. text ed. 25.00 (ISBN 0-87765-048-9); 34 slides incl. (ISBN 0-685-62584-2). Natl Fire Prot.

NFPA Committee on Fire Department Equipment. Fire Apparatus Maintenance. 136p. 1966. 5.00 (ISBN 0-685-46057-6). Natl Fire Prot.

NFPA Forest Committee. Chemicals for Forest Fire Fighting. 2nd ed. 112p. 1967. 3.00 (ISBN 0-685-46049-5). Natl Fire Prot.

--Chemicals for Forest Fire Fighting. 3rd ed. Lyons, Paul, ed. LC 77-814121. 1977. pap. text ed. 6.50 (ISBN 0-87765-104-3, FSP-19A). Natl Fire Prot.

O'Hagan, John T. High Rise Fire & Life Safety. (Illus.). 1977. 21.95 (ISBN 0-912212-08-X). Fire Eng.

Plastics & Plastic Products. LC 75-39854. (Illus.). 126p. 1975. pap. 5.50 (ISBN 0-87765-064-0, SPP-35). Natl Fire Prot.

Proprietary Protective Signaling Systems. (Seventy Ser.). 56p. 1974. pap. 3.00 (ISBN 0-685-44175-X, 72D). Natl Fire Prot.

Protection from Exposure Fires. (Eighty-Ninety Ser.). 1970. pap. 2.00 (ISBN 0-685-58146-2, 80A). Natl Fire Prot.

Public Fire Service Communications. (Seventy Ser.). 68p. 1973. pap. 2.00 (ISBN 0-685-44176-8, 73). Natl Fire Prot.

Purington, Robert G. Hydraulics for the Fire Service: Pumps & Pumpers, Unit 4. Lyons, Paul R., ed. LC 78-50007. (Illus.). 1979. pap. text ed. 42.50 (ISBN 0-87765-148-5). Natl Fire Prot.

Pyle, Ernest W. New Techniques for Welding & Extending Sprinkler Pipes. 1976. 2.50 (ISBN 0-686-17608-1, TR 76-2). Society Fire Protect.

Respiratory Protective Equipment for Fire Fighters. (Ten Ser). 1971. pap. 2.00 (ISBN 0-685-58123-3, 19B). Natl Fire Prot.

Screw Threads & Gaskets for Fire Hose Connections. (Ten Ser). 1974. pap. 2.00 (ISBN 0-685-58131-4, 194). Natl Fire Prot.

Shaw, J. Principles of Wildfire Management. 352p. 1984. 32.95 (ISBN 0-07-056481-7). McGraw.

Sherad, Shirley E., ed. Fire-Fighting Foams & Foam Systems. LC 77-74657. (Illus.). 1977. pap. 6.00 (ISBN 0-87765-094-2, SPP-44). Natl Fire Prot.

Simon, Andrew. Fire Hydraulics. LC 82-7012. 232p. 1983. text ed. 27.95 (ISBN 0-471-09183-9); solutions manual 2.50 (ISBN 0-471-09179-0). Wiley.

Society for Fire Protection Engineers. Engineering Applications of Fire Technology Workshop: Proceedings. 1983. 44.75 (ISBN 0-318-00471-2). Society Fire Protect.

Standard Operating Procedures, Aircraft Rescue & Fire Fighting. (Four Hundred Ser.). 140p. 1973. pap. 2.00 (ISBN 0-685-44137-7, 402). Natl Fire Prot.

Standpipes & Hose Systems. (Ten Ser). 1981. pap. 6.00 (ISBN 0-685-58128-4, 14). Natl Fire Prot.

Stavitskiy, M. G., et al. Structural Design & Fire Extinguishing Systems. LC 83-1763. (Fire Fighting Aboard Ships Ser.: Vol. 2). 582p. (Orig.). 1983. pap. 69.95x (ISBN 0-87201-307-3). Gulf Pub.

Sylvia, Richard P. A Study Guide to Fire Service Hydraulics: Questions & Answers. 1971. pap. 12.95 (ISBN 0-912212-03-9). Fire Eng.

Synthetic Foam & Combined Agent Systems. (Ten Ser.). 1974. pap. 2.00 (ISBN 0-685-58132-2, 11B). Natl Fire Prot.

Training Standard on Initial Fire Attack. (Ten Ser). 1966. pap. 2.00 (ISBN 0-685-58119-5, 197). Natl Fire Prot.

University of Missouri, Division of Fire Training. Combating Vehicle Fires. Instructional Media Associates, Inc. & National Fire Protection Association, eds. LC 79-720176. (Illus.). 1979. pap. text ed. 49.50 (ISBN 0-87765-145-0). Natl Fire Prot.

Walsh, Charles V. & Marks, Leonard. Firefighting Strategy & Leadership. 2nd ed. (Illus.). 1976. text ed. 30.95 (ISBN 0-07-068026-4). McGraw.

Whitman, Lawrence E. Fire Safety in the Atomic Age. LC 79-17265. 288p. 1980. 24.95x (ISBN 0-88229-529-2); pap. 13.95x (ISBN 0-88229-732-5). Nelson-Hall.

FIRE EXTINCTION–EXAMINATIONS, QUESTIONS, ETC.

Goldwater, Sam. Five Hundred Competencies for Firefighter Certification. LC 83-62587. 140p. 1983. pap. text ed. 10.00 (ISBN 0-87939-050-6). Intl Fire Serv.

Rudman, Jack. Administrative Fire Alarm Dispatcher. (Career Examination Ser.: C-2602). (Cloth bdg. avail. on request). pap. 12.00 (ISBN 0-8373-2602-8). Natl Learning.

--Administrative Fire Marshall (Uniformed) (Career Examination Ser.: C-2603). (Cloth bdg. avail. on request). pap. 12.00 (ISBN 0-8373-2603-6). Natl Learning.

--Assistant Fire Marshal. (Career Examination Ser.: C-1105). (Cloth bdg. avail on request). pap. 12.00 (ISBN 0-8373-1105-5). Natl Learning.

--Battalion Chief-Fire Department. (Career Examination Ser.: C-81). (Cloth bdg. avail. on request). pap. 14.00 (ISBN 0-8373-0081-9). Natl Learning.

--Captain, Fire Department. (Career Examination Ser.: C-120). (Cloth bdg. avail. on request). pap. 14.00 (ISBN 0-8373-0120-3). Natl Learning.

--Deputy Chief, Fire Department. (Career Examination Ser.: C-195). (Cloth bdg. avail. on request). pap. 12.00 (ISBN 0-8373-0195-5). Natl Learning.

--Fire Alarm Dispatcher. (Career Examination Ser.: C-256). (Cloth bdg. avail. on request). pap. 12.00 (ISBN 0-8373-0256-0). Natl Learning.

--Fire Control Mechanic. (Career Examination Ser.: C-257). (Cloth bdg. avail. on request). pap. 12.00 (ISBN 0-8373-0257-9). Natl Learning.

--Fire Fighter. (Career Examination Ser.: C-1287). (Cloth bdg. avail. on request). pap. 10.00 (ISBN 0-8373-1287-6). Natl Learning.

--Fireman Examinations - All States. (Career Examination Ser.: C-258). (Cloth bdg. avail. on request). pap. 10.00 (ISBN 0-8373-0258-7). Natl Learning.

--Fireman, Fire Department. (Career Examination Ser.: C-259). (Cloth bdg. avail. on request). pap. 10.00 (ISBN 0-8373-0259-5). Natl Learning.

--Fireman-Laborer. (Career Examination Ser.: C-1289). (Cloth bdg. avail. on request). pap. 8.00 (ISBN 0-8373-1289-2). Natl Learning.

--Housing Fireman. (Career Examination Ser.: C-336). (Cloth bdg. avail. on request). pap. 8.00 (ISBN 0-8373-0336-2). Natl Learning.

FIRE EXTINCTION–HISTORY

Lyons, Paul R. Fire in America. LC 75-29598. (Illus.). 1976. 19.95 (ISBN 0-685-68872-0, SPP-33). Natl Fire Prot.

FIRE FIGHTING

see Fire Extinction

FIRE INVESTIGATION

Bates, Edward B. Elements of Fire & Arson Investigation. 1975. 8.50 (ISBN 0-89368-313-2). Davis Pub Co.

Carroll, John R. Physical & Technical Aspects of Fire & Arson Investigation. (Illus.). 470p. 1983. 44.50x (ISBN 0-398-03785-X). C C Thomas.

Cole, Lee S. The Investigation of Motor Vehicle Fires. 65p. 1980. pap. 5.00 (ISBN 0-939818-04-3). Lee Bks.

DeHaan, John D. Kirk's Fire Investigation. 2nd ed. LC 82-16078. 352p. 1983. text ed. 29.95 (ISBN 0-471-09279-7). Wiley.

Dennett, M. F. Fire Investigation: A Practical Guide for Fire Students & Officers, Insurance Investigators, Loss Adjustors, & Police Officers. (Illus.). 80p. 1980. 20.00 (ISBN 0-08-024741-5); pap. 9.75 (ISBN 0-08-024742-3). Pergamon.

IFSTA Committee. Fire Cause Determination. LC 82-62125. 159p. 1982. 10.00 (ISBN 0-87939-048-4). Intl Fire Serv.

Kennedy, John. Fire, Arson & Explosion Investigation. LC 77-76032. (Illus.). 1163p. 1977. 50.00 (ISBN 0-9607876-0-7). Investigations.

Kennedy, John & Kennedy, Patrick. Fires & Explosions: Determining Cause & Origin. LC 84-62332. (Illus.). 1562p. 1985. text ed. 50.00 (ISBN 0-9607876-1-5). Investigations.

Phillips, Calvin & McFadden, David. Investigating the Fireground. LC 82-1290. (Illus.). 288p. 1982. pap. 16.95 (ISBN 0-89303-074-0). Brady Comm.

Roblee, C. & McKechnie, A. Investigation of Fires. 1981. 24.95 (ISBN 0-13-503169-9). P-H.

FIRE PREVENTION

see also Fire Extinction; Fireproofing; Forest Fires; Lightning Arresters

also subdivision Fires and Fire Prevention under various classes of institutions and buildings, e.g. Schools–Fires and Fire Prevention

Aircraft Electrical Systems Maintenance Operations. (Four Hundred Ser). 1968. pap. 2.00 (ISBN 0-685-58061-X, 410A). Natl Fire Prot.

Alpert, Ronald L. & Ward, Edward J. Evaluating Unsprinklered Fire Hazards. 5.35 (ISBN 0-318-00407-0, TR83-2). Society Fire Protect.

Automatic Fire Detectors. (Seventy Ser.). 1974. pap. 3.00 (ISBN 0-685-58150-0, 72E). Natl Fire Prot.

Auxiliary Protective Signaling Systems. (Seventy Ser.). 1974. pap. 3.00 (ISBN 0-685-58063-6, 72B). Natl Fire Prot.

Babcock, Denise L. NFPA Fire Protection Reference Directory, 1979. 4th ed. 1980. pap. 8.00. Natl Fire Prot.

Bahme, Charles W. Fire Officer's Guide to Dangerous Chemicals. Lyons, Paul R., ed. LC 77-76481. (Illus.). 1978. 10.50 (ISBN 0-87765-101-9, FSP-36A). Natl Fire Prot.

Bare, William K. Fundamentals of Fire Prevention. LC 76-23221. (Fire Science Ser.). 213p. 1977. text ed. 27.95 (ISBN 0-471-04835-6). Wiley.

--Introduction to Fire Science & Fire Prevention. LC 77-14002. (Fire Science Ser.). 290p. 1978. text ed. 26.95x (ISBN 0-471-01708-6); tchrs. manual (ISBN 0-471-03779-6). Wiley.

Belles, Donald W. Fire Hazard Analysis from Plastic Insulation in Exterior Walls of Buildings. 1982. 5.35 (ISBN 0-686-37665-X, TR 82-1). Society Fire Protect.

Bhatnagar, Vijay M., ed. Advances in Fire Retardants, Pt. Two. LC 72-91704. (Progress in Fire Retardancy Ser.: Vol. 3). 200p. 1974. pap. 9.95 (ISBN 0-87762-111-X). Technomic.

--Fire Retardants: Proceedings of the First European Conference on Flammability & Fire Retardants. LC 78-66105. 1979. pap. 19.00 (ISBN 0-87762-264-7). Technomic.

Blair, William. Fire! Survival & Prevention. (Illus.). 192p. (Orig.). 1983. pap. 3.80i (ISBN 0-06-465147-9, P-BN 5147). B&N NY.

Brannigan, Francis L. Building Construction for the Fire Service. 2nd ed. McKinnon, Gordon P. & Matson, Debra, eds. LC 78-178805. (Illus.). 392p. 1982. text ed. 20.00 (ISBN 0-87765-227-9, FSP-33A). Natl Fire Prot.

Bryan, John L. Fire Suppression & Detections Systems. 2nd ed. 464p. 1982. text ed. write for info. (ISBN 0-02-471300-7). Macmillan.

Bugbee, Percy. Principles of Fire Protection. Tower, Keith & Dean, Amy, eds. LC 76-50848. 1978. text ed. 16.50 (ISBN 0-87765-084-5, TXT-4); instr. manual 3.50 (ISBN 0-87765-122-1, TXT-4A). Natl Fire Prot.

Butcher, D. G. & Parnell, A. C. Smoke Control in Fire Safety Design. 1979. 42.00x (ISBN 0-419-11190-5, Pub. by E & FN Spon, NO. 6558). Methuen Inc.

Butcher, E. G. & Parnell, A. C. Designing for Fire Safety. 372p. 1983. 54.95 (ISBN 0-471-10239-3). Wiley.

Campbell, John A. Adding Logic to Fire Prevention Systems. 1982. 4.65 (ISBN 0-686-37669-2, TR 82-5). Society Fire Protect.

--Estimating the Magnitude of Macro-Hazards. 1981. 3.75 (ISBN 0-686-31894-3, TR 81-2). Society Fire Protect.

--Expanding Fire Safety Management Systems in High-Rise Buildings. 4.65 (ISBN 0-318-00406-2, TR83-4). Society Fire Protect.

Central Station Signaling Systems. (Seventy Ser.). 1974. pap. 3.00 (ISBN 0-685-58066-0, 71). Natl Fire Prot.

Coakley, Deirdre, et al. The Day the MGM Grand Hotel Burned. LC 81-14511. (Illus.). 1982. 11.95 (ISBN 0-8184-0318-7). Lyle Stuart.

Code for Unmanned Rockets: 1982. 1982. 8.00 (ISBN 0-317-07396-6, NFPA 1122). Natl Fire Prot.

Colburn, Robert E. Fire Protection & Suppression. Williams, Carlton, ed. (Illus.). 352p. 1975. text ed. 29.95 (ISBN 0-07-011680-6, 11680-6). McGraw.

Coleman, Ron J. Opportunities in Fire Protection Services. (VGM Career Bks.). (Illus.). 160p. 1983. 7.95 (ISBN 0-8442-6264-1, 6264-1, Passport Bks.); pap. 5.95 (ISBN 0-8442-6266-8, 6266-8). Natl Textbk.

Commerce & Community Affairs Dept. Fire Protection Administration for Small Communities & Fire Protection Districts. LC 79-93086. (Illus.). 330p. 1980. pap. text ed. 15.00 (ISBN 0-87939-037-9). Intl Fire Serv.

Committee on Fire Research, National Research Council. Fire Detection for Life Safety. LC 76-53105. 1977. pap. 9.25 (ISBN 0-309-02600-8). Natl Acad Pr.

Connor, Joseph. Marine Fire Prevention, Fire Fighting & Fire Safety. (Illus.). 404p. 1979. pap. text ed. 16.95 (ISBN 0-87618-994-X). Brady Comm.

Critser, James R., Jr. Flame Retardants for Plastics, Rubber & Textiles: Including Indexes & Abstracts 1967 to 1971. Incl. 315.00 (ISBN 0-914428-03-9). (Ser. 2-6771b). 1971. Lexington Data.

Dean, Amy E. & Tower, Keith. Fire Protection Guide on Hazardous Materials. 7th ed. LC 78-59832. 1978. pap. 12.50 (ISBN 0-87765-130-2, SPP-1D). Natl Fire Prot.

Dean, Amy E., ed. Flash Point Index of Trade Liquids. 9th ed. LC 78-54003. 1978. pap. text ed. 5.50 (ISBN 0-87765-127-2, SPP-51). Natl Fire Prot.

DeCicco, Paul R. Life Safety Considerations in Atrium Buildings. 1982. 4.35 (ISBN 0-686-37667-6, TR 82-3). Society Fire Protect.

Design of Buildings for Fire Safety, STP 685. 290p. 1979. 28.00x (ISBN 0-8031-0320-4, 04-685000-31). ASTM.

DiNenno, Philip J. Simplified Radiation Heat Transfer Calculations from Large Open Hydrocarbon Fires. 1982. 5.35 (ISBN 0-686-37674-9, TR 82-9). Society Fire Protect.

Drysdale, D. D. Ignition: The Material, the Source & Subsequent Fire Growth. 5.35 (ISBN 0-318-00408-9, TR83-5). Society Fire Protect.

Earnest, Ernest. The Volunteer Fire Company. LC 78-8785. (Illus.). 224p. 1980. pap. 8.95 (ISBN 0-8128-6094-2). Stein & Day.

European Convention of Constructional Steelwork. European Recommendations for the Fire Safety of Steel Structures. 106p. 1983. 70.25 (ISBN 0-444-42120-3). Elsevier.

Explosion Prevention Systems. (Sixty Ser). 60p. 1973. pap. 2.00 (ISBN 0-685-44174-1, 69). Natl Fire Prot.

Explosives Motor Vehicle Terminals. (Forty Ser). 1970. pap. 2.00 (ISBN 0-685-58095-4, 498). Natl Fire Prot.

Fire Prevention & Suppression, Part 2. (Fire & Flammability Ser.: Vol. 18). 140p. 1981. 25.00 (ISBN 0-87762-297-3). Technomic.

Fire Protection Handbook. 13th ed. (Illus.). 2128p. 1969. 29.50 (ISBN 0-685-58184-5, FPH1369). Natl Fire Prot.

Fire Protection Library, 24 bks. 1147p. includes protective case 53.30 (ISBN 0-685-58054-7, FLP-A). Natl Fire Prot.

Fire Safety Educator's Handbook: A Comprehensive Guide to Planning, Designing, & Implementing Fire Safety Programs. LC 82-62828. 150p. 1983. 19.00 (ISBN 0-87765-231-7, FSP-61). Natl Fire Prot.

Fire Safety in Boarding Homes. LC 82-61904. 82p. 1982. pap. text ed. 10.50 (ISBN 0-87765-236-8, SPP-76). Natl Fire Prot.

Fire Standards & Safety - STP 614. 343p. 1977. 27.75 (ISBN 0-8031-0352-2, 04-614000-31). ASTM.

Glenn, Gary A. & Glenn, Peggy. Don't Get Burned: A Family Fire-Safety Guide. LC 82-6872. (Illus.). 210p. (Orig.). 1982. lib. bdg. 10.95 (ISBN 0-936930-81-0); pap. 7.95. Aames-Allen.

Gold, David T. Fire Brigade Training Manual: Emergency Forces Training for Work Environments. Carwile, Ruth, ed. LC 82-82125. (Illus.). 236p. 1982. pap. text ed. 17.00 (ISBN 0-87765-224-4, SPP-73); training manual 21.50 (SPP-73M). Natl Fire Prot.

Guard Operations in Fire Loss Prevention. (Six Hundred Ser). 1968. pap. 2.00 (ISBN 0-685-58227-2, 601A). Natl Fire Prot.

Guard Service in Fire Loss Prevention. (Six Hundred Ser). 1968. pap. 2.00 (ISBN 0-685-58226-4, 601). Natl Fire Prot.

Gupta, R. S. A Handbook of Fire Technology. 292p. 1981. 30.00x (ISBN 0-86125-113-X, Pub. by Orient Longman India); cloth with jacket 30.00x (ISBN 0-86125-088-5). State Mutual Bk.

Hazardous Locations. (Illus.). 160p. 1974. pap. 4.00 (ISBN 0-685-58192-6, 70C). Natl Fire Prot.

Health Care Facilities Code. LC 83-110354. 1984. 32.50; member 29.25. Natl Fire Prot.

Heskestad, Gunnar. Engineering Relations for Fire Plumes. 1982. 4.65 (ISBN 0-686-37673-0, TR 82-8). Society Fire Protect.

High Rise Fire Alarm Systems - Recommendations for State & Local Codes. 5.00 (ISBN 0-318-18045-6). Natl Elec Mfrs.

Household Fire Warning Equipment. (Seventy Ser). 1974. pap. 5.25 (ISBN 0-685-58149-7, 74). Natl Fire Prot.

Hydraulics for Fire Protection. LC 79-91611. (Illus.). 340p. 1980. text ed. 16.50 (ISBN 0-87765-170-1, TXT-6). Natl Fire Prot.

Hydraulics for the Fire Service: Hydraulic Field Equations, Vol. VI. LC 78-50007. (Illus.). 72p. (Orig.). 1980. pap. text ed. 42.50 (ISBN 0-87765-171-X, SL-60). Natl Fire Prot.

IFSTA Committee. Fire Prevention & Inspection. 4th ed. Hudiburg, Everett & Thomas, Charles, eds. (Illus.). 182p. 1974. pap. text ed. 8.00 (ISBN 0-87939-010-7). Intl Fire Serv.

--Forcible Entry, Rope & Portable Extinguisher Practices. 6th ed. Peige, John, et al, eds. LC 77-94425. (Illus.). 199p. 1978. pap. text ed. 10.00 (ISBN 0-87939-032-8). Intl Fire Serv.

--Industrial Fire Protection. LC 82-70085. (Illus.). 223p. 1982. 24.95 (ISBN 0-87939-047-6); pap. 17.95. Intl Fire Serv.

--Private Fire Protection & Detection Systems. Carlson, Gene P., ed. LC 79-55670. (Illus.). 184p. (Orig.). 1979. pap. 10.00 (ISBN 0-87939-036-0). Intl Fire Serv.

--Water Supplies for Fire Protection. 3rd ed. Laughlin, Jerry & Williams, Connie E., eds. LC 78-58881. (Illus.). 147p. 1978. pap. text ed. 10.00 (ISBN 0-87939-029-8). Intl Fire Serv.

Indoor General Storage. (Two Hundred Ser.). 1974. pap. 2.00 (ISBN 0-685-58169-1, 231). Natl Fire Prot.

Juillerat, Ernest. Campus Firesafety. new ed. Lyons, Paul R., ed. LC 77-82037. (Illus.). 1977. pap. 8.50 (ISBN 0-87765-106-X, SPP-46). Natl Fire Prot.

Klevan, Jacob B. Modeling of Available Egress Time from Assembly Spaces or Estimating the Advance of the Fire Threat. 1982. 4.65 (ISBN 0-686-37666-8, TR 82-2). Society Fire Protect.

Kuvshinoff, B. W., et al, eds. Fire Sciences Dictionary. LC 77-3489. 439p. 1977. 26.95x (ISBN 0-471-51113-7, Pub. by Wiley-Interscience). Wiley.

Laboratories in Health-Related Institutions. (Fifty Ser.). 1973. pap. 2.00 (ISBN 0-685-58087-3, 56C). Natl Fire Prot.

Levine, Robert S. & Pagni, Patrick J. Fire Science for Fire Saftey. (Combustion Science & Technology Ser.). 510p. 1984. pap. text ed. 75.00 (ISBN 2-88124-115-8). Gordon.

Local Protective Signaling Systems. (Seventy Ser.). 1974. pap. 3.00 (ISBN 0-685-58064-4, 72A). Natl Fire Prot.

Lucht, David A. Fire Prevention Planning & Leadership for Small Communities. Harmon, Ruth L., ed. LC 80-80229. (Illus.). 80p. (Orig.). 1980. pap. text ed. 4.95 (ISBN 0-87765-177-9, FSP-54). Natl Fire Prot.

Lyons, Paul R. Testing Fire Apparatus: Acceptance & Service Tests for Aerial Ladders, Pt. II. LC 78-59790. (Illus.). 50p. (Orig.). 1979. pap. text ed. 65.00 (ISBN 0-87765-136-1, SL-31). Natl Fire Prot.

--Testing Fire Apparatus: Acceptance & Service Tests for Elevating Platforms, Pt. III. LC 78-59790. (Illus.). 54p. (Orig.). 1979. pap. text ed. 65.00 (ISBN 0-87765-137-X). Natl Fire Prot.

--Testing Fire Apparatus: Acceptance & Service Tests for Pumpers, Pt. 1. LC 78-59790. 1979. pap. text ed. 65.00 (ISBN 0-87765-129-9). Natl Fire Prot.

MacGillivray, Lois. Decision-Related Research on the Organization of Service Delivery Systems in Metropolitan Areas: Fire Protection. LC 79-83819. 1979. codebook write for info. (ISBN 0-89138-985-7). ICPSR.

Manufacture, Transportation, Storage of Fireworks. (Fourty Ser). 52p. 1974. pap. 3.00 (ISBN 0-685-44169-5, 44A). Natl Fire Prot.

Marchant. Design for Fire Safety. Date not set. text ed. price not set (ISBN 0-408-00487-8). Butterworth.

Marine Publications Intl. Ltd., ed. Ships Firefighting Manual. 1981. 50.00x (ISBN 0-906314-03-8, Pub. by Marine Pubns Intl England). State Mutual Bk.

Meldrum, D. H. Fighting Fire with Foam: Basics of Effective Systems. 1979. 3.50 (ISBN 0-686-25956-4, TR 79-2). Society Fire Protect.

Melott, Ronald K. Is Energy Conservation Firesafe? 2.50 (ISBN 0-686-12081-7, TR 78-8). Society Fire Protect.

Moulton, Gene. Conducting Fire Inspections: A Guidebook for Field Use. LC 82-61920. 302p. 1982. 18.00 (ISBN 0-87765-230-9, SPP-75). Natl Fire Prot.

Mowrer, David S. Costing Data for Fire Protection in Complex Industrial Occupancies. 1982. 4.65 (ISBN 0-686-37671-4, TR 82-7). Society Fire Protect.

Nao, T. Van. Forest Fire Prevention & Control. 1982. text ed. 39.50 (ISBN 90-247-3050-3, Pub. by Martinus Nijhoff). Kluwer Academic.

National Electrical Code Handbook: 1981. 1981. 25.00 (ISBN 0-317-07377-X, SPC-6C). Natl Fire Prot.

National Fire Code Supplement, 2 vols. 1978. Set. 30.00 (ISBN 0-685-66909-2, NFC-S78). Natl Fire Prot.

National Fire Codes, 1978, 18 vols. rev. ed. 1978. Set. pap. 90.00 (ISBN 0-685-66908-4, NFC). Natl Fire Prot.

National Fire Protection Association. Danger! Fire Fighters at Work Safety One. LC 79-720640. (Illus.). 1979. pap. text ed. 60.00 (ISBN 0-87765-163-9, SL-53). Natl Fire Prot.

--Electrical Code for One & Two-Family Dwellings: 1981. 1981. 9.50 (ISBN 0-317-07379-6, NFPA 70A). Natl Fire Prot.

--The Fire Department Safety Program: Safety Two. LC 79-720641. (Illus.). 1979. pap. text ed. 60.00 (ISBN 0-87765-164-7, SL-54). Natl Fire Prot.

--Flammable & Combustible Liquids Code: 1981. 1981. 10.00 (ISBN 0-317-07372-9, NFPA 30). Natl Fire Prot.

--Guide to NFPA National Building Fire Safety Standards. Moulton, Gene A., ed. LC 83-61644. 60p. 1983. pap. text ed. 12.00 (ISBN 0-87765-260-0, SPP-78). Natl Fire Prot.

--Handling Pipeline Transportation Emergencies. Harmon, Ruth & Tower, Keith, eds. LC 79-720296. 1979. pap. text ed. 115.00 (ISBN 0-87765-149-3). Natl Fire Prot.

--Hydraulics for the Fire Sevice: Operating the Pumper, Vol. V. Lyons, Paul R., ed. LC 78-50007. (Illus.). 1979. text ed. 42.50 (ISBN 0-87765-157-4, SL-51). Natl Fire Prot.

--National Electrical Code Handbook: 1984. 1074p. 1983. 27.50 (ISBN 0-317-07356-7, SPP-6D). Natl Fire Prot.

NFPA & U.S. Department of Transportation. Handling Hazardous Materials Transportation Emergencies. Dean, Amy E., ed. LC 78-54010. 1978. pap. text ed. 350.00 (ISBN 0-87765-126-4, SL-29); wkbk. 10.00 (ISBN 0-87765-125-6, SL-29WB). Natl Fire Prot.

Operation Skyline. 1975. pap. 3.25 (ISBN 0-685-61258-9, SPP-27). Natl Fire Prot.

Osborn, Richard W. & Flach, George W. Tapping in to the NEC. Osborn, Richard W., ed. LC 82-82124. (Illus.). 178p. 1982. pap. text ed. 8.50 (ISBN 0-87765-226-0, NEC-QUE). Natl Fire Prot.

Outdoor General Storage. (Two Hundred Ser.). 1970. pap. 2.00 (ISBN 0-685-58170-5, 231A). Natl Fire Prot.

Powers, W. Robert. Sprinkler Experience in High-Rise Buildings. 1979. 3.25 (ISBN 0-686-26148-8, TR 79-1). Society Fire Protect.

Prevention of Fire & Dust Explosions in Grain Elevators & Bulk Grain Handling Facilities. (Sixty Ser.). 1973. pap. 2.00 (ISBN 0-685-58080-6, 61B). Natl Fire Prot.

Prevention of Furnace Explosions in Fuel-Oil & Natural Gas-Fired Watertube Boiler Furnaces with One Burner. (Eighty-Ninety Ser.). 68p. 1973. pap. 2.00 (ISBN 0-685-44149-0, 85). Natl Fire Prot.

Prevention of Furnace Explosions in Fuel Oil-Fired Multiple Burner Boiler-Furnaces. (Eighty-Ninety Ser.). 84p. 1974. pap. 3.50 (ISBN 0-685-44131-8, 85D). Natl Fire Prot.

Prevention of Furnace Explosions in Natural Gas-Fired Multiple Burner Boiler-Furnaces. (Eighty-Ninety Ser.). 68p. 1973. pap. 3.50 (ISBN 0-685-44130-X, 85B). Natl Fire Prot.

Prevention of Furnace Explosions in Pulverized Coal-Fired Multiple Burner Boiler-Furnaces. (Eighty-Ninety Ser.). 68p. 1974. pap. 3.50 (ISBN 0-685-44132-6, 85E). Natl Fire Prot.

Purington, Robert G. Hydraulics for the Fire Service: Unit I - Characteristics of Water. Lyons, Paul R., ed. LC 78-50007. (Illus.). 1978. pap. text ed. 42.50 (ISBN 0-87765-117-5, SL-27). Natl Fire Prot.

--Hydraulics for the Fire Service: Unit II - Water Flow, Friction Loss, Engine Pressure. Lyons, Paul R., ed. LC 78-50007. (Illus.). 1978. pap. text ed. 42.50 (ISBN 0-685-63021-8, SL-28). Natl Fire Prot.

Purpura, Philip. Security & Loss Prevention. LC 83-10044. 512p. 1983. text ed. 22.95 (ISBN 0-409-95075-0). Butterworth.

Recommended System for the Indentification of the Fire Hazards of Materials. (Seven Hundred Ser.). 1969. pap. 2.00 (ISBN 0-685-58213-2, 704M). Natl Fire Prot.

Remote Station Protective Signaling Systems. (Seventy Ser.). 1974. pap. 3.00 (ISBN 0-685-58065-2, 72C). Natl Fire Prot.
Rushbrook, F. Fire Aboard: The Problems of Prevention & Control in Ships, Port Installations & Offshore Structures. 2nd ed. (Illus.). 1979. 75.00 (ISBN 0-686-77984-3). Heinman.
Schainblatt, Al & Koss, Margo. Fire Code Inspections & Fire Prevention: What Methods Lead to Success? (Illus.). 122p. (Orig.). 1979. pap. text ed. 6.95x. Urban Inst.
Schwartz, Kenneth J. Effects of Thermal Insulation on Fire Resistive Assemblies. 1981. 4.00 (ISBN 0-686-31892-7, TR 81-7). Society Fire Protect.
Sherad, Shirley E., ed. Interior Finish & Fire Spread. LC 77-85254. 1977. pap. 11.00 (ISBN 0-87765-108-6, SPP-47). Natl Fire Prot.
Soros, Charles C. & Lyons, Paul R. Safety in the Fire Service. LC 79-84757. (Illus.). 1979. pap. 21.00 (ISBN 0-87765-147-7). Natl Fire Prot.
Standard Methods of Fire Tests for Flame Resistant Textiles & Films. (Seven Hundred Ser.). 1969. pap. 2.00 (ISBN 0-685-58210-8, 701). Natl Fire Prot.
Summers, Wilford. NFPA Handbook of the National Electrical Code. Tasner, Paul & Hill, Mary, eds. LC 77-93950. (Illus.). 1978. 15.50 (ISBN 0-87765-115-9, SPP-6B). Natl Fire Prot.
Tasner, Paul, et al, eds. Industrial Fire Hazards. LC 79-66427. (Illus.). 1979. 30.00 (ISBN 0-87765-155-8, SPP-57). Natl Fire Prot.
Telecommunications Systems. (Illus.). 1975. pap. 3.50 (ISBN 0-685-54122-3). Natl Fire Prot.
Tentative Standard for Evaluating Fire Protection at a New Facility. 1970. pap. 2.00 (ISBN 0-685-58200-0, 5A-T). Natl Fire Prot.
Tentative Standard on Fire Protection for Limited Access Highways, Tunnels, Bridges & Elevated Structures. 1972. pap. 2.00 (ISBN 0-685-58191-8, 502-T). Natl Fire Prot.
Thompson, Norman J. Fire Behavior & Sprinklers. 3rd ed. (Illus.). 167p. 1964. pap. text ed. 3.95 (ISBN 0-87765-052-7, SPP-2). Natl Fire Prot.
Thornberry, Richard P. Designing Stair Pressurization Systems. 1982. 4.65 (ISBN 0-686-37668-4, TR 82-4). Society Fire Protect.
Trade & Technical Press Editors. Handbook of Industrial Fire Protection & Security. 600p. 1976. 83.00x (ISBN 0-85461-059-6, Pub by Trade & Tech England). Brookfield Pub Co.
Trade & Technical Press Ltd, ed. Handbook of Industrial Fire Protection & Security. 150.00x (ISBN 0-85461-059-6). Intl Ideas.
Traister, John E. Design & Application of Security-Fire-Alarm Systems. (Illus.). 176p. 1981. 21.00 (ISBN 0-07-065114-0). McGraw.
Transue, Ralph E. Impact of Modern Electronics on Fire Protection. 1982. 3.35 (ISBN 0-686-37670-6, TR 82-6). Society Fire Protect.
Tuck, Charles A., Jr., ed. NFPA Inspection Manual. 5th ed. LC 76-5194. (Illus.). 387p. 1982. 20.00 (ISBN 0-87765-239-2, SPP-11C). Natl Fire Prot.
Vervalin, Charles H., ed. Fire Protection Manual for Hydrocarbon Processing Plants, Vol. 1. 3rd ed. LC 84-8989. (Illus.). 630p. 1985. 83.95x (ISBN 0-87201-333-2). Gulf Pub.
--Fire Protection Manual for Hydrocarbon Processing Plants, Vol. 2. LC 72-94065. 430p. 1981. 59.95x (ISBN 0-87201-288-3). Gulf Pub.
Water Spray Fixed Systems. (Ten Ser). 68p. 1973. pap. 2.00 (ISBN 0-685-44163-6, 15). Natl Fire Prot.
Whitman, Lawrence. Fire Prevention. LC 78-26894. (Illus.). 329p. 1979. 24.95x (ISBN 0-88229-359-1). Nelson-Hall.
Whitman, Lawrence E. Fire Safety in the Atomic Age. LC 79-17265. 288p. 1980. 24.95x (ISBN 0-88229-529-2); pap. 13.95x (ISBN 0-88229-732-5). Nelson-Hall.

FIRE PREVENTION–RESEARCH

Bhatnagar, Vijay M. Flammability of Apparel. LC 72-91704. (Progress in Fire Retardancy Ser.: Vol. 7). (Illus.). 230p. 1975. pap. 14.95 (ISBN 0-87762-165-9). Technomic.
Castino & Harmathy, eds. Fire Risk Assessment - STP 762. 112p. 1982. pap. 15.00 (ISBN 0-8031-0724-2, 04-762000-31). ASTM.
Committee on Fire Research, National Research Council. Directory of Fire Research. 8th ed. 1978. pap. text ed. 9.95 (ISBN 0-309-02799-3). Natl Acad Pr.
International Symposium on Flammability & Fire Retardants, 1974. Fire Retardants: Proceedings. Bhatnagar, Vijay M., ed. LC 72-33842. 200p. (Orig.). 1974. pap. 9.95x (ISBN 0-87762-196-9). Technomic.
Plane, Donald R., et al. Simulation of the Denver Fire Department for Development Policy Analysis. 1975. 2.50 (ISBN 0-686-64196-5). U CO Busn Res Div.

FIRE PROOFING
see Fireproofing
FIRE PUMPS
see Fire-Engines
FIRE RESEARCH
see Fire Prevention–Research

FIRE RESISTANT POLYMERS

Bhatnager, Vijay M., ed. Proceedings: 1976 International Symposium on Flammability & Fire Retardants. LC 75-25478. (Illus.). 1977. pap. 14.95x (ISBN 0-87762-215-9). Technomic.
Critser, James R., Jr. Flame, Retardants for Plastics, Rubber, Textiles & Paper (July 1978-June 1979) (Ser. 2-7879). 1979. 123.00 (ISBN 0-914428-61-6). Lexington Data.
--Flame Retardants for Plastics, Rubber, Textiles & Paper (July 1975-June 1976) (Ser. 2 - 7576). 1976. 123.00 (ISBN 0-914428-37-3). Lexington Data.
--Flame Retardants for Plastics, Rubber, Textiles & Paper (July 1979-June 1980) (Ser. 2-7980). 136p. 1980. refer. 130.00 (ISBN 0-914428-73-X). Lexington Data.
--Flame Retardants for Plastics, Rubber, Textiles & Paper (July 1980-June 1981) (Ser. 2-8081). 152p. 130.00 (ISBN 0-914428-82-9). Lexington Data.
Flame Retardant Additives for Thermoplastics & Thermosets. 158p. 1983. 78.00 (ISBN 0-317-12675-X, LS129). T-C Pubns CA.
Flame Retardant Report. 61p. 1972. 25.00 (ISBN 0-318-01524-2, 17050). Indus Fabrics.
Hilado, Carlos J., ed. Flammability of Cellulosic Materials, Part 2, Vol. 11. LC 73-82115. (Fire & Flammability Ser.). (Illus.). 1976. pap. 9.95x (ISBN 0-87762-171-3). Technomic.
International Symposium on Flammability & Fire Retardants, 1977. Fire Retardants: Proceedings. Bhatnagar, Vijay M., ed. LC 77-90574. (Illus.). 1977. pap. 14.95x (ISBN 0-87762-246-9). Technomic.
Kuryla, W. C. & Pappa, A. J. Flame Retardancy of Polymeric Materials, Vol. 5. 1979. 65.00 (ISBN 0-8247-6778-0). Dekker.
Kuryla, William C. & Papa, Anthony J., eds. Flame Retardancy of Polymeric Materials, Vol. 1. 334p. 1973. 65.00 (ISBN 0-8247-6012-3). Dekker.
--Flame Retardancy of Polymeric Materials, Vol. 2. 256p. 1973. 65.00 (ISBN 0-8247-6013-1). Dekker.
--Flame Retardancy of Polymeric Materials, Vol. 3. 376p. 1975. 65.00 (ISBN 0-8247-6235-5). Dekker.
Lewin, Menachem, et al, eds. Flame-Retardant Polymeric Materials, Vol. 1. LC 75-26781. 457p. 1975. 65.00x (ISBN 0-306-30840-1, Plenum Pr). Plenum Pub.
Melhotra, H. L. Design of Fire Resisting Structures. 1982. 49.95x (ISBN 0-412-00121-7, NO. 5019, Pub. by Chapman & Hall). Methuen Inc.
National Academy of Sciences. Elements of Polymer Fire Safety & Guide to the Designer, Vol. 5. LC 77-79218. (Fire Safety Aspects of Polymeric Materials Ser.). 151p. 1979. 17.00 (ISBN 0-87762-226-4). Technomic.
--Materials: State of the Art, Vol. 1. LC 77-79218. (Fire Safety Aspects of Polymeric Materials Ser.). 1977. text ed. 15.00x (ISBN 0-87762-222-1). Technomic.
--Ships. LC 77-79218. (Fire Safety Aspects of Polymeric Materials: Vol. 9). 236p. 1980. 19.00 (ISBN 0-87762-230-2). Technomic.
--Smoke & Toxicity: Combustion Toxicology of Polymers. LC 77-79218. (Fire Safety Aspects of Polymeric Materials Ser.: Vol. 3). 55p. 1978. 15.00 (ISBN 0-87762-224-8). Technomic.
--Test Methods, Specifications, & Standards. LC 77-79218. (Fire Safety Aspects of Polymeric Materials Ser.: Vol. 2). 99p. 1979. 18.00 (ISBN 0-317-17383-9). Technomic.
NFPA. The Fire Fighter & Plastics in a Changing Environment. 1977. 35.00 (ISBN 0-87765-093-4, SL-25). Natl Fire Prot.
Progress in Fire Safety: Regulations, Polymers, Chemicals, Markets - Fire Retardant Chemicals Association Conference, March 1982-Oct. 1982. 242p. 1983. 35.00 (ISBN 0-317-17385-5). Technomic.
Society of Plastics Engineers. Flame Retardant Needs of the Future: Building & Construction. (Illus.). pap. 62.30 (ISBN 0-317-10869-7, 2017600). Bks Demand UMI.
Yehaskel, A. Fire & Flame Retardant Polymers: Recent Developments. LC 78-70742. (Chemical Technology Review Ser: No. 122). (Illus.). 1979. 45.00 (ISBN 0-8155-0733-X). Noyes.

FIREARMS
see also Air Guns; Pistols; Revolvers; Rifles; Shooting; Shot-Guns
also names of specific kinds of firearms, e.g. Colt Revolver; Machine Guns; Mauser Rifle; Winchester Rifle

Anderson, Robert S. Metallic Cartridge Reloading. LC 81-70996. (Illus.). 320p. 1982. pap. 13.95 (ISBN 0-910676-39-9). DBI.
Askins, Charles. Askins on Pistols & Revolvers. Bryant, Ted & Askins, Bill, eds. 144p. 1980. text ed. 25.00 (ISBN 0-935998-22-5); pap. 9.95 (ISBN 0-935998-21-7). Natl Rifle Assn.
Automatic & Concealable Firearms Design Book, Vol. II. (Illus.). 64p. 1979. pap. 12.00 (ISBN 0-87364-177-9). Paladin Pr.
Barwick, Humphrey. Concerning the Force & Effect of Manual Weapons of Fire. LC 74-80163. (English Experience Ser.: No. 643). 86p. 1974. Repr. of 1594 ed. 8.00 (ISBN 90-221-0643-8). Walter J Johnson.
Bell, Bob. Scopes & Mounts: Gun Digest Bk. LC 83-72345. 224p. 1983. pap. 11.95 (ISBN 0-910676-61-5). DBI.
Bristow, Allen P. The Search for an Effective Police Handgun. (Illus.). 256p. 1973. 26.75x (ISBN 0-398-02554-1). C C Thomas.
Browne, Bellmore H. Guns & Gunning. (Shorey Lost Arts Ser.). (Illus.). 122p. pap. 4.95 (ISBN 0-8466-6014-8, U14). Shorey.
Cameron, Frank. Micro Guns. (Illus.). 48p. 1982. 24.00 (ISBN 0-88014-049-6). Mosaic Pr OH.
Carlisle, G. L. & Stanbury, Percy. Shotgun & Shooter. Rev. ed. 232p. 1981. 35.00x (ISBN 0-686-87325-4, Pub. by Hutchinson). State Mutual Bk.
Carmichel, Jim. Women's Guide to Handguns. 190p. 1983. pap. 8.95 (ISBN 0-88317-118-X). Stoeger Pub Co.
Chant, Chris. Armed Forces of the United Kingdom. LC 80-66428. (Illus.). 80p. 1980. 14.95 (ISBN 0-7153-8024-9). David & Charles.
Chomsky, Noam. Some Concepts & Consequences of the Theory of Government & Binding. (Linguistic Inquiry Monographs). 96p. 1982. 20.00x (ISBN 0-262-03090-X); pap. text ed. 7.95x (ISBN 0-262-53042-2). MIT Pr.
The Compleat Gunner: Sixteen Seventy-Two. 250p. 1983. 17.50 (ISBN 0-87556-430-5). Saifer.
Cromwell, Giles. The Virginia Manufactory of Arms. LC 74-8802. 1975. 20.00 (ISBN 0-8139-0573-7). U Pr of Va.
Daehnhardt, Rainer & Neal, W. Keith, eds. Espingarda Perfeyta; or the Perfect Gun: Rules for Its Use Together with Necessary Instructions for Its Construction & Precepts for Good Aiming. (Illus.). 480p. 1975. 48.00x (ISBN 0-85667-014-6, Pub by Sotheby Pubns England). Biblio Dist.
Davis, John E. An Introduction to Tool Marks, Firearms & the Striagraph. 302p. 1958. photocopy ed. 25.50x (ISBN 0-398-00402-1). C C Thomas.
Daw, George. Gun Patents 1864. 1982. 15.00x (ISBN 0-87556-251-5). Saifer.
Dunlap, Roy. The Gunowner's Book of Care, Repair & Maintenance. LC 73-92404. (Outdoor Life). (Illus.). 320p. 1974. 12.95i (ISBN 0-06-011137-2, HarpT). Har-Row.
Edsall, James. The Story of Firearm Ignition. 3.50 (ISBN 0-913150-27-4). Pioneer Pr.
--Volcanic Firearms & Their Successors. 2.50 (ISBN 0-913150-28-2). Pioneer Pr.
Erickson, Wayne R. & Pate, Charles E. The Broomhandle Pistol, Eighteen Ninety-Six to Nineteen Thirty-Six. 300p. 1985. 49.95x (ISBN 0-9614095-0-9). E & P Enter.
Ezell, Edward C. Handguns of the World. LC 81-8575. (Illus.). 704p. 1981. 39.95 (ISBN 0-8117-0816-0). Stackpole.
--Small Arms Today: Latest Reports on the World's Weapons & Ammunition. 256p. (Orig.). 1984. pap. 16.95 (ISBN 0-8117-2197-3). Stackpole.
Gambordella, Ted. Weapons of the Street. (Illus.). 80p. (Orig.). 1984. pap. 8.00 (ISBN 0-87364-281-3). Paladin Pr.
George, John N. English Pistols & Revolvers. 1979. 20.00x (ISBN 0-87556-153-5). Saifer.
Gore, Gerry. Handguns for Self Defense: A South African Guide. (Illus.). 164p. 1982. pap. 12.95x (ISBN 0-86954-079-3, Pub. by Macmillan S Africa). Intl Spec Bk.
Hatcher. The Book of the Garand. 17.95 (ISBN 0-88227-014-1). Gun Room.
Hatcher, Julian S. Hatcher's Notebook. rev. ed. LC 62-12654. (Illus.). 646p. 1962. 19.95 (ISBN 0-8117-0795-4). Stackpole.
Hatcher, Julian S., et al. Firearms Investigation, Identification & Evidence. (Illus.). 548p. 1977. Repr. 26.95 (ISBN 0-8117-0612-5). Stackpole.
Hoffschmidt, Edward J. Know Your Gun Set. Incl. Know Your .45 Auto Pistols. pap. 5.95; Know Your Walther P. 38 Pistols. pap. 5.95; Know Your Walther P. P. & P. P. K. Pistols. pap. 5.95; Know Your MI Garand Rifles. pap. 5.95; Know Your Mauser Broomhandle Pistol. pap. 6.95; Know Your Anti Tank Rifle. pap. 5.95. 1976. pap. Borden.
Hogg, Brig., frwd. by. The Compleat Gunner. (Illus.). 1976. Repr. 10.50x (ISBN 0-85409-677-9). Charles River Bks.
Hogg, Ivan V. Guns & How They Work. LC 78-53013. (Illus.). 1979. 16.95 (ISBN 0-89696-023-4, An Everest House Book). Dodd.
Home Workshop Silencers I. (Illus.). 72p. 1980. pap. 12.00 (ISBN 0-87364-193-0). Paladin Pr.
Howe, Walter J. Professional Gunsmithing. (Illus.). 416p. 1946. 24.95 (ISBN 0-8117-1375-X). Stackpole.
Huebner, Siegfried F. Silencers for Hand Firearms. LC 76-13260. (Illus.). 100p. 1976. pap. 11.95 (ISBN 0-87364-055-1). Paladin Pr.
Huntington, R. T. Hall's Breechloaders: John H. Hall's Invention & Development of a Breechloading Rifle with Precision-Made Interchangeable Parts, & Its Introduction into the United States Service. LC 71-91843. (Illus.). 369p. 1972. pap. 20.00 softbound (ISBN 0-87387-049-2). Shumway.
Irwin, John R. Guns & Gunmaking Tools of Southern Appalachia. 2nd ed. (Illus.). 118p. 1983. pap. 9.95 (ISBN 0-916838-81-1). Schiffer.
Jackson & Whitelaw. European Hand Firearms. 1978. 25.00 (ISBN 0-87556-154-3). Saifer.
James, Garry, ed. Guns for Home Defense. LC 74-25603. (Petersen Books Sports & Hobbies Ser.). (Illus.). 1975. pap. 3.95 (ISBN 0-8227-0088-3). Petersen Pub.
Kates, Don B., Jr. Firearms & Violence: Issues of Public Policy. (Pacific Institute on Public Policy Research Ser.). 608p. 1984. prof ref 38.00 (ISBN 0-88410-922-4); pap. write for info. (ISBN 0-88410-923-2). Ballinger Pub.
Kennedy, Monty. Checkering & Carving of Gunstocks. rev. ed. (Illus.). 352p. 1952. 27.95 (ISBN 0-8117-0630-3). Stackpole.
Larson, E. Dixon. Remington Tips. 4.95 (ISBN 0-913150-34-7). Pioneer Pr.
Lauber, Georg. How to Build Your Own Flintlock Rifle or Pistol. Seaton, Lionel, tr. from Ger. LC 75-11043. (Sports Library). (Illus.). 1976. pap. text ed. 6.95 (ISBN 0-89149-003-5). Jolex.
--How to Build Your Own Wheellock Rifle or Pistol. Seaton, Lionel, tr. from Ger. LC 75-11042. (Sports Library). (Illus.). 1976. pap. 12.50 (ISBN 0-89149-002-7). Jolex.
Lenk, Torsten. Flintlock: Its Origin & Development. 45.00 (ISBN 0-87556-149-7). Saifer.
Lewis, Jack. Black Powder Gun Digest. 3rd ed. LC 72-86645. (Illus.). 256p. 1982. pap. 11.95 (ISBN 0-910676-41-0). DBI.
--Law Enforcement Handgun Digest. 3rd ed. LC 73-186804. (Illus.). 288p. 1980. pap. 10.95 (ISBN 0-695-81413-3). DBI.
Lewis, Jack & Mitchell, Jack. Combat Handgunnery. LC 83-72347. 288p. 1983. pap. 11.95 (ISBN 0-910676-62-3). DBI.
Lindsay, Merrill. Twenty Great American Guns. (Illus.). 34p. 1976. pap. 1.75 (ISBN 0-686-15689-7). Arma Pr.
Murtz, Harold A., ed. Exploded Firearms Drawings. 3rd ed. LC 73-91584. (Illus.). 480p. 1982. pap. 14.95 (ISBN 0-910676-45-3). DBI.
Myatt, F. An Illustrated Guide to Rifles & Automatic Weapons. LC 80-70977. (Illustrated Military Guides Ser.). (Illus.). 160p. 1981. 9.95 (ISBN 0-668-05229-5, 5229). Arco.
Nation Muzzle Loading Rifle Association. Muzzle Blasts: Early Years Plus Vol I & II 1939-41. LC 74-11637. 352p. 1974. pap. 18.00 softbound (ISBN 0-87387-069-7). Shumway.
Nonte, George C., Jr. Combat Handguns. Jurras, Lee F., ed. LC 79-21398. (Illus.). 352p. 1980. 19.95 (ISBN 0-8117-0409-2). Stackpole.
--Home Guide to Muzzle Loaders. LC 74-16168. (Illus.). 224p. 1982. pap. 14.95 (ISBN 0-8117-2101-9). Stackpole.
Nonte, George C., Jr. & Jurras, Lee E. Handgun Hunting. (Illus.). 256p. pap. 7.95 (ISBN 0-88317-070-1). Stoeger Pub Co.
Paladin Press Books Editors. Automatic & Concealable Firearms Design Book, III. (Illus.). 64p. 1982. pap. 12.00 (ISBN 0-87364-224-4). Paladin Pr.
Pollard, Hugh B. The History of Firearms. LC 72-82385. 1974. lib. bdg. 29.50 (ISBN 0-686-57680-2, Artemis); pap. 8.95 (ISBN 0-89102-091-8). B Franklin.
Price, Robert M. Firearms Self-Defense: An Introductory Guide. (Illus.). 160p. 1981. 19.95 (ISBN 0-87364-218-X). Paladin Pr.
Reese, Michael, II. Nineteen Hundred Luger-U.S. Test Trials. 2nd rev. ed. Pioneer Press, ed. LC 71-117532. (Illus.). pap. 4.95 (ISBN 0-913150-35-5). Pioneer Pr.
Reilly, Robert M. United States Military Small Arms, 1816-1865. 1983. 35.00 (ISBN 0-88227-019-2). Gun Room.
Riling, Ray. Guns & Shooting: A Bibliography. (Illus.). 1981. 75.00 (ISBN 0-9603094-3-8). Ray Riling.
The Ruger Pistol Exotic Weapons System. (Exotic Weapons Systems Ser.). (Illus.). 96p. (Orig.). 1984. pap. 12.00 (ISBN 0-87364-286-4). Paladin Pr.
Ryan, J. W. Guns, Mortars & Rockets. (Brassey's Battlefield Weapons Systems & Technology: Vol. 2). (Illus.). 236p. 1982. 26.00 (ISBN 0-08-028324-1, P110); pap. 13.00 (ISBN 0-08-028325-X). Pergamon.
Sell. Handguns Americana. 1973. 8.50 (ISBN 0-87505-102-2). Borden.
Shelsby, Earl, ed. NRA Gunsmithing Guide: Updated. rev. ed. (Illus.). 336p. (Orig.). 1980. pap. text ed. 11.95 (ISBN 0-935998-47-0). Natl Rifle Assn.

Stanford, J. K. Complex Gun. 19.50x (ISBN 0-392-00519-0, SpS). Sportshelf.
Steindler, R. A. Reloader's Guide. 3rd ed. (Illus.). 224p. pap. 8.95 (ISBN 0-88317-021-3). Stoeger Pub Co.
Steiner, Bradley. The Death Dealer's Manual. (Illus.). 112p. (Orig.). 1982. pap. 10.00 (ISBN 0-87364-247-3). Paladin Pr.
Stockbridge, V. D. Digest of U. S. Patents Relating to Breech-Loading & Magazine Small Arms, 1836-1873. (Illus.). 1963. 12.50 (ISBN 0-910598-02-9). Flayderman.
Sybertz, Gustav. Technical Dictionary for Weaponry. (Ger. & Eng.). 1969. pap. 120.00 (ISBN 3-7888-0081-X, M-7642, Pub. by Neumann-Neudamm). French & Eur.
Thielen, Thomas W. The Complete Guide to Gun Shows. 1980. pap. 6.95 (ISBN 0-686-30707-0). Loompanics.
Thomas, Donald G. Silencer Patents, Vol. III: European Patents 1901-1978. (Illus.). 253p. 1978. pap. 15.00 (ISBN 0-87364-102-7). Paladin Pr.
Traister, John E. How to Buy & Sell Used Guns. 192p. (Orig.). 1982. pap. 9.95 (ISBN 0-88317-114-7). Stoeger Pub Co.
U. S. Army Sniper Training Manual. (Illus.). 196p. 1969. pap. 14.95 (ISBN 0-87364-120-5). Paladin Pr.
Van Rensselaer, S. American Firearms. (Illus.). 1948. pap. 15.00 (ISBN 0-87282-093-9). CHB-ALF.
West, Bill. Winchester Encyclopedia. (Winchester for Over a Century Ser.). (Illus.). 15.00x (ISBN 0-911614-02-8). B West.
--Winchester Lever-Action Handbook. (Winchester for Over a Century Ser.). (Illus.). 25.00x (ISBN 0-911614-06-0). B West.
--The Winchester Single Shot. (Winchester for Over a Century Ser.). (Illus.). 15.00x (ISBN 0-911614-03-6). B West.
--Winchesters, Cartridges, & History. (Winchester for Over a Century Ser.). (Illus.). 36.00x (ISBN 0-911614-04-4). B West.
Weston, Paul B. The New Handbook of Handgunning. (Illus.). 112p. 1980. 12.95x (ISBN 0-398-04092-3). C C Thomas.
Williams, John J. Survival Guns & Ammo: Raw Meat. (Illus.). 52p. 1979. pap. 15.00 (ISBN 0-934274-00-2). Consumertronics.
Williams, Mason. The Law Enforcement Book of Weapons, Ammunition & Training Procedures: Handguns, Rifles & Shotguns. (Illus.). 544p. 1977. photocopy 55.50x (ISBN 0-398-03576-8). C C Thomas.
Wood, J. B. Gun Digest Book of Firearms Assembly - Disassembly: Pt. VI: Law Enforcement Weapons. LC 79-54271. (Illus.). 288p. 1981. pap. 12.95 (ISBN 0-910676-31-3). DBI.

FIREARMS INDUSTRY AND TRADE
see also Gunsmithing
Farley, Philip J., et al. Arms Across the Sea. LC 77-91804. 1978. 22.95 (ISBN 0-8157-2746-1); pap. 8.95 (ISBN 0-8157-2745-3). Brookings.
Grancsay, Stephen V. & Lindsay, Merrill. Illustrated British Firearms Patents 1718-1853. limited ed. LC 77-99750. (Illus.). 450p. 1969. 75.00 (ISBN 0-87691-008-8). Arma Pr.
Hartzler, Daniel D. Arms Makers of Maryland. LC 74-24434. (Longrifle Ser.). (Illus.). 312p. 1977. 40.00 (ISBN 0-87387-054-9). Shumway.
Kirkland, Turner. Southern Derringers of the Mississippi Valley. 2.00 (ISBN 0-913150-00-2). Pioneer Pr.
Noel-Baker, Philip. The Private Manufacture of Armaments. LC 78-145399. 1971. pap. 7.00 (ISBN 0-486-22736-7). Dover.
West, Bill. Browning Arms & History, Eighteen Forty-Two to Date. LC 72-81300. (West Arms Library). (Illus.). 380p. 1972. 29.00x (ISBN 0-911614-12-5). B West.

FIREFLIES
Arnett, Ross H., Jr. Checklist of the Beetles of North & Central America & the West Indies: The Click Beetles, Fireflies, Checkered Beetles, & Related Groups, Vol. 4. 215p. 1983. 23.00x (ISBN 0-916846-17-2). Flora & Fauna.

FIREPLACES
Baden-Powell, Charlotte. Fireplace Design & Construction. LC 83-5449. (Illus.). 224p. text ed. 40.00 (ISBN 0-7114-5619-4). Longman.
Bortz, Paul. Getting More Heat from Your Fireplace. LC 81-13389. (Illus.). 156p. 1982. pap. 7.95 (ISBN 0-88266-254-6). Garden Way Pub.
Brann, Donald R. How to Install a Fireplace, Bk. 674. LC 67-15264. (Illus.). 1978. pap. 7.95 (ISBN 0-87733-674-1). Easi-Bild.
Danz, Ernst & Menges, Axel. Modern Fireplaces. (Illus.). 1979. 29.95 (ISBN 0-8038-0165-3). Architectural.
Harrington, Geri. Fireplace Stoves, Hearths, & Inserts. LC 80-7587. (Illus.). 192p. 1980. 20.00i (ISBN 0-06-011821-0, HarpT). Har-Row.
--Fireplace Stoves, Hearths, & Inserts: A Guide & Catalog. LC 80-7587. (Illus.). 192p. 1980. pap. 8.95i (ISBN 0-06-090804-1, CN 804, CN). Har-Row.
Hills, Nicholas. The English Fireplace: Its Architecture & the Working Fire. 158p. 1984. 19.95 (ISBN 0-907621-22-8, Pub. by Salem Hse Ltd). Merrimack Pub Cir.
Jones, Robert E. & Burch, Monte. Fireplaces. Horowitz, Shirley M. & Auer, Marilyn M., eds. LC 80-67153. (Illus.). 128p. (Orig.). 1980. 19.95 (ISBN 0-932944-25-6); pap. 6.95 (ISBN 0-932944-26-4). Creative Homeowner.
Kern & Magers. Fireplaces. 200p. 7.95 (ISBN 0-686-31218-X). Owner-Builder.
Kern, Ken & Magers, Steve. Fireplaces: The Owner-Builder's Guide. 1978. pap. 7.95 (ISBN 0-684-15885-X, ScribT). Scribner.
Ladd, Paul R. Early American Fireplaces. (Illus.). 1977. 16.95 (ISBN 0-8038-1930-7). Hastings.
Lytle, R. J. & Little, Marie J. Fireplaces. rev. ed. (Successful Home Improvement Ser.). 96p. 1981. pap. 3.95 (ISBN 0-8249-6105-6). Ideals.
Orton, Vrest. The Forgotten Art of Building a Good Fireplace. LC 70-9285. (Forgotten Arts Ser.). (Illus.). 64p. (Orig.). 1969. pap. 4.95 (ISBN 0-911658-53-X). Yankee Bks.
Self, Charles R. Wood Heating Handbook. 2nd ed. 1983. 16.95 (ISBN 0-8306-0096-5); pap. 9.95 (ISBN 0-8306-1472-9, 1472). TAB Bks.
Stedman, Myrtle. Adobe Fireplaces. rev. ed. LC 77-78520. (Illus., Orig.). 1977. pap. 2.50 (ISBN 0-913270-32-6). Sunstone Pr.
Sunset Editors. Fireplaces: How to Plan & Build. 4th ed. LC 79-90337. 96p. 1980. pap. 5.95 (ISBN 0-376-01157-2, Sunset Bks). Sunset-Lane.
Taylor, A. D. Campstoves, Fireplaces & Chimneys. (Shorey Lost Arts Ser.). (Illus.). 112p. pap. 9.95 (ISBN 0-8466-6055-5, U-55). Shorey.

FIREPROOF BUILDING
see Building, Fireproof

FIREPROOFING
see also Fire Resistant Polymers
Bhatnagar, Vijay M., ed. Advances in Fire Retardant Textiles. LC 72-91704. (Progress in Fire Retardancy Ser.: Vol. 5). 500p. 1974. pap. 14.95 (ISBN 0-87762-143-8). Technomic.
--Fire Retardant Polyurethanes: Formulations Handbook, Vol. 8. LC 72-91704. (Progress in Fire Retardancy Ser.). (Illus.). 1977. pap. 9.95x (ISBN 0-87762-217-5). Technomic.
--Fire Retardants: Proceedings of the First European Conference on Flammability & Fire Retardants. LC 78-66105. 1979. pap. 19.00 (ISBN 0-87762-264-7). Technomic.
Bhatnager, Vijay M., ed. Proceedings: 1976 International Symposium on Flammability & Fire Retardants. LC 75-25478. (Illus.). 1977. pap. 14.95x (ISBN 0-87762-215-9). Technomic.
Building Services Library, 15 bks. 1300p. includes protective case 38.70 (ISBN 0-685-58049-0, BSL-A). Natl Fire Prot.
Critser, James R., Jr. Flame, Retardants for Plastics, Rubber, Textiles & Paper (July 1978-June 1979) (Ser. 2-7879). 1979. 123.00 (ISBN 0-914428-61-6). Lexington Data.
--Flame Retardants for Plastics, Rubber, Textiles & Paper (July 1974-June 1975) (Ser. 2-7475). 1975. 123.00 (ISBN 0-914428-30-6). Lexington Data.
--Flame Retardants for Plastics, Rubber, Textiles & Paper (July 1976-June 1977) (Ser. 2-7677). 1977. 123.00 (ISBN 0-914428-49-7). Lexington Data.
--Flame Retardants for Plastics, Rubber, Textiles & Paper (July 1977-June 1978) (Ser. 2-7778). 1978. 123.00 (ISBN 0-914428-55-1). Lexington Data.
Dean, Amy E., ed. Flash Point Index of Trade Liquids. 9th ed. LC 78-54003. 1978. pap. text ed. 5.50 (ISBN 0-87765-127-2, SPP-51). Natl Fire Prot.
Fire & Smoke Retardant Chemicals Outlook. 1984. 1500.00 (ISBN 0-89336-205-0, C-004N). BCC.
Fire Protection by Sprinklers. LC 75-21643. (Illus.). 100p. 1975. pap. 4.75 (ISBN 0-87765-047-0, SPP-30). Natl Fire Prot.
Fire Resistance: Fire Safety of Concrete Structures. 308p. 1983. 42.50 (ISBN 0-317-37046-4); members 32.25 (ISBN 0-317-37047-2). ACI.
Hilado, Carlos J., ed. Flame Retardants, Part 2, Vol. 16. LC 73-82115. (Fire & Flammability Ser.). (Illus.). 1976. pap. 9.95x (ISBN 0-87762-176-4). Technomic.
--Flooring & Floor Covering Materials, Vol. 12. LC 73-82115. (Fire & Flammability Ser.). (Illus.). 1976. pap. 9.95x (ISBN 0-87762-172-1). Technomic.
Marchant. Design for Fire Safety. Date not set. text ed. price not set (ISBN 0-408-00487-8). Butterworth.
Progress in Fire Safety: Regulations, Polymers, Chemicals, Markets - Fire Retardant Chemicals Association Conference, March 1982-Oct. 1982. 242p. 1983. 35.00 (ISBN 0-317-17385-5). Technomic.
Society of Fire Protection Engineers. Computer Applications in Fire Protection: Analysis, Modeling & Design, Proceedings from the 1984 Annual Symposium. 243p. 1985. 49.75 (ISBN 0-318-12115-8). Society Fire Protect.
Thiery, P. Fireproofing: Chemistry, Technology & Applications. (Illus.). 156p. 1970. 24.00 (ISBN 0-444-20062-2, Pub. by Elsevier Applied Sci England). Elsevier.
Thiery, P. & Goundry, J. H. Fireproofing: Chemistry, Technology, & Applications. (Illus.). 1970. 22.30x (ISBN 0-444-20062-2, Pub. by Applied Science). Burgess-Intl Ideas.
Trade & Technical Press Editors. Handbook of Industrial Fire Protection & Security. 600p. 1976. 83.00x (ISBN 0-85461-059-6, Pub by Trade & Tech England). Brookfield Pub Co.
United Nations Economic Commission for Europe, Timber Committee. Behaviour of Wood Products in Fire: Proceedings, Oxford, 1977. 1977. pap. text ed. 35.00 (ISBN 0-08-021990-X). Pergamon.
Williams, Alec. Flame Resistant Fabrics. LC 74-79393. (Chemical Technology Review Ser: No. 36). (Illus.). 339p. 1975. 36.00 (ISBN 0-8155-0544-2). Noyes.

FIRES
see also Fire Extinction; Fire Investigation; Fire Prevention; Forest Fires
also subdivision Fires and Fire Prevention under various classes of institutions and buildings, e.g. Schools–Fires and Fire Prevention; Particular conflagrations are entered under names of place, e.g. London–Fire, 1666
American Society for Testing & Materials. Fire Risk Assessment: A Symposium. Castino, G. T. & Harmathy, T. Z., eds. LC 81-68807. (ASTM Special Technical Publication: No. 762). pap. 27.80 (ISBN 0-317-26540-7, 2023990). Bks Demand UMI.
Coakley, Deirdre, et al. The Day the MGM Grand Hotel Burned. LC 81-14511. (Illus.). 1982. 11.95 (ISBN 0-8184-0318-7). Lyle Stuart.
DiNenno, Philip J. Simplified Radiation Heat Transfer Calculations from Large Open Hydrocarbon Fires. 1982. 5.35 (ISBN 0-686-37674-9, TR 82-9). Society Fire Protect.
A Hazard Study: Natural Gas Fires & Explosions. (Illus.). 1974. pap. 2.00 (ISBN 0-685-58193-4, HS-9). Natl Fire Prot.
Hotel Fires Behind the Headlines. LC 82-51056. 161p. 1982. pap. text ed. 13.50 (ISBN 0-87765-228-7, SPP-74). Natl Fire Prot.
Investigation Report on the Westchase Hilton Hotel Fire. LC 82-61906. 64p. 1982. pap. text ed. 10.00 (ISBN 0-87765-238-4, LS-7). Natl Fire Prot.
Kennedy, John & Kennedy, Patrick. Fires & Explosions: Determining Cause & Origin. LC 84-62332. (Illus.). 1562p. 1985. text ed. 50.00 (ISBN 0-9607876-1-5). Investigations.
Klevan, Jacob B. Modeling of Available Egress Time from Assembly Spaces or Estimating the Advance of the Fire Threat. 1982. 4.65 (ISBN 0-686-37666-8, TR 82-2). Society Fire Protect.
Kravontka, Stanley J. Elevator Use During Fires in Megastructures. 1976. 2.50 (ISBN 0-686-22737-9, TR-76-1). Society Fire Protect.
LP-Gas Fires & Explosions. 52p. 1961. pap. 1.50 (ISBN 0-685-44152-0, Q55-5). Natl Fire Prot.
Planer, R. Fire Loss Control. (Occupational Safety Ser.: Vol. 3). 1979. 39.75 (ISBN 0-8247-6890-6). Dekker.
Powers, W. Robert. Electrical Fires in New York City - 1976. 1977. 2.50 (ISBN 0-686-22739-5, TR 77-3). Society Fire Protect.
Shpilberg, David. Statistical Decomposition of Industrial Fire Loss. LC 80-52616. (S. S. Huebner Foundation Monographs: No. 11). 102p. (Orig.). 1982. pap. 14.95 (ISBN 0-918930-11-1). Huebner Foun Insur.
Swab, Steven E. Incendiary Fires: A Reference Manual for Fire Analysis. LC 82-25313. (Illus.). 244p. 1983. pap. 19.95 (ISBN 0-89303-540-8). Brady Comm.

FIREWOOD
see Wood As Fuel

FIREWORKS
see also Military Fireworks
Barbour, Richard T. Pyrotechnics in Industry. LC 80-11152. (Illus.). 190p. 1981. 25.95 (ISBN 0-07-003653-5). McGraw.
Conkling. Chemistry & Pyrotechnics: Basic Principles & Theory. 216p. 1985. 49.75 (ISBN 0-8247-7443-4). Dekker.
Lancaster, Ronald, et al. Fireworks Principles & Practice. (Illus.). 1972. 22.50 (ISBN 0-8206-0216-7). Chem Pub.
McLain, Joseph H. Pyrotechnics. (Illus.). 225p. 1980. 15.95 (ISBN 0-89168-032-2). L Erlbaum Assocs.
Manufacture, Transportation, Storage of Fireworks. (Fourty Ser). 52p. 1974. pap. 3.00 (ISBN 0-685-44169-5, 44A). Natl Fire Prot.
Model State Fireworks Law. (Forty Ser). 1974. pap. 2.00 (ISBN 0-685-58097-0, 494L). Natl Fire Prot.
Weingart, George W. Pyrotechnics. (Illus.). 1968. Repr. of 1947 ed. 18.50 (ISBN 0-8206-0112-8). Chem Pub.

FISH
see Fishes

FISH, CANNED
Blackwood, C. M. Water Supplies for Fish Processing Plants. (Fisheries Technical Papers: No. 174). (Eng., Fr. & Span.). 86p. 1978. pap. 7.50 (ISBN 92-5-100685-7, F1595, FAO). Unipub.
Farah, Nuruddin. Sardines. 256p. 1982. 13.95 (ISBN 0-8052-8126-6, Pub. by Allison & Busby England). Schocken.
Higgins, John. North Pacific Deckhand's & Alaska Cannery Worker's Handbook. 1978. pap. 7.50 (ISBN 0-686-32919-8). Albacore Pr.
Recommended International Code of Practice for Canned Fish. 3rd ed. (CAC-RCP Ser.). 42p. 1983. pap. 4.50 (ISBN 92-5-100278-9, F1582, FAO). Unipub.

FISH AS FOOD
see also Sea Food
Billmeyer, Patricia. The Encyclopedia of Wild Game & Fish Cleaning & Cooking. LC 79-54388. 116p. pap. 3.95 (ISBN 0-9606262-0-4). Yesnaby Inc.
Borgstrom, G., ed. Fish As Food, 4 vols. Incl. Vol. 1. Production, Biochemistry & Microbiology. 1961. 90.00 (ISBN 0-12-118501-X); Vol. 2. Nutrition, Sanitation & Utilization. 1962. 85.00 (ISBN 0-12-118502-8); Vol. 3. Processing, Part 1. 1965. 75.00 (ISBN 0-12-118503-6); Vol. 4. Processing, Part 2. 1965. 75.00 (ISBN 0-12-118504-4). Acad Pr.
Davy, B. & Graham, M., eds. Disease of Fish Cultured for Food in Southeast Asia: Report of a Workshop Held in Cisarua, Bogor, Indonesia, 28 Nov.-1-Dec. 1978. 32p. 1979. pap. 5.00 (ISBN 0-88936-226-2, IDRC139, IDRC). Unipub.
Gastell, J. D. & Tiews, K. Report on Standardization of Methodology in Fish Nutrition Research: EIFAC, UNIS, ICES Working Group on Standardization of Methodology, Hamburg, Fed. Rep. of Germany, March 1979. (European Inland Fisheries Advisory Commission (EIFAC): Technical Papers: No. 36). (Eng. & Fr.). 30p. 1980. pap. 8.25 (ISBN 92-5-100918-X, F2048, FAO). Unipub.
Kreuzer, Rudolf, ed. Freezing & Irradiation of Fish. (Illus.). 548p. 56.25 (ISBN 0-85238-008-9, FN50, FNB). Unipub.
Mutkoski, Stephen A. & Schurer, Marcia L. Meat & Fish Management. 1981. text ed. write for info. (ISBN 0-534-00907-7, Breton Pubs). Wadsworth Pub.
Nakamura, Hiroshi. Tuna: Distribution & Migration. 1978. 40.00x (ISBN 0-685-63462-0). State Mutual Bk.
O'Farrell, R. C. Seafood Fishing for Amateur & Professional. (Illus.). 196p. 15.75 (ISBN 0-85238-097-6, FN70, FNB). Unipub.
Organic Recycling in Africa: Papers Presented at the FAO-SIDA Workshop on the Use of Organic Materials as Fertilizers in Africa, Buea, Cameroon, Dec. 5-14, 1977. (Soils Bulletins: No. 43). 308p. 1980. pap. 22.00 (ISBN 92-5-100945-7, F2096, FAO). Unipub.
Orr, A. P. & Marshall, S. M. The Fertile Sea. 1978. 40.00 (ISBN 0-685-63407-8). State Mutual Bk.
Pariser, E. R., et al. Fish Protein Concentrate: Panacea for Protein Malnutrition? LC 77-28112. (International Nutrition Policy Ser.: N0. 3). 1978. text ed. 35.00x (ISBN 0-262-16069-2). MIT Pr.
Production of Fish-Protein Concentrate, Pt. 2. pap. 3.50 (ISBN 0-686-94419-4, UN72/2B/1, UN). Unipub.
Recommended International Code of Practice for Frozen Fish. (CAC-RCP Ser.: No. 16-1978). 58p. 1980. pap. 8.25 (ISBN 92-5-100985-6, F2124, FAO). Unipub.
Report of the FAO-NORAD Round Table Discussion on Expanding the Utilization of Marine Fishery Resources for Human Consumption: Svany, Norway, 1975. (Fisheries Reports: No. 175). 53p. 1975. pap. 7.50 (ISBN 0-686-93990-5, F825, FAO). Unipub.
Suzuki, Taneko. Fish & Krill Protein: Processing Technology. (Illus.). 260p. 1981. 42.75 (ISBN 0-85334-954-1, Pub. by Elsevier Applied Sci England). Elsevier.
WHO Expert Committee. Fish & Shellfish Hygiene. 62p. 1975. pap. 6.00 (ISBN 0-685-54032-4, F170, FAO). Unipub.

FISH AS LABORATORY ANIMALS
Kirpichnikov, V. S. Genetic Bases of Fish Selection. Gause, G. G., tr. from Rus. (Illus.). 430p. 1981. 54.00 (ISBN 0-387-10911-0). Springer Verlag.
Neuhaus, O. W. & Halver, J. E., eds. Fish in Research. LC 74-107020. 1969. 49.50 (ISBN 0-12-515850-5). Acad Pr.

FISH BY-PRODUCTS
see Fishery Products

FISH-CULTURE

see also Animal Introduction; Aquariums; Tropical Fish Breeding

Allen, Lochie J. & Kinney, Edward C., eds. Bio-Engineering Symposium for Fish Culture: Proceedings. 307p. 1981. text ed. 24.00 (ISBN 0-913235-25-3). AM Fisheries Soc.

Axelrod, Herbert R. Breeding Aquarium Fishes, Bk. 4. (Illus.). 320p. 1976. 16.95 (ISBN 0-87666-451-6, H-963). TFH Pubns.

--Breeding Aquarium Fishes, Bk.6. (Illus.). 288p. 1980. 16.95 (ISBN 0-87666-536-9, H-995). TFH Pubns.

Better Freshwater Fish Farming: The Pond, 1981 Edition. (Better Farming Ser.: No. 29). 43p. 1981. pap. 7.50 (ISBN 92-5-101127-3, F2316, FAO). Unipub.

Boyd, C. E. Water Quality Management for Pond Fish Culture. (Developments in Aquaculture & Fisheries Science Ser.: Vol. 9). 318p. 1982. 64.00 (ISBN 0-444-42054-1). Elsevier.

Brown, E. Evan & Gratzek, J. B. Fish Farming Handbook. (Illus.). 1980. 29.50 (ISBN 0-87055-341-0). AVI.

Burczynski, J. Introduction to the Use of Sonar Systems for Estimating Fish Biomass. (Fisheries Technical Papers: No. 191, Rev. 1). (Eng., Fr. & Span.). 109p. 1982. pap. 8.00 (ISBN 92-5-101161-3, F2301, FAO). Unipub.

Connell, J. J. Control of Fish Quality. 2nd ed. (Illus.). 240p. 1980. 33.25 (ISBN 0-85238-105-0, FN83, FNB). Unipub.

Davis, H. S. Culture & Diseases of Game Fishes. (Illus.). 1953. 34.00x (ISBN 0-520-00293-8). U of Cal Pr.

Davy, B. & Graham, M., eds. Disease of Fish Cultured for Food in Southeast Asia: Report of a Workshop Held in Cisarua, Bogor, Indonesia, 28 Nov.-1-Dec. 1978. 32p. 1979. pap. 5.00 (ISBN 0-88936-226-2, IDRC139, IDRC). Unipub.

Davy, F. B. & Chouinard, A., eds. Induced Fish Breeding in Southeast Asia: Report of a Workshop Held in Singapore, 25-28 Nov. 1980. 48p. 1981. pap. 7.50 (ISBN 0-88936-306-4, IDRC178, IDRC). Unipub.

Dow, Steven. Breeding Angelfish. (Illus.). 1977. pap. 4.95 (ISBN 0-668-04055-6). Arco.

Educational Research Council of America. Fish Biologist. Kunze, Linda J. & Marchak, John P., eds. (Real People at Work Ser.: G). (Illus.). 36p. 1974. pap. text ed. 2.70 (ISBN 0-89247-056-9, 9336). Changing Times.

Elementary Guide to Fish Culture in Nepal. (Illus.). 131p. 1976. pap. 8.50 (ISBN 0-685-62391-2, F772, FAO). Unipub.

Fish Culture in Central East Africa. pap. 16.25 (F176, FAO). Unipub.

Fish Farming International, Vol. 3. pap. 8.25 (FN34, FNB). Unipub.

Freshwater Fish Farming: How to Begin. (Better Farming Ser.: No. 27). 43p. 1979. pap. 5.50 (ISBN 92-5-100606-7, F1834, FAO). Unipub.

Gerking, Shelby D., ed. Ecology of Freshwater Fish Production. LC 77-92407. 520p. 1978. 104.95x (ISBN 0-470-99362-6). Halsted Pr.

Head, William & Splane, Jon. Fish Farming in Your Solar Greenhouse. Lamson, Sabin, ed. LC 83-22361. (Illus.). 50p. 1984. pap. text ed. 5.00 (ISBN 0-9612716-1-2). Amity Found.

Hepher, Dalfour & Pruginin, Yoel. Commercial Fish Farming: With Special Reference to Fish Culture in Israel. LC 80-28593. 261p. 1981. 42.95x (ISBN 0-471-06264-2, Pub. by Wiley-Interscience). Wiley.

Hjul, P., ed. Fish Farming International, No. 2. 1978. 60.00 (ISBN 0-685-63410-8). State Mutual Bk.

Huet, Marcel. Textbook of Fish Culture: Breeding & Cultivation of Fish. (Illus.). 454p. 56.75 (ISBN 0-85238-020-8, FN16, FNB). Unipub.

Huisman, E. A. Report of the EIFAC Workshop on Mass Rearing of Fry & Fingerlings of Freshwater Fishes. (European Inland Fisheries Advisory Commission (EIFAC): Technical Papers: No. 35). (Eng. & Fr.). 23p. 1979. pap. 7.50 (ISBN 92-5-100829-9, F1874, FAO). Unipub.

Iwamoto, Robert N. & Sower, Stacia, eds. Salmonid Reproduction: Review Papers from an International Symposium. LC 85-13764. (Illus.). viii, 167p. (Orig.). 1985. pap. text ed. 10.00 (ISBN 0-934539-00-6). Wash Sea Grant.

Jhaveri, S. & Montecalvo, J., Jr. Abstracts of Methods Used to Assess Fish Quality. (Technical Report Ser.: No. 69). 104p. 1978. 3.00 (ISBN 0-938412-00-0, P777). URI Mas.

Kirpichnikov, V. S. Genetic Bases of Fish Selection. Gause, G. G., tr. from Rus. (Illus.). 430p. 1981. 54.00 (ISBN 0-387-10911-0). Springer Verlag.

Korringa, P. Farming Marine Fishes & Shrimps: A Multidisciplinary Treatise. (Developments in Aquaculture & Fisheries Science: Vol. 4). 208p. 1976. 55.50 (ISBN 0-444-41335-9). Elsevier.

Lewis, William M. Maintaining Fishes for Experimental & Instructional Purposes. LC 62-15001. 109p. 1963. 5.95x (ISBN 0-8093-0077-X); pap. 3.95 (ISBN 0-8093-0078-8). S Ill U Pr.

McLarney, William. The Freshwater Aquaculture Book: A Handbook for Small Scale Fish Culture in North America. LC 84-80961. 583p. 1984. text ed. 40.00 (ISBN 0-88179-002-8). Hartley & Marks.

McNeil, William J. & Himsworth, Daniel C., eds. Salmonid Ecosystems of the North Pacific. LC 80-17800. (Illus.). 348p. 1980. pap. 19.95x (ISBN 0-87071-335-3). Oreg St U Pr.

Manual of Methods for Fish Stock Assessment, Report on Marking. (Fisheries Technical Papers: No. 51). 19p. 1965. pap. 7.50 (ISBN 0-686-93244-7, F1727, FAO). Unipub.

May, R. C., et al, eds. Summary Report of the Asian Regional Workshop on Carp Hatchery & Nursery Technology: Manila, Philippines, 1-3 February 1984. (ICLARM Conference Proceedings Ser.: No. 1). 38p. (Orig.). 1984. pap. 5.00x (ISBN 0-317-17298-0, Pub. by ICLARM Philippines). Intl Spec Bk.

Mills, Dick. A Fishkeeper's Guide to Coldwater Fishes. (Fishkeeper's Guide Ser.). (Illus.). 120p. 1985. 7.95 (ISBN 0-668-06349-1). Arco.

--A Fishkeeper's Guide to Community Fishes. (Fishkeeper's Guide Ser.). (Illus.). 120p. 1985. 7.95 (ISBN 0-668-06352-1). Arco.

--A Fishkeeper's Guide to the Tropical Aquarium. (Fishkeeper's Guide Ser.). (Illus.). 120p. 1985. 7.95 (ISBN 0-668-06347-5). Arco.

Milne, P. H. Fish & Shellfish Farming in Coastal Waters. 1978. 40.00 (ISBN 0-685-63408-6). State Mutual Bk.

Paysan, Klaus. Larousse Guide to Aquarium Fishes. LC 81-81045. (Larousse Nature Guide Ser.). (Illus.). 240p. (Orig.). 1981. pap. text ed. 10.95 (ISBN 0-88332-257-9, 8186). Larousse.

Pitcher, Tony J. & Hart, Paul J. Fisheries Ecology. (Illus.). 1982. text ed. 36.00 (ISBN 0-87055-405-0). AVI.

Pullin, Roger S. & Shehadeh, Ziad H., eds. Integrated Agriculture-Aquaculture Farming Systems. (Illus.). 208p. 1983. pap. text ed. 25.00 (ISBN 0-89955-385-0, Pub. by ICLARM Philippines). Intl Spec Bk.

Report of the Technical Consultation on Methodologies Used for Fish Age-Reading: Montpellier, Oct. 1981. (Fisheries Reports: No. 257). (Eng. & Fr.). 112p. 1982. pap. 8.00 (ISBN 92-5-001207-1, F2305, FAO). Unipub.

Report on the Fourth Session of the Cooperative Programme of Research on Aquaculture of the General Fisheries Council for the Mediterranean. (Fisheries Reports: No. 232). (Eng. & Fr.). 32p. 1981. pap. 7.50 (ISBN 92-5-100927-9, F2068, FAO). Unipub.

Schoitz & Dahlstrom. Collins Guide to Aquarium Fishes & Plants. 29.95 (ISBN 0-00-219165-2, Collins Pub England). Greene.

Sedgwick, Stephen D. The Salmon Handbook. (Illus.). 1982. 26.50 (ISBN 0-233-97331-1). Scholium Intl.

Shell, E. W. Fish Farming Research. (Illus.). 108p. (Orig.). 1983. pap. 12.50 (ISBN 0-8173-0277-8). U of Ala Pr.

Smith, P. E. & Richardson, S. L. Standard Techniques for Pelagic Fish Egg & Larva Surveys. (Fisheries Technical Papers: No. 175). (Eng. & Span.). 108p. (2nd Printing 1979). 1977. pap. 8.00 (ISBN 92-5-100515-X, F1439, FAO). Unipub.

Spotte, Stephen. Fish & Invertebrate Culture: Water Management in Closed Systems. 2nd ed. LC 78-10276. 179p. 1979. 23.50x (ISBN 0-471-02306-X, Pub. by Wiley-Interscience). Wiley.

Symposium on the Development & Exploitation of Artificial Lakes: Proceedings, Dominican Republic, Nov.-Dec. 1981. (Fisheries Reports: No. 273). (Eng. & Span.). 22p. 1982. pap. 7.50 (ISBN 92-5-001246-2, F2347, FAO). Unipub.

Taverner, John. Certaine Experiments Concerning the Fish & the Fruite. LC 76-6030. (English Experience Ser.: No. 75). 38p. 1968. Repr. of 1600 ed. 7.00 (ISBN 90-221-0075-8). Walter J Johnson.

Textbook of Fish Culture: Breeding & Cultivation of Fish. 1978. 40.00x (ISBN 0-685-63460-4). State Mutual Bk.

Thorpe, John, ed. Salmon Ranching. 1981. 78.00 (ISBN 0-12-690660-2). Acad Pr.

Todd, Nancy J. & Todd, John. Bioshelters, Ocean Arks, City Farming: Ecology as the Basis of Design. LC 83-51436. (Illus.). 256p. 1984. 25.00 (ISBN 0-87156-348-7); pap. 10.95 (ISBN 0-87156-814-4). Sierra.

Watanabe, W. O., et al. Experimental Rearing of Nile Tilapia Fry: Oreochromis Niloticus for Saltwater Culture. (ICLARM Technical Reports Ser.: 14). (Illus.). 28p. (Orig.). 1984. pap. 6.00x (ISBN 0-317-17293-X, Pub. by ICLARM Philippines). Intl Spec Bk.

Water Quality Criteria for European Freshwater Fish: Report on Copper and Freshwater Fish. pap. 7.50 (F768, FAO). Unipub.

World Symposium on Warm-Water Pond Fish Culture: Proceedings, Rome, 1966, 2 Vols. (Fisheries Reports: No. 44, Vols. 3-4). 1967-68. Vol. 3, 426p. pap. 25.50 (ISBN 0-686-92950-0, F1395, FAO); Vol. 4, 495p. pap. 29.25 (ISBN 0-686-98807-8, F1664). Unipub.

FISH FARMING

see Fish-Culture

FISH HATCHERIES

see Fish-Culture

FISH-OIL

Barlow, S. M. & Stansby, M. E., eds. Nutritional Evaluation of Long-Chain Fatty Acids in Fish Oil. 1982. 45.00 (ISBN 0-12-078920-5). Acad Pr.

FISH POPULATIONS

Cjosaeter, J. & Kawaguchi, K. A Review of the World Resources of Mesopelagic Fish. (Fisheries Technical Papers: No. 193). 156p. 1980. pap. 11.50 (ISBN 92-5-100924-4, F2074, FAO). Unipub.

Cushing, D. H. Marine Ecology & Fisheries. LC 74-82218. (Illus.). 228p. 1975. 62.50 (ISBN 0-521-20501-8); pap. 22.95 (ISBN 0-521-09911-0). Cambridge U Pr.

Cushing, D. H., intro. by. Key Papers on Fish Population. (Illus.). 426p. (Orig.). 1983. pap. 42.00 (ISBN 0-904147-58-4). IRL Pr.

Deacon, James E. Fish Populations, Following a Drought, in the Neosho & Marais Des Cygnes Rivers of Kansas. (Museum Ser.: Vol. 13, No. 9). 69p. 1961. pap. 3.75 (ISBN 0-686-79822-8). U of KS Mus Nat Hist.

The Design of Fisheries Statistical Surveys - Inland Waters: Populations in Non-Random Order Sampling Methods for Echo Surveys, Double Sampling. (Fisheries Technical Papers: No. 133, Suppl. 1). 52p. 1976. pap. 7.50 (ISBN 92-5-100660-1, F869, FAO). Unipub.

Gulland, J. A. Manual of Methods for Fish Stock Assessment: Fish Population Analysis, Pt. 1. (Fisheries Ser.: No. 3). (Illus.). 154p. (Orig., 4th Printing 1976). 1969. pap. 13.25 (ISBN 92-5-100204-5, F262, FAO). Unipub.

Gulland, John A. Fish Population Dynamics. LC 75-45094. 372p. 1977. 74.95 (ISBN 0-471-01575-X). Wiley.

Mills, Dick. A Fishkeeper's Guide to Coldwater Fishes. (Fishkeeper's Guide Ser.). (Illus.). 120p. 1985. 7.95 (ISBN 0-668-06349-1). Arco.

--A Fishkeeper's Guide to Community Fishes. (Fishkeeper's Guide Ser.). (Illus.). 120p. 1985. 7.95 (ISBN 0-668-06352-1). Arco.

--A Fishkeeper's Guide to the Tropical Aquarium. (Fishkeeper's Guide Ser.). (Illus.). 120p. 1985. 7.95 (ISBN 0-668-06347-5). Arco.

Nikolskii, G. V. Theory of Fish Population Dynamics As the Biological Background for Rational Exploitation & Management of Fishery Resources. Jones, R., ed. Bradley, J. E., tr. from Rus. (Illus.). 323p. 1980. Repr. of 1969 ed. lib. bdg. 28.00x (ISBN 3-87429-171-5). Lubrecht & Cramer.

Report of the Indo-Pacific Fisheries Council & Indian Ocean Fishery Commission, Special Committee on Indian Ocean Tuna. Incl. Joint Session, Rome, 1971. Indo-Pacific Fisheries Council Committee on Management of Tuna, 1st Session & Indian Ocean Fishery Commission on Management of Indian Ocean Tuna, 2nd Session. (No. 104). 21p. 1971. pap. 7.50 (ISBN 0-686-92734-6, F1695); Joint Session, Mombasa, Kenya, July 1975. Indo-Pacific Fisheries Council Committee on Management of Tuna, 3rd Session & Indian Ocean Fishery Commission Committee on Management of Indian Ocean Tuna, 4th Session. (No. 174). (Illus.). 47p. 1976. pap. 7.50 (ISBN 0-685-68361-3, F824). (Fisheries Reports, FAO). Unipub.

Report on the Symposium on Methodology for the Survey, Monitoring & Appraisal of Fishery Resources in Lakes & Large Rivers. pap. 7.50 (ISBN 92-5-102075-2, F763, FAO). Unipub.

Stokes, F. Joseph. Handguide to the Coral Reef Fishes of the Caribbean. LC 79-27224. (Illus.). 160p. 1980. 9.95i (ISBN 0-690-01919-X). Harrow.

FISH TRADE

see also Fishery Products

Ben-Yami, M. Fishing with Light. 1978. 16.00 (ISBN 0-685-63423-X). State Mutual Bk.

Bombace, G. Preliminary Report on Fish Distribution & Marketing in Sicily. (General Fisheries Council of the Mediterranean (GFCM): Studies & Reviews: No. 28). (Eng. & Fr.). 28p. 1966. pap. 7.50 (ISBN 92-5-101946-0, F1789, FAO). Unipub.

Connell, J. J. Control of Fish Quality. 1978. 40.00 (ISBN 0-685-63397-7). State Mutual Bk.

Forrest, David M. Eel Capture, Culture, Processing & Marketing. 1978. 40.00 (ISBN 0-685-63399-3). State Mutual Bk.

Gersuny, Carl, et al. Some Effects of Technological Change on New England Fishermen. (Marine Technical Report Ser.: No. 42). 1975. pap. 1.00 (ISBN 0-938412-14-0). URI MAS.

International Directory of Fish Inspection & Quality Control Institutes. (Fisheries Technical Papers: No. 244). 139p. 1984. pap. 10.75 (ISBN 92-5-002088-0, F2635, FAO). Unipub.

International Labour Office. Small-Scale Processing of Fish. (Technology Series Technical Memorandum: No. 3). xi, 118p. (Orig.). 1982. pap. 8.55 (ISBN 92-2-103205-1). Intl Labour Office.

Jones, Rodney. The Use of Marking Data in Fish Population Analysis. (Fisheries Technical Papers: No. 153). (Illus.). 47p. 1976. pap. 7.50 (ISBN 92-5-100051-4, F886, FAO). Unipub.

Mead, John T. Marine Refrigeration & Fish Preservation. rev. ed. LC 80-25359. (Illus.). 1980. 25.00 (ISBN 0-912524-19-7). Busn News.

Motte, G. A. & Iitaka, Y. Evaluation of Trawl Performance by Statistical Inference of the Catch. (Marine Technical Report Ser.: No. 36). 1975. pap. 2.00 (ISBN 0-938412-08-6). URI MAS.

Nowak, W. S. The Marketing of Shellfish. (Fisheries Ser.: No. 13). (Illus.). 280p. 22.50 (ISBN 0-85238-010-0, FN59, FAO). Unipub.

OECD. Financial Support to the Fishing Industry. (Illus.). 161p. (Orig.). 1980. pap. 6.50x (ISBN 92-64-12087-4, 53-80-01-1). OECD.

Sainsbury, John C. Commercial Fishing Methods. 1978. 30.00 (ISBN 0-685-63396-9). State Mutual Bk.

Usui, Atsushi. Eel Culture. 1978. 40.00 (ISBN 0-685-63400-0). State Mutual Bk.

Vibert, R., ed. Fishing with Electricity. 1978. 20.00 (ISBN 0-685-63422-1). State Mutual Bk.

FISH WASTE

see Fishery Products

FISHERIES

see also Cod-Fisheries; Fish Trade; Fishes; Fishing Boats; Lobster Fisheries; Trawls and Trawling

Across-Beach Operations in the Small-Scale Fishery. (Fisheries Technical Papers: No. 157). 118p. 1977. pap. 8.00 (ISBN 92-5-100188-X, F889, FAO). Unipub.

Advisory Committee on Marine Resources Research. Report on Marine Resources Research on Biological Accumulators: First Session, Rome, December 1974. (Fisheries Reports: No. 160). 18p. 1976. pap. 7.50 (ISBN 0-685-67377-4, F803, FAO). Unipub.

--Report on Marine Resources Research: 7th Session, Rome, 1973. (Fisheries Reports: No. 142). 49p. 1974. pap. 7.50 (ISBN 0-686-93972-7, F788, FAO). Unipub.

The Aquatic Sciences & Fisheries Information System (ASFIS) Summary Report & Recommendations of the 2nd Session of the Joint FAO/IOC Panel of Experts, Paris, France, Oct. 1976. (Fisheries Reports: No. 186). 26p. (2nd Printing 1977). 1976. pap. 7.50 (ISBN 92-5-100179-0, F834, FAO). Unipub.

An Assessment of the Fish Stocks & Fisheries of the Campeche Bank. (Western Central Atlantic Fishery Commission Studies: No. 5). 1976. pap. 7.50 (ISBN 92-5-100043-3, F1213, FAO). Unipub.

Beverton, R. J. H., et al, eds. Marine Mammals & Fisheries. (Illus.). 350p. 1985. text ed. 55.00x (ISBN 0-04-639003-0). Allen Unwin.

Biological Monitoring of Inland Fisheries. (Illus., Applied science pub). 1978. pap. 52.90 (ISBN 0-85334-719-0, AS2, AS). Unipub.

Blackford, Mansel G. Pioneering a Modern Small Business: Wakefield Seafoods & the Alaskan Frontier. Porter, Glenn, ed. LC 77-7794. (Industrial Development & the Social Fabric Ser.: Vol. 6). 222p. 1979. 29.50 (ISBN 0-686-74079-3). Jai Pr.

Brandt, A. von. Fish Catching Methods of the World. 3rd ed. (Illus.). 418p. 1984. 66.00 (ISBN 0-85238-125-5, FN106, FNB). Unipub.

Brown, E. Evan. World Fish Farming: Cultivation & Economics. 2nd ed. (Illus.). 1983. text ed. 47.50 (ISBN 0-87055-427-1). AVI.

Browning, Robert J. Fisheries of the North Pacific: History, Species, Gear & Processes. rev. ed. LC 80-17194. (Illus.). 432p. 1980. pap. 24.95 (ISBN 0-88240-128-9). Alaska Northwest.

Carlton, Frank E. Marine Recreational Fisheries, Vol. 3. Clepper, Henry, ed. LC 76-22389. 1978. 15.00 (ISBN 0-686-65030-1). Sport Fishing.

--Marine Recreational Fisheries, Vol. 4. Clepper, Henry, ed. LC 76-22389. 1979. 15.00 (ISBN 0-686-65031-X). Sport Fishing.

--Marine Recreational Fisheries, Vol. 5. Clepper, Henry, ed. LC 76-22389. 1980. 15.00 (ISBN 0-686-70340-5). Sport Fishing.

Chaston, Ian. Business Management in Fisheries & Aquaculture. (Illus.). 128p. 1985. pap. 18.00 (ISBN 0-85238-132-8, FN109, FNB). Unipub.

Childerhose, R. J. & Trim, Marj. Pacific Salmon & Steelhead Trout. LC 78-65830. (Illus.). 166p. 1979. pap. 16.95 (ISBN 0-295-95866-9). U of Wash Pr.

Clark, C. W. Bioeconomic Modelling & Fisheries Management. 352p. 1985. 47.95 (ISBN 0-471-87394-2). Wiley.

Coche, A. G. Report of the Symposium on Finfish Nutrition & Feed Technology: Hamburg, Fed. Rep. of Germany, 20-23 June 1978. (European Inland Fisheries Advisory Commission (EIFAC): Technical Papers: No. 31). (Eng. & Fr.). 41p. 1978. pap. 7.50 (ISBN 92-5-100642-3, F1514, FAO). Unipub.

Coche, A. G. & Wal, H. Van der. Water for Freshwater Fish Culture: Simple Methods for Aquaculture. (Training Ser.: No. 4). 111p. 1981. pap. text ed. 20.25 (ISBN 92-5-101112-5, F2409, FAO). Unipub.

Code of Practice for Fresh Fish. (Fisheries Reports: No. 74). 39p. 1969. pap. 7.50 (ISBN 0-686-93159-9, F1681, FAO). Unipub.

Comparative Studies on Fresh-Water Fisheries: Report of a Workshop Held at the Instituto Italiano di Idrobiologia, Pallanza, Italy, Sept. 4-8, 1978. (Fisheries Technical Papers: No. 198). 54p. 1980. pap. 7.50 (ISBN 92-5-100952-X, F2085, FAO). Unipub.

Conference on Fish Behavior in Relation to Fishing Techniques & Tactics: Proceedings, Bergen, Norway, 1968-69, Vols. 1 & 3. (Fisheries Reports: No. 62). Vol. 1, 51p. pap. 7.50 (ISBN 0-686-92921-7, F1674, FAO); Vol. 3, 427p. pap. 25.50 (ISBN 0-686-98784-5). Unipub.

Connell, J. J., ed. Advances in Fish Science & Technology. 528p. 1980. cloth 118.50x (ISBN 0-85238-108-5, Pub. by Fishing News England). State Mutual Bk.

Conroy, D. A. Evaluation of the Present State of World Trade in Ornamental Fish. (Fisheries Technical Papers: No. 146). 133p. (2nd Printing 1976). 1975. pap. 9.00 (ISBN 92-5-101911-8, F877, FAO). Unipub.

Crutchfield, James A. & Pontecorvo, Giulio. The Pacific Salmon Fisheries: A Study of Irrational Conservation. LC 72-75180. (Resources for the Future Ser). (Illus.). 220p. 1969. 14.00x (ISBN 0-8018-1025-6). Johns Hopkins.

Cushing, D. H. Climate & Fisheries. 1983. 49.50 (ISBN 0-12-199720-0). Acad Pr.

--Fisheries Biology: A Study in Population Dynamics. 2nd ed. LC 79-5405. (Illus.). 320p. 1981. 19.95x (ISBN 0-299-08110-9). U of Wis Pr.

--Marine Ecology & Fisheries. LC 74-82218. (Illus.). 228p. 1975. 62.50 (ISBN 0-521-20501-8); pap. 22.95 (ISBN 0-521-09911-0). Cambridge U Pr.

Cushing, David H. Recruitment & Parent Stock in Fishes. (Washington Sea Grant). 197p. 1973. pap. 12.50x (ISBN 0-295-95311-X). U of Wash Pr.

Dipl-Ling, V. & Bensch, Erhard. Dictionary of Shipbuilding, Shipping & Fisheries. 784p. 1980. vinyl 150.00x (ISBN 0-686-30016-5, Pub. by Collet's). State Mutual Bk.

Directory of Fishing Technology Institutions & Services. (Fisheries Technical Papers: No. 205). (Trilingual.). 109p. 1980. pap. 8.00 (ISBN 92-5-001018-4, F2163, FAO). Unipub.

Eddie, G. The Harvesting of Krill. (Southern Ocean Fisheries Survey Programmes: GLO-SO-77-2). (Eng. & Span.). 82p. (2nd Printing 1978). 1977. pap. 7.50 (ISBN 92-5-100415-3, F1309, FAO). Unipub.

Eddie, G. C. Road Transport of Fish & Fishery Products. (Fisheries Technical Paper Ser.: No. 232). 54p. (Orig.). 1984. pap. 7.50 (ISBN 92-5-101362-4, F2570, FAO). Unipub.

Everhart, W. Harry & Youngs, William D. Principles of Fishery Science. 2nd ed. (Illus.). 343p. 1981. 22.50x (ISBN 0-8014-1334-6). Cornell U Pr.

FAO-ICES-ICNAF-ICCAT: Report of the Coordinating Working Party on Atlantic Fishery Statistics, 7th Session, Rome, 1971. (Fisheries Reports: No. 121). 49p. 1971. pap. 7.50 (ISBN 0-686-93226-9, F1704, FAO). Unipub.

Fisheries & Aquatic Sciences in Canada: An Overview. (Fisheries Research Board of Canada Reports). 53p. 1979. pap. 4.75 (ISBN 0-660-01195-6, SSC134, SSC). Unipub.

Fisheries Dictionaries & Encyclopedias 1945-1973. pap. 7.50 (F1204, FAO). Unipub.

Fisheries in the Food Economy. (Freedom from Hunger Campaign Basic Studies: No. 19). 79p. (Orig.). 1968. pap. 4.75 (ISBN 92-5-101611-9, F177, FAO). Unipub.

Fisheries Management & the Limitation of Fishing. (Fisheries Technical Papers: No. 93). 16p. 1969. pap. 7.50 (ISBN 0-686-92779-6, F1743, FAO). Unipub.

Fisheries 1945-1969, 2 vols. pap. 24.00 (F944, FAO). Unipub.

Fishery Harbour Planning. (Fisheries Technical Papers: No. 123). 36p. 1973. pap. 7.50 (ISBN 0-686-92785-0, F857, FAO). Unipub.

Report of the IUCN Workshop on Marine Mammals Fishery Interactions. pap. 7.00 (IUCN). Unipub.

Fishing Vessel Data: 1965. (Fisheries Reports: No. 28, Vol. 1). 237p. 1965. pap. 15.50 (ISBN 0-686-92771-0, F1653, FAO). Unipub.

Fishing Vessel Data: 1969. (Fisheries Reports: No. 28, Vol. 2). 362p. 1969. pap. 23.75 (ISBN 0-686-92773-7, F1654, FAO). Unipub.

Forbes, S. T. & Nakken, O., eds. Manual of Methods for Fisheries Resource Survey & Appraisal: The Use of Acoustic Instruments for Fish Detection & Abundance Estimation, Pt. 2. (Manuals in Fisheries Science: No. 5). (Illus.). 138p. (Orig.). 1972. pap. 11.00 (ISBN 92-5-101604-6, F263, FAO). Unipub.

La Funcion Consultative Scientifique dans les Organismes Internationaux D'Amenagement et de Developpement des Peches: Supplement 1, Rome, Octobre 17-24, 1973. (Fisheries Reports: No. 142, Suppl. 1). (Fr.). pap. 8.25 (F1282, FAO). Unipub.

La Funcion de Asesoramiento Tecnico en Los Organismos Internacionales de Ordenacion y Desarrollo Pesqueros: Supplemento 1, Roma, Octubre 17-24, 1973. (Fisheries Reports: No. 142, Suppl. 1). (Span. only.). pap. 8.25 (F1283, FAO). Unipub.

General Fisheries Council for the Mediterranean. Establishment, Structure, Functions & Activities of International Fisheries Bodies, Pt. 5. 39p. 1968. pap. 7.50 (ISBN 0-686-92808-3, F1737, FAO). Unipub.

German, Andrew W. Down on T Wharf: The Boston Fisheries as Seen Through The Photographs of Henry D. Fisher. (American Maritime Library: Vol. 10). (Illus.). 160p. 1982. 20.00 (ISBN 0-913372-26-9). Mystic Seaport.

Gopalakrishnan, Chennat, ed. Emerging Marine Economy of the Pacific. (Illus.). 256p. 1984. text ed. 39.95 (ISBN 0-250-40637-3). Butterworth.

Grantham, G. J. The Utilization of Krill. (Southern Ocean Fisheries Survey Programmes: GLO-SO-77-3). (Eng. & Span.). 67p. 1977. pap. 7.50 (ISBN 92-5-100416-1, F1314, FAO). Unipub.

Grantham, G. J. & Tuna, Charley. Minced Fish Technology: A Review. (Fisheries Technical Papers: No. 216). 79p. 1981. pap. 7.50 (ISBN 92-5-101130-3, F2242, FAO). Unipub.

Gregory, Homer E. & Barnes, Kathleen. North Pacific Fisheries, with Special Reference to Alaska Salmon. 1976. Repr. of 1939 ed. 23.00 (ISBN 0-527-35850-9). Kraus Repr.

Guide to Fishery Education & Training. (Fisheries Technical Papers: No. 128). 349p. 1973. pap. 22.50 (ISBN 0-686-92866-0, F1749, FAO). Unipub.

Gulland, J. A. Manual of Methods for Fish Stock Assessment: Fish Population Analysis, Pt. 1. (Fisheries Ser.: No. 3). (Illus.). 154p. (Orig., 4th Printing 1976). 1969. pap. 13.25 (ISBN 92-5-100204-5, F262, FAO). Unipub.

--Manual of Methods for Fisheries Resource Survey & Appraisal: Objectives & Basic Methods, Pt. 4. (Fisheries Technical Papers: No. 145). (Illus.). 33p. (3rd Printing 1977). 1975. pap. 7.50 (ISBN 92-5-100118-9, F876, FAO). Unipub.

--Some Problems of the Management of Shared Stocks. (Fisheries Technical Papers: No. 206). (Eng. & Fr.). 29p. (2nd Printing 1981). 1980. pap. 7.50 (ISBN 92-5-101022-6, F2149, FAO). Unipub.

Haley, K. Brian, ed. Applied Operations Research in Fishing. LC 80-27780. (NATO Conference Series II-Systems Science: Vol. 10). 506p. 1981. 72.50x (ISBN 0-306-40634-9, Plenum Pr). Plenum Pub.

Hamabe, Mototsugu, et al. Squid Jigging from Small Boats: An FAO Fishing Manual. 84p. 1982. pap. 19.00 (ISBN 0-85238-122-0, FN99, FNB). Unipub.

Harden-Jones, F. R. Sea Fisheries Research. 510p. 1974. 58.95x (ISBN 0-470-35142-X). Halsted Pr.

Hazleton, J. E. & Bell, F. W. Recent Developments & Research in Fisheries Economics: Papers. LC 66-27364. 233p. 1967. 15.00 (ISBN 0-379-00317-1). Oceana.

Hester, F. J. Economic Aspects of the Effects of Pollution on the Marine & Anadromous Fisheries of the Western United States of America. (Fisheries Technical Papers: No. 162). (Illus.). 41p. 1976. pap. 7.50 (ISBN 92-5-100116-2, F894, FAO). Unipub.

Higgins, John. North Pacific Deckhand's & Alaska Cannery Worker's Handbook. 1978. pap. 7.50 (ISBN 0-686-32919-8). Albacore Pr.

Hillard, A. & Jhaveri, S. Fish Preservation: An Annotated Bibliography. (Technical Report Ser.: No. 82). 50p. 1981. 2.00 (ISBN 0-938412-24-8, P909). URI MAS.

Hjul, P., ed. Fish Farming International, No. 2. 1978. 60.00 (ISBN 0-685-63410-8). State Mutual Bk.

Ice in Fisheries. (Fisheries Reports: No. 59, Rev. 1). (Illus.). 57p. 1975. pap. 7.50 (ISBN 0-685-55203-9, F779, FAO). Unipub.

Idyll, C. P. The Sea Against Hunger. new, rev. ed. LC 77-2655. (Apollo Eds.). (Illus.). 1978. pap. 6.95i (ISBN 0-8152-0422-1, A-422). T Y Crowell.

Indo-Pacific Fishery Commission (IPFC), Report of the Second Session of the IPFC Working Party on Inland Fisheries. (Fisheries Reports: No. 312). 56p. 1985. pap. 7.50 (ISBN 92-5-102126-0, F2652, FAO). Unipub.

International Directory of Fish Inspection & Quality Control Institutes. (Fisheries Technical Papers: No. 244). 139p. 1984. pap. 10.75 (ISBN 92-5-002088-0, F2635, FAO). Unipub.

International Directory of Fish Technology Institutes. (Fisheries Technical Papers: No. 152, Rev. 1). 114p. 1980. pap. 8.50 (ISBN 92-5-101002-1, F2031, FAO). Unipub.

International Fishery Bodies: Papers Presented at the First Session of the Committee on Fisheries, Rome. 1966. pap. 7.50 (F1729, FAO). Unipub.

Introduction to Accounting & Management for Sea Fishermen: Manual for Extension Workers. (Fisheries Technical Papers: No. 127). 44p. 1974. pap. 7.50 (ISBN 0-686-93262-5, F1748, FAO). Unipub.

IOFC Ad Hoc Committee of Nations. Mechanics of Tuna Research & Management: Report of the IOFC Ad Hoc Committee of Nations, 2nd Session, Bangkok, 1975. (Fisheries Reports: No. 184). 8p. 1976. pap. 7.50 (ISBN 92-5-100045-X, F832, FAO). Unipub.

Irish Academic Press Editors. Fisheries, 7 vols. 1971. text ed. 684.00x (ISBN 0-7165-1435-4, Pub. by Irish Academic Pr Ireland). Biblio Dist.

Johannesson, K. A. & Mitson, R. B. Fisheries Acoustics: A Practical Manual for Aquatic Biomass Estimation. (Fisheries Technical Papers: No. 240). 249p. 1984. pap. text ed. 18.50 (ISBN 92-5-101449-3, F2533, FAO). Unipub.

Johnston, Paul F. The New England Fisheries: A Treasure Greater Than Gold. (Illus.). 80p. 1984. pap. 15.00 (ISBN 0-87577-151-3). Peabody Mus Salem.

Jones, R. Materials & Methods Used in Marking Experiments in Fishery Research. (Fisheries Technical Papers: No. 190). 139p. (2nd Printing 1980). 1979. pap. 10.00 (ISBN 92-5-100773-X, F1636, FAO). Unipub.

Kapetsky, James M. Some Considerations for the Management of Coastal Lagoon & Estuarine Fisheries. (Fisheries Technical Papers: No. 218). (Eng., Fr & Span.). 54p. 1981. pap. 7.50 (ISBN 92-5-101136-2, F2260, FAO). Unipub.

Kasahara, Hiroshi & Burke, William. North Pacific Fisheries Management. LC 77-86401. (Program of International Studies of Fishery Arrangements. Papers: No. 2). Repr. of 1973 ed. 14.00 (ISBN 0-404-60337-8). AMS Pr.

Konovalov, S. M. Differentiation of Local Populations of Sockeye Salmon Oncorhynchus Nerka. Sagen, Leda V., tr. from Rus. LC 75-14733. (Publications in Fisheries, Ser.: No. 6). (Illus.). 256p. (Orig.). 1975. pap. text ed. 20.00x (ISBN 0-295-95406-X). U of Wash Pr.

Korringa, P. Farming Cupped Oysters of the Genus Crassostrea. (Developments in Aquaculture & Fisheries Science Ser.: Vol. 2). 224p. 1976. 55.50 (ISBN 0-444-41333-2). Elsevier.

--Farming Marine Organisms Low in the Food Chain. (Developments in Aquaculture & Fisheries Science: Vol. 1). 264p. 1976. 55.50 (ISBN 0-444-41332-4). Elsevier.

--Farming the Flat Oyster of the Genus Ostrea. (Developments in Aquaculture & Fisheries Science Ser.: Vol. 3). 238p. 1976. 55.50 (ISBN 0-444-41334-0). Elsevier.

Kuhns, John F., ed. Codex of Fishery Chemicals. 1983. looseleaf 50.00X (ISBN 0-318-00766-5). Written Word.

Lackey, Robert T. & Nielsen, Larry A. Fisheries Management. LC 80-20028. 422p. 1980. 42.95x (ISBN 0-470-27056-X). Halsted Pr.

Laevastu, Taivo & Hayes, Murray L. Fisheries Oceanography & Ecology. (Illus.). 216p. 1981. 66.25 (ISBN 0-85238-117-4, FN94, FNB). Unipub.

--Fisheries Oceanography & Ecology. 1981. 79.00x (ISBN 0-686-78648-3, Pub. by Fishing News England). State Mutual Bk.

Laevastu, Taivo & Larkins, Herbert A. Marine Fisheries Ecosystem: Its Quantitative Evaluation & Management. (Illus.). 176p. 1981. 42.00 (ISBN 0-85238-116-6, FN93, FNB). Unipub.

Landing & Marketing Facilities at Selected Sea Fishing Ports. (Fisheries Reports: No. 36). 345p. 1966. pap. 22.25 (ISBN 0-686-92943-8, F1659, FAO). Unipub.

Lang, Varley. Follow the Water. LC 61-16637. (Illus.). 1961. 6.95 (ISBN 0-910244-24-3). Blair.

Lanier, B. V. The World Supply & Demand Picture for Canned Small Pelagic Fish. (Fisheries Technical Papers: No. 220). 123p. 1981. pap. 9.00 (ISBN 92-5-101143-5, F2264, FAO). Unipub.

Leopold, M. Glossary of Inland Fishery Terms. (European Inland Fisheries Advisory Commission (EIFAC): Technical Papers: No. 12). (Eng. & Fr.). 129p. 1978. pap. 9.50 (ISBN 92-5-000724-8, F1558, FAO). Unipub.

Lewis, Mary J., ed. Directory of North American Fisheries Scientists. 450p. 1984. pap. text ed. 30.00 (ISBN 0-913235-18-0). Am Fisheries Soc.

Lewis, Tracy R. Stochastic Modeling of Ocean Fisheries Resource Management. LC 81-51282. (Illus.). 118p. 1983. 30.00x (ISBN 0-295-95838-3). U of Wash Pr.

Lima dos Santos, C A, et al. Guidelines for Chilled Fish Storage Experiments. (Fisheries Technical Papers: No. 210). 29p. 1981. pap. 7.50 (ISBN 92-5-101078-1, F2187, FAO). Unipub.

Lutz, R. A. Mussel Culture & Harvest: A North American Perspective. (Developments in Acquaculture & Fisheries Science Ser.: Vol. 7). 350p. 1980. 70.25 (ISBN 0-444-41866-0). Elsevier.

McHugh, J. L. Fishery Management. (Lecture Notes on Coastal & Estuarine Studies: Vol. 10). vii, 207p. 1984. pap. 17.00 (ISBN 0-387-96062-7). Springer-Verlag.

Manpower Planning in Fisheries Development Programs. (Fisheries Technical Papers: No. 65). 40p. 1967. pap. 7.50 (ISBN 0-686-93246-3, F1730, FAO). Unipub.

Manual of Fisheries Science, Pt. 2: Methods of Resource Investigation & Their Application. (Fisheries Technical Papers: No. 115, Rev. 1). 224p. 1979. pap. 16.00 (ISBN 92-5-100842-6, F854, FAO). Unipub.

Manual of Methods for Fish Stock Assessment, Report on Marking. (Fisheries Technical Papers: No. 51). 19p. 1965. pap. 7.50 (ISBN 0-686-93244-7, F1727, FAO). Unipub.

Manual of Methods for Fish Stock Assessment: Tables of Yield Functions, Pt. 2. Rev. ed. (Fisheries Technical Papers: No. 38, Rev. 1). 1980. pap. 7.50 (ISBN 92-5-000840-6, F848, FAO). Unipub.

Manual on Fishermen's Cooperatives. 124p. (Orig.). 1971. pap. 9.25 (ISBN 0-685-30137-0, F264, FAO). Unipub.

Manual on the Identification & Preparation of Fishery Investment Projects. (Fisheries Technical Papers: No. 149). 1976. pap. 7.50 (ISBN 0-685-71575-2, F882, FAO). Unipub.

Marr, John C. Fishery & Resource Management in Southeast Asia. LC 75-36946. (Resources for the Future Ser). 76p. 1976. pap. 5.00x (ISBN 0-8018-1826-5). Johns Hopkins.

May, R. M., ed. Exploitation of Marine Communities. (Dahlem Workshop Reports Ser.: Vol. 32). (Illus.). 370p. 1984. 20.00 (ISBN 0-387-15028-5). Springer-Verlag.

Milne, P. H. Fish & Shellfish Farming in Coastal Waters. 1978. 40.00 (ISBN 0-685-63408-6). State Mutual Bk.

Mitchell, Edward. Porpoise, Dolphin & Small Whale Fisheries of the World: Status & Problems. (Illus.). 129p. 1975. pap. 12.00 (ISBN 2-88032-027-5, IUCN6, IUCN). Unipub.

Mitson, R. B. Fisheries Sonar. 287p. 1984. 49.95 (ISBN 0-85238-124-7, FN100, FNB). Unipub.

Monitoring of Fish Stock Abundance: The Use of Catch & Effort Data: A Report of the ACMRR Working Party on Fishing Effort & Monitoring of Fish Abundance, Rome, Italy, Dec. 16-20, 1975. (Fisheries Technical Papers: No. 155). (Illus.). 105p. (2nd Printing). 1976. pap. 7.75 (ISBN 92-5-100050-6, F888, FAO). Unipub.

Muzinic, R. On the Use of Anesthetics in the Transportation of Sardines. (General Fisheries Council of the Mediterranean (GFCM): Studies & Reviews: No. 47). 23p. 1970. pap. 6.00 (ISBN 92-5-101966-5, F1806, FAO). Unipub.

Neilsen, Larry A. & Johnson, David L. Fisheries Techniques. 468p. 1984. text ed. 30.00 (ISBN 0-913235-00-8); members 25.00. Am Fisheries Soc.

Novikov, V. M., ed. Handbook of Fishery Technology, Vol. 1. 504p. 1983. lib. bdg. 28.00 (ISBN 90-6191-409-4, Pub. by Balkema RSA). IPS.

OECD. Financial Support to the Fishing Industry. (Illus.). 161p. (Orig.). 1980. pap. 6.50x (ISBN 92-64-12087-4, 53-80-01-1). OECD.

O'Farrell, R. C. Seafood Fishing for Amateur & Professional. 1978. 25.00 (ISBN 0-685-63452-3). State Mutual Bk.

Panayotou, Theodore. Management Concepts for Small-Scale Fisheries: Economic & Social Aspects. (Fisheries Technical Papers: No. 228). (Eng., Fr & Span.). 58p. 1982. pap. text ed. 7.50 (ISBN 92-5-101279-2, F2431, FAO). Unipub.

Panel Reviews & Relevant Papers: Symposium on the Methodology for the Survey, Monitoring & Appraisal of Fishery Resources in Lakes & Larger Rivers, Vol. 2. (European Inland Fisheries Advisory Commission (EIFAC): Technical Papers: No. 23, Supp. 1). (Eng. & Fr.). 750p. 1975. pap. 29.50 (ISBN 92-5-000326-9, F764, FAO). Unipub.

Paquette, Gerald N. Fish Quality Improvement: A Manual for Plant Operators. Practical Everyday Procedures to Benefit Performance & Quality. LC 82-24677. (Orig.). 1983. pap. text ed. 17.50x (ISBN 0-943738-05-9). Osprey Bks.

Permanent Commission of the Conference on the Use & Conservation of the Marine Resources of the South Pacific. Establishment, Structure, Functions & Activities of International Fisheries Bodies, Pt. 4. 44p. 1968. pap. 7.50 (ISBN 0-686-92803-2, F1736, FAO). Unipub.

Piper, Robert G., et al. Fish Hatchery Management. 517p. 1983. pap. 27.00 (ISBN 0-913235-03-2). Am Fisheries Soc.

Platteau, J., et al. Technology, Credit & Indebtness in Marine Fishing. 406p. 1985. text ed. 30.00x (ISBN 0-391-03350-6, Pub. by Hindustan India). Humanities.

The Prevention of Losses in Cured Fish. (Fisheries Technical Papers: No. 219). 98p. 1981. pap. 7.50 (ISBN 92-5-101140-0, F2248, FAO). Unipub.

The Production & Storage of Dried Fish: Proceedings of the Workshop on the Production & Storage of Dried Fish, Serdang, Malaysia, Nov. 1982. (Fisheries Reports: No. 279 supp.). 271p. 1983. pap. text ed. 19.50 (ISBN 92-5-101343-8, F2450, FAO). Unipub.

Recommended International Code of Practice for Fresh Fish. 3rd ed. (CAC-RCP Ser.: No. 9-1976). 40p. 1982. pap. 4.50 (ISBN 92-5-100277-0, F1583, FAO). Unipub.

Reintjes, John W., ed. Improving Multiple Use of Coastal & Marine Resources. 96p. 1983. pap. 10.00 (ISBN 0-913235-01-6); 8.00. AM Fisheries Soc.

Report of an FAO-Norway Expert Consultation on International Cooperation in Fishery Development in Developing Countries: Svany, Norway, 1977. (Fisheries Reports: No. 201). 52p. 1977. pap. 7.50 (ISBN 0-686-93998-0, F1414, FAO). Unipub.

Report of the ACMRR Working Party on the Scientific Basis of Determining Management Measures: Hong Kong, 10-15 Dec. 1979. (Fisheries Reports: No. 236). (Eng., Fr. & Span.). 154p. 1980. pap. 11.75 (ISBN 92-5-100938-4, F2051, FAO). Unipub.

Report of the Committee on Fisheries. Incl. Fourteenth Session, Rome, 26-30 May 1981. (No. 256). (Eng., Fr & Span.). 43p. 1981. pap. 7.50 (ISBN 92-5-101106-0, F2209); Twelfth Session. (No. 208). 32p. 1979. pap. 7.50 (ISBN 92-5-100656-3, F1518). (Fisheries Reports, FAO). Unipub.

Report of the Eighth Session of the Fishery Committee for the Eastern Central Atlantic (CECAF) Lome, Tago, Sept. 1982. (Fisheries Reports: No. 282). (Eng. & Fr.). 44p. 1983. pap. text ed. 7.50 (ISBN 92-5-101357-8, F2451, FAO). Unipub.

Report of the Eighth Session of the Indian Ocean Fishery Commission Executive Committee for the Implementation of the International Indian Ocean Fishery Survey & Development Programme: Rome, 23-24 April 1979. (Fisheries Reports: No. 221). (Eng. & Fr.). 18p. 1979. pap. 7.50 (ISBN 92-5-100776-4, F1828, FAO). Unipub.

Report of the Eleventh Session of the Committee on Fisheries: Rome, 9-26 April 1977. (Fisheries Reports: No. 196). (Eng., Fr. & Span.). 58p. 1977. pap. 7.50 (ISBN 92-5-100336-X, F1178, FAO). Unipub.

Report of the Eleventh Session of the Coordinating Working Party on Atlantic Fishery Statistics: Luxembourg, July 1982. (Fisheries Reports: No. 274). 46p. 1982. pap. 7.50 (ISBN 92-5-101257-1, F2370, FAO). Unipub.

Report of the Eleventh Session of the European Inland Fisheries Advisory Commission: Stavanger, Norway, 28 May - 3 June 1980. (Fisheries Reports: No. 248). (Eng. & Fr.). 63p. 1981. pap. 7.50 (ISBN 92-5-101062-5, F2181, FAO). Unipub.

Report of the Expert Consultation on Quantitative Analysis in Fishery Industries Development. Rome, Italy, 16-24 January 1975: A Review of Quantitative Methods for Marketing Management, Vol. 6. pap. 7.50 (F814, FAO). Unipub.

Report of the FAO-NORAD Round Table Discussion on Expanding the Utilization of Marine Fishery Resources for Human Consumption: Svany, Norway, 1975. (Fisheries Reports: No. 175). 53p. 1975. pap. 7.50 (ISBN 0-686-93990-5, F825, FAO). Unipub.

Report of the Fifteenth FAO Regional Conference for Asia & the Pacific, New Delhi 5-13 March 1980. 97p. 1981. pap. 7.50 (ISBN 92-5-100963-5, F2084, FAO). Unipub.

Report of the Fifteenth Session of the General Fisheries Council for the Mediterranean, Palma de Mallorca, Spain, 18-26 September 1980. 91p. 1980. pap. 12.50 (ISBN 92-5-101026-9, F2126, FAO). Unipub.

Report of the Fifth Session of the Fishery Committee for the Eastern Central Atlantic (CECAF) Lome, Tago, 7-11 March 1977. (Fisheries Reports: No. 195). (Eng. & Fr.). 57p. 1977. pap. 7.50 (ISBN 92-5-100308-4, F8419, FAO). Unipub.

Report of the Fifth Session of the IPFC-IOFC Joint Working Party of Experts on Indian Ocean & Western Pacific Fishery Statistics: Manila, Philippines, 1-3 March 1978. (Fisheries Reports: No. 218). (Eng. & Fr.). 28p. 1979. pap. 7.50 (ISBN 92-5-100733-0, F1827, FAO). Unipub.

Report of the First Session of the Committee for the Development & Management of Fisheries in the Southwest Indian Ocean: Le Chaland, Mauritius, April 1981. (Fisheries Reports: No. 254). (Eng. & Fr.). 65p. 1981. pap. 7.50 (ISBN 92-5-101097-8, F2223, FAO). Unipub.

Report of the First Technical Consultation on Stock Assessment in the Central Mediterranean: Tunis, 19-23 April 1982. (Fisheries Reports: No. 266). (Eng. & Fr., Illus.). 132p. 1982. pap. text ed. 10.75 (ISBN 92-5-001268-3, F2373, FAO). Unipub.

Report of the Fishery Committee for the Eastern Central Atlantic (CECAF) Working Party on Resources Evaluation: Rome, 9-13 Feb. 1976. (Fisheries Reports: No. 183). (Eng. & Fr., Illus.). 138p. 1976. pap. 9.00 (ISBN 92-5-100085-9, F831, FAO). Unipub.

Report of the Fishery Committee for the Eastern Central Atlantic (CECAF), Subcommittee on Fishery Development: 1st Session, Dakar, Senegal, 1974. (Fisheries Reports: No. 145). 40p. 1974. pap. 7.50 (ISBN 0-686-93973-5, F1713, FAO). Unipub.

Report of the Fishery Committee for the Eastern Central Atlantic (CECAF) 4th Session, Rome, 1974. (Fisheries Reports: No. 151). 28p. 1974. pap. 7.50 (ISBN 0-686-93978-6, F1714, FAO). Unipub.

Report of the Fishery Committee for the Eastern Central Atlantic (CECAF), Working Party on Resources Evaluation: 2nd Session, Rome, 1973. (Fisheries Reports: No. 158). 95p. 1975. pap. 7.50 (ISBN 0-686-93981-6, F800, FAO). Unipub.

Report of the Fishery Committee for the Eastern Central Atlantic (CECAF), Working Party on Resource Evaluation: 5th Session, Dakar, Senegal, 1980. (Fisheries Reports: No. 244). (Eng. & Fr.). 127p. 1981. pap. 9.75 (ISBN 92-5-101061-7, F2169, FAO). Unipub.

Report of the Fishery Committee for the Eastern Central Atlantic (CECAF), Sub-Committee on Management of Resources Within the Limits of National Jurisdiction: 3rd Session, Dakar, Sengal, 1981. (Fisheries Reports: No. 250). (Eng. & Fr.). 47p. 1981. pap. 7.50 (ISBN 92-5-101063-3, F2170, FAO). Unipub.

Report of the Fourth Joint Meeting of the Indo-Pacific Fisheries Council Special Committee on Management of Indo-Pacific Tuna, 4th Session, & the Indian Ocean Fishery Commission on Management of Indian Ocean Tuna, 5th Session, Colombo, Sri Lanka, 1976. (Fisheries Reports: No. 190). (Eng. & Fr.). 17p. 1977. pap. 7.50 (ISBN 92-5-100251-7, F838, FAO). Unipub.

Report of the Fourth Session of the Indian Ocean Fishery Commission Committee for the Development & Management of the Fishery Resources of the Gulfs: Doha, Qatar, 17-21 April 1982. (Fisheries Reports: No. 276). (Eng. & Ar.). 24p. 1983. pap. text ed. 7.50 (ISBN 92-5-001318-3, F2436, FAO). Unipub.

Report of the Fourth Session of the Indo-Pacific Fishery Commission Working Party on Aquaculture & the Environment: Manila, Philippines, 1-2 March 1978. (Fisheries Reports: No. 215). 12p. 1979. pap. 7.50 (F1830, FAO). Unipub.

Report of the Fourth Session of the Working Party on Resource Evaluation of the CECAF Evaluation of the Fishery Resources of the Eastern Central Atlantic: Dakar, Senegal, 23-27 April 1979. (Fisheries Reports: No. 220). (Eng. & Fr.). 203p. pap. 14.75 (ISBN 92-5-100800-0, F1873, FAO). Unipub.

Report of the Government Consultation on Codes of Practice for Fish & Fishery Products: Rome, October, 1975. (Fisheries Reports: No. 173). 6p. 1976. pap. 7.50 (ISBN 0-685-68360-5, F823, FAO). Unipub.

Report of the Indian Ocean Fishery Commission Special Working Party on Stock Assessment of Shrimp of the Indian Ocean Area: 1st Session, Bahrain, 1971. (Fisheries Reports: No. 138). 44p. 1973. pap. 7.50 (ISBN 0-686-93969-7, F781, FAO). Unipub.

Report of the Indo-Pacific Fishery Commission, Working Party on Aquaculture & Environment: 5th Session, Jakarta, Indonesia, 1980. (Fisheries Reports: No. 241). 12p. 1980. pap. 7.50 (ISBN 92-5-100962-7, F2081, FAO). Unipub.

Report of the Informal Consultation on Antarctic Kill, 1974. (Fisheries Reports: No. 153). 153p. 1974. pap. 7.50 (ISBN 0-686-93980-8, F794, FAO). Unipub.

Report of the International Symposium on the Early Life History of Fish: Obun, Scotland. (Fisheries Reports: No. 141). 61p. 1973. pap. 7.50 (ISBN 0-686-93971-9, F786, FAO). Unipub.

Report of the IPFC Ad Hoc Committee to Review the Functions & Responsibilities of IPFC: Bagnou, 1975. (Fisheries Reports: No. 181). 21p. 1976. pap. 7.50 (ISBN 0-686-93991-3, F829, FAO). Unipub.

Report of the IPFC Group of Experts on the Indian Ocean. 1967. pap. 7.50 (F1670, FAO). Unipub.

Report of the IUCN Workshop on Marine Mammals-Fishery Interactions. 68p. 1980. pap. 10.00 (IUCN123, IUCN). Unipub.

Report of the Joint Session of the Indian Ocean Fisheries Commission (IOFC) (Seventh Session) & the Indo-Pacific Fisheries Commission (IPFC) (Twentieth Session) Bali, Indonesia, November 1982. (Fisheries Reports: No. 281). (Eng. & Fr.). 198p. 1984. pap. 7.90 (ISBN 92-5-001378-7, F2493, FAO). Unipub.

Report of the of the Indian Ocean Fishery Commission: 5th Session, Cohin, India, 1977. (Fisheries Reports: No. 199). (Eng. & Fr.). 41p. 1977. pap. 7.50 (ISBN 92-5-100549-4, F1420, FAO). Unipub.

Report of the Second Session of the Indian Ocean Fishery Commission Committee for the Development & Management of Fishery Resources of the Gulfs: Doha, Qatar, 18-20 Sept. 1979. (Fisheries Reports: No. 223). (Eng. & Fr.). 19p. 1979. pap. 9.00 (ISBN 92-5-100841-8, F1895, FAO). Unipub.

Report of the Sixth Session of the Fishery Committee for the Eastern Central Atlantic (CECAF) Agadir, Morocco, Dec. 1979. (Fisheries Reports: No. 229). (Eng. & Fr.). 70p. 1980. pap. 7.50 (ISBN 92-5-100900-7, F1952, FAO). Unipub.

Report of the Sixth Session of the Indian Ocean Fishery Commission: Perth, Australia, 25-29 Feb. 1980. (Fisheries Reports: No. 234). (Eng. & Fr.). 35p. 1980. pap. 7.50 (ISBN 92-5-100930-9, F2088, FAO). Unipub.

Report of the Symposium on Stock Enhancement in the Management of Freshwater Fisheries: Budapest, Hungary, 31 May - 2 June 1982. (European Inland Fisheries Advisory Commission (EIFAC): Technical Papers: No. 42). 48p. 1982. pap. text ed. 7.50 (ISBN 92-5-101280-6, F2397, FAO). Unipub.

Report of the Technical Conference on Fishery Products, Tokyo, 1973. (Fisheries Reports: No. 146). 59p. 1974. pap. 7.50 (ISBN 0-686-93977-8, F789, FAO). Unipub.

Report of the Technical Consultation on Methodologies Used for Fish Age-Reading: Montpellier, Oct. 1981. (Fisheries Reports: No. 257). (Eng. & Fr.). 112p. 1982. pap. 8.00 (ISBN 92-5-001207-1, F2305, FAO). Unipub.

Report of the Technical Consultation on Stock Assessment in the Adriatic: Split, Yugoslavia, 2-6 June 1980. (Fisheries Reports: No. 239). (Eng. & Fr.). 71p. 1981. pap. 7.50 (ISBN 92-5-100970-8, F2144, FAO). Unipub.

Report of the Third Session of the Committee on Resource Management of the General Fisheries Council for the Mediterranean: Rome, 17-19 June 1980. (Fisheries Reports: No. 240). (Eng. & Fr.). 20p. 1980. pap. 7.50 (ISBN 92-5-100966-X, F2087, FAO). Unipub.

Report of the Third Session of the Indian Ocean Fishery Commission Committee for the Development & Management of the Fishery Resources of the Gulfs: Doha, Qatar, 28-30 Sept. 1980. (Fisheries Reports: No. 247). (Eng. & Arabic.). 45p. 1981. pap. 7.50 (ISBN 92-5-001057-5, F2210, FAO). Unipub.

Report of the Third Session of the Standing Committee on Resources Research and Development, Indo-Pacific Fishery Committee (IPFC) (Fisheries Reports: No. 275). pap. 10.00 (ISBN 92-5-101256-3, F2354, FAO). Unipub.

Report of the Third Session of the Western Central Atlantic Fishery Commission: Havana, Cuba, 18-22 Nov. 1980. (Fisheries Reports: No. 246). (Eng., Fr & Span.). 52p. 1981. pap. 7.50 (ISBN 92-5-101044-7, F2182, FAO). Unipub.

Report of the Thirteenth Session of the Committee on Fisheries: Rome, 8-12 Oct. 1979. (Fisheries Reports: No. 228). (Eng., Fr. & Span.). 51p. 1979. pap. 9.00 (ISBN 92-5-100877-9, F1896, FAO). Unipub.

Report of the Working Party on the Promotion of Fishery Resources Research in Developing Countries: Floro, Norway, Sept. 1979 & Rome, Italy, Sept. 1980. (Fisheries Reports: No. 251). (Trilingual.). 245p. 1981. pap. 17.75 (F2226, FAO). Unipub.

Report of the Workshop on the Phenomenon Known as "El Nino". Ecuador, 1974. (Fisheries Reports: No. 163). 24p. 1975. pap. 7.50 (ISBN 0-686-93985-9, F806, FAO). Unipub.

Report on Atlantic Fishery Statistics: Coordinating Working Party, 8th Session. (Fisheries Reports: No. 156). (Illus.). 39p. 1976. pap. 7.50 (ISBN 0-685-74969-X, F797, FAO). Unipub.

Report on Fisheries: Committee on Fisheries, 10th Session, Rome, 1975. (Fisheries Reports: No. 162). 45p. 1975. pap. 7.50 (ISBN 0-686-93983-2, F805, FAO). Unipub.

Report on Fisheries: Committee on Fisheries, 9th Session, Rome, October 15-22, 1974. (Fisheries Reports: No. 154). 39p. 1976. pap. 7.50 (ISBN 0-685-68359-1, F795, FAO). Unipub.

Report on Marine Research Resources: 8th Session, Sesimbra, Portugal, 1975. (Fisheries Reports: No. 171). 24p. 1975. pap. 7.50 (ISBN 0-686-93988-3, F819, FAO). Unipub.

Report on Quantitative Analysis in Fishery Industries Development: Expert Consultation held at Rome, Italy, 1975. (Fisheries Reports: No. 167). 1975. pap. 7.50 ea. (F809, FAO); Vol. 1, 22p. pap. (F809); Vol. 2, 24p. pap. (F810); Vol. 3, 12p. pap. (F811); Vol. 4, 14p. pap. (F812); Vol. 5, 11p. pap. (F813); Vol. 6, 7p. pap. (F814). Unipub.

Report on Selective Shrimp Trawls: Expert Consultation Held at the Netherlands, 1973. (Fisheries Reports: No. 139). 71p. 1973. pap. 7.50 (ISBN 0-686-93970-0, F784, FAO). Unipub.

Report on Small-Scale Fisheries Development: Expert Consultation, Rome, 1975. (Fisheries Reports: No. 169). 16p. 1975. pap. 7.50 (ISBN 0-686-93987-5, F816, FAO). Unipub.

Report on the Government Consultation on Codes of Practice for Fish & Fishery Products: Rome, 1974. (Fisheries Reports: No. 155). 5p. 1976. pap. 10.50 (ISBN 0-685-68965-4, F796, FAO). Unipub.

Report on the Seventh Session of the Fishery Committee for the Eastern Central Atlantic (CECAF) Lagos, Nigeria, 10-14 April 1981. (Fisheries Reports: No. 255). (Eng. & Fr.). 95p. 1982. pap. 7.75 (ISBN 92-5-101109-5, F2228, FAO). Unipub.

Report on the Symposium on Methodology for the Survey, Monitoring & Appraisal of Fishery Resources in Lakes & Large Rivers. pap. 7.50 (ISBN 92-5-102075-2, F763, FAO). Unipub.

Report on the Training Course on Quality Aspects in the Handling & Storage of Fish. (Danish Funds-in-Trust Ser.: No. 143). 26p. 1975. pap. 7.50 (ISBN 0-685-55200-4, F1094, FAO). Unipub.

Reports of the Fourth Session of the Committee on Resource Management: Rome, 17-18 June 1982 & the Technical Consultation on Regulation of Efforts in Trawl Fisheries in the Mediterranean. (Fisheries Reports: No. 270). (Eng. & Fr.). 83p. 1983. pap. text ed. 7.50 (ISBN 92-5-001266-7, F2376, FAO). Unipub.

Rettig, R. Bruce & Ginter, Jay J., eds. Limited Entry as a Fishery Management Tool. (Washington Sea Grant Ser.). 584p. 1980. pap. 17.50x (ISBN 0-295-95741-7). U of Wash Pr.

A Review of Quantitative Analysis of Vessels & Fishing Operations, Vol. 2. pap. 7.50 (F810, FAO). Unipub.

A Review of Quantitative Methods as Applied to Fishery Harbour Planning, Design & Operation, Vol. 3. pap. 7.50 (F811, UN). Unipub.

A Review of Quantitative Methods for the Management of Fish Distribution & Storage Systems, Vol. 5. pap. 7.50 (F813, FAO). Unipub.

A Review of Quantitative Methods for the Management of Fish Processing Plants, Vol. 4. pap. 7.50 (F812, FAO). Unipub.

A Review of the Fishery Resources in the Western Central Atlantic. (WECAF Studies Ser.: No. 3). (Illus.). 1976. pap. 7.50 (ISBN 92-5-100015-8, F1212, FAO). Unipub.

Rothchild, B. J., ed. Global Fisheries: Perspectives for the 1980's. (Springer Series on Environmental Management Ser.). (Illus.). 289p. 1983. 37.00 (ISBN 0-387-90772-6). Springer-Verlag.

Russell-Hunter, W. D. Aquatic Productivity: An Introduction to Some Basic Aspects of Biological Oceanography & Limnology. (Illus.). 1970. text ed. 12.95x (ISBN 0-685-04258-8). Macmillan.

Sara, R. Light Fishing. (General Fisheries Council of the Mediterranean (GFCM): Studies & Reviews: No. 19). (Eng. & Fr.). 34p. (2nd Printing 1966). 1962. pap. 7.50 (ISBN 0-686-92941-1, F1782, FAO). Unipub.

Scientific Basis for the Conservation of Non-Ocean Living Aquatic Resources. (Fisheries Reports: No. 82). 19p. 1968. pap. 6.00 (ISBN 0-686-92705-2, F1740, FAO). Unipub.

Smith, Ian R. Research Framework for Traditional Fisheries. (Illus.). 40p. 1983. pap. text ed. 6.50x (ISBN 0-89955-391-5, Pub. by ICLARM Philippines). Intl Spec Bk.

Some Geotechnical & Geophysical Systems & their Applications to the Planning of Fishery Harbour Development Programmes in Developing Countries. (Fisheries Technical Papers: No. 91). 28p. 1969. pap. 7.50 (ISBN 0-686-92743-5, F1742, FAO). Unipub.

Some Scientific Problems of Multispecies Fisheries: Report of the Expert Consultation on Management of Multispecies Fisheries, Rome, Italy, Sept. 1977. (Fisheries Technical Papers: No. 181). (Eng. & Fr.). 48p. 1978. pap. 7.50 (ISBN 92-5-100573-7, F1419, FAO). Unipub.

State of World Fisheries. pap. 4.50 (F448, FAO). Unipub.

Stevenson, David K. A Review of the Marine Resources of the Western Central Atlantic Fisheries Commission (WECAFC) Region. (Fisheries Technical Papers: No. 211). (Eng. & Span.). 142p. 1981. pap. 10.50 (ISBN 92-5-101153-2, F2286, FAO). Unipub.

Stock Assessment of Shrimp in the Indian Ocean Area (Bahrain, Iran, Iraq, Kuwait, Oman, Qatar, Saudi Arabia, United Arab Emirates) Report of the Meeting of the Ad Hoc Group of the IOFC Special Working Party on Stock Assessment of Shrimp in the Indian Ocean Area, to Consider the Stocks in the Area Covered by the UNDP-FAO Regional Fishery Survey & Development Project REM-71-278. Doha, Qatar, 26-29 April 1976. (Eng. & Fr.). 28p. pap. 7.50 (ISBN 92-5-100287-8, F840, FAO). Unipub.

Stuart, Erling. Preserving the Catch. LC 81-21495. (Illus.). 176p. 1982. 16.95 (ISBN 0-8117-1285-0). Stackpole.

Summary Report and Recommendations of the First Session of the Joint FAO-IOC Panel of Experts on the Aquatic Sciences & Fisheries Information System (ASFIS). New York, U.S.A., September 2-5, 1975. pap. 7.50 (F815, FAO). Unipub.

Symposium on Investigations & Resources of the Caribbean Sea & Adjacent Regions (CICAR) Proceedings. (Fisheries Reports: No. 71.2). 353p. 1971. pap. 19.00 (ISBN 0-686-92975-6, F1678, FAO). Unipub.

Symposium on the Development & Exploitation of Artificial Lakes: Proceedings, Dominican Republic, Nov.-Dec. 1981. (Fisheries Reports: No. 273). (Eng. & Span.). 22p. 1982. pap. 7.50 (ISBN 92-5-001246-2, F2347, FAO). Unipub.

Templeton, Robin G., ed. Freshwater Fisheries Management. 190p. 1985. pap. 30.00 (ISBN 0-85238-130-1, FN107, FNB). Unipub.

Tomczak, G. H. Environmental Analyses in Marine Fisheries Research. (Fisheries Technical Papers: No. 17). 152p. 1977. pap. 9.75 (ISBN 92-5-100494-3, F1341, FAO). Unipub.

Toward a Relevant Science: Fisheries & Aquatic Scientific Resource Needs in Canada. (Fisheries Research Board of Canada Reports: No. 14). 29p. 1978. pap. 5.50 (ISBN 0-685-60676-7, SSC103, SSC). Unipub.

Training Course on Quality Aspects in the Handling & Storage of Fish: 1975. pap. 7.50 (F1260, FAO). Unipub.

Trilingual Dictionary of Fisheries Technological Terms: Curing. 85p. 1960. pap. 11.50 (ISBN 92-5-000856-2, F483, FAO). Unipub.

Tropical Forest Resources Assessment. Tropical Forest Resources Assessment Project: Forest Resources of Tropical Africa, Part 1 Regional Synthesis, 2 Pts. (Eng. & Fr.). 115p. 1981. pap. 8.50 (ISBN 92-5-101087-0, F2199, FAO); pap. 42.00 (ISBN 92-5-101090-0, F2200). Unipub.

Ulltang, O. Methods of Measuring Stock Abundance Other Than by the Use of Commercial Catch & Effort Data. (Fisheries Technical Papers: No. 176). (Eng., Fr. & Span.). 30p. 1977. pap. 7.50 (ISBN 92-5-100397-1, F1323, FAO). Unipub.

U. S. Department of the Interior, Federal Water Pollution Control Administration, Committee on Water Quality Criteria, 1968. Facsimile of Section Three: Fish, Other Aquatic Life, & Wildlife - Report. (Fisheries Technical Papers: No. 94). 113p. 1969. pap. 7.50 (ISBN 0-686-92755-9, F1744, FAO). Unipub.

Waugh, Geoffrey. Aquaculture: Fisheries Management. 225p. 1983. 23.00x (ISBN 0-86531-983-9). Westview.

Welcomme, R. L. Fishery Management in Large Rivers. (Fisheries Technical Papers: No. 194). (Eng. & Span.). 65p. 1979. pap. 7.50 (ISBN 92-5-100764-0, F1637, FAO). Unipub.

Welcomme, Robin L. Fisheries Ecology of Floodplain Rivers. (Illus.). 1979. text ed. 50.00x (ISBN 0-582-46310-6). Longman.

Western Central Atlantic Fishery Commission: Report of the Third Session of the Working Party on Assessment of Marine Fishery Resources, Kingston, Jamaica, May 1982. (Fisheries Reports: No. 278). (Eng., Fr. & Span.). 40p. 1983. pap. text ed. 7.50 (ISBN 92-5-101319-5, F2417, FAO). Unipub.

Wharton, James. Bounty of the Chesapeake: Fishing in Colonial Virginia. (Illus.). 78p. (Orig.). 1957. pap. 2.95 (ISBN 0-8139-0137-5). U Pr of Va.

White, Donald J. New England Fishing Industry: A Study in Price & Wage Setting. LC 54-7065. (Wertheim Publications in Industrial Relations Ser). (Illus.). 1954. 14.00x (ISBN 0-674-61200-0). Harvard U Pr.

Windsor, Malcolm & Barlow, Stuart. Introduction to Fishery By-Products. (Illus.). 208p. 1981. 36.00 (ISBN 0-85238-115-8, FN91, FNB). Unipub.

Working Party on Tuna & Billfish Tagging in the Atlantic & Adjacent Seas. Final Report. (Fisheries Reports: No. 118, Suppl. 1). 40p. 1971. pap. 6.00 (ISBN 0-686-92814-8, F1702, FAO). Unipub.

World List of Aquatic Sciences & Fisheries Serial Titles. (Fisheries Technical Papers: No. 147, Suppl. 3). 158p. 1978. pap. 11.50 (ISBN 92-5-100617-2, F1490, FAO). Unipub.

World Review of Interactions Between Marine Mammals & Fisheries. (Fisheries Technical Papers: No. 251). 190p. 1985. pap. 16.00 (ISBN 92-5-102145-7, F2709 5071, FAO). Unipub.

Woynarovich, E. & Horvath, L. The Artificial Propagation of Warm-Water Finfishes: A Manual for Extension. (Fisheries Technical Papers: No. 201). (Eng., Fr., & Span.). 192p. (2nd Printing 1980). 1980. pap. 14.00 (ISBN 92-5-100999-6, F2125, FAO). Unipub.

FISHERIES–BIBLIOGRAPHY

Advisory Committee on Marine Resources Research, 7th Session, Rome, 1973. The Scientific Advisory Function in International Fishery Management & Development Bodies: Report, Supplement 1. (Fisheries Reports: No. 142, Suppl. 1). 14p. 1974. pap. 7.50 (ISBN 0-686-93096-7, F787, FAO). Unipub.

Alabaster, John S. Report of the EIFAC Workshop on Fish-Farm Effluents: Silkeborg, Denmark, May 26-28, 1981. (European Inland Fisheries Advisory Commission (EIFAC): Technical Papers: No. 41). 174p. 1982. pap. 12.75 (ISBN 92-5-101162-1, F2285, FAO). Unipub.

Bibliography of Living Marine Resources. (Regional Fishery Survey & Development Project). 47p. 1977. pap. 7.50 (ISBN 92-5-100200-2, F727, FAO). Unipub.

FAO Fisheries Department. FAO Fisheries Department List of Publications & Documents: 1948-1978. 3rd, Rev. ed. (Fisheries Reports: No. 100). 241p. 1979. pap. 7.50 (ISBN 0-686-93225-0, F2053, FAO). Unipub.

Gastell, J. D. & Tiews, K. Report on Standardization of Methodology in Fish Nutrition Research: EIFAC, UNIS, ICES Working Group on Standardization of Methodology, Hamburg, Fed. Rep. of Germany, March 1979. (European Inland Fisheries Advisory Commission (EIFAC): Technical Papers: No. 36). (Eng. & Fr.). 30p. 1980. pap. 8.25 (ISBN 92-5-100918-X, F2048, FAO). Unipub.

North Atlantic Bibliography & Citation Index: Subject Index - Physical Oceanography. (Fisheries Technical Papers: No. 54, Suppl. 1). 5p. 1968. pap. 7.50 (ISBN 0-686-92781-8, F1818, FAO). Unipub.

North Atlantic Bibliography & Citation Index. (Fisheries Technical Papers: No. 54). 260p. 1968. pap. 17.00 (ISBN 0-686-92778-8, F1728, FAO). Unipub.

Report of an FAO Expert Panel for the Facilitation of Tuna Research: 3rd Session, 1969. (Fisheries Reports: No. 80). 97p. 1969. pap. 7.50 (ISBN 0-686-93036-3, F1683, FAO). Unipub.

Report of an FAO Expert Panel for the Facilitation of Tuna Research: 4th Session, La Jolla, 1971. (Fisheries Reports: No. 118). 26p. 1972. pap. 7.50 (ISBN 0-686-93074-6, F1701, FAO). Unipub.

Report of an FAO-SIDA Experts Consultation on Policies & Institutions for Integrated Rural Development: Nairobi, Kenya, 1976. (Development Documents: No. 30). 1976. Set. pap. 13.00 (ISBN 0-686-92832-6, F1205, FAO); Vol. 1, 43p. pap. Vol. 2, 95p. Unipub.

Report of the Committee on Fisheries. (Fisheries Reports). 17p. 1967. pap. 7.50 (ISBN 0-686-93093-2, F1667, FAO). Unipub.

Report of the Conference on Fish Finding, Pruse Seining & Aimed Trawling, Reykjavik, 1970. (Fisheries Reports: No. 110). 47p. 1971. pap. 7.50 (ISBN 0-686-93069-X, F1699, FAO). Unipub.

Report of the FAO Technical Conference on Fish Inspection & Quality Control: Halifax, 1969. (Fisheries Reports: No. 81). 73p. 1969. pap. 7.50 (ISBN 0-686-93041-X, F1684, FAO). Unipub.

Report of the FAO Technical Conference of Fishery Representatives of the Near East Countries: Kuwait, 1966. (Fisheries Reports: No. 39). 36p. 1966. pap. 7.50 (ISBN 0-686-92934-9, F1660, FAO). Unipub.

Report of the FAO Technical Conference on the Freezing & Irradiation of Fish: Madrid, 1967. (Fisheries Reports: No. 53). 60p. 1968. pap. 7.50 (ISBN 0-686-93012-6, F1669, FAO). Unipub.

Report of the Fishery Committee for the Eastern Central Atlantic (CECAF) 1st Session, Ohana, 1969. (Fisheries Reports: No. 69). 42p. 1969. pap. 7.50 (ISBN 0-686-93019-3, F1676, FAO). Unipub.

Report of the Fishery Committee for the Eastern Central Atlantic (CECAF) 2nd Session, Casablanca, 1971. (Fisheries Reports: No. 107). 25p. 1971. pap. 7.50 (ISBN 0-686-93061-4, F1697, FAO). Unipub.

Report of the Fishery Committee for the Eastern Central Atlantic (CECAF) Working Party on Regulatory Measures for Demersal Stocks: 2nd Session, Rome, 1971. (Fisheries Reports: No. 109). 113p. 1971. pap. 8.00 (ISBN 0-686-93066-5, F1698, FAO). Unipub.

Report of the Fishery Committee for the Eastern Central Atlantic (CECAF) Sub-Committee on Implementation of Management Measures: 1st Session, Rome, 1972. (Fisheries Reports: No. 125). 14p. 1972. pap. 7.50 (ISBN 0-686-93080-0, F1706, FAO). Unipub.

Report of the Fishery Committee for the Eastern Central Atlantic (CECAF) 3rd Session, Canary Islands, 1972. (Fisheries Reports: No. 132). 26p. 1973. pap. 7.50 (ISBN 0-686-93089-4, F1710, FAO). Unipub.

Report of the Fishery Committee for the Eastern Central Atlantic (CECAF) Working Party on Resource Evaluation: Rome, 1972. (Fisheries Reports: No. 136). 73p. 1973. pap. 7.50 (ISBN 0-686-93095-9, F782, FAO). Unipub.

Report of the International Commission for the Conservation of Atlantic Tunas: 1st Meeting, Rome 1969. (Fisheries Reports: No. 84). 47p. 1970. pap. 7.50 (ISBN 0-686-93046-0, F1686, FAO). Unipub.

Report of the International Conference on Investment in Fisheries: Rome, 1969, Vol. 1. (Fisheries Reports: No. 83,). 78p. 1970. pap. 7.50 (ISBN 0-686-93042-8, F1685, FAO). Unipub.

Report of the IPFC-IOFC Ad Hoc Working Party of Scientists on Assessment of Tuna. Incl. First Session, Rome, 1972. (No. 137). 20p. 1973. pap. 7.50 (ISBN 0-686-93097-5, F783); Second Session, Nates, 1974. (No. 152). 22p. 1974. pap. 7.50 (ISBN 0-686-93979-4, F793). (Fisheries Reports, FAO). Unipub.

Report of the IPFC-IOFC Joint Working Party of Experts on Indian Ocean & Western Pacific Fishery Statistics. Incl. First Session, Bangkok. (No. 120). 14p. 1971. pap. 6.00 (ISBN 0-686-93077-0, F1703); Third Session. (No. 157). (Illus.). 1976. pap. 7.50 (ISBN 0-685-74970-3, F798); Fourth Session, Colombo, Sri Lanka, 1976. (No. 189). (Eng. & Fr.). 19p. 1977. pap. 7.50 (ISBN 92-5-100260-6, F837). (Fisheries Reports, FAO). Unipub.

Report of the Man-Made Lakes Stock Assessment Working Group: Jinji, Uganda, 1970. (Fisheries Reports: No. 87). 13p. 1970. pap. 7.50 (ISBN 0-686-93051-7, F1688, FAO). Unipub.

Report of the Meeting for Consultations on Underwater Noise: Rome, 1968. (Fisheries Reports: No. 76). 35p. 1970. pap. 7.50 (ISBN 0-686-93032-0, F1682, FAO). Unipub.

Report of the Technical Conference on Fishery Management & Development: Vancouver, 1973. (Fisheries Reports: No. 134). 83p. 1973. pap. 7.50 (ISBN 0-686-93091-6, F785, FAO). Unipub.

Report on Codes of Practice for Fish & Fishery Products: Ad Hoc Consultation, 2nd, Rome, 1969. (Fisheries Reports: No. 73). 6p. 1969. pap. 7.50 (ISBN 0-686-93029-0, F1680, FAO). Unipub.

Report on Fish Toxicity Testing Procedures: Prepared by the EIFAC Working Party on Toxicity Testing Procedures. (European Inland Fisheries Advisory Commission (EIFAC): Technical Papers: No. 24). (Eng. & Fr.). 1975. pap. 7.50 (ISBN 92-5-102076-0, F765, FAO). Unipub.

Report on Fisheries: Committee on Fisheries, Rome, 1967. 2nd ed. (Fisheries Reports: No. 46). 44p. 1967. pap. 7.50 (ISBN 0-686-93005-3, F1666, FAO). Unipub.

Report on Fisheries: 5th Session, Committee on Fisheries, Rome, 1970. (Fisheries Reports: No. 86). 44p. 1970. pap. 7.50 (ISBN 0-686-93050-9, F1687, FAO). Unipub.

Report on Fisheries: 6th Session, Committee on Fisheries, Rome, 1971. (Fisheries Reports: No. 103). 50p. 1971. pap. 7.50 (ISBN 0-686-93054-1, F1694, FAO). Unipub.

Report on Fisheries: 8th Session, Committee on Fisheries, Rome, 1973. (Fisheries Reports: No. 135). 47p. 1973. pap. 6.00 (ISBN 0-686-93094-0, F1711, FAO). Unipub.

Report on Fishery Administration & Services: Conference, Rome, 1966, 3 vols. (Fisheries Reports: No. 43, Vols. 1-3). 1967. Vol. 1, 169p. pap. 11.50 (ISBN 0-686-92992-6, F1661, FAO); Vol. 2, 310p. pap. 20.25 (ISBN 0-686-98836-1, F1662); Vol. 3, 286p. pap. 18.75 (ISBN 0-686-98837-X, F1663). Unipub.

Report on Fishery Statistics in the North Atlantic Area: Continuing Working Party on Fishery Statistics, 5th Session, 1967. (Fisheries Reports: No. 45). 33p. 1967. pap. 7.50 (ISBN 0-686-93002-9, F1665, FAO). Unipub.

Report on the FAO-MARMAP International Training Course on Fish Egg & Larval Studies: La Jolla, Calif., 1973. (Fisheries Reports: No. 144). 23p. 1974. pap. 7.50 (ISBN 0-686-93064-9, F1328, FAO). Unipub.

The Role of FAO in the Development of Inland Fishery Resources. (Fisheries Technical Papers: No. 81). 73p. 1969. pap. 7.50 (ISBN 0-686-92749-4, F1739, FAO). Unipub.

Workshop on Controlled Reproduction of Cultivated Fishes. Reports & Relevant Papers. (European Inland Fisheries Advisory Commission (EIFAC): Technical Papers: No. 25). 180p. 1975. pap. 11.75 (ISBN 0-686-93008-8, F766, FAO). Unipub.

World Conference on Agrarian Reform & Rural Development: Report, Rome, 1979. (Development Documents: No. 62). 67p. 1979. pap. 7.50 (ISBN 0-686-92900-4, F1846, FAO). Unipub.

World List of Aquatic Sciences & Fisheries Serial Titles. (Fisheries Technical Papers: No. 147, Suppl. 4). 128p. 1980. pap. 9.50 (ISBN 92-5-100904-X, F1946, FAO). Unipub.

World List of Aquatic Sciences & Fisheries Serial Titles. (Fisheries Technical Papers: No. 148, Suppl. 4). 128p. 1980. pap. 8.00 (ISBN 92-5-000882-1, F1947, FAO). Unipub.

World List of Aquatic Sciences & Fisheries Serial Titles. (Fisheries Technical Papers: No. 147, Suppl. 1). 173p. 1976. pap. 12.50 (ISBN 92-5-100124-3, F879, FAO). Unipub.

World List of Aquatic Sciences & Fisheries Serial Titles. (Fisheries Technical Papers: No. 147, Suppl. 2). (Illus.). 159p. 1977. pap. 11.75 (ISBN 92-5-100341-6, F880, FAO). Unipub.

World List of Aquatic Sciences & Fisheries Serial Titles. (Fisheries Technical Papers: No. 147, Suppl. 5). 96p. 1981. pap. 7.75 (ISBN 92-5-101129-X, F2263, FAO). Unipub.

FISHERIES–EQUIPMENT AND SUPPLIES

see also Fishing–Implements and Appliances

FAO Technical Conference on Fishery Research Craft: Proceedings, Seattle, 1968. (Fisheries Reports: No. 64). 56p. 1968. pap. 7.50 (ISBN 0-686-92946-2, F1675, FAO). Unipub.

Lozano Cabo, F. Graphic Documentation on Some Fishing Gear Used in Spanish Coastal Lagoons. (General Fisheries Council of the Mediterranean (GFCM): Studies & Reviews: No. 9). (Eng. & Fr., Illus.). 5p. (2nd Printing 1966). 1959. pap. 7.50 (ISBN 92-5-101927-4, F1773, FAO). Unipub.

FISHERIES–STATISTICS

Applied Fishery Statistics. (Fisheries Technical Papers: No. 135). 174p. 1974. pap. 13.00 (ISBN 92-5-100086-7, F865, FAO). Unipub.

Applied Fishery Statistics: Vectors & Matrices. (Fisheries Technical Papers: No. 135, Suppl. 1). 39p. 1975. pap. 7.50 (ISBN 0-686-93137-8, F863, FAO). Unipub.

Armantrout, Neil B., ed. Acquisition & Utilization of Aquatic Habitat Inventory Information. 376p. 1982. pap. 22.00 (ISBN 0-913235-19-9). Am Fisheries Soc.

Bazigos, G. P. Mathematics for Fishery Statisticians. (Fisheries Technical Papers: No. 169). 193p. (2nd Printing 1978). 1977. pap. 14.00 (ISBN 92-5-100314-9, F1241, FAO). Unipub.

The Design of Fisheries Statistical Surveys - Inland Waters: Populations in Non-Random Order Sampling Methods for Echo Surveys, Double Sampling. (Fisheries Technical Papers: No. 133, Suppl. 1). 52p. 1976. pap. 7.50 (ISBN 92-5-100660-1, F869, FAO). Unipub.

Garcia, S. & LeReste, L. Life Cycles, Dynamics, Exploitation & Management of Coastal Penaeid Shrimp Stocks. (Fisheries Technical Papers: No. 203). (Eng. & Fr.). 215p. 1981. pap. 16.00 (ISBN 92-5-101069-2, F2205, FAO). Unipub.

Gulland, J. A. Fish Stock Assessment: A Manual of Basic Methods. (FAO Wiley Food & Agriculture Ser.). 223p. 1983. 37.95x (ISBN 0-471-90027-3, Pub. by Wiley-Interscience). Wiley.

BOOKS - SUBJECT INDEX FISHERIES–ISLANDS OF THE PACIFIC

Report of the Eleventh Session of the Committee on Fisheries: Rome, 9-26 April 1977. (Fisheries Reports: No. 196). (Eng., Fr. & Span.). 58p. 1977. pap. 7.50 (ISBN 92-5-100336-X, F1178, FAO). Unipub.
Report of the First Session of the Working Party on Fishery Statistics: Dakar, Senegal, 13-14 Oct. 1980. (Fisheries Reports: No. 245). (Eng. & Fr.). 148p. 1981. pap. 10.75 (ISBN 92-5-101056-0, F2135, FAO). Unipub.
Report of the Second Joint Meeting of the Working Party on Assessment of Fish Resources & the Working Party on Stock Assessment of Shrimp & Lobster Resources (WECAF) Mexico City, Mexico, 26-29 Nov. 1979. (Fisheries Reports: No. 235). (Eng. & Span.). 49p. 1981. pap. 7.50 (ISBN 92-5-101049-8, F2143, FAO). Unipub.
Report of the Second Session of the Working Party on Fishery Statistics: Western Central Atlantic Fishery Commission, Miami, Florida, USA, 18-22 October 1982. (Fisheries Reports: No. 280). (Eng., Fr & Span.). 32p. 1983. pap. text ed. 7.50 (ISBN 92-5-101326-8, F2395, FAO). Unipub.
Report of the Technical Consultation on the Assessment & Management of the Black Sea Turbot (GFCM) Working Party on Resource Evaluation & Fishery Statistics, Istanbul, Turkey, 11-15 June 1979. (Fisheries Reports: No. 226). (Eng. & Fr.). 23p. (2nd Printing 1980). 1979. pap. 9.00 (ISBN 92-5-100879-5, F1964, FAO). Unipub.
Troadec, J. P. & Garcia, S. The Fish Resources of the Eastern Central Atlantic: The Resources of the Gulf of Guinea from Angola to Mauritania, Pt. 1. (Fisheries Technical Papers: No. 186). (Eng. & Fr.). 171p. 1980. pap. 12.50 (ISBN 92-5-100851-5, F2028, FAO). Unipub.
Yearbook of Fishery Statistics. annual Incl. Vol. 51. Fishery Commodities, 1980. (No. 17). 178p. 1981. 36.50 (ISBN 92-5-001135-0, F2237); Catches & Landings, 1980. (No. 38). 386p. 47.25 (ISBN 92-5-001134-2, F2283); Vol. 53. Fishery Commodities, 1981. (No. 19). 151p. 1983. text ed. 36.50 (ISBN 92-5-001284-5, F2400); Vol. 52. Catches and Landings, 1981. (No. 18). 357p. 47.25 (ISBN 92-5-001262-4, F2401, FAO); Vol. 12. 1960. pap. 16.25 (F529); Vol. 49. Fishery Commodities. 1981. pap. 36.50 (ISBN 92-5-001015-X, F2172); Vol. 54. Catches & Landings, 1982. (Fisheries Ser.: No. 21). (Eng., Fr & Span.). 393p. 1984. 47.50 (ISBN 92-5-001437-6, F2553); Vol. 55. Fishery Commodities. (Fisheries Ser.: No. 22). (Eng., Fr. & Span.). 162p. 1984. 30.50 (ISBN 92-5-001438-4, F2554, FAO). (Statistics & Fisheries Ser.). (Eng., Fr & Span., Orig., FAO). Unipub.

FISHERIES–AFRICA

AM Design & Operation to Optimize Fish Production in Impounded River Basins: Based on a Review of the Ecological Effects of Large Dams in Africa. (Commission for Inland Fisheries of Africa (CIFA): Technical Papers: No. 11). 98p. 1984. pap. 7.50 (ISBN 92-5-101485-X, F2637, FAO). Unipub.
Committee For Inland Fisheries Of Africa (CIFA) Report of the First Session of the Sub-Committee for the Development & Management of the Fisheries of Lake Victoria, Mwanza, Tanzania, Oct. 1981. (Fisheries Reports: No. 262). (Eng. & Fr.). 78p. 1982. pap. 7.50 (ISBN 92-5-101189-3, F2326, FAO). Unipub.
FAO Expert Consultation on Fish Technology in Africa: Proceedings, Casablanca, Morocco, 7-11 June 1982. (Fisheries Reports: No. 268 Suppl.). (Eng. & Fr.). 295p. 1982. pap. text ed. 21.00 (ISBN 92-5-001287-X, F2393, FAO). Unipub.
The Fisheries Ecology of African Floodplains. (Committee for Inland Fisheries of Africa (CIFA): Technical Papers: No. 3). 51p. 1975. pap. 7.50 (ISBN 92-5-101917-7, F1816, FAO). Unipub.
The Freedom from Hunger Campaign (FFHC) Outboard Mechanization Projects in Dahomey & Togo. (Fisheries Technical Papers: No. 80). 23p. 1968. pap. 7.50 (ISBN 0-686-92833-4, F1738, FAO). Unipub.
Organic Recycling in Africa: Papers Presented at the FAO-SIDA Workshop on the Use of Organic Materials as Fertilizers in Africa, Buea, Cameroon, Dec. 5-14, 1977. (Soils Bulletins: No. 43). 308p. 1980. pap. 22.00 (ISBN 92-5-100945-7, F2096, FAO). Unipub.
Report of the FAO Expert Consultation on Fish Technology in Africa: Dar-es-Salaam, Tanzania, 11-15 Feb. 1980. (Fisheries Reports: No. 237). (Eng. & Fr.). 23p. 1981. pap. 7.50 (ISBN 92-5-100981-3, F2101, FAO). Unipub.
Report of the FAO Expert Consultation on Fish Technology in Africa: Casablanca, Morocco, 7-11 June 1982. (Fisheries Reports: No. 268). (Eng. & Fr.). 24p. 1982. pap. 7.50 (ISBN 92-5-101236-9, F2337, FAO). Unipub.
Report of the Fifth Session of the Committee for Inland Fisheries of Africa: Cairo, Egypt, Jan. 1983. (Fisheries Reports: No. 283). (Eng. & Fr.). 28p. 1983. pap. text ed. 7.50 (ISBN 92-5-101347-0, F2452, FAO). Unipub.
Report on the CIDA-FAO-CECAF Seminar on the Changing Law of the Sea & the Fisheries of West Africa. 1979. pap. 10.75 (ISBN 92-5-100634-2, F1500, FAO). Unipub.
Role of Fishery Technology in the Management & Development of Freshwater Fisheries in Africa. (Commission for Inland Fisheries of Africa (CIFA): Technical Papers: No. 6). (Eng. & Fr.). 71p. 1979. pap. 9.00 (ISBN 92-5-100831-0, F1888, FAO). Unipub.
Welcomme, R. L. Symposium on River & Floodplain Fisheries in Africa: Review & Experience Papers, Bujumbura, Burundi, 21-23 November 1977. (Commission for Inland Fisheries of Africa (CIFA): Technical Papers: No. 5). (Eng. & Fr.). 390p. 1978. pap. 28.00 (ISBN 92-5-000674-8, F1561, FAO). Unipub.

FISHERIES–ASIA

Aquaculture Development in China: Report on an FAO-UNEP Aquaculture Study Tour to the People's Republic of China, 2 May - 1 June 1978. 74p. 1981. pap. 7.50 (ISBN 92-5-100811-6, F1861, FAO). Unipub.
Aquaculture Economics Research in Asia: Proceedings of a Workshop Held in Singapore, 2-5 June 1981. 152p. 1982. pap. 15.00 (ISBN 0-88936-330-7, IDRC193, IDRC). Unipub.
Baluyut, E. A. Stocking & Introduction of Fish in Lakes & Reservoirs in the ASEAN Countries. (Fisheries Technical Paper Ser.: No. 236). 82p. (Orig.). 1984. pap. 7.50 (ISBN 92-5-101366-7, F2591, FAO). Unipub.
Bhukaswan, Thirophan. Management of Asian Reservoir Fisheries. (Fisheries Technical Papers: No. 207). 78p. 1980. pap. 7.50 (ISBN 92-5-101023-4, F2156, FAO). Unipub.
Chen, T. P. Aquaculture Practices in Taiwan. 1978. 30.00x (ISBN 0-685-63392-6). State Mutual Bk.
Chonchuenchob, Pradit, et al. Hanging Culture of the Green Mussel in Thailand (Mytilus Smaragdinus Chemnitz) (Illus.). 1983. pap. 2.00 (ISBN 0-89955-383-4, Pub. by ICLARM Philippines). Intl Spec Bk.
Emmerson, Donald K. Rethinking Artisanal Fisheries Development: Western Concepts, Asian Experiences. (Working Paper: No. 423). x, 97p. 1980. 5.00 (ISBN 0-686-36074-5, WP-0423). World Bank.
Freshwater Aquaculture Development in China: Report of the FAO/UNDP Study Tour Organized for French-speaking African Countries April-May 1980. (Fisheries Technical Papers: No. 215). (Eng. & Fr.). 137p. 1983. pap. 5.50 (ISBN 92-5-101113-3, FAO). Unipub.
Oldeman, L. R. & Frere, M. A Study of the Agroclimatology of the Humid Tropics of Southeast Asia: An FAO-UNESCO-WHO Inter-Agency Project on Agroclimatology. (Technical Note Ser.: No. 179). lxi, 259p. 1982. pap. 45.00 (ISBN 92-63-10597-9, W547, WMO). Unipub.
Pauly, Daniel. Theory & Management of Tropical Multispecies Stock: A Review, with Emphasis on the Southeast Asian Demersal Fisheries. (ICLARM Studies & Reviews: No. 1). (Illus.). 35p. 1983. pap. text ed. 6.50x (ISBN 0-89955-398-2, Pub. by ICLARM Philippines). Intl Spec Bk.
Pritchard, G. I. Fisheries & Aquaculture in the People's Republic of China. (Illus.). 32p. 1980. pap. 7.50 (ISBN 0-88936-189-4, IDRC115, IDRC). Unipub.
Report of the Second Session of the Committee for the Development & Management of Fisheries in the Southwest Indian Ocean: Indian Ocean Fisheries Commission (IOFC), Make, Seychelles, Dec. 1982. (Fisheries Reports: No. 285). (Eng. & Fr.). 56p. 1983. pap. text ed. 7.50 (ISBN 92-5-101352-7, F2453, FAO). Unipub.
Report on Credit for Artisanal Fishermen in Southeast Asia. (Fisheries Reports: No. 122). 67p. 1972. pap. 7.50 (ISBN 0-686-93018-5, F1705, FAO). Unipub.
Smith, Ian R., et al. Philippine Municipal Fisheries: A Review of Resources Technology & Socioeconomics. (Illus.). 87p. 1983. pap. text ed. 12.00x (ISBN 0-89955-388-5, Pub. by ICLARM Philippines). Intl Spec Bk.

FISHERIES–AUSTRALIA

Egloff, Brian J. Wreck Bay: An Aboriginal Fishing Community. (AIAS New Ser.: No. 28). 52p. 1981. pap. text ed. 7.50x (ISBN 0-391-02240-7, Pub. by Australian Inst Australia). Humanities.
Greenber, Fridaz. Great Barrier Reef Fishwatcher's Field Guide. (Illus.). 1984. plastic card 3.95x (ISBN 0-913008-15-X). Seahawk Pr.
Pownall, Peter. Fisheries of Australia. (Illus.). 160p. 1979. 27.25 (ISBN 0-85238-101-8, FN79, FNB). Unipub.
--Fisheries of Australia. 1978. 40.00x (ISBN 0-685-63414-0). State Mutual Bk.

FISHERIES–EUROPE

Bagenal, T. B., et al. EIFAC Experiments on Pelagic Fish Stocks: Assessment by Acoustic Methods in Lake Konnevesi, Finland. (European Inland Fisheries Advisory Commission (EIFAC): Technical Papers: No. 14). 22p. 1982. pap. 7.50 (ISBN 92-5-101234-2, F2349, FAO). Unipub.
Bombace, G. Preliminary Report on Fish Distribution & Marketing in Sicily. (General Fisheries Council of the Mediterranean (GFCM): Studies & Reviews: No. 28). (Eng. & Fr.). 28p. 1966. pap. 7.50 (ISBN 92-5-101946-0, F1789, FAO). Unipub.
Fishery Committee for the Eastern Central Atlantic (CECAF) Report of the Second Session of the Working Party on Fishery Statistics, Dakar, Senegal, 8-10 February 1982. (Fisheries Reports: No. 265). (Eng. & Fr.). 80p. 1982. pap. 7.50 (ISBN 92-5-101215-6, F2339, FAO). Unipub.
Fishery of the Green Crab (Carcinus Maenus L.) & Soft Crab Cultivation in the Lagoon of Venice. (General Fisheries Council of the Mediterranean (GFCM): Studies & Reviews: No. 37). 44p. 1968. pap. 7.50 (ISBN 92-5-101956-8, F1797, FAO). Unipub.
Gaudet, J. L. Organization of Inland Fisheries Administration in Europe. Rev. ed. (European inland Fisheries Advisory Commission (EIFAC): Technical Papers: No. 5). (Eng. & Fr.). 86p. 1974. pap. 7.50 (ISBN 92-5-102055-8, F1718, FAO). Unipub.
The Reduction of Fish in Poland. (Fisheries Technical Papers: No. 69). 20p. 1969. pap. 7.50 (ISBN 0-686-92837-7, F1731, FAO). Unipub.
Report of the Ninth Session of European Inland Fisheries Commission. (Fisheries Reports: No. 178). 1977. pap. 7.50 (ISBN 92-5-000120-7, F826, FAO). Unipub.
Report of the Second Technical Consultation on Stock Assessment in the Balearic & Gulf of Lions Statistical Division: Casablanca, Morocco, Dec. 1981. (Fisheries Reports: No. 263). (Eng. & Fr.). 174p. 1982. pap. 12.75 (ISBN 92-5-001211-X, F2304, FAO). Unipub.
Report of the Twelfth Session of the European Inland Fisheries Advisory Commission: Budapest, Hungary, May-June 1982. (Fisheries Reports: No. 267). (Eng. & Fr.). 47p. 1982. pap. 7.50 (ISBN 92-5-101250-4, F2353, FAO). Unipub.
Symposium on New Development in Carp & Trout Nutrition, European Inland Fisheries Advisory Commission: Proceedings, 5th Session, Rome, 1968. (European Inland Fisheries Advisory Commission (EIFAC): Technical Papers: No. 9). 213p. 1969. pap. 14.25 (ISBN 0-686-92982-9, F755, FAO). Unipub.
Symposium on the Major Communicable Fish Diseases in Europe & Their Control. Panel Reviews & Relevant Papers. (European Inland Fisheries Advisory Commission (EIFAC): Technical Papers: No. 17, Suppl. 2). (Eng. & Fr.). 255p. 1973. pap. 18.50 (ISBN 92-5-002069-4, F759, FAO). Unipub.

FISHERIES–GREAT BRITAIN

Benham, Hervey. The Codbangers. 35.00x (ISBN 0-9505944-1-5, Pub. by Essex County England). State Mutual Bk.
Edwards, Eric. The Edible Crab & Its Fishery in British Waters. (Illus.). 144p. 1979. pap. 13.25 (ISBN 0-85238-100-X, FN78, FNB). Unipub.
FAO Fisheries Technology Service & Hamabe, Mototsugu, eds. Squid Jigging from Small Boats. 84p. 1982. 42.95x (ISBN 0-85238-122-0, Pub. by Fishing News England). State Mutual Bk.
Harris, G. S. Salmon Progagation in England Wales. 62p. 1982. 30.00x (ISBN 0-904561-39-9, Pub. by Natl Water England). State Mutual Bk.
Mills, Derek. Scotland's King of Fish. 74p. 1981. 10.00x (ISBN 0-85158-134-X, Pub. by Blackwood & Sons England). State Mutual Bk.
O'Conner, R., et al. Development of the Irish Sea Fishing Industry & Its Regional Implications. 1981. 50.00x (ISBN 0-686-75526-X, Pub. by ESRI Ireland). State Mutual Bk.
Report on Fisheries Legislation & Administration in the United Kingdom (England & Wales) (Fisheries Reports: No. 98). 33p. 1971. pap. 6.00 (ISBN 0-686-93039-8, F1692, FAO). Unipub.
Scallop & Queen Fisheries in the British Isles. 141p. 1983. pap. text ed. 16.75 (ISBN 0-85238-128-X, FN104, FNB). Unipub.

FISHERIES–INDIA

Fish Silage Production & Its Use: Papers Presented at the Indo-Pacific Fisheries Commission Workshop on Fish Silage Production & Its Use, Djakarta, Indonesia, September 17-21, 1979. (Fisheries Reports: No. 230). 109p. 1980. pap. 8.00 (ISBN 92-5-100921-X, F1940, FAO). Unipub.
Indian Ocean Fishery Commission (IOFC) Report of the First Session of the Committee for the Development and Management of Fisheries in the Bay of Bengal, Colombo, Sri Lanka, December 7-9, 1981. Incl. Indian Ocean Fishery Commission (IOFC) Report of the Second Session of the Committee for the Development & Management of Fisheries in the Bay of Bengal. (Fisheries Reports: No. 296). (Eng. & Fr.). 15p. 1983. pap. text ed. 7.50 (ISBN 92-5-101435-3, F2524); Indian Ocean Fishery Commission (IOFC) Report of thr Third Session of the Committee for the Development & Management of Fisheries in the Southwest Indian Ocean: Mombasa, Kenya, Nov. 14-16, 1984. (Fisheries Reports: No. 320). 36p. 1985. pap. 7.50 (ISBN 92-5-102206-2, F2727 5091). (Fisheries Reports: No. 260). (Eng. & Fr.). 15p. 1982. pap. 7.50 (ISBN 92-5-101195-8, F2300, FAO). Unipub.
IPCP Group of Experts on the Indian Ocean, Rome, 1967. The Present Status of Fisheries & Assessment of Potential Resources of the Indian Ocean & Adjacent Seas. (Fisheries Reports: No. 54). 33p. 1967. pap. 7.50 (ISBN 0-686-92888-1, F1679, FAO). Unipub.
Report of the Eighth Session of the Indian Ocean Fishery Commission Executive Committee for the Implementation of the International Indian Ocean Fishery Survey & Development Programme: Rome, 23-24 April 1979. (Fisheries Reports: No. 221). (Eng. & Fr.). 18p. 1979. pap. 7.50 (ISBN 92-5-100776-4, F1828, FAO). Unipub.
Report of the Indian Ocean Fishery Commission Executive Committee for Implementation of the International Indian Ocean Fishing Survey & Development Programme. Incl. First Session. (No. 105). 18p. 1971. pap. 7.50 (ISBN 0-686-93056-8, F1696); Second Session, Rome 1971. (No. 111). 36p. 1971. pap. 7.50 (ISBN 0-686-93070-3, F1700); Third Session, Colombo, Sri Lanka 1972. (No. 126). 10p. 1972. pap. 7.50 (ISBN 0-686-93082-7, F1707); Seventh Session. (No. 205). (Eng. & Fr.). 26p. 1978. pap. 7.50 (ISBN 92-5-100631-8, F1496). (Fisheries Reports, FAO). Unipub.
Report of the Indian Ocean Fishery Commission. Incl. First Session, Rome, 1968. (No. 60). 35p. 1968. pap. 7.50 (ISBN 0-686-93015-0, F1673); Third Session, Colombo, Sri Lanka, 1972. (No. 130). 28p. 1973. pap. 7.50 (ISBN 0-686-93088-6, F1709); Fourth Session, Mobasa, Kenya, July 1975. (No. 166). 27p. 1976. pap. 7.50 (ISBN 0-685-66330-2, F808). (Fisheries Reports, FAO). Unipub.
Report of the Indian Ocean Fishery Commission Special Working Party on Stock Assessment of Shrimp of the Indian Ocean Area: 1st Session, Bahrain, 1971. (Fisheries Reports: No. 138). 44p. 1973. pap. 7.50 (ISBN 0-686-93969-7, F781, FAO). Unipub.
Report of the IPFC-IOFC Joint Working Party of Experts on Indian Ocean & Western Pacific Fishery Statistics. Incl. First Session, Bangkok. (No. 120). 14p. 1971. pap. 6.00 (ISBN 0-686-93077-0, F1703); Third Session. (No. 157). (Illus.). 1976. pap. 7.50 (ISBN 0-685-74970-3, F798); Fourth Session, Colombo, Sri Lanka, 1976. (No. 189). (Eng. & Fr.). 19p. 1977. pap. 7.50 (ISBN 92-5-100260-6, F837). (Fisheries Reports, FAO). Unipub.
Report of the of the Indian Ocean Fishery Commission: 5th Session, Cohin, India, 1977. (Fisheries Reports: No. 199). (Eng. & Fr.). 41p. 1977. pap. 7.50 (ISBN 92-5-100549-4, F1420, FAO). Unipub.
Report of the Sixth Joint Meeting of the Indian Ocean Fishery Commission, Committee on Management of Indian Ocean Tuna, 7th Session: Indo-Pacific Fishery Commission, Special Committee on Management of Indo-Pacific Tuna, 6th Session, Perth, Australia, Feb. 1980. (Fisheries Reports: No. 233). (Eng. & Fr.). 22p. 1980. pap. 7.50 (ISBN 92-5-100939-2, F2045, FAO). Unipub.
UNDP-FAO Pelagic Fishery Investigation Project FIRS IND-75-038, 1977. Report of Acoustic Survey Along the Southwest of India, November 1976: Phase II, Progress Report. (Fisheries Reports: No. 6). 50p. 1977. pap. 7.50 (ISBN 0-686-93083-5, F1826, FAO). Unipub.

FISHERIES–ISLANDS OF THE PACIFIC

Bleeker, Pieter. Atlas Ichtyologique Indes Orientales Neerlandaises, Vols. 11-14. (Atlas of Fishes of the Dutch East Indies). (Illus.). 200p. 1983. text ed. 250.00x (ISBN 0-87474-240-4). Smithsonian.
Report of the First Session of the Indo-Pacific Fishery Commission Working Party of Experts on Inland Fisheries: Bangkok, Thailand, 17-19 January 1978. (Fisheries Reports: No. 214). 24p. 1979. pap. 7.50 (ISBN 92-5-100747-0, F1621, FAO). Unipub.

FISHERIES–LATIN AMERICA

Goulding, Michael. Man & Fisheries of an Amazon Frontier. (Developments in Hydrobiology Ser.: Vol. 4). 140p. 1982. 47.50 (ISBN 90-6193-755-8, Pub. by Junk Pubs Netherlands). Kluwer Academic.

Merluza Trawlers for Peru: A Techno-Economic Evaluation. (Fisheries Technical Papers: No. 132). 57p. 1974. pap. 7.50 (ISBN 0-686-92756-7, F1750, FAO). Unipub.

Report of the Regional Conference for Latin America: 4th Session, Santiago, 1956. 89p. 1957. pap. 4.75 (ISBN 0-686-92898-9, F378, FAO). Unipub.

Report of the Second Session of the Commission for Island Fisheries of Latin America: Santo Domingo, Dominican Republic, December 2-4, 1981. (Fisheries Reports: No. 261). (Eng. & Span.). 46p. 1982. pap. 7.50 (ISBN 92-5-101191-5, F2309, FAO). Unipub.

Report of the Technical Consultation on the Latin American Hake Industry: Montevideo, Uruguay, October 24-28, 1977. (Fisheries Reports: No. 203). (Eng. & Span.). 76p. 1978. pap. 7.50 (ISBN 0-686-94000-8, F1484, FAO). Unipub.

Report on Manpower in the Fisheries Sector of Chile, Present Status & Prospects of Education. (Fisheries Reports: No. 94). 72p. 1971. pap. 7.50 (ISBN 0-686-93045-2, F1691, FAO). Unipub.

Zeisler, R. & Ardizzone, G. D. The Inland Waters of Latin America. (Commission for Inland Fisheries of Latin America (COPESCAL): Technical Papers: No. 1). (Eng. & Span.). 179p. 1979. pap. 13.00 (ISBN 92-5-000780-9, F1831, FAO). Unipub.

FISHERIES–MEDITERRANEAN AREA

Controlled Breeding & Larval Rearing of Selected Mediterranean Marine Species. (General Fisheries Council of the Mediterranean (GFCM): Studies & Reviews: No. 55). (Eng., Fr., Illus.). 177p. (2nd Printing, 1980). 1976. pap. 11.75 (ISBN 92-5-000059-6, F923, FAO). Unipub.

Dremiere, P. Y. & Nedelec, C. Data on Fishing Vessels & Gear in the Mediterranean. (General Fisheries Council of the Mediterranean (GFCM): Studies & Reviews: No. 56). (Eng. & Fr., Illus.). 188p. 1977. pap. 12.00 (ISBN 92-5-000350-1, F1257, FAO). Unipub.

Everson, I. The Living Resources of the Southern Ocean. (Southern Ocean Fisheries Survey Programmes: No. 77-1). (Eng. & Span.). 160p. 1977. pap. 10.50 (ISBN 92-5-100428-5, F1321, FAO). Unipub.

Existing Regulations for Sardine Fishing in the Mediterranean. (General Fisheries Council of the Mediterranean (GFCM): Studies & Reviews: No. 20). (Eng. & Fr.). 24p. 1963. pap. 7.50 (ISBN 92-5-101938-X, F1783, FAO). Unipub.

Explorations of the Possible Deep-Water Trawling Grounds in the Levant Basin. (General Fisheries Council of the Mediterranean (GFCM): Studies & Reviews: No. 49). (Eng. & Fr.). 71p. 1971. pap. 7.50 (ISBN 92-5-001968-8, F1807, FAO). Unipub.

General Fisheries Council for the Mediterranean (GFCM), Report of the Fifth Session of the Committee on Resource Management: Rome, 23-25 July 1984. (Fisheries Reports: No. 314). (Illus.). 42p. 1985. pap. 7.50 (ISBN 92-5-102142-2, F2653, FAO). Unipub.

General Fisheries Council for the Mediterranean (GFCM) Report of the Seventeenth Session: Rome, 17-21 September 1984. (GFCM Reports: No. 17). 62p. 1985. pap. 12.50 (ISBN 92-5-102162-7, F2680 5071, FAO). Unipub.

General Fisheries Council for the Mediterranean: Report of the Fourteenth Session, Nantes, France, 16-20 October 1978. 42p. 1978. pap. 9.50 (ISBN 92-5-100690-3, F1617, FAO). Unipub.

General Fisheries Council for the Mediterranean: Report of the Sixteenth Session, Held at Rome, September 27-October 1, 1982. 47p. 1983. pap. text ed. 12.50 (ISBN 92-5-101313-6, F2402, FAO). Unipub.

General Fisheries Council for the Mediterranean: Statistical Bulletin, No. 2. 116p. 1980. pap. 7.50 (ISBN 0-686-72310-4, F2065, FAO). Unipub.

General Fisheries Council for the Mediterranean, Statistical Bulletin, No. 1: Nominal Catches, 1964 - 1974. 1976. pap. 8.00 (ISBN 92-5-000026-X, F904, FAO). Unipub.

Investigations of Mullet Fisheries by Beach Seine on the U. A. R. Mediterranean Coast. (General Fisheries Council of the Mediterranean (GFCM): Studies & Reviews: No. 35). 52p. 1968. pap. 7.50 (ISBN 92-5-001954-8, F1795, FAO). Unipub.

Kapetsky, James A. & Lassere, G., eds. Management of Coastal Lagoon Fisheries, Vols. 1 & 2. (General Fisheries Council for the Mediterranean (GFCM): Studies & Reviews: No. 61). (Illus.). 776p. 1985. Set. pap. 57.00 (F2662, FAO). Vol. 1 (ISBN 92-5-002134-8). Vol. 2 (ISBN 92-5-002135-6). Unipub.

Management of Living Resources in the Mediterranean Coastal Area. (General Fisheries Council of the Mediterranean (GFCM): Studies & Reviews: No. 58). (Eng. & Fr.). 356p. 1981. pap. 26.50 (ISBN 92-5-101064-1, F2261, FAO). Unipub.

Rafail, S. Z., et al. Long Line Mediterranean Fisheries Studies, West of Alexandria. (General Fisheries Council of the Mediterranean (GFCM): Studies & Reviews: No. 42). (Eng.). 16p. (With French Summary). 1969. pap. 8.50 (ISBN 92-5-101961-4, F1802, FAO). Unipub.

Report of the General Fisheries Council for the Mediterranean. Incl. Tenth Session. 80p. 1970. pap. 7.25 (ISBN 0-686-92914-4, F206); Eleventh Session. 71p. 1972. pap. 7.25 (ISBN 0-686-92911-X, F207); Twelfth Session. 53p. 1974. pap. 5.25 (ISBN 0-686-92917-9, F208); Thirteenth Session, Rome 1976. 1977. pap. 9.50 (ISBN 92-5-100099-9, F209). FAO). Unipub.

Report of the General Fisheries Council for the Mediterranean, Committee on Resource Management. (Fisheries Reports: No. 207). 42p. 1978. pap. 7.50 (ISBN 92-5-100632-6, F1498, FAO). Unipub.

Report of the Second Technical Consultation on Stock Assessment in the Adriatic: Ancona, Italy, May 1981. (Fisheries Reports: No. 253). (Eng. & Fr.). 195p. 1981. pap. 14.00 (ISBN 92-5-001082-6, F2256, FAO). Unipub.

Report of the Sixth Session of the Working Party on Resources Appraisal & Fishery Statistics of the General Fisheries Council for the Mediterranean (GFCM) Rome, 10-14 Nov. 1975. (Fisheries Reports: No. 182). (Eng. & Fr.). 68p. 1976. pap. 7.50 (ISBN 92-5-100027-1, F830, FAO). Unipub.

Report of the Technical Consultation on Stock Assessment in the Balearic & Gulf of Lions Statistical Divisions: Palma de Mallorca, Spain, 1-5 Oct. 1979. (Fisheries Reports: No. 227). (Eng. & Fr.). 154p. 1981. pap. 11.50 (ISBN 92-5-100894-9, F2145, FAO). Unipub.

Report of the Technical Consultation on the Assessment & Management of the Black Sea Turbot (GFCM) Working Party on Resource Evaluation & Fishery Statistics, Istanbul, Turkey, 11-15 June 1979. (Fisheries Reports: No. 226). (Eng. & Fr.). 23p. (2nd Printing 1980). 1979. pap. 9.00 (ISBN 92-5-100879-5, F1964, FAO). Unipub.

FISHERIES–NEWFOUNDLAND

Lounsbury, Ralph G. British Fishery at Newfoundland, 1634-1763. LC 69-19217. viii, 398p. 1969. Repr. of 1934 ed. 25.00 (ISBN 0-208-00795-4, Archon). Shoe String.

Reeves, John. History of the Government of the Island of Newfoundland. 1793. 18.00 (ISBN 0-384-50131-1). Johnson Repr.

Report of the Technical Consultation on the Utilization of Small Pelagic Species in the Mediterranean Area: Madrid, Spain, May 1981. (Fisheries Reports: No. 252). (Eng. & Fr.). 203p. 1981. pap. 14.75 (ISBN 92-5-001124-5, F2227, FAO). Unipub.

FISHERIES–NORWAY

Edwards, David J. Salmon & Trout Farming in Norway. (Illus.). 208p. 1978. 26.00 (ISBN 0-85238-093-3, FN75, FNB). Unipub.

--Salmon & Trout Farming in Norway. 1978. 50.00x (ISBN 0-685-63450-7). State Mutual Bk.

Kobayashi, Teruo. Anglo-Norwegian Fisheries Case of 1951 & the Changing Law of the Territorial Sea. LC 65-64000. (University of Florida Social Sciences Monographs: No. 26). 1965. pap. 3.50 (ISBN 0-8130-0133-1). U Presses Fla.

Underal, Arild. The Politics of International Fisheries Management. 234p. 1981. pap. 20.00x (ISBN 0-686-69763-4). Universitet.

FISHERIES–NOVA SCOTIA

Denys, Nicolas. Description: Natural History of the Coasts of North America. Ganong, William F., ed. LC 68-28597. 1968. Repr. of 1908 ed. lib. bdg. 42.25x (ISBN 0-8371-3873-6, DEDH). Greenwood.

FISHERIES–TROPICS

Report of the ACMRR Working Party on the Management of Living Resources in Near-Shore Tropical Waters: Adviser Committee on Marine Resources Research (ACMRR), Rome, February-March 1983. (Fisheries Reports: No. 284). 84p. 1984. pap. 7.50 (ISBN 92-5-101393-4, F2491, FAO). Unipub.

Report of the Western Central Atlantic Fishery Commission. Incl. First Session, Port of Spain, Trinidad & Tobago, 1975. (No. 172). 31p. 1976. pap. 7.50 (ISBN 0-685-66354-X, F822); Second Session, Panama, 22-26 May 1978. (No. 209). (Eng., Fr & Span.). 54p. 1978. pap. 7.50 (ISBN 92-5-100665-2, F1537); Fourth Session, Managua, Nicaragua, May 1983. (No. 292). (Eng. & Span.). 39p. 1984. pap. 7.50 (ISBN 92-5-101391-8, F2498). (Fisheries Reports, FAO). Unipub.

FISHERY PRODUCTS

see also Canning and Preserving; Cold Storage; Fish-Oil

Available Amino Acid Content of Fish Meals. (Fisheries Reports: No. 92). 71p. 1970. pap. 7.50 (ISBN 0-686-93148-3, F1689, FAO). Unipub.

Chichester, C. O. & Graham, H. D., eds. Microbial Aspects of Fishery Products. 1973. 50.00 (ISBN 0-12-172740-8). Acad Pr.

Connell, J. J. & Hardy, R. Trends in Fish Utilization. (Illus.). 116p. 1982. pap. 19.00 (ISBN 0-85238-120-4, FN96, FNB). Unipub.

Dore, Ian, ed. Frozen Seafood-the Buyer's Handbook: A Guide to Profitable Buying for Commercial Users. LC 82-12513. (Osprey Seafood Handbks.). 308p. 1982. text ed. 48.00x (ISBN 0-943738-00-8). Osprey Bks.

Eddie, G. C. Road Transport of Fish & Fishery Products. (Fisheries Technical Paper Ser.: No. 232). 54p. (Orig.). 1984. pap. 7.50 (ISBN 92-5-101362-4, F2570, FAO). Unipub.

Fermented Fish Products. (Fisheries Reports: No. 100). 58p. 1971. pap. 7.50 (ISBN 0-686-93223-4, F1693, FAO). Unipub.

Fish Silage Production & Its Use: Papers Presented at the Indo-Pacific Fisheries Commission Workshop on Fish Silage Production & Its Use, Djakarta, Indonesia, September 17-21, 1979. (Fisheries Reports: No. 230). 109p. 1980. pap. 8.00 (ISBN 92-5-100921-X, F1940, FAO). Unipub.

Fishing News Books Ltd., ed. Introduction to Fishery by-Products. 208p. 1981. 70.00x (ISBN 0-686-86774-2, Pub. by Fishing News England). State Mutual Bk.

Grantham, G. J. & Tuna, Charley. Minced Fish Technology: A Review. (Fisheries Technical Papers: No. 216). 79p. 1981. pap. 7.50 (ISBN 92-5-101130-3, F2242, FAO). Unipub.

Hanson, S. W. & Horner, W. F. Fish Processing: It's Science & Technology. 1985. write for info. (ISBN 0-913655-30-9, Pub. by Ellis Horwood LTD UK). VCH Pubs.

Klust, Gerhard. Fibre Ropes for Fishing Gear: An FAO Fishing Manual. (Illus.). 200p. 1984. 30.00 (ISBN 0-85238-123-9, FN101, FNB). Unipub.

Kreuzer, Rudolf, ed. Fishery Products. 1978. 59.00 (ISBN 0-685-63415-9). State Mutual Bk.

Lanier, B. V. The World Supply & Demand Picture for Canned Small Pelagic Fish. (Fisheries Technical Papers: No. 220). 123p. 1981. pap. 9.00 (ISBN 92-5-101143-5, F2264, FAO). Unipub.

Multilingual Dictionary of Fish & Fish Products, Pt. 1. (Eng., Fr. & Rus.). 1978. 60.00 (ISBN 0-85238-086-0, FN64, FNB). Unipub.

OECD. Multilingual Dictionary of Fish & Fish Products. 1978. 59.00 (ISBN 0-685-63442-6). State Mutual Bk.

OECD Staff. International Trade in Fish Products: Effects on the 200-Mile Limit. 192p. (Orig.). 1982. pap. 17.50 (ISBN 92-64-12318-0). OECD.

Orr, A. P. & Marshall, S. M. The Fertile Sea. 1978. 40.00 (ISBN 0-685-63407-8). State Mutual Bk.

The Prevention of Losses in Cured Fish. (Fisheries Technical Papers: No. 219). 98p. 1981. pap. 7.50 (ISBN 92-5-101140-0, F2248, FAO). Unipub.

Report of the Fifth Session of the Working Party on Fish Technology & Marketing (IPFC) Serdang, Malaysia, 2-5 November 1982. (Fisheries Reports: No. 279). 28p. 1983. pap. text ed. 7.50 (ISBN 92-5-101323-3, F2443, FAO). Unipub.

Report of the Technical Conference on Fishery Products, Tokyo, 1973. (Fisheries Reports: No. 146). 59p. 1974. pap. 7.50 (ISBN 0-686-93977-8, F789, FAO). Unipub.

Report on the CIDA-FAO-CECAF Regional Seminar of Senior Fish Processing Technologists: Dakar, Senegal, October 1977. 2nd ed. (Fisheries Reports: No. 202). (Eng. & Fr.). 35p. 1978. pap. 7.50 (ISBN 92-5-100561-3, F1417, FAO). Unipub.

Scheuer, Paul J., ed. Marine Natural Products: Chemical & Biological Perspectives, Vol. 4. 1981. 45.00 (ISBN 0-12-624004-3). Acad Pr.

Waterman, J. J. The Production of Dried Fish. (Fisheries Technical Papers: No. 160). (Eng., Fr & Span.). 57p. (2nd Printing 1978). 1976. pap. 7.50 (ISBN 92-5-100103-0, F892, FAO). Unipub.

FISHERY PRODUCTS–PRESERVATION

Burgess, G. H., et al. Fish Handling & Processing. (Illus.). 1967. 25.00 (ISBN 0-8206-0045-8). Chem Pub.

FISHES

see also Aquariums; Fish As Food; Fish-Culture; Fisheries; Fishing; Tropical Fish;
also names of classes, orders, etc. of fishes, e.g. Bass, salmon

Ali, M. A. & Anctil, M. Retinas of Fishes: An Atlas. LC 76-22204. (Illus.). 1976. 71.00 (ISBN 0-387-07840-1). Springer-Verlag.

Allen, Gerald R. Damselfishes. (Illus.). 240p. 1975. 19.95 (ISBN 0-87666-034-0, H-950). TFH Pubns.

Allyn, Rube. Dictionary of Fishes. LC 52-334. (Orig.). pap. 4.95 (ISBN 0-8200-0101-5). Great Outdoors.

Artedi, P. Genera Piscium: Emendata & Aucta. 1967. Repr. of 1792 ed. 42.00 (ISBN 3-7682-0190-2). Lubrecht & Cramer.

--Ichthyolgia. Linnaeus, C., ed. 1961. Repr. of 1738 ed. 35.00 (ISBN 3-7682-0082-5). Lubrecht & Cramer.

Axelrod, Herbert R. & Burgess, Warren E. Freshwater Angelfish. (Illus.). 1979. 4.95 (ISBN 0-87666-516-4, KW-048). TFH Pubns.

Baardseth, E. Synopsis of Biological Data on Kobbed Wrack: Ascophyllum Nodosum (Linnaeus) Le Jolis. (Fisheries Synopses: No. 38, Rev. 1). 41p. 1970. pap. 7.50 (ISBN 92-5-101895-2, F1825, FAO). Unipub.

Backiel, T. & Zawisza, J. Synopsis of Biological Data on the Bream: Abramis Brama (Linnaeus, 1758) (Fisheries Synopses: No. 36). 110p. 1968. pap. 8.00 (ISBN 0-686-93027-4, F1763, FAO). Unipub.

Bagenal, T. B. Ageing of Fish. 240p. 1982. 40.00 (ISBN 0-686-84445-9, Pub. by Gresham England). State Mutual Bk.

Balon, E. K. Early Life Histories of Fishes: Developmental, Ecological & Evolutionary Perspectives. (Developments in Environmental Biology of Fishes Ser.). 1985. lib. bdg. 75.00 (ISBN 90-6193-514-8, Pub. by Junk Pub Netherlands). Kluwer-Academic.

Balon, Eugene, ed. Charrs: Salmonid Fishes of the Genus Salvelinus. (Perspectives in Vertebrate Science: No. 1). (Illus.). 919p. 1980. lib. bdg. 210.50 (ISBN 90-6193-701-9, Pub. by Junk Pubs Netherlands). Kluwer Academic.

Benirschke, K. & Hsu, T. C., eds. Chromosome Atlas: Fish, Amphibians, Reptiles & Birds, Vol. 1. LC 73-166079. (Illus.). 225p. 1972. loose leaf 25.00 (ISBN 0-387-05507-X). Springer-Verlag.

The Biology & Status of Stocks of Small Tunas: Report of an Ad Hoc Committee of Specialists, Honolulu, Hawaii, 15-18 Dec. 1975. (Fisheries Technical Papers: No. 154). 29p. 1976. pap. 7.50 (ISBN 92-5-100020-4, F887, FAO). Unipub.

Blouch, Ralph I. & Blouch, Ralph I., eds. International Association of Fish & Wildlife Agencies 69th Convention: Proceedings. (Orig.). 1980. 11.00 (ISBN 0-932108-04-0). IAFWA.

Bone, Q. & Marshall, N. B. Biology of Fishes. (Teritiary Level Biology Ser.). 253p. 1983. pap. 25.00 (ISBN 0-412-00151-9, NO. 5008). Methuen Inc.

Bullen, Frank T. Creatures of the Sea: Sea Birds, Beasts, & Fishes. 1977. lib. bdg. 69.95 (ISBN 0-8490-1682-7). Gordon Pr.

Cailliet, Gregor M. & Love, Milton, eds. Readings in Ichthyology. LC 78-16654. (Illus.). 1978. pap. 21.70x (ISBN 0-673-16249-4). Scott F.

Colby, P. J. & McNicol, R. E. Synopsis of Biological Data on the Walleye: Stizostedion V. Vitreum (Mitchell 1818) (Fisheries Synopses: No. 119). (Illus.). 147p. 1979. pap. 11.75 (ISBN 92-5-100757-8, F1622, FAO). Unipub.

Collette, Bruce B. & Nauen, Cornelia E. FAO Species Catalogue: Vol. 2: Scombrids of the World: An Annotated & Illustrated Catalogue of Tunas, Mackerels, Bonitos & Related Species Known to Date. (Fisheries Synopsis Ser.: No. 125, Vol. 2). 137p. (Orig.). 1984. pap. text ed. 10.50 (ISBN 92-5-101381-0, F2546, FAO). Unipub.

Computation & Interpretation of Biological Statistics of Fish Populations. (Illus.). 382p. 1975. pap. 19.50 (ISBN 0-686-93207-2, SSC22, SSC). Unipub.

Connell, J. J., ed. Advances in Fish Science & Technology. (Illus.). 528p. 1980. pap. 150.00 (ISBN 0-85238-108-5, FN87, FNB). Unipub.

Curtis, Brian. Life of the Fish: His Manners & Morals. (Illus.). 12.75 (ISBN 0-8446-1933-7). Peter Smith.

--Life Story of the Fish. 2nd ed. 1949. pap. 5.95 (ISBN 0-486-20929-6). Dover.

De Carli, Franco. The World of Fish. Richardson, Jean, tr. LC 79-1436. (Abbeville Press Encyclopedia of Natural Science). (Illus.). 1979. 13.95 (ISBN 0-89659-035-6); pap. 7.95 (ISBN 0-89659-029-1). Abbeville Pr.

Encyclopedie Illustree Des Poissons. (Fr.). 600p. 14.95 (ISBN 0-686-57157-6, M-6216). French & Eur.

Fishes: A Guide to Their Structure, Systemics, & Natural History. 300p. 1985. pap. text ed. write for info. (ISBN 0-534-05556-7). Wadsworth Pub.

Gammon, Clive. A Tide of Fish. 14.50x (ISBN 0-392-06417-0, SpS). Sportshelf.

Goode, G. Brown. Game Fishes of the United States. (Illus.). 1972. Repr. of 1879 ed. 75.00x (ISBN 0-8329-0851-7, Pub. by Winchester Pr). New Century.

Gordon, Bernard L. Secret Lives of Fishes. rev. ed. (Illus.). 306p. 1980. pap. text ed. 7.95 (ISBN 0-910258-12-0). Book & Tackle.

Gosline, William A. Functional Morphology & Classification of Teleostean Fishes. LC 77-151454. (Illus.). 216p. 1971. pap. text ed. 10.00x (ISBN 0-87022-300-3). UH Pr.

Greenberg, Idaz. Guide to Corals & Fishes. (Illus.). 1977. saddlestitched 4.95x (ISBN 0-913008-08-7). Seahawk Pr.

--Waterproof Guide to Corals & Fishes. (Illus.). 1977. soft plastic pages, rust-proof bdg. 9.95x (ISBN 0-913008-07-9). Seahawk Pr.

Greenfield, David, ed. Systemic Ichthyology: A Collection of Readings. 1972. 39.50x (ISBN 0-8422-5024-7); pap. text ed. 17.50x (ISBN 0-8290-0674-5). Irvington.

Greenwood, Peter H. & Norman, J. R. A History of Fishes. 3rd ed. 467p. 1976. pap. 26.95x (ISBN 0-470-99012-0). Halsted Pr.

Guia de Peces y Plantas de Acuario. (Span.). Date not set. Leatherette 44.95 (ISBN 0-686-97406-9, S-36344). French & Eur.

Hardy, David. Scallops & the Diver-Fisherman. (Illus.). 144p. 1981. pap. 23.50 (ISBN 0-85238-114-X, FN90, FNB). Unipub.

Hempel, Gotthilf. Early Life History of Marine Fish: The Egg Stage. LC 79-14549. (Washington Sea Grant). 86p. 1980. pap. 7.50x (ISBN 0-295-95672-0). U of Wash Pr.

Hennessen, W., ed. International Symposium on Fish Biologics: Serodiagnostics & Vaccines. (Developments in Biological Standardization: Vol. 49). (Illus.). xii, 496p. 1981. pap. text ed. 40.00 (ISBN 3-8055-3471-X). S Karger.

Hocutt, Charles H., et al. Power Plants: Effects on Fish & Shellfish Behavior. 1980. 38.50 (ISBN 0-12-350950-5). Acad Pr.

Hydrodynamics & Energetics of Fish Propulsion. (Illus.). 159p. 1975. pap. 9.25 (ISBN 0-686-93212-9, SSC51, SSC). Unipub.

International Association of Fish & Wildlife Agencies, 70th Convention: Proceedings. 1981. 13.00 (ISBN 0-932108-05-9). IAFWA.

Jankovic, D. Synopsis of Biological Data on European Grayling: Thymallus Thymallus (Linnaeus, 1758) (Fisheries Synopses: No. 24, Rev. 1). 50p. 1964. pap. 7.50 (ISBN 0-686-92726-5, F1754, FAO). Unipub.

Jhingram, Y. G. Synopsis of Biological Data on Catla: Catla Catla (Hamilton, 1822) (Fisheries Synopses: No. 32). 78p. 1966. pap. 7.50 (ISBN 0-686-92723-0, F1759, FAO). Unipub.

Jocher, Willy. Spawning Problem Fishes. Incl. Book 1 (ISBN 0-87666-146-0, PS-302); Book 2 (ISBN 0-87666-147-9, PS-302). (Illus.). 1972. pap. 4.95 ea. TFH Pubns.

Jordan, David S. Genera of Fishes & a Classification of Fishes. 1963. 55.00x (ISBN 0-8047-0201-2). Stanford U Pr.

Klausewitz, W. Die Erforshung der Ichthyofauna Des Roten Meeres. pap. 6.25 (ISBN 3-7682-7115-3). Lubrecht & Cramer.

Klunzinger, C. B. Synopsis der Fische Des Rothen Meeres, 2 parts in 1 vol. (Illus.). 1964. Repr. of 1871 ed. 35.00 (ISBN 3-7682-7115-3). Lubrecht & Cramer.

Lagler, Karl F., et al. Ichthyology. 2nd ed. LC 76-50114. 506p. 1977. 38.50 (ISBN 0-471-51166-8). Wiley.

Lampman, Ben H. Coming of the Pond Fishes. 1946. 12.50 (ISBN 0-8323-0341-0). Binford.

Langlois, T. H. A Study of the Small-Mouth Bass, Micropterus dolomieu (Lacepede) in Rearing Ponds in Ohio. 1936. 2.00 (ISBN 0-86727-032-2). Ohio Bio Survey.

Lanham, Url N. The Fishes. LC 62-9366. (Illus.). 116p. 1967. pap. 9.00x (ISBN 0-231-08581-8). Columbia U Pr.

Longhurst, A. R. Synopsis of Biological Data on West African Croakers: Pseudotolithus Typus, P. Elongatus. (Fisheries Synopses: No. 35). 44p. 1966. pap. 7.50 (ISBN 0-686-93037-1, F1762, FAO). Unipub.

Love, R. M. The Chemical Biology of Fishes: Vol. 2, Advances 1968-1977. 1980. 98.00 (ISBN 0-12-455852-6). Acad Pr.

McNeil, William J. & Himsworth, Daniel C., eds. Salmonid Ecosystems of the North Pacific. LC 80-17800. (Illus.). 348p. 1980. pap. 19.95x (ISBN 0-87071-335-3). Oreg St U Pr.

Marshall, N. B. Explorations in the Life of Fishes. LC 75-129122. (Books in Biology Ser: No. 7). 1971. 15.00x (ISBN 0-674-27951-4). Harvard U Pr.

Miller, P. J., ed. Fish Phenology: Anabolic Adaptiveness in Teleosts, No. 44. LC 79-40966. (Symposia of the Zoological Society of London). 1980. 60.00 (ISBN 0-12-613344-1). Acad Pr.

Moyle, Peter B. & Cech, Joseph J. Fishes: An Introduction to Ichthyology. (Illus.). 720p. 1982. 39.95 (ISBN 0-13-319723-9). P-H.

Multilingual Dictionary of Fish & Fish Products, Pt. 1. (Eng., Fr. & Rus.). 1978. 60.00 (ISBN 0-85238-086-0, FN64, FNB). Unipub.

Munzinic, R. The Value of Sharp Rings for the Age Determination of Sardine (Sardina Pilchardus Walb.) (General Fisheries Council of the Mediterranean (GFCM): Studies & Reviews: No. 25). (Eng. & Fr.). 8p. 1964. pap. 7.50 (ISBN 92-5-101943-6, F1786, FAO). Unipub.

Nelson, Joseph S. Fishes of the World. 2nd ed. LC 83-19684. 523p. 1984. 44.95x (ISBN 0-471-86475-7, Pub. by Wiley-Interscience). Wiley.

Neugebauer, Wilbert. Marine Aquarium Fish Identifier. LC 74-82341. (Illus.). 256p. 1982. pap. 6.95 (ISBN 0-8069-7614-4). Sterling.

Nikolsky, G. V. The Ecology of Fishes. rev ed. Orig. Title: The Biology of Fishes. (Illus.). 1978. pap. 19.95 (ISBN 0-87666-505-9, H-999). TFH Pubns.

Noakes, D. L. & Ward, J. A., eds. Ecology & Ethology of Fishes. (Developments in Environmental Biology of Fishes Ser.: No. 1). 144p. 1981. 34.00 (ISBN 90-6193-896-1, Pub. by Junk Pubs Netherlands). Kluwer Academic.

Norton, T. A. Synopsis of Biological Data on Saccorhiza Polyschides. (Fisheries Synopses: No. 83). 28p. 1970. pap. 7.50 (ISBN 92-5-101899-5, F1766, FAO). Unipub.

OECD. Multilingual Dictionary of Fish & Fish Products. 1978. 59.00 (ISBN 0-685-63442-6). State Mutual Bk.

Olah, J. Fish, Pathogens & Environment in European Polyculture. (Symposium Biologica Hungarica: Vol. 23). 1984. text ed. 28.00 (ISBN 0-9910001-7-X, Pub. by Akademiai Kaido Hungary). Heyden.

Oren, O. H., ed. Aquaculture of Grey Mullets. LC 79-53405. (International Biological Programme: No. 26). (Illus.). 450p. 1981. 140.00 (ISBN 0-521-22926-X). Cambridge U Pr.

Orme, Frank W. Cyclopaedia of Coldwater Fish & Pond Life. (Illus.). 152p. 1981. 14.95 (ISBN 0-904558-84-3). Saiga.

Ostrow, Marshal E. Breeding Killifishes. (Illus.). 1981. 4.95 (ISBN 0-87666-540-7, KW-129). TFH Pubns.

Perlmutter, Alfred. Guide to Marine Fishes. LC 60-14491. (Illus.). 431p. 1961. 40.00x (ISBN 0-8147-0336-4); pap. 20.00x (ISBN 0-8147-6561-0). NYU Pr.

Peters, Hans M. Fecundity, Egg Weight & Oocyte Development in Tilapias: Cichlidae, Teleostei. Pauly, Daniel, tr. (ICLARM Translations Ser.: No. 2). (Illus.). 28p. (Orig.). 1983. pap. 5.35x (ISBN 0-89955-381-8, Pub. by ICLARM Philippines). Intl Spec Bk.

Potts, Geoffrey W. & Wooton, R. J., eds. Fish Reproduction. 1984. 55.00 (ISBN 0-12-563660-1). Acad Pr.

Raitt, D. F. Synopsis of Biological Data on the Norway Pout: Trisopterus Esmarkii (Nilsson, 1855) (Fisheries Synopses: No. 33, Rev. 1). 27p. 1968. pap. 7.50 (ISBN 92-5-101892-8, F1760, FAO). Unipub.

Ray, John. Synopsis Methodica Avium & Piscium. Derham, William & Sterling, Keir B., eds. LC 77-81111. (Biologists & Their World Ser.). (Latin.). 1978. Repr. of 1713 ed. lib. bdg. 35.50x (ISBN 0-405-10695-5). Ayer Co Pubs.

Relyea, Kenneth. Inshore Fishes of the Arabian Gulf. (Natural History of the Arabian Gulf Ser.). (Illus.). 96p. 1981. text ed. 19.50x (ISBN 0-04-597003-3). Allen Unwin.

Russell, F. S. Eggs & Planktonic Stages of Marine Fishes. 1976. 83.50 (ISBN 0-12-604050-8). Acad Pr.

Santer, R. M. Morphology & Innervation of the Fish Heart. (Advances in Anatomy, Embryology & Cell Biology Ser.: Vol. 89). (Illus.). 110p. 1985. pap. 24.00 (ISBN 0-387-13995-8). Springer-Verlag.

Study of Fish Populations by Capture Data & the Value of Tagging Experiments. (General Fisheries Council of the Mediterranean (GFCM): Studies & Reviews: No. 54). (Eng. & Fr.). 75p. 1974. pap. 7.50 (ISBN 92-5-001973-4, F924, FAO). Unipub.

Study of Hake (Merluccius Merluccius L.) Biology & Population Dynamics in the Adriatic. (General Fisheries Council of the mediterranean (GFCM): Studies & Reviews: No. 32). 24p. (Summary in Fr., 2nd Printing 1969). 1968. pap. 7.50 (ISBN 92-5-101951-7, F1793, FAO). Unipub.

Symposium on Icthygenetics, 1st. Genetics & Mutagenesis of Fish: Proceedings. Schroeder, J. H., ed. LC 73-11601. 330p. 1974. 45.00 (ISBN 0-387-06419-2). Springer-Verlag.

Synopsis of Biological Data on Anchovy: Engraulis Encrasicolus (Linnaeus, 1758) (Mediterranean & Adjacent Seas) (Fisheries Synopses: No. 26). 41p. 1965. pap. 7.50 (ISBN 92-5-101889-8, F1755, FAO). Unipub.

Synopsis of Biological Data on Indian Mackerel, Rastrelliger Kanagurta (Cuvier, 1817) & Short-Bodied Mackerel, Rastrelliger Brachymosa (Bleeker, 1851) (Fisheries Synopses: No. 29). 34p. 1965. pap. 7.50 (ISBN 92-5-101890-1, F1758, FAO). Unipub.

Tanyolac, Julide. Morphometric Variation & Life History of the Cyprinid Fish Notropis Stramineus (Cope) (Occasional Papers: No. 12). 28p. 1973. pap. 1.75 (ISBN 0-686-79831-7). U of KS Mus Nat Hist.

Terofol, Fritz. Fishes. (Nature Guide Ser.). (Illus.). 144p. 1979. pap. 5.95 (ISBN 0-7011-2460-1, Pub. by Chatto & Windus). Merrimack Pub Cir.

Turner, Bruce J., ed. Evolutionary Genetics of Fishes. (Monographs in Evolutionary Biology). 616p. 1984. 85.00x (ISBN 0-306-41520-8, Plenum Pr). Plenum Pub.

Tyler, James C. A Monograph of Plectognath Fishes of the Superfamily Triacanthoidea. (Monograph: No. 16). (Illus.). 364p. 1968. lib. bdg. 22.00 (ISBN 0-910006-24-5). Acad Nat Sci Phila.

Walker, Braz. Angelfish. (Illus.). 1974. 7.95 (ISBN 0-87666-755-8, PS-711). TFH Pubns.

Walker, Charlotte. Fish & Shellfish. (Illus.). 160p. 1984. pap. 7.95 (ISBN 0-89586-258-1). H P Bks.

Welcomme, R. L. Register of International Transfers of Inland Fish Species. (Fisheries Technical Papers: No. 213). (Trilingual.). 130p. 1981. pap. 9.50 (ISBN 92-5-001098-2, F2196, FAO). Unipub.

Western Central Atlantic Fishery Commission (WECAFC) National Reports & Selected Papers Presented at the Third Session of the Working Party on Assessment of Marine Fishery Resources: Held at Kingston, Jamaica, May 17-21, 1982. (Fisheries Reports: No. 278 Supp.). (Eng., Fr. & Span.). 313p. 1983. pap. text ed. 23.00 (ISBN 92-5-001332-9, F2415, FAO). Unipub.

WHO Expert Committee. Geneva, 1973. Fish & Shellfish Hygiene: Report. (Technical Report Ser.: No. 550). (Also avail. in French & Spanish). 1974. pap. 2.40 (ISBN 92-4-120550-4). World Health.

Willughby, Francis. De Historia Piscium & Icthyographia ad Amplisimum Virum Dnum: Samuelem Pepys, Presidem Soc. Reg, 2 vols in one. Sterling, Keir B., ed. LC 77-81089. (Biologists & Their World Ser.). (Illus.). 1978. Repr. of 1685 ed. lib. bdg. 58.50x (ISBN 0-405-10667-X). Ayer Co Pubs.

Wootton. The Biology of the Sticklebacks. 1977. 59.50 (ISBN 0-12-763650-1). Acad Pr.

A World List of Experts Concerned with the Study of the Biology & Culture of Shrimps & Prawns. (Fisheries Technical Papers: No. 44). 23p. 1965. pap. 7.50 (ISBN 0-686-92972-1, F1723, FAO). Unipub.

Wourms, John P., et al. Genetic Studies of Fish, Vol. 2. Ridgway, George S. & Morrison, William J., eds. LC 74-516. 179p. 1974. text ed. 22.50x (ISBN 0-8422-7207-0). Irvington.

FISHES–ANATOMY

see also Electric Organs in Fishes

Bond, Carl E. Biology of Fishes. LC 77-84665. (Illus.). 1979. text ed. 37.95 (ISBN 0-7216-1839-1). HR&W.

Fay, et al, eds. Hearing & Sound Communication in Fishes: Proceedings in Life Sciences Ser. (Illus.). 704p. 1981. 59.00 (ISBN 0-387-90590-1). Springer-Verlag.

Gans, Carl & Parsons, Thomas S. A Photographic Atlas of Shark Anatomy: The Gross Morphology of Squalas Acanthias. LC 80-24528. (Illus.). 106p. 1981. spiral bnd. 8.00x (ISBN 0-226-28120-5). U of Chicago Pr.

Gilbert, Stephen G. Pictorial Anatomy of the Dogfish. LC 74-152331. (Illus.). 66p. (Orig.). 1973. pap. text ed. 7.95x (ISBN 0-295-95148-6). U of Wash Pr.

Harder, Wilhelm. Anatomy of Fishes, 2 vols. 2nd rev. ed. (Illus.). 1976. Set. text ed. 90.50 (ISBN 3-510-65067-0). Lubrecht & Cramer.

Hoar, W. S. & Randall, D. J., eds. Fish Physiology, Vol. 10: Gills. 1984. 59.00 (ISBN 0-12-350460-0). Acad Pr.

Houlihan, D. F., et al, eds. Gills. LC 81-21778. (Society for Experimental Biology Seminar Ser.: No. 16). (Illus.). 250p. 1982. 57.50 (ISBN 0-521-24083-2). Cambridge U Pr.

International Symposium on Fish Biologics. Serodiagnostics & Vaccines: Proceedings. Andersen, D. P., et al, eds. (Developments in Biological Standardization: Vol. 49). (Illus.). xii, 496p. 1981. pap. text ed. 40.00 (ISBN 3-8055-3471-X). S Karger.

Kilgen, Ronald H. & Ragan, James G. Laboratory Manual for Ichthyology. (Illus.). 72p. 1983. 9.95x (ISBN 0-88136-014-7). Jostens.

Kindred, James E. Skull of Amiurus. (Illus.). 1919. 12.00 (ISBN 0-384-29415-4). Johnson Repr.

Poplin, Cecil M. Discovery of Intracranial Ossicles in a Carboniferous North American Paleoniscid: Pisces: Actinopterygii. (Occasional Papers: No. 99). 17p. 1982. 1.75 (ISBN 0-317-04811-2). U of KS Mus Nat Hist.

Satchell, G. H. Circulation in Fishes. LC 77-149561. (Cambridge Monographs in Experimental Biology: No. 18). pap. 35.30 (ISBN 0-317-26688-8, 2024544). Bks Demand UMI.

Smeets, W. J., et al. The Central Nervous System of Cartilaginous Fish: Structure & Functional Correlations. (Illus.). 266p. 1983. 160.00 (ISBN 0-387-12146-3). Springer-Verlag.

Tchernavin, V. V. The Feeding Mechanism of a Deep Sea Fish, Chauliodus Sloani Schneider. (Illus.). 1953. pap. 22.50 (ISBN 0-565-00111-6, Pub. by Brit Mus Nat Hist). Sabbot-Natural Hist Bks.

FISHES–BEHAVIOR

Aquarium Tagging Experiments on Sardines with Anchor Tags by Use of Tricaine Methane Sulfonate. (General Fisheries Council of the Mediterranean (GFCM): Studies & Reviews: No. 36). 31p. (2nd Printing 1969). 1968. pap. 7.50 (ISBN 92-5-101955-X, F1796, FAO). Unipub.

Conference on Fish Behavior in Relation to Fishing Techniques & Tactics: Proceedings, Bergen, Norway, 1968-69, Vols. 1 & 3. (Fisheries Reports: No. 62). Vol. 1, 51p. pap. 7.50 (ISBN 0-686-92921-7, F1674, FAO); Vol. 3, 427p. pap. 25.50 (ISBN 0-686-98784-5). Unipub.

Fay, et al, eds. Hearing & Sound Communication in Fishes: Proceedings in Life Sciences Ser. (Illus.). 704p. 1981. 59.00 (ISBN 0-387-90590-1). Springer-Verlag.

Fish Behavior & Its Use in the Capture & Culture of Fishes. (Illus.). 512p. 1982. pap. 25.00x (ISBN 9-71020-003-8, Pub. by ICLARM Philippines). Intl Spec Bk.

Hasler, A. D. Olfactory Imprinting & Homing in Salmon: Investigations into the Mechanism of the Imprinting Process. (Zoophysiology Ser.: Vol. 14). (Illus.). 150p. 1983. 29.00 (ISBN 0-387-12519-1). Springer-Verlag.

Kennleyside, M. H. Diversity & Adaptation in Fish Behaviour. (Zoophysiology Ser.: Vol. 11). (Illus.). 1979. 45.00 (ISBN 0-387-09587-X). Springer-Verlag.

Pauly, Daniel. Fish Population Dynamics in Tropical Waters: A Manual for Use with Programmable Calculators. (ICLARM Studies & Reviews: 8). (Illus.). 325p. 1984. 29.50x (ISBN 971-1022-03-6, Pub. by ICLARM Philippines); pap. 25.00 (ISBN 971-1022-04-4). Intl Spec Bk.

Reese, Ernst S. & Lighter, Frederick J. Contrasts in Behavior: Adaptations in the Aquatic & Terrestrial Environments. LC 78-8284. 406p. 1978. 50.95 (ISBN 0-471-71390-2, Pub. by Wiley-Interscience). Wiley.

Report of the International Symposium on the Early Life History of Fish: Obun, Scotland. (Fisheries Reports: No. 141). 61p. 1973. pap. 7.50 (ISBN 0-686-93971-9, F786, FAO). Unipub.

Tavolga, W. N., ed. Sound Reception in Fishes, 2 vols. LC 76-13525. (Benchmark Papers in Animal Behavior: Vol. 7). 1976. 66.00 (ISBN 0-12-787516-6). Acad Pr.

Tavolga, William N., ed. Sound Production in Fishes. LC 76-28352. (Benchmark Papers in Animal Behavior: Vol. 9). 1977. 66.00 (ISBN 0-12-787515-8). Acad Pr.

FISHES–BIBLIOGRAPHY

Dean, Bashford. A Bibliography of Fishes, 3 vols. 1973. Set. 112.00 (ISBN 3-87429-036-0). Lubrecht & Cramer.

Hureau, J. C. & Monod, T., eds. Check-List of the Fishes of the North-Eastern Atlantic & the Mediterranean, 2 vols. (Eng. & Fr., Illus., 2nd Printing with Suppl. 1979). 1973. Set. pap. 89.25 (ISBN 92-3-001762-0, U71, UNESCO). Vol. 1, 683p. Vol. 2, 394p. Unipub.

Huver, Charles W., compiled by. A Bibliography of the Genus Fundulus. 1973. lib. bdg. 23.00 (ISBN 0-8161-0976-1, Hall Reference). G K Hall.

Leopold, Marian. Problems of Fish Culture Economics with Special Reference to Carp Culture in Eastern Europe. (European Inland Fisheries Advisory Commission (EIFAC): Technical Papers: No. 40). 107p. 1981. pap. 7.75 (ISBN 92-5-101152-4, F2284, FAO). Unipub.

Matthes, H., compiled by. A Bibliography of African Freshwater Fish. 299p. (Orig.). 1973. pap. 26.25 (ISBN 92-5-101595-3, F89, FAO). Unipub.

Selected Terms in Fish Culture. (Terminology Bulletins: No. 19). (Eng., Fr., Span. & Arabic.). 158p. 1981. pap. 11.50 (ISBN 92-5-000910-0, F2277, FAO). Unipub.

FISHES–COLLECTION AND PRESERVATION

Billard, Ruth S. Ralph Morrill's in Museum Quality Fish Taxidermy: A Guide to Molding with Plaster, Casting with Resin, Painting with an Airbrush. LC 84-70664. (Illus.). 275p. 1984. lib. bdg. 30.00x (ISBN 0-9611112-0-8). Bill Art.

Bohlke, Eugenia B. Catalog of Type Specimens in the Ichthyological Collection of the Academy of Natural Sciences of Philadelphia. (Special Publication: No. 14). 246p. 1984. pap. 15.00 (ISBN 0-910006-41-5). Acad Nat Sci Phila.

Caddy, J. F. Advances in Assessment of World Cephalopod Resources. (Fisheries Technical Papers: No. 231). (Eng., Fr., & Span.). 452p. (Orig.). 1984. pap. text ed. 33.50 (ISBN 92-5-001431-7, F2552, FAO). Unipub.

Guenther, Albert. Catalogue of the Fishes in the British Museum (Natural History, 8 vols. 4368p. 1981. lib. bdg. 295.00 (ISBN 3-7682-7109-9). Lubrecht & Cramer.

Gulland, J. A. Manual of Methods for Fish Stock Assessment: Fish Population Analysis, Pt. 1. (Fisheries Ser.: No. 3). (Illus.). 154p. (Orig., 4th Printing 1976). 1969. pap. 13.25 (ISBN 92-5-100204-5, F262, FAO). Unipub.

Migdalski, Edward C. Fish Mounts & Other Fish Trophies: The Complete Book of Taxidermy. 2nd ed. LC 80-27829. 212p. 1981. 21.95x (ISBN 0-471-07990-1). Wiley.

Preservation of Fish by Irradiation. (Panel Proceedings Ser.). (Illus.). 176p. (Orig.). 1970. pap. 14.50 (ISBN 92-0-111070-7, ISP196, IAEA). Unipub.

FISHES–DISTRIBUTION

see Fishes–Geographical Distribution

FISHES–EMBRYOLOGY

see Embryology–Fishes

FISHES–FOOD

Connell, J. J. Control of Fish Quality. 2nd ed. (Illus.). 240p. 1980. 33.25 (ISBN 0-85238-105-0, FN83, FNB). Unipub.

Fish Feed Technology: Lectures Presented at the FAO-UNDP Training Course in Fish Feed Technology. (Agricultural Development & Coordination Programme). 400p. 1980. pap. 28.75 (ISBN 92-5-100901-5, F1944, FAO). Unipub.

National Research Council Commission on Natural Resources. Nutrient Requirements of Coldwater Fishes. 63p. 1981. pap. text ed. 8.95 (ISBN 0-309-03187-7). Natl Acad Pr.

Price, John W. Food Habits of Some Lake Erie Fishes. 1963. 3.00 (ISBN 0-86727-048-9). Ohio Bio Survey.

Sano, Mituhiko, et al. Food Habits of Teleostean Reef Fishes in Okinawa Island, Southern Japan. 128p. 1985. 32.50x (ISBN 0-86008-368-3, Pub. by U of Tokyo Japan). Columbia U Pr.

Schwiebert, Ernest. Nymphs. LC 82-62597. (Illus.). 368p. 1983. pap. 19.95 (ISBN 0-8329-0340-X, Pub. by Winchester Pr). New Century.

Symposium on New Development in Carp & Trout Nutrition, European Inland Fisheries Advisory Commission: Proceedings, 5th Session, Rome, 1968. (European Inland Fisheries Advisory Commission (EIFAC): Technical Papers: No. 9). 213p. 1969. pap. 14.25 (ISBN 0-686-92982-9, F755, FAO). Unipub.

FISHES–GEOGRAPHICAL DISTRIBUTION

see also Fish Populations

Courtenay, Walter R., Jr. & Stauffer, Jay R., Jr., eds. Distribution, Biology & Management of Exotic Fishes. LC 83-18723. 448p. 1984. 40.00x (ISBN 0-8018-3037-0). Johns Hopkins.

Echelle, Anthony & Kornfield, Irv, eds. Evolution of Fish Species Flocks. LC 84-51502. 257p. 1984. 28.95 (ISBN 0-89101-058-0); pap. 20.95 (ISBN 0-89101-057-2). U Maine Orono.

Moyle, Peter B. & Smith, Jerry J. Distribution & Ecology of Stream Fishes of the Sacramento-San Joaquin Drainage System, California. LC 81-13072. (University of California Publications in Zoology Ser.: Vol. 115). 264p. 1982. 18.50x (ISBN 0-520-09650-9). U of Cal Pr.

Nakamura, Hiroshi. Tuna: Distribution & Migration. 1978. 40.00x (ISBN 0-685-63462-0). State Mutual Bk.

Taxonomy & Distribution of the Stomioid Fish Genus Eustomias (Melanostomiidae), I: Subgenus Nominostomias. LC 83-600023. (Smithsonian Contributions to Zoology: No. 380). pap. 36.00 (ISBN 0-317-29925-5, 2021730). Bks Demand UMI.

FISHES–MIGRATION

Hay, John. The Run. (Illus.). 1979. 9.95 (ISBN 0-393-01269-7); pap. 3.95 (ISBN 0-393-00946-7). Norton.

McCleave, James D., et al, eds. Mechanisms of Migration in Fishes. (NATO Conference Series IV-Marine Sciences: Vol. 14). 584p. 1984. 85.00x (ISBN 0-306-41676-X, Plenum Pr). Plenum Pub.

McKeown, Brian A. Fish Migration. (Illus.). 224p. 1985. 29.00x (ISBN 0-917304-99-3). Timber.

Nakamura, Hiroshi. Tuna: Distribution & Migration. 1978. 40.00x (ISBN 0-685-63462-0). State Mutual Bk.

Smith, R. J. The Control of Fish Migration. (Zoophysiology Ser.: Vol. 17). (Illus.). 270p. 1985. 49.50 (ISBN 0-387-13707-6). Springer-Verlag.

FISHES–NOMENCLATURE

Names of Fishes, Shellfish & Marine Animals. (Terminology Bulletin: No. 38C). (Eng., Lat. & Chinese.). 142p. 1979. pap. 5.70 (ISBN 92-5-000788-4, FAO). Unipub.

FISHES–PARASITES

see Parasites–Fishes

FISHES–PHYSIOLOGY

The Aging of Fish. (Illus.). 234p. 1975. pap. 36.00 (ISBN 0-9502121-1-3, UBL1, FAO). Unipub.

Ali, M. A., ed. Environmental Physiology of Fishes. LC 80-22156. (NATO ASI Series A, Life Sciences: Vol. 35). 734p. 1981. 89.50x (ISBN 0-306-40574-1, Plenum Pr). Plenum Pub.

--Vision in Fishes - New Approaches in Research. LC 75-8570. (Nato ASI Series A, Life Sciences: Vol. 1). 850p. 1975. 89.50x (ISBN 0-306-35601-5, Plenum Pr). Plenum Pub.

Bone, Q. & Marshall, N. B. Biology of Fishes. (Teritiary Level Biology Ser.). 253p. 1983. pap. 25.00 (ISBN 0-412-00151-9, NO. 5008). Methuen Inc.

Conservation of the Genetic Resources of Fish: Problems & Recommendations: Report of the Expert Consultation on the Genetic Resources of Fish, Rome, 9-13 June 1980. (Fisheries Technical Papers: No. 217). 43p. 1981. pap. 7.50 (ISBN 92-5-101173-7, F2275, FAO). Unipub.

Hara, T. J. Chemoreception in Fishes. (Developments in Agriculture & Fisheries Science Ser.: Vol. 8). 434p. 1982. 91.50 (ISBN 0-444-42040-1). Elsevier.

Hasler, A. D. Olfactory Imprinting & Homing in Salmon: Investigations into the Mechanism of the Imprinting Process. (Zoophysiology Ser.: Vol. 14). (Illus.). 150p. 1983. 29.00 (ISBN 0-387-12519-1). Springer-Verlag.

Hoar, W. S. & Randall, D. J., eds. Fish Physiology. Vol. 1, 1969. 76.00 (ISBN 0-12-350401-5); Vol. 2, 1969. 76.00 (ISBN 0-12-350402-3); Vol. 3, 1969. 76.00 (ISBN 0-12-350403-1); Vol. 4, 1970. 76.00 (ISBN 0-12-350404-X); Vol. 5, 1971. 84.00 (ISBN 0-12-350405-8); Vol. 6, 1971. 84.00 (ISBN 0-12-350406-6); Vol. 7, 1979. 60.50 (ISBN 0-12-350407-4). Acad Pr.

--Fish Physiology, Vol. 10: Gills. 1984. 59.00 (ISBN 0-12-350460-0). Acad Pr.

--Fish Physiology Vol. 8: Bioenergetics & Growth. LC 76-84233. 1979. 79.50 (ISBN 0-12-350408-2). Acad Pr.

Hoar, W. S., et al. Fish Physiology, Vol. 9: Reproduction, Pt. A: Endocrine Tissues & Hormones. 1983. 65.00 (ISBN 0-12-350409-0). Acad Pr.

--Fish Physiology, Vol. 9: Reproduction, Part B: Behavior & Fertility Control. 1983. 55.00 (ISBN 0-12-350429-5). Acad Pr.

Love, R. The Chemical Biology of Fishes: With a Key to Literature. 1970. 87.00 (ISBN 0-12-455850-X). Acad Pr.

Matty, A. J. Fish Endocrinology. 272p. 1985. 27.95 (ISBN 0-88192-024-X, Dist. by Intl Spec Bk). Timber.

Neuhaus, O. W. & Halver, J. E., eds. Fish in Research. LC 74-107020. 1969. 49.50 (ISBN 0-12-515850-5). Acad Pr.

Northcutt, Glenn & Davis, Roger, eds. Fish Neurobiology, Vol. 1: Brain Stem & Sense Organs. (Illus.). 368p. 1983. text ed. 45.00x (ISBN 0-472-10005-X). U of Mich Pr.

Nybelin, Orvar. On the Tooth-Bearing Bone Element in the Lower Jaw of Some Primitive Recent Teleostean Fishes. (Acta- Goteborg Zoologica Ser.: No. 13). (Illus.). 36p. 1982. pap. text ed. 12.50x (ISBN 91-85252-28-X, Pub. by Goteborg Sweden). Humanities.

Rankin, J. C., et al. Control Processes in Fish Physiology. 298p. 1983. 39.95x (ISBN 0-471-88404-9, Pub. by Wiley-Interscience). Wiley.

Reproductive Physiology of Fish. 256p. 1983. 27.75 (ISBN 90-220-0818-5, PDC251, Pudoc). Unipub.

Reproductive Physiology of Teleost Fishes: A Review of Present Knowledge & Needs for Future Research. (Agricultural Development & Coordination Programme). 89p. 1981. pap. 7.50 (ISBN 92-5-101145-1, F2257, FAO). Unipub.

Reutter, K. Taste Organ in the Bullhead (Teleostei) (Advances in Anatomy, Embryology & Cell Biology: Vol. 55, Pt. 1). (Illus.). 1978. pap. 32.00 (ISBN 0-387-08880-6). Springer-Verlag.

Satchell, G. H. Circulation in Fishes. (Cambridge Monographs in Experimental Biology: No. 18). (Illus.). 1971. 29.95 (ISBN 0-521-07973-X). Cambridge U Pr.

Schuijf, A. & Hawkins, A. D., eds. Sound Reception in Fish. LC 76-54648. (Developments in Agriculture & Fisheries Science: Vol. 5). 288p. 1977. 61.75 (ISBN 0-444-41540-8). Elsevier.

Sharp, Gary D. & Dizon, Andrew E., eds. Physiological Ecology of the Tunas. LC 78-26514. 1979. 56.00 (ISBN 0-12-639180-7). Acad Pr.

Silva, Tony & Kotlar, Barbara. Discus. (Illus.). 98p. 1980. 4.95 (ISBN 0-87666-535-0, KW-097). TFH Pubns.

Smith, Lynwood S. Introduction to Fish Physiology. (Illus.). 256p. 1982. 29.95 (ISBN 0-87666-549-0, PS-785). TFH Pubns.

Thorpe, J. E., ed. Rhythmic Activity of Fishes. 1978. 47.50 (ISBN 0-12-690650-5). Acad Pr.

Thresher, R. E. Reproduction in Reef Fishes. (Illus.). 400p. 1984. 39.95 (ISBN 0-87666-808-2, H-1048). TFH Pubns.

Tyler, Peter & Calow, Peter, eds. Fish Energetics: New Perspectives. LC 82-26. 352p. 1985. text ed. 32.50x (ISBN 0-8018-2792-2). Johns Hopkins.

Van Muiswinkel, W. B., ed. Immunology & Immunization of Fish: Proceedings of the Conference Held June 22-24, 1981 In Wageningen Netherlands. (Developmental & Comparative Immunology Ser.). 256p. 1982. 39.00 (ISBN 0-08-028831-6). Pergamon.

Webb, Paul W. & Weihs, Daniel, eds. Fish Biomechanics. 414p. 1983. 46.95x (ISBN 0-03-059461-8). Praeger.

Wooten, R. J. A Functional Biology of Sticklebacks. LC 84-8864. (Functional Biology Ser.). (Illus.). 272p. 1985. 29.75x (ISBN 0-520-05381-8). U of Cal Pr.

FISHES–AFRICA

Boulenger, G. A. Fishes of the Nile. 1964. Repr. of 1907 ed. 129.50 (ISBN 3-7682-0241-0). Lubrecht & Cramer.

Brichard, Pierre. Fishes of Lake Tanganyika. (Illus.). 1978. 29.95 (ISBN 0-87666-464-8, H-972). TFH Pubns.

Greenwood, P. H. The Cichlid Fishes of Lake Victoria, East Africa: Biology & Evolution of a Species Flock. (Bulletin of the British Museum Natural History Zool. Ser.: No. 6). (Illus.). 1974. text ed. 22.50x (ISBN 0-565-00761-0, Pub. by Brit Mus Nat Hist); pap. text ed. 15.00x (ISBN 0-8277-4357-2). Sabbot-Natural Hist Bks.

--The Haplochromine Fishes of the East African Lakes. (Illus.). 764p. 1981. 85.00x (ISBN 0-8014-1346-X). Cornell U Pr.

Playfair, R. Lambert & Guenther, Albert C. The Fishes of Zanzibar. (Hand Colored Reprint Ser). (Illus.). xiv, 154p. 1971. Repr. of 1866 ed. 125.00 (ISBN 0-912318-00-7). N K Gregg.

Stiassny, M. L. Phylogenetic Versus Convergent Relationship Between Piscivorous Cichlid Fishes from Lakes Malawai & Tangayika. 40.00x (ISBN 0-686-78660-2, Pub. by Brit Mus Pubns England). State Mutual Bk.

Voss, J. Color Patterns of African Cichlids. Orig. Title: Les Livrees Ou Patrons De Coloration Chezles Poissons Chichlides Africains. (Illus.). 128p. 1980. 9.95 (ISBN 0-87666-503-2, PS-755). TFH Pubns.

FISHES–ATLANTIC COAST

Annotated Bibliography on Albacore Thunnus Alalunga of the Atlantic Ocean, 1962-72. (Fisheries Reports: No. 6, Vol. 4, Suppl. 1). 94p. 1974. pap. 6.00 (ISBN 0-686-93119-X, F778, FAO). Unipub.

Perlmutter, Alfred. Guide to Marine Fishes. LC 60-14491. (Illus.). 431p. 1961. 40.00x (ISBN 0-8147-0336-4); pap. 20.00x (ISBN 0-8147-6561-0). NYU Pr.

FISHES–AUSTRALIA

Allen, G. R. A Field Guide to Inland Fishes of Western Australia. (Illus.). 92p. 1982. pap. 15.00x (ISBN 0-7244-8409-4, Pub. by U of West Austral Pr). Intl Spec Bk.

Deas, Walter. Australian Fishes in Color. (Illus.). 1973. 6.00 (ISBN 0-912728-47-7). Newbury Bks.

Thomson, J. M. A Field Guide to the Common Sea & Estuary Fishes of Non-Tropical Australia. 144p. 1980. 17.95x (ISBN 0-00-219271-3, Pub. by W Collins Ausftralia). Intl Spec Bk.

Watanabe, W. O., et al. Experimental Rearing of Nile Tilapia Fry: Oreochromis Niloticus for Saltwater Culture. (ICLARM Technical Reports Ser.: 14). (Illus.). 28p. (Orig.). 1984. pap. 6.00x (ISBN 0-317-17293-X, Pub. by ICLARM Philippines). Intl Spec Bk.

Weil, Martin. Puli. (Illus.). 128p. 1982. 4.95 (ISBN 0-87666-740-X, KW-141). TFH Pubns.

FISHES–CANADA

Freshwater Fishes of Canada. pap. 46.50 (SSC42, SSC). Unipub.

McAllister, D. E. & Crossman, E. J. A Guide to the Freshwater Sport Fishes of Canada. (Illus.). 1973. pap. 4.95 (ISBN 0-660-00048-2, 56365-0, Pub. by Natl Mus Canada). U of Chicago Pr.

Pacific Fishes of Canada. pap. 37.00 (SSC66, SSC). Unipub.

FISHES–CHINA

IDRC, Ottawa. Science of the Culture of Freshwater Fish Species in China, 17 Microfiches. 1981. Set (IDRC). Unipub.

FISHES–EUROPE

European Inland Water Fish: A Multilingual Catalogue. (Eng., Fr., Span. & Ger., Illus.). 196p. 1972. 43.25 (ISBN 0-85238-056-9, FN10, FNB). Unipub.

FAO. European Inland Water Fish. 1978. 35.00 (ISBN 0-685-63401-9). State Mutual Bk.

Miller & Nicholls. The Fishes of Britain & Europe. pap. 8.95 (ISBN 0-00-219751-0, Collins Pub England). Greene.

Muus & Dahlstrom. Collins Guide to the Fresh Water Fishes of Britain & Europe. 29.95 (ISBN 0-00-219270-5, Collins Pub England). Greene.

--Collins Guide to the Sea Fishes of Britain & Northwestern Europe. 29.95 (ISBN 0-00-219258-6, Collins Pub England). Greene.

Wheeler, Alwyne. Fishes of the British Isles & Northwest Europe. LC 69-19148. 672p. 1969. text ed. 25.00x (ISBN 0-87013-134-6). Mich St U Pr.

FISHES–GREAT BRITAIN

Cope, Ken. Fishing Canals. LC 79-55994. (Illus.). 1980. 17.95 (ISBN 0-7153-7887-2). David & Charles.

Donovan, Edward. The Natural History of British Fishes: Scientific & General Descriptions of the Most Interesting Species, 2 vols. Sterling, Keir B., ed. LC 77-81091. (Biologists & Their World Ser.). (Illus.). 1978. Repr. of 1808 ed. Set. lib. bdg. 62.00x (ISBN 0-405-10668-8); lib. bdg. 31.50x ea. Vol. 1 (ISBN 0-405-10669-6). Vol. 2 (ISBN 0-405-10670-X). Ayer Co Pubs.

Houghton, W. British Freshwater Fishes. 256p. 1981. 55.00x (ISBN 0-906671-06-X, Pub. by Webb & Bower). State Mutual Bk.

--British Freshwater Fishes. (Illus.). 256p. 1981. 35.00 (ISBN 0-03-059832-X). Webb & Bower.

Kabata, Z. Parasitic Copepoda of British Fishes. (Illus.). 670p. 1979. 65.00x (ISBN 0-903874-05-9, Pub. by Brit Mus Nat Hist England). Sabbot-Natural Hist Bks.

Miller & Nicholls. The Fishes of Britain & Europe. pap. 8.95 (ISBN 0-00-219751-0, Collins Pub England). Greene.

Muus & Dahlstrom. Collins Guide to the Fresh Water Fishes of Britain & Europe. 29.95 (ISBN 0-00-219270-5, Collins Pub England). Greene.

--Collins Guide to the Sea Fishes of Britain & Northwestern Europe. 29.95 (ISBN 0-00-219258-6, Collins Pub England). Greene.

Varley, Margaret. British Freshwater Fishes. 1978. 29.00x (ISBN 0-685-63394-2). State Mutual Bk.

--British Freshwater Fishes: Factors Affecting Their Distribution. (Illus.). 148p. 12.00 (ISBN 0-85238-107-7, FN4, FNB). Unipub.

Wheeler, Alwyne. Fishes of the British Isles & Northwest Europe. LC 69-19148. 672p. 1969. text ed. 25.00x (ISBN 0-87013-134-6). Mich St U Pr.

Woodward, A. Smith. The Fishes of the English Chalk, Part 1-7, Vols. 56-56, 61-65, Nos. 263, 266, 291, 300, 308, 313, 320. Repr. of 1912 ed. Set. 64.00 (ISBN 0-384-69212-5). Johnson Repr.

FISHES–JAPAN

Marr, John, ed. Kuroshio: A Symposium on the Japan Current. 624p. 1970. 30.00x (ISBN 0-8248-0090-7, Eastwest Ctr). UH Pr.

Sano, Mituhiko, et al. Food Habits of Teleostean Reef Fishes in Okinawa Island, Southern Japan. 128p. 1985. 32.50x (ISBN 0-86008-368-3, Pub. by U of Tokyo Japan). Columbia U Pr.

FISHES–LATIN AMERICA

Smith, Nigel J. Man, Fishes, & the Amazon. 176p. 1981. 32.00x (ISBN 0-231-05156-5). Columbia U Pr.

Whitehead, Peter J. The Clupeoid Fishes of the Guianas. (Illus.). 227p. 1973. pap. text ed. 32.50X (ISBN 0-565-00900-1, Pub. by Brit Mus Nat Hist England). Sabbot-Natural Hist Bks.

Zeisler, R. Bibliography of Latin American Freshwater Fish. (Commission for Inland Fisheries of Latin America Technical Papers: No. 2). (Eng. & Span.). 195p. 1979. pap. 14.00 (ISBN 92-5-000781-7, F1832, FAO). Unipub.

FISHES–NEW ZEALAND

Arnitage, R. O., et al, eds. Guide to New Zealand Fish Species. LC 83-15132. (Illus.). 1984. Repr. of 1981 ed. 55.00x (ISBN 0-943738-10-5). Osprey Bks.

Ayling, Tony & Cox, Geoffrey J. The Collins Guide to the Sea Fishes of New Zealand. (Illus.). 384p. 1983. 19.95x (ISBN 0-00-216987-8, Pub. by W Collins New Zealand). Intl Spec Bk.

FISHES–NORTH AMERICA

Carlander, Kenneth D. Handbook of Freshwater Fishery Biology, Vol. 2. 1977. text ed. 21.50x (ISBN 0-8138-0670-4). Iowa St U Pr.

Hocutt, C. H. & Wiley, E. O. The Zoogeography of North American Freshwater Fishes. 1985. 80.00 (ISBN 0-471-86419-6). Wiley.

Hubbs, Carl L., et al. Memoir VII: Hydrographic History & Relict Fishes of the North-Central Great Basin. Kessel, Edward L., ed. (Memoirs of the California Academy of Sciences Ser.). (Illus.). 259p. (Orig.). 1974. pap. 10.00 (ISBN 0-940228-11-4). Calif Acad Sci.

BOOKS - SUBJECT INDEX FISHES, FRESH-WATER

McClane, A. J. McClane's Field Guide to Saltwater Fishes of North America. LC 77-14417. pap. 10.95 (ISBN 0-03-021121-2, Owl Bks.). HR&W.
Mitchell, Robert W., et al. Mexican Eyeless Characin Fishes, Genus Astyanax: Environment, Distribution, & Evolution. (Special Publications: No. 12). (Illus.). 89p. (Orig.). 1977. pap. 5.00 (ISBN 0-89672-038-1). Tex Tech Pr.
Olund, Leonard J. & Cross, Frank B. Geographic Variation in the North American Cyprinid Fish, Hybopsis Gracilis. (Museum Ser.: Vol. 13, No. 7). 26p. 1961. pap. 1.50 (ISBN 0-686-79826-0). U of KS Mus Nat Hist.
Ono, Dana R., et al. Vanishing Fishes of North America. LC 82-62896. (Illus.). 268p. 1983. 29.95 (ISBN 0-913276-43-X). Stone Wall Pr.
Richardson, John. Fauna Boreali-Americana: Zoology of the Northern Parts of British America, the Fish, Pt. 3. Sterling, Keir B., ed. LC 77-81088. (Biologists & Their World Ser.). (Illus.). 1978. Repr. of 1836 ed. lib. bdg. 31.00x (ISBN 0-405-10664-5). Ayer Co Pubs.
Schell, Stewart. Trematodes of North America North of Mexico. (Illus.). 260p. (Orig.). 1985. pap. 25.95 (ISBN 0-317-26191-6). U Pr of Idaho.
Soltz, David L. & Naiman, Robert. The Natural History of Native Fishes in the Death Valley System. (Science Ser.: No. 30). (Illus.). 76p. 1978. 7.50 (ISBN 0-938644-10-6). Nat Hist Mus.
Whyte, Mal. North American Sealife Coloring Album. (Wildlife Ser.). (Illus.). 1973. pap. 3.95 (ISBN 0-8431-1713-3, 27-2). Troubador Pr.

FISHES-PACIFIC OCEAN

Bleeker, Pieter. Atlas Ichtyologique des Indes Orientales Neerlandaises, Vol. IV: Murenes, Symbranches, et Leptocephales. 2nd ed. LC 82-80033. (Fr., Illus.). 132p. 1985. Repr. of 1862 ed. 50.00x (ISBN 0-87474-226-9, BLA4). Smithsonian.
Brouard, F., et al. Notes on Observations of Daily Rings on Otoliths of Deepwater Snappers. (ICLARM Translations Ser.: No. 3). Orig. Title: Note sur les lectures de stries journalieres observees sur les otolithes de poissons. (Illus.). 8p. (Orig.). 1984. pap. 2.00x (ISBN 0-317-17297-2, Pub. by ICLARM Philippines). Intl Spec Bk.
Burgess, Warren E. & Axelrod, Herbert R. Fishes of California & Western Mexico. (Pacific Marine Fishes Ser.: Bk. 8). (Illus.). 267p. 1985. text ed. 29.95 (ISBN 0-86622-012-7, PS-724). TFH Pubns.
--Pacific Marine Fishes, Bk. 5. (Illus.). 271p. 1975. 29.95 (ISBN 0-87666-127-4, PS-721). TFH Pubns.
Chong, K. C., et al. Inputs as Related to Output in Milkfish Production in the Philippines. (ICLARM Technical Reports Ser.: No. 3). (Illus.). 82p. (Orig.). 1982. pap. 10.00x (ISBN 0-89955-421-0, Pub. by ICLARM Philippines). Intl Spec Bk.
--Milkfish Production Dualism in the Philippines: A Multi-Disciplinary Perspective on Continous Low Yields & Constraints to Aquaculture Development. (ICLARM Technical Reports Ser.: No. 15). (Illus.). 70p. (Orig.). 1984. pap. 10.50 (ISBN 0-317-17296-4, Pub. by ICLARM Philippines). Intl Spec Bk.
Eschmeyer, William N. & Herald, Earl S. Field Guide to the Pacific Coast Fishes of North America. 1983. 19.95 (ISBN 0-395-26873-7); pap. 11.95 (ISBN 0-395-33188-9). HM.
Fowler, H. R. The Fishes of Oceania: With Supplements 1-3. 1967. Repr. of 1881 ed. 105.00 (ISBN 3-7682-0444-8). Lubrecht & Cramer.
Fowler, H. W. Fishes of Guam, Hawaii, Samoa, & Tahiti. (BMB). pap. 8.00 (ISBN 0-527-02125-3). Kraus Repr.
--The Fishes of Oceania, 1927. (BMB). (Orig.). Repr. of 1949 ed. 98.00 (ISBN 0-527-01664-0). Kraus Repr.
--Fishes of the Tropical Central Pacific. (BMB). pap. 8.00 (ISBN 0-527-02141-5). Kraus Repr.
Fowler, H. W. & Ball, S. C. Fishes of Hawaii, Johnston Island, & Wake Island. (BMB). pap. 8.00 (ISBN 0-527-02129-6). Kraus Repr.
Fowler, Henry W. The Fishes of Oceania, 4 Vols. in 1. (Illus.). Repr. of 1949 ed. 140.00 (ISBN 0-384-16535-4). Johnson Repr.
--The Fishes of the George Vanderbilt South Pacific Expedition, 1937. (Monograph: No. 2). (Illus.). 349p. (Orig.). 1938. pap. 23.00 (ISBN 0-910006-09-1). Acad Nat Sci Phila.
Gotshall, Daniel W. Pacific Coast Inshore Fishes. rev. ed. LC 80-53027. (Illus.). 96p. 1981. ltd. ed. 22.95 (ISBN 0-930118-07-3); pap. 12.95 (ISBN 0-930118-06-5). Sea Chall.
Gotshall, Daniel W. & Zimbleman. Fishes of the Pacific Coast: An Underwater Guide, Alaske to the Baja. (Illus.). 96p. 1974. text ed. 12.50 (ISBN 0-87098-060-2). Livingston.
Greenberg, Idaz. Hawaiian Fishwatcher's Field Guide. (Illus.). 1983. plastic card 3.95x (ISBN 0-913008-13-3). Seahawk Pr.
Guenther, A. Andrew Garrett's Fische der Suedsee, 3 vols. in 1. (Illus.). 1966. 126.00 (ISBN 3-7682-0351-4). Lubrecht & Cramer.
Hobson, Edmund & Chave, Edith H. Hawaiian Reef Animals. LC 72-84060. (Illus.). 159p. 1979. pap. 15.95 (ISBN 0-8248-0653-0). UH Pr.
Howard, John K. & Ueyanagi, Shoji. Distribution & Relative Abundance of Billfishes (Istiophoridae) of the Pacific Ocean. (Studies in Tropical Oceanography: No. 2). 1965. 5.50x (ISBN 0-87024-083-8). U Miami Marine.
Jordan, David S. & Evermann, Barton W. The Shore Fishes of Hawaii. LC 73-77578. (Illus.). 1973. pap. 8.50 (ISBN 0-8048-1106-7). C E Tuttle.
Pacific Fishes of Canada. pap. 37.00 (SSC66, SSC). Unipub.
Pietschmann, V. Remarks on Pacific Fishes. (BMB). pap. 8.00 (ISBN 0-527-02179-2). Kraus Repr.
Randall, John E. The Underwater Guide to Hawaiian Reef Fishes. LC 79-27625. (Illus.). 1980. plastic bdg. 9.95 (ISBN 0-915180-02-2). Harrowood Bks.
Report of the Indo-Pacific Fisheries Council & Indian Ocean Fishery Commission, Special Committee on Indian Ocean Tuna. Incl. Joint Session, Rome, 1971. Indo-Pacific Fisheries Council Committee on Management of Tuna, 1st Session & Indian Ocean Fishery Commission on Management of Indian Ocean Tuna, 2nd Session. (No. 104). 21p. 1971. pap. 7.50 (ISBN 0-686-92734-6, F1695); Joint Session, Mombasa, Kenya, July 1975. Indo-Pacific Fisheries Council Committee on Management of Tuna, 3rd Session & Indian Ocean Fishery Commission Committee on Management of Indian Ocean Tuna, 4th Session. (No. 174). (Illus.). 47p. 1976. pap. 7.50 (ISBN 0-685-68361-3, F824). (Fisheries Reports, FAO). Unipub.
Schindler, O. Sexually Mature Larval Hemiramphidae from the Hawaiian Islands. (BMB). pap. 8.00 (ISBN 0-527-02203-9). Kraus Repr.
Smith, E. R., et al, eds. Summary Report of the PCARRD-ICLARM Workshop on Philippine Tilapia Economics. (ICLARM Conference Proceedings Ser.: No. 10). (Illus.). 45p. (Orig.). 1984. pap. 5.00x (ISBN 0-317-17300-6, Pub. by ICLARM Philippines). Intl Spec Bk.
Somerton, David & Murray, Craig. Field Guide to the Fish of Puget Sound & the Northwest Coast. LC 75-40884. (Washington Sea Grant Ser.). (Illus.). 80p. 1976. pap. 8.95 (ISBN 0-295-95497-3). U of Wash Pr.
Springer, Victor G. Pacific Plate Biogeography, with Special Reference to Shorefishes. LC 82-600146. (Contributions to Zoology Ser.: No. 367). (Illus.). 182p. 1982. pap. text ed. 7.95x (ISBN 0-87474-883-6). Smithsonian.
Tinker, Spencer W. Fishes of Hawaii. LC 77-93337. (Illus.). 1978. 29.95 (ISBN 0-930492-02-1); soft bdg. 22.50 (ISBN 0-930492-14-5). Hawaiian Serv.
Walford, Lionel A. Marine Game Fishes of the Pacific Coast from Alaska to the Equator. LC 74-80976. 205p. 1975. Repr. of 1937 ed. 15.00x (ISBN 0-87474-153-X). Smithsonian.

FISHES-RED SEA

Greenberg, Idaz. Red Sea Fishwatcher's Field Guide. (Illus.). 1982. plastic card 3.95x (ISBN 0-913008-12-5). Seahawk Pr.

FISHES-TROPICS

see also Tropical Fish

Brittan, Martin. Rasbora. (Illus.). 1972. 19.95 (ISBN 0-87666-136-3, PS-681). TFH Pubns.
Howard, John K. & Starck, Walter A., 2nd. Distribution & Relative Abundance of Billfishes (Istiophoridae) of the Indian Ocean. LC 75-4747. (Studies in Tropical Oceanography: No. 13). (Illus.). 1975. 10.00x (ISBN 0-87024-276-8). U Miami Marine.
Kabats. Parasites & Diseases & Fish Cultures. 1985. 54.00 (ISBN 0-85066-285-0, Pub. by Falmer Pr). Taylor & Francis.
Leis, J. M. & Rennis, D. S. The Larvae of Indo-Pacific Coral Reef Fishes: A Guide to Identification. (Illus.). 280p. 1983. text ed. 25.00X (ISBN 0-8248-0910-6). UH Pr.
Myers, George. Piranhas. 9.95 (ISBN 0-87666-771-X, M539). TFH Pubns.
Weil, Martin. Puli. (Illus.). 128p. 1982. 4.95 (ISBN 0-87666-740-X, KW-141). TFH Pubns.

FISHES-UNITED STATES

Allyn, Rube. Florida Fishes. Allyn, Charles, ed. LC 74-14516. (Illus., Orig.). 1969. pap. 2.95 (ISBN 0-8200-0108-2). Great Outdoors.
Burgess, Warren E. & Axelrod, Herbert R. Fishes of California & Western Mexico. (Pacific Marine Fishes Ser.: Bk. 8). (Illus.). 267p. 1985. text ed. 29.95 (ISBN 0-86622-012-7, PS-724). TFH Pubns.
--Pacific Marine Fishes, Bk. 4. (Illus.). 272p. 1974. 29.95 (ISBN 0-87666-126-6, PS-720). TFH Pubns.
Carpenter, Russell & Carpenter, Blyth. Fish Watching in Hawaii. (Illus.). 120p. (Orig.). 1981. pap. 7.95 (ISBN 0-939560-00-3). Natural World.
Cooper, Edwin L. Fishes of Pennsylvania & the Northeastern United States. LC 82-18052. (Illus.). 256p. 1983. 32.50x (ISBN 0-271-00337-5). Pa St U Pr.
Cross, Frank B. & Collins, Joseph T. Fishes in Kansas. (Public Education: No. 3). 189p. 1975. pap. 8.00 (ISBN 0-686-79820-1). U of KS Mus Nat Hist.
Davis, Jackson. Management of Channel Catfish in Kansas. (Miscellaneous Publications: No. 21). 56p. 1959. pap. 3.00 (ISBN 0-686-79821-X). U of KS Mus Nat Hist.
Deacon, James E. & Metcalf, Artie L. Fishes of the Wakarusa River in Kansas. (Museum Ser.: Vol. 13, No. 6). 14p. 1961. 1.25 (ISBN 0-317-04824-4). U of KS Mus Nat Hist.
Echols, Joan. A New Genus of Pennsylvanian Fish (Grossopterygii, Coelacanthiformes) from Kansas. (Museum Ser.: Vol. 12, No. 10). 27p. 1963. pap. 1.25 (ISBN 0-686-79815-5). U of KS Mus Nat Hist.
Fitch, John E. & Lavenberg, Robert J. Marine Food & Game Fishes of California. (California Natural History Guides: No. 28). (Illus.). 1971. pap. 5.95 (ISBN 0-520-01831-1). U of Cal Pr.
--Tidepool & Nearshore Fishes of California. (Illus.). 1976. pap. 3.95 (ISBN 0-520-02845-7). U of Cal Pr.
Fowler, Henry W. A Study of the Fish of the Southern Piedmont & Coastal Plain. (Monograph: No. 7). (Illus.). 408p. (Orig.). 1945. pap. 26.00 (ISBN 0-910006-16-4). Acad Nat Sci Phila.
Gordon, Bernard L. The Marine Fishes of Rhode Island. (Illus.). 148p. 1974. pap. 5.00 (ISBN 0-910258-00-7). Book & Tackle.
Hoese, H. Dickson, et al. Fishes of the Gulf of Mexico: Texas, Louisiana & Adjacent Waters. LC 76-51654. (W. L. Moody, Jr Natural History Ser.: No.1). (Illus.). 346p. 1977. 18.95 (ISBN 0-89096-027-5); pap. 9.95 (ISBN 0-89096-028-3). Tex A&M Univ Pr.
Jordan, David S. & Evermann, Barton W. The Shore Fishes of Hawaii. LC 73-77578. (Illus.). 1973. pap. 8.50 (ISBN 0-8048-1106-7). C E Tuttle.
Kumpf, H. E. Economic Impact of the Effects of Pollution on the Coastal Fisheries of the Atlantic & Gulf of Mexico Regions of the United States of America. (Fisheries Technical Papers: No. 172). (Illus.). 86p. 1977. pap. 7.50 (ISBN 92-5-100380-7, F1238, FAO). Unipub.
McGinnis, Samuel M. Freshwater Fishes of California. LC 83-5113. (California Natural History Guides Ser.: No. 49). (Illus.). 350p. 1985. 22.50 (ISBN 0-520-04881-4). U of Cal Pr.
Metcalf, Artie L. Fishes of Chautauqua, Cowley & Elk Counties, Kansas. (Museum Ser.: Vol. 11, No. 6). 56p. 1959. pap. 3.00 (ISBN 0-686-79823-6). U of KS Mus Nat Hist.
--Fishes of the Kansas River System in Relation to Zoogeography of the Great Plains. (Museum Ser.: Vol. 17, No. 3). 167p. 1966. pap. 8.50 (ISBN 0-686-79824-4). U of KS Mus Nat Hist.
Miller, Daniel J. & Lea, Robert N. Guide to the Coastal Marine Fishes of California. 1976. pap. 5.00x (ISBN 0-931876-13-3, 4065). Ag & Nat Res.
Minckley, W. L. Fishes of the Big Blue River Basis, Kansas. (Museum Ser.: Vol. 11, No. 7). 42p. 1959. pap. 2.25 (ISBN 0-686-79825-2). U of KS Mus Nat Hist.
Moyle, Peter B. Inland Fishes of California. 1976. 24.00 (ISBN 0-520-02975-5). U of Cal Pr.
Moyle, Peter B. & Smith, Jerry J. Distribution & Ecology of Stream Fishes of the Sacramento-San Joaquin Drainage System, California. LC 81-13072. (University of California Publications in Zoology Ser.: Vol. 115). 264p. 1982. 18.50x (ISBN 0-520-09650-9). U of Cal Pr.
Petit, Gedeon D. Effects of Dissolved Oxygen on Survival & Behavior of Selected Fishes of Western Lake Erie. 1973. 3.00 (ISBN 0-86727-063-2). Ohio Bio Survey.
Pflieger, William L. A Distributional Study of Missouri Fishes. (Museum Ser.: Vol. 20, No. 3). 346p. 1971. pap. 14.00 (ISBN 0-686-79829-5). U of KS Mus Nat Hist.
Phillips, Gary L., et al. Fishes of the Minnesota Region. LC 81-14693. (Illus.). 200p. 1982. 25.00 (ISBN 0-8166-0979-9); pap. 12.95 (ISBN 0-8166-0982-9). U of Minn Pr.
Price, John W. Food Habits of Some Lake Erie Fishes. 1963. 3.00 (ISBN 0-86727-048-9). Ohio Bio Survey.
Rafinesque, Constantine. Ichthyologia Ohiensis, or, Natural History of the Fishes Inhabiting the River Ohio & Its Tributary Streams. LC 72-125760. (American Environmental Studies). 1970. Repr. of 1820 ed. 18.00 (ISBN 0-405-02686-2). Ayer Co Pubs.
Shurrager, P. Sheridan. An Ecological Study of the Fishes of the Hocking River. 1932. 1.00 (ISBN 0-86727-027-6). Ohio Bio Survey.
Simpson, James C. & Wallace, Richard L. Fishes of Idaho. 2nd ed. LC 81-71495. 237p. 1982. 10.95 (ISBN 0-89301-084-7). U Pr of Idaho.
Smith, Jerome V. C. Natural History of the Fishes of Massachusetts. (Illus.). 400p. 1970. boxed 10.75 (ISBN 0-88395-002-2). Freshet Pr.
Smith, Philip W. The Fishes of Illinois. LC 78-12741. 343p. 1978. 27.50x (ISBN 0-252-00682-8). U of Ill Pr.
Trautman, Milton B. The Fishes of Ohio. rev. 2nd ed. LC 80-29521. (Illus.). 793p. 1982. 32.50 (ISBN 0-8142-0213-6). Ohio St U Pr.
Varley, John D., et al. Fresh Water Wilderness: Yellowstone Fishes & Their World. (Illus.). 130p. 1982. write for info. Yellowstone Lib.
Werner, Robert G. Freshwater Fishes of New York State: A Field Guide. LC 80-17942. (York State Bks.). (Illus.). 270p. 1980. 20.00x (ISBN 0-8156-2233-3); pap. 11.95 (ISBN 0-8156-2222-8). Syracuse U Pr.
Wydoski, Richard S. & Whitney, Richard R. Inland Fishes of Washington. LC 78-21759. (Illus.). 284p. 1979. 25.00x (ISBN 0-295-95643-7); pap. 12.50 (ISBN 0-295-95644-5). U of Wash Pr.

FISHES, ELECTRIC

see Electric Organs in Fishes

FISHES, FOSSIL

Herre, Albert. Notes on Fishes in the Zoological Museum of Stanford University. 102p. 1974. 6.95 (ISBN 0-912318-02-3). N K Gregg.
Stensio, Erik A. The Downtonian & Devonian Vertebrates of Spitsbergen: Pt. 1, Family Cephalaspidea, Det Norske Videnskaps-Akademii Oslo, Skrifter M Svalbard G Nordishav et, Nr. 12, 2 vols. Gould, Stephen J., ed. LC 79-8553. (History of Paleontology Ser.). (Illus.). 1980. Repr. of 1927 ed. lib. bdg. 80.00x (ISBN 0-405-12746-4); lib. bdg. 35.00x ea. Vol. 1 (ISBN 0-405-12747-2). Vol. 2 (ISBN 0-405-12748-0). Ayer Co Pubs.
Teller, Susan & Bardack, David. Post-Glacial Fishes from a Lake Michigan Drainage in Milwaukee Wisconsin. 20p. 1977. 1.40 (ISBN 0-89326-028-2). Milwaukee Pub Mus.
Traquair, R. H. The Fishes of the Old Red Sandstone, Pt. 2, Nos. 2-4. Repr. of 1914 ed. Set. 20.00 (ISBN 0-384-61370-5). Johnson Repr.
--Ganoid Fishes of British Carboniferous Formations, Pt. 1., Nos. 2-7. Repr. of 1914 ed. Set. 41.00 (ISBN 0-384-61380-2). Johnson Repr.
Woodward, A. Smith. Wealden & Purbeck Fishes, Pts. 1-3. Set. 47.00 (ISBN 0-384-69219-2). Johnson Repr.

FISHES, FRESH-WATER

see also names of classes, orders, etc. of fresh water fishes

Ardizzone, D. A Bibliography of African Freshwater Fish: Supplement 1, 1968-1975. (Commission for Inland Fisheries of Africa (CIFA): Technical Papers: No. 5). (Eng. & Fr.). 52p. 1976. pap. 7.50 (ISBN 92-5-000092-8, F737, FAO). Unipub.
Axelrod, Herbert R., et al. Dr. Axelrod's Atlas of Freshwater Aquarium Fishes. (Illus.). 780p. 1985. text ed. 49.95 (ISBN 0-86622-052-6, H-1077). TFH Pubns.
Berra, Tim M. An Atlas of Distribution of the Freshwater Fish Families of the World. LC 80-24666. (Illus.). xxx, 197p. 1981. 26.50x (ISBN 0-8032-1411-1); pap. 12.50x (ISBN 0-8032-6059-8, BB 768, Bison). U of Nebr Pr.
Branson, Branley A. & Batch, Donald L. Fishes of the Red River Drainage, Eastern Kentucky. LC 73-80459. (Illus.). 76p. 1974. pap. 5.00x (ISBN 0-8131-1295-8). U Pr of Ky.
Cross, Frank B. & Minckley, W. L. Five Natural Hybrid Combinations in Minnows (Cyprinidae) (Museum Ser.: Vol. 13, No. 1). 18p. 1960. pap. 1.25 (ISBN 0-686-79819-8). U of KS Mus Nat Hist.
Dinha, V. R. The European Freshwater Eel. 134p. 1975. 50.00x (ISBN 0-85323-190-7, Pub. by Liverpool Univ England). State Mutual Bk.
Documents Presented at the Symposium on Stock Enhancement in the Management of Freshwater Fish. Rev. ed. (EIFAC Technical Papers: No. 42, Suppl. 1). (Eng. & Fr.). 284p. 1985. pap. 21.00 (ISBN 92-5-002101-1, F2686 5071, FAO). Unipub.
Documents Presented at the Symposium on Stock Enhancement in the Management of Freshwater Fish. (EIFAC Technical Papers: No. 42, Suppl. 2). (Eng. & Fr.). 557p. 1985. pap. 20.50 (ISBN 92-5-002102-X, F2687 5071, FAO). Unipub.
Eddy, Samuel & Underhill, James C. How to Know the Freshwater Fishes. 3rd ed. (Pictured Key Nature Ser.). 224p. 1978. text ed. wire coil avail. (ISBN 0-697-04750-4). Wm C Brown.
Everett, Charles. Fresh Water Fishes. (Illus.). 45p. pap. 1.00 (ISBN 0-8323-0126-4). Binford.

Hocutt, C. H. & Wiley, E. O. The Zoogeography of North American Freshwater Fishes. 1985. 80.00 (ISBN 0-471-86419-6). Wiley.

Houghton, W. British Freshwater Fishes. (Illus.). 256p. 1981. 35.00 (ISBN 0-03-059832-X). Webb & Bower.

Lackiel, T. & Welcome, R. L. Guidelines for Sampling Fish in Inland Waters. (European Inland Fisheries Advisory Commission (EIFAC): Technical Papers: No. 33). 184p. 1980. 13.50 (ISBN 92-5-100973-2, F2037, FAO). Unipub.

Lee, D. S., et al. Atlas of North American Freshwater Fishes. LC 80-620039. (Illus.). 867p. 1981. 25.00x (ISBN 0-917134-03-6). NC Natl Hist.

--Atlas of North American Freshwater Fishes: 1983 Supplement. (Occasional Papers of the North Carolina Biological Survey: 1983-6). (Illus.). 67p. 5.00 (ISBN 0-317-19673-1). NC Natl Hist.

Liu, H. Mei. Biology & Pathology of Nerve Growth. LC 81-3630. 1981. 45.00 (ISBN 0-12-452960-7). Acad Pr.

McClane, A. J. McClane's Field Guide to Freshwater Fishes of North America. LC 77-11967. (Illus.). 1978. pap. 9.95 (ISBN 0-03-021116-6, Owl Bks.). HR&W.

McGinnis, Samuel M. Freshwater Fishes of California. LC 83-5113. (California Natural History Guides Ser.: No. 49). (Illus.). 350p. 1985. 22.50 (ISBN 0-520-04881-4). U of Cal Pr.

Maitland, Peter S. A Key to British Freshwater Fishes. 1972. 20.00x (ISBN 0-900386-18-5, Pub. by Freshwater Bio). State Mutual Bk.

Morrow, James E. The Freshwater Fishes of Alaska. LC 80-1116. (Illus.). 272p. (Orig.). 1980. pap. 24.95 (ISBN 0-88240-134-3). Alaska Northwest.

Moyle, Peter B. Inland Fishes of California. 1976. 24.00 (ISBN 0-520-02975-5). U of Cal Pr.

Page, Lawrence M. & Braach, Marvin E. Systematic Studies of Darters of the Subgenus Catonotus (Percidae), with the Description of a New Species from the Lower Cumberland & Tennessee River Systems. (Occasional Papers: No. 60). 18p. 1976. pap. 1.25 (ISBN 0-686-79828-7). U of KS Mus Nat Hist.

Page, Lawrence M. & Braasch, Marvin E. Systematic Studies of Darters of the Subgenus Catonotus with the Description of a New Species from the Duck River System. (Occasional Papers: No. 63). 18p. 1977. pap. 1.25 (ISBN 0-686-79827-9). U of KS Mus Nat Hist.

Scott, W. B. Freshwater Fishes of Eastern Canada. 2nd ed. LC 67-101255. (Illus.). 1967. pap. 10.95 (ISBN 0-8020-6074-9). U of Toronto Pr.

Water Quality Criteria for European Freshwater Fish: Report on Chromium & Freshwater Fish. (European Inland Fisheries Advisory Commission (EIFAC): Technical Papers: No. 43). (Eng. & Fr.). 37p. 1983. pap. text ed. 7.50 (ISBN 92-5-101350-0, F2458, FAO). Unipub.

Wiley, E. O. The Phylogeny & Systematics of the Fundulus Nottii Species Group (Teleostei: Cyprinodontidae) (Occasional Papers: No. 66). 31p. 1977. pap. 1.75 (ISBN 0-686-79833-3). U of KS Mus Nat Hist.

FISHES, TROPICAL
see Tropical Fish

FISHING
see also Salt-Water Fishing

Amos, D. A Fisherman's Guide to Echo Soundings & Sonar Equipment: Acoustic Fish Detection Instruments. (Marine Bulletin Ser.: No. 41). 68p. 1980. 2.00 (ISBN 0-938412-30-2, P870). URI MAS.

Apte, Stuart C. Stu Apte's Fishing in the Florida Keys & Flamingo. 3rd ed. (Illus.). 1982. pap. 4.95 (ISBN 0-89317-019-4). Windward Pub.

Bates, Joseph D., Jr. How to Find Fish & Make Them Strike. LC 73-93268. (An Outdoor Life Bk). (Illus.). 224p. 1975. 11.49i (ISBN 0-06-010241-1, HarpT). Har-Row.

Beard, Henry & McKie, Roy. Fishing. LC 82-40498. 96p. 1983. pap. 4.95 (ISBN 0-89480-355-7, 355). Workman Pub.

Ben-Yami, M., ed. Tuna Fishing with Pole & Line: An FAO Fishing Manual. (Illus.). 168p. 1981. pap. 24.50 (ISBN 0-85238-111-5, FN88, FNB). Unipub.

Brabant, J. C. & Nedelec, C. Bottom Trawls for Small-Scale Fishing: Adaptation for Pair Trawling. (Fisheries Technical Papers: No. 189). (Eng. & Fr., Illus.). 27p. 1983. pap. text ed. 7.50 (ISBN 92-5-101235-0, F2420, FAO). Unipub.

Brandt, A. von. Fish Catching Methods of the World. 3rd ed. (Illus.). 418p. 1984. 66.00 (ISBN 0-85238-125-5, FN106, FNB). Unipub.

Cushing, D. H. Detection of Fish. 220p. 1973. text ed. 50.00 (ISBN 0-08-017123-0). Pergamon.

Dalrymple, Byron W. How to Rig & Fish Natural Baits. (Funk & W Bk.). (Illus.). 1976. pap. 4.50i (ISBN 0-308-10291-6, TYC-T). T Y Crowell.

Dremiere, P. Y. & Nedelec, C. Data on Fishing Vessels & Gear in the Mediterranean. (General Fisheries Council of the Mediterranean (GFCM): Studies & Reviews: No. 56). (Eng. & Fr., Illus.). 188p. 1977. pap. 12.00 (ISBN 92-5-000350-1, F1257, FAO). Unipub.

Electrical Fishing. (Fishery Studies: No. 7). pap. 4.50 (F120, FAO). Unipub.

Evanoff, Vlad. One Thousand & One Fishing Tips & Tricks. (Illus.). 1966. 10.95i (ISBN 0-06-070738-0, HarpT). Har-Row.

Fishing News Books Ltd., ed. Seine Fishing: Bottom Fishing with Rope Warps & Wing Trawls. 224p. 1981. 50.00x (ISBN 0-85238-113-1, Pub. by Fishing News England). State Mutual Bk.

Garrison, Chuck. Offshore Fishing: In Southern California & Baja. LC 80-27579. (Illus., Orig.). 1980. pap. 4.95 (ISBN 0-87701-166-4). Chronicle Bks.

Grey, Zane. Fresh Water Fishing. 298p. Repr. lib. bdg. 16.95x (ISBN 0-89190-762-9, Pub. by River City Pr). Amereon Ltd.

--Seafishing Yarns. 276p. Repr. lib. bdg. 16.95x (ISBN 0-89190-766-1, Pub. by River City Pr). Amereon Ltd.

Hadson, Alfred. The Fishing Cadet's Handbook. 1978. 25.00 (ISBN 0-685-63420-5). State Mutual Bk.

Haig-Brown, Roderick. Bright Waters, Bright Fish. 1980. ltd. ed. o.p. 75.00x (ISBN 0-918400-05-8, Pub. by Champoeg Pr). Intl Spec Bk.

--Bright Waters, Bright Fish. (Illus.). 160p. 1980. 19.95 (ISBN 0-917304-59-4). Timber.

Haley, K. Brian, ed. Applied Operations Research in Fishing. LC 80-27780. (NATO Conference Series II-Systems Science: Vol. 10). 506p. 1981. 72.50x (ISBN 0-306-40634-9, Plenum Pr). Plenum Pub.

Hardy, David. Scallops & the Diver-Fisherman. (Illus.). 144p. 1981. pap. 23.50 (ISBN 0-85238-114-X, FN90, FNB). Unipub.

Hayden, Mike. Pier Fishing on San Francisco Bay. LC 81-3799. (Illus.). 116p. (Orig.). 1982. pap. 5.95 (ISBN 0-87701-138-9). Chronicle Bks.

Hillard, A. & Jhaveri, S. Fish Preservation: An Annotated Bibliography. (Technical Report Ser.: No. 82). 50p. 1981. 2.00 (ISBN 0-938412-24-8, P909). URI MAS.

Hodson, Alfred. The Fishing Cadet's Handbook. (Illus.). 108p. 9.00 (ISBN 0-85238-011-9, FN44, FNB). Unipub.

Homemade Fishing. 2.95 (ISBN 0-686-31392-5). Outdoor Pubns.

Housby, Trevor. Fishing for Food. pap. 2.95 (ISBN 0-7153-7546-6). David & Charles.

Iversen, Edwin S. Farming the Edge of the Sea. 2nd ed. (Illus.). 440p. 50.75 (ISBN 0-85238-079-8, FN30, FNB). Unipub.

Judd, Stan. Inshore Fishing: Its Skills, Risks, Rewards. (Illus.). 144p. 17.50 (ISBN 0-85238-096-8, FN55, FNB). Unipub.

Lambuth, Letcher. The Angler's Workshop. 212p. 1979. 49.50x (ISBN 0-918400-01-5, Pub. by Champoeg Pr). Intl Spec Bk.

Lee, Jasper S. Commercial Catfish Farming. 2nd ed. (Illus.). 310p. 1981. text ed. 19.35 (ISBN 0-8134-2156-X, 2156); text ed. 14.50. Interstate.

McClane, A. J. Fishing With McClane. Reiger, George, ed. (Illus.). 266p. 1982. pap. 7.95 (ISBN 0-13-319624-0). P-H.

--McClane's Secrets of Successful Fishing. LC 78-24367. (Illus.). 288p. 1980. (Owl Bks.); pap. 7.95 (ISBN 0-03-021126-3). HR&W.

Marshall, Mel. Steelhead. (Illus.). 186p. 1980. 12.95 (ISBN 0-8329-0932-7, Pub. by Winchester Pr). New Century.

Martin, A. The Ring-Net Fishermen. 263p. 1981. pap. text ed. 31.75x (ISBN 0-85976-064-2, Pub. by John Donald England). Humanities.

The Mechanization of Small Fishing Craft. pap. 7.00 (FN47, FNB). Unipub.

Milne, P. H. Fish & Shellfish Farming in Coastal Waters. (Illus.). 208p. 30.00 (ISBN 0-85238-022-4, FN32, FNB). Unipub.

Moraski, Art. Complete Guide to Walleye Fishing. 1980. pap. 9.95 (ISBN 0-932558-12-7). Willow Creek.

Nathan, Bill, ed. The Sea Fisherman's Bedside Book. (Illus.). 166p. 1982. text ed. 12.95x (ISBN 0-7156-1537-8, Pub. by Duckworth England). Biblio Dist.

Norling, D. Economic Evaluation of Inland Sport Fishing. (European Inland Fisheries Advisory Commission (EIFAC): Technical Papers: No. 7). (Eng. & Fr.). 96p. (2nd Printing 1973). 1968. pap. 7.50 (ISBN 92-5-002057-0, F1720, FAO). Unipub.

Norling, I. & Gaudet, J. L. Summary of the Organized Discussion on the Economic Evaluation of Sport Fishing: Dublin, October 1967. (European Inland Fisheries Advisory Commission (EIFAC): Technical Papers: No. 1). 27p. (2nd Printing 1973). 1968. pap. 7.50 (ISBN 92-5-102040-X, F1808, FAO). Unipub.

O'Farrell, R. C. Seafood Fishing for Amateur & Professional. (Illus.). 196p. 15.75 (ISBN 0-85238-097-6, FN70, FNB). Unipub.

Olson, Fred. Successful Downrigger Fishing. 184p. 1981. 18.95 (ISBN 0-8329-3400-3, Pub. by Winchester Pr). New Century.

Otter Board Design & Performance. (Fishing Manuals). (Illus.). 79p. (Orig.). 1974. pap. 4.75 (ISBN 92-5-101596-1, F307, FAO). Unipub.

Ovington, Ray. Basic Fishing. LC 82-5436. (Illus.). 168p. (Orig.). 1982. pap. 9.95 (ISBN 0-8117-2141-8). Stackpole.

Pagliazzi, P. Situation of the Fishing Industry in Italy, Particularly Regarding Distribution. (General Fisheries Council of the Mediterranean (GFCM): Studies & Reviews: No. 8). (Eng. & Fr.). 22p. (2nd Printing 1966). 1959. pap. 7.50 (ISBN 92-5-101926-6, F1772, FAO). Unipub.

Parrish Rogers International, ed. The Fishing Handbook. 1985. 75.00x (ISBN 0-906358-12-4, Pub. by Parrish-Rogers England). State Mutual Bk.

Perry, W. H., ed. Fishermen's Handbook. 344p. 1980. cloth 29.95x (ISBN 0-85238-106-9, Pub. by Fishing News England). State Mutual Bk.

Pfleuger, Al. Fisherman's Handbook. 96p. 1981. pap. 5.95 (ISBN 0-89317-035-6). Windward Pub.

Pike, Dag. Fishing Boats & Their Equipment. 192p. 1980. pap. 18.00 (ISBN 0-85238-090-9, FN81, FNB). Unipub.

Pratt, Mary M. Better Angling with Simple Science. (Illus.). 144p. 13.50 (ISBN 0-85238-069-0, FN3, FNB). Unipub.

Punola, John A. Fishing & Canoeing the Upper Delaware River. rev. for 1982 ed. (Illus.). 112p. (Orig.). 1981. pap. 4.95 (ISBN 0-939888-04-1). Path Pubns NJ.

Report on Fishing for Squid & Other Cephalopods: Expert Consultation on Fishing, Tokyo & Hakodat, Japan, 1975. (Fisheries Reports: No. 170). 11p. 1976. pap. 7.50 (ISBN 0-685-66350-7, F817, FAO). Unipub.

Sainsbury, John C. Commercial Fishing Methods: An Introduction to Vessels & Gear. (Illus.). 120p. 21.75 (ISBN 0-85238-076-3, FN5, FNB). Unipub.

Swainbank, Todd, ed. Taking Gamefish: From Dry Flies to Downrigger Freshwater Fishing. LC 79-20982. (Illus.). 1979. 18.95 (ISBN 0-89594-026-4); pap. 8.95 (ISBN 0-89594-025-6). Crossing Pr.

Taylor, Buck. The Complete Guide to Using Depthfinders. (Illus.). 272p. (Orig.). 1981. pap. 9.95 (ISBN 0-940022-00-1). Outdoor Skills.

Tedone, David. Complete Shellfisherman's Guide. (Illus.). 200p. 1981. pap. 7.95 (ISBN 0-933614-09-8). Peregrine Pr.

Thomson, David. Seine Fishing: Bottom Fishing with Rope Warps & Wing Trawls. (Illus.). 224p. 1981. pap. 50.50 (ISBN 0-85238-113-1, FN89, FNB). Unipub.

Three Books on Fishing: Associated with the Complete Angler by Izaac Walton. LC 62-7054. 1962. Repr. of 1659 ed. 35.00x (ISBN 0-8201-1017-5). Schol Facsimiles.

Torbett, Harvey. Coarse Fishing. 15.00x (ISBN 0-392-06501-0, SpS). Sportshelf.

Vanderweide, Harry & Delorme, David. Maine Fishing Maps, Vol. 1: Lakes & Ponds. (Illus.). 96p. (Orig.). 1980. pap. 8.95 (ISBN 0-89933-007-X). DeLorme Pub.

--Maine Fishing Maps, Vol. 2: Rivers & Streams. (Illus.). 96p. (Orig.). 1983. pap. 8.95 (ISBN 0-89933-038-X). DeLorme Pub.

Von Brandt, Andres. Fish Catching Methods of the World. 1984. 150.00 (ISBN 0-685-63409-4). State Mutual Bk.

Walker, Richard. Catching Fish: Knowing Their Feeding Habits. LC 81-65961. (Illus.). 160p. 1981. 15.95 (ISBN 0-7153-8198-9). David & Charles.

Walton, Izaak. Compleat Angler. 1975. o.p 8.95x (ISBN 0-460-00070-5, Evman); pap. 2.95x (ISBN 0-460-01070-0, Evman). Biblio Dist.

Wisner, Bill. The Fishermen's Sourcebook. (Illus.). 352p. 1983. 24.95 (ISBN 0-02-630570-4). Macmillan.

Woods, Craig & Seybold, David, eds. Waters Swift & Still. LC 82-1840. (Illus.). 152p. 1982. 17.95 (ISBN 0-8329-3575-1, Pub. by Winchester Pr). New Century.

Woolner, Frank & Lyman, Hal. Striped Bass Fishing. LC 82-20300. 192p. 1983. 18.95 (ISBN 0-8329-0279-9, Pub. by Winchester Pr); pap. 12.95 (ISBN 0-8329-0281-0). New Century.

Zenanko, Tom. Walleye Fishing Today. Zenanko, Tom, ed. (Illus.). 212p. (Orig.). 1982. pap. 9.95 (ISBN 0-9610296-0-9). Zenanko Outdoors.

Zwirz, Bob. Digest Book of Fresh Water Fishing. LC 79-50066. 96p. pap. 3.95 (ISBN 0-695-81283-1). DBI.

FISHING--DICTIONARIES

Bridger, J. P. & Foster, J. J. Glossary of United Kingdom Fishing Gear Terms. 128p. 1981. 47.25 (ISBN 0-85238-119-0, FN95, FNB). Unipub.

Dictionary of Fishing Terms: Japanese-English, English-Japanese. (Japanese & Eng.). 443p. 1980. 39.95 (ISBN 0-686-92534-3, M-9344). French & Eur.

Glossary of UK Fishing Gear Terms. 1980. 39.50x (ISBN 0-686-64737-8, Pub. by Fishing News England). State Mutual Bk.

Greenberg, Idaz. Fishwatcher's Field Guide. (Illus.). 1979. plastic card 3.95x (ISBN 0-913008-10-9). Seahawk Pr.

Perry, W. H., ed. Fisherman's Handbook. (Illus.). 344p 1980. 26.50 (ISBN 0-85238-106-9, FN85, FNB). Unipub.

Schreiner, Jean, et al. Le Nouveau Dictionnaire de la Peche. (Fr.). 384p. 1975. 35.95 (ISBN 0-686-57331-5). French & Eur.

Taggart, Robert. A Fisherman's Guide: An Assessment of Training & Remediation Strategies. LC 81-16209. 373p. (Orig.). 1981. pap. text ed. 14.95 (ISBN 0-911558-92-6). W E Upjohn.

FISHING--IMPLEMENTS AND APPLIANCES

Bagenal, T. B. EIFAC Fishing Gear Intercalibration Experiments. (European Inland Fisheries Advisory Commission (EIFAC): Technical Papers: No.34). (Eng. & Fr., Illus.). 92p. 1979. pap. 9.00 (ISBN 92-5-100864-7, F1954, FAO). Unipub.

Bridger, J. P. & Foster, J. J. Glossary of United Kingdom Fishing Gear Terms. 128p. 1981. 47.25 (ISBN 0-85238-119-0, FN95, FNB). Unipub.

Clemens, Dale P. Fiberglass Rod Making. (Illus.). 212p. pap. 8.95 (ISBN 0-88317-042-6). Stoeger Pub Co.

Fisheries Technology Service. Echo Sounding & Sonar for Fishing. 1980. pap. 50.00x (ISBN 0-85238-110-7, Pub. by Fishing News England). State Mutual Bk.

Garner, John. Modern Inshore Fishing Gear. 1978. 40.00 (ISBN 0-685-63440-X). State Mutual Bk.

Graumont, Raoul & Wenstrom, Elmer. Fisherman's Knots & Nets. LC 48-423. (Illus.). 218p. 1948. pap. 6.95 (ISBN 0-87033-024-1). Cornell Maritime.

IPC Business Press, ed. Fishing Electronics. 65.00x (ISBN 0-617-00314-9, Pub. by IPC Busin England). State Mutual Bk.

--World Fishing Equipment Guide. 75.00x (ISBN 0-686-79380-3, Pub. by IPC Busn England). State Mutual Bk.

Klust, Gerhard. Fibre Ropes for Fishing Gear: An FAO Fishing Manual. (Illus.). 200p. 1984. 30.00 (ISBN 0-85238-123-9, FN101, FNB). Unipub.

Kristjonsson, Hilmar, ed. Modern Fishing Gear of the World One. 1981. 170.00 (ISBN 0-685-63437-X). State Mutual Bk.

--Modern Fishing Gear of the World Three. 1981. 170.00 (ISBN 0-685-63439-6). State Mutual Bk.

--Modern Fishing Gear of the World Two. 1981. 170.00 (ISBN 0-685-63438-8). State Mutual Bk.

Larocco, Rich. Shopping at Home for Hunting & Fishing Equipment. 192p. 1982. 15.95 (ISBN 0-87196-539-9); pap. 9.95 (ISBN 0-87196-533-X). Facts on File.

Liu, Allan J. The American Sporting Collector's Handbook. (Illus.). 256p. pap. 5.95 (ISBN 0-88317-040-X). Stoeger Pub Co.

McNally, Tom. Complete Book of Fisherman's Knots. (Illus.). 1975. 7.95 (ISBN 0-89149-024-8); pap. 4.95 (ISBN 0-89149-020-5). Jolex.

Manual of Methods for Fish Stock Assessment: Selectivity of Fishing Gear, Pt. 3. (Fisheries Technical Papers: No. 41, Rev. 1). (Illus.). 65p. 1976. pap. 7.50 (ISBN 92-5-100409-9, F849, FAO). Unipub.

Mutton, Brian. Engineering Applications: Hauling Devices for Small Fishing Craft. (Fisheries Technical Papers: No. 229). 157p. 1982. pap. text ed. 11.50 (ISBN 92-5-101281-4, F2425, FAO). Unipub.

Nedelec, C. Definition & Classification of Fishing Gear Categories. (Fisheries Technical Papers: No. 222). (Eng. & Fr.). 59p. (2nd Printing 1983). 1982. pap. 7.50 (ISBN 92-5-101219-9, F2314, FAO). Unipub.

Nedelec, C., ed. FAO Catalogue of Small Scale Fishing Gear. (Eng., Fr. & Span., Illus.). 192p. 25.25 (ISBN 0-85238-077-1, FN29, FNB). Unipub.

Oberrecht, Kenn. Angler's Guide to Jigs & Jigging. LC 81-23998. 256p. 1982. 14.95 (ISBN 0-8329-3656-1, Pub. by Winchester Pr). New Century.

Report of the EIFAC Consultation on Eel Fishing Gear & Techniques: Hamburg, 1970. (European Inland Fisheries Advisory Commission (EIFAC): Technical Papers: No. 14). (Eng. & Fr.). 192p. 1971. pap. 12.75 (ISBN 92-5-002064-3, F757, FAO). Unipub.

Rosman, I. Fishing with Bottom Gillnets. (Training Ser.: No. 3). 39p. 1980. pap. 10.25 (ISBN 92-5-100906-6, F2167, FAO). Unipub.

Fraser, F. C. Odonata: Vol. 1 - Coenagriidae. (Fauna of British India Ser.). (Illus.). xiv, 424p. 1977. Repr. of 1933 ed. 30.00 (ISBN 0-88065-086-9, Pub. by Messers Today & Tomorrows Printers & Publishers India). Scholarly Pubns.

--Odonata: Vol. 2 - Agriidae & Gomphida. (Illus.). xxiv, 416p. 1977. Repr. of 1934 ed. 30.00 (ISBN 0-88065-087-7, Pub. by Messers Today & Tomorrows Printers & Publishers India). Scholarly Pubns.

--Odonata: Vol. 3 - Cordulegasteridae, Aeshnidae, Labellulidae. (Fauna of British India Ser.). (Illus.). xii, 472p. 1977. Repr. of 1936 ed. 30.00 (ISBN 0-88065-088-5, Pub. by Messers Today & Tomorrows Printers & Publishers India). Scholarly Pubns.

Freeman, Paul & De Meillon, Botha. Simuliide of the Ethiopian Region. (Illus.). vii, 224p. 1953. Repr. of 1968 ed. 24.00x (ISBN 0-565-00194-9, Pub. by Brit Mus Nat Hist). Sabbot-Natural Hist Bks.

Griffiths, G. C. Flies of the Nearctic Region: Cyclorhapha II (Schizophora, Calyptratae) Part 2 Anthomiidae, Vol. VIII, No. 1. (Illus.). 600p. 1984. pap. text ed. 51.85x (ISBN 3-51070-009-0). Lubrecht & Cramer.

--Flies of the Nearctic Region Vol. VIII: Cyclorrhapha II (Schizophora. Calyptratae, Pt. 2 Anthomyiidae, No. 1. (Illus.). 160p. (Orig.). 1982. pap. text ed. 53.76 (ISBN 3-510-70004-X). Lubrecht & Cramer.

Griffiths, Graham C. Flies of the Nearctic Region: Vol. VIII-Cyclorrhapha II Schizophora: Calyptratae Pt. 2-Anthomylidae. (Illus.). 1984. pap. text ed. 38.14 (ISBN 3-510-70007-4). Lubrecht & Cramer.

Hall, J. C. & Evenhuis, M. L. Flies of the Neartic Region: Vol. V-Homeodactyla & Asilomorpha Pt. 13-Bombylliidae, No. 4. Griffiths, Graham C., ed. (Illus.). 1984. pap. text ed. 15.21 (ISBN 3-510-70008-2). Lubrecht & Cramer.

Hall, Jack C. & Evenhuis, N. L. Flies of the Nearctic Region: Bombyliidae, Vol. V, Pt. 13. Griffiths, Grahm C., ed. (Monograph: No. 2). (Illus.). 184p. 1982. pap. text ed. 35.90x (ISBN 3-510-70003-1). Lubrecht & Cramer.

--Flies of the Nearctic Region: Volume V part 13: Bombyliidae No. 3. Griffiths, Graham C., ed. (Illus.). 280p. 1982. pap. text ed. 38.64 (ISBN 3-510-70005-8). Lubrecht & Cramer.

Hall, Jack C. & Evenhuis, Neal L. Flies of the Nearctic Region: Volume V, Part 13: Bombyliidae, No. 1. Griffiths, Graham C., ed. (Illus.). 96p. 1980. pap. text ed. 35.90x (ISBN 3-510-70002-3). Lubrecht & Cramer.

Hull, Frank M. Bee Flies of the World: The Genera of the Family Bombyliidae. 1973 ed. LC 73-1581. (Illus.). 687p. 75.00x (ISBN 0-87474-131-9). Smithsonian.

Johnson, Ned K. Character Variation & Evolution of Sibling Species in the Empidonax Difficilis-Flavescens Complex (Aves: Tyrannidae) (University of California Publications in Zoology: Vol. 112). 1979. monograph 18.00x (ISBN 0-520-09599-5). U of Cal Pr.

Laird, Marshall, ed. Blackflies: The Future for Biological Methods in Integrated Control. LC 81-66373. 1982. 59.50 (ISBN 0-12-434060-1). Acad Pr.

Loosjes, M. Ecology & Genetic Control of the Onion Fly. (Agricultural Research Reports: No. 857). 1976. pap. 20.00 (ISBN 90-220-0611-5, PDC103, PUDOC). Unipub.

Mathis, Wayne N. Studies of Parydrinae (Diptera: Ephydridae) Revision of the Shore Fly Genus Pelinoides Cresson, Pt. 2. LC 84-600299. (Smithsonian Contributions to Zoology Ser.: No. 410). pap. 20.00 (ISBN 0-317-30174-8, 2025356). Bks Demand UMI.

Muirhead-Thomson, E. C. Behaviour Patterns of Blood-Sucking Flies. (Illus.). 240p. 1982. 55.00 (ISBN 0-08-025497-7). Pergamon.

Pal, R. & Wharton, R. H., eds. Control of Arthropods: Medical & Veterinary Importance. LC 74-4172. 143p. 1974. 32.50x (ISBN 0-306-30790-1, Plenum Pr). Plenum Pub.

Price, S. D. Taff Price's Complete Stillwater Flies. 276p. 1982. 75.00x (ISBN 0-510-22546-2, Pub. by Benn Pubns). State Mutual Bk.

A Revisionary Study of Leaf-Mining Flies: Agromyzidae of California. LC 81-70585. 1981. pap. text ed. 20.00x (ISBN 0-931876-53-2, 3273). Ag & Nat Res.

Shorrocks, B. Drosophila. (Illus.). 144p. 1980. 13.25 (ISBN 0-08-025941-3). Pergamon.

Stone, Alan. Flies of the Nearctic Region: Volume 1, Handbook, Part 1: History of Nearctic Dipterology. Griffiths, Graham C., ed. (Illus.). 76p. 1981. pap. text ed. 36.75x (ISBN 3-510-7000-15). Lubrecht & Cramer.

Strausfeld, N. J. Atlas of an Insect Brain. LC 75-19499. (Illus.). 250p. 1975. 150.00 (ISBN 0-387-07343-4). Springer-Verlag.

Theodor, Oskar. Diptera: Asilidae Insecta II. (Fauna Palaestina Ser.: No. 2). (Illus.). 448p. 1981. text ed. 40.00x (ISBN 0-87474-910-7, Pub. by the Israel Academy of Sciences & Humanities). Smithsonian.

Townes, Henry & Townes, Marjorie. Ichneumon-Flies of America North of Mexico: Pt. 7 Subfamily Banchinae, Tribes Lissonotini & Banchini. (Memoir Ser: No. 26). (Illus.). 614p. 1978. 40.00x (ISBN 0-686-30712-7). Am Entom Inst.

FLIGHT

see also Aeronautics; Flying-Machines; Stability of Airplanes

Bernstein, Burton. Plane Crazy: A Celebration of Flying. (Illus.). 192p. 1985. 16.95 (ISBN 0-89919-390-0). HM.

Brink, Randall. Restoring & Flying a Sport Plane on a Budget. (Illus.). 192p. 1982. pap. 8.95 (ISBN 0-8306-2319-1, 2319). TAB Bks.

Buck, Robert N. Weather Flying. rev. ed. (Illus.). 1978. 16.95 (ISBN 0-02-518020-7). Macmillan.

Dalton. The Miracle of Flight. 1977. 16.95 (ISBN 0-07-015207-1). McGraw.

Dole, Charles E. Flight Theory & Aerodynamcs: A Practical Guide for Operational Safety. LC 81-3009. 299p. 1981. 42.95x (ISBN 0-471-09152-9, Pub. by Wiley-Interscience). Wiley.

Downie, Don & Downie, Julia. Your Mexican Flight Plan. (Illus.). 272p. (Orig.). 1983. pap. 12.95 (ISBN 0-8306-2337-X, 2337). TAB Bks.

Dwiggins, Don. Man-Powered Aircraft. (Illus.). 1979. 9.95 (ISBN 0-8306-9851-5); pap. 5.95 (ISBN 0-8306-2254-3, 2254). TAB Bks.

Dwyer, James. Private Pilot's Blue Book. LC 76-41837. 1977. 9.95 (ISBN 0-685-81548-X). Macmillan.

Etkin, Bernard. Dynamics of Atmospheric Flight. LC 73-165946. (Illus.). 579p. 1972. text ed. 49.00x (ISBN 0-471-24620-4). Wiley.

--Dynamics of Flight Stability & Control. 2nd ed. LC 81-13058. 370p. 1982. text ed. 43.45 (ISBN 0-471-08936-2). Wiley.

Fillingham, Paul. Basic Guide to Flying. 1977. pap. 5.95 (ISBN 0-8015-0526-7, Hawthorn). Dutton.

Garrison, Paul. Cross-Country Flying. (Illus.). 192p. 1980. 9.95 (ISBN 0-8306-9966-X); pap. 11.95 (ISBN 0-8306-2284-5, 2284). TAB Bks.

--Lift, Thrust & Drag: A Primer of Modern Flying. (Illus.). 224p. 1982. pap. 8.95 (ISBN 0-8306-2309-4, 2309). TAB Bks.

Garrison, Peter. Long Distance Flying. LC 80-2049. (Illus.). 1981. 14.95 (ISBN 0-385-14595-0). Doubleday.

Griffin, Jeff W. Cold Weather Flying. (Modern Aviation Ser.). 1980. 9.95 (ISBN 0-8306-9711-X). TAB Bks.

--Foundations of Flying. (Illus.). 144p. 1982. pap. 9.95 (ISBN 0-8306-2345-0, 2345). TAB Bks.

Haldon Books. Flight Maneuver Manual. (Illus.). 1981. spiral bdg. 15.00 (ISBN 0-940766-06-X, Pub. by Haldon Bks). Aviation.

Hartill, William R., ed. World Free Flight Review. LC 78-64742. (Illus.). 1978. 30.00 (ISBN 0-933066-01-5). World Free Flight.

Kimberley, Gareth J. Fun Flying! A Total Guide to Ultralights. (Illus.). 176p. 1984. pap. 10.25 (ISBN 0-8306-2350-7, 2350). TAB Bks.

Langewiesche, Wolfgang. Stick & Rudder. (Illus.). 1944. 16.95 (ISBN 0-07-036240-8). McGraw.

Lert, Peter. Flying Advanced Multi-Engine Aircraft. (Illus.). 224p. 1982. pap. 7.95 (ISBN 0-8306-2299-3, 2299). TAB Bks.

Sarpolus, Dick. Building & Flying Ducted-Fan Radio Control Aircraft. Angle, Burr, ed. LC 81-83268. (Illus.). 52p. 1981. pap. 6.95 (ISBN 0-89024-038-8). Kalmbach.

Taylor, Richard L. Instrument Flying. 2nd ed. 1978. 17.95 (ISBN 0-02-616670-4). Macmillan.

Traister, Robert J. The Joy of Flying. (Illus.). 272p. 1982. pap. 10.25 (ISBN 0-8306-2321-3, 2321). TAB Bks.

Urry, David & Urry, Katie. Flying Birds. LC 74-110974. 1969. 7.95 (ISBN 0-910294-20-8). Brown Bk.

Von Mises, Richard. Theory of Flight. 17.00 (ISBN 0-8446-2599-X). Peter Smith.

FLIGHT, UNPOWERED

see Gliding and Soaring

FLIGHT ENGINEERING

Aircraft Fueling Ramp Drainage. (Four Hundred Ser.). 1973. pap. 2.00 (ISBN 0-685-58234-5, 415). Natl Fire Prot.

Aviation Maintenance Publishers. Aircraft Logbook. 74p. 1975. pap. 4.95 (ISBN 0-89100-190-5, EA-AFL-1). Aviation Maintenance.

Aviation Supplies & Academics. Flight Engineer Test Prep Program. 1978. 3-ring binder 49.95 (ISBN 0-940732-26-2, Pub. by ASA). Aviation.

Federal Aviation Administration. Flight Engineer Turboset-Basic Written Test Guide. 144p. 1977. pap. text ed. 4.00 (ISBN 0-939158-18-3). Flightshops.

Griffin, Jeff W. How to Become a Flight Engineer. (Illus.). 160p. 1982. pap. 6.95 (ISBN 0-8306-2318-3, 2318). TAB Bks.

Mises, Richard Von. Theory of Flight. pap. 10.95 (ISBN 0-486-60541-8). Dover.

Nykorowitsch, P., ed. Return Passage of Multi-Stage Turbomachinery. 66p. 1983. pap. text ed. 20.00 (ISBN 0-317-02644-5, G00225). ASME.

Vinh, Nguyen X., et al. Hypersonic & Planetary Entry Flight Mechanics. 376p. 1980. 29.95x (ISBN 0-472-10004-1). U of Mich Pr.

FLIGHT SIMULATORS

Garrison, Paul. Flying Without Wings: A Flight Simulation Manual. (Illus.). 144p. (Orig.). 1985. pap. 14.95 (ISBN 0-8306-2366-3, 2366). TAB Bks.

Ingersoll Engineers. The FMS Report. Rev. ed. Mortimer, J., ed. 180p. 1984. pap. 61.00 (ISBN 0-387-13556-1). Springer-Verlag.

Network Editors, ed. History: The Role of the Flight Simulation in Training & Research User Requirements, Successes, Failures & Prospects. 1982. 75.00x (ISBN 0-904999-60-2, Pub. by Network). State Mutual Bk.

--The Role of Flight Simulation: To Train or Assess? 1982. 50.00x (ISBN 0-904999-47-5, Pub. by Network). State Mutual Bk.

--What Makes the Simulator Fly Like the Aircraft? 1982. 50.00x (ISBN 0-904999-46-7, Pub. by Network). State Mutual Bk.

FLIGHT TESTING OF AIRPLANES

see Airplanes–Flight Testing

FLIGHT TO MARS

see Space Flight to Mars

FLIGHT TO THE MOON

see Space Flight to the Moon

FLIGHT TRACKING

see Artificial Satellites–Tracking

FLIGHT TRAINING

see also Airplanes–Piloting; Flight Simulators

Advanced Pilot Manual. 1st ed. (Pilot Training Ser.). (Illus.). 480p. 1981. text ed. 24.49 (ISBN 0-88487-068-5, JS314298). Jeppesen Sanderson.

Baxter, Gordon. How to Fly. (Illus.). 224p. 1981. 12.95 (ISBN 0-671-44801-3). Summit Bks.

Bellomo, Chas & Lynch, John. Crash, Fire & Rescue Handbook. (Pilot Training Ser.). 94p. (Orig.). 1984. pap. text ed. 8.95 (ISBN 0-89100-250-2, EA-250-2). Aviation Maintenance.

Brink, Randall. The Flight School Handbook. (Illus.). 210p. 1982. pap. 8.95 (ISBN 0-8306-2329-9, 2329). TAB Bks.

Carrier, Rick. Ultralights: The Complete Book of Flying, Training & Safety. LC 83-40143. (Illus.). 144p. 1985. pap. 12.95 (ISBN 0-385-19290-8, Dolp). Doubleday.

Coleman, John E. Flight Instructor: Questions, Answers, Explanations. rev. ed. (Illus.). 220p. 1985. pap. text ed. 12.95 (ISBN 0-941272-23-0). Astro Pubs.

Crane, Dale. So You Think You Know...? Quiz Book. (Aviation Training Ser.). (Illus.). 297p. 1980. pap. 10.95 (ISBN 0-89100-071-2, EA-QB). Aviation Maintenance.

Delp, Frank. Commercial Pilot Question Book Including Answers, Explanations, & References. rev. ed. (Pilot Training Ser.). 475p. 1985. pap. text ed. 12.95 (ISBN 0-89100-261-8, EA-FAA-T-8080-2C). Aviation Maintenance.

--Flight Instructor Question Book Including Answers, Explanations, & References. rev. ed. (Pilot Training Ser.). 300p. 1985. pap. text ed. 10.95 (ISBN 0-89100-263-4, EA-FAA-T-8080-3C). Aviation Maintenance.

Department of Aviation Education. Manual of Flight: Private & Commercial Pilot. 332p. 1973. pap. 14.95 (ISBN 0-685-62814-0). Aero Products.

Federal Aviation Administration. Aviation Instructor's Handbook (AC-60-14) 1977. pap. text ed. 6.00 (ISBN 0-86677-017-8, Pub. by Cooper Aviation). Aviation.

--Commercial Pilot Question Book. (Pilot Training Ser.). (Illus.). 228p. 1984. pap. 6.50 (ISBN 0-89100-260-X, EA-FAA-T-8080-2). Aviation Maintenance.

--Flight Instructor Practical Test Guide (AC 61-58A) 1979. pap. 1.75 (ISBN 0-86677-011-9, Pub. by Cooper Aviation). Aviation.

--Flight Instructor Question Book. (Pilot Training Ser.). (Illus.). 150p. 1984. pap. 5.50 (ISBN 0-89100-262-6, EA-FAA-T-8080-3). Aviation Maintenance.

--Flight Test Guide, Instrument, Airplane AC 61-56A) 1976. pap. text ed. 1.75 (ISBN 0-86677-009-7, Pub. by Cooper Aviation). Aviation.

--Flight Training Handbook. 2nd ed. (Pilot Training Ser.). (Illus.). 325p. 1980. pap. 9.00 (ISBN 0-89100-165-4, EA-AC61-21A). Aviation Maintenance.

--Flight Training Handbook. LC 80-70552. (Illus.). 352p. 1981. 15.95 (ISBN 0-385-17599-X). Doubleday.

--Private Pilot Question Book. (Pilot Training Ser.). (Illus.). 138p. 1984. pap. 5.00 (ISBN 0-89100-258-8, EA-FAA-T-8080-1). Aviation Maintenance.

--Private Pilot Question Book & References. (Pilot Training Ser.). (Illus.). 234p. 1984. pap. 9.95 (ISBN 0-89100-259-6, EA-FAA-T-8080-1C). Aviation Maintenance.

--Student Pilot Guide (AC 61-12J) 1979. pap. text ed. 3.95 (ISBN 0-939158-05-1, Pub. by Natl Flightshops). Aviation.

Federal Aviation Administration & Aviation Book Company Editors. IFR Pilot Exam-O-Grams. (Illus.). 96p. 1984. pap. 3.25 (ISBN 0-911721-79-7). Aviation.

Federal Aviation Administration, Dept. of Transportation. Private Pilot-Airplane: Practical Test Standards for Airplane, Single-Engine, Land. 118p. (Orig.). 1984. pap. text ed. 4.95 (ISBN 0-941272-25-7). Astro Pubs.

Federal Aviation Administration Staff. Private Pilot: Practical Test Standards for Airplane, Single-Engine, Land. 112p. 1984. pap. 3.95 (ISBN 0-916413-01-2). Aviation.

Federal Aviation Agency. Pilot Instruction Manual. 1961. 12.95 (ISBN 0-385-01046-X). Doubleday.

Flight Instructor Manual. 1st ed. (Pilot Training Ser.). (Illus.). 240p. 1981. pap. text ed. 14.95 (ISBN 0-88487-066-9, JS314126). Jeppesen Sanderson.

Flight Instructor Practical Test Guide. (Federal Aviation Administration Ser.). 17p. 1975. pap. text ed. 3.50 (ISBN 0-89100-175-1, EA-AC61-58A). Aviation Maintenance.

Foster, Timothy R. Flying in Congested Airspace. (Illus.). 192p. 1983. pap. 10.25 (ISBN 0-8306-2358-2, 2358). TAB Bks.

Fowler, Ron. Making Perfect Landings in Light Airplanes. (Illus.). 128p. 1984. 12.95 (ISBN 0-8138-1081-7). Iowa St U Pr.

Fundamentals of Instructing & Ground Instructor Basic-Advanced Question Book. (Pilot Training Ser.). 108p. 1984. pap. text ed. 4.25 (ISBN 0-89100-264-2, EA-FAA-T-8080-4). Aviation Maintenance.

Fundamentals of Instructing & Ground Instructor: Basic-Advanced Question Book Including Answers, Explanations & References. (Pilot Training Ser.). 220p. 1985. pap. text ed. 7.95 (ISBN 0-89100-265-0, EA-FAA-T-8080-4C). Aviation Maintenance.

Garrison, Peter. Flying Airplanes: The First Hundred Hours. Parke, Robert B., ed. LC 80-7476. (Illus.). 240p. 1980. 11.95 (ISBN 0-385-14594-2). Doubleday.

Glaeser, et al. Invitation to Fly. 2nd ed. 640p. 1985. write for info. (ISBN 0-534-04800-5). Wadsworth Pub.

Ground Studies for Pilots, Vol. 2: Plotting & Flight Planning. 3rd ed. 144p. 1979. 19.95x (ISBN 0-246-11176-3, Pub. by Granada England). Sheridan.

Ground Studies for Pilots, Vol. 3: Navigation General. 3rd ed. 240p. 1979. 22.50x (ISBN 0-246-11177-1, Pub. by Granada England). Sheridan.

Haldon Books. Visualized Flight Maneuvers Handbook for Instructors & Students. (Illus.). 172p. 1980. ringbound softcover 15.00 (ISBN 0-940766-05-1, Pub. by Haldon). Aviation.

Instrument-Pilot-Airplane Flight Test Guide. (Pilot Training Ser.). 23p. 1976. pap. text ed. 3.75 (ISBN 0-89100-173-5, EA-AC61-56A). Aviation Maintenance.

Instrument Rating Manual. 5th ed. (Pilot Training Ser.). (Illus.). 344p. 1981. pap. text ed. 21.95 (ISBN 0-88487-069-3, JS314299). Jeppesen Sanderson.

Kershner, William K. Flight Instructor's Manual. 2nd ed. (Illus.). 400p. 1981. pap. 23.95 (ISBN 0-8138-0635-6). Iowa St U Pr.

Larson, George C. Fly on Instruments. LC 79-7602. (Illus.). 240p. 1980. 12.95 (ISBN 0-385-14619-1). Doubleday.

Melton, James E. Your Right to Fly. LC 80-82961. (Illus.). 218p. 1979. pap. 6.95 (ISBN 0-9604752-0-6). Global Pubns CA.

Middlekauf, Dana & Horowitz, Milton. Instrument Rating Question Book Including Answers, Explanations, & References. rev. ed. (Pilot Training Ser.). 450p. 1984. pap. text ed. 12.95 (ISBN 0-89100-267-7, EA-FAA-T-8080-7C). Aviation Maintenance.

Multi-Engine Pilot Manual. 1st ed. (Pilot Training Ser.). (Illus.). 128p. 1981. pap. text ed. 16.95 (ISBN 0-88487-070-7, JS314127). Jeppesen Sanderson.

Nelson, John L. The Beginner's Guide to Flight Instruction. (Illus.). 304p. (Orig.). 1983. pap. 13.50 (ISBN 0-8306-2324-8, 2324). TAB Bks.

Private & Commercial Pilot Helicopter Flight Test Guide. (Pilot Training Ser.). 37p. 1977. 4.50 (ISBN 0-89100-176-X, EA-AC61-59A). Aviation Maintenance.

Private Pilot Manual. (Pilot Training Ser.). (Illus.). 400p. 1983. text ed. 20.95 (ISBN 0-88487-081-2, JS314301). Jeppesen Sanderson.

Professional Instrument Courses, Inc. & Dogan, Peter. Instrument Flight Training Manual. (Illus.). 208p. 1985. pap. 16.95t (ISBN 0-916413-02-0). Aviation.

BOOKS - SUBJECT INDEX

FLOW CHARTS

Ramsey, Dan. Budget Flying. (McGraw-Hill Series in Aviation). (Illus.). 176p. 1980. 20.25 (ISBN 0-07-051202-7). McGraw.
--How to Earn Your Private Pilot License. LC 83-6404. 1984. pap. 7.95 (ISBN 0-668-05856-0, 5856). Arco.
Smith, Robert T. Your FAA Flight Exam: Private & Commercial. (Modern Aircraft Ser). (Illus.). 1978. 7.95 (ISBN 0-8306-9893-0). TAB Bks.
Stoffel, Robert & LaValle, Patrick. Survival Sense for Pilots. LC 80-70906. (Illus.). 160p. 1980. pap. 7.95 (ISBN 0-913724-24-6, Pub. by Emergency Response). Aviation.
Taylor, Albert J. How to Teach Flying. (Illus.). 304p. 1983. pap. 12.50 (ISBN 0-8306-2343-4, 2343). TAB Bks.
Taylor, Richard L. Recreational Flying: The Complete Guide to Earning & Enjoying the New Recreational Pilot Certificate. Eggspuehler, Jack, intro. by. (Illus.). 1985. 18.95 (ISBN 0-02-616620-8). Macmillan.
Type Rating Airplane Flight Test Guide. (Pilot Training Ser.). 29p. 1975. 4.25 (ISBN 0-89100-174-3, EA-AC61-57A). Aviation Maintenance.
Underwood, John W. The Light Plane Since 1909. new rev. 2nd ed. (Illus.). 80p. 1975. pap. 10.95 (ISBN 0-911834-07-9, Pub. by Collingwood). Aviation.
Vasko, Donna M. I'd Rather Be Flying. 100p. (Orig.). 1980. pap. 6.95. Calligraphy Donna.
Vitale, Barbara M. Free Flight: Riding the Wind in a Right-Brained Way. 160p. 1985. 9.95 (ISBN 0-915190-43-5); pap. write for info (ISBN 0-915190-44-3). Jalmar Pr.

FLINT

Sieveking, G. & Hart, M. B., eds. The Scientific Study of Flint & Chert: Proceedings of the Fourth International Flint Symposium. 350p. Date not set. price not set. (ISBN 0-521-26252-6). Cambridge U Pr.

FLINT IMPLEMENTS

see Stone Implements

FLOCCULATION

Ives, K. J., ed. The Scientific Basis of Flocculation. 375p. 1978. 36.00x (ISBN 90-286-0758-7). Sijthoff & Noordhoff.

FLOOD CONTROL

see also Flood Dams and Reservoirs

The Application of Computers in Analysis of Various Problems Relating to Irrigation & Drainage Systems: Proceedings of a Symposium, Mexico. 202p. 1969. 12.00 (ISBN 0-318-16969-X); members 8.00 (ISBN 0-318-16970-3). US Comm Irrigation.
Australian Rainfall & Runoff Flood Analysis & Design. 159p. (Orig.). 1977. pap. text ed. 27.00x (ISBN 0-85825-077-2, Pub. by Inst Engineering Australia). Brookfield Pub Co.
Baker, V. R., ed. Catastrophic Flooding: The Origin of the Channeled Scabland. LC 79-22901. (Benchmark Papers in Geology: Vol. 55). 384p. 1981. 51.95 (ISBN 0-87933-360-X). Van Nos Reinhold.
Bosch, Vanden, et al. Urban Watershed Management: Flooding & Water Quality. Bedient, Philip B. & Rowe, Peter G., eds. (Rice University Studies: Vol. 65, No. 1). 205p. 1979. pap. 10.00x (ISBN 0-89263-240-2). Rice Univ.
De Vore, R. William & Haan, Charles T., eds. International Symposium on Urban Storm Water Management: Proceedings 1978. 348p. 1978. pap. text ed. 33.50 (ISBN 0-89779-002-2, UKY BU116). OES Pubns.
Estimation of Maximum Floods. (Technical Note Ser.: No. 98). 288p. 1969. pap. 45.00 (ISBN 0-685-22303-5, W66, WMO). Unipub.
Flood Damage Prevention & Control in China. (Natural Resources-Water Ser.: No. 11). 121p. 1983. pap. text ed. 13.50 (ISBN 0-317-00313-5, UN82/2A13, UN). Unipub.
Frank, Arthur D. Development of the Federal Program of Flood Control on the Mississippi River. LC 68-58572. (Columbia University. Studies in the Social Sciences: No. 323). Repr. of 1930 ed. 21.00 (ISBN 0-404-51323-9). AMS Pr.
Hall, A. J. Flash Flood Forecasting. (Operational Hydrology Reports: No. 18). 38p. 1981. pap. 6.00 (ISBN 92-63-10577-4, W511, WMO). Unipub.
Hammer, Thomas R. Empirical Estimation of Flood-Detention Capacity Needed to Offset Effects of Urbanization on Peak Streamlining. (Discussion Paper Ser.: No. 57). 1972. pap. 4.50 (ISBN 0-686-32224-X). Regional Sci Res Inst.
Kemper, J. P. Rebellious River. LC 72-2848. (Use & Abuse of America's Natural Resources Ser). 284p. 1972. Repr. of 1949 ed. 20.00 (ISBN 0-405-04514-X). Ayer Co Pubs.
Kerns, Walson R. & Underwood, Richard C., eds. Implementation of Non-Structural Alternatives in Flood Damage Abatement: Proceedings of a Two-day Research Needs Identification Conference, May 24-25, 1976. pap. 29.50 (ISBN 0-317-10796-8, 2011995). Bks Demand UMI.
Leuchtenburg, William E. Flood Control Politics: The Connecticut River Valley Problem, 1927-1950. LC 73-38834. (FDR & the Era of the New Deal Ser.). (Illus.). 1972. Repr. of 1953 ed. lib. bdg. 39.50 (ISBN 0-306-70446-3). Da Capo.
Mahmood, K., et al, eds. Unsteady Flow in Open Channels, 3 vols. LC 75-9251. 1975. Set. 48.00 (ISBN 0-686-67936-9); Vol. 1. (ISBN 0-918334-09-8); Vol. 2. (ISBN 0-918334-10-1); Vol. 3. (ISBN 0-918334-11-X). WRP.
Methods & Problems of Flood Control in Asia & the Far East. (Water Resources Development Ser.: No. 2). pap. 2.00 (ISBN 0-686-94780-0, UN51/2F5, UN). Unipub.
National Research Council. Safety of Dams: Flood & Earthquake Criteria. 320p. 1985. pap. 16.50 (ISBN 0-309-03532-5). Natl Acad Pr.
Peregrine, D. H., ed. Floods Due to High Winds & Tides. (IMA Conference Ser.). 1982. 26.00 (ISBN 0-12-551820-X). Acad Pr.
Peterson, Elmer T. Big Dam Foolishness. 1954. 9.50 (ISBN 0-8159-5107-8). Devin.
Rational Methods of Flood Control Planning in River Basin Development. pap. 6.00 (ISBN 0-686-94434-8, UN76/2E26, UN). Unipub.
Symposium on Inland Waterways for Navigation, Flood Control & Water Diversions. Inland Waterways for Navigation, Flood Control & Water Diversions: Third Annual Symposium of the Waterways, Harbors & Coastal Engineering Division of ASCE, Colorado State University, Fort Collins, Colorado, August 10-12, 1976, 2 vols. Vol. 1. pap. 160.00 (ISBN 0-317-28778-8, 2017762); Vol. 2. pap. 160.00 (ISBN 0-317-28779-6). Bks Demand UMI.
Vance, Mary. Flood Damage Prevention: Monographs. (Public Administration Ser.: Bibliography P 1639). 1985. pap. 3.00 (ISBN 0-89028-329-X). Vance Biblios.

FLOOD DAMS AND RESERVOIRS

see also Sea-Walls

Baker, V. R., ed. Catastrophic Flooding: The Origin of the Channeled Scabland. LC 79-22901. (Benchmark Papers in Geology: Vol. 55). 384p. 1981. 51.95 (ISBN 0-87933-360-X). Van Nos Reinhold.
National Research Council. Safety of Dams: Flood & Earthquake Criteria. 320p. 1985. pap. 16.50 (ISBN 0-309-03532-5). Natl Acad Pr.
Peterson, Elmer T. Big Dam Foolishness. 1954. 9.50 (ISBN 0-8159-5107-8). Devin.
Symposium on Inland Waterways for Navigation, Flood Control & Water Diversions. Inland Waterways for Navigation, Flood Control & Water Diversions: Third Annual Symposium of the Waterways, Harbors & Coastal Engineering Division of ASCE, Colorado State University, Fort Collins, Colorado, August 10-12, 1976, 2 vols. Vol. 1. pap. 160.00 (ISBN 0-317-28778-8, 2017762); Vol. 2. pap. 160.00 (ISBN 0-317-28779-6). Bks Demand UMI.

FLOODS

see also Flood Control; Reclamation of Land; Rivers;
also subdivision floods under names of rivers, cities, etc.

Brown, J. P. The Economic Effects of Floods. LC 72-86100. (Lecture Notes in Economics & Mathematical Systems: Vol. 70). v, 87p. 1972. pap. 9.00 (ISBN 0-387-05925-3). Springer-Verlag.
Burton, Ian, et al. The Human Ecology of Coastal Flood Hazards in Megalopolis. LC 68-57967. (Research Papers Ser.: No. 115). 196p. 1968. pap. 10.00 (ISBN 0-89065-023-3). U Chicago Dept Geog.
Clark, Champ. Flood. (Planet Earth Ser.). 1982. 14.95 (ISBN 0-8094-4308-2). Time-Life.
Eckert, Allan W. A Time of Terror: The Great Dayton Flood. LC 65-12444. (Illus.). 341p. 1981. Repr. of 1965 ed. 9.95 (ISBN 0-913428-02-7). Landfall Pr.
Institution of Civil Engineers Staff, ed. Flood Studies Conference. 112p. 1975. 50.25x (ISBN 0-7277-0014-6). Am Soc Civil Eng.
--Flood Studies Report - Five Years on. 166p. 1981. 48.00x (ISBN 0-7277-0120-7). Am Soc Civil Eng.
--Floods & Reservoir Safety: An Engineering Guide. 64p. 1978. pap. 10.00x (ISBN 0-7277-0033-2). Am Soc Civil Eng.
Kozlowski, T. T. & Riker, A. J., eds. Flooding & Plant Growth. LC 83-15811. (Physiological Ecology Ser.). 1984. 60.00 (ISBN 0-12-424120-4). Acad Pr.
Martin, John H., ed. The Corning Flood: Museum Under Water. LC 77-73627. (Illus.). 72p. 1977. pap. 6.00 (ISBN 0-87290-063-0). Corning.
Penning-Rowsell, Edmund C., et al. Floods & Drainage: British Policies for Hazard Reduction, Agricultural Improvement & Wetland Conservation. (Risks & Hazards Ser.: No. 2). (Illus.). 192p. 1985. text ed. 30.00x (ISBN 0-04-627001-9). Allen Unwin.
Schultz, E. F., et al, eds. Floods & Droughts: Proceedings. LC 73-80676. 1973. 21.00 (ISBN 0-918334-03-9). WRP.
Shank, W. H. Great Floods of Pennsylvannia. 1981. 3.75 (ISBN 0-933788-38-X). Am Canal & Transport.
Tufty, Barbara. One Thousand & One Questions Answered about Earthquakes, Avalanches, Floods, & Other Natural Disasters. LC 78-51736. 1978. lib. bdg. 12.50x (ISBN 0-88307-612-8). Gannon.
--One Thousand & One Questions Answered about Earthquakes, Avalanches, Floods & Other Natural Disasters. 14.25 (ISBN 0-8446-5826-X). Peter Smith.

FLOOR COVERINGS

Crawshaw, G. H. & Ince, J. Textile Floorcoverings. 84p. 1977. 70.00x (ISBN 0-686-63800-X). State Mutual Bk.
Gray, Jerry E. Floor Covering: The Only Complete Installation Guide. LC 83-70255. (Illus.). 188p. 1983. pap. 12.95 (ISBN 0-9610814-0-6). Cameo Pub.
Hilado, Carlos J., ed. Flooring & Floor Covering Materials, Vol. 12. LC 73-82115. (Fire & Flammability Ser.). (Illus.). 1976. pap. 9.95x (ISBN 0-87762-172-1). Technomic.
Sunset Editors, ed. Flooring: Do it Yourself. LC 81-82872. (Illus.). 112p. (Orig.). 1982. pap. 4.95 (ISBN 0-376-01141-6). Sunset-Lane.

FLOORING

see also Floor Coverings

Hilado, Carlos J., ed. Flooring & Floor Covering Materials, Vol. 12. LC 73-82115. (Fire & Flammability Ser.). (Illus.). 1976. pap. 9.95x (ISBN 0-87762-172-1). Technomic.
Sunset Editors, ed. Flooring: Do it Yourself. LC 81-82872. (Illus.). 112p. (Orig.). 1982. pap. 4.95 (ISBN 0-376-01141-6). Sunset-Lane.

FLOORS

see also Flooring

Design of Industrial Floors. 178p. 1983. 24.00 (ISBN 0-317-37034-0); members 18.00 (ISBN 0-317-37035-9). ACI.
Off Center Spliced Floor Joists, Vol. 4. (Research Report Ser.). 58p. 1982. pap. 8.00 (ISBN 0-86718-143-5); pap. 6.00 members. Natl Assn Home.
Time Life Books Editors. Floors & Stairways. (Home Repair Ser.). (Illus.). 1978. 11.95 (ISBN 0-8094-2394-4). Time-Life.

FLOORS, CONCRETE

Slab Thickness Design for Industrial Floors on Grade. 1976. pap. 1.25 (ISBN 0-89312-158-4, IS195D). Portland Cement.

FLOORS AND FLOORING

American Institute of Maintenance. Floor Care Guide. 149p. 1982. pap. 5.95x (ISBN 0-9609052-1-9). Am Inst Maint.
Fairchild Market Research Division. Soft Surface Floor Coverings. (Fairchild Fact Files Ser.). (Illus.). 51p. 1982. pap. 15.00 (ISBN 0-87005-421-X). Fairchild.
Salter, W. L. Floors & Floor Maintenance. (Illus.). 360p. 1974. 18.50 (ISBN 0-85334-586-4, Pub. by Elsevier Applied Sci England). Elsevier.

FLORA

see Botany; Plants

FLORA, ANTARCTIC

see Botany–Antarctic Regions

FLORA, ARCTIC

see Botany–Arctic Regions

FLORICULTURE

see also Annuals (Plants); Bulbs; Flowers; Greenhouses; Orchid Culture; Perennials; Plant-Breeding; Plant Propagation
also particular varieties of plants and flowers, e.g. Aquatic Plants, Chrysanthemums, Climbing Plants, Dahlias, Roses

Brickell, C., et al. Petaloid Monocotyledons: Horticultural & Botanical Research. (Linnean Society Symposium Ser.: No.8). 1980. 75.00 (ISBN 0-12-133950-5). Acad Pr.
Carter, Jack, ed. Sunflower Science & Technology. 1978. 17.50 (ISBN 0-89118-054-0). Am Soc Agron.
Janick, Jules, ed. Horticultural Reviews, Vol. 1. (Horticultural Reviews Ser.). (Illus.). 1979. lib. bdg. 45.00 (ISBN 0-87055-314-3). AVI.
Larson, Roy A. Introduction to Floriculture. 1980. 29.50 (ISBN 0-12-437650-9). Acad Pr.
Laurie, Alex, et al. Commercial Flower Forcing. 8th ed. (Illus.). 1979. text ed. 39.95x (ISBN 0-07-036633-0). McGraw.
Mastalerz, John W. The Greenhouse Environment: The Effect of Environmental Factors on Flower Crops. LC 77-6793. 629p. 1977. 39.50x (ISBN 0-471-57606-9). Wiley.
Miller, H. A. & Whittier, H. O. Prodromus Florae Hepaticarum Polynesiae. (Bryophytorum Bibliotheca Ser.: Vol. 25). 422p. 1983. lib. bdg. 52.50x (ISBN 3-7682-1373-0). Lubrecht & Cramer.
Nelson, Kennard S. Flower & Plant Production in the Greenhouse. 3rd ed. LC 77-79741. (Illus.). 336p. 1978. 19.35 (ISBN 0-8134-1965-4); text ed. 14.50x. Interstate.
Phillips, Harry R. Growing & Propagating Wild Flowers. Moore, J. Kenneth, ed. LC 84-25734. (Illus.). x, 331p. 1985. 24.95 (ISBN 0-8078-1648-5); pap. 14.95 (ISBN 0-8078-4131-5). U of NC Pr.
Roberts, Marvin L. & Stuckey, Ronald L. Bibliography of Theses & Dissertations on Ohio Floristics & Vegetation in Ohio Colleges & Universities. 1974. 2.00 (ISBN 0-86727-074-8). Ohio Bio Survey.
Roest, S. Flowering & Vegetative Propagation of Pyrethrum (Chrysanthemum Cinerariaefolium Vis.) in Vivo & in Vitro. (Agricultural Research Reports: No. 860). (Illus.). 1976. pap. 14.00 (ISBN 90-220-0622-0, PDC35, PUDOC). Unipub.

FLOTATION

Fuerstenau, M. C. & Miller, J. D. Chemistry of Flotation. LC 84-52209. (Illus.). 177p. 1985. 22.00x (ISBN 0-89520-436-3, 436-3). Soc Mining Eng.
Fuerstenau, M. C., ed. Flotation, 2 vols. LC 76-19745. 1976. 39.00x (ISBN 0-89520-032-5). Soc Mining Eng.
Glembotskii, V. A., et al. Flotation. LC 63-21692. (Illus.). 1963. 37.00x (ISBN 0-911184-07-4). Primary.
Ives, K. J. The Scientific Basis of Flotation. 1984. lib. bdg. 56.00 (ISBN 90-247-2907-6, Pub. by Martinus Nijhoff Netherlands). Kluwer Academic.
Leja, Jan. Surface Chemistry of Froth Flotation. 744p. 1981. 89.50x (ISBN 0-306-40588-1, Plenum Pr). Plenum Pub.
Plaksin, I. N., ed. Flotation Properties of Rare Metal Minerals. LC 67-16333. (Illus.). 91p. 1967. 8.75x (ISBN 0-911184-03-1). Primary.
Ranney, M. W., ed. Flotation Agents & Processes: Technology & Applications. LC 80-19191. (Chemical Tech. Rev. 172). (Illus.). 372p. 1981. 48.00 (ISBN 0-8155-0821-2). Noyes.
Schulze, W. J. & Hans, J. M. Physico-Chemical Elementary Processes in Flotation: An Analysis from the Point of View of Colloid Science Including Process Engineering Considerations. (Developments in Numeral Processing Ser.: Vol. 4). 320p. 1984. 67.50 (ISBN 0-444-99643-5, I-400-83). Elsevier.

FLOUNDERS

see Flatfishes

FLOUR

see also Corn; Grain; Oats; Wheat

D'Appolonia, B. L. & Kunerth, W. H. The Farinograph Handbook. 3rd ed. 80p. 1984. 33.50 (ISBN 0-913250-37-6). Am Assn Cereal Chem.

FLOUR AND FEED TRADE

American Feed Manufacturers Association. Feed Manufacturing Technology. Pfost, Harry, ed. 1976. 50.00 (ISBN 0-686-00374-8). AG Pr.

FLOUR MILLS

Bennett, Richard & Elton, John. History of Corn Milling, 4 Vols. (Illus.). 1964. Repr. of 1904 ed. Set. 91.00 (ISBN 0-8337-0230-0). B Franklin.
Colonial Williamsburg Foundation Staff. Miller in Eighteenth Century Virginia. (Williamsburg Craft Ser). (Illus.). 32p. (Orig.). 1958. pap. 1.25 (ISBN 0-910412-19-7). Williamsburg.
Eastman, P. An End to Pounding: A New Mechanical Flour Milling System in Use in Africa. (Eng. & Fr.). 64p. 1980. pap. 5.00 (ISBN 0-88936-246-7, IDRC152, IDRC). Unipub.
Evans, Oliver. The Young Mill-Wright & Miller's Guide. LC 72-5047. (Technology & Society Ser.). (Illus.). 438p. 1972. Repr. of 1850 ed. 32.00 (ISBN 0-405-04699-5). Ayer Co Pubs.
Kuhlman, Charles B. Development of the Flour Milling Industry in the United States. LC 68-56240. Repr. of 1929 ed. 29.50x (ISBN 0-678-00932-5). Kelley.
McGrain, John W. Grist Mills in Baltimore County, Maryland. (Baltimore County Heritage Publication). (Illus.). 40p. 1980. pap. 4.95 (ISBN 0-937076-00-7). Baltimore Co Pub Lib.
Moritz, L. A. Grain-Mills & Flour in Classical Antiquity. Finley, Moses, ed. LC 79-4994. (Ancient Economic History Ser.). (Illus.). 1980. Repr. of 1958 ed. lib. bdg. 24.50x (ISBN 0-405-12381-7). Ayer Co Pubs.

FLOW, MULTIPHASE

see Multiphase Flow

FLOW, TWO-PHASE

see Two-Phase Flow

FLOW CHARTS

Agarwal, K. K. Programming with Structured Flowcharts. 160p. 1984. pap. 12.00. Van Nos Reinhold.
Agarwal, Krishna K. Programming with Structured Flowcharts. 142p. 1984. pap. 12.00 (ISBN 0-89433-226-0). Petrocelli.
Arjani, K. A. Structured Programming Flowcharts. 1978. pap. text ed. 6.95 (ISBN 0-89669-000-8). Collegium Bk Pubs.
Asanuma, T. Flow Visualization. 1979. 69.50 (ISBN 0-07-002378-6). McGraw.
Benedek, P., ed. Steady-State Flow-Sheeting of Chemical Plants. (Chemical Engineering Monographs: Vol. 12). 410p. 1981. 72.50 (ISBN 0-444-99765-2). Elsevier.
Bohl, Marilyn. Flowcharting Techniques. 208p. 1971. pap. text ed. 11.95 (ISBN 0-574-16096-5, 13-1440). SRA.

Boillot, Michel H., et al. Essentials of Flowcharting. 4th. ed. 176p. 1985. pap. text ed. write for info. (ISBN 0-697-00420-1). Wm C Brown.
Clayton, C. G., ed. Modern Developments in Flow Measurement: Proceedings of the International Conference Held at Harwell, 21st-23rd September, 1971. LC 73-173002. (PPL Conference Publication Ser.: No. 10). (Illus.). pap. 103.80 (ISBN 0-317-09262-6, 2011896). Bks Demand UMI.
DeMarco, Tom. Structured Analysis & System Specification. LC 78-51285. (Illus.). 368p. (Orig.). 1979. pap. 27.50 (ISBN 0-917072-07-3). Yourdon.
Edwards, Perry. Flowcharting & FORTRAN IV. (Illus.). 132p. 1973. 14.15 (ISBN 0-07-019042-9, G). McGraw.
Edwards, Perry & Broadwell, Bruce. Flowcharting & BASIC. 214p. (Orig.). 1974. pap. text ed. 11.95 (ISBN 0-15-527661-1, HC). HarBraceJ.
Farina, Mario V. Flowcharting. 1970. pap. 14.95 ref. ed. (ISBN 0-13-322750-2). P-H.
Flow Diagrams. (Fossil Power Plant Startup Training: Module 4). (Illus.). 316p. 1984. pap. text ed. 12.00x spiral binding (ISBN 0-87683-361-X). G P Courseware.
Flowchart Symbols & Their Usage in Micrographics: ANSI-AIIM MS4-1972 (R1978) (Standards & Recommended Practices Ser.). 21p. 1972. pap. 6.00 (ISBN 0-89258-003-8, M004); pap. 5.25 member. Assn Inform & Image Mgmt.
Haskell, Richard E. FORTRAN Programming Using Structured Flowcharts. LC 77-23931. 320p. 1978. pap. text ed. 19.95 (ISBN 0-574-21135-7, 13-4135). SRA.
Hecht, Matthew S. Flow Analysis of Computer Programs. (Programming Languages Ser.: Vol. 5). 232p. 1977. 30.75 (ISBN 0-444-00210-3, North Holland). Elsevier.
I Know Flow Charting. (First Look Bks.). 1983. pap. 2.50 (ISBN 0-440-04153-8). Dell.
Jones, Jerry L. Structured Programming Logic: A Flowcharting Approach. (Illus.). 144p. 1986. pap. text ed. 17.95 (ISBN 0-318-11865-3). P H.
Kazlauskas, Edward. Flow Charting for Information Services. (Consulting Report Ser.). (Illus.). 75p. (Orig.). 1983. pap. text ed. 18.50x (ISBN 0-913203-06-8). Pacific Info.
McQuigg, James D. & Harness, Alta M. Flowcharting. (Modern Mathematics Ser). (Illus.). 1970. pap. 7.08 (ISBN 0-395-03244-X). HM.
Merzkirch, W. Flow Visualization. 1974. 67.00 (ISBN 0-12-491350-4). Acad Pr.
Passen, Barry J. Program Flowcharting for Business Data Processing. LC 77-25509. 251p. 1978. pap. text ed. 29.00 (ISBN 0-471-01410-9). Wiley.
Patankar, S. V., et al, eds. Numerical Prediction of Flow, Heat Transfer Turbulence, & Combustion: Selected Works of Professor D. Brian Spalding. LC 83-12172. 444p. 1983. 100.00 (ISBN 0-08-030937-2, 11). Pergamon.
Patient Care Magazine. Patient Care Flow Chart Manual. 3rd ed. 1982. 42.95 (ISBN 0-87489-295-3). Med Economics.
Schriber, Thomas J. Fundamentals of Flowcharting. LC 79-21692. 1981. pap. 13.50 (ISBN 0-89874-023-1). Krieger.
--Fundamentals of Flowcharting. LC 73-91159. pap. 34.30 (ISBN 0-317-08459-3, 2011886). Bks Demand UMI.
Shelly, Gary B. & Cashman, Thomas J. Introduction to Flowcharting & Computer Programming Logic. LC 72-95674. (Illus.). 251p. 1972. pap. text ed. 21.95 (ISBN 0-88236-345-X). Anaheim Pub Co.
Singlemann, Jay & Longhurst, Jean. Business Programming Logic: A Structured Approach. 2nd ed. (Illus.). 288p. 1982. text ed. 18.95. P-H.
Stern, Nancy. Flowcharting: A Tool for Understanding Computer Logic. LC 75-11600. (Self Teaching Guides Ser.). 341p. 1975. pap. 9.95 (ISBN 0-471-82331-7). Wiley.
Structured Analysis & System Specification. 1979. 37.50 (ISBN 0-13-854380-1). P-H.
Symposium on Flow, Its Measurement & Control in Science & Industry, Pittsburgh, Pa., 1971. Flow, Its Measurement & Control in Science & Industry. Dowdell, Rodger B., ed. LC 74-77995. Vol. 1, Pt. 1. pap. 125.30 (ISBN 0-317-10565-5, 2051607); Vol. 1, Pt. 2. pap. 159.00 (ISBN 0-317-10566-3); Vol. 1, Pt. 3. pap. 137.00 (ISBN 0-317-10567-1). Bks Demand UMI.
Van Hoozer, Helen L. & Ruther, Lavonne M. Introduction to Charting. 151p. 1982. pap. text ed. 8.75 (ISBN 0-397-54400-6, 64-03414, Lippincott Nursing). Lippincott.
Wen-Jei Yang, ed. Flow Visualization Three. LC 84-19737. (Illus.). 800p. 1985. 95.00 (ISBN 0-89116-377-8). Hemisphere Pub.
Westerberg, A. W., et al. Process Flowsheeting. LC 78-51682. (Illus.). 1979. 39.50 (ISBN 0-521-22043-2). Cambridge U Pr.

FLOW GRAPHS
see Flowgraphs

FLOW METERS
American Water Works Association. Water Meters: Selection, Installation, Testing, & Maintenance - M6. (AWWA Manuals). (Illus.). 112p. 1973. pap. text ed. 9.60 (ISBN 0-89867-064-0). Am Water Wks Assn.
Clayton, C. G., ed. Modern Developments in Flow Measurement: Proceedings of the International Conference Held at Harwell, 21st-23rd September, 1971. LC 73-173002. (PPL Conference Publication Ser.: No. 10). (Illus.). pap. 103.80 (ISBN 0-317-09262-6, 2011896). Bks Demand UMI.
DeCarlo, Joseph P. Fundamentals of Flow Measurement: An Independent Learning Module of the Instrument Society of America. LC 83-12686. 288p. 1984. text ed. 39.95x (ISBN 0-87664-627-5). Instru Soc.
Dowden, R. Rosemary, ed. Fluid Flow Measurement Bibliography. 1972. microfiche 24.00x (ISBN 0-900983-21-3, Dist. by Air Science Co.). BHRA Fluid.
Fundamentals of Eddy Current Testing, Module 32-5. (Nondestructive Examination Techniques II Ser.). (Illus.). 46p. 1979. spiral bdg. 7.00x (ISBN 0-87683-102-1). G P Courseware.
Hayward, Alan T. Flowmeters: A Basic Guide & Source-Book for Users. LC 79-15530. 197p. 1979. 44.95x (ISBN 0-470-26732-1). Halsted Pr.
PTC 19.5-1972 Application, Part Two of Fluid Meters: Interim Supplement on Instruments & Apparatus. 1972. pap. text ed. 14.00 (ISBN 0-685-30666-6, G00018). ASME.
Scott, R. W., ed. Developments in Flow Measurement, Vol. 1. (Illus.). 333p. 1982. 72.25 (ISBN 0-85334-976-2, Pub. by Elsevier Applied Sci England). Elsevier.
Symposium on Flow, Its Measurement & Control in Science & Industry, Pittsburgh, Pa., 1971. Flow, Its Measurement & Control in Science & Industry. Dowdell, Rodger B., ed. LC 74-77995. Vol. 1, Pt. 1. pap. 125.30 (ISBN 0-317-10565-5, 2051607); Vol. 1, Pt. 2. pap. 159.00 (ISBN 0-317-10566-3); Vol. 1, Pt. 3. pap. 137.00 (ISBN 0-317-10567-1). Bks Demand UMI.

FLOW OF GAS
see Gas Flow

FLOW OF WATER
see Hydraulics

FLOWCHARTS
see Flow Charts

FLOWERING OF PLANTS
see Plants, Flowering Of

FLOWERING PLANTS
see Angiosperms

FLOWERING TREES
Donkin, R. A. Manna: An Historical Geography. (Biogeographica Ser.: No. 17). (Illus.). vii, 160p. 1980. lib. bdg. 47.50 (ISBN 90-6193-218-1, Pub. by Junk Pubs Netherlands). Kluwer Academic.
Flowering Trees. 2.25 (ISBN 0-686-21136-7). Bklyn Botanic.
Lancaster, Roy. Arbres, ornements de nos jardins. (Collection "Flore"). (Fr., Illus.). 145p. 1974. 15.95x (ISBN 2-03-074704-1). Larousse.

FLOWERS
see also Annuals (Plants); Botany; Fertilization of Plants; Floriculture; Plants; Plants, Flowering of; Wild Flowers
also names of flowers, e.g. Carnations, Roses, Violets
Arnberger, Leslie P. Flowers of the Southwest Mountains. 6th ed. Jackson, Earl, ed. LC 74-84444. (Popular Ser.: No. 7). 1974. pap. 7.50 (ISBN 0-911408-00-2). SW Pks Mnmts.
--Flowers of the Southwest Mountains. rev. ed. Priehs, T. J., ed. Dodson, Carolyn. LC 81-86380. 1983. pap. 7.95 (ISBN 0-911408-61-4). SW Pks Mnmts.
Baker, Douglas. Bach Flower Remedy Repertoires, Pts. 1 & 2. 1982. Set. 50.00x (ISBN 0-686-45415-4, Pub. by Baker Pubns England); Pt. 1. 30.00 (ISBN 0-906006-60-0); Pt. 2. 30.00 (ISBN 0-906006-61-9). State Mutual Bk.
Baker, K. Wild Flowers of Western Australia. (Illus.). 1973. 6.00 (ISBN 0-912728-45-0). Newbury Bks.
Beek, M. & Foster, D. Wild Flowers of South Australia. (Illus.). 1973. 6.00 (ISBN 0-912728-46-9). Newbury Bks.
Blundell. Wild Flowers of Kenya. 29.95 (ISBN 0-00-219317-5, Collins Pub England). Greene.
Carr, Samuel, ed. Poetry of Flowers. LC 77-26728. 1977. 7.50 (ISBN 0-8008-6393-3). Taplinger.
Compton, Joan. Enjoy Your Flowers. 14.50 (ISBN 0-392-02805-0, LTB). Sportshelf.
Croft, J. R. & Kanis, A. Handbooks of the Flora of Papua New Guinea, Vol. II. (Illus.). 276p. 1982. text ed. 37.95x (ISBN 0-522-84204-6, Pub. by Melbourne U Pr Australia). Intl Spec Bk.
Darwin, Charles R. The Different Forms of Flowers on Plants of the Same Species. LC 72-3900. (Illus.). viii, 352p. 1972. 42.50 (ISBN 0-404-08414-1). AMS Pr.
Davis, P. H. & Cullen, J. The Identification of Flowering Plant Families. LC 78-8125. (Illus.). 1979. 29.95 (ISBN 0-521-22111-0); pap. 8.95x (ISBN 0-521-29359-6). Cambridge U Pr.
Dean, Blanche, et al. Wildflowers of Alabama & Adjoining States. LC 73-10585. (Illus.). 230p. 1973. pap. 14.75 1983 (ISBN 0-8173-0147-X). U of Ala Pr.
Diamond, Denise. Living with Flowers: A Guide to Bringing Flowers into Your Daily Life. LC 81-18879. (Illus.). 288p. 1982. 19.95 (ISBN 0-688-00990-5). Morrow.
--Living with the Flowers: A Guide to Bringing Flowers into Your Daily Life. LC 81-18552. (Illus.). 288p. (Orig.). 1982. pap. 11.95 (ISBN 0-688-00991-3, Quill NY). Morrow.
Durant, Mary. Who Named the Daisy? Who Named the Rose? A Roving Dictionary of North American Wildflowers. LC 83-1781. (Illus.). 224p. 1983. pap. 8.95 (ISBN 0-312-92944-7). Congdon & Weed.
Eichler, A. W. Bluethendiagramme, 2 vols. (Illus.). 1954. 57.75 (ISBN 3-87429-003-4). Lubrecht & Cramer.
Erdtman, G. World Pollen Flora, 4 vols. Incl. Vol. 1. Coriariaceae. 1970. pap.; Vol. 2. Gyrostemonaceae. Prijanto, B. 1970. pap.; Vol. 3. Batidacene. Prijanto, B. 1970. pap.; Vol. 4. Globularioceae. Praglowski, J. & Gyllander, K. 1971. pap.. (Illus.). Set. pap. 39.95x (ISBN 0-02-844210-5). Hafner.
Fish, Margery. Cottage Garden Flowers. 208p. 1980. pap. 7.95 (ISBN 0-571-11462-8). Faber & Faber.
Flora: Enciclopedia Salvat De la Jardineria, 12 vols. (Espn.). 3600p. 1977. Set. 336.00 (ISBN 84-345-3786-9, S-50537). French & Eur.
Flower Essence Society. The Flower Essence Journal, Issue 1. rev. ed. Katz, Richard A., ed. (Illus.). 36p. 1982. pap. 3.00 (ISBN 0-943986-01-X). Gold Circle.
--The Flower Essence Journal, Issue 2. rev. ed. Katz, Richard A., ed. (Illus.). 36p. 1983. pap. 3.00 (ISBN 0-943986-02-8). Gold Circle.
--The Flower Essence Journal, Issue 3. rev. ed. Katz, Richard A., ed. (Illus.). 48p. 1983. pap. 3.00 (ISBN 0-943986-03-6). Gold Circle.
--The Flower Essence Journal, Issue 4. Katz, Richard A. & Kaminski, Patricia A., eds. (Illus.). 80p. (Orig.). 1982. pap. 7.00 (ISBN 0-943986-04-4). Gold Circle.
Gibbons, Bob. How Flowers Work: A Guide to Plant Biology. (Illus.). 160p. 1984. 15.95 (ISBN 0-7137-1278-3, Pub. by Blandford Pr England). Sterling.
Grey-Wilson & Blamey. The Alpine Flowers of Britain & Europe. 1979. pap. 19.95 (ISBN 0-00-219288-8, Collins Pub England). Greene.
Guedes, M. Teratological Modifications & the Meaning of Flower Parts. (International Bioscience Monographs: No. 7). 62p. 1979. 8.00 (ISBN 0-88065-093-1, Pub. by Messers Today & Tomorrows Printers & Publishers India). Scholarly Pubns.
Halevy, Abraham H., ed. CRC Handbook of Flowering. 584p. 1985. Set. 624.75. Vol. I (ISBN 0-8493-3911-1). Vol. II (ISBN 0-8493-3912-X). CRC Pr.
Hargreaves, Dorothy & Hargreaves, Bob. Hawaii Blossoms. LC 58-46974. (Illus.). 1958. pap. 3.00 (ISBN 0-910690-01-4). Hargreaves.
--Tropical Blossoms of the Caribbean. LC 60-15513. (Illus.). 1960. pap. 3.00 (ISBN 0-910690-03-0). Hargreaves.
Hay, Roy & Synge, Patrick M. The Color Dictionary of Flowers & Plants for Home & Garden. (Illus.). 584p. 1982. pap. 12.95 (ISBN 0-517-52456-2). Crown.
Heiser, Charles B. The Sunflower. LC 74-15906. 1980. Repr. of 1976 ed. 10.95 (ISBN 0-8061-1229-8). U of Okla Pr.
Kelland, Rufus A. The Illustrated Book in Full Colors of Pansies, Violas & Violets. (Illus.). 117p. 1981. 195.00 (ISBN 0-86650-013-8). Gloucester Art.
Mathias, Mildred E., ed. Flowering Plants in the Landscape. LC 81-16310. (Illus.). 215p. 1982. 16.95 (ISBN 0-520-04350-2). U of Cal Pr.
Miller, Millie. Saguaro: The Desert Flower Book. new ed. (Orig.). 1982. pap. 3.95 (ISBN 0-933472-69-2). Johnson Bks.
Moggi, Guido, et al. Simon & Schuster's Guide to Garden Flowers. Schuler, Stanley, ed. (Illus.). 1983. 19.95 (ISBN 0-671-46674-7); pap. 9.95 (ISBN 0-671-46678-X). S&S.
Mohlenbrock, Robert H. Flowering Plants: Flowering Rush to Rushes. LC 69-16117. (Illustrated Flora of Illinois Ser.). (Illus.). 286p. 1970. 22.95x (ISBN 0-8093-0407-4). S Ill U Pr.
Oldham, Kathleen I. The Annals of Flowerland. 1982. 7.95 (ISBN 0-533-05235-1). Vantage.
Percival, M. Floral Biology. 1965. pap. 7.75 (ISBN 0-08-010609-9). Pergamon.
Perrero, Laurie. World of Tropical Flowers. LC 76-12926. (Illus.). 64p. (Orig.). 1976. pap. 3.50 (ISBN 0-89317-008-9). Windward Pub.
Perry, Frances, ed. Simon & Schuster's Complete Guide to Plants & Flowers. (Illus.). 1976. pap. 10.95 (ISBN 0-671-22247-3). S&S.
Pizetti, I. & Cocker, H. Flowers: A Guide for Your Garden, 2 vols. (Illus.). 24.95 set (ISBN 0-517-22044-X). Crown.
Polunin, O. & Everard. Flowers of Europe: A Field Guide. 1981. 50.00x (ISBN 0-686-78775-7, Pub. by RHS Ent England). State Mutual Bk.
Polunin, Oleg. The Concise Flowers of Europe. (Illus.). 1972. pap. 14.95x (ISBN 0-19-217630-7). Oxford U Pr.
--Flowers of Greece & the Balkans: A Field Guide. 1980. 125.00x (ISBN 0-19-217626-9). Oxford U Pr.
Polunin, Oleg & Huxley, Anthony. Flowers of the Mediterranean. LC 79-670242. (Illus.). 260p. 1979. 15.95 (ISBN 0-7011-1029-5, Pub. by Chatto & Windus); pap. 9.95 (ISBN 0-7011-2284-6). Merrimack Pub Cir.
Smith, L. D. Flowers from Foreign Fields. PLB 59.95 (ISBN 0-8490-0175-7). Gordon Pr.
Sprengel, Christian K. Das Entdeckte Geheimnis der Natur Im Bau & der Befruchtung der Blumen. 1973. Repr. of 1793 ed. 35.00 (ISBN 3-7682-0828-1). Lubrecht & Cramer.
Stocken, C. M. Andalusian Flowers & Countryside. pap. 10.00 (ISBN 0-8283-1326-1). Branden Pub Co.
Synge, P. & Hay, R. Dictionary of Garden Plants & Flowers in Colour: May 1981. 1981. 60.00x (ISBN 0-686-78769-2, Pub. by RHS Ent England). State Mutual Bk.
Urmi-Koenig, K. Bluetentragende Spross-Systeme Einiger Chenopodiaceae. (No.63, Dissertationes Botanica). (Illus.). 240p. pap. text ed. 16.00x (ISBN 3-7682-1322-6). Lubrecht & Cramer.
Vilmorin, Roger de. L' Encyclopedie Des Fleurs et Des Jardins, 3 vols. (Fr.). 2000p. 1975. Set. 95.00 (ISBN 0-686-57140-1, M-6197). French & Eur.
Watts, Phoebe. Redwood Region Flower Finder. (Illus.). 1979. pap. 1.50 (ISBN 0-912550-08-2). Nature Study.
White, Helen A. & Williams, Maxcine, eds. The Alaska-Yukon Wild Flowers Guide. LC 74-79085. (Illus.). 218p. 1974. pap. 12.95 (ISBN 0-88240-032-0). Alaska Northwest.
Wills, Mary M. & Irwin, Howard S. Roadside Flowers of Texas. (Elma Dill Russell Spencer Foundation Ser.: No. 1). (Illus.). 257p. 1961. pap. 9.95 (ISBN 0-292-77009-X). U of Tex Pr.
Withering, William. An Account of the Foxglove & Some of Its Uses. LC 77-6995. 1977. Repr. of 1785 ed. lib. bdg. 30.00 (ISBN 0-89341-146-9). Longwood Pub Group.

FLOWERS, FORCING OF
see Forcing (Plants)

FLOWERS, WILD
see Wild Flowers

FLOWGRAPHS
Ackers, P., et al. Weirs & Fumes for Flow Measurement. LC 78-317. 327p. 1978. cloth 91.95x (ISBN 0-471-99637-8, Pub. by Wiley-Interscience). Wiley.
Furman, William B. Continuous Flow Analysis: Theory & Practice. (Clinical & Biochemical Analysis Ser.: Vol. 3). 1976. 59.75 (ISBN 0-8247-6320-3). Dekker.
Hecht, Matthew S. Flow Analysis of Computer Programs. (Programming Languages Ser.: Vol. 5). 232p. 1977. 30.75 (ISBN 0-444-00210-3, North Holland). Elsevier.
Spencer, E. A., ed. Flow Measurement. (Proceedings of FLOMEKO 1983, IMEKO Conference on Flow Measurement, Budapest, Hungary, 20-22 September 1983). 328p. 1985. 60.00 (ISBN 0-444-87562-X, North-Holland). Elsevier.

FLOWMETERS
see Flow Meters

FLOWOFF
see Runoff

FLUID AMPLIFIERS
Brock, T. E., ed. Fluidics Applications Bibliography. 1968. text ed. 23.00x (ISBN 0-900983-00-0, Dist. by Air Science Co.). BHRA Fluid.
Fluidics Quarterly, Vol. 1. (Illus.). 1968-69. 85.00 (ISBN 0-88232-001-7). Delbridge Pub Co.
Fluidics Quarterly, Vol. 2. (Illus.). 1970. 125.00 (ISBN 0-88232-006-8). Delbridge Pub Co.
Fluidics Quarterly, Vol. 3. (Illus.). 1971. 100.00 (ISBN 0-88232-012-2). Delbridge Pub Co.
Fluidics Quarterly, Vol. 9. (Illus.). 1977. 115.00 (ISBN 0-88232-042-4). Delbridge Pub Co.
Humphrey, E. F. & Tarumoto, D. H., eds. Fluidics: A Comprehensive Examination. rev ed. 1968. 28.00 (ISBN 0-88232-000-9). Delbridge Pub Co.

FLUID BED PROCESSES
see Fluidization

Pichal, M., ed. Optical Methods in Dynamics of Fluids & Solids. (International Union of Theoretical & Applied Mechanics). (Illus.). xxii, 383p. 1985. 45.00 (ISBN 0-387-15247-4). Springer-Verlag.
Reynolds, W. C. & MacCormack, R. W., eds. Seventh International Conference on Numerical Methods in Fluid Dynamics. Proceedings. (Lecture Notes in Physics Ser.: Vol. 141). 485p. 1981. pap. 30.00 (ISBN 0-387-10694-4). Springer-Verlag.
Rhodes, E. & Scott, D. E., eds. Cocurrent Gas-Liquid Flow. LC 76-80084. 698p. 1969. 57.50x (ISBN 0-306-30404-X, Plenum Pr). Plenum Pub.
Riggs, H. C. Streamflow Characteristics: Developments in Water Science. (No. 22). 250p. 1985. 53.75 (ISBN 0-444-42480-6). Elsevier.
Roache, Patrick J. Computational Fluid Dynamics. rev. ed. 1976. 26.50 (ISBN 0-913478-05-9). Hermosa.
Robinson, Peter G. Marine Engineer's Guide to Fluid Flow. LC 75-25933. (Illus.). 86p. 1975. pap. 5.00x (ISBN 0-87033-215-5). Cornell Maritime.
Roe, P. L. Numerical Methods in Aeronautical Fluid Dynamics. (IMA Conference Ser.). 1983. 55.50 (ISBN 0-12-592520-4). Acad Pr.
Roedder, Edwin, ed. Fluid Inclusion Research: Proceedings of COFFI, 1973, Vol. 6. 216p. 1973. pap. text ed. 15.00x (ISBN 0-472-02006-4). U of Mich Pr.
--Fluid Inclusion Research: Proceedings of COFFI, 1974, Vol. 7. 300p. 1976. pap. text ed. 15.00x (ISBN 0-472-02007-2). U of Mich Pr.
--Fluid Inclusion Research: Proceedings of COFFI, 1975, Vol. 8. 240p. 1978. pap. text ed. 15.00x (ISBN 0-472-02008-0). U of Mich Pr.
--Fluid Inclusion Research: Proceedings of COFFI, 1975, Vol. 9. 280p. 1978. pap. text ed. 15.00x (ISBN 0-472-02009-9). U of Mich Pr.
Rohsenow, Warren M. & Choi, H. Heat, Mass & Momentum Transfer. (Illus.). 1961. text ed. 41.95 (ISBN 0-13-385187-7). P-H.
Rothfus, Robert R. Working Concepts of Fluid Flow. (Illus.). 96p. (Orig.). pap. 3.75x (ISBN 0-685-23655-2). Bek Tech.
Saad, Michel A. Compressible Fluid Flow. (Illus.). 528p. 1985. text ed. 41.95 (ISBN 0-13-163486-0). P-H.
Sabersky, Rolf H., et al. Fluid Flow: First Course in Fluid Mechanics. 2nd ed. 1971. text ed. write for info. (ISBN 0-02-404970-0). Macmillan.
Second IFAC Symposium on Fluidics. Fluidics Quarterly: Selected Papers, Vol. 3, Issue 4, Pt. 1. 1971. 26.00 (ISBN 0-88232-016-5). Delbridge Pub Co.
Seeger, Raymond J. & Temple, G., eds. Research Frontiers in Fluid Dynamics. LC 65-14246. (Interscience Monographs & Texts in Physics & Astronomy: Vol. 15). pap. 160.00 (ISBN 0-317-08477-1, 2051478). Bks Demand UMI.
Shapiro, A. H. The Dynamics & Thermodynamics of Compressible Fluid Flow, Vol. 1. 647p. 1953. 46.00x (ISBN 0-471-06691-5). Wiley.
Shapiro, Ascher H. The Dynamics & Thermodynamics of Compressible Fluid Flow, Vol. 2. LC 82-17967. 550p. 1983. Repr. of 1954 ed. lib. bdg. 36.00 (ISBN 0-89874-566-7). Krieger.
Shin, Y. W. & Moody, F. J., eds. Fluid Transients & Fluid-Structure Interaction. (PVP Ser.: Vol. 64). 381p. 1982. 60.00 (H00221). ASME.
Shivamoggi, Bhimsen K. Theoretical Fluid Dynamics. 1984. lib. bdg. 78.00 (ISBN 90-247-2999-8, Pub. by Martinus Nijhoff Netherlands). Kluwer Academic.
Short Course Held at the Von Karman Institute for Fluid Dynamics, Rhode-St.-Genese, Belgium, Feb. 11-15, 1974. Progress in Numerical Fluid Dynamics. Wirz, H. J., ed. (Lecture Notes in Physics: Vol. 41). 480p. 1975. pap. 26.00 (ISBN 0-387-07408-2). Springer-Verlag.
Smith, Charles E., ed. Dynamics Exam File. LC 84-24699. (Exam File Ser.). 346p. (Orig.). 1985. pap. 9.95 (ISBN 0-910554-44-7). Engineering.
Sorensen, Smith T., ed. Dynamics & Instability of Fluid Interfaces. (Lecture Notes in Physics: Vol. 105). 1979. pap. 20.00 (ISBN 0-387-09524-1). Springer-Verlag.
Soubbaramayer, J. P., ed. Ninth International Conference on Numerical Methods in Fluid Dynamics. (Lecture Notes in Physics Ser.: Vol. 218). x, 612p. 1985. pap. 32.00 (ISBN 0-387-13917-6). Springer-Verlag.
Specialist Symposium on Geophysical Fluid Dynamics, European Geophysical Society, Fourth Meeting, Munich September, 1977. Proceedings. Davies, P. A. & Roberts, P. H., eds. 156p. 1978. 30.25 (ISBN 0-677-40115-9). Gordon.
Stewart, Harry L. & Storer, John M. Fluid Power. 3rd ed. LC 79-9123. 1980. scp 28.44 (ISBN 0-672-97224-7); scp instructor's manual 3.67 (ISBN 0-672-97226-3); scp student manual 13.24 (ISBN 0-672-97225-5); scp transparency masters 51.43 (ISBN 0-672-97228-X). Bobbs.
Storvick, Truman S. & Sandler, Stanley I., eds. Phase Equilibria & Fluid Properties in the Chemical Industry: Estimation & Correlation. LC 77-13804. (ACS Symposium Ser.: No. 60). 1977. 49.95 (ISBN 0-8412-0393-8). Am Chemical.
Streeter, Victor L. Handbook of Fluid Dynamics. 1961. 84.50 (ISBN 0-07-062178-0). McGraw.
Symposium at Pittsburgh, Penn., June, 1974. Turbulence in Mixing Operations: Theory & Application to Mixing & Reaction. Brodkey, Robert S., ed. 1975. 57.50 (ISBN 0-12-134450-9). Acad Pr.
Symposium in Applied Mathematics, College, Park Md., 1951. Fluid Dynamics. Martin, M. H., ed. LC 50-1183. (Proceedings of Symposia in Applied Mathematics: Vol. 4). 86p. 1953. 24.00 (ISBN 0-8218-1304-8, PSAPM-4). Am Math.
Symposium in Applied Mathematics, New York, 1960. Hydrodynamic Instability: Proceedings. Bellman, R., et al, eds. LC 50-1183. (Vol. 13). 319p. 1962. pap. 25.00 (ISBN 0-8218-1313-7, PSAPM-13). Am Math.
Symposium on Cavity Flows (1975: Minneapolis). Cavity Flows: Presented at the Fluids Engineering Conference, Minneapolis, Minnesota, May 5-7, 1975. Parkin, Blaine R. & Morgan, W. B., eds. LC 75-8089. (Illus.). pap. 36.30 (ISBN 0-317-08133-0, 2016869). Bks Demand UMI.
Symposium On The Dynamics Of Fluids And Plasmas. Dynamics of Fluids & Plasmas: Proceedings. Pai, S. I., ed. 1967. 84.00 (ISBN 0-12-544250-5). Acad Pr.
Symposium on Thermophysical Properties, 8th. Thermophysical Properties of Fluids: Proceedings, 2 Vols, Vol. 1. 1981. 65.00 (I00151). ASME.
Szekely, Julian. Fluid Flow Phenomena in Metals Processing. 1979. 67.50 (ISBN 0-12-680840-6). Acad Pr.
Thomasset, F. Implementation of Finite Element Methods for Navier-Stokes Equations. (Springer Series in Computational Phsyics). (Illus.). 160p. 1981. 36.00 (ISBN 0-387-10771-1). Springer Verlag.
Tipei, Nicolae. Theory of Lubrication: With Applications to Liquid & Gas-Film Lubrication. Gross, William A., ed. 1962. 35.00x (ISBN 0-8047-0028-1). Stanford U Pr.
Tritton, D. J. Physical Fluid Dynamics. 1977. pap. 16.95 (ISBN 0-442-30132-4). Van Nos Reinhold.
Truesdell, C., ed. Continuum Mechanics, 4 vols. Incl. Vol. 1. Mechanical Foundations of Elasticity. 324p. 1966. 46.25x (ISBN 0-677-00820-1); Vol. 2. Rational Mechanics of Materials. 446p. 1965. 54.50x (ISBN 0-677-00830-9); Vol. 3. Foundations of Elasticity Theory. 320p. 1965. 49.95x (ISBN 0-677-00840-6); Vol. 4. Problems of Nonlinear Elasticity. 276p. 1965. 46.25x (ISBN 0-677-00850-3). (International Science Review Ser.). (Illus.). 1965. Gordon.
Turner, J. S. Buoyancy Effects in Fluids. LC 79-7656. (Cambridge Monographs on Mechanics & Applied Mathematics). (Illus.). 1980. pap. 24.95 (ISBN 0-521-29726-5). Cambridge U Pr.
Von Mises, Richard & Friedrichs, K. O. Fluid Dynamics. LC 73-175242. (Applied Mathematical Sciences Ser.: Vol. 5). 360p. 1971. pap. 39.50 (ISBN 0-387-90028-4). Springer-Verlag.
Von Schwind, J. Geophysical Fluid Dynamics for Oceanographers. 1980. 36.95 (ISBN 0-13-352591-0). P-H.
Ward-Smith, A. J. Internal Fluid Flow: The Fluid Dynamics of Flow in Pipes & Ducts. (Illus.). 1980. 98.00x (ISBN 0-19-856325-6). Oxford U Pr.
Wasp, Edward J., et al. Solid-Liquid Flow Slurry Pipeline Transportation. LC 78-75080. 240p. 1979. 44.95x (ISBN 0-87201-809-1). Gulf Pub.
Wegener, Peter P., ed. Nonequilibrium Flows, Vol. 1. LC 71-78829. (Illus.). pap. 68.00 (ISBN 0-317-07990-5, 2055070). Bks Demand UMI.
Wiegel, F. W. Fluid Flow Through Macromolecular Systems. (Lecture Notes in Physics: Vol. 121). 102p. 1980. pap. 13.00 (ISBN 0-387-09973-5). Springer-Verlag.
Wirz, Hans J. & Smolderen, J. J., eds. Numerical Methods in Fluids Dynamics. LC 77-18145. (Series in Thermal & Fluids Engineering). pap. 78.90 (ISBN 0-317-09136-0, 2016697). Bks Demand UMI.
Woods, L. C. The Thermodynamics of Fluid Systems. (Oxford Engineering Science Ser). (Illus.). 1975. 65.00x (ISBN 0-19-856125-3). Oxford U Pr.
Wylie, E. Benjamin & Streeter, Victor L. Fluid Transients. LC 82-84215. 384p. 1983. Repr. of 1978 ed. 25.00x (ISBN 0-9610144-0-7). F E B Pr.
Yanenko, N. & Shokin, Yu. Numerical Methods in Fluid Dynamics. 335p. 1985. pap. 8.95 (ISBN 0-8285-2882-9, Pub by Mir Pubs USSR). Imported Pubns.
Yuan, Shao. Foundations of Fluid Mechanics. 1967. text ed. 38.95 (ISBN 0-13-329813-2). P-H.
Zakin, J. L. & Patterson, C. K., eds. Turbulence in Liquids: Proceedings of the Fourth Biennial Symposium on Turbulence in Liquids. LC 76-52537. 1977. lib. bdg. 35.00 (ISBN 0-89500-000-8). Sci Pr.

FLUID FILM BEARINGS

see also Gas-Lubricated Bearings

Fluid Film Bearing Committee of the Lubrication Division. Topics in Fluid Film Bearing & Rotor Bearing Systems Design & Optimization: Presented at the Design Engineering Conference, Chicago, Ill., April 17-20, 1978. Rohde, S. M., et al, eds. LC 78-52526. pap. 70.00 (ISBN 0-317-11248-1, 2017648). Bks Demand UMI.
Gross, William A., et al. Fluid Film Lubrication. LC 80-36889. 773p. 1980. 57.95x (ISBN 0-471-08357-7). Wiley.
Rohde, S. M., et al, eds. Fundamentals of the Design of Fluid Film Bearings. (Bk. no. H00145). 1979. 24.00 (ISBN 0-685-95760-8). ASME.

FLUID MECHANICS

see also Diaphragms (Mechanical Devices); Fluid Dynamics; Fluids; Hydraulic Engineering; Hydraulics; Hydrodynamics; Hydrometer; Hydrostatics

Albertson, Maurice L., et al. Fluid Mechanics for Engineers. 1960. text ed. 37.95 (ISBN 0-13-322578-X). P-H.
American Society of Mechanical Engineers, et al. Flow Studies in Air & Water Pollution: Presented at the Joint Meeting of the Fluids Engineering Division & the Applied Mechanics Division, Georgia Institute of Technology, Atlanta, GA, June, 1973. Arndt, Roger E., ed. LC 73-80154. pap. 58.00 (ISBN 0-317-11237-6, 2016839). Bks Demand UMI.
American Society of Mechanical Engineering. Fluids Engineering Division. Fluid Mechanics of Combustion: Papers Presented at Joint Fluids Engineering & CSME Conference, Montreal, Quebec, May 13-15, 1974. Dussourd, J. L., et al, eds. LC 74-78505. pap. 68.30 (ISBN 0-317-08509-3, 2051718). Bks Demand UMI.
Anderson, D. A., et al. Computational Fluid Mechanics & Heat Transfer. LC 83-18614. (Series in Computational Methods in Mechanics & Thermal Sciences). 624p. 1984. 45.00 (ISBN 0-07-050328-1). McGraw.
Au-Yang, M. K. & Brown, S. J., Jr., eds. Fluid-Structure Interaction Phenomena in Pressure Vessel & Piping Systems, Series PVP-PB-026. 1977. pap. text ed. 16.00 (ISBN 0-685-86866-4, G00130). ASME.
Au-Yang, M. K., et al, eds. Dynamics of Fluid-Structure Systems in the Energy Industry. (PVP-39). (Orig.). 1979. 30.00 (ISBN 0-685-96305-5, H00153). ASME.
Belytschko, T. & Geers, T. L., eds. Computational Methods for Fluid-Structure Interaction Problems: Presented at the Winter Annual Meeting of the American Society of Mechanical Engineers, Atlanta, Georgia, Nov. 27-Dec. 2, 1977. LC 77-88000. (American Society of Mechanical Engineers Ser. - Applied Mechanics Division: Vol. 26). (Illus.). pap. 43.50 (ISBN 0-317-09990-6, 2011589). Bks Demand UMI.
Bertin, John J. Engineering Fluid Mechanics. (Illus.). 576p. 1984. 38.95 (ISBN 0-13-278812-8). P-H.
Binder, Raymond C. Fluid Mechanics. 5th ed. (Illus.). 448p. 1973. ref. ed. 38.95 (ISBN 0-13-322594-1). P-H.
Bradbury, L. J. & Durst, F., eds. Turbulent Shear Flows Four. (Illus.). 370p. 1985. 58.00 (ISBN 0-387-13744-0). Springer-Verlag.
Buckmaster, J. D., ed. Fluid Mechanics in Energy Conversion. LC 80-65817. (SIAM-SIMS Conference Ser.: No. 7). ix, 315p. 1980. pap. 31.00 (ISBN 0-89871-165-7). Soc Indus-Appl Math.
Cermak, Jack E. Applications of Fluid Mechanics to Wind Engineering: Presented at the Winter Annual Meeting of ASME, New York, N. Y. November 17-21, 1974. pap. 20.00 (ISBN 0-317-08137-3, 2016871). Bks Demand UMI.
Chang, Paul K. Control of Flow Separation: Energy Conservation, Operational Efficiency & Safety. (McGraw-Hill Series in Thermal & Fluids Engineering). (Illus.). 1976. text ed. 65.00x (ISBN 0-07-010513-8). McGraw.
--Recent Development in Flow Separation. LC 83-72431. (Illus.). 300p. 1983. write for info. (ISBN 0-9612410-6-3). P K Chang.
Chapman, R. E. Geology & Water: An Introduction to Fluid Mechanics for Geologists. 1982. 44.50 (ISBN 90-247-2455-4, Pub. by Martinus Nijhoff Netherlands). Kluwer Academic.
Chemical Engineering Magazine. Fluid Movers: Pumps, Compressors, Fans & Blowers. (Chemical Engineering Bks.). (Illus.). 384p. 1980. 39.50 (ISBN 0-07-010769-6). McGraw.
Cheremisinoff, Nicholas P., ed. Encyclopedia of Fluid Mechanics, Vol. 1: Flow Phenomena & Measurement. LC 85-9742. (Illus.). 1500p. 1985. 149.95x (ISBN 0-87201-513-0). Gulf Pub.
--Encyclopedia of Fluid Mechanics, Vol. 2: Dynamics of Single-Fluid Flows & Mixing. LC 85-9742. (Illus.). 1500p. 1985. 149.95x (ISBN 0-87201-514-9). Gulf Pub.
--Encyclopedia of Fluid Mechanics, Vol. 3: Gas-Liquid Flows. (Illus.). 1600p. 1985. 149.95x (ISBN 0-87201-515-7). Gulf Pub.
Chermisinoff, Nicholas P. Fluid Flow: Pumps, Pipes & Channels. LC 81-68034. (Illus.). 702p. 1981. 45.00 (ISBN 0-250-40432-X). Butterworth.
Cherry, R. C., et al, eds. Materials of Construction of Fluid Machinery & Their Relationship to Design & Performance. 104p. 1981. 24.00 (ISBN 0-686-34499-5, H00208). ASME.
Childress, Stephen. Mechanics of Swimming & Flying. LC 80-23364. (Cambridge Studies in Mathematical Biology: No. 2). (Illus.). 170p. 1981. 39.50 (ISBN 0-521-23613-4); pap. 16.95 (ISBN 0-521-28071-0). Cambridge U Pr.
Chorin, A. J. & Marsden, J. E. A Mathematical Introduction to Fluid Mechanics. (Universitexts Ser.). (Illus.). 1979. pap. 22.00 (ISBN 0-387-90406-9). Springer-Verlag.
Chuen-Yen, Chow. An Introduction to Computational Fluid Mechanics. Rev. ed. (Illus.). 400p. 1983. Repr. text ed. 35.00 (ISBN 0-9612302-0-7). Seminole Pub Co.
CISM (International Center for Mechanical Sciences) Fluidic Applications. Belforte, G., ed. (CISM Intl. Centre for Mechanical Sciences, Courses & Lectures Ser.: No. 60). (Illus.). 156p. 1974. pap. 16.90 (ISBN 0-387-81220-2). Springer-Verlag.
--Physiological Fluid Mechanics. Lighthill, J., ed. (CISM Pubns. Ser: No. 111). 59p. 1973. pap. 9.80 (ISBN 0-387-81133-8). Springer Verlag.
Corey, Arthur T. Mechanics of Heterogeneous Fluids in Porous Media. LC 77-71937. 1977. 25.00 (ISBN 0-918334-17-9). WRP.
Cormack, D. Criteria for the Selection of Oil Spill Containment & Recovery Equipment for Use at Sea, 1979. 1981. 40.00x (ISBN 0-686-97051-9, Pub. by W Spring England). State Mutual Bk.
Croxton, Clive A. Statistical Mechanics of the Liquid Surface. LC 79-40819. 345p. 1980. 89.95 (ISBN 0-471-27663-4, Pub. by Wiley-Interscience). Wiley.
Currie, I. G., ed. Fundamental Mechanics of Fluids. 480p. 1974. text ed. 49.00 (ISBN 0-07-014950-X). McGraw.
Daughtery, R. L. & Franzini, J. B. Fluid Mechanics with Engineering Applications. 8th ed. LC 84-10050. 640p. 1985. 40.95 (ISBN 0-07-015441-4). McGraw.
Davis, S. H., ed. Frontiers in Fluid Mechanics. Lumley, J. L. (Illus.). 340p. 1985. 34.00 (ISBN 0-387-15361-6). Springer-Verlag.
DeNevers, Noel. Fluid Mechanics. LC 78-91144. (Engineering Ser). 1970. text ed. 31.95 (ISBN 0-201-01497-1). Addison-Wesley.
Denn, M. Process Fluid Mechanics. 1980. 39.95 (ISBN 0-13-723163-6). P-H.
Douglas, J. F., et al. Fluid Mechanics. (Civil Engineering Ser.). 721p. 1979. 37.95 (ISBN 0-273-00461-1). Pitman Pub MA.
Douglas, J. G., et al. Fluid Mechanics. 2nd ed. 768p. 1985. pap. text ed. 24.95 (ISBN 0-273-02134-6). Pitman Pub MA.
Duckworth, Roger A. Mechanics of Fluids. LC 76-10368. (Introductory Engineering Ser.). (Illus.). pap. 71.30 (ISBN 0-317-08297-3, 2019602). Bks Demand UMI.
Eskinazi, S. Fluid Mechanics & Thermodynamics of Our Environment. 1975. 55.50 (ISBN 0-12-242540-5). Acad Pr.
Fluid Inclusion Research: Proceedings of COFFI, Vol. 12, 1979. 304p. 1983. pap. 15.00x (ISBN 0-472-02012-9). U of Mich Pr.
Fluid Movers. (Principles of Steam Generation Ser.). (Illus.). 70p. 1982. spiral bdg. 10.00x (ISBN 0-87683-255-9); instr's. manual 15.00x (ISBN 0-87683-276-1). G P Courseware.
Fluidics Quarterly, Vol. 4. (Illus.). 1972. 100.00 (ISBN 0-88232-017-3). Delbridge Pub Co.
Fluidics Quarterly, Vol. 6. (Illus.). 1974. 100.00 (ISBN 0-88232-027-0). Delbridge Pub Co.
Fluidics Symposium, Chicago, 1967. Advances in Fluidics. Brown, Forbes T., ed. LC 67-23027. (Illus.). pap. 116.50 (ISBN 0-317-11130-2, 2013308). Bks Demand UMI.

Van Dyke, M. & Wehausen, J. V., eds. Annual Review of Fluid Mechanics, Vol. 9. LC 74-80866. (Illus.). 1977. text ed. 20.00 (ISBN 0-8243-0709-7). Annual Reviews.
--Annual Review of Fluid Mechanics, Vol. 10. LC 74-80866. (Illus.). 1978. text ed. 20.00 (ISBN 0-8243-0710-0). Annual Reviews.
--Annual Review of Fluid Mechanics, Vol. 11. LC 74-80866. (Illus.). 1979. text ed. 20.00 (ISBN 0-8243-0711-9). Annual Reviews.
--Annual Review of Fluid Mechanics, Vol. 12. LC 74-80866. (Illus.). 1980. text ed. 20.00 (ISBN 0-8243-0712-7). Annual Reviews.
--Annual Review of Fluid Mechanics, Vol. 13. LC 74-80866. (Illus.). 1983. text ed. 20.00 (ISBN 0-8243-0713-5). Annual Reviews.
--Annual Review of Fluid Mechanics, Vol. 14. LC 74-80866. (Illus.). 1982. text ed. 22.00 (ISBN 0-8243-0714-3). Annual Reviews.
--Annual Review of Fluid Mechanics, Vol. 15. LC 74-80866. (Illus.). 1983. text ed. 28.00 (ISBN 0-8243-0715-1). Annual Reviews.
--Annual Review of Fluid Mechanics, Vol. 17. LC 74-80866. (Illus.). 630p. 1985. text ed. 28.00 (ISBN 0-8243-0717-8). Annual Reviews.
--Annual Review of Fluid Mechanics, Vol. 18. LC 74-808866. (Illus.). 520p. 1986. text ed. 32.00 (ISBN 0-8243-0718-6). Annual Reviews.
Van Dyke, M., et al, eds. Annual Review of Fluid Mechanics, Vol. 16. (Illus.). 1984. text ed. 28.00 (ISBN 0-8243-0716-X). Annual Reviews.
Van Dyke, Milton. An Album of Fluid Motion. LC 81-83088. (Illus.). 176p. 1982. text ed. 20.00x (ISBN 0-915760-03-7); pap. text ed. 10.00x (ISBN 0-915760-02-9). Parabolic Pr.
--Perturbation Methods in Fluid Mechanics. LC 75-15072. 1975. 10.00x (ISBN 0-915760-01-0). Parabolic Pr.
Vennard, John K. & Street, Robert L. Elementary Fluid Mechanics. 6th ed. LC 81-4427. 689p. 1982. text ed. 43.00x (ISBN 0-471-04427-X). Wiley.
Verhulst, F., ed. Asymptotic Analysis: From Theory to Application. (Lecture Notes in Mathematics Ser.: Vol. 711). 1979. pap. 17.00 (ISBN 0-387-09245-5). Springer-Verlag.
Verruijt, A. Grounderwater Flow. 2nd ed. (Illus.). 145p. 1982. text ed. 35.00x (ISBN 0-333-32958-9); pap. text ed. 20.00x (ISBN 0-333-32959-7). Scholium Intl.
Webb, D. R. & Papadakis, C. N., eds. Small Hydro Power Fluid Machinery. 1982. 40.00 (H00233). ASME.
Webber, N. B. Fluid Mechanics for Civil Engineers. 354p. 1971. pap. 13.95x (ISBN 0-412-10600-0, NO. 6585, Pub. by Chapman & Hall England). Methuen Inc.
Wells, C. Sinclair, ed. Viscous Drag Reduction. LC 77-76496. 500p. 1969. 45.00x (ISBN 0-306-30398-1, Plenum Pr). Plenum Pub.
Wesfreid, J. E. & Zaleski, S., eds. Cellular Structures in Instabilites. (Lecture Notes in Physics Ser.: Vol. 210). vi, 389p. 1984. 21.00 (ISBN 0-387-13879-X). Springer-Verlag.
Whitaker, Stephen. Introduction to Fluid Mechanics. LC 81-1620. 476p. 1981. Repr. of 1968 ed. 31.50 (ISBN 0-89874-337-0). Krieger.
White, Frank M. Fluid Mechanics. (Illus.). 1979. text ed. 43.95 (ISBN 0-07-069667-5). McGraw.
Wighton, John L. An Experimentation Approach to the Fluids Laboratory: A Lab Manual. LC 78-23968. (Illus.). 224p. 1979. pap. 15.95x (ISBN 0-910554-26-9). Engineering.
Yih, Chia-Shun. Fluid Mechanics. 1979. text ed. 25.00x (ISBN 0-9602190-0-5). West River.
Zierep, Juergen & Oertel, Herbert, Jr., eds. Convective Transport & Instability Phenomena. (Illus.). 577p. 1982. text ed. 65.00x (ISBN 3-7650-1114-2). Sheridan.

FLUID MECHANICS–PROBLEMS, EXERCISES, ETC.

Ingham, D. B. & Kelmanson, M. A. Boundary Integral Equation Analysis of Singular, Potential & Biharmonic Problems. (Lecture Notes in Engineering Ser.: Vol. 7). (Illus.). iv, 173p. 1984. pap. 12.50 (ISBN 0-387-13646-0). Springer-Verlag.

FLUID METERS

see Flow Meters

FLUID POWER TECHNOLOGY

see also Hydraulic Machinery; Pneumatic Control; Pneumatic Machinery

Aerospace Fluid Power & Control Systems, 8 papers. 112p. 1983. pap. 22.00 (ISBN 0-89883-325-6, SP554). Soc Auto Engineers.
Chemical Engineering Magazine. Fluid Movers: Pumps, Compressors, Fans & Blowers. (Chemical Engineering Bks.). (Illus.). 384p. 1980. 39.50 (ISBN 0-07-010769-6). McGraw.
Esposito, Anthony. Fluid Power with Applications. (Illus.). 1980. text ed. 28.95 (ISBN 0-13-322701-4). P-H.
Fluid Power Symposium, 5th. Proceedings, 2 vols. Stephens, H. S. & Stapleton, C. A., eds. (Illus.). 1979. Set. lib. bdg. 69.00x (ISBN 0-900983-96-5, Dist by Air Science Co.). BHRA Fluid.
Fluid Power Systems & Components. 1983. 495.00 (ISBN 0-318-00503-4). Busn Trend.
Gabow, Patricia A. Fluids & Electrolytes: Clinical Problems & Their Solutions. 1983. pap. 15.95 (ISBN 0-316-30114-0). Little.
Hedges, Charles S. Electrical Control of Fluid Power. LC 77-156757. (Illus.). 160p. 1984. pap. 11.95 (ISBN 0-9605644-6-2). Womack Educ Pubns.
--Industrial Fluid Power, Vol. 1. 3rd ed. LC 82-199733. (Illus.). 288p. 1984. pap. 11.95 (ISBN 0-9605644-5-4). Womack Educ Pubns.
--Industrial Fluid Power, Vol. 2. 3rd ed. LC 82-199733. (Illus.). 256p. 1982. pap. 11.95 (ISBN 0-9605644-1-1). Womack Educ Pubns.
--Industrial Fluid Power, Vol. 3. 2nd ed. LC 82-199733. (Illus.). 224p. 1979. pap. 11.95 (ISBN 0-9605644-2-X). Womack Educ Pubns.
Hedges, Charles S. & Womack, R. C. Fluid Power in Plant & Field. 2nd ed. LC 68-22573. 232p. 1985. pap. 11.95 (ISBN 0-9605644-7-0). Womack Educ Pubns.
Henke, R. W. Introduction to Fluid Mechanics. 1966. 25.95 (ISBN 0-201-02809-3). Addison-Wesley.
Institute of Energy. Fluidised Combustion: Systems & Applications. (Institute of Energy Symposium Ser.: No. 4). 450p. 1982. pap. 66.00x (ISBN 0-8448-1418-0). Crane-Russak Co.
Instruments & Computers for Cost Effective Fluid Power Testing. 95p. 1979. pap. 37.00 (ISBN 0-85298-436-7, MEP105). Soc Auto Engineers.
Johnson, Olaf A. Fluid Power for Industrial Use: Hydraulics. LC 80-12953. 272p. 1983. lib. bdg. 14.50 (ISBN -89874-048-7). Krieger.
McCloy, D. Control of Fluid Power: Analysis & Design. 2nd rev. ed. LC 80-40027. (Ser. in Engineering Science: Civil Engineering). 505p. 1980. 100.00x (ISBN 0-470-27012-8). Halsted Pr.
Merrill, Samuel W. Fluid Power for Aircraft: Modern Hydraulic Technology. 3rd ed. 1974. pap. 11.75x (ISBN 0-914680-01-3). Intermtn Air.
Morgan-Grampian Books, ed. Fluid Power Equipment Locator, 1985. 210p. 125.00x (ISBN 0-686-75513-8, Pub. by Morgan-Grampian Bk). State Mutual Bk.
Pippenger, John & Hicks, Tyler. Industrial Hydraulics. 3rd ed. (Illus.). 1979. text ed. 36.30 (ISBN 0-07-050140-8). McGraw.
Proceedings of the Symposium on Degassing. 1978. pap. 47.00x (ISBN 0-900983-89-2, Dist. by Air Science Co.). BHRA Fluid.
Reed, Edward W. & Larman, Ian S. Fluid Power with Microprocessor Control: An Introduction. 208p. 1985. text ed. 36.95 (ISBN 0-13-322488-0). P-H.
Stephens, H. S. & Radband, D. Papers Presented at the Sixth Fluid Power Symposium. (Orig.). 1981. pap. 69.00x library ed. (ISBN 0-906085-53-5). BHRA Fluid.
Stephens, H. S. & Jarvis, B., eds. Papers Presented at the Fifth International Symposium on Jet Cutting. (Illus.). 438p. (Orig.). 1980. pap. 87.00x (ISBN 0-906085-41-1). BHRA Fluid.
Stewart, Harry L. Hydraulic & Pneumatic Power for Production. 4th ed. LC 76-28238. (Illus.). 435p. 1977. 29.95 (ISBN 0-8311-1114-3). Indus Pr.
Tucker, Allen E. Pressure Rating, Vol. B. rev. ed. (Fluid Power Standards 1984 Ser.). (Illus.). 259p. 1984. 45.00 (ISBN 0-942220-72-2). Natl Fluid Power.
Tucker, Allen E., ed. Bibliographies, Vol. K. rev. ed. (Fluid Power Standards 1984 Ser.). 95p. 1984. 30.00 (ISBN 0-942220-80-3). Natl Fluid Power.
--Communications, Vol. A. rev. ed. (Fluid Power Standards 1984 Ser.). (Illus.). 219p. 1984. 25.50 (ISBN 0-942220-71-4); Set. write for info. Natl Fluid Power.
--Conductors & Associated Products, Vol. E. rev. ed. (Fluid Power Standards 1984 Ser.). (Illus.). 224p. 1984. 48.00 (ISBN 0-942220-75-7); Set. write for info. Natl Fluid Power.
--Control Products, Vol. F. rev. ed. (Fluid Power Standards 1984 Ser.). (Illus.). 445p. 1984. 106.50 (ISBN 0-942220-76-5); Set. write for info. Natl Fluid Power.
--Cylinders & Accumulators, Vol. G. rev. ed. (Fluid Power Standards 1984 Ser.). (Illus.). 368p. 1984. 81.50 (ISBN 0-942220-77-3); Set. write for info. Natl Fluid Power.
--Filtration & Contamination, Vol. D. rev. ed. (Fluid Power Standards 1984 Ser.). (Illus.). 300p. 1984. 83.00 (ISBN 0-942220-74-9); Set. write for info. Natl Fluid Power.
--Fluids, Lubricants & Sealing Devices, Vol. H. rev. ed. (Fluid Power Standards 1984 Ser.). (Illus.). 147p. 1984. 40.00 (ISBN 0-942220-78-1); Set. write for info. Natl Fluid Power.
--Pumps, Motor Power Units & Reservoirs, Vol. C. rev. ed. (Fluid Power Standards 1984 Ser.). (Illus.). 1984. 56.00 (ISBN 0-942220-73-0); Set. write for info. Natl Fluid Power.
--Testing, Vol. J. rev. ed. (Fluid Power Standards 1984 Ser.). (Illus.). 421p. 1984. 96.00 (ISBN 0-942220-79-X); Set. write for info. Natl Fluid Power.
Wolansky, William D., et al. Fundamentals of Fluid Power. LC 76-13963. (Illus.). 1977. text ed. 34.95 (ISBN 0-395-18956-X). HM.
Yeaple. Fluid Power Design Handbook. (Fluid Power & Control Ser.). 464p. 1984. 69.75 (ISBN 0-8247-7196-6). Dekker.

FLUIDIZATION

Davidson, J. F., ed. Fluidization. Keairns, D. L. LC 77-82495. (Illus.). 1978. 69.50 (ISBN 0-521-21943-4). Cambridge U Pr.
Davidson, John F. & Harrison, O. Fluidised Particles. LC 63-22979. (Illus.). pap. 46.30 (ISBN 0-317-10893-X, 2050790). Bks Demand UMI.
Grace, John R. & Matsen, John M., eds. Fluidization. LC 80-16314. 622p. 1980. 89.50x (ISBN 0-306-40458-3, Plenum Pr). Plenum Pub.
Knowlton, T. M., ed. Fluidization & Fluid-Particle Systems: Theories & Applications. (AICHE Symposium: Vol. 79). 109p. 1983. pap. 34.00 (ISBN 0-8169-0246-1, S-222); pap. 17.00. Am Inst Chem Eng.
--Fluidization & Fluid Particle Systems: Theories & Application. LC 84-6165. (AIChE Symposium Ser.: Vol. 80, No. 234). 128p. 1984. pap. 36.00 (ISBN 0-8169-0319-0); Member. pap. 18.00. Am Inst Chem Eng.
Kunii, Daizo & Levenspiel, Octave. Fluidization Engineering. LC 77-2885. (Illus.). 556p. 1977. Repr. of 1969 ed. lib. bdg. 34.50 (ISBN 0-88275-542-0). Krieger.
Kunii, Daizo & Toei, Ryozo, eds. Fluidization, Fourth International Fluidization Conference, Japan, May 29. LC 83-83069. 718p. 1984. text ed. 60.00 (ISBN 0-8169-0264-X); Member. text ed. 45.00. Am Inst Chem Eng.
Kwauk, M. & Kunii, D., eds. Fluidization: Science & Technology. (Chinese Academy of Sciences Joint Symposium Ser.). 348p. 1982. 161.75 (ISBN 0-677-31010-2). Gordon.
Kwauk, M., et al, eds. Fluidization Nineteen Eighty-Five: Science & Engineering Conference Papers, Second China-Japan Symposium, Kumming, China, April 10-15, 1985. 488p. 1985. 135.25 (ISBN 0-444-99568-4). Elsevier.
Patterson, G. A. Basic Fluid System Analysis: With HP-25 & SR-56 Pocket Calculator Programs. LC 76-21585. 95p. 1977. 12.95 (ISBN 0-917410-00-9). Basic Sci Pr.
Punwani, D. V., ed. Recent Advances in Fluidization & Fluid-Particle Systems. LC 81-3525. (AIChE Symposium: Vol. 77). 198p. 1981. pap. 36.00 (ISBN 0-8169-0201-1, S-205); pap. 19.00 members (ISBN 0-686-47544-5). Am Inst Chem Eng.
Radovanovic, M., ed. Combustion in Fluidized Beds. (Proceedings of the International Centre for Heat & Mass Transfer). 350p. 1985. 80.00 (ISBN 0-89116-409-X). Hemisphere Pub.
Roedder, Edwin & Kozlowski, Andrezj, eds. Fluid Inclusion Research: Proceedings of COFFI, Vol. 10, 1977. 270p. 1980. pap. 15.00x (ISBN 0-472-02010-2). U of Mich Pr.
Schwieger, Robert G., ed. Fluidized Bed Combustion & Applied Technology: The First International Symposium. (Illus.). 644p. 1984. 95.00 (ISBN 0-07-606902-8). McGraw.
Sheahan, Richard T. Fluidized Bed Combustion: Technical, Financial & Regulatory Issues. (Illus.). 281p. 1983. 3-ring binder 48.00 (ISBN 0-86587-105-1). Gov Insts.
Yates, J. G. Fundamentals of Fluidized Bed Chemical Processes. 224p. 1983. text ed. 49.95. Butterworth.
Zabrodsky, S. S. Hydrodynamics & Heat Transfer in Fluidized Beds. 1966. 40.00x (ISBN 0-262-24007-6). MIT Pr.

FLUIDIZED SYSTEMS

see Fluidization

FLUIDS

see also Drops; Fluid Dynamics; Fluid Mechanics; Gases; Hydraulic Engineering; Hydraulic Fluids; Hydrostatics; Liquids; Osmosis; Permeability; Rotating Masses of Fluid; Solvents

Angus, S. International Thermodynamic Tables of the Fluid State. Incl. Vol. 1. Argon. 39.00 (ISBN 0-08-020822-3); Vol. 3. Carbon Dioxide. 88.00 (ISBN 0-08-020924-6); Vol. 4. Helium. 56.00 (ISBN 0-08-020957-2). Pergamon.
Bain, D. C. & Baker, P. J. A Technical & Market Survey of Fluidic Applications. 1969. text ed. 32.00x (ISBN 0-900983-02-7, Dist. by Air Science Co.). BHRA Fluid.
Cheremisinoff, Nicholas P. & Azbel, David S., eds. Liquid Filtration. LC 82-46063. (Illus.). 400p. 1983. 59.95 (ISBN 0-250-40600-4). Butterworth.
Cranfield Fluidics Conference, 2nd. Proceedings. 1967. text ed. 36.00x (ISBN 0-685-85166-4, Dist. by Air Science Co.). BHRA Fluid.
Cranfield Fluidics Conference, 3rd. Proceedings. 1968. text ed. 47.00x (ISBN 0-900983-01-9, Dist. by Air Science Co.). BHRA Fluid.
Cranfield Fluidics Conference, 4th. Proceedings. 1970. text ed. 54.00x (ISBN 0-900983-08-6, Dist. by Air Science Co.). BHRA Fluid.
Cranfield Fluidics Conference, 5th. Proceedings. 1972. text ed. 54.00x (ISBN 0-900983-24-8, Dist. by Air Science Co.). BHRA Fluid.
Duckworth, Roger A. Mechanics of Fluids. LC 76-10368. (Introductory Engineering Ser.). (Illus.). pap. 71.30 (ISBN 0-317-08297-3, 2019602). Bks Demand UMI.
European Federation of Chemical Engineering, 2nd Intl. Conference on Phase Equilibria & Fluid Properties in the Chemical Industry, Berlin, 1980. Phase Equilibria & Fluid Properties in the Chemical Industry: Proceedings, Pts. 1 & 2. (EFCE Publication Ser.: No. 11). 1012p. 1980. text ed. 92.50x (ISBN 3-921567-35-1, Pub. by Dechema Germany). Scholium Intl.
Fluid Mixing: Proceedings, No. 64. 200p. 1981. 70.00x (ISBN 0-85295-135-3, Pub. by Inst Chem Eng England). State Mutual Bk.
Fluid Power Symposium, 1st. Proceedings. 1969. text ed. 27.00x (ISBN 0-900983-03-5, Dist. by Air Science Co.). BHRA Fluid.
Fluid Power Symposium, 2nd. Proceedings. 1971. text ed. 43.00x (ISBN 0-900983-11-6, Dist. by Air Science Co.). BHRA Fluid.
Fluid Power Symposium, 3rd. Proceedings. 1973. text ed. 47.00x (ISBN 0-900983-30-2, Dist. by Air Science Co.). BHRA Fluid.
Fluid Power Symposium, 4th. Proceedings. 1975. text ed. 50.00x (ISBN 0-900983-45-0, Dist. by Air Science Co.). BHRA Fluid.
Fluidics Quarterly, Vol. 5. (Illus.). 1973. 100.00 (ISBN 0-88232-022-X). Delbridge Pub Co.
Fluidics Quarterly, Vol. 7. (Illus.). 1975. 100.00 (ISBN 0-88232-032-7). Delbridge Pub Co.
Fluidics Quarterly, Vol. 10. (Illus.). 1978. 115.00 (ISBN 0-88232-047-5). Delbridge Pub Co.
Fluidics Quarterly: The Journal of Fluid Control, Vol. 13. (Illus.). 1981. 124.00 (ISBN 0-88232-062-9). Delbridge Pub Co.
Gallagher, R. H., et al, eds. Finite Elements in Fluids, 3 vols. Incl. Vol. 1. Viscous Flow & Hydrodynamics. 290p. 1975. 79.95x (ISBN 0-471-29045-9); Vol. 2. Mathematical Foundations, Aerodynamics, & Lubrication. 287p. 1975. 79.95x (ISBN 0-471-29046-7); Vol. 3. 1978. 79.95x (ISBN 0-471-99630-0). LC 74-13573 (Pub. by Wiley-Interscience). Wiley.
Genet, Edmond C. Memorial on the Upward Motion of Fluids. (Illus.). 7.50 (ISBN 0-8363-0069-6). Jenkins.
Gray, C. G. & Gubbins, K. E. Theory of Molecular Fluids: Fundamentals, Vol. 1. (International Series of Monographs on Chemistry). (Illus.). 1984. 79.00x (ISBN 0-19-855602-0). Oxford U Pr.
Hiza, M. J. & Kidnay, A. J., eds. Equilibrium Properties of Fluid Mixtures: A Bibliography of Experimental Data on Selected Fluids. rev. ed. LC 82-7643. (NSRDS Bibliographic Ser.). 254p. 1982. 115.00x (ISBN 0-306-66002-4, IFI Plenum). Plenum Pub.
International Conference on Fluid Sealing, 5th. Proceedings. 1971. text ed. 45.00x (ISBN 0-900983-12-4, Dist. by Air Science Co.). BHRA Fluid.
International Conference on Fluid Sealing, 6th. Proceedings. 1973. text ed. 47.00x (ISBN 0-900983-27-2, Dist. by Air Science Co.). BHRA Fluid.
Johnson, Julian & Porter, Roger, eds. Liquid Crystals & Ordered Fluids. Incl. Vol. 1. LC 76-110760. 494p. 1970. 75.00x (ISBN 0-306-30466-X); Vol. 2. LC 74-1269. 783p. 1974. 95.00x (ISBN 0-306-35182-X); Vol. 3. LC 74-1269. 559p. 1978. 85.00x (ISBN 0-306-35183-8). Plenum Pr). Plenum Pub.
Marsden, Jerrold E., ed. Fluids & Plasmas: Geometry & Dynamics. LC 84-3011. (Contemporary Mathematics Ser.: Vol. 28). 448p. 1984. pap. 35.00 (ISBN 0-8218-5028-8). Am Math.
Metheny, Norma M. Quick Reference to Fluid Balance. (Quick Reference for Nurses Ser.). (Illus.). 368p. 1984. pap. text ed. 13.75 (ISBN 0-397-54448-0, 64-03893, Lippincott Nursing). Lippincott.
Montroll, E. W. & Lebowitz, J. L., eds. The Liquid State of Matter: Fluids, Simple & Complex. (Studies in Statistical Mechanics: Vol. 8). 250p. 1982. 45.00 (ISBN 0-444-86334-6, North-Holland). Elsevier.
Nicksic, Esther. The Plus & Minus of Fluids & Electrolytes. 1981. text ed. 21.00 (ISBN 0-8359-5561-3); pap. text ed. 15.95 (ISBN 0-8359-5560-5). Reston.
Opachak, Mark, ed. Industrial Fluids: Controls, Concerns & Costs. LC 82-60442. (Manufacturing Update Ser.). 262p. 1982. 32.00 (ISBN 0-87263-086-2). SME.
Prausnitz, John M., et al. Molecular Thermodynamics of Fluid-Phase Equilibria. 2nd ed. (Illus.). 720p. 1985. text ed. 44.95 (ISBN 0-13-599564-7). P-H.

BOOKS - SUBJECT INDEX FLYING SAUCERS

Ranney, M. William, ed. Functional Fluids for Industry, Transportation & Aerospace. LC 80-10550. (Chemical Technology Review Ser.: No. 155). (Illus.). 364p. 1980. 45.00 (ISBN 0-8155-0789-5). Noyes.
Research & Education Association Staff. Fluid Mechanics Dynamics Problem Solver. rev. ed. LC 83-62278. (Illus.). 960p. 1984. pap. text ed. 23.85 (ISBN 0-87891-547-8). Res & Educ.
Review & Bibliography on Aspects of Fluid Sealing. 1972. text ed. 32.00x (ISBN 0-900983-16-7, Dist. by Air Science Co.). BHRA Fluid.
Rimon, S. G. Fluids & Applied Mathematics. pap. 49.00 (ISBN 0-08-030531-8). Pergamon.
Riste, T., ed. Ordering in Strongly Fluctuating Condensed Matter Systems. LC 79-28173. (NATO ASI Series B, Physics: Vol. 50). 490p. 1980. 75.00x (ISBN 0-306-40341-2, Plenum Pr). Plenum Pub.
Seals in Fluid Power Symposium. Proceedings. 1973. pap. 27.00x (ISBN 0-900983-31-0, Dist. by Air Science Co.). BHRA Fluid.
Second IFAC Symposium on Fluidics. Fluidics Quarterly: Selected Papers, Vol. 4, Issue 1, Pt. 2. 1971. 26.00 (ISBN 0-88232-018-1). Delbridge Pub Co.
Second Review & Bibliography on Aspects of Fluid Sealing. 1975. text ed. 43.00x (ISBN 0-900983-49-3, Dist. by Air Science Co.). BHRA Fluid.
Seventh International Conference on Fluid Sealing. Proceedings. 1976. text ed. 56.00x (ISBN 0-900983-48-5, Dist. by Air Science Co.). BHRA Fluid.
Southwestern Federation of Geological Societies. Fluids in Subsurface Environments, a Symposium. Young, Addison & Galley, John F., eds. LC 65-26430. (American Association of Petroleum Geologists. Memoir: No. 4). (Illus.). pap. 107.00 (ISBN 0-317-09975-2, 2050021). Bks Demand UMI.
Stokes, V. K. Theories of Fluids with Microstructure: An Introduction. (Illus.). 230p. 1984. 32.00 (ISBN 0-387-13708-4). Springer-Verlag.
Supercritical Fluids Processing: Emerging Opportunities. LC 85-50685. (Emerging Technologies Ser.: No. 15). (Illus.). 200p. 1985. spiral bdg. 635.00 (ISBN 0-914993-13-5). Tech Insights.
Tatsumi. Turbulence & Chaotic Phenomena in Fluids. 1984. 65.00 (ISBN 0-444-87594-8). Elsevier.
Tenth Anniversary Fluidics Symposium. Fluidics Quarterly: Special Issue, Vol. 2, Pts. 4 & 5. 1970. Set. 52.00 (ISBN 0-88232-067-X). Pt. 4 (ISBN 0-88232-010-6). Pt. 5 (ISBN 0-88232-011-4). Delbridge Pub Co.
Trefil, James S. Introduction to the Physics of Fluids & Solids. 320p. 1975. text ed. 33.00 (ISBN 0-08-018104-X). Pergamon.
Tucker, Allen E., ed. Fluids, Lubricants & Sealing Devices, Vol. H. rev. ed. (Fluid Power Standards 1984 Ser.). (Illus.). 147p. 1984. 40.00 (ISBN 0-942220-78-1); Set. write for info. Natl Fluid Power.
Turner, J. S. Bouyancy Effects in Fluids. LC 72-76085. (Cambridge Monographs on Mechanics & Applied Mathematics). (Illus.). 350p. 1973. 62.50 (ISBN 0-521-08623-X). Cambridge U Pr.
Vogel, Stephen. Life in Moving Fluids. 368p. 1981. text ed. write for info. (ISBN 0-87150-749-8, 40N 4351, Pub. by Willard Grant Pr). PWS Pubs.
Vogel, Steven. Life in Moving Fluids: The Physical Biology of Flow. LC 83-60465. (Illus.). 368p. 1983. pap. 9.95 (ISBN 0-691-02378-6). Princeton U Pr.

FLUIDS, DRILLING
see Drilling Muds

FLUORESCENCE
see also Fluorescent Lighting; Fluorimetry; Moessbauer Effect
Chen, R. F. & Edelhoch, H., eds. Biochemical Fluorescence: Concepts, Vol. 1. 424p. 1975. 75.00 (ISBN 0-8247-6222-3). Dekker.
--Biochemical Fluorescence: Concepts, Vol. 2. 336p. 1976. 75.00 (ISBN 0-8247-6223-1). Dekker.
Conference on Particle Induced X-Ray Emissions & Its Applications, Lund, August 23-26, 1976 & Johansson, S. E. Particle Induced X-Ray Emission & Its Analytical Applications: Proceedings. (Nuclear Instruments & Methods Ser.: Vol. 142 Pts. 1-2). Date not set. price not set (ISBN 0-7204-0715-X, North-Holland). Elsevier.
Gillespie, Allesia M. A Manual of Fluorometric & Spectrophotometric Experiments. 146p. 1985. pap. text ed. 25.00 (ISBN 2-88124-005-4). Gordon.
Guilbault, G. G. Practical Fluorescence: Theory, Methods, & Techniques. 680p. 1973. 99.75 (ISBN 0-8247-1263-3). Dekker.
Guilbault, G. G., ed. Fluorescence: Theory, Instrumentation, & Practice. 1967. 95.00 (ISBN 0-8247-1260-9). Dekker.
International Symposium on Fluorescin Angiography, Miami, 1970. Photography in Ophthalmology: Proceedings. Ferrer, O., ed. (Modern Problems in Ophthalmology: Vol. 9). 1971. 29.25 (ISBN 3-8055-1165-5). S Karger.
Kottow, Michael H. Anterior Segment Fluorescein Angiography. LC 77-16572. 268p. 1978. 27.50 (ISBN 0-683-04757-4). Krieger.
Passwater, R. A. Guide to Fluorescence Literature. Incl. Vol. 1. LC 67-18075. 367p. 1967. 75.00x (ISBN 0-306-68261-3); Vol. 2. LC 67-18075. 370p. 1970. 75.00x (ISBN 0-306-68262-1); Vol. 3. LC 67-18075. 365p. 1974. 75.00x (ISBN 0-306-68263-X). IFI Plenum). Plenum Pub.
Pesce, Amadeo J., et al, eds. Fluorescence Spectroscopy: An Introduction for Biology & Medicine. LC 76-154611. pap. 65.50 (ISBN 0-317-29566-7, 2021509). Bks Demand UMI.
Schulman, Stephen G. Fluorescence & Phosphorescence Spectroscopy: Physicochemical Principles & Practice. 1977. text ed. 53.00 (ISBN 0-08-020499-6). Pergamon.
Tertian & Claiss. Principles of Quantitative X-Ray Fluorescence. 404p. 1982. 64.95 (ISBN 0-471-26199-8). Wiley.
Udenfriend, Sidney. Fluorescence Assay in Biology & Medicine, 2 Vols. (Molecular Biology: Vol. 3). (Illus.). Vol. 1, 1962. 75.00 (ISBN 0-12-705850-8); Vol. 2. 77.50 (ISBN 0-12-705802-8). Acad Pr.
Wehry, E. L. Modern Fluorescence Spectroscopy, Vol. 1. LC 75-43827. (Modern Analytical Chemistry Ser.). (Illus.). 238p. 1976. 37.50x (ISBN 0-306-33903-X, Plenum Pr). Plenum Pub.
Wehry, E. L., ed. Modern Fluorescence Spectroscopy, 2 vols. LC 75-43827. (Modern Analytical Chemistry Ser.). Vol. 1. pap. 63.50 (ISBN 0-317-10684-8, 2019650); Vol. 2. pap. 119.80 (ISBN 0-317-10685-6). Bks Demand UMI.
--Modern Fluorescence Spectroscopy, Vol. 4. LC 75-43827. (Modern Analytical Chemistry Ser.). 300p. 1981. 45.00 (ISBN 0-306-40691-8, Plenum Pr). Plenum Pub.
--Modern Fluorescence Spectroscopy, Vol. 2. LC 75-43827. (Modern Analytical Chemistry Ser.). (Illus.). 459p. 1976. 59.50x (ISBN 0-306-33904-8, Plenum Pr). Plenum Pub.
Zahradnik, Milos. The Production & Application of Fluorescent Brightening Agents. LC 81-16355. 147p. 1982. 34.95 (ISBN 0-471-10125-7, Pub. by Wiley-Interscience). Wiley.

FLUORESCENCE ANALYSIS
see Fluorimetry

FLUORESCENCE MICROSCOPY
see also Fluorescent Antibody Technique
Conference on Quantitative Flourescence Techniques As Applied to Cell Biology, Seattle, Wash. Fluorescence Techniques in Cell Biology: Proceedings. Thaer, A. & Sernetz, M., eds. LC 73-11950. (Illus.). 450p. 1973. 35.00 (ISBN 0-387-06421-4). Springer-Verlag.
Valenzuela, Rafael, et al. Interpretation of Immunofluorescent Patterns in Skin Diseases. LC 83-22320. 176p. 1984. text ed. 55.00 (ISBN 0-89189-177-3, 16-A-004-00); 153 35mm slides 145.00 (ISBN 0-89189-186-2, 15-A-004-00). Am Soc Clinical.

FLUORESCENT ANTIBODY TECHNIQUE
Goldman, Morris. Fluorescent Antibody Methods. LC 68-14660. 1968. 55.00 (ISBN 0-12-289050-7). Acad Pr.
Kawamura, A., Jr., ed. Fluorescent Antibody Techniques. 2nd ed. (Illus.). 310p. 1977. text ed. 37.00 (ISBN 0-8391-0855-9). Univ Park.
Voss, Edward W., Jr., ed. Fluorescein Hapten: An Immunological Probe. 208p. 1984. 59.00 (ISBN 0-8493-5070-0). CRC Pr.

FLUORESCENT LIGHTING
Butler, Keith H. Fluorescent Lamp Phosphors. LC 79-11829. (Illus.). 1980. lib. bdg. 45.00x (ISBN 0-271-00219-0). Pa St U Pr.
IES Approved Method for Life Performance Testing of Fluorescent Lamps. 5.00 (ISBN 0-686-47891-6, LM-40). Illum Eng.
IES Approved Method for Life Testing HID Lamps. 5.00 (ISBN 0-686-47898-3). Illum Eng.
IES Approved Method for Photometric Testing of Indoor Fluorescent Luminaires. 4.00 (ISBN 0-686-47893-2, LM-41). Illum Eng.
IES Approved Method for the Electrical & Photometric Measurements of Fluorescent Lamps. 6.50 (ISBN 0-686-47879-7, LM-9). Illum Eng.
Miller, Samuel C. Neon Techniques & Handling: Handbook of Neon Sign & Cold Cathode Lighting. 1977. 24.00 (ISBN 0-911380-41-8). Signs of Times.

FLUORIDATION OF WATER
see Water–Fluoridation

FLUORIDES
see also Water–Fluoridation
Adler, P., et al. Fluorides & Human Health. (Monograph Ser: No. 59). 364p. 1970. 13.60 (ISBN 92-4-140059-5, 423). World Health.
Ciba Foundation. Carbon-Fluorine Compounds: Chemistry, Biochemistry & Biological Activities. LC 72-76005. (Ciba Foundation Symposium Ser.: No. 2). pap. 106.30 (ISBN 0-317-28328-6, 2022135). Bks Demand UMI.
Committee on Animal Nutrition. Effects of Fluorides in Animals. LC 74-4061. (Illus.). 76p. 1974. pap. 5.75 (ISBN 0-309-02219-3). Natl Acad Pr.
Fluoride, Teeth & Health. 112p. 1976. 30.00x (ISBN 0-272-79373-6, Pub. by Pitman Bks England). State Mutual Bk.
Fluoride: The Cause of the Poisoning of America. pap. 2.00 (ISBN 0-318-04803-5). Top-Ecol Pr.
Fluoride: The Missing Link in Acid Rain. pap. 2.00 (ISBN 0-318-04802-7). Top-Ecol Pr.
Hagenmuller, Paul, ed. Inorganic Solid Fluorides. (Candidate for Materials Science Ser.). 1985. 99.00 (ISBN 0-12-313370-X). Acad Pr.
Hawkins, Donald T., et al, eds. Binary Fluorides: Free Molecular Structures & Force Fields, a Bibliography, 1957-1975. LC 76-40174. 250p. 1976. 65.00x (ISBN 0-306-66011-3, IFI Plenum). Plenum Pub.
Murray, Frank, ed. Fluoride Emissions: Their Monitoring & Effects on Vegetation & Ecosystems. 234p. 1982. 36.00 (ISBN 0-12-511980-1). Acad Pr.
Production of Yellow Cake & Uranium Fluorides. (Panel Proceedings Ser.). (Illus.). 355p. 1981. pap. 50.25 (ISBN 92-0-041080-4, ISP553, IAEA). Unipub.
Public Interest Report: Fluoride Fallout from Factories Making Man the Endangered Species, No. 1. pap. 1.50 (ISBN 0-318-03955-9). Top Ecol Pr.
Public Interest Report, No. Two: Fluoride Industry's Phantom Air Pollutant Poisoning Animals, Farm & Forest. pap. 1.50 (ISBN 0-318-03956-7). Top Ecol Pr.
Smith, F. A., ed. Pharmacology of Fluorides. (Handbook of Experimental Pharmacology: Vol. 20). (Illus.). 1966-70. Pt. 1. 103.30 (ISBN 0-387-03537-0); Pt. 2. 97.40 (ISBN 0-387-04846-4). Springer-Verlag.
Wei, Stephen H., ed. Clinical Uses of Fluorides: A State of the Art Conference on the Uses of Fluorides in Clinical Dentistry. LC 84-19374. (Illus.). 232p. 1985. text ed. 29.00 (ISBN 0-8121-0970-8). Lea & Febiger.
Workshop on Cariostatic Mechanism of Fluorides, Naples, Florida, April 1976. Proceedings. Koenig, K. G., ed. (Caries Research: Vol. 11, Suppl. 1). 1976. 33.00 (ISBN 3-8055-2430-7). S Karger.
Yiamouyiannis, John. Fluoride: The Aging Factor. (Illus.). 210p. 1983. 11.95 (ISBN 0-913571-00-8). Health Act Pr.

FLUORIMETRY
Cline Love, L. J. & Eastwood, Delyle, eds. Advances in Luminesince Spectroscopy - STP 863. LC 84-71320. (Illus.). 129p. 1985. pap. text ed. 26.00 (ISBN 0-8031-0412-X, 04-863000-39). ASTM.
International Commission on Radiation Units & Measurements. Cameras for Image Intensifier Fluorography. LC 73-97641. 1969. 8.00 (ISBN 0-913394-08-4). Intl Comm Rad Meas.
Kaufman, Leon. Medical Applications of Fluorescent Excitation Analysis. 176p. 1979. 49.95 (ISBN 0-8493-5507-9). CRC Pr.
Pesez, M. & Bartos, J. Colorimetric & Fluorimetric Analysis of Organic Compounds & Drugs. (Clinical & Biochemical Analysis Ser.: Vol. 1). 688p. 1974. 99.75 (ISBN 0-8247-6105-7). Dekker.
Schulman, Stephen G., ed. Molecular Luminescence Spectroscopy Methods & Applications. (Chemical Analysis Ser.: No. 1-075). 1985. text ed. 85.00 (ISBN 0-471-86848-5, Pub by Wiley-Interscience). Wiley.
Snell, Forster D. Photometric & Fluorometric Methods of Analysis: Metals, 2 pts. LC 77-25039. 2192p. 1978. Set. 395.95 (ISBN 0-471-81014-2, Pub. by Wiley-Interscience). Wiley.
Wehry, E. L., ed. Modern Fluorescence Spectroscopy, Vol. 4. LC 75-43827. (Modern Analytical Chemistry Ser.). 300p. 1981. 45.00 (ISBN 0-306-40691-8, Plenum Pr). Plenum Pub.
--Modern Fluorescence Spectroscopy, Vol. 3. LC 75-43827. (Modern Analytical Chemistry Ser.). 375p. 1981. 55.00x (ISBN 0-306-40690-X, Plenum Pr). Plenum Pub.
White, Charles E. & Argauer, R. J. Fluorescence Analysis: A Practical Approach. 1970. 85.00 (ISBN 0-8247-1781-3). Dekker.

FLUORINE
see also Organofluorine Compounds
Chambers, Richard D. Fluorine in Organic Chemistry. LC 73-7824. (Interscience Monographs on Organic Chemistry). pap. 101.50 (ISBN 0-317-26348-X, 2055982). Bks Demand UMI.
Committee on Animal Nutrition. Effects of Fluorides in Animals. LC 74-4061. (Illus.). 76p. 1974. pap. 5.75 (ISBN 0-309-02219-3). Natl Acad Pr.
Eagers, R. Y. Toxic Properties of Inorganic Flourine Compounds. 1969. 26.00x (ISBN 0-444-20044-4, Pub. by Applied Science). Burgess-Intl Ideas.
--Toxic Properties of Inorganic Fluorine Compounds. 152p. 1969. 22.25 (ISBN 0-444-20044-4, Pub. by Elsevier Applied Sci England). Elsevier.
Emeleus, H. J. Chemistry of Fluorine & Its Compounds. (Current Chemical Concepts Monograph). 1969. 44.50 (ISBN 0-12-238150-5). Acad Pr.
Largent, Edward J. Fluorosis: The Health Aspects of Fluorine Compounds. LC 60-16601. 160p. 1961. 3.50 (ISBN 0-8142-0079-6). Ohio St U Pr.
Robinson, J. B. Flourine-Its Occurrence, Analysis, Effects on Plants: Diagnosis & Control. 36p. 1978. 30.00x (ISBN 0-85198-431-2, Pub. by CAB Bks England). State Mutual Bk.
Simons, J. H., ed. Fluorine Chemistry, 5 vols. 1950-64. Vol. 1, 1950. 85.00 (ISBN 0-12-643901-X); Vol. 2, 1954. 85.00 (ISBN 0-12-643902-8); Vol. 3, 1963. 70.00 (ISBN 0-12-643903-6); Vol. 4, 1965. 95.00 (ISBN 0-12-643904-4); Vol. 5, 1964. 80.00 (ISBN 0-12-643905-2). Acad Pr.
Tarrant, Paul, ed. Fluorine Chemistry Reviews, Vol. 1. 1967. 65.00 (ISBN 0-8247-1645-0). Dekker.
--Fluorine Chemistry Reviews, Vol. 2. 1968. 65.00 (ISBN 0-8247-1646-9). Dekker.
--Fluorine Chemistry Reviews, Vol. 3. LC 67-30920. 1969. 65.00 (ISBN 0-8247-1647-7). Dekker.
--Flourine Chemistry Reviews, Vol. 4. 1969. 65.00 (ISBN 0-8247-1648-5). Dekker.
--Fluorine Chemistry Reviews, Vol. 7. 256p. 1974. 65.00 (ISBN 0-8247-6091-3). Dekker.
--Fluorine Chemistry Reviews, Vol. 8. 1977. 65.00 (ISBN 0-8247-6578-8). Dekker.
Young, A. S. Sulfur Dioxide, Chlorine, Fluorine & Chlorine Oxides. 1983. 100.00x (ISBN 0-08-026218-X). Pergamon.

FLUOROCARBONS
Banks, R. E., ed. Fluorocarbon & Related Chemistry, Vols. 1-3. Barlow, M. G. Incl. Vol. 1. 1969-70 Literature. 1971. 38.00 (ISBN 0-85186-504-6); Vol. 2. 1971-72 Literature. 1974. 49.00 (ISBN 0-85186-514-3); Vol. 3. 1973-74 Literature. 1976. 90.00 (ISBN 0-85186-524-0, Pub. by Royal Soc Chem London). LC 72-78530. Am Chemical.
Knunyants, I. L. & Yakobson, G. G., eds. Syntheses of Fluororganic Compounds. 260p. 1985. 69.00 (ISBN 0-387-15077-3). Springer-Verlag.
Sugden, T. M. & West, T. F., eds. Chlorofluorocarbons in the Environment: The Aerosol Controversy. 183p. 1980. 79.95 (ISBN 0-470-26937-5). Halsted Pr.

FLUOROMETRY
see Fluorimetry

FLUXIONS
see Calculus

FLY
see Flies

FLYING
see Flight

FLYING BOATS
see Seaplanes

FLYING BOMBS
see V-One Bomb; V-Two Rocket

FLYING CLASSES
see Flight Training

FLYING FORTRESS (BOMBERS)
see B-Seventeen Bomber

FLYING-MACHINES
see also Aeronautics; Airplanes; Autogiros; Gliders (Aeronautics); Helicopters; Propellers, Aerial; Rockets (Aeronautics)
Chanute, Octave. Progress in Flying Machines. 1976. Repr. 12.50 (ISBN 0-916494-00-4). Lorenz & Herweg.
Goldstein, Laurence. The Flying Machine & Modern Literature. LC 84-48043. (Illus.). 288p. 1985. 27.50 (ISBN 0-253-32218-9). Ind U Pr.
Taylor, Michael. Fantastic Flying Machines. (Illus.). 144p. 1982. 12.95 (ISBN 0-86720-552-0). Jane's Pub Inc.

FLYING SAUCERS
Adamski, George. Inside the Spaceships: UFO Experiences of George Adamski 1952-1955. LC 80-80385. (Illus.). 296p. pap. 9.95 (ISBN 0-942176-01-4). GAF Intl.
Beckley, Timothy G. Book of Space Contacts. 72p. 1981. pap. 7.95 (ISBN 0-938294-05-9). Global Comm.
--Psychic & UFO Revelations in Last Days. 2nd ed. (Illus.). 72p. 1981. pap. 7.95 (ISBN 0-938294-01-6). Global Comm.
Berthold & Schwarz. UFO-Dynamics: Psychiatric & Psychic Aspects of the UFO Syndrome, Bk. 2. (Illus.). 260p. 1983. pap. 14.95 (ISBN 0-935834-13-3). Rainbow Books.
Billig, Otto. Flying Saucers: Magic in the Skies. 256p. 1982. 16.95x (ISBN 0-87073-833-X); pap. 9.95 (ISBN 0-87073-940-9). Schenkman Bks Inc.

Brom, Elgar. Sagasha: Mysterious Dust from Space. (Illus.). 72p. 1981. pap. 7.95 (ISBN 0-938294-00-8). Global Comm.

Buhler, Walter K., et al. U. F. O. Abduction from Mirassol: A Biogenetic Experiment. Stevens, Wendelle C., ed. (Factbooks Ser.). (Illus.). 416p. 1985. lib. bdg. 16.95 (ISBN 0-9608558-8-2). UFO Photo.

Cathie, Bruce L. & Temm, Peter N. UFOs & Anti-Gravity. LC 77-8718. (A Walnut Hill Book). (Illus.). 1971. pap. 6.95 (ISBN 0-89407-011-8). Strawberry Hill.

Catoe, Lynn E., ed. UFOs & Related Subjects: An Annotated Bibliography. LC 78-26124. 1979. Repr. of 1969 ed. 66.00x (ISBN 0-8103-2021-5). Gale.

Cazeau, C. J. & Scott, S. D. Exploring the Unknown: Great Mysteries Re-Examined. LC 78-27413. (Illus.). 295p. 1979. (full discount avail.) 18.95 (ISBN 0-306-40210-6, Plenum Pr). Plenum Pub.

Cohen, Daniel. The Great Airship Mystery: A UFO of the 1890's. LC 81-5529. (Illus.). 256p. 1981. 9.95 (ISBN 0-396-07990-3). Dodd.

Constable, Trevor J. The Cosmic Pulse of Life: The Revolutionary Biological Power Behind UFO's. 432p. 25.00x (ISBN 0-85435-194-9, Pub. by Spearman England). State Mutual Bk.

Coundakis, Anthony L. Mannerism on Space Communication. 194p. 1981. 12.50 (ISBN 0-682-49734-7). Exposition Pr FL.

Denaerde, Stefan & Stevens, Wendelle C. UFO... Contact from Planet Iarga. Lodge, Jim, tr. from Dutch. (UFO Fact Bks.). Orig. Title: Buitenaardse Beschaving. (Illus.). 368p. 1982. lib. bdg. 15.95 (ISBN 0-9608558-1-5). UFO Photo.

Eberhart, George M. & Hynek, J. Allen. UFO's & the Extraterrestrial Contact Movement: A Bibliography. LC 84-48874. 600p. 1985. lib. bdg. 50.00 (ISBN 0-8240-8755-0). Garland Pub.

Fowler, R. UFOs: Interplanetary Visitors. 1979. pap. 4.95 (ISBN 0-13-935569-3, Reward). P-H.

Gansberg, Judith & Gansberg, Alan. Direct Encounters: Personal Histories of UFO Abductees. (Illus.). 1980. 11.95 (ISBN 0-8027-0639-8). Walker & Co.

Haines, Richard F. Observing UFO's: An Investigative Handbook. LC 79-13418. 320p. 1980. 23.95x (ISBN 0-88229-540-3). Nelson-Hall.

Haines, Richard F., ed. UFO Phenomena & the Behavioral Scientist. LC 79-14878. 464p. 1979. 22.00 (ISBN 0-8108-1228-2). Scarecrow.

Hopkins, Budd. Missing Time: A Documented Study of UFO Abductions. 272p. 1983. Berkley Pub.

Hynek, Allen. The Hynek UFO Report. 304p. pap. 1.95 (ISBN 0-440-19201-3). Dell.

Messier, Charles. The Messier Catalogue. Niles, P. H., ed. LC 80-70586. 52p. (Orig.). 1981. pap. 1.50 (ISBN 0-9602738-2-4). Auriga.

Moore, Alvin E. The Mystery of the Skymen. 1979. pap. 15.00 (ISBN 0-685-67589-0). G Barker Bks.

Oberg, James. UFOs & Space Mysteries. LC 81-3193. 1982. pap. 6.95 (ISBN 0-89865-102-6). Donning Co.

Pawlicki, T. How to Build a Flying Saucer: And Other Proposals in Speculative Engineering. 1980. pap. 5.95 (ISBN 0-13-402461-3). P-H.

Randles, Jenny & Warrington, Peter. Science & the UFOs. 250p. 1985. 17.95 (ISBN 0-631-13563-4). Basil Blackwell.

Rutledge, Harley D. Project Identification: The First Scientific Field Study of UFO Phenomena. (Illus.). 1981. 10.95 (ISBN 0-13-730713-6); pap. 6.95 (ISBN 0-13-730705-5). P-H.

Sagan, Carl & Page, Thornton, eds. UFO's: A Scientific Debate. LC 72-4572. (Illus.). 341p. 1973. 24.95x (ISBN 0-8014-0740-0). Cornell U Pr.

--UFO's: A Scientific Debate. (Illus.). 344p. 1974. pap. 7.95 (ISBN 0-393-00739-1, Norton Lib). Norton.

Sanchez-Ocejo, Virgilio & Stevens, Wendelle C. UFO Contact from Undersea. (UFO Factbooks). (Illus.). 190p. 1982. lib. bdg. 14.95 (ISBN 0-9608558-0-7). UFO Photo.

Seers, Stan. UFO's: The Case for Scientific Myopia. 1982. 10.00 (ISBN 0-533-05271-8). Vantage.

Sheaffer, Robert. The UFO Verdict: Examining the Evidence. LC 80-84406. (Science & the Paranormal Ser.). 242p. 1981. 18.95 (ISBN 0-87975-146-0). Prometheus Bks.

Short, Robert. UFOs: Atlantis to Armageddon. (Illus.). 72p. 1981. pap. 7.95 (ISBN 0-938294-08-3). Global Comm.

Shuttlewood, Arthur. UFO Prophecy. 2nd ed. (Illus.). 72p. 1981. pap. 8.95 (ISBN 0-938294-03-2). Global Comm.

--UFOs: Visions of a New Age. (Illus.). 72p. 1981. pap. 8.95 (ISBN 0-938294-04-0). Global Comm.

Stevens, Wendelle & Herrmann, William J. UFO...Contact from Reticulum. (UFO Factbooks). (Illus.). 398p. 1981. lib. bdg. 16.95 (ISBN 0-686-84864-0). UFO Photo.

Story, Ronald D. Sightings: UFOs & the Limits of Science. LC 81-15773. (Illus.). 224p. 1982. pap. 7.25 (ISBN 0-688-00802-X, Quill NY). Morrow.

Story, Ronald D., ed. The Encyclopedia of UFOs. LC 77-15174. (Illus.). 1980. 29.95 (ISBN 0-385-13677-3). Doubleday.

--The Encyclopedia of UFOs. LC 77-15174. (Illus.). 1980. pap. 12.95 (ISBN 0-385-11681-0, Dolp). Doubleday.

Stranges, Frank E. My Friend from Beyond Earth. 3rd, rev. ed. (Illus.). 64p. 1981. pap. 4.50x (ISBN 0-686-30008-4). Intl Evang.

--Nazi UFO Secrets & Bases Exposed. 34p. 1982. pap. 2.95 (ISBN 0-686-37108-9). Intl Evang.

--UFO Conspiracy. 2nd ed. (Illus.). 122p. 1985. pap. 8.95 (ISBN 0-933470-02-9). Intl Evang.

Vallee, Jacques. The Messengers of Deception. LC 78-73378. 1979. pap. 6.95 (ISBN 0-915904-38-1). And-Or Pr.

FM RADIO

see Radio Frequency Modulation

FOAM RUBBER

Moody & Thomas. Chromatographic Separation with Foamed Plastics & Rubbers. (Chromatographic Science Ser.). 176p. 1982. 35.00 (ISBN 0-8247-1549-7). Dekker.

Storage of Cellular Rubber & Plastics. (Two Hundred Ser). 1974. pap. 2.00 (ISBN 0-685-58171-3, 231B). Natl Fire Prot.

FOAMED MATERIALS

see also Foam Rubber; Plastic Foams; Urethane Foam

Mooney, Peter. Structural Foams. 1982. 1750.00 (ISBN 0-89336-196-8, P-006). BCC.

Structural Foam: The Expanding Challenge of the 80's: 8th Conference 1980. 105p. 1980. pap. 25.00 (ISBN 0-87762-294-9). Technomic.

Wendle, Bruce C. Structural Foam: A Purchasing & Design Guide. (Plastics Engineering Ser.). 192p. 1985. 49.50 (ISBN 0-8247-7398-5). Dekker.

FODDER

see Feeds

FOLDS (GEOLOGY)

Hansen, E. Strain Facies. LC 72-89551. (Minerals, Rocks & Inorganic Materials Ser.: Vol. 2). (Illus.). 1971. 33.00 (ISBN 0-387-05204-6). Springer-Verlag.

Jaroszewski, W. Fault & Fold Tectonics. (Geology Ser.: I-528). 550p. 1984. 97.00x (ISBN 0-470-27478-6). Halsted Pr.

Johnson, A. M. Styles of Folding: Mechanics & Mechanisms of Folding of Natural Elastic Materials. (Developments in Geotectonics: Vol. 11). 406p. 1977. 76.75 (ISBN 0-444-41496-7). Elsevier.

Ramsay, John G. Folding & Fracturing of Rocks. (International Ser. in Earth & Planetary Sciences). (Illus.). 1967. text ed. 66.95 (ISBN 0-07-051170-5). McGraw.

FOLIAGE

see Leaves

FOLIC ACID

Adams, Ruth & Murray, Frank. Vitamin B-Twelve & Folic Acid. 176p. (Orig.). 1981. pap. 2.95 (ISBN 0-915962-31-4). Larchmont Bks.

Botez, M. I. & Reynolds, E. H., eds. Folic Acid in Neurology, Psychiatry, & Internal Medicine. LC 78-57243. 550p. 1979. text ed. 71.00 (ISBN 0-89004-338-8). Raven.

Food & Nutrition Board. Folic Acid: Biochemistry & Physiology in Relation to the Human Nutrition Requirement. LC 77-8182. 1977. 14.50 (ISBN 0-309-02605-9). Natl Acad Pr.

FOOD

see also Animal Food; Animals, Food Habits of; Beverages; Cereals As Food; Diet; Farm Produce; Fish as Food; Flavoring Essences; Food, Natural; Fruit; Grain; Meat; Nutrition; Nuts; Sea Food; Vegetables

also headings beginning with the word Food; also particular foods and beverages, e.g. Bread, Milk; also subdivision Food under subjects, e.g. Fishes–Food; Indians of North America–Food

Altschul, Aaron A., ed. New Protein Foods Vol. 4. LC 72-12188. (Food Science & Technology Ser.). 1981. Pt. B. 65.00 (ISBN 0-12-054804-6). Acad Pr.

Bach, W., ed. Interactions of Food & Climate. 1982. 58.50 (ISBN 90-277-1353-7, Pub. by Reidel Holland); pap. 28.50 (ISBN 90-277-1354-5, Pub. by Reidel Holland). Kluwer Academic.

Basic Texts of the FAO, Vols. 1 & 2. 1978. Set. pap. 27.00 (ISBN 92-5-100568-0, F1556, FAO). Unipub.

Bauer, Cathy & Andersen, Juel. The Tofu Cookbook. 1979. 9.95 (ISBN 0-87857-246-5). Rodale Pr Inc.

Bennion, Marion. The Science of Food. 1980. text ed. 24.50 scp (ISBN 0-06-453532-0, HarpC). Har-Row.

Birch, C. G. & Parker, K. J., eds. Control of Food Quality & Food Analysis. 320p. 1984. 64.75 (ISBN 0-85334-239-3, I-525-83, Pub. by Elsevier Applied Sci England). Elsevier.

Birch, G. G., et al, eds. Food from Waste. (Illus.). 301p. 1976. 70.50 (ISBN 0-85334-659-3, Pub. by Elsevier Applied Sci England). Elsevier.

--Sensory Properties of Foods. (Illus.). 326p. 1977. 53.75 (ISBN 0-85334-744-1, Pub. by Elsevier Applied Sci England). Elsevier.

Blaxter, K., ed. Food, Nutrition & Climate. Fowden, L. (Illus.). 422p. 1982. 72.25 (ISBN 0-85334-107-9, Pub. by Elsevier Applied Sci England). Elsevier.

Border, Barbara. Food Safety & Sanitation. (Careers in Home Economics Ser.). (Illus.). 1979. pap. text ed. 12.92 (ISBN 0-07-006511-X). McGraw.

Borlaug, Norman E. & Bente, Paul F., Jr. Land Use, Food, Energy & Recreation. 15p. (Orig.). 1983. pap. 6.00 (ISBN 0-940222-07-8). Bio Energy.

Business Communications Staff. Healthy Foods: Markets, Trends. 1982. 975.00 (ISBN 0-89336-245-X, GA-047). BCC.

Cameron, Allan. The Science of Food & Cooking. 3rd ed. (Illus.). 1973. pap. 19.95x (ISBN 0-7131-1791-5). Intl Ideas.

Casas, Penelope. Foods & Wines of Spain. LC 82-47830. (Illus.). 1982. 18.95 (ISBN 0-394-51348-7). Knopf.

Chandra, R. K., ed. Progress in Food & Nutrition Science. (Illus.). 198p. 1984. pap. 84.00 (ISBN 0-08-030928-3). Pergamon.

Charley, Helen. Food Science. 2nd ed. LC 81-11366. 564p. 1982. 29.00 (ISBN 0-471-06206-5); text ed. 26.95 (ISBN 0-471-06160-3). Wiley.

--Food Study Manual. 3rd ed. LC 79-75636. (Illus.). 275p. (Orig.). 1971. 26.95 (ISBN 0-471-06160-3). Wiley.

Chichester, C. O., ed. Advances in Food Research, Vol. 27. (Serial Publication Ser.). 1981. 60.00 (ISBN 0-12-016427-2). Acad Pr.

--Advances in Food Research, Vol. 28. 403p. 1982. 60.00 (ISBN 0-12-016428-0). Acad Pr.

Chichester, C. O., et al, eds. Advances in Food Research, Vol. 26. LC 48-7808. 1980. 55.00 (ISBN 0-12-016426-4). Acad Pr.

--Advances in Food Research, Vol. 25. 1979. 60.00 (ISBN 0-12-016425-6). Acad Pr.

Clydesdale, Fergus M. & Francis, Frederick J. Human Ecological Issues: A Reader. 320p. (Orig.). 1980. pap. text ed. 9.95 (ISBN 0-8403-2197-X). Kendall-Hunt.

Clydesdale, Fergus S. & Francis, F. J. Food, Nutrition & You. (Illus.). 1977. lib. bdg. 17.95 (ISBN 0-13-323048-1); pap. text ed. 16.95 (ISBN 0-13-323030-9). P-H.

Combination Processes in Food Irradiation. (Proceedings Ser.). (Illus.). 467p. 1981. pap. 64.50 (ISBN 92-0-110081-7, ISP568, IAEA). Unipub.

Commission on International Relations, National Research Council. World Food & Nutrition Study: Interim Report. LC 75-37120. xix, 82p. 1975. pap. 6.95 (ISBN 0-309-02436-6). Natl Acad Pr.

Connolly, Pat. Guide to Living Foods. rev. ed. LC 78-70856. (Illus.). 10.00 (ISBN 0-916764-05-2). Price-Pottenger.

Convenience & Take-Away Foods. 120p. 1981. 150.00x (ISBN 0-686-71863-1, Pub. by Euromonitor). State Mutual Bk.

Deatherage, F. E. Food for Life. LC 75-15502. (Illus.). 434p. 1975. 24.50x (ISBN 0-306-30816-9, Plenum Pr). Plenum Pub.

Debry, G., ed. Nutrition, Food & Drug Interactions in Man. (World Review of Nutrition & Dietetics: Vol. 43). (Illus.). x, 210p. 1984. 70.75 (ISBN 3-8055-3800-6). S Karger.

A Decade of Learning: International Development Research Centre, Agriculture, Food & NutritionSciences Division: The First Ten Years. (Eng., Fr. & Span.). 180p. 1981. pap. 9.00 (ISBN 0-88936-297-1, IDRC170, IDRC). Unipub.

De Kruif, Paul. Hunger Fighters. LC 67-32084. 1967. pap. 0.95 (ISBN 0-15-642430-4, Harv). HarBraceJ.

Doyle, Rodger P. & Redding, James L. The Complete Food Handbook. LC 79-52123. (Illus.). 320p. (Revised & Updated ed.). 1980. pap. 3.50 (ISBN 0-394-17398-8, B431, BC). Grove.

Duckworth, R. B., ed. Water Relations of Foods. (Food Science & Technology Ser.). 1975. 95.00 (ISBN 0-12-223150-3). Acad Pr.

Eskin, N. A., et al. Biochemistry of Foods. 1971. 45.00 (ISBN 0-12-242350-X). Acad Pr.

Fennema, Owen. Principles of Food Science, Pt. 1. (Food Sci. Ser.: Vol. 4). 1976. 79.75 (ISBN 0-8247-6350-5); text ed. 34.75. Dekker.

Fetterman, Elsie. Buying Food. (Consumer Casebook Ser.). (Illus.). 80p. 1981. pap. text ed. 5.00 (ISBN 0-87005-268-3). Fairchild.

Food, Nutrition & Agriculture Guidelines for Agriculture Training Curricula in Africa. (Food & Nutrition Papers: No. 22). (Eng. & Fr.). 205p. 1982. pap. 15.50 (ISBN 92-5-101176-1, F2293, FAO). Unipub.

Fox, Brian A. & Cameron, Allan G. Food Science: A Chemical Approach. 382p. 1982. pap. 19.50x (ISBN 0-8448-1451-2). Crane-Russak Co.

Francis, F. J. & Clydesdale, F. M. Food Colorimetry: Theory & Applications. (Illus.). 1975. text ed. 60.00 (ISBN 0-87055-183-3). AVI.

Gaman, P. M. & Sherrington, K. B. The Science of Food: An Introduction to Food Science, Nutrition & Microbiology. 2nd ed. (Illus.). 224p. 1981. pap. 13.75 (ISBN 0-08-025895-6). Pergamon.

Ganmaster. Food Irradiation Now. 1982. 22.00 (ISBN 90-247-2763-4, Pub. by Martinus Nijhoff Netherlands). Kluwer Academic.

Garvy, John W., Jr. Introducing the Five Phases of Food: How to Begin. Liebermann, Jeremiah, ed. (Illus., Orig.). 1982. pap. 3.00 (ISBN 0-943450-00-4). Wellbeing Bks.

Gates, June. Basic Foods. 2nd ed. LC 80-26409. 636p. 1981. text ed. 28.95 (ISBN 0-03-049846-5, HoltC). HR&W.

Goforth, Allene, ed. Food & Nutrition: A Bibliographic Guide to the Microform Collection. 96p. 1981. pap. text ed. 50.00 (ISBN 0-667-00591-9). Microfilming Corp.

Harper, John C. Elements of Food Engineering. (Illus.). 1976. pap. text ed. 21.00 (ISBN 0-87055-299-6). AVI.

Howell, Edward. Food Enzymes for Health & Longevity. (Illus.). 154p. 1981. pap. text ed. 5.95 (ISBN 0-933278-06-3). Twen Fir Cent.

IDRC, Ottawa. Agriculture, Food & Nutrition Sciences Division: The First Five Years. 49p. 1977. pap. 5.00 (ISBN 0-88936-130-4, IDRC89, IDRC). Unipub.

International Congress of Food & Science Technology-1st-London, 1962. Food Science & Technology, 5 vols. Leitch, J. M., ed. Incl. Vol. 1. Chemical & Physical Aspects of Foods. 838p. 1969 (ISBN 0-677-10240-2); Vol. 2. Biological & Microbiological Aspects of Foods. 670p. 1966 (ISBN 0-677-10250-X); Vol. 3. Quality Analysis & Composition of Foods. 750p. 1966 (ISBN 0-677-10260-7); Vol. 4. Manufacture & Distribution of Foods. 834p. 1967 (ISBN 0-677-10270-4); Vol. 5. Proceedings. 364p. 1967. (Illus.). 3456p. Set. 809.75x (ISBN 0-677-10290-9); each 153.95. Gordon.

Johnston, B. F. & Greaver, J. P. Manual on Food & Nutrition Policy. (Food & Nutrition Papers: No. 15). 95p. 1969. pap. 5.50 (ISBN 92-5-100436-6, F265, FAO). Unipub.

Karmas, Endel. Meat, Poultry & Seafood Technology: Recent Developments. LC 81-18932. (Food Technology Review Ser.: No. 56). (Illus.). 427p. 1982. 45.00 (ISBN 0-8155-0887-5). Noyes.

Knorr, Dietrich. Sustainable Food Systems. (Illus.). 1983. pap. text ed. 29.50 (ISBN 0-87055-398-4). AVI.

Labuza, Theodore P. & Sloan, A. Elizabeth. Food for Thought. 2nd ed. (Illus.). 1977. pap. text ed. 9.50 (ISBN 0-87055-244-9). AVI.

Lawrence. Food Constituents & Food Residues. (Food Science & Technology Ser.). 608p. 1984. 99.50 (ISBN 0-8247-7076-5). Dekker.

Lee, Royal & Lee Foundation Staff. The Effect of Aluminum Compounds in Foods. 1983. pap. 4.95x (ISBN 0-911238-94-8, Regent House). B of A.

Lolfas, T. Food & Environment. 44p. (2nd Printing 1978). 1976. pap. 6.25 (ISBN 92-5-101516-3, F187, FAO). Unipub.

Lowenberg, Miriam E., et al. Food & People. 3rd ed. LC 78-19172. 382p. 1979. 33.95 (ISBN 0-471-02690-5). Wiley.

McWilliams, M. Food Fundamentals. 4th ed. 624p. Date not set. price not set (ISBN 0-471-81369-9). Wiley.

McWilliams, Margaret. Food Fundamentals. 3rd ed. LC 78-65888. 670p. 1979. 27.95 (ISBN 0-471-02691-3). Wiley.

Martens, H. & Russwurm, H., Jr., eds. Food Research & Data Analysis: Proceedings of the IUFOST Symposium, Sept. 1982, Oslo, Norway. (Illus.). 535p. 1983. 74.00 (ISBN 0-85334-206-7, Pub. by Elsevier Applied Sci England). Elsevier.

Mohsenin, N. N. Physical Properties of Plant & Animal Materials. 758p. 1970. 128.50x (ISBN 0-677-02300-6). Gordon.

Mohsenin, Nuri N. Thermal Properties of Food & Agricultural Materials. 418p. 1980. 74.25 (ISBN 0-677-05450-5). Gordon.

Mrak, E. M. & Stewart, G. F., eds. Advances in Food Research, Vol. 29. (Serial Publication Ser.). 1984. 49.00 (ISBN 0-12-016429-9). Acad Pr.

Morris, B. A. & Clifford, M. N., eds. Immunoassays in Food Analysis. 240p. 1985. 37.50 (ISBN 0-85334-321-7, Pub. by Elsevier Applied Sci England). Elsevier.

Nickerson, John T. & Ronsivalli, Louis J. Elementary Food Science. 2nd ed. 1980. pap. text ed. 21.50 (ISBN 0-87055-318-6). AVI.

OECD Staff. Food Margins Analysis: Aims Methods & Uses. 90p. (Orig.). 1981. pap. 8.00x (ISBN 92-64-12166-8). OECD.

O'Mahoney, Michael. Sensory Evaluation of Food: Statistical Methods & Procedures. (Food Science & Technology Ser.). 520p. 1985. write for info. (ISBN 0-8247-7337-3). Dekker.

Osborne, D. R. & Voogt, P. The Analysis of Nutrients in Foods. (Food Science & Technology Ser.). 1978. 44.00 (ISBN 0-12-529150-7). Acad Pr.

Peleg, Micha & Bagley, Edward B., eds. Physical Properties of Food. (IFT Ser.). 1983. text ed. 55.00 (ISBN 0-87055-418-2). AVI.

Pigden, W. J. & Balch, C. C., eds. Standardization of Analytical Methodology for Feeds: Proceedings of a Workshop Held in Ottawa, Canada, 4-12 Mar. 1979. 128p. 1980. pap. 13.00 (ISBN 0-88936-217-3, IDRC134, IDRC). Unipub.

Piggott, John R., ed. Sensory Analysis of Food. 396p. 1984. 57.00 (ISBN 0-85334-272-5, I-263-84, Pub. by Elsevier Applied Sci England). Elsevier.

Pomeranz, Y. & Meloan, Clifton E. Food Analysis: Theory & Practice. rev. ed. 1978. 32.00 (ISBN 0-87055-238-4). AVI.

Recommended International Standard for Concentrated Apple Juice & Concentrated Orange Juice Preserved Exclusively by Physical Means. (CAC-RS Ser.: Nos. 63-64 - 1972). 15p. (Orig.). 1975. pap. 5.50 (ISBN 92-5-101794-8, F604, FAO). Unipub.

Recommended International Standard for Pineapple Juice Preserved Exclusively by Physical Means. (CAC-RS Ser.: No. 85-1976). 7p. 1978. pap. 4.50 (ISBN 92-5-101803-0, F575, FAO). Unipub.

Regenstein, Joe M. & Regenstein, Carrie E. Food Protein Chemistry. LC 83-12320. (Food Science Ser.). 1984. 52.00 (ISBN 0-12-585820-5). Acad Pr.

Santos, W. J., et al, eds. Nutrition & Food Science: Present Knowledge & Utilization, 3 vols. LC 79-27952. 1980. Vol. 1, 822p. 89.50x (ISBN 0-306-40342-0, Plenum Pr); Vol. 2, 968p. 95.00x (ISBN 0-306-40343-9); Vol. 3, 832p. 89.50x (ISBN 0-306-40344-7). Plenum Pub.

Sapeika, N. Food Pharmacology. (Illus.). 200p. 1969. 19.50x (ISBN 0-398-01648-8). C C Thomas.

Sharpe, A. N. Food Microbiology. (Illus.). 238p. 1980. 24.75x (ISBN 0-398-04017-6). C C Thomas.

Stewart, Kent K. & Whitaker, J. R., eds. Modern Methods of Food Analysis. (IFT Symposia Ser.). (Illus.). lib. bdg. 55.00 (ISBN 0-87055-462-X). AVI.

Stone, Herbert & Sidel, Joel L. Sensory Evaluation Practices. Monograph ed. (Food Science & Technology Ser.). 1985. 39.50 (ISBN 0-12-672480-6). Acad Pr.

Symposium on Analytical Methods in the Food Industry, San Francisco, 1949. Analytical Methods in the Food Industry: A Collection of the Papers. LC 50-12845. (American Chemical Society Advances in Chemistry Ser.: No. 3). (Illus.). pap. 20.00 (ISBN 0-317-10306-7, 2011562). Bks Demand UMI.

Teranishi, Roy. Agricultural & Food Chemistry: Past, Present, Future. (Illus.). 1978. lib. bdg. 49.50 (ISBN 0-87055-231-7). AVI.

Toxicological Evaluation of Some Food Additives Including Anticaking Agents, Antimicrobials, Antioxidants, Emulsifiers & Thickening Agents. (Food Additive Ser.: No. 5). (Also avail. in French). 1974. pap. 9.20 (ISBN 92-4-166005-8). World Health.

Toxicological Evaluation of Some Food Colours, Enzymes, Flavour Enhancers, Thickening Agents & Certain Other Food Additives. (Food Additive Ser.: No. 6). (Also avail. in French). 1975. pap. 5.20 (ISBN 92-4-166006-6). World Health.

Toxicological Evaluation of Some Food Colours, Thickening Agents & Certain Other Substances. (Food Additive Ser.: No. 8). (Also avail. in French). 1975. pap. 4.80 (ISBN 92-4-166008-2). World Health.

Tressler, Donald K. & Sultan, William J. Food Products Formulary, Vol. 2: Cereals, Baked Goods, Dairy & Egg Products. (Illus.). 1975. lib. bdg. 55.00 (ISBN 0-87055-170-1). AVI.

U. S. Department of Agriculture. Guide to the Sodium Contents of Your Food. (Cookery Ser.). 48p. 1985. pap. 1.75 (ISBN 0-486-24829-1). Dover.

Vaughan, J. G., ed. Food Microscopy. (Food Science & Technology Ser.). 1979. 85.00 (ISBN 0-12-715350-0). Acad Pr.

Whitaker, John R., ed. Food Related Enzymes: A Symposium Sponsored by the Division of Agricultural & Food Chemistry at the 166th Meeting of the American Chemical Society, Chicago. LC 74-20861. (American Chemical Society Advances in Chemistry Ser.: No. 136). pap. 93.30 (ISBN 0-317-10534-5, 2019529). Bks Demand UMI.

Woods, A. E. & Aurand, L. W. Laboratory Manual in Food Chemistry. (Illus.). 1977. pap. text ed. 12.00 (ISBN 0-87055-220-1). AVI.

Working Conference.Deutsches Krebsforschungszentrum, Heidelberg, Germany.Oct. 13-15, 1971. N-Nitroso Compounds-Analysis & Formation: Proceedings. Bogovski, P., et al, eds. (IARC Scientific Pub.: No. 3). 1972. 10.00 (ISBN 0-686-16787-2). World Health.

Zapsalis, Charles & Beck, Robert A. Food Chemistry & Nutritional Biochemistry. 1216p. Date not set. price not set (ISBN 0-471-86129-4). Wiley.

FOOD–BACTERIOLOGY

Allen, J. C. & Hamilton, R. J., eds. Rancidity in Foods. 198p. 1984. 44.50 (ISBN 0-85334-219-9, Pub. by Elsevier Applied Sci England). Elsevier.

Ayres, J. C., et al, eds. Chemical & Biological Hazards in Food. (Illus.). 1970. Repr. of 1962 ed. 17.95x (ISBN 0-02-840650-8). Hafner.

Fletcher, Madilyn M. & Floodgate, George D., eds. Bacteria in Their Natural Environments. (Society for General Microbiology Special Publications: Vol. 16). Date not set. price not set (ISBN 0-12-260560-8). Acad Pr.

Foodborne Disease & Food Safety. 1981. 18.00 (ISBN 0-89970-106-X, OP-150). AMA.

Simatos, D. & Multon, J. L., eds. Properties of Water in Foods in Relation to Quality & Stability. 1985. lib. bdg. 79.50 (ISBN 90-247-3153-4, Pub. by Martinus Nijhoff Netherlands). Kluwer Academic.

Stumbo, C. R. Thermobacteriology in Food Processing. 2nd ed. (Food, Science & Technology Ser.). 1973. 59.50 (ISBN 0-12-675352-0). Acad Pr.

FOOD–BIBLIOGRAPHY

FAO Library Select Catalogue of Books, 1951-58. 1961. 22.50 (ISBN 0-685-09379-4, F155, FAO). Unipub.

Food & Nutrition: Annotated Bibliography, Author & Subject Index (1945-1972) (Special Index Ser.: No. 26). (Orig.). 1974. pap. 8.00 (ISBN 0-685-41433-7, FAO). Unipub.

Food & Nutrition Bibliography. 9th ed. 352p. 1980. pap. text ed. 40.00x (ISBN 0-912700-77-7). Oryx Pr.

Food & Nutrition Bibliography. 10th ed. 480p. 1983. pap. text ed. 40.00 (ISBN 0-912700-78-5). Oryx Pr.

Food & Nutrition Bibliography. 11th ed. 568p. 1984. pap. text ed. 40.00 (ISBN 0-89774-009-2). Oryx Pr.

Freedman, Robert L., compiled by. Human Food Uses: A Cross-Cultural, Comprehensive Annotated Bibliography. LC 81-469. xxxvii, 552p. 1981. lib. bdg. 75.00 (ISBN 0-313-22901-5, FHU/). Greenwood.

FOOD–COMPOSITION

see also Food–Analysis

ACS Committee on Chemistry & Public Affairs. Chemistry & the Food System. LC 80-11194. 1980. 19.95 (ISBN 0-8412-0557-4); pap. 12.95 (ISBN 0-8412-0563-9). Am Chemical.

Antonetti, Vincent. The Computer Diet. LC 73-80174. (Illus.). 284p. 1973. 6.95 (ISBN 0-87131-122-4). M Evans.

Bechtel, D. B., ed. New Frontiers in Food Microstructure. LC 83-70795. (Illus.). 392p. 1983. text ed. 48.00 nonmember (ISBN 0-913250-32-5); text ed. 44.00 member. Am Assn Cereal Chem.

Bender, Arnold & Nash, Tony. Pocket Encyclopedia of Calories & Nutrition. 1979. pap. 4.95 (ISBN 0-671-24839-1). S&S.

Berk, Z. Braverman's Introduction to the Biochemistry of Foods. 2nd, rev. ed. 316p. 1976. 41.50 (ISBN 0-444-41450-9, Biomedical Pr). Elsevier.

Block, Richard J. & Bolling, Diana. The Amino Acid Composition of Proteins & Foods: Analytical Methods & Results. 2nd ed. (Illus.). 584p. 1951. 48.50x (ISBN 0-398-04210-1). C C Thomas.

Breimer, T. Environmental Factors & Cultural Measures Affecting the Nitrate of Spinach. 1982. pap. text ed. 22.00 (ISBN 90-247-3053-8, Pub. by Martinus Nijhoff Netherlands). Kluwer Academic.

Charalambous, George, ed. Analysis & Control of Less-Desirable Flavors in Foods & Beverages. 1980. 35.00 (ISBN 0-12-169065-2). Acad Pr.

Counsell, J. N. Natural Colours for Food & Other Uses. (Illus.). 173p. 1981. 29.75 (ISBN 0-85334-933-9, Pub. by Elsevier Applied Sci England). Elsevier.

Dadd, Debra L., et al. Nutritional Analysis System: A Physician's Manual for Evaluation of Therapeutic Diets. 154p. 1982. pap. 19.50x spiral (ISBN 0-398-04681-6). C C Thomas.

DeMan, J. M. Principles of Food Chemistry. Rev. ed. (Illus.). 1980. pap. 27.50 (ISBN 0-87055-287-2). AVI.

Ericksson, C. Maillard Reactions in Food: Proceedings of the International Symposium, Uddevalla, Sweden, September 1979. (Progress in Food & Nutrition Science Ser.: Vol. 5). (Illus.). 500p. 1982. 155.00 (ISBN 0-08-025496-9). Pergamon.

Fisher, Patty & Bender, A. E. The Value of Food. 3rd ed. (Illus.). 1979. pap. 8.95x (ISBN 0-19-859465-8). Oxford U Pr.

Food Composition Table for Use in East Asia. 1979. pap. 25.00 (ISBN 0-685-95365-3, F1546, FAO). Unipub.

Furia, Thomas E. Current Aspects of Food Colorants. LC 77-10088. 100p. (Orig.). 1977. 32.50 (ISBN 0-8493-5395-5). Krieger.

Glicksman, Martin. Food Hydrocolloids, Vol. II. 208p. 1983. 72.00 (ISBN 0-8493-6042-0). CRC Pr.

Hawthorn, John. Foundations of Food Science. (Illus.). 195p. 1981. text ed. 27.95 (ISBN 0-7167-1295-4); pap. text ed. 14.95 (ISBN 0-7167-1296-2). W H Freeman.

Hayes, P. R. Food Microbiology & Hygiene. 400p. 1985. 72.00 (ISBN 0-85334-355-1, Pub. by Elsevier Applied Sci England). Elsevier.

Heimann, Werner. Fundamentals of Food Chemistry. (Illus.). 1980. pap. text ed. 24.50 (ISBN 0-87055-356-9). AVI.

Holas, J. & Kratochvil, J., eds. Progress in Cereal Chemistry & Technology: Proceedings of the VII World Cereal & Bread Congress, Prague, Czechoslovakia, June 28-July 2, 1982, 2 vols. (Developments in Food Science Ser.: No. 5). 1300p. 1983. Set. 159.75 (ISBN 0-444-99649-4). Elsevier.

Howard, Rosanne B. Nutrition in Clinical Care. 2nd ed. Herbold, Nancy H., ed. (Illus.). 800p. 1982. 36.00x (ISBN 0-07-030514-5). McGraw.

Hunter, Beatrice. Food Additives: The Mirage of Safety. 322p. 9.95 (ISBN 0-318-15658-X). Natl Health Fed.

Iglesias, Hector A. & Chirife, Jorge, eds. Handbook of Food Isotherms: Water Sorption Parameters for Food & Food Components (Monographs) (Food Science & Technology Ser.). 1982. 49.00 (ISBN 0-12-370380-8). Acad Pr.

Improvement of Food Quality by Irradiation. (Panel Proceedings Ser.). (Illus.). 188p. (Orig.). 1974. pap. 16.25 (ISBN 92-0-011174-2, ISP370, IAEA). Unipub.

Inglett, G. E. & Charalambous, George, eds. Tropical Foods: Chemistry & Nutrition, Vol. 1. 1979. 39.50 (ISBN 0-12-370901-6). Acad Pr.

Kiss, Istvan, et al, eds. Microbial Associations & Interactions in Food. 1985. lib. bdg. 66.50 (ISBN 90-277-1802-4, Pub. by Reidel Holland). Kluwer Academic.

Kraus, Barbara. Dictionary of Sodium, Fats & Cholesterol. LC 72-90848. (Illus.). 256p. 1974. 9.95 (ISBN 0-448-01371-1); pap. 6.95 (ISBN 0-399-50945-3, G&D). Putnam Pub Group.

Leveille, et al. Nutrients in Foods. 1983. 29.95 (ISBN 0-938550-00-4). Acad Guild.

Liener, I. Toxic Constituents in Plant Foodstuffs. (Food Science & Technology Ser). 1969. 85.00 (ISBN 0-12-449950-3). Acad Pr.

Liener, Irvin E. Toxic Constituents of Plant Foodstuffs. 2nd ed. LC 79-51681. (Food Science & Technology Ser.). 1980. 43.50 (ISBN 0-12-449960-0). Acad Pr.

Long, Lucy, et al. Food Products Formulary, Vol. 1: Meats, Poultry, Fish & Shellfish. 2nd ed. (Illus.). 1982. lib. bdg. 69.50 (ISBN 0-87055-392-5). AVI.

Meyer, Lillian Hoagland. Food Chemistry. Rev. ed. (Illus.). 1978. 17.50 (ISBN 0-87055-171-X). AVI.

Mondy, Nell I. Experimental Food Chemistry. (Illus.). 1980. pap. text ed. 17.50 (ISBN 0-87055-343-7). AVI.

Morgan-Grampian Books, ed. Food Ingredient & Machinery Survey, 1985. 142p. 1984. 150.00x (ISBN 0-686-75514-6, Pub. by Morgan-Grampian Bk). State Mutual Bk.

Morr, Mary L. & Irmiter, Theodore F. Introductory Foods: A Laboratory Manual of Food Preparation & Evaluation. 3rd ed. (Illus.). 1980. pap. text ed. write for info. (ISBN 0-02-384120-6). Macmillan.

Nickerson, John T. & Ronsivalli, Louis J. Elementary Food Science. 2nd ed. 1980. pap. text ed. 21.50 (ISBN 0-87055-318-6). AVI.

O'Mahoney, Michael. Sensory Evaluation of Food: Statistical Methods & Procedures. (Food Science & Technology Ser.). 520p. 1985. write for info. (ISBN 0-8247-7337-3). Dekker.

On the Relationship Between Chemical Composition & Digestibility in Vivo of Roughage. 1973. pap. 4.00 (ISBN 90-220-0429-5, PDC204, PUDOC). Unipub.

On the Relationship Between Chemical Composition & Digestibility in Vivo of Roughage. (Agricultural Research Reports: No. 736). 1970. pap. 4.00 (PDC179, PUDOC). Unipub.

Paul, A. A. & Southgate, D. A. McCance & Widdowson's Composition of Foods. 4th ed. 418p. 1978. 71.00 (ISBN 0-444-80027-1, Biomedical Pr). Elsevier.

Paul, A. A., et al, eds. McCance & Widdowson's Composition of Food: First Supplement. 114p. 1981. 35.75 (ISBN 0-444-80220-7, Biomedical Pr). Elsevier.

Pomeranz, Y. Functional Properties of Food Components: Monograph. LC 83-21434. (Food Science & Technology Ser.). 1985. 69.00 (ISBN 0-12-561280-X). Acad Pr.

Rockland, Louis B. & Stewart, George F., eds. Water Activity: Influences on Food Quality: Proceedings of Second International Symposium on Properties of Water Affecting Food Quality. LC 79-26632. 1981. 75.50 (ISBN 0-12-591350-8). Acad Pr.

Safety Evaluation of Chemicals in Food: Toxicological Data Profiles for Pesticides, Pt. 1: Carbamate & Organophosphorus Insecticides Used in Agriculture & Public Health. (Progress in Standardization: No. 3). (WHO bulletin vol. 52, supp. no. 2). 1975. pap. 4.00 (ISBN 92-4-068522-7). World Health.

Sapeika, N. Food Pharmacology. (Illus.). 200p. 1969. 19.50x (ISBN 0-398-01648-8). C C Thomas.

Schwimmer, Sigmund. Source Book of Food Enzymology. (Illus.). 1981. lib. bdg. 89.50 (ISBN 0-87055-369-0). AVI.

Sharpe, A. N. Food Microbiology. (Illus.). 238p. 1980. 24.75x (ISBN 0-398-04017-6). C C Thomas.

Sodium & Potassium in Foods & Drugs. pap. 6.00 (ISBN 0-89970-007-1, OP-080). AMA.

Souci, S. W. & Fachmann, W. Food Composition & Nutrition Tables. 1982. 75.00 (ISBN 0-9960099-8-1, Pub. by Wissenschaftliche W Germany). Heyden.

Southgate, D. A., ed. Guidelines for the Preparation of Tables of Food Composition. 80p. 1974. pap. 8.25 (ISBN 3-8055-1780-7). S Karger.

U. S. Department of Agriculture. Guide to the Sodium Contents of Your Food. (Cookery Ser.). 48p. 1985. pap. 1.75 (ISBN 0-486-24829-1). Dover.

Wedzicha, B. L., ed. Chemistry of Sulphur Dioxide in Foods. (Illus.). 384p. 1984. 57.00 (ISBN 0-85334-267-9, I-264-84, Pub. by Elsevier Applied Sci England). Elsevier.

Whitaker, John R. & Tannenbaum, Steven R., eds. Food Proteins. (IFT Symposia Ser.). (Illus.). 1977. lib. bdg. 55.00 (ISBN 0-87055-230-9). AVI.

Zapsalis, Charles & Beck, Robert A. Food Chemistry & Nutritional Biochemistry. 1216p. Date not set. price not set (ISBN 0-471-86129-4). Wiley.

FOOD–CONTAMINATION

see Food Contamination

FOOD–DICTIONARIES

Adrian, J., ed. Dictionary of Food, Nutrition & Biochemsitry. (Illus.). 240p. 1985. 29.00 (ISBN 0-89573-404-4, Pub. by Ellis Horwood Ltd UK). VCH Pubs.

Ashley, Richard & Duggal, Heidi. Dictionary of Nutrition. 1983. pap. 3.50 (ISBN 0-671-49407-4). PB.

Considine, Douglas M. & Considine, Glenn D. Foods & Food Production Encyclopedia. LC 81-19728. (Illus.). 2560p. 1982. 195.00 (ISBN 0-442-21612-2). Van Nos Reinhold.

Diccionario de los Alimentos: Vitaminas, Calories, Coccion, Conservacion, Etc. 2nd ed. (Span.). 758p. 1979. pap. 41.95 (ISBN 84-352-0338-7, S-13671). French & Eur.

Food & Nutrition Terminology: Definitions of Selected Terms & Expressions in Current Use. (Terminology Bulletins: No. 28). (Eng., Fr. & Span.). 55p. (2nd Printing 1976). 1974. pap. 7.50 (ISBN 92-5-000061-8, F1194, FAO). Unipub.

Foods & Nutrition Encyclopedia, 2 vols. 79.95. Ency Brit Inc.

Hauser, Gaylord & Berg, Ragnar. Dictionary of Foods. 156p. 1971. pap. 2.25 (ISBN 0-87904-008-4). Lust.

Igoe, Robert S. The Dictionary of Food Ingredients. 192p. 1982. 19.95 (ISBN 0-442-24002-3). Van Nos Reinhold.

Lindberg, G. U. Multilingual Dictionary of Names of Marine Food-Dishes of World Fauna. 562p. 1980. 79.00x (ISBN 0-686-44732-8, Pub. by Collets). State Mutual Bk.

Peterson, Martin S. & Johnson, Arnold H. Encyclopedia of Food Science, Vol. 3. (Technologic Food Encyclopedia). (Illus.). 1978. lib. bdg. 89.50 (ISBN 0-87055-227-9). AVI.

Ward, Artemus. Encyclopedia of Food, Vol. 1. 22.50 (ISBN 0-8446-1464-5). Peter Smith.

FOOD–DRYING

Borella, Anne. How to Book: Canning, Freezing, Drying. 1977. 1.95 (ISBN 0-87502-051-8). Benjamin Co.

Recommended International Standard for Fruit & Vegetable Products. (Codex Alimentarius Commission Reports: No. 2). (Orig.). 1969. pap. 4.50 (ISBN 0-685-36282-5, F1886, FAO). Unipub.

FOOD, CHEMISTRY OF

see Food–Analysis; Food–Composition

FOOD, DRIED

see also Food–Drying; Food–Preservation

Recommended International Code of Hygienic Practice for Dried Fruits. (CAC-RCP Ser.: No. 3). 1969. pap. 4.50 (ISBN 0-685-36294-9, F661, FAO). Unipub.

FOOD, EFFECT OF RADIATION ON

Application of Food Irradiation in Developing Countries. (Technical Reports Ser.: No. 54). (Illus.). 183p. (Orig.). 1966. pap. 13.00 (ISBN 92-0-115066-0, IDC54, IAEA). Unipub.

Aspects of the Introduction of Food Irradiation in Developing Countries. (Illus.). 113p. (Orig.). 1974. pap. 9.75 (ISBN 92-0-111673-X, ISP362, IAEA). Unipub.

Enzymological Aspects of Food Irradiation. (Panel Proceedings Ser.). (Illus.). 110p. (Orig.). 1969. pap. 9.25 (ISBN 92-0-111169-X, ISP216, IAEA). Unipub.

Factors Influencing the Economical Application of Food Irradiation. (Panel Proceedings Ser.). (Illus.). 137p. (Orig.). 1973. pap. 12.75 (ISBN 92-0-111373-0, ISP331, IAEA). Unipub.

Food Irradiation. (Proceedings Ser.). (Eng., Fr., Rus. & Span., Illus.). 957p. (Orig.). 1966. pap. 53.00 (ISBN 92-0-010166-6, ISP127, IAEA). Unipub.

International Acceptance of Irradiated Food: Legal Aspects. (Legal Ser.: No. 11). 70p. 1979. pap. 10.75 (ISBN 92-0-176079-5, ISP530, IAEA). Unipub.

Manual of Food Irradiation Dosimetry. (Technical Reports Ser.: No. 178). (Illus.). 161p. 1978. pap. 19.25 (ISBN 92-0-115277-9, IDC178, IAEA). Unipub.

Microbiological Specifications & Testing Methods for Irradiated Food. (Technical Reports Ser.: No. 104). (Illus.). 121p. (Orig.). 1970. pap. 11.00 (ISBN 92-0-115170-5, IDC104, IAEA). Unipub.

Mohsenin, Nuri N. Electromagnetic Radiation Properties of Foods & Agricultural Products. 560p. 1984. 103.95. Gordon.

Radiation Control of Salmonellae in Food & Feed Products. (Technical Reports Ser.: No. 22). (Illus.). 148p. pap. 10.50 (ISBN 92-0-015063-2, IDC22, IAEA). Unipub.

Recommended International General Standard for Irradiated Foods & Recommended International Code of Practice for the Operation of Radiation Facilities for the Treatment of Foods. (CAC-RCP Ser.: No. 19-1979). 19p. 1980. pap. 7.50 (ISBN 92-5-100993-7, F2157, FAO). Unipub.

Training Manual on Food Irradiation Technology & Techniques. (Technical Reports Ser.: No. 114). (Illus., Orig.). 1970. pap. 13.00 (ISBN 92-0-115570-0, IDC114, IAEA). Unipub.

Training Manual on Food Irradiation Technology & Techniques. (Technical Reports Ser.: No. 114). (Illus.). 220p. 1982. pap. 30.50 (ISBN 92-0-115082-2, IDC114/2, IAEA). Unipub.

Wholesomeness of Irradiated Food. (Food & Nutrition Papers: No. 6). 44p. 1977. pap. 6.25 (ISBN 92-5-100282-7, F495, FAO). Unipub.

FOOD, FROZEN

Borella, Anne. How to Book: Canning, Freezing, Drying. 1977. 1.95 (ISBN 0-87502-051-8). Benjamin Co.

Convenience & Take-Away Foods. 120p. 1981. 150.00x (ISBN 0-686-71863-1, Pub. by Euromonitor). State Mutual Bk.

Desrosier, Norman W. & Tressler, Donald K. Fundamentals of Food Freezing. (Illus.). 1977. pap. text ed. 26.50 (ISBN 0-87055-290-2). AVI.

Fennema, O., et al, eds. Low Temperature Preservation of Foods & Living Matter. (Food Science Ser: Vol. 3). 592p. 1973. 95.00 (ISBN 0-8247-1185-8). Dekker.

Glanfield, P. Applied Cook-Freezing. (Illus.). 203p. 1980. 33.50 (ISBN 0-85334-888-X, Pub. by Elsevier Applied Sci England). Elsevier.

International Symposium, Karlsruhe, August 23-24, 1977. How Ready Are Ready-to-Serve Foods? Proceedings. Paulus, K., ed. (Illus.). 1978. pap. 53.00 (ISBN 3-8055-2884-1). S Karger.

McWilliam, J. Book of Freezing. 1977. Repr. 20.00 (ISBN 0-85941-010-2). State Mutual Bk.

Methods of Analysis for Quick Frozen Fruits & Vegetables 43-1971 54-1974, 1 Vol. pap. 4.50 (F637, FAO). Unipub.

Recommended International Code of Practice for Frozen Fish. (CAC-RCP Ser.: No. 16-1978). 58p. 1980. pap. 8.25 (ISBN 92-5-100985-6, F2124, FAO). Unipub.

Recommended International Code of Practice for the Processing & Handling of Quick Frozen Foods, Appendix I: Method for Checking Product Temperature. 8p. 1978. pap. 4.50 (ISBN 92-5-100697-0, F1426, FAO). Unipub.

Recommended International Standard Procedures for Thawing of Quick Frozen Fruits & Vegetables & Cooking of Quick-Frozen Vegetables for Examination Purposes. (CAC-RM Ser.: No. 32-33). 9p. 1972. pap. 4.50 (ISBN 92-5-101746-8, F634, FAO). Unipub.

Robinson, R. K., ed. Microbiology of Frozen Foods. 304p. 1985. 49.50 (ISBN 0-85334-335-7, Pub. by Elsevier Applied Sci England). Elsevier.

Tressler, Donald K., et al. Freezing Preservation of Foods, 4 vols. 4th ed. Incl. Vol. 1. Principles of Refrigeration; Equipment for Freezing & Transporting Food. 50.00 (ISBN 0-87055-044-6); Vol. 2. Factors Affecting Quality in Frozen Foods. 55.00 (ISBN 0-87055-045-4); Vol. 3. Commercial Freezing Operations; Fresh Foods; Vol. 4. Freezing of Precooked & Prepared Foods. (Illus.). 1968. AVI.

United Nations Economic Commission for Europe & United Nations, Food & Agricultural Organization. Frozen & Quick-Frozen Food: New Agricultural Production & Marketing Aspects, Proceedings of a Joint Symposium, Budapest, 1977. LC 77-30194. 1977. pap. 42.00 (ISBN 0-08-022031-2). Pergamon.

United States Department of Agriculture. Complete Guide to Home Canning, Preserving & Freezing. LC 72-92754. (Illus.). 215p. 1973. pap. 3.95 (ISBN 0-486-22911-4). Dover.

U. S. Dept. of Agriculture. Home Freezing of Fruits & Vegetables. (Shorey Lost Arts Ser.). (Illus.). 48p. pap. 1.95 (ISBN 0-8466-6056-3). Shorey.

Walker, Charlotte. Freezing & Drying. Coolman, Anne, ed. Ortho Books Staff, tr. LC 83-62653. (Illus.). 1984. pap. 5.95 (ISBN 0-89721-027-1). Ortho.

FOOD, NATURAL

ecker, Gail R. Cooking for the Health of It. LC 81-67070. (Orig.). pap. 5.95 (ISBN 0-87502-090-9). Benjamin Co.

Business Communications Staff. Microwave. 1985. pap. 1500.00 (ISBN 0-89336-449-5, GO20N). BCC.

Center for Self Sufficiency Research Division. International Directory of Herb, Health, Vitamin & Natural Food Catalogs. 200p. 1985. pap. text ed. 3.50 (ISBN 0-910811-36-9, Pub. by Center Self Suff). Prosperity & Profits.

Herbert, Victor & Barrett, Stephen. Vitamins & "Health" Foods: The Great American Hustle. 200p. 1981. 11.95 (ISBN 0-89313-054-0). G F Stickley.

Herz, W., et al, eds. Progress in the Chemistry of Organic Natural Products, Vol. 36. (Illus.). 1979. 115.70 (ISBN 0-387-81472-8). Springer-Verlag.

Hunter, Beatrice T. Fact-Book on Fermented Foods & Beverages. LC 73-76229. (Pivot Original Health Book). 128p. 1973. pap. 1.25 (ISBN 0-87983-055-7). Keats.

Nakamura, Hiroshi. Spirulina: Food for a Hungry World; A Pioneer's Story in Aquaculture. Hills, Christopher, ed. Wargo, Robert, tr. from Japanese. LC 82-4816. (Illus.). 224p. (Orig.). 1982. pap. 10.95 (ISBN 0-916438-47-3). Univ of Trees.

Norris, P. About Honey: Nature's Elixir for Health. 1982. pap. 2.95 (ISBN 0-87904-043-2). Lust.

Wade, Carlson. Catalytic Hormones: Key to Extraordinary Weight Loss. 285p. 1982. 16.95 (ISBN 0-13-120857-8, Parker). P-H.

Wilson, Frank A. Food Fit for Humans. 1980. 15.00x (ISBN 0-85207-132-9, Pub. by Daniel Co England). State Mutual Bk.

FOOD, PURE

see Food Adulteration and Inspection

FOOD, RAW

Gerras, Charles, ed. Feasting on Raw Foods. (Illus.). 1980. 16.95 (ISBN 0-87857-271-6); pap. 11.95 (ISBN 0-87857-272-4). Rodale Pr Inc.

Munroe, Esther. Sprouts to Grow & Eat. LC 74-23609. (Illus.). 128p. 1974. pap. 6.95 (ISBN 0-8289-0226-7). Greene.

Szekely, Edmond B. Treasury of Raw Foods. (Illus.). 48p. 1981. pap. 2.95 (ISBN 0-89564-042-2). IBS Intl.

FOOD, WILD

see also Game and Game-Birds

Benoliel, Doug. Northwest Foraging: Wild Edibles of the Pacific Northwest. (Illus., With recipes). 1974. pap. 5.95 (ISBN 0-913140-13-9). Signpost Bk Pubns.

Furlong, Marjorie & Pill, Virginia. Wild Edible Fruits & Berries. LC 74-32015. (Illus.). 64p. 1974. 11.95 (ISBN 0-87961-033-6); pap. 5.95 (ISBN 0-87961-032-8). Naturegraph.

Stewart, Hilary. Wild Teas, Coffees, & Cordials. (Illus.). 128p. 1981. pap. 8.95 (ISBN 0-295-95804-9). U of Wash Pr.

Tomikel, John. Edible Wild Plants of Pennsylvania & New York. LC 72-89403. 1973. 5.00 (ISBN 0-910042-14-4); pap. 2.50 (ISBN 0-910042-13-6). Allegheny.

FOOD ADDITIVES

Benarde, Melvin A. The Food Additives Dictionary. 96p. 1981. pap. 4.95 (ISBN 0-671-42837-3, Wallaby). S&S.

Bicknell, Franklin. Chemicals in Your Food. LC 61-11031. 1970. 9.95 (ISBN 0-87523-130-6). Emerson.

Birch, G. G., et al, eds. Sweetness & Sweeteners. (Illus.). 176p. 1971. 26.00 (ISBN 0-85334-503-1, Pub. by Elsevier Applied Sci England). Elsevier.

Conners, C. Keith. Food Additives for Hyperactive Children. LC 80-66. 180p. 1980. 22.50x (ISBN 0-306-40400-1, Plenum Pr). Plenum Pub.

Coulston, Frederick, ed. Regulatory Aspects of Carcinogenesis & Food Additives: The Delaney Clause. (Ecotoxicology & Environmental Quality Ser.). 1979. 48.50 (ISBN 0-12-192750-4). Acad Pr.

Evaluation of Certain Food Additives, & of the Contaminants Mercury, Lead & Cadmium. (Nutrition Meetings Reports: No. 51). 32p. (Orig.). 1972. pap. 4.50 (ISBN 92-5-101809-X, F127, FAO). Unipub.

Evaluation of Certain Food Additives: 20th Report of the Joint FAO-WHO Expert Committee of Food Additives, Rome, 1976. (Food & Nutrition Papers: No. 1). 32p. (2nd Printing). 1976. pap. 6.75 (ISBN 92-5-100109-X, F130, FAO). Unipub.

Evaluation of Food Additives, 14th Report: Specifications for the Identity & Purity of Food Additives & Their Toxicological Evaluation. (Nutrition Meetings Reports: No. 48). (Orig.). 1971. pap. 4.50 (ISBN 0-685-02923-9, F131, FAO). Unipub.

Evaluation of Mercury, Lead, Cadmium & the Food Additives Amaranth, Diethylpyrocarbonate, & Octyl Gallate. pap. 8.25 (F775, FAO). Unipub.

Evaluation of the Toxicity of a Number of Antimicrobials & Antioxidants. (Nutrition Meetings Reports: No. 31). 104p. (2nd Printing 1974). 1962. pap. 4.75 (ISBN 92-5-101812-X, F133, FAO). Unipub.

FAO Nutrition Meetings. Specifications for the Identity & Purity of Some Food Additives: Including Food Colors, Flavour Enhancers, Thickening Agents, & Others. (Nutrition Meetings Reports: No. 54b). 216p. 1976. pap. 22.00 (ISBN 0-685-66331-0, F1181, FAO). Unipub.

FAO-WHO Expert Committee on Food Additives. Rome, 1974, 18th. Evaluation of Certain Food Additives: Report. (Technical Report Ser.: No. 557). (Also avail. in French & Spanish). 1974. pap. 2.00 (ISBN 92-4-120557-1). World Health.

FAO-WHO Expert Committee on Food Additives. Geneva, 1972, 16th. Evaluation of Certain Food Additives & the Contaminants Mercury, Lead, & Cadmium: Report. (Technical Report Ser.: No. 505). (Also avail. in French & Spanish). 1972. pap. 1.60 (ISBN 92-4-120505-9). World Health.

FAO-WHO Expert Committee on Food Additives. Geneva, 1975, 19th. Evaluation of Certain Food Additives; Some Food Colours, Thickening Agents, Smoke Condensates & Certain Other Substances: Report. (Technical Report Ser.: No. 576). (Also avail. in French & Spanish). 1975. pap. 2.00 (ISBN 92-4-120576-8). World Health.

FAO-WHO Expert Committee on Food Additives. Rome, 1971, 15th. Evaluation of Food Additives. Some Enzymes, Modified Starches & Certain Other Substances; Toxicological Evaluations & Specifications & a Review of the Technological Efficacy of Some Antioxidants: Report. (Technical Report Ser.: No. 488). (Also avail. in French, Russian & Spanish). 1972. pap. 1.60 (ISBN 92-4-120488-5). World Health.

FAO-WHO Expert Committee on Food Additives. Geneva, 1970, 14th. Evaluation of Food Additives: Specifications for the Identity & Purity of Food Additives & Their Toxocological Evaluation: Some Extraction Solvents & Certain Other Substances & a Review of the Technological Efficacy of Some Antimicrobial Agent: Report. (Technical Report Ser.: No. 462). (Also avail. in French, Russian & Spanish). 1971. pap. 2.00 (ISBN 92-4-120462-1). World Health.

FAO-WHO Joint Expert Committee on Food Additives, Geneva, 1975. Evaluation of Certain Food Additives: 19th Report of the Joint FAO-WHO Expert Committee on Food Additives, Geneva, 1975. (Nutrition Meetings Reports: No. 55). 23p. 1975. pap. 4.75 (ISBN 92-5-101811-1, F129, FAO). Unipub.

FAO - WHO Joint Expert Committee on Food Additives. Evaluation of Mercury, Lead, Cadmium & the Food Additives Amaranth, Diethylpyrocarbonate, & Octyl Gallate. (WHO Food Additives Ser: No. 4). 84p. 1972. pap. 2.40 (ISBN 92-4-166004-X). World Health.

FAO-WHO Joint Expert Committee on Food Additives, 1st Session, Rome, 1956. General Principles Governing the Use of Food Additives: Report. (Nutrition Meetings Reports: No. 15). 22p. 1957. pap. 4.50 (ISBN 92-5-101824-3, F376, FAO). Unipub.

FAO - WHO Joint Expert Committee on Food Additives. Review of the Technological Efficiency of Some Antioxidants & Synergists. (WHO Food Additives Ser: No. 3). 144p. 1972. pap. 3.20 (ISBN 92-4-166003-1). World Health.

--Specifications for the Identity & Purity of Some Enzymes & Certain Other Substances. (WHO Food Additives Ser: Vol. 2). 174p. 1972. pap. 3.60 (ISBN 92-4-166002-3). World Health.

--Toxicological Evaluation of Some Enzymes, Modified Starches & Certain Other Substances. (WHO Food Additives Ser: Vol. 1). 109p. 1972. pap. 2.40 (ISBN 92-4-166001-5). World Health.

Farrer, K. T. Fancy Eating That! A Closer Look at Food Additives & Contaminants. (Illus.). 194p. (Orig.). 1984. pap. 11.25x (ISBN 0-522-84243-7, Pub. by Melbourne U Pr Australia). Intl Spec Bk.

Flavors & Fragrances (U. S.) 1985. write for info. (ISBN 0-86621-413-5, A1488). Frost & Sullivan.

Flavours & Fragrances Markets. 279p. 1983. 1400.00 (ISBN 0-86621-545-X, E621). Frost & Sullivan.

Fondu, M., et al, eds. Food Additive Tables III: Classes IX-XII, Vol. 1. rev. ed. 224p. 1985. 166.75 (ISBN 0-444-42286-2). Elsevier.

Fondu, M. H., et al, eds. Food Additives Tables, Pt. 1: Updated Edition, Classes I-IV. (Vol. 1). 162p. 1981. 117.00 (ISBN 0-444-41937-3). Elsevier.

Food Additive Control in Canada. (Food Additive Control Ser.: No. 1). pap. 4.50 (F178, FAO). Unipub.

Food Additive Control in France. (Food Additive Control Ser.). pap. 4.50 (F179, FAO). Unipub.

Food Additive Control in The Netherlands. (Food additive Control Ser.: No. 3). pap. 4.50 (F181, FAO). Unipub.

Food Additive Control in the United Kingdom. (Food Additive Control Ser.: No. 2). pap. 4.50 (F182, FAO). Unipub.

Food & Nutrition Board. Food Chemicals Codex. 3rd ed. (Illus.). 735p. 1981. 65.00 (ISBN 0-309-03090-0). Natl Acad Pr.

Food Enhancers Market. 314p. 1984. 1500.00 (ISBN 0-86621-267-1). Frost & Sullivan.

Furia, Thomas E., ed. Handbook of Food Additives, Vol. 1. 2nd ed. LC 68-21741. (Handbook Ser.). 432p. 1979. Vol. 1. 76.50 (ISBN 0-8493-0542-X). CRC Pr.

Gortner, Willis A. & Freydberg, Nicholas. The Food Additives Book. 1982. 17.95 (ISBN 0-553-05012-5). Bantam.

Gray, William D. The Use of Fungi As Food & in Food Processing, Pt. 2. LC 76-141883. (Monotopic Reprint Ser.). 1973. 19.95 (ISBN 0-8493-0118-1). CRC Pr.

Guide to the Safe Use of Food Additives. (CAC-FAL Ser.: 5-1979). 104p. 1979. pap. 7.25 (ISBN 92-5-100759-4, F1835, FAO). Unipub.

Houben, Milton & Kropf, William. Harmful Food Additives: The Eat-Safe Guide. LC 79-13879. 1980. 13.95 (ISBN 0-87949-161-2). Ashley Bks.

How Safe Is Safe? The Design of Policy on Drugs & Food Additives. LC 74-5981. (Academy Forum Ser). 250p. 1974. pap. 10.25 (ISBN 0-309-02222-3). Natl Acad Pr.

Hulse, J. H., ed. Polyphenols in Cereals & Legumes: Proceedings of a Symposium Held During the 36th Annual Meeting of the Institute of Food Technologists, St. Louis, Missouri June 1979. 72p. 1979. pap. 8.00 (ISBN 0-88936-234-3, IDRC145, IDRC). Unipub.

Hunter, Beatrice T. Additives Book. rev. ed. LC 79-93436. 144p. 1980. pap. 2.25 (ISBN 0-87983-223-1). Keats.

--Whole-Grain Baking Sampler. LC 74-190457. 320p. 1972. 6.95 (ISBN 0-87983-013-1). Keats.

Inglett, George E., ed. Symposium: Sweeteners: Proceedings. (Illus.). 1974. 50.00 (ISBN 0-87055-153-1). AVI.

Jacobson, Michael F. Eater's Digest: The Consumer's Factbook of Food Additives. LC 75-186030. 1972. pap. 4.95 (ISBN 0-385-05341-X, Anch). Doubleday.

--Eater's Digest: The Consumer's Factbook of Food Additives. 260p. 1976. 5.00 (ISBN 0-385-05341-X, Pub. by Achor Bks.). Ctr Sci Public.

Johnson, J. C., ed. Food Additives: Recent Developments. LC 83-2205. (Food Technology Review 58). 412p. (Orig.). 1983. 45.00 (ISBN 0-8155-0935-9). Noyes.

Joint FAO-WHO Committee on Food Additives. Specifications for the Identity & Purity of Food Colours, Flavouring Agents & Other Food Additives. (Food & Nutrition Papers: No. 12). (Eng. & Fr.). 155p. 1979. pap. 12.75 (ISBN 92-5-100812-4, F1878, FAO). Unipub.
--Specifications for the Identity & Purity of Thickening Agents, Anticaking Agents, Antimicrobials, Antioxidants & Emulsifiers. (Food & Nutrition Papers: No. 4). 331p. 1978. pap. 21.75 (ISBN 92-5-100503-6, F1425, FAO). Unipub.
Karnola, Josepha M. Food Additives: Medical Subject Analysis & Research Index with Bibliography. LC 83-48719. 151p. 1984. 29.95 (ISBN 0-88164-082-4); pap. 21.95 (ISBN 0-88164-083-2). ABBE Pubs Assn.
Labuza, Theodore P. Food & Your Well-Being. (Illus.). 1977. pap. text ed. 17.95 (ISBN 0-8299-0129-9); instrs.' manual & study guide 7.50 (ISBN 0-8299-0162-0). West Pub.
Lipske, Michael & Center for Science in the Public Interest Staff. Chemical Additives in Booze. Jacobson, Michael, ed. 133p. (Orig.). 1983. pap. 4.95 (ISBN 0-89329-098-X). Ctr Sci Public.
List of Additives Evaluated for Their Safety-in-Use in Food. (CAC-FAL Ser.: No. 1). 88p. (Orig.). 1973. pap. 4.50 (ISBN 92-5-100530-3, F648, FAO). Unipub.
Lueck, E. Antimicrobial Food Additives: Characteristics, Uses, Effects. (Illus.). 280p. 1980. 45.00 (ISBN 0-387-10056-3). Springer-Verlag.
Markakis, Pericles, ed. Anthocyanins As Food Colors. LC 81-22902. (Food Science & Technology Ser.). 1982. 39.50 (ISBN 0-12-472550-3). Acad Pr.
Morella, J. Additives Directory. 1986. cancelled (ISBN 0-442-26297-3). Van Nos Reinhold.
NRC Committee on Food Protection. The Use of Chemicals in Food Production, Processing, Storage & Distribution. 40p. 1973. pap. 3.75 (ISBN 0-309-02136-7). Natl Acad Pr.
Packard, Vernal S., Jr. Processed Foods & the Consumer: Additives, Labeling, Standards & Nutrition. LC 75-32670. 312p. 1976. pap. text ed. 8.95 (ISBN 0-8166-0784-2). U of Minn Pr.
Phillips, G., et al, eds. Gums & Stabilisers for the Food Industry II: Application fo Hydrocolliods; Proceedings of the International Conference, Clwyd, Wales, U. K., 11-15 July, 1983. LC 82-3863. (Illus.). 578p. 1984. 95.00 (ISBN 0-08-029819-2). Pergamon.
Procedures for the Testing of International Food Additives to Establish Their Safety for Use. (Nutrition Meetings Reports: No. 17). 19p. (2nd Printing 1974). 1958. pap. 4.50 (ISBN 92-5-101822-7, F336, FAO). Unipub.
Report of an FAO-WHO Joint Conference on Food Additives: Geneva, Sept. 1975. (Nutrition Meetings Reports: No. 11). 14p. (2nd printing). 1974. pap. 4.50 (ISBN 0-686-92802-4, F246, FAO). Unipub.
Report of the Second Joint FAO-WHO Conference on Food Additives: Rome, June, 1963. (Nutrition Meetings Reports: No. 34). 13p. 1974. pap. 5.00 (ISBN 92-5-101825-1, F381, FAO). Unipub.
Roe, Francis J., ed. Metabolic Aspects of Food Safety. LC 72-142181. 1971. 76.50 (ISBN 0-12-592550-6). Acad Pr.
Specifications for Identity & Purity & Toxicological Evaluation of Food Colours, Dec 17, 1964. (Nutrition Meetings Reports: No. 38B). pap. 17.50 (F1208, FAO). Unipub.
Specifications for Identity and Purity of Buffering Agents, Salts, Emulsifers, Thickening Agents, Stabilizers, Flavouring Agents, Food Colours, Sweetening Agents and Miscellaneous Food Additives: Prepared by the 26th Session of the Joint FAO/WHO Expert Committee on Food Additives, Rome, April 19-28, 1982. (Food & Nutrition Papers: No. 25). 1982. pap. 17.50 (ISBN 92-5-101239-3, F2351, FAO). Unipub.
Specifications for the Identity & Purity of Food Additives & Their Toxicological Evaluation: Emulsifiers, Stabilizers, Bleaching & Maturing Agents. (Nutrition Meetings Reports: No. 35). 189p. (Orig.). 1964. pap. 8.75 (ISBN 0-685-48300-2, 92-5-101830-8, FAO). Unipub.
Specifications for the Identity & Purity of Food Additives & Their Toxicological Evaluation: Food Colours & Some Antimicrobials & Antioxidants. (Nutrition Meetings Reports: No. 38). 25p. (Orig.). 1965. pap. 10.00 (ISBN 92-5-101831-6, F430, FAO). Unipub.
Specifications for the Identity & Purity of Food Additives & Their Toxicological Evaluation: Some Antimicrobials, Antioxidants, Emulsifiers, Stabilizers, Flour-Treatment Agents, Acids, & Bases. (Nutrition Meetings Reports: No. 40). 24p. (Orig.). 1966. pap. 4.50 (ISBN 92-5-101832-4, F431, FAO). Unipub.
Specifications for the Identity & Purity of Food Additives & Their Toxicological Evaluation: Some Antibiotics. (Nutrition Meetings Reports: No. 45). 49p. (Orig.). 1969. pap. 5.00 (ISBN 92-5-101835-9, F210, FAO). Unipub.
Specifications for the Identity & Purity of Food Additives & Their Toxicological Evaluation: Some Flavouring Substances & Non-Nutritive Sweetening Agents. (Nutrition Meetings Reports: No. 44). 18p. (Orig.). 1968. pap. 4.50 (ISBN 92-5-101834-0, F433, FAO). Unipub.
Specifications for the Identity & Purity of Food Additives & Their Toxicological Evaluation: Antimicrobial Preservatives & Antioxidants, Vol. 1. 1962. 11.00 (ISBN 0-685-36337-6, F429, FAO). Unipub.
Specifications for the Identity & Purity of Sweeting Agents, Emulsifying Agents, Flavouring Agents & Other Food Additives: Twenty-Fourth Session of the FAO-WHO Expert Committee on Food Additives, Rome, 24 March - 2 April 1980. (Food & Nutrition Papers: No. 17). (Eng., Fr. & Span.). 167p. 1980. pap. 13.00 (ISBN 92-5-100984-8, F2150, FAO). Unipub.
Specifications for the Identity & Purity of Some Food Additives, Including Acids, Bases, Buffers, Flour & Dough Conditioning Agents. (Nutrition Meetings Reports: No. 55 B). 1977. pap. 8.00 (ISBN 92-5-100218-5, F1192, FAO). Unipub.
Specifications for the Identity & Purity of Some Food Colours, Flavour Enhancers, Thickening Agents & Certain Other Food Additives. (Food Additive Ser.: No. 7). (Also avail. in French). 1976. pap. 8.80 (ISBN 92-4-166007-4). World Health.
Stenberg, A. J., et al. Food Additive Control in the U. S. S. R. (Food Additive Control Ser.: No. 8). 45p. (Orig.). 1969. pap. 4.50 (ISBN 92-5-101814-6, F183, FAO). Unipub.
Sullivan, George. Additives in Your Food. 1976. 1.95 (ISBN 0-346-12225-2). Cornerstone.
Taylor, R. J. Food Additives. LC 79-42729. (The Institution of Environmental Sciences Ser.). 126p. 1980. 39.95 (ISBN 0-471-27684-7, Pub. by Wiley Interscience); pap. 19.95 (ISBN 0-471-27683-9). Wiley.
Toxicological Evaluation of Certain Food Additives with a Review of General Principles & of Specifications. (Nutrition Meetings Reports: No. 53). 40p. (Orig.). 1974. pap. 4.50 (ISBN 92-5-101837-5, F466, FAO). Unipub.
Toxicological Evaluation of Some Extraction Solvents & Certain Other Substances. (Nutrition Meetings Reports: No. 48A). pap. 8.50 (F1250, FAO). Unipub.
Toxicological Evaluation of Some Flavouring Substances & Non-nutritive Sweetening Agents. (Nutrition Meetings Reports: No. 44A). pap. 8.25 (F1258, FAO). Unipub.
Toxicological Evaluation of Some Food Additives; Including Food Colors, Thickening Agents & Others. (Nutrition Meetings Reports: No. 55a). (Illus.). 89p. 1977. pap. 9.75 (ISBN 92-5-100060-3, F1217, FAO). Unipub.
Toxicological Evaluation of Some Food Additives, Including Food Colors, Enzymes, Flavour Enhancers, Thickening Agents & Others. (Nutrition Meetings Reports: No. 54a). (Illus.). 204p. 1976. pap. 13.25 (ISBN 92-4-166006-6, F1243, FAO). Unipub.
Toxicological Evaluation of Some Food Colors, Emulsifiers, Stabilizers, Anti-caking Agents & Certain Other Substances. (Nutrition Meetings Reports: No. 46). pap. 13.25 (F1216, FAO). Unipub.
Vetter, J. L., ed. Adding Nutrients to Foods: Where Do We Go from Here? LC 81-71373. 150p. 1982. pap. text ed. 24.00 (ISBN 0-913250-25-2); pap. text ed. 18.00 members. Am Assn Cereal Chem.
Wilson, David A. Sugar & Food Additives. 40p. (Orig.). 1975. pap. 2.00 (ISBN 0-934852-14-6). Lorien Hse.
Winter, Ruth. A Consumers's Dictionary of Food Additives. new rev. ed. 1984. pap. 8.95 (ISBN 0-517-55287-6). Crown.
Zweig, Gunter, ed. Analytical Methods for Pesticides, Plant Growth Regulators & Food Additives, 11 vols. Incl. Vol. 1. Principles, Methods & General Applications. 1963. 86.50 (ISBN 0-12-784301-9); Vol. 2. Insecticides. 1964.. 86.50 (ISBN 0-12-784302-7); Vol. 3. Fungicides, Nematocides & Soil Fumigants, Rodenticides, & Food & Feed Additives. 1964; Vol. 4. Herbicides (Plant Growth Regulators) 1964. 50.50 (ISBN 0-12-784304-3); Vol. 5. 1967. 82.50 (ISBN 0-12-784305-1); Vol. 6. 1970. 89.50 (ISBN 0-12-784306-X); Vol. 7. Thin-Layer & Liquid Chromatography & Analysis of Pesticides of International Importance. 1973. 89.50 (ISBN 0-12-784307-8); Vol. 8. Government Regulations, Pheromone Analyses, Additional Pesticides. Zweig, Gunter & Sharma, Joseph, eds. 1976. 86.50 (ISBN 0-12-784308-6); Vol. 10. Newer & Updated Methods. Zweig, Gunter & Sharma, Joseph, eds. 1978. 73.50 (ISBN 0-12-784310-8); Vol. 11. 1980. 66.00 (ISBN 0-12-784311-6). Acad Pr.

FOOD ADULTERATION AND INSPECTION

see also Food Contamination

Filby, Frederick A. A History of Food Adulteration & Analysis. LC 75-23707. 1976. Repr. of 1934 ed. 21.00 (ISBN 0-404-13259-6). AMS Pr.
Food & Drug Administration. FDA Device Inspections Manual. Hadley, Richard D., ed. 141p. 1983. pap. text ed. 27.00 (ISBN 0-914176-21-8). Wash Busn Info.
Food Safety Council, Columbia, U. S. A., ed. Proposed System for Food Safety Assessment: A Comprehensive Report on the Issues of Food Ingredient Testing. new ed. LC 78-40901. (Illus.). 1979. 25.00 (ISBN 0-08-023752-5). Pergamon.
Frigerio, A. & Milon, H., eds. Chromatography & Mass Spectrometry in Nutrition Science & Food Safety: Proceedings of the International Symposium in Chromatography & Mass Spectrometry in Nutrition Science & Food Safety, Montreux, June 19-22, 1983. (Analytical Chemistry Symposium Ser.: No. 21). 306p. 1985. 109.25 (ISBN 0-444-42339-7, I-315-84). Elsevier.
Goodman, Robert L. A Quick Guide to Food Additives. (Orig.). 1982. pap. 4.00 (ISBN 0-940988-00-3). Gnosis Pubns.
Graham, Horace D. Safety of Foods. 2nd ed. (Illus.). 1980. lib. bdg. 59.00 (ISBN 0-87055-337-2). AVI.
Herschdoerfer, S. M. Quality Control in the Food Industry, 4 vols. 2nd ed. (Food Science & Technology Ser.). 1985. Vol. 1. 45.00 (ISBN 0-12-343001-1); Vol. 2. write for info. (ISBN 0-12-343002-X); Vol. 3. write for info. (ISBN 0-12-343003-8); Vol. 4. write for info. (ISBN 0-12-343004-6). Acad Pr.
Herschdoerfer, S. M., ed. Quality Control in the Food Industry, Vol. 3. 2nd ed. (Food Science & Technology Ser.). write for info. (ISBN 0-12-343003-8). Acad Pr.
Imholte, Thomas J. Engineering for Food Safety & Sanitation. (Illus.). 326p. 1984. 54.95 (ISBN 0-918351-00-6). Thompson & Co.
Joint FAO-WHO Expert Committee on Food Additives. Specifications for the Identity & Purity of Carrier Solvents, Emulsifiers & Stabilizers, Enzyme Preparations, Flavouring Agents, Food Colours, Sweetening Agents & Other Food Additives. (Food & Nutrition Papers: No. 19). (Eng & Fr.). 265p. 1981. pap. 19.00 (ISBN 92-5-101126-5, F2246, FAO). Unipub.
Kallet, Arthur & Schlink, F. J. One Hundred Million Guinea Pigs: Dangers in Everyday Foods, Drugs, & Cosmetics. LC 75-39252. (Getting & Spending: the Consumer's Dilemma). 1976. Repr. of 1933 ed. 24.50x (ISBN 0-405-08025-5). Ayer Co Pubs.
Lamb, Ruth D. American Chamber of Horrors: The Truth About Food & Drugs. LC 75-39255. (Getting & Spending: the Consumer's Dilemma). (Illus.). 1976. Repr. of 1936 ed. 32.00x (ISBN 0-405-08028-X). Ayer Co Pubs.
Lehman, S. C. Nutrition & Food Preparation & Preventive Care & Maintenance. (Lifeworks Ser.). 1981. 7.96 (ISBN 0-07-037094-X). McGraw.
Mycotoxin Surveillance: Prepared in Cooperation with the United Nations Environment Programme. (Food & Nutrition Papers: No. 21). 68p. 1982. pap. 7.50 (ISBN 92-5-101180-X, F2306, FAO). Unipub.
Nader, Ralph & Fortun, Michael, eds. Eating Clean: Food Safety & the Chemical Harvest. 294p. 1982. 6.50 (ISBN 0-936758-05-8). Ctr Responsive Law.
Ninemeier, Jack. Food & Beverage Security: Control of Cash, Food & Beverage. 208p. 1982. 3-ring binder 64.95 (ISBN 0-8436-2250-4). Van Nos Reinhold.
Recommended International Code of Hygienic Practice for Food for Infants & Children. (CAC-RCP Ser.: 21-1979). 13p. 1980. pap. 7.50 (ISBN 92-5-101014-5, F2158, FAO). Unipub.
Rha, Chokyun, ed. Theory, Determination & Control of Physical Properties of Food Materials. LC 74-76481. (Food Material Science Ser: No. 1). xi, 315p. 1975. lib. bdg. 68.50 (ISBN 90-277-0468-6, Pub. by Reidel Holland). Kluwer Academic.
Roberts, Howard R. Food Safety. LC 80-25335. 339p. 1981. 58.95 (ISBN 0-471-06458-0, Pub. by Wiley-Interscience). Wiley.
Roe, Francis J., ed. Metabolic Aspects of Food Safety. LC 72-142181. 1971. 76.50 (ISBN 0-12-592550-6). Acad Pr.
Rudman, Jack. Food Inspector. (Career Examination Ser.: C-2543). (Cloth bdg. avail. on request). pap. 8.00 (ISBN 0-8373-2543-9). Natl Learning.
--Senior Food Inspector. (Career Examination Ser.: C-2051). (Cloth bdg. avail. on request). pap. 12.00 (ISBN 0-8373-2051-8). Natl Learning.
--Supervising Food Inspector. (Career Examination Ser.: C-2055). (Cloth bdg. avail. on request). pap. 10.00 (ISBN 0-8373-2055-0). Natl Learning.
Speck, Marvin L., ed. Compendium of Methods for the Microbiological Examination of Foods. 2nd ed. 914p. 1984. 50.00x (ISBN 0-87553-117-2). Am Pub Health.
Turner, James S. Chemical Feast: Report on the Food & Drug Administration. LC 73-112515. (Ralph Nader Study Group Reports). 1970. 12.50 (ISBN 0-670-21428-0, N2, Grossman). Viking.
Wolfe, Margaret R. Lucius Polk Brown & Progressive Food & Drug Control: Tennessee & New York City,1908-1920. LC 77-6637. 1978. 22.50x (ISBN 0-7006-0163-5). U Pr of KS.

FOOD CHAINS (ECOLOGY)

Pimm, S. L. Food Web. LC 82-1306. (Population & Community Biology Ser.). 1982. 37.00x (ISBN 0-412-23100-X, NO. 6438, Pub. by Chapman & Hall); pap. 18.95 (ISBN 0-412-23110-7, NO. 6575). Methuen Inc.

FOOD CHEMISTRY

see Food–Analysis; Food–Composition

FOOD CONSERVATION

see also Canning and Preserving; Food Contamination

Robinson, R. K. The Vanishing Harvest: A Study of Food & its Conservation. (Illus.). 1983. 39.95x (ISBN 0-19-854713-7). Oxford U Pr.

FOOD CONSUMPTION

Alexis, Marcus, et al. Black Consumer Profiles: Food Purchasing in the Inner City. (Illus.). 106p. 1980. pap. 4.00 (ISBN 0-87712-195-8). U Mich Busn Div Res.
Baxter, M. W. Food in Fiji: The Produce & Processed Foods Distribution Systems. (Development Studies Centre-Monographs: No. 22). 282p. 1980. pap. text ed. 9.00 (ISBN 0-909150-03-6, 0064, Pub. by ANUP Australia). Australia N U P.
Burk, M. & Pas, E. Analysis of Food Consumption Survey Data for Developing Countries. (Food & Nutrition Papers: No. 16). (Eng., Fr., & Span.). 146p. 1980. pap. 9.50 (ISBN 92-5-100968-6, F2118, FAO). Unipub.
Changes in Food Habits in Relation to Increase of Productivity. 370p. 1973. 13.75 (ISBN 0-686-70974-8, APO14, APO). Unipub.
Christensen, Raymond P. Efficient Use of Food Resources in the United States. LC 75-26300. (World Food Supply Ser). (Illus.). 1976. Repr. of 1948 ed. 12.00x (ISBN 0-405-07772-6). Ayer Co Pubs.
A Comparative Study of Food Consumption Data from Food Balance Sheets & Household Surveys. (Economic & Social Development Paper: No. 34). 33p. 1984. pap. text ed. 7.50 (ISBN 92-5-101426-4, F2549, FAO). Unipub.
Den Hartog, Adel P. & Van Staveren, Wija A. Manual for Social Surveys on Food Habits & Consumption in Developing Countries. 114p. 1984. pap. text ed. 7.50 (ISBN 90-220-0838-X, PDC265, Pudoc). Unipub.
McGee, T. G., et al. Food Distribution in the New Herbrides. (Development Studies Centre-Monographs: No. 25). 268p. 1981. pap. text ed. 9.00 (ISBN 0-909150-19-2, 0068, Pub. by ANUP Australia). Australia N U P.
National Research Council Assembly of Life Sciences-Food & Nutrition Board. Assessing Changing Food Consumption Patterns. 296p. 1981. pap. text ed. 16.00 (ISBN 0-309-03135-4). Natl Acad Pr.
OECD. Food Consumption Statistics 1973-1982. 564p. (Orig.). 1985. pap. 56.00x (ISBN 92-64-02674-6). OECD.
Rao, K. K., ed. Food Consumption & Planning. 1976. 110.00 (ISBN 0-08-016459-5). Pergamon.
Rao, V. K. Food, Nutrition & Poverty. x, 154p. 1982. text ed. 25.00x (ISBN 0-7069-1886-X, Pub. by Vikas India). Advent NY.
Rechcigl, Miloslav, Jr. Man, Food & Nutrition: Strategies & Technological Measures for Alleviating the World Food Problem. LC 82-6560. 352p. (Orig.). 1982. Repr. of 1973 ed. 44.95 (ISBN 0-89874-509-8). Krieger.
Reh, E. Manual on Household Food Consumption Surveys. (Food & nutrition Papers: No. 3). 96p. (4th Printing 1976). 1962. pap. 8.00 (ISBN 92-5-100080-8, F266, FAO). Unipub.
Talbot, Ross B., ed. World Food Problem & U. S. Food Politics & Policies: 1978. (A Readings Bk.: Vol. 3). 1979. pap. text ed. 9.75x (ISBN 0-8138-1155-4). Iowa St U Pr.
Wortman, Sterling & Cummings, Ralph W., Jr. To Feed this World: The Challenge & the Strategy. LC 78-8478. 480p. (Orig.). 1978. pap. text ed. 12.95x (ISBN 0-8018-2137-1). Johns Hopkins.

FOOD CONTAMINATION

see also Radioactive Contamination of Food

Alpert, M. E., et al. Chemical & Radionuclide Food Contamination. (Illus.). 220p. 1973. text ed. 29.50x (ISBN 0-8422-7091-4). Irvington.
Ayres, J. C., et al, eds. Chemical & Biological Hazards in Food. (Illus.). 1970. Repr. of 1962 ed. 17.95x (ISBN 0-02-840650-8). Hafner.
Beuchat, L. R. Food & Beverage Mycology. (Illus.). 1978. pap. text ed. 28.50 (ISBN 0-87055-293-7). AVI.

FAO-WHO Experts on Pesticide Residues. Geneva, 1968. Pesticide Residues in Food: Report. (Technical Report Ser.: No. 417). (Also avail. in French & Spanish). 1969. pap. 2.00 (ISBN 92-4-120417-6). World Health.

FAO-WHO Experts on Pesticide Residues. Rome, 1970. Pesticide Residues in Food: Report. (Technical Report Ser.: No. 474). (Also avail. in French & Spanish). 1971. pap. 2.00 (ISBN 92-4-120474-5). World Health.

FAO-WHO Experts on Pesticide Residues. Geneva, 1971. Pesticide Residues in Food: Report. (Technical Report Ser.: No. 502). (Also avail. in French, Russian & Spanish). 1972. pap. 1.60 (ISBN 92-4-120502-4). World Health.

FAO-WHO Experts on Pesticide Residues. Rome, 1972. Pesticide Residues in Food: Report. (Technical Report Ser.: No. 525). (Also avail. in french & spanish). 1973. pap. 1.60 (ISBN 92-4-120525-3). World Health.

FAO-WHO Experts on Pesticide Residues. Geneva, 1973. Pesticide Residues in Food: Report. (Technical Report Ser.: No. 545). (Also avail. in French, Russian & Spanish). 1974. pap. 2.40 (ISBN 92-4-120545-8). World Health.

FAO-WHO Experts on Pesticide Residues. Rome, 1975. Pesticide Residues in Food: Report. (Technical Report Ser.: No. 574). (Also avail. in French & Spanish). 1975. pap. 2.40 (ISBN 92-4-120574-1). World Health.

Farrer, K. T. Fancy Eating That! A Closer Look at Food Additives & Contaminants. (Illus.). 194p. (Orig.). 1984. pap. 11.25x (ISBN 0-522-84243-7, Pub. by Melbourne U Pr Australia). Intl Spec Bk.

Food & Nutrition Board. Toxicants Occurring Naturally in Foods. rev. 2nd ed. (Illus.). 704p. 1973. 19.25 (ISBN 0-309-02117-0). Natl Acad Pr.

Food & Nutrition Board, National Research Council. Prevention of Microbial & Parasitic Hazard Associated with Processed Foods: A Guide for the Food Processor. 164p. 1975. pap. 7.25 (ISBN 0-309-02345-9). Natl Acad Pr.

Gilbert, J., ed. Analysis of Food Contaminants. (Illus.). 400p. 1984. 74.00 (ISBN 0-85334-255-5, I-168-84, Pub. by Elsevier Applied Sci England). Elsevier.

Gunther, F. A., ed. Residue Reviews, Vols. 1-11. Incl. Vol. 1. (Illus.). iv, 162p. 1962; Vol. 2. (Illus.). iv, 156p. 1963; Vol. 3. (Illus.). iv, 170p. 1963; Vol. 4. (Illus.). iv, 175p. 1963; Vol. 5. Instrumentation for the Detection & Determination of Pesticides & Their Residues in Foods. (Illus.). viii, 176p. 1964; Vol. 6. (Illus.). iv, 165p. 1964; Vol. 7. vi, 161p. 1964; Vol. 8. (Illus.). viii, 183p. 1965. 25.00 (ISBN 0-387-03390-4); Vol. 9. (Illus.). viii, 175p. 1965; Vol. 10. With Comprehensive Cumulative Contents, Subjectmatter, & Author Indexes of Volume 1-10. (Illus.). viii, 159p. 1965; Vol. 11. (Illus.). viii, 164p. 1965. 25.00 (ISBN 0-387-03393-9). LC 62-18595. (Eng, Fr, Ger.). Springer-Verlag.

--Residue Reviews, Vols. 13-24. Incl. Vol. 13. (Illus.). viii, 136p. 1966; Vol. 14. (Illus.). viii, 131p. 1966. 25.00 (ISBN 0-387-03649-0); Vol. 15. (Illus.). vi, 121p. 1966. 25.00 (ISBN 0-387-03650-4); Vol. 16. (Illus.). viii, 158p. 1966. 29.00 (ISBN 0-387-03651-2); Vol. 17. (Illus.). viii, 184p. 1967. 29.00 (ISBN 0-387-03963-5); Vol. 18. (Illus.). viii, 227p. 1967; Vol. 19. (Illus.). viii, 155p. 1967; Vol. 20. With Cumulative Table of Subjects Covered, Detailed Subject-Matter Index, & Author Index of Volumes 11-20. x, 214p. 1968. 39.00 (ISBN 0-387-04310-1); Vol. 21. (Illus.). viii, 128p. 1968. 36.00 (ISBN 0-387-04311-X); Vol. 22. (Illus.). viii, 120p. 1968. 39.00 (ISBN 0-387-04312-8); Vol. 23. (Illus.). viii, 152p. 1968. 39.00 (ISBN 0-387-04313-6); Vol. 24. vii, 173p. 1968. 39.00 (ISBN 0-387-04314-4). LC 62-18595. (Eng, Fr, Ger.). Springer-Verlag.

--Residue Reviews, Vols. 25-35. Incl. Vol. 25. Special Volume: Seminar on Experimental Approaches to Pesticide Metabolism, Degradation & Mode of Action. United States-Japan Seminar, August 16-19, 1967, Nikko, Japan. (Illus.). x, 364p. 1969. 52.00 (ISBN 0-387-04687-9); Vol. 26. (Illus.). vii, 142p. 1969. 39.00 (ISBN 0-387-04688-7); Vol. 27. (Illus.). vii, 143p. 1969. 37.00 (ISBN 0-387-04689-5); Vol. 28. Insecticide Residues in California Citrus Fruits & Products. (Illus.). vii, 127p. 1969. 39.00 (ISBN 0-387-04690-9); Vol. 29. Special Volume: Symposium on Decontamination of Pesticide Residues in the Environment. Atlantic City Meetings of the ACS, Sept. 1968. (Illus.). viii, 213p. 1969. 43.00 (ISBN 0-387-04691-7); Vol. 30. With Cumulative Table of Subjects Covered, Detailed Subject-Matter Index & Author Index of Vols. 21-30. (Illus.). ix, 169p. 1969. 43.00 (ISBN 0-387-04692-5); Vol. 31. Leaf Structure As Related to Absorption of Pesticides & Other Compounds. Hull, H. M. vii, 155p. 1970. 42.50 (ISBN 0-387-05000-0); Vol. 32. Single-Pesticide Volume: Trianzine Herbicides. (Illus.). 420p. 1970. 42.00 (ISBN 0-387-05235-6); Vol. 33. (Illus.). 160p. 1970. 43.00 (ISBN 0-387-05236-4); Vol. 34. 160p. 1971. 43.00 (ISBN 0-387-05237-2); Vol. 35. (Illus.). viii, 156p. 1971. 39.00 (ISBN 0-387-05238-0). LC 62-18595. (Eng, Fr, Ger.). Springer-Verlag.

--Residue Reviews, Vols. 36-45. Incl. Vol. 36. Chemistry of Pesticides. Melnikov, N. N. (Illus.). xii, 492p. 1971; Vol. 37. (Illus.). 144p. 1971. 49.00 (ISBN 0-387-05374-3); Vol. 38. (Illus.). 144p. 1971; Vol. 39. The Carbinole Acaricides, Chlorobenzilate & Chloropropylate. 1971. 49.00 (ISBN 0-387-05409-X); Vol. 40. With Cumulative Table of Subjects, Vols. 31-40. (Illus.). 144p. 1971. 43.00 (ISBN 0-387-05410-3); Vol. 41. Rueckstandsberichte. (Illus.). 1972. 24.00 (ISBN 0-387-05568-1); Vol. 42. (Illus.). 1972. 24.00 (ISBN 0-387-05627-0); Vol. 43. (Illus.). 1972. 25.00 (ISBN 0-387-05779-X); Vol. 44. (Illus.). 1973. 39.50 (ISBN 0-387-90058-6); Vol. 45. 1972. 39.50 (ISBN 0-387-90059-4). LC 62-18595. (Eng, Fr, Ger,.). Springer-Verlag.

--Residue Reviews, Vol. 50. x, 192p. 1974. 39.50 (ISBN 0-387-90082-9). Springer-Verlag.

--Residue Reviews, Vol. 51. viii, 203p. 1974. 39.50 (ISBN 0-387-90079-9). Springer-Verlag.

Hagstad, Harry V. & Hubbert, William T. Food Quality Control: A Syllabus for Veterinary Students. (Illus.). 148p. 1982. pap. text ed. 11.95x (ISBN 0-8138-0701-8). Iowa St U Pr.

Hunter, Beatrice T. How Safe Is Food in Your Kitchen? 96p. 1981. 7.95 (ISBN 0-684-16752-2, ScribT); pap. 3.95 (ISBN 0-684-17480-4). Scribner.

Institut National De Recherche Chimique Appliguee. Pollution by the Food Processing Industries in the EEC. 193p. 1977. 33.00x (ISBN 0-86010-074-X, Pub. by Graham & Trotman England). State Mutual Bk.

Liener, I. Toxic Constituents in Plant Foodstuffs. (Food Science & Technology Ser). 1969. 85.00 (ISBN 0-12-449950-3). Acad Pr.

Liener, Irvin E. Toxic Constituents of Plant Foodstuffs. 2nd ed. LC 79-51681. (Food Science & Technology Ser.). 1980. 43.50 (ISBN 0-12-449960-0). Acad Pr.

List of Maximum Levels Recommended for Contaminants by the Joint FAO-WHO Codex Alimentarius Commission. (Third Ser.: No. 4). 9p. 1978. pap. 4.50 (ISBN 92-5-100693-8, F1603, FAO). Unipub.

List of Maximum Levels Recommended for Contaminants by the Joint FAO-WHO Codes Alimentarius Commission. (CAC-FAL Ser.: No. 3). 8p. 1976. pap. 4.50 (ISBN 92-5-101819-7, F664, FAO). Unipub.

Magallona, E. D., et al. Residue Reviews, Vol. 56. (Illus.). 160p. 1975. 25.00 (ISBN 0-387-90115-9). Springer-Verlag.

Methods of Sampling & Analysis of Contaminants in Food: Report of a Joint FAO-WHO Expert Consultation. 19p. 1978. pap. 7.50 (ISBN 92-5-100572-9, F1472, FAO). Unipub.

Mycotoxin Surveillance: A Guideline. (Food Additive Control Ser.: No. 4). 1978. pap. 7.50 (ISBN 92-5-100315-7, F1229, FAO). Unipub.

Nader, Ralph, et al, eds. Who's Poisoning America: Corporate Polluters & Their Victims in the Chemical Age. LC 80-29608. 320p. 1981. 12.95 (ISBN 0-87156-276-6). Sierra.

Natural Resources & the Human Environment for Food & Agriculture. (Environment Papers: No. 1). (Eng., Fr. & Span.). 70p. 1980. pap. 7.50 (ISBN 92-5-100967-8, F2132, FAO). Unipub.

Peakall, D. B. Residue Reviews, Vol. 54. LC 62-18595. (Illus.). x, 190p. 1975. 39.00 (ISBN 0-387-90099-3). Springer-Verlag.

Pesticides Residues in Food: Report of the Joint Meeting, Geneva, December 1968. (Agricultural Planning Studies: No. 78). 40p. 1969. pap. 6.00 (ISBN 92-5-101532-5, F309, FAO). Unipub.

Riemann, Hans & Bryan, Frank L., eds. Food-Borne Infections & Intoxication. 2nd ed. LC 79-14935. (Food Science & Technology Ser.). 1979. 85.00 (ISBN 0-12-588360-9). Acad Pr.

Roberts, Howard R. Food Safety. LC 80-25335. 339p. 1981. 58.95 (ISBN 0-471-06458-0, Pub. by Wiley-Interscience). Wiley.

Roe, Francis J., ed. Metabolic Aspects of Food Safety. LC 72-142181. 1971. 76.50 (ISBN 0-12-592550-6). Acad Pr.

Trace Contaminants of Agriculture, Fisheries & Food in Developing Countries. LC 76-8895. (Panel Proceedings Ser.). (Illus.). 108p. 1977. pap. 12.00 (ISBN 92-0-111576-8, ISP454, IAEA). Unipub.

FOOD HABITS OF ANIMALS

see Animals, Food Habits of

FOOD HANDLING

Boykin-Smith, Lorraine & Williams, Barbara K., eds. A Comprehensive Review of Food Preparation & Storage Application. LC 82-50386. 124p. 1982. pap. 14.95x (ISBN 0-938860-04-6). Westville Pub Co.

Guthrie, Rufus K. Food Sanitation. 2nd ed. (Illus.). 1980. lib. bdg. 24.50 (ISBN 0-87055-361-5). AVI.

Jernigan, Anna K. Food Sanitation: Study Course. LC 73-146936. (Illus.). 78p. 1971. pap. text ed. 7.50x (ISBN 0-8138-0815-4). Iowa St U Pr.

Longree, Karla. Quantity Food Sanitation. 3rd ed. LC 80-11551. 456p. 1980. 35.50 (ISBN 0-471-06424-6, Pub. by Wiley Interscience). Wiley.

--Sanitary Techniques in Food Service. 2nd ed. LC 81-3047. 271p. 1982. 26.00 (ISBN 0-471-08820-X). Wiley.

NIFI, ed. Applied Foodservice Sanitation. 2nd ed. LC 81-68719. 272p. 1978. Repr. of 1974 ed. text ed. 16.95 (ISBN 0-669-00792-7); 29.75 (ISBN 0-669-02106-7). Wm C Brown.

--Applied Foodservice Sanitation. 3rd ed. 272p. 1985. text ed. price not set (ISBN 0-697-00315-9); certification coursebook avail. (ISBN 0-697-00836-3). Wm C Brown.

Rajagopalan, S. Guide to Simple Sanitary Measures for the Control of Enteric Diseases. (Also avail. in French, supl. with a chapter on food sanitation). 1974. 12.80 (ISBN 92-4-154047-8). World Health.

Rimmer, Peter J. & Drakakis-Smith, David W., eds. Food Shelter & Transport. (Department of Human Geography Publications Ser.). 1978. pap. 7.00 (ISBN 0-7081-0670-6). Australia N U P.

Rudman, Jack. Food Service Worker. (Career Examination Ser.: C-260). (Cloth bdg. avail. on request). pap. 8.00 (ISBN 0-8373-0260-9). Natl Learning.

--Institution Food Administrator. (Career Examination Ser.: C-2121). (Cloth bdg. avail. on request). 1977. pap. 10.00 (ISBN 0-8373-2121-2). Natl Learning.

Safety & Quality in Food. (Developments in Animal & Veterinary Sciences Ser.: Vol. 17). 1984. 35.25 (ISBN 0-444-42409-1). Elsevier.

Scriven, Carl & Stevens, James. Food Equipment Facts. new ed. LC 80-67617. (First Ser.). 429p. (Orig.). 1980. pap. 13.95 (ISBN 0-9604902-0-5). Concept Design.

Stewart, George F. & Amerine, Maynard A. Introduction to Food Science & Technology. 2nd ed. (Food Science & Technology Ser.). 1982. 24.00 (ISBN 0-12-670256-X). Acad Pr.

Troller, John A., ed. Sanitation in Food Processing. LC 82-16291. (Food Science & Technology Ser.). 1983. 34.50 (ISBN 0-12-700660-5). Acad Pr.

FOOD INDUSTRY AND TRADE

see also Farm Produce; Food Additives; Food Supply

also individual processed food and processing industries, e.g. Cheese and Dairying; Meat Industry and Trade

Allen, Peter, ed. Processed Foods Packaging. 250p. 1982. pap. 985.00 (ISBN 0-931634-25-3). FIND-SVP.

Altschul, Aaron A., ed. New Protein Foods. (Food Science & Technology Ser.). 1974. Vol. 1A, 1974. 85.00 (ISBN 0-12-054801-1); Vol. 2B 1976. 70.00 (ISBN 0-12-054802-X). Acad Pr.

Appropriate Technology for Employment Creation in the Food Processing & Drink Industries of Developing Countries: Second Tripartite Technical Meeting for the Food Products & Drink Industries, Report 3. 1978. pap. 8.75 (ISBN 92-2-101880-6, ILO110, ILO). Unipub.

Ayres, John C. & Kirschman, John C., eds. Impact of Toxiology on Food Processing. (Institute of Food Technologists Basic Symposia Ser.). (Illus.). 1981. lib. bdg. 55.00 (ISBN 0-87055-387-9). AVI.

Baron, C. Technology, Employment & Basic Needs in Food Processing in Developing Countries. 44.00 (ISBN 0-08-025228-1). Pergamon.

Batty, J. Clair & Folkman, Steven L. Food Engineering Fundamentals. 300p. 1983. text ed. 35.45x (ISBN 0-471-05694-4). Wiley.

Bender, Arnold. Food Processing & Nutrition. (Food Science & Technology Ser.). 1978. 41.50 (ISBN 0-12-086450-9). Acad Pr.

Bibliography of Food & Agricultural Marketing in the Developing Countries. (No. 5). 114p. 1983. pap. text ed. 8.75 (ISBN 92-5-101263-6, F2382, FAO). Unipub.

Birch, G. G. & Blakebrough. Enzymes & Food Processing: An Industry-University Co-Operation Symposium. Reading, England, April 1980. (Illus.). 295p. 1980. 48.00 (ISBN 0-85334-935-5, Pub. by Elsevier Applied Sci England). Elsevier.

Bishop, D. & Carter, L. P. Crop Science & Food Production. 416p. 1983. text ed. 19.60 (ISBN 0-07-005431-2); activity guide 6.76 (ISBN 0-07-005432-0). McGraw.

Bloom, Gordon F. Productivity in the Food Industry: Problems & Potential. 240p. 1972. 25.00x (ISBN 0-262-02088-2). MIT Pr.

Braton, Norman R. Cryogenic Recycling & Processing. 256p. 1980. 78.00 (ISBN 0-8493-5779-9). CRC Pr.

Brennan, J. G., et al. Food Engineering Operations. 2ND ed. (Illus.). 532p. 1976. 44.50 (ISBN 0-85334-694-1, Pub. by Elsevier Applied Sci England). Elsevier.

Bruinsma, Domien H., et al. Selection of Technology for Food Processing in Developing Countries. 199p. 1984. pap. text ed. 7.50 (ISBN 90-220-0837-1, PDC264, Pudoc). Unipub.

Business Communications Staff. Convenience Foods & Microwave: Directions. 1980. 725.00 (ISBN 0-89336-227-1, GA-044). BCC.

--Foods under Glass. 1980. 675.00 (ISBN 0-89336-229-8, GA-046). BCC.

--Specialty Foods: New Developments. 1985. text ed. 1250.00 (ISBN 0-89336-357-X, GA-042R). BCC.

Cantor, Sidney M., ed. Use of Sugars & Other Carbohydrates in the Food Industry. LC 55-4135. (Advances in Chemistry Ser: No. 12). 1955. pap. 10.95 (ISBN 0-8412-0013-0). Am Chemical.

Casper, M. E. Energy-Saving Techniques for the Food Industry. LC 77-71931. (Energy Technology Rev. 13; Food Technology Rev. 42). (Illus.). 657p. 1977. 39.00 (ISBN 0-8155-0663-5). Noyes.

Charalambous, George, ed. Analysis of Foods & Beverages: Headspace Techniques. 1978. 49.50 (ISBN 0-12-169050-4). Acad Pr.

Charm, Stanley E. Fundamentals of Food Engineering. 3rd ed. 1978. pap. text ed. 35.00 (ISBN 0-87055-313-5). AVI.

Chiba, H., et al, eds. Food Science & Technology: Proceedings of the 5th International Congress. LC 79-20898. (Developments in Food Science Ser.: Vol. 2). 448p. 1980. 106.50 (ISBN 0-444-99770-9). Elsevier.

Chou, Marylin & Harmon, David P., Jr. Critical Food Issues of the Nineteen Eighties. LC 79-14718. (Pergamon Policy Studies). (Illus.). 1979. 52.00 (ISBN 0-08-024611-7); pap. 9.95 (ISBN 0-08-024639-7). Pergamon.

Ciobanu, A. Cooling Technology in the Food Industry. 1976. 41.00 (ISBN 0-9961000-1-6, Pub. by Abacus England). Heyden.

Clement, Jean-Michel. Dictionnaire des Industries Alimentaires. (Fr.). 361p. 1978. 32.50 (ISBN 0-686-56949-0, M-6071). French & Eur.

Clydesdale, Fergus M. & Francis, Frederick J. Human Ecological Issues: A Reader. 320p. (Orig.). 1980. pap. text ed. 9.95 (ISBN 0-8403-2197-X). Kendall-Hunt.

Code of Ethics for International Trade in Food. (CAC-RCP Ser.: 20-1979). 5p. 1980. pap. 7.50 (ISBN 92-5-101004-8, F2159, FAO). Unipub.

Codex Alimentarius Commission Reports. Incl. Vol. 3l. Methods of Analysis for Processed Fruits & Vegetables. 14p. 1980. pap. 4.50 (ISBN 92-5-100813-2, F1886); Recommended International Standards for Canned Tropical Fruit Salad. 14p. 1980. pap. 4.50 (ISBN 92-5-100809-4, F1884); Recommended International Standard for Quick Frozen Leeks. 12p. 1980. pap. 3.00 (ISBN 92-5-100808-6, F1885); Recommended International Code of Hygenic Practice for Egg Products: Section 5 - End Product Specification; Annex 2 - Microbiologic Specifications for Pasteurized Egg Products. 35p. pap. 7.50 (ISBN 92-5-100818-3, F1891). 1979 (FAO). Unipub.

Considine, Douglas M. & Considine, Glenn D. Foods & Food Production Encyclopedia. LC 81-19728. (Illus.). 2560p. 1982. 195.00 (ISBN 0-442-21612-2). Van Nos Reinhold.

Coons, Kenelm. Seasons for the Seafood Buyer-How to Plan Profitable Purchasing of Fish & Shellfish: A Guide to Natural Cycles & Regulatory Controls. Dore, Ian, ed. LC 84-2385. (Osprey Seafood Handbooks). 1986. 54.00x (ISBN 0-943738-02-4). Osprey Bks.

Cooperative Processing of Agricultural Products. 52p. 1975. pap. 7.50 (ISBN 0-685-54186-X, F744, FAO). Unipub.

Wright, Becky A., ed. Food Industry Institute Proceedings April 18-21, 1982. 99p. (Orig.). 1982. pap. 10.00 (ISBN 0-89154-197-7). Intl Found Employ.

FOOD INDUSTRY AND TRADE–DATA PROCESSING

Alvarez, J., et al. Microcomputers As Management Tools in the Sugar Cane Industry. 206p. 1985. 55.75 (ISBN 0-444-42425-3). Elsevier.

West, C. E., ed. Eurofoods: Towards Compatibility of Nutrient Data Banks in Europe. (Journal: Annals of Nutrition & Metabolism: Vol. 29, Suppl. 1, 1985). (Illus.). 72p. 1985. pap. 10.25 (ISBN 3-8055-4209-7). S Karger.

FOOD INDUSTRY AND TRADE–VOCATIONAL GUIDANCE

Appropriate Technology for Employment Creation in the Food Processing & Drink Industries of Developing Countries: Second Tripartite Technical Meeting for the Food Products & Drink Industries, Report 3. 1978. pap. 8.75 (ISBN 92-2-101880-6, ILO110, ILO). Unipub.

Endres, Joseph G. Opportunities in Food Science & Technology. 1969. pap. 1.25 (ISBN 0-8442-6480-6). Natl Textbk.

FOOD INSPECTION
see Food Adulteration and Inspection

FOOD PLANTS
see Plants, Edible

FOOD PRESERVATION
see Food–Preservation

FOOD SANITATION
see Food Handling

FOOD SERVICE
Here are entered works on quantity preparation and service of food for outside the home. Works dealing solely with quantity food preparation are entered under Quantity Cookery.
see also School Lunchrooms, Cafeterias, Etc.

Avery, Arthur C. A Modern Guide to Foodservice Equipment. LC 79-20831. (Illus.). 560p. 1980. text ed. 29.95 (ISBN 0-8436-2179-6). Van Nos Reinhold.

Barker, Lewis M., et al, eds. Learning Mechanisms in Food Selection. LC 77-76779. 632p. 1977. 40.00 (ISBN 0-918954-19-3). Baylor Univ Pr.

Birchfield, John C. Foodservice Operations Manual. LC 79-15622. 250p. 1979. spiral bd. 59.95 (ISBN 0-8436-2145-1). Van Nos Reinhold.

Border, Barbara. Food Safety & Sanitation. (Careers in Home Economics Ser.). (Illus.). 1979. pap. text ed. 12.92 (ISBN 0-07-006511-X). McGraw.

Boykin-Smith, Lorraine & Williams, Barbara K., eds. A Comprehensive Review of Food Preparation & Storage Application. LC 82-50386. 124p. 1982. pap. 14.95x (ISBN 0-938860-04-6). Westville Pub Co.

Boykin-Stith, Lorraine & Williams, Barbara K. A Basic Primer of Food Service Administration. LC 82-50566. 260p. 1982. pap. 19.95x (ISBN 0-938860-04-6). Westville Pub Co.

--A Comprehensive Review of Food Service Administration. LC 81-50668. 138p. 1981. pap. 14.95x (ISBN 0-938860-01-1). Westville Pub Co.

Business Communications Staff. Restaurant & Institutional Food Industry. 1985. 1250.00 (ISBN 0-89336-426-6, GA-039R). BCC.

Davis, Bernard. Food Commodities-Catering, Processing, Storing. 1978. pap. 16.50 (ISBN 0-434-90297-7, Pub. by W Heinemann Ltd). David & Charles.

Eison, Irving L. Strategic Marketing in Food Service: Planning for Change. LC 80-16264. 1980. 20.95 (ISBN 0-86730-231-3). Lebhar Friedman.

Gottlieb, Leon. The Best of Gottlieb's Bottom Line: A Practical Profit Guide for Today's Food Service Operator. LC 80-16535. 1980. 19.95 (ISBN 0-86730-229-1). Lebhar Friedman.

Griffin, W. R. Food Service: Health, Sanitation & Safety. (Illus.). lab. manual 26.00 (ISBN 0-9601054-4-1). Cleaning Consultant.

Haines, Robert G. Math Principles for Food Service Occupations. LC 77-88118. 1979. pap. text ed. 13.00 (ISBN 0-8273-1680-1); instr's. guide 5.25 (ISBN 0-8273-1681-X). Delmar.

Houston, Joseph & Glenesk, Neil. The Professional Service of Food & Beverage in Britain. (Illus.). 144p. 1982. 12.50 (ISBN 0-7134-3529-1, Pub. by Batsford England). David & Charles.

Imholte, Thomas J. Engineering for Food Safety & Sanitation. (Illus.). 326p. 1984. 54.95 (ISBN 0-918351-00-6). Thompson & Co.

Jernigan, Anna K. & Ross, Lynne N. Food Service Equipment. 2nd ed. (Illus.). 132p. 1980. pap. text ed. 7.50x (ISBN 0-8138-0550-3). Iowa St U Pr.

Kahrl, William L. Food Preparation. LC 78-57194. 1978. 6.95 (ISBN 0-86730-207-0). Lebhar Friedman.

--Food Service Cost Control. LC 78-57196. 1978. 6.95 (ISBN 0-86730-206-2). Lebhar Friedman.

--Food Service Equipment. LC 77-95260. 1977. 6.95 (ISBN 0-86730-203-8). Lebhar Friedman.

--Food Service Sanitation-Safety. LC 78-57192. 1978. 6.95 (ISBN 0-86730-205-4). Lebhar Friedman.

--Food Service Warehandling. LC 78-50680. 1978. 6.95 (ISBN 0-86730-204-6). Lebhar Friedman.

--Improving Food Service. LC 78-57193. 1978. 6.95 (ISBN 0-86730-209-7). Lebhar Friedman.

--Menu Planning Merchandising. LC 78-57195. 1978. 6.95 (ISBN 0-912016-71-X). Lebhar Friedman.

Kazarian, Edward A. Foodservice Facilities Planning. 2nd ed. (Illus.). 1983. text ed. 26.50 (ISBN 0-87055-436-0). AVI.

Keister, D. C. Food & Beverage Control. 1977. 27.95 (ISBN 0-13-323022-8). P-H.

Knoll, Anne P. Food Service Management: A Human Relations Approach. 1975. 21.30 (ISBN 0-07-035183-X). McGraw.

Kotschevar, Lendal H. & Terrell, Margaret E. Foodservice Planning: Layout Planning & Equipment Selection for Public Foodservice Facilities. 3rd ed. 600p. 1985. 27.95 (ISBN 0-471-81678-7). Wiley.

Levinson, Charles. Food & Beverage Operation: Cost Controls & Systems Management. (Illus.). 320p. 1976. 25.95 (ISBN 0-13-322958-0). P-H.

Livingston, G. E. & Chang, Charlotte M., eds. Food Service Systems: Analysis, Design & Implementation. 1979. 49.50 (ISBN 0-12-453150-4). Acad Pr.

Longree, Karla. Sanitary Techniques in Food Service. 2nd ed. LC 81-3047. 271p. 1982. 26.00 (ISBN 0-471-08820-X). Wiley.

Minor, Lewis J. L. J. Minor Foodservice Standards Series: Vol. 1-Nutritional Standards. (Illus.). 1983. text ed. 19.50 (ISBN 0-87055-425-5). AVI.

--L. J. Minor Foodservice Standards Series: Vol. 2-Sanitation, Safety, Environmental Standards. (Illus.). 1983. text ed. 19.50 (ISBN 0-87055-428-X). AVI.

Morgan, William J., Jr. Supervision & Management of Quantity Preparation: Principles & Procedures. 2nd, rev ed. LC 80-83876. (Illus.). 1981. 26.00 (ISBN 0-8211-1254-6); text ed. 23.00x 10 or more copies. McCutchan.

Morton, Ian D. & Morton, C. Elsevier's Dictionary of Food Science & Technology. (Eng., Fr., Span., Ger. & Lat.). 208p. 1977. 47.00 (ISBN 0-444-41559-9). Elsevier.

Mutkoski, Stephen A. & Schurer, Marcia L. Meat & Fish Management. 1981. text ed. write for info. (ISBN 0-534-00907-7, Breton Pubs). Wadsworth Pub.

National Institute for Food Service Industry, et al. Financial Ingredient in Foodservice Management. 224p. 1981. pap. text ed. write for info. (ISBN 0-697-00473-2); instrs.' manual avail. (ISBN 0-697-05229-X); student manual avail. (ISBN 0-697-05228-1). Wm C Brown.

National Institute for Food Service Industry & Axler, Bruce H. Foodservice: A Managerial Approach. 512p. 1981. text ed. write for info. (ISBN 0-669-00079-5); instrs.' manual avail. (ISBN 0-669-02723-5); student guide avail. (ISBN 0-669-02722-7). Wm C Brown.

National Institute for Food Service Industry Applied Foodservice Sanitation. 2nd ed. 272p. 1981. text ed. write for info. (ISBN 0-697-00792-8); pap. certification course book avail. (ISBN 0-697-02106-8); instr.' guide avail. (ISBN 0-697-02730-9). Wm C Brown.

NIFI, ed. Applied Foodservice Sanitation. 2nd ed. LC 81-68719. 272p. 1978. Repr. of 1974 ed. text ed. 16.95 (ISBN 0-669-00792-7); 29.75 (ISBN 0-669-02106-7). Wm C Brown.

--Applied Foodservice Sanitation. 3rd ed. 272p. 1985. text ed. price not set (ISBN 0-697-00315-9); certification coursebook avail. (ISBN 0-697-00836-3). Wm C Brown.

Ninemeier, Jack. Food & Beverage Security: Control of Cash, Food & Beverage. 208p. 1982. 3-ring binder 64.95 (ISBN 0-8436-2250-4). Van Nos Reinhold.

Posner, Barbara M. Nutrition & the Elderly: Policy Development, Program Planning, & Evaluation. LC 77-17683. 208p. 1979. 24.50x (ISBN 0-669-02085-0). Lexington Bks.

Powers, T. F. & Powers, J. M. Food Service Operations: Planning & Control. (Service Management Ser.). 372p. 1984. 29.95 (ISBN 0-471-06107-7). Wiley.

Ross, Lynne N. Work Simplification in Food Service: Individualized Instruction. LC 73-171164. (Orig., Prog. Bk.). 1972. text ed. 6.95x (ISBN 0-8138-0785-9). Iowa St U Pr.

--Work Simplification in Food Service: Individualized Instruction. 1st ed. LC 73-171164. pap. 33.50 (ISBN 0-317-27203-9, 2023865). Bks Demand UMI.

Rudman, Jack. Assistant Cook. (Career Examination Ser.: C-1101). (Cloth bdg. avail. on request). pap. 10.00 (ISBN 0-8373-1101-2). Natl Learning.

--Food Service Supervisor. (Career Examination Ser.: C-1411). (Cloth bdg. avail. on request). pap. 10.00 (ISBN 0-8373-1411-9). Natl Learning.

Spears, M. C. & Vaden, A. G. Foodservice Organizations: A Systems Approach. 850p. 1985. write for info. (ISBN 0-471-81849-6). Wiley.

Terrell, M. E. Professional Food Preparation. 2nd ed. LC 78-16985. 741p. 1979. 41.00 (ISBN 0-471-85202-3). Wiley.

Thorner, Marvin E. & Manning, Peter B. Quality Control in Foodservice. rev. ed. (Illus.). 1983. 29.50 (ISBN 0-87055-431-X). AVI.

Tolve, Arthur. Standardizing Foodservice for Quality & Efficiency. (Illus.). 1984. text ed. 27.50 (ISBN 0-87055-437-9). AVI.

Unklesbay, Nan & Unklesbay, Kenneth, eds. Energy Management in Foodservice. (Illus.). 1982. text ed. 32.50 (ISBN 0-87055-403-4). AVI.

Wilkinson, Jule. Complete Book of Cooking Equipment. 2nd ed. 336p. 1981. 26.95 (ISBN 0-8436-2186-9). Van Nos Reinhold.

FOOD SERVICE–DATA PROCESSING

Kasavana, Michael L. Computer Systems for Foodservice Operations. 272p. 1984. 24.95 (ISBN 0-8436-2274-1, CBI). Van Nos Reinhold.

FOOD SERVICE–VOCATIONAL GUIDANCE

Winn, Charles S. & Baker, M. C. Exploring Occupations in Food Service & Home Economics. (Careers in Focus Ser.). 1975. text ed. 12.52 (ISBN 0-07-071041-4). McGraw.

FOOD SUBSTITUTES

Specifications for the Identity & Purity of Sweeting Agents, Emulsifying Agents, Flavouring Agents & Other Food Additives: Twenty-Fourth Session of the FAO-WHO Expert Committee on Food Additives, Rome, 24 March - 2 April 1980. (Food & Nutrition Papers: No. 17). (Eng., Fr. & Span.). 167p. 1980. pap. 13.00 (ISBN 92-5-100984-8, F2150, FAO). Unipub.

FOOD SUBSTITUTES–PATENTS

Maltz, M. A., ed. Protein Food Supplements: Recent Advances. LC 81-38327. (Food Tech. Rev. 54). (Illus.). 404p. 1982. 48.00 (ISBN 0-8155-0865-4). Noyes.

FOOD SUPPLY

see also Agriculture–Statistics; Food–Preservation; Food Consumption; Food Industry and Trade; Meat Industry and Trade

Agricultural Production Team. Report on India's Food Crisis & Steps to Meet It. LC 75-26294. (World Food Supply Ser). 1976. Repr. of 1959 ed. 21.00x (ISBN 0-405-07767-X). Ayer Co Pubs.

Amidei, Nancy. Hunger in the Eighties: A Primer. Perry, Cecilia, ed. 166p. (Orig.). 1984. pap. write for info. (ISBN 0-934220-06-9). Food Res Action.

Approaches to World Food Security. (Economic & Social Development Papers: No. 32). 180p. 1984. pap. text ed. 13.50 (ISBN 92-5-101364-0, F2535, FAO). Unipub.

Beresford-Peirse, H. Forests, Food & People. (Freedom from Hunger Campaign Basic Studies: No. 20). 72p. (Orig.). 1968. pap. 4.50 (ISBN 0-685-09384-0, F199, FAO). Unipub.

Brown, Lester R. Food or Fuel: New Competition for the World's Cropland. LC 80-50216. (Worldwatch Papers). 1980. pap. 2.00 (ISBN 0-916468-34-8). Worldwatch Inst.

--Increasing World Food Output. LC 75-26298. (World Food Supply Ser). (Illus.). 1976. Repr. of 1965 ed. 14.00x (ISBN 0-405-07770-X). Ayer Co Pubs.

--The Worldwide Loss of Cropland. LC 78-64454. (Worldwatch Papers). 1978. pap. 2.00 (ISBN 0-916468-23-2). Worldwatch Inst.

Caird, James. Landed Interest & the Supply of Food. 4th ed. LC 67-16346. Repr. of 1880 ed. 25.00x (ISBN 0-678-05034-1). Kelley.

Chou, Marylin & Harmon, David P., Jr. Critical Food Issues of the Nineteen Eighties. LC 79-14718. (Pergamon Policy Studies). (Illus.). 1979. 52.00 (ISBN 0-08-024611-7); pap. 9.95 (ISBN 0-08-024639-7). Pergamon.

Chrispeels, Maarten J. & Sadava, David. Plants, Food, & People. LC 76-46498. (Illus.). 278p. 1977. text ed. 25.95 (ISBN 0-7167-0378-5); pap. text ed. 13.95 (ISBN 0-7167-0377-7). W H Freeman.

Christensen, Raymond P. Efficient Use of Food Resources in the United States. LC 75-26300. (World Food Supply Ser). (Illus.). 1976. Repr. of 1948 ed. 12.00x (ISBN 0-405-07772-6). Ayer Co Pubs.

Clydesdale, Fergus S. & Francis, F. J. Food, Nutrition & You. (Illus.). 1977. lib. bdg. 17.95 (ISBN 0-13-323048-1); pap. text ed. 16.95 (ISBN 0-13-323030-9). P-H.

Cohen, Joel E. Food Webs & Niche Space. (Monographs in Population Biology: No. 11). 1978. text ed. 23.00 (ISBN 0-691-08201-4); pap. 9.95 (ISBN 0-691-08202-2). Princeton U Pr.

Commission on International Relations. World Food & Nutrition Study: Supporting Papers, 5 vols. 1977. Vol. I. pap. 8.25 (ISBN 0-309-02647-4); Vol. II. pap. 8.25 (ISBN 0-309-02726-8); Vol. III. pap. 8.50 (ISBN 0-309-02730-6); Vol. IV. pap. 7.50 (ISBN 0-309-02727-6); Vol. V. pap. 7.50 (ISBN 0-309-02646-6). Natl Acad Pr.

Croxall, Harold E. & Smith, Lionel P. The Fight for Food: Factors Limiting Agricultural Production. 232p. 1984. text ed. 25.00 (ISBN 0-04-630011-2); pap. text ed. 7.95 (ISBN 0-04-630012-0). Allen Unwin.

Dahlberg, Kenneth A., ed. Beyond the Green Revolution: The Ecology & Politics of Global Agricultural Development. LC 78-11271. (Illus.). 270p. 1979. 25.00x (ISBN 0-306-40120-7, Plenum Pr). Plenum Pub.

Darby, W. J., ed. Food: the Gift of Osiris. 1977. Vol. 1. 69.50 (ISBN 0-12-203401-5); Vol.2. 69.50 (ISBN 0-12-203402-3). Acad Pr.

Deatherage, F. E. Food for Life. LC 75-15502. (Illus.). 434p. 1975. 24.50x (ISBN 0-306-30816-9, Plenum Pr). Plenum Pub.

De Kruif, Paul. Hunger Fighters. LC 67-32084. 1967. pap. 0.95 (ISBN 0-15-642430-4, Harv). HarBraceJ.

Development of Airborne Equipment to Intensify World Food Production. 218p. 1981. pap. 16.00 (ISBN 0-686-97574-X, UN81/2E24, UN). Unipub.

Ethyl Corporation. Food for America's Future. LC 72-14156. (Essay Index Reprint Ser.). Repr. of 1960 ed. 15.25 (ISBN 0-518-10009-X). Ayer Co Pubs.

Fyson, Bance L. Feeding the World. (Today's World Ser.). (Illus.). 72p. 1984. 14.95 (ISBN 0-7134-4264-6, Pub. by Batsford England). David & Charles.

Githens, Thomas S. & Wood, Carroll E. Jr. Food Resources of Africa. (African Handbooks Ser.: Vol. 3). (Illus.). 105p. 1943. 7.50x (ISBN 0-686-24087-1). Univ Mus of U PA.

Halcrow, Harold G. Food Policy for America. (TBD Ser.). (Illus.). 1977. text ed. 37.95 (ISBN 0-07-025550-4). McGraw.

Hills, Christopher & Nakamura, Hiroshi. Food from Sunlight. new ed. LC 78-9582. (Illus.). 384p. (Orig.). 1978. pap. 14.95 (ISBN 0-916438-13-9). Univ of Trees.

Idyll, C. P. The Sea Against Hunger. new, rev. ed. LC 77-2655. (Apollo Eds.). (Illus.). 1978. pap. 6.95i (ISBN 0-8152-0422-1, A-422). T Y Crowell.

International Congress of Pesticides Chemistry, 4th, Zurich, July 1978. World Food Production--Environment--Pesticides: Plenary Lectures. Geissbuehler, H., et al, eds. (IUPAC Symposia). 1979. text ed. 35.00 (ISBN 0-08-022374-5). Pergamon.

Knight, C. Gregory & Wilcox, R. Paul. Triumph or Triage? The World Food Problem in Geographical Persective. Natoli, Salvatore J., ed. LC 76-29265. (Resource Papers for College Geography Ser.). 1977. pap. text ed. 4.00 (ISBN 0-89291-115-8). Assn Am Geographers.

Let There Be Bread. (Eng., Fr., Span. & Arabic., Double frame, FAO). Unipub.

Manocha, S. L. Nutrition & Our Overpopulated Planet. (Illus.). 488p. 1975. spiral 49.50x (ISBN 0-398-03180-0). C C Thomas.

Byrne, John M., et al, eds. Families & the Energy Transition. LC 85-17706. (Marriage & Family Review Ser.: Vol. 9, Nos. 1-2). 300p. 1985. text ed. 29.95 (ISBN 0-86656-451-9, B451); pap. 22.95 (ISBN 0-86656-494-2, B494). Haworth Pr.

Cannon, Don L. Understanding Electronic Control of Energy Systems. Luecke, Gerald & Battle, Charles, eds. LC 81-85602. (Understanding Ser.). (Illus.). 272p. 1982. pap. 9.95 (ISBN 0-89512-051-8, LCB6642). Tex Instr Inc.

Carey, Helen, ed. Playing with Energy. 106p. (Orig.). 1981. pap. 5.00 (ISBN 0-87355-020-X). Natl Sci Tchrs.

Central Intelligence Agency. CIA Energy Information Reprint Series, 5 vols. Bereny, J. A., ed. Incl. Vol. I. The International Energy Situation: Outlook to 1985; Vol. 2. Prospects for Soviet Oil Production; Vol. 3. Prospects for Soviet Oil Production: A Supplemental Analysis; Vol. 4. China: Oil Production Prospects; Vol. 5. World Petroleum Outlook. 189p. 1979. Set. pap. 54.00x (ISBN 0-89934-000-8, V-050). Solar Energy Info.

Chigier, N. A., ed. Progress in Energy & Combustion Science, Vol. 6. (Illus.). 388p. 1981. 130.00 (ISBN 0-08-027153-7). Pergamon.

Chigier, Norman A., ed. Progress in Energy & Combustion Science, Vols. 1-2. Incl. Vol. 1, Pt. 1. pap. 15.50 (ISBN 0-08-019931-3); Vol. 1, Pts. 2-3. pap. 25.00 (ISBN 0-08-021023-6); Vol. 1, Pt. 4. pap. 22.00 (ISBN 0-08-021041-4); Vol. 1, Complete. Pollution Formation & Destruction in Flames. 97.50 (ISBN 0-08-020307-8); Vol. 2, Pt. 1. pap. 14.00 (ISBN 0-08-021211-5); Vol. 2, Pt. 2. pap. 14.00 (ISBN 0-08-021213-1); Vol. 2, Pt. 3. pap. 12.50 (ISBN 0-08-021215-8); Vol. 2, Pt. 4. 97.50 (ISBN 0-08-021217-4); Vol. 2 Complete, 1978. 50.00 (ISBN 0-08-021219-0). LC 75-24822. 1976-78. pap. write for info. Pergamon.

Commission of the European Communities, ed. Energy Research & Development Programme, Status Report 1977. 1977. pap. 24.00 (ISBN 90-247-2059-1, Pub. by Martinus Nijhoff Netherlands). Kluwer Academic.

Community Energy Self-Reliance. Incl. Vol. I, Alchohol Fuels, Water Power, Wind Energy. 65p. 1981. 2.75 (ISBN 0-89988-021-5); Vol. II. Sheehan, Jim, et al. (Illus.). 42p. 1981. 2.75 (ISBN 0-89988-089-4); Vol. III. McKensie, Keith & Bossong, Ken. (Illus.). 50p. 1981. 3.00 (ISBN 0-89988-090-8). Citizens Energy.

Corey, D. Q. & Maas, J. P. The Energy Couple: The New Sexuality. (Illus.). 160p. 1980. 9.95 (ISBN 0-398-03964-X). C C Thomas.

Counihan, Martin. A Dictionary of Energy. (Illus.). 200p. 1981. 16.95x (ISBN 0-7100-0847-3). Routledge & Kegan.

Cross, Michael, ed. Grow Your Own Energy. (New Scientist Guides Ser.). (Illus.). 256p. 1984. 24.95 (ISBN 0-85520-731-0); pap. 8.95x (ISBN 0-85520-730-2). Basil Blackwell.

Dalpiaz, P., et al, eds. Fundamental Interactions in Low-Energy Systems. (Ettore Majorana International Sciences Series-Physical Science: Vol. 23). 1985. 85.00x (ISBN 0-317-20605-2, Plenum Pr). Plenum Pub.

Davies, Paul. Superforce: The Search for a Grand Unified Theory of Nature. LC 84-5473. 288p. 1984. 16.95 (ISBN 0-671-47685-8). S&S.

Davis, John. Energy, to Use or Abuse. 192p. 1980. softcover 10.00x (ISBN 0-905381-00-9, Pub. by Gresham England). State Mutual Bk.

Dilavore, Philip. Energy: Insights from Physics. LC 83-19840. 414p. 1984. text ed. 30.95 (ISBN 0-471-89683-7); write for info. (ISBN 0-471-88494-4). Wiley.

Doolittle, Jesse S. Energy-a Crisis, a Dilemma, or Just Another Problem. 2nd ed. 316p. pap. 16.95 (ISBN 0-916460-33-9). Matrix Pub.

Eden, Jerome. Orgone Energy: The Answer to Atomic Suicide. LC 72-75477. 1972. 8.95 (ISBN 0-682-47477-0). Exposition Pr FL.

Emmerich, Werner, et al. Energy Does Matter. (Illus.). 1963. 7.95 (ISBN 0-8027-0096-9). Walker & Co.

Energy in Texas: Electric-Power Generation, No. 13. (Policy Research Project Reports). 125p. 1976. 3.50 (ISBN 0-89940-608-4). LBJ Sch Pub Aff.

Energy in Texas: Policy Alternatives, No. 7. (Policy Research Project Reports). 120p. 1974. 3.50 (ISBN 0-89940-603-3). LBJ Sch Pub Aff.

Fenn, John B. Engines, Energy, & Entropy: A Thermodynamics Primer. LC 81-17305. (Illus.). 293p. 1982. text ed. 19.95 (ISBN 0-7167-1281-4); pap. text ed. 12.95 (ISBN 0-7167-1282-2). W H Freeman.

Fowler, John M. Energy & the Environment. 2nd ed. 672p. 1984. pap. text ed. 27.95 (ISBN 0-07-021722-X). McGraw.

--Energy-Environment Source Book: Energy, Society, & the Environment; Energy, Its Extraction, Conversion, & Use, 2 vols. rev. ed. (Illus.). 1980. Set. pap. 9.00 (ISBN 0-87355-022-6). Natl Sci Tchrs.

Frampton, Paul & Glashow, Sheldon, eds. First Workshop on Grand Unification: University of New Hampshire, April, 1980. 370p. 1980. text ed. 30.00 (ISBN 0-915692-31-7). Birkhauser.

Gattegno, Caleb. Forms of Energy. (The Study of Energy. Vol. 1). 1963. 3.85 (ISBN 0-85225-682-5). Ed Solutions.

Gibson, Duncan. Energy Graphics. (Illus.). 144p. 1983. 21.95 (ISBN 0-13-277624-3). P-H.

Goodman, G. T. & Rowe, W. D., eds. Energy Risk Management. LC 79-42931. 1980. 53.50 (ISBN 0-12-289680-7). Acad Pr.

Hesse, Mary B. Forces & Fields. LC 74-106693. (Illus.). 318p. Repr. of 1962 ed. lib. bdg. 24.75x (ISBN 0-8371-3366-1, HEFF). Greenwood.

Hill, Richard F., ed. Energy Technology V: Challenges to Technology. LC 78-55582. (Illus.). 1063p. 1978. pap. text ed. 38.00 (ISBN 0-86587-004-7). Gov Insts.

--Energy Technology X: A Decade of Progress, X. LC 80-66431. (Energy Technology Ser.). (Illus.). 1475p. 1983. pap. text ed. 56.00 (ISBN 0-86587-011-X). Gov Insts.

Hirst, D. M. Potential Energy Surfaces. 200p. 1985. 35.00 (ISBN 0-85066-275-3). Taylor & Francis.

Hollander, Jack M. & Brooks, Harvey, eds. Annual Review of Energy, Vol. 10. (Illus.). 612p. 1985. text ed. 56.00 (ISBN 0-8243-2310-6). Annual Reviews.

Hollander, Jack M., et al, eds. Annual Review of Energy, Vol. 1. Incl. Vol. 1. Hollander, Jack M., et al, eds. (Illus.). 1976. text ed. 20.00 (ISBN 0-8243-2301-7); Vol. 2. Hollander, Jack M., et al, eds. (Illus.). 1977. text ed. 20.00 (ISBN 0-8243-2302-5); Vol. 3. Hollander, Jack M., et al, eds. 1978. text ed. 20.00 (ISBN 0-8243-2303-3); Vol. 4. Hollander, Jack M., et al, eds. (Illus.). 1979. text ed. 20.00 (ISBN 0-8243-2304-1); Vol. 5. Hollander, Jack M., et al, eds. (Illus.). 1980. text ed. 20.00 (ISBN 0-8243-2306-8); Vol. 6. Hollander, Jack M., et al, eds. (Illus.). 1981. text ed. 20.00 (ISBN 0-8243-2306-8); Vol. 7. Hollander, Jack M., et al, eds. (Illus.). 1982. text ed. 22.00 (ISBN 0-8243-2307-6); Vol. 8. Hollander, Jack M., et al, eds. (Illus.). 1983. text ed. 56.00 (ISBN 0-8243-2308-4); Vol 9. Hollander, Jack M., et al, eds. (Illus.). ix, 577p. 1984. text ed. 56.00 (ISBN 0-8243-2309-2); Vol. 10. Hollander, Jack M., et al, eds. (Illus.). 1985. text ed. 56.00 (ISBN 0-8243-2310-6). (Illus.). 1976. text ed. 20.00 (ISBN 0-8243-2301-7). Annual Reviews.

--Annual Review of Energy, Vol. 7. (Illus.). 1982. text ed. 22.00 (ISBN 0-8243-2307-6). Annual Reviews.

Hottel, H. C. & Howard, J. B. New Energy Technology - Some Facts & Assessments. 384p. 1972. pap. 6.95x (ISBN 0-262-58019-5). MIT Pr.

Inglis, K. A., ed. Energy: From Surplus to Scarcity. (Illus.). 242p. 1974. 37.00 (ISBN 0-85334-463-9, Pub. by Elsevier Applied Sci England). Elsevier.

Jammer, Max. Concepts of Force: A Study in the Foundations of Dynamics. LC 57-7610. (Illus.). Repr. of 1957 ed. 69.80 (ISBN 0-8357-9154-8, 2002782). Bks Demand UMI.

Jardine, Jim. Energy. (Heinemann Science & Technical Readers Ser.). (Orig.). 1980. pap. text ed. 2.95x (ISBN 0-435-29002-9). Heinemann Ed.

Johnson, Patti L. Acu-Energy. 17.95 (ISBN 0-89557-059-9). Bi World Indus.

Kaliaguine, S. & Mahay, A., eds. Catalysis on the Energy Scene: Proceedings of the Canadian Symposium on Catalysis, 9th, Quebec, P. Q., Sept. 30-Oct. 3, 1984. (Studies in Surface Science & Catalysis: Vol. 19). 602p. 1984. 105.75 (ISBN 0-444-42402-4). Elsevier.

Kaplan, Seymour. Energy, Economics, & the Environment. (Illus.). 448p. 1983. 42.00 (ISBN 0-07-033286-X). McGraw.

Krockel, H., et al, eds. Ceramics in Advanced Energy Technologies. 568p. 1984. lib. bdg. 79.50 (ISBN 90-277-1787-7, Pub. by Reidel Holland). Kluwer Academic.

Lawley, K. P., ed. Potential Energy Surfaces. LC 81-466015. pap. 154.50 (ISBN 0-317-26346-3, 2025196). Bks Demand UMI.

Lax, Peter D., ed. Mathematical Aspects of Production & Distribution of Energy. LC 77-7174. (Proceedings of Symposia in Applied Mathematics Ser.: No. 21). 137p. 1979. pap. 18.00 with corrections (ISBN 0-8218-0121-X, PSAPM-21). Am Math.

Lee, Kaiman & Masloff, Jacqueline. Kaiman's Encyclopedia of Energy Topics, 2 vols. LC 79-104541. (Illus.). 1979. Set. 150.00x (ISBN 0-915250-31-4). Environ Design.

Libowitz, G. G. & Whittingham, M. S., eds. Materials Science in Energy Technology. LC 78-51235. (Materials Science & Technology Ser.). 1979. 70.00 (ISBN 0-12-447550-7). Acad Pr.

Lindsay, B. R., ed. Applications of Energy: Nineteenth Century. (Benchmark Papers in Energy: Vol. 2). 1976. 71.00 (ISBN 0-12-786961-1). Acad Pr.

Lindsay, R. Bruce, ed. Energy: Historical Development of the Concept. LC 75-30719. (Benchmark Papers on Energy Ser.: Vol 1). 369p. 1975. 67.00 (ISBN 0-12-786963-8). Acad Pr.

McVeigh, J. C. Energy Around the World: An Introduction to Energy Studies: Global Resources, Needs, Utilization. (Illus.). 253p. 1984. 35.00 (ISBN 0-08-031649-2); pap. 15.00 (ISBN 0-08-031650-6). Pergamon.

Miller, David H. Energy at the Surface of the Earth: An Introduction to the Energetics of Ecosystems. (International Geophysics Ser.). 1981. 59.50 (ISBN 0-12-497150-4); student ed. 30.00 (ISBN 0-12-497152-0). Acad Pr.

Miller, Raymond C. The Force of Energy: A Business History of the Detroit Edison Company. (Illus.). 350p. 1971. 12.50 (ISBN 0-87013-164-8). Mich St U Pr.

Moore, Desmond F. Thermodynamic Principles of Energy Degrading. (Illus.). 155p. 1981. text ed. 32.50x (ISBN 0-333-29506-4, Pub. by Macmillan England); pap. 19.50x (ISBN 0-333-29504-8, Pub. by Macmillan England). Scholium Intl.

Moray, John E. The Sea of Energy. 5th ed. (Illus.). 275p. 1978. 22.50 (ISBN 0-9606374-0-0, 264-334); pap. 9.35 (ISBN 0-9606374-1-9). Cosray Res.

Morrison, Denton E. Energy: A Bibliography of Social Science & Related Literature. LC 74-4800. (Reference Library of Social Science: No. 9). 185p. 1975. lib. bdg. 28.00 (ISBN 0-8240-1096-5). Garland Pub.

Mott-Smith, Morton. Concept of Energy Simply Explained. Orig. Title: Story of Energy, Il. 1934. pap. 3.95 (ISBN 0-486-21071-5). Dover.

--The Concept of Energy Simply Explained. LC 63-19496. 1964. lib. bdg. 10.50x (ISBN 0-88307-626-8). Gannon.

Nardi, V., et al, eds. Energy Storage, Compression, & Switching, Vol. 2. 1036p. 1982. 135.00x (ISBN 0-306-41014-1, Plenum Pr). Plenum Pub.

Panvini, R. S. & Word, G. B., eds. High Energy-Interactions (Vanderbilt, 1984) AIP Conference Proceedings. LC 84-72632. (No. 121). 429p. Date not set. 43.75 (ISBN 0-88318-320-X). Am Inst Physics.

Payne, F. William, ed. The Cogeneration Sourcebook. LC 84-48530. 380p. 1985. 36.00 (ISBN 0-88173-002-5). Fairmont Pr.

Perlmutter, A., et al. Coral Cables Conference on Fundamentals Interactions at High Energy, Vol. 2. 380p. 1970. 84.75 (ISBN 0-677-14380-X). Gordon.

Perrine, Richard L. & Ernst, W. G., eds. Energy: For Ourselves & Our Posterity. (Rubey Ser.: Vol. III). (Illus.). 640p. 1986. text ed. 37.95 (ISBN 0-13-277278-7). P-H.

Ramage, Janet. Energy: A Guidebook. (Illus.). 345p. 1983. pap. 12.95x (ISBN 0-19-289157-X). Oxford U Pr.

Rieger, Heinz. Power & Energy in Alternating-Current Circuits. (Siemens Programmed Instruction Ser.: No. 14). pap. 20.00 (ISBN 0-317-27750-2, 2052090). Bks Demand UMI.

Romer, Robert H. Energy: An Introduction to Physics. LC 75-35591. (Illus.). 628p. 1976. 27.95x (ISBN 0-7167-0357-2); tchr's guide avail. W H Freeman.

Ruedisili, Lon C. & Firebaugh, Morris, eds. Perspectives on Energy: Issues, Ideas, & Environmental Dilemmas. 3rd ed. (Illus.). 1982. pap. text ed. 16.95x (ISBN 0-19-503038-9); cloth 25.95x (ISBN 0-19-503289-6). Oxford U Pr.

San Pietro, Anthony G., ed. Biochemical & Photosynthetic Aspects of Energy Production. 1980. 28.50 (ISBN 0-12-618980-3). Acad Pr.

Schuder, Charles B. Energy Engineering Fundamentals: With Residential & Commercial Applications. 176p. 1982. 22.95 (ISBN 0-442-28109-9). Van Nos Reinhold.

Scientific American Editors. Energy & Power: A Scientific American Book. LC 75-180254. (Illus.). 144p. 1971. pap. text ed. 10.95x (ISBN 0-7167-0938-4). W H Freeman.

Sih, G. & Czoboly, E. Absorbed Specific Energy & or Strain Energy Density Criterion. 1982. lib. bdg. 65.00 (ISBN 90-247-2598-4, Pub. by Martinus Nijhoff Netherlands). Kluwer Academic.

Silverman, Sanford L. & Silverman, Martin G. Theory of Relationships. LC 63-13349. 1964. 6.00 (ISBN 0-8022-1571-8). Philos Lib.

Simpson, Jan. Citizens' Energy Directory. 2nd, rev. ed. (Illus.). 185p. 1980. pap. 3.00 (ISBN 0-89988-055-X). Citizens Energy.

Slattery, John C. Momentum, Energy, & Mass Transfer in Continua. 2nd ed. LC 80-22746. 702p. 1981. text ed. 36.50 (ISBN 0-89874-212-9). Krieger.

Sneider & Picciotto. Energy. (Science in Action Ser.). (Illus.). 48p. 1984. pap. text ed. 2.85 (ISBN 0-88102-020-6). Janus Bks.

Stoker, H. Stephen, et al. Energy: From Source to Use. 1975. pap. 10.80 (ISBN 0-673-07947-3). Scott F.

Striedieck, Werner F. Energie: Von der Tretmuhle zum Kernreaktor. LC 65-12034. (Ger., Orig.). 1965. pap. text ed. 4.95x (ISBN 0-89197-141-6). Irvington.

Studies in Atmospheric Energetics Based on Aerospace Probings. Incl. Annual Report-1966. 129p. 1967. pap. 5.00 (ISBN 0-299-97024-8); Annual Report-1967. 231p. 1968. pap. 7.50x (ISBN 0-299-97025-6); Annual Report-1968. 162p. 1969. pap. 5.00 (ISBN 0-299-97026-4). pap. U of Wis Pr.

Swartz, Clifford & Goldfarb, Theodore. A Search for Order in the Physical Universe. LC 73-19743. (Illus.). 315p. 1974. text ed. 24.95x (ISBN 0-7167-0345-9). W H Freeman.

Taube, M. Evolution of Matter & Energy. (Illus.). 290p. 1985. pap. 24.00 (ISBN 0-387-13399-2). Springer-Verlag.

Thielheim, K. O., ed. Primary Energy: Present Status & Future Perspectives. (Illus.). 440p. 1982. pap. 36.00 (ISBN 0-387-11307-X). Springer-Verlag.

VanGool, W., et al, eds. Energy & Time in the Economic & Physical Sciences: Papers & Comments; Workshop Held June 1984 Wolfheze, the Netherlands. 386p. 1985. 59.25 (ISBN 0-444-87748-7, North Holland). Elsevier.

Van Koevering, Thomas E. & Sell, Nancy J. Energy: A Conceptual Approach. (Illus.). 336p. 1986. text ed. 21.95 (ISBN 0-13-277765-7); pap. text ed. 14.95 (ISBN 0-13-277757-6). P-H.

Veziroglu, Nejat, ed. Hydrogen Energy. LC 74-34483. 1436p. 1975. 150.00x (ISBN 0-306-34301-0, Plenum Pr). Plenum Pub.

White, Carol. Energy Potential: Toward a New Electromagnetic Field Theory. Cleary, James, tr. 305p. 1978. pap. 7.95 (ISBN 0-918388-04-X, QC665.E4W45, Univ Edns). New Benjamin.

Youmans, Edward L. The Correlation & Conservation of Forces. Cohen, I. Bernard, ed. LC 80-2152. (Development of Science Ser.). (Illus.). 1981. lib. bdg. 40.00 (ISBN 0-405-13961-6). Ayer Co Pubs.

Zamir, Yecheskiel. Avkoan Theory & the Nature of Energy & Temperature, Vol. 3. Date not set. price not set (ISBN 0-9614730-3-7). Y Z Pubns.

--Avkoan Theory & the Universal Order, Vol. 2. Date not set. price not set (ISBN 0-9614730-2-9). Y Z Pubns.

FORCE PUMPS

see Pumping Machinery

FORCING (PLANTS)

see also Greenhouses

Laurie, Alex, et al. Commercial Flower Forcing. 8th ed. (Illus.). 1979. text ed. 39.95x (ISBN 0-07-036633-0). McGraw.

Zweig, Gunter & Lawrence, James, eds. Analytical Methods for Pesticides & Plant Growth Regulators, Vol. 12: High Performance Liquid Chromatography (HPLC) of Pesticides. LC 63-16560. 1982. 45.00 (ISBN 0-12-784312-4). Acad Pr.

FORD AUTOMOBILE

see Automobiles–Types–Ford

FORD MOTOR COMPANY

Arnold, Horace L. & Faurote, Fay L. Ford Methods & the Ford Shops. LC 72-5029. (Technology & Society Ser.). (Illus.). 450p. 1972. Repr. of 1915 ed. 38.50 (ISBN 0-405-04682-0). Ayer Co Pubs.

Dominguez, Henry. The Ford Agency: A Pictorial History. 1981. pap. 14.95 (ISBN 0-87938-095-0). Motorbooks Intl.

Meyer, Stephen, III. The Five Dollar Day: Labor Management & Social Control in the Ford Motor Company, 1908-1921. LC 80-22795. (American Social History Ser.). 230p. 1981. 39.50x (ISBN 0-87395-508-0); pap. 11.95x (ISBN 0-87395-509-9). State U NY Pr.

Post, Dan R., ed. Ford, Closing the Years of Tradition. 1975. 14.95 (ISBN 0-911160-35-3). Post-Era.

Sorensen, Lorin. The American Ford. (Fordiana Ser.). (Illus.). 263p. 1975. 49.50 (ISBN 0-87938-079-9). Silverado.

Wilkins, Mira & Hill, Frank E. American Business Abroad: Ford on Six Continents. LC 64-12747. (Illus.). 559p. 1964. 14.95x (ISBN 0-8143-1227-6). Wayne St U Pr.

FORECASTING

Anderson, M. G. & Burt, T. P. Hydrological Forecasting. (Geomorphology Ser.). 1985. 54.95 (ISBN 0-471-90614-X). Wiley.

Clarke, Arthur C. Profiles of the Future. 304p. (Orig.). 1985. pap. 3.50 (ISBN 0-446-32107-9). Warner Bks.

Cleary, James P. & Levenbach, Hans. The Professional Forecaster: The Forecasting Process Through Data Analysis. 402p. 1982. 31.50 (ISBN 0-534-97960-2). Van Nos Reinhold.

Nao, T. Van. Forest Fire Prevention & Control. 1982. text ed. 39.50 (ISBN 90-247-3050-3, Pub. by Martinus Nijhoff). Kluwer Academic.
NFPA Forest Committee. Chemicals for Forest Fire Fighting. 3rd ed. Lyons, Paul, ed. LC 77-814121. 1977. pap. text ed. 6.50 (ISBN 0-87765-104-3, FSP-19A). Natl Fire Prot.
Shaw, J. Principles of Wildfire Management. 352p. 1984. 32.95 (ISBN 0-07-056481-7). McGraw.
Spring, Ira & Fish, Byron. Lookouts: Firewatchers of the Cascades & Olympics. (Illus.). 208p. (Orig.). 1981. pap. 9.95 (ISBN 0-89886-014-8). Mountaineers.
Systems for Evaluating & Predicting the Effects of Weather & Climate on Wildland Fires. (Special Environmental Reports: No. 11). 40p. 1978. pap. 10.00 (ISBN 92-63-10496-4, W389, WMO). Unipub.
Wolffsohn, A. Fire Control in Tropical Pine Forests. 1981. 30.00x (ISBN 0-85074-056-8, Pub. by For Lib Comm England). State Mutual Bk.

FOREST FLORA
see also Woody Plants
Dawkins, H. C. & Field, D. R. A Long-Term Surveillance System for British Woodland Vegetation. 1978. 40.00x (ISBN 0-85074-038-X, Pub. by For Lib Comm England). State Mutual Bk.
Longman, K. A. Vegetative Propagation of Trees in the 1980s. 1980. 30.00x (ISBN 0-85074-055-X, Pub. by For Lib Comm England). State Mutual Bk.
Wiegers, J. Succession in Fen Woodland Ecosystems in the Dutch Haf District with Special Reference to Betula Pubescens Ehrh. (Dissertationes Botanicae Ser.: No. 86). (Illus.). 152p. 1985. pap. text ed. 21.00x (ISBN 3-7682-1441-9). Lubrecht & Cramer.

FOREST GENETICS
see also Tree Breeding
Burley, J. & Nikles, D. C. Selection & Breeding to Improve Some Tropical Conifers, 2 Vols, Vol. 1. 1972. Vol. 1. 90.00x (ISBN 0-85074-026-6, Pub. by For Lib Comm England); Vol. 2. 95.00x (ISBN 0-85074-027-4). State Mutual Bk.
Burley, J. & Styles, B. T., eds. Tropical Trees: Variation Breeding & Conservation. 1976. 49.50 (ISBN 0-12-145150-X). Acad Pr.
Cannell, M. G. & Last, F. T., eds. Tree Physiology & Yield Improvement. 1977. 80.50 (ISBN 0-12-158750-9). Acad Pr.
Forest Genetic Resources Information: 1977, No. 6. (Forestry Papers: No. 1). (Illus.). 1977. pap. 8.00 (ISBN 0-685-80147-0, F917, FAO). Unipub.
Krugman, Stanley L., et al. Forest Genetics & Tree Improvement in the People's Republic of China. LC 82-62310. 84p. (Orig.). 1983. pap. 3.00 (ISBN 0-939970-19-8, SAF 83-02). Soc Am Foresters.
The Methodology of Conservation of Forest Genetic Resources: Report on a Pilot Study. (Illus.). 127p. 1976. pap. 11.50 (ISBN 0-685-62394-7, F1136, FAO). Unipub.
Miksche, J. P., ed. Modern Methods in Forest Genetics. LC 76-8828. (Illus.). 1976. 36.00 (ISBN 0-387-07708-1). Springer-Verlag.
Nikles, D. G., et al. Progress & Problems of Genetic Improvement of Tropical Forest Trees, 2 Vols. 1978. 165.00x (ISBN 0-85074-020-7, Pub. by For Lib Comm England). State Mutual Bk.
Report of the Fourth Session of the FAO Panel of Experts on Forest Gene Resources Held in Canberra, Australia. 1977. pap. 7.50 (ISBN 92-5-100379-3, F1338, FAO). Unipub.
Wright, Jonathan W. Introduction to Forest Genetics. 1976. 35.00 (ISBN 0-12-765250-7). Acad Pr.

FOREST INDUSTRIES
see Wood-Using Industries

FOREST INFLUENCES
see also Forests and Forestry; Vegetation and Climate
Beresford-Peirse, H. Forests, Food & People. (Freedom from Hunger Campaign Basic Studies: No. 20). 72p. (Orig.). 1968. pap. 4.50 (ISBN 0-685-09384-0, F199, FAO). Unipub.

FOREST MACHINERY–DIRECTORIES
FAO & ILO. Chainsaws in Tropical Forests. (Training Ser.: No. 2). 96p. 1980. pap. 10.25 (ISBN 92-5-100932-5, F2116, FAO). Unipub.
International Directory of Manufacturers of Forestry Instruments & Hand Tools. 1967. pap. 6.00 (F245, FAO). Unipub.

FOREST MANAGEMENT
see Forest Policy; Forests and Forestry

FOREST MENSURATION
see Forests and Forestry–Mensuration

FOREST PLANTING
see Forests and Forestry

FOREST PLANTS
see Forest Flora

FOREST POLICY
see also Forests and Forestry
Cameron, Jenks. Development of Governmental Forest Control in the United States. (Brookings Institution Reprint Ser.). Repr. of 1928 ed. lib. bdg. 29.00x (ISBN 0-697-00153-9). Irvington.
Earl, D. E. Forest Energy & Economic Development. (Illus.). 1975. 27.50x (ISBN 0-19-854521-5). Oxford U Pr.
Gane, M. Priorities in Planning. 1969. 30.00x (ISBN 0-85074-007-X, Pub. by For Lib Comm England). State Mutual Bk.
Pinchot, Gifford. Adirondack Spruce, A Study of the Forest in Ne-Ha-Sa-Ne Park. LC 77-125756. (American Environmental Studies). 1971. Repr. of 1907 ed. 14.00 (ISBN 0-405-02682-X). Ayer Co Pubs.
--Biltmore Forest. LC 70-125757. (American Environmental Studies). 1970. Repr. of 1893 ed. 13.00 (ISBN 0-405-02683-8). Ayer Co Pubs.
Sedjo, Roger A., ed. Investments in Forestry: Resources, Land Use & Public Policy. (Westview Special Studies in Natural Resources & Energy Management). 250p. 1985. soft cover 23.50x (ISBN 0-8133-7039-6). Westview.
Waring, R. H. & Schlesinger, W. H. Forest Ecosystems: Concepts & Management. Date not set. 45.00 (ISBN 0-12-735440-9). Acad Pr.
Williams, M. R. Decision-Making in Forest Management. (Forestry Research Press Ser.). 143p. 1981. 48.95x (ISBN 0-471-10097-8, Pub. by Res Stud Pr). Wiley.

FOREST PRODUCTS
see also Gums and Resins; Lumber; Lumber Trade; Rubber; Timber; Wood; Wood-Pulp; Wood-Using Industries
Baker, Andrew J., ed. Advances in Production of Forest Products. (AIChE Symposium Ser.: Vol. 79). 87p. 1983. pap. 30.00 (ISBN 0-8169-0247-X, S-223); pap. 15.00 (ISBN 0-317-03718-8). Am Inst Chem Eng.
Classification & Definitions of Forest Products. (Forestry Papers: No. 32). (Eng., Fr., Span. & Arabic.). 256p. 1982. pap. 18.50 (ISBN 92-5-001209-8, F2325, FAO). Unipub.
Davis, Richard C., compiled by. Inventory of the Records of the National Forest Products Association. (Guides to Forest & Conservation History of North America, No. 3). 1976. pap. 1.00 (ISBN 0-89030-031-3). Forest Hist Soc.
Estimated Production of Pulp, Paper & Paperboard in Certain Countries in 1981: FAO Advisory Committee on Pulp and Paper, 23rd Session, Rome, 9-12 June 1982. 30p. 1982. pap. 7.50 (ISBN 0-686-84613-3, F2327, FAO). Unipub.
Ford-Robertson, F. C. & Winters, Robert K., eds. Terminology of Forest Science, Technology, Practice & Products. rev. ed. LC 82-61327. (The Multilingual Forestry Terminology Ser.). 370p. 1983. pap. 15.00 (ISBN 0-939970-16-3, SAF 83-01). Soc Am Foresters.
Forest Products Prices, 1961-1980. (Forestry Papers: No. 23). (Eng., Fr & Span.). 113p. 1981. pap. 8.00 (ISBN 92-5-001042-7, F2140, FAO). Unipub.
Haygreen, John G. & Bowyer, James L. Forest Products & Wood Science: An Introduction. (Illus.). 496p. 1982. text ed. 24.95 (ISBN 0-8138-1800-1). Iowa St U Pr.
Hillis, W. E. & Brown, A. G., eds. Eucalypts for Wood Production. 434p. 1980. 90.00x (ISBN 0-643-02245-7, Pub. by CSIRO Australia). State Mutual Bk.
Phillips, F. H. The Pulping & Papermaking Potential of Tropical Hardwoods, Vol. 1. 1980. 20.00x (ISBN 0-643-00339-8, Pub. by CSJRO). State Mutual Bk.
Reese, Richard M. Marketing of a Forest Product: A Chance-Constrained Transportation Model. LC 74-4903. (Studies in Marketing: No. 20). (Illus.). 80p. 1974. pap. 4.00 (ISBN 0-87755-189-8). Bureau Busn UT.
The Saurus of Forest Products Terms. 167p. 1980. 30.00 (ISBN 0-935018-21-2). Forest Prod.
Sedjo, Roger A. & Radcliffe, Samuel J. Postwar Trends in U. S. Forest Products Trade: A Global, National & Regional View. LC 80-8886. (Resources for the Future Research Paper: R-22). (Illus.). 622p. 1981. pap. text ed. 18.00x (ISBN 0-8018-2635-7). Johns Hopkins.
Sedjo, Roger A., ed. Issues in U. S. International Forest Products Trade: Proceedings of a Workshop. LC 80-8885. (Resources for the Future Research Paper: R-23). (Illus.). 276p. 1981. pap. text ed. 12.95x (ISBN 0-8018-2634-9). Johns Hopkins.
World Forest Products Demand & Supply, 1990-2000. (Forestry Papers: No. 29). (Eng., Fr & Span.). 366p. 1982. pap. 26.00 (ISBN 92-5-101167-2, F2274, FAO). Unipub.
Yearbook of Forest Products Statistics. annual Incl. 1950. pap. 5.25 (F559); 1952. pap. 5.25 (ISBN 0-685-48284-7, F555); 1953. pap. 0.10.25 (ISBN 0-685-48285-5); 1954; 1955. pap. 5.25 (F557); 1956; 1957. pap. 10.25 (ISBN 0-685-48288-X, F558); 1961. pap. 10.25 (ISBN 0-685-48289-8, F560); 1964. pap. 12.75 (ISBN 0-685-48290-1, F561); 1965. 132p. pap. 12.75 (F562); 1966. 144p. pap. 5.75 (ISBN 92-5-001682-4, F563); 1967. 156p. pap. 12.75 (92-5-001683-2); 1968. pap. 10.25 (F565); 1969. 216p. pap. 19.25 (ISBN 92-5-001684-0, F1924); 1970. 228p. pap. 16.00 (92-5-001685-9); 1972: Review 1961-1972. 371p. 1972. 30.25 (ISBN 92-5-001686-7, F568); 1973: Review 1962-1973. 371p. 1973. 30.25 (ISBN 92-5-001687-5, F569); 1974: Review 1963-1974. 407p. 1976. 33.00 (ISBN 92-5-001688-3, F570, FAO); 1976: Review 1965-1976. (No. 14). 392p. 1978. 29.50 (ISBN 92-5-000542-3, F1400); 1977: Review 1966-1977. (No. 21). 462p. 1979. 37.00 (ISBN 92-5-000732-9, F1577, FAO); 1978: Review 1967-1978. (No. 27). 428p. 1980. 40.50 (ISBN 92-5-000888-0, F1906); 1968-1979. 430p. 1981. 44.25 (F2168, FAO); 1981: Review 1970-1981. 408p. 1983. 44.25 (F2403). (Statistical Ser.). (Orig.). pap. (FAO). Unipub.
Yearbook of Forest Products, 1980: 1969-1980. (Economic & Social Development Papers: No. 15). 414p. 1982. 44.25 (ISBN 92-5-001175-X, F2270, FAO). Unipub.

FOREST PROTECTION
see also Plants, Protection of; Trees–Diseases and Pests
McFadden, Max W., et al. Forest Pest Management in the People's Republic of China. LC 82-50539. 86p. (Orig.). 1982. pap. 5.00 (ISBN 0-939970-14-7, SAF 82-03). Soc Am Foresters.
Seidensticker, John. Managing Elephant Depredation in Agricultural & Forestry Projects. 50p. 3.00 (ISBN 0-318-02824-7, BK0297). World Bank.
Smith, W. H. Air Pollution & Forests. (Springer Series on Environmental Management). (Illus.). 379p. 1981. 35.00 (ISBN 0-387-90501-4). Springer-Verlag.

FOREST REPRODUCTION
see Forests and Forestry

FOREST SOILS
Acidic Deposition & Forests. (SAF Resource Policy Ser.). 56p. (Orig.). 1984. pap. 4.50 (ISBN 0-939970-25-2, SAF 84-14). Soc Am Foresters.
Bowman, Isaiah. Forest Physiography: Physiography of the United States & Principles of Soils in Relation to Forestry. LC 78-125732. (American Environmental Studies). 1970. Repr. of 1911 ed. 52.00 (ISBN 0-405-02659-5). Ayer Co Pubs.
Pritchett, William L. Properties & Management of Forest Soils. LC 78-23196. 500p. 1979. text ed. 43.50 (ISBN 0-471-03718-4). Wiley.
Wambeke, A. van. Management Properties of Ferralsols. (Soils Bulletins: No. 23). 120p. (2nd Printing 1979). 1980. pap. 8.75 (ISBN 92-5-100754-3, F1165, FAO). Unipub.

FOREST SURVEYS
Husch, Bertram, et al. Forest Mensuration. 3rd ed. LC 82-4811. 402p. 1982. 36.50 (ISBN 0-471-04423-7). Wiley.
Wilson, A. L. Elementary Forest Surveying & Mapping, Two. 1982. pap. text ed. 7.95x (ISBN 0-88246-136-2). Oreg St U Bkstrs.
Wilson, R. L. Elementary Forest Surveying & Mapping. 1985. pap. text ed. 5.45x (ISBN 0-88246-135-4). Oreg St U Bkstrs.

FORESTATION
see Forests and Forestry

FORESTRY EDUCATION
see Forestry Schools and Education

FORESTRY ENGINEERING
see also Lumbering
Appropriate Technology in Forestry: Report of the Consultation on Intermediate Technology in Forestry, New Delhi and Dehra Dun, October 18-November 7, 1981. (Forestry Papers: No. 31). 140p. 1982. pap. 10.00 (ISBN 92-5-101185-0, F2297, FAO). Unipub.
Ford-Robertson, F. C. & Winters, Robert K., eds. Terminology of Forest Science, Technology, Practice & Products. rev. ed. LC 82-61327. (The Multilingual Forestry Terminology Ser.). 370p. 1983. pap. 15.00 (ISBN 0-939970-16-3, SAF 83-01). Soc Am Foresters.
Maddison, Bernard H. Handbook of Timber Engineering Design. (Illus.). 83p. 1982. pap. text ed. 15.95x (ISBN 0-9593488-0-8, Pub. by U of W Austral Pr). Intl Spec Bk.

FORESTRY RESEARCH
Bonga, J. M. & Durzan, D. J. Tissue Culture in Forestry. 1982. lib. bdg. 49.50 (ISBN 90-247-2660-3, Pub. by Martinus Nijhoff Netherlands). Kluwer Academic.
Romberger, J. A. & Mikola, P., eds. International Review of Forestry Research, Vols. 1-3. 60.00. Vol. 1, 1964 (ISBN 0-12-365501-3). Vol. 3, 1970. 60.00 (ISBN 0-12-365503-X). Acad Pr.
Sanger, C. & Lessard, G. Trees for People: An Account of Forestry Research Program Supported by IDRC. 52p. 1977. pap. 5.00 (ISBN 0-88936-139-8, IDRC94, IDRC). Unipub.

FORESTRY SCHOOLS AND EDUCATION
Demmon, E. L. Opportunities in Forestry Careers. rev. ed. LC 74-25903. (Illus.). 1975. text ed. 6.60 (ISBN 0-8442-6442-3); pap. text ed. 4.95 (ISBN 0-8442-6441-5). Natl Textbk.
Graves, Henry S. & Guise, C. H. Forest Education. 1932. 59.50x (ISBN 0-686-51388-6). Elliots Bks.
McCulloch, Walter F. Forest Management Education in Oregon. (Studies in Education & Guidance: No. 2). 136p. 1949. pap. 5.95x (ISBN 0-87071-042-7). Oreg St U Pr.
Mason, Earl G. Functional Curriculum in Professional Forestry. (Studies in Education & Guidance Ser: No. 1). 100p. 1944. pap. 5.95x (ISBN 0-87071-041-9). Oreg St U Pr.
Report on Forestry Education: Advisory Commission, 9th Session, Jakarta, 1978. (Forestry Papers: No. 48). 139p. 1979. pap. 9.50 (ISBN 0-686-93009-6, F1848, FAO). Unipub.
Summary Record of the Eighth Session of FAO Advisory Committee on Forestry Education. 47p. 1980. pap. 9.00 (ISBN 92-5-100480-3, F1968, FAO). Unipub.
Trask, Samuel, et al. Forestry Education in America Today & Tomorrow. LC 63-21251. (Illus.). 402p. 1963. 5.00 (ISBN 0-939970-12-0). Soc Am Foresters.

FORESTS AND FORESTRY
see also Aeronautics in Forestry; Botany–Ecology; Flood Control; Forest Flora; Hardwoods; Lumber; Lumber Trade; Lumbering; Natural History–Outdoor Books; Pruning; Rain Forests; Tree Planting; Trees; Wood
Adlard, P. G. & Richardson, K. F. Stand Density & Stem Taper in Pinus Patula: Schiede & Deppe. 1978. 30.00x (ISBN 0-85074-047-9, Pub. by For Lib Comm England). State Mutual Bk.
Adlard, P. G. & Smith, J. P. Growth & Growing Space. 1981. 30.00x (ISBN 0-85074-054-1, Pub. by For Lib Comm England). State Mutual Bk.
AGRIS Forestry: World Catalogue of Information & Documentation Services. (Forestry Papers: No. 15). (Eng., Fr & Span.). 152p. 1979. pap. 11.00 (ISBN 92-5-000810-4, F1876, FAO). Unipub.
Ahlgren, Clifford & Ahlgren, Isabel. Lob Trees in the Wilderness. LC 83-16809. (Illus.). 232p. 1984. 29.50x (ISBN 0-8166-1264-1); pap. 12.95 (ISBN 0-8166-1262-5). U of Minn Pr.
Allison, Philip. The New Forest. 1981. 45.00x (ISBN 0-686-75453-0, Pub. by Cave Pubns England). State Mutual Bk.
American Foresters Society & Wildlife Society. Choices in Silviculture for American Forests. LC 81-51229. (Illus.). 88p. (Orig.). 1981. pap. 4.00 (ISBN 0-939970-09-0). Soc Am Foresters.
America's Hardwood Forests: Opportunities Unlimited. LC 83-60910. 352p. (Orig.). 1983. pap. 17.00 (ISBN 0-939970-19-8, SAF 83-04). Soc Am Foresters.
Anderson, David & Holland, I. I., eds. Forests & Forestry. 3rd ed. 1982. 19.65 (ISBN 0-8134-2169-1); text ed. 14.75x. Interstate.
Armson, K. A. Forest Soils: Properties & Processes. 1977. 27.50 (ISBN 0-8020-2265-0). U of Toronto Pr.
Basic Technology in Forest Operations. (Forestry Papers: No. 36). (Eng., Fr & Span.). 137p. 1982. pap. text ed. 10.00 (ISBN 92-5-101260-1, F2380, FAO). Unipub.
Bernatzky, A. Tree Ecology & Preservation. (Developments in Agricultural & Managed-Forest Ecology Ser.: Vol. 2). 358p. 1978. 72.50 (ISBN 0-444-41606-4). Elsevier.
Biology Colloquium, 40th, Oregon State University, 1979. Forests: Fresh Perspectives from Ecosystem Analysis: Proceedings. Waring, Richard H., ed. LC 80-14883. (Illus.). 210p. 1979. pap. 15.95x (ISBN 0-87071-179-2). Oreg St U Pr.
Bowman, Isaiah. Forest Physiography: Physiography of the United States & Principles of Soils in Relation to Forestry. LC 78-125732. (American Environmental Studies). 1970. Repr. of 1911 ed. 52.00 (ISBN 0-405-02659-5). Ayer Co Pubs.
Braun, E. L. Deciduous Forests of Eastern North America. 1967. Repr. of 1950 ed. 31.95x (ISBN 0-02-841910-3). Hafner.
Braun, Thomas B., et al, eds. In Place Resource Inventories: Principles & Practices. LC 82-61437. 1101p. (Orig.). 1982. pap. 20.00 (ISBN 0-939970-17-1, SAF 82-02). Soc Am Foresters.
Brown, G. W. Forestry & Water Quality. 1983. pap. text ed. 8.65x (ISBN 0-88246-007-2). Oreg St U Bkstrs.
Cable Logging Systems. (Forestry Papers: No. 24). 104p. 1981. pap. 8.00 (ISBN 92-5-101046-3, F2178, FAO). Unipub.

Prats-Llaurado, J. & Speidel, G. Public Forestry Administration in Latin America. (Forestry Papers: No. 25). 185p. 1981. pap. 13.50 (ISBN 92-5-101051-X, F2179, FAO). Unipub.

Purcell, L. E., ed. Forest Resource Management in the States. 112p. 1982. pap. 8.00 (ISBN 0-87292-028-3). Coun State Govts.

Rakestraw, Lawrence W. A History of the United States Forest Service in Alaska. LC 81-620020. (Alaska Historical Commission Studies in History: No. 6). (Illus.). 221p. (Orig.). 1981. pap. text ed. 8.50 (ISBN 0-943712-06-8); microfiche 4.00 (ISBN 0-943712-05-X). Alaska Hist.

Raphael, Ray. Tree Talk: The People & Politics of Timber. (Illus.). 304p. (Orig.). 1981. pap. 12.00 (ISBN 0-933280-10-6). Island Ca.

Redfield, Alfred C. & Maunder, Elwood R. The Recollections of an Ecologist on the Origins of the Natural Resources Council of America. (Illus.). 74p. 1974. 25.00 (ISBN 0-89030-004-6). Forest Hist Soc.

Reifsnyder, William E. & Lull, Howard W. Radiant Energy in Relation to Forests. LC 77-10239. (U. S. Department of Agriculture. Technical Bulletin: 1344). Repr. of 1965 ed. 15.00 (ISBN 0-404-16217-7). AMS Pr.

Report of the Fifteenth Session of the Intergovernmental Group on Jute, Kenaf & Allied Fibres to the CCP. 18p. 1980. pap. 9.00 (ISBN 92-5-100863-9, F1908, FAO). Unipub.

Report of the North American Forestry Commission: 8th Session. (Illus., Orig.). 1976. pap. 7.50 (ISBN 92-5-100025-5, F1111, FAO). Unipub.

Report of the Tenth Session of the Asia-Pacific Forestry Commission. 33p. 1978. pap. 7.50 (ISBN 92-5-100370-X, F1349, FAO). Unipub.

Report on the Second FAO SIDA Training Course on Forest Inventory: Ibadan, Nigeria, Aug. 12 - Sept. 13, 1974. (Swedish.). pap. 13.50 (F1096, FAO). Unipub.

Richards, John F. & Tucker, Richard P. Global Deforestation & the Nineteenth Century World Economy. LC 82-18273. (Duke Press Policy Studies). 232p. 1983. 35.75 (ISBN 0-8223-0482-1). Duke.

Richardson, Curtis J., ed. Pocosin Wetlands: An Integrated Analysis of Coastal Plain Freshwater Bogs in North Carolina. LC 81-7158. 364p. 1981. 28.50 (ISBN 0-87933-418-5). Van Nos Reinhold.

Rigby, G. R., intro. by. Expanding Horizons in Chemical Engineering. (Chemeca Ser.). 241p. (Orig.). 1979. pap. text ed. 54.00x (ISBN 0-85825-116-7, Pub. by Inst Engineering Australia). Brookfield Pub Co.

Robbie, T. A. Teach Yourself Forestry. 10.00x (ISBN 0-392-08216-0, SpS). Sportshelf.

Roth, Filibert. Forest Regulation. 1925. 4.95x (ISBN 0-685-21784-1). Wahr.

Rudman, Jack. Forester. (Career Examination Ser.: C-289). (Cloth bdg. avail. on request). pap. 10.00 (ISBN 0-8373-0289-7). Natl Learning.

--Forestry Technician. (Career Examination Ser.: C-1424). (Cloth bdg. avail. on request). pap. 10.00 (ISBN 0-8373-1424-0). Natl Learning.

--Senior Forestry Technician. (Career Examination Ser.: C-2715). (Cloth bdg. avail. on request). 1980. pap. 14.00 (ISBN 0-8373-2715-6). Natl Learning.

--Urban Forester. (Career Examination Ser.: C-2905). (Cloth bdg. avail. on request). pap. 12.00 (ISBN 0-8373-2905-1). Natl Learning.

Safety & Health in Forestry Work: ILO Code of Practice. 1969. 5.15 (ISBN 92-2-100017-6). Intl Labour Office.

Saltman, David. Paper Basics: Forestry, Manufacture, Selection, Purchasing, Mathematics & Metrics, Recycling. 1978. 16.95 (ISBN 0-442-25121-1). Van Nos Reinhold.

Sands, Anne, ed. Riparian Forests in California. LC 80-53162. (Illus.). 121p. pap. 4.00x (ISBN 0-931876-41-9, 4101). Ag & Nat Res.

Scheduling the Harvest of Old Growth. (SAF Resource Policy Ser.). 50p. 1984. pap. 4.50 (ISBN 0-939970-24-4, SAF 84-09). Soc Am Foresters.

Schwab, Judith L. Recreation as a Forest Product. (Public Administration Ser.: Bibliography P 1096). 57p. 1982. pap. 8.25 (ISBN 0-88066-286-7). Vance Biblios.

Sedjo, Roger A. & Ostermeier, David M. Policy Alternatives for Nonindustrial Private Forests. LC 78-53432. 71p. (Orig.). 1978. pap. 4.00 (ISBN 0-939970-10-4). Soc Am Foresters.

Sedjo, Roger A., ed. Investments in Forestry: Resources, Land Use & Public Policy. (Westview Special Studies in Natural Resources & Energy Management). 250p. 1985. soft cover 23.50x (ISBN 0-8133-7039-6). Westview.

Shands, William E., et al. National Forest Policy: From Conflict Toward Consensus. LC 79-88975. 1979. pap. 4.00 (ISBN 0-89164-054-1). Conservation Foun.

Sharpe, G. W. & Hendes, C. Introduction to Forestry. 5th ed. (Forest Resources Ser.). 576p. 1986. price not set (ISBN 0-07-056482-5). McGraw.

Sharpe, Grant W., et al. Introduction to Forestry. 4th ed. (Forest Resources Ser.). 1976. text ed. 37.95 (ISBN 0-07-056480-9). McGraw.

Shugart, H. H. A Theory of Forest Dynamics: The Ecological Implications of Forest Succession Models. (Illus.). 305p. 1984. 39.50 (ISBN 0-387-96000-7). Springer-Verlag.

Smith, David M. The Practice of Silviculture. 7th ed. LC 62-16244. 578p. 1962. 39.50 (ISBN 0-471-80017-1). Wiley.

Smith, W. Ramsay, ed. Energy from Forest Biomass. LC 82-20745. (Symposium). 1983. 33.50 (ISBN 0-12-652780-6). Acad Pr.

Society of American Foresters. Town Meeting Forestry: Issues for the 1980's. Evans, H. H., ed. (SAF Convention Proceedings Ser. -1979). (Illus.). 320p. (Orig.). 1980. pap. 17.00 (ISBN 0-939970-06-6). Soc Am Foresters.

Sonnenfeld, Jeffrey A. Corporate Views of the Public Interest: Perceptions of the Forest Products Industry. 304p. 1981. 24.95 (ISBN 0-86569-060-X). Auburn Hse.

Springer, John S. Forest Life & Forest Trees. rev. ed. (Illus.). 292p. 1971. Repr. of 1851 ed. 7.50x (ISBN 0-912274-08-5). O'Brien.

Standiford, Richard B. & Ramacher, Shirley I., eds. Cumulative Effects of Forest Management on California Watersheds: An Assessment of Status & Need for Information. LC 81-68328. 109p. (Orig.). 1981. pap. 4.00x (ISBN 0-931876-48-6, 3268). Ag & Nat Res.

Stoddard, Charles H. Essentials of Forestry Practice. 3rd ed. LC 78-6652. 387p. 1978. text ed. 31.50 (ISBN 0-471-07262-1). Wiley.

--The Small Private Forest in the United States. LC 77-86414. Repr. of 1961 ed. 17.50 (ISBN 0-404-60345-9). AMS Pr.

Sutton, Ann & Sutton, Myron. Eastern Forest. Elliott, Charles, ed. LC 84-48671. (The Audubon Society Nature Guides Ser.). (Illus.). 638p. 1985. pap. 14.95 (ISBN 0-394-73126-3). Knopf.

--Wildlife of the Forests. (Wildlife Habitat Ser.). (Illus.). 1979. 19.95 (ISBN 0-8109-1759-9). Abrams.

Symposium on Forest Meteorology. Symposium on Forest Meteorology: Proceedings. 233p. 1980. pap. text ed. 10.00 (ISBN 92-63-00527-3, W447, WMO). Unipub.

Tiwari, K. M. Social Forestry for Rural Development. (Illus.). 108p. 1983. text ed. 21.25x (Pub. by Intl Bk Dist). Intl Spec Bk.

Tripartite Technical Meeting for the Timber Industry, Third, Geneva, 1981. Employment Promotion & Vocational Training in the Timber Industry, with Particular Reference to Developing Countries, Report III. International Labour Office, ed. iii, 77p. (Orig.). 1981. pap. 7.15 (ISBN 92-2-102766-X). Intl Labour Office.

--Occupational Safety & Health Problems in the Timber Industry, Report II. International Labour Office, ed. iii, 78p. (Orig.). 1981. pap. 7.15 (ISBN 92-2-102765-1). Intl Labour Office.

U. S. Dept. of Agriculture-Forest Service. Timber Resources for America's Future: Forest Resource Report No. 14. LC 72-2872. (Use & Abuse of America's Natural Resources Ser). 728p. 1972. Repr. of 1958 ed. 41.00 (ISBN 0-405-04538-7). Ayer Co Pubs.

U. S. Senate. A National Plan for American Forestry, 2 vols. Brouchey, Stuart, ed. LC 78-53554. (Development of Public Land Law in the U. S. Ser.). (Illus.). 1979. Repr. of 1933 ed. Set. lib. bdg. 109.00 (ISBN 0-405-11389-7). Ayer Co Pubs.

V. Weck, Johannes. Woerterbuch der Forstwirtschaft. (Ger., Eng., Fr., Span. & Rus., Dictionary of Forestry). 1966. 99.50 (ISBN 3-405-10494-7, M-7005). French & Eur.

Watt, G. The Planning & Evaluation of Forestry Projects. 1973. 30.00x (ISBN 0-85074-014-2, Pub. by For Lib Comm). State Mutual Bk.

Weck, J. Dictionary of Forestry. (Eng., Ger., Fr., Span. & Rus.). 513p. 1966. 113.00 (ISBN 0-444-40626-3). Elsevier.

Wenger, Karl F. Forestry Handbook. 2nd ed. LC 83-17110. 1335p. 1984. 49.95x (ISBN 0-471-06227-8, Pub. by Wiley-Interscience). Wiley.

Williston, Ed M., ed. Small Log Sawmills: Profitable Product Selection, Process Design & Operation. LC 80-84893. (A Forest Industries Bk.). (Illus.). 368p. 1981. 52.50 (ISBN 0-87930-091-4); pap. 42.50. Miller Freeman.

Yavchenko, P. Interrelations of Forest & Bog. 1981. 50.00x (ISBN 0-686-76646-6, Pub. by Oxford & IBH India). State Mutual Bk.

Young, R. A. Introduction to Forest Science. LC 81-16031. 554p. 1982. 35.95 (ISBN 0-471-06438-6). Wiley.

FORESTS AND FORESTRY–BIBLIOGRAPHY

Adams, P. H. & Entwistle, P. F. An Annotated Bibliography of Gilpinia Hercyniae (Hartig) European Spruce. 1981. 30.00x (ISBN 0-85074-051-7, Pub. by For Lib Comm England). State Mutual Bk.

Cannell, M. G., ed. World Forest Biomass & Primary Production Data. 1982. 55.00 (ISBN 0-12-158780-0). Acad Pr.

Eldridge, K. G. An Annotated Bibliography of Genetic Variation in Eucalyptus Camaldulensis. 1975. 30.00x (ISBN 0-85074-023-1, Pub. by For Lib Comm England). State Mutual Bk.

Fortmann, Louise & Riddell, James. Trees & Tenure: An Annotated Bibliography for Agroforesters & Others. xvii, 135p. (Orig.). 1985. pap. 8.00 (ISBN 0-934519-00-5). U of Wis Land.

Hughes, Katherine W., et al. Forestry Theses Accepted in the United States, 1900-1952. (Bibliographic Ser.: No. 3). 140p. 1953. pap. 3.95x (ISBN 0-87071-123-7). Oreg St U Pr.

Kinch, Michael P., compiled by. Forestry Theses Accepted by Colleges & Universities in the United States 1956-June 1966. (Bibliographic Ser.: No. 13). 214p. 1978. pap. 5.95x (ISBN 0-87071-133-4). Oreg St U Pr.

Osborn, Katherine H., compiled by. Forestry Theses Accepted by Colleges & Universities in the United States, Supplement 1953-55. (Bibliographic Ser: No. 5). 44p. 1957. pap. 3.95x (ISBN 0-87071-125-3). Oreg St U Pr.

Yale University. Henry S. Graves Memorial Library. Dictionary Catalogue of the Yale Forestry Library, 12 Vols. 1962. Set. lib. bdg. 1185.00 (ISBN 0-8161-0631-2, Hall Library). G K Hall.

FORESTS AND FORESTRY–DATA PROCESSING

Moser, John W., Jr., ed. Microcomputers: A New Tool for Foresters. 159p. (Orig.). 1983. pap. 8.00 (ISBN 0-317-18181-5, SAF 83-15). Soc Am Foresters.

FORESTS AND FORESTRY–ECOLOGY

see Forest Ecology

FORESTS AND FORESTRY–ECONOMIC ASPECTS

see also Forest Policy

Assessment of Logging Costs from Forest Inventories in the Tropics, 2 Parts. Swedish International Development Authority, tr. Incl. Vol. 1. Principles & Methodology. 56p; Vol. 2. Data Collections & Calculations. 76p (ISBN 92-5-100599-0). (Forestry Papers: No. 10). (Eng., Fr. & Span.). 1978. Set. pap. 14.50 (ISBN 0-686-93608-6, F1492, FAO). Unipub.

Beresford-Peirse, H. Forests, Food & People. (Freedom from Hunger Campaign Basic Studies: No. 20). 72p. (Orig.). 1968. pap. 4.50 (ISBN 0-685-09384-0, F199, FAO). Unipub.

Douglas, J. Sholto & Hart, Robert A. Forest Farming: Towards a Solution to Problems of World Hunger & Conservation. 2nd ed. (Illus.). 207p. (Orig.). 1984. pap. 11.50x (ISBN 0-946688-30-3, Pub. by Intermediate Tech England). Intermediate Tech.

Duerr, William A. Economic Problems of Forestry in the Appalachian Region. LC 49-8873. (Economic Studies: No. 84). (Illus.). 1949. 18.50x (ISBN 0-674-22950-9). Harvard U Pr.

Earl, D. E. Forest Energy & Economic Development. (Illus.). 1975. 27.50x (ISBN 0-19-854521-5). Oxford U Pr.

Economic Analysis of Forestry Projects: Readings. (Forestry Papers: No. 17, Suppl. 2). 224p. (2nd Printing 1983). 1980. pap. 16.00 (ISBN 92-5-100955-4, F2105, FAO). Unipub.

Estimated Production of Pulp, Paper, & Paperboard in Certain Countries in 1974. (Forestry Papers: No. 11). 49p. 1975. pap. 11.50 (ISBN 0-686-92796-6, F773, FAO). Unipub.

Estimated Production of Pulp, Paper, & Paperboard in Certain Countries in 1976. (Forestry Papers: No. 28). 48p. 1977. pap. 7.50 (ISBN 0-686-92798-2, F1269, FAO). Unipub.

Fernow, Bernhard E. Economics of Forestry: A Reference Book for Students of Political Economy & Professional & Lay Students of Forestry. LC 72-2836. (Use & Abuse of America's Natural Resources Ser). 536p. 1972. Repr. of 1902 ed. 33.00 (ISBN 0-405-04505-0). Ayer Co Pubs.

Forestry & Rural Development. (Forestry Papers: No. 26). (Eng., Fr. & Span.). 38p. (2nd Printing 1982). 1981. pap. 7.50 (ISBN 92-5-101083-8, F2217, FAO). Unipub.

Gregerson, Hans & Contreras, Arnoldo H. Economic Analysis of Forestry Projects: Case Studies. (Forestry Papers: No. 17). (Eng., Fr. & Span.). 208p. (2nd Printing 1981). 1979. pap. 15.00 (ISBN 92-5-100827-2, F1907, FAO). Unipub.

Gregory, G. Robinson. Forest Resource Economics. 548p. 1972. 37.50 (ISBN 0-471-06833-0, 40503). Wiley.

Heinsdijk, D. Forest Assessment. 395p. (1800 references). 1975. 33.25 (ISBN 90-220-0550-X, PDC36, Pub. by PUDOC). Unipub.

Lorrain-Smith, R. An Economic Analysis of Silvicultural Options for Broadleaved Woodlands, Vol. II. 1982. 42.00x (ISBN 0-85074-042-8, Pub. by For Lib Comm England). State Mutual Bk.

MacGregor, J. J. Forest Economic Research at Oxford: 1945-1974. 1974. 32.00x (ISBN 0-686-45514-2, Pub. by For Lib Comm England). State Mutual Bk.

Openshaw, K. Cost & Financial Accounting in Forestry. 1980. text ed. 39.00 o. p. (ISBN 0-08-021456-8); pap. text ed. 15.00 (ISBN 0-08-021455-X). Pergamon.

Pryor, S. N. An Economic Analysis of Silvicultural Options for Broadleaved Woodlands, Vol. I. 1982. 42.00x (ISBN 0-85074-041-X, Pub. by For Lib Comm England). State Mutual Bk.

Reese, Richard M. Marketing of a Forest Product: A Chance-Constrained Transportation Model. LC 74-4903. (Studies in Marketing: No. 20). (Illus.). 80p. 1974. pap. 4.00 (ISBN 0-87755-189-8). Bureau Busn UT.

Report of the FAO-Norway Seminar on Storage, Transport & Shipping of Wood: Singapore, 8-28 May 1977. 229p. 1977. pap. 15.00 (ISBN 92-5-100351-3, F1249, FAO). Unipub.

Roth, Filibert. Forest Valuation. 1926. 4.95x (ISBN 0-685-21785-X). Wahr.

State Taxation of Forest & Land Resources: Symposium Proceedings. (Lincoln Institute Monograph: No. 80-6). 149p. 1980. pap. text ed. 12.00 (ISBN 0-686-29507-2). Lincoln Inst Land.

FORESTS AND FORESTRY–MENSURATION

see also Lumber Trade–Tables and Ready-Reckoners

Avery, Thomas E. & Burkhart, Harold E. Forest Measurements. 3rd ed. (McGraw-Hill Ser. in Forest Measurements). (Illus.). 384p. 1983. text ed. 37.95 (ISBN 0-07-002503-7). McGraw.

Dilworth, J. R. Log Scaling & Timber Cruising. 1984. pap. text ed. 11.95x (ISBN 0-88246-031-5). Oreg St U Bkstrs.

Husch, Bertram, et al. Forest Mensuration. 3rd ed. LC 82-4811. 402p. 1982. 36.50 (ISBN 0-471-04423-7). Wiley.

Merchant, Roger L. The Maine Forest. (Literacy Volunteers of America Readers Ser.). 32p. (Orig.). 1983. pap. 2.46 (ISBN 0-8428-9611-2). Cambridge Bk.

FORESTS AND FORESTRY–STATISTICS

World Forest Inventory: 1963. (Orig.). 1966. pap. 9.25 (ISBN 0-685-09415-4, F508, FAO). Unipub.

FORESTS AND FORESTRY–STUDY AND TEACHING

see Forestry Schools and Education

FORESTS AND FORESTRY–SURVEYING

see Forest Surveys

FORESTS AND FORESTRY–VOCATIONAL GUIDANCE

McCulloch, W. F. Forester on the Job. 1972. pap. text ed. 7.95x (ISBN 0-88246-081-1). Oreg St U Bkstrs.

Nyland, Ralph D. & Larson, Charles C. Forestry & Its Career Opportunities. 4th ed. (Illus.). 400p. 1983. text ed. 37.00x (ISBN 0-07-056979-7). McGraw.

Rudman, Jack. Principal Forestry Technician. (Career Examination Ser.: C-2716). (Cloth bdg. avail. on request). 1980. pap. 12.00 (ISBN 0-8373-2716-4). Natl Learning.

Wille, Christopher M. Opportunities in Forestry. (VGM Career Bks.). (Illus.). 160p. 1983. 7.95 (ISBN 0-8442-6321-4, 6321-4, Passport Bks.); pap. 5.95 (ISBN 0-8442-6322-2, 6322-2). Natl Textbk.

FORESTS AND FORESTRY–AFRICA

Adland, P. G. Growing Stock Levels & Productivity Cclusions from Thinning & Spacing Trails in Young Pinus Patula Stands in Southern Tanzania. 1978. 40.00x (ISBN 0-85074-048-7, Pub. by For Lib Comm England). State Mutual Bk.

Report of the African Forestry Commission: 4th Session. 34p. 1976. pap. 7.50 (ISBN 92-5-100039-5, F1104, FAO). Unipub.

Report on the Information Mission of Forest Operations in Africa. 25p. 1978. pap. 7.50 (ISBN 92-5-100498-6, F1346, FAO). Unipub.

Savanna Afforestation in Africa: Lecture Notes for the FAO-DANIDA Training Course on Forest Nursery & Establishment Techniques for African Savannas & Papers from the Symposium on Savanna Afforestation, Kaduna, Nigeria, 1976. (Forestry Papers: No. 11). (Eng. & Fr., Illus.). 318p. 1977. pap. 22.75 (ISBN 92-5-100273-8, F1176, FAO). Unipub.

Shantz, Homer L. & Marbut, Curtis F. Vegetation & Soils of Africa. LC 70-170848. Repr. of 1923 ed. 19.00 (ISBN 0-404-05953-8). AMS Pr.

FORTRAN (COMPUTER PROGRAM LANGUAGE)

see also GASP (Computer Program Language); SIMSCRIPT (Computer Program Language)

Petersen, T. M. Elementary FORTRAN. (Illus.). 176p. 1976. pap. text ed. 17.50x (ISBN 0-7121-0548-4, Pub. by Macdonald & Evans England). Trans-Atlantic.

Press, William, et al. Numerical Recipes: The Art of Scientific Computing. 700p. Date not set. price not set. (ISBN 0-521-30811-9). Cambridge U Pr.

Radford, A. S. Computer Programming-FORTRAN. (Teach Yourself Ser.). 1975. pap. 5.95 (ISBN 0-679-10378-3). McKay.

Ramden, H. JCL & Advanced FORTRAN Programming. (Methods in Geomathematics Ser.: Vol. 2). 170p. 1976. pap. 53.25 (ISBN 0-444-41415-0). Elsevier.

Rao, P. V. Computer Programming in FORTRAN & Other Languages. 1982. 3.00 (ISBN 0-07-096569-2). McGraw.

Ridler, P. Pocket Guide to... FORTRAN. 64p. spiral bdg. 6.95 (ISBN 0-201-07746-9). Addison-Wesley.

SAS Institute Inc., ed. SAS Programmer's Guide, 1981 Edition. (SAS Programmer's Guide). 208p. (Orig.). 1980. pap. 9.95 (ISBN 0-917382-17-X). SAS Inst.

Schallert, William F. & Clark, Carol R. Programming in FORTRAN. LC 78-74039. 1979. pap. text ed. 23.95 (ISBN 0-201-06716-1). Addison-Wesley.

Schmidt, B. GPSS FORTRAN. LC 80-40968. (Computing Ser.). 523p. 1980. 53.95 (ISBN 0-471-27881-5, Pub. by Wiley-Interscience). Wiley.

Schott, Brian. RISKM: A FORTRAN Computer Program. (Research Monograph: No. 66 B). 1975. 50.00 (ISBN 0-88406-100-0). Ga St U Busn Pub.

Schwar, James P. & Best, Charles L. Applied FORTRAN for Engineering & Science. 304p. 1982. pap. text ed. 19.95 (ISBN 0-574-21365-1, 13-4365); instr's guide avail. (ISBN 0-574-21366-X, 13-4366). SRA.

Sears, Joel L. Optimization Techniques in FORTRAN. (Illus.). 96p. (Orig.). 1979. pap. text ed. 10.00 (ISBN 0-89433-034-9). Petrocelli.

Sinha, Mihir K. & Padgett, Larry. Reservoir Engineering Techniques Using FORTRAN. (Illus.). 225p. 1984. text ed. 45.00 (ISBN 0-934634-50-5). Intl Human Res.

Smetana, Frederick O. & Smetana, Andrew O. FORTRAN Codes for Classical Methods in Linear Dynamics. 408p. 1982. 20.00 (ISBN 0-07-058440-0). McGraw.

Smith, Robert E. & Johnson, Dora E. FORTRAN Autotester: A Self-Training Course Designed to Emancipate the Scientist & Engineer from the Need for the Professional Programmer. LC 63-827. pap. 48.00 (ISBN 0-317-09144-1, 2016483). Bks Demand UMI.

Spath. Cluster Dissection & Analysis Theory FORTRAN Programs Examples. 226p. 1985. 49.95 (ISBN 0-470-20129-0). Wiley.

Specialized Systems Consultants. FORTRAN Seventy Seven Reference. 10p. 1984. pap. 2.50 (ISBN 0-317-17130-5). Specialized Sys.

Spencer, Donald D. FORTRAN Programming. 2nd ed. 1980. pap. 8.95 (ISBN 0-89218-042-0); tchr's manual 3.95x (ISBN 0-686-80432-5). Camelot Pub.

--Problem Solving with FORTRAN. LC 76-26040. (Illus.). 1977. pap. text ed. 21.95 (ISBN 0-13-720094-3). P-H.

Standard FORTRAN Programming Manual. 150p. 1980. 27.50x (ISBN 0-85012-239-2). Intl Pubns Serv.

Starkey, J. Denbigh & Ross, Rockford. Fundamental Programming: FORTRAN. 352p. 1982. pap. text ed. write for info. (ISBN 0-314-71812-5). West Pub.

Stuart, Frederic. FORTRAN Programming. LC 68-30922. 371p. 1970. Repr. 40.50 (ISBN 0-471-83466-1). Wiley.

--WATFOR WATFIV FORTRAN Programming. LC 78-162424. 239p. 1971. pap. 30.50 (ISBN 0-471-83471-8). Wiley.

Taylor, Fred I. & Smith, Steve L. Digital Signal Processing in FORTRAN. LC 75-28940. 432p. 1976. 35.00x (ISBN 0-669-00330-1). Lexington Bks.

Tremblay, Jean P. & Bunt, Richard B. Structured FORTRAN WATFIV-S Programming. 1979. pap. text ed. 24.95 (ISBN 0-07-065171-X). McGraw.

Tucker, Allen B., Jr. Programming Languages. (Computer Science Ser.). (Illus.). 1978. text ed. 36.95 (ISBN 0-07-065415-8). McGraw.

Tuggle, Francis D. How to Program a Computer, Using FORTRAN IV. LC 74-31654. pap. 43.80 (ISBN 0-317-30129-2, 2025312). Bks Demand UMI.

Valentino, James. FORTRAN for Engineers & Technologists. 1985. pap. text ed. 23.95x (ISBN 0-03-060569-5). HR&W.

Walker, Henry M. Problems for Computer Solutions Using FORTRAN. 203p. (Orig.). 1980. pap. text ed. 15.95 (ISBN 0-316-91833-4). Little.

Wolfe, Carvel. Linear Programming with BASIC & FORTRAN. LC 84-24758. 1985. pap. text ed. 19.95 (ISBN 0-8359-4082-9); instr's manual avail. (ISBN 0-8359-4083-7). Reston.

Worth, T. Non-Technical FORTRAN. 1976. pap. 18.95 (ISBN 0-13-623678-2). P-H.

Zinsmeister, George E., et al. FORTRAN on Time-Sharing. LC 78-26269. 103p. 1979. pap. 9.95x (ISBN 0-910554-27-7). Engineering.

Zwass, Vladimir. Programming in FORTRAN. 224p. 1980. pap. 5.95i (ISBN 0-06-460194-3, CO 194, COS). B&N NY.

FORTRAN (COMPUTER PROGRAM LANGUAGE)–PROGRAMMED INSTRUCTION

Boillot, Michel. Understanding FORTRAN-77 with Structured Problem Solving. (Illus.). 320p. 1984. pap. text ed. 23.95 (ISBN 0-314-77845-4); write for info. instr's guide (ISBN 0-314-77846-2). West Pub.

Dock, V. Thomas. Structured FORTRAN IV Programming. (Data Processing & Information System Ser.). (Illus.). 1979. pap. text ed. 22.95 (ISBN 0-8299-0249-X). West Pub.

Meek, B. FORTRAN, PL-I & the ALGOLS. 385p. 1979. 29.50 (ISBN 0-444-19464-9, North Holland). Elsevier.

Rule, Wilfred. FORTRAN: A Practical Approach with Style & Structure. 3rd ed. 1980. write for info. (ISBN 0-87150-290-9, 2292, Prindle). PWS Pubs.

Spencer, Donald D. Visual Masters for Teaching FORTRAN Programming. 1978. 9.95x (ISBN 0-89218-035-8). Camelot Pub.

FORTRAN 77 (COMPUTER PROGRAM LANGUAGE)

Ashcroft, J., et al. Programming with FORTRAN 77. 304p. 1981. pap. 18.50x (ISBN 0-246-11573-4, Pub. by Granada England). Sheridan.

Balfour, A. & Marwick, D. H. Programming in Standard FORTRAN 77. LC 79-7450. (Heinemann Educational Bks.). 388p. 1979. 25.75 (ISBN 0-444-19465-7, North Holland). Elsevier.

Boillot, Michel. Understanding FORTRAN-77 with Structured Problem Solving. (Illus.). 320p. 1984. pap. text ed. 23.95 (ISBN 0-314-77845-4); write for info. instr's guide (ISBN 0-314-77846-2). West Pub.

Boillot, Michel & Boillot, Mona. Understanding FORTRAN-77 with Structured Problem Solving. International ed. 525p. 1984. 17.00 (ISBN 0-314-77847-0). West Pub.

Borse. FORTRAN 77 & Numerical Methods for Engineers. 1985. text ed. write for info. (ISBN 0-534-04638-X, 22R2105, Pub. by PWS Engineering). PWS Pubs.

Brainerd, Walter S., et al. FORTRAN 77 Fundamentals & Style. (Programming Language Ser.). (Illus.). 448p. 1985. pap. text ed. 21.00 (ISBN 0-87835-143-4); write for info. tchr's. manual (ISBN 0-87835-146-9). Boyd & Fraser.

Chivers, Ian D. & Clark, Malcolm W. Interactive FORTRAN Seventy-Seven: A Hands on Approach. (Computers & Their Applications Ser.). 231p. 1984. text ed. 29.95x (ISBN 0-470-20101-0). Halsted Pr.

Cole, J. W. Perry. ANSI FORTRAN IV with FORTRAN 77 Extensions: A Sructured Programming Approach. 2nd ed. 720p. 1983. pap. write for info. (ISBN 0-697-08172-9); instr's. manual avail. (ISBN 0-697-08177-X). Wm C Brown.

Davis, Gordon B. & Hoffman, Thomas R. FORTRAN 77: A Structured Disciplined Style. 2nd ed. 416p. 1983. pap. text ed. 26.95 (ISBN 0-07-015903-3). McGraw.

Dillman, Richard W. Problem Solving with FORTRAN 77. 1985. pap. text ed. 23.95 (ISBN 0-03-063734-1). HR&W.

Durgin, Max W. FORTRAN 77. (Illus.). 316p. (Orig.). 1982. pap. text ed. 22.50 (ISBN 0-935920-04-8). Natl Pub Black Hills.

--Subset FORTRAN-77. (Illus.). 320p. (Orig.). 1983. pap. text ed. 22.50 (ISBN 0-935920-11-0). Natl Pub Black Hills.

Dyck, V. A., et al. FORTRAN 77: A Structured Approach to Problem Solving. 1983. text ed. 25.95 (ISBN 0-8359-3163-3). Reston.

Ellis, T. M. A Structured Approach to FORTRAN 77 Programming. 1982. pap. text ed. 19.95 (ISBN 0-201-13790-9). Addison-Wesley.

Etter, D. M. Problem Solving Software Supplement to "Problem Solving with Structured FORTRAN 77". 1984. pap. 10.00 (ISBN 0-8053-2526-3). Benjamin Cummings.

--Problem Solving with Structured FORTRAN 77. 1984. 24.95 (ISBN 0-8053-2522-0); instr's. manual 5.95 (ISBN 0-8053-2523-9); software supplement package 50.00 (ISBN 0-8053-2524-7). Benjamin-Cummings.

--Structured FORTRAN 77 for Engineers & Scientists. 1982. 22.95 (ISBN 0-8053-2520-4); instr's guide 5.95 (ISBN 0-8053-2521-2); software supplement package 50.00 (ISBN 0-8053-2517-4); application software supplement 12.00 (ISBN 0-8053-2518-2). Benjamin-Cummings.

Fleming-Redish. The U. S. McMaster Glossary of FORTRAN-77. 64p. 1983. pap. text ed. 3.95 (ISBN 0-8403-3052-9). Kendall-Hunt.

Fuori, William. FORTRAN 77 Programming for the IBM PC & PC XT. 224p. 1984. 19.95 (ISBN 0-8359-2096-8). Reston.

--Pascal Programming for the IBM PC & PC XT. 1984. cancelled (ISBN 0-317-06174-7). Reston.

Gibson, Glenn A. & Young, James R. Introduction to Programming Using FORTRAN 77. (Illus.). 480p. 1982. pap. text ed. 22.95 (ISBN 0-13-493551-9). P-H.

Grout, Jarrell C. Fundamental Computer Programming Using FORTRAN 77. (Software Ser.). (Illus.). 432p. 1983. pap. text ed. 21.95 (ISBN 0-13-335141-6). P-H.

Holoien, Martin O. & Behforooz, Ali. Problem Solving & Structured Programming with FORTRAN 77. LC 82-24436. 560p. 1983. pap. text ed. 19.00 pub net (ISBN 0-534-01275-2). Brooks-Cole.

--Problem Solving & Structured Programming with FORTRAN 77. 514p. 1983. pap. write for info. Wadsworth Pub.

Hume, J. N. & Holt, R. C. Programming FORTRAN 77. (Illus.). 1979. pap. text ed. 19.95 (ISBN 0-8359-5671-7). Reston.

Katzan, Harry, Jr. FORTRAN 77. (Computer Science Ser.). (Illus.). 224p. 1982. pap. 12.95 (ISBN 0-442-25428-8). Van Nos Reinhold.

Law, Victor J. ANSI FORTRAN 77: An Introduction to Software Design. 400p. 1983. pap. write for info. (ISBN 0-697-08167-2); instr's manual avail. (ISBN 0-697-08175-3); wkbk. avail. (ISBN 0-697-08176-1). Wm C Brown.

Lehman, Richard S., ed. Programming for the Social Sciences: Algorithms & FORTRAN 77 Coding. 1985. text ed. write for info. (ISBN 0-89859-588-6). L Erlbaum Assocs.

Lehmkuhl, Nonna. FORTRAN 77. 576p. 1983. pap. text ed. write for info. (ISBN 0-02-369390-8). Macmillan.

McCracken, Daniel D. Computing for Engineers & Scientists with FORTRAN 77. LC 83-23473. 361p. 1984. 23.45x (ISBN 0-471-09701-2); tchrs' manual avail. (ISBN 0-471-80090-2). Wiley.

McKeown, Patrick G. Structured Programming Using FORTRAN 77. 482p. 1985. pap. text ed. 20.95 (ISBN 0-15-584411-3, HC). HarBraceJ.

Meissner, Loren P. & Organick, Elliot I. FORTRAN 77: Featuring Structured Programming. 3rd ed. LC 78-74689. 1980. pap. text ed. 24.95 (ISBN 0-201-05499-X). Addison-Wesley.

Merchant, Michael. FORTRAN 77: Language & Style. 464p. 1981. pap. text ed. write for info. (ISBN 0-534-00920-4). Wadsworth Pub.

Monro, Donald M. FORTRAN 77. 368p. 1982. pap. text ed. 19.95 (ISBN 0-7131-2794-5). E Arnold.

Nanney, T. Ray. Computing: A Problem-Solving Approach Using FORTRAN 77. (Illus.). 432p. 1981. text ed. 22.95 (ISBN 0-13-165209-5). P-H.

Nickerson, Robert C. Fundamentals of FORTRAN 77 Programming: A Structured Approach. 3rd ed. 1985. pap. text ed. 23.95 (ISBN 0-316-60653-7); tchr's. ed. avail. Little.

Nyhoff, Larry & Leestma, Sanford. FORTRAN 77 for Engineers & Scientists. 388p. 1985. pap. text ed. write for info. (ISBN 0-02-388620-X). Macmillan.

--Problem Solving with FORTRAN 77. 368p. 1983. pap. text ed. write for info. (ISBN 0-02-388720-6). Macmillan.

Page, Rex & Didday, Richard. FORTRAN 77 for Humans. 2nd ed. (Illus.). 464p. 1983. pap. text ed. 21.95 (ISBN 0-314-69672-5); instr's. manual avail. (ISBN 0-314-71115-5). West Pub.

Page, Ulive. Pocket Guide: FORTRAN 77. (Pitman Programming Pocket Guides Ser.). 64p. (Orig.). 1984. pap. 6.95 (ISBN 0-273-01973-2). Pitman Pub MA.

Pollack, Seymour V. Structured FORTRAN 77 Programming. LC 82-70214. 504p. (Orig.). 1982. pap. text ed. 25.00x (ISBN 0-87835-095-0); write for info. solutions manual. Boyd & Fraser.

--Structured FORTRAN 77 Programming for Hewlett-Packard Computers. 512p. (Orig.). 1983. pap. text ed. 25.00x (ISBN 0-87835-130-2). Boyd & Fraser.

Ratzer, Gerald. A FORTRAN 77 Course. 144p. 1981. pap. text ed. 9.95 (ISBN 0-8403-2427-8). Kendall-Hunt.

Rouse, Robert A. & Bugnitz, Thomas L. Introduction to FORTRAN 77. 1986. pap. text ed. 19.95 (ISBN 0-03-063634-5). HR&W.

--Programming the IBM Personal Computer: FORTRAN 77. LC 82-23235. 304p. 1983. pap. 17.50 (ISBN 0-03-063668-X); incl. diskette 40.45 (ISBN 0-03-063979-4). HR&W.

Rule, Wilfred P. FORTRAN 77: A Practical Approach. 4th ed. 486p. 1983. pap. text ed. write for info. (ISBN 0-87150-390-5, 8030, Prindle). PWS Pubs.

Sass, C. Joseph. A Structured Approach to FORTRAN 77 Programming: With WATFIV. 350p. 1983. scp 25.00 (ISBN 0-205-07918-0, 207918). Allyn.

Seeds, Harice L. Structured FORTRAN 77 for Business & General Applications. LC 81-125. 512p. 1981. text ed. 28.00 (ISBN 0-471-07836-0). Wiley.

Shelly, John. FORTRAN 77: An Introduction. 204p. 1984. 12.95 (ISBN 0-471-90502-X). Wiley.

Smith, Marilyn Z. FORTRAN 77: A Problem-Solving Approach. LC 84-81083. 416p. 1984. pap. text ed. 23.95 (ISBN 0-395-35041-7); instr's. manual 2.00 (ISBN 0-395-35042-5). HM.

Wagener, Jerrold L. Principles of FORTRAN 77 Programming. LC 79-17421. 370p. 1980. pap. text ed. 25.00 (ISBN 0-471-04474-1); tchr's manual 5.50x (ISBN 0-471-07831-X). Wiley.

Wu, Nesa L. ANSI FORTRAN IV & FORTRAN 77: Programming with Business Applications. 3rd ed. 352p. 1982. pap. 16.95 (ISBN 0-697-08153-2); solutions manual avail. (ISBN 0-697-08156-7). Wm C Brown.

FORTRAN IV (COMPUTER PROGRAM LANGUAGE)

Alexander, Daniel E. & Messer, Andrew C. FORTRAN IV Pocket Handbook. 96p. (Orig.). 1972. pap. 4.95 (ISBN 0-07-001015-3). McGraw.

Anderson, Decima M. Computer Programming: FORTRAN IV. (Illus., Orig.). 1966. pap. 24.95 (ISBN 0-13-164822-5). P-H.

Ayatey, Siegfried B. Elementary FORTRAN IV Microeconomics Programs. LC 84-5155. 238p. (Orig.). 1984. pap. text ed. 12.00 (ISBN 0-8191-3950-5). U Pr of Amer.

Bauer, C. R. & Peluso, A. P. Basic FORTRAN IV with WATFOR & WATFIV. 1974. 21.95 (ISBN 0-201-00411-9). Addison-Wesley.

Beech, Graham. FORTRAN IV in Chemistry: An Introduction to Computer-Assisted Methods. LC 75-2488. 303p. 1975. 67.95x (ISBN 0-471-06165-4, Pub. by Wiley-Interscience). Wiley.

Calderbank, V. J. Course in Programming in FORTRAN IV. 2nd ed. 1983. 25.00 (ISBN 0-412-24270-2, NO. 6737, Pub. by Chapman & Hall); pap. 9.95x (ISBN 0-412-23790-3, NO. 6738). Methuen Inc.

Carnahan, Brice & Wilkes, James O. Digital Computing & Numerical Methods with FORTRAN IV WATFOR & WATFIV Programming. LC 72-13010. 477p. 1973. text ed. 45.45 (ISBN 0-471-13500-3). Wiley.

Chopra, M. G. & Kumar, Ram. FORTRAN IV Programming. 248p. 1981. pap. 15.00x (ISBN 0-7069-1535-6, Pub. by Vikas India). Advent NY.

Cole, J. W. Perry. ANSI FORTRAN IV with FORTRAN 77 Extensions: A Sructured Programming Approach. 2nd ed. 720p. 1983. pap. write for info. (ISBN 0-697-08172-9); instr's. manual avail. (ISBN 0-697-08177-X). Wm C Brown.

Cress, P., et al. FORTRAN IV with WATFOR & WATFIV. 1970. ref. ed. 22.95 (ISBN 0-13-329433-1). P-H.

Dickson, G. W. & Smith, H. R. Introduction to FORTRAN IV Programming: A Self-Paced Approach. LC 74-189809. 1972. pap. text ed. 17.95 (ISBN 0-03-088088-2, HoltC). HR&W.

Dock, V. Thomas. Structured FORTRAN IV Programming. (Data Processing & Information System Ser.). (Illus.). 1979. pap. text ed. 22.95 (ISBN 0-8299-0249-X). West Pub.

Dorn, William S. & McCracken, Daniel D., eds. Numerical Methods with FORTRAN IV Case Studies. LC 77-37365. 477p. 1972. 44.50 (ISBN 0-471-21918-5). Wiley.

Duchane, Emma, ed. User's Manual, Advanced FORTRAN IV Utilities for Data General Computers. (Illus.). viii, 223p. 1980. pap. 20.00 (ISBN 0-938876-03-1). Entropy Ltd.

Edwards, Perry. Flowcharting & FORTRAN IV. (Illus.). 132p. 1973. 14.15 (ISBN 0-07-019042-9, G). McGraw.

Farina, Mario V. FORTRAN IV Self-Taught. 1966. pap. 18.95 (ISBN 0-13-329722-5). P-H.

Forsythe, Alexandra I., et al. Computer Science: Programming in FORTRAN IV with WATFOR-WATFIV. LC 74-96044. 210p. 1975. pap. 14.00x (ISBN 0-471-26685-X). Wiley.

Friedmann, J., et al. FORTRAN-IV. 2nd ed. LC 80-21709. (Self Teaching Guide Ser.: No. 1-581). 499p. 1981. pap. 14.95 (ISBN 0-471-07771-2, Pub. by Wiley Pr). Wiley.

Gottfried, Byron S. Programming with FORTRAN IV. 2nd ed. (Illus.). 384p. 1984. pap. text ed. 19.95 (ISBN 0-13-729699-1). P-H.

Grout, Jarrell C. Fundamental Computer Programming Using FORTRAN 77. (Software Ser.). (Illus.). 432p. 1983. pap. text ed. 21.95 (ISBN 0-13-335141-6). P-H.

Steel Foundry Workplace Improvement Guidebooks. Incl. Section I. General Engineering Principles. 10.00 (ISBN 0-686-44980-0); Section V. Cleaning & Finishing. 10.00 (ISBN 0-686-44981-9); Appendices. 10.00 (ISBN 0-686-44982-7). 10.00 (ISBN 0-686-44978-9); 3-Ring Binder 4.00 (ISBN 0-686-44979-7). Steel Founders.
Stolzel, K. Dictionary of Metallurgy & Foundry Technology: English-German. 1984. 92.75 (ISBN 0-444-99612-5, I-423-84). Elsevier.
Strauss, K. Applied Science in the Casting of Metals. 1970. 59.00 (ISBN 0-08-015711-4). Pergamon.
Surface Indicator Scale: Elecroformed Nickel - includes Standard. 50.00 (ISBN 0-686-44990-8). Steel Founders.
Surface Indicator Scale: Plastic Replica. 1.00 (ISBN 0-686-44992-4). Steel Founders.
Sylvia, J. Gerin. Cast Metals Technology. LC 74-153067. 1972. text ed. 26.95 (ISBN 0-201-07395-1). Addison-Wesley.
Taylor, F., et al. Foundry Engineering. LC 59-11811. 407p. 1959. 46.50 (ISBN 0-471-84843-3). Wiley.
Technical Insights Inc. Robots in Industry: Applications for Foundries. LC 82-99924. 180p. 1984. 125.00 (ISBN 0-89671-055-6). Tech Insights.
Vocabulary de la Fonderie, Francais-Anglais. (Fr. & Eng., French-English Vocabulary of Foundries). pap. 14.95 (ISBN 0-686-56719-6, M-6557). French & Eur.
Vocabulary de la Fonderie, Francais-Anglais. (Fr. & Eng., French-English Vocabulary of Foundries). pap. 12.50 (ISBN 0-686-56720-X, M-6556). French & Eur.
Webster, P. D., ed. Fundamentals of Foundry Technology. 496p. 1981. 99.50x (ISBN 0-86108-078-5, Pub. by Portcullio Pr). State Mutual Bk.

FOUNDRY PRACTICE
see Founding

FOUR-COLOR PROBLEM
Saaty, Thomas L. & Kainen, Paul C. The Four-Color Problem: Assaults & Conquest. (Illus.). 1977. text ed. 41.95x (ISBN 0-07-054382-8). McGraw.

FOURIER ANALYSIS
see also Fourier Series; Fourier Transformations; Functions, Orthogonal; Orthogonal Polynomials
Argabright, Loren & De Lamadrid, Jesus G. Fourier Analysis of Unbounded Measures on Locally Compact Abelian Groups. LC 74-6499. (Memoirs: No. 145). 53p. 1974. pap. 10.00 (ISBN 0-8218-1845-7, MEMO-145). Am Math.
Beals, R. Michael. LP Boundedness of Fourier Integral Operators. LC 82-8740. (Memoirs of the American Mathematical Society: Vol. 264). 1982. pap. 9.00 (ISBN 0-8218-2264-0, MEMO-264). Am Math.
Birch, J. R., ed. Fourier Transform Spectroscopy: Proceedings of the International Conference, Durham, U. K., 19-22 September, 1983. 290p. 1984. pap. 64.00 (ISBN 0-08-030265-3). Pergamon.
De Guzman, Miguel & Miguel. Real Variable Methods in Fourier Analysis. (Mathematical Studies Ser.: Vol. 46). 392p. 1981. 61.75 (ISBN 0-444-86124-6, North-Holland). Elsevier.
Fourier Coefficients of Automorphic Forms. (Lecture Notes in Mathematics: Vol. 865). 201p. 1981. pap. 16.00 (ISBN 0-387-10839-4). Springer-Verlag.
Henrici, P. Applied & Computational Complex Analysis: Discrete Fourier Analysis, Cauchy Integrals, Construction of Conformal Maps, Univalent Functions. (Pure & Applied Mathematics Ser.). 1985. write for info. (ISBN 0-471-08703-3). Wiley.
Hsu. Applied Fourier Analysis. (College Outline Ser.). 1984. pap. text ed. 9.95 (ISBN 0-15-601609-5, BFP). HarBraceJ.
Peral, I & De Francia, Rubio J., eds. Recent Progress in Fourier Analysis: Proceedings of the Seminar on Fourier Analysis Held in El Escorial, Spain, June 30 to July 5 1983. (Mathematics Studies: Vol. III). 268p. 1985. 37.00 (ISBN 0-444-87745-2, North Holland). Elsevier.
Rees, C., et al, eds. Theory & Applications of Fourier Analysis. (Pure & Applied Mathematics Ser.: Vol. 59). 1980. 39.75 (ISBN 0-8247-6903-1). Dekker.
Salem, Raphael & Carleson, Lennart. Algebraic Numbers & Fourier Analysis & Selected Problems on Exceptional Set. LC 82-20053. (Wadsworth Mathematics Ser.). 224p. Repr. write for info (ISBN 0-534-98049-X). Wadsworth Pub.
Stein, Elias M. & Weiss, Guido. Introduction to Fourier Analysis on Euclidean Spaces. LC 73-106394. (Mathematical Ser.: No. 32). 1971. 33.00 (ISBN 0-691-08078-X). Princeton U Pr.
Steward, E. G. Fourier Optics: An Introduction. LC 83-9052. (Physics Series-Ellis Horwood: I-674). 185p. 1983. 26.95x (ISBN 0-470-27454-9). Halsted Pr.
Stuart, R. D. Introduction to Fourier Analysis. 1966. pap. 8.50x (ISBN 0-412-20200-X, NO.6282, Pub. by Chapman & Hall). Methuen Inc.
Taibleson, M. H. Fourier Analysis on Local Fields. LC 74-32047. (Mathematical Notes Ser.: No. 15). 308p. 1977. 27.00 (ISBN 0-691-08165-4). Princeton U Pr.
Weaver, Joseph H. Applications of Discrete & Continuous Fourier Analysis. LC 83-3651. 375p. 1983. 37.50x (ISBN 0-471-87115-X, Pub. by Wiley-Interscience). Wiley.

FOURIER INTEGRALS
see Fourier Series

FOURIER SERIES
see also Almost Periodic Functions; Harmonic Analysis; Harmonic Functions
Bari, N. K., et al. Series & Approximation, Vol. 3. (Translations Ser.: No. 1). 1962. 24.00 (ISBN 0-8218-1603-9, TRANS 1-3). Am Math.
Bloomfield, Peter. Fourier Analysis of Time Series: An Introduction. LC 75-34294. (Probability & Mathematical Statistics Ser.). 258p. 1976. 33.95x (ISBN 0-471-08256-2, Pub. by Wiley-Interscience). Wiley.
Boas, R. P., Jr. Integrability Theorems for Trigonometric Transforms. (Ergebnisse der Mathematik und Ihrer Grenzgebiete: Vol. 38). 1967. 19.50 (ISBN 0-387-03780-2). Springer-Verlag.
Bochner, Salomon. Fouriersche Integrale. LC 49-22695. (Ger). 10.50 (ISBN 0-8284-0042-3). Chelsea Pub.
Britton, W. Conjugate Duality & the Exponential Fourier Spectrum. (Lecture Notes in Statistics: Vol. 18). (Illus.). 226p. 1983. pap. 18.00 (ISBN 0-387-90826-9). Springer-Verlag.
Carslaw, Horatio S. Introduction to the Theory of Fourier's Series & Integrals. 3rd ed. (Illus.). 1952. pap. 7.50 (ISBN 0-486-60048-3). Dover.
Chazarain, J. Fourier Integral Operators & Partial Differential Equations. (Lecture Notes in Mmathematics: Vol. 459). 372p. 1975. pap. 21.00 (ISBN 0-387-07180-6). Springer-Verlag.
Churchill, Ruel V. & Brown, James W. Fourier Series & Boundary Value Problems. 3rd ed. 1978. text ed. 40.95 (ISBN 0-07-010843-9). McGraw.
Coifman, Ronald & Weiss, Guido. Transference Methods in Analysis. LC 77-24098. (Conference Board of the Mathematical Sciences Ser.: No. 31). 59p. 1977. pap. 13.00 (ISBN 0-8218-1681-0, CBMS 31). Am Math.
Dym, H. & McKean, H. P. Fourier Series & Integrals. (Probability & Mathematical Statistics Ser). 1972. 55.00 (ISBN 0-12-226450-9). Acad Pr.
Edwards, R. Fourier Series: A Modern Introduction. LC 79-11932. (Graduate Texts in Mathematics: Pt. 1, Vol. 64). 1979. 24.00 (ISBN 0-387-90412-3). Springer-Verlag.
Gelbart, Stephen S. Fourier Analysis on Matrix Space. LC 52-42839. (Memoirs: Vol. 108). 77p. 1971. pap. 9.00 (ISBN 0-8218-1808-2, MEMO-108). Am Math.
Hirschman, I. I. Decomposition of Walsh & Fourier Series. LC 52-42839. (Memoirs Ser.: No. 15). 65p. pap. 13.00 (ISBN 0-8218-1215-7, MEMO-15). Am Math.
Jeffery, Ralph L. Trigonometric Series: A Survey. LC 56-59071. (Canadian Mathematical Congress Lecture Ser.: No. 2). pap. 20.00 (ISBN 0-317-08877-7, 2014260). Bks Demand UMI.
Kawata, Tatsuo. Fourier Analysis in Probability Theory. (Probability & Mathematical Statistics Ser.). 1972. 91.50 (ISBN 0-12-403650-3). Acad Pr.
Levinson, Norman. Gap & Density Theorems. LC 41-6147. (Colloquium, Pbns. Ser.: Vol. 26). 246p. 1963. Repr. of 1940 ed. 23.00 (ISBN 0-8218-1026-X, COLL-26). Am Math.
Lighthill, M. J. Introduction to Fourier Analysis & Generalized Functions. (Cambridge Monographs on Mechanics & Applied Mathematics). 24.95 (ISBN 0-521-05556-3); pap. text ed. 11.95 (ISBN 0-521-09128-4). Cambridge U Pr.
Marcus, Michael B. & Pisier, Gilles. Random Fourier Series with Application to Harmonic Analysis. LC 81-47145. (Annals of Mathematical Studies: No.101). 192p. 1981. 22.50 (ISBN 0-691-08289-8); pap. 8.95 (ISBN 0-691-08292-8). Princeton U Pr.
Oberhettinger, Fritz. Fourier Expansions: A Collection of Formulas. 1973. 34.50 (ISBN 0-12-523640-9). Acad Pr.
Okuyama, Y. Absolute Summability of Fourier Series & Orthogonal Series. (Lecture Notes in Mathematics Ser.: Vol. 1067). vi, 118p. 1984. pap. 10.00 (ISBN 0-387-13355-0). Springer-Verlag.
Olevsky, A. M. Fourier Series with Respect to General Orthogonal Systems, Vol. 86. LC 74-32297. (Ergebnisse der Mathematik und Ihrer Grenzgebiete). 160p. 1975. 48.00 (ISBN 0-387-07103-2). Springer-Verlag.
Rogosinski, Werner. Fourier Series. 2nd ed. LC 50-6214. 7.95 (ISBN 0-8284-0067-9). Chelsea Pub.
Spiegel, Murray R. Fourier Analysis. 1974. pap. text ed. 9.95 (ISBN 0-07-060219-0). McGraw.
Steklov Institute of Mathematics, Academy of Sciences, USSR. Limits of Interdeterminacy in Measure of Trigonometric & Orthogonal Series: Proceedings. (Proceedings of the Steklov Institute of Mathematics: No. 99). 1968. 23.00 (ISBN 0-8218-1899-6, STEKLO-99). Am Math.
Titchmarsh, Edward Charles. Introduction to the Theory of Fourier Integrals. 2nd ed. pap. 100.80 (ISBN 0-317-28050-3, 2055776). Bks Demand UMI.
Tolstov, Georgi P. Fourier Series. Silverman, Richard A., tr. from Russian. LC 75-41883. 352p. 1976. pap. 6.00 (ISBN 0-486-63317-9). Dover.
Wainger, Stephen. Special Trigonometric Series in K Dimensions. LC 52-42839. (Memoirs: No. 59). 102p. 1965. pap. 9.00 (ISBN 0-8218-1259-9, MEMO-59). Am Math.
Walsh, Thomas. On Summability Methods for Conjugate Fourier-Steiltjes Integrals in Several Variables & Generalizations. LC 73-2729. (Memoirs: No. 131). 103p. 1973. pap. 12.00 (ISBN 0-8218-1831-7, MEMO-131). Am Math.
Wiener, Norbert. Fourier Integral & Certain of Its Applications. 1933. pap. text ed. 4.50 (ISBN 0-486-60272-9). Dover.
Wilcox, Howard & Myers, David L. An Introduction to Lebesgue Integration & Fourier Analysis. LC 77-12013. 168p. 1977. pap. 13.50 (ISBN 0-88275-614-1). Krieger.
Young, Robert M. An Introduction to Nonharmonic Fourier Series. LC 79-6807. (Pure & Applied Ser.). 1980. 39.50 (ISBN 0-12-772850-3). Acad Pr.
Zygmund, A. Trigonometric Series. LC 77-82528. 1977. 105.00 (ISBN 0-521-07477-0). Cambridge U Pr.

FOURIER TRANSFORMATIONS
see also Digital Filters (Mathematics)
Bell, R. J. Introductory Fourier Transform Spectroscopy. 1972. 59.50 (ISBN 0-12-085150-4). Acad Pr.
Berenstein, C. A. & Dostal, M. A. Analytically Uniform Spaces & Their Applications to Convolution Equations. LC 70-189386. (Lecture Notes in Mathematics: Vol. 256). 137p. 1972. pap. 9.00 (ISBN 0-387-05746-3). Springer-Verlag.
Bochner, S. & Chandrasekharan, K. Fourier Transforms. (Annals of Math Studies). 1949. 15.00 (ISBN 0-527-02735-9). Kraus Repr.
Bracewell, R. The Fourier Transform & Its Applications. 2nd ed. (Electrical Engineering Ser.). (Illus.). 1978. text ed. 48.00 (ISBN 0-07-007013-X). McGraw.
Brigham, E. Oran. Fast Fourier Transform. (Illus.). 304p. 1973. ref. ed. 32.95 (ISBN 0-13-307496-X). P-H.
Champeney, D. C. Fourier Transforms & Their Physical Applications. (Techniques of Physics Ser.: No. 1). 1973. 47.50 (ISBN 0-12-167450-9). Acad Pr.
--Fourier Transforms in Physics. (Student Monographs in Physics). 64p. (Orig.). 1985. pap. text ed. 5.00 (ISBN 0-85274-794-2, 990300609, Pub. by Adam Hilger Techo Hse UK). Heyden.
Duffieux, P. M. The Fourier Transform & Its Applications to Optics. 2nd ed. LC 82-20302. (Pure & Applied Optics Ser.). 197p. 1982. 36.50 (ISBN 0-471-09589-3, Pub. by Wiley-Interscience). Wiley.
Ehrenpreis, Leon. Fourier Analysis in Several Complex Variables. (Pure & Applied Mathematics Ser.). 506p. 1970. 64.95x (ISBN 0-471-23400-1, Pub. by Wiley-Interscience). Wiley.
Ferraro, John R., ed. Fourier Transform: Applications to Chemical Systems, Vol. 1. 1978. 59.50 (ISBN 0-12-254101-4). Acad Pr.
Ferraro, John R. & Basile, Louis J., eds. Fourier Transform Infared Spectroscopy, Vol. 3: Techniques Using Fourier Transform Interferometry. 1982. 39.00 (ISBN 0-12-254103-0). Acad Pr.
--Fourier Transform Infrared Spectroscopy: Applications to Chemical Systems, Vol. 2. LC 78-26956. 1979. 55.00 (ISBN 0-12-254102-2). Acad Pr.
--Fourier Transform Infrared Spectroscopy, Vol. 4. 1985. 74.50 (ISBN 0-12-254104-9). Acad Pr.
Gaskill, Jack D. Linear Systems, Fourier Transforms & Optics. LC 78-1118. (Pure & Applied Optics Ser.). 554p. 1978. 44.50x (ISBN 0-471-29288-5, Pub. by Wiley-Interscience). Wiley.
Geckinli, N. C. & Yavus, D., eds. Discrete Fourier Transformation & Its Applications to Power Spectra Estimation. (Studies in Electrical & Electronic Engineering: No. 8). 340p. 1983. 78.75 (ISBN 0-444-41713-3). Elsevier.
Griffiths, Peter R. Chemical Infrared Fourier Transform Spectroscopy. LC 75-6505. (Chemical Analysis: A series of Monographs on Analytical Chemistry & Its Applications: Vol. 43). 340p. 1975. 58.00x (ISBN 0-471-32786-7, Pub by Wiley-Interscience). Wiley.
Hanna, J. Ray. Fourier Series & Integrals of Boundary Value Problems. LC 81-16063. (Pure & Applied Mathematics Ser.). 271p. 1982. 37.50x (ISBN 0-471-08129-9, Pub. by Wiley-Interscience). Wiley.
Mattson, James S., et al, eds. Infrared Correlation & Fourier Transform Spectroscopy. (Computers in Chemistry & Instrumentation Ser.: Vol. 7). 1976. 69.75 (ISBN 0-8247-6369-6). Dekker.
Mullen, K. & Pregosin, P. S. Fourier Transform Nuclear Magnetic Resonance Techniques: A Practical Approach. 1977. 37.00 (ISBN 0-12-510450-2). Acad Pr.
Nussbaumer, H. Fast Fourier Transform & Convolution Algorithms. 2nd ed. (Springer Series in Information Sciences). (Illus.). 280p. 1982. pap. 31.00 (ISBN 0-387-11825-X). Springer-Verlag.
Oberhettinger. Fourier Transformations of Distributions & Their Inverses: A Collection of Tables. 1973. 52.00 (ISBN 0-12-523650-6). Acad Pr.
Paley, Raymond E. & Wiener, Norbert. Fourier Transforms in the Complex Domain. LC 35-3273. (Colloquium, Pbns. Ser.: Vol. 19). 183p. 1982. pap. 33.00 (ISBN 0-8218-1019-7, COLL-19). Am Math.
Petersen, B. & Oregon State University. Introduction to the Fourier Transform & Pseudofferential Operators. (Monographs & Studies in Mathematics: No. 19). 368p. 1983. text ed. 48.00 (ISBN 0-273-08600-6). Pitman Pub MA.
Rudin, Walter. Fourier Analysis on Groups. (Pure & Applied Mathematics Ser.). 285p. 1962. 45.50x (ISBN 0-470-74481-2). Wiley.
Shaw, Derek. Fourier Transform N.M.R. Spectroscopy. 2nd, rev. ed. (Studies in Physical & Theoretical Chemistry: Vol. 30). 304p. 1984. 72.25 (ISBN 0-444-42285-4, I-248-84). Elsevier.
Silberger, A. J. PGL-2, Over the P-Adics: Its Representations, Spherical Functions, & Fourier Analysis. LC 70-139951. (Lecture Notes in Mathematics: Vol. 166). 1970. pap. 14.00 (ISBN 0-387-05193-7). Springer-Verlag.
Stark, Henry, ed. Applications of Optical Fourier Transforms. 1982. 71.50 (ISBN 0-12-663220-0). Acad Pr.
Szmydt, Zofia. Fourier Transformation & Linear Differential Equations. new ed. PWN, Polish Scientific Pb., ed. (Symposia of the Intl. Astronomical Union: No. 71). 1976. lib. bdg. 47.50 (ISBN 90-277-0622-0, Pub. by Reidel Holland). Kluwer Academic.
Wrinch, Dorothy. Fourier Transforms & Structure Factors. 96p. 1966. pap. 3.00 (ISBN 0-686-60368-0). Polycrystal Bk Serv.

FOWLS
see Poultry

FOX
see Foxes

FOXES
see also Red Fox
Ashbrook, Frank G. Silver-Fox Farming. facs. ed. (Shorey Lost Arts Ser.). 68p. pap. 5.95 (ISBN 0-8466-6047-4, U47). Shorey.
Taketazu, Minoru. Fox Family. LC 79-9286. (Illus.). 1979. 25.00 (ISBN 0-8348-1039-5). Weatherhill.

FRACTIONAL DISTILLATION
see Distillation, Fractional

FRACTIONS
The Arithmetic Classroom: Fraction - Addition & Subtraction. (Courses by Computers Ser.). Apple. 49.95 (ISBN 0-88408-201-6); IBM-PC, PCjr. 49.95; Acom. 49.95 (ISBN 0-88408-346-2). Sterling Swift.
The Arithmetic Classroom: Fraction - Multiplication & Division, 3 pts. (Courses by Computers Ser.). Apple. 49.95 (ISBN 0-88408-202-4); IBM-PC, PCjr. 49.95 (ISBN 0-88408-290-3); Acom. 49.95 (ISBN 0-88408-347-0). Sterling Swift.
The Arithmetic Classroom: Fractions - Basic Concepts, 3 pts. (Courses by Computers Ser.). Apple. 49.95 (ISBN 0-88408-200-8); IBM-PC, PCjr. 49.95 (ISBN 0-88408-293-8); Acom. 49.95 (ISBN 0-88408-345-4). Sterling Swift.
Gatje, Charles T. & Gatje, John F. A Math Activity Packet for Fractions. (Orig.). 1976. pap. text ed. 1.95 (ISBN 0-937534-01-3). G&G Pubs.
Gregorich, Barbara & Odom, Clark. Fractions. LC 79-730045. (Illus.). 1978. 135.00 (ISBN 0-89290-094-6, A510-SATC). Soc for Visual.
Howett, J. Basic Skills with Fractions. 128p. 1980. pap. text ed. 3.67 (ISBN 0-8428-2117-1). Cambridge Bk.
McLean & Anderson. Applied Factorical & Fractional Designs. (Statistics - Textbooks & Monographs). 360p. 1984. 65.00 (ISBN 0-8247-7154-0). Dekker.

Mick, Beverly J. Multiplication Facts & Basic Fractions. 1981. Set. 8.50 (ISBN 0-932786-01-4); Bk. 1. 4.25 (ISBN 0-932786-02-2); Bk. 2. 4.25 (ISBN 0-932786-03-0). Bellefontaine.

Rasmussen. Key to Fractions Reproducible Tests. 32p. 1985. pap. 9.95 (ISBN 0-317-31629-X). HM.

Rasmussen, Steven. Key to Fractions Series. Incl. Bk. 1. Fraction Concepts. 40p. 1.50 (ISBN 0-913684-91-0); Bk. 2. Multiplying & Dividing. 40p. 1.50 (ISBN 0-913684-92-9); Bk. 3. Adding & Subtracting. 40p. 1.50 (ISBN 0-913684-93-7); Bk. 4. Mixed Numbers. 1.50 (ISBN 0-913684-94-5); Key to Fractions Answer Book. pap. 1.75 (ISBN 0-913684-97-X). 1980. pap. Key Curr Project.

Resource Systems International. Applied Math: II. 1982. pap. text ed. 15.00 (ISBN 0-8359-0141-6). Reston.

FRACTIONS–PROGRAMMED INSTRUCTION

Bezuszka, Stanley, et al. Fraction Action 1. (Motivated Math Project Activity Booklets). 47p. (Orig.). 1976. pap. text ed. 2.00 (ISBN 0-917916-12-3). Boston Coll Math.

--Fraction Action 2. (Motivated Math Project Activity Booklets). 68p. (Orig.). 1976. pap. text ed. 2.00 (ISBN 0-917916-13-1). Boston Coll Math.

Gatje, Charles T. & Gatje, John F. A MAP for Fractions. Marcos, Rafael, tr. (Span., Orig.). 1981. pap. text ed. 1.95 (ISBN 0-937534-07-2). G&G Pubs.

FRACTIONS, CONTINUED
see also Processes, Infinite

Freiman & Fuller, eds. Fracture Mechanics for Ceramics, Rocks, & Concrete - STP 745. 278p. 1981. 29.00 (ISBN 0-8031-0731-5, 04-745000-30). ASTM.

Jones, William B. & Thron, W. J. Encyclopedia of Mathematics & Its Applications: Continued Fractions, Vol. 11. 1984. 47.50 (ISBN 0-521-30231-5). Cambridge U Pr.

Khinchin, Aleksandr J. Continued Fractions. Eagle, Herbert, ed. LC 64-15819. pap. 28.00 (ISBN 0-317-09464-5, 2016988). Bks Demand UMI.

Lewis & Sines, eds. Fracture Mechanics: Fourteenth Symposium - STP 791: Volume 1, Theory & Analysis. 610p. 1983. 75.00 (ISBN 0-8031-0728-5, 04-791001-30). ASTM.

--Fracture Mechanics: Fourteenth Symposium-STP 791, 2 vols. 1983. Set. 135.00 (ISBN 0-8031-0730-7, 04-791000-30). ASTM.

--Fracture Mechanics: Fourteenth Symposium - STP 791, Vol. 11. 639p. 1983. 75.00 (ISBN 0-8031-0729-3, 04-791002-30). ASTM.

Olds, Carl D. Continued Fractions. LC 61-12185. (New Mathematical Library: No. 9). 162p. 1975. pap. 10.00 (ISBN 0-88385-609-3). Math Assn.

Shohat, J. A. & Tamarkin, J. D. Problem of Moments. LC 51-96. (Mathematical Surveys Ser.: No. 1). 144p. 1983. Repr. of 1950 ed. 30.00 (ISBN 0-8218-1501-6, SURV-1). Am Math.

Wall, H. S. Analytic Theory of Continued Fractions. LC 66-24296. 17.50 (ISBN 0-8284-0207-8). Chelsea Pub.

FRACTURE MECHANICS
see also Brittleness; Materials–Fatigue; Metals–Fracture; Polymers and Polymerization–Fracture; Yield-Line Analysis

Allgower, M., et al, eds. ASIF - Technique for Internal Fixation of Fractures. 1975. ring binder 187.00 (ISBN 0-387-92105-2). Springer-Verlag.

American Society for Materials & Testing. Crack Arrest Methodology & Applications, STP 711. 452p. 1980. 44.75x (ISBN 0-8031-0317-4, 04-711000-30). ASTM.

American Society for Metal. Wear & Fracture Prevention: Proceedings of a Conference Held May 21-22, 1980, Peoria, Illinois. LC 81-67226. (Materials-Metalworking Technology Ser.). pap. 79.80 (ISBN 0-317-26752-3, 2024351). Bks Demand UMI.

American Society for Metals Staff. Prevention of Structural Failures: The Role of NDT, Fracture Mechanics & Failure Analysis: Proceedings of Two Annual Forums, 19-22 June, 1977 & 14-16 June 1976, Tarpon Springs, Florida. LC 78-15388. (Materials-Metalworking Technology Ser.). (Illus.). pap. 90.00 (ISBN 0-317-09726-1, 2019489). Bks Demand UMI.

--Source Book on Failure Analysis: A Discriminative Selection of Outstanding Articles & Case Histories from the Periodical Literature. American Society for Metals Staff, the Periodical Publication Department, ed. LC 74-22347. (ASM Engineering Bookshelf Ser.). (Illus.). pap. 103.50 (ISBN 0-317-09642-7, 2019492). Bks Demand UMI.

American Society for Testing & Materials. Progress in Flaw Growth & Fracture Toughness Testing: Proceedings of the 1972 National Symposium on Fracture Mechanics, Philadelphia, PA, 28-30, 1972. LC 73-76198. (American Society for Testing & Materials Special Technical Publication: No. 536). pap. 125.30 (ISBN 0-317-10700-3, 2022546). Bks Demand UMI.

ASTM Committee E-24 on Fracture Testing. Fracture Mechanics: Fifteenth Symposium - STP 833. Sanford, R. J., ed. LC 83-72816. 750p. 1984. text ed. 74.00 (ISBN 0-8031-0208-9, 04-833000-30). ASTM.

Bonis, L. J., et al, eds. Fracture of Metals, Polymers & Glasses. (Fundamental Phenomena in the Materials Science Ser.: Vol. 4). 310p. 1967. 32.50x (ISBN 0-306-38604-6, Plenum Pr). Plenum Pub.

Bradt, Richard C., et al, eds. Fracture Mechanics of Ceramics, 4 vols. Incl. Vol. 1. Concepts, Flaws & Fractography. 471p. 1974. 75.00x (ISBN 0-306-37591-5); Vol. 2. Microstructure, Materials & Applications. 504p. 1974. 75.00x (ISBN 0-306-37592-3); Vol. 3. Flaws & Testing. 528p. 1978. 75.00x (ISBN 0-306-37593-1); Vol. 4. Crack Growth & Microstructure. 504p. 1978. 75.00x (ISBN 0-306-37594-X). LC 73-20399 (Plenum Pr). Plenum Pub.

Broek, D. Elementary Engineering Fracture Mechanics. rev. ed. 450p. 1978. 60.00x (ISBN 90-286-0208-9); pap. 20.00x (ISBN 90-286-0218-6). Sijthoff & Noordhoff.

Broek, David. Elementary Engineering Fracture Mechanics. 1982. lib. bdg. 69.00 (ISBN 90-247-2580-1, Pub. by Martinus Nijhoff Netherlands); pap. 29.50 (ISBN 90-247-2656-5, Pub. by Martinus Nijhoff Netherlands). Kluwer Academic.

Burke, J. J. & Weiss, V., eds. Application of Fracture Mechanics to Design. LC 78-14819. (Sagamore Army Materials Research Conference Proceedings Ser.: Vol. 22). 347p. 1978. 55.00x (ISBN 0-306-40040-5, Plenum Pr). Plenum Pub.

Burridge, Robert, ed. Fracture Mechanics. LC 78-24473. (SIAM-AMS Proceedings: Vol. 12). 1979. 20.00 (ISBN 0-8218-1332-3). Am Math.

Caddell, Robert M. Deformation & Fracture of Solids. (Illus.). 1980. text ed. 37.95 (ISBN 0-13-198309-1). P-H.

Campell, J. E. & Inderwood, J. H., eds. Application of Fracture Mechanics for Selection of Metallic Structural Materials. 1982. 83.00 (ISBN 0-87170-136-7). ASM.

Carlsson, J., ed. Mechanical Behaviour of Materials: Proceedings of the Fourth International Conference on Mechanical Behaviour of Materials, Stockholm, Sweden, August 15-19, 1983, 2 Vols, No. IV. (International Series on Strength & Fracture of Materials & Structures). (Illus.). 1175p. 1984. 225.00 (ISBN 0-08-029340-9). Pergamon.

Carpinteri, A., ed. Fracture Mechanics of Concrete: Material Characterization & Testing. 1984. lib. bdg. 49.50 (ISBN 90-247-2959-9, Pub. by Martinus Nijhoff Netherlands). Kluwer Academic.

Chell, G. G., ed. Developments in Fracture Mechanics, Vols. 1 & 2. Vol. 1, 1979. 52.00 (ISBN 0-85334-858-8, Pub. by Elsevier Applied Sci England); Vol. 2, 1981. 57.50 (ISBN 0-85334-973-8, Pub. by Elsevier Applied Sci England). Elsevier.

Cherepanov, C. P. Mechanics of Brittle Fracture. 1980. 150.00 (ISBN 0-07-010739-4). McGraw.

Conway, J. B. Numerical Methods for Creep & Rupture Analysis. 212p. 1967. 57.75 (ISBN 0-677-01090-7). Gordon.

Cyclic Stress-Strain Behavior: Analysis, Experimentation & Failure Prediction, STP 519. 289p. 1973. 28.00 (ISBN 0-8031-0078-7, 04-519000-30). ASTM.

Developments in Fracture Mechanics Test Methods Standardization - STP 632. 290p. 1977. 24.75 (ISBN 0-8031-0321-2, 04-632000-30). ASTM.

Drucker, Daniel C. & Gilman, J. J., eds. Fracture of Solids: Proceedings of an International Conference, Maple Valley, Washington, August 21-24, 1962. LC 63-13590. (Metallurgical Society Conferences Ser.: Vol. 20). pap. 160.00 (ISBN 0-317-11259-7, 2001508). Bks Demand UMI.

Easterling, K., ed. Mechanisms of Deformation & Fracture: Proceedings of the Interdisciplinary Conference, Held at the University of Lulea-Sweden, 20-22, September 1978. (Strength & Fracture of Materials & Structures). 1979. 105.00 (ISBN 0-08-024258-8). Pergamon.

Effects of Environment & Complex Load History on Fatigue Life, STP 462. 332p. 1970. 22.00 (ISBN 0-8031-0032-9, 04-462000-30). ASTM.

Evans, A. G., ed. Fracture in Ceramic Materials: Toughening Mechanisms, Machining Damage, Shock. LC 84-14763. (Illus.). 420p. 1985. 42.00 (ISBN 0-8155-1005-5). Noyes.

Ewalds, H. L. & Wanhill, R. J. Fracture Mechanics. 304p. 1984. pap. text ed. 24.50 (ISBN 0-7131-3515-8). E Arnold.

Fatigue Crack Growth Under Spectrum Loads-STP 595. 352p. 1976. 34.50 (ISBN 0-8031-0344-1, 04-595000-30). ASTM.

Ford, Hugh, et al. Fracture Mechanics in Design & Service. (Phil Trans of the Royal Soc., Series A: Vol. 299). (Illus.). 239p. 1981. lib. bdg. 67.00x (ISBN 0-85403-152-9, Pub. by Royal Soc London). Scholium Intl.

Fractography & Materials Science - STP 733. 450p. 1981. 46.50 (ISBN 0-8031-0733-1, 04-733000-30). ASTM.

Fracture Analysis: 8th Conference, STP 560. 262p. 1974. 22.75 (ISBN 0-8031-0361-1, 04-560000-30). ASTM.

Fracture Mechanics - STP 677: 11th Conference. 802p. 1979. 60.00x (ISBN 0-8031-0364-6, 04-677000-30). ASTM.

Fracture Mechanics Applied to Brittle Measurements: 11th Conference, STP 678. 232p. 1979. 25.00x (ISBN 0-8031-0365-4, 04-678000-30). ASTM.

Fracture Mechanics, STP 700: 12th Conferecne. 587p. 1980. 53.25x (ISBN 0-8031-0363-8, 04-700000-30). ASTM.

Fracture Toughness & Slow-Stable Cracking: 8th Conference, STP 559. 318p. 1974. 25.25 (ISBN 0-8031-0367-0, 04-559000-30). ASTM.

Fracture Toughness Testing & Its Applications, STP 381. 418p. 1965. 19.50 (ISBN 0-8031-0105-8, 04 381000 30). ASTM.

Freiman & Hudson, eds. Methods for Assessing the Structural Reliability of Brittle Materials - STP 844. 226p. 1984. 39.00 (ISBN 0-8031-0265-8, 04-844000-30). ASTM.

Friedrich, K. Fracture Mechanical Behavior of Short Fiber Reinforced Thermoplastic. (Progress Report of the VDI-Z: No. 18). 114p. 1984. pap. 30.00 (ISBN 0-9907000-9-7, Pub. by VDI Verlag Gmbh Dusseldorf). Heyden.

Garrett, G. G. & Marriott, D. L., eds. Engineering Applications of Fracture Analysis: Proceedings of the First National Conference on Fracture Held in Johannesburg, South Africa, 1979. LC 80-41074. (International Ser. on the Strength & Fractures of Materials & Structures). (Illus.). 440p. 1980. 72.00 (ISBN 0-08-025437-3). Pergamon.

Gdoutos, E. E. Problems of Mixed Mode Crack Propagation. 250p. 1984. lib. bdg. 53.00 (ISBN 90-247-3055-4, Pub. by Martinus Nijhoff Netherlands). Kluwer Academic.

Hellan, Kare. Introduction to Fracture Mechanics. (Illus.). 352p. 1984. text ed. 45.00 (ISBN 0-07-028048-7). McGraw.

Hertzberg, Richard W. Deformation & Fracture Mechanics of Engineering Materials. 2nd ed. LC 83-5881. 697p. 1983. 46.50 (ISBN 0-471-08609-6); write for info (ISBN 0-471-89367-6). Wiley.

Hierholzer, G., et al. Manual on the AO-ASIF Tubular External Fixator. (Illus.). 1985. 37.50 (ISBN 0-387-13518-9). Springer-Verlag.

Huazong, H. Li. Fracture Mechanics in China: A Selection of Chinese Papers & Abstracts. 158p. 1982. pap. 62.00 (ISBN 0-08-028726-3, A115, A145). Pergamon.

Jaeger, J. C. Elasticity, Fracture & Flow: With Engineering & Geological Applications. 3rd ed. 1971. pap. 10.95 (ISBN 0-412-20890-3, NO.6164, Pub. by Chapman & Hall). Methuen Inc.

Jagannadham, K. & Marcinkowski, M. J. Unified Theory of Fracture. (Materials Science Surveys Ser.: Vol. 1). 800p. 1983. 86.00 (ISBN 0-87849-523-1). Trans Tech.

Jayatilaka, Ayal De S. Fracture of Engineering Brittle Materials. (Illus.). 378p. 1979. 68.50 (ISBN 0-85334-825-1, Pub. by Elsevier Applied Sci England). Elsevier.

Kobayashi, Albert S., ed. Experimental Techniques in Fracture Mechanics. LC 72-13967. (Society for Experimental Stress Analysis Ser.: No. 1). (Illus.). 150p. 1973. 8.50x (ISBN 0-8138-0710-7). Iowa St U Pr.

--Experimental Techniques in Fracture Mechanics, No. 2. (Society for Experimental Stress Analysis Ser.: No.2). (Illus.). 204p. 1975. text ed. 9.95x (ISBN 0-8138-0735-2). Iowa St U Pr.

Lane & Otten, eds. Fracture Mechanics: 13th Conference - STP 743. 650p. 1981. 58.50 (ISBN 0-8031-0732-3, 04-743000-30). ASTM.

Larsson, L. H., ed. Subcritical Crack Growth Due to Fatigue, Stress Corrosion & Creep: Selected Proceedings of the Third Advanced Seminar on Fracture Mechanics (ASFM 3), Joint Research Centre, Ispra, Italy, 19-23 October 1981. (Illus.). 640p. 1985. 112.50 (ISBN 0-85334-289-X, Pub. by Elsevier Applied Sci England). Elsevier.

Latzko, D. G., ed. Post-Yield Fracture Mechanics. (Illus.). 349p. 1979. 77.75 (ISBN 0-85334-775-1, Pub. by Elsevier Applied Sci England). Elsevier.

Latzko, D. G., et al, eds. Post-Yield Fracture Mechanics. 2nd ed. (Illus.). 512p. 1985. 90.00 (ISBN 0-85334-276-8, Pub. by Elsevier Applied Sci England). Elsevier.

Lawn, B. R. & Wilshaw, T. R. Fracture of Brittle Solids. LC 74-12970. (Cambridge Solid State Science Ser.). (Illus.). 160p. 1975. pap. 21.95x (ISBN 0-521-09952-8). Cambridge U Pr.

Liebowitz, H., ed. Progress in Fatigue & Fracture, Vol. 8 No. 1. 1976. text ed. 66.00 (ISBN 0-08-020866-5). Pergamon.

Liebowitz, Harold A. A Treatise on Fracture, 7 vols. Incl. Vol. 1. Microscopic & Macroscopic Fundamentals of Fracture. 1969. 86.00 (ISBN 0-12-449701-2); Vol. 2. Mathematical Fundamentals of Fracture. 1969. 90.00 (ISBN 0-12-449702-0); Vol. 3. Engineering Fundamentals & Environmental Effects. 1971. 90.00 (ISBN 0-12-449703-9); Vol. 4. 1969. 72.00 (ISBN 0-12-449704-7); Vol. 5. 1969. 80.50 (ISBN 0-12-449705-5); Vol. 6. 1969. 80.50 (ISBN 0-12-449706-3); Vol. 7. 1972. 134.00 (ISBN 0-12-449707-1). Acad Pr.

Mechanics of Crack Growth- STP 590. 502p. 1976. 45.25 (ISBN 0-8031-0509-6, 04-590000-30). ASTM.

National Symposium Fracture Mechanics. Stress Analysis & Growth of Cracks-STP 513. 307p. 1972. 27.50x (ISBN 0-8031-0362-X, 04-513000-30). ASTM.

Nemat-Nasser, S., ed. Three Dimensional Constitutive Relationships & Ductile Fracture. 440p. 1981. 83.00 (ISBN 0-444-86108-4, North Holland). Elsevier.

Panasyuk, V. V. Limiting Equilibrium of Brittle Solids with Fractures. LC 75-135093. 325p. 1969. 39.00 (ISBN 0-403-04527-4). Scholarly.

Parker, A. P. Mechanics of Fracture & Fatigue: An Introduction. 1981. 33.00x (ISBN 0-419-11460-2, NO. 6495, Pub. by E & FN Spon); pap. 16.95x (ISBN 0-419-11470-X, NO. 6494). Methuen Inc.

Part-Through Crack Fatigue Life Prediction - STP 687. 226p. 1979. 26.25x (ISBN 0-8031-0532-0, 04-687000-30). ASTM.

Parton, V. Elastic-Plastic Fracture Mechanics. 233p. 1978. 10.00 (ISBN 0-8285-0678-7, Pub. by Mir Pubs USSR). Imported Pubns.

Perrone, N. & Atluri, S. N., eds. Nonlinear & Dynamic Fracture Mechanics, Bk. No. G00152. LC 79-54425. (Applied Mechanics Division Ser.: Vol. 35). 220p. 1979. 30.00 (ISBN 0-686-62962-0). ASME.

Radon, J. C. Fracture & Fatigue-Elasto-Plasticity, Thin Sheet & Micro-Mechanisms: Proceedings of the Third European Colloquium on Fracture, London, 8-10 September 1980. LC 80-40915. (Illus.). 450p. 1980. 72.00 (ISBN 0-08-026161-2). Pergamon.

Rolfe, Stan & Barson, John. Fracture & Fatigue Control in Structures: Applications of Fracture Mechanics. (Illus.). 1977. text ed. 45.00 (ISBN 0-13-329953-8). P-H.

Rybicki, Edmund F. & Benzley, Steven E., eds. Computational Fracture Mechanics: Presented at the Second National Congress on Pressure Vessels & Piping, San Francisco, CA, June 23-27 1975. LC 75-149. pap. 55.50 (ISBN 0-317-08124-1, 2016859). Bks Demand UMI.

Shah, S. P., ed. Application of Fracture Mechanics to Cementitious Composites. 1985. lib. bdg. 89.50 (ISBN 90-247-3176-3, Pub. by Martinus). Kluwer Academic.

Sih, G. C. & Tamus, V. P. Fracture of Composite Materials. 429p. 1979. 35.00x (ISBN 90-286-0289-5). Sijthoff & Noordhoff.

Sih, G. C., ed. Analytical & Experimental Fracture Mechanics. Mirabile, M. 970p. 1981. 97.50x (ISBN 90-286-0890-7, Pub. by Martinus Nijhoff Netherlands). Kluwer Academic.

--Fracture Mechanics & Technology, 2 vols. 1636p. 1977. 125.00x (ISBN 90-286-0934-2). Sijthoff & Noordhoff.

Sih, G. C. & DiTomasso, A., eds. Fracture Mechanics of Concrete: Structural Application & Numerical Calculation. 1984. lib. bdg. 57.50 (ISBN 90-247-2960-2, Pub. by Martinus Nijhoff Netherlands). Kluwer Academic.

Sih, G. C. & Faria, L., eds. Fracture Mechanics Methodology: Evaluation of Structural Components Integrity. 250p. 1984. lib. bdg. 45.00 (ISBN 90-247-2941-6, Pub. by Martinus Nijhoff Netherlands). Kluwer Academic.

Sih, G. C. & Francois, D., eds. Progress in Fracture Mechanics: Fracture Mechanics Research & Technological Activities of Nations Around the World. (International Series on Strength & Fracture of Materials). (Illus.). 96p. 1983. 35.00 (ISBN 0-08-028691-7). Pergamon.

Sih, G. C. & Provan, J. W., eds. Defects, Fracture & Fatigue. 1983. lib. bdg. 69.50 (ISBN 90-247-2804-5, Pub. by Martinus Nijhoff Netherlands). Kluwer Academic.

Sih, G. C. & Skudra, A. M., eds. Failure Mechanics of Composites. (Handbook of Composites: Vol. 3). 444p. 1985. 95.00 (ISBN 0-444-86879-8, North-Holland). Elsevier.

Sih, G. C. & Theocaris, P. S., eds. Mixed Mode Crack Propagation. 410p. 1981. 50.00x (ISBN 90-286-2691-3, Pub. by Martinus Nijhoff Netherlands). Kluwer Academic.

Sih, G. C., et al, eds. Application of Fracture Mechanics to Materials & Structures. 1984. lib. bdg. 125.00 (ISBN 90-247-2958-0, Pub. by Martinus Nijhoff Netherlands). Kluwer Academic.

Simpson, L. A., ed. Fracture Problems & Solutions in the Energy Industry: Proceedings of the 5th Canadian Fracture Conference (CFC5), Winnipeg, Canada, September 3-4, 1981. (Illus.). 260p. 1982. 55.00 (ISBN 0-08-028671-2, A145, B110). Pergamon.

Smith, R. A., ed. Fracture Mechanics, Current Status, Future Prospects: Proceedings of a Conference Held at Cambridge University, March 16, 1979. (Illus.). 128p. 1979. 65.00 (ISBN 0-08-024766-0). Pergamon.

Swedlow, J. L., ed. The Surface Crach: Physical Problems & Computational Solutions. Presented at the Winter Annual Meeting of ASME, New York, N. Y., November 26-30, 1972. LC 72-88547. pap. 52.00 (ISBN 0-317-08113-6, 2016841). Bks Demand UMI.

Taplin, D. M. Advances in Research on the Strength & Fracture of Materials, 6 Vols. Incl. Vol. 1. An Overview. 100.00 (ISBN 0-08-022136-X); Vol. 2a. Physical Metallurgy of Fracture. 100.00 (ISBN 0-08-022138-6); Vol. 2b. Fatigue. 100.00 (ISBN 0-08-022140-8); Vol. 3a. 100.00 (ISBN 0-08-022142-4); Vol. 3b. Applications & Non-Metals. incl. index 100.00 (ISBN 0-08-022144-0). 1978. 530.00 (ISBN 0-08-022130-0). Pergamon.

Tetelman, A. S. & McEvily, A. J. Fracture of Structural Materials. LC 67-12573. (Wiley Series on the Science & Technology of Materials Ser.). Repr. of 1967 ed. 120.00 (ISBN 0-8357-9893-3, 2055171). Bks Demand UMI.

VDI, ed. European Colloquium on Fracture: Proceedings of the 2nd Colloquium. 1978. 87.00 (ISBN 0-9961073-6-3, Pub. by VDI W Germany). Heyden.

Wittmann, F. H., ed. Fracture Mechanics of Concrete. (Developments in Civil Engineering Ser.: No. 7). 680p. 1983. 138.50 (ISBN 0-444-42199-8, I-303-83). Elsevier.

Wright, M. Fracture Mechanics. 1984. write for info. (ISBN 0-442-29386-0). Van Nos Reinhold.

Yokobori, T. Interdisciplinary Approach to Fractures & Strength of Solids. 328p. 1968. 87.95 (ISBN 0-677-61320-2). Gordon.

FRACTURE OF METALS
see Metals–Fracture

FRACTURE OF POLYMERIC MATERIALS
see Polymers and Polymerization–Fracture

FRACTURE OF SOLIDS
see Fracture Mechanics

FRAMES (STRUCTURES)
see Structural Frames

FRAMEWORK (COMPUTER PROGRAM)

Ashley, Ruth & Fernandez, Judi N. Essential Framework: A Self-Teaching Guide. 1985. pap. 19.95 (ISBN 0-471-82048-2). Wiley.

Blake, Robert M. Measured Doses of Framework. (Illus.). 320p. (Orig.). 1985. plastic comb bdg. 24.95. Macmillan.

Curtin, Dennis P. Manager's Guide to Framework: An Illustrated Short Course. 160p. 1985. pap. 18.95 (ISBN 0-13-550070-2). P-H.

Dinerstein, Nelson T. The Dynamics of Framework. 300p. 1985. pap. cancelled (ISBN 0-87094-671-4). Dow Jones-Irwin.

Expert Systems Staff. Framework: On-the-Job Application. 265p. 1985. pap. 29.95 incl. disk (ISBN 0-912677-50-3). Ashton-Tate Bks.

--Framework: On-the-Job Applications. Ashton-Tate, ed. (Framework Books). 300p. 1984. pap. 19.95 incl. disk (ISBN 0-912677-22-8). Ashton-Tate Bks.

Forefront Corporation Staff. Framework: A Developer's Handbook. (Framework Bks.). 300p. 1985. pap. 24.95 (ISBN 0-912677-24-4). Ashton-Tate Bks.

--Framework: A Programmer's Reference. Ashton-Tate, ed. 300p. 1984. pap. 24.95 (ISBN 0-912677-21-X). Ashton-Tate Bks.

--Framework: An Introduction to Programming. (Framework Bks.). 300p. 1985. pap. 24.95 (ISBN 0-912677-23-6). Ashton-Tate Bks.

Framework. (Workbook Ser.). 1985. Introduction to Framework, Level One Course. pap. write for info. (ISBN 0-912677-59-7). Using Framework, Level Two Course (ISBN 0-912677-65-1). Programming with Framework, Level Three Course (ISBN 0-912677-65-1). Ashton-Tate Bks.

Granoff, Steve, et al. Framework Made Easier. 200p. 1985. 14.95 (ISBN 0-13-330531-7). P-H.

Graves-Smith, Tom R. Linear Analysis of Frameworks. (Series in Engineering Science). (Illus.). 451p. 1983. 64.95 (ISBN 0-470-27449-2). Halsted Pr.

Harrison, Bill. Framework: An Introduction. (Framework Bks.). 300p. 1984. pap. 15.95 (ISBN 0-912677-20-1). Ashton-Tate Bks.

--Framework: An Introduction. 15.95 (ISBN 0-317-13749-2). P-H.

Hoenig, Alan. Framework with Applications for the IBM Personal Computer. (Micropower Ser.). 200p. 1985. pap. 17.95 (ISBN 0-697-00725-1); deluxe ed., incl. diskette 29.95 (ISBN 0-697-00726-X). Wm C Brown.

King, Brian L. & Philips, Sheldon W. Framework: The Decision Maker's Guide to Business Applications. 205p. 1985. pap. 14.95 (ISBN 0-394-72961-7, RanC). Random.

Kruglinski, David. FrameWork Book. 224p. (Orig.). 1985. pap. 17.95 (ISBN 0-07-881164-3, 164-3). Osborne-McGraw.

Matthews, Carole B. & Matthews, Martin S. Framework Business Solutions. LC 84-45892. 336p. (Orig.). 1985. pap. 19.95 (ISBN 0-8019-7617-0). Chilton.

Myers, Mary. Presenting Framework. (Illus.). 128p. 1984. pap. cancelled (ISBN 0-88056-363-X). Dilithium Pr.

Osgood, William R. & Curtin, Dennis P. Preparing Your Business Budget with Framework. 160p. 1985. pap. 18.95 (ISBN 0-13-698770-2). P-H.

Prague, Cary N. & Kasevich, Lawrence. Using Framework: A Pictorial Guide. (Illus.). 320p. 1985. pap. 18.95 (ISBN 0-8306-1966-6, 1966); text ed. 26.95 (ISBN 0-8306-0966-0). TAB Bks.

Seybold, P. B. & Marshak, R. T. Integrated Desk-Top Environments: Symphony, Framework, Visi-On & DesQ. 208p. 1985. pap. 15.95 (ISBN 0-07-056324-1). McGraw.

Simpson, Alan. The Best Book of Framework. 15.95 (ISBN 0-672-22421-6, 22421). Sams.

Stinson, Craig. Framework: Tips & Techniques. (Illus.). 384p. 1985. pap. 19.95 (ISBN 0-89303-491-6). Brady Comm.

Stone, Deborah L. The Illustrated Framework Book. (Illustrated Ser.). 280p. (Orig.). pap. 19.95 (ISBN 0-915381-76-1). Wordware Pub.

Weber Systems, Inc. Staff. Framework User's Handbook. (Orig.). 1985. pap. 14.95 (ISBN 0-345-32377-7). Ballantine.

Weber Systems Inc. Staff, et al. Framework Programmer's Guide. 300p. (Orig.). pap. cancelled. Weber Systems.

Williams, Frederick. Framework for Writers. 1985. pap. 15.95 (ISBN 0-912677-54-6). Ashton-Tate Bks.

FRAMING (BUILDING)
see also Roofs

Henrych, J. The Dynamics of Arches & Frames. (Developments in Civil Engineering Ser.: Vol. 2). 464p. 1981. 104.25 (ISBN 0-444-99792-X). Elsevier.

Jones, R. Framing, Sheathing & Insulation. LC 73-1847. 227p. 1973. pap. 12.40 (ISBN 0-8273-0096-4); answer book 3.00 (ISBN 0-8273-0097-2). Delmar.

Kani, Gaspar. Analysis of Multistory Frames. Hyman, Charles J., tr. LC 57-6114. 1967. 8.50 (ISBN 0-8044-4486-2). Ungar.

FRANCE–AIR FORCE

Farre, Henry. Sky Fighters of France: Aerial Warfare, Nineteen Fourteen to Nineteen Eighteen. Gilbert, James, ed. Rush, Catharine, tr. LC 79-7252. (Flight: Its First Seventy-Five Years Ser.). (Illus.). 1979. Repr. of 1919 ed. lib. bdg. 19.00x (ISBN 0-405-12164-4). Ayer Co Pubs.

Hall, James N. High Adventure: A Narrative of Air Fighting in France. Gilbert, James, ed. LC 79-7267. (Flight: Its First Seventy-Five Years Ser.). 1979. Repr. of 1918 ed. lib. bdg. 23.00x (ISBN 0-405-12177-6). Ayer Co Pubs.

FRANKLIN, BENJAMIN, 1706-1790

Amacher, Richard E. Benjamin Franklin. (Twayne's United States Authors Ser.). 1962. pap. 5.95x (ISBN 0-8084-0059-2, T12, Twayne). New Coll U Pr.

Baker, Jim. Benjamin Franklin: The Uncommon Man. (Illus.). 1976. pap. 1.00 (ISBN 0-914482-13-0). Ohio Hist Soc.

Clark, Ronald W. Benjamin Franklin: A Biography. LC 82-40115. (Illus.). 480p. 1983. 22.95 (ISBN 0-394-50222-1). Random.

Conner, Paul W. Poor Richard's Politicks: Benjamin Franklin & His New American Order. LC 80-21490. xiv, 285p. 1980. Repr. of 1965 ed. lib. bdg. 29.75x (ISBN 0-313-22695-4, COPRP). Greenwood.

Crowther, James G. Famous American Men of Science. facs. ed. LC 69-18925. (Essay Index Reprint Ser). 1937. 27.50 (ISBN 0-8369-0040-5). Ayer Co Pubs.

Franklin, Benjamin. The Autobiography of Benjamin Franklin: A Genetic Text. Lemay, J. A. & Zall, P. M., eds. LC 78-25907. 352p. 1981. 29.95x (ISBN 0-87049-256-X). U of Tenn Pr.

--The Papers of Benjamin Franklin: March 23, 1775 Through October 27, 1776; October 27, 1776-April 30, 1977, 2 Vols, Vols. 22, 23. Willcox, William B., ed. LC 59-12697. 1982, 768 55.00x (ISBN 0-300-02618-8); text ed. 55.00x 1983 752pp (ISBN 0-300-02897-0). Yale U Pr.

Goodman, Nathan G., ed. The Ingenious Dr. Franklin: Selected Scientific Letters of Benjamin Franklin. LC 74-81751. 256p. 1974. 22.00x (ISBN 0-8122-7680-9); pap. 7.95 (ISBN 0-8122-1067-0). U of Pa Pr.

Granger, Bruce I. Benjamin Franklin: An American Man of Letters. LC 76-8167. 1976. pap. 6.95 (ISBN 0-8061-1336-7). U of Okla Pr.

Johansen, Bruce E. Forgotten Founders: Benjamin Franklin, the Iroquois & the Rationale for American Revolution. LC 81-83027. 167p. 1982. 10.95 (ISBN 0-87645-111-3, Pub. by Gambit). Harvard Common Pr.

Morse, John T., Jr. Benjamin Franklin. LC 74-128926. (American Statesmen: No. 1). Repr. of 1898 ed. 35.00 (ISBN 0-404-50851-0). AMS Pr.

Oswald, John C. Benjamin Franklin, Printer. LC 74-3020. 1974. Repr. of 1917 ed. 48.00x (ISBN 0-8103-3642-1). Gale.

Scudder, Evarts S. Benjamin Franklin: A Biography. facsimile ed. LC 79-150199. (Select Bibliographies Reprint Ser). Repr. of 1939 ed. 21.00 (ISBN 0-8369-5712-1). Ayer Co Pubs.

Seeger, Raymond J. Benjamin Franklin. LC 73-7981. 200p. 1973. 19.50 (ISBN 0-08-017648-8). Pergamon.

Van Doren, Carl. Benjamin Franklin & Jonathan Edwards. 1979. Repr. of 1920 ed. lib. bdg. 20.00 (ISBN 0-8495-5525-6). Arden Lib.

Van Doren, Carl C. Benjamin Franklin. LC 73-8566. (Illus.). 845p. 1973. Repr. of 1938 ed. lib. bdg. 47.25x (ISBN 0-8371-6964-X, VABF). Greenwood.

Weems, Mason L. The Life of Benjamin Franklin. LC 75-31137. Repr. of 1822 ed. 21.00 (ISBN 0-404-13611-7). AMS Pr.

Zall, P. M., ed. Ben Franklin Laughing: Anecdotes from Original Sources by & About Benjamin Franklin. 1980. 12.95 (ISBN 0-520-04026-0). U of Cal Pr.

FREDHOLM'S EQUATION
see Integral Equations

FREE ELECTRON THEORY OF METALS
see also Electric Conductivity; Electrons–Emission; Fermi Surfaces

Brandt, N. B. & Chudinov, S. M. Electronic Structure of Metals. 336p. 1973. 6.45 (ISBN 0-8285-0778-3, Pub. by Mir Pubs USSR). Imported Pubns.

Metallurgical Society of AIME. Electro & Thermo-transport in Metals & Alloys: A Symposium. Hummel, R. E. & Huntington, H. B., eds. LC 77-76059. pap. 41.30 (ISBN 0-317-26079-0, 2023771). Bks Demand UMI.

Platzman, P. M. & Wolff, P. A. Waves & Interactions in Solid State Plasmas. (Solid State Physics Ser.: Suppl. 13). 1973. 35.00 (ISBN 0-12-607773-8). Acad Pr.

Timmerhaus, K. D., et al, eds. Low Temperature Physics - LT-13, 4 vols. Incl. Vol. 1. Quantum Fluids. 669p. 95.00x (ISBN 0-306-35121-8); Vol. 2. Quantum Crystals & Magnetism. 668p. 95.00x (ISBN 0-306-35122-6); Vol. 3. Superconductivity. 834p. 105.00x (ISBN 0-306-35123-4); Vol. 4. Electronic Properties, Instrumentation, & Measurement. 684p. 95.00x (ISBN 0-306-35124-2). LC 73-81092. (Illus.). 1974 (Plenum Pr). Plenum Pub.

FREE ENERGY RELATIONSHIP, LINEAR
see Linear Free Energy Relationship

FREE FALL–PHYSIOLOGICAL EFFECT
see Weightlessness

FREEWAYS
see Express Highways

FREEZE-DRYING

Copson, David A. Microwave Heating. 2nd ed. (Illus.). 1975. lib. bdg. 50.00 (ISBN 0-87055-182-5). AVI.

Goldblith, S. A., et al, eds. Freeze Drying & Advanced Food Technology. 1975. 95.00 (ISBN 0-12-288450-7). Acad Pr.

Hower, Rolland O. Freeze-Drying Biological Specimens: A Laboratory Manual. LC 78-10750. (Illus.). 196p. 1979. 27.50x (ISBN 0-87474-532-2). Smithsonian.

Mellor, J. D. Fundamentals of Freeze Drying. 1979. 69.50 (ISBN 0-12-490050-X). Acad Pr.

Sunset Editors. Canning, Freezing & Drying. 2nd ed. LC 80-53480. (Illus.). 128p. 1981. pap. 4.95 (ISBN 0-376-02213-2, Sunset Books). Sunset-Lane.

FREEZING
see Cryobiology; Ice; Refrigeration and Refrigerating Machinery

FREEZING AND OPENING OF RIVERS, LAKES, ETC.
see Ice on Rivers, Lakes, Etc.

FREEZING POINTS OF SOLUTIONS
see Molecular Weights

FREIGHT PLANES
see Transport Planes

FREIGHT SHIPS
see Cargo Ships

FREIGHT VESSELS
see Cargo Ships

FRENCH CLOVER
see Alfalfa

FRENCH LANGUAGE–TECHNICAL FRENCH

Locke, William N. Scientific French: A Concise Description of the Structural Elements of Scientific & Technical French. LC 78-11669. 124p. 1979. pap. 6.50 (ISBN 0-88275-771-7). Krieger.

FRENCH SCIENCE
see Science, French

FREQUENCIES OF OSCILLATING SYSTEMS
see also Doppler Effect; Radio Frequency

Boszany. Bracketing of Eigenfrequencies of Continuous Structures. 1981. 55.00 (ISBN 0-9960071-2-1, Pub. by Akademiai Kaido Hungary). Heyden.

Frerking, Marvin E. Crystal Oscillator Design & Temperature Compensation. 1978. 24.95 (ISBN 0-442-22459-1). Van Nos Reinhold.

Gerber, Eduard A. & Ballato, Arthur, eds. Precision Frequency Control, Vol. 2: Oscillators & Standards. 1985. 69.50 (ISBN 0-12-280602-6). Acad Pr.

Kartaschoff, P. Frequency & Time. (Monographs in Physical Measurement). 1978. 47.50 (ISBN 0-12-400150-5). Acad Pr.

MacFarlane, A. G., ed. Frequency: Response Methods in Control Systems. LC 79-90572. 1979. 56.10 (ISBN 0-87942-125-8, PC01206). Inst Electrical.

Ord, J. K. Families of Frequency Distributions. 1972. pap. 16.25x (ISBN 0-02-849910-7). Hafner.

Skudrzyk, Eugen. Simple & Complex Vibratory Systems. LC 66-18222. (Illus.). 1968. 36.75x (ISBN 0-271-73127-3). Pa St U Pr.

FREQUENCY ANALYSIS (DYNAMICS)
see Frequencies of Oscillating Systems

FREQUENCY CHANGERS
see also Frequency Multipliers

Heller, Samuel. Frequency Changers: Rotating Type-Designing, Reconnecting & Testing with Design of Induction Regulators. LC 68-57467. (Illus., Orig.). 1968. 22.50 (ISBN 0-911740-05-8). Datarule.

Manassewitsch, Vadim. Frequency Synthesizers: Theory & Design. 2nd ed. LC 80-13345. 544p. 1980. 50.95x (ISBN 0-471-07917-0, Pub. by Wiley Interscience). Wiley.

Thomson, J., et al. Frequency Coversion. (Wykeham Science Ser.: No. 1). 216p. 1969. pap. cancelled (ISBN 0-85109-030-3). Taylor & Francis.

FREQUENCY CONVERTERS
see Frequency Changers

FREQUENCY CURVES

Elderton, William & Johnson, Norman L. Systems of Frequency Curves. LC 69-10571. pap. 56.00 (ISBN 0-317-26324-2, 2024451). Bks Demand UMI.

Haberman, Shelby J. The Analysis of Frequency Data. LC 74-7558. (Statistical Research Monographs). (Midway Reprints). 1974. pap. text ed. 17.00x (ISBN 0-226-31185-6). U of Chicago Pr.

FREQUENCY DISTRIBUTION
see Distribution (Probability Theory)

FREQUENCY MODULATION, RADIO
see Radio Frequency Modulation

FREQUENCY MULTIPLIERS

Gyugyi, L. & Pelly, B. R. Static Power Frequency Changers: Theory, Performance & Application. LC 76-6088. 442p. 1976. 66.95x (ISBN 0-471-67800-7, Pub. by Wiley-Interscience). Wiley.

FREQUENCY OF OSCILLATION
see Frequencies of Oscillating Systems

FRESH WATER
see Drinking Water; Saline Waters–Demineralization

FRESH-WATER BIOLOGY
see also Aquarium Plants; Aquariums; Aquatic Plants; Fresh-Water Fauna; Fresh-Water Flora; Limnology

Bardach, John E., et al. Aquaculture: The Farming & Husbandry of Freshwater & Marine Organisms. LC 72-2516. 868p. 1972. pap. 34.95x (ISBN 0-471-04826-7, Pub. by Wiley-Interscience). Wiley.

Barica, J. & Mur, L., eds. Hypertrophic Ecosystems. (Developments in Hydrobiology Ser.: No. 2). 330p. 1981. PLB 87.00 (ISBN 90-6193-752-3, Pub. by Junk Pubs. Netherlands). Kluwer Academic.

Bonomi, G. & Erseus, C., eds. Aquatic Oligochaeta. (Developments in Hydrobiology Ser.). 1984. lib. bdg. 68.50 (ISBN 90-6193-775-2, Pub. by Junk Pubs Netherlands). Kluwer Academic.

Brinkhurst, Ralph O. British & Other Marine & Estuarine Oligochaetes. LC 81-3854. (Synopses of the British Fauna: No. 21). (Illus.). 100p. 1982. 37.50 (ISBN 0-521-24258-4). Cambridge U Pr.

Cairns, John, Jr., ed. The Structure & Function of Fresh-Water Microbial Communities. 301p. 1971. 15.00x (ISBN 0-8139-0541-9). U Pr of Va.

Cash, J. & Hopkinson, J. British Freshwater Rhizopoda & Heliozoa, 5 Vols. 1905-21. Set. 92.00 (ISBN 0-384-07835-4). Johnson Repr.

Casper, S. Jost, ed. Lake Stachlin. (Monographiae Biologicae). 1985. lib. bdg. 95.00 (ISBN 90-6193-512-1, Pub. by Junk Pubs Netherlands). Kluwer Academic.

Christensen, C. M. E. C. Stakman, Statesman of Science. LC 84-70114. (Illus.). 156p. 1984. text ed. 18.00 (ISBN 0-89054-056-X). Am Phytopathol Soc.

Dawes, John. The Freshwater Aquarium Questions & Answers. 128p. 1984. 29.00x (ISBN 0-947728-00-7, Pub. by R Royce UK). State Mutual Bk.

Fassett, Norman C. Manual of Aquatic Plants. rev. ed. (Illus.). 416p. 1957. 17.50x (ISBN 0-299-01450-9). U of Wis Pr.

Freshwater Biological Association, Cumbria England. Catalogue of the Library of the Freshwater Biological Association. 1979. lib. bdg. 660.00 (ISBN 0-8161-0289-9, Hall Library). G K Hall.

Gunnison, D., ed. Microbial Processes in Reservoirs. (Developments in Hydrobiology Ser.). 1985. lib. bdg. 52.50 (ISBN 90-6193-525-3, Pub. by Junk Pub Netherlands). Kluwer-Academic.

Heip, C., ed. Biology of Meiofauna. (Developments in Hydrobiology Ser.). 1985. lib. bdg. 40.00 (ISBN 90-6193-513-X, Pub. by Junk Pub Netherlands). Kluwer-Academic.

Hosking, Eric, et al. Eric Hosking's Waders. (Illus.). 184p. 1983. 24.95 (ISBN 0-7207-1430-3, Pub by Michael Joseph). Merrimack Pub Cir.

Johannsen, Oskar A. Aquatic Diptera. LC 78-7782. (Illus.). 370p. 1969. 17.50 (ISBN 0-911836-01-2). Entomological Repr.

Jones, Gwynfryn. A Guide to Methods for Estimating Microbial Numbers & Biomass in Fresh Water. 1979. 25.00x (ISBN 0-900386-37-1, Pub. by Freshwater Bio). State Mutual Bk.

Kofoid, Charles A. The Plankton of the Illinois River, 1894-1899: Quantitative Investigations & General Results, Pt.1. Egerton, Frank N., 3rd, ed. LC 77-74235. (History of Ecology Ser.). (Illus.). 1978. Repr. of 1903 ed. lib. bdg. 46.50x (ISBN 0-405-10404-9). Ayer Co Pubs.

Maitland, Peter S. Biology of Fresh Waters. (Tertiary Level Biology Ser.). 244p. 1978. pap. text ed. 34.95x (ISBN 0-470-26986-3). Halsted Pr.

Mason, C F. Biology of Freshwater Pollution. LC 80-41551. (Illus.). 240p. (Orig.). 1982. pap. 12.95x (ISBN 0-582-45596-0). Longman.

Muenscher, W. C. Aquatic Plants of the United States. (HANH Ser.). (Illus.). 384p. 1944. 32.50x (ISBN 0-8014-0306-5). Comstock.

Muller, Paul, ed. Verhandlungen der Gesellschaft fur Okologie, Gottingen 1976. 1977. pap. 60.50 (ISBN 90-6193-568-7, Pub. by Junk Pubs Netherlands). Kluwer Academic.

Needham, James G. & Lloyd, J. T. The Life of Inland Waters: An Elementary Textbook of Fresh-Water Biology for Students. 2nd ed. (Illus.). 438p. 1930. photocopy ed. 19.75x (ISBN 0-398-04378-7). C C Thomas.

Needham, James G. & Needham, Paul R. A Guide to the Study of Fresh-Water Biology: With Special Reference to Aquatic Insects & Other Invertebrate Animals. (Illus.). 88p. 1930. spiral 19.75x (ISBN 0-398-04377-9). C C Thomas.

--Guide to the Study of Freshwater Biology. 5th ed. LC 62-20742. (Illus.). 1962. pap. 8.95x (ISBN 0-8162-6310-8). Holden-Day.

Pascoe, D. & Edwards, R. W., eds. Freshwater Biological Monitoring: Proceedings of a Specialized Conference Held in Cardiff, UK 12-14 Sept.1984. LC 82-645900. (Advances in Water Pollution Control Ser.). 168p. 1984. 39.00 (ISBN 0-08-032313-8). Pergamon.

Prescott, G. W. How to Know the Freshwater Algae. 3rd ed. (Pictured Key Nature Ser.). 300p. 1978. write for info. wire coil (ISBN 0-697-04754-7). Wm C Brown.

Russian-English Glossary of Hydrobiology. (Rus. & Eng.). 113p. 1958. 35.00x (ISBN 0-306-10599-3, Consultants). Plenum Pub.

Salanki, J. & Biro, P., eds. Human Impacts on Life in Fresh Waters. 1979. 22.50 (ISBN 0-9960013-5-2, Pub. by Akademiai Kaido Hungary). Heyden.

Straskraba, M. & Gnauck, A. H. Freshwater Ecosystems: Modelling & Simulation: Developments in Environmental Modelling, No. 8. 300p. 1985. 78.00 (ISBN 0-444-99567-6). Elsevier.

Stroud, Richard H. & Clepper, Henry, eds. Black Bass Biology & Management. 1975. 25.00 (ISBN 0-686-21850-7); pap. 20.00 (ISBN 0-686-21851-5). Sport Fishing.

Uhlmann, Dietrich. Hydrobiology: A Text for Engineers & Scientists. LC 77-24258. 313p. 1979. 71.95x (ISBN 0-471-99557-6, Pub. by Wiley-Interscience). Wiley.

Van Damme, Dirk. The Freshwater Mollusca of Northern Africa. (Developments in Hydrobiologia Ser.). 1985. lib. bdg. 55.00 (ISBN 90-6193-502-4, Pub. by Junk Pubs Netherlands). Kluwer Academic.

Water Quality Criteria for European Freshwater Fish: Report on Copper and Freshwater Fish. pap. 7.50 (F768, FAO). Unipub.

Williams, W. D. Life in Inland Waters. (Illus.). 262p. 1983. pap. text ed. 20.00x (ISBN 0-86793-088-8). Blackwell Pubns.

Willoughby, L. C. Freshwater Biology. LC 76-20405. (Studies in the Biological Sciences). (Illus.). 1977. 12.50x (ISBN 0-87663-721-7). Universe.

Winberg, G. G. Methods for the Estimation of Production of Aquatic Animals. 1971. 36.00 (ISBN 0-12-758350-5). Acad Pr.

Woods, Cedric S. Freshwater Life in Ireland. 128p. 1974. 7.00x (ISBN 0-7165-2280-2, BBA 02193, Pub. by Irish Academic Pr Ireland); pap. 2.50x o. p. (ISBN 0-7165-2281-0). Biblio Dist.

FRESH-WATER ECOLOGY

see also Marsh Ecology; Pond Ecology; Thermal Pollution of Rivers, Lakes, etc.

Andrews, W. Guide to the Study of Freshwater Ecology. 1971. 11.36 (ISBN 0-13-370866-7); pap. text ed. 10.84 (ISBN 0-13-370759-8). P-H.

Bick, H. Ciliated Protozoa: An Illustrated Guide to the Species Used As Biological Indicators in Fresh Water Biology. 198p. 1972. pap. 9.60 (ISBN 92-4-154028-1, 1308). World Health.

Curds, C. R. & Hawkes, H. A., eds. Ecological Aspects of Used Water Treatment, Vol. 1. 1976. 66.00 (ISBN 0-12-199501-1). Acad Pr.

Furtado, J. I. & Mori, S. Tasek Bera: The Ecology of a Freshwater Swamp. 1982. text ed. 79.00 (ISBN 90-6193-100-2, Pub. by Junk Pubs Netherlands). Kluwer Academic.

Gomella, C & Mounier, J. P., eds. Eutrophication & Water Supply: Proceedings of the Specialised Conference of the IWSA held in Vienna, Austria, Oct. 7-9, 1981. (Illus.). 284p. 1983. pap. 66.00 (ISBN 0-08-030419-2). Pergamon.

Good, Ralph E., et al, eds. Freshwater Wetlands: Ecological Processes & Management Potential. LC 78-2836. 1978. 45.00 (ISBN 0-12-290150-9). Acad Pr.

Hart, C. W. & Fuller, Samuel. Pollution Ecology of Freshwater Invertebrates. 1974. 66.00 (ISBN 0-12-328450-3). Acad Pr.

Hynes, H. B. Ecology of Running Waters. 1970. 37.50c (ISBN 0-8020-1689-8). U of Toronto Pr.

Le Cren, E. D. & Lowe-McConnell, R. H., eds. The Functioning of Freshwater Ecosystems. LC 79-50504. (International Biological Programme Ser.: No. 22). (Illus.). 1980. 110.00 (ISBN 0-521-22507-8). Cambridge U Pr.

Lillehammer, Albert, ed. Ecology & Regulated Streams. 275p. 1984. pap. 22.00 (ISBN 82-00-06195-7). Universitet.

Moss, Brian. The Ecology of Fresh Waters. 332p. 1980. pap. 37.95 (ISBN 0-470-26942-1). Halsted Pr.

Ogden, C. G. An Atlas of Freshwater Testate Amoebae. (Illus.). 1980. text ed. 49.50x (ISBN 0-19-858502-0). Oxford U Pr.

Reynolds, C. S. The Ecology of Freshwater Photoplankton. LC 83-7211. (Cambridge Studies in Ecology). (Illus.). 300p. 1984. 57.50 (ISBN 0-521-23782-3); pap. 24.95 (ISBN 0-521-28222-5). Cambridge U Pr.

Riemer, Donald N. Introduction to Freshwater Vegetation. (Illus.). 1984. lib. bdg. 35.00 (ISBN 0-87055-448-4). AVI.

Snow, John. Secrets of Ponds & Lakes. Jack, Susan, ed. (Secrets of Ser.). (Illus.). 96p. (Orig.). 1982. pap. 5.95 (ISBN 0-930096-30-4). G Gannett.

Ward, James V. & Stanford, Jack A., eds. The Ecology of Regulated Streams. LC 79-21632. 412p. 1979. 49.50 (ISBN 0-306-40317-X, Plenum Pr). Plenum Pub.

Water Quality Criteria for European Freshwater Fish: Report on Copper and Freshwater Fish. pap. 7.50 (F768, FAO). Unipub.

Weller, Milton W. Freshwater Marshes: Ecology & Wildlife Management. LC 81-14714. (Illus.). 161p. 1981. 22.50x (ISBN 0-8166-1061-4); pap. 8.95 (ISBN 0-8166-1062-2). U of Minn Pr.

FRESH-WATER FAUNA

see also Aquariums; Fishes, Fresh-Water; Insects, Aquatic

Annandale, N. Coelenterata, Polyzoa: Freshwater Sponges, Hydroids, & Polyzoa. (Illus.). vii, 262p. 1972. Repr. of 1911 ed. 10.00 (ISBN 0-88065-015-X, Pub. by Messers Today & Tomorrows Printers & Publishers India). Scholarly Pubns.

Baker, F. C. The Fresh Water Mollusca of Wisconsin. 1973. Repr. of 1928 ed. lib. bdg. 70.00 (ISBN 3-7682-0764-1). Lubrecht & Cramer.

Boulenger, G. A. Fishes of the Nile. 1964. Repr. of 1907 ed. 129.50 (ISBN 3-7682-0241-0). Lubrecht & Cramer.

Brauer, A. Die Suesswasserfauna Deutchlands. (Illus.). 1961. Repr. of 1909 ed. 122.50 (ISBN 3-7682-0045-0). Lubrecht & Cramer.

Cavaliere, A. R., et al. Field Guide to the Conspicuous Flora & Fauna of Bermuda. (Special Publication: No. 26). 60p. (Orig.). 1983. pap. 6.00 (ISBN 0-917642-26-0). Bermuda Bio.

Ellis, A. E. British Freshwater Bivalve Mollusca: Keys & Notes for the Identification of the Species. (A Volume in the Synopses of the British Fauna Ser.). 1978. pap. 12.00 (ISBN 0-12-236950-5). Acad Pr.

Engle, R. W. Shallow-Water Crabs. LC 82-9706. (Synopses of the British Fauna Ser.: No. 25). (Illus.). 220p. 1983. 42.50 (ISBN 0-521-24963-5). Cambridge U Pr.

Evanoff, Viad. Fresh-Water Fisherman's Bible. rev. ed. LC 79-7684. (Outdoor Bible Ser.). (Illus.). 1980. pap. 5.95 (ISBN 0-385-14405-9). Doubleday.

Fitzpatrick, Joseph F., Jr. How to Know the Freshwater Crustacea. (Pictured Key Nature Ser.). 240p. 1982. write for info wire coil (ISBN 0-697-04783-0). Wm C Brown.

Forel, Francois A. La Faune Profonde Des Lags Suisses: The Bottom Fauna of Swiss Lakes. Egerton, Frank N., 3rd, ed. LC 77-74224. (History of Ecology Ser.). 1978. Repr. of 1884 ed. lib. bdg. 19.00x (ISBN 0-405-10394-8). Ayer Co Pubs.

Holdich, D. M. & Jones, J. A. Tanaids. LC 82-12761. (Synopses of the British Fauna Ser.: No. 27). (Illus.). 64p. 1983. 32.50 (ISBN 0-521-27203-3). Cambridge U Pr.

Ogden, C. G. An Atlas of Freshwater Testate Amoebae. (Illus.). 1980. text ed. 49.50x (ISBN 0-19-858502-0). Oxford U Pr.

Pennak, Robert W. Fresh-Water Invertebrates of the U. S. 2nd ed. LC 78-8130. 803p. 1978. 42.50x (ISBN 0-471-04249-8, Pub. by Wiley-Interscience). Wiley.

Russo, Ron & Olhausen, Pam. Pacific Intertidal. (A Guide to Organisms of Rocky Reefs & Tide Pools of the Pacific Coast). 1981. pap. 1.50 (ISBN 0-912550-10-4). Nature Study.

Wesenberg-Lund, C. Biologie der Suesswassertiere: Wirbellose Tiere. (Illus.). 1967. 56.00 (ISBN 3-7682-0426-X). Lubrecht & Cramer.

Whitford, L. A. & Schumacher, George. Manual of Freshwater Algae. 20.00 (ISBN 0-916822-01-X). Sparks Pr.

Zeisler, R. Bibliography of Latin American Freshwater Fish. (Commission for Inland Fisheries of Latin America Technical Papers: No. 2). (Eng. & Span.). 195p. 1979. pap. 14.00 (ISBN 92-5-000781-7, F1832, FAO). Unipub.

FRESH-WATER FLORA

see also Phytoplankton

Aquatic Plants of Australia. 1973. pap. 40.00x (ISBN 0-522-84044-2, Pub. by Melbourne U Pr Australia). Intl Spec Bk.

Cavaliere, A. R., et al. Field Guide to the Conspicuous Flora & Fauna of Bermuda. (Special Publication: No. 26). 60p. (Orig.). 1983. pap. 6.00 (ISBN 0-917642-26-0). Bermuda Bio.

Haslam, S. M. River Plants. LC 76-46857. (Illus.). 1978. 99.00 (ISBN 0-521-21493-9); pap. 29.95x (ISBN 0-521-29172-0). Cambridge U Pr.

Hotchkiss, Neil. Common Marsh, Underwater & Floating-Leaved Plants of the United States & Canada. (Illus.). 15.50 (ISBN 0-8446-4558-3). Peter Smith.

Magee, Dennis W. Freshwater Wetlands: A Guide to Common Indicator Plants of the Northeast. LC 80-26876. (Illus.). 240p. 1981. lib. bdg. 20.00x (ISBN 0-87023-316-5); pap. text ed. 9.95x (ISBN 0-87023-317-3). U of Mass Pr.

Riemer, Donald N. Introduction to Freshwater Vegetation. (Illus.). 1984. lib. bdg. 35.00 (ISBN 0-87055-448-4). AVI.

FRICTION

see also Aerodynamic Heating; Bearings (Machinery); Internal Friction; Lubrication and Lubricants; Mechanical Wear; Rolling Contact; Surfaces (Technology)

Bowden, Frank P. & Tabor, David. Friction: An Introduction to Tribology. LC 82-110. 192p. 1982. Repr. of 1973 ed. lib. bdg. 12.50 (ISBN 0-89874-474-1). Krieger.

Charnley, J. Low Friction Arthroplasty of the Hip: Theory & Practice. (Illus.). 1978. 59.00 (ISBN 0-387-08893-8). Springer-Verlag.

Hausner, Henry H., et al, eds. Friction & Antifriction Materials. LC 74-127937. (Perspectives in Powder Metallurgy: Fundamentals, Methods, & Applications Ser.: Vol. 4). pap. 87.50 (ISBN 0-317-10432-2, 2019460). Bks Demand UMI.

Kragelskii, Igor V. Friction & Wear. LC 65-5310. pap. 90.00 (ISBN 0-317-08539-5, 2051729). Bks Demand UMI.

Kragelsky, I. V. Friction Wear Methods. 110.00 (ISBN 0-08-025461-6). Pergamon.

Kragelsky, I. V. & Alisin, V. V., eds. Friction, Wear & Lubrication: A Complete Handbook of Tribology, 3 Vols. (Illus.). 800p. 1982. 130.00 (ISBN 0-08-027591-5, A115); firm 60.00 (ISBN 0-686-97493-X). Pergamon.

Kragelsky, I. V., et al. Friction & Wear: Calculation Methods. LC 80-41669. (Illus.). 450p. 1982. 110.00 (ISBN 0-08-025461-6). Pergamon.

Lubrication, Friction & Wear. 332p. (Orig.). 1980. pap. text ed. 60.00x (ISBN 0-85825-148-5, Pub. by Inst Engineering Australia). Brookfield Pub Co.

Newman, L. B. Friction Materials: Recent Advances. LC 77-15219. (Chemical Technology Review Ser.: No. 100). (Illus.). 358p. 1978. 36.00 (ISBN 0-8155-0688-0). Noyes.

Rigney, D. A. Fundamentals of Friction & Wear of Materials. 1980. 85.00 (ISBN 0-87170-115-4). ASM.

Sarkar, A. D. Friction & Wear. LC 80-40526. 1980. 86.50 (ISBN 0-12-619260-X). Acad Pr.

Schey, John A., ed. Metal Deformation Processes: Friction & Lubrication. LC 75-107756. (Monographs & Textbooks in Material Science: No. 1). (Illus.). pap. 160.00 (ISBN 0-317-07845-3, 2055018). Bks Demand UMI.

FRIEDEL-CRAFTS REACTION

Roberts. A Century of Friedel-Crafts Alkylations & Re-Arrangements. 1984. 165.00 (ISBN 0-8247-6433-1). Dekker.

FRINGILLIDAE

see Finches; Sparrows

FROGS

Adler, Kraig & Dennis, David M. New Tree Frogs of the Genus Hyla from the Cloud Forests of Western Guerrero, Mexico. (Occasional Papers: No. 7). 19p. 1972. pap. 2.25 (ISBN 0-686-79834-1). U of KS Mus Nat Hist.

Bohensky, Fred. Photo Manual & Dissection Guide of the Frog. (Avery's Anatomy Ser.). (Illus.). 88p. (Orig.). 1982. lab manual 5.95x (ISBN 0-89529-162-2). Avery Pub.

Deuchar, Elizabeth M. Xenopus: The South African Clawed Frog. LC 73-18927. pap. 64.00 (ISBN 0-317-28860-1, 2020972). Bks Demand UMI.

Dickerson, Mary C. Frog Book. (Illus.). 1969. pap. 8.95 (ISBN 0-486-21973-9). Dover.

--The Frog Book: North American Toads & Frogs, with a Study of the Habits & Life Histories of Those of the Northeastern States. (Illus.). 18.00 (ISBN 0-8446-0582-4). Peter Smith.

Duellman, William E. Centrolenid Frogs from Peru. (Occasional Papers: No. 52). 11p. 1976. pap. 1.25 (ISBN 0-686-80349-3). U of KS Mus Nat Hist.

--Description of New Hylid Frogs from Mexico & Central America. (Museum Ser.: Vol. 17, No. 13). 20p. 1968. pap. 1.25 (ISBN 0-686-80341-8). U of KS Mus Nat Hist.

--Descriptions of Two Species of Frogs, Genus Ptychohyla: Studies of American Hylid Frogs, Vol. V. (Museum Ser.: Vol. 13, No. 8). 9p. 1961. pap. 1.25 (ISBN 0-686-80336-1). U of KS Mus Nat Hist.

--The Genera of Phyllomedusine Frogs (Anura Hylidae) (Museum Ser.: Vol. 18, No. 1). 10p. 1968. pap. 1.25 (ISBN 0-686-80342-6). U of KS Mus Nat Hist.

--A New Species of Fringed-Limbed Tree Frog, Genus Hyla, from Darien, Panama. (Museum Ser.: Vol. 17, No. 5). 6p. 1966. 1.25 (ISBN 0-317-04850-3). U of KS Mus Nat Hist.

--On the Classification of Frogs. (Occasional Papers: No. 42). 14p. 1975. 1.25 (ISBN 0-317-04852-X). U of KS Mus Nat Hist.

--A Reassessment of the Taxonomic Status of Some Neotropical Hylid Frogs. (Occasional Papers: No. 27). 27p. 1974. pap. 1.50 (ISBN 0-686-80348-5). U of KS Mus Nat Hist.

--A Review of the Frogs of the Hyla Bistincta Group. (Museum Ser.: Vol. 15, No. 9). 23p. 1964. pap. 1.25 (ISBN 0-686-80338-8). U of KS Mus Nat Hist.

--A Review of the Neotropical Frogs of the Hyla Bogotensis Group. (Occasional Papers: No. 11). 31p. 1972. pap. 1.75 (ISBN 0-686-80345-0). U of KS Mus Nat Hist.

--A Systematic Review of the Marsupial Frogs (Hylidae Gastrotheca) of the Andes of Ecuador. (Occasional Papers: No. 22). 27p. 1974. pap. 1.50 (ISBN 0-686-80347-7). U of KS Mus Nat Hist.

--Taxonomic Notes on Some Mexican & Central American Hylid Frogs. (Museum Ser.: Vol. 17, No. 6). 17p. 1966. pap. 1.25 (ISBN 0-686-80339-6). U of KS Mus Nat Hist.

--A Taxonomic Review of South American Hylid Frogs, Genus Phrynohyas. (Occasional Papers: No. 4). 21p. 1971. pap. 1.25 (ISBN 0-686-80343-4). U of KS Mus Nat Hist.

--Three New Species of Centrolenid Frogs from the Pacific Versant of Ecuador & Colombia. (Occasional Papers: No. 88). 9p. 1981. 1.25 (ISBN 0-317-04856-2). U of KS Mus Nat Hist.

Duellman, William E. & Crump, Martha L. Speciation in Frogs of the Hyla Parviceps Group in the Upper Amazon Basin. (Occasional Papers: No. 23). 40p. 1974. pap. 2.25 (ISBN 0-686-32527-3). U of KS Mus Nat Hist.

Duellman, William E. & Foquette, M. J., Jr. Middle American Frogs of the Hyla Microcephala Group. (Museum Ser.: Vol. 17, No. 12). 41p. 1968. pap. 2.25 (ISBN 0-686-80340-X). U of KS Mus Nat Hist.

Duellman, William E. & Fritts, Thomas H. A Taxonomic Review of the Southern Andean MarsupialFrogs (Hylidae Gastrotheca) (Occasional Papers: No. 9). 37p. 1972. pap. 2.00 (ISBN 0-686-80344-2). U of KS Mus Nat Hist.

Duellman, William E. & Leseure, Jean. Life History & Ecology of the Hylid Frog Osteocephalus Taurinus, with Observations on Larval Behavior. (Occasional Papers: No. 13). 12p. 1973. pap. 1.25 (ISBN 0-686-80346-9). U of KS Mus Nat Hist.

Duellman, William E. & Pyles, Rebecca A. A New Marsupial Frog (Hylidae: Gastrotheca) from the Andes of Ecuador. (Occasional Papers: No. 84). 13p. 1980. 1.25 (ISBN 0-317-04854-6). U of KS Mus Nat Hist.

Duellman, William E. & Trueb, Linda. The Systematic Status & Relationships of the Hylid Frog Nyctimantis Rugiceps Boulenger. (Occasional Papers: No. 58). 14p. 1976. pap. 1.25 (ISBN 0-686-80350-7). U of KS Mus Nat Hist.

Ecker. The Anatomy of the Frog. Haslam, G., tr. from Ger. 1971. 36.80 (ISBN 90-6123-240-6). Lubrecht & Cramer.

Edwards, Stephen R. Taxonomic Notes on South American Dendrobatid Frogs of the Genus Colostethus. (Occasional Papers: No. 30). 14p. 1974. pap. 1.25 (ISBN 0-686-80354-X). U of KS Mus Nat Hist.

Gilbert, Stephen G. Pictorial Anatomy of the Frog. LC 65-14843. (Illus.). 71p. 1965. pap. 7.95x (ISBN 0-295-73878-2). U of Wash Pr.

Kamin, Franz. Egz Book of Frogs. (Illus.). 24p. (Orig.). 1982. 3.95 (ISBN 0-930794-70-2). Station Hill Pr.

La Marca, Enrique. A New Frog of the Genus Atelopus (Anura-Bufonidae) from a Venezuelan Cloud Forest. (Illus.). 1983. pap. 4.25 (ISBN 0-89326-096-7). Milwaukee Pub Mus.

Leon, Juan R. The Systematics of the Frogs of the Hyla Rubra Group in Middle America. (Museum Ser.: Vol. 18, No. 6). 41p. 1969. 2.25 (ISBN 0-317-04876-7). U of KS Mus Nat Hist.

Llinas, R. & Precht, W., eds. Frog Neurobiology: A Handbook. LC 75-46505. 1976. 263.00 (ISBN 0-387-07606-9). Springer-Verlag.

Lutz, Bertha & Lutz, Gualter. Brazilian Species of "Hyla". LC 70-39502. (Illus.). 286p. 1973. 25.00x (ISBN 0-292-70704-5). U of Tex Pr.

Lynch, John D. Evolutionary Relationships, Osteology & Zoogeography of Leptodactyloid Frogs. (Miscellaneous Publications Ser.: No. 53). 238p. 1971. pap. 12.25 (ISBN 0-686-80374-4). U of KS Mus Nat Hist.

--Genera of Leptodactylid Frogs in Mexico. (Museum Ser.: Vol. 17, No. 11). 13p. 1968. pap. 1.25 (ISBN 0-686-80368-X). U of KS Mus Nat Hist.

--Leptodactylid Frogs of the Genus Eleutherodactylus from the Andes of Southern Ecuador. (Miscellaneous Publications Ser.: No. 66). 62p. 1979. pap. 3.25 (ISBN 0-686-80375-2). U of KS Mus Nat Hist.

--New Species of Frogs (Leptodactylidae Eleutherodactylus) from the Pacific Versant of Ecuador. (Occasional Papers: No. 55). 33p. 1976. pap. 2.00 (ISBN 0-686-80372-8). U of KS Mus Nat Hist.

--A Re-Assessment of the Telmatobiine Leptodactylid Frogs of Patagonia. (Occasional Papers: No. 72). 57p. 1978. pap. 3.00 (ISBN 0-686-80373-6). U of KS Mus Nat Hist.

--A Review of the Andean Leptodactylid Frog Genus Phrynopus. (Occasional Papers: No. 35). 51p. 1975. pap. 2.75 (ISBN 0-686-80370-1). U of KS Mus Nat Hist.

--A Review of the Broad-Headed Eleutherodactyline Frogs of South America (Leptodactylidae) (Occasional Papers: No. 38). 46p. 1975. pap. 2.50 (ISBN 0-686-80371-X). U of KS Mus Nat Hist.

--The Species Groups of South American Frogs of the Genus Eleutherodactylus: (Leptodactylidae) (Occasional Papers: No. 61). 24p. 1976. 1.50 (ISBN 0-317-04878-3). U of KS Mus Nat Hist.

--Systematic Status of a South American Frog, Allophryne Ruthveni Gaige. (Museum Ser.: Vol. 17, No. 10). 10p. 1966. pap. 1.25 (ISBN 0-686-80367-1). U of KS Mus Nat Hist.

--A Taxonomic Revision of the Leoptodactylid Frog Genus Syrrhophus Cope. (Museum Ser.: Vol. 20, No. 1). 45p. 1970. pap. 2.50 (ISBN 0-686-80369-8). U of KS Mus Nat Hist.

Lynch, John D. & Duellman, William E. A Review of the Centrolenid Frogs of Ecuador: With Descriptions of New Species. (Occasional Papers: No. 16). (Illus.). 66p. 1973. 4.50 (ISBN 0-317-04877-5). U of KS Mus Nat Hist.

Lynch, John O. New Species of Frogs (Leptodactylidae Eleutherodactylus) from Amazonian Lowlands of Ecuador. (Occasional Papers: No. 31). 22p. 1974. pap. 1.25 (ISBN 0-686-32528-1). U of KS Mus Nat Hist.

McCranie, James R. & Wilson, Larry D. A New Hylid Frog of the Genus Plectrohyla from a Cloud Forest in Honduras. (Occasional Papers: No. 92). 7p. 1981. 1.25 (ISBN 0-317-04882-1). U of KS Mus Nat Hist.

Parker, H. W. Monograph of the Frogs of the Family Microhylidae. Repr. of 1934 ed. 18.00 (ISBN 0-384-44850-X). Johnson Repr.

Smith, Hobart M. The Tadpoles of Bufo Cognatus Say. (Museum Ser.: Vol. 1, No. 3). 4p. 1946. pap. 1.25 (ISBN 0-686-80379-5). U of KS Mus Nat Hist.

Taylor, Edward H. New Hylid Frogs from Eastern Mexico. (Museum Ser.: Vol. 1, No. 15). 8p. 1948. 1.50 (ISBN 0-317-04891-0). U of KS Mus Nat Hist.

Trueb, Linda. Cranial Osteology of the Hylid Frog: Smilisca Baudini. (Museum Ser.: Vol. 18, No. 2). 25p. 1968. 1.50 (ISBN 0-317-04895-3). U of KS Mus Nat Hist.

--Evolutionary Relationships of Casque-Headed Tree Frogs with Co-Ossified Skulls: Family Hylidae. (Museum Ser.: Vol. 18, No.7). 170p. 1970. pap. 8.75 (ISBN 0-317-04571-7). U of KS Mus Nat Hist.

--Systematic Relationships of Neotropical Horned Frogs, Genus Hemiphractus (Anura: Hylidae) (Occasional Papers: No. 29). 60p. 1974. pap. 3.25 (ISBN 0-686-80386-8). U of KS Mus Nat Hist.

Trueb, Linda & Duellman, William E. A Synopsis of Neotropical Hylid Frogs, Genus Osteocephalus. (Occasional Papers: No. 1). 47p. 1971. pap. 2.50 (ISBN 0-686-80384-1). U of KS Mus Nat Hist.

Trueb, Linda & Tyler, Michael J. Systematics & Evolution of the Greater Antillean Hylid Frogs. (Occasional Papers: No. 24). 60p. 1974. pap. 3.25 (ISBN 0-686-80385-X). U of KS Mus Nat Hist.

Tyler, Michael J. Frogs. (Illus.). 256p. 1983. pap. 12.50 (ISBN 0-00-216450-7, Pub. by W Collins Australia). Intl Spec Bk.

--The Phylogenetic Significance of Vocal Sac Structure in Hylid Frogs. (Museum Ser.: Vol. 19, No. 4). 42p. 1971. pap. 2.25 (ISBN 0-686-80388-4). U of KS Mus Nat Hist.

Tyler, Michael J., ed. The Gastric Brooding Frog. (Illus.). 180p. 1983. 33.00 (ISBN 0-7099-2425-9, Pub. by Croom Helm Ltd). Longwood Pub Group.

Underhill, Raymond A. Laboratory Anatomy of the Frog. 4th ed. (Laboratory Anatomy Ser.). 72p. 1980. write for info. wire coil (ISBN 0-697-04645-1). Wm C Brown.

Villa, Jaime. Biology of a Neotropical Glass Frog, Centrolenella Fleischmanni (Boettger), with Special Reference to its Frogfly Associates. (Illus.). 60p. 1984. 8.50 (ISBN 0-89326-098-3). Milwaukee Pub Mus.

--Synopsis of the Biology of the Middle American Highland Frog Rana Maculata Brocchi. 1979. 1.00 (ISBN 0-89326-037-1). Milwaukee Pub Mus.

Walker, Charles F. A New Genus & Species of Microhylid Frog from Educador. (Occasional Papers: No. 20). 7p. 1973. pap. 1.25 (ISBN 0-317-04572-5). U of KS Mus Nat Hist.

Walker, Charles F. & Duellman, William E. Description of a New Species of Microhylid Frog, Chiasmocleis, from Ecuador. (Occasional Papers: No. 26). 6p. 1974. pap. 1.25 (ISBN 0-317-04573-3). U of KS Mus Nat Hist.

Wright, Albert H. & Wright, Anna A. Handbook of Frogs & Toads of the United States & Canada. 3rd ed. (HANH Ser.). (Illus.). 652p. 1949. 36.50x (ISBN 0-8014-0462-2). Comstock.

FROST PROTECTION

Bagdonas, A & Georg, J. c. Techniques of Frost Prediction & Methods of Frost & Cold Protection. (Technical Note Ser.: No. 157). x, 101p. 1978. pap. 37.00 (ISBN 92-63-10487-5, W403, WMO). Unipub.

Hurst, G. W. & Rumney, R. P. Protection of Plants Against Adverse Weather. (Technical Note Ser.: No. 118). x, 64p. (Orig.). 1972. pap. 12.00 (ISBN 0-685-02934-4, W94, WMO). Unipub.

Protection Against Frost Damage. (Technical Note Ser.: No. 51). (Illus.). 62p. 1963. pap. 11.00 (ISBN 0-685-22333-7, W23, WMO). Unipub.

FROZEN FOOD

see Food, Frozen

FROZEN GROUND

Brown, Roger J. Permafrost in Canada: Its Influence on Northern Development. LC 70-464841. (Illus.). 1970. 27.50x (ISBN 0-8020-1602-2). U of Toronto Pr.

Building Research Advisory Board. Permafrost. 2nd ed. (Illus.). 744p. 1973. 50.00 (ISBN 0-309-02115-4). Natl Acad Pr.

--Permafrost: Russian Papers. 1978. pap. 19.50 (ISBN 0-309-02746-2). Natl Acad Pr.

Johnston, G. H. Permafrost: Engineering Design & Construction. 540p. 1981. 56.95x (ISBN 0-471-79918-1, Pub. by Wiley-Interscience). Wiley.

Jumikis, Alfred R. Thermal Geotechnics. 1977. 50.00x (ISBN 0-8135-0824-X). Rutgers U Pr.

Linell, Kenneth A. & Tedrow, C. F. Soil & Permafrost Surveys in the Arctic. (Monographs on Soil Survey). (Illus.). 1981. 55.00x (ISBN 0-19-857557-2). Oxford U Pr.

National Academy of Sciences. Permafrost Fourth International Conference: Final Proceedings. 413p. 1985. text ed. 32.50 (ISBN 0-309-03533-3). Natl Acad Pr.

National Research Council. Permafrost: Fourth International Conference, Proceedings. 1524p. 1983. text ed. 65.00 (ISBN 0-309-03435-3). Natl Acad Pr.

Pewe, Troy L. Permafrost & Its Effect on Life in the North. LC 52-19235. (Illus.). 40p. 1970. pap. 3.95x (ISBN 0-87071-141-5). Oreg St U Pr.

FROZEN STARS

see Black Holes (Astronomy)

FRUIT

see also Berries; Citrus Fruits; Fruit-Culture; Fruit Juices

also particular fruits, e.g. Apple, Orange

Appel, L. Lexique des Fruits et Legumes. (Fr. & Eng.). 133p. Date not set. pap. 9.95 (ISBN 0-686-97410-7, M-9238). French & Eur.

Appel, Louise. Lexique Anglais-Francais Des Fruits et Legumes. rev. ed. (Eng. & Fr.). 128p. 1974. pap. 9.95 (ISBN 0-686-56897-4, M-6007). French & Eur.

Carrol, Frieda. Pick Your Own Fruits & Vegetables & More: A Reference Guide. LC 80-70861. 1981. 7.95 (ISBN 0-939476-12-6, Pub. by Biblio Pr GA); pap. 4.95 (ISBN 0-939476-11-8); wkbk. 6.95 (ISBN 0-939476-82-7). Prosperity & Profits.

Crispo, Dorothy. The Story of Our Fruits & Vegetables. pap. 4.95 (ISBN 0-8159-6826-4). Devin.

Dennis, Colin, ed. Post-Harvest Pathology of Fruits & Vegatables. (Food Science & Technology Ser.). 1983. 46.00 (ISBN 0-12-210680-6). Acad Pr.

Flood, R. B. Home Fruit & Vegetable Production. LC 78-4214. 175p. 1978. 16.00 (ISBN 0-8108-1132-4). Scarecrow.

Friend, John, ed. Recent Advances in Biochemistry of Fruits & Vegetables. (Phytochemical Society of Europe Symposia Ser.: No. 18). 1982. 49.50 (ISBN 0-12-268420-6). Acad Pr.

Hedrick, U. P. Fruits for the Home Garden. (Illus.). 14.50 (ISBN 0-8446-4753-5). Peter Smith.

International Standardiation of Fruit & Vegetables: Peaches. rev. ed. 40p. 1979. 9.00x (ISBN 92-64-01994-4). OECD.

Kadans, Joseph N. Encyclopedia of Fruits, Vegetables, Nuts & Seeds for Healthful Living. 1973. 12.95 (ISBN 0-13-275412-6, Reward); pap. 4.95 (ISBN 0-13-275420-7). P-H.

McCoy, Doyle. Roadside Wild Fruits of Oklahoma. LC 79-6705. (Illus.). 96p. (Orig.). 1980. pap. 10.95 (ISBN 0-8061-1626-9). U of Okla Pr.

Martin, Franklin W., et al. Cultivation of Neglected Tropical Fruits with Promise. (Studies in Tropical Agriculture). 1980. lib. bdg. 59.95 (ISBN 0-8490-3074-9). Gordon Pr.

Popenoe, Wilson. Manual of Tropical & Subtropical Fruits: Excluding the Banana, Coconut, Pineapple, Citrus Fruits, Olive & Fig. (Illus.). 1974. Repr. 23.95x (ISBN 0-02-850280-9). Hafner.

Salunkhe, D. K. Storage, Processing & Nutritional Quality of Fruits & Vegetables. LC 74-20660. (Monotopic Reprint Ser.). 176p. 1974. Repr. 19.95 (ISBN 0-8493-0123-8). CRC Pr.

Samson, J. A. Tropical Fruits. LC 74-40498. (Tropical Agriculture Ser.). (Illus.). 288p. 1980. text ed. 40.00x (ISBN 0-582-46032-8). Longman.

Sinclair, Walton B. The Biochemistry & Physiology of the Lemon & Other Citrus Fruits. LC 83-72137. (Illus.). 1000p. (Orig.). 1983. 55.00x (ISBN 0-931876-64-8, 3306). Ag & Nat Res.

Teranishi, Roy & Barrera-Benitez, Heriberto, eds. Quality of Selected Fruits & Vegetables of North America. LC 81-14853. (ACS Symposium Ser.: No. 170). 1981. 29.95 (ISBN 0-8412-0662-7). Am Chemical.

Turner, Nancy J. & Szczawinski, Adam F. Edible Wild Fruits & Nuts of Canada. (Illus.). 1979. pap. 9.95 spiral bdg. (ISBN 0-660-00128-4, 56328-6, Pub. by Natl Mus Canada). U of Chicago Pr.

Westwood, Melvin N. Temperate-Zone Pomology. LC 77-26330. (Illus.). 428p. 1978. text ed. 38.95x (ISBN 0-7167-0196-0). W H Freeman.

FRUIT–DISEASES AND PESTS

see also Fruit-Flies; Insects, Injurious and Beneficial; Plant Diseases; Scale-Insects;

also subdivision Diseases and Pests under particular fruits, and names of diseases and pests

Alford, D. V. & Upstone, M. E. Pests & Disease Control in Fruit & Hops. 105p. 1980. 30.00x (ISBN 0-901436-60-7, Pub. by CAB Bks England). State Mutual Bk.

Alford, David V. A Colour Atlas of Fruit Pests: Their Recognition, Biology & Control. (Illus.). 310p. 1984. text ed. 58.00x (ISBN 0-7234-0816-5, Pub. by Wolfe Medical England). Sheridan.

Bethell, Richard S., ed. Pear Pest Management. LC 78-67293. 1978. 3-ring polymer bndr. 20.00x (ISBN 0-931876-26-5, 4086). Ag & Nat Res.

Croft, B. A. & Hoyt, S. C., eds. Integrated Management of Insect Pests of Pome & Stone Fruit. LC 82-13659. (Environemental Science & Technology Texts & Monographs). 454p. 1983. 52.50x (ISBN 0-471-05334-1, Pub. by Wiley-Interscience). Wiley.

Frazier, N. W., ed. Virus Diseases of Small Fruits & Grapevines. 1970. 7.50x (ISBN 0-931876-21-4, 4056). Ag & Nat Res.

Hall, E. G. & Scott, K. J. Storage & Market Diseases of Fruit. (Illus.). 1978. pap. 5.00x (ISBN 0-643-00217-0, Pub. by CSIRO). Intl Spec Bk.

--Storage & Market Diseases of Fruit. 1982. 35.00x (ISBN 0-686-97896-X, Pub. by CSIRO Australia). State Mutual Bk.

--Storage & Market Diseases of Fruit: Collected Supplements I-XXIV Reprinted from CSIRO Food Research Quarterly. 52p. 1977. pap. 6.50 (ISBN 0-643-00217-0, C039, CSIRO). Unipub.

International Organization of Citrus Virologists - 2nd Conference. Proceedings. Price, W. C., ed. LC 61-64183. 1961. 11.50 (ISBN 0-8130-0189-7). U Presses Fla.

Nel, P. J. Deciduous Fruits & Vines: Pests & Diseases & Their Control. LC 85-1340. (Illus.). 224p. 1985. 22.50x (ISBN 0-389-20568-0). B&N Imports.

Stover, R. H. Banana, Plantain & Abaca Diseases. 316p. 1972. 70.00x (ISBN 0-686-45707-2, Pub. by CAB Bks England). State Mutual Bk.

FRUIT–PESTS

see Fruit–Diseases and Pests

FRUIT–PRESERVATION

Flack, Dora D. Fun with Fruit Preservation: Leather, Drying, & Other Methods. LC 74-78025. (Illus.). 98p. 1973. pap. 5.95 (ISBN 0-88290-023-4). Horizon Utah.

Goodenough, P. W. & Atkin, R. K. Quality of Stored & Processed Vegetables & Fruit. LC 81-66382. 1981. 62.00 (ISBN 0-12-289740-4). Acad Pr.

Hope, G. W. & Vitale, D. G. Osmotic Dehydration: A Cheap & Simple Method of Preserving Mangoes, Bananas & Plantains. 12p. 1972. pap. 5.00 (ISBN 0-88936-004-9, IDRC4, IDRC). Unipub.

Jagtiani, Duru, ed. Fruit Preservation. 128p. 1980. pap. 3.95x (ISBN 0-7069-1039-7, Pub. by Vikas India). Advent NY.

McBean, D. M. Drying & Processing Tree Fruits. (Illus.). 20p. 1977. pap. 1.50x (ISBN 0-643-00181-6, Pub. by CSIRO). Intl Spec Bk.

Peters, Frank. Fruit Jar Manual. rev. ed. 120p. 1981. pap. 8.95 (ISBN 0-89288-003-1). Maverick.

Phelan, Chas. Dried Fruit: Its Care, Protection from Worms, Packing, Storing, Etc. facs. ed. (Shorey Lost Arts Ser.). 48p. pap. 1.95 (ISBN 0-8466-6049-0, U49). Shorey.

Preservation of Fruit & Vegetables by Radiation. (Panel Proceedings Ser.). (Illus.). 152p. 1968. pap. 10.00 (ISBN 92-0-111068-5, ISP149, IAEA). Unipub.

Recommended International Standard for Apple Juice Preserved Exclusively by Physical Means. 2nd ed. (CAC-RS Ser.: No. 48-1971). 1973. pap. 4.50 (ISBN 92-5-100231-2, F589, FAO). Unipub.

Recommended International Standard for Orange, Grapefruit & Lemon Juices Preserved Exclusively by Physical Means. 1972. pap. 4.50 (ISBN 0-685-36312-0, F588, FAO). Unipub.

FRUIT–STORAGE

Haard, Norman F. & Salunkhe, D. K. Postharvest Biology & Handling of Fruits & Vegetables. (Illus.). 1975. text ed. 40.00 (ISBN 0-87055-187-6). AVI.

Hall, E. G. & Scott, K. J. Storage & Market Diseases of Fruit. 1982. 35.00x (ISBN 0-686-97896-X, Pub. by CSIRO Australia). State Mutual Bk.

--Storage & Market Diseases of Fruit: Collected Supplements I-XXIV Reprinted from CSIRO Food Research Quarterly. 52p. 1977. pap. 6.50 (ISBN 0-643-00217-0, C039, CSIRO). Unipub.

Ryall, A. Lloyd & Lipton, Werner J. Handling, Transportation & Storage of Fruits & Vegetables, Vol. 1. 2nd ed. (Illus.). 1979. text ed. 62.50 (ISBN 0-87055-264-3). AVI.

Ryall, A. Lloyd & Pentzer, W. T. Handling, Transportation & Storage of Fruits & Vegetables: Fruits & Tree Nuts, Vol. 2. 2nd ed. (Illus.). 1982. lib. bdg. 62.50 (ISBN 0-87055-410-7). AVI.

FRUIT-VARIETIES

Brooks, Reid M. & Olmo, Harold P. Register of New Fruit & Nut Varieties. 2nd rev. & enl. ed. LC 76-100017. 512p. 1972. 37.50x (ISBN 0-520-01638-6). U of Cal Pr.

FRUIT, FORCING OF

see Forcing (Plants)

FRUIT-CULTURE

see also Berries; Dwarf Fruit Trees; Fungi in Agriculture; Grafting; Horticulturists; Nurseries (Horticulture); Olive Industry and Trade; Plant Propagation; Pruning; Viticulture; also names of fruits

Alexander, D. M. Some Avocado Varieties for Australia. 1980. 20.00x (ISBN 0-643-02276-7, Pub. by CSIRO Australia). State Mutual Bk.

Bailey, Liberty H. Sketch of the Evolution of Our Native Fruits. LC 72-89072. (Rural America Ser.). 1973. Repr. of 1898 ed. 36.00 (ISBN 0-8420-1473-X). Scholarly Res Inc.

CAB Books, ed. Herbicides in British Fruit Growing. 1973. 39.00x (ISBN 0-901436-29-1, Pub. by CAB Bks England). State Mutual Bk.

Childers, Norman B. Modern Fruit Science. 9th ed. (Illus.). 600p. 1983. 40.00 (ISBN 0-317-03711-0); pap. 35.00 (ISBN 0-317-03712-9). Horticult Pubns.

Childers, Norman F. & Zutter, Hans. Modern Fruit Science Lab Manual. 250p. 1975. pap. 8.75 (ISBN 0-317-03713-7). Horticult Pubns.

Clarke, Harold. Growing Berries & Grapes at Home. 384p. 1976. pap. 4.50 (ISBN 0-486-23274-3). Dover.

Control of Bitter Pit & Breakdown by Calcium in the Apples Cox's Orange Pippin & Jonathan. (Agricultural Research Reports: No. 711). 43p. 1968. pap. 4.00 (ISBN 0-686-71855-0, PDC173, PUDOC). Unipub.

Fogg, H. G. Soft Fruit Growing. 160p. 1981. pap. 12.00x (ISBN 0-906379-01-6, Pub. by Jupiter England). State Mutual Bk.

Fruit-Bearing Forest Trees: Technical Notes. (Forestry Papers: No. 34). (Eng., Fr. & Span.). 182p. 1982. pap. 13.50 (ISBN 92-5-101218-0, F2368, FAO). Unipub.

Geiser, Samuel W. Horticulture & Horticulturists in Early Texas. LC 46-161. 1945. pap. 4.95 (ISBN 0-87074-058-X). SMU Press.

Gilbert, Zoe. Fruit Growing in Southern Africa. 1980. 32.00x (ISBN 0-686-69982-3, Pub. by Bailey & Swinton South Africa). State Mutual Bk.

Griggs, William H. & Iwakiri, Ben T. Asian Pear Varieties in California. 1977. pap. 3.00 (ISBN 0-931876-00-1, 4068). Ag & Nat Res.

Growing Fruits & Berries. (Illus.). 304p. (Orig.). 1983. 18.95 (ISBN 0-8306-0118-X, 1518); pap. 12.95 (ISBN 0-8306-0518-5). TAB Bks.

Jackson, D. Temperate & Subtropical Fruit Production. 1985. text ed. 39.95 (ISBN 0-409-70149-1). Butterworth.

Janick, Jules & Moore, James N. Advances in Fruit Breeding. LC 73-76916. (Illus.). 640p. 1975. 30.00 (ISBN 0-911198-36-9). Purdue U Pr.

Knight, R. L. Abstract Bibliography of Fruit Breeding & Genetics to 1960: Malus & Pyrus. 535p. 1963. 50.00x (ISBN 0-686-45685-8, Pub. by CAB Bks England). State Mutual Bk.

Knight, R. L. & Parker, J. H. Abstract Bibliography of Fruit Breeding & Genetics, 1956-1969: Rubus & Ribes. 449p. 1972. 76.00x (ISBN 0-85198-202-6, Pub. by CAB Bks England). State Mutual Bk.

McBean, D. M. Drying & Processing Tree Fruits. 20p. 1976. pap. 6.00 (ISBN 0-643-00181-6, C040, CSIRO). Unipub.

Mascall, Leonard. A Booke of the Arte & Manner How to Plant & Graffe All Sortes of Trees. LC 74-80200. (English Experience Ser.: No. 679). 90p. 1974. Repr. of 1572 ed. 13.00 (ISBN 90-221-0679-9). Walter J Johnson.

Moore, James N. & Janick, Jules, eds. Methods in Fruit Breeding. LC 81-80945. (Illus.). 464p. 1983. 40.00 (ISBN 0-911198-63-6). Purdue U Pr.

Nijjar, G. S. Fruit Breeding in India. 219p. 1981. 15.00x (ISBN 0-686-76637-7, Pub. by Oxford & IBH India). State Mutual Bk.

Ortho Books Staff. All about Growing Fruits & Berries. rev. ed. Ferguson, Barbara J., ed. LC 82-82156. (Illus.). 112p. 1982. pap. 5.95 (ISBN 0-89721-009-3). Ortho.

Pearce, S. C. Field Experiments with Fruit Tree & other Perennial Plants. 182p. 1976. 89.00x (ISBN 0-85198-354-5, Pub. by CAB Bks England). State Mutual Bk.

Popenoe, Wilson. Manual of Tropical & Subtropical Fruits: Excluding the Banana, Coconut, Pineapple, Citrus Fruits, Olive & Fig. (Illus.). 1974. Repr. 23.95x (ISBN 0-02-850280-9). Hafner.

Ramos, David. Prune Orchard Management. LC 80-71944. (Illus.). 144p. (Orig.). 1981. pap. 10.00x (ISBN 0-931876-45-1, 3269). Ag & Nat Res.

Rice, R. P. & Rice, L. W. Fruit & Vegetable Production in Tropical Africa. LC 82-23698. 250p. 1985. 34.95 (ISBN 0-471-10362-4, Pub. by Wiley-Interscience); pap. write for info. (ISBN 0-471-90138-5). Wiley.

Ruck, H. C. Deciduous Fruit Tree Cultivars for Tropical & Subtropical Regions. 91p. 1975. 30.00x (ISBN 0-85198-341-3, Pub. by CAB Bks England). State Mutual Bk.

Ryugo. Fruit Culture: Its Arts & Science. 1986. write for info. (ISBN 0-471-89191-6). Wiley.

Salunkhe, D. K. & Desai, B. B. Postharvest Biotechnology of Fruits, 2 vols. LC 83-7770. 1984. Vol. I, 240p. 72.00 (ISBN 0-8493-6121-4); Vol. II, 176p. 60.00 (ISBN 0-8493-6122-2). CRC Pr.

Scheer, Arnold H. & Juergenson, E. M. Approved Practices in Fruit & Vine Production. 2nd ed. (Illus.). 590p. 1976. 19.95 (ISBN 0-8134-1704-X, 1704); text ed. 14.95x. Interstate.

Shoemaker, James S. Small Fruit Culture. 5th ed. (Illus.). 1978. lib. bdg. 26.50 (ISBN 0-87055-248-1). AVI.

Sunset Editors. Fruits, Nuts & Berries: How To Grow. LC 84-80621. (Illus.). 112p. (Orig.). 1984. pap. 5.95 (ISBN 0-376-03092-5). Sunset Lane.

Taverner, John. Certaine Experiments Concerning the Fish & the Fruite. LC 76-6030. (English Experience Ser.: No. 75). 38p. 1968. Repr. of 1600 ed. 7.00 (ISBN 90-221-0075-8). Walter J Johnson.

Top Rated Berries. (Golden Gardening Ser.). (Illus.). 64p. 1984. pap. 3.95 (ISBN 0-307-46641-8, Golden Pr). Western Pub.

Turner, David & Muir, Ken. The Handbook of Soft Fruit Growing. LC 85-3812. (Illus.). 208p. 1985. 22.50 (ISBN 0-7099-3538-2, Pub. by Croom Helm Ltd); pap. 13.50 (ISBN 0-7099-2496-8). Longwood Pub Group.

Westwood, Melvin N. Temperate-Zone Pomology. LC 77-26330. (Illus.). 428p. 1978. text ed. 38.95x (ISBN 0-7167-0196-0). W H Freeman.

Wills, Ron, et al. Postharvest: An Introduction to the Physiology & Handling of Fruit & Vegetables. (Illus.). 1981. pap. text ed. 17.50 (ISBN 0-87055-402-6). AVI.

FRUIT-CULTURE–GREAT BRITAIN

Roach, F. A. Cultivated Fruits of Britain: Their Origins & History. 320p. 1985. 50.00x (ISBN 0-631-13969-9). Basil Blackwell.

FRUIT-CULTURE–HAWAII

Miller, Carey D., et al. Fruits of Hawaii: Description, Nutritive Value, & Recipes. 4th ed. 1976. pap. 7.95 (ISBN 0-8248-0448-1). UH Pr.

FRUIT-FLIES

Ashburner, M. & Novitski, E., eds. The Genetics & Biology of Drosophila. Incl. Vol. 1, 3 pts. 1976. Pt. A. 82.50 (ISBN 0-12-064901-2); Pt. B. 75.00 (ISBN 0-12-064902-0); Pt. C. 89.50 (ISBN 0-12-064903-9); Vol. 2, 5 pts. 1978-79. Pt. A. 90.00 (ISBN 0-12-064940-3); Pt. B. 90.00 (ISBN 0-12-064941-1); Pt. C. 89.50 (ISBN 0-12-064942-X); Pt. D. 99.00 (ISBN 0-12-064943-8); Pt. E. write for info. (ISBN 0-12-064944-6). Acad Pr.

Ashburner, M., et al, eds. The Genetics & Biology of Drosophila, Vol. 3B. 1982. 88.50 (ISBN 0-12-064946-2). Acad Pr.

Clark, Arnold M., et al. Aging in Insects. (Aging Ser.). 201p. 1976. text ed. 24.50x (ISBN 0-8422-7269-0). Irvington.

Controlling Fruit Flies by the Sterile-Insect Technique. (Panel Proceedings Ser.). (Illus.). 175p. 1976. pap. 19.00 (ISBN 92-0-111575-X, ISP392, IAEA). Unipub.

King, Robert C. Ovarian Development in Drosophila Melanogaster. 1970. 50.50 (ISBN 0-12-408150-9). Acad Pr.

Lindsley, Dan L. & Grell, E. H. Genetic Variations of Drosophila Melanogaster. LC 68-15915. (Illus.). 472p. 1968. 16.50 (ISBN 0-87279-638-8, 627). Carnegie Inst.

Lints, F. A., et al. Aging in Drosophila. (Aging Ser.). 179p. 1977. text ed. 24.50x (ISBN 0-8422-7244-5). Irvington.

Siddiqui, O., et al, eds. Development & Neurobiology of Drosophila. LC 80-19900. (Basic Life Sciences Ser.: Vol. 16). 485p. 1980. 59.50x (ISBN 0-306-40559-8, Plenum Pr). Plenum Pub.

Sterile-Male Technique for Control of Fruit Flies. (Panel Proceedings Ser.). (Illus., Orig.). 1970. pap. 14.50 (ISBN 92-0-111570-9, ISP276, IAEA). Unipub.

FRUIT JUICES

Bielig, Hans J. Fruit Juice Processing. (Agricultural Services Bulletins: No. 13). (Eng. & Span., Illus.). 108p. (3rd Printing 1977). 1973. pap. 8.00 (ISBN 92-5-100174-X, F708, FAO). Unipub.

Kirschner, H. E. Live Food Juices. 4.95x (ISBN 0-686-29769-5). Cancer Control Soc.

Krop, J. J. The Mechanism of Cloud Loss in Orange Juice. (Agricultural Research Reports: No. 830). (Illus.). vi, 107p. 1975. pap. 14.00 (ISBN 90-220-0545-3, PDC53, PUDOC). Unipub.

Nelson, Philip E. & Tressler, Donald K. Fruit & Vegetable Juice Processing Technology. 3rd ed. (Illus.). 1980. text ed. 57.50 (ISBN 0-87055-362-3). AVI.

Newman, Laura. Make Your Juicer Your Drug Store. LC 66-125414. (Illus.). 192p. 1978. pap. 3.95 (ISBN 0-87904-001-7). Lust.

Recommended International Standard for Apple Juice Preserved Exclusively by Physical Means. 2nd ed. (CAC-RS Ser.: No. 48-1971). 1973. pap. 4.50 (ISBN 92-5-100231-2, F589, FAO). Unipub.

Recommended International Standard for Apricot, Peach & Pear Nectars Preserved Exclusively by Physical Means. (CAC-RS Ser.: No. 44-1971). 17p. (Orig.). 1972. pap. 4.50 (ISBN 92-5-101787-5, F587, FAO). Unipub.

Recommended International Standard for Concentrated Apple Juice & Concentrated Orange Juice Preserved Exclusively by Physical Means. (CAC-RS Ser.: Nos. 63-64 - 1972). 15p. (Orig.). 1975. pap. 5.50 (ISBN 92-5-101794-8, F604, FAO). Unipub.

Recommended International Standard for Orange, Grapefruit & Lemon Juices Preserved Exclusively by Physical Means. 1972. pap. 4.50 (ISBN 0-685-36312-0, F588, FAO). Unipub.

Recommended International Standard for Tomato Juice Preserved Exclusively by Physical Means. 3rd ed. (CAC-RS Ser.: No. 49-1971). 17p. 1974. pap. 4.50 (ISBN 92-5-101788-3, F590, FAO). Unipub.

Tressler, Donald K., et al. Freezing Preservation of Foods, 4 vols. 4th ed. Incl. Vol. 1. Principles of Refrigeration; Equipment for Freezing & Transporting Food. 50.00 (ISBN 0-87055-044-6); Vol. 2. Factors Affecting Quality in Frozen Foods. 55.00 (ISBN 0-87055-045-4); Vol. 3. Commercial Freezing Operations; Fresh Foods; Vol. 4. Freezing of Precooked & Prepared Foods. (Illus.). 1968. AVI.

FRUIT PESTS

see Fruit–Diseases and Pests

FRUIT TREES

see also Dwarf Fruit Trees

Fruit Trees & Shrubs. 2.25 (ISBN 0-686-21159-6). Bklyn Botanic.

McBean, D. M. Drying & Processing Tree Fruits. 20p. 1976. pap. 6.00 (ISBN 0-643-00181-6, C040, CSIRO). Unipub.

Mohlenbrock. Growing Tropical Fruit Trees. (Illus.). 1979. pap. 3.95 (ISBN 0-8200-0409-X). Great Outdoors.

Pearce, S. C. Field Experiments with Fruit Tree & other Perennial Plants. 182p. 1976. 89.00x (ISBN 0-85198-354-5, Pub. by CAB Bks England). State Mutual Bk.

Stebbins, Robert L. & Walheim, Lance. Western Fruit, Berries & Nuts: How to Select, Grow & Enjoy. (Illus.). 192p. (Orig.). 1981. pap. 9.95 (ISBN 0-89586-078-3). H P Bks.

Stefanile, Felix. A Fig Tree in America. 1970. 6.00 (ISBN 0-685-01012-0). Elizabeth Pr.

Teskey, Benjamin J. & Shoemaker, James S. Tree Fruit Production. 3rd ed. (Illus.). 1978. text ed. 26.50 (ISBN 0-87055-265-1). AVI.

FUCHSIA

Boullemier, Leo. The Checklist of Species, Hybrids & Cultivars of the Genus Fuchsia. (Illus.). 352p. 1985. 17.95 (ISBN 0-7137-1594-4, Pub. by Blandford Pr England). Sterling.

Clapham, Sidney. Fuchsias for House & Garden. LC 82-8401. (Illus.). 152p. 1982. text ed. 15.00x (ISBN 0-87663-404-8). Universe.

Jennings, K. & Miller, V. Growing Fuchsias. LC 80-471699. (Illus.). 170p. 1982. pap. 10.95 (ISBN 0-917304-45-4). Timber.

Munz, Phillip A. Revision of the Genus Fuchsia: Onagraceae. LC 44-30622. 1971. Repr. of 1943 ed. 20.00 (ISBN 0-384-40590-8). Johnson Repr.

Proudley, Brian & Proudley, Valerie. Fuchsias in Color. (Illus.). 206p. 1981. 12.95 (ISBN 0-7137-0754-2, Pub. by Blandford Pr England). Sterling.

FUCUS

Esper, E. J. Icones Fucorum Cum Characteribus Systematicis Synonymis Auctorum & Descriptionibus Novarum Specierum. 1966. Repr. of 1797 ed. 84.00 (ISBN 3-7682-0262-3). Lubrecht & Cramer.

FUEL

see also Biomass Energy; Charcoal; Coal; Coke; Heating; Lignite; Liquid Fuels; Motor Fuels; Peat; Petroleum As Fuel; Smoke; Synthetic Fuels; Wood As Fuel

Additives for Fuels & Lubricants: An Important & Growing Market. 1983. 1250.00 (ISBN 0-89336-239-5, C-027). BCC.

Alternative Fuels for Compression & Spark Ignition Engines. 136p. 1984. 25.00 (ISBN 0-317-17705-2, SP587). Soc Auto Engineers.

American Chemical Society, Division of Fuel Chemistry. Environmental Control in Synfuels Processes: Catalytic Reactions Involving Synthesis Gas. (Preprints of Papers: Vol. 25, No. 2). pap. 54.00 (ISBN 0-317-28249-2, 2012122). Bks Demand UMI.

American Chemical Society Division of Fuel Chemistry. Physical Methods for Fossil Fuels Characterization, Coal Gasification, Pyrolysis & Biomass: Presented at Miami Beach, FL, April 28 May 3, 1985, Vol. 7. (American Chemical Society Division of Fuel Chemistry Preprints of Papers Ser.: Vol. 30). pap. 108.80 (ISBN 0-317-28033-3, 2025564). Bks Demand UMI.

Anderson, Larry L. & Tillman, David A. Synthetic Fuels from Coal: Overview & Assessment. LC 79-17786. 158p. 1979. 40.00 (ISBN 0-471-01784-1, Pub. by Wiley-Interscience). Wiley.

Axelson, David E. Solid State Nuclear Magnetic Resonance of Fossil Fuels. 320p. 1985. text ed. 56.00x (ISBN 0-919868-25-8, Pub. by Multisci Pubns Ltd). Brookfield Pub Co.

Bach, W., et al, eds. Renewable Energy Prospects: Proceedings of the Conference on Non-Fossil Fuel & Non-Nuclear Fuel Energy Strategies, Honolulu, USS, January 1979. 340p. 1980. 26.00 (ISBN 0-08-024252-9). Pergamon.

Battelle Columbus Laboratories. Preliminary Environmental Assessment of Biomass Conversion to Synthetic Fuels. 346p. 1980. pap. 49.95x (ISBN 0-89934-049-0, B049-PP). Solar Energy Info.

Bisio, Attilio. Encyclopedia of Energy Technology. 4000p. 1983. Set. 350.00x (ISBN 0-471-89039-1, Pub. by Wiley-Interscience). Wiley.

Bogach, Susan V. Wood As Fuel: Energy for Developing Countries. LC 84-26640. 176p. 1985. 39.95 (ISBN 0-03-001649-5). Praeger.

Brown, Lester R. Food or Fuel: New Competition for the World's Cropland. LC 80-50216. (Worldwatch Papers). 1980. pap. 2.00 (ISBN 0-916468-34-8). Worldwatch Inst.

Business Communications Staff. Fuel & Lubricant Additives. 1983. 1250.00 (ISBN 0-89336-239-5, C-027). BCC.

Clark, J. S. & De Corso, S. M., eds. Stationary Gas Turbine Alternative Fuels - STP 809. LC 82-73767. 360p. 1983. 43.00 (ISBN 0-8031-0199-6, 04-809000-13). ASTM.

Commoner, Barry & Boksenbaum, Howard, eds. Energy & Human Welfare: Alternative Technologies for Power Production, Vol. 2. LC 75-8987. 1975. 14.95 (ISBN 0-02-468430-9). Macmillan Info.

Cooper, John A. & Malek, Dorothy, eds. Residential Solid Fuels: Environmental Impacts & Solutions. (Proceedings of the 1981 International Conference on Residential Solid Fuels, Portland, Oregon, June 1-4, 1981). (Illus.). 1300p. 1981. lib. bdg. 80.00x (ISBN 0-686-46045-6, Pub. by OGC). Scholium Intl.

Cusumano, James A. & Farkas, Adalbert, eds. Catalysis in Coal Conversion. LC 77-25620. 1978. 47.50 (ISBN 0-12-199935-1). Acad Pr.

Energy Technology VIII: New Fuels Era. LC 80-66431. (Illus.). 1454p. 1981. 48.00 (ISBN 0-86587-008-X). Gov Insts.

Environmental Science of Fossil Fuels, General Papers: Presented at Miami Beach, FL, April 28-May 3, 1985. (American Chemical Society, Division of Fuel Chemistry, Preprints of Papers Ser.: No. 30, No. 2). pap. 96.30 (ISBN 0-317-28037-6, 2025563). Bks Demand UMI.

ESCAP-FAO-UNEP Expert Group Meeting on Fuelwood & Charcoal: Proceedings. (Energy Resources & Development Ser.: No. 24). 120p. 1985. pap. 11.00 (UN82/2F10, UN). Unipub.

Fabrication of Water Reactor Fuel Elements. (Proceedings Ser.). (Illus.). 595p. 1978. pap. 83.50 (ISBN 9-2005-0079-X, ISP499, IAEA). Unipub.

Francis, W. Fuels & Fuel Technology, 2 Vols. 2nd ed. 1965. Vol. 1. 125.00 (ISBN 0-08-025249-4); Vol. 2. text ed. 125.00 (ISBN 0-08-025250-8); Vol. 1. pap. 38.00 (ISBN 0-08-010753-2); Vol. 2. pap. 34.50 (ISBN 0-08-010755-9). Pergamon.

Francis, W. & Peters, M. C. Fuels & Fuel Technology. 2nd ed. (Illus.). 608p. 1980. 125.00 (ISBN 0-08-025249-4); pap. 38.00 (ISBN 0-08-025250-8). Pergamon.

Fry, L. John. Practical Building of Methane Power Plants for Rural Energy Independence. Knox, D. Anthony, ed. LC 76-16224. (Illus.). 1974. pap. text ed. 12.00 (ISBN 0-9600984-1-0). L J Fry.

Fuels & Combustion. (Principles of Steam Generation Ser.: Module 6). (Illus.). 70p. 1982. spiral bdg. 10.00x (ISBN 0-87683-256-7); instr's. manual 15.00x (ISBN 0-87683-277-X). G P Courseware.

Fuels & Lubricants Technology: An Overview. 1985. 25.00 (ISBN 0-89883-825-8, SP603). Soc Auto Engineers.

Gilchrist, J. D. Fuel, Furnaces & Refractories. 2nd ed. 1977. text ed. 37.00 (ISBN 0-08-020430-9); pap. text ed. 12.75 (ISBN 0-08-020429-5). Pergamon.

Gillies, M. T., ed. Chemical Additives for Fuels: Developments Since 1978. LC 81-18939. (Chemical Technology Review: No. 203, Energy Technology Review: No. 76). (Illus.). 308p. 1982. 48.00 (ISBN 0-8155-0886-7). Noyes.

Goodger, E. M. Alternative Fuels: Chemical Energy Resources. LC 80-11796. 238p. 1980. 53.95 (ISBN 0-470-26952-9). Halsted Pr.

Hollaender, A., et al, eds. Trends in the Biology of Fermentations for Fuels & Chemicals. LC 81-5928. (Basic Life Sciences Ser.). 604p. 1981. 85.00x (ISBN 0-306-40752-3, Plenum Pr). Plenum Pub.

Horton, K. E., et al, eds. International Symposium Fuels Technology. (Nuclear Metallurgy Ser.: Vol. 13). pap. 134.00 (ISBN 0-317-09256-1, 2001101). Bks Demand UMI.

Institute of Gas Technology. Nonpetroleum Vehicular Fuel: IV Symposium. 292p. 1984. 50.00 (ISBN 0-910091-51-X). Inst Gas Tech.

IPC Business Press. Marine Propulsion & Future Fuels. 1980. 55.00x (ISBN 0-686-79381-1, Pub. by IPC Busn England). State Mutual Bk.

Jackson & Wright, eds. Analysis of Waters Associated with Alternative Fuel Production - STP 720. 205p. 1981. 23.00 (ISBN 0-8031-0763-3, 04-720000-16). ASTM.

Kaupp, A. Rice Hull Gasification: Theory & Praxis. (Illus.). 303p. (Orig.). 1984. 40.00 (ISBN 0-942914-05-8); lib. bdg. 40.00 (ISBN 0-942914-06-6); pap. 20.00 (ISBN 0-942914-04-X). Tipi Wkshp Bks.

Kaupp, A. & Goss, J. R. State of the Art: Small Scale (to 50 kw) Gas Producer Engine Systems. (Illus.). 278p. (Orig.). 1983. 40.00 (ISBN 0-942914-03-1); pap. 20.00 (ISBN 0-942914-02-3). Tipi Wkshp Bks.

Keith, Lawrence H., ed. Energy & Environmental Chemistry, 2 vols. LC 81-69255. (Illus.). 1982. Set. text ed. 75.00 (ISBN 0-250-40486-9); text ed. 49.95 ea. Vol. 1: Fossil Fuels, 425p (ISBN 0-250-40401-X). Vol. 2: Acid Rain, 350p (ISBN 0-250-40402-8). Butterworth.

Klass, Donald L., ed. Biomass As a Nonfossil Fuel Source. LC 80-26044. (ACS Symposium Ser.: No. 144). 1981. 44.95 (ISBN 0-8412-0599-X). Am Chemical.

Klein, George D. Sandstone Depositional Models for Exploration for Fossil Fuels. 3rd ed. (Illus.). 218p. 1985. text ed. 48.00 (ISBN 0-934634-82-3). Intl Human Res.

Knowles, Don. Alternative Automotive Fuels. 1984. text ed. 29.95 (ISBN 0-8359-0120-3); pap. 18.95 (ISBN 0-8359-0119-X). Reston.

Lefond, Stanley J., ed. Industrial Minerals & Rocks: (Nonmetallics Other Than Fuels) rev., 4th ed. LC 73-85689. (Seeley W. Mudd Ser.). pap. 160.00 (ISBN 0-317-29747-3, 2017421). Bks Demand UMI.

Maritime Transportation Research Board, National Research Council. Alternative Fuels for Maritime Use. 1983. pap. text ed. 11.25 (ISBN 0-309-03088-9). Natl Acad Pr.

Methane Digesters for Fuel Gas & Fertilizer. (Illus.). 1973. pap. text ed. 4.00 (ISBN 0-9600984-2-9). L J Fry.

Monroe, Elmer S., Jr. Saving Fuel with Furnaces. Gyftopoulos, Elias P. & Cohen, Karen C., eds. (Industrial Energy-Conservation Manuals: No. 6). 56p. 1982. loose-leaf 20.00x (ISBN 0-262-13171-4). MIT Pr.

Nathan, R. A., ed. Fuels from Sugar Crops. 137p. 1980. pap. 19.95x (ISBN 0-930978-91-9, B.036). Solar Energy Info.

Nathan, Richard A., ed. Fuels from Sugar Crops: Systems Study for Sugarcane, Sweet Sorghum, & Sugar Beets. LC 78-19127. (DOE Critical Review Ser.). 148p. 1978. pap. 11.75 (ISBN 0-87079-111-7, TID-22781); microfiche 4.50 (ISBN 0-87079-212-1, TID-22781). DOE.

National Industrial Fuel Efficiency Service Ltd. Fuel Economy Handbook. 300p. 1979. 27.50x (ISBN 0-86010-130-4, Pub. by Graham & Trotman England). State Mutual Bk.

Nonaqueous Reprocessing of Irradiated Fuels. (Bibliographical Ser.: No. 264). 2364p. 1976. pap. write for info. (ISBN 92-0-044167-X, STI/PUB/21/26, IAEA). Unipub.

Odgers, J. & Kretschmer, D. Gas Turbine Fuels & Their Influence on Combustion. (Energy & Engineering Science Ser.). 1984. 40.00 (ISBN 0-9901004-7-2, Pub. by Abacus England). Heyden.

OECD. Safety Aspects of Fuel Behavior in Off-Normal & Accident Conditions. 658p. (Orig.). 1981. pap. text ed. 28.00x (ISBN 92-64-02234-1). OECD.

Parent, Joseph D. A Survey of United States & Total World Production, Proved Reserves, & Remaining Recoverable Resources of Fossil Fuels & Uranium, as of December 31, 1982. xviii, 250p. 1984. 30.00 (ISBN 0-910091-52-8). Inst Gas Tech.

Platt, Hugh. A New, Cheape & Delicate Fire of Cole-Balles. LC 72-7838. (English Experience Ser.: No. 550). 32p. 1972. Repr. of 1603 ed. 7.00 (ISBN 90-221-0550-4). Walter J Johnson.

The Potential for Production of "Hydrocarbon" Fuels from Crops in Australia. 86p. 1983. pap. 7.25 (ISBN 0-643-02931-1, CO67, CSIRO). Unipub.

Pugh, Brinley. Fuel Calorimetry. 196p. 1966. 22.50x (ISBN 0-306-30654-9, Plenum Pr). Plenum Pub.

Redmayne, R. Fuel. 1979. Repr. of 1929 ed. lib. bdg. 12.50 (ISBN 0-8495-4623-0). Arden Lib.

--Fuel: Its Origin & Use. 1979. Repr. of 1929 ed. lib. bdg. 12.50 (ISBN 0-8492-2399-7). R West.

Reed, T. B., ed. Biomass Gasification: Principles & Technology. LC 81-9667. (Energy Tech. Rev.: No. 67). (Illus.). 401p. 1981. 42.00 (ISBN 0-8155-0852-2). Noyes.

Robinson, Colin. Policy for Fuel. (Institute of Economic Affairs, Occasional Papers Ser.: No. 31). pap. 2.50 technical (ISBN 0-255-27607-9). Transatlantic.

Rocks, Lawrence. Fuels for Tomorrow. 190p. 1980. 34.95x (ISBN 0-87814-135-9). Pennwell Bks.

Rose, J. W. & Cooper, J., eds. Technical Data on Fuel: S. I. Units. 7th rev. ed. LC 77-24872. 343p. 1978. 106.95x (ISBN 0-470-99239-5). Halsted Pr.

Semenza, G. Of Oxygen, Fuels & Living Matter, Vol. 2, Pt. 2. (Evolving Life Sciences: Recollections on Scientific Ideas & Events Ser.). 508p. 1982. text ed. 74.95x (ISBN 0-471-27924-2, Pub. by Wiley-Interscience). Wiley.

Shelton, Jay. Jay Shelton's Solid Fuels Encyclopedia. Chesman, Andrea, ed. LC 82-15648. (Illus.). 268p. 1982. pap. 12.95 (ISBN 0-88266-307-0). Garden Way Pub.

Short, W., et al. Questions & Answers on Cutting Fuel Costs. 104p. 1975. 11.00x (ISBN 0-86010-019-7, Pub. by Graham & Trotman England). State Mutual Bk.

Solar Energy Research Institute. Fuel from Farms: A Guide to Small-Scale Ethanol Production. 161p. 1980. 34.95x (ISBN 0-89934-050-4, B947-PP); pap. 19.95x (ISBN 0-89934-051-2, B047-PP). Solar Energy Info.

Stavinoha & Henry, eds. Distillate Fuel Stability & Cleanliness - STP 751. 168p. 1981. 20.00 (ISBN 0-8031-0762-5, 04-751000-12). ASTM.

Storage, Handling & Movement of Fuel & Related Components at Nuclear Power Plants. (Technical Reports Ser.: No. 189). 56p. 1979. pap. 11.75 (ISBN 92-0-125279-X, IDC189, IAEA). Unipub.

Swedish Academy of Engineering. Gengas: The Swedish Classic on Wood Powered Vehicles. 2nd ed. Reed, Thomas B. & Jantzen, Dan, eds. Geuther, Maria, tr. from Swedish. (Illus.). 329p. 1982. pap. 15.00 (ISBN 0-942914-01-5). Tipi Wkshp Bks.

Veziroglu, T. Nejat, ed. Renewable Energy Sources: International Progress, Vols. 4 A & B. (Energy Research Ser.). 1984. Set. 222.25 (ISBN 0-444-42363-X); Vol. A, 456 pgs. 129.75 (ISBN 0-444-42361-3, I-313-84); Vol. B, 498 pgs. 129.75 (ISBN 0-444-42362-1). Elsevier.

Weisz, P. B. & Marshall, J. F., eds. Fuels from Biomass. 136p. 1980. 435.00 (ISBN 0-8247-6964-3). Dekker.

Wilson, Richard, et al. Health Effects of Fossil Fuel Burning: Assessment & Mitigation. 416p. 1980. prof ref 37.50 (ISBN 0-88410-714-0). Ballinger Pub.

FUEL CELLS

Bagotskii, V. S. & Vasil'ev, Yu B., eds. Fuel Cells: Their Electrochemical Kinetics. LC 64-66348. 121p. 1966. 30.00x (ISBN 0-306-10741-4, Consultants). Plenum Pub.

Baker, Bernard S., ed. Hydrocarbon Fuel Cell Technology: A Symposium. (Illus.). 1966. 89.50 (ISBN 0-12-074250-0). Acad Pr.

Breiter, M. W. Electrochemical Processes in Fuel Cells. LC 69-17789. (Illus.). 1969. 34.00 (ISBN 0-387-04418-3). Springer-Verlag.

Faust, Charles L., ed. Fundamentals of Electrochemical Machining. LC 72-150646. pap. 92.80 (ISBN 0-317-08009-1, 2051971). Bks Demand UMI.

Industrial Batteries & Fuel Cells (Europe) 1985. write for info. (ISBN 0-86621-711-8, E783). Frost & Sullivan.

Koryta, J. Medical & Biological Applications of Electrochemical Devices. 331p. 1980. 91.95 (ISBN 0-317-00283-X). Wiley.

--Medical & Biological Applications of Electrochemical Devices. LC 79-41212. 331p. 1980. 105.95 (ISBN 0-471-27678-2). Wiley.

Linden, D. Handbook of Batteries & Fuel Cells. 1088p. 1983. 78.50 (ISBN 0-07-037874-6). McGraw.

Mantell, Charles L. Batteries & Energy Systems. 2nd ed. (Illus.). 352p. 1983. 36.50 (ISBN 0-07-040031-8). McGraw.

Oniciu. Fuel Cells. 25.00 (ISBN 0-9961000-6-7, Pub. by Abacus England). Heyden.

Sandstede, G., ed. From Electrocatalysis to Fuel Cells. LC 79-38116. (Illus.). 441p. 1972. 30.00x (ISBN 0-295-95178-8). U of Wash Pr.

Vielstich, Wolf. Fuel Cells: Modern Processes for the Electrochemical Production of Energy. LC 76-114088. pap. 130.80 (ISBN 0-317-09146-8, 2019671). Bks Demand UMI.

Workshop of the Electrocatalysis of Fuel Cell Reactions (1978: Brookhaven National Laboratory) The Electrocatalysis of Fuel Cell Reactions. O'Grady, W. E. & Srinivasan, S., eds. LC 79-51633. (Electrochemical Society Proceedings Ser.: Vol. 79-2). (Illus.). pap. 59.00 (ISBN 0-317-09592-7, 2051701). Bks Demand UMI.

FUEL ELEMENTS

see Nuclear Fuel Elements

FUEL OIL

see Petroleum As Fuel

FUEL OIL BURNERS

see Oil Burners

FUEL PUMPS

see also Automobiles–Fuel Systems

Pulverized Fuel Systems. (Sixty Ser.). Orig. Title: Installation & Operation of Pulverized Fuel Systems. 68p. 1973. pap. 2.00 (ISBN 0-685-44173-3, 60). Natl Fire Prot.

FUEL TRADE

see also Coal Trade; Coke; Wood

De Montalembert, M. R. & Clement, J. Fuelwood Supplies in the Developing Countries. (Forestry Papers: No. 42). (Eng., Fr. & Span.). 134p. 1983. pap. text ed. 9.75 (ISBN 92-5-101252-0, F2429, FAO). Unipub.

Johnson, Charles J. Coal Demand in the Electric Utility Industry, Nineteen Forty-Six to Nineteen Ninety. Bruchey, Stuart, ed. LC 78-22689. (Energy in the American Economy Ser.). (Illus.). 1979. lib. bdg. 23.00x (ISBN 0-405-11992-5). Ayer Co Pubs.

Striner, Herbert E. An Analysis of the Bituminous Coal Industry in Terms of Total Energy Supply & a Synthetic Oil Program. Bruchey, Stuart, ed. LC 78-22752. (Energy in the American Economy Ser.). (Illus.). 1979. lib. bdg. 24.50x (ISBN 0-405-12016-8). Ayer Co Pubs.

FULLERS EARTH

see also Filters and Filtration

Hasruddin Siddiqui, M. K. Bleaching Earths. 1968. text ed. 23.00 (ISBN 0-08-012738-X). Pergamon.

FULLING (TEXTILES)

see Textile Finishing

FUME CONTROL

see also Smoke Prevention

Ames, J. Systems Study of Odorous Industrial Processes, 1979. 1981. 75.00x (ISBN 0-686-97144-2, Pub. by W Spring England). State Mutual Bk.

Bailey, J. C. & Bedborough, D. R. Tests on the Efficiency of Odour Removal of a Pilot-Scale Boiler Incinerator at an Activated Carbon Plant, 1979. 1981. 40.00x (ISBN 0-686-97145-0, Pub. by W Spring England). State Mutual Bk.

Carleton, A. J. Odour Control by Thermal Incineration, 1978. 1981. 75.00x (ISBN 0-686-97130-2, Pub. by W Spring England). State Mutual Bk.

Irwin, J. G. Odour Removal by Catalytic Oxidation Nineteen Seventy Eight. 1982. 75.00x (ISBN 0-686-97132-9, Pub. by W Spring England). State Mutual Bk.

User Guide to Dust & Fume Control. 130p. 1981. 75.00x (ISBN 0-85295-125-6, Pub. by IChemE). State Mutual Bk.

Warren Spring Laboratory, ed. Odours Control: A Concise Guide, Nineteen Eighty. 1981. 85.00x (ISBN 0-686-97135-3, Pub. by W Spring England). State Mutual Bk.

Welding Fume Control: A Demonstration Project WFDP. 65p. 1982. 24.00 (ISBN 0-686-43388-2). Am Welding.

FUMIGATION

see also Disinfection and Disinfectants

Standards on Fumigation. 1973. pap. 2.00 (ISBN 0-685-58082-2, 57). Natl Fire Prot.

FUNCTION ALGEBRAS

Greene, R. E. & Krantz, S. G. Function Theory of One Complex Variable. 1985. 64.95 (ISBN 0-471-80468-1). Wiley.

Simon, Barry. Functional Integration & Quantum Physics. (Pure & Applied Mathematics Ser.). 1979. 44.50 (ISBN 0-12-644250-9). Acad Pr.

FUNCTION SPACES

see also Functional Analysis

Baker, J. & Cleaver, C., eds. Banach Spaces of Analytic Functions, Kent 1976: Proceedings of a Conference Held at Kent State University July 12-16, 1976. LC 77-11202. (Lecture Notes in Mathematics: Vol. 604). 1977. pap. text ed. 14.00 (ISBN 0-387-08356-1). Springer-Verlag.

Bekken, O. B., et al, eds. Spaces of Analytic Functions. (Lecture Notes in Mathematics Ser.: Vol. 512). 1976. pap. 16.00 (ISBN 0-387-07682-4). Springer-Verlag.

Ciesielski, Z. Approximation & Function Spaces: Proceedings of the International Conference in Gdansk, Aug. 1979. 898p. 1982. 117.00 (ISBN 0-444-86143-2, North-Holland). Elsevier.

Cwikel, M. & Peetre, J. Interpolation Spaces & Allied Topics in Analysis: Proceedings of the Conference Held in Lund, Sweden, August 29 - September 1, 1983. (Lecture Notes in Mathematics Ser.: Vol. 1070). iii, 239p. 1984. pap. 13.50 (ISBN 0-387-13363-1). Springer-Verlag.

Fisher, S. W. & Jerome, J. W. Minimum Norm Extremals in Function Spaces: With Applications to Classical & Modern Analysis. (Lecture Notes in Mathematics: Vol. 479). viii, 209p. (Orig.). 1975. pap. 16.00 (ISBN 0-387-07394-9). Springer-Verlag.

Hamilton, R. S. Harmonic Maps of Manifolds with Boundary. (Lecture Notes in Mathematics Ser.: Vol. 471). 168p. 1975. pap. 14.00 (ISBN 0-387-07185-7). Springer-Verlag.

Hogbe-Nlend, H. & Moscatelli, V. B. Nuclear & Conuclear Spaces: An Introductory Course. (Mathematics Studies: Vol. 52). 276p. 1981. pap. 47.00 (ISBN 0-444-86207-2). Elsevier.

Kalton, N. J., et al. An F-Space Sampler. 252p. 1985. not set 24.95 (ISBN 0-521-27585-7). Cambridge U Pr.

Katz, M. B. Questions of Uniqueness & Resolution in Reconstruction of 2-D & 3-D Objects from Their Projections. (Lecture Notes in Biomathematics: Vol. 26). 1978. pap. 15.00 (ISBN 0-387-09087-8). Springer-Verlag.

Kaucher, Edgar W. & Miranker, Willard L. Self-Validating Numerics For Function Space Problems: Computation With Guarantees For Differential & Integral Equations. Monograph ed. (Notes & Reports in Computer Science & Applied Mathematics Ser.). 1984. 28.00 (ISBN 0-12-402020-8). Acad Pr.

Maz'ja, V. G. Sobolev Spaces. Saposnikova, T. O., tr. from Rus. (Springer Series in Soviet Mathematics). (Illus.). 510p. 1985. 59.00 (ISBN 0-387-13589-8). Springer-Verlag.

Maz'ya, V. G. & Shaposhnikova, T. V. Theory of Multipliers in Spaces of Differential Functions. (Monographs & Studies: No. 23). 320p. 1985. text ed. 49.95 (ISBN 0-273-08638-3). Pitman Pub Ma.

Musielak, J. Orlicz Spaces & Modular Spaces. (Lecture Notes in Mathematics: Vol. 1034). 222p. 1983. pap. 13.00 (ISBN 0-387-12706-2). Springer Verlag.

Schmets, J. Spaces of Vector-Valued Continuous Functions. (Lecture Notes in Mathematics: Vol. 1003). 117p. 1983. pap. 10.00 (ISBN 0-387-12327-X). Springer-Verlag.

Semadeni, Z. Schauder Bases in Banach Spaces of Continuous Functions. (Lecture Notes in Mathematics Ser.: Vol. 918). 136p. 1982. pap. 12.00 (ISBN 0-387-11481-5). Springer-Verlag.

Triebel, Hans. Recent Developments in the Theory of Function Spaces. 286p. 1983. text ed. 34.95 (ISBN 3-7643-1381-1). Birkhauser.

FUNCTIONAL ANALYSIS

see also Approximation Theory; Digital Filters (Mathematics); Distributions, Theory of (Functional Analysis); Function Spaces; Functor Theory; Hardy Spaces; Hilbert Algebras; Integral Equations; Perturbation (Mathematics); Spectral Theory (Mathematics); Topological Algebras; Vector Spaces

Abramov, L. M., et al. Ten Papers on Functional Analysis & Measure Theory. LC 51-5559. (Translations Ser.: No. 2, Vol. 49). 1966. 24.00 (ISBN 0-8218-1749-3, TRANS 2-49). Am Math.

Agranovic, Z. S., et al. Thirteen Papers on Functional Analysis. LC 51-5559. (Translations Ser.: No. 2, Vol. 90). 1970. 32.00 (ISBN 0-8218-1790-6, TRANS 2-90). Am Math.

Ahiezer, N. I. & Krein, M. G. Some Questions in the Theory of Moments. LC 63-22077. (Translations of Mathematical Monographs: Vol. 2). 1974. Repr. of 1962 ed. 30.00 (ISBN 0-8218-1552-0, MMONO-2). Am Math.

Aizerman, M. A., et al. Sixteen Papers on Differential & Difference Equations, Functional Analysis, Games & Control. LC 51-5559. (Translations Ser.: No. 2, Vol. 87). 1970. 36.00 (ISBN 0-8218-1787-6, TRANS 2-87). Am Math.

Aleksandrov, A. D., et al. Ten Papers on Differential Equations & Functional Analysis. LC 51-5559. (Translations Ser.: No. 2, Vol. 68). 1968. 35.00 (ISBN 0-8218-1768-X, TRANS 2-68). Am Math.

Aliprantis, C. D. & Burkinshaw, O. Principles of Real Analysis. 288p. 1981. 33.50 (ISBN 0-444-00448-3). Elsevier.

Altman. Contractors & Contractor Direction Theory & Applications: A New Approach to Solving Equations. (Lecture Notes in Pure & Applied Math Ser.: Vol. 32). 1977. 55.00 (ISBN 0-8247-6672-5). Dekker.

Mathematical Society of Japan. Functional Analysis & Related Topics, 1969: Proceedings of the International Conference. 423p. 1970. 40.00 (ISBN 0-86008-026-9, Pub. by U of Tokyo Japan). Columbia U Pr.

Maz'ja, V. G. Sobolev Spaces. Saposnikova, T. O., tr. from Rus. (Springer Series in Soviet Mathematics). (Illus.). 510p. 1985. 59.00 (ISBN 0-387-13589-8). Springer-Verlag.

Milne, R. D. Applied Functional Analysis: An Introductory Treatment. (Applicable Math Ser.). 528p. 1980. text ed. 52.95 (ISBN 0-273-08404-6). Pitman Pub MA.

MRC Symposium-1971. Contributions to Nonlinear Functional Analysis: Proceedings. Zarantonello, Eduardo H., ed. 1971. 31.00 (ISBN 0-12-775850-X). Acad Pr.

Mukherjea, A. & Pothoven, K. Real & Functional Analysis: Part A: Real Analysis. 2nd ed. (Mathematical Concepts & Methods in Science & Engineering Ser.: Vol. 27). 351p. 1984. 49.50x (ISBN 0-306-41557-7, Plenum Pr). Plenum Pub.

--Real & Functional Analysis: Part B: Functional Analysis. 2nd ed. (Mathematical Concepts & Methods in Science & Engineering Ser.: Vol. 28). 275p. 1985. 39.50x (ISBN 0-306-41558-5, Plenum Pr). Plenum Pub.

Nachbin, Leopoldo. Introduction to Functional Analysis: Banach Spaces & Different Calculus. (Pure & Applied Mathematics: Monographs & Textbooks: Vol. 60). (Illus.). 184p. 1981. 35.00 (ISBN 0-8247-6984-8). Dekker.

Nagel, A. & Stein, E. M. Lectures on Pseudo-Differential Operators: Regularity Theorems & Applications to Non-Elliptic Problems. LC 79-19388. (Mathematical Notes Ser.: No. 24). 1980. 15.95 (ISBN 0-691-08247-2). Princeton U Pr.

Nashed, M. Z., ed. Functional Analysis Methods in Numerical Analysis: Proceeding, St. Louis, Mo., 1977. (Lecture Notes in Mathematics: Vol. 701). 1979. pap. 20.00 (ISBN 0-387-09110-6). Springer-Verlag.

Novozhilov, Y. V. & Tulub, A. V. The Method of Functionals in the Quantum Theory of Fields. (Russian Tracts on the Physical Sciences Ser.). 90p. 1961. 20.95x (ISBN 0-677-20410-8). Gordon.

Nowinski, J. L. Applications of Functional Analysis in Engineering. LC 81-5213. (Mathematical Concepts & Methods in Science & Engineering Ser.: Vol.22). 320p. 1981. 42.50x (ISBN 0-306-40693-4, Plenum Pr). Plenum Pub.

Oden, J. T. Applied Functional Analysis: A First Course for Students of Mechanics & Engineering Science. LC 78-541. (Illus.). 1979. ref. 48.95 (ISBN 0-13-040162-5). P-H.

Packel, Edward W. Functional Analysis: A Short Course. Anderson, Richard D. & Rosenberg, Alex, eds. LC 79-21888. 192p. 1980. Repr. of 1974 ed. lib. bdg. 12.50 (ISBN 0-89874-019-3). Krieger.

Pelczynski, Aleksander. Banach Spaces of Analytic Functions & Absolutely Summing Operators. LC 77-9884. (Conference Board of the Mathematical Sciences Ser.: No. 30). 1980. pap. 10.00 (ISBN 0-8218-1680-2, CBMS30). Am Math.

Power, S. C., ed. Operators & Function Theory. 1985. lib. bdg. 49.00 (ISBN 90-277-2008-8, Pub. by Reidel Netherlands). Kluwer Academic.

Prolla, J. B. Approximation Theory & Functional Analysis. (Mathematical Studies: Vol. 35). 450p. (Proceedings). 1979. 70.25 (ISBN 0-444-85264-6, North-Holland). Elsevier.

Rall, Louis B., ed. Nonlinear Functional Analysis & Applications: Proceedings. 1971. 28.00 (ISBN 0-12-576350-6). Acad Pr.

Reddy, J. N. Applied Functional Analysis & Variational Methods in Engineering. 560p. 1986. text ed. price not set (ISBN 0-07-051348-1). McGraw.

Rellich, Franz. Perturbation Theory of Eigenvalue Problems. (Notes on Mathematics & Its Applications Ser). 138p. (Orig.). 1969. 37.25 (ISBN 0-677-00680-2). Gordon.

Rudin, Walter. Functional Analysis. LC 71-39686. (McGraw-Hill Series in Higher Mathematics). 1972. text ed. 45.95 (ISBN 0-07-054225-2). McGraw.

Sard, Arthur. Linear Approximation. LC 63-11988. (Mathematical Surveys Ser.: No. 9). 544p. 1982. pap. 50.00 (ISBN 0-8218-1509-1, SURV-9). Am Math.

Sawyer, W. W. A First Look at Numerical Functional Analysis. (Oxford Applied Mathematics & Computing Science Ser.). (Illus.). 1978. pap. 15.95x (ISBN 0-19-859629-4). Oxford U Pr.

Schwartz, Jacob T. Nonlinear Functional Analysis. (Notes on Mathematics & Its Applications Ser.). 244p. 1969. 44.00x (ISBN 0-677-01500-3). Gordon.

Segal, I. E. & Kunze, R. A. Integrals & Operators. 2nd rev ed. LC 77-16682. (Grundlehren der Mathematischen Wissenschaften: Vol. 228). 1978. Repr. 44.00 (ISBN 0-387-08323-5). Springer-Verlag.

Seminar on Functional Operators & Equations, Zurich, 1965-66 & Targonski, G. I. Proceedings. (Lecture Notes in Mathematics: Vol. 33). 1967. pap. 10.70 (ISBN 0-387-03904-X). Springer-Verlag.

Simon, Barry. Trace Ideals & Their Applications. LC 78-20867. (London Mathematical Society Lecture Notes Ser.: No. 35). 1979. pap. 21.95x (ISBN 0-521-22286-9). Cambridge U Pr.

Singer, Ivan. The Theory of Best Approximation & Functional Analysis. (CBMS-NSF Regional Conference Ser.: No. 13). vii, 95p. (Orig.). 1974. pap. text ed. 13.00 (ISBN 0-89871-010-3). Soc Indus-Appl Math.

Sobolev, Sergei L. & Browder, F E, trs. Applications of Functional Analysis in Mathematical Physics. LC 63-15658. (Translations of Mathematical Monographs: Vol. 7). 239p. 1982. pap. 35.00 (ISBN 0-8218-1557-1). Am Math.

Steklov Institute of Mathematics, Academy of Sciences, U S S R, No. 96. Automatic Programming, Numerical Methods & Functional Analysis: Proceedings. Faddeeva, V. N., ed. (Proceedings of the Steklov Institute of Mathematics: No. 96). 1970. 47.00 (ISBN 0-8218-1896-1, STEKLO-96). Am Math.

Steklov Institute of Mathematics, Academy of Sciences, U.S.S.R., No. 114. Some Questions in Constructive Functional Analysis: Proceedings. LC 73-21929. (No. 114). 238p. 1974. 68.00 (ISBN 0-8218-3014-7, STEKLO-114). Am Math.

Steklov Institute of Mathematics, Academy of Sciences, U S S R. Theory & Applications of Differentiable Functions of Several Variables: Proceedings. Nikol'skii, S. M., ed. (Proceedings of the Steklov Institute of Mathematics: No. 77). 1967. 46.00 (ISBN 0-8218-1877-5, STEKLO-77). Am Math.

--Theory & Applications of Differentiable Functions of Several Variables, 2: Proceedings. Nikol'skii, S. M., ed. (Proceedings of the Steklov Institute of Mathematics: No. 89). 1968. 67.00 (ISBN 0-8218-1889-9, STEKLO-89). Am Math.

Sundaresan, K. & Swaminathan, S. Geometry & Nonlinear Analysis in Banach Spaces. (Lecture Notes in Mathematics: Vol. 1131). iii, 116p. 1985. pap. 9.80 (ISBN 0-387-15237-7). Springer-Verlag.

Swaminathan, S., ed. Fixed Point Theory & Its Applications. 1976. 34.00 (ISBN 0-12-678650-X). Acad Pr.

Tammi, O. Extremum Problems for Bounded Univalent Functions. (Lecture Notes in Mathematics: Vol. 646). 1978. pap. 19.00 (ISBN 0-387-08756-7). Springer-Verlag.

Taylor, A. & Lay, D. Introduction to Functional Analysis. 2nd ed. LC 79-13658. 467p. 1980. 42.50 (ISBN 0-471-84646-5). Wiley.

Taylor, Angus E. General Theory of Functions & Integration. 448p. 1985. pap. 10.95 (ISBN 0-486-64988-1). Dover.

Temam, R. Navier-Stokes Equations & Nonlinear Functional Analysis. LC 82-62216. (CBMS-NSF Regional Conference Ser.: No. 41). xii, 122p. 1983. pap. text ed. 15.50 (ISBN 0-89871-183-5). Soc Indus-Appl Math.

Thirty-Five Scientific Communications from the All-Union Conference on Functional Analysis & Its Applications & Five Papers on Analysis. LC 51-5559. (Translations Ser.: No. 2, Vol. 16). 1960. 36.00 (ISBN 0-8218-1716-7, TRANS 2-16). Am Math.

Treves, Francois. Linear Partial Differential Equations with Constant Coefficients. (Mathematics & Its Applications Ser.). 544p. 1966. 132.95x (ISBN 0-677-01190-3). Gordon.

Van Rooij. Non-Archimedian Functional Analysis. (Pure & Applied Mathematics Ser.: Vol. 51). 1978. 65.00 (ISBN 0-8247-6556-7). Dekker.

Varga, Richard S. Functional Analysis & Approximation Theory in Numerical Analysis. (CBMS-NSF Regional Conference Ser.: No. 3). v, 76p. (Orig.). 1971. pap. text ed. 8.00 (ISBN 0-89871-003-0). Soc Indus-Appl Math.

Von Neumann, J. Functional Operators, Vol. 2, Geometry Of Orthogonal Spaces. (Annals of Mathematics Studies). Repr. of 1950 ed. 11.00 (ISBN 0-527-02738-3). Kraus Repr.

Von Neumann, John. Functional Operators: Measures & Integrals. (Annals of Mathematics Studies: No. 21). (Orig.). 1950. pap. 27.00 (ISBN 0-691-07966-8). Princeton U Pr.

Voronovskaja, E. V. Functional Method & Its Applications. LC 70-138816. (Translations of Mathematical Monographs: Vol. 28). 1970. 39.00 (ISBN 0-8218-1578-4, MMONO-28). Am Math.

Wilansky, A. Summability Through Functional Analysis. (Mathematics Studies: Vol. 85). 1984. 42.50 (ISBN 0-444-86840-2, I-550-83, North-Holland). Elsevier.

--Topics in Functional Analysis. (Lecture Notes in Mathematics: Vol. 45). 1967. pap. 10.70 (ISBN 0-387-03916-3). Springer-Verlag.

Wilde, Carroll O., ed. Functional Analysis: Proceedings. 1970. 42.50 (ISBN 0-12-751750-2). Acad Pr.

Wong, Y. C. The Topology of Uniform Convergence on Order-Bounded Sets. (Lecture Notes in Mathematics: Vol. 531). 1976. pap. 13.00 (ISBN 0-387-07800-2). Springer-Verlag.

Wouk, A. A Course of Applied Functional Analysis. LC 78-15026. (Pure & Applied Mathematics Ser.). 443p. 1979. 53.50x (ISBN 0-471-96238-4, Pub. by Wiley-Interscience). Wiley.

Wright, Charles. Constructions of Deviance in Sociological Theory: The Problem of Commensurability. LC 84-7501. 224p. (Orig.). 1984. lib. bdg. 22.50 (ISBN 0-8191-3993-9); pap. text ed. 12.50 (ISBN 0-8191-3994-7). U Pr of Amer.

Zapata, G. I. Functional Analysis, Holomorphy & Approximation Theory, Vol. II. (Mathematics Studies: Vol. 86). 1984. 57.75 (ISBN 0-444-86845-3, North-Holland). Elsevier.

Zeidler, E. Nonlinear Functional Analysis & Its Applications III: Variational Methods & Optimization. Boron, L. L., tr. from German. (Illus.). 600p. 1985. 59.00 (ISBN 0-387-90915-X). Springer-Verlag.

Zemanian, A. H. Realizability Theory for Continuous Linear Systems. (Mathematics in Science & Engineering Ser.: Vol. 97). 1972. 60.00 (ISBN 0-12-779550-2). Acad Pr.

FUNCTIONAL CALCULUS

see Functional Analysis

FUNCTIONAL EQUATIONS

see also Differential-Difference Equations; Functional Analysis; Functional Equations; Integral Equations; Invariant Imbedding; Programming (Mathematics)

Aczel, J. Lectures on Functional Equations & Their Applications. (Mathematics in Science & Engineering). 1966. 82.00 (ISBN 0-12-043750-3). Acad Pr.

--On Applications & Theory of Functional Equations. 1969. 22.50 (ISBN 0-12-043756-2). Acad Pr.

Aczel, J., ed. Functional Equations: History, Applications & Theory. 1984. lib. bdg. 47.50 (ISBN 90-277-1706-0, Pub. by Reidel Holland). Kluwer Academic.

Golubitsky, M. & Guillemin, V. W. Stable Mappings & Their Singularities: Second Corrected Printing. (Graduate Texts in Mathematics: Vol. 14). (Illus.). 209p. 1974. 29.50 (ISBN 0-387-90072-1). Springer-Verlag.

Hale, Jack & Meyer, K. R. Class of Functional Equations of Neutral Type. LC 52-42839. (Memoirs: No. 76). 65p. 1967. pap. 9.00 (ISBN 0-8218-1276-9, MEMO-76). Am Math.

Japan - United States Seminar on Ordinary Differential & Functional Equations, Kyoto, 1971. Proceedings. Urabe, M., ed. (Lecture Notes in Mathematics: Vol. 243). viii, 332p. 1971. pap. 13.00 (ISBN 0-387-05708-0). Springer-Verlag.

Langlands, R. P. On the Functional Equations Satisfied by Eisenstein Series. (Lecture Notes in Mathematics: Vol. 544). 1976. soft cover 21.00 (ISBN 0-387-07872-X). Springer-Verlag.

Prouse, G. & Amerio, L. Almost-Periodic Functions & Functional Equations. LC 72-112713. viii, 183p. 1971. 24.00 (ISBN 0-387-90119-1). Springer-Verlag.

Salamon, D. Control & Observation of Neutral Systems. (Research Notes in Mathematics: No. 91). 220p. 1984. pap. text ed. 19.95 (ISBN 0-273-08618-9). Pitman Pub MA.

Schmitt, Klaus, ed. Delay & Functional Differential Equations & Their Applications. 1972. 77.50 (ISBN 0-12-627250-6). Acad Pr.

Truesdell, Clifford A. Unified Theory of Special Functions. (Annals of Math Studies). 1948. 15.00 (ISBN 0-527-02734-0). Kraus Repr.

Warga, J. Optimal Control of Differential & Functional Equations. 1972. 77.00 (ISBN 0-12-735150-7). Acad Pr.

FUNCTIONALS

see Functional Analysis

FUNCTIONS

see also Asymptotic Expansions; Calculus; Cluster Set Theory; Convergence; Distributions, Theory of (Functional Analysis); Riemann Surfaces

Abel, Niels H. Oeuvres Completes, 2 vols in 1. Sylow, L. & Lie, S., eds. Set. 65.00 (ISBN 0-384-00103-3). Johnson Repr.

Abramowitz, M. & Stegun, I. A. Pocketbook of Mathematical Functions. 468p. (Orig.). 1984. pap. 15.00 (ISBN 0-317-14892-3, Pub. by Verlagharri-Deutsch W Germany). Heyden.

Abramowitz, Milton & Stegun, Irene A., eds. Handbook of Mathematical Functions with Formulas, Graphs & Mathematical Tables. (Illus.). 1964. pap. 19.95 (ISBN 0-486-61272-4). Dover.

Ahiezer, N. I., et al. Fifteen Papers on Real & Complex Functions, Series, Differential & Integral Equations. LC 51-5559. (Translations Ser.: No. 2, Vol. 86). 1970. 34.00 (ISBN 0-8218-1786-8, TRANS 2-86). Am Math.

Aleksandrov, A. D., et al. Eleven Papers on Topology, Function Theory, & Differential Equations. LC 51-5559. (Translations Ser.: No. 2, Vol. 1). 1955. 26.00 (ISBN 0-8218-1701-9, TRANS 2-1). Am Math.

Allendoerfer, Carl B., et al. Elementary Functions. 1976. text ed. 27.95 (ISBN 0-07-001371-3). McGraw.

Andreev, A. E., et al. Twelve Papers on Function Theory, Probability, & Differential Equations. LC 51-5559. (Translations Ser.: No. 2, Vol. 8). 1957. 43.00 (ISBN 0-8218-1708-6, TRANS 2-8). Am Math.

Arson, I. S., et al. Eighteen Papers on Logic & Theory of Functions. LC 51-5559. (Translations Ser.: No. 2, Vol. 83). 1969. 33.00 (ISBN 0-8218-1783-3, TRANS 2-83). Am Math.

Babenko, K. I. On the Theory of Extremal Problems for Univalent Functions of Class S. (Proceedings of the Steklov Institute of Mathematics: No. 101). 1974. 90.00 (ISBN 0-8218-3001-5, STEKLO-101). Am Math.

Beckenbach, Edwin & Grady, Mike. Functions & Graphs. 3rd ed. 592p. 1982. text ed. write for info. (ISBN 0-534-01180-2). Wadsworth Pub.

Bieberach, Ludwig, tr. Lehrbuch der Funktionentheorie, 2 Vols. (Bibliotheca Mathematica Teubneriana Ser: Nos. 21, 22). Repr. of 1921 ed. Set. 50.00 (ISBN 0-384-04244-9). Johnson Repr.

Bohr, Harald. Almost Periodic Functions. LC 47-5500. 1980. 7.95 (ISBN 0-8284-0027-X). Chelsea Pub.

Bonar, D. D. On Annular Functions. (Math. Forschungsberichte, No.24). (Illus.). 1971. pap. 15.00x (ISBN 0-685-37412-2). Adlers Foreign Bks.

Bruckner, A. M. Differentiation of Real Functions. (Lecture Notes in Mathematics: Vol. 659). 1978. pap. 17.00 (ISBN 0-387-08910-1). Springer-Verlag.

Buckley, A. G. & Goffin, J. L. Algorithms for Constrained Minimumization of Smooth Nonlinear Functions. (Mathematical Programming Studies: Vol. 16). 190p. 1982. Repr. 25.75 (ISBN 0-444-86390-7, North-Holland). Elsevier.

Butkovskiy, A. G. Green's Functions & Transfer Functions Handbook. (Mathematics & Its Applications Ser.). 260p. 1982. 74.95 (ISBN 0-470-27344-5). Halsted Pr.

Cameron, R. H. & Storvick, D. A. A Simple Definition of the Feynman Integral, with Applications. LC 83-15605. (Memoirs Ser.: No. 288). 48p. 1983. paper 9.00 (ISBN 0-8218-2288-8). Am Math.

Caratheodory, Constantin. Vorlesungen Ueber Reelle Funktionen. 3rd ed. LC 63-11321. (Ger). 1968. 17.95 (ISBN 0-8284-0038-5). Chelsea Pub.

Carter, David S. & Vogt, Andrew. Collinearity-Preserving Functions Between Affine Desarguesian Planes. LC 80-20427. (Memoirs: No. 235). 98p. 1980. pap. 9.00 (ISBN 0-8218-2235-7). Am Math.

Cernikov, S. N., et al. Twelve Papers on Algebra & Real Functions. LC 51-5559. (Translations Ser.: No. 2, Vol. 17). 1961. 30.00 (ISBN 0-8218-1717-5, TRANS 2-17). Am Math.

Chandrasekharan, K. Arithmetical Functions. LC 72-102384. (Die Grundlehren der Mathematischen Wissenschaften: Vol. 167). (Illus.). 1971. 39.00 (ISBN 0-387-05114-7). Springer-Verlag.

Christy, Dennis T. Elementary Functions. (Illus.). 1978. text ed. 23.50 scp (ISBN 0-06-041297-6, HarpC); avail. answers to even number excercises (ISBN 0-06-361191-0). Har-Row.

Church, Alonzo. Calculi of Lambda Conversion. (Annals of Math). 1941. pap. 10.00 (ISBN 0-527-02722-7). Kraus Repr.

Cohn, L. Analytic Theory of the Harishchandra C-Function. LC 74-23331. (Lecture Notes in Mathematics Ser.: Vol. 429). 167p. 1974. pap. 13.00 (ISBN 0-387-07017-6). Springer-Verlag.

Conway, J. B. Functions of One Complex Variable. 2nd ed. (Graduate Texts in Mathematics Ser.: Vol. 11). (Illus.). 1978. 29.80 (ISBN 0-387-90328-3). Springer-Verlag.

Davis, Harold T. & Fisher, Vera. Tables of Mathematical Functions, Vol. 3. 1962. 8.75 (ISBN 0-911536-17-5). Trinity U Pr.

De Koninck & Ivic. Topics in Arithmetical Functions. (Mathematics Studies Ser.: Vol. 43). 262p. 1980. 47.00 (ISBN 0-444-86049-5, North Holland). Elsevier.

Duren, P. L. Univalent Functions. (Grundlehern der Mathematischen Wissenschaften Ser.: Vol. 259). (Illus.). 382p. 1983. 48.00 (ISBN 0-387-90795-5). Springer-Verlag.

FUNCTIONS (FUNCTIONAL ANALYSIS)
see Distributions, Theory of (Functional Analysis)

FUNCTIONS, ABELIAN
see also Geometry, Algebraic

FUNCTIONS, ALGEBRAIC

FUNCTIONS, ALMOST PERIODIC
see Almost Periodic Functions

FUNCTIONS, ANALYTIC
see Analytic Functions

FUNCTIONS, AUTOMORPHIC

FUNCTIONS, BESSELIAN
see Bessel's Functions

FUNCTIONS, BETA

Hamilton-Miller, J. M. T. & Smith, J. T., eds. Beta Lactamases. 1979. 76.50 (ISBN 0-12-321550-1). Acad Pr.

Pearson, K. Tables of the Incomplete Beta-Function. 505p. 1968. 60.00x (ISBN 0-85264-704-2, Pub. by England Griffin). State Mutual Bk.

Pearson, Karl. Tables of the Incomplete Beta Function. 205p. 1968. lib. bdg. 35.95x (ISBN 0-521-05922-4). Lubrecht & Cramer.

FUNCTIONS, CHEBYSHEV'S

see Chebyshev Polynomials

FUNCTIONS, CIRCULAR

see Trigonometrical Functions

FUNCTIONS, CONTINUOUS

Burckel, R. B. Characterization of C(X) Among Its Subalgebras. (Lecture Notes in Pure & Applied Mathematics Ser: Vol. 6). 176p. 1972. 35.00 (ISBN 0-8247-6038-7). Dekker.

De Vore, R. A. The Approximation of Continuous Functions by Positive Linear Operators. LC 72-91891. (Lecture Notes in Mathematics: Vol. 293). viii, 289p. 1972. pap. 13.00 (ISBN 0-387-06038-3). Springer-Verlag.

Mandelkern, Mark. Constructive Continuity. LC 82-24358. (Memoirs of the American Mathematical Society: MEMO No. 277). 122p. 1983. pap. 10.00 (ISBN 0-8218-2277-2). Am Math.

Owen, T. C. Characterization of Organic Compounds by Chemical Methods: An Introductory Laboratory Textbook. 256p. 1969. 22.75 (ISBN 0-8247-1510-1). Dekker.

Semadeni, Z. Schauder Bases in Banach Spaces of Continuous Functions. (Lecture Notes in Mathematics Ser.: Vol. 918). 136p. 1982. pap. 12.00 (ISBN 0-387-11481-5). Springer-Verlag.

Zalcman, L. Analytic Capacity & Rational Approximation. LC 68-19414. (Lecture Notes in Mathematics: Vol. 50). (Orig.). 1968. pap. 10.70 (ISBN 0-387-04220-2). Springer-Verlag.

FUNCTIONS, COULOMB

see Coulomb Functions

FUNCTIONS, ELLIPTIC

see also Functions, Modular; Functions of Complex Variables

Birkhoff, Garrett & Scheonstadt, Arthur. Elliptic Problem Solvers, No. II: Symposium. 1984. 44.00 (ISBN 0-12-100560-7). Acad Pr.

Byrd, P. F. & Friedman, M. D. Handbook of Elliptic Integrals for Engineers & Scientists. 2nd ed. LC 72-146515. (Die Grundlehren der Mathematischen Wissenschaften: Vol. 67). (Illus.). 1971. 42.00 (ISBN 0-387-05318-2). Springer-Verlag.

Chandrasekharan, K. Elliptic Functions. (Grundlehren der Mathematischen Wissenschaften: Vol. 281). (Illus.). 190p. 1985. 48.00 (ISBN 0-387-15295-4). Springer Verlag.

Ciarlet, P. G. The Finite Element Method for Elliptic Problems. (Studies in Mathematics & Its Applications: Vol. 4). 530p. 1978. 85.00 (ISBN 0-444-85028-7, North-Holland); pap. 36.25 (ISBN 0-444-86016-9). Elsevier.

Fricke, Robert. Die Elliptischen Funktionen und Ihre Anwendungen, 2 Vols. LC 5-33590. 1971. Repr. of 1922 ed. Set. 95.00 (ISBN 0-384-16860-4). Johnson Repr.

Gilbert, Robert P. & Buchanan, James. First-Order Elliptic Systems: A Functional Theoretic Approach. 1983. 49.50 (ISBN 0-12-283280-9). Acad Pr.

Grisvard, P. Elliptic Problems in Nonsmooth Domains. (Monographs & Studies in Mathematics: No. 24). 384p. 1985. text ed. 49.95 (ISBN 0-273-08647-2). Pitman Pub MA.

Ivanov. Quasilinear Degenerate & Nonuniformly Elliptic & Parabolic Equations of Second Order. (Proceedings of the Steklov Institute of Mathematics). 1983. write for info (ISBN 0-8218-3080-5). Am Math.

Katz, Nicholas & Mazur, Barry. Arithmetic Moduli of Elliptic Curves. LC 83-43079. (Annals of Mathematics Studies: No. 108). 700p. 1984. 60.00x (ISBN 0-691-08349-5); pap. 22.50x (ISBN 0-691-08352-5). Princeton U Pr.

Lang, S. Elliptic Curves: Diophantine Analysis. LC 77-21139. (Grundlehren der Mathematischen Wissenschaften: Vol 231). 1978. 45.00 (ISBN 0-387-08489-4). Springer-Verlag.

Masser, D. W. Elliptic Functions & Transcendence. (Lecture Notes in Mathematics: Vol. 437). xiv, 143p. 1975. pap. 13.00 (ISBN 0-387-07136-9). Springer-Verlag.

Rice, J. & Boisvert, R. F. Solving Elliptic Problems Using ELLPACK. (Springer Series in Computational Mathematics: Vol. 2). (Illus.). 350p. 1985. 39.00 (ISBN 0-387-90910-9). Springer Verlag.

Schoeneberg, B. Elliptic Modular Functions: An Introduction. Smart, J. R. & Schwandt, E., trs. from Ger. LC 73-8486. (Grundlehren der Mathematischen Wissenschaften: Vol. 203). (Illus.). 233p. 1974. 42.00 (ISBN 0-387-06382-X). Springer-Verlag.

Tannery, Jules & Molk, Jules. Elements de la Theorie des Fonctions Elliptiques, 4 vols. in 2. 2nd ed. LC 70-113152. (Fr.). 1145p. 1972. Set. text ed. 49.50 (ISBN 0-8284-0257-4). Chelsea Pub.

Weber, Heinrich. Lehrbuch der Algebra, Vols. 1, 2, & 3. 3rd ed. LC 61-6890. 1979. Repr. of 1962 ed. Set. text ed. 95.00 (ISBN 0-8284-0144-6). Chelsea Pub.

Weil, A. Elliptic Functions According to Eisenstein & Kronecker. LC 75-23200. (Ergebnisse der Mathematik und Ihrer Grenzgebiete: Vol. 88). 105p. 1976. 26.00 (ISBN 0-387-07422-8). Springer-Verlag.

Wendland, W. L. Elliptic Systems in the Plane. (Monographs & Studies Ser.: No. 3). 404p. 1979. text ed. 77.95 (ISBN 0-273-01013-1). Pitman Pub MA.

FUNCTIONS, ENTIRE

see also Value Distribution Theory

Boas, Ralph P., Jr. Entire Functions. (Pure & Applied Mathematics Ser.: Vol. 5). 1954. 59.50 (ISBN 0-12-108150-8). Acad Pr.

Daniljuk, I. I., ed. On Integral Functionals with Variable Domain of Integration. (Proceedings of the Steklov Institute of Mathematics: No. 118). 1976. 39.00 (ISBN 0-8218-3018-X, STEKLO-118). Am Math.

Evgrafov, M. A. Asymptotic Estimates & Entire Functions. (Russian Tracts on the Physical Sciences Ser.). (Illus.). 192p. 1962. 49.95 (ISBN 0-677-20070-6). Gordon.

Holland, A. S. Introduction to the Theory of Entire Functions. (Pure & Applied Mathematics Ser.). 1973. 59.00 (ISBN 0-12-352750-3). Acad Pr.

Levin, Boris J. Distribution of Zeros of Entire Functions. rev. ed. LC 80-36891. (Translations of Mathematical Monographs: Vol. 5). 524p. 1980. pap. 50.00 (ISBN 0-8218-4505-5, MMONO-5). Am Math.

Novikov, S. P., et al. Integrable Systems: Selected Papers. LC 81-6093. (London Mathematical Society Lecture Note Ser.: No. 60). 272p. 1981. pap. 32.50 (ISBN 0-521-28527-5). Cambridge U Pr.

Ronkin, L. I. Introduction to the Theory of Entire Functions of Several Variables. LC 74-12068. (Translations of Mathematical Monographs: Vol. 44). 1974. 59.00 (ISBN 0-8218-1594-6, MMONO-44). Am Math.

Stoll, Wilhelm. Holomorphic Functions of Finite Order in Several Variables. LC 74-8213. (CBMS Regional Conference Series in Mathematics: No. 21). 82p. 1974. pap. 12.00 (ISBN 0-8218-1671-3, CBMS-21). Am Math.

Symposium in Pure Mathematics - San Diego - 1966. Entire Functions & Related Parts of Analysis. Chern, S. S., et al, eds. LC 68-10458. (Proceedings of Symposia in Pure Mathematics: Vol. 11). 1968. 38.00 (ISBN 0-8218-1411-7, PSPUM-11). Am Math.

FUNCTIONS, ERROR

see Error Functions

FUNCTIONS, EXPONENTIAL

Britton, W. Conjugate Duality & the Exponential Fourier Spectrum. (Lecture Notes in Statistics: Vol. 18). (Illus.). 226p. 1983. pap. 18.00 (ISBN 0-387-90826-9). Springer-Verlag.

Exponents, Roots, & Polynomials: Level Three Texts. rev. ed. (Math Components Ser.). 64p. 1983. 3.00 (ISBN 0-88336-833-1). New Readers.

Jeffrey, Alan. Quasilinear Hyperbolic Systems & Waves. (Research Notes in Mathematics Ser.: No. 5). 203p. (Orig.). 1976. pap. text ed. 22.95 (ISBN 0-273-00102-7). Pitman Pub MA.

Levinson, Norman. Gap & Density Theorems. LC 41-6147. (Colloquium, Pbns. Ser.: Vol. 26). 246p. 1963. Repr. of 1940 ed. 23.00 (ISBN 0-8218-1026-X, COLL-26). Am Math.

Paley, Raymond E. & Wiener, Norbert. Fourier Transforms in the Complex Domain. LC 35-3273. (Colloquium, Pbns. Ser.: Vol. 19). 183p. 1982. pap. 33.00 (ISBN 0-8218-1019-7, COLL-19). Am Math.

Shiffer, M. M. & Bowden, Leon. The Role of Mathematics in Science. (New Mathematical Library: No. 30). 150p. 1984. pap. 0.14.00 (ISBN 0-88385-630-1). Math Assn.

FUNCTIONS, GAMMA

Nielsen, Niels. Die Gammafunktion, 2 vols. in 1. Incl. Integrallogarithmus. LC 64-13785. (Ger.). 1965. 19.50 (ISBN 0-8284-0188-8). Chelsea Pub.

Pearson, K. Tables of the Incomplete Gamma-Function. 164p. 1965. 30.00x (ISBN 0-85264-703-4, Pub. by Griffin England). State Mutual Bk.

Pearson, Karl. Tables of the Incomplete Gamma Function. 164p. 1965. lib. bdg. 17.50x (ISBN 0-521-05924-0). Lubrecht & Cramer.

FUNCTIONS, GENERALIZED

see Distributions, Theory of (Functional Analysis)

FUNCTIONS, GREEN'S

see Green's Functions

FUNCTIONS, HARMONIC

see Harmonic Functions

FUNCTIONS, HOLOMORPHIC

see Analytic Functions

FUNCTIONS, HYPERBOLIC

see Functions, Exponential

FUNCTIONS, HYPERGEOMETRIC

see also Weber Functions

Buchholz, H. Confluent Hypergeometric Function with Special Emphasis on Its Applications. Lichtblau, H. & Wetzel, K., trs. LC 69-16291. (Springer Tracts in Natural Philosophy: Vol. 15). 1969. 42.00 (ISBN 0-387-04715-8). Springer-Verlag.

Erdelyi, Arthur & Swanson, Charles A. Asymptotic Forms of Whittaker's Confluent Hypergeometric Functions. (Memoirs: No. 25). 49p. 1967. pap. 9.00 (ISBN 0-8218-1225-4, MEMO-25). Am Math.

Exton, H. Q Hypergeometric Functions & Applications. (Mathematics & its Applications). 355p. 1983. 53.95x (ISBN 0-470-27453-0). Halsted Pr.

Exton, Harold. Handbook of Hypergeometric Integrals: Theory, Applications, Tables, Computer Programs. LC 78-40120. (Mathematics & Its Applications Ser.). 316p. 1978. 79.95x (ISBN 0-470-26342-3). Halsted Pr.

--Multiple Hypergeometric Functions & Applications. LC 76-20720. (Mathematics & It's Applications Ser.). 312p. 1977. 56.95x (ISBN 0-470-15190-0). Halsted Pr.

Lieberman, Gerald J. & Owen, Donald B. Tables of the Hypergeometric Probability Distribution. 1961. 45.00x (ISBN 0-8047-0057-5). Stanford U Pr.

Mathai, A. M. & Saxena, R. K. Generalized Hypergeometric Functions with Applications in Statistics & Physical Sciences. LC 73-13489. (Lecture Notes in Mathematics: Vol. 348). 1973. pap. 19.00 (ISBN 0-387-06482-6). Springer-Verlag.

Slater, Lucy J. Confluent Hypergeometric Functions. LC 60-4198. pap. 64.80 (ISBN 0-317-08557-3, 2051427). Bks Demand UMI.

--Generalized Hypergeometric Functions. LC 66-10050. pap. 71.80 (ISBN 0-317-11003-9, 2051492). Bks Demand UMI.

FUNCTIONS, INTEGRAL

see Functions, Entire

FUNCTIONS, INVERSE

McLaughlin, D. W., ed. Inverse Problems: SIAM-AMS Proceedings. LC 84-392. (S I A M-A M S Proceedings: Vol. 14). 192p. 1984. 33.00 (ISBN 0-8218-1334-X). Am Math.

Nashed, M. Z., ed. Recent Applications of Generalized Inverses. (Research Notes in Mathematics Ser.: No. 23). (Illus.). pap. cancelled (ISBN 0-685-96564-3, Pub. by Pitman Bks Ltd UK). Pitman Pub MA.

Sabatier, P. C., ed. Applied Inverse Problems: Lectures Presented at the RCP 264 in Montpellier. (Lecture Notes in Physics: Vol. 85). 1978. pap. 27.00 (ISBN 0-387-09094-0). Springer-Verlag.

Smith, C. Ray & Grandy, W. T., Jr., eds. Maximum-Entropy & Bayesian Methods in Inverse Problems. 1985. lib. bdg. 44.50 (ISBN 90-277-2074-6, Pub. by Reidel Holland). Kluwer Academic.

FUNCTIONS, LAME'S

see Lame's Functions

FUNCTIONS, LIAPUNOV

see Liapunov Functions

FUNCTIONS, MATHIEU

see Mathieu Functions

FUNCTIONS, MEROMORPHIC

see also Value Distribution Theory

Andreotti, A. & Stoll, W. Analytic & Algebraic Dependence of Meromorphic Functions. (Lecture Notes in Mathematics: Vol. 234). iii, 390p. 1971. pap. 13.00 (ISBN 0-387-05670-X). Springer-Verlag.

McDonald, Alvis E. A Multiplicity-Independent, Global Iteration for Meromorphic Functions. LC 75-130610. 116p. 1969. 19.00 (ISBN 0-403-04516-9). Scholarly.

Namba, M. Families of Meromorphic Functions on Compact Riemann Surfaces. (Lecture Notes in Mathematics: Vol. 767). 284p. 1979. pap. 20.00 (ISBN 0-387-09722-8). Springer-Verlag.

Weyl, Hermann. Meromorphic Functions & Analytic Curves. (Annals of Math Studies). 1943. 19.00 (ISBN 0-527-02728-6). Kraus Repr.

Wu, Hung-Hsi. Equidistribution Theory of Holomorphic Curves. LC 78-100997. (Annals of Mathematics Studies: No. 64). 1970. 23.00 (ISBN 0-691-08073-9). Princeton U Pr.

FUNCTIONS, MODULAR

Gunning, Robert C. Lectures on Modular Forms. (Annals of Mathematics Studies: No. 48). (Orig.). 1963. pap. 13.50 (ISBN 0-691-07995-1). Princeton U Pr.

International Summer School, Univ. of Antwerp, RUCA, July-Aug., 1972. Modular Functions of One Variable Four: Proceedings. Birch, B. J. & Kuyk, W., eds. (Lecture Notes in Mathematics: Vol. 476). v, 151p. (Orig.). 1975. pap. text ed. 14.00 (ISBN 0-387-07392-2). Springer-Verlag.

Klein, Felix & Fricke, Robert. Vorlesungen Ueber Die Theorie der Elliptischen Modulfunktionen, 2 Vols. 1890-1892. 95.00 (ISBN 0-384-29734-X). Johnson Repr.

Narkiewicz, W. Uniform Distribution of Sequences of Integers in Residue Classes. (Lecture Notes in Mathematics Ser.: Vol. 1087). vii, 125p. 1984. pap. 10.00 (ISBN 0-387-13872-2). Springer-Verlag.

Rankin, R. A. Modular Forms. (Mathematics & Its Applications Ser.). 1985. 54.95 (ISBN 0-470-20099-5). Halsted Pr.

--Modular Forms & Functions. LC 76-11089. (Illus.). 1977. 85.00 (ISBN 0-521-21212-X). Cambridge U Pr.

Serre, J. P. & Zagier, D. B., eds. Modular Functions of One Variable 5: Proceedings. LC 77-22148. (Lecture Notes in Mathematics: Vol. 601). 1977. pap. text ed. 18.00 (ISBN 0-387-08348-0). Springer-Verlag.

Stratila, S. Modular Theory in Operator Algebras. 1981. 55.00 (ISBN 0-9961004-7-4, Pub. by Abacus England). Heyden.

FUNCTIONS, MONOGENIC

see Analytic Functions

FUNCTIONS, ORTHOGONAL

see also Orthogonal Polynomials; Series, Orthogonal

Dautov, Sh. A. & Aizenberg, L. A. Differential Forms Orthogonal to Holomorphic Functions or Forms, &Their Properties. (Translations of Mathematical Monographs: Vol. 56). 38.00 (ISBN 0-8218-4508-X). Am Math.

Eichler, Martin & Zagier, Don. The Theory of Jacobi Forms. (Progress in Mathematics Ser.: No. 55). 155p. 1985. text ed. write for info. (ISBN 0-8176-3180-1). Birkhauser.

Geramita & Seberry. Orthogonal Designs: Quad. Forms & Had. Matrices. (Lecture Notes in Pure & Applied Mathematics Ser.: Vol. 45). 1979. 65.00 (ISBN 0-8247-6774-8). Dekker.

Jackson, Dunham. Fourier Series & Orthogonal Polynomials. (Carus Monograph: No. 6). 234p. 1941. 19.00 (ISBN 0-88385-006-0). Math Assn.

Milin, Isaak M. Univalent Functions & Orthonormal Systems. LC 77-1198. (Translations of Mathematical Monographs: Vol. 49). 1977. 46.00 (ISBN 0-8218-1599-7, MMONO-49). Am Math.

Olevsky, A. M. Fourier Series with Respect to General Orthogonal Systems, Vol. 86. LC 74-32297. (Ergebnisse der Mathematik und Ihrer Grenzgebiete). 160p. 1975. 48.00 (ISBN 0-387-07103-2). Springer-Verlag.

Sansone, G., et al. Orthogonal Functions, Vol. 9. rev. ed. LC 75-11888. 424p. 1977. Repr. of 1959 ed. 23.50 (ISBN 0-88275-303-7). Krieger.

FUNCTIONS, PARABOLIC CYLINDER

see Weber Functions

FUNCTIONS, POTENTIAL

see Differential Equations, Partial; Harmonic Analysis; Potential, Theory Of; Spherical Harmonics

FUNCTIONS, RECURSIVE

see Recursive Functions

FUNCTIONS, REGULAR

see Analytic Functions

FUNCTIONS, SPECIAL

see also names of special functions, e.g. Functions, Orthogonal

Advanced Seminar, the University of Wisconsin, Madison, March-April, 1975. Theory & Application of Special Functions: Proceedings. Askey, Richard A., ed. (University of Wisconsin Mathematics Research Center Publications: No. 35). 1975. 29.50 (ISBN 0-12-064850-4). Acad Pr.

Askey, Richard. Orthogonal Polynomials & Special Functions. (CBMS-NSF Regional Conference Ser.: No. 21). vii, 110p. (Orig.). 1975. pap. text ed. 16.00 (ISBN 0-89871-018-9). Soc Indus-Appl Math.

Dieudonne, Jean. Special Functions & Linear Representations of Lie Groups. LC 79-22180. (CBMS Regional Conference Ser. in Mathematics: No. 42). 59p. 1982. pap. 11.00 (ISBN 0-8218-1692-6, CBMS-42). Am Math.

Feinsilver, P. J. Special Functions, Probability Semigroups, & Hamiltonian Flows. (Lecture Notes in Mathematics Ser.: Vol. 696). 1978. pap. 14.00 (ISBN 0-387-09100-9). Springer-Verlag.

Geronimus, Ja L. & Szego, Gabor. Two Papers on Special Functions. LC 76-30843. (Translations Ser. 2: Vol. 108). 1977. 34.00 (ISBN 0-8218-3058-9, TRANS2108). Am Math.

Higgins, J. R. Completeness & Basis Properties of Sets of Special Functions. LC 76-19630. (Cambridge Tracts in Mathematics Ser.: No. 72). (Illus.). 1977. 59.50 (ISBN 0-521-21376-2). Cambridge U Pr.

Lebedev, N. N. Special Functions & Their Applications. rev. ed. Silverman, Richard A., tr. from Rus. LC 72-86228. 320p. 1972. pap. 6.00 (ISBN 0-486-60624-4). Dover.

Luke, Yudell L. Special Functions & Their Approximations, 2 Vols. LC 68-23498. (Mathematics in Science & Engineering Ser.,: Vol. 53). 1969. Vol. 1. 70.00 (ISBN 0-12-459901-X); Vol. 2. 80.00 (ISBN 0-12-459902-8). Acad Pr.
McBride, E. B. Obtaining Generating Functions. LC 72-138811. (Springer Tracts in Natural Philosophy: Vol. 21). 1969. 34.00 (ISBN 0-387-05255-0). Springer-Verlag.
Olver, F. W. J. Asymptotics & Special Functions. (Computer Science & Applied Mathematics Ser.). 1974. 70.00 (ISBN 0-12-525850-X). Acad Pr.
Rainville, Earl D. Special Functions. LC 70-172380. (Illus.). xii, 365p. 1972. Repr. of 1960 ed. text ed. 15.95 (ISBN 0-8284-0258-2). Chelsea Pub.
Vilenkin, N. Ja. Special Functions & the Theory of Group Representations. Rev. ed. LC 68-19438. (Translations of Mathematical Monographs: Vol. 22). 613p. 1983. pap. 53.00 (ISBN 0-8218-1572-5, MMONO-22). Am Math.

FUNCTIONS, SPHEROIDAL
see also Mathieu Functions
Connett, W. C. & Schwartz, Alan Lee. The Theory of Ultraspherical Multipliers. LC 76-58958. (Memoirs: No. 183). 92p. 1977. pap. 13.00 (ISBN 0-8218-2183-0, MEMO-183). Am Math.
John, F. Plane Waves & Spherical Means Applied to Partial Differential Equations. (Illus.). 172p. 1981. pap. 23.00 (ISBN 0-387-90565-0). Springer-Verlag.
Meixner, J., et al. Mathieu Functions & Spheroidal Functions & Their Mathematical Foundations. (Lecture Notes in Mathematics Ser.: Vol. 837). 126p. 1980. pap. 12.00 (ISBN 0-387-10282-5). Springer-Verlag.

FUNCTIONS, SYMMETRIC
see Symmetric Functions

FUNCTIONS, THETA
Accola, R. D. Riemann Surfaces, Theta Functions, & Abelian Automorphisms Groups. LC 75-25928. (Lecture Notes in Mathematics: Vol. 483). iii, 105p. 1975. pap. text ed. 13.00 (ISBN 0-387-07398-1). Springer-Verlag.
Auslander, L. Lecture Notes on Nil-Theta Functions. LC 77-16471. (Conference Board of the Mathematical Sciences Ser.: No. 34). 96p. 1984. pap. 10.00 (ISBN 0-8218-1684-5, CBMS34). Am Math.
Gunning, R. C. Riemann Surfaces & Generalized Theta Functions. (Illus.). 1976. 31.00 (ISBN 0-387-07744-8). Springer-Verlag.
Hejhal, Dennis A. Theta Functions, Kernel Functions, & Abelian Integrals. LC 72-6824. (Memoirs: No. 129). 112p. 1972. pap. 10.00 (MEMO-129). Am Math.
Krazer, Adolph. Lehrbuch der Thetafunktionen. LC 75-113132. (Ger). 1970. Repr. of 1903 ed. 25.00 (ISBN 0-8284-0244-2). Chelsea Pub.
Lion, Gerard & Vergne, Michele, eds. The Weil Representation, Maslov Index & Theta Series. (Progress in Mathematics Ser.: No. 6). 346p. 1980. pap. text ed. 24.00x (ISBN 0-8176-3007-4). Birkhauser.
Mumford, David. Tata Lecture Notes on Theta Functions, 2 vols. (Progress in Mathematics Ser.: Vol.43). 1983. Vol. 1, 220pp. text ed. 20.00x (ISBN 0-8176-3109-7); Vol. 2, 200pp. text ed. 20.00 (ISBN 0-8176-3110-0). Birkhauser.

FUNCTIONS, TRANSCENDENTAL
see also names of specific transcendental functions, e.g. Bellel Functions; Functions, Gamma
Marichev, O. I. Handbook of Integral Transforms of Higher Transcendental Functions: Theory & Algorithmic Tables. LC 82-15849. (Mathematics & Its Applications Ser.). 336p. 1983. 81.95x (ISBN 0-470-27364-X). Halsted Pr.

FUNCTIONS, TRIGONOMETRICAL
see Trigonometrical Functions

FUNCTIONS, WEBER
see Weber Functions

FUNCTIONS, ZETA
Christian, U. Selberg's Zeta-, L-, & Eisensteinseries. (Lecture Notes in Mathematics: Vol. 1030). 196p. 1983. pap. 13.00 (ISBN 0-387-12701-1). Springer Verlag.
Edwards, Harold M. Riemann's Zeta Function. (Pure & Applied Mathematics: A Series of Monographs & Textbooks, Vol. 59). 1974. 55.00 (ISBN 0-12-232750-0). Acad Pr.
Godement, R. & Jacquet, H. Zeta-Functions of Simple Algebras. LC 72-76391. (Lecture Notes in Mathematics: Vol. 260). 197p. 1972. pap. 10.00 (ISBN 0-387-05797-8). Springer-Verlag.
Hunter, R. J. Zeta Potential in Colloid Science. LC 80-42268. 1981. 84.00 (ISBN 0-12-361960-2). Acad Pr.
Ivic, A. The Riemann Zeta-Function. (Pure & Applied Mathematics Ser.). 336p. 1985. 49.95 (ISBN 0-471-80634-X). Wiley.
Koblitz, N. P-Adic Numbers, P-Adic Analysis & Zeta Functions. 2nd ed. (Graduate Tests in Mathematics Ser.: Vol. 58). (Illus.). 288p. 1984. 28.00 (ISBN 0-387-96017-1). Springer-Verlag.
Thomas, A. D. Zeta-Functions: An Introduction to Algebraic Geometry. (Research Notes in Mathematics Ser.: No. 12). 230p. 1977. pap. text ed. 23.95 (ISBN 0-273-01038-7). Pitman Pub MA.

FUNCTIONS OF COMPLEX VARIABLES
see also Analytic Functions; Banach Spaces; Boundary Value Problems; Functions, Elliptic; Functions, Entire; Functions of Real Variables; Functions of Several Complex Variables; Global Analysis (Mathematics); Hardy Spaces
Abramov, L. M., et al. Fourteen Papers on Logic, Algebra, Complex Variables & Topology. LC 51-5559. (Translations Ser.: No. 2, Vol. 48). 1965. 32.00 (ISBN 0-8218-1748-5, TRANS 2-48). Am Math.
Adjan, S., et al. Eleven Papers on Number Theory, Algebra & Functions of a Complex Variable. LC 51-5559. (Translations, Ser.: No. 2, Vol. 46). 1965. 25.00 (ISBN 0-8218-1746-9, TRANS 2-46). Am Math.
Alenicyn, Ju. E., et al. Fifteen Papers on Series & Functions of Complex Variables. LC 51-5559. (Translations Ser.: No. 2, Vol. 43). 1964. 27.00 (ISBN 0-8218-1743-4, TRANS 2-43). Am Math.
Azarin, V. S., et al. Thirteen Papers on Functions of Real & Complex Variables. LC 51-5559. (Translations Ser.: No. 2, Vol. 80). 1969. 36.00 (ISBN 0-8218-1780-9, TRANS 2-80). Am Math.
Bazilevic, I. E., et al. Thirteen Papers on Algebra, Topology, Complex Variables, & Linear Programming. LC 51-5559. (Translations Ser.: No. 2, Vol. 71). 1968. 32.00 (ISBN 0-8218-1771-X, TRANS 2-71). Am Math.
Beardon, A. F. Complex Analysis: The Argument Principle in Analysis & Topology. LC 78-8540. 239p. 1979. 69.95x (ISBN 0-471-99671-8, Pub. by Wiley-Interscience). Wiley.
Bieberbach, Ludwig. Conformal Mapping. LC 53-7209. 6.95 (ISBN 0-8284-0090-3); pap. 2.95 o. p. (ISBN 0-8284-0176-4). Chelsea Pub.
Brannan, D. A. & Clunie, J. G., eds. Aspects of Contemporary Complex Analysis. LC 80-40887. 1981. 75.00 (ISBN 0-12-125950-1). Acad Pr.
Caratheodory, Constantin. Theory of Functions. 2nd ed. LC 60-16838. Vol. 1. 12.95 (ISBN 0-8284-0097-0); Vol. 2. 12.95 (ISBN 0-8284-0106-3). Chelsea Pub.
Carin, V. S., et al. Nine Papers on Foundations, Algebra, Topology, Functions of a Complex Variable. (Translations Ser.: No. 2, Vol. 15). 1960. 29.00 (ISBN 0-8218-1715-9, TRANS 2-15). Am Math.
Chevalley, Claude C. Introduction to the Theory of Algebraic Functions of One Variable. LC 51-4714. (Mathematical Surveys Ser.: No. 6). 188p. 1979. pap. 25.00 (ISBN 0-8218-1506-7, SURV-6). Am Math.
Complex Analysis & Its Application, 3 vols. Vol. 1. pap. 38.50 (ISBN 92-0-130376-9, ISP428-1, IAEA); Vol. 2. pap. 35.00 (ISBN 92-0-130476-5, ISP428-2); Vol. 3. pap. 35.00 (ISBN 92-0-130576-1, ISP428-3); pap. 108.50 (ISBN 0-685-79710-4). Unipub.
Conway, J. B. Functions of One Complex Variable. Halmos, P. R., ed. LC 72-96938. (Lecture Notes in Mathematics: Vol. 11). (Illus.). xiv, 314p. 1975. text ed. 10.70 (ISBN 0-387-07028-1). Springer-Verlag.
Dettman, John W. Applied Complex Variables. (Mathematics Ser.). 481p. 1984. pap. 10.00 (ISBN 0-486-64670-X). Dover.
Dzrbasjan, M. M., et al. Seventeen Papers on Functions of Complex Variables. LC 51-5559. (Translations Ser.: No. 2, Vol. 32). 1963. 32.00 (ISBN 0-8218-1732-9, TRANS 2-32). Am Math.
Funciones De Variable Compleja. rev. ed. (Serie De Matematica: No. 8). (Span.). 1973. pap. 3.50 (ISBN 0-8270-6260-5). OAS.
Gilbert, R. P. Function Theoretic Methods in Partial Differential Equations. (Mathematics in Science & Engineering Ser: Vol. 54). 1969. 75.00 (ISBN 0-12-283050-4). Acad Pr.
Goluzin, G. M. Geometric Theory of Functions of a Complex Variable. LC 70-82894. (Translations of Mathematical Monographs: Vol. 26). 676p. 1983. pap. 71.00 (ISBN 0-8218-1576-8, MONO-26). Am Math.
Hawkins, F. M. & Hawkins, J. Q. Complex Numbers & Elementary Complex Functions. 154p. 1970. 41.75 (ISBN 0-677-61110-2). Gordon.
Hromadka, T. V. The Complex Variable Boundary Element Method. (Lecture Notes in Engineering Ser.: Vol. 9). xi, 243p. 1984. pap. 15.50 (ISBN 0-387-13743-2). Springer-Verlag.
Kirwan, W. E. & Zalcman, L., eds. Advances in Complex Function Theory. LC 75-45187. (Lecture Notes in Mathematics Ser: Vol. 505). 1976. pap. 16.00 (ISBN 0-387-07548-8). Springer-Verlag.
Landkof, N. S. Foundations of Modern Potential Theory. Doohovskoy, A. P., tr. from Rus. LC 77-186131. (Grundlehren der Mathematischen Wissenschaften: Vol. 180). 440p. 1972. 58.00 (ISBN 0-387-05394-8). Springer-Verlag.
Levinson, Norman. Gap & Density Theorems. LC 41-6147. (Colloquium, Pbns. Ser.: Vol. 26). 246p. 1963. Repr. of 1940 ed. 23.00 (ISBN 0-8218-1026-X, COLL-26). Am Math.
Levinson, Norman & Redheffer, Raymond. Complex Variables. LC 76-113833. (Illus.). 1970. text ed. 37.00x (ISBN 0-8162-5104-5); sol. man. 6.00 (ISBN 0-8162-5114-2). Holden-Day.
Luecking, D. H. & Rubel, L. A. Complex Analysis: A Functional Analysis Approach. (Illus.). 180p. 1984. pap. 18.00 (ISBN 0-387-90993-1). Springer-Verlag.
Marden, Morris. Geometry of Polynomials. rev. ed. LC 49-48816. (Mathematical Surveys Ser.: Vol. 3). 1966. 35.00 (ISBN 0-8218-1503-2, SURV-3). Am Math.
Marsden, Jerrold E. Basic Complex Analysis. LC 72-89894. (Illus.). 472p. 1973. text ed. 29.95x (ISBN 0-7167-0451-X). W H Freeman.
Morse, Marston. Topological Methods in the Theory of Functions of a Complex Variable. 1947. 11.00 (ISBN 0-527-02731-6). Kraus Repr.
Paliouras, John D. Complex Variables for Scientists & Engineers. (Illus.). 416p. 1975. text ed. write for info. (ISBN 0-02-390550-6). Macmillan.
Polya, George, et al. Complex Variables. LC 73-14882. pap. 65.20 (ISBN 0-317-09340-1, 2055266). Bks Demand UMI.
Shankar, Hari, ed. Mathematical Essays Dedicated to A. J. MacIntyre. LC 68-20937. xvi, 377p. 1970. 22.50x (ISBN 0-8214-0061-4, 82-80679). Ohio U Pr.
Silverman, Richard A. Complex Analysis with Applications. 274p. 1984. pap. 6.50 (ISBN 0-486-64762-5). Dover.
Spiegel, Murray R. Complex Variables. (Orig.). 1964. pap. 9.95 (ISBN 0-07-060230-1). McGraw.
Steklov Institute of Mathematics, Academy of Sciences, U S S R, No. 94. External Problems of the Geometric Theory of Functions: Proceedings. Alenicyn, J. E., ed. (Proceedings of the Steklov Institute of Mathematics: No. 94). 1969. 44.00 (ISBN 0-8218-1894-5, STEKLO-94). Am Math.
Stolzenberg, G. Volumes, Limits & Extensions of Analytic Varieties. (Lecture Notes in Mathematics: Vol. 19). (Orig.). 1966. pap. 10.70 (ISBN 0-387-03602-4). Springer-Verlag.
Symposium in Pure Mathematics - San Diego - 1966. Entire Functions & Related Parts of Analysis. Chern, S. S., et al, eds. LC 68-10458. (Proceedings of Symposia in Pure Mathematics: Vol. 11). 1968. 38.00 (ISBN 0-8218-1411-7, PSPUM-11). Am Math.

FUNCTIONS OF REAL VARIABLES
see also Functions of Complex Variables
Alexandrov, Paul S. Introduction to the Theory of Sets & Functions. write for info. (ISBN 0-685-07980-5). Chelsea Pub.
Azarin, V. S., et al. Thirteen Papers on Functions of Real & Complex Variables. LC 51-5559. (Translations Ser.: No. 2, Vol. 80). 1969. 36.00 (ISBN 0-8218-1780-9, TRANS 2-80). Am Math.
Bernstein, Serge & Poussin, Charles D. Approximation, 2 Vols. in 1. LC 69-16996. (Fr). 15.95 (ISBN 0-8284-0198-5). Chelsea Pub.
Boas, Ralph P., Jr. A Primer of Real Functions. 3rd ed. LC 81-82669. (Carus Monograph: No. 13). 232p. 1981. 16.50 (ISBN 0-88385-022-2). Math Assn.
Fischer, E. Intermediate Real Analysis. (Undergraduate Texts in Mathematics Ser.). (Illus.). 770p. 1983. 32.00 (ISBN 0-387-90721-1). Springer-Verlag.
Fleming, W. H. Functions of Several Variables. 2nd ed. LC 76-40029. (Undergraduate Texts in Mathematics Ser.). (Illus.). 1977. Repr. 33.00 (ISBN 3-540-90206-6). Springer-Verlag.
Goldberg, Richard R. Methods of Real Analysis. 2nd ed. LC 75-30615. 402p. 1976. text ed. 41.00x (ISBN 0-471-31065-4). Wiley.
Golovkin, K. K., et al. Four Papers on Functions of Real Variables. LC 51-5559. (Translations Ser.: No. 2, Vol. 81). 1969. 36.00 (ISBN 0-8218-1781-7, TRANS 2-81). Am Math.
Handscomb, D. C., ed. Multivariate Approximation. 1979. 50.00 (ISBN 0-12-323350-X). Acad Pr.
Jeffery, R. L. The Theory of Functions of a Real Variable. (Mathematics Ser.). 256p. 1985. pap. 6.00 (ISBN 0-486-64781-1). Dover.
Karlin, Samuel. Total Positivity: Vol. 1. 1968. 35.00x (ISBN 0-8047-0314-0). Stanford U Pr.
Kolmogorov, A. N. & Fomin, S. V. Introductory Real Analysis. Silverman, Richard A., ed. & tr. from Rus. LC 74-18669. 416p. 1975. pap. 7.50 (ISBN 0-486-61226-0). Dover.
Natanson, I. P. Theory of Functions of a Real Variable, 2 vols. Boron, Leo F. & Hewitt, Edwin, eds. LC 61-14620. 278p. Vol. 1. 15.00 (ISBN 0-8044-4702-0). Ungar.
Olmsted, John M. Intermediate Analysis: An Introduction to Theory of Functions of One Real Variable. LC 56-5844. (Illus.). 1981. Repr. of 1956 ed. 29.50x (ISBN 0-89197-796-1). Irvington.
Shapiro, Victor L. Topics in Fourier & Geometric Analysis. LC 52-42839. (Memoirs: No. 39). 100p. 1968. pap. 10.00 (ISBN 0-8218-1239-4, MEMO-39). Am Math.
Spiegel, Murray R. Real Variables. 1969. pap. 9.95 (ISBN 0-07-060221-2). McGraw.
Stein, E. M. Singular Integrals & Differentiability Properties of Functions. (Mathematical Ser.: No. 30). 1971. 32.50x (ISBN 0-691-08079-8). Princeton U Pr.
Steklov Institute of Mathematics, Academy of Sciences, U S S R. Theory & Applications of Differentiable Functions of Several Variables: Proceedings. Nikol'skii, S. M., ed. (Proceedings of the Steklov Institute of Mathematics: No. 77). 1967. 46.00 (ISBN 0-8218-1877-5, STEKLO-77). Am Math.
--Theory & Applications of Differentiable Functions of Several Variables, 2: Proceedings. Nikol'skii, S. M., ed. (Proceedings of the Steklov Institute of Mathematics: No. 89). 1968. 67.00 (ISBN 0-8218-1889-9, STEKLO-89). Am Math.
Walsh, Thomas. On Summability Methods for Conjugate Fourier-Steiltjes Integrals in Several Variables & Generalizations. LC 73-2729. (Memoirs: No. 131). 103p. 1973. pap. 12.00 (ISBN 0-8218-1831-7, MEMO-131). Am Math.
Williamson, Richard, et al. Calculus of Vector Functions. 3rd ed. LC 75-167788. (Illus.). 576p. 1972. ref. ed. 41.95 (ISBN 0-13-112367-X). P-H.

FUNCTIONS OF SEVERAL COMPLEX VARIABLES
see also Analytic Continuation; Automorphic Forms
Amar, E., et al, eds. Analyse Complexe. (Lecture Notes in Mathematics Ser.: Vol. 1094). ix, 185p. 1984. pap. 12.00 (ISBN 0-387-13886-2). Springer-Verlag.
De Arrillano, E. Ramirez & Sundararaman, D. Topics in Several Complex Variables. (Research Notes in Mathematics Ser.: No. 112). 300p. 1985. pap. text ed. 18.95 (ISBN 0-273-08656-1). Pitman Pub MA.
Ehrenpreis, Leon. Fourier Analysis in Several Complex Variables. (Pure & Applied Mathematics Ser.). 506p. 1970. 64.95x (ISBN 0-471-23400-1, Pub. by Wiley-Interscience). Wiley.
Fuks, Boris A. Introduction to the Theory of Analytic Functions of Several Complex Variables. LC 63-15662. (Translations of Mathematical Monographs: Vol. 8). pap. 99.50 (ISBN 0-317-08581-6, 2012206). Bks Demand UMI.
Grauert, H. & Remmert, R. Theory of Stein Spaces. LC 79-1430. (Grundlehren der Mathematischen Wissenschaften: Vol. 236). (Illus.). 1979. 55.00 (ISBN 0-387-90388-7). Springer-Verlag.
Handscomb, D. C., ed. Multivariate Approximation. 1979. 50.00 (ISBN 0-12-323350-X). Acad Pr.
Henkin, Gennadi M. & Leiterer, Jurgen. Theory of Functions on Complex Manifolds. (Monographs in Mathematics). 240p. 1983. text ed. 29.95 (ISBN 3-7643-1477-X). Birkhauser.
International Mathematical Conference, College Park, 1970. Several Complex Variables 2: Proceedings. Horvath, J., ed. (Lecture Notes in Mathematics: Vol. 185). 1971. pap. 14.00 (ISBN 0-387-05372-7). Springer-Verlag.
Kujala, Robert O. & Vitter, Albert L., III, eds. Value Distribution Theory: Deficit & Bezout Estimates, Pt. B. (Pure & Applied Mathematics Ser.: Vol. 25). 288p. 1973. 45.00 (ISBN 0-8247-6125-1). Dekker.
Lelong, P. Fonctions Plurisousharmoniques et Formes Differentielles Positives. (Cours & Documents de Mathematiques & de Physique Ser.). 90p. 1968. 24.50x (ISBN 0-677-50220-6). Gordon.
--Plurisubharmonic Functions & Positive Differential Forms. (Notes on Mathematics & Its Applications Ser.). 88p. 1969. 24.50 (ISBN 0-677-30220-7). Gordon.
Malgrange, B. Lectures on the Theory of Functions of Several Complex Variables. (Tata Institute Lectures on Mathematics Ser.). iii, 132p. 1984. pap. 7.10 (ISBN 0-387-12875-1). Springer-Verlag.
Narasimhan, Raghavan. Several Complex Variables. LC 75-166949. (Chicago Lectures in Mathematics Ser). (Orig.). 1971. text ed. 7.00x (ISBN 0-226-56816-4). U of Chicago Pr.

Nikol'skii, S. M., ed. Theory & Applications of Differentiable Functions of Several Variables, 8: 1983, No.2. LC 68-1677. (Proceedings of the Steklov Institute of Mathematics: No. 156). 285p. 1983. pap. text ed. 86.00 (ISBN 0-8218-3017-1). Am Math.

Phillips, Edgar Giraldus. Functions of a Complex Variable: With Applications. (Longman Mathematical Texts Ser.). pap. 38.50 (ISBN 0-317-08527-1, 2013562). Bks Demand UMI.

Ronkin, L. I. Introduction to the Theory of Entire Functions of Several Variables. LC 74-12068. (Translations of Mathematical Monographs: Vol. 44). 1974. 59.00 (ISBN 0-8218-1594-6, MMONO-44). Am Math.

Wells, R. O., ed. Several Complex Variables: Proceedings, 2 pts. LC 77-23168. (Proceedings of Symposia in Pure Mathematics: Vol. 30). 1977. Set. 74.00 (ISBN 0-685-74775-1, PSPUM-30); Pt. 1. 42.00 (ISBN 0-8218-0249-6, PSPUM 30-1); Pt. 2. 42.00 (ISBN 0-8218-0250-X, PSPUM 30-2). Am Math.

Wermer, J. Banach Algebras & Several Complex Variables. (Graduate Texts in Mathematics Ser.: Vol. 35). 185p. 1976. 27.50 (ISBN 0-387-90160-4). Springer-Verlag.

FUNCTOR THEORY

see also Categories (Mathematics)

Arbib, Michael A. & Manes, Ernest G., eds. Arrows, Structures & Functors: The Categorical Imperative. 1975. 33.50 (ISBN 0-12-059060-3). Acad Pr.

Dubuc, E. J. Kan Extensions in Enriched Category Theory. LC 77-131542. (Lecture Notes in Mathematics: Vol. 145). 1970. pap. 11.00 (ISBN 0-387-04934-7). Springer-Verlag.

Kamps, K. H., et al, eds. Category Theory, Applications to Algebra, Logic, & Topology: Proceedings, Gummersbach, FRG, 1981. (Lecture Notes in Mathematics Ser.: Vol. 962). 322p. 1982. pap. 18.00 (ISBN 0-387-11961-2). Springer-Verlag.

Lane, S. Mac, ed. Coherence in Categories. LC 72-87920. (Lecture Notes in Mathematics: Vol. 281). vii, 235p. 1972. pap. 11.00 (ISBN 0-387-05963-6). Springer-Verlag.

Michor, P. W. Functors & Categories of Banach Spaces: Tensor Products, Operator Ideals & Functors on Categories of Banach Spaces. (Lecture Notes in Mathematics: Vol. 651). 1978. pap. 12.00 (ISBN 0-387-08764-8). Springer-Verlag.

Midwest Category Seminar, 1st. Reports. Benabou, J., et al, eds. (Lecture Notes in Mathematics: Vol. 47). (Orig.). 1967. pap. 10.70 (ISBN 0-387-03918-X). Springer-Verlag.

Moss, R. M. & Thomas, C. B. Algebraic K-Theory & Its Geometric Applications. LC 74-97991. (Lecture Notes in Mathematics Ser.). 1969. pap. 10.70 (ISBN 0-387-04627-5). Springer-Verlag.

Schubert, H. Categories. Gray, J., tr. from Ger. LC 72-83016. 390p. 1972. 48.00 (ISBN 0-387-05783-8). Springer-Verlag.

Sidney Category Theory Seminar, 1972-1973. Category Seminar: Proceedings. Kelly, G. M., ed. (Lecture Notes in Mathematics Ser.: Vol. 420). 650p. 1974. pap. 21.00 (ISBN 0-387-06966-6). Springer-Verlag.

FUNCTORIAL REPRESENTATION

see Functor Theory

FUNDULUS HETEROCLITUS

Pickford, Grace E., et al. Studies on the Blood Serum of the Euryhaline Cyprinodont Fish, Fundulus Heteroclitus, Adapted to Fresh or to Salt Water. (Transactions of the Connecticut Academy of Arts & Sciences Ser.: Vol. 43). 1969. pap. 10.50 (ISBN 0-208-00907-8). Shoe String.

FUNGAL GENETICS

see Fungi–Genetics

FUNGAL TOXINS

see Mycotoxins

FUNGI

see also Ascomycetes; Bacteriology; Basidiomycetes; Discomycetes; Gasteromycetes; Lichens; Molds (Botany); Mushrooms; Myxomycetes; Phycomycetes; Pyrenomycetes; Soil Micro-Organisms; Truffles; Thermophilic Fungi

Ainsworth & Bisby. Dictionary of the Fungi. 663p. 1971. 75.00x (ISBN 0-85198-075-9, Pub. by CAB Bks England). State Mutual Bk.

Ainsworth & Bisby's. Dictionary of the Fungi. 663p. 1978. 75.00 (ISBN 0-85198-075-9, M-9711). French & Eur.

Ainsworth, Geoffrey C. & Sussman, A. S., eds. Fungi: An Advanced Treatise, 4 vols. LC 65-15769. Vol. 2, 1966. 90.00 (ISBN 0-12-045602-8); Vol. 3, 1968. 90.00 (ISBN 0-12-045603-6); Vol. 4A, 1973. 75.00 (ISBN 0-12-045604-4); Vol. 4B, 1973. 70.00 (ISBN 0-12-045644-3). Acad Pr.

Alexopoulos, Constantine J. & Bold, Harold C. Algae & Fungi. 1967. pap. 12.95x (ISBN 0-02-301700-7, 30170). Macmillan.

Arx, J. A. von. Pilzkunde: Ein Kurzer Abriss der Mykologie Unter Besonderer Beruecksichtigung der Pilze in Reinkultur. 3rd ed. (Illus.). 1976. 10.50 (ISBN 3-7682-1067-7). Lubrecht & Cramer.

Baldwin, Richard S. The Fungus Fighters: Two Women Scientists & Their Discovery. (Illus.). 184p. 1981. 18.95x (ISBN 0-8014-1355-9). Cornell U Pr.

Bataille, F. Les Reactions Macrochimiques chez les Champignons Suives d'Indications sur la Morphologie des Spores. 1969. Repr. of 1948 ed. 14.00 (ISBN 3-7682-0654-8). Lubrecht & Cramer.

Batra, Lekh R., ed. Insect-Fungus Symbiosis: Nutrition, Mutualism & Commensalism. LC 78-20640. (Illus.). 276p. 1979. text ed. 44.95x (ISBN 0-470-26671-6). Halsted Pr.

Bennett & Ciegler. Secondary Metabolism & Differentiation in Fungi. (Mycology Ser.). 472p. 1983. 75.00 (ISBN 0-8247-1819-4). Dekker.

Berlese, A. N. Icones Fungorum Omnium Hucusque Cognitorum: Ad usum sylloges Saccardianae accomodatae, 4 vols. 1968. 126.00 (ISBN 3-7682-0575-4). Lubrecht & Cramer.

Bessey, Ernest A. Morphology & Taxonomy of Fungi. (Illus.). 1973. Repr. of 1950 ed. 21.95x (ISBN 0-02-841320-2). Hafner.

Bilgrami, K. S. & Jamaluddin, eds. Fungi of India: Host Index & Addenda. (Pt. II). 250p. 1981. 30.00 (ISBN 0-88065-060-5, Pub. by Messers Today & Tomorrows Printers & Publishers India). Scholarly Pubns.

--Fungi of India: List & References. (Pt. I). 466p. 1979. 50.00 (ISBN 0-88065-059-1, Pub. by Messers Today & Tomorrows Printers & Publishers India). Scholarly Pubns.

Brandenburger, W. Vademekum zum Sammeln Parasitischer Pilze. (Ger.). 1963. pap. 14.95 (ISBN 3-8001-3412-8, M-7136). French & Eur.

Brodie, H. J. The Bird's Nest Fungi. LC 75-18476. 1975. 25.00x (ISBN 0-8020-5307-6). U of Toronto Pr.

Burnett, J. H. & Trinci, A. P., eds. Fungal Walls & Hyphal Growth. LC 78-72082. (Illus.). 1980. 82.50 (ISBN 0-521-22499-3). Cambridge U Pr.

Coker, William C. The Club & Coral Mushrooms (Clavarias) of the United States & Canada. LC 74-82202. (Illus.). 320p. 1975. pap. 7.95 (ISBN 0-486-23101-1). Dover.

Cole, G. T. & Kendrick, B. Biology of Conidial Fungi, 2 vols. 1981. Vol. 1. 49.50 (ISBN 0-12-179501-2); Vol. 2. 69.50 (ISBN 0-12-179502-0); Set. 101.50. Acad Pr.

Cole, Garry T. & Samson, Robert A. Patterns of Development in Conidial Fungi. (Pitman International Ser. in Bioscience). 190p. 1979. text ed. 75.95 (ISBN 0-273-08407-0). Pitman Pub MA.

Cooke, W. Bridge. Ecology of Fungi. 288p. 1979. 84.50 (ISBN 0-8493-5343-2). CRC Pr.

Corda, A. C. Icones Fungorum Hucusque Cognitorum. 1963. 133.00 (ISBN 3-7682-7050-5). Lubrecht & Cramer.

Dermek, Aurel. Mushrooms & Other Fungi. (Illus.). 224p. 1985. 8.95 (ISBN 0-668-06304-1). Arco.

Dube, H. C. An Introduction to Fungi. 616p. 1983. text ed. 45.00x (ISBN 0-7069-1896-7, Pub. by Vikas India). Advent NY.

Fries, Elias M. Systema Mycologicum, Sistens Fungorum Ordines, Genera et Species, 6 vols. in 4. 160.00 (ISBN 0-384-16960-0). Johnson Repr.

Garraway, Michael O. & Evans, Robert C. Fungal Nutrition & Physiology. LC 83-23450. 401p. 1984. 44.95x (ISBN 0-471-05844-0, Pub. by Wiley-Interscience). Wiley.

Griffin, David H. Fungal Physiology. LC 81-3344. 383p. 1981. 37.50x (ISBN 0-471-05748-7). Wiley.

Grund, D. W. & Harrison, K. A. Nova Scotian Boletes. (Bibliotheca Mycologica Ser.: No. 47). 1976. text ed. 21.00 (ISBN 3-7682-1062-6). Lubrecht & Cramer.

Gupta, J. S. Textbook of Fungi. 305p. 1981. 60.00x (ISBN 0-686-84469-6, Pub. by Oxford & I B H India). State Mutual Bk.

Hawker, Lilian E. Physiology of Fungi. (Illus.). 1968. Repr. of 1950 ed. 28.00 (ISBN 3-7682-0530-4). Lubrecht & Cramer.

Heath, I. B., ed. Nuclear Division in the Fungi. 1978. 39.50 (ISBN 0-12-335950-3). Acad Pr.

Hoffman, P. Genetische Grundlagen der Artbildung in der Gattung Polyporus. (Bibliotheca Mycologica Ser.: No. 65). (Illus.). 1978. pap. text ed. 11.20x (ISBN 3-7682-1210-6). Lubrecht & Cramer.

Horak, E. Fungi Austroamericani. pap. 6.00 (ISBN 3-7682-0226-7). Lubrecht & Cramer.

Howard. Fungi Pathogenic for Humans & Animals, Vol. A. 672p. 1983. 85.00 (ISBN 0-8247-1875-5). Dekker.

--Fungi Pathogenic for Humans & Animals, Vol. B. 576p. 1983. 85.00 (ISBN 0-8247-1144-0). Dekker.

Ingold, Cecil T. Biology of Fungi. 3rd rev. ed. (Hutchinson Biology Monographs). (Illus., Orig.). 1973. pap. text ed. 11.00x (ISBN 0-09-105120-7, Hutchinson U Lib). Humanities.

International Congress of Botany, Edinburgh, 1964. Incompatability in Fungi: A Symposium. Raper, J. R. & Esser, K., eds. (Illus.). viii, 124p. 1965. pap. 32.00 (ISBN 0-387-03334-3). Springer Verlag.

Jennings, D. H. & Rayner, A. D., eds. The Ecology & Physiology of the Fungal Mycelium. (British Mycological Society Symposia Ser.: No. 8). (Illus.). 400p. 1984. 99.50 (ISBN 0-521-25413-2). Cambridge U Pr.

Karling, J. S. Chytridiomycetarum Iconographia: Illustrated & Descriptive Guide to the Chytridiomycetous Genera with a Suppl. of the Hyphochytriomycetes. (Illus.). 1978. lib. bdg. 70.00 (ISBN 3-7682-1111-8). Lubrecht & Cramer.

--The Simple Biflagellate Holocarpic Phycomycetes. 2nd ed. (Illus.). 1981. lib. bdg. 52.50x (ISBN 0-686-31663-0). Lubrecht & Cramer.

Kohlmeyer, J. Index Alphabecticus Klotzschii & Rabenhorstii Herbarii Mycologici. 1962. pap. 14.00 (ISBN 3-7682-5404-6). Lubrecht & Cramer.

Kohlmeyer, J. E. Icones Fungorum Maris, 7 parts. 1969. 70.00 (ISBN 3-7682-2000-1). Lubrecht & Cramer.

Kueck, H. U. Struktur und Funktionen Mitochondrialer dna Bei Pilzen. (No. 84, Bibliotheca Mycologica Ser.). (Ger., Illus.). 148p. pap. text ed. 14.70x (ISBN 3-7682-1323-4). Lubrecht & Cramer.

Lawrey, James D. & Hale, Mason. Biology of Lichenized Fungi. LC 84-9908. 416p. 1984. 39.95x (ISBN 0-03-060047-2). Praeger.

Marasas, W. F., et al. Toxigenic Fusarium Species: Identity & Mycotoxicology. LC 82-42779. 350p. 1984. 39.50x (ISBN 0-271-00348-0). Pa St U Pr.

Mehrotra, B. S. The Fungi. 1981. 17.00x (ISBN 0-686-76638-5, Pub. by Oxford & IBH India). State Mutual Bk.

Meinhardt, F. Untersuchungen Zur Genetik Des Fortpflanzungsverhaltens und der Fruchtkoerper- und Antibiotikabbildung Des Basidiomyceten Agrocybe Aegerita. (Bibliotheca Mycologica: No. 75). (Ger., Illus.). 128p. 1981. pap. text ed. 14.00x (ISBN 3-7682-1275-0). Lubrecht & Cramer.

Metlitsky, L. V. & Ozeretskovskaya, O. L. Plant Immunity. LC 68-25383. 114p. 1968. 29.50x (ISBN 0-306-30344-2, Plenum Pr). Plenum Pub.

Michael, E. Handbuch fuer Pilzfreunde: Volume 4: Blaetterilze-Dunkelblaettler. Kreisel, H, ed. (Illus.). 472p. text ed. 23.25 (ISBN 3-437-30349-X). Lubrecht & Cramer.

Moore-Landecker, Elizabeth. Fundamentals of the Fungi. 2nd ed. (Illus.). 544p. 1982. 43.95 (ISBN 0-13-339200-7). P-H.

Moser, M. Fungorum Rariorum Icones Coloratae, Part 7. (Illus.). 1979. pap. text ed. 14.00x (ISBN 3-7682-0413-8). Lubrecht & Cramer.

Nag Raj, T. R. & DiCosmo, F. A Monograph of Herknessia & Mastigospoella with Notes on Associated Teleomorphs. (Bibliotheca Mycologica Ser.: Vol. 80). (Illus.). 160p. 1981. text ed. 17.50x (ISBN 3-7682-1300-5). Lubrecht & Cramer.

Neuner, Andreas. Mushrooms & Fungi. LC 78-316610. (Nature Guides Ser.). (Illus.). 144p. 1979. pap. 5.95 (ISBN 0-7011-2328-1, Pub. by Chatto & Windus). Merrimack Pub Cir.

New York Botanical Garden. Mycologia Index: Volumes 1-58, 1909-1966. LC 57-51730. (Mycologia Ser.). 1968. 20.00x (ISBN 0-89327-215-9). NY Botanical.

Nilsson, S. T., ed. Atlas of Airborne Fungal Spores in Europe. (Illus.). 145p. 1983. 55.00 (ISBN 0-387-11900-0). Springer-Verlag.

Peberdy, et al. Fungal Protoplasts: Applications in Biochemistry & Genetics. (Mycology Ser.). 408p. 1985. 69.75 (ISBN 0-8247-7112-5). Dekker.

Persoon, Christiaan H. Synopsis Methodica Fungorum, 3 vols. in 1. 1952. Repr. of 1808 ed. incl. index botanicus 46.00 (ISBN 0-384-45820-3). Johnson Repr.

Petersen, R. H. Ramaria, Subgenus Lentoramaria, with Emphasis on North American Taxa. (Bibliotheca Mycologica Ser.: No. 43). 1975. text ed. 17.50 (ISBN 3-7682-0961-X). Lubrecht & Cramer.

Petrak, F. & Sydow, H. Die Gattungen der Pyrenomyceten, Sphaeropsideen und Melanconieen, Pt. 1. (Feddes Repertorium: Beiheft 27). (Ger.). 551p. 1979. Repr. of 1926 ed. lib. bdg. 63.00x (ISBN 3-87429-071-9). Lubrecht & Cramer.

Quintanilha, A. La Probleme de la Sexualite Chez les Champignons: Recherches Sur le Genre Coprinus. (Illus.). 1968. pap. 14.00 (ISBN 3-7682-0556-8). Lubrecht & Cramer.

Ramsbottom, J. Fungi: An Introduction to Mycology. 1979. Repr. of 1929 ed. lib. bdg. 12.50 (ISBN 0-8495-4608-7). Arden Lib.

Rattan, S. S. Resupinate Aphyllophorales of the Northwestern Himalayas. (Bibliotheca Mycologica Ser.: No. 60). (Illus.). 1977. lib. bdg. 42.00x (ISBN 3-7682-1172-X). Lubrecht & Cramer.

Reid, Derek A. A Monograph of the Stipitate Steroid Fungi. (Illus.). 1965. pap. 56.00 (ISBN 3-7682-5418-6). Lubrecht & Cramer.

Remler, P. Ascomyceten auf Ericaceen in den Ostalpen. (Bibliotheca Mycologica: No. 68). (Ger., Illus.). 1980. lib. bdg. 28.00x (ISBN 3-7682-1248-3). Lubrecht & Cramer.

Ricken, H. Vademecum fuer Pilzfreunde: Taschenbuch Zur Bequemen Bestimmung Aller in Mittel-Europa Vorkommenden Ansehnlichen Pilzkoerper. 1969. Repr. of 1920 ed. 14.00 (ISBN 3-7682-0603-3). Lubrecht & Cramer.

Robinson, Peter M. Practical Fungal Physiology. LC 78-4243. 123p. 1978. pap. 19.95 (ISBN 0-471-99656-4, Pub. by Wiley-Interscience). Wiley.

Rolfe, R. T. & Rolfe, F. W. The Romance of the Fungus World. (Illus.). Repr. of 1925 ed. 25.00 (ISBN 0-384-51830-3). Johnson Repr.

--The Romance of the Fungus-World: An Account of Fungus Life in Its Numerous Guises, Both Real & Legendary. LC 74-81401. (Illus.). 352p. 1974. pap. 6.95 (ISBN 0-486-23105-4). Dover.

Romagnesi, H. Petit Atlas Des Champignons, 2 vols. (Illus.). 1964. Vols. 1 & 2. 25.00 (ISBN 0-934454-91-4). Lubrecht & Cramer.

Saccardo, Pier A. Sylloge Fungorum Omnium Hucusque Cognitorum, Vols. 1-25. Set. 1950.00 (ISBN 0-384-52831-7); Set. pap. 1800.00 (ISBN 0-384-52830-9); Vols. 1-4, 6, 7, 10, 11, 18, 21. pap. 66.00 ea.; Vols. 5, 8, 9, 12-14, 16, 17, 19, 20, 23, 25. pap. 72.00 ea.; Vol. 15. pap. 42.00 suppl. to vols. 1-4 (ISBN 0-685-13610-8); Vols. 22, 24 In 2 Pts, Ea. pap. 115.00 ea.; Vol. 26. 210.00 (ISBN 0-685-13612-4). Johnson Repr.

Samuels, Gary J. A Revision of the Fungi Formerly Classified As Nectria Subgenus Hyphonectria. LC 66-6394. (Memoirs of the New York Botanical Garden Ser.: Vol. 26, No. 3). 1976. pap. 12.00x (ISBN 0-89327-008-3). NY Botanical.

Schenck, N. C., ed. Methods & Principles of Mycarrhizal Research. (Illus.). 244p. 1982. text ed. 24.00 (ISBN 0-89054-046-2). Am Phytopathol Soc.

Schroeter, J. Die Pilze Schlesiens, 2 vols. (Illus.). 1973. Repr. of 1908 ed. Set. 87.50 (ISBN 3-7682-0761-7). Lubrecht & Cramer.

Smith. Fungal Differentiations. (Mycology Ser.). 600p. 1983. 85.00 (ISBN 0-8247-1734-1). Dekker.

Smith, J. E., ed. Fungal Biotechnology, No. 3. (British Mycological Society Symposia Ser.). 1980. 44.00 (ISBN 0-12-652950-7). Acad Pr.

Soothill, Eric & Fairhurst, Alan. The New Field Guide to Fungi. (Illus.). 1979. 22.00 (ISBN 0-7181-1620-8). Transatlantic.

Stevens, F. L. Hawaiian Fungi. (BMB). Repr. of 1925 ed. 24.00 (ISBN 0-527-02122-9). Kraus Repr.

Stevens, Frank L. The Genus Meliola in Porto Rico. (University of Illinois Biological Monographs: Vol. 2, No. 4). pap. 8.00 (ISBN 0-384-58110-2). Johnson Repr.

Sutton, B. C. The Coelomycetes, Fungi Imperfecti with Pycnidia, Acervuli & Stromata. 696p. 1980. 110.00x (ISBN 0-85198-446-0, Pub. by CAB Bks England). State Mutual Bk.

Sydow, Hans & Sydow, Paul. Monographia Uredinearum: Seu Specierum Omnium As Hunc Usque Diem Cognitarum Descripto & Adumbratio Systematica, Vols. 1-4. pap. 306.25 (ISBN 3-7682-0730-7). Lubrecht & Cramer.

Tavares, Isabelle I. Laboulbeniales (Fungi, Ascomycetes) (Mycologia Memoir Ser.: No. 9). (Illus.). 700p. 1985. lib. bdg. 60.00x (ISBN 3-7682-1389-7). Lubrecht & Cramer.

Trinci, A. P. & Ryley, J. F., eds. Mode of Action of Antifungal Agents. (British Mycological Society Symposium Ser.: No. 9). 390p. 1984. 79.50 (ISBN 0-521-26171-6). Cambridge U Pr.

Turner, W. B. Fungal Metabolites. 1971. 71.00 (ISBN 0-12-704550-3). Acad Pr.

Turner, W. B. & Aldridge, D. C. Fungal Metabolites, Vol. II. 1983. 80.00 (ISBN 0-12-704556-2). Acad Pr.

Ueno, Y., ed. Trichothecenes: Chemical, Biological & Toxicological Aspects. (Developments in Food Science: Vol. 4). 312p. 1983. 85.00 (ISBN 0-444-99661-3). Elsevier.

Vanbreuseghem, R. & Devroey, C., eds. Sexuality & Pathogenicity of Fungi. 250p. 1980. 59.50 (ISBN 0-89352-187-6). Masson Pub.

Von Arx, J. A. A Revision of the Fungi Described As Gloesporium. 1970. 28.00 (ISBN 3-7682-0667-X). Lubrecht & Cramer.

Siegel, Malcolm R. & Sisler, Hugh D., eds. Antifungal Compounds: Discovery & Development, Vol. 1. 1977. 89.75 (ISBN 0-8247-6557-5). Dekker.
--Antifungal Compounds: Interactions in Biological & Ecological Systems, Vol.2. 1977. 99.75 (ISBN 0-8247-6558-3). Dekker.
Sixth British Insecticide & Fungicide Conference: Vol. 1, 2 & 3. 1971. Set. 100.00x (ISBN 0-901436-07-0, Pub. by BCPC Pubns England). State Mutual Bk.
Torgeson, Dewayne C., ed. Fungicides: An Advanced Treatise, Vols. 1-2. 1969. Vol. 1. 90.00 (ISBN 0-12-695601-4); Vol. 2. 90.00 (ISBN 0-12-695602-2). Acad Pr.
U. S. Environmental Protection Agency, ed. Federal Insecticide, Fungicide, & Rodenticide Act: Compliance-Enforcement Guidance Manual. (Illus.). 512p. 1984. pap. 64.00 (ISBN 0-86587-032-2). Gov Insts.
Zehr, Eldon I., ed. Methods for Evaluating Plant Fungicides, Nematicides, & Bactericides. LC 78-63414. 141p. 1978. lib. bdg. 18.00 (ISBN 0-89054-025-X). Am Phytopathol Soc.

FUNGUS DISEASES OF PLANTS
see Fungi, Phytopathogenic

FUNICULAR RAILROADS
see Railroads, Cable

FUR

Bachrach, Max. Fur - a Practical Treatise: Geography of the Fur World. 1977. lib. bdg. 75.00 (ISBN 0-8490-1873-0). Gordon Pr.
Ewing, Elizabeth. Fur in Dress. (Illus.). 192p. 1981. 32.00 (ISBN 0-7134-1741-2, Pub. by Batsford England). David & Charles.

FUR-BEARING ANIMALS
see also Fur Farming; Fur Trade; also Names of Fur-Bearing Animals

Coues, Elliott. Fur-Bearing Animals of North America. LC 79-125735. (American Environmental Studies). (Illus.). 1970. Repr. of 1877 ed. 24.50 (ISBN 0-405-02660-9). Ayer Co Pubs.
Deems, Eugene F., Jr. & Pursley, Duane. North American Furbearers: A Contemporary Reference. (Illus.). 217p. 1983. text ed. 14.00 (ISBN 0-932108-08-3). IAFWA.
McCracken, Harold & Van Cleve, Harry. Trapping. (Illus.). 1974. 8.95 (ISBN 0-498-08272-5). A S Barnes.
Martin, Calvin. Keepers of the Game: Indian-Animal Relationships & the Fur Trade. (Illus.). 238p. 1982. pap. 6.95 (ISBN 0-520-04637-4). U of Cal Pr.
Rue, Leonard L. Furbearing Animals of North America. (Illus.). 352p. 1981. 6.98 (ISBN 0-517-53942-X, Michelman Books). Crown.

FUR FARMING
see also names of Fur-Bearing Animals

Harding, A. R. Fur Farming. (Illus.). 442p. pap. 5.00 (ISBN 0-936622-08-3). A R Harding Pub.

FUR SEAL
see Sealing

FUR TRADE

Ashley, William H. British Establishments on the Columbia & the State of the Fur Trade. 60p. 1981. 9.95 (ISBN 0-87770-255-1). Ye Galleon.
Gates, Charles M., ed. Five Fur Traders of the Northwest. LC 65-63528. 296p. 1965. Repr. of 1933 ed. 7.25 (ISBN 0-87351-024-0). Minn Hist.
Irving, Washington. Astoria. LC 67-25439. (Illus.). 1967. 12.50 (ISBN 0-8323-0101-9). Binford.
Johnson, Ida A. The Michigan Fur Trade. LC 74-155928. 1981. Repr. of 1919 ed. 17.50 (ISBN 0-912382-07-4). Black Letter.
Krech, Shepard, ed. Indians, Animals, & the Fur Trade: A Critique of "Keepers of the Game". LC 81-1351. 214p. 1981. 14.00x (ISBN 0-8203-0563-4). U of Ga Pr.
McDonald, Lois H. Fur Trade Letters of Francis Ermatinger. LC 80-65050. (Northwest Historical Ser.: Vol. 15). (Illus.). 317p. 1980. 29.00 (ISBN 0-87062-130-0). A H Clark.
Mitchell, Elaine A. Fort Timiskaming & the Fur Trade. LC 76-51782. 1977. 25.00x (ISBN 0-8020-2234-0). U of Toronto Pr.
Musgrove, Bill & Blair, Gerry. Fur Trapping. (Illus.). 1979. pap. write for info. (Pub. by Winchester Pr). New Century.
Ogden, Adele. The California Sea Otter Trade: 1784-1848. (California Library Reprint Ser.). 1975. 32.50x (ISBN 0-520-02806-6). U of Cal Pr.
Russell, Carl P. Firearms, Traps & Tools of the Mountain Men. LC 77-81984. (Illus.). 448p. 1977. pap. 9.95 (ISBN 0-8263-0465-6). U of NM Pr.
Weber, David J. The Taos Trappers: The Fur Trade in the Far Southwest, 1540-1846. LC 75-145508. (Illus.). 280p. 1980. pap. 7.95 (ISBN 0-8061-1702-8). U of Okla Pr.

FURNACES
see also Electric Furnaces; Kilns; Solar Furnaces

Bartok, John W., Jr. Solid Fuel Furnaces & Boilers: Low-Cost Central Heating Systems. LC 82-1003. (Illus.). 224p. (Orig.). 1982. pap. 8.95 (ISBN 0-88266-264-3). Garden Way Pub.
Cone, Carroll. Energy Management for Industrial Furnaces. LC 80-10435. 201p. 1980. 49.50x (ISBN 0-471-06037-2, Pub. by Wiley-Interscience). Wiley.
Gasoline Blow Torches & Plumber's Furnaces. (Thirty Ser.). 1974. pap. 2.00 (ISBN 0-685-58104-7, 393). Natl Fire Prot.
Gilchrist, J. D. Fuel, Furnaces & Refractories. 2nd ed. 1977. text ed. 37.00 (ISBN 0-08-020430-9); pap. text ed. 12.75 (ISBN 0-08-020429-5). Pergamon.
Glinkov, M. A. & Glinkov, G. M. A General Theory of Furnaces. 1980. 8.45 (ISBN 0-8285-1799-1, Pub. by Mir Pubs USSR). Imported Pubns.
Installation & Operation of Solid-Fuel-Burning Appliances. 1.50 (ISBN 0-318-00063-6). Intl Conf Bldg Off.
Khalil, E. E. Modelling of Furnaces & Combustors. 1982. 41.00 (ISBN 0-9961005-3-9, Pub. by Abacus England). Heyden.
Monroe, Elmer S., Jr. Saving Fuel with Furnaces. Gyftopoulos, Elias P. & Cohen, Karen C., eds. (Industrial Energy-Conservation Manuals: No. 6). 56p. 1982. loose-leaf 20.00x (ISBN 0-262-13171-4). MIT Pr.
Ovens & Furnaces, Design, Location & Equipment. (Eighty-Ninety Ser). 156p. 1973. pap. 2.50 (ISBN 0-685-44133-4, 86A). Natl Fire Prot.
Prevention of Furnace Explosions in Fuel-Oil & Natural Gas-Fired Watertube Boiler Furnaces with One Burner. (Eighty-Ninety Ser.). 68p. 1973. pap. 2.00 (ISBN 0-685-44149-0, 85). Natl Fire Prot.
Prevention of Furnace Explosions in Natural Gas-Fired Multiple Burner Boiler-Furnaces. (Eighty-Ninety Ser.). 68p. 1973. pap. 3.50 (ISBN 0-685-44130-X, 85B). Natl Fire Prot.
Prevention of Furnace Explosions in Pulverized Coal-Fired Multiple Burner Boiler-Furnaces. (Eighty-Ninety Ser.). 68p. 1974. pap. 3.50 (ISBN 0-685-44132-6, 85E). Natl Fire Prot.
Reed, Robert D. Furnace Operations. 3rd ed. LC 80-26274. 230p. 1981. 29.95x (ISBN 0-87201-301-4). Gulf Pub.
Slavin, W., ed. Graphite Furnace Technology & Atomic Absorption Spectroscopy: Commemorating the 25th Anniversary of the Publication of the First Paper by B. V. L'vov. 400p. 1984. pap. 55.00 (ISBN 0-08-031405-8). Pergamon.
Talmor, E. Combustion Hot Spot Analysis for Fired Process Heaters: Prediction, Control, Troubleshooting. LC 82-3037. 162p. 1982. 37.95 (ISBN 0-87201-362-6). Gulf Pub.
Trinks, Willibald & Mawhinney, M. H. Industrial Furnaces, 2 vols. 5th ed. Vol. 1: Principles of Design & Operations. pap. 121.50 (ISBN 0-317-26260-2, 2055713); Vol. 2: Fuels, Furnace Types & Furnace Equipment. pap. 93.50 (ISBN 0-317-26261-0, 2055713). Bks Demand UMI.
White, Bill. Build Your Own Woodburning Furnace. LC 78-66818. (Illus.). 1978. pap. 3.50 (ISBN 0-9601794-2-9). FireBuilders.
--Convert Your Oil Furnace to Wood. 2nd ed. LC 76-58642. (Illus.). 1977. 3.50 (ISBN 0-9601794-1-0). FireBuilders.

FURNITURE–BUILDING
see Furniture Making

FURNITURE BUILDING
see Furniture Making

FURNITURE INDUSTRY AND TRADE

Furniture & Joinery Industry. (UNIDO Guides to Information Sources: No. 4). pap. 4.00 (ISBN 0-686-93248-X, UNID188, UN). Unipub.
Glossop, R. H. Method Study & the Furniture Industry. LC 75-112711. 1970. 25.00 (ISBN 0-08-015653-3). Pergamon.
Mason, Billy. A Furniture Stripping Business for the Small Man. 1975. pap. text ed. 5.00 (ISBN 0-942140-03-6). Kelso.
Taylor, Lonn & Warren, David B. Texas Furniture: The Cabinetmakers & Their Work, 1840-1880. LC 75-20391. (Illus.). 399p. 1975. 60.00 (ISBN 0-292-73801-3). U of Tex Pr.

FURNITURE MAKING
see also Cabinet-Work; Upholstery

Alexander, John D., Jr. Make a Chair from a Tree: An Introduction to Working Green Wood. LC 78-58222. (Illus.). 128p. 1978. pap. 8.95 (ISBN 0-918804-01-9, Dist. by W W Norton). Taunton.
Artist's Furniture You Can Make. 1986. cancelled (ISBN 0-442-25948-4). Van Nos Reinhold.
Blandford, Percy W. Fifty-Three Space-Saving Built-In Furniture Projects. (Illus.). 400p. (Orig.). 1983. pap. 17.50 (ISBN 0-8306-1504-0). TAB Bks.
--Sixty-Six Children's Furniture Projects. (Illus.). 1979. pap. 9.95 (ISBN 0-8306-1188-6, 1188). TAB Bks.
Brann, Donald R. How to Build Bars. rev. ed. LC 67-15263. 1976. lib. bdg. 5.95 (ISBN 0-87733-090-5). Easi-Bild.
--How to Build Kitchen Cabinets, Room Dividers & Cabinet Furniture. rev. ed. LC 65-27708. 1978. lib. bdg. 5.95 (ISBN 0-87733-058-1); pap. 3.50 (ISBN 0-87733-658-X). Easi-Bild.
Carrell, Al. The Superhandyman's Fix & Finish Furniture Guide. 180p. 1982. pap. 5.95 (ISBN 0-13-875971-5); 7.95 (ISBN 0-13-875997-9). P-H.
Center for Self Sufficiency Learning Institute Staff. At Your Own Pace Bibliography on Making Your Own Furniture. 35p. 1983. pap. text ed. 2.75 (ISBN 0-910811-70-9, Pub. by Center Self Suff). Prosperity & Profits.
D'Addario, Joseph D. Build It: Out of Sight Sewing Center. 1972. pap. 5.95 (ISBN 0-686-01898-2). Classic Furn Kits.
Daniele, Joseph W. Building Early American Furniture. LC 74-10953. (Illus.). 256p. 1974. 19.95. Stackpole.
Dodds, Margaret K. Easy-to-Build Wooden Chairs for Children: Measured Drawings & Illustrated Step-by-Step Instructions for Traditional Chairs. (Woodworking Ser.). (Illus.). 32p. (Orig.). 1984. pap. 2.00 (ISBN 0-486-24579-9). Dover.
Douglass, J. Harvey. Projects in Wood Furniture. rev. ed. LC 67-21721. (Illus.). 1967. text ed. 16.64 (ISBN 0-87345-027-2). McKnight.
Dunbar, Michael. Make a Windsor Chair with Michael Dunbar. LC 83-50681. (Illus.). 176p. 1984. pap. 13.95 (ISBN 0-918804-21-3, Dist. by W W Norton). Taunton.
Durney, Charles M. Building Free-Form Furniture. (Illus.). 224p. 1982. o.p 15.95 (ISBN 0-8306-1340-4, 1440); pap. 9.95 (ISBN 0-8306-1440-0). TAB Bks.
Endacott, G. W. Woodworking & Furniture Making. (Drake Home Craftman Ser.). (Illus.). 1976. pap. 5.95 (ISBN 0-8069-8804-5). Sterling.
Family Handyman Magazine Editors. The Furniture Maker's Handbook. (Illus.). 282p. 1981. pap. 15.95 (ISBN 0-684-17313-1, ScribT). Scribner.
Family Handyman Staff. The Early American Furniture-Making Handbook. LC 72-38945. (Illus.). 160p. 1972. 14.95 (ISBN 0-684-12869-1, ScribT); pap. 9.95 (ISBN 0-684-15060-3). Scribner.
Feirer & Hutchings. Advanced Woodwork & Furniture Making. rev. ed. 1982. text ed. 22.20 (ISBN 0-02-662110-X). Bennett IL.
--Advanced Woodwork & Furniture Making. 1978. text ed. 18.60 (ISBN 0-02-662080-4); student guide 5.28 (ISBN 0-02-662120-7); visual masters 20.00 (ISBN 0-02-662070-7); tchr's. guide 3.96 (ISBN 0-02-662150-9). Bennett IL.
Feirer, John. Furniture & Cabinet Making. 1983. text ed. 17.76 (ISBN 0-02-664050-3). Bennett Il.
Feirer, John & Hutchings, Gilbert R. Advanced Woodwork & Furniture-Making. 4th. rev ed. (Illus.). 538p. 1978. 35.00 (ISBN 0-684-17475-8, ScribT). Scribner.
Feirer, John L. Furniture & Cabinet Making. (Illus.). 512p. 1983. pap. 19.95 (ISBN 0-684-17965-2, ScribT). Scribner.
Fine Woodworking Magazine Editors. Fine Woodworking on Making Period Furniture. LC 84-52101. (Illus.). 128p. (Orig.). 1985. pap. 6.95 (ISBN 0-918804-30-2, Dist. by W W Norton). Taunton.
Furniture Made in America, Eighteen Seventy five-Nineteen Hundred five. (Illus.). 320p. 17.95. Apollo.
Geary, Don. Build It with Plywood: Eighty-Eight Furniture Projects. (Illus.). 304p. 1983. 18.95 (ISBN 0-8306-0330-1, 1430); pap. 13.50 (ISBN 0-8306-0230-5). TAB Bks.
Gottshall, Franklin H. Masterpiece Furniture Making. LC 79-12. (Illus.). 224p. 1979. 24.95 (ISBN 0-8117-0974-4). Stackpole.
Huth, Hans. Roentgen Furniture: Abraham & David Roentgen, European Cabinet Makers. (Illus.). 260p. 1974. 100.00x (ISBN 0-85667-003-0, Pub. by Sotheby Pubns England). Biblio Dist.
Joyce, Ernest. Encyclopedia of Furniture Making. LC 76-49087. (Illus.). 1979. 19.95 (ISBN 0-8069-8302-7). Sterling.
Make Your Own Furniture. 176p. 1979. 35.00x (ISBN 0-563-16262-7, Pub. by BBC Pubns). State Mutual Bk.
Margon, Lester. Construction of American Furniture Treasures. (Illus.). 14.00 (ISBN 0-8446-5220-2). Peter Smith.
Marlow, A. W. Classic Furniture Projects. (Illus.). 1979. pap. 9.95 (ISBN 0-8128-6034-9). Stein & Day.
Moser, Thomas. How to Build Shaker Furniture. LC 76-46809. (Illus.). 224p. 1980. pap. 9.95 (ISBN 0-8069-8392-2). Sterling.
--Measured Shop Drawings for American Furniture. LC 84-26872. (Illus.). 328p. 1985. 24.95 (ISBN 0-8069-5712-3). Sterling.
Palmer, Bruce. Making Children's Furniture & Play Structures. LC 75-8813. (Parents & Children Together Ser.). (Illus.). 160p. 1974. o.p 8.95 (ISBN 0-911104-24-0, 014); pap. 3.95 (ISBN 0-911104-25-9, 015). Workman Pub.
Roberts, Nadine H. One Hundred & One Children's Furniture Projects. (Illus.). 192p. (Orig.). 1984. 18.95 (ISBN 0-8306-0228-3); pap. 10.95 (ISBN 0-8306-1528-8, 1528). TAB Bks.
Schmultzhart, Berthold. The Handmade Furniture Book. (Illus.). 144p. 1981. 13.95 (ISBN 0-13-383638-X); pap. 5.95 (ISBN 0-13-383620-7). P-H.
Spielman, Patrick. Making Country-Rustic Furniture: Original Designs from Spielmans Wood Works. LC 85-2690. (Illus.). 164p. (Orig.). 1985. pap. 8.95 (ISBN 0-8069-6210-0). Sterling.
Sunset Editors, ed. Children's Furniture. LC 84-82286. (Illus.). 96p. (Orig.). 1985. pap. 5.95 (ISBN 0-376-01268-4). Sunset-Lane.
Taylor, V. J. How to Build Period Country Furniture. LC 79-3731. (Illus.). 1980. pap. 11.95 (ISBN 0-8128-6047-0). Stein & Day.
Taylor, Victor J. Constructing Modern Furniture. LC 79-91383. (A Home Craftsman Bk.). (Illus.). 144p. 1980. pap. 6.95 (ISBN 0-8069-8888-6). Sterling.
The Family Workshop. How to Make PVC Pipe Furniture for Indoors & Outdoors. LC 85-6871. (Family Workshop Bk.). 144p. 1985. pap. 12.95 (ISBN 0-385-23219-5). Doubleday.
Trussell, John. Making Furniture. (Illus.). 144p. 1984. text ed. 9.95 (ISBN 0-85219-591-5, Pub. by Batsford England). David & Charles.
Watson, Aldren A. & Poulos, Theodora. Furniture Making Plain & Simple. (Illus.). 328p. 1984. 24.95 (ISBN 0-393-01812-1). Norton.
Watts, Simon. Building a Houseful of Furniture: 43 Plans with Comments on Design & Construction. LC 82-60352. (Illus.). 224p. 1983. pap. 18.95 (ISBN 0-918804-16-7, Dist. by W. W. Norton). Taunton.
Windsor, H. H. Mission Furniture: How to Make It. LC 76-16111. (Illus.). 120p. 1976. pap. 7.95 (ISBN 0-87905-064-0, Peregrine Smith). Gibbs M Smith.
Wolverton, Mike & Wolverton, Ruth. One Hundred & Forty-Nine One-Evening Furniture Projects. (Illus.). 420p. (Orig.). 1982. pap. 11.95 (ISBN 0-8306-1469-9). TAB Bks.

FURNITURE MAKING–AMATEURS' MANUALS

Adams, Florence. Make Your Own Baby Furniture. LC 80-10495. (Illus.). 224p. 1980. pap. 9.95 (ISBN 0-87131-320-0). M Evans.
Brann, Donald R. How to Build Collectors' Display Cases. LC 78-57773. (Illus.). 194p. 1979. pap. 6.95 (ISBN 0-87733-792-6). Easi-Bild.
--How to Build Colonial Furniture. LC 74-24602. 1982. pap. 7.95 (ISBN 0-87733-761-6). Easi-Bild.
--How to Build Outdoor Furniture. LC 76-14045. 1983. pap. 7.95 (ISBN 0-87733-754-3). Easi-Bild.
Buckley, Larry. Easy-to-Make Slotted Furniture. (Illus.). 52p. (Orig.). 1980. pap. 2.25 (ISBN 0-486-23983-7). Dover.
Fabbro, Mario D. How to Make Children's Furniture & Play Equipment. 2nd ed. LC 83-15856. (Illus.). 208p. (Orig.). 1984. pap. 8.95 (ISBN 0-668-05925-7). Arco.
Gottshall, Franklin H. How to Make Colonial Furniture. LC 79-20825. 1980. 17.95 (ISBN 0-02-544840-4). Macmillan.
Hennessey, James & Papanek, Victor. Nomadic Furniture One. LC 72-342. 1973. pap. 9.95 (ISBN 0-394-70228-X). Pantheon.
Johnston, David. The Craft of Furniture Making. 1979. 11.95 (ISBN 0-7134-1546-0, Pub. by Batsford England); pap. 9.95 (ISBN 0-7134-1547-9, Pub. by Batsford England). David & Charles.
Kramer, Jack. Fold-Away Furniture. (Illus.). 1978. pap. 4.95 (ISBN 0-346-12341-0). Cornerstone.
Makepeace, John, et al. The Art of Making Furniture. LC 80-52623. (Illus.). 192p. 1981. 21.95 (ISBN 0-8069-5426-4). Sterling.
Martensson, Alf. The Book of Furniture Making. 1980. 25.95 (ISBN 0-312-08973-2). St Martin.
Ouimet, Ronald P. Contemporary Furniture Plans: One Hundred Fourteen Projects You Can Build Yourself. LC 81-8811. (A Home Craftsman Bk.). (Illus.). 160p. (Orig.). 1981. pap. text ed. 8.95 (ISBN 0-8069-7546-6). Sterling.
Peterson, Franklynn. The Build-It-Yourself Furniture Catalog. LC 76-6567. 1976 (Reward). pap. 4.95 (ISBN 0-13-085902-8). P-H.
Stamberg, Peter. Build Your Own Furniture. LC 81-66174. 1981. pap. 8.95 (ISBN 0-345-29553-6). Ballantine.
Stiles, David. Easy-to-Make Children's Furniture. (Illus.). 1980. 7.95 (ISBN 0-394-73871-3). Pantheon.

G

Symposium of the International Astronomical Union, No. 77. Structure & Properties of Nearby Galaxies: Proceedings. Berkhuijsen, Elly M. & Wielebinski, Richard, eds. 1978. lib. bdg. 39.50 (ISBN 90-277-0874-6, Pub. by Reidel Holland); pap. text ed. 26.00 (ISBN 90-277-0875-4). Kluwer Academic.
Tayler, R. J. & Everest, A. S. Galaxies: Structure & Evolution. LC 78-52248. (Wykeham Science Ser.: No. 49). 204p. 1979. 21.00x (ISBN 0-8448-1356-7). Crane-Russak Co.
Taylor, R. J. Galaxies: Structure & Evolution. (Wykeham Science Ser.: No. 49). 204p. cancelled (ISBN 0-85109-680-8); pap. cancelled (ISBN 0-85109-670-0). Taylor & Francis.
Vehrenberg, Hans. Atlas of Deep Sky Splendors. 4th ed. Orig. Title: Mein Messier-Buch. Tr. of Mein Messier-Buch. (Illus.). 240p. 1983. 39.95 (ISBN 0-933346-03-4). Sky Pub.
Webb Society & Jones, Kenneth G., eds. Webb Society Deep-Sky Observer's Handbook: Galaxies, Vol. IV. LC 77-359099. 256p. 1981. pap. 16.95x (ISBN 0-89490-050-1). Enslow Pubs.
Westerlund, Bengt E., ed. Stars & Star Systems. (Astrophysics & Space Science Library: No. 75). 1979. lib. bdg. 34.00 (ISBN 90-277-0983-1, Pub. by Reidel Holland). Kluwer Academic.
Woltjer, Lodewijk, ed. Galaxies & the Universe: Lectures. LC 68-20445. (Vetlesen Symposium, 1966). (Illus.). 1968. 24.00x (ISBN 0-231-03110-6). Columbia U Pr.

GALAXY (MILKY WAY)
see Milky Way

GALES
see Storms; Winds

GALILEO (GALILEO GALILEI), 1564-1642
Bernkopf, Michael. Science of Galileo, Level 3. McConochie, Jean, ed. (Regents Readers Ser.). (Illus.). 80p. 1983. pap. text ed. 2.50 (ISBN 0-88345-457-2, 21092). Regents Pub.
Brophy, James & Paolucci, Henry, eds. The Achievement of Galileo. 1962. pap. 7.95x (ISBN 0-8084-0389-3). New Coll U Pr.
Butts, Robert E. & Pitt, Joseph C., eds. New Perspectives on Galileo. (Western Ontario Ser: No. 14). 1978. lib. bdg. 39.50 (ISBN 90-277-0859-2, Pub. by Reidel Holland); pap. 15.80 (ISBN 90-277-0891-6). Kluwer Academic.
Campanella, Thomas. The Defense of Galileo. LC 74-26254. (History, Philosophy & Sociology of Science Ser.). 1975. Repr. 14.00 (ISBN 0-405-06582-5). Ayer Co Pubs.
Drake, Stillman. Galileo. (Past Masters Ser.). 1980. pap. 3.95 (ISBN 0-19-287526-4). Oxford U Pr.
--Galileo at Work: His Scientific Biography. LC 78-5239. xxiv, 536p. 1981. pap. 9.95 (ISBN 0-226-16227-3). U of Chicago Pr.
--Telescopes, Tides, & Tactics: A Galilean Dialogue about the "Starry Messenger" & Systems of the World. LC 82-24790. 256p. 1983. lib. bdg. 22.50x (ISBN 0-226-16231-1). U of Chicago Pr.
Fahie, J. J. Galileo: His Life & Work. (Illus.). Repr. of 1903 ed. lib. bdg. 47.00x (ISBN 0-697-00003-6). Irvington.
Galilei, Galileo. Dialogue Concerning the Two Chief World Systems-Ptolemaic & Copernican. 2nd rev. ed. Drake, Stillman, tr. 1967. 40.00x (ISBN 0-520-00449-3); pap. 10.95x (ISBN 0-520-00450-7, CAL66). U of Cal Pr.
--Galileo Galilei: Operations of the Geometric & Military Compass. Drake, Stillman, tr. from Ital. & intro. by. LC 78-606002. (Illus.). 1978. pap. text ed. 6.95x (ISBN 0-87474-383-4). Smithsonian.
Galileo. Discoveries & Opinions of Galileo. LC 57-6305. 1957. pap. 5.50 (ISBN 0-385-09239-3, A94, Anch). Doubleday.
Gebler, Karl Von. Galileo Galilei & the Roman Curia from Authentic Sources. Sturge, Jane, tr. LC 76-1124. 1977. Repr. of 1897 ed. lib. bdg. 28.50x (ISBN 0-915172-11-9). Richwood Pub.
Golino, Carlo L., ed. Galileo Reappraised. LC 66-15485. (UCLA Center for Medieval & Renaissance Studies). 1966. 26.00x (ISBN 0-520-00490-6). U of Cal Pr.
Koyre, Alexandre. Galileo Studies. Mepham, J., tr. (European Philosophy & the Human Sciences Ser.). 1978. text ed. 46.75x (ISBN 0-391-00760-2). Humanities.
Langford, Jerome J. Galileo, Science & the Church. rev. ed. 1971. pap. 6.95x (ISBN 0-472-06173-9, 173, AA). U of Mich Pr.
Lijegren, Sten. Studies in Milton. LC 67-30816. (Studies in Milton, No. 22). 1969. Repr. of 1918 ed. lib. bdg. 49.95x (ISBN 0-8383-0718-3). Haskell.
Santillana, Giorgio. The Crime of Galileo. LC 55-7400. (Midway Reprint Ser). (Illus.). xvi, 339p. 1955. pap. 13.00x (ISBN 0-226-73481-1). U of Chicago Pr.
Wallace, William A. Galileo & His Sources: The Heritage of the Collegio Romano in Galileo's Science. LC 84-42556. 470p. 1984. text ed. 42.50x (ISBN 0-691-08355-X). Princeton U Pr.
--Galileo's Early Notebooks. LC 77-89766. 1977. text ed. 24.95x (ISBN 0-268-00998-8). U of Notre Dame Pr.

GALIUM
Dempster, Lauramay T. The Genus Galium (Rubiaceae) in Mexico & Central America. (Publications in Botany Ser.: No. 73). 1978. pap. 14.00x (ISBN 0-520-09578-2). U of Cal Pr.
Institute of Physics. Gallium Arsenide. (Institute of Physics Conference Ser.: No. 3). 1967. 24.50 (ISBN 0-9960028-2-0, Pub. by Inst Physics England). Heyden.
--Gallium Arsenide. (Institute of Physics Conference Ser.: No. 7). 1969. 55.00 (ISBN 0-9960028-6-3, Pub. by Inst Physics England). Heyden.
--Gallium Arsenide & Related Compounds. (Institute of Physics Conference Ser.: No. 9). 1971. 55.00 (ISBN 0-9960028-8-X, Pub. by Inst Physics England). Heyden.

GALLIFORMES
see also Pheasants; Turkeys
Bent, Arthur C. Life Histories of North American Gallinaceous Birds. (Illus.). 1932. pap. 8.00 (ISBN 0-486-21028-6). Dover.
--Life Histories of North American Gallinaceous Birds. (Illus.). 15.25 (ISBN 0-8446-1635-4). Peter Smith.

GALLIUM
Johnston, Gerald & Jones, A. E. Atlas of Gallium - 67 Scintigraphy: A New Method of Radioisotope Diagnosis. LC 73-18375. 232p. 1974. 32.50x (ISBN 0-306-30769-3, Plenum Pr). Plenum Pub.

GALLIUM ARSENIDE
Ferry, David K. Gallium Arsenide Technology. Date not set. 44.95 (ISBN 0-672-22375-9, 22375). Sams.
Gallium Arsenide & Related Compounds. (Reports on Progress in Physics Ser.: No. 56). 1981. 87.50 (ISBN 0-9960033-6-3, Pub. by Inst Physics England). Heyden.
Gallium Arsenide & Related Compounds: 1972. (Institute of Physics Conference Ser.: No. 17). 1972. 60.00 (ISBN 0-9960029-6-0, Pub. by Inst Physics England). Heyden.
Gallium Arsenide & Related Compounds: 1974. (Institute of Physics Conference Ser.: No. 24). 1974. 75.00 (ISBN 0-9960030-3-7, Pub. by Inst Physics England). Heyden.
Gallium Arsenide & Related Compounds: Edinburgh 1976. (Institute of Physics Conference Ser.: No. 33A). 1977. 75.00 (ISBN 0-9960031-2-6, Pub. by Inst Physics England). Heyden.
Gallium Arsenide & Related Compounds: St. Louis 1976. (Institute of Physics Conference Ser.: No. 33B). 1977. 75.00 (ISBN 0-9960031-3-4, Pub. by Inst Physics England). Heyden.
Gallium Arsenide & Related Compounds 1978: St. Louis. (Institute of Physics Conference Ser.: No. 45). 1979. 87.50 (ISBN 0-9960032-5-8, Pub. by Inst Physics England). Heyden.
Howes, M. J. & Morgan, D. V. Gallum Arsenide: Materials, Devices & Circuits. (Solid State Devices & Circuits Ser.). 1985. 57.00 (ISBN 0-471-90048-6). Wiley.
International Conference, Albuquerque, New Mexico, 1982. Gallium Arsenide & Related Compounds: 10th. Stillman, G. E., ed. 1983. 65.00 (ISBN 0-9960040-1-7, Pub. by A Hilger England). Heyden.
International Symposium, 9th, Oiso, Japan Sept. 1981. Galium Arsenide & Related Compounds: Proceedings. Sugano, T., ed. 1982. 75.00 (ISBN 0-9960039-9-1, Pub. by A Hilger England). Heyden.
Pearsall, T. P., ed. GaInAsP Alloy Semiconductors. LC 81-15922. 468p. 1982. text ed. 52.95x (ISBN 0-471-10119-2). Wiley.

GALLS (BOTANY)
see also Insects, Injurious and Beneficial
Russo, Ronald A. Plant Galls of the California Region. (Illus.). 1979. pap. 8.95 (ISBN 0-910286-71-X). Boxwood.
Shorthouse, Joe D. & Rohfritsch, O., eds. Biology of Insect-Induced Galls. 250p. 1986. 31.50x (ISBN 0-03-060476-1). Praeger.

GALOIS THEORY
see also Modular Fields
Artin, Emil. Galois Theory. (Mathematical Lectures Ser.: No. 2). (Orig.). 1966. pap. 3.95 (ISBN 0-268-00108-1). U of Notre Dame Pr.
Bastida, Julio R. Encyclopedia of Mathematics & Its Applications: Field Extensions & Galois Theory, Vol. 22. 1984. 47.50 (ISBN 0-317-14400-6, 30242-0). Cambridge U Pr.
Buhler, J. P. Icosahedral Galois Representations. (Lecture Notes in Mathematics Ser.: Vol. 654). 1978. pap. 12.00 (ISBN 0-387-08844-X). Springer-Verlag.
Chase, S. U., et al. Galois Theory & Cohomology of Commutative Rings. LC 52-42839. (Memoirs: No. 52). 79p. 1978. pap. 9.00 (ISBN 0-8218-1252-1, MEMO-52). Am Math.
Edwards, Harold H. Galois Theory. (Graduate Texts in Mathematics: Vol. 101). (Illus.). 240p. 1984. 22.00 (ISBN 0-387-90980-X). Springer-Verlag.
Frohlich, A. Central Extensions, Galois Groups, & Ideal Class Groups of Numbers Fields. LC 83-19685. (Contemporary Mathematics Ser.: Vol. 24). 86p. 1983. pap. 17.00 (ISBN 0-8218-5022-9). Am Math.
Gaal, Lisl. Classical Galois Theory. 3rd ed. LC 73-649. viii, 248p. 1979. text ed. 11.95 (ISBN 0-8284-1268-5). Chelsea Pub.
Haberland, K. Galois Cohomology of Algebraic Number Fields. 1978. 30.75x (ISBN 0-685-87204-1). Adlers Foreign Bks.
Joyal, Andre & Tierney, Myles. An Extension of the Galois Theory of Grothendieck. LC 84-14587. (Memoirs of the American Mathematical Society: No. 309). 71p. 1984. pap. 11.00 (ISBN 0-8218-2312-4). Am Math.
Kaplansky, Irving. Fields & Rings. rev. 2nd ed. LC 72-78251. (Chicago Lectures in Mathematics Ser). 224p. 1972. text ed. 12.50x (ISBN 0-226-42450-2); pap. text ed. 9.00x (ISBN 0-226-42451-0). U of Chicago Pr.
Lang, S. & Trotter, H. F. Frobenius Distributions in GL-Two Extensions. (Lecture Notes in Mathematics: Vol. 504). 274p. 1976. pap. 17.00 (ISBN 0-387-07550-X). Springer-Verlag.
Magid, A. R. Separable Galois Theory of Commutative Rings. (Pure & Applied Mathematics Ser.: Vol. 27). 1974. 35.00 (ISBN 0-8247-6163-4). Dekker.
Postnikov, M. M. Fundamentals of Galois Thoery. (Russian Tracts on the Physical Sciences Ser.). 196p. 1964. 57.75x (ISBN 0-677-20440-X). Gordon.
Stewart, I. N. Galois Theory. 1973. pap. 15.95x (ISBN 0-412-10800-3, NO. 6274, Pub. by Chapman & Hall). Methuen Inc.
Winter, D. J. The Structure of Fields. LC 73-21824. (Graduate Texts in Mathematics Ser.: Vol. 16). (Illus.). 320p. 1974. 28.00 (ISBN 0-387-90074-8). Springer-Verlag.

GALVANIC BATTERIES
see Electric Batteries

GALVANIC CORROSION
see Electrolytic Corrosion

GALVANISM
see Electricity

GALVANIZING
see also Metals–Pickling; Tin Plate; Zinc Coating
Zinc Development Association, ed. Hot Dip Galvanizing. 442p. 1981. 60.00x (ISBN 0-86108-033-5, Pub. by Portcullio Pr). State Mutual Bk.
--Intergalva Seventy-Nine. 361p. 1981. 150.00x (ISBN 0-86108-091-2, Pub. by Portcullio Pr). State Mutual Bk.
--Intergalva Seventy-Six. 272p. 1981. 76.00x (ISBN 0-86108-024-6, Pub. by Portcullio Pr). State Mutual Bk.

GALVANOMAGNETIC EFFECTS
see also Hall Effect
Weiss, H. Structure & Application of Galvanomagnetic Devices. 1969. 72.00 (ISBN 0-08-012597-2). Pergamon.

GALVANOPLASTY
see Electrometallurgy; Electroplating

GAMBLING–DATA PROCESSING
George, F. H. Casino Games with the Commodore 64. (Illus.). 160p. 1984. pap. 13.95 (ISBN 0-00-383013-6, Pub. by Collins England). Sheridan.
--Football Pools with the Commodore 64. (Illus.). 160p. 1984. pap. 13.95 (Pub. by Collins England). Sheridan.
Sagan, Hans. Beat the Odds: Microcomputer Simulations of Casino Games. 192p. 1983. pap. 9.50 (ISBN 0-8104-5181-6). Hayden.

GAME AND GAME-BIRDS
see also Animal Introduction; Dogs–Training; Game Protection; Shooting; Shore Birds; Trapping; Water-Birds; Waterfowl
also Particular Animals and Birds, e.g. Deer, Grouse, Rabbits, Woodcock
Atkinson, Herbert. Cockfighting & Game Fowl. (Illus.). 288p. 1977. 24.95 (ISBN 0-904558-23-1). Saiga.
Beasom, Sam L. & Roberson, Sheila F., eds. Game Harvest Management. (Illus.). 300p. 1985. 20.00 (ISBN 0-912229-08-X); pap. 15.00 (ISBN 0-912229-09-8). CK Wildlife Res.
Billmeyer, Patricia. The Encyclopedia of Wild Game & Fish Cleaning & Cooking. LC 79-54388. 116p. pap. 3.95 (ISBN 0-9606262-0-4). Yesnaby Inc.
Blair, Gerry. Predator Caller's Companion. LC 81-497. 280p. 1981. 18.95 (ISBN 0-8329-3362-7, Pub. by Winchester Pr). New Century.
Hagerbaumer, David. Selected American Game Birds. LC 74-137773. 1972. 30.00 (ISBN 0-87004-213-0). Caxton.
Marchington, John. The Natural History of Game. (Illus.). 256p. 1984. 22.50 (ISBN 0-85115-196-5, Pub. by Boydell & Brewer). Longwood Pub Group.
Mettler, John J. Basic Butchering of Livestock & Game. LC 85-70195. (Illus.). 160p. 1985. pap. 9.95 (ISBN 0-88266-391-7). Garden Way Pub.
Oldham, J. The West of England Flying Tumbler. 120p. 1980. 13.50 (ISBN 0-904558-90-8). Saiga.
Robbins, Charles T. Wildlife Feeding & Nutrition. LC 82-13720. 1983. 31.50 (ISBN 0-12-589380-9). Acad Pr.
Scott, P. A Coloured Key to the Wildfowl of the World. rev. ed. (Illus.). 1972. 15.00 (ISBN 0-685-12001-5). Heinman.
Sherwood, Morgan. Big Game in Alaska. LC 81-3005. (Yale Western Americana Ser.: No. 33). (Illus.). 224p. 1981. 33.00x (ISBN 0-300-02625-0). Yale U Pr.
Smith, Guy N. Gamekeeping & Shooting for Amateurs. 1981. 13.00 (ISBN 0-904558-17-7). Saiga.
--Ratting & Rabbiting for Amateur Gamekeepers. 196p. 1979. 13.50 (ISBN 0-904558-64-9). Saiga.

GAME PROTECTION
see also Birds, Protection of
Coles, C. L. Game Conservation in a Changing Countryside. 16.50x (ISBN 0-273-40133-5, SpS). Sportshelf.
Grinnell, George B. & Sheldon, Charles, eds. Hunting & Conservation. LC 71-125741. (American Environmental Studies). 1970. Repr. of 1925 ed. 33.00 (ISBN 0-405-02666-8). Ayer Co Pubs.
Hornaday, William T. Thirty Years War for Wild Life. LC 71-125768. (American Environmental Studies). 1970. Repr. of 1931 ed. 14.00 (ISBN 0-405-02675-7). Ayer Co Pubs.
Rudman, Jack. Game Warden. (Career Examination Ser.: C-2012). (Cloth bdg. avail. on request). pap. 12.00 (ISBN 0-8373-2012-7). Natl Learning.
Spottiswoode, J. Moorland Gamekeeper. LC 77-74356. 1977. 7.50 (ISBN 0-7153-7384-6). David & Charles.
Steele, Melba. Cowboy, Game Warden & Longhorns. 104p. 1981. 6.95 (ISBN 0-686-72645-6). Dorrance.
Tillet, Paul. Doe Day: The Antlerless Deer Controversy in New Jersey. 1963. pap. 9.00 (ISBN 0-8135-0419-8). Rutgers U Pr.
Weitz, Chauncey. A Game Warden's Diary: Nineteen Thirty-Three to Nineteen Sixty-Five. 1983. deluxe ed. 15.00 (ISBN 0-932558-16-X). Willow Creek.

GAME THEORY
see also Decision-Making; Games of Chance (Mathematics); Games of Strategy (Mathematics); Statistical Decision
Aizerman, M. A., et al. Sixteen Papers on Differential & Difference Equations, Functional Analysis, Games & Control. LC 51-5559. (Translations Ser.: No. 2, Vol. 87). 1970. 36.00 (ISBN 0-8218-1787-6, TRANS 2-87). Am Math.
Aubin, J. P. Mathematical Methods of Game & Economic Theory. 2nd ed. (Studies in Mathematics & Its Applications: Vol. 7). 616p. 1982. 98.00 (ISBN 0-444-85184-4, North-Holland). Elsevier.
Aubin, Jean-Pierre. Applied Abstract Analysis. LC 77-2382. (Pure & Applied Mathematics Ser.). 263p. 1977. 47.50x (ISBN 0-471-02146-6, Pub. by Wiley-Interscience). Wiley.
Aumann, R. J. & Harsanyi, J. C., eds. Essays in Game Theory & Mathematical Economics. 196p. 1981. pap. text ed. 21.95x (ISBN 3-411-01609-4). Birkhauser.
Bailey, Norman & Feder, Stuart. Operational Conflict Analysis. 1973. 9.00 (ISBN 0-8183-0145-7). Pub Aff Pr.
Bartos, Otomar J. Simple Models of Group Behavior. LC 67-21498. (Illus.). 345p. 1967. 36.00x (ISBN 0-231-02894-6); pap. 18.00x (ISBN 0-231-02893-8). Columbia U Pr.
Borch, Karl H. Economics of Uncertainty. LC 68-10503. (Princeton Studies in Mathematical Economics: Vol. 2). 1968. 32.00x (ISBN 0-691-04124-5). Princeton U Pr.
Border, Kim C. Fixed Point Theorems with Applications to Economics & Game Theory. (Illus.). 128p. 1985. 29.95 (ISBN 0-521-26564-9). Cambridge U Pr.
Brams, S. J. Superior Beings-If They Exist, How Would We Know? Game-Theoretic Implications of Omniscience, Immortality, & Incomprehensibility. (Illus.). 192p. 1983. 23.00 (ISBN 0-387-91223-1); pap. 11.95 (ISBN 0-387-90877-3). Springer-Verlag.
Brams, Steven J. Superpower Games: Applying Game Theory to Superpower Conflict. LC 84-21876. (Illus.). 192p. 1985. text ed. 22.50x (ISBN 0-300-03323-0, Y-529); pap. 6.95x (ISBN 0-300-03364-8). Yale U Pr.
Collatz, L. & Wetterling, W. Optimization Problems. Hadsack, P. R., tr. from Ger. (Applied Mathematical Sciences Ser.: Vol. 17). (Illus.). 370p. (Orig.). 1975. pap. text ed. 22.00 (ISBN 0-387-90143-4). Springer-Verlag.
Conway, John. On Numbers & Games. (London Mathematical Society Monographs). 1976. 34.50 (ISBN 0-12-186350-6). Acad Pr.
Dresher, Melvin, et al, eds. Advances in Game Theory. (Annals of Mathematics Studies, Vol. 52). (Orig.). 17.50 (ISBN 0-691-07902-1). Princeton U Pr.

Hunt, V. Daniel. The Gasohol Handbook. LC 81-6543. (Illus.). 580p. 1981. 45.00 (ISBN 0-8311-1137-2). Indus Pr.
Medard, L. Gas Encyclopedia. 1150p. 1976. 191.50 (ISBN 0-444-41492-4). Elsevier.
Nineteen Eighty-One Gas Research Conference Proceedings. LC 81-86225. (Illus.). 1830p. 1982. 56.00 (ISBN 0-86587-094-2). Gov Insts.
Ozima, Minoru & Podosek, Frank A. Noble Gas Geochemistry. LC 83-5226. 400p. 1984. 79.50 (ISBN 0-521-23939-7). Cambridge U Pr.
Satriana, M., ed. New Developments in Flue Gas Desulfurization Technology. LC 81-11045. (Pollution Tech. Rev. 82). (Illus.). 326p. 1982. 45.00 (ISBN 0-8155-0863-8). Noyes.
United Nations Institute for Training & Research. International Conference on the Future Supply of Nature-Made Petroleum & Gas: Proceedings. 1977. pap. text ed. 61.00 (ISBN 0-08-021735-4). Pergamon.

GAS-ANALYSIS
see Gases–Analysis

GAS, BOTTLED
see Liquefied Petroleum Gas

GAS, NATURAL
see also Boring; Gas Industry; Liquefied Natural Gas; Liquefied Petroleum Gas; Oil Fields

Alperovitch, I. M., et al. Magnetotellurics in Oil Exploration in the U.S.S.R. Keller, G. V., tr. Vozoff, K. & Asten, M., eds. 65p. 1982. pap. 12.00 (ISBN 0-931830-19-2). Soc Exploration.
American Gas Association & Payne, F. William. Guide to New Natural Gas Utilization Technologies. LC 83-49499. 300p. 1984. text ed. 39.00 (ISBN 0-915586-94-0). Fairmont Pr.
American Gas Association. Policy Evaluation & Analysis Group. New Technologies for Gas Energy Supply & Efficient Use: 1983 Update. LC 83-174168. (Illus.). 43p. Date not set. price not set. Am Gas Assn.
Beebe, B. W., et al, eds. Natural Gases of North America: A Symposium. LC 68-15769. (American Association of Petroleum Geologists Memoir Ser.: No. 9). Vol. 1. pap. 160.00 (ISBN 0-317-10363-6, 2050025); Vol. 2. pap. 160.00 (ISBN 0-317-10364-4). Bks Demand UMI.
Brown, Keith C., ed. Regulation of the Natural Gas Producing Industry. LC 71-186502. (Resources for the Future Ser.). (Illus.). 271p. 1972. pap. 10.00x (ISBN 0-8018-1383-2). Johns Hopkins.
Chaballe, L. Y. & Masuy, L. Elsevier's Oil & Gas Field Dictionary. 672p. (in 6 languages plus Arabic suppl.). 1980. 138.50 (ISBN 0-444-41833-4). Elsevier.
Challa, Krishna. Investment & Returns in Exploration & the Impact on the Supply of Oil & Natural Gas Reserves. Bruchey, Stuart, ed. LC 78-22667. (Energy in the American Economy Ser.). (Illus.). 1979. lib. bdg. 16.00x (ISBN 0-405-11971-2). Ayer Co Pubs.
Committee on Gas Production Opportunities. Potential for Increasing Production of Natural Gas from Existing Fields in the Near Term. 1978. pap. 7.75 (ISBN 0-309-02784-5). Natl Acad Pr.
Conference on Natural Gas Research & Technology (2nd: 1972: Atlanta) Staff. Proceedings of the Second Conference on Natural Gas Research & Technology Sponsored by American Gas Association & Institute of Gas Technology, Atlanta, Georgia, June 5-7, 1972. White, Jack W. & Kragulski, Maryann, eds. pap. 160.00 (ISBN 0-317-26319-6, 2024236). Bks Demand UMI.
Consumers Power Company. Fundamentals of Natural Gas. LC 74-100858. (Supervision Ser.). 1970. pap. text ed. 14.95 (ISBN 0-201-01180-8). Addison-Wesley.
Curry, R. N. Fundamentals of Natural Gas Conditioning. 118p. 1981. 39.95x (ISBN 0-87814-162-6). Pennwell Bks.
Davis, J. D. Blue Gold: The Political Economy of Natural Gas. (World Industry Studies: No. 3). 300p. 1984. text ed. 29.50 (ISBN 0-04-338112-X). Allen Unwin.
Development of Petroleum & Natural Gas Resources in Asia & the Far East: Proceedings, Vols. 1 & 3. (Mineral Resources Development Ser.: No. 41). Vol. 1. pap. 19.00 (ISBN 0-686-93048-7, UN73/2F/14V2, UN); Vol. 3. pap. 8.50 (ISBN 0-686-98882-5). Unipub.
Effect of Leaking Natural Gas on Soil & Vegetation in Urban Areas. (Agricultural Research Reports: 778). 1972. pap. 14.00 (ISBN 90-220-0401-5, PDC30, PUDOC). Unipub.
Ffooks, Roger. Natural Gas by Sea: The Development of a New Technology. 248p. 1982. 99.00x (ISBN 0-85614-054-6, Pub. by Gentry England); pap. 50.00x. State Mutual Bk.
Field Handling of Natural Gas. 3rd ed. (Illus.). 143p. 1972. pap. text ed. 6.00 (ISBN 0-88698-077-1, 3.10030). PETEX.
Hawkins, Clark A. The Field Price Regulation of Natural Gas. LC 70-79582. ix, 268p. 1969. 12.00 (ISBN 0-8130-0427-6). U Presses Fla.
Herman, Stephen A., et al. Natural Gas Users' Handbook. LC 76-27247. pap. 32.00 (ISBN 0-317-29428-8, 2024301). Bks Demand UMI.
Ikoku, Chi U. Natural Gas Production Engineering. LC 83-21617. 517p. 1984. 39.50 (ISBN 0-471-89483-4). Wiley.
--Natural Gas Reservoir Engineering. LC 84-7260. 503p. 1984. text ed. 34.95 (ISBN 0-471-89482-6, Pub. by Wiley); Solutions Manual avail. (ISBN 0-471-87813-8). Wiley.
Kash, Don E., et al. Energy Under the Ocean: A Technology Assessment. LC 73-8374. (Illus.). 350p. 1973. pap. 12.95x (ISBN 0-8061-1145-3). U of Okla Pr.
Katz, D. L. Handbook of Natural Gas Engineering. 1959. 99.50 (ISBN 0-07-033384-X). McGraw.
Kruse, Curtis & Haas, Hank. Plant Processing of Natural Gas. (Illus.). 114p. (Orig.). 1980. pap. text ed. 6.00 (ISBN 0-88698-115-8). Petex.
Lawrence, Anthony G. Pricing & Planning in the U. S. Natural Gas Industry: An Econometric & Programming Study. Bruchey, Stuart, ed. LC 78-22693. (Energy in the American Economy Ser.). (Illus.). 1979. lib. bdg. 17.00x (ISBN 0-405-11996-8). Ayer Co Pubs.
Lovejoy, Wallace F. Methods of Estimating Reserves of Crude Oil, Natural Gas, & Natural Gas Liquids. LC 65-24790. pap. 45.50 (ISBN 0-317-26470-2, 2023805). Bks Demand UMI.
Makogon, Yuri F. Hydrates of Natural Gas. Cieslewicz, W. J., tr. from Russian. 237p. 1981. 37.95x (ISBN 0-87814-165-0). Pennwell Bks.
Mangan, Frank. Pipeliners. LC 77-73481. (Illus.). 1977. 20.00 (ISBN 0-930208-06-4, Pub. by Guynes Press). Mangan Bks.
Mangone, Gerard J. The Future of Gas & Oil from the Sea. 240p. 1983. 35.00 (ISBN 0-442-26164-0). Van Nos Reinhold.
Marcus, Kenneth K. The National Government & the Natural Gas Industry, 1946-56: A Study in the Making of a National Policy. Bruchey, Stuart, ed. LC 78-22697. (Energy in the American Economy Ser.). (Illus.). 1979. lib. bdg. 83.00x (ISBN 0-405-12000-1). Ayer Co Pubs.
Natural Gas Processing & Utilization: Proceedings, No. 44, Dublin, April 1976. 420p. 1981. 160.00x (ISBN 0-85295-011-X, Pub. by Inst Chem Eng England). State Mutual Bk.
Netschert, Bruce C. The Future Supply of Oil & Gas: A Study of the Availability of Crude Oil, Natural Gas, & Natural Gas Liquids in the United States in the Period Through 1975. LC 77-23269. (Resources for the Future Ser.). 1977. Repr. of 1958 ed. lib. bdg. 18.75 (ISBN 0-8371-9473-3, NEOG). Greenwood.
OECD Staff. Natural Gas Prospects to 2000. 173p. 1982. pap. 24.00 (ISBN 92-64-12309-1). OECD.
Oil & Natural Gas Resources of Canada 1976: Oil Sands & Heavy Oils - the Prospects, 2 pts. 1978. pap. 5.50 set (ISBN 0-685-89403-7, SSC97, SSC); Vol. 1. pap. (ISBN 0-660-00859-9); Vol. 2. pap. (ISBN 0-685-89404-5). Unipub.
Oppenheimer, Ernest J. Natural Gas: The New Energy Leader. rev. ed. 188p. 1982. pap. 10.00 (ISBN 0-9603982-3-6). Pen & Podium.
Page, John. Cost Estimating Man-Hour Manual for Pipelines & Marine Structures. LC 76-40868. 336p. 1977. 39.95x (ISBN 0-87201-157-7). Gulf Pub.
Pierce, Richard J., Jr. Natural Gas Regulation Handbook. 1980. pap. 75.00 (ISBN 0-917386-29-9). Exec Ent Inc.
Riva, Joseph P., Jr., et al. Prospects for U. S. Conventional Oil & Gas Production to the Year 2000. (WVSS in Natural Resources & Energy Management Ser.). 150p. 1985. pap. text ed. 22.50x (ISBN 0-8133-7067-1). Westview.
Satriana, M. Unconventional Natural Gas: Resources, Potential & Technology. LC 80-15215. (Energy Technology Review: No. 56). 358p. (Orig.). 1980. 42.00 (ISBN 0-8155-0808-5). Noyes.
Smith, R. V. Practical Natural Gas Engineering. LC 82-24684. 248p. 1983. 49.95x (ISBN 0-87814-225-8, P-4331). Pennwell Bks.
Spann, Robert M. The Supply of Natural Resources: The Case of Oil & Natural Gas. Bruchey, Stuart, ed. LC 78-22748. (Energy in the American Economy Ser.). (Illus.). 1979. lib. bdg. 12.00x (ISBN 0-405-12013-3). Ayer Co Pubs.
Spooner, Robert D. Response of Natural Gas & Crude Oil Exploration & Discovery to Economic Incentives. Bruchey, Stuart, ed. LC 78-22749. (Energy in the American Economy Ser.). (Illus.). 1979. lib. bdg. 21.00x (ISBN 0-405-12014-1). Ayer Co Pubs.
Starratt, Patricia E. The Natural Gas Shortage & the Congress. LC 74-29378. 1975. pap. 4.25 (ISBN 0-8447-3148-X). Am Enterprise.
Stern, Jonathan P. Soviet Natural Gas Development to Nineteen Ninety: The Implications for the CMEA & the West. LC 79-2705. 208p. 1980. 27.50x (ISBN 0-669-03233-6). Lexington Bks.
Tenneco Oil Company. Operators Handbook. LC 61-13964. 210p. 1961. 19.95x (ISBN 0-87201-643-9). Gulf Pub.
Tiratsoo, E. N. Natural Gas. 3rd ed. LC 79-92137. 360p. 1980. 49.95x (ISBN 0-87201-578-5). Gulf Pub.
--Natural Gas: A Study. LC 67-28865. 386p. 1967. 59.50 (ISBN 0-306-30317-5, Plenum Pr). Plenum Pub.
Tussing, Arlon R. & Barlow, Connie. The Natural Gas Industry: Evolution, Structure, & Economics. LC 83-22520. 304p. 1984. 29.95x (ISBN 0-88410-975-5). Ballinger Pub.
United Nations Economic Commission for Europe. Gas Situation in the EEC Region Around the Year 1990. (European Committee for Economic Perspectives: Vol. 18). 1979. 81.00 (ISBN 0-08-024465-3). Pergamon.
U. S. Dept. of the Interior. Hearings Before the Secretary of the Interior on Leasing of Oil Lands & Natural-Gas Wells in Indian Territory & Territory of Oklahoma: May 8, 24, 25 & 29, & June 7, & 19, 1906. LC 72-2841. (Use & Abuse of America's Natural Resources Ser.). 92p. 1972. Repr. of 1906 ed. 14.00 (ISBN 0-405-04509-3). Ayer Co Pubs.
World Natural Gas-Two Thousand. 232p. 1978. 180.00 (ISBN 0-686-76143-X). Barrows Co.

GAS AND OIL ENGINES
see also Diesel Motor; Jet Propulsion; Motor-Boats

Anderson, Edwin P. Gas Engine Manual. 3rd ed. LC 76-45883. 1985. 12.95 (ISBN 0-8161-1707-1). Audel.
Ayres, Robert U. & McKenna, Richard P. Alternatives to the Internal Combustion Engine: Impacts on Environmental Quality. LC 74-181555. (Resources for the Future Ser). 340p. 1972. 27.50x (ISBN 0-8018-1369-7). Johns Hopkins.
Baxa, Donald E. & Petska, Darrell E. Noise Control in Internal Combustion Engines. 511p. 1982. 68.50 (ISBN 0-471-05870-X). Wiley.
Benson, Rowland S. Thermodynamics & Gas Dynamics of Internal Combustion Engines, Vol. 1. Horlock, J. H. & Winterbone, D., eds. (Illus.). 1982. text ed. 125.00x (ISBN 0-19-856210-1). Oxford U Pr.
Benson, Rowland S. & Whitehouse, N. D. Internal Combustion Engines, 2 vols. LC 79-40359. (Thermodynamics & Fluid Mechanics for Mechanical Engineers). (Illus.). 1979. Set. 28.00 set (ISBN 0-08-031630-1); Vol. 1. pap. 15.75 (ISBN 0-08-022718-X); Vol. 2. pap. 15.75 (ISBN 0-08-022720-1). Pergamon.
Billiet, Walter E. Small Gas Engines & Power Transmission Systems: A Repair & Maintenance Handbook. LC 82-3866. (Illus.). 281p. 1982. 20.95 (ISBN 0-13-814327-7); pap. 12.95 (ISBN 0-13-814319-6). P-H.
Brown, Arlen D. & Strickland, R. Mack. Tractor & Small Engine Maintenance. 5th ed. 350p. 1983. 17.00 (ISBN 0-8134-2258-2); text ed. 12.75x. Interstate.
Campbell, Ashley S. Thermodynamic Analysis of Combustion Engines. LC 84-12203. 376p. 1985. Repr. of 1979 ed. lib. bdg. 40.00 (ISBN 0-89874-774-0). Krieger.
Combustion, Emission & Analysis. 1985. 42.00 (ISBN 0-89883-723-5, P162). Soc Auto Engineers.
Critser, James R., Jr. Air Pollution Control: Internal Combustion Engines - Exhaust Treatment 1976. (Ser. 4IC-76). 1977. 115.00 (ISBN 0-914428-40-3). Lexington Data.
Crouse, William H. Small Engines: Operation & Maintenance. (Automotive Technology Ser.). (Illus.). 448p. 1973. pap. text ed. 22.85 (ISBN 0-07-014691-8). McGraw.
Crouse, William H. & Anglin, Donald L. Small Engine Mechanics. 2nd ed. LC 79-4658. (Illus.). 1979. pap. text ed. 22.85 (ISBN 0-07-014795-7). McGraw.
Cummins, C. Lyle, Jr. Internal Fire: The Internal Combustion Engine, 1673-1900. LC 75-40701. (Illus.). 1976. 20.00x (ISBN 0-917308-01-8). Carnot Pr.
Darack, Arthur & Consumer Group, Inc. Staff. Small Engine Maintenance & Repair for Outdoor Power Equipment. (Illus.). 192p. 1984. 18.95 (ISBN 0-13-813148-1); pap. 9.95 (ISBN 0-13-813130-9). P-H.
Dempsey, Paul. How to Repair Small Gasoline Engines. 2nd ed. LC 76-45056. 1976. pap. 9.95 (ISBN 0-8306-5917-X, 917). TAB Bks.
Drake, George. Small Gas Engines: Maintenance, Troubleshooting & Repair. 500p. 1981. text ed. 21.95 (ISBN 0-8359-7014-0); soln. manual avail. (ISBN 0-8359-7015-9). Reston.
Ferguson, Colin R. Internal Combustion Engines: Applied Thermosciences. 560p. Date not set. 36.00 (ISBN 0-471-88129-5). Wiley.
Goring, Loris. The Care & Repair of Marine Gasoline Engines. LC 80-84623. (Illus.). 146p. 1981. 17.50 (ISBN 0-87742-139-0). Intl Marine.
Gray, J. A. & Barrow, R. W. Small Gas Engines. 357p. 1976. pap. text ed. 19.95 (ISBN 0-13-813113-9). P-H.
Hickling, Robert & Kamal, Mounir M. Engine Noise: Excitation, Vibration, & Radiation. LC 82-160708. (General Motors Research Laboratories Symposia Ser.). 506p. 1982. 69.50x (ISBN 0-306-41168-7, Plenum Pr). PLenum Pub.
Hoerner, Harry & Bear, W. Forrest. Small Gasoline Engines, Operation & Maintenance. rev. ed. (Illus.). 136p. 1984. pap. 5.80x (ISBN 0-913163-17-1). Hobar Pubns.
Kates, Edgar J. & Luck, W. E. Diesel & High Compression Gas Engines. 3rd ed. (Illus.). 1974. pap. 18.95 (ISBN 0-8269-0203-0). Am Technical.
Kaupp, A. & Goss, J. R. State of the Art: Small Scale (to 50 kw) Gas Producer Engine Systems. (Illus.). 278p. (Orig.). 1983. 40.00 (ISBN 0-942914-03-1); pap. 20.00 (ISBN 0-942914-02-3). Tipi Wkshp Bks.
Kowalewicz, A. Combustion Systems of High-Speed Piston I. C. Engines. (Studies in Mechanical Engineering: Vol. 3). 1984. 90.75 (ISBN 0-444-99637-0, I-097-84). Elsevier.
Lewis, Alexander D. Gas Power Dynamics. LC 77-15095. 544p. 1978. Repr. of 1962 ed. lib. bdg. 34.00 (ISBN 0-88275-629-X). Krieger.
Lucke, Charles E. & Woodward, S. M. The Use of Alcohol & Gasoline in Farm Engines. (Illus.). 100p. 1980. pap. 4.95 (ISBN 0-936222-04-2). Rutan Pub.
MacDonald, K. L. Small Gasoline Engines Student's Workbook. 2nd ed. 1973. pap. 4.24 scp (ISBN 0-672-97632-3). Bobbs.
Mason, L. C. Model Four Stroke Petrol Engines. rev. ed. (Illus.). 116p. 1983. pap. 9.95 (ISBN 0-85242-431-0, Pub. by Argus). Aztex.
Multicylinder Test Sequences for Evaluating Automotive Engine Oils, Pt. II, STP 315H: Sequence IIID. 115p. 1980. soft cover 13.00x (ISBN 0-8031-0522-3, 04-315090-12); 16.00 (ISBN 0-8031-0523-1, 04-315091-12). ASTM.
Multicylinder Test Sequences for Evaluating Engine Oils, Pt. I: Sequence ID- STP 315H. 111p. 1980. soft cover 13.00x (ISBN 0-686-76072-7, 04-315080-12); looseleaf 16.00x (ISBN 0-686-76073-5, 04-315081-12). ASTM.
OECD Staff. Annual Oil & Gas Statistics, 1980-1981. (Fr. & Eng.). 524p. (Orig.). 1983. pap. 36.00x (ISBN 92-64-02417-4). OECD.
Potter, Philip J. Power Plant Theory & Design. 2nd ed. (Illus.). 710p. 1959. 47.50 (ISBN 0-471-06689-3). Wiley.
Reed, T. B., ed. Biomass Gasification: Principles & Technology. LC 81-9667. (Energy Tech. Rev.: No. 67). (Illus.). 401p. 1981. 42.00 (ISBN 0-8155-0852-2). Noyes.
Rogowski, Augustus R. Elements of Internal Combustion Engines. (Illus.). 1953. text ed. 45.00 (ISBN 0-07-053575-2). McGraw.
Rudman, Jack. Small Engine Repair. (Occupational Competency Examination Ser.: OCE-32). (Cloth bdg. avail. on request). pap. 13.95 (ISBN 0-8373-5732-2). Natl Learning.
Scheel, Lyman F. Gas Machinery. LC 70-149760. pap. 67.50 (ISBN 0-317-26815-5, 2024312). Bks Demand UMI.
Schilling, A. Automobile Engine Lubrication. (Illus.). 480p. 1972. text ed. 55.00x (ISBN 0-900645-00-8). Scholium Intl.
Shear Stability of Multigrade Crankcase Oil, DS49. 1973. pap. 7.75 (ISBN 0-8031-0090-6, 05-049000-12). ASTM.
Single Cylinder Engine Tests, Part II: Caterpillar 1H2 Test Method- STP 509A. 94p. 1979. looseleaf 12.75 (ISBN 0-8031-0572-X, 04-509021-12); pap. 9.75 (ISBN 0-8031-0571-1, 04-509020-12). ASTM.
Stephenson, George. Small Gasoline Engines. 4th ed. (Illus.). 288p. 1984. pap. text ed. 13.80 (ISBN 0-8273-2242-9); instr's guide 3.00 (ISBN 0-8273-2243-7). Delmar.
Stone, Richard. Introduction to Internal Combustion Engines. (Illus.). 330p. 1985. text ed. 55.00x (ISBN 0-333-37593-9, Pub. by Macmillan London); pap. text ed. 24.50x (ISBN 0-333-37594-7, Pub. by Macmillan London). Sheridan.
Swedish Academy of Engineering. Gengas: The Swedish Classic on Wood Powered Vehicles. 2nd ed. Reed, Thomas B. & Jantzen, Dan, eds. Geuther, Maria, tr. from Swedish. (Illus.). 329p. 1982. pap. 15.00 (ISBN 0-942914-01-5). Tipi Wkshp Bks.
Taylor, Charles F. The Internal Combustion Engine in Theory & Practice: Combustion, Fuels, Materials, Design, Vol. 2. 2nd, rev. ed. 800p. 1984. pap. text ed. 19.50x (ISBN 0-262-70017-X). MIT Pr.
--The Internal-Combustion Engine in Theory & Practice, Vol. 2: Combustion, Fuels, Materials, Design. 1968. 38.00x (ISBN 0-262-20052-X); pap. 18.50x (ISBN 0-262-70016-6). MIT Pr.

Uzkan, T., ed. Flows in Internal Combustion Engines. 1982. 24.00 (H00245). ASME.
Watson, N. & Janota, M. S. Turbocharging the Internal Combustion Engine. 608p. 1982. 96.50 (ISBN 0-471-87072-2, Pub. by Wiley-Interscience). Wiley.
Weathers & Hunter. Fundamentals of Small Gas Engines. 1983. text ed. 26.95 (ISBN 0-8359-2192-1); pap. text ed. 20.95 (ISBN 0-8359-2191-3). Reston.
Weissler, Paul. Small Gas Engines: How to Repair & Maintain Them. LC 75-13334. (A Popular Science Bk). (Illus.). 288p. 1975. 15.34i (ISBN 0-06-014564-1, HarpT). Har-Row.
Wendel, Charles H. American Gasoline Engines Since 1872. Dammann, George H., ed. LC 83-71594. (Agricultural Ser.). (Illus.). 584p. 1983. 34.95 (ISBN 0-912612-22-3). Crestline.
Zinner, K. A. Supercharging of Internal Combustion Engines. (Illus.). 290p. 1978. pap. 32.40 (ISBN 0-387-08544-0). Springer-Verlag.

GAS AND OIL ENGINES–CARBURETORS
see Carburetors

GAS APPLIANCES
see also Gas Flow
Meyerink, George. Appliance Service Handbook. (Illus.). 464p. 1973. ref. ed. 29.95x (ISBN 0-13-038844-0). P-H.
National Fuel Gas Code. (Fifty Ser.). 146p. 1974. pap. 7.50 (ISBN 0-685-46069-X, 54). Natl Fire Prot.

GAS AS FUEL
see also Liquefied Petroleum Gas
Kaupp, A. Gasification of Rice Hulls: Theory & Praxis. 330p. 1984. pap. 27.00 (ISBN 3-528-02002-4, Pub. by Vieweg & Sohn Germany). Heyden.
Kaupp, A. & Goss, J. R. Small Scale Gas Producer Engine Systems. 290p. 1984. pap. 24.00 (ISBN 3-528-02001-6, Pub. by Vieweg & Sohn Germany). Heyden.
Lyons, T. P., ed. A Step to Energy Independence: Gasohol. LC 81-68334. (Illus.). 346p. 1982. 45.00x (ISBN 0-412-00241-8, NO. 6710, Pub. by Chapman & Hall). Methuen Inc.
National Fire Protection Association. National Fuel Gas Code: 1980. 1980. 9.50 (ISBN 0-317-07374-5, NFPA 54). Natl Fire Prot.
Pritchard, R. Guy & Connor, N. E. Handbook of Industrial Gas Utilization: Engineering Principles & Practice. LC 77-22278. 794p. 1977. 47.50 (ISBN 0-442-26635-9). Krieger.
Wise, Donald L., ed. Fuel Gas Developments. 264p. 1984. 77.00 (ISBN 0-8493-6092-7). CRC Pr.
--Fuel Gas Systems. 272p. 1983. 79.00 (ISBN 0-8493-6091-9). CRC Pr.

GAS BEARINGS
see Gas-Lubricated Bearings

GAS CHROMATOGRAPHY
Ambrose, D. Gas Chromatography. 2nd ed. LC 72-169709. 227p. 1971. 16.50 (ISBN 0-442-20362-4, Pub. by Van Nos Reinhold). Krieger.
Analysis of Drugs & Metabolites by Gas Chromatography - Mass Spectometry: Natural, Pyrolytic & Metabolic Products of Tobacco & Marijuana, Vol. 7. 1980. 89.75 (ISBN 0-8247-6861-2). Dekker.
Bailey, J. C. & Viney, N. J. Analysis of Odours by Gas Chromatography & Allied Techniques, 1979. 1981. 75.00x (ISBN 0-686-97023-3, Pub. by W Spring England). State Mutual Bk.
Baiulescu, G. E. & Ilie, A. V. Stationary Phases in Gas Chromatography. 1975. text ed. 65.00 (ISBN 0-08-018075-2). Pergamon.
Berezkin, V. G. Chemical Methods in Gas Chromatography. (Journal of Chromatography Library: No. 24). 314p. 1983. 81.00 (ISBN 0-444-41951-9, I-383-83). Elsevier.
Berezkin, V. G. & Tatarinskii, V. S. Gas-Chromatographic Analysis of Trace Impurities. LC 78-16035. 288p. 1973. 45.00 (ISBN 0-306-10879-8, Consultants). Plenum Pub.
Berezkin, Viktor G. Analytical Reaction Gas Chromatography. LC 68-21473. (Illus.). 193p. 1968. 29.50x (ISBN 0-306-30338-8, Plenum Pr). Plenum Pub.
Brenner, N., ed. International Gas Chromatography Symposium, Third. 1962. 109.00 (ISBN 0-12-131650-5). Acad Pr.
Budde, William L. & Eichelberger, James W., eds. Organics Analysis Using Gas Chromatography-Mass Spectrometry: A Techniques & Procedures Manual. LC 79-88484. (Illus.). 1979. 39.95 (ISBN 0-250-40318-8). Butterworth.
Butlin, A. G. & D'Oyly-Watkins, C., eds. Gas Chromatography Abstracts: Cumulative Indexes, 1958-1963, Inclusive. LC 63-22896. pap. 78.80 (ISBN 0-317-29011-8). Bks Demand UMI.
Coates, Donald R., ed. Gas Chromatography. 1960. 79.50 (ISBN 0-12-177350-7). Acad Pr.
Conder, John R. & Young, Colin L. Physiochemical Measurements by Gas Chromatography. LC 78-9899. 1979. 139.95 (ISBN 0-471-99674-2, Pub. by Wiley-Interscience). Wiley.
Crippen, Raymond C. GC-LC, Instruments, Derivatives in Identifying Pollutants & Unknowns. (Illus.). 452p. 1983. 83.00 (ISBN 0-08-027185-5). Pergamon.
Crompton, T. R. Gas Chromatography of Organometallic Compounds. LC 82-523. 600p. 1982. 85.00x (ISBN 0-306-40987-9, Plenum Pr). Plenum Pub.
Domsky, I. & Perry, J., eds. Recent Advances in Gas Chromatography. 1971. 85.00 (ISBN 0-8247-1146-7). Dekker.
Drozd, J. Chemical Derivatization in Gas Chromatography. (Journal of Chromatography Library: Vol. 19). 232p. 1981. 57.50 (ISBN 0-444-41917-9). Elsevier.
Drucker, D. B. Microbiological Applications of Gas Chromatography. LC 80-40447. 300p. 1981. 110.00 (ISBN 0-521-22365-2). Cambridge U Pr.
Eik-Nes, K. B. & Horning, E. C. Gas Phase Chromatography of Steroids. LC 68-18620. (Monographs on Endocrinology: Vol. 2). (Illus.). 1968. 29.00 (ISBN 0-387-04277-6). Springer-Verlag.
Ettre, L. S. Open Tubular Columns in Gas Chromatography. LC 65-13583. 164p. 1965. 25.00x (ISBN 0-306-30188-1, Plenum Pr). Plenum Pub.
Federal Institute for Biology in Agriculture & Forestry, Institute for Plant Protection Agent Research, Berlin-Dahlem & Ebing, Winifried. Gaschromatographie der Pflanzenschutzmittel: Tabellarische Literaturreferate, 5 vols. new ed. (Ger.). Vol. I, 1970. 20.00 (ISBN 0-913106-09-7); Vol. II, 1972. 15.00 (ISBN 0-913106-10-0); Vol. III. 15.00 (ISBN 0-913106-11-9); Vol. IV. 15.00 (ISBN 0-913106-12-7); Vol. V, 1975. 15.00 (ISBN 0-913106-13-5). PolyScience.
Fowler, L., ed. Gas Chromatography. 1963. 65.00 (ISBN 0-12-263150-1). Acad Pr.
Gas Chromatographic Data Compilation: First Supplement, AMD 25 A-S1. 726p. 1971. 40.00 (ISBN 0-8031-0806-0, 10-025011-39). ASTM.
Gas Chromatography Institute, 3rd Annual Buffalo, N. Y. April 4-6, 1961. Progress in Industrial Gas Chromatography: Proceedings, Vol. 1. LC 61-15520. pap. 59.80 (ISBN 0-317-10634-1, 2020700). Bks Demand UMI.
Goodman, Stephen I. & Markey, Sanford P., eds. Diagnosis of Organic Acidemias by Gas Chromatography-Mass Spectrometry. LC 81-8228. (Laboratory & Research Methods in Biology & Medicine Ser.: Vol. 6). 170p. 1981. 28.00 (ISBN 0-8451-1655-X). A R Liss.
Grob, R. L. Modern Practice of Gas Chromatography. 2nd ed. 912p. 1985. 65.00 (ISBN 0-471-87157-5). Wiley.
Grob, Robert L., ed. Modern Practice of Gas Chromatography. 654p. 1977. text ed. 58.00 (ISBN 0-471-01564-4). Wiley.
Gudzinowicz, B. J. Analysis of Drugs & Metabolites by Gas Chromatography - Mass Spectrometry: Antipsychotic, Antiemetic & Antidepressant Drugs, Vol. 3. 1977. 49.75 (ISBN 0-8247-6586-9). Dekker.
--Gas Chromatographic Analysis of Drugs & Pesticides. (Chromatographic Science Ser: Vol. 2). 1967. 125.00 (ISBN 0-8247-1255-2). Dekker.
Gudzinowicz, B. J., et al. Fundamentals of Integrated Gc-Ms, Pt. III: The Integrated Gc-Ms Analytical System. (Chromotographic Science Ser.: Vol. 7). 1977. 125.00 (ISBN 0-8247-6431-5). Dekker.
--Fundamentals of Integrated Gc-Ms, Pt. I: Gas Chromatograpghy. (Chromatographic Science Ser.: Vol. 7). 1976. 95.00 (ISBN 0-8247-6365-3). Dekker.
Gudzinowicz, Michael J. & Gudzinowicz, Benjamin J. The Analysis of Drugs & Related Compounds by Gas Chromotography-Mass Spectometry: Respiratory Gases, Volatile Anesthetics, Ethyl Alcohol, & Related Toxicological Materials, Vol. 1. 1977. 89.75 (ISBN 0-8247-6576-1). Dekker.
Hachenberg, H. & Schmidt, A. P. Gas Chromatographic Head Space Analysis. 136p. 1977. 49.95 (ISBN 0-471-25753-2, Pub. by Wiley Heyden). Wiley.
Haken, J. K. Gas Chromatography of Coating Materials. 352p. 1974. 85.00 (ISBN 0-8247-6123-5). Dekker.
Institute of Petroleum. Gas Chromatography Abstracts: Cumulative Indexes. 1971. Indexes 1958-63. 40.75 (ISBN 0-444-39952-6, Pub. by Applied Sci England); Indexes 1964-68. 44.50 (ISBN 0-85334-484-1). Elsevier.
--Gas Chromatography Abstracts: 1963. 286p. 1963. 31.50 (ISBN 0-444-39990-9, Pub. by Elsevier Applied Sci England). Elsevier.
--Gas Chromatography Abstracts: 1964-67 & 1969-72. 1964-73. 1964 31.50 (ISBN 0-444-39976-3, Pub. by Elsevier Applied Sci England); 1965 31.50 (ISBN 0-444-39960-7); 1966 31.50 (ISBN 0-444-39954-2); 1967 31.50 (ISBN 0-444-39947-X); 1969 31.50 (ISBN 0-444-39930-5); 1970 44.50 (ISBN 0-85334-497-3); 1971 46.25 (ISBN 0-85334-478-7); 1972 44.50 (ISBN 0-85334-472-8). Elsevier.
Institute of Petroleum, et al. Gas Chromotography Symposia. 1964 44.50 (ISBN 0-444-39975-5); 1966 50.00 (ISBN 0-444-39957-7); 1968 o.p. 50.00 (ISBN 0-444-39939-9); 1970 50.00 (ISBN 0-85334-492-2); 1972 50.00 (ISBN 0-85334-479-5). Elsevier.
International Symposium on Gas Chromatography (7th: 1968: Copenhagen) Staff. Gas Chromatography, Nineteen Sixty-Eight. Harbourn, C. L., ed. pap. 134.80 (ISBN 0-317-29018-5, 2023686). Bks Demand UMI.
International Symposium on Gas Chromatography (5th: 1964: Brighton) Staff. Gas Chromatography, Nineteen Sixty-Four. Goldup, A., ed. pap. 99.50 (ISBN 0-317-29014-2, 2023685). Bks Demand UMI.
International Symposium on Gas Chromatography, 1966. Gas Chromatography 1966. Littlewood, A. B., ed. pap. 119.00 (ISBN 0-317-27251-9, 2023708). Bks Demand UMI.
International Symposium on Gas Chromatography, 1970. Gas Chromatography 1970. Stock, R., ed. pap. 115.80 (ISBN 0-317-27250-0, 2023709). Bks Demand UMI.
International Symposium, 3rd, Amsterdam, Sept. 1976. Analytical Pryolysis: Proceedings. Jones, C. E. & Cramers, C. A., eds. 424p. 1977. 83.00 (ISBN 0-444-41558-0). Elsevier.
The Interpretation of Vapor-Phase Infrared Spectra. Vol. 1 Group Frequency Data. 120.00 (ISBN 0-8456-0092-3); Vol. 2 Corresponding Spectra. 350.00 (ISBN 0-8456-0100-8); Set. 425.00. Sadtler Res.
Ioffe, B. V. & Vitenberg, A. G. Head Space Analysis & Related Methods in Gas Chromatography. LC 83-10632. 276p. 1984. 65.00 (ISBN 0-471-06507-2, Wiley-Interscience). Wiley.
Jack, David B. Drug Analysis by Gas Chromatography. 1984. 49.50 (ISBN 0-12-378250-3). Acad Pr.
Jennings. Applications of Glass Capillary Gas Chromatography. (Chromotographic Science Ser.: Vol. 14). 648p. 1981. 89.75 (ISBN 0-8247-1223-4). Dekker.
Jennings, Walter, ed. Gas Chromatography with Glass Capillary Columns. 2nd ed. LC 79-8851. 1980. 35.00 (ISBN 0-12-384360-X). Acad Pr.
Jones, R. A. Introduction to Gas-Liquid Chromatography. 1970. 39.50 (ISBN 0-12-389850-1). Acad Pr.
Kiselev, A. V. & Yashin, Ya I. Gas-Adsorption Chromatography. LC 69-12531. 250p. 1969. 34.50x (ISBN 0-306-30370-1, Plenum Pr). Plenum Pub.
Knapman, C. E., ed. Gas Chromatography Abstracts, 1966. LC 63-22896. pap. 81.80 (ISBN 0-317-27255-1, 2023704). Bks Demand UMI.
--Gas Chromatography Abstracts, 1967. LC 63-22896. pap. 75.00 (ISBN 0-317-27254-3, 2023705). Bks Demand UMI.
--Gas Chromatography Abstracts, 1969. LC 63-22896. pap. 76.80 (ISBN 0-317-27253-5, 2023706). Bks Demand UMI.
Knapman, C. E. & Maggs, R. J., eds. Gas & Liquid Chromatography Abstacts, 1970. LC 63-22896. pap. 93.00 (ISBN 0-317-27252-7, 2023707). Bks Demand UMI.
Knapman, C. E. H., ed. Gas & Liquid Chromatography Abstracts: Cumulative Indexes 1969-73. 381p. 1976. 70.50 (ISBN 0-85334-643-7, Pub. by Elsevier Applied Sci England). Elsevier.
Kolb, B. Applied Headspace Gas Chromatography. 224p. 1980. 49.95 (ISBN 0-471-25838-5, Pub. by Wiley Heyden). Wiley.
Laub, R. J. & Pecsok, R. L. Physicochemical Applications of Gas Chromatography. LC 78-5493. 300p. 1978. 41.50 (ISBN 0-471-51838-7). Krieger.
Lee, Milton L. & Yang, Frank J. Open Tubular Column Gas Chromatography Theory & Practice. LC 83-14780. 445p. 1984. 52.00X (ISBN 0-471-88024-8, Pub. by Wiley-Interscience). Wiley.
Lipsett, Mortimer, ed. Gas Chromatography of Steroids in Biological Fluids. LC 65-25243. 315p. 1965. 34.50x (ISBN 0-306-30204-7, Plenum Pr). Plenum Pub.
Lowe, P. G. Basic Principles of Plate Theory. (Illus.). 180p. 1982. 55.00x (ISBN 0-903384-26-4); pap. text ed. 32.50x (ISBN 0-903384-25-6). Intl Ideas.
McFadden, W. H. Techniques of Combined Gas Chromatography - Mass Spectrometry: Applications in Organic Analysis. LC 73-6916. 463p. 1973. 60.00x (ISBN 0-471-58388-X, Pub. by Wiley-Interscience). Wiley.
McReynolds, W. O. Gas Chromatographic Retention Data. 1966. 45.00 (ISBN 0-912474-01-7). Preston Pubns.
Message, Gordon M. Practical Aspects of Gas Chromotography-Mass Spectrometry. LC 83-23475. 351p. 1984. 59.95x (ISBN 0-471-06277-4, Pub. by Wiley-Interscience). Wiley.
Mitruka, Brij M. Gas Chromatographic Applications in Microbiology & Medicine. LC 74-18002. 492p. 1975. 55.50 (ISBN 0-471-61183-2). Krieger.
Noebels, H. J., ed. Gas Chromatography. 1961. 79.50 (ISBN 0-12-520450-7). Acad Pr.
Novak, Josef. Quantitative Analysis by Gas Chromatography. (Chromatographic Science Ser.: Vol. 5). 224p. 1975. 38.50 (ISBN 0-8247-6311-4). Dekker.
Odham, Goran, et al, eds. Gas Chromatography - Mass Spectroscopy: Applications in Microbiology. 436p. 1984. 59.50x (ISBN 0-306-41314-0, Plenum Pr). Plenum Pub.
Onuska, Francis I. & Karasek, Francis W. Open Tubular Column Gas Chromatography in Environmental Sciences. LC 84-4806. 294p. 1984. 42.50x (ISBN 0-306-41589-5, Plenum Pr). Plenum Pub.
Paryjczak. Gas Chromatography in Adsorption & Catalysis. 1986. 75.00 (ISBN 0-470-20131-2). Wiley.
Perry, J. A. Introduction to Analytical Gas Chromatography: History, Principles, & Practice. 1981. 39.75 (ISBN 0-8247-1537-3). Dekker.
Polvani, Filippo, et al, eds. Meeting on Gas Chromatographic Determination of Hormonal Steroids. LC 68-19262. (Illus.). 1968. 60.00 (ISBN 0-12-561240-0). Acad Pr.
Preston, Seaton T. & Pankratz, Ronald. A Guide to the Analysis of Pesticides by Gas Chromatography. 1981. spiral plastic bdg. 35.00 (ISBN 0-913106-15-1). PolyScience.
--A Guide to the Analysis of Thioalcohols & Thioethers: (Mercaptans & Alkyl Sulfides) by Gas Chromatography. rev. ed. 1981. spiral plastic bdg. 25.00 (ISBN 0-913106-16-X). PolyScience.
Preston, Seaton T., Jr. Guide to Selected Liquid Phases & Absorbents Used in Gas Chromatography. 194p. 1969. PolyScience.
--A Guide to the Analysis of Fatty Acids and Their Esters by Gas Chromatography. 1971. spiral bdg 25.00 (ISBN 0-913106-08-9). PolyScience.
--A Guide to the Analysis of Hydro-Carbons by Gas Chromatography. 2nd ed. 1976. spiral bdg 35.00 (ISBN 0-913106-02-X). PolyScience.
Preston, Seaton T., Jr. & Pandratz, Ronald. A Guide to the Analysis of Alcohols by Gas Chromatography. 3rd ed. 190p. 1984. pap. 35.00 (ISBN 0-913106-25-9). Polyscience.
Preston, Seaton T., Jr. & Pankratz, Ronald. A Guide to the Analysis of Alcohols by Gas Chromatography. 2nd ed. 1976. 25.00 (ISBN 0-913106-06-2). PolyScience.
--A Guide to the Analysis of Amines by Gas Chromatography. 3rd rev. ed. 1981. spiral bdg 25.00 (ISBN 0-913106-20-8). PolyScience.
--A Guide to the Analysis of Ketones by Gas Chromatography. 2nd rev. ed. 1975. spiral 25.00 (ISBN 0-913106-07-0). PolyScience.
--A Guide to the Analysis of Phenols by Gas Chromatography. 1978. spiral bdg 25.00 (ISBN 0-913106-04-6). PolyScience.
Preston, Seaton T., Jr., et al. Qualitative Analysis by Gas Chromatography. 30p. 1982. write for info. (ISBN 0-913106-18-6). PolyScience.
Scholler, R. & Jayle, M. F. Gas Chromatography of Hormonal Steroids. 574p. 1968. 151.50 (ISBN 0-677-13280-8). Gordon.
Signeur, Austin V. Guide to Gas Chromatography Literature, 4 vols. Incl. Vol. 1. 351p. 1964. 95.00x (ISBN 0-306-68201-X); Vol. 2. 379p. 1967. 95.00x (ISBN 0-306-68202-8); Vol. 3. 1100p. 1974. 150.00x (ISBN 0-306-68203-6). LC 64-20743 (IFI Plenum). Plenum Pub.
Snyder, Lloyd R. Principles of Adsorption Chromatography: The Separation of Nonionic Organic Compounds. LC 68-17426. (Chromatographic Science: Vol. 3). (Illus.). pap. 107.30 (ISBN 0-317-08018-0, 2017858). Bks Demand UMI.
Stevens, Malcolm P. Characterization & Analysis of Polymers by Gas Chromatography. LC 74-84778. (Techniques & Methods of Polymer Education: Vol. 3). (Illus.). pap. 52.50 (ISBN 0-317-07829-1, 2055033). Bks Demand UMI.
Syzmanski, Herman A., ed. Lectures on Gas Chromatography, 1962: Based on Lectures Presented at the Advanced Session of the 4th Annual Gas Chromatography Institute Held at Canisius College, Buffalo, New York, April 23-26, 1962. LC 61-15520. (Illus.). pap. 72.00 (ISBN 0-317-10951-0, 2019391). Bks Demand UMI.
Szymanski, H. A. & Mattick, L. R. Lectures on Gas Chromatography, Vol. 3. LC 61-15520. 227p. 1967. 32.50x (ISBN 0-306-30289-6, Plenum Pr). Plenum Pub.

Szymanski, Herman A., ed. Biomedical Applications of Gas Chromatography, 2 vols. Incl. Vol. 1. 324p. 1964. 37.50x (ISBN 0-306-37581-8); Vol. 2. 198p. 1968. 32.50x (ISBN 0-306-37582-6). LC 64-13147 (Plenum Pr). Plenum Pub.

Tsuji, Kiyoshi, ed. GLC & HPLC: Determination of Therapeutic Agents, Pt. III. (Chromatographic Science Ser.: Vol. 9). 1979. 85.00 (ISBN 0-8247-6693-8). Dekker.

Tsuji, Kiyoshi & Morozowich, Walter, eds. GLC & HPLC: Determination of Therapeutic Agents, Pt. II. (Chromatographic Science Ser.: Vol. 9). 1978. 85.00 (ISBN 0-8247-6664-4). Dekker.

--GLC & HPLC: Determination of Therapeutic Agents, Pt. I. (Chromatographic Science Ser.: Vol. 9). 1978. 85.00 (ISBN 0-8247-6641-5). Dekker.

GAS CHROMATOGRAPHY–BIBLIOGRAPHY

Knapman, C. E., ed. Gas Chromatography Abstracts. LC 63-22896. 1965. pap. 78.50 (ISBN 0-317-26002-2, 2023703). Bks Demand UMI.

--Gas Chromatography Abstracts. LC 63-228996. 1963. pap. 74.00 (ISBN 0-317-26004-9, 2023702). Bks Demand UMI.

Signeur, Austin V. Guide to Gas Chromatography Literature, Vol. 4. 1330p. 1979. 195.00x (ISBN 0-306-68204-4, IFI Plenum). Plenum Pub.

GAS COOLED REACTORS

Advanced & High-Temperature Gas-Cooled Reactors. (Proceedings Ser.). (Illus.). 917p. (Orig.). 1968. pap. 62.75 (ISBN 92-0-050768-9, ISP197, IAEA). Unipub.

British Nuclear Energy Society, ed. Optimisation of Sodium-Cooled Fast Reactors. 470p. 1978. 125.00x (ISBN 0-7277-0054-5, Pub. by Brit Nuclear England). State Mutual Bk.

Fickeisen, D. H. & Schneider, M. J., eds. Gas Bubble Disease: Proceedings. AEC Technical Information Center. LC 75-619327. 123p. 1967. pap. 11.00 (ISBN 0-87079-023-4, CONF-741033); microfiche 4.50 (ISBN 0-87079-213-X, CONF-741033). DOE.

Gas-Cooled Reactors with Emphasis on Advanced Systems: Proceedings of an IAEA-NEA Symposium, Julich, Oct. 13-17, 1975, Vol. 1. (Proceedings Ser.). (Illus.). 419p. 1976. Vol. 1. pap. 46.50 (ISBN 92-0-050076-5, ISP407/1, IAEA); Vol.2. pap. 59.25 (ISBN 92-0-050176-1, ISP407/2). Unipub.

GAS DISTRIBUTION

see also Gases, Compressed

Kellogg, Orson. Every Pilot's Guide to Fuel Economy. 1980. pap. 4.95 (ISBN 0-935802-00-2, Pub. by Taxlogs Unltd). Aviation.

Koch, G. H. & Thompson, N. G., eds. Corrosion in Flue Gas Desulfurization Systems. LC 84-61873. 479p. 35.00 (ISBN 0-915567-05-9); 28.00. Natl Corrosion Eng.

GAS DYNAMICS

see also Aerodynamics; Gas Flow; Jets–Fluid Dynamics

Becker, Ernst. Gas Dynamics. 1969. 70.50 (ISBN 0-12-084450-8). Acad Pr.

Beloserkovskii, O. M., et al, eds. Rarefied Gas Dynamics. 1418p. 1985. 195.00x (ISBN 0-306-41932-7, Plenum Pr). Plenum Pub.

Benedict, Robert P. Fundamentals of Gas Dynamics. LC 83-1273. 272p. 1983. text ed. 37.45 (ISBN 0-471-09193-6); solutions avail. (ISBN 0-471-87340-3). Wiley.

Benedict, Robert P. & Carlucci, Nicola A. Handbook of Specific Losses in Flow Systems. LC 65-25129. 193p. 1966. 32.50x (ISBN 0-306-65122-X, IFI Plenum). Plenum Pub.

Benedict, Robert P. & Steltz, W. G. Handbook of Generalized Gas Dynamics. LC 65-25128. 243p. 1966. 52.50x (ISBN 0-306-65118-1, IFI Plenum). Plenum Pub.

Bogoyavlensky, O. I. Methods in the Qualitative Theory of Dynamical Systems in Astrophysics & Gas Dynamics. Gokhman, D., tr. from Russ. (Soviet Mathematics Ser.). (Illus.). 320p. 1985. 49.00 (ISBN 0-387-13614-2). Springer-Verlag.

Brutsaert, Wilfried & Jirka, Gerhard H., eds. Gas Transfer at Water Surfaces. 1984. lib. bdg. 78.00 (ISBN 0-318-00439-9, Pub. by Reidel Holland). Kluwer Academic.

Burgers, J. M. Flow Equations for Composite Gases. (Applied Mathematics & Mechanics Ser.: Vol. 11). 1969. 85.00 (ISBN 0-12-143250-5). Acad Pr.

Cannon, C. J. The Transfer of Spectral Line Radiation. (Illus.). 650p. 1985. 99.50 (ISBN 0-521-25995-9). Cambridge U Pr.

CISM (International Center for Mechanical Sciences) Introduction to Gasdynamics of Explosions. Oppenheim, A. K., ed. (CISM Pubns. Ser.: No. 48). (Illus.). 220p. 1972. pap. 23.80 (ISBN 0-387-81083-8). Springer-Verlag.

--Lectures on Radiating Gasdynamics: General Equations & Boundary Conditions. Ferrari, C., ed. (CISM Pubns. Ser.: No. 146). (Illus.). 83p. 1975. pap. 12.40 (ISBN 0-387-81204-0). Springer-Verlag.

CISM (International Center for Mechanical Sciences), Dept. of Hydro & Gas Dynamics, 1970. Shock Waves in Real Gases. Bazhenova, T. V., ed. (CISM International Center for Mechanical Sciences Ser.: No. 37). (Illus.). 78p. 1974. pap. 12.40 (ISBN 3-211-81219-9). Springer-Verlag.

Constantinescu, Virgiliu N. Gas Lubrication. Wehe, Robert L., ed. Scripta Technica, tr. LC 78-93540. pap. 160.00 (ISBN 0-317-26212-2, 2052120). Bks Demand UMI.

Davies, Donald G. & Barnes, Charles D., eds. Regulation of Ventilation & Gas Exchange. (Research Topics in Physiology). 1978. 49.50 (ISBN 0-12-204650-1). Acad Pr.

Dosanjh, Darshan S., ed. Modern Optical Methods in Gas Dynamic Research. LC 75-155352. 295p. 1971. 45.00 (ISBN 0-306-30537-2, Plenum Pr). Plenum Pub.

Emmons, Howard W., ed. Fundamentals of Gas Dynamics. LC 57-6331. (High Speed Aerodynamics & Jet Propulsion Ser.: Vol. 3). pap. 160.00 (ISBN 0-317-09255-3, 2000878). Bks Demand UMI.

Goodman, Frank O & Wachman, Harold Y. Dynamics of Gas-Surface Scattering. 1976. 76.00 (ISBN 0-12-290450-8). Acad Pr.

John, James E. Gas Dynamics. 2nd ed. 1985. text ed. 42.91 (ISBN 0-205-08014-6, 328014); student manual incl. (ISBN 0-205-08015-4). Allyn.

Johnston, Harold S. Gas Phase Reaction Rate Theory. LC 66-21855. (Modern Concepts in Chemistry Ser.). pap. 93.00 (ISBN 0-317-09414-9, 2020599). Bks Demand UMI.

Karamcheti, K., ed. Rarefield Gas Dynamics. 1974. 71.00 (ISBN 0-12-398150-6). Acad Pr.

Klinzing, George E. Gas-Solid Transport. (Chemical Engineering Ser.). (Illus.). 358p. 1981. text ed. 44.00 (ISBN 0-07-035047-7). McGraw.

Kogan, M. N. Rarefied Gas Dynamics. LC 69-12532. 515p. 1969. 52.50x (ISBN 0-306-30361-2, Plenum Pr). Plenum Pub.

Kondratiev, V. N. & Nikitin, E. E. Gas-Phase Reactions: Kinetics & Mechanisms. (Illus.). 250p. 1981. 70.00 (ISBN 0-387-09956-5). Springer-Verlag.

Ladenburg, R. W., et al, eds. Physical Measurements in Gas Dynamics & Combustion. LC 54-13127. pap. 151.50 (ISBN 0-317-09134-4, 2000097). Bks Demand UMI.

Liepmann, Hans W. & Roshko, A. Elements of Gasdynamics. LC 56-9823. 439p. 1957. text ed. 50.45 (ISBN 0-471-53460-9). Wiley.

Lodding, William, ed. Gas Effluent Analysis. LC 67-19950. (Thermal Analysis Ser.: Vol. 13). (Illus.). pap. 57.80 (ISBN 0-317-07981-6, 2055006). Bks Demand UMI.

Loh, W. H. Modern Developments in Gas Dynamics. LC 69-14561. 386p. 1969. 42.50x (ISBN 0-306-30377-9, Plenum Pr). Plenum Pub.

Losev, S. A. Gasdynamic Laser. (Springer Series in Chemical Physics: Vol. 12). (Illus.). 300p. 1981. 49.00 (ISBN 0-387-10503-4). Springer-Verlag.

Napolitano, L. G. & Belotserkovsky, O. M. Computational Gasdynamics. (International Centre for Mechanical Sciences, Courses & Lectures: Vol. 40). (Illus.). 1975. pap. 40.80 (ISBN 0-387-81428-0). Springer-Verlag.

Oguchi, Hakuro. Rarefied Gas Dynamics, 2 vols. 1130p. 1985. 100.00x (ISBN 0-86008-383-7, Pub. by U of Tokyo Japan). Columbia U Pr.

Oppenheim, A. K., ed. Gasdynamics of Explosions & Reactive Systems: Proceedings of the Sixth International Colloquium Held in Stockholm, Sweden, 22-26 August 1977. (Illus.). 782p. 1980. 265.00 (ISBN 0-08-025442-X). Pergamon.

Oswatitsch. Contributions to the Development of Gas Dynamics. 1980. 85.00 (ISBN 0-9940012-9-0, Pub. by Vieweg & Sohn Germany). Heyden.

Predvoditelev, A. S., ed. Physics of Heat Exchange & Gas Dynamics. LC 62-12858. 99p. 1963. 25.00x (ISBN 0-306-10574-8, Consultants). Plenum Pub.

Robertson, A. J. Catalysis of Gas Reactions by Metals. (Illus.). 1970. 19.50 (ISBN 0-387-91031-X). Springer-Verlag.

Rozdestvenskii, B. L. & Janenko, N. N. Systems of Quasilinear Equations & Their Applications to Gas Dynamics. LC 82-24488. (Translations of Mathematical Monographs: Vol. 55). 147.00 (ISBN 0-8218-4509-8). Am Math.

Shalan, M. & Nasser, A. Gas Dynamics. 450p. 1985. pap. 17.00 (ISBN 0-471-87899-5). Wiley.

Steklov Institute of Mathematics, Academy of Sciences, U S S R. Unsteady Motions of Compressible Media with Blast Waves: Proceedings. Sedov, Leond I., ed. (Proceedings of the Steklov Institute of Mathematics: No. 87). 1967. 36.00 (ISBN 0-8218-1887-2, STEKLO-87). Am Math.

Steklov Institute of Mathematics, No. 122. Difference Methods of Solving Problems of Mathematical Physics II: Proceedings. Janenko, N. N., ed. LC 75-20006. (Proceedings of the Steklov Institutue of Mathematics: No. 122). 99p. 1975. 39.00 (ISBN 0-8218-3022-8, STEKLO-122). Am Math.

Symposium on Cosmical Gas Dynamics,6th, et al. Interstellar Gas Dynamics: Proceedings. Habing, H. J., ed. LC 78-124849. (IAU Symposia: No.39). 388p. 1970. lib. bdg. 42.00 (ISBN 90-277-0172-5, Pub. by Reidel Holland). Kluwer Academic.

Vincenti, W. G. & Kruger, C. H. Introduction to Physical Gas Dynamics. LC 75-5806. 556p. 1975. Repr. of 1965 ed. 33.50 (ISBN 0-88275-309-6). Krieger.

Wegener, P., ed. Molecular Beams & Low Density Gasdynamics. (Gasdynamics Ser.: Vol. 4). 1974. 62.00 (ISBN 0-8247-6199-5). Dekker.

Zierep, Jhurgen. Similarity Laws & Modeling. LC 74-157835. (Gasdynamics: Vol. 2). pap. 41.80 (ISBN 0-317-28555-6, 2055016). Bks Demand UMI.

Zucrow, Maurice J. & Hoffman, Joe D. Gas Dynamics, 2 vols. LC 76-6855. 480p. 1977. Vol. 1. 64.50 (ISBN 0-471-98440-X). Wiley.

--Gas Dynamics: Multidimensional Flow, Vol. 2. LC 84-29719. 490p. 1985. Repr. of 1977 ed. lib. bdg. 64.50 (ISBN 0-89874-840-2). Krieger.

GAS DYNAMICS–TABLES, ETC.

Zierep, Jhurgen. Similarity Laws & Modeling. LC 74-157835. (Gasdynamics: Vol. 2). pap. 41.80 (ISBN 0-317-28555-6, 2055016). Bks Demand UMI.

GAS ENGINES

see Gas and Oil Engines

GAS EQUIPMENT AND APPLIANCES

see Gas Appliances

GAS FLOW

see also Air Flow; Gas-Lubricated Bearings

Bauer, Frantisek, et al. Isentropic Gas Flow: Tables & Correction Nomograms. LC 62-28534. pap. 160.00 (ISBN 0-317-09432-7, 2019388). Bks Demand UMI.

Bird, G. A. Molecular Gas Dynamics. (Oxford Engineering & Science Ser.). 1976. text ed. 72.00x (ISBN 0-19-856120-2). Oxford U Pr.

Cheremisinoff, Nicholas P. Fluid Flow Pocket Handbook. LC 83-22619. 330p. 1984. Flexibound 21.95x (ISBN 0-87201-707-9). Gulf Pub.

Cheremisinoff, Nicholas P. & Cheremisinoff, Paul N. Hydrodynamics of Gas-Solids Fluidization. LC 83-18555. 1000p. 1984. 89.95x (ISBN 0-87201-352-9). Gulf Pub.

Fiszdon, W., ed. Rarefied Gas Flows: Theory & Experiment. (CISM-International Centre for Mechanical Sciences, Courses & Lectures: Vol. 224). (Illus.). 524p. 1982. pap. 45.60 (ISBN 0-387-81595-3). Springer-Verlag.

Gas Flow & Chemical Laser 1984. (Institute of Physics Conference Ser.: No. 75). 520p. 1985. 65.00 (ISBN 0-85498-163-2, Pub. by A Hilger England). Heyden.

Onorato, Michele. Gas Flow & Chemical Lasers. 774p. 1985. 115.00x (ISBN 0-306-41478-3, Plenum Pr). Plenum Pub.

Rhodes, E. & Scott, D. E., eds. Cocurrent Gas-Liquid Flow. LC 76-80084. 698p. 1969. 57.50x (ISBN 0-306-30404-X, Plenum Pr). Plenum Pub.

Sellin, R. H. Flow in Channels. 160p. 1970. 44.25x (ISBN 0-677-61650-3). Gordon.

GAS INDUSTRY

Here are entered general works on industries based on natural or manufactured gas.

see also Gas, Natural; Gas Appliances; Gas Manufacture and Works;

also other headings beginning with the word Gas

Allain, Louis J. Capital Investment Models of the Oil & Gas Industry: A Systems Approach. Bruchey, Stuart, ed. LC 78-22654. (Energy in the American Economy Ser.). (Illus.). 1979. lib. bdg. 42.00x (ISBN 0-405-11959-3). Ayer Co Pubs.

Annual Bulletin of Gas Statistics for Europe: 1966-1980, Vols. 12-26. Incl. Vol. 12. 1966. pap. 3.00 (ISBN 0-686-93361-3, UN68/2E8); Vol. 13. 1967. pap. 2.00 (ISBN 0-686-93362-1, UN69/2E4); Vol. 14. 1968. pap. 2.00 (ISBN 0-686-93363-X, UN69/2E/16); Vol. 15. 1969. pap. 2.00 (ISBN 0-686-93364-8, UN70/2E/11); Vol. 16. 1970. pap. 3.00 (ISBN 0-686-93365-6, UN71/2E4); Vol. 17. 1971. pap. 3.00 (ISBN 0-686-93366-4, UN72/2E/10); Vol. 18. 1972. pap. 5.00 (ISBN 0-686-93367-2, UN73/2E/17); Vol. 19. 1973. pap. 6.00 (ISBN 0-686-93368-0, UN74/2E/16); Vol. 20. 1974. pap. 6.00 (ISBN 0-686-93369-9, UN75/2E/17); Vol. 21. 1975. pap. 7.00 (ISBN 0-686-93370-2, UN76/2E20); Vol. 22. 1976. pap. 7.00 (ISBN 0-686-93371-0, UN77/2E19); Vol. 23. 1977. pap. 7.00 (ISBN 0-686-93372-9, UN78/2E21); Vol. 24. 1978. 97p. 1979. pap. 8.00 (ISBN 0-686-68941-0, UN792E26); Vol. 25. 1979. pap. 9.00 (UN80 2E21); Vol. 26. 1980. 107p. 1981. pap. 10.00 (ISBN 0-686-96512-4, UN81/2E21); Vol. 27. 1981. 101p. 1983. pap. text ed. 11.00 (UN82/2E22); Vol. 28. 1982. (Eng., Fr. & Rus., UN.). 104p. 1984. pap. text ed. 11.00 (UN83/2E26). (Eng., Fr. & Rus., UN). Unipub.

Arab Petroleum Research Center. Arab Oil & Gas Directory: 1985. 450p. 1980. 175.00x (ISBN 0-686-64697-5, Pub. by Graham & Trotman England). State Mutual Bk.

Brown, Keith C., ed. Regulation of the Natural Gas Producing Industry. LC 71-186502. (Resources for the Future Ser.). (Illus.). 271p. 1972. pap. 10.00x (ISBN 0-8018-1383-2). Johns Hopkins.

Buialov, N. I., et al. Quantitative Evaluation of Predicted Reserves of Oil & Gas (Authorized Translation from the Russian) LC 64-7759. pap. 20.00 (ISBN 0-317-10640-6, 2003359). Bks Demand UMI.

Business Communications Staff. The Changing Gas Industry: Good & Bad. 1982. 950.00 (ISBN 0-89336-018-X, E-019R). BCC.

California-Alaska Oil & Gas Review for 1969. 1970. 40.00 (ISBN 0-686-28269-8). Munger Oil.

California-Alaska Oil & Gas Review for 1971. 40.00 (ISBN 0-686-28270-1). Munger Oil.

California-Alaska Oil & Gas Review for 1972. 40.00 (ISBN 0-686-28271-X). Munger Oil.

California-Alaska Oil & Gas Review for 1973. 1974. 40.00 (ISBN 0-686-28272-8). Munger Oil.

California-Alaska Oil & Gas Review of 1975. 1976. 40.00 (ISBN 0-686-28273-6). Munger Oil.

California Gas & Oil Exploration: 1963 Annual. 1964. 40.00 (ISBN 0-686-28263-9). Munger Oil.

California Oil & Gas Exploration: 1960 Annual. 1961. 40.00 (ISBN 0-686-28261-2). Munger Oil.

California Oil & Gas Exploration: 1962 Annual. 1963. 40.00 (ISBN 0-686-28262-0). Munger Oil.

California Oil & Gas Exploration: 1964 Annual. 1965. 40.00 (ISBN 0-686-28264-7). Munger Oil.

California Oil & Gas Exploration: 1965 Annual. 1966. 40.00 (ISBN 0-686-28265-5). Munger Oil.

California Oil & Gas Exploration: 1966 Annual. 1967. 40.00 (ISBN 0-686-28266-3). Munger Oil.

California Oil & Gas Exploration: 1967 Annual. 1968. 40.00 (ISBN 0-686-28267-1). Munger Oil.

California Oil & Gas Exploration: 1968 Annual. 1969. 40.00 (ISBN 0-686-28268-X). Munger Oil.

California Oil & Gas Review, 1977. 1978. 40.00 (ISBN 0-686-16192-0). Munger Oil.

Commission of the European Communities. New Technologies for Exploration & Exploitation of Oil & Gas Resources, Vol. 1. 800p. 1979. 90.00x (ISBN 0-86010-158-4, Pub. by Graham & Trotman England). State Mutual Bk.

Commisssion of the European Communities. Oil & Gas Multilingual Glossary. 500p. 1979. 44.00x (ISBN 0-86010-170-3, Pub. by Graham & Trotman England). State Mutual Bk.

Donnelly, Richard W. Project Development for Gas Processing Plants & Facilities. 2nd ed. Stelzner, Karen L., ed. (Illus.). 347p. (Orig.). 1982. pap. write for info binder (ISBN 0-88698-047-X, 3.80010). PETEX.

Giuliano, Francis A., ed. Introduction to Oil & Gas Technology. 2nd ed. (Short Course Handbooks). (Illus.). 194p. 1981. text ed. 32.00 (ISBN 0-934634-48-3); pap. text ed. 24.00. Intl Human Res.

Harris, D. J., et al. Coal, Gas & Electricity Industries. (Reviews of United Kingdom Statistical Sources Ser.: Vol. XI). 1979. 65.00 (ISBN 0-08-022461-X). Pergamon.

Kruse, Curtis & Haas, Hank. Plant Processing of Natural Gas. (Illus.). 114p. (Orig.). 1980. pap. text ed. 6.00 (ISBN 0-88698-115-8). Petex.

Lawrence, Anthony G. Pricing & Planning in the U. S. Natural Gas Industry: An Econometric & Programming Study. Bruchey, Stuart, ed. LC 78-22693. (Energy in the American Economy Ser.). (Illus.). 1979. lib. bdg. 17.00x (ISBN 0-405-11996-8). Ayer Co Pubs.

Metal Structures in the Mining, Gas & Oil Industries: Metal Stuctures Conferences, 1978. 114p. (Orig.). 1978. pap. text ed. 31.50 (ISBN 0-85825-104-3, Pub. by Inst Engineering Australia). Brookfield Pub Co.

OECD Staff. Annual Oil & Gas Statistics, 1979-1980. (Eng. & Fr.). 532p. (Orig.). 1982. pap. text ed. 33.50x (ISBN 92-64-02287-2). OECD.

Oil & Gas Journal Databook. 1985. write for info; pap. 19.95 (ISBN 0-317-18736-8). Pennwell Bks.

Oil & Gas Statistics Annual 1978 to 1979. 557p. (Orig.). 1981. pap. 32.50x (ISBN 92-64-02182-5). OECD.

Shell UK Exploration & Production Ltd. Winning Supply & Service Business in Offshore Oil & Gas Markets. 112p. 1976. 77.00x (ISBN 0-86010-025-1, Pub. by Graham & Trotman England). State Mutual Bk.

Starratt, Patricia E. The Natural Gas Shortage & the Congress. LC 74-29378. 1975. pap. 4.25 (ISBN 0-8447-3148-X). Am Enterprise.

State & Federal Exploratory Wells & Core Holes Drilled off the West Coast of Continental U.S.A. Prior to 1974. 1975. 40.00 (ISBN 0-686-28277-9). Munger Oil.

Stern, Jonathan P. International Gas Trade in Europe. (British Institutes' Joint Energy Policy Programme - Energy Papers: No. 8). x, 204p. 1984. text ed. 40.00x (ISBN 0-435-84341-9). Gower Pub Co.

United Nations Economic Commission for Europe, Commission on Gas, Minsk, USSR, 1977. The Gas Industry & the Environment: Proceedings. 1978. text ed. 61.00 (ISBN 0-08-022412-1). Pergamon.

Wedemeyer, Karl E. Interstate Natural Gas Supply & Intrastate Market Behavior. Bruchey, Stuart, ed. LC 78-22714. (Energy in the American Economy Ser.). (Illus.). 1979. lib. bdg. 14.00x (ISBN 0-405-12024-9). Ayer Co Pubs.

Williams, Trevor I. A History of the British Gas Industry. 1981. 49.00x (ISBN 0-19-858157-2). Oxford U Pr.

GAS LIQUID CHROMATOGRAPHY
see Gas Chromatography

GAS-LUBRICATED BEARINGS

Constantinescu, V. N. Gas Lubrication: Translated from the Rumanian. Wehe, Robert L., ed. Technica, Scripta, tr. LC 78-93540. 630p. 1969. pap. 19.50 (ISBN 0-685-06526-X, G00015). ASME.

Gas Bearing Symposium. 4th ed. 1969. text ed. 27.50x (ISBN 0-686-63954-5, Dist. by Air Science Co.). BHRA Fluid.

Gross, William A., et al. Fluid Film Lubrication. LC 80-36889. 773p. 1980. 57.95x (ISBN 0-471-08357-7). Wiley.

International Gas Bearing Symposium, 7th. Proceedings. 1977. pap. 47.00x (ISBN 0-900983-57-4, Dist. by Air Science Co.). BHRA Fluid.

International Gas Bearing Symposium, 6th. Proceedings. 1974. pap. 47.00x (ISBN 0-900983-36-1, Dist. by Air Science Co.). BHRA Fluid.

International Gas Bearings Symposium, 5th. Proceedings. 1969. lib. bdg. 27.00x (ISBN 0-686-71063-0). BHRA Fluid.

International Gas Bearings Symposium, 2nd. Proceedings. 1965. 25.00x (ISBN 0-686-71064-9). BHRA Fluid.

Stout, K., ed. Papers Presented at the Eight International Gas Bearing Symposium. (Illus.). 325p. 1981. pap. 54.00x (ISBN 0-906085-54-3). BHRA Fluid.

GAS MANUFACTURE AND WORKS
see also Coal Gasification; Gas Industry

American Gas Association. Gas Engineers Handbook. Segeler, C. George, ed. LC 65-17328. (Illus.). 1550p. 1965. 75.00 (ISBN 0-8311-3011-3). Indus Pr.

Bhattacharyya, S. & Torok, J., eds. A Critical Study of Materials for Synthetic Gas Quench Systems: Proceedings of the International Gas Research Conference, June 13-16, 1983, London, United Kingdom. LC 81-86225. write for info. Metal Prop Coun.

Donnelly, Richard W. Project Development for Gas Processing Plants & Facilities. 2nd ed. Stelzner, Karen L., ed. (Illus.). 347p. (Orig.). 1982. pap. write for info binder (ISBN 0-88698-047-X, 3.80010). PETEX.

International Gas Union. Elsevier's Dictionary of the Gas Industry, 2 vols. (Eng., Fr., Span., Ital., Ger., Port. & Dutch.). 1961. Set. 95.75 (ISBN 0-444-40758-8); pap. 42.50 suppl. (ISBN 0-444-41174-7). Elsevier.

Paxson, Jeanette, ed. Reciprocating Gas Compressors. (Oil & Gas Production Ser.). (Illus.). 107p. (Orig.). 1982. pap. text ed. 5.00 (ISBN 0-88698-119-0, 3.30210). PETEX.

PETEX. Well Cleanout & Repair Methods. (Well Servicing & Workover Ser.: Lesson 8). (Illus.). 32p. 1971. pap. text ed. 4.50 (ISBN 0-88698-064-X, 3.70810). PETEX.

UNITAR Staff. Shallow Oil & Gas Resources. (Illus.). 600p. 1985. 59.95x (ISBN 0-87201-833-4). Gulf Pub.

Well Logging Methods. (Well Servicing & Workover: Lesson 3). (Illus.). 46p. 1971. pap. text ed. 4.50 (ISBN 0-88698-059-3, 3.70310). PETEX.

GAS-PIPES
see also Electrolytic Corrosion

National Fuel Gas Code. (Fifty Ser.). 146p. 1974. pap. 7.50 (ISBN 0-685-46069-X, 54). Natl Fire Prot.

An Overview of the Alaska Highway Gas Pipeline. 136p. 1978. pap. 11.00x (ISBN 0-87262-130-8). Am Soc Civil Eng.

GAS-PRODUCERS
see also Coal Gasification; Gas and Oil Engines; Gas Manufacture and Works

Kaupp, A. & Goss, J. R. State of the Art: Small Scale (to 50 kw) Gas Producer Engine Systems. (Illus.). 278p. (Orig.). 1983. 40.00 (ISBN 0-942914-03-1); pap. 20.00 (ISBN 0-942914-02-3). Tipi Wkshp Bks.

Reed, T. B., ed. Biomass Gasification: Principles & Technology. LC 81-9667. (Energy Tech. Rev.: No. 67). (Illus.). 401p. 1981. 42.00 (ISBN 0-8155-0852-2). Noyes.

Stafford, D. A., et al. Methane Production from Waste Organic Matter. LC 78-31274. 304p. 1980. 86.50 (ISBN 0-8493-5223-1). CRC Pr.

Swedish Academy of Engineering. Gengas: The Swedish Classic on Wood Powered Vehicles. 2nd ed. Reed, Thomas B. & Jantzen, Dan, eds. Geuther, Maria, tr. from Swedish. (Illus.). 329p. 1982. pap. 15.00 (ISBN 0-942914-01-5). Tipi Wkshp Bks.

Wise, Donald L., ed. Fuel Gas Production from Biomass, 2 vols. 1981. Vol. I, 280 Pgs. 83.00 (ISBN 0-8493-5990-2); Vol. II, 296 Pgs. 91.50 (ISBN 0-8493-5991-0). CRC Pr.

GAS-PURIFICATION

Kohl, Arthur L. & Riesenfeld, Fred C. Gas Purification. 4th ed. LC 85-4148. (Illus.). 912p. 1985. 59.95x (ISBN 0-87201-314-6). Gulf Pub.

GAS STATIONS
see Automobiles–Service Stations

GAS-TURBINE AUTOMOBILES
see Automobiles, Gas-Turbine

GAS-TURBINES
see also Automotive Gas Turbines

American Society for Testing & Materials. Hot Corrosion Problems Associated with Gas Turbines. LC 67-17473. (American Society for Testing & Materials Special Technical Publication Ser.: No. 421). pap. 75.80 (ISBN 0-317-10925-1, 2001123). Bks Demand UMI.

American Society of Mechanical Engineers. Fatigue Life Technology: Presented at the 22nd Annual International Gas Turbine Conference, Philadelphia, Pa., March 27-31, 1977. Cruse, T. A. & Gallagher, J. P., eds. LC 77-70040. pap. 30.50 (ISBN 0-317-29901-8, 2019350). Bks Demand UMI.

--Turbomachinery Developments in Steam & Gas Turbines: Presented at the Winter Annual Meeting of the American Society of Mechanical Engineers, Atlanta, Georgia, November 27-December 2, 1977. Steltz, W. G., ed. LC 77-88002. (Illus.). pap. 26.00 (ISBN 0-317-11146-9, 2013321). Bks Demand UMI.

Bathie, William W. Fundamentals of Gas Turbines. LC 83-21609. 358p. 1984. text ed. 37.50 (ISBN 0-471-86285-1). Wiley.

Boyce, Meherwan P. Gas Turbine Engineering Handbook. LC 82-6158. 604p. 1982. 69.95x (ISBN 0-87201-878-4). Gulf Pub.

Cohen, H., et al. Gas Turbine Theory. 2nd ed. 337p. 1979. 39.95 (ISBN 0-470-26781-X). Halsted Pr.

Coutsouradis, D., et al, eds. High Temperature Alloys for Gas Turbines. (Illus.). 901p. 1978. 96.25 (ISBN 0-85334-815-4, Pub. by Elsevier Applied Sci England). Elsevier.

Dictionary of Gas Turbine Installation. (Eng. & Chinese.). 170p. 1973. pap. 3.95 (ISBN 0-686-92296-4, M-9566). French & Eur.

Erickson, V. L. & Julien, H. L., eds. Gas Turbine Heat Transfer: 1978. 1978. 18.00 (ISBN 0-685-66801-0, H00125). ASME.

Harman, Richard T. Gas Turbine Engineering: Applications Cycles & Characteristics. LC 80-21003. 270p. 1981. 32.95x (ISBN 0-470-27065-9). Halsted Pr.

Hart, A. B. & Cutler, A. J., eds. Deposition & Corrosion in Gas Turbines. (Illus.). 425p. 1973. 59.25 (ISBN 0-85334-575-9, Pub. by Elsevier Applied Sci England). Elsevier.

Lefebvre, Arthur H. Gas Turbine Combustion. (Energy, Combustion, & Environment Ser.). (Illus.). 416p. 1983. text ed. 45.00 (ISBN 0-07-037029-X). McGraw.

Lefebvre, Arthur H., ed. Gas Turbine Combustor Design Problems. LC 79-22350. 431p. 1979. text ed. 79.95 (ISBN 0-89116-177-5). Hemisphere Pub.

Manual on Requirements, Handling & Quality Control of Gas Turbine Fuel-STP 531. 200p. 1973. 20.00 (ISBN 0-8031-0764-1, 04-531000-12). ASTM.

Meetham, G. W. Development of Gas Turbine Materials. LC 81-13127. 306p. 1981. 52.95x (ISBN 0-470-27273-2). Halsted Pr.

Sawyer, John W. & Japikse, David, eds. Sawyer's Gas Turbine Engineering Handbook, 3 Vols. 3rd ed. Set. 248.50 (ISBN 0-937506-13-3); Vol. 1: Theory & Design. 89.50 (ISBN 0-937506-14-1); Vol. 2: Selection & Application. 79.50 (ISBN 0-937506-15-X); Vol. 3: Accessories & Support. 79.50 (ISBN 0-937506-16-8). Turbo Intl Pubn.

Stationary Combustion Engines & Gas Turbines. (Thirty Ser). 1970. pap. 2.00 (ISBN 0-685-58106-3, 37). Natl Fire Prot.

Stodola, A. Steam & Gas Turbines, 2 vols. 6th ed. 48.00 set (ISBN 0-8446-1424-6). Peter Smith.

Whittle, Frank. Gas Turbine Aero-Thermodynamics: With Special Reference to Aircraft Propulsion. LC 80-41372. 240p. 1981. 35.00 (ISBN 0-08-026719-X); pap. 19.75 (ISBN 0-08-026718-1). Pergamon.

Woodward, John B. Marine Gas Turbines. LC 74-31383. (Ocean Engineering Ser). 390p. 1975. 57.50x (ISBN 0-471-95962-6, Pub. by Wiley-Interscience). Wiley.

GAS-TURBINES, AIRCRAFT
see Airplanes–Turbojet Engines

GAS WELDING
see Oxyacetylene Welding and Cutting

GAS WELLS

Donohue, David A. & Ertekin, Turqay. Gaswell Testing: Theory, Practice & Regulation. LC 81-80726. (Illus.). 214p. 1981. text ed. 35.00 (ISBN 0-934634-10-6); pap. text ed. 26.00 (ISBN 0-934634-12-2). Intl Human Res.

Longley, Mark. Analysis for Well Completion. Leecraft, Jodie, ed. (Oil & Gas Production Ser.). (Illus.). 80p. (Orig.). 1984. pap. text ed. 5.00 (ISBN 0-88698-084-4, 3.31110). Petex.

GASDYNAMICS
see Gas Dynamics

GASEOUS PLASMA
see Plasma (Ionized Gases)

GASES
see also Bubbles; Combustion Gases; Osmosis; Pneumatics
also Specific gases, e.g. Acetylene, Helium, Hydrogen, Nitrogen, Oxygen

Arnot, Frederick L. Collision Processes in Gases. 4th ed. LC 50-12768. (Methuen's Monographs on Physical Subjects). pap. 29.00 (ISBN 0-317-08481-X, 2013148). Bks Demand UMI.

Bamford, C. H. & Tipper, C. F. Reactions of Solids with Gases. (Comprehensive Chemical Kinetics Ser.: Vol. 21). 1984. 79.75 (ISBN 0-444-42288-9, I-450-84). Elsevier.

--Simple Processes at the Gas-Solid Interface. (Comprehensive Chemical Kinetics Ser.: Vol. 19). 1984. 135.25 (ISBN 0-444-42287-0, I-147-84). Elsevier.

Berecz, E. & Balla-Ach, S. M. Gas Hydrates. (Studies in Inorganic Chemistry: Vol. 4). 330p. 1984. 75.00 (ISBN 0-444-99657-5, I-318-83). Elsevier.

Bird, R. B., et al. Fundamental Physics of Gases. Donaldson, C. D., ed. (Princeton Aeronautical Paperbacks Ser.: Vol. 7). 1961. pap. 13.95 (ISBN 0-691-07968-4). Princeton U Pr.

Business Communications Staff. Gas Separation. 1985. pap. 1950.00 (ISBN 0-89336-422-3, C-062). BCC.

Canjar, Lawrence N. & Manning, Francis S. Thermodynamic Properties & Reduced Correlations for Gases. LC 66-30022. pap. 64.50 (ISBN 0-317-08041-5, 2051874). Bks Demand UMI.

Christophorou, L. G., ed. Gaseous Dielectrics III: Proceedings of the Third International Symposium on Gaseous Dielectrics, Knoxville, Tennessee, USA, March 7-11, 1982. LC 82-9825. (Illus.). 600p. 1982. 105.00 (ISBN 0-08-029381-6, A110). Pergamon.

Christophorou, Loucas G., ed. Gaseous Dielectrics II: Proceedings of the Second International Symposium on Gaseous Dielectrics, Knoxville, Tenn., U.S.A., March 9-13, 1980. 506p. 1980. 30.00 (ISBN 0-08-025978-2). Pergamon.

Cohen, I. Bernard, ed. Laws of Gases. LC 80-2099. (Development of Science Ser.). (Illus.). 1981. lib. bdg. 35.00x (ISBN 0-405-13864-4). Ayer Co Pubs.

Cullis, C. F. & Firth, J. G., eds. Detection & Measurement of Hazardous Gases. LC 81-2785. 1981. text ed. 35.00x (ISBN 0-435-71030-3). Heinemann Ed.

Degen, H. & Cox, Raymond P., eds. Gas Enzymology. 1985. lib. bdg. 44.00 (ISBN 90-277-1900-4, Pub. by Reidel Holland). Kluwer Academic.

Dymond, J. H. & Smith, E. B. The Second Virial Coefficients of Pure Gases & Mixtures: A Critical Compilation. (Oxford Science Research Papers Ser.). (Illus.). 1980. pap. text ed. 79.00x (ISBN 0-19-855361-7). Oxford U Pr.

Elementary Science Study Staff. Gases & Airs. 1975. tchr's. guide 17.88 (ISBN 0-07-018519-0). McGraw.

Emelus, K. G. & Woolsey, G. A., eds. Discharges in Electronegative Gases. 162p. 1970. cancelled (ISBN 0-85066-035-1). Taylor & Francis.

Fast, Johan D. Interaction of Metals & Gases, Vol. 1. Thermodynamics & Phase Relations. 1965. 64.00 (ISBN 0-12-249801-1). Acad Pr.

First International Gas Research Conference, 1980: Proceedings. LC 80-83454. (Illus.). 992p. 1980. 48.50 (ISBN 0-86587-085-3). Gov Insts.

Gerrard, W. Solubility of Gases & Liquids: A Graphic Approach. LC 76-10676. (Illus.). 275p. 1976. 49.50x (ISBN 0-306-30866-5, Plenum Pr). Plenum Pub.

Gruschka, H. & Wecken, F. Gasdynamic Theory of Detonation: Combustion Science & Technology. 210p. 1971. 57.75 (ISBN 0-677-03370-2). Gordon.

Gugan, Keith. Unconfined Vapor Cloud Explosions. LC 78-74101. 168p. 1979. 37.50x (ISBN 0-87201-887-3). Gulf Pub.

Henzel, D. S., et al. Handbook for Flue Gas Desulfurization Scrubbing with Limestone. LC 82-7926. (Pollution Technology Rev. 94). (Illus.). 424p. 1983. 44.00 (ISBN 0-8155-0912-X). Noyes.

Hildebrand, Joel, et al. Regular & Related Solutions: The Solubility of Gases, Liquids & Solids. LC 79-122670. 238p. 1970. 15.95 (ISBN 0-442-15665-0). Krieger.

Holub, Robert & Vonka, Petr. The Chemical Equilibrium of Gaseous Systems. LC 75-34393. 1976. PLB 47.50 (ISBN 90-277-0556-9, Pub. by Reidel Holland). Kluwer Academic.

International Conference on the Control of Sulphur & Other Gaseous Emissions, 3rd, University of Salford, 1979. The Control of Sulphur & Other Gaseous Emissions: Proceedings, No. 57. 460p. 1981. 80.00x (ISBN 0-85295-117-5, Pub. by Inst Chem Eng England). State Mutual Bk.

Jeans, James H. The Dynamical Theory of Gases. LC 26-14895. pap. 112.00 (ISBN 0-317-08728-2, 2055295). Bks Demand UMI.

Jeans, James S. An Introduction to the Kinetic Theory of Gases. LC 40-3353. (Cambridge Science Classics). 319p. 1982. pap. 17.95 (ISBN 0-521-09232-9). Cambridge U Pr.

Krypton Eighty-Five in the Atmosphere: Accumulation, Biological Significance, & Control Technology. LC 75-11458. (NCRP Reports Ser.: No. 44). 1975. 8.00 (ISBN 0-913392-26-X). NCRP Pubns.

Mason, D. McA. & Hakewill, H., Jr. Identification & Determination of Organic Sulfur in Utility Gases. (Research Bulletin Ser.: 5). iv, 51p. 1959. 5.00 (ISBN 0-317-34308-4). Inst Gas Tech.

Noakes, G. R., ed. Sources of Physics Teaching: Gravity. Liquids. Gases, Vol. 5. 1970. pap. text ed. 18.50x (ISBN 0-85066-040-8). Intl Ideas.

Reintjes, John F. Nonlinear Optical Parametric Processes in Liquids & Gases. LC 82-11603. 1984. 67.00 (ISBN 0-12-585980-5). Acad Pr.

Saakyan, G. S. Equilibrium Configurations of Degenerate Gaseous Masses. Hall, C. F., tr. from Rus. LC 74-13583. 294p. 1974. 71.95x (ISBN 0-470-74805-2). Halsted Pr.

Saltsburg, Howard, et al, eds. Fundamentals of Gas-Surface Interactions: Proceedings. 1967. 72.00 (ISBN 0-12-616950-0). Acad Pr.

Schneider, G. M., et al, eds. Extraction with Supercritical Gases. (Illus.). 189p. 1980. 48.80x (ISBN 3-527-25854-X). VCH Pubs.

Setser, D. W., ed. Reactive Intermediates in the Gas Phase: Generation & Monitoring. LC 79-51698. 1979. 44.00 (ISBN 0-12-637450-3). Acad Pr.

Short, W. L. Flue Gas Desulfurization. Date not set. price not set. Elsevier.

Smith, B. L. The Inert Gases: Model Systems for Science. (The Wykeham Science Ser.: No. 16). 176p. 1971. pap. cancelled (ISBN 0-85109-220-9). Taylor & Francis.

Steklov Institute of Mathematics, Academy of Sciences, USSR. Problems in the Theory of Point Explosion in Gases: Proceedings. Korobeinikov, V. P., ed. (Proceedings of the Steklov Institute of Mathematics: No. 113). 311p. 1976. 67.00 (ISBN 0-8218-3019-8, STEKLO-119). Am Math.

Storch, O. Industrial Separators for Gas Cleaning. LC 78-10916. (Chemical Engineering Monographs: Vol. 6). 388p. 1979. 66.00 (ISBN 0-444-99808-X). Elsevier.

Strauss, Werner. Industrial Gas Cleaning. 2nd, rev. ed. LC 74-8066. 632p. 1976. text ed. 97.00 (ISBN 0-08-017004-8); 29.50 (ISBN 0-08-019933-X). Pergamon.

Symposium on Heavy Gas, Frankfurt-Main, September 3-4, 1979. Heavy Gas & Risk Assessment: Proceedings. Hartwig, Sylvius, ed. 355p. 1980. lib. bdg. 37.00 (ISBN 90-277-1108-9, Pub. by Reidel Holland). Kluwer Academic.

Thompson, Richard L. Equilibrium States on Thin Energy Shells. LC 74-14723. (Memoirs Ser.: No. 150). 110p. 1974. pap. 11.00 (ISBN 0-8218-1850-3, MEMO-150). Am Math.

GASES–ABSORPTION AND ADSORPTION

Arkharov, V. I., ed. Surface Interactions Between Metals & Gases. LC 65-23067. 163p. 1966. 35.00x (ISBN 0-306-10738-4, Consultants). Plenum Pub.

Gregg, S. J. & Sing, K. S. Absorption, Surface Area & Porosity. 2nd ed. 1982. 55.00 (ISBN 0-12-300956-1). Acad Pr.

McCartney, E. J. Absorption & Emission by Atmospheric Gases: The Physical Processes. 320p. 1983. 52.95x (ISBN 0-471-04817-8). Wiley.

Rouquerol, J. & Sing, K. S., eds. Adsorption at the Gas-Solid Interface: Proceedings of the International Symposium at Auxen - Provence, Sept. 1981. (Studies in Surface Science & Catalysis: Vol. 10). 512p. 1982. 93.75 (ISBN 0-444-42087-8). Elsevier.

Tompkins, F. C. Chemisorption of Gases on Metals. 1978. 62.00 (ISBN 0-12-694650-7). Acad Pr.

Touloukian, Y. S. & Ho, C. Y. Thermal Accommodation & Adsorption Coefficients of Gases, Vol. II-1. 1st ed. (McGraw-Hill-CINDAS Data Ser. on Material Properties). 448p. (Orig.). 1981. 56.00 (ISBN 0-07-065031-4). McGraw.

GASES–ANALYSIS

Astbury, N. F., et al. Experimental Gas Explosions: Report of Further Tests at Potters Marston. 1972. 25.00x (ISBN 0-900910-17-8, Pub. by Brit Ceramic Soc England). State Mutual Bk.

Bochkova, O. P. & Shreyder, E. Y. Spectroscopic Analysis of Gaseous Mixtures. 1966. 74.50 (ISBN 0-12-109450-2). Acad Pr.

Cowper, C. J. & Derose, A. J. The Analysis of Gases by Chromatography. LC 83-6207. (Pergamon Series in Analytical Chemistry: Vol. 7). (Illus.). 159p. 1983. 25.00 (ISBN 0-08-024027-5). Pergamon.

Hill, D. W. & Powell, T. Non-Dispersive Infrared Gas Analysis in Science, Medicine, & Industry. LC 68-56425. 222p. 1968. 32.50x (ISBN 0-306-30374-4, Plenum Pr). Plenum Pub.

Korte, Friedhelm & Zimmer, Hans, eds. Methodicum Chimicum: A Critical Survey of Proven Methods & Their Applications in Chemistry, Natural Science & Medicine, Vol. 7: Group Elements & Their Compounds, Pt. A: Main Group O to IV Elements & Their Compounds. 1978. 195.00 (ISBN 0-12-460707-1). Acad Pr.

Meek, J. M. & Craggs, J. D. Electrical Breakdown of Gases. LC 77-2784. Repr. of 1978 ed. 120.00 (ISBN 0-8357-9879-8, 2019472). Bks Demand UMI.

Rabinovich, Viktor Abramovich. Thermophysical Properties of Gases & Liquids. (Physical Constants & Properties of Substances No.1). pap. 53.80 (ISBN 0-317-08438-0, 2004605). Bks Demand UMI.

Touloukian, Y. S. & Ho, C. Y. Thermal Accommodation & Adsorption Coefficients of Gases, Vol. II-1. 1st ed. (McGraw-Hill-CINDAS Data Ser. on Material Properties). 448p. (Orig.). 1981. 56.00 (ISBN 0-07-065031-4). McGraw.

GASES–DIFFUSION

see Diffusion

GASES–IONIZATION

see Ionization of Gases

GASES–LIQUEFACTION

see also Hydrogen; Liquefied Natural Gas; Liquefied Petroleum Gas; Liquid Helium; Liquid Hydrogen; Low Temperature Research

Arnot, Frederick L. Collision Processes in Gases. 4th ed. LC 50-12768. (Methuen's Monographs on Physical Subjects). pap. 29.00 (ISBN 0-317-08481-X, 2013148). Bks Demand UMI.

Liquefaction Problems in Geotechnical Engineering. 394p. 1976. pap. 16.50x (ISBN 0-87262-324-6). Am Soc Civil Eng.

Touloukian, Y. S. & Ho, C. Y. Properties of Nonmetallic Fluid Elements, Vol. III. (M-H-CINDAS Data Series on Material Properties). 224p. 1981. text ed. 56.00 (ISBN 0-07-065033-0). McGraw.

United Nations Economic Commission for Europe, Geneva, Switzerland. Oils & Gases from Coal: A Review of the State-of-the-Art in Europe & North America Based on the Work of the Symposium on the Gasification & Liquefaction of Coal Held Under the Auspices of the UNECE, Katowice, Poland. 23-27 April 1979. (ECE Seminars & Symposia Ser.). (Illus.). 316p. 1980. 69.00 (ISBN 0-08-025678-3). Pergamon.

Vargaftik, N. B. Handbook of Physical Properties of Liquids & Gases: Pure Substances & Mixtures. 2nd ed. LC 82-25857. 758p. 1983. text ed. 69.50 (ISBN 0-89116-356-5). Hemisphere Pub.

GASES–SPECTRA

Business Communications Staff. Gas Separation. 1985. pap. 1950.00 (ISBN 0-89336-422-3, C-062). BCC.

Murcray, David G., ed. Handbook of High Resolution Infrared Laboratory Spectra of Gases of Atmospheric Interest. 288p. 1981. 56.00 (ISBN 0-8493-2950-7). CRC Pr.

Weber, A., ed. Raman Spectroscopy of Gases & Liquids. (Topics in Current Physics Ser.: Vol. 11). (Illus.). 1979. 37.00 (ISBN 0-387-09036-3). Springer-Verlag.

GASES–VISCOSITY

see Viscosity

GASES–TABLES, CALCULATIONS, ETC.

Canjar, Lawrence & Manning, Francis. Thermodynamic Properties & Reduced Correlations for Gases. LC 66-30022. 222p. 1967. pap. text ed. 6.95x abridged student (ISBN 0-87201-868-7). Gulf Pub.

Keenan, Joseph H., et al. Gas Tables: Thermodynamic Properties of Air Products of Combustion & Component Gases Compressible Flow Functions Including Those of Ascher H. Shapiro & Gilbert M. Edelman. 2nd ed. LC 79-15098. 217p. 1983. 45.50x (ISBN 0-471-02207-1, Pub. by Wiley-Interscience); si version 45.50x (ISBN 0-471-08874-9). Wiley.

Melzer, Dorothy G. Introduction & Computations for Gases. (AIChEMI Modular Instruction F. Ser.: Vol. 1). 51p. 1981. pap. 30.00 (ISBN 0-8169-0175-9, J-6); pap. 15.00 members (ISBN 0-317-03836-2). Am Inst Chem Eng.

GASES, ASPHYXIATING AND POISONOUS

see also Carbon Dioxide; Carbon Monoxide; Chemical Warfare; Fume Control; Mine Gases

Fiserova-Bergerova, Vera, ed. Modeling of Inhalation Exposure to Vapors: Uptake, Distribution. & Elimination, 2 Vols. 1983. Vol. I, 184pp. 54.00 (ISBN 0-8493-6315-2); Vol. II, 208pp. 58.00 (ISBN 0-8493-6316-0). CRC Pr.

Thain, William. Monitoring Toxic Gases in the Atmosphere. 1980. 30.00 (ISBN 0-08-023810-6). Pergamon.

The Welding Environment. LC 72-95119. (Illus.). 169p. (Orig.). 1973. pap. text ed. 30.00 (ISBN 0-87171-103-6). Am Welding.

GASES, COMPRESSED

see also Liquefied Petroleum Gas

Compressed Gas Association. Handbook of Compressed Gases. 2nd ed. 1981. 46.50 (ISBN 0-442-25419-9). Van Nos Reinhold.

GASES, ELECTRIC DISCHARGES THROUGH

see Electric Discharges through Gases

GASES, FLOW OF

see Gas Flow

GASES, IONIZATION OF

see Ionization of Gases

GASES, KINETIC THEORY OF

Al'pert, Y. L., et al. Space Physics with Artificial Satellites. LC 64-23253. 240p. 1965. 42.50x (ISBN 0-306-10727-9, Consultants). Plenum Pub.

Bamford, C. H. & Tipper, C. F. Reactions of Solids with Gases. (Comprehensive Chemical Kinetics Ser.: Vol. 21). 1984. 79.75 (ISBN 0-444-42288-9, I-450-84). Elsevier.

--Simple Processes at the Gas-Solid Interface. (Comprehensive Chemical Kinetics Ser.: Vol. 19). 1984. 135.25 (ISBN 0-444-42287-0, I-147-84). Elsevier.

Brush, S. G. The Kind of Motion We Call Heat: A History of the Kinetic Theory of Gases in the Nineteenth Century, 2 bks. (Studies in Statistical Mechanics: Vol. 6). 1976. Bk. 1. 53.25 (ISBN 0-7204-0370-7, North-Holland); Bk. 2. 93.75 (ISBN 0-7204-0482-7); Set. 121.25 (ISBN 0-686-67836-2). Elsevier.

Cercignani, Carlo. Mathematical Methods in Kinetic Theory. LC 69-15832. (Illus.). 227p. 1969. 29.50x (ISBN 0-306-30386-8, Plenum Pr). Plenum Pub.

Chapman, S. & Cowling, T. G. Mathematical Theory of Non-Uniform Gases. 3rd ed. LC 70-77285. (Illus.). 1970. 54.50 (ISBN 0-521-07577-7). Cambridge U Pr.

Collie, C. H. Kinetic Theory & Entropy. LC 81-8332. (Illus.). 416p. 1983. pap. text ed. 21.95x (ISBN 0-582-44368-7). Longman.

Dushman, Saul & Lafferty, J. M., eds. Scientific Foundations of Vacuum Technique. 2nd ed. LC 61-17361. 1962. 78.95x (ISBN 0-471-22803-6, Pub. by Wiley-Interscience). Wiley.

Gatignol, T. Theorie Cinetique des Gaz a Repartition Descrete De Vitesses. 206p. 1975. pap. 14.70 (ISBN 0-387-07156-3). Springer-Verlag.

Heer, C. V. Statistical Mechanics, Kinetic, Theory & Stochastic Process. 1972. 31.50 (ISBN 0-12-336550-3). Acad Pr.

Klimontovich, Yu L. Kinetic Theory of Nonideal Gases & Nonideal Plasmas, Vol. 105. Bakescu, R., tr. LC 82-9044. (International Series in Natural Philosophy). (Illus.). 328p. 1982. 72.00 (ISBN 0-08-021671-4). Pergamon.

Liboff, Richard L. Introduction to the Theory of Kinetic Equations. corr. ed. LC 76-30383. (Illus.). 410p. 1979. Repr. of 1969 ed. lib. bdg. 24.00 (ISBN 0-88275-496-3). Krieger.

Nozdrev, V. F. Application of Ultrasonics to Molecular Physics. (Russian Monographs). (Illus.). 542p. 1963. 132.95 (ISBN 0-677-20360-8). Gordon.

Pack, Donald C. & Neunzert, Helmut, eds. Mathematical Problems in the Kinetic Theory of Gases: Proceedings of a Conference-Oberwolfach, May 20-26, 1979. (Methoden und Verfahren der mathematischen Physik Ser.: Vol. 19). 159p. 1980. pap. 18.95 (ISBN 3-8204-6151-5). P Lang Pubs.

Resibois, P. & De Leener, M. F. Classical Kinetic Theory of Fluids. LC 76-58852. 412p. 1977. 63.50 (ISBN 0-471-71694-4, Pub. by Wiley-Interscience). Wiley.

Sears, Francis W. & Salinger, Gerhard L. Thermodynamics, the Kinetic Theory of Gases & Statistical Mechanics. 3rd ed. 464p. 1975. text ed. 36.95 (ISBN 0-201-06894-X). Addison-Wesley.

Tabor, D. Gases, Liquids & Solids. 2nd ed. LC 78-26451. (Illus.). 1980. 59.50 (ISBN 0-521-22383-0); pap. 19.95 (ISBN 0-521-29466-5). Cambridge U Pr.

Towse, G., ed. Progress with Domperidone: A Gastrokinetic & Anti-Emitic Agent. (Royal Society of Medicine International Congress & Symposium Ser.: No. 36). 110p. 1981. 20.00 (ISBN 0-8089-1350-6, 794643); pap. 10.50. Grune.

Truesdell, C. & Muncaster, R. G. Fundamentals of Maxwell's Kinetic Theory of a Simple Monatomic Gas: Treated As a Branch of Rational Mechanics. (Pure & Applied Mathematics Ser.). 1980. 69.50 (ISBN 0-12-701350-4). Acad Pr.

GASES, PHOTOIONIZATION OF

see Photoionization of Gases

GASES, RARE

see also Argon; Helium; Radon

Clever. Helium & Neon. 1979. 100.00 (ISBN 0-08-022351-6). Pergamon.

--Krypton, Xenon, & Radon: Gas Solubilities. (Solubility Data Ser.: Vol. 2). 1979. 100.00 (ISBN 0-08-022352-4). Pergamon.

Hawkins, Donald T., et al, eds. Noble Gas Compounds, a Bibliography 1962-1976. LC 77-26721. 185p. 1978. 85.00x (ISBN 0-306-65171-8, IFI Plenum). Plenum Pub.

Hyman, Herbert H., ed. Noble Gas Compounds. LC 63-20907. 1963. 15.00x (ISBN 0-226-36540-9). U of Chicago Pr.

Klein, M. L., ed. Inert Gases: Potentials, Dynamics & Energy Transfer in Doped Crystals. (Springer Series in Chemical Physics: Vol. 34). (Illus.). 280p. 1984. 32.00 (ISBN 0-387-13128-0). Springer-Verlag.

Klein, M. L. & Venables, J. A., eds. Rare Gas Solids, Vol. 1. 1976. 99.00 (ISBN 0-12-413501-3). Acad Pr.

--Rare Gas Solids, Vol. 2. 1977. 81.00 (ISBN 0-12-413502-1). Acad Pr.

Macdonald, A. G. & Wann, K. T. Physiological Aspects of Anaesthetics & Inert Gases. 1978. 55.00 (ISBN 0-12-464150-4). Acad Pr.

Marine Publications Intl. Ltd., ed. Inert Gas System Manual. 1981. 100.00x (ISBN 0-686-75502-2, Pub. by Marine Pubns Intl England). State Mutual Bk.

Rare Gas Solids. (Springer Tracts in Modern Physics Ser.: Vol. 103). (Illus.). 115p. 1984. 26.00 (ISBN 0-387-13272-4). Springer-Verlag.

Schwentner, N., et al. Electronic Excitations in Condensed Rare Gases. (Tracts in Modern Physics Ser.: Vol. 107). (Illus.). 250p. 1985. 34.00 (ISBN 0-387-15382-9). Springer Verlag.

Smith, B. L. & Webb, J. P. The Inert Gases: Model Systems for Science. (Wykeham Science Ser: No. 16). 176p. 1971. 9.95x (ISBN 0-8448-1118-1). Crane Russak Co.

Tungsten Inert Gas (TIG), Metal Inert Gas (MIG) & Submerged Arc Welding. (Welding Inspection Ser.: Module 28-3). (Illus.). 58p. 1979. spiral bdg. 8.00x (ISBN 0-87683-107-2). G P Courseware.

GASES AT HIGH TEMPERATURES

Cambel, Ali B., et al. Real Gases. 1963. 44.00 (ISBN 0-12-155950-5). Acad Pr.

Fox, Robert. Caloric Theory of Gases from Lavoisier to Regnault. (Illus.). 1971. 32.00x (ISBN 0-19-858131-9). Oxford U Pr.

Zel'Dovich, Ya B., et al. Physics of Shock Waves & High Temperature Hydrodynamic Phenomena, 2 Vols. Vol. 1 1966. 76.50 (ISBN 0-12-778701-1); Vol. 2 1967. 76.50 (ISBN 0-12-778702-X). Acad Pr.

GASES IN METALS

Arkharov, V. I., ed. Surface Interactions Between Metals & Gases. LC 65-23067. 163p. 1966. 35.00x (ISBN 0-306-10738-4, Consultants). Plenum Pub.

Fast, Johan D. Interaction of Metals & Gases, Vol. 1. Thermodynamics & Phase Relations. 1965. 64.00 (ISBN 0-12-249801-1). Acad Pr.

Gulaev, B. B., ed. Gases in Cast Metals. LC 65-15007. 257p. 1965. 45.00x (ISBN 0-306-10726-0, Consultants). Plenum Pub.

Roberts, M. W. Chemistry of the Metal-Gas Interface. McKee, C. S., ed. (Monographs on the Physics & Chemistry of Materials). (Illus.). 1979. 59.00x (ISBN 0-19-851339-9). Oxford U Pr.

GASES IN MINES

see Mine Gases

GASIFICATION OF COAL

see Coal Gasification

GASOLINE

see also Airplanes–Fuel

Allvine, Fred C. & Patterson, James M. Competition Ltd, the Marketing of Gasoline. LC 70-180491. pap. 65.40 (ISBN 0-317-28578-5, 2055197). Bks Demand UMI.

Effect of Automotive Emission Requirements on Gasoline Characteristics, STP 487. 165p. 1971. pap. 9.50 (ISBN 0-8031-0004-3, 04-487000-12). ASTM.

Fleming, Harold M. Gasoline Prices & Competition. LC 65-26736. 1966. 27.00x (ISBN 0-89197-187-4). Irvington.

Hopkins, Robert A. Living Without Gasoline. LC 76-19477. 1979. 10.95 (ISBN 0-917240-06-5). Am Metric.

McGillivray, Robert G. Automobile Gasoline Conservation. 67p. 1976. pap. 6.00x (ISBN 0-87766-162-6, 14100). Urban Inst.

Scardino, Vince, et al. Impact of the FEA-EPA Fuel Economy Information Program: Final Report. 1976. pap. 11.80x (ISBN 0-89011-488-9, ECR-112). Abt Bks.

--Impact of the FEA-EPA Fuel Economy Information Program: Summary. 1976. pap. 1.90x (ISBN 0-89011-487-0, ECR-111). Abt Bks.

Tenneco Oil Company. Operators Handbook. LC 61-13964. 210p. 1961. 19.95x (ISBN 0-87201-643-9). Gulf Pub.

GASOLINE ENGINES

see Gas and Oil Engines

GASOLINE STATIONS

see Automobiles–Service Stations

GASP (COMPUTER PROGRAM LANGUAGE)

Horn, Carin E. & Poirot, James L. Computer Literacy: Problem-Solving with Computers. 2nd ed. 304p. (Orig.). 1984. 21.95; pap. 18.95; tchrs. manual 8.95. Sterling Swift.

Pritsker, A. Alan. The Gasp IV Simulation Language. LC 74-3281. 451p. 1974. 41.50x (ISBN 0-471-70045-2, Pub. by Wiley-Interscience). Wiley.

GASTEROMYCETES

see also Puffballs

Burk, W. R. A Bibliography of North American Gasteromycetes I: Phalales. 200p. 1981. pap. text ed. 16.00x (ISBN 3-7682-1262-9). Lubrecht & Cramer.

Coker, William C. & Couch, John N. The Gasteromycetes of Eastern United States & Canada. Bd. with The Gasteromycetes of Ohio. Johnson, Minne M. (Illus.). 11.25 (ISBN 0-8446-5017-X). Peter Smith.

--The Gasteromycetes of the Eastern United States & Canada. LC 73-91490. (Illus.). 447p. 1974. pap. 8.95 (ISBN 0-486-23033-3). Dover.

Johnson, Minnie M. The Gasteromycetae of Ohio: Puffballs, Bird's Nest Fungi & Stinkhorns. 1929. 1.50 (ISBN 0-86727-021-7). Ohio Bio Survey.

GASTEROPODA

see also Opisthobranchiata; Snails

Davis, George M. The Origin & Evolution of the Gastropod Family Pomatiopsidae, with Emphasis on the Mekong River Triculinae. (Monograph: No. 20). (Illus.). 120p. 1979. pap. 14.00 (ISBN 0-910006-28-8). Acad Nat Sci Phila.

Farmer, Wesley M. Sea-Slug Gastropods. (Illus.). 177p. (Orig.). 1980. pap. 9.57 (ISBN 0-937772-00-3). Farmer Ent.

Fretter, V. & Peake, J., eds. Pulmonates: Functional Anatomy & Physiology, Vol. 1. 1975. 64.50 (ISBN 0-12-267501-0). Acad Pr.

Keen, A. Myra & Doty, Charlotte L. Annotated Checklist of the Gastropods of Cape Arago, Oregon. (Studies in Zoology Ser.: No. 3). 16p. 1942. pap. 3.95x (ISBN 0-87071-103-2). Oreg St U Pr.

Macan, T. T. A Key to the British Fresh - & Brackish - Water Gastropods. 4th ed. 1977. 20.00x (ISBN 0-900386-30-4, Pub. by Freshwater Bio). State Mutual Bk.

Thompson, Fred G. Aquatic Snails of the Family Hydrobiidae of Peninsular Florida. LC 68-9707. 1968. 10.00 (ISBN 0-8130-0273-7). U Presses Fla.

Welch, D'Alte A. Distribution of Variation of Achatinella Mustelina Mighels in the Waianae Mountains, Oahu. (BMB). Repr. of 1938 ed. 22.00 (ISBN 0-527-02260-8). Kraus Repr.

Arber, Werner, et al. Genetic Manipulation: Impact on Man & Society. LC 83-26166. 250p. 1984. 34.50 (ISBN 0-521-26417-0). Cambridge U Pr.

Bennett, J. W. & Lasure, Linda L., eds. Gene Manipulation in Fungi. Edited Treatise ed. Date not set. 75.00 (ISBN 0-12-088640-5). Acad Pr.

Blank, Robert H. The Political Implications of Human Genetic Technology. (Special Studies in Science, Technology, & Public Policy). 209p. (Orig.). 1981. lib. bdg. 28.50x (ISBN 0-89158-975-9); pap. text ed. 12.95x (ISBN 0-86531-193-5). Westview.

Cherfas, Jeremy. Man-Made Life: An Overview of the Science, Technology & Commerce of Genetic Engineering. 279p. 1983. 15.45 (ISBN 0-394-52926-X). Pantheon.

Collins, Glenn B. & Petolino, Joseph G., eds. Applications of Genetic Engineering to Corp Improvement. (Advances in Agricultural Biotechnology Ser.). 1985. lib. bdg. 75.00 (ISBN 90-247-3084-8, Pub. by Martinus Nijhoff Netherlands). Kluwer-Academic.

Downey, Kathleen, et al. Advances in Gene Technology: Molecular Genetics of Plants & Animals. LC 83-21371. 1984. 55.00 (ISBN 0-12-221480-3). Acad Pr.

Garland, P. B. & Williamson, R., eds. Biochemistry of Genetic Engineering. (Symposia Ser.: No. 44). 145p. 1981. 27.50x (ISBN 0-904498-08-5, Pub. by Biochemical England). State Mutual Bk.

Gleba, Y. Y. & Sytnik, K. M. Protoplast Fusion: Genetic Engineering in Higher Plants. (Monographs on Theoretical & Applied Genetics: Vol. 8). (Illus.). 245p. 1984. 55.00 (ISBN 0-387-13284-8). Springer-Verlag.

Glover, D. M. Genetic Engineering. (Outline Studies in Biology). 79p. 1980. pap. 6.95 (ISBN 0-412-16170-2, NO. 6394, Pub. by Chapman & Hall). Methuen Inc.

Gupta, Akshey K. Genetics & Wheat Improvement. 268p. 1981. 80.00x (ISBN 0-686-76640-7, Pub. by Oxford & IBH India). State Mutual Bk.

Hanson, Earl D., ed. Recombinant DNA Research & the Human Prospect. (Other Technical Bks.). 129p. 1983. text ed. 19.95 (ISBN 0-8412-0750-X); pap. text ed. 14.95 (ISBN 0-8412-0754-2). Am Chemical.

Harnden, D. G., et al, eds. An International System for Human Cytogenetic Nomenclature: High-Resolution Banding, 1981, ISCN, 1981, Vol. 31, No.1. (Illus.). 32p. 1981. pap. 10.00 (ISBN 3-8055-3484-1). S Karger.

Hollaender, Alexander, ed. Genetic Engineering of Microorganisms for Chemicals. LC 81-21166. (Basic Life Sciences Ser.: Vol. 19). 500p. 1982. text ed. 59.50 (ISBN 0-306-40912-7, Plenum Pr). Plenum Pub.

Huang, P. C. & Kuo, T. T., eds. Genetic Engineering Techniques: Recent Developments (Symposium) LC 82-20687. 1983. 37.50 (ISBN 0-12-358250-4). Acad Pr.

Inouye, Masayori. Experimental Manipulation of Gene Expression. 1983. 44.00 (ISBN 0-12-372380-9). Acad Pr.

Johnston, James B. & Robinson, Susan G. Genetic Engineering & New Pollution Control Technologies. LC 83-22077. (Pollution Technology Review Ser., No. 106; Biotechnology Review Ser., No. 3). (Illus.). 131p. 1984. 32.00 (ISBN 0-8155-0973-1). Noyes.

Kosuge, Tsune, et al, eds. Genetic Engineering of Plants: An Agricultural Perspective. (Basic Life Sciences Ser.: Vol. 26). 512p. 1983. 69.50x (ISBN 0-306-41353-1, Plenum Pr). Plenum Pub.

Levin, Morris A., et al. Applied Genetic Engineering: Future Trends & Problems. LC 82-14401. (Illus.). 191p. 1983. 24.00 (ISBN 0-8155-0925-1, Noyes Pubns). Noyes.

Lurquin, Paul F. & Kleinhofs, A., eds. Genetic Engineering in Eukaryotes. (NATO ASI Series A, Life Sciences: Vol. 61). 292p. 1983. 45.00x (ISBN 0-306-41275-6, Plenum Pr). Plenum Pub.

McCuen, Gary E., ed. Manipulating Life: Debating the Genetic Revolution. (Ideas in Conflict Ser.). (Illus.). 136p. 1985. lib. bdg. 10.95 (ISBN 0-86596-054-2). GEM McCuen Pubns.

MacGregor, Herbert C. & Varley, Jennifer M. Working with Animal Chromosomes. LC 82-23788. 250p. 1983. 44.95x (ISBN 0-471-10295-4, Pub. by Wiley-Interscience). Wiley.

Magnien, E. & De Nettancourt, D., eds. Genetic Engineering of Plants & Micro-Organisms Important for Agriculture. (Advances in Argicultural Biotechnology Ser.). 1985. lib. bdg. 36.00 (ISBN 90-247-3131-3, Pub. by Martinus Nijhoff Netherlands). Kluwer Academic.

Menditto, Joseph & Kirsch, Debbie. Genetic Engineering, DNA & Cloning: A Bibliography in the Future of Genetics. LC 82-50417. 790p. 1982. 50.00 (ISBN 0-87875-241-2). Whitston Pub.

Mitsuhashi, S., et al, eds. Transferable Antibiotic Resistance; Plasmids & Gene Manipulation: Fifth International Symposium on Antibiotic Resistance & Plasmids, Castle of Smolenice, Czechoslovakia, 1983. 420p. 1984. 41.50 (ISBN 0-387-13141-8). Springer-Verlag.

Moraczewski, Albert S., ed. Genetic Medicine & Engineering: Ethical & Social Dimensions. LC 82-22019. (Orig.). 1983. pap. 17.50 (ISBN 0-87125-077-2). Cath Health.

National Council of Churches Staff. Genetic Engineering: Social & Ethical Consequences. 96p. 1984. pap. 5.95 (ISBN 0-8298-0701-2). Pilgrim NY.

Newsletter Publications Center. Genetic Engineering-Biotechnology Sourcebook. Pergolizzi, Robert, ed. 333p. 1982. pap. 99.95 (ISBN 0-07-049321-9). McGraw.

Nossal, G. J. V. Reshaping Life: Key Issues in Genetic Engineering. 150p. 1985. pap. 11.95 (ISBN 0-521-31603-0). Cambridge U Pr.

Old, R. W. & Primrose, S. B. Principles of Gene Manipulation. 3rd ed. (Illus.). 414p. 1985. pap. text ed. 24.00x (ISBN 0-632-01318-4). Blackwell Pubns.

Oliver, S. G. & Ward, J. M. A Dictionary of Genetic Engineering. (Illus.). 256p. 1985. 19.95 (ISBN 0-521-26080-9). Cambridge U Pr.

Omenn, Gilbert & Hollaender, Alexander, eds. Genetic Control of Environmental Pollutants. (Basic Life Sciences Ser.: Vol. 28). 418p. 1984. 55.00x (ISBN 0-306-41624-7, Plenum Pr). Plenum Pub.

Owens, Lowell D. Genetic Engineering: Applications to Agriculture. LC 83-3252. (Beltsville Symposia in Agricultural Research: No. 7). (Illus.). 352p. 1983. text ed. 42.50x (ISBN 0-86598-112-4). Rowman & Allanheld.

Panopoulos, Nickolas J. Genetic Engineering in the Plant Sciences. LC 81-10564. 288p. 1981. 45.95 (ISBN 0-03-057026-3). Praeger.

Paul, J. K., ed. Genetic Engineering Applications for Industry. LC 81-14028. (Chemical Technical Review: No. 197). (Illus.). 580p. 1982. 72.00 (ISBN 0-8155-0869-7). Noyes.

Rains, Donald W., et al, eds. Genetic Engineering of Osmoregulation: Impact of Plant Productivity for Food, Chemicals, & Energy. LC 80-14972. (Basic Life Sciences Ser.: Vol. 14). 395p. 1980. 49.50x (ISBN 0-306-40454-0, Plenum Pr). Plenum Pub.

Research & Education Association Staff. Genetic Engineering. LC 82-62129. (Illus.). 352p. 1982. 14.30 (ISBN 0-87891-544-3). Res & Educ.

Roy, A. K. & Clark, J. H., eds. Gene Regulation by Steroid Hormones II. (Illus.). 384p. 1983. 65.00 (ISBN 0-387-90784-X). Springer-Verlag.

Roy, David J. & De Wachter, Maurice A. The Second Genesis: New Human Reproductive & Genetic Technologies & the Public Policy Questions They Raise. (Orig.). Date not set. pap. text ed. write for info (ISBN 0-88645-007-1, Pub. by Inst Res Pub Canada). Brookfield Pub Co.

Russell, Gordon E., ed. & intro. by. Biotechnology & Genetic Engineering Reviews, Vol. 1. (Biotechnology & Genetic Engineering Reviews Ser.). (Illus.). 438p. 1984. text ed. 79.50x (ISBN 0-946707-01-4). Scholium Intl.

--Biotechnology & Genetic Engineering Reviews, Vol. 2. (Biotechnology Genetic & Engineering Reviews Ser.). (Illus.). 466p. 1984. text ed. 79.50x (ISBN 0-946707-02-2). Scholium Intl.

--Biotechnology & Genetic Engineering Reviews, Vol. 3. (Biotechnology & Genetic Engineering Reviews Ser.). (Illus.). 450p. 1985. text ed. 99.50 (ISBN 0-946707-04-9). Scholium Intl.

Samal, B. Gene Expression in Higher Organisms, Vol. 3. Horrobin, D. F., ed. (Annual Research Reviews Ser.). 272p. 1984. 38.00 (ISBN 0-88831-115-X). Eden Pr.

Scott, Walter A., et al, eds. Advances in Gene Technology: Human Genetic Disorders, Proceedings of the 16th Miami Winter Symposium, 16th. Schultz, Julius & Whelan, William J. (International Council of Scientific Unions Short Reports: No. 1). (Illus.). 300p. 1984. 39.50 (ISBN 0-521-26749-8). Cambridge U Pr.

Setlow, Jane K. & Hollaender, Alexander, eds. Genetic Engineering: Principles & Methods, Vol. 4. 298p. 1982. 39.50x (ISBN 0-306-41113-X, Plenum Pr). Plenum Pub.

--Genetic Engineering: Vol. 6 Principles & Methods. 346p. 1984. 49.50x (ISBN 0-306-41710-3, Plenum Pr). Plenum Pub.

Shannan, Thomas A. What Are They Saying about Genetic Engineering. (W. A. T. S. A. Ser.). 96p. (Orig.). 1986. pap. 4.95 (ISBN 0-8091-2743-1). Paulist Pr.

Silhavy, Thomas J., et al, eds. Experiments with Gene Fusions. LC 83-15230. 350p. 1984. pap. 40.00x (ISBN 0-87969-163-8). Cold Spring Harbor.

Skamene, Emil, ed. Genetic Control of Natural Resistance to Infection & Malignancy. (Perspectives in Immunology Ser.). 1980. 49.50 (ISBN 0-12-647680-2). Acad Pr.

Stableford, Brian. Future Man: Brave New World or Genetic Nightmare? LC 84-4955. (Illus.). 1984. 17.95 (ISBN 0-517-55248-5); pap. 12.95 (ISBN 0-517-55249-3). Crown.

Starlinger, P. & Schell, J., eds. The Impact of Gene Transfer Techniques in Eucaryotic Cell Biology. (Colloquium der Gesellschaft fur Biologische Chemie Ser.: Vol. 35). (Illus.). 230p. 1985. 33.50 (ISBN 0-387-13836-6). Springer-Verlag.

Subtelny, Stephen & Sussex, Ian M., eds. The Clonal Basis of Development. (Thirty Sixth Symposia of the Society for Developmental Biology Ser.). 1979. 41.00 (ISBN 0-12-612982-7). Acad Pr.

Technical Insights Inc. Drug Delivery Systems: A Technology Survey. LC 84-50989. 288p. 1984. 710.00 (ISBN 0-914993-03-8). Tech Insights.

--Monoclonal Antibodies: Technical Opportunities. LC 83-51745. (Emerging Technology Ser.: No. 10). 1984. 645.00 (ISBN 0-914993-02-X). Tech Insights.

Technical Insights, Inc. Staff. Genetic Technology: A Guide to Key R & D Projects. rev. ed. LC 84-52608. 280p. 1985. 337.00 (ISBN 0-914993-10-0). Tech Insights.

Walton, A. G. & Hammer, S. K., eds. Genetic Engineering & Biotechnology Yearbook, 1985. 1060p. 1985. 750.00 (ISBN 0-444-42461-X). Elsevier.

Whelan, W. J., et al. From Genetic Experimentation to Biotechnology: The Critical Transition. LC 81-19838. 266p. 1982. 44.95x (ISBN 0-471-10148-6, Pub. by Wiley-Interscience). Wiley.

Williamson, R., ed. Genetic Engineering, Vol. 3. (Serial Publication). 192p. 1982. 27.00 (ISBN 0-12-270303-0). Acad Pr.

Williamson, Robert, ed. Genetic Engineering, Vol. 4. (Serial Publication). 1983. pap. 24.50 (ISBN 0-12-270304-9). Acad Pr.

Witt, Steven C. Briefbook: Biotechnology & Genetic Diversity. (Illus.). 140p. (Orig.). 1985. pap. 9.95 (ISBN 0-317-19451-8). CA Agri Lnd Pr.

--QuickBook: Genetic Engineering of Plants. (Illus.). 53p. (Orig.). 1983. pap. 7.95 (ISBN 0-912005-02-5). CA Agri Lnd Pr.

Yoxen, Edward. The Gene Business: Who Should Control Biotechnology? LC 83-48809. 230p. 1984. 15.34 (ISBN 0-06-015303-2, HarpT). Har-Row.

GENETIC PSYCHOLOGY

Here are entered works on the evolutionary psychology of man in terms of origin and development, whether in the individual or in the species. Works on the psychological development of the individual from infancy to old age are entered under Developmental Psychology.

see also Sociobiology

Baldwin, James M. Development & Evolution: Including Psychophysical Evolution, Evolution by Orthoplasy & the Theory of Genetic Modes. LC 75-3022. (Philosophy in America Ser.). Repr. of 1902 ed. 42.50 (ISBN 0-404-59017-9). AMS Pr.

Broughton, John M. & Freeman-Moir, John D. The Cognitive Developmental Psychology of James Mark Baldwin: Current Theory & Research in Genetic Epistemology. LC 81-7885. (Publications for the Advancement of Theory & History in Psychology (PATH) Ser.). 480p. 1982. 42.50x (ISBN 0-89391-043-0). Ablex Pub.

Cold Spring Harbor Symposia on Quantitative Biology: Population Genetics, Vol. 20. LC 34-8174. (Illus.). 362p. 1956. 38.00x (ISBN 0-87969-019-4). Cold Spring Harbor.

Conrad, Herbert S., ed. Studies in Human Development: Selections from the Publications & Addresses of Harold Ellis Jones. (Century Psychology Ser.). (Illus.). 1966. 46.50x (ISBN 0-89197-581-0). Irvington.

Crow, James F. & Denniston, Carter. Genetic Distance. LC 74-23683. 203p. 1974. 35.00x (ISBN 0-306-30827-4, Plenum Pr). Plenum Pub.

Eysenck, H. J. The Inequality of Man. 1975. 10.95 (ISBN 0-912736-16-X). EDITS Pubs.

Gary, A. L. & Glover, John A. Eye Color, Sex, & Children's Behavior. LC 76-3642. 186p. 1976. 19.95x (ISBN 0-88229-213-7). Nelson-Hall.

Gershon, E. S., et al, eds. Genetic Research Strategies in Psychobiology & Psychiatry. 470p. 1981. 65.50 (ISBN 0-444-80350-5, Biomedical Pr). Elsevier.

--Genetic Research Strategies in Psychobiology & Psychiatry. (Psychobiology & Psychopathology Ser.: Vol. 1). 1981. 38.50x (ISBN 0-910286-84-1). Boxwood.

Griffin, Donald R. The Question of Animal Awareness: Evolutionary Continuity of Mental Experience. LC 76-18492. 144p. 1976. 7.00x (ISBN 0-87470-020-5). Rockefeller.

Grinder, Robert E. A History of Genetic Psychology: The First Science of Human Development. LC 67-21330. (Illus.). pap. 65.30 (ISBN 0-317-10457-8, 2012527). Bks Demand UMI.

Hobhouse, Leonard T. Mind in Evolution. Repr. of 1915 ed. 30.00 (ISBN 0-89987-057-0). Darby Bks.

Lumsden, Charles J. & Wilson, Edward O. Promethean Fire: Reflections on the Origin of Mind. (Illus.). 256p. 1983. 17.50 (ISBN 0-674-71445-8). Harvard U Pr.

--Promethean Fire: Reflections on the Origin of Mind. 224p. 1984. pap. 6.95 (ISBN 0-674-71446-6). Harvard U Pr.

Milunsky, Aubrey. Prevention of Genetic Disease & Mental Retardation. LC 74-21015. (Illus.). Repr. of 1975 ed. 130.50 (ISBN 0-8357-9554-3, 2016674). Bks Demand UMI.

Piaget, Jean. The Child & Reality: Problems of Genetic Psychology. Rosin, Arnold, tr. from Fr. 182p. 1973. text ed. 8.95. Beekman Pubs.

Symons, Donald. The Evolution of Human Sexuality. 1979. 27.50x (ISBN 0-19-502535-0); pap. 9.95 (ISBN 0-19-502907-0, GB 638). Oxford U Pr.

GENETIC SURGERY

see Genetic Engineering

GENETICS

see also Adaptation (Biology); Bacterial Genetics; Behavior Genetics; Biology; Chemical Genetics; Chromosomes; Cytogenetics; Developmental Genetics; Epigenesis; Evolution; Genetic Psychology; Heredity; Human Genetics; Linkage (Genetics); Molecular Genetics; Mutation (Biology); Natural Selection; Origin of Species; Population Genetics; Radiogenetics; Variation (Biology)

Alaeddinoglue, Gurdal N., et al, eds. Industrial Aspects of Biochemistry & Genetics, Volume 87. (NATO ASI Series A, Life Sciences). 227p. 1985. 45.00x (ISBN 0-306-41934-3, Plenum Pr). Plenum Pub.

Animal Genetic Resources Conservation & Management: Proceedings of the UNEP Technical Consultation. (Animal Production & Health Papers: No. 24). 399p. (With Summaries in French & Spanish). 1981. pap. 28.75 (ISBN 92-5-101118-4, F2249, FAO). Unipub.

Applewhite, Steven R., et al, eds. Genetic Screening & Counseling-A Multidisciplinary Perspective. (Illus.). 260p. 1981. 19.50x (ISBN 0-398-04080-X). C C Thomas.

Ashburner, M., et al, eds. The Genetics of Drosphila, Vol. 3, Pt. A. Carson, H. L. 1981. 86.50 (ISBN 0-12-064945-4). Acad Pr.

Atkinson, B. G. & Walden, S. B., eds. Changes in Gene Expression in Response to Environmental Stress. 1985. 65.00 (ISBN 0-12-066290-6). Acad Pr.

Auerbach, Charlotte. Notes for Introductory Courses in Genetics. rev. ed. 1965. pap. 2.25 (ISBN 0-910824-02-9). Kallman.

Avers, Charlotte J. Genetics. 2nd ed. 700p. 1984. text ed. write for info (ISBN 0-87150-779-X, 4541, Pub. by Willard Grant Pr). PWS Pubs.

Ayala. Evolutionary & Population Genetics: A Primer. 1982. 19.95 (ISBN 0-8053-0315-4). Benjamin-Cummings.

Ayala, F. J. Genetic Variation & Evolution. Head, J. J., ed. LC 81-67985. (Carolina Biology Readers Ser.). (Illus.). 16p. 1983. pap. 1.60 (ISBN 0-89278-326-5, 45-9726). Carolina Biological.

Ayala, F. J. & Kiger, J. A., Jr. Modern Genetics. 2nd ed. 1984. 36.95 (ISBN 0-8053-0316-2); solutions manual 4.95 (ISBN 0-8053-0317-0). Benjamin-Cummings.

Baer, Adela S. The Genetic Perspective. 1977. text ed. 24.95 (ISBN 0-7216-1471-X, CBS C). SCP.

Balakrishman, V., et al. Genetic Diversity Among Australian Aborigines. (AIAS Research & Regional Ser.: No. 3). (Illus.). 1975. pap. text ed. 7.75x (ISBN 0-85575-043-X). Humanities.

Balk, Melvin W. & Melby, Edward C., Jr. Importance of Laboratory Animal Genetics: Health & Environment in Biomedical Research. 1984. 28.00 (ISBN 0-12-489520-4). Acad Pr.

Baraitser, Michael. The Genetics of Neurological Disorders. 1982. text ed. 69.00x (ISBN 0-19-261155-0). Oxford U Pr.

Barker, J. S., ed. Future Developments in the Genetic Improvement of Animals. 256p. 1983. 29.00 (ISBN 0-12-078830-6). Acad Pr.

Barker, J. S. & Starmer, T., eds. Ecological Genetics & Evolutions: The Cactus-Yeast-Drosophila Model. LC 82-72224. 376p. 1982. 52.50 (ISBN 0-12-078820-9). Acad Pr.

Bartsocas, Christos S. & Papadatos, Constantine J., eds. The Management of Genetic Disorders: Proceedings. LC 79-5298. (Progress in Clinical & Biological Research Ser.: Vol. 34). 430p. 1979. 42.00x (ISBN 0-8451-0034-3). A R Liss.

Baskin, Yvonne. The Gene Doctors: Medical Genetics at the Frontier. LC 83-61743. 288p. 1984. 13.95 (ISBN 0-688-02645-1). Morrow.

Bateson. Problems of Genetics. LC 79-15467. 1979. text ed. 33.00x (ISBN 0-300-02435-5); pap. 9.95x (ISBN 0-300-02436-3, Y-350). Yale U Pr.

Fincham, John R. Genetics. 643p. 1983. text ed. write for info (ISBN 0-86720-026-X). Jones & Bartlett.

Ford, E. B. Ecological Genetics. 4th ed. 1979. 29.95x (ISBN 0-412-16130-3, NO.6110, Pub. by Chapman & Hall). Methuen Inc.

--Understanding Genetics. LC 79-63132. (Illus.). 1979. text ed. 15.00x (ISBN 0-87663-728-4, Pica Pr). Universe.

Fraenkel-Conrat, H. & Wagner, R. R., eds. Comprehensive Virology, Vol. 10: Viral Gene Expression & Integeration. (Illus.). 512p. 1977. 55.00x (ISBN 0-306-35150-1, Plenum Pr). Plenum Pub.

--Comprehensive Virology, Vol. 11: Genetics of Plant Viruses. LC 77-7908. (Illus.). 364p. 1977. 39.50x (ISBN 0-306-35151-X, Plenum Pr). Plenum Pub.

Francis Galton Laboratory for National Eugenics Staff, et al. Eugenics Laboratory Lecture Series. Rosenberg, Charles, ed. LC 83-48563. (The History of Hereditarian Thought Ser.). 434p. 1985. lib. bdg. 52.00 (ISBN 0-8240-5815-1). Garland Pub.

Fristrom, James W. & Clegg, Michael T. Principles of Genetics. 2nd ed. LC 80-65757. (Illus.). 700p. 1986. text ed. 29.95tx (ISBN 0-913462-05-5). Chiron Pr.

Garber, Edward. Genetic Pespectives in Biology & Medicine. LC 85-8454. 500p. 1985. 30.00 (ISBN 0-317-28530-0); pap. 12.00 (ISBN 0-226-28216-3). U of Chicago Pr.

Gardner, E. John & Snustad, D. Peter. Principles of Genetics. 7th ed. LC 83-21798. 672p. 1984. text ed. 34.45 (ISBN 0-471-87610-0, Pub by Wiley). Wiley.

Gardner, Eldon & Mertens, Thomas R. Genetics Laboratory Investigations. 8th ed. 1985. write for info. (ISBN 0-8087-4146-2). Burgess.

Gedda, Luigi & Brenci, Gianni. Chronogenetics: The Inheritance of Biological Time. (Illus.). 232p. 1978. 32.75x (ISBN 0-398-03641-1). C C Thomas.

Genetica y la Revolucion en las Ciencias Biologicas. rev. ed. (Serie De Biologia: No. 1). (Span.). 1975. pap. 3.50 (ISBN 0-8270-6045-9). OAS.

Genetics - New Frontiers: Proceedings, International Congress of Genetics, 15th, Dec. 1983, 4 Vols. 1600p. 1984. Set. pap. 185.00 (ISBN 0-89059-037-0, OIB101, UPB). Unipub.

Genetics & Reproduction. 124p. 1972. 35.00x (ISBN 0-686-45150-3, Pub. by Biochemical England). State Mutual Bk.

Giblett, Eloise R. Genetic Markers in Human Blood. (Illus.). 1969. 25.25 (ISBN 0-632-05290-2, B 1814-2, Blackwell). Mosby.

Gibson, J. B. & Oakeshoff, J. G., eds. Genetic Studies of Drosophila Populations. 267p. (Orig.). 1981. pap. text ed. 10.00 (ISBN 0-686-30658-9, 0069, Pub. by ANUP Australia). Australia N U P.

Ginsberg, Harold S. & Vogel, Henry J., eds. Transfer & Expression of Eukaryotic Genes. (P & S Biomedical Symposia Ser.). 1984. 65.00 (ISBN 0-12-284650-8). Acad Pr.

Glover, S. W. & Hopwood, D. A., eds. Genetics As a Tool in Microbiology. (Society for General Microbiology Symposium: No. 31). (Illus.). 450p. 1981. text ed. 75.00 (ISBN 0-521-23748-3). Cambridge U Pr.

Goldberger, Robert F., ed. Biological Regulation & Development, Vol. 1: Gene Expression. LC 78-21893. 576p. 1978. 55.00x (ISBN 0-306-40098-7, Plenum Pr). Plenum Pub.

Goodenough, Ursula. Genetics. 3rd ed. LC 83-4438. 894p. 1984. text ed. 37.95x (ISBN 0-03-058212-1). SCP.

Grant, Verne. The Origin of Adaptations. LC 63-11695. (Illus.). 606p. 1963. 54.00x (ISBN 0-231-02529-7); pap. 22.00x (ISBN 0-231-08648-2). Columbia U Pr.

Green, Earl L. Genetics & Probability. (Illus.). 1981. text ed. 45.00x (ISBN 0-19-520159-0). Oxford U Pr.

Greene, Mark I. & Nisonoff, Alfred, eds. The Biology of Idiotypes. 524p. 1984. 59.50x (ISBN 0-306-41646-8, Plenum Pr). Plenum Pub.

Grell, Rhoda F., ed. Mechanisms in Recombination. LC 74-20987. 471p. 1974. 47.50x (ISBN 0-306-30823-1, Plenum Pr). Plenum Pub.

Griffin, John R. & Fatt, Helene. Genetics for the Primary Eye Care Practitioner. LC 83-61488. 1983. 28.00 (ISBN 0-87873-037-0). Prof Press.

Hackel, Emanuel & Mallory, Delores, eds. Theoretical Aspects of HLA. (Illus.). 141p. 1982. 22.70 (ISBN 0-914404-71-7). Am Assn Blood.

Hall, Jeffrey C. & Greenspan, Ralph J. Genetic Neurobiology. 1982. 40.00x (ISBN 0-262-08111-3). MIT Pr.

Hamer, Dean H. & Rosenberg, Martin G. Gene Expression. LC 83-16280. (UCLA Symposia on Molecular & Cellular Biology Ser.: Vol. 8). 612p. 1983. 76.00 (ISBN 0-8451-2607-5). A R Liss.

Harris, Harry & Hirschhorn, Kurt, eds. Advances in Human Genetics, Vol. 14. 381p. 1985. 49.50x (ISBN 0-306-41752-9, Plenum Pr). Plenum Pub.

Harsanyi, Zsolt & Hutton, Richard. Genetic Prophecy: Beyond the Double Helix -- Genes That Predict the Future. 294p. 1981. 3.95 (ISBN 0-89256-163-7). Rawson Assocs.

Hartl, Daniel. Our Uncertain Heritage: Genetics & Human Diversity. 2nd ed. 468p. 1984. text ed. 30.50 scp (ISBN 0-06-042684-5, HarpC). Har-Row.

Hayden, M. R. Huntington's Chorea. (Illus.). 216p. 1981. 49.50 (ISBN 0-387-10588-3). Springer Verlag.

Hecht, Max K. & Steere, William C., eds. Essays in Evolution & Genetics in Honor of Theodosius Dobzhansky: A Supplement to Evolutionary Biology. LC 74-105428. 594p. 1970. 42.50x (ISBN 0-306-50034-5, Plenum Pr). Plenum Pub.

Herrmann, Klaus & Somerville, Ronald. Amino-Acid Biosynthesis & Genetic Regulation. (Biotechnology Ser.: No. 3). (Illus.). 330p. 1983. text ed. 42.95x (ISBN 0-201-10520-9). Addison-Wesley.

Herskowitz, Irwin H. The Elements of Genetics. 1979. write for info. (ISBN 0-02-353950-X). Macmillan.

--Principles of Genetics. 2nd ed. 672p. 1977. write for info. (ISBN 0-02-353930-5). Macmillan.

Hou, Ching T. Methylotrophs: Microbiology, Biochemistry & Genetics. 192p. 1984. 65.00 (ISBN 0-8493-5992-9). CRC Pr.

Hsu, T. C. Human & Mammalian Cytogenetics: A Historical Perspective. (Heidelberg Science Library Ser.). (Illus.). 1979. pap. 18.00 (ISBN 0-387-90364-X). Springer-Verlag.

Huber, A. & Klein, D., eds. Neurogenetics & Neuro-Opthalmology. (Developments in Neurology Ser.: Vol. 5). 432p. 1982. 78.75 (ISBN 0-444-80378-5, I-499-82, Biomedical Pr). Elsevier.

Hutt, Frederick B. Genetics for Dog Breeders. LC 79-15169. (Illus.). 245p. 1979. text ed. 23.95 (ISBN 0-7167-1069-2). W H Freeman.

Hutt, Frederick B. & Rasmusen, Benjamin. Animal Genetics. 2nd ed. LC 81-19561. 582p. 1982. text ed. 36.95 (ISBN 0-471-08497-2). Wiley.

Huxley, Julian S. Heredity, East & West: Lysenko & World Science. LC 49-50254. 1969. Repr. of 1949 ed. 16.00 (ISBN 0-527-43810-3). Kraus Repr.

Hyde, Margaret O. & Hyde, Lawrence E. Cloning & the New Genetics. LC 83-20727. (Illus.). 128p. 1984. PLB 11.95 (ISBN 0-89490-084-6). Enslow Pubs.

ICLAS Staff. ICLAS Manual for Genetic Monitoring of Inbred Mice. 200p. 1985. pap. 25.00x (ISBN 0-86008-366-7, Pub. by U of Tokyo Japan). Columbia U Pr.

ICN-UCLA Symposia on Molecular & Cellular Biology. Eukaryotic Genetics Systems. Wilcox, Gary, et al, eds. 1977. 47.50 (ISBN 0-12-751550-X). Acad Pr.

Ingram, Vernon M. Hemoglobins in Genetics & Evolution. LC 63-10416. (Biology Ser.). (Illus.). 1963. 24.00x (ISBN 0-231-02585-8). Columbia U Pr.

International Symposium on Molecular Biology Staff. Cellular Modification & Genetic Transformation by Exogenous Nucleic Acids. LC 73-5909. (The John Hopkins Medical University Ser.: No. 2). pap. 87.50 (ISBN 0-317-28474-6, 2020738). Bks Demand UMI.

Ionasescu, Victor & Zellweger, Hans. Genetics in Neurology. 520p. 1983. text ed. 71.50 (ISBN 0-89004-775-8). Raven.

Islam, A. S. Fundamentals of Genetics. 2nd ed. 520p. 1982. text ed. 30.00x (ISBN 0-7069-1798-7, Pub. by Vikas India). Advent NY.

Jackson, Laird G. & Schimke, R. Neil, eds. Clinical Genetics: A Sourcebook for Physicians. LC 78-24414. 652p. 1979. 70.00 (ISBN 0-471-01943-7, Pub. by Wiley Medical). Wiley.

Jacob, Francois. The Possible & the Actual. 1982. pap. 4.95 (ISBN 0-394-70671-4). Pantheon.

Jacob, Francois & Wollman, E. Sexuality & the Genetics of Bacteria. rev. ed. 1961. 64.50 (ISBN 0-12-379450-1). Acad Pr.

Jacquard, A. The Genetic Structure of Populations. Charlesworth, B. & Charlesworth, D., trs. from Fr. LC 73-80868. (Biomathematics Ser.: Vol. 5). (Illus.). xviii, 569p. 1974. text ed. 26.00 (ISBN 0-387-06329-3). Springer-Verlag.

Jaenicke, L., ed. Biochemistry of Differentiation & Morphogenosis. (Collequium Mosbach: Vol. 33). (Illus.). 301p. 1982. 42.00 (ISBN 0-387-12010-6). Springer-Verlag.

Jameson, D. L., ed. Evolutionary Genetics. (Benchmark Papers in Genetics: Vol. 8). 1977. 56.00 (ISBN 0-12-786755-4). Acad Pr.

Johnson, K. E. Histology: Microscopic Anatomy & Embryology. 415p. 1982. pap. 25.00 (ISBN 0-471-08092-6, Pub. by Wiley Med). Wiley.

Jorgenson, Ronald J. Dentition: Genetic Effects. LC 82-24935. (Birth Defects: Original Article Ser.: Vol. 19, No. 1). 202p. 1983. 42.00 (ISBN 0-8451-1053-5). A R Liss.

Jude, Albert C. Cat Genetics. new ed. (Illus.). 1977. 12.95 (ISBN 0-87666-172-X, AP-4600). TFH Pubns.

Karp, Lawrence E. Genetic Engineering: Threat or Promise? LC 76-3497. (Illus.). 253p. 1976. 22.95x (ISBN 0-88229-261-7); pap. 11.95x (ISBN 0-88229-460-1). Nelson-Hall.

Kenney, F. T., et al. Gene Expression & Its Regulation. LC 72-90334. (Basic Life Sciences Ser.: Vol. 1). 588p. 1973. 57.50x (ISBN 0-306-36501-4, Plenum Pr). Plenum Pub.

Kety, Seymour S., et al, eds. Genetics of Neurological & Psychiatric Disorders. (Association for Research in Nervous & Mental Disease (ARNMD) Research Publications Ser.: Vol. 60). 312p. 1983. text ed. 52.00 (ISBN 0-89004-626-3). Raven.

Kevles, Daniel J. In the Name of Eugenics: Genetics & the Uses of Human Heredity. LC 84-47810. 1985. 22.95 (ISBN 0-394-50702-9). Knopf.

Kiger, Ayala & Kiger, J. Modern Genetics. 1985. 37.95 (ISBN 0-8053-0314-6). Benjamin-Cummings.

King, James C. The Biology of Race. rev. ed. LC 81-1345. (Illus.). 220p. 1982. 18.95 (ISBN 0-520-04223-9); pap. 6.95 (ISBN 0-520-04224-7, CAL 539). U of Cal Pr.

King, Robert C. Genetics. 2nd ed. (Illus.). 1965. 12.50x (ISBN 0-19-500932-0). Oxford U Pr.

King, Robert C. & Stansfield, William D. Dictionary of Genetics. 3rd ed. (Illus.). 496p. 1985. 35.00x (ISBN 0-19-503494-5); pap. 16.95 (ISBN 0-19-503495-3). Oxford U Pr.

King, Robert C., ed. Handbook of Genetics. Incl. Vol. 1. Bacteria, Bacteriophages, & Fungi. LC 74-8867. (Illus.). 691p. 65.00x (ISBN 0-306-37611-3); Vol. 2. Plants, Plant Viruses, & Protists. LC 74-23531. (Illus.). 642p. 1974. 65.00x (ISBN 0-306-37612-1); Vol. 3. Invertebrates of Genetic Interest. 888p. 1975. 65.00x (ISBN 0-306-37613-X); Vol. 4. Vertebrates of Genetic Interest. 683p. 1975. 65.00x (ISBN 0-306-37614-8); Vol. 5. Molecular Genetics. 675p. 1976. 65.00x (ISBN 0-306-37615-6). (Illus., Plenum Pr). Plenum Pub.

Kirk, R. L. The Distribution of Genetic Markers in Australian Aborigines. (AIAS Human Biology Ser.: No. 1). (Illus.). 1965. pap. text ed. 5.00x (ISBN 0-85575-099-5). Humanities.

Klingmuller, W., ed. Azospirillum II: Genetics, Physiology, Ecology, Vol. 48. (Experimentia Supplementa Ser.). 196p. 1984. 27.95 (ISBN 3-7643-1576-8). Birkhauser.

Klug, William S. & Cummings, Michael R. Concepts of Genetics. 1983. text ed. 32.95 (ISBN 0-675-20010-5). Additional supplements may be obtained from publisher. Merrill.

Koger, Marvin, et al, eds. Crossbreeding Beef Cattle: Series II. LC 73-8847. 470p. 1973. 17.50 (ISBN 0-8130-0364-4). U Presses Fla.

Kohn, Alexander & Shatkay, Adam, eds. Control of Gene Expression. LC 74-3157. (Advances in Experimental Medicine & Biology Ser.: Vol. 44). 447p. 1974. 55.00 (ISBN 0-306-39044-2, Plenum Pr). Plenum Pub.

Korochkin, L. I. Gene Interactions in Development. (Monographs on Theoretical & Applied Genetics: Vol. 4). (Illus.). 340p. 1981. 62.00 (ISBN 0-387-10112-8). Springer-Verlag.

Kowles, Richard V. Genetics, Society & Decisions. 480p. 1985. text ed. 28.95 (ISBN 0-675-20374-0). Additional supplements may be obtained from publisher. Merrill.

Kroon, A. M., ed. Genes: Structure & Expression, Vol. 7. (Environmental & Applied Microbiology Ser.: 1-675). 362p. 1983. 49.95x (ISBN 0-471-90264-0, 1-575, Pub. by Wiley-Interscience). Wiley.

Krumphanzl, V., et al, eds. Overproduction of Microbial Products. 1982. 75.00 (ISBN 0-12-426920-6). Acad Pr.

Kushev, V. V. Mechanisms of Genetic Recombination. LC 73-83989. (Studies in Soviet Science-Life Sciences). (Illus.). 266p. 1974. 35.00x (ISBN 0-306-10891-7, Consultants). Plenum Pub.

Lakovaara, Seppo, ed. Advances in Genetics, Development, & Evolution of Drosophila. LC 82-9154. 480p. 1982. 57.50x (ISBN 0-306-41106-7, Plenum Pr). Plenum Pub.

Lande, Rivian & Knox, Marlys. Concepts of Genetics. (Orig.). 1980. 8.95x (ISBN 0-8087-3826-7). Burgess.

Lauder, Jean & Nelson, Phillip, eds. Gene Expression & Cell-Cell Interactions in the Developing Nervous System. 274p. 1985. 42.50x (ISBN 0-306-41836-3, Plenum Pr). Plenum Pub.

Lebacqz, Karen. Genetics, Ethics & Parenthood. 128p. (Orig.). 1983. pap. 7.95 (ISBN 0-8298-0671-7). Pilgrim NY.

Lerner, I. M. & Donald, H. P. Modern Developments in Animal Breeding. 1966. 59.00 (ISBN 0-12-444350-8). Acad Pr.

Lerner, I. Michael. The Genetic Basis of Selection. LC 73-19295. (Illus.). 298p. 1974. Repr. of 1958 ed. lib. bdg. 24.75x (ISBN 0-8371-7315-9, LEGB). Greenwood.

Lester, Lane & Bohlin, Raymond G. The Natural Limits to Biological Change. 160p. 1984. pap. 6.95 (ISBN 0-310-44511-6, 12211P, Pub. by Academie Bks). Zondervan.

Levine, Louis. Biology of the Gene. 3rd ed. LC 80-10730. (Illus.). 542p. 1980. pap. text ed. 23.95 (ISBN 0-8016-2988-8). Mosby.

Lewin, Benjamin. Gene Expression, Vol. 3: Plasmids & Phages. LC 73-14382. 925p. 1977. 53.50x (ISBN 0-471-53170-7, Pub. by Wiley-Interscience); pap. 32.50 (ISBN 0-471-02715-4). Wiley.

Lipkin, Mack, Jr. & Rowley, Peter T., eds. Genetic Responsibility: On Choosing Our Children's Genes. LC 74-12149. 185p. 1974. 27.50x (ISBN 0-306-30813-4, Plenum Pr). Plenum Pub.

Lipski, Alexander. Thomas Merton & Asia: His Quest for Utopia. (Cistercian Studies: No. 74). 1983. 17.95 (ISBN 0-87907-874-X); pap. 7.95 (ISBN 0-87907-974-6). Cistercian Pubns.

Luce, Thomas G. Genetics with a Computer. 1977. pap. 16.95 (ISBN 0-87567-076-8); incl. diskette 80.00. Entelek.

Lucy, J. A., et al. Mammalian Cell Hybridization, II. (Illus.). 220p. 1973. text ed. 25.50x (ISBN 0-8422-7102-3). Irvington.

Lygre, David. Life Manipulation: From Test Tube Babies to Aging. 1979. 9.95 (ISBN 0-8027-0632-0). Walker & Co.

Lynch, Henry T. Genetics & Breast Cancer. 256p. 1981. 27.50 (ISBN 0-442-24919-5). Van Nos Reinhold.

Maciejowski, J. & Zieba, J. Genetic & Animal Breeding, 2 pts. (Developments in Animal & Veterinary Science Ser.: Vol. 10). 1983. Pt. A, Biological & Genetic Foundation of Animal Breeding. 57.50 (ISBN 0-444-99696-6); Pt. B, Stock Improvement Methods. 57.50 (ISBN 0-444-99732-6, I-528-82); 115.00 set (ISBN 0-444-99676-1). Elsevier.

Mackean, D. J. Introduction to Genetics. 3rd ed. 1978. pap. text ed. 8.95 (ISBN 0-7195-3346-5). Transatlantic.

McKinnell, Robert G. Cloning: Nuclear Transplantation in Amphibia. LC 78-3195. (Illus.). 1978. 27.50x (ISBN 0-8166-0831-8). U of Minn Pr.

Maclean, N. Control of Gene Expression. 1976. 44.00 (ISBN 0-12-464950-5). Acad Pr.

Maclean, N., et al. Eukaryotic Genes: Structure, Activity & Regulation. 1983. text ed. 99.95 (ISBN 0-408-10824-X). Butterworth.

Maclean, Norman, ed. Oxford Surveys on Eukaryotic Genes 1984, Vol. 1. 219p. 1985. 35.00 (ISBN 0-19-854157-0). Oxford U Pr.

McNiel, N. A. & Magill, C. W. Genetics. 2nd ed. (Illus.). 225p. 1977. pap. text ed. 8.95x (ISBN 0-89641-004-8). American Pr.

Manyoni, Angelika. Consistency of Phenotype: A Study of Gottfried Benn's Views on Lyrical Poetry. LC 83-5462. (American Universtiy Studies I: Vol. 9). 346p. (Orig.). 1983. pap. text ed. 36.30 (ISBN 0-8204-0011-4). P Lang Pubs.

Maragos, George D., ed. Seminar on Human Genetics. (Paediatrician: Vol. 6, No. 6). (Illus.). 1978. 13.25 (ISBN 3-8055-2909-0). S Karger.

Massarik, Fred & Kaback, Michael M. Genetic Disease Control: A Social Psychological Approach. LC 80-28219. (Sage Library of Social Research: Vol. 116). (Illus.). 168p. 1981. 24.00 (ISBN 0-8039-1054-1); pap. 12.00 (ISBN 0-8039-1055-X). Sage.

Mather, K. & Jinks, J. L. Introduction to Biometrical Genetics. LC 77-76809. 220p. 1978. 29.95x (ISBN 0-8014-1123-8). Cornell U Pr.

Mather, K. & Links, J. L. Biometrical Genetics. 3rd ed. 1982. 53.00 (ISBN 0-412-22890-4, NO. 6715, Pub. by Chapman & Hall). Methuen Inc.

Maxson, Linda & Daugherty, Charles. Genetics: A Human Perspective. 496p. 1985. pap. text ed. write for info. (ISBN 0-697-00074-5); instr's. manual avail. (ISBN 0-697-00614-X); transparencies avail. (ISBN 0-697-00645-X). Wm C Brown.

Mays, Laura. Genetics: A Molecular Approach. 1981. text ed. write for info. (ISBN 0-02-378320-6). Macmillan.

Medvedev, Zhores. The Rise & Fall of T. D. Lysenko. Lawrence, Lucy G., ed. Lerner, I. Michael, tr. LC 79-77519. pap. 76.00 (ISBN 0-317-26082-0, 2023770). Bks Demand UMI.

Meier, Hans. Experimental Pharmacogenetics: Physiopathology of Heredity & Pharmacologic Responses. 1963. 49.50 (ISBN 0-12-488450-4). Acad Pr.

Merrell, David J. Ecological Genetics. LC 81-14789. (Illus.). 512p. 1981. 25.00x (ISBN 0-8166-1019-3). U of Minn Pr.

Tsukada, Y., ed. Genetic Approaches to Development Neurobiology. 269p. 1982. 46.00 (ISBN 0-387-11872-1). Springer-Verlag.

Van Brink, J. M. & Vorontsov, N. N., eds. Animal Genetics & Evolution: Selected Papers. (Illus.). 393p. 1980. lib. bdg. 99.00 (ISBN 90-6193-602-0, Pub. by Junk Pubs Netherlands). Kluwer Academic.

Van der Awevera, Johan, ed. The Semantics of Determiners. 320p. 1980. text ed. 37.00 (ISBN 0-8391-1627-6). Univ Park.

Van Peenen, Hubert J. Biochemical Genetics. (Illus.). 352p. 1966. photocopy ed. 34.50x (ISBN 0-398-01971-1). C C Thomas.

Voeller, Bruce R., ed. The Chromosome Theory of Inheritance. LC 68-19963. 229p. 1968. pap. 15.00x (ISBN 0-306-50080-9, Plenum Pr). Plenum Pub.

Von Blum, Ruth C., et al. Mendelian Genetics: A Problem-Solving Approach. 1979. pap. text ed. 6.95x (ISBN 0-933694-00-8). COMPress.

Von Der Pahle, Alejo. Genetica. 1979. text ed. 6.00 (ISBN 0-06-319200-4, IntlDept). Har-Row.

Wagner, R. P., et al. Introduction to Modern Genetics. LC 79-1414. 573p. 1980. text ed. 36.45x (ISBN 0-471-91430-4). Wiley.

Wagner, Robert P., ed. Genes & Proteins. LC 75-8851. (Benchmark Papers in Genetics Ser: Vol. 2). 395p. 1975. 70.00 (ISBN 0-12-787710-X). Acad Pr.

Wallace, Bruce. Chromosomes, Giant Molecules, & Evolution. (Illus.). 1966. 5.00x (ISBN 0-393-06343-7); (NortonC). Norton.

Wallace, Bruce & Srb, Adrian M. Adaption. LC 77-18812. (Foundations of Modern Biology Ser.). 1978. Repr. of 1964 ed. lib. bdg. 19.75x (ISBN 0-313-20212-5, WAAD). Greenwood.

Warr, Roger J. Genetic Engineering in Higher Organisms. (Studies in Biology: No. 162). 64p. 1984. pap. text ed. 8.95 (ISBN 0-7131-2885-2). E Arnold.

Watanabe, S., et al, eds. Anthropological & Genetic Studies on the Japanese, Vol. 2. (Japan International Biological Program Synthesis Ser.). 337p. 1975. 41.00x (ISBN 0-86008-212-1, Pub. by U of Tokyo Japan). Columbia U Pr.

Watson, Jack E. Introductory Genetics: A Laboratory Textbook. 2nd ed. 1976. pap. text ed. 9.95 (ISBN 0-8403-0838-8). Kendall-Hunt.

Westerveld, A. & Marin, G. Mammalian Cell Hybridization I. (Illus.). 220p. 1973. text ed. 25.50x (ISBN 0-8422-7096-5). Irvington.

Whitehouse, H. L. Towards an Understanding of the Mechanism of Heredity. 3rd ed. LC 73-82629. 513p. 1973. pap. 16.95 (ISBN 0-312-81095-4). St Martin.

Whitehouse, Harold L. Genetic Recombination: Understanding Mechanisms. LC 81-21981. 415p. 1982. 61.95 (ISBN 0-471-10205-9, Pub. by Wiley-Interscience). Wiley.

Wilkins, N. P. & Gosling, E. M., eds. Genetics in Aquaculture. (Developments in Aquaculture & Fisheries Science Ser.: Vol. 12). 436p. 1983. 91.50 (ISBN 0-444-42209-9). Elsevier.

Wilson, John H., ed. Genetic Recombination & Rearrangement. 1985. text ed. 29.95 (ISBN 0-8053-9790-6). Benjamin-Cummings.

Winchester, A. M. Genetics: A Survey of the Principles of Heredity. 5th ed. LC 76-14001. (Illus.). 1977. text ed. 31.95 (ISBN 0-395-24557-5); instr's. manual & solutions 1.90 (ISBN 0-395-24559-1). HM.

Wohlfarth, G. W. & Hulata, G. I. Applied Genetics of Tilapias. 26p. 1982. pap. text ed. 5.25 (ISBN 0-89955-375-3, Pub. by ICLARM Philippines). Intl Spec Bk.

Woods, R. A. Biochemical Genetics. 2nd ed. LC 79-41695. (Outline Studies in Biology). 80p. 1980. pap. 7.50x (ISBN 0-412-22400-3, NO.6340, Pub. by Chapman & Hall England). Methuen Inc.

Wourms, John P., et al. Genetic Studies of Fish, Vol. 2. Ridgway, George S. & Morrison, William J., eds. LC 74-516. 179p. 1974. text ed. 22.50x (ISBN 0-8422-7207-0). Irvington.

Wright, James E., et al. Genetic Studies of Fish, Vol. 1. Ridgway, George J. & Morrison, William J., eds. LC 74-516. 172p. 1974. text ed. 22.50x (ISBN 0-8422-7177-5). Irvington.

Wright, Sewall. Evolution & the Genetics of Populations: Experimental Results & Evolutionary Deductions, Vol. 3. LC 67-25533. (Illus.). viii, 614p. 1984. lib. bdg. 44.00x (ISBN 0-226-91051-2). U of Chicago Pr.

--Evolution & the Genetics of Populations, 4 vols. Incl. Vol. I. Genetic & Biometric Foundations. 1968. Repr. pap. 15.00X (ISBN 0-226-91038-5); Vol. II. Theorie of Gene Frequencies. 1969. Repr. 15.00X (ISBN 0-226-91039-3); Vol. 3. Experimental Results & Evolutionary Deductions. 1977. Repr. pap. 15.00X (ISBN 0-226-91040-7); Vol. 4. Variability Within & Among Natural Populations. 1978. Repr. 15.00x (ISBN 0-226-91041-5). LC 67-25533. U of Chicago Pr.

Zaleski, Marek B., et al. Immunogenetics. 512p. 1983. text ed. 39.95 (ISBN 0-273-01925-2). Pitman Pub MA.

Zilinskas, Raymond A. & Zimmerman, Burke K., eds. The Gene Splicing Wars, Nineteen Seventy-Four to Nineteen Seventy-Eight: Reflections on the Recombinant DNA Controversy. 320p. 1985. 24.95x (ISBN 0-02-948560-6). Macmillan.

Zimmerman, Burke K. Biofuture: Confronting the Genetic Era. (Illus.). 318p. 1984. (full discount avail.) 16.95 (ISBN 0-306-41315-9, Plenum Pr). Plenum Pub.

Zomaely-Neurath, Claire & Walker, William A. Gene Expression in the Brain. LC 84-11918. 320p. 1985. text ed. 42.50 (ISBN 0-471-86209-6, Pub. by Wiley-Interscience). Wiley.

GENETICS–DATA PROCESSING

Crosby, Jack L. Computer Simulation in Genetics. LC 72-5715. pap. 122.30 (ISBN 0-317-28345-6, 2016182). Bks Demand UMI.

GENETICS–DICTIONARIES

Biass-Ducroux, Francoise. Glossary of Genetics. (Glossaria Inetrpretum: Vol. 16). (Eng., Fr., Span., Ital., Ger. & Rus.). 436p. 1970. 76.75 (ISBN 0-444-40712-X). Elsevier.

Rieger, R., et al. Glossary of Genetics & Cytogenetics. 4th rev. ed. LC 76-16183. (Illus.). 1976. pap. 20.00 (ISBN 3-540-07668-9). Springer-Verlag.

Sawicki, Eugene, ed. Handbook of Environmental Genotoxicology: Dictionary of Environ Gene, Vol. I. (Handbook Ser.). 336p. 1982. 83.50 (ISBN 0-8493-3401-2). CRC Pr.

GENETICS–LABORATORY MANUALS

Stine, Gerald J. Laboratory Experiments in Genetics. (Illus.). 256p. 1973. pap. text ed. 12.95x (ISBN 0-02-417520-X). Macmillan.

Winchester, A. M. Laboratory Manual: Genetics. 3rd ed. 160p. 1979. write for info. wire coil (ISBN 0-697-04677-X). Wm C Brown.

GENETICS–MATHEMATICAL MODELS

Akin, Ethan. Hopf Bifurcation in the Two Locus Genetic Model. LC 83-6438. (Memoirs of the American Mathematical Society: No. 284). 192p. 1983. pap. 16.00 (ISBN 0-8218-2284-5). Am Math.

Ballanoff, Paul A., ed. Genetics & Social Structure: Mathematical Structuralism in Population Genetics & Social Theory. LC 73-20412. (Benchmark Papers in Genetics Ser.: Vol. 1). 504p. 1975. 53.50 (ISBN 0-87933-067-8). Van Nos Reinhold.

Bodmer, W. F. & Kingman, J. F., eds. Mathematical Genetics. (Proceedings of the Royal Society: Ser. B, Vol. 219). (Illus.). 133p. 1984. Repr. lib. bdg. 30.00x (ISBN 0-85403-219-3, Pub. by Royal Soc London). Scholium Intl.

English, Darrel S., et al. Genetic & Reproductive Engineering. LC 73-22048. 1974. 29.75x (ISBN 0-8422-5157-X); pap. text ed. 9.50x (ISBN 0-8422-0383-4). Irvington.

Kingman, J. F. C. Mathematics of Genetic Diversity. LC 80-51290. (CBMS-NSF Regional Conference Ser.: No. 34). vii, 70p. 1980. pap. text ed. 16.00 (ISBN 0-89871-166-5). Soc Indus-Appl Math.

Silver, Herbert, ed. Probability of Inclusion in Paternity Testing. 106p. 1982. 15.30 (ISBN 0-914404-77-6). Am Assn Blood.

GENETICS–PROGRAMMED INSTRUCTION

Duran, John C. Exercises in Genetics. (EMI Programed Biology Ser). (Orig.). 1969. pap. 3.00 (ISBN 0-88462-022-0, 3304-22, Ed Methods). Longman USA.

Kaplan, Barbara J. Preparation of the Normal Giemsa-Trypsin-Banded Karyotype: A Monograph. Evans, Leonard A., ed. LC 81-720284. (Illus.). 56p. 1982. tchrs. ed. 85.00 (ISBN 0-89189-148-X, 21-9-016-00); monograph 18.00 (ISBN 0-89189-149-8, 21-9-016-20). Am Soc Clinical.

GENSTAT (COMPUTER SYSTEM)

Alvey, N. G. & Galwey, P. Lane. An Introduction to Genstat. 1982. 18.00 (ISBN 0-12-055550-6). Acad Pr.

GEOBOTANY

see Phytogeography

GEOCHEMICAL PROSPECTING

Brooks, J., ed. Petroleum Geochemistry & Exploration of Europe. (Illus.). 396p. 1983. text ed. 60.00x (ISBN 0-632-01076-2). Blackwell Pubns.

Ettinger, L. J. The Rockhound & Prospector's Bible: A Reference & Study Guide to Rocks, Minerals, Gemstones & Prospecting. (Illus.). 140p. 1985. pap. price not set (ISBN 0-9614840-0-4). Ettinger.

Foldvar, Maria V. Theory & Practice of Regional Geochemical Exploration. 1978. 26.50 (ISBN 0-9960009-3-3, Pub. by Akademiai Kaido Hungary). Heyden.

Galloway, W. E., et al. Depositional & Ground-Water Flow Systems in the Exploration for Uranium: Syllabus for Research Colloquium Held in Austin, 1978. (Illus.). 267p. 1979. 6.00 (ISBN 0-318-03374-7). Bur Econ Geology.

Parslow, G. R. Geochemical Exploration, 1982. (Developments in Economic Geology Ser.: Vol. 17). 1984. 86.75 (ISBN 0-444-42268-4). Elsevier.

Sittig, Marshall, ed. Geophysical & Geochemical Techniques for Exploration of Hydrocarbons & Minerals. LC 79-24469. (Energy Technology Review Ser.: No. 52). (Illus.). 300p. 1980. 40.00 (ISBN 0-8155-0782-8). Noyes.

GEOCHEMISTRY

see also Chemical Oceanography; Geochemical Prospecting; Geothermal Resources; Mineralogical Chemistry; Mineralogy, Determinative; Rocks–Analysis

Abelson, Philip H., ed. Researches in Geochemistry, Vol. 2. LC 59-6755. 678p. 1967. 38.50 (ISBN 0-471-00167-8). Krieger.

Adler, Isidore. X-Ray Emission Spectrography in Geology. (Methods in Geochemistry & Geophysics: Vol. 4). xii, 258p. 1966. 68.00 (ISBN 0-444-40004-4). Elsevier.

Aiken, G. R., et al. Humic Substances in Soil, Sediment & Water: Geochemistry, Isolation & Characterization. 688p. 1985. 59.95 (ISBN 0-471-88274-7). Wiley.

Akimoto, S. & Manghnani, M. H. High Pressure Research in Geophysics. 1982. 113.00 (ISBN 90-277-1439-8, Pub. by Reidel Holland). Kluwer Academic.

Allegre, C. J. & Michard, G. Introduction to Geochemistry. Varney, R. N., tr. from Fr. LC 74-83871. (Geophysics & Astrophysics Monographs: No. 10). 1974. lib. bdg. 31.50 (ISBN 90-277-0497-X, Pub. by Reidel Holland); pap. text ed. 18.50 (ISBN 90-277-0498-8, Pub. by Reidel Holland). Kluwer Academic.

American Chemical Society, Division of Fuel Chemistry. Chemistry & Geochemistry of Oil Shales: Preprints of Papers Presented at Seattle, Washington, March 20-25, 1983. (American Chemical Society, Division of Fuel Chemistry, Preprints of Papers Ser.: Vol. 28, No. 3). pap. 62.80 (ISBN 0-317-28800-8, 2020320). Bks Demand UMI.

Angino, E. D. & Long, D. T., eds. Geochemistry of Bismuth. LC 78-24291. (Benchmark Papers in Geology: Vol. 49). 432p. 1979. 58.95 (ISBN 0-87933-234-4). Van Nos Reinhold.

Aramaki, S. & Kushiro, I., eds. Arc Volcanism: Selected Papers from the International Symposium on "Arc Volcanism" Held in Tokyo & Hakone & Sponsored by the Volcanological Society of Japan & the International Association of Volcanology & Chemistry of the Earth's Interior, Aug. 31-Sept. 5, 1981. (Developments in Volcanology Ser.: Vol. 2). 634p. 1984. Repr. 88.50 (ISBN 0-444-42234-X, I-307-83). Elsevier.

Aston, S. R. Silicon Geochemistry & Biogeochemistry. 1983. 44.50 (ISBN 0-12-065620-5). Acad Pr.

Atherton, M. P. & Tarney, J., eds. Origin of Granite Batholiths: Geochemical Evidence. 150p. (Orig.). 1981. pap. text ed. 11.95x (ISBN 0-906812-00-3). Birkhauser.

Back, W. & Letolle, R., eds. Geochemistry of Groundwater: Proceedings of thd 26th International Geological Congress, Paris, France-July 1980. (Developments in Water Science Ser.: Vol. 16). 370p. 1982. 64.00 (ISBN 0-444-42036-3). Elsevier.

Back, William R. & Freeze, Allan, eds. Chemical Hydrogeology. LC 81-11853. (Benchmark Papers in Geology Ser.: Vol. 73). 416p. 1983. 49.00 (ISBN 0-87933-440-1). Van Nos Reinhold.

Berdichevsky, M. N. & Zhdanov, M. S. Advanced Theory of Deep Geomagnetic Sounding. (Methods in Geochemistry & Geophysics Ser.: Vol. 19). 400p. 1984. 94.50 (ISBN 0-444-42189-0). Elsevier.

Beus, A. A. Geochemistry of the Lithosphere. 1976. 10.00 (ISBN 0-8285-1817-3, Pub. by Mir Pubs USSR). Imported Pubns.

Beus, A. A. & Grigorian, S. V. Geochemical Exploration Methods for Mineral Deposits. Levinson, A. A., ed. Teteruk-Schneider, Rita, tr. LC 77-75045. (Illus.). 1977. 32.00x (ISBN 0-915834-03-0). Applied Pub.

Bjorklund, A., ed. Geochemical Exploration, 1983: Selected Papers from the International Geochemical Explorational Symposium, 10th, Symposium on Methods of Geochemical Prospecting, 3rd, Held in Espoo, Finland, Aug.29-Sept. 2, 1983. 1984. Repr. 89.00 (ISBN 0-444-42385-0). Elsevier.

Bouska, V. Geochemistry of Coal. (Coal Science & Technology Ser.: Vol. 1). 1982. 64.00 (ISBN 0-444-99738-5). Elsevier.

Bowie, S. H. & Webb, J. S. Environmental Geochemistry & Health. (Royal Society Ser.). (Illus.). 216p. 1980. Repr. of 1979 ed. text ed. 63.00x (ISBN 0-85403-114-6, Pub. by Royal Society London). Scholium Intl.

Bowie, S H. & Thornton, I., eds. Environmental Geochemistry & Health. 1985. lib. bdg. 27.50 (ISBN 90-277-1879-2, Pub. by Reidel Holland). Kluwer Academic.

Brown, G. C. & Mussett, A. E. The Inaccessible Earth. (Illus.). 272p. 1981. pap. text ed. 22.50x (ISBN 0-04-550028-2). Allen Unwin.

Brownlow, Arthur H. Geochemistry. (Illus.). 1979. text ed. 38.95 (ISBN 0-13-351064-6). P-H.

Butt, C. R. & Smith, R. E., eds. Conceptual Models in Exploration Geochemistry: Australia. (Developments in Economic Geology: Vol. 13). 276p. 1980. 68.00 (ISBN 0-444-41902-0). Elsevier.

Cannon, Helen L. & Hopps, Howard C., eds. Environmental Geochemistry in Health & Disease: American Association for Advancement of Science Symposium. LC 78-111440. (Geological Society of America Ser.: No. 123). pap. 60.00 (ISBN 0-317-28384-7, 2025465). Bks Demand UMI.

Chayes, Felix. Ratio Correlation: A Manual for Students of Petrology & Geochemistry. LC 71-146110. 1971. text ed. 7.00x (ISBN 0-226-10218-1); pap. text ed. 3.00x (ISBN 0-226-10220-3). U of Chicago Pr.

Chen, C. H. Seismic Signal Analysis & Discrimination. (Methods in Geochemistry & Geophysics: Vol. 17). 196p. 1983. 53.25 (ISBN 0-444-42136-X). Elsevier.

Chen, C. H., ed. Seismic Signal Analysis & Discrimination III. (Methods in Geochemistry & Geophysics Ser.: Vol. 22). 170p. 1985. Repr. 46.50 (ISBN 0-444-42430-X). Elsevier.

Committee on Env. Geochem., National Research Council. Geochemistry & the Environment: Distribution of Trace Elements Related to the Occurrence of Certain Cancers, Cardiovascular Diseases, & Urolithiasis, Vol. III. (Geochemistry & the Environment Ser.). 1978. pap. text ed. 15.50 (ISBN 0-309-02795-0). Natl Acad Pr.

Davy, R. & Mazzucchelli, R. H., eds. Geochemical Exploration in Arid & Deeply Weathered Environments: Proceedings of the Regional Meeting of the Australian Branch of the Association of Exploration Geochemists Held in Perth, Western Australia, May 1983. 376p. 1984. Repr. 81.50 (ISBN 0-444-42412-1). Elsevier.

Drever, James I. The Geochemistry of Natural Waters. (Illus.). 400p. 1982. 37.95 (ISBN 0-13-351403-X). P-H.

Eglinton, G. & Murphy, Sr. M. T., eds. Organic Geochemistry: Methods & Results. LC 70-107318. (Illus.). 1969. 115.00 (ISBN 0-387-04669-0). Springer-Verlag.

Ellis, A. J. & Mahon, W. A., eds. Chemistry & Geothermal Systems. 1977. 65.00 (ISBN 0-12-237450-9). Acad Pr.

Ernst, W. G. Earth Materials. 1969. pap. text ed. 15.95 (ISBN 0-13-222604-9). P-H.

Fairbridge, R. W., ed. The Encyclopedia of Geochemistry & Environmental Sciences. LC 75-152326. (Encyclopedia of Earth Sciences Ser.: Vol. IVA). 1321p. 1972. 98.00 (ISBN 0-87933-180-1). Van Nos Reinhold.

Fletcher, W. K. Analytical Methods in Geochemical Prospecting. (Handbook of Exploration Geochemistry Ser.: Vol. 1). 256p. 1981. 64.00 (ISBN 0-444-41930-6). Elsevier.

Fortescue, J. A. Environmental Geochemistry: A Holistic Approach. (Ecological Studies: Vol. 35). (Illus.). 347p. 1980. text ed. 44.00 (ISBN 0-387-90454-9). Springer-Verlag.

Fritz, P. Handbook of Environmental Isotope Geochemistry, Vol. 2: The Terrestrial Environment, B. Date not set. write for info. (ISBN 0-444-42225-0). Elsevier.

Fyfe, W. S., et al. Fluids in the Earth's Crust: Their Significance in Metamorphic, Tectonic, & Chemical Transport Process. (Developments in Geochemistry Ser.: Vol. 1). 384p. 1978. 72.50 (ISBN 0-444-41636-6). Elsevier.

Galloway, W. E. & Kaiser, W. R. Catahoula Formation of the Texas Coastal Plain: Origin, Geochemical Evolution, & Characteristics of Uranium Deposits. (Report of Investigations Ser.: RI 100). (Illus.). 81p. 1980. 3.00 (ISBN 0-318-03235-X). Bur Econ Geology.

Geochemistry of Water in Relation to Cardiovascular Disease. 1979. pap. 12.25 (ISBN 0-309-02884-1). Natl Acad Pr.

Golubev, V. S. & Garibyants, A. A. Heterogeneous Processes of Geochemical Migration. LC 73-140829. 145p. 1971. 27.50x (ISBN 0-306-10860-7, Consultants). Plenum Pub.

Govett, G. J. Rock Geochemistry in Mineral Exploration. (Handbook of Mineral Exploration Geology Ser.: Vol. 3). 462p. 1983. 100.00 (ISBN 0-444-42021-5). Elsevier.

Henderson, P., ed. Rare Earth Element Geochemistry. (Developments in Geochemistry: Vol. 2). 510p. 1984. 84.75 (ISBN 0-444-42148-3). Elsevier.

Henry, C. D. Geologic Setting & Geochemistry of Thermal Water & Geothermal Assessment, Trans-Pecos Texas & Adjacent Mexico with Tectonic Map of the Rio Grande Area, Trans-Pecos Texas. (Report of Investigations Ser.: RI 96). (Illus.). 48p. 1979. 2.25 (ISBN 0-318-03232-5). Bur Econ Geology.

Penck, Walther. Morphological Analysis of Land Forms: A Contribution to Physical Geology. Czech, Hella & Boswell, Katharine Cumming, trs. from Ger. Orig. Title: Die Morphologische Analyse. 443p. 1972. Repr. of 1953 ed. deluxe ed. 24.95x (ISBN 0-02-850130-6). Hafner.

Saxena, S. K. & Bhattacharji, S., eds. Energetics of Geological Processes. LC 76-30859. 1977. 47.00 (ISBN 3-540-08119-4). Springer-Verlag.

Scheidegger, A. E. Principles of Geodynamics. 3rd, rev. ed. (Illus.). 380p. 1982. 78.00 (ISBN 0-387-11323-1). Springer-Verlag.

Shimer, John A. This Sculptured Earth: The Landscape of America. LC 59-10628. (Illus.). 255p. 1959. 34.00x (ISBN 0-231-02331-6). Columbia U Pr.

Storr, Eric D., ed. Geomechanics: Interaction. 300p. 1984. pap. text ed. 30.00x (ISBN 0-85825-208-2, Pub. by Inst Engineering Australia). Brookfield Pub Co.

Turcotte, Donald L. & Schubert, Gerald. Geodynamics: Application of Continuum Physics to Geological Problems. LC 81-15965. 450p. 1982. text ed. 39.50x (ISBN 0-471-06018-6). Wiley.

U. S. Program for the Geodynamics Project: Scope & Objectives. 1973. pap. 5.95 (ISBN 0-309-02211-8). Natl Acad Pr.

Uyeda, S., et al, eds. Geodynamics of the Western Pacific. (Advances in Earth & Planetary Sciences Ser.: Pt. 6). 592p. 1980. 49.50x (ISBN 0-89955-315-X, Pub. by Japan Sci Soc Japan). Intl Spec Bk.

Windley, Brian F. The Evolving Continents. 2nd ed. 404p. 1984. 49.95 (ISBN 0-471-90376-0); pap. 24.95 (ISBN 0-471-90390-6). Wiley.

GEO-ELECTRIC PROSPECTING

see Electric Prospecting

GEOGNOSY

see Geology

GEOGRAPHERS

Association of Pacific Coast Geographers. Yearbook of the Association of Pacific Coast Geographers: 1982, Vol. 44. Scott, James, ed. LC 37-13376. (Illus.). 144p. 1983. pap. 7.00x (ISBN 0-87071-244-6). Oreg St U Pr.

Directory of Applied Geographers, 1981. 9.00 (ISBN 0-89291-157-3). Assn Am Geographers.

Freeman, T. W. Geographers: Bibliographical Studies. (The Geographers Ser.: Vol. 8). 159p. 1984. pap. 34.00x (ISBN 0-7201-1705-4). Mansell.

--Geographers: Biobibliographical Studies, Vol. 7. 176p. 1983. 34.00x (ISBN 0-7201-1684-8). Mansell.

Taylor, Eva G. Tudor Geography, 1485-1583. 1968. lib. bdg. 23.50x (ISBN 0-374-97847-6). Octagon.

GEOGRAPHICAL DISTRIBUTION OF ANIMALS

see Zoogeography

GEOGRAPHICAL DISTRIBUTION OF ANIMALS AND PLANTS

see also Forest Ecology; Phytogeography; Zoogeography;

also subdivisions Geographical Distribution or Migration under names of organisms, e.g. Fishes–Geographical Distribution; Birds–Migration

Biology Colloquium, 37th, Oregon State University, 1976. Historical Biogeography, Plate Tectonics, & the Changing Environment: Proceedings. Gray, Jane & Boucot, Arthur J., eds. LC 78-31376. (Illus.). 512p. 1979. 69.50x (ISBN 0-87071-176-8). Oreg St U Pr.

Brown, James H. & Gibson, Arthur C. Biogeography. LC 82-14124. (Illus.). 653p. 1983. text ed. 32.95 (ISBN 0-8016-0824-4). Mosby.

Browne, Janet. The Secular Ark: Studies in the History of Biogeography. LC 82-17497. (Illus.). 273p. 1983. text ed. 31.00x (ISBN 0-300-02460-6). Yale U Pr.

Cox, C. B. & Moore, P. D. Biogeography: An Ecological & Evolutionary Approach. 4th ed. (Illus.). 272p. 1985. pap. text ed. 19.00x (ISBN 0-632-01332-X). Blackwell Pubns.

Donkin, R. A. Manna: An Historical Geography. (Biogeographica Ser.: No. 17). (Illus.). vii, 160p. 1980. lib. bdg. 47.50 (ISBN 90-6193-218-1, Pub. by Junk Pubs Netherlands). Kluwer Academic.

Fernando, C. H. Ecology & Biogeography of Sri Lanka. (Monographiae Biologicae: No. 57). 520p. 1984. 110.00 (ISBN 90-6193-109-6, Pub. by Junk Pubs Netherlands). Kluwer Academic.

Gilbertson, David, et al. Practical Ecology for Geography & Biology: Survey, Mapping & Data Analysis. (Illus.). 350p. (Orig.). 1985. pap. 11.95 (ISBN 0-09-162651-X, Pub. by Hutchinson Educ). Longwood Pub Group.

Gressitt, J. L. Biogeography & Ecology of New Guinea, 2 vols. 1982. lib. bdg. 195.00 (ISBN 90-6193-094-4, Pub. by Junk Pubs Netherlands). Kluwer Academic.

Grinnell, Joseph. An Account of the Mammals & Birds of the Lower Colorado Valley, with Especial Reference to the Distributional Problems Presented. Sterling, Keir B., ed. LC 77-81116. (Biologists & Their World Ser.). (Illus.). 1978. Repr. of 1914 ed. lib. bdg. 22.00x (ISBN 0-405-10708-0). Ayer Co Pubs.

Heckman, Charles W. Rice Field Ecology in Northeastern Thailand. (Monographiae Biologicae: Vol. 34). (Illus.). 1979. lib. bdg. 38.00 (ISBN 90-6193-086-3, Pub. by Junk Pubs Netherlands). Kluwer Academic.

Hopkins, David M., ed. The Bering Land Bridge. (Illus.). 1967. 42.50x (ISBN 0-8047-0272-1). Stanford U Pr.

Hudson, John C. Geographical Diffusion Theory: Studies in Geography. (No. 19). 1972. pap. 5.95 (ISBN 0-8101-0398-2). Northwestern U Pr.

Jones, R. L. Biogeography: Structure, Process, Pattern & Change Within the Biosphere. (Illus.). 192p. 1980. pap. 16.95 (ISBN 0-7175-0872-2). Dufour.

Jungbluth, Jurgen H. Der Tiergeographicshe Undokologische Beitrag Zur Okologischen Landschaftsforschung. (Biogeographica: No. 13). 1978. lib. bdg. 55.00 (ISBN 90-6193-214-9, Pub. by Junk Pubs Netherlands). Kluwer Academic.

Loffler, H., ed. Neusiedlersee: The Limnology of a Shallow Lake in Central Europe. (Monographiae Biologicae Ser.: No. 37). (Illus.). x, 559p. 1980. lib. bdg. 103.00 (ISBN 90-6193-089-8, Pub. by Junk Pubs Netherlands). Kluwer Academic.

Lowe, Charles H., Jr., ed. The Vertebrates of Arizona: With Major Section on Arizona Habitats. LC 63-11981. 270p. 1964. pap. 8.95x (ISBN 0-8165-0348-6). U of Ariz Pr.

MacArthur, Roger H. & Wilson, Edward O. Theory of Island Biogeography. (Monographs in Population Biology: Vol. 1). (Illus.). 1967. 23.50x (ISBN 0-691-08049-6); pap. 9.95x (ISBN 0-691-08050-X). Princeton U Pr.

Morafka, David J. A Biogeographical Analysis of the Chihuahuan Desert Through Its Herpetofauna. (Biogeographica: No. 9). (Illus.). 1977. lib. bdg. 50.00 (ISBN 90-6193-210-6, Pub. by Junk Pubs Netherlands). Kluwer Academic.

Morain, Stanley. Systematic & Regional Biogeography. 300p. 1984. 32.50 (ISBN 0-442-26186-1). Van Nos Reinhold.

Muller, P. & Rathjens, C., eds. Landscape Ecology: In Honor of Prof. Dr. J. Schmithusen. (Biogeographica: No. 16). 1980. lib. bdg. 53.00 (ISBN 90-6193-217-3, Pub. by Junk Pubs Netherlands). Kluwer Academic.

Muller, Paul, ed. Ecosystem Research in South America. (Biogeographica Ser: Vol. 8). 1977. lib. bdg. 24.00 (ISBN 90-6193-209-2, Pub. by Junk Pubs. Netherlands). Kluwer Academic.

Neill, Wilfred T. Geography of Life. LC 68-8877. (Illus.). 48p. 1969. 34.00x (ISBN 0-231-02876-8). Columbia U Pr.

Nelson, Gareth & Platnick, Norman I. Systematics & Biogeography: Cladistics & Vicariance. LC 80-20828. (Illus.). 592p. 1981. 55.00x (ISBN 0-231-04574-3). Columbia U Pr.

Nelson, Gareth & Rosen, Donn E., eds. Vicariance Biogeography: A Critique. LC 80-15351. (Illus.). 616p. 1981. 55.00x (ISBN 0-231-04808-4). Columbia U Pr.

Pears, Nigel V. Basic Biogeography. (Illus.). pap. text ed. 17.95x (ISBN 0-582-30120-3). Longman.

Q A S General Secretariat, Dept. of Echnological & Scientific Affairs. Biogeografia de America Latina. 2nd ed. (Biologia: No. 13). (Span., Illus.). 122p. 1980. pap. 3.50 (ISBN 0-8270-1233-0). OAS.

Radovsky, Frank J., et al, eds. Biogeography of the Tropical Pacific: Proceedings of a Symposium. (Illus.). 228p. 1984. 45.00 (ISBN 0-942924-08-8); pap. 35.00 (ISBN 0-942924-09-6). Assn Syst Coll.

Rapoport, Eduardo H. Areography: Geographical Strategies of Species. (Publications of Fundacion Bariloche: Vol. 1). (Illus.). 250p. 1982. 32.00 (ISBN 0-08-028914-2, G135, H110). Pergamon.

Romans, Robert C., ed. Geobotany II. LC 81-13992. 271p. 1981. text ed. 45.00x (ISBN 0-306-40832-5, Plenum Pr). Plenum Pub.

Sauer, Jonathan D. Cayman Islands Seashore Vegetation: A Study in Comparative Biogeography. LC 82-2608. (Publications in Geography: Vol. 25). 166p. 1983. pap. 15.00x (ISBN 0-520-09656-8). U of Cal Pr.

Selections from the Literature of American Biogeography. LC 73-17844. (Natural Sciences in America Ser.). (Illus.). 512p. 1974. 26.00x (ISBN 0-405-05766-0). Ayer Co Pubs.

Simmons, I. G. Biogeography: Natural & Cultural. 416p. 1979. pap. text ed. 19.95 (ISBN 0-7131-6246-5). E Arnold.

Springer, Victor G. Pacific Plate Biogeography, with Special Reference to Shorefishes. LC 82-600146. (Contributions to Zoology Ser.: No. 367). (Illus.). 182p. 1982. pap. text ed. 7.95x (ISBN 0-87474-883-6). Smithsonian.

Taylor, J. A., ed. Biogeography: Recent Advances & Future Directions. LC 84-12428. 432p. 1984. 36.50x (ISBN 0-389-20507-9, BNB-08065). B&N Imports.

Wallace, Alfred R. Island Life. 3rd, rev. ed. LC 72-1667. Repr. of 1911 ed. 34.50 (ISBN 0-404-08183-5). AMS Pr.

Walter, H. Vegetation of the Earth & Ecological Systems of the Geobiosphere. 3rd, rev. ed. Muise, O., tr. from Ger. (Heidelberg Science Library). (Illus.). 340p. 1985. pap. 17.00 (ISBN 0-387-13748-3). Springer-Verlag.

Walter, H. & Breckle, S. W. Ecological Systems of the Geobiosphere. Gruber, S., tr. from Ger. (Illus.). 260p. 1985. 34.50 (ISBN 0-387-13792-0). Springer-Verlag.

Werger, M. J. A., ed. Biogeography & Ecology of Southern Africa, 2 vols. (Monographiae Biologicae: No. 31). 1977. lib. bdg. 192.00 set (ISBN 90-6193-083-9, Pub. by Junk Pubs Netherlands). Kluwer Academic.

Whitmore, T. C. & Prance, G. T., eds. Biogeography & Quaternary History in Tropical Latin America. (Oxford Monographs in Biogeography). (Illus.). 220p. 1984. 39.95x (ISBN 0-19-854546-0). Oxford U Pr.

GEOGRAPHICAL DISTRIBUTION OF PLANTS

see Phytogeography

GEOGRAPHICAL DISTRIBUTION OF PLANTS AND ANIMALS

see Geographical Distribution of Animals and Plants

GEOGRAPHY

see also Geographers; Man–Influence of Environment; Maps; Physical Geography also subdivision Description and Travel under names of countries, e.g. France–Description and Travel; and subdivision Description, Geography under names of countries of antiquity, e.g. Greece–Description, Geography; and subdivision Maps under names of places, e.g. France–Maps

AAG Consulting Services Panel. Suggestions for Self-Evaluation of Geography Programs with Self-Study Data Forms. 1974. pap. 2.00 (ISBN 0-89291-141-7). Assn Am Geographers.

AAG Denver: Field Trip Guide 1983. (Illus.). 104p. (Orig.). 1983. pap. 2.00 (ISBN 0-89291-169-7). Assn Am Geographers.

Andreae, Bernd. Allgemeine Agrargeographie. (Sammlung Goeschen Ser.: No. 2624). (Ger., Illus.). 219p. 1984. pap. text ed. 11.90x (ISBN 3-11-010076-2). De Gruyter.

Annual Meeting Program, 1984. 1984. 1.00 (ISBN 0-89291-179-4). Assn Am Geographers.

Association of American Geographers. Field Trip Guide, 1984. 1984. 2.00 (ISBN 0-89291-180-8). Assn Am Geographers.

--Program Abstracts, 1984. write for info. (ISBN 0-89291-176-X). Assn Am Geographers.

Banner, F. T., et al, eds. The North-West European Shelf Seas: The Sea-Bed & the Sea in Motion, Vol. 1, Geology & Sedimentology. LC 78-14524. (Elsevier Oceanography Ser.: Vol. 24b). 300p. 1979. 74.50. Elsevier.

Birkeland, Peter W. & Larson, Edwin E., eds. Putnam's Geology. 4th ed. (Illus.). 1982. text ed. 27.95x (ISBN 0-19-503002-8); tchr's manual avail. (ISBN 0-19-503004-4); study guide 8.95x (ISBN 0-19-503003-6). Oxford U Pr.

Buttimer, Anne. The Practice of Geography. LC 82-13091. (Illus.). 1984. text ed. 29.95 (ISBN 0-582-30087-8). Longman.

Cuningham, William. The Cosmographical Glasse, Conteinyng the Principles of Cosmographie, Etc. LC 68-54632. (English Experience Ser.: No. 44). 1968. Repr. of 1559 ed. 49.00 (ISBN 90-221-0044-8). Walter J Johnson.

De Cardonda, Nicolas. Geographic & Hydrographic Descriptions... of the Kingdom of California (1632) Mathes, Michael, ed. & tr. (Baja California Travels Ser.: No. 35). (Illus.). 111p. 1974. 18.00 (ISBN 0-87093-235-7). Dawsons.

Dutton, Geoffrey, ed. Harvard Papers on Geographic Information Systems, 8 vols. 1979. Set. text ed. 180.00 (ISBN 0-201-03920-6). Addison-Wesley.

Eckel, Edwin B. The Geological Society of America: Life History of a Learned Society. LC 82-15412. (Memoir Ser.: No. 155). (Illus.). 1982. 24.50 (ISBN 0-8137-1155-X). Geol Soc.

English, Paul W. World Regional Geography: A Question of Place. 2nd ed. LC 84-3497. 583p. 1984. text ed. 30.95x (ISBN 0-471-09295-9). Wiley.

Gerasimov, I. P. Geography & Ecology. 167p. 1983. 5.95 (ISBN 0-8285-2394-0, 095, Pub. by Progress Pubs USSR). Imported Pubns.

Griffith, Daniel A. Evolving Geographical Structures. 1983. lib. bdg. 65.00 (ISBN 90-2472-858-4, Pub. by Martinus Nijhoff Netherlands). Kluwer Academic.

Harper, Schmudde. Between Two Worlds: An Introduction to Geography. 544p. 1984. pap. text ed. 23.95 (ISBN 0-8403-3165-7). Kendall Hunt.

International Geographical Congress, 1st: Antwerp, 1871, Compte-Rendu, 2 vols. Repr. Set. 140.00 (ISBN 0-317-15302-1). Kraus Repr.

International Geographical Congress, 15th: Amsterdam, 1938, Comptes-Rendus, 2 vols. in 6. Set. 462.00 (ISBN 0-317-15376-5). Kraus Repr.

International Geographical Congress, 11th: Cairo, 1925, Compte-Rendu, 5 vols. in 2. Repr. Set. 166.00. Kraus Repr.

International Geographical Congress, 12th: Cambridge, 1928 (Report) Repr. 60.00 (ISBN 0-317-15369-2). Kraus Repr.

International Geographical Congress, 16th: Lisbon, 1949, Comptes-Rendus, 4 vols. Set. 305.00 (ISBN 0-317-15377-3). Kraus Repr.

International Geographical Congress, 13th: Paris, 1931, Comptes-Rendus, 3 vols. Repr. Set. 287.00 (ISBN 0-317-15372-2). Kraus Repr.

International Geographical Congress, 10th: Rome, 1913, Atti, 2 vols. Repr. Set. 180.00 (ISBN 0-317-15366-8). Kraus Repr.

International Geographical Congress, 14th: Warsaw, 1934, Comptes-Rendus, 4 vols. Repr. Set. 285.00 (ISBN 0-317-15375-7). Kraus Repr.

International Geographical Congress, 2nd: Paris, 1875, Compte-Rendu, 2 vols. Set. 140.00 (ISBN 0-317-15303-X). Kraus Repr.

International Geographical Congress, 3rd: Venice, 1881, Atti Report, 3 vols. Repr. Set. 185.00. Kraus Repr.

International Geographical Congress, 4th: Paris, 1889, Compte-Rendu, 2 vols. Repr. Set. 116.00 (ISBN 0-317-15305-6). Kraus Repr.

International Geographical Congress, 5th: Berne, 1891 (Compte-Rendu) Repr. 120.00 (ISBN 0-317-15306-4). Kraus Repr.

International Geographical Congress, 6th: London, 1895 (Report) Repr. 120.00 (ISBN 0-317-15357-9). Kraus Repr.

International Geographical Congress, 7th: Berlin, 1899, Verhandlungen, 3 vols. Repr. Set. 202.00 (ISBN 0-317-15359-5). Kraus Repr.

International Geographical Congress, 9th: Geneva, 1908, Compte-Rendu, 3 vols. Repr. Set. 191.00 (ISBN 0-317-15364-1). Kraus Repr.

Johnston, R. J. Multivariate Statistical Analysis in Geography: A Primer of the General Linear Model. (Illus.). 1980. 13.95x (ISBN 0-582-30034-7). Longman.

Lowe, John C. & Moryadas, S. The Geography of Movement. (Illus.). 333p. 1984. Repr. of 1975 ed. text ed. 24.95x (ISBN 0-88133-100-7). Waveland Pr.

Mitchell & Draper. Relevance & Ethics in Geography. LC 81-19386. (Illus.). 256p. 1982. text ed. 28.50x (ISBN 0-582-30035-5). Longman.

Mitchell, Bruce. Geography & Resource Analysis. (Illus.). 1979. text ed. 36.00x (ISBN 0-582-48732-3); pap. text ed. 19.95x (ISBN 0-582-48733-1). Longman.

Norwine, Jim & Anderson, Thomas D. Geography As Human Ecology? LC 80-8148. 70p. 1980. pap. text ed. 7.50 (ISBN 0-8191-1249-6). U Pr of Amer.

Pickles, John. Phenomenology, Science & Geography: Towards a Hermeneutic Ontology of Spatiality for the Human Sciences. (Human Geography Ser.). 256p. 1985. 44.50 (ISBN 0-521-26540-1). Cambridge U Pr.

Pitty, A. F. Geography & Soil Properties. 1979. 15.95 (ISBN 0-416-75380-9, NO. 2374); pap. 15.95x (ISBN 0-416-71540-0, NO. 2375). Methuen Inc.

Saarinen, Thomas F., et al, eds. Environmental Perception & Behavior: An Inventory & Prospect. LC 84-2492. (Research Papers: No. 209). 263p. 1984. pap. 10.00 (ISBN 0-89065-114-0). U Chicago Dept Geog.

Stamp, Laurence D. & Wooldridge, Sidney W. London Essays in Geography. facs. ed. LC 76-80399. (Essay Index Reprint Ser). 1951. 23.75 (ISBN 0-8369-1050-8). Ayer Co Pubs.

Stern, Eliahu & Krackover, Shaul, eds. Geography Research Forum, Vol. 8. 230p. 1985. pap. text ed. 19.95x (ISBN 0-88738-625-3). TRansaction Bks.

Tomlinson, R. F. & Calkins, H. W. Computer Handling of Geographical Data: An Examination of Selected Geographic Information Systems. (Natural Resources Research Ser.: Vol. 13). (Illus.). 214p. 1976. pap. 17.50 (ISBN 92-3-101340-8, U97, UNESCO). Unipub.

Vincentius, Bellovacensis. Hier Begynneth the Table of the Rubrices of This Presente Volume Namde the Myrrour of the Worlde or Thymage of the Same. Caxton, William, tr. from Fr. LC 79-84143. (English Experience Ser.: No. 960). (Eng.). 204p. 1979. Repr. of 1481 ed. lib. bdg. 30.00 (ISBN 90-221-0960-7). Walter J Johnson.

Cuvier, Georges. Essay on the Theory of the Earth: Mineralogical Notes, & an Account of Cuvier's Geological Discoveries. Albritton, Claude C., Jr., ed. Kerr, Robert, tr. LC 77-6517. (History of Geology Ser.). (Illus.). 1978. Repr. of 1817 ed. lib. bdg. 32.00 (ISBN 0-405-10439-1). Ayer Co Pubs.

Daly, Reginald A. Our Mobile Earth. LC 80-2889. (BCL Ser.: I & II). (Illus.). Repr. of 1926 ed. 47.50 (ISBN 0-404-18066-3). AMS Pr.

Dapples, Edward C. Basic Geology for Science & Engineering. LC 59-5880. 620p. 1973. Repr. of 1959 ed. 29.50 (ISBN 0-88275-106-9). Krieger.

Darwin, Charles. Journal of Researches into the Natural History & Geology of the Countries Visited During the Voyage of H. M. S. "Beagle" Round the World, under the Command of Capt. Fitz Roy, R. A. 1977. Repr. of 1892 ed. lib. bdg. 30.00 (ISBN 0-8482-0544-8). Norwood Edns.

--Voyage of the Beagle. LC 62-2990. 1962. 6.95 (ISBN 0-385-02767-2, Anchor). Natural Hist.

Davis, Stanley, et al. Geology: Our Physical Environment. 1975. text ed. 36.95 (ISBN 0-07-015680-8). McGraw.

De Marsily, G., et al, eds. Predictive Geology with Emphasis on Nuclear-Waste Disposal: Proceedings of Papers Presented at Sessions Sponsored by the International Association for Mathematical Geology at the 26th International Geological Congress in Paris, July 1980. (Computers & Geology Ser.: Vol. 4). (Illus.). 222p. 1981. 39.00 (ISBN 0-08-026246-5). Pergamon.

Dennis, J. G., ed. Orogeny. LC 81-6436. (Benchmark Papers in Geology: Vol. 62). 380p. 1982. 47.95 (ISBN 0-87933-394-4). Van Nos Reinhold.

Dennison, John M. Analysis of Geologic Structures. (Illus.). 1968. text ed. 14.95x (ISBN 0-393-09801-X, NortonC). Norton.

Dietrich, Richard V. & Skinner, Brian J. Rocks & Rock Minerals. LC 79-12111. 319p. 1979. 28.50 (ISBN 0-471-02934-3). Wiley.

Donnelly, Thomas W., ed. Earth Sciences: Problems & Progress in Current Research. LC 63-20901. 1963. 12.50x (ISBN 0-226-15656-7). U of Chicago Pr.

Doomkamp, J. C., et al, eds. Geology, Geomorphology & Pedology of Bahrain. 443p. 150.00x (ISBN 0-86094-021-7, Pub. by GEO Abstracts England). State Mutual Bk.

Dorr, John A., Jr. & Eschman, Donald F. Geology of Michigan. LC 69-17351. (Illus.). 1970. 19.95x (ISBN 0-472-08280-9). U of Mich Pr.

Eastern Kentucky University, Dept. of Geology. Principles of Physical Geology Laboratory Manual. 80p. 1980. pap. text ed. 5.50 (ISBN 0-8403-2285-2). Kendall-Hunt.

Elder, John. The Bowels of the Earth. (Illus.). 1976. 21.95x (ISBN 0-19-854412-X); pap. 8.95x (ISBN 0-19-854413-8). Oxford U Pr.

Emerson, B. K., et al. Geology & Paleontology. (Harriman Alaska Expedition, 1899 Ser.). Repr. of 1904 ed. 41.00 (ISBN 0-527-38164-0). Kraus Repr.

Emmons, Ebenezer. American Geology: Statement of the Principles of the Science, with Full Illustrations of the Characteristic American Fossils, 2 vols. in one. LC 73-17818. (Natural Sciences in America Ser.). (Illus.). 544p. 1974. Repr. 37.50x (ISBN 0-405-05734-2). Ayer Co Pubs.

Ernst, W. G. Earth Materials. 1969. pap. text ed. 15.95 (ISBN 0-13-222604-9). P-H.

Ervin, M. C., ed. In-situ Testing for Geotechnical Investigation: Proceedings of an Extension Course on In-situ Testing for Geotechnical Investigations, Sydney, May-June 1983. 140p. 1983. lib. bdg. 26.00 (ISBN 90-6191-506-6, Pub. by Balkema RSA). IPS.

Eveland, H. E. & Tennissen, A. C. Physical Geology Laboratory Manual. 4th ed. 96p. 1979. pap. text ed. 8.95 (ISBN 0-8403-2565-7, 40256502). Kendall-Hunt.

Farquhar, Oswald C., ed. Geotechnology in Massachusetts. LC 82-70207. (Illus.). 626p. 1982. text ed. 25.00 (ISBN 0-9604712-0-0). Univ Mass Grad.

Faure, Gunter. Principles of Isotope Geology. LC 77-4479. (Intermediate Geology Ser.). 464p. 1977. text ed. 48.50 (ISBN 0-471-25665-X). Wiley.

Flint, Richard F. & Skinner, Brian J. Physical Geology. 2nd ed. LC 76-23206. 671p. 1977. text ed. 35.45 (ISBN 0-471-26442-3); study guide, 185p. 11.45 (ISBN 0-471-02593-3); tchrs.' manual avail. (ISBN 0-471-03075-9). Wiley.

Foster, Robert J. General Geology. 3rd ed. (Physical Science Ser.). 1978. study guide 8.95 (ISBN 0-675-08447-4). Merrill.

--General Geology. 4th ed. 672p. 1983. text ed. 28.50 (ISBN 0-675-20020-2). Merrill.

--Geology. 5th, rev. ed. 224p. 1985. pap. text ed. 9.95 (ISBN 0-675-20414-3). Merrill.

Fraser, Donald, ed. Thermodynamics in Geology. (Nato Adv. Study Inst. Ser. C: No. 30). 1977. lib. bdg. 50.00 (ISBN 90-277-0794-4, Pub. by Reidel Holland); pap. 16.00 (ISBN 90-277-0834-7). Kluwer Academic.

Friedland, Mary. Earth Resources. (Science in Action Ser.). (Illus.). 48p. 1984. pap. text ed. 2.85 (ISBN 0-88102-025-7). Janus Bks.

Garver, John B., et al. Atlas of Landforms. 3rd ed. LC 83-675974. 165p. 1984. text ed. 35.95 (ISBN 0-471-87434-5). Wiley.

Gastil, R. Gordon, et al. Reconnaissance Geology of the State of Baja California. LC 74-83806. (Geological Society of America Memoir Ser.: No. 140). pap. 62.00 (ISBN 0-317-29112-2, 2023734). Bks Demand UMI.

Gerfin, Richard & Koch, Robert. Physical Geology: Student Handbook & Study Guide. 6th ed. 320p. 1982. pap. text ed. 8.95 (ISBN 0-13-669788-7). P-H.

Gillen, Cornelius. Metamorphic Geology: An Introduction to Tectonic & Metamorphic Processes. (Special Topics in Geology Ser.). (Illus.). 160p. (Orig.). 1982. text ed. 25.00x (ISBN 0-04-551057-1); pap. text ed. 9.95x (ISBN 0-04-551058-X). Allen Unwin.

Gilluly, James, et al. Principles of Geology. 4th ed. LC 74-23076. (Geology Ser.). (Illus.). 527p. 1975. text ed. 30.95 (ISBN 0-7167-0269-X). W H Freeman.

Glass, Billy P. Introduction to Planetary Geology. LC 81-17057. (Planetary Science Ser.: No. 2). (Illus.). 1982. 32.50 (ISBN 0-521-23579-0); pap. cancelled (ISBN 0-521-28052-4). Cambridge U Pr.

Goguel, Jean. Geologie, 2 vols. (Methodique Ser.). 53.95 ea. French & Eur.

Gorshkov, G. & Yakushova, A. Physical Geology. Gurevich, A., tr. (Russian Monographs Ser.). 596p. 1969. 125.95x (ISBN 0-677-20790-5). Gordon.

Gorshkov, G. S. Volcanism & the Upper Mantle: Investigations in the Kurile Island Arc. LC 69-12530. (Monographs in Geoscience Ser.). 385p. 1970. 39.50x (ISBN 0-306-30407-4, Plenum Pr). Plenum Pub.

Gorshkov, George & Yakushova, Alexandra. Physical Geology. (Illus.). 596p. 1975. text ed. 17.50x (ISBN 0-8464-0718-3). Beekman Pubs.

Greenough, George B. A Critical Examination of the First Principles of Geology. Albritton, Claude C., Jr., ed. LC 77-6520. (History of Geology Ser.). 1978. Repr. of 1819 ed. lib. bdg. 27.50x (ISBN 0-405-10442-1). Ayer Co Pubs.

Gregory, Herbert E. Military Geology & Topography. 1918. 49.50x (ISBN 0-686-83626-X). Elliots Bks.

Guest, John. Planetary Geology. LC 79-+011. 208p. 1979. 25.95x (ISBN 0-470-26887-5). Halsted Pr.

Gupta, A. & Yagi, K. Petrology & Genesis of Leucite-Bearing Rocks. (Minerals & Rocks Ser.: Vol. 14). (Illus.). 250p. 1980. 44.00 (ISBN 0-387-09864-X). Springer-Verlag.

Habberjam, G. M. Apparent Resistivity Observations & the Use of Square Array Techniques. (Geoexploration Monographs, I-9). (Illus.). 1979. lib. bdg. 36.00 (ISBN 3-443-13013-5). Lubrecht & Cramer.

Hallam, A. Great Geological Controversies. 1983. pap. 14.95x (ISBN 0-19-854430-8). Oxford U Pr.

Hamblin, Kenneth W. The Earth's Dynamic Systems: A Textbook of Physical Geology. 3rd ed. LC 80-68323. (Illus.). 544p. 1982. text ed. 29.95x (ISBN 0-8087-3172-6). Burgess.

Hamblin, W. Kenneth & Howard, James D. Exercises in Physical Geology. 5th ed. 1980. pap. text ed. 15.95x (ISBN 0-8087-3154-8). Burgess.

--Exercises in Physical Geology. 6th, rev. ed. (Illus.). 192p. 1986. pap. price not set lab manual (ISBN 0-8087-4769-X). Burgess.

Hancock, P. L., et al, eds. Planar & Linear Fabrics of Deformed Rocks: A Selection of Papers Delivered at an International Conference held at ETH Zurich 30 August to 2 September 1982. 218p. 1984. pap. 44.00 (ISBN 0-08-031428-7). Pergamon.

Handbuch der Regionalen Geologie, Nos. 1-30. 1910-44. 400.00 (ISBN 0-384-21285-9). Johnson Repr.

Hansen, E. Strain Facies. LC 72-89551. (Minerals, Rocks & Inorganic Materials Ser.: Vol. 2). (Illus.). 1971. 33.00 (ISBN 0-387-05204-6). Springer-Verlag.

Hardy, H. R., Jr. & Leighton, F. W., eds. Acoustic Emission & Microseismic Activity in Geologic Structures & Materials. LC 83-81165. 680p. 1984. 50.00x (ISBN 0-87201-546-7). Gulf Pub.

Hardy, H. Reginald, Jr. First Conference on Acoustic Emission (Microseismic Activity) in Geologic Structures & Materials. new ed. (Illus.). 500p. 1977. text ed. 40.00x (ISBN 0-87849-017-5). Trans Tech.

Harvey, John C. Geology for Geotechnical Engineers. (Illus.). 136p. 1983. 27.95 (ISBN 0-521-24629-6); pap. 9.95 (ISBN 0-521-28862-2). Cambridge U Pr.

Hassan, M. Y., et al. General Geology. (Arabic.). 550p. 1983. pap. 17.00 (ISBN 0-471-86092-1). Wiley.

Hatheway, Allen W. & McClure, Cole R., Jr., eds. Reviews in Engineering Geology, Vol. 4: Geology in the Siting of Nuclear Power Plants. LC 62-51690. (Illus.). 1979. 41.00 (ISBN 0-8137-4104-1). Geol Soc.

Hay, Edward A. & McAlester, A. Lee. Physical Geology: Principles & Perspectives. 2nd ed. (Illus.). 432p. 1984. 28.95 (ISBN 0-13-669549-3). P-H.

Heckman, Carol, et al, eds. GeoRef Thesaurus & Guide to Indexing. 2nd ed. LC 78-65083. 1978. pap. 35.00 (ISBN 0-913312-07-X) (ISBN 0-913312-40-1). Am Geol.

Heirtzler, J. R., et al, eds. Indian Ocean Geology & Biostratigraphy. LC 77-88320. (Special Publication Ser.). (Illus.). 616p. 1978. 25.00 (ISBN 0-87590-208-1). Am Geophysical.

Hobson, G. D., ed. Developments in Petroleum Geology, 2 vols. Vol. 1, 1977. 72.25 (ISBN 0-85334-745-X, Pub. by Elsevier Applied Sci England); Vol. 2, 1980. 72.25 (ISBN 0-85334-907-X). Elsevier.

Holmes, A. Principles of Physical Geology. 3rd ed. 1978. pap. 35.00 (ISBN 0-442-30780-2). Van Nos Reinhold.

Holzer, Thomas L., ed. Man-Induced Land Subsidence. (Review in Engineering Geology Ser.: Vol. VI). (Illus.). 1984. 28.00. Geol Soc.

Horowitz, A. S. & Potter, P. E. Introductory Petrography of Fossils. LC 73-142385. (Illus.). 1971. 56.00 (ISBN 0-387-05275-5). Springer-Verlag.

Howard, Arthur D. & Remson, Irwin. Geology in Environmental Planning. (Illus.). 1977. text ed. 47.95 (ISBN 0-07-030510-2). McGraw.

Hutton, James. Theory of the Earth, 2 vols. 1960. Repr. of 1795 ed. 50.75 (ISBN 3-7682-0025-6). Lubrecht & Cramer.

Huxley, Thomas H. Discourses Biological & Geological. 1896. 12.00 (ISBN 0-8274-4221-1). R West.

Institution of Civil Engineers Staff, ed. Manual of Applied Geology for Engineers. 414p. 1976. pap. 30.25x (ISBN 0-7277-0038-3). Am Soc Civil Eng.

Jackson, Bob. The Rockhound's Guide to Washington, Vol. IV. (Illus.). 50p. (Orig.). 1985. pap. 3.95 (ISBN 0-918499-07-0). Jackson Mtn.

Jagoda, Susan. Changing Earth. (Science in Action Ser.). (Illus.). 48p. 1984. pap. text ed. 2.85 (ISBN 0-88102-024-9). Janus Bks.

Johnson, Arvid M. Physical Processes in Geology. LC 70-119373. 1984. pap. text ed. 23.00x (ISBN 0-87735-320-4). Freeman Cooper.

Judson, S. & Deffeyes. Physical Geology. (Illus.). 592p. 1976. study guide 7.95 (ISBN 0-13-669630-9). P-H.

Jumikis, Alfreds R. Rock Mechanics II. (Rock & Soil Mechanics Ser.). (Illus.). 1983. 58.00x (ISBN 0-87849-038-8). Trans Tech.

Keller, Edward A. Environmental Geology. 4th, rev. ed. 500p. 1985. text ed. 27.95 (ISBN 0-675-20373-2). Merrill.

Kelly, A., et al, eds. Creep of Engineering Materials & of the Earth. (Philosophical Transactions of the Royal Society). (Illus.). 1978. 57.50x (ISBN 0-85403-099-9). Scholium Intl.

Khan, M. A. Global Geology. (The Wykeham Science Ser.: No. 41). 178p. 1976. pap. cancelled (ISBN 0-85109-510-0). Taylor & Francis.

Khan, M. A. & Matthews, B. Global Geology. LC 75-38616. (Wykeham Science Ser.: No. 41). 178p. 1976. 8.60x (ISBN 0-8448-1168-8). Crane Russak Co.

Kingma, Jacobus. The Geological Structure of New Zealand. LC 73-22454. 407p. 1974. 73.50 (ISBN 0-471-47900-4, Pub. by Wiley). Krieger.

Kirwan, Richard. Geological Essays. Albritton, Claude C., ed. LC 77-6523. (History of Geology Ser.). Repr. lib. bdg. 40.00 (ISBN 0-405-10444-8). Ayer Co Pubs.

Kitts, David B. The Structure of Geology. LC 77-7395. 1977. pap. 9.95 (ISBN 0-87074-162-4). SMU Press.

Klins, Mark A. Carbon Dioxide Flooding: Basic Mechanisms & Project Design. 279p. 1984. 58.00 (ISBN 0-934634-44-0). Intl Human Res.

Knill, J. L., ed. Industrial Geology. (Illus.). 1979. 39.50x (ISBN 0-19-854520-7). Oxford U Pr.

Kokelaar, B. P. & Howells, Malcolm, eds. Marginal Basin Geology: Volcanic & Associated Sedimentary & Tectonic Processes in Modern & Ancient Marginal Basins. (Illus.). 328p. 1984. text ed. 70.00x (ISBN 0-632-01073-8). Blackwell Pubns.

Kolisko, Eugen. Geology. 1979. pap. 3.95 (ISBN 0-906492-01-7, Pub. by Kolisko Archives). St George Bk Serv.

Kopp, Otto C. An Introduction to Physical Geology. 3rd ed. (Illus.). 144p. 1980. 8.95x (ISBN 0-89459-103-7). Hunter Textbks.

Kostov, I. & Stefanova, J. M. Sulphide Minerals. Crystal Chemistry, Parageneses and Systematics. (Illus.). 212p. 1982. text ed. 26.50x (ISBN 3-510-65110-3). Lubrecht & Cramer.

Kovari, K., ed. Field Measurements in Geomechanics: Proceedings of an International Symposium, Zurich, 5-8 September 1983. 1100p. 1983. lib. bdg. 95.00 (ISBN 90-6191-500-7, Pub. by Balkema RSA). IPS.

Krauskopf, Konrad B. The Third Planet: An Invitation to Geology. LC 74-77823. (Illus.). 528p. 1974. text ed. 17.50x (ISBN 0-87735-359-X); pap. text ed. 11.00 (ISBN 0-87735-360-3). Freeman Cooper.

Krynine, Dimitri P. & Judd, William R. Principles of Engineering Geology & Geotechnics. (Soil Mechanics & Foundations Library). (Illus.). 1957. text ed. 50.00 (ISBN 0-07-035560-6). McGraw.

Kulm, LaVerne D., et al, eds. Nazca Plate: Crustal Formation & Andean Convergence. (Memoir Ser: 154). (Illus.). 1981. 18.00 (ISBN 0-8137-1154-1). Geol Soc.

Laporte, Leo F. Ancient Environments. 2nd ed. (Foundations of the Earth Ser.). (Illus.). 1979. ref. o.p. 23.95 (ISBN 0-13-036392-8); pap. 15.95 ref. (ISBN 0-13-036384-7). P-H.

Larson, R. L., et al. The Bedrock Geology of the World. (Illus.). 1985. 34.95 (ISBN 0-7167-1702-6). W H Freeman.

LeRoy, L. W. & LeRoy, D. O., eds. Subsurface Geology: Petroleum, Mining, Construction. 4th ed. LC 76-51265. 941p. 1977. 21.00 (ISBN 0-918062-00-4). Colo Sch Mines.

Leveson, David J. A Sense of the Earth. LC 82-11437. (Illus.). 176p. 18.00 (ISBN 0-404-19149-5). AMS Pr.

Levin, Harold. Contemporary Physical Geology. 2nd ed. (Illus.). 608p. 1986. text ed. 35.95 (ISBN 0-03-057803-5, CBS C). SCP.

Libby, Leona M. & Bergle, Rainer, eds. Life Work of Noble Laureate Willard Frank Libby, 7 vols. 1982. Set. pap. 15.00 (ISBN 0-941054-00-4); Vol. I, 640p. pap. 15.00 (ISBN 0-941054-01-2); Vol. II, 540p. pap. 15.00 (ISBN 0-941054-02-0); Vol. III, 500p. pap. 15.00 (ISBN 0-941054-03-9); Vol. IV, 400p. pap. 15.00 (ISBN 0-941054-04-7); Vol. V, 500p. pap. 15.00 (ISBN 0-941054-05-5); Vol. VI, 550p. pap. 15.00 (ISBN 0-941054-06-3); Vol. VII, 600p. pap. 15.00 (ISBN 0-941054-07-1). GeoScience Anal.

Long, Leon E. Geology. (Illus.). 526p. 1982. pap. text ed. 18.95x (ISBN 0-89641-110-9). American Pr.

Low-Flow, Low-Permeability Measurements in Largely Impermeable Rocks. 1979. 16.00x (ISBN 92-64-01955-3). OECD.

Lowman, Paul D., Jr. The Third Planet. LC 77-128348. (Illus.). 170p. 1972. 40.00x (ISBN 0-8139-0577-X). U Pr of Va.

Ludman, Allan, et al. Physical Geology. (Illus.). 576p. 1982. text ed. 37.95x (ISBN 0-07-011510-9). McGraw.

Lundgren, Lawrence. Environmental Geology. (Illus.). 528p. 1986. text ed. 30.95 (ISBN 0-13-283300-X). P-H.

Lyell, Charles. Principles of Geology, 3 vols. (Illus.). 1970. Repr. of 1833 ed. Set. text ed. 91.00 (ISBN 3-7682-0685-8). Lubrecht & Cramer.

--Principles of Geology: Being an Attempt to Explain the Former Changes of the Earth's Surface by Reference to Causes Now in Operation, 3 Vols. 1970. Repr. of 1830 ed. Set. 145.00 (ISBN 0-384-34524-7). Johnson Repr.

Mabbutt, J. A. Desert Landforms. 1977. 25.00x (ISBN 0-262-13131-5). MIT Pr.

McAlester, A. Earth: An Introduction to the Geological & Geophysical Sciences. 1973. 29.95 (ISBN 0-13-222422-4); instr. res. bk. 1.95 (ISBN 0-13-222695-2); study guide o.p. 5.95 (ISBN 0-13-222380-5). P-H.

McAlester, A. Lee & Hay, Edward A. Physical Geology: Principles & Perspectives. (Illus.). 448p. 1975. 26.95. P-H.

McCall, G. J. H., ed. Ophiolitic & Related Melanges. LC 81-13490. (Benchmark Papers in Geology: Vol. 66). 464p. 1983. 56.00 (ISBN 0-87933-421-5). Van Nos Reinhold.

MacGregor, A. R. Fife & Angus Geology. 1974. 15.00x (ISBN 0-7073-0054-1, Pub. by Scottish Academic Pr Scotland). Columbia U Pr.

McLean, Adam C. & Gribble, Colin D. Geology for Civil Engineers. (Illus.). 1979. text ed. 30.00x (ISBN 0-04-624001-2); pap. text ed. 15.95x. Allen Unwin.

McPhee, John. Basin & Range. (Illus.). 216p. 1981. 10.95 (ISBN 0-374-10914-1); pap. 6.25 (ISBN 0-374-51690-1). FS&G.

McQuillin, R. & Ardus, D. A. Exploring the Geology of Shelf Seas. 234p. 1977. 24.00x (ISBN 0-86010-070-7, Pub. by Graham & Trotman England). State Mutual Bk.

Mahadeuan, C. Mahadevan Volume: A Collection of Geological Papers in Commeration of the Sixty-First Birthday of Pr. C. Mahadevan. Krishman, M. S., ed. (Illus.). 1961. 5.00 (ISBN 0-934454-59-0). Lubrecht & Cramer.

Mason, Shirley L. Source Book in Geology, Fourteen Hundred to Nineteen Hundred. Mather, Kirtley F., ed. (Source Books in the History of the Sciences Ser). (Illus.). 1970. text ed. 40.00x (ISBN 0-674-82277-3). Harvard U Pr.

Mathewson, Christopher C. Engineering Geology. (Illus.). 416p. 1981. text ed. 32.95 (ISBN 0-675-08032-0). Additional supplements may be obtained from publisher. Merrill.

Matthews, William H., III. Geology Made Simple. rev. ed. (Made Simple Ser.). (Illus.). 240p. 1982. pap. 4.95 (ISBN 0-385-17142-0). Doubleday.

Menard, H. W. Geology, Resources & Society: An Introduction to Earth Science. LC 73-17151. (Geology Ser.). (Illus.). 621p. 1974. text ed. 30.95x (ISBN 0-7167-0260-6); instr's. guide avail. W H Freeman.

Merriam, D. Random Processes in Geology. LC 75-6848. 1976. 28.00 (ISBN 0-387-07277-2). Springer Verlag.

Miller, Keith. Continents in Collision: The International Karakoram Project. (Illus.). 212p. 1982. 29.95 (ISBN 0-540-01066-9, Pub. by G Philip). Sheridan.

Milnes, A. G. Geology & Radwaste. Date not set. 60.00 (ISBN 0-12-498070-8); pap. 39.95 (ISBN 0-12-498071-6). Acad Pr.

Mitchell-Thome, Raoul C. Geology of the South Atlantic Islands. (Beitraege zur regionalen Geologie der Erde: Vol. 10). (Illus.). 366p. 1970. lib. bdg. 90.05x (ISBN 3-443-11010-X, Pub by Gebrueder Borntraeger Germany). Lubrecht & Cramer.

Morey, G. B. & Hanson, Gilbert N., eds. Selected Studies of Archean Gneisses & Lower Proterozoic Rocks, Southern Canadian Shield. LC 80-67113. (Special Paper Ser.: No. 182). (Illus., Orig.). 1980. pap. 26.00 (ISBN 0-8137-2182-2). Geol Soc.

Moullade, M. & Nairn, A. E., eds. Phanerozoic Geology of the World: The Mesozoic, Vol. 2B. 450p. 1983. 113.00 (ISBN 0-444-41672-2, I-343-83). Elsevier.

Mulvihill, John, ed. Bibliography & Index of Geology: Users Guide. 160p. (Orig.). 1982. pap. text ed. 8.95 (ISBN 0-913312-66-5). Am Geol.

Murray, John. A Comparative View of the Huttonian & Neptunian Systems of Geology: In Answer to the Illustrations of the Huttonian Theory of the Earth. Albritton, Claude C., Jr., ed. LC 77-6533. (History of Geology Ser.). 1978. Repr. of 1802 ed. lib. bdg. 24.50 (ISBN 0-405-10453-7). Ayer Co Pubs.

Nilsson. The Pleistocene. 1982. lib. bdg. 115.00 (ISBN 90-277-1466-5, Pub. by Reidel Holland). Kluwer Academic.

Northeastern Women's Geoscientists Conference, First. Women in Geology: Proceedings. Halsey, S. D., et al, eds. LC 76-21580. (Illus.). 1976. pap. 2.00 (ISBN 0-915492-02-4). Ash Lad Pr.

Park, Charles F. & Guilbert, John M. The Geology of Ore Deposits. 4th ed. LC 85-10099. (Illus.). 768p. 1985. text ed. write for info. (ISBN 0-7167-1456-6). W H Freeman.

Pearl, Richard M. Turquoise. 1976. pap. 1.35 (ISBN 0-940566-08-7). R M Pearl Bks.

Peters, William C. Exploration & Mining Geology. LC 77-14006. 696p. 1978. text ed. 44.50 (ISBN 0-471-68261-6). Wiley.

Phillips, William. An Outline of Mineralogy & Geology: Intended for the Use of Those Who May Desire to Become Acquainted with the Elements of Those Sciences. Albritton, Claude C., Jr., ed. LC 77-6536. (History of Geology Ser.). (Illus.). 1978. Repr. of 1816 ed. lib. bdg. 17.00x (ISBN 0-405-10456-1). Ayer Co Pubs.

Pitts, J. A Manual of Geology for Civil Engineers. 1985. 24.95 (ISBN 0-470-20096-0). Halsted Pr.

Plummer, Charles C. & McGeary, David. Physical Geology. 2nd ed. 520p. 1982. pap. text ed. write for info. (ISBN 0-697-05038-6); instrs.' manual avail. (ISBN 0-697-05021-1); study guide avail. (ISBN 0-697-05039-4); lab manual avail. (ISBN 0-697-05041-6); slides avail. (ISBN 0-697-05022-X). Wm C Brown.

--Physical Geology. 3rd ed. 528p. 1985. pap. write for info. (ISBN 0-697-05046-7); instr's. manual avail. (ISBN 0-697-00566-6); student study guide avail. (ISBN 0-697-00564-X); lab manual avail. (ISBN 0-697-00351-5); transparencies avail. (ISBN 0-697-00565-8); slides avail. (ISBN 0-697-00596-8); instr's. lab manual avail. (ISBN 0-697-00595-X). Wm C Brown.

Poirier, J. P. Creep of Crystals. (Cambridge Earth Science Ser.). (Illus.). 275p. 1985. 49.50 (ISBN 0-521-26177-5); pap. 22.95 (ISBN 0-521-27851-1). Cambridge U Pr.

Potter, A. W. R. & Robinson, H. Geology. 2nd ed. (Illus.). 296p. 1983. pap. text ed. 14.95x (ISBN 0-7121-0742-8). Trans-Atlantic.

Price, George M. Evolutionary Geology & the new Catastrophism. (Illus.). 352p. 1984. Repr. of 1926 ed. photocopy 16.95x (ISBN 0-915554-13-5). Sourcebook.

Putnis, A. & McConnell, J. D. Principles of Mineral Behavior. (Geological Studies: Vol. 1). 258p. 1980. 62.50 (ISBN 0-444-00439-4); pap. 32.50 (ISBN 0-444-00444-0). Elsevier.

Quennell, Albert M., ed. Rift Valley: Afro-Arabian. (Benchmark Papers in Geology: Vol. 60). 419p. 1982. 52.95 (ISBN 0-87933-383-9). Van Nos Reinhold.

Rapp, George & Gifford, John A., eds. Archaeological Geology. LC 84-40201. (Illus.). 448p. 1985. text ed. 35.00 (ISBN 0-300-03142-4). Yale U Pr.

Ray, Santosh. A Textbook of Geology. 480p. 1981. 25.00x (ISBN 0-86125-280-2, Pub. by Orient Longman India). State Mutual Bk.

Raymo, Chet. The Crust of Our Earth: An Armchair Traveller's Guide to the New Geology. (Illus.). 136p. 1983. 22.95 (ISBN 0-13-195107-6); pap. 12.95 (ISBN 0-13-195099-1). P-H.

Read, H. H. & Watson, Janet. Introduction & Geology, 2 vols. Incl. Vol. 1. Principles. 2nd ed. LC 76-50637. 693p. 1977. 39.95x (ISBN 0-470-99031-7); Vol. 2, 2 pts. LC 75-501. 1975; Pt. 1. Early Stages of Earth History. 221p. 24.95 (ISBN 0-470-71165-5); Pt. 2. Later Stages of Earth History. 371p. Halsted Pr.

Reeves, C. C., Jr. Caliche-Origin Classification, Morphology & Uses. LC 76-2234. 1976. text ed. 39.95x (ISBN 0-686-16733-3). Estacado Bks.

Reyer, Edward. Questions on Geologic Principles. Keller, Allen, et al, trs. LC 79-89374. (Microform Publication: No. 9). (Illus.). 1979. 4.00 (ISBN 0-8137-6009-7). Geol Soc.

Rhodes & Stone. The Language of the Earth. 350p. 1981. text ed. 39.00 (ISBN 0-08-025981-2); pap. text ed. 19.25 (ISBN 0-08-025980-4). Pergamon.

Riban, David M. Introduction to Physical Science. (Illus.). 656p. 1981. text ed. 32.95 (ISBN 0-07-052140-9). McGraw.

Rigby, J. Keith. Field Guide: Southern Colorado Plateau. LC 75-32499. (Geology Field Guide Ser.). (Illus.). 1977. pap. text ed. 8.95 (ISBN 0-8403-1314-4). Kendall-Hunt.

Robinson, Edwin S. Basic Physical Geology. LC 81-16384. 686p. 1982. 36.00x (ISBN 0-471-72809-8); tchr's. manual 7.50 (ISBN 0-471-86926-0). Wiley.

Rolfe, Ian, ed. Geological Howlers. (Illus.). 60p. 1983. pap. 4.95 (ISBN 0-04-550032-0). Allen Unwin.

Ross, C. A., ed. Paleobiogeography. LC 76-12969. (Benchmark Papers in Geology Ser.: Vol. 31). 1976. 68.00 (ISBN 0-12-787365-1). Acad Pr.

Rowbotham, Fred. The Severn Bore. (Illus.). 108p. 1983. 12.95 (ISBN 0-7153-8508-9). David & Charles.

Rudman, Jack. Geology. (Undergraduate Program Field Test Ser.: UPFT-11). (Cloth bdg. avail. on request). pap. 9.95 (ISBN 0-8373-6011-0). Natl Learning.

Salem, M. J. & Busrewil, M. T., eds. The Geology of Libya, 3 vols. 1981. 59.00 ea. Vol. 1 (ISBN 0-12-615501-1). Vol. 2 (ISBN 0-12-615502-X). Vol. 3 (ISBN 0-12-615503-8). Acad Pr.

Salop, L. J. Precambrian of the Northern Hemisphere. (Developments in Paleontology & Stratigraphy Ser.: Vol. 3). 382p. 1977. 93.75 (ISBN 0-444-41510-6). Elsevier.

Sanders, John E. & Carola, R. Principles of Physical Geology. LC 81-50125. 624p. 1981. 35.45 (ISBN 0-471-08424-7); tchr's manual avail. (ISBN 0-471-09378-5). Wiley.

Schultz, John R. & Cleaves, A. B. Geology in Engineering. LC 55-7317. 592p. 1955. text ed. 47.50 (ISBN 0-471-76461-2). Wiley.

Schwab, F. L., ed. Geosynclines: Concept & Place Within Plate Tectonics. (Benchmark Papers in Geology Ser.: Vol. 50). 432p. 1982. 54.50 (ISBN 0-87933-410-X). Van Nos Reinhold.

Schwartz, M. L., ed. Spits & Bars. LC 72-88983. (Benchmark Papers in Geology: Vol. 3). 452p. 1973. 57.95 (ISBN 0-87933-012-0). Van Nos Reinhold.

Scott-LaDochy. Climate & Landforms: A Laboratory Manual in Physical Geography. 288p. 1983. pap. 12.95 (ISBN 0-8403-3168-1). Kendall-Hunt.

Shelton, John S. Geology Illustrated. LC 66-16380. (Illus.). 434p. 1966. text ed. 31.95x (ISBN 0-7167-0229-0). W H Freeman.

Shrock, Robert. Geology at MIT Eighteen Sixty-five to Nineteen Sixty-five: A History of the First Hundred Years of Geology at Massachusetts Institute of Technology. Vol. I: The Faculty & Supporting Staff. LC 77-71235. (Illus.). 1977. 40.00x (ISBN 0-262-19161-X). MIT Pr.

Siegal, B. S. & Gillespie, A. R. Remote Sensing in Geology. 702p. 1980. text ed. 61.95 (ISBN 0-471-79052-4). Wiley.

Siegfried, Robert & Dott, Robert H., Jr., eds. Humphry Davy on Geology: The 1805 Lectures for the General Audience. LC 79-5022. 192p. 1980. 25.00x (ISBN 0-299-08030-7). U of Wis Pr.

Singhal, B. B., ed. Engineering Geosciences: Professor R.S. Mithal Commerorative Volume. LC 82-905257. 225p. 1982. 44.00 (ISBN 0-9605004-8-0, Pub. by Sarita Prakashan India). Eng Pubns.

Site Selection Factors for Repositories of Solid High-Level & Alpha Bearing Wastes in Geological Formations. (Illus.). 64p. 1978. pap. 10.75 (ISBN 92-0-125177-7, IDC177, IAEA). Unipub.

Spencer, Edgar W. Physical Geology. (Biology Ser.). (Illus.). 656p. 1983. text ed. 34.95 (ISBN 0-201-06423-5); Laboratory Manual avail.; Instr's Manual 2.00 (ISBN 0-201-06424-3); Study Guide avail. Addison-Wesley.

Spurr, Josia E., ed. Political & Commercial Geology & the World's Mineral Resources. LC 82-48322. (The World Economy Ser.). 562p. 1982. lib. bdg. 66.00 (ISBN 0-8240-5378-8). Garland Pub.

Squyres, Coy H., ed. Geology of Italy, 2 vols. 1975. Set. 135.00x (ISBN 0-8002-1458-7). Intl Pubns Serv.

Stauffer, M. R., ed. Fabric of Ducile Strain. (Illus.). 399p. 1983. 48.00 (ISBN 0-87933-442-8). Van Nos Reinhold.

Steinhart, J. S. & Smith, T. J., eds. The Earth Beneath the Continents. LC 66-62581. (Geophysical Monograph Ser.: Vol. 10). 663p. 1966. 21.00 (ISBN 0-87590-010-0). Am Geophysical.

Stirrup, M. N. Geology: The Science of the Earth. LC 78-73233. (Illus.). 1980. pap. 12.95 (ISBN 0-521-22567-1). Cambridge U Pr.

Stokes, William L., et al. Introduction to Geology: Physical & Historical. 2nd ed. LC 77-21570. 1978. text ed. 32.95 (ISBN 0-13-484352-5). P-H.

Strahler, Arthur N. Physical Geology. 612p. 1981. text ed. 28.95 scp (ISBN 0-06-046462-3, HarpC); instr's. manual avail. (ISBN 0-06-366461-5). Har-Row.

Summerson, Charles H., ed. Sorby on Geology, Vol. III. (Geological Milestones Ser.). (Illus.). 241p. 1978. 8.50 (ISBN 0-932981-28-3). Univ Miami CSL.

Sweeting, M. M., ed. Karst Geomorphology. LC 81-6558. (Benchmark Papers in Geology Ser.: Vol. 59). 448p. 1981. 56.00 (ISBN 0-87933-379-0). Van Nos Reinhold.

Tank, Ronald W. Environmental Geology: Text & Readings. 3rd ed. 1983. pap. 16.95x (ISBN 0-19-503288-8). Oxford U Pr.

--Legal Aspects of Geology. 580p. 49.50x (ISBN 0-306-41159-8); pap. 19.95 (ISBN 0-306-41215-2). Plenum Pub.

Tarbuck, Edward J. & Lutgens, Frederick K. The Earth: An Introduction to Physical Geology. 1984. text ed. 28.95 (ISBN 0-675-20051-2); additional supplements avail. Merrill.

Techter, David. Stereogram Book of Rocks, Minerals & Gems. 64p. (Orig.). 1970. pap. text ed. 6.95 (ISBN 0-8331-1701-7). Hubbard Sci.

Tennissen, Anthony C. Nature of Earth Materials. (Illus.). 448p. 1983. prof. ref. 25.95 (ISBN 0-13-610527-0). P-H.

Uyeda, Seiya. The New View of the Earth: Moving Continents & Moving Oceans. Ohnuki, Masako, tr. LC 77-9900. (Geology Ser.). (Illus.). 217p. 1978. pap. text ed. 10.50x (ISBN 0-7167-0282-7). W H Freeman.

Vasiliev, Y. M. General & Historical Geology. 382p. 1981. 15.00 (ISBN 0-8285-2070-4, Pub. by Mir Pubs USSR). Imported Pubns.

Velikovsky, Immanuel. Earth in Upheaval. 1980. pap. 3.95 (ISBN 0-671-52465-8). PB.

Venturini, W. S. Boundary Element Method in Geomechanics. (Lecture Notes in Engineering: Vol. 4). (Illus.). 246p. 1983. pap. 21.00 (ISBN 0-387-12653-8). Springer-Verlag.

Visser, W. A., ed. Geological Nomenclature. 568p. 1980. lib. bdg. 95.00 (ISBN 90-247-2403-1, Pub. by Martinus Nijhoff Netherlands). Kluwer Academic.

Vuke, Susan. Processes of the Earth's Surface. 96p. 1980. pap. 5.00 (ISBN 0-87842-125-4). Mountain Pr.

Walker, John. Lectures on Geology. Scott, Harold W., ed. LC 65-24986. Repr. of 1966 ed. 82.50 (ISBN 0-8357-9647-7, 2015764). Bks Demand UMI.

Warren, Erasmus. Geologia: Discourse Concerning the Earth Before the Deluge, Wherein the Form & Properties Ascribed to It. LC 77-6546. (History of Geology Ser.). (Illus.). 1978. Repr. of 1690 ed. lib. bdg. 34.50x (ISBN 0-405-10470-7). Ayer Co Pubs.

Watson, Janet. Geology & Man: An Introduction to Applied Earth Science. (Illus.). 176p. 1983. text ed. 25.00x (ISBN 0-04-553001-7); pap. text ed. 11.95x (ISBN 0-04-553002-5). Allen Unwin.

Wauschkuhn, A., et al, eds. Syngenesis & Epigenesis in the Formation of Mineral Deposits. (Illus.). 660p. 1984. 61.50 (ISBN 0-387-13845-5). Springer-Verlag.

Weber, Jon N., ed. Geochemistry of Germanium. LC 73-12621. (Benchmark Papers in Geology Ser). 480p. 1974. 62.50 (ISBN 0-87933-058-9). Van Nos Reinhold.

Wermund, E. G., ed. Approaches to Environmental Geology: A Colloquium & Workshop. (Report of Investigations Ser.: RI 81). (Illus.). 268p. 1974. 3.50 (ISBN 0-318-03211-2). Bur Econ Geology.

Whitehurst, John. An Inquiry into the Original State & Formation of the Earth: Deduced from Facts & the Laws of Nature. 2nd rev. ed. Albritton, Claude C., Jr., ed. LC 77-6548. (History of Geology Ser.). 1978. Repr. of 1786 ed. lib. bdg. 27.50x (ISBN 0-405-10465-0). Ayer Co Pubs.

Wilson, Gilbert. Introduction to Small Scale Geological Structures. Cosgrove, John, ed. (Illus.). 160p. 1982. pap. text ed. 9.95x (ISBN 0-04-551052-0). Allen Unwin.

Wood, B. J. & Fraser, D. G. Elementary Thermodynamics for Geologists. (Illus.). 1976. pap. text ed. 16.95x (ISBN 0-19-859927-7). Oxford U Pr.

Woodford, Alfred O. Historical Geology. LC 65-19557. pap. 128.00 (ISBN 0-317-29239-0, 2055544). Bks Demand UMI.

Woodward, John. An Essay Toward a Natural History of the Earth, & Terrestrial Bodies Especially Minerals of the Sea, Rivers, & Springs: An Account of the Universal Deluge & of the Effects That It Had Upon the Earth. Albritton, Claude C., Jr., ed. LC 77-7406. (History of Geology Ser.). 1978. Repr. of 1695 ed. lib. bdg. 27.50 (ISBN 0-405-10468-5). Ayer Co Pubs.

World Petroleum Congress. Proceedings of the Ninth World Petroleum Congress: Geology, Vol. 2. 383p. 1975. 111.00 (ISBN 0-85334-664-X, Pub. by Elsevier Applied Sci England). Elsevier.

Wyllie, Peter J. The Way the Earth Works: An Introduction to the New Global Geology & Its Revolutionary Development. LC 75-23197. 296p. 1976. pap. text ed. 21.95x (ISBN 0-471-96896-X). Wiley.

Yong, Raymond N., ed. Geological Environment & Soil Properties. 453p. 1983. pap. 36.00x (ISBN 0-87262-381-5). Am Soc Civil Eng.

Young, Louise B. The Blue Planet. 304p. 1984. pap. 8.95 (ISBN 0-452-00708-9, Mer). NAL.

Zenger, D. H. & Mazzullo, S. J., eds. Dolomitization. LC 81-7133. (Benchmark Papers in Geology: Vol. 65). 427p. 1982. 54.00 (ISBN 0-87933-416-9). Van Nos Reinhold.

Zumberge, James H. & Nelson, Clemens A. Elements of Physical Geology. LC 75-26843. 412p. 1972. 34.95x (ISBN 0-471-98674-7). Wiley.

Zumberge, James H. & Rutford, Robert H. Laboratory Manual for Physical Geology. 6th ed. 200p. 1983. write for info. wire coil (ISBN 0-697-05043-2); instrs.' manual avail. (ISBN 0-697-05045-9). Wm C Brown.

GEOLOGY–BIBLIOGRAPHY

Aggasiz, Jean L. Bibliographia Zoologiae Et Geologiae, 4 Vols. (Sources of Science Ser.: No. 20). Set. 275.00 (ISBN 0-384-00404-0). Johnson Repr.

Bibliography & Index of Texas Geology. Incl. 1933-1950. Girard, R. M. (Publication Ser.: No. 5910). 238p. 1959. 1.50 (ISBN 0-318-12074-7); 1951-1960. Moore, E. T. & Brown, M. D. 575p. 1979. Repr. 11.00 (ISBN 0-318-12075-5); 1961-1974. Moore, E. T. 446p. 1976. 7.00 (ISBN 0-318-12076-3); 1975-1980. Masterson, Amanda R. 334p. 8.00 (ISBN 0-318-12077-1). Bur Econ Geology.

Bibliography & Index of the Geology & Mineral Resources of Washington, 1937-1956: 1937-1956. Reichert, William H. (Bulletin Ser.: No. 46). 721p. 1960. 3.00 (ISBN 0-686-34699-8). Geologic Pubns.

Corbin, John B., compiled by. An Index of State Geological Survey Publications Issued in Series: Supplement, Nineteen Sixty-Three to Nineteen Eighty. LC 81-18501. 461p. 1982. 37.50 (ISBN 0-8108-1501-X). Scarecrow.

Editerral Editor's Handbook. 1980. pap. 10.51 (ISBN 0-686-27381-8, Pub. by GEO Abstracts England). State Mutual Bk.

Goodman, G. T. & Bray, S. An Annotated Bibliography of Ecological Aspects of the Reclamation of Derelict & Disturbed Land. (Bibliography Ser.). 351p. 1980. 14.95x (ISBN 0-902246-52-6, Pub. by GEO Abstracts England). State Mutual Bk.

Harvard University Museum of Comparative Zoology. Catalogue of the Library of the Museum of Comparative Zoology, First Supplement. 1976. lib. bdg. 125.00 (ISBN 0-8161-0811-0, Hall Library). G K Hall.

Hazen, R. M. & Hazen, M. Hindle, eds. American Geological Literature 1669-1850. LC 79-25898. 448p. 1980. 37.95 (ISBN 0-87933-371-5). Van Nos Reinhold.

Kieffer, F. V. An Annotated Bibliography of Geology & Land Use Planning, No. 1230. 1977. 6.00 (ISBN 0-686-19687-2). CPL Biblios.

Northrop, Stuart A. University of New Mexico Contributions in Geology, 1898-1964. LC 66-14777. (Geology Ser.: No. 7). 1966. pap. 2.00x (ISBN 0-8263-0117-7). U of NM Pr.

Reichert, William H. Bibliography & Index of the Geology & Mineral Resources of Washington, 1957-1962. (Bulletin Ser.: No. 59). 375p. 1969. 3.00 (ISBN 0-686-34714-5). Geologic Pubns.

Richards, Horace G. & Shapiro, Earl A. Annotated Bibliography of Quaternary Shorelines: Third Supplement (1974-1977) (Bibliography Ser.). 245p. 1980. 21.00x (ISBN 0-86094-025-X, Pub. by GEO Abstracts England). State Mutual Bk.

U. S. Department of the Interior - U. S. Geological Survey, Washington, D. C. Catalog of the United States Geological Survey Library, 25 vols. 1964. Set. lib. bdg. 2470.00 (ISBN 0-8161-0712-2, Hall Library). G K Hall.

U. S. Department of the Interior - U. S. Geological Survey, Washington D. C. Catalog of the United States Geological Survey Library - Supplement 1, 11 vols. 1972. Set. 1200.00 (ISBN 0-8161-0876-5, Hall Library). G K Hall.

U. S. Department of the Interior, Washington, D. C. Catalog of the United States Geological Survey 3rd Suppl, 6 vols. 1976. lib. bdg. 660.00 (ISBN 0-8161-0051-9, Hall Library). G K Hall.

Ward, Dederick C., et al. Geologic Reference Sources: A Subject & Regional Bibliography of Publications & Maps in the Geological Sciences. 2nd ed. LC 81-4770. 590p. 1981. 35.00 (ISBN 0-8108-1428-5). Scarecrow.

Whitaker, C. R. A Bibliography of Pediments. (Bibliography Ser.). 95p. 1980. pap. 3.50x (ISBN 0-686-27380-X, Pub. by GEO Abstracts England). State Mutual Bk.

GEOLOGY–DATA PROCESSING

Arya, V. K. & Aggarwal, J. K., eds. Deconvolution of Seismic Data. LC 81-6311. (Benchmark Papers in Electrical Engineering & Computer Science Ser.: Vol. 24). 336p. 1982. 49.95 (ISBN 0-87933-406-1). Van Nos Reinhold.

Computer-Assisted Land Resources Planning. 44p. 1979. 12.00. Am Plan Assn.

Computers for Professionals Staff, ed. Geoscience Software Directory for IBM-PC & Compatibles, 1985. 112p. 1985. pap. 45.00 (ISBN 0-88746-064-X). Intl Human Res.

Cutbill, J. L. Data Processing in Biology & Geology. (Systematics Association Ser.: Special Vol. 3). 1971. 59.50 (ISBN 0-12-199750-2). Acad Pr.

Davis, John C. Statistics & Data Analysis in Geology. LC 72-6792. (Illus.). 550p. 1973. 48.50 (ISBN 0-471-19895-1). Wiley.

Fabbri, Andrea G. Image Processing of Geological Data. 272p. 1984. 32.50 (ISBN 0-442-22536-9). Van Nos Reinhold.

Harbaugh, John W. & Bonham-Carter, Graeme. Computer Simulation in Geology. LC 80-22433. 590p. 1981. Repr. of 1970 ed. lib. bdg. 39.50 (ISBN 0-89874-125-4). Krieger.

Lin, Cunshen & Harbaugh, John W. Graphic Display of Two & Three Dimensional Markov Computer Models in Geology. 192p. 1984. 29.50 (ISBN 0-442-25924-7). Van Nos Reinhold.

Loudon, T. V. Computer Methods in Geology. 1979. 49.50 (ISBN 0-12-456950-1). Acad Pr.

Mather, P. M. Computational Methods of Multivariate Analysis in Physical Geography. 532p. 1976. 84.95x (ISBN 0-471-57626-3, Pub. by Wiley-Interscience). Wiley.

Merriam, D. F., ed. Capture, Management & Display of Geological Data: With Special Emphasis on Energy & Mineral Resources. LC 76-56893. 1977. pap. text ed. 45.00 (ISBN 0-08-021422-3). Pergamon.

--Computer Assisted Instruction in Geology: Proceedings of the 4th Geochautauqua, Syracuse University, 1975. 1976. pap. text ed. 45.00 (ISBN 0-08-021040-6). Pergamon.

--Geostatistics. LC 71-142040. (Computer Applications in the Earth Sciences Ser.). 177p. 1970. 35.00x (ISBN 0-306-30519-4, Plenum Pr). Plenum Pub.

--Management, Analysis & Display of Geoscience Data: Proceedings of the First Annual Conference, Golden, CO, January 27-29, 1982. 60p. 1983. pap. 52.00 (ISBN 0-08-030248-3). Pergamon.

Robinson, Joseph E., ed. Computer Applications in Petroleum Geology. LC 82-3113. (Computer Methods in the Geosciences Ser.). 164p. 1982. 26.95 (ISBN 0-87933-444-4); pap. 16.95 (ISBN 0-87933-432-0). Van Nos Reinhold.

Simaan, Marwaan, ed. Advances in Geophysical Data Processing, Vol. 1. 57.50 (ISBN 0-89232-401-5). Jai Pr.

Vallee, Jacques & Askevold, Gerald. Computer Conferencing in the Geo Sciences. 93p. 1977. 9.00 (ISBN 0-318-14411-5). Inst Future.

GEOLOGY–DICTIONARIES

American Geological Institute. Dictionary of Geological Terms. 3rd rev. ed. LC 82-45315. (Illus.). 576p. 1984. 19.95 (ISBN 0-385-18100-0, Anchor Pr); pap. 7.95 (ISBN 0-385-18101-9, Anchor Pr). Doubleday.

Bates, Robert L. & Jackson, Julia A. Dictionary of Geologic Terms. 571p. 1984. 7.95 (ISBN 0-385-18101-9). Am Geol.

Bates, Robert L. & Jackson, Julia A., eds. Glossary of Geology. 2nd ed. LC 79-57360. 749p. 1980. 60.00 (ISBN 0-913312-15-0). Am Geol.

Cagnacci-Schwicker, Angelo. Dictionnaire International de Metallurgie, Mineralogie, Geologie et Industries Extractives, 2 vols. (Fr.). 1530p. 1969. Set. 95.00 (ISBN 0-686-56933-4, M-6054). French & Eur.

Cailleux, E. Elements de Geologie en Six Langues. (Fr., Ger., Rus., Span. & Eng.). 191p. (Elements of Geology in Six Languages). 1965. pap. 19.95 (ISBN 0-686-56735-8, M-6055). French & Eur.

Challinor, John. A Dictionary of Geology. 5th ed. 1978. text ed. 14.95x (ISBN 0-19-520063-2). Oxford U Pr.

Chesnel De La Charbouclais, L. P. Dictionnaire de Geologie... et Dictionnaire de Chronologie Universelle par M. Champagnac, Vol. 50. Migne, J. P., ed. (Encyclopedie Theologique Ser.). (Fr.). 728p. Repr. of 1849 ed. lib. bdg. 192.50x (ISBN 0-89241-253-4). Caratzas.

Diccionario Rioduero: Geologia y Mineralogia. 2nd ed. (Span.). 1978. leatherette 9.95 (ISBN 0-686-57363-3). French & Eur.

Dybovskaia, V. & Kirillova, I. Dictionnaire Geologique: Francais-Russe. (Fr. & Rus.). 406p. 1958. leatherette 4.95 (ISBN 0-686-92570-X, M-9099). French & Eur.

Entwicklungsgeschichte der Erde Mit Einem ABC der Geologie, 2 vols. (Ger.). 800p. 1970. Set. 22.50 (ISBN 3-7684-6026-6, M-7363, Pub. by W. Dausien). French & Eur.

Fairbridge, R. Encyclopedia of World Regional Geology, Pt. 3. 1986. price not set (ISBN 0-87933-266-2). Van Nos Reinhold.

Fairbridge, Rhodes W., ed. Encyclopedia of World Regional Geology: Part I: Western Hemisphere Including Australia & Antarctica, Pt. 1. LC 75-1406. (Encyclopedia of Earth Sciences Ser: Vol. 8A). 1975. 76.00 (ISBN 0-12-786461-X). Acad Pr.

Finkl, Charles W., Jr., ed. The Encyclopedia of Applied Geology. 832p. 1984. 75.00 (ISBN 0-442-22537-7). Van Nos Reinhold.

Four Languages Dictionary of Geological Terms. (Eng., Fr., Ger. & Rus.). 703p. 1980. 19.95 (ISBN 0-686-97380-1). French & Eur.

Gagnacci-Schwicker, A. & Schwicker. International Dictionary of Metallurgy, Mineralogy, Geology & the Mining & Oil Industries. (Eng., Fr., Ger. & Ital.). 1530p. 1970. 88.00 (ISBN 3-7625-0751-1, M-7482, Pub. by Bauverlag). French & Eur.

Gary, M., et al. Glossary of Geology. (Eng. & Rus.). 1717p. 1977. 75.00 (ISBN 0-686-92556-4, M-9113). French & Eur.

Hallam, A., ed. Planet Earth Encyclopedia of Geology. 320p. 1977. 40.00x (ISBN 0-7290-0055-9, Pub. by Phaidon Pr). State Mutual Bk.

Heckman, Carol, et al, eds. GeoRef Thesaurus & Guide to Indexing. 2nd ed. LC 78-65083. 1978. pap. 35.00 (ISBN 0-913312-07-X) (ISBN 0-913312-40-1). Am Geol.

Klein, J. Herder-Lexikon Geologie und Mineralogie. (Ger.). 238p. 1975. 15.95 (ISBN 3-451-16452-3, M-7457, Pub. by Herder). French & Eur.

Murawski, H. Geologisches Woerterbuch. 7th ed. (Ger.). 1977. pap. 10.95 (ISBN 3-432-84107-8, M-7418, Pub. by DTV). French & Eur.

Murawski, Hans. Geologisches Woerterbuch. (Ger.). 1972. pap. 10.95 (ISBN 0-686-56476-6, 7419, Pub. by DTV). French & Eur.

Riley, Sharon J., ed. GeoRef Thesaurus & Guide to Indexing. 3rd ed. 468p. 1981. 45.00 (ISBN 0-913312-53-3). Am Geol.

Rosenfeld, V. Kleines Fachwoerterbuch Geologie. (Ger.). 197p. 1966. 14.50 (ISBN 3-443-39048-X, M-7500, Pub. by Borntaeger). French & Eur.

Russian-English Geological Dictionary. 559p. 1983. 18.95 (ISBN 0-317-02600-3). Am Geol.

Thompson, Reginald C. A Dictionary of Assyrian Chemistry & Geology. LC 78-72768. (Ancient Mesopotamian Texts & Studies). (Assyrian.). Repr. of 1936 ed. 24.50 (ISBN 0-404-18222-4). AMS Pr.

Verbic, Ing S. English-Serbocroat & Serbocroat-English Geological & Mining Dictionary. (Eng. & Serbocroatian.). 528p. 1981. 90.00x (ISBN 0-686-44714-X, Pub. by Collets). State Mutual Bk.

Watt, Alec. Barnes & Noble Thesaurus of Geology. (Illus.). 192p. 1983. 13.41i (ISBN 0-06-015177-3, EH 579); pap. 6.68i (ISBN 0-06-463579-1). B&N NY.

Watznauer, A. Woerterbuch Geowissenschaften, Vol. 2. (Ger. & Eng., German-English Dictionary of Geo-Sciences). 1973. 45.00 (ISBN 3-87144-140-6, M-6916). French & Eur.

Whitten & Brooks. Dictionary of Geology. (Reference Ser.). 1973. pap. 5.95 (ISBN 0-14-051049-4). Penguin.

Wilmarth, Mary G. Lexicon of Geologic Names in the U. S, 2 Vols. 1968. Repr. of 1938 ed. 175.00x (ISBN 0-403-00128-5). Scholarly.

Woerterbuch fuer Metallurgie, Mineralogie, Geologie, Bergbau und die Oelindustrie. (Eng., Fr., Ger. & Ital., Dictionary of Metallurgy, Mineralogy, Geology, Mining and Oil Industry). 1970. 88.00 (ISBN 3-7625-0751-1, M-6912). French & Eur.

Wyllie, R. J. & Argall, George O., Jr., eds. World Mining Glossary of Mining, Processing & Geological Terms. LC 74-20169. (A World Mining Book). 432p. 1975. 55.00 (ISBN 0-87930-031-0). Miller Freeman.

GEOLOGY–EXAMINATIONS, QUESTIONS, ETC.

Pipkin, Bernard & Cummings, David. Environmental Geology: Practical Exercises. (Illus.). 240p. 1983. pap. 15.95 (ISBN 0-89863-058-4). Star Pub CA.

Rudman, Jack. Earth Science & General Science - Sr. H.S. (Teachers License Examination Ser.: T-14). (Cloth bdg. avail. on request). pap. 13.95 (ISBN 0-8373-8014-6). Natl Learning.

--Geologist. (Career Examination Ser.: C-301). (Cloth bdg. avail. on request). pap. 12.00 (ISBN 0-8373-0301-X). Natl Learning.

--Geology. (College Level Examination Ser.: CLEP-15). (Cloth bdg. avail. on request). pap. 9.95 (ISBN 0-8373-5207-X). Natl Learning.

--Geology. (College Proficiency Examination Ser.: CPEP-13). (Cloth bdg. avail. on request). pap. 9.95 (ISBN 0-8373-5413-7). Natl Learning.

--Geology. (Graduate Record Examination Ser.: GRE-8). (Cloth bdg. avail. on request). pap. 13.95 (ISBN 0-8373-5208-8). Natl Learning.

--Junior Geologist. (Career Examination Ser.: C-414). (Cloth bdg. avail. on request). pap. 12.00 (ISBN 0-8373-0414-8). Natl Learning.

--Senior Geologist. (Career Examination Ser.: C-1006). (Cloth bdg. avail. on request). pap. 12.00 (ISBN 0-8373-1006-7). Natl Learning.

GEOLOGY–FIELD WORK

Ahmed, F. & Almond, D. C. Field Mapping for Geology Students. (Illus.). 88p. 1983. pap. 6.95x (ISBN 0-04-550031-2). Allen Unwin.

Bonney, Orrin H. & Bonney, Lorraine. Field Book. Incl. The Teton Range & the Gros Ventre Range: Climbing Routes & Back Country. rev., 2nd ed. LC 76-189201. 263p. pap. 7.95 (ISBN 0-8040-0578-8, 82-73096); Yellowstone Park: Absaroka Range. rev. 2nd ed. LC 70-189202. 162p. pap. 7.95 (ISBN 0-8040-0579-6, 82-73104); Big Horn Range. LC 72-132589. 172p. pap. 7.95 (ISBN 0-8040-0536-2, 82-72726). (Illus.). 1977. (SB). Ohio U Pr.

Compton, R. R. Manual of Field Geology. LC 61-17357. 378p. 1962. 28.95 (ISBN 0-471-16698-7). Wiley.

Feldmann, Rodney M. & Heimlich, Richard A. Geology Field Guide: The Black Hills. 208p. (Orig.). 1980. pap. 10.95 (ISBN 0-8403-2193-7). Kendall-Hunt.

Feldmann, Rodney M., et al. Field Guide: Southern Great Lakes. LC 77-75770. (Geology Field Guide Ser). (Illus.). 1977. pap. text ed. 9.95 (ISBN 0-8403-1730-1). Kendall-Hunt.

Kiersch, George A., et al, eds. Engineering Geology Case Histories, Nos. 6-10 In One Volume. LC 74-77141. (Illus.). 1974. 12.50 (ISBN 0-8137-4202-1). Geol Soc.

Koefoed, O. The Application of the Kernel Function in Interpreting Geoelectrical Resistivity Measurements. (Geoexploration Monographs: No. 2). (Illus.). 111p. 1968. text ed. 17.60x (ISBN 3-4431-3002-X). Lubrecht & Cramer.

Lahee, Frederick H. Field Geology. 6th ed. 1961. text ed. 56.95 (ISBN 0-07-035808-7). McGraw.

Lozo, Frank E., ed. Woodbine & Adjacent Strata of the Waco Area of Central Texas: A Symposium. LC 52-10665. (Fondreu Science Ser.: No. 4). (Illus.). 1951. 17.95 (ISBN 0-87074-091-1); pap. 14.95 (ISBN 0-87074-092-X). SMU Press.

Moseley, Frank. Methods in Field Geology. (Illus.). 211p. 1981. text ed. 32.95x (ISBN 0-7167-1293-8); pap. text ed. 17.95x (ISBN 0-7167-1294-6). W H Freeman.

Smith, Robert D., II & Hoff, Donald T. Geology & Mineralogy of Copper-Uranium Occurrences in the Picture Rocks & Sonestown Quadrangles, Lycoming & Sullivan Counties Pennsylvania. (Mineral Resource Report: No. 80). (Illus.). 271p. 1984. pap. 18.35 (ISBN 0-8182-0023-5). Commonweal PA.

Socolow, Arthur A. Geologic Interpretation of Aeromagnetic Maps of Southeastern Pennsylvania. (Information Circular Ser.: No. 77). (Illus.). 85p. 1984. pap. 3.25 (ISBN 0-8182-0050-2). Commonweal PA.

Suchman, J. Richard. Idea Book for Geological Inquiry. 96p. 1981. pap. 10.00 wkbk. (ISBN 0-89824-024-7). Trillium Pr.

Weiss, L. E. The Minor Structures of Deformed Rocks: A Photographic Atlas. LC 72-79582. (Illus.). 440p. 1972. 41.00 (ISBN 0-387-05828-1). Springer-Verlag.

World Petroleum Congress. Proceedings of Eighth World Petroleum Congress: Geological & Exploration, Vol. 2. 362p. 1971. 89.00 (ISBN 0-85334-517-1, Pub. by Elsevier Applied Sci England). Elsevier.

GEOLOGY–GRAPHIC METHODS

Geoscience Information Society. Proceedings of the Ninth Annual Meeting of the Geoscience Information Society, November 18, 1974, Miami Beach, Florida. LC 73-16672. pap. 24.80 (ISBN 0-317-30046-6, 2025048). Bks Demand UMI.

McCammon, R. B., ed. Concepts in Geostatistics. LC 74-23669. (Illus.). xvi, 184p. 1975. pap. 20.00 (ISBN 0-387-06892-9). Springer-Verlag.

Merriam, D. F., ed. Management, Analysis & Display of Geoscience Data: Proceedings of the First Annual Conference, Golden, CO, January 27-29, 1982. 60p. 1983. pap. 52.00 (ISBN 0-08-030248-3). Pergamon.

GEOLOGY–HISTORY

Albritton, Claude C., ed. History of Geology Series, 37 vols. (Illus.). 1978. lib. bdg. 1286.50x (ISBN 0-405-10429-4). Ayer Co Pubs.

Contributions to Geology, 1928. (Bulletin Ser.: Bull 2801). 202p. 1928. 1.00 (ISBN 0-318-03302-X). Bur Econ Geology.

Contributions to Geology, 1929. (Bull 2901). 226p. 1929. 1.00 (ISBN 0-318-03303-8). Bur Econ Geology.

Contributions to Geology, 1930. (Bulletin Ser: Bull 3001). 207p. 1930. 1.00 (ISBN 0-318-03304-6). Bur Econ Geology.

Contributions to Geology, 1932. (Bulletin Ser.: Bull 3201). (Illus.). 216p. 1932. 1.00 (ISBN 0-318-03306-2). Bur Econ Geology.

Drake, Ellen, ed. History of Geology. (DNAG Special Volumes Ser.: Vol. 1). (Illus.). 1985. write for info. Geol Soc.

Dudich, E. Contributions to the History of Geological Mapping: Proceedings. 441p. 1984. text ed. 40.00 (ISBN 0-9910001-6-1, Pub. by Aluminium W Germany). Heyden.

Faul, Henry & Faul, Carol. It Began with a Stone: A History of Geology from the Stone Age to the Age of Plate Tectonics. LC 83-3683. 1983. 230p. 38.95x (ISBN 0-471-89735-3, Pub. by Wiley-Interscience); pap. 19.95x 264p. (ISBN 0-471-89605-5). Wiley.

Fenton, Carroll L. & Fenton, Mildred. Story of the Great Geologists. facs. ed. LC 73-84306. (Essay Index Reprint Ser.). 1945. 22.00 (ISBN 0-8369-1130-X). Ayer Co Pubs.

Ferguson, W. K. History of the Bureau of Economic Geology, 1909-1960. (Illus.). 329p. 1981. 11.00 (ISBN 0-318-03330-5); pap. 6.00 (ISBN 0-318-03331-3). Bur Econ Geology.

Greene, Mott T. Geology in the Nineteenth Century: Changing Views of a Changing World. LC 82-7456. (Illus.). 320p. 1982. 34.50x (ISBN 0-8014-1467-9). Cornell U Pr.

--Geology in the Nineteenth Century: Changing Views of a Changing World. LC 82-7456. (Illus.). 328p. (Orig.). 1985. 34.50x (ISBN 0-8014-1467-9); pap. text ed. 12.95x (ISBN 0-8014-9295-5). Cornell U Pr.

Hagood, Allen. Dinosaur: The Story Behind the Scenery. LC 75-157460. (Illus.). 1972. 8.95 (ISBN 0-916122-35-2); pap. 3.75 (ISBN 0-916122-10-7). KC Pubns.

Harrington, John W. Dance of the Continents: Adventures with Rocks & Time. LC 82-16979. (Illus.). 256p. 1983. 15.00 (ISBN 0-87477-168-4); pap. 9.95 (ISBN 0-87477-247-8). J P Tarcher.

Jameson, Robert. The Wernerian Theory of the Neptunian Origin of Rocks: A Facsimile Reprint of Elements of Geognosy, 1808. White, George W., ed. LC 75-43364. (Contributions to the History of Geology Ser.). (Illus.). 1976. Repr. of 1808 ed. 31.95x (ISBN 0-02-847160-1). Hafner.

Leveson, David J. Geology & the Urban Environment. (Illus.). 1980. text ed. 21.95x (ISBN 0-19-502578-4). Oxford U Pr.

Mintz, Leigh W. Historical Geology: The Science of a Dynamic Earth. 3rd ed. (Illus.). 576p. 1981. text ed. 26.95 (ISBN 0-675-08028-2). Additional supplements may be obtained from publisher. Merrill.

Schneer, Cecil J., ed. Two Hundred Years of Geology in America: Proceedings of the New Hampshire Bicentennial Conference. LC 78-63149. (Illus.). 401p. 1979. 35.00x (ISBN 0-87451-160-7). U Pr of New Eng.

--Geology & Palaeontology of Southeast Asia, Vol. 5. 320p. 1968. 37.50x (ISBN 0-86008-013-7, Pub. by U of Tokyo Japan). Columbia U Pr.

--Geology & Palaeontology of Southeast Asia, Vol. 6. 420p. 1969. 46.00 (ISBN 0-86008-014-5, Pub. by U of Tokyo Japan). Columbia U Pr.

--Geology & Palaeontology of Southeast Asia, Vol. 7. 240p. 1970. 37.50x (ISBN 0-86008-015-3, Pub. by U of Tokyo Japan). Columbia U Pr.

--Geology & Palaeontology of Southeast Asia, Vol. 8. 360p. 1971. 49.50x (ISBN 0-86008-016-1, Pub. by U of Tokyo Japan). Columbia U Pr.

--Geology & Palaeontology of Southeast Asia, Vol. 9. 260p. 1971. 34.50 (ISBN 0-86008-017-X, Pub. by U of Tokyo Japan). Columbia U Pr.

--Geology & Palaeontology of Southeast Asia, Vol. 11. 200p. 1973. 37.50x (ISBN 0-86008-019-6, Pub. by U of Tokyo Japan). Columbia U Pr.

--Geology & Palaeontology of Southeast Asia, Vol. 12. 300p. 1973. 39.50x (ISBN 0-86008-020-X, Pub. by U of Tokyo Japan). Columbia U Pr.

--Geology & Palaeontology of Southeast Asia, Vol. 13. 230p. 1974. 39.50x (ISBN 0-86008-099-4, Pub. by U of Tokyo Japan). Columbia U Pr.

--Geology & Palaeontology of Southeast Asia, Vol. 15. 480p. 1975. 45.00x (ISBN 0-86008-137-0, Pub. by U of Tokyo Japan). Columbia U Pr.

--Geology & Palaeontology of Southeast Asia, Vol. 16. 1976. 37.50x (ISBN 0-86008-154-0, Pub. by U of Tokyo Japan). Columbia U Pr.

--Geology & Palaeontology of Southeast Asia, Vol. 17. 240p. 1976. 42.50x (ISBN 0-86008-175-3, Pub. by U of Tokyo Japan). Columbia U Pr.

--Geology & Palaeontology of Southeast Asia, Vol. 18. 220p. 1977. 42.50x (ISBN 0-86008-177-X, Pub. by U of Tokyo Japan). Columbia U Pr.

--Geology & Palaeontology of Southeast Asia, Vol. 19. 260p. 1978. 52.50x (ISBN 0-86008-202-4, Pub. by U of Tokyo Japan). Columbia U Pr.

--Geology & Palaeontology of Southeast Asia, Vol. 20. 270p. 1979. 59.50x (ISBN 0-86008-244-X, Pub. by U of Tokyo Japan). Columbia U Pr.

--Geology & Palaeontology of Southeast Asia, Vol. 21. 1980. 59.50x (ISBN 0-86008-263-6, Pub. by U of Tokyo Japan). Columbia U Pr.

--Geology & Paleontology of Southeast Asia, Vol. 10. 400p. 1972. 44.00x (ISBN 0-86008-018-8, Pub. by U of Tokyo Japan). Columbia U Pr.

--Geology & Paleontology of Southeast Asia, Vol. 14. 230p. 1975. 42.50x (ISBN 0-86008-125-7, Pub. by U of Tokyo Japan). Columbia U Pr.

Movius, Hallam L. Early Man & Pleistocene Stratigraphy in Southern & Eastern Asia. (HU PMP Ser.). (Illus.). 1944. 21.00 (ISBN 0-527-01249-1). Kraus Repr.

Philippson, Alfred. Kleinasien. Repr. of 1915 ed. 30.00 (ISBN 0-384-46300-2). Johnson Repr.

Sengor, A. M., ed. The Cimmeride Orogenic System & the Tectonics of Eurasia. (Special Paper Ser.: No. 195). (Illus.). 1984. 17.00 (ISBN 0-8137-2195-4). Geol Soc.

Wolfart, R. & Wittekind, H. Geologie von Afghanistan. (Beitraege z. Regionalen Geologie der Erde Ser.: Vol. 14). Tr. of Ger. (Illus.). 500p. 1980. lib. bdg. 97.30x (ISBN 3-443-11014-2). Lubrecht & Cramer.

GEOLOGY–AUSTRALIA

Brown, D. S. W., et al. The Geological Evolution of Australia & New Zealand. 1968. pap. 17.00 (ISBN 0-08-012277-9). Pergamon.

Lands of the Alligator Rivers Area: Northern Territory. (Land Research Ser.: No. 38). (Illus.). 173p. 1976. pap. 13.50 (ISBN 0-643-00208-1, C019, CSIRO). Unipub.

Veevers, J. J. Phanerozoic Earth History of Australia. (Oxford Geological Sciences Ser.). (Illus.). 1984. 75.00x (ISBN 0-19-854459-6). Oxford U Pr.

GEOLOGY–BURMA

Bender, Friedrich. Geology of Burma. (Beitraege zur Regionalen Geologie der Erde: Vol. 16). (Illus.). 293p. 1983. lib. bdg. 74.50x (ISBN 3-443-11016-9). Lubrecht & Cramer.

Chhibber, Harbans L. The Geology of Burma. LC 77-87011. Repr. of 1934 ed. 38.50 (ISBN 0-404-16803-5). AMS Pr.

GEOLOGY–CALIFORNIA

Cady, John W. Magnetic & Gravity Anomalies in the Great Valley & Western Sierra Nevada Metamorphic Belt, California. LC 75-19540. (Geological Society of America Special Paper Ser.: No. 168). pap. 20.00 (ISBN 0-317-30055-5, 2025031). Bks Demand UMI.

Howard, Arthur D. Geological History of Middle California. LC 78-57299. (California Natural History Guide: No. 43). (Illus.). 1979. 14.95x (ISBN 0-520-03707-3); pap. 3.95 (ISBN 0-520-03874-6). U of Cal Pr.

Johnson, A. M. Styles of Folding: Mechanics & Mechanisms of Folding of Natural Elastic Materials. (Developments in Geotectonics: Vol. 11). 406p. 1977. 76.75 (ISBN 0-444-41496-7). Elsevier.

Merrill, George P. The Geology & Natural History of Lower California. (Shorey Historical Ser.). (Illus.). 40p. 1975. pap. 2.95 (ISBN 0-8466-0158-3). Shorey.

Norris, R. M. & Webb, R. W. Geology of California. 379p. 1976. 34.50 (ISBN 0-471-61566-8). Wiley.

Oakeshott, Gordon B. California's Changing Landscapes. 2nd ed. (Illus.). 1978. pap. text ed. 37.95 (ISBN 0-07-047584-9). McGraw.

GEOLOGY–CANADA

Borns, Harold W., Jr., et al, eds. Late Pleistocene History of NE New England & Adjacent Quebec. (Special Paper Ser.: No. 197). (Illus.). 160p. 1985. 22.50 (ISBN 0-8137-2197-0). Geol Soc.

Cady, Wallace M. Regioanl Tectonic Synthesis of Northwestern New England & Adjacent Quebec. LC 77-98020. (Geological Society of America Ser.: No. 120). pap. 62.00 (ISBN 0-317-28385-5, 2025466). Bks Demand UMI.

The Estimation of Seismic Risk in Canada: A Review. pap. 4.65 (SSC37, SSC). Unipub.

Geology & Economic Minerals of Canada, 3 pts. (Illus.). 1978. pap. 44.50 set (ISBN 0-660-00553-0, SSC96, SSC). Unipub.

Geology & Minerals of Canada, Sec. 2. (Maps & Charts). pap. 14.80 (SSC46, SSC). Unipub.

Geology of Iron Deposits in Canada: Iron Ranges of the Labrador Geosyncline, Vol. 3. pap. 14.80 (SSC44, SSC). Unipub.

Hind, Henry Y. Narrative of the Canadian Red River Exploring Expedition of 1857, & of the Assiniboine & Saskatchewan Exploring Expedition of 1858, 2 Vols. LC 68-55195. (Illus.). 1968. Repr. of 1860 ed. Set. lib. bdg. 35.00x (ISBN 0-8371-3896-5, HIRR). Greenwood.

Teichert, Curt. Tillite Occurence on the Canadian Shield, Vol. 1. LC 76-21824. (Thule Expedition, 5th, 1921-1924: No. 6). Repr. of 1937 ed. 20.00 (ISBN 0-404-58306-7). AMS Pr.

Tesmer, Irving H., ed. Colossal Cataract: The Geological History of Niagara Falls. LC 80-26858. (Illus.). 210p. 1981. 39.50x (ISBN 0-87395-522-6); pap. 13.95x (ISBN 0-87395-523-4). State U NY Pr.

GEOLOGY–CARIBBEAN AREA

Bonini, William E., et al, eds. The Caribbean-South American Plate Boundary & Regional Tectonics. (Memoir Ser.: No. 162). (Illus.). 1984. 47.50. Geol Soc.

Khudoley, K. M. & Meyerhoff, A. A. Paleogeography & Geological History of Greater Antilles. LC 77-129999. (Geological Society of America Memoir Ser.: No. 129). pap. 53.80 (ISBN 0-317-29130-0, 2025024). Bks Demand UMI.

Kinghor, Marion. Bibliography of Jamaican Geology. (Bibliography Ser.). 150p. 1980. 6.90x (ISBN 0-686-27379-6, Pub. by GEO Abstracts England). State Mutual Bk.

Land, Lynton S. & Mackenzie, Fred T. Field Guide to Bermuda Geology. (Bermuda Biological Station Special Pubn.: No. 4). (Illus.). 35p. 1970. pap. 4.00 (ISBN 0-917642-04-X). Bermuda Bio.

Liddell, W. D. & Ohlhorst, S. L. Modern & Ancient Carbonate Enivronments of Jamaica. Ginsburg, Robert N., ed. (Sedimenta Series-Sedimenta X). (Illus.). 100p. (Orig.). 1984. pap. 12.00 (ISBN 0-932981-09-7). Univ Miami CSL.

Mattson, Peter H., ed. West Indies Island Arcs. (Benchmark Papers in Geology Ser.: Vol. 33). 1977. 68.00 (ISBN 0-12-787060-1). Acad Pr.

Moore, Hilary B. Ecological Guide to Bermuda Inshore Water. (Bermuda Biological Station Special Pubn.: No. 5). (Illus.). ii, 42p. pap. 4.00 (ISBN 0-917642-05-8). Bermuda Bio.

Woodring, Wendell. Geology of the Republic of Haiti. lib. bdg. 69.95 (ISBN 0-8490-1882-X). Gordon Pr.

GEOLOGY–CHINA

En-Zhi, Mu, et al. Correlation of the Chinese Silurian. Berry, W. B., ed. (Special Paper Ser.: No. 202). (Illus.). 1985. write for info. (ISBN 0-8137-2202-0). Geol Soc.

Milliman, J. D. & Qingming, J., eds. Sediment Dynamics on the Changjiang Estuary & the Adjacent East China Sea: A Selection of Edited Papers from the International Symposium Held in Hangzhou, People's Republic of China, April 1983. 236p. 1985. pap. 40.00 (ISBN 0-08-030257-2, Pub. by Aberdeen Scotland). Pergamon.

Sonegiao, Zhao, ed. Physical Geography of China. 1984. text ed. 29.95 (ISBN 0-471-09597-4). Wiley.

GEOLOGY–EGYPT

Butzer, Karl W. & Hansen, Carl L. Desert & River in Nubia: Geomorphology & Prehistoric Environments at the Aswan Reservoir. LC 67-20761. (Illus.). 1968. 45.00x (ISBN 0-299-04770-9); Set Of 15 Maps. 20.00x (ISBN 0-685-20706-4). U of Wis Pr.

Said, R. The Geological Evolution of the River Nile. (Illus.). 176p. 1981. 69.00 (ISBN 0-387-90484-0). Springer-Verlag.

Sandford, Kenneth S. & Arkell, W. J. Paleolithic Man & the Nile-Faiyum Divide, Vol. 1. LC 30-8240. (Illus.). 1930. 20.00X (ISBN 0-226-62104-9, OIP10). U of Chicago Pr.

GEOLOGY–EUROPE

Ager, Derek V. The Geology of Europe. LC 80-40318. 535p. 1980. 53.95x (ISBN 0-470-26990-1). Halsted Pr.

Anderson, J. G. The Structure of Western Europe. 1978. pap. text ed. 14.00 (ISBN 0-08-022046-0). Pergamon.

Bailey, E. B. Tectonic Essays, Mainly Alpine. 1935. 39.50x (ISBN 0-19-854368-9). Oxford U Pr.

Burchfiel, B. C. Geology of Romania. LC 75-32832. (Geological Society of America Ser.: No. 158). pap. 28.00 (ISBN 0-317-28366-9, 2025469). Bks Demand UMI.

Freytet, P. & Plaziat, J. Continental Carbonate Sedimentation & Pedogenesis: Late Cretaceous & Early Tertiary of Southern France. (Contributions to Sedimentology Ser.: No. 12). (Illus.). 213p. 1982. pap. text ed. 49.60x (ISBN 3-510-57012-X). Lubrecht & Cramer.

Godwin, Harry. Fenland: Its Ancient Past & Uncertain Future. LC 77-8824. (Illus.). 1978. 37.50 (ISBN 0-521-21768-7). Cambridge U Pr.

International Geological Map of Europe & the Mediterranean Region. (Illus.). 67p. (Co-published by UNESCO with the Bundesanstalt, Hanover). 1971. pap. 34.75 (ISBN 0-686-93984-0, M4, UNESCO). Unipub.

International Hydrogeological Map of Europe: Explanatory Notes. Incl. Berlin. 1979; Berne; London. 1979. pap. 31.50 (M109); Paris. pap. 31.50 (M70); Sheet E3. International Hydrogeological Map of Europe-Moskova. 1979. (Co-published by UNESCO, Bundesanstalt, Hanover, UNESCO). Unipub.

John, David, et al. Geology & Landscape in Britain & Western Europe. (Illus.). 1983. 19.95x (ISBN 0-19-217686-2). Oxford U Pr.

Meeting of European Geological Societies. Europe from Crust to Core. Ager, D. V. & Brooks, M., eds. LC 76-40096. (A Wiley-Interscience Publication). pap. 52.50 (ISBN 0-317-26153-3, 2025193). Bks Demand UMI.

Moore, Peter. European Mires. 1984. 75.00 (ISBN 0-12-505580-3). Acad Pr.

Naylor, D. & Mounteney, N. Geology of the North West European Continental Shelf: The West British Shelf, Vol. 1. 162p. 1975. 20.00x (ISBN 0-86010-009-X, Pub. by Graham & Trotman England). State Mutual Bk.

Pomerol, Charles, et al. Geology of France. (Illus.). 256p. 1980. 30.00x (ISBN 2-225-67001-3). Masson Pub.

Schneider, H. J., ed. Mineral Deposits of the Alps & of the Alpine Epoch in Europe. (Special Publicaton of the Society for Geology Applied to Mineral Deposits: No. 3). (Illus.). 410p. 1983. 45.00 (ISBN 0-387-12231-1). Springer-Verlag.

Scrope, George P. The Geology & Extinct Volcanos of the Central France. 2nd rev. ed. Albritton, Claude C., Jr., ed. LC 77-6540. (History of Geology Ser.). (Illus.). 1978. Repr. of 1858 ed. lib. bdg. 27.00 (ISBN 0-405-10459-6). Ayer Co Pubs.

Sengor, A. M., ed. The Cimmeride Orogenic System & the Tectonics of Eurasia. (Special Paper Ser.: No. 195). (Illus.). 1984. 17.00 (ISBN 0-8137-2195-4). Geol Soc.

Trumpy, Rudolf, et al. Geology of Switzerland: A Guide Book, Pt. A. (Illus.). 104p. 1980. pap. 19.00 (ISBN 3-8597-7062-4, Pub. by Wepf & Co). Interbk Inc.

--Geology of Switzerland: A Guide Book, Pt. B. (Illus.). 232p. 1980. pap. 40.00 (ISBN 3-8597-7063-2, Pub. by Wepf & Co). Interbk Inc.

West, R. G. The Pre-Glacial Pleistocene of the Norfolk & Suffolk Coasts. LC 77-90191. (Illus.). 1980. 125.00 (ISBN 0-521-21962-0). Cambridge U Pr.

GEOLOGY–GREAT BRITAIN

Anderson, J. G. & Owen, T. R. The Structure of the British Isles. 2nd ed. LC 80-41075. (Illus.). 242p. 1980. 35.00 (ISBN 0-08-023998-6); pap. 14.50 (ISBN 0-08-023997-8). Pergamon.

Bate, R. H. & Robinson, E., eds. A Stratigraphical Index of British Ostracoda: Geological Journal Special Issue, Vol. 8. (Liverpool Geological Society & the Manchester Geological Association Ser.). 552p. 1978. 159.95x (ISBN 0-471-27755-X, Pub. by Wiley-Interscience). Wiley.

Bowes, D. R. & Leake, B. E., eds. Crustal Evolution in Northwestern Britain & Adjacent Regions: Geological Journal Special Issue, No. 10. (Liverpool Geological Society & the Manchester Geological Association Ser). 508p. 1978. 143.95x (ISBN 0-471-27757-6, Pub. by Wiley-Interscience). Wiley.

Campbell, John B. The Upper Palaeolithic of Britain: A Study of Man & Nature in the Late Ice Age, Vols. I & II. (Illus.). 1978. 84.00 set (ISBN 0-19-813188-7). Oxford U Pr.

Conybeare, W. D. & Phillips, William. Outlines of the Geology of England & Wales: General Principles of That Science, & Comparative Views of the Structure of Foreign Countries. Albritton, Claude C., Jr., ed. LC 77-6516. (History of Geology Ser.). 1978. Repr. of 1822 ed. lib. bdg. 37.50x (ISBN 0-405-10438-3). Ayer Co Pubs.

Craig, C. Y., ed. Geology of Scotland. 2nd ed. 400p. 1983. 54.95x (ISBN 0-470-27260-0). Halsted Pr.

Dreghorn, William. Geology Explained in the Severn Vale & Cotswolds. (Illus.). 192p. 1974. 14.95 (ISBN 0-7153-4102-2). David & Charles.

Ford, Trevor D. Limestone & Caves of the Peak District. 469p. 1980. pap. 26.45x (ISBN 0-86094-004-7, Pub. by GEO Abstracts England). State Mutual Bk.

Hancock, P., ed. The Variscan Fold Belt in the British Isles. 1983. 68.00 (ISBN 0-9960024-4-8, Pub. by A Hilger England). Heyden.

Harris, A. L., ed. Nature & Timing of Orogenic Activity in the Caledonian & Hercynian Rocks of the British Isles. (Illus.). 64p. 1984. pap. text ed. 25.00x (ISBN 0-632-01298-6). Blackwell Pubns.

John, David, et al. Geology & Landscape in Britain & Western Europe. (Illus.). 1983. 19.95x (ISBN 0-19-217686-2). Oxford U Pr.

Middlemiss, Frank A. British Stratigraphy. 2nd ed. (Intoducing Geology Ser.: No. 2). (Illus.). 48p. 1985. pap. text ed. 4.95x (ISBN 0-04-550023-1). Allen Unwin.

Miller, Hugh. The Old Red Sandstone, or New Walks in an Old Field. Albritton, Claude C., Jr., ed. LC 77-6531. (History of Geology Ser.). (Illus.). 1978. Repr. of 1851 ed. lib. bdg. 34.50x (ISBN 0-405-10451-0). Ayer Co Pubs.

Naylor, D. Geology of Offshore Ireland & West Britain. Shann, P, ed. 250p. 1982. 90.00x (ISBN 0-86010-247-5, Pub. by Graham & Trotman England). State Mutual Bk.

Naylor, D. & Shannon, P. Geology of Offshore Ireland & West Britain. 250p. 1983. 42.00x (ISBN 0-8448-1425-3). Crane-Russak Co.

Naylor, D. & Shannon, P. M. Geology of Offshore Ireland & West Britain. 174p. 1982. 100.00x (ISBN 0-86010-340-4, Pub. by Order Dept Graham Trotman England). State Mutual Bk.

Owen, T. R. The Geological Evolution of the British Isles. 1976. pap. text ed. 34.00 (ISBN 0-08-020461-9); pap. text ed. 11.95 (ISBN 0-08-020460-0). Pergamon.

--Geology Explained in South Wales. (Geology Explained Ser.). (Illus.). 192p. 1973. 14.95 (ISBN 0-7153-5860-X). David & Charles.

Parkins, John W. Geology Explained in Dorset. LC 76-54070. (Geology Explained Ser.). (Illus.). 1977. 8.95 (ISBN 0-7153-7319-6). David & Charles.

Perkins, John. Geology Explained: Dartmoor & the Tamar Valley. (Geology Explained Ser). 1972. 10.50 (ISBN 0-7153-5516-3). David & Charles.

Porter, Roy. The Making of Geology: Earth Science in Britain, 1660-1815. LC 76-56220. pap. 75.00 (ISBN 0-317-27575-5, 2024515). Bks Demand UMI.

Prosser, Robert. Geology Explained in the Lake District. (Geology Explained Ser.). 1977. 14.95 (ISBN 0-7153-7397-8). David & Charles.

Roberts, B. The Geology of Snowdonia & Llyn: An Outline & Field Guide. (Illus.). 1979. pap. 43.50 (ISBN 0-686-25752-9, Pub. by A Hilger England). Heyden.

Smith, A. J. The Geology of the Seas Around the British Isles. 1986. 30.00 (ISBN 0-08-022062-2); flexi-cover 16.80 (ISBN 0-08-022061-4). Pergamon.

Sparks, B. W. & West, R. G. The Ice Age in Britain. (Methuen Library Reprint Ser.). (Illus.). 320p. 1981. 49.95x (ISBN 0-416-32160-7, 3583). Methuen Inc.

Thomas, A. T., et al. Trilobites in British Stratigraphy. (Illus.). 80p. 1984. pap. text ed. 17.00x (ISBN 0-632-01201-3). Blackwell Pubns.

GEOLOGY–HAWAII

Hinds, N. E. Geology of Kauai & Niihau. (BMB). Repr. of 1930 ed. 30.00 (ISBN 0-527-02177-6). Kraus Repr.

Macdonald, Gordon & Macdonald, Kyselka. Anatomy of an Island: A Geological History of Oahu. LC 66-30400. (Special Publication Ser.: No. 55). (Illus.). 37p. 1967. pap. 3.25 (ISBN 0-910240-14-0). Bishop Mus.

Stark, J. T. & Howland, A. L. Geology of Borabora Society Islands. (BMB). 1941. pap. 10.00 (ISBN 0-527-02277-2). Kraus Repr.

Williams, H. Geology of Tahiti, Moorea, & Maiao. (BMB). Repr. of 1933 ed. 14.00 (ISBN 0-527-02211-X). Kraus Repr.

GEOLOGY–SCANDINAVIA

Gee, D. G. & Sturt, B. A. The Caledonide Orogen: Scandinavia & Related Areas. 110p. 1984. 186.95 (ISBN 0-471-10504-X). Wiley.

In Situ Heating Experiments in Geological Formations, Ludvika, Sweden, September, 1978. 1979. 16.50x (ISBN 92-64-01872-7). OECD.

Rasmussen, A., et al. Geological Survey of Norway, No. 369, Bulletin 63. 96p. 1982. pap. 20.00x (ISBN 82-00-31438-3). Universitet.

Rutherford, G. K. The Physical Environment of the Faeroe Islands. 1982. 39.50 (ISBN 90-6193-099-5, Pub. by Junk Pubs Netherlands). Kluwer Academic.

Strand, Trygve & Kulling, O. Scandinavian Caledonides. LC 77-78474. (Regional Geology Ser.). pap. 80.80 (ISBN 0-317-29870-4, 2016158). Bks Demand UMI.

GEOLOGY–SOUTH AMERICA

Bonini, William E., et al, eds. The Caribbean-South American Plate Boundary & Regional Tectonics. (Memoir Ser.: No. 162). (Illus.). 1984. 47.50. Geol Soc.

Geology & Metallogenesis of Uranium Deposits of South America: Proceedings of a Working Group Meeting, San Luis, Argentina, Sept. 21-23, 1981. 275p. (Orig.). 1984. pap. 44.00 (ISBN 92-0-041084-7, ISP641, IAEA). Unipub.

GEOLOGY–SOVIET UNION

Klein, Richard G. Ice-Age Hunters of the Ukraine. LC 73-77443. (Prehistoric Archaeology & Ecology Ser). 1973. 12.50x (ISBN 0-226-43945-3); pap. text ed. 4.50x (ISBN 0-226-43946-1). U of Chicago Pr.

Velichko, A. A., et al, eds. Late Quaternary Environments of the Soviet Union. LC 83-25892. (Illus.). 320p. 1984. 45.00x (ISBN 0-8166-1250-1). U of Minn Pr.

GEOLOGY–UNITED STATES

Here are entered works on the geology of the United States as a whole, together with works on individual states or specific areas.

Allison, Ira S. Geology of Pluvial Lake Chewaucan, Lake County, Oregon. LC 81-22415. (Studies in Geology: No. 11). (Illus.). 80p. 1982. pap. 7.95x (ISBN 0-87071-069-9). Oreg St U Pr.

Alt, David & Hyndman, Donald. Roadside Geology of Oregon. LC 77-2581. (Roadside Geology Ser.). (Illus.). 268p. 1978. pap. 9.95 (ISBN 0-87842-063-0). Mountain Pr.

American Geological Institute. Directory of the Geologic Division, U.S. Geological Survey. (Illus.). 144p. 1980. pap. 10.00 (ISBN 0-913312-45-2). Am Geol.

Archibald, David J. A Study of Mammalia & Geology Across the Cretaceous-Tertiary Boundary in Garfield County, Montana. (Publications in Geological Sciences: Vol. 122). 1982. pap. 36.00x (ISBN 0-520-09639-8). U of Cal Pr.

Association of American Geologists & Naturalists at Philadelphia, 1840 & 1841. Proceedings. Albritton, Claude C., ed. LC 77-6507. (History of Geology Ser.). Repr. of 1843 ed. lib. bdg. 46.50x (ISBN 0-405-10430-8). Ayer Co Pubs.

Baker, Frank C. Life of the Pleistocene or Glacial Period. LC 74-80996. (BCL Ser. I). 1969. Repr. of 1920 ed. 37.50 (ISBN 0-404-00449-0). AMS Pr.

Baldwin, Ewart M. Geology of Oregon. 3rd ed. LC 76-4346. (Illus.). 1981. perfect bdg. 12.95 (ISBN 0-8403-2321-2). Kendall-Hunt.

Barnes, F. A. Canyon Country Geology for the Layman & Rockhound. new ed. LC 77-95050. (Illus.). 1978. pap. 4.50 (ISBN 0-915272-17-2). Wasatch Pubs.

Barnes, V. E. Geologic Atlas of Texas: Amarillo Sheet, Leroy Thompson Patton Memorial Edition. 1969. Repr. 4.00 (ISBN 0-686-36619-0). Bur Econ Geology.

--Geologic Atlas of Texas: Austin Sheet, Francis Luther Whitney Memorial Edition. rev ed. 1981. 4.00 (ISBN 0-686-36621-2). Bur Econ Geology.

Barnes, V. E. & Bell, W. C. The Moore Hollow Group of Central Texas. (Report of Investigations Ser.: RI 88). (Illus.). 169p. 1977. 5.00 (ISBN 0-318-03228-7). Bur Econ Geology.

Barnes, V. E. & Schofield, D. A. Potential Low-Grade Iron Ore & Hydraulic-Fracturing Sand in Cambrian Sandstones, Northwestern Llano Region, Texas. (Report of Investigations Ser.: RI 53). (Illus.). 58p. 1964. 2.00 (ISBN 0-686-29335-5). Bur Econ Geology.

Barnes, V. E., et al. Geology of the Llano Region & Austin Area. rev. ed. (Guidebook Ser.: GB 13). 154p. 1983. Repr. of 1972 ed. 2.50 (ISBN 0-686-29321-5). Bur Econ Geology.

Bassett, Allen M. & O'Dunn, Shannon. General Geology of the Western United States: A Laboratory Manual. rev. ed. (Illus.). 176p. 1980. pap. text ed. 13.95x (ISBN 0-917962-67-2). Peek Pubns.

Baumgardner, Robert W., et al. Formation of the Wink Sink, a Salt Dissolution & Collapse Feature, Winkler County, Texas. (Report of Investigations Ser.: RI 114). (Illus.). 50p. 1982. 1.50 (ISBN 0-686-37544-0). Bur Econ Geology.

Bebout, D. G. & Loucks, R. G., eds. Cretaceous Carbonates of Texas & Mexico: Applications to Subsurface Exploration. (Report of Investigations Ser.: No. 89). 322p. 1977. Repr. 8.50 (ISBN 0-686-36611-5). Bur Econ Geology.

Bebout, D. G., et al. Depositional & Diagenetic History of the Sligo & Hosston Formations (Lower Cretaceous) in South Texas. (Report of Investigations Ser.: No. 109). (Illus.). 69p. 1981. 4.00 (ISBN 0-686-36993-9). Bur Econ Geology.

Bernard, H. A. & LeBlanc, R. J., Sr. Recent Sediments of Southeast Texas - a Field Guide to the Brazos Alluvial & Deltaic Plains & the Galveston Barrier Island Complex: Resume of the Quaternary Geology of the Northwestern Gulf of Mexico Province. (Guidebook Ser.: GB 11). 132p. 1970. Repr. 7.00 (ISBN 0-686-29319-3). Bur Econ Geology.

Bezy, John V. A Guide to the Desert Geology of the Lake Mead National Recreation Area. new ed. Jackson, Earl, ed. LC 78-56673. (Popular Ser.: No. 24). (Illus., Orig.). 1979. pap. 1.75x (ISBN 0-911408-51-7). SW Pks Mnmts.

Blackwelder, E. United States of North America. 1912. 30.00 (ISBN 0-384-04645-2). Johnson Repr.

Borns, Harold W., Jr., et al, eds. Late Pleistocene History of NE New England & Adjacent Quebec. (Special Paper Ser.: No. 197). (Illus.). 160p. 1985. 22.50 (ISBN 0-8137-2197-0). Geol Soc.

Brand, J. P. Cretaceous of Llano Estacado of Texas. (Illus.). 59p. 1953. 0.70 (ISBN 0-686-29330-4, RI 20). Bur Econ Geology.

Brown, L. F., et al. Pennsylvanian Depositional Systems in North-Central Texas: A Guide for Interpreting Terrigenous Clastic Facies in a Cratonic Basin. (Guidebook Ser.: GB 14). (Illus.). 122p. 1973. Repr. 4.00 (ISBN 0-686-29322-3). Bur Econ Geology.

Bryant, Vaughn M. & Holloway, Richard G., eds. Pollen Records of Late Quaternary North American Sediments. (Illus.). 350p. 1985. 35.00 (ISBN 0-931871-01-8). Am Assn Strat.

Buchanan, Rex, ed. Kansas Geology: An Introduction to Landscapes, Rocks, Minerals & Fossils. LC 83-23546. 1984. pap. 12.95 (ISBN 0-7006-0240-2). U Pr of KS.

Budd, D. A. & Loucks, R. G. Smackover & Lower Buckner Formations, Jurassic, South Texas: Depositional Systems on a Carbonate Ramp. (Report of Investigations Ser.: No. 112). (Illus.). 38p. 1981. 2.25 (ISBN 0-686-36593-3). Bur Econ Geology.

Bullard, F. M. The Geology of Grayson County, Texas. (Illus.). 72p. 1931. 0.50 (ISBN 0-686-29350-9, BULL 3125). Bur Econ Geology.

Campbell, Charles D. Introduction to Washington Geology & Resources. (Information Circular Ser.: No. 22r). (Illus.). 44p. 1962. 0.25 (ISBN 0-686-34733-1). Geologic Pubns.

Caran, S. C., et al. Lineament Analysis & Inference of Geologic Structure: Examples from the Balcones-Ouachita Trent of Texas. (Geological Circular Ser.: GC 82-1). 1982. Repr. 1.00 (ISBN 0-686-37545-9). Bur Econ Geology.

Carter, George F. Pleistocene Man at San Diego. LC 77-74811. Repr. of 1957 ed. 37.00 (ISBN 0-404-14885-9). AMS Pr.

Caughey, C. A. Depositional Systems in the Paluxy Formation (Lower Cretaceous), Northeast Texas: Oil, Gas, & Ground-Water Resources. (GC 77-8). (Illus.). 59p. 1977. Repr. 2.50 (ISBN 0-686-29327-4, GC 77-8). Bur Econ Geology.

Chadwick, George H. Rocks of Greene County. 1973. pap. 2.00 (ISBN 0-685-40640-7). Hope Farm.

Chamberlain, Barbara B. These Fragile Outposts. 327p. 1981. pap. 9.95 (ISBN 0-940160-12-9). Parnassus Imprints.

Chapman, Carleton A. Geology of Acadia National Park. LC 73-107079. (Illus.). 1970. 12.95 (ISBN 0-87638-012-7); pap. 5.95 (ISBN 0-85699-010-8). Chatham Pr.

Chronic, Halka. Time, Rocks & the Rockies: The Geology of Rocky Mountain National Park. (Roadside Geology Ser.). (Illus.). 200p. (Orig.). 1984. pap. 7.95 (ISBN 0-87842-172-6). Mountain Pr.

Contributions to Geology, 1928. (Bulletin Ser.: Bull 2801). 202p. 1928. 1.00 (ISBN 0-318-03302-X). Bur Econ Geology.

Contributions to Geology, 1930. (Bulletin Ser: Bull 3001). 207p. 1930. 1.00 (ISBN 0-318-03304-6). Bur Econ Geology.

Contributions to Geology, 1932. (Bulletin Ser.: Bull 3201). (Illus.). 216p. 1932. 1.00 (ISBN 0-318-03306-2). Bur Econ Geology.

Corgan, James X., ed. The Geological Sciences in the Antebellum South. LC 81-2993. (Illus.). 208p. 1982. 17.50 (ISBN 0-8173-0076-7). U of Ala Pr.

Crandall, D. R. & Mullineaux, D. R. Pleistocene Sequence in Southeastern Part of the Puget Sound Lowland, Washington. (Reprint Ser.: No. 2). (Illus.). 14p. 1958. 0.25 (ISBN 0-686-36910-6). Geologic Pubns.

Crolier, M. J. & Bingham, J. W. Geology of Parts of Grant, Adams, & Franklin Counties, East-Central Washington. (Illus.). 91p. 1978. 1.50 (ISBN 0-686-34720-X). Geologic Pubns.

Dietrich, Richard V. Geology & Virginia. LC 76-110752. (Illus.). xiv, 213p. 1971. 16.95x (ISBN 0-8139-0289-4). U Pr of Va.

Diver, Bradford B. van. Roadside Geology of New York. (Roadside Geology Ser.). (Illus.). 320p. 1985. pap. 9.95 (ISBN 0-87842-180-7). Mountain Pr.

Dorr, John A., Jr., et al. Deformation & Deposition Between a Foreland Uplift & an Impinging Thrust Belt: Hoback Basin, Wyoming. LC 77-70022. (Special Paper: No. 177). (Illus.). 1977. pap. 10.00 (ISBN 0-8137-2177-6). Geol Soc.

Dutton, S. P., et al. Geology & Geohydrology of the Palo Duro Basin, Texas Panhandle: A Report on the Progress of Nuclear Waste Isolation Feasibility Studies (1978) (Geological Circular Ser.: 79-1). (Illus.). 99p. 1979. 2.50 (ISBN 0-686-29328-2, GC 79-1). Bur Econ Geology.

Eargle, D. H., et al. Uranium Geology & Mines, South Texas. (GB 12 Ser.). (Illus.). 59p. 1971. 1.75 (ISBN 0-686-29320-7). Bur Econ Geology.

Edmund, Rudolph W. Structural Geology & Physiography of the Northern End of the Teton Range, Wyoming. LC 52-3353. (Augustana College Library Publication Ser.: No. 23). 82p. 1951. pap. 3.50x (ISBN 0-910182-18-3). Augustana Coll.

Ekman, Leonard C. Scenic Geology of the Pacific Northwest. 2nd. ed. LC 61-13278. (Illus.). 1970. 8.95 (ISBN 0-8323-0130-2). Binford.

Ellison, S. P., Jr. Sulfur in Texas. (Illus.). 48p. 1971. 2.00 (ISBN 0-686-29324-X, HB 2). Bur Econ Geology.

Emmons, Ebenezer. American Geology: Statement of the Principles of the Science, with Full Illustrations of the Characteristic American Fossils, 2 vols. in one. LC 73-17818. (Natural Sciences in America Ser.). (Illus.). 544p. 1974. Repr. 37.50x (ISBN 0-405-05734-2). Ayer Co Pubs.

Evans, T. J. Bituminous Coal in Texas. (Illus.). 65p. 1974. Repr. 3.50 (ISBN 0-686-29325-8, HB 4). Bur Econ Geology.

Feldmann, Rodney M. & Heimlich, Richard A. Geology Field Guide: The Black Hills. 208p. (Orig.). 1980. pap. 10.95 (ISBN 0-8403-2193-7). Kendall-Hunt.

Finley, R. J. & Gustavson, T. C. Climatic Controls on Erosion in the Rolling Plains along the Caprock Escarpment of the Texas Panhandle: Geological Circular 80-11. (Illus.). 50p. 1980. 1.75 (ISBN 0-686-36578-X). Bur Econ Geology.

Finley, Robert J. & Gustavson, Thomas C. Lineament Analysis Based on Landsat Imagery, Texas Panhandle. (Geological Circular Ser.: No. 81-5). (Illus.). 37p. 1981. 2.25 (ISBN 0-686-35723-X). Bur Econ Geology.

Fisher, W. L. & Rodda, P. U. Lower Cretaceous Sands of Texas: Stratigraphy & Resources. (Report of Investigations: RI 59). (Illus.). 116p. 1967. 1.75 (ISBN 0-686-29340-1). Bur Econ Geology.

Flawn, P. T., et al. The Ouachita System. (Illus.). 401p. 1982. Repr. of 1980 ed. 12.00 (ISBN 0-318-03315-1, PUB 6120). Bur Econ Geology.

Folk, R. L. Field Excursion, Central Texas: Tertiary Bentonites of Central Texas. 53p. 1978. Repr. of 1961 ed. 1.25 (ISBN 0-686-29312-6, GB 3). Uranium-Bearing Clays & Tuffs of South-Central Texas, by D. H. Eargle & A. D. Weeks. Vermiculite Deposits Near Liano, by V. E. Barnes & S. E. Clabaugh. Bur Econ Geology.

Frey, Robert W., ed. Excursions in Southeastern Geology: Field Trip Guidebooks, 2 vols. Incl. Vol. I. Field Trips-1-13. pap. 25.00 (ISBN 0-913312-48-7); Vol. II. Field Trips-14-23. pap. 25.00 (ISBN 0-913312-49-5). (Illus., Orig.). 1980. Set. pap. 40.00 (ISBN 0-913312-50-9). Am Geol.

Galloway, W. E. Catahoula Formation of the Texas Coastal Plain: Depositional Systems, Composition, Structural Development, Ground-Water Flow History, & Uranium Distribution. (Report of Investigations Ser.: RI 87). (Illus.). 59p. 1977. 3.25 (ISBN 0-686-36608-5). Bur Econ Geology.

Galloway, W. E., et al. South Texas Uranium Province, Geologic Perspective. (Guidebook Ser.: GB 18). (Illus.). 81p. 1979. 3.00 (ISBN 0-686-29323-1, GB 18). Bur Econ Geology.

Gilbert, Grove K. Report of the Geology of the Henry Mountains: U.S. Geographical & Geological Survey of the Rocky Mounntain Region. Albritton, Claude C., Jr., ed. LC 77-6519. (History of Geology Ser.). (Illus.). 1978. Repr. of 1877 ed. lib. bdg. 21.00x (ISBN 0-405-10441-3). Ayer Co Pubs.

Girard, R. M. Texas Rocks & Minerals: An Amateur's Guide. (Illus.). 109p. 1964. Repr. 2.50 (ISBN 0-686-29314-2, GB 6). Bur Econ Geology.

Goldich, Samuel S., et al. Precambrian Geology & Geochronology of Minnesota. LC 61-8016. (Bulletin: No. 41). (Illus.). 1961. 4.00x (ISBN 0-8166-0224-7). Minn Geol Survey.

Graves, R. W., Jr. Geology of Hood Spring Quadrangle, Brewster County, Texas. (Report of Investigations Ser.: RI 21). (Illus.). 51p. 1954. 2.25 (ISBN 0-686-29331-2). Bur Econ Geology.

Grout, Frank F. & Wolff, J. Fred. Geology of the Cuyuna District, Minnesota: A Progress Report. LC 55-9000. (Bulletin: No. 36). (Illus.). 1955. 3.00x (ISBN 0-8166-0106-2). Minn Geol Survey.

Gundersen, James N. & Schwartz, George M. Geology of the Metamorphosed Biwabik Iron Formation, Eastern Mesabi District, Minnesota. LC 62-9302. (Bulletin: No. 43). 1962. 4.25x (ISBN 0-8166-0274-3). Minn Geol Survey.

Hamblin, W. Kenneth, et al. Roadside Geology of U. S. Interstate 80 Between Salt Lake City & San Francisco. 53p. 1975. pap. 3.00 (ISBN 0-913312-43-6). Am Geol.

Handford, C. Robertson, et al. Regional Cross Sections of the Texas Panhandle: Precambrian to Mid-Permian. (Illus.). 1981. Repr. 3.00 (ISBN 0-686-36995-5). Bur Econ Geology.

Harris, Ann G. Geology of National Parks. 2nd ed. LC 74-25041. (Illus.). 1982. pap. text ed. 24.95 (ISBN 0-8403-2810-9, 40281001). Kendall-Hunt.

Henry, C. D. & Gluck, J. K. A Preliminary Assessment of the Geologic Setting, Hydrology, & Geochemistry of the Hueco Tanks Geothermal Area, Texas & New Mexico. (Geological Circular Ser.: No. 81-1). (Illus.). 48p. 1981. 2.00. Bur Econ Geology.

Hill, Mary. Geology of the Sierra Nevada. LC 73-93053. (California Natural History Guides Ser.). (Illus.). 1975. 14.95x (ISBN 0-520-02801-5); pap. 6.95 (ISBN 0-520-02698-5). U of Cal Pr.

Hoffmeister, J. Edward. Land from the Sea: The Geologic Story of South Florida. LC 73-20120. (Illus.). 128p. 1974. 9.95 (ISBN 0-87024-268-7). U of Miami Pr.

Horberg, Leland. The Structural Geology & Physiography of the Teton Pass Area, Wyoming. LC 39-7044. (Augustana College Library Publication Ser.: No. 16). 86p. 1938. pap. 3.50x (ISBN 0-910182-11-6). Augustana Coll.

Hunt, Charles B. Death Valley: Geology, Ecology, Archaeology. LC 74-2460. 256p. 1975. 19.95 (ISBN 0-520-02460-5); pap. 9.95 (ISBN 0-520-03013-3, CAL 315). U of Cal Pr.

Johnson, A. M. Styles of Folding: Mechanics & Mechanisms of Folding of Natural Elastic Materials. (Developments in Geotectonics: Vol. 11). 406p. 1977. 76.75 (ISBN 0-444-41496-7). Elsevier.

King, P. B. The Geology of the Glass Mountains, Texas: Part I, Descriptive Geology. (Bull Ser.: 3038). (Illus.). 167p. 1930. 2.50 (ISBN 0-686-29348-7). Bur Econ Geology.

King, R. E. The Geology of the Glass Mountains, Texas: Part II, Faunal Summary & Correlation of the Permian Formations with Description of Brachiopoda. (Bull Ser.: 3042). (Illus.). 146p. 1930. 2.50 (ISBN 0-686-29349-5). Bur Econ Geology.

Kreitler, C. W., et al. Geology & Geohydrology of the East Texas Basin: A Report on the Progress of Nuclear Waste Isolation Feasibility Studies(1979) Incl. A/Report on the Progress of Nuclear Waste Isolation Feasibility Studies. Kreitler, C. W., et al. (Geological Circular Ser. of Nuclear Waste Isolation Feasibility Studies: No. 81-7). (Illus.). 207p. 1981. 5.00 (ISBN 0-686-36595-X); A/Report on the Progress of Nuclear Waste Isolation Feasibility Studies, 1979. Kreitler, C. W., et al. (Geological Circular Ser.: No. 80-12). (Illus.). 112p. 1980. 2.50 (ISBN 0-318-03140-X); A/Report on the Progress of Nuclear Waste Isolation Feasibility Studies 1980. Kreitler, C. W., et al. (Geological Circular: No. 81-7). 207p. 5.00. (Geological Circular Ser.: 80-12). (Illus.). 112p. 1980. 2.50 (ISBN 0-318-03140-X). Bur Econ Geology.

GEOLOGY, CHEMICAL

see Geochemistry; Mineralogical Chemistry; Mineralogy, Determinative; Rocks–Analysis

GEOLOGY, DYNAMIC

see Geodynamics

GEOLOGY, ECONOMIC

see also Coal; Engineering Geology; Gas, Natural; Mineral Oils; Mines and Mineral Resources; Mining Geology; Ores; Petroleum; Petroleum–Geology; Quarries and Quarrying; Soils; also other geological products, e.g. Asbesto-Graphite, Quartz

Bebout, D. G., et al. Depositional & Diagenetic History of the Sligo & Hosston Formations (Lower Cretaceous) in South Texas. (Report of Investigations Ser.: No. 109). (Illus.). 69p. 1981. 4.00 (ISBN 0-686-36993-9). Bur Econ Geology.

Bischoff, J. L. & Piper, D. Z., eds. Marine Geology & Oceanography of the Pacific Manganese Nodule Province. LC 79-12475. (Marine Science Ser.: Vol. 9). 855p. 1979. 89.50x (ISBN 0-306-40187-8, Plenum Pr). Plenum Pub.

Bjorklund, A., ed. Geochemical Exploration, 1983: Selected Papers from the International Geochemical Explorational Symposium, 10th, Symposium on Methods of Geochemical Prospecting, 3rd, Held in Espoo, Finland, Aug.29-Sept. 2, 1983. 1984. Repr. 89.00 (ISBN 0-444-42385-0). Elsevier.

Geochemical Exploration, 1984: Proceedings of the 5th International Symposium, Vancouver 1974. LC 74-21855. (Development in Economic Geology Ser: Vol. 1). 720p. 1975. 121.50 (ISBN 0-444-41280-8). Elsevier.

Given, P. H. & Cohen, A. D., eds. Interdisciplinary Studies of Peat & Coal Origins. LC 77-71662. (Microform Publication: No. 7). (Illus.). 1977. 4.00 (ISBN 0-8137-6007-0). Geol Soc.

Handford, C. Robertson, et al. Regional Cross Sections of the Texas Panhandle: Precambrian to Mid-Permian. (Illus.). 1981. Repr. 3.00 (ISBN 0-686-36995-5). Bur Econ Geology.

Jenkins, G. Oil Economists' Handbook: 1984. 292p. 1983. 77.75 (ISBN 0-85334-207-5, I-264-83, Pub. by Elsevier Applied Sci England). Elsevier.

Kesler, S. E. Our Finite Resources. 1975. 19.95 (ISBN 0-07-034245-8). McGraw.

Knill, J. L., ed. Industrial Geology. (Illus.). 1979. 39.50x (ISBN 0-19-854520-7). Oxford U Pr.

Knopf, Adolph. Sitka Mining District, Alaska. fasc. ed. (Geology Ser.). (Illus.). 32p. pap. 3.95 (ISBN 0-8466-8002-5, G2). Shorey.

Kuzvart, M. Industrial Minerals & Rocks. (Developments in Economic Geology Ser.: Vol. 18). 454p. 1984. 74.00 (ISBN 0-444-99605-2). Elsevier.

Riley, Charles M. Our Mineral Resources: An Elementary Textbook in Economic Geology. 4th ed. LC 76-57669. (Illus.). 348p. 1977. Repr. of 1967 ed. lib. bdg. 19.50 (ISBN 0-88275-530-7). Krieger.

Stratigraphic Correlation Between Sedimentary Basins of the ESCAP Region, Vols. 3-7. Incl. Vols. 3 & 4. (No. 42). pap. 17.00 (ISBN 0-686-94391-0, UN77/2F11); Vol. 5. (No. 44). pap. 11.00 (ISBN 0-686-99360-8, UN78/2F17); Vol. 6. (No. 45). 64p. 1979. pap. 6.00 (ISBN 0-686-99361-6, UN79 2F15); Vol. 7. (No. 46). pap. 9.00 (ISBN 0-686-99362-4, UN80 2F2); Vol. 8. (No. 48). pap. 13.00 (UN82/2F6). (Mineral Resources Development Ser., UN). Unipub.

Tarling, D. H., ed. Economic Geology & Geotectonics. LC 81-673. 213p. 1981. 58.95x (ISBN 0-470-27145-0). Halsted Pr.

GEOLOGY, HISTORICAL

see Geology, Stratigraphic; Paleontology

GEOLOGY, LUNAR

see Lunar Geology

GEOLOGY, STRATIGRAPHIC

see also Borings; Glacial Epoch; Oil Well Logging; Paleontology; Paleontology, Stratigraphic

Ager, Derek V. Nature of the Stratigraphical Record. 2nd ed. LC 80-22559. 136p. 1981. 19.95x (ISBN 0-470-27052-7). Halsted Pr.

Andrews, P. B. Facies & Genesis of a Hurricane-Washover Fan, St. Joseph Island, Central Texas Coast. (Report of Investigations Ser.: RI 67). (Illus.). 147p. 1970. 3.00 (ISBN 0-318-03167-1). Bur Econ Geology.

Bradbury, John P. Diatom Stratigraphy & Human Settlement in Minnesota. LC 75-21066. (Geological Society of America Special Papers: No. 171). pap. 20.00 (ISBN 0-317-29090-8, 2023739). Bks Demand UMI.

Brown, D. S. W., et al. The Geological Evolution of Australia & New Zealand. 1968. pap. 17.00 (ISBN 0-08-012277-9). Pergamon.

Cubitt, J. M. & Reyment, R. A., eds. Quantitative Stratigraphic Correlation. LC 81-21926. (International Geological Correlation Programme Ser.). 301p. 1982. 59.95 (ISBN 0-471-10171-0, Pub. by Wiley-Interscience). Wiley.

D'Orbigny, Alcide. Cours Elementaire de Paleontologie et de Geologie Stratgraphiques, Vol. 2, Pt. 2. (Fr.). 33.00 (ISBN 0-405-12744-8). Ayer Co Pubs.

D'Orbigny, Alcide D. Cours Elementaire de Paleontologie et de Geologie Stratigraphiques: Beginning Course in Paleontology & Stratigraphic Geology, 2 vols. in 3. Gould, Stephen J., ed. LC 79-8339. (The History of Paleontology Ser.). (Fr., Illus.). 1980. Repr. of 1849 ed. Set. lib. bdg. 98.00x (ISBN 0-405-12725-1); Vol. 1. 33.00 (ISBN 0-405-12726-X); Vol. 2. 33.00 (ISBN 0-405-12727-8). Ayer Co Pubs.

Douglas, Ian. Humid Landforms. (Illus.). 1977. text ed. 22.50x (ISBN 0-262-04054-9). Mit Pr.

Downie, C. H. Acritarchs in British Stratigraphy. (Illus.). 28p. 1984. pap. text ed. 11.95x (ISBN 0-632-01225-0). Blackwell Pubns.

Dunbar, Carl O. & Waage, Karl M. Historical Geology. 3rd ed. LC 72-89681. (Illus.). 556p. 1969. text ed. 39.95x (ISBN 0-471-22507-X). Wiley.

Einsele, G. & Soilacher, A., eds. Cyclic & Event Stratification. (Illus.). 550p. 1982. pap. 32.00 (ISBN 0-387-11373-8). Springer-Verlag.

Englund, Kenneth J., et al. Proposed Pennsylvanian System Stratotype. West Virginia & Virginia. LC 78-74893. (AGI Selected Guidebook Ser.: No. 1). 1979. pap. 20.00 (ISBN 0-913312-08-8). Am Geol.

Evitt, William R. Sporopollenin Dinoflagellate Cysts: Their Morphology & Interpretation. LC 84-72457. (Illus.). 349p. 1985. 30.00 (ISBN 0-317-19725-8). Am Assn Strat.

Fabre, J., ed. Afrique de l'Ouest West Africa: Introduction Geologique et Termes Stratigraphiques-Geological Introduction & Stratigraphic Terms. LC 83-13418. (Lexique Stratigraphique International: Nouvelle Series No. 1). (Illus.). 426p. 1983. 65.00 (ISBN 0-08-030267-X); pap. 22.00 (ISBN 0-08-030277-7). Pergamon.

Galloway, W. E., et al. Depositional Framework, Hydrostratigraphy & Uranium Mineralization of the Oakville Sandstone (Miocene), Texas Coastal Plain. (Report of Investigations Ser.: RI 113). (Illus.). 51p. 1982. 2.50 (ISBN 0-318-03245-7). Bur Econ Geology.

Gentile, Richard J. Influence of Structural Movement on Sedimentation During the Pennsylvanian Period in Western Missouri. LC 74-4528. 108p. 1968. 10.00x (ISBN 0-8262-7619-9). U of Mo Pr.

Gondwana Stratigraphy: IUGS Symposium, Buenos Aires, 1967. (Earth Sciences Ser.: No. 2). (Eng. & Span., Illus.). 173p. (Orig.). 1969. pap. 28.25 (ISBN 92-3-000770-6, U267, UNESCO). Unipub.

Hallam, A. Facies Interpretation & the Stratigraphic Record. LC 80-24276. (Illus.). 291p. 1981. text ed. 36.95 (ISBN 0-7167-1291-1). W H Freeman.

Haq, Bilal U., ed. Calcareous Nannoplankton. LC 83-4366. (Benchmark Papers in Geology: Vol. 79). 368p. 1983. 46.50 (ISBN 0-87933-090-2). Van Nos Reinhold.

Heirtzler, J. R., et al, eds. Indian Ocean Geology & Biostratigraphy. LC 77-88320. (Special Publication Ser.). (Illus.). 616p. 1978. 25.00 (ISBN 0-87590-208-1). Am Geophysical.

Huber, G. C. Stratigraphy & Uranium Deposits, Lisbon Valley District, San Juan County, Utah. Raese, Jon W., ed. LC 80-18873. (CSM Quarterly Ser.: Vol. 75, No. 2). (Illus.). 45p. (Orig.). 1980. pap. 8.00 (ISBN 0-686-63163-3). Colo Sch Mines.

Ikebe, Nobuo & Tsuchi, Ryuichi, eds. Pacific Neogene Datum Planes: Contributions to Biostratigraphy & Chronology. 283p. 1984. 64.50x (ISBN 0-86008-354-3, Pub. by U of Tokyo Japan). Columbia U Pr.

International Subcommission on Stratigraphic Classification. International Stratigraphic Guide: A Guide to Stratlcalss Terminology & Procedure (A Guide to Stratigraphic Classification, Terminology & Procedure) LC 75-33086. 390p. 1976. 21.50x (ISBN 0-471-36743-5, Pub. by Wiley-Interscience). Wiley.

Kay, Marshall & Colbert, Edwin H. Stratigraphy & Life History. LC 64-20072. pap. 160.00 (ISBN 0-317-28755-9, 2055486). Bks Demand UMI.

Keller, Fred, et al. Introduction to Historical Geology. (Illus.). 1979. lab manual 8.95x (ISBN 0-89459-194-0). Hunter Textbks.

Klemm, D. D. & Schneider, H. J., eds. Time- & Strata- Bound Ore Deposits. (Illus.). 1979. 59.00 (ISBN 0-387-08502-5). Springer-Verlag.

Krishtalka, L. & West, Robert M. Paleontology & Geology of the Bridger Formation, Southern Green River Basin, Southwestern Wyoming: Part Two - The Bridgerian Insectivore Entomolestes Granseri. 1977. 0.75 (ISBN 0-89326-027-4). Milwaukee Pub Mus.

Krishtalka, Leonard & West, R. M. Paleonology & Geology of the Bridger Formation, Southern Green River Basin, Southwestern Wyoming: Part Four - The Geolabididae (Mammalia, Insectivora) 1979. 0.75 (ISBN 0-89326-050-9). Milwaukee Pub Mus.

Krumbein, William C. & Sloss, L. L. Stratigraphy & Sedimentation. 2nd ed. LC 61-11422. (Illus.). 660p. 1963. 35.95 (ISBN 0-7167-0219-3). W H Freeman.

Level, Howard R. Illustrated Guide for Physical Geology. 88p. 1983. pap. 7.95 (ISBN 0-8403-3164-9). Kendall-Hunt.

Levorsen, Arville I. Stratigraphic Type Oil Fields, 2 vols. 1976. lib. bdg. 250.00 (ISBN 0-8490-2694-6). Gordon Pr.

Lind, Aulis O. Coastal Landforms of Cat Island, Bahamas: A Study of Holocene Accretionary Topography & Sea Level Change. LC 76-77892. (Research Papers Ser.: No. 122). 156p. 1969. pap. 10.00 (ISBN 0-89065-029-2). U Chicago Dept Geog.

Matter, Albert & Tucker, Maurice E., eds. Modern & Ancient Lake Sediments. (International Association of Sedimentologists & the Societas Internationalis Limnologiae Symposium Proceding Ser.). 290p. 1979. 39.95x (ISBN 0-470-26571-X). Halsted Pr.

Matthews, Robley K. Dynamic Stratigraphy: An Introduction to Sedimentation & Stratigraphy. 2nd ed. (Illus.). 512p. 1984. 36.95 (ISBN 0-13-222109-8). P-H.

Merriam, D. F., ed. Computer Assisted Instruction in Geology: Proceedings of the 4th Geochautauqua, Syracuse University, 1975. 1976. pap. text ed. 45.00 (ISBN 0-08-021040-6). Pergamon.

--Quantitative Stratigraphic Correlation: Proceedings of the 6th Geochautauqua, Syracuse University, October 1977. (Illus.). 112p. 1979. pap. 45.00 (ISBN 0-08-023979-X). Pergamon.

Middlemiss, Frank A. British Stratigraphy. 2nd ed. (Intoducing Geology Ser.: No. 2). (Illus.). 48p. 1985. pap. text ed. 4.95x (ISBN 0-04-550023-1). Allen Unwin.

Miller, Hugh. The Old Red Sandstone, or New Walks in an Old Field. Albritton, Claude C., Jr., ed. LC 77-6531. (History of Geology Ser.). (Illus.). 1978. Repr. of 1851 ed. lib. bdg. 34.50x (ISBN 0-405-10451-0). Ayer Co Pubs.

Page, Lincoln R., ed. Contributions to the Stratigraphy of New England. LC 76-9220. (Memoir: No. 148). (Illus.). 1976. 30.00 (ISBN 0-8137-1148-7). Geol Soc.

Pearson, Ronald. Climate & Evolution. 1979. 49.00 (ISBN 0-12-548250-7). Acad Pr.

Poort, Jon M. Historical Geology: Interpretations & Applications. 3rd ed. 1980. pap. text ed. 15.95x (ISBN 0-8087-3303-6). Burgess.

Purser, B. H., ed. The Persian Gulf. LC 72-97023. (Illus.). viii, 471p. 1973. 55.00 (ISBN 0-387-06156-8). Springer-Verlag.

Quarternary Stratigraphy Symposium, 1975. Quarternary Stratigraphy of North America: Proceedings. Mahaney, W. C., ed. 1976. 71.00 (ISBN 0-12-787045-8). Acad Pr.

Ramondetta, P. J. Facies & Stratigraphy of the San Andres Formation, Northern & Northwestern Shelves of the Midland Basin, Texas & New Mexico. (Report of Investigations Ser.: RI 128). (Illus.). 56p. 1982. 2.50 (ISBN 0-318-03277-5). Bur Econ Geology.

Rau, Weldon W. Foraminifera, Stratigraphy & Paleoecology of the Quinault Formation, Point Grenville-Raft River Coastal Area, Washington. (Bulletin Ser.: No. 62). (Illus.). 41p. 1970. 3.00 (ISBN 0-686-34711-0). Geologic Pubns.

--Stratigraphy & Foraminifera of the Satsop River Area, Southern Olympic Peninsula, Washington: Southern Olympic Peninsula, Washington. (Bulletin Ser.: No. 53). (Illus.). 66p. 1966. 1.50 (ISBN 0-686-34706-4). Geologic Pubns.

Rayner, Dorothy H. Stratigraphy of the British Isles. 2nd ed. LC 79-8523. (Illus.). 400p. 1981. 77.00 (ISBN 0-521-23452-2). Cambridge U Pr.

Ross, Charles A. & Ross, June R. P., eds. Geology of Coal. LC 83-8521. (Benchmark Papers in Geology: Vol. 77). 368p. 1983. 36.00 (ISBN 0-87933-099-6). Van Nos Reinhold.

Sharma. Geophysical Methods in Geology. 2nd ed. Date not set. write for info. (ISBN 0-444-00836-5). Elsevier.

Snelling, N. J., ed. The Chronology of the Geological Record. (Illus.). 400p. 1985. text ed. 60.00x (ISBN 0-632-01285-4). Blackwell Pubns.

Swain, F. M., ed. Stratigraphic Micropaleontology of Atlantic Basin & Borderlands. (Developments in Paleontology & Stratigraphy Ser.: Vol. 6). 604p. 1977. 85.00 (ISBN 0-444-41554-8). Elsevier.

Van Houten, Franklyn B., ed. Ancient Continental Deposits. (Bench Mark Papers in Geology Ser.). 1977. 61.50 (ISBN 0-12-787650-2). Acad Pr.

Van Landingham, S. L. Paleoecology & Microfloristics of Miocene Diatomites from the Otis Basin-Juntura Region of Harney & Malheur Counties, Oregon. (Illus.). 1967. pap. 14.00 (ISBN 3-7682-5426-7). Lubrecht & Cramer.

Visher, Glenn S. Exploration Stratigraphy. 350p. 1984. 74.95 (ISBN 0-87814-251-7). Pennwell Bks.

West, R. M. Paleontology & Geology of the Bridger Formation, Southern Green River Basin, Southwestern Wyoming: Part Three - Notes on Hyopsodus. 52p. 1979. 3.50 (ISBN 0-89326-046-0). Milwaukee Pub Mus.

West, Robert M. Paleontology & Geology of the Bridger Formation, Southern Green River Basin, Southwestern Wyoming: Part One - History of Field Work & Geological Setting. 1976. 0.75 (ISBN 0-89326-018-5). Milwaukee Pub Mus.

West, Robert M. & Hutchison, J. Howard. Geology & Palentology of the Bridger Formation, Southern Green River Basin, Southwestern Wyoming: Part Six - The Fauna & Correlation of Bridge E. 8p. 1981. 1.00 (ISBN 0-89326-074-6). Milwaukee Pub Mus.

Wolf, K. H. Handbook of Strata-Bound & Stratiform Ore Deposits, Pt. 4. Date not set. write for info. (ISBN 0-444-42248-X). Elsevier.

Wonderly, Daniel E. God's Time-Records in Ancient Sediments: Evidences of Long Time Spans in Earth's History. LC 77-85681. (Illus.). 258p. (Orig.). 1977. pap. 7.00 (ISBN 0-930402-01-4). Crystal MI.

Wright, J. B., et al. Geology & Mineral Resources of West Africa. (Illus.). 176p. 1985. text ed. 40.00x (ISBN 0-04-556001-3). Allen Unwin.

GEOLOGY, STRATIGRAPHIC–ARCHAEAN

McCall, G. J., ed. The Archean: Search for the Beginning. LC 76-11015. 1977. 77.00 (ISBN 0-12-787025-3). Acad Pr.

GEOLOGY, STRATIGRAPHIC–CALEDONIAN

see Geology, Stratigraphic–Paleozoic

GEOLOGY, STRATIGRAPHIC–CAMBRIAN

Cook, P. J. & Shergold, J. H., eds. Proterozoic-Cambrian Phosphorites. 1979. pap. text ed. 6.00 (ISBN 0-7081-1159-9, 0522, Pub. by ANUP Australia). Australia N U P.

Vugrinovich, R. G. Precambrian Geochronology of North America: An Annotated Bibliography,1951-1977. LC 80-68063. (Microform Publication: No. 11). 1980. 4.00 (ISBN 0-8137-6011-9). Geol Soc.

GEOLOGY, STRATIGRAPHIC–CARBONIFEROUS

Beus, Stanley S. & Rawson, Richard R., eds. Carboniferous Stratigraphy in the Grand Canyon Country, Northern Arizona & Southern Nevada. LC 78-74894. (AGI Selected Guidebook Ser.: No. 2). 1979. pap. 20.00 (ISBN 0-913312-09-6). Am Geol.

Cameron, Barry, ed. Carboniferous Basins of Southeastern New England. LC 79-51602. 1979. pap. 10.00 (ISBN 0-913312-14-2). Am Geol.

Dutro, J. Thomas, Jr., ed. Carboniferous of the Northern Rocky Mountains. LC 78-74895. (AGI Selected Guidebook Ser.: No. 3). 1979. pap. 12.00 (ISBN 0-913312-10-X). Am Geol.

Muir-Wood, Helen M. Malayan Lower Carboniferous Fossils & Their Bearing on the Visean Palaeogeography of Asia. (Illus.). 118p. 1948. 14.00x (ISBN 0-565-00374-7, Pub. by Brit Mus Nat Hist England). Sabbot-Natural Hist Bks.

Ninth International Congress of Carboniferous Stratigraphy & Geology: Compte Rendu, Vol. 1. LC 83-19147. 159p. 1984. pap. 25.00x (ISBN 0-8093-1168-2). S Ill U Pr.

GEOLOGY, STRATIGRAPHIC–CENOZOIC

see also Geology, Stratigraphic–Quaternary; Geology, Stratigraphic–Tertiary

Andel, Tjeerd H., et al. Cenozoic History & Paleoceanography of the Central Equatorial Pacific Ocean: A Regional Synthesis Deep Sea Drilling Project Data. LC 75-20815. (Geological Society of America Memoir Ser.: No. 143). pap. 57.80 (ISBN 0-317-29104-1, 2023732). Bks Demand UMI.

Anderson, John J., et al. Cenozoic Geology of Southwestern High Plateaus of Utah. LC 75-10395. (Geological Society of America Ser.: No. 160). pap. 33.50 (ISBN 0-317-28376-6, 2025457). Bks Demand UMI.

Armentrout, John M., ed. Pacific Northwest Cenozoic Biostratigraphy. LC 80-82937. (Special Paper: No. 184). (Illus., Orig.). 1981. pap. 26.00 (ISBN 0-8137-2184-9). Geol Soc.

Carnegie Institution Of Washington. Studies on Cenozoic Vertebrates of Western America. Repr. of 1938 ed. 28.00 (ISBN 0-685-02176-9). Johnson Repr.

Cenozoic Stratigraphy of the Transverse Ranges & Adjacent Areas, Southern California. LC 75-2953. (Geological Society of America Ser.: No. 162). pap. 34.30 (ISBN 0-317-28374-X, 2025455). Bks Demand UMI.

Frost, Stanley H. & Langenheim, Ralph L., Jr. Cenozoic Reef Biofacies: Tertiary Larger Foraminifera & Scleractinian Corals from Chiapas, Mexico. LC 72-7513. (Illus.). 388p. 1974. 50.00 (ISBN 0-87580-027-0). N Ill U Pr.

Pomerol, C. Cenozoic Era. LC 80-42073. (Geology Ser.). 280p. 1982. 69.95x (ISBN 0-470-27140-X). Halsted Pr.

Smith, Robert B. & Eaton, Gordon P., eds. Cenozoic Tectonics & Regional Geophysics of the Western Cordillera. LC 78-55296. (Memoir Ser.: No. 152). (Illus.). 1978. 55.00 (ISBN 0-8137-1152-5). Geol Soc.

Turekian, Karl K., ed. The Late Cenozioc Glacial Ages. LC 70-140540. (Yale University, Mrs. Hepse Ely Silliman Memorial Lectures). pap. 154.50 (ISBN 0-317-29710-4, 2022045). Bks Demand UMI.

GEOLOGY, STRATIGRAPHIC–CRETACEOUS

Bebout, D. G. & Loucks, R. G. Stuart City Trend, Lower Cretaceous, South Texas: A Carbonate Shelf-Margin for Hydrocarbon Exploration. (Report of Investigations Ser.: RI 78). (Illus.). 80p. 1980. Repr. of 1974 ed. 3.00 (ISBN 0-318-03198-1). Bur Econ Geology.

Bebout, D. G., et al. Depositional & Diagenetic History of the Sligo & Hosston Formations (Lower Cretaceous) in South Texas. (Report of Investigations Ser.: No. 109). (Illus.). 69p. 1981. 4.00 (ISBN 0-686-36993-9). Bur Econ Geology.

International Symposium on the Boreal Lower Cretaceous (1972: London) Staff. The Boreal Lower Cretaceous: The Proceedings of an International Symposium Organized by Queen Mary College, University of London, & the Institute of Geological Sciences, 17-30 September, 1972. Casey, R. & Rawson, P. F., eds. LC 75-302015. (Geological Journal Special Issue Ser.: No. 5). pap. 130.00 (ISBN 0-317-26139-8, 2024275). Bks Demand UMI.

Kauffman, Erle G., et al. Stratigraphic, Paleontologic, & Paleoenvironmental Analysis of the Upper Cretaceous Rocks of Cimarron County, Northwestern Oklahoma. LC 76-47800. (Memoir Ser.: No. 149). (Illus.). 1977. 19.00 (ISBN 0-8137-1149-5). Geol Soc.

MacNeal, Donald L. The Flora of the Upper Cretaceous Woodbine Sand in Denton County, Texas. (Monograph: No. 10). (Illus.). 152p. (Orig.). 1958. pap. 11.00 (ISBN 0-910006-17-2). Acad Nat Sci Phila.

Matthews, Vincent, ed. Laramide Folding Associated with Basement Block Faulting in the Western United States. LC 78-54346. (Geological Society of America Memoir Ser.: No. 151). pap. 100.00 (ISBN 0-317-28993-4, 2023731). Bks Demand UMI.

Pessagno, E. A., Jr. Radiolarian Zonation & Stratigraphy of the Upper Cretaceous Portion of the Great Valley Sequence, California Coast Ranges. (Micropaleontology Special Publications Ser.: No. 2). 95p. 1976. 20.00 (ISBN 0-686-84250-2). Am Mus Natl Hist.

Renz, O. The Cretaceous Amonites of Venezuela. (Illus.). 216p. 1982. 73.95x (ISBN 0-8176-1364-1). Birkhauser.

Reyment, R. A. & Bengston, P., eds. Aspects of Mid-Cretaceous Regional Geology. LC 80-42379. 1981. 72.00 (ISBN 0-12-587040-X). Acad Pr.

Rose, P. R. Edwards Group, Surface & Subsurface, Central Texas. (Report of Investigations Ser.: RI 74). (Illus.). 198p. 1978. Repr. of 1972 ed. 5.50 (ISBN 0-318-03178-7). Bur Econ Geology.

Saul, LouElla. The North Pacific Cretaceous Trigoniid Genus Yaadia. (Publications in Geological Science Ser.: Vol. 119). 1978. pap. 17.00x (ISBN 0-520-09582-0). U of Cal Pr.

Schlanger, S. O. & Cita, M. B., eds. Nature & Origin of Cretaceous Carbonrich Facies. 1983. 43.50 (ISBN 0-12-624950-4). Acad Pr.

Smith, C. I. Lower Cretaceous Stratigraphy, Northern Coahuila, Mexico. (Report of Investigations: RI 65). (Illus.). 101p. 1970. 4.00 (ISBN 0-318-03166-3). Bur Econ Geology.

Stewart, Ralph B. Gabb's California Cretaceous & Tertiary Type Lamellibranchs. (Special Publication: No. 3). (Illus.). 314p. (Orig.). 1930. pap. 15.00 (ISBN 0-910006-31-8). Acad Nat Sci Phila.

GEOLOGY, STRATIGRAPHIC–DEVONIAN

Murphy, Michael & Matti, Jonathan C. Lower Devonian Conodonts-Hesperius-Kindlei Zones. LC 82-8638. (Publications in Geological Sciences Ser.: Vol. 123). 94p. 1983. pap. text ed. 10.25x (ISBN 0-520-09661-4). U of Cal Pr.

GEOLOGY, STRATIGRAPHIC–EOCENE

Fisher, W. L., et al. Evolution of Athleta Petrosa Stock (Eocene, Gastropoda) of Texas. (Pub. Ser: 6413). (Illus.). 117p. 1964. 4.00 (ISBN 0-318-03318-6). Bur Econ Geology.

Henriksen, Donald A. Eocene Stratigraphy of the Lower Cowlitz River-Eastern Willapa Hill Area, Southwestern Washington. (Bulletin Ser.: No. 43). (Illus.). 122p. 1956. 1.50 (ISBN 0-686-34698-X). Geologic Pubns.

Lillegraven, Jason A., et al. Evolutionary Relationships of Middle Eocene & Younger Species of Centetodon (Mammalia, Insectivora, Geolabididae) with a Description of the Dentition of Ankylodon (Adapisoricidae) LC 81-53020. (Illus.). 116p. 1981. pap. 12.50 (ISBN 0-941570-00-2). U of Wyoming.

Vine, James D. Stratigraphy of Eocene Rocks in a Part of King County, Washington. (Report of Investigations Ser.: No. 21). (Illus.). 20p. 1962. 0.50 (ISBN 0-686-34728-5). Geologic Pubns.

Weaver, Charles E. Eocene & Paleocene Deposits at Martinez, California. LC 53-9284. (Publications in Geology: No. 7). (Illus.). 102p. 1953. pap. 20.00x (ISBN 0-295-73772-7). U of Wash Pr.

GEOLOGY, STRATIGRAPHIC–MESOZOIC

see also Geology, Stratigraphic–Cretaceous; Geology, Stratigraphic–Triassic

Bjaerke, Tor & Manum, Svein B. Mesozoic Palynology of Svalbard. (Norsk Polarinstitutt Skrifter: No. 165). (Illus.). 1978. pap. 8.00x (ISBN 82-00-29719-5, Dist. by Columbia U Pr). Universitet.

Hsu, Kenneth J. Paleoceanography of the Mesozoic Alpine-Tethys. LC 75-32124. (Special Papers: No. 170). (Illus., Orig.). 1976. pap. 7.00x (ISBN 0-8137-2170-9). Geol Soc.

Moullade, M. & Nairn, A. E., eds. The Phanerozoic Geology of the World: The Mesozoic, Vol. 2A. 530p. 1978. 110.75 (ISBN 0-444-41671-4). Elsevier.

GEOLOGY, STRATIGRAPHIC–OLIGOCENE

Frost, S. H., et al. Oligocene Reef-Tract Development, Southwestern Puerto Rico: Part 1 Text; Part 2, Field Guide to Reprsentative Exposures & Modern Analog. (Sedimenta IX). (Illus.). 180p. 1983. 12.00 (ISBN 0-932981-08-9). Univ Miami CSL.

Rensberger, John M. Successions of Meniscomyine & Allomyine Rodents (Aplodontidae) in the Oligo-Miocene John Day Formation, Oregon. LC 83-1403. (Geological Sciences Ser.: Vol. 124). 176p. 1984. pap. text ed. 21.50x (ISBN 0-520-09668-1). U of Cal Pr.

GEOLOGY, STRATIGRAPHIC–ORDOVICIAN

Bruton, David L., ed. Aspects of the Ordovician System. (Illus.). 275p. 1984. pap. 19.00x (ISBN 82-00-06319-4). Universitet.

Budge, D. R. & Sheehan, P. M. The Upper Ordovician Through Middle Silurian of the Eastern Great Basin: Part Two - Lithologic Descriptions. 80p. 1980. 5.50 (ISBN 0-89326-041-X). Milwaukee Pub Mus.

Sheehan, P. M. The Late Ordovician & Silurian of the Eastern Great Basin: Part Three - Brachiopods of the Tony Grove Lake Member of the Laketown Dolomite. 23p. 1980. 2.25 (ISBN 0-89326-054-1). Milwaukee Pub Mus.

Sheehan, Peter M. The Late Ordovician & Silurian of the Eastern Great Basin: Part Four - Late Llandovery & Wenlock Brachiopods. 83p. 1982. 7.95. Milwaukee Pub Mus.

GEOLOGY, STRATIGRAPHIC–PALEOCENE

Rau, Weldon W. Foraminifera, Stratigraphy & Paleoecology of the Quinault Formation, Point Grenville-Raft River Coastal Area, Washington. (Bulletin Ser.: No. 62). (Illus.). 41p. 1970. 3.00 (ISBN 0-686-34711-0). Geologic Pubns.

Weaver, Charles E. Eocene & Paleocene Deposits at Martinez, California. LC 53-9284. (Publications in Geology: No. 7). (Illus.). 102p. 1953. pap. 20.00x (ISBN 0-295-73772-7). U of Wash Pr.

GEOLOGY, STRATIGRAPHIC–PALEOZOIC

see also Geology, Stratigraphic–Cambrian; Geology, Stratigraphic–Carboniferous; Geology, Stratigraphic–Devonian; Geology, Stratigraphic–Ordovician; Geology, Stratigraphic–Permian; Geology, Stratigraphic–Silurian

Barnes, V. E., et al. Stratigraphy of the Pre-Simpson Paleozoic Subsurface Rocks of Texas & Southeast New Mexico, 2 Vols. (Pub. Ser.: 5924). (Illus.). 836p. 1959. 7.75 (ISBN 0-318-03311-9). Bur Econ Geology.

Campbell, John B. The Upper Palaeolithic of Britain: A Study of Man & Nature in the Late Ice Age, Vols. I & II. (Illus.). 1978. 84.00 set (ISBN 0-19-813188-7). Oxford U Pr.

Gee, D. G. & Sturt, B. A. The Caledonide Orogen: Scandinavia & Related Areas. 110p. 1984. 186.95 (ISBN 0-471-10504-X). Wiley.

Holland, C. H. Lower Paleozoic of North-Western & West-Central Africa. (Lower Palaezoic Rocks of the World Ser.: 1-166). 552p. 1984. 130.00 (ISBN 0-471-10357-8, 1166, Pub. by Wiley-Interscience). Wiley.

Holland, C. H., ed. Lower Palaeozoic of the Middle East, Eastern & Southern Africa & Antarctica: With Essays on Lower Palaeozoic Trace Fossils of Africa & Lower Palaeozoic Palaeoclimatology, Vol. 3. LC 80-41688. (Lower Palaeozoic Rocks of the World Ser.). 331p. 1981. 115.00 (ISBN 0-471-27945-5, Pub. by Wiley-Interscience). Wiley.

McElhinny, M. W., et al. Global Reconstruction & the Geomagnetic Field During the Palaeozoic. 1981. 29.50 (ISBN 90-277-1231-X, Pub. by Reidel Holland). Kluwer Academic.

Thomas, A. T., et al. Trilobites in British Stratigraphy. (Illus.). 80p. 1984. pap. text ed. 17.00x (ISBN 0-632-01201-3). Blackwell Pubns.

Van der Voo, R., et al, eds. Plate Reconstruction from Paleozoic Paleomagnetism. (Geodynamics Ser.: Vol. 12). 136p. 1984. 20.00 (ISBN 0-87590-512-9). Am Geophysical.

Webster, G. D. Bibliography & Index of Paleozoic Crinoids, Nineteen Sixty-Nine to Nineteen Seventy-Three. LC 77-76475. (Microform Publication: No. 8). 1977. 4.50 (ISBN 0-8137-6008-9). Geol Soc.

Webster, Gary D. Bibliography & Index of Paleozoic Crinoids, 1942-1968. LC 73-76885. (Geological Society of America Memoir Ser.: No. 137). pap. 88.30 (ISBN 0-317-29085-1, 2023737). Bks Demand UMI.

Zharkov, M. A. History of Paleozoic Salt Accumulation. (Illus.). 308p. 1981. 42.00 (ISBN 0-387-10614-6). Springer-Verlag.

GEOLOGY, STRATIGRAPHIC–PERMIAN

Falke, Horst, ed. The Continental Permian in West, Central, & South Europe. (Nato Mathematical & Physical Sciences Ser.: No. 22). 1976. lib. bdg. 53.00 (ISBN 90-277-0664-6, Pub. by Reidel Holland). Kluwer Academic.

Handford, C. Robertson, et al. Regional Cross Sections of the Texas Panhandle: Precambrian to Mid-Permian. (Illus.). 1981. Repr. 3.00 (ISBN 0-686-36995-5). Bur Econ Geology.

GEOLOGY, STRATIGRAPHIC–PLEISTOCENE

Axelrod, Daniel I. New Pleistocene Conifer Records: Coastal California. LC 83-6874. (Geological Sciences Ser.: Vol. 127). 120p. 1984. pap. text ed. 11.00x (ISBN 0-520-09707-6). U of Cal Pr.

Baker, Frank C. Life of the Pleistocene or Glacial Period. LC 74-80996. (BCL Ser. I). 1969. Repr. of 1920 ed. 37.50 (ISBN 0-404-00449-0). AMS Pr.

Borns, Harold W., Jr., et al, eds. Late Pleistocene History of NE New England & Adjacent Quebec. (Special Paper Ser.: No. 197). (Illus.). 160p. 1985. 22.50 (ISBN 0-8137-2197-0). Geol Soc.

Butzer, Karl W. Environment & Archeology: An Ecological Approach to Prehistory. 2nd ed. LC 74-115938. (Illus.). 703p. 1971. text ed. 39.95x (ISBN 0-202-33023-0). Aldine Pub.

Carnegie Institution Of Washington. Papers Concerning the Palaeontology of the Pleistocene of California & the Tertiary of Oregon. Repr. of 1925 ed. 19.00 (ISBN 0-685-02123-8). Johnson Repr.

--Studies of the Pleistocene Palaeobotany of California. Repr. of 1934 ed. 19.00 (ISBN 0-685-02051-7). Johnson Repr.

Carter, George F. Pleistocene Man at San Diego. LC 77-74811. Repr. of 1957 ed. 37.00 (ISBN 0-404-14885-9). AMS Pr.

Coleman, Arthur P. The Last Million Years: A History of the Pleistocene in North America. LC 75-41062. (BCL Ser.: Ii). Repr. of 1941 ed. 21.50 (ISBN 0-404-14656-2). AMS Pr.

Crandall, D. R. & Mullineaux, D. R. Pleistocene Sequence in Southeastern Part of the Puget Sound Lowland, Washington. (Reprint Ser.: No. 2). (Illus.). 14p. 1958. 0.25 (ISBN 0-686-36910-6). Geologic Pubns.

Daly, Reginald A. The Changing World of the Ice Age. 1963. Repr. of 1934 ed. 21.75x (ISBN 0-02-843500-1). Hafner.

Gray, J. M. & Lowe, J. J., eds. Studies in the Scottish Lateglacial Environment. 1977. text ed. 35.00 (ISBN 0-08-020498-8). Pergamon.

Hambrey, M. J. & Harland, W. B. Earth's Pre-Pleistocene Glacial Record. LC 80-41613. (Cambridge Earth Science Ser.). (Illus.). 1009p. 1981. 220.00 (ISBN 0-521-22860-3). Cambridge U Pr.

Healy-Williams, Nancy, ed. Principles of Pleistocene Stratigraphy Applied to the Gulf of Mexico. (Illus.). 252p. 1984. 39.00 (ISBN 0-934634-72-6). Intl Human Res.

James, N. P. & Schenk, P. E. Field Guide to Pleistocene & Modern Carbonates of Bermuda. (Special Publication: No. 25). 72p. 1983. pap. 6.00 (ISBN 0-917642-25-2). Bermuda Bio.

Movius, Hallam L. Early Man & Pleistocene Stratigraphy in Southern & Eastern Asia. (HU PMP Ser.). (Illus.). 1944. 21.00 (ISBN 0-527-01249-1). Kraus Repr.

Newcomb, R. C. Ringold Formation of Pleistocene Age in Type Locality, The White Bluffs, Washington. (Reprint Ser.: No. 1). (Illus.). 13p. 1958. 0.25 (ISBN 0-686-36909-2). Geologic Pubns.

Reynolds, S. H. The Pleistocene Mustelidae. Repr. of 1912 ed. 16.00 (ISBN 0-384-50426-4). Johnson Repr.

Sandford, Kenneth S. & Arkell, W. J. Paleolithic Man & the Nile-Faiyum Divide, Vol. 1. LC 30-8240. (Illus.). 1930. 20.00X (ISBN 0-226-62104-9, OIP10). U of Chicago Pr.

Schneider, Allan F. Pleistocene Geology of the Randall Region, Central Minnesota. LC 61-63788. (Bulletin: No. 40). 1961. 4.25x (ISBN 0-8166-0244-1). Minn Geol Survey.

Stock, Chester. Rancho La Brea: A Record of Pleistocene Life in California. 6th ed. (Science Ser.: No. 20). (Illus.). 81p. 1972. 7.00 (ISBN 0-938644-01-7); softcover 4.00 (ISBN 0-938644-00-9). Nat Hist Mus.

Stuart, A. J. Pleistocene Vertebrates in the British Isles. (Illus.). 288p. 1982. 38.00x (ISBN 0-582-30069-X). Longman.

West, R. G. Pleistocene Geology & Biology. 2nd ed. LC 76-28353. (Illus.). 1977. pap. text ed. 21.95x (ISBN 0-582-44620-1). Longman.

Williams, Howell & Curtis, G. H. The Sutter Buttes of California: A Study of Plio-Pleistocene Volcanism. (Library Reprint Ser.: No. 97). 1979. Repr. of 1977 ed. 16.50x (ISBN 0-520-03808-8). U of Cal Pr.

Wright, Herbert E., ed. Late Quaternary Environments of the United States, Volume 1: The Late Pleistocene. LC 83-5804. (Illus.). 480p. 1983. 45.00x (ISBN 0-8166-1169-6). U of Minn Pr.

GEOLOGY, STRATIGRAPHIC–PLIOCENE

Berggren, W. F. & Van Couvering, J. Late Neogene. 1975. 29.50 (ISBN 0-444-41246-8). Elsevier.

Sandford, Kenneth S. & Arkell, W. J. Paleolithic Man & the Nile-Faiyum Divide, Vol. 1. LC 30-8240. (Illus.). 1930. 20.00X (ISBN 0-226-62104-9, OIP10). U of Chicago Pr.

GEOLOGY, STRATIGRAPHIC–PRE-CAMBRIAN

see also Geology, Stratigraphic–Archaean

Bickford, Marion E. & Mose, D. G. Geochronology of Precambrian Rocks in the St. Francois Mountains, Southeastern Missouri. LC 75-25345. (Geological Society of America Special Paper Ser.: No. 165). pap. 20.00 (ISBN 0-317-30059-8, 2025033). Bks Demand UMI.

Condie, K. C. Archean Greenstone Belts. (Developments in Pre-Cambrian Geology Ser.: Vol. 3). 434p. 1981. 110.75 (ISBN 0-444-41854-7). Elsevier.

Doe, B. R. & Smith, D. K., eds. Studies in Mineralogy & Precambrian Geology: A Volume in Honor of John W. Gruner. LC 70-190173. (Geological Society of America Memoir Ser.: No. 135). pap. 93.00 (ISBN 0-317-30052-0, 2025029). Bks Demand UMI.

French, Bevan M. Progressive Contact Metamorphism of the Biwabik Iron-Formation, Mesabi Range, Minnesota. LC 68-66592. (Bulletin: No. 45). (Illus.). 1968. 4.50x (ISBN 0-8166-0478-9). Minn Geol Survey.

Goldich, Samuel S., et al. Precambrian Geology & Geochronology of Minnesota. LC 61-8016. (Bulletin: No. 41). (Illus.). 1961. 4.00x (ISBN 0-8166-0224-7). Minn Geol Survey.

Gundersen, James N. & Schwartz, George M. Geology of the Metamorphosed Biwabik Iron Formation, Eastern Mesabi District, Minnesota. LC 62-9302. (Bulletin: No. 43). 1962. 4.25x (ISBN 0-8166-0274-3). Minn Geol Survey.

Handford, C. Robertson, et al. Regional Cross Sections of the Texas Panhandle: Precambrian to Mid-Permian. (Illus.). 1981. Repr. 3.00 (ISBN 0-686-36995-5). Bur Econ Geology.

Hunter, D. R., ed. Precambrian of the Southern Hemisphere. (Developments in Precambrian Geology Ser.: Vol. 2). 882p. 1981. 149.00 (ISBN 0-444-41862-8). Elsevier.

Killeen, P. G. & Heier, K. S. Radioelement Distribution & Heat Production in Precambrian Granitic Rocks, Southern Norway. 1975. pap. 11.00x (ISBN 8-200-01463-0, Dist. by Columbia U Pr). Universitet.

Kroner, A., ed. Precambrian Plate Tectonics. (Developments in Precambrian Geology Ser.: Vol. 4). 782p. 1981. 161.75 (ISBN 0-444-41910-1). Elsevier.

Medaris, L. G., Jr., ed. Early Proterozoic Geology of the Great Lakes Region. (Memoir Ser.: No. 160). (Illus.). 1983. 28.00 (ISBN 0-8137-1160-6). Geol Soc.

Medaris, L. G., Jr., et al, eds. Proterozoic Geology: Selected Papers from an International Proterozoic Symposium. (Memoir Ser.: No. 161). (Illus.). 1983. 49.00 (ISBN 0-8137-1161-4). Geol Soc.

Melnik, Y. P., ed. Precambrian Banded Iron Formations: Physicochemical Conditions of Formations. (Developments in Precambrian Geology Ser.: Vol. 5). 310p. 1982. 72.50 (ISBN 0-444-41934-9). Elsevier.

Salop, L. J. Precambrian of the Northern Hemisphere. (Developments in Paleontology & Stratigraphy Ser.: Vol. 3). 382p. 1977. 93.75 (ISBN 0-444-41510-6). Elsevier.

Vidal, Gonzalo. Late Precambrian Microfossils from the Visingso Beds in Southern Sweden. (Fossils & Strata: No.9). 1976. pap. text ed. 18.00x (ISBN 8-200-09418-9, Dist. by Columbia U Pr). Universitet.

GEOLOGY, STRATIGRAPHIC–QUATERNARY

see also Geology, Stratigraphic–Pleistocene

Al-Sayari, S. S. & Zoetl, J. G., eds. Quaternary Period in Saudi Arabia One. (Illus.). 1978. 61.00 (ISBN 0-387-81448-5). Springer-Verlag.

Andrews, John T. & Andrews, Martha, eds. Quaternary Studies on Baffin Island, West Greenland & Baffin Bay. 400p. cancelled (ISBN 0-08-027559-1). Pergamon.

Bowen, D. Q., ed. Quaternary Science Reviews, Vol. 1. (Illus.). 340p. 1984. 84.00 (ISBN 0-08-031491-0). Pergamon.

Bryant, Vaughn M. & Holloway, Richard G., eds. Pollen Records of Late Quaternary North American Sediments. (Illus.). 350p. 1985. 35.00 (ISBN 0-931871-01-8). Am Assn Strat.
Butzer, Karl W. Quaternary Stratigraphy & Climate in the Near East. 1958. pap. 20.00 (ISBN 0-384-06790-5). Johnson Repr.
Cline, R. M. & Hays, J. D., eds. Investigation of Late Quaternary Paleoceanography & Paleoclimatology. LC 75-40899. (Memoir: No. 145). (Illus.). 1976. 30.00 (ISBN 0-8137-1145-2). Geol Soc.
Douglas, Ian & Spencer, Tom, eds. Environmental Change & Tropical Geomorphology. (Illus.). 400p. 1985. text ed. 45.00x (ISBN 0-04-551074-1). Allen Unwin.
Enos, Paul & Perkins, R. D. Quaternary Sedimentation in South Florida. LC 76-44123. (Memoir: No. 147). (Illus.). 1977. 34.00 (ISBN 0-8137-1147-9). Geol Soc.
Flint, Richard F. Glacial & Quaternary Geology. LC 74-141198. (Illus.). 892p. 1977. 52.95x (ISBN 0-471-26435-0). Wiley.
Hulten, E. Outline of the History of the Arctic & Boreal Biota During the Quaternary Period. (Illus.). 1972. Repr. of 1937 ed. 28.00 (ISBN 3-7682-0006-X). Lubrecht & Cramer.
Jado, A. R. & Zotl, J. G., eds. Quaternary Period in Saudi Arabia, Sedimentological, Hydrogeological, Hydrochemical, Geochronological, & Climatological Investigations in Western Saudi Arabia, Vol. 2. (Illus.). 420p. 1984. 59.00 (ISBN 0-387-81749-2). Springer Verlag.
Lowe, J. J. & Walker, J. C. Reconstructing Quaternary Environments. (Illus.). 352p. 1985. pap. text ed. 24.95 (ISBN 0-582-30070-3). Longman.
McCalpin, James P. Quaternary Geology & Neotectonics of the West Flank of the Northern Sangre de Cristo Mountains, South-Central Colorado. Raese, Jon W. & Goldberg, J. H., eds. LC 82-17899. (Colorado School of Mines Quarterly Ser.: Vol. 77, No. 3). 97p. 1983. pap. text ed. 12.00 (ISBN 0-686-82132-7). Colo Sch Mines.
Mahaney, W. C. Quaternary Dating Methods. (Developments in Palaeontology & Stratigraphy Ser.: Vol. 7). 1984. 72.25 (ISBN 0-444-42392-3). Elsevier.
Neale, J. & Flenley, J., eds. The Quaternary in Britain: Essays Reviews & Original Work on the Quarternary Published in Honour of Lewis Penny on His Retirement. (Illus.). 278p. 1981. 37.00 (ISBN 0-08-026254-6). Pergamon.
Richards, Horace G. Annotated Bibliography of Quarternary Shorelines: Supplement 1965-1969. (Special Publication: No. 10). 240p. 1970. lib. bdg. 17.00 (ISBN 0-910006-37-7); pap. 14.00 (ISBN 0-910006-44-X). Acad Nat Sci Phila.
--Annotated Bibliography of Quaternary Shorelines: Second Supplement 1970-1973. (Special Publication: No. 11). 214p. 1974. lib. bdg. 24.00 (ISBN 0-910006-38-5); pap. 21.00 (ISBN 0-910006-45-8). Acad Nat Sci Phila.
Richards, Horace G. & Fairbridge, Rhodes W. Annotated Bibliography of Quaternary Shorelines (1945-1964) (Special Publication: No. 6). 280p. (Orig.). 1965. pap. 11.00 (ISBN 0-910006-34-2). Acad Nat Sci Phila.
Velichko, A. A., et al, eds. Late Quaternary Environments of the Soviet Union. LC 83-25892. (Illus.). 320p. 1984. 45.00x (ISBN 0-8166-1250-1). U of Minn Pr.
Wright, Herbert E., ed. Late Quaternary Environments of the United States, Volume 1: The Late Pleistocene. LC 83-5804. (Illus.). 480p. 1983. 45.00x (ISBN 0-8166-1169-6). U of Minn Pr.
Wright, Herbert E., Jr., ed. Late Quaternary Environments of the United States, Volume 2: The Holocene. LC 83-5804. (Illus.). 384p. 1983. 45.00x (ISBN 0-8166-1171-8). U of Minn Pr.
Wynne-Edwards, Hugh R. Terracy: Reconciliation with the Earth. (Illus.). 1986. text ed. write for info. (ISBN 0-87735-031-0). Freeman Cooper.

GEOLOGY, STRATIGRAPHIC–SILURIAN

Bassett, Michael G. & Cocks, Leonard R. A Review of Silvrian Brachiopods from Gotland. (Fossils & Strata Ser: No. 3). 1974. 10.50x (ISBN 8-200-09349-2, Dist. by Columbia U Pr). Universitet.
Budge, D. R. & Sheehan, P. M. The Upper Ordovician Through Middle Silurian of the Eastern Great Basin: Part Two - Lithologic Descriptions. 80p. 1980. 5.50 (ISBN 0-89326-041-X). Milwaukee Pub Mus.
Larsson, Kent. Silurian Tentaculitids from Gotland & Scania. (Fossils & Strata Ser.: No. 11). 1979. pap. 35.00x (ISBN 82-00-09483-9, Dist. by Columbia U Pr.). Universitet.
Sheehan, P. M. The Late Ordovician & Silurian of the Eastern Great Basin: Part Three - Brachiopods of the Tony Grove Lake Member of the Laketown Dolomite. 23p. 1980. 2.25 (ISBN 0-89326-054-1). Milwaukee Pub Mus.
Sheehan, Peter M. The Late Ordovician & Silurian of the Eastern Great Basin: Part Four - Late Llandovery & Wenlock Brachiopods. 83p. 1982. 7.95. Milwaukee Pub Mus.

GEOLOGY, STRATIGRAPHIC–TERTIARY

see also Geology, Stratigraphic–Eocene; Geology, Stratigraphic–Paleocene; Geology, Stratigraphic–Pliocene

Mallory, Virgil S. Lower Tertiary Biostratigraphy of the California Coast Ranges. LC 59-1390. pap. 115.00 (ISBN 0-317-29061-4, 2023745). Bks Demand UMI.
Oaks, Robert Q., Jr. & DuBar, Jules R., eds. Post-Miocene Stratigraphy Central & Southern Atlantic Coastal Plain. 275p. 1974. 13.00 (ISBN 0-87421-065-8). Utah St U Pr.
Paleopedology & Stratigraphy on the Condrusian Peneplain: Belguim. (Agricultural Research Reports: 766). 1972. pap. 9.00 (ISBN 90-220-0377-9, PDC62, PUDOC). Unipub.
Stewart, Ralph B. Gabb's California Cretaceous & Tertiary Type Lamellibranchs. (Special Publication: No. 3). (Illus.). 314p. (Orig.). 1930. pap. 15.00 (ISBN 0-910006-31-8). Acad Nat Sci Phila.
Tertiary Stratigraphic Papers, Southwestern Washington. (Reprint Ser.: No. 3). (Illus.). 45p. 1959. 0.25 (ISBN 0-686-36911-4). Geologic Pubns.
Weaver, Charles E. Tertiary Stratigraphy of Western Washington & Northwestern Oregon. (Publications in Geology: No. 4). 266p. 1937. pap. 17.50x (ISBN 0-295-73962-2). U of Wash Pr.
West, R. M. & Lukacs, J. R. Geology & Vertebrate-Fossil Localities, Tertiary Continental Rocks, Kala-Chitta Hills, Attock District, Pakistan. 20p. 1979. 1.50 (ISBN 0-89326-047-9). Milwaukee Pub Mus.

GEOLOGY, STRATIGRAPHIC–TRIASSIC

Kier, Porter M. Echinoids from the Triassic (St. Cassian) of Italy, Their Lantern Supports, & a Revised Physogeny of Triassic Echinoids. LC 83-600346. (Smithsonian Contributions to Paleobiology: No. 56). pap. 20.00 (ISBN 0-317-20101-8, 2023162). Bks Demand UMI.
Nichols, K. M. & Silberling, N. J. Stratigraphy & Depositional History of the Star Peak Group (Triassic) Northwestern Nevada. LC 77-89753. (Special Paper: No. 178). (Illus.). 1977. pap. 7.75 (ISBN 0-8137-2178-4). Geol Soc.

GEOLOGY, STRUCTURAL

see also Domes (Geology); Faults (Geology); Folds (Geology); Geomorphology; Mountains; Plate Tectonics; Rifts (Geology)

Bailey, E. B. Tectonic Essays, Mainly Alpine. 1935. 39.50x (ISBN 0-19-854368-9). Oxford U Pr.
Baker, Wallace H., ed. Grouting in Geotechnical Engineering. LC 81-71798. 1028p. 1982. pap. 69.00x (ISBN 0-87262-295-9). Am Soc Civil Eng.
Banerjee, P. K. & Butterfield, R., eds. Developments in Soil Mechanics & Foundation Engineering, Vol. 1. (Illus.). 266p. 1984. 59.25 (ISBN 0-85334-222-9, Pub. by Elsevier Applied Sci England). Elsevier.
Belousov, V. V. Geotectonics. (Illus.). 330p. 1980. 34.00 (ISBN 0-387-09173-4). Springer-Verlag.
Berner, Robert A. Early Diagenesis: A Theoretical Approach. LC 80-7510. (Princeton Series in Geochemistry: No. 1). (Illus.). 256p. 1980. 35.00 (ISBN 0-691-08258-8); pap. 15.50 (ISBN 0-691-08260-X). Princeton U Pr.
Billings, Marland P. Structural Geology. 3rd ed. (Illus.). 1972. 37.95 (ISBN 0-13-853846-8). P-H.
Bott, Martin H. & Saxov, Svend, eds. Structure & Development of the Greenland-Scotland Ridge: New Methods & Concepts. (NATO Conference Ser. IV, Marine Sciences: Vol. 8). 696p. 1982. 95.00x (ISBN 0-306-41019-2, Plenum Pr). Plenum Pub.
Carreras, J., et al. Shear Zones in Rocks: Papers Presented at the International Conference Held at the University of Barcelona, May 1979. 200p. 1980. pap. 44.00 (ISBN 0-08-026244-9). Pergamon.
Cermak, V. & Rybach, L., eds. Terrestrial Heat Flow in Europe. (Illus.). 1979. 59.00 (ISBN 0-387-09440-7). Springer-Verlag.
Clark, George B. Geotechnical Centrifuges for Model Studies & Physical Property Testing of Rock & Rock Structures. Raese, Jon W., ed. LC 81-21614. (Colorado School of Mines Quarterly Ser.: Vol. 76, No. 4). (Illus.). 63p. 1982. pap. text ed. 12.00 (ISBN 0-686-79746-9). Colo Sch Mines.
Clark, Sydney P. Structure of the Earth. (Foundations of Earth Science Ser). 1971. pap. text ed. 15.95 (ISBN 0-13-854646-0). P-H.
Cloos, Ernst. Microtectonics along the Western Edge of the Blue Ridge, Maryland, & Virginia. LC 77-156828. (Johns Hopkins University Studies in Geology Ser.: No. 20). pap. 65.30 (ISBN 0-317-29738-4, 2015688). Bks Demand UMI.
Das, Braja M. Principles of Geotechnical Engineering. 1985. text ed. write for info. (ISBN 0-534-03765-8, 21R4400, Pub. by PWS Engineering). PWS Pubs.
Davis, George H. Structural Geology of Rocks & Regions. LC 83-17076. 492p. 1984. text ed. 37.45 (ISBN 0-471-09267-3). Wiley.
Dennis, J. G. & Murawski, H. International Tectonic Lexicon: A Prodrome. (International Union of Geological Sciences Ser.). 153p. 1979. pap. text ed. 24.00x (ISBN 3-510-65092-1). Lubrecht & Cramer.
Dennis, John G. Structural Geology. 532p. 1972. 38.95 (ISBN 0-471-06746-6). Wiley.
Donn, William L. & Shimer, John A. Graphic Methods in Structual Geology. LC 58-5315. (The Century Earth Science Ser.). pap. 45.00 (ISBN 0-317-26222-X, 2055684). Bks Demand UMI.
Dorr, John A., Jr., et al. Deformation & Deposition Between a Foreland Uplift & an Impinging Thrust Belt: Hoback Basin, Wyoming. LC 77-70022. (Special Paper: No. 177). (Illus.). 1977. pap. 10.00 (ISBN 0-8137-2177-6). Geol Soc.
Ernst, W. G., ed. The Geotectonic Development of California, Vol. 1. (Illus.). 720p. 1981. text ed. 45.95 (ISBN 0-13-353938-5). P-H.
Geddes, James D. Large Ground Movements & Structures. LC 78-19092. 1064p. 1978. 96.95x (ISBN 0-470-26460-8). Halsted Pr.
Geomechanics. (AMD Ser.: Vol. 57). 78p. 1983. pap. text ed. 20.00 (ISBN 0-317-02622-4, G00229). ASME.
Goguel, Jean. Tectonics. Thalmann, H. E., tr. LC 62-7477. (Geology Ser.). (Illus.). 384p. 1962. 38.95 (ISBN 0-7167-0217-7). W H Freeman.
Hanrahan, E. A. Geotechnics of Real Materials: The E-G, E-K Method. (Developments in Geotechnical Engineering Ser.: Vol. 39). 254p. 1985. 50.00 (ISBN 0-444-42470-9). Elsevier.
Harmon, R. S., et al, eds. Andean Magmatism: Chemical & Isotopic Constraints. 300p. 1984. 39.95 (ISBN 0-906812-60-7); pap. 19.95s (ISBN 0-906812-61-5). Birkhauser.
Hills, E. S. Elements of Structural Geology. 2nd ed. 1972. pap. 23.95x (ISBN 0-412-20750-8, NO.6300, Pub. by Chapman & Hall). Methuen Inc.
Hobbs, B. E., et al. An Outline of Structural Geology. LC 75-20393. 571p. 1976. text ed. 38.45 (ISBN 0-471-40156-0). Wiley.
King, Philip B. Tectonics of Middle North America: Middle North America East of the Cordilleran Systems. (Illus.). 1969. Repr. 19.95x (ISBN 0-02-847920-3). Hafner.
La Pointe, P. R. & Hudson, J. A., eds. Characterization & Interpretation of Rock Mass Joint Patterns. (Special Paper Ser.: No. 199). (Illus.). 45p. 1985. 10.50 (ISBN 0-8137-2199-7). Geol Soc.
Lee, J. S. Introduction to Geomechanics. 2nd ed. 140p. 1983. 68.00 (ISBN 0-677-31070-6). Gordon.
Lewin, Benjamin M. Genes. LC 84-15350. 1985. 38.95 (ISBN 0-471-80789-3). Wiley.
Liquefaction Problems in Geotechnical Engineering. 394p. 1976. pap. 16.50x (ISBN 0-87262-324-6). Am Soc Civil Eng.
Lowell, James D. Structural Styles in Petroleum Exploration. 460p. 1985. 45.00 (ISBN 0-930972-08-2). Oil & Gas.
McCall, G. J. H., ed. Astroblemes-Cryptoexplosion Structures. LC 79-10991. (Benchmark Papers in Geology: Vol. 50). 437p. 1979. 57.95 (ISBN 0-87933-342-1). Van Nos Reinhold.
Mainwaring, William L. Exploring Oregon's Central & Southern Cascades. LC 79-64841. (Illus.). 1979. pap. 7.95 (ISBN 0-918832-02-0). Westridge.
Matsumoto, T. Age & Nature of the Circum-Pacific Orogenesis. 1967. 42.50 (ISBN 0-686-43415-3). Elsevier.
Miyashiro, Akiho, et al. Orogeny. LC 82-8499. 242p. 1982. (Pub. by Wiley-Interscience); 21.95 (ISBN 0-471-10377-2). Wiley.
Neumann, Else-Ragnhild & Ramberg, Ivar B., eds. Petrology & Geochemistry of Continental Rifts. (Nato Advanced Study Institute Ser. C: No. 36). 1978. lib. bdg. 42.00 (ISBN 90-277-0866-5, Pub. by Reidel Holland). Kluwer Academic.
Park, R. G. Foundations of Structural Geology. (Illus.). 135p. 1982. 38.00 (ISBN 0-412-00181-0, NO. 5025, Chapman & Hall); pap. 17.95 (ISBN 0-412-00191-8, NO. 5026, Chapman & Hall). Methuen Inc.
Peter, P. Canal & River Levees. (Developments in Geotechnical Engineering Ser.: Vol. 29). 540p. 1982. 104.25 (ISBN 0-444-99726-1). Elsevier.
Platt, John & Challinor, John. Simple Geological Structures. 1974. pap. text ed. 4.95x (ISBN 0-04-550020-7). Allen Unwin.
Price, N. J. Fault & Joint Development in Brittle & Semi-Brittle Rock. 1966. pap. 13.00 (ISBN 0-08-011274-9). Pergamon.
Ragan, D. M. Structural Geology: An Introduction to Geometrical Techniques. 3rd ed. 405p. 1984. pap. 21.95 (ISBN 0-471-08043-8). Wiley.
Ragan, Donal M. Structural Geology: An Introduction to Geometrical Techniques. 2nd ed. LC 73-3335. (Illus.). 288p. 1973. pap. text ed. 25.45 (ISBN 0-471-70481-4). Wiley.
Ramberg, Ivar B. & Neumann, Else-Ragnhild, eds. Tectonics & Geophysics of Continental Rifts. (NATO Advanced Study Institute Ser.: No. 37). 1978. lib. bdg. 42.00 (ISBN 90-277-0867-3, Pub. by Reidel Holland). Kluwer Academic.
Ramsay, John G. & Huber, Martin. The Techniques of Modern Structural Geology, Vol. 1. 1984. 55.00 (ISBN 0-12-576901-6); pap. 28.00 (ISBN 0-12-576921-0); instrs' manual 1.50 (ISBN 0-12-576911-3). Acad Pr.
Raymond, Loren A., ed. Melanges: Their Nature, Origin, & Significance. (Special Paper Ser.: No. 198). (Illus.). 175p. 1985. 22.00 (ISBN 0-8137-2198-9). Geol Soc.
Rowland, Stephen M. Structural Analysis & Synthesis: A Laboratory Course in Structural Geology. (Illus.). 200p. 1986. pap. text ed. 14.95x (ISBN 0-86542-308-3). Blackwell Sci.
Sanglerat, G. Penetrometer & Soil Exploration. (Developments in Geotechnical Engineering Ser.: Vol. 1). 464p. 1972. 72.50 (ISBN 0-444-40976-9). Elsevier.
Sengor, A. M., ed. The Cimmeride Orogenic System & the Tectonics of Eurasia. (Special Paper Ser.: No. 195). (Illus.). 1984. 17.00 (ISBN 0-8137-2195-4). Geol Soc.
Sheinmann, Yu. M. Tectonics & the Formation of Magmas. LC 70-136981. 173p. 1971. 30.00x (ISBN 0-306-10859-3, Consultants). Plenum Pub.
Sommerville, Paul. Dictionary of Geotechnics. 1983. text ed. 49.95 (ISBN 0-408-00437-1). Butterworth.
Spencer, Edgar W. Introduction to the Structure of the Earth. 2nd ed. 1977. text ed. 43.95 (ISBN 0-07-060197-6). McGraw.
Suppe, John. Principles of Structural Geology. (Illus.). 560p. 1985. text ed. 38.95 (ISBN 0-13-710500-2). P-H.
Tarling, D. H., ed. Economic Geology & Geotectonics. LC 81-673. 213p. 1981. 58.95x (ISBN 0-470-27145-0). Halsted Pr.
Tatsch, J. H. The Earth's Tectonosphere: Its Past Development & Present Behavior. 2nd ed. LC 74-78917. (Illus.). 468p. 1977. 30.00 (ISBN 0-912890-03-7). Tatsch.
Thornbury, William D. Principles of Geomorphology. 2nd ed. LC 68-8323. 594p. 1969. text ed. 41.50x (ISBN 0-471-86197-9). Wiley.
Uemura, Takeshi & Mizuta, Shinjiro. Geological Structures. (Texts in Earth Sciences: 1-713). 309p. 1984. 39.95 (ISBN 0-471-90411-2). Wiley.
Vyskcosil, P. & Green, R., eds. Recent Crustal Movements, 1979. (Developments in Geotectonics: Vol. 16). 356p. 81. Repr. 83.00 (ISBN 0-444-41953-5). Elsevier.
Vyskocil, P., et al, eds. Recent Crustal Movements, 1982: Proceedings of the 3rd Symposium on Recent Crustal Movements & Phenomena Associated with Earthquakes & Volcanism, May 12-13, 1982, Tokyo, at the General Meeting of the International Association of Geodesy. (Developments in Geotectonophysics Ser.: Vol. 20). 352p. 1983. Repr. 89.50 (ISBN 0-444-42243-9, I-315-83). Elsevier.
Whitten, C. A., et al, eds. Recent Crustal Movement, 1977. (Developments in Geotectonics: Vol. 13). 664p. 1979. 89.50 (ISBN 0-444-41783-4). Elsevier.
Yong, R. N. & Selig, E. T., eds. Application of Plasticity & Generalized Stress-Strain in Geotechnical Engineering. LC 81-71796. 359p. 1982. pap. 27.25x (ISBN 0-87262-294-0). Am Soc Civil Eng.

GEOLOGY, SUBMARINE

see Submarine Geology

GEOLOGY AS A PROFESSION

American Geological Institute. Geology: Science & Profession. 1976. pap. 1.00 (ISBN 0-913312-19-3). Am Geol.
Rossbacher, Lisa A. Career Opportunities in Geology & the Earth Sciences. LC 82-1799. 192p. 1983. 12.95 (ISBN 0-668-05205-8); pap. 7.95 (ISBN 0-668-05220-1). Arco.
Snelgrove, Alfred K. Opportunities in Geology & Geological Engineering. LC 72-111531. 1970. pap. 1.25 (ISBN 0-8442-6474-1). Natl Textbk.

GEOMAGNETISM

see Magnetism, Terrestrial

GEOMETRICAL DRAWING

see also Geometry, Descriptive; Graphic Methods; Mechanical Drawing; Projection

Adcock, Carol P. Geometric Maze Designs. (International Design Library). (Illus.). 48p. (Orig.). 1984. pap. 3.50 (ISBN 0-88045-048-7). Stemmer Hse.
Agarwal, D. D., et al. Geometrical Drawing. 1984. text ed. 22.50x (ISBN 0-7069-0802-3, Pub. by Vikas India). Advent NY.

Jablonski, Sergeiv. Diskrete Mathematik und Mathematische Fragen der Kybernetik. (Mathematische Reihe Ser.: No. 71). (Ger.). 260p. 1979. 45.95x (ISBN 0-8176-1071-5). Birkhauser.

Jacobs, Harold R. Geometry. LC 73-20024. (Illus.). 701p. 1974. text ed. 17.95 (ISBN 0-7167-0456-0); tchr's guide 7.95 (ISBN 0-7167-0460-9); test masters 6.00 (ISBN 0-7167-0459-5); transparency masters 45.00x (ISBN 0-7167-0458-7). W H Freeman.

--Geometry. LC 85-7034. 1986. price not set (ISBN 0-7167-1745-X). W H Freeman.

Jeger, M. & Eckmann, M. Einfuehrung in die Vektorielle Geometrie und Lineare Algebra fur Ingenieure und Naturwissenschafter. (Ger.). 252p. 1967. 38.95x (ISBN 0-8176-0198-8). Birkhauser.

Johnson, Delvin J. Solutions to the Three Historical Problems by Compass & Straightedge. 1982. 6.95 (ISBN 0-533-05050-2). Vantage.

Keedy, Mervin & Bittinger, Marvin. Functions & Basic Geometry. rev. ed. (Algebra, a Modern Introduction Ser.). 1980. pap. text ed. 4.32 (ISBN 0-201-03985-0, Sch Div). Addison-Wesley.

Kelly, Paul J. & Weiss, Max L. Geometry & Convexity: A Study in Mathematical Methods. LC 78-21919. (Pure & Applied Mathematics Ser.). 261p. 1979. 48.50x (ISBN 0-471-04637-X, Pub. by Wiley-Interscience). Wiley.

Klein, Felix. Vorlesungen Ueber Hoehere Geometrie. 3rd ed. LC 51-3040. 1976. text ed. 9.95 (ISBN 0-8284-0065-2). Chelsea Pub.

Kluge, Eike-Henner, tr. from Ger. Gottlob Frege on the Foundations of Geometry & Formal Theories of Arithmetic. LC 74-140533. Repr. of 1971 ed. 39.00 (ISBN 0-8357-9190-4, 2016768). Bks Demand UMI.

Kogan, B. Yu. The Applications of Mechanics to Geometry. LC 73-89789. (Popular Lectures in Mathematics Ser). 66p. 1975. pap. text ed. 4.50x (ISBN 0-226-45016-3). U of Chicago Pr.

Kutepov, A. Problems in Geometry. 208p. 1975. 5.45 (ISBN 0-8285-0739-2, Pub. by Mir Pubs USSR). Imported Pubns.

Lang, Serge & Murrow, Gene. Geometry. (Illus.). 464p. 1982. pap. text ed. 26.00 (ISBN 0-387-90727-0). Springer-Verlag.

Lawlor, Robert. Sacred Geometry: Philosophy & Practice. Purce, Jill, ed. LC 81-67703. (The Illustrated Library of Sacred Imagination Ser.). (Illus.). 96p. 1982. pap. 9.95 (ISBN 0-8245-0067-9). Crossroad NY.

Ledermann, W. & Vajda, S. Handbook of Applicable Mathematics: Geometry & Combinatorics, 2 pts. (Handbook of Applicable Mathematics Ser.). 550p. 1985. Set. 170.00 (ISBN 0-471-90023-0); Pt. A. 85.00 (ISBN 0-471-90567-4); Pt. B. 85.00 (ISBN 0-471-90568-2). Wiley.

Leff. Geometry the Easy Way. 1984. pap. 7.95 (ISBN 0-8120-2718-3). Barron.

Leithold, Louis. The Calculus with Analytic Geometry, 2 vols. 4th ed. Incl. Vol. I. Functions of One Variable, Plane Analytic Geometry, & Infinite Series. 819p. text ed. 27.50 scp (ISBN 0-06-043936-X); scp outline to accompany text vol. I 11.50 (ISBN 0-06-044543-2); Vol. II. Infinite Series, Vectors, & Functions of Several Variables. 410p. text ed. 27.50 scp (ISBN 0-06-043937-8); scp outline to accompany text Vol II 11.50 (ISBN 0-06-044544-0); Vol. III. text ed. 11.50 scp outline to accompany text (ISBN 0-06-044545-9). 1981. Set, 2 vols. in 1. text ed. 27.50 scp (ISBN 0-06-043935-1, HarpC); scp solutions manual 18.95 (ISBN 0-06-043938-6); answer key avail. (ISBN 0-06-363958-0). Har-Row.

Levi, Howard. Topics in Geometry. LC 75-19477. 112p. 1975. Repr. of 1968 ed. 8.50 (ISBN 0-88275-280-4). Krieger.

Lines & Angles: Level Four Texts. rev. ed. (Math Components Ser.). 40p. 1983. 2.25 (ISBN 0-88336-840-4). New Readers.

Locher-Ernst, L. Einfuehrung in die Freie Geometrie Ebener Kurven. (Elemente der Mathematik Vom Hoeheren Standpunkt Aus: Vol. 1). (Ger.). 85p. 1952. pap. 13.95x (ISBN 0-8176-0252-6). Birkhauser.

Looijenga, E., et al, eds. Geometry Symposium, Utrecht Nineteen Eighty: Proceedings. (Lecture Notes in Mathematics Ser.: Vol. 894). 153p. 1981. pap. 14.00 (ISBN 0-387-11167-0). Springer-Verlag.

Lueneburg, H., ed. Translation Planes. 256p. 1980. 38.00 (ISBN 0-387-09614-0). Springer-Verlag.

Luneburg, H. Kombinatorik. (Elemente der Mathematik Vom Hoeheren Standpunkt Aus Ser.: Band 6). (Ger.). 108p. 1971. pap. 18.95x (ISBN 0-8176-0548-7). Birkhauser.

MacLane, Saunders. Selected Papers: Saunders MacLane. Kaplansky, I., ed. LC 79-10105. 1979. 39.50 (ISBN 0-387-90394-1). Springer-Verlag.

McLeod, Robin J. & Wachspress, Eugene L., eds. Frontiers of Applied Geometry: Proceedings of a Symposium, Las Cruces, New Mexico, 1980. 128p. 1981. pap. 26.00 (ISBN 0-08-026487-5). Pergamon.

Martin, Clyde & Hermann, Robert, eds. Ames Research Center (NASA) Conference on Geometric Control Theory, 1976. (Lie Groups: History, Frontiers & Applications Ser.: Vol. 7). 1977. 44.00 (ISBN 0-915692-21-X). Math Sci Pr.

Martin, G. E. Transformation Geometry: An Introduction to Symmetry. (Undergraduate Texts in Mathematics Ser.). (Illus.). 240p. 1982. 29.95 (ISBN 0-387-90636-3). Springer-Verlag.

Math Review. pocket ed. 150p. pap. text ed. cancelled (ISBN 0-8120-2198-3). Barron.

Matzner, Richard A. & Shepley, L. C., eds. Spacetime & Geometry: The Alfred Schild Lectures. 199p. 1982. text ed. 37.50x (ISBN 0-292-77567-9). U of Tex Pr.

Melzak, Z. A. Invitation to Geometry. LC 82-17483. (Pure & Applied Mathematics Ser.). 225p. 1983. 34.95x (ISBN 0-471-09209-6, Pub. by Wiley Interscience). Wiley.

Meserve, Bruce E. Fundamental Concepts of Geometry. (Illus.). 352p. 1983. pap. 7.50 (ISBN 0-486-63415-9). Dover.

Michael, W. Ortskurvengeometrie in der Komplexen Zahlenebene. (Ger., Illus.). 96p. 1950. 15.95x (ISBN 0-8176-0266-6). Birkhauser.

Millman, R. S. & Parker, G. D. Geometry: A Metric Approach with Models. (Undergraduate Texts in Mathematics Ser.). (Illus.). 355p. 1981. 29.80 (ISBN 0-387-90610-X). Springer-Verlag.

Mitchell, Robert & Prickel, Donald. Number Power Four: Geometry. (Number Power Ser.). 176p. (Orig.). 1983. pap. 4.95 (ISBN 0-8092-5517-0). Contemp Bks.

Moise, Edwin E. Elementary Geometry from an Advanced Standpoint. 2nd ed. LC 73-2347. 1974. text ed. 24.95 (ISBN 0-201-04793-4). Addison-Wesley.

Nagano, Tadashi. Homotopy Invariants in Differential Geometry. LC 52-42839. (Memoirs: No. 100). 41p. 1970. 9.00 (ISBN 0-8218-1800-7, MEMO-100). Am Math.

Nash, Charles & Sen, Siddartha. Topology & Geometry for Physicists. 1983. 43.00 (ISBN 0-12-514080-0). Acad Pr.

National Council of Teachers of Mathematics. Geometry in the Mathematics Curriculum: 36th Yearbook. LC 73-16458. (Illus.). 480p. 1973. 16.90 (ISBN 0-87353-016-0). NCTM.

Nevanlinna, R. Raum, Zeit und Relativitat. (Science & Civilization Ser.: No. 19). (Ger., Illus.). 229p. 1964. 29.95 (ISBN 0-8176-0277-1). Birkhauser.

Nevanlinna, R. & Kustaanheimo, P. Grundlagen der Geometrie. rev. 2nd ed. (Mathematische Reihe Ser.: No. 43). (Ger.). 136p. 1977. 29.95x (ISBN 0-8176-0958-X). Birkhauser.

Nichols, Eugene D., et al. Holt Geometry. 1982. text ed. 18.52 (ISBN 0-03-053866-1, HoltE); tchr's ed. 27.68 (ISBN 0-03-053871-8); testmasters 30.64 (ISBN 0-03-053881-5); skillmasters o.p. 54.60 (ISBN 0-03-053886-6); solutions manual 8.96 (ISBN 0-03-053876-9). HR&W.

--Holt Geometry. 1978. text ed. 18.32 (ISBN 0-03-018921-7); tchr's ed. 27.16 (ISBN 0-03-018926-8); testmasters 32.00 (ISBN 0-03-019756-2); skillmasters o.p. 39.39 (ISBN 0-03-019751-1). HR&W.

Nielsen, Kaj L. Mathematics for Practical Use. (Orig.). 1962. pap. 5.72i (ISBN 0-06-463212-1, EH 212, EH). B&N NY.

O'Neill, Barrett. Semi-Riemannian Geometry: With Applications to Relativity. (Pure & Applied Mathematics Ser.). 1983. 49.50 (ISBN 0-12-526740-1). Acad Pr.

Osserman, Robert & Weinstein, Alan, eds. Geometry of the LaPlace Operator. LC 79-26934. (Proceedings of Symposia in Pure Mathematics Ser.: Vol. 36). 323p. 1982. pap. 30.00 (ISBN 0-8218-1439-7). Am Math.

Palis, J., Jr., ed. Geometric Dynamics. (Lecture Notes in Mathematics Ser.: Vol. 1007). 827p. 1983. pap. 35.00 (ISBN 0-387-12336-9). Springer Verlag.

Pare, E. G., et al. Descriptive Geometry. 7th ed. 1986. text ed. price not set (ISBN 0-02-391320-7). Macmillan.

Pedoe, Dan. Geometry & the Visual Arts. (Illus.). 353p. 1983. pap. 5.95 (ISBN 0-486-24458-X). Dover.

Penna, Michael A. & Patterson, Richard R. Projective Geometry & Its Applications to Computer Graphics. (Illus.). 592p. 1986. text ed. 37.50 (ISBN 0-13-730649-0). P-H.

Polya, G. & Szego, G. Problems & Theorems in Analysis II: Theory of Functions, Zeros, Polynomials, Determinants, Number Theory, Geometry. Billigheimer, C. E., tr. (Illus.). 1977. pap. text ed. 24.00 (ISBN 0-387-90291-0). Springer-Verlag.

Porteous, I. R. Topological Geometry. 2nd ed. LC 79-41611. 1981. 67.50 (ISBN 0-521-23160-4); pap. 29.95 (ISBN 0-521-29839-3). Cambridge U Pr.

Postnikov, M. Lectures in Geometry: Linear Algebra & Differential Geometry. 319p. 1982. 8.45 (ISBN 0-8285-2461-0, Pub. by Mir Pubs USSR). Imported Pubns.

Prenowitz, W. & Jantosciak, J. The Theory of Join Spaces: A Contemporary Approach to Convex Sets & Linear Geometry. (Undergraduate Texts in Mathematics). (Illus.). 1979. 29.00 (ISBN 0-387-90340-2). Springer-Verlag.

Rado, Tibor. Length & Area. (American Mathematical Society, Colloquim Publications Ser.: Vol. 30). pap. 144.80 (ISBN 0-317-08616-2, 2004936). Bks Demand UMI.

Raleigh, A. S. Occult Geometry. 2nd ed. 80p. 1981. pap. 3.95 (ISBN 0-87516-448-X). De Vorss.

Rees, Paul K. Analytic Geometry. 3rd ed. 1970. ans. suppl. 0.50 (ISBN 0-13-034272-6). P-H.

Ringenberg, Lawrence A. College Geometry. LC 77-2631. (Illus.). 320p. 1977. Repr. of 1968 ed. lib. bdg. 19.50 (ISBN 0-88275-545-5). Krieger.

Robinson, Gilbert de Beauregard. The Foundations of Geometry. 4th ed. LC 48-3776. (Mathematical Expositions: No. 1). pap. 46.00 (ISBN 0-317-08573-5, 2020515). Bks Demand UMI.

Row, Sundara T., et al. Geometric Exercises in Paper Folding. Beman, Wooster W. & Smith, David E., eds. 162p. 1958. 17.95 (ISBN 0-87548-165-5). Open Court.

Row, T. S. Geometric Exercises in Paper Folding. rev. ed. Berman, W. W. & Smith, D. E., eds. (Illus.). 13.25 (ISBN 0-8446-2840-9). Peter Smith.

Row, T. Sundara. Geometric Exercises in Paper Folding. (Illus.). pap. 2.95 (ISBN 0-486-21594-6). Dover.

Rucker, Rudolf v. B. Geometry, Relativity & the Fourth Dimension. LC 76-22240. 1977. lib. bdg. 10.50x (ISBN 0-88307-584-9). Gannon.

Runion, Garth E. & Lockwood, James R. Deductive Systems: Finite & Non-Euclidean Geometries. LC 78-17827. (Illus.). 90p. 1978. pap. 4.00 (ISBN 0-87353-129-9). NCTM.

Ryskov, S. S., ed. The Geometry of Positive Quadratic Forms. LC 82-24328. (Proceedings of the Steklov Institute of Mathematics: No. 152). 88.00 (ISBN 0-8218-3070-8). Am Math.

Saxon, John H., Jr. Geometry & Trigonometry: An Incremental Development. 800p. 1985. text ed. 24.00 (ISBN 0-939798-12-3); tchr's. ed. avail. (ISBN 0-939798-13-1). Grassdale.

Schmidt, H. J. Axiomatic Characterization of Physical Geometry. (Lecture Notes in Physics Ser.: Vol. 111). 163p. 1979. pap. 16.00 (ISBN 0-387-09719-8). Springer-Verlag.

Schutz, B. Geometrical Methods of Mathematical Physics. LC 80-40211. (Illus.). 300p. 1980. 49.50 (ISBN 0-521-23271-6); pap. 18.95 (ISBN 0-521-29887-3). Cambridge U Pr.

Schwerdtfeger, Hans. Geometry of Complex Numbers. LC 79-52529. 1980. pap. text ed. 5.95 (ISBN 0-486-63830-8). Dover.

Semple, J. G. & Roth, L. Introduction to Algebraic Geometry. (Illus.). 480p. 1985. pap. 23.95 (ISBN 0-19-853363-2). Oxford U Pr.

Serre, Jean-Pierre & Shimura, Goro, eds. Geometry & Number Theory: A Volume in Honor of Andre Weil. LC 83-48062. 608p. 1983. text ed. 48.00x (ISBN 0-8018-3091-5). Johns Hopkins.

Seydel, Ken. Geometry: An Exercise in Reasoning. 1980. text ed. 27.95 (ISBN 0-7216-8070-4, CBS C). SCP.

Slaby, S. M. Fundamentals of Three-Dimensional Geometry. 2nd ed. LC 76-18152. 416p. 1976. 40.45x (ISBN 0-471-79621-2); wkbk. 20.45x (ISBN 0-471-79622-0); solns. wkbk. avail. (ISBN 0-471-01914-3); solns. manual avail. (ISBN 0-471-01913-5). Wiley.

Smart, Margaret A. & Laycock, Mary. Focus on Geometry. (Illus.). 1982. pap. 6.50 (ISBN 0-918932-78-5). Activity Resources.

Smith, Vincent E., tr. Saint Thomas & the Object of Geometry. (Aquinas Lecture). 1953. 7.95 (ISBN 0-87462-118-6). Marquette.

Sokolnikoff, Ivan S. Tensor Analysis: Theory & Applications to Geometry & Mechanics of Continua. 2nd ed. LC 64-13223. (Applied Mathematics Ser.). pap. 93.30 (ISBN 0-317-08559-X, 2055264). Bks Demand UMI.

Springer, Charles E. Geometry & Analysis of Projective Spaces. LC 64-21148. (Books in Mathematics Ser.). pap. 77.50 (ISBN 0-317-08705-3, 2055552). Bks Demand UMI.

Srivastava, H. M. & Karlsson, P. W. Multiple Gaussian Hypergeometric Series. (Mathematics & Its Applications Ser.). 1985. 74.95 (ISBN 0-470-20100-2). Halsted Pr.

Stasheff, J. H-Spaces from a Homotopy Point of View. LC 71-134651. (Lecture Notes in Mathematics: Vol. 161). 1970. pap. 12.00 (ISBN 0-387-04940-1). Springer-Verlag.

Steiner, Jacob. Gesammelte Werke, 2 Vols. 2nd ed. LC 76-113151. (Ger). 1971. text ed. 59.50 set (ISBN 0-8284-0233-7). Chelsea Pub.

Stiefel, E. Lehrbuch der Darstellenden Geometrie. 3rd ed. (Mathematische Reihe Ser.: No. 6). (Ger.). 177p. 1971. 32.95x (ISBN 0-8176-0368-9). Birkhauser.

Stokes, William T. Gems of Geometry. rev. ed. (Illus.). 1978. pap. text ed. 6.95 (ISBN 0-914534-02-5). Stokes.

Strambach, K. & Plaumann, P., eds. Geometry: Von Staudt's Point of View. xii, 426p. 1981. 58.00 (ISBN 90-277-1283-2, Pub. by Reidel Holland). Kluwer Academic.

Sulanke, R. & Wintgen, P. Differentialgeometrie und Faserbundel. (Mathematische Reihe Ser.: No. 48). (Ger.). 299p. 1972. 44.95x (ISBN 0-8176-0646-7). Birkhauser.

Sweet, M. V. Algebra, Geometry & Trigonometry in Science Engineering & Mathematics. 617p. 1984. 45.00 (ISBN 0-470-20102-9). Halsted Pr.

Thompson, J. E. Geometry for the Practical Worker. 2nd ed. 256p. 1982. pap. 7.95 (ISBN 0-442-28272-9). Van Nos Reinhold.

Triangles & Quadrangles: Level Four Texts. rev. ed. (Math Components Ser.). 56p. 1983. 2.75 (ISBN 0-88336-841-2). New Readers.

Uspenskii, V. A. Pascal's Triangle. McLarnan, Timothy & Sookne, David J., trs. from Rus. LC 73-90941. (Popular Lectures in Mathematics Ser). 42p. 1975. pap. text ed. 3.50x (ISBN 0-226-84316-5). U of Chicago Pr.

Vaisman. Foundations of Three Dimensional Euclidean Geometry. (Lecture Notes in Pure & Applied Mathematics Ser.: Vol. 56). 1980. 44.75 (ISBN 0-8247-6901-5). Dekker.

Wilson, Grace, et al. Geometry for Architects. 2nd ed. (Illus.). 1975. spiral bdg. 9.80x (ISBN 0-87563-092-8). Stipes.

Wyant, Lin & Stakkestad, James. Introduction to Geometry. Date not set. text ed. price not set (ISBN 0-12-766140-9). Acad Pr.

Yaglom, I. M. Geometric Transformations, Vol. 2. LC 67-20607. (New Mathematical Library: No. 21). 1968. pap. 10.00 (ISBN 0-88385-621-2). Math Assn.

Yakovlev, G. Geometry. 288p. 1982. 7.45 (ISBN 0-8285-2330-4, Pub. by Mir Pubs USSR). Imported Pubns.

Young, J. W. Projective Geometry. (Carus Monograph: No. 4). 185p. 1930. 16.50 (ISBN 0-88385-004-4). Math Assn.

Zlot, William, et al. Elementary Geometry. LC 78-25633. 1979. pap. 6.95 (ISBN 0-88275-820-9). Krieger.

GEOMETRY–ADDRESSES, ESSAYS, LECTURES

Barrow, Isaac. The Geometrical Lectures. Child, J. M., ed. 218p. 14.95 (ISBN 0-912050-54-3). Open Court.

Borel, A. Oevres- Collected Papers, 3 Vols. 2240p. 1983. Set. 150.00 (ISBN 0-387-12126-9). Springer-Verlag.

Brouwer, L. E. & Freudenthal, H. L. E. J. Brouwer, Collected Works, Vol. 2: Geometry, Analysis, Topology & Mechanics. 706p. 1976. 127.75 (ISBN 0-7204-2805-X, North-Holland). Elsevier.

Hoffman, Banesh, ed. Perspectives in Geometry & Relativity: Essays in Honor of Vaclav Hlavaty. LC 65-19704. (Illus.). pap. 127.00 (ISBN 0-317-07881-X, 2005745). Bks Demand UMI.

White, A., ed. Anomalies, Geometry & Topology: Proceedings of the Symposium on Anomalies, Geometry & Topology. 540p. 1985. 65.00x (ISBN 0-317-27182-2, Pub. by World Sci Singapore). Taylor & Francis.

GEOMETRY–CURIOSA AND MISCELLANY

Pottage, J. Geometrical Investigations: Illustrating the Art of Discovery in the Mathematical Field. 1982. text ed. 45.95 (ISBN 0-201-05733-6). Addison-Wesley.

GEOMETRY–EARLY WORKS TO 1800

see also Mathematics, Greek

Babington, John. A Short Treatise of Geometrie. LC 76-25837. (English Experience Ser.: No. 296). 200p. Repr. of 1635 ed. 35.00 (ISBN 90-221-0296-3). Walter J Johnson.

Bibiena, Ferdinando G. Da. Architettura Civile. LC 68-57184. (Illus., It). 1969. 50.00 (ISBN 0-405-08268-1, Blom Pubns). Ayer Co Pubs.

Descartes, Rene. La Geometrie. (Illus.). 96p. 5.95 (ISBN 0-686-55671-2). French & Eur.

--La Geometrie. Smith, David E. & Latham, Marcia L., trs. from Fr. & Lat. (Illus.). xiii, 259p. 1952. 7.95 (ISBN 0-87548-168-X). Open Court.

Euclid. Elements. Todhunter, Isaac, ed. 1967. Repr. of 1933 ed. 12.95x (ISBN 0-460-00891-9, Evman). Biblio Dist.

--The Elements, 3 vols. Heath, Thomas L., ed. 1926. Vol. 1. pap. 7.50 (ISBN 0-486-60088-2); Vol. 2. pap. 7.50 (ISBN 0-486-60089-0); Vol. 3. pap. 7.50 (ISBN 0-486-60090-4). Dover.

Record, Robert. The Path-Way to Knowledge, Containing the First Principles of Geometrie. LC 74-80206. (English Experience Ser.: No. 687). 1974. Repr. of 1551 ed. 18.50 (ISBN 90-221-0687-X). Walter J Johnson.

Milnor, John W. Singular Points of Complex Hypersurfaces. (Annals of Mathematics Studies: No. 61). 1969. pap. 16.50x (ISBN 0-691-08065-8). Princeton U Pr.

Moise, E. E. Geometric Topology in Dimensions 2 & 3. LC 76-49892. (Graduate Texts in Mathematics Ser.: Vol. 47). 1977. 34.00 (ISBN 0-387-90220-1). Springer-Verlag.

Mumford, D. Algebraic Geometry I: Complex Projective Varieties, I. (Grundlehren der Mathematischen Wissenschaften: Vol. 221). (Illus.). 186p. 1976. 29.80 (ISBN 0-387-07603-4). Springer-Verlag.

Mumford, D. & Fogarty, J., eds. Geometric Invariant Theory. 2nd ed. (Ergebnisse der Mathematik Ser.: Vol. 34). 240p. 1982. 36.00 (ISBN 0-387-11290-1). Springer-Verlag.

Namba. Geometry of Projective Algebraic Curves. (Pure & Applied Mathematics Ser.). 232p. 1984. 69.75 (ISBN 0-8247-7222-9); text ed. 39.75. Dekker.

Olson, L. D., ed. Algebraic Geometry: Proceedings, Tromso Symposium, June 27-July 8,1977. (Lecture Notes in Mathematics: Vol. 687). 1978. pap. 18.00 (ISBN 0-387-08954-3). Springer-Verlag.

Pham, F. Singularities des Systemes Differentiels de Gauss-Manin. (Progress in Mathematics Ser.: No. 2). (Fr.). 340p. 1979. pap. 24.00x (ISBN 0-8176-3002-3). Birkhauser.

Pognoli, A. Institutiones Mathematicae: Algebraic Geometry & Nash Functions, Vol. III. 1981. 19.50 (ISBN 0-12-363603-5). Acad Pr.

Popp, H., ed. Moduli Theory & Classification Theory of Algebraic Varieties. (Lecture Notes in Mathematics: Vol 620). 1977. pap. 14.00 (ISBN 0-387-08522-X). Springer-Verlag.

Poston, T. & Woodcock, A. E. A Geometrical Study of the Elementary Catastrophes. LC 73-22575. (Lectures Notes in Mathematics: Vol. 373). (Illus.). v, 257p. 1974. pap. 18.00 (ISBN 0-387-06681-0). Springer-Verlag.

Ranicki, A., et al, eds. Algebraic & Geometric Topology. (Lecture Notes in Mathematics: Vol. 1126). v, 423p. 1985. pap. 25.80 (ISBN 0-387-15235-0). Springer Verlag.

Raynaud, M. & Shioda, T., eds. Algebraic Geometry. (Lecture Notes in Mathematics Ser.: Vol. 1016). 528p. 1983. pap. 26.00 (ISBN 0-387-12685-6). Springer-Verlag.

Segre, Beniamino. Some Properties of Differentiable Varieties & Transformations: With Special Reference to the Analytic & Algebraic Cases. 2nd ed. LC 72-137498. (Ergebnisse der Mathematik und Ihrer Grenzgebiete: Vol. 13). 1971. pap. 34.00 (ISBN 0-387-05085-X). Springer-Verlag.

Seidenberg, Abraham, ed. Studies in Algebraic Geometry. LC 80-81041. (MAA Studies in Mathematics: No. 20). 1980. 16.00 (ISBN 0-88385-120-2). Math Assn.

Severi, Francesco. Vorlesungen Uber Algebraische Geometrie. (Bibliotheca Mathematica Teubneriana Ser.: No. 32). (Ger). Repr. of 1921 ed. 45.00 (ISBN 0-384-54945-4). Johnson Repr.

Shafarevich, I. R. Basic Algebraic Geometry. LC 77-6425. (Springer Study Edition). 1977. pap. 29.50 (ISBN 0-387-08264-6). Springer-Verlag.

Slodowy, P. Simple Singularities & Simple Algebraic Groups. (Lecture Notes in Mathematics: Vol. 815). 175p. 1980. pap. 15.00 (ISBN 0-387-10026-1). Springer-Verlag.

Snyder, Virgil, et al. Selected Topics in Algebraic Geometry, 2 Vols in 1. 2nd ed. LC 78-113149. 1970. text ed. 15.95 (ISBN 0-8284-0189-6). Chelsea Pub.

Sot, Richard. Simple Morphisms in Algebraic Geometry. (Lecture Notes in Mathematics: Vol. 935). 146p. 1982. pap. 11.00 (ISBN 0-387-11564-1). Springer-Verlag.

Strange, Jerry D. & Rice, Bernard J. Analytical Geometry & Calculus: With Technical Applications. 462p. 1970. 31.95 (ISBN 0-471-83190-5). Wiley.

Symposium in Pure Mathematics, Humboldt State University, Arcata, Calif., July 29-August 16, 1974. Algebraic Geometry - Arcata 1974: Proceedings. Hartstone, Robin, ed. LC 75-9530. (Proceedings of Symposia in Pure Mathematics: Vol. 29). 642p. 1982. Repr. of 1979 ed. with corrections 46.00 (ISBN 0-8218-1429-X, PSPUM-29). Am Math.

Toelke, J., ed. Contributions to Geometry: Proceedings of the Geometry-Symposium Seigen 1978. Willis, J. 404p. 1979. softcover 56.95x (ISBN 0-8176-1048-0). Birkhauser.

Van Oystaeyen, F. M. & Verschoren, A. Non-Commutative Algebraic Geometry. (Lecture Notes in Mathematics Ser.: Vol. 887). 404p. 1981. pap. 24.00 (ISBN 0-387-11153-0). Springer-Verlag.

Vogel, W. Lectures on Results on Bezout's Theorem. (Tata Institute Lectures on Mathematics Ser.). viii, 136p. 1984. pap. 9.50 (ISBN 0-387-12679-1). Springer-Verlag.

Walker, R. J. Algebraic Curves. LC 78-11956. 1978. pap. 19.50 (ISBN 0-387-90361-5). Springer-Verlag.

Weil, Andre. Foundations of Algebraic Geometry. rev. ed. LC 62-7794. (Colloquium Pbns. Ser.: Vol. 29). 363p. 1978. pap. 29.00 (ISBN 0-8218-1029-4, COLL-29). Am Math.

Zariski, O. Algebraic Surfaces. 2nd ed. LC 70-148144. (Ergebnisse der Mathematik & Ihrer Grenzgebiete: Vol. 61). 1971. 37.00 (ISBN 0-387-05335-2). Springer-Verlag.

GEOMETRY, ANALYTIC

see also Conic Sections; Curves; Surfaces

Anton, H. Calculus: With Analytic Geometry. brief, 2nd ed. 738p. 1984. 32.95 (ISBN 0-471-88817-6); student's manual 10.95 (ISBN 0-471-80732-X). Wiley.

Anton, Howard. Calculus with Analytic Geometry. LC 79-11469. 1220p. 1980. 40.45 (ISBN 0-471-03248-4); solution manual 11.95 (ISBN 0-471-04498-9). Wiley.

Badescu, L. & Popescu, D., eds. Algebraic Geometry, Bucharest 1982: Proceedings of the International Conference, Held in Bucharest, Romania, August 2-7, 1982. (Lecture Notes in Mathematics Ser.: Vol. 1056). vii, 380p. 1984. 18.50 (ISBN 0-387-12930-8). Springer-Verlag.

Blaschke, W. Analytische Geometrie. 2nd ed. (Mathematics Reihe Ser.: No. 16). (Ger.). 190p. 1954. 23.95x (ISBN 0-8176-0031-0). Birkhauser.

Bohuslov, Ronald L. Analytic Geometry: A Precalculus Approach. (Illus.). 1970. text ed. write for info. (ISBN 0-02-311810-5, 31181). Macmillan.

Brieskorn, E. & Knorrer, H. Ebene Algebraische Kurven. (Ger.). 928p. 1981. text ed. 29.95x (ISBN 0-8176-3030-9). Birkhauser.

Bugrov, Y. S. & Nikolsky, S. M. Fundamentals of Linear Algebra & Analytical Geometry. Levant, Leonid, tr. 189p. 1982. pap. 3.45 (ISBN 0-8285-2445-9, Pub. by Mir Pubs USSR). Imported Pubns.

Campbell, Howard E. & Dierker, Paul F. Calculus with Analytic Geometry. 3rd ed. 912p. 1982. text ed. write for info. (ISBN 0-87150-331-X, 2641, Prindle). PWS Pubs.

--Student Supplement to Accompany Calculus with Analytic Geometry. 3rd ed. 341p. 1982. pap. text ed. write for info. (ISBN 0-87150-353-0, 2646, Prindle). PWS Pubs.

Carico, Charles C. & Drooyan, Irving. Analytic Geometry. LC 79-21633. 310p. 1980. 31.50x (ISBN 0-471-06435-1); student supplement, 175 p. 14.45 (ISBN 0-471-06378-9). Wiley.

Chasen, Sylvan H. Geometric Principles & Procedures for Computer Graphic Applications. LC 78-7998. (Illus.). 1978. 37.50 (ISBN 0-13-352559-7). P-H.

Clebsch, Rudolph F., tr. Vorlesungen Ueber Geometrie Mit Besonderer Benutzung der Vortrage Von Clebsch, 2 Vols. in 3 Pts. (Bibliotheca Mathematica Teubneriana Ser. 43-44). (Ger). 1969. Repr. Set. 140.00 (ISBN 0-384-09295-0). Johnson Repr.

Coble, A. B. Algebraic Geometry & Theta Functions. LC 30-12679. (Colloquium Pbns. Ser.: Vol. 10). 289p. 1982. Repr. of 1929 ed. 46.00 (ISBN 0-8218-1010-3, COLL-10). Am Math.

Crowell, Richard H. & Slesnick, William E. Calculus with Analytic Geometry. (Illus.). 1968. 26.95x (ISBN 0-393-09782-X). Norton.

Dadourian, H. M. Introduction to Analytic Geometry & the Calculus. LC 80-39791. 256p. 1983. Repr. of 1949 ed. bds. 15.00 (ISBN 0-89874-267-6). Krieger.

Descartes, Rene. La Geometrie. (Illus.). 96p. 5.95 (ISBN 0-686-55671-2). French & Eur.

--La Geometrie. Smith, David E. & Latham, Marcia L., trs. from Fr. & Lat. (Illus.). xiii, 259p. 1952. 7.95 (ISBN 0-87548-168-X). Open Court.

--Geometry. (Eng. & Fr.). 1925. pap. 4.50 (ISBN 0-486-60068-8). Dover.

Edwards, C. H. & Penney, David E. Calculus & Analytic Geometry. 1120p. 1982. 36.95 (ISBN 0-13-111609-6). P-H.

Edwards, C. H., Jr. & Penney, David E. Calculus & Analytic Geometry. 2nd ed. (Illus.). 1088p. 1986. text ed. 39.95 (ISBN 0-317-29669-8). P-H.

--Calculus & Analytic Geometry, Student Manual. (Illus.). 352p. 1982. pap. 9.95 student manual (ISBN 0-13-111583-9). P-H.

Espacios Vectoriales y Geometria Analitica. rev. ed. (Serie De Matematica: No. 2). (Span.). 1974. pap. 3.50 (ISBN 0-8270-1096-6). OAS.

Federer, Herbert & Jonsson, Bjarni. Analytic Geometry & Calculus. LC 61-6325. pap. 160.00 (ISBN 0-317-08413-5, 2012452). Bks Demand UMI.

Fischer, G. Complex Analytic Geometry. (Lecture Notes in Mathematics: Vol. 538). 1976. soft cover 16.00 (ISBN 0-387-07857-6). Springer-Verlag.

Fraleigh, John B. Calculus with Analytic Geometry. LC 79-18693. (Illus.). 1980. text ed. 37.95 (ISBN 0-201-03041-1); student supplement 10.95 (ISBN 0-201-03042-X); solutions manual 10.95. Addison-Wesley.

--Calculus with Analytic Geometry. 2nd ed. 1985. text ed. 38.95 (ISBN 0-201-12010-0). Addison-Wesley.

Fresnel, Jean. Geometrie Analytique Rigide et Applications. (Progress in Mathematics Ser.: No. 18). (Fr.). 150p. 1981. text ed. 17.50x (ISBN 0-8176-3069-4). Birkhauser.

Fuller, Gordon. Analytic Geometry. 5th ed. LC 78-55820. 1979. text ed. 26.95 (ISBN 0-201-02414-4); ans. bk. 1.50 (ISBN 0-201-02415-2). Addison-Wesley.

Geometry & Analysis: Papers Dedicated to the Memory of V. K. Patodi. (Tata Institute Studies in Mathematics). 166p. 1981. 15.00 (ISBN 0-387-10270-1). Springer-Verlag.

Gillett, Philip. Calculus & Analytic Geometry. 928p. 1981. text ed. 34.95 (ISBN 0-669-00641-6); solutions guide, vol. 1 8.95 (ISBN 0-669-00642-4); solutions guide vol. 2 8.95 (ISBN 0-669-03212-3); solutions guide vol. 3 8.95 (ISBN 0-669-03213-1); selected study & solutions guide 9.95 (ISBN 0-669-05170-5); linear algebra suppl. 2.95 (ISBN 0-669-05142-X); revised problem sets 2.95 (ISBN 0-669-06334-7). Heath.

--Calculus & Analytic Geometry. 2nd ed. 992p. text ed. 35.95 (ISBN 0-669-06059-3). Heath.

Gondin, William R. & Sohmer, Bernard. Intermediate Algebra & Analytic Geometry Made Simple. (Made Simple Ser.). pap. 4.95 (ISBN 0-385-00437-0). Doubleday.

Goodman, A. W. Analytic Geometry & the Calculus. 4th ed. (Illus.). 1980. text ed. write for info.. (ISBN 0-02-344960-8). Macmillan.

--Analytic Geometry & the Calculus: Student Study Guide, 2 vols. 4th ed. (Illus.). 1980. pap. text ed. write for info. Vol. I (ISBN 0-02-344970-5). Vol. II (ISBN 0-02-344980-2). Macmillan.

Greco, S. & Strano, R., eds. Complete Intersections. (Lecture Notes in Mathematics Ser.: Vol. 1092). vii, 299p. 1984. pap. 18.50 (ISBN 0-387-13884-6). Springer-Verlag.

Griffiths, Phillip. Topics in Algebraic & Analytic Geometry. LC 74-2968. (Mathematical Notes Ser.: No. 13). 227p. 1974. 22.00x (ISBN 0-691-08151-4). Princeton U Pr.

Guillou, Louis A. Calculus with Analytic Geometry. 4th ed. (Illus.). 368p. 1984. 15.95 (ISBN 0-13-111824-2). P-H.

Gunning, Robert C. Lectures on Complex Analytic Varieties: Finite Analytic Mappings. LC 74-2969. (Mathematical Notes Ser.: No. 14). 170p. 1974. 19.95 (ISBN 0-691-08150-6). Princeton U Pr.

Ilyin, V. A., et al. Analytic Geometry. 232p. 1985. 7.95 (Pub. by Mir Pubns USSR). Imported Pubns.

Johnson, Richard E., et al. Calculus with Analytic Geometry. 6th ed. 1978. text ed. 41.43 (ISBN 0-205-05917-1, 565917); tchr's. manual 7.23 (ISBN 0-205-05918-X, 565918); study guide 13.57 (ISBN 0-205-05919-8, 565919). Allyn.

Kindle, Joseph H. Analytic Geometry. (Orig.). 1950. pap. 6.95 (ISBN 0-07-034575-9). McGraw.

Kletenik, D. Problems in Analytic Geometry. MIR Publishers, tr. from Rus. (Illus.). 298p. 1975. text ed. 14.00x (ISBN 0-8464-0757-4). Beekman Pubs.

Krasnosel'skii, M. M. & Zabreiko, P. P. Geometrical Methods of Nonlinear Analysis. (Grundlehren der Mathematischen Wissenschaften: Vol. 263). xix, 409p. 1984. 48.00 (ISBN 0-387-12945-6). Springer-Verlag.

Kuhfittig, Peter. Technical Calculus with Analytic Geometry. LC 82-9714. (Mathematics Ser.). 512p. 1982. text ed. 23.00 pub net (ISBN 0-534-01191-8). Brooks-Cole.

Larson, Roland E. & Hostetler, Robert P. Calculus with Analytic Geometry. text ed. 31.95 (ISBN 0-669-01301-3); solution manuals 7.95 ea. Vol. 1 (ISBN 0-669-03187-9). Vol. 2 (ISBN 0-669-03188-7). Vol. 3 (ISBN 0-669-03189-5). differential equations suppl. 1.95 (ISBN 0-669-03204-2); student manual 8.95 (ISBN 0-669-01705-1); appendix d 1.95 (ISBN 0-669-03190-9); instructor's manual to adopters 1.95 (ISBN 0-669-01302-1). Heath.

Leithold, Louis. Before Calculus: Functions, Graphs, & Analytic Geometry. 666p. 1985. text ed. 27.50 scp (ISBN 0-06-043928-9, HarpC). Har-Row.

Longley, William R., et al. Analytic Geometry & Calculus. LC 60-3940. pap. 146.50 (ISBN 0-317-09333-9, 2055267). Bks Demand UMI.

Middlemiss, Ross R., et al. Analytic Geometry. 3rd ed. LC 68-15472. 1968. text ed. 35.95 (ISBN 0-07-041896-9). McGraw.

Miller, Eldon. Student Solutions for Calculus & Analytic Geometry, Vol. I. 208p. 1983. pap. text ed. write for info. (ISBN 0-534-00980-8). Wadsworth Pub.

Mizrahi & Sullivan. Calculus & Analytic Geometry. 2nd ed. 1985. text ed. write for info (ISBN 0-534-05454-4). Wadsworth Pub.

Mizrahi, Abshalom & Sullivan, Michael J. Calculus & Analytic Geometry. 1136p. 1982. text ed. write for info (ISBN 0-534-00978-6); write for info study guide (ISBN 0-534-00979-4). Wadsworth Pub.

Pease, Edward M. & Wadsworth, George P. Calculus: With Analytic Geometry. LC 68-56150. pap. 120.00 (ISBN 0-317-08689-8, 2012457). Bks Demand UMI.

Pedoe, Daniel. A Geometric Introduction to Linear Algebra. 2nd ed. LC 72-78369. xi, 224p. 1976. text ed. 9.95 (ISBN 0-8284-0286-8). Chelsea Pub.

Pogrelov, A. V. Analytical Geometry. 240p. 1984. pap. 7.95 (ISBN 0-8285-2816-0, Pub. by Mir Pubs USSR). Imported Pubns.

Postnikov, M. Lectures in Geometry: Analytic Geometry. 343p. 1982. 8.45 (ISBN 0-8285-2393-2, Pub. by Mir Pubs USSR). Imported Pubns.

Protter, Murray H. & Morrey, Charles B., Jr. Analytic Geometry. 2nd ed. (Illus.). 432p. 1975. text ed. 24.95 (ISBN 0-201-05997-5). Addison-Wesley.

--Calculus with Analytic Geometry: A First Course. 3rd ed. LC 76-12801. (Mathematics Ser.). 1977. text ed. 27.95 (ISBN 0-201-06037-X); instr's manual 3.50 (ISBN 0-201-06031-0); student suppl. 9.95 (ISBN 0-201-06032-9). Addison-Wesley.

--Calculus with Analytic Geometry: A Second Course. LC 70-153066. (Mathematics Ser.). 1971. text ed. 27.95 (ISBN 0-201-06021-3). Addison-Wesley.

--College Calculus with Analytic Geometry. 3rd ed. LC 76-12800. (Mathematics Ser.). 1977. text ed. 39.95 (ISBN 0-201-06030-2); study guide 5.95 (ISBN 0-201-06036-1); study supplemental 9.95 (ISBN 0-201-06032-9). Addison-Wesley.

Purcell, Edwin J. Analytic Geometry. LC 58-5609. (Century Mathematics Ser.). (Illus.). 1958. 37.50x (ISBN 0-89197-605-1). Irvington.

Purcell, Edwin J. & Varberg, Dale. Calculus with Analytic Geometry. 4th ed. (Illus.). 896p. 1984. text ed. 39.95 (ISBN 0-13-111807-2). P-H.

Rees, Paul K. & Sparks, Fred W. Algebra, Trigonometry & Analytic Geometry. 2nd ed. (Illus.). 512p. 1975. text ed. 34.95 (ISBN 0-07-051720-7). McGraw.

--Calculus with Analytic Geometry. LC 68-17508. (Illus.). 1969. text ed. 44.95 (ISBN 0-07-051675-8). McGraw.

Resnikoff, H. L. & Wells, R. O., Jr., eds. Complex Analysis, 1972, Vol. 1: Geometry of Singularities. (Rice University Studies: Vol. 59, No. 1). 162p. 1973. pap. 10.00x (ISBN 0-89263-215-1). Rice Univ.

--Complex Analysis, 1972, Vol. 2: Analysis on Singularities. (Rice University Studies: Vol. 59, No. 2). 163p. 1973. pap. 10.00x (ISBN 0-89263-216-X). Rice Univ.

Riddle, Douglas F. Analytic Geometry with Vectors. 3rd ed. 1978. write for info (ISBN 0-534-01030-X). Wadsworth Pub.

--Calculus & Analytic Geometry. 1116p. 1984. text ed. write for info. (ISBN 0-534-01198-5). Wadsworth Pub.

--Calculus & Analytic Geometry. 4th ed. 1248p. write for info. (ISBN 0-534-01468-2). Wadsworth Pub.

Rudman, Jack. Calculus with Analytical Geometry. (College Level Examination Ser.: CLEP-43). (Cloth bdg. avail. on request). 1977. pap. 9.95 (ISBN 0-8373-5393-9). Natl Learning.

Salas, S. L. & Hille, E. Calculus: One & Several Variables with Analytic Geometry, 2 pts. 4th ed. LC 81-21975. (Bahasa-Malaysia.). 1982. Pt. 1, 671p. text ed. 32.45 (ISBN 0-471-08055-1); Pt. 1, 600p. pap. text ed. 10.95 (ISBN 0-471-86622-9); Pt. 2, 613. text ed. 32.45 (ISBN 0-471-08054-3); Cloth combined, 1136p. text ed. 39.45 (ISBN 0-471-04660-4); student supplement 17.45 (ISBN 0-471-05383-X); student solutions manual 16.45 (ISBN 0-471-08008-X); transparencies 18.50 (ISBN 0-471-04698-1). Wiley.

Schachter, H. Calculus & Analytic Geometry. 1972. text ed. 35.50 (ISBN 0-07-055056-5). McGraw.

Selby, Peter H. Geometry & Trigonometry for Calculus. LC 74-23936. (Self-Teaching Guides Ser). 424p. 1975. pap. text ed. 9.95x (ISBN 0-471-77558-4, Pub. by Wiley Pr). Wiley.

Shenk, Al. Calculus & Analytic Geometry. 3rd ed. 1984. text ed. 39.30x (ISBN 0-673-16582-5). Scott F.

Shockley, James E. Calculus & Analytic Geometry. 1212p. 1982. text ed. 39.95x (ISBN 0-03-018886-5). SCP.

Simmons, G. F. Calculus with Analytic Geometry. LC 84-14359. 1056p. 1985. 40.95 (ISBN 0-07-057419-7). McGraw.

Simon, Arthur B. Algebra & Trigonometry with Analytic Geometry. LC 78-23409. (Mathematical Sciences Ser.). (Illus.). 533p. 1979. text ed. 24.95x (ISBN 0-7167-1016-1); solutions manual avail. W H Freeman.

--Calculus with Analytic Geometry. 1982. text ed. 39.30x (ISBN 0-673-16044-0). Scott F.
Steffensen, Arnold R. & Johnson, L. M. Trigonometry with Analytic Geometry. 1983. pap. text ed. 21.70x (ISBN 0-673-15633-8). Scott F.
Stein, S. K. Calculus & Analytical Geometry. 3rd ed. (Illus.). 1248p. 1982. 44.95x (ISBN 0-07-061153-X). McGraw.
Stein, Sherman K. Calculus & Analytic Geometry. 2nd ed. (Illus.). 1977. text ed. 34.95 (ISBN 0-07-061008-8). McGraw.
Strange & Rice. Technical Calculus with Analytic Geometry. 1986. text ed. write for info. Breton Pubs.
Swokowski, Earl W. Algebra & Trigonometry with Analytic Geometry. 5th ed. LC 80-29056. 544p. 1981. text ed. write for info. (ISBN 0-87150-310-7, 33L 2471, Prindle). PWS Pubs.
--Algebra & Trigonometry with Analytic Geometry. 5th ed. write for info. (ISBN 0-87150-310-7, Prindle). PWS Pubs.
--Calculo Con Geometria Analitica. 2nd ed. Smith, Richard, ed. Abreu, Jose L. & Fetter, Helga, trs. from Eng. (Span.). 1064p. 1982. pap. text ed. write for info (ISBN 84-534-0001-6). Wadsworth Pub.
--Calculus with Analytic Geometry. 2nd ed. (Illus.). 1979. text ed. write for info. (ISBN 0-87150-268-2, PWS 2181, Prindle). PWS Pubs.
--Elements of Calculus with Analytic Geometry. (Illus.). 636p. text ed. write for info. (ISBN 0-87150-504-5, Prindle); write for info. tchr's manual (ISBN 0-87150-507-X); write for info. calulator wkbk. (ISBN 0-686-64031-4); write for info. test bank (ISBN 0-686-64032-2); write for info. solutions manual (ISBN 0-87150-508-8). PWS Pubs.
Thomas, George B., Jr. & Finney, Ross L. Calculus & Analytic Geometry. 5th ed. LC 78-55832. (Illus.). 1979. Combined Ed. text ed. 38.95 (ISBN 0-201-07540-7); Pt. 1. o. p. 24.95 (ISBN 0-201-07541-5); Pt. 2. o. p. 26.95 (ISBN 0-201-07542-3); avail. student suppl. 10.95 (ISBN 0-201-07543-1); avail. self study guide 10.95 (ISBN 0-201-07655-1); solutions manual 13.95 (ISBN 0-201-07544-X). Addison-Wesley.
--Calculus & Analytic Geometry. 6th ed. LC 83-2569. (Illus.). 1100p. 1984. 39.95 (ISBN 0-201-16290-3); student suppl. 14.95 (ISBN 0-201-16298-9). Addison-Wesley.
--Calculus & Analytic Geometry: Functions of One Variable, Pt. 1. 6th ed. (Analytic Geometry & Infinite Ser.). 760p. 1984. 29.95 (ISBN 0-201-16291-1). Addison-Wesley.
--Calculus & Analytic Geometry: Vectors, Functions of Several Variables, Pt. 1. (Infinite Series & Differential). 520p. 1984. 27.95 (ISBN 0-201-16292-X). Addison-Wesley.
Wade, Thomas L. & Taylor, Howard E. Contemporary Analytic Geometry. LC 79-22955. 338p. 1980. Repr. of 1969 ed. lib. bdg. 19.50 (ISBN 0-89874-034-7). Krieger.
Washington, Allyn J. Technical Calculus with Analytical Geometry. 2nd ed. 1980. 28.95 (ISBN 0-8053-9519-9); instr's. guide 4.95 (ISBN 0-8053-9533-4). Benjamin-Cummings.
Wong, Yung-Chow. Isoclinic N-Planes in Euclidean 2n-Space, Clifford Parallels in Elliptic(2n-1) Space & the Hurwitz Matrix Equations. LC 52-42839. (Memoirs: No. 41). 114p. 1971. pap. 11.00 (ISBN 0-8218-1241-6, MEMO-41). Am Math.
Yefimov, N. Brief Course in Analytical Geometry. (Illus.). 1965. 12.95x (ISBN 0-8464-1080-X). Beekman Pubs.
Zill, Dennis G. Calculus with Analytic Geometry. 939p. 1984. text ed. write for info. (ISBN 0-87150-432-4, 33L2820, Prindle). PWS Pubs.

GEOMETRY, ANALYTIC–PLANE

Graham, Walter W. & Rowan, William H. Plane Analytic Geometry. (Quality Paperback Ser.: No. 47). 169p. (Orig.). 1968. pap. 3.50 (ISBN 0-8226-0047-1). Littlefield.
Salmon, George. Conic Sections. 6th ed. LC 55-3390. 9.95 (ISBN 0-8284-0099-7); pap. 6.95 (ISBN 0-8284-0098-9). Chelsea Pub.
Scott, Charlotte A. Projective Methods in Plane Analytical Geometry. 3rd ed. LC 49-4920. 11.95 (ISBN 0-8284-0146-2). Chelsea Pub.

GEOMETRY, ANALYTIC–SOLID

Albert, Abraham A. Solid Analytic Geometry. pap. 43.50 (ISBN 0-317-09471-8, 2016983). Bks Demand UMI.
Salmon, George. Analytic Geometry of Three Dimensions, Vol. II. LC 56-13057. 1979. text ed. 12.95 (ISBN 0-8284-0196-9). Chelsea Pub.

GEOMETRY, DESCRIPTIVE

see also Engineering Graphics; Projection

Bennett, Joseph A. Problems in Descriptive Geometry, Bk. 2. pap. 20.00 (ISBN 0-317-08629-4, 2007319). Bks Demand UMI.
Earle, James H. Geometry for Engineers. LC 83-2793. (Illus.). 336p. 1983. 25.95 (ISBN 0-201-11315-5). Addison-Wesley.
Gordon, V. O. A Course in Descriptive Geometry. 1980. 10.00 (ISBN 0-8285-1870-X, Pub. by Mir Pubs USSR). Imported Pubns.
Grant, Hiram E. Practical Descriptive Geometry. 2nd ed. LC 65-16867. pap. 72.00 (ISBN 0-317-08784-3, 2004354). Bks Demand UMI.
Guillemin, Victor & Sternberg, Shlomo. Geometric Asymptotics. LC 77-8210. (Mathematical Surveys Ser.: No. 14). 474p. 1977. 58.00 (ISBN 0-8218-1514-8, SURV-14). Am Math.
Hawk, M. C. Descriptive Geometry. (Orig.). 1962. pap. 7.95 (ISBN 0-07-027290-5). McGraw.
Hector, G. & Hirsch, U. Introduction to the Geometry of Foliations, Pt. C. Date not set. 22.00 (ISBN 0-9940018-0-0, Pub. by Vieweg & Sohn Germany). Heyden.
Kamthan, P. K. & Gupta, M. Theory of Bases & Cones. (Research Notes in Mathematics Ser.: No. 117). 250p. 1985. pap. text ed. 17.95 (ISBN 0-273-08657-X). Pitman Pub MA.
Lamit, Gary. Descriptive Geometry. (Illus.). 464p. 1983. 26.95 (ISBN 0-13-199802-1); pap. 16.95 (ISBN 0-13-199828-5). P-H.
Lord, E. A. & Wilson, C. B. The Mathematical Description of Shape & Form. LC 83-26685. (Mathematics & Its Applications Ser.: 1-176). 323p. 1984. text ed. 59.95x (ISBN 0-470-20043-X). Halsted Pr.
Moschovakis, Y. N. Descriptive Set Theory. (Studies in Logic & the Foundations of Mathematics: Vol. 100). 638p. 1980. 93.75 (ISBN 0-444-85305-7, North Holland). Elsevier.
Pare, E. G. & Loving, R. O. Descriptive Geometry Worksheets, 6th ed. 83p. 1986. pap. price not set (ISBN 0-02-390960-9). Macmillan.
Pare, E. G., et al. Descriptive Geometry-Metric. 6th ed. 1982. text ed. write for info. (ISBN 0-02-390930-7). Macmillan.
Pare, Eugene G. & Shook, Micheal. Computer Graphics Project for Design & Descriptive Geometry. 149p. 1985. pap. write for info. (ISBN 0-02-390980-3). MacMillan.
Rusinoff, Samuel E. Practical Descriptive Geometry. LC 47-24789. pap. 67.00 (ISBN 0-317-12987-2, 2004562). Bks Demand UMI.
Shafer, Steven A. Shadows & Silhouettes in Computer Vision. 1985. lib. bdg. 34.50 (ISBN 0-89838-167-3). Kluwer Academic.
Slaby, Steve M. Engineering Descriptive Geometry. (Orig.). 1969. pap. 5.72i (ISBN 0-06-460101-3, CO 101, COS). B&N NY.
Wellman, B. Leighton. Technical Descriptive Geometry. 2nd ed. 1957. text ed. 36.00 (ISBN 0-07-069234-3). McGraw.

GEOMETRY, DESCRIPTIVE–PROBLEMS, EXERCISES, ETC.

Gordon, V. O. & Ivanov, Y. A. Worked Problems in Descriptive Geometry. 332p. 1979. 9.45 (ISBN 0-8285-1536-0, Pub. by Mir Pubs USSR). Imported Pubns.
Pare, E. G., et al. Descriptive Geometry Worksheets. 5th ed. (A). 1982. text ed. write for info. (ISBN 0-02-390910-2). Macmillan.
Warner, Frank M. & McNeary, M. Applied Descriptive Geometry. 5th ed. (Illus.). 1959. text ed. 35.00 (ISBN 0-07-068298-4). McGraw.

GEOMETRY, DIFFERENTIAL

see also Calculus of Tensors; Congruences (Geometry); Convex Bodies; Convex Domains; Coordinates; Curves; Differential Forms; Differential Topology; Geometry, Riemannian; Hyperspace; Riemannian Manifolds; Spaces, Generalized; Surfaces; Transformations (Mathematics)

Abraham, Ralph & Marsden, Jerrold E. Foundations of Mechanics: A Mathematical Exposition of Classical Mechanics with An Introduction to the Qualitative Theory of Dynamical Systems & Applications to the Three-Body Problem. 2nd rev. & enl. ed. 1978. 59.95 (ISBN 0-8053-0102-X). Benjamin-Cummings.
Aleksandrov, A. D. & Zalgaller, V. A. Intrinsic Geometry of Surfaces. LC 66-30492. (Translations of Mathematical Monographs: Vol. 15). 1967. 32.00 (ISBN 0-8218-1565-2, MMONO-15). Am Math.
Ancikov, A. M., et al. Seventeen Papers on Topology & Differential Geometry. LC 51-5559. (Translations Ser.: No. 2, Vol. 92). 1970. 35.00 (ISBN 0-8218-1792-2, TRANS 2-92). Am Math.
Andersson, S. I. & Doebner, H. D., eds. Non-linear Partial Differential Operators & Quantization Procedures. (Lecture Notes in Mathematics: Vol. 1037). 334p. 1983. pap. 17.00 (ISBN 0-387-12710-0). Springer Verlag.
Arnold, V. I. Geometrical Methods in the Theory of Ordinary Differential Equations. (Grundlehren der Mathematischen Wissenschaften: Vol. 250). (Illus.). 384p. 1983. 39.50 (ISBN 0-387-90681-9). Springer-Verlag.
Artzy, R. & Vaisman, I., eds. Geometry & Differential Geometry. (Lecture Notes in Mathematics: Vol. 792). 443p. 1980. pap. 28.00 (ISBN 0-387-09976-X). Springer-Verlag.
Atkin, E. The Metric Theory of Banach Manifolds. LC 78-14728. (Lecture Notes in Mathematics: Vol. 662). 1978. pap. 19.00 (ISBN 0-387-08915-2). Springer-Verlag.
Baker & Batten. Finite Geometrics. (Lecture Notes in Pure & Applied Mathematics). 392p. 1986. price not set (ISBN 0-8247-7488-4). Dekker.
Bieberbach, Ludwig. Differentialgeometrie. (Bibliothecha Mathematica Teubneriana Ser: No. 35). (Ger). 1969. 20.00 (ISBN 0-384-04240-6). Johnson Repr.
Bleuler, K., et al, eds. Differential Geometrical Methods in Mathematical Physics II: Proceedings, University of Bonn, July 13-16, 1977. (Lecture Notes in Mathematics Ser.: Vol. 676). 1978. pap. 37.00 (ISBN 0-387-08935-7). Springer-Verlag.
Bloom, F. Modern Differential Geometric Techniques in the Theory of Continuous Distributions of Dislocations. Dold, A. & Eckmann, B., eds. (Lecture Notes in Mathematics: Vol. 733). 1979. pap. 17.00 (ISBN 0-387-09528-4). Springer-Verlag.
Brockett, Roger & Millman, Richard, eds. Differential Geometric Control Theory. (Progress in Mathematics: Vol. 27). 340p. 1983. 25.00x (ISBN 0-8176-3091-0). Birkhauser.
Brooks, Robert & Gray, Alfred, eds. Differential Geometry: Proceedings, Special Year, Maryland 1981-1982. (Progress in Mathematics). 263p. 1983. 18.95 (ISBN 0-8176-3134-8). Birkhauser.
Buchin, Su. Affine Differential Geometry. 250p. 1982. 63.75 (ISBN 0-677-31060-9). Gordon.
Buchin, Su, et al, eds. Lectures on Differential Geometry. 220p. pap. text ed. 17.00 (ISBN 0-317-01578-8, DIFF GEOM). Am Math.
Burke, William L. Applied Differential Geometry. (Illus.). 400p. 1985. 54.50 (ISBN 0-521-26317-4); pap. 19.95 (ISBN 0-521-26929-6). Cambridge U Pr.
Buseman, Herbert. Geometry of Geodesics. (Pure and Applied Mathematics: Vol. 6). 1955. 69.50 (ISBN 0-12-148350-9). Acad Pr.
Busemann, H. Recent Synthetic Differential Geometry. LC 13-120381. (Ergebnisse der Mathematik und Ihrer Grenzgebiete: Vol. 54). 1970. 26.00 (ISBN 0-387-04810-3). Springer-Verlag.
Cahen, M. & Flato, M., eds. Differential Geometry & Relativity. new ed. (Mathematical Physics & Applied Mathematics Ser: No. 3). 1976. lib. bdg. 42.00 (ISBN 90-277-0745-6, Pub. by Reidel Holland). Kluwer Academic.
Calenko, M. S., et al. Twenty-Two Papers on Algebra, Number Theory, & Differential Geometry. LC 51-5559. (Translations Ser.: No. 2, Vol. 37). 1964. 34.00 (ISBN 0-8218-1737-X, TRANS 2-37). Am Math.
Chavel, I. & Farkas, H. M., eds. Differential Geometry & Complex Analysis. (Illus.). 225p. 1985. 32.00 (ISBN 0-387-13543-X). Springer-Verlag.
Colloquium Held at Dijon, June 17-22, 1974, et al. Differential Topology & Geometry: Proceedings. Joubert, G. P. & Moussu, R. P., eds. LC 75-25927. (Lecture Notes in Mathematics: Vol. 484). ix, 287p. 1975. pap. 14.70 (ISBN 0-387-07405-8). Springer-Verlag.
Coolidge, Julian L. Treatise on the Circle & the Sphere. LC 78-128872. 1971. text ed. 27.50 (ISBN 0-8284-0236-1). Chelsea Pub.
Do Carmo, Manfredo. Differential Geometry of Curves & Surfaces. 1976. 37.95 (ISBN 0-13-212589-7). P-H.
Doebner, H. D., ed. Differential Geometric Methods in Mathematical Physics: Proceedings. (Lecture Notes in Physics Ser.: Vol. 139). 329p. 1981. pap. 22.00 (ISBN 0-387-10578-6). Springer-Verlag.
Eberlein, Patrick. Surfaces of Nonpositive Curvature. LC 79-15112. (Memoirs: No. 218). 90p. 1979. pap. 10.00 (ISBN 0-8218-2218-7, MEMO-218). Am Math.
Efimov, N. V., et al. Differential Geometry & Calculus of Variations. (Translations Ser.: No. 1 Vol. 6). 1970. Repr. of 1962 ed. 30.00 (ISBN 0-8218-1606-3, TRANS 1-6). Am Math.
Eisenhart, L. P. Non-Riemannian Geometry. LC 28-28413. (Colloquium Pbns. Ser.: Vol. 8). 184p. 1981. pap. 29.00 (ISBN 0-8218-1008-1, COLL-8). Am Math.
Ferus, D., et al, eds. Global Differential Geometry & Global Analysis: Proceedings. (Lecture Notes in Mathematics: Vol. 838). 299p. 1981. pap. 22.00 (ISBN 0-387-10285-X). Springer-Verlag.
Freed, D. S. & Uhlenbeck, K. K. Instantons & Four-Manifolds. (Mathematical Sciences Research Institute Publications Ser.: Vol. 1). (Illus.). x, 232p. 1984. 15.00 (ISBN 0-387-96036-8). Springer-Verlag.
Garcia, P. L., et al, eds. Differential Geometrical Methods in Mathematical Physics: Proceedings. (Lecture Notes in Mathematics: Vol. 836). 538p. 1980. 32.00 (ISBN 0-387-10275-2). Springer-Verlag.
Guggenheimer, Heinrich. Differential Geometry. pap. text ed. 6.95 (ISBN 0-486-63433-7). Dover.
Guillemin, Victor & Sternberg, Shlomo. Symplectic Techniques in Physics. LC 83-7762. 464p. 1984. 49.50 (ISBN 0-521-24866-3). Cambridge U Pr.
Hale, J. K. & Magalhaes, L. T. An Introduction to Infinite Dimensional Dynamical Systems-Geometry Theory. (Applied Mathematical Sciences Ser.: Vol. 47). (Illus.). vii, 195p. 1984. pap. 19.50 (ISBN 0-387-90931-1). Springer-Verlag.
Hejhal, D. A. The Selberg Trace Formula for PSL; 2, IR, Vol. 2. (Lecture Notes in Mathematics: Vol. 1001). 806p. 1983. pap. 38.00 (ISBN 0-387-12323-7). Springer-Verlag.
Helgason, Sigurdur. Differential Geometry, Lie Groups & Symmetric Spaces. (Pure & Applied Mathematics Ser.). 1978. 29.50 (ISBN 0-12-338460-5). Acad Pr.
Hermann, Robert. Diffferential Geometry & the Calculus of Variations. 2nd ed. LC 68-14664. (Intermath Ser.: No. 17). 724p. 1977. 52.00 (ISBN 0-915692-23-6, 991600320). Math Sci Pr.
--Gauge Fields & Cartan-Enresmann Connections: Part A. LC 75-12199. (Interdisciplinary Mathematics Ser.: No. 10). 515p. 1975. 44.00 (ISBN 0-915692-09-0, 991600193). Math Sci Pr.
--Geometric Structure of Systems Control Theory & Physics: Part B. LC 74-30856. (Interdisciplinary Mathematics Ser.: No. 11). 484p. 1976. 49.00 (ISBN 0-915692-14-7, 991600185). Math Sci Pr.
--Quantum & Fermion Differential Geometry, Pt. A. (Interdisciplinary Mathematics Ser.: No. 16). 196p. 1977. 24.00 (ISBN 0-915692-22-8, 991600339). Math Sci Pr.
Hoff, H. Differential Geometry in the Large: Seminar Lectures New York University 1946 & Stanford University 1956. (Lecture Notes in Mathematics: Vol. 1000). 184p. 1983. pap. 12.00 (ISBN 0-387-12004-1). Springer-Verlag.
Hsiung, Chuan-Chih. A First Course in Differential Geometry. LC 80-22112. (Pure & Applied Mathematics Ser.). 343p. 1981. 49.95 (ISBN 0-471-07953-7, Pub. by Wiley-Interscience). Wiley.
Hurt, Norman & Hermann, R. Quantum Statistical Mechanics & Lie Group Harmonic Analysis, Pt. A. LC 80-13949. (Lie Groups; History, Frontiers & Applications: Vol. 10). 250p. 1980. text ed. 36.00 (ISBN 0-915692-30-9, 991600118). Math Sci Pr.
Isidori, A. Nonlinear Control Systems: An Introduction. (Lecture Notes in Control & Information Sciences: Vol. 72). 300p. 1985. pap. 19.00 (ISBN 0-387-15595-3). Springer-Verlag.
Kamber, F. & Tondeur, P. Flat Manifolds. LC 68-55623. (Lecture Notes in Mathematics: Vol. 67). 1968. pap. 10.70 (ISBN 0-387-04237-7). Springer-Verlag.
Kenmotsu, K. Differential Geometry of Submanifolds. (Lecture Notes in Mathematics: Vol. 1090). vi, 132p. 1984. pap. 10.00 (ISBN 0-387-13873-0). Springer-Verlag.
Kenner, Hugh. Geodesic Math & How to Use It. LC 74-27292. 150p. 1976. 22.00x (ISBN 0-520-02924-0); pap. 5.95 (ISBN 0-520-03054-0, CAL 323). U of Cal Pr.
Kobayashi, S. Transformation Groups in Differential Geometry. LC 72-80361. (Ergebnisse der Mathematik und Ihrer Grenzgebiete: Vol. 70). 182p. 1972. 28.00 (ISBN 0-387-05848-6). Springer-Verlag.
Kobayashi, Shoshichi & Nomizu, K. Foundations of Differential Geometry, 2 Vols. LC 63-19209. (Pure & Applied Mathematics Ser.). Pt. 1, 1963, 329p. 50.50x (ISBN 0-470-49647-9); Pt. 2, 1969, 470p. 54.95x (ISBN 0-470-49648-7, Pub. by Wiley-Interscience). Wiley.
Kobayshi, Shoshichi. Complex Differential Geometry. (Deutche Mathemaiker-Vereinigung Ser.: Vol. 3). 148p. 1983. text ed. 14.95 (ISBN 3-7643-1494-X). Birkhauser.
Kock, Anders. Synthetic Differential Geometry. LC 81-6099. (London Mathematical Society Lecture Note Ser.: No. 51). 328p. 1981. pap. 34.50 (ISBN 0-521-24138-3). Cambridge U Pr.
Kompaniec, V. P., et al. Fourteen Papers on Algebra, Topology, Algebraic & Differential Geometry. LC 51-5559. (Translations Ser.: No. 2, Vol. 73). 1968. 35.00 (ISBN 0-8218-1773-6, TRANS 2-73). Am Math.
Laugwitz, D. Differential & Riemannian Geometry. Steinhardt, F., tr. 1965. 53.00 (ISBN 0-12-437750-5). Acad Pr.
Lipschutz, Martin. Differential Geometry. (Schaum's Outline Ser). 1969. pap. 7.95 (ISBN 0-07-037985-8). McGraw.
Matsushima, Yozo. Holomorphic Vector Fields on Compact Kaehler Manifolds. LC 77-145641. (CBMS Regional Conference Series in Mathematics: No. 7). 38p. 1971. pap. 9.00 (ISBN 0-8218-1656-X, CBMS-7). Am Math.

Millman, Richard S. & Parker, George D. Elements of Differential Geometry. LC 76-28497. (Illus.). 1977. 28.95 (ISBN 0-13-264143-7). P-H.

Milnor, John W. Morse Theory. (Annals of Mathematics Studies: Vol. 51). (Orig.). 1963. pap. 18.00x (ISBN 0-691-08008-9). Princeton U Pr.

NATO Advanced Study Institute, 1973. Geometric Methods in System Theory: Proceedings. Mayne, D. Q. & Brockett, R. W., eds. LC 73-91206. (NATO Advanced Study Institutes: No. C-3). 1973. lib. bdg. 39.50 (ISBN 90-277-0415-5, Pub. by Reidel Holland). Kluwer Academic.

Naveira, A. M., ed. Differential Geometry. (Lecture Notes in Mathematics: Vol. 1045). viii, 194p. 1984. pap. 13.00 (ISBN 0-387-12882-4). Springer-Verlag.

Niemark, Ju. I. & Fufaev, N. A. Dynamics of Nonholonomic Systems. LC 72-3274. (Translations of Mathematical Monographs: No. 33). 1972. 90.00 (ISBN 0-8218-1583-0, MMONO-33). Am Math.

O'Neill, Barrett. Elementary Differential Geometry. 1966. text ed. 22.50i (ISBN 0-12-526750-9); answer bklt. 2.50i (ISBN 0-12-526756-8). Acad Pr.

Poor, Walter A. Differential Geometric Structures. (Illus.). 320p. 1981. text ed. 52.95 (ISBN 0-07-050435-0). McGraw.

Poston, T. & Woodcock, A. E. A Geometrical Study of the Elementary Catastrophes. LC 73-22575. (Lectures Notes in Mathematics: Vol. 373). (Illus.). v, 257p. 1974. pap. 18.00 (ISBN 0-387-06681-0). Springer-Verlag.

Prakash, N. Differential Geometry: An Integrated Approach. 1982. 7.00 (ISBN 0-07-096560-9). McGraw.

Rassias. Differential Geometry: Calculus of Variations & Their Applications. (Lecture Notes In Pure & Applied Mathematics Ser.). 480p. 1985. 75.00 (ISBN 0-8247-7267-9). Dekker.

Rauzy, G., ed. Repartition Modulo 1. LC 75-20300. (Lecture Notes in Mathematics: Vol. 475). 258p. 1975. pap. 14.70 (ISBN 0-387-07388-4). Springer-Verlag.

Reinhart, B. L. Differential Geometry of Folitations: The Fundamental Integrability Problem. (Ergebnisse der Mathematik: Folge 2, Vol. 99). 195p. 1983. 44.00 set (ISBN 0-387-12269-9). Springer-Verlag.

Romanov, V. G. Integral Geometry & Inverse Problems for Hyperbolic Equations. (Springer Tracts in Natural Philosophy: Vol. 26). (Illus.). 152p. 1974. 39.00 (ISBN 0-387-06429-X). Springer-Verlag.

Schwartz, Jacob T. Differential Geometry & Topology. (Notes on Mathematics & Its Applications Ser.). 180p. 1968. 47.75 (ISBN 0-677-01510-0). Gordon.

Shing-Tung Yau, ed. Seminar on Differential Geometry. LC 81-8631. (Annals of Mathematics Studies: No. 102). 832p. 1981. 62.50x (ISBN 0-691-08268-5); pap. 15.00x (ISBN 0-691-08296-0). Princeton U Pr.

Singer, I. M. & Thorpe, J. A. Lecture Notes on Elementary Topology & Geometry. LC 76-26137. (Undergraduate Texts in Mathematics). 1976. 26.50 (ISBN 0-387-90202-3). Springer-Verlag.

Soos, G. & Szenthe, J., eds. Differential Geometry. (Colloquia Mathematica Societatis Janos Bolyai: Vol. 31). 830p. 1982. 136.25 (ISBN 0-444-86197-1, North Holland). Elsevier.

Spivak, Michael. A Comprehensive Introduction to Differential Geometry, 5 vols. 2nd ed. LC 78-71771. (Illus.). 1979. Set. text ed. 120.00 (ISBN 0-914098-83-7); Vols. 1-2 Set. text ed. 40.00 (ISBN 0-914098-81-0); Vols. 3-5 Set. text ed. 85.00 (ISBN 0-914098-82-9); Vol. 1. pap. text ed. 18.00x (ISBN 0-914098-79-9); Vol. 2. pap. text ed. 15.00x (ISBN 0-914098-80-2). Publish or Perish.

Steklov Institute of Mathematics, Academy of Sciences, U S S R. Two-Dimensional Manifolds of Bounded Curvature: Proceedings. Aleksandrov, A. D. & Zalgaller, V. A., eds. (Proceedings of the Steklov Institute of Mathematics: No. 76). 1967. 42.00 (ISBN 0-8218-1876-7, STEKLO-76). Am Math.

Sternberg, Shlomo. Lectures on Differential Geometry. 2nd ed. LC 81-71141. xvii, 438p. 1983. text ed. 25.00 (ISBN 0-8284-0316-3, 316). Chelsea Pub.

Stoker, James. Differential Geometry. LC 69-16131. (Pure & Applied Mathematics Ser.). 404p. 1969. 48.50x (ISBN 0-471-82825-4, Pub. by Wiley-Interscience). Wiley.

Svec, A. Global Differential Geometry of Surfaces. 1982. lib. bdg. 28.50 (ISBN 90-277-1295-6, Pub. by Reidel Holland). Kluwer Academic.

Symposium in Pure Mathematics, - Stanford, Calif., 1973. Differential Geometry, 2 pts. Chern, S. S. & Osserman, R., eds. LC 75-6593. (Proceedings of Symposia in Pure Mathematics: Vol. 27). 1982. Set. pap. 84.00 (ISBN 0-685-55822-3, PSPUM-27); Pt. 1 451 p. pap. 47.00 (ISBN 0-8218-0247-X, PSPUM-27.1); Pt. 2 443 p. 53.00 (ISBN 0-8218-0248-8, PSPUM-27.2). Am Math.

Symposium in Pure Mathematics, - Tempe, Ariz., - 1960. Differential Geometry: Proceedings. Allendoerfer, C. B., ed. LC 50-1183. (Proceedings of Symposia in Pure Mathematics: Vol. 3). 1961. 27.00 (ISBN 0-8218-1403-6, PSPUM-3). Am Math.

Thorpe, J. Elementary Topics in Differential Geometry. (Undergraduate Texts in Mathematics Ser.). (Illus.). 1979. pap. 23.00 (ISBN 0-387-90357-7). Springer-Verlag.

Vaisman. A First Course in Differential Geometry. (Pure & Applied Mathematics Ser.). 232p. 1983. 32.50 (ISBN 0-8247-7063-3). Dekker.

Van Tiel, Jan. Convex Analysis: An Introductory Text. LC 83-10176. 125p. 1984. text ed. 21.95x (ISBN 0-471-90263-2). Wiley.

Yano, K. & Bochner, S. Curvature & Betti Numbers. (Annals of Math Studies). 1953. 14.00 (ISBN 0-527-02748-0). Kraus Repr.

Yano, Kentaro & Ishihara, Shigeru. Tangent & Cotangent Bundles: Differential Geometry. LC 72-91438. (Pure & Applied Mathematics Ser.: 16). pap. 108.00 (ISBN 0-317-07841-0, 2055025). Bks Demand UMI.

GEOMETRY, DIFFERENTIAL–PROJECTIVE

Asten, H. Keller-von. Encounters with the Infinite: Geometrical Experiences Through Active Contemplation. Juhr, Gerald, tr. from Germ. (Illus.). 364p. 1971. 19.95 (ISBN 0-88010-040-0, Pub. by Verlag Walter Keller Switzerland). Anthroposophic.

GEOMETRY, ENUMERATIVE

see also Curves; Surfaces

LeBarz, P. & Hervier, Y., eds. Enumerative Geometry & Classical Algebra. (Progress in Mathematics Ser.: Vol. 24). 246p. 1982. text ed. 20.00 (ISBN 0-8176-3106-2). Birkhauser.

GEOMETRY, HYPERBOLIC

Kelly, P. & Matthews, G. The Non-Euclidean Hyperbolic Plane. (Universitexts Ser.). (Illus.). 350p. 1981. pap. 29.50 (ISBN 0-387-90552-9). Springer-Verlag.

Smogovzhevsky, A. Lobachevskian Geometry. 71p. 1976. pap. 1.95 (ISBN 0-8285-0729-5, Pub. by Mir Pubs USSR). Imported Pubns.

GEOMETRY, MODERN

see also Geometry, Affine; Geometry, Projective

Adler, Claire F. Modern Geometry. 2nd ed. 1967. text ed. 27.95 (ISBN 0-07-000421-8). McGraw.

Dubrovin, B. A., et al. Modern Geometry: Methods & Applications Pt. I: The Geometry of Surface, of Transformation Groups & of Fields. Burns, R. G., tr. (Graduate Texts in Mathematics Ser.: Vol. 93). (Rus., Illus.). 495p. 1984. 48.00 (ISBN 0-387-90872-2). Springer-Verlag.

Ellis, A. J. Basic Algebra & Geometry for Scientists & Engineers. 187p. 1982. 28.95x (ISBN 0-471-10174-5). Wiley.

Rees, E. G. Notes in Geometry. (Universitexts). (Illus.). 109p. 1983. pap. 16.00 (ISBN 0-387-12053-X). Springer-Verlag.

Smart, James R. Modern Geometries. 2nd ed. Wisner, Robert J., ed. LC 77-15784. (Contemporary Undergraduate Mathematics Ser.). (Illus.). 1978. text ed. 21.75 pub net (ISBN 0-8185-0265-7); inst. manual upon adoption of text free (ISBN 0-685-86623-8). Brooks-Cole.

Torretti, R. Relativity & Geometry. (Foundations & Philosophy of Science & Technology Ser.). (Illus.). 400p. 1983. 50.00 (ISBN 0-08-026773-4). Pergamon.

GEOMETRY, MODERN–PLANE

Gustafson, Roy D. & Frisk, Peter D. Elementary Plane Geometry. 2nd ed. LC 84-7259. 358p. 1985. 26.95 (ISBN 0-471-89047-2). Wiley.

GEOMETRY, NON-EUCLIDEAN

see also Geometry–Foundations; Geometry, Hyperbolic; Geometry, Riemannian; Hyperspace; Parallels (Geometry); Screws, Theory of; Spaces, Generalized

Ball, W. Rouse, et al, eds. String Figures & Other Monographs, 4 vols. in 1. Incl. String Figures. Ball, W. R; History of the Slide Rule. Cajori, F; Non Euclidean Geometry. Carslaw, Horatio S; Methods Geometrical Construction. Petersen, Julius. LC 59-11780. 15.95 (ISBN 0-8284-0130-6). Chelsea Pub.

Boehm, J. & Hertel, E. Polyedergeometrie in n-dimensionalen Raeumen konstanter Kruemmung. (LMW-MA Ser.: No. 70). 288p. 1980. 51.95x (ISBN 0-8176-1160-6). Birkhauser.

Bonola, Roberto. Non-Euclidean Geometry. Carslaw, H. S., ed. 1954. pap. 7.00 (ISBN 0-486-60027-0). Dover.

Coxeter, H. S. Non-Euclidean Geometry. 5th ed. 1965. 30.00 (ISBN 0-8020-1068-7). U of Toronto Pr.

Engel, Friederich & Stackel, Paul. Urkunden Zur Geschichte Der Nichteuklidischen Geometrie, 2 Vols. (Ger). Repr. of 1913 ed. Set. 95.00 (ISBN 0-384-63370-6). Johnson Repr.

Greenberg, Marvin J. Euclidean & Non-Euclidean Geometries: Development & History. 2nd ed. LC 79-19348. (Illus.). 400p. 1980. text ed. 26.95 (ISBN 0-7167-1103-6); instrs. manual & answer book avail. W H Freeman.

Henderson, Linda D. The Fourth Dimension & Non-Euclidean Geometry in Modern Art. LC 82-15076. (Illus.). 496p. 1983. 60.00x (ISBN 0-691-04008-7); pap. 18.50 L.P.E. (ISBN 0-691-10142-6). Princeton U Pr.

Hess, Adrien L. Four-Dimensional Geometry: Introduction. LC 77-4310. (Illus.). 32p. 1977. pap. 2.50 (ISBN 0-87353-117-5). NCTM.

Kelly, P. & Matthews, G. The Non-Euclidean Hyperbolic Plane. (Universitexts Ser.). (Illus.). 350p. 1981. pap. 29.50 (ISBN 0-387-90552-9). Springer-Verlag.

Klein, Felix. Nicht-Euklidische Geometrie. LC 59-10281. (Ger). 9.95 (ISBN 0-8284-0129-2). Chelsea Pub.

Magnus, Wilhelm. Noneuclidian Tesselations & Their Groups. 1974. 44.00 (ISBN 0-12-465450-9). Acad Pr.

Martin, G. E. Foundations of Geometry & the Non-Euclidean Plane. (Undergraduate Texts in Mathematics Ser.). 509p. 1982. 27.00 (ISBN 0-387-90694-0). Springer-Verlag.

Rucker, Rudolf V. Geometry, Relativity & the Fourth Dimension. LC 76-22240. (Illus.). 1977. pap. text ed. 2.75 (ISBN 0-486-23400-2). Dover.

Sommerville, Duncan Y. Bibliography of Non-Euclidean Geometry. 2nd ed. LC 72-113150. 1960. text ed. 22.50 (ISBN 0-8284-0175-6). Chelsea Pub.

Yaglom, I. M. A Simple Noneuclidean Geometry & Its Physical Basis. (Heidelberg Science Library). (Illus.). 1979. pap. 28.00 (ISBN 0-387-90332-1). Springer-Verlag.

GEOMETRY, PLANE

see also Area Measurement; Circle; Conic Sections; Geometry, Analytic–Plane; Geometry, Modern–Plane; Triangle

Baker, H. F. Introduction to Plane Geometry. LC 70-141879. 1971. text ed. 18.50 (ISBN 0-8284-0247-7). Chelsea Pub.

Ball, W. Rouse, et al, eds. String Figures & Other Monographs, 4 vols. in 1. Incl. String Figures. Ball, W. R; History of the Slide Rule. Cajori, F; Non Euclidean Geometry. Carslaw, Horatio S; Methods Geometrical Construction. Petersen, Julius. LC 59-11780. 15.95 (ISBN 0-8284-0130-6). Chelsea Pub.

Gomes Teixeira, Francisco. Traite des Courbes Speciales Remarquables Planes et Gauches, 3 vols. 2nd ed. LC 73-113153. (Fr.). 1337p. 1972. text ed. 65.00 set (ISBN 0-8284-0255-8). Chelsea Pub.

Hemmerling, Edwin M. Fundamentals of College Geometry. 2nd ed. (Illus.). 464p. 1969. text ed. 32.50x (ISBN 0-471-37034-7). Wiley.

Hughes, D. R. & Piper, F. C. Projective Planes. 2nd ed. (Graduate Texts in Mathematics Ser.: Vol. 6). 291p. 1982. 37.50 (ISBN 0-387-90043-8). Springer-Verlag.

Kavanau, J. Lee. Structural Equation Geometry. LC 83-72284. (Illus.). 534p. (Orig.). 1983. pap. text ed. 19.95x (ISBN 0-937292-02-8). Science Software.

Kunz, E. Ebene Geometrie: Grundlagen der Geometrie. (Ger.). 147p. 1976. pap. 8.00x. Birkhauser.

Lacret-Subirat, Fabian. Lacret Plane Geometry: Grade 9-12. rev. enl. ed. (Illus.). 510p. 1985. text ed. 15.00x (ISBN 0-943144-15-9); pap. text ed. 13.00x (ISBN 0-943144-14-0). Lacret Pub.

Pickett, Hale C. An Analysis of Proofs & Solutions of Exercises Used in Plane Geometry Tests. LC 78-177153. (Columbia University. Teachers College. Contributions to Education: No. 747). Repr. of 1938 ed. 22.50 (ISBN 0-404-55747-3). AMS Pr.

Pritulenko, P. V. Plane Figures & Sections: How to Construct Them Given Specific Conditions. 1980. 8.45 (ISBN 0-8285-1778-9, Pub. by Mir Pubs USSR). Imported Pubns.

Rich, Barnett. Plane Geometry. (Shaum Outline Ser.). (Orig.). 1963. pap. 6.95 (ISBN 0-07-052245-6). McGraw.

Selby, Peter H. Geometry & Trigonometry for Calculus. LC 74-23936. (Self-Teaching Guides Ser). 424p. 1975. pap. text ed. 9.95x (ISBN 0-471-77558-4, Pub. by Wiley Pr). Wiley.

Touton, Frank C. Solving Geometric Originals. LC 76-177698. (Columbia University. Teachers College. Contributions to Education: No. 146). Repr. of 1924 ed. 22.50 (ISBN 0-404-55146-7). AMS Pr.

GEOMETRY, PROJECTIVE

Adams, George & Whicher, Olive. The Plant Between Sun & Earth & the Science Physical & Ethereal Spaces. 2nd ed. (Illus.). 1980. pap. 33.95 (ISBN 0-85440-360-4, Pub. by Steinerbooks). Anthroposophic.

Ayres, Frank, Jr. Projective Geometry. (Schaum's Outline Ser). (Orig.). 1967. pap. 7.95 (ISBN 0-07-002657-2). McGraw.

Baer, Reinhold. Linear Algebra & Projective Geometry. (Pure and Applied Mathematics Ser.: Vol. 2). 1952. 59.50 (ISBN 0-12-072250-X). Acad Pr.

Buseman, Herbert & Kelly, Paul J. Projective Geometry & Projective Metrics. (Pure & Applied Mathematics Ser.: Vol. 3). 1953. 65.00 (ISBN 0-12-148356-8). Acad Pr.

Coxeter, H. S. Projective Geometry. 2nd ed. LC 73-86992. 1974. 17.50 (ISBN 0-8020-2104-2). U of Toronto Pr.

Coxeter, Harold & Macdonald, Scott. The Real Projective Plane. 2nd ed. LC 60-3540. pap. 59.50 (ISBN 0-317-09189-1, 2050796). Bks Demand UMI.

Fishback, W. T. Projective & Euclidean Geometry. 2nd ed. LC 76-81329. Repr. of 1969 ed. 78.00 (ISBN 0-8357-9967-0, 2051602). Bks Demand UMI.

Garner, L. E. Outline of Projective Geometry. 220p. 1981. 36.75 (ISBN 0-444-00423-8, North-Holland). Elsevier.

Grunbaum, B. Arrangements & Spreads. LC 71-38926. (CBMS Regional Conference Series in Mathematics: No. 10). 114p. 1980. pap. 11.00 (ISBN 0-8218-1659-4, CBMS-10). Am Math.

Heyting, A. Axiomatic Projective Geometry. 2nd, rev. ed. 150p. 1980. 42.75 (ISBN 0-444-85431-2, North-Holland). Elsevier.

Hughes, D. R. & Piper, F. C. Projective Planes. 2nd ed. (Graduate Texts in Mathematics Ser.: Vol. 6). 291p. 1982. 37.50 (ISBN 0-387-90043-8). Springer-Verlag.

Lazarsfeld & Van de Ven, eds. Topics in the Geometry of Projective Space: Recent Work of F. L. Zak. (DMV Seminars Ser.: Band 4). 52p. 1984. pap. 9.95 (ISBN 0-317-18426-1). Birkhauser.

Okonek, Christian, et al. Vector Bundles on Complex Projective Spaces. (Progress in Mathematics Ser.: No. 3). 396p. 1980. pap. text ed. 26.00x (ISBN 0-8176-3000-7). Birkhauser.

Pickert, G. Projektive Ebenen. 2nd ed. LC 75-9953. (Die Grundlehren der Mathematischen Wissenschaften: Vol. 80). (Illus.). 371p. 1975. 57.90 (ISBN 0-387-07280-2). Springer-Verlag.

Steiner, Jacob. Gesammelte Werke, 2 Vols. 2nd ed. LC 76-113151. (Ger). 1971. text ed. 59.50 set (ISBN 0-8284-0233-7). Chelsea Pub.

Stevenson, Frederick W. Projective Planes. LC 72-156824. (Illus.). 416p. 1972. text ed. 32.95x (ISBN 0-7167-0443-9); teacher's manual avail. W H Freeman.

Von Neumann, John. Continuous Geometry. (Mathematical Ser.: Vol. 25). 1960. 33.00x (ISBN 0-691-07928-5). Princeton U Pr.

GEOMETRY, PROJECTIVE DIFFERENTIAL

see Geometry, Differential–Projective

GEOMETRY, RIEMANNIAN

Blair, D. E. Contact Manifold in Riemannian Geometry. (Lecture Notes in Mathematics Ser: Vol. 509). 1976. pap. 13.00 (ISBN 0-387-07626-3). Springer-Verlag.

Boothby, William M. An Introduction to Differentiable Manifolds & Riemannian Geometry. (Pure & Applied Mathematics Ser.). 424p. 1975. Acad Pr.

Cartan, Elie. Geometry of Riemannian Spaces. (LIE Groups Ser.: Vol. XIII). 506p. 1983. 55.00 (ISBN 0-317-18190-4, 991600010). Math Sci Pr.

Cheeger, J. & Ebin, D. G. Comparison Theorems in Riemannian Geometry. LC 74-83725. (Mathematical Library: Vol. 9). 174p. 1975. 47.00 (ISBN 0-444-10764-9, North-Holland). Elsevier.

Eisenhart, Luther P. Riemannian Geometry. rev. ed. 1950. 30.00x (ISBN 0-691-08026-7). Princeton U Pr.

Goldberg, Samuel I. Curvature & Homology. (Illus.). xviii, 315p. pap. 6.50 (ISBN 0-486-64314-X). Dover.

Klingenberg, Wilhelm. Riemannian Geometry. LC 82-9772. (De Gruyter Studies in Mathematics). x, 396p. 1982. 39.20 (ISBN 3-11-008673-5). De Gruyter.

Laugwitz, D. Differential & Riemannian Geometry. Steinhardt, F., tr. 1965. 53.00 (ISBN 0-12-437750-5). Acad Pr.

White, J. Enrico. Method of Integrated Tangents with Applications in Local Riemannian Geometry. (Monographs & Studies: No. 13). 256p. 1982. text ed. 48.50 (ISBN 0-273-08515-8). Pitman Pub MA.

Willmore, T. J. Total Curvature in Riemannian Geometry. LC 82-15670. (Mathematics & Its Applications Ser.). 168p. 1982. 42.95x (ISBN 0-470-27354-2). Halsted Pr.

BOOKS - SUBJECT INDEX GEOPHYSICAL RESEARCH

Willmore, Thomas J. & Hitchin, N. J. Global Riemannian Geometry. LC 83-26675. (Mathematics & Its Applications Ser.). 213p. 1984. 64.95x (ISBN 0-470-20017-0). Halsted Pr.
Yano, Kentaro. Integral Formulas in Riemannian Geometry. LC 74-121180. (Pure & Applied Mathematics Ser.: No. 1). pap. 41.30 (ISBN 0-317-08364-3, 2055285). Bks Demand UMI.

GEOMETRY, SOLID
see also Crystallography; Cube; Geometry, Analytic–Solid; Polyhedra; Sphere; Surfaces
Court, Nathan A. Modern Pure Solid Geometry. 2nd ed. LC 64-18134. 1979. text ed. 17.95 (ISBN 0-8284-0147-0). Chelsea Pub.
Wheeler, David. Presenting the Gattegno Prisms & Cubes. 1974. pap. 1.25 (ISBN 0-87825-029-8). Ed Solutions.
Zameeruddin, Qazi & Khanna, V. K. Solid Geometry. 1977. 25.00x (ISBN 0-7069-0560-1, Pub. by Vikas India). Advent NY.

GEOMETRY CONCEPT
Brunelle, Wallace & O'Neill, Robert. Constructional Geometry: Student Syllabus. 2nd ed. Gray, Allan W., ed. 1972. pap. text ed. 8.35 (ISBN 0-89420-229-4, 350299); cassette recordings 108.05 (ISBN 0-89420-201-4, 350300). Natl Book.
Piaget, Jean, et al. Child's Conception of Geometry. Lunzer, E. A., tr. LC 60-7177. (Illus.). 1960. 13.95x (ISBN 0-465-01078-4). Basic.
--The Child's Conception of Geometry. Lunzer, E. A., tr. 432p. 1981. pap. 8.95 (ISBN 0-393-00057-5). Norton.

GEOMETRY OF NUMBERS
see also Numbers, Theory of
Cassels, J. W. Introduction to the Geometry of Numbers. 2nd ed. LC 75-154801. (Grundlehren der Mathematischen Wissenschaften: Vol. 99). (Illus.). 1971. 47.00 (ISBN 0-387-02397-6). Springer-Verlag.
Hiller, H. Geometry of Coxeter Groups. (Research Notes in Mathematics Ser.: No. 54). 232p. (Orig.). 1982. pap. text ed. 23.95 (ISBN 0-273-08517-4). Pitman Pub MA.

GEOMETRY OF PATHS
see Spaces, Generalized

GEOMORPHOLOGY
see also Erosion; Landforms; Physical Geography; Volcanism
Andrews, John T. A Geomorphological Study of Post-Glacial Uplift: With Particular Reference to Arctic Canada. (Special Publication of the Institute of British Geographers Ser.: No. 2). 1980. 25.00 (ISBN 0-12-058580-4). Acad Pr.
Baker, Victor R. The Channels of Mars. (Illus.). 212p. 1982. text ed. 45.00x (ISBN 0-292-71068-2). U of Tex Pr.
Birkeland, Peter W. Soils & Geomorphology. (Illus.). 1984. text ed. 37.50x (ISBN 0-19-503398-1); pap. 22.95x (ISBN 0-19-503435-X). Oxford U Pr.
Bloom, A. L. Surface of the Earth. pap. text ed. 15.95 (ISBN 0-13-877944-9). P-H.
Bloom, Arthur L. Geomorphology: A Systematic Analysis of Late Cenozoic Landforms. LC 77-25816. (Illus.). 1978. ref. ed. 40.95 (ISBN 0-13-353086-8). P-H.
Brown, E. H. & Waters, R. S., eds. Progress in Geomorphology: Papers in Honour of David L. Linton. (Special Publication of the Institute of British Geographers: No. 7). 1980. 27.50 (ISBN 0-12-137780-6). Acad Pr.
Brunsden, Denys, et al, eds. The Unquiet Landscape. LC 77-15583. (The Geographical Magazine Ser.). 168p. 1975. Repr. of 1972 ed. 29.95x (ISBN 0-470-99345-6). Halsted Pr.
Budel, Julius. Climatic Geomorphology. Fischer, Lenore & Busche, Detlef, trs. LC 81-47909. (Illus.). 443p. 1982. 55.00x (ISBN 0-691-08294-4); pap. 20.00x (ISBN 0-691-08295-2). Princeton U Pr.
Butzer, Karl W. Geomorphology from the Earth. (Meinig Ser.). (Illus.). 512p. 1976. text ed. 31.50 scp (ISBN 0-06-041097-3, HarpC). Har-Row.
--Geomorphology of the Lower Illinois Valley As a Spatial-Temporal Context for the Koster Archaic Site. (Reports of Investigations Ser.: No. 34). (Illus.). 60p. 1977. pap. 3.50 (ISBN 0-89792-067-8). Ill St Museum.
Carson, M. A. & Kirkby, M. J. Hillslope Form & Process. (Cambridge Geographical Studies). 67.50 (ISBN 0-521-08234-X). Cambridge U Pr.
Chikishev, A. G., ed. Landscape Indicators. LC 72-88886. (Illus.). 165p. 1973. 35.00x (ISBN 0-306-10875-5, Consultants). Plenum Pub.
Chorley, R. J., et al. History of the Study of Landforms; or, the Development of Geomorphology, Vol. 2: The Life & Work of William Morris Davis. 874p. 1973. 75.00x (ISBN 0-416-26890-0, NO. 2139). Methuen Inc.
Chorley, Richard J., et al. Geomorphology. (Orig.). 1985. pap. text ed. 30.00 (ISBN 0-416-32590-4, 9361). Methuen Inc.
Coates, D. R., ed. Environmental Geomorphology & Landscape Conservation: Non-Urban, Vol. 3. LC 72-77882. (Benchmark Papers in Geology: Vol. 8). 483p. 1973. 57.95 (ISBN 0-87933-040-6). Van Nos Reinhold.
--Environmental Geomorphology & Landscape Conservation: Prior to 1900, Vol. 1. LC 72-77882. (Benchmark Papers in Geology: Vol.1). 485p. 1972. 57.95 (ISBN 0-87933-005-8). Van Nos Reinhold.
Coates, Donald R., ed. Environmental Geomorphology & Landscape Conservation, 2. V. LC 72-77882. (Benchmark Papers in Geology Ser.). (Illus.). 1974. 66.00 (ISBN 0-12-786242-0). Acad Pr.
--Geomorphology & Engineering. (Binghamton Symposia in Geomorphology: International Ser.: No. 7). (Illus.). 384p. 1980. text ed. 45.00x (ISBN 0-04-551040-7). Allen Unwin.
Coates, Donald R & Vitek, John D., eds. Thresholds in Geomorphology. (Binghamton Symposia in Geomorphology Ser.: Vol. 9). (Illus.). 512p. (Orig.). 1980. text ed. 50.00x (ISBN 0-04-551033-4). Allen Unwin.
Cooke, R. U. Geomorphological Hazards in Los Angeles: A Study of Slope & Sediment Problems in a Metropolitan County. LC 84-9234. (London Research Series in Geography: No. 7). (Illus.). 192p. 1984. text ed. 35.00x (ISBN 0-04-551090-3). Allen Unwin.
Cooke, R. U. & Brunsden, D. Urban Geomorphology in Drylands. 1982. 32.00x (ISBN 0-19-823239-X). Oxford U Pr.
Cooke, Ronald U. & Doornkamp, John C. Geomorphology in Environmental Management: An Introduction. (Illus.). 1974. pap. text ed. 15.95x (ISBN 0-19-874021-2). Oxford U Pr.
Cooke, Ronald U. & Warren, Andrew. Geomorphology in Deserts. 1974. 40.00x (ISBN 0-520-02280-7). U of Cal Pr.
Costa, J. E. & Fleisher, p. J., eds. Developments & Applications of Geomorphology. (Illus.). 300p. 1984. 44.00 (ISBN 0-387-13457-3). Springer Verlag.
Craig, R. G. & Craft, J. L., eds. Applied Geomorphology. (Binghamton Symposia in Geomorphology, International Ser.: No. 11). (Illus.). 272p. 1982. text ed. 35.00x (ISBN 0-04-551050-4). Allen Unwin.
Cullingford, R. A., et al. Timescales in Geomorphology. LC 79-40517. 360p. 1980. 103.95 (ISBN 0-471-27600-6, Pub. by Wiley-Interscience). Wiley.
Derbyshire, Edward, ed. Geomorphology & Climate. LC 75-4523. Repr. of 1976 ed. 99.80 (ISBN 0-8357-9899-2, 2016026). Bks Demand UMI.
Diskit, K. R., ed. Contributions to Indian Geography: Geomorphology, Vol. 2. 1983. 37.50x (ISBN 0-8364-1038-6, Pub. by Heritage India). South Asia Bks.
Doehring, Donald O., ed. Geomorphology in Arid Regions. (Binghamton Symposia in Geomorphology: International Ser.: No. 8). (Illus.). 276p. 1980. pap. text ed. 30.00x (ISBN 0-04-551041-5). Allen Unwin.
Doomkamp, J. C., et al, eds. Geology, Geomorphology & Pedology of Bahrain. 443p. 150.00x (ISBN 0-86094-021-7, Pub. by GEO Abstracts England). State Mutual Bk.
Douglas, Ian & Spencer, Tom, eds. Environmental Change & Tropical Geomorphology. (Illus.). 400p. 1985. text ed. 45.00x (ISBN 0-04-551071-1). Allen Unwin.
Embleton, C. & King, C. A. Glacial & Periglacial Morphology, 2 vols. 2nd ed. Incl. Vol. 1. Glacial Geomorphology. LC 75-14188; Vol. 2. Periglacial Geomorphology. LC 75-14187. 1975. pap. Halsted Pr.
Embleton, Clifford, ed. The Geomorphology of Europe. 465p. 1984. 79.95 (ISBN 0-471-80070-8, Pub. by Wiley-Interscience). Wiley.
Embleton, Clifford & Thornes, John, eds. Process in Geomorphology. LC 79-18747. 436p. 1979. pap. 32.95x (ISBN 0-470-26808-5). Halsted Pr.
Embleton, Clifford, et al, eds. Geomorphology: Present Problems & Future Prospects. (Illus.). 1978. text ed. 32.50x (ISBN 0-19-874078-6). Oxford U Pr.
Fairbridge, R. W., ed. The Encyclopedia of Geomorphology. LC 68-58342. (Encyclopedia of Earth Sciences Ser.: Vol. III). 1295p. 1968. 98.00 (ISBN 0-87933-179-8). Van Nos Reinhold.
Faniran. Humid Tropical Geomorphology. LC 82-14896. 1984. text ed. 35.00 o. p. (ISBN 0-582-64346-5); pap. text ed. 17.95 (ISBN 0-582-64351-1). Longman.
Fookes, P. G. & Vaughan, P. R., eds. A Handbook of Engineering Geomorphology. (Illus.). 320p. 1985. 66.00 (ISBN 0-412-00591-3, 9022, Pub by Chapman & Hall). Methuen Inc.
Fuchs, K., et al, eds. Plateau Uplift: The Rhenish Shield-a Case History. (Illus.). 420p. 1983. 52.00 (ISBN 0-387-12577-9). Springer-Verlag.
Gardiner, V. & Dackombe, R. Geomorphological Field Manual. (Illus.). 272p. 1982. pap. text ed. 14.95x (ISBN 0-04-551062-8). Allen Unwin.
Gardner, Rita & Scoging, Helen. Mega-Geomorphology. (Illus.). 1983. 42.00x (ISBN 0-19-823244-6). Oxford U Pr.
Gladfelter, Bruce G. Meseta & Campina Landforms in Central Spain. LC 75-133028. (Research Papers Ser.: No. 130). (Illus., Orig.). 1971. pap. 10.00 (ISBN 0-89065-037-3, 130). U Chicago Dept Geog.
Goudie, A. S. & Pye, K., eds. Chemical Sediments & Geomorphology. 1983. 58.00 (ISBN 0-12-293480-6). Acad Pr.
Goudie, Andrew, ed. Geomorphological Techniques. (Illus.). 395p. 1981. text ed. 60.00x (ISBN 0-04-551042-3); pap. text ed. 29.95x (ISBN 0-04-551043-1). Allen Unwin.
Hack, J. T. & Morisawa, M., eds. Tectronic Geomorphology. (Binghamton Symposia in Geomorphology International Ser.: No. 15). 400p. 1985. text ed. 40.00x (ISBN 0-04-551098-9). Allen Unwin.
Hails, John R., ed. Applied Geomorphology. 418p. 1977. pap. text ed. 55.50 (ISBN 0-444-41317-0). Elsevier.
Hart, M. G. Geomorphology: Pure & Applied. (Illus.). 160p. 1985. text ed. 25.00x (ISBN 0-04-551087-3); pap. text ed. 11.95 (ISBN 0-04-551088-1). Allen Unwin.
Helgren, David M. Rivers of Diamonds: An Alluvial History of the Lower Vaal Basin, South Africa. LC 79-17790. (Research Papers Ser.: No. 185). (Illus.). 388p. 1979. pap. 10.00 (ISBN 0-89065-092-6). U Chicago Dept Geog.
Hill, Mary. California Landscape: Origin & Evolution. 200p. 1984. 16.95 (ISBN 0-520-04831-8). U of Cal Pr.
Howard, J. & Mitchell, C. W. Phytogeomorphology. 1985. 37.50 (ISBN 0-471-09914-7). Wiley.
Hurlbut, Cornelius S., Jr. & Switzer, George S. Geomology. LC 78-13262. 272p. 1979. 39.95 (ISBN 0-471-42224-X, Pub. by Wiley-Interscience). Wiley.
Jackson, Roscoe G., II & Day, T. J. Mass Wasting, Nineteen Seventy-Five. (Guelph Geomorphology Ser.). 202p. 1980. 10.35x (ISBN 0-902246-58-5, Pub. by GEO Abstracts England). State Mutual Bk.
--Research in Fluvial Systems Nineteen Seventy-Seven. (Guelph Geomorphology Ser.). 214p. 1980. 11.50x (ISBN 0-86094-013-6, Pub. by GEO Abstracts England). State Mutual Bk.
--Research in Polar & Alpine Geomorphology, 1973. 206p. 1980. 11.50x (ISBN 0-902246-22-4, Pub. by GEO Abstracts England). State Mutual Bk.
--Research Methods in Pleistocene Geomorphology, 1971. (Guelph Geomorphology Ser.). 285p. 1980. 13.80x (ISBN 0-902246-17-8, Pub. by GEO Abstracts England). State Mutual Bk.
Johnson, R. H., ed. The Geomorphology of North-West England. LC 85-275. 1985. write for info. (ISBN 0-7190-1745-9, Pub. by Manchester Univ Pr); pap. write for info. (ISBN 0-7190-1790-4). Longwood Pub Group.
King, Cuchlaine, ed. Landforms & Geomorphology: Concepts & History. LC 76-3489. (Benchmark Papers in Geology Ser.: Vol. 28). 400p. 1976. 67.50 (ISBN 0-12-786845-3). Acad Pr.
King, Lester C. South African Scenery, a Textbook of Geomorphology. 3rd rev. ed. (Illus.). 1967. 17.95x (ISBN 0-02-847900-9). Hafner.
King, Philip B. & Schumm, Stanley A. The Physical Geography (Geomorphology) of William Morris Davis. 217p. 1980. 37.00x (ISBN 0-86094-046-2, Pub. by GEO Abstracts England). State Mutual Bk.
LaFleur, Robert G., ed. Groundwater As a Geomorphic Agent. (Binghamton Symposia in Geomorphology: International Ser.: No. 13). (Illus.). 384p. 1984. text ed. 50.00x (ISBN 0-04-551069-5). Allen Unwin.
Leopold, Luna B., et al. Fluvial Processes in Geomorphology. LC 64-10919. (Geology Ser.). (Illus.). 522p. 1964. 38.95 (ISBN 0-7167-0221-5). W H Freeman.
Loffler, E. Explanatory Notes to the Geomorphological Map of Papua New Guinea. (Land Pesearch Ser.: No. 33). (Illus.). 19p. 1977. pap. 10.00x (ISBN 0-643-00092-5, Pub. by CSIRO). Intl Spec Bk.
McFarlane, J. M. Laterite & Landscape. 1977. 33.00 (ISBN 0-12-484450-2). Acad Pr.
Michael, Henry N., ed. The Archaeology & Geomorphology of Northern Asia: Selected Works. LC 65-1456. (Arctic Institute of North America-Anthropology of the North; Translation from Russian Sources Ser.: No. 5). pap. 132.00 (ISBN 0-317-10857-3, 2019174). Bks Demand UMI.
Morisawa, Marie. Geomorphology Laboratory Manual. 2nd ed. 253p. 1983. pap. text ed. 20.45 (ISBN 0-471-89806-6). Wiley.
Mukkopadhyay, S. C. The Tista Basin: A Study in Fluvial Geomorphology. 308p. 1984. 49.00x (ISBN 0-317-20278-2, Pub. by K P Bagchi & Co India). State Mutual Bk.
Pethick, John S. Introduction to Coastal Geomorphology. 300p. 1984. pap. text ed. 16.95 (ISBN 0-7131-6391-7). E Arnold.
Pitty, Alistair, ed. Geomorphology: Themes & Trends. LC 84-24436. (Illus.). 286p. 1985. 28.50x (ISBN 0-389-20537-0, BNB-08099). B&N Imports.
Pitty, Alistair F. Introduction to Geomorphology. 1971. pap. 18.95x (ISBN 0-416-29760-9, NO.2376). Methuen Inc.
--The Nature of Geomorphology. 150p. 1982. pap. 8.95x (ISBN 0-416-32120-8, NO. 3737). Methuen Inc.
Price, R. J. & Sugen, D. E., eds. Polar Geomorphology. (Institute of British Geographers Special Publication Ser.: No. 4). 1980. 25.00 (ISBN 0-12-564550-3). Acad Pr.
Richards, K., et al, eds. Geomorphology & Soils. (Illus.). 500p. 1985. text ed. 50.00x (ISBN 0-04-551093-8). Allen Unwin.
Ritter, Dale F. Process Geomorphology. 616p. 1978. text ed. write for info. (ISBN 0-697-05035-1). Wm C Brown.
--Process Geomorphology. 2nd ed. 608p. 1985. text ed. price not set (ISBN 0-697-05047-5). Wm C Brown.
Robbins, R. G., ed. Lands of the Ramu - Madang Area, Papua New Guinea. (Land Research Ser.: No. 37). (Illus.). 1977. pap. 10.00x (ISBN 0-643-00175-1, Pub. by CSIRO). Intl Spec Bk.
Scheidegger, Adrian E. Theoretical Geomorphology. 2nd ed. LC 70-110153. (Illus.). 1970. 69.10 (ISBN 0-387-05005-1). Springer-Verlag.
Selby, M. J. Earth's Changing Surface. (Illus.). 480p. 1985. text ed. 32.50x (ISBN 0-19-823252-7); pap. text ed. 12.95x (ISBN 0-19-823251-9). Oxford U Pr.
Sharma, H. S., ed. Perspectives in Geomorphology, 4 vols. 1500p. 1982. text ed. 185.50x (ISBN 0-391-02636-4, Pub. by Concept India). Humanities.
Sissons, J. B. Evolution of Scotland's Scenery. (Illus.). ix, 259p. 1967. 21.00 (ISBN 0-208-00163-8, Archon). Shoe String.
Small, R. J. The Study of Landforms. 2nd ed. LC 77-71427. 1978. pap. 27.95x (ISBN 0-521-29238-7). Cambridge U Pr.
Snead, R. World Atlas of Geomorphic Features. 1980. 46.50 (ISBN 0-442-28973-1). Van Nos Reinhold.
Snead, Rodman E. World Atlas of Geomorphic Features. LC 77-28009. 320p. 1980. 39.50 (ISBN 0-88275-272-3). Krieger.
Steers, Alfred J. Coastal Features of England & Wales: Eight Essays. (Illus.). 240p. 1981. 35.00 (ISBN 0-900891-70-X). Oleander Pr.
Steers, J. A., ed. Applied Coastal Geomorphology. 1971. 25.00x (ISBN 0-262-19088-5). MIT Pr.
Thom, B. G., ed. Coastal Geomorphology in Australia. 360p. 1984. 45.00 (ISBN 0-12-687880-3). Acad Pr.
Thorn, Colin E., ed. Space & Time in Geomorphology. (The Binghamton' Symposia in Geomorphology, International Ser.: No. 12). (Illus.). 350p. 1982. text ed. 45.00x (ISBN 0-04-551056-3). Allen Unwin.
Thornes, John & Brunsden, Denys. Geomorphology & Time. 1977. 15.95x (ISBN 0-416-80080-7, NO. 6289). Methuen Inc.
Tinkler, Keith J. A Short History of Geomorphology. LC 84-24364. (Illus.). 336p. 1985. 25.00x (ISBN 0-389-20544-3, BNB-08108). B&N Imports.
Verstappen, H. Applied Geomorphology: Geomorphological Surveys for Environmental Development. 1983. 95.75 (ISBN 0-444-42181-5, I-198-83). Elsevier.
Vocabulaire Franco-Anglo-Allemand De Geomorphologie. (Fr., Eng. & Ger.). 1970. pap. 14.95 (ISBN 0-686-57278-5, F-136940). French & Eur.
Weyman, Darrell & Weyman, Valerie. Landscape Processes: An Introduction to Geomorphology. (Processes in Physical Geography Ser). (Illus.). 1977. pap. text ed. 7.95x (ISBN 0-04-551026-1). Allen Unwin.
Woldenberg, M. Models in Geomorphology. (Binghamton Symposia in Geomorphology International Ser.: No. 14). 400p. 1985. text ed. 45.00x (ISBN 0-04-551075-X). Allen Unwin.

GEOPHYSICAL PROSPECTING
see Prospecting–Geophysical Methods

GEOPHYSICAL RESEARCH
Cassinis, R., ed. The Solution of the Inverse Problem in Geophysical Interpretation. LC 81-4067. 392p. 1981. 65.00x (ISBN 0-306-40735-3, Plenum Pr). Plenum Pub.
Fitch, A. A., ed. Developments in Geophysical Exploration Methods, Vol. 3. (Illus.). 320p. 1982. 57.50 (ISBN 0-85334-126-5, Pub. by Elsevier Applied Sci England). Elsevier.

--Developments in Geophysical Exploration Methods, Vol. 5. 262p. 1983. 63.00 (ISBN 0-85334-216-4, Pub. by Elsevier Applied Sci England). Elsevier.

--Developments in Geophysical Exploration Methods, Vol. 6. (Illus.). 280p. 1985. 57.00 (ISBN 0-85334-334-9, Pub. by Elsevier Applied Sci England). Elsevier.

Geophysics Research Board & Division Of Earth Sciences. Solid-Earth Geophysics: Survey & Outlook. 1964. pap. 5.00 (ISBN 0-309-01231-7). Natl Acad Pr.

Geophysics Research Board, National Research Council. Geophysical Predictions. LC 78-8147. (Studies in Geophysics Ser.). 1978. 14.25 (ISBN 0-309-02741-1). Natl Acad Pr.

Gronlie, Gisle. Geophysical Studies in the Norwegian-Greenland Sea. (Norsk Polarinstitutt Skrifter: Vol. 170). (Illus.). 117p. 1980. pap. 10.00 (ISBN 82-90307-05-5). Universitet.

Kearey, P. & Brooks, M. Introduction to Geophysical Exploration. (Illus.). 310p. 1984. pap. text ed. 21.00 (ISBN 0-632-01049-5). Blackwell Pubns.

Persen, L. N. Rock Dynamics & Geophysical Exploration. LC 74-21865. (Developments in Geotechnical Engineering: Vol. 8). 276p. 1975. 68.00 (ISBN 0-444-41284-0). Elsevier.

Pesek, John, ed. Agronomy: Science in Action. 1979. pap. write for info. (ISBN 0-89118-059-1). Am Soc Agron.

Silvia, M. T. & Robinson, E. A. Deconvolution of Geophysical Time Series in the Exploration of Oil & Natural Gas. (Developments in Petroleum Science Ser.: Vol. 10). 252p. 1979. 61.75 (ISBN 0-444-41679-X). Elsevier.

GEOPHYSICS

see also Atmospheric Electricity; Auroras; Continents; Earth Movements; Earth Tides; Geodynamics; Geology; Geophysical Research; Magnetism; Magnetohydrodynamics; Meteorology; Nuclear Geophysics; Oceanography; Plate Tectonics; Prospecting–Geophysical Methods; Radiative Transfer; Seismology; Solifluction; Van Allen Radiation Belts

Akimoto, S. & Manghnani, M. H. High Pressure Research in Geophysics. 1982. 113.00 (ISBN 90-277-1439-8, Pub. by Reidel Holland). Kluwer Academic.

American Meteorological Society - Boston. Cumulated Bibliography & Index to Meteorological & Geoastrophysical Abstracts: 1950-1969. 1972. Author Sequence, 9 Vols. 1395.00 (ISBN 0-8161-0942-7, Hall Library); Dec. Class, 4 Vols. 835.00 (ISBN 0-8161-0183-3). G K Hall.

Annals of the International Geophysical Year. Vols. 1-20, 1973. 690.00 (ISBN 0-08-019913-5); Vols. 1-24. 830.00 (ISBN 0-08-019911-9); Vols. 21-22 Separately, 1974. 360.00 (ISBN 0-08-018913-X); Vols. 23-48, 1975. 750.00 (ISBN 0-08-019914-3). Single Vols. 2, 5. 28.00 ea. Pergamon.

Athay, R. G. Radiation Transport in Spectral Lines. LC 72-188002. (Geophysics & Astrophysics Monographs: No. 1). 266p. 1972. lib. bdg. 39.50 (ISBN 90-277-0228-4, Pub. by Reidel Holland); pap. 21.50 (ISBN 90-277-0241-1, Pub. by Reidel Holland). Kluwer Academic.

Augustithis, S. S. Atlas of the Textural Patterns of Basic & Ultrabasic Rocks & Their Genetic Significance. 1979. 102.00x (ISBN 3-11-006571-1). De Gruyter.

Baguelin, F., et al. The Pressuremeter & Foundation Engineering. (Rock & Soil Mechanics Ser.). (Illus.). 1978. 58.00x (ISBN 0-87849-019-1). Trans Tech.

Ballantyne, E. J., Jr., et al, eds. Manual of Geophysical Hand-Calculator Programs TI & HP Volumes. 1981. TI Vol. looseleaf 50.00 (ISBN 0-931830-20-6); HP Vol. 50.00 (ISBN 0-931830-17-6); Set, TI & HP. 90.00 (ISBN 0-317-12576-1). Soc Exploration.

Baranov, Wladimir. Potential Fields & Their Transformations in Applied Geophysics. (Geoexploration Monographs: Series 1, No. 6). (Illus.). 121p. 1975. lib. bdg. 23.10x (ISBN 3-4431-3008-9). Lubrecht & Cramer.

Bates, C. C. & Gaskell, T. F. Geophysics in the Affairs of Man: A Personalized History of Exploration Geophysics & Its Allied Sciences of Seismology & Oceanography. (Illus.). 536p. 1982. 66.00 (ISBN 0-08-024026-7); pap. 25.00 (ISBN 0-08-024025-9). Pergamon.

Bath, M. Spectral Analysis in Geophysics. (Developments in Solid Earth Geophysics: Vol. 7). 563p. 1974. Repr. of 1974 ed. 106.50 (ISBN 0-444-41222-0). Elsevier.

Beck, A. E. Physical Principles of Exploration Methods: An Introductory Text for Geology & Geophysics Students. LC 81-80411. 234p. 1981. pap. 17.95 (ISBN 0-470-27128-0). Halsted Pr.

Berdichevsky, M. N. & Zhdanov, M. S. Advanced Theory of Deep Geomagnetic Sounding. (Methods in Geochemistry & Geophysics Ser.: Vol. 19). 400p. 1984. 94.50 (ISBN 0-444-42189-0). Elsevier.

Beynon, Granville, ed. Solar-Terrestrial Physics: Proceedings of an International Symposium, Innsbruck, Austria, 1978. (Illus.). 240p. 1979. pap. 47.00 (ISBN 0-08-025054-8). Pergamon.

Billings, S. A., ed. Identification & System Parameter Estimation: Proceedings of the 7th TFAC-IFORS Symposium, York, UK, July 3-7 1985, 2 vol. (IFAC Proceedings Ser.). (Illus.). 1800p. 1985. 450.00 (ISBN 0-08-032560-2). Pergamon.

Bisztricsany, E. & Szeidovitz, G., eds. Proceedings: Assembly of European Seismological Commission, 17th, Budapest, 24-29 Aug. 1980. (Developments in Solid Earth Geophysics: Vol. 15). 690p. 1983. 117.00 (ISBN 0-444-99662-1). Elsevier.

Borehole Geophysics Applied to Metallic Mineral Prospecting. pap. 4.95 (SSC9, SSC). Unipub.

Bowhill, S. A., ed. Review Papers: International Solar-Terrestrial Physics Symposium, Sao-Paolo, June, 1974. 212p. 1976. pap. 50.00 (ISBN 0-08-019959-3). Pergamon.

Bradford, James N. Escape Route: Surviving the Earth Changes. 180p. Date not set. pap. 10.00 (ISBN 0-89540-135-5, SB-135). Sun Pub.

Bruzek, Anton & Durrant, Christopher J., eds. Illustrated Glossary for Solar & Solar-Terrestrial Physics. (Astrophysics & Space Science Library: No. 69). 1977. lib. bdg. 34.00 (ISBN 90-277-0825-8, Pub. by Reidel Holland). Kluwer Academic.

Buntebarth, G. Geothermics: An Introduction. Chapman, I. M. & Chapman, D. S., trs. from Ger. (Universitext Ser.). (Illus.). 150p. 1984. pap. 22.50 (ISBN 0-387-12751-8). Springer-Verlag.

Cassinis, R., ed. Problems & Methods for Lithospheric Exploration. (Ettore Majorana International Science Series, Physical Sciences: Vol. 19). 230p. 1984. 49.50x (ISBN 0-306-41721-9, Plenum Pr). Plenum Pub.

Cermak, V. & Rybach, L., eds. Terrestrial Heat Flow in Europe. (Illus.). 1979. 59.00 (ISBN 0-387-09440-7). Springer-Verlag.

Chen, C. H., ed. Seismic Signal Analysis & Discrimination III. (Methods in Geochemistry & Geophysics Ser.: Vol. 22). 170p. 1985. Repr. 46.50 (ISBN 0-444-42430-X). Elsevier.

Claerbout, Jon F. Fundamentals of Geophysical Data Processing. (Illus.). 274p. 1985. pap. text ed. 39.95x (ISBN 0-86542-305-9). Blackwell Pubns.

Clark, Sydney P. Structure of the Earth. (Foundations of Earth Science Ser). 1971. pap. text ed. 15.95 (ISBN 0-13-854646-0). P-H.

Clayton, C. G., ed. Nuclear Geophysics: Selected Papers on Applications of Nuclear Techniques in Minerals Exploration, Mining & Process Control. (Illus.). 500p. 1983. 60.00 (ISBN 0-08-029158-9, 82-24570). Pergamon.

Corliss, William R. Earthquakes, Tides, Unidentified Sounds & Related Phenomena. LC 83-50781. (Catalog of Geophysical Anomalies Ser.). (Illus.). 214p. 1983. 12.95 (ISBN 0-915554-11-9). Sourcebook.

--Rare Halos, Mirages, Anomalous Rainbows, & Related Electromagnetic Phenomena. (Catalog of Geophysical Anomalies Ser.). (Illus.). 244p. 1984. 12.95 (ISBN 0-915554-12-7). Sourcebook.

Coulsen, Kinsell L. Solar & Terrestrial Radiation. 1975. 35.75 (ISBN 0-12-192950-7). Acad Pr.

DeBremaecker, J. Geophysics: The Earth's Interior. 352p. 1985. 29.95 (ISBN 0-471-87815-4). Wiley.

Dohr, Gerhard. Applied Geophysics: Introduction to Geophysical Prospecting. 2nd ed. LC 80-28695. (Geology of Petroleum Ser.). 231p. 1981. pap. 23.95x (ISBN 0-470-99102-X). Halsted Pr.

Donn, William. The Earth: Our Physical Environment. LC 79-37431. Repr. of 1972 ed. 158.00 (ISBN 0-8357-9875-5, 2055110). Bks Demand UMI.

Durrani, Robinson. Geophysical Signal Processing. (Illus.). 560p. 1986. text ed. 46.95 (ISBN 0-13-352667-4). P-H.

Ebel, A. & Simon, P. C., eds. Middle Atmosphere Sciences: A Selection of Papers from the Symposium Organised by the IAMAP & IAGA on the Occasion of the XVIII General Assembly of the IUGG, Hamburg, Federal Republic of Germany, August 1983. 120p. 1985. pap. 33.00 (ISBN 0-08-032592-0). Pergamon.

Egeland, Alv, et al, eds. Cosmical Geophysics. (Illus.). 360p. 1973. 33.50x (ISBN 8-200-02256-0, Dist. by Columbia U Pr). Universitet.

Eskinazi, S. Fluid Mechanics & Thermodynamics of Our Environment. 1975. 55.50 (ISBN 0-12-242540-5). Acad Pr.

Fedotov, S. A. & Markhinin, Y. K., eds. The Great Tolbachik Fissure Eruption: Geological & Geophysical Data, 1975-1976. LC 82-9586. (Cambridge Earth Science Ser.). 300p. 1983. 72.50 (ISBN 0-521-24345-9). Cambridge U Pr.

Fitch, A. A., ed. Developments in Geophysical Exploration Methods, Vol. 1. (Illus.). 310p. 1979. 50.00 (ISBN 0-85334-835-9, Pub. by Elsevier Applied Sci England). Elsevier.

--Developments in Geophysical Exploration Methods, Vol. 2. (Illus.). 235p. 1981. 40.75 (ISBN 0-85334-930-4, Pub. by Elsevier Applied Sci England). Elsevier.

Fluegge, S. Encyclopedia of Physics, Vol. 49, Pt. 5: Geophysics 3, Pt. 5. LC 56-2942. (Eng, Fr, & Ger., Illus.). 420p. 1976. 116.90 (ISBN 0-387-07512-7). Springer-Verlag.

Fluegge, S., ed. Geophysics Three. (Encyclopedia of Physics Ser.: Vol. 49, Pt. 6). (Illus.). 429p. 1982. 118.60 (ISBN 0-387-07080-X). Springer-Verlag.

Foster, Robert J. Physical Geology. 4th ed. 460p. 1983. text ed. 25.95 (ISBN 0-675-20021-0). Additional supplments may be obtained from publisher. Merrill.

Fritz, P. & Fontes, J. C. Handbook of Environmental Isotope Chemistry: Terrestrial Environment, Vol. 1. 546p. 1980. 93.75 (ISBN 0-444-41780-X). Elsevier.

Galperin, E. I. The Polarization Method of Seismic Studies. 1983. lib. bdg. 58.00 (ISBN 90-277-1555-6, Pub. by Reidel Holland). Kluwer Academic.

Garland, George D. Introduction to Geophysics: Mantle, Core & Crust. 2nd ed. LC 78-54516. (Illus.). 1979. text ed. 42.95 (ISBN 0-7216-4026-5). HR&W.

Geophysics in the Americas: A Symposium of the Geophysics Commission of the Pan American Inst. of Geography & History Ottawa, Canada, Sept. 76. (Illus.). 1978. pap. 18.50 (ISBN 0-660-00702-9, SSC102, SSC). Unipub.

Geophysics Research Board. Impact of Technology on Geophysics. xii, 121p. 1979. pap. 11.75 (ISBN 0-309-02887-6). Natl Acad Pr.

Geophysics Research Board, National Research Council. Climate in Earth History. 1982. pap. text ed. 16.25 (ISBN 0-309-03329-2). Natl Acad Pr.

Geophysics Study Committee. Estuaries, Geophysics, & the Environment. LC 77-82812. (Studies in Geophysics). (Illus.). 1977. pap. text ed. 9.95 (ISBN 0-309-02629-6). Natl Acad Pr.

Goguel, Jean. Geophysique. (Methodique Ser.). 1336p. 53.95 (ISBN 0-686-56430-8). French & Eur.

Gordon, C. W. & Canuto, V. The Earth One: The Upper Atmosphere, Ionisphere & Magnetosphere. (Handbook of Astronomy, Astrophysics & Geophysics Ser.: Vol. I). 420p. 1978. 103.95 (ISBN 0-677-16100-X). Gordon.

Grant, F. S. & West, G. F. Interpretation Theory in Applied Geophysics. (Illus.). 1965. text ed. 69.95 (ISBN 0-07-024100-7). McGraw.

Griffiths, D. H. & King, R. F. Applied Geophysics for Engineers & Geologists. 2nd ed. 1965. 33.00 (ISBN 0-08-022071-1); pap. 14.50 (ISBN 0-08-022072-X). Pergamon.

--Applied Geophysics for Geologists & Engineers: The Elements of Geophysical Prospecting. 2nd ed. (Illus.). 224p. 1981. 33.00 (ISBN 0-08-022071-1); pap. 14.50 (ISBN 0-08-022072-X). Pergamon.

Gy, P. M. Sampling of Particulate Materials. 2nd ed. LC 79-16075. (Developments in Geomathematics Ser.: Vol. 4). 432p. 1982. 59.75 (ISBN 0-444-42079-7). Elsevier.

Habberjam, G. M. Apparent Resistivity Observations & the Use of Square Array Techniques. (Geoexploration Monographs: No. 9). (Illus.). 1979. 55.00xcancelled (ISBN 3-443-13013-5). Intl Pubns Serv.

Haenel, Ralph, ed. The Urach Geothermal Project: Swabian Alb, Germany. (Illus.). 419p. 1982. pap. text ed. 64.80x (ISBN 3-510-65107-3). Lubrecht & Cramer.

Hardy, H. Reginald & Leighton, Frederick W. Proceedings of the Second Conference on Acoustic Emission: Microseismic Activity in Geologic Structures & Materials. (Rock & Soil Mechanics Ser.). (Illus.). 500p. 1980. 45.00x (ISBN 0-87849-032-9). Trans Tech.

Hart, P. J., ed. The Earth's Crust & Upper Mantle. LC 75-600572. (Geophysical Monograph Ser.: Vol. 13). (Illus.). 735p. 1969. pap. 10.00 (ISBN 0-87590-013-5). Am Geophysical.

Howell, Benjamin F., Jr. Introduction to Geophysics. rev. ed. LC 77-814. (International Ser. in the Earth & Planetary Sciences). (Illus.). 412p. 1978. lib. bdg. 24.50 (ISBN 0-88275-540-4). Krieger.

Hutter, Kolumban. Theoretical Glaciology. 1983. lib. bdg. 104.00 (ISBN 90-2771-473-8, Pub. by Reidel Holland). Kluwer Academic.

Illes, J. H., ed. Mechanism of Graben Formation. (Developments in Geotechtonics Ser.: Vol. 17). 266p. 1981. Repr. 64.00 (ISBN 0-444-41956-X). Elsevier.

Johnson, Francis S., ed. Satellite Environment Handbook. rev. ed. (Illus.). 1965. 15.00x (ISBN 0-8047-0090-7). Stanford U Pr.

Josephs, Melvin J. & Sanders, Howard J. Chemistry & the Environment. LC 67-30718. 1967. 9.95 (ISBN 0-8412-0103-X). Am Chemical.

Kibel, Ivan A., ed. A Collection of Articles on Dynamic Meteorology. LC 60-9255. (Soviet Research in Geophysics in English Translation Ser.: Vol. 1). pap. 46.80 (ISBN 0-317-28718-4, 2020660). Bks Demand UMI.

King, J. W. & Newman, W. S. Solar Terrestrial Physics. 1967. 62.00 (ISBN 0-12-407850-8). Acad Pr.

Kleyn, A. H. Seismic Reflection Interpretation. (Illus.). xii, 269p. 1983. 55.50 (ISBN 0-85334-161-3, Pub. by Elsevier Applied Sci England). Elsevier.

Kovacs, William D. & Holtz, Robert D. An Introduction to Geotechnical Engineering. (Illus.). 720p. 1981. text ed. 38.95 (ISBN 0-13-484394-0). P-H.

Kulhanek, O. Introduction to Digital Filtering in Geophysics. (Developments in Solid Earth Geophysics Ser.: Vol. 8). 168p. 1976. 59.75 (ISBN 0-444-41331-6). Elsevier.

Kunetz, Geza. Principles of Direct Current Resistivity Prospecting. Van Nostrans, R., tr. from Fr. (Geoexploration Monographs: Ser. 1, No. 1). (Illus.). 103p. 1966. text ed. 13.70x (ISBN 3-4431-3001-1). Lubrecht & Cramer.

Landsberg, H. E., ed. Advances in Geophysics, 19 vols. Incl. Vol. 1. 1952 (ISBN 0-12-018801-5); Vol. 2. 1955 (ISBN 0-12-018802-3); Vol. 3. 1956 (ISBN 0-12-018803-1); Vol. 4. Landsberg, H. E & Van Mieghen, J., eds. 1958 (ISBN 0-12-018804-X); Vol. 5. 1958 (ISBN 0-12-018805-8); Vol. 6. Atmospheric Diffusion & Air Pollution: Proceedings. Frenkiel, F. N. & Sheppard, P. A., eds. 1959 (ISBN 0-12-018806-6); Vol. 7. 1961 (ISBN 0-12-018807-4); Vol. 8. 1961 (ISBN 0-12-018808-2); Vol. 9. 1962 (ISBN 0-12-018809-0); Vol. 10. 1964 (ISBN 0-12-018810-4); Vol. 11. 1965 (ISBN 0-12-018811-2); Vol. 12. 1967 (ISBN 0-12-018812-0); Vol. 13. 1969 (ISBN 0-12-018813-9); Vol. 14. 1970 (ISBN 0-12-018814-7); Vol. 15. 1971 (ISBN 0-12-018815-5); Suppl. 1. Biometeorological Methods. Munn, R. E. 1966. 43.50 (ISBN 0-12-018861-9); Vol. 16. 1973 (ISBN 0-12-018816-3); Vol. 17. 1974 (ISBN 0-12-018817-1); Vol. 18A. 1974. 36.00 (ISBN 0-12-018818-X); Vol. 19. 1976. 85.00 (ISBN 0-12-018819-8). Vols. 1-17. 85.00 ea. Acad Pr.

--Advances in Geophysics, Vol. 26. (Serial Publication Ser.). 1984. 62.00 (ISBN 0-12-018826-0). Acad Pr.

Lee, W. H. & Steward, S. W. Advances in Geophysics, Supplement 2: Principles & Applications of Microearthquake Networks. LC 80-70588. 1981. 32.00 (ISBN 0-12-018862-7). Acad Pr.

McAlester, A. Earth: An Introduction to the Geological & Geophysical Sciences. 1973. 29.95 (ISBN 0-13-222422-4); instr. res. bk. 1.95 (ISBN 0-13-222695-2); study guide o.p. 5.95 (ISBN 0-13-222380-5). P-H.

Magnetic Properties of Pyrrhotite & Their Use in Applied Geology & Geophysics. pap. 5.55 (SSC59, SSC). Unipub.

Manghnani, Merli H. High Pressure Research: Applications to Geophysics. 1977. 69.50 (ISBN 0-12-468750-4). Acad Pr.

Mares, S. Introduction to Applied Geophysics. 556p. 1984. 89.00 (ISBN 90-277-1424-X, Pub. by Reidel Holland). Kluwer Academic.

Meissner, Rolf. The Continental Crust: A Geophysical Approach. (International Geophysics Ser.). Date not set. price not set (ISBN 0-12-488950-6). Acad Pr.

Mitchell, R. L., ed. Agronomy: Solving Problems & Serving People. 1979. pap. write for info (ISBN 0-89118-060-5). Am Soc Agron.

Nelson, H. Roice, Jr. New Technologies in Exploration Geophysics. LC 82-21120. 282p. 1983. 36.95x (ISBN 0-87201-321-9). Gulf Pub.

Nieto, Michael M. & Haxton, W. C., eds. Science Underground. LC 83-70377. (AIP Conference Proceedings No. 96). 446p. 1983. lib. bdg. 38.75 (ISBN 0-88318-195-9). Am Inst Physics.

Officer, C. B. Introduction to Theoretical Geophysics. LC 73-15605. (Illus.). 300p. 1974. 32.00 (ISBN 0-387-06485-0). Springer-Verlag.

Paoletti, A., ed. Physics of Magnetic Garnets. (Enrico Fermi International Summer School of Physics Ser.: Course 70, 1977). 546p. 1979. 102.25 (ISBN 0-444-85200-X, North Holland). Elsevier.

Parasnis, D. S. Mining Geophysics. 2nd ed. (Methods in Geochemistry & Geophysics Ser.: Vol. 3). 395p. 1975. pap. 51.00 (ISBN 0-444-41324-3). Elsevier.

--Principles of Applied Geophysics. 3rd ed. 1979. 32.00 (ISBN 0-412-15140-5, NO. 6304, Pub. by Chapman & Hall); pap. 15.95x (ISBN 0-412-15810-8, NO. 6387). Methuen Inc.

Pedlosky, J. Geophysical Fluid Dynamics. (Illus.). 1979. 49.50 (ISBN 0-387-90368-2). Springer-Verlag.

--Geophysical Fluid Dynamics: Springer Study Edition. (Illus.). 624p. 1982. pap. 26.00 (ISBN 0-387-90745-9). Springer-Verlag.

Parker, Joni M. & Maurer, Ruth A. An Economic Feasibility Study for a Geothermal-Coal Hybrid Power Plant in Chaffee County, Colorado. Raese, Jon W. & Goldberg, J. H., eds. LC 83-1922. (Colorado School Mines Quarterly Ser.: Vol. 78, No. 1). (Illus.). 34p. 1983. pap. 12.00 (ISBN 0-686-45174-0). Colo Sch Mines.

Rapolla, Antonio & Keller, George V., eds. Geophysics of Geothermal Areas: State of the Art & Future Development: Proceedings of the Third Course Held at the School of Geophysics, International Centre for Scientific Culture, Erice, Italy, May 1980. (Illus.). 306p. 1984. text ed. 35.00 (ISBN 0-918062-57-8). Colo Sch Mines.

Rinehart, J. S. Geysers & Geothermal Energy. (Illus.). 223p. 1980. 24.00 (ISBN 0-387-90489-1). Springer-Verlag.

Rybach, L. & Muffler, L. J. Geothermal Systems: Principles & Case Histories. LC 80-40290. 359p. 1981. 79.95 (ISBN 0-471-27811-4, Pub. by Wiley-Interscience). Wiley.

Rybach, Ladislaus & Stegena, Lajos, eds. Geothermics & Geothermal Energy. (Contributions to Current Research in Geophysics: No. 7). (Illus.). 341p. 1979. 61.95x (ISBN 0-8176-1062-6). Birkhauser.

Schultz, Robert J., et al, eds. Geothermal: Energy for the Eighties. (Transactions Ser.: Vol. 4). (Illus.). 835p. 1980. 28.00 (ISBN 0-934412-54-5). Geothermal.

Strub, A. S. & Ungemach, P., eds. Advances in European Geothermal Research. 1096p. 1980. lib. bdg. 63.00 (ISBN 90-277-1138-0, Pub. by Reidel Holland). Kluwer Academic.

--European Geothermal Update. 1985. lib. bdg. 79.00 (ISBN 90-277-2048-7, Pub. by Reidel Netherlands). Kluwer Academic.

Training Needs in Geothermal Energy: Report of the Workshop, Laugarvatu, Iceland, July 1978. 51p. 1980. pap. 5.00 (ISBN 92-808-0017-5, TUNU004, UNU). Unipub.

U. S. Dept. of Energy. Solar, Geothermal, Electric & Storage Systems Program Summary Document. 475p. 1979. pap. 34.50x (ISBN 0-89934-053-9, V071-PP). Solar Energy Info.

Wagner, Sharon C. State Taxation of Geothermal Resources Compared with State Taxation of Other Energy Minerals. (Special Report Ser.: No. 4). (Illus.). 86p. (Orig.). 1979. pap. 6.00 (ISBN 0-934412-04-9). Geothermal.

Wharton, James C. Geothermal Resource Development: Laws & Regulation. 1980. 35.00x. Bks Business.

Zapffe, Carl A. Geohydrothermodynamics of a Water Planet, Vol. 1: Quaternary Glaciation Theories. LC 82-91044. (Illus.). 170p. (Orig.). 1984. pap. text ed. 20.00 (ISBN 0-9601448-3-8). C A Zapffe.

GERANIUMS

Shellard, Alan. Geraniums for Home & Garden. (Illus.). 200p. 1981. 22.50 (ISBN 0-7153-8124-5). David & Charles.

GERBILS

How to Raise & Train Gerbils. pap. 2.95 (ISBN 0-87666-195-9, M-524). TFH Pubns.

Ostrow, Marshall. The T.F.H Book of Gerbils. (Illus.). 64p. 1981. 6.95 (ISBN 0-87666-824-4, HP-009). TFH Pubns.

Paradise, Paul. Gerbils. (Illus.). 96p. 1980. 4.95 (ISBN 0-87666-927-5, KW-037). TFH Pubns.

Robinson, D. G., Jr. Gerbils. (Illus.). 80p. 1984. pap. 3.95 (ISBN 0-86622-240-5, PB-110). TFH Pubns.

Robinson, David. Encyclopedia of Gerbils. 224p. 1980. 12.95 (ISBN 0-87666-915-1, H-974). TFH Pubns.

GERM CELLS

see also Oogenesis; Ovum; Spermatozoa

McLaren, Anne & Wylie, C. C., eds. Current Problems in Germ Cell Differentiation. LC 83-1845. (British Society for Developmental Biology Symposium: No. 7). 350p. 1983. 85.00 (ISBN 0-521-25329-2). Cambridge U Pr.

Nieuwkoop, P. D. & Sutasurya, L. A. Primordial Germ Cells in the Chordates. LC 78-18101. (Developmental & Cell Biology Ser.: No. 7). (Illus.). 1979. 42.50 (ISBN 0-521-22303-2). Cambridge U Pr.

GERM FREE LIFE

see Germfree Life

GERMAN LANGUAGE–TEXTBOOKS FOR FOREIGNERS

Condoyannis, George E. Scientific German. LC 77-16570. 174p. 1978. pap. 9.50 (ISBN 0-88275-644-3). Krieger.

GERMAN POLICE DOGS

see Dogs–Breeds–German Shepherd Dogs

GERMANIUM

Basov, N. G., ed. Microwave Studies of Exciton Condensation in Germanium. LC 78-10160. (P. N. Lebedev Physics Institute Ser.: Vol. 100). (Illus.). 98p. 1979. 55.00 (ISBN 0-306-10952-2, Consultants). Plenum Pub.

Brownridge, I. C. Lithium-Drifted Germanium Detectors: Their Fabrication & Use. LC 73-183565. 216p. 1972. 65.00x (ISBN 0-306-65180-7, IFI Plenum). Plenum Pub.

Davydov, V. I. Germanium. 422p. 1966. 106.50 (ISBN 0-677-20610-0). Gordon.

Glockling, Frank. Chemistry of Germanium. 1969. 44.00 (ISBN 0-12-286450-6). Acad Pr.

Samsonov, G. V. & Bondarev, V. N. Germanides. LC 70-79918. 155p. 1969. 35.00x (ISBN 0-306-10823-2, Consultant). Plenum Pub.

--Germanides. LC 70-125852. (Illus.). 220p. 1970. 22.50x (ISBN 0-911184-03-1). Primary.

Weber, Jon N., ed. Geochemistry of Germanium. LC 73-12621. (Benchmark Papers in Geology Ser). 480p. 1974. 62.50 (ISBN 0-87933-058-9). Van Nos Reinhold.

GERMFREE LIFE

Coates, Marie E. Germ-Free Animal in Research. LC 68-24698. (Illus.). 1968. 49.00 (ISBN 0-12-177150-4). Acad Pr.

Luckey, Thomas D. Germfree Life & Gnotobiology. 1963. 76.50 (ISBN 0-12-458750-X). Acad Pr.

Mirand, E. A. & Back, N., eds. Germ Free Biology. LC 69-16518. (Advances in Experimental Medicine & Biology Ser.: Vol. 3). 435p. 1969. 55.00 (ISBN 0-306-39003-5, Plenum Pr). Plenum Pub.

Wostmann, Bernard S., et al. Germfree Research: Microflora Control & Its Application to the Biomedical Sciences. LC 84-4306. (Progress in Clinical & Biological Research Ser.: Vol. 181). 538p. 1985. 78.00 (ISBN 0-8451-5031-6). A R Liss.

GERMICIDES

see Disinfection and Disinfectants; Fungicides

GERMINATION

Bewley, D. & Black, M. Physiology & Biochemistry of Seeds in Relation to Germination Vol. 1: Development, Germination, & Growth. LC 77-7953. (Illus.). 1978. 56.00 (ISBN 0-387-08274-3). Springer-Verlag.

Bewley, J. Derek & Black, Michael, eds. Seeds: Physiology of Development & Germination. 382p. 1985. 45.00x (ISBN 0-306-41687-5, Plenum Pr). Plenum Pub.

Black, M. & Bewley, J. D. Physiology & Biochemistry of Seeds in Relation to Germination: Viability, Dormancy, & Environmental Control, Vol. 2. (Illus.). 380p. 1982. 56.00 (ISBN 0-387-11656-7). Springer-Verlag.

Heslop-Harrison, J. Aspects of the Structure, Cytochemistry & Germination of the Pollen of Rye. LC 79-41655. 1980. 26.50 (ISBN 0-12-344950-2). Acad Pr.

Khan, A. A., ed. The Physiology & Biochemistry of Seed Dormancy & Germination. 548p. 1983. 119.25 (ISBN 0-444-80423-4, I-439-82, Biomedical Pr). Elsevier.

Knapp, Ruediger. Gegenseitige Beeinflussung und Temperatur-Wirkung bei tropischen und subtropischen Pflanzen: Bericht ueber neue experimentelle Untersuchungen an Nutzpflanzen und Arten der spontanen Vegetation. (Illus.). 1967. pap. 6.00 (ISBN 3-7682-0576-2). Lubrecht & Cramer.

Levinson, Hillel S., et al, eds. Sporulation & Germination: Proceedings. (Illus.). 316p. 1981. 25.00 (ISBN 0-914826-35-2). Am Soc Microbio.

Mayer, A. M. & Poljakoff-Mayber, A. The Germination of Seeds. 3rd ed. (Illus.). 212p. 1982. pap. 19.00 (ISBN 0-08-028853-7). Pergamon.

On the Seed Production of Tropical Grasses in Kenya: Agricultural Research Reports Ser. 1973. pap. 4.00 (PDC61, PUDOC). Unipub.

Rubenstein, Irwin, et al, eds. The Plant Seed: Development, Preservation & Germination. 1979. 35.00 (ISBN 0-12-602050-7). Acad Pr.

GERMS

see Bacteria; Bacteriology; Micro-Organisms

GESNERIACEAE

James, Theodore, Jr. African Violets & Other Gesneriads: How to Select & Grow. (Illus.). 144p. 1983. pap. 7.95 (ISBN 0-89586-222-0). H P Bks.

GESTATION

see Pregnancy

GIBBERELLIN

Crozier, Alan. Biochemistry & Physiology of Gibberellins, 2 vols. LC 83-13862. 576p. 1983. Vol. 1. 62.50 (ISBN 0-03-059054-X); Vol. 2. 59.50x (ISBN 0-03-059056-6). Praeger.

Merritt, James M., ed. Gibberellins. LC 61-11135. (Advances in Chemistry Ser: No. 28). 1961. 14.95 (ISBN 0-8412-0029-7). Am Chemical.

GIBBONS

Carpenter, Clarence R. A Field Study in Siam of the Behavior & Social Relations of the Gibbon. LC 76-44702. (Illus.). 224p. Repr. of 1941 ed. 37.50 (ISBN 0-404-15855-2). AMS Pr.

Rumbaught, Duane M., ed. Gibbon & Siamang: A Series of Volumes on the Lesser Apes, 4 vols. Incl. Vol. 1. Evolution, Ecology, Behavior & Captive Maintenance. 1972. 57.50 (ISBN 3-8055-1362-3); Vol. 2. Anatomy, Dentition, Taxonomy & Molecular Evolution & Behavior. 1973. 57.50 (ISBN 3-8055-1341-0); Vol. 3. Natural History, Social Behavior, Reproduction, Vocalizations, Prehension. 1974. 55.50 (ISBN 3-8055-1602-9); Vol. 4. Suspensory Behavior, Locomotion, & Other Behaviors of Captive Gibbons; Cognition. 1976. 100.00 (ISBN 3-8055-1658-4). (Illus.). Set. 270.25 (ISBN 3-8055-2308-4). S Karger.

Whitten, Tony. The Gibbons of Siberut. 224p. 1982. 45.00x (ISBN 0-460-04476-1, Pub. by Dent Australia). State Mutual Bk.

GIBBS, JOSIAH WILLARD, 1839-1908

Crowther, James G. Famous American Men of Science. facs. ed. LC 69-18925. (Essay Index Reprint Ser). 1937. 27.50 (ISBN 0-8369-0040-5). Ayer Co Pubs.

Donnan, Frederick G. & Haas, Arthur, eds. Commentary on the Scientific Writings of Josiah-Willard Gibbs: A Propos de la Publication Des Ses Memories Scientifiques, 3 vols. in 2. LC 79-7963. (Three Centuries of Science in America Ser.). 1980. Repr. of 1936 ed. Set. lib. bdg. 115.00x (ISBN 0-405-12544-5); lib. bdg. 57.50x ea. Vol. 1 (ISBN 0-405-12611-5). Vol. 2 (ISBN 0-405-12612-3). Ayer Co Pubs.

Seeger, Raymond J. Josiah Willard Gibbs-American Physicist Par Excellance. (Men of Physics Ser.). 1974. 41.00 (ISBN 0-08-018013-2). Pergamon.

GINGERBREAD

see Cake

GINSENG

Dixon, Pamela. Ginseng. 102p. 1976. 16.00 (ISBN 0-7156-1006-6, Pub. by Duckworth England); pap. 4.50 (ISBN 0-7156-1007-4, Pub. by Duckworth England). Biblio Dist.

Fulder, Stephen. About Ginseng: The Magical Herb of the East. (About Ser.). 64p. (Orig.). 1984. pap. 1.95 (ISBN 0-7225-1000-4). Thorsons Pubs.

Hardacre, Val. Ginseng. 2nd ed. LC 74-27603. (Illus.). 1975. 14.95 (ISBN 0-913042-07-2). Holland Hse Pr.

Harding, A. R. Ginseng & Other Medicinal Plants. rev. ed. 386p. 1972. pap. 4.50 (ISBN 0-936622-09-1, A399155). A R Harding Pub.

Harris, Ben C. Ginseng: What It Is, What It Can Do for You. LC 78-59174. 1978. pap. 2.25 (ISBN 0-87983-179-0). Keats.

Hou, Joseph P. Ginseng: The Myth & Truth. 1979. 3.00 (ISBN 0-87980-367-3). Wilshire.

GIPSY-MOTH

Gerardi, Michael H. & Grimm, James K. The History, Biology, Damage & Control of the Gypsy Moth. LC 72-20321. 233p. 1978. 21.50 (ISBN 0-8386-2023-X). Fairleigh Dickinson.

Howard, Leland O. & Fiske, William F. The Importation into the United States of the Parasites of the Gypsy Moth & the Brown-Tail Moth: Report of Progress of Previous & Concurrent Efforts of This Kind. Egerton, Frank N., 3rd, ed. LC 77-74230. (History of Ecology Ser.). (Illus.). 1978. Repr. of 1911 ed. lib. bdg. 32.00x (ISBN 0-405-10400-6). Ayer Co Pubs.

GIRAFFES

Dagg, Anne I & Foster, J. Bristol. The Giraffe: Its Biology, Behavior, & Ecology. LC 80-21839. 248p. 1982. Repr. of 1976 ed. text ed. 16.50 (ISBN 0-89874-275-7). Krieger.

GIRDERS

see also Bridges; Building, Iron and Steel; Graphic Statics; Influence Lines; Roofs; Steel, Structural

Chen Wai-Fah & Atsuta, Toshio. Theory of Beam Columns, Vol. 2: Space Behavior & Design. 1977. text ed. 78.00x (ISBN 0-07-010759-9). McGraw.

Donnell, Lloyd H. Beams, Plates & Shells. (Engineering Societies Monograph Ser.). 1976. text ed. 60.00 (ISBN 0-07-017593-4). McGraw.

Fatigue Tests of Pretensioned Girders with Blanketed & Draped Strands. (PCI Journal Reprints Ser.). 16p. pap. 6.00 (ISBN 0-686-40122-0, JR214). Prestressed Concrete.

Hetenyi, Miklos. Beams on Elastic Foundation: Theory with Applications in the Fields of Civil & Mechanical Engineering. (Illus.). 1946. 20.00x (ISBN 0-472-08445-3). U of Mich Pr.

Heyman, J. Beams & Framed Structures. 2nd ed. LC 74-2234. 160p. 1974. pap. text ed. 10.25 (ISBN 0-08-017946-0). Pergamon.

Kani, Gaspar. Analysis of Multistory Frames. Hyman, Charles J., tr. LC 57-6114. 1967. 8.50 (ISBN 0-8044-4486-2). Ungar.

Kristek, Vladimir. Theory of Box Girders. LC 78-8637. 371p. 1980. 59.95 (ISBN 0-471-99678-5, Pub. by Wiley-Interscience). Wiley.

Narayanan, R., ed. Beams & Beam Columns: Stability & Strength. (Illus.). 252p. 1983. 70.50 (ISBN 0-85334-205-9, Pub. by Elsevier Applied Sci England). Elsevier.

Practical Engineering Applications Software. Beam Analysis. 1985. IBM-PC Version. incl. disk 125.00 (ISBN 0-471-80302-2); Apple Version. incl. disk 125.00 (ISBN 0-471-88420-0). Wiley.

White, G. W. Elementary Beam Theory & the Ship Girder. 124p. 1979. 15.00x (ISBN 0-540-07352-0). Sheridan.

GIRDERS–TABLES, CALCULATIONS, ETC.

Griffel, William. Beam Formulas. LC 68-31449. 1970. 15.00 (ISBN 0-8044-4338-6). Ungar.

Iyengar, J. T., et al. Design Tables for Beams on Elastic Foundations & Related Structural Problems. (Illus.). 140p. 1979. 42.75 (ISBN 0-85334-841-3, Pub. by Elsevier Applied Sci England). Elsevier.

Rogers, Paul. Tables & Formulas for Fixed End Moments of Members of Constant Moment of Inertia & for Simply Supported Beams. 2nd ed. LC 65-28016. 1965. 10.50 (ISBN 0-8044-4850-7). Ungar.

GIRDERS, CONTINUOUS

see also Influence Lines

Baum, Gunter. Basic Values on Single Span Beams: Tables for Calculating Continuous Beams & Frame Constructions, Including Prestressed Beams. (Illus.). 1966. 28.00 (ISBN 0-387-03464-1). Springer-Verlag.

Hahn, J. Structural Analysis of Beams & Slabs. Amerongen, C. V., tr. LC 68-20516. 1967. 18.50 (ISBN 0-8044-4368-8). Ungar.

GLACIAL EPOCH

see also Geology, Stratigraphic–Pleistocene

America's Ice Age Hunters. (Wonders of Learning Kits Ser.). 1980. incl. cassette & tchrs. guide 24.95 (ISBN 0-686-74402-0, 04966). Natl Geog.

Chorlton, Windsor. Ice Ages. LC 82-16765. (Planet Earth Ser.). 1983. lib. bdg. 19.94 (ISBN 0-8094-4329-5, Pub. by Time-Life). Silver.

Coleman, Arthur P. Ice Ages Recent & Ancient. LC 77-105678. (BCL Ser.: Ii). Repr. of 1926 ed. 24.50 (ISBN 0-404-01596-4). AMS Pr.

--The Last Million Years: A History of the Pleistocene in North America. LC 75-41062. (BCL Ser.: Ii). Repr. of 1941 ed. 21.50 (ISBN 0-404-14656-2). AMS Pr.

Daly, Reginald A. The Changing World of the Ice Age. 1963. Repr. of 1934 ed. 21.75x (ISBN 0-02-843500-1). Hafner.

Daly, Reginald D. Changing World of the Ice Age. 1934. 19.50x (ISBN 0-686-83502-6). Elliots Bks.

Denton, G. H. & Hughes, T. J., eds. The Last Great Ice Sheets. LC 79-27808. 484p. 1980. 128.50 (ISBN 0-471-06006-2, Pub. by Wiley-Interscience). Wiley.

Eyles, N., ed. Glacial Geology: An Introduction for Engineers & Earth Scientists. LC 83-17418. (Illus.). 431p. 1983. 60.00 (ISBN 0-08-030264-5); pap. 17.95 (ISBN 0-08-030263-7). Pergamon.

Goldthwait, Richard P., ed. Till: A Symposium. LC 70-153422. (Illus.). 414p. 1972. 20.00x (ISBN 0-8142-0148-2). Ohio St U Pr.

Gray, J. M. & Lowe, J. J., eds. Studies in the Scottish Lateglacial Environment. 1977. text ed. 35.00 (ISBN 0-08-020498-8). Pergamon.

Hadingham, Evans. Secrets of the Ice Age: A Reappraisal of Prehistoric Man. 342p. 1981. pap. 9.95 (ISBN 0-8027-7192-0). Walker & Co.

Hoyle, Fred. Ice: The Ultimate Human Catastrophe. (Illus.). 192p. 1981. 14.95 (ISBN 0-8264-0064-7). Continuum.

Imbrie, John & Imbrie, Katherine P. Ice Ages: Solving the Mystery. LC 78-13246. 224p. 1979. 16.95x (ISBN 0-89490-015-3). Enslow Pubs.

Lyell, Charles. Geological Evidence of the Antiquity of Man. 4th ed. LC 72-1728. (Illus.). Repr. of 1873 ed. 35.00 (ISBN 0-404-08138-X). AMS Pr.

Matsch, Charles L. North America & the Great Ice Age. new ed. (Earth Science Paperback Ser.). (Illus.). 1976. pap. text ed. 15.95 (ISBN 0-07-040935-8). McGraw.

Schultz, Gwen. Glaciers & the Ice Age. 128p. 1963. Holt, Rinehart & Winston. 6.00 (ISBN 0-915988-04-6). Reading Gems.

--Glaciers & the Ice Age. 128p. 1963. Holt, Rinehart & Winston. pap. 5.00 (ISBN 0-915988-05-4). Reading Gems.

--Ice Age Lost. LC 73-13280. 342p. 1974. 10.00 (ISBN 0-385-05759-8, Pub. by Anchor Pr-Doubleday). Reading Gems.

Sparks, B. W. & West, R. G. The Ice Age in Britain. (Methuen Library Reprint Ser.). (Illus.). 320p. 1981. 49.95x (ISBN 0-416-32160-7, 3583). Methuen Inc.

West, R. G. Pleistocene Geology & Biology. 2nd ed. LC 76-28353. (Illus.). 1977. pap. text ed. 21.95x (ISBN 0-582-44620-1). Longman.

GLACIERS

see also Erosion

Doremus, Robert H. Glass Science. LC 73-4713. (Science & Technology of Materials Ser). 349p. 1973. 46.95x (ISBN 0-471-21900-2, Pub. by Wiley-Interscience). Wiley.

Doyle, P. J., ed. Glass-Making Today. 343p. 1981. 79.00x (ISBN 0-86108-047-5, Pub. by Portcullio Pr). State Mutual Bk.

Duffy, J. I., ed. Glass Technology: Developments Since 1978. LC 80-26045. (Chemical Tech. Rev.: 184). (Illus.). 323p. 1981. 48.00 (ISBN 0-8155-0838-7). Noyes.

Farrar, Estelle S. H. P. Sinclaire, Jr., Glassmaker, Vol. 2: The Manufacturing Years. (Illus.). viii, 119p. 1975. pap. 10.00 (ISBN 0-686-10549-4). Corning.

Giegerich, W. & Trier, W., eds. Glass Machines: Construction & Operation of Machines for the Forming of Hot Glass. Kreidl, Norbert J., tr. LC 68-56941. (Illus.). 1969. 56.00 (ISBN 0-387-04493-0). Springer-Verlag.

Gunther, R. Glass Melting Tank Furnaces. 232p. 1954. 69.00x (ISBN 0-686-79277-7, Pub. by Soc Glass Tech England). State Mutual Bk.

Hoffmann, E. Fachwoerterbuch Fuer die Glasindustriel. (Ger. & Eng.). 160p. (Dictionary doe the Glass Industry). 1963. 36.00 (ISBN 3-540-03007-7, M-7396, Pub. by Springer). French & Eur.

Honeywell, Marie-Anne. Index Journal of Glass Studies, 1959-1973: Volumes 1-15. LC 59-12390. 1976. pap. 8.00 (ISBN 0-87290-061-4). Corning.

International Commission on Glass. Dictionary of Glass Making. (Eng., Fr. & Ger.). 402p. 1983. 106.50 (ISBN 0-444-42048-7). Elsevier.

Journal of Glass Studies. LC 59-12390. 1972-81. 15.00x ea. Vol. 14 (ISBN 0-87290-014-2). Vol. 15 (ISBN 0-87290-015-0). Vol. 16 (ISBN 0-87290-016-9). Vol. 17 (ISBN 0-87290-017-7). Vol. 18 (ISBN 0-87290-018-5). Vol. 19 (ISBN 0-87290-019-3). Vol. 20 (ISBN 0-87290-020-7). Vol. 21 (ISBN 0-87290-021-5). Corning.

McKearin, Helen & McKearin, George S. American Glass. (Illus.). 1941. 22.50 (ISBN 0-517-00111-X). Crown.

Matson, F. B. & Rindone, G. E., eds. Advances in Glass Technology: Pt. 2, Historical Papers & Discussions of the Technical Papers. 410p. 1963. 49.50x (ISBN 0-306-37002-6, Plenum Pr). Plenum Pub.

Matsumura, Takao. The Labour Aristocracy Revisited: The Victorian Flint Glass Makers, 1850-80. LC 83-7951. 196p. 1984. 25.00 (ISBN 0-7190-0931-6, Pub. by Manchester Univ Pr). Longwood Pub Group.

Mazelev, L. Ye. Borate Glasses: Thermochemical Processes in Glass Formation, Crystallo-Optics, Technology, Physicochemical Properties, & Structure of Glasses with the Composition B203-Li20-MeO. LC 60-8719. pap. 39.80 (ISBN 0-317-28016-3, 2055799). Bks Demand UMI.

Mazurin, O. V. & Poraikoshits, E. A., eds. Phase Separation in Glass. 1985. 78.00 (ISBN 0-444-86810-0). Elsevier.

Miller, Richard K. Noise Control Solutions for the Glass Industry. 120p. pap. text ed. 90.00 (ISBN 0-89671-016-5). SEAI Tech Pubns.

Pincus, Alexis G. Combustion Melting in the Glass Industry. LC 78-55358. (Processing in the Glass Industry Ser.). 300p. 1980. 29.95 (ISBN 0-911993-11-8). Ashlee Pub Co.

--Electric Melting in the Glass Industry. LC 76-44898. (Processing in the Glass Industry Ser.). 138p. 1976. 29.95 (ISBN 0-911993-12-6). Ashlee Pub Co.

--Melting Furnace Design in the Glass Industry. LC 78-55352. (Processing in the Glass Industry Ser.). 269p. 1980. 24.95 (ISBN 0-911993-08-8). Ashlee Pub Co.

--Melting Furnace Operation in the Glass Industry. LC 77-55374. (Processing in the Glass Industry Ser.). 250p. 1980. 24.95 (ISBN 0-911993-10-X). Ashlee Pub Co.

--The Melting Process in the Glass Industry. LC 78-55368. (Processing in the Glass Industry Ser.). 257p. 1980. 24.95 (ISBN 0-911993-19-3). Ashlee Pub Co.

--Refractories in the Glass Industry. LC 78-55364. (Provessing in the Glass Industry Ser.). 280p. 1980. 24.95 (ISBN 0-911993-09-6). Ashlee Pub Co.

Pincus, Alexis G. & Chang, S. H. Joining in the Glass Industry. LC 83-73581. (Processing in the Glass Industry Ser.). (Illus.). 282p. 1985. 34.95 (ISBN 0-911993-16-9). Ashlee Pub Co.

--Secondary Manufacturing in the Glass Industry. LC 78-55369. (Processing in the Glass Industry Ser.). 314p. 1978. 34.95 (ISBN 0-911993-14-2). Ashlee Pub Co.

Pincus, Alexis G. & Davies, David H. Batching in the Glass Industry. LC 81-67427. (Processing in the Glass Industry Ser.). 217p. 1981. 24.95 (ISBN 0-911993-07-X). Ashlee Pub Co.

Pincus, Alexis G. & Holmes, Thomas R. Annealing & Strengthening in the Glass Industry. LC 77-83834. (Processing in the Glass Industry Ser.). 332p. 1977. 34.95 (ISBN 0-911993-06-1). Ashlee Pub Co.

Pincus, Alexis G., ed. Forming in the Glass Industry, Pt. II: Accessories in Glass Forming. LC 83-70120. (Processing in the Glass Industry Ser.). (Illus.). 254p. Set. text ed. 69.95 (ISBN 0-911993-04-5). Ashlee Pub Co.

--Forming in the Glass Industry, Pts. I: Forming Machines & Methods. (Processing in the Glass Industry Ser.). (Illus.). 248p. 1983. Set. text ed. 69.95 (ISBN 0-911993-03-7). Ashlee Pub Co.

Pincus, Alexis G. & Davies, David H., eds. Raw Materials in the Glass Industry: Minor Ingredients, 2 pts. LC 83-70137. (Processing in the Glass Industry). (Illus.). 454p. 1983. Set. text ed. 59.90 (ISBN 0-911993-02-9). Ashlee Pub Co.

--Raw Materials in the Glass Industry, Pt. I: Major Ingredients. LC 83-70137. (Processing in the Glass Industry Ser.). (Illus.). 254p. 1983. text ed. 29.95 (ISBN 0-911993-00-2). Ashlee Pub Co.

Refractories & Glass-Making. 1982. 35.00x (ISBN 0-686-44581-3, Pub. by Brit Ceramic Soc England). State Mutual Bk.

Rindone, G. E., ed. Advances in Glass Technology: Pt. 1, Technical Papers. LC 61-15176. 639p. 1962. 55.00x (ISBN 0-306-37001-8, Plenum Pr). Plenum Pub.

Scoville, Warren C. Revolution in Glassmaking: Entrepreneurship & Technological Change in the American Industry, 1880-1920. LC 76-38264. (The Evolution of Capitalism Ser.). 440p. 1972. Repr. of 1948 ed. 30.00 (ISBN 0-405-04144-6). Ayer Co Pubs.

Spillman, Jane S. Glassmaking: America's First Industry. LC 76-17354. (Illus.). 35p. 1976. pap. 1.40 (ISBN 0-87290-062-2). Corning.

Tooley, Fay V., ed. Handbook of Glass Manufacture, 2 Vols, Vols. I & II. LC 84-70587. 1500p. 1985. Set. text ed. 195.00 (ISBN 0-911993-22-3); Vol. I. text ed. write for info. (ISBN 0-911993-20-7); Vol. II. text ed. write for info. (ISBN 0-911993-21-5). Ashlee Pub Co.

Walton, J. D., Jr., ed. Radome Engineering Handbook: Design & Principles. LC 74-131300. (Ceramics & Glass: Science & Technology Ser.). (Illus.). pap. 152.80 (ISBN 0-317-07833-X, 2055030). Bks Demand UMI.

Weatherman, Hazel M. Fostoria: Its First Fifty Years. (Illus.). 320p. 1972. 18.00 (ISBN 0-913074-02-0). Weatherman.

Weyl, Woldemar A. The Constitution of Glasses: A Dynamic Interpretation. LC 62-19684. Vol. 1. pap. 111.80 (ISBN 0-317-10914-6, 2055162); Vol. 2, Pt. 1. pap. 121.20 (ISBN 0-317-10915-4); Vol. 2, Pt. 2. pap. 160.00 (ISBN 0-317-10916-2). Bks Demand UMI.

GLASS REINFORCED PLASTICS

see also Fiberglass Boats

Glass Reinforced Epoxy Systems, Part 2. (Materials Technology Ser.: Vol. 10). 203p. 1982. pap. 35.00 (ISBN 0-87762-319-8). Technomic.

Hilado, Carlos J., ed. Glass Reinforced Polyester Systems. LC 74-83231. (Materials Technology Ser.: Vol. 14). 182p. 1984. pap. 35.00 (ISBN 0-87762-344-9). Technomic.

Hollaway, L. Glass Reinforced Plastics in Construction: Engineering Aspects. LC 77-13952. 228p. 1978. 52.95x (ISBN 0-470-99338-3). Halsted Pr.

GLASS RESEARCH

Duffy, J. I., ed. Glass Technology: Developments Since 1978. LC 80-26045. (Chemical Tech. Rev.: 184). (Illus.). 323p. 1981. 48.00 (ISBN 0-8155-0838-7). Noyes.

Herman, Herbert & Tomozawa, Minoru, eds. Treatise on Materials Science & Technology: Vol. 22, Glass III. LC 77-378180. 1982. 59.50 (ISBN 0-12-341822-4). Acad Pr.

Martin, John H. & Edwards, Charleen K., eds. Journal of Glass Studies, Vol. 26. LC 59-12390. (Illus.). 225p. (Orig.). 1984. pap. 20.00 (ISBN 0-87290-026-6). Corning.

Persson, Rune. Flat Glass Technology. LC 72-83172. 177p. 1969. 17.50x (ISBN 0-306-30649-2, Plenum Pr). Plenum Pub.

Porai-Koshits, E. A., ed. Phase-Separation Phenomena in Glasses. LC 58-44503. (The Structure of Glass Ser.: Vol. 8). 208p. 1973. 39.50 (ISBN 0-306-18308-0, Consultants). Plenum Pub.

Pye, L. D., et al, eds. Introduction to Glass Science. LC 72-76933. 722p. 1972. 65.00x (ISBN 0-306-30596-8, Plenum Pr). Plenum Pub.

Rawson, H. Properties & Applications of Glass. (Glass Science & Technology Ser.: Vol. 3). 318p. 1980. 64.00 (ISBN 0-444-41922-5). Elsevier.

GLASSY ALLOYS

see Metallic Glasses

GLASSY METALS

see Metallic Glasses

GLIDERS (AERONAUTICS)

see also Gliding and Soaring

Knauff, Thomas L. Glider Basics from First Flight to Solo. 2nd ed. Northcut, Allan & Northcut, Debbie, eds. (Illus.). 1982. text ed. 16.95 (ISBN 0-9605676-1-5). Knauff.

Perna, Albert F. Glider Gladiators of World War Two. LC 70-91840. (Illus.). 398p. 1970. 25.00 (ISBN 0-9600302-0-4). Podiatric Educ.

Piggott, Derek. Gliding: A Handbook on Soaring Flight. 4th ed. (Illus.). 270p. 1976. 26.95x (ISBN 0-06-495570-2). B&N Imports.

Schroder, Jack E. How to Build & Fly Radio Control Gliders. Angle, Burr, ed. (Illus., Orig.). 1980. pap. 4.00 (ISBN 0-89024-549-5). Kalmbach.

Wills, Maralys. Manbirds: Hang Gliders & Hang Gliding. 320p. 1981. 17.95 (ISBN 0-13-551101-1). P-H.

GLIDING AND SOARING

see also Gliders (Aeronautics)

Bowers, Pete. Modern Soaring Guide. 2nd ed. (Illus.). 1979. 9.95 (ISBN 0-8306-9781-0); pap. 6.95o.p (ISBN 0-8306-2257-8, 2257). TAB Bks.

Byars, Ed & Holbrook, Bill. Soaring Cross Country. new ed. LC 74-78637. (Illus.). 180p. 1974. 9.95 (ISBN 0-914600-00-1). Ridge Soaring.

Handbook of Meteorological Forecasting for Soaring Flight. (Technical Note Ser.: No. 158). (Eng. & Fr.). x, 101p. 1978. pap. 18.00 (ISBN 92-63-10495-6, W399, WMO). Unipub.

Lincoln, Joseph C., ed. On Quiet Wings: A Soaring Anthology. LC 70-174993. (Illus.). 1972. 30.00 (ISBN 0-87358-082-6). Northland.

Piggott, Derek. Beginning Gliding: The Fundamentals of Soaring Flight. (Illus.). 208p. 1982. 26.95x (ISBN 0-06-495569-9). B&N Imports.

--Going Solo: A Simple Guide to Soaring. (Illus.). 112p. 1978. pap. 10.95x (ISBN 0-06-495571-0). B&N Imports.

--Understanding Gliding: The Principles of Soaring Flight. LC 77-371531. (Illus.). 259p. 1977. 26.95x (ISBN 0-06-495568-0). B&N Imports.

Scull, Bill. Soaring Across Country. (Illus.). 192p. 1981. 17.95 (ISBN 0-7207-1153-3, Pub. by Michael Joseph). Merrimack Pub Cir.

Stanton, David. Flying High: The Beginner's Guide to Daring Airsports. (Illus., Orig.). 1980. pap. 3.00 (ISBN 0-939468-01-8). Sportsbks.

Wallington, C. E. Meteorology for Glider Pilots. 3rd ed. (Illus.). 331p. 1980. 30.00 (ISBN 0-7195-3303-1). Transatlantic.

Wolters, Richard A. Art & Technique of Soaring. 1971. 19.95 (ISBN 0-07-071560-2). McGraw.

GLOBAL ANALYSIS (MATHEMATICS)

see also Differential Topology; Functions of Complex Variables; Geometry, Algebraic

Delves, L. M. & Freeman, T. L. Analysis of Global Expansion Methods: Weakly Asymtotically Diagonal Systems. LC 80-42084. (Computational Mathematics & Application Ser.). 1981. 55.00 (ISBN 0-12-208880-8). Acad Pr.

Ferus, D., et al, eds. Global Differential Geometry & Global Analysis: Proceedings. (Lecture Notes in Mathematics: Vol. 838). 299p. 1981. pap. 22.00 (ISBN 0-387-10285-X). Springer-Verlag.

Hamilton, R. S. Harmonic Maps of Manifolds with Boundary. (Lecture Notes in Mathematics Ser.: Vol. 471). 168p. 1975. pap. 14.00 (ISBN 0-387-07185-7). Springer-Verlag.

Kahn, Donald W. Introduction to Global Analysis: Pure & Applied Mathematics Ser. LC 79-8858. 1980. 37.50 (ISBN 0-12-394050-8). Acad Pr.

Kotus, Janina, et al. Global Structural Stability of Flows on Open Surfaces. LC 81-22941. (Memoirs: 261). 109p. 1982. pap. 9.00 (ISBN 0-8218-2261-6). Am Math.

Morse, Marston. Global Variational Analysis: Weierstrass Integrals on a Riemannian Manifold. LC 76-836. (Mathematical Notes: No. 16). 264p. 1976. pap. 26.50 (ISBN 0-691-08181-6). Princeton U Pr.

Spencer, D. C. & Iyanaga, S., eds. Global Analysis: Papers in Honor of K. Kodaira. (Mathematical Ser: Vol. 29). (Published jointly with the University of Tokyo). 1970. 42.00 (ISBN 0-691-08077-1). Princeton U Pr.

Willmore, Thomas J. & Hitchin, N. J. Global Riemannian Geometry. LC 83-26675. (Mathematics & Its Applications Ser.). 213p. 1984. 64.95x (ISBN 0-470-20017-0). Halsted Pr.

GLOBAL SATELLITE COMMUNICATIONS SYSTEMS

see Artificial Satellites in Telecommunication

GLOBULAR PROTEINS

see Proteins

GLOW-LAMPS

see Electric Lamps

GLOW-WORMS

see Fireflies

GLUCINIUM

see Beryllium

GLUCOSE

Birch, G. G., et al, eds. Glucose Syrups & Related Carbohydrates. (Illus.). 118p. 1971. 20.50 (ISBN 0-444-20103-3, Pub. by Elsevier Applied Sci England). Elsevier.

Board of Education & Training. Identification of Glucose-Nonfermenting Gram-Negative Rods. (Continuing Education Manual Ser.). 1977. 12.00 (ISBN 0-686-95697-4). Am Soc Microbio.

Dziedzic, S. Z. & Kearsley, M. W., eds. Glucose Syrups: Science & Technology. (Illus.). 272p. 1985. 52.50 (ISBN 0-85334-299-7, Pub. by Elsevier Applied Sci England). Elsevier.

WHO Scientific Group, Geneva, 1966. Standardization of Procedures for the Study of Glucose-6-Phosphate Dehydrogenase: A Report. (Technical Report Ser: No. 366). (Eng, Fr, Rus, & Span.). 53p. 1967. pap. 2.00 (ISBN 92-4-120366-8). World Health.

GLUCURONIC ACID

Dutton, G. J. Glucuronidation of Drugs & Other Compounds. 288p. 1980. 86.00 (ISBN 0-8493-5295-9). CRC Pr.

Dutton, Geoffrey J., ed. Glucuronic Acid: Free & Combined Chemistry, Biochemistry, Pharmacology & Medicine. 1966. 95.00 (ISBN 0-12-225350-7). Acad Pr.

GLUE

see also Adhesives

Giles, Carl & Giles, Barbara. Glue It! (Illus.). 112p. (Orig.). 1984. 14.95 (ISBN 0-8306-0201-1); pap. 8.95 (ISBN 0-8306-1801-5, 1801). TAB Bks.

GLUTAMIC ACID

Davidson, Neil. Neurotransmitter Amino Acids. 1976. 33.00 (ISBN 0-12-205950-6). Acad Pr.

Mora, Jaime & Palacios, Rafael, eds. Glutamine: Metabolism, Enzymology & Regulation. 1980. 37.50 (ISBN 0-12-506040-8). Acad Pr.

Najjar, V. A. The Biological Effects of Glutamic Acid & Its Derivatives. 1982. lib. bdg. 85.00 (ISBN 90-6193-841-4, Pub. by Junk Pubs Netherlands). Kluwer Academic.

Roberts, P. J., et al, eds. Glutamate: Transmitter in the Central Nervous System. LC 80-42300. 228p. 1981. 52.95x (ISBN 0-471-27951-X, Pub. by Wiley-Interscience). Wiley.

Santen, R. J. & Henderson, I. C., eds. A Comprehensive Guide to the Therapeutic Use of Aminoglutethimide. (Pharmanual: Vol. 2). (Illus.). vi, 162p. 1981. pap. 18.50 (ISBN 3-8055-2871-X). S Karger.

Sies, H. & Haussinger, D., eds. Glutamine Metabolism in Mammalian Tissues. (Illus.). 295p. 1984. 44.00 (ISBN 0-387-13454-9). Springer Verlag.

GLUTATHIONE

Colowick, Sidney P., et al, eds. Glutathione: A Symposium. 1954. 65.00 (ISBN 0-12-181876-4). Acad Pr.

Larsson, Agne, et al, eds. Functions of Glutathione: Biochemical, Physiological, Toxicological, & Clinical Aspects: Fifth Karolinska Institute Nobel Conference. (Illus.). 424p. 1983. text ed. 65.00 (ISBN 0-89004-908-4). Raven.

Sies, H. & Wendel, A., eds. Functions of Glutathione in Liver & Kidney. (Proceedings in Life Sciences Ser.). (Illus.). 1978. 39.00 (ISBN 0-387-09127-0). Springer-Verlag.

GLYCERIN

Ashworth, M. R. Analytical Methods for Glycerol. 1979. 61.00 (ISBN 0-12-065050-9). Acad Pr.

GLYCOGEN

see also Polysaccharides

Horowitz, Martin, ed. The Glycoconjugates: Glyconproteins, Glycolipides & Proteoglycans. LC 77-4086. 392p. 1982. 60.00 ea. Vol. III: Pt. A: 392 pgs (ISBN 0-12-356103-5). Vol. IV: Pt. B: 82-45134: 384 pgs (ISBN 0-12-356104-3). Acad Pr.

International Symposium on Glycoconjugates, Fourth. Glycoconjugate Research, Vol. 2. Jeanloz, Roger & Gregory, John, eds. LC 79-15164. 1979. 60.00 (ISBN 0-12-301302-X). Acad Pr.

International Symposium on Glycoconjugates, Sixth, Tokyo, Japan, September 20-25, 1981. Glycoconjugates: Proceedings. Yamakawa, T., et al, eds. 531p. pap. 43.00x (ISBN 0-686-86933-8, Pub. by Japan Sci Soc Japan). Intl Spec Bk.

Lennarz, William J., ed. The Biochemistry of Glycoproteins & Proteoglycans. LC 79-9176. (Illus.). 395p. 1980. 39.50x (ISBN 0-306-40243-2, Plenum Pr). Plenum Pub.

Makita, Akira, et al, eds. New Vistas in Glycolipid Research. LC 82-11221. (Advances in Experimental Medicine & Biology Ser.: Vol. 152). 504p. 1982. 62.50x (ISBN 0-306-41108-3, Plenum Pr). Plenum Pub.

GLYCOLYSIS

Phillips, David, et al, eds. The Enzymes of Glycolysis: Structure, Activity & Evolution. (Royal Society of London Ser.). (Illus.). 214p. 1981. lib. bdg. 58.00x (ISBN 0-85403-169-3, Pub. by Royal Soc London). Scholium Intl.

GLYCOSIDES

Bochkov, A. E. & Zaikov, G. E. Chemistry of the O-Glycosidic Bond: Formation & Cleavage. 1979. 53.00 (ISBN 0-08-022949-2). Pergamon.

Horowitz, Martin, ed. The Glycoconjugates: Glyconproteins, Glycolipides & Proteoglycans. LC 77-4086. 392p. 1982. 60.00 ea. Vol. III: Pt. A: 392 pgs (ISBN 0-12-356103-5). Vol. IV: Pt. B: 82-45134: 384 pgs (ISBN 0-12-356104-3). Acad Pr.

Piras, Romano & Piras, Horatio G., eds. Biochemistry of the Glycosidic Linkage: An Integrated View, Proceedings. 1972. 67.50 (ISBN 0-12-557250-6). Acad Pr.

Smith, Thomas W., ed. Digitalis Glycosides: Mechanisms & Management of Toxicity. LC 79-4146. 1985. 39.50 (ISBN 0-8089-1731-5). Grune.

Wiegandt, H., et al, eds. Glycolipids. (New Comprehensive Biochemistry Ser.: Vol. 10). 312p. 1985. 59.00 (ISBN 0-444-80595-8). Elsevier.

GNOMONICS
see Sun-Dials

GNOTOBIOLOGY
see Germfree Life

GOATS

Acharya, R. M. Sheep & Goat Breeds of India. (Animal Production & Health Papers: No. 30). 197p. 1982. pap. 14.50 (ISBN 92-5-101212-1, F2340, FAO). Unipub.

Belanger, Jerry. Raising Milk Goats the Modern Way. LC 75-3493. (Illus.). 160p. 1975. pap. 5.95 (ISBN 0-88266-062-4). Garden Way Pub.

Carlson, Paul H. Texas Woollybacks: The Range Sheep & Goat Industry. LC 82-40311. (Illus.). 256p. 1982. 19.50 (ISBN 0-89096-133-6). Tex A&M Univ Pr.

Chadwick, Douglas H. A Beast the Color of Winter: The Mountain Goat Observed. LC 83-4737. (Illus.). 288p. 1983. 15.95 (ISBN 0-87156-805-5). Sierra.

Dairy Goats: Breeding-Feeding Management. 3.00 (ISBN 0-686-26685-4). Dairy Goat.

Eberhardt, Jo. Good Beginnings with Dairy Goats. 15.00 (ISBN 0-686-26687-0). Dairy Goat.

Ensminger, M. Eugene. Sheep & Wool Science. 4th ed. LC 73-79612. 1970. text ed. 27.35 (ISBN 0-8134-1113-0); text ed. 20.50x. Interstate.

French, M. H. Observations on the Goat. (Animal Production & Health Papers: No. 14). 204p. 1970. pap. 15.50 (ISBN 92-5-100848-5, F303, FAO). Unipub.

Gall, C., ed. Goat Production: Breeding & Management. LC 81-66393. 1981. 80.00 (ISBN 0-12-273980-9). Acad Pr.

Hall, Alice. The Pygmy(Goat) in America. (Illus.). 100p. (Orig.). 1982. pap. 7.50x (ISBN 0-932218-13-X). Hall Pr.

Herman, Harry A. Artificial Insemination of Dairy Goat. 5.00 (ISBN 0-686-26684-6). Dairy Goat.

Jackson, Robert A. & Hall, Alice G. Fundamentals of Improved Dairy Goat Management. (Illus.). 74p. (Orig.). 1985. pap. 10.00 (ISBN 0-932218-14-8). Hall Pr.

Leach, C. E. The Goat Owners' Scrapbook. 12.50 (ISBN 0-686-26682-X). Dairy Goat.

Leach, Corl A. Aids to Goatkeeping. 15.00 (ISBN 0-686-26686-2). Dairy Goat.

Mackenzie, David. Goat Husbandry. 4th ed. Laing, Jean, ed. (Illus.). 336p. 1981. 23.00 (ISBN 0-571-18024-8); pap. 9.95 (ISBN 0-571-11322-2). Faber & Faber.

National Research Council Commission on Natural Resources. Nutrient Requirements of Goats: Angora, Dairy, & Meat Goats in Temperate & Tropical Countries. 91p. 1981. pap. text ed. 7.75 (ISBN 0-309-03185-0). Natl Acad Pr.

Nievergelt, B. Ibexes in an African Environment. (Ecological Studies Ser.: Vol. 40). (Illus.). 230p. 1981. 53.00 (ISBN 0-387-10592-1). Springer-Verlag.

Owen, Nancy L. The Illustrated Standard of the Dairy Goat. 11.00 (ISBN 0-686-26679-X). Dairy Goat.

Rogers, Ferial & Minter, Phyllis V. Goats: Their Care & Breeding. (Illus.). 103p. 1980. 5.95 (ISBN 0-686-85660-0, 4948-0, Pub. by K & R Bks England). Arco.

Salmon, Jill. The Goatkeeper's Guide. 14.95 (ISBN 0-686-26681-1). Dairy Goat.

--The Goatkeeper's Guide. LC 80-69354. (Illus.). 152p. 1981. 14.95 (ISBN 0-7153-8055-9). David & Charles.

Sheep & Goat Breeding. (Better Farming Ser.: No. 12). 51p. 1977. pap. 7.50 (ISBN 92-5-100152-9, F70, FAO). Unipub.

Shields, Joan. Exhibition & Practical Goatkeeping. 2nd ed. (Illus.). 194p. 1982. 18.95 (ISBN 0-86230-057-6). Triplegate.

Shields, John. Exhibition & Practical Goatkeeping. 1981. 14.50 (ISBN 0-904558-26-6). Saiga.

Weems, David B. Raising Goats: The Backyard Dairy Alternative. (Illus.). 208p. (Orig.). 1983. pap. 12.95 (ISBN 0-8306-1534-2, 1534). TAB Bks.

Wilkinson, J. M. & Stark, Barbara. Commercial Goat Production. 256p. 1986. 20.00x (ISBN 0-00-383052-7, Pub. by Collins England). Sheridan.

GODEL'S THEOREM
see Goedel's Theorem

GOEDEL'S THEOREM

Davis, M., ed. The Undecidable: Basic Papers on Undecidable Propositions, Unsolvable Problems & Computable Functions. LC 65-3996. 440p. 1965. 36.50 (ISBN 0-911216-01-4). Raven.

Gensler, Harry J. Godel's Theorem Simplified. 88p. (Orig.). 1984. lib. bdg. 13.50 (ISBN 0-8191-3868-1); pap. text ed. 7.25 (ISBN 0-8191-3869-X). U Pr of Amer.

Mostowski, A. Sentences Undecidable in Formalized Arithmetic. 118p. 1952. 25.00 (ISBN 0-7204-2220-5, North Holland). Elsevier.

Mostowski, Andrej. Sentences Undecidable in Formalized Arithmetic: An Exposition of the Theory of Kurt Godel. LC 82-11886. (Studies in Logic & the Foundations of Mathematics). viii, 117p. 1982. Repr. of 1952 ed. lib. bdg. 27.50x (ISBN 0-313-23151-6, MOSU). Greenwood.

Siefkes, D. Decidable Theories: Buechi's Monadic Second Order Successor Arithmetic. LC 70-111900. (Lecture Notes in Mathematics: Vol. 120). 1970. pap. 10.70 (ISBN 0-387-04909-6). Springer-Verlag.

GOLD
see also Alchemy; Gold Mines and Mining; Jewelry

Branson, O. T. What You Need to Know about Your Gold & Silver. (Illus.). 56p. (Orig.). 1980. pap. 4.95 (ISBN 0-918080-44-4). Treasure Chest.

Emmons, William H. Gold Deposits of the World: With a Section on Prospecting. LC 74-350. (Vol. 13). (Illus.). 562p. 1974. Repr. of 1937 ed. gold 43.00x (ISBN 0-405-05912-4). Ayer Co Pubs.

Foster, R. P., ed. Gold: Proceedings of the International Symposium, Zimbabwe, May 1982. 500p. 1983. lib. bdg. 40.00 (ISBN 90-6191-504-X, Pub. by Balkema RSA). IPS.

Frank, Susan. Glass & Archaeology. (Studies in Archaeological Science). 1982. 26.00 (ISBN 0-12-265620-2). Acad Pr.

Fuerstenau, Maurice C. & Palmer, R. B., eds. Gold, Silver, Uranium & Coal - Geology, Mining, Extraction, & Environment. LC 82-73914. (Illus.). 526p. 1983. pap. text ed. 40.00x (ISBN 0-89520-406-1, 406-1). Soc Mining Eng.

Gajda, George. Gold Refining. 2nd rev. ed. 1980. 25.50 (ISBN 0-9608018-2-0). G Gajda.

The Geochemistry of Gold & Its Deposits. (Geological Survey Bulletins: No. 280). 584p. 1980. pap. 83.50 (ISBN 0-660-01769-5, SSC136, SSC). Unipub.

Gold: Historical & Economic Aspects, 18 vols. facsimile ed. 1974. Set. 435.00 (ISBN 0-405-05910-8). Ayer Co Pubs.

Greene, Vaughn. Diving for Gold. rev. ed. (Illus.). 120p. 1985. pap. 5.95 (ISBN 0-89288-040-6). Maverick.

Lippard, Stephen J., ed. Platinum, Gold, & Other Metal Chemotherapeutic Agents. LC 82-24333. (Symposium Ser.: No. 209). 453p. 1983. lib. bdg. 59.95 (ISBN 0-8412-0758-5). Am Chemical.

Martin, James. Recreational Gold Prospecting. (Illus.). 138p. 1983. pap. 8.95 (ISBN 0-933506-12-0). Darwin Pubns.

Merton, Henry A. Your Gold & Silver: An Easy Guide to Appraising Household Objects, Coins, Heirlooms & Jewelry. (Illus.). 96p. 1981. pap. 5.95 (ISBN 0-02-077410-9, Collier). Macmillan.

Milton, Charles & Milton, Daniel J. Nickel-Gold Ore of the Mackinaw Mine, Snohomish County, Washington. (Reprint Ser.: No. 4). (Illus.). 22p. 1959. 0.25 (ISBN 0-686-36913-0). Geologic Pubns.

Puddephatt, Richard J. The Chemistry of Gold. (Topics in Inorganic & General Chemistry: Vol. 16). 274p. 1978. 64.00 (ISBN 0-444-41624-2). Elsevier.

Rapson, W. S. & Groenewald, T. Gold Usage. 1978. 54.00 (ISBN 0-12-581250-7). Acad Pr.

Tatsch, J. H. Gold Deposits: Origin, Evolution, and Present Characteristics. LC 75-1947. (Illus.). 275p. 1975. 72.00 (ISBN 0-912890-07-X). Tatsch.

Von Mueller, Karl. Gold Refiner's Manual. (Placer Miner's Manual Ser.: Vol. 5). 1984. write for info. (ISBN 0-89316-628-6). Exanimo Pr.

GOLD MINES AND MINING
see also Hydraulic Mining; Prospecting

Angier, Bradford. Looking for Gold. LC 74-23258. (Illus.). 224p. 1981. pap. 8.95 (ISBN 0-8117-2034-9). Stackpole.

Boericke, William F. Prospecting & Operating Small Gold Placers. 2nd ed. 144p. 1936. 15.95 (ISBN 0-471-08514-6, Pub. by Wiley-Interscience). Wiley.

Brown, Robert L. The Great Pikes Peak Gold Rush. LC 85-5767. (Illus.). 1985. 12.95 (ISBN 0-87004-311-0); pap. 7.95 (ISBN 0-87004-323-4). Caxton.

Byers, William N. & Kellom, John H. Hand-book to the Gold Fields of Nebraska & Kansas. LC 72-9432. (The Far Western Frontier Ser.). (Illus.). 122p. 1973. Repr. of 1859 ed. 11.00 (ISBN 0-405-04963-3). Ayer Co Pubs.

Campbell, Gilbert L. Wet Plates & Dry Gulches. LC 71-41602. (Wild & Woolly West Ser., No. 8). (Illus., Orig.). 1973. 8.00 (ISBN 0-910584-94-X); pap. 2.00 (ISBN 0-910584-11-7). Filter.

Carpenter, Kenneth E., ed. Gold Mining Company Prospect Uses: California, Alaska, Arizona, Colorado, Idaho, Utah, 2 pts. LC 74-365. (Vol. 6). (Illus.). 1974. gold 32.00 (ISBN 0-405-05926-4). Ayer Co Pubs.

Cash, Joseph H. Working the Homestake. (Illus.). 142p. 1973. 6.95 (ISBN 0-8138-0755-7). Iowa St U Pr.

Emmons, William H. Gold Deposits of the World: With a Section on Prospecting. LC 74-350. (Vol. 13). (Illus.). 562p. 1974. Repr. of 1937 ed. gold 43.00x (ISBN 0-405-05912-4). Ayer Co Pubs.

Faulk, Terry R. Simple Methods of Mining Gold. 2nd ed. (Wild & Woolly West Ser. No. 10). (Illus., Orig.). 1981. 8.00 (ISBN 0-910584-97-4); pap. 1.50 (ISBN 0-910584-98-2). Filter.

Furst, P. T. Gold Before Columbus. (Illus.). 80p. 1964. 5.00 (ISBN 0-938644-16-5). Nat Hist Mus.

Gerrick, David J. Gold Prospecting in Ohio. 84p. 1980. pap. 4.95 (ISBN 0-916750-25-6). Dayton Labs.

Green, Timothy. The New World of Gold. 1982. 15.95 (ISBN 0-8027-0692-4). Walker & Co.

An Illinois Gold Hunter in the Black Hills: The Diary of Jerry Bryan. 1960. pap. 2.00 (ISBN 0-912226-02-1). Ill St Hist. Soc.

Miller, Tron. Gold Rocker Handbook. 1980. pap. 4.00 (ISBN 0-89316-619-7); plastic bdg. 6.00 (ISBN 0-686-70739-7). Exanimo Pr.

Neese, Harvey, ed. Gold Mining for Recreation. LC 81-3831. (Illus., Orig.). 1981. pap. 4.95 (ISBN 0-87701-182-6). Chronicle Bks.

Paul, Rodman W. California Gold: The Beginning of Mining in the Far West. LC 47-54111. (Illus.). xx, 380p. 1965. pap. 3.95 (ISBN 0-8032-5149-1, BB 313, Bison). U of Nebr Pr.

Petralia, Joseph F. Gold! Gold!-A Beginners Handbook & Recreational Guide: How to Prospect for Gold, Vol. 4. 2nd ed. LC 81-126200. (Illus.). 112p. (Orig.). 1982. 10.95 (ISBN 0-9605890-2-3); pap. 6.95 (ISBN 0-9605890-3-1). Sierra Trading.

Ransom, Jay E. The Gold Hunter's Field Book: How & Where to Find Gold in the United States & Canada. LC 74-20409. 1980. pap. 8.61i (ISBN 0-06-090775-4, CN 775, CN). Har-Row.

Santschi, R. J. Treasure Trails. (Doodlebug Edition Ser.). 1974. 6.00 (ISBN 0-89316-612-X); pap. 4.00 (ISBN 0-89316-601-4). Exanimo Pr.

Schlitt, W. J. & Larson, W. C., eds. Gold & Silver Leaching, Recovery & Economics. LC 81-68558. (Illus.). 148p. 1981. text ed. 20.00x (ISBN 0-89520-289-1). Soc Mining Eng.

Stone, Gregory V. Placer Gold. 72p. 1982. pap. 6.95 (ISBN 0-8059-2833-2). Dorrance.

Stultz, Arthur L. Gold Rush Eighty, Vol. 1. (Getting Rich Ser.: No. 1). (Illus.). 300p. 1981. 17.00 (ISBN 0-9605958-0-5); lib. bdg. 20.00 (ISBN 0-9605958-2-1); pap. 10.00x (ISBN 0-9605958-1-3, GR-801). Ophir Intl.

Van Onselen, Charles. Chibaro: African Mine Labour in Southern Rhodesia 1900-1933. 326p. 1980. text ed. 16.95 (ISBN 0-902818-88-0, Pub. by Pluto Pr). Longwood Pub Group.

Volcanogenic Gold Deposits. 1982. 82.60 (ISBN 0-942218-19-1). Minobras.

Von Mueller, Karl. Gold Dredger's Handbook. 2nd, rev. ed. 1980. pap. 5.00 (ISBN 0-89316-609-X); plastic bdg. 6.00 (ISBN 0-89316-610-3). Exanimo Pr.

--Vibrating Gold Concentrators. 1980. pap. 4.00 (ISBN 0-89316-617-0); plastic bdg. 6.00 (ISBN 0-89316-618-9). Exanimo Pr.

Voynick, Stephen M. In Search of Gold. (Illus.). 216p. 1982. 15.95 (ISBN 0-87364-238-4). Paladin Pr.

Wagner, Jack R. Gold Mines of California. LC 79-115852. 1970. 25.00 (ISBN 0-8310-7002-1). Howell-North.

Wiltsee, Ernest A. The Pioneer Miner & the Pack Mule Express. LC 76-4134. (Illus.). 160p. 1976. Repr. 35.00x (ISBN 0-88000-084-8). Quarterman.

GOLD MINES AND MINING-AFRICA, SOUTH

Letcher, Owen. The Gold Mines of Southern Africa: The History Technology & Statistics of the Gold Industry. LC 74-353. (Vol. 18). (Illus.). 580p. 1974. Repr. 43.00x (ISBN 0-405-05915-9). Ayer Co Pubs.

Reunert, Theodore. Diamonds & Gold in South Africa. LC 72-3916. (Black Heritage Library Collection Ser.). Repr. of 1893 ed. 29.50 (ISBN 0-8369-9106-0). Ayer Co Pubs.

GOLDEN EAGLE

Everett, Michael. The Golden Eagle. 60p. 1981. 10.00x (ISBN 0-85158-119-6, Pub. by Blackwood & Sons England). State Mutual Bk.

Tomkies, Mike. Golden Eagle Years. (Illus.). 208p. (Orig.). 1982. 24.95 (ISBN 0-434-78801-5, Pub. by W Heinemann Ltd). David & Charles.

True, Dan. Flying Free. (Illus.). 160p. 1984. 13.95 (ISBN 0-396-08413-3). Dodd.

GOLDEN HAMSTER
see Hamsters

GOLDEN RETRIEVERS
see Dogs-Breeds-Golden Retrievers

GOLDEN SECTION

Cook, Theodore A. The Curves of Life. 1979. pap. 6.95 (ISBN 0-486-23701-X). Dover.

GOLDFISH

Gannon, Robert. Start Right with Goldfish. (Orig.). pap. 2.95 (ISBN 0-87666-081-2, M-504). TFH Pubns.

Matsui, Yoshiichi. Goldfish Guide. (Illus.). 256p. 1981. 14.95 (ISBN 0-87666-545-8, PL-2011). TFH Pubns.

Orme, Frank W. Fancy Goldfish Culture. 284p. 1979. 14.95 (ISBN 0-904558-63-0). Saiga.

--Goldfish & Koi. (Illus.). 80p. 1982. pap. 2.75 (ISBN 0-86230-020-7). Triplegate.

Paradise, Paul R., ed. Goldfish. (Illus.). 1979. 4.95 (ISBN 0-87666-511-3, KW-014). TFH Pubns.

Powers, Edwin B. The Goldfish (Carassius Carassius) As a Test Animal in the Study of Toxicity. pap. 8.00 (ISBN 0-384-47495-0). Johnson Repr.

Wolburg, H. Axonal Transport, Degeneration, & Regeneration in the Visual System of the Goldfish. (Advances in Anatomy, Embryology & Cell Biology Ser.: Vol. 67). (Illus.). 100p. 1981. pap. 22.90 (ISBN 0-387-10336-8). Springer-Verlag.

GOLDSCHMIDT, RICHARD BENEDICT 1878-

Pitternick, L. K., ed. Richard Goldschmidt: Controversial Geneticist & Creative Biologist. (Experientia Supplementa: No. 35). 154p. 1980. 16.95x (ISBN 0-8176-1093-6). Birkhauser.

GOLGI APPARATUS

Whaley, W. G. The Golgi Apparatus. LC 75-20055. (Cell Biology Monographs: Vol. 2). (Illus.). 200p. 1975. 55.00 (ISBN 0-387-81315-2). Springer-Verlag.

GONADOTROPIN

Flamigni, C. & Givens, J. R., eds. The Gonadotropins. (Serono Symposium Ser.: No. 42). 512p. 1982. 66.00 (ISBN 0-12-258550-X). Acad Pr.

Institute of Endocrinology, Gunma University, ed. Evolutionary Aspects of Gonadotropins. (Gunma Symposia on Endocrinology Ser.: Vol. 21). (Illus.). 210p. 1984. 28.00x (ISBN 4-905648-05-X, Pub. by Japan Sci Soc Pr Japan). Intl Spec Bk.

McKerns, Kenneth W., ed. Structure & Function of the Gonadotropins. LC 78-12372. (Biochemical Endocrinology Ser.). (Illus.). 646p. 1978. 75.00x (ISBN 0-306-40097-9, Plenum Pr). Plenum Pub.

Rosemberg, Eugenia, ed. Gonadotropins Nineteen Sixty-Eight: Proceedings of the Workshop Conference Held at Vista Hermosa, Mor., Mexico, June 24-26, 1968. LC 68-59129. (Illus.). 1968. text ed. 12.00x (ISBN 0-87672-004-1). Geron-X.

Runnebaum, B., et al, eds. Secretion & Action of Gonadotropins. (Illus.). 105p. 1984. pap. 18.00 (ISBN 0-387-13854-4). Springer-Verlag.

GOOSE
see Geese

GOPHERS
see Ground Squirrels; Pocket Gophers

GORDIUS

May, Henry G. Contributions to the Life Histories of Gordius Robustus Leidy & Paragordius Varius: Leidy. (Illus.). Repr. of 1920 ed. 12.00 (ISBN 0-384-36060-2). Johnson Repr.

GORDON SETTER
see Dogs-Breeds-Gordon Setter

GORILLAS

Dixson, A. F. The Natural History of the Gorilla. 202p. 1985. pap. 10.95 (ISBN 0-231-05319-3). Columbia U Pr.

Fossey, Dian. Gorillas in the Mist: A Remarkable Woman's Thirteen Year Adventure in Remote African Rain Forests with the Greatest of the Great Apes. LC 82-23332. (Illus.). 325p. 1983. 19.95 (ISBN 0-395-28217-9); pap. 10.95. HM.

Jones, C. & Sabater Pi, J. Comparative Ecology of Gorilla & Pan Troglodytes in Rio Muni, West Africa. (Bibliotheca Primatologica: No. 13). 1971. pap. 10.75 (ISBN 3-8055-0293-1). S Karger.

Maple, Terry & Hoff, M. P. Gorilla Behavior. (VNR Primate Behavior & Development Ser.). 272p. 1981. 34.50 (ISBN 0-442-25152-1). Van Nos Reinhold.

Patterson, Francine & Linden, Eugene. The Education of Koko. LC 81-1325. (Illus.). 240p. 1981. 15.95 (ISBN 0-03-046101-4); pap. 7.95 (ISBN 0-03-063551-9). HR&W.

Schaller, George B. The Mountain Gorilla: Ecology & Behavior. LC 63-11401. (Illus.). 1976. pap. 9.00x (ISBN 0-226-73636-9). U of Chicago Pr.

--Year of the Gorilla. LC 64-13946. (Illus.). 1964. pap. 5.50 (ISBN 0-226-73638-5, P209, Phoen). U of Chicago Pr.

GOSSE, PHILIP HENRY, 1810-1888

Gosse, Edmund. Father & Son. 1963. pap. 6.95 (ISBN 0-393-00195-4, Norton Lib). Norton.

GPS (COMPUTER PROGRAM)

Ernst, George W. & Newell, Allen. G. P. S. A Case Study in Generality & Problem Solving. (ACM Monograph Ser). 1969. 70.00 (ISBN 0-12-241050-5). Acad Pr.

GPSS (COMPUTER PROGRAM LANGUAGE)

Bobillier, P. A., et al. Simulation with Gpss & Gpssv. LC 75-40316. 1976. 37.50 (ISBN 0-13-810549-9). P-H.

Gordon, Geoffrey. The Application of GPSS Five to Discrete System Simulation. (Illus.). 336p. 1975. 35.00 (ISBN 0-13-039057-7). P-H.

Maisel, Herbert & Gnugnoli, Guiliano. Simulation of Discrete Stochastic Systems. LC 72-80761. (Illus.). 465p. 1972. 29.95 (ISBN 0-574-16133-3, 13-1565). SRA.

Schmidt, B. GPSS FORTRAN. LC 80-40968. (Computing Ser.). 523p. 1980. 53.95 (ISBN 0-471-27881-5, Pub. by Wiley-Interscience). Wiley.

GRAFTING

see also Plant Propagation

Johnston, Patricia Irwin. Perspectives on a Grafted Tree. (Illus.). 144p. 1983. 12.95 (ISBN 0-9609504-0-0). Perspect Indiana.

Mascall, Leonard. A Booke of the Arte & Manner How to Plant & Graffe All Sortes of Trees. LC 74-80200. (English Experience Ser.: No. 679). 90p. 1974. Repr. of 1572 ed. 13.00 (ISBN 90-221-0679-9). Walter J Johnson.

GRAIN

see also Cereals As Food;

also names of the various cereal plants, e.g. Corn; Rye; Wheat

Adams, Ruth & Murray, Frank. Seeds, Grains, Nuts. 1.75x (ISBN 0-915962-07-1). Cancer Control Soc.

Babakina, V. S., ed. Grain & Pulse Crops. 255p. 1981. 60.00x (ISBN 0-686-76641-5, Pub. by Oxford & IBH India). State Mutual Bk.

Bland, Brian F. Crop Production: Cereals & Legumes. 1971. 73.50 (ISBN 0-12-104050-X). Acad Pr.

Broekhuizen, S. & Thran, P., eds. Atlas of Cereal Growing in Europe. (Agro-Ecological Atlas Ser.: Vol. 2). 156p. 1970. 159.50 (ISBN 0-444-40819-3). Elsevier.

Brooker, Donald B., et al. Drying Cereal Grains. (Illus.). 1974. pap. text ed. 25.00 (ISBN 0-87055-303-8). AVI.

Brown, Lester R. Increasing World Food Output. LC 75-26298. (World Food Supply Ser). (Illus.). 1976. Repr. of 1965 ed. 14.00x (ISBN 0-405-07770-X). Ayer Co Pubs.

Bumgarner, Marlene A. Book of Whole Grains. (Illus.). 256p. 1976. pap. 7.95 (ISBN 0-312-09240-7). St Martin.

Bushuk, W. Rye: Production, Chemistry, & Technology. LC 76-29382. (AACC Monograph: No. V). 181p. 1976. text ed. 32.00 (ISBN 0-913250-11-2); text ed. 24.00 members. Am Assn Cereal Chem.

Cereal & Grain-Legume Seed Processing: Technical Guidelines. (Plant Production & Protection Papers: No. 21). 156p. 1981. pap. 20.25 (ISBN 92-5-100980-5, F2296, FAO). Unipub.

Cereal Grain Protein Improvement: Proceedings of the Final Research Co-ordination Meeting of the FAO-IAEA-GSF-SIDA Co-ordinated Research Programme, Vienna, 6-10 December 1982. (Panel Proceedings Ser.). (Illus.). 388p. 1984. pap. 61.00 (ISBN 92-0-111184-3, ISP664, IAEA). Unipub.

Cereals. (Better Farming Ser.: No. 15). 51p. 1977. pap. 7.50 (ISBN 92-5-100150-2, F72, FAO). Unipub.

China: Post-Harvest Grain Technology: Report of a Study Group in the People's Republic of China September-October 1977. (Agricultural Services Bulletins: No. 50). 70p. 1982. pap. 7.50 (ISBN 92-5-101196-6, F2324, FAO). Unipub.

Coarse Grains. (Commodity Projections: 1985). 1979. pap. 6.00 (ISBN 0-686-59425-8, F1611, FAO). Unipub.

Grossbard, Eerna, ed. Straw Decay & Its Effect on Disposal & Utilization. LC 79-42841. 337p. 1979. 66.95x (ISBN 0-471-27694-4). Wiley.

High-Yielding Varieties of Grain. LC 75-26315. (World Food Supply Ser.). (Illus.). 1976. 15.00x (ISBN 0-405-07800-5). Ayer Co Pubs.

Hu, H., ed. The Nature & Behavior of Grain Boundaries. LC 72-81907. 440p. 1972. 65.00x (ISBN 0-306-30704-9, Plenum Pr). Plenum Pub.

Hunter, Beatrice T. Wheat, Millet & Other Grains. (Good Health Guide Ser.). 1982. pap. 1.45 (ISBN 0-87983-289-4). Keats.

Karel, Leonard. Dried Grasses, Grains, Gourds, Pods & Cones. LC 74-31178. (Illus.). 209p. 1975. 15.00 (ISBN 0-8108-0792-0). Scarecrow.

Kent, N. L. Technology of Cereals: An Introduction for Students of Food Science & Agriculture. 3rd ed. LC 75-6654. (Illus.). 200p. 1983. 24.50 (ISBN 0-08-029801-X); pap. 13.50 (ISBN 0-08-029800-1). Pergamon.

Knobel, Edward. Field Guide to the Grasses, Sedges & Rushes of the United States. LC 77-72531. (Illus.). 1977. pap. 2.75 (ISBN 0-486-23505-X). Dover.

Laidman, D. L. & Jones, R. G., eds. Recent Advances in the Biochemistry of Cereals. 1979. 69.50 (ISBN 0-12-433950-6). Acad Pr.

Laszity, Radmoir & Hidvegi, Mate, eds. Amino Acid Composition & Biological Value of Cereal Proteins. 1985. lib. bdg. 76.00 (ISBN 90-277-1937-3, Pub. by Reidel Holland). Kluwer Academic.

Lasztity, R. The Chemistry of Cereal Proteins. 216p. 1984. 65.00 (ISBN 0-8493-5140-5). CRC Pr.

Leonard, Warren H. & Martin, John H. Cereal Crops. 1963. text ed. write for info. (ISBN 0-02-369830-6). Macmillan.

Peryt, T., ed. Coated Grains. (Illus.). 600p. 1983. 58.00 (ISBN 0-387-12071-8). Springer-Verlag.

Pomeranz, Y., ed. Cereals Seventy-Eight: Better Nutrition for the World's Millions. LC 78-69838. 272p. 1978. lib. bdg. 9.00 member (ISBN 0-913250-13-9). Am Assn Cereal Chem.

Quick, G. & Buchele, W. The Grain Harvesters. (Illus.). 280p. pap. 13.95 (ISBN 0-916150-13-5). Am Soc Ag Eng.

Report of the Twentieth Session of the Intergovernmental Group on Grains to the Committee on Commodity Problems. 30p. 1980. pap. 7.50 (ISBN 92-5-100919-8, F1953, FAO). Unipub.

Salunkhe, D. K., et al, eds. Postharvest Biotechnology of Cereals. 224p. 1985. 67.00 (ISBN 0-8493-6288-1). CRC Pr.

Shejbal, J. Controlled Atmosphere Storage of Grains. (Developments in Agricultural Engineering Ser.: Vol. 1). 608p. 1981. 93.75 (ISBN 0-444-41939-X). Elsevier.

Solar Energy Research Institute. Fermentation Guide for Common Grains: A Step-by-Step Procedure for Small-Scale Ethanol Fuel Production. 1982. pap. 9.95 (ISBN 0-89934-157-8, B-026). Solar Energy Info.

Stoskopf, Neil. Cereal Grain Crops. 1985. text ed. 34.95 (ISBN 0-8359-0733-3); instr's. manual avail. (ISBN 0-8359-0734-1). Reston.

Summerfield, R. J. & Roberts, E. H., eds. Grain Legume Crops. 600p. 1985. text ed. 85.00x (ISBN 0-00-383037-3, Pub. by Collins England). Sheridan.

Thran, P. & Brockhuizen, S., eds. Agro-Climatic Atlas of Europe. (Agro-Ecological Atlas Ser.: Vol. 1). 294p. 1965. 202.25 (ISBN 0-444-40569-0). Elsevier.

Time-Life Books, ed. Dried Beans & Grains. 176p. 1982. 13.95 (ISBN 0-8094-2920-9). Time-Life.

Titow, J. Z. Winchester Yields: A Study in Medieval Agricultural Productivity. LC 72-171685. (Cambridge Studies in Economic History). 1972. 32.50 (ISBN 0-521-08349-4). Cambridge U Pr.

GRAIN–BREEDING

see also Rice Breeding

Carter, N. & Dixon, A. F. Cereal Aphid Population: Biology, Simulation & Prediction. 94p. 1982. pap. 14.50 (ISBN 90-220-0804-5, PDC252, Pudoc). Unipub.

Feistritzer, W. P., ed. Cereal Seed Technology: A Manual of Cereal Seed Production, Quality, Control & Distribution. (Plant Production & Protection Papers: No. 10). 238p. (2nd printing, 1977). 1975. pap. 17.00 (ISBN 92-5-100460-9, F94, FAO). Unipub.

Hardarson, G. & Lie, T. A., eds. Breeding Legumes for Enhanced Symbiotic Nitrogen Fixation. (Advances in Agricultural Biotechnology Ser.). 1985. lib. bdg. 36.00 (ISBN 90-247-3123-2, Pub. by Martinus Nijhoff Netherlands). Kluwer-Academic.

Maximizing the Efficiency of Fertilizer Use by Grain Crops. (Fertilizer Bulletins: No. 3). (Eng. & Fr.). 40p. 1980. pap. 7.50 (ISBN 92-5-100954-6, F2131, FAO). Unipub.

Nuclear Techniques for Seed Protein Improvement. (Panel Proceedings Ser.). (Illus.). 442p. (Orig.). 1973. pap. 33.75 (ISBN 92-0-111073-1, ISP320, IAEA). Unipub.

GRAIN–DISEASES AND PESTS

Attwood, P., ed. Crop Protection Handbook: Cereals. 85.00x (ISBN 0-901436-72-0, Pub. by CAB Bks England). State Mutual Bk.

Egerton, Frank N., 3rd, ed. Phytopathological Classics of the Eighteenth Century: An Originial Anthology. LC 77-74247. (History of Ecology Ser.). (Illus.). 1978. lib. bdg. 47.50x (ISBN 0-405-10416-2). Ayer Co Pubs.

Graham, et al. A Compendium of Alfalfa Disease. LC 79-88555. (Illus.). 65p. 1979. saddle stitched 17.00 (ISBN 0-89054-026-8). Am Phytopathol Soc.

Jenkyn, J. F. & Plumb, R. T. Strategies for the Control of Cereal Disease: Organized by the British Plant Pathologist, Vol. 2. (Federation of British Plant Pathologists Ser.: Vol. 9). 219p. 1981. 57.95x (ISBN 0-470-27049-7). Halsted Pr.

Jones, D. Gareth & Clifford, Brian C. Cereal Diseases: Their Pathology & Control. 2nd ed. LC 82-24783. 309p. 1983. text ed. 79.95x (ISBN 0-471-10501-5, Pub. by Wiley-Interscience). Wiley.

Judenko, E. Analytical Method for Assessing Yield Losses Caused by Pests on Cereal Crops with & Without Pesticides. 1973. 35.00x (ISBN 0-85135-061-5, Pub. by Centre Overseas Research). State Mutual Bk.

Shurtleff, M. C. Compendium of Corn Diseases. 2nd ed. LC 80-67517. (Illus.). 105p. 1980. 17.00 (ISBN 0-89054-029-2); members 14.00. Am Phytopathol Soc.

Zadoks, J. C. & Rijsdijk, F. H. Atlas of Cereal Diseases & Pests in Europe. (Agro-ecological Atlas of Cereal Growing in Europe: Vol. 3). (Illus.). 169p. 1985. 30.50 (ISBN 90-220-0863-0, PDC281, Pudoc). Unipub.

GRAIN–MILLING

see also Flour; Flour Mills; Milling Machinery

Association of Operative Millers. Cereal Miller's Handbook. 1963. 25.00 (ISBN 0-686-00364-0). AG Pr.

--Technical Bulletins: 1944-1974, Vol. 3. 1975. 25.00 (ISBN 0-686-00376-4). AG Pr.

--Technical Bulletins: 1944-1975, Vol. 4. 1977. 25.00 (ISBN 0-686-00375-6). AG Pr.

Engineering Foundation Conference on Modeling of Casting & Welding Processes II, New Hampshire, July 31 - August 5, 1983. Grain Refinement in Castings & Welds. David, S. A. & Abbaschian, G. J., eds. (Proceedings). 458p. 45.00 (ISBN 0-89520-477-0, 247); members 30.00 (ISBN 0-317-37161-4); student members 15.00 (ISBN 0-317-37162-2). Metal Soc.

International Labour Office Staff. Small Scale Maize Milling: Technical Memorandum, No. 7. (Technology Ser.). xii, 143p. (Orig.). 1984. pap. 10.00 (ISBN 92-2-103640-5). Intl Labour Office.

Moritz, L. A. Grain-Mills & Flour in Classical Antiquity. Finley, Moses, ed. LC 79-4994. (Ancient Economic History Ser.). (Illus.). 1980. Repr. of 1958 ed. lib. bdg. 24.50x (ISBN 0-405-12381-7). Ayer Co Pubs.

Small-Scale Maize Milling. (Technology Series: Technical Memorandums: No. 7). 143p. 1985. pap. 10.00 (ISBN 92-2-103640-5, ILO359, ILO). Unipub.

GRAIN–STORAGE

Boumans, G. Grain Handling & Storage. (Developments in Agricultural Engineering Ser.: Vol. 4). 442p. 1985. 94.50 (ISBN 0-444-42439-3). Elsevier.

China: Grain Storage Structures: Report on an FAO/UNDP Workshop Study Tour in the People's Republic of China: October 18 - November 16, 1979. (Agricultural Services Bulletins: No. 49). (Illus.). 122p. 1982. pap. 14.50 (ISBN 92-5-101154-0, F2311, FAO). Unipub.

Christensen, C. M., ed. Storage of Cereal Grains & Their Products. 3rd ed. LC 82-72829. (Illus.). 544p. 1982. text ed. 85.00 (ISBN 0-913250-23-6); text ed. 69.00 members. Am Assn Cereal Chem.

Christensen, Clyde M. & Kaufmann, Henry H. Grain Storage: The Role of Fungi in Quality Loss. LC 70-76174. (Illus.). 1969. 10.95x (ISBN 0-8166-0518-1). U of Minn Pr.

Labuza, Theodore P. Moisture Sorption: Practical Aspects of Isotherm Measurement & Use. 150p. 1984. 28.50 (ISBN 0-913250-34-1); member 22.50. Am Assn Cereal Chem.

Midwest Plan Service Personnel. Low Temperature & Solar Grain Drying Handbook. 1st ed. (Illus.). 86p. 1980. pap. 5.00 (ISBN 0-89373-048-3, MWPS-22). Midwest Plan Serv.

O'Kelly, Elizabeth & Forster, R. H. Processing & Storage of Foodgrains by Rural Families. (Agricultural Services Bulletins: No. 53). (Eng. & Fr.). 129p. 1983. pap. text ed. 9.95 (ISBN 92-5-101276-8, F2447, FAO). Unipub.

Ripp, B. E., ed. Controlled Atmosphere & Fumigation in Grain Storages: Proceedings of an International Symposium Held from 11-12 April, 1983, in Perth, Western Australia. (Developments in Agricultural Engineering Ser.: No. 5). 798p. 1984. 105.75 (ISBN 0-444-42417-2). Elsevier.

Shejbal, J. Controlled Atmosphere Storage of Grains. (Developments in Agricultural Engineering Ser.: Vol. 1). 608p. 1981. 93.75 (ISBN 0-444-41939-X). Elsevier.

Storage of Food Grain: A Guide for Extension Workers. (Illus.). 33p. 1976. pap. 7.50 (ISBN 0-685-66340-X, F1206, FAO). Unipub.

GRAIN ELEVATORS

Patton, Harold S. Grain Growers' Cooperation in Western Canada. LC 71-100529. Repr. of 1928 ed. 29.50 (ISBN 0-404-00630-2). AMS Pr.

GRAIN PESTS

see Grain–Diseases and Pests

GRAIN SORGHUM

see Sorghum

GRANITE

Cameron, Eugene N., et al. Internal Structure of Granitic Pragmatites. (Economic Geology Monograph: No. 2). pap. 43.00 (ISBN 0-317-28808-3, 2020336). Bks Demand UMI.

Didier, J. Granites & Their Enclaves. LC 76-179999. (Developments in Petrology Ser.: Vol. 3). 412p. 1973. 93.75 (ISBN 0-444-40974-2). Elsevier.

Hammers on Stone: The History of Cape Ann Granite. (Illus.). 18.95 (ISBN 0-317-15142-8). Peter Smith.

Marmo, V. Granite Petrology & the Granite Problem. (Developments in Petrology Ser.: Vol. 2). 244p. 1971. 85.00 (ISBN 0-444-40852-5). Elsevier.

Symposium on the Granites of West Africa, Ivory Coast, Nigeria, Cameroon, 1965: Proceedings. 1968. 17.50 (ISBN 0-685-20791-9, U488, UNESCO). Unipub.

Twidale, C. R. Granite Landforms. 372p. 1982. 115.00 (ISBN 0-444-42116-5). Elsevier.

GRANULAR MATERIALS

Broersma, G. Behavior of Granular Materials. 266p. 1972. 50.00x (ISBN 0-85950-045-4, Pub. by Stam Pr England). State Mutual Bk.

Litwiniszyn, J. Stochastic Methods in Mechanics of Granular Bodies. (CISM - International Centre for Mechanical Sciences, Courses & Lectures: Vol. 93). (Illus.). 93p. 1975. pap. 13.30 (ISBN 0-387-81310-1). Springer-Verlag.

Shahinpoor, M. Advances in the Flow of Granular Materials, Vol. 1. 1983. 45.00x (ISBN 0-87849-049-3). Trans Tech.

--Advances in the Flow of Granular Materials, Vol. 2. 1983. 45.00x (ISBN 0-87849-050-7). Trans Tech.

Shahinpoor, Mohsen, ed. Advances in the Mechanics & Flow of Granular Materials, Vol. II. LC 83-80567. 500p. 1983. 48.50x (ISBN 0-87201-013-9). Gulf Pub.

--Advances in the Mechanics & Flow of Granular Materials, Vol. I. LC 83-80567. 500p. 1983. 48.50x (ISBN 0-87201-010-4). Gulf Pub.

Sherrington, P. J. & Oliver, R. Granulation: Powder Advisory Centre Publication Ser. (POWTECH) 196p. 1980. 49.95 (ISBN 0-471-26019-3, Pub. by Wiley Heyden). Wiley.

GRAPES

see also Viticulture

Antcliff, A. J. Major Wine Grape Varieties of Australia. 62p. 1979. pap. 6.50 (ISBN 0-643-02517-0, C012, CSIRO). Unipub.

--Some Wine Grape Varieties for Australia. 50p. 1976. pap. 6.00 (ISBN 0-643-00180-8, C009, CSIRO). Unipub.

Bosqui & Co. Grapes & Grapevines of California. LC 81-4775. (Illus.). 64p. 1981. 29.95 (ISBN 0-15-136786-8). HarBraceJ.

Brandt, Johanna. The Grape Cure. 2.00x (ISBN 0-686-29874-8). Cancer Control Soc.

Flaherty, Donald L., et al, eds. Grape Pest Management. LC 80-70846. (Illus.). 312p. (Orig.). 1981. pap. 25.00x (ISBN 0-931876-44-3, 4105). Ag & Nat Res.

Frazier, N. W., ed. Virus Diseases of Small Fruits & Grapevines. 1970. 7.50x (ISBN 0-931876-21-4, 4056). Ag & Nat Res.

Recommended International Standard for Grape Juice, Concentrated Grape Juice, & Sweetened Concentrated Labrusca Type Grape Juice Preserved Exclusively by Physical Means. (CAC-RS Ser.: Nos. 82-84 -1976). 17p. 1976. pap. 4.50 (ISBN 92-5-101802-2, F579, FAO). Unipub.

GRAPES–VARIETIES

Kasimatis, A. N., et al. Wine Grape Varieties in the North Coast Counties of California. 1977. pap. 3.00 (ISBN 0-931876-22-2, 4069). Ag & Nat Res.

--Wine Grape Varieties in the San Joaquin Valley. 1972. pap. 5.00 (ISBN 0-931876-23-0, 4009). Ag & Nat Res.

Ramey, Bern C. The Great Wine Grapes & the Wines They Make. 1978. 49.95 (ISBN 0-8436-2257-1). Van Nos Reinhold.

Wagner, Philip M. Wine-Grower's Guide. rev ed. (Illus.). 1965. 14.95 (ISBN 0-394-40183-2). Knopf.

GRAPH THEORY

see also Bond Graphs; Four-Color Problem; Network Analysis (Planning)

Alavi, Y. & Lick, D. R., eds. Theory & Applications of Graphs: Proceedings, Michigan, May 11-15, 1976. (Lecture Notes in Mathematics: Vol. 642). 1978. pap. 31.00 (ISBN 0-387-08666-8). Springer-Verlag.

Biggs, Norman, et al. Graph Theory: Seventeen Thirty-Six to Nineteen Thirty-Six. (Illus.). 1976. 55.00x (ISBN 0-19-853901-0). Oxford U Pr.
Broekhuizen, Richard. Graphic Communications. 380p. 1979. text ed. 17.28 (ISBN 0-87345-246-1); study guide 6.00 (ISBN 0-87345-247-X); ans. key free (ISBN 0-87345-248-8). McKnight.
Cameron, P. J. & Van Lint, J. H. Graphs, Codes & Designs. (London Mathematical Society Lecture Notes Ser.: No. 43). 180p. 1980. 24.95 (ISBN 0-521-23141-8). Cambridge U Pr.
Centre De Mathematique Sociale Ecole Des Hautes Etudes En Sciences Sociales. Combinatorics Graphs & Algebra. (Methods & Models in the Social Sciences: No. 5). (Illus., Orig.). 1976. text ed. 16.80x (ISBN 90-2797-511-6). Mouton.
Coxeter, H. S., et al. Zero-Symmetric Graphs: Trivalent Graphical Regular Representations of Groups. LC 81-4604. 1981. 21.50 (ISBN 0-12-194580-4). Acad Pr.
Crow, Wendell C. Communication Graphics. (Illus.). 336p. 1986. text ed. 26.95 (ISBN 0-13-153792-X). P-H.
Cvetlovic, Dragos, et al, eds. Spectra of Graphs: Theory & Applications. LC 79-50490. (Pure & Applied Mathematics Ser.). 1980. 67.50 (ISBN 0-12-195150-2). Acad Pr.
DeWilde, Marc. Closed Graph Theorems & Webbed Spaces. (Research Notes in Mathematics: No. 19). 158p. (Orig.). 1978. pap. text ed. 21.50 (ISBN 0-273-08403-8). Pitman Pub MA.
Dlab, Vlastimil & Ringel, Claus M. Indecomposable Representations of Graphs & Algebras. LC 76-18784. (Memoirs: No. 173). 57p. 1976. pap. 12.00 (ISBN 0-8218-1873-2, MEMO-173). Am Math.
Enrick, Norbert L. Handbook of Effective Graphic & Tabular Communication. LC 79-4483. 224p. 1980. 13.75 (ISBN 0-88275-914-0). Krieger.
Fiorini, S. & Wilson, R. J. Edge-Colourings of Graphs. (Research Notes in Mathematics Ser.: No. 16). 154p. (Orig.). 1977. pap. text ed. 22.95 (ISBN 0-273-01129-4). Pitman Pub MA.
Fitts, Gary. Module XI: Graphing Functions. Ablon, Leon J., ed. LC 76-62884. (Ser. in Mathematics Modules). 1977. pap. 8.95 (ISBN 0-8465-0265-8). Benjamin-Cummings.
Garland, Ken. Illustrated Graphics Glossary. 192p. 1981. 30.00x (ISBN 0-09-141511-X, Pub. by Barrie & Jenkins England). State Mutual Bk.
Gelfand, I. M., et al. Functions & Graphs. (Pocket Mathematical Library). 110p. 1968. 24.50 (ISBN 0-677-20690-9). Gordon.
Grant, Donald P. The Dual Graph Approach: How to Use Planar Graphs & Their Duals As Design Aids. (Illus.). iii, 26p. (Orig.). 1983. pap. 3.60x (ISBN 0-911215-02-6). Small Master.
Graphic Symbols for Distributed Control Shared Display Instrumentation, Logic & Computer Systems: ISA Standard S5.3. 15p. 1982. pap. text ed. 16.00x (ISBN 0-87664-707-7). Instru Soc.
Graphs & Charts. (Basic Academic Ser.: Module 5). (Illus.). 110p. 1982. spiral bdg. 10.00x (ISBN 0-87683-229-X); instr's. manual 15.00 (ISBN 0-87683-240-0). G P Courseware.
Grossman, I. & Magnus, W. Groups & Their Graphs. LC 64-8512. (New Mathematical Library: No. 14). 1975. pap. 10.00 (ISBN 0-88385-614-X). Math Assn.
Hackworth, Robert D. & Howland, Joseph. Introductory College Mathematics: Tables & Graphs. LC 75-23628. (Illus.). 62p. 1976. pap. text ed. 9.95 (ISBN 0-7216-4421-X). HR&W.
Hansen, P. Studies on Graphs & Discreet Programming. (Mathematics Studies: Vol. 59). 396p. 1982. 93.75 (ISBN 0-444-86216-1, North Holland). Elsevier.
Hypergraph Seminar, Ohio State University, 1972. Proceedings. Berge, C. & Ray-Chaudhuri, D., eds. (Lecture Notes in Mathematics: Vol. 411). x, 287p. 1974. pap. 19.00 (ISBN 0-387-06846-5). Springer-Verlag.
Kepler, Harold B. Basic Graphical Kinematics. 2nd ed. (Illus.). 384p. 1973. text ed. 35.50 (ISBN 0-07-034171-0). McGraw.
Leblanc, John F., et al. Mathematics-Methods Program: Graphs, the Picturing of Information. (Mathematics Ser.). (Illus.). 160p. 1976. pap. text ed. 4.25 (ISBN 0-201-14622-3). Addison-Wesley.
Lefferts, Robert. Elements of Graphics: How to Prepare Charts & Graphs for Effective Reports. (Illus.). 176p. (Orig.). 1982. pap. 4.76i (ISBN 0-06-463545-7, EH 545, EH). B&N NY.
--Elements of Graphics: How to Prepare Charts & Graphs for Effective Reports. LC 80-8209. (Illus.). 192p. 1981. 14.37i (ISBN 0-06-012578-0, HarpT). Har-Row.
--How to Prepare Charts & Graphs for Effective Reports. 1982. pap. 4.76 (ISBN 0-06-463545-7, EH-545). Har-Row.
Leithold, Louis. Before Calculus: Functions, Graphs, & Analytic Geometry. 666p. 1985. text ed. 27.50 scp (ISBN 0-06-043928-9, HarpC). Har-Row.
Levens, A. S. Graphical Methods in Research. rev ed. LC 75-15676. 256p. 1975. Repr. of 1965 ed. 15.00 (ISBN 0-88275-316-9). Krieger.
MacGregor, A. J. Graphics Simplified: How to Plan & Prepare Effective Charts, Graphs, Illustrations, & Other Visual Aids. LC 79-10358. 1979. pap. 5.00 (ISBN 0-8020-6363-2). U of Toronto Pr.
Martin, James & McClure, Carma. Diagramming Techniques for Analysts & Programmers. (Illus.). 416p. 1984. text ed. 42.95 (ISBN 0-13-208794-4). P-H.
Maxwell, Lee M. & Reed, Myril B. The Theory of Graphs: A Basis for Network Theory. LC 77-106387. 181p. 1975. 19.00 (ISBN 0-08-016321-1). Pergamon.
Mitchell, Robert & Prickel, Donald. Number Power Five: Graphs, Tables, Schedules & Maps. (Number Power Ser.). 176p. (Orig.). 1983. pap. 4.95 (ISBN 0-8092-5516-2). Contemp Bks.
Mulhearn, Henry J. Graphing, Charting Simplified. 105p. 1976. 6.00 (ISBN 0-87526-221-X). Gould.
Muller-Brockmann, Josef. Grid Systems in Graphic Design: A Visual Communications Manual. (Visual Communications Bks.). (Eng. & Ger., Illus.). 176p. 1981. 45.00 (ISBN 0-8038-2711-3). Hastings.
Munce, Howard. Graphics Handbook. LC 82-8278. 160p. 1982. pap. 11.95 (ISBN 0-89134-049-1). North Light Pub.
Neurath, Otto. Graphic Communication Through Isotype. 48p. 1981. 25.00x (ISBN 0-7049-0480-2, Pub. by Dept Typography England). State Mutual Bk.
Newcomb, John. The Book of Graphic Problem Solving: How to Get Visual Ideas When You Need Them. 259p. 1984. 29.95 (ISBN 0-8352-1895-3). Bowker.
Ore, Oystein. Graphs & Their Use. LC 63-9345. (New Mathematical Library: No. 10). 131p. 1975. pap. 8.75 (ISBN 0-88385-610-7). Math Assn.
Palmer, E. M. Graphical Evolution. (Discrete Mathematics Ser.). 177p. 1985. 34.95 (ISBN 0-471-81577-2). Wiley.
Porter, Tom & Goodman, Sue. Manual of Graphic Techniques 3: For Architects, Graphic Designers & Artists, No. 3. (Illus.). 128p. 1983. pap. 10.95 (ISBN 0-684-18018-9, ScribT). Scribner.
Rival, Ivan, ed. Graphs & Order: The Role of Graphs in the Theory of Ordered Sets & Its Applications. 1985. lib. bdg. 99.00 (ISBN 90-277-1943-8, Pub. by Reidel Holland). Kluwer Academic.
Robinson, D. F. & Foulds, L. R. Diagraphs: Theory & Technique. 272p. 1980. 47.50 (ISBN 0-677-05470-X). Gordon.
Rudman, Jack. Director of Graphics & Production. (Career Examination Ser.: C-1795). (Cloth bdg. avail. on request). pap. 14.00 (ISBN 0-8373-1795-9). Natl Learning.
Schmid, Calvin F. Statistical Graphics: Design Principles & Practices. LC 82-19971. 212p. 1983. 28.50x (ISBN 0-471-87525-2, Pub. by Wiley Interscience). Wiley.
Simmonds, D. D., ed. Charts & Graphs. 1981. lib. bdg. 13.50 (ISBN 0-85200-293-9, Pub. by MTP Pr England). Kluwer Academic.
Swokowski, Earl W. Functions & Graphs. 3rd ed. 507p. 1980. write for info (ISBN 0-87150-283-6, 2221, Prindle). PWS Pubs.
--Functions & Graphs. 4th ed. 1984. text ed. write for info. (ISBN 0-87150-443-X, Prindle). PWS Pubs.
Swokowsti, Earl W. Functions & Graphs. 4th ed. 544p. 1984. text ed. write for info (ISBN 0-87150-460-X, 2840, Prindle). PWS Pubs.
Temperley, H. N. Graph Theory & Applications. LC 81-6933. (Mathematics & Its Applications Ser.). 130p. 1981. 49.95x (ISBN 0-470-27296-1); pap. 14.95 (ISBN 0-470-20120-7). Halsted Pr.
Wellman, Bernard L. Introduction to Graphical Analysis & Design. LC 65-28137. pap. 141.80 (ISBN 0-317-10844-1, 2003760). Bks Demand UMI.
White, A. T. Graphs, Groups & Surfaces. 2nd, rev. & enl. ed. (Mathematics Studies: Vol. 8). 314p. 1985. 30.00 (ISBN 0-444-87643-X, North-Holland). Elsevier.
White, Jan V. Using Charts & Graphs: One Thousand Ideas for Getting Attention. 208p. 1984. pap. 24.95 (ISBN 0-8352-1894-5). Bowker.

GRAPHIC STATICS

see also Bridges; Building, Iron and Steel; Girders; Girders, Continuous; Influence Lines; Mechanical Drawing; Nomography (Mathematics); Roofs; Strains and Stresses; Strength of Materials

Henneberg, L. E. Graphische Statik der Starren Systeme. (Bibliotheca Mathematica Teubneriana, Ser: No. 38). (Ger). 1969. Repr. of 1911 ed. 57.00 (ISBN 0-384-22325-7). Johnson Repr.

GRAPHICS, COMPUTER

see Computer Graphics

GRAPHICS, ENGINEERING

see Engineering Graphics

GRAPHITE

American Society of Mechanical Engineers. Rubber & Plastic Division. Symposium on Graphite Fiber Composites: An Integrated Approach to Their Development & Use Presented at ASME Winter Meeting, Pittsburgh, PA., Nov. 1967. LC 67-31228. pap. 20.00 (ISBN 0-317-08656-1, 2012303). Bks Demand UMI.
ASTM Standards on Manufactured Carbon & Graphite Products. 115p. 1981. pap. 3.50 (ISBN 0-8031-0821-4, 06-305001-00). ASTM.
Carbon & Graphite Fibers & Fiber Composites, March 1982-May 1983. 272p. 1983. 78.00 (ISBN 0-686-48273-5, LS108). T-C Pubns CA.
Delmonte, John. Technology of Carbon & Graphite Fiber Composites. (Illus.). 464p. 1981. 36.50 (ISBN 0-686-48237-9, 0213). T-C Pubns CA.
Dresselhaus, M. S. & Dresselhaus, G., eds. Intercalated Graphite. (Materials Research Society Symposia Proceedings Ser.: Vol. 20). 428p. 1983. 77.00 (ISBN 0-444-00781-4, North Holland). Elsevier.
Mantell, Charles L. Carbon & Graphite Handbook. LC 78-21468. 548p. 1979. Repr. of 1968 ed. lib. bdg. 37.50 (ISBN 0-88275-796-2). Krieger.
Reynolds, W. N. Physical Properties of Graphite. (Illus.). 193p. 1968. 31.50 (ISBN 0-444-20012-6, Pub. by Elsevier Applied Sci England). Elsevier.

GRAPHS

see Graphic Methods

GRAPTOLITES

Berry, W. B. Graptolite Faunas of the Marathon Region, West Texas. (Pub Ser.: 6005). (Illus.). 179p. 1960. 3.00 (ISBN 0-318-03312-7). Bur Econ Geology.
Bjerreskov, Merete. Llandoverian & Wenlockian Graptolites from Bornholm. (Fossils & Strata: No.8). 1975. 25.00x (ISBN 8-200-09392-1, Dist. by Columbia U Pr). Universitet.
Braithwaite, Lee F. Graptolites from the Lower Ordovician Pogonip Group of Western Utah. LC 75-31373. (Special Paper: No. 166). (Illus., Orig.). 1976. pap. 9.75 (ISBN 0-8137-2166-0). Geol Soc.
Bulman, O. M. The Caradoc Balclatchie Graptolites from Limestones in Laggan Burn, Ayrshire, Pts. 1-3. (Illus.). 1945-47. Set. pap. 30.00 (ISBN 0-384-06325-X). Johnson Repr.
--The Dendroid Graptolites, Pts. 1-3. 1927-34. Set. pap. 25.00 (ISBN 0-384-06335-7). Johnson Repr.
Elles, Gertrude L. & Wood, Ethel M. British Graptolites. 1901-1918. Set. pap. 72.00 (ISBN 0-384-14155-2). Johnson Repr.

GRASS PARAKEET

see Budgerigars

GRASS TETANY

Grunes, D. L. & Rendig, V. V., eds. Grass Tetany. (Illus.). 1979. pap. 5.00 (ISBN 0-89118-056-7). Am Soc Agron.

GRASSES

see also Forage Plants; Grasslands; Grazing; Pastures;
also names of grasses

Arber, A. The Gramineae: A Study of Cereal, Bamboo & Grass. (Illus.). 1973. Repr. of 1934 ed. 28.00 (ISBN 3-7682-0276-3). Lubrecht & Cramer.
Barnard, Carolyn & Potter, Loren D. New Mexico Grasses: A Vegetative Key. LC 83-21901. (Illus.). 160p. 1984. pap. 8.95 (ISBN 0-8263-0744-2). U of NM Pr.
Beard, J. Turfgrass: Science & Culture. (Illus.). 1972. ref. ed. 30.95 (ISBN 0-13-933002-X). P-H.
Bews, John W. The World's Grasses: Their Differention, Distribution, Economics. 1977. lib. bdg. 59.95 (ISBN 0-8490-2848-5). Gordon Pr.
Bor, N. L. Grasses of India, Burma & Ceylon: Excluding Bambuseae. (Illus.). 1973. Repr. of 1960 ed. 77.00 (ISBN 3-87429-043-3). Lubrecht & Cramer.
Brown, Lauren. Grasses: An Identification Guide. (Peterson Native Library). 1979. 9.95 (ISBN 0-395-27624-1). HM.
Butler, G. W. & Bailey, R. W., eds. Chemistry & Biochemistry of Herbage, 3 vols. Incl. Vol. 1. 1973. 90.00 (ISBN 0-12-148101-8); Vol. 2. 1974; Vol. 3. 1974. 55.00 (ISBN 0-12-148103-4). Acad Pr.
Cation Selectivity & Cation-Anion Balance as Factors Governing Mineral Composition of Pasture Herbage. 1959. pap. 4.00 (ISBN 90-220-0027-3, PDC155, PUDOC). Unipub.
Chase, Agnes. First Book of Grasses: The Structure of Grasses Explained for Beginners. 3rd ed. LC 76-48919. (Illus.). 127p. 1977. text ed. 8.95x (ISBN 0-87474-307-9). Smithsonian.
Clifford, H. T. & Watson, L. Identifying Grasses: Data, Methods & Illustrations. 1977. text ed. 35.00x (ISBN 0-7022-1312-8). U of Queensland Pr.
Competition Between Legumes & Grasses. (Agricultural Research Reports: No. 687). 1966. pap. 4.00 (PDC166, PUDOC). Unipub.
Crampton, Beecher. Grasses in California. (California Natural History Guides Ser.). (Illus., Orig.). 1974. pap. 5.95 (ISBN 0-520-02507-5). U of Cal Pr.
Emmons, Robert D. Turfgrass Science & Management. (Illus.). 384p. 1984. text ed. 23.00; instr's guide 2.85. Delmar.
Gould, Frank W. Common Texas Grasses: An Illustrated Guide. LC 78-6368. (W. L. Moody, Jr. Natural History Ser.: No. 3). (Illus.). 280p. 1978. 15.95 (ISBN 0-89096-057-7); pap. 8.95 (ISBN 0-89096-058-5). Tex A&M Univ Pr.
--The Grasses of Texas. LC 75-18688. (Illus.). 672p. 1975. 27.50 (ISBN 0-89096-005-4). Tex A&M Univ Pr.
--Grasses of the Southwestern United States. (Illus.). 352p. 1973. pap. 8.95 (ISBN 0-8165-0406-7). U of Ariz Pr.
Grounds, Roger. Ornamental Grasses. 216p. 1981. 18.95 (ISBN 0-442-24707-9). Van Nos Reinhold.
Hackel, Eduard. The True Grasses. Lamson-Scribner, F. & Southworth, E. A., trs. from Ger. (Illus.). 228p. 1982. Repr. of 1896 ed. text ed. 12.00 (ISBN 0-934454-98-1). Lubrecht & Cramer.
Hanson, A. A. & Juska, F. V., eds. Turfgrass Science. (Illus.). 1969. 12.50 (ISBN 0-89118-015-X). Am Soc Agron.
Harrington, H. D. How to Identify Grasses & Grasslike Plants. LC 76-17744. (Illus.). 142p. 1977. pap. 8.95x (ISBN 0-8040-0746-2, 82-74144, Pub. by Swallow). Ohio U Pr.
Hiesey, William & Nobs, Malcolm A. Interspecific Hybrid Derivatives Between Facultatively Apomictic Species of Bluegrasses & Their Responses to Contrasting Environments. LC 40-14859. (Experimental Studies on the Nature of Species: Vol. 6). (Illus.). 129p. 1982. 11.00 (ISBN 0-87279-656-6). Carnegie Inst.
Hitchcock, A. S. Manual of Grasses of the United States, 2 vols. 2nd ed. (Illus.). 30.00 set (ISBN 0-8446-0309-0). Peter Smith.
--Manual of the Grasses of the United States, 2 Vols. 2nd ed. (Illus.). 1971. pap. 8.50 ea.; Vol. 1. pap. (ISBN 0-486-22717-0); Vol. 2. pap. (ISBN 0-486-22718-9). Dover.
Humphrey, Robert R. Arizona Range Grasses. LC 61-63166. 159p. 1970. pap. 5.95x (ISBN 0-8165-0254-4). U of Ariz Pr.
Hunter, Peter J. Peter Hunter's Guide to Grasses, Clovers, & Weeds. (Illus.). 80p. pap. 7.50 (ISBN 0-938670-02-6). By Hand & Foot.
Jones. C4 Grasses & Cereals: Growth, Development, & Stress Response. 1985. 50.00 (ISBN 0-471-82409-7). Wiley.
Kahlenberg, Mary H. & Schwartz, Mark. The Book of Grass Crafts: Its Beauty & Uses. (Illus.). 1982. 24.95 (ISBN 0-525-06983-6, 02422-730). Dutton.
Karel, Leonard. Dried Grasses, Grains, Gourds, Pods & Cones. LC 74-31178. (Illus.). 209p. 1975. 15.00 (ISBN 0-8108-0792-0). Scarecrow.
Knobel, Edward. Field Guide to the Grasses, Sedges & Rushes of the United States. LC 77-72531. (Illus.). 1977. pap. 2.75 (ISBN 0-486-23505-X). Dover.
--Field Guide to the Grasses, Sedges & Rushes of the United States. 12.75 (ISBN 0-8446-5593-7). Peter Smith.
Knobloch, Irving W. A Check List of Crosses in the Gramineae. 1968. pap. 10.00 (ISBN 0-934454-22-1). Lubrecht & Cramer.
Koch, Stephen D. The Eragrostis Pectinacea-Pilosa Complex in North & Central America (Gramineae Erogrostoideae) LC 73-2454. (Biological Monographs Ser: No. 48). (Illus.). 86p. 1974. pap. 9.95x (ISBN 0-252-00389-6). U of Ill Pr.
Kucera, Clair L. Grasses of Missouri. LC 61-5880. (Illus.). 241p. 1961. 19.00x (ISBN 0-8262-0544-5). U of Mo Pr.
Kuelen, Van H. Simulation of Water Use & Herbage Growth in Arid Regions. 180p. 1981. 105.00x (ISBN 0-686-76664-4, Pub. by Oxford & IBH India). State Mutual Bk.
Lazarides, M. The Tropical Grasses of Southeast Asia: Excluding Bamboos. 350p. 1980. lib. bdg. 28.00 (ISBN 3-7682-1255-6). Lubrecht & Cramer.
Mohlenbrock, Robert H. Grasses: Bromus to Paspalum. LC 71-156793. (Illustrated Flora of Illinois Ser.). (Illus.). 352p. 1972. 22.95x (ISBN 0-8093-0520-8). S Ill U Pr.
--Grasses: Panicum to Danthonia. LC 73-6807. (Illustrated Flora of Illinois Ser). (Illus.). 398p. 1973. 22.95x (ISBN 0-8093-0521-6). S Ill U Pr.

On the Seed Production of Tropical Grasses in Kenya: Agricultural Research Reports Ser. 1973. pap. 4.00 (PDC61, PUDOC). Unipub.

Patunkar, B. W. Grasses of Marathwada, Maharashtra State. 1979. 49.00x (ISBN 0-686-45807-9, Pub. by United Bk Traders India). State Mutual Bk.

Phillips, Roger. Grasses, Ferns, Mosses & Lichens of Britain. 1981. 30.00x (ISBN 0-686-78776-5, Pub. by RHS Ent England). State Mutual Bk.

--Grasses, Ferns, Mosses & Lichens of Great Britain & Ireland. (Illus.). 181p. (Orig.). 1980. pap. text ed. 14.95x (ISBN 0-916422-38-0, Pub. by Pan Bks England). Mad River.

Pohl, Richard W. How to Know the Grasses. 3rd ed. (Pictured Key Nature Ser.). 208p. 1978. wire coil (ISBN 0-697-04876-4). Wm C Brown.

Rattray, J. M. Grass Cover of Africa. (Plant Production & Protection Papers: No. 9). 168p. (Orig., 3rd Printing 1978). 1960. pap. 13.50 (ISBN 92-5-100386-6, F211, FAO). Unipub.

Roberts, E. C., ed. International Turfgrass Research Conference, 2nd: Proceedings. (Illus.). 1974. 17.00 (ISBN 0-89118-007-9). Am Soc Agron.

Rotar, Peter P. Grasses of Hawaii. (Illus.). 364p. 1968. text ed. 17.50x (ISBN 0-87022-715-7). UH Pr.

Schaffner, John H. The Grasses of Ohio. 1917. 1.50 (ISBN 0-86727-008-X). Ohio Bio Survey.

Shantz, Homer L. & Marbut, Curtis F. Vegetation & Soils of Africa. LC 70-170848. Repr. of 1923 ed. 19.00 (ISBN 0-404-05953-8). AMS Pr.

Smith, James P. Key to the Genera of Grasses of the Conterminus United States. (Illus.). 40p. 1980. pap. 8.95x (ISBN 0-916422-22-4). Mad River.

Smithsonian Institution, Washington, D. C. Index to Grass Species, 3 Vols. Chase, Agnes & Niles, Cornelia D., eds. 1963. Set. 300.00 (ISBN 0-8161-0445-X, Hall Library). G K Hall.

Spedding, C. R. & Diekmahns, E. C., eds. Grasses & Legumes in British Agriculture. 511p. 1972. 89.00x (ISBN 0-85198-016-3, Pub. by CAB Bks England). State Mutual Bk.

Sund, Robert. Bunch Grass. LC 70-94014. 88p. 1969. pap. 5.95 (ISBN 0-295-95005-6). U of Wash Pr.

Trinius, K. B. Species Graminum Iconibus et Descriptionbus Illustravit, 3 vols. in 1. (Illus.). 1970. Repr. of 1836 ed. 96.25 (ISBN 3-7682-0669-6). Lubrecht & Cramer.

Turgeon, Al. Turfgrass Management. rev. ed. 1985. text ed. 26.95 (ISBN 0-8359-7883-4); tchr's ed. avail. (ISBN 0-8359-7888-5); lab manual 14.95 (ISBN 0-8359-7887-7). Reston.

Ward, H. M. Grasses: Field & Lab Handbook. 1979. 39.00x (ISBN 0-686-45806-0, Pub. by United Bk Traders India). State Mutual Bk.

Weishaupt, Clara G. A Descriptive Key to the Grasses of Ohio Based on Vegetative Characters. Cafazzo, Veda M., ed. (Ohio Biological Survey Bulletin, New Ser.: Vol. 7, No. 1). (Illus.). 100p. (Orig.). 1985. pap. text ed. 15.00 (ISBN 0-86727-098-5). Ohio Bio Survey.

Whyte, R. O. & Noir, T. R. Grasses in Agriculture. (Agricultural Planning Studies: No. 42). 418p. (5th Printing 1975). 1959. pap. 26.25 (ISBN 92-5-101529-5, F212, FAO). Unipub.

Youngner, V. B. & McKell, C. M., eds. The Biology & Utilization of Grasses. (Physiological Ecology Ser.). 1971. 70.00 (ISBN 0-12-774750-8). Acad Pr.

GRASSES–DISEASES AND PESTS

Couch, Houston B. Diseases of Turfgrasses. 3rd ed. 1986. price not set (ISBN 0-89874-211-0). Krieger.

Smiley, R. W., ed. Compendium of Turfgrass Diseases. LC 82-73593. (Illus.). 102p. 1983. pap. 14.00 member (ISBN 0-89054-049-7). Am Phytopathol Soc.

GRASSHOPPERS

see Locusts

GRASSLAND ECOLOGY

African Pastureland Ecology. (Pasture & Fodder Crop Studies: No. 7). 203p. 1980. pap. 13.95 (ISBN 92-5-100873-6, F2099, FAO). Unipub.

Brodie, Juliet. Grassland Studies. (Practical Ecology Ser.). (Illus.). 88p. 1985. pap. text ed. 9.95x (ISBN 0-04-574020-8). Allen Unwin.

Coupland, R. T., ed. Grassland Ecosystems of the World. LC 77-83990. (International Biological Programme Ser.: No. 18). 1979. 89.50 (ISBN 0-521-21867-5). Cambridge U Pr.

De V. Booysen, P. & Tainton, N. M., eds. Ecological Effects of Fire in South African Ecosystems. (Ecological Studies: Analysis & Synthesis: Vol. 48). (Illus.). 440p. 1984. 33.50 (ISBN 0-387-13501-4). Springer-Verlag.

Estes, James R., et al. Grasses & Grasslands: Systematics & Ecology. LC 81-40294. (Illus.). 400p. 1982. 27.50x (ISBN 0-8061-1776-1); pap. 13.50x (ISBN 0-8061-1778-8). U of Okla Pr.

French, N. R., ed. Perspectives in Grassland Ecology: Results & Applications of the US-IBP Grassland Biome Study. LC 78-13971. (Ecological Studies: Vol. 32). (Illus.). 1979. 39.00x (ISBN 0-387-90384-4). Springer-Verlag.

Gutierrez, Luis T. & Fey, Willard R. Ecosystem Succession: A General Hypothesis & a Test Model of a Grassland. (Illus.). 1980. text ed. 35.00x (ISBN 0-262-07075-8). MIT Pr.

Heath, Maurice E., et al, eds. Forages: The Science of Grassland Agriculture. 4th ed. 644p. 1985. text ed. 34.95x (ISBN 0-8138-0680-1). Iowa St U Pr.

Huntley, B. J. & Walker, B. H., eds. Ecology of Tropical Savannas. (Ecological Studies: Vol. 42). (Illus.). 669p. 1982. 52.00 (ISBN 0-387-11885-3). Springer-Verlag.

Innis, G. S., ed. Grassland Simulation Model. LC 77-23016. (Ecological Studies: Vol. 26). (Illus.). 1978. 39.00 (ISBN 0-387-90269-4). Springer-Verlag.

Kowal, J. M. & Kassam, A. H. Agricultural Ecology of Savanna: A Study of West Africa. LC 77-30412. (Illus.). 1978. 60.00x (ISBN 0-19-859462-3). Oxford U Pr.

Malin, James C. History & Ecology: Studies of the Grassland. Swierenga, Robert P., ed. LC 83-16951. xxx, 376p. 1984. 28.50x (ISBN 0-8032-4144-5); pap. 13.95x (ISBN 0-8032-8125-0, BB 882, Bison). U of Nebr Pr.

Numata, Makoto, ed. Ecology of Grasslands & Bamboolands in the World. 1980. lib. bdg. 53.00 (ISBN 90-6193-601-2, Pub. by Junk Pubs Netherlands). Kluwer Academic.

Thompson, Paul W. Vegetation & Common Plants of Sleeping Bear. Fletcher, Margaret C., ed. LC 67-28209. (Bulletin Ser.: No. 52). (Illus.). 47p. (Orig.). 1984. pap. 3.50x (ISBN 0-87737-029-X). Cranbrook.

Van Dyne, G. M. Grasslands, Systems Analysis & Man. Breymeyer, A. I., ed. LC 77-28249. (International Biological Programme Ser.: No. 19). 1980. 165.00 (ISBN 0-521-21872-1). Cambridge U Pr.

Yadava, P. S. & Singh, J. S. Grassland Vegetation, Vol. 2. (Progress in Ecology Ser.: Vol. 2). (Illus.). 138p. 1977. 12.00 (ISBN 0-88065-211-X, Pub. by Messers Today & Tomorrows Printers & Publishers India). Scholarly Pubns.

GRASSLANDS

see also Pampas; Prairies; Steppes

Accumulation of Organic Matter Under Grassland & Its Effects on Grassland & on Arable Land. (Agricultural Research Reports: No. 806). 1973. pap. 4.00 (ISBN 90-220-0481-3, PDC192, PUDOC). Unipub.

Arnolds, Eef. Ecology & Coenology of Macrofungi in Grasslands & Moist Heathlands in Drenthe, the Netherlands: Pt. 1: Introduction & Synecology. (Bibliotheca Mycologica: Vol. 83). (Illus.). 410p. 1981. text ed. 48.00x (ISBN 3-7682-1314-5). Lubrecht & Cramer.

--Ecology & Coenology of Macrofungi in Grasslands & Moist Heathlands in Drenthe, the Netherlands. (Illus.). 510p. (Orig.). 1982. Pt. 3 Taxonomy. lib. bdg. 70.00 (ISBN 3-7682-1346-3). Lubrecht & Cramer.

Brown, Lauren. Grasslands. Elliott, Charles, ed. LC 84-48675. (The Audubon Society Nature Guides Ser.). (Illus.). 606p. 1985. pap. 14.95 (ISBN 0-394-73121-2). Knopf.

Crowder, L. V. & Chheda, H. R. Tropical Grassland Husbandry. Wrigley, G., ed. (Tropical Agriculture Ser.). (Illus.). 562p. 1983. text ed. 60.00x (ISBN 0-582-46677-6). Longman.

Curry-Lindahl, Kai. Wildlife of the Prairies & Plains. LC 80-27927. (Wildlife Habitat Ser.). (Illus.). 232p. 1981. 19.95 (ISBN 0-8109-1766-1). Abrams.

Hoogerkamp, M. Ley, Periodically Reseeded Grassland, or Permanent Grassland. (Agricultural Research Reports: No. 81). 35p. 1974. pap. 5.75 (ISBN 90-220-0500-3, PDC51, PUDOC). Unipub.

Krause, W., ed. Application of Vegetation Science to Grassland Husbandry. (Handbook of Vegetation Science: No. 13). (Illus.). 1977. lib. bdg. 79.00 (ISBN 90-6193-194-0, Pub. by Junk Pubs Netherlands). Kluwer Academic.

Management & the Use of Grasslands, Democratic Republic of the Congo. 152p. 1966. pap. 9.75 (ISBN 0-686-70623-4, F1918, FAO). Unipub.

Mannetje, L., ed. Measurement of Grassland Vegetation & Animal Production. 270p. 1978. 60.00x (ISBN 0-85198-404-5, Pub. by CAB Bks England). State Mutual Bk.

Parry, John & Butterworth, Bill. Grassland Mangement. 208p. 1981. 35.00x (ISBN 0-7198-2518-0, Pub. by Northwood Bks). State Mutual Bk.

Prins, W. H. & Arnold, G. H., eds. The Role of Nitrogen in Intensive Grassland Production: Proceedings of an International Symposium of the European Grassland Federation, Wageningen, 25-29 Aug. 1980. 171p. 1980. pap. 16.00 (ISBN 90-220-0734-0, PDC214, Pudoc). Unipub.

Smith, J. Allan & Hays, Virgil, eds. International Grassland Congress, Fourteenth: Proceedings. 1000p. 1982. lib. bdg. 42.00x (ISBN 0-86531-280-X). Westview.

Sprague, Howard B., ed. Grasslands of the United States: Their Economic & Ecological Importance. (Illus.). 220p. 1974. text ed. 10.50x (ISBN 0-8138-0745-X). Iowa St U Pr.

Whitehead, D. C. The Role of Nitrogen in Grassland Productivity: A Review of Information from Temperate Regions. 203p. 1970. 39.00x (ISBN 0-85198-015-5, Pub. by CAB Bks England). State Mutual Bk.

Yadava, P. S. & Singh, J. S. Grassland Vegetation, Vol. 2. (Progress in Ecology Ser.: Vol. 2). (Illus.). 138p. 1977. 12.00 (ISBN 0-88065-211-X, Pub. by Messers Today & Tomorrows Printers & Publishers India). Scholarly Pubns.

GRATES

see Fireplaces; Furnaces

GRAVIMETRIC ANALYSIS

see Chemistry, Analytic–Quantitative

GRAVITATION

Here are entered theoretical works on the phenomenon of gravitation. Works relating to measurement of the intensity and direction of the earth's force of attraction are entered under the heading Gravity.

see also Ether (Of Space); Mass (Physics); Matter; Potential, Theory of; Relativity (Physics); Weightlessness

Airy, George B. & Cohen, I. Bernard, eds. Gravitation. LC 80-2113. (Development of Science Ser.). (Illus.). 1981. lib. bdg. 20.00x (ISBN 0-405-13833-4). Ayer Co Pubs.

Benedikt, E. T., ed. Weightlessness: Physical Phenomena & Biological Effects. special vol ed. 1960. 20.00x (ISBN 0-87703-000-6, Pub. by Am Astronaut). Univelt Inc.

Bergmann, Peter G. Riddle of Gravitation. LC 68-11537. 1968. lib. bdg. 25.00 (ISBN 0-684-15378-5, ScribT). Scribner.

Bergmann, Peter G. & De Sabbath, Venzo, eds. Cosmology & Gravitation: Spin, Torsion, Rotation, & Supergravity. LC 80-23742. (NATO ASI Series B, Physics: Vol. 58). 519p. 1980. 75.00x (ISBN 0-306-40478-8, Plenum Pr). Plenum Pub.

Berry, M. Principles of Cosmology & Gravitation. LC 75-22559. (Illus.). 200p. 1976. 44.50 (ISBN 0-521-21061-5); pap. 14.95 (ISBN 0-521-29028-7). Cambridge U Pr.

Bertotti, B., ed. Experimental Gravitation. (Italian Physical Society: Course 56). 1974. 92.50 (ISBN 0-12-368856-6). Acad Pr.

Bettotti, B., et al, eds. General Relativity & Gravitation. 1984. lib. bdg. 69.00 (ISBN 90-277-1819-9, Pub. by Reidel Holland). Kluwer Academic.

Birrell, N. D. & Davies, P. C. Quantum Fields in Curved Space. LC 81-3851. (Cambridge Monographs on Mathematical Physics: No. 7). (Illus.). 340p. 1982. 57.50 (ISBN 0-521-23385-2). Cambridge U Pr.

Braginsky, V. B. & Manukin, A. B. Measurement of Weak Forces in Physics Experiments. Douglass, David H., ed. LC 76-22953. (Illus.). 1977. lib. bdg. 11.00x (ISBN 0-226-07070-0). U of Chicago Pr.

Breuer, R. A. Gravitational Perturbation Theory & Synchrotron Radiation. (Lecture Notes in Physics: Vol. 44). 210p. 1975. pap. 14.00 (ISBN 0-387-07530-5). Springer-Verlag.

Burt, R. O. & Mills, C. Gravity Concentration Technology. (Developments in Mineral Processing Ser.: No. 5). 606p. 1984. 120.50 (ISBN 0-444-42411-3). Elsevier.

Cohen, I. Bernard, ed. Gravitation, Heat & X-Rays. LC 80-2104. (Development of Science Ser.). (Illus.). 1981. lib. bdg. 35.00x (ISBN 0-405-13869-5). Ayer Co Pubs.

Constant, James. Gravitational Action. 114p. 1978. pap. 15.00 (ISBN 0-914330-16-0). RCS Assocs.

Dal Cin, Mario, et al, eds. Fundamental Interactions at High Energy Three: Tracts in Mathematics & Natural Sciences, 5 vols. Incl. Vol. 1. Nonpolynomial Lagrangians Renormalization & Gravity. Salam, Abdus. 156p. 41.75 (ISBN 0-677-12050-8); Vol. 2. Broken Scale Variance & the Light Cone. Gell-Mann, M. & Wilson, K. 158p. 45.25 (ISBN 0-677-12060-5); Vol. 3. Invited Papers. Hamermesh, M. 166p. 44.25 (ISBN 0-677-12070-2); Vol. 4. Troubles in the External Field Problem for Invariant Wave Equations. Wightman, A. S. 76p. 30.25 (ISBN 0-677-12080-X); Vol. 5. Multiperipheral Dynamics. Chew, G. 90p. 30.25 (ISBN 0-677-12090-7). LC 79-85472. (Illus.). 646p. 1971. Set. 169.75 (ISBN 0-677-12100-8). Gordon.

Dicke, Robert H. Gravitation & the Universe. LC 78-107344. (Memoirs Ser.: Vol. 78). (Illus.). 1970. 5.00 (ISBN 0-87169-078-0). Am Philos.

Ehlers, J., ed. Isolated Gravitating Systems in General Relativity. (Enrico Fermi Ser.: Vol. 67). 500p. 1979. 106.50 (ISBN 0-444-85329-4, North Holland). Elsevier.

Evans, D. J., ed. Sparsity & Its Applications. 352p. 1985. 39.50 (ISBN 0-521-26272-0). Cambridge U Pr.

Fock, V. A. The Theory of Space, Time & Gravitation. 2nd ed. 1964. 62.00 (ISBN 0-08-010061-9). Pergamon.

Fridman, A. M. & Polyachenko, V. I. Physics of Gravitating Systems: Vol. 1 - Equilibrium & Stability of Gravitating Systems. Aries, A. B. & Poliakoff, I. N., trs. from Rus. (Illus.). 480p. 1984. 84.00 (ISBN 0-387-11045-3). Springer Verlag.

Fridman, A. M. & Polyachenko, V. L. Physics of Gravitating Systems: Vol. 2 - The Nonlinear Theory of Collective Processes in a Gravitating Medium: Astrophysical Application. Aries, A. B. & Poliakoff, I. N., trs. from Rus. (Illus.). 385p. 1984. 60.00 (ISBN 0-387-13103-5). Springer Verlag.

Gravitation, Geometry & Relativistic. (Lecture Notes in Physics Ser.: Vol. 212). vi, 336p. 1984. pap. 19.00 (ISBN 0-387-13881-1). Springer-Verlag.

Harrigan, Gregory L. The Great Gravity Myth. rev. ed. LC 84-50399. 125p. 1986. 8.95 (ISBN 0-916403-03-3); pap. 5.95 (ISBN 0-916403-01-7). Shanty Pr.

--The Great Gravity Myth. 112p. (Orig.). 1983. pap. 5.95 (ISBN 0-916403-00-9). Shanty Pr.

Harrison, B. Kent, et al. Gravitation Theory & Gravitational Collapse. LC 65-17293. 1965. 11.00x (ISBN 0-226-31802-8). U of Chicago Pr.

Haynes, Kingsley E. & Fotheringham, A. Stewart. Gravity & Spatial Interaction Models. LC 84-50799. 88p. 1984. pap. 6.50 (ISBN 0-8039-2326-0). Sage.

Held, A., ed. General Relativity & Gravitation: One Hundred Years After the Birth of Albert Einstein, 2 vols. LC 79-27748. (Illus.). 1980. Set. 135.00x (ISBN 0-686-58609-3, Plenum); 75.00 ea. (ISBN 0-306-40265-3). Vol. 2, 558p (ISBN 0-306-40266-1). Plenum Pub.

Hoffer, K. Permanent Fasteners for Light-Weight Structures. (Illus.). 220p. pap. 51.00 (ISBN 0-9911001-4-X, Pub. by Aluminium W Germany). Heyden.

Hoyle, Fred & Narlikar, J. V. Action at a Distance in Physics & Cosmology. LC 74-4158. (Astronomy & Astrophysics Ser.). (Illus.). 266p. 1974. text ed. 38.95 (ISBN 0-7167-0346-7). W H Freeman.

Hu Ning, ed. General Relativity: Proceedings of the Third Marcel Grossman Meeting, 30 Aug-3 Sept. 1982, Shanghai, China, 2 vols. 1524p. 1985. Set. 150.00 (ISBN 0-444-86746-5, North Holland). Elsevier.

I.A.U. Symposium No. 64, Warsaw, Poland, 5-8 September 1973. Gravitational Radiation & Gravitational Collapse: Proceedings. DeWitt-Morette, Cecile, ed. LC 73-91436. (Symposium of the International Astronomical Union: No. 64). 226p. 1974. lib. bdg. 39.50 (ISBN 90-277-0435-X, Pub. by Reidel Holland); pap. 29.00 (ISBN 90-277-0436-8, Pub. by Reidel Holland). Kluwer Academic.

International Conference, 7th, Tel Aviv, June 23-28, 1974. General Relativity & Gravitation: Proceedings. Shaviv, G., ed. LC 75-33824. 1976. 69.95x (ISBN 0-470-77939-X). Halsted Pr.

Kramer, D., et al. Exact Solutions of Einstein's Field Equations. (Cambridge Monographs on Mathematical Physics). 400p. 1981. 85.00 (ISBN 0-521-23041-1). Cambridge U Pr.

Kuper, C. G. & Peres, A. Relativity & Gravitation. 336p. 1971. 93.75 (ISBN 0-677-14300-1). Gordon.

Larson, Dewey B. Beyond Newton. LC 63-22695. (Illus.). 1964. 5.00 (ISBN 0-913138-03-7). North Pacific.

Levy, M. & Deser, S., eds. Recent Developments in Gravitation: Cargese 1978. LC 79-9174. (NATO ASI Series B, Physics: Vol. 44). 604p. 1979. 89.50x (ISBN 0-306-40198-3, Plenum Pr). Plenum Pub.

Lightman, Alan P., et al. Problem Book in Relativity & Gravitation. 500p. 1975. 48.50 (ISBN 0-691-08160-3); pap. 17.50 (ISBN 0-691-08162-X). Princeton U Pr.

Logunov, A. A., ed. Gravitation & Elementary Particle Physics. Ilyushchenko, Valerii, tr. 294p. 1984. pap. 8.95 (Pub. by Mir Pubs USSR). Imported Pubns.

Maeterlinck, Maurice. Supreme Law. LC 75-86042. (Essay & General Literature Index Reprint Ser). 1969. Repr. of 1935 ed. 14.50x (ISBN 0-8046-0571-8, Pub. by Kennikat). Assoc Faculty Pr.

Marlow, A. R. Quantum Theory & Gravitation. LC 79-277837. 1980. 30.00 (ISBN 0-12-473260-7). Acad Pr.

Mehra, J. Einstein, Hilbert & the Theory of Gravitation. LC 73-91833. 1974. pap. 10.00 (ISBN 90-277-0440-6, Pub. by Reidel Holland). Kluwer Academic.

Milewski, B. Supersymmetry & Supergravity, 1983: Proceedings of the XIX Winter School & Workshop Theoretical Physics, Karpacz, Poland, February 14-26, 1983. 588p. 1983. 60.00x (ISBN 9971-950-23-5, Pub. by World Sci Singapore); pap. 33.00x (ISBN 9971-950-97-9, Pub. by World Sci Singapore). Taylor & Francis.

Misner, Charles W., et al. Gravitation. LC 78-156043. (Physics Ser.). (Illus.). 1279p. 1973. pap. text ed. 47.95x (ISBN 0-7167-0344-0). W H Freeman.

Moller, C. Evidence for Gravitational Theories. (Italian Physical Society: Course 20). 1963. 65.00 (ISBN 0-12-368820-5). Acad Pr.

Ohanian, Hans C. Gravitation & Space Time. new ed. (Illus.). 400p. 1976. text ed. 24.95x (ISBN 0-393-09198-8). Norton.

Posada, E. & Violini, G., eds. Workshop on the Search of Gravitational Waves: Proceedings of the Workshop Held in Bogota, Columbia, March 30-April 7, 1982. (ACIF Ser.: Vol. 2). vi, 238p. 1983. 25.00x (ISBN 9971-950-78-2, Pub. by World Sci Singapore). Taylor & Francis.

Prasanna, A. R., et al, eds. Gravitation & Relativistic Astrophysics: Proceedings of the Workshop held in Ahmedabad, India, Jan. 18-20, 1982. 160p. 1984. 28.00x (ISBN 9971-966-67-0, Pub. by World Sci Singapore). Taylor & Francis.

Ramsey, Arthur S. An Introduction to the Theory of Newtonian Attraction. LC 41-15935. pap. 48.50 (ISBN 0-317-08670-7, 2051354). Bks Demand UMI.

Schmutzer, E., ed. Ninth International Conference on General Relativity & Gravitation: Proceedings. LC 83-7366. 304p. 1984. 72.50 (ISBN 0-521-24669-5). Cambridge U Pr.

Schrodinger, Erwin. Space-Time Structure. (Illus.). 119p. Date not set. price not set (ISBN 0-521-31520-4). Cambridge U Pr.

Smarr, Larry. Sources of Gravitational Radiation. LC 79-50177. (Illus.). 1979. 37.50 (ISBN 0-521-22778-X). Cambridge U Pr.

Stephani, Hans. General Relativity. (Illus.). 312p. 1985. pap. 24.95 (ISBN 0-521-31534-4). Cambridge U Pr.

Wald, Robert M. Space, Time & Gravity: The Theory of the Big Bang & Black Holes. LC 77-4038. (Illus.). 1977. 10.95x (ISBN 0-226-87030-8); pap. 5.95 (ISBN 0-226-87031-6). U of Chicago Pr.

Weinberg, Steven. Gravitation & Cosmology; Principles & Applications of the General Theory of Relativity. LC 78-37175. 750p. 1972. 49.45x (ISBN 0-471-92567-5). Wiley.

West, B. J. On the Simpler Aspects of Nonlinear Fluctuating Deep Gravity Waves: Weaker Interaction Theory. (Lecture Notes in Physics Ser.: Vol. 146). 341p. 1981. pap. 20.00 (ISBN 0-387-10852-1). Springer Verlag.

Will, Clifford M. Theory & Experiment in Gravitational Physics. LC 80-39642. (Illus.). 272p. 1981. 82.50 (ISBN 0-521-23237-6). Cambridge U Pr.

--Theory & Experiment in Gravitational Physics. (Illus.). 384p. 1985. pap. 24.95 (ISBN 0-521-31710-X). Cambridge U Pr.

GRAVITY

Applewhite, James. Following Gravity. LC 80-21578. 1980. 9.95x (ISBN 0-8139-0885-X). U Pr of Va.

Bowin, Carl. Caribbean Gravity Field & Plate Tectonics. LC 76-16261. (Geological Society of America Special Papers: No. 169). pap. 33.80 (ISBN 0-317-29080-0, 2023738). Bks Demand UMI.

Caputo, Michele. Gravity Field of the Earth: Classical & Modern Methods. (International Geophysics Ser.: Vol. 10). 1967. 49.50 (ISBN 0-12-159050-X). Acad Pr.

Christensen, S. M. Quantum Theory of Gravity. 500p. 1984. 54.00 (ISBN 0-9960042-1-1, Pub. by A Hilger England). Heyden.

Cook, A. H. Gravity & the Earth. (The Wykeham Science Ser.: No. 6). 108p. 1969. pap. cancelled (ISBN 0-85109-070-2). Taylor & Francis.

Cook, A. H. & Saunders, V. T. Gravity & the Earth. (Wykeham Science Ser.: No. 6). 108p. 1969. 9.95x (ISBN 0-8448-1108-4). Crane Russak Co.

Davies, P. C. The Search for Gravity Waves. (Illus.). 160p. 1980. 15.95 (ISBN 0-521-23197-3). Cambridge U Pr.

Dehlinger, P. Marine Gravity. (Oceanography Ser.: Vol. 22). 322p. 1978. 83.00 (ISBN 0-444-41680-3). Elsevier.

Domokos, G. & Kovesi-Domokos, S., eds. Particles & Gravity: Proceedings of the Johns Hopkins Workshop on Current Problems in Particle Theory, June 8, 1984. 400p. 1984. 44.00x (ISBN 9971-966-78-6, Pub. by World Sci Singapore). Taylor & Francis.

Dow, T. W. Reshape Newton's Laws. LC 64-19218. 1965. 5.00 (ISBN 0-910340-03-X). Celestial Pr.

Farrar, Glennys & Henyey, Frank, eds. Problems in Unification & Supergravity: Conference Proceedings, La Jolla Institute, 1983. LC 84-71246. (AIP Conference Proceedings Ser.: No. 116). 185p. 1984. lib. bdg. 35.50 (ISBN 0-88318-315-3). Am Inst Physics.

Ferrara, S. & Taylor, J. G., eds. Supergravity Nineteen Eighty One. LC 82-1204. 512p. 1982. 47.50 (ISBN 0-521-24738-1). Cambridge U Pr.

Garland, G. D. Earth's Shape & Gravity. 1965. Pergamon.

Gordon, Solon A. & Cohen, Melvin J., eds. Gravity & the Organism. LC 70-156302. pap. 121.00 (ISBN 0-317-20702-4, 2024116). Bks Demand UMI.

Halpern, Leopold. On the Measurement of Cosmological Variations of the Gravitational Constant: Proceedings of the Workshop Meetings Held Nov. 12-14, 1975, at the Dept. of Physics, Florida State University, Tallahassee. LC 78-8350. (Monograph Publishing on Demand: Imprint Ser.). pap. 31.50 (ISBN 0-317-29818-6, 2016494). Bks Demand UMI.

McCally, Michael, et al, eds. Hypodynamics & Hypogravics: The Physiology of Inactivity & Weightlessness. LC 68-18675. (Illus.). 1968. 63.00 (ISBN 0-12-482050-6). Acad Pr.

Molodenskii, M. S., et al. Methods for Study of the External Gravitational Field & Figure of the Earth. LC 62-61244. pap. 63.50 (ISBN 0-317-07809-7, 2002332). Bks Demand UMI.

Napolitano, L. G. Microgravity Sciences & Processes. pap. 34.00 (ISBN 0-08-029985-7). Pergamon.

Narlikar, Jayant V. The Lighter Side of Gravity. LC 81-19496. (Illus.). 194p. 1982. 20.95 (ISBN 0-7167-1343-8); pap. text ed. 11.95 (ISBN 0-7167-1344-6). W H Freeman.

Nicolson, I. Gravity: Black Holes & the Universe. 264p. 1981. 31.95x (ISBN 0-470-27111-6). Halsted Pr.

Nilsen, Tor. Washington Gravity Base Station Network. 83p. 1976. 2.00 (ISBN 0-686-34729-3). Geologic Pubns.

Noakes, G. R., ed. Sources of Physics Teaching: Gravity. Liquids. Gases, Vol. 5. 1970. pap. text ed. 18.50x (ISBN 0-85066-040-8). Intl Ideas.

Pearse, M. J. Gravity Thickening Theories: A Review, 1977. 1981. 60.00x (ISBN 0-686-97084-5, Pub. by W Spring England). State Mutual Bk.

Pick, M., et al. Theory of the Earth's Gravity Field. 538p. 1973. 106.50 (ISBN 0-444-40939-4). Elsevier.

Ramberg, Hans. Gravity, Deformation & the Earth's Crust: In Theory, Experiments & Geological Application. 2nd ed. LC 80-41317. 1981. 55.00 (ISBN 0-12-576860-5). Acad Pr.

Smith, Tony E. Spatial Discounting & the Gravity Hypothesis. (Discussion Paper Ser.: No. 82). 1975. pap. 3.25 (ISBN 0-686-32248-7). Regional Sci Res Inst.

Tsuboi, Chuji. Gravity. (Illus.). 256p. 1983. text ed. 40.00x (ISBN 0-04-551072-5); pap. text ed. 19.95x (ISBN 0-04-551073-3). Allen Unwin.

Van Nieuwenhuizen, P. & Freedman, D. Z., eds. Supergravity. 342p. 1980. 68.00 (ISBN 0-444-85438-X, North-Holland). Elsevier.

Wess, Julius & Bagger, Jonathan. Supersummetry & Supergravity. (Princeton Series in Physics). 192p. 1983. 42.50 (ISBN 0-691-08327-4); pap. 12.50 (ISBN 0-691-08326-6). Princeton U Pr.

Wesson, Paul, ed. Gravity, Particles, & Astrophysics. (Astrophysics & Space Science Library Ser.: No. 79). 276p. 1980. lib. bdg. 34.00 (ISBN 90-277-1083-X, Pub. by Reidel). Kluwer Academic.

GRAVITY, SPECIFIC

see Specific Gravity

GRAVITY-FREE STATE, PHYSIOLOGICAL EFFECT OF

see Weightlessness

GRAY, ASA, 1810-1888

Gray, Asa. Letters of Asa Gray, 2 vols. Gray, Jane L., ed. LC 73-170952. 1973. Repr. of 1893 ed. Set. lib. bdg. 47.00 (ISBN 0-8337-1430-9). B Franklin.

GRAY SNAPPER

Starck, Walter A., 2nd & Schroeder, Robert E. Investigations on the Gray Snapper, Lutianus Grisevs. LC 70-125664. (Studies in Tropical Oceanography Ser: No. 10). 1971. 12.00x (ISBN 0-87024-181-8). U Miami Marine.

GRAZING

see also Forage Plants; Pastures; Stock-Ranges

Arnold, G. W. & Dudzinski, M. L. Ethology of Free Ranging Domestic Animals. (Developments in Animal & Veterinary Sciences Ser.: Vol. 2). 198p. 1979. 57.50 (ISBN 0-444-41700-1). Elsevier.

Christian, K. R., et al. Simulation of Grazing Systems. 121p. 1978. pap. 14.50 (ISBN 0-686-93181-5, PDC106, Pudoc). Unipub.

Foss, Phillip O. Politics & Grass: The Administration of Grazing on the Public Domain. LC 75-90508. (Illus.). ix, 236p. Repr. of 1960 ed. lib. bdg. 15.00x (ISBN 0-8371-2136-1, FOPG). Greenwood.

Meijs, J. A. Herbage Intake by Grazing Dairy Cows. (Agricultural Research Reports: No. 909). 280p. 1981. pap. 22.00 (ISBN 90-220-0764-2, PDC229, PUDOC). Unipub.

Morley, F. H. W., ed. Grazing Animals. (World Animal Science Ser.: Vol. 1B). 412p. 1981. 93.75 (ISBN 0-444-41835-0). Elsevier.

Voigt, William, Jr. Public Grazing Lands: Use & Misuse by Industry & Government. LC 75-42250. (Illus.). 365p. 1976. 35.00x (ISBN 0-8135-0819-3). Rutgers U Pr.

GREASE

see Lubrication and Lubricants; Oils and Fats

GREAT BARRIER REEF, AUSTRALIA

Cribb, A. B. & Cribb, J. W. Plant Life of the Great Barrier Reef & Adjacent Shores. LC 84-3704. (Illus.). 294p. 1985. text ed. 25.00x (ISBN 0-7022-1984-3). U of Queensland Pr.

Endean, Robert. Australia's Great Barrier Reef. LC 82-2063. (Illus.). 348p. 1983. text ed. 29.95x (ISBN 0-7022-1678-X). U of Queensland Pr.

Greenber, Fridaz. Great Barrier Reef Fishwatcher's Field Guide. (Illus.). 1984. plastic card 3.95x (ISBN 0-913008-15-X). Seahawk Pr.

Hopley, David. The Geomorphology of the Great Barrier Reef: Quaternary Development of Coral Reefs. LC 81-163336. 453p. 1982. 66.95x (ISBN 0-471-04562-4, Pub. by Wiley-Interscience). Wiley.

Stoddart, D. R. & Yonge, Maurice, eds. The Northern Great Barrier Reaf. (Proceedings of the Royal Society). (Illus.). 364p. 1979. text ed. 100.00x (ISBN 0-85403-102-2, Pub. by Royal Soc London). Scholium Intl.

GREAT CRESTED GREBE

Huxley, Julian. Courtship Habits of the Great Crested Grebe. LC 68-55824. (Cape Editions Ser). 1968. 6.95 (ISBN 0-670-24426-0, Grossman). Viking.

GREAT DANE DOGS

see Dogs–Breeds–Great Dane

GREAT PYRENEES (DOGS)

see Dogs–Breeds–Great Pyrenees

GREENHEAD

see Striped Bass

GREENHOUSES

see also Artificial Light Gardening; Forcing (Plants)

Alward, Ron & Shapiro, Andy. Low-Cost Passive Solar Greenhouses: A Design & Construction Guide. (Illus.). 176p. 1982. pap. 10.95 (ISBN 0-684-17503-7, ScribT). Scribner.

Batts, H. Lewis & Evans, Monica A., eds. Proceedings: Great Lakes Solar Greenhouse Conference IV. Kalamazoo, Michigan, Nov. 6-7, 1981. 177p. 1982. pap. 10.00 (ISBN 0-939294-05-2, SB-416-G7). Beech Leaf.

Boodley, James W. The Commercial Greenhouse. LC 78-74806. (Agriculture Ser.). 568p. 1981. 22.80 (ISBN 0-8273-1719-0); instr's. guide 3.60 (ISBN 0-8273-1718-2). Delmar.

Brann, Donald R. How to Build Greenhouses-Sun Houses. rev ed. LC 72-91056. (Illus.). 1976. lib. bdg. 5.95 (ISBN 0-87733-011-5); pap. 3.50 (ISBN 0-87733-611-3). Easi-Bild.

--How to Build Greenhouses-Walk-in, Window, Sun House, Garden Tool House. LC 80-67650. 210p. 1980. pap. 7.95 (ISBN 0-87733-811-6). Easi-Bild.

Clegg, Peter & Watkins, Derry. The Complete Greenhouse Book: Building & Using Greenhouses from Cold Frames to Solar Structures. LC 78-24572. (Illus.). 288p. 1978. pap. 10.95 (ISBN 0-88266-141-8). Garden Way Pub.

Downs, R. G. & Hellmers, H. Environment & the Experimental Control of Plant Growth. (Experimental Botany Ser.). 1975. 31.50 (ISBN 0-12-221450-1). Acad Pr.

Fletcher, J. T. Diseases of Greenhouse Plants. (Illus.). 1984. text ed. 39.95 (ISBN 0-582-44263-X). Longman.

Geery. Solar Greenhouses: Underground. (Illus.). 416p. 1982. o.p 19.95 (ISBN 0-8306-0069-8); pap. 12.95 (ISBN 0-8306-1272-6, 1272). TAB Bks.

Greenhouse Handbook for the Amateur. 2.25 (ISBN 0-686-21137-5). Bklyn Botanic.

Head, William D. Gardening Under Cover: A Northwest Guide to Solar Greenhouses, Coldframes & Cloches. Stewart, Kay, ed. LC 83-22383. (Illus.). 104p. 1984. pap. 9.95 (ISBN 0-9612716-0-4). Amity Found.

Hellyer, Arthur. Dobies Book of Greenhouses. (Illus.). 1981. pap. 12.50 (ISBN 0-434-32626-7, Pub. by W Heinemann Ltd). David & Charles.

Kozai, T. & Goudriaan, J. Light Transmission & Phitisynthesis in Greenhouses. 105p. 1978. pap. 13.25 (ISBN 0-686-93165-3, PDC104, Pudoc). Unipub.

Kramer, Jack. Your Homemade Greenhouse. 1980. pap. 5.95 (ISBN 0-346-12442-5). Cornerstone.

Langhans, Robert W. Greenhouse Management: A Guide to Structures, Environmental Control, Materials Handling, Crop Programming, & Business Analysis. 2nd ed. (Illus.). 270p. 1983. 19.50 (ISBN 0-9604006-1-3). Halcyon Ithaca.

Laurie, Alex, et al. Commercial Flower Forcing. 8th ed. (Illus.). 1979. text ed. 39.95x (ISBN 0-07-036633-0). McGraw.

Magee, Tim, et al. A Solar Greenhouse Guide for the Pacific Northwest. 2nd ed. Stewart, Annie & Sassaman, Richard, eds. (Illus.). 91p. 1979. pap. 6.00 (ISBN 0-934478-26-0). Ecotope.

Marier, Donald & Stoiaken, Larry. Alternative Sources of Energy: Solar Energy, No. 59, Jan-Feb. 83. 44p. (Orig.). 1983. pap. 3.50 (ISBN 0-917328-49-3). ASEI.

Mastalerz, John W. The Greenhouse Environment: The Effect of Environmental Factors on Flower Crops. LC 77-6793. 629p. 1977. 39.50x (ISBN 0-471-57606-9). Wiley.

Menage, Ronald H. The Practical Book of Greenhouse Gardening. 168p. 1983. 7.95 (ISBN 0-312-63461-7). St Martin.

Minar, William M. Greenhouse Gardening in the South. LC 76-1685. (Illus.). 96p. (Orig.). 1976. pap. 6.95x (ISBN 0-88415-327-4, Pub. by Pacesetter Pr). Gulf Pub.

Nearing, Scott & Nearing, Helen K. Building & Using Our Sun-Heated Greenhouse. (Illus.). 1979. pap. 8.00 (ISBN 0-88266-112-4). Soc Sci Inst.

Nelson, Kennard S. Flower & Plant Production in the Greenhouse. 3rd ed. LC 77-79741. (Illus.). 336p. 1978. 19.35 (ISBN 0-8134-1965-4); text ed. 14.50x. Interstate.

--Greenhouse Management for Flower & Plant Production. 2nd ed. 252p. 1980. 17.35 (ISBN 0-8134-2070-9, 2070); text ed. 13.00x. Interstate.

Nelson, Paul V. Greenhouse Operations & Management. 3rd ed. LC 84-22256. 1985. text ed. 27.95 (ISBN 0-8359-2583-8); instr's. manual avail. (ISBN 0-8359-2584-6). Reston.

Nicholls, Richard. The Handmade Greenhouse: From Windowsill to Backyard. LC 74-31541. (Illus.). 128p. (Orig.). 1975. lib. bdg. 12.90 (ISBN 0-914294-11-3); pap. 5.95 (ISBN 0-914294-12-1). Running Pr.

Northen, Henry T. & Northen, Rebecca T. Greenhouse Gardening. 2nd ed. LC 75-190208. (Illus.). Repr. of 1973 ed. 75.30 (ISBN 0-8357-9900-X, 2055118). Bks Demand UMI.

Ortho Books Editorial Staff, ed. How to Build & Use Greenhouses. LC 78-57889. (Illus.). 1979. pap. 5.95 (ISBN 0-917102-74-6). Ortho.

Pierce, John H. Greenhouse Grow How. (Illus.). 1982. 19.95 (ISBN 0-918730-01-5, ScribT). Scribner.

Selected Papers in Greenhouse & Nursery Engineering. 117p. 1984. 30.00 (ISBN 0-317-06801-6). Am Soc Ag Eng.

Selected Papers in Greenhouse & Nursery Mechanization Concepts. 112p. 1984. 27.00 (ISBN 0-317-06802-4). Am Soc Ag Eng.

Shapiro, Andrew M. The Homeowner's Complete Handbook for Add-On Solar Greenhouses & Sunspaces. 1985. 19.95 (ISBN 0-87857-507-3); pap. 13.95 (ISBN 0-87857-508-1). Rodale Pr Inc.

Sherrill Britz, Billie. The Greenhouse at Lyndhurst: Construction & Development of the Gould Greenhouse, 1881. LC 76-50813. (Illus.). 50p. (Orig.). 1977. pap. 5.00 (ISBN 0-89133-046-1). Preservation Pr.

Shumack, Ronald L. & Williams, George S. Greenhouse Flowers & Bedding Plants for Agribusiness Studies. 2nd ed. xiv, 282p. 1983. text ed. 13.00 (ISBN 0-8134-2262-0, 2262); pap. text ed. 9.75. Interstate.

Smith, Shane. The Bountiful Solar Greenhouse: A Guide to Year-Round Food Production. (Illus.). 224p. (Orig.). 1982. pap. 8.00 (ISBN 0-912528-08-7). John Muir.

Steinbrunner. Greenhouses: From Design to Harvest. (Illus.). 304p. 1982. 19.95 (ISBN 0-8306-0056-6); pap. 11.95 (ISBN 0-8306-1307-2, 1307). TAB Bks.

Virhammar, Kjell. Plastic Greenhouses for Warm Climates. (Agricultural Services Bulletins: No. 48). 52p. 1982. pap. 7.50 (ISBN 92-5-101168-0, F2302, FAO). Unipub.

Walls, Ian. Making the Most of Your Greenhouse. LC 77-90053. (Illus.). 1978. pap. 3.95 (ISBN 0-8120-0869-3). Barron.

Willmott, P. K. Scientific Greenhouse Gardening. 200p. 1982. 40.00x (ISBN 0-7158-0663-7, Pub. by EP Pub England). State Mutual Bk.

Yanda, Bill & Fisher, Rick. The Food & Heat Producing Solar Greenhouse. rev. ed. LC 79-91276. (Illus.). 208p. (Orig.). 1980. pap. 8.00 (ISBN 0-912528-20-6). John Muir.

Yanda, W. F. & Yanda, Susan. An Attached Solar Greenhouse. (Sp. & Eng.). 1976. pap. 2.00 (ISBN 0-89016-028-7). Lightning Tree.

BOOKS - SUBJECT INDEX

GROUPS, THEORY OF

GREEN'S FUNCTIONS
Doniach, S. & Sondheimer, E. G. Green's Functions for Solid State Physicists. LC 73-13723. (Frontiers in Physics Ser.: No. 44). (Illus.). 304p. 1974. pap. text ed. 30.95 (ISBN 0-8053-2397-X). Benjamin-Cummings.
Rickayzen, G. Green's Functions & Condensed Matter. 1981. 55.00 (ISBN 0-12-587950-4). Acad Pr.
Rickayzen, Gerald. Greens Function & Condensed Matter. 1984. pap. 29.50 (ISBN 0-12-587952-0). Acad Pr.
Stakgold, Ivar. Green's Functions & Boundary Value Problems. LC 78-27259. (Pure & Applied Mathematics Ser.). 638p. 1979. 53.50 (ISBN 0-471-81967-0, Pub. by Wiley-Interscience). Wiley.
GREGARINIDA
Kamm, Minnie E. Studies on Gregarines. 1916. 22.00 (ISBN 0-384-28550-3). Johnson Repr.
--Studies on Gregarines 2: Synopsis of the Polycystid Gregarines of the World, Excluding Those from the Myriapoda, Orthoptera and Coleoptera. (Illinois Biological Monographs: Vol. 7, No. 1). 1922. 8.00 (ISBN 0-384-28560-0). Johnson Repr.
GREYHOUNDS
see Dogs–Breeds–Greyhounds
GRIDWORK (STRUCTURAL ENGINEERING)
see Grillages (Structural Engineering)
GRILLAGES (STRUCTURAL ENGINEERING)
Ghia, K. & Ghia, U., eds. Advances in Grid Generation. (FED Ser.: Vol. 5). 219p. 1983. pap. text ed. 40.00 (ISBN 0-317-02550-3, G00222). ASME.
Thompson, J. F., et al. Numerical Grid Generation: Foundations & Applications. 504p. 1985. pap. text ed. 34.95 (ISBN 0-444-00985-X, North Holland). Elsevier.
GRINDING AND POLISHING
see also Metals–Finishing; Sharpening of Tools
Allen, J., et al, eds. Grinding, Vol. 1. (Engineering Craftsmen: No. H5). 1968. spiral bdg. 38.50x (ISBN 0-85083-013-3). Trans-Atlantic.
Barlow, D. W., et al, eds. Grinding, Vol. 2. (Engineering Craftsmen: No. H.31). 1972. spiral bdg. 49.95x (ISBN 0-85083-380-9). Trans-Atlantic.
Beke, B. The Process of Fine Grinding. 1981. 29.50 (ISBN 90-247-2462-7, Pub. by Martinus Nijhoff Netherlands). Kluwer Academic.
Bellows, Guy. Low Stress Grinding. (Machining Process Ser.: MDC 83-103). (Illus.). 136p. 1983. pap. 17.50 (ISBN 0-936974-09-5). Metcut Res Assocs.
Bhateja, Chander & Lindsay, Richard, eds. Grinding: Theory, Techniques & Trouble Shooting. LC 81-84502. (Manufacturing Update Ser.). (Illus.). 230p. 1982. 32.00 (ISBN 0-87263-077-3). SME.
Burkar, W. & Schmortz, K. Grinding & Polishing. 345p. 1981. 100.00x (ISBN 0-86108-079-3, Pub. by Portcullio Pr). State Mutual Bk.
Coes, L. Abrasives. LC 78-153451. (Applied Minerology: Vol. 1). (Illus.). 1971. 31.00 (ISBN 0-387-80968-6). Springer-Verlag.
Drozda, Tom, ed. Manufacturing Engineering Reviews Grinding. LC 82-50273. 208p. 1982. text ed. 18.50 (ISBN 0-87263-082-X). SME.
Farago, Francis T. Abrasive Methods Engineering, Vol. 1. LC 76-14970. (Illus.). 366p. 1976. 45.00 (ISBN 0-8311-1112-7). Indus Pr.
Grinding. 1983. enlarged ed. 50.00x (ISBN 0-85083-160-1, Pub. by Engineering Ind). State Mutual BK.
Grinding One. 50.00x (ISBN 0-85083-013-3, Pub. by Engineering Ind). State Mutual Bk.
Kibbe, Richard R. Grinding Machine Operations. LC 84-11815. 294p. 1985. spiral 17.95 (ISBN 0-471-89021-9). Wiley.
Krar, S. F. & Oswald, J. W. Grinding Technology. LC 72-7935. 1974. pap. text ed. 14.80 (ISBN 0-8273-0208-8). Delmar.
Malaghan, Subhas G. Ultrafine Grinding & Separation of Industrial Minerals. LC 83-82078. 177p. 1983. pap. 32.00x (ISBN 0-89520-419-3, 419-3). Soc Mining Eng.
Pinkstone, William G. The Abrasive Ages. LC 74-23797. (Illus.). 136p. 1975. 10.00 (ISBN 0-915010-01-1). Sutter House.
Springborn, R. K., ed. Cutting & Grinding Fluids: Selection & Application. LC 67-17077. (Manufacturing Data Ser). 1967. pap. 8.75 (ISBN 0-87263-001-3). SME.
Turner, Susan. Wheels & Grindstones. LC 80-53022. 1980. pap. 4.95 (ISBN 0-87397-180-9). Strode.
GRIST-MILLS
see Flour Mills
GRIZZLY BEAR
Brown, David E. The Grizzly in the Southwest: Documentary of an Extinction. LC 80-40684. (Illus.). 280p. 1985. 19.95 (ISBN 0-8061-1930-6). U of Okla Pr.
Haynes, Bessie D. & Haynes, Edgar. The Grizzly Bear: Portraits from Life. (Illus.). 396p. 1979. pap. 9.95 (ISBN 0-8061-1481-9). U of Okla Pr.
Wright, William H. The Grizzly Bear: The Narrative of a Hunter-Naturalist. LC 77-1772. (Illus.). xii, 290p. 1977. 21.50x (ISBN 0-8032-0927-4); pap. 5.95 (ISBN 0-8032-5865-8, BB 646, Bison). U of Nebr Pr.
Young, Ralph W. Grizzlies Don't Come Easy. (Illus.). 200p. 1981. 15.95 (ISBN 0-8329-3494-1, Pub. by Winchester Pr). New Century.
GROSSULIARIA
Hutchinson, G. E. Some Continental European Aberrations of Abraxas Grossulariata Linn, Lepidoptera: With a Note on the Theoretical Significance of the Variation Observed in the Species. (Connecticut Academy of Arts & Sciences - Transaction: Vol. 43). (Illus.). 1969. pap. 9.50 (ISBN 0-208-00832-2). Shoe String.
GROUND-EFFECT MACHINES
see also Helicopters; Vertically Rising Aircraft
Symposium on Air Cushion Handling. Proceedings. 1974. pap. 32.00x (ISBN 0-900983-34-5, Dist. by Air Science Co.). BHRA Fluid.
GROUND HOGS
see Marmots
GROUND NUTS
see Peanuts
GROUND PROXIMITY MACHINES
see Ground-Effect Machines
GROUND SQUIRRELS
Murie, Jan O. & Michener, Gail R., eds. The Biology of Ground-Dwelling Squirrels: Annual Cycles, Behavioral Ecology, & Sociality. LC 83-26035. xvi, 459p. 1984. 25.95x (ISBN 0-8032-3090-7). U of Nebr Pr.
GROUND SUPPORT SYSTEMS (ASTRONAUTICS)
American Society of Civil Engineers, Aero-Space Transport Division Staff. Space Age Facilities: Papers, Specialty Conference, Cocoa Beach, Fl., November 17-19, 1965. LC 68-23. pap. 99.50 (ISBN 0-317-10983-9, 2004908). BKs Demand UMI.
Geddes, James D. Ground Movements & Structures. 964p. 1981. 85.95x (ISBN 0-470-27208-2). Halsted Pr.
Irvine, Jerry. Ground Support Equipment. (Ace Information Report Ser.: No. 7). 1984. 2.50 (ISBN 0-912468-05-X). CA Rocketry.
Space Age Facilities Conference. Space Age Facilities Conference: Second Aero Space Transport Division Specialty Conference, April 24-26, 1968, Los Angeles, California. LC 74-15643. pap. 115.30 (ISBN 0-317-10926-X, 2007869). Bks Demand UMI.
GROUND TEMPERATURE
see Earth Temperature
GROUND WATER
see Water, Underground
GROUP REPRESENTATION (MATHEMATICS)
see Representations of Groups
GROUPS
see Discrete Groups
GROUPS, CONTINUOUS
see also Differential Forms; Differential Invariants; Ergodic Theory; Fiber Bundles (Mathematics); Topological Groups; Transformations, Infinitesimal
Campbell, John R. Introductory Treatise on Lie's Theory. LC 65-28441. 16.95 (ISBN 0-8284-0183-7). Chelsea Pub.
Dieudonne, Jean & Hua, L. K. On the Automorphisms of the Classical Groups. LC 52-42839. (Memoirs: No. 2). 123p. 1980. pap. 13.00 (ISBN 0-8218-1202-5, MEMO-2). Am Math.
Ferraro, John R. & Ziomek, Joseph S. Introductory Group Theory & Its Applications to Molecular Structure. 2nd ed. LC 75-33752. 292p. 1975. 35.00x (ISBN 0-306-30768-5, Plenum Pr). Plenum Pub.
Loewner, Charles, et al. Charles Loewner: Theory of Continuous Groups. (Mathematicians of Our Time Ser). 1971. 30.00x (ISBN 0-262-06041-8). MIT Pr.
Palais, Richard S. Global Formulation of the Lie Theory of Transformation Groups. LC 52-42839. (Memoirs: No. 22). 123p. 1971. pap. 10.00 (ISBN 0-8218-1222-X, MEMO-22). Am Math.
Sehgal, Sudarshan K. Topics in Group Rings, Vol. 50. (Pure & Applied Mathematics Ser.). (Illus.). 264p. 1978. 45.00 (ISBN 0-8247-6755-1). Dekker.
Tondeur, Philippe. Introduction to Lie Groups & Transformation Groups. 2nd ed. LC 78-99012. (Lecture Notes in Mathematics: Vol. 7). 1969. pap. 10.70 (ISBN 0-387-04599-6). Springer-Verlag.
Von Neumann, John. Continuous Geometry. (Mathematical Ser.: Vol. 25). 1960. 33.00x (ISBN 0-691-07928-5). Princeton U Pr.
Weyl, Hermann. Classical Groups, Their Invariants & Representations. rev ed. (Mathematical Ser.: Vol. 1). 1946. 35.00x (ISBN 0-691-07923-4). Princeton U Pr.
GROUPS, LIE
see Lie Groups
GROUPS, REPRESENTATION THEORY OF
see Representations of Groups
GROUPS, THEORY OF
see also Abelian Groups; Algebra, Boolean; Categories (Mathematics); Crystallography, Mathematical; Finite Groups; Fourier Transformations; Functions, Modular; Galois Theory; Games of Strategy (Mathematics); Lattice Theory; Matrix Groups; Representations of Groups; Semigroups; Transformation Groups; Transformations (Mathematics)
Adian, S. I. The Burnside Problem & Identities in Groups. Lennox, J. & Wiegold, J., trs. from Russian. (Ergebnisse der Mathematik und Ihrer Grenzgebiete: Vol. 95). 1979. 46.00 (ISBN 0-387-08728-1). Springer-Verlag.
American Mathematical Society Special Session, San Francisco, Jan, 1974. A Crash Course on Kleinian Groups: Proceedings. Bers, L. & Kra, I., eds. (Lecture Notes in Mathematics Ser.: Vol. 400). vii, 130p. 1974. pap. 13.00 (ISBN 0-387-06840-6). Springer-Verlag.
Andrianov, A. N., et al. Thirteen Papers on Group Theory, Algebraic Geometry & Algebraic Topology. LC 51-5559. (Translations Ser.: No. 2, Vol. 66). 1968. 35.00 (ISBN 0-8218-1766-3, TRANS 2-66). Am Math.
Arad, Z. & Herzog, M., eds. Products of Conjugacy Classes in Groups. (Lecture Notes in Mathematics: Vol. 1112). v, 244p. 1985. pap. 14.40 (ISBN 0-387-13916-8). Springer-Verlag.
Araki, et al, eds. Group Theoretical Methods in Physics: Proceedings, Istanbul, Turkey, 1982. (Lecture Notes in Physics: Vol. 180). 569p. 1983. pap. 32.00 (ISBN 0-387-12291-5). Springer-Verlag.
Arbib, Michael A. Algebraic Theory of Machines, Languages & Semigroups. LC 68-18654. 1968. 76.00 (ISBN 0-12-059050-6). Acad Pr.
Arkowitz, M. & Curjel, C. R. Groups of Homotopy Classes: Rank Formualas & Homotopy - Commutativity. 2nd ed. (Lecture Notes in Mathematics: Vol. 4). (Orig.). 1967. pap. 10.70 (ISBN 0-387-03900-7). Springer-Verlag.
Aschbacher, Michael. The Finite Simple Groups & Their Classifications. LC 79-20927. (Yale Mathematical Monograph: No. 7). (Orig.). 1980. pap. text ed. 8.95x (ISBN 0-300-02449-5). Yale U Pr.
Aschbacher, Michael, et al, eds. Future Directions in Finite Group Theory. 400p. 1984. 39.50 (ISBN 0-521-26493-6). Cambridge U Pr.
Atkinson, Michael, ed. Computational Group Therapy. 1984. 60.00 (ISBN 0-12-066270-1). Acad Pr.
Bacry, Henri. Lecons Sur la Theorie des Groupes & les Symetries des Particules Elementaires. (Cours & Documents de Mathematiques & de Physique Ser.). 466p. (Orig.). 1967. 94.95 (ISBN 0-677-50190-0). Gordon.
--Lectures on Group Theory & Particle Theory. LC 72-78879. (Documents on Modern Physics Ser.). (Illus.). 598p. 1977. 132.95 (ISBN 0-677-30190-1). Gordon.
Bargmann, V., ed. Group Representations in Mathematics & Physics: Battelle Seattle 1969 Rencontres. LC 75-146233. (Lecture Notes in Physics: Vol. 6). 1970. pap. 18.30 (ISBN 0-387-05310-7). Springer-Verlag.
Baumslag, Gilbert. Lecture Notes on Nilpotent Groups. LC 78-145636. (CBMS Regional Conference Series in Mathematics: No. 2). 73p. 1971. 10.00 (ISBN 0-8218-1651-9, CBMS-2). Am Math.
Beaumont, Ross A. & Pierce, Richard S. Torsion Free Groups of Rank Two. LC 52-42839. (Memoirs: No. 38). 44p. 1968. pap. 9.00 (ISBN 0-8218-1238-6, MEMO-38). Am Math.
Beiglboeck, W., et al, eds. Group Theoretical Methods in Physics, Vol. 94. (Lecture Notes in Physics Ser.). 1979. pap. 28.00 (ISBN 0-387-09238-2). Springer-Verlag.
Berman, S. D., et al. Nine Papers on Logic & Group Theory. LC 51-5559. (Translations Ser.: No. 2, Vol. 64). 1967. 34.00 (ISBN 0-8218-1764-7, TRANS 2-64). Am Math.
Beyl, F. R. & Tappe, J. Group Extensions, Representations, & the Schur Multiplicator. (Lecture Notes in Mathematics: Vol. 958). 278p. 1982. pap. 16.00 (ISBN 0-387-11954-X). Springer-Verlag.
Bhagavantam, S. & Venkatarayudu, T. Theory of Groups & Its Application to Physical Problems. 1969. 32.00 (ISBN 0-12-095460-5). Acad Pr.
Birkhoff, Garrett. Hydrodynamics: A Study in Logic, Fact, & Similitude. LC 77-18143. (Illus.). 1978. Repr. of 1960 ed. lib. bdg. 24.75x (ISBN 0-313-20118-8, BIHY). Greenwood.
Bishop, David M. Group Theory & Chemistry. (Illus.). 1973. 49.00x (ISBN 0-19-855140-1). Oxford U Pr.
Boruvka, O. Foundations of the Theory of Groupoids & Groups. 216p. 1975. 39.95x (ISBN 0-8176-0780-3). Birkhauser.
Bruck, R. H. Survey of Binary Systems. 3rd ed. LC 79-143906. (Ergebnisse der Mathematik und Ihrer Grenzebiete: Vol. 20). 1971. 22.00 (ISBN 0-387-03497-8). Springer-Verlag.
Bryce, R. A., et al. Group Theory. (Lectures Notes in Mathematics: Vol. 573). 1977. pap. 13.00 (ISBN 0-387-08131-3). Springer-Verlag.
Burns, Gerald. Introduction to Group Theory with Applications. (Material Science & Technology Ser.). 1977. 29.00 (ISBN 0-12-145750-8). Acad Pr.
Butzer, P. L. & Berens, H. Semi-Groups of Operators & Approximation. LC 68-11980. (Grundlehren der Mathematischen Wissenschaften: Vol. 145). 1967. 39.00 (ISBN 0-387-03832-9). Springer-Verlag.
Camina, A. R. & Whelan, E. A. Linear Groups & Permutations. (Research Notes in Mathematics Ser.: No. 118). 168p. 1985. pap. text ed. 15.95 (ISBN 0-273-08672-3). Pitman Pub Ma.
Campbell, C. M. & Robertson, E. F., eds. Groups: St. Andrew's 1981. LC 82-4427. (London Mathematical Society Lecture Note Ser.: No. 71). 360p. 1982. pap. 39.50 (ISBN 0-521-28974-2). Cambridge U Pr.
Carmeli, Moshe. Group Theory & General Relativity. (Pure & Applied Physics Ser.). (Illus.). 1977. text ed. 56.95x (ISBN 0-07-009986-3). McGraw.
Carrell, J. B., ed. Group Actions & Vector Fields: Vancouver, Canada, 1981, Proceedings. (Lecture Notes in Mathematics: Vol. 956). 144p. 1982. pap. 10.00 (ISBN 0-387-11946-9). Springer-Verlag.
Carrell, James B., et al. Topics in the Theory of Algebraic Groups. LC 82-17329. (Notre Dame Mathematical Lectures Ser.: No. 10a). 192p. (Orig.). 1982. pap. text ed. 9.95x (ISBN 0-268-01843-X, 85-18433). U of Notre Dame Pr.
Cernikov, S. N., et al. Fourteen Papers on Groups & Semigroups. LC 51-5559. (Translations Ser.: No. 2, Vol. 36). 1964. 32.00 (ISBN 0-8218-1736-1, TRANS 2-36). Am Math.
Clifford, A. H. & Preston, G. B. Algebraic Theory of Semigroups, 2 Vols. LC 61-15686. (Mathematical Surveys Ser.: Vol. 7). 1977. Repr. of 1961 ed. Vol. 1, 224p. with corrections 27.00 (ISBN 0-8218-0271-2, SURV-7-1); Vol. 2, 352p. with corrections 35.00 (ISBN 0-8218-0272-0, SURV-7.2). Am Math.
Conference in Orders, Group Rings & Related Topics. Proceedings. Hsia, J. S., et al, eds. (Lecture Notes in Mathematics: Vol. 353). 224p. 1973. pap. 16.00 (ISBN 0-387-06518-0). Springer-Verlag.
Conference on Group Theory, University of Wisconsin-Parkside, 1972. Proceedings. Gatterdam, R. W. & Weston, K. W., eds. LC 73-76679. (Lecture Notes in Mathematics: Vol. 319). v, 188p. 1973. pap. 13.00 (ISBN 0-387-06205-X). Springer-Verlag.
Conference, 5th, Oberwolfach, Germany, Jan. 29 - Feb. 4, 1978. Probability Measures on Groups: Proceedings. Heyer, H., ed. (Lecture Notes in Mathematics: Vol. 706). 1979. pap. 22.00 (ISBN 0-387-09124-6). Springer-Verlag.
Cornwell, John F. Group Therapy in Physics, Vol. 1. (Techniques of Physics Ser.). 1984. 75.00 (ISBN 0-12-189801-6). Acad Pr.
Cotton, F. Albert. Chemical Applications of Group Theory. 2nd ed. LC 76-129657. 386p. 1971. 38.50x (ISBN 0-471-17570-6, Pub. by Wiley-Interscience). Wiley.
Coxeter, H. S. & Moser, W. O. Generators & Relations for Discrete Groups. 3rd rev. ed. LC 72-79063. (Ergebnisse der Mathematik und Ihrer Grenzgebiete: Vol. 14). (Illus.). ix, 169p. 1980. 39.00 (ISBN 0-387-09212-9). Springer-Verlag.
Demazure, M. & Gabriel, P. Introduction to Algebraic Geometry & Algebraic Groups. (Mathematics Studies: Vol. 39). 358p. 1980. 44.75 (ISBN 0-444-85443-6, North-Holland). Elsevier.
DeWitt, Bryce S. Dynamical Theory of Groups & Fields. (Documents on Modern Physics Ser.). 258p. 1965. pap. 69.50 (ISBN 0-677-00985-2). Gordon.
Dieudonne, Jean & Hua, L. K. On the Automorphisms of the Classical Groups. LC 52-42839. (Memoirs: No. 2). 123p. 1980. pap. 13.00 (ISBN 0-8218-1202-5, MEMO-2). Am Math.
Dixon, John D. Problems in Group Theory. LC 72-76597. 1973. pap. 4.00 (ISBN 0-486-61574-X). Dover.
Dunkl, Charles F. & Ramirez, Donald E. Topics in Harmonic Analysis. LC 73-153387. (Century Mathematics Ser.). 1971. 34.50x (ISBN 0-89197-454-7); pap. text ed. 16.95x (ISBN 0-89197-969-7). Irvington.
Dynkin, E. B., et al. Five Papers on Algebra & Group Theory. LC 51-5559. (Translations Ser.: No. 2, Vol. 6). 1957. 55.00 (ISBN 0-8218-1706-X, TRANS 2-6). Am Math.

Edwards, R. E., ed. Integration & Harmonic Analysis on Compact Groups. LC 77-190412. (London Mathematical Society Lecture Notes Ser.: No. 8). 228p. 1972. 24.95 (ISBN 0-521-09717-7). Cambridge U Pr.

Evanston Conference, Oct. 11-15, 1975. Brauer Groups: Proceedings. Zelinsky, D., ed. (Lecture Notes in Mathematics: Vol. 549). 1976. soft cover 13.00 (ISBN 0-387-07989-0). Springer-Verlag.

Figa-Talamanca & Picardello. Harmonic Analysis on Free Groups. (Lecture Notes in Pure & Applied Mathematics). 224p. 1983. 35.00 (ISBN 0-8247-7042-0). Dekker.

Flato, Moshe, et al, eds. Applications of Group Theory in Physics & Math. Incl. Large-Scale Computations in Fluid Mechanics. Osher, Stanley, ed. (Lectures in Applied Mathematics: Vol. 21). 1984. write for info. Am Math.

Fossum, R. M. The Divisor Class Group of a Krull Domain. LC 72-918901. (Ergebnisse der Mathematik und Ihrer Grenzgebiete: Vol. 74). (Illus.). 148p. 1973. 31.00 (ISBN 0-387-06044-8). Springer-Verlag.

Fulkerson, D. R., ed. Studies in Graph Theory: Part II. LC 75-24987. (MAA Studies: No. 12). 212p. 1976. 16.50 (ISBN 0-88385-112-1). Math Assn.

Gallo, D. M. & Porter, R. M., eds. Kleinian Groups & Related Topics: Proceedings, Oaxtepec, Mexico, 1981. (Lecture Notes in Mathematics: Vol. 971). 117p. 1983. pap. 11.00 (ISBN 0-387-11975-2). Springer-Verlag.

Gel'fand, I. M., et al. Eight Papers on Group Theory. LC 51-5559. (Translations, Ser.: No. 2, Vol. 2). 1956. 27.00 (ISBN 0-8218-1702-7, TRANS 2-2). Am Math.

Gerardin, P. Construction de Series Discretes p-Adiques. LC 75-16187. (Lecture Notes in Mathematics: Vol. 462). 180p. 1975. pap. 10.70 (ISBN 0-387-07172-5). Springer-Verlag.

Gersten, S. M. Topology of the Automorphism: Group of a Free Group. (London Mathematical Society Lecture Note Ser.: No. 102). 200p. Date not set. pap. price not set. (ISBN 0-521-31523-9). Cambridge U Pr.

Golubitsky, M. & Schaeffer, D. Bifurcations & Groups in Bifurcation Theory I. (Applied Mathematical Sciences Ser.: Vol. 51). (Illus.). 320p. 1985. 38.00 (ISBN 0-387-90999-0). Springer-Verlag.

Goodman, R. W. Nilpotent Lie Groups: Structure & Applications to Analysis. (Lecture Notes on Mathematics Ser.: Vol. 562). 1976. soft cover 17.00 (ISBN 0-387-08055-4). Springer-Verlag.

Grothendieck, A. & Murre, J. P. Tame Fundamental Group of a Formal Neighbourhood of a Divisor with Normal Crossing on a Scheme. (Lecture Notes in Mathematics: Vol. 208). 1971. pap. 11.00 (ISBN 0-387-05499-5). Springer-Verlag.

Gruenberg, Karl W. Cohomological Topics in Group Theory. LC 70-127042. (Lecture Notes in Mathematics: Vol. 143). 1970. pap. 14.70 (ISBN 0-387-04932-0). Springer-Verlag.

Gruenberg, Karl W. & Roseblade, James E., eds. Group Theory: Essays for Phillip Hall. 1985. 65.00 (ISBN 0-12-304880-X). Acad Pr.

Guillemin, V. W. & Sternberg, Shlomo. Deformation Theory of Pseudogroup Structures. LC 52-42839. (Memoirs Ser.: No. 64). 80p. 1966. pap. 9.00 (ISBN 0-8218-1264-5, MEMO-64). Am Math.

Hall, George G. Applied Group Theory. LC 67-73110. (Mathematical Physics Ser.). pap. 34.00 (ISBN 0-317-08613-8, 2004946). Bks Demand UMI.

Hall, Lowell H. Group Theory & Symmetry in Chemistry. LC 69-13607. pap. 96.00 (ISBN 0-317-08736-3, 2004355). Bks Demand UMI.

Hall, Marshall, Jr. The Theory of Groups. 2nd ed. LC 75-42306. xiii, 434p. text ed. 14.95 (ISBN 0-8284-0288-4). Chelsea Pub.

Hamermesh, Morton. Group Theory & Its Application to Physical Problems. (Illus.). 1962. 36.95 (ISBN 0-201-02780-1). Addison-Wesley.

Heine, V. Group Theory in Quantum Mechanics. 1963. 35.00 (ISBN 0-08-009242-X). Pergamon.

Hermann, Robert. Lie Groups for Physicists. (Mathematical Physics Monographs: No. 5). 1966. pap. 27.95 (ISBN 0-8053-3951-5). Benjamin-Cummings.

Hewitt, E. & Ross, K. A. Abstract Harmonic Analysis: Vol. 2, Structure & Analysis for Compact Groups, Analysis on Locally Compact Abelian Groups. LC 63-12898. (Grundlehren der Mathematischen Wissenschaften: Vol. 152). 1970. 79.00 (ISBN 0-387-04832-4). Springer-Verlag.

Hill, Victor E. Groups, Representations & Characters. LC 75-43362. 1976. text ed. 16.95x (ISBN 0-02-846790-6). Hafner.

Hilton, P. J., ed. Localization in Group Theory & Homotopy Theory & Related Topics. (Lecture Notes in Mathematics: Vol. 418). 185p. 1974. pap. 14.00 (ISBN 0-387-06963-1). Springer-Verlag.

Hochschild, G. H. Basic Theory of Algebraic Groups & Line Algebras. (Graduate Texts in Mathematics Ser.: Vol. 75). 350p. 1981. 39.00 (ISBN 0-387-90541-3). Springer-Verlag.

Hoffmann, C. M. Group-Theoretic Algorithms & Graph Isomorphism. (Lecture Notes in Computer Science Ser.: Vol. 136). 311p. 1982. pap. 20.00 (ISBN 0-387-11493-9). Springer-Verlag.

Horvath, Juan & Riera, Emilio L. Introduccion a la Topologia General. (Serie de Matematica Monografia: No. 9). 149p. 1981. pap. text ed. 3.50 (ISBN 0-8270-1412-0). OAS.

Humphreys, J. E. Ordinary & Modular Representations of Chevalley Groups. (Lecture Notes in Mathematics: Vol. 528). 1976. soft cover 13.00 (ISBN 0-387-07796-0). Springer-Verlag.

Husseini, S. Y. The Topology of Classical Groups & Related Topics. (Notes on Mathematics & Its Applications Ser.). 136p. 1968. 28.95x (ISBN 0-677-02160-7). Gordon.

International Conference on the Theory of Groups, 2nd. Proceedings. Newman, M. F., ed. (Lecture Notes in Mathematics Ser.: Vol. 372). vii, 740p. 1974. pap. 31.00 (ISBN 0-387-06845-7). Springer-Verlag.

Istanbul Summer School Of Theoretical Physics - 1962. Group Theoretical Concepts & Methods in Elementary Particle Physics. Gursey, F., ed. (Quantum Physics & Its Applications Ser.). 434p. 1964. 106.50 (ISBN 0-677-10140-6). Gordon.

Joshi, A. W. Elements of Group Theory for Physicists. 3rd ed. 334p. 1982. 18.95x (ISBN 0-470-27306-2). Halsted Pr.

Kambayashi, T., et al. Unipotent Algebraic Groups. (Lecture Notes in Mathematics: Vol. 414). vi, 165p. 1974. pap. 14.00 (ISBN 0-387-06960-7). Springer-Verlag.

Kargapolov, M. I. & Merzljakov, Ju. I. Fundamentals of the Theory of Groups, Vol. 62. Burns, R., tr. from Rus. (Graduate Texts in Mathematics Ser.). 1979. 25.00 (ISBN 0-387-90396-8). Springer-Verlag.

Kervaire, M. & Ojanguren, M., eds. Groupe de Brauer: Proceedings. (Lecture Notes in Mathematics Ser.: Vol. 844). 274p. 1981. pap. 19.00 (ISBN 0-387-10562-X). Springer-Verlag.

Kettle, S. A. Symmetry & Structure. 1985. 34.95 (ISBN 0-471-90501-1). Wiley.

Kim, A. C. & Neumann, B. H., eds. Groups-Korea 1983. (Lecture Notes in Mathematics Ser.: Vol. 1098). vii, 183p. 1984. pap. 9.50 (ISBN 0-387-13890-0). Springer-Verlag.

Kletzing, D. Structure & Representations of Q-Groups. (Lecture Notes in Mathematics: Vol. 1084). vi, 290p. 1984. pap. 16.00 (ISBN 0-387-13865-X). Springer-Verlag.

Kolchin, E. R. Differential Algebra & Algebraic Groups. (Pure & Applied Mathematics Ser.: Vol. 55). 1973. 79.50 (ISBN 0-12-417650-X). Acad Pr.

Koster, George F. Space Groups & Their Representations. (Solid State Reprint Ser.). 1964. 18.00 (ISBN 0-12-608468-8). Acad Pr.

Kowalewski, Gerhard. Kontinuierliche Gruppen. LC 51-3003. (Ger). 16.95 (ISBN 0-8284-0070-9). Chelsea Pub.

Kramer, P. & Rieckers, A., eds. Group Theoretical Methods in Physics: Sixth International Colloquium, Tuebingen 1977. (Lecture Notes in Physics: Vol. 79). 1978. pap. 32.00 (ISBN 0-387-08848-2). Springer-Verlag.

Kurosh, Alexander G. Group Theory, Vol. 1. LC 60-8965. 1979. text ed. 12.50 (ISBN 0-8284-0107-1). Chelsea Pub.

--Group Theory, Vol. 2. 2nd ed. LC 60-8965. 1979. text ed. 12.50 (ISBN 0-8284-0109-8). Chelsea Pub.

Lazard, M. P. Communative Formal Groups. (Lecture Notes in Mathematics Ser.: Vol. 443). ii, 236p. 1975. pap. 16.00 (ISBN 0-387-07145-8). Springer-Verlag.

Ledermann, W. Introduction to Group Theory. (Illus.). 176p. 1973. pap. 8.95x (ISBN 0-06-494125-6). B&N Imports.

Lee, Chung-Nim & Wasserman, Arthur G. On the Groups JO(G) (Memoirs: No. 159). 62p. 1975. pap. 10.00 (ISBN 0-8218-1859-7, MEMO-159). Am Math.

Ljapin, E. S. Semigroups. 4th ed. LC 63-15659. (Translations of Mathematical Monographs: Vol. 3). 519p. 1978. paper 46.00 (ISBN 0-8218-1553-9, MMONO-3). Am Math.

Loebl, Ernest M., ed. Group Theory & Its Applications, 3 vols. LC 67-23166. Vol. 1 1968. 81.00 (ISBN 0-12-455150-5); Vol. 2 1971. 71.50 (ISBN 0-12-455152-1); 98.50 (ISBN 0-12-455153-X). Vol. 3, 1975. Acad Pr.

Lusztig, George. Characters of Reductive Groups Over a Finite Field. LC 83-43083. (Annals of Mathematics Studies, 107). 495p. 1984. 50.00 (ISBN 0-691-08350-9); pap. 19.50 (ISBN 0-691-08351-7). Princeton U Pr.

--The Discrete Series Representations of the General Linear Groups Over a Finite Field. (Annals of Mathematics Studies: No. 81). 150p. 1974. 15.00 (ISBN 0-691-08154-9). Princeton U Pr.

Lyapin, E. S., et al. Exercises in Group Theory. LC 78-141243. 240p. 1972. 35.00x (ISBN 0-306-30505-4, Plenum Pr). Plenum Pub.

Lyndon, R. & Schapp, P. E. Combinatorial Group Theory. (Ergebnisse der Mathematik und Ihrer Grenzgebiete: Vol. 89). 1977. 48.00 (ISBN 0-387-07642-5). Springer-Verlag.

Lyndon, Roger. Groups & Geometry. (London Mathematical Society Lecture Note Ser.: No. 101). 225p. 1985. 19.95 (ISBN 0-521-31694-4). Cambridge U Pr.

MacDonald, Ian D. Theory of Groups. 1968. pap. 16.95x (ISBN 0-19-853138-9). Oxford U Pr.

Mackenzie. A Theory of Group Structures, 2 vols. 550p. 1976. Set. 75.25 (ISBN 0-677-05330-4). Gordon.

Magnus, Wilhelm. Noneuclidian Tesselations & Their Groups. 1974. 44.00 (ISBN 0-12-465450-9). Acad Pr.

Magnus, Wilhelm, et al. Combinational Group Theory: Presentations of Groups in Terms of Generators & Relations. 1976. pap. text ed. 7.95 (ISBN 0-486-63281-4). Dover.

Mann, Henry B. Addition Theorems: The Addition Theorems of Group Theory & Number Theory. LC 76-16766. 124p. 1976. Repr. of 1965 ed. text ed. 12.50 (ISBN 0-88275-418-1). Krieger.

Meijer, P. H., ed. Group Theory & Solid State Physics. (International Science Review Ser.). 304p. 1964. 55.75x (ISBN 0-677-00530-X). Gordon.

Mennicke, J. L., ed. Burnside Groups. (Lecture Notes in Mathematics: Vol. 806). 274p. 1980. pap. 20.00 (ISBN 0-387-10006-7). Springer-Verlag.

Miller, Charles F., 3rd. On Group-Theoretic Decision Problems & Their Classification. (Annals of Mathematics Studies: No. 68). 1971. 17.50x (ISBN 0-691-08091-7). Princeton U Pr.

Moshinsky, M. Group Theory & the Many-Body Problem. 188p. 1968. 37.25 (ISBN 0-677-01740-5, DMP). Gordon.

Mura, R. & Rhemtulla, A., eds. Orderable Groups. (Lecture Notes in Pure & Applied Mathematics: Vol. 27). 1977. 35.00 (ISBN 0-8247-6579-6). Dekker.

Napier, Rodney & Gershenfeld, Matti. Groups: Theory & Experience. 2nd ed. LC 80-82844. (Illus.). 448p. 1981. text ed. 25.50 (ISBN 0-395-29703-6); instr's manual 1.00 (ISBN 0-395-29704-4). HM.

Netto, Eugen. Theory of Substitutions. 2nd ed. LC 64-10289. 1964. 13.95 (ISBN 0-8284-0165-9). Chelsea Pub.

Neumann, B. H., et al, eds. The International Conference on the Theory of Groups: Proceedings. 418p. 1967. 60.00 (ISBN 0-677-10780-3). Gordon.

Neumann, H. Varieties of Groups. (Ergebnisse der Mathematik und Ihrer Grenzgebiete: Vol. 37). 1967. 33.00 (ISBN 0-387-03779-9). Springer-Verlag.

Neuwirth, L. P., ed. Knots, Groups, & 3-Manifolds: Papers Dedicated to the Memory of R. H. Fox. LC 75-5619. (Annals of Mathematics Studies: No. 84). 345p. 1975. 35.00 (ISBN 0-691-08170-0); pap. 13.50 (ISBN 0-691-08167-0). Princeton U Pr.

Newman, Morris. Integral Matrices. (Pure & Applied Mathematics Ser.: Vol. 45). 1972. 49.50 (ISBN 0-12-517850-6). Acad Pr.

Okamoto, K., ed. Group Representations & Systems of Differential Equations: Proceedings of the Symposium Tokyo, Japan, 20-27 Dec. 1982. (Advanced Studies in Pure Mathematics: Vol. 4). 498p. 1985. 99.00 (ISBN 0-444-87710-X, North-Holland). Elsevier.

Pfeuty, Pierre & Toulouse, Gerard. Introduction to the Renormalization Group & to Critical Phenomena. LC 76-26111. pap. 50.50 (ISBN 0-317-29389-3, 2024283). Bks Demand UMI.

Pleskin, W., ed. Group Rings of Finite Groups over p-adic Integers. (Lecture Notes in Mathematics: Vol. 1026). 151p. 1983. pap. 12.00 (ISBN 0-387-12728-3). Springer Verlag.

Pyatekskii-Shapiro, I. I. Automorphic Functions & the Geometry of Classical Domains. (Mathematics & Its Applications Ser.). 272p. 1969. 56.75x (ISBN 0-677-20310-1). Gordon.

Reiner, I. & Roggenkamp, K. W. Integral Representations. (Lecture Notes in Mathematics: Vol. 744). 1979. pap. 19.00 (ISBN 0-387-09546-2). Springer-Verlag.

Robinson, D. J. A Course in the Theory of Groups. (Graduate Texts in Mathematics Ser.: Vol. 80). 480p. 1982. 44.00 (ISBN 0-387-90600-2). Springer-Verlag.

--Finiteness Conditions & Generalized Soluble Groups, Pt. 1. (Ergebnisse der Mathematik und Ihrer Grenzgebiete: Vol. 62). (Illus.). 240p. 1972. 27.00 (ISBN 0-387-05620-3). Springer-Verlag.

Rose, John S. A Course on Group Theory. LC 76-22984. (Illus.). 1978. 59.50 (ISBN 0-521-21409-2); pap. 22.95x (ISBN 0-521-29142-9). Cambridge U Pr.

Rotman. An Introduction of the Theory of Groups. 3rd ed. 1985. 40.71 (ISBN 0-205-07963-6, 567963). Allyn.

Rotman, Joseph J. An Introduction to the Theory of Groups. 3rd ed. 1984. text ed. 40.71 (ISBN 0-205-07963-6, EDP 567963). Allyn.

Satake, I. Classification Theory of Semi-Simple Algebraic Groups, Vol. 3. (Lecture Notes in Pure & Applied Mathematics Ser.: Vol. 3). 1971. 29.75 (ISBN 0-8247-1607-8). Dekker.

Singmaster, David. Notes on Rubik's Magic Cube. LC 80-27751. (Illus.). 73p. 1981. text ed. 11.95x (ISBN 0-89490-057-9); pap. 5.95 (ISBN 0-89490-043-9). Enslow Pubs.

Smith, J., et al, eds. Ordered Groups. (Lecture Notes in Pure & Applied Mathematics: Vol. 62). 192p. 1980. 35.00 (ISBN 0-8247-6943-0). Dekker.

Springer, T. A. Jordan Algebras & Algebraic Groups. LC 72-96718. (Ergebnisse der Mathematik und Ihrer Grenzgebiete: Vol. 75). vii, 169p. 1973. 33.00 (ISBN 0-387-06104-5). Springer-Verlag.

--Linear Algebraic Groups. (Progress in Mathematics Ser.: No. 9). 312p. 1981. 22.00x (ISBN 0-8176-3029-5). Birkhauser.

Stallings, John R. Group Theory & Three-Dimensional Manifolds. LC 70-151590. (Yale Mathematical Monagraphs Ser.: Vol. 4). pap. 20.00 (ISBN 0-317-09475-0, 2016792). Bks Demand UMI.

Stammbach, U. Homology in Group Theory. LC 73-19547. (Lecture Notes in Mathematics: Vol. 359). 183p. 1973. pap. 14.00 (ISBN 0-387-06569-5). Springer-Verlag.

Steinberg, Robert. Endomorphisms of Linear Algebraic Groups. LC 52-42839. (Memoirs: No. 80). 1968. pap. 9.00 (ISBN 0-8218-1280-7, MEMO-80). Am Math.

Steklov Institute of Mathematics, Academy of Sciences, USSR, No. 85. Defining Relations & Algorithmic Problems for Groups & Semigroups: Proceedings. Adjan, S I., ed. (Proceedings of the Steklov Institute of Mathematics: No. 85). 1967. 36.00 (ISBN 0-8218-1885-6, STEKLO-85). Am Math.

Stillwell, J. Classical Topology & Combinatorial Group Theory. (Graduate Texts in Mathematics Ser.: Vol. 72). (Illus.). 301p. 1980. 39.50 (ISBN 0-387-90516-2). Springer-Verlag.

Suprenenko, F. A. Soluble & Nilpotent Linear Groups. LC 63-20676. (Translations of Mathematical Monographs: Vol. 9). 1970. Repr. of 1963 ed. 23.00 (ISBN 0-8218-1559-8, MMONO-9). Am Math.

Suprunenko, D. A. Matrix Groups. LC 75-45115. (Translations of Mathematical Monographs: Vol. 45). 1976. 56.00 (ISBN 0-8218-1595-4, MMONO-45). Am Math.

Suzuk., M. Group Theory I. (Grundlehren der Mathematischen Wissenschaften: Vol. 247). (Illus.). 440p. 1981. 54.00 (ISBN 0-387-10915-3). Springer-Verlag.

Swamy, N. V. & Samuel, Mark A. Group Theory Made Easy for Scientists & Engineers. LC 78-11733. 174p. 1979. 32.95x (ISBN 0-471-05128-4, Pub. by Wiley-Interscience). Wiley.

Symposia in Pure Mathematics, New York, 1959. Finite Groups: Proceedings. Albert, A. A. & Kaplansky, I., eds. LC 50-1183. (Proceedings of Symposia in Pure Mathematics: Vol. 1). 110p. 1979. pap. 23.00 (ISBN 0-8218-1401-X, PSPUM-1). Am Math.

Symposium in Pure Mathematics-Boulder, 1965. Algebraic Groups & Discontinous Subgroups: Proceedings. Borel, A. & Mostow, G. D., eds. LC 66-18581. (Proceedings of Symposia in Pure Mathematics: Vol. 9). 426p. 1966. pap. 35.00 (ISBN 0-8218-1409-5, PSPUM-9). Am Math.

Symposium in Pure Mathematics. Monterey, Calif. 1959. Lattice Theory: Proceedings. Dilworth, R. P., ed. LC 50-1183. (Proceedings of Symposia in Pure Mathematics: Vol. 2). 1961. 24.00 (ISBN 0-8218-1402-8, PSPUM-2). Am Math.

Thomas, A. D. & Wood, G. V. Group Tables. (Shiva Mathematics Ser.: 2). 190p. 1981. pap. text ed. 13.95x (ISBN 0-906812-02-X). Birkhauser.

Tinkham, Michael. Group Theory & Quantum Mechanics. (International Series in Pure & Applied Physics). 1964. text ed. 54.95 (ISBN 0-07-064895-6). McGraw.

Tomkinson, M. J. FC-Groups. (Research Notes in Mathematics Ser.: No. 96). 208p. 1984. pap. text ed. 19.95 (ISBN 0-273-08566-2). Pitman Pub MA.

Tung, Ku-Ki. Group Theory in Physics: An Introduction to Symmetry Principles, Group Representations, & Special Functions in Classical & Quantum Physics. 280p. 1984. 30.00x (ISBN 9971-966-56-5, Pub. by World Sci Singapore); pap. 19.00x (ISBN 9971-966-57-3, Pub. by World Sci Singapore). Taylor & Francis.

Wareing, P. F. & Phillips, I. D. The Control of Growth & Differentiation in Plants. 3rd ed. LC 76-109055. 1981. 40.00 (ISBN 0-08-026351-8); pap. 20.00 (ISBN 0-08-026350-X). Pergamon.
--Growth & Differentiation in Plants. Orig. Title: The Control of Growth & Differentiation in Plants. (Illus.). 176p. 1981. pap. 20.00 (ISBN 0-08-026350-X). Pergamon.
Wareing, P. F., ed. Plant Growth Substances. 1982. 49.00 (ISBN 0-12-735380-1). Acad Pr.
Whatley, F. R. & Whatley, J. M. Light & Plant Life. (Studies in Biology: No. 124). 96p. 1980. pap. text ed. 8.95 (ISBN 0-7131-2785-6). E Arnold.
Williams, R. F. The Shoot Apex & Leaf Growth. (Illus.). 280p. 1975. 44.50 (ISBN 0-521-20453-4). Cambridge U Pr.
Zweig, Gunter & Lawrence, James, eds. Analytical Methods for Pesticides & Plant Growth Regulators, Vol. 12: High Performance Liquid Chromatography (HPLC) of Pesticides. LC 63-16560. 1982. 45.00 (ISBN 0-12-784312-4). Acad Pr.

GROWTH PROMOTING SUBSTANCES

see also Plant Hormones

Hillman, John R., ed. Isolation of Plant Growth Substances. LC 78-1641. pap. 41.80 (ISBN 0-317-29374-5, 2024477). Bks Demand UMI.
International Conference on Plant Growth Substances, 7th, Canberra, 1970. Plant Growth Substances, 1970: Proceedings. Carr, D. J., ed. LC 72-80291. (Illus.). 849p. 1972. pap. 31.00 (ISBN 0-387-05850-8). Springer-Verlag.
Leffert, H. L., ed. Growth Regulation by Ion Fluxes. LC 80-13986. (Annals of the New York Academy of Sciences: Vol. 339). 335p. pap. 62.00x (ISBN 0-89766-049-8). NY Acad Sci.
McLaren. Chemical Manipulation of Crop Growth. 1982. text ed. 99.95 (ISBN 0-408-10767-7). Butterworth.
Opportunities for Chemical Plant Growth Regulation. 222p. 1978. 42.00x (ISBN 0-686-45037-X, Pub. by BCPC Pubns England). State Mutual Bk.
Roberts, J. A. & Tucker, G. A. Ethylene & Plant Development. (Illus.). 448p. 1985. text ed. 99.95 (ISBN 0-407-00920-5). Butterworth.
Thomas, T. H., ed. Plant Growth Regulators: Potential & Practice. 250p. 1982. 40.00x (ISBN 0-901436-69-0, Pub. by CAB Bks England). State Mutual Bk.
Van Keulen, H. & Van Heemst, H. D. J. Crop Response to the Supply of Macronutrients. (Agricultural Research Reports: No. 916). 52p. 1982. pap. 6.75 (ISBN 90-220-0807-X, PDC247, PUDOC). Unipub.

GUAIANOLIDES

Sorm, Frantisek & Dolejs, Ladislaw. Guaianolides & Germacranolides. LC 66-16515. 1966. 38.00x (ISBN 0-8162-8261-7). Holden-Day.

GUIDANCE SYSTEMS (FLIGHT)

Here are entered works on systems for supervising the navigation of aircraft and space vehicles from one location to another.

Culp, Robert D. & Stafford, Parker S., eds. Guidance & Control 1984. LC 57-43769. (Advances in the Astronautical Sciences Ser.: Vol. 55). 500p. (Orig.). 1984. lib. bdg. 60.00x (ISBN 0-87703-199-1, Pub. by Am Astro Soc); pap. text ed. 50.00 (ISBN 0-87703-200-9); microfiche suppl. 15.00x (ISBN 0-87703-201-7). Univelt Inc.
Culp, Robert D., et al, eds. Guidance & Control 1985: Feb. 2-6, 1985, Keystone, CO. LC 57-43769. (Advances in the Asronautical Sciences Ser.: Vol. 57). (Illus.). 618p. (Orig.). 1985. lib. bdg. 65.00 (ISBN 0-87703-211-4, Pub By Am Astro Soc); pap. text ed. 50.00 (ISBN 0-87703-212-2). Univelt Inc.
Guidance & Control. 75.00 (ISBN 0-317-06664-1). AIAA.
Gysbers, N. & Moore, E. Improving Guidance Programs. 1981. 18.95 (ISBN 0-13-452656-2). P-H.
Pallett, E. H. Automatic Flight Control. 2nd ed. (Illus.). 236p. 1983. text ed. 30.00x (ISBN 0-246-12048-7, Pub. by Granada England). Sheridan.

GUIDED MISSILES

see also Ballistic Missiles; Rockets (Aeronautics) also names of specific missiles

Bellany, Ian & Blacker, Coit D., eds. Antiballistic Missile Defense in the 1980s. 100p. 1983. text ed. 27.50x (ISBN 0-7146-3207-4, F Cass Co). Biblio Dist.
Betts, Richard. Cruise Missiles & U.S. Policy. LC 82-72704. 61p. 1982. pap. 6.95 (ISBN 0-8157-0933-1). Brookings.
Betts, Richard K., ed. Cruise Missiles: Technology, Strategy, Politics. LC 81-18149. 612p. 1981. 32.95 (ISBN 0-8157-0932-3); pap. 15.95 (ISBN 0-8157-0931-5). Brookings.
Champion, Brian. Advanced Weapons Systems: An Annotated Bibliography of the Cruise Missile, MX Missile, Laser & Space Weapons, & Stealth Technology. LC 84-48398. (Referance Library of Social Science). 100p. 1985. lib. bdg. 35.00 (ISBN 0-8240-8793-3). Garland Pub.
Forty, George. Missile Systems. (Illus.). 120p. 1985. 14.95 (ISBN 0-87052-153-5, Pub. by Ian Allan England). Hippocrene Bks.
Gunston, Bill. An Illustrated Guide to Modern Airborne Missiles. LC 82-74478. (Illustrated Military Guides Ser.). (Illus.). 160p. 1983. 9.95 (ISBN 0-668-05822-6). Arco.
Hoover, Robert A. The MX Controversy: A Guide to Issues & References. LC 81-23393. (Guides to Contemporary Issues Ser.: No. 1). 110p. 1982. 16.50x (ISBN 0-941690-00-8); pap. 9.95x (ISBN 0-941690-01-6); pap. text ed. 6.95x. Regina Bks.
Huisken, Ron. The Cruise Missile & Arms Control. LC 80-68052. (Canberra Papers on Strategy & Defence: No. 13). 84p. (Orig.). 1980. pap. text ed. 9.00 (ISBN 0-908160-54-2, 0370). Australia N U P.
Huisken, Ronald. The Origin of the Strategic Cruise Missile. LC 81-4921. 220p. 1981. 32.95 (ISBN 0-03-059378-6). Praeger.
Kennedy, Gregory P. Vengeance Weapon Two: The V-2 Guided Missile. LC 82-600400. (Illus.). 168p. 1983. pap. text ed. 9.95x (ISBN 0-87474-573-X). Smithsonian.
Kennedy, Gregory P., compiled by. Rockets, Missiles, & Spacecraft of the National Air & Space Museum, Smithsonian Institution. LC 83-600049. (Illus.). 165p. 1983. pap. 6.50 (ISBN 0-87474-573-1). Smithsonian.
Lee, et al. Guided Weapons. (Brassey's Battlefield Weapons Systems & Technology: Vol. 8). 160p. 1983. 27.00 (ISBN 0-08-028336-5); pap. 12.50 (ISBN 0-08-028337-3). Pergamon.
Pfaltzgraff, Robert L., Jr. & Davis, Jacquelyn K. The Cruise Missile: Bargaining Chip or Defense Bargain? LC 76-51854. (Special Reports Ser.). 53p. 1977. 3.00 (ISBN 0-89549-001-3). Inst Foreign Policy Anal.
Scoville, Herbert, Jr. The MX: Prescription for Disaster. (Illus.). 224p. 1981. pap. 6.95 (ISBN 0-262-69077-2). MIT Pr.
Slow to Take Offense: Bombers, Cruise Missles & Prudent Deterrence. 2nd ed. 136p. 1980. pap. 15.00 (ISBN 0-89206-015-8, CSIS017, CSIS). Unipub.
Williams, Tim. The Ground Launched Cruise Missile: A Technical Assessment. 36p. 1983. lib. bdg. 12.95 (ISBN 0-88286-138-7); pap. 2.50 (ISBN 0-88286-113-1). C H Kerr.

GUIDED MISSILES–DESIGN AND CONSTRUCTION

Edwards, John. Superweapon: The Making of MX. 288p. 1982. 16.95 (ISBN 0-393-01523-8). Norton.

GUIDED MISSILES–GUIDANCE SYSTEMS

Blakelock, John H. Automatic Control of Aircraft & Missiles. LC 65-16402. 348p. 1965. 64.50x (ISBN 0-471-07930-8, Pub. by Wiley-Interscience). Wiley.

GUINEA-PIGS

Axelrod, Jennifer. Breeding Guinea Pigs. 1980. 4.95 (ISBN 0-87666-929-1, KW-073). TFH Pubns.
Bleier, Ruth. The Hypothalmus of the Guinea Pig: A Cytoarchitectronic Atlas. LC 83-47756. (Illus.). 176p. 1984. text ed. 50.00x (ISBN 0-299-09040-X). U of Wis Pr.
Cooper, Gale & Schiller, Alan L. Anatomy of the Guinea Pig. LC 74-81866. (Commonwealth Fund Ser.). (Illus.). 432p. 1975. text ed. 40.00x (ISBN 0-674-03159-8). Harvard U Pr.
Denham, Ken. Guinea Pigs & Chinchillas. (Illus.). 93p. 1977. pap. 3.95 (ISBN 0-7028-1075-4). Avian Pubns.
Elward, Margaret & Whiteway, Catherine E. Encyclopedia of Guinea Pigs. (Illus.). 224p. 1980. 12.95 (ISBN 0-87666-916-X, H-975). TFH Pubns.
Hammer, Gunnar. A Quantitative Cytochemical Study of Shock Wave Effects on Spiral Ganglion Cells. 1956. 12.00 (ISBN 0-384-21250-6). Johnson Repr.
Ragland, Kay. Guinea Pigs. (Illus.). 1979. 4.95 (ISBN 0-87666-925-9, KW-016). TFH Pubns.
Ritter, William. The T.F.H Book of Guinea Pigs. (Illus.). 80p. 1982. 6.95 (ISBN 0-87666-823-6, HP-008). TFH Pubns.
Roberts, Mervin F. Guinea Pigs for Beginners. (Illus.). 1972. pap. 2.95 (ISBN 0-87666-198-3, M-541). TFH Pubns.
Wagner, Joseph E. & Manning, Patrick J., eds. The Biology of the Guinea Pig. 1976. 75.00 (ISBN 0-12-730050-3). Acad Pr.
Wersall, Jan. Studies in the Structure & Innervation of the Sensory Epithelium of the Cristae Ampullares in the Guinea Pig. Repr. of 1956 ed. 12.00 (ISBN 0-384-66900-X). Johnson Repr.

GULF STREAM

Stommmel, Henry. The Gulf Stream: A Physical & Dynamical Description. (California Library Reprint Ser). 1977. Repr. of 1964 ed. 34.50x (ISBN 0-520-03307-8). U of Cal Pr.

GULLS

see also California Gull

Barnard, C. J. & Thompson, D. B. Gulls & Plovers: The Ecology of Mixed-Species Feeding Groups. 320p. 1985. 30.00x (ISBN 0-231-06262-1). COlumbia U Pr.
Grant, P. J. Gulls: A Guide to Identification. 280p. 1982. 60.00x (ISBN 0-85661-030-5, Pub. by T & AD Boyser England). State Mutual Bk.
Grant, Peter J. Gulls: A Guide to Identification. LC 81-71625. (Illus.). 408p. 32.50 (ISBN 0-931130-08-5). Buteo.

GUM ELASTIC

see Rubber

GUMBRIN

see Bentonite

GUMS AND RESINS

see also Ion Exchange Resins; Polyesters also names of specific gums and resins

Ash, M. & Ash, I. Encyclopedia of Plastics, Polymers & Resins Vol. 1, A-G. 1981. 75.00 (ISBN 0-8206-0290-6). Chem Pub.
--Encyclopedia of Plastics, Polymers & Resins Vol. 2, H-O. 1982. 75.00 (ISBN 0-8206-0296-5). Chem Pub.
--Encyclopedia of Plastics, Polymers & Resins Vol. 3, P-Z. 1983. 75.00 (ISBN 0-8206-0303-1). Chem Pub.
Davidson, R. L. Handbook of Water-Soluble Gums & Resins. 1980. 57.50 (ISBN 0-07-015471-6). McGraw.
Davidson, Robert L. & Sittig, Marshall, eds. Water-Soluble Resins. 2nd ed. LC 68-9136. 240p. 1968. 15.95 (ISBN 0-686-86267-8). Krieger.
Future for Water-Soluble Polymers. 1985. 1750.00 (ISBN 0-89336-423-1, C-012R). BCC.
Gillies, M. T., ed. Stabilizers for Synthetic Resins: Recent Developments. LC 81-16758. (Chemical Technology Review: No. 199). (Illus.). 356p. 1982. 54.00 (ISBN 0-8155-0872-7). Noyes.
Glicksman, M. Gum Technology in the Food Industry. (Food Science & Technology Ser). 1969. 85.00 (ISBN 0-12-286350-X). Acad Pr.
K. G. Roberts Associates. Resinkit: A Working Guide. 125.00 (ISBN 0-686-48150-X, 2201). T-C Pubns CA.
May, Clayton A., ed. Resins for Aerospace. LC 80-15342. (ACS Symposium Ser.: No. 132). 1980. 49.95 (ISBN 0-8412-0567-1). Am Chemical.
Riew, C. Keith & Gillham, John K., eds. Rubber-Modified Thermoset Resins. LC 84-21566. (Advances in Chemistry Ser.: No. 208). 372p. 1984. lib. bdg. 89.95x (ISBN 0-8412-0828-X). Am Chemical.
Whistler, R. L. & BeMiller, J. N., eds. Industrial Gums: Polysaccharides & Their Derivatives. 2nd ed. 1973. 89.50 (ISBN 0-12-746252-X). Acad Pr.

GUNITE

Ryan, T. F. Gunite, a Handbook for Engineers. 1973. pap. 14.50 (ISBN 0-7210-0820-8). Scholium Intl.

GUNN OSCILLATORS

see Oscillators, Microwave

GUNSMITHING

Angier, R. H. Firearm Blueing & Browning. 160p. 1936. 12.95 (ISBN 0-686-76905-8). Stackpole.
Carmichel, Jim. Do-It-Yourself Gunsmithing. LC 77-12450. (Outdoor Life Book). (Illus.). 1978. 18.22i (ISBN 0-06-010638-7, HarpT). Harrow.
Dunlap, Roy F. Gunsmithing. LC 63-21755. (Illus.). 848p. 1963. 27.95 (ISBN 0-8117-0770-9). Stackpole.
Hartzler, Daniel D. Arms Makers of Maryland. LC 74-24434. (Longrifle Ser.). (Illus.). 312p. 1977. 40.00 (ISBN 0-87387-054-9). Shumway.
Howe, J. V. Modern Gunsmith. (Illus.). 1982. 14.98 (ISBN 0-517-38583-X, Bonanza). Outlet Bk Co.
Howe, Walter J. Professional Gunsmithing. (Illus.). 416p. 1946. 24.95 (ISBN 0-8117-1375-X). Stackpole.
Irwin, John R. Guns & Gunmaking Tools of Southern Appalachia. 2nd ed. (Illus.). 118p. 1983. pap. 9.95 (ISBN 0-916838-81-1). Schiffer.
Masterpieces of Tula Gunsmiths (Shedevry Tul'skikh Oruzheynikov) 144p. 1981. 60.00x (ISBN 0-317-14254-2, Pub. by Collet's). State Mutual Bk.
Mitchell, Jack. Gun Digest Book of Pistolsmithing. LC 80-66470. (Illus.). 288p. (Orig.). 1980. pap. 11.95 (ISBN 0-910676-18-6). DBI.
--The Gun Digest Book of Riflesmithing. LC 82-72293. (Illus.). 256p. 1982. pap. 11.95 (ISBN 0-910676-47-X). DBI.
Shelsby, Earl, ed. NRA Gunsmithing Guide: Updated. rev. ed. (Illus.). 336p. (Orig.). 1980. pap. text ed. 11.95 (ISBN 0-935998-47-0). Natl Rifle Assn.
Stelle & Harrison. The Gunsmith's Manual: A Complete Handbook for the American Gunsmith. (Illus.). Repr. of 1883 ed. 15.00 (ISBN 0-88227-002-8). Gun Room.
Traister, John. Modern Gunsmithing. LC 81-39911. (Illus.). 608p. 1981. 24.95 (ISBN 0-8117-0983-3). Stackpole.
Traister, John E. Basic Gunsmithing. (Illus.). 1979. pap. 9.95 (ISBN 0-8306-1140-1, 1140). TAB Bks.
--First Book of Gunsmithing. LC 81-14509. (Illus.). 192p. 1981. 18.95 (ISBN 0-8117-0633-8). Stackpole.
--Gun Digest Book of Gunsmithing Tools...& Their Uses. LC 80-67793. 256p. 1980. pap. 10.95 (ISBN 0-910676-08-9). DBI.
--Gunsmithing at Home. 256p. 1985. pap. 11.95 (ISBN 0-88317-122-8). Stoeger Pub Co.
Walker, Ralph. Shotgun Gunsmithing: Gun Digest Bk. LC 83-70144. 256p. 1983. pap. 11.95 (ISBN 0-910676-54-2). DBI.
Wood, J. B. Gunsmithing: The Tricks of the Trade. LC 82-72294. (Illus.). 288p. (Orig.). 1982. pap. 11.95 (ISBN 0-910676-46-1). DBI.

GUNTER'S LINE

see Slide-Rule

GYMNOSPERMS

see also Coniferae

Chamberlain, Charles J. Gymnosperms: Structure & Evolution. (Illus.). 1935. 40.00 (ISBN 0-384-08415-X). Johnson Repr.
Kern, Frank D. A Revised Taxonomic Account of Gymnosporangium. LC 79-165358. (Illus.). 136p. 1973. 17.95x (ISBN 0-271-01105-X). Pa St U Pr.
Ramanujam, C. G. Indian Gymnosperms in Time & Space. (Illus.). 50p. 1976. Repr. 8.00 (ISBN 0-88065-178-4, Pub. by Messers Today & Tomorrows Printers & Publishers India). Scholarly Pubns.
Rendle, Alfred B. Classification of Flowering Plants, 2 bks. Incl. Bk. 1. Gymnosperms & Monocotyledons; Bk. 2. Dicotyledons. 90.00 (ISBN 0-521-06057-5). Cambridge U Pr.
Singh, Hardev. Embryology of Gymnosperms. (Encyclopedia of Plant Anatomy: Vol. X, No. 2). (Illus.). 302p. 1978. lib. bdg. 84.20x (ISBN 3-443-14011-4). Lubrecht & Cramer.

GYPSY-MOTH

see Gipsy-Moth

GYRO COMPASS

Frost, A. Marine Gyro Compasses for Ships Officers. (Illus.). 145p. 1982. text ed. 21.50x (ISBN 0-85174-426-5, Pub. by Brown Son Ferguson). Sheridan.

GYRODYNAMICS

see Rotational Motion

GYROPLANES

see Autogiros

GYROSCOPE

see also Gyro Compass; Gyroscopic Instruments; Stability of Airplanes; Stability of Ships

CISM (International Center for Mechanical Sciences), Dept. for General Mechanics, 1970. Critical Speeds of Gyroscopes. Schweitzer, G., ed. (CISM Pubns. Ser.: No. 55). (Illus.). 95p. 1973. pap. 13.50 (ISBN 0-387-81150-8). Springer-Verlag.
CISM (International Center for Mechanical Sciences), Dept. for General Mechanics, Vienna, 1970. Gas-Lubricated Bearings of Gyroscopes. Heinrich, G., ed. (CISM Pubns. Ser.: No. 43). (Illus.). 57p. 1973. pap. 10.00 (ISBN 0-387-81147-8). Springer-Verlag.
CISM (International Center for Mechanical Sciences) Gyrodynamics. Magnus, K., ed. (CISM Intl. Centre for Mechanical Science, Courses & Lectures Ser.: No. 53). (Illus.). x, 280p. 1974. pap. 15.40 (ISBN 0-387-81229-6). Springer-Verlag.
Crabtree, Harold. Spinning Tops & Gyroscopic Motion. LC 66-23755. (Illus.). 1977. text ed. 12.95 (ISBN 0-8284-0204-3). Chelsea Pub.
Euromech 38 Colloquium, Louvain-la-Neuve, Belgium, 3-5 September, 1973. Gyrodynamics: Proceedings. Willems, P. Y., ed. (Illus.). 300p. 1974. 28.40 (ISBN 0-387-06776-0). Springer-Verlag.
Greenhill, George. Gyroscopic Theory. LC 66-30616. 22.50 (ISBN 0-8284-0205-1). Chelsea Pub.
Klein, Felix. Ueber Die Theorie Des Kreisels. 1965. 60.00 (ISBN 0-384-29720-X). Johnson Repr.
Leimanis, E. General Problem of the Motion of Coupled Rigid Bodies About a Fixed Point. (Springer Tracts in Natural Philosophy: Vol. 7). (Illus.). 1965. 36.00 (ISBN 0-387-03408-0). Springer-Verlag.

GYROSCOPIC INSTRUMENTS

see also Astronautical Instruments;

also names of specific instruments and uses, e.g. Automatic Pilot (Airplanes); Gyro Compass; Inertial Navigation

CISM (International Center for Mechanical Sciences), Dept. for General Mechanics, 1970. Special Problems in Gyrodynamics. Muller, P. C., ed. (CISM Pubns. Ser.: No. 63). (Illus.). 96p. 1973. pap. 14.20 (ISBN 0-387-81085-4). Springer-Verlag.

Siff, Elliott J. & Emmerich, Claude L. Engineering Approach to Gyroscopic Instruments. 1961. 12.95 (ISBN 0-8315-0028-X). Speller.

GYROSTATIC COMPASS

see Gyro Compass

H

HABER, FRITZ, 1868-1934

Goran, Morris. Story of Fritz Haber. (Illus.). 1967. 15.95x (ISBN 0-8061-0756-1). U of Okla Pr.

HABITS OF ANIMALS

see Animals, Habits and Behavior Of

HACKS (CARRIAGES)

see Carriages and Carts

HADRONS

Cabibbo, N. & Sertorio, L., eds. Hadronic Matter at Extreme Energy Density. LC 79-18446. (Ettore Majoana International Science Ser., Physical Sciences: Vol. 2). 365p. 1980. 59.50x (ISBN 0-306-40303-X, Plenum Pr). Plenum Pub.

Danos, M. & Gillet, V. Relativistic Bound Hadrons. Date not set. 85.00. Elsevier.

Donnachie, A. & Shaw, G., eds. Electromagnetic Interactions of Hadrons. LC 77-17811. (Nuclear Physics Monographs). (Illus.). 1978. Vol. 1, 458 Pp. 65.00x (ISBN 0-306-31052-X, Plenum Pr); Vol. 2, 590 Pp. 85.00x (ISBN 0-306-31106-2). Plenum Pub.

Fries, D. E. C. & Wess, J., eds. New Phenomena in Lepton-Hadron Physics. LC 79-19005. (NATO ASI, Ser. B, Physics: Vol. 49). 444p. 1979. 65.00x (ISBN 0-306-40301-3, Plenum Pr). Plenum Pub.

Hofmann, W. Jets of Hadrons. (Springer Tracts in Modern Physics Ser.: Vol. 90). (Illus.). 210p. 1981. 36.00 (ISBN 0-387-10625-1). Springer-Verlag.

Humpert, B., ed. Dynamical Concepts on Scaling Violation & the New Resonances in E Positive E Negative Annihilation. (Lecture Notes in Physics Ser: Vol. 45). 1975. pap. 17.00 (ISBN 0-387-07539-9). Springer-Verlag.

Hwang, W-Y. P. & Macfarlane, M. H., eds. Hadron Substructure in Nuclear Physics: Indiana University 1983. LC 84-70165. (AIP Conference Proceedings Ser.: No. 110). 398p. 1984. lib. bdg. 43.00 (ISBN 0-88318-309-9). Am Inst Physics.

Leader, Elliot & Predazzi, Enrico. An Introduction to Gauge Theories & the "New Physics". LC 81-3860. (Illus.). 400p. 1982. 75.00 (ISBN 0-521-23375-5); pap. 32.50 (ISBN 0-521-29937-3). Cambridge U Pr.

Levy, et al, eds. Hadron Structure & Lepton-Hadron Interactions. LC 78-24027. (NATO ASI Series B, Physics: Vol. 39). 742p. 1979. 110.00x (ISBN 0-306-40072-3, Plenum Pr). Plenum Pub.

Lichtenberg, D. B. & Rosen, S. P., eds. Development in the Quark Theory of Hadrons. 502p. (Orig.). 1980. pap. text ed. 50.00x (ISBN 0-911767-02-9). Hadronic Pr Inc.

Morpurgo, G., ed. Quarks & Hadronic Structure. LC 76-47490. 328p. 1977. 52.50 (ISBN 0-306-38141-9, Plenum Pr). Plenum Pub.

Mukunda, N., et al. Relativistic Models of Extended Hadrons Obeying a Mas-Spin Trajectory Constraint. (Lecture Notes in Physics: Vol. 165). 163p. 1982. pap. 11.00 (ISBN 0-387-11586-2). Springer-Verlag.

Perl, Martin L. High Energy Hadron Physics. LC 74-6348. 584p. 1974. 52.50x (ISBN 0-471-68049-4, Pub. by Wiley-Interscience). Wiley.

Preparata, G. & Aubert, J. J., eds. Probing Hadrons with Leptons. LC 80-12024. (Ettore Majorana International Science Ser., Physical Sciences: Vol. 5). 517p. 1980. 79.50 (ISBN 0-306-40438-9, Plenum Pr). Plenum Pub.

Santilli, Ruggero M. Lie Admissible Approach to the Hadronic Structure, 2 Vols. 1982. Set. pap. text ed. 100.00x (ISBN 0-911767-05-3). Hadronic Pr Inc.

--Lie Admissible Approach to the Hadronic Structure: Covering of the Galilei & Einstein Relativites, Vol. 2. 575p. 1982. pap. 50.00x (ISBN 0-911767-07-X). Hadronic Pr Inc.

--Lie Admissible Approach to the Hadronic Structure: Non Applicability of the Galilei & Einstein Relativities, Vol.1. 485p. 1978. pap. 50.00x (ISBN 0-911767-06-1). Hadronic Pr Inc.

Satz, H., ed. Statistical Mechanics of Quarks & Hadrons: Proceedings of the International Symposium, University of Bieleveld, France, Aug., 1980. 480p. 1981. 74.50 (ISBN 0-444-86227-7, North-Holland). Elsevier.

Scheck, F. Leptons, Hadrons & Nuclei. 400p. 1984. 61.75 (ISBN 0-444-86719-8, I-006-83, North Holland). Elsevier.

Thomas, A. W., ed. Modern Three-Hadron Physics. (Topics in Current Physics: Vol. 2). 1977. 45.00 (ISBN 3-540-07950-5). Springer-Verlag.

Zichichi, A., ed. Laws of Hadronic Matter: Proceedings. Ettore Majorana Course on Subnuclear Physics, Eleventh, Held at Erice, Italy, July 1973. 1975. 111.00 (ISBN 0-12-780588-5). Acad Pr.

Zichichi, Antonio, ed. Pointlike Structures Inside & Outside Hadrons. LC 80-25632. (The Subnuclear Ser.: Vol. 17). 747p. 1982. 110.00 (ISBN 0-306-40568-7, Plenum Pr). Plenum Pub.

HAFNIUM

Atomic Energy Review, Special Issue Hafnium: Physico-Chemical Properties of its Compounds & Alloys. (No. 8). 407p. 1981. pap. 50.50 (IAER8, IAEA). Unipub.

Hafnium: Physico-Chemical Properties of its Compounds & Alloys. (Atomic Energy Review Ser.: No. 8, Special Issue). (Eng.). 407p. 1981. pap. 55.75 (ISBN 92-0-149181-6, IAEA8, IAEA). Unipub.

Manual on Zirconium & Hafnium, STP 639. 108p. 1977. 9.50x (ISBN 0-8031-0505-3, 04-639000-35). ASTM.

HAIL

Aviation Hail Problem: Includes Other Notes on Forecasting for Jet Aircraft. (Technical Note Ser.: Nos. 37-40). pap. 17.00 (ISBN 0-685-57276-5, W25, WMO). Unipub.

Flora, Snowden D. Hailstorms of the United States. (Illus.). 216p. 1956. 13.50x (ISBN 0-8061-0359-0). U of Okla Pr.

Gokhale, Narayan R. Hailstorms & Hailstone Growth. LC 75-19480. 550p. 1976. 49.50x (ISBN 0-87395-313-4). State U NY Pr.

HAIR

see also Wigs and Wigmakers

Bragg, Paul C. & Bragg, Patricia. Your Health & Your Hair. 13th, rev. ed. LC 84-82235. pap. 4.95 (ISBN 0-87790-034-5). Health Sci.

Dale, Alexander. Healthy Hair & Common Sense. 11.95x (ISBN 0-911638-02-4). Cancer Control Soc.

Ferriman, David. Human Hair Growth in Health & Disease. (Illus.). 76p. 1971. 11.75x (ISBN 0-398-00560-5). C C Thomas.

How to Keep Your Hair on. 1980. 15.00x (ISBN 0-85032-191-3, Pub. by Daniel Co England). State Mutual Bk.

Huffaker, Sandy. The Bald Book: Miracle Cures & More. LC 82-21000. (Illus.). 64p. 1983. pap. 3.95 (ISBN 0-87131-401-0). M Evans.

International Association of Trichologists Staff, ed. Applied Trichology & the Use of the Microscope, 2 pts. (Trichology Educational Program Ser.: Modules 5 & 6). 200p. 1984. Set. 20.00 (ISBN 0-318-02108-0). Intl Assn Trichologists.

Law, Donald. How to Keep Your Hair On. 70p. 1968. pap. 4.95x (ISBN 0-8464-1025-7). Beekman Pubs.

LuBowe, Irwin I. & Huss, Barbara. A Teenage Guide to Healthy Skin & Hair. 224p. 1983. pap. 6.95 (ISBN 0-8290-1159-5). Irvington.

Norris, Clarice. Classroom Experiments in Hair Structure & Chemistry. (Illus.). 1976. 31.50 (ISBN 0-87350-068-7). Milady.

Ortonne, Jean-Paul & Mosher, David B. Vitiligo & Other Hypomelanoses of Hair & Skin. (Topics in Dermatology Ser.). 700p. 1983. 79.50x (ISBN 0-306-40974-7, Plenum Med Bk). Plenum Pub.

Passwater, Richard. Hair Analysis. 1982. 14.95x (ISBN 0-87983-265-7). Cancer Control Soc.

Passwater, Richard A. & Cranton, Elmer M. Trace Elements, Hair Analysis & Nutrition: Fact & Myth. LC 81-83892. 1983. 18.95 (ISBN 0-87983-348-3); pap. 14.95 (ISBN 0-87983-265-7). Keats.

Powitt, A. H. Hair Structure & Chemistry Simplified. new ed. (Illus.). 300p. 1977. text ed. 20.20 (ISBN 0-87350-080-6). Milady.

--Lectures in Hair Structure & Chemistry for Cosmetology Teachers. (Illus.). 1983. 18.00 (ISBN 0-87350-013-X). Milady.

Robbins, Clarence R. The Chemical & Physical Behavior of Human Hair. 1979. 32.50 (ISBN 0-442-26818-1). Van Nos Reinhold.

Savage, John. The Biodynamics of Hair Growth. 88p. 1977. pap. 8.95x (ISBN 0-8464-0996-8). Beekman Pubs.

--The Biodynamics of Hair Growth. 1980. 17.50x (ISBN 0-686-64691-6, Pub. by Daniel Co England). State Mutual Bk.

Sims, Naomi. All about Hair Care for the Black Woman. LC 81-43267. (Illus.). 224p. 1982. 12.95 (ISBN 0-385-14819-4). Doubleday.

Yahm, J. J. Lesson Plans for Hair Structure & Chemistry. 1973. 39.75 (ISBN 0-87350-052-0); wkbk. 12.45 (ISBN 0-87350-053-9). Milady.

HAIR, REMOVAL OF

Hinkel, Arthur R. & Lind, Richard W. Electrolysis, Thermolysis & the Blend: The Principles & Practice of Permanent Hair Removal. LC 68-19191. (Illus.). 1968. 24.00x (ISBN 0-9600284-1-2). Arroway.

Horchem, Sophie K. All about Permanent Hair Removal. LC 76-11436. 1976. pap. 5.00 (ISBN 0-8283-1671-6). Branden Pub Co.

Shapiro, Julius. Electrolysis: Beauty & Confidence Through Permanent Hair Removal. LC 80-24691. (Illus.). 207p. 1981. 10.95 (ISBN 0-396-07903-2). Dodd.

HAIRDRESSING

Bowser, Milton. Chemical Hair Straightening. (Illus.). 130p. 1979. softbound 5.00 (ISBN 0-940178-00-1). Sitare Inc.

Kilgour, O. F. & McGarry, Marguerite. Complete Hairdressing Science. (Illus.). 208p. 1985. pap. 14.95 (ISBN 0-434-91058-9, Pub. by W Heinemann Ltd). David & Charles.

Kingsley, Philip. The Complete Hair Book: The Ultimate Guide to Your Hairs Health & Beauty. (A Fred Jordan Bk.). (Illus.). 1982. pap. 10.95 (ISBN 0-394-17981-1, Ever). Grove.

Lee, C. M. & Inglis, J. K. Science for Hairdressing Students. 3rd ed. (Illus.). 200p. 1983. 44.00 (ISBN 0-08-027440-4); pap. 15.00 (ISBN 0-08-027439-0). Pergamon.

Masters, T. W. Hairdressing in Theory & Practice. 5th ed. (Illus.). 280p. 1981. pap. text ed. 18.95x (ISBN 0-291-39624-0). Intl Ideas.

--Hairdressing in Theory & Practice. 280p. 1980. 25.00x (ISBN 0-291-39618-6, Pub. by Tech Pr). State Mutual Bk.

Robbins, Stephen P. Organizational Behavior: Concepts, Controversies & Applications. 2nd ed. (Illus.). 608p. 1983. 28.95 (ISBN 0-13-641480-X). P-H.

Salter, Mary & Sturtivant, Doreen. Health for Hairdressers: Notes for Hairdressing Students & Apprentices. 144p. 1981. pap. 25.00x (ISBN 0-291-39613-5, Pub. by Tech Pr). State Mutual Bk.

Yahm, J. J. Lesson Plans for Hair Structure & Chemistry. 1973. 39.75 (ISBN 0-87350-052-0); wkbk. 12.45 (ISBN 0-87350-053-9). Milady.

HALDANE, JOHN BURDON SANDERSON, 1892-1964

Clark, Ronald. J. B. S. The Life & Work of J. B. S. Haldane. (Illus., Orig.). 1984. pap. 7.95 (ISBN 0-19-281430-3). Oxford U Pr.

HALES, STEPHEN, 1677-1761

Allan, D. G. & Schofield, R. E. Stephen Hales: Scientist & Philanthropist. 1980. 50.00 (ISBN 0-85967-482-7). Scolar.

Darwin, Francis. Rustic Sounds & Other Studies in Literature & Natural History. facs. ed. LC 69-17572. (Essay Index Reprint Ser). 1917. 17.00 (ISBN 0-8369-0069-3). Ayer Co Pubs.

HALF-TIMBERED HOUSES

see also Framing (Building)

Harris, Richard. Discovering Timber-Framed Buildings. (Discovering Ser.: No. 242). (Illus.). 96p. 1982. pap. 4.95 (ISBN 0-85263-481-1, Pub. by Shire Pubns England). Seven Hills Bks.

HALF TONE PROCESS

see Photoengraving

HALIBUT FISHERIES

Bell, F. Howard. Pacific Halibut: The Resource & the Fishery. LC 80-29218. (Illus.). 288p. 1981. 24.95 (ISBN 0-88240-158-0); pap. 19.95 (ISBN 0-88240-141-6). Alaska Northwest.

HALIDES

Abraham, S. Tetraalkyl Halides. 1986. 100.00 (ISBN 0-08-026188-4). Pergamon.

Gerrard, W. Hydrogen Halides in Non-Aqueous Solvents: Gas Solubilities. (Solubility Data Ser.). 1986. 100.00 (ISBN 0-08-023925-0). Pergamon.

Huang, C. C., et al. Molecular Studies on Halogenated Deoxynucleosides. 256p. 1972. text ed. 36.50x (ISBN 0-8422-7013-2). Irvington.

Patai, S. The Chemistry of Halides, Pseudohalides & Azides: Supplement D. (Chemistry of Functional Groups Ser.). 1983. Pt. 1, 931p. 288.95 (ISBN 0-471-10087-0); Part 2, 936p. 288.95 (ISBN 0-471-10088-9); Set. 577.95 (ISBN 0-471-10089-7). Wiley.

Wilcox. Lead Tin Telluride, Silver Halides & Czochralski Growth. (Preparation & Properties of Solid State Materials Ser.: Vol. 6). 344p. 1981. 65.00 (ISBN 0-8247-1367-2). Dekker.

HALITE

see Salt

HALL EFFECT

Campell, Leslie L. Galvanomagnetic & Thermogmagnetic Effects: The Hall & Allied Phenomena. (Illus.). 1923. 23.00 (ISBN 0-384-07280-1). Johnson Repr.

Chien, C. L. & Westgate, C. R., eds. The Hall Effect & Its Applications. LC 80-18566. 560p. 1980. 79.50x (ISBN 0-306-40556-3, Plenum Pr). Plenum Pub.

Hurd, Colin M. The Hall Effect in Metals & Alloys. LC 76-157936. (International Cryogenics Monographs). 400p. 1972. 65.00x (ISBN 0-306-30530-5, Plenum Pr). Plenum Pub.

HALLEY'S COMET

Asimov, Isaac. Asimov's Guide to Halley's Comet. (Illus.). 61p. 1985. 12.95 (ISBN 0-8027-0836-6); pap. cancelled (ISBN 0-8027-7281-1). Walker & Co.

--Asimov's Guide to Halley's Comet. 1985. pap. 5.95 (ISBN 0-440-50434-1, Dell Trade Pbks). Dell.

Baldwin, Louis. Edmond Halley & His Comet. (Illus.). 170p. (Orig.). 1985. 14.95 (ISBN 0-89288-115-1); pap. 7.95 (ISBN 0-89288-107-0). Maverick.

Doherty, Paul. The Arrival of Halley's Comet, 1985-1986. 1985. pap. 8.95 (ISBN 0-8120-3632-8). Barron.

Edberg, Stephen J. International Halley Watch: Amateurs Observers' Manual for Scientific Comet Studies. (Illus.). 192p. 1983. pap. 9.95 (ISBN 0-933346-40-9). Sky Pub.

Etter, Roberta & Schneider, Stuart. Halley's Comet: Memories of 1910. 96p. 1985. 19.95 (ISBN 0-89659-588-9). Abbeville Pr.

Flaste, Richard, et al. The New York Times Guide to the Return of Halley's Comet. LC 84-40420. (Illus.). 288p. 1985. 16.95 (ISBN 0-8129-1148-2); pap. 7.95 (ISBN 0-8129-6347-4). Times Bks.

Greiner, Keith. Halley's Comet: The Viewer's Essential Guide & Notebook. (Illus.). 33p. 1984. pap. 6.95 (ISBN 0-9614258-0-6); European Edition. pap. 6.95 (ISBN 0-9614258-1-4). Better Life.

Gropman, Donald & Mirvis, Kenneth. Comet Fever. 1985. pap. 7.95 (ISBN 0-671-60307-8, Fireside). S&S.

Harper, Brian. The Official Halley's Comet Book. (Illus.). 192p. 1985. 15.95 (ISBN 0-340-36511-0, Pub. by Hodder & Stoughton UK). David & Charles.

Hart, Matthew. A Viewers Guide to Halley's Comet. 1985. pap. 2.95 (ISBN 0-671-49841-X). PB.

Lancaster-Brown, Peter. Halley & His Comet. (Illus.). 192p. 1985. 12.95 (ISBN 0-7137-1447-6, Pub. by Blandford Pr England). Sterling.

Metz, Jerred. Halley's Comet, Nineteen Ten: Fire in the Sky. (Illus., Orig.). 1985. 13.95 (ISBN 0-933439-00-8); pap. 8.95 (ISBN 0-933439-01-6). Singing Bone Pr.

Moore, Patrick & Mason, John. Return of Halley's Comet. 128p. 1985. pap. 6.95 (ISBN 0-446-38303-1). Warner Bks.

Peterson, Richard B. The Wonderful Apparition: Halley's Comet. Lighthouse Writer's Guild Staff, ed. 200p. 1985. 24.95x (ISBN 0-935125-00-0). Lighthouse Writers.

Reddy, Francis. Halley's Comet! LC 85-1396. (Illus.). 58p. (Orig.). 1985. pap. 9.95 (ISBN 0-913135-02-X). AstroMedia Corp.

Sagan, Carl. Comet. 1985. 24.95 (ISBN 0-317-20762-8). Random.

Sky & Telescope Editors. Mr. Halley's Comet. LC 84-52261. (Illus.). 32p. (Orig.). 1984. saddle stitch 2.00 (ISBN 0-933346-41-7). Sky Pub.

Tattersfield, Donald. Halley's Comet. (Illus.). 166p. 1985. 12.95x (ISBN 0-631-13558-8). Basil Blackwell.

Tullius, John. The Science Digest Book of Halley's Comet. 122p. 1985. pap. 9.95 (ISBN 0-380-89527-7). Avon.

HALLUCINOGENIC DRUGS

Byck, Robert. The Mood Modifiers. (Encyclopedia of Psychoactive Drugs Ser.). (Illus.). 1985. PLB 15.95x. Chelsea Hse.

De Rios, Marlene D. Hallucinogens: Cross-Cultural Perspectives. LC 84-7244. 224p. 1984. 22.50x (ISBN 0-8263-0737-X). U of NM Pr.

Furst, Peter E. Mushrooms: Psychedelic Fungi. (Encyclopedia of Psychoactive Drugs Ser.). (Illus.). 1985. PLB 15.95x (ISBN 0-87754-767-X). Chelsea Hse.

Glowa, John R. Inhalants: Glue, Gas & Sniff. (Encyclopedia of Psychoactive Drugs Ser.). (Illus.). 1985. PLB 15.95x (ISBN 0-87754-758-0). Chelsea Hse.

Guzman, Gaston. The Genus Psilocybe: Revision of the Known Species (Hallucinogenic Species) (Beiheft to Nova Hedwigia Ser.: No. 74). (Illus.). 650p. 1983. lib. bdg. 70.00 (ISBN 3-7682-1319-6). Lubrecht & Cramer.

McLellan, Tom & Bragg, Alicia. Escape from Anxiety & Stress. (Encyclopedia of Psychoactive Drugs Ser.). (Illus.). 1985. PLB 15.95x (ISBN 0-87754-772-6). Chelsea Hse.

Richardson, P. Mick. Flowering Plants: Magic in Bloom. (Encyclopedia of Psychoactive Drugs Ser.). (Illus.). 1985. PLB 15.95x (ISBN 0-87754-757-2). Chelsea Hse.

Schultes, Richard E. & Hofmann, Albert. The Botany & Chemistry of Hallucinogens. 2nd ed. (Illus.). 464p. 1980. photocopy 46.50x (ISBN 0-398-03863-5). C C Thomas.

Stafford, Peter. Psychedelics Encyclopedia. LC 82-10482. (Illus.). 416p. 1982. pap. 12.95 (ISBN 0-87477-231-1). J P Tarcher.

HALOGENATION

De La Mare, Peter. Electrophilic Halogenation: Reaction Pathways Involving Attack by Electrophilic Halogens on Unsaturated Compounds. LC 75-13451. (Cambridge Chemistry Texts Ser.). pap. 60.80 (ISBN 0-317-20854-3, 2024444). Bks Demand UMI.

HALOGENS

see also Chlorine; Fluorine; Iodine

Gutmann, Viktor, ed. International Review of Halogen Chemistry, 3 Vols. LC 66-30147. (Illus.). Vol. 1, 1967. 81.00 (ISBN 0-12-310901-9); Vol. 2, 1967. 76.00 (ISBN 0-12-310902-7); Vol. 3, 1968. 81.00 (ISBN 0-12-310903-5). Acad Pr.

Khan, M. A. & Stanton, R. H., eds. Toxicology of Halogenated Hydrocarbons: Health & Ecological Effects. (Illus.). 350p. 1981. 66.00 (ISBN 0-08-027530-3). Pergamon.

MacDiarmid, Alan G. The Bond to Halogens & Halogenoids, Pt. 1. (Organometalic Compounds of the Group IV Elements Ser.: Vol. 2). (Illus.). pap. 98.00 (ISBN 0-317-12973-2, 2055068). Bks Demand UMI.

Nicholson, William J. & Moore, John A., eds. Health Effects of Halogenated Aromatic Hydrocarbons. LC 79-12253. (Annals of the New York Academy of Sciences: Vol. 320). 730p. 1979. 117.00x (ISBN 0-89766-008-0). NY Acad Sci.

HALOPHYTES

Sen, D. N. Contributions to the Ecology of Halophytes. 1982. 69.50 (ISBN 90-6193-942-9, Pub. by Junk Pubs Netherlands). Kluwer Academic.

Waisel, Yoav. Biology of Halophytes. (Physiological Ecology Ser). 1972. 67.50 (ISBN 0-12-730850-4). Acad Pr.

HAMILTON, WILLIAM ROWAN, SIR, 1805-1865

Hankins, Thomas L. Sir William Rowan Hamilton: A Biography. LC 80-10627. 496p. 1980. text ed. 38.00x (ISBN 0-8018-2203-3). Johns Hopkins.

Mill, John S. An Examination of Sir William Hamilton's Philosophy. Robson, John M., ed. LC 63-25976. (Collected Works of John Stuart Mill). 1979. 45.00x (ISBN 0-8020-2329-0). U of Toronto Pr.

HAMSTERS

Hamsters. rev. ed. Folk, Edgar G. Jr., ed. (Illus.). 80p. 1984. pap. 3.95 (ISBN 0-86622-228-6, PB-114). TFH Pubns.

Keyser, A. The Development of the Diencephalon of the Chinese Hamster: An Investigation of the Validity of the Criteria of Subdivision of the Brain. (Acta Anatomica: Vol. 83, Suppl.). (Illus.). 1972. pap. 15.50 (ISBN 3-8055-1593-6). S Karger.

Ostrow, Marshall. Breeding Hamsters. (Illus.). 96p. 1982. 4.95 (ISBN 0-87666-935-6, KW-134). TFH Pubns.

Reznik, G., et al. Clinical Anatomy of the European Hamster Cricetus Cricetus, L. 248p. 1980. 67.00x (ISBN 0-7194-0064-3, Pub. by Castle Hse England). State Mutual Bk.

Roberts, Mervin F. Teddy Bear Hamsters. (Illus.). 96p. (Orig.). 1974. 4.95 (ISBN 0-87666-776-0, PS-710). TFH Pubns.

--The T.F.H Book of Hamsters. (Illus.). 80p. 1981. 6.95 (ISBN 0-87666-848-1, HP-003). TFH Pubns.

Siegel, Harold I., ed. The Hamster: Reproduction & Behavior. 458p. 1984. 59.50x (ISBN 0-306-41791-X, Plenum Pr). Plenum Pub.

Streilein, Jacob W., et al, eds. Hamster Immune Responses in Infectious & Oncologic Diseases. LC 80-29639. (Advances in Experimental Medicine & Biology Ser.: Vol. 134). 486p. 1981. 65.00x (ISBN 0-306-40642-X, Plenum Pr). Plenum Pub.

Symposium on the Syrian Hamster in Toxicology & Carcinogenesis Research, Boston, November 30-December 2, 1977. The Syrian Hamster in Toxicology & Carcinogenesis: Proceedings. Homburger, F., ed. (Progress in Experimental Tumor Research: Vol. 24). (Illus.). 1979. 69.50 (ISBN 3-8055-2890-6). S Karger.

HAND PLANES

see Planes (Hand Tools)

HAND PRESS

see Handpress

HANDLING OF BULK SOLIDS

see Bulk Solids Handling

HANDLING OF FOOD

see Food Handling

HANDLING OF MATERIALS

see Materials Handling

HANDPRESS

see also Printing, Practical; Printing Press

Mason, Billy. How to Build Your Own Rubber Stamp Press. 1978. 5.00 (ISBN 0-686-23414-6). Kelso.

HANGING ROOFS

see Roofs, Suspension

HARBORS

see also Docks; Piers; Pilots and Pilotage; Shore Protection; Wharves

Agerschou, Hans & Lundgren, Helge. Planning & Design of Ports & Marine Terminals. LC 83-7032. 320p. 1983. 74.95x (ISBN 0-471-90191-1, Pub. by Wiley-Interscience). Wiley.

American Society of Civil Engineers Staff, compiled by. Ports '77, 2 Vols. 997p. 1977. pap. 36.00x (ISBN 0-87262-084-0). Am Soc Civil Eng.

American Society of Civil Engineers, compiled by. Report on Small Craft Harbors. (Manual & Report on Engineering Practice Ser.: No. 50). 145p. 1969. pap. 10.00x (ISBN 0-87262-224-X). Am Soc Civil Eng.

Bruun, Per. Port Engineering. 3rd ed. LC 81-603. 800p. 1981. 79.95x (ISBN 0-87201-739-7). Gulf Pub.

Clark, John, et al. Small Seaports: Revitalization Through Conserving Heritage Resources. LC 79-67736. (Illus.). 64p. (Orig.). 1979. pap. 6.50 (ISBN 0-89164-059-2). Conservation Foun.

Cornick, H. F. Dock & Harbour Engineering: The Design of Docks, Vol. 1. 338p. 200.00x (ISBN 0-85264-037-4, Pub. by Griffin England). State Mutual Bk.

Dock & Harbour Engineering: The Design of Harbours, Vol. 2. 352p. 1969. 200.00x (ISBN 0-85264-041-2, Pub. by Griffin England). State Mutual Bk.

Fishery Harbour Planning. (Fisheries Technical Papers: No. 123). 36p. 1973. pap. 7.50 (ISBN 0-686-92785-0, F857, FAO). Unipub.

Hoyle, B. S. & Hilling, D., eds. Seaport Systems & Spatial Change: Technologies, Industries & Developmental Strategies. LC 89-16987. 481p. 1984. 49.95x (ISBN 0-471-90354-X, Pub. by Wiley-Interscience). Wiley.

Hoyle, Brian & Pinder, David, eds. Cityport Industrialization: Spatial Analysis & Planning Strategies Cityport Industrialization, 15-18 Nov. 1978, Univ. Of Southampton. LC 80-40837. (Urban & Regional Planning Ser.). (Illus.). 350p. 1981. 60.00. Pergamon.

Inland & Maritime Waterways & Ports: Proceedings of the XXV Congress of the Permanent International Association of Navigation Congresses, (PIANC) Edinburgh, Scotland, 11 vols. Incl. Section 1: Inland Waterways & Ports. 190.00 (ISBN 0-08-026753-X); Section 2: Maritime Ports & Seaways. 190.00 (ISBN 0-08-027278-9). (Illus.). 2750p. 1981. 400.00 (ISBN 0-08-026750-5). Pergamon.

Porteous, J. Douglas. Canal Ports: The Urban Achievement of the Canal Age. 1977. 47.50 (ISBN 0-12-561950-2). Acad Pr.

Ports of the World, 1984. 1985. 330.00x (ISBN 0-686-98230-4, Pub. by Lloyds London Pr). State Mutual Bk.

A Review of Quantitative Methods as Applied to Fishery Harbour Planning, Design & Operation, Vol. 3. pap. 7.50 (F811, UN). Unipub.

Source Book on Environmental & Safety Considerations for Planning & Design of LNG Marine Terminals. 46p. 1976. pap. 7.00x (ISBN 0-87262-158-8). Am Soc Civil Eng.

Winters, Tobey L. Deepwater Ports in the United States: An Economic & Environmental Impact Study. LC 76-12885. (Special Studies). 220p. 1977. 38.95x (ISBN 0-275-23250-6). Praeger.

HARD WOODS

see Hardwoods

HARDBOARD

see also Particle Board

Plywood, Fibreboard & Particle Board. (Terminology Bulletins: No. 30). (Eng., Fr., Ital., Ger. & Span.). 162p. 1976. pap. 11.75 (F1218, FAO). Unipub.

HARDNESS

see also Precipitation Hardening

Almond, E. A., et al, eds. Science of Hard Materials 1984. Warren, R. R. (Institute of Conference Ser.: 75). 1000p. 1985. 120.00 (ISBN 0-85498-166-7, Pub. by A Hilger England). Heyden.

American Society for Testing & Materials. Plane Strain Crack Toughness: Testing of High Strength Metallic Materials. LC 66-29517. (American Society for Testing & Materials, Special Technical Publication Ser.: No. 410). pap. 34.00 (ISBN 0-317-08331-7, 2051707). Bks Demand UMI.

Ghose, Rabindra N. EMP Environment & System Hardness Design. LC 83-51067. (Illus.). 250p. 1984. text ed. 42.00 (ISBN 0-932263-16-X). White Consult.

VDE, ed. Hardness Testing in Theory & Practice VDI 308. 1978. 57.00 (ISBN 0-9961073-9-8, Pub. by VDI W Germany). Heyden.

Westbrook, J. H. & Conrad, H., eds. The Science of Hardness Testing & Its Research Applications: Papers Presented at a Symposium of the American Society for Metals, Oct. 18-20, 1971. LC 72-95851. (Illus.). pap. 133.50 (ISBN 0-317-08332-5, 2019482). Bks Demand UMI.

HARDWARE

see also Building Fittings; Cutlery; Knives; Locks and Keys; Saws; Tools

Beeson, Richard D. & Crutcher, Ernest R. Hardware Cleaning & Sampling for Cleanliness Verification & Contamination Control Microscopy. LC 61-38584. 34p. 1983. pap. text ed. 25.00 (ISBN 0-915414-72-4). Inst Environ Sci.

Eastwood, Maud L. Antique Builders Hardware: Knobs & Accessories. (Illus.). 224p. (Orig.). 1982. 19.50 (ISBN 0-9610800-2-7); pap. 17.50 (ISBN 0-9610800-1-9). Ant Doorknob Pub.

Marine Fabric & Hardware Directory. 20.00 (ISBN 0-318-01516-1, 12080). Indus Fabrics.

Roberts, Kenneth D., ed. Stanley Rule & Level Co. 1879 Price List of Tools & Hardware. 1973. 5.00 (ISBN 0-913602-05-1). K Roberts.

Ryder, G. H., ed. Gates' Jigs, Fixtures, Tools & Gauges. 6th ed. (Illus.). 1973. 35.00x (ISBN 0-291-39432-9). Intl Ideas.

Schiffer, Herbert F. Early Pennsylvania Hardware. (Illus.). 64p. 1966. pap. 3.75 (ISBN 0-916838-42-0). Schiffer.

Stanley Rule & Level Co. 1870 Catalogue of Tools & Hardware. 1973. 5.50 (ISBN 0-913602-04-3). K Roberts.

Tinkham, Sandra S., ed. Catalog of Tools, Hardware, Firearms & Vehicles. (Index of American Design Ser.: Pt. 4). (Orig.). 1979. pap. 36.00x (ISBN 0-914146-69-6); incl. color microfiche 480.00x (ISBN 0-914146-68-8). Chadwyck-Healey.

HARDWOODS

see also names of hardwoods, e.g. Mahogany

America's Hardwood Forests: Opportunities Unlimited. LC 83-60910. 352p. (Orig.). 1983. pap. 17.00 (ISBN 0-939970-19-8, SAF 83-04). Soc Am Foresters.

Directory of Hardwood Plywood Manufacturers: U. S. & Canada. 46p. 30.00 (ISBN 0-686-34549-5). Hardwd Ply.

Fine Hardwoods Selectorama: FH-AWA. 57p. 10.00 (ISBN 0-686-34553-3). Hardwd Ply.

The How & Why of Hardwood Paneling: Set of Slides with Script. 30.00 (ISBN 0-686-34556-8). Hardwd Ply.

Nutting, Wallace. Furniture Treasury, 3 Vols. (Illus.). Vols. 1 & 2 In 1. 29.95 (ISBN 0-02-590980-0); Vol. 3. 24.95 (ISBN 0-02-591040-X). Macmillan.

Phillips, F. H. & Logan, A. F. The Pulping & Paper Making Potential of Tropical Hardwoods VI: Mixed Species from the Gogol Timber Area, Papua New Guinea. (Division of Chemical Technology Technical Papers: No. 10). 32p. 1979. 6.00 (ISBN 0-643-00339-8, C064, CSIRO). Unipub.

Usher, M. B. & Ocloo, J. K. The Natural Resistance of Eighty-Five West African Hardwood Timbers to Attack by Termites & Micro-Organisms. 1979. 35.00x (ISBN 0-85135-103-4, Pub. by Centre Overseas Research). State Mutual Bk.

HARDY SPACES

see also Functional Analysis; Functions of Complex Variables

Garcia-Cuerva & Rubio De Francia, J. L. Weighted Norm Inequalities & Related Topics. (Mathematics Studies: Vol. 116). 604p. 1985. 65.00 (ISBN 0-444-87804-1, North-Holland). Elsevier.

Neville, Charles W. Invariant Subspaces of Hardy Classes on Infinitely Connected Open Surfaces. (Memoirs: No. 160). 151p. 1975. pap. 12.00 (ISBN 0-8218-1860-0, MEMO-160). Am Math.

HARES

see also Rabbits

Kingdon, Jonathan. East African Mammals: An Atlas of Evolution in Africa. Vol. II, Pt. B: Hares & Rodents. LC 83-24174. (Illus.). 428p. 1984. pap. 25.00 (ISBN 0-226-43720-5). U of Chicago Pr.

HARIOT, THOMAS, 1560-1621

Shirley, John W. A Source Book for the Study of Thomas Harriot. Cohen, I. Bernard, ed. LC 80-2111. (Development of Science Ser.). (Illus.). 1981. lib. bdg. 50.00x (ISBN 0-405-13831-8). Ayer Co Pubs.

--Thomas Harriott: Renaissance Scientist. (Illus.). 1974. 37.50x (ISBN 0-19-858140-8). Oxford U Pr.

Stevens, Henry. Thomas Hariot, the Mathematician, the Philosopher & the Scholar. LC 72-82433. 213p. 1972. Repr. of 1900 ed. 19.50 (ISBN 0-8337-3399-0). B Franklin.

HARLEY-DAVIDSON MOTORCYCLE

Arman, Mike & Heinrichs, Kurt. What Fits What on Harley Davidson Nineteen Thirty-Six to Nineteen Eighty-Three. 6th ed. (Illus.). 1983. pap. 5.00 (ISBN 0-933078-11-0). M Arman.

Clew, Jeff. Harley Davidson Owners Workshop Manual: Sportster '70 Thru '76. (Owners Workshop Manuals Ser.: No. 250). 1979. 10.50 (ISBN 0-85696-250-3, Pub. by J H Haynes England). Haynes Pubns.

Clymer Publications. Harley-Davidson Service-Repair Handbook: Sportster Series, 1959-1984. Robinson, Jeff, ed. (Illus.). pap. 13.95 (ISBN 0-89287-126-1, M419). Clymer Pubns.

Harley Davidson Owners Workshop Manual: Super & Electraglide '74 Thru '77. (Owners Workshop Manuals Ser.: No. 330). 1979. 10.50 (ISBN 0-85696-330-5, Pub. by J H Haynes England). Haynes Pubns.

Jorgensen, Eric, ed. Harley-Davidson Service, Repair Handbook: All 74 and 80 Cu. in. models, V-Twins 1959-1984. (Illus.). pap. 13.95 (ISBN 0-89287-190-3, M420). Clymer Pubns.

Sucher, Harry V. Harley-Davidson: The Milwaukee Marvel. rev. ed. (Illus.). 283p. 1982. 22.95 (ISBN 0-85429-261-6, F261). Haynes Pubns.

HARMONIC ANALYSIS

see also Bessel's Functions; Fourier Series; Fourier Transformations; Harmonic Functions; Lame's Functions; Spherical Harmonics; Time-Series Analysis

Ash, Marshall J., ed. Studies in Harmonic Analysis. LC 76-16431. (MAA Studies Ser.: No. 13). 319p. 1976. 21.00 (ISBN 0-88385-113-X). Math Assn.

Baird, P. Harmonic Maps with Symmetry, Harmonic Morphisms & Deformation of Metrics. (Research Notes in Mathematics Ser.: No. 87). 208p. 1983. pap. text ed. 17.95 (ISBN 0-273-08603-0). Pitman Pub MA.

Beckner, William, et al, eds. Conference on Harmonic Analysis in Honor of Antoni Zygmund. LC 82-11172. (Mathematics Ser.: Vols. I & II). 837p. 1983. write for info. (ISBN 0-534-98043-0). Wadsworth Pub.

Benedetto, J. Harmonic Analysis on Totally Disconnected Sets. LC 77-163741. (Lecture Notes in Mathematics: Vol. 202). 1971. pap. 14.00 (ISBN 0-387-05488-X). Springer-Verlag.

Benedetto, J. J., ed. Euclidean Harmonic Analysis: Proceedings. (Lecture Notes in Mathematics: Vol. 779). 177p. 1980. pap. 15.00 (ISBN 0-387-09748-1). Springer-Verlag.

Berg, C. & Christensen, J. P. Harmonic Analysis on Semigroups: Theory of Positive Definite & Related Functions. (Graduate Texts in Mathematics Ser.: Vol. 100). (Illus.). 335p. 1984. 39.00 (ISBN 0-387-90925-7). Springer-Verlag.

Bochner, Salomon. Fouriersche Integrale. LC 49-22695. (Ger). 10.50 (ISBN 0-8284-0042-3). Chelsea Pub.

Bracewell, R. The Fourier Transform & Its Applications. 2nd ed. (Electrical Engineering Ser.). (Illus.). 1978. text ed. 48.00 (ISBN 0-07-007013-X). McGraw.

Brezin, J. P. Harmonic Analysis on Compact Solvmanifolds. LC 77-22142. (Lecture Notes in Mathematics: Vol. 602). 1977. pap. text ed. 14.00 (ISBN 0-387-08354-5). Springer-Verlag.

Carmona, J. & Vergne, M., eds. Non-Commutative Analysis: Proceedings. (Lecture Notes in Mathematics: Vol. 728). 1979. pap. 17.00 (ISBN 0-387-09516-0). Springer-Verlag.

--Non-Commutative Harmonic Analysis. (Lecture Notes in Mathematics Ser.: Vol. 587). 1977. soft cover 18.00 (ISBN 0-387-08245-X). Springer-Verlag.

--Non-Commutative Harmonic Analysis & Lie Group: Proceedings. (Lecture Notes in Mathematics Ser.: Vol. 830). 553p. 1981. pap. 32.00 (ISBN 0-387-10872-6). Springer-Verlag.

Carmona, J., et al, eds. Non-Commutative Harmonic Analysis. 231p. 1975. pap. 16.00 (ISBN 0-387-07183-0). Springer-Verlag.

Chao & Woyczynski. Probability Theory & Harmonic Analysis. (Pure & Applied Mathematics Ser.). 320p. 1986. price not set (ISBN 0-8247-7473-6). Dekker.

Coifman, Ronald & Weiss, Guido. Transference Methods in Analysis. LC 77-24098. (Conference Board of the Mathematical Sciences Ser.: No. 31). 59p. 1977. pap. 13.00 (ISBN 0-8218-1681-0, CBMS 31). Am Math.

Conference on Harmonic Analysis, College Park, Md., 1971. Proceedings. Gulick, D. & Lipsman, R. L., eds. LC 72-80302. (Lecture Notes in Mathematics: Vol. 266). 329p. 1972. pap. 13.00 (ISBN 0-387-05856-7). Springer-Verlag.

Dobrev, V. K., et al. Harmonic Analysis. (Lecture Notes in Physics: Vol. 63). 1977. pap. 18.00 (ISBN 0-387-08150-X). Springer-Verlag.

Dunkl, Charles F. & Ramirez, Donald E. Topics in Harmonic Analysis. LC 73-153387. (Century Mathematics Ser.). 1971. 34.50x (ISBN 0-89197-454-7); pap. text ed. 16.95x (ISBN 0-89197-969-7). Irvington.

Figa-Talamanca & Picardello. Harmonic Analysis on Free Groups. (Lecture Notes in Pure & Applied Mathematics). 224p. 1983. 35.00 (ISBN 0-8247-7042-0). Dekker.

Graham, C. C. & McGehee, O. C. Essays in Commutative Harmonic Analysis. LC 79-13096. (Grundlehren der Mathematischen Wissenschaften: Vol. 238). (Illus.). 1979. 58.00 (ISBN 0-387-90426-3). Springer-Verlag.

Gross, Leonard. Harmonic Analysis on Hilbert Space. LC 52-42839. (Memoirs: No. 46). 62p. 1983. pap. 9.00 (ISBN 0-8218-1246-7, MEMO-46). Am Math.

Harrington, Roger F. Time-Harmonic Electromagnetic Fields. (Electronic & Electrical Engineering Ser.). 1961. text ed. 58.00 (ISBN 0-07-026745-6). McGraw.

Helgason, Sigurdur. Topics in Harmonic Analysis on Homgeneous Spaces. (Progress in Math. Ser.: No. 13). 160p. 1981. text ed. 14.50x (ISBN 0-8176-3051-1). Birkhauser.

Helson, Henry. Ahrmonic Analysis. 190p. 1983. 31.95 (ISBN 0-201-12752-0). Addison-Wesley.

Hewitt, E. & Ross, K. A. Abstract Harmonic Analysis: Vol. 2, Structure & Analysis for Compact Groups, Analysis on Locally Compact Abelian Groups. LC 63-12898. (Grundlehren der Mathematischen Wissenschaften: Vol. 152). 1970. 79.00 (ISBN 0-387-04832-4). Springer-Verlag.

Heyer, H. Probability Measures on Locally Compact Groups. (Ergebnisse der Mathematik und ihrer Grenzgbiete: Vol. 94). 1977. 78.00 (ISBN 0-387-08332-4). Springer-Verlag.

Hua, L. K. Harmonic Analysis of Functions of Several Complex Variables in the Classical Domains. rev. ed. LC 63-16769. (Translations of Mathematical Monographs: Vol. 6). 186p. 1979. pap. 27.00 (ISBN 0-8218-1556-3, MMONO-6). Am Math.

Jost, J. Harmonic Maps Between Surfaces. (Lecture Notes in Mathematics Ser.: Vol. 1062). ix, 133p. 1984. pap. 10.50 (ISBN 0-387-13339-9). Springer-Verlag.

Katznelson, Yitzhak. An Introduction to Harmonic Analysis. 264p. 1976. pap. text ed. 5.00 (ISBN 0-486-63331-4). Dover.

Knill, R. J., et al, eds. Harmonic Maps, Tulane: 1980, Proceedings. (Lecture Notes in Mathematics Ser.: Vol. 949). 158p. 1982. pap. 12.00 (ISBN 0-387-11595-1). Springer-Verlag.

Levinson, Norman. Gap & Density Theorems. LC 41-6147. (Colloquium, Pbns. Ser.: Vol. 26). 246p. 1963. Repr. of 1940 ed. 23.00 (ISBN 0-8218-1026-X, COLL-26). Am Math.

Lindahl, L. A. & Poulsen, F. Thin Sets in Harmonic Analysis. (Lecture Notes in Pure & Applied Mathematics Ser.: Vol. 2). 1971. 35.00 (ISBN 0-8247-1317-6). Dekker.

Local Analysis of Selberg's Trace Formula. (Lecture Notes in Mathematics: Vol. 1040). iii, 128p. 1983. pap. 10.00 (ISBN 0-387-12713-5). Springer-Verlag.

Mandrekar, V. & Salehi, H., eds. Prediction Theory & Harmonic Analysis. 446p. 1983. 68.00 (ISBN 0-444-86597-7, I-121-83, North Holland). Elsevier.

Marcus, Michael B. & Pisier, Gilles. Random Fourier Series with Application to Harmonic Analysis. LC 81-47145. (Annals of Mathematical Studies: No.101). 192p. 1981. 22.50 (ISBN 0-691-08289-8); pap. 8.95 (ISBN 0-691-08292-8). Princeton U Pr.

Mauceri, G., et al, eds. Harmonic Analysis. (Lecture Notes in Mathematics: Vol. 992). 449p. 1983. pap. 24.00 (ISBN 0-387-12299-0). Springer-Verlag.

Moshinsky, M. Harmonic Oscillator in Modern Physics: From Atoms to Quarks. (Documents on Modern Physics Ser.). 100p. 1969. 31.25x (ISBN 0-677-02450-9). Gordon.

Paley, Raymond E. & Wiener, Norbert. Fourier Transforms in the Complex Domain. LC 35-3273. (Colloquium, Pbns. Ser.: Vol. 19). 183p. 1982. pap. 33.00 (ISBN 0-8218-1019-7, COLL-19). Am Math.

Petridis, N., et al, eds. Harmonic Analysis, Iraklion Nineteen Seventy-Eight: Proceedings. (Lecture Notes in Mathematics: Vol. 781). 213p. 1980. pap. text ed. 17.00 (ISBN 0-387-09756-2). Springer-Verlag.

Ricci, F. & Weiss, G., eds. Harmonic Analysis Minneapolis 1981: Proceedings. (Lecture Notes in Mathematics: Vol. 908). 325p. 1982. pap. 20.00 (ISBN 0-387-11188-3). Springer-Verlag.

Riesz, Frigyes & Sz-Nagy, Bela. Functional Analysis. Boron, Leo. F, tr. LC 55-8437. xii, 468p. 25.00 (ISBN 0-8044-4821-3); appendix 2.50 (ISBN 0-8044-4822-1). Ungar.

Schempp, W. Harmonic Analysis on the Heisenberg Nol Patent Group with Applications to Signal Theory. (Research Notes in Mathematics Ser.). 192p. 1985. pap. text ed. write for info. (ISBN 0-273-08542-5). Pitman Pub MA.

Silberger, Allan J. Introduction to Harmonic Analysis on Reductive P-Adic Groups. LC 79-19020. (Mathematical Notes Ser.: 23). 376p. 1980. pap. 24.00 (ISBN 0-691-08246-4). Princeton U Pr.

Stein, E. M. Singular Integrals & Differentiability Properties of Functions. (Mathematical Ser.: No. 30). 1971. 32.50x (ISBN 0-691-08079-8). Princeton U Pr.

Stein, Elias M. Topics in Harmonic Analysis Related to the Littlewood-Paley Theory. LC 72-83688. (Annals of Mathematics Studies: No. 63). 1969. 22.00x (ISBN 0-691-08067-4). Princeton U Pr.

Stein, Elias M. & Weiss, Guido. Introduction to Fourier Analysis on Euclidean Spaces. LC 73-106394. (Mathematical Ser.: No. 32). 1971. 33.00 (ISBN 0-691-08078-X). Princeton U Pr.

Terras, A. Harmonic Analysis on Symmetric Spaces & Applications I. (Illus.). 355p. 1985. pap. 39.00 (ISBN 0-387-96159-3). Springer-Verlag.

Varadarajan, V. S. Harmonic Analysis on Real Reductive Groups. LC 77-2216. (Lecture Notes in Mathematics: Vol. 576). 1977. pap. 26.00 (ISBN 0-387-08135-6). Springer-Verlag.

Weiss, Guido & Wainger, Steve, eds. Harmonic Analysis in Euclidean Spaces, 2 pts. LC 79-12726. (Proceedings of Symposia in Pure Mathematics: Vol. 35). 1979. Set. pap. 57.00 (ISBN 0-8218-1436-2); Pt. 1. 34.00 (PSPUM 35, 1); Pt. 2. pap. 32.00 (ISBN 0-8218-1438-9, PSPUM 35, 2). Am Math.

Whittaker, Edmund T. & Watson, George N. A Course of Modern Analysis. 4th ed. 1927. pap. text ed. 29.95 (ISBN 0-521-09189-6). Cambridge U Pr.

Williams, F. L. Tensor Products of Principal Series Representations, Reduction of Tensor Products of Principal Series Representations of Complex Semisimple Lie Groups. LC 73-19546. (Lecture Notes in Mathematics: Vol. 358). 132p. 1973. pap. 12.00 (ISBN 0-387-06567-9). Springer-Verlag.

HARMONIC FUNCTIONS

see also Bessel's Functions; Fourier Series; Functions, Spheroidal; Harmonic Analysis; Lame's Functions; Spherical Harmonics

Agrest, M. M. & Maksimov, M. S. Theory of Incomplete Cylindrical Functions & Their Applications. Fettis, H. E., et al, trs. from Rus. LC 78-139673. (Die Grundlehren der Mathematischen Wissenschaften: Vol. 160). (Illus.). 1971. 50.00 (ISBN 0-387-05111-2). Springer-Verlag.

Aronszajn, N. & Creese, T. M. Polyharmonic Functions. (Mathematical Monographs). 1983. 59.00x (ISBN 0-19-853906-1). Oxford U Pr.

Arrillaga. Power System Harmonics. LC 84-22097. 1985. 39.95 (ISBN 0-471-90640-9). Wiley.

Chao, J. A. & Woyczynski, W. A., eds. Martingale Theory in Harmonic Analysis & Banach Spaces, Cleveland, Ohio 1981: Proceedings. (Lecture Notes in Mathematics: Vol. 939). 225p. 1982. pap. 14.00 (ISBN 0-387-11569-2). Springer-Verlag.

Constantinescu, C. & Cornea, A. Potential Theory on Harmonic Spaces. LC 72-86117. (Die Grundlehren der Mathematischen Wissenschaften: Vol. 158). 1972. 65.00 (ISBN 0-387-05916-4). Springer-Verlag.

Doob, J. L. Classical Potential Theory & Its Probabilistic Counterpart. (Grundelehren der Mathematischen Wissenschaften Ser.: Vol. 262). 750p. 1984. 64.00 (ISBN 0-387-90881-1). Springer-Verlag.

Fuglede, B. Finely Harmonic Functions. LC 72-90194. (Lecture Notes in Mathematics: Vol. 289). 188p. 1972. pap. 10.00 (ISBN 0-387-06005-7). Springer-Verlag.

Glasner, M. S. Proximal Flows. (Lecture Notes in Mathematics: Vol. 517). 1976. pap. 13.00 (ISBN 0-387-07689-1). Springer-Verlag.

Hayman, W. K. & Kennedy, P. B. Subharmonic Functions, Vol. 1. (London Mathematical Society Ser.). 1977. 49.50 (ISBN 0-12-334801-3). Acad Pr.

Herve, M. Analytic & Plurisubharmonic Functions in Finite & Infinite Dimensional Spaces. (Lecture Notes in Mathematics: Vol. 198). 1971. pap. 11.00 (ISBN 0-387-05472-3). Springer-Verlag.

Lelong, P. Fonctions Plurisousharmoniques et Formes Differentielles Positives. (Cours & Documents de Mathematiques & de Physique Ser.). 90p. 1968. 24.50x (ISBN 0-677-50220-6). Gordon.

--Plurisubharmonic Functions & Positive Differential Forms. (Notes on Mathematics & Its Applications Ser.). 88p. 1969. 24.50 (ISBN 0-677-30220-7). Gordon.

Maeda, F. Y. Dirichlet Integrals on Harmonic Spaces. (Lecture Notes in Mathematics: Vol. 803). 180p. 1980. pap. 15.00 (ISBN 0-387-09995-6). Springer-Verlag.

Rado, T. On the Problem of Plateau - Subharmonic Functions. LC 71-160175. (Illus.). 1971. pap. 22.50 (ISBN 0-387-05479-0). Springer-Verlag.

Ronkin, L. I. Introduction to the Theory of Entire Functions of Several Variables. LC 74-12068. (Translations of Mathematical Monographs: Vol. 44). 1974. 59.00 (ISBN 0-8218-1594-6, MMONO-44). Am Math.

Sario, L., et al. Classification Theory of Riemannian Manifolds. LC 77-22197. (Lecture Notes in Mathematics: Vol. 605). 1977. pap. text ed. 26.00 (ISBN 0-387-08358-8). Springer-Verlag.

Stein, E. M. Boundary Behavior of Holomorphic Functions of Several Complex Variables. LC 71-183062. (Mathematical Notes Ser.: No. 11). 84p. 1972. pap. 12.00 (ISBN 0-691-08109-3). Princeton U Pr.

Stein, Elias M. & Weiss, Guido. Introduction to Fourier Analysis on Euclidean Spaces. LC 73-106394. (Mathematical Ser.: No. 32). 1971. 33.00 (ISBN 0-691-08078-X). Princeton U Pr.

Steklov Institute of Mathematics. Selected Problems of Weighted Approximation & Spectral Analysis: Proceedings. Nikolskii, N. K., ed. LC 76-46375. (Proceeding of the Steklov Institute of Mathematics: No. 120). 1976. 67.00 (ISBN 0-8218-3020-1, STEKLO-120). Am Math.

Sternberg, Wolfgang & Smith, Turner L. The Theory of Potential & Spherical Harmonics. LC 44-9717. (Mathematical Expositions: No. 3). pap. 80.50 (ISBN 0-317-09115-8, 2014421). Bks Demand UMI.

Stockman, Harry E. Steinmetz & Laplace Solutions to Modern Network Problems. 1977. pap. 4.00 (ISBN 0-918332-07-9). Sercolab.

Tsuji, Masatugu. Potential Theory in Modern Function Theory. 2nd ed. LC 74-4297. 600p. 1975. text ed. 23.50 (ISBN 0-8284-0281-7). Chelsea Pub.

Walsh, Joseph L. Location of Critical Points of Analytic & Harmonic Functions. LC 50-12177. (Colloquium Pbns. Ser.: Vol. 34). 394p. 1950. 38.00 (ISBN 0-8218-1034-0, COLL-34). Am Math.

HARMONY

Aldwell, Edward & Schachter, Carl. Harmony & Voice Leading, Vol. 2. 276p. 1979. text ed. 17.95 (ISBN 0-15-531517-X, HC); wkbk. 7.95 (ISBN 0-15-531518-8). HarBraceJ.

Levarie, Siegmund. Fundamentals of Harmony. LC 84-67829. xiii, 151p. 1984. Repr. of 1954 ed. lib. bdg. 25.00x (ISBN 0-313-24526-6, LEFU). Greenwood.

Schoenberg, Arnold. Theory of Harmony. Carter, Roy E., tr. (Calif. Library Reprint: No. 121). 1983. 57.50x (ISBN 0-520-04945-4); pap. 14.95 (ISBN 0-520-04944-6). U of Cal Pr.

HARMONY, KEYBOARD

Frackenpohl, Arthur. Harmonization at the Piano. 5th. ed. 288p. 1985. write for info. plastic comb bdg. (ISBN 0-697-03574-3). Wm C Brown.

McLean, Gary N., et al. Keyboarding for Everyone. LC 84-70836. (Illus.). 160p. (Orig.). 1984. pap. text ed. 12.95 (ISBN 0-88236-122-8). Anaheim Pub Co.

HARNESS MAKING AND TRADE

Hasluck, Paul N. Saddlery & Harness Making. (Illus.). 9.95 (ISBN 0-85131-148-2, BL6610, Dist. by Miller). J A Allen.

--Saddlery & Harness Making. 160p. 1981. 30.00x (ISBN 0-85131-148-2, Pub. by Allen & Co). State Mutual Bk.

HARVESTERS

see Harvesting Machinery

HARVESTING MACHINERY

see also Mowing Machines

Casson, Herbert N. Cyrus Hall McCormick: His Life & Work. LC 74-152977. (Select Bibliographies Reprint Ser.). 1972. Repr. of 1909 ed. 24.50 (ISBN 0-8369-5729-6). Ayer Co Pubs.

Fruit, Nut, & Vegetable Harvesting Mechanization. 424p. 1984. 38.50 (ISBN 0-317-06789-3). Am Soc Ag Eng.

Hutchinson, William T. Cyrus Hall McCormick, 2 Vols. 2nd ed. LC 68-8127. (American Scene Ser). 1968. Repr. of 1935 ed. Set. lib. bdg. 95.00 (ISBN 0-306-71162-1). Da Capo.

McCormick, Cyrus. The Century of the Reaper: An Account of Cyrus Hall McCormick, the Inventor of the Reaper, of the McCormick Harvesting Machine Company, the Business He Created & of the International Harvester Company, His Heir & Chief Memorial. LC 31-9940. Repr. of 1931 ed. 28.00 (ISBN 0-384-34740-1). Johnson Repr.

Status of Harvest Mechanization of Horticultural Crops. 78p. 1984. 10.25 (ISBN 0-317-06793-1). Am Soc Ag Eng.

Status of Harvest Mechanization of Horticultural Crops. 78p. pap. 12.75 (ISBN 0-916150-50-X, 903CO383). Am Soc Ag Eng.

HAWKER AIRCRAFT, LIMITED

Rice, Michael S. Pilot's Manual for Hawker Hurricane. (Illus.). 56p. 1974. pap. 3.95 (ISBN 0-87994-030-1, Pub. by AvPubns). Aviation.

HAWKS

Craighead, John J. & Craighead, Frank C., Jr. Hawks, Owls & Wildlife. LC 74-81670. 1969. pap. 7.95 (ISBN 0-486-22123-7). Dover.

Cupper, Jack & Cupper, Lindsay. Hawks in Focus: A Study of Australia's Birds of Prey. (Illus.). 208p. 1982. 30.00 (ISBN 0-686-97177-9). Buteo.

Fisher, Albert K. The Hawks & Owls of the United States in Their Relation to Agriculture. LC 73-17820. (Natural Sciences in America Ser.). (Illus.). 266p. 1974. Repr. 18.00x (ISBN 0-405-05736-9). Ayer Co Pubs.

Fitch, Henry S. Observations on the Mississippi Kite in Southwestern Kansas. (Museum Ser.: Vol. 12, No. 11). 17p. 1963. pap. 1.25 (ISBN 0-317-04587-3). U of KS Mus Nat Hist.

Harting, J. E. Hints on the Management of Hawks & Practical Falconry. (Illus.). 288p. 1981. 16.95 (ISBN 0-86230-031-2). Saiga.

Heintzelman, Donald S. A Guide to Hawk Watching in North America. LC 78-21003. (Keystone Bks.). (Illus.). 1979. 18.95x (ISBN 0-271-00212-3); pap. 9.75 (ISBN 0-271-00217-4). Pa St U Pr.

Holly, H. H. Sparrow Hawk. 1969. 1.25 (ISBN 0-940628-39-2). Pilgrim Hall.

HAZARDOUS SUBSTANCES

see also Inflammable Materials

Allen, Peter, ed. Hazardous Waste Management. 300p. 1984. pap. 985.00 (ISBN 0-931634-41-5). FIND-SVP.

American Trucking Assn. ATA Hazardous Materials Tariff. 1983. pap. text ed. 18.25 (ISBN 0-88711-061-4). Am Trucking Assns.

--Fundamentals of Transporting Hazardous Materials. 174p. 1982. pap. text ed. 4.50 (ISBN 0-88711-051-7). Am Trucking Assns.

--Fundamentals of Transporting Hazardous Wastes. 173p. 1980. pap. text ed. 4.50 (ISBN 0-88711-049-5). Am Trucking Assns.

--Hazardous Materials Handbook. 239p. 1982. pap. text ed. 4.50 (ISBN 0-88711-050-9). Am Trucking Assns.

American Water Works Association. Hazardous Materials Spills. (AWWA Handbooks - Proceedings). (Illus.). 72p. 1977. pap. text ed. 8.40 (ISBN 0-89867-054-3). Am Water Wks Assn.

Angerer, J. & Schaller, K. H., eds. Analyses of Hazardous Substances in Biological Materials, Vol. 1. (Commission for the Investigation of Health Hazards of Chemical Compounds in the Work Area Ser.). 222p. 1985. lib. bdg. 36.00 (ISBN 0-89573-075-8). VCH Pubs.

ASTM Committee F-20, Division on Hazardous Materials Spill Response, ed. A Guide to the Safe Handling of Hazardous Materials Accidents- STP 825-A. LC 83-71801. 55p. 1983. pap. text ed. 15.00 (ISBN 0-8031-0261-5, 04-825000-31). ASTM.

Belfiglio, Jeff, et al. Hazardous Waste Disposal Sites: A Handbook for Public Input & Review. LC 82-121857. x, 168p. 1981. 10.00. Stanford Enviro.

Bennett, Gary F., et al. Handbook of Hazardous Materials Spills. LC 82-123. (Illus.). 704p. 1982. 57.50 (ISBN 0-07-004680-8). McGraw.

Bhatt, H. G., et al. Management of Toxic & Hazardous Wastes. (Illus.). 548p. 1985. 49.95 (ISBN 0-87371-023-1). Lewis Pubs Inc.

BNA's Environmental & Safety Information Services. Hazardous Materials Transportation. write for info. BNA.

Bonner, T., et al. Hazardous Waste Incineration Engineering. LC 81-14223. (Pollution Technology Review Ser.: No. 88). (Illus.). 432p. 1982. 45.00 (ISBN 0-8155-0877-8). Noyes.

Bowman. Handbook of Carcinogens & Hazardous Substances. 766p. 1982. 99.50 (ISBN 0-8247-1683-3). Dekker.

Bretherick, L. Handbook of Reactive Chemical Hazards. 2nd ed. 1979. text ed. 175.00 (ISBN 0-408-70927-8). Butterworth.

Bretherick, Leslie. Handbook of Reactive Chemical Hazards. 3rd ed. 1280p. 1985. text ed. 139.95 (ISBN 0-408-01388-5). Butterworth.

Breuel, A., ed. How to Dispose of Oil & Hazardous Chemical Spill Debris. LC 81-14235. (Pollution Technical Review: No. 87). (Illus.). 420p. 1982. 48.00 (ISBN 0-8155-0876-X). Noyes.

Brown. Hazardous Waste Land Treatment. 49.95 (ISBN 0-250-40636-5). Butterworth.

Canadian Law & the Control of Exposure to Hazards. (Science Council of Canada Background Studies: No. 39). 1978. pap. 7.50 (ISBN 0-660-01484-X, SSC110, SSC). Unipub.

Cashman, John R. Hazardous Materials Emergencies. LC 82-74318. 400p. 1983. 45.00 (ISBN 0-87762-324-4). Technomic.

Castellani, Amleto, ed. The Use of Human Cells for the Evaluation of Risk from Physical & Chemical Agents. (NATO ASI Series, Series A, Life Science: Vol. 60). 822p. 1983. 110.00x (ISBN 0-306-41274-8, Plenum Pr). Plenum Pub.

Chapman, David W., et al. Hazardous Wastes & the Consumer Connection: A Guide for Educators & Citizens Concerned with the Role of Consumers in the Generation of Hazardous Wastes. (Hazardous Chemicals Education Project Ser.). 36p. (Orig.). 1984. pap. write for info.; pap. text ed. write for info. Sci Citizens.

Cheremisinoff, Paul N., et al. Leachate from Hazardous Wastes Sites. LC 83-50748. 92p. 1983. 18.00 (ISBN 0-87762-334-1). Technomic.

Cicalese, Michael. Emergency Response Directory for Hazardous Materials Accidents. LC 83-63323. 251p. 1984. pap. text ed. 34.00 (ISBN 0-930500-01-6). Odin Pr.

Code for Storage of Gaseous Oxidizing Materials: 1980. 1980. 7.00 (ISBN 0-317-07373-7, NFPA 43C). Natl Fire Prot.

Committee on Hazardous Substances in the Laboratory, National Research Council. Prudent Practices for Handling Hazardous Chemicals in Laboratories. 291p. 1981. 16.95 (ISBN 0-309-03128-1); pap. text ed. 9.95 (ISBN 0-309-03234-2). Natl Acad Pr.

Control of Hazardous Material Spills. (Illus.). 1978. 20.00 (ISBN 0-318-01364-9); pap. 15.00 (ISBN 0-318-01365-7). Hazardous Mat Control.

Control of Hazardous Material Spills, Nineteen Seventy-Eight. (Illus.). 1978. 20.00x (ISBN 0-686-26028-7); softcover 15.00x (ISBN 0-686-26029-5). Info Transfer.

Conway & Malloy, eds. Hazardous Solid Waste Testing: First Conference - STP 760. 352p. 1982. 39.00 (ISBN 0-8031-0795-1, 04-760000-16). ASTM.

Conway, R. A. & Gulledge, W. P., eds. Hazardous & Industrial Solid Waste Testing: 2nd Symposium. LC 84-70420. (Special Technical Publications: No. 805). 332p. 1983. text ed. 44.00 (ISBN 0-8031-0246-1, 04-805000-16). ASTM.

Cope, C. B. & Fuller, W. H. The Scientific Management of Hazardous Wastes. LC 82-14650. (Illus.). 375p. 1983. 75.00 (ISBN 0-521-25100-1). Cambridge U Pr.

Corson, Lynn A. Statistical Report of Compensable Injuries in Michigan's Hazardous Waste Processing & Transporting Industry: 1982. LC 83-720023. 1983. 2.00 (ISBN 0-941872-46-7). MSU Comm Dev.

--A Statistical Report of Hazardous Materials Transportation Incidents in Michigan Communities: January 1979 to September 1981. LC 82-620021. 1982. 1.50 (ISBN 0-941872-39-4). MSU Comm Dev.

Corson, Lynn A. & Johnson, Melinda O. Report of Rail Incidents Involving Cars Carrying Hazardous Materials: State of Michigan, 1977-1982. LC 83-620021. 1983. 1.50 (ISBN 0-941872-47-5). MSU Comm Dev.

Dabberdt, Walter F., ed. Atmospheric Dispersion of Hazardous-Toxic Materials from Transport Accidents: Proceedings of a Course, International Center for Transportation Studies, Amalfi, Italy, 20-24 Sept., 1983. 200p. 1985. 52.00 (ISBN 0-444-87518-2, I-244-84). Elsevier.

Dalton, Thomas F. The Effects of Heat & Stress on Cleanup Personnel Working with Hazardous Materials. 1984. 25.00 (ISBN 0-318-01766-0). Spill Control Assn.

Dangerous Goods Panel of Air Avigation Commission of ICAO. Instructions Techniques pour la Securite du Transport Aerien des Marchandises Dangereuses, 1984. Tr. of Technical Instructions for the Transport of Dangerous Good by Air, 1984. (Fr.). 1983. fabric cover 35.00 (ISBN 0-940394-10-3). Intereg.

Dangerous Goods Panel of Air Navigation Commission of ICAO. Instrucciones Technicas para el Transporte sin Riesgos de Mercancias Peligrosas por Via Aerea, 1984. Tr. of Technical Instructions for the Safe Transport of Dangerous Goods by Air, 1984. (Sp.). 1983. fabric cover 35.00x (ISBN 0-940394-09-X). Intereg.

--Technical Instructions for the Safe Transport of Dangerous Goods by Air, 1984. 1983. fabric cover 35.00 (ISBN 0-940394-08-1). Intereg.

DePol, Dennis R. & Cheremisinoff, Paul N. Emergency Response to Hazardous Materials Incidents. LC 84-51633. 121p. 1984. pap. 19.00 (ISBN 0-87762-371-6). Technomic.

De Renzo, D. J., ed. Biodegradation Techniques for Industrial Organic Wastes. LC 80-12834. (Pollution Technology Review Ser. 65; Chemical Technology Review Ser. 158). (Illus.). 358p. 1980. 28.00 (ISBN 0-8155-0800-X). Noyes.

Dow's Fire & Explosion Index: Hazard Classification Guide. (CEP Technical Manual). 57p. 1981. pap. 22.00 (ISBN 0-8169-0194-5); 12.00 (ISBN 0-317-03758-7). Am Inst Chem Eng.

Ecology & Environment, Inc. Toxic Substance Storage Tank Containment. LC 84-22697. (Pollution Technology Review Ser.: No. 116). (Illus.). 274p. 1985. 36.00 (ISBN 0-8155-1018-7). Noyes.

Edwards, B. H., et al. Emerging Technologies for the Control of Hazardous Wastes. LC 83-4022. (Pollution Tech. Rev.: No. 99). (Illus.). 146p. (Orig.). 1983. 24.00 (ISBN 0-8155-0943-X). Noyes.

Ehrenfeld, John & Bass, Jeffrey. Evaluation of Remedial Action Unit Operations at Hazardous Waste Disposal Sites. LC 84-14834. (Pollution Technology Review Ser.: No. 110). (Illus.). 434p. 1985. 39.00 (ISBN 0-8155-0998-7). Noyes.

Epstein, Samuel S., et al. Hazardous Waste in America: Our Number One Environmental Crisis. LC 82-3304. (The Sierra Club Paperback Library). 640p. 1983. 27.50 (ISBN 0-87156-294-4); pap. 12.95 (ISBN 0-87156-807-1). Sierra.

Exner, Jurgen H., ed. Detoxication of Hazardous Waste. LC 82-70696. (Illus.). 362p. 1982. 39.95 (ISBN 0-250-40521-0). Butterworth.

Fawcett, Howard. Hazardous & Toxic Materials: Safe Handling & Disposal. LC 84-5148. 296p. 1984. text ed. 35.00x (ISBN 0-471-80483-5, Pub. by Wiley Interscience). Wiley.

Greenberg, Michael R. & Anderson, Richard F. Hazardous Waste Sites: The Credibility Gap. 293p. 1984. 15.00x (ISBN 0-88285-102-0). Ctr Urban Pol Res.

Grisham, J. W., ed. Health Aspects of the Disposal of Waste Chemicals. 560p. 1985. 85.00 (ISBN 0-08-033159-9, Pub by PPI). Pergamon.

A Guide for Control & Cleanup of Hazardous Material. 20p. 1975. pap. 1.00 (ISBN 0-686-32375-0, GCM). AASHTO.

Guide to Managing Industrial Hazardous Waste. 29.95 (ISBN 0-317-04496-6). Butterworth.

Handling Hazardous Materials. 113p. 1977. pap. text ed. 7.00 (ISBN 0-88711-046-0). Am Trucking Assns.

Handling of Tritium-Bearing Wastes. (Technical Reports Ser.: No. 203). (Illus.). 137p. 1981. pap. 21.25 (ISBN 92-0-125081-9, IDC203, IAEA). Unipub.

Harris, Judith C., et al. Combustion of Hazardous Wastes: Sampling & Analysis Methods. LC 84-22690. (Pollution Technology Review Ser.: No. 117). (Illus.). 419p. 1985. 42.00 (ISBN 0-8155-1019-5). Noyes.

Harthill, Michalann, ed. Hazardous Waste Management: In Whose Backyard? (AAAS Selected Symposium, Ser.: No. 88). 212p. 1984. 24.00x (ISBN 0-86531-748-8). Westview.

Hazardous Chemicals Data. (Forty Ser). 298p. 1973. pap. 3.50 (ISBN 0-685-44170-9, 49). Natl Fire Prot.

Hazardous Liquids Pumps & Valves Market. 343p. 1983. 1200.00 (ISBN 0-86621-068-7). Frost & Sullivan.

Hazardous Material Control Directory. (Illus.). 1985. text ed. 45.00 (ISBN 0-318-02813-1). Hazardous Mat Control.

Hazardous Material Risk Assessment, Disposal & Management. (Illus.). 1979. 20.00 (ISBN 0-318-01363-0). Hazardous Mat Control.

Hazardous Materials Control Directory. (Illus.). 1984. text ed. 35.00 (ISBN 0-318-01362-2). Hazardous Mat Control.

Hazardous Waste Management Markets. 370p. 1984. 1775.00 (ISBN 0-86621-302-3, A1380). Frost & Sullivan.

Hazardous Wastes & Environmental Emergencies: Management-Prevention-Cleanup-Control. (Illus.). 1984. text ed. 45.00 (ISBN 0-318-01361-4). Hazardous Mat Control.

Hurford, N. A Review of the IMCO Standards for Procedures & Arrangements for the Noxious Liquid Substances from Ships, 1980. 1981. 65.00x (ISBN 0-686-97160-4, Pub. by W Spring England). State Mutual Bk.

International Technical Information Institute. Toxic & Hazardous Industrial Chemicals Safety Manual. 450p. 1984. 88.00 (ISBN 0-318-04390-4). Media Intl Promo.

J. J. Keller & Associates, Inc, ed. Driver's Pocket Guide to Hazardous Materials. 5th ed. LC 77-90372. (ORS-2). (Orig.). 1984. pap. 2.25 (ISBN 0-934674-26-4). J J Keller.

J. J. Keller & Associates, Inc., ed. Hazardous Materials Guide: Shipping, Materials Handling & Transportation. rev. ed. LC 76-40627. (20G). 900p. 1985. looseleaf 95.00 (ISBN 0-934674-10-8). J J Keller.

--Hazardous Waste Audit Program. LC 81-86197. (10M). 400p. 1984. 3-ring binder 65.00 (ISBN 0-934674-41-8). J J Keller.

--Hazardous Waste Regulatory Guide. LC 81-86200. (26G). 500p. 1985. 3-ring binder 95.00 (ISBN 0-934674-44-2). J J Keller.

Jackson, et al, eds. Hazardous & Industrial Waste Management & Testing: Third Symposium-STP 851. 400p. 1984. 46.00 (ISBN 0-8031-0405-7, 04-851000-16). ASTM.

Lagrega, ed. Toxic & Hazardous Waste. (Fifteenth Mid-Atlantic Conference on Industrial Waste). 1983. text ed. 49.95 (ISBN 0-250-40591-1). Butterworth.

Lehman, John P., ed. Hazardous Waste Disposal. (NATO-Challenges of Modern Society Ser.: Vol. 4). 400p. 1983. 49.50x (ISBN 0-306-41171-7, Plenum Press). Plenum Pub.

Long, F. A. & Schweitzer, Glenn E., eds. Risk Assessment at Hazardous Waste Sites. LC 82-16376. (Symposium Ser.: No. 204). 128p. 1982. lib. bdg. 29.95 (ISBN 0-8412-0747-X). Am Chemical.

Lowry, George G. & Lowry, Robert C. Handbook of Hazard Communication & OSHA Requirements. (Illus.). 130p. 1985. 24.95 (ISBN 0-87371-022-3). Lewis Pubs Inc.

Mallow, Alex. Hazardous Waste Regulations: An Interpretive Guide. 640p. 1981. 44.00 (ISBN 0-442-21935-0). Van Nos Reinhold.

Management of Alpha-Contaminated Wastes. (Proceedings Ser.). (Illus.). 714p. 1981. pap. 95.50 (ISBN 92-0-020081-8, ISP562, IAEA). Unipub.

Management of Hazardous Wastes & Environmental Emergencies. (Illus.). 1985. text ed. 45.00 (ISBN 0-318-02812-3). Hazardous Mat Control.

Management of Uncontrolled Hazardous Waste Sites. (Illus.). 1984. text ed. 45.00 (ISBN 0-318-02811-5). Hazardous Mat Control.

Marine Board. Responding to Casualties of Ships Bearing Hazardous Cargoes. 1979. pap. 8.75 (ISBN 0-309-02935-X). Natl Acad Pr.

Meidl, James. Hazardous Materials Handbook. (Fire Science Ser). 1972. pap. text ed. write for info. (ISBN 0-02-476370-5, 47637). Macmillan.

Morell, David & Magorian, Christopher. Siting Hazardous Waste Facilities: Local Opposition & the Myth of Preemption. 288p. 1982. prof ref 27.50 (ISBN 0-88410-906-2). Ballinger Pub.

Natale, Anthony & Levins, Hoag. Asbestos Removal & Control: An Insider's Guide to the Business. LC 84-5371. (Illus.). 400p. 1984. 280.00 (ISBN 0-917097-00-9). SourceFinders.

National Research Council. Reducing Hazardous Waste Generation. 88p. 1985. pap. text ed. 4.95 (ISBN 0-309-03498-1). Natl Acad Pr.

National Research Council (U. S.) Transportation Research Board. Atmospheric Emergencies: Existing Capabilities & Future Needs. LC 83-13464. (Transportation Research Record Ser.: No. 902). 1983. 6.40 (ISBN 0-309-03516-3). Natl Acad Pr.

OECD Staff. Hazardous Waste "Problem" Sites. 62p. (Orig.). 1983. pap. 9.50x (ISBN 92-64-12401-2). OECD.

Parr, James F., et al, eds. Land Treatment of Hazardous Wastes. LC 82-14402. (Illus.). 422p. 1983. 45.00 (ISBN 0-8155-0926-X, Noyes Pubns). Noyes.

Peirce, J. Jeffery, et al. Hazardous Waste Management. LC 81-67509. 200p. 1981. text ed. 34.95 (ISBN 0-250-40459-1). Butterworth.

Perkins, R., ed. Hazardous Materials Management. 350p. 1985. pap. 40.00 (ISBN 0-913061-00-X). Morgan-Rand.

Pishdad, A. Alan, ed. Hazardous Waste Sites in the U. S. 175p. 1981. pap. 42.00 (ISBN 0-08-026274-0). Pergamon.

Porteous, Andrew. Hazardous Waste Management Handbook. (Illus.). 304p. 1985. text ed. 64.95 (ISBN 0-408-01379-6). Butterworth.

Quarles, John R. Federal Regulation of Hazardous Wastes: A Guide to RCRA. LC 82-84040. 1982. 24.00 (ISBN 0-911937-04-8). Environ Law Inst.

Regulatory Processes & Jurisdictional Issues in the Regulation of Hazardous Products in Canada. (Science Council of Canada Background Studies: No. 41). 1978. pap. 10.25 (ISBN 0-660-01490-4, SSC108, SSC). Unipub.

Rishel, H. L., et al. Costs of Remedial Response Actions at Uncontrolled Hazardous Waste Sites. LC 83-21976. (Pollution Technology Review Ser.: No. 105). (Illus.). 144p. 1984. 32.00 (ISBN 0-8155-0969-3). Noyes.

Robinson, J. S., ed. Hazardous Chemical Spill Cleanup. LC 79-16362. (Pollution Technology Review Ser.: No. 59). (Illus.). 406p. 1980. 48.00 (ISBN 0-8155-0767-4). Noyes.

Royal Society of London. Long-Term Hazards from Environmental Chemicals. Doll, Richard & McClean, A. E., eds. 1979. 25.00x (ISBN 0-85403-110-3, Pub. by Royal Soc London). Scholium Intl.

Sax, N. Irving. Cancer Causing Chemicals. 400p. 1981. 42.95 (ISBN 0-442-21919-9). Van Nos Reinhold.

Sax, N. Irving & Feiner, Benjamin. Dangerous Properties of Industrial Materials. 6th ed. 3136p. 1984. 225.00 (ISBN 0-442-28304-0). Van Nos Reinhold.

Saxena, J. Hazard Assessment of Chemicals: Current Developments, Vol. 3. (Serial Publication). 1984. 65.00 (ISBN 0-12-312403-4). Acad Pr.

Saxena, Jitendra, ed. Hazard Assessment of Chemicals, Vol. 2. (Serial Publication). 332p. 1983. 47.50 (ISBN 0-12-312402-6). Acad Pr.

Schweitzer, Glenn E. & Santolucito, John A., eds. Environmental Sampling for Hazardous Wastes. LC 84-20480. (ACS Symposium Ser.: No. 267). 134p. 1984. lib. bdg. 34.95x (ISBN 0-8412-0884-0). Am Chemical.

Shuckrow, Alan J., et al. Hazardous Waste Leachate Management Manual. LC 82-7924. (Pollution Technology Review Ser.: No. 92). (Illus.). 379p. 1983. 36.00 (ISBN 0-8155-0910-3). Noyes.

Sittig, Marshall. Handbook of Toxic & Hazardous Chemicals & Carcinogens. 2nd ed. LC 84-22755. 950p. 1985. 96.00 (ISBN 0-8155-1009-8). Noyes.

--Landfill Disposal of Hazardous Wastes & Sludges. LC 79-20359. (Pollution Technology Review: No. 62). (Illus.). 369p. 1980. 48.00 (ISBN 0-8155-0773-9). Noyes.

Sobetzer, John G. & Corson, Lynn A. Hazardous Waste Management in Michigan: A Guide for Local Government & Citizens. LC 82-620008. 1982. 5.00 (ISBN 0-941872-34-3). MSU Comm Dev.

Sweeney, Thomas L. & Bhatt, Harasiddhiprasad D., eds. Hazardous Waste Management for the Eighties. LC 82-71532. (Illus.). 553p. 1982. 59.95 (ISBN 0-250-40429-X). Butterworth.

Terrien, Ernest J. Hazardous Materials & Natural Disaster Emergencies: Incident Action Guidebook. LC 84-51388. 64p. 1984. pap. 20.00 (ISBN 0-87762-365-1). Technomic.

Toxic Substances & Hazardous Wastes: Tenth Annual Airlie House Conference on the Environment. 25p. 1982. pap. 5.00 (ISBN 0-317-30672-3). Amer Bar Assn.

Transporting Hazardous Waste. 51p. 1981. pap. text ed. 4.50 (ISBN 0-88711-045-2). Am Trucking Assns.

Treatment & Disposal of Hazardous Wastes from Industry: Some Experiences. 197p. 1983. pap. text ed. 14.75 (ISBN 92-833-2005-0, APO140, APO). Unipub.

Turner & McCreery. Chemistry of Fire & Hazardous Materials. 1980. text ed. 29.29 (ISBN 0-205-06912-6, 826912-2); instrs' manual avail. (ISBN 0-205-06913-4). Allyn.

United Nations Economic & Social Council Staff. Transport of Dangerous Goods: 1983 Edition. rev. ed. (Illus.). 1984. 40.00 (ISBN 0-940394-12-X). INTEREG.

Vouk, V. B., et al. Methods for Estimating Risk of Chemical Injury: Human & Non-Human Biota & Ecosystems; Scope 26. (Scope Ser.). 1985. write for info. (ISBN 0-471-90546-1). Wiley.

Walters, Douglas B., ed. Safe Handling of Chemical Carcinogens, Mutagens Teratogens & Highly Toxic Substances. LC 79-88922. 1980. Vol. 1. 59.95 (ISBN 0-250-40303-X); Vol. 2. 59.95 (ISBN 0-250-40354-4). Butterworth.

Ward, et al. Hazardous Wastes: Confronting the Challenge. 200p. 1985. write for info. (ISBN 0-911937-17-X). Environ Law Inst.

Watson, et al. Hazardous Waste Handbook. 5th ed. 796p. 1984. 98.00 (ISBN 0-86587-121-3). Gov Insts.

Watson, Thomas & Davidson, Jeffrey. Hazardous Wastes Handbook. 4th, rev. ed. 681p. 1984. Wkbk. 95.00 (ISBN 0-86587-097-7). Gov Insts.

Wood, Eric F. & Princeton Water Resorces Group. Groundwater Contamination from Hazardous Wastes. (Illus.). 192p. 1984. 30.95 (ISBN 0-13-366286-1). P-H.

Young, R. E. Control in Hazardous Environments. (IEE Control Engineering Ser.: No. 17). 128p. 1982. pap. 34.00 (ISBN 0-906048-69-9, CE017). Inst Elect Eng.

Zajic, J. E. & Himmelman, W. A. Highly Hazardous Material Spills & Emergency Planning. (Hazardous & Toxic Substances Ser.: Vol. 1). 1978. pap. 55.00 (ISBN 0-8247-7228-8). Dekker.

HAZARDOUS SUBSTANCES–LAW AND LEGISLATION

Birnbaum, Sheila & Phelan, Richard J. Special Problems in Toxic Substances Litigation after Manville, 1983. LC 83-60146. (Litigation Course Handbook Ser.: No. 220). (Illus.). 552p. 1983. 35.00. PLI.

Brickman, Ronald, et al. Controlling Chemicals: The Politics of Regulation in Europe & the United States. LC 84-29340. 336p. 1985. 34.95x (ISBN 0-8014-1677-9). Cornell U Pr.

Dawson, Gaynor W. Harzardous Waste Management. 1985. 60.00 (ISBN 0-471-82268-X). Wiley.

Hamline University. Advanced Legal Education. Hazardous Waste. LC 85-138256. 488p. Date not set. 37.10 (ISBN 0-317-27336-1). Hamline Law.

Henry, Cleopatra E. The Carriage of Dangerous Goods by Sea: The Role of the International Maritime Organisation in International Legislation. 240p. 1985. 29.95 (ISBN 0-312-12258-6). St Martin.

Institute for Continuing Education-New Jersey. Trying the Toxic Tort Case (3-84) LC 84-150007. (Illus.). ii, 312p. 1985. incl. cassettes 75.00. NJ Inst CLE.

Judicial Administration Working Group on Asbestos Litigation. Asbestos Litigation: Final Report with Recommendations. LC 84-3293. 62p. 1984. pap. text ed. 8.00 (ISBN 0-89656-074-0, R-087). Natl Ctr St Courts.

Lowry, George G. & Lowry, Robert C. Handbook of Hazard Communication & OSHA Requirements. (Illus.). 130p. 1985. 24.95 (ISBN 0-87371-022-3). Lewis Pubs Inc.

Otway, Harry J., et al. Regulating Industrial Risks: Public, Experts, & Media. LC 85-14946. write for info. (ISBN 0-408-00740-0). Butterworth.

Piasecki, Bruce, ed. Beyond Dumping: New Strategies for Controlling Toxic Contamination. LC 83-24510. (Quorum Ser.). (Illus.). xix, 239p. 1984. lib. bdg. 35.00 (ISBN 0-89930-056-1, PIT/, Quorum). Greenwood.

Speer, R. D. Speer's Digest of Toxic Substances State Law: 1984 to '85 Trends, Summaries & Forecasts. 2nd ed. (Speer's Digest Series of Policy & Law). (Illus.). 300p. (Orig.). 1985. lib. bdg. 95.00x (ISBN 0-915669-02-1); pap. 80.00x (ISBN 0-915669-03-X). Strategic Assessments.

Speer, R. D. & Bulanowski, Gerard A., eds. Speer's Digest of Toxic Substances State Law 1983-1984: Trends, Summaries, & Forecasts. (Speer's Digest Series of Policy & Law). (Illus.). 372p. 1983. 100.00 (ISBN 0-915669-01-3); pap. 85.00 perfect bdg. (ISBN 0-915669-00-5). Strategic Assessments.

Weinberg, David. Hazardous Waste Regulation Handbook. 1982. pap. 90.00 (ISBN 0-88057-007-5). Exec Ent Inc.

White, Anthony G. Financial, Planning, & Intergovernmental Aspects of Hazardous Waste Materials Handling: A Selected Bibliography. LC 82-209377. (Public Administration Ser.: P-1027). 7p. 1982. pap. 2.00. Vance Biblios.

HAZARDOUS SUBSTANCES–TRANSPORTATION

Calabrese, E. J. The Environmental Gender Gap: Sex Differences in Response to Toxic Substances. (Environmental Science & Technology Ser.). 424p. 1985. 45.00 (ISBN 0-471-80903-9). Wiley.

Dangerous Goods Panel of Air Navigations Commissions of ICAO. Technical Instructions for the Safe Transport of Dangerous Goods by Air, 1986. 525p. 1985. 37.00 (ISBN 0-940394-18-9). Intereg.

Dawson, Gaynor W. Harzardous Waste Management. 1985. 60.00 (ISBN 0-471-82268-X). Wiley.

Regulations Respecting the Handling, Offering for Transport & Transporting of Dangerous Goods. 250p. 1985. pap. text ed. 29.95 (ISBN 0-317-28532-7, Pub. by Canadian Govt Pub Ctr). Brookfield Pub Co.

HEAD

see also Brain; Ear; Eye; Hair; Mouth; Skull

Batsakis, John G. Tumors of the Head & Neck: Clinical & Pathological Considerations. 2nd ed. (Illus.). 584p. 1979. 62.00 (ISBN 0-683-00476-X). Williams & Wilkins.

Gerrick, David J. Surface Anatomy: The Head. (Illus.). 1978. 20.00 (ISBN 0-916750-60-4). Dayton Labs.

Hiatt, James L. & Gartner, Leslie P. Textbook of Head & Neck Anatomy. (Illus.). 350p. 1981. 32.50 (ISBN 0-8385-8876-X). ACC.

Lang, J. Clinical Anatomy of the Head: Neurocranium, Orbita, Craniocervical Regions. (Illus.). 489p. 1983. 490.00 (ISBN 0-387-11014-3). Springer-Verlag.

McMinn, R. M. Color Atlas of Head & Neck Anatomy. 1981. 47.50 (ISBN 0-8151-5826-2). Year Bk Med.

Paff, George H. Anatomy of the Head & Neck. LC 72-93117. pap. 61.30 (ISBN 0-317-26123-1, 2125000). Bks Demand UMI.

Palacios, Enrique, et al. Multiplanar Anatomy of the Head & Neck for Computed Tomography. LC 80-11368. 206p. 1980. 185.00 (ISBN 0-471-05820-3, Pub. by WileyMed). Wiley.

Pernkopf, Eduard. Atlas of Topographical & Applied Human Anatomy, 2 vols. 2nd ed. Ferner, Helmut, ed. Monsen, Harry, tr. from Ger. LC 79-25264. Orig. Title: Atlas der Topographischen und Angewamdten Anatomie Des Menschen. (Illus.). 1980. Repr. of 1963 ed. Set. text ed. 196.00 (ISBN 0-7216-7196-9); Vol. 1: Head & Neck. text ed. 98.00 (ISBN 0-7216-7198-5); Vol. 2: Thorax, Abdomen & Extremities. text ed. 98.00 (ISBN 0-7216-7199-3). Saunders.

Potter, Guy D. Sectional Anatomy & Tomography of the Head. LC 71-158948. (Illus.). 352p. 1971. 99.00 (ISBN 0-8089-0700-X, 793370). Grune.

Reed, Gretchen M. & Sheppard, Vincent F. Basic Structures of the Head & Neck: A Programmed Instruction in Clinical Anatomy for Dental Professionals. LC 75-298. (Illus.). 640p. 1976. pap. text ed. 28.00 (ISBN 0-7216-7516-6). Saunders.

Schnitzlein, H. Norman, et al. Computed Tomography of the Head & Spine: A Photographic Atlas of CT, Gross & Microscopic Anatomy. LC 82-13515. (Illus.). 126p. 1982. text ed. 65.00 (ISBN 0-8067-1771-8). Urban & S.

HEALEY AUTOMOBILE

see Automobiles, Foreign–Types–Healey

HEARING

see also Audiometry; Ear; Labyrinth (Ear)

Altschuler, Richard A., et al, eds. Neurobiology of Hearing: The Cochlea. 1985. text ed. price not set (ISBN 0-89004-925-4). Raven.

Arnst, Dennis & Katz, Jack, eds. Central Auditory Assessment: The SSW Test. LC 81-17987. (Illus.). 538p. 1982. pap. 32.50 (ISBN 0-933014-66-X). College-Hill.

Bateman, Hugh E., et al. Applied Anatomy & Physiology of the Speech & Hearing Mechanism. (Illus.). 644p. 1984. 39.75x (ISBN 0-398-04912-2). C C Thomas.

Berlin, Charles I., ed. Hearing Science: Recent Advances. LC 84-11424. (Illus.). 380p. 1984. 49.50 (ISBN 0-933014-96-1). College-Hill.

Dallos, Peter. The Auditory Periphery: Biophysics & Physiology. 1973. 78.00 (ISBN 0-12-200750-6). Acad Pr.

Davis, Audrey B. & Merzbach, Uta C. Early Auditory Studies: Activities in the Psychology Laboratories of American Universities. LC 75-619025. (Smithsonian Studies in History & Technology: No. 31). (Illus.). pap. 20.00 (ISBN 0-317-08276-0, 2004230). Bks Demand UMI.

Drescher, Dennis G., ed. Auditory Biochemistry. (Illus.). 536p. 1985. 64.50x (ISBN 0-398-05122-4). C C Thomas.

Facts about Hearing & Hearing Aids. 1984. lib. bdg. 79.95 (ISBN 0-87700-534-6). Revisionist Pr.

Feldman, Alan S. & Grimes, Charles I. Hearing Conservation in Industry. 352p. 1985. 35.00 (ISBN 0-683-03112-0). Williams & Wilkins.

Gerber, Sanford E. Introductory Hearing Science: Physical & Psychological Concepts. LC 73-89177. pap. 77.80 (ISBN 0-317-26432-X, 2024988). Bks Demand UMI.

Gerber, Sanford E. & Mencher, George. The Development of Auditory Behavior. 368p. 1983. 25.50 (ISBN 0-8089-1598-3, 791546). Grune.

Hinchcliffe, Ronald, ed. Hearing & Balance in the Elderly. LC 82-14787. (Medicine in Old Age Ser.). (Illus.). 521p. 1983. text ed. 65.00 (ISBN 0-443-02075-2). Churchill.

Holmes, M. H. & Rubenfield, L. A., eds. Mathematical Modeling of the Hearing Process: Proceedings. (Lecture Notes in Biomathematics Ser.: Vol. 43). 104p. 1981. pap. 12.00 (ISBN 0-387-11155-7). Springer-Verlag.

How We Hear. 1977. tchrs'. guide 8.00 (ISBN 0-87453-155-1). Denoyer.

International Congress of Logopedics & Phoniatrics, 17th, Copenhagen, August 1977. Main Lectures: Proceedings. Loebell, E., et al, eds. (Folia Phoniatrics: Vol. 29, No. 1). (Illus.). 1977. 14.25 (ISBN 3-8055-2780-2). S Karger.

Keidel, Wolfgang D. The Physiological Basis of Hearing. (Illus.). 262p. 1983. 25.00 (ISBN 0-86577-072-7). Thieme-Stratton.

Kuroda, Ryo. Experimental Researches Upon the Sense of Hearing in Lower Vertebrates, Including Reptiles, Amphibians, & Fishes. LC 26-12355. (Comp Psych Memoirs). 1926. pap. 8.00 (ISBN 0-527-24851-7). Kraus Repr.

Lasky, Elaine Z. & Katz, Jack, eds. Central Auditory Processing Disorders: Problems of Speech, Language & Learning. (Illus.). 368p. 1983. text ed. 30.00 (ISBN 0-8391-1802-3, 18368). Univ Park.

Lutman, M. E. & Haggard, M. P., eds. Hearing Science & Hearing Disorders. 1983. 29.50 (ISBN 0-12-460440-4). Acad Pr.

Miller, Maurice H. & Silverman, Carol A., eds. Occupational Hearing Conservation. (Illus.). 304p. 1984. 38.95 (ISBN 0-13-629386-7). P-H.

Moore, B. C. An Introduction to the Psychology of Hearing. 2nd ed. LC 81-69595. 1982. 36.00 (ISBN 0-12-505620-6); pap. 16.00 (ISBN 0-12-505622-2). Acad Pr.

Ogden, Robert M. Hearing. LC 73-97562. Repr. of 1924 ed. 19.50 (ISBN 0-404-04812-9). AMS Pr.

--Hearing. LC 75-124248. (Select Bibliographies Reprint Ser.). 1924. 29.00 (ISBN 0-8369-5137-9). Ayer Co Pubs.

Palmer, John M. Anatomy for Speech & Hearing. 3rd ed. 247p. 1983. pap. text ed. 18.50 scp (ISBN 0-06-044974-8, HarpC). Har-Row.

Paparella, Michael M. Biochemical Mechanisms in Hearing & Deafness. (Illus.). 416p. 1970. photocopy ed. 44.50x (ISBN 0-398-01445-0). C C Thomas.

Pickles, J. O. An Introduction to the Physiology of Hearing. 1982. 37.50 (ISBN 0-12-554750-1); pap. 19.50 (ISBN 0-12-554752-8). Acad Pr.

Schneiderman, Carl R. Basic Anatomy & Physiology In Speech & Hearing. LC 83-26290. (Illus.). 228p. 1984. pap. text ed. 17.50 (ISBN 0-933014-05-8). College Hill.

Schuijf, A. & Hawkins, A. D., eds. Sound Reception in Fish. LC 76-54648. (Developments in Agriculture & Fisheries Science: Vol. 5). 288p. 1977. 61.75 (ISBN 0-444-41540-8). Elsevier.

Stevens, Stanley S. & Davis, Hallowell. Hearing: Its Psychology & Physiology. 512p. 1983. pap. 15.00 prepaid (ISBN 0-88318-426-5). Acoustical Soc Am.

Szende, O. Intervallic Hearing: Its Nature & Pedagogy. 1977. 13.00 (ISBN 0-9960013-3-6, Pub. by Akademiai Kaido Hungary). Heyden.

Yost, William A. Directional Hearing. 210p. 1985. pap. text ed. 30.00 (ISBN 0-8391-2041-9, 21512). Univ Park.

Yost, William A. & Nielsen, Donald W. Fundamentals of Hearing: An Introduction. 2nd ed. LC 76-54247. 1984. text ed. 24.95 (ISBN 0-03-069621-6, HoltC). HR&W.

Zemlin, Eileen & Zemlin, W. R. Study Guide-Workbook to Accompany Speech & Hearing Science Anatomy & Physiology. (Illus.). 300p. 1983. 12.80x (ISBN 0-87563-240-8). Stipes.

HEARING–TESTING

see Audiometry

HEART

see also Blood–Circulation

American Heart Association, Scientific Sessions, 52nd. Abstracts. (AHA Monograph: No. 65). 1979. pap. 8.00 (ISBN 0-686-58031-1). Am Heart.

Bane, Bernard M. A Schematic Replica of the Cardiac Cycle. 45p. 1981. pap. 3.00 (ISBN 0-930924-11-8). BMB Pub Co.

Bishop, Vernon S. Cardiac Performance, Vol. 1. Granger, Harris J., ed. (Annual Research Reviews). 1979. 18.00 (ISBN 0-88831-060-9). Eden Pr.

Buhler, Fritz R., ed. Alpha-Adrenoceptors in Cardiovascular Regulation. 192p. 1982. Repr. of 1982 ed. text ed. 25.50 (ISBN 0-89004-858-4). Raven.

Critser, James R., Jr. Cardiac Technology. (Ser. 10CT-82). 100p. 1983. 100.00 (ISBN 0-88178-010-3). Lexington Data.

Davies. Conduction System of the Heart. 1982. text ed. 119.95 (ISBN 0-407-00133-6). Butterworth.

De Mello, Walmor C., ed. Electrical Phenomena in the Heart. (Clinical Engineering Ser). 1972. 70.00 (ISBN 0-12-208950-2). Acad Pr.

Dhalla, N. S., ed. Methods in Studying Cardiac Membranes, Vol. II. 344p. 1984. 98.00 (ISBN 0-8493-5996-1). CRC Pr.

Gey, H. F., et al. Structure & Chemistry of the Aging Heart. 238p. 1974. text ed. 24.00x (ISBN 0-8422-7168-6). Irvington.

Harvey, William. De Motu Cordis: Anatomical Studies on the Motion of the Heart & Blood. 5th ed. Leake, Chauncey D., tr. (Illus.). 186p. 1978. pap. 6.75x (ISBN 0-398-00793-4). C C Thomas.

Higgins, Charles B. & Carlsson, Erik, eds. C.T. of the Heart & Great Vessels: Experimental Evaluation & Clinical Application. LC 82-71767. (Illus.). 416p. 1982. 68.00 (ISBN 0-87993-180-9). Futura Pub.

Hurst, J. Willis, ed. The Heart: Update I. 1979. text ed. 35.00 (ISBN 0-07-031490-X). McGraw.

Hurst, J. Willis, et al. The Heart. 5th ed. (Illus.). 352p. 1982. 85.00 (ISBN 0-07-031481-0). McGraw.

--The Heart, 2 vol. ed. 5th ed. 2120p. 1982. Set. 95.00 (ISBN 0-07-079033-7); Vol. 1. (ISBN 0-07-031483-7); Vol. 2. (ISBN 0-07-031484-5). McGraw.

Johnson, J. Alan & Anderson, Ralph R., eds. The Renin-Angiotensin System. LC 80-17962. (Advances in Experimental Medicine & Biology Ser.: Vol. 130). 315p. 1980. 45.00x (ISBN 0-306-40469-9, Plenum Pr). Plenum Pub.

Katz, Arnold M. Physiology of the Heart. LC 75-14580. 464p. 1977. o. p. 31.00 (ISBN 0-89004-053-2); pap. 23.00 (ISBN 0-686-67627-0). Raven.

Laane, Henk-Maarten. The Arterial Pole of the Embryonic Heart. 160p. 1978. pap. text ed. 26.50 (ISBN 90-265-0297-4, Pub. by Swets Pub Serv Holland). Swets North Am.

Legato, Marianne J., ed. The Developing Heart. 1984. lib. bdg. 52.50 (ISBN 0-89838-672-1, Pub. by Martinus Nijhoff Netherlands). Kluwer Academic.

Little. Physiology of the Heart & Circulation. 2nd ed. (Illus.). 352p. 1981. pap. 18.95 (ISBN 0-8151-5476-3). Year Bk Med.

Luederitz, B., ed. Cardiac Pacing: Diagnostic & Therapeutic Tools. (Illus.). 1976. 29.00 (ISBN 0-387-07711-1). Springer-Verlag.

McAlpine, W. A. Heart & Coronary Arteries. LC 74-20634. (Illus.). 240p. 1974. 99.50 (ISBN 0-387-06985-2). Springer-Verlag.

Meerson, Felix Z. The Failing Heart: Adaptation & Deadaptation. Katz, Arnold M., ed. (Illus.). 342p. 1983. text ed. 58.00 (ISBN 0-89004-550-X). Raven.

Morgan, H. E., ed. Cellular Biology of the Heart: Supplement to Journal of Molecular & Cellular Cardiology. 1982. 19.00 (ISBN 0-12-506960-X). Acad Pr.

National Heart, Lung & Blood Institute. A Handbook of Heart Terms. LC 81-12490. (Illus.). 64p. 1982. 10.95 (ISBN 0-89490-052-8). Enslow Pubs.

Ornish, Dean. Stress, Diet, & Your Heart. LC 81-24003. (Illus.). 400p. 1982. 16.95 (ISBN 0-03-049011-1). HR&W.

Paes de Caravalho, Antonio, et al, eds. Normal & Abnormal Conduction in the Heart: Biophysics, Physiology, Pharmacology & Ultrastructure. LC 81-71154. (Illus.). 512p. 1982. 68.00 (ISBN 0-87993-172-8). Futura Pub.

Phibbs, Brendan. The Human Heart: A Guide to Heart Disease. 4th ed. LC 79-17665. 272p. 1979. pap. text ed. 15.95 (ISBN 0-8016-3917-4). Mosby.

Sambhi, Mohinder P., ed. Renin-Substrate Reaction. (AHA Monograph: No. 56). 1977. pap. 4.00 (ISBN 0-87493-058-8, 73-042A). Am Heart.

Sano, T., et al, eds. Electrophysiology & Ultrastructure of the Heart. (Illus.). 267p. 1968. 86.00 (ISBN 0-8089-0613-5, 793780). Grune.

Tillmans, H., et al, eds. Microcirculation of the Heart: Theoretical & Clinical Problems. (Illus.). 360p. 1982. pap. 49.00 (ISBN 0-387-11346-0). Springer-Verlag.

Vassalle, Mario. The Human Heart. rev. ed. Head, J. J., ed. LC 76-62985. (Carolina Biology Readers Ser.). (Illus.). 16p. 1979. pap. 1.60 (ISBN 0-89278-208-0, 45-9608). Carolina Biological.

Zabriskie, John, et al. Clinical Immunology of the Heart. LC 80-17927. (Perspectives in Clinical Immunology Ser.). 238p. 1981. 65.00x (ISBN 0-471-02676-X, Pub. by Wiley Med). Wiley.

Zelenin, V. Strengthen Your Heart. 110p. 1979. pap. 4.45 (ISBN 0-8285-0835-6, Pub. by Mir Pubs USSR). Imported Pubns.

HEART–INNERVATION

Abraham, A. Microscopic Innervation of the Heart & Blood Vessels in Vertebrates Including Man. 1969. 76.00 (ISBN 0-08-012342-2). Pergamon.

Hainsworth, R., et al, eds. Cardiac Receptors. LC 77-12404. (Illus.). 1980. 99.50 (ISBN 0-521-21853-5). Cambridge U Pr.

Khabarova, A. Y. The Afferent Innervation of the Heart. LC 62-15548. 175p. 1963. 25.00x (ISBN 0-306-10656-6, Consultants). Plenum Pub.

Santer, R. M. Morphology & Innervation of the Fish Heart. (Advances in Anatomy, Embryology & Cell Biology Ser.: Vol. 89). (Illus.). 110p. 1985. pap. 24.00 (ISBN 0-387-13995-8). Springer-Verlag.

HEAT

see also Aerodynamic Heating; Animal Heat; Atmospheric Temperature; Calorimeters and Calorimetry; Cold; Combustion; Entropy; Fire; Gases–Liquefaction; Heat Engineering; High Temperatures; Metals at High Temperatures; Pyrometers and Pyrometry; Solidification; Steam; Temperature; Thermochemistry; Thermodynamics; Thermoelectricity; Thermography (Copying Process); Thermomagnetism; Thermometers and Thermometry; Waste Heat

Andronov, A. A., et al. Seven Papers on Equations Related to Mechanics & Heat. LC 51-5559. (Translations Ser.: No. 2, Vol. 75). 1968. 34.00 (ISBN 0-8218-1775-2, TRANS 2-75). Am Math.

Beggerow, G. Heats of Mixing & Solution. (Landolt-Bornstein New Ser.: Group IV, Vol. 2). 1976. 268.80 (ISBN 0-387-07443-0). Springer-Verlag.

Chapple, M. A Level Physics: Mechanics & Heat, Vol. 1. 2nd ed. (Illus.). 336p. (Orig.). 1979. pap. text ed. 14.95x (ISBN 0-7121-0154-3, Pub. by Macdonald & Evans England). Trans-Atlantic.

Cohen, I. Bernard, ed. Gravitation, Heat & X-Rays. LC 80-2104. (Development of Science Ser.). (Illus.). 1981. lib. bdg. 35.00x (ISBN 0-405-13869-5). Ayer Co Pubs.

Cornwall, Keith. The Flow of Heat. 1977. pap. 14.95 (ISBN 0-442-30168-5). Van Nos Reinhold.

Frautschi, Steven C., et al. The Mechanical Universe: Mechanics & Heat, Advanced Edition. (Illus.). 450p. Date not set. price not set (ISBN 0-521-30432-6). Cambridge U Pr.

Gay, Larry. Heating the Home Water Supply: Wood, Coal, Solar. Griffith, Roger, ed. LC 82-24224. (Illus.). 128p. 1983. pap. 7.95 (ISBN 0-88266-311-9). Garden Way Pub.

Hannequin, Arthur. Essai Critique sur L'hypothese Atomesdans La Sciene Contemporaine. Cohen, I. Bernard, ed. LC 80-2127. (Development of Science Ser.). (Illus.). 1981. lib. bdg. 40.00x (ISBN 0-405-13876-8). Ayer Co Pubs.

In Situ Heating Experiments in Geological Formations, Ludvika, Sweden, September, 1978. 1979. 16.50x (ISBN 92-64-01872-7). OECD.

Larsen, David C., ed. Thermal Expansion 7. LC 82-9083. 224p. 1982. 49.50x (ISBN 0-306-41031-1, Plenum Pr). Plenum Pub.

Lavoisier, A. L. & Laplace, P. S. Memoir on Heat. Guerlac, Henry, ed. Tr. of Memoire sur la Chaleur. 1981. 14.95 (ISBN 0-88202-195-8). Watson Pub Intl.

McKenzie, Arthur E. Physics. 4th ed. 1970. 18.95x (ISBN 0-521-07698-6). Cambridge U Pr.

Maxwell, James C. Theory of Heat. 3rd ed. LC 77-173064. Repr. of 1872 ed. 11.25 (ISBN 0-404-04277-5). AMS Pr.

--Theory of Heat. 3rd ed. Repr. of 1872 ed. lib. bdg. 18.75x (ISBN 0-8371-4097-8, MATH). Greenwood.

Mott-Smith, Morton. Concept of Heat & Its Workings. Orig. Title: Heat & Its Workings. 1933. pap. 3.95 (ISBN 0-486-20978-4). Dover.

Olenick, Richard, et al. The Mechanical Universe: Introduction to Mechanics & Heat. (Illus.). 576p. 1985. 24.95 (ISBN 0-521-30429-6). Cambridge U Pr.

Olszewski. Utilization of Reject Heat. (Energy, Power & Environment Ser.: Vol. 10). 189p. 1980. 39.75 (ISBN 0-8247-1168-8). Dekker.

Portman, Donald J. & Ryznar, Edward. An Investigation of Heat Exchange. (International Indian Ocean Expedition Meteorological Monographs: No. 5). 88p. 1971. text ed. 15.00x (ISBN 0-8248-0097-4, Eastwest Ctr). UH Pr.

Roller, Duane E. The Early Development of the Concepts of Temperature & Heat: The Rise & Decline of the Caloric Theory. LC 50-8653. (Harvard Case Histories in Experimental Science Ser.: Case 3). pap. 27.50 (ISBN 0-317-09176-X, 2011607). Bks Demand UMI.

Saha, M. N. & Srivastava, B. N. A Textbook of Heat for Junior Students. 368p. 1981. 29.00x (ISBN 0-86125-639-5, Pub. by Orient Longman India). State Mutual Bk.

Sears, Francis W. Mechanics, Heat, & Sound. 2nd ed. (Illus.). 1950. 23.95 (ISBN 0-201-06905-9). Addison-Wesley.

Symposium on Optical Spectrometric Measurements of High Temparatures. Optical Spectrometric Measurements of High Temperatures. Dickerman, Philip J., ed. LC 61-5607. pap. 99.30 (ISBN 0-317-08417-8, 2005139). Bks Demand UMI.

Tong, L. S. Boiling Crisis & Critical Heat Flux. LC 72-600190. (AEC Critical Review Ser.). 89p. 1972. pap. 10.25 (ISBN 0-87079-154-0, TID-25887); microfiche 4.50 (ISBN 0-87079-155-9, TID-25887). DOE.

Truesdell, C. & Bharatha, S. The Concept & Logic of Classical Thermodynamics As a Theory of Heat Engines. Rigorously Constructed Upon Foundations Laid by S. Carnot & F. Reech. LC 76-48115. (Texts & Monographs in Physics). (Illus.). 1977. 41.00 (ISBN 0-387-07971-8). Springer-Verlag.

United Nations Economic Commission for Europe. Combined Production of Electric Power & Heat: Proceedings of a Seminar Organized by the Committee on Electric Power of the United Nations Economic Commission for Europe, Hamburg, FR Germany, 6-9 November 1978. LC 80-755. (Illus.). 150p. 1980. 37.00 (ISBN 0-08-025677-5). Pergamon.

Widder, D. V. The Heat Equation. (Pure & Applied Mathematics Ser.). 1975. 56.00 (ISBN 0-12-748540-6). Acad Pr.

Wilkinson, Bruce W. & Barnes, Richard W. Cogeneration of Electricity & Useful Heat. 272p. 1980. 84.00 (ISBN 0-8493-5615-6). CRC Pr.

Zemansky, Mark & Dittman, Richard. Heat & Thermodynamics. 6th ed. (Illus.). 560p. 1981. text ed. 40.95 (ISBN 0-07-072808-9). McGraw.

HEAT–ABSORPTION

see Heat–Radiation and Absorption

HEAT–CONDUCTION

Arpaci, Vedat S. Conduction Heat Transfer. 1966. 38.95 (ISBN 0-201-00359-7). Addison-Wesley.

Beck, James V. & St. Clair, C. R. Inverse Heat Conduction. 336p. 1985. 34.50 (ISBN 0-471-08319-4). Wiley.

Berman, R. Thermal Conductions in Solids. (Oxford Studies in Physics). (Illus.). 1976. 39.95x (ISBN 0-19-851429-8); pap. 19.95x (ISBN 0-19-851430-1). Oxford U Pr.

Carslaw, Horatio S. & Jaeger, J. C. Conduction of Heat in Solids. 2nd ed. (Illus.). 1959. 45.00x (ISBN 0-19-853303-9). Oxford U Pr.

CISM (International Center for Mechanical Sciences) Structural Dynamics Heat Conduction. De Veubeke, B. F., et al, eds. (CISM Pubns. Ser.: No. 126). (Illus.). 256p. 1974. pap. 25.60 (ISBN 0-387-81201-6). Springer-Verlag.

Grigull, U. & Sandner, H. Heat Conduction. Kestin, Joseph, tr. from Ger. LC 83-16616. (International Series in Heat & Mass Transfer). Orig. Title: Warmeleitung. (Illus.). 187p. 1984. text ed. 34.00 (ISBN 0-89116-358-1); pap. text ed. 22.50 (ISBN 0-89116-366-2). Hemisphere Pub.

Heat. (Tops Cards Ser.: No. 15). 1978. pap. 6.95 (ISBN 0-941008-15-0). Tops Learning.

Ho, C. Y. & Taylor, R. D. Thermal Conductivity. LC 79-80957. 1169p. 1969. 95.00x (ISBN 0-306-30413-9, Plenum Pr). Plenum Pub.

Hust, J. G., ed. Thermal Conductivity 17. 793p. 1983. 120.00x (ISBN 0-306-41177-6, Plenum Press). Plenum Pub.

Kakac, Sadik & Yener, Yaman. Heat Conduction. 2nd ed. LC 84-27975. (Illus.). 397p. 1985. 37.50 (ISBN 0-89116-391-3); pap. 26.95. Hemisphere Pub.

Klemens, P. G. & Chu, T. K. Thermal Conductivity 14. LC 76-10951. 566p. 1976. 85.00x (ISBN 0-306-33114-4, Plenum Pr). Plenum Pub.

Mirkovich, V. V., ed. Thermal Conductivity 15. LC 78-12943. 511p. 1978. 75.00x (ISBN 0-306-40054-5, Plenum Pr). Plenum Pub.

Ozisik, M. Necati. Heat Conduction. LC 79-990. 687p. 1980. 53.50x (ISBN 0-471-05481-X, Pub. by Wiley-Interscience). Wiley.

Pal, L. & Pal, L., eds. Organic Conductors & Semiconductors: Proceedings of the International Conference Siofok, Hungary,1976. (Lecture Notes in Physics: Vol. 65). 1977. pap. text ed. 33.00 (ISBN 0-387-08255-7). Springer-Verlag.

Peggs, I. D., ed. Thermal Expansion 6. LC 78-11252. 302p. 1977. 55.00x (ISBN 0-306-40056-1, Plenum Pr). Plenum Pub.

HEAT–CONVECTION

Bergles, A. E. & Webb, R. L., eds. Augmentation of Convective Heat & Mass Transfer. LC 75-143215. pap. 42.00 (ISBN 0-317-10889-1, 2015856). Bks Demand UMI.

Burmeister, L. C. Convective Heat Transfer. 790p. 1982. 51.95 (ISBN 0-471-09141-3). Wiley.

Cattan, I. & Smith, R. N., eds. Natural Convection. (HTD Ser.: Vol. 16). 150p. 1981. 24.00 (ISBN 0-686-34495-2, G00205). ASME.

Cebeci, T. & Bradshaw, P. Physical & Computational Aspects of Convective Heat Transfer. (Illus.). 345p. 1984. 57.00 (ISBN 0-387-12097-1). Springer-Verlag.

International Heat Transfer Conference, 6th, Toronto, Aug. 1978. Heat Transfer Nineteen Seventy-Eight: Proceedings, 8 vols. Banerjee, S. & Rogers, J. T., eds. (Illus.). 3770p. 1979. Set. text ed. 395.00 (ISBN 0-89116-130-9). Hemisphere Pub.

Jaluria, Y. Natural Convection Heat & Mass Transfer. LC 79-41176. (HMT Ser.). (Illus.). 400p. 1980. 50.00 (ISBN 0-08-025432-2). Pergamon.

Kakac, Sadik & Spalding, D. Brian, eds. Turbulent Forced Convection in Channels & Bundles: Theory & Applications to Heat Exchangers & Nuclear Reactors, 2 vols. LC 79-12842. (Illus.). 1132p. 1979. Set. text ed. 185.00 (ISBN 0-89116-148-1). Hemisphere Pub.

Kakac, Sadik, et al. Handbook of Single-Phase Convective Heat Transfer. 1985. 70.00 (ISBN 0-471-81702-3). Wiley.

Launder, B. E., ed. Studies in Convection: Theory Measurement & Applications, Vol. 2. 1978. 44.00 (ISBN 0-12-438002-6). Acad Pr.

Shah, Ramesh & London, A. L. Laminar Flow Forced Convection in Ducts: Supplement 1 to Advances in Heat Transfer. (Supplement I to Advances in Heat Transfer). 1978. 82.50 (ISBN 0-12-020051-1). Acad Pr.

Spalding, D. Brian & Afgan, N., eds. Heat Transfer & Turbulent Buoyant Convection: Studies & Applications for Natural Environment, Buildings, Engineering Systems, Vol. 2. LC 77-1868. (Thermal & Fluids Engineering Ser.). (Illus.). Repr. of 1977 ed. 82.90 (ISBN 0-8357-9188-2, 2016696). Bks Demand UMI.

HEAT–PHYSIOLOGICAL EFFECT

Aldrete, J. Antonio & Britt, Beverly A., eds. The International Symposium on Malignant Hyperthermia, Second, 1978: International Symposium. 592p. 1978. 54.00 (ISBN 0-8089-1073-6, 790035). Grune.

Bicher, Haim I. & Bruley, Duane F., eds. Hyperthermia. LC 82-18047. (Advances in Experimental Medicine & Biology Ser.: Vol. 157). 202p. 1982. 39.50x (ISBN 0-306-41172-5, Plenum Pr). Plenum Pub.

Dalton, Thomas F. The Effects of Heat & Stress on Cleanup Personnel Working with Hazardous Materials. 1984. 25.00 (ISBN 0-318-01766-0). Spill Control Assn.

Dintenfass, Leopold. Hyperviscosity in Hypertension. (Illus.). 192p. 1981. 42.00 (ISBN 0-08-024816-0). Pergamon.

Hornback, Ned B. & Shupe, Robert. Hyperthermia & Cancer: Human Clinical Trail Experience, Vol. II. 176p. 1984. 54.00 (ISBN 0-8493-5676-8). CRC Pr.

Hornback, Ned B. & Shupe, Robert E. Hyperthermia & Cancer: Human Clinical Trail Experience, Vol. I. 160p. 1984. 48.00 (ISBN 0-8493-5675-X). CRC Pr.

Kerslake, D. M. The Stress of Hot Environments. LC 74-168896. (Physiological Society Monographs: No. 29). (Illus.). 300p. 1972. 85.00 (ISBN 0-521-08343-5). Cambridge U Pr.

Kirmiz, John P. Adaptation to Desert Environment: A Study of the Jerboa, Rat & Man. 168p. 1962. 24.50x (ISBN 0-306-30658-1, Plenum Pr). Plenum Pub.

Schlesinger, Milton J., et al, eds. Heat Shock: From Bacteria to Man. LC 82-61222. 440p. 1982. 57.00X (ISBN 0-87969-158-1). Cold Spring Harbor.

Schmidt-Nielsen, Knut. Desert Animals: Physiological Problems of Heat & Water. 11.75 (ISBN 0-8446-5811-1). Peter Smith.

HEAT–RADIATION AND ABSORPTION

see also Radiative Transfer

Giordano, Carmelo, ed. Sorbents & Their Clinical Applications. 1980. 67.50 (ISBN 0-12-285250-8). Acad Pr.

Gray, W. A. & Muller, R. Engineering Calculations in Radiative Heat Transfer. LC 73-17321. 176p. 1974. text ed. 34.00 (ISBN 0-08-017786-7); pap. text ed. 14.50 (ISBN 0-08-017787-5). Pergamon.

Ritchie, Ralph W. & Ritchie, Fern J. Electric Kiln Handbook, Vol. 6. LC 81-90074. (Energy Conservation in the Crafts-a Craft Monograph). (Illus.). 60p. (Orig.). 1981. pap. 5.00 (ISBN 0-939656-05-1). Studios West.

Svet, Darii Y. Thermal Radiation: Metals, Semiconductors, Ceramics, Partly Transparent Bodies, & Films. LC 65-25260. 93p. 1965. 25.00x (ISBN 0-306-10737-6, Consultants). Plenum Pub.

HEAT–TABLES

Christensen, James J., et al. Handbook of Heats of Mixing. 1586p. 1982. 159.95 (ISBN 0-471-07960-X). Wiley.

HEAT–TRANSMISSION

see also Heat Exchangers

American Society for Testing & Materials. Thermal Transmission Measurements of Insulation - STP 660. 458p. 1979. 39.50x (ISBN 0-8031-0589-4, 04-660000-10). ASTM.

American Society of Mechanical Engineers, Heat Transfer Division Staff. Environmental Effects of Thermal Discharges: The Elements in Formulating a Rational Public Policy. LC 77-139496. pap. 20.00 (ISBN 0-317-11241-4, 2016910). Bks Demand UMI.

American Society of Mechanical Engineers. Heat Transfer in Low Reynolds Number Flow. Brown, George A & Moszynski, Jerzy R, eds. LC 70-180676. pap. 20.00 (ISBN 0-317-08519-0, 2010126). Bks Demand UMI.

American Society of Mechanical Engineers. Heat Transfer Division. Heat Transfer in Solar Energy Systems: Presented at the Winter Annual Meeting of the American Society of Mechanical Engineers, Atlanta, Georgia, Nov. 27-Dec. 2, 1977. Howell, J. R. & Min, T., eds. LC 77-89012. pap. 35.30 (ISBN 0-317-08530-1, 2051730). Bks Demand UMI.

American Society of Mechanical Engineers, Committee on Nucleonics Heat Transfer. Survey of Nucleonic Heat Transfer Research & Development. LC 72-185848. (American Society of Mechanical Engineers, Heat Transfer Division Ser.: Vol. 1). pap. 20.00 (ISBN 0-317-09936-1, 2016900). Bks Demand UMI.

AMSE. Spent Nuclear Fuel Heat Transfer; Fuel Casks & Transfer Operations: Proceedings of AMSE, Annual Winter Meeting, December 1971. Groetch, D. J. & Todreas, N., eds. LC 79-180673. (American Society of Mechanical Engineers, Heat Transfer Division Ser.: Vol. 2). pap. 20.00 (ISBN 0-317-09924-8, 2016901). Bks Demand UMI.

Anderson, D. A., et al. Computational Fluid Mechanics & Heat Transfer. LC 83-18614. (Series in Computational Methods in Mechanics & Thermal Sciences). 624p. 1984. 45.00 (ISBN 0-07-050328-1). McGraw.

Arpaci, Verdat S. & Larsen, Paul S. Convection Heat Transfer. (Illus.). 544p. 1984. text ed. 47.95 (ISBN 0-13-172346-4). P-H.

Azbel, David. Fundamentals of Heat Transfer for Process Engineering. LC 84-4213. (Illus.). 382p. 1984. 36.00 (ISBN 0-8155-0982-0). Noyes.

--Heat Transfer Applications in Process Engineering. LC 84-14781. (Illus.). 584p. 1985. 39.00 (ISBN 0-8155-0996-0). Noyes.

Bankoff, S. G., ed. Topics in Two-phase Heat Transfer & Flow: Presented at the Winter Annual Meeting of ASME, San Francisco, CA, Dec. 10-15, 1978. LC 78-68087. pap. 59.80 (ISBN 0-317-08175-6, 2013876). Bks Demand UMI.

Bankoff, S. George & Afgan, Naim H., eds. Heat Transfer in Nuclear Reactor Safety. (International Centre for Heat & Mass Transfer Ser.). (Illus.). 964p. 1982. text ed. 115.00 (ISBN 0-89116-223-2). Hemisphere Pub.

Beck, J. V. & Yao, L. S., eds. Heat Transfer in Porous Media. (HTD Ser.: Vol. 22). 1982. 24.00 (H00250). ASME.

Begell, William, ed. Glossary of Terms in Heat Transfer, Fluid Flow & Related Topics. LC 82-3153. (A Hemisphere Engineering Paperback Ser.). (Eng., Rus., Ger., Fr. & Japanese.). 112p. 1983. pap. 32.95 (ISBN 0-89116-261-5). Hemisphere Pub.

Bejan, Adrian. Convection Heat Transfer. LC 84-3583. 477p. 1984. text ed. 39.95x (ISBN 0-471-89612-8, Pub. by Wiley-Interscience). Wiley.

Bergles, A. E., et al. Two-Phase Flow & Heat Transfer in the Power & Process Industries. (Illus.). 695p. 1981. 69.50 (ISBN 0-07-004902-5). McGraw.

Bergles, Arthur E. & Ishigai, Seiken, eds. Two-Phase Flow Dynamics & Reactor Safety: The Japan-U. S. Seminar 1979. LC 81-4295. (Illus.). 554p. 1981. text ed. 87.50 (ISBN 0-89116-198-8). Hemisphere Pub.

Bergles, Arthur E., et al. Two-Phase Flow & Heat Transfer in the Power & Process Industries. LC 80-22025. (Illus.). 707p. 1980. text ed. 69.50 (ISBN 0-89116-197-X). Hemisphere Pub.

Bishop, A. A. & Kulacki, F. A., eds. Nuclear Reactor Safety Heat Transfer: Presented at the Winter Meeting of the ASME. LC 77-87329. pap. 20.00 (ISBN 0-317-09185-9, 2016904). Bks Demand UMI.

Catton, I. & Torrance, K. E., eds. Natural Convection in Enclosures. (Bound Conference Volumes in Heat Transfer Ser.: Vol. 26). 113p. 1983. pap. text ed. 24.00 (ISBN 0-317-02635-6, H00270). ASME.

Chapman, Alan J. Heat Transfer. 4th ed. (Illus.). 620p. 1984. text ed. write for info. (ISBN 0-02-321470-8). Macmillan.

Chemical Engineering Magazine. Process Heat Exchange. (Chemical Engineering Book Ser.). (Illus.). 624p. 1980. 47.50 (ISBN 0-07-010742-4). McGraw.

Chen, John C. & Bishop, A. A., eds. Liquid-Metal Heat Transfer & Fluid Dynamics: Presented at the Annual Winter Meeting of ASME, New York,N. Y., November 30, 1970. LC 76-141816. pap. 46.30 (ISBN 0-317-09992-2). Bks Demand UMI.

Chenoweth, J. M., et al, eds. Advances in Enhanced Heat Transfer. 168p. 1979. 24.00 (ISBN 0-686-59659-5, I00122). ASME.

Cheremisinoff, Nicholas P. Heat Transfer Pocket Handbook. LC 84-654. (Illus.). 240p. 1984. flex-bound 24.95x (ISBN 0-87201-379-0). Gulf Pub.

Cheremisinoff, Nicholas P., ed. Handbook of Heat & Mass Transfer, Vol. 1: Heat Transfer Operations. LC 84-25338. (Illus.). 1350p. 1985. 149.95x (ISBN 0-87201-411-8). Gulf Pub.

--Handbook of Heat & Mass Transfer, Vol. 2: Mass Transfer & Reactor Design. LC 84-25338. (Illus.). 1400p. 1985. 149.95x (ISBN 0-87201-412-6). Gulf Pub.

Chew, J. C. & Bawkoff, S. G., eds. Interfacial Transport Phenomena. (Bound Conference Volumes in Heat Transfer Ser.: Vol. 23). 109p. 1983. pap. text ed. 24.00 (ISBN 0-317-02628-3, H00269). ASME.

Collier, J. G. Convective Boiling & Condensation. 2nd ed. (Illus.). 460p. 1981. text ed. 85.00 (ISBN 0-07-011798-5). McGraw.

Dalrymple, Paul, et al. A Year of Snow Accumulation at Plateau Station; Thermal Properties & Heat Transfer Processes of Low-Temperature Snow; Radiative Heat Transfer; Process in Snow & Ice; Papers 1, 2, 3 & 4: Meteorological Studies at Plateau Station, Antarctica. Businger, Joost A., ed. (Antarctic Research Ser.: Vol. 25). (Illus.). 1977. pap. 13.50 (ISBN 0-87590-125-5). Am Geophysical.

DiNenno, Philip J. Simplified Radiation Heat Transfer Calculations from Large Open Hydrocarbon Fires. 1982. 5.35 (ISBN 0-686-37674-9, TR 82-9). Society Fire Protect.

Durst, Franz, et al, eds. Two-Phase Momentum, Heat & Mass Transfer in Chemical, Process, & Energy Engineering Systems, 2 vols. LC 79-12405. (Thermal & Fluids Engineering,International Centre for Heat & Mass Transfer Ser.). (Illus.). 1079p. 1979. Set. text ed. 179.50 (ISBN 0-89116-154-6). Hemisphere Pub.

Dwyer, O. E. Boiling Liquid-Metal Heat Transfer. LC 75-11012. (Nuclear Science Technology Ser.). (Illus.). 1976. text ed. 37.95 (ISBN 0-89448-000-6, 300008). Am Nuclear Soc.

Eckert, E. R. & Irvine, T. F., Jr. Heat Transfer Reviews, Nineteen Seventy to Nineteen Seventy-One. 42.00 (ISBN 0-08-021737-0). Pergamon.

Schrock, V. F., ed. Two-Phase Flow & Heat Transfer in Rod Bundles: Presented at the Winter Annual Meeting of the American Society of Mechanical Engineers, Los Angeles, November, 18, 1969. LC 73-28391. pap. 25.00 (ISBN 0-317-08165-9, 2013315). Bks Demand UMI.

Seagrave, Richard C. Biomedical Applications of Heat & Mass Transfer. LC 71-146930. (Illus.). 1971. 9.95x (ISBN 0-8138-0195-8). Iowa St U Pr.

Seely, John H. & Chu, R. C. Heat Transfer in Microelectronic Equipment: Practical Guide. LC 77-188302. (Illus.). pap. 89.30 (ISBN 0-317-07885-2, 2055000). Bks Demand UMI.

Shitzer, Avraham & Eberhart, Robert C., eds. Heat Transfer in Medicine & Biology: Analysis & Applications, 2 vols. 849p. 1985. Set. 110.00 (Plenum Pr); Vol. 1. 65.00x (ISBN 0-306-41597-6, Plenum Pr); Vol. 2. 65.00x (ISBN 0-306-41695-6, Plenum Pr). Plenum Pub.

Siegel, Robert & Howell, John R. Thermal Radiation Heat Transfer. 2nd ed. LC 79-17242. (Thermal & Fluids Engineering Hemisphere Ser.). (Illus.). 928p. 1980. text ed. 48.00 (ISBN 0-07-057316-6). McGraw.

Simulation of Heat & Mass Transfer in Spray Drying. (Agricultural Research Reports: No. 845). 1975. pap. 14.50 (ISBN 90-220-0595-X, PDC200, PUDOC). Unipub.

Singh. Heat Transfer Fluids & Systems for Process & Energy Applications. (Mechanical Engineering Ser.). 304p. 1985. 59.75 (ISBN 0-8247-7191-5). Dekker.

Soloukhin, R. I. & Afgan, N., eds. Measurement Techniques in Heat & Mass Transfer. LC 84-15655. (International Centre for Heat & Mass Transfer Ser.). (Illus.). 750p. 1985. 84.50 (ISBN 0-89116-381-6). Hemisphere Pub.

Somerscales, Euan F. & Knudsen, James G., eds. Fouling of Heat Transfer Equipment. LC 80-28694. (Illus.). 743p. 1981. text ed. 98.50 (ISBN 0-89116-199-6). Hemisphere Pub.

Soumerai, Henri. A Unified Thermodynamic Treatment of Heat, Mass & Momentum Exchange. Date not set. 60.00 (ISBN 0-471-81854-2). Wiley.

Space Technology & Heat Transfer Conference, 1970, Los Angeles. Space Systems & Thermal Technology for the 70's. LC 72-17650. pap. 123.30 (ISBN 0-317-10961-8, 2005682). Bks Demand UMI.

Space Technology & Heat Transfer Conference, Los Angeles, 1970. Space Systems & Thermal Technology for the 70's, Pt. 2. LC 72-17650. pap. 101.50 (ISBN 0-317-10230-3, 2013322). Bks Demand UMI.

Spalding, D. Brian & Afgan, N., eds. Heat Transfer & Turbulent Buoyant Convection: Studies & Applications for Natural Environment, Buildings, Engineering Systems, Vol. 2. LC 77-1868. (Thermal & Fluids Engineering Ser.). (Illus.). Repr. of 1977 ed. 82.90 (ISBN 0-8357-9188-2, 2016696). Bks Demand UMI.

Spalding, D. Brian & Afgan, Naim H., eds. Heat & Mass Transfer in Metallurgical Systems. LC 80-27193. (International Centre for Heat & Mass Transfer Ser.). (Illus.). 758p. 1981. text ed. 118.00 (ISBN 0-89116-169-4). Hemisphere Pub.

Spalding, Dudley B., ed. Progress in Heat & Mass Transfer, Vol. 19, No. 10 - Alan Ede Memorial Issue: Developments in Heat & Mass Transfer. 1977. pap. 35.00 (ISBN 0-08-021285-9). Pergamon.

Sparrow, E. M. & Cess, R. D. Radiation Heat Transfer: Augmented Edition. LC 77-24158. (McGraw-Hill Series in Thermal & Fluids Engineering). (Illus.). 1978. text ed. 48.00 (ISBN 0-07-059910-6). McGraw.

Stein, Ralph P., ed. Heat Transfer: Milwaukee Nineteen Eighty-One. LC 81-10921. (AIChE Symposium: Vol. 77). 425p. 1981. pap. 36.00 (ISBN 0-8169-0199-6, S-208); pap. 19.00 members (ISBN 0-686-47541-0). Am Inst Chem Eng.

Styrikovich, M. A., et al. Heat & Mass Transfer Source Book: Fifth All-Union Conference, Minsk, 1976. LC 77-22337. 480p. 1977. 45.95x (ISBN 0-470-99234-4). Halsted Pr.

Sucec, James. Heat Transfer. 896p. 1985. text ed. write for info. (ISBN 0-697-00257-8); write for info. solutions manual (ISBN 0-697-00506-2). Wm C Brown.

Sukhatme, S. P. A Textbook on Heat Transfer. 238p. 1981. 40.00x (Pub. by Orient Longman India). State Mutual Bk.

Symposium on Basic Mechanisms in Two-phase Flow & Heat Transfer, 1980, Chicago. Basic Mechanisms in Two-phase Flow & Heat Transfer. Rothe, P. H. & Lahey, R. T., eds. LC 80-69186. pap. 33.80 (ISBN 0-317-27790-1, 2024181). Bks Demand UMI.

Symposium on Heat Transfer in Rod Bundles, New York, 1968. Heat Transfer in Rod Bundles: Papers Presented at the Winter Annual Meeting of the American Society of Mechanical Engineers, New York, December 3, 1968. LC 68-58742. pap. 44.00 (ISBN 0-317-12986-4, 2011326). Bks Demand UMI.

Thermal Properties: Chapter 5. 1984. 25.00 (ISBN 0-8169-0329-8); ALCHE members 18.00 (ISBN 0-317-17536-X); sponsor 12.50 (ISBN 0-317-17537-8). Am Inst Chem Eng.

Thomas, Lindon. Fundamentals of Heat Transfer. (Illus.). 1980. text ed. 39.95 (ISBN 0-13-339903-6). P-H.

Tien-Mo Shih. Numerical Heat Transfer. LC 83-18469. (Computational Methods in Mechanics & Thermal Sciences Ser.). (Illus.). 563p. 1984. text ed. 42.00 (ISBN 0-89116-257-7). Hemisphere Pub.

Tien-Mo Shih, ed. Numerical Properties & Methodologies in Heat Transfer: Proceedings of the Second Annual Symposium. LC 82-6187. (Computational Methods in Mechanics & Thermal Sciences Ser.). (Illus.). 554p. 1983. text ed. 69.50 (ISBN 0-89116-257-7). Hemisphere Pub.

Todd, James P. & Ellis, Herbert B. Applied Heat Transfer. 546p. 1982. text ed. 29.50 scp (ISBN 0-06-046635-9, HarpC); sol. manual avail. (ISBN 0-06-366670-7). Har-Row.

Tong, L. S. Boiling Heat Transfer & Two-Phase Flow. LC 74-26607. 256p. 1975. Repr. of 1965 ed. 18.50 (ISBN 0-88275-251-0). Krieger.

Tong, L. S. & Weisman, Joel. Thermal Analysis of Pressurized Water Reactors. LC 77-119001. (ANS Monographs). 320p. 1983. Repr. of 1970 ed. 24.00 (ISBN 0-89448-005-7, 300015). Am Nuclear Soc.

Turner, G. Alan. Heat & Concentration Waves: Analysis & Applications. 1972. 57.50 (ISBN 0-12-704050-1). Acad Pr.

Two-Phase Flow & Heat Transfer Workshop, Ft. Lauderdale, Oct. 1976. Two-Phase Transport & Reactor Safety: Proceedings, 4 vols. Veziroglu, T. N. & Kakac, S., eds. LC 77-14094. 1416p. 1978. Set. text ed. 385.00 (ISBN 0-89116-168-6). Hemisphere Pub.

Van Swaaij, W. P. & Afgan, N., eds. Heat & Mass Transfer in Fixed & Fluidized Beds. (Proceedings of the International Centre for Heat & Mass Transfer). 750p. 1985. 125.00 (ISBN 0-89116-417-0). Hemisphere Pub.

Veziroglu, T. N. & Bergles, A. E. Multi-Phase Flow & Heat Transfer III, Vols. 1A & 1B. 1984. 333.50 (ISBN 0-444-42381-8); 183.50 (ISBN 0-444-42379-6); 183.50 (ISBN 0-444-42380-X). Elsevier.

Wakao, N. & Kaguei, S. Heat & Mass Transfer in Packed Beds. (Topics in Chemical Engineering Ser.: Vol. 1). 386p. 1983. 73.50 (ISBN 0-677-05860-8). Gordon.

Webb, R. L., et al, eds. Advances in Enhanced Heat Transfer, 1981. (HTD Ser.: Vol. 18). 153p. 1981. 24.00 (ISBN 0-686-34491-X, G00207). ASME.

Webb, Ralph L. & Barry, Robert E., eds. Dry & Wet-Dry Cooling Towers for Power Plants: Presented at the Winter Annual Meeting of the ASME, Detroit, MI, November 11-15, 1973 (Sponsored by the Heat Division, ASME) LC 73-89077. (American Society of Mechanical Engineers, Heat Transfer Division HTD: Vol. 6). pap. 39.80 (ISBN 0-317-11240-6, 2016895). Bks Demand UMI.

Welty, James R. Engineering Heat Transfer. LC 73-22315. pap. 131.80 (ISBN 0-317-08524-7, 2055114). Bks Demand UMI.

Welty, James R. & Wicks, Charles E. Fundamentals of Momentum, Heat, & Mass Transfer. 3rd ed. LC 83-17065. 803p. 1984. text ed. 40.45 (ISBN 0-471-87497-3); write for info. solutions (ISBN 0-471-88242-9). Wiley.

Whitaker, S. Elementary Heat Transfer Analysis (in SI-Metric Units) LC 74-3246. 1976. text ed. 18.25 (ISBN 0-08-018959-8). Pergamon.

Whitaker, Stephen. Fundamental Principles of Heat Transfer. LC 82-13031. 574p. 1983. Repr. of 1977 ed. PLB 40.00 (ISBN 0-89874-543-8). Krieger.

Wolf, Helmut. Heat Transfer. 522p. 1983. text ed. 36.50 scp (ISBN 0-06-047181-6, HarpC); sol. manual avail. (ISBN 0-06-367180-8). Har-Row.

Xuejun Chen & Veziroglu, T. Nejat, eds. Two-Phase Flow & Heat Transfer: China-U. S. Progress. LC 84-27908. (Illus.). 1000p. 1985. 175.00 (ISBN 0-89116-432-4). Hemisphere Pub.

Zabrodsky, S. S. Hydrodynamics & Heat Transfer in Fluidized Beds. 1966. 40.00x (ISBN 0-262-24007-6). MIT Pr.

Zaric, Z. Structure of Turbulence in Heat & Mass Transfer. 1982. 90.00 (ISBN 0-07-072731-7). McGraw.

Zaric, Z., ed. Heat & Mass Transfers in Flows with Separated Regions. LC 72-85858. 232p. 1975. pap. text ed. 34.00 (ISBN 0-08-017156-7). Pergamon.

Zaric, Zoran P., ed. Structure of Turbulence in Heat & Mass Transfer. LC 81-23730. (The International Centre for Heat & Mass Transfer Ser.). 608p. 1982. text ed. 76.50 (ISBN 0-89116-233-X). Hemisphere Pub.

Zukauskas, A. & Ziugzda, J. Heat Transfer of a Cylinder in Crossflow. Hewitt, G. F., ed. Bogdanaite, E. I., tr. from Rus. LC 84-19169. (Experimental & Applied Heat Transfer Equipment Ser.). (Illus.). 300p. 1985. 59.50 (ISBN 0-89116-365-4). Hemisphere Pub.

HEAT, SPECIFIC

see Specific Heat

HEAT ABSORPTION

see Heat–Radiation and Absorption

HEAT BARRIER

see Aerodynamic Heating; High Temperatures

HEAT ENGINEERING

see also Heat-Engines; Heating

Arpaci, Vedat S. Conduction Heat Transfer. 1966. 38.95 (ISBN 0-201-00359-7). Addison-Wesley.

Barber, H. Electroheat. (Illus.). 300p. 1983. pap. 26.50x (ISBN 0-246-11739-7, Pub. by Granad England). Sheridan.

Bridgwater, Anthony V., ed. Thermochemical Processing of Biomass. (Illus.). 340p. 1984. text ed. 49.95 (ISBN 0-408-01469-5). Butterworth.

Burghardt, M. David. Engineering Thermodynamics with Applications. 2nd. ed. (Illus.). 571p. 1982. text ed. 36.50 scp (ISBN 0-06-041042-6, HarpC); sol. manual avail. (ISBN 0-06-361041-8). Har-Row.

Chernov, A. & Bessrebrennikov, N. Fundamentals of Heat Engineering & Hydraulics. Troitsky, A., tr. from Rus. (Illus.). 407p. 1969. 17.00x (ISBN 0-8464-0437-0). Beekman Pubs.

Cofield, Roger E., Jr. Design Manual for High Temperature Hot Water & Steam Systems. LC 83-1135. 340p. 1984. 46.50x (ISBN 0-471-89363-3, Pub. by Wiley-Interscience). Wiley.

Dean, Thomas S. Thermal Storage. LC 78-3211. (Solar Ser). (Illus.). 1977. pap. text ed. 3.50 (ISBN 0-89168-005-5). L Erlbaum Assocs.

Duffie, John A. & Beckman, William A. Solar Energy Thermal Processes. LC 74-12390. 386p. 1974. 44.95 (ISBN 0-471-22371-9, Pub. by Wiley-Interscience). Wiley.

Granet, Irving. Thermodynamics & Heat Power. 3rd ed. 1985. text ed. 36.95 (ISBN 0-8359-7674-2); instrs'. manual avail. Reston.

Mori, Y. & Yang, W., eds. Thermal Engineering Joint Conference: Proceedings of the ASME-JSME, 4. 2005p. 1983. pap. text ed. 150.00 set (ISBN 0-317-02652-6, I00158); Vol. 1. pap. text ed. 50.00 (ISBN 0-317-02653-4, I00158A); Vol. 2. pap. text ed. 40.00 (ISBN 0-317-02654-2, I00158B); Vol. 3. pap. text ed. 50.00 (ISBN 0-317-02655-0, I00158C); Vol. 4. pap. text ed. 50.00 (ISBN 0-317-02656-9, I00158D). ASME.

Preobrazhensky, V. Measurements & Instrumentation in Heat Engineering, 2 vols. 1980. Set. 18.00 (ISBN 0-8285-1804-1, Pub. by Mir Pubs USSR). Imported Pubns.

Reiter, Sydney. Industrial & Commercial Heat Recovery Systems. 256p. 1983. 27.50 (ISBN 0-442-27943-4). Van Nos Reinhold.

Rohsenow, Warren M. & Choi, H. Heat, Mass & Momentum Transfer. (Illus.). 1961. text ed. 41.95 (ISBN 0-13-385187-7). P-H.

Schaetzle. Thermal Energy Storage in Aquifiers. (Design & Applications). 275p. 1980. text ed. 29.00 (ISBN 0-08-025977-4). Pergamon.

Solberg, Harry L., et al. Thermal Engineering. LC 60-11730. 649p. 1960. text ed. 34.95 (ISBN 0-471-81147-5). Wiley.

Turner, Robert H. High Temperature Thermal Energy Storage. LC 77-18603. (Solar Ser.). (Illus.). 1978. 4.20 (ISBN 0-89168-007-1). L Erlbaum Assocs.

Wahl, Edward F. Geothermal Energy Utilization. LC 77-546. 302p. 1977. 60.00x (ISBN 0-471-02304-3, Pub. by Wiley-Interscience). Wiley.

HEAT-ENGINES

see also Gas and Oil Engines; Heat Engineering; Heat Pumps; Steam-Engines; Thermodynamics

Bennett, J. V. Heat Engines: Questions & Answers. (Marine Engineering Ser.). 116p. 1975. pap. 9.95x (ISBN 0-540-07340-7). Sheridan.

Jones, James B. & Hawkins, George A. Engineering Thermodynamics: An Introductory Textbook. LC 60-10316. (Illus.). 724p. 1960. text ed. 47.50 (ISBN 0-471-44946-6). Wiley.

Mott-Smith, Morton. Concept of Energy Simply Explained. Orig. Title: Story of Energy, Il. 1934. pap. 3.95 (ISBN 0-486-21071-5). Dover.

Sandfort, John F. Heat Engines: Thermodynamics in Theory & Practice. LC 78-25847. (Illus.). Repr. of 1962 ed. lib. bdg. 27.50x (ISBN 0-313-20784-4, SAEN). Greenwood.

Walker, G. & Senft, J. R. Free Piston Stirling Engines. (Lecture Notes in Engineering Ser.: Vol. 12). 290p. 1985. pap. 21.00 (ISBN 0-387-15495-7). Springer-Verlag.

HEAT EQUATION

Cannon. The One-Dimensional Heat Equation. 1984. 68.00 (ISBN 0-201-13522-1). Cambridge U Pr.

HEAT EXCHANGERS

Afgan, N. H. & Schlunder, E. U. Heat Exchangers: Design & Theory. (Illus.). 928p. 1974. 89.50 (ISBN 0-07-000460-9). McGraw.

Bliem, C., et al. Ceramic Heat Exchanger Concepts & Materials Technology. LC 85-4914. (Illus.). 385p. 1985. 45.00 (ISBN 0-8155-1030-6). Noyes.

Bott, R. Fouling of Heat Exchange Surfaces. Date not set. write for info. Elsevier.

Bott, T. R. Fouling of Heat Exchangers. 1984. write for info. Elsevier.

Chenoweth, J. M. & Impagliazzo, M., eds. Fouling in Heat Exchange Equipment. 105p. 1981. 20.00 (ISBN 0-686-34494-4, G00206). ASME.

Chisholm, D., ed. Developments in Heat Exchanger Technology, Vol. 1. (Illus.). 294p. 1980. 64.75 (ISBN 0-85334-913-4, Pub. by Elsevier Applied Sci England). Elsevier.

Coen, V. & Holtbecker, H. Post Accident Heat Removal. (European Applied Research Reports Special Topics Ser.). 402p. 1980. pap. text ed. 129.50 (ISBN 3-7186-0025-0). Harwood Academic.

Garrett-Price, B. A., et al. Fouling of Heat Exchangers: Characteristics, Costs, Prevention, Control, & Removal. LC 84-22689. (Illus.). 417p. 1985. 45.00 (ISBN 0-8155-1016-0). Noyes.

Gupta, J. P. Fundamentals of Heat Exchanger & Pressure Vessel Technology. LC 84-12865. (Illus.). 675p. 1985. 45.00 (ISBN 0-89116-344-1). Hemisphere Pub.

Kakac, S., et al, eds. Heat Exchangers: Thermal-Hydraulic Fundamentals & Design. 1144p. 1985. Repr. 95.00 (ISBN 0-89116-225-9). Hemisphere Pub.

Kakac, Sadik, et al, eds. Low Reynolds Number Flow Heat Exchangers. LC 82-3036. (Illus.). 1016p. 1983. text ed. 125.00 (ISBN 0-89116-254-2). Hemisphere Pub.

Kays, W. M. & London, A. L. Compact Heat Exchangers. 3rd ed. 352p. 1984. 39.50 (ISBN 0-07-033418-8). McGraw.

Kays, William M. & London, A. L. Compact Heat Exchangers. 2nd ed. (Mechanical Engineering Ser.). 1964. text ed. 42.50 (ISBN 0-07-033391-2). McGraw.

Kitto, J. B. & Robertson, J. R., eds. Heat Exchangers for Two-Phase Applications. 167p. 1983. 34.00 (H00271). ASME.

Kraus, Allan D. Analysis & Evaluation of Extended Surface Thermal Systems. LC 82-980. (Illus.). 560p. 1982. text ed. 79.95 (ISBN 0-89116-252-6). Hemisphere Pub.

Manzoor, M. Heat Flow Through Extended Surface Heat Exchangers. (Lecture Notes in Engineering: Vol. 5). 277p. 1983. pap. 21.00 (ISBN 0-387-13047-0). Springer-Verlag.

Palen, J. W., ed. Heat Exchanger Sourcebook. 750p. 1985. 89.95 (ISBN 0-89116-451-0). Hemisphere Pub.

Ranney, M. W. Heat Exchange Fluids & Techniques. LC 79-20336. (Energy Tech Review, No. 50, Chemical Review Ser.: No. 143). (Illus.). 392p. 1980. 42.00 (ISBN 0-8155-0778-X). Noyes.

Research & Education Association Staff. Heat Transfer Problem Solver. LC 84-61813. (Illus.). 800p. 1984. pap. text ed. 23.85 (ISBN 0-87891-557-5). Res & Educ.

Schlunder, E. U., et al, eds. Heat Exchanger Design Handbook, Supplement 1. LC 82-9267. (Illus.). 100p. 1984. looseleaf 115.00 (ISBN 0-89116-368-9). Hemisphere Pub.

--Heat Exchanger Design Handbook: Supplement 2. LC 82-9267. (Illus.). 100p. 1985. looseleaf 115.00 (ISBN 0-89116-384-0). Hemisphere Pub.

Schlunder, E. U, et al, eds. Heat Exchanger Design Handbook, 5 vols. LC 82-9267. (Illus.). 2080p. 1983. Set. looseleaf 600.00 (ISBN 0-89116-125-2). Hemisphere Pub.

Shah, R. K. & Metzger, D. E., eds. Regenerative & Recuperative Heat Exchangers. (HTD Ser.: Vol. 21). 86p. 1981. 22.00 (ISBN 0-686-34497-9, H00207). ASME.

Shurcliff, W. A. Air-To-Air Heat Exchanges for Houses: How to Build Fresh Air into Your Home & Expel Polluted Air, While Recovering Valuable Heat. 224p. 1982. 29.95 (ISBN 0-471-88649-1). Wiley.

Shurcliff, William A. Air to Air Heat Exchanges for Houses. (Illus.). 224p. 1983. pap. 12.95 (ISBN 0-931790-40-9). Brick Hse Pub.

Singh, Krishna & Soler, Alan. Mechanical Design of Heat Exchangers & Pressure Vessel Components. (Illus.). 1100p. 1984. 95.00 (ISBN 0-916877-00-0); incl. software user guide, examples & magnetic tape 2500.00 (ISBN 0-916877-01-9). Arcturus Pubs.

Shaw, E. W. Heating & Hot Water Services. 1979. 32.95 (ISBN 0-8464-0048-0); pap. 18.95 (ISBN 0-8464-0049-9). Beekman Pubs.
--Heating & Hot-Water Services: Selected Subjects with Worked Examples in SI Units. 4th ed. 241p. pap. text ed. 25.00x (ISBN 0-246-11229-8, Pub. by Granada England). Brookfield Pub Co.
Shelton, Jay W. Wood Heat Safety. LC 79-17951. (Illus.). 1979. pap. 9.95 (ISBN 0-88266-160-4). Garden Way Pub.
Simplified Energy Analysis Using the Modified Bin Method. (Illus.). 472p. 1984. pap. text ed. 40.00 nonmember price (ISBN 0-910110-39-5); pap. text ed. 20.00 member price (ISBN 0-318-01915-9). Am Heat Ref & Air Eng.
Stoecker, W. F. Using SI Units (Standard International Metric) in Heating, Air Conditioning, & Refrigeration. LC 74-26697. (Illus.). 1975. 7.50 (ISBN 0-912524-12-X). Busn News.
Swenson, S. D. Heating Technology: Principles Equipment & Application. text ed. write for info. (ISBN 0-534-01481-X, Breton Pubs). Wadsworth Pub.
Talmor, E. Combustion Hot Spot Analysis for Fired Process Heaters: Prediction, Control, Troubleshooting. LC 82-3037. 162p. 1982. 37.95 (ISBN 0-87201-362-6). Gulf Pub.
Time-Life Books, ed. Heating & Cooling. (Home Repair & Improvement Ser.). 1977. 11.95 (ISBN 0-8094-2378-2). Time-Life.
Traister, John E. Residential Heating Operations & Troubleshooting. (Illus.). 240p. 1985. text ed. 24.95 (ISBN 0-13-774696-2). P-H.
Urban District Heating Using Nuclear Heat. (Panel Proceedings Ser.). (Illus.). 207p. 1977. pap. text ed. 25.25 (ISBN 92-0-051077-9, ISP461, IAEA). Unipub.
Vermont Castings. The Book of Heat: A Four Season Guide to Heating with Wood & Coal. Busha, William & Morris, Stephen, eds. LC 82-12064. 224p. 1982. 18.95 (ISBN 0-8289-0488-X); pap. 10.95 (ISBN 0-8289-0491-X). Greene.
Warm Air Heating & Air Conditioning System. (Eighty-Ninety Ser). 1973. pap. 6.00 (ISBN 0-685-58162-4, 90B). Natl Fire Prot.
Whillier, Austin. Solar Energy Collection & Its Utilization for House Heating. Bruchey, Stuart, ed. LC 78-22712. (Energy in the American Economy Ser.). (Illus.). 1979. lib. bdg. 16.00x (ISBN 0-405-12022-2). Ayer Co Pubs.
Zurick, Timothy. Air Conditioning, Heating & Refrigeration Dictionary. LC 77-10318. 1977. sewn lexotone 5.95 (ISBN 0-912524-16-2). Busn News.

HEATING–TABLES, CALCULATIONS, ETC.

Stamper, Eugene & Koral, Richard L., eds. Handbook of Air Conditioning, Heating & Ventilating. 3rd ed. LC 78-71559. (Illus.). 1420p. 1979. 70.00 (ISBN 0-8311-1124-0). Indus Pr.

HEATING, AERODYNAMIC

see Aerodynamic Heating

HEATING FROM CENTRAL STATIONS

Diamant, R. M. & Kut, David. District Heating & Cooling for Energy Conservation. LC 81-4110. 464p. 1981. 63.95x (ISBN 0-470-27182-5). Halsted Pr.
Din Standards for Central-Heating & Ventilation Plants. 248.00 (ISBN 0-01-005732-3, 10057-5/23). Heyden.
Federal Construction Council - Building Research Advisory Board. Supplementary Field Investigation of Underground Heat Distribution Systems. 1966. pap. 4.25 (ISBN 0-309-01481-6). Natl Acad Pr.
MacKenzie. District Heating Thermal Generation & Distribution. 1979. text ed. 44.00 (ISBN 0-08-022711-2). Pergamon.
Standards for Central Heating & Central Raw Water Heating Systems. (DIN Standards Ser.). 342.00 (ISBN 0-686-31844-7, 11350-1/84). Heyden.

HEATING-PIPES

Here are entered works on pipes which are components of heating installations in structures. Works on heat transfer cylinders that absorb heat at one end by vaporization of a liquid and release heat by condensation of the liquid at the other end are entered under Heat Pipes.

Building Research Advisory Board. Criteria for Underground Heat Distribution Systems. LC 74-32581. 1975. pap. 6.25 (ISBN 0-309-02320-3). Natl Acad Pr.

HEAVISIDE LAYER

see Ionosphere

HEAVY ELECTRONS

see Mesons

HEAVY HYDROGEN

see Hydrogen–Isotopes

HEAVY IONS

Balian, R., et al, eds. Nuclear Physics with Heavy Ions & Mesons, 2 vols. (Les Houches Summer Session Ser.: No. 30). (Proceedings). 1979. Set. 172.50 (ISBN 0-444-85232-8); Vol. 1. 91.50 (ISBN 0-444-85122-4); Vol. 2. 115.00 (ISBN 0-444-85231-X). Elsevier.
Brink, D. M. Semi-Classical Methods for Nucleus-Nucleus Scattering. (Cambridge Monographs on Mathematical Physics). 300p. Date not set. price not set. (ISBN 0-521-23940-0). Cambridge U Pr.
Broglia, R. A. & Winther, Aage. Heavy Ion Reactions: Elastic & Inelastic Reactions, Vol. 1. 1980. 46.95 (ISBN 0-8053-1302-8). Benjamin-Cummings.
Bromley, D. Allan, ed. Treatise on Heavy-Ion Science: Vol. 1, Elastic & Quasi-Elastic Phenomena. LC 84-8384. 750p. 1984. 95.00x (ISBN 0-306-41571-2, Plenum Pr). Plenum Pub.
--Treatise on Heavy-Ion Science, Vol. 2: Fusion & Quasi-Fusion Phenomena. 752p. 1985. 95.00x (ISBN 0-306-41572-0, Plenum Pr). Plenum Pub.
--Treatise on Heavy-Ion Science, Vol. 3: Compound Systems Phenomena. 610p. 1985. 89.50x (ISBN 0-306-41573-9, Plenum Pr). Plenum Pub.
--Treatise on Heavy Ion Science, Vol. 6: Astrophysics, Chemistry, & Condensed Matter, Volume 6. 452p. 1985. 69.50x (ISBN 0-306-41786-3, Plenum Pr). Plenum Pub.
--Treatise on Heavy Ion Science, Vol. 7: Instrumentation & Techniques. 494p. 1985. 79.50x (ISBN 0-306-41787-1, Plenum Pr). Plenum Pub.
Cindro, N., et al, eds. Dynamics of Heavy-Ion Collisions: Proceedings of Adriatic Europhysics Conference on the Dynamics of Heavy-Ion Collisions, 3rd, Hvar Croatia, Yugoslavia, May 25-30, 1981. 382p. 1982. 68.00 (ISBN 0-444-86332-X, North-Holland). Elsevier.
Janev, R. K., et al. Physics of Highly Charged Ions. (Springer Series in Electrophysics: Vol. 13). (Illus.). 350p. 1985. 52.00 (ISBN 0-387-12559-0). Springer-Verlag.
McVoy, K. W. & Friedman, W. A., eds. Theoretical Methods in Medium-Energy Heavy Iron Physics. LC 78-11583. (NATO ASI Series B, Physics: Vol. 38). 761p. 1978. 110.00x (ISBN 0-306-40062-6, Plenum Pr). Plenum Pub.
Madurga, G. & Lozano, M. Heavy-Ion Collision, La Rabida, Spain, 1982: Proceedings. (Lecture Notes in Physics: Vol. 168). 429p. 1982. pap. 23.00 (ISBN 0-387-11945-0). Springer-Verlag.
Moretto, L. G. & Ricci, R. A., eds. Nuclear Structure & Heavy Ion Dynamics: Proceedings of the International School of Physics "Enrico Fermi" Course LXXXVII, Varenna, Italy, 27 July-6 Aug, 1982. (Enrico Fermi International Summer School of Physics Ser.: Vol. 87). 492p. 1984. 102.00 (ISBN 0-444-86826-7, North Holland). Elsevier.
Noerenberg, W. & Weidenmueller, H. -A. Introduction to the Theory of Heavy-Ion Collisions. 2nd enl ed. (Lecture Notes in Physics: Vol. 51). 345p. 1980. pap. 23.00 (ISBN 3-540-09753-8). Springer-Verlag.
Tamura, T., et al, eds. Continuum Spectra of Heavy-Ion Reactions. (Nuclear Science Research Conference Ser.: Vol. 2). 490p. 1980. 68.25 (ISBN 3-7186-0028-5). Harwood Academic.
Von Oertzen, W., ed. Deep Inelastic & Fusion Reactions with Heavy Ions. (Lecture Notes in Physics: Vol. 117). 410p. 1980. pap. 33.00 (ISBN 0-387-09965-4). Springer-Verlag.
--Detectors in Heavy-Ion Reactions. Berlin, 1982: Proceedings. (Lecture Notes in Physics Ser.: Vol. 178). 258p. 1983. pap. 18.00 (ISBN 0-387-12001-7). Springer-Verlag.

HEAVY METALS

Moore, J. W. & Ramamoorthy, S. Heavy Metals in Natural Waters. (Springer Series on Environmental Management). (Illus.). 255p. 1984. 40.00 (ISBN 0-387-90885-4). Springer Verlag.

HEAVY WATER REACTORS

Heavy Water Lattices. (Illus., Orig.). 1960. pap. 5.50 (ISBN 92-0-151060-8, ISP17, IAEA). Unipub.
Heavy Water Lattices: Second Panel Report. (Technical Reports Ser.: No. 20). (Illus., Orig.). 1963. pap. 34.75 (ISBN 92-0-051063-9, IDC20, IAEA). Unipub.
Heavy-Water Power Reactors. (Eng. & Fr., Illus.). 981p. (Orig.). 1968. pap. 64.50 (ISBN 92-0-050268-7, ISP163, IAEA). Unipub.

HEDGEHOGS

Poduschka, Walter & Poduschka, Christl. Dearest Prickles: The Story of a Hedgehog Family. LC 72-2182. (Illus.). 128p. 1972. 6.50 (ISBN 0-8008-2124-6). Taplinger.
Rich, Thomas H. & Rasmussen, Donald L. New North American Erinaceine Hedgehogs: Mammalia: Insectivora. (Occasional Papers: No. 21). 54p. 1973. pap. 3.00 (ISBN 0-317-04904-6). U of KS Mus Nat Hist.

HEDGES

see also Shrubs

Howland, Joseph E. How to Select & Care for Shrubs & Hedges. Ortho Books Editorial Staff, ed. LC 80-66346. (Illus.). 96p. (Orig.). 1981. pap. 5.95 (ISBN 0-917102-88-6). Ortho.
Pollard, E., et al. Hedges. LC 75-5816. (New Naturalist Ser). (Illus.). 256p. 1974. text ed. 14.95x (ISBN 0-8008-3828-9). Taplinger.

HEINKEL (FIGHTER PLANES)

Aeronautical Staff of Aero Publishers, et al. Heinkel HE162. LC 65-26827. (Aero Ser.: Vol. 4). 1965. pap. 3.95 (ISBN 0-8168-0512-1). Aero.
Feist, Uwe & Hirsch, R. S. Heinkel HE100, 112. LC 67-16730. (Aero Ser.: Vol. 12). (Illus.). 1967. pap. 3.95 (ISBN 0-8168-0544-X). Aero.

HEINKEL ONE HUNDRED SEVENTY-SEVEN (BOMBERS)

Feist, Uwe & Hirsch, R. S. Heinkel HE177 Greif. LC 67-16732. (Aero Ser: Vol. 13). (Illus.). 1967. pap. 3.95 (ISBN 0-8168-0548-2). Aero.

HEISENBERG, WERNER, 1901-

Baker-Cassidy, Martha & Cassidy, David, eds. Werner Heisenberg: A Bibliography of His Writings. LC 82-60498. (Berkeley Papers in History of Science). 200p. (Orig.). 1984. pap. 10.00x (ISBN 0-918102-10-3). U Cal Hist Sci Tech.

HELICOPTERS

see also Heliports

Basic Helicopter Handbook. rev. ed. (AC 61-13B. Advisory Circular 61-13 B Ser.). (Illus.). 1978. pap. 5.50 (ISBN 0-318-11707-X). Gov Printing Office.
Beall, James R. & Downing, Robert E. Helicopter Utilization in Municipal Law Enforcement: Administrative Considerations. (Illus.). 96p. 1973. 14.75x (ISBN 0-398-02780-3). C C Thomas.
Boyne, Walter J. & Lopez, Donald S., eds. Vertical Flight: The Age of the Helicopter. (Illus., Orig.). 1984. pap. 15.00 (ISBN 0-87474-279-X). Smithsonian.
Branch, Melville C. Urban Air Traffic & City Planning: Case Study of Los Angeles County. LC 73-1090. (Special Studies in U.S. Economic, Social & Political Issues). 1973. 49.50x (ISBN 0-275-28701-7). Irvington.
Drake, John. Radio Control Helicopter Models. rev. ed. (Illus.). 144p. 1983. pap. 9.95 (Pub. by Argus). Aztex.
Dzik, Stanley J. Helicopter Design & Data Manual. 2nd rev. ed. (Illus.). 120p. 1974. pap. 9.95 (ISBN 0-87994-010-7, Pub. by AvPubns). Aviation.
Everett-Heath, John. Soviet Helicopters: Design, Development & Tactics. 1983. 24.95 (ISBN 0-86720-662-4). Jane's Pub Inc.
Fay, John. The Helicopter: History, Piloting & How It Flies. LC 76-54073. (Illus.). 1977. 15.95 (ISBN 0-7153-7249-1). David & Charles.
Gerding, Mildred, ed. Helicopter Safety. rev. ed. (Rotary Drilling Ser.: Unit 5, Lesson 7). (Illus.). 37p. (Orig.). 1980. pap. text ed. 4.50 (ISBN 0-88698-075-5, 2.50710). PETEX.
Gessow, Alfred & Myers, Garry C., Jr. Aerodynamics of the Helicopter. LC 67-26126. 1967. 28.00 (ISBN 0-8044-4275-4). Ungar.
Gunston, Bill. An Illustrated Guide to Military Helicopters. LC 81-67084. (Illus.). 160p. 1981. 9.95 (ISBN 0-668-05345-3, 5345). Arco.
Harrison, P. G. Military Helicopters. (Battlefields Weapons Systems & Technology Ser.: Vol. XI). 200p. 1985. 27.00 (ISBN 0-08-029958-X); pap. 15.00 (ISBN 0-08-029959-8). Pergamon.
Helicopter Design & Data Manual. (Illus.). 118p. 1974. pap. 9.95 (ISBN 0-87994-010-7). Aviat Pub.
Jane's Pocket Books. Jane's Pocket Book of Helicopters. (Illus.). 260p. 1981. pap. 8.95 (ISBN 0-02-080680-9, Collier). Macmillan.
Johnson, Wayne. Helicopter Theory. LC 79-83995. 1000p. 1980. 110.00 (ISBN 0-691-07971-4). Princeton U Pr.
Lavalla, Rick. Helirescue Manual: Personal Safety & SAR Operations Around Helicopters. (Illus.). 73p. pap. 5.00 (ISBN 0-913724-27-0). Survival Ed Assoc.
Military Helicopters. (Illus.). 9.95 (ISBN 0-668-05345-3). Arco.
Peoples, Kenneth D. OH-6A Loach: Hughes Helicopter. Gentle, Ernest J., ed. (Illus.). 104p. (Orig.). 1985. pap. 9.95 (ISBN 0-8168-0615-2). Aero.
Polmar, Norman & Kennedy, Floyd. Military Helicopters of the World: Military Rotary-Wing Aircraft Since 1917. LC 80-84060. 1981. 31.95 (ISBN 0-87021-383-0). Naval Inst Pr.
Saunders, George H. Dynamics of Helicopter Flight. LC 74-30261. (Illus.). 304p. 1975. 41.50 (ISBN 0-471-75509-5, Pub. by Wiley-Interscience). Wiley.
Schafer, Joseph. Helicopter Fundamentals. (Aviation Technician Training Course Ser.). (Illus.). 459p. 1980. pap. text ed. 19.95 (ISBN 0-89100-118-2, EA-HF); Study Guide 5.95 (ISBN 0-89100-270-7, EA-HF-SG). Aviation Maintenance.
Warbirds Illustrated: Military Helicopters, No. 13. 1982. 9.95 (ISBN 0-85368-572-X, Pub. by Arms & Armour Pr). Sterling.
Young, Warren. The Helicopters. (The Epic Flight Ser.). (Illus.). 176p. 1983. 14.95 (ISBN 0-8094-3350-8). Time Life.

HELICOPTERS–PILOTING

Collier, Larry. How to Fly Helicopters. (Modern Aviation Ser.). (Illus.). 1979. pap. 10.95 (ISBN 0-8306-2264-0, 2264). TAB Bks.
Federal Aviation Administration. Basic Helicopter Handbook. 3rd ed. (Pilot Training Ser.). (Illus.). 111p. 1978. pap. 5.50 (ISBN 0-89100-162-X, EA-AC61-13B). Aviation Maintenance.
McDonald, John J. Flying the Helicopter. (Illus.). 256p. 1982. pap. 11.95 (ISBN 0-8306-2326-4, 2326). TAB Bks.
Private & Commercial Pilot Helicopter Flight Test Guide. (Pilot Training Ser.). 37p. 1977. 4.50 (ISBN 0-89100-176-X, EA-AC61-59A). Aviation Maintenance.
Saunders, George H. Dynamics of Helicopter Flight. LC 74-30261. (Illus.). 304p. 1975. 41.50 (ISBN 0-471-75509-5, Pub. by Wiley-Interscience). Wiley.

HELIOCHROMY

see Color Photography

HELIOMETER

Lietze, Ernst. Modern Heliographic Processes: A Manual of Instruction. Lyons, Nathan, ed. LC 73-22265. (Visual Studies Reprint Ser.). 1974. 12.50 (ISBN 0-87992-001-7); pap. 7.95 (ISBN 0-87992-000-9). Light Impressions.

HELIOZOA

Cash, J. & Hopkinson, J. British Freshwater Rhizopoda & Heliozoa, 5 Vols. 1905-21. Set. 92.00 (ISBN 0-384-07835-4). Johnson Repr.

HELIPORTS

see also Aeronautics, Commercial; Airports; Helicopters

Roof-Top Heliport Construction & Protection. (Four Hundred Ser.). 1973. pap. 2.00 (ISBN 0-685-58237-X, 418). Natl Fire Prot.

HELIUM

see also Liquid Helium; Solid Helium

Armitage, J. G. Jubilee Conference on the Helium-4: Proceedings of the 75th Meeting, St. Andrew, Scotland, Aug.1-5, 1983. 232p. 1983. 26.00x (ISBN 9971-966-23-9, Pub. by World Sci Singapore). Taylor & Francis.
Armitage, Jonathan G. & Farquhar, Ian E., eds. The Helium Liquid. (A NATO Advanced Study Institute). 1976. 89.50 (ISBN 0-12-062550-4). Acad Pr.
Benneman, K. H. & Ketterson, J. B., eds. The Physics of Solid and Liquid Helium, Pt. 2. LC 75-20235. 760p. Repr. of 1978 ed. text ed. 80.95 (ISBN 0-471-06601-X). Krieger.
Clever. Helium & Neon. 1979. 100.00 (ISBN 0-08-022351-6). Pergamon.
Daunt, John G. Helium Three: Proceedings of the Second Symposium on Liquid & Solid Helium Three. 198p. 1960. 4.50 (ISBN 0-8142-0042-7). Ohio St U Pr.
Daunt, John G. & Lerner, E., eds. Monolayer & Submonolayer Helium Films. LC 73-12930. 160p. 1973. 35.00x (ISBN 0-306-30757-X, Plenum Pr). Plenum Pub.
Galasiewicz, Z. M. Helium Four. 1971. 30.00 (ISBN 0-08-015816-1). Pergamon.
Helium Study Committee. Helium: A Public Policy Program. 1978. pap. 11.95 (ISBN 0-309-02742-X). Natl Acad Pr.
Lifshits, Evgenii M. & Andronikashvili, E. L. A Supplement of "Helium". LC 59-8465. pap. 44.00 (ISBN 0-317-08930-7, 2003365). Bks Demand UMI.
Ziegler, James F., ed. Helium: Stopping Powers & Ranges in All Elemental Matter, Vol. 4. LC 77-13219. 1978. text ed. 47.00 (ISBN 0-08-021606-4). Pergamon.

HELIUM–ISOTOPES

Keller, William E. Helium-Three & Helium-Four. LC 68-25382. (International Cryogenics Monographs). (Illus.). 431p. 1969. 59.50x (ISBN 0-306-30346-9, Plenum Pr). Plenum Pub.
Mamyrin, B. A. & Tolstikhin, I. N. Helium Isotopes in Nature. (Developments in Geochemistry Ser.: No. 3). 274p. 1984. 54.00 (ISBN 0-444-42180-7, I-0073-84). Elsevier.

HELMINTHOLOGY

Frith, Mary, ed. Albendazole in Helminthiasis. (Royal Society Medicine International Congress & Symposia Ser.: No. 57). 106p. 1983. 10.00 (ISBN 0-8089-1553-3). Grune.
The Microsporidian Paradites of Platyleminthes: EU Canning. 32p. 1975. 49.00x (ISBN 0-85198-380-4, Pub. by CAB Bks England). State Mutual Bk.
Pozniak, G. I., ed. Dictionary of Helminthology & Plant Nematology. (Rus. & Eng.). 108p. 1979. 35.00 (ISBN 0-85198-447-9). French & EUr.
Pozniak, G. J. Russian-English Dictionary of Helminthology & Plant Nematology. (Rus. & Eng.). 108p. 1979. 60.00x (ISBN 0-85198-447-9, Pub. by CAB Bks England). State Mutual Bk.
Rysavy, B. & Ryzhikov, K. M., eds. Helminths of Fish Eating Birds of the Palaearctic Region: Volume 1, Nematoda. (Illus.). 1978. lib. bdg. 50.00 (ISBN 90-6193-551-2, Pub. by Junk Pubs Nethherlands). Kluwer Academic.

HELMONT, JEAN BAPTISTE VAN

Pagel, Walter. Joan Baptista Van Helmont: Reformer of Science & Medicine. LC 81-24193. (Cambridge Monographs on the History of Medicine). (Illus.). 192p. 1982. 34.50 (ISBN 0-521-24807-8). Cambridge U Pr.

HEMATOLOGY

see also Blood

Baum, S. J., ed. Current Methodology in Experimental Hematology. (Bibliotheca Haematologica: No. 48). (Illus.). vi, 418p. 1985. 105.75 (ISBN 3-8055-3722-0). S Karger.

Brain, Michael C. & McCulloch, Peter B. Current Therapy in Hematology-Oncology 1983-1984: 1983 to 1984. LC 82-83696. 326p. 1983. text ed. 44.00 (ISBN 0-941158-05-5, D07809). Mosby.

DeLoach, et al, eds. Red Blood Cells As Carriers for Drugs. (Bibliotheca Haematologica: No. 51). (Illus.). viii, 162p. 1985. 44.25 (ISBN 3-8055-3940-1). S Karger.

Dimitriv, Nikolay V. & Nodine, John H., eds. Drugs & Hematologic Reactions: The Twenty-Ninth Hahnemann Symposium. 416p. 1974. 87.50 (ISBN 0-8089-0812-X, 791048). Grune.

Fascicle II: Hematology. 160p. 15.00 (ISBN 0-930304-27-6). Coll Am Pathol.

Ferrone, Soldano & Solheim, Bjarte G., eds. HLA Typing: Methodology & Clinical Aspects, 2 vols. 1982. 59.00 ea. Vol. I, 208 pp (ISBN 0-8493-6410-8). Vol. II, 200 pp (ISBN 0-8493-6411-6). 59.00. CRC Pr.

Figueroa, William G., ed. Hematology. LC 81-10310. 430p. 1981. 40.00 (ISBN 0-471-09515-X). Krieger.

Fulwood, Robinson & Johnson, Clifford L. Hematological & Nutritional Biochemistries References Data of Persons 6 Months-74 Years of Age: United States, 1976-1980. Cox, Klaudia, tr. (Ser. 11: No. 232). 60p. 1982. pap. 1.95 (ISBN 0-8406-0267-7). Natl Ctr Health Stats.

Gross, R., ed. Strategies in Clinical Hematology. (Recent Results in Cancer Research Ser.: Vol. 69). (Illus.). 1979. 32.00 (ISBN 0-387-09578-0). Springer-Verlag.

Hansen, H. G. & Graucob, E. Hematologic Cytology of Storage Diseases. Cooper-Schluter, H. K., tr. from Ger. 115p. 1985. 58.00 (ISBN 0-387-13825-0). Springer-Verlag.

Heckner, Fritz. Practical Microscopic Hematology. 2nd ed. Lehmann, Peter & Yuan Kao, eds. Lehmann, H. L., tr. from Ger. LC 82-4738. Tr. of Praktikum der Mikroskopischen Hamatologie. (Illus.). 140p. 1982. pap. text ed. 19.50 (ISBN 0-8067-0812-3). Urban & S.

Hematology & the Lymphatic Immune Systems. 2nd ed. (Medical Ser.). (Illus.). 72p. 12.95x (ISBN 0-935920-21-8, Pub. by Natl Medical Careers). Natl Pub Black Hills.

Hocking, William G. Practical Hematology. LC 82-20087. (Family Practice Today: A Comprehensive Postgraduate Library: A Comprehensive Postgraduate Library). 275p. 1983. 35.00 (ISBN 0-471-09563-X, Pub. by Wiley Med). Wiley.

Hollan, S., et al, eds. Recent Advances in Haemotology, Immunology & Blood Transfusion. 418p. 1983. text ed. 45.00x (ISBN 0-471-90164-4, Pub. by Wiley Med). Wiley.

Huser, H. J. Atlas of Comparative Primate Hematology. 1970. 74.50 (ISBN 0-12-362750-8). Acad Pr.

Koepke, John A., ed. Laboratory Hematology, 2 vol. (Illus.). 1344p. 1984. Set. text ed. 125.00 (ISBN 0-443-08191-3). Churchill.

Livingstone, Frank B. Data on the Abnormal Hemoglobins & Glucose-Six-Phosphate Dehydrogenase Deficiency in Human Populations. (Technical Reports: No. 3). (Contribution 1 in Contributions in Human Biology). 1973. pap. 2.50x (ISBN 0-932206-12-3). U Mich Mus Anthro.

Murano, Genesio. Reviews of Hematology, Vol. II. 1985. 59.95 (ISBN 0-915340-14-3). PJD Pubns.

Prasad, Ananda S.. Trace Elements & Iron in Human Metabolism. LC 78-13446. (Topics in Hematology Ser.). (Illus.). 408p. 1978. 45.00x (ISBN 0-306-31142-9, Plenum Med Bk). Plenum Pub.

Reeves, G. W., ed. Recent Developments in Clinical Immunology. (Research Monographs in Immunology: Vol. 6). 216p. 1984. 59.25 (ISBN 0-444-80554-0, I-273-84). Elsevier.

Reizenstein, Peter. Hematologic Stress Syndrome: The Biological Response to Disease. Erslev, Allan, frwd. by. 204p. 1983. 29.95 (ISBN 0-03-059802-8). Praeger.

Roath, S., ed. Topical Reviews in Haematology, Vol. 2. (Illus.). 232p. 1982. text ed. 37.00 (ISBN 0-7236-0615-3). PSG Pub Co.

Schmid-Schoenbein, H., et al, eds. Hemodilution & Flow Improvement: Bibliotheca Haematologica, No. 47. (Illus.). viii, 356p. 1982. pap. 80.50 (ISBN 3-8055-2899-X). S Karger.

Schumacher, Harold R., et al. Introduction to Laboratory Hematology & Hematopathology. LC 84-3969. 624p. 1984. 49.50 (ISBN 0-8451-0235-4). A R Liss.

Seiverd, Charles E. Hematology for Medical Technologists. 5th. ed. LC 81-8265. (Illus.). 946p. 1983. text ed. 37.50 (ISBN 0-8121-0805-1). Lea & Febiger.

Szirmai, E., ed. Nuclear Hematology. 1965. 88.00 (ISBN 0-12-681650-6). Acad Pr.

Tsieh Sun, et al. Atlas of Cytochemistry & Immunochemistry of Hematologic Neoplasms. LC 84-24164. (Illus.). 264p. 1985. text ed. 80.00 (ISBN 0-89189-185-4, 16- 5-002-00); incl. slide set 160.00 (ISBN 0-89189-193-5, 15-5-002-00). Am Soc Clinical.

Williams, W. Hematology: Pretest Self-Assessment & Review. Prestest Service Inc., ed. 240p. Date not set. write for info. (ISBN 0-07-051930-7). McGraw-Pretest.

Wintrobe, Maxwell M. Blood, Pure & Eloquent. new ed. (Illus.). 1980. text ed. 50.00 (ISBN 0-07-071135-6). McGraw.

--Hematology, the Blossoming of a Science: A Story of Inspiration & Effort. LC 84-26095. (Illus.). 564p. 1985. text ed. write for info. (ISBN 0-8121-0961-9). Lea & Febiger.

HEMATOPOIESIS

see also Blood; Hematopoietic System

Albert, Solomon N., et al. The Hematocrit in Clinical Practice. (Illus.). 80p. 1965. 9.75x (ISBN 0-398-00025-5). C C Thomas.

Cronkite, E. P. & Carstens, A. L. Diffusion Chamber Culture: Hemopoiesis, Cloning of Tumors, Cytogenetic & Carinogenic Assays. (Illus.). 270p. 1980. pap. 51.00 (ISBN 0-387-10064-4). Springer-Verlag.

Golde, David W., ed. Hematopoiesis. (Methods in Hematology Ser.: Vol. 11). (Illus.). 358p. 1984. text ed. 55.00 (ISBN 0-443-08286-3). Churchill.

Keleman, E., et al. Atlas of Human Hemopoietic Development. (Illus.). 1979. 230.00 (ISBN 0-387-08741-9). Springer-Verlag.

Killmann, Aa., et al, eds. Hemopoietic Stem Cells: Characterization, Proliferation, Regulation. (Alfred Benzon Symposium Ser.: Vol. 18). 428p. 1983. text ed. 51.50 (ISBN 0-317-19790-8). Raven.

Metcalf, D. Clonal Culture of Hemopoietic Cells: Techniques & Applications. 168p. 1984. 37.00 (ISBN 0-444-80565-6). Elsevier.

--The Hemopoietic Colony Stimulating Factors. 493p. 1984. 120.50 (ISBN 0-444-80564-8). Elsevier.

Weiss, Leon. The Blood Cells & Hematopoietic Tissues. 2nd ed. 224p. 1984. pap. text ed. 27.95 (ISBN 0-444-00926-4). Elsevier.

HEMATOPOIETIC SYSTEM

see also Reticulo-Endothelial System

Ciba Foundation. Haemopoietic Stem Cells. LC 73-76975. (Ciba Foundation Symposium: New Ser.: No. 13). pap. 88.80 (ISBN 0-317-28301-4, 2022144). Bks Demand UMI.

Golde, David W., et al, eds. Hematopoietic Cell Differentiation. (ICN-UCLA Symposia on Molecular Biology, 1978 Ser.: Vol. 10). 1978. 55.00 (ISBN 0-12-287750-0). Acad Pr.

Luriya, E. A., ed. Hematopoietic & Lymphoid Tissue in Cultures. LC 76-55703. (Studies in Soviet Science: Life Science). (Illus.). 194p. 1977. 49.50 (ISBN 0-306-10934-4, Consultants). Plenum Pub.

Marchesi, Vincent T. & Gallo, Robert C., eds. Differentiation & Function of Hematopoietic Cell Surfaces. LC 82-6557. (UCLA Symposia on Molecular & Cellular Biology Ser.: Vol. 1). 320p. 1982. 56.00 (ISBN 0-8451-2600-8). A R Liss.

Palek, Jiri, et al. Hematopoietic Stem Cell Physiology. (PCBR Ser.). 510p. 1985. 84.00 (ISBN 0-8451-5034-0). A R Liss.

HEME

Bishop, D. F. & Desnick, R. J., eds. Assays of the Heme Biosynthetic Enzymes. (Journal: Enzyme: Vol. 28, No. 2-3). (Illus.). vi, 144p. 1982. pap. 41.50 (ISBN 3-8055-3573-2). S Karger.

Chance, Britton, et al, eds. Hemes & Hemoproteins. 1967. 80.00 (ISBN 0-12-167856-3). Acad Pr.

Matteis, F. De & Aldridge, W. N., eds. Heme & Hemoproteins. LC 77-13134. (Handbook of Experimental Pharmacology Ser.: Vol. 44). (Illus.). 1977. 113.00 (ISBN 0-387-08460-6). Springer-Verlag.

HEMIPTERA

see also Homoptera; Scale-Insects

Furth, David G. The Stink Bugs of Ohio (Hemiptera: Pentatomidae) 1974. 3.00 (ISBN 0-86727-069-1). Ohio Bio Survey.

Hungerford, H. B. The Corixidae of the Western Hemisphere (Hemiptera) LC 75-43673. (Illus.). 827p. 1977. Repr. of 1948 ed. 25.00 (ISBN 0-911836-07-1). Entomological Repr.

McPherson, J. E. The Pentatomoidea (Hemiptera) of Northeastern North America With Emphasis on the Fauna of Illinois. LC 81-9167. (Illus.). 253p. 1982. 30.00x (ISBN 0-8093-1040-6). S Ill U Pr.

Slater, James A. & Baranowski, Richard M. How to Know the True Bugs: (Hemiptera: Heteroptera) (Pictured Key Nature Ser). 300p. 1978. wire coil avail. (ISBN 0-697-04894-2). Wm C Brown.

Usinger, R. L. Genus Nysius & Its Allies in the Hawaiian Islands. (BMB). Repr. of 1942 ed. 22.00 (ISBN 0-527-02281-0). Kraus Repr.

Van Duzee, E. P. Checklist of Hemiptera (Excepting the Aphididae, Aleurodidae & Coccidae) of America, North of Mexico. 1916. pap. 5.00 (ISBN 0-934454-23-X). Lubrecht & Cramer.

Weber, H. Biologie der Hemipteren. (Illus.). 1968. 31.00 (ISBN 90-6123-179-5). Lubrecht & Cramer.

HEMOGLOBIN

see also Anoxemia

Abraham. Glycosylated Hemoglobins: Methods of Analysis & Clinical Applications. (Clinical & Biochemical Analysis Ser.). 280p. 1985. write for info. (ISBN 0-8247-7356-X). Dekker.

Bowman, J. E., ed. Distribution & Evolution of Hemoglobin & Globin Loci: Proceedings of the Comprehensive Sickle Cell Center Symposium, Fourth Annual, University of Chicago, Oct. 10-12, 1982. (The University of Chicago Sickle Cell Center Hemoglobin Symposia Ser.: No. 4). 618p. 1983. 86.00 (ISBN 0-444-00793-8, Biomedical Pr). Elsevier.

Goldwasser, E., ed. Regulation of Hemoglobin Biosynthesis. (Proceedings of the Third Annual Comprehensive Sickle Cell Center Symposium, Chicago: Vol. 3). 428p. 1983. 83.00 (ISBN 0-444-00768-7, Biomedical Pr). Elsevier.

Goslinga, H. Blood Viscosity & Shock: The Role of Hemodilution, Hemoconcentration & Defibrination. (Anaesthesiology & Intensive Care Medicine Ser.: Vol. 160). (Illus.). 215p. 1984. pap. 30.60 (ISBN 0-387-12620-1). Springer-Verlag.

Ho, C. & Eaton, W. A., eds. Hemoglobin & Oxygen Binding. 486p. 1982. 95.00 (ISBN 0-444-00571-4, Biomedical Pr). Elsevier.

Ingram, Vernon M. Hemoglobins in Genetics & Evolution. LC 63-10416. (Biology Ser.). (Illus.). 1963. 24.00x (ISBN 0-231-02585-8). Columbia U Pr.

Schroeder & Huisman. The Chromatography of Hemoglobin. (Clinical & Biochemical Analysis Ser.: Vol. 9). 256p. 1980. 45.00 (ISBN 0-8247-6941-4). Dekker.

HENRY, JOSEPH, 1797-1878

Crowther, James G. Famous American Men of Science. facs. ed. LC 69-18925. (Essay Index Reprint Ser). 1937. 27.50 (ISBN 0-8369-0040-5). Ayer Co Pubs.

Molella, Arthur P., et al. A Scientist in American Life: The Essays & Lectures of Joseph Henry. LC 80-19367. (Illus.). 136p. 1981. pap. 6.95 (ISBN 0-87474-641-8). Smithsonian.

Reingold, Nathan, ed. The Papers of Joseph Henry. Incl. Volume One: The Albany Years, December 1797-October 1832. LC 72-2005. 496p. 30.00x (ISBN 0-87474-123-8); Volume Two: The Princeton Years, November 1832-December 1835. LC 72-2005. 539p. 35.00x (ISBN 0-87474-164-5). (Illus.). Smithsonian.

--The Papers of Joseph Henry: The Princeton Years, January 1838-1840, Vol. 4. LC 72-2005. (The Papers of Joseph Henry Ser.). (Illus.). 475p. 1981. text ed. 35.00x (ISBN 0-87474-792-9). Smithsonian.

HENS

see Poultry

HERBAGE

see Grasses

HERBALS

see Botany–Pre-Linnean Works; Botany, Medical; Herbs

HERBARIA

see also Plants–Collection and Preservation

Jain, S. K. & Rao, R. R. A Handbook of Field & Herbarium Methods. (Illus.). 150p. 1977. 7.00 (ISBN 0-88065-139-3, Pub. by Messers Today & Tomorrows Printers & Publishers India). Scholarly Pubns.

Lasegue, A. Musee Botanique de M. Benjamin Delessert. 1970. Repr. of 1845 ed. 35.00 (ISBN 3-7682-0686-6). Lubrecht & Cramer.

Womersley, J. S. Plant Collecting & Herbarium Development: A Manual. (Plant Production & Protection Papers: No. 33). 148p. 1981. pap. 10.75 (ISBN 92-5-101144-3, F2283, FAO). Unipub.

HERBICIDES

Aquatic Herbicides: Monograph Ser. (No. 16). 115p. (Orig.). 1976. pap. 14.00x (ISBN 0-901436-49-6, Pub. by BCPC England). Intl Spec Bk.

Ashton, Floyd M. & Crafts, Alden S. Mode of Action of Herbicides. 2nd ed. LC 80-23077. 525p. 1981. 58.95x (ISBN 0-471-04847-X, Pub. by Wiley-Interscience). Wiley.

Audus, L. J., ed. Herbicides: Physiology, Biochemistry Ecology. 2nd ed. Vol. 1, 1976. 95.00 (ISBN 0-12-067701-6); Vol. 2, 1977. 90.00 (ISBN 0-12-067702-4). Acad Pr.

Beste, C. E. & Humburg, N. E. Herbicide Handbook of the Weed Science Society of America. rev., 5th ed. 664p. pap. 10.00 (ISBN 0-686-39882-3). Weed Sci Soc.

CAB Books, ed. Herbicides in British Fruit Growing. 1973. 39.00x (ISBN 0-901436-29-1, Pub. by CAB Bks England). State Mutual Bk.

Chlorpropham, Propham. (Specifications for Plant Protection Products). 9p. 1978. pap. 7.50 (ISBN 92-5-100539-7, F1374, FAO). Unipub.

Critser, James R., Jr. Herbicides. (Ser. 12-77). 1978. 80.00 (ISBN 0-914428-48-9). Lexington Data.

Directory of Herbicides for Use in Home Gardens. 138p. 1980. pap. 6.00x (ISBN 0-931876-42-7, 4102). Ag & Nat Res.

Eagle, D. J. & Caverly, D. J. Diagnosis of Herbicide Damage to Crops. (Illus.). 1981. 35.00 (ISBN 0-8206-0294-9). Chem Pub.

Fedtke, Carl. Biochemistry & Physiology of Herbicide Action. (Illus.). 250p. 1982. 70.00 (ISBN 0-387-11231-6). Springer-Verlag.

Forests, Herbicides & People. 1985. 17.95 (ISBN 0-87871-017-5). CEP.

Grossbard, E. & Atkinson, D. Herbicide Glyphosate. 400p. 1984. text ed. 109.95 (ISBN 0-408-11153-4). Butterworth.

Hance, R. J., ed. Interactions Between Herbicides & the Soil. 1981. 59.50 (ISBN 0-12-323840-4). Acad Pr.

Harnly, Caroline D. Agent Orange & the Vietnam Veteran: An Annotated Bibliography. (Public Administration Ser.: Bibliography P 1623). 160p. 1985. pap. 18.25 (ISBN 0-89028-293-5). Vance Biblios.

Hatzios, Kriton K. & Penner, Donald. Metabolism of Organic Herbicides in Higher Plants. LC 81-68903. 142p. (Orig.). 1982. text ed. 29.95x (ISBN 0-8087-2987-X). Burgess.

Isotopes in Weed Research. (Proceedings Ser.). (Illus.). 237p. (Orig.). 1966. pap. 14.50 (ISBN 92-0-010066-X, ISP113, IAEA). Unipub.

Johnson, J. C., ed. Plant Growth Regulators & Herbicide Antagonists: Recent Advances. LC 82-7966. (Chemical Technology Rev. 212). (Illus.). 303p. 1983. 45.00 (ISBN 0-8155-0915-4). Noyes.

Kearney, Philip C. & Kaufman, D., eds. Herbicides: Chemistry, Degradation, & Mode of Action, Vol.1. rev. 2nd ed. 512p. 1975. 99.75 (ISBN 0-8247-6175-8). Dekker.

--Herbicides: Chemistry, Degradation, & Mode of Action, Vol. 2. rev.2nd ed. 1976. 99.75 (ISBN 0-8247-6301-7). Dekker.

Life Sciences Symposium Held in New York, Oct 19-20, 1983. Public Health Risks of the Dioxins: Proceedings. Lowrance, William W., ed. 168p. 1984. pap. text ed. 25.00 (ISBN 0-86576-076-4). W Kaufmann.

Moreland, Donald E. & St. John, Judith B., eds. Biochemical Responses Induced by Herbicides. LC 81-20645. (ACS Symposium Ser.: No. 181). 1982. 39.95 (ISBN 0-8412-0699-6). Am Chemical.

Newton, Michael. Handbook of Weed & Insect Control Chemicals for Forest Resource Managers. 160p. 1981. 24.95x (ISBN 0-917304-25-X); pap. 17.95x (ISBN 0-917304-63-2). Timber.

Page, B. G. & Thompson, W. T. The Insecticide, Herbicide, Fungicide Quick Guide, 1985. 140p. pap. 12.00 (ISBN 0-913702-30-7). Thomson Pub CA.

Pallos, Ferenc M. & Casida, John E., eds. Chemistry & Action of Herbicide Antidotes (Symposium) (MS-REPRO) 1978. 29.50 (ISBN 0-12-544050-2). Acad Pr.

Que Hee, Shane S. & Sutherland, Ronald G. The Phenoxyalkanoic Herbicides: Volume 1 Chemistry, Analysis & Environmental Pollution. 321p. 1981. 91.50 (ISBN 0-8493-5851-5). CRC Pr.

Summers, L. A. The Bipyridinium Herbicides. LC 79-41550. 1980. 79.50 (ISBN 0-12-676450-6). Acad Pr.

Thomson, W. T. Agricultural Chemicals: Herbicides 1983-84, Bk. II. rev. ed. 285p. 1983. pap. 13.50 (ISBN 0-913702-23-4). Thomson Pub CA.

Torrey, S., ed. Preemergence Herbicides: Recent Advances. LC 82-7954. (Chemical Technology Review: No. 211). (Illus.). 335p. 1983. 48.00 (ISBN 0-8155-0914-6). Noyes.

Tucker, Richard E. & Young, Alvin L., eds. Human & Environmental Risks of Chlorinated Dioxins & Related Compounds. (Enviornmental Science Research Ser.: Vol. 26). 800p. 1983. 95.00x (ISBN 0-306-41170-9, Plenum Press). Plenum Pub.

Weaver, Robert J. Plant Growth Substances in Agriculture. LC 71-166964. (Plant Science Ser.). (Illus.). 594p. 1972. text ed. 45.95x (ISBN 0-7167-0824-8). W H Freeman.

Westing, Arthur, ed. Herbicides in War: The Long Term Ecological & Human Consequences. LC 84-2468. (Peace Studies). (Illus.). 290p. 1984. 33.00x (ISBN 0-85066-265-6, Pub. by SIPRI). Taylor & Francis.

Wilcox, Fred A. Waiting for an Army to Die: The Tragedy of Agent Orange. LC 82-42791. 256p. 1983. pap. 6.95 (ISBN 0-394-71518-7, Vin). Random.

HERBIVORA

see also names of herbivorous animals

Coombs, Margery C. Large Mammalian Clawed Herbivores: A Comparative Study. LC 83-71301. (Transactions Ser.: Vol. 73, Pt. 7). 1983. 20.00 (ISBN 0-87169-737-8). Am Philos.

Crawley, Michael J. Herbivory: The Dynamics of Animal Plant Interactions. LC 82-45903. (Studies in Ecology: Vol. 10). 420p. 1983. text ed. 45.00x (ISBN 0-520-05042-8). U of Cal Pr.

Denno, Robert F. & McClure, Mark S. Variable Plants & Herbivores in Natural & Managed Systems. 1983. 64.00 (ISBN 0-12-209160-4). Acad Pr.

Rosenthal, G. Herbiovores. 1982. pap. 37.00 (ISBN 0-12-597182-6). Acad Pr.

Rosenthal, Gerald A. & Janzen, Daniel, eds. Herbivores: Their Interaction with Secondary Plant Metabolites. LC 79-6944. 1979. 69.00 (ISBN 0-12-597180-X). Acad Pr.

HERBS

see also Botany–Pre-Linnean Works; Botany, Medical

Andrews, Theodora, et al. Bibliography on Herbs, Herbal Remedies, Natural Foods, & Unconventional Treatment. LC 82-128. 344p. 1982. lib. bdg. 30.00 (ISBN 0-87287-288-2). Libs Unl.

Askham, Anthony. A Little Herball of the Properties of the Herbes. LC 77-6848. (English Experience Ser.: No. 843). 1977. Repr. of 1561 ed. lib. bdg. 11.50 (ISBN 90-221-0843-0). Walter J Johnson.

Bacon, Richard M. The Forgotten Arts: Growing, Gardening & Cooking with Herbs. LC 72-91864. (Forgotten Arts Ser.). (Illus.). 128p. (Orig.). 1972. pap. 6.95 (ISBN 0-911658-51-3). Yankee Bks.

Bamer, Donald. Applied Iridology & Herbology. pap. 12.95 (ISBN 0-89557-053-X). Bi World Indus.

Beckett, Kenneth A. The Garden Library: Herbs. Dorling Kindersley Ltd., ed. 96p. 1984. pap. 4.95 (ISBN 0-345-30907-3). Ballantine.

Binding, G. J. Vegetables & Herbs with a Difference. 1980. 19.50x (ISBN 0-85032-178-6, Pub. by Daniel Co England). State Mutual Bk.

Biokinesiology Institute & Barton, John. Which Vitamin - Which Herb Do You Need? 2nd ed. (Illus.). 64p. 1981. pap. 2.00 (ISBN 0-937216-16-X). Biokinesiology.

Bonar, Ann. How to Book of Herbs & Herb Gardening. (How-To Ser.). (Illus.). 96p. (Orig.). 1982. pap. 3.95 (ISBN 0-7137-1290-2, Pub. by Blandford Pr England). Sterling.

--The Macmillan Treasury of Herbs. 144p. 1985. 14.95 (ISBN 0-02-513470-1). Macmillan.

Britten, James, et al, eds. William Turner, Libellus de re Herbaria 1538, the Names of Herbes 1548. ix, 275p. 1965. Repr. of 1548 ed. 22.50x (ISBN 0-318-02524-8, Pub by Brit Mus Nat Hist England). Sabbot-Natural Hist Bks.

Brother Aloysius. Comfort to the Sick: A Recipe Book of Medicinal Herbs. LC 82-60161. 416p. pap. price not set (ISBN 0-87728-525-X). Weiser.

Brown, O. Phelps. The Complete Herbalist or the People Their Own Physicians. 504p. Date not set. pap. 25.00 (ISBN 0-89540-118-5, SB-118). Sun Pub.

Center for Self-Sufficiency Research Division, compiled by. Herbs: A Bibliography Index. LC 83-90711. 35p. 1985. pap. text ed. 2.95 (ISBN 0-910811-04-0, Pub. by Center Self Suff). Prosperity & Profits.

Center for Self Sufficiency Research Division. International Directory of Herb, Health, Vitamin & Natural Food Catalogs. 200p. 1985. pap. text ed. 3.50 (ISBN 0-910811-36-9, Pub. by Center Self Suff). Prosperity & Profits.

Challem, Jack & Lewin-Challem, Renate. What Herbs Are All about. LC 80-82913. 150p. (Orig.). 1980. pap. 2.95 (ISBN 0-87983-204-5). Keats.

Clair, Colin. Dictionnaire des Herbes et des Epices. (Fr.). 259p. 1963. pap. 6.95 (ISBN 0-686-56842-7, M-6621). French & Eur.

Clarkson, Rosetta E. The Golden Age of Herbs & Herbalists. (Illus.). 352p. 1972. pap. 5.95 (ISBN 0-486-22869-X). Dover.

--The Golden Age of Herbs & Herbalists. Orig. Title: Green Enchantment. (Illus.). 11.25 (ISBN 0-8446-4623-7). Peter Smith.

Dawson, Adele. Health, Happiness & the Pursuit of Herbs. LC 79-21182. (Illus.). 1980. pap. 9.95 (ISBN 0-8289-0363-8). Greene.

De Bairacli-Levy, Juliette. Common Herbs for Natural Health. LC 73-91335. (Illus.). 198p. 1974. pap. 3.95 (ISBN 0-8052-0436-9). Schocken.

--The Complete Herbal Book for the Dog. LC 72-3339. 1973. 8.95 (ISBN 0-668-02649-9); pap. 5.95 (ISBN 0-668-04181-1). Arco.

De Waal, M. Medicinal Herbs in the Bible. Meijlink, Jane, tr. from Dutch. 96p. 1984. pap. 5.95 (ISBN 0-87728-527-6). Weiser.

Duncan, Thomas. A Taxonomic Study of the Ranunculus Hispidus. (U. C. Publications in Botany V Ser.: Vol. 77). 1980. 14.00x (ISBN 0-520-09617-7). U of Cal Pr.

Frompovich, Catherine J. & Hay, Joanne M. Everyday Herbs for Cooking & Healing. 1980. 100 frame filmstrip, cassette, text 25.00 (ISBN 0-935322-11-6). C J Frompovich.

Genders, Roy. Complete Book of Herbs & Herb Growing. LC 79-93206. (Illus.). 160p. 1980. pap. 9.95 (ISBN 0-8069-3930-3). Sterling.

Gerard, John. The Herball or General Historie of Plants, 2 vols. LC 74-80179. (English Experience Ser.: Nos. 660a-660b). 1974. Repr. of 1597 ed. Set. 214.00 (ISBN 90-221-0660-8). Walter J Johnson.

Gerarde, John. The Herball or Generall Historie of Plantes. 303p. 1984. Repr. of 1597 ed. text ed. 85.00x (ISBN 0-86590-238-0). Apt Bks.

Giles, F. A. Herbaceous Perennials. (Illus.). 1980. text ed. 21.95 (ISBN 0-8359-2822-5). Reston.

Grieve, M. Culinary Herbs & Condiments. 13.00 (ISBN 0-8446-0117-9). Peter Smith.

--A Modern Herbal. Leyel, Mrs. C. F., ed. LC 72-169784. (Illus.). 1971. pap. 7.95; Vol. 1. pap. 7.95 (ISBN 0-486-22798-7); Vol. 2. pap. 8.50 (ISBN 0-486-22799-5). Dover.

Grieve, Mrs. M. A Modern Herbal, 2 vols. LC 72-169782. (Illus.). Set. 32.00 (ISBN 0-8446-0302-3). Peter Smith.

Griffin, LaDean. No Side Effects: Return to Herbal Medicine. 7.95x (ISBN 0-89036-073-1). Cancer Control Soc.

Grounds, Roger. Growing Vegetables & Herbs. (Orig.). 1980. pap. 6.95x (ISBN 0-8464-1016-8). Beekman Pubs.

Hamilton, Geoff. Herbs: How to Grow Them. 1980. pap. 4.50 (ISBN 0-7153-7897-X). David & Charles.

Harris, Ben C. Eat the Weeds. LC 69-12302. 1969. pap. 3.95 (ISBN 0-517-51730-2). Barre.

Harris, Ben C., ed. The Compleat Herbal. LC 77-185615. 248p. (Orig.). 1972. pap. 3.95 (ISBN 0-915962-15-2). Larchmont Bks.

Hayes, Elizabeth S. Spices & Herbs: Lore & Cookery. 13.00 (ISBN 0-8446-5772-7). Peter Smith.

Heinerman, John. Science of Herbal Medicine. 19.95x (ISBN 0-89557-044-0). Cancer Control Soc.

Hemphill, John & Hemphill, Rosemary. Herbs: Their Cultivation & Usage. (Illus.). 128p. (Orig.). 1985. pap. 7.95 (ISBN 0-7137-1451-4, Pub. by Blandford Pr England). Sterling.

Hiesey, William M., et al. Biosystematics, Genetics, & Physiological Ecology of the Erythranthe Section of Mimulus. LC 40-14859. (Experimental Studies on the Nature of Species: Vol. 5). (Illus.). 219p. 1971. 13.75 (ISBN 0-87279-639-6, 628). Carnegie Inst.

Huson, Paul. Mastering Herbalism. LC 73-90704. 1975. pap. 10.95 (ISBN 0-8128-1847-4). Stein & Day.

Hylton, William, ed. The Rodale Herb Book: How to Use, Grow & Buy Nature's Miracle Plants. LC 73-18902. (Illus.). 656p. 1974. 16.95 (ISBN 0-87857-076-4); deluxe ed. 19.95 (ISBN 0-87857-196-5). Rodale Pr Inc.

Jacobs, Betty E. Growing & Using Herbs Successfully. LC 80-28802. (Illus.). 240p. 1981. pap. 8.95 (ISBN 0-88266-249-X). Garden Way Pub.

Kaaiakamanu, D. M. & Akina, J. K. Hawaiian Herbs of Medicinal Value. Akana, Akaiko, tr. LC 76-177367. 1972. pap. 4.75 (ISBN 0-8048-1019-2). C E Tuttle.

Kadans, Joseph. Modern Encyclopedia of Herbs. 1970. 9.95 (ISBN 0-13-593798-1, Reward); pap. 4.95 (ISBN 0-13-593780-9). P-H.

Kamm, Minnie W. Old Time Herbs for Northern Gardens. (Illus.). 1971. pap. 4.95 (ISBN 0-486-22695-6). Dover.

--Old-Time Herbs for Northern Gardens. (Illus.). 8.25 (ISBN 0-8446-0162-4). Peter Smith.

Kerr, Ralph W. Herbalism Through the Ages. 7th ed. LC 74-96813. 1980. 12.50 (ISBN 0-912057-24-6, G635). AMORC.

Keys, John. Chinese Herbs: Their Botany, Chemistry & Pharmacodynamics. LC 75-35399. 1976. 19.50 (ISBN 0-8048-1179-2). C E Tuttle.

Kirschner, H. E. Nature's Healing Grasses. 3.00x (ISBN 0-686-29771-7). Cancer Control Soc.

Kloppenburg-Versteegh, J. The Traditional Use of Malay Plants & Herbs. Kaufman, Aileen, tr. from Dutch. LC 79-89939. Orig. Title: Het Gebruik Van Indische Planten. (Illus.). 1985. cancelled (ISBN 0-86164-152-3, Pub by Momenta Publishing Ltd U. K.). Hunter Hse.

Kohlein, Fritz. Saxifrages. (Saxifragen., Illus.). 289p. 1985. 34.95 (ISBN 0-88192-008-8). Timber.

Law, Donald. Concise Herbal Encyclopedia. 256p. 1981. 30.00x (ISBN 0-7028-1046-0, Pub. by Collet's). State Mutual Bk.

Lazow, Alfred & Nelson, Pearl A. The ABC's of Herbs. (Illus.). 1977. 2.95 (ISBN 0-914634-48-8, 7718). DOK Pubs.

Lee, William. Herbs & Herbal Medicine. Passwater, Richard A. & Mindell, Earl, eds. (Good Health Guide Ser.). 1982. pap. 1.95 (ISBN 0-87983-294-0). Keats.

Leek, Sybil. Sybil Leek's Book of Herbs. 1980. pap. 3.95 (ISBN 0-346-12435-2). Cornerstone.

Loewenfeld, Claire & Back, Philippa. The Complete Book of Herbs & Spices. 1976. pap. 9.70i (ISBN 0-316-53070-0). Little.

Lowenfeld, Claire & Back, Philippa. The Complete Book of Herbs & Spices. (Illus.). 319p. 1980. 19.95 (ISBN 0-7153-7656-X). David & Charles.

Lust, Benedict. Kneipp Herbs & Their Uses. (Illus.). 1968. pap. 1.00 (ISBN 0-87904-009-2). Lust.

Lust, John B. The Herb Book. LC 74-75368. (Illus.). 640p. 1974. 15.95 (ISBN 0-87904-007-6). Lust.

MacLeod, Dawn. Popular Herbs: Their History, Growth & Use. 2nd ed. (Illus.). 204p. 1981. pap. 10.00x (ISBN 0-7156-1526-2, Pub. by Duckworth England). Biblio Dist.

March, Kathryn G. & March, Andrew L. The Wild Plant Companion: A Fresh Understanding of Herbal Food & Medicine. (Illus.). 200p. (Orig.). 1985. pap. 10.00 (ISBN 0-940206-03-X). Meridian Hill.

Meyer, Joseph E. Herbalist. 10.95x (ISBN 0-916638-01-4). Meyerbooks.

--The Herbalist. (Illus.). 304p. 1981. 14.95 (ISBN 0-8069-3902-8). Sterling.

Miller, Richard A. The Magical & Ritual Use of Herbs. LC 83-7457. 144p. 1983. pap. 6.95 (ISBN 0-89281-047-5). Destiny Bks.

Minster, Margaret, ed. Herbs: From Cultivation to Cooking. (Illus.). 228p. 1981. Repr. of 1980 ed. spiral bdg. 9.95 (ISBN 0-88289-288-6). Pelican.

Morton, Julia F. Herbs & Spices. (Golden Guide Ser.). (Illus.). 1977. pap. 2.95 (ISBN 0-307-24364-8, Golden Pr). Western Pub.

Moulton, LeArta. Herb Walk, No. 1. 398p. 1979. 35.00 (ISBN 0-935596-02-X); perfect bdg. 25.00 (ISBN 0-935596-03-8). Gluten Co.

Muenscher, Walter C. & Rice, Myron A. Garden Spice & Wild Pot-Herbs: An American Herbal. LC 78-56899. (Illus.). 218p. 1978. pap. 12.95 (ISBN 0-8014-9174-6). Comstock.

Neblekopf, Ethan. The Herbal Connection. 1980. 12.95 (ISBN 0-89557-048-3). Bi World Indus.

O'Hanlon, Daniel P., tr. from Lat. Macer's Virtue of Herbs. Orig. Title: Macer Floridus De Viribus Herbarum. 125p. 12.95 (ISBN 0-89744-243-1). Auromere.

Pond, Barbara. A Sampler of Wayside Herbs: Rediscovering Old Uses for Familiar Wild Plants. LC 73-89773. (Illus.). 1974. 32.00 (ISBN 0-85699-096-5). Chatham Pr.

Rishel, Jonas. The Indian Physician. 132p. 1980. 5.95 (ISBN 0-88215-048-0). Ohio St U Lib.

Rohde, Eleanor S. Culinary & Salad Herbs: Their Cultivation & Food Values with Recipes. (Illus.). 10.75 (ISBN 0-8446-4602-4). Peter Smith.

Rohde, Eleanour S. Garden of Herbs. LC 75-81736. 1969. pap. 4.50 (ISBN 0-486-22308-6). Dover.

--Herbs & Herb Gardening. LC 70-180975. (Illus.). 1976. Repr. of 1936 ed. 48.00x (ISBN 0-8103-4303-7). Gale.

Rollins, Reed C. & Shaw, Elizabeth A. Genus Lesquerella (Cruciferae) in North America. LC 72-87777. (Illus.). 385p. 1973. 20.00x (ISBN 0-674-34775-7). Harvard U Pr.

Romanne-James, Constance. Herb-Lore for Housewives. LC 71-180978. (Illus.). 264p. 1974. Repr. of 1938 ed. 40.00x (ISBN 0-8103-3976-5). Gale.

Rose, Jeanne. Jeanne Rose's Herbal Guide to Inner Health. (Illus.). 1980. (G&D); pap. 6.95 1980 (ISBN 0-448-14522-7). Putnam Pub Group.

--Kitchen Cosmetics: Using Plants & Herbs in Cosmetics. LC 77-17077. 128p. 1978. 10.95 (ISBN 0-915572-25-7); pap. 5.95 (ISBN 0-915572-24-9). Panjandrum.

Sanecki, Kay N. Discovering Herbs. (Discovering Ser.: No. 89). (Illus., Orig.). 1985. pap. 4.95 (ISBN 0-85263-719-5, Pub. by Shire Pubns England). Seven Hills Bks.

Simon, et al. Herbs: An Indexed Bibliography, 1971-1980. Date not set. price not set (ISBN 0-444-99626-5). Elsevier.

Smith, Alan R. Taxonomy of Thelyptęris Subgenus Steiropteris (Including Glaphyropteris) (U. C. Publications in Botany Ser.: Vol. 76). 1980. pap. 12.50x (ISBN 0-520-09602-9). U of Cal Pr.

Twitchell, Paul. Herbs, the Magic Healers. 1971. pap. 3.95 (ISBN 0-914766-10-4). IWP Pub.

--Les Plantes: Guerisseuses Magiques. Lasnier, Denis R., et al, trs. (Fr.). 240p. (Orig.). 1980. pap. 3.95 (ISBN 0-914766-59-7, 0308). IWP Pub.

Weiner, Michael A. Weiner's Herbal. LC 78-26616. (Illus.). 1979. pap. 11.95 (ISBN 0-8128-6023-3). Stein & Day.

HERCULES (CONSTELLATION)

see Stars–Clusters

HEREDITY

see also Biometry; Chromosomes; Eugenics; Evolution; Hybridization; Genetics; Linkage (Genetics); Mendel's Law; Natural Selection; Population Genetics; Variation (Biology)

Adams, Joseph. A Treatise on the Supposed Hereditary Properties of Diseases...(London, 1814) Rosenberg, Charles, ed. LC 83-48528. (The History of Hereditarian Thought Ser.). 125p. 1985. Repr. of 1814 ed. lib. bdg. 22.00 (ISBN 0-8240-5800-3). Garland Pub.

Beckwith, Jon, et al, eds. Gene Function in Prokaryotes. LC 83-15229. (Monograph Ser.: Vol. 15). 328p. 1984. pap. 30.00 (ISBN 0-87969-176-X). Cold Spring Harbor.

Bennett, J. H. Natural Selection, Heredity & Eugenics. 1983. 47.50x (ISBN 0-19-858177-7). Oxford U Pr.

Brody, Elizabeth G. Genetic Basis at Spontaneous Activity in the Albino Rat. (Comparative Psychology Monographs). 1942. pap. 5.00 (ISBN 0-527-24924-6). Kraus Repr.

Cattell, Raymond B. The Inheritance of Personality & Ability: Research Methods & Findings. LC 80-70667. (Personality & Psychopathology Ser.). 1982. 49.50 (ISBN 0-12-164260-7). Acad Pr.

Cavalier-Smith, T. & Smith. The Evolution of Genome Size. 1985. 59.95 (ISBN 0-471-10272-5). Wiley.

Cold Spring Harbor Symposia on Quantitative Biology: Genes & Chromosomes, Vol. 9. LC 34-8174. (Illus.). 325p. 1941. 38.00x (ISBN 0-87969-008-9). Cold Spring Harbor.

Cold Spring Harbor Symposia on Quantitative Biology: Genes & Mutations, Vol. 16. LC 34-8174. (Illus.). 537p. 1952. 38.00x (ISBN 0-87969-015-1). Cold Spring Harbor.

Conklin, Edwin G. Heredity & Environment in the Development of Men. 533p. 1984. Repr. of 1915 ed. lib. bdg. 45.00 (ISBN 0-89984-025-6). Century Bookbindery.

Cowan, Ruth S. Sir Francis Galton & the Study of Heredity in the Nineteenth Century. Rosenberg, Charles, ed. LC 83-48624. (The History of Hereditarian Thought Ser.). 289p. 1985. lib. bdg. 35.00 (ISBN 0-8240-5802-X). Garland Pub.

Cravens, Hamilton. Triumph of Evolution: American Scientists & the Heredity-Environment Controversy, 1900-1941. LC 77-20570. (Illus.). 1978. 26.00x (ISBN 0-8122-7744-9). U of Pa Pr.

Dampier, William C. & Whetham, Catherine. The Family & the Nation: A Study in the Natural Inheritance & Social Responsibility. Rosenberg, Charles, ed. LC 83-48562. (The History of Hereditarian Thought Ser.). 233p. 1985. Repr. of 1909 ed. lib. bdg. 30.00 (ISBN 0-8240-5831-3). Garland Pub.

Davenport, Charles B. The Feebly Inhibited: Nomadism, or the Wandering Impulse, with Special Reference. Rosenberg, Charles, ed. LC 83-48533. (The History of Hereditarian Thought Ser.). 156p. 1985. Repr. of 1915 ed. lib. bdg. 25.00 (ISBN 0-8240-5804-6). Garland Pub.

DeVries, Hugo. Intracellular Pangenesis. Gager, C. S, tr. from Ger. 1910. 19.95 (ISBN 0-87548-209-0). Open Court.

Fishman, William H. & Sell, Stewart, eds. Onco-Developmental Gene Expression. 1976. 75.00 (ISBN 0-12-257660-8). Acad Pr.

Fowler, Orson. Hereditary Descent: Its Laws & Facts Applied to Human Improvement. Rosenberg, Charles, ed. LC 83-48538. (The History of Hereditarian Thought Ser.). 288p. 1985. Repr. of 1847 ed. lib. bdg. 35.00 (ISBN 0-8240-5812-7). Garland Pub.

Fox, L. Raymond & Elliott, Paul R. Heredity & You. LC 76-51113. 1983. pap. text ed. 9.50 (ISBN 0-8403-3215-7). Kendall-Hunt.

Galton, Francis. Hereditary Genius. LC 82-62300. (Classics in Psychology & Psychiatry Ser.). 390p. 1978. 20.00 (ISBN 0-86187-307-6); pap. 8.50 (ISBN 0-86187-308-4). F Pinter Pubs.

--Natural Inheritance. LC 72-1633. Repr. of 1889 ed. 22.00 (ISBN 0-404-08129-0). AMS Pr.

--Natural Inheritance. Bd. with Darwinism. (Contributions to the History of Psychology Ser., Vol. IV, Pt. D: Comparative Psychology). 1978. Repr. of 1889 ed. 30.00 (ISBN 0-89093-173-9). U Pubns Amer.

Glass, Robert E. Gene Function: E. Coli & Its Heritable Elements. LC 81-69893. (Illus.). 480p. 1982. 42.50x (ISBN 0-520-04619-6); pap. 20.00 (ISBN 0-520-04654-4, CAMPUS 297). U of Cal Pr.

Glover, David M. Gene Cloning: The Mechanics of DNA Manipulation. 1985. 29.95 (ISBN 0-412-26600-8, NO. 9338, Pub. by Chapman & Hall); pap. 11.95 (ISBN 0-412-25430-1, NO. 9161, Pub. by Chapman & Hall). Methuen Inc.

Gobineau, A. de. The Moral & Intellectual Diversity of Races. Rosenberg, Charles, ed. LC 83-48534. (The History of Hereditarian Thought Ser.). 512p. 1984. Repr. of 1856 ed. lib. bdg. 60.00 (ISBN 0-317-14533-9). Garland Pub.

Hyatt, Alpheus. Phylogeny of an Acquired Characteristic: Proceedings of American Philosophical Society, Vol.xxxii, No. 143. Gould, Stephen J., ed. LC 79-8333. (The History of Paleontology Ser.). (Illus.). 1980. Repr. of 1893 ed. lib. bdg. 32.50x (ISBN 0-405-12714-6). Ayer Co Pubs.

Jacob, Francois. The Logic of Life: A History of Heredity. 1982. pap. 7.95 (ISBN 0-394-71007-X). Pantheon.

--The Logic of Life: A History of Heredity. Spillman, Betty E., tr. from Fr. 1976. (Vin); pap. 7.95 (ISBN 0-394-71007-X). Random.

Jinks, J. L. Cytoplasmic Inheritance. rev ed. Head, J. J., ed. LC 77-90233. (Carolina Biology Readers Ser.). (Illus.). 16p. 1978. pap. 1.60 (ISBN 0-89278-272-2, 45-9672). Carolina Biological.

Kemp, Brenda & Pillitteri, Adele. Fundamentals of Nursing: A Framework for Practice. 1984. text ed. 33.95 (ISBN 0-316-48818-6); tchr's. manual avail. (ISBN 0-316-48819-4). Little.

Kevles, Daniel J. In the Name of Eugenics: Genetics & the Uses of Human Heredity. LC 84-47810. 1985. 22.95 (ISBN 0-394-50702-9). Knopf.

Kumar, A., ed. Eukaryotic Gene Expression. LC 83-24721. (GWUMC Annual Spring Symposia Ser.). 229p. 1984. 35.00x (ISBN 0-306-41532-1, Plenum Pr). Plenum Pub.

Lee, Sherry, et al. Chromosomes & Genes: An Interracial Anthology. 54p. (Orig.). 1982. pap. 4.25x (ISBN 0-940248-12-3). Guild Pr.

Lewin, Benjamin. Gene Expression: Eucaryotic Chromosomes, 1 of 3 vols, Vol. 2. 2nd ed. LC 80-10849. 1160p. 1980. 59.95x (ISBN 0-471-01977-1, Pub. by Wiley-Interscience); pap. 34.50x (ISBN 0-471-01976-3, Pub. by Wiley-Interscience). Wiley.

--Gene Expression, Vol. 1: Bacterial Genomes. LC 73-14382. (Illus.). 642p. 1974. (Pub. by Wiley-Interscience); pap. 27.95x (ISBN 0-471-53168-5). Wiley.

Little, Clarence C. Inheritance of Coat Color in Dogs. LC 67-8658. (Illus.). 208p. 1984. 15.95 (ISBN 0-87605-621-4). Howell Bk.

M. D. Anderson Symposia on Fundamental Cancer Research, 33rd. Genes, Chromosomes, & Neoplasia. Arrighi, Frances E., et al, eds. 550p. 1981. 88.00 (ISBN 0-89004-532-1). Raven.

McKusick, Victor A., ed. Mendelian Inheritance in Man: Catalogs of Autosomal Dominant, Autosomal Recessive & X-linked Phenotypes. 6th ed. LC 82-47975. 1448p. 1983. lib. bdg. write for info. (ISBN 0-8018-2744-2). Johns Hopkins.

Medvedev, Zhores A. Protein Biosynthesis & Problems of Heredity Development & Aging. LC 67-71423. pap. 151.50 (ISBN 0-317-28826-1, 2020702). Bks Demand UMI.

Mitsuhashi, S., et al, eds. Plasmids: Medical & Theoretical Aspects. (Illus.). 1977. 63.00 (ISBN 0-387-07946-7). Springer-Verlag.

Morgan, Thomas H. The Theory of the Gene. (Illus.). 343p. 1985. Repr. of 1926 ed. lib. bdg. 100.00 (ISBN 0-8492-6843-5). R West.

Nagle, James J. Heredity & Human Affairs. 2nd ed. LC 78-27066. (Illus.). 380p. 1979. pap. text ed. 18.95 (ISBN 0-8016-3621-3). Mosby.

Ohno, S. Major Sex-Determining Genes. LC 78-10285. (Monographs on Endocrinology: Vol. 11). (Illus.). 1979. 24.00 (ISBN 0-387-08965-9). Springer-Verlag.

O'Malley, Bert W., ed. Gene Regulation: UCLA Symposium Molecular Cellular Biology. LC 82-20709. (Vol. 26). 1982. 42.50 (ISBN 0-12-525960-3). Acad Pr.

Padilla, George & McCarty, Kenneth, eds. Genetic Expression in the Cell Cycle. (Cell Biology Ser.). 1982. 65.00 (ISBN 0-12-543720-X). Acad Pr.

Parker, Gary, et al. Heredity. 2nd ed. (Programed Biology Studies). 1977. 6.95 (ISBN 0-88462-014-X, Ed Methods). Longman USA.

Pendleton, Hester. The Parents Guide: Or, Human Development Through Inherited Tendencies. Rosenberg, Charles, ed. LC 83-48554. (The History of Hereditarian Thought Ser.). 203p. 1985. Repr. of 1871 ed. lib. bdg. 27.00 (ISBN 0-8240-5824-0). Garland Pub.

Pettersson, R. F., ed. Expression of Eukaryotic Viral & Cellular Genes. LC 81-68257. 1981. 55.00 (ISBN 0-12-553120-6). Acad Pr.

Pierce, Carl W. & Cullen, Susan E., eds. IR Genes: Past, Present, & Future. LC 82-4291. (Experimental Biology & Medicine Ser.). (Illus.). 640p. 1983. 69.50 (ISBN 0-89603-050-4). Humana.

Ribot, Theodule A. Heredity: A Psychological Study of Its Phenomena, Laws, Causes, & Consequences. R. W., intro. by. LC 78-72821. (Brainedness, Handedness, & Mental Abilities Ser.). Repr. of 1875 ed. 40.00 (ISBN 0-404-60890-6). AMS Pr.

Rosenthal, S., et al, eds. Gene Function: Proceedings of the 12th FEBS Meeting, Dresden, 1978. (Federation of European Biochemical Society Ser.: Vol. 51). (Illus.). 1979. 72.00 (ISBN 0-08-023175-6). Pergamon.

Russell, E. S. Interpretation of Development & Heredity: A Study in Biological Method. LC 70-39699. (Select Bibliographies Reprint Ser.). 312p. 1972. Repr. of 1930 ed. 17.25 (ISBN 0-8369-9943-6). Ayer Co Pubs.

Sheppard, Philip M. Natural Selection & Heredity. 4th ed. 1975. text ed. 11.25x (ISBN 0-09-036801-0, Hutchinson U Lib); pap. text ed. 8.25x (ISBN 0-09-036802-9). Humanities.

Stoddard, Lothrop. The Revolt Against Civilization, the Menace of the Under-Man. Rosenberg, Charles, ed. LC 83-48558. (The History of the Hereditarian Thought Ser.). 225p. 1985. Repr. of 1923 ed. lib. bdg. 32.00 (ISBN 0-8240-5828-3). Garland Pub.

Taylor, Howard F. The I.Q. Game: A Methodological Inquiry into the Heredity-Environment Controversy. 300p. 1980. 25.00x (ISBN 0-8135-0902-5). Rutgers U Pr.

Voeller, Bruce R., ed. The Chromosome Theory of Inheritance: Classic Papers in Development & Heredity. LC 68-19963. pap. 61.50 (ISBN 0-317-26284-X). Bks Demand UMI.

Wagner, Robert P., ed. Genes & Proteins. LC 75-8851. (Benchmark Papers in Genetics Ser: Vol. 2). 395p. 1975. 70.00 (ISBN 0-12-787710-X). Acad Pr.

Weinstein, I. Bernard & Vogel, Henry J. Genes & Proteins in Oncogenesis. (P & S Biomedical Science Ser.). 1983. 60.00 (ISBN 0-12-742420-2). Acad Pr.

Weismann, August, et al. Germ Plasm: A Theory of Heredity. LC 72-1659. Repr. of 1893 ed. 31.00 (ISBN 0-404-08191-6). AMS Pr.

Winchester, Albert. Heredity, Evolution & Humankind. LC 75-45130. (Illus.). 350p. 1976. text ed. 24.95 (ISBN 0-8299-0106-X). West Pub.

Winchester, Albert M. Heredity: An Introduction to Genetics. pap. 4.95 (ISBN 0-06-460167-6, CO 167, COS). B&N NY.

Winterton, Bert W. The Processes of Heredity. 304p. (Orig.). 1980. pap. 15.95 (ISBN 0-8403-2835-4). Kendall-Hunt.

HERMAPHRODITISM

Jirasek, Jan E. Development of the Genital System & the Male Pseudohermaphroditism. Cohen, M. Michael, Jr., ed. LC 72-128825. pap. 37.50 (ISBN 0-317-19868-8, 2023106). Bks Demand UMI.

Lepori, N. G. Sex Differentiation, Hermaphroditism & Intersexuality in Vertebrates Including Man. (Illus.). 372p. 1980. text ed. 49.50x (ISBN 88-212-0747-1, Pub. by Piccin Italy). J K Burgess.

Reinboth, R. Intersexuality in the Animal Kingdom. (Illus.). 510p. 1975. 59.00 (ISBN 0-387-07118-0). Springer-Verlag.

HERODIONES

Bent, Arthur C. Life Histories of North American Marsh Birds. (Illus.). 1927. pap. 7.50 (ISBN 0-486-21082-0). Dover.

--Life Histories of North American Marsh Birds. (Illus.). 15.00 (ISBN 0-8446-1639-7). Peter Smith.

HERPETOLOGY

see also Amphibians; Reptiles

A, Peters J. Dictionary of Herpetology: Description of Words & Terms. (Illus.). 392p. 1981. lib. bdg. 15.00x (ISBN 0-02-850230-2). Lubrecht & Cramer.

Carroll, R. L. & Kuhn, O. Batrachosauria (Anthrosauria), Gephyrostegida-Chronlosuchide. (Encyclopedia of Paleoherpetology Ser.: Pt. 5-B). (Illus.). 81p. 1972. text ed. 27.25 (ISBN 3-437-30136-5). Lubrecht & Cramer.

Charig, A. J. & Krebs, B. Theodontia. (Encyclopedia of Paleoherpetology Ser.: Pt. 13). (Illus.). 137p. 1976. lib. bdg. 54.20x (ISBN 3-437-30184-5). Lubrecht & Cramer.

Chiszar, David & Smith, Rozella. Fifty Years of Herpetology Publications of Hobart M. Smith. 90p. 1982. pap. text ed. 4.00x (ISBN 0-910914-17-6). J Johnson.

Collins, Joseph T., ed. Amphibians & Reptiles in Kansas. (University of Kansas, Museum of Natural History Public Education Ser. No. 8). (Illus.). 356p. (Orig.). 1982. 17.00 (ISBN 0-89338-013-X); pap. 12.00 (ISBN 0-89338-012-1). U of KS Mus Nat Hist.

Estes, R. Gymnophions, Caudata. (Encyclopedia of Paleoherpetology: Pt. 2). (Illus.). 115p. 1976. pap. text ed. 59.35 (ISBN 3-437-30339-2). Lubrecht & Cramer.

--Sauria terrestria, Amphisbaenia. (Encyclopedia of Paleoherpetology Ser.: Pt. 10A). (Illus.). 249p. 1983. lib. bdg. 100.80 (ISBN 0-318-04101-4). Lubrecht & Cramer.

Girard, Charles. United States Exploring Expedition During the Years 1838, 1839, 1840, 1841, 1842 Under the Command of Charles Wilkes, U.S.N. Herpetology, 2 vols, Vol. 20. Srling, Keir B., ed. LC 77-81095. (Biologists & Their World Ser.). (Illus.). 1978. Repr. of 1858 ed. lib. bdg. 50.00x (ISBN 0-405-10678-5). Ayer Co Pubs.

Goin, Coleman J., et al. Introduction to Herpetology. 3rd ed. LC 77-13554. (Illus.). 378p. 1978. text ed. 26.95 (ISBN 0-7167-0020-4). W H Freeman.

Haubold, H. Ichnia Amphibiorum et Reptiliorum Fossilium. (Encyclopedia of Paleoherpetology Ser.: Pt. 18). (Illus.). 124p. 1971. lib. bdg. 36.15x (ISBN 3-437-30112-8). Lubrecht & Cramer.

Kuhn, O. Proganasauria, Bolosauria, Placedontia, Aeraeoscelidia, Trilophosauria, Weigeltisauria, Millerosauria, Rhincocephalia, Protorosauria. (Encyclopedia of Paleoherpetology: Pt. 9). (Illus.). 74p. 1969. text ed. 24.00 (ISBN 3-437-30027-X). Lubrecht & Cramer.

McKeown, Sean & Honolulu Zoo. Hawaiian Reptiles & Amphibians. 1979. pap. 3.50 (ISBN 0-932596-07-X, Pub. by Oriental). Intl Spec Bk.

Minarski, M. Testudines. (Encyclopedia of Paleoherpetology Ser.: Pt. 7). (Illus.). 130p. 1976. text ed. 40.85 (ISBN 3-437-30236-1). Lubrecht & Cramer.

Panchen, A. L. Batrachosauria (Anthrosauria) (Encyclopedia of Paleoherpetology Ser.: Pt. 5-A). (Illus.). 1970. pap. text ed. 31.00 (ISBN 3-437-30111-X). Lubrecht & Cramer.

Pregill, Gregory. Late Pleistocene Herpetofaunas from Puerto Rico. (Miscellaneous Papers: No. 71). 72p. 1981. 4.25 (ISBN 0-317-04884-8). U of KS Mus Nat Hist.

Rage, Jean-Claude. Serpentes. (Encyclopedia of Paleoherpetology: Pt. 11). (Illus.). 80p. 1984. pap. text ed. 38.50 (ISBN 3-437-30448-8). Lubrecht & Cramer.

Steel, R. Ornithischia. (ENcyclopedia of Paleoherpetology: Pt. 15). (Illus.). 84p. 1969. pap. text ed. 31.85x (ISBN 3-437-30028-8). Lubrecht & Cramer.

--Saurischia. (Encyclopedia of Paleoherpetology Ser.: Pt. 14). (Illus.). 87p. 1970. pap. text ed. 31.85x (ISBN 3-437-30030-X). Lubrecht & Cramer.

Sterling, Keir B., ed. Early Herpetological Studies & Surveys in the Eastern United States: Original Anthology. LC 77-81101. (Biologists & Their World Ser.). (Illus.). 1978. lib. bdg. 53.00x (ISBN 0-405-10685-8). Ayer Co Pubs.

--Herpetological Explorations of the Great American West: Original Anthology, 2 vols. LC 77-81100. (Biologists & Their World Ser.). (Eng. Fr. Ger. & Span., Illus.). 1978. Set. lib. bdg. 100.00x (ISBN 0-405-10682-3); lib. bdg. 50.00x ea. Vol. 1 (ISBN 0-405-10683-1). Vol. 2 (ISBN 0-405-10684-X). Ayer Co Pubs.

Taylor, Edward H, et al. Edward H. Taylor: Recollections of an Herpetologist. (Monographs Ser.: No. 4). 160p. 1975. pap. 4.00 (ISBN 0-686-80382-5). U of KS Mus Nat Hist.

Trueb, Linda. Catalogue of Publications in Herpetology. (Special Publications Ser.: No. 1). 15p. 1976. pap. 1.00 (ISBN 0-686-80387-6). U of KS Mus Nat Hist.

Weishampel, D. B. Evolution of Jaw Mechanisms in Ornithopod Dinosaurs. (Advances in Anatomy, Embryology, & Cell Biology Ser.: Vol. 87). (Illus.). 110p. 1984. pap. 24.00 (ISBN 0-387-13114-0). Springer-Verlag.

Welch, K. R. Herpetology of Europe & Southwest Asia: A Checklist & Bibliography of the Orders Amphisbaenia, Sauria & Serpentes. LC 82-12645. 1983. lib. bdg. 14.50 (ISBN 0-89874-533-0). Krieger.

Welch, Kenneth R. Herpetology of Africa: A Checklist & Bibliography of the Orders Amphisbaenia, Sauria & Serpentes. LC 81-17233. 304p. 1982. text ed. 19.50 (ISBN 0-89874-428-8). Krieger.

Wellnhofer, P. Pterosauria. (Handbook of Paleoherpatology: Pt. 19). (Illus.). 82p. 1978. pap. text ed. 39.55 (ISBN 3-437-30269-8). Lubrecht & Cramer.

HERSCHEL, JOHN FREDERICK WILLIAM, BART., 1792-1871

Herschel, John F. & Scheber, Silvan S. Aspects of the Life & Thought of Sir John Frederick Herschel. LC 80-2110. (Development of Science Ser.). (Illus.). 1981. lib. bdg. 95.00x (ISBN 0-405-13829-6). Ayer Co Pubs.

Leech, James, compiled by. John Herschel & Victorian Science. (Illus., Orig.). 1966. pap. 5.00 (ISBN 0-87959-005-X). U of Tex H Ransom Ctr.

HERSCHEL, WILLIAM, SIR, 1738-1822

Sime, James. William Herschel & His Work. 1978. Repr. of 1900 ed. lib. bdg. 35.00 (ISBN 0-8492-8049-4). R West.

HERTZIAN WAVES

see Electric Waves; Microwaves; Radio Waves

HERTZLER, ARTHUR EMANUAL, 1870-1946

Coe, Edith C. Hertzler Heritage. Vandergriff, James, ed. LC 75-32001. (Illus.). 172p. 1975. 7.50x (ISBN 0-686-13109-6). Emporia State.

HESPERIA (BUTTERFLIES)

Albrecht, Carl W. & Watkins, Reed A. Cross-Reference to Names of Ohio Skippers & Butterflies: Insecta, Lepidoptera, Hesperoidea & Papilionoidea. 1983. 4.00 (ISBN 0-86727-095-0). Ohio Bio Survey.

HETEROCERA

see Moths

HETEROCYCLIC COMPOUNDS

Abramovitch, R. A., ed. Chemistry of Heterocyclic Compounds. LC 73-9800. (A Series of Monographs Pyridine & Its Derivitives: Vol. 14, Pt. 1). 451p. 1974. 59.00 (ISBN 0-471-37913-1). Krieger.

--Chemistry of Heterocyclic Compounds. LC 73-9800. (A Series of Monographs Pyridine & Its Derivitives: Vol. 14, Pt. 3). 1249p. 1974. 105.00 (ISBN 0-471-37915-8). Krieger.

Acheson, R. M. An Introduction to the Chemistry of Heterocyclic Compounds. 3rd ed. LC 76-21319. 501p. 1976. 57.50 (ISBN 0-471-00268-2, Pub. by Wiley-Interscience). Wiley.

Albert, Adrien. Heterocyclic Chemistry: An Introduction. 547p. 1968. 62.00 (ISBN 0-485-11092-X, Pub. by Athlone Pr Ltd). Longwood Pub Group.

Allcock, H. R. Heteroatom Ring Systems & Polymers. 1967. 73.50 (ISBN 0-12-050550-9). Acad Pr.

Allen, C. F., et al. Heterocyclic Compounds, Vol. 12. LC 45-8533. 646p. 83.50 (ISBN 0-470-37851-4). Krieger.

Ansell, M. F. & Pattenden, G. Saturated Heterocyclic Chemistry, Vols. 2-5. LC 72-83454. Vol. 2 1974. 47.00 (ISBN 0-85186-532-1); Vol. 3 1975. 1973 literature 43.00 (ISBN 0-85186-562-3); Vol. 4 1977. 1974 literature 77.00 (ISBN 0-85186-592-5); Vol. 5 1978. 66.00 (ISBN 0-85186-622-0). Am Chemical.

Armarego, W. Stereochemistry of Heterocyclic Compounds: Part II-Oxygen; Sulfur; Mixed N, O, & S; & Phosophorus Heterocycles. LC 76-26023. 512p. 1977. 66.50 (ISBN 0-471-03322-7). Krieger.

Bambas, L. L. Heterocyclic Compounds, Vol. 4. LC 52-6640. 416p. 1952. 58.50. Krieger.

Barlin, G. B. Chemistry of Heterocyclic Compounds: Pyrazines - A Series of Monographs, Vol. 41. 712p. 1982. 193.50 (ISBN 0-471-38119-5, Pub. by Wiley-Interscience). Wiley.

Batterham, T. J. NMR Spectra of Simple Heterocycles. LC 80-11724. 560p. 1982. Repr. of 1973 ed. lib. bdg. 64.50 (ISBN 0-89874-140-8). Krieger.

Beilstein Institute for Literature of Organic Chemistry. Heterocyclische Verbindungen. Boit, H. G., ed. (Beilsteins Handbuch der Organischen Chemie, 4th Ed., 3rd & 4th Suppl.: Vol. 17, Pt. 6). 868p. 1975. 495.60 (ISBN 0-387-07359-0). Springer-Verlag.

--Heterocyclische Verbindungen. (Beilsteins Handbuch der Orgnaischen Chemie, 4th Ed.,: Vol. 17, Pts. 3-5). 1975. Pt. 3. 505.70 (ISBN 0-387-07084-2); Pt. 4. 701.40 (ISBN 0-387-07220-9); Pt. 5. 446.90 (ISBN 0-387-07310-8). Springer-Verlag.

Berdy, Janos. Heterocyclic Antibiotics. (CRC Handbook of Antibiotic Compounds: Vol. 5). 576p. 1982. 82.00 (ISBN 0-8493-3456-X). CRC Pr.

Chesseman, G. W. & Cookson, R. F. Condensed Pyrazines, Vol. 35. 835p. 1979. 275.95 (ISBN 0-471-38204-3, Pub. by Wiley-Interscience). Wiley.

Coffey, ed. Rodd's Chemistry of Carbon Compounds, Vol. 4, Pt. G: Heterocyclic Compounds - 6 Membered Heterocyclic Compounds with a Single Nitrogen Atom from Group V of the Periodic Table. 1977. 136.25 (ISBN 0-444-41644-7). Elsevier.

Dryhurst, Glenn, ed. Electrochemistry of Biological Molecules: Purines, Pyrimidines, Pteridines, Flavins, Pyrroles, Porphyrins and Pyridines. 1977. 95.00 (ISBN 0-12-222650-X). Acad Pr.

The Eighth Symposium on the Chemistry of Heterocyclic Compounds & the Sixth Symposium on Nucleic Acid Components. (Nucleic Acids Symposium Ser.: No. 14). (Illus.). 331p. (Orig.). 1984. pap. 50.00 (ISBN 0-904147-75-4). IRL Pr.

Elguero, J., et al. The Tautomerism of Heterocycles: Supplement I to Advances in Heterocyclic Chemistry. (Serial Publication). 1976. 95.00 (ISBN 0-12-020651-X). Acad Pr.

Ellis, G. P., ed. Chromenes, Chromanones, & Chromones: Chemistry of Heterocyclic Compounds-A Series of Monographs. (Vol. 31). 1196p. 1977. 301.50 (ISBN 0-471-38212-4). Wiley.

Ellis, Gwynn P. & Lockhart, Ian M., eds. Chromans & Tocopherols. LC 80-16902. (The Chemistry of Heterocyclic Compounds: Vol. 36). 1981. 198.95 (ISBN 0-471-03038-4, Pub. by Wiley-Interscience). Wiley.

Finley, K. T. Triazoles. LC 80-13323. (Chemistry of Heterocyclic Compounds, Series of Monographs: Vol. 39). 349p. 1980. 156.50x (ISBN 0-471-07827-1). Wiley.

Finley, K. Thomas. Triazoles-One-Two-Three. (Chemistry of Heterocyclic Compounds Monographs). 349p. 1980. 179.50 (ISBN 0-471-07827-1). Wiley.

Fitton, A. O. & Smalley, R. K. Practical Heterocyclic Chemistry. LC 68-19255. 1968. 26.00 (ISBN 0-12-257850-3). Acad Pr.

Hartough, Howard D. Thiophene & Its Derivatives. LC 51-13781. (The Chemistry of Heterocyclic Compounds). pap. 137.80 (ISBN 0-317-08757-6, 2007400). Bks Demand UMI.

Hasner, Alfred, ed. Small Ring Heterocycles: Oxiranes, Areneoxides, Oxaridines, Dioxetanes, Thietanes, Thietes, Thiazetes, Vol. 42. (Chemistry of Heterocyclic Compounds Monographs). 874p. 1983. 215.00 (ISBN 0-471-05624-3). Wiley.

Hassner, Alfred, ed. Small Ring Heterocycles, Vol. 42: Aziridines, Azirines, Thiiranes, Thiirenes, Vol. 42, Pt. 1. LC 82-4790. (The Chemistry of Heterocyclic Compounds, A Series of Monographs). 696p. 1983. 203.50 (ISBN 0-471-05626-X, Pub. by Wiley-Interscience); Pt. 2. 189.95 (ISBN 0-471-05625-1). Wiley.

Heterocyclic Compounds, Vol. 39. 167.50 (ISBN 0-471-07827-1). Wiley.

Houlihan, William J. Indoles. LC 76-154323. (Chemistry of Heterocyclic Compounds, a Series of Monographs: Vol. 25, Pt. 3). 586p. 1979. 187.50 (ISBN 0-471-05132-2, Pub. by Wiley-Interscience). Wiley.

Jones, Gurnos, ed. Quinolines: Chemistry of Metrocyclic Compounds, A Series of Monographs, 2 pts, Vol. 32. rev. ed. (Orig.). 1982. Pt. 1, 898 P. 243.95 (ISBN 0-471-99437-5, Pub. by Wiley-Interscience); Pt. 2, 685p. 189.95 (ISBN 0-471-28055-0). Wiley.

Joule, J. A. & Smith, G. F. Heterocyclic Chemistry. 2nd ed. 1978. pap. 14.95 (ISBN 0-442-30212-6). Van Nos Reinhold.

Katrikzky, A. R., ed. Advances in Heterocyclic Chemistry. Incl. Vol. 17. 1974. 95.00 (ISBN 0-12-020617-X); Vol. 18. 1975. 107.00 (ISBN 0-12-020618-8) (ISBN 0-12-020675-7); Vol. 20. 1976. 74.50 (ISBN 0-12-020620-X); Vol. 21. 1977. 95.50 (ISBN 0-12-020621-8); lib. ed. 122.00 (ISBN 0-12-020680-3); 68.00 (ISBN 0-12-020681-1). (Serial Publication Ser.). Acad Pr.

Katritsky. Physical Methods in Heterocyclic Chemistry, Vol. 6. 1974. 68.50 (ISBN 0-12-401106-3). Acad Pr.

Katritsky, Alan, ed. Advances in Heterocyclic Chemistry, Vol. 32. 396p. 1982. 74.50 (ISBN 0-12-020632-3); lib. ed. 97.00 (ISBN 0-12-020738-9); microfiche 52.50 (ISBN 0-12-020739-7). Acad Pr.

Katritzky, A. R. Advances in Heterocyclic Chemistry, Vol. 35. (Serial Publication Ser.). 1984. 89.00 (ISBN 0-12-020635-8). Acad Pr.

Katritzky, A. R., ed. Advances in Heterocyclic Chemistry, Vols. 1-16, 22-24. Incl. Vol. 1. 1963. 89.00 (ISBN 0-12-020601-3); Vol. 2. 1963. 89.00 (ISBN 0-12-020602-1); Vol. 3. 1964. 89.00 (ISBN 0-12-020603-X); Vol. 4. 1965. 89.00 (ISBN 0-12-020604-8); Vol. 5. 1965. 89.00 (ISBN 0-12-020605-6); Vol. 6. Katritzky, A. R. & Boulton, A. J., eds. 1966. 89.00 (ISBN 0-12-020606-4); Vol. 7. 1967. 89.00 (ISBN 0-12-020607-2); Vol. 8. 1967. 89.00 (ISBN 0-12-020608-0); Vol. 9. 1968. 89.00 (ISBN 0-12-020609-9); Vol. 10. 1969. 89.00 (ISBN 0-12-020610-2); Vol. 11. 1970 (ISBN 0-12-020611-0); Vol. 12. 1970. 89.00 (ISBN 0-12-020612-9); Vol. 13. 1971. 89.00 (ISBN 0-12-020613-7); Vol. 14. 1972. 89.00 (ISBN 0-12-020614-5); Vol. 15. 1973. 89.00 (ISBN 0-12-020615-3); Vol. 16. 1974. 89.00 (ISBN 0-12-020616-1); Vol. 22. 1978. 90.00 (ISBN 0-12-020622-6); Vol. 23. 77.00 (ISBN 0-12-020623-4); Vol. 24. 1979. 80.00 (ISBN 0-12-020624-2). Vols. 1-16. 89.00 ea. Acad Pr.

--Advances in Heterocyclic Chemistry, Vol. 28. (Serial Publication Ser.). 1981. 75.00 (ISBN 0-12-020628-5). Acad Pr.

--Advances in Heterocyclic Chemistry, Vol. 34. (Serial Publication Ser.). 1983. 89.00 (ISBN 0-12-020634-X). Acad Pr.

--Advances in Heterocyclic Chemistry, Vol. 36. (Serial Publication Ser.). 1984. 95.00 (ISBN 0-12-020636-6). Acad Pr.

--Advances in Heterocyclic Chemistry, Vol. 37. 1984. 85.00 (ISBN 0-12-020637-4). Acad Pr.

Katritzky, A. R. & Boulton, A. J., eds. Advances in Heterocyclic Chemistry, Vol. 26. LC 62-13037. 1980. 50.00 (ISBN 0-12-020626-9); lib. ed. 60.00 (ISBN 0-12-020726-5); microfiche ed. 30.00 (ISBN 0-12-020727-3). Acad Pr.

--Advances in Heterocyclic Chemistry, Vol. 27. (Serial Publication). 1981. 70.00 (ISBN 0-12-020627-7). Acad Pr.

--Advances in Heterocyclic Chemistry, Vol. 29. LC 62-13037. (Serial Publication Ser.). 1981. 75.00 (ISBN 0-12-020629-3). Acad Pr.

--Advances in Heterocyclic Chemistry Supplement, No. 2. 432p. 1982. 75.00 (ISBN 0-12-020652-8). Acad Pr.

Katritzky, Alan. Advances in Heterocyclic Chemistry, Vol. 31. (Serial Publication). 1982. 80.00 (ISBN 0-12-020631-5). Acad Pr.

Katritzky, Alan R., ed. Advances in Heterocyclic Chemistry, Vol. 30. (Serial Publication Ser.). 1982. 85.00 (ISBN 0-12-020630-7). Acad Pr.

--Advances in Heterocyclic Chemistry, Vol. 33. (Serial Publication Ser.). 1983. 65.00 (ISBN 0-12-020633-1). Acad Pr.

Mitra, R. B., ed. New Trends in Heterocyclic Chemistry. (Studies in Organic Chemistry: Vol. 3). 408p. 1979. 83.00 (ISBN 0-444-41816-4). Elsevier.

Mndzhoian, A. L. Synthesis of Heterocyclic Compounds, 4 vols. LC 59-11346. 155p. 1959. Vols. 1 & 2, 1959, 155p. 32.50x (ISBN 0-306-17033-7, Consultants); Vols. 3 & 4, 1961, 156p. 32.50 (ISBN 0-306-17034-5, Consultants). Plenum Pub.

Neunhoeffer, Hans & Wiley, Paul F. Chemistry of One, Two, Three-Triazines & One, Two, Four-Triazines, Tetrazines & Pentazines. LC 77-18932. (Chemistry of Heterocyclic Compounds Ser.: Vol. 33). 1335p. 1978. 263.50 (ISBN 0-471-03129-1, Pub. by Wiley-Interscience). Wiley.

Newkome, G. R. & Paudler, W. W. Contemporary Heterocyclic Chemistry: Syntheses, Reactions & Applications. 422p. 1982. 39.50x (ISBN 0-471-06279-0, Pub. by Wiley-Interscience). Wiley.

Padwa, Albert, ed. One, Three-Dipolar Cycloaddition Chemistry, 2 vols. (General Heterocyclic Chemistry Ser.: 1-128). 1552p. 1984. Set. 295.00 (ISBN 0-471-08364-X, Wiley-Interscience). Wiley.

Penczek, S., et al. Cationic Ring-Opening Polymerization of Heterocyclic Monomers. (Advances in Polymer Science Ser.: Vol. 37). (Illus.). 156p. 1980. 48.00 (ISBN 0-387-10209-4). Springer-Verlag.

Preston, P. N. Benzimidazoles & Congeneric Tricyclic Compounds, Pt. 1, Vol. 40. LC 80-17383. (Chemistry of Heterocyclic Compounds Ser.). 687p. 1981. 278.50 (ISBN 0-471-03792-3, Pub. by Wiley-Interscience). Wiley.

--Benzimidazoles & Congeneric Tricyclic Compounds, Vol. 40, Pt. 2. LC 80-17383. (Chemistry of Heterocyclic Compounds Ser.). 581p. 1980. 278.50 (ISBN 0-471-08189-2, Pub. by Wiley-Interscience). Wiley.

Pullman, B. & Bergman, E., eds. Quantum Aspects of Heterocyclic Compounds in Chemistry & Biochemistry: Proceedings. 1970. 72.00 (ISBN 0-12-567050-8). Acad Pr.

Renfroe, Burt. Azepines, Vol. 43, Pt. 1. Rosowsky, Andre & Proctor, George H., eds. LC 83-3497. (Chemistry of Heterocyclic Compounds, a Series of Monographs: No. 1-079). 822p. 1984. 225.00x (ISBN 0-471-01878-3, Pub. by Wiley-Interscience). Wiley.

Riddell, Frank. The Conformational Analysis of Heterocyclic Compounds. LC 79-41514. 1980. 55.00 (ISBN 0-12-588160-6). Acad Pr.

Rosowsky, Andre, ed. Seven-Membered Heterocyclic Compounds Containing Oxygen & Sulfur, Vol. 26. (Heterocyclic Compounds Ser.). 949p. 1972. 109.00 (ISBN 0-471-38210-8). Krieger.

Tomasik, Piotr & Ratajewicz, Zbigniew. Pyridine-Metal Compounds, Vol. 14, Pt. 6. Newkome, ed. (The Chemistry of Heterocyclic Compounds Ser.). 2160p. 1985. 400.00x (ISBN 0-471-05073-3, Pub. by Wiley-Interscience). Wiley.

Van Der Plas, H. C. Ring Transformation of Heterocycles, 2 vols. 1973. Vol. 2. 66.00 (ISBN 0-12-711702-4). Acad Pr.

Vogl, Otto & Furukawa, Junji, eds. Polymerization of Heterocyclics: Papers Presented at the XXIII IUPAC Congress. LC 73-76028. pap. 56.80 (ISBN 0-317-08378-3, 2055023). Bks Demand UMI.

Watthey, Jeffrey W. & Peet, Norton P. Azepines, Vol. 43, Pt. 2. (Chemistry of Heterocyclic Compounds Ser.: No. 1-079). 889p. 1984. 225.00x (ISBN 0-471-89592-X, Pub. by Wiley-Interscience). Wiley.

Weissberger, Arnold & Taylor, Edward, eds. Special Topics in Heterocyclic Chemistry. LC 76-10672. (Chemistry of Heterocyclic Compounds Ser.: Vol. 30). 616p. 1977. 85.00 (ISBN 0-471-67253-X). Krieger.

Young, Douglas W. Heterocyclic Chemistry. LC 75-11739. (Illus.). pap. 35.30 (ISBN 0-317-09438-6, 2019610). Bks Demand UMI.

HETEROGENESIS

see Generations, Alternating; Life–Origin; Spontaneous Generation

HETEROPTERA

Distant, W. L. Rhynchota: Heteroptera, Vol. 1. (Fauna of British India Ser,). xxxviii, 438p. 1977. Repr. of 1902 ed. 25.00 (ISBN 0-88065-048-6, Pub. by Messers Today & Tomorrows Printers & Publishers India). Scholarly Pubns.

--Rhynchota: Heteroptera, Vol. 2. (Fauna of British India Ser.). xviii, 504p. 1977. Repr. of 1902 ed. 25.00 (ISBN 0-88065-049-4, Pub. by Messers Today & Tomorrows Printers & Publishers India). Scholarly Pubns.

--Rhynchota: Heteroptera - Appendix, Vol. 5. (Fauna of British India Ser.). xii, 362p. 1977. Repr. of 1910 ed. 20.00 (ISBN 0-88065-077-X, Pub. by Messers Today & Tomorrows Printers & Publishers India). Scholarly Pubns.

--Rhynchota: Heteroptera-Homoptera, Vol. 3. (Fauna of British India Ser.). iiv, 504p. 1977. Repr. of 1906 ed. 25.00 (ISBN 0-88065-075-3, Pub. by Messers Today & Tomorrows Printers & Publishers India). Scholarly Pubns.

Evolutionary Trends in Heteroptera: Eggs (Architecture of Shell, Gross Embryology & Eclosion, Pt. 1. (Agricultural Research Reports: No. 707). 1968. pap. 44.25 (ISBN 90-220-0169-5, PDC171, PUDOC). Unipub.

Miller, N. C. The Biology of the Heteroptera. 204p. 1971. 45.00x (ISBN 0-317-07044-4, Pub. by EW Classey UK). State Mutual Bk.

Slater, James A. & Baranowski, Richard M. How to Know the True Bugs: (Hemiptera: Heteroptera) (Pictured Key Nature Ser). 300p. 1978. wire coil avail. (ISBN 0-697-04894-2). Wm C Brown.

HETEROSIS

Frankel, R., ed. Heterosis. (Monographs on Theoretical & Applied Genetics: Vol. 6). (Illus.). 320p. 1983. 63.00 (ISBN 0-387-12125-0). Springer-Verlag.

Manwell, Clyde & Baker, C. M. Molecular Biology & the Origin of Species: Heterosis, Protein Polymorphism, & Animal Breeding. LC 70-103299. (Biology Ser). (Illus.). 446p. 1970. 20.00x (ISBN 0-295-95065-X). U of Wash Pr.

HETEROTROPIA

Hobbie, John E. & Williams, Peter J., eds. Heterotrophic Activity in the Sea. (NATO Conference Series IV, Marine Sciences: Vol. 15). 586p. 1984. 85.00x (ISBN 0-306-41724-3, Plenum Pr). Plenum Pub.

Macan, T. T. A Revised Key to the British Water Bugs (Hempitera-Heteroptera) 2nd ed. 1976. 20.00x (ISBN 0-900386-07-X, Pub. by Freshwater Bio). State Mutual Bk.

HEWLETT-PACKARD COMPUTERS

see also Hp-33e (Calculating-Machine); Hp-41 (Calculating-Machine); Hp-150 (Computer); Hp-1000 (Computer)

Anbarlian, Harry. An Introduction to Multiplan: Spreadsheeting on the Hewlett Packard 75C. 1984. pap. 22.95 (ISBN 0-07-079407-3). McGraw.

Flanagan, Dale. The HP 110 Portable: Power to Go! LC 84-61401. 250p. 1985. 16.95 (ISBN 0-88022-135-6, 165). Que Corp.

Harper, Steve, et al. The HP-IL System: An Introductory Guide to the Hewlett-Packard Interface Loop. 106p. (Orig.). 1982. pap. 17.95 (ISBN 0-07-931077-X, 77-X). Osborne-McGraw.

Hewlett-Packard Company Staff. Series Eighty Software Catalog. 4th ed. 15.95 (ISBN 0-317-13082-X). P-H.

Horn, Joseph K. HP 71 BASIC Made Easy. Jarett, Keith, ed. LC 84-51753. 1985. pap. text ed. 18.95 (ISBN 0-9612174-3-X). Synthetix.

Pollack, Seymour V. Structured FORTRAN 77 Programming for Hewlett-Packard Computers. 512p. (Orig.). 1983. pap. text ed. 25.00x (ISBN 0-87835-130-2). Boyd & Fraser.

HEXAPODA

see Insects

HI-FI SYSTEMS

see High-Fidelity Sound Systems

HIBERNATION

see also Animals, Habits and Behavior of; Dormancy in Plants

Lyman, Charles, et al. Hibernation & Torpor in Mammals & Birds. (Physiological Ecology Ser.). 317p. 1982. 43.50 (ISBN 0-12-460420-X). Acad Pr.

Mrosovsky, Nicholas. Hibernation & the Hypothalamus. 287p. 1971. 22.50x (ISBN 0-306-50058-2, Plenum Pr). Plenum Pub.

HIGH ALTITUDE ROCKET RESEARCH

see Atmosphere, Upper–Rocket Observations

HIGH ENERGY FORMING

see also Explosive Forming; Metals–Extrusion

Bruno, E. J., ed. High-Velocity Forming of Metals. rev. ed. LC 68-23027. (Manufacturing Data Ser.). 1968. pap. 10.75 (ISBN 0-87263-009-9). SME.

Ferbel, Thomas, ed. Techniques & Concepts of High-Energy Physics I. LC 81-13767. (NATO ASI Series B, Physics: Vol. 66). 554p. 1981. 79.50x (ISBN 0-306-40721-3, Plenum Pr). Plenum Pub.

Hot Working & Forming Processes. 290p. 1980. text ed. 30.00x (ISBN 0-904357-28-7, Metals Soc). Brookfield Pub Co.

Month, Melvin. Physics of High Energy Particle Accelerators: SLAC Summer School, 1982, No. 105. LC 83-72986. (AIP Conference Proceedings: No. 105). 1102p. 1983. lib. bdg. 55.50 (ISBN 0-88318-304-8). Am Inst Physics.

Newby & Niemeier, eds. Formability of Metallic Materials, 2,000 A.D. - STP 753. 331p. 1981. 39.50 (ISBN 0-8031-0742-0, 04-753000-23). ASTM.

Panvini, R. S. & Word, G. B., eds. High Energy-Interactions (Vanderbilt, 1984) AIP Conference Proceedings. LC 84-72632. (No. 121). 429p. Date not set. 43.75 (ISBN 0-88318-320-X). Am Inst Physics.

--High Energy Interactions: Vanderbilt 1984. LC 84-72632. (Conference Proceedings Ser.: No. 121). 429p. 1984. lib. bdg. 43.75 (ISBN 0-88318-320-X). Am Inst Physics.

Perlmutter, Arnold, et al, eds. High-Energy Physics in the Einstein Centennial Year. LC 79-18441. (Studies in the Natural Science: Vol. 16). 533p. 1979. 75.00 (ISBN 0-306-40297-1, Plenum Pr). Plenum Pub.

Schroeder, J. W., ed. High Energy Rate Fabrication. (PVP Ser.: Vol. 70). 1982. 20.00 (H00246). ASME.

Zichichi, Antonio, ed. The High-Energy Limit. (The Subnuclear Ser.: Vol. 18). 1116p. 1982. 135.00x (ISBN 0-306-41036-2, Plenum Pr). Plenum Pub.

HIGH-FIDELITY SOUND SYSTEMS

see also Stereophonic Sound Systems

Audio Equipment. rev. ed. (Illus.). pap. 1.95 (ISBN 0-89552-006-0). DMR Pubns.

Baber, Alfred W. Handbook of Hi-Fi Audio Systems & Projects. 235p. 1981. 18.95 (ISBN 0-13-378307-3, Parker). P-H.

Clifford, Martin. The Complete Guide to High Fidelity. LC 82-50014. 15.95 (ISBN 0-672-21892-5). Sams.

Cohen, Abraham. Hi-Fi Loudspeakers & Enclosures. 2nd, rev. ed. (Illus.). 1968. 11.60 (ISBN 0-8104-0721-3). Hayden.

Davey, Gilbert. Fun with Hi-Fi. Cox, Jack, ed. (Learning with Fun). (Illus.). 64p. 1974. 13.50x (ISBN 0-7182-0083-7, SpS). Sportshelf.

Johnson, Kenneth W. & Walker, Willard C. Hi-Fidelity: Concepts & Components for Consumers. (Illus.). 1979. pap. 9.95 (ISBN 0-8403-1992-4). Kendall-Hunt.

--The Science of Hi-Fidelity Laboratory Manual. 1978. pap. text ed. 9.50 (ISBN 0-8403-2964-4). Kendall-Hunt.

Johnson-Walker, Kenneth W., et al. The Science of Hi-Fidelity. LC 81-81012. (Illus.). 1981. pap. text ed. 21.95 (ISBN 0-8403-2297-6). Kendall-Hunt.

Rosenthal, Murray P. How to Select & Use Hi-Fi & Stereo Amplifiers. LC 79-2361. 1979. pap. 6.50 (ISBN 0-8104-0832-5). Hayden.

--How to Select & Use Hi-Fi & Stereo Equipment. 1979. pap. 9.85 (ISBN 0-8104-0424-9). Hayden.

Sturridge, Helen, et al. The Arco Book of Electronics. LC 84-2868. (Illus.). 140p. 1984. 11.95 (ISBN 0-668-06154-5, 6154-5). Arco.

HIGH-FREQUENCY RADIO

see Radio, Short Wave

HIGH PRESSURE (SCIENCE)

see also Compressibility; High Pressure (Technology); High Pressure Research; Pressure Vessels

Beggerow, O. High-Pressure Properties of Matter. (Landolt-Boernstein Ser.: Group IV, Vol. 4). (Illus.). 1980. 201.60 (ISBN 0-387-09370-2). Springer-Verlag.

Bradley, C. C. High-Pressure Methods in Solid State Research. 184p. 1969. 15.00x (ISBN 0-306-30693-X, Plenum Pr). Plenum Pub.

Caldirola, P. & Knoepfel, H., eds. Physics of High Energy Density. (Italian Physical Society: Course 48). 1971. 80.00 (ISBN 0-12-368848-5). Acad Pr.

Colin, Henri, et al. A Guide to the HPLC Literature: 1966-1979, Vol. 1. 900p. 1984. text ed. 125.00 (ISBN 0-471-87993-2, Pub. by Wiley-Interscience). Wiley.

Homan, C., et al. High Pressure in Science & Technology, 3 pts. (Materials Research Society Ser.: Vol. 22, Pts. 1-3). 1984. Set. 149.00 (ISBN 0-444-00932-9); Pt. 1. 59.00 (ISBN 0-444-00929-9); Pt. 2. 59.00 (ISBN 0-444-00930-2); Pt. 3. 59.00 (ISBN 0-444-00931-0). Elsevier.

International AIRAPT Conference, Le Creuset, France, July 30-Aug. 3, 1979. High Pressure Science & Technology: Proceedings. Vodar, B. & Marteau, P., eds. (Illus.). 1200p. 1980. 270.00 (ISBN 0-08-024774-1). Pergamon.

Tomizuka, Carl & Emrick, Roy, eds. Physics of Solids at High Pressures. 1965. 82.50 (ISBN 0-12-693850-4). Acad Pr.

Ulmer, G. C., ed. Research Techniques for High Pressure & High Temperature. (Illus.). 384p. 1971. 25.00 (ISBN 0-387-05594-0). Springer-Verlag.

Friedrichs, K. O. Perturbation of Spectra in Hilbert Space. LC 60-12712. (Lectures in Applied Mathematics Ser.: Vol. 3). 178p. 1967. Repr. of 1965 ed. 27.00 (ISBN 0-8218-1103-7, LAM-3). Am Math.
--Spectral Theory of Operators in Hilbert Space. rev. ed. LC 73-13721. (Applied Mathematical Sciences: Vol. 9). x, 246p. 1973. pap. 23.95 (ISBN 0-387-90076-4). Springer-Verlag.
Gohberg, I. & Goldberg, S. Basic Operator Theory. 304p. 1981. 14.95x (ISBN 3-7643-3028-7). Birkhauser.
Gohberg, I. C. & Krein, M. G. Theory & Applications of Volterra Operators in Hilbert Space. LC 71-120134. (Translations of Mathematical Monographs: Vol. 24). 1970. 64.00 (ISBN 0-8218-1574-1, MMONO-24). Am Math.
Gross, Leonard. Harmonic Analysis on Hilbert Space. LC 52-42839. (Memoirs: No. 46). 62p. 1983. pap. 9.00 (ISBN 0-8218-1246-7, MEMO-46). Am Math.
Gudkov, D. A. & Utkin, G. A. Nine Papers on Hilbert's Sixteenth Problem. LC 78-10201. (American Mathematical Society Translations Ser. 2: Vol. 112). 1978. 43.00 (ISBN 0-8218-3062-7, TRANS2-112). Am Math.
Guichardet, A. Symmetric Hilbert Spaces & Related Topics. LC 72-76390. (Lecture Notes in Mathematics: Vol. 261). 102p. 1972. pap. 10.00 (ISBN 0-387-05803-6). Springer-Verlag.
Gustafson, Karl E. Introduction to Partial Differential Equations & Hilbert Space Methods. LC 80-331. 270p. 1980. text ed. 38.50 (ISBN 0-471-04089-4). Wiley.
Halmos, P. R. A Hilbert Space Problem Book. rev., enl. ed. (Graduate Texts in Mathematics Ser.: Vol. 19). 369p. 1982. 34.00 (ISBN 0-387-90685-1). Springer-Verlag.
--Introduction to Hilbert Space. 2nd ed. LC 57-12834. 9.95 (ISBN 0-8284-0082-2). Chelsea Pub.
Helmberg, Gilbert M. Introduction to Spectral Theory in Hilbert Space. (Applied Mathematics & Mechanics Ser: Vol. 6). 346p. 1969. 64.00 (ISBN 0-444-10211-6, North-Holland). Elsevier.
Herrero, D. A. Approximation of Hilbert Space Operators, Vol. 1. (Research Notes in Mathematics Ser.: No. 72). 255p. 1982. pap. 21.95 (ISBN 0-273-08579-4). Pitman Pub MA.
Minkhlin, Solomon G. The Problem of the Minimum of a Quadratic Functional. Feinstein, A., tr. LC 64-24626. (Holden-Day Series in Mathematical Physics). pap. 41.00 (ISBN 0-317-09170-0, 2016292). Bks Demand UMI.
Murray, Francis J. Introduction to Linear Transformations in Hilbert Space. (Annals of Math Studies). 1941. 11.00 (ISBN 0-527-02720-0). Kraus Repr.
Nagszy, Bela. Unitary Dilations of Hilbert Space Operators & Related Topics. LC 73-17332. (CBMS Regional Conference Series in Mathematics: No. 19). 54p. 1982. pap. 14.00 (ISBN 0-8218-1669-1, CBMS-19). Am Math.
Nagy, B. Sz. & Foias, C. Harmonic Analysis of Operators on Hilbert Space. LC 78-97933. 390p. 1971. 51.00 (ISBN 0-7204-2035-0, North-Holland). Elsevier.
Nikodym, Otton M. Mathematical Apparatus for Quantum-Theories. (Grundlehren der Mathematischen Wissenschaften: Vol. 129). 1966. 95.00 (ISBN 0-387-03523-0). Springer-Verlag.
Oda, Takayuki. Periods of Hilbert Modular Surfaces. (Progress in Mathematics Ser.: Vol. 19). 1981. text ed. 12.50x (ISBN 0-8176-3084-8). Birkhauser.
Prugovecki, Eduard. Quantum Mechanics in Hilbert Space. 2nd ed. LC 80-534. (Pure & Applied Mathematics Ser.). 1981. 42.00 (ISBN 0-12-566060-X). Acad Pr.
Putnam, Calvin R. Commutation Properties of Hilbert Space Operators & Related Topics. (Ergebnisse der Mathematik und Ihrer Grenzgebiete: Vol. 36). 1967. 29.50 (ISBN 0-387-03778-0). Springer-Verlag.
Radjavi, H. & Rosenthal, P. Invariant Subspaces. LC 73-77570. (Ergebnisse der Mathematik und Ihrer Gremzgebiete: Vol. 77). (Illus.). 230p. 1973. 34.00 (ISBN 0-387-06217-3). Springer-Verlag.
Reid, Constance. Hilbert. LC 76-97989. (Illus.). 1970. 29.50 (ISBN 0-387-04999-1). Springer-Verlag.
Rektorys, Karel. Variational Methods in Mathematics, Sciences & Engineering. new ed. SNTL, ed. LC 74-80530. 1976. lib. bdg. 71.00 (ISBN 90-277-0488-0, Pub. by Reidel Holland). Kluwer Academic.
Sarason, Donald. H-To-The-P Spaces of Annulus. LC 52-42839. (Memoirs: No. 56). 78p. 1982. pap. 14.00 (ISBN 0-8218-1256-4, MEMO-56). Am Math.
Schatten, Robert. Norm Ideals of Completely Continuous Operators. (Ergebnisse der Mathematik und Ihrer Grenzebiete: Vol. 27). 1970. Repr. 26.00 (ISBN 0-387-04806-5). Springer-Verlag.
Showalter, R. E. Hilbert Space Methods for Partial Differential Equations. (Monographs & Studies: No. 1). 196p. 1977. pap. 49.50 (ISBN 0-273-08440-2). Pitman Pub MA.
Simon, Barry. Trace Ideals & Their Applications. LC 78-20867. (London Mathematical Society Lecture Notes Ser.: No. 35). 1979. pap. 21.95x (ISBN 0-521-22286-9). Cambridge U Pr.
Skorohod, A. V. Integration in Hilbert Space. Wickwire, T., tr. from Rus. LC 73-82356. (Ergebnisse der Mathematik und Ihrer Grenzgebiete: Vol. 79). 190p. 1974. 33.00 (ISBN 0-387-06322-6). Springer-Verlag.
Sleeman, Brian D. Multiparameter Spectral Theory in Hilbert Space. (Research Notes in Mathematics Ser.: No. 22). 118p. (Orig.). pap. text ed. 18.95 (ISBN 0-273-08414-3). Pitman Pub MA.
Soule, J. L. Linear Operators in Hilbert Space. (Notes on Mathematics & Its Applications Ser.). 50p. (Orig.). 1968. 24.50 (ISBN 0-677-30170-7). Gordon.
--Operateurs Lineaires Dans l'Espace Hilbert. (Cours & Documents de Mathematiques & de Physique Ser.). (Fr.). 50p. (Orig.). 1967. 24.50x (ISBN 0-677-50170-6). Gordon.
Stone, M. H. Linear Transformations in Hilbert Space & Their Applications to Analysis. LC 33-2746. (Colloquium Publications Ser.: Vol. 15). 622p. 1979. pap. 53.00 (ISBN 0-8218-1015-4, COLL-15). Am Math.
Takesaki, M. Tomita's Theory of Modular Hilbert Algebras & Its Applications. LC 79-117719. (Lecture Notes in Mathematics: Vol. 128). 1970. pap. 10.70 (ISBN 0-387-04917-7). Springer-Verlag.
Weidmann, J. Linear Operators in Hilbert Spaces. Szuecs, J., tr. from Ger. (Graduate Texts in Mathematics Ser.: Vol 68). 400p. 1980. 42.00 (ISBN 0-387-90427-1). Springer-Verlag.
Weinert, H. L., ed. Reproducing Kernel Hilbert Spaces: Applications in Statistical Signal Processing. LC 82-9332. (Benchmark Papers in Electrical Engineering & Computer Science: Vol. 25). 655p. 1982. 63.50 (ISBN 0-87933-434-7). Van Nos Reinhold.

HINDENBURG (AIR-SHIP)

Dick, Harold G. & Robinson, Douglas H. The Golden Age of the Great Passenger Airships, Graf Zeppelin & Hindenburg. LC 84-600298. (Illus.). 200p. 1985. 24.95 (ISBN 0-87474-364-8, D1GA). Smithsonian.
Mooney, Michael M. The Hindenburg. LC 75-184190. (Illus.). 288p. 1972. 8.95 (ISBN 0-396-06502-3). Dodd.
Robinson, Douglas H. LZ-129 Hindenburg. (Famous Aircraft Ser.). (Illus.). 52p. 1981. pap. 6.95 (ISBN 0-8168-5652-4). Aero.

HINDERED ROTATION THEORY

see Molecular Rotation

HINDU MATHEMATICS

see Mathematics, Hindu

HIPPOLOGY

see Horses

HIPPOPOTAMUS

Reynolds, S. H. Pleistocene Hippopotamus. Repr. of 1922 ed. 14.00 (ISBN 0-384-50420-5). Johnson Repr.

HIRUNDINIDAE

see Swallows

HISTAMINE

Beaven, M. A. Histamine: Its Role in Physiological & Pathological Processes. (Monographs in Allergy: Vol. 13). (Illus.). 1978. pap. 16.25 (ISBN 3-8055-2887-6). S Karger.
Maslinski, C., ed. Histamine: Mechanisms of Regulation of the Biogenic Amines Level in the Tissues with Special Reference to Histamine. LC 72-95941. 370p. 1974. 58.50 (ISBN 0-12-787052-0). Acad Pr.
Schachter, M., ed. Histamine & Antihistamines. LC 72-10535. 196p. 1973. text ed. 36.00 (ISBN 0-08-016390-4). Pergamon.
Torsoli, A. & Lucchelli, P. E. Further Experience with H-Two-Receptor Antagonists in Peptic Ulcer Disease & Progress in Histamine Research. (International Congress Ser.: Vol. 521). 372p. 1980. 69.00 (ISBN 0-444-90147-7, Excerpta Medica). Elsevier.
Uvnas, B. & Tasaka, K., eds. Advances in Histamine Research: Proceedings of a Satellite Symposium to the 8th International Congress of Pharmacology, July 26-27, 1981, Okayama, Japan. (Illus.). 260p. 1982. 72.00 (ISBN 0-08-028006-4, H130). Pergamon.

HISTOCHEMISTRY

see also Biological Chemistry; Molecular Biology; Physiological Chemistry

Chang, Louis W. A Color Atlas & Manual for Applied Histochemistry. (Illus.). 126p. 1979. photocopy ed. spiral 17.50x (ISBN 0-398-03914-3). C C Thomas.
Chayen, Joseph, et al. Practical Histochemistry. LC 72-8596. 271p. 1973. 42.95 (ISBN 0-471-14950-0, Pub. by Wiley-Interscience). Wiley.
Chouchkov, C. N. Cutaneous Receptors. (Advances in Anatomy, Embryology & Cell Biology Ser.: Vol. 54, Part 5). (Illus.). 1978. pap. 22.00 (ISBN 0-387-08826-1). Springer-Verlag.
Ciba Foundation. Trends in Enzyme Histochemistry & Cytochemistry. LC 80-11757. (Ciba Foundation Symposium, New Ser.: 73). pap. 80.50 (ISBN 0-317-29754-6, 2022192). Bks Demand UMI.
Cuello, A. C., ed. Immunohistochemistry. (IBRO Handbook Ser.: Methods in the Neurosciences). 501p. 1983. 95.00 (ISBN 0-471-10245-8, Pub. by Wiley-Interscience); pap. 39.95 498p (ISBN 0-471-90052-4). Wiley.
Dubach, U C. & Schmidt, U. Recent Advances in Quantitative Histo & Cytochemistry. 363p. 90.00 (ISBN 3-456-00038-3, Pub. by Holdan Bk Ltd UK). State Mutual Bk.
Eranko, Olavi, et al, eds. Histochemistry & Cell Biology of Autonomic Neurons: Sif Cells, & Paraneurons. (Advances in Biochemical Psychopharmacology Ser.: Vol. 25). (Illus.). 410p. 1980. text ed. 64.50 (ISBN 0-89004-495-3). Raven.
Gahan, Peter B. Plant Histochemistry. (Experimental Botany: An International Series of Monographs). 1984. 41.00 (ISBN 0-12-273270-7). ACad Pr.
Giorno, Ralph C. Immunohistology & Histochemistry of the Lymphoid System. (Illus.). 180p. 1984. 28.50x (ISBN 0-398-04898-3). C C Thomas.
Goldsby, Richard A. Cells & Energy. 2nd ed. 1977. pap. text ed. write for info. (ISBN 0-02-344300-6, 34430). Macmillan.
Hack, M. H. & Helmy, F. M. An Introduction to Comparative, Correlative Histochemical Principles. (Illus.). 90p. 1974. 19.00x (ISBN 0-685-50594-4). Adlers foreign Bks.
High, Olga B. Lipid Histochemistry. (Royal Microscopy Handbooks Ser.). (Illus.). 1984. pap. 9.95x (ISBN 0-317-04826-0). Oxford U Pr.
Humason, Gretchen L. Animal Tissue Techniques. 4th ed. LC 78-17459. (Illus.). 661p. 1979. text ed. 33.95 (ISBN 0-7167-0299-1). W H Freeman.
Pearse, A. G. Histochemistry, Vol. 1: Theoretical & Applied. 4th ed. (Illus.). 439p. 1980. text ed. 62.50 (ISBN 0-443-01998-3). Churchill.
--Histochemistry, Vol 2: Theoretical & Applied. 4th ed. (Illus.). 614p. 1985. text ed. 125.00 (ISBN 0-443-02997-0). Churchill.
Stoward, P. J. & Polak, J. M., eds. Histochemistry: The Widening Horizons. LC 81-14704. (Horizons in Biochemistry & Biophysics Ser.). 293p. 1982. 74.95x (ISBN 0-471-10010-2, Pub. by Wiley-Interscience). Wiley.
Thompson, Samuel W. Selected Histochemical & Histopathological Methods. (Illus.). 1680p. 1974. 90.50x (ISBN 0-398-03132-0). C C Thomas.
Troyer, Henry. Principles & Techniques of Histochemistry. LC 80-80592. 1980. text ed. 24.95 (ISBN 0-316-85310-0). Little.
Vacca, Linda L. Laboratory Manual of Histochemistry. 596p. 1985. 28.50 Spiral Bd (ISBN 0-89004-540-2). Raven.
Wied, George. Introduction to Quantitative Cytochemistry. 1966. 90.00 (ISBN 0-12-748850-2). Acad Pr.
Wied, George & Bahr, Gunter F. Introduction to Quantitative Cytochemistry, 2. 1970. 86.50 (ISBN 0-12-748852-9). Acad Pr.

HISTOCOMPATIBILITY

Carpenter, Charles B., ed. Clinical Histocompatibility Testing, Vol. 4. (Transplantation Proceedings Reprint Ser.). 336p. 1980. 52.00 (ISBN 0-8089-1275-5, 790794). Grune.
Dorf, Martin E. The Role of the Major Histocompatibility Complex in Immunobiology. LC 80-772. 525p. 1981. lib. bdg. 66.00 (ISBN 0-8240-7129-8). Garland Pub.
Gotz, D., ed. The Major Histocompatibility System in Man & Animals. 1977. 46.00 (ISBN 0-387-08097-X). Springer-Verlag.
Klein, J. Biology of the Mouse Histocompatibility - 2 Complex: Principles of Immunogenetics Applied to a Single System. LC 74-14843. (Illus.). xiv, 618p. 1975. 69.00 (ISBN 0-387-06733-7). Springer-Verlag.
Parham, B. & Stominger, J. S., eds. Histocompatability Antigens. (Receptors & Recognition Series B.: Vol. 14). 350p. 1982. 62.00 (ISBN 0-412-22410-0, NO. 6717, Pub. by Chapman & Hall). Methuen Inc.
Pernis, Benvenuto & Vogel, Henry J., eds. Cell Biology of the Major Histocompatibility Complex. Edited Treatise ed. (P & S Biomedical Sciences Symposia Ser.). Date not set. 75.00; pap. 39.95 (ISBN 0-12-550871-9). Acad Pr.
Reisfeld, Ralph A. & Ferrone, Soldano, eds. Current Trends in Histocompatability, 2 vols. Incl. Vol. 1. Immunogenetic & Molecular Profiles. 565p. 57.50x (ISBN 0-306-40480-X); Vol. 2. Biological & Clinical Concepts. 325p. 39.50x (ISBN 0-306-40481-8). LC 80-18211. 1981 (Plenum Pr). Plenum Pub.
Selwood, Neville & Hedges, Alan. Transplantation Antigens: A Study in Serological Data Analysis. LC 78-5708. Repr. of 1978 ed. 38.30 (ISBN 0-8357-9995-6, 2016180). Bks Demand UMI.
Snell, George D. & Hildemann, W. H. Cell Surface Antigens: Studies in Mammals Other Than Man. LC 72-13690. (Illus.). 220p. 1973. text ed. 23.00x (ISBN 0-8422-7100-7). Irvington.
Terasaki, Paul I. Histocompatibility Testing Nineteen Eighty, Vol. 1. LC 80-36737. (Illus.). 1980. 59.00 (ISBN 0-9604606-0-8). UCLA Tissue.
Zaleski, M. B., et al, eds. Immunobiology of the Major Histocompatibility Complex. (Illus.). xii, 396p. 1981. 84.25 (ISBN 3-8055-1896-X). S Karger.

HISTOLOGY

see also Botany–Anatomy; Cells; Histochemistry; Microscope and Microscopy; Tissues; also names of particular tissues or organs, e.g. Muscle, Nerves

Amenta, Peter S. Histology & Embryology Review. 2nd ed. LC 82-11322. (Illus.). 208p. 1983. pap. 13.95 (ISBN 0-668-05486-7). ACC.
Amenta, Peter S., ed. Histology. 3rd ed. (Medical Outline Ser.). 1983. spiral bdg. 16.50 (ISBN 0-87488-662-7). Med Exam.
Arey, Leslie B. Human Histology: A Textbook in Outline Form. 4th ed. LC 73-88256. (Illus.). 338p. 1974. text ed. 20.00 (ISBN 0-7216-1392-6). Saunders.
Bancroft, John D. & Stevens, Alan, eds. Theory & Practice of Histological Techniques. 2nd ed. (Illus.). 662p. 1982. text ed. 79.00 (ISBN 0-443-02006-X). Churchill.
Banks, William J. Histology & Comparative Organology: A Text-Atlas. LC 79-24569. 296p. 1980. Repr. of 1974 ed. lib. bdg. 25.50 (ISBN 0-89874-084-3). Krieger.
Bevelander, Gerrit & Ramaley, Judith A. Essentials of Histology. 8th ed. LC 78-4847. 400p. 1979. text ed. 25.95 (ISBN 0-8016-0669-1). Mosby.
Bhaskar, S. N. Orban's Oral Histology & Embryology. 9th ed. LC 80-11972. (Illus.). 486p. 1980. pap. text ed. 39.95 (ISBN 0-8016-4609-X). Mosby.
Bloom, William & Fawcett, Don W. A Textbook of Histology. 10th ed. LC 73-77935. (Illus.). 1040p. 1975. text ed. 45.95 (ISBN 0-7216-1757-3). Saunders.
Borysenko, Myrin & Beringer, Theodore. Functional Histology. 2nd ed. 400p. 1984. pap. text ed. 24.95 (ISBN 0-316-10304-7). Little.
Brown, Geoffrey G. An Introduction to Histotechnology: A Manual for the Student, Practicing Technologist, & Resident in Pathology. 2nd ed. (Illus.). 480p. 1978. 29.95 (ISBN 0-8385-4340-5). ACC.
Carleton's Histological Technique. 5th ed. Wallington, E. A., ed. (Illus.). 1980. text ed. 65.00x (ISBN 0-19-261310-3). Oxford U Pr.
Coleman, Raymond. Multiple Choice Questions in Histology. 285p. (Orig.). 1983. pap. text ed. 10.50 (ISBN 0-272-79733-2, Pub. by Pitman Bks Ltd UK). Urban & S.
Constantinides, Paris. Functional Electronic Histology. 244p. 1974. 110.25 (ISBN 0-444-40998-X, Biomedical Pr). Elsevier.
Cormack, David H. Introduction to Histology. (Illus.). 512p. 1984. text ed. 19.75 (ISBN 0-397-52114-6, 65-07338, Lippincott Medical). Lippincott.
Dodd, E. E. Atlas of Histology. 1979. 45.00 (ISBN 0-07-017230-7). McGraw.
Elias, Hans, et al. Histology & Human Microanatomy. 4th ed. LC 78-9108. 607p. 1978. 36.50 (ISBN 0-471-04929-8, Pub. by Wiley Medical). Wiley.
Fejerskov, Ole & Mjor, Aarhus J. Histology of the Human Tooth. 2nd rev. ed. 174p. 1979. 79.00x (ISBN 0-686-44530-9, Pub. by Munksgaard Denmark). State Mutual Bk.
Fonts, Alfredo R. Histology & Embryology Notes for Dental Assistants & Dental Hygienists. 1980. pap. text ed. 8.50 (ISBN 0-89669-029-6). Collegium Bk Pubs.
Gabe, M. Histological Techniques. Blackith, R. E. & Kovoor, A., trs. from Fr. (Illus.). 1976. 65.80 (ISBN 0-387-90162-0). Springer-Verlag.
Giorno, Ralph C. Immunohistology & Histochemistry of the Lymphoid System. (Illus.). 180p. 1984. 28.50x (ISBN 0-398-04898-3). C C Thomas.
Ham, Arthur W. & Cormack, David H. Histology. 8th ed. LC 79-13185. 1979. text ed. 47.50 (ISBN 0-397-52089-1, Lippincott Medical). Lippincott.
Histology & Embryology. (National Medical Ser.: 1-635). 297p. 1984. pap. 16.00 (ISBN 0-471-86826-4, Pub. by Wiley Med). Wiley.

Menzel. Fingerprint Detection with Lasers. 1980. 25.75 (ISBN 0-8247-6974-0). Dekker.
Noakes, G. R., ed. Sources of Physics Teaching: Atomic Energy. Holography. Electrostatics, Vol. 4. 1970. pap. text ed. 18.50x (ISBN 0-85066-038-6). Intl Ideas.
Okoshi, T. Three-Dimensional Imaginary Techniques. 1976. 47.50 (ISBN 0-12-525250-1). Acad Pr.
Ostrovsky, Y. I., et al. Interferometry by Holography. (Springer Ser. in Optical Sciences: Vol. 20). (Illus.). 280p. 1980. 42.00 (ISBN 0-387-09886-0). Springer-Verlag.
Schumann, W. & Dubas, M. Holographic Interferometry: From the Scope of Deformation Analysis of Opaque Bodies. (Springer Ser. in Optical Sciences: Vol. 16). (Illus.). 1979. 40.00 (ISBN 0-387-09371-0). Springer-Verlag.
Smith, H. M., ed. Holographic Recording Materials. LC 77-24503. (Topics in Applied Physics: Vol. 20). (Illus.). 1977. 50.00 (ISBN 0-387-08293-X). Springer-Verlag.
Smith, Howard M. Principles of Holography. 2nd ed. LC 75-5631. 279p. 1975. 37.50x (ISBN 0-471-80341-3, Pub. by Wiley-Interscience). Wiley.
Society of Photo-Optical Instrumentation Engineers. Engineering Applications of Holography. 28.00 (ISBN 0-89252-097-3). Photo-Optical.
Soroko, L. M. Holography & Coherent Optics. LC 78-4479. (Illus.). 834p. 1978. 99.50x (ISBN 0-306-40101-0, Plenum Pr). Plenum Pub.
Stoll, W. Value Distribution of Holomorphic Maps into Compact Complex Manifolds. LC 75-121987. (Lecture Notes in Mathematics: Vol. 135). 1970. pap. 14.70 (ISBN 0-387-04924-X). Springer-Verlag.
Stroke, George W. Introduction to Coherent Optics & Halography. 2nd ed. (Illus.). 1969. 47.50 (ISBN 0-12-673956-0). Acad Pr.
Symposium on Applications of Holography in Mechanics (1971: University ofSouthern California) Applications of Holography in Mechanics: Symposium. Gottenberg, W. G., ed. LC 78-172086. pap. 23.50 (ISBN 0-317-08117-9, 2016842). Bks Demand UMI.
Symposium on Engineering Applications of Holography 1972, Los Angeles. Engineering Applications of Holography: Proceedings. pap. 100.00 (ISBN 0-317-09018-6, 2016751). Bks Demand UMI.
Unterseher, Fred, et al. The Holographic Handbook. new ed. (Illus.). 408p. (Orig.). 1982. pap. 16.95 (ISBN 0-89496-017-2). Ross Bks.
Vest, Charles M. Holographic Interferometry. LC 78-14883. (Wiley Series in Pure & Applied Optics). 465p. 1979. 51.95x (ISBN 0-471-90683-2, Pub. by Wiley-Interscience). Wiley.
Von Bally, G., ed. Holography in Medicine & Biology. (Springer Ser. in Optical Sciences: Vol. 18). (Illus.). 269p. 1979. 46.00 (ISBN 0-387-09793-7). Springer-Verlag.
Wenyon, Michael. Understanding Holography. LC 78-965. (Illus.). 176p. 1984. 14.95 (ISBN 0-668-06414-5); pap. 8.95 (ISBN 0-668-06203-7). Arco.
Yaroslavskii, L. P. & Merzlyakov, N. S. Methods of Digital Holography. LC 80-16286. 182p. 1980. 49.50 (ISBN 0-306-10963-8, Consultants). Plenum Pub.

HOME AIR CONDITIONING
see Dwellings–Air Conditioning

HOME CONSTRUCTION
see House Construction

HOME REPAIRS
see Dwellings–Maintenance and Repair

HOMEOSTASIS

Biro, Z., et al, eds. Homeostasis in Injury & Shock: Proceedings of a Satellite Symposium of the 28th International Congress of Physiological Sciences, Budapest, Hungary, 1980. LC 80-42104. (Advances in Physiological Sciences: Vol. 26). (Illus.). 360p. 1981. 44.00 (ISBN 0-08-027347-5). Pergamon.
Darrow, Frank M. Cybernetics versus Homeostasis. (Illus.). 42p. 1977. pap. 4.00 (ISBN 0-686-82893-3). Darrow.
Davis, Bernard B. & Wood, W. Gibson, eds. Homeostatic Function & Aging. (Aging Ser.: Vol. 30). 1985. text ed. write for info. (ISBN 0-88167-139-8). Raven.
Dilman, Vladimir M. Law of Deviation of Homeostasis & Diseases of Aging. LC 79-21456. (Illus.). 392p. 1981. 44.50 (ISBN 0-88416-250-8). PSG Pub Co.
Gardiner, Sheila M. & Bennett, Terence. Cardiovascular Homeostasis: Intrarenal & Extrarenal Mechanisms. (Illus.). 1981. text ed. 37.50x (ISBN 0-19-261178-X). Oxford U Pr.
Hardy, R. N. Homeostasis. 2nd ed. (Studies in Biology: No. 63). 64p. 1983. pap. text ed. 8.95 (ISBN 0-7131-2871-2). E Arnold.
Korneva, Elena A., et al. Neurohumoral Maintenance of Immune Homeostasis. Corson, Samuel A. & Corson, Elizabeth O., eds. LC 84-8771. (Illus.). 184p. 1985. lib. bdg. 32.00x (ISBN 0-226-45042-2). U of Chicago Pr.
Langley, Lee L. Homeostasis: Origins of the Concept. (Benchmark Papers in Human Physiology Ser.: Vol. 1). 362p. 1973. 49.50 (ISBN 0-87933-007-4). Van Nos Reinhold.
Lord, B. I. & Potten, C. S., eds. Stem Cells & Tissue Homeostasis. LC 77-80844. (British Society for Cell Biology Symposium Ser.). (Illus.). 1978. 85.00 (ISBN 0-521-21799-7). Cambridge U Pr.
Trojan, P. Ecosystem Homeostasis. 1984. pap. text ed. 32.50 (ISBN 90-6193-622-5, Pub. by Junk Pubs Netherlands). Kluwer Academic.

HOMING PIGEONS
see Pigeons

HOMOLOGICAL ALGEBRA
see Algebra, Homological

HOMOLOGY THEORY
see also Algebra, Homological; K-Theory; Sheaves, Theory of

Barratt, M. B. & Mahowald, M. E., eds. Geometric Applications of Homotopy Theory II: Proceedings, Evanston, March 21-26, 1977. LC 78-16038. (Lecture Notes in Mathematics: Vol. 658). 1978. pap. 25.00 (ISBN 0-387-08859-8). Springer-Verlag.
Battelle Memorial Institute Conference - Seattle - 1968. Category Theory, Homology Theory & Their Applications, 1: Proceedings. Hilton, P. J., ed. LC 75-75931. (Lecture Notes in Mathematics: Vol. 86). 1969. pap. 14.70 (ISBN 0-387-04605-4). Springer-Verlag.
--Category Theory, Homology Theory & Their Applications, 2: Proceedings. Hilton, Peter J., ed. LC 75-75931. (Lecture Notes in Mathematics: Vol. 92). (Orig.). 1969. pap. 18.30 (ISBN 0-387-04611-9). Springer-Verlag.
--Category Theory, Homology Theory, & Their Applications, 3: Proceedings. Hilton, Peter J., ed. LC 75-75931. (Lecture Notes in Mathematics: Vol. 99). (Orig.). 1969. pap. 21.90 (ISBN 0-387-04618-6). Springer-Verlag.
Berthelot, Pierre & Ogus, Arthur. Notes on Crystalline Coholomology. LC 78-57039. (Mathematical Notes Ser.: No. 21). 1979. 16.50x (ISBN 0-691-08218-9). Princeton U Pr.
Borel, A. & Wallach, N. Continuous Cohomology, Discrete Subgroups, & Representation of Reductive Groups. LC 79-19858. (Annals of Mathematics Studies: 94). 352p. 1980. 35.00x (ISBN 0-691-08248-0); pap. 16.50 (ISBN 0-691-08249-9). Princeton U Pr.
Borel, Armand, et al. Intersection Cohomology. (Progress in Mathematics Ser.: No. 50). 235p. 1984. text ed. 19.95 (ISBN 0-8176-3274-3). Birkhauser.
Brown, K. S. Cohomology of Groups. (Graduate Text in Mathematics Ser.: Vol. 87). (Illus.). 336p. 1982. 33.00 (ISBN 0-387-90688-6). Springer-Verlag.
Buoncristiano, S., et al. A Geometric Approach to Homology Theory. LC 75-22980. (London Mathematical Society Lecture Note Ser.: No. 18). (Illus.). 216p. 1976. pap. text ed. 21.95x (ISBN 0-521-20940-4). Cambridge U Pr.
Cohen, F. R. The Homology of Iterated Loop Spaces. (Lecture Notes in Mathematics: Vol. 533). 1976. soft cover 34.00 (ISBN 0-387-07984-X). Springer-Verlag.
Conner, Pierre E. & Floyd, E. E. Relation of Corbordism to K-Theories. (Lecture Notes in Mathematics: Vol. 28). 1966. pap. 10.70 (ISBN 0-387-03610-5). Springer-Verlag.
Duskin, J. Simplical Methods & the Interpretation of "Triple" Cohomolgy. LC 75-20008. (Memoirs: No. 163). 135p. 1975. pap. 13.00 (ISBN 0-8218-1863-5, MEMO-163). Am Math.
Erven, J. & Falkowski, B. J. Low Order Cohomology & Applications. (Lecture Notes in Mathematics Ser.: Vol. 877). 126p. 1981. pap. 12.00 (ISBN 0-387-10864-5). Springer-Verlag.
Franks, John M. Homology & Dynamical Systems. LC 82-8897. (Conference Board of the Mathematical Sciences Ser.: Vol. 49). 120p. 1982. pap. 15.00 (ISBN 0-8218-1700-0). Am Math.
Goldberg, Samuel I. Curvature & Homology. (Illus.). xviii, 315p. pap. 6.50 (ISBN 0-486-64314-X). Dover.
Grothendieck, A. Local Cohomology: A Seminar Given by A. Grothendieck at Harvard University, 1961. Hartshorne, ed. (Lecture Notes in Mathematics: Vol. 41). 1967. pap. 10.70 (ISBN 0-387-03912-0). Springer-Verlag.
Gruenberg, Karl W. Cohomological Topics in Group Theory. LC 70-127042. (Lecture Notes in Mathematics: Vol. 143). 1970. pap. 14.70 (ISBN 0-387-04932-0). Springer-Verlag.
Hartshorne, R. Residues & Duality. (Lecture Notes in Mathematics: Vol. 20). 1966. pap. 21.90 (ISBN 0-387-03603-2). Springer-Verlag.
Hilton, Peter J. & Wylie, Shaun. Homology Theory. 1961. 67.50 (ISBN 0-521-05266-1); pap. 27.95x (ISBN 0-521-09422-4). Cambridge U Pr.
Hochster, Melvin. Topics in the Homological Theory of Modules over Commutative Rings. LC 75-1325. (CBMS Regional Conference Series in Mathematics: No. 24). 75p. 1979. pap. 10.00 (ISBN 0-8218-1674-8, CBMS-24). Am Math.
Hofmann, K. H. & Mostert, P. S. Cohomology Theories for Compact Abelian Groups. 200p. 1973. 34.00 (ISBN 0-387-05730-7). Springer-Verlag.
Illman, Soren. Equivariant Singular Homology & Cohomology I. (Memoirs Ser.: No. 156). 74p. 1975. pap. 10.00 (ISBN 0-8218-1856-2, MEMO-156). Am Math.
Johnson, B. E. Cohomology in Banach Algebras. LC 72-4561. (Memoirs Ser.: No. 127). 96p. 1972. pap. 10.00 (ISBN 0-8218-1827-9, MEMO-127). Am Math.
Kamber, Franz W. & Tondeur, Philippe. Invariant Differential Operators & Cohomology of Lie Algebra Sheaves. LC 52-42839. (Memoirs: No. 113). 1971. pap. 9.00 (ISBN 0-8218-1813-9, MEMO-113). Am Math.
Kirwan, Francis C. & Freidlin, Mark. Cohomology of Quotients in Symplectic & Algebraic Geometry. LC 84-15143. (Mathematical Notes Ser.: No. 31). 827p. 1985. 17.50x (ISBN 0-691-08370-3). Princeton U Pr.
Kleinerman, Samuel N. The Cohomology of Chevalley Groups of Exceptional Lie Type. LC 82-11545. (Memoirs Ser.: No. 268). 9.00 (ISBN 0-8218-2268-3). Am Math.
Knutson, D. Algebraic Spaces. (Lecture Notes in Mathematics: Vol. 203). 1971. pap. 12.00 (ISBN 0-387-05496-0). Springer-Verlag.
Lubkin. Cohomology of Completions. (Mathematics Studies: Vol. 42). 802p. 1980. 85.00 (ISBN 0-444-86042-8, North Holland). Elsevier.
Massey, W. S. Singular Homology Theory. LC 79-23309. (Graduate Texts in Mathematics: Vol. 70). (Illus.). 280p. 1980. 33.00 (ISBN 3-540-90456-5). Springer-Verlag.
Massey, William S. Homology & Cohomology Theory. (Monographs in Pure & Applied Math: Vol. 46). 1978. 59.75 (ISBN 0-8247-6662-8). Dekker.
Milne, J. S. Etale Cohomolgy. LC 79-84003. (Princeton Series in Mathematics: 33). 1980. 32.00 (ISBN 0-691-08238-3). Princeton U Pr.
Mostow, Mark A. Continuous Cohomology of Spaces with Two Topologies. LC 76-25187. (Memoirs of the American Mathematical Society: No. 175). 142p. 1976. pap. 14.00 (ISBN 0-8218-2175-X, MEMO 175). Am Math.
Northcott, Douglas G. Introduction to Homological Algebra. 1960. 44.50 (ISBN 0-521-05841-4). Cambridge U Pr.
Sanders, Jack P. The Category of H-Modules Over a Spectrum. LC 73-22409. (Memoirs: No. 141). 136p. 1974. pap. 11.00 (ISBN 0-8218-1841-4, MEMO-141). Am Math.
Schwartz, Jacob T. Differential Geometry & Topology. (Notes on Mathematics & Its Applications Ser.). 180p. 1968. 47.75 (ISBN 0-677-01510-0). Gordon.
Seminar on Triples & Categorical Homology. Proceedings. Eckmann, B., ed. LC 68-59303. (Lecture Notes in Mathematics: Vol. 80). 1969. pap. 18.30 (ISBN 0-387-04601-1). Springer-Verlag.
Shatz, Stephen S. Profinite Groups, Arithmetic, & Geometry. LC 77-126832. (Annals of Mathematics Studies: No. 67). 1972. 26.50 (ISBN 0-691-08017-8). Princeton U Pr.
Stammbach, U. Homology in Group Theory. LC 73-19547. (Lecture Notes in Mathematics: Vol. 359). 183p. 1973. pap. 14.00 (ISBN 0-387-06569-5). Springer-Verlag.
Stong, R. E. Unoriented Bordism & Actions of Finite Groups. LC 52-42839. (Memoirs: No. 103). 80p. 1970. pap. 9.00 (ISBN 0-8218-1803-1, MEMO-103). Am Math.
Thomas, Emery. Generalized Pontrjagin Cohomology Operations & Rings with Divided Powers. LC 52-42839. (Memoirs: No. 27). 1968. pap. 10.00 (ISBN 0-8218-1227-0, MEMO-27). Am Math.
Vasconcelos, Wolmer V., ed. The Rings of Dimension II. (Lecture Notes in Pure & Applied Mathematics Ser.: Vol. 22). 1976. 29.75 (ISBN 0-8247-6447-1). Dekker.
Vick, James W. Homology Theory: An Introduction to Algebraic Topology. (Pure & Applied Mathematics Ser., Vol. 54). 1973. text ed. 23.25i (ISBN 0-12-721250-7). Acad Pr.
Whitehead, G. Elements of Homotopy Theory. (Graduate Texts in Mathematics Ser.: Vol. 61). (Illus.). 1978. 44.00 (ISBN 0-387-90336-4). Springer-Verlag.
Wilson, W. Stephen. Brown-Peterson Homology: An Introduction & Sampler. LC 81-20619. (Conference Board of Mathematical Sciences Ser.: No. 48). 86p. 1982. pap. 11.00 (ISBN 0-8218-1699-3). Am Math.

HOMOPTERA
see also Cicada; Scale-Insects

Caldwell, John S. The Jumping Plant-Lice of Ohio (Homoptera: Chermidae) 1938. 1.00 (ISBN 0-86727-033-0). Ohio Bio Survey.
Distant, W. L. Rhynchota: Homoptera - Appendix, Vol. 4. (Fauna of British India Ser.). xiv, 502p. 1977. Repr. of 1908 ed. 25.00 (ISBN 0-88065-076-1, Pub. by Messers Today & Tomorrows Printers & Publishers India). Scholarly Pubns.
--Rhynchota: Homoptera - Appendix, Vol. 6. (Fauna of British India Ser.). viii, 250p. 1977. Repr. of 1916 ed. 15.00 (ISBN 0-88065-078-8, Pub. by Messers Today & Tomorrows Printers & Publishers India). Scholarly Pubns.
--Rhynchota: Homoptera - Appendix, Heteroptera - Addenda, Vol. 7. (Fauna of British India Ser.). viii, 212p. 1977. Repr. of 1918 ed. 15.00 (ISBN 0-88065-079-6, Pub. by Messers Today & Tomorrows Printers & Publishers India). Scholarly Pubns.
Distant, William L. Synonymic Catalogue of Homoptera, Pt. 1, Cicadidae. 1906. 19.00 (ISBN 0-384-11870-4). Johnson Repr.
Duffels, J. P. & Van der Laan, P. A. Catalogue of the Cicadoidea (Homoptera, Auchenorhyncha) 1956-1980. 1985. lib. bdg. 65.00 (ISBN 90-6193-522-9, Pub. by Junk Pub Netherlands). Kluwer-Academic.
Feeding & Multiplication of Three Cereal Aphid Species & Their Effect on Yield of Winter Wheat. (Agricultural Research Reports: 888). 1979. pap. 10.00 (ISBN 90-220-0694-8, PDC113, PUDOC). Unipub.
Fennah, R. G. Fulgoroidea of Fiji. (BMB). 1950. pap. 8.00 (ISBN 0-527-02310-8). Kraus Repr.
Ghauri, M. S. The Morphology & Taxonomy of Male Scale Insects (Homoptera: Coccoidea) (Illus.). vii, 221p. 1962. 24.50x (ISBN 0-565-00580-4, Pub. by British Mus Nat Hist England). Sabbot-Natural Hist Bks.
McKenzie, Howard L. Mealybugs of California: With Taxonomy, Biology, & Control of North American Species. (Illus.). 1968. 78.50x (ISBN 0-520-00844-8). U of Cal Pr.
Mound, L. A. & Halsey, S. H. Whitefly of the World: A Systematic Catalogue of the Aleyrodidoe (Homoptera) with Host Plant & Natural Enemy Data. 340p. 1978. 62.95x (ISBN 0-471-99634-3, Pub. by Wiley-Interscience). Wiley.
Osborn, H. Cicadellidae of Hawaii. (BMB). pap. 10.00 (ISBN 0-527-02240-3). Kraus Repr.
Osborn, Herbert. The Fulgoridae of Ohio. 1938. 1.50 (ISBN 0-86727-034-9). Ohio Bio Survey.
--The Membracidae of Ohio. 1940. 1.00 (ISBN 0-86727-036-5). Ohio Bio Survey.
Watson, S. A. The Miridae of Ohio. 1928. 1.00 (ISBN 0-86727-015-2). Ohio Bio Survey.

HOMOTOPY THEORY

Adams, J. Frank. Infinite Loop Spaces. (Annals of Mathematics Studies Ser.: No. 90). 1978. 26.50 (ISBN 0-691-08207-3); pap. 12.50 (ISBN 0-691-08206-5). Princeton U Pr.
--Stable Homotopy. (Chicago Lectures in Mathematics Ser). 384p. 1974. pap. text ed. 10.00x (ISBN 0-226-00524-0). U of Chicago Pr.
--Stable Homotopy Theory. 3rd ed. LC 70-90867. (Lecture Notes in Mathematics: Vol. 3). 1969. pap. 10.70 (ISBN 0-387-04598-8). Springer-Verlag.
Antonelli, P. L., et al. Concordance-Homotopy Groups of Geometric Automorphism Groups. LC 73-171479. (Lecture Notes in Mathematics: Vol. 215). 1971. pap. 11.00 (ISBN 0-387-05560-6). Springer-Verlag.
Arkowitz, M. & Curjel, C. R. Groups of Homotopy Classes: Rank Formualas & Homotopy - Commutativity. 2nd ed. (Lecture Notes in Mathematics: Vol. 4). (Orig.). 1967. pap. 10.70 (ISBN 0-387-03900-7). Springer-Verlag.
Barratt, M. B. & Mahowald, M. E., eds. Geometric Applications of Homotopy Theory I: Proceedings, Evanston, March 21-26, 1977. LC 78-16038. (Lecture Notes in Mathematics: Vol. 657). 1978. pap. 25.00 (ISBN 0-387-08858-X). Springer-Verlag.
Boardman, J. M. & Vogt, R. M. Homotopy Invariant Algebraic Structures on Topological Spaces. LC 73-13427. (Lecture Notes in Mathematics: Vol. 347). 1975. pap. 17.00 (ISBN 0-387-06479-6). Springer-Verlag.
Boltyanskii, V. G. & Postnikov, M. M. Two Papers on Homotopy Theory of Continuous Mappings. LC 51-5559. (Translation Ser.: No. 2, Vol. 7). 1957. 27.00 (ISBN 0-8218-1707-8, TRANS 2-7). Am Math.
Burghelea, D. & Lashof, R. Groups of Automarphisms of Manifolds. (Lecture Notes in Mathematics Ser.: Vol. 473). 156p. 1975. pap. 13.00 (ISBN 0-387-07182-2). Springer-Verlag.
Chapman, T. A. Controlled Simple Homotopy Theory & Applications. (Lecture Notes in Mathematics: Vol. 1009). 94p. 1983. pap. 10.00 (ISBN 0-387-12338-5). Springer-Verlag.

Antoniades, Harry N., ed. Hormones in Human Blood: Detection & Assay. 1976. 60.00x (ISBN 0-674-40635-4, ANHH). Harvard U Pr.

Austin, C. R. & Short, R. V., eds. Mechanisms of Hormone Action. LC 79-16287. (Reproduction in Mammals Ser.: Bk. 7). (Illus.). 1980. 42.50 (ISBN 0-521-22945-6); pap. 11.95 (ISBN 0-521-29737-0). Cambridge U Pr.

Balthazart, J., et al, eds. Hormones & Behavior in Higher Vertebrates. (Proceedings in Life Sciences Ser.). (Illus.). 500p. 1983. 57.00 (ISBN 0-387-12576-0). Springer-Verlag.

Barrington, E. J., ed. Hormones & Evolution. Vol. 1, 1979. 79.50 (ISBN 0-12-079401-2); Vol. 2, 1980. 79.50 (ISBN 0-12-079402-0). Acad Pr.

Benagiano, Giuseppe, et al, eds. Progestogens in Therapy. (Serono Symposia Publications Ser.: Vol. 3). (Illus.). 280p. 1983. text ed. 67.00 (ISBN 0-89004-856-8). Raven.

Berde, E. & Eichler, O., eds. Neurohypophysial Hormones & Similar Polypeptides. (Handbook of Experimental Pharmacology: Vol. 23). (Illus.). 1968. 135.70 (ISBN 0-387-04149-4). Springer-Verlag.

Bradshaw, Ralph A. Evolution of Hormone-Receptor Systems. LC 83-16185. (UCLA Symposia on Molecular & Celular Biology Ser.: Vol. 6). 526p. 1983. 88.00 (ISBN 0-8451-2605-9). A R Liss.

Brain, Paul F. Hormones & Aggression. Horrobin, D. F., ed. (Hormone Research Review Ser.: Vol. I). 126p. 1977. Repr. of 1977 ed. 22.95 (ISBN 0-87705-963-2). Human Sci Pr.

Brain, Paul F., ed. Hormones, Drugs & Aggression. (Hormone Research Review Ser.: Vol. 3). 173p. 1980. Repr. of 1979 ed. 24.95 (ISBN 0-87705-959-4). Human Sci Pr.

Brandenburg, D., ed. Insulin: Chemistry, Structure & Function of Insulin & Related Hormones. text ed. 68.00 (ISBN 3-11-008156-3). De Gruyter.

Brenner, Barry M. & Stein, Jay H., eds. Hormonal Function & the Kidney. (Contemporary Issues in Nephrology: Vol. 4). (Illus.). 1979. text ed. 40.00 (ISBN 0-443-08039-9). Churchill.

Brooks, Chandler M., et al. Humors, Hormones, & Neurosecretions: The Origins & Development of Man's Present Knowledge of the Humoral Control of Body Functions. LC 61-14336. 1962. 39.00x (ISBN 0-87395-006-2). State U NY Pr.

Buckle, John W. Animal Hormones. (Studies in Biology: No. 158). 80p. 1983. pap. text ed. 8.95 (ISBN 0-7131-2874-7). E Arnold.

Burdette, W. J., ed. Invertebrate Endocrinology & Hormonal Heterophylly. (Illus.). 438p. 1974. 39.00 (ISBN 0-387-06594-6). Springer-Verlag.

Catt, K. J. & Dufau, Maria L., eds. Hormone Action & Testicular Function. (Annals of The New York Academy of Science Ser.: Vol. 438). 708p. 1984. lib. bdg. 163.00x (ISBN 0-89766-270-9); pap. 163.00x (ISBN 0-89766-271-7). NY Acad Sci.

Charyulu. Homones & Cancer. 1979. 32.50 (ISBN 0-8151-1644-6). Year Bk Med.

Choh Hao Li, ed. Hormonal Proteins & Peptides: Gonadotropic Hormones, Vol. XI. LC 82-22770. 1983. 47.50 (ISBN 0-12-447211-7). Acad Pr.

--Hormonal Proteins & Peptides: Techniques in Protein Chemistry, Vol. 9. LC 80-11061. (Hormonal Proteins & Peptides Ser.). 1980. 49.50 (ISBN 0-12-447209-5). Acad Pr.

Clark, J. H., et al, eds. Hormone & Antihormone, Action at the Target Cell. (Dahlem Workshop Reports Ser.: L.S.R.R. No.3). 228p. 1976. 26.50x (ISBN 0-89573-087-1). VCH Pubs.

Cohn, D. V., et al, eds. Hormonal Control of Calcium Metabolism. (International Congress Ser.: No. 511). 506p. 1981. 98.75 (ISBN 0-444-90193-0, Excerpta Medica). Elsevier.

Cold Spring Harbor Symposia On Quantitative Biology. Relation of Hormones to Development: Proceedings, Vol. 10. Repr. of 1942 ed. 27.00 (ISBN 0-384-50250-4). Johnson Repr.

Collu, R., et al, eds. Brain Neurotransmitters & Hormones. 428p. 1982. text ed. 66.00 (ISBN 0-89004-763-4). Raven.

Copinschi, G. & Jaquet, P., eds. Lipo-Corticotropic Hormones & Cushing's Disease. (Journal: Hormone Research: Vol. 13, No. 4-5). (Illus.). 152p. 1981. pap. 28.25 (ISBN 3-8055-3410-8). S Karger.

Corbin, Jackie D. & Hardman, Joel D., eds. Methods in Enzymology: Hormone Action: Protein Kinases, Vol. 99, Pt F. 1983. 55.00 (ISBN 0-12-181999-X). Acad Pr.

Corvilain, H. & Fuss, M., eds. Hormones & Calcium Metabolism. (Journal: HormoneResearch: Vol. 20, No. 1). 92p. 1984. pap. 16.75 (ISBN 3-8055-3888-X). S Karger.

De Brux, J., et al, eds. The Endometrium: Hormonal Impacts. LC 81-8529. 176p. 1981. 35.00x (ISBN 0-306-40749-3, Plenum Pr). Plenum Pub.

Dellman, H. D., et al, eds. Comparative Endocrinology of Prolactin. LC 77-1871. (Advances in Experimental Medicine & Biology: Vol. 80). 229p. 1977. 35.00x (ISBN 0-306-39080-9, Plenum Pr). Plenum Pub.

DeWeid. Hormones & the Brain. (Illus.). 352p. 1981. text ed. 42.50 (ISBN 0-8391-1645-4). Univ Park.

Dumont, J. & Nunez, J., eds. Hormones & Cell Regulation, Vol. 6. 320p. 1982. 66.00 (ISBN 0-444-80419-6, Biomedical Pr). Elsevier.

Dumont, J. E. & Nunez, J. Hormones & Cell Regulation. (European Symposium Ser.: Vol. 8). 1984. 68.00 (ISBN 0-444-80583-4, I-253-84). Elsevier.

Dumont, J. E., et al, eds. Hormones & Cell Regulation, Vol. 7. 360p. 1983. 64.00 (ISBN 0-444-80500-1, Biomedical Pr). Elsevier.

Eisenbach, G. M. & Brod, J., eds. Vasoactive Renal Hormones. (Contributions to Nephrology: Vol. 12). (Illus.). 1978. pap. 29.00 (ISBN 3-8055-2839-6). S Karger.

Eisenbach, G. M. & Brod, Jan, eds. Non-Vasoactive Renal Hormones. (Contributions to Nephrology: Vol. 13). (Illus.). 1978. pap. 29.00 (ISBN 3-8055-2895-7). S Karger.

Eleftheriou, Basil E. & Sprott, Richard L., eds. Hormonal Correlates of Behavior. Incl. Vol. 1. Lifespan View. 456p. 1975. 45.00x (ISBN 0-306-37504-4); Vol. 2, an Organismic View. 382p. 45.00 (ISBN 0-306-37505-2). LC 75-5938. 1975 (Plenum Pr). Plenum Pub.

Elias, Alan N. Gamma-Aminobutyric Acid in the Regulation of Hormone Secretion. (Endocrinology & Metabolism Ser.: Vol. 6). 142p. 1985. 36.50 (ISBN 0-03-069744-1). Praeger.

Endroczi, E. & De Wied, D., eds. Integrative Neurohumoral Mechanisms. (Developments in Neuroscience Ser.: Vol. 16). 560p. 1983. 40.00 (ISBN 0-444-80487-0, I-093-83, Biomedical Pr). Elsevier.

Engle, Earl T. & Pincus, Gregory, eds. Hormones & the Aging Process. 1956. 55.00 (ISBN 0-12-239050-4). Acad Pr.

Fischer, G. & Weiser, R. J., eds. Hormonally Defined Media: A Tool in Cell Biology. (Proceedings in Life Sciences Ser.). (Illus.). 460p. 1983. 33.00 (ISBN 0-387-12668-6). Springer-Verlag.

Forsling, Mary. Anti-Diuretic Hormone, Vol. 3. Horrobin, D. F., ed. (Annual Research Reviews Ser.). 1979. 26.00 (ISBN 0-88831-044-7). Eden Pr.

Forsling, Mary L. Anti-Diuretic Hormone, Vol. 1. (Annual Research Reviews Ser.). 1977. 19.20 (ISBN 0-904406-51-2). Eden Pr.

--Anti-Diuretic Hormone, Vol. 2. LC 78-309279. (Annual Research Reviews). 1978. 24.00 (ISBN 0-88831-016-1). Eden Pr.

Fotherby, K. & Pal, S. B., eds. Hormones in Normal & Abnormal Human Tissues, Vol. 1. 1980. 58.00x (ISBN 3-11-008031-1). De Gruyter.

Gilbert, L. I., ed. Juvenile Hormones. LC 76-21097. 582p. 1976. 65.00x (ISBN 0-306-30959-9, Plenum Pr). Plenum Pub.

Goldberger, Robert F. & Yamamoto, Keith, eds. Biological Regulation & Development, Vol. 3B. (Hormone Action Ser.). 326p. 1984. 42.50x (ISBN 0-306-41442-2, Plenum Pr). Plenum Pub.

--Biological Regulation & Development, Vol. 3A: Hormone Action. LC 82-8941. 360p. 1982. 45.00x (ISBN 0-306-40925-9, Plenum Pr). Plenum Pub.

Gray, C. H. & James, V. H. T. Hormones in Blood, Vol. 3. 3rd ed. LC 78-73882. 1980. 90.00 (ISBN 0-12-296203-6). Acad Pr.

Gray, C. H. & James, V. H., eds. Hormones in Blood, Vol. 4. 3rd ed. 1983. 77.50 (ISBN 0-12-296204-4). Vol. 5th. 55.00 (ISBN 0-12-296205-2). Acad Pr.

Gray, C. H. & James, V. H. T., eds. Hormones in Blood, Vol. 1. 3rd ed. 1979. 90.00 (ISBN 0-12-296201-X). Acad Pr.

--Hormones in Blood, Vol. 2. 3rd ed. 1979. 80.00 (ISBN 0-12-296202-8). Acad Pr.

Greenhalgh, R. M. Hormones & Vascular Disease. 346p. text ed. cancelled (ISBN 0-272-79622-0, Pub. by Pitman Bks Ltd UK). Pitman Pub MA.

Greenhalgh, Roger M., ed. Hormones & Vascular Disease. 345p. 1981. text ed. 57.95x (ISBN 0-8464-1222-5). Beekman Pubs.

Greep, Roy O., ed. Recent Progress in Hormone Research, Vol. 35. 1979. 70.00 (ISBN 0-12-571135-2). Acad Pr.

--Recent Progress in Hormone Research, Vol. 36. (Serial Pub.). 1980. 75.00 (ISBN 0-12-571136-0). Acad Pr.

Gupta, Derek & Voelter, Wolfgang. Hypothalamic Hormones: Chemistry, Physiology & Clinical Applications. (Illus.). 766p. 1978. 75.30x (ISBN 3-527-25712-8). VCH Pubs.

--Hypothalamic Hormones: Structure, Synthesis, & Biological Activity. (Illus.). 328p. 1975. 34.20x (ISBN 3-527-25589-3). VCH Pubs.

Habenicht, U. F. & Neumann, F. Hormonal Regulation of Testicular Descent. (Advances in Anatomy, Embryology & Cell Biology: Vol. 81). (Illus.). 70p. 1983. pap. 21.00 (ISBN 0-387-12439-X). Springer-Verlag.

Haller, Jurgen. Hormonal Contraception. rev. 2nd ed. Gottfried, Herbert, tr. from Third Ger. Ed. LC 71-188791. (Illus.). 1972. 13.00x (ISBN 0-87672-034-3). Geron-X.

Hamburgh, Max & Barrington, E. J., eds. Hormones in Development. LC 72-116424. 854p. 1971. 69.50x (ISBN 0-306-50028-0, Plenum Pr). Plenum Pub.

Hansen, G. N. Cell Types in the Adenohypophysis of the Primitive Actinopterygians: With Special Reference to Immunocytochemical Identification of Pituitary Hormone Producing Cells in the Distal Lobe. (Illus.). 88p. 1983. pap. 20.00 (ISBN 0-08-029827-3). Pergamon.

Hoffmann, J. & Porchet, M., eds. Biosynthesis, Metabolism & Mode of Action of Inverterbrate Hormones. (Proceedings in Life Sciences Ser.). (Illus.). 570p. 1984. 59.00 (ISBN 0-387-13667-3). Springer-Verlag.

Horrobin, David F. Prolactin, Vol. 2. (Annual Research Reviews Ser.). 1974. 19.20 (ISBN 0-85200-120-7). Eden Pr.

--Prolactin, Vol. 4. (Annual Research Reviews Ser.). 1976. 24.00 (ISBN 0-904406-47-4). Eden Pr.

--Prolactin, Vol. 5. LC 77-369577. (Annual Research Reviews Ser.). 1977. 24.00 (ISBN 0-88831-009-9). Eden Pr.

--Prolactin, Vol. 6. (Annual Research Reviews Ser.). 1979. 21.60 (ISBN 0-88831-041-2). Eden Pr.

--Prolactin, Vol. 8. (Annual Research Reviews Ser.). 152p. 1981. 24.00 (ISBN 0-88831-093-5). Eden Pr.

Iacobelli, Stefano, et al, eds. Hormones & Cancer. (Progress in Cancer Research & Therapy Ser.: Vol. 14). 589p. 1980. text ed. 92.00 (ISBN 0-89004-486-4). Raven.

Imura, H. & Kuzuya, H., eds. Hormone Receptors & Receptor Diseases: Proceedings of the International Symposium on Hormone Receptors & Receptor Diseases, Kyoto, Aug. 29-30, 1982. (International Congress Ser.: No. 603). 220p. 1983. 49.00 (ISBN 0-444-90298-8, I-209-83, Excerpta Medica). Elsevier.

International Society of Psychoneuroendocrinology-Brooklyn-1970. Influence of Hormones on the Nervous System: Proceedings. Ford, D. H., ed. (Illus.). 1971. 55.75 (ISBN 3-8055-1216-3). S Karger.

Ishii, S., ed. Hormones, Adaptation & Evolution: International Symposium. 300p. 1980. 51.00 (ISBN 0-387-10033-4). Springer-Verlag.

Jaffe. Prolactin, Vol. 3. 81. 45.75 (ISBN 0-444-00555-2). Elsevier.

Jaffe, Bernard & Behrman, Harold, eds. Methods of Radioimmunoassay. 1974. 48.00 (ISBN 0-12-379250-9). Acad Pr.

Kato, Junzo, et al. Hormone Receptors in the Brain. (Illus.). 220p. 1973. text ed. 26.50x (ISBN 0-8422-7078-7). Irvington.

Kellen, John A. & Hilf, Russell. Influences of Hormones in Tumor Development, 2 vols. 1979. Vol. 1, 192p. 58.00 (ISBN 0-8493-5351-3); Vol. 2, 224p. 61.00 (ISBN 0-8493-5352-1). CRC Pr.

Klachko, D. M., et al, eds. Hormones & Energy Metabolism. LC 78-23943. (Advances in Experimental Medicine & Biology Ser.: Vol. 111). 212p. 1979. 35.00x (ISBN 0-306-40070-7, Plenum Pr). Plenum Pub.

Klachko, David M., et al, eds. Hormone Receptors. LC 77-25856. (Advances in Experimental Medicine & Biology Ser.: Vol. 96). 224p. 1978. 35.00x (ISBN 0-306-32696-5, Plenum Pr). Plenum Pub.

Lamberts, Steven W. & MacLeod, Robert M. Physiological & Pathological Aspects of Prolactin Secretion, Vol. 1. Horrobin, David F., ed. (Annual Research Reviews Ser.). 1978. 19.20 (ISBN 0-88831-034-X). Eden Pr.

Leavitt, Wendell W., ed. Hormones & Cancer. LC 81-15743. (Advances in Experimental Medicine & Biology: Vol. 138). 432p. 1982. 57.50 (ISBN 0-306-40831-7, Plenum Pr). Plenum Pub.

Levey, Gerald S. Hormone Receptor Interaction: Molecular Aspects. (Modern Pharmacology-Toxicology Ser.: Vol. 9). 488p. 1976. 79.75 (ISBN 0-8247-6438-2). Dekker.

Levine, Seymour. Hormones & Behavior. 1972. 64.50 (ISBN 0-12-445450-X). Acad Pr.

Li, Choh H., ed. Hormonal Proteins & Peptides, 7 vols. Incl. Vol. 1. 1973. 49.50 (ISBN 0-12-447201-X); Vol. 2. 1973. 59.50 (ISBN 0-12-447202-8); Vol. 3. 1975. 67.50 (ISBN 0-12-447203-6); Vol. 4. 1977. 49.50 (ISBN 0-12-447204-4); Vol. 5. Lipotropin & Related Peptides. 1978. 47.50 (ISBN 0-12-447205-2); Vol. 6. Thyroid Hormones. 1978. 71.50 (ISBN 0-12-447206-0); Vol. 7. Hypothalmic Hormones. 1979. 49.50 (ISBN 0-12-447207-9). LC 78-5444. Acad Pr.

Litwack, G., ed. Biochemical Actions of Hormones, Vol. 8. 1981. 64.00 (ISBN 0-12-452808-2). Acad Pr.

Litwack, Gerald, ed. Biochemical Actions of Hormones, 7 vols. Incl. Vol. 1. 1970. 73.00 (ISBN 0-12-452801-5); Vol. 2. 1972. 73.00 (ISBN 0-12-452802-3); Vol. 3. 1975. 71.00 (ISBN 0-12-452803-1); Vol. 4. 1977. 71.00 (ISBN 0-12-452804-X); Vol. 5. 1978. 66.00 (ISBN 0-12-452805-8); Vol. 6. 1979. 59.00 (ISBN 0-12-452806-6); Vol. 7. 1980. 59.00 (ISBN 0-12-452807-4). LC 70-107567. Acad Pr.

--Biochemical Actions of Hormones, Vol. 9. LC 70-107567. 374p. 1982. 49.50 (ISBN 0-12-452809-0). Acad Pr.

Litwak, Gerald. Biochemical Actions of Hormones, Vol. 11. LC 70-107567. 1984. 63.00 (ISBN 0-12-452811-2). Acad Pr.

Litwick, Gerald, ed. Biochemical Actions of Hormones, Vol. 12. 1985. 89.00 (ISBN 0-12-452812-0). Acad Pr.

McKerns, Kenneth W., ed. Hormonal Control of the Hypothalamo-Pituitary-Gonadal Axis. (Biochemical Endocrinology Ser.). 636p. 1984. 85.00x (ISBN 0-306-41800-2, Plenum Pr). Plenum Pub.

McQuillan, Mary T. Somatostatin, Vol. 1. Horrobin, D. F., ed. (Annual Research Reviews Ser.). 1979. 24.00 (ISBN 0-88831-040-4). Eden Pr.

Mahesh, V. B. & Muldoon, T. G., eds. Functional Correlates of Hormone Receptors in Reproduction. (Developments in Endocrinology Ser.: Vol. 12). 594p. 1981. 122.00 (ISBN 0-444-00604-4, Biomedical Pr). Elsevier.

Malkinson, A. M. Hormone Action. (Outline Studies in Biology Ser.). 1975. pap. 7.50 (ISBN 0-412-13070-X, 6185, Pub. by Chapman & Hall). Methuen Inc.

Mena, Flavio & Valverde, Carlos M., eds. Prolactin Secretion: A Multidisciplinary Approach. 1984. 44.50 (ISBN 0-12-490620-6). Acad Pr.

Menon, K. M. & Reel, Jerry R., eds. Steroid Hormone Action & Cancer. LC 76-25873. (Current Topics in Molecular Endocrinology Ser.: Vol. 4). 190p. 1976. 39.50x (ISBN 0-306-34004-6, Plenum Pr). Plenum Pub.

Middlebrook, John H. & Kohn, Leonard D., eds. Receptor-Mediated Binding & Internalization of Toxins & Hormones. 1981. 44.00 (ISBN 0-12-494850-2). Acad Pr.

Munson, P. L., et al, eds. Vitamins & Hormones, Vol. 38. (Serial Publication Ser.). 1981. 61.50 (ISBN 0-12-709838-0). Acad Pr.

Munson, Paul L., et al, eds. Vitamins & Hormones: Advances in Research & Applications, Vol. 37. LC 43-10535. 1980. 60.00 (ISBN 0-12-709837-2). Acad Pr.

Nieschlag, E., ed. Hormone Assays in Reproductive Medicine. (Hormone Research: Vol. 9, No. 6). (Illus.). 1978. pap. 13.25 (ISBN 3-8055-2975-9). S Karger.

Nitzan, Menachem, ed. The Influence of Maternal Hormones on the Fetus & Newborn. (Pediatric & Adolescent Endocrinology: Vol. 5). (Illus.). 1979. pap. 42.25 (ISBN 3-8055-2902-3). S Karger.

O'Malley, B. W. & Birnbaumer, Lutz, eds. Receptors & Hormone Action, Vol. 3. 1978. 77.50 (ISBN 0-12-526303-1). Acad Pr.

O'Malley, Bert & Means, Anthony, eds. Receptors for Reproductive Hormones. LC 73-81095. (Advances in Experimental Medicine & Biology Ser.: Vol. 36). 470p. 1973. 57.50x (ISBN 0-306-39036-1, Plenum Pr). Plenum Pub.

O'Malley, Bert W., ed. Hormone Action, Vol. 2. 1978. 78.00 (ISBN 0-12-526302-3). Acad Pr.

Pal, S. B., ed. Enzyme Labelled Immunoassay of Hormones & Drugs. 1978. 64.00x (ISBN 3-11007-539-3). De Gruyter.

Palkovic, M. Hormones, Lipoproteins & Atherosclerosis: Proceedings of a Satelite Symposium of the 28th International Congress of Physiological Sciences, Bratislava, Czechoslovakia, 1980. LC 80-41926. (Advances in Physiological Sciences Ser.: Vol. 35). (Illus.). 300p. 1981. 44.00 (ISBN 0-08-027357-2). Pergamon.

Pecile, A. & Muller, E., eds. Growth Hormones & Other Biologically Active Peptides: Proceedings, Milan, Sept. 1979. (International Congress Ser.: Vol. 495). 282p. 1980. 58.50 (ISBN 0-444-90122-1, Excerpta Medica). Elsevier.

Pennington, G. W. & Naik, Sandra. Hormone Analysis: Methodology & Clinical Intrepretation, Vol. 1. 320p. 1981. 89.50 (ISBN 0-8493-5539-7). CRC Pr.

Pincus, Gregory, ed. Hormones & Atherosclerosis: Proceedings. 1959. 61.00 (ISBN 0-12-557050-3). Acad Pr.

Pratt, G. E. & Brooks, G. T., eds. Juvenile Hormone Biochemistry. (Developments in Endocrinology Ser.: Vol. 15). 456p. 1982. 79.75 (ISBN 0-444-80390-4, Biomedical Pr). Elsevier.

BOOKS - SUBJECT INDEX HORSES

Raabe, Marie. Insect Neurohormones. Marshall, Nissim, tr. LC 82-7535. (Fr.). 366p. 1982. 42.50 (ISBN 0-306-40782-5, Plenum Pr). Plenum Pub.
Randle, P. J. & Denton, R. M. Hormones & Cell Metabolism. rev. ed. Head, J. J., ed. LC 78-69515. (Carolina Biology Readers Ser.). (Illus.). 16p. 1982. pap. 1.60 (ISBN 0-89278-279-X, 45-9679). Carolina Biological.
Rosner, Martic C. Hormones & Hyacinths. LC 79-82087. 1980. 5.95 (ISBN 0-87212-126-7). Libra.
Sawin, Clark T. The Hormones: Endocrine Physiology. (Illus.). 308p. 1969. 19.95 (ISBN 0-316-77170-8). Little.
Saxena, Brij B., et al, eds. Hormone Receptors in Growth & Reproduction. LC 84-3341. (Serono Symposia Publications from Raven Press Ser.: Vol. 9). (Illus.). 416p. 1984. text ed. 99.00 (ISBN 0-89004-964-5). Raven.
Schindler, A. E. Hormones in Human Amniotic Fluid. (Monographs on Endocrinology: Vol. 21). (Illus.). 190p. 1982. 48.00 (ISBN 0-387-10810-6). Springer-Verlag.
Schmidt-Gollwitzer, Manfred & Schley, Rosemarie, eds. LH-RH & Its Analogues: Fertility & Anti-Fertility Aspects. (New Developments in Biosciences Ser.). (Illus.). x, 357p. 1985. 39.20x (ISBN 3-11-010055-X). De Gruyter.
Schulster, D. & Levitzki, A. Cellular Receptors for Hormones & Neurotransmitters. LC 79-41216. 412p. 1980. 94.95x (ISBN 0-471-27682-0, Pub. by Wiley-Interscience). Wiley.
Scott, Walter N. & Goodman, David B., eds. Hormonal Regulation of Epithelial Transport of Ions & Water, Vol. 372. LC 81-14068. 660p. 1981. 142.00x (ISBN 0-89766-133-8). NY Acad Sci.
Selye, H. Hormones & Resistance, 2 vols. LC 78-155342. (Illus.). 1971. Set. 99.50 (ISBN 0-387-05411-1). Springer-Verlag.
Shire, John G. Genetic Variation in Hormone Systems, 2 vols. 1979. Vol. 1, 208p. 59.00 (ISBN 0-8493-5283-5); Vol. 2, 192p. 54.00 (ISBN 0-8493-5284-3). CRC Pr.
Sowers, J. R., ed. Hypothalmic Hormones. (Benchmark Papers in Human Physiology Ser.: Vol. 14). 368p. 1980. 46.00 (ISBN 0-87933-358-8). Van Nos Reinhold.
Svare, Bruce B., ed. Hormones & Aggrssive Behavior. 610p. 1983. 59.50x (ISBN 0-306-41055-9, Plenum Pr). Plenum Pub.
Taylor, William N. Hormonal Manipulation: A New Era of Monstrous Athletes. LC 85-42523. 136p. 1985. pap. 14.95 (ISBN 0-89950-166-4). McFarland & Co.
Tolis, George, et al, eds. Prolactin & Prolactinomas. (Illus.). 504p. 1983. text ed. 79.00 (ISBN 0-89004-804-5). Raven.
Verndakis, A. Hormones in Development & Aging. 718p. 1981. text ed. 75.00 (ISBN 0-89335-140-7). SP Med & Sci Bks.
Vitamins & Hormones, Vol. 39. 1982. 65.00 (ISBN 0-12-709839-9). Acad Pr.
Voitkevick, A. A. Feather & Plumage of Birds. 1966. 10.50 (ISBN 0-8079-0050-8). October.
Wade, Carlson. Catalytic Hormones: Key to Extraordinary Weight Loss. 285p. 1982. 16.95 (ISBN 0-13-120857-8, Parker). P-H.
--Natural Hormones: Secret of Youthful Health. 4.95x (ISBN 0-13-609958-0). Cancer Control Soc.
Weaver, Robert J. Plant Growth Substances in Agriculture. LC 71-166964. (Plant Science Ser.). (Illus.). 594p. 1972. text ed. 45.95x (ISBN 0-7167-0824-8). W H Freeman.
Weisbart, Melvin, et al. Isolation & Purification of Hormones. (Illus.). 220p. 1973. text ed. 20.00x (ISBN 0-8422-7107-4). Irvington.
White, A., et al. Hormones & Metabolic Control. 160p. 1984. pap. text ed. 11.95 (ISBN 0-7131-4437-8). E Arnold.
Wigglesworth, V. B. Insect Hormones. (Illus.). 159p. 1970. text ed. 13.95x (ISBN 0-7167-0688-1). W H Freeman.
Wolff, E., ed. Hormones et Differenciation Sexuelle Chez les Invertebres. (Cours & Documents De Biologie Ser.). (Fr.). 276p. 1972. 67.25 (ISBN 0-677-50430-6). Gordon.
Workshop Conference, Basel 1971, et al. Thyrotrophin Releasing Hormone: Proceedings. Marois, M. & Werner, I., eds. (Frontiers of Hormone Research: Vol. 1). (Illus.). 196p. 1972. 22.25 (ISBN 3-8055-1288-0). S Karger.

HORMONES (PLANTS)
see Plant Hormones

HORMONES, SEX
see also names of hormones, e.g. Androgens, Testosterone
Alcaraz, Manuel, et al. Sexual Hormones: Influence on the Electrophysiology of the Brain. LC 74-4137. 223p. 1974. text ed. 28.00x (ISBN 0-8422-7214-3). Irvington.
Austin, C. R. & Short, R. V., eds. Hormones in Reproduction. LC 73-178279. (Reproduction in Mammals Ser.: Bk. 3). (Illus.). 1972. Cambridge U Pr.
Baulieu, E. E. Etude sur le Mode D'Action des Hormones Steroides Sexuelles: Metabolisme Au Niveau des Organes Cibles et Liaison a Des Proteines Specifiques. LC 74-185798. (Cours & Documents de Biologie Ser.). (Illus.). 150p. 1974. 52.00 (ISBN 0-677-50650-3). Gordon.
Bigazzi, M. F. & Greenwood, F. C., eds. Biology of Relaxin & Its Role in the Human: Proceedings of the 1st International Conference on Human Relaxin, Florence, Italy, September 30 - October 2, 1983. (International Congress Ser.: No. 610). xiv, 424p. 1983. 93.75 (ISBN 0-444-90303-8, I-362-83, Excerpta Medica). Elsevier.
CIBA Foundation. Sex, Hormones & Behaviour. (CIBA Foundation Symposium: No. 62). 1979. 47.00 (ISBN 0-444-90045-4). Elsevier.
Clark, J. H. & Peck, E. J. Female Sex Steroids: Receptors & Function. (Monographs on Endocrinology: Vol. 14). (Illus.). 1979. 50.00 (ISBN 0-387-09375-3). Springer-Verlag.
Dufau, Maria & Means, Anthony, eds. Hormone Binding & Target Cell Activation in the Testis. LC 74-23709. (Current Topics in Molecular Endocrinology: Vol. 1). 380p. 1974. 47.50x (ISBN 0-306-34001-1, Plenum Pr). Plenum Pub.
French, Frank S., et al, eds. Hormonal Regulation of Spermatogenesis. LC 75-32541. (Current Topics in Molecular Endocrinology Ser.: Vol. 2). 537p. 1975. 59.50x (ISBN 0-306-34002-X, Plenum Pr). Plenum Pub.
International Seminar on Reproductive Physiology & Sexual Endocrinology, 3rd, Brussels, 1970. Basic Actions of Sex Steroids on Target Organs: Proceedings. Hubinont, P. O., et al, eds. 1971. 24.25 (ISBN 3-8055-1156-6). S Karger.
James, V. H. T., et al, eds. Endocrine Function of the Human Ovary. 1976. 71.00 (ISBN 0-12-380150-8). Acad Pr.
Lisk, R. D., et al. Neonatal Hormone Treatment & Adult Sexual Behavior in Rodents. (Biology of Sex Ser.). 230p. 1974. text ed. 25.50x (ISBN 0-8422-7125-2). Irvington.
Moudgil, V. K., ed. Molecular Mechanism of Steroid Hormone Action: Recent Advances. (Illus.). xii, 824p. 1985. 116.00x (ISBN 3-11-010118-1). De Gruyter.
O'Malley, Bert & Means, Anthony, eds. Receptors for Reproductive Hormones. LC 73-81095. (Advances in Experimental Medicine & Biology Ser.: Vol. 36). 470p. 1973. 57.50x (ISBN 0-306-39036-1, Plenum Pr). Plenum Pub.
Regulatory Mechanisms Affecting Gonadal Hormone Action. (Advances in Sex Hormone Research Ser.: Vol. 3). pap. 89.00 (ISBN 0-317-27715-4, 2052098). Bks Demand UMI.
Salhanick, Hilton A., et al. Metabolic Effects of Gonadal Hormones & Contraceptive Steroids. LC 71-89792. 762p. 1969. 49.50x (ISBN 0-306-30422-8, Plenum Pr). Plenum Pub.
Schirren, C. Praktische Andrologie. 2nd ed. (Illus.). 1982. pap. 17.25 (ISBN 3-8055-3474-4). S Karger.
Silver, Rae, intro. by. Hormones & Reproductive Behavior: Readings from Scientific American. LC 79-1192. (Illus.). 181p. 1979. text ed. 20.95x (ISBN 0-7167-1093-5); pap. text ed. 11.95x (ISBN 0-7167-1094-3). W H Freeman.
Thomas, John A., ed. Advances in Sex Hormone Research, Vol. 4. Singhal, Radhey L. LC 79-25717. (Illus.). 376p. 1980. text ed. 35.00 (ISBN 0-8067-1914-1). Urban & S.
Wolff, E., ed. Hormones et Differenciation Sexuelle Chez les Invertebres. (Cours & Documents De Biologie Ser.). (Fr.). 276p. 1972. 67.25 (ISBN 0-677-50430-6). Gordon.

HORNED TOADS
Sherbrook, Wade C. Horned Lizards, Unique Reptiles of Western North America. Jackson, Earl, ed. LC 81-51078. (Popular Ser.: No. 31). (Illus.). 48p. 1981. pap. 4.95 (ISBN 0-911408-59-2). SW Pks Mnmts.

HORNSTONE
see Chert

HOROLOGY
see also Chronometer; Clocks and Watches; Sun-Dials; Time
Belin, Peter. Horology on the Half-Shell. LC 78-55929. (Illus.). 77p. 1978. 12.50 (ISBN 0-8048-1482-1). C E Tuttle.
Britten, F. W. Horological Hints & Helps. (Illus.). 1977. 21.50 (ISBN 0-902028-64-2). Apollo.
Bromley, John, ed. The Clockmakers' Library: The Catalogue of the Books & Manuscripts in the Library of the Worshipful Company of Clockmakers. (Illus.). 136p. 1977. 52.50x (ISBN 0-85667-033-2, Pub. by Sotheby Pubns England). Biblio Dist.
Gerschler, Malcolm C. The Clock & Watch Pronunciary. LC 82-91052. (Illus.). 256p. 1983. pap. 11.95 (ISBN 0-9609628-1-6). Wag on Wall.
Haswell, J. Eric. Horology. (Illus.). 1976. 25.00 (ISBN 0-7158-1146-0). Charles River Bks.

HORSE
see Horses

HORSE BREEDING
see also Horse Breeds
Blood-Horse, ed. Sires of Runners of 1979. (Annual Supplement). 1980. lib. bdg. 20.00 (ISBN 0-936032-19-7); pap. 10.00 (ISBN 0-936032-20-0). Blood-Horse.
Blood Horse, ed. Stallion Register, 1981. (Illus.). 900p. 1980. 20.00 (ISBN 0-936032-33-2); pap. 10.00 (ISBN 0-936032-34-0). Blood-Horse.
Blood-Horse-Thoroughbred Owners & Breeders Association, ed. The Breeder's Guide for 1979. (Bound Supplements of the Blood-Horse). 1980. 51.75 (ISBN 0-936032-01-4). Blood-Horse.
Blood-Horse Thoroughbred Owners & Breeders Association, ed. The Breeder's Guide for 1981. 1982. 47.50 (ISBN 0-936032-51-0). Blood-Horse.
Breeders Guide for Nineteen Eighty-Four: Bound Supplements, 3 vols. in one. 1985. 64.00 (ISBN 0-936032-80-4). Blood-Horse.
The Breeder's Guide for 1978. 46.75 (ISBN 0-936032-00-6). Blood-Horse.
Conn, George H. Horse Selection & Care for Beginners. pap. 5.00 (ISBN 0-87980-193-X). Wilshire.
Denhardt, Robert M. Foundation Dams of the American Quarter Horse. 240p. 1982. 22.95 (ISBN 0-8061-1820-2). U of Okla Pr.
Edwards, Elwyn H., ed. A Standard Guide to Horse & Pony Breeds. LC 79-23921. (Illus.). 352p. 1980. 24.95 (ISBN 0-07-019035-6). McGraw.
Equine Reproduction. 776p. 1975. 100.00x (ISBN 0-686-45144-9, Pub. by Biochemical England). State Mutual Bk.
Equine Reproduction II. 652p. 1979. 100.00x (ISBN 0-906545-03-X, Pub. by Biochemical England). State Mutual Bk.
Feeding the Horse. (Illus.). 127p. 1974. lib. bdg. 10.75 (ISBN 0-936032-04-9). Blood-Horse.
Hardman, A. C. The Amateur Horse Breeder. (The Pelham Horsemaster Ser.). (Illus.). 125p. 1983. 12.95 (ISBN 0-7207-1177-0, Pub. by Michael Joseph). Merrimack Pub Cir.
Hardman, A. Leighton. The Amateur Horse Breeder. 2nd ed. (Illus.). 240p. 1980. cancelled (ISBN 0-7207-1177-0). Transatlantic.
--Amateur Horse Breeder. pap. 5.00 (ISBN 0-87980-181-6). Wilshire.
Hardman, Ann C. The Amateur Horse Breeder. LC 72-132207. (Illus.). 1970. 6.95 (ISBN 0-668-02743-6). Arco.
Jones, William E. Genetics & Horsebreeding. LC 81-6059. (Illus.). 660p. 1982. text ed. 38.50 (ISBN 0-8121-0721-7). Lea & Febiger.
Leicester, Chas. Bloodstock Breeding: Theory & Practice. (Illus.). 40.00x (ISBN 0-87556-148-9). Saifer.
Lesh, Donald. Treatise on Thoroughbred Selection. new ed. 7.95 (ISBN 0-85131-296-9, BL6783, Dist. by Miller). J A Allen.
Lorch. An Amateur's Guide to Foaling. (Illus.). 1978. 3.50 (ISBN 0-85131-302-7, BL2340, Dist. by Miller). J A Allen.
Males, Ron & Males, Val. Foaling. (Illus.). 80p. 1981. 13.95x (ISBN 0-85131-314-0, Pub. by Allen & Co). State Mutual Bk.
Napier, Miles. Breeding a Racehorse. pap. 4.95 (ISBN 0-85131-224-1, BL6798, Dist. by Miller). J A Allen.
Rosedale, Peter. Horse Breeding. (Illus.). 320p. 1981. 32.00 (ISBN 0-7153-7987-9). David & Charles.
Rossdale, P. D. & Ricketts, S. W. Equine Stud Farm Medicine. 2nd ed. (Illus.). 564p. 1980. text ed. 58.50 (ISBN 0-8121-0750-0). Lea & Febiger.
Rowlands, J. W., et al. Equine Reproduction, No. III. 1982. 179.00x (ISBN 0-906545-08-0, Pub. by Journals Repro England). State Mutual Bk.
Self, Margaret C. Horses - Their Selection, Care & Handling. pap. 5.00 (ISBN 0-87980-195-6). Wilshire.
Sutcliffe, Anne. Breeding & Training a Horse or Pony. (Illus.). 165p. 1981. 14.95 (ISBN 0-7153-7953-4). David & Charles.
Tesio, Frederico. Breeding the Racehorse. Spinola, Edward, ed. & tr. (Illus.). 9.95 (ISBN 0-85131-028-1, BL2493, Dist. by Miller). J A Allen.
Thoroughbred Owners & Breeders Association. The Breeder's Guide for 1980. 1981. 57.50 (ISBN 0-936032-41-3). Blood-Horse.
Thrall, Ellen. American Tarpan Studbook, Vol. 1. (Illus.). 1975. 12.50 (ISBN 0-912830-32-8). Printed Horse.
Tottenham, Katharine. Horse & Pony Breeding Explained. LC 78-9001. (Horseman's Handbook Ser.). (Illus.). 1979. pap. 3.95 (ISBN 0-668-04584-1). Arco.
Wharton, Mary E. & Bowen, Edward L. The Horse World of the Bluegrass, Vol. 1. Denbo, Bruce F. & Wharton, Mary E., eds. 246p. 1980. 30.00 (ISBN 0-934554-00-5). Host Assoc.
Willis, Larryann C. The Horse Breeding Farm. (Illus.). 426p. 1983. Repr. of 1973 ed. text ed. 19.95 (ISBN 0-914327-00-3). Breakthrough.
Wynmalen, Henry. Horse Breeding & Stud Management. (Illus.). 13.95 (ISBN 0-85131-139-3, 13.95, Dist. by Miller). J A Allen.

HORSE BREEDS
see also names of specific breeds
Chivers, Keith. The Shire Horse. (Illus.). 36.00 (ISBN 0-85131-245-4, BL176, Dist. by Miller). J A Allen.
Dent, Anthony. Cleveland Bay Horses. (Illus.). 1978. 4.95 (ISBN 0-85131-283-7, NL51, Dist. by Miller). J A Allen.
Edwards, Elwyn H. The Larousse Guide to Horses & Ponies of the World. LC 77-71167. (The Larousse Guide Bks.). (Illus.). 1979. pap. 7.95 (ISBN 0-88332-121-1). Larousse.
Edwards, Elwyn H., ed. A Standard Guide to Horse & Pony Breeds. LC 79-23921. (Illus.). 352p. 1980. 24.95 (ISBN 0-07-019035-6). McGraw.
Flanigan, Karen C. Those Magnificent Clydesdales: The Gentle Giants. 1977. 6.95 (ISBN 0-517-53426-6). Crown.
Hayes, M. Horace. Points of the Horse. rev. ed. LC 69-10649. 1969. 15.00 (ISBN 0-668-01811-9). Arco.
Haynes, Glynn W. The American Paint Horse. LC 75-9645. (Illus.). 375p. 1976. 22.95 (ISBN 0-8061-1293-X). U of Okla Pr.
McCarr, Ken. The Kentucky Harness Horse. LC 75-3548. (Kentucky Bicentennial Bookshelf Ser.). (Illus.). 152p. 1978. 6.95 (ISBN 0-8131-0213-8). U Pr of Ky.
Montgomery, E. S. The Thoroughbred. LC 72-93791. (Illus.). 1971. 15.00 (ISBN 0-668-02824-6). Arco.
Rudofsky, Herbert. Trakehnen Horses. (Breed Ser.). 1977. pap. 1.95 (ISBN 0-88376-011-8). Dreenan Pr.

HORSE FLIES
see Horseflies

HORSE RACE BETTING–DATA PROCESSING
Brecher, Steven L. Beating the Races with a Computer. LC 80-11311. 105p. (Orig.). 1980. pap. 14.95 (ISBN 0-9603792-0-7). Software Supply.
George, F. H. Horse Racing with the Commodore 64. (Illus.). 160p. (Orig.). 1985. pap. 13.95 (ISBN 0-246-12577-2, Pub. by Collins England). Sheridan.

HORSEFLIES
Chvala, M., et al. The Horse Flies of Europe (Tabanidae) 1972. 125.00x (ISBN 0-317-07096-7, Pub. by EW Classey UK). State Mutual Bk.

HORSEPOWER (MECHANICS)
Advani, L. T. Horsepower Tables for Agitator Impellers. LC 76-2964. 175p. 1976. 29.95x (ISBN 0-87201-368-5). Gulf Pub.
Lessiter, Frank D. Horsepower. LC 76-45044. 1977. 9.95 (ISBN 0-89821-018-6). Reiman Assocs.
Veinott, Cyril G. Fractional & Subfractional Horsepower Electric Motors. 3rd ed. LC 79-85117. (Illus.). 1970. 42.50 (ISBN 0-07-067390-X). McGraw.

HORSES
see also Draft Horses; Horse Breeds; Mustang; Ponies; Quarter Horse
Ainslie, Tom & Ledbetter, Bonnie. The Body Language of Horses: Revealing the Nature of Equine Needs, Wishes & Emotions & How Horses Communicate Them - for Owners, Breeders, Trainers, Riders & All Other Horse Lovers (Including Handicappers) LC 79-26995. (Illus.). 224p. 1980. 15.95 (ISBN 0-688-03620-1). Morrow.
Alexander, A. S. Horse Secrets. (Shorey Lost Arts Ser.). (Illus.). 68p. pap. 4.95 (ISBN 0-8466-6024-5, U24). Shorey.
Andrist, Friedrich. Mares, Foals & Foaling. Dent, A., tr. pap. 2.75 (ISBN 0-85131-053-2, BL714, Dist. by Miller). J A Allen.
Arab Horse Society. The Arab Horse Stud Book: Containing the Entries of Arab Stallions & Mares, 6 vols. 1976. lib. bdg. 634.95 (ISBN 0-8490-1445-X). Gordon Pr.
Best, Heidi. How to Book of Riding & Horse Care. (How to Bks.). (Illus.). 96p. (Orig.). 1981. pap. 3.95 (ISBN 0-8069-9694-3, Pub. by Blandford Pr England). Sterling.
Bigler, Alexander. Equestrian Facilities: Planning & Design Handbook. 1986. cancelled (ISBN 0-442-20739-5). Van Nos Reinhold.
Bowen, Edward. Thoroughbreds of 1976. 1979. 46.25 (ISBN 0-936032-14-6). Blood-Horse.
--Thoroughbreds of 1978. 1979. 36.25 (ISBN 0-936032-15-4). Blood-Horse.
Bradley, Melvin. Horses: A Practical & Scientific Approach. (Illus.). 560p. 1981. text ed. 31.95x (ISBN 0-07-007065-2). McGraw.
Brown, Jeremy & Powell-Smith, Vincent. Horse & Stable Management. 256p. 1984. 19.50 (ISBN 0-246-11217-4, Pub. by Granada England). Sheridan.
Burt, Olive W. Horse in America. LC 73-6187. (Illus.). 1940. 12.45i (ISBN 0-381-99630-1, JD-J). Har-Row.

Codrington, W. S. Know Your Horse. (Illus.). 7.95 (ISBN 0-85131-207-1, BL6839, Dist. by Miller); pap. 9.75 (ISBN 0-85131-208-X). J A Allen.

Coldsmith, Don. Horsin' Around Again. LC 81-67743. (Illus.). 188p. 1981. 14.00 (ISBN 0-931722-13-6); pap. 7.95 (ISBN 0-931722-14-4). Corona Pub.

Cunha, Tony J. Horse Feeding & Nutrition. LC 80-531. (Animal Feeding & Nutrition Ser.). 1980. 33.00 (ISBN 0-12-196560-0). Acad Pr.

Denhardt, Robert M. The Horse of the Americas. LC 74-5955. 1975. pap. 10.95 (ISBN 0-8061-1724-9). U of Okla Pr.

Disston, Harry. Know All about Horses. 1975. pap. 3.00 (ISBN 0-87980-294-4). Wilshire.

Dougall, Neil. Horses & Ponies on Small Areas. (Illus.). pap. 1.50 (ISBN 0-85131-273-X, NL51, Dist. by Miller). J A Allen.

--Stallions: Their Management & Handling. pap. 5.95 (ISBN 0-85131-256-X, NL51, Dist. by Miller). J A Allen.

Ensminger, M. E. Horses & Horsemanship. 5th ed. LC 76-45238. (Illus.). 537p. 1977. 26.50 (ISBN 0-8134-1888-7); text ed. 19.95x. Interstate.

Evans, J. Warren. Horses: A Guide to Selection, Care, & Enjoyment. LC 80-29070. (Illus.). 683p. 1981. text ed. 29.95 (ISBN 0-7167-1253-9). W H Freeman.

Evans, J. Warren, et al. The Horse. LC 76-22686. (Animal Science Ser.). (Illus.). 766p. 1977. 34.95 (ISBN 0-7167-0491-9). W H Freeman.

Ewers, John C. The Horse in Blackfoot Indian Culture. LC 55-60591. (Classics in Smithsonian Anthropology Ser.: No. 3). (Illus.). 374p. 1980. pap. text ed. 15.00x (ISBN 0-87474-419-9). Smithsonian.

Feeding the Horse. (Illus.). 127p. 1974. lib. bdg. 10.75 (ISBN 0-936032-04-9). Blood-Horse.

Field, Walter L. Tale of the Horse. LC 76-482750. (Illus.). 50p. 1978. 5.95 (ISBN 0-8143-1607-7). Wayne St U Pr.

Flower, William H. The Horse: A Study in Natural History. 1978. Repr. of 1892 ed. lib. bdg. 25.00 (ISBN 0-8482-0824-2). Norwood Edns.

Gorman, John A. Western Horse. LC 66-12997. (Illus.). 1967. 16.50 (ISBN 0-8134-0126-7); text ed. 12.50x. Interstate.

Green, Ben K. The Color of Horses. LC 74-79459. (Illus.). 120p. 1974. O.P. 25.00 (ISBN 0-87358-131-8); softcover 12.95 (ISBN 0-87358-327-2). Northland.

--Horse Conformation: As to Soundness & Performance. LC 74-82362. (Illus.). 1974. Repr. 9.95 (ISBN 0-87358-135-0). Northland.

Grimshaw, Anne. The Horse: A Bibliography of British Books 1851-1976. (Illus.). 508p. 1982. 110.00x (ISBN 0-89774-067-X, Pub. by Lib Assn England). Oryx Pr.

Hanauer, Elsie V. Horse Owner's Concise Guide. pap. 3.00 (ISBN 0-87980-192-1). Wilshire.

Hartigan, Joe. Your First Point to Point Horse. pap. 3.50 (ISBN 0-85131-212-8, NL51, Dist. by Miller). J A Allen.

Hayes, M. Horace. Points of the Horse. rev. ed. LC 69-10649. 1969. 15.00 (ISBN 0-668-01811-9). Arco.

Henschel, Georgie. The Illustrated Guide to Horses & Ponies. LC 81-68189. 192p. 1982. 16.95 (ISBN 0-668-05353-4, 5353). Arco.

Hickman, J. Farriery. 240p. 1981. 49.00x (ISBN 0-85131-228-4, Pub. by Allen & Co). State Mutual Bk.

Hyland, Ann. Foal to Five Years. LC 80-11310. 128p. 1980. 14.95 (ISBN 0-668-04952-9, 4952-9). Arco.

Jones, Dave. The Western Horse: Advice & Training. LC 73-7422. (Illus.). 184p. 1974. 14.95 (ISBN 0-8061-1130-5). U of Okla Pr.

Jones, Howard A. Hooked on Horses: Bits of This & That about People & Horses after 21 Years in the Racing Game. (Illus.). 256p. 1982. 12.50 (ISBN 0-682-49791-6, Banner). Exposition Pr FL.

Jones, William E., ed. Basic First Aid for Horses. (Horse Health & Care Ser.). (Illus.). 1973. pap. 4.95 (ISBN 0-912830-04-2). Printed Horse.

--A Descriptive Bibliography of One Thousand One Horse Books. 128p. 1972. pap. 4.95 (ISBN 0-912830-10-7). Printed Horse.

Kidd, Jane. The Better Horse: Breeding & Training for Equestrian Sports. LC 84-70188. (Illus.). 160p. 1984. 19.95 (ISBN 0-668-06037-9, 6037-9). Arco.

--An Illustrated Guide to Horse & Pony Care. LC 81-68162. 240p. 1982. 9.95 (ISBN 0-668-05368-2, 5368). Arco.

Lewis, Lon D. Feeding & Care of the Horse. LC 81-8137. (Illus.). 248p. 1982. text ed. 16.00 (ISBN 0-8121-0803-5). Lea & Febiger.

Macdonald, Janet W. The Right Horse: An Owner's & Buyers' Guide. LC 84-6240. (Illus.). 160p. 1984. 9.95 (ISBN 0-668-06246-0, 6246-0). Arco.

Magner, D. The Classic Encyclopedia of the Horse. (Illus.). 1981. 6.98 (ISBN 0-517-32168-8, Bonanza). Outlet Bk Co.

Midwest Plan Service Personnel. Horse Housing & Equipment Handbook. 1st ed. (Illus.). 60p. 1971. pap. 5.00 (ISBN 0-89373-009-2, MWPS-15). Midwest Plan Serv.

Mohr, Erna. The Asiatic Wild Horse. Goodall, Daphne M., tr. (Illus.). 7.50 (ISBN 0-85131-013-3, Dist. by Sporting Book Center). J A Allen.

Money, Keith. Salute the Horse. (Illus.). 14.50 (ISBN 0-392-04473-0, SpS). Sportshelf.

Mulder. Imported Foundation Stock of North American Arabian Horses, Vol. 2. 15.00 (ISBN 0-87505-111-1). Borden.

Nutrient Requirements of Horses. 1978. 5.95 (ISBN 0-309-02760-8). Natl Acad Pr.

Phillips, Lance. The Saddle Horse. LC 64-14315. (Illus.). 1964. 8.95 (ISBN 0-668-02814-9). Arco.

Posey, Jeanne K. The Horsekeeper's Handbook. LC 75-6971. (Illus.). 288p. 1975. pap. 6.95 (ISBN 0-02-063550-8, 06355, Collier). Macmillan.

Potter, Murray A. Four Essays. (Harvard Studies in Romance Languages). 1917. 12.00 (ISBN 0-527-01101-0). Kraus Repr.

Practical Horse Psychology. pap. 4.00 (ISBN 0-87980-247-2). Wilshire.

Price, Steven D. Practical Guide to Owning Your Own Horse. 1974. pap. 3.00 (ISBN 0-87980-292-8). Wilshire.

Price, Steven D., et al, eds. The Whole Horse Catalog. (Illus.). 288p. 1983. (Fireside); pap. 12.95 (ISBN 0-671-54196-X). S&S.

Prince, Leslie. The Farrier & His Craft. 280p. 1981. 60.00x (ISBN 0-85131-353-1, Pub. by Allen & Co). State Mutual Bk.

Rayner, Nick & Chivers, Keith. The Heavy Horse Manual. LC 80-85501. (Illus.). 207p. 1981. 23.50 (ISBN 0-7153-8057-5). David & Charles.

Rossdale, P. D. Das Pferd. Fortpflanzung und Entwicklung. Gerber, H., ed. (Illus.). 120p. 1975. 17.25 (ISBN 3-8055-2030-1). S Karger.

Rossdale, Peter. The Horse. (Illus.). pap. 17.50 (ISBN 0-87556-609-X). Saifer.

Rossdale, Peter D. & Wreford, Susan M. Horses' Health A to Z. LC 73-89678. 256p. 1974. 24.95 (ISBN 0-668-03414-9). Arco.

Rudofsky, Herbert. Young Horses. (Breed Ser.). 1977. pap. 1.95 (ISBN 0-88376-009-6). Dreenan Pr.

Rudofsky, Hubert. Horses. (Breed Ser.). 1977. pap. 1.95 (ISBN 0-88376-015-0). Dreenan Pr.

Saunders, Ray. Horsekeeping: Ownership, Stabling & Feeding. (Illus.). 120p. 1982. 12.95 (ISBN 0-8069-3748-3); pap. 6.95 (ISBN 0-8069-7616-0). Sterling.

Saurel, E. Le Cheval: Equitation et sports hippiques. (La Vie active). (Fr., Illus.). 34.95x (ISBN 0-685-13827-5). Larousse.

Sheatz, Guy C. Missie, Equus Sapiens. LC 81-81613. 1983. 7.95 (ISBN 0-87212-159-3). Libra.

Silver, Caroline. Guide to Horses of the World. (Illustrated Natural History Guides). (Illus.). 1977. pap. 4.95 (ISBN 0-8467-0365-3, Pub. by Two Continents). Hippocrene Bks.

Smythe, R. H. The Horse: Structure & Movement. 2nd ed. (Illus.). pap. 6.95 (ISBN 0-85131-242-X, BL2401, Dist. by Miller). J A Allen.

Smythe, Reginald H. Mind of the Horse. LC 65-22225. 1965. 9.95 (ISBN 0-8289-0042-6). Greene.

--The Mind of the Horse. (Illus.). Repr. write for info. (ISBN 0-85131-150-4, BL2339, Dist. by Miller). J A Allen.

Sponenberg, D. Phillip & Beaver, Bonnie V. Horse Color. LC 83-45102. (Illus.). 144p. 1983. 25.00 (ISBN 0-89096-155-7). Tex A&M Univ Pr.

Summerhays, R. S. The Problem Horse. (Illus.). pap. write for info. (ISBN 0-85131-225-X, NL51, Dist. by Miller). J A Allen.

Thiffault, Mark. Digest Book of Horse Care. LC 79-51755. 96p. pap. 3.95 (ISBN 0-695-81325-0). DBI.

Thoroughbred Owners & Breeders Directory, 1976. 1977. 97.50 (ISBN 0-936032-12-X). Blood-Horse.

Thoroughbred Owners & Breeders Directory, 1978. 1979. 27.50 (ISBN 0-936032-13-8). Blood-Horse.

Trahan, Ronald. Careers for Horse Lovers. (Illus.). 288p. 1981. 13.95 (ISBN 0-395-31331-7) HM.

Tuke, Diane R. Feeding Your Horse. (Illus.). 104p. (Orig.). 1980. pap. 7.95 (ISBN 0-85131-334-5, BL6605). J A Allen.

Weikel, Bill, ed. Farnam Horse Library Series. Incl. Understanding Horse Psychology; How to Become a Better Rider; Know Practical Horse Feeding; How to Break & Train the Western Horse; Know the American Quarter Horse; How to Recognize Horse Health Problems; Know the Anatomy of a Horse; Riding the Show Ring Hunter; Know Practical Horse Breeding; How to Shoe Your Horse; Know the Arabian Horse; How to Buy the Right Horse; Know First Aid for Your Horse; Riding the Gymkana Winner; Know the English Equitation & Training; How to Correct the Problem Horse; Know All About Tack; How to Show Your Horse & Win; Know Stable Design & Management; Know All About Trail Riding; How to Raise a Foal; How to Train the Roping Horse; Know the Appaloosa Horse; How to Train the Reining Horse; Between Mare & Foal. Coen, Sue; Book of Bad Habits. Jones, Dave; The Save Your Horse Handbook: Care & Treatment of Sick Horses. Bailey, Nevajac; Happiness Is a Well Trained Horse. Gray, Patsy; Winning Through Grooming. Self, Charles. (Illus.). pap. 3.95 ea. Borden.

Wiederhold, Hermann. Your Pony Book. pap. 2.00 (ISBN 0-87980-331-2). Wilshire.

Williams, M. Horse Psychology. 1978. 17.50 (ISBN 0-87556-616-2). Saifer.

Williams, Moyra. Horse Psychology. (Illus.). pap. write for info (ISBN 0-85131-238-1, NL51, Dist. by Miller). J A Allen.

Wyman, Walker D. Wild Horse of the West. LC 66-17457. (Illus.). 348p. 1963. pap. 7.50 (ISBN 0-8032-5223-4, BB 144, Bison). U of Nebr Pr.

HORSES–ANATOMY

Bradley, Melvin. Horses: A Practical & Scientific Approach. (Illus.). 560p. 1981. text ed. 31.95x (ISBN 0-07-007065-2). McGraw.

Edwards, Gladys B. Anatomy & Conformation of the Horse. LC 73-77060. 224p. 1973. pap. 5.95 (ISBN 0-88376-025-8). Dreenan Pr.

Geurts, Reiner. Hair Colour in the Horse. Dent, Anthony, tr. from Dutch. (Illus.). pap. 9.95 (ISBN 0-85131-290-X, BL189). J A Allen.

Goody, Peter. Horse Anatomy. (Illus.). 11.95 (ISBN 0-85131-230-6, BL2351, Dist. by Miller). J A Allen.

Jones, William E., ed. Anatomy of the Horse. (Horse Health & Care Ser.). (Illus.). 1973. pap. 7.95 (ISBN 0-912830-07-7). Printed Horse.

--Teeth of the Horse. (Horse Health & Care Ser.). (Illus.). 1973. pap. 4.95 (ISBN 0-912830-15-8). Printed Horse.

Milne, Dennis W. & Turner, Simon. An Atlas of Surgical Approaches to the Bones of the Horse. (Illus.). 210p. 1979. 34.00 (ISBN 0-7216-6362-1). Saunders.

Schebitz, H. & Wilkens, H. Atlas of Radiographic Anatomy of the Horse. 3rd ed. (Illus.). 100p. 1979. 35.00 (ISBN 0-7216-7964-1). Saunders.

Smythe, R. H. The Horse; Structure & Movement. 17.50x (ISBN 0-87556-321-X). Saifer.

Stubbs, George. The Anatomy of the Horse. McCunn, J. C. & Ottaway, C. W., eds. LC 76-17945. (Illus.). 128p. 1977. pap. 8.95 (ISBN 0-486-23402-9). Dover.

--The Anatomy of the Horse. 19.00 (ISBN 0-8446-5663-1). Peter Smith.

Way, Robert F. Horse Anatomy. LC 73-77063. (Illus.). 1973. pap. 3.95 (ISBN 0-88376-007-X). Dreenan Pr.

Way, Robert F. & Lee, Donald G. The Anatomy of the Horse. (Illus.). 214p. 1983. pap. 14.95 (ISBN 0-914327-03-8). Breakthrough.

HORSES–BREEDING

see Horse Breeding

HORSES–BREEDS

see Horse Breeds

HORSES–DICTIONARIES

Baranowski, Zdzislaw. Woerterbuch Pferd und Reiter. (Eng., Fr. & Ger., Dictionary of Horses and Horsemanship). 1977. 24.95 (ISBN 0-273-00937-0, M-6910). French & Eur.

Blood Horse, ed. Stallion Register, 1981. (Illus.). 900p. 1980. 20.00 (ISBN 0-936032-33-2); pap. 10.00 (ISBN 0-936032-34-0). Blood-Horse.

Cassart, C. & Moirant, R. Dictionnaire du Cheval et du Chevalier. (Fr.). 288p. 1979. 49.95 (ISBN 0-686-56942-3, M-6064). French & Eur.

Ensminger, M. E. The Complete Encyclopedia of Horses. LC 74-9282. (Illus.). 720p. 1977. 29.50 (ISBN 0-498-01508-4). A S Barnes.

Kays, John M. The Horse. 3rd ed. LC 82-11496. (Illus.). 416p. 1982. 19.95 (ISBN 0-668-05469-7). Arco.

Lexikon Fuer Pferdefreunde. (Ger.). 1976. 25.00 (ISBN 3-7658-0221-2, M-7197). French & Eur.

Marcenac, Louis N. & Aublet, Henri. Encyclopedie du Cheval. 3rd ed. (Fr.). 1244p. 1974. 125.00 (ISBN 0-686-57037-5, M-6397). French & Eur.

Rousselet-Blanc, Pierre, ed. Larousse du cheval. new ed. (Larousse des animaux familiers). (Fr., Illus.). 260p. 1975. 43.95x (ISBN 2-03-014855-5). Larousse.

--Larousse Du Chevel. (Fr.). 1976. 47.50 (ISBN 0-686-56997-0, M-6337). French & Eur.

Taylor, Louis. Harper's Encyclopedia for Horsemen: The Complete Book of the Horse. LC 72-79697. (Illus.). 572p. 1973. 24.95i (ISBN 0-06-014226-X, HarpT). Har-Row.

HORSES–HISTORY

Anderson, J. K. Ancient Greek Horsemanship. LC 61-6780. (Illus.). 1961. 42.00x (ISBN 0-520-00023-4). U of Cal Pr.

Denhardt, Robert M. The Horse of the Americas. LC 74-5955. 1975. pap. 10.95 (ISBN 0-8061-1724-9). U of Okla Pr.

Grimshaw, Anne. The Horse: A Bibliography of British Books 1851-1976. (Illus.). 508p. 1982. 110.00x (ISBN 0-89774-067-X, Pub. by Lib Assn England). Oryx Pr.

Hart, Edward. Heavy Horses. (Illus.). 64p. 1981. pap. 5.50 (ISBN 0-7134-3805-3, Pub. by Batsford England). David & Charles.

Poska, Valentine J. Miniature Horses. (Illus.). 48p. 1981. 18.00 (ISBN 0-88014-026-7). Mosaic Pr OH.

Ridgeway, William. The Origin & Influence of the Thoroughbred Horse. LC 73-174446. (Illus.). Repr. of 1905 ed. 27.50 (ISBN 0-405-08890-6, Blom Pubns). Ayer Co Pubs.

Seth-Smith, Michael. The Horse. (Illus.). 1980. 35.00 (ISBN 0-7064-1024-6, Mayflower Bks). Smith Pubs.

Wallace, John H. The Horse in America in His Derivation, History, & Development. LC 72-89083. (Rural America Ser.). 1973. Repr. of 1897 ed. 38.00 (ISBN 0-8420-1502-7). Scholarly Res Inc.

HORSESHOEING

Butler, Doug. The Principles of Horseshoeing. LC 73-88039. (Illus.). 428p. 1974. 29.95 (ISBN 0-916992-01-2). Doug Butler.

Hickman, J. Farriery. (Illus.). 1976. 23.95 (ISBN 0-85131-228-4, BL2141, Dist. by Miller). J A Allen.

--Farriery. 240p. 1981. 49.00x (ISBN 0-85131-228-4, Pub. by Allen & Co). State Mutual Bk.

Jones, William E., ed. Horseshoeing. (Horse Health & Care Ser.). (Illus.). 1973. pap. 4.95 (ISBN 0-912830-03-4). Printed Horse.

Practical Guide to Horseshoeing. pap. 5.00 (ISBN 0-87980-239-1). Wilshire.

Prince, Leslie. The Farrier & His Craft. 280p. 1981. 60.00x (ISBN 0-85131-353-1, Pub. by Allen & Co). State Mutual Bk.

Sparkes, Ivan G. Old Horseshoes. (Shire Album Ser.: No. 19). (Illus.). 32p. (Orig.). pap. 2.95 (ISBN 0-85263-348-3, Pub. by Shire Pubns England). Seven Hills Bks.

Springhall, John. Elements of Horseshoeing. 3rd ed. (Illus.). 50p. 1985. 9.95 (ISBN 0-7022-1827-8). U of Queensland Pr.

Wiseman, Robert F. The Complete Horseshoeing Guide. rev. ed. LC 72-9279. (Illus.). 304p. 1973. 16.95 (ISBN 0-8061-1049-X). U of Okla Pr.

HORTICULTURE

see also Agricultural Pests; Bulbs; Floriculture; Forcing (Plants); Frost Protection; Fruit-Culture; Grafting; Greenhouses; Horticulturists; Hydroponics; Insects, Injurious and Beneficial; Mulching; Mushroom Culture; Nurseries (Horticulture); Organic Farming; Plant Propagation; Pruning; Truck Farming; Vegetable Gardening

Adams, Charles & Bamford, Katherine. Principles of Horticulture. (Illus.). 264p. 1984. pap. 23.00 (ISBN 0-434-90008-7, Pub. by W Heinemann Ltd). David & Charles.

Adriance, Guy W. & Brison, Fred R. Propagation of Horticultural Plants. 2nd ed. LC 79-9753. 308p. 1979. Repr. of 1955 ed. lib. bdg. 19.50 (ISBN 0-88275-965-5). Krieger.

American Horticultural Society. North American Horticulture. 448p. 1982. 50.00 (ISBN 0-684-17604-1, ScribT). Scribner.

Bailey, Liberty H. Hortus Third: A Concise Dictionary of Plants Cultivated in the United States & Canada. (Illus.). 1976. 125.00 (ISBN 0-02-505470-8). Macmillan.

Ballard, Edward B., et al, eds. A Technical Glossary of Horticultural & Landscape Terminology. LC 78-165521. 1971. text ed. 5.50 (ISBN 0-935336-00-1); tchr's. ed. 4.00 (ISBN 0-935336-00-1). Horticult Research.

Baudendistel. Horticulture: A Basic Awareness. 2nd ed. 368p. 1982. pap. text ed. 18.95 (ISBN 0-8359-2895-0); instr's. manual free (ISBN 0-8359-2896-9). Reston.

Bienz, D. R. The Why & How of Home Horticulture. LC 79-19915. (Illus.). 513p. 1980. text ed. 25.95 (ISBN 0-7167-1078-1). W H Freeman.

Bleasdale, J. K. Plant Physiology in Relation to Horticulture. 1977. text ed. 13.50 (ISBN 0-87055-239-2). AVI.

Bourke, D. O. French-English Horticultural Dictionary. 196p. 1974. 59.00x (ISBN 0-85198-308-1, Pub. by CAB Bks England). State Mutual Bk.

--Horticultural Dictionary: French-English. (Fr. & Eng.). 1974. 49.95 (ISBN 0-85198-308-1, M-9713). French & Eur.

Wass, Alonzo. Estimating Residential Construction. (Illus.). 1980. text ed. 30.95 (ISBN 0-13-289942-6). P-H.

Wass, Alonzo & Sanders, Gordon. Materials & Procedures for Residential Construction. (Illus.). text ed. 25.95 (ISBN 0-8359-4284-8). Reston.

Wilson, J. Douglas. Practical House Carpentry: Simplified Methods for Building. 3rd ed. (Illus.). 1979. pap. 5.95 (ISBN 0-07-070889-4). McGraw.

Woodframe Houses: Construction & Maintenance. LC 81-50025. (Illus.). 223p. 1981. pap. 8.95 (ISBN 0-8069-7512-1). Sterling.

Zink, William. How to Build a House Simply for One-Third Cost. 2nd ed. LC 75-46405. (Illus.). 1977. 7.50 (ISBN 0-916666-02-6); pap. 4.95 (ISBN 0-916666-01-8). Jay Pubns.

HOUSE DRAINAGE

see Drainage, House; Plumbing; Sanitation; Sewerage

HOUSE FITTINGS

see Building Fittings

HOUSE-FLIES

see Flies

HOUSE PAINTING

see also Painting, Industrial

Brushwell, William, ed. Painting & Decorating Encyclopedia. LC 81-13513. (Illus.). 272p. 1982. text ed. 16.00 (ISBN 0-87006-404-5). Goodheart.

Demske, Dick. Painting, Paneling, & Wallpapering. Wolf, Donald D. & Wolf, Margot L., eds. LC 76-8373. (Adventures in Home Repair Ser.). (Illus.). 1977. pap. 3.95 (ISBN 0-8326-2212-5, 7702). Delair.

Goodier, J. H. Dictionary of Painting & Decorating. 308p. 1974. 39.50x (ISBN 0-85264-224-5, Pub. by Griffin England). State Mutual Bk.

Gundrey, Elizabeth. Painting & Decorating. (Orig.). 1980. pap. 8.95x (ISBN 0-8464-1036-2). Beekman Pubs.

Harbeck, Kirk. How to Paint Your House: A Step by Step Guide. (Illus.). 80p. (Orig.). 1982. pap. 6.95 (ISBN 0-943650-00-3). McDaniel House.

How to Paint Interiors. (Home Care Guides Ser.). (Illus.). 1981. pap. 2.50 (ISBN 0-686-71128-9). S&S.

Hurst, A. E. & Goodier, J. M. Painting & Decorating. 620p. 1980. 75.00x (ISBN 0-85264-243-1, Pub. by Griffin England). State Mutual Bk.

Rudman, Jack. House Painter. (Career Examination Ser.: C-354). (Cloth bdg. avail. on request). pap. 10.00 (ISBN 0-8373-0354-0). Natl Learning.

HOUSE PLANS

see Architecture, Domestic–Designs and Plans

HOUSE SANITATION

see Sanitation, Household

HOUSE-SPARROWS

see Sparrows

HOUSE STYLE

see Industrial Design Coordination

HOUSEHOLD APPLIANCES–MAINTENANCE AND REPAIR

Anderson, Edwin P. Home Appliance Servicing. 4th ed. LC 83-5984. (Audel Ser.). 608p. 15.95 (ISBN 0-672-23379-7). G K Hall.

Heiserman, D. L. Handbook of Major Appliance Trouble-Shooting & Repair. LC 76-10684. (Illus.). 1977. 29.95 (ISBN 0-13-380295-7). P-H.

Lee, R. R. Pocket Guide to Electrical Equipment & Instrumentation. LC 84-25340. (Illus.). 320p. (Orig.). 1985. 17.95x (ISBN 0-87201-246-8). Gulf Pub.

Meyerink, George. Appliance Service Handbook. (Illus.). 464p. 1973. ref. ed. 29.95x (ISBN 0-13-038844-0). P-H.

Popular Mechanics Home Appliance Repair Manual. LC 80-29670. (Illus.). 320p. 1981. 23.00 (ISBN 0-910990-75-1). Hearst Bks.

Powell, Evan. The Complete Guide to Home Appliance Repair. 2nd ed. LC 80-5262. (A Popular Science Bk.). (Illus.). 480p. 1984. pap. 14.37 (ISBN 0-06-091190-5, CN). Har-Row.

Scharff, B. Basics of Electric Appliance Servicing. 1976. 32.95 (ISBN 0-07-055141-3). McGraw.

HOUSEHOLD PESTS

see also specific pests, e.g. Flies

Von Frisch, Karl. Twelve Little Housemates. Sugar, A. T., tr. LC 78-40341. 1979. text ed. 17.00 (ISBN 0-08-021959-4); pap. text ed. 7.75 (ISBN 0-08-021958-6). Pergamon.

HOUSEHOLD SANITATION

see Sanitation, Household

HOUSEKEEPING, INDUSTRIAL

see Industrial Housekeeping

HOUSES

see Dwellings

HOUSES, APARTMENT

see Apartment Houses

HOUSES, DEMOUNTABLE

see Buildings, Prefabricated

HOUSES, PREFABRICATED

see Buildings, Prefabricated

HOVERCRAFT

see Ground-Effect Machines

HP-33E (CALCULATING-MACHINE)

Henrici, P. & Henrici, M. L. Numerical Analysis Demonstrations on the HP-33E. 234p. 1982. pap. 15.00 (ISBN 0-471-05943-9). Wiley.

HP-41 (CALCULATING-MACHINE)

Dodin, Jean-Daniel. Enter. Jarett, Keith, ed. Dodin, Mary-Denise, tr. from Fr. LC 84-51380. 142p. 1984. pap. text ed. 12.95 (ISBN 0-9612174-2-1). Synthetix.

--Inside the HP-41. Holes, W. W., ed. Dodin, Mary D., tr. from Fr. LC 84-51921. 256p. 1985. pap. text ed. 18.95 (ISBN 0-9612174-4-8). Synthetix.

Emery, Ken. HP-41 M-Code for Beginners. Jarett, Keith, ed. LC 85-61881. 200p. 1985. pap. text ed. 18.95 (ISBN 0-9612174-7-2). Synthetix.

Flight Deck Uses for the HP-41C Series: Vol. 4, Tornado Block Forecasting (Via NWS Facsimile Charts) 50p. 1984. 15.00 (ISBN 0-938880-03-9); 2 magnetic cards incl. MNP Star.

Garb, Forrest A. Waterflood Manual for Hewlett Packard Calculators. LC 81-20274. (Illus.). 94p. (Orig.). 1982. 21.95x (ISBN 0-87201-895-4). Gulf Pub.

Garrison, Paul. Programming the TI-59 & HP-41 Calculators. (Illus.). 300p. (Orig.). 1982. 18.95 (ISBN 0-8306-2442-2); pap. 13.50 (ISBN 0-8306-1442-7, 1442). TAB Bks.

Jarett, Keith. HP-41 Synthetic Programming Made Easy. LC 82-62786. (Illus.). 192p. (Orig.). 1982. pap. text ed. 16.95 (ISBN 0-9612174-0-5). Synthetix.

McCornack, Alan. Advance Programming on the HP-41. Jarett, Keith, ed. 125p. (Orig.). Date not set. pap. text ed. 18.95x (ISBN 0-9612174-6-4). Synthetix.

Phillips, William C. Data Processing on the HP-41C-CV. LC 83-81097. (EduCALC Technical Ser.). 1983. pap. 16.95 (ISBN 0-936356-02-2). EduCALC Pubns.

Wadman, Ted & Coffin, Chris. An Easy Course in Programming the HP-41. (Easy Course Ser.). (Illus., Orig.). 1985. pap. 18.00 (ISBN 0-931011-00-0). Grapevine Pubns.

Wentworth, Ross. HP-41 Microcode Made Easy. Jarett, Keith, ed. 150p. Date not set. pap. 18.95 (ISBN 0-9612174-5-6). Synthetix.

HP-150 (COMPUTER)

Smith, Leslie S. HP-150 User's Guide. LC 84-50246. 256p. 1984. pap. 15.95 (ISBN 0-672-22329-5, 22329). Sams.

HP-1000 (COMPUTER)

Conference on the HP-1000 International Users Group, 1st. Minicomputer Research & Applications: Proceedings. Brown, H. K., ed. LC 81-5134. (Illus.). 392p. 1981. 44.00 (ISBN 0-08-027567-2). Pergamon.

HULLS (NAVAL ARCHITECTURE)

Mansir, A. Richard. A Modeller's Guide to Hull Construction. (Illus.). 64p. (Orig.). 1980. pap. 10.95 (ISBN 0-940620-01-4). Moonraker.

HUMAN ANATOMY

see Anatomy, Human

HUMAN BEINGS ON OTHER PLANETS

see Life on Other Planets

HUMAN BIOLOGY

see also Physical Anthropology

Balaban, Miriam. Biological Foundations & Human Nature. (Aharon Katzir-Katchalsky Lectures Ser.). 1984. 39.50 (ISBN 0-12-076150-5). Acad Pr.

Barnett, S. A. The Human Species: The Biology of Man. (Illus.). 12.75 (ISBN 0-8446-0477-1). Peter Smith.

Bates, Marston. Gluttons & Libertines: Human Problems of Being Natural. LC 66-11978. 1971. pap. 2.95 (ISBN 0-394-71267-6, V-267, Vin). Random.

Baum, Harold. Human Biology: Biorhythms, No. 1. Shade, Peter, ed. 78p. 1984. pap. 17.95 bk & cassette (ISBN 0-85066-291-5). Taylor & Francis.

Bittles, A. H. & Collins, K. J., eds. The Biology of Human Ageing. (Illus.). 350p. Date not set. price not set (ISBN 0-521-30485-7). Cambridge U Pr.

Borek, Ernest. The Atoms Within Us. rev. ed. LC 80-19010. 272p. 1980. 29.00x (ISBN 0-231-04386-4); pap. 11.00x (ISBN 0-231-04387-2). Columbia U Pr.

Borms, J., et al, eds. Human Growth & Development. 952p. 1984. 125.00x (ISBN 0-306-41518-6, Plenum Pr). Plenum Pub.

British Museum. Human Biology: An Exhibition of Ourselves. 2nd ed. LC 81-7641. (Natural History Ser.). 124p. 1982. 29.95 (ISBN 0-521-23832-3); pap. 9.95 (ISBN 0-521-28247-0). Cambridge U Pr.

Chiarenza, Loretta & Burkart, John, eds. Human Biology. 2nd ed. 316p. 1984. pap. text ed. 16.95 (ISBN 0-89529-134-7). Avery Pub.

Cunningham, John D. Human Biology. 449p. 1983. text ed. 27.50 scp (ISBN 0-06-041451-0, HarpC); instr's. manual avail.; test bank avail. (ISBN 0-06-361454-5). Har-Row.

Currie, Gregory & Musgrave, Alan, eds. Popper & the Human Sciences. 1985. lib. bdg. 41.50 (ISBN 90-247-2998-X, Pub. by Martinus Nijhoff Netherlands); pap. text ed. 14.95 (ISBN 90-247-3141-0, Pub. by Martinus Nijhoff Netherlands). Kluwer Academic.

Damon, Albert. Human Biology & Ecology. LC 77-559. (Illus.). 1977. pap. text ed. 8.95x (ISBN 0-393-09103-1). Norton.

Edwards, Gabrielle. Man & Woman: Inside Homo Sapiens. 8.97 (ISBN 0-8239-0445-8). Rosen Group.

From Biology to Human Values. (Aharon Katzir-Katchalsky Lecture Ser.). (Illus.). 200p. 1983. 30.00 (ISBN 0-86689-017-3). Balaban Intl Sci Serv.

Gunstream, Stanley E. Human Biology: Laboratory Explorations. (Illus.). 288p. 1986. pap. price not set lab manual (ISBN 0-8087-4148-9). Burgess.

Harrison, G. A., et al. Human Biology: An Introduction to Human Evolution, Variation, Growth, & Ecology. 2nd ed. (Illus.). 1977. pap. text ed. 18.95x (ISBN 0-19-857165-8). Oxford U Pr.

Hubbard, Ruth, et al. Biological Woman: The Convenient Myth. 376p. 1982. 18.95 (ISBN 0-87073-702-3); pap. 11.95 (ISBN 0-87073-703-1). Schenkman Bks Inc.

Inglis, J. K. A Textbook of Human Biology. 2nd rev. ed. LC 73-21696. 1974. pap. text ed. 8.25 (ISBN 0-08-017847-2). Pergamon.

Kellogg, Vernon. Human Life As the Biologist Sees It. 1922. 20.00 (ISBN 0-8274-4227-0). R West.

Khan, Aman U. Men & Women in Biological Perspective: A Review of the Literature. LC 84-6802. 240p. 1984. 29.95 (ISBN 0-03-063664-7). Praeger.

Kirk, R. L., ed. The Human Biology of Aborigines in Cape York. (AIAS Human Biology Ser.: No. 5). (Illus., Orig.). 1973. pap. text ed. 11.00x (ISBN 0-85575-028-6). Humanities.

Konner, Melvin. The Tangled Wing: Biological Constraints on the Human Spirit. LC 81-47464. 1982. 19.95 (ISBN 0-03-057062-X). HR&W.

Mader, Sylvia S. Inquiry into Life. 4th ed. 864p. 1985. text ed. write for info. (ISBN 0-697-04798-9); instr's. manual avail. (ISBN 0-697-04951-5); student's guide avail. (ISBN 0-697-04933-7); transparencies avail. (ISBN 0-697-04945-0); lab manual avail. (ISBN 0-697-04940-X). Wm C Brown.

Mason, William H. & Marshall, Norton L. The Human Side of Biology. 576p. 1983. text ed. 27.50 scp (ISBN 0-06-044239-5, HarpC); instr's. manual avail. (ISBN 0-06-364170-4); study guide scp 9.50 (ISBN 0-06-044242-5). Har-Row.

Open University Health & Disease Course Team. The Biology of Health & Disease. (Health & Disease Ser.). 168p. 1985. pap. text ed. 11.00x (ISBN 0-335-15053-5, Open Univ Pr). Taylor & Francis.

Rowlinson, Pat & Jenkins, Morton. Human Biology: An Activity Approach. (Illus.). 304p. 1982. pap. text ed. 10.95 (ISBN 0-521-28200-4). Cambridge U Pr.

Santos, Miguel A., ed. Readings in Biology & Man. LC 73-12020. 1974. 29.00x (ISBN 0-8422-5048-4); pap. text ed. 9.75x (ISBN 0-8422-0334-6). Irvington.

Schoeninger, Margaret J. Dietary Reconstruction at Chalcatzingo, a Formative Period Site in Morelos, Mexico. (Technical Reports Ser.: No. 9). (Illus., Orig., Contribution 2 in contributions in human biology). 1979. pap. 3.50x (ISBN 0-932206-78-6). U Mich Mus Anthro.

Shapiro, Mark. The Sociobiology of Homo Sapiens. LC 78-60932. 1978. 9.95 (ISBN 0-9601858-0-1). Pinecrest Fund.

Shephard, R. J. Human Physiological Work Capacity. LC 77-80847. (International Biological Programme Ser.: No. 15). (Illus.). 1978. 79.50 (ISBN 0-521-21781-4). Cambridge U Pr.

Sherman, Irwin W. & Sherman, Vilia G. Biology: A Human Approach. 3rd ed. (Illus.). 1983. 28.95x (ISBN 0-19-503176-8); tchrs.' companion free (ISBN 0-19-503296-9). Oxford U Pr.

Singer, Sam & Hilgard, Henry R. The Biology of People. LC 77-17893. (Biology Ser.). (Illus.). 546p. 1978. text ed. 28.95x (ISBN 0-7167-0026-3); tchr's resource bk. 2.95x. W H Freeman.

Sloane, Ethel, ed. Biology of Women. 600p. 1984. pap. text ed. 18.95 (ISBN 0-471-87939-8, Pub. by Wiley Med). Wiley.

Sterling, Anne F. Myths of Gender: Biological Theories about Women & Men. LC 85-47561. 236p. 1985. 18.95 (ISBN 0-465-04790-4). Basic.

Vorster, D. J., ed. Human Biology of Environmental Change. 1972. pap. text ed. 28.95x (ISBN 0-89563-007-9). Intl Ideas.

Watanabe, Hitoshi, ed. Human Activity System: Its Spatiotemporal Structure. 260p. 1977. 42.50x (ISBN 0-86008-183-4, Pub. by U of Tokyo Japan). Columbia U Pr.

Weiner, J. S. & Lourie, J. A. Practical Human Biology. LC 81-66372. 1981. 43.00 (ISBN 0-12-741960-8). Acad Pr.

Weiss & Mann. Human Biology & Behavior. 3rd ed. 1981. text ed. 22.95 (ISBN 0-316-92891-7); tchr's manual avail. (ISBN 0-316-92892-5). Little.

Wever, R. A. The Circadian System of Man: Results of Experiments Under Temporal Isolation. Schaefer, K. E., ed. (Topics in Environmental Physiology & Medicine Ser.). (Illus.). 1979. 63.00 (ISBN 0-387-90338-0). Springer-Verlag.

Wittman, Karl S. Basic Sciences for Health Careers. 1976. text ed. 26.70 (ISBN 0-07-071195-X). McGraw.

Zanden, James V. Human Development. 3rd ed. 1985. study guide 9.00 (ISBN 0-394-34752-8, KnopfC). Knopf.

HUMAN CENTRIFUGE

Sheeler, P. Centrifugation in Biology & Medical Science. 269p. 1981. 48.50 (ISBN 0-471-05234-5, Pub. by Wiley-Interscience). Wiley.

HUMAN CHROMOSOMES

Berg, Kare, ed. Genetic Damage in Man Caused by Environmental Agents. LC 79-414. 1979. 47.50 (ISBN 0-12-089550-1). Acad Pr.

Borgaonkar, Digamber S. Chromosomal Variation in Man: A Catalog of Chromosomal Variants & Anomalies. 4th ed. LC 83-25526. 1002p. 1984. 95.00 (ISBN 0-8451-0231-1). A R Liss.

Buckton, K. E. & Evans, H. J. Methods for the Analysis of Human Chromosome Aberrations. (Also avail. in French & Russian). 1973. 4.80 (ISBN 92-4-154031-1). World Health.

De Grouchy, Jean & Turleau, Catherine. Clinical Atlas of Human Chromosomes. 2nd ed. LC 83-16839. 487p. 1984. 65.00 (ISBN 0-471-89205-X, Pub. by Wiley Med). Wiley.

Giannelli, F. Human Chromosomes DNA Synthesis. Beckman, L. & Hauge, M., eds. (Monographs in Human Genetics: Vol. 5). 1970. 20.00 (ISBN 3-8055-0448-9). S Karger.

Klinger, H. P., et al, eds. Chromosome Mutations: Their Potential Relevance to the Genetic Risks in Man. (Journal: Cytogenetics & Cell Genetics: Vol. 33, No. 1-2). (Illus.). 202p. 1982. pap. 54.50 (ISBN 3-8055-3569-4). S Karger.

Obe, G., ed. Mutations in Man. (Illus.). 350p. 1984. 44.50 (ISBN 0-387-13113-2). Springer-Verlag.

Persaud, T. V. Genetic Disorders, Syndromology & Prenatal Diagnosis. LC 81-84816. (Advances in the Study of Birth Defects: Vol. 5). 268p. 1982. 38.00 (ISBN 0-8451-3002-1). A R Liss.

Schinzel, Albert. Catalogue of Unbalanced Chromosome Aberrations in Man. LC 83-7645. (Illus.). xviii, 886p. 1983. 136.00x (ISBN 3-11-008370-1). De Gruyter.

Yunis, G. J. New Chromosomal Syndromes. 1977. 70.00 (ISBN 0-12-775165-3). Acad Pr.

Yunis, Jorge J., ed. Human Chromosome Methodology. 2nd ed. 1974. 55.00 (ISBN 0-12-775155-6). Acad Pr.

HUMAN COLD STORAGE

see Cryonics

HUMAN ECOLOGY

see also Environmental Policy; Man–Influence of Environment; Man–Influence on Nature

Adams, Robert M., et al. The Fitness of Man's Environment. LC 68-20988. (Smithsonian Annual, No. 2). 205p. 1968. 17.50x (ISBN 0-87474-058-4). Smithsonian.

Altman, Irwin & Wohlwill, J. F., eds. Human Behavior & Environment, Vol. 1. (Illus.). 316p. 1976. 32.50x (ISBN 0-306-33301-5, Plenum Pr). Plenum Pub.

--Human Behavior & Environment, Vol. 3: Children & the Environment. (Illus.). 316p. 1978. 32.50x (ISBN 0-306-40090-1, Plenum Pr). Plenum Pub.

American Enterprise Institute for Public Policy Research. How Can Our Physical Environment Best be Controlled & Developed? (American Enterprise Institute for Public Policy Research. High School Debate Ser.). pap. 31.30 (ISBN 0-317-09965-5, 2017087). Bks Demand UMI.

Anderson, Walter. A Place of Power: The American Episode in Human Evolution. LC 76-12809. 1976. pap. text ed. 15.80 (ISBN 0-673-16268-0). Scott F.

Anthropogenic Compounds. (The Handbook of Environmental Chemistry Ser.: Vol. 3, Part C). (Illus.). 250p. 1984. 61.00 (ISBN 0-387-13019-5). Springer-Verlag.

Armstrong, R. W. & Lewis, H. T., eds. Human Ecology: North Kohala Studies. (Social Science & Linguistics Institute Special Publications). (Illus.). 144p. 1972. pap. 8.00x (ISBN 0-8248-0247-0). UH Pr.

Asimov, Isaac, ed. Isaac Asimov Presents Living in the Future. (Illus.). 288p. 1985. 19.95 (ISBN 0-8253-0225-0). Beaufort Bks NY.

Barker, Roger G., et al. Habitats, Enviroments, & Human Behavior: Studies in Ecological Psychology & Eco-Behavioral Science. LC 77-82912. (Social & Behavioral Science Ser.). 1978. text ed. 27.95x (ISBN 0-87589-356-2). Jossey-Bass.

Bates, Marston. Jungle in the House: Essays in Natural & Unnatural History. LC 70-103375. 1970. 7.50 (ISBN 0-8027-0159-0). Walker & Co.

Baum, Andrew & Singer, Jerome E., eds. Environment & Health. (Advances in Environmental Psychology Ser.: Vol. 4). (Illus.). 352p. 1982. text ed. 39.95x (ISBN 0-89859-174-0). L Erlbaum Assocs.

Bayliss-Smith, Timothy & Feachem, Richard, eds. Subsistence & Survival: Rural Ecology in the Pacific. 1978. 68.00 (ISBN 0-12-083250-X). Acad Pr.

Bennett, John W. The Ecological Transition. 1976. pap. text ed. 17.50 (ISBN 0-08-017868-5). Pergamon.

Benoit, Emile. Progress & Survival: An Essay on the the Future of Mankind. Gohn, Jack B., ed. 144p. 1980. 29.95 (ISBN 0-03-056911-7). Praeger.

Bilsky, Lester J., ed. Historical Ecology: Essays on Environment & Social Change. (National University Pubns. Ser.). 1980. 16.95x (ISBN 0-8046-9247-5, Pub. by Kennikat). Assoc Faculty Pr.

Birch, Charles & Cobb, John B. The Liberation of Life: From the Cell to the Community. 361p. 1985. pap. 17.95 (ISBN 0-521-31514-X). Cambridge U Pr.

Bird, C. F. & Ongkosongo, Otto S. Environmental Changes on the Coasts of Indonesia. 52p. 1981. pap. 10.00 (ISBN 92-808-0197-X, TUNU128, UNU). Unipub.

Boughey, Arthur S. Man & the Environment. 2nd ed. (Illus.). 480p. 1975. pap. text ed. write for info. (ISBN 0-02-312770-8, 31277). Macmillan.

Brierley, John. A Natural History of Man. 184p. 1970. 15.00 (ISBN 0-8386-7819-X). Fairleigh Dickinson.

Bronfenbrenner, Urie. Reality & Research in the Ecology of Human Development. (Master Lectures on Developmental Psychology: Manuscript No. 1333). 9.50x (ISBN 0-912704-30-6). Am Psychol.

Brubaker, Sterling. To Live on Earth: Man & His Environment in Perspective. LC 75-185514. (Resources for the Future Ser.). 218p. 1972. 16.50x (ISBN 0-8018-1378-6). Johns Hopkins.

Calabrese, Edward J. Pollutants & High Risk Groups: The Biological Basis of Increased Human Susceptibility to Environmental & Occupational Pollutants. LC 77-13957. (Environmental Science & Technology: Wiley-Interscience Series of Texts & Monographs). 266p. 1977. 58.95 (ISBN 0-471-02940-8, Pub. by Wiley-Inerscience). Wiley.

Carter, Vernon G. & Dale, Tom. Topsoil & Civilization. rev. ed. (Illus.). 240p. 1974. 12.95 (ISBN 0-8061-0332-9); pap. 8.95x (ISBN 0-8061-1107-0). U of Okla Pr.

Catton, William R., Jr. Overshoot: The Ecological Basis of Revolutionary Change. LC 80-13443. (Illus.). 250p. 1980. 16.50 (ISBN 0-252-00818-9); pap. 8.95x (ISBN 0-252-00988-6). U of Ill Pr.

Chapman, Graham P. Human & Environmental Systems: A Geographer's Appraisal. 1978. 67.00 (ISBN 0-12-168650-7). Acad Pr.

Clapham, W. B., Jr. Human Ecosystems. 1981. pap. write for info. (ISBN 0-02-322510-6). Macmillan.

Cody, Martin L. & Diamond, Jared M., eds. Ecology & Evolution of Communities. LC 74-27749. (Illus.). 838p. 1975. (Belknap Pr); pap. 15.00x (ISBN 0-674-22446-9). Harvard U Pr.

Collier, George A. Fields of the Tzotzil: The Ecological Bases of Tradition in Highland Chiapas. LC 75-12840. (Texas Pan American Ser.). (Illus.). 270p. 1975. 17.50x (ISBN 0-292-72412-8). U of Tex Pr.

Committee on the Alaska Earthquake. Great Alaska Earthquake of 1964: Human Ecology. 1970. 31.00 (ISBN 0-309-01607-X). Natl Acad Pr.

Conference on the Human Environment, Founex, Switzerland, June 4-12, 1971. Development & Environment: Proceedings. Strong, Maurice F., ed. LC 72-75446. (Illus.). 225p. (Orig.). 1973. pap. text ed. 12.80x (ISBN 90-2796-990-6). Mouton.

Conklin, Edwin G. Heredity & Environment in the Development of Men. 533p. 1984. Repr. of 1915 ed. lib. bdg. 45.00 (ISBN 0-89984-025-6). Century Bookbindery.

Conservation Education Association. Critical Index of Films on Man & His Environment. LC 65-23951. 32p. 1972. pap. text ed. 1.25x (ISBN 0-8134-1374-5, 1374). Interstate.

Croll, Neil A. & Cross, John H., eds. Human Ecology & Infectious Diseases. 1983. 49.50 (ISBN 0-12-196880-4). Acad Pr.

Curtis, R. K. Evolution or Extinction: The Choice Before Us-A Systems Approach to the Study of the Future. 420p. 1982. 55.00 (ISBN 0-08-027933-3); pap. 28.00 (ISBN 0-08-027932-5). Pergamon.

Damon, Albert. Human Biology & Ecology. LC 77-559. (Illus.). 1977. pap. text ed. 8.95x (ISBN 0-393-09103-1). Norton.

Dansereau, Pierre, ed. Challenge for Survival: Land, Air, & Water for Man in Megalopolis. LC 78-98397. 235p. 1970. 29.00x (ISBN 0-231-03267-6); pap. 15.00x (ISBN 0-231-08638-5). Columbia U Pr.

Dasgupta, Partha. The Control of Resources. (Illus.). 240p. 1983. text ed. 18.50x (ISBN 0-674-16980-8). Harvard U Pr.

Dice, Lee R. Man's Nature & Nature's Man: The Ecology of Human Communities. LC 72-9607. 329p. 1973. Repr. of 1955 ed. lib. bdg. 20.75x (ISBN 0-8371-6594-6, DIMN). Greenwood.

Dreifuss, Kurt. The Endangered Human Animal. LC 84-52235. (First Serial Rights Ser.). 320p. 23.50 (ISBN 0-9614149-0-1). Soc Wld Serv.

Dubos, Rene. A God Within. LC 76-37224. 320p. 1972. text ed. 29.50x (ISBN 0-684-12768-7). Irvington.

--So Human an Animal. LC 68-27794. (The Scribner Library of Contemporary Classics). 228p. 1984. pap. 7.95 (ISBN 0-684-71753-0, SL195, ScribT). Scribner.

Eckholm, Erik P. Down to Earth: Environment & Human Needs. 220p. 1982. 14.95 (ISBN 0-393-01600-5). Norton.

Ehrlich, Paul R., et al. Human Ecology: Problems & Solutions. LC 72-12828. (Illus.). 304p. 1973. pap. 13.95 (ISBN 0-7167-0595-8). W H Freeman.

Eiseley, Loren. The Invisible Pyramid. 1983. 14.25 (ISBN 0-8446-5980-0). Peter Smith.

Emery, F. E. & Trist, E. L. Towards a Social Ecology: Contextual Appreciation of the Future in the Present. LC 70-178778. 256p. 1973. 25.00x (ISBN 0-306-30563-1, Plenum Pr). Plenum Pub.

Emery, Frederick E. & Trist, E. L. Towards a Social Ecology. LC 74-26842. 256p. 1975. pap. 5.95x (ISBN 0-306-20015-5, Rosetta). Plenum Pub.

Enthoven, Alain C. & Freeman, A. Myrick, 3rd, eds. Pollution, Resources & the Environment. new ed. (Illus.). 1973. pap. 7.95x (ISBN 0-393-09933-4). Norton.

Fields, Brian A. The Impact of Shifting Ecologies upon the Dental Biology of Precolumbian Populations of the Illinois River Valley: A Case Study in Human Ecosystems Dynamics. Lee, Don Y., ed. LC 84-70885. 384p. 1984. text ed. 62.50x (ISBN 0-939758-08-3). Eastern Pr.

Foley, Robert. Hominid Evolution & Community Ecology. LC 83-72771. (Studies in Archaeology). 1984. 37.50 (ISBN 0-12-261920-X). Acad Pr.

Fowler, John M. Energy & the Environment. 2nd ed. 672p. 1984. pap. text ed. 27.95 (ISBN 0-07-021722-X). McGraw.

Freedman, Daniel G. Human Sociobiology: A Holistic Approach. LC 78-73025. (Illus.). 1979. 16.95 (ISBN 0-02-910660-5). Free Pr.

Garlick, J. P., ed. Human Ecology in the Tropics. (Symposia of the Society for the Study of Human Biology Ser.: Vol. 16). 172p. 1976. cancelled (ISBN 0-85066-098-X). Taylor & Francis.

Glacken, Clarence J. Traces on the Rhodian Shore: Nature & Culture in Western Thought from Ancient Times to the End of the Eighteenth Century. LC 67-10970. 1967. pap. 13.95x (ISBN 0-520-03216-0, CAMPUS 170). U of Cal Pr.

Golden-Wolfe, Malka. Malka - A Total Celebration (A Survival Manual) LC 80-53000. (Illus., Orig.). 1980. pap. 9.95 (ISBN 0-937496-00-1). Univ Goddess.

Goldman, Charles R., et al, eds. Environmental Quality & Water Development. LC 72-83739. (Illus.). 510p. 1973. 46.95 (ISBN 0-7167-0256-8). W H Freeman.

Goyal, Bhagwat S. The Strategy of Survival. 244p. 1975. text ed. 13.50x (ISBN 0-391-02714-X, Pub. by UBS India). Humanities.

Greenwood, Ned J. & Edwards, J. M. Human Environments & Natural Systems. 2nd ed. LC 78-13082. (Illus.). 1979. write for info. (ISBN 0-87872-168-1). Wadsworth Pub.

Guha, A. Evolutionary Theory of Economic Growth. 1981. 21.95x (ISBN 0-19-828431-4). Oxford U Pr.

Gyorgy, P. & Kline, O. L., eds. Malnutrition Is a Problem of Ecology. (Bibliotheca Nutritio et Dieta: No. 14). 1970. pap. 14.50 (ISBN 3-8055-0164-1). S Karger.

Halprin, Lawrence. The RSVP Cycles. 1970. pap. 13.95 (ISBN 0-8076-0628-6). Braziller.

Hardesty, Donald L. Ecological Anthroplogy. 310p. 1977. text ed. 29.95 (ISBN 0-394-34407-3, RandC). Random.

Harris, D. R. Human Ecology in Savanna Environments. LC 80-40210. 1980. 59.50 (ISBN 0-12-326550-9). Acad Pr.

Hawley, Amos H. Human Ecology: A Theory of Community Structure. LC 50-7591. pap. 118.50 (ISBN 0-317-09573-0, 2013570). Bks Demand UMI.

Hoyt, Joseph B. Man & the Earth. 3rd ed. (Illus.). 512p. 1973. text ed. 36.95 (ISBN 0-13-550947-5). P-H.

Hughes, J. Donald. American Indian Ecology. LC 82-74273. (Illus.). 228p. 1983. 20.00 (ISBN 0-87404-070-1). Tex Western.

The Human Environment: Past, Present, & Future. 1983. 11.00 (ISBN 0-318-02041-6). NCRP Pubns.

Inger, Robert F., et al, eds. Man in the Living Environment. (Illus.). 312p. 1972. 20.00x (ISBN 0-299-06050-0); pap. 5.95x (ISBN 0-299-06054-3). U of Wis Pr.

Jamison, P. L. & Zegura, S. L., eds. The Eskimo of Northwestern Alaska: A Biological Perspective. LC 77-18941. (US-IBP Synthesis Ser.: Vol. 8). 319p. 1978. 47.95 (ISBN 0-87933-319-7). Van nos Reinhold.

Jochim, Michael. Strategies for Survival: Cultural Behavior in an Ecological Context. LC 81-7887. 1981. 19.50 (ISBN 0-12-385460-1). Acad Pr.

Johnson, Warren A. Muddling Toward Frugality. LC 78-8595. 256p. 1978. 7.95 (ISBN 0-87156-214-6). Sierra.

Jones, J. Owen & Rogers, Paul, eds. Human Ecology & the Development of Settlements. LC 76-10301. (Frontiers in Human Ecology Ser.: Vol. 3). 158p. 1976. 27.50 (ISBN 0-306-30941-6, Plenum Pr). Plenum Pub.

Jones, Orville E. & Swan, Malcolm D. Discovering Your Environment. 1971. text ed. 9.25x (ISBN 0-8134-1169-6, 1169). Interstate.

Jones, Owen J. Index of Human Ecology. LC 73-90302. 150p. 1974. 16.00x (ISBN 0-900362-66-9). Intl Pubns Serv.

Jorgensen, S. E., ed. Handbook of Environmental Data & Ecological Parameters. rev. ed. LC 78-41207. (Enviromental Sciences & Applications Ser.: Vol. 6). (Illus.). 1100p. 1979. 265.00 (ISBN 0-08-023436-4). Pergamon.

Kaplan, S. J. & Kivy-Rosenberg, E. Ecology & the Quality of Life. (Illus.). 308p. 1973. 31.00x (ISBN 0-398-02828-1). C C Thomas.

Kaplan, Stephen & Kaplan, Rachel. Humanscape: Environments for People. LC 77-27531. 1978. pap. text ed. write for info. (ISBN 0-87872-163-0). Wadsworth Pub.

--Humanscape: Environments for People. LC 77-27531. 480p. pap. text ed. 12.95 (ISBN 0-914004-49-2). Ulrich.

Karlin, Samuel, et al, eds. Population Genetics & Ecology: Proceedings. 1976. 65.00 (ISBN 0-12-398560-9). Acad Pr.

Kneese, Allen V. & Bower, Blair T., eds. Environmental Quality Analysis: Theory & Method in the Social Sciences. LC 78-181556. (Resources for the Future Ser). (Illus.). 420p. 1972. 29.00x (ISBN 0-8018-1332-8). Johns Hopkins.

Krebs, John R. & Davies, Nicholas B. An Introduction to Behavioural Ecology. LC 80-25843. (Illus.). 300p. 1981. pap. text ed. 18.50x (ISBN 0-87893-432-4). Sinauer Assoc.

LaConte, P. & Gibson, J. E. Human & Energy Factors: Factors in Urban Planning; A Systems Approach. 1982. 50.00 (ISBN 90-247-2688-3, Pub. by Martinus Nijhoff Netherlands). Kluwer Academic.

Langbein, Laura I. & Lichtman, Allan J. Ecological Inference. LC 77-93283. (University Papers Ser.: Quantitative Applications in the Social Sciences, No. 10). 70p. 1978. pap. 5.00 (ISBN 0-8039-0941-1). Sage.

Lehmann, Dietrich & Callaway, Enoch, eds. Human Evoked Potentials: Applications & Problems. LC 79-4320. (NATO Conference Series III: Human Factors: Vol. 9). 511p. 1979. 59.50x (ISBN 0-306-40160-6, Plenum Pr). Plenum Pub.

Lillard, Richard. Eden in Jeopardy: Man's Prodigal Meddling with His Environment-the Southern California Experience. LC 76-1842. (Illus.). 1977. Repr. of 1966 ed. lib. bdg. 22.75x (ISBN 0-8371-8181-X, LIEJ). Greenwood.

Living in Our Environment: Proceedings. LC 62-38584. (Illus.). 1971. pap. text ed. 20.00 (ISBN 0-915414-11-2). Inst Environ Sci.

McClary, Andrew. Biology & Society: The Evolution of Man & His Technology. (Illus.). 352p. 1975. pap. text ed. write for info. (ISBN 0-02-378510-1). Macmillan.

McGurk, H., ed. Ecological Factors in Human Development. LC 76-30321. (Illus.). 296p. 1977. 42.75 (ISBN 0-7204-0488-6, North-Holland). Elsevier.

McHale, John. The Ecological Context. new ed. LC 77-132200. 1970. 7.95 (ISBN 0-8076-0562-X). Braziller.

McHarg, Ian L. Design with Nature. LC 76-77344. 1971. pap. 12.95 (ISBN 0-385-05509-9). Natural Hist.

McKenzie, Roderick D. Roderick D. McKenzie on Human Ecology. Hawley, Amos H., ed. LC 68-9728. (Heritage of Sociology Ser.). 1969. pap. 3.45x (ISBN 0-226-31982-2, P326, Phoen). U of Chicago Pr.

Man's Home: Background Readings in Issues Before the United Nations Conference on the Human Environment, 1972. pap. 2.00 (ISBN 0-686-94802-5, UN72/1/5, UN). Unipub.

Margenau, Henry & Sellon, Emily B., eds. Nature, Man & Society. 1976. 16.00 (ISBN 0-89254-005-2). Nicolas-Hays.

Marois, Maurice, ed. Towards a Plan of Actions for Mankind, 5 vols. Incl. Vol. 1. Long Range Mineral Resources & Growth. text ed. 60.00 (ISBN 0-08-021445-2); Vol. 2. Long Range Energetic Resources & Growth. text ed. 40.00 (ISBN 0-08-021446-0); Vol. 3. Biological Balance & Thermal Modification. text ed. 105.00 (ISBN 0-08-021447-9); Vol. 4. Design of Global System Models & Their Limitations. text ed. 55.00 (ISBN 0-08-021448-7); Vol. 5. Conclusions & Perspectives. text ed. 100.00 (ISBN 0-08-021449-5). 1977. Set. 530.00 (ISBN 0-08-021850-4). Pergamon.

Marten, Gerald G., ed. The Human Ecology of Traditional Agriculture in the Tropics. 275p. 1985. 27.50 (ISBN 0-8133-7026-4). Westview.

Maxwell, Kenneth E., et al. Environment of Life. 4th ed. LC 84-19875. (Biology Ser.). 500p. 1985. pap. text ed. 15.00 pub. net (ISBN 0-534-04089-6). Brooks-Cole.

Medvedkov, Yuri, ed. Amelioration of the Human Environment: IGU Congress, Moscow, 1976, Proceedings, Pt. 1. 1977. pap. text ed. 21.00 (ISBN 0-08-021322-7). Pergamon.

Metress, James, ed. Man in Ecological Perspective. 1972. 29.50x (ISBN 0-8422-5022-0); pap. text ed. 12.50x (ISBN 0-8422-0125-4). Irvington.

Mitchell, Henry. The Essential Earthman. (Illus.). 244p. 1981. pap. 6.95 (ISBN 0-374-51765-7). FS&G.

Mohtadi, M. F., ed. Man & His Environment, Vol. 2: Proceedings of the Second Banff Conference. 216p. 1976. text ed. 44.00 (ISBN 0-08-019922-4). Pergamon.

Montgomery, David. Imperial Science & National Survival. LC 80-70692. 1981. 2.50x (ISBN 0-87081-094-4). Colo Assoc.

Moos, Rudolf & Brownstein, Robert. Environment & Utopia: A Synthesis. LC 77-23275. (Plenum Social Ecology Ser.). 293p. 1977. 30.00x (ISBN 0-306-30985-8, Plenum Pr). Plenum Pub.

Moran, Emilio F. Human Adaptability: An Introduction to Ecological Anthropology. 1979. write for info. (ISBN 0-87872-192-4). Wadsworth Pub.

Moran, Emilio R. Human Adaptability: An Introduction to Ecological Anthropology. (Illus.). 404p. 1982. lib. bdg. 26.50x (ISBN 0-86531-430-6); pap. text ed. 14.00x (ISBN 0-86531-431-4). Westview.

Moran, Joseph M., et al. An Introduction to Environmental Sciences. 464p. 1973. text ed. 14.95 (ISBN 0-316-58218-2); instructor's manual free (ISBN 0-316-58204-2). Little.

Moser, Leo J. The Technology Trap. LC 78-26034. 288p. 1979. 23.95x (ISBN 0-88229-419-9); pap. 11.95 (ISBN 0-88229-669-8). Nelson-Hall.

National Geographic Society, ed. As We Live & Breathe: The Challenge of Our Environment. LC 74-151945. (Special Publications Ser.). (Illus.). 1971. 6.95, avail. only from Natl Geog (ISBN 0-87044-097-7). Natl Geog.

Netting, Robert M. Balancing on an Alp: Ecological Change & Continuity in a Swiss Mountain Community. LC 81-358. (Illus.). 436p. 1981. 49.50 (ISBN 0-521-23743-2); pap. 17.95 (ISBN 0-521-28197-0). Cambridge U Pr.

Norwine, Jim. Climate & Human Ecology. LC 78-52975. (Illus.). 1978. pap. 9.95 (ISBN 0-918464-19-6). D Armstrong.

O'Brien, Michael J., et al. Grassland, Forest, & Historical Settlement: An Analysis of Dynamics in Northeast Missouri. LC 84-3660. (Studies in North American Archaeology). (Illus.). xxii, 345p. 1984. 25.00x (ISBN 0-8032-3551-8). U of Nebr Pr.

Odum, Howard T. Environment Power & Society. LC 78-129660. (Environmental Science & Technology Ser). 331p. 1971. pap. text ed. 19.95x (ISBN 0-471-65275-X, Pub. by Wiley-Interscience). Wiley.

Odum, Howard T. & Odum, Elisabeth C. Energy Basis for Man & Nature. 2nd ed. (Illus.). 352p. 1981. text ed. 22.50 (ISBN 0-07-047511-3); pap. text ed. 22.50 (ISBN 0-07-047510-5, C). McGraw.

Olson, Mancur & Landsberg, Hans H., eds. The No-Growth Society. 259p. 1974. 10.00x (ISBN 0-393-01111-9); pap. text ed. 4.95x (ISBN 0-393-09260-7). Norton.

Orr, David W. & Soroos, Marvin S., eds. The Global Predicament: Ecological Perspectives on World Order. LC 78-10207. xvi, 398p. 1979. 26.00x (ISBN 0-8078-1346-X); pap. 9.95x (ISBN 0-8078-1349-4). U of NC Pr.

Peeke, Harman V. & Petrinovich, Lewis. Habituation, Sensitization & Behavior. 1984. 59.00 (ISBN 0-12-549860-8). Acad Pr.
Peter, Laurence J. The Peter Plan: A Proposal for Survival. LC 75-22327. (Illus.). 224p. 1976. 6.95 (ISBN 0-688-02972-8). Morrow.
Polgar, Steven, ed. Culture & Population: A Collection of Current Studies. LC 80-20070. (Carolina Population Center, Monograph: 9). vi, 195p. 1980. Repr. of 1971 ed. lib. bdg. 22.50x (ISBN 0-313-22620-2, POCP). Greenwood.
Rambo, A Terry. Conceptual Approaches to Human Ecology. LC 83-16460. (East-West Environment & Policy Institute Research Report). (Orig.). 1983. pap. text ed. 3.00 (ISBN 0-86638-049-3). E W Center HI.
Randolph, Theron G. Human Ecology & Susceptibility to the Chemical Environment. (Illus.). 160p. 1981. 19.75x (ISBN 0-398-01548-1). C C Thomas.
ReVelle, Charles & ReVelle, Penelope. The Environment: Issues & Choices for Society. 2nd ed. 650p. 1984. text ed. write for info (ISBN 0-87150-788-9, 4571, Pub. by Willard Grant Pr). PWS Pubs.
Ritterbush, Philip C. The Built Environment: Ideas in Engineering for Human Adaptive Potential. (Illus.). 150p. (Orig.). 1983. pap. 27.00x (ISBN 0-942776-04-6). Inst Cult Prog.
Robertson, Thomas. Human Ecology, 2 Vols. 560p. 1973. 200.00 (ISBN 0-87968-340-6). Gordon Pr.
Rogers, Dorothy. Life-Span Human Development. LC 80-25158. 512p. 1981. text ed. 21.75 pub net (ISBN 0-8185-0389-0). Brooks-Cole.
Schaeffer, Francis. Pollution & the Death of Man. 1970. pap. 5.95 (ISBN 0-8423-4840-9). Tyndale.
Schwab, William A. Urban Sociology: A Human Ecological Perspective. LC 81-5006. 576p. 1982. text ed. 24.95 (ISBN 0-394-34850-8, RanC). Random.
Scott, Allan & Lorraine, John, eds. Here Today... World Outlooks from the Centre of Human Ecology. 120p. 1979. 30.00x (ISBN 0-904919-34-X, Pub. by Polygon Bks Scotland). State Mutual Bk.
Shaler, Nathaniel S. Man & the Earth. Repr. of 1905 ed. 20.00 (ISBN 0-384-54960-8). Johnson Repr.
Sibly, R. M. & Smith, R. H., eds. Behavioural Ecology: Ecological Consequences of Adaptive Behaviour. (Illus.). 420p. 1985. text ed. 96.00x (ISBN 0-632-01359-1); pap. text ed. 39.00x (ISBN 0-632-01413-X). Blackwell Pubns.
Slack, Walter H. The Surplus Species: Need Man Prevail? LC 81-40833. 172p. (Orig.). 1982. lib. bdg. 25.00 (ISBN 0-8191-2231-9); pap. text ed. 11.25 (ISBN 0-8191-2232-7). U Pr of Amer.
Stapp, William B. & Liston, Mary D., eds. Environmental Education: A Guide to Information Sources. LC 73-17542. (Man & the Environment Information Guide Ser.: Vol. 1). 350p. 1975. 60.00x (ISBN 0-8103-1337-5). Gale.
Strong, Maurice, ed. Who Speaks for Earth? 160p. 1973. 6.95 (ISBN 0-393-06392-5); pap. 1.95 (ISBN 0-393-09341-7). Norton.
Tappan, Mel. Tappan on Survival. LC 81-82264. 1982. 7.95 (ISBN 0-916172-04-X). Janus Pr.
Theodorson, George A., ed. Urban Patterns: Studies in Human Ecology. rev. ed. LC 81-83145. (Illus.). 475p. 1982. 26.75x (ISBN 0-271-00297-2). Pa St U Pr.
Theory Development in Environment & Aging. 294p. 1974. 4.00 (ISBN 0-318-02259-1). Gerontological Soc.
Tinker, Irene & Buvinic, Mayra, eds. The Many Facets of Human Settlement: Science & Society. LC 77-6307. 1977. text ed. 155.00 (ISBN 0-08-021994-2). Pergamon.
Todd, Nancy J. & Todd, John. Bioshelters, Ocean Arks, City Farming: Ecology as the Basis of Design. LC 83-51436. (Illus.). 256p. 1984. 25.00 (ISBN 0-87156-348-7); pap. 10.95 (ISBN 0-87156-814-4). Sierra.
Treshow, Michael. The Human Environment. (Population Biology Ser.). 1976. text ed. 29.95 (ISBN 0-07-065136-1). McGraw.
Tullar, Richard M. The Human Species: Its Nature, Evolution & Ecology. (Illus.). 1976. pap. text ed. 34.95 (ISBN 0-07-065423-9). McGraw.
Turnbull, Colin M. The Human Cycle. 320p. (Orig.). 1983. pap. 6.95 (ISBN 0-671-50599-8, Touchstone Bks). S&S.
Tybout, Richard A., ed. Environmental Quality & Society. LC 75-2244. (Illus.). 327p. (Orig.). 1975. pap. 7.50x (ISBN 0-8142-0214-4). Ohio St U Pr.
Unispace International Round Table, New York, 8-10 March 1982 & Karnik, K. Alternative Space Futures & the Human Condition: Proceedings. 180p. 1982. 22.00 (ISBN 0-08-029969-5). Pergamon.
United Nations Statistical Office, compiled by. United Nations Conference on Human Settlements, Vancouver, B. C., 1976: Human Settlements Factbook Statistical Annex, 2 vols. 1976. text ed. 195.00 (ISBN 0-08-021045-7). Pergamon.
Vayda, Andrew P. War in Ecological Perspective. LC 75-40272. (Illus.). 143p. 1976. 27.50x (ISBN 0-306-30876-2, Plenum Pr). Plenum Pub.
Waddington, C. H. The Man-Made Future. LC 77-29043. 1978. 26.00 (ISBN 0-312-51045-4). St Martin.
Wagner, Philip L. Human Use of the Earth. LC 60-7092. 1964. pap. text ed. 3.00 (ISBN 0-02-933570-1). Free Pr.
Wagner, Richard H. Environment & Man. 3rd ed. (Illus.). 606p. 1978. text ed. 22.95x (ISBN 0-393-09066-3). Norton.
Wapner, Seymour, et al, eds. Experiencing the Environment. LC 75-37839. (Illus.). 252p. 1976. 29.50x (ISBN 0-306-30873-8, Plenum Pr). Plenum Pub.
Ward, Barbara & Dubos, Rene. Only One Earth: The Care & Maintenance of a Small Planet. 1972. 13.95 (ISBN 0-393-06391-7). Norton.
Waterman, Laura & Waterman, Guy. Backwoods Ethics: Environmental Concerns for Hikers & Campers. LC 79-16684. (Illus.). 192p. (Orig.). 1979. pap. 7.95 (ISBN 0-913276-28-6). Stone Wall Pr.
Wicker, Allan W. An Introduction to Ecological Psychology. 300p. 1985. pap. text ed. 14.95x (ISBN 0-8290-1291-5). Irvington.
Wilson, Edward O., intro. by. Ecology, Evolution, & Population Biology: Readings from Scientific American. LC 73-17448. (Illus.). 315p. 1974. text ed. 23.95x (ISBN 0-7167-0888-4); pap. text ed. 11.95x (ISBN 0-7167-0887-6). W H Freeman.
Witters, Weldon L. & Jones-Witters, Patricia. Environmental Biology: The Human Factor. 2nd ed. LC 75-35412. 1982. perfect bdg. 9.95 (ISBN 0-8403-2812-5). Kendall Hunt.
Wittman, James S., ed. Selected Articles in Social Ecology. LC 73-609. 295p. 1973. text ed. 34.50x (ISBN 0-8422-5086-7); pap. text ed. 12.50x (ISBN 0-8422-0293-5). Irvington.
Woodbury, Angus M. Notes on the Human Ecology of Glen Canyon. (Glen Canyon Ser.: No. 26). Repr. of 1965 ed. 20.00 (ISBN 0-404-60674-1). AMS Pr.
Young, Gerald L., ed. Origins of Human Ecology. LC 83-39. (Benchmark Papers in Ecology: Vol. 12). 432p. 1983. 49.95 (ISBN 0-87933-104-6). Van Nos Reinhold.

HUMAN ECOLOGY–BIBLIOGRAPHY

Berry, Peter S., ed. Sourcebook for Environmental Studies. 1975. pap. text ed. 11.00x (ISBN 0-8464-0865-1). Beekman Pubs.
Boucher, Doug A., ed. The Biology of Mutualism: Ecology & Evolution. 400p. 1985. 49.95 (ISBN 0-19-520483-2). Oxford U Pr.
Chicorel, Marietta, ed. Chicorel Index to Environment & Ecology, 2 vols. LC 75-306805. (Index Ser.). 1000p. 1974. Set. 250.00 (ISBN 0-934598-21-5). Vol. 16 (ISBN 0-934598-25-8). Vol. 16A (ISBN 0-934598-26-6). Am Lib Pub Co.
Hammond, Kenneth A., et al. Sourcebook on the Environment: A Guide to the Literature. LC 77-17407. 1978. lib. bdg. 27.50x (ISBN 0-226-31522-3). U of Chicago Pr.
Kruse, Lenelis & Arlt, Lenelis. Environment & Behavior: An International Multidisciplinary Bibliography 1970-1981, 2 vols. (Illus.). 1420p. 1984. lib. bdg. 75.00 (ISBN 3-598-10494-4). K G Saur.
Lee, Kaiman, ed. Bibliography of the Computer in Environmental Design, 3 Vols. 2nd ed. LC 73-158197. 650p. 1973. Set. 110.00x (ISBN 0-915250-03-9). Environ Design.
O'Brien, Michael, et al, eds. The Cannon Reservoir Human Ecology Project: An Archaeological Study of Cultural Adaptations in the Southern Prairie Peninsula. (Studies in Archaeology). 1982. 50.00 (ISBN 0-12-523980-7). Acad Pr.
Owings, Loren C., ed. Environmental Values, Eighteen Sixty to Nineteen Seventy-Two: A Guide to Information Sources. LC 73-17539. (Man & the Environment Information Guide Ser.: Vol. 4). 593p. 1976. 60.00x (ISBN 0-8103-1343-X). Gale.
Sargent, Frederick, II, ed. Human Ecology: A Guide to Information Sources. (Health Affairs Information Guide Series, Gale Information Guide Library: Vol. 10). 300p. 1982. 60.00x (ISBN 0-8103-1504-1). Gale.

HUMAN ECOLOGY–STUDY AND TEACHING

see also Nature Study

Stapp, William B. & Liston, Mary D., eds. Environmental Education: A Guide to Information Sources. LC 73-17542. (Man & the Environment Information Guide Ser.: Vol. 1). 350p. 1975. 60.00x (ISBN 0-8103-1337-5). Gale.

HUMAN EMBRYOLOGY

see Embryology, Human

HUMAN ENGINEERING

see also Human Information Processing; Life Support Systems (Space Environment); Man-Machine Systems

Applied Ergonomics Handbook. 126p. 1974. 21.95 (ISBN 0-902852-38-8). Butterworth.
Bailey, Robert W. & Human Performance Associates. Human Performance Engineering: A Guide for System Designers. (Illus.). 672p. 1982. text ed. 44.95 (ISBN 0-13-445320-4); wkbk 9.95 (ISBN 0-13-445338-7). P-H.
Biotechnology Directory. 1984. 50.00 (DIR103). Market Res Co.
Bootzin, David & Muffley, Harry C., eds. Biomechanics. LC 69-16519. 185p. 1969. 35.00x (ISBN 0-306-30392-2, Plenum Pr). Plenum Pub.
British Library Staff. European Biotechnology Information Project (EBIP) Biotechnology Information Seminar Course Book. 1984. 30.00 (Pub. by British Lib). Longwood Pub Group.
--European Biotechnology Information Project (EBIP) Business Information Sources in Biotechnology. 1984. 15.00 (ISBN 0-317-26872-4, Pub. by British Lib). Longwood Pub Group.
--European Biotechnology Information Project (EBIP) Culture Collections. 1984. 7.50 (ISBN 0-317-26875-9, Pub. by British Lib). Longwood Pub Group.
--European Biotechnology Information Project (EBIP) Forthcoming Conferences. 1984. 7.50 (ISBN 0-317-26881-3, Pub. by British Lib). Longwood Pub Group.
--European Biotechnology Information Project (EBIP) Market Research Reports. 2nd ed. 1984. 7.50 (ISBN 0-317-26879-1, Pub. by British Lib). Longwood Pub Group.
Burch, John L., ed. Computers: The Non-Technological (Human) Factors: A Recommended Reading List on Computer Ergonomics & User Friendly Design. LC 84-60013. 101p. 1984. pap. 34.95 (ISBN 0-916313-00-X). Report.
--Ergonomics: The Science of Productivity & Health: Capsule Reviews of the Principal Literature on Present-Day Ergonomics & Human Factors Engineering. LC 84-60949. 125p. 1984. pap. 37.50 (ISBN 0-916313-01-8). Report.
Chapanis, Alfred R. E. Research Techniques in Human Engineering. LC 59-10765. pap. 82.00 (ISBN 0-317-10928-6, 2002276). Bks Demand UMI.
Chapanis, Alphonse, ed. Ethnic Variables in Human Factors Engineering. LC 74-24393. 310p. 1975. 27.50x (ISBN 0-8018-1668-8). Johns Hopkins.
Clarke, T. S. & Corlett, E. N. The Ergonomics of Workspaces & Machines: A Design Manual. LC 84-242. (Illus.). 100p. 1984. 31.00x (ISBN 0-85066-246-X). Taylor & Francis.
Computers, Ergonomics, & User Friendly System Design. cancelled. Report.
Critser, James R., Jr. Biotechnical Engineering: Equipment & Processes. (Ser. 14-83). 318p. 1984. 210.00 (ISBN 0-88178-012-X). Lexington Data.
--Biotechnical Engineering: Equipment & Processes. (Series 14-84). 293p. 1985. 210.00 (ISBN 0-88178-023-5). Lexington Data.
Daly, Peter. The Biotechnology Business: A Strategic Analysis. 150p. 1985. 25.00x (ISBN 0-8476-7460-6). Rowman.
Damon, Albert, et al. Human Body in Equipment Design. LC 65-22067. (Illus.). 1966. 25.00x (ISBN 0-674-41450-0). Harvard U Pr.
DECHEMA, Deutsche Gesellschaft Fuer Chemisches Apparatewesen E. V., ed. Biotechnology: Proceedings of the First European Congress on Biotechnology. (Dechema Monographs: Vol. 82). 304p. 1979. pap. 37.50x (ISBN 3-527-10765-7). VCH Pubs.
Eastman Kodak Company Staff. Ergonomic Design for People at Work: The Design of Jobs, Vol. II. 1984. 42.00t (ISBN 0-534-03111-0). Lifetime Learn.
Eberts, R. E. & Eberts, C. G., eds. Trends in Ergonomics Human Factors II. 652p. 1985. 74.00 (ISBN 0-444-87751-7, North Holland). Elsevier.
Ergonomics Society, UK. Proceedings of the Ergonomics Society's Conference, 1983. Coombes, Karenna, ed. LC 83-6165. 214p. 1982. pap. 47.50x (ISBN 90-313-0500-6). Taylor & Francis.
Floyd, W. F. & Welford, A. T., eds. Symposium on Fatigue & Symposium on Human Factors in Equipment Design, 2 vols. in one. LC 77-70494. (Work Ser.). (Illus.). 1977. Repr. of 1954 ed. lib. bdg. 32.00x (ISBN 0-405-10165-1). Ayer Co Pubs.
Fraser, T. M. Ergonomic Principles in the Design of Hand Tools. (Occupational Safety & Health Ser.: No. 44). 97p. 1981. pap. 8.55 (ISBN 92-2-102356-7, ILO155, ILO). Unipub.
Gallopin, Giberte. Planning Methods & the Human Environment. (Socio-Economic Studies: No. 4). 68p. 1981. pap. 7.50 (ISBN 92-3-101894-9, U1106, UNESCO). Unipub.
Grainger, J. M. & Lynch, J. M., eds. Microbiological Methods for Environmental Biotechnology. (Society for Applied Bacteriology, Technical Ser.: No. 19). 1984. 65.00 (ISBN 0-12-295040-2). ACad Pr.
Grandjean, Etienne. Ergonomics of the Home. LC 73-13221. (Illus.). 344p. 1973. 32.00x (ISBN 0-85066-067-X). Taylor & Francis.
--Fitting the Task to the Man: An Ergonomic Approach. 3rd ed. LC 79-3855. 379p. 1980. 42.00x (ISBN 0-8002-2225-3); pap. 25.00x (ISBN 0-85066-192-7). Taylor & Francis.
Grandjean, Etienne, ed. Ergonomics & Health in Modern Offices. LC 84-8470. 510p. 1984. pap. 77.00 (ISBN 0-85066-270-2). Taylor & Francis.
Hammond, John. Understanding Human Engineering: An Introduction to Ergonomics. 1979. 14.95 (ISBN 0-7153-7670-5). David & Charles.
Higgins, I. J., et al, eds. Biotechnology: Principles & Applications. (Illus.). 300p. 1985. text ed. 50.00x (ISBN 0-632-01029-0); pap. text ed. 27.00x (ISBN 0-632-01034-7). Blackwell Sci.
Hollaender, Alexander, et al, eds. Basic Biology of New Developments in Biotechnology. (Basic Life Sciences Ser.: Vol. 25). 579p. 1983. 75.00x (ISBN 0-306-41244-6, Plenum Pr). Plenum Pub.
Houwink, E. H. & Van Der Meer, R. R., eds. Innovations in Biotechnology: Proceedings of a Poster Symposium, Delft, the Netherlands, Nov. 22, 1983. (Progress in Industrial Microbiology Ser.: No. 20). 530p. 1984. 90.75 (ISBN 0-444-42275-7, I-309-84). Elsevier.
Hutchinson, R. Anthony. Computer Eye Stress: How to Avoid It, How to Alleviate It. Heffernen, Maureen, ed. (Illus.). 96p. (Orig.). 1985. pap. text ed. 4.95 (ISBN 0-87131-457-6). M Evans.
Institution of Chemical Engineers, ed. Ergonomics Problems in Process Operations: Proceedings of the Symposium Held in Birmingham, UK, 11-13 July 1984. (Institution of Chemical Engineers Symposium Ser.: Vol. 90). 235p. 1984. 28.00 (ISBN 0-08-030282-3). Pergamon.
International Conference on Machine Pacing & Occupational Stress, 1st, Purdue Univ., Mar. 1981. Machine Pacing & Occupational Stress. Salvendy, Gavriel & Smith, M. J., eds. (Illus.). 374p. 1981. 53.00x (ISBN 0-85066-255-9). Taylor & Francis.
International on the Commercial Applications & Implementations of Biotechnology. Biotech: Proceedings. 1100p. (Orig.). 1983. pap. text ed. 210.00x (ISBN 0-86353-000-1, Pub. by Online Conferences England). Brookfield Pub Co.
Ivergard, Toni. Information Ergonomics. 228p. (Orig.). 1982. pap. text ed. 29.95 (ISBN 0-86238-032-4, Pub. by Chartwell-Bratt England). Brookfield Pub Co.
Kvalseth, Tarald O., ed. Ergonomics of Workstation Design. 304p. 1983. text ed. 89.95 (ISBN 0-408-01253-6). Butterworth.
Lampton, Christopher. DNA & the Creation of New Life. LC 82-6874. (How It Works Ser.). (Illus.). 224p. 1982. 12.95 (ISBN 0-668-05396-8, 5396). Arco.
Lenihan, John. Human Engineering: The Body Re-Examined. LC 74-25318. 212p. 1975. 7.95 (ISBN 0-8076-0782-7); pap. 4.95 (ISBN 0-8076-0969-2). Braziller.
Levinson, Risha W. & Haynes, Karen S., eds. Accessing Human Services. LC 84-16012. 320p. 1985. 29.95 (ISBN 0-8039-2388-0); pap. 14.00 (ISBN 0-8039-2389-9). Sage.
Loellgen, H. & Mellerowicz, H., eds. Progress in Ergometry: Quality Control & Test Criteria, Fifth International Seminar on Ergometry. (Illus.). 260p. 1984. pap. 19.00 (ISBN 0-387-13570-7). Springer-Verlag.
McCormick, E. J. & Sanders, M. S. Human Factors in Engineering & Design. 5th ed. 1982. 43.95 (ISBN 0-07-044902-3). McGraw.
Mandel, Janice K. Biotechnology Emerges: The Key Years, 1973-1980. 295.00 (ISBN 0-89947-019-X). EIC Intell.
Mandel, Janice K., ed. Telegen Index & Yearbook, 1982. write for info. (ISBN 0-89947-021-1). EIC Intell.
--Telegen Index & Yearbook, 1983. write for info. EIC Intell.
Marsh, George P. The Earth As Modified by Human Action. (American Environmental Studies). Repr. of 1876 ed. 33.00 (ISBN 0-405-02677-3). Ayer Co Pubs.
Megaw, E. D., ed. Contemporary Ergonomics 1984: Proceedings of the Ergonomics Society's Conference held in Exeter UK, April 2-5, 1984. (Illus.). 282p. 1984. pap. 44.00x (ISBN 0-85066-268-0). Taylor & Francis.
Meister, David. Behavioral Foundations of System Development. 2nd ed. LC 83-19964. 392p. 1985. Repr. of 1976 ed. 49.50 (ISBN 0-89874-703-1). Krieger.

--Human Factors: Theory & Practice. LC 77-148505. (Human Factors Ser). 1971. 57.50 (ISBN 0-471-59190-4, Pub. by Wiley-Interscience). Wiley.

Microencapsulation & Artificial Cells. Chang, T. M., ed. 328p. 65.00 (ISBN 0-89603-073-3). Humana.

Mital, A., ed. Advances in Ergonomics: Human Factors I. 368p. 1984. 55.75 (ISBN 0-444-87659-6, North-Holland). Elsevier.

Moo-Young. Advances in Biotechnology: Fermentation & Yeasts--Proceedings of the 6th International Fermentation Symposium-5th International Symposium on Yeasts, London, Canada, July 20-25, 1980, 4 vols. (Illus.). 2900p. 1981. Set. 385.00 (ISBN 0-08-025365-2); Vol. 1. 110.00 (ISBN 0-08-025383-0); Vol. 2. 110.00 (ISBN 0-08-025384-9); Vol. 3. 110.00 (ISBN 0-08-025385-7); Vol. 4. 105.00 (ISBN 0-08-025382-2). Pergamon.

Moraal, J. & Kraiss, F. K., eds. Manned Systems Design: Methods, Equipment, & Applications. LC 81-10732. (NATO Conference Series III, Human Factors: Vol. 17). 498p. 1981. 59.50x (ISBN 0-306-40804-X, Plenum Pr). Plenum Pub.

Murrell, K. F. Ergonomics: Man In His Working Environment. 1980. 21.00x (ISBN 0-412-07800-7, NO. 2181, Pub. by Chapman & Hall); pap. 19.95x (ISBN 0-412-21990-5, NO. 6207). Methuen Inc.

Oborne, D. J., ed. Contemporary Ergonomics 1985: Proceedings of the Ergonomics Society's Conference. 246p. 1985. 36.00x (ISBN 0-85066-295-8). Taylor & Francis.

Office of Technology Assessment. Commercial Biotechnology: An International Analysis. Date not set. write for info. (ISBN 0-444-99586-2). Elsevier.

Office of Technology Assessment, Congress of the United States Staff, ed. Commercial Biotechnology: An International Analysis. (Illus.). 624p. 1984. 66.00 (ISBN 0-08-031620-4). Pergamon.

Organisation for Economic Co-Operation & Development. Biotechnology-International Trends & Perspectives. 84p. (Orig.). 1982. pap. 11.00x (ISBN 92-64-12362-8). OECD.

Perrone, Nicholas. Dynamic Response of Biomechanical Systems: Papers Presented at the Winter Annual Meeting of the ASME, N.Y, N.Y., Dec. 2, 1970. LC 78-143213. pap. 39.00 (ISBN 0-317-08321-X, 2016913). Bks Demand UMI.

Rehm, H. J. & Reed, G., eds. Biotechnology: Vol. 3 Biomass, Microorganisms for Special Applications, Microbial Products I, Energy from Renewable Resources. (Illus.). 642p. 1983. 298.00x (ISBN 0-89573-043-X). VCH Pubs.

Rubinstein, Richard & Hersh, Harry. The Human Factor: Designing Computer Systems for People. 256p. 1984. 25.00 (ISBN 0-932376-44-4, EY-00013-DP). Digital Pr.

Rudman, Jack. Human Resources Specialist. (Career Examination Ser.: C-356). (Cloth bdg. avail. on request). pap. 8.00 (ISBN 0-8373-0356-7). Natl Learning.

--Supervising Human Resources Specialist. (Career Examination Ser.: C-1046). (Cloth bdg. avail. on request). pap. 10.00 (ISBN 0-8373-1046-6). Natl Learning.

Salvendy, G., ed. Human-Computer Interaction: Proceedings of the U. S. A.-Japan Conference on Human-Computer Interaction, 1st Honolulu, Hawaii, Aug. 18-20, 1984. (Advances in Human Factors-Ergonomics Ser.: Vol. 1). 1984. 74.50 (ISBN 0-444-42395-8). Elsevier.

Symposium on Thermal Problems in Biotechnology (1968: New York) Thermal Problems in Biotechnology: Presented at the Winter Annual Meeting of ASME, New York, NY, December 3, 1968. LC 68-58741. (Illus.). pap. 33.00 (ISBN 0-317-08429-1, 2016822). Bks Demand UMI.

Teich, Albert H., et al, eds. Biotechnology & the Environment: Risk & Regulation. 1985. pap. text ed. 12.95 (ISBN 0-87168-279-6). AAAS.

Terminello, Joanne, ed. The New Biotechnology Marketplace: Japan. 1983. 395.00 (ISBN 0-317-07625-6). EIC Intell.

--The New Biotechnology Marketplace: U. S. & Canada. 2nd ed. 1984. 295.00. EIC Intell.

Tichauer, E. R. The Biochemical Basis of Ergonomics: Anatomy Applied to the Design of Work Situations. LC 77-28807. 99p. 1978. pap. 22.00 (ISBN 0-471-03644-7, Pub. by Wiley-Interscience). Wiley.

Umbers, I. G. A Review of Human Factors Data on Input Devices Used for Process Computer Communication, 1977. 1981. 40.00x (ISBN 0-686-97156-6, Pub. by W Spring England). State Mutual Bk.

Van Loon, J. H. & Staudt, F. J., eds. Ergonomics in Tropical Agriculture & Forestry: Proceedings. 136p. 1979. pap. 14.00 (ISBN 0-686-93162-9, PDC148, Pudoc). Unipub.

Wickens, Christopher. Engineering Psychology & Human Performance. (No. 309). 544p. 1984. 36.95 (ISBN 0-675-20156-X). Merrill.

Woodson, Wesley E. Human Factors Design Handbook: Information & Guidelines for the Design of Systems, Facilities, Equipment, & Products for Human Use. LC 80-13299. (Illus.). 1049p. 1981. 94.00 (ISBN 0-07-071765-6). McGraw.

Woodson, Wesley E. & Conover, Donald W. Human Engineering Guide for Equipment Designers. 2nd rev ed. (Illus.). 1965. 42.00x (ISBN 0-520-01363-8). U of Cal Pr.

The World Biotech Report Nineteen Eighty-Four: Europe, Vol. 1. 691p. 1984. pap. text ed. 150.00x (ISBN 0-86353-003-6, Pub. by Online). Brookfield Pub Co.

The World Biotech Report Nineteen Eighty-Four: U. S. A, Vol. 2. 967p. 1984. pap. text ed. 220.00x (ISBN 0-86353-004-4, Pub. by Online). Brookfield Pub Co.

HUMAN ENVIRONMENT

see Human Ecology

HUMAN EVOLUTION

see also Fossil Man; Sociobiology

Bajema, Carl J., ed. Natural Selection in Human Populations: The Measurement of Ongoing Genetic Evolution in Contemporary Societies. LC 76-50639. (Illus.). 416p. 1977. Repr. of 1971 ed. lib. bdg. 19.50 (ISBN 0-88275-476-9). Krieger.

Benjamin, Elsie. Man at Home in the Universe: A Study of the Great Evolutionary Cycle: the "Globes", the "Rounds", "Races", "Root-Races" & "Sub-Races". (Study Ser.: No. 8). 36p. 1981. pap. 3.00 (ISBN 0-913004-43-X). Point Loma Pub.

Birdsell, J. B. Human Evolution. 3rd ed. 1981. 29.50 (ISBN 0-395-30784-8); instr's manual 1.50 (ISBN 0-395-30785-6). HM.

Bodmer, W. F. & Cavalli-Sforza, L. L. Genetics, Evolution, & Man. LC 75-33990. (Illus.). 782p. 1976. 30.95 (ISBN 0-7167-0573-7). W H Freeman.

Boughey, Arthur S. Man & the Environment. 2nd ed. (Illus.). 480p. 1975. pap. text ed. write for info. (ISBN 0-02-312770-8, 31277). Macmillan.

Boyce, A. J., ed. Chromosome Variations in Human Evolution. (Symposia of the Society for the Study of Human Biology Ser.: Vol. 14). 136p. 1975. cancelled (ISBN 0-85066-081-5). Taylor & Francis.

Brierley, John. A Natural History of Man. 184p. 1970. 15.00 (ISBN 0-8386-7819-X). Fairleigh Dickinson.

Bronfenbrenner, Urie. The Ecology of Human Development: Experiments by Nature & Design. LC 78-27232. 1979. text ed. 25.00x (ISBN 0-674-22456-6). Harvard U Pr.

Campbell, Bernard, ed. Sexual Selection & the Descent of Man. LC 70-169510. 388p. 1972. 39.95x (ISBN 0-202-02005-3). Aldine Pub.

Campbell, Bernard G. Humankind Emerging. 4th ed. 1985. pap. text ed. 23.95 (ISBN 0-316-12553-9); tchr's. ed. avail. (ISBN 0-316-12554-7). Little.

Clark, W. E. The Fossil Evidence for Human Evolution: An Introduction to the Study of Paleoanthropology. 3rd rev. ed. Campbell, Bernard G., ed. LC 78-529. (Illus.). 1979. 16.00x (ISBN 0-226-10937-2); pap. 4.95x (ISBN 0-226-10938-0, P502, Phoen). U of Chicago Pr.

Cold Spring Harbor Symposia on Quantitative Biology: Origin & Evolution of Man, Vol. 15. LC 34-8174. (Illus.). 437p. 1951. 38.00x (ISBN 0-87969-014-3). Cold Spring Harbor.

Darwin, Charles. The Descent of Man & Selection in Relation to Sex. LC 80-8679. (Illus.). 935p. 1981. 45.00x (ISBN 0-691-08278-2); pap. 12.50x (ISBN 0-691-02369-7). Princeton U Pr.

--The Illustrated Origin of Species. (Illus.). 240p. 1979. 25.00 (ISBN 0-8090-5735-2); pap. 12.95 (ISBN 0-8090-1397-5). Hill & Wang.

Day, M. H., ed. Human Evolution. (Symposia of the Society for the Study of Human Biology Ser.: Vol. II). 162p. 1973. 19.00x (ISBN 0-85066-061-0). Taylor & Francis.

Dobzhansky, Theodosius. Mankind Evolving: The Evolution of the Human Species. (Silliman Memorial Lectures Ser.). (Illus.). 1962. 33.00x (ISBN 0-300-00427-3); pap. 8.95x 1964 (ISBN 0-300-00070-7, Y116). Yale U Pr.

Dubos, Rene. Celebrations of Life. 1981. 12.95 (ISBN 0-07-017893-3). McGraw.

Dunn, Leslie C. Heredity & Evolution in Human Populations. rev. ed. LC 65-11617. (Books in Biology: No. 1). (Illus.). 1965. 8.95x (ISBN 0-674-38950-6). Harvard U Pr.

Edwards, Gabrielle. Man & Woman: Inside Homo Sapiens. 8.97 (ISBN 0-8239-0445-8). Rosen Group.

Eldredge, Niles & Tattersall, Ian. The Myths of Human Evolution. LC 82-1118. 192p. 1982. 20.00 (ISBN 0-231-05144-1); pap. 11.95 (ISBN 0-231-05145-X). Columbia U Pr.

Elliott, Scott F. Evolution & the Rediscovery of Prehistoric Man, 2 vols. (A Great Currents of History Library Bk.). (Illus.). 239p. 1985. Set. 189.75 (ISBN 0-89266-534-3). Am Classical Coll Pr.

Engels, Friedrich. The Part Played by Labour in the Transition from Ape to Man. 16p. 1972. pap. 0.75 (ISBN 0-8285-0044-4, Pub. by Progress Pubs USSR). Imported Pubns.

Foley, Robert. Hominid Evolution & Community Ecology. LC 83-72771. (Studies in Archaeology). 1984. 37.50 (ISBN 0-12-261920-X). Acad Pr.

Geist, V. Life Strategies, Human Evolution, Environmental Design: Toward a Biological Theory of Health, Vol. I. LC 78-10807. (Illus.). 1978. 39.50 (ISBN 0-387-90363-1). Springer-Verlag.

Greenwood, Davydd J. The Taming of Evolution: The Persistence of NonEvolutionary Views in the Study of Humans. LC 84-45147. (Illus.). 232p. 1984. 24.95x (ISBN 0-8014-1743-0). Cornell U Pr.

Haviland, William A. Human Evolution & Prehistory. 2nd ed. 1983. text ed. 23.95 (ISBN 0-03-062129-1). HR&W.

Higham, Charles. Life in the Old Stone Age. 2nd ed. (Cambridge Introduction to the History of Mankind). (Illus.). 1971. 4.50 (ISBN 0-521-21869-1). Cambridge U Pr.

Hooton, Earnest A. Apes, Men & Morons. LC 76-134095. (Essay Index Reprint Ser). 1937. 21.50 (ISBN 0-8369-1956-4). Ayer Co Pubs.

Huntington, Ellsworth. The Character of Races: Influenced by Physical Environment, Natural Selection & Historical Development. Grob, Gerald, ed. LC 76-46082. (Anti-Movements in America). 1977. lib. bdg. 31.00x (ISBN 0-405-09955-X). Ayer Co Pubs.

Itzkoff, Seymour W. The Form of Man: The Evolutionary Origins of Human Intelligence. LC 83-62230. (Illus.). 340p. 1983. 18.00 (ISBN 0-913993-00-X). Paideia MA.

--Triumph of the Intelligent: The Creation of Homo Sapiens. LC 84-19110. (Illus.). 223p. 1985. 16.00 (ISBN 0-913993-01-8). Paideia MA.

Kierkegaard, Soren A. Internal Development of Man in Dynamic Representational Expressions. Karlweiss, Joseph R., ed. (Illus.). 107p. 1981. 69.75 (ISBN 0-89266-273-5). Am Classical Coll Pr.

Korn, Noel. Human Evolution: Readings for Physical Anthropology. 4th ed. LC 77-27086. 1978. pap. 17.95 (ISBN 0-03-019321-4, HoltC). HR&W.

Leakey, Richard & Lewin, Roger. Origins: What New Discoveries Reveal About the Emergence of Our Species & Its Possible Future. 1982. pap. 7.95 (ISBN 0-525-48013-7, 0772-230). Dutton.

Lerner, I. Michael & Libby, William J. Heredity, Evolution, & Society. 2nd ed. LC 75-33968. (Illus.). 431p. 1976. text ed. 27.95 (ISBN 0-7167-0576-1); tchr's manual avail. W H Freeman.

Lewin, R. Human Evolution. (Illus.). 104p. 1984. text ed. 27.95 (ISBN 0-7167-1635-6); pap. text ed. 14.95 (ISBN 0-7167-1636-4). W H Freeman.

Lewis, John. Uniqueness of Man. 1974. pap. 7.95x (ISBN 0-8464-0948-8). Beekman Pubs.

MacCurdy, George G. Human Origins: A Manual of Prehistory, 2 Vols. 1978. Repr. of 1924 ed. lib. bdg. 80.00 (ISBN 0-8482-1724-1). Norwood Edns.

Morris, Richard. Evolution & Human Nature. 208p. 1984. pap. 3.75 (ISBN 0-380-69120-5, 69120-5, Discus). Avon.

Morris-Wu, Eleanor B. Human Efflorescence: A Study in Man's Evolutionary & Historical Development. 352p. 1983. 27.50 (ISBN 0-87527-323-8). Green.

Mother & Satprem. Mother's Agenda-1962, Vol. 3. LC 80-472990. Orig. Title: L' Agenda De Mere 1962. 540p. (Orig.). 1982. pap. text ed. 12.50 (ISBN 0-938710-02-8). Inst Evolutionary.

National Science Foundation. Human Evolution. Kornberg, Warren, ed. (Mosaic Reader Ser.). 64p. (Orig.). 1982. pap. text ed. 5.00 (ISBN 0-89529-174-6). Avery Pub.

Oxnard, Charles. Form & Pattern in Human Evolution. 256p. 1973. 17.00x (ISBN 0-226-64251-8). U of Chicago Pr.

--Uniqueness & Diversity in Human Evolution: Morphometric Studies of Australopithecines. LC 74-16689. viii, 134p. 1975. text ed. 17.50x (ISBN 0-226-64253-4). U of Chicago Pr.

Pawson, Ivan G. Physical Anthropology: Human Evolution. LC 77-2412. (Self-Teaching Guides). Repr. of 1977 ed. 48.70 (ISBN 0-8357-9954-9, 2011877). Bks Demand UMI.

Pfeiffer, John E. The Emergence of Humankind. 4th ed. 440p. 1985. pap. text ed. 19.50 scp (ISBN 0-06-045201-3, HarpC); instr's. manual avail. (ISBN 0-06-365200-5). Har-Row.

--The Emergence of Man. 3rd ed. LC 77-12804. (Illus.). 1978. pap. text ed. 18.50 scp (ISBN 0-06-045196-3, HarpC); inst. manual avail. (ISBN 0-06-365188-2). Har-Row.

Pilbeam, David. The Ascent of Man: An Introduction to Human Evolution. (Illus.). 224p. 1972. pap. text ed. write for info. (ISBN 0-02-395270-9). Macmillan.

Pringle, J. W., ed. Biology & the Human Sciences. 1972. pap. 3.50x (ISBN 0-19-857122-4). Oxford U Pr.

Rensch, Bernhard. Homo Sapiens: From Man to DemiGod. LC 72-80482. 1972. 30.00x (ISBN 0-231-03683-3). Columbia U Pr.

Schrodinger, Erwin. What Is Life? Bd. with Mind & Matter. pap. 11.95x (ISBN 0-521-09397-X). Cambridge U Pr.

Sigmon, Becky A. & Cybulski, Jerome S., eds. Homo Erectus: Papers in Honor of Davidson Black. 336p. 1981. 32.50x (ISBN 0-8020-5511-7). U of Toronto Pr.

Simons, Elwyn L. Primate Evolution: An Introduction to Man's Place in Nature. (Illus.). 352p. 1972. pap. text ed. write for info. (ISBN 0-02-410680-1). Macmillan.

Smith, G. E. Evolution of Man. 2nd ed. Repr. of 1927 ed. 22.00 (ISBN 0-527-84020-3). Kraus Repr.

Steele, E. J. Somatic Selection & Adaptive Evolution. 100p. 1980. 30.00x (ISBN 0-686-69937-8, Pub. by Croom Helm England). State Mutual Bk.

Steiner, Rudolf. Christianity in Human Evolution. 1979. pap. 1.50 (ISBN 0-88010-095-8). Anthroposophic.

Stringer, C. D., ed. Aspects of Human Evolution. LC 81-139420. (Symposia of the Society for the Study of Human Biology Ser.: Vol. 21). 234p. 1981. text ed. 33.00x (ISBN 0-85066-209-5). Taylor & Francis.

Swanson, Carl P. Ever-Expanding Horizons: The Dual Informational Sources of Human Evolution. LC 82-21750. (Illus.). 176p. 1983. lib. bdg. 13.50x (ISBN 0-87023-391-2); pap. 7.50 (ISBN 0-87023-392-0). U of Mass Pr.

Teilhard De Chardin, Pierre. Phenomenon of Man. pap. 6.68i (ISBN 0-06-090495-X, CN495, CN). Har-Row.

Underwood, Jane H. Human Variation & Human Microevolution. (Illus.). 1979. pap. 21.95 (ISBN 0-13-447573-9). P-H.

Vorzimmer, Peter J. Charles Darwin, the Years of Controversy: The Origin of SPecies & Its Critics, 1859-82. LC 78-118377. 300p. 1970. 17.95 (ISBN 0-87722-001-8). Temple U Pr.

Washburn, Sherwood L., ed. Classification & Human Evolution. LC 63-18184. (Viking Fund Publications in Anthropology: No. 37). pap. 95.30 (ISBN 0-317-26251-3, 2052136). Bks Demand UMI.

Weidenreich, Franz. Apes, Giants & Man. (Illus.). 1946. 10.00x (ISBN 0-226-88147-4). U of Chicago Pr.

Weiss, Mark L. & Mann, Alan E. Human Biology & Behavior: An Anthropological Perspective. 4th ed. 1985. text ed. 22.95 (ISBN 0-316-92894-1); tchr's. ed. avail. (ISBN 0-316-92896-8). Little.

Wilber, Ken. Up from Eden: A Transpersonal View of Human Evolution. LC 82-42678. (Illus.). 384p. 1983. pap. 8.95 (ISBN 0-87773-228-0). Shambhala Pubns.

Williams, B. J. Evolution & Human Origins: An Introduction to Physical Anthropology. 2nd ed. (Illus.). 1979. text ed. 18.50 scp (ISBN 0-06-047121-2, HarpC). Har-Row.

Wilson, Glenn. The Coolidge Effect: An Evolutionary Account of Human Sexuality. LC 81-16760. 252p. 1982. 12.50 (ISBN 0-688-01023-7). Morrow.

Wilson, Peter J. Man, the Promising Primate: The Conditions of Human Evolution. 2nd ed. LC 83-5791. 1983. text ed. 26.00 (ISBN 0-300-03106-8); pap. 7.95 (ISBN 0-300-02988-8, Y-479). Yale U Pr.

Wolsky, M. I. & Wolsky, A. The Mechanism of Evolution: A New Look at Old Ideas. (Contributions to Human Development: Vol. 4). (Illus.). 160p. 1976. 18.75 (ISBN 3-8055-2347-5). S Karger.

Young, Louise B., ed. Evolution of Man. (Orig.). 1970. text ed. 12.95x (ISBN 0-19-501107-4). Oxford U Pr.

HUMAN GENETICS

see also Genetic Psychology; Genetics; Human Chromosomes

Ananthakrishnan, R., et al. Human Biochemical Genetics. LC 73-645. 147p. 1973. text ed. 22.50x (ISBN 0-8422-7095-7). Irvington.

Armendares, S. & Lisker, R. Human Genetics. (International Congress Ser.: No. 411). 1978. 98.00 (ISBN 0-444-15252-0, Excerpta Medica). Elsevier.

Bajema, Carl J., ed. Natural Selection in Human Populations: The Measurement of Ongoing Genetic Evolution in Contemporary Societies. LC 76-50639. (Illus.). 416p. 1977. Repr. of 1971 ed. lib. bdg. 19.50 (ISBN 0-88275-476-9). Krieger.

HUMAN INFORMATION PROCESSING

Kardos, L., ed. Problems of Information Processing & Perceptual Organization. 1978. casebound 7.00 (ISBN 0-9960009-6-8, Pub. by Kiado Hungary). Heyden.
Klatzky, Roberta L. Memory & Awareness. 155p. 1984. text ed. 18.95 (ISBN 0-7167-1599-6); pap. text ed. 9.95 (ISBN 0-7167-1600-3). W H Freeman.
Ledgard, H., et al. Directions in Human Factors for Interactive Systems. (Lecture Notes in Computer Science Ser.: Vol. 103). 190p. 1981. pap. 14.95 (ISBN 0-387-10574-3). Springer-Verlag.
Lindsay, Norman, ed. Human Information Processing: Study Guide. 2nd ed. 1977. 7.25i (ISBN 0-12-450962-2). Acad Pr.
Marteniuk, R. G. Information Processing in Motor Skills. LC 75-43982. 1976. text ed. 25.95 (ISBN 0-03-006091-5, HoltC). HR&W.
Mayzner, Mark S. & Dolan, Terrence R. Minicomputers in Sensory & Information Processing Research. LC 78-15762. 280p. 1978. 18.00x (ISBN 0-470-26488-8). Halsted Pr.
Mayzner, Mark S. & Dolan, Terrence R., eds. Minicomputers in Sensory & Information-Processing Research. 288p. 1978. text ed. 29.95x (ISBN 0-89859-478-2). L Erlbaum Assocs.
Newell, Allen & Simon, Herbert. Human Problem Solving. LC 79-152528. (Illus.). 1972. 37.95 (ISBN 0-13-445403-0). P-H.
Rumelhart, D. E. Introduction to Human Information Processing. LC 76-54653. 306p. 1977. text ed. 28.95 (ISBN 0-471-74500-6). Wiley.
Saito, Shuzo & Nakata, Kazuo, eds. Fundamentals of Speech Signal Processing: Monograph. LC 83-9237. Date not set. 59.00 (ISBN 0-12-614880-5). Acad Pr.
Schatz, A. E. & Funk, B. M. Transcription Skills for Information Processing, Unit 4. 1981. pap. 5.28 text workbook (ISBN 0-07-055203-7). McGraw.
--Transcription Skills for Information Processing, Unit 5. 1981. pap. 5.28 text workbook (ISBN 0-07-055204-5). McGraw.
--Transcription Skills for Information Processing, Unit 6. 1981. pap. 5.28 text workbook (ISBN 0-07-055205-3). McGraw.
--Transcription Skills for Information Processing, Unit 7. 1981. pap. 5.28 text workbook (ISBN 0-07-055206-1). McGraw.
--Transcription Skills for Information Processing, Unit 8. 1981. pap. 5.28 text workbook (ISBN 0-07-055207-X). McGraw.
Simon. Models of Thought. LC 78-31744. 1979. text ed. 60.00x (ISBN 0-300-02347-2); pap. 22.00x (ISBN 0-300-02432-0, Y-352). Yale U Pr.
Solso, Robert L, ed. Information Processing & Cognition: The Loyola Symposium. LC 75-14324. (Loyola Symposium Ser.). 438p. 1975. 19.95x (ISBN 0-470-81230-3). Halsted Pr.
Sowa, John F. Conceptual Structures: Information Processing in Mind & Machine. LC 82-20720. (Systems Programming Ser.). 300p. 1983. text ed. 31.95 (ISBN 0-201-14472-7). Addison-Wesley.
Torda, Clara. Information Processing: The Central Nervous System & the Computer. Walters, ed. (Illus.). 157p. 1982. pap. 9.50 (ISBN 0-686-35738-8). Walters Pub.
Underwood, Geoffrey, ed. Strategies of Information Processing. 1979. 64.00 (ISBN 0-12-708950-0). Acad Pr.
Van Der Heijden, A. H. Short-Term Visual Information Forgetting. (International Library of Psychology). 224p. 1982. 29.95x (ISBN 0-7100-0851-1). Routledge & Kegan.

HUMAN MAGNETISM
see Animal Magnetism

HUMAN OPERATORS (SYSTEMS ENGINEERING)
see Man-Machine Systems

HUMAN PALEONTOLOGY
see Fossil Man

HUMAN SUBSYSTEMS (SYSTEMS ENGINEERING)
see Man-Machine Systems

HUMANITIES–DATA PROCESSING
Hockey, Susan. A Guide to Computer Applications in the Humanities. LC 79-3378. 248p. 1980. pap. 8.95x (ISBN 0-8018-2891-0). Johns Hopkins.
--SNOBOL Programming for the Humanities. 190p. 1985. 32.50 (ISBN 0-19-824675-7); pap. 14.95 (ISBN 0-19-824676-5). Oxford U Pr.

HUMBLEBEES
see Bumblebees

HUMIDITY
see also Moisture
Povoledo, D. & Golterman, H., eds. Humic Substances: Their Structure & Function in the Biosphere. 300p. 1975. pap. 60.00 (ISBN 90-220-0552-6, PDC41, Pub. by PUDOC). Unipub.
Wexler, Arnold, ed. Humidity & Moisture: Measurement & Control in Science & Industry, Vol. 3. 1965. (Pub. by UNR); Vol. 3, 1977 576 Pgs. 32.50 (ISBN 0-88275-080-1, Pub. by UNR). Krieger.

HUMMING-BIRDS
Mobbs, A. J. Hummingbirds. (Illus.). 200p. 1982. 32.50 (ISBN 0-86230-049-5). Triplegate.
Tyrrell, Esther Q. Hummingbirds: Their Life & Behavior. (Illus.). 1985. 35.00 (ISBN 0-517-55336-8). Crown.
Wildlife Education, Ltd. Hummingbirds. (Orig.). 1984. pap. 1.95 (ISBN 0-937934-31-3). Wildlife Educ.

HUMUS
see also Compost; Forest Soils
Buurman, Peter, ed. Podzols: Temperate Regions. (Benchmark Papers in Soil Science). 464p. 1984. 49.50 (ISBN 0-442-21129-5). Van Nos Reinhold.
Choudhry, Ghulam G. Humic Substances: Structural, Photophysical, Photochemical & Free Radial Aspects & Interactions with Environmental Chemistry. (Current Topics in Environmental & Toxicological Chemistry Ser.: Vol. 7). 180p. 1984. 44.00 (ISBN 0-677-06440-3). Gordon.
Christman, Russell F. & Gjessing, Egil, eds. Aquatic & Terrestrial Humic Materials. LC 82-71526. (Illus.). 538p. 1982. 49.95 (ISBN 0-250-40550-4). Butterworth.
Darwin, Charles. Darwin on Earthworms: The Formation of Vegetable Mould Through the Action of Worms. (Illus.). 160p. 1976. 7.95 (ISBN 0-916302-10-5); pap. 5.95 (ISBN 0-916302-06-7). Bookworm Pub.
--The Formation of Vegetable Mould, Through the Action of Worms: With Observations on Their Habits. 10/1985 ed. (Illus.). 348p. pap. 11.95 (ISBN 0-226-13663-9). U of Chicago Pr.
Darwin, Charles R. The Formation of Vegetable Mould, Through the Action of Worms, with Observations on Their Habits. LC 72-3903. (Illus.). vii, 326p. 1972. 42.50 (ISBN 0-404-08416-8). AMS Pr.
Flaig, W., et al. Organic Materials & Soil Productivity. (Soils Bulletins: No. 35). 127p. (2nd Printing). 1977. pap. 9.50 (ISBN 92-5-100510-9, F1404, FAO). Unipub.
Goring, Cleve A. & Hamaker, John W., eds. Organic Chemicals in the Soil Environment. LC 71-179384. (Books in Soils & the Environment Ser.: Vol. 1). pap. 114.00 (ISBN 0-317-28661-7, 2055084). Bks Demand UMI.
Handreck, K. A. Organic Matter & Soils. (Discovering Soils Ser.: No. 7). 51p. 1979. pap. 6.00 (ISBN 0-686-71837-2, C047, CSIRO). Unipub.
Isotopes & Radiation in Soil Organic-Matter Studies. (Proceedings Ser.). (Eng., Fr., Rus. & Span., Illus.). 584p. (Orig.). 1968. pap. 36.00 (ISBN 92-0-010368-5, ISP190, IAEA). Unipub.
Schnitzer, M. & Khan, S. U. Humic Substances in the Environment. LC 72-76064. (Books in Soils & the Environment). pap. 63.50 (ISBN 0-317-28553-X, 2055014). Bks Demand UMI.
Soil Organic Matter Studies, 2 Vols. (Proceedings Ser.). 1978. pap. 49.25 (ISBN 92-0-010077-5, ISP438-1, IAEA); pap. 46.50 (ISBN 92-0-010177-1, 438-2). Unipub.
Stevenson, F. J. Humus Chemistry: Genesis, Composition, Reactions. LC 81-12933. 443p. 1982. 42.95x (ISBN 0-471-09299-1, Pub. by Wiley-Interscience). Wiley.
Vaughan, D. & Malcolm, R. E., eds. Soil Organic Matter & Biological Activity. (Developments in Plant & Soil Sciences). 1985. lib. bdg. 59.50 (ISBN 90-247-3154-2, Pub. by Martinus Nijhoff Netherlands). Kluwer Academic.

HURRICANE PROTECTION
see also Flood Control; Hydraulic Engineering; Shore Protection
Regional Association IV (North & Central America) Hurricane Operational Plan. (Eng. & Fr.). 1979. pap. 23.00 loose-leaf (ISBN 92-63-10524-3, W429, WMO). Unipub.

HURRICANES
Here are entered mainly works on storms in the neighborhood of the West Indies.
see also Storms; Typhoons
Allen, Everett S. A Wind to Shake the World: The Story of the 1938 Hurricane. (Illus.). 1976. 17.45 (ISBN 0-316-03426-6). Little.
Chantz, N. E. Just Pick a Murricane? (Oleander Language & Literature Ser.: Vol. 3). 1.25 (ISBN 0-902675-11-7). Oleander Pr.
Douglass, Herbert. Parable of the Hurricane. (Uplook Ser.). 1980. pap. 0.79 (ISBN 0-8163-0356-8). Pacific Pr Pub Assn.
Gordon, Bernard L., ed. Hurricane in Southern New England: An Analysis of the Great Storm of 1938. LC 75-38912. (Illus.). 64p. 1976. pap. 4.00 (ISBN 0-910258-05-8). Book & Tackle.
Nalivkin, D. V., ed. Hurricanes, Storms & Tornadoes: Geographic Characteristics & Geological Activity. Bhattacharya, B. B., tr. from Rus. 605p. 1983. lib. bdg. 26.50 (ISBN 90-6191-408-6, Pub. by Balkema RSA). IPS.
Simpson, Robert H. & Riehl, Herbert. The Hurricane & Its Impact. LC 80-13911. (Illus.). 420p. 1981. 25.00x (ISBN 0-8071-0688-7). La State U Pr.
Tannehill, Ivan R. Hurricanes, Their Nature & History, Particularly Those of the West Indies & the Southern Coasts of the United States. Repr. of 1938 ed. lib. bdg. 24.75x (ISBN 0-8371-2316-X, TAHU). Greenwood.

HUSBANDRY
see Agriculture

HUTTON, JAMES, 1726-1797
Donovan, Arthur & Prentiss, Joseph. James Hutton's Medical Dissertation. LC 80-65850. (Transaction Ser.: Vol. 70). 1980. 8.00 (ISBN 0-87169-706-8). Am Philos.

HUXLEY, JULIAN SORELL, 1887-
Baker, J. R. Julian Huxley: Scientist & World Citizen, 1887-1975: A Bibliographic Memoir. 184p. (Bibliography compiled by Jens-Peter-Green). 1978. pap. 7.00 (ISBN 92-3-101461-7, U894, UNESCO). Unipub.

HUXLEY, THOMAS HENRY, 1825-1895
Ainsworth-Davis, James R. Thomas H. Huxley. LC 70-158236. (English Men of Science: No. 2). Repr. of 1907 ed. 21.50 (ISBN 0-404-07892-3). AMS Pr.
Clodd, Edward. Thomas Henry Huxley. LC 75-30018. Repr. of 1902 ed. 14.50 (ISBN 0-404-14023-8). AMS Pr.
--Thomas Henry Huxley. LC 74-2491. 1902. lib. bdg. 15.00 (ISBN 0-685-45595-5). Folcroft.
DeBeer, Gavin. Autobiographies: Charles Darwin & Thomas Henry Huxley. (Illus.). 1983. pap. 5.95 (ISBN 0-19-285131-4). Oxford U Pr.
Di Gregorio, Mario A. T. H. Huxley's Place in Natural Science. LC 84-2375. 280p. 1984. 25.00x (ISBN 0-300-03062-2). Yale U Pr.
Huxley, Leonard. Life & Letters of Thomas Henry Huxley, 2 vols. LC 75-41152. (BCL Ser. II). Repr. of 1900 ed. 85.00 set (ISBN 0-404-14980-4). AMS Pr.
--Life & Letters of Thomas Henry Huxley, 2 vols. 1979. Repr. of 1901 ed. Set. lib. bdg. 75.00 (ISBN 0-8492-5317-9). R West.
--Thomas Henry Huxley. LC 76-102247. (Select Bibliographies Reprint Ser). 1920. 18.00 (ISBN 0-8369-5132-8). Ayer Co Pubs.

HYBRID COMPUTERS
see Electronic Analog Computers; Electronic Digital Computers
Hyndman, D. E. Analog & Hybrid Computing. LC 75-120691. 1970. pap. 14.50 (ISBN 0-08-015572-3). Pergamon.
IEEE Standard 166-1977: Standard Definitions of Terms for Hybrid Computer Linkage Components. 1977. 5.00 (ISBN 0-317-03953-9, SH06502). IEEE.

HYBRID VIGOR
see Heterosis

HYBRIDIZATION
see also Genetics; Heterosis; Mendel's Law
Cottam, Walter P., et al. Oak Hybridization at the University of Utah. (State Arboretum of Utah Ser.: Publication No. 1, 1982). (Illus.). 96p. 1982. 15.00 (ISBN 0-942830-00-8); pap. 10.00x (ISBN 0-942830-01-6). State Arbor.
Ephrussi, Boris. Hybridization of Somatic Cells. LC 79-39783. (Illus.). 192p. 1972. 22.00 (ISBN 0-691-08114-X); pap. 8.50 (ISBN 0-691-08117-4). Princeton U Pr.
Knobloch, Irving W. A Check List of Crosses in the Gramineae. 1968. pap. 10.00 (ISBN 0-934454-22-1). Lubrecht & Cramer.
Levin, Donald A., ed. Hybridization: An Evolutionary Perspective. LC 78-10947. (Benchmark Papers in Genetics: Vol. 11). 321p. 1979. 49.95 (ISBN 0-87933-341-3). Van Nos Reinhold.
Protides of the Biological Fluids: Proceedings of the 28th Colloquium on Protides of the Biological Fluids, Brussels, 5-8 May 1980. LC 58-5908. (Illus.). 600p. 1980. 120.00 (ISBN 0-08-026370-4). Pergamon.
Stace, C. A., ed. Hybridization & the Flora of the British Isles. 1975. 96.50 (ISBN 0-12-661650-7). Acad Pr.
Stern, Norman J. & Gamble, H. Ray, eds. Hybridoma Technology in Agricultural & Veterinary Research. LC 84-17795. (Illus.). 354p. 1984. 52.50x (ISBN 0-8476-7362-6). Rowman & Allanheld.

HYBRIDIZATION, VEGETABLE
Cooperative Hybrid Maize Tests in Europe & Mediterranean Countries: 1952. (Agricultural Development Papers: No. 42). pap. 7.50 (F105, FAO). Unipub.
De Vries, H. Mutation Theory, 2 Vols. in 1. Farmer, J. B. & Darbishire, trs. 1909-1910. 58.00 (ISBN 0-527-93470-4). Kraus Repr.
Fehr, W. R. & Hadley, H. H., eds. Hybridization of Crop Plants. (Illus.). 1980. 25.00 (ISBN 0-89118-034-6). Am Soc Agron.
Herbert, William. Amaryllidacea...&...a Treatise on Cross-Bred Vegetables. (Illus.). 1970. 56.00 (ISBN 3-7682-0672-6). Lubrecht & Cramer.
Mendel, G. Versuche ueber Pflanzenhybriden. 1966. pap. 7.50 (ISBN 3-7682-0013-2). Lubrecht & Cramer.
Mendel, Gregor. Experiments in Plant-Hybridisation. LC 67-9611. 1965. pap. 3.50x (ISBN 0-674-27800-3). Harvard U Pr.
Moir, W. W. & Moir, May A. Laeliinae Intergenerics. LC 82-4887. (Illus.). 61p. 1982. pap. text ed. 12.00x (ISBN 0-8248-0814-2). UH Pr.
Roberts, Herbert F. Plant Hybridization Before Mendel. (Illus.). 1965. Repr. of 1929 ed. 15.95x (ISBN 0-02-851000-3). Hafner.

HYDRA
Burnett, Allison L., ed. Biology of Hydra. 1973. 72.00 (ISBN 0-12-145950-0). Acad Pr.
Lenhoff, Howard M., ed. Hydra: Research Methods. LC 82-24648. 496p. 1983. 59.50x (ISBN 0-306-41086-9). Plenum Pub.
Lenhoff, Howard M. & Loomis, W. Farnsworth, eds. Biology of Hydra & of Some Other Coelenterates. LC 61-18157. 1961. 9.95x (ISBN 0-87024-010-2). U of Miami Pr.

HYDRATION
Conway, B. E. Ionic Hydration in Chemistry & Biophysics. (Studies in Physical & Theoretical Chemistry: Vol. 12). 774p. 1981. 132.00 (ISBN 0-444-41947-0). Elsevier.
Taylor, R. E., ed. Advances in Obsidian Glass Studies: Archaeological & Geochemical Perspectives. LC 76-43192. (Illus.). 36p. 1977. 32.00 (ISBN 0-8155-5050-2, NP). Noyes.

HYDRAULIC CEMENT
see Cement

HYDRAULIC CONTROL
Dransfield, P. Hydraulic Control Systems: Design & Analysis of the Dynamics. (Lecture Notes in Control & Information Sciences Ser.: Vol. 33). 227p. 1981. pap. 18.00 (ISBN 0-387-10890-4). Springer-Verlag.
Fluidics Quarterly, Vol. 1. (Illus.). 1968-69. 85.00 (ISBN 0-88232-001-7). Delbridge Pub Co.
Fluidics Quarterly, Vol. 2. (Illus.). 1970. 125.00 (ISBN 0-88232-006-8). Delbridge Pub Co.
Fluidics Quarterly, Vol. 3. (Illus.). 1971. 100.00 (ISBN 0-88232-012-2). Delbridge Pub Co.
Fluidics Quarterly, Vol. 9. (Illus.). 1977. 115.00 (ISBN 0-88232-042-4). Delbridge Pub Co.
Merritt, Herbert E. Hydraulic Control Systems. LC 66-28759. 358p. 1967. 54.95x (ISBN 0-471-59617-5, Pub. by Wiley-Interscience). Wiley.
Pippenger, John J. Hydraulic Valves & Controls: Selection & Application. (Fluid Power & Control: Vol. 4). (Illus.). 272p. 1984. 35.00 (ISBN 0-8247-7087-0). Dekker.

HYDRAULIC CONVEYING
Carleton, A. J. & French, R. J. Hydraulic Transport of Limestone Aggregates & Colliery Spoil, 1978. 1981. 80.00x (ISBN 0-686-97086-1, Pub. by W Spring England). State Mutual Bk.
Linderman, Charles W., ed. International Technical Conference on Slurry Tranportation, 2nd: Proceedings. LC 77-81416. (Illus.). 152p. 1977. pap. 40.00 (ISBN 0-932066-02-X). Slurry Tech.
Round, Gilbert F., ed. Solid-Liquid Flow Abstracts, 3 Vols. 1064p. 1969. Set. 283.00x (ISBN 0-677-40120-5); Vol. 1, 448p. 127.25x (ISBN 0-677-40080-2); Vol. 2, 460p. 130.75 (ISBN 0-677-40090-X); Vol. 3, 156p. 62.50x (ISBN 0-677-40100-0). Gordon.
Stepanoff, Alexely. Gravity Flow & Transportation of Solids in Suspension. LC 72-91156. (Materials Handling & Packaging Ser). 1969. text ed. 12.50 (ISBN 0-471-82202-7, Pub. by Wiley). Krieger.
Stephens, H. S. & Stephen, H. S., eds. Hydrotransport Seven: Papers Presented at the Seventh International Conference on the Hydraulic Transport of Solids in Pipes. (Illus., Orig.). 1980. pap. 98.00x (ISBN 0-906085-46-2). BHRA Fluid.

HYDRAULIC ENGINEERING
see also Boring; Channels (Hydraulic Engineering); Drainage; Flood Control; Hydraulic Machinery; Hydraulic Measurements; Hydraulic Mining; Hydraulic Structures; Hydraulics; Hydrodynamics; Hydrostatics; Irrigation; Offshore Structures; Pumping Machinery; Reclamation of Land; Rivers; Shore Protection; Stream Measurements; Underwater Drilling; Water-Jet; Water-Supply Engineering; Wells
American Society of Civil Engineers & O'Neill, Michale W., eds. Drilled Piers & Caissons. LC 81-69227. 159p. 1981. 17.25x (ISBN 0-87262-285-1). Am Soc Civil Eng.
American Society of Civil Engineers, compiled by. Hydraulic Engineering & the Environment. 474p. 1973. pap. 12.50x (ISBN 0-87262-054-9). Am Soc Civil Eng.
ASCE Conference, Hydraulics Division, 1980. Computer & Physical Modeling in Hydraulic Engineering. Ashton, George, ed. LC 80-67878. 500p. 1980. pap. 36.00x (ISBN 0-87262-252-5). Am Soc Civil Eng.
Australasian Conference on Hydraulics & Fluid Mechanic, 1977: Sixth Conference. 627p. (Orig.). 1977. pap. text ed. 67.50x (ISBN 0-85825-088-8, Pub. by Inst Engineering Australia). Brookfield Pub Co.

Australasian Conference on Hydraulics & Fluid Mechanics, 1980: Seventh Conference. 575p. (Orig.). 1980. pap. text ed. 67.50x (ISBN 0-85825-136-1, Pub. by Inst Engineering Australia). Brookfield Pub Co.

Bartlett, R. E. & Madill, W. Hydraulics for Public Health Engineers. (Illus.). 198p. 1982. 33.50 (ISBN 0-85334-148-6, I-431-82, Pub. by Elsevier Applied Sci England). Elsevier.

Bergeron, Louis J. Water Hammer in Hydraulics & Wave Surges in Electricity. pap. 84.30 (ISBN 0-317-10793-3, 2011588). Bks Demand UMI.

Bras, Rafael & Rodriquez-Itube, I. Hydraulic Analysis & Synthesis. 704p. 1985. text ed. 42.95 (ISBN 0-201-05865-0). Addison-Wesley.

Brebbia, C. A., et al, eds. Hydrosoft '84; Hydraulic Engineering Software: Proceedings of the International Conference, Protoroz, Yugoslavia, Sept. 10-14, 1984. 1984. 129.75 (ISBN 0-444-99607-9). Elsevier.

Bretschneider, Charles L. Topics in Ocean Engineering, 3 vols. Incl. Vol. 1. 428p. 1969 (ISBN 0-87201-598-X); Vol. 2. (Illus.). 229p. 1970 (ISBN 0-87201-599-8); Vol. 3. 328p. 1976 (ISBN 0-87201-600-5). LC 78-87230. 29.50x ea. Gulf Pub.

Carleton, A. J. & French, R. J. Hydraulic Transport of Limestone Aggregates & Colliery Spoil, 1978. 1981. 80.00x (ISBN 0-686-97086-1, Pub. by W Spring England). State Mutual Bk.

Cunge, J. A. & Holley, F. M. Practical Aspects of Computational River Hydraulics. LC 79-25810. (Water Resources Engineering Ser.). 420p. 1981. text ed. 82.95 (ISBN 0-273-08442-9). Pitman Pub MA.

Davis, Calvin V. & Sorensen, K. E. Handbook of Applied Hydraulics. 3rd ed. (Illus.). 1968. 87.50 (ISBN 0-07-015538-0). McGraw.

Deere & Company. Hydraulics: Compact Equipment. (Fundamentals of Service Compact Equipment Ser.). (Illus.). 124p. 1983. pap. text ed. 8.80 (ISBN 0-86691-029-8); wkbk. 3.80 (ISBN 0-86691-032-8). Deere & Co.

Droze, Wilmon H. High Dams & Slack Waters: TVA Rebuilds a River. LC 65-14533. pap. 46.00 (ISBN 0-317-09202-2, 2007179). Bks Demand UMI.

The Efficient Use of Water in the Manufacturing Industries: Proceedings, No. 52, Leeds, September 1977. 208p. 1981. 80.00x (ISBN 0-85295-105-1, Pub. by Inst Chem Eng England). State Mutual Bk.

Fawcett, J. R. Hydraulic Circuits & Control Systems. 240p. 1982. 110.00x (ISBN 0-85461-078-2, Pub. by Trade & Tech). State Mutual Bk.

Featherstone, R. E. & Nalluri, C. Civil Engineering Hydraulics: Essential Theory with Worked Examples. (Illus.). 384p. 1982. text ed. 23.50x (ISBN 0-246-11483-5). Sheridan.

Fox, J. The Hydraulic Analysis of Unsteady Flow in Pipe Networks. 216p. 1977. 49.95 (ISBN 0-470-27037-3). Halsted Pr.

Gyorke, Olivier. European Hydraulics Laboratories: A Survey. (Engineering Laboratories Ser.: No. 3). (Illus.). 128p. (Orig.). 1973. pap. 6.25 (ISBN 92-3-101064-6, U217, UNESCO). Unipub.

Hwang, Ned H. Fundamentals of Hydraulic Engineering Systems. (P-H Ser. in Environmental Sciences). (Illus.). 352p. 1981. text ed. 38.95 (ISBN 0-13-340000-X). P-H.

Institution of Chemical Engineers. Interflow Eighty. 52.50 (ISBN 0-08-028758-1). Pergamon.

International Conference on the Hydraulic Transport of Solids in Pipes, 6th. Hydrotransport Six: Proceedings, 2 vols. Stephens, H. S., ed. 400p. 1979. Set. pap. 98.00x lib. ed. (ISBN 0-906085-21-7, Dist. by Air Science Co.). BHRA Fluid.

International Conference on the Hydraulic Transport of Solids in Pipes. Proceedings, 2 vols. Stephens, H. S. & Gittins, L., eds. (Illus.). 1978. Set. pap. text ed. 76.00x (ISBN 0-900983-82-5, Dist by Air Science Co.). BHRA Fluid.

International Conference on Underground Pumped Hydro & Compressed Air Energy Storage. 1982. 50.00 (ISBN 0-317-06668-4). AIAA.

Jaeger, Charles. Fluid Transients in Hydro-Electric Engineering Practice. (Illus.). 1977. 75.00x (ISBN 0-216-90225-8). Intl Ideas.

Jansen, P. P., et al. Principles of River Engineering: The Non-Tidal Alluvial River. LC 79-40141. (Water Resources Engineering Ser.). 509p. 1979. text ed. 139.95 (ISBN 0-273-01139-1). Pitman Pub MA.

Johnson, et al, eds. Water for Subsurface Injection - STP 735. 150p. 1981. 14.00 (ISBN 0-8031-0800-1, 04-735000-16). ASTM.

Kinori, B. Z. Manual of Surface Drainage Engineering, Vol. 1. 224p. 1970. 55.50 (ISBN 0-444-40851-7). Elsevier.

Kobus, Helmut. Hydraulic Modelling. (Water Resoures Engineering Ser.). 323p. 1980. pap. text ed. 30.95 (ISBN 0-273-08519-0). Pitman Pub MA.

Kovacs, G. Seepage Hydraulics. (Developments in Water Science Ser.: Vol. 10). 730p. 1981. 127.75 (ISBN 0-444-99755-5). Elsevier.

Lajos, Ivicsics. Hydraulic Models. 1980. 32.00 (ISBN 0-918334-38-1). WRP.

Li, R. Wen-Hsiung. Fluid Mechanics in Water Resources Engineering. 1983. text ed. 43.24 scp (ISBN 0-205-07895-8, 327895); write for info. solution manual (ISBN 0-205-07896-6). Allyn.

Maass, Arthur. Muddy Waters: The Army Engineers & the Nation's Rivers. LC 73-20238. (FDR & the Era of the New Deal Ser). 306p. 1974. Repr. of 1951 ed. lib. bdg. 39.50 (ISBN 0-306-70607-5). Da Capo.

Morris, Henry M. & Wiggert, James M. Applied Hydraulics in Engineering. 2nd ed. 629p. 1972. 45.50 (ISBN 0-471-06669-9); solutions avail. (ISBN 0-471-07503-5). Wiley.

National Association of Home Builders, et al. Residential Storm Water Management: Objectives, Principles & Design Considerations. LC 75-34759. 64p. 1975. pap. 6.00 (ISBN 0-87420-564-6, R04); pap. 4.50 members. Natl Assn Home.

Naudascher, E. & Rockwell, D., eds. Practical Experiences with Flow-Induced Vibrations: Symposium Proceedings. (International Association for Hydraulic Research - International Union of Theoretical & Applied Mechanics). (Illus.). 850p. 1980. 82.60 (ISBN 0-387-10314-7). Springer-Verlag.

Neese, Bill. Aircraft Hydraulic Systems. LC 83-22168. 204p. 1984. 16.50 (ISBN 0-89874-688-4). Krieger.

Nemat-Nasser, S., ed. Hydraulic Fracturing & Geothermal Energy. 1983. lib. bdg. 78.50 (ISBN 90-247-2855-X, Pub. by Martinus Nijhoff Netherlands). Kluwer Academic.

Novak, P. Developments in Hydraulic Engineering, Vol. 1. (Illus.). 240p. 1984. 55.50 (ISBN 0-85334-227-X, I-338-83, Pub. by Elsevier Applied Sci England). Elsevier.

Novak, P. & Cabelka, J. Models in Hydraulic Engineering. LC 80-22383. (Water Resources Engineering Ser.). 480p. 1981. text ed. 89.95 (ISBN 0-273-08436-4). Pitman Pub MA.

Novak, P., ed. Developments in Hydraulic Engineering, Vol. 2. 256p. 45.50 (ISBN 0-85334-228-8, I-007-84, Pub. by Elsevier Applied Sci England). Elsevier.

Petersen, Margaret S. River Engineering. (Illus.). 480p. 1986. text ed. 41.95 (ISBN 0-13-781352-X). P-H.

Robb, Louis A. Engineers' Dictionary, Spanish-English, English-Spanish. 2nd ed. LC 40-50261. (Span. & Eng.). 664p. 1949. 56.95 (ISBN 0-471-72501-3, Pub. by Wiley-Interscience). Wiley.

Rudman, Jack. Hydraulic Engineer. (Career Examination Ser.: C-357). (Cloth bdg. avail. on request). pap. 10.00 (ISBN 0-8373-0357-5). Natl Learning.

Schwab, G. O., et al. Elementary Soil & Water Engineering. 2nd ed. LC 76-132224. 316p. 1979. 40.00 (ISBN 0-471-76526-0); Arabic Translation 9.80 (ISBN 0-471-04504-7). Wiley.

Shen, Hsieh W. Modeling of Rivers. LC 79-3913. 1000p. 1979. 79.95x (ISBN 0-471-05474-7, Pub. by Wiley-Interscience). Wiley.

Shen, Hung T., ed. Frontiers in Hydraulic Engineering. 632p. 1983. pap. 47.75x (ISBN 0-87262-371-8). Am Soc Civil Eng.

Smith, P. E., ed. Applying Research to Hydraulic Practice. LC 82-72777. 743p. 1982. pap. 53.00x (ISBN 0-87262-316-5). Am Soc Civil Eng.

Society of Manufacturing Engineers. Hydraulic Accessories. (Productivity Equipment Ser.). 1984. 38.00 (ISBN 0-87263-151-6). SME.

Studien Zur Hydronymie des Savesystems: Woerterbuch der Gewaessernamen, Auswertung. 2nd ed. (Ger.). 1966. pap. 32.50 (ISBN 3-533-00810-X, M-7629, Pub. by Carl Winter). French & Eur.

Swift, W. L, et al, eds. Performance Characteristics of Hydraulic Turbines & Pumps. (FED Ser.: Vol. 6). 296p. 1983. pap. text ed. 40.00 (ISBN 0-317-02639-9, H00280). ASME.

Symposium on Hydraulic System Cleanliness. Hydraulic System Cleanliness: A Symposium Presented At the 73rd Annual Meeting American Society for Testing & Materials, Toronto, Ont., Canada, 21-26 June 1970. LC 70-151113. (American Society for Testing & Materials Special Technical Publication Ser.: No. 491). pap. 22.30 (ISBN 0-317-29436-9, 2024294). Bks Demand UMI.

Thomas, Jean. Modern Oil-Hydraulic Engineering. 350p. 1982. 40.00x (ISBN 0-85461-043-X, Pub. by Trade & Tech England). Brookfield Pub Co.

Threlfall, A. J. Design Charts for Water Retaining Structures: BS 5337. (Viewpoint Publication Ser). (Illus.). 1978. pap. text ed. 16.50x (ISBN 0-7210-1104-7). Scholium Intl.

U. S. Dept. of Agriculture-Soil Conservation Service & Forest Service. Headwaters Control & Use: A Summary of Fundamental Principles & Their Application in the Conservation & Utilization of Waters & Soils Throughout Headwater Areas. LC 72-2871. (Use & Abuse of America's Natural Resources Ser). (Illus.). 290p. 1972. Repr. of 1937 ed. 26.50 (ISBN 0-405-04539-5). Ayer Co Pubs.

Verification of Mathematical & Physical Models in Hydraulic Engineering. 898p. 1978. pap. 40.00x (ISBN 0-87262-131-6). Am Soc Civil Eng.

Viersma, T. J. Analysis Synthesis & Design Hydraulic Servosystem & Pipelines. (Studies in Mechanical Engineering: Vol. 1). 280p. 1980. 66.00 (ISBN 0-444-41869-5). Elsevier.

Walski, Thomas M. Analysis of Water Distribution Systems. 400p. 1984. 42.50 (ISBN 0-442-29192-2). Van Nos Reinhold.

Warnick, Calvin C. Hydropower Engineering. (Illus.). 1984. 36.95 (ISBN 0-13-448498-3). P-H.

Zimmie & Riggs, eds. Permeability & Groundwater Contaminant Transport - STP 746. 245p. 1981. 28.00 (ISBN 0-8031-0797-8, 04-746000-38). ASTM.

HYDRAULIC ENGINEERING–PROBLEMS, EXERCISES, ETC.

Anders, James E., Sr. Industrial Hydraulics Troubleshooting. (Illus.). 192p. 1983. 29.75 (ISBN 0-07-001592-9). McGraw.

HYDRAULIC FLUIDS

see also Petroleum Products

Tourret, R. & Wright, E. P., eds. Performance Testing of Hydraulic Fluids. 544p. 1979. 95.95 (ISBN 0-471-26059-2, Wiley Heyden). Wiley.

Trade & Technical Press Editors. Fluids for Power Systems. 250p. 1970. 35.00x (ISBN 0-85461-040-5, Pub by Trade & Tech England). Brookfield Pub Co.

HYDRAULIC MACHINERY

see also Centrifugal Pumps; Hydraulic Control; Hydraulic Servomechanisms; Oil Hydraulic Machinery; Pumping Machinery; Turbines

Hydraulic & Pneumatic Cylinders. 200p. 1982. 75.00x (ISBN 0-85461-049-9, Pub. by Trade & Tech). State Mutual Bk.

Jarvis, Adrian. Hydraulic Machines. (Shire Album Ser.: No. 144). (Orig.). 1985. pap. 3.50 (ISBN 0-85263-751-9, Pub. by Shire Pubns England). Seven Hills Bks.

Lambeck. Hydraulic Pumps & Motors. (Mechanical Engineering Ser.). 240p. 1983. 24.95 (ISBN 0-8247-7014-5). Dekker.

Manohar, M. & Krishnamachar, P. Fluid Mechanics: Vol. 2: Hydraulic Machinery & Advanced Hydraulics. 600p. 1983. text ed. 45.00x (ISBN 0-7069-2078-3, Pub. by Vikas India). Advent NY.

Prokes, J. Hydraulic Mechanisms in Automation. 334p. 1977. 64.00 (ISBN 0-444-99829-2). Elsevier.

Society of Automotive Engineers. Topics on Contamination in Hydraulic Systems. LC 79-67067. 60p. 1979. Eight papers. pap. 18.00 (ISBN 0-89883-218-7, SP447). Soc Auto Engineers.

Troskolanski, A. T. Dictionary of Hydraulic Machinery. (Eng., Ger., Span., Fr. & Ital. & Rus.). 736p. 1983. 117.00 (ISBN 0-444-99728-8). Elsevier.

Watt, Simon B. A Manual on the Automatic Hydraulic Ram for Pumping Water. rev. ed. (Illus.). 40p. 1978. pap. 7.75x (ISBN 0-903031-15-9, Pub. by Intermediate Tech England). Intermediate Tech.

HYDRAULIC MEASUREMENTS

see also Flow Meters; Hydrometer; Stream Measurements; Water-Meters

Herschy, R. W., ed. Hydrometry: Principles & Practices. LC 78-4101. 511p. 1978. 120.95 (ISBN 0-471-99649-1, Pub. by Wiley-Interscience). Wiley.

Kolupaila, Steponas. Bibliography of Hydrometry. 1961. 40.00x (ISBN 0-268-00021-2). U of Notre Dame Pr.

Modern Developments in Hydrometry: Introductory Reports on the Topics of the Seminar, Vol. 1. (Illus.). 71p. 1975. pap. 16.00 (ISBN 92-63-10427-1, W191, WMO). Unipub.

HYDRAULIC MINING

see also Gold Mines and Mining; Manganese Mines and Mining, Submarine

Evans, Taliesin. Hydraulic Mining in California in Eighteen Eighty-Three. Jones, William R., ed. (Illus.). 1981. pap. 1.00 (ISBN 0-89646-052-5). Outbooks.

MacDonald, E. H. Alluvial Mining: The Geology, Technology & Economics of Placers. LC 82-22215. (Illus.). 580p. 1983. 79.95 (ISBN 0-412-24630-9, NO. 6791). Methuen Inc.

May, Philip R. Origins of Hydraulic Mining in California. limited ed. (Illus.). 88p. 1970. octavo 6.95 (ISBN 0-910740-17-8). Holmes.

Placer Mining. facs. ed. (Shorey Prospecting Ser.). (Illus.). 147p. pap. 8.95 (ISBN 0-8466-0106-0, S106). Shorey.

HYDRAULIC POWER PLANTS

see Water-Power; Water-Power Electric Plants

HYDRAULIC PRESSES

Idelchik, I. E. Handbook of Hydraulic Resistance. 2nd, rev., and aug. ed. Fried, Erwin, ed. Malyavskaya, Greta R., tr. from Rus. (Illus.). 650p. 1985. 89.95 (ISBN 0-89116-284-4). Hemisphere Pub.

Mueller, E. Hydraulic Forging Presses. 3rd ed. (Illus.). 1968. 56.00 (ISBN 0-387-04286-5). Springer-Verlag.

HYDRAULIC SERVOMECHANISMS

Fawcett, J. R. Hydraulic Servo-Mechanisms & Their Applications. 130p. 1979. 65.00x (ISBN 0-85461-026-X, Pub. by Trade & Tech). State Mutual Bk.

HYDRAULIC STRUCTURES

see also Aqueducts; Canals; Dams; Docks; Flood Dams and Reservoirs; Harbors; Lighthouses; Piers; Pipe Lines; Reservoirs; Sea-Walls; Sewerage; Structural Engineering; Tunnels and Tunneling; Wharves

Grishin, M. Hydraulic Structures, 2 vols. 732p. 1982. 15.45 (ISBN 0-8285-2448-3, Pub. by Mir Pubs USSR). Imported Pubns.

McCormick, Michael E. Ocean Engineering Wave Mechanics. LC 72-12756. (Ocean Engineering Ser.). 179p. 1973. 43.95x (ISBN 0-471-58177-1, Pub. by Wiley-Interscience). Wiley.

Muga, Bruce J. & Wilson, James F. Dynamic Analysis of Ocean Structures. LC 77-122021. 377p. 1970. 52.50x (ISBN 0-306-30483-X, Plenum Pr). Plenum Pub.

Small Hydraulic Structures, 2 vols. (Irrigation & Drainage Papers: No. 26 1-2). (Eng., Fr. & Span., Illus., 2nd Printing 1982). 1975. Set. pap. 26.00 (ISBN 0-685-54184-3, F995, FAO). Vol. 1, 422p (ISBN 92-5-100160-X). Vol. 2, 308p (ISBN 0-686-77065-X). Unipub.

Wiegel, Robert L. Oceanographical Engineering. 1964. ref. ed. O.P. 43.95 (ISBN 0-13-629600-9). P-H.

HYDRAULIC TRANSMISSION

see Oil Hydraulic Machinery

HYDRAULICS

see also Channels (Hydraulic Engineering); Fire Extinction; Fluids; Hydraulic Engineering; Hydraulic Measurements; Hydrostatics; Seepage; Water Hammer

Abbott, M. B. Computational Hydraulics: Elements of the Theory of Free Surface Flows. LC 78-40148. (Water Resources Engineering Ser.). 324p. 1979. text ed. 64.95 (ISBN 0-273-01140-5). Pitman Pub MA.

Abbott, M. B. & Cunge, J. A. Engineering Applications of Computational Hydraulics. LC 81-2327. (Water Resources Engineering Ser.). 288p. 1982. 66.50 (ISBN 0-273-08512-3). Pitman Pub MA.

American Society of Civil Engineers, Special Committee on Irrigation. Letter Symbols & Glossary for Hydraulics: With Special Reference to Irrigation. LC 42-233. (American Society of Civil Engineers, Manuals of Engineering Practice: No. 11). pap. 20.00 (ISBN 0-317-29810-0, 2052000). Bks Demand UMI.

American Society of Civil Engineers, compiled by. Reaeration Research. 376p. 1979. pap. 26.00x (ISBN 0-87262-142-1). Am Soc Civil Eng.

American Water Works Association. Op Flow: Vol. 6, 1980. (Illus.). 104p. 1981. text ed. 19.20 (ISBN 0-89867-254-6). Am Water Wks Assn.

Applied Hydraulics & Pneumatics in Industry. 260p. 1982. 75.00x (ISBN 0-686-92052-X, Trade & Tech). State Mutual Bk.

ASCE Conference, Hydraulics Division, 1980. Urban Stormwater Management in Coastal Areas. Kuo, Chin Y., ed. LC 80-66949. 442p. 1980. pap. 32.00x (ISBN 0-87262-247-9). Am Soc Civil Eng.

Aviation Maintenance Foundation. Aircraft Hydraulics Systems. Crane, Dale, ed. (Aviation Technician Training Ser.). (Illus.). 87p. 1975. pap. text ed. 5.95 (ISBN 0-89100-058-5, EA-AH-1). Aviation Maint.

Azevedo, J. M. Manual De Hidraulica. (Span.). 1976. pap. text ed. 17.00 (ISBN 0-06-310007-X, IntlDept). Har-Row.

Benque, J. P., et al. Engineering Applications of Computational Hydraulics, Vol. 2. Abbott, M. & Cunge, J. A., eds. (Water Resources Engineering Ser.). 224p. 1982. text ed. 48.95 (ISBN 0-273-08543-3). Pitman Pub MA.

Binder, Raymond C. Fluid Mechanics. 5th ed. (Illus.). 448p. 1973. ref. ed. 38.95 (ISBN 0-13-322594-1). P-H.

Bouthillier, Patrick H. Hydraulic Tables for Water Supply & Drainage. LC 81-69115. (Illus.). 150p. 1981. pap. text ed. 17.50 (ISBN 0-250-40517-2). Butterworth.

Brater, E. F. Handbook of Hydraulics. 6th ed. (Handbook Ser.). 1976. 51.50 (ISBN 0-07-007243-4). McGraw.

Brown, W. Elgar. Hydraulics for Operators. rev. ed. 145p. 1985. pap. text ed. 19.95 (ISBN 0-250-40650-0). Butterworth.

Brown, William E. Hydraulics Manual for Operators. LC 81-68896. (Illus.). 145p. 1981. pap. text ed. 19.95 (ISBN 0-250-40503-2). Butterworth.

Chernov, A. & Bessrebrennikov, N. Fundamentals of Heat Engineering & Hydraulics. Troitsky, A., tr. from Rus. (Illus.). 407p. 1969. 17.00x (ISBN 0-8464-0437-0). Beekman Pubs.

Chow Ven Te, ed. Advances in Hydroscience, 12 vols. Incl. Vol. 1. 1964. 87.50 (ISBN 0-12-021801-1); Vol. 2. 1966. 87.50 (ISBN 0-12-021802-X); Vol. 3. 1967. 87.50 (ISBN 0-12-021803-8); Vol. 4. 1968. 87.50 (ISBN 0-12-021804-6); Vol. 5. 1969. 87.50 (ISBN 0-12-021805-4); Vol. 6. 1970. 87.50 (ISBN 0-12-021806-2); Vol. 7. 1971. 87.50 (ISBN 0-12-021807-0); Vol. 8. 1972. 87.50 (ISBN 0-12-021808-9); Vol. 9. 1973. 87.50 (ISBN 0-12-021809-7); Vol. 10. 1975. 90.00 (ISBN 0-12-021810-0); Vol. 11. 1978. 90.00 (ISBN 0-12-021811-9); lib. bdg. 120.00 o.p (ISBN 0-12-021876-3); Vol. 12. 1981. 80.00 (ISBN 0-12-021812-7). Acad Pr.

Classic Papers in Hydraulics. 672p. 1982. pap. 49.00x (ISBN 0-87262-310-6). Am Soc Civil Eng.

Davis, Calvin V. & Sorensen, K. E. Handbook of Applied Hydraulics. 3rd ed. (Illus.). 1968. 87.50 (ISBN 0-07-015538-0). McGraw.

De Laat, P. J. M. Model for Unsaturated Flow Above a Shallow Water-Table, Applied to a Regional Subsurface Flow Problem. (Agricultural Research Reports: No. 895). 133p. 1980. pap. 11.00 (ISBN 90-220-0725-1, PDC244, PUDOC). Unipub.

DeVore, R. William & Huffsey, R. Nineteen Eighty-Five International Symposium on Urban Hydrology, Hydraulic & Infrastructures & Water Quality Control: Proceedings. (Illus.). 335p. (Orig.). 1985. pap. 33.50 (ISBN 0-89779-063-4, UKY BU138). OES Pubns.

De Vore, R. William & Huffsey, R., eds. Nineteen Eighty-Four International Symposium on Urban Hydrology, Hydrolics & Sediment Control: Proceedings. LC 83-60965. (Illus.). 284p. (Orig.). 1984. pap. 33.50 (ISBN 0-89779-060-X, UKY BU135). OES Pubns.

De Vore, R. William & Wood, Don J., eds. Proceedings 1981 International Symposium on Urban Hydrology, Hydraulics & Sediment Control. LC 81-82243. (Illus.). 473p. (Orig.). 1981. pap. 33.50 (ISBN 0-89779-047-2, UKY BU125). OES Pubns.

Dingman, S. Lawrence. Fluvial Hydrology. 1983. text ed. 31.95 (ISBN 0-7167-1452-3); pap. text ed. write for info (ISBN 0-7167-1453-1). W H Freeman.

Drago, John J. Hydraulics: A New Approach. LC 78-67464. (Illus.). 1978. pap. 3.00x (ISBN 0-89368-301-9). Davis Pub Co.

Erven, Lawrence. Techniques of Fire Hydraulics. (Fire Science Ser). 1972. text ed. write for info. (ISBN 0-02-473000-9, 47300). Macmillan.

Essers, J. A., ed. Computational Methods for Turbulent, Transonic, & Viscous Flows. LC 83-187. (A Von Karman Institute Bk.). 360p. 1983. text ed. 49.95 (ISBN 0-89116-273-9). Hemisphere Pub.

Ewbank, Thomas. A Descriptive & Historical Account of Hydraulic & Other Machines for Raising Water, Ancient & Modern. LC 72-5048. (Technology & Society Ser.). 598p. 1972. Repr. of 1842 ed. 33.00 (ISBN 0-405-04700-2). Ayer Co Pubs.

Fogg, G. E. & Kreitler, C. W. Ground-Water Hydraulics & Hydrochemical Facies in Eocene Aquifers of the East Texas Basin. (Report of Investigations Ser.: RI 127). (Illus.). 75p. 1982. 3.00 (ISBN 0-318-03274-0). Bur Econ Geology.

Frankenfield, T. C. Using Industrial Hydraulics. LC 84-81279. (Illus.). 406p. 1985. 35.00 (ISBN 0-932905-01-3). Penton IPC.

French, R. H. Open-Channel Hydraulics. 704p. 1985. 49.95 (ISBN 0-07-022134-0). McGraw.

Giles, Ronald V. Fluid Mechanics & Hydraulics. (Schaum's Outline Ser). (Orig.). 1962. pap. 9.95 (ISBN 0-07-023234-2). McGraw.

Glover, Robert E. Transient Ground Water Hydraulics. 1978. 21.00 (ISBN 0-918334-24-1). WRP.

Graf, W. H. Hydraulics of Sediment Transport. LC 79-128788. 513p. 1984. 45.00 (ISBN 0-918334-81-0). WRP.

Hjorth, Peder, et al, eds. Hydraulic Problems Solved by Stochastic Methods. LC 77-78941. 1977. 18.00 (ISBN 0-918334-22-5). WRP.

Hydraulics for the Fire Service: Hydraulic Field Equations, Vol. VI. LC 78-50007. (Illus.). 72p. (Orig.). 1980. pap. text ed. 42.50 (ISBN 0-87765-171-X, SL-60). Natl Fire Prot.

Hydraulics in the Coastal Zone. 372p. 1977. pap. 19.75x (ISBN 0-87262-085-9). Am Soc Civil Eng.

Institute for Power System. Hydraulic Standards, Lexicon & Data. 200p. 1979. 35.00x (ISBN 0-85461-005-7). State Mutual Bk.

--Hydraulic Technical Data, Vol. 3. 117p. 1979. 25.00x (ISBN 0-85461-047-2). State Mutual Bk.

Interafrican Committee for Hydraulic Studies. Catalog of the Documentation Center Interafrican Committee for Hydraulic Studies. 1977. lib. bdg. 200.00 (ISBN 0-8161-0091-8, Hall Library). G K Hall.

International Conference on Hydraulics, Pneumatics & Fluidics in Control & Automation. Proceedings. 1977. text ed. 58.00x (ISBN 0-900983-53-1, Dist. by Air Science Co.). BHRA Fluid.

King, Horace W., et al. Hydraulics. 5th ed. LC 79-25379. 364p. 1980. Repr. of 1941 ed. 21.50 (ISBN 0-89874-106-8). Krieger.

Koutitas, Christopher. Elements of Computational Hydraulics. 148p. 1982. 29.95 (ISBN 0-412-00361-9, NO. 6788, Chapman & Hall). Methuen Inc.

A List of Translations of Foreign Literature on Hydraulics. (ASCE Manual & Report on Engineering Practice Ser.: No. 35). 140p. 1968. pap. 6.00x (ISBN 0-87262-212-6). Am Soc Civil Eng.

McWhorter, David B. & Sunada, Daniel K. Ground Water Hydrology & Hydraulics. LC 77-74259. 1981. 27.00 (ISBN 0-918334-18-7). WRP.

Mahoney, Eugene F. Fire Department Hydraulics. 1978. casebound 31.77 (ISBN 0-205-06563-5, 826563). Allyn.

Manohar, M. & Krishnamachar, P. Fluid Mechanics: Vol. 2: Hydraulic Machinery & Advanced Hydraulics. 600p. 1983. text ed. 45.00x (ISBN 0-7069-2078-3, Pub. by Vikas India). Advent NY.

Mariotte, Edme. The Motion of Water & Other Fluids: Being a Treatise of Hydrostaticks. Albritton, Claude C., ed. Desaguliers, J. T., tr. (History of Geology Ser.). (Illus.). 1978. Repr. of 1718 ed. lib. bdg. 27.50x (ISBN 0-405-10449-9). Ayer Co Pubs.

Mataix, Claudio. Mecanica de Fluidos y Maquinas Hidraulicas. 2nd ed. (Span.). 640p. 1982. pap. text ed. write for info. (ISBN 0-06-315591-5, Pub. by HarLA Mexico). Har-Row.

Muir-Wood, A. M. & Fleming, C. A. Coastal Hydraulics. 2nd ed. LC 81-2992. 280p. 1981. 59.95x (ISBN 0-470-27198-1). Halsted Pr.

National Fire Protection Association. Hydraulics for the Fire Sevice: Operating the Pumper, Vol. V. Lyons, Paul R., ed. LC 78-50007. (Illus.). 88p. 1979. text ed. 42.50 (ISBN 0-87765-157-4, SL-51). Natl Fire Prot.

Neubert, G. Dictionary of Hydraulics & Pneumatics: English-German-Russian-Slovene. (Eng., Ger., Rus. & Slovene.). 226p. 1973. 75.00 (ISBN 0-686-92602-1, M-9896). French & Eur.

Neubert, Gunter. Dictionary of Hydraulics & Pneumatics. 226p. 1980. 40.00x (ISBN 0-569-08523-3, Pub. by Collet's). State Mutual Bk.

Nichil, P. Lexique Francais-Anglais et Anglais-Francais des Termes d'usage Courant En Hydraulique et Pneumatique. (Fr. & Eng.). 42p. (French-English, English-French Lexicon of Commonly Used Terms in Hydraulics and Pneumatics). 1974. pap. 8.95 (ISBN 0-686-56790-0, M-6426). French & Eur.

Pippenger, John & Hicks, Tyler. Industrial Hydraulics. 3rd ed. (Illus.). 1979. text ed. 36.30 (ISBN 0-07-050140-8). McGraw.

Polubarinova-Kochina, P. Theory of Ground Water Movement. De Wiest, R., tr. 1962. 62.50x (ISBN 0-691-08048-8). Princeton U Pr.

Purington, Robert G. Hydraulics for the Fire Service: Pumps & Pumpers, Unit 4. Lyons, Paul R., ed. LC 78-50007. (Illus.). 1979. pap. text ed. 42.50 (ISBN 0-87765-148-5). Natl Fire Prot.

--Hydraulics for the Fire Service: Unit I - Characteristics of Water. Lyons, Paul R., ed. LC 78-50007. (Illus.). 1978. pap. text ed. 42.50 (ISBN 0-87765-117-5, SL-27). Natl Fire Prot.

--Hydraulics for the Fire Service: Unit II - Water Flow, Friction Loss, Engine Pressure. Lyons, Paul R., ed. LC 78-50007. (Illus.). 1978. pap. text ed. 42.50 (ISBN 0-685-63021-8, SL-28). Natl Fire Prot.

Purington, Robert G., et al. Hydraulics for the Fire Service Unit III, Multiple Lines, Unequal Layouts. Lyons, Paul R., ed. LC 78-50007. (Illus.). 1979. pap. 42.50 (ISBN 0-87765-132-9, SL-33). Natl Fire Prot.

Pytkowicz, Ricardo M. Equilibria, Nonequilibria, & Natural Waters. 2nd ed. 1983. Set, 400p. 84.95x (ISBN 0-471-87831-6, Pub. by Wiley-Interscience); Vol. 1, 351p. 49.95x (ISBN 0-471-86192-8); Vol. 2, 353. 49.95x (ISBN 0-471-89111-8). Wiley.

Rhodes, Dallas D., ed. Adjustments of the Fluvial System. Williams, Garnett P. (Binghamton Symposia in Geomorphology International Ser.: No. 10). (Illus.). 372p. 1982. Repr. of 1979 ed. text ed. 35.00x (ISBN 0-04-551059-8). Allen Unwin.

Rouse, Hunter, ed. Engineering Hydraulics. 1039p. 1950. 88.50x (ISBN 0-471-74283-X, Pub. by Wiley-Interscience). Wiley.

Sharp, J. J. Hydraulic Modelling: Theory & Practice. 1981. text ed. 59.95 (ISBN 0-408-00482-7, Newnes-Butterworth). Butterworth.

Simon, A. Practical Hydraulics. 3rd ed. 31.95 (ISBN 0-471-88488-X). Wiley.

Simon, Andrew L. Practical Hydraulics. 2nd ed. LC 79-27270. 403p. 1981. text ed. 29.95 (ISBN 0-471-05381-3); tchrs.' ed. avail. (ISBN 0-471-07783-6). Wiley.

Some Aspects of Hydraulics in Mechanical Handling & Mobile Equipment. 120p. 1982. 75.00x (ISBN 0-85461-006-5, Pub. by Trade & Tech). State Mutual Bk.

Stewart, Harry L. Hydraulics for Off-the-Road Equipment. 2nd ed. LC 77-93790. 1985. 13.95 (ISBN 0-8161-1701-2, Dist. by G. K. Hall). Audel.

--Pneumatics & Hydraulics. 3rd ed. LC 75-36658. (Illus.). 1976. 10.95 (ISBN 0-672-23237-5, 23237). Audel.

Stoker, James J. Water Waves. LC 56-8228. (Pure & Applied Mathematics Ser.). (Illus.). 595p. 1957. 61.95x (ISBN 0-470-82863-3, Pub. by Wiley-Interscience). Wiley.

Switzer, Stephen. An Introduction to a General System of Hydrostaticks & Hydraulics Philosophical & Practical. Hunt, John D., ed. LC 79-57002. 499p. 1982. lib. bdg. 107.00 (ISBN 0-8240-0161-3). Garland Pub.

Trade & Techinical Press Editors. Applied Hydraulics & Pneumatics in Industry. 260p. 1968. 32.50x (ISBN 0-85461-077-4, Pub by Trade & Tech England). Brookfield Pub Co.

Trade & Technical Press Editors. Hydraulic Handbook. 7th ed. 900p. 1981. 190.00x (ISBN 0-85461-074-X, Pub. by Trade & Tech). State Mutual Bk.

--Hydraulic Technical Data, Vol. 4. 117p. 1977. 22.00x (Pub by Trade & Tech England). Brookfield Pub Co.

--Principles of Hydraulics. 150p. 1963. 25.00x (ISBN 0-85461-002-2, Pub by Trade & Tech England). Brookfield Pub Co.

--Some Aspects of Hydraulics in Mechanical Handling & Mobile Equipment. 120p. 1970. 20.00x (ISBN 0-85461-006-5, Pub by Trade & Tech England). Brookfield Pub Co.

Vollmer, Ernst. Encyclopaedia of Hydraulics, Soil & Foundation Engineering. 398p. 1967. 89.50 (ISBN 0-444-40615-8). Elsevier.

Warring, R. H. Hydraulic Handbook. 8th ed. LC 83-80066. 1983. 77.50x (ISBN 0-87201-349-9). Gulf Pub.

HYDRAZENE

Schmidt, Eckart W. Hydrazine & Its Derivatives: Preparation, Properties, Applications. LC 83-14663. 1088p. 1984. 85.00 (ISBN 0-471-89170-3, Pub. by Wiley-Interscience). Wiley.

HYDRIDES

Andresen, A. F. & Maeland, A., eds. Hydrides for Energy Storage: Proceedings of an International Symposium Held in Norway, Aug. 1977. 1978. text ed. 105.00 (ISBN 0-08-022715-5). Pergamon.

Bambakidis, Gust, ed. Metal Hydrides. LC 81-17761. (NATO ASI Series B, Physics: Vol. 76). 393p. 1981. 65.00x (ISBN 0-306-40891-0, Plenum Pr). Plenum Pub.

Fogg, A. S. & Young. Ammonia Amines, Phosphides, Arsin. 1985. 100.00 (ISBN 0-08-026177-9). Pergamon.

Gaylord, Norman G. Reduction with Complex Metal Hydrides. LC 55-8227. (Illus.). 1062p. 1956. text ed. 45.00 (ISBN 0-470-29436-1, Pub. by Wiley). Krieger.

Hajos, A. Complex Hydrides & Related Reducing Agents in Organic Synthesis. LC 78-14524. (Studies in Organic Chemistry: Vol. 1). 398p. 1979. 74.50 (ISBN 0-444-99791-1). Elsevier.

HYDROAIRPLANES

see Seaplanes

HYDROBIIDAE

Thompson, Fred G. Aquatic Snails of the Family Hydrobiidae of Peninsular Florida. LC 68-9707. 1968. 10.00 (ISBN 0-8130-0273-7). U Presses Fla.

HYDROBIOLOGY

see Fresh-Water Biology; Marine Biology

HYDROBOTANY

see Aquatic Plants

HYDROCARBON RESEARCH

American Petroleum Institute, Research Project 42. Properties of Hydrocarbons of High Molecular Weight Synthesized by Research Project 42 of the American Petroleum Institute, the Pennsylvania State University College of Science, University Park, Penn., 1940-1961. LC 72-8620. pap. 20.00 (ISBN 0-317-10723-2, 2004349). Bks Demand UMI.

Horvath. Halogenated Hydrocarbons. 920p. 1982. 145.00 (ISBN 0-8247-1166-1). Dekker.

Nicholson, William J. & Moore, John A., eds. Health Effects of Halogenated Aromatic Hydrocarbons. LC 79-12253. (Annals of the New York Academy of Sciences: Vol. 320). 730p. 1979. 117.00x (ISBN 0-89766-008-0). NY Acad Sci.

Pucknat, A. W., ed. Health Impacts of Polynuclear Aromatic Hydrocarbons. LC 80-28039. (Environmental Health Review: No. 5). (Illus.). 271p. 1981. 39.00 (ISBN 0-8155-0840-9). Noyes.

HYDROCARBONS

see also Alkylation; Cracking Process; Hydrocarbon Research; Mineral Oils; Paraffins; Petroleum Products

Afghan, B. K. & Mackay, D., eds. Hydrocarbons & Halogenated Hydrocarbons in the Aquatic Environment. LC 79-26462. (Environmental Science Research Ser.: Vol. 16). 602p. 1980. 79.50x (ISBN 0-306-40329-3, Plenum Pr). Plenum Pub.

Albaiges, J., et al, eds. Chemistry & Analysis of Hydrocarbons in the Environment. LC 83-1603. (Current Topics in Environmental & Toxicological Chemistry Ser.: Vol. 5). 326p. 1983. 57.75 (ISBN 0-677-06140-4). Gordon.

American Chemical Society, Division of Organic Chemistry. & Industrial & Engineering Chemistry. System of Nomenclature for Terpene Hydrocarbons: Acyclics, Monocyclics, Bicyclics. LC 55-4170. (American Chemical Society Advances in Chemistry Series: No. 14). pap. 37.50 (ISBN 0-317-08703-7, 2050183). Bks Demand UMI.

American Society of Mechanical Engineers. Risers, Arctic Design Criteria, Equipment Reliability in Hydrocarbon Processing: A Workbook for Engineers, Presented at 37th Petroleum Mechanical Engineering Workshop & Conference, September 13-15, 1981, Dallas, Texas. Kozik, Thomas J., ed. LC 81-186405. pap. 62.50 (ISBN 0-317-29899-2, 2019351). Bks Demand UMI.

Andrew, William G. & Williams, H. B. Applied Instrumentation in the Process Industries, Vol. 3: Engineering Data & Resource Material. 2nd ed. LC 79-9418. 520p. 1982. 45.95x (ISBN 0-87201-384-7). Gulf Pub.

Baker, Bernard S., ed. Hydrocarbon Fuel Cell Technology: A Symposium. (Illus.). 1966. 89.50 (ISBN 0-12-074250-0). Acad Pr.

Bingham, R. C. & Von Schleyer, P. R. Chemistry of Adamantanes: Recent Developments in the Chemistry of Adamantane & Related Polycyclic Hydrocarbons. (Topics in Current Chemistry: Vol. 18). (Illus.). 1971. pap. 32.50 (ISBN 0-387-05387-5). Springer-Verlag.

Bjorseth, Alf & Dennis, Anthony J., eds. Polynuclear Aromatic Hydrocarbons: Chemistry & Biological Effects. (Illus.). 1097p. 1980. 49.95 (ISBN 0-935470-05-0). Battelle.

Compressor Handbook for the Hydrocarbon Processing Industries. LC 79-50252. 258p. (Orig.). 1979. pap. 19.95x (ISBN 0-87201-131-3). Gulf Pub.

Cooke, M. & Dennis, A. J., eds. Polynuclear Aromatic Hydrocarbons V: Chemical & Biological Fate Symposium. 770p. 1982. 49.95 (ISBN 0-387-47009-3). Springer-Verlag.

Cooke, Marcus & Dennis, Anthony J. Polynuclear Aromatic Hydrocarbons: Formation, Metabolism & Measurement. (International Poynuclear Aromatic Symposium on Hydrocarbons). 1301p. 1983. 65.00 (ISBN 0-935470-16-6). Battelle.

--Polynuclear Aromatic Hydrocarbons: Mechanisms, Methods & Metabolism. (International Symposium on Polynuclear Aromatic Hydrocarbons Ser.). 1504p. 1984. 75.00 (ISBN 0-935470-22-0). Battelle.

Cooke, Marcus & Dennis, Anthony J., eds. Chemical Analysis & Biological Fate: Polynuclear Aromatic Hydrocarbons. (International Symposium on Polynuclear Aromatic Hydrocarbons Ser.). 770p. 1981. 59.95 (ISBN 0-935470-09-3). Battelle.

--Polynuclear Aromatic Hydrocarbons: Physical & Biological Chemistry. (International Symposium on Polynuclear Aromatic Hydrocarbons, Sixth). 947p. 1982. 65.00 (ISBN 0-935470-13-1). Battelle.

Edmister, Wayne C. & Lee, Byung Ik. Applied Hydrocarbon Thermodynamics, Vol. 1. 2nd ed. LC 83-22654. 234p. 1984. 59.95x (ISBN 0-87201-855-5). Gulf Pub.

Emanuel, N. M., et al. Liquid-Phase Oxidation of Hydrocarbons. LC 66-12888. 350p. 1967. 39.50x (ISBN 0-306-30292-6, Plenum Pr). Plenum Pub.

Emanuel, Nikolai, et al. Liquid-phase Oxidation of Hydrocarbons. LC 66-12888. pap. 91.00 (ISBN 0-317-27888-6, 2055792). Bks Demand UMI.

Environmental Studies Board. Polychlorinated Biphenyls. 1979. pap. 8.75 (ISBN 0-309-02885-X). Natl Acad Pr.

Ferris, Seymour W. Handbook of Hydrocarbons. 1955. 56.00 (ISBN 0-12-254050-6). Acad Pr.

Tuve, Merle A. & Lundsager, Soren. Velocity Structures in Hydrogen Profiles: A Sky Atlas of Neutral Hydrogen Emission. (Carnegie Institution of Washington Ser.: No. 630). (Illus.). pap. 47.00 (ISBN 0-317-09033-X, 2007901). Bks Demand UMI.

Van Kranendonk, Jan. Solid Hydrogen: Theory of the Properties of Solid H2, HD, & D2. LC 82-18054. 322p. 1983. 45.00x (ISBN 0-306-41080-X, Plenum Pr). Plenum Pub.

Veziroglu, Nejat, ed. Hydrogen Energy. LC 74-34483. 1436p. 1975. 150.00x (ISBN 0-306-34301-0, Plenum Pr). Plenum Pub.

Veziroglu, T. N., ed. Metal-Hydrogen Systems: Proceedings of the International Symposium, Miami Beach, Florida, USA, 13-15 April 1981. (Illus.). 750p. 1982. 165.00 (ISBN 0-08-027311-4); pap. 100.00 (ISBN 0-08-027316-5). Pergamon.

Veziroglu, T. N. & Taylor, J. B., eds. Hydrogen Energy Progress V: Proceedings of the 5th World Hydrogen Energy Conference, Toronto, Canada, 15-20 July 1984, 4 vols. (Advances in Hydrogen Energy Ser.: No.4). 1968p. 1984. 275.00 (ISBN 0-08-030953-4, Intl Assn Hydro Energy). Pergamon.

Veziroglu, T. Nejat, ed. Proceedings of the Clean Energy Research Institute, 1st, Miami Beach, 1976. 1977. pap. text ed. 265.00 (ISBN 0-08-021561-0). Pergamon.

Williams, L. O. Hydrogen Power: An Introduction to Hydrogen Energy & Its Applications. LC 80-40434. (Illus.). 200p. 1980. 32.00 (ISBN 0-08-024783-0); pap. 11.00 (ISBN 0-08-025422-5). Pergamon.

World Hydrogen Energy Conference, Fourth & Veziroglu, T. N. Hydrogen Energy Process IV: Proceedings of the World Hydrogen Energy Conference, Fourth, Pasadena, CA 13-17 June, 1982. Van Vorst, W. D., et al, eds. (Advances in Hydrogen Energy Ser.: No. 3). 2000p. 1982. 385.00 (ISBN 0-08-028699-2). Pergamon.

World Hydrogen Energy Conference Papers, 4th, California, USA, 13-17 June 1982 & Veziroglu, T. N. Hydrogen: Today, Tomorrow & Beyond. 132p. 1983. pap. 50.00 (ISBN 0-08-031139-3). Pergamon.

World Hydrogen Energy Conference, 2nd, Zurich, Aug. 1978. Hydrogen Energy System: Proceedings, 5 Vols. Veziroglu, T. N. & Seifritz, W., eds. LC 78-40507. 1979. Set. text ed. 485.00 (ISBN 0-08-023224-8). Pergamon.

World Hydrogen Energy Conference, 3rd, Tokyo, Japan 23-26 June 1980, et al. Hydrogen Energy Progress: Proceedings, 4 vols. Veziroglu, T. N., et al, eds. LC 80-40559. (Advances in Hydrogen Energy Ser.: 2). (Illus.). 2500p. 1981. 425.00 set (ISBN 0-08-024729-6). Pergamon.

Young. Hydrogen & Deuterium, 2 Vols. (IUPAC Solubility Data Ser.: Vol. 5 & 6). 670p. 1981. 200.00 (ISBN 0-08-023927-7). Pergamon.

HYDROGEN–ISOTOPES

see also Deuterium

Rae, Howard K., ed. Separation of Hydrogen Isotopes. LC 78-760. (ACS Symposium Ser.: No. 68). 1978. 22.95 (ISBN 0-8412-0420-9). Am Chemical.

Shatenshtein, A. I. Isotopic Exchange & the Replacement of Hydrogen in Organic Compounds. LC 62-12859. 308p. 1962. 35.00x (ISBN 0-306-10547-0, Consultants). Plenum Pub.

HYDROGEN BOMB

see also Atomic Bomb; Radioactive Fallout

De Volpi, A., et al. Born Secret: The H-Bomb, the "Progressive" Case & National Security. (Illus.). 320p. 1981. 19.25 (ISBN 0-08-025995-2). Pergamon.

Shepley, James R. & Blair, Clay. Hydrogen Bomb: The Men, the Menace, the Mechanism. LC 70-136085. 1971. Repr. of 1954 ed. lib. bdg. 18.75 (ISBN 0-8371-5235-6, SHHY). Greenwood.

HYDROGEN BONDING

Covington, A. K. & Jones, P., eds. Hydrogen-Bonded Solvent Systems. 366p. 1968. cancelled (ISBN 0-85066-025-4). Taylor & Francis.

Green, R. D. Hydrogen Bonding by C-H Groups. LC 74-11310. 207p. 1974. 58.95 (ISBN 0-470-32478-3). Halsted Pr.

Joesten, Melvin D. & Schaad, L. Hydrogen Bonding. 632p. 1974. 115.00 (ISBN 0-8247-6211-8). Dekker.

Schuster, P., ed. Hydrogen Bonds. (Topics in Current Chemistry Ser.: Vol. 120). (Illus.). 120p. 1984. 25.50 (ISBN 0-387-12785-2). Springer Verlag.

Schuster, Peter, et al. The Hydrogen Bond: Recent Developments in Theory & Experiments, 3 vols. LC 76-373671. (Illus.). 1782p. 1976. Set. 266.00 (ISBN 0-444-10805-X, North-Holland). Elsevier.

HYDROGEN-ION CONCENTRATION

see also Ionization

Bates, Roger G. Determination of PH: Theory & Practice. 2nd ed. LC 72-8779. (Illus.). pap. 123.80 (ISBN 0-317-09107-7, 2019293). Bks Demand UMI.

Behrendt, Hans & Green, Marvin. Patterns of Skin PH from Birth Through Adolescence: With a Synopsis on Skin Growth. (Illus.). 116p. 1971. 14.75x (ISBN 0-398-00125-1). C C Thomas.

Kasbekar, Dinkar K., et al, eds. Gastric Hydrogen Ion Secretion. (Nutrition & Clinical Nutrition Ser.: Vol. 3). 1976. 89.75 (ISBN 0-8247-6432-3). Dekker.

Kroc Foundation, Santa Ynez Valley, CA, July 20-24, 1981 & Nuccitelli, Richard. Intracellular PH: Its Measurement, Regulation, & Utilization in Cellular Functions: Proceedings. LC 81-18616. (Kroc Foundation Ser.: Vol. 15). 622p. 1982. 88.00 (ISBN 0-8451-0305-9). A R Liss.

McMillan, Gregory K. PH Control: An Independent Learning Module of the Instrument Society of America. 272p. 1985. pap. text ed. 39.95 (ISBN 0-87664-725-5). Instru Soc.

Perrin, D. D. & Dempsey, B. Buffers for PH & Metal Ion Control. 1979. (Pub. by Chapman & Hall England); pap. 15.95 (ISBN 0-412-21890-9, NO.6218). Methuen Inc.

Ricci, John E. Hydrogen Ion Concentration. 1952. 46.00 (ISBN 0-691-07981-1). Princeton U Pr.

HYDROGEN NUCLEUS

see Protons

HYDROGENATION

see also Coal Liquefaction

Carbonization & Hydrogenation. pap. 3.50 (ISBN 0-686-94711-8, UN72/2B/26, UN). Unipub.

Freifelder, Morris. Catalytic Hydrogenation in Organic Synthesis: Procedures & Commentary. LC 78-9458. 191p. 1978. 34.95 (ISBN 0-471-02945-9, Pub. by Wiley-Interscience). Wiley.

--Practical Catalytic Hydrogenation: Techniques & Applications. LC 76-123740. 1971. 42.50 (ISBN 0-471-27800-9, Pub. by Wiley-Interscience). Wiley.

Harriman, A. & West, M. A., eds. Photogeneration of Hydrogen. 1983. 26.50 (ISBN 0-12-326380-8). Acad Pr.

Henrici-Olive, G. & Olive, S. The Chemistry of the Catalyzed Hydrogenation of Carbon Monoxide. (Illus.). 230p. 1984. 56.00 (ISBN 0-387-13292-9). Springer-Verlag.

James, Brian R. Homogeneous Hydrogenation. LC 84-5778. 542p. 1985. Repr. of 1973 ed. write for info. (ISBN 0-89874-740-6). Krieger.

Kursanov, et al. Ionic Hydrogenation & Related Reactions. (Chemistry Reviews Supplement Ser.: Soviet Scientific Reviews, Section B, Vol. 1). 230p. 1984. text ed. 112.00 (ISBN 3-7186-0145-1). Harwood Academic.

McQuillin, F. J., ed. Homogeneous Hydrogenation in Organic Chemistry. LC 75-37874. (Homogeneous Catalysis in Organic & Inorganic Chemistry: No. 1). vi, 146p. 1976. lib. bdg. 26.00 (ISBN 90-277-0646-8, Pub. by Reidel Holland). Kluwer Academic.

Patterson, H. B. Hydrogeneration of Fats & Oils. (Illus.). 300p. 1983. 70.50 (ISBN 0-85334-201-6, Pub. by Elsevier Applied Sci England). Elsevier.

Rylander, Paul N. Catalytic Hydrogenation Over Platinum Metals. 1967. 81.00 (ISBN 0-12-605350-2). Acad Pr.

--Hydrogenation Methods. Date not set. 48.00 (ISBN 0-12-605365-0). Acad Pr.

Satriana, M. J., ed. Hydroprocessing Catalysts for Heavy Oil & Coal. LC 81-18933. (Chemical Technology Review: No. 202, Energy Technology Review Ser: No. 74). (Illus.). 308p. 1982. 45.00 (ISBN 0-8155-0883-2). Noyes.

Whitehurst, D. D., ed. Coal Liquefaction Fundamentals. LC 80-20585. (ACS Symposium Ser.: No. 139). 1980. 39.95 (ISBN 0-8412-0587-6). Am Chemical.

Whitehurst, D. D., et al. Coal Liquefaction: The Chemistry & Technology of Thermal Process. 1980. 28.00 (ISBN 0-12-747080-8). Acad Pr.

HYDROGEOLOGY

Back, W. & Stephenson, D. A., eds. Contemporary Hydrogeology: The George Burke Maxey Memorial. (Developments in Water Science Ser.: Vol. 12). 570p. 1980. Repr. 85.00 (ISBN 0-444-41848-2). Elsevier.

Back, William R. & Freeze, Allan, eds. Chemical Hydrogeology. LC 81-11853. (Benchmark Papers in Geology Ser.: Vol. 73). 416p. 1983. 49.00 (ISBN 0-87933-440-1). Van Nos Reinhold.

Bassett, R. L., et al. Deep Brine Aquifers in the Palo Duro Basin: Regional Flow & Geochemical Constraints. (Report of Investigations Ser.: RI 130). (Illus.). 59p. 1983. 2.50 (ISBN 0-318-03280-5). Bur Econ Geology.

Bebout, D. G., et al. Frio Sandstone Reservoirs in the Deep Subsurface Along the Texas Gulf Coast: Their Potential for the Production of Geopressured Geothermal Energy. (Report of Investigations Ser.: RI 91). (Illus.). 92p. 1983. Repr. of 1978 ed. 5.50 (ISBN 0-318-03230-9). Bur Econ Geology.

Bogomolov, Yu. G. & Zhabin, V. F., eds. Effect of Reclamation on Hydrogeological Conditions. Erastov, Konstantin, tr. from Rus. 300p. 1983. 101.95 (ISBN 0-677-06070-X). Gordon.

Bulletin du Centre D'Hydrogeologie, Vol. 4. (Ger.). 270p. 1983. 18.40 (ISBN 3-261-03335-5). P Lang Pubs.

Cermak, V. & Rybach, L., eds. Terrestrial Heat Flow in Europe. (Illus.). 1979. 59.00 (ISBN 0-387-09440-7). Springer-Verlag.

Dutton, S. P. Depositional Systems & Hydrocarbon Resource Potential of the Pennsylvanian System, Palo Duro & Dalhart Basins, Texas Panhandle. (Illus.). 49p. 1980. 1.50 (ISBN 0-318-03136-1, GC80-8). Bur Econ Geology.

Erxleben, A. W. Depositional Systems in the Canyon Group (Pennsylvanian System), North-Central Texas. (Report of Investigations Ser.: RI 82). (Illus.). 76p. 1980. Repr. of 1975 ed. 4.00 (ISBN 0-318-03216-3). Bur Econ Geology.

Fetter, Charles W., Jr. Applied Hydrogeology. (Physics & Physical Science Ser.). 448p. 1980. text ed. 37.50 (ISBN 0-675-08126-2). Merrill.

Fogg, G. E. & Kreitler, C. W. Ground-Water Hydraulics & Hydrochemical Facies in Eocene Aquifers of the East Texas Basin. (Report of Investigations Ser.: RI 127). (Illus.). 75p. 1982. 3.00 (ISBN 0-318-03274-0). Bur Econ Geology.

Fogg, G. E., et al. Three-Dimensional Ground-Water Modeling in Depositional Systems, Wilcox Group, Oakwood Salt Dome Area, East Texas. (Report of Investigations Ser.: RI 133). (Illus.). 55p. 1983. 3.25 (ISBN 0-318-03289-9). Bur Econ Geology.

Freeze, R. A. & Back, W., eds. Physical Hydrogeology. LC 82-2976. (Benchmark Papers in Geology: Vol. 72). 431p. 1983. 48.00 (ISBN 0-87933-431-2). Van Nos Reinhold.

Galloway, W. E. & Brown, L. F., Jr. Depositional Systems & Shelf-Slope Relationships in Upper Pennsylvanian Rocks, North-Central Texas. (Report of Investigations Ser.: RI 75). (Illus.). 62p. 1981. Repr. of 1972 ed. 3.00 (ISBN 0-318-03182-5). Bur Econ Geology.

Galloway, W. E., et al. Frio Formation of the Texas Gulf Coast Basin: Depositional Systems, Structural Framework, & Hydrocarbon Origin, Migration, Distribution & Exploration Potential. (Report of Investigations Ser.: RI 122). (Illus.). 78p. 1982. 4.50 (ISBN 0-318-03263-5). Bur Econ Geology.

--Depositional & Ground-Water Flow Systems in the Exploration for Uranium: Syllabus for Research Colloquium Held in Austin, 1978. (Illus.). 267p. 1979. 6.00 (ISBN 0-318-03374-7). Bur Econ Geology.

Gheorghe, A. Processing & Synthesis of Hydrogeological Data. 1978. 43.00 (ISBN 0-9961002-7-X, Pub. by Abacus England). Heyden.

Halasi-Kun, George J., ed. Pollution & Water Resources: Hydrogeology & Other Selected Reports. (Columbia University Seminar Ser.: Vol. XIV-1, 1981). (Illus.). 195p. 39.00 (ISBN 0-08-028792-1). Pergamon.

Henry, C. D., et al. Geochemistry of Ground Water in the Miocene Oakville Sandstone: A Major Aquifer & Uranium Host of the Texas Coastal Plain. (Report of Investigations Ser.: RI 118). (Illus.). 63p. 1982. 2.50 (ISBN 0-318-03256-2). Bur Econ Geology.

Hydrogeological Considerations in Northern Pipeline Development. pap. 5.00 (SSC50, SSC). Unipub.

Hydrogeological Investigations of the Peel Region & Its Environs. (Agricultural Research Reports: 684). 1967. pap. 9.75 (ISBN 0-686-51208-1, PDC42, PUDOC). Unipub.

International Hydrogeological Map of Europe: Explanatory Notes. Incl. Berlin. 1979; Berne; London. 1979. pap. 31.50 (M109); Paris. pap. 31.50 (M70); Sheet E3. International Hydrogeological Map of Europe-Moskova. 1979. (Co-published by UNESCO, Bundesanstalt, Hanover, UNESCO). Unipub.

Klimentov, P. General Hydrogeology. Gurevich, K. G., tr. 239p. 1983. 7.95 (ISBN 0-8285-2740-7, Pub. by Mir Pubs USSR). Imported Pubns.

Kreitler, C. W. Determining the Source of Nitrate in Ground Water by Nitrogen Isotope Studies. (Report of Investigations Ser.: RI 83). (Illus.). 57p. 1975. 2.00 (ISBN 0-318-03223-6). Bur Econ Geology.

Kreitler, C. W., et al. Geology & Geohydrology of the East Texas Basin: A Report on the Progress of Nuclear Waste Isolation Feasibility Studies(1979) Incl. A/Report on the Progress of Nuclear Waste Isolation Feasibility Studies. Kreitler, C. W., et al. (Geological Circular Ser. of Nuclear Waste Isolation Feasibility Studies: No. 81-7). (Illus.). 207p. 1981. 5.00 (ISBN 0-686-36595-X); A/Report on the Progress of Nuclear Waste Isolation Feasibility Studies, 1979. Kreitler, C. W., et al. (Geological Circular Ser.: No. 80-12). (Illus.). 112p. 1980. 2.50 (ISBN 0-318-03140-X); A/Report on the Progress of Nuclear Waste Isolation Feasibility Studies 1980. Kreitler, C. W., et al. (Geological Circular: No. 81-7). 207p. 5.00. (Geological Circular Ser.: 80-12). (Illus.). 112p. 1980. 2.50 (ISBN 0-318-03140-X). Bur Econ Geology.

Legends for Geohydrochemical Maps. (Technical Papers in Hydrology). (Illus.). 61p. 1976. pap. 6.00 (ISBN 92-3-001207-6, U351, UNESCO). Unipub.

McGowen, M. K. & Lopez, C. M. Depositional Systems in the Nacatoch Formation (Upper Cretaceous), Northeast Texas & Southwest Arkansas. (Report of Investigations Ser.: RI 137). (Illus.). 59p. 1983. 2.00 (ISBN 0-318-03297-X). Bur Econ Geology.

Milanovic, Petar J. Karst Hydrogeology. LC 80-54287. 1981. 29.00 (ISBN 0-918334-36-5). WRP.

Morton, R. A. & McGowen, J. H. Modern Depositional Environments of the Texas Coast. (Guidebook Ser.: GB 20). (Illus.). 167p. 1983. Repr. of 1980 ed. 4.50 (ISBN 0-318-03129-9). Bur Econ Geology.

Narasimhan, T. N. & Freeze, R. Allan, eds. Recent Trends in Hydrogeology. (Special Paper: No. 189). 1982. 32.00 (ISBN 0-8137-2189-X). Geol Soc.

Pfannkuch, Hans-Olaf. Elsevier's Dictionary of Hydrogeology. (Eng., Fr., & Ger.). 168p. 1969. 42.75 (ISBN 0-444-40717-0). Elsevier.

Pinneker, E. V., ed. General Hydrogeology. Howard, D. E., tr. LC 82-9499. (Earth Science Ser.). (Illus.). 250p. 1983. 47.50 (ISBN 0-521-24905-8). Cambridge U Pr.

Presley, M. W. & McGillis, K. A. Coastal Evaporite & Tidal-Flat Sediments of the Upper Clear Fork & Glorieta Formations, Texas Panhandle. (Report of Investigations Ser.: RI 115). (Illus.). 50p. 1982. 2.00 (ISBN 0-318-03248-1). Bur Econ Geology.

Raghunath, H. M. Ground Water Hydrology: Hydroeconomics, Ground Water Survey & Pumping Tests, Rural Water Supply & Irrigation Systems. LC 81-23162. 456p. 1982. 32.95x (ISBN 0-470-27315-1). Halsted Pr.

Rona, P. A. & Lowell, R. P. Seafloor Spreading Centers: Hydrothermal Systems. LC 79-18265. (Bench Papers in Geology: Vol. 56). 424p. 1980. 57.50 (ISBN 0-87933-363-4). Van Nos Reinhold.

Rosenshein, Joseph & Bennett, Gordon D., eds. Groundwater Hydraulics. (Water Resources Monograph: Vol. 9). (Illus.). 416p. (Orig.). 1984. 18.00 (ISBN 0-87590-310-X). Am Geophysical.

Smith, G. E. Depositional Systems, San Angelo Formation (Permian), North Texas: Facies Control of Red-Bed Copper Mineralization. (Report of Investigations Ser.: RI 80). (Illus.). 74p. 1974. Repr. 3.00 (ISBN 0-318-03206-6). Bur Econ Geology.

Solis, R. F. Upper Tertiary & Quaternary Depositional Systems, Central Coastal Plain, Texas: Regional Geology of the Coastal Aquifer & Potential Liquid-Waste Repositories. (Illus.). 89p. 1981. 3.00 (ISBN 0-318-03239-2). Bur Econ Geology.

Thompson, D. M. Atoka Group (Lower-Middle Pennsylvanian), Northern Fort Worth Basin, Texas: Terrigenous Depositional Systems, Diagenesis, Reservoir Distribution, & Quality. (Report of Investigations Ser.: RI 125). (Illus.). 62p. 1982. 2.50 (ISBN 0-318-03270-8). Bur Econ Geology.

Tolson, J. S. & Doyle, F. L., eds. Karst Hydrogeology. (Eng. & Fr., Illus.). 1977. 15.00 (ISBN 0-933958-03-X). UAH Pr.

White, W. A., et al. Submerged Lands of Texas, Corpus Christi Area: Sediments, Geochemistry, Benthic Macroinvertebrates, & Associated Wetlands. (Submerged Lands Ser.). (Illus.). 154p. 1983. 9.50 (ISBN 0-318-03338-0). Bur Econ Geology.

Winker, C. D., et al. Depositional Setting, Structural Style, & Sandstone Distribution in Three Geopressured Geothermal Areas, Texas Gulf Coast. (Report of Investigations Ser.: RI 134). (Illus.). 60p. 1983. 2.50 (ISBN 0-318-03292-9). Bur Econ Geology.

HYDROGRAPHIC CHARTS

see Nautical Charts

HYDROGRAPHIC SURVEYING

see also Hydrography; Navigation

ASCE Task Committee on Hydrographic Investigations. Measurement of Hydrographic Parameters in Large Sand-Bed Streams from Boats. 84p. 1983. pap. 13.50x (ISBN 0-87262-354-8). Am Soc Civil Eng.
Ingham, A. E. Sea Surveying. LC 74-3066. 539p. 1975. 143.95x (ISBN 0-471-42729-2, Pub. by Wiley-Interscience). Wiley.
Ingham, Alan. Hydrography for the Surveyor & Engineer. 2nd ed. 132p. 1984. text ed. 21.50x (ISBN 0-471-80535-1, Wiley-Interscience). Wiley.
Institution of Civil Engineers Staff, ed. Hydraulic Modelling in Maritime Engineering. 152p. 1982. 34.50x (ISBN 0-7277-0154-1). Am Soc Civil Eng.
Milne, P. H. Underwater Engineering Surveys. LC 80-65129. (Illus.). 370p. 1980. 49.95x (ISBN 0-87201-884-9). Gulf Pub.
Morris, Byron F. & Schroeder, Elizabeth. Hydrographic Observations in the Sargasso Sea off Bermuda: 1967-1973. (Bermuda Biological Station Special Pubn. Ser.: No. 12). 105p. 1973. pap. 4.00 (ISBN 0-917642-12-0). Bermuda Bio.

HYDROGRAPHY
see also Coastwise Navigation; Harbors; Hydrographic Surveying; Hydrology; Inland Navigation; Lakes; Navigation; Ocean Currents; Rivers; Stream Measurements; Submarine Topography; Sounding and Soundings; Tides
De Cardonda, Nicolas. Geographic & Hydrographic Descriptions... of the Kingdom of California (1632) Mathes, Michael, ed. & tr. (Baja California Travels Ser.: No. 35). (Illus.). 111p. 1974. 18.00 (ISBN 0-87093-235-7). Dawsons.
Foerstner, U. & Wittman, G. T. Metal Pollution in the Aquatic Environment. 2nd ed. (Illus.). 486p. 1983. pap. 31.00 (ISBN 0-387-12856-5). Springer-Verlag.
Galtsoff, P. S. Pearl & Hermes Reef, Hawaii, Hydrographical & Biographical Observations. (BMB). pap. 10.00 (ISBN 0-527-02213-6). Kraus Repr.
Hubbs, Carl L., et al. Memoir VII: Hydrographic History & Relict Fishes of the North-Central Great Basin. Kessel, Edward L., ed. (Memoirs of the California Academy of Sciences Ser.). (Illus.). 259p. (Orig.). 1974. pap. 10.00 (ISBN 0-940228-11-4). Calif Acad Sci.
Morel-Seytoux, Hubert J., et al, eds. Modeling Hydrologic Processes. LC 78-68497. 1979. 28.00 (ISBN 0-918334-27-6). WRP.
--Surface & Subsurface Hydrology. LC 78-68496. 1979. 28.00 (ISBN 0-918334-28-4). WRP.

HYDROLOGIC CYCLE
see also Energy Budget (Geophysics)
Askew, A. J., et al, eds. Logistics & Benefits of Using Mathematical Models of Hydrologic & Water Resource Systems: Selected Papers from an International Symposium, IIASA Laxenburg, Austria. 270p. 1981. 55.00 (ISBN 0-08-025662-7). Pergamon.
Hollis, G. E. Man's Influence on the Hydrological Cycle in the United Kingdom. 278p. 1981. 40.00x (ISBN 0-86094-024-1, Pub. by GEO Abstracts England); pap. 19.55x (ISBN 0-86094-018-7). State Mutual Bk.
Man's Influence on the Hydrological Cycle: A Draft Report of the UNESCO-FAO Working Group on the International Hydrological Decade. (Irrigation & Drainage Papers: No. 17). (Eng., Fr. & Span., Illus.). 78p. 1973. pap. 13.00 (ISBN 0-686-93249-8, F986, FAO). Unipub.
Singh, Vijay P., ed. Modeling Components of Hydrologic Cycle. LC 81-71291. 1982. 36.00 (ISBN 0-918334-46-2). WRP.
Tuan, Yi-fu. The Hydrologic Cycle & the Wisdom of God: A Theme in Geoteleology. LC 68-135693. (University of Toronto Dept. of Geography Research Publications, Scholarly Research Ser.: No. 1). pap. 43.50 (ISBN 0-317-26960-7, 2023675). Bks Demand UMI.
Wendt, Charles. Water Transfer from Soil to the Atmosphere As Related to Climate & Soil Properties. LC 73-136103. 101p. 1970. 19.00 (ISBN 0-403-04546-0). Scholarly.

HYDROLOGY
see also Hydrogeology; Hydrography; Oceanography; Radioisotopes in Hydrology; Water;
also headings beginning with the word Water
Abridged Final Report of the Sixth Session Commission for Hydrology. 129p. 1981. pap. 25.00 (ISBN 0-686-73317-7, W489, WMO). Unipub.
Advisory Group Meeting, Vienna, Jan. 27-31, 1975. Interpretation of Environmental Isotope & Hydrochemical Data in Groundwater Hydrology: Proceedings. (Panel Proceedings Ser.). (Illus.). 228p. (Orig.). 1976. pap. 25.25 (ISBN 92-0-141076-X, ISP429, IAEA). Unipub.
Anderson, M. G. & Burt, T. P. Hydrological Forecasting. (Geomorphology Ser.). 1985. 54.95 (ISBN 0-471-90614-X). Wiley.
Application of Results from Representative & Experimental Basins. (Studies & Reports in Hydrology: No. 32). (Illus.). 477p. 1982. pap. 22.50 (ISBN 92-3-101949-X, U1215, UNESCO). Unipub.
Applications of Remote Sensing to Hydrology. 52p. (Joint WMO-UNESCO Publication). 1979. pap. 10.00 (ISBN 92-63-10513-8, W453, WMO). Unipub.
Aquifer Contamination & Protection. (Studies & Reports in Hydrology: No. 30). 442p. 1980. pap. 46.50 (ISBN 92-3-101886-8, U1102, UNESCO). Unipub.
Arid-Zone Hydrology: Investigations with Isotope Techniques. (Panel Proceedings Ser.). (Illus.). 265p. 1981. pap. 29.50 (ISBN 92-0-141180-4, ISP547, IAEA). Unipub.
Automatic Collection & Transmission of Hydrological Observations. (Operational Hydrology Reports: No. 2). (Illus.). 70p. 1973. pap. 15.00 (ISBN 0-685-39016-0, W258, WMO). Unipub.
Balek, J. Hydrology & Water Resources in Tropical Regions. (Developments in Water Science Ser.: Vol. 18). 272p. 1983. 70.25 (ISBN 0-444-99656-7, I-304-83). Elsevier.
Balek, Jaroslav. Hydrology & Water Resources in Tropical Africa. (Developments in Water Science Ser.: Vol. 8). 208p. 1977. 70.25 (ISBN 0-444-99814-4). Elsevier.
Berthelot, R. M. Socio-Economic Aspects of Urban Hydrology: Prepared at a Workshop in Lund, Sweden. (Studies & Reports in Hydrology: No. 27). (Illus.). 88p. 1979. pap. 10.00 (ISBN 92-3-101702-0, U965, UNESCO). Unipub.
Bilateral U. S.-Japan Seminar in Hydrology, 1st, Honolulu, Jan. 11-17, 1971. Systems Approach to Hydrology: Proceedings. Yevjevich, Vujica, ed. LC 71-168496. 1971. 21.00 (ISBN 0-918334-02-0). WRP.
Boegli, A. Karst Hydrology & Physical Speleology. (Illus.). 300p. 1980. 41.00 (ISBN 0-387-10098-9). Springer-Verlag.
Bouwer, Herman. Groundwater Hydrology. (Environment Water & Resources Ser). (Illus.). 1978. text ed. 45.00x (ISBN 0-07-006715-5). McGraw.
Branson, Farrell A., et al. Rangeland Hydrology. 2nd ed. 352p. 1981. pap. text ed. 15.00 (ISBN 0-8403-2408-1). Kendall-Hunt.
Bras, Rafael & Rodriquez-Itube, I. Hydraulic Analysis & Synthesis. 704p. 1985. text ed. 42.95 (ISBN 0-201-05865-0). Addison-Wesley.
Casebook of Examples of Organization & Operation of Hydrological Services. (Operational Hydrology Reports: No. 9). 1977. pap. 22.00 (ISBN 92-63-10461-1, W367, WMO). Unipub.
Casebook of Methods of Computation of Quantitative Changes in the Hydrological Regime of River Basins Due to Human Activities. (Studies & Reports in Hydrology: No. 28). (Illus.). 330p. 1980. pap. 24.25 (ISBN 92-3-101798-5, U1037, UNESCO). Unipub.
Chandra, Satish & Masterman, L., eds. Curricula & Syllabi in Hydrology. 2nd ed. (Technical Papers in Hydrology: No. 22). (Illus.). 111p. 1983. pap. text ed. 12.25 (ISBN 92-3-102106-0, U1310, UNESCO). Unipub.
Chorley, Richard J., ed. Introduction to Geographical Hydrology. (Illus.). 1971. pap. 12.95 (ISBN 0-416-68830-6, NO.2134). Methuen Inc.
--Introduction to Physical Hydrology. 1971. pap. 12.95 (ISBN 0-416-68810-1, NO.2135). Methuen Inc.
Chow, Ven Te, ed. Advances in Hydroscience, Vol. 13. 393p. 1982. 77.00 (ISBN 0-12-021813-5). Acad Pr.
Chow Ven-Te. Handbook of Applied Hydrology: A Compendium of Water Resources Technology. 1964. 83.95 (ISBN 0-07-010774-2). McGraw.
Chow Ven Te, ed. Advances in Hydroscience, 12 vols. Incl. Vol. 1. 1964. 87.50 (ISBN 0-12-021801-1); Vol. 2. 1966. 87.50 (ISBN 0-12-021802-X); Vol. 3. 1967. 87.50 (ISBN 0-12-021803-8); Vol. 4. 1968. 87.50 (ISBN 0-12-021804-6); Vol. 5. 1969. 87.50 (ISBN 0-12-021805-4); Vol. 6. 1970. 87.50 (ISBN 0-12-021806-2); Vol. 7. 1971. 87.50 (ISBN 0-12-021807-0); Vol. 8. 1972. 87.50 (ISBN 0-12-021808-9); Vol. 9. 1973. 87.50 (ISBN 0-12-021809-7); Vol. 10. 1975. 90.00 (ISBN 0-12-021810-0); Vol. 11. 1978. 90.00 (ISBN 0-12-021811-9); lib. bdg. 120.00 o.p (ISBN 0-12-021876-3); Vol. 12. 1981. 80.00 (ISBN 0-12-021812-7). Acad Pr.
Ciriani, Tito A., et al, eds. Mathematical Models for Surface Water Hydrology: Proceedings of the Workshop Held at the IBM Scientific Center, Pisa Italy. LC 76-13457. 423p. 1977. 109.95x (ISBN 0-471-99400-6, Pub. by Wiley-Interscience). Wiley.
Combined Heat, Ice & Water Balance at Selected Glacier Basins, 2 Pts. Incl. Pt. 2. Specifications, Standards & Data Exchange. 32p. pap. 5.00 (ISBN 92-3-101050-6, U738). (Technical Papers in Hydrology Ser.: No. 5). (Co-published with IAHS). 1973. pap. (UNESCO). Unipub.
Compendium of Training Facilities for Meterology & Operational Hydrology. 6th ed. 590p. 1982. pap. 50.00 (ISBN 92-63-16240-9, W530, WMO). Unipub.
Compendium of Training Facilities in Environmental Problems Related to Meteorological & Operational Hydrology. (Illus.). 192p. 1977. pap. 22.00 (ISBN 92-63-10489-1, W363, WMO). Unipub.
Davis, George H. & Velikanov. Hydrological Problems Arising from the Development of Energy: A Preliminary Report. (Technical Papers in Hydrology: No. 17). (Illus.). 32p. 1979. pap. 5.00 (ISBN 92-3-101685-7, U912, UNESCO). Unipub.
Deju, Raul A. Regional Hydrology Fundamentals. (Illus.). 222p. 1971. 57.75 (ISBN 0-677-03860-7). Gordon.
DeVore, R. William & Graves, Donald H. Nineteen Eighty-Five Symposium on Surface Mining, Hydrology, Sedimentology & Reclamation: Proceedings. LC 83-60966. (Illus.). 600p. (Orig.). 1985. text ed. 45.00 (ISBN 0-89779-064-2, UKY BU139). OES Pubns.
DeVore, R. William & Huffsey, R. Nineteen Eighty-Five International Symposium on Urban Hydrology, Hydraulic & Infrastructures & Water Quality Control: Proceedings. (Illus.). 335p. (Orig.). 1985. pap. 33.50 (ISBN 0-89779-063-4, UKY BU138). OES Pubns.
DeVore, R. William & Graves, Donald H., eds. Nineteen Eighty-Four Symposium on Surface Mining, Hydrology, Sedimentology & Reclamation: Proceedings. LC 83-60966. (Illus.). 492p. (Orig.). 1984. pap. 45.00 (ISBN 0-89779-062-6, UKY BU136). OES Pubns.
--Proceedings, Symposium on Surface Mining, Hydrology, Sedimentology, & Reclamation, 1982. LC 82-51182. (Illus.). 728p. (Orig.). 1982. pap. 45.00 (ISBN 0-89779-054-5, UKY BU129). OES Pubns.
De Vore, R. William & Graves, Donald H., eds. Proceedings, 1983 Symposium on Surface Mining, Hydrology, Sedimentology & Reclamation. LC 83-60966. (Illus.). 554p. (Orig.). 1983. pap. 45.00 (ISBN 0-89779-058-8, UKY BU 133). OES Pubns.
De Vore, R. William & Huffsey, R., eds. Nineteen Eighty-Four International Symposium on Urban Hydrology, Hydrolics & Sediment Control: Proceedings. LC 83-60965. (Illus.). 284p. (Orig.). 1984. pap. 33.50 (ISBN 0-89779-060-X, UKY BU135). OES Pubns.
De Vries, J. J. Inleiding Tot De Hydrologie Van Nederland. (Chemie En Technick Ser.: No. 2). (Ger., Illus.). 78p. 1976. pap. text ed. 6.50x (ISBN 90-6203-149-8). Humanities.
Dingman, S. Lawrence. Fluvial Hydrology. 1983. text ed. 31.95 (ISBN 0-7167-1452-3); pap. text ed. write for info (ISBN 0-7167-1453-1). W H Freeman.
Discharge of Selected Rivers of the World. Incl. Vol. 1. General & Regime Characteristics of Stations Selected. 70p. 1969. pap. 9.25 (ISBN 92-3-001164-9, U165); Vol. 2. Monthly & Annual Discharges Recorded at Various Selected Stations (From Start of Observations up to 1964) 194p. 1971. pap. 12.50 (ISBN 92-3-000847-8, U166); Vol. 3, Pt. 1. Mean Monthly & Extreme Discharges (1965-1969) 98p. 1971; Vol. 3, Pt. 2. Mean Monthly & Extreme Discharges (1969-1972) 214p. 1974. pap. 13.25 (ISBN 92-3-001178-9, U168); Vol. 3, Pt. 3. Mean Monthly & Extreme Discharges (1972-1975) 123p. 1979. pap. 9.25 (ISBN 92-3-001569-5, U916). (Studies & Reports in Hydrology: No. 5). (Eng., Fr., Span. & Rus., Orig., UNESCO). Unipub.
Dubreuil, P. Recueil Quadrilingue de Mots Usuels en Hydrologie. 113p. (Quadrilingual Collection of Commonly Used Words in Hydrology). 1969. pap. 9.95 (ISBN 0-686-56767-6, M-6176). French & Eur.
Eichert, B. S., et al, eds. Methods of Hydrological Computations for Water Projects: A Contribution to the International Hydrological Programme. (Studies & Reports in Hydrology: No. 38). (Illus.). 122p. 1982. pap. 17.00 (ISBN 92-3-102005-6, U1236, UNESCO). Unipub.
El-Shaarawi, A. H., ed. Time Series Methods in Hydrosciences: Proceedings of the International Conference, Burlington, Ontario, Canada, October 6-8, 1981. (Developments in Water Science Ser.: No. 17). 614p. 1982. 85.00 (ISBN 0-444-42102-5). Elsevier.
Engelen, G. B. & Van Lissa, R. V. Aqua-Vu Three: Hydrological Surveys in the Algarve, Portugal, Part I. (Communications of the Institute of Earth Sciences, Ser A: No. 3). 1979. pap. text ed. Cancelled (ISBN 90-6203-009-2). Humanities.
Engineering Foundation Conference, 1979. Improved Hydrologic Forecastings: Why & How. 458p. 1980. pap. 32.50x (ISBN 0-87262-203-7). Am Soc Civil Eng.
Eschner, Arthur R. & Black, Peter E., eds. Readings in Forest Hydrology. (Illus.). 293p. 1975. text ed. 27.50x (ISBN 0-8422-5228-2). Irvington.
Farraday, R. V. & Charlton, F. G. Hydraulic Factors in Bridge Design. 110p. 1983. 29.75x (ISBN 0-946466-00-9). Am Soc Civil Eng.
Fleming, George. Computer Simulation Techniques in Hydrology. (Environmental Science Ser.). 352p. 1975. 42.50 (ISBN 0-444-00157-3). Elsevier.
Fox, Cyril S. Water. LC 75-138233. (Illus.). 148p. 1972. Repr. of 1951 ed. lib. bdg. 15.00x (ISBN 0-8371-5590-8, FOWA). Greenwood.
Fritz, Jack. Small & Mini Hydropower Systems: Resource Assessment & Project Feasibility. Allen-Browne, Patricia, ed. (Illus.). 464p. 1983. 47.95 (ISBN 0-07-022470-6). McGraw.
Further Hydrologic Studies in the Mackenzie Valley. 1975. pap. 6.95 (SSC43, SSC). Unipub.
Gillman, K. & Newson, M. D. Soil Pipes & Pipeflow. (Bgrg Research Monography Ser.). 1980. pap. 9.90x (ISBN 0-686-27388-5, Pub. by GEO Abstracts England). State Mutual Bk.
Glenn, Ronald E. & Blinn, James E. Mobile Hydraulic Testing. LC 79-107426. (Illus.). pap. 84.00 (ISBN 0-317-10998-7, 2004564). Bks Demand UMI.
Glossaire International d'Hydrologie. (Fr.). 393p. 1974. pap. 29.95 (ISBN 0-686-57304-8, M-6281). French & Eur.
Gray, D. M., ed. Handbook on the Principles of Hydrology. LC 73-82157. (Illus.). 720p. 1973. pap. text ed. 28.00 (ISBN 0-912394-07-2). Water Info.
Gregory, K. J., ed. Background to Palaeohydrology: A Perspective. 408p. 1983. 59.95x (ISBN 0-471-90179-2, Pub. by Wiley-Interscience). Wiley.
Guide to Hydrological Practices: Analysis, Forecasting & Other Applications, Vol. II. (WMO Ser.: No. 168). 150p. 1983. pap. text ed. 40.00 (ISBN 92-63-14168-1, W578, WMO). Unipub.
Guide to Hydrological Practices: Supplement. 3rd ed. pap. 55.00 (W36, WMO). Unipub.
Guide to World Inventory of Sea, Lake & River Ice. (Technical Papers in Hydrology: No. 9). 23p. (Orig., Co-published with IAHS). 1972. pap. 5.25 (ISBN 92-3-100958-3, U276, UNESCO). Unipub.
Guidebook on Nuclear Techniques in Hydrology. (Technical Reports Ser.: No. 91). 439p. 1983. pap. text ed. 56.00 (ISBN 92-0-145083-4, IDC91/2, IAEA). Unipub.
Guidelines for the Education & Training of Personnel in Meteorology & Operational Hydrology. 2nd ed. (Eng. & Fr., Illus.). 236p. 1977. pap. 20.00 (ISBN 92-63-12258-X, W373, WMO). Unipub.
Guidelines for the Education & Training of Personnel in Meteorology & Operational Hydrology, 3 pts. Incl. Part 1. 2nd ed. pap. 20.00 (ISBN 92-6-312258-X, W532, WMO); Education & Training of Personnel in Operating Hydrology. pap. 3.00 (ISBN 0-686-93854-2, W532); Addendum to Part 2. 35p. 1982. pap. 5.00 (W532). (Illus.). 1977 (WMO). Unipub.
Gupta, S. K., ed. Current Trends in Arid Zone Hydrology: Proceedings of Symposium Held at Physical Research Laboratory, Ahmedabad, April 5-8, 1978. 540p. 1979. 40.00 (ISBN 0-88065-097-4, Pub. by Messers Today & Tomorrows Printers & Publishers India). Scholarly Pubns.
Haan, C. T. Statistical Methods in Hydrology. 1977. text ed. 16.50x (ISBN 0-8138-1510-X). Iowa St U Pr.
Hall, M. J. Urban Hydrology. 304p. 1984. 42.00 (ISBN 0-85334-268-7, I-217-84, Pub. by Elsevier Applied Sci England). Elsevier.
Hammer, Mark J. & Mackichan, Kenneth A. Hydrology & Quality of Water Resources. LC 80-209. 486p. 1981. 31.95 (ISBN 0-471-02681-6); solutions manual avail. (ISBN 0-471-08573-1); problem papers avail. Wiley.
Hansen, E. G. Hydronic System Design & Operation. 544p. 1985. 46.50 (ISBN 0-07-026065-6). McGraw.
Henry, C. D. & Gluck, J. K. A Preliminary Assessment of the Geologic Setting, Hydrology, & Geochemistry of the Hueco Tanks Geothermal Area, Texas & New Mexico. (Geological Circular Ser.: No. 81-1). (Illus.). 48p. 1981. 2.00. Bur Econ Geology.
Hewlett, John D. Principles of Forest Hydrology. LC 81-16371. 192p. 1982. pap. text ed. 7.00x (ISBN 0-8203-0608-8). U of Ga Pr.
Hjelmfelt, A. T., Jr. & Cassidy, J. J. Hydrology for Engineers & Planners. (Illus.). 1975. text ed. 17.95x (ISBN 0-8138-0795-6). Iowa St U Pr.

Hromadka, Theodore V., II. Computer Methods in Urban Hydrology: Rational Methods & Unit Hydrograph Methods. LC 83-81435. (Illus.). 280p. 1983. pap. text ed. 36.50 (ISBN 0-914055-00-3). Lighthouse Pubns.
Hydrological Atlas of Canada. 1978. pap. 65.00 (ISBN 0-660-01591-9, SSC122, SSC). Unipub.
Hydrological Effects of Urbanization. (Studies & Reports in Hydrology: No. 18). (Illus.). 280p. 1975. pap. 35.75 (ISBN 92-3-101223-1, U290, UNESCO). Unipub.
Hydrological Forecasting Practices: Prepared by the Working Group on Hydrological Forecasting of the Commission for Hydrology. (Operational Hydrology Reports: No. 6). (Illus.). 134p. 1975. pap. 21.00 (ISBN 92-63-10425-5, W262, WMO). Unipub.
Hydrological Forecasting: Proceedings of the Queensland Symposium, 1967. 325p. 1969. pap. write for info (ISBN 92-3-100767-X, U1355, UNESCO). Unipub.
Hydrology & Water Resources Symposium 83. 341p. (Orig.). 1984. pap. text ed. 28.00x (ISBN 0-85825-213-9, Pub. by Inst. Engineering Australia). Brookfield Pub Co.
Hydrology Symposium. 189p. (Orig.). 1978. pap. text ed. 36.00x (ISBN 0-85825-096-9, Pub. by Inst Engineering Australia). Brookfield Pub Co.
Institution of Civil Engineers Staff, ed. Engineering Hydrology Today. 150p. 1975. 50.25x (ISBN 0-7277-0012-X). Am Soc Civil Eng.
--Hydraulic Modelling in Maritime Engineering. 152p. 1982. 34.50x (ISBN 0-7277-0154-1). Am Soc Civil Eng.
Intercomparison of Conceptual Models Used in Operational Hydrological Forecasting. (Operational Hydrology Reports: No. 7). (Illus.). 172p. 1975. pap. 22.00 (ISBN 92-63-10429-8, W263, WMO). Unipub.
International Glossary of Hydrology. (Eng., Fr., Span. & Rus.). xx, 394p. 1974. pap. 40.00 (ISBN 92-63-00385-8, W155, WMO). Unipub.
International Hydrological Programme (IHP) Third Session of the Intergovernmental Council, Paris, 9-16 November 1979. 72p. 1981. pap. 10.00 (ISBN 0-686-69436-8, U1051, UNESCO). Unipub.
International Symposium in Hydrology, 2nd, Colorado State Univ., Sep. 11-13, 1972. Decision with Inadequate Hydrologic Data: Proceedings. Woolhiser, David A., ed. LC 73-80677. 1973. 14.00 (ISBN 0-918334-04-7). WRP.
International Symposium, 1983. Proceedings, 1983 International Symposium on Urban Hydrology, Hydraulics & Sediment Control. De Vore, R. William, ed. LC 83-60965. (Illus.). 531p. (Orig.). 1983. pap. 33.50 (ISBN 0-89779-056-1, UKY BU 131). OES Pubns.
Isotopes in Hydrology. (Proceedings Ser.). (Eng., Fr. & Rus., Illus.). 740p. (Orig.). 1967. pap. 43.25 (ISBN 92-0-040067-1, ISP141, IAEA). Unipub.
Jones, K. & Berney, O. Arid Zone Hydrology for Agricultural Development. (Irrigation & Drainage Papers: No. 37). 383p. 1981. pap. 27.50 (ISBN 92-5-101079-X, F2204, FAO). Unipub.
Keller, George R. Hydraulic System Analysis. LC 78-52991. (Illus.). 201p. 1985. 25.00 (ISBN 0-932905-00-5). Penton IPC.
Kirkby, M. J., ed. Hillslope Hydrology. LC 77-2669. (Geomorphology Ser.). 389p. 1978. 96.95x (ISBN 0-471-99510-X, Pub. by Wiley-Interscience). Wiley.
Kite, G. W. Frequency & Risk Analyses in Hydrology. 1977. 15.00 (ISBN 0-918334-23-3). WRP.
Knapp, B. J. Elements of Geographical Hydrology. (Illus.). 1978. pap. text ed. 7.95x (ISBN 0-04-551030-X). Allen Unwin.
Kovacs, G., et al. Subterranean Hydrology. LC 80-54120. 1981. 49.00 (ISBN 0-918334-35-7). WRP.
Kunkle, S. H. & Thames, J. L., eds. Hydrological Techniques for Upstream Conservation. (Conservation Guides: No. 2). (Eng. & Fr.). 145p. (2nd Printing 1979). 1976. pap. 9.75 (ISBN 92-5-100115-4, F742, FAO). Unipub.
LaFleur, Robert G., ed. Groundwater As a Geomorphic Agent. (Binghamton Symposia in Geomorphology: International Ser.: No. 13). (Illus.). 384p. 1984. text ed. 50.00x (ISBN 0-04-551069-5). Allen Unwin.
Lal, R. & Russell, E. W., eds. Tropical Agricultural Hydrology: Watershed Management & Land Use. LC 80-41590. 482p. 1981. 74.95x (ISBN 0-471-27931-5, Pub. by Wiley-Interscience). Wiley.
La Moreaux, P. E. & Wilson, B. M., eds. Guide to the Hydrology of Carbonate Rocks. (Studies and Reports in Hydrology: No. 41). (Illus.). 345p. 1984. pap. 44.75 (ISBN 92-3-102206-7, U1377, UNESCO). Unipub.
Lexique Trilingue des Termes de l'Eau. (Fr.). 224p. (Trilingual Lexicon of Water Terminology). 1975. pap. 29.95 (ISBN 0-686-56724-2, M-6372). French & Eur.
Linsley, Ray K., et al. Hydrology for Engineers. 3rd ed. (Water Resources & Environmental Engineering Ser.). (Illus.). 496p. 1982. 43.00 (ISBN 0-07-037956-4). McGraw.
McCuen, Richard H. A Guide to Hydrologic Analysis Using SCS Methods. (Illus.). 160p. 1982. 32.95 (ISBN 0-13-370205-7). P-H.
McCuen, Richard H. & Snyder, Willard M. Hydrologic Modeling: Statistical Methods & Applications. (Illus.). 496p. 1986. text ed. 39.95 (ISBN 0-13-448119-4). P-H.
McMahon, T. A. & Diaz, Arenas A., eds. Methods of Computation of Low Stream-flow. (Studies & Reports in Hydrology: No. 36). (Illus.). 95p. 1982. pap. 11.50 (ISBN 92-3-102013-7, U1252, UNESCO). Unipub.
McPherson, M. B. & Zuidema, F. C. Urban Hydrological Modeling & Catchment Research: International Summary. (Technical Papers in Hydrology: No. 18). (Illus.). 48p. 1979. pap. 5.00 (ISBN 0-685-95367-X, U896, UNESCO). Unipub.
McPherson, M. B., ed. Research on Urban Hydrology, 3 vols. Incl. Vol. 1. State-of-the-Art Reports from Australia, Canada, U.S.S.R., United Kingdom & United States. (No. 15). 185p. 1977. pap. 13.75 (ISBN 92-3-101488-9, U763); Vol. 2. State-of-the Art Reports from France, the Federal Republic of Germany, India, the Netherlands, Norway, Poland & Sweden. (No. 16). (Illus.). 265p. 1978. pap. 13.75 (ISBN 92-3-101555-9, U849); Vol. 3. Follow-up Reports from Eleven Countries 1979. (No. 21). 144p. 1981. pap. 14.50 (ISBN 92-3-101984-8, U1230). (Technical Papers in Hydrology Ser.). (Illus., UNESCO). Unipub.
McWhorter, David B. & Sunada, Daniel K. Ground Water Hydrology & Hydraulics. LC 77-74259. 1981. 27.00 (ISBN 0-918334-18-7). WRP.
Majewski, W. & Miller, D., eds. Predicting Effects of Power Plant On-Through Cooling on Aquatic Systems: A State-of-the-Art Report of IHP Working Group 6.2 on the Effects of Thermal Discharges. (Technical Papers in Hydrology: No. 20). (Illus.). 171p. 1979. pap. 17.00 (ISBN 92-3-101704-7, U939, UNESCO). Unipub.
Mathematical Models in Hydrology. (Irrigation & Drainage Papers: No. 19). 292p. (4th Printing 1978). 1973. pap. 21.00 (ISBN 92-5-100641-5, F988, FAO). Unipub.
Maxwell, H. C., ed. Frontiers of Hydrology. Beard, L. R. LC 83-50244. 1984. 32.00 (ISBN 0-918334-54-3). WRP.
Measurement of River Sediments. (Operational Hydrology Reports: No. 16). 61p. 1981. pap. 7.00 (ISBN 92-63-10561-8, W506, WMO). Unipub.
Miller, D. H. Water at the Surface of the Earth: An Introduction to Ecosystem Hydrodynamics. 1977. 74.50 (ISBN 0-12-496750-7). Acad Pr.
Modern Developments in Hydrometry: Papers Submitted by Author & Discussion of Introductory Reports & Papers, Vol. 2. (Illus.). 510p. 1976. pap. 16.00 (ISBN 92-63-10427-1, W356, WMO). Unipub.
Moss, H. Concepts & Techniques in Hydrological Network Design. (Operational Hydrology Reports: No. 19). 30p. 1982. pap. 6.00 (ISBN 92-63-10580-4, W522, WMO). Unipub.
National Water Summary, 1983: Hydrologic Events & Issues. 249p. 1984. pap. 9.00 (ISBN 0-318-11740-1). Gov Printing Office.
Neal, James T., ed. Playas & Dried Lakes: Occurrence & Development. LC 74-31134. (Benchmark Papers in Geology Ser: No. 20). 411p. 1975. 69.00 (ISBN 0-12-787110-1). Acad Pr.
Nuclear Well Logging in Hydrology. (Technical Reports Ser.: No. 126). (Illus., Orig.). 1971. pap. 10.75 (ISBN 92-0-145071-0, IDC126, IAEA). Unipub.
Peixoto, J. Atmosheric Vapour Flux Computations for Hydrological Purposes. (WMO-IHD Reports: No. 20). xii, 100p. 1973. pap. (WMO). Unipub.
Pinder, G. F. & Gray, W. G. Finite Element Simulation in Surface & Subsurface Hydrology. 1977. 43.00 (ISBN 0-12-556950-5). Acad Pr.
Pitty, A. F. A Geographical Approach to Fluvial Processes. 300p. 1980. text ed. 29.50x (ISBN 0-86094-027-6, Pub. by GEO Abstracts England); pap. text ed. 15.55 (ISBN 0-86094-026-8, Pub. by GEO Abstracts England). State Mutual Bk.
Raabe, J. Hydro Power. 600p. 1984. 71.00 (ISBN 3-18-400616-6, 990700054, Pub. by VDI Verlag Gmbh Dusseldorf). Heyden.
Raghunath, H. M. Hydrology: Principles, Analysis & Design. 480p. 1985. 34.95 (ISBN 0-470-20036-7). Halsted Pr.
Rasmusson, E. M. Hydrological Application of Atmospheric Vapour-Flux Analyses. (Operational Hydrology Reports: No. 11). (Illus.). x, 50p. 1977. pap. 10.00 (ISBN 92-63-10476-X, W354, WMO). Unipub.
Raudkivi, A. J. Hydrology. 1979. 80.00 (ISBN 0-08-024261-8). Pergamon.
Rodda, John C. Facets of Hydrology, Vol. 2. 400p. 1985. text ed. 66.00 (ISBN 0-471-90338-8, Pub by Wiley-Interscience). Wiley.
Rodda, John C., ed. Facets of Hydrology. LC 75-26568. pap. 96.00 (ISBN 0-317-09887-X, 2019670). Bks Demand UMI.
Salas, J. D., et al. Applied Modeling of Hydrologic Time Series. LC 80-53334. 1981. 32.00 (ISBN 0-918334-37-3). WRP.
Saleem, Zubair A., ed. Advances in Groundwater Hydrology. LC 77-92093. pap. 85.30 (ISBN 0-317-28827-X, 2017812). Bks Demand UMI.
Schulz, E. F. Problems in Applied Hydrology. 1974. 25.00 (ISBN 0-918334-07-1). WRP.
Scientific Papers Presented at the Technical Conference of Hydrological & Meteorological Services: Geneva, 28 Sept.-6 Oct. 1970. (Eng. & Fr., Illus.). 124p. (Orig.). 1971. pap. 10.00 (ISBN 0-685-24966-2, W107, WMO). Unipub.
Sevruk, B. Methods of Correction for Systematic Error in Point Precipitation Measurement for Operational Use. (Operational Hydrology Reports: No. 21). 91p. 1982. pap. 10.00 (ISBN 92-63-10589-8, W529, WMO). Unipub.
Shahin, M. M. Hydrology of the Nile Basin. (Developments in Water Science Ser.: Vol. 21). 575p. 1985. 92.75 (ISBN 0-444-42433-4). Elsevier.
Sharp, James J. & Sawden, P. G. Basic Hydrology. (Basic Ser.). (Illus.). 180p. 1984. pap. text ed. 15.95 (ISBN 0-408-01363-X). Butterworth.
Shaw, Elizabeth M. Hydrology in Practice. 1983. 43.50 (ISBN 0-442-30565-6). Van Nos Reinhold.
Simeons, Charles. Hydro-Power: The Use of Water As an Alternative Source. (Illus.). 560p. 1980. 105.00 (ISBN 0-08-023269-8). Pergamon.
Singh, Vijay P., ed. Applied Modeling in Catchment Hydrology. LC 81-71292. 1982. 34.00 (ISBN 0-918334-43-8). WRP.
Smith, D. I. & Stopp, P. The River Basin. LC 77-85688. (Topics in Geography Ser.). (Illus.). 1979. 22.95 (ISBN 0-521-21900-0); pap. 10.95x (ISBN 0-521-29307-3). Cambridge U Pr.
Storr, Eric D., ed. Hydraulics in Civil Engineering. 300p. 1984. pap. text ed. 20.00x (ISBN 0-85825-211-2, Pub. by Inst Engineers Australia). Brookfield Pub Co.
Street-Perrot & Beran. Variations in the Global Water Budget. 1983. lib. bdg. 69.50 (ISBN 90-277-1364-2, Pub. by Reidel Holland). Kluwer Academic.
Svanidze, G. G. Mathematical Modeling of Hydrologic Series. LC 79-57578. 1980. 18.00 (ISBN 0-918334-32-2). WRP.
Symposium on Karst Hydrology & Water Resources, Dubrovnik, Yugo., Jun 2-7, 1975. Karst Hydrology & Water Resources, 2 vols. Yevjevich, V., ed. LC 76-12972. 1976. Set. 25.00 (ISBN 0-686-67935-0); Vol. 1. (ISBN 0-918334-15-2); Vol. 2. (ISBN 0-918334-16-0). WRP.
Tercentenary of Scientific Hydrology, Paris, 1974. Three Centuries of Scientific Hydrology, 1674-1974: Papers. (Eng., Fr., Span. & Rus.). 123p. 1974. pap. 9.50 (ISBN 0-686-94189-6, U680, UNESCO). Unipub.
Todd, David K. Groundwater Hydrology. 2nd ed. LC 80-11831. 535p. 1980. 45.45x (ISBN 0-471-87616-X). Wiley.
Toebes, C. & Ouryvaer, V., eds. Representative & Experimental Basins: An International Guide for Research & Practice. (Studies & Reports in Hydrology: No. 4). (Illus.). 348p. (Orig.). 1970. 24.25 (ISBN 92-3-100808-0, U551, UNESCO). Unipub.
Torno, Harry C. Urban Hydrology. 270p. 1983. pap. 23.00x (ISBN 0-87262-388-2). Am Soc Civil Eng.
Unny, T. E. & McBean, Edward A., eds. Decision Making for Hydrosystems: Forecasting & Operation. LC 82-50384. 1982. 37.00 (ISBN 0-918334-50-0). WRP.
Use of WWW Facilities for Hydrology. (World Weather Watch Planning Reports: No. 35). (Illus.). 34p. 1976. pap. 10.00 (ISBN 92-63-10451-4, W247, WMO). Unipub.
Van der Leeden, Frits. Water Resources of the World. LC 75-20952. (Illus.). 1975. 60.00 (ISBN 0-912394-14-5). Water Info.
Verstraten, J. M. Water-Rock Interactions. (Bgrg Research Monograph Ser.). 1980. pap. 9.90x (ISBN 0-686-27389-3, Pub. by GEO Abstracts England). State Mutual Bk.
Viessman, Warren, et al. Introduction to Hydrology. 2nd ed. 1977. text ed. 35.50 scp (ISBN 0-7002-2497-1, HarpC). Har-Row.
Wiin-Nielsen, A., ed. Compendium of Meteorology for Use by Class I & Class II Meteorological Personnel, 2 Vols. in 7 Pts. Incl. Vol. 1, Pt. 1. Dynamic Meteorology. Wiin-Nielsen, A. (Eng. & Span.). vi, 334p. 1973. pap. 35.00 (W138); Vol. 1, Pt. 2. Physical Meteorology. Retallack, B. (Eng. & Span.). vi, 212p. 1973. pap. 25.00 (W139); Vol. 1, Pt. 3. Synoptic Meteorology. Defant, F. & Morth, H. xiv, 276p. 1978. 32.00 (W405); Vol. 2, Pt. 1. General Hydrology. Cheborateu, A. vi, 43p. 1977. pap. 10.00 (W359); Vol. 2, Pt. 2. Aeronautical Meteorology. Revalack, B. vi, 126p. 1978. pap. 14.00 (W416); Vol. 2, Pt. 3. Marine Meteorology. Fatheringham, R. x, 121p. 1979. pap. 11.00 (W441); Vol. 2, Pt. 4. Tropical Meteorology. Krishnamiirthi, T. xvii, 428p. 1979. pap. 30.00 (W484). WMO). Unipub.
Williams, W. D. Salt Lakes. (Developments in Hydrobiology Ser.: No. 5). 458p. 1982. 95.00 (ISBN 90-6193-756-6, Pub. by Junk Pubs Netherlands). Kluwer Academic.
Yevjevich, Vujica. Probability & Statistics in Hydrology. LC 74-168494. 1972. 25.00 (ISBN 0-918334-00-4). WRP.
--Stochastic Processes in Hydrology. LC 78-168495. 25.00 (ISBN 0-918334-01-2). WRP.
--Structure of Daily Hydrologic Series. (Illus.). 264p. (Orig.). 1984. pap. 25.00 (ISBN 0-918334-55-1). WRP.

HYDROLOGY–DATA PROCESSING

American Water Works Association. Computer-Based Automation in Water Systems. (AWWA Handbooks-General Ser.). (Illus.). 104p. 1980. pap. text ed. 12.00 (ISBN 0-89867-230-9). Am Water Wks Assn.
Automation & Instrumentation: M2. (AWWA Manuals Ser.). (Illus.). 160p. 1977. pap. text ed. 19.20 (ISBN 0-89867-060-8). Am Water Wks Assn.
Case Studies of National Hydrological Data Banks: Planning, Development & Organization. (Operational Hydrology Reports: 17). 134p. 1981. pap. 10.00 (ISBN 92-63-10576-6, W523, WMO). Unipub.
Deterministic Models in Hydrology. (Irrigation & Drainage Papers: No. 32). 85p. 1979. pap. 7.50 (ISBN 92-5-100708-X, F1842, FAO). Unipub.
Flanders, H. F. Hydrological. (Operational Hydrology Reports: No. 14). 34p. 1981. pap. 6.00 (ISBN 92-63-10559-6, W499, WMO). Unipub.
Fleming, George. Computer Simulation Techniques in Hydrology. (Environmental Science Ser.). 352p. 1975. 42.50 (ISBN 0-444-00157-3). Elsevier.
Hromadka, Theodore V., II. Computer Methods in Urban Hydrology: Rational Methods & Unit Hydrograph Methods. LC 83-81435. (Illus.). 280p. 1983. pap. text ed. 36.50 (ISBN 0-914055-00-3). Lighthouse Pubns.
Hydrological Bench Marks. (WMO-IHD Reports: No. 8). 8p. 1968. pap. (WMO). Unipub.
Hydrological Network Design & Information Transfer: Proceedings of the International Seminar, Newcastle Upon Tyme, U.R., Aug. 1974. (Operational Hydrology Reports: No. 8). (Illus.). 185p. 1976. pap. 30.00 (ISBN 92-63-10433-6, W264, WMO). Unipub.
Narayana, Dhruva, et al. Analog Computer Simulation of the Runoff Characteristics of an Urban Watershed. LC 77-141023. 88p. 1969. 19.00 (ISBN 0-403-04522-3). Scholarly.
Pinder, G. F. & Gray, W. G. Finite Element Simulation in Surface & Subsurface Hydrology. 1977. 43.00 (ISBN 0-12-556950-5). Acad Pr.
Roving Seminar on the Use of Computers in Hydrology & Water Resources Planning - Proceedings: Asian Economy. (Water Resources Development Ser.: No. 52). pap. 21.00 (UN80/2F17, UN). Unipub.
Technical Regulations: Hydrology & International Codes. 129p. 1980. pap. 20.00 loose leaf (ISBN 92-63-10555-3, W477, WMO). Unipub.
Use of Analog & Digital Computers in Hydrology: Proceedings of the Tucson Symposium, 2 Vols. (Studies & Reports in Hydrology: No. 1). (Illus.). 1969. Set. 46.25 (ISBN 92-3-000734-X, U711, UNESCO). Vol. 1, 344p. Vol. 2, 411p. Unipub.
Water Plant Instrumentation & Automation. (AWWA Handbooks-Proceedings Ser.). (Illus.). 304p. 1976. pap. text ed. 14.40 (ISBN 0-89867-049-7). Am Water Wks Assn.

HYDROLYSIS

see also Lysosomes

Baes, Charles F., Jr. & Mesmer, Robert E. The Hydrolysis of Cations. 512p. 1986. Repr. of 1976 ed. lib. bdg. price not set (ISBN 0-89874-892-5). Krieger.
Fishman, William H., ed. Metabolic Conjugation & Metabolic Hydrolysis, 3 vols. LC 79-107556. Vol. 1, 1970. 90.00 (ISBN 0-12-257601-2); Vol. 2, 1971. 95.00 (ISBN 0-12-257602-0); Vol. 3, 1973. 90.00 (ISBN 0-12-257603-9). Acad Pr.

HYDROMAGNETIC WAVES

see Magnetohydrodynamics

Dods, John B. Philosophy of Electrical Psychology. (Hypnosis & Altered States of Consciousness Ser.). 252p. 1982. Repr. of 1850 ed. lib. bdg. 29.50 (ISBN 0-306-76077-0). Da Capo.

Edmonston, William E. Hypnosis & Relaxation: Modern Verification of an Old Equation. LC 80-22506. (Personality Processes Ser.). 255p. 1981. 35.00 (ISBN 0-471-05903-X, Pub. by Wiley-Interscience). Wiley.

Edmonston, William E., Jr., ed. Conceptual & Investigative Approaches to Hypnosis & Hypnotic Phenomena, Vol. 296. (Annals of the New York Academy of Sciences). 619p. 1977. 24.00x (ISBN 0-89072-042-8). NY Acad Sci.

Edmunds, Simeon. Hypnotism & Psychic Phenomena. pap. 4.00 (ISBN 0-87980-077-1). Wilshire.

--The Psychic Power of Hypnosis. (Paths to Inner Power Ser). 1968. pap. 2.50 (ISBN 0-85030-291-9). Weiser.

Erickson, Milton H. Hypnotic Alteration of Sensory, Perceptual & Psychophysiological Processes. Rossi, Ernest L., ed. (The Collected Papers of Milton H. Erickson on Hypnosis: Vol. II). 368p. 1980. text ed. 29.95x (ISBN 0-8290-0543-9). Irvington.

--The Hypnotic Investigation of Psychodynamic Processes. Rossi, Ernest L., ed. (The Collected Papers of Milton H. Erickson on Hypnosis: Vol. III). 368p. 1980. text ed. 29.95x (ISBN 0-8290-0544-7). Irvington.

--The Nature of Hypnosis & Suggestion. Rossi, Ernest L., ed. (The Collected Papers of Milton H. Erickson on Hypnosis: Vol. I). 570p. 1980. text ed. 37.50x (ISBN 0-8290-0542-0). Irvington.

Erickson, Milton H. & Rossi, Ernest, eds. Hypnotic Investigation of Psychodynamic Processes. LC 79-15939. (Collected Papers of Milton H. Erickson on Hypnosis: Vol. 3). 367p. 1980. 29.95x (ISBN 0-470-26723-2). Halsted Pr.

Erickson, Milton H., et al. Hypnotic Realities: The Induction of Clinical Hypnosis & Forms of Indirect Suggestion. LC 76-20636. 1976. incl. audio cassette 27.95x (ISBN 0-8290-0112-3). Irvington.

Frankel, F. H. & Zamansky, H., eds. Hypnosis at Its Bicentennial. LC 78-16605. 320p. 1978. 34.50x (ISBN 0-306-40029-4, Plenum Pr). Plenum Pub.

Frankel, Fred H., ed. Hypnosis: Trance As a Coping Mechanism. LC 76-14856. 195p. 1976. 24.50x (ISBN 0-306-30932-7, Plenum Pr). Plenum Pub.

Fromm, Erika & Shor, Ronald E. Hypnosis: Developments in Research & New Perspectives. 2nd ed. LC 79-89279. (Illus.). 793p. 1979. lib. bdg. 59.95x (ISBN 0-202-26085-2). Aldine Pub.

Gibbons, D. E. Applied Hypnosis & Hyperempiria. LC 79-20879. 227p. 1979. 24.50x (ISBN 0-306-40271-8, Plenum Pr). Plenum Pub.

Gibson, H. B. Hypnosis: Its Nature & Therapeutic Uses. LC 77-92821. 1980. pap. 4.95 (ISBN 0-8008-4043-7). Taplinger.

Gindes, B. New Concepts in Hypnosis. 4.00x (ISBN 0-685-22059-1). Wehman.

Gindes, Bernard C. New Concepts of Hypnosis. pap. 5.00 (ISBN 0-87980-108-5). Wilshire.

Gray & Hidalgo. How to Hypnotize. 3.00 (ISBN 0-87505-083-2). Borden.

Grinder, John & Bandler, Richard. Trance-Formations: Neuro-Linguistic Programming & the Structure of Hypnosis. Andreas, Connirae, ed. 252p. (Orig.). 1981. 10.00 (ISBN 0-911226-22-2); pap. 6.50 (ISBN 0-911226-23-0). Real People.

Grossack, Martin. Hypnosis & Self-Hypnosis. pap. 2.50 (ISBN 0-8283-1526-4). Inst Rat Liv.

Hibbard, Whitney & Worring, Raymond. Forensic Hypnosis: The Practical Application of Hypnosis in Criminal Investigations. (Illus.). 400p. 1981. 34.75x (ISBN 0-398-04098-2). C C Thomas.

Hilgard, Josephine R. Personality & Hypnosis: A Study of Imaginative Involvement. 2nd ed. LC 79-13387. 1979. lib. bdg. 19.50x (ISBN 0-226-33443-0); pap. 5.95 (ISBN 0-226-33442-2, P852). U of Chicago Pr.

Hudson, Jay T. The Magical Powers of Hypnotism & Mesmerism & How to Acquire Them. (Illus.). 131p. 1983. 87.45 (ISBN 0-89920-064-8). Am Inst Psych.

Kappas, John. Professional Hypnotism Manual: Introducing Physical & Emotional Suggestibility & Sexuality. rev. ed. 1978. pap. 14.95 (ISBN 0-87505-250-9). Borden.

Krafft-Ebbing, Richard Von. An Experimental Study in the Domain of Hypnotism. (Hypnosis & Altered States of Consciousness Ser.). 129p. 1982. Repr. of 1893 ed. lib. bdg. 19.50 (ISBN 0-306-76162-9). Da Capo.

LeCron, Leslie M. The Complete Guide to Hypnosis. 240p. 1976. pap. 4.33 (ISBN 0-06-465069-3, P/BN 5069, BN). B&N NY.

Moll, Albert. Hypnotism. (Hypnosis & Altered States of Consciousness Ser.). 626p. 1982. Repr. of 1902 ed. lib. bdg. 49.50 (ISBN 0-306-76079-7). Da Capo.

O'Hara, M. New Hope through Hypnotherapy: The Joe Keeton Phenomenon. 1980. 12.00 (ISBN 0-9961002-1-0, Pub. by Abacus England); pap. 8.00 (ISBN 0-9961002-2-9). Heyden.

Overholser, Lee C. Ericksonian Hypnosis: A Handbook of Clinical Practice. 250p. 1985. text ed. 29.95x (ISBN 0-8290-0738-5). Irvington.

Sackett, Patrick L. The Power of Autosuggestion & How to Master It. (Illus.). 1979. deluxe ed. 89.85 (ISBN 0-930582-61-6). Gloucester Art.

Segal, Robert M. Hypnotism Fundamentals. (Illus.). 64p. 1982. 10.95 (ISBN 0-87396-095-5). Stravon.

Shaftesbury, Edmund. Universal Magnetism, Vol. 2. 14.95x (ISBN 0-685-22150-4). Wehman.

Sheehan, P. W. & McConkey, K. M. Hypnosis & Experience: The Exploration of Phenomena & Process. (Illus.). 320p. 1982. text ed. 29.95x (ISBN 0-89859-195-3). L Erlbaum Assocs.

Tinterow, Maurice M. Foundations of Hypnosis: From Mesmer to Freud. (Illus.). 620p. 1970. 59.75x (ISBN 0-398-01928-2). C C Thomas.

Wallace, Benjamin. Applied Hypnosis: An Overview. LC 79-65. 144p. 1979. 18.95x (ISBN 0-88229-415-6); pap. 9.95x (ISBN 0-88229-771-6). Nelson-Hall.

HYPOTHALAMUS

Behavioral Studies of the Hypothalamus, Pt. A. 512p. 1980. 99.75 (ISBN 0-8247-6904-X). Dekker.

Bleier, Ruth. The Hypothalamus of the Guinea Pig: A Cytoarchitectonic Atlas. LC 83-47756. (Illus.). 176p. 1984. text ed. 50.00x (ISBN 0-299-09040-X). U of Wis Pr.

--The Hypothalmus of the Rhesus Monkey: A Cytoarchitectonic Atlas. LC 84-40146. (Illus.). 136p. 1984. text ed. 50.00x (ISBN 0-299-09890-7). U of Wis Pr.

Cushing, Harvey. Papers Relating to the Pituitary Body, Hypothalamus & Parasympathetic Nervous System. (Illus.). 234p. 1932. photocopy ed. 25.75x (ISBN 0-398-04237-3). C C Thomas.

Everitt, Arthur V. & Burgess, John A. Hypothalamus, Pituitary & Aging. (Illus.). 808p. 1976. 67.50x (ISBN 0-398-03346-3). C C Thomas.

Gupta, Derek & Voelter, Wolfgang. Hypothalamic Hormones: Chemistry, Physiology & Clinical Applications. (Illus.). 766p. 1978. 75.30x (ISBN 3-527-25712-8). VCH Pubs.

--Hypothalamic Hormones: Structure, Synthesis, & Biological Activity. (Illus.). 328p. 1975. 34.20x (ISBN 3-527-25589-3). VCH Pubs.

Handbook of the Hypothalmus, Vol. 3, Pt. B. 99.75 (ISBN 0-8247-6905-8). Dekker.

Haymaker, Webb, et al. Hypothalamus. (Illus.). 820p. 1969. 57.00x (ISBN 0-398-00810-8). C C Thomas.

Hypothalmic Control of Fertility. 180p. 1973. 60.00x (ISBN 0-686-45152-X, Pub. by Biochemical England). State Mutual Bk.

Labrie, Fernand, et al, eds. Hypothalamus & Endocrine Functions. LC 76-13912. (Current Topics in Molecular Endocrinology Ser.: Vol. 3). 519p. 1976. 59.50x (ISBN 0-306-34003-8, Plenum Pr). Plenum Pub.

Locke, William & Schally, Andrew V., eds. The Hypothalamus & Pituitary in Health & Disease. (Illus.). 624p. 1972. 41.75x (ISBN 0-398-02526-6). C C Thomas.

Martini, L. & Meites, J., eds. Neurochemical Aspects of Hypothalmic Function. 1971. 39.00 (ISBN 0-12-475560-7). Acad Pr.

Martini, L., et al, eds. Hypothalamus. 1971. 90.00 (ISBN 0-12-475550-X). Acad Pr.

Morgane, P. & Panksepp, J., eds. Anatomy of the Hypothalmus. (Handbook of the Hypothalmus Ser.: Vol. 1). 756p. 155.00 (ISBN 0-8247-6834-5). Dekker.

Motta, M., et al. Hypothalamic Hormones: Chemistry, Physiology, Pharmacology & Clinical Uses. (Serono Symposia Ser.). 1976. 59.50 (ISBN 0-12-509150-8). Acad Pr.

Mrosovsky, Nicholas. Hibernation & the Hypothalamus. 287p. 1971. 22.50x (ISBN 0-306-50058-2, Plenum Pr). Plenum Pub.

Sowers, J. R., ed. Hypothalmic Hormones. (Benchmark Papers in Human Physiology Ser.: Vol. 14). 368p. 1980. 46.00 (ISBN 0-87933-358-8). Van Nos Reinhold.

Sulman, F. G. Hypothalamic Control of Lactation. LC 70-125281. (Monographs on Endocrinology: Vol. 3). (Illus.). 1970. 39.00 (ISBN 0-387-04973-8). Springer-Verlag.

Watkins, Wayne. Hypothalamic Releasing Factors, Vol. 1. 1977. 19.20 (ISBN 0-88831-002-1). Eden Pr.

--Hypothalamic Releasing Factors, Vol. 3. Horrobin, D. F., ed. (Annual Research Reviews Ser.). 1979. 20.00 (ISBN 0-88831-046-3). Eden Pr.

Watkins, Wayne B. Hypothalamic Releasing Factors, Vol. 2. Horrobin, David F., ed. (Annual Research Reviews Ser.). 1978. 21.60 (ISBN 0-88831-033-1). Eden Pr.

Zaborszky, L. Afferent Connections of the Medial Basal Hypothalmus. (Advances in Anatomy, Embryology, & Cell Biology Ser.: Vol. 69). (Illus.). 107p. 1982. pap. 27.00 (ISBN 0-387-11076-3). Springer-Verlag.

HYPOTHESIS TESTING (STATISTICS)

see Statistical Hypothesis Testing

I

IBM 360 (COMPUTER)

Brooks, Frederick P., et al. Automatic Data Processing: System-360 Edition. LC 68-31293. pap. 122.50 (ISBN 0-317-09380-0, 2055097). Bks Demand UMI.

Brown, Gary D. System-360 Job-Control Language. 292p. 1970. pap. 23.50 (ISBN 0-471-10870-7, Pub. by Wiley-Interscience). Wiley.

Cashman, Thomas J. & Shelly, Gary B. IBM System-360 Assembler Language Workbook. LC 75-23969. (Illus.). 237p. 1973. pap. text ed. 11.95 (ISBN 0-88236-051-5). Anaheim Pub Co.

--Introduction to Computer Programming IBM System-360 Assembler Language. LC 75-4790. 327p. 1969. pap. text ed. 24.95x (ISBN 0-88236-050-7). Anaheim Pub Co.

Chapin, Ned. Three-Sixty-Three-Seventy Programming in Assembly Language. 1973. text ed. 44.50 (ISBN 0-07-010552-9). McGraw.

Essick, Edward L. RPG for System 360 & System 370. (Orig.). 1973. pap. text ed. 20.95 scp (ISBN 0-06-382625-9, HarpC). Har-Row.

Feingold, Carl. Introduction to Assembler Language Programming. 427p. 1978. pap. text ed. write for info. (ISBN 0-697-08124-9); instrs.' manual avail. (ISBN 0-697-08158-3). Wm C Brown.

Fisher, Franklin M., et al. IBM & the U. S. Data Processing Industry: An Economic History. LC 83-3988. (Select Basic Industries Studies). (Illus.). 544p. 1983. 42.95x (ISBN 0-03-063059-2). Praeger.

Hannula, Reino. System 360-370 Job Control Language & the Access Methods. LC 76-23986. (Illus.). 1977. pap. text ed. 21.95 (ISBN 0-201-02755-0). Addison-Wesley.

Kapur, Gopal K. IBM 360 Assembler Language Programming. LC 76-12572. 560p. 1971. 40.50 (ISBN 0-471-45840-6). Wiley.

Kudlick, Michael D. Assembly Language Programming for the IBM Systems 360 & 370 for OS-DOS. 2nd ed. 624p. 1983. write for info. (ISBN 0-697-08166-4); instr's. manual avail. (ISBN 0-697-08184-2). Wm C Brown.

Lane, Ron. An Introduction to Utilities. LC 75-19284. pap. 44.00 (ISBN 0-317-08595-6, 2010397). Bks Demand UMI.

Loschetter, Richard F. RPG for IBM Systems-360, 370 & System 3. (Illus.). 448p. 1975. ref. ed. 29.95 (ISBN 0-13-773713-0). P-H.

Murach, Mike. System-Three-Sixty RPG. LC 70-178830. (Illus.). 297p. 1972. pap. text ed. 20.95 (ISBN 0-574-16097-3, 13-1415); instr's guide avail. (ISBN 0-574-16128-7, 13-1416); transparency masters avail. (ISBN 0-574-16129-5, 13-1417). SRA.

Parker, A. J. VS BASIC for Business: For the IBM 360-370. 1982. pap. text ed. 12.95 (ISBN 0-8359-8439-7). Reston.

Passen, Barry J. Introduction to IBM System 360-Assembler Language Programming: A Problem Analysis Approach for Business Data Processing. 334p. 1973. pap. text ed. write for info. (ISBN 0-697-08108-7); student manual avail. (ISBN 0-697-08109-5); instr's manual avail. (ISBN 0-697-08223-7). Wm C Brown.

Rattenbury, Judith. Introduction to the IBM 360 Computer & OS-JCL (Job Control Language) rev. ed. LC 73-620248. 103p. 1974. 8.00x (ISBN 0-87944-011-2). Inst Soc Res.

Rindfleisch. Debugging System 360-370 Programs Using OS & VS Storage Dumps. 1976. 37.00 (ISBN 0-13-197632-X). P-H.

Rudd, Walter G. Assembly Language Programming & the IBM 360 & 370 Computers. 1976. 28.95 (ISBN 0-13-049536-0); wkbk. 12.95 (ISBN 0-13-049510-7). P-H.

Schriber, Thomas J. Simulation Using GPSS. LC 73-21896. 533p. 1974. 45.50 (ISBN 0-471-76310-1). Wiley.

Spencer, Richard E., et al, eds. MERMAC Manual: Test & Questionnaire Analysis Programs Written for the IBM System-360. LC 71-131006. 1971. pap. 10.00 (ISBN 0-252-00131-1); computer program 800.00 (ISBN 0-252-00227-X); non-profit institions 460.00 (ISBN 0-252-00205-9); supplement to manual 4.95 (ISBN 0-252-00651-8). U of Ill Pr.

Stabley, Don H. Logical Programming with System 360. LC 75-96047. 579p. 1970. 45.50 (ISBN 0-471-81945-X); supplementary materials avail. (ISBN 0-471-02856-8). Wiley.

--System 360 Assembler Language. LC 67-30037. 129p. 1967. pap. 25.50x (ISBN 0-471-81950-6, Pub. by Wiley-Interscience). Wiley.

Struble, George W. Assembler Language Programming: The IBM System 360. 2nd ed. 496p. 1975. text ed. 27.95 (ISBN 0-201-07322-6). Addison-Wesley.

IBM 370 (COMPUTER)

Brown, Gary D. System-370 Job Control Language. LC 77-24901. 297p. 1977. pap. 23.50x (ISBN 0-471-03155-0, Pub. by Wiley-Interscience). Wiley.

Feingold, Carl. Introduction to Assembler Language Programming. 427p. 1978. pap. text ed. write for info. (ISBN 0-697-08124-9); instrs.' manual avail. (ISBN 0-697-08158-3). Wm C Brown.

Hannula, Reino. System 360-370 Job Control Language & the Access Methods. LC 76-23986. (Illus.). 1977. pap. text ed. 21.95 (ISBN 0-201-02755-0). Addison-Wesley.

Hebditch, D. Teleprocessing Monitor Packages for IBM 370. 1978. pap. 47.50x (ISBN 0-85012-196-5). Intl Pubns Serv.

Kudlick, Michael D. Assembly Language Programming for the IBM Systems 360 & 370 for OS-DOS. 2nd ed. 624p. 1983. write for info. (ISBN 0-697-08166-4); instr's. manual avail. (ISBN 0-697-08184-2). Wm C Brown.

Lane, Ron. An Introduction to Utilities. LC 75-19284. pap. 44.00 (ISBN 0-317-08595-6, 2010397). Bks Demand UMI.

Parker, A. J. VS BASIC for Business: For the IBM 360-370. 1982. pap. text ed. 12.95 (ISBN 0-8359-8439-7). Reston.

Rindfleisch. Debugging System 360-370 Programs Using OS & VS Storage Dumps. 1976. 37.00 (ISBN 0-13-197632-X). P-H.

Rudd, Walter G. Assembly Language Programming & the IBM 360 & 370 Computers. 1976. 28.95 (ISBN 0-13-049536-0); wkbk. 12.95 (ISBN 0-13-049510-7). P-H.

Stoddard, S. D. Principles of Assembler Language Programming for the IBM 370. 656p. 1985. 33.95 (ISBN 0-07-061561-6). McGraw.

IBM 1130 (COMPUTER)

Jamison, Robert V. FORTRAN IV Programming: Based on the IBM System 1130. LC 70-96241. (Illus.). 1970. text ed. 31.25 (ISBN 0-07-032270-8). McGraw.

Louden, Robert K. & Ledin, George. Programming the IBM 1130. 2nd ed. (Illus.). 448p. 1972. pap. 22.95 ref. ed. (ISBN 0-13-730275-4). P-H.

IBM COMPUTERS

Bashe, Charles, et al. IBM's Early Computers: A Technical History. (History of Computing Ser.). (Illus.). 650p. 1985. text ed. 27.50x (ISBN 0-262-02225-7). MIT Pr.

Greenblatt, David. The IBM System 36: What's In It for You? (Illus.). 99p. (Orig.). 1984. pap. text ed. 59.00 (ISBN 0-930941-01-2). D G C Assocs Inc.

--Insights into the IBM System 38. (Illus.). 137p. (Orig.). 1984. pap. text ed. 95.00 (ISBN 0-930941-00-4). D G C Assocs Inc.

Infotech. Die IBM 4300 Series. 370p. 1980. 430.00 (ISBN 0-08-028553-8). Pergamon.

Leben, J. & Arnold, J. IBM CPU & Storage Architecture: System-370-Mode & 370-XA Mode. (Data Processing Training Ser.). 256p. 1984. pap. 49.95 (ISBN 0-471-80142-9). Wiley.

Tabler, D. N., et al. IBM OS Assembler Language-Arithmetic Operations. (Data Processing Training Ser.). 384p. 1985. pap. 49.95 (ISBN 0-471-80135-6). Wiley.

IBM DISPLAYWRITER

see Displaywriter (Computer Program)

IBM PC (COMPUTER)

see Ibm Personal Computer

Arkin, H. & Arkin, R. Statistical Sampling Software for Auditing & Accounting, IBM Version. 160p. 1985. 295.00 (ISBN 0-07-852135-1). McGraw.

California State University. Miranda: Understanding Poetry-Alliteration & Assonance; Images; Metaphors; Similies & Symbols for Use with IBM-PC, Pt. 2. 1984. write for info. (ISBN 0-07-831003-2). McGraw.

Murray, William H. & Pappas, Chris H. An Introduction to APL for the IBM PC & Xt. (Illus.). 224p. 1985. 29.95 (ISBN 0-89303-567-X). Brady Comm.

PC Magazine Editors. The PC Guide to Database Management for the IBM PC. 240p. pap. cancelled (ISBN 0-916688-86-0, 86-0). Creative Comp.

IBM PC AT

Byers, T. J. Inside the IBM PC AT. 288p. 1985. 19.95 (ISBN 0-07-009520-5, BYTE Bks). McGraw.

Schwieder, Pete H. How to Repair & Maintain Your Own IBM PC XT to the Component Level Using an Oscilloscope. (Illus.). 120p. 1985. pap. 29.95 (ISBN 0-915097-01-X). Personal Sys Pubns.

IBM PERSONAL COMPUTER

Abel, Peter. Assembler for the IBM PC & PC XT. (Illus.). 1983. text ed. 21.95 (ISBN 0-8359-0110-6); pap. text ed. 18.95 (ISBN 0-8359-0153-X). Reston.

Adamis, Eddie. BASIC Keywords for the IBM PC. (IBM Personal Computer Ser.). 150p. 1984. pap. 14.95 (ISBN 0-471-88402-2, Pub. by Wiley Pr). Wiley.

--Business BASIC for the IBM PC. (IBM PC Ser.: No. 1-646). 200p. 1984. pap. 14.95 (ISBN 0-471-88401-4, Pub. by Wiley Pr). Wiley.

Adams, N. Douglas. PC Wizardry on Wall Street: How to Use Your IBM & Compatibles to Invest in the Stock Market. 224p. 1985. 21.95 (ISBN 0-13-655010-X); pap. 14.95 (ISBN 0-13-655002-9). P-H.

Algebra Arcade. 1983. Apple II Plus or Apple IIe. write for info; IBM-PC. write for info (ISBN 0-534-02973-6); Atari 800. write for info; Commodore 64. write for info (ISBN 0-686-46802-3). Wadsworth Pub.

Allen, Brandt R. VisiCalc: IBM. 1984. pap. text ed. 10.95 (ISBN 0-8359-8408-7). Reston.

Alvernaz, Bill. Expanding Your IBM PC: A Guide for Beginners. (Illus.). 256p. 1984. pap. 16.95 (ISBN 0-89303-445-2). Brady Comm.

Alves, Jeff & Curtin, Dennis. Planning & Budgeting for Higher Profits: An IBM-PC Business User's Guide. 156p. 1983. pap. 14.95 (ISBN 0-930764-61-7). Van Nos Reinhold.

Alves, Jeffrey & Curtin, Dennis. Planning & Budgeting-IBM Version. (Illus.). 224p. (Orig.). 1983. pap. 15.50 (ISBN 0-930764-61-7). Curtin & London.

Anbarlian, Harry. An Introduction to VisiCalc Matrixing for Apple & IBM. (Personal Computing Ser.). 260p. 1982. pap. 26.95 (ISBN 0-07-001605-4, BYTE Bks). McGraw.

Angell, I. O. Advanced Graphics with the IBM Personal Computer. 1985. pap. 24.95 (ISBN 0-470-20134-7). Wiley.

Anthony, Robert N. Teach Yourself Essentials of Accounting on the IBM PC. incl. documentation & four disks for the IBM PC 129.95 (ISBN 0-201-15328-9); incl. documentation & four disks for the Apple II, II Plus & IIe 79.95. Addison-Wesley.

--Teach Yourself Essentials of Accounting on the IBM PC. 80p. 1983. write for info. (ISBN 0-201-15329-7); write for info. incl. disk (ISBN 0-201-15328-9); write for info. incl. disk (ISBN 0-201-15331-9). Addison-Wesley.

Arnold, David & PC World Staff. Getting Started with the IBM PC & XT. 256p. 1984. pap. 14.95 (ISBN 0-671-49277-2, Pub. by Computer Bks). S&S.

Ashley, Ruth. PC-DOS: Using IBM-PC Operating System. LC 82-24720. (IBM Personal Computer Ser.: No. 1646). 225p. 1983. pap. text ed. 16.95 (ISBN 0-471-89718-3, Pub. by Wiley Pr). Wiley.

Atwater, Dorothea. First Aid for Your IBM PC. 144p. (Orig.). 1985. pap. 6.95 (ISBN 0-345-31943-5). Ballantine.

Avante-Garde Publishing Corporation Staff & Thiel, James R. Getting Graphic on the IBM-PC. 192p. 1985. pap. 14.95 (ISBN 0-13-354069-3). P-H.

Avery, Rachel R. LOGO & the IBM PC. (Illus.). 240p. 1985. pap. 16.95 (ISBN 0-13-539941-6). P-H.

Barden, William, Jr. Assembly Language Programming for the IBM PC & PCjr. 500p. pap. cancelled (ISBN 0-88134-146-0, 146-0). Osborne-McGraw.

Barnett, Michael P. & Barnett, Graham K. Personal Graphics for Profit & Pleasure on the IBM Personal Computer. (Little, Brown Microcomputer Bookshelf Ser.). 225p. (Orig.). 1984. pap. 14.50 (ISBN 0-316-08220-1). Little.

Beacham, Walton & Beacham, Deborah. Using Displaywrite. LC 84-62131. 280p. 1985. 16.95 (ISBN 0-88022-127-5, 158). Que Corp.

Beechhold, Henry F. The Plain English Maintenance & Repair Guide for the IBM PC & PCjr. 288p. 1985. pap. 14.95 (ISBN 0-671-52864-5, Pub. by Computer Bks). S&S.

Beekman, George & Folts, Jim. The IBM PC Home Companion. (Home Companion Ser.). (Illus.). 360p. (Orig.). Date not set. pap. 19.95 (ISBN 0-88190-314-0, BO314). Datamost.

Bennet, Michael. IBM Personal Computer Handbook, Vol. I. 1986. 19.95 (ISBN 0-89303-544-0). Brady Comm.

Bent, Robert & Sethares, George. Microsoft BASIC: Programming the IBM PC. LC 84-23765. (Computer Science Ser.). 350p. 1985. pap. text ed. 20.00 pub net (ISBN 0-534-04770-X). Brooks-Cole.

Berenbon, Howard. Mostly BASIC: Applications for Your IBM-PC, 2 Vols. 1983. Bk. 1. 12.95 (ISBN 0-672-22076-8, 22093); Bk. 2. 14.95 (ISBN 0-672-22093-8). Bobbs.

--Mostly BASIC: Applications for Your IBM-PC, 2 vols. LC 83-61072. 1983. Bk. 1, 192 pp. 12.95 (ISBN 0-672-22076-8, 22076); Bk. 2, 248 pp. 14.95 (ISBN 0-672-22093-8, 22093). Sams.

Berk, Joseph & Berk, Susan. Financial Analysis on the IBM PC. LC 84-12130. 222p. (Orig.). 1984. pap. 12.95 (ISBN 0-8019-7546-8). Chilton.

Bitter, G. & Watson, N. IBM PC & PCjR LOGO Primer. 1985. 17.95 (ISBN 0-8359-3180-3). Reston.

Bitter, Gary G. & Cook, Paul M. IBM BASIC for Business. (Illus.). 192p. 1986. pap. text ed. 19.95 (ISBN 0-13-448093-7). P-H.

The Blue Book for the IBM PC Computer. 24.95 (ISBN 0-684-17939-3). WIDL Video.

Blumberg, Donald F. & Dooley, Brian J. The IBM PC Guide to Risk & Decision Making: Acting Wisely in An Uncertain World. 320p. 1985. pap. 49.95 incl. disk (ISBN 0-88693-064-2). Banbury Bks.

Boggs, Roy A. Advanced BASIC for the IBM PC. 1985. pap. 16.95 (ISBN 0-8359-9142-3). Reston.

Bolocan, David. The WORD Book. LC 85-2528. (Illus.). 240p. (Orig.). 1985. 24.95 (ISBN 0-8306-0958-X, 1958); pap. 16.95 (ISBN 0-8306-1958-5). TAB Bks.

Bolocan, David & Microtrend, Inc. Visi-On on the IBM PC. (Microtrend Ser.). 1984. 14.95 (ISBN 0-13-942301-X). P-H.

Bonynge, David B. MicroMansion: Using Your IBM-PC Computer to Have a Safer, More Convenient Home. (Illus.). 176p. (Orig.). 1985. pap. 11.95 (ISBN 0-8306-1926-7, 1926). TAB Bks.

Booth, Ada. Get More from Your IBM-PC & PCjr & Save Money. (Illus.). 224p. 1984. pap. 8.95 (ISBN 0-86582-163-1, EN79215). Enrich.

Bowyer, Kevin & Tomboulian, Sherryl. Pascal Programming for the IBM PC: IBM DOS, Pascal & UCSD P-System Pascal. LC 83-3921. (Illus.). 352p. 1983. pap. 19.95 (ISBN 0-89303-280-8); bk. & diskette 49.95 (ISBN 0-89303-761-3); disk 30.00 (ISBN 0-89303-762-1). Brady Comm.

Brenner, Robert. IBM PC Troubleshooting & Repair Guide. LC 84-52214. 18.95 (ISBN 0-672-22358-9). Sams.

Bretz, Jeff & Craig, John C. One Hundred Ready-to-Run Programs & Subroutines for the IBM PC. (Illus.). 320p. (Orig.). 1983. 22.95 (ISBN 0-8306-0540-1); pap. 16.50 (ISBN 0-8306-1540-7, 1540). TAB Bks.

Bridges, George. IBM Personal Computer Program Writing Workbook. 96p. 1983. 4.95 (ISBN 0-86668-818-8). ARCsoft.

Brown, J. R. & Finkel, L. IBM PC: Data File Programming. 367p. 1983. pap. 14.95 (ISBN 0-471-89717-5). Wiley.

Brown, Jerald R. & Finkel, LeRoy. IBM PC, Data File Programming: IBM Data File Set. LC 82-24849. (IBM Personal Computing Ser.). 320p. 1983. pap. 39.90 (ISBN 0-471-88904-0, Pub by Wiley Pr); programming disk incl. Wiley.

Budin, Howard. Speed Walker: Fun to Program Your IBM-PC. 89p. (Orig.). 1984. pap. 2.95 (ISBN 0-523-42246-6). Pinnacle Bks.

Burns, Robert V. & Johnson, Rees C. Sixty Forms for the Entrepreneur: Forms Generator - IBM-PC, PCjr & PC XT. 192p. 1985. pap. cancelled (ISBN 0-88056-258-7). Dilithium Pr.

--Sixty Forms for the Landlord: Forms Generator - IBM-PC, PCjr & PC XT. 192p. 1985. pap. cancelled (ISBN 0-88056-255-2). Dilithium Pr.

--Sixty Forms for Your Household: Forms Generator for Your IBM-PC, IBM-PCjr & IBM-PC XT. 192p. 1985. pap. 29.95 incl. disk (ISBN 0-88056-252-8). Dilithium Pr.

Buscaino, Dale & Daniel, Scott. IBM BASIC Decoded & Other Mysteries. 29.95 (ISBN 0-317-06580-7). Blue Cat.

--Superzap: IBM-PC Version 1.0. Moore, David & Trapp, Charles, eds. (Illus.). 104p. 1985. softcover & disk 49.95 (ISBN 0-932679-00-5). Blue Cat.

Busch, David D. IBM PC & PCjr Subroutine Cookbook. (Illus.). 224p. 1984. pap. 12.95 (ISBN 0-89303-542-4). Brady Comm.

--PC-DOS Customized: Create Your Own DOS Commands for the IBM-PC, XT & AT. 176p. 1985. pap. 14.95 (ISBN 0-89303-753-2). Brady Comm.

Calabrese, Charles A. Understanding the IBM Personal Computer, Vol. 1. (Calabrese Understanding Ser.). (Illus.). 288p. (Orig.). 1982. pap. 14.95 (ISBN 0-911699-01-5). Calabrese Pubns.

California State University. Constructing the Paragraph: The Ramblestones on the Road for Use with IBM-PC. 1984. 39.95 (ISBN 0-07-831013-X). McGraw.

--Contestination: Developing Successful Estimating Abilities for Use with IBM-PC. 1984. 49.95 (ISBN 0-07-831021-0). McGraw.

--Introduction to Language for Use with IBM PC. 1984. 49.95 (ISBN 0-07-831035-0). McGraw.

--Miranda: Understanding Poetry-Meter, Rhythm, Rhyme for Use with the IBM-PC, Pt. 1. 1984. write for info. (ISBN 0-07-831011-3). McGraw.

--Ten Common Inferences: Oscar-The Big Escape for Use with IBM-PC, Pt. 2. 1984. write for info. (ISBN 0-07-831015-6). McGraw.

Carlson, Edward. Kids & the IBM. 1984. pap. 19.95 (ISBN 0-8359-3675-9). Reston.

Carr, Joseph L. Sixty-Eight Scientific & Engineering Programs for the IBM PC & PC XT. 1984. 19.95 (ISBN 0-8359-6921-5). Reston.

Cassel, Don. The dBASE II Simplified for the IBM Personal Computer. (Illus.). 176p. 1985. text ed. 22.95 (ISBN 0-13-195942-5); 14.95 (ISBN 0-13-195934-4). P-H.

--EasyWriter Simplified for the IBM Personal Computer. 208p. 1984. text ed. 21.95 (ISBN 0-13-222449-6); pap. text ed. 12.95 (ISBN 0-13-222431-3). P-H.

--Lotus 1-2-3 Simplified for the IBM Personal Computer. (Illus.). 208p. 1985. pap. 14.95 (ISBN 0-13-541012-6). P-H.

--WordStar Simplified for the IBM Personal Computer. (Illus.). 160p. 1984. text ed. 22.95 (ISBN 0-13-963620-X); pap. text ed. 12.95 (ISBN 0-13-963612-9). P-H.

Chance, David W. Thirty-Three Adult Computer Games in BASIC for the IBM PC, Apple II, IIe & TRS-80. (Illus.). 378p. 1983. 18.95 (ISBN 0-8306-0627-0, 1627); pap. 13.50 (ISBN 0-8306-1627-6). TAB Bks.

Chase, Cochran, et al. Solving Marketing Problems with VisiCalc on the IBM PC. 300p. (Orig.). 1984. pap. 29.95 incl. disc (ISBN 0-8019-7542-5). Chilton.

Chaya, Ruth K. & Miller, Joan M. More BASIC Programming for the Classroom & Home Teacher (IBM PC, IBM PCjr, Commodore, Apple, Macintosh) 262p. (Orig.). 1985. pap. text ed. 17.95X (ISBN 0-8077-2780-6). Tchrs Coll.

Chertok, Barbara L., et al. IBM PC & XT Owner's Manual: A Practical Guide to Operations. LC 83-15576. 224p. 1983. pap. 14.95 (ISBN 0-89303-531-9). Brady Comm.

Chien. Using BASIC for Business: IBM-PC. 250p. 1985. pap. text ed. write for info. (ISBN 0-8087-6403-9). Burgess.

Chien, Chao. Programming the IBM Personal Computer: Assembly Language. 1984. 17.95 (ISBN 0-03-070442-1). HR&W.

Clark, Roger E. Executive VisiCalc for the IBM Personal Computer. 192p. 1983. pap. 12.95 (ISBN 0-201-10243-9). Addison-Wesley.

Cobb, Douglas F. & Cobb, Gena B. VisiCalc Models for Business. LC 82-42767. (Que's IBM-PC Library). (Illus.). 210p. (Orig.). 1983. pap. 16.95 (ISBN 0-88022-017-1, 7); software disk 79.90 ea. IBM-PC format (225). Apple II (226). Apple III format (227). Que Corp.

Coffron, James W. The IBM PC Connection. LC 83-51571. (Illus.). 264p. 1984. pap. 16.95 (ISBN 0-89588-127-6). SYBEX.

The Complete Book of Random Access & Data File Programming for the IBM PC, Vol. I. 1984. 29.95 (ISBN 0-910985-09-X); Program Disk Pack avail. D S C Pub.

Compute Editors. Compute's First Book of IBM. (Orig.). 1985. pap. 14.95 (ISBN 0-87455-010-6). Compute Pubns.

Computers for Professionals Staff, ed. Geoscience Software Directory for IBM-PC & Compatibles, 1985. 112p. 1985. pap. 45.00 (ISBN 0-88746-064-X). Intl Human Res.

Conklin, Dick. PC Graphics: Charts, Graphs, Games, & Art on the IBM-PC. LC 83-5797. (IBM Personal Computer Ser.). 182p. 1983. pap. text ed. 15.95 (ISBN 0-471-89207-6, 1-646, Pub. by Wiley Pr); book & program disk 40.90 (ISBN 0-471-88541-X). Wiley.

Conlan, Jim. IBM PC Pascal. (IBM Personal Computer Ser.). 318p. 1984. pap. 17.95 (ISBN 0-471-87936-3). Wiley.

Continental Software. The Home Accountant - IBM PC. 1985. manual 9.95 (ISBN 0-538-01012-6, A013). SW Pub.

Corchado, Veronica & McHugh, Kathleen. Selecting the Right Word Processing Software for the IBM PC. LC 84-50991. 96p. 1984. pap. 11.95 (ISBN 0-89588-177-2). SYBEX.

Corsi, Jerome R. & Hills, William F. Debugging Techniques for IBM PC BASIC. (Illus.). 288p. 1985. pap. 18.95 (ISBN 0-89303-587-4). Brady Comm.

Cortesi, David & Cherry, George. Personal Pascal: Compiled Pascal for the IBM Personal Computer. (Illus.). 1983. text ed. 24.95 (ISBN 0-8359-5523-0); pap. text ed. 17.95 (ISBN 0-8359-5522-2). Reston.

Cortesi, David E. Your IBM Personal Computer: Use, Applications, & BASIC. LC 82-15671. 304p. 1983. pap. 19.95 (ISBN 0-03-061979-3). HR&W.

Craig, John C. & Bretz, Jeff. IBM PC Graphics. LC 84-8893. (Illus.). 250p. (Orig.). 1984. 19.95 (ISBN 0-8306-0860-5); pap. 13.95 (ISBN 0-8306-1860-0, 1860). TAB Bks.

Cratch, Stephen C. & Johansson, Anders B. The Hindu Vedic Master Operations Guide: Astrological Software for the IBM PC. Johansson, Lilian M., ed. (Illus.). 200p. (Orig.). 1985. 30.00 (ISBN 0-914725-12-2); pap. 18.00 (ISBN 0-914725-10-6); spiral 24.00 (ISBN 0-914725-11-4). Astro Dynasty Pub Hse.

Crowley, Robert. The IBM PC: VisiCalc. 256p. 1984. pap. 20.45 (ISBN 0-03-062634-X); pap. 40.45 with diskette (ISBN 0-03-063982-4). HR&W.

--Using the IBM PC: PFS Files-PFS Report. 1984. 19.95 (ISBN 0-03-063994-8). HR&W.

--Using the IBM Personal Computer: PFS File-Report. 1984. 18.45 (ISBN 0-03-069399-3). HR&W.

Cuellar, Gabriel. Fancy Programming in IBM PC BASIC. 17.95 (ISBN 0-8359-1860-2); incl. disk 29.95 (ISBN 0-8359-1854-8). Reston.

--Games for the IBM-PC. 1984. 19.95 (ISBN 0-8359-2420-3). Reston.

--Graphics Made Easy for the IBM PC or PC XT. (Illus.). 1984. pap. 18.95 (ISBN 0-8359-2569-2). Reston.

Culp, George & Nickles, Herbert. Instructional Computing Fundamentals for IBM Microcomputers. LC 84-7661. (Computer Science Ser.). 320p. 1984. pap. text ed. 15.00 pub net (ISBN 0-534-03364-4). Brooks-Cole.

Curtin, Dennis & Alves, Jeff. Controlling Financial Performance for Higher Profits: An IBM-PC Business User's Guide. 160p. 1983. pap. 14.95 (ISBN 0-930764-57-9); software disk 29.95 (ISBN 0-930764-68-4); bk. & disk 39.95 (ISBN 0-930764-78-1). Van Nos Reinhold.

Curtin, Dennis & Alves, Jeffrey. Controlling Financial Performance: An IBM-PC Business Users Guide. (Illus.). 160p. (Orig.). 1983. pap. 15.50 (ISBN 0-930764-57-9). Curtin & London.

Curtis, Richard. WordStar on the IBM PC. (A BYTE Bk.). 208p. 1984. pap. 11.95 (ISBN 0-07-014978-X). McGraw.

Datapro-McGraw-Hill. Datapro-McGraw-Hill Guide to IBM PC Software. 2nd ed. 1985. 22.95 (ISBN 0-07-015407-4). McGraw.

Datapro Research Corporation. Datapro-McGraw-Hill Guide to IBM PC Software. 2nd ed. LC 84-20021. 390p. 1984. pap. 22.95 (ISBN 0-07-015407-4). Datapro Res.

Datz & Datz. Processing Words with Your IBM PC, PC XT or PC Compatible. 232p. 1984. 15.95 (ISBN 0-317-06579-3, 6359). Hayden.

Davis, Frederic E. & PC World Editors. Hardware for the IBM PC & XT. 256p. 1985. pap. 16.95 (ISBN 0-671-49278-0, Pub. by Computer Bks). S&S.

Derfler, Frank J., Jr. & InfoWorld Editors. InfoWorld's Essential Guide to the IBM PC. (InfoWorld's Essential Guides Ser.). 250p. (Orig.). 1984. pap. 16.95 (ISBN 0-06-669002-1). Har Row.

Desautels, Edouard J. Lotus 1-2-3 for the IBM Personal Computer & XT. (Microcomputer Power Ser.). 288p. 1984. pap. 16.95 (ISBN 0-697-09997-0); incl. disk 29.95 (ISBN 0-697-00337-X). Wm C Brown.

--Symphony for the IBM Personal Computer & Compatible Computers. (Micropower Ser.). 200p. 1985. pap. 17.95 (ISBN 0-697-00600-X). Wm C Brown.

--VisiCalc for the IBM Personal Computer. (Microcomputer Power Ser.). 156p. 1982. plastic comb 16.95 (ISBN 0-697-00344-2); deluxe ed. bk. & diskette 27.95 (ISBN 0-697-00327-2). Wm C Brown.

DeVoney, Chris. IBM's Personal Computer. 2nd ed. 318p. (Orig.). 1983. pap. 17.95 (ISBN 0-88022-026-0, 14). Que Corp.

D'Ignazio, Fred & PC World Editors. Learning & Having Fun with the IBM PC & PCjr. 244p. 1985. pap. 16.95 (ISBN 0-671-49281-0, Pub. by Computer Bks). S&S.

Directories from InfoSource Inc. Business Software for the IBM PC: An Applications Directory. LC 83-45380. 336p. (Orig.). 1984. pap. 12.95 (ISBN 0-8019-7432-1). Chilton.

Directory of Public Domain (& User-Supported) Software for the IBM Personal Computer. 1984. pap. 4.95 (ISBN 0-915835-01-0). PC Software.

DLW Corporation. My Computer Guide: An Introduction to the IBM-PC. 1984. write for info. (ISBN 0-07-031740-2). McGraw.

Dorf, Richard C. A Guide to the Best Business Software for the IBM PC. (Illus.). 192p. 1983. pap. 12.95 (ISBN 0-201-10256-0). Addison-Wesley.

Dorner, Joe. Assembly Language Routines for the IBM PC. (Illus.). 192p. 1985. pap. 17.95 (ISBN 0-89303-409-6). Brady Comm.

Douglass, Bruce P. Applications Programming in IBM BASIC. LC 84-45166. 390p. (Orig.). 1985. pap. 29.95 (ISBN 0-8019-7622-7). Chilton.

--BASIC Applications Programming for the IBM PC. LC 84-45166. 250p. (Orig.). 1985. pap. 17.95 (ISBN 0-8019-7524-7). Chilton.

Dravnieks, Dzintar E., et al, eds. IBM Personal Computer Handbook. LC 83-9953. (Illus.). 448p. (Orig.). 1983. pap. 19.95 (ISBN 0-915904-66-7). And-Or Pr.

Duncan, Ray. IBM PC-DOS Programmer's Reference Guide. Date not set. pap. price not set postponed (ISBN 0-89303-523-8). Brady Comm.

Dunn, Seamus & Morgan, Valerie. The IBM Personal Computer for Beginners. (Illus.). 320p. 1984. pap. 15.95 (ISBN 0-13-448259-X). P-H.

Durr, Michael. Networking IBM PCs: A Practical Guide. 320p. 1984. pap. 18.95 (ISBN 0-88022-106-2, 125). Que Corp.

Dwyer, Thomas A. & Critchfield, Margot. A Bit of IBM BASIC. 240p. 1984. pap. 12.95 (ISBN 0-201-11162-4). Addison-Wesley.

Eckhardt, Richard A., et al, eds. The IBM PC Enhancement Handbook for Scientists & Engineers. (The IBM PC Enhancement Handbook: Vol. 1, No. 2). (Illus.). 196p. (Orig.). 1985. pap. 18.95 (ISBN 0-931193-00-1). Cyber Res Inc.

Eggebrecht, Lewis C. Interfacing to the IBM Personal Computer. LC 83-61065. 272p. 1983. pap. 15.95 (ISBN 0-672-22027-X, 22027). Sams.

Elliott, Alan C. The PC Programming Techniques: Creative BASIC Skills for IBM Personal Computers. (Illus.). 176p. 1984. pap. 14.95 (ISBN 0-89303-755-9). Brady Comm.

Emerson, Sandra L. & Darnovsky, Marcy. Database for the IBM PC. LC 84-9377. 1438p. 1984. pap. 14.95 (ISBN 0-201-10483-0). Addison-Wesley.

Fabbri, Tony. Animation, Games & Sound for the IBM Personal Computer. (Illus.). 224p. 1983. pap. text ed. 19.50 (ISBN 0-13-037689-2). P-H.

Fassnacht, Philip R., et al. The IBM PC Microcomputer. (Nanos Reference Cards Ser.). 24p. (Orig.). 1984. 5.95 (ISBN 0-915069-24-5). Nanos Sys.

Faulk, Ed. How to Write an IBM PC Program. (How to Write Ser.). (Illus.). 1982. pap. 14.95 (ISBN 0-88190-028-1, BO028). Datamost.

Fernandez, Judi N. & Ashley, Ruth. CP-M-86. (A Self-Teaching & Wiley IBM-PC Ser.: No. 1-646). 261p. 1983. pap. text ed. 14.95 (ISBN 0-471-89719-1, Pub. by Wiley Pr). Wiley.

Finifter, Ada. Using the IBM Personal Computer: IBM Easywriter. 1984. 17.95 (ISBN 0-03-063736-8). HR&W.

Flanders, Dennis. BASIC Programming for the IBM PC. 1985. cancelled (ISBN 0-89303-240-9). Brady Comm.

Flanders, Robert & Flanders, Dennis. Systems Made Simple on the IBM PC: How to Design & Develop Applications Programs. 1984. cancelled (ISBN 0-89303-242-5). Brady Comm.

Flast, Robert H. Fifty-Four SuperCalc Models: Finance, Statistics, Mathematics. 288p. (Orig.). 1983. pap. 15.95 (ISBN 0-07-881118-X, 118-X). Osborne-McGraw.

Ford, Nelson. Business Graphics for the IBM PC. LC 83-51567. (Illus.). 259p. 1984. pap. 18.95 (ISBN 0-89588-124-1). SYBEX.

Foster, Dennis L. & D. L. Foster Book Company Editors. The Addison-Wesley Book of IBM Software 1985. 416p. 1985. pap. 19.95 (ISBN 0-201-12021-6). Addison-Wesley.

Fox, Michael. Ninety-Nine Programming Tips & Tricks for the IBM Personal Computer. 128p. 1984. 8.95 (ISBN 0-86668-046-2). ARCsoft.

--Practical IBM Personal Computer Programs for Beginners. 96p. 1984. 8.95 (ISBN 0-86668-045-4). ARCsoft.

--Quick 'n Fun Games for the IBM Personal Computer. 96p. 1984. 8.95 (ISBN 0-86668-044-6). ARCsoft.

Franklin, Mark. Programming the IBM Personal Computer: Organization & Assembly Language Programming. 1984. 19.95 (ISBN 0-03-062862-8). HR&W.

Frenzel, Louis E., Jr., et al. Handbook for the IBM P C. LC 83-50939. 352p. 1984. pap. 15.95 (ISBN 0-672-22004-0, 22004). Sams.

Friedman, Herb. The Complete Guide to Care & Maintenance for the IBM. (Illus.). 224p. 1986. pap. 15.95 (ISBN 0-13-160508-9). P H.

--Supercharging the IBM PC Portable. 244p. 1985. pap. 15.95 (ISBN 0-13-875790-9). P H.

Fugate, James K. Programming Tools for the IBM PC: Screen Design, Code Generator & High Memory Access. (Illus.). 272p. 1985. pap. 19.95 (ISBN 0-89303-784-2); diskette 30.00 (ISBN 0-89303-785-0). Brady Comm.

Fuori, William. COBOL Programming for the IBM PC & PC XT: Vol. 1. 275p. 1984. 19.95 (ISBN 0-8359-0779-1). Reston.

--COBOL Programming for the IBM PC & PC XT: Vol. 2. 250p. 1984. 19.95 (ISBN 0-8359-0780-5). Reston.

--FORTH Programming for the IBM PC & PC XT. 224p. 19.95 (ISBN 0-8359-2099-2). Reston.

--FORTRAN 77 Programming for the IBM PC & PC XT. 224p. 1984. 19.95 (ISBN 0-8359-2096-8). Reston.

--Pascal Programming for the IBM PC & PC XT. 1984. cancelled (ISBN 0-317-06174-7). Reston.

Gaber, Walter A. PC Abstracts: Abstracts & Index of Periodical Literature for the IBM-PC & PC Compatible User. (Reference Library of the Humanities). 400p. 1985. lib. bdg. 60.00 (ISBN 0-8240-8720-8). Garland Pub.

Gader, Bertram & Nodar, Manuel V. Free Software for the IBM PC. 480p. (Orig.). 1984. pap. 10.95 (ISBN 0-446-38198-5). Warner Bks.

Germain, Clarence B. Programming the IBM PC & XT: A Guide to Languages. LC 84-289. (Illus.). 352p. 1984. pap. 19.95 (ISBN 0-89303-783-4). Brady Comm.

Gilder, Jules H. IBM Programs in Science & Engineering. 256p. pap. 16.95 (6356). Hayden.

Glazer, Amihai. Managing Money with Your IBM PC. (Illus.). 208p. 1985. pap. 16.95 (ISBN 0-13-550658-1). P-H.

Goldstein, Larry J. Advanced BASIC & Beyond for the IBM PC. LC 83-15725. (Illus.). 384p. 1983. pap. text ed. 19.95 (ISBN 0-89303-324-3); bk. & diskette 49.95 (ISBN 0-89303-325-1); diskette 30.00 (ISBN 0-89303-326-X). Brady Comm.

--The Graphics Generator: Business & Technical Graphics for the IBM Personal Computer. (Illus.). 155p. 1982. 95.00 (ISBN 0-89303-266-2); diskettes o.p. 95.00 (ISBN 0-89303-495-9). Brady Comm.

Goldstein, Larry J. & Goldstein, Martin. IBM Personal Computer: An Introduction to Operating System, BASIC Programming & Applications. rev. ed. LC 83-11780. (Illus.). 400p. 1983. 18.95 (ISBN 0-89303-530-0); diskette 25.00 (ISBN 0-89303-526-2); bk. & diskette 43.95 (ISBN 0-89303-527-0). Brady Comm.

Good, Phillip. The Critic's Guide to Word Processing for the IBM PC & PC Compatable Computers. 19.95 (ISBN 0-8019-7530-1). Chilton.

Good, Phillip I. A Critical Guide to Software for the IBM PC & PC Compatible Computers: Computers for Professionals in Business, Agriculture, Law & Health. LC 83-17148. (Illus.). 284p. 1983. pap. 12.95 (ISBN 0-8019-7413-5). Chilton.

--Critic's Guide to Software for the IBM PC & PC Compatible Computers. 2nd ed. LC 83-17148. 310p. (Orig.). 1984. pap. 14.95 (ISBN 0-8019-7538-7). Chilton.

--A Critic's Guide to Word Processing for the IBM-PC & PC Compatible Computers. LC 84-45160. 120p. (Orig.). 1984. pap. 10.95 (ISBN 0-8019-7530-1). Chilton.

Goodman, Danny. How to Buy An IBM PC Or Compatible Computer. PC World Editors, ed. 224p. 1984. pap. 14.95 (ISBN 0-671-49282-9, Pub. by Computer Bks). S&S.

--Word Processing on the IBM Personal Computer. 1983. pap. 19.95 (ISBN 0-672-22081-4). Bobbs.

--Word Processing on the IBM Personal Computer. LC 83-50376. 464p. 1983. pap. 19.95 (ISBN 0-672-22081-4, 22081). Sams.

Graham, L. J. & Field, T. Your IBM PC. 400p. 1983. 17.95 (ISBN 0-88134-120-7, 112-6, Osborne-McGraw). Mcgraw.

Graham, Lyle & Field, Tim. Your IBM PC: A Guide to the IBM PC (D05 2.0) and XT. 600p. (Orig.). 1983. pap. 17.95 (ISBN 0-07-881120-1, 120-1). Osborne-McGraw.

Graham, Lyle J. Your IBM PC: A Guide to the IBM Personal Computer. 384p. (Orig.). 1983. pap. text ed. 17.95 (ISBN 0-07-931085-0, 85-0). Osborne-McGraw.

Graham, Neill. Programming the IBM Personal Computer: Fundamentals of BASIC. 1984. 17.95 (ISBN 0-03-059561-4). HR&W.

--Programming the IBM Personal Computer: BASIC. LC 82-11706. 256p. 1983. 17.50 (ISBN 0-03-063667-1). HR&W.

--Programming the IBM Personal Computer: COBOL. 1984. 20.45 (ISBN 0-03-059563-0); 40.50. HR&W.

--Programming the IBM Personal Computer: Pascal. 1984. 19.45 (ISBN 0-03-061982-3). HR&W.

Grauer, Robert T. The IBM COBOL Environment. (Illus.). 384p. 1984. text ed. 25.00 (ISBN 0-13-448654-4). P-H.

Grauer, Robert T., et al. BASIC Is Child's Play: IBM-PC Edition. (Illus.). 112p. 1984. pap. text ed. 18.95 (ISBN 0-13-058793-1). P-H.

--More BASIC Is Child's Play: IBM Edition. (Illus.). 256p. 1985. pap. 21.95 (ISBN 0-13-601097-0). P-H.

Grillo, John P. & Robertson, J. D. Data & File Management for the IBM Personal Computer. (Microcomputer Power Ser.). 191p. 1983. pap. 16.95 (ISBN 0-697-00349-3); incl. disk 32.95 (ISBN 0-697-00335-3). Wm C Brown.

Hahn, Harley. Using Your IBM PC AT. 1985. pap. 19.95 (ISBN 0-673-18262-2). Scott F.

Halpern, Richard. Microcomputer Graphics Using Pascal: IBM Version. 238p. 1985. pap. text ed. 24.95 scp (ISBN 0-06-042584-9, HarpC). Harper Row.

Hamilton, J. David & Trenary, Robert G. Macro-86: Programming Algorithms. Hubbard, John D., ed. LC 84-12805. (Macro-86 Software Design Ser.). (Illus.). 498p. 1984. 3 ring-binder 59.95 (ISBN 0-87119-089-3, EC-1202). HeathKit-Zenith Ed.

Harris, J. Mel & Scofield, Michael L. IBM PC Conversion Handbook of BASIC. LC 83-13977. 176p. 1983. pap. text ed. 15.95 (ISBN 0-13-448481-9). P-H.

Hart, Jack, et al. Cross Reference Utility (CRF) A Programming Aid for the IBM Personal Computer. (Illus.). 192p. 1983. pap. 29.95 (ISBN 0-13-194746-X, Spec). P-H.

Hartnell, Tim. How to Program Your IBM PC: If You've Never Programmed a Computer Before. (Tim Hartnell's Computer Programming Ser.). 101p. (Orig.). 1984. pap. 6.95 (ISBN 0-345-31661-4). Ballantine.

--Tim Hartnell's Executive Games for the IBM PC & XT. 288p. (Orig.). 1984. pap. 9.95 (ISBN 0-345-31940-0). Ballantine.

Haskell, Richard. IBM PC Assembly Language Tutor. 240p. 1985. pap. cancelled (ISBN 0-13-448662-5). P-H.

Haskell, Richard & Jackson, Glenn A. IBM PC BASIC Programming. (Illus.). 184p. 1984. 19.95 (ISBN 0-13-448432-0); pap. 13.95 (ISBN 0-13-448424-X). P-H.

Hearn, D. Donald & Baker, M. Pauline. Computer Graphics for the IBM Personal Computer. (Illus.). 320p. 1983. text ed. 24.95 (ISBN 0-13-164335-5); pap. text ed. 19.95 (ISBN 0-13-164327-4). P-H.

--Microcomputer Graphics for the IBM Personal Computer: Techniques & Applications. (Illus.). 272p. 1983. text ed. 24.95 (ISBN 0-13-580670-4); pap. text ed. 18.95 (ISBN 0-13-580662-3). P-H.

Hecht, Myron. File & Database Management Programs for the IBM PC. (IBM PC Ser.). 304p. 1985. pap. 16.95 (ISBN 0-471-80975-6). Wiley.

Heiserman, David L. Programming in BASIC for the IBM PC. (Illus.). 416p. 1984. text ed. 25.95 (ISBN 0-13-729450-6); pap. text ed. 16.95 (ISBN 0-13-729443-3). P-H.

--Programming Surprises & Tricks for Your IBM PC Computer. (Illus.). 208p. (Orig.). 1984. pap. 11.50 (ISBN 0-8306-1711-6, 1711). TAB Bks.

Held. IBM PC User's Reference Manual. 432p. 1984. 24.95 (6262). Hayden.

Held, Gil. IBM User's Manual. 384p. 1984. pap. 24.95 (6262). Hayden.

Held, Gilbert. IBM PC AT Networking Strategies. 300p. (Orig.). 1986. pap. cancelled (ISBN 0-938862-34-0). Weber Systems.

--IBM PC BASIC: A Quick Reference Guide. (Illus.). 80p. 1982. Set of 10. 29.50 (ISBN 0-471-87045-5). Wiley.

Henderson, Joe. Running Your Best Race Computerized Edition: IBM-PC Version. 224p. 1984. plastic comb 19.95 (ISBN 0-697-00460-0). Wm C Brown.

Hergert, Douglas. IBM PC Spreadsheets to Graphics. 250p. 1984. pap. 16.95 (ISBN 0-89588-163-2). SYBEX.

Hesse, Rick. Decision Making: A Management Science Guide for the IBM-PC. (IBM-PC Ser.: 1-646). 224p. 1984. pap. 16.95 (ISBN 0-471-89206-8, Wiley Professional Software); disk 29.95 (ISBN 0-471-89026-X); bk. & disk 46.90 (ISBN 0-471-89003-0). Wiley.

Hewes, Jeremy & Grout, Bill. Word Processing with the IBM PC. LC 84-11966. (IBM Personal Computer Ser.: 1-646). 224p. 1984. pap. 12.95 (ISBN 0-471-88663-7). Wiley.

Hildebrand, George. Business Program Portfolio for Your IBM PC. 242p. pap. 15.95 (6351); disk & documentation 59.95 (7305). Hayden.

Hime, Robert. QuickWrite: IBMPC & PCjr. 128p. 1984. cancelled (ISBN 0-88056-219-6). Dilithium Pr.

Hindelang, Thomas J. & Dascher, Paul E. IBM PC Guide to Marginal Analysis: Business Thinking at the Cutting Edge. 320p. 1984. pap. cancelled (ISBN 0-88693-058-8). Banbury Bks.

Hindelang, Thomas J., et al. The IBM PC Guide to Accounting for the Manager: The Latest Accounting Principles on Disk. (Business Applications Library). 320p. 1984. pap. cancelled (ISBN 0-88693-159-2). Banbury Bks.

Hite, Eugene & Close, Kenneth S. Spreadsheets: Principles & Applications Using VisiCalc - IBM Version. 1986. pap. text ed. 14.95 wkbk. & template diskette (ISBN 0-538-10210-1, J21). SW Pub.

Hoenig, Alan. Framework with Applications for the IBM Personal Computer. (Micropower Ser.). 200p. 1985. pap. 17.95 (ISBN 0-697-00725-1); deluxe ed., incl. diskette 29.95 (ISBN 0-697-00726-X). Wm C Brown.

--Introduction to Microsoft Word for the IBM PC. (Microcomputer Power Ser.). 208p. 1984. deluxe ed. 28.95 plastic comb, incl. diskette (ISBN 0-697-00441-4); pap. 17.95 (ISBN 0-697-00437-6). Wm C Brown.

--WordStar for the IBM PC & Compatible Computers. (Microcomputer Power Ser.). 224p. 1984. pap. 16.95 (ISBN 0-697-00437-6); deluxe ed. 27.95 incl. diskette (ISBN 0-697-00394-9). Wm C Brown.

Holzner, Steven. Indispensible Utilities: Ten Best for the IBM PC & XT. (Illus.). 320p. 1985. pap. 19.95 (ISBN 0-89303-584-X). Brady Comm.

How to Use the IBM Personal Computer. 1983. pap. 3.50 (ISBN 0-88284-234-X). Alfred Pub.

Hume, J. N. & Holt, R. C. Better BASIC for the IBM PC. 1983. pap. text ed. 17.95 (ISBN 0-8359-0467-9). Reston.

Hunt, Greg. Great Games for the IBM PC: A Buyer's Guide to Challenging Games of Strategy & Skill. 320p. 1984. pap. 7.95 (ISBN 0-88693-100-2). Banbury Bks.

Hunter, Beverly, et al. Guide to Managing Information with Your Personal Computer. 1985. 14.95 (ISBN 0-673-18092-1). Scott F.

Hurley, Richard B. Decision Tables in Software Engineering. (VNR Data Processing Ser.). 184p. 1982. text ed. 22.95 (ISBN 0-442-23599-2); disks for Apple II & IBM-PC 59.50 ea. (ISBN 0-442-23666-2). Van Nos Reinhold.

Hurwicz, Michael. Networking with the IBM Cluster. (Illus.). 224p. (Orig.). 1985. 29.95 (ISBN 0-8306-0929-6, 1929); pap. 19.95 (ISBN 0-8306-1929-1). TAB Bks.

Hyman, Michael I. Advanced IBM PC Graphics: State of the Art. (Illus.). 320p. 1985. pap. 21.95 (ISBN 0-89303-476-2); diskette 30.00 (ISBN 0-89303-474-6). Brady Comm.

IBM PC & Compatible Device Hardware Add-On Market. 298p. 1985. 1675.00 (ISBN 0-86621-349-X, A1433). Frost & Sullivan.

IBM PC & Compatible Device Software Market. 289p. 1984. 1550.00 (ISBN 0-86621-257-4, A1329). Frost & Sullivan.

IBM PC Enhancement Handbook for Scientists & Engineers, Vol. 2: Infrastructure & Applications. 388p. 1985. 18.95 (ISBN 0-317-31763-6). Cyber Res Inc.

IBM Software Directory 1985. Date not set. pap. text ed. 29.95 (ISBN 0-8352-1972-0). Bowker.

The IBM User Show. 354p. 1983. 114.00x (ISBN 0-903796-97-X, Pub. by Online). Taylor & Francis.

Illowsky, Dan & Abrash, Michael. Graphics for the IBM PC. LC 83-51617. 14.95 (ISBN 0-672-22191-8). Sams.

International Resource Development Inc. Market for Add-On Boards, Systems & Services for the IBM PC. 241p. 1984. 1850.00x (ISBN 0-88694-603-4). Intl Res Dev.

Isaacson, Dan, et al. Skill Builders: For Your IBM-PC & IBM-PCjr, 2 bks. (Illus.). 64p. 1984. Bk. 1. pap. cancelled (ISBN 0-88056-215-3); Bk. 2. pap. cancelled (ISBN 0-88056-216-1). Dilithium Pr.

Jensen, Paul A. Microsolve-Operations Research. 186p. 1985. IBM Version. 65.00 (ISBN 0-8162-4503-7). Apple Version (ISBN 0-8162-4502-9). Holden-Day.

Jordan, Larry E. & Churchill, Bruce. Communications & Networking for the IBM PC. LC 83-12250. (Illus.). 256p. 1983. pap. 21.95 (ISBN 0-89303-385-5). Brady Comm.

Jourbain, Robert L. Programmer's Problem Solver for the IBM PC, XT & AT. (Illus.). 320p. 1985. pap. 22.95 (ISBN 0-89303-787-7). Brady Comm.

Kassob, Vincent. BASIC Programming for the IBM Personal Computer with Technical Applications. (Illus.). pap. text ed. 15.95 (ISBN 0-13-066218-6). P-H.

Kearsley, Gregory, et al. Guide to Telecommunications with Your IBM PC. 1985. pap. 39.95 incl. diskette (ISBN 0-673-15944-2). Scott F.

Kelley. An Accounting Experience with the IBM Microcomputer: A Service Firm. 2nd ed. 1985. pap. 16.95x (ISBN 0-256-03437-0). Business Pubns.

Kelley, James E., Jr. The IBM PC & Business Software: VisiCalc, dBASE II & WordStar Explained. 320p. 1983. pap. 39.95 incl. 2 floppy disks (ISBN 0-88693-000-6). Banbury Bks.

--The IBM PC & 1-2-3: Real World Applications of the IBM-PC's Most Popular Software Package. 320p. 1983. pap. 39.95 incl. disk (ISBN 0-88693-032-4). Banbury Bks.

--The IBM Personal Computer User's Guide. 352p. 1983. spiral bdg., incl. disk 29.95 (ISBN 0-440-03946-0, Banbury). Dell.

Kelley, Jane. An Accounting Experience with the IBM Microcomputer: A Merchandising Firm. 1985. 16.95x (ISBN 0-256-03438-9). Business Pubns.

Kelly, Brian W. & Grimes, Dennis J. IBM PC Compatible Computer Directory: Hardware, Software & Peripherals. (Kelly-Grimes Buyers Guide Ser.: No. 1702). 581p. 1985. pap. 26.95 (ISBN 0-471-87819-7, Pub. by Wiley Pr). Wiley.
--IBM Personal Computer Directory: Hardware, Software, & Peripherals. (Kelly-Grimes Buyers Guide Ser.: No. 1-702). 581p. 1985. pap. 26.95 (ISBN 0-471-87821-9, Pub. by Wiley Pr). Wiley.
Kepner, Terry & Robinson, Mark. Fifty-Eight Business Programs for the IBM PC. 1985. pap. 18.95 (ISBN 0-673-18286-X). Scott F.
King, Richard A. IBM PC-DOS Handbook. LC 83-61387. (Illus.). 296p. 1983. pap. 16.95 (ISBN 0-89588-103-9). SYBEX.
Klein, Mike. The IBM PC Experience. (Experience Ser.). 240p. (Orig.). 1984. pap. text ed. 14.95 (ISBN 0-88190-370-1, BO370). Datamost.
Knight, Timothy O. Graphics & Sounds on the IBM PC. LC 83-50941. 128p. 1984. pap. 8.95 (ISBN 0-672-22172-1, 22172). Sams.
Krakow, Ira H. Lotus 1-2-3 Self-Taught on the IBM PC. (Illus.). 304p. 1984. pap. 15.95 (ISBN 0-89303-628-5); bk. diskette 45.95 (ISBN 0-89303-629-3); bk. diskette 30.00 (ISBN 0-89303-630-7). Brady Comm.
Kruglinski, David. The Osborne-McGraw-Hill Guide to Your IBM PC Communications. 250p. (Orig.). 15.95 (ISBN 0-07-881126-0, 126-0). Osborne-McGraw.
Krukow, Ira. Project Management with the IBM PC. 128p. 1985. 11.95 (ISBN 0-89303-774-5). Brady Comm.
Lambert, Steve. Presentation Graphics on the IBM PC: How to use Microsoft Chart to Create Dazzling Graphics for Corporate & Professional Applications. (Illus.). 320p. (Orig.). 1986. pap. 19.95 (ISBN 0-914845-12-8). Microsoft.
Lamoitier, J. P. BASIC Exercises for the IBM Personal Computer. LC 82-60234. (Illus.). 251p. (Orig.). 1982. pap. 15.95 (ISBN 0-89588-088-1). SYBEX.
Landberg, Ramona. Getting Started with Word Processing on the IBM-PC. 1984. cancelled (ISBN 0-89303-488-6). Brady Comm.
Lansing, David. The Quick & Easy Guide to Wordprocessing with the IBM PC. 128p. 1984. pap. 4.95 (ISBN 0-912003-25-1). Bk Co.
Laric, Michael V. & Stiff, M. R. Multiplan for the IBM Personal Computer. (Microcomputer Power Ser.). 150p. 1984. pap. 16.95 (ISBN 0-697-00230-6); incl. disk 27.95 (ISBN 0-697-00330-2). Wm C Brown.
Laric, Michael V. & Stiff, Ronald. Marketing & Business Planning with the IBM PCs: A Guide to the Productive Use of Personal Computers for Business & Marketing Professionals. (Illus.). 224p. 1985. pap. 16.95 (ISBN 0-13-557067-0). P H.
Larsen, Elmer. Icons & Images. Compute!, ed. (Orig.). 1985. pap. 14.95 (ISBN 0-942386-84-1). Compute Pubns.
Lasselle, Joan & Ramsay, Carol. The ABC's of the IBM PC. LC 83-61383. (Illus.). 143p. 1983. pap. 13.95 (ISBN 0-89588-102-0). SYBEX.
Latif, Rebecca C. WordStar on the IBM PC. 1985. pap. text ed. 19.95 (ISBN 0-8359-8818-X). Reston.
Lauderdale, Leslie. The Home Accountant Plus: A Handholding Guide for IBM-PC Users. 1985. pap. write for info (ISBN 0-912003-44-8). Bk Co.
Leithauser, David. Programs for Electronic Circuit Design. (Illus.). 128p. (Orig.). 1984. IBM-PC. pap. 24.95 spiral bound incl. disk (ISBN 0-88006-080-8, CC7410). Green Pub Inc.
Lemmons, Phillip. A Buyer's Guide to Software for the IBM Personal Computer. 1983. pap. 18.95 (ISBN 0-07-037150-4, BYTE Bks). McGraw.
Lemone. Assembly Language & Systems for the IBM PC. 1985. 16.45i (ISBN 0-316-52069-1). Little.
Leonsis, Ted & List Magazine Editors. Software Master for the PFS. 336p. (Orig.). Apple Version. pap. 39.95 (ISBN 0-446-38177-2). Warner Bks.
Lesser, M. L. Using the Microsoft Business BASIC Compiler on the IBM PC. 256p. 1985. price not set (ISBN 0-07-037299-3, BYTE Bks). McGraw.
Levitan, Arlan R. & Leemon, Sheldon. Compute's Telecomputing on the IBM. Compute Editors, ed. (Orig.). 1985. pap. 14.95 (ISBN 0-942386-96-5). Compute Pubns.
Lewart, Cass. Science & Engineering Programs for the IBM PC. (Illus.). 150p. 1983. 18.95 (ISBN 0-13-794925-1). P-H.
Lewart, Cass R. Science & Engineering Programs for the IBM PC. (Illus.). 240p. 1984. incl. diskette 39.95 (ISBN 0-13-794934-0). P-H.
Lewis, Richard. Software Plus for the IBM Personal Computer. 1983. pap. 2.00 (ISBN 0-913929-00-X). UOI Co.
Lewis, T. G. Using the IBM Personal Computer. 1982. text ed. 19.95 O.P. (ISBN 0-8359-8140-1); pap. text ed. 16.95 (ISBN 0-8359-8138-X). Reston.
Lewis, Ted. Microbook-Database Management for the IBM PC. 310p. 1983. pap. 19.95 (ISBN 0-88056-114-9); pap. 39.95 incl. disk (ISBN 0-88056-165-3). Dilithium Pr.
Lewis, Ted G. Pascal for the IBM Personal Computer. LC 82-22750. 288p. 1983. pap. 15.95 (ISBN 0-201-05464-7). Addison-Wesley.
Lien, David A. BASIC Programming for the IBM Personal Computer. (Data Processing Ser.). 560p. 1984. pap. text ed. write for info. (ISBN 0-697-00414-7); write for info. solution manuals (ISBN 0-697-00439-2). Wm C Brown.
--The IBM BASIC Handbook. LC 84-71386. (Illus.). 237p. (Orig.). 1984. pap. 14.95 (ISBN 0-932760-23-6). CompuSoft.
--Learning IBM BASIC for the Personal Computer. rev. ed. LC 82-73471. (CompuSoft Learning Ser.). (Illus.). 494p. (Orig.). 1984. pap. 19.95 (ISBN 0-932760-13-9). CompuSoft.
--Learning IBM PC Disk BASIC. (CompuSoft Learning Ser.). 250p. Date not set. pap. 17.95 (ISBN 0-932760-25-2). CompuSoft.
Lord, Kenniston W., Jr. Graphics with the IBM-PC. 1985. pap. 19.95 (ISBN 0-673-15971-X). Scott F.
--Learning to Use the IBM Personal Computer. LC 83-60185. 175p. 1983. pap. 14.95 (ISBN 0-89435-066-8). QED Info Sci.
--Using the IBM Personal Computer. 336p. 1983. 19.95 (ISBN 0-442-25815-1); pap. 12.95 (ISBN 0-442-26078-4). Van Nos Reinhold.
Luehrmann, Arthur & Peckham, Herbert. Hands-on Pascal: For the IBM Personal Computer. (Personal Programmimg Ser.). 448p. 1984. pap. text ed. write for info. (ISBN 0-07-049176-3). McGraw.
Lyn, E. Ray. IBM PC & XT Handy Reference Guide. 96p. (Orig.). cancelled (ISBN 0-8306-0797-8); pap. cancelled (ISBN 0-8306-1797-3, 1797). TAB Bks.
McBeth. IBM Assembler: An Intuitive Approach. 1986. price not set (ISBN 0-471-82424-0). Wiley.
McCunn, Donald. Stretch Your IBM PC: For Multilingual Word Processing, Math & Scientific Notation, Music Composition, & Typesetting. 300p. 1985. 24.95 (ISBN 0-932538-63-0); pap. 14.95 (ISBN 0-932538-64-9). Design Ent SF.
McCunn, Donald H. Computer Programming for the Compleat Idiot: IBM-PC Edition. 2nd ed. (Illus.). 192p. 1984. 18.95 (ISBN 0-932538-13-4); pap. 10.95 (ISBN 0-932538-14-2). Design Ent SF.
Mackie, Peter. The World of PC-DOS. 125p. 1984. pap. 9.95 (ISBN 0-88056-145-9); IBM-PC, IBM-PC XT, Compaq. incl. disk 29.95. Dilithium Pr.
Mackie, Peter H. & Griffin, John R. PC to Mac & Back: A File Transfer Utility for the IBM-PC & Macintosh. (Illus.). 165p. incl. disk 49.95 (ISBN 0-88056-224-2). Dilithium Pr.
McMahan, Mike. Graphics & Sound for Your IBM-PC. Berliner, Thomas H., ed. LC 85-719. (Illus.). 240p. 1984. pap. 19.95 (ISBN 0-915381-66-4). WordWare Pub.
McMullen, John & McMullen, Barbara. One-Two-Three User's Guide for the IBM PC. cancelled 18.95 (ISBN 0-89303-740-0). Brady Comm.
McNichols, Charles. IBM PC Statistics: BASIC Programs & Applications. pap. text ed. 16.95 (ISBN 0-8359-3014-9). Reston.
--Microcomputer Based Data Analysis for the IBM Personal Computer. 1984. pap. text ed. 21.95 (ISBN 0-8359-4349-6); instr's manual avail. (ISBN 0-8359-4350-X). Reston.
McNichols, Charles W. IBM PC Statistics: Basic Programs & Applications. 1984. write for info. P-H.
McWilliams, Peter A. Word Processing on the IBM. 224p. 1983. pap. 9.95 (ISBN 0-345-31530-8). Ballantine.
Magid, Lawrence J. & Boeschen, John. The Electronic Link: Using the IBM-PC to Communicate. LC 84-11929. (IBM-PC Ser.: 1-646). 224p. 1984. pap. 15.95 (ISBN 0-471-88382-4). Wiley.
Malitz, Issac. The Super Computer Snooper for the IBM PC. (Orig.). 1983. pap. 14.95 (ISBN 0-88190-344-2, BO344). Datamost.
Mandell, Steven L. Introduction to Computers Using the IBM PC. 550p. text ed. 25.95 (ISBN 0-314-85267-0). West Pub.
Manus, Steven. Everything You Can Do with Your IBM PC. (Everything You Can Do with Your... Ser.). 1984. pap. 9.95 (ISBN 0-88284-279-X). Alfred Pub.
Markowsky, George. A Comprehensive Guide to the IBM Personal Computer. (Illus.). 640p. 1984. pap. text ed. 19.95 (ISBN 0-13-164203-0). P-H.
Martin, Donald, et al. IBM PC & PCjr LOGO Programming Primer. LC 84-51654. 24.95 (ISBN 0-672-22379-1); Book & Software Pack. 24.95. Sams.
Massie, Paul. Programming IBM Assembly Language. (Illus.). 500p. 1985. pap. text ed. write for info. (ISBN 0-8087-6405-5). Burgess.
Matthews, Carol B. & Matthews, Martin S. Word Processing for the IBM PC & PCjr & Compatible Computers. (Illus.). 428p. 1985. pap. 18.95 (ISBN 0-07-040952-8, Byte Bks). McGraw.
Mayer, John S. IBM PC Survivor's Manual: A Primer for the IBM Personal Computer. 35p. (Orig.). 1982. pap. 11.95 (ISBN 0-9609092-0-6). Mayer Assocs.
Mears, Peter. Introduction to the IBM Personal Computer: Keyboarding. 1984. with diskette 40.45 (ISBN 0-03-064134-9). HR&W.
Mellin, Michael & Hays, Nancy, eds. The Book of IBM Software 1985. 550p. (Orig.). 1984. 19.95 (ISBN 0-912003-38-3). Bk Co.
Metcalf, Chris & Sugiyama, Marc. Compute's Beginner's Guide to Machine Language on the IBM PC & PCjr. Compute!, ed. (Orig.). 1985. pap. 14.95 (ISBN 0-942386-83-3). Compute Pubns.
Meyer, Edwin W. & Oldfield, Molly. WordStar for the IBM PC: A Self-Guided Tutorial. LC 83-21375. (Illus.). 384p. 1984. pap. 15.95 (ISBN 0-89303-956-X). Brady Comm.
Microtrend Inc. C Language on the IBM PC. 1984. 14.95. P-H.
Microtrend, Inc. DESQ on the IBM PC. (Microtrend Ser.). 1984. write for info. (ISBN 0-13-202094-7). P-H.
--Microsoft Windows on the IBM PC. (Microtrend Ser.). 1984. cancelled (ISBN 0-13-581661-0). P-H.
Microtrend Inc. UCSD P-System on the IBM PC. (Microtrend Ser.). 1984. 14.95 (ISBN 0-13-935404-2). P-H.
Microtrend Inc. & Jackson, Charles H. MS-DOS & PC-DOS on the IBM PC. (Microtrend Ser.). 1984. 14.95 (ISBN 0-13-604281-3). P-H.
Miller, David. IBM Data Files: A Basic Tutorial. 1983. 16.95 (ISBN 0-8359-3026-2). Reston.
Miller, Larry & Viands, Leon. Introduction to CICS Programming. 1983. 24.95 (ISBN 0-13-479212-2, Spec). P-H.
Morgan, Christopher L. Bluebook of Assembly Routines for the IBM PCjr & XT. (Plume-Waite Computer Ser.). (Illus.). 1984. pap. 19.95 (ISBN 0-452-25498-1, Plume). NAL.
Moron, John & Hilbush, Mark. IBM PC Guide to Artificial Intelligence: Making Computers Think Like People. 272p. 1984. pap. 19.95 (ISBN 0-88693-158-4). Banbury Bks.
Morrill, Harriet. BASIC Programming for the IBM Personal Computer. (Microcomputer Bookshelf Ser.). 175p. (Orig.). 1983. pap. 14.50 (ISBN 0-316-58402-9); tchr's. manual avail. (ISBN 0-316-58403-7). Little.
Murdock, Everett & Sudbury, Susan. School & Home Guide to IBM Compatible Personal Computers. LC 84-24786. 292p. 1985. pap. 18.95 (ISBN 0-13-793662-1). P-H.
MVP-FORTH Assembly Source Code: For CP-M, IBM-PC & Apple. (MVP-FORTH Books: Vol. 2). 20.00 (ISBN 0-318-01342-8). Mountain View Pr.
Myers, Roy E. Microcomputer Graphics for the IBM PC. 1438p. 1984. pap. 14.95 (ISBN 0-201-05158-3); apple disk package 29.95 (ISBN 0-201-05312-8). Addison-Wesley.
Naiman, Arthur. IBM Personal Computer Made Easy. 1983. 11.95 (ISBN 0-395-34413-1); pap. 5.95 (ISBN 0-395-34933-8). HM.
Nashelsky, Louis & Boylestad, Robert. IBM PC XT: BASIC Programming & Applications. (Illus.). 304p. 1984. pap. 14.95 (ISBN 0-13-448325-1); incl. disk 39.95 (ISBN 0-13-448341-3). P-H.
Newman, Barry. Magic Picture for the IBM & IBM PCjr. (Illus.). 160p. 1984. pap. cancelled (ISBN 0-88056-222-6). Dilithium Pr.
Newrock, Melody. Here Comes the Clones: A Guide to IBM-PC Compatible Computers & Software. (A BYTE Book). (Illus.). 1984. pap. 18.95 (ISBN 0-07-046458-8). McGraw.
Norton, Peter. Inside the IBM PC: Access to Advanced Features & Programming Techniques. LC 83-3775. (Illus.). 320p. 1983. pap. 19.95 (ISBN 0-89303-556-4); bk. & diskette 86.95 (ISBN 0-89303-561-0); diskette 65.00 (ISBN 0-89303-559-9). Brady Comm.
--Mastering the IBM PC. 1985. cancelled (ISBN 0-671-55780-7). Microsoft.
--The Peter Norton Programmer's Guide to the IBM PC. (Illus.). 368p. (Orig.). 1985. pap. 19.95 (ISBN 0-914845-46-2). Microsoft.
Orwig, Gary W. & Hodges, William S. The Computer Tutor for the IBM Personal Computers: Learning Activities for Homes & Schools. (Little, Brown Microcomputer Bookshelf Ser.). 1984. 15.95 (ISBN 0-316-66503-7). Little.
Osgood, William & Molloy, James, Jr. Business Decision Making: An IBM PC User's Guide. 1983. 14.95; pap. 29.95 disk (ISBN 0-930764-98-6); pap. 39.95 disk set (ISBN 0-930764-97-8). Van Nos Reinhold.
Owens, James. Handbook for New IBM PC Users. LC 84-60128. 160p. (Orig.). 1984. pap. 39.00 (ISBN 0-943170-06-0). Management Ed.
Pardee, Michael. Pascal Primer for the IBM PC. (Plume-Waite Computer Ser.). (Illus.). 1984. pap. 17.95 (ISBN 0-452-25496-5, Plume). NAL.
Parker, Alan J. BASIC for Business for the IBM Personal Computer. 1983. text ed. 21.95 (ISBN 0-8359-0356-7); pap. text ed. 17.95 (ISBN 0-8359-0355-9). Reston.
Payne, Donald T. IBM BASIC. 234p. 1983. 22.95 (ISBN 0-13-448696-X, Spec); pap. 15.95 (ISBN 0-13-448688-9). P-H.
PC Magazine Editors, ed. The PC Guide to Printers. (Illus.). 240p. (Orig.). pap. cancelled (ISBN 0-916688-96-8, 96-8). Creative Comp.
The PC Telemart-VanLoves IBM Software Directory. 964p. 1984. pap. 24.95 (ISBN 0-8352-1969-0). Bowker.
PC World Editors & Myers, David. LOGO for IBM Personal Computers. 1985. pap. 16.95 (ISBN 0-671-49284-5). S&S.
Peckham, H. Structured BASIC for the IBM PC. (Personal Programming Ser.). 320p. 1985. 22.00 (ISBN 0-07-049162-3). McGraw.
Peckham, Herbert D. Hands-on BASIC: For the IBM Personal Computer. LC 82-81497. 352p. 1982. pap. text ed. 23.95 (ISBN 0-07-049178-X, BYTE Bks). McGraw.
Peiperl, Maury. The IBM PC & XT Sourcebook. 288p. 1985. pap. 15.95 (ISBN 0-671-47474-X, Pub. by Computer Bks). S&S.
Person, Ron. Animation Magic with Your IBM PC & PCjr. LC 84-22639. 250p. 1984. pap. 16.95 (ISBN 0-07-881145-7, 145-7). Osborne-McGraw.
Personal Computer Software Directory for IBM 1985. 1000p. 1985. 49.95 (ISBN 0-912603-17-8). Micro Info.
Phillips, Gary. IBM PC Public Domain Software, Vol. 1. Thomson, Monet, ed. 547p. 1983. pap. 24.95 (ISBN 0-912677-06-6). Ashton-Tate Bks.
--IBM Public Domain Software, Vol. 1. 1984. 24.95 (ISBN 0-8359-3042-4). Reston.
Phillips, Gary & Phillips, Karen. The Reference Encyclopedia for the IBM Personal Computer, 2 vols. 2nd ed. 700p. 1983. Set. 69.95 (ISBN 0-912677-01-5). Ashton-Tate Bks.
Phillips, Gary, ed. Reference Encyclopedia for the IBM Personal Computer, 2 Vols. 1984. 69.95 (ISBN 0-317-03007-8). P-H.
Pirisino, Jim. Minute Manual for PFS: File'Report'Graph'Write'Proof for IBM. 175p. Date not set. pap. 12.95 (ISBN 0-913131-06-7). Minuteware.
Pitter, K. & Pitter, R. Using Microcomputers: An IBM PC Lab Manual. 280p. 1984. pap. text ed. 14.95 (ISBN 0-938188-22-4). Mitchell Pub.
Plemmons, Patrick & PC World Editors. Essential Applications for the IBM PC & XT. 244p. 1984. pap. 16.95 (ISBN 0-671-49279-9, Pub. by Computer Bks). S&S.
Pollack, Seymour V. Programming the IBM Personal Computer: UCSD Pascal. LC 82-21249. 400p. 1983. pap. 40.45 with diskette (ISBN 0-03-063669-8); pap. 20.95 (ISBN 0-03-062637-4). HR&W.
Poole, Lon. Using Your IBM Personal Computer. LC 82-62203. 328p. 1983. pap. 16.95 (ISBN 0-672-22000-8, 22000). Sams.
Posdamer, Jeffrey. Using the IBM Personal Computer: Graphics. 1984. 18.45 (ISBN 0-03-063167-X). HR&W.
Post, Dan. Profit From the IBM PC. 2nd ed. (Illus.). 192p. 1985. 14.95 (ISBN 0-317-28835-0, Pub. by Microtrend). Slawson Comm.
Post, Dan W. Profit from the IBM PC: A Non-Technical Guide to Selling User Services. LC 83-82632. (Illus.). 192p. 1984. 14.95 (ISBN 0-911160-89-2, Edge Press). Post-Era.
Presley, Bruce. A Guide to Programming the IBM Personal Computers. 2nd ed. 1985. pap. 19.95 (ISBN 0-931717-11-6); drilled for a 3ring binder tchr's guide 19.95 (ISBN 0-931717-12-4). Lawrenceville Pr.
Press, Laurence. The IBM PC & Its Applications. LC 83-25939. (Wiley IBM PC Series: 354). 354p. 1984. pap. 14.95 (ISBN 0-471-88440-5, Pub. by Wiley Pr). Wiley.
Price, Wilson T. Programming the IBM Personal Computer: Business BASIC. 318p. 1984. pap. text ed. 17.95 (ISBN 0-03-063746-5). HR&W.
Puotinen, C. J. Using the IBM PC: WordStar. 357p. 1983. pap. 40.95 with diskette (ISBN 0-03-063981-6); pap. 18.45 (ISBN 0-03-062857-1). HR&W.
--Using the IBM Personal Computer: MultiMate. 352p. 1984. pap. 20.45 (ISBN 0-03-071411-7). HR&W.
Purcell, W. R. Decision Graphs for Profit & Cash Flow Planning with an IBM PC. 256p. 1986. pap. text ed. price not set (ISBN 0-07-050951-4). McGraw.
Que Staff. IBM PC Expansion & Software Guide. 5th ed. LC 84-62134. 1000p. 1985. pap. 21.95 (ISBN 0-88022-096-1, 169). Que Corp.

Weber Systems, Inc. Staff. IBM Portable PC User's Handbook. LC 84-25628. (WSI's User's Handbooks to Personal Computers Ser.). 350p. (Orig.). 1985. pap. 15.95 (ISBN 0-938862-17-0). Weber Systems.
--Sourcebook of IBM Compatible Hardware, Software & Peripherals. 608p. (Orig.). 1985. pap. 18.95 (ISBN 0-345-31843-9). Ballantine.
Weber Systems Staff. IBM Color Printer User's Handbook. (WSI's User's Handbook to Personal Computers Ser.). 300p. (Orig.). pap. cancelled (ISBN 0-938862-18-9). Weber Systems.
--IBM PC Business Software in BASIC. LC 84-51354. (Applications Software Ser.). 300p. 1985. pap. 17.95 (ISBN 0-938862-35-9); incl. disk 20.00 (ISBN 0-938862-36-7). Weber Systems.
White, Howard. Data File Handling for the IBM PC & XT. 192p. 1985. pap. 16.95 (ISBN 0-89303-402-9). Brady Comm.
White, R., Jr. WordStar with Style for the IBM PC. 1984. 15.95 (ISBN 0-8359-8817-1). Reston.
Whittaker, Elizabeth. Advanced dBASE II with Applications for the IBM Personal Computer. (Micropower Ser.). 200p. 1985. pap. 17.95 (ISBN 0-697-00712-X); deluxe ed., incl. diskette 29.95 (ISBN 0-697-00720-0). Wm C Brown.
--The dBASE III for the IBM Personal Computer. (Micropower Ser.). 200p. 1985. pap. 17.95 (ISBN 0-697-00710-3); deluxe ed., incl. diskette 29.95 (ISBN 0-697-00736-7). Wm C Brown.
Williams, Andrew T. What If? A User's Guide to Spreadsheets on the IBM-PC. (IBM Personal Computer Ser.: Nos. 1-646). 281p. (Orig.). 1984. pap. text ed. 16.95 (ISBN 0-471-89218-1, Pub. by Wiley Pr). Wiley.
Williams, Gene B. Repair & Maintenance for the IBM PC. LC 84-45156. 220p. (Orig.). 1984. pap. 12.95 (ISBN 0-8019-7537-9). Chilton.
Willis, Jerry & Manning, William. How to Use the IBM PC. (How to Use Ser.). (Illus.). 128p. 1984. pap. 5.95 (ISBN 0-88056-308-7). Dilithium Pr.
Willis, Jerry, et al. Things to Do with Your IBM PC. 1984. pap. 3.95 (ISBN 0-451-13183-5, Sig). NAL.
--Things to Do with Your IBM Personal Computer. 1983. pap. 3.95 (ISBN 0-451-12849-4, Sig). NAL.
Willmott, Thomas. Software Solutions for the IBM PC: A Practical Guide to dBASE, Lotus 1-2-3, VisiCalc, WordStar & More. 230p. 1983. 21.95 (ISBN 0-13-822395-5); pap. 14.95 (ISBN 0-13-822387-4). P-H.
Wolfe, Philip & Koelling, C. Patrick. Basic Engineering & Scientific Programs for the IBM PC. LC 83-7100. (Illus.). 356p. 1983. pap. text ed. 21.95 (ISBN 0-89303-330-8); bk. & diskette 46.95 (ISBN 0-89303-331-6); 25.00 (ISBN 0-89303-333-2). Brady Comm.
Woodis, Amy & Lim, Evan. The Quick & Easy Guide to Database Management on the IBM PC. 128p. 1984. pap. 4.95 (ISBN 0-912003-23-5). Bk Co.
Wyatt, Allen L. BASIC Tricks for the IBM. LC 83-51185. 136p. 1984. pap. 7.95 (ISBN 0-672-22250-7, 22250). Sams.
Zaks, Rodnay. Your First IBM PC Program. LC 83-51190. (Illus.). 182p. (Orig.). 1983. pap. 14.95 (ISBN 0-89588-171-3). SYBEX.
Zimmerman, Steven & Conrad, Leo. Business Applications for the IBM Personal Computer. LC 83-3823. (Illus.). 320p. 1983. pap. 19.95 (ISBN 0-89303-243-3); incl. diskette 49.95 (ISBN 0-89303-351-0); diskette 30.00 (ISBN 0-89303-352-9). Brady Comm.
Zimmerman, Steven, et al. Electronic Spreadsheets for the IBM PC. 320p. pap. 16.95 (6357). Hayden.
Zussman, John & Cortesi, David. Executive Computing: The IBM Personal Computer. 1985. pap. text ed. 19.95 (ISBN 0-03-068914-7). HR&W.

IBM PERSONAL COMPUTER XT

Arnold, David & PC World Staff. Getting Started with the IBM PC & XT. 256p. 1984. pap. 14.95 (ISBN 0-671-49277-2, Pub. by Computer Bks). S&S.
Bowyer, Kevin W. & Tomboulian, Sherryl J. Pascal for the IBM-PC: Turbo Pascal, PC-DOS Pascal, & UCSD p-System Pascal. rev. & expanded ed. (Illus.). 438p. 1984. pap. 19.95 (ISBN 0-89303-766-4). Brady Comm.
Burns, Robert V. & Johnson, Rees C. Sixty Forms for the Entrepreneur: Forms Generator - IBM-PC, PCjr & PC XT. 192p. 1985. pap. cancelled (ISBN 0-88056-258-7). Dilithium Pr.
--Sixty Forms for the Landlord: Forms Generator - IBM-PC, PCjr & PC XT. 192p. 1985. pap. cancelled (ISBN 0-88056-255-2). Dilithium Pr.
Busch, David D. PC-DOS Customized: Create Your Own DOS Commands for the IBM-PC, XT & AT. 176p. 1985. pap. 14.95 (ISBN 0-89303-753-2). Brady Comm.
Carr, Joseph L. Sixty-Eight Scientific & Engineering Programs for the IBM PC & PC XT. 1984. 19.95 (ISBN 0-8359-6921-5). Reston.
Chertok, Barbara L., et al. IBM PC & XT Owner's Manual: A Practical Guide to Operations. LC 83-15576. 224p. 1983. pap. 14.95 (ISBN 0-89303-531-9). Brady Comm.
Crop, Sheldon. Local Area Networks for the IBM PC XT. 225p. 1984. pap. 14.95 (ISBN 0-89588-243-4). SYBEX.
Cuellar, Gabriel. Graphics Made Easy for the IBM PC or PC XT. (Illus.). 1984. pap. 18.95 (ISBN 0-8359-2569-2). Reston.
Datz & Datz. Processing Words with Your IBM PC, PC XT or PC Compatible. 232p. 1984. 15.95 (ISBN 0-317-06579-3, 6359). Hayden.
Desautels, Edouard J. Lotus 1-2-3 for the IBM Personal Computer & XT. (Microcomputer Power Ser.). 288p. 1984. pap. 16.95 (ISBN 0-697-09997-0); incl. disk 29.95 (ISBN 0-697-00337-X). Wm C Brown.
Fowler, John. The IBM PC XT Graphics Book. (Illus.). 300p. 1984. 16.95 (ISBN 0-13-448408-8); pap. 34.95 incl. disk (ISBN 0-13-448416-9). P-H.
Fuori, William. COBOL Programming for the IBM PC & PC XT: Vol. 1. 275p. 1984. 19.95 (ISBN 0-8359-0779-1). Reston.
--COBOL Programming for the IBM PC & PC XT: Vol. 2. 250p. 1984. 19.95 (ISBN 0-8359-0780-5). Reston.
--FORTH Programming for the IBM PC & PC XT. 224p. 19.95 (ISBN 0-8359-2099-2). Reston.
--FORTRAN 77 Programming for the IBM PC & PC XT. 224p. 1984. 19.95 (ISBN 0-8359-2096-8). Reston.
--Pascal Programming for the IBM PC & PC XT. 1984. cancelled (ISBN 0-317-06174-7). Reston.
Germain, Clarence B. Programming the IBM PC & XT: A Guide to Languages. LC 84-289. (Illus.). 352p. 1984. pap. 19.95 (ISBN 0-89303-783-4). Brady Comm.
Holzner, Steven. Indispensible Utilities: Ten Best for the IBM PC & XT. (Illus.). 320p. 1985. pap. 19.95 (ISBN 0-89303-584-X). Brady Comm.
How to Repair & Maintain Your Own PC XT. 19.95 (ISBN 0-317-05234-9). Personal Sys Pubns.
Jourbain, Robert L. Programmer's Problem Solver for the IBM PC, XT & AT. (Illus.). 320p. 1985. pap. 22.95 (ISBN 0-89303-787-7). Brady Comm.
Lyn, E. Ray. IBM PC & XT Handy Reference Guide. 96p. (Orig.). cancelled (ISBN 0-8306-0797-8); pap. cancelled (ISBN 0-8306-1797-3, 1797). TAB Bks.
Murray, William H. & Pappas, Chris H. An Introduction to APL for the IBM PC & Xt. (Illus.). 224p. 1985. 29.95 (ISBN 0-89303-567-X). Brady Comm.
Nashelsky, Louis & Boylestad, Robert. IBM PC XT: BASIC Programming & Applications. (Illus.). 304p. 1984. pap. 14.95 (ISBN 0-13-448325-1); incl. disk 39.95 (ISBN 0-13-448341-3). P-H.
Plemmons, Patrick & PC World Editors. Essential Applications for the IBM PC & XT. 244p. 1984. pap. 16.95 (ISBN 0-671-49279-9, Pub. by Computer Bks). S&S.
Scanlon, Leo J. IBM PC & XT Assembly Language: A Guide for Programmers. rev. & expanded ed. (Illus.). 352p. 1985. pap. 21.95 (ISBN 0-89303-575-0). Brady Comm.
Schwieder, Pete H. How to Repair & Maintain Your Own IBM PC-XT. (Illus.). 186p. (Orig.). 1984. pap. 29.95x (ISBN 0-915097-00-1). Personal Sys Pubns.
Seyer, Martin. The IBM PC XT: Making the Right Connections. (Illus.). 288p. 1985. text ed. 24.95 (ISBN 0-13-449026-6); pap. text ed. 16.95 (ISBN 0-13-448978-0). P-H.
SPSS Inc. Staff & Norusis, Marija J. SPSS PC: SPSS for the IBM-PC XT. LC 84-42824. 576p. (Orig.). 1984. pap. 34.95 (ISBN 0-918469-00-7). SPSS Inc.
Stahr, Lisa & PC World Editors. Communications for the IBM PC & XT. 1984. pap. 16.95 (ISBN 0-671-49280-2, Pub. by Computer Bks). S&S.
Startz, Richard. Eighty Eighty Seven Applications & Programming for the IBM PC, XT, & AT Revised & Expanded. (Illus.). 320p. 1985. pap. 22.95 (ISBN 0-89303-485-1). Brady Comm.
Stein, Barry. Dr. LOGO for the IBM PC XT. cancelled 12.95 (ISBN 0-89303-410-X). Brady Comm.
VanDiver, Gerald. The IBM PC & XT Business Software Guide. 231p. 1984. 19.95 (ISBN 0-912603-12-7). Micro-Info.
--The IBM PC & XT Educational Software Guide. 124p. 1984. 5.95 (ISBN 0-912603-03-8). Micro Info.
--The IBM PC & XT Software Guide. 1036p. (Orig.). 1983. pap. 24.95 (ISBN 0-912603-00-3). Micro Info.
--The IBM PC & XT Word Processing Software Guide. 187p. 1984. 9.95 (ISBN 0-912603-11-9). Micro Info.
--The IBM PC XT Software Directory Update. 320p. 19.95 (ISBN 0-317-05311-6). Micro Info.
Vickers, Ralph. IBM PC BASIC: A Guide to Programming Your IBM PC, XT, PCjr & PC Compatible Computer. (Hands On! Computer Bks.). 300p. 1984. pap. 16.95 (ISBN 0-06-669013-7). Har-Row.
Waite Group. BASIC Primer for the IBM PC & XT. (Plume-Waite Computer Ser.). (Illus.). 1984. pap. 16.95 (ISBN 0-452-25495-7, Plume). NAL.
Waite, Mitchell, et al. DOS Primer for the IBM PC & XT. (Plume-Waite Computer Ser.). (Illus.). 1984. pap. 14.95 (ISBN 0-452-25494-9, Plume). NAL.
Weber Systems, Inc. Staff. IBM PC & XT User's Handbook. 304p. 1984. pap. 9.95 (ISBN 0-345-31592-8). Ballantine.
Weber Systems Inc. Staff. IBM PC AT User's Handbook. LC 85-5343. 350p. (Orig.). 1985. pap. 17.95 (ISBN 0-938862-06-5). Weber Systems.
White, Howard. Data File Handling for the IBM PC & XT. 192p. 1985. pap. 16.95 (ISBN 0-89303-402-9). Brady Comm.

ICE

see also Glaciers

Colbeck, Samuel C. Dynamics of Snow & Ice Masses. LC 79-17949. 1980. 55.00 (ISBN 0-12-179450-4). Acad Pr.
Fletcher, Neville H. Chemical Physics of Ice. LC 74-75825. (Monographs on Physics). (Illus.). 1970. 49.50 (ISBN 0-521-07597-1). Cambridge U Pr.
Hobbs, Peter V. Ice Physics. (Illus.). 1974. 115.00x (ISBN 0-19-851936-2). Oxford U Pr.
Ice in Fisheries. (Fisheries Reports: No. 59, Rev. 1). (Illus.). 57p. 1975. pap. 7.50 (ISBN 0-685-55203-9, F779, FAO). Unipub.
Klein, Donald A. Environmental Impacts of Artificial Ice Nucleating Agents. LC 78-7985. 256p. 1978. 36.00 (ISBN 0-87933-334-0). Van Nos Reinhold.
Noone, Richard W. Ice: The Ultimate Disaster. LC 83-81272. 380p. (Orig.). 1983. 19.95 (ISBN 0-910285-00-4); pap. 10.95 (ISBN 0-913331-00-7). Genesis Pubs Inc.
Symposium Copenhagen, Technical University of Denmark, August 6-10, 1979. Physics & Mechanics of Ice: Proceedings. Tryde, P., ed. (IUTAM Ser.). (Illus.). 378p. 1980. 43.70 (ISBN 3-540-09906-9). Springer-Verlag.
U. S. National Committee for the International Hydrological Decade. Advanced Concepts & Techniques in the Study of Snow & Ice Resources. Santeford, H. & Smith, J., eds. x, 789p. 1974. pap. 16.75 (ISBN 0-309-02235-5). Natl Acad Pr.

ICE-MANUFACTURE

see Refrigeration and Refrigerating Machinery

ICE AGE

see Glacial Epoch

ICE CREAM, ICES, ETC.

see also Confectionery

Hoffman, Mable & Hoffman, Gar. Ice Cream. LC 81-80744. 1981. pap. 7.95 (ISBN 0-89586-040-6). H P Bks.

ICE CRYSTALS

see also Snow Crystals

Fletcher, Neville H. Chemical Physics of Ice. LC 74-75825. (Monographs on Physics). (Illus.). 1970. 49.50 (ISBN 0-521-07597-1). Cambridge U Pr.
Riehl, N., et al, eds. Physics of Ice. LC 72-81281. 642p. 1969. 49.50x (ISBN 0-306-30412-0, Plenum Pr). Plenum Pub.

ICE ON RIVERS, LAKES, ETC.

Pivovarov, A. A. Thermal Conditions in Freezing Lakes & Rivers. Vilim, E., tr. from Rus. LC 73-12269. 136p. 1973. 42.95x (ISBN 0-470-69103-4). Halsted Pr.
--Thermal Conditions in Freezing Lakes & Rivers. LC 73-12269. 136p. 1973. 21.95 (ISBN 0-470-69103-4, Pub. by Wiley). Krieger.

ICES

see Ice Cream, Ices, etc.

ICHNEUMODIDAE

Bhat, Shama & Gupta, V. K. Ichneumonologia Orientalis, Pt. VI: The Subfamily Agathidinae (Hym: Braconidae) (Oriental Insects Monograph: No. 6). 1977. 45.00x (ISBN 0-318-01584-6). Oriental Insects.
Chandra, Girish & Gupta, V. K. Ichneumonologia Orientalis, Pt. VII: The Tribes Lissonotini & Banchini (Hym: Ichneumonidae) (Oriental Insects Monograph: No. 7). 1977. 45.00x (ISBN 0-318-01585-4). Oriental Insects.
Dasch, Clement E. Ichneumon-Flies of America North of Mexico: Pt. 8. Subfamily. Cremastinae Memoir 29. (Illus.). 702p. 1979. 50.00x (ISBN 0-686-40424-6). Am Entom Inst.
--Ichneumonidae of America North of Mexico: Pt. 5 Subfamily Diplazontinae. (Memoirs Ser: No. 3). (Illus.). 1964. 25.00x (ISBN 0-686-00422-1). Am Entom Inst.
Gauld, I. D. An Introduction to the Ichneumonidae of Australia. (Illus.). 420p. 1984. pap. 80.00x (ISBN 0-565-00896-X, Pub. by Brit Mus Nat Hist England). Sabbot-Natural Hist Bks.
Gupta, V. K. & Gupta, M. L. Ichneumonologia Orientalis, Pt. V: Genus Dusona Cameron (Hym: Ichneumonidae) (Oriental Insects Monographs: No. 8). 1977. 45.00x (ISBN 0-318-01583-8). Oriental Insects.
Gupta, V. K. & Maheshwary, Sharda. Ichneumonolgia Orientalis, Pt. IV: The Tribe Porizontini (Hym: Ichneumonidae) (Oriental Insects Monographs: No. 5). 1977. 45.00x (ISBN 0-318-01582-X). Oriental Insects.
Gupta, V. K. & Tikar, D. T. Ichneumonologia Orientalis, Pt. I: The Tribe Pimplini (Hym: Ichneumonidae) (Oriental Insects Monograph: No. 1). 1976. 45.00x (ISBN 0-318-01579-X). Oriental Insects.
Jonathan, J. K. & Gupta, V. K. Ichneumonologia Orientalis, Pt. III: The Gorypus Complex (Hym: Ichneumonidae) (Oriental Insects Monographs: No.3). 1973. 45.00x (ISBN 0-318-01580-3). Oriental Insects.
Kamath, M. K. & Gupta, V. K. Ichneumonologia Orientalis, Pt. II: The Tribe Rhyssini (Hym: Ichneumonidae) (Oriental Insects Monographs: No. 2). 1972. 45.00x (ISBN 0-318-01581-1). Oriental Insects.
Kaur, Raminder & Jonathan, J. K. Ichneumonologia Orientalis, Pt. VIII: The Tribe Phytodietini (Hym: Ichneumonidae) (Oriental Insects Monograph: No. 9). 1979. 45.00 (ISBN 0-318-01586-2). Oriental Insects.
Short, John. The Final Larval Instars of the Ichneumonidae. (Memoir Ser.: No. 25). (Illus.). 508p. 1978. 35.00 (ISBN 0-686-26663-3). Am Entom Inst.
Townes, Henry. The Genera of Ichneumonidae, Pt. 1, Ephialtinae To Agriotypinae. (Memoirs Ser: No. 11). (Illus.). 300p. 1969. 25.00x (ISBN 0-686-00418-3). Am Entom Inst.
--The Genera of Ichneumonidae, Pt. 2, Gelinae. (Memoirs Ser: No. 12). (Illus.). 537p. 1970. 40.00x (ISBN 0-686-00419-1). Am Entom Inst.
--The Genera of Ichneumonidae, Pt. 3, Lycorininae To Porizontinae. (Memoirs Ser: No. 13). (Illus.). 307p. 1970. 25.00x (ISBN 0-686-00420-5). Am Entom Inst.
--Genera of Ichneumonidae, Pt. 4, Cremastinae To Diplazontinae. (Memoirs Ser: No. 17). (Illus.). 372p. 1971. 35.00x (ISBN 0-686-01268-2). Am Entom Inst.
Townes, Henry & Gupta, Virendra K. Ichneumonidae of America North of Mexico: Pt. 4 Subfamily Gelinae, Tribe Hemigasterini. (Memoirs Ser: No. 2). (Illus.). 30.00x (ISBN 0-686-00421-3). Am Entom Inst.
Townes, Henry & Townes, Marjorie. Catalogue & Reclassification of the Neotropic Ichneumonidae. (Memoirs Ser: No. 8). 1966. 30.00x (ISBN 0-686-00416-7). Am Entom Inst.
Townes, Henry, et al. Catalogue & Reclassification of the Eastern Palearctic Ichneumonidae. (Memoirs Ser.: No. 5). 661p. 1965. 45.00x (ISBN 0-686-00414-0). Am Entom Inst.
--Catalogue & Reclassification of the Indo-Australian Ichneumonidae. (Memoirs Ser: No. 1). 522p. 1961. 35.00x (ISBN 0-686-00415-9). Am Entom Inst.

ICHTHYOLOGY

see Fishes

IDEALS (ALGEBRA)

Jategaonkar, A. V. Left Principal Ideal Rings. LC 74-114015. (Lecture Notes in Mathematics: Vol. 123). 1970. pap. 10.70 (ISBN 0-387-04912-6). Springer-Verlag.
Kaplansky, Irving. Commutative Rings. rev. ed. LC 74-5732. 192p. 1974. text ed. 12.00x (ISBN 0-226-42454-5). U of Chicago Pr.
Larsen, Max D. & McCarthy, Paul J. Multiplicative Theory of Ideals. (Pure & Applied Mathematics Ser.: Vol. 43). 1971. 68.00 (ISBN 0-12-436850-6). Acad Pr.
Reiner, I. Maximal Orders. (London Mathematical Society Monographs). 1975. 70.00 (ISBN 0-12-586650-X). Acad Pr.
Simon, Barry. Trace Ideals & Their Applications. LC 78-20867. (London Mathematical Society Lecture Notes Ser.: No. 35). 1979. pap. 21.95x (ISBN 0-521-22286-9). Cambridge U Pr.

IDENTIFICATION OF PLANTS

see Plants–Identification

IGNEOUS ROCKS

see Rocks, Igneous

IGNITION DEVICES

see Automobiles–Ignition

IGUANAS

see Lizards

ILLUMINATION

see Lighting

ILLUSTRATION, BIOLOGICAL
see Biological Illustration
ILLUSTRATION, SCIENTIFIC
see Scientific Illustration
ILLUSTRATION, TECHNICAL
see Technical Illustration
IMAGE CONVERTERS

Advances in Image Transmission II: Proceedings of the SPIE Annual Technical Symposium, 24th, San Diego, 1980. (SPIE Seminar Proceedings: Vol. 249). 212p. 39.00 (ISBN 0-89252-278-X); 31.00, members (ISBN 0-317-34582-6). SPIE.

Advances in Image Transmisson Techniques One: Proceedings of the SPIE Annual Technical Symposium, 20th, San Diego, 1976. (SPIE Seminar Proceedings: Vol. 87). 280p. 10.00 (ISBN 0-89252-114-7); members 8.00 (ISBN 0-317-34583-4). SPIE.

Aggarwal, J. K., et al, eds. Computer Methods in Image Analysis. LC 76-50335. 1977. pap. 24.90 (ISBN 0-87942-090-1, PP00919). Inst Electrical.

Applications of Electronic Imaging Systems: Proceedings of the SPIE Technical Symposium East, Washington, D.C., 1978. (SPIE Seminar Proceedings: Vol. 143). 194p. 21.00 (ISBN 0-89252-170-8); members 14.00 (ISBN 0-317-34595-8). SPIE.

Cardiovascular Imaging & Image Processing - Theory & Practice: Proceedings of the SPIE Seminar, Stanford, 1975. (SPIE Seminar Proceedings: Vol. 72). 374p. 21.00 (ISBN 0-89252-084-1); members 19.00 (ISBN 0-317-34607-5). SPIE.

Computerized Imaging Techniques: Proceedings of the SPIE Seminar, Washington, D.C., 1967. (SPIE Seminar Proceedings: Vol. 10). 212p. 29.00 (ISBN 0-89252-013-2); members 14.00 (ISBN 0-317-34611-3). SPIE.

Electronic Image Processing. (IEE Conference Publications Ser.: No. 214). 251p. 1982. pap. 64.00 (ISBN 0-85296-262-2, IC214). Inst Elect Eng.

Fu, K. S. & Pavlidis, T., eds. Biomedical Pattern Recognition & Image Processing. (Dahlem Workshop Reports-Life Sciences Reseach Report Ser.: No. 15). 443p. 1979. 33.80x (ISBN 0-89573-097-9). VCH Pubs.

Green, William B. Digital Image Processing: A Systems Approach. (Van Nostrand Reinhold Electrical-Computer Science & Engineering Ser.). (Illus.). 204p. 1982. 34.50 (ISBN 0-442-28801-8). Van Nos Reinhold.

Herman, G. T., ed. Image Reconstruction from Projections Implementation & Applications. LC 79-13823. (Topics in Applied Physics Ser.: Vol. 32). (Illus.). 1979. 59.00 (ISBN 0-387-09417-2). Springer-Verlag.

Hord, Michael. Digital Image Processing of Remotely Sensed Data. (Notes & Reports in Computer Science & Applied Mathematics Ser.). 221p. 1982. 29.50 (ISBN 0-12-355620-1). Acad Pr.

Image Information Recovery: Proceedings of the SPIE Seminar, Philadelphia, 1968. (SPIE Seminar Proceedings: Vol. 16). 170p. 29.00 (ISBN 0-317-34653-9); members 14.00 (ISBN 0-317-34654-7). SPIE.

Infrared Image Sensor Technology: Proceedings 1001 SPIE Technical Symposium East, Washington, D.C., 1980. (SPIE Seminar Proceedings: Vol. 225). 174p. 37.00 (ISBN 0-89252-254-2); members 30.00 (ISBN 0-317-34666-0). SPIE.

Kittler, J. & Duff, M. Image Processing System Architectures. (Pattern Recognition & Image Processing Research Studies). 1985. 34.95 (ISBN 0-471-90681-6). Wiley.

Shaw, Rodney, ed. Selected Readings in Image Evaluation. 509p. 1976. 45.00 (ISBN 0-317-34757-8); members 35.00 (ISBN 0-317-34758-6). SPIE.

IMAGE INTENSIFIERS
see also Electron Microscope; Image Converters; Television Picture Tubes

International Resource Development Inc. Electronic Imaging: The Impact on Traditional Photography Markets. 214p. 1984. 1650.00x (ISBN 0-88694-600-X). Intl Res Dev.

Jain, Anil K. Multidimensional Techniques in Digital Images Processing. 1986. cancelled (ISBN 0-442-24089-9). Van Nos Reinhold.

Kittler, J. & Duff, M. Image Processing System Architectures. (Pattern Recognition & Image Processing Research Studies). 1985. 34.95 (ISBN 0-471-90681-6). Wiley.

Machine-Aided Image Analysis 1978: Oxford. (Institute of Physics Conference Ser.: No. 44). 1979. 75.00 (ISBN 0-9960032-4-X, Pub. by Inst Physics England). Heyden.

Machine Perception of Patterns & Pictures: 1972. (Institute of Physics Conference Ser.: No. 13). 1972. 55.00 (ISBN 0-9960029-2-8, Pub. by Inst Physics England). Heyden.

Serra, Jean. Image Analysis & Mathematical Morphology. 1984. pap. 39.50 (ISBN 0-12-637242-X). Acad Pr.

Society of Photographic Scientists & Engineers Staff. Image Technology, Nineteen Eighty-Four: SPSE's 37th Annual Conference: Advanced Printing of Paper Abstracts, May 20-24, 1984, Park Plaza Hotel, Boston, Massachusetts. pap. 37.30 (ISBN 0-317-29119-X, 2025038). Bks Demand UMI.

Society of Photographic Scientists & Engineers. Image Technology, Nineteen Eighty-Three: SPSE's 36th Annual Conference, the Fairmont Hotel, San Francisco, CA, May 31-June 3, 1983: Advanced Printing of Paper Summaries. pap. 29.00 (ISBN 0-317-28764-8, 2020628). Bks Demand UMI.

Talmi, Yair, ed. Multichannel Image Detectors, Vol. 2. LC 79-12441. (ACS Symposium Ser.: No. 236). 332p. 1983. lib. bdg. 49.95x (ISBN 0-8412-0814-X). Am Chemical.

Ullman, Shimon & Richards, Whitman, eds. Image Understanding, 1984. (Illus.). 288p. 1984. text ed. 35.00 (ISBN 0-89391-254-9). Ablex Pub.

Watson, B. W., ed. Medical Imaging Techniques. (IEE Medical Electronics Monographs: No. 6). (Illus.). 1979. 52.00 (ISBN 0-906048-20-6). Inst Elect Eng.

IMAGING SYSTEMS

Ahsen, Akhter & Dolan, A. T., eds. Handbook of Imagery Research & Practice. LC 82-73889. 400p. (Orig.). 1985. pap. 45.00 (ISBN 0-913412-19-8). Brandon Hse.

Alais, Pierre & Metherell, Alexander F., eds. Acoustical Imaging, Vol. 10. LC 69-12533. 842p. 1981. 115.00x (ISBN 0-306-40725-6, Plenum Pr). Plenum Pub.

Andrews, Harry C. Computer Techniques in Image Processing. 1970. 44.00 (ISBN 0-12-058550-2). Acad Pr.

--Tutorial & Selected Papers in Digital Image Processing. 748p. 1978. 25.00 (ISBN 0-317-34769-1); 19.00, members (ISBN 0-317-34770-5). SPIE.

Applications of Digital Image Processing. Incl. No. I. Proceedings of the SPIE Annual Technical Symposium, 21st, San Diego, 1977. (SPIE Seminar Proceedings:: Vol. 119.). 320p. 22.00 (ISBN 0-89252-146-5); members 19.00 (ISBN 0-317-34591-5); No. II. Proceedings of the SPIE Annual Technical Symposium, 22nd, San Diego, 1978. (SPIE Seminar Proceedings:: Vol. 149.). 254p. 26.00 (ISBN 0-89252-176-7); members. 19.00 (ISBN 0-317-34592-3); No. III. Proceedings of the SPIE Annual Techenical Symposiun, 23rd, San Diego, 1979. (SPIE Seminar Proceedings:: Vol. 207.). 336p. 38.00 (ISBN 0-89252-235-6); members. 30.00 (ISBN 0-317-34593-1). SPIE.

Applications of Digital Image Processing to Astronomy: Proceedings. (SPIE Seminar Proceedings: Vol. 264). 314p. 35.00 (ISBN 0-89252-293-3); members 27.00 (ISBN 0-317-34594-X). SPIE.

Applied Machine Vision: Conference Proceedings. 300p. 1984. 50.00 (ISBN 0-87263-140-0, 812). SME.

Assessment of Imaging Systems I: Proceedings of the SPIE Seminar, London, 1976. (SPIE Seminar Proceedings: Vol. 98). 144p. 27.00 (ISBN 0-89252-125-2); members 19.00 (ISBN 0-317-34601-6). SPIE.

Automation & Inspection Applications of Image Processing Techniques: Proceedings. (SPIE Seminar Proceedings: Vol. 130). 112p. 27.00 (ISBN 0-89252-157-0); members 23.00 (ISBN 0-317-34603-2). SPIE.

Ballard, Dana H. & Brown, Christopher M. Computer Vision. (Illus.). 544p. 1982. text ed. 46.95 (ISBN 0-13-165316-4). P-H.

Baxes, Gary. Digital Image Processing. 1983. 22.95 (ISBN 0-13-214064-0, Spec); pap. 14.95 (ISBN 0-13-214056-X). P-H.

Beck, Jacob, et al, eds. Human & Machine Vision: Symposium. LC 83-9976. (Notes & Reports in Computer Science & Applied Mathematics Ser.). 1983. 47.00 (ISBN 0-12-084320-X). Acad Pr.

Bernstein, R., ed. Digital Image Processing for Remote Sensing. LC 77-94520. 1978. 49.85 (ISBN 0-87942-105-3, PC01024). Inst Electrical.

Bisconte, J. C. & Sklansky, J., eds. Biomedical Images & Computers: St. Pierre de Chartreuse, France 1980, Proceedings. (Lecture Notes in Medical Informatics: Vol. 17). 332p. 1982. pap. 23.00 (ISBN 0-387-11579-X). Springer-Verlag.

Bolc, L. & Kulpa, Z., eds. Digital Image Processing Systems: Proceedings. (Lecture Notes in Computer Science Ser.: Vol. 109). 353p. 1981. pap. 22.00 (ISBN 0-387-10705-3). Springer-Verlag.

Braddick, O. J. & Sleigh, A. C., eds. Physical & Biological Processing of Images: London, England, 1982, Proceedings. (Springer Series in Information Sciences: Vol. 11). (Illus.). 403p. 1983. 36.00 (ISBN 0-387-12108-0). Springer-Verlag.

Castleman, Kenneth R. Digital Image Processing. LC 78-27578. (Illus.). 1979. text ed. 44.95 (ISBN 0-13-212365-7). P-H.

Chang, Ning-San. Image Analysis & Image Database Management. Stone, Harold S., ed. LC 81-10406. (Computer Science: Artificial Intelligence Ser.: No. 9). 154p. 1981. 34.95 (ISBN 0-8357-1217-6). UMI Res Pr.

Chellappa, Rama & Sawchuk, Alexander. Tutorial: Digital Image Processing & Analysis, 2 vols. Incl. Vol. 2. Digital Image Analysis. 66.00 (ISBN 0-8186-0666-5); prepub. 32.95 (ISBN 0-317-31786-5); Vol. 1. Digital Image Processing. Set. 132.00 (ISBN 0-317-31784-9); prepub. 72.00 (ISBN 0-317-31785-7). IEEE Comp Soc.

Cottrall, M. B. Fundamentals of Clinical Radionuclide Imaging. 1982. 25.00x (ISBN 0-686-92013-9, Pub. by Brit Inst Radiology England). State Mutual Bk.

Coulam, Craig M., ed. Physical Basis of Medical Imaging. (Illus.). 416p. 1981. 62.00 (ISBN 0-8385-7844-6). ACC.

Duff, M. J. & Leviadi, S., eds. Languages & Architectures for Image Processing. LC 81-67909. 1981. 49.50 (ISBN 0-12-223320-4). Acad Pr.

Duff, Michael J., ed. Computing Structures for Image Processing. 1983. 33.00 (ISBN 0-12-223340-9). Acad Pr.

Easton, Edward J. Magnetic Resonance Imaging. LC 85-61596. 175p. Date not set. 49.50 (ISBN 0-943432-54-5). Slack Inc.

Ekstrom, Michael P., ed. Digital Image Processing Techniques. LC 83-22321. (Computer Techniques Ser.). 1984. 49.50 (ISBN 0-12-236760-X). Acad Pr.

Esser, Peter, et al, eds. Digital Imaging: Clinical Advances in Nuclear Medicine. LC 82-16941. (Illus.). 304p. 1983. 37.50 (ISBN 0-932004-13-X). Soc Nuclear Med.

Faugeras, O. D. Fundamentals in Computer Vision. LC 82-14624. 500p. 1983. 42.50 (ISBN 0-521-25099-4). Cambridge U Pr.

Fu, K. S., ed. VLSI for Pattern Recognition & Image Processing. (Springer Series in Information Sciences: Vol. 13). (Illus.). 255p. 1984. 23.00 (ISBN 0-387-13268-6). Springer-Verlag.

Goris, Michael L. & Briandet, Philippe A. A Clinical & Mathematical Introduction to Computer Processing of Scintigraphic Images. (Illus.). 308p. 1983. text ed. 77.00 (ISBN 0-89004-766-9). Raven.

Gray. Quality Control in Diagnostic Imaging. (Illus.). 264p. 1982. text ed. 38.00 (ISBN 0-8391-1681-0). Univ Park.

Green, William B. Digital Image Processing: A Systems Approach. (Van Nostrand Reinhold Electrical-Computer Science & Engineering Ser.). (Illus.). 204p. 1982. 34.50 (ISBN 0-442-28801-8). Van Nos Reinhold.

Hall, Ernest L. Computer Image Processing & Recognition. (Computer Science & Applied Mathematics Ser.). 1979. 36.50 (ISBN 0-12-318850-4). Acad Pr.

Hamilton, Betty, ed. Medical Diagnostic Imaging Systems: Technology & Applications. (Health Care Economics & Technology Ser.). (Illus.). 230p. 1982. 39.50 (ISBN 0-86621-003-2). F&S Pr.

Haralick, R. M., ed. Pictorial Data Analysis. (NATO ASI Series F: Computer & Systems Sciences, No. 4). 480p. 1983. 49.70 (ISBN 0-387-12288-5). Springer-Verlag.

Hawkes, P. W., ed. Computer Processing of Electron Microscope Images. (Topics in Current Physics: Vol. 13). (Illus.). 300p. 1980. 40.00 (ISBN 0-387-09622-1). Springer-Verlag.

Hildreth, Ellen C. The Measurement of Visual Motion. (ACM Distinguished Dissertation Ser.). (Illus.). 190p. 1984. text ed. 32.50 (ISBN 0-262-08143-1). MIT Pr.

Hoehne, K. H., ed. Digital Image Processing in Medicine: Proceedings. (Lecture Notes in Medical Informatics Ser.: Vol. 15). 197p. 1981. pap. 21.00 (ISBN 0-387-10877-7). Springer-Verlag.

Hralick, R. M. & Simon, J. C., eds. Issues in Digital Image Processing. LC 80-50682. (NATO Advanced Study Institute Ser.: No. 34). 356p. 1980. 40.75x (ISBN 90-286-0460-X). Sijthoff & Noordhoff.

Huang, T. S. Picture Processing & Digital Filtering. LC 75-5770. (Illus.). 270p. 1979. 26.00 (ISBN 0-387-09339-7). Springer-Verlag.

Huang, Thomas S., ed. Advances in Computer & Image Processing, Vol. 1. 350p. 1983. 57.50 (ISBN 0-89232-280-2). Jai Pr.

Image Processing Computers & Systems. 186p. 1983. 985.00. Intl Res Dev.

Imaging Spectroscopy: Proceedings of the SPIE Technical Symposium, Los Angeles, 1981. (SPIE Seminar Proceedings: Vol. 268). 208p. 40.00 (ISBN 0-89252-300-X); members 34.00 (ISBN 0-317-34656-3). SPIE.

Imaging Through the Atmosphere: Proceedings of the SPIE-SPSE Technical Symposium East, Reston, VA, 1976. (SPIE Seminar Proceedings: Vol. 75). 176p. 17.00 (ISBN 0-89252-102-3); members 12.00 (ISBN 0-317-34657-1). SPIE.

Imaging X-Ray Optics Workshop: Proceedings of the SPIE Technical Symposium, Huntsville, 1979. (SPIE Seminar Proceedings: Vol. 184). 302p. 32.00 (ISBN 0-89252-212-7); members 24.00 (ISBN 0-317-34658-X). SPIE.

Infrared Imaging Systems Technology: Proceedings 1001 SPIE Technical Symposium East, Washington, D.C., 1980. (SPIE Seminar Proceedings: Vol. 226). 166p. 37.00 (ISBN 0-89252-255-0); members 30.00 (ISBN 0-317-34667-9). SPIE.

International Conference on Low Light & Thermal Imaging Systems, London, 1975. Low Light & Thermal Imaging Systems: March 3-5, 1975. (Institution of Electrical Engineers Conference Publication Ser.: No. 124). pap. 61.00 (ISBN 0-317-10166-8, 2012130). Bks Demand UMI.

International Symposium on Acoustical Imaging, et al. Acoustical Imaging: Proceedings of the International Symposium on Acoustical Imaging, 13th, Minneapolis, Minn., Oct. 26-28, 1984, Vol. 13. Kaveh, M., et al, eds. 576p. 1984. 89.50x (ISBN 0-306-41717-0, Plenum Pr). Plenum Pub.

Jackson, Daphne F. Imaging with Non-Ionizing Radiations. (Progress in Medical & Environmental Physics Ser.: Vol. 2). (Illus.). 240p. 1983. text ed. 58.00x (ISBN 0-911378-46-4, Pub. by Surrey Univ Pr UK). Sheridan.

Johansen, Peter & Becker, Peter W., eds. Third Scandinavian Conference on Image Analysis: Proceedings. 426p. (Orig.). 1983. pap. text ed. 29.95x (ISBN 0-86238-039-1, Pub. by Chartwell-Bratt England). Brookfield Pub Co.

Kak, A. C. & Slaney, M. Tomographic Imaging with Non-Diffracting & Diffracting Sources. 200p. 1985. avail. (ISBN 0-87942-198-3). IEEE.

--Tomographic Imaging with Non-Diffracting & Diffracting Sources. 200p. 1985. write for info. (ISBN 0-87942-198-3). Inst Electrical.

Kazam, Benjamin, ed. Advances in Image Pickup & Display, Vol. 5. 298p. 1982. 59.95 (ISBN 0-12-022105-5). Acad Pr.

Kazan, Benjamin, ed. Advances in Image Pickup & Display, Vol. 6. (Serial Publication Ser.). 1983. 66.00 (ISBN 0-12-022106-3). Acad Pr.

Kim, E. E. & Haynie, T. P. Nuclear Imaging in Oncology. 256p. 1984. 52.50 (ISBN 0-8385-6973-0). ACC.

Klinger, E., ed. Imagery: Concepts, Results, & Applications, Vol. 2. LC 81-8680. 410p. 1981. 39.50x (ISBN 0-306-40748-5, Plenum Pr). Plenum Pub.

Kouris, K., et al. Imaging with Ionizing Radiations. (Progress in Medical & Environmental Physics Ser.: Vol. 1). (Illus.). 204p. 1982. text ed. 55.00x (ISBN 0-903384-30-2, Pub. by Surrey Univ Pr UK). Sheridan.

Lalli, A. F. Tailored Urologic Imaging. 1981. 51.95 (ISBN 0-8151-5276-0). Year Bk Med.

Larsen, L. E., ed. Electromagnetic Imaging of Biological Systems. 200p. 1985. avail. (ISBN 0-87942-196-7). IEEE.

--Electromagnetic Imaging of Biological Systems. 200p. 1985. write for info. (ISBN 0-87942-196-7). Inst Electrical.

Lawrence, V. B. & LoCicero, J. L., eds. IEEE Communications Society's Tutorials in Modern Communication. LC 82-10599. 348p. 1982. text ed. 36.95 (ISBN 0-914894-48-X). Computer Sci.

Leach, K. G. The Physical Aspects of Radioisotopic Organ Imaging. 1976. 25.00x (ISBN 0-686-99803-0, Pub. by Brit Inst Radiology England). State Mutual Bk.

Lee, Hua & Wade, Glen, eds. Imaging Technology. 300p. 1985. avail. (ISBN 0-87942-199-1). IEEE.

--Imaging Technology. (Reprint Ser.). 300p. 1985. write for info. (ISBN 0-87942-199-1). Inst Electrical.

Levasldi, S. Digital Image Analysis. 392p. 1984. pap. text ed. 36.95 (ISBN 0-273-08616-2). Pitman Pub MA.

Levialdi, S., ed. Parallel Integrated Technology for Image Processing. 1985. 39.50 (ISBN 0-12-444820-8). Acad Pr.

Machine Vision for Robotics & Automated Inspection: Technical Report for Engineers & Managers, 3 Vols. Incl. Vol. 1. Fundamentals; Vol. 2. Applications; Vol. 3. Manufacturers-Systems. 1984. Set. 185.00 (ISBN 0-89671-046-7). SEAI Tech Pubns.

Marks, David F. Theories of Image Formation. 1985. lib. bdg. 45.00 (ISBN 0-913412-18-X). Brandon Hse.

Musha, T., et al, eds. Noise & Clutter Rejection in Radars & Imaging Sensors, 1984: Proceedings of the 1984 International Symposium Held in Tokyo, Japan, October 22-24, 1984. 750p. 1985. 125.00 (ISBN 0-444-87674-X, North-Holland). Elsevier.

Onoe, Morio, et al, eds. Real-Time Medical Image Processing. LC 80-23779. 257p. 1980. 45.00x (ISBN 0-306-40551-2, Plenum Pr). Plenum Pub.

--Real-Time-Parallel Computing: Imaging Analysis. LC 80-28025. 424p. 1981. 59.50x (ISBN 0-306-40639-X, Plenum Pr). Plenum Pub.
Partain, Leon C., ed. Nuclear Magnetic Resonance & Correlative Imaging Modalities. 312p. (Orig.). 1984. text ed. 49.50 (ISBN 0-932004-17-2). Soc Nuclear Med.
Pau, L. F. & Nahas, M. Y. El. An Introduction to Infrared Image Acquistion & Classification Systems. 268p. 1983. 61.95x (ISBN 0-471-90151-2, Pub. by Wiley-Interscience). Wiley.
Pratt, William K. Digital Image Processing. LC 77-20888. 750p. 1978. 61.95 (ISBN 0-471-01888-0, Pub. by Wiley-Interscience). Wiley.
Preston, Kendall, et al, eds. Medical Imaging Techniques: A Comparison. LC 79-4424. 396p. 1979. 59.50x (ISBN 0-306-40161-4, Plenum Pr). Plenum Pub.
Preston, Kendall, Jr. & Uhr, Leonard, eds. Multicomputers & Image Processing: Algorithms & Programs; Based on a Symposium held in Madison, Wisc., May 26-29, 1981. LC 82-1623. (Notes & Reports in Computer Science & Applied Mathematics Ser.). 1982. 47.50 (ISBN 0-12-564480-9). Acad Pr.
Proceedings of the First Scandinavian Conference on Image Analysis. 388p. 1980. pap. text ed. 29.95x (ISBN 0-86238-001-4, Pub. by Chartwell-Bratt England). Brookfield Pub Co.
Reba, Richard & Goodenough, David J. Diagnostic Imaging Medicine. 1983. 87.00 (ISBN 90-247-2798-7, Pub. by Martinus Nijhoff Netherlands). Kluwer Academic.
Recent & Future Developments in Medical Imaging I: Proceedings of the SPIE Annual Technical Symposium, 22nd, San Diego, 1978. (SPIE Seminar Proceedings: Vol. 152). 142p. 19.00 (ISBN 0-89252-179-1); 11.00, members (ISBN 0-317-34751-9). SPIE.
Recent & Future Developments in Medical Imaging II: Proceedings of the SPIE Annual Technical Symposium, 23rd, San Diego, 1979. (SPIE Seminar Proceedings: Vol. 206). 268p. 38.00 (ISBN 0-89252-234-8); 30.00, members (ISBN 0-317-34752-7). SPIE.
Roberts, J. A., ed. Indirect Imaging: Measurement & Processing. LC 83-26348. 464p. 1984. 54.50 (ISBN 0-521-26282-8). Cambridge U Pr.
Ronse, Christian & Devijver, Pierre A. Connected Components in Binary Images: The Detection Problem. LC 84-3312. (Pattern Recognition & Image Processing Research Studies (1-516)). 165p. 1984. 44.95x (ISBN 0-471-90456-2, Pub.by Res Stud Pr). Wiley.
Rosenfeld, A., ed. Multiresolution Image Processing & Analysis. (Springer Series in Information Sciences: Vol. 12). (Illus.). 400p. 1984. 32.00 (ISBN 0-387-13006-3). Springer Verlag.
Rosenfeld, Azriel, ed. Image Modeling. LC 81-3562. 1981. 35.00 (ISBN 0-12-597320-9). Acad Pr.
Rosenthal, David A. An Inquiry Driven Vision System Based on Visual & Conceptual Hierarchies. Stone, Harold, ed. LC 81-7616. (Computer Science Ser.: Artificial Intelligence: No. 7). 198p. 1981. 39.95 (ISBN 0-8357-1214-1). UMI Res Pr.
Saxton, W. O. & Cavendish Laboratory, Electron Microscopy Section. Computer Techniques for Image Processing in Electron Microscopy: Supplement 10 to Advances in Electronics & Electron Physics. 1978. 70.00 (ISBN 0-12-014570-7). Acad Pr.
Schowengerdt, Robert A. Techniques for Image Processing & Classification in Remote Sensing. LC 83-11769. 272p. 1983. 29.00 (ISBN 0-12-628980-8). Acad Pr.
Simon, J. C. & Haralick, R. M., eds. Digital Image Processing. 608p. 1982. 69.50 (ISBN 90-277-1329-4, Pub. by Reidel Holland). Kluwer Academic.
Simon, J. C. & Rosenfeld, A., eds. Digital Image Processing & Analysis, No.22. (NATO Advanced Study, Applied Science Ser.). 524p. 1978. 47.50x (ISBN 90-286-0467-7). Sijthoff & Noordhoff.
Society of Photographic Scientists & Engineers. Image Analysis Techniques & Applications Technical Digest. Slater, Philip N. & Wagner, Robert F., eds. pap. 45.80 (ISBN 0-317-11058-6, 2015860). Bks Demand UMI.
--Unconventional Imaging, Science & Technology: Advanced Printing of Paper Summaries, the 22nd Fall Symposium, November 15-18, 1982, Key Bridge Marriott Hotel, Arlington, Virginia. pap. 21.50 (ISBN 0-317-29897-6, 2019357). Bks Demand UMI.
Steinberg, Bernard D. Microwave Imaging with Large Antenna Arrays: Radio Camera Principles & Techniques. LC 83-6705. 269p. 1983. 39.95x (ISBN 0-471-89173-8, Pub. by Wiley-Interscience). Wiley.
Stoffel, J. C. Graphical & Binary Image Processing. (Illus.). 350p. 1982. pap. 39.00 (ISBN 0-89006-111-4). Artech Hse.
Stucki, P., ed. Advances in Digital Image Processing: Theory, Application, Implementation. LC 79-21443. (IBM Research Symposia Ser.). 1979. 55.00x (ISBN 0-306-40314-5, Plenum Pr). Plenum Pub.
Sutton, David. Textbook of Radiology & Imaging. 3rd ed. 1981. text ed. 149.00 i vol. set (ISBN 0-443-01700-X); text ed. 175.00 2 vol. set (ISBN 0-443-02371-9). Churchill.
Tanimoto, S. & Klinger, A., eds. Structured Computer Vision: Machine Perception Through Hierarchical Computation Structures. LC 80-14878. 1980. 29.50 (ISBN 0-12-683280-3). Acad Pr.
Trends in Optical & Video Disks. (Special Interest Packages Ser.). pap. 23.00 (ISBN 0-317-06201-8, PO23); pap. 18.00 member. Assn Inform & Image Mgmt.
Twogood, Richard. Image Processing with Minicomputers. 1986. price not set (ISBN 0-442-21199-6). Van Nos Reinhold.
Wells, P. N., ed. Scientific Basis of Medical Imaging. (Illus.). 284p. 1982. text ed. 55.00 (ISBN 0-443-01986-X). Churchill.

IMAGING SYSTEMS IN MEDICINE

Bragg, D. G., et al, eds. Oncologic Imaging. (Illus.). 650p. 1985. 95.00 (ISBN 0-08-031967-X). Pergamon.
Buda, Andrew J. & Delp, Edward J., eds. Digital Cardiac Imaging. 1985. lib. bdg. 60.00 (ISBN 0-89838-697-7, Pub. by Martinus Nijhoff Netherlands). Kluwer Academic.
Capp, M. Paul. Digital Radiographic Imaging. (Illus.). 500p. Date not set. price not set (ISBN 0-7216-1117-6). Saunders.
Finlay, David, et al. MOQ's in Imaging Sciences. 128p. 1982. pap. 9.95 (ISBN 0-7216-0806-X, Pub. by Bailliere-Tindall). Saunders.
Friedman, William F. & Higgins, Charles B. Pediatric Cardiac Imaging. (Illus.). 350p. 1984. 40.00 (ISBN 0-7216-1287-3). Saunders.
Gerstenbrand, F., et al. Neuroimaging. (Illus.). 327p. 1985. pap. 49.00 (ISBN 3-437109-41-3, Pub. by Gustav Fisher Verlag). VCH Pubs.
Goodman, Lawrence R. & Putnam, Charles E. Intensive Care Radiology: Imaging of the Critically Ill. 2nd ed. (Saunders Monographs in Clinical Radiology: Vol. 20). (Illus.). 352p. 1983. 47.50 (ISBN 0-7216-4166-0). Saunders.
Hillman, Bruce J. Imaging & Hypertension. (Saunders Monographs in Clinical Radiology: Vol. 22). (Illus.). 192p. 1983. 42.95 (ISBN 0-7216-4678-6). Saunders.
Kelley, Michael J., et al. Cardiac Imaging in Infants & Children. (Saunders Monographs in Clinical Radiology: Vol. 18). (Illus.). 464p. 1982. 52.00 (ISBN 0-7216-5361-8). Saunders.
Kovac, Alexander & Haddad, Farid. Guide to Diagnostic Imaging: Lower Urinary & Male Genital Tract, Vol. 5. 1984. pap. text ed. write for info (ISBN 0-87488-418-7). Med Exam.
Mancuso, Anthony & Hanafee, William. Computed Tomography & Magnetic Resonance Imaging of the Head & Neck. 2nd ed. 436p. 1985. 84.75 (ISBN 0-683-05476-7). Williams & Wilkins.
Medical Electronic Imaging. 1985. write for info. (ISBN 0-86621-663-4). Frost & Sullivan.
Meschan, Isadore. Roentgen Signs in Diagnostic Imaging: Abdomen, Vol. 1. 2nd ed. (Illus.). 992p. 1984. 85.00 (ISBN 0-7216-6302-8). Saunders.
Meschan, Isadore & Ott, David J. Introduction to Diagnostic Imaging. (Illus.). 416p. 1984. 24.95 (ISBN 0-7216-6277-3). Saunders.
Nalcioglu, O. & Cho, Z. H., eds. Selected Topics in Image Science. (Lecture Notes in Medical Informatics: Vol. 23). ix, 308p. 1984. 27.50 (ISBN 0-387-12898-0). Springer-Verlag.
Partain, C. Leon, et al. Nuclear Magnetic Resonance (NMR) Imaging. (Illus.). 592p. 1983. 79.50 (ISBN 0-7216-7098-9). Saunders.
Penning, L. & Thijn, C. J. Liber Amicorum Presented to Prof. Dr. J. R. Blickman. (Journal: Diagnostic Imaging in Clinical Medicine: Vol. 53, No. 4). (Illus.). 56p. 1984. 18.75 (ISBN 3-8055-3934-7). S Karger.
Powers, Thomas A. & James, A. Everette. Nuclear Imaging. 2nd ed. (Exercises in Diagnostic Radiology Ser.: Vol. 6). (Illus.). 250p. 1984. 18.95 (ISBN 0-7216-5109-7). Saunders.
Robb, Robert. Three-Dimensional Biomedical Imaging, Vol. I & II. 1985. Vol. I, 184 pp. 55.00 (ISBN 0-8493-5264-9); Vol. II, 160 pp. 63.00 (ISBN 0-8493-5265-7). CRC Pr.
Seeram, Euclid. X-Ray Imaging Equipment: An Introduction. (Illus.). 610p. 1985. 44.50x (ISBN 0-398-05078-3). C C Thomas.
Sideman, Samuel & Beyar, Rafael, eds. Simulation & Imaging of the Cardiac System. (Developments in Cardiovascular Medicine Ser.). 1985. lib. bdg. 75.00 (ISBN 0-89838-687-X, Pub. by Martinus Nijhoff Netherlands). Kluwer Academic.
Sprawls, Perry. Physical Principles of Medical Imaging. 1985. pap. text ed. 38.00 (ISBN 0-8391-2057-5, 21695). Univ Park.

IMBEDDINGS, TOPOLOGICAL

see Topological Imbeddings

IMIDOYL HALIDES

Ulrich, Henri. Chemistry of Imidoyl Halides. LC 68-26773. 238p. 1968. 35.00x (ISBN 0-306-30353-1, Plenum Pr). Plenum Pub.

IMINES

see also Polyamines

Patai, Saul. The Chemistry of Amidines & Imidates. LC 75-6913. (Chemistry of Functional Groups Ser.). 677p. 1976. 155.95 (ISBN 0-471-66923-7, Pub by Wiley-Interscience). Wiley.

IMMUNITY (PLANTS)

see Plants–Disease and Pest Resistance

IMMUNOCHEMISTRY

Boguslaski, Robert C., et al, eds. Clinical Immunochemistry: Principles of Methods & Applications. 296p. 1984. text ed. 39.50 (ISBN 0-316-10087-0). Little.
Bullock, G. R. & Petrusz, P., eds. Techniques in Immunocytochemistry, Vol. 1. 1982. 55.00 (ISBN 0-12-140401-3). Acad Pr.
Bullock, Gillian R. & Petrusz, Peter. Techniques in Immunocytochemistry, Vol. 3. Date not set. 46.00 (ISBN 0-12-140403-X). Acad Pr.
Cantor, Harvey, et al. Regulation of the Immune System. (UCLA Symposium on Molecular & Cellular Biology, New Ser.: Vol. 18). 1008p. 1984. 160.50 (ISBN 0-8451-2617-2). A R Liss.
Colowick, Sidney P. & Kaplan, Nathan O., eds. Methods in Enzymology: Immunochemical Techniques, Conventional Antibodies, FC Receptors & Cytotoxicity, Vol. 93, Pt. F. 393p. 1983. 55.00 (ISBN 0-12-181993-0). Acad Pr.
--Methods in Enzymology: Monoclonal Antibodies & General Immonoassay Methods, Vol. 92, Pt. E. 1983. 69.50 (ISBN 0-12-181992-2). Acad Pr.
Cuello, A. C., ed. Immunohistochemistry. (IBRO Handbook Ser.: Methods in the Neurosciences). 501p. 1983. 95.00 (ISBN 0-471-10245-8, Pub. by Wiley-Interscience); pap. 39.95 498p (ISBN 0-471-90052-4). Wiley.
DeLellis, Ronald A., ed. Advances in Immunohistochemistry. (Monographs in Diagnostic Pathology: Vol. 7). (Illus.). 384p. 1984. 69.50 (ISBN 0-89352-215-5). Masson Pub.
Glynn, L. E. & Steward, M. W. Immunochemistry: An Advanced Textbook. LC 77-1630. 628p. 1977. 149.95x (ISBN 0-471-99508-8, Pub. by Wiley-Interscience). Wiley.
Glynn, L. E. & Steward, M. W., eds. Immunochemistry: An Advanced Textbook. LC 77-1630. pap. text ed. 159.50 (ISBN 0-317-28975-6, 2052064). Bks Demand UMI.
Griscelli, C. & Vossen, J. Progress in Immunodeficiency Research & Therapy, Vol. 1. (International Congress Ser.: Vol. 645). 1984. 94.50 (ISBN 0-444-80602-4). Elsevier.
Kabat, Elvin A. Experimental Immunochemistry. 2nd ed. (Illus.). 920p. 1971. photocopy ed. 90.50x (ISBN 0-398-00956-2). C C Thomas.
Kuhlmann, Wolf D., ed. Immuno Enzyme Techniques in Cytochemistry. 170p. 1984. text ed. 56.90x (ISBN 0-89573-071-5). VCH Pubs.
Kwapinski, George. The Methodology of Investigative & Clinical Immunology. LC 78-26882. 528p. 1982. text ed. 42.50 (ISBN 0-88275-828-4). Krieger.
McGhee, Jerry R. & Mestecky, Jiri, eds. Secretory Immune System. 1983. 175.00x (ISBN 0-89766-210-5); pap. 175.00x (ISBN 0-89766-211-3, VOL. 409). NY Acad Sci.
Najjar, V. A. Immunologically Active Peptides. 1982. lib. bdg. 55.00 (ISBN 90-6193-842-2, Pub by Junk Pubs Netherlands). Kluwer Academic.
Penn, Gerald M. Resolution of Monoclonal Gammopathy Problems by Electrophoresis & Associated Immunonchemical Techniques. LC 82-720308. (Illus.). 52p. 1982. includes slides & tape 40.00 (ISBN 0-89189-166-8, 21-2-002-07); monograph only 10.00 (ISBN 0-89189-183-8, 21-2-007-00). Am Soc Clinical.
Polak & Van Noorden. Immunocytochemistry. 2nd ed. 1986. price not set. PSG Pub Co.
Polak, J. M. & Varndel, I. M. Immunolabelling for Electron Microscopy. 1984. 49.50 (ISBN 0-444-80563-X, I-431-84). Elsevier.
Polak, Julia M. & Van Noorden, Susan. An Introduction to Immunocytochemistry: Current Techniques & Problems. (Royal Microscopical Society Microscopy Handbooks Ser.). (Illus.). 1984. pap. 7.95x (ISBN 0-19-856411-2). Oxford U Pr.
Porter, R. R. Chemical Aspects of Immunology. Head, J. J., ed. LC 76-28269. (Carolina Biology Readers Ser.). (Illus.). 16p. 1976. pap. 1.60 (ISBN 0-89278-285-4, 45-9685). Carolina Biological.
Sternberger, Ludwig A. Immunocytochemistry. 512p. Date not set. 60.00 (ISBN 0-471-86721-7). Wiley.
Van Regenmortal, M. H. Serology & Immunochemistry of Plant Viruses. LC 81-17631. 1982. 47.00 (ISBN 0-12-714180-4). Acad Pr.
Williams, Curtis A. & Chase, Merrill W., eds. Methods in Immunology & Immunochemistry, 5 vols. Vol. 1. 1968. 77.50 (ISBN 0-12-754401-1); Vol. 2. 1968. 77.50 (ISBN 0-12-754402-X); Vol. 3. 1971. 77.50 (ISBN 0-12-754403-8); Vol. 4 1977. 77.50 (ISBN 0-12-754404-6); Vol. 5 1976. 77.50 (ISBN 0-12-754405-4). Acad Pr.

IMMUNOELECTROPHORESIS

Osterman, L. A. Methods of Protein & Nucleic Acid Research: Immunoelectrophoresis - Application of Radioisotopes. (Illus.). 220p. 1984. 38.00 (ISBN 0-387-13094-2). Springer-Verlag.
Penn, Gerald M. Resolution of Monoclonal Gammopathy Problems by Electrophoresis & Associated Immunonchemical Techniques. LC 82-720308. (Illus.). 52p. 1982. includes slides & tape 40.00 (ISBN 0-89189-166-8, 21-2-002-07); monograph only 10.00 (ISBN 0-89189-183-8, 21-2-007-00). Am Soc Clinical.

IMMUNOGLOBULINS

see also Antigens; Fluorescent Antibody Technique

August, J. T., ed. Monoclonal Antibodies in Drug Development. (Illus.). 237p. (Orig.). 1982. lexitone 24.00 (ISBN 0-9609094-0-0). Am Phar & Ex.
Battisto, J. R. & Knight, K. L. Immunoglobulin Genes & B Cell Differentiation. (Developments in Immunology Ser.: Vol. 12). 212p. 1980. 61.00 (ISBN 0-444-00580-3). Elsevier.
Bizollon, C. A., ed. Monoclonal Antibodies & New Trends in Immunoassays: Proceedings of the 6th International Symposium on Radioimmunology Held in Lyon, France, 12-14 April, 1984. 310p. 1984. 59.25 (ISBN 0-444-80619-9). Elsevier.
Bona, Constantin A. & Kohler, Heinz, eds. Immune Networks, Vol. 418. 80.00x (ISBN 0-89766-230-X); pap. 80.00x (ISBN 0-89766-231-8). NY Acad Sci.
Campbell, A. M. Monoclonal Antibody Technology: Production & Characterization of Rodent & Human Hybridomas. (Laboratory Techniques in Biochemistry & Molecular Biology Ser.: Vol. 13). 1984. pap. 25.75 (ISBN 0-444-80575-3). Elsevier.
Colowick, Sidney P. & Kaplan, Nathan O., eds. Methods in Enzymology: Immunochemical Techniques, Conventional Antibodies, FC Receptors & Cytotoxicity, Vol. 93, Pt. F. 393p. 1983. 55.00 (ISBN 0-12-181993-0). Acad Pr.
Fellows, Robert & Eisenbarth, George, eds. Monoclonal Antibodies in Endocrine Research. 212p. 1981. text ed. 34.00 (ISBN 0-89004-687-5). Raven.
Hammerling, G. L., et al, eds. Monoclonal Antibodies & T-Cell Hybridomas: Perspectives & Technical Notes. (Research Monographs in Immunology: Vol. 3). 588p. 1982. 107.75 (ISBN 0-444-80351-3, Biomedical Pr). Elsevier.
Haynes, Barton F. & Eisenbarth, George S., eds. Monoclonal Antibodies: Probes for the Study of Autoimmmunity & Immunodeficiency. LC 83-3909. 1983. 49.50 (ISBN 0-12-334880-3). Acad Pr.
Hennessen, W., ed. Monoclonal Antibodies: Standardization of Their Characteristization & Use. (Developments in Biological Standardization: Vol. 57). (Illus.). xii, 430p. 1985. pap. 51.25 (ISBN 3-8055-3971-1). S Karger.
Janeway, Charles, et al. Immunoglobulin Idiotypes. LC 81-12895. (ICN-UCLA Symposia on Molecular & Cellular Biology Ser.: Vol. 20). 1981. 65.00 (ISBN 0-12-380380-2). Acad Pr.
Katz, David H., ed. Monoclonal Antibodies & T Cell Products. 184p. 1982. 68.50 (ISBN 0-8493-6580-5). CRC Pr.
Kennett, Roger H., et al, eds. Monoclonal Antibodies & Functional Cell Lines: Progress & Applications, Vol. 1. 444p. 1984. 49.50x (ISBN 0-306-41567-4, Plenum Pr). Plenum Pub.
Koenig, U. D. & Thrun, A., eds. Immunglobine in der Therapie. (Illus.). viii, 96p. 1985. 14.25 (ISBN 3-8055-4048-5). S Karger.
Kohler, Heinz, et al. Idiotypy in Biology & Medicine. 1984. 78.00 (ISBN 0-12-417780-8). Acad Pr.
Marchalonis, J. J. & Warr, G. W. Antibody as Tool: The Applications of Immunochemistry. 568p. 1982. 64.95x (ISBN 0-471-10084-6). Wiley.
Melchers, F. & Potter, M., eds. Lymphocyte Hybridomas: Second Workshop on "Functional Properties of Tumors of T & B Lymphocytes" Sponsored by the National Cancer Institute (NIH) April 3-5, 1978, Bethesda, MD, USA. (Current Topics in Microbiology & Immunology: Vol. 81). (Illus.). 1978. 35.00 (ISBN 0-387-08810-5). Springer-Verlag.

Milgrom, F., et al, eds. Antibodies: Protective, Destructive & Regulatory Role: Ninth International Convocation on Immunology, Amherst, N.Y., June 1984. (Illus.). xiv, 462p. 1985. 159.75 (ISBN 3-8055-3990-8). S Karger.

Ritzmann, Stephan E., ed. Pathology of Immunoglobulins: Diagnostic & Clinical Aspects. LC 82-18021. (Protein Abnormalities Ser.: Vol. 2). 408p. 1982. 38.00 (ISBN 0-8451-2801-9). A R Liss.

Ritzmann, Stephen E., ed. Physiology of Immunoglobulins: Diagnostic & Clinical Aspects. LC 82-13101. (Protein Abornormalities Ser.: Vol. 1). 376p. 1982. 38.00 (ISBN 0-8451-2800-0). A R Liss.

Schmidt, R. E. & Stroehmann, I., eds. Immunglobulintherapie. (Beitraege zu Infusionstherapie und klinische Ernaehrung: Vol. 11). viii, 96p. 1983. pap. 10.75 (ISBN 3-8055-3660-7). S Karger.

Seiler, F. R. & Geursen, R. G., eds. Sieben S-Immunglobulin zur intravenoesen Anwendung. (Beitraege zu Infusionstherapie und klinische Ernaehrung: Vol. 9). (Illus.). viii, 176p. 1982. pap. 21.50 (ISBN 3-8055-3632-1). S Karger.

Sikora, Karol & Smedley, Howard. Monoclonal Antibodies. (Illus.). 146p. 1984. pap. text ed. 13.00x (ISBN 0-632-01166-1). Blackwell Pubns.

Steward, M. W. Antibodies: Their Structure & Function. (Outline Studies in Biology). 96p. 1984. pap. 7.80x (ISBN 0-412-25640-1, NO. 6897, Pub. by Chapman & Hall). Methuen Inc.

Streilein, J., ed. Advances in Gene Technology, Molecular Biology of the Immune System: Proceedings of the 17th Miami Winter Symposium. (Illus.). 300p. 1985. 59.50 (ISBN 0-521-30486-5). Cambridge U Pr.

Thorbecke, G. Jeanette & Leslie, Gerrie, eds. Immunoglobulin D: Structure & Function. (Annals of The New York Academy of Science Ser.: Vol. 399). 410p. 1982. lib. bdg. 80.00x (ISBN 0-89766-188-5); pap. 80.00x (ISBN 0-89766-189-3). NY Acad Sci.

Tom, Baldwin H. & Allison, James P., eds. Hybridomas & Cellular Immortality. 326p. 1983. 35.00x (ISBN 0-306-41467-8, Plenum Pr). Plenum Pub.

Venter, J. Craig, et al. Monoclonal & Anti-Idiotypic Antibodies: Probes for Receptor Structure & Function. LC 84-12254. (Receptor Biochemistry & Methodology Ser.: Vol. 4). 206p. 1984. 46.00 (ISBN 0-8451-3703-4). A R Liss.

Work, T. S. & Campbell, A. M., eds. Monoclonal Antibody Technology. (Laboratory Techniques in Biochemistry & Molecular Biology Ser.: Vol. 13). 1984. 70.50 (ISBN 0-444-80592-3, I-446-84, Biomedical Pr). Elsevier.

Wright. Monoclonal Antibodies & Cancer. (Immunology Ser.). 432p. 1984. 85.00 (ISBN 0-8247-7073-0). Dekker.

IMMUNOLOGY

see also Radiation Immunology

Ablin, Richard J. Immunobiology of the Prostate. LC 79-50200. 320p. 1985. 22.50 (ISBN 0-87527-178-2). Green.

Adams, Dolph O. & Hanna, Michael G., Jr., eds. Contemporary Topics in Immunobiology, Vol. 13: Macrophage Action. 280p. 1984. 39.50 (ISBN 0-306-41536-4, Plenum Pr). Plenum Pub.

Advances in Immunology, Vol. 32. 372p. 1982. 60.00 (ISBN 0-12-022432-1). Acad Pr.

Agarwal, M. K. & Yoshida, M., eds. Immunopharmacology of Endotoxicosis: Proceedings of the 5th International Congress of Immunology Satellite Workshop. Kyoto, Japan, August 27, 1983. LC 84-7650. (Illus.). xiv, 376p. 1984. 68.00x (ISBN 3-11-009887-3). De Gruyter.

Albert, E. D., et al, eds. Histocompatibility Testing, 1984. 820p. 1984. 98.00 (ISBN 0-387-13464-6). Springer-Verlag.

Alder, William H. & Nordin, Albert A. Immunological Techniques Applied to Aging Research. 256p. 1981. 77.00 (ISBN 0-8493-5809-4). CRC Pr.

Allansmith, Mathea R. The Eye & Immunology. LC 81-14163. (Illus.). 209p. 1982. text ed. 37.95 (ISBN 0-8016-0117-7). Mosby.

Amos, D. Bernard, et al, eds. Immune Mechanisms & Disease. LC 79-19241. 1979. 44.00 (ISBN 0-12-055850-5). Acad Pr.

Amos, W. M. Basic Immunology. 210p. 1981. text ed. 14.95 (ISBN 0-407-00178-6). Butterworth.

Arber, W., ed. Current Topics in Microbiology & Immunology, Vol. 72. LC 15-12910. (Illus.). 200p. 1976. 50.00 (ISBN 0-387-07564-X). Springer-Verlag.

--Current Topics in Microbiology & Immunology, Vol. 78. LC 15-12910. (Illus.). 1977. 56.00 (ISBN 0-387-08499-1). Springer-Verlag.

Arber, W., et al. Current Topics in Microbiology & Immunology, Vol. 75. LC 15-12910. (Illus.). 1976. 54.00 (ISBN 3-540-08013-9). Springer-Verlag.

--Current Topics in Microbiology & Immunology, Vol. 79. LC 15-12910. 1978. 63.00 (ISBN 0-387-08587-4). Springer-Verlag.

Arber, W., et al, eds. Current Topics in Microbiology & Immunology, Vols. 40-55. Incl. Vols. 40-50 & 52-55. Chronic Infections Neuropathic Agents & Other Slow Virus Infections. Brody, J. A., et al, eds. (Illus.). vii, 74p. 1967; Vol. 41. (Illus.). iv, 183p. 1967. 49.00 (ISBN 0-387-03755-1); Vol. 42. Insect Viruses. Maramorosch, K., ed. (Illus.). viii, 192p. 1968. 31.00 (ISBN 0-387-04071-4); Vol. 43. (Illus.). iii, 233p. (Incl. 32 pp. in German). 1968. 52.00 (ISBN 0-387-04072-2); Vol. 44. (Illus.). iii, 175p. 1968. 52.00 (ISBN 0-387-04073-0); Vol. 45. (Illus.). iii, 237p. (Incl. 61 pp. in German). 1968. 52.00 (ISBN 0-387-04074-9); Vol. 46. (Illus.). iii, 203p. (Incl. 90 pp. in German). 1968. 57.90 (ISBN 0-387-04075-7); Vol. 47. (Illus.). iii, 222p. (Incl. 29 pp. in German). 1969. 55.50 (ISBN 0-387-04445-0); Vol. 48. (Illus.). iii, 206p. 1969. 55.50 (ISBN 0-387-04446-9); Vol. 49. (Illus.). iii, 250p. 1969. 55.50 (ISBN 0-387-04447-7); Vol. 50. (Illus.). iii, 238p. 1969. 55.50 (ISBN 0-387-04448-5); Vol. 52. (Illus.). iv, 197p. 1970. 55.50 (ISBN 0-387-04787-5); Vol. 53. (Illus.). 236p. 1970. 58.50 (ISBN 0-387-05069-8); Vol. 54. (Illus.). 230p. 1971. 58.50 (ISBN 0-387-05289-5); Vol. 55. Arthropod Cell Cultures & Their Application to the Study of Viruses: Arthropod Cell Cultures & Their Application to the Study of Viruses. Weiss, E., ed. (Illus.). 340p. 1971. 58.00 (ISBN 0-387-05451-0). (Eng. & Ger., Illus.). Springer-Verlag.

--Current Topics in Microbiology & Immunology, Vol. 62. LC 73-17985. (Illus.). 170p. 1973. 43.00 (ISBN 0-387-06598-9). Springer-Verlag.

--Current Topics in Microbiology & Immunology, Vol. 63. LC 73-20915. (Illus.). 230p. 1974. 50.00 (ISBN 0-387-06599-7). Springer-Verlag.

--Current Topics in Microbiology & Immunology, Vol. 64. LC 74-3541. (Illus.). 190p. 1974. 48.00 (ISBN 0-387-06713-2). Springer-Verlag.

--Current Topics in Microbiology & Immunology, Vol. 65. LC 15-12910. (Illus.). 165p. 1974. 47.00 (ISBN 0-387-06774-4). Springer-Verlag.

--Current Topics in Microbiology & Immunology, Vol. 66. LC 15-12910. (Illus.). 130p. 1974. 36.00 (ISBN 3-540-06831-7). Springer-Verlag.

--Current Topics in Microbiology & Immunology, Vol. 67. LC 15-12910. (Illus.). iv, 162p. 1974. 46.00 (ISBN 3-540-06838-4). Springer-Verlag.

--Current Topics in Microbiology & Immunology, Vol. 76. LC 15-12910. (Illus.). 1977. 54.00 (ISBN 3-540-08238-7). Springer-Verlag.

--Current Topics in Microbiology & Immunology, Vol. 77. LC 15-12910. (Illus.). 1977. 51.00 (ISBN 0-387-08401-0). Springer-Verlag.

--Current Topics in Microbiology & Immunology, Vol. 82. LC 15-12910. (Illus.). 1978. 43.00 (ISBN 0-387-08981-0). Springer-Verlag.

--Current Topics in Microbiology & Immunology, Vol. 83. LC 15-12910. (Illus.). 1978. 45.00 (ISBN 0-387-09034-7). Springer-Verlag.

--Current Topics in Microbiology & Immunology, Vol. 85. (Illus.). 1979. 57.00 (ISBN 0-387-09410-5). Springer-Verlag.

--Current Topics in Microbiology & Immunology, Vols. 86-87. (Illus.). 1980. Vol. 86. 45.00 (ISBN 0-387-09432-6); Vol. 87. 42.00 (ISBN 0-387-09433-4). Springer-Verlag.

--Current Topics in Microbiology & Immunology, Vol. 90. (Illus.). 147p. 1980. 58.00 (ISBN 0-387-10181-0). Springer-Verlag.

--Current Topics in Microbiology & Immunology, Vol. 91. (Illus.). 250p. 1981. 59.00 (ISBN 0-387-10722-3). Springer-Verlag.

Arnold, P., et al, eds. Marker Proteins in Inflammation: Proceedings of the Second Symposium, Lyon, France, June 27-30, 1983, Vol. 2. LC 84-9462. (Illus.). xix, 687p. 1984. 98.00x (ISBN 3-11-009872-5). De Gruyter.

Atassi, M. Z. & Benjamini, E., eds. Immunobiology of Proteins & Peptides II. (Advances in Experimental Medicine & Biology: Vol. 150). 238p. 1982. 35.00x (ISBN 0-306-41110-5, Plenum Pr). Plenum Pub.

Azzolina, L. S., ed. Comparative Immunology: Proceedings of the Verona Workshop, 16-17 July 1980, Verona, Italy. (Illus.). 180p. 1982. pap. 28.00 (ISBN 0-08-028019-6). Pergamon.

Bach, Jean-Francois, et al, eds. Immunology. 2nd ed. LC 81-11503. 1014p. 1982. 80.00 (ISBN 0-471-08044-6, Pub. by Wiley Med). Wiley.

Banker, D. D. Modern Practice in Immunization. rev. 3rd ed. xii, 384p. 1980. pap. text ed. 12.95 (ISBN 0-86590-007-8, Pub. by Popular Prakashan India). Apt Bks.

Barriga, Omar O. Immunology of Parasitic Infections. (Illus.). 368p. (Orig.). 1981. pap. text ed. 31.50 (ISBN 0-8391-1621-7). Univ Park.

Baumgarten, Alexander & Richards, Frank F. Handbook Series in Clinical Laboratory Science, CRC: Section F, Immunology, 2 pts, Vol. 1. 1978-79. Pt. 1. 63.95 (ISBN 0-8493-7021-3); Pt. 2, 480p. 62.95 (ISBN 0-8493-7022-1). CRC Pr.

Behan, P. O., et al. Immunology of Nervous System Infections. (Progress in Brain Research Ser.: Vol. 59). 1983. 104.25 (ISBN 0-444-80443-9, I-350-83). Elsevier.

Behan, P. O., et al, eds. Immunology of Nervous System Infections: Proceedings of the Noble Bodman Symposia, London, U.K., November 12-13, 1981. (Progress in Brain Research Ser.). 59p. 1983. 104.25 (ISBN 0-444-80443-9, Biomedical Pr). Elsevier.

Bellanti, Joseph A. Immunology: Basic Process. new ed. LC 79-3947. (Illus.). 1979. pap. text ed. 14.95 (ISBN 0-7216-1677-1). Saunders.

--Immunology II. 2nd ed. LC 77-72808. (Illus.). 1978. text ed. 32.50 (ISBN 0-7216-1681-X). Saunders.

Benedict, A. A., ed. Avian Immunology. LC 77-2732. (Advances in Experimental Medicine & Biology Ser.: Vol. 88). 423p. 1977. 55.00x (ISBN 0-306-32688-4, Plenum Pr). Plenum Pub.

Bertazzoni, Umberto & Bollum, Fred J., eds. Terminal Transferase in Immunobiology & Leukemia. LC 82-3691. (Advances in Experimental Medicine & Biology: Vol. 145). 405p. 1982. 55.00x (ISBN 0-306-40989-5, Plenum Pr). Plenum Pub.

Bier, O. G., et al. Fundamentals of Immunology. (Illus.). 442p. 1981. pap. 19.50 (ISBN 0-387-90529-4). Springer-Verlag.

Bigley, Nancy J. Immunologic Fundamentals. 2nd ed. 1980. 20.95 (ISBN 0-8151-0801-X). Year Bk Med.

Blough, H. A., et al. Current Topics in Microbiology & Immunology, Vol. 70. LC 75-12910. (Illus.). 140p. 1975. 40.00 (ISBN 0-387-07223-3). Springer-Verlag.

Boehmer, H. V., et al, eds. T Cell Hybridomas: A Workshop at the Basle Institute for Immunology. (Current Topics in Microbiology & Immunology Ser.: Vol. 100). 262p. 1982. 26.00 (ISBN 0-387-11535-8). Springer-Verlag.

Bona, Constantin. Idiotypes & Lymphocytes. LC 81-10759. (Immunology: An International Series of Monographs & Treatise). 1981. 35.00 (ISBN 0-12-112950-0). Acad Pr.

Bowry, T. R. Immunology Simplified. 2nd ed. (Illus.). 1984. pap. 12.50x (ISBN 0-19-261340-5). Oxford U Pr.

Brockes, Jeremy, ed. Neuroimmunology. LC 82-3679. (Current Topics in Neurobiology Ser.). 272p. 1982. 29.50x (ISBN 0-306-40955-0, Plenum Pr). Plenum Pub.

Bruni, C., ed. Systems Theory in Immunology. (Lecture Notes in Biomathematics: Vol. 32). 273p. 1979. pap. 19.00 (ISBN 0-387-09728-7). Springer-Verlag.

Burrell, Robert. Experimental Immunology. 5th ed. 1979. spiral bdg. 9.95x (ISBN 0-8087-2876-8). Burgess.

Butt. Practical Immunoassay. (Clinical & Biochemical Analysis Ser.). 360p. 1984. 55.00 (ISBN 0-8247-7094-3). Dekker.

Celada, Franco, et al, eds. Protein Conformation As an Immunological Signal. 510p. 1983. 69.50x (ISBN 0-306-41463-5, Plenum Pr). Plenum Pub.

Chedid, L., ed. Immunostimulation. (Illus.). 236p. 1980. 26.00 (ISBN 0-387-10354-6). Springer-Verlag.

Ciba Foundation. Enzyme Defects & Immune Dysfunction. LC 79-17092. (Ciba Foundation Symposium, New Ser.: No. 68). pap. 74.80 (ISBN 0-317-29762-7, 2022188). Bks Demand UMI.

Clark, William R. The Experimental Foundations of Modern Immunology. 2nd ed. LC 80-13565. 453p. 1983. text ed. 36.50x (ISBN 0-471-86534-6). Wiley.

Cohen, Alan S., ed. Rheumatology & Immunology. (The Science & Practice of Clinical Medicine Ser.). 464p. 1979. 46.50 (ISBN 0-8089-1118-X, 790875). Grune.

Cohen, Edward P. & Kohler, Heinz, eds. Membranes, Receptors, & the Immune Response: Eighty Years after Ehrlich's Side Chain Theory. LC 80-7811. (Progress in Clinical & Biological Research Ser.: Vol. 42). 404p. 1980. 45.00 (ISBN 0-8451-0042-4). A R Liss.

Cohen, S. & Cross, G. A., eds. Towards the Immunological Control of Human Protozoal Diseases: Proceedings of a Royal Society Discussion Meeting Held February 22-23, 1984. (Illus.). 206p. 1985. lib. bdg. 65.00x (ISBN 0-85403-235-5). Scholium Intl.

Colloquium of the Workshop for Biological Chemistry, April 29 - May 1, 1976, Mosbach-Baden. The Immune System: Proceedings. Melchers, F., ed. (Illus.). 1976. 49.00 (ISBN 0-387-07976-9). Springer-Verlag.

Cooper, E. L. General Immunology. LC 80-42218. (Illus.). 300p. 1982. 53.00 (ISBN 0-08-026368-2); pap. 22.00 (ISBN 0-08-026369-0). Pergamon.

Cooper, Edwin & Brazier, Mary. Developmental Immunology: Clinical Problems & Aging. LC 82-4035. (UCLA Forum in Medical Sciences Ser.: No. 25). 1982. 35.00 (ISBN 0-12-188040-0). Acad Pr.

Cooper, Edwin L., ed. Contemporary Topics in Immunobiology, Vol. 4: Invertebrate Immunology. LC 78-165398. (Illus.). 316p. 1974. 32.50x (ISBN 0-306-37804-3, Plenum Pr). Plenum Pub.

Cooper, M., et al, eds. Current Topics in Microbiology & Immunology, Vol. 102. (Illus.). 152p. 1983. pap. 38.00 (ISBN 0-387-12133-1). Springer-Verlag.

--B Lymphocytes in the Immune Response. (Developments in Immunology Ser.: Vol. 3). 396p. 1979. 76.50 (ISBN 0-444-00319-3, Biomedical Pr). Elsevier.

Cooper, Max D. & Warner, Noel L., eds. Contemporary Topics in Immunobiology, Vol. 3. LC 68-26769. (Illus.). 281p. 1974. 32.50x (ISBN 0-306-37803-5, Plenum Pr). Plenum Pub.

Crighton, D. B., ed. Immunological Aspects of Reproduction in Mammals. (Nottingham Easter School Ser.: No. 38). 448p. 1984. text ed. 135.00 (ISBN 0-408-10865-7). Butterworth.

Cruse, J. M. & Lewis, R. E., Jr., eds. The Year in Immunology, 1984-85. (The Year in Immunology Ser.: Vol. 1). (Illus.). vi, 234p. 1985. 67.25 (ISBN 3-8055-4025-6). S Karger.

Current Topics in Microbiology & Immunology, Vol. LC 15-12910. (Illus.). 1978. 45.00 (ISBN 0-387-08781-8). Springer-Verlag.

Current Topics in Microbiology & Immunology, Vol. 114. (Illus.). 245p. 1985. 49.00 (ISBN 0-387-15103-6). Springer-Verlag.

Current Topics in Microbiology & Immunology, Vol. 71. LC 15-12910. (Illus.). 1975. 44.00 (ISBN 0-387-07369-8). Springer-Verlag.

Current Topics in Microbiology & Immunology, Vol. 88. (Illus.). 142p. 1979. 40.00 (ISBN 0-387-09415-6). Springer-Verlag.

Curtis, A. S., ed. Cell-Cell Recognition. LC 77-28646. (Society for Experimental Biology: Symposia No. 32). (Illus.). 1978. 82.50 (ISBN 0-521-22020-3). Cambridge U Pr.

Dean, Jack H., et al, eds. Immunotoxicology & Pharmacology. (Target Organ Toxicology Ser.). 520p. 1985. text ed. 98.00 (ISBN 0-89004-838-X). Raven.

Dixon, Frank J., ed. Advances in Immunology, Vol. 37. 1985. 49.50 (ISBN 0-12-022437-2). Acad Pr.

Dixon, Frank J. & Fisher, David W., eds. Biology of Immunologic Disease. LC 83-4780. (Illus.). 399p. 1983. text ed. 32.50x (ISBN 0-87893-148-1). Sinauer Assoc.

Dixon, Frank J. & Kunkel, Henry G., eds. Advances in Immunology, Vol. 34. (Serial Publication Ser.). 1983. 45.00 (ISBN 0-12-022434-8). Acad Pr.

Dubin, N. A Stochastic Model for Immunological Feedback in Carcinogenesis: Analysis & Approximations. (Lecture Notes in Biomathematics: Vol. 9). 1976. soft cover 14.00 (ISBN 0-387-07786-3). Springer-Verlag.

Eickenberg, H. U., ed. The Influence of Antibiotics on the Host-Parasite Relationship. (Illus.). 270p. 1982. pap. 27.00 (ISBN 0-387-11680-X). Springer-Verlag.

Eisen, H. N. & Reisfeld, R. A., eds. Contemporary Topics in Molecular Immunology, Vol. 5. (Illus.). 249p. 1976. 35.00x (ISBN 0-306-36105-1, Plenum Pr). Plenum Pub.

Eisen, Herman N. Immunology. 2nd ed. (Illus.). 259p. 1980. pap. text ed. 19.25x (ISBN 0-06-140781-X, 14-07816, Harper Medical). Lippincott.

Emerson, S. U., et al. Current Topics in Microbiology & Immunology, Vol. 73. LC 15-12910. 1976. 49.00 (ISBN 0-387-07593-3). Springer-Verlag.

Engelfriet, C. P., et al, eds. Immunoheamatology. (Research Monographs in Immunology: Vol. 5). 400p. 1984. 96.50 (ISBN 0-444-80541-9, I-272-84). Elsevier.

Escobar, M. R. & Friedman, H., eds. Macrophages & Lymphocytes: Nature, Functions, & Interaction, Pt. A. LC 79-9566. (Advances in Experimental Medicine & Biology Ser.: Vol. 121A). 660p. 1980. 75.00x (ISBN 0-306-40285-8, Plenum Pr). Plenum Pub.

Fabris, N. Immunology & Ageing. 1982. lib. bdg. 37.50 (ISBN 90-247-2640-9, Pub. by Martinus Nijhoff Netherlands). Kluwer Academic.

Fauci, Anthony S. & Ballieux, Rudy, eds. Human B-Lymphocyte Function: Activation & Immunoregulation. 352p. 1982. text ed. 71.50 (ISBN 0-89004-620-4). Raven.

Fenichel & Chirogos. Immune Modulation Agents & Their Mechanisms. (Immunology Ser.). 792p. 1984. 99.50 (ISBN 0-8247-7178-8). Dekker.

Folds. Laboratory Procedures in Diagnostic Immunology. Date not set. write for info. (ISBN 0-444-00855-1). Elsevier.

Fougereau, M. & Dausset, J., eds. Immunology Eighty: Progress in Immunology IV (Fourth International Congress of Immunology) 1500p. 1981. pap. 98.00 (ISBN 0-12-262940-X). Acad Pr.

Fougereau, M. & Daussett, J., eds. Immunology, 1980. LC 80-49682. 1981. Vol. 1. 63.00 (ISBN 0-12-262901-9); Vol. 2. 63.00 (ISBN 0-12-262902-7); Vol. 3. 63.00 (ISBN 0-12-262903-5). Acad Pr.

Fraenkel-Conrat, H. & Wagner, R. R., eds. Comprehensive Virology, Vol. 15: Virus - Host Interactions - Immunity to Viruses. LC 79-26533. (Illus.). 309p. 1979. 35.00x (ISBN 0-306-40262-9, Plenum Pr). Plenum Pub.

Franklin, E. C. Clinical Immunology Update, 1981: Reviews for Physicians. 428p. 1980. 42.50 (ISBN 0-444-00416-5, Biomedical Pr). Elsevier.

Frazer, A. C., et al. Current Topics in Microbiology & Immunology, Vol. 69. (Illus.). 200p. 1975. 46.00 (ISBN 0-387-07195-4). Springer-Verlag.

Friedman, Herman, et al, eds. Immunomodulation by Bacteria & Their Products. LC 81-17888. 320p. 1982. 42.50 (ISBN 0-306-40885-6, Plenum Pr). Plenum Pub.

Fudenberg, H. Hugh & Ambrogi, Fabio, eds. Immunomodulation: New Frontiers & Advances. 468p. 1984. 65.00x (ISBN 0-306-41493-7, Plenum Pr). Plenum Pub.

Fulginiti, Vincent A. Immunization in Clinical Practice: A Useful Guideline to Vaccines, Sera, & Immune Globulins in Clinical Practice. (Illus.). 192p. 1982. pap. text ed. 24.75 (ISBN 0-397-50539-6, 65-06869, Lippincott Medical). Lippincott.

Galbraith, Robert M. Immunological In Diabetes Mellitus. 96p. 1979. 34.95 (ISBN 0-8493-5365-3). CRC Pr.

Gillis, Steven & Inman, F. P., eds. Contemporary Topics in Molecular Immunology, Vol. 10: The Interleukins. 316p. 1985. 42.50x (ISBN 0-306-41776-6, Plenum Pr). Plenum Pub.

Gilmore, Norbert & Wainberg, Mark A. Viral Mechanisms of Immunosuppression. LC 85-5788. (Progress in Leukocyte Biology Ser.: Vol. 1). 302p. 1985. 44.00 (ISBN 0-8451-4100-7). A R Liss.

Gleicher, Norbert. Reproductive Immunology. LC 81-11812. (Progress in Clinical & Biological Research Ser.: Vol. 70). 510p. 1981. 86.00 (ISBN 0-8451-0070-X). A R Liss.

Golub, Edward S. The Cellular Basis of the Immune Response. rev. & 2nd ed. LC 80-28080. (Illus.). 325p. 1981. pap. text ed. 18.95x (ISBN 0-87893-212-7). Sinauer Assoc.

Goodman, Joel M., et al. Phylogenetic Development of Vertebrate Immunity, No. 2. new ed. (Illus.). 220p. 1972. text ed. 28.50x (ISBN 0-8422-7057-4). Irvington.

Graf, T. & Jaenisch, R., eds. Tumorviruses, Neoplastic Transformation & Differentiation. (Current Topics in Microbiology & Immunology: Vol. 101). (Illus.). 198p. 1982. 42.00 (ISBN 0-387-11665-6). Springer-Verlag.

Habermehl, K. O., ed. Rapid Methods & Automation in Microbiology & Immunology. (Illus.). 780p. 1985. 87.00 (ISBN 0-387-13695-9). Springer-Verlag.

Hadden, J., et al. Advances in Immunopharmacology: Proceedings of the First International Conference on Immunopharmacology, 29 July-1 August 1980, Brighton. (Illus.). 538p. 1981. 88.00 (ISBN 0-08-026384-4); pap. 39.00 (ISBN 0-08-027974-0). Pergamon.

Haeney, Mansel. Introduction to Clinical Immunology. (Illus.). 160p. 1985. text ed. 19.95 (ISBN 0-407-00362-2). Butterworth.

Hamilton, Helen, ed. Immune Disorders. (Illus.). 192p. 1985. text ed. 19.95 (ISBN 0-916730-76-X). Springhouse Corp.

Hanna, M. G., Jr., ed. Contemporary Topics in Immunobiology, Vol. 1. LC 68-26769. 202p. 1972. 29.50x (ISBN 0-306-37801-9, Plenum Pr). Plenum Pub.

Hay, J. B., ed. Animal Models of Immunological Processes. 1982. 53.50 (ISBN 0-12-333520-5). Acad Pr.

Henle, W., et al. Current Topics in Microbiology & Immunology, Vols. 94 & 95. (Illus.). 308p. 1981. 62.00 (ISBN 0-387-10803-3). Springer-Verlag.

Henle, W., et al, eds. Current Topics in Microbiology & Immunology, Vol. 97. (Illus.). 220p. 1982. 46.00 (ISBN 0-387-11118-2). Springer-Verlag.

Hennessen, W. & Huygelen, C., eds. Immunization: Benefit Versus Risk Factors. (Developments in Biological Standardization: Vol. 43). (Illus.). 1979. pap. 42.75 (ISBN 3-8055-2816-7). S Karger.

Hesch, R. D., ed. Peptide Hormones As Mediators in Immunology & Oncology. (Serono Symposia Publications Ser.). Date not set. text ed. write for info. (ISBN 0-89004-609-3). Raven.

Hildemann, W. H. & Benedict, A. A., eds. Immunologic Phylogeny. LC 75-35524. (Advances in Experimental Medicine & Biology Ser.: Vol. 64). 499p. 1975. 59.50x (ISBN 0-306-39064-7, Plenum Pr). Plenum Pub.

Hogarth, Peter J. Immunological Aspects of Mammalian Reproduction. LC 81-86329. 204p. 1982. 43.95 (ISBN 0-03-061903-3). Praeger.

Hollan, S., et al, eds. Recent Advances in Haemotology, Immunology & Blood Transfusion. 418p. 1983. text ed. 45.00x (ISBN 0-471-90164-4, Pub. by Wiley Med). Wiley.

Hood, Leroy, et al. Immunology. 1978. 25.95 (ISBN 0-8053-4405-5). Benjamin-Cummings.

Hoshino, T. & Uchida, A. Clinical & Experimental Studies in Immunotherapy. (Current Clinical Practice Ser.: Vol. 17). 1984. 37.00 (ISBN 4-9003-9225-1, I-289-84). Elsevier.

Hudson, Leslie & Hay, Frank C. Practical Immunology. 2nd ed. (Illus.). 368p. 1981. pap. text ed. 22.95 (ISBN 0-632-00353-7, B-2311-1). Mosby.

Hume, D. A. & Weidmann, M. J. Mitogenic Lymphocyte Transformation. (Research Monographs in Immunology: Vol. 2). 252p. 1981. 67.25 (ISBN 0-444-80219-3, Biomedical Pr). Elsevier.

Immunological Aspects of Fertility. 196p. 1974. 60.00x (ISBN 0-686-45153-8, Pub. by Biochemical England). State Mutual Bk.

Inchley, Christopher. Immunobiology. (Studies in Biology: No. 128). 88p. 1981. pap. text ed. 8.95 (ISBN 0-7131-2808-9). E Arnold.

Inglis, J. R., ed. T Lymphocytes Today. 200p. 1983. 19.50 (ISBN 0-444-80524-9, I-331-83, Biomedical Pr). Elsevier.

Inman, F. P. & Kindt, T. J., eds. Contemporary Topics in Molecular Immunology, Vol. 9. 262p. 1983. 39.50x (ISBN 0-306-41304-3, Plenum Pr). Plenum Pub.

Inman, F. P. & Mandy, W. J., eds. Contemporary Topics in Molecular Immunology, Vol. 8. 240p. 1981. 32.50x (ISBN 0-306-40661-6, Plenum Pr). Plenum Pub.

International Congress of Allergology, 10th, Jerusalem, Israel, Nov. 1979. Advances in Allergology & Applied Immunology: Proceedings. Oehling, A., et al, eds. (Illus.). 680p. 1980. 170.00 (ISBN 0-08-025519-1). Pergamon.

International Planned Parenthood Federation, ed. Immunology & Reproduction. 1969. 14.00x (ISBN 0-686-87110-3, Pub. by Intl Planned Parent). State Mutual Bk.

International Society for Cell Biology. Differentiation & Immunology. Warren, Katherine B., ed. (Proceedings: Vol. 7). 1969. 67.50 (ISBN 0-12-611907-4). Acad Pr.

International Symposium on Yersinia, 3rd, Montreal, September 1977. Yersinia Enterocolitica. Carter, Philip B., et al, eds. (Contributions to Microbiology & Immunology: Vol. 5). (Illus.). 1979. 66.00 (ISBN 3-8055-2927-9). S Karger.

International Symposium on Yersinia, Pasteurella & Francisella, Malmoe, April 1972. Yersinia, Pasteurella & Francisella: Proceedings. Winblad, ed. (Contributions to Microbiology & Immunology: Vol. 2). 1973. 32.00 (ISBN 3-8055-1636-3). S Karger.

Isojima, S. & Billington, W. D., eds. Reproductive Immunology 1983: Proceedings of the Second International Congress of Reproductive Immunology, Kyoto, Japan, August 17-20, 1983. 276p. 1984. 69.25 (ISBN 0-444-80551-6). Elsevier.

Karcher, D., et al, eds. Humoral Immunity in Neurological Diseases. LC 79-15096. (NATO ASI Series A, Life Sciences: Vol. 24). 684p. 1979. 79.50x (ISBN 0-306-40195-9, Plenum Pr). Plenum Pub.

Khan, Amanullah, et al, eds. Immune Regulators in Transfer Factor. LC 79-1464. 1979. 59.50 (ISBN 0-12-406060-9). Acad Pr.

Kimball, John W. Introduction to Immunology. 496p. 1983. text ed. write for info. (ISBN 0-02-363820-6). Macmillan.

Kindt, Thomas J. & Capra, J. Donald. The Antibody Enigma. 228p. 1984. 35.00x (ISBN 0-306-41581-X, Plenum Pr). Plenum Pub.

Kirkpatrick, Charles H. & Burger, Denis R., eds. Immunobiology of Transfer Factor. (Symposium). 1983. 39.50 (ISBN 0-12-409850-9). Acad Pr.

Kirkwood, Evelyne M. & Lewis, Catriona J. Understanding Medical Immunology. LC 82-13444. 128p. 1984. pap. 17.50 (ISBN 0-471-10529-5, Pub. by Wiley Med). Wiley.

Klein, Thomas, et al, eds. Biological Response Modifiers in Human Oncology & Immunology. (Advances in Experimental Medicine & Biology Ser.: Vol. 166). 334p. 1983. 45.00x (ISBN 0-306-41391-4, Plenum Pr). Plenum Pub.

Klinman, et al. B Lymphocytes in the Immune Response. (Developments in Immunology Ser.: Vol. 15). 540p. 1981. 96.00 (ISBN 0-444-00611-7, Biomedical Pr). Elsevier.

Korneva, Elena A., et al. Neurohumoral Maintenance of Immune Homeostasis. Corson, Samuel A. & Corson, Elizabeth O., eds. LC 84-8771. (Illus.). 184p. 1985. lib. bdg. 32.00x (ISBN 0-226-45042-2). U of Chicago Pr.

Krakauer, R. S. & Cathcart, M. K., eds. Immunoregulation & Autoimmunity. (Developments in Immunology Ser.: Vol. 13). 258p. 1980. 68.50 (ISBN 0-444-00579-X, Biomedical Pr). Elsevier.

Kunkel, Henry & Dixon, Frank, eds. Advances in Immunology, Vol. 31. (Serial Publication Ser.). 1981. 60.00 (ISBN 0-12-022431-3). Acad Pr.

--Advances in Immunology, Vol. 33. 367p. 1982. 63.00 (ISBN 0-12-022433-X). Acad Pr.

Kwapinski, George. The Methodology of Investigative & Clinical Immunology. LC 78-26882. 528p. 1982. text ed. 42.50 (ISBN 0-88275-828-4). Krieger.

Larralde, Carlos, et al, eds. Molecules, Cells & Parasites in Immunology. 1980. 31.50 (ISBN 0-12-436840-9). Acad Pr.

Lefkovits, Ivan, ed. Immunological Methods, Vol. 2. LC 78-3342. 1981. 65.00 (ISBN 0-12-442702-2). Acad Pr.

Lefkovits, Ivan & Pernis, Benvenuto, eds. Immunological Methods. LC 78-3342. 1979. 44.00 (ISBN 0-12-442750-2). Acad Pr.

Lindahl-Kiessling, K., et al, eds. Morphological & Functional Aspects of Immunity. LC 75-148822. (Advances in Experimental Medicine & Biology Ser.: Vol. 12). 721p. 1971. 75.00x (ISBN 0-306-39012-4, Plenum Pr). Plenum Pub.

Litman, Gary W. & Good, Robert A., eds. Immunoglobulins. LC 78-1439. (Comprehensive Immunology Ser.: Vol. 5). (Illus.). 397p. 1978. 45.00x (ISBN 0-306-33105-5, Plenum Med Bk). Plenum Pub.

Locke, Steven E., et al, eds. Foundations of Psychoneuroimmunology. LC 84-24559. 504p. 1985. lib. bdg. 59.95x (ISBN 0-202-25138-1). Aldine Pub.

Loke, Y. W. Immunology & Immunopathology of the Human Foetal-Maternal Interaction. 328p. 1978. 87.25 (ISBN 0-444-80055-7, Biomedical Pr). Elsevier.

McConnell, Ian, et al. The Immune System: A Course on the Molecular & Cellular Basis of Immunity. 2nd. ed. (Illus.). 352p. 1981. pap. text ed. 21.95 (ISBN 0-632-00626-9, B 3224-2). Mosby.

McCullough, Jeffrey & Sandler, Gerald S. Advances in Immunobiology: Blood Cell Antigens & Bone Marrow Transplantation. LC 84-945. (Progress in Clinical & Biological Research Ser.: Vol. 149). 462p. 1984. 58.00 (ISBN 0-8451-0149-8). A R Liss.

McGrady, Pat. New Immunology. 3.00x (ISBN 0-686-29802-0). Cancer Control Soc.

Maggio, Edward T. Enzyme Immunoassay. 304p. 1980. 79.00 (ISBN 0-8493-5617-2). CRC Pr.

Makinodan, Takashi & Kay, Marguerite M., eds. CRC Handbook of Immunology of Aging. (Series in Aging). 328p. 1981. 62.00 (ISBN 0-8493-3144-7). CRC Pr.

Manning, M. J. Phylogeny of Immunological Memory. (Developments in Immunology Ser.: Vol. 10). 1980. 58.00 (ISBN 0-444-80255-X). Elsevier.

Marchalonis, John J., ed. Contemporary Topics in Immunobiology, Vol. 12: Immunobiology of Parasites & Parasitic Infections. 490p. 1984. 59.50x (ISBN 0-306-41418-X, Plenum Pr). Plenum Pub.

Marchalonis, John J. & Cohen, Nicholas, eds. Contemporary Topics in Immunobiology, Vol. 9: Self-Non Self Discrimination. LC 79-179761. (Illus.). 309p. 1980. 35.00x (ISBN 0-306-40263-7, Plenum Pr). Plenum Pub.

Marchuk, G. I. & Belykh, L. N., eds. Mathematical Modeling in Immunology & Medicine. 396p. 1983. 51.00 (ISBN 0-444-86588-8, I-36-83, North-Holland). Elsevier.

Matthews, C. & Burnie, J. P. MCQ Tutor: Medical Immunology. 208p. 1984. 14.00 (ISBN 0-433-20347-1, Pub. by W Heinemann Med Bks). Sheridan Med Bks.

Midwest Autumn Immunology Conference, 7th Meeting, Michigan, Nov. 1978. Immunologic Tolerance & Macrophage Function: Proceedings. Baram, R., et al, eds. LC 79-243. (Developments in Immunology Ser.: Vol. 4). 266p. 1979. 65.00 (ISBN 0-444-00316-9, Biomedical Pr). Elsevier.

Miller, Michael E. Host Defenses in the Human Neonate. (Monographs in Neonatology). 144p. 1978. text ed. 29.50 (ISBN 0-8089-1094-9, 792925). Grune.

Mishell, Barbara B. & Shiigi, Stanley M., eds. Selected Methods in Cellular Immunology. LC 79-19990. (Illus.). 486p. 1980. 39.95x (ISBN 0-7167-1106-0). W H Freeman.

Mitchison, N. Avrion, ed. Manipulation of the Immune Response in Cancer. (Perspectives in Immunology Ser.). 1979. 49.00 (ISBN 0-12-500250-5). Acad Pr.

Mnarchuk, G. I. Mathematical Models in Immunology. (Illus.). xxv, 351p. 1983. pap. 46.00 (ISBN 0-387-90901-X). Springer-Verlag.

Montagna, W. & Billingham, R. E., eds. Immunology & the Skin. LC 75-133174. (Advances in Biology of Skin Ser.: Vol. 11). 396p. 1971. 32.50x (ISBN 0-306-50055-8, Plenum Pr). Plenum Pub.

Muftuoglu, Asuman U. & Barlas, Nefise, eds. Recent Advances in Immunology. 252p. 1984. 39.50x (ISBN 0-306-41515-1, Plenum Pr). Plenum Pub.

Mullen, P. W., ed. Immunotoxicology. (NATO ASI Series G - Ecological Studies: No. 2). (Illus.). vii, 161p. 1984. 24.50 (ISBN 0-387-13382-8). Springer-Verlag.

Muller-Ruchholtz, Wolfgang & Muller-Hermelink, Hans K., eds. Function & Structure of the Immune System. LC 79-4272. (Advances in Experimental Medicine and Biology Ser.: Vol. 114). 872p. 1979. 95.00x (ISBN 0-306-40158-4, Plenum Pr). Plenum Pub.

Myrvik, Quentin N., ed. Fundamentals of Immunology. 2nd ed. Weiser, Russell S. LC 83-12051. 510p. 1984. text ed. 24.50 (ISBN 0-8121-0866-3). Lea & Febiger.

Nahmias, Andre J. & O'Reilly, Richard, eds. Immunology of Human Infection. Incl. Pt. 1, Bacteria, Mycoplasmae, Chlamydiae, & Fungi. 678p. 1981. 57.50x (ISBN 0-306-40257-2); Pt. 2, Viruses & Parasites Immunodiagnosis & Presentation of Infectious Disease. 632p. 1982. 52.50x (ISBN 0-306-40258-0). (Comprehensive Immunology Ser.: Vols. 8 & 9, Plenum Pr). Plenum Pub.

Najjar, Victor A. & Fridkin, Mati, eds. Antineoplastic, Immunogenic & Other Effects of the Tetrapeptide Tuftsin, Vol. 419. 55.00 (ISBN 0-89766-232-6); pap. 55.00x (ISBN 0-89766-233-4). NY Acad Sci.

Nakamura, R. M., et al, eds. Immunoassays: Clinical Laboratory Techniques for the 1980's. LC 80-21230. (Laboratory & Research Methods in Biology & Medicine: Vol. 4). 482p. 1980. 70.00 (ISBN 0-8451-1653-3). A R Liss.

--Immunoassays in the Clinical Laboratory: Proceedings of the First Annual Conference on Immunoassays in the Clinical Laboratory, La Jolla, Calif., Mar.-Apr. 1978. LC 79-1649. (Laboratory & Research Methods in Biology & Medicine: Vol. 3). 394p. 1979. 48.00x (ISBN 0-8451-1652-5). A R Liss.

Neidermeier, William, et al. Phylogenetic Development of Vertebrate Immunity, No. 1. (Illus.). 206p. 1973. text ed. 28.50x (ISBN 0-8422-7056-6). Irvington.

Neubauer, Russell H. Naturally Occuring Biological Immunosuppressive Factors & Their Relationship to Disease. 304p. 1979. 74.50 (ISBN 0-8493-5243-6). CRC Pr.

Nisonoff, Alfred. Introduction to Molecular Immunology. 2nd Rev. ed. LC 83-20259. (Illus.). 225p. (Orig.). 1984. pap. text ed. 16.50x (ISBN 0-87893-595-9). Sinauer Assoc.

Norman, P. S., ed. Pathology & Physiology of Allergic Reactions. (Journal: International Archives of Allergy & Applied Immunology: Vol. 77 No. 1-2). (Illus.). 280p. 1985. pap. 49.50 (ISBN 3-8055-4056-6). S Karger.

Notkins, Abner L., ed. Viral Immunology & Immunopathology. 1975. 55.00 (ISBN 0-12-522050-2). Acad Pr.

O'Connor, G. Richard & Chandler, John W., eds. Advances in Immunology & Immunopathology of the Eye. (Illus.). 304p. 1985. text ed. write for info. (ISBN 0-89352-224-4). Masson Pub.

Oppenheim, J. J., et al. Cellular Functions in Immunity & Inflammation. 1984. pap. 35.00 (ISBN 0-444-00951-5). Elsevier.

Parrish, John A., et al, eds. Photoimmunology. 320p. 1983. 39.50x (ISBN 0-306-41280-2, Plenum Pr). Plenum Pub.

Paul, William E., ed. Fundamental Immunology. (Illus.). 830p. 1984. text ed. 88.00 (ISBN 0-89004-923-8). Raven.

Paul, William E., et al, eds. Annual Review of Immunology, Vol. 3. (Illus.). 584p. 1985. text ed. 27.00 (ISBN 0-8243-3003-X). Annual Reviews.

Peeters, H., ed. Protides of the Biological Fluids, Proceedings of the 29th Colliquium on Protides of the Biological Fluids, Brussels, Belgium, May 1981. (Illus.). 993p. 1982. 165.00 (ISBN 0-08-027988-0, H220). Pergamon.

Pick, Edgar, ed. Lymphokine Reports: A Forum for Nonantibody Lymphocyte Products, Vol. 1. 1980. 39.50 (ISBN 0-12-432001-5). Acad Pr.

Porter, R. R. & Ada, G. L., eds. Contemporary Topics in Molecular Immunology, Vol. 6. (Illus.). 265p. 1977. 35.00x (ISBN 0-306-36106-X, Plenum Pr). Plenum Pub.

Pruitt, Tenovuo. The Lactoperoxidas System. (Immunology Ser.). 280p. 1985. 55.00 (ISBN 0-8247-7298-9). Dekker.

Ray, Prasanta K., ed. Immunobiology & Transplantation, Cancer & Pregnancy. 500p. 1983. text ed. 94.00 (ISBN 0-08-025994-4). Pergamon.

Reeves, G. W., ed. Recent Developments in Clinical Immunology. (Research Monographs in Immunology: Vol. 6). 216p. 1984. 59.25 (ISBN 0-444-80554-0, I-273-84). Elsevier.

Reisfeld, R. A. & Inman, F. P., eds. Contemporary Topics in Molecular Immunology, Vol. 7. 447p. 1978. 42.50x (ISBN 0-306-40081-2, Plenum Pr). Plenum Pub.

Reisfeld, R. A. & Mandy, W. J., eds. Contemporary Topics in Molecular Immunology, Vol. 2. LC 73-186260. (Illus.). 291p. 1973. 35.00x (ISBN 0-306-36102-7, Plenum Pr). Plenum Pub.

Reiss. Fungal Antigens & the Immune Response. Date not set. write for info. (ISBN 0-444-00856-X). Elsevier.

Rimon, A., et al. Current Topics in Microbiology & Immunology, Vol. 74. LC 15-12910. 1976. 48.00 (ISBN 0-387-07657-3). Springer-Verlag.

Ritchie, Robert F., ed. Automated Immunoanalysis, 2 pts. (Clinical Chemistry & Biochemical Analysis Ser.: Vol. 7). (Illus.). 656p. 1978. Pt. I. 59.75 (ISBN 0-8247-6678-4); Pt. II. 59.75 (ISBN 0-8247-6679-2). Dekker.

Roesel, Catherine E. Immunology: A Self-Instructional Approach. 1978. pap. text ed. 26.00 (ISBN 0-07-053411-X). McGraw.

Roitt, Ivan M. Essential Immunology. (Illus.). 368p. 1981. pap. text ed. 17.50 (ISBN 0-632-00739-7, B-4160-8, Blackwell). Mosby.

Rose, N. R., et al, eds. Genetic Control of Autoimmune Disease: Proceedings of the 1978 Conference in Bloomfield Hills, Mich. (Developments in Immunology Ser.: Vol. 1). 466p. 1979. 82.75 (ISBN 0-444-00297-9, Biomedical Pr). Elsevier.

Rose, Noel R. & Bigazzi, Pierluigi E., eds. Methods in Immunodiagnosis. 2nd ed. LC 80-15273. (Techniques in Pure & Applied Microbiology Ser.). 269p. 1980. 29.50 (ISBN 0-471-02208-X, Pub. by Wiley Med). Wiley.

Rose, Noel R. & Milgrom, Felix, eds. Principles of Immunology. 2nd ed. (Illus.). 1979. pap. text ed. write for info. (ISBN 0-02-403610-2). Macmillan.

Rothfield, Lawrence I. & Ward, Peter A. Microbiology & Immunology Review. 2nd ed. LC 79-23991. (Medical Review Ser.). (Illus.). 176p. 1981. pap. 12.95 (ISBN 0-668-04882-4, 4882). ACC.

Rudbach, B. & Baker, R., eds. Immunology of Bacterial Polysaccharides. LC 78-31961. (Developments in Immunology Ser.: Vol. 2). 158p. 1979. 45.50 (ISBN 0-444-00315-0, Biomedical Pr). Elsevier.

Safai, Bijan & Good, Robert A., eds. Immunodermatology. LC 80-15102. (Comprehensive Immunology Ser.: Vol. 7). (Illus.). 759p. 1981. 65.00x (ISBN 0-306-40380-3, Plenum Pr). Plenum Pub.

Sandler, S. Gerald & Nusbacher, Jacob, eds. Immunobiology of the Erythrocyte. LC 80-81465. (Progress in Clinical & Biological Research Ser.: Vol. 43). 360p. 1980. 53.00 (ISBN 0-8451-0043-2). A R Liss.

Sarma, P. S., et al. Current Topics in Microbiology & Immunology, Vol. 68. LC 75-12910. (Illus.). 180p. 1974. 46.00 (ISBN 0-387-07074-5). Springer-Verlag.

Schell, Musher. Pathogenesis & Immunology of Treponemal Infections. (Immunology Ser.). 424p. 1983. 65.00 (ISBN 0-8247-1384-2). Dekker.

Schuppli, R. Immunbiologie: Einfuehrung in die allergologischen und immunologischen Grundlagen der klinischen Medizin. (Ueberarbeitete Auflage). (Illus.). 1979. pap. 9.00 (ISBN 3-8055-3000-5). S Karger.

Schwartz, Lazar M. & Schwartz, Paula. An Exercise Manual iu Immunology. LC 75-14774. 324p. 1975. pap. 18.50 (ISBN 0-317-06892-X). Krieger.

Schwartz, Lazarm. Compendium of Immunology. LC 77-83914. (Medical Pocketbook Library). 1977. pap. 5.00 (ISBN 0-930728-01-7). Educ Medical.

Sell, Stewart. Immunologia Inmunopatologia. (Span.). 1981. pap. text ed. 18.30 (ISBN 0-06-317151-1, Pub. by HarLA Mexico). Har-Row.

--Immunology, Immunopathology & Immunity. 3rd ed. (Illus.). 600p. 1980. pap. text ed. 35.00x (ISBN 0-06-142369-6, 14-23698, Harper Medical). Lippincott.

Sercarz, Eli E. & Cunningham, Alastair J., eds. Strategies of Immune Regulation. LC 79-28392. 1980. 59.50 (ISBN 0-12-637140-7). Acad Pr.

Serrou, B. & Rosenfeld, S., eds. New Immunomodulating Agents & Biological Response Modifiers. (Human Cancer Immunology Ser.: Vol. 3). 400p. 1982. 106.50 (ISBN 0-444-80401-3, Biomedical Pr). Elsevier.

Sharma, R. P., ed. Immunologic Considerations in Toxicology, Vols. I & II. 1981. Vol. I, 184p. 66.00 (ISBN 0-8493-5271-1); Vol. II, 184p. 66.00 (ISBN 0-8493-5272-X). CRC Pr.

Shatkin, A. J., ed. Initiation Signals in Viral Gene Expression. (Current Topics in Microbiology & Immunology Ser.: Vol. 93). (Illus.). 212p. 1981. 41.00 (ISBN 0-387-10804-1). Springer Verlag.

Shulman, Sidney, et al, eds. Immunological Factors in Human Reproduction. (Serono Symposia Ser.: No. 45). 1982. 44.00 (ISBN 0-12-640780-0). Acad Pr.

Siskind, Gregory W., ed. Developmental Immunobiology. 272p. 1979. 29.50 (ISBN 0-8089-1191-0, 794091). Grune.

Skamene, Emil, ed. Genetic Control of Natural Resistance to Infection & Malignancy. (Perspectives in Immunology Ser.). 1980. 49.50 (ISBN 0-12-647680-2). Acad Pr.

Smolin, Gilbert & O'Connor, G. Richard. Ocular Immunology. LC 81-8218. (Illus.). 322p. 1981. text ed. 27.50 (ISBN 0-8121-0688-1). Lea & Febiger.

Solomon, J. B., ed. Aspects of Developmental & Comparative Immunology I: First Congress of Developmental & Comparative Immunology, 27 July-1 August 1980, Aberdeen. (Illus.). 580p. 1981. 120.00 (ISBN 0-08-025922-7). Pergamon.

Stansfield. Serology & Immunology. 1981. write for info. (ISBN 0-02-415740-6). Macmillan.

Sternberger, Ludwig A. Immunocytochemistry. 2nd ed. LC 78-13263. (Basic & Clinical Immunology Ser.). 354p. 1979. 50.00x (ISBN 0-471-03386-3, Pub. by Wiley Medical). Wiley.

Stewart, et al. Microbiology & Immunology for the Health Team. 1984. pap. write for info. (ISBN 0-471-33385-9). Wiley.

Stewart-Tull, D. E. Immunology of the Bacterial Cell Envelope. Davies, M., ed. LC 84-20993. 1985. price not set (ISBN 0-471-90552-6). Wiley.

Strauss, E. G. & Strauss, J. H. Current Topics in Microbiology & Immunology, Vol. 105. (Illus.). 220p. 1983. 46.50 (ISBN 0-387-12492-6). Springer-Verlag.

Streilein, J., ed. Advances in Gene Technology, Molecular Biology of the Immune System: Proceedings of the 17th Miami Winter Symposium. (Illus.). 300p. 1985. 59.50 (ISBN 0-521-30486-5). Cambridge U Pr.

Streilein, Wayne J. & Hughes, John D. Immunology: A Programmed Text. 1977. pap. text ed. 14.95 (ISBN 0-316-81919-0, Little Med Div). Little.

Strickland, Thomas G. Immunoparasitology: Principles & Methods in Malaria & Schistosomiasis Research. Hunter, Kenneth W., ed. LC 82-626. 304p. 1982. 45.95 (ISBN 0-03-061499-6). Praeger.

Taliaferro, W. H. & Humphrey, J. H., eds. Advances in Immunology, Vol. 35. (Serial Publication). 1984. 40.00 (ISBN 0-12-022435-6). Acad Pr.

Talmadge, James E., et al. Screening for Biological Response Modifiers: Methods & Rationale. (Developments in Oncology Ser.). 1985. lib. bdg. 32.50 (ISBN 0-89838-712-4, Pub. by Martinus Nijhoff Netherlands). Kluwer Academic.

Talwar, G. P., ed. Non-Isotopic Immunoassays & Their Applications. (Workshop & Symposia Series, National Institute of Immunology, New Delhi: No. 1). (Illus.). xv, 436p. 1983. text ed. 45.00 (ISBN 0-7069-1900-9, Pub. by Vikas India). Advent NY.

Terry, W. D. & Yamamura, Y., eds. Immunobiology & Immunotherapy of Cancer. LC 79-19197. (Developments in Immunobiology Ser.: Vol. 6). 432p. 1980. 68.50 (ISBN 0-444-00356-8, Biomedical Pr). Elsevier.

Thompson, R. A. & Rose, Noel R., eds. Recent Advances in Clinical Immunology, No. 3. LC 77-30129. (Illus.). 318p. 1983. text ed. 60.00 (ISBN 0-443-02641-6). Churchill.

Tizard, Ian R. Immunology: An Introduction. LC 83-15096. 428p. 1984. text ed. 31.95x (ISBN 0-03-060277-7). SCP.

Toder, V. & Beer, A. E., eds. Immunology & Immunopathology of Reproduction. (Contributions to Gynecology & Obstetics: Vol. 14). (Illus.). viii, 180p. 1985. 52.50 (ISBN 3-8055-4059-0). S Karger.

Touraine, J. L., et al, eds. Transplantation & Clinical Immunology: Proceedings of the 9th International Course, Lyon, 1977. (International Congress Ser.: No. 447). 1979. 66.50 (ISBN 0-444-90042-X, Excerpta Medica). Elsevier.

--Transplantation & Clinical Immunology: Immunosuppression, Vol. 15. (Symposia Foundation Merieux Ser.: Vol. 9). 294p. 1984. 59.75 (ISBN 0-444-90373-9, I-019-84, Excerpta Medica). Elsevier.

Trautner, T. A., ed. Methylation of DNA. (Current Topics in Microbiology & Immunology Ser.: Vol. 108). (Illus.). 180p. 1984. 36.00 (ISBN 0-387-12849-2). Springer-Verlag.

Twomey, J. J. & Good, R. A., eds. Immunopathology of Lymphoreticular Neoplasms. LC 77-27315. (Comprehensive Immunology Ser.: Vol. 4). (Illus.). 781p. 1978. 65.00x (ISBN 0-306-33104-7, Plenum Med Bk). Plenum Pub.

Unanue, Emil R. & Benacerraf, Baruj. Textbook of Immunology. 2nd ed. (Illus.). 324p. 1984. pap. 17.50 (ISBN 0-317-18555-1, 8504-2). Williams & Wilkins.

Understanding the Immune System: The Immune System in the Human Body & How It Works. 1984. lib. bdg. 79.95 (ISBN 0-87700-620-2). Revisionist Pr.

Vandenbark, A. & Raus, J., eds. Immunoregulatory Processes in Multiple Sclerosis & Experimental Allergic Encephalomyelitis. (Research Monographs in Immunology: Vol. 7). 288p. 1984. 72.25 (ISBN 0-444-80570-2). Elsevier.

Van Muiswinkel, W. B., ed. Immunology & Immunization of Fish: Proceedings of the Conference Held June 22-24, 1981 In Wageningen Netherlands. (Developmental & Comparative Immunology Ser.). 256p. 1982. 39.00 (ISBN 0-08-028831-6). Pergamon.

Vilcek, J., et al, eds. Interferon & the Immune System, Vol. 2. 272p. 1984. 72.25 (ISBN 0-444-80543-5). Elsevier.

Vogt, P. K. & Koprowski, H., eds. Mouse Mammary Tumor Virus. (Current Topics in Microbiology & Immunology Ser.: Vol. 106). (Illus.). 105p. 1983. 25.00 (ISBN 0-387-12828-X). Springer-Verlag.

--Retroviruses, Vol. 2. (Current Topics in Microbiology & Immunology: Vol. 107). (Illus.). 185p. 1983. 39.50 (ISBN 0-387-12384-9). Springer-Verlag.

Volker-Dieben, H. J. The Effect of Immunological & Non-Immunological Factors on Corneal Graft Survival. (Monographs in Opthalmology). 1984. lib. bdg. 45.50 (ISBN 90-6193-808-2, Pub. by Junk Pubs Netherlands). Kluwer Academic.

Voller, A. & Bartlett, A., eds. Immunoassays for the Eighties. (Illus.). 500p. 1981. text ed. 42.00 (ISBN 0-8391-1672-1). Univ Park.

Waksman, Byron H. Atlas of Experimental Immunobiology & Immunopathology. LC 73-81434. (Illus.). 1970. 67.00x (ISBN 0-300-01154-7). Yale U Pr.

Warner, Noel L., ed. Contemporary Topics in Immunobiology, Vol. 11. (Illus.). 312p. 1980. 35.00x (ISBN 0-306-40419-2, Plenum Pr). Plenum Pub.

Warner, Noel L. & Cooper, Max D., eds. Contemporary Topics in Immunobiology, Vol. 8. LC 79-17961. (Illus.). 286p. 1978. 32.50x (ISBN 0-306-37808-6, Plenum Pr). Plenum Pub.

Webb, David R., ed. Immunopharmacology & the Regulation of Leukocyte Function. (Immunology Ser.: Vol. 19). (Illus.). 312p. 1982. 55.00 (ISBN 0-8247-1707-4). Dekker.

Weigle, William O., ed. Contemporary Topics in Immunobiology, Vol. 5. 357p. 1976. 39.50 (ISBN 0-306-37805-1, Plenum Pr). Plenum Pub.

Weir. Handbook of Experimental Immunology: Application of Immunological Methods, Vol. 3. 3rd ed. 1978. pap. 44.00 (ISBN 0-632-00186-0, B 5396-7, Blackwell Scientific). Mosby.

Weir, D. M., ed. Handbook of Experimental Immunology: Cellular Immunology, Vol. 2. 3rd ed. 1978. pap. 41.50 (ISBN 0-8016-5395-9, Blackwell Scientific). Mosby.

Weissman, Irving, compiled by. Annual Reviews Reprints: Immunology, 1977-1979. (Illus.). 1980. soft cover 12.00 (ISBN 0-8243-2502-8). Annual Reviews.

Weissman, Irving, et al. Essential Concepts in Immunology. LC 78-57262. 1978. 21.95 (ISBN 0-8053-4406-3). Benjamin-Cummings.

Weksler, Marc E., et al. Immune Effector Mechanisms in Disease. 272p. 1978. 34.00 (ISBN 0-8089-1069-8, 794790). Grune.

Williams, Curtis A. & Chase, Merrill W., eds. Methods in Immunology & Immunochemistry, 5 vols. Vol. 1. 1968. 77.50 (ISBN 0-12-754401-1); Vol. 2. 1968. 77.50 (ISBN 0-12-754402-X); Vol. 3. 1971. 77.50 (ISBN 0-12-754403-8); Vol. 4 1977. 77.50 (ISBN 0-12-754404-6); Vol. 5 1976. 77.50 (ISBN 0-12-754405-4). Acad Pr.

Wright, C. A., ed. Biochemical & Immunological Taxonomy of Animals. 1975. 76.00 (ISBN 0-12-765350-3). Acad Pr.

Yoshitsugi, Hokama & Nakamura, Robert M. Immunology & Immunopathology: Basic Concepts. 1981. write for info. (ISBN 0-316-36932-2). Little.

Zaleski, Marek B., et al. Immunogenetics. 512p. 1983. text ed. 39.95 (ISBN 0-273-01925-2). Pitman Pub MA.

IMPACT, ION

see Ion Bombardment

IMPACT PHENOMENA (NUCLEAR PHYSICS)

see Collisions (Nuclear Physics)

IMPELLERS

Advani, L. T. Horsepower Tables for Agitator Impellers. LC 76-2964. 175p. 1976. 29.95x (ISBN 0-87201-368-5). Gulf Pub.

IMPLANTATION, ION

see Ion Implantation

IMPLANTATION OF OVUM

see Ovum Implantation

IMPREGNATION, ARTIFICIAL

see Artificial Insemination

INAUDIBLE SOUND

see Ultrasonics

INBREEDING

Inbreeding Heterosis Fertility Plasmon Differentiation & Phytophtora - Resistance in Solanum Verrucosum Schlechte & Some Interspecific Crosses in Solanum. (Agricultural Research Reports: No. 748). 1970. pap. 21.50 (ISBN 90-220-0326-4, PDC182, PUDOC). Unipub.

Shields, William M. Philopatry, Inbreeding & the Evolution of Sex. 250p. 1982. 49.00x (ISBN 0-87395-617-6); pap. 16.95x (ISBN 0-87395-618-4). State U NY Pr.

INCANDESCENT LAMPS

see Electric Lamps

INCINERATORS

Bonner, T., et al. Hazardous Waste Incineration Engineering. LC 81-14223. (Pollution Technology Review Ser.: No. 88). (Illus.). 432p. 1982. 45.00 (ISBN 0-8155-0877-8). Noyes.

Brunner, Calvin R. Design of Sewage Sludge Incineration Systems. LC 80-21916. (Pollution Technology Review Ser.: No. 71). (Illus.). 380p. 1981. 48.00 (ISBN 0-8155-0825-5). Noyes.

--Hazardous Air Emissions from Incineration. 250p. 1985. text ed. 35.00 (ISBN 0-412-00721-5, NO. 9093, Pub. by Chapman & Hall England). Methuen Inc.

--Incineration Systems: Selection & Design. LC 83-26124. (Illus.). 417p. 1984. 52.50 (ISBN 0-442-21192-9). Van Nos Reinhold.

--Incineration Systems Seminar Notebook. 477p. 1982. Wkbk. 95.00 (ISBN 0-86587-111-6). Gov Insts.

Combustion Fundamentals for Waste Incineration. 212p. 1974. 30.00 (ISBN 0-685-48047-X, H00087). ASME.

Hooper, G. V., ed. Offshore Ship & Platform Incineration of Hazardous Wastes. LC 81-38372. (Pollution Tech. Rev. 79). (Illus.). 468p. 1981. 42.00 (ISBN 0-8155-0854-9). Noyes.

Incinerators, Rubbish Handling. (Eighty-Ninety Ser.). 1972. pap. 2.00 (ISBN 0-685-58144-6, 82). Natl Fire Prot.

Kiang, Yen-Hsiung & Ross, Richard. Handbook of Incineration Technology. 1986. cancelled (ISBN 0-442-24401-0). Van Nos Reinhold.

National Incinerator Conference. Resource Recovery Through Incineration: Proceedings; Papers Presented at 1974 National Incinerator Conference, Miami, Florida, May 12-15, 1974. LC 70-124402. pap. 95.00 (ISBN 0-317-29795-3, 2016866). Bks Demand UMI.

National Materials Advisory Board, National Research Council. Materials of Construction for Shipboard Waste Incinerators. 1977. pap. 10.25 (ISBN 0-309-02606-7). Natl Acad Pr.

Niessen, Walter R. Combustion & Incineration. (Pollution Engineering & Technology Ser.: Vol. 7). 1978. 75.00 (ISBN 0-8247-6656-3). Dekker.

Rubel, Fred N. Incineration of Solid Wastes. LC 74-77723. (Pollution Technology Review Ser: No. 13). (Illus.). 246p. 1975. 24.00 (ISBN 0-8155-0551-5). Noyes.

Rudman, Jack. Incinerator Plant Foreman. (Career Examination Ser.: C-2163). (Cloth bdg. avail. on request). 1976. pap. 10.00 (ISBN 0-8373-0362-1). Natl Learning.

--Incinerator Plant Maintenance Foreman. (Career Examination Ser.: C-2773). (Cloth bdg. avail. on request). 1980. pap. 10.00 (ISBN 0-8373-2773-3). Natl Learning.

--Incinerator Plant Supervisor. (Career Examination Ser.: C-2164). (Cloth bdg. avail. on request). 1976. pap. 10.00 (ISBN 0-8373-2164-6). Natl Learning.
--Incinerator Stationary Engineer. (Career Examination Ser.: C-2636). (Cloth bdg. avail. on request). pap. 10.00 (ISBN 0-8373-2636-2). Natl Learning.
--Senior Incinerator Stationary Engineer. (Career Examination Ser.: C-2637). (Cloth bdg. avail. on request). pap. 12.00 (ISBN 0-8373-2637-0). Natl Learning.
--Supervising Incinerator Stationary Engineer. (Career Examination Ser.: C-2638). pap. 12.00 (ISBN 0-8373-2638-9). Natl Learning.
Sittig, Marshall. Incineration of Industrial Hazardous Wastes & Sludges. LC 79-21252. (Pollution Technology Review: No. 63). (Illus.). 348p. 1980. 48.00 (ISBN 0-8155-0774-7). Noyes.
Stephenson, J. W., et al, eds. Incinerator & Solid Waste Technology, 1962-1975. 415p. 1975. pap. text ed. 60.00 (ISBN 0-685-62568-0, I00092). ASME.
Waymat, E. C. Portable Beach Incinerator, 1977. 1981. 25.00x (ISBN 0-686-97141-8, Pub. by W Spring England). State Mutual Bk.

INDETERMINATE ANALYSIS
see Diophantine Analysis

INDIA-RUBBER
see Rubber

INDIA-RUBBER INDUSTRY
see Rubber Industry and Trade

INDIAN CORN
see Corn

INDICATING INSTRUMENTS
see Recording Instruments

INDICATOR PLANTS
see Plant Indicators

INDICATORS AND TEST-PAPERS
see also Chemical Tests and Reagents
Bishop, E. Indicators. 756p. 1973. text ed. 125.00 (ISBN 0-08-016617-2). Pergamon.

INDOLE
Erspamer, V., ed. Five-Hydroxytryptamine & Related Indolealkylamines. (Handbook of Experimental Pharmacology: Vol. 19). (Illus.). 1966. 106.00 (ISBN 0-387-03536-2). Springer-Verlag.
Houlihan, William, ed. Indoles, Vol. 25, Pt. 2. 616p. 1972. 77.00 (ISBN 0-471-37501-2). Krieger.
Robinson, Brian. The Fischer-Indole Synthesis. LC 81-14749. 923p. 1982. 214.95 (ISBN 0-471-10009-9, Pub. by Wiley-Interscience). Wiley.
Sundberg, Richard J. Chemistry of Indoles. (Organic Chemistry Ser.: Vol. 18). 1970. 81.00 (ISBN 0-12-676950-8). Acad Pr.

INDORE PROCESS
see Compost

INDUCTION (ELECTRICITY)
Kiltie, Ordean. Design Shortcuts & Procedures for Electronics Power Transformers & Inductors. 2nd, rev. ed. LC 81-81620. (Illus.). 274p. (Orig.). 1981. 39.50 (ISBN 0-916512-27-4). Kiltie.
Waters, William E. Electrical Induction from Distant Current Surges. (Illus.). 224p. 1983. text ed. 41.95 (ISBN 0-13-247254-6). P-H.

INDUCTION (LOGIC)
see also Induction (Mathematics)
Bogdan, R. J., ed. Local Induction. LC 75-34922. (Synthese Library: No. 93). 1975. lib. bdg. 58.00 (ISBN 90-277-0649-2, Pub. by Reidel Holland). Kluwer Academic.
Burks, Arthur W. Chance, Cause, Reason: An Inquiry into the Nature of Scientific Evidence. LC 74-11617. (Illus.). 688p. 1977. lib. bdg. 27.50x (ISBN 0-226-08087-0). U of Chicago Pr.
Christensen, R. Foundations of Inductive Reasoning. (Entropy Minimax Sourcebook Ser.: Vol. VII). xii, 363p. 1964. 34.95 (ISBN 0-938876-00-7). Entropy Ltd.
Cohen, L. J. & Hesse, M. B., eds. Applications of Inductive Logic: Proceedings of a Conference at the Queen's College, Oxford, August 1978. (Illus.). 1980. 59.00x (ISBN 0-19-824584-X). Oxford U Pr.
Coyne, Anthony M. Introduction to Inductive Reasoning. LC 84-3560. 294p. (Orig.). 1984. pap. text ed. 13.50 (ISBN 0-8191-3883-5). U Pr of Amer.
Goodman, Nelson. Fact, Fiction & Forecast. 4th ed. 176p. 1983. text ed. 10.00x (ISBN 0-674-29070-4); pap. text ed. 4.95x (ISBN 0-674-29071-2). Harvard U Pr.
Gratry, A. Logic. Singer, Helen & Singer, Milton, trs. from Fr. xii, 640p. 1944. 34.95x (ISBN 0-87548-035-7). Open Court.
Jeffrey, Richard C., ed. Studies in Inductive Logic & Probability, Vol. II. 312p. 1980. 30.00x (ISBN 0-520-03826-6). U of Cal Pr.
Minto, William. Logic, Inductive & Deductive. 16.75 (ISBN 0-8369-6997-9, 7814). Ayer Co Pubs.
Niiniluoto, I. & Tuomela, R. Theoretical Concepts & Hypothetico-Inductive Inference. LC 73-83567. (Synthese Library: No. 53). 1973. lib. bdg. 39.50 (ISBN 90-277-0343-4, Pub. by Reidel Holland). Kluwer Academic.
Rescher, Nicholas. Induction. LC 80-52598. xii, 225p. 1981. 34.95x (ISBN 0-8229-3431-0). U of Pittsburgh Pr.
Rosenkrantz, Roger D. Foundations & Applications of Inductive Probability. xiv, 326p. (Orig.). 1981. lib. bdg. 29.00x (ISBN 0-917930-23-1); pap. text ed. 15.00x (ISBN 0-917930-03-7). Ridgeview.
Skyrms, Brian. Choice & Chance: An Introduction to Inductive Logic. 3rd ed. LC 85-7131. 192p. 1985. pap. text ed. write for info. (ISBN 0-534-05190-1). Wadsworth Pub.
Venn, John. Principles of Empirical or Inductive Logic. 2nd ed. LC 77-165344. 604p. 1973. Repr. of 1907 ed. 33.50 (ISBN 0-8337-3625-6). B Franklin.
--The Principles of Inductive Logic. 2nd ed. LC 72-119162. Orig. Title: The Principles of Empirical, or Inductive Logic. 624p. 1973. 19.50 (ISBN 0-8284-0265-5). Chelsea Pub.
Von Wright, Georg H. The Logical Problem of Induction. 2nd ed. LC 78-24370. 1979. Repr. of 1957 ed. lib. bdg. 24.75x (ISBN 0-313-20830-1, WRLP). Greenwood.
Wesleyan Conference on Induction. Induction: Some Current Issues. Kyburg, Henry E. & Nagel, Ernest, eds. LC 63-8860. pap. 60.50 (ISBN 0-317-08262-0, 2001965). Bks Demand UMI.

INDUCTION (MATHEMATICS)
Edwards, A. W. Likelihood. (Cambridge Sciences Classics). (Illus.). 235p. 1985. pap. 16.95 (ISBN 0-521-31871-8). Cambridge U Pr.
Gelfand, S. I., et al. Sequences & Combinatorial Problems. (Pocket Mathematical Library). 92p. 1968. 24.50 (ISBN 0-677-20730-1). Gordon.
Golovina, L. & Yaglom, I. Induction in Geometry. 133p. 1979. pap. 2.95 (ISBN 0-8285-1534-4, Pub. by Mir Pubs USSR). Imported Pubns.
Golovina, L. I. & Yaglom, I. M. Induccion en la Geometria. (Span.). 126p. 1976. pap. 2.95 (ISBN 0-8285-1687-1, Pub. by Mir Pubs USSR). Imported Pubns.
Hacking, Ian M. The Emergence of Probability. LC 74-82224. 216p. 1975. 37.50 (ISBN 0-521-20460-7). Cambridge U Pr.
Nicas, Andrew J. Induction Theorems for Groups of Homotopy Manifold Structures. LC 82-11546. (Memoirs of the American Mathematical Society Ser.: No. 267). 108p. pap. 9.00 (ISBN 0-8218-2267-5, MEMO/267). Am Math.

INDUCTION MOTORS
see Electric Motors, Induction

INDUSTRIAL ARTS
see also Agriculture; Artisans; Bookbinding; Engineering; Inventions; Machinery; Machinery in Industry; Manufactures; Mechanical Engineering; Mills and Mill-Work; Patents; Research, Industrial; Technical Education; Technology
also names of specific industries, arts, trades, etc., e.g. Bookbinding; Printing; Ship-building
Adkins, Jan. Inside: Seeing Beneath the Surface. 32p. 1984. pap. 4.95 (ISBN 0-8027-7215-3). Walker & Co.
Balkham, K. & Mills, R. Introductory Design Problems. 1979. pap. text ed. 7.50x (ISBN 0-435-75860-8). Heinemann Ed.
Bragg, William H. Creative Knowledge. facs. ed. LC 74-134057. (Essay Index Reprint Ser). 1926. 33.00 (ISBN 0-8369-2104-6). Ayer Co Pubs.
Clark, Edie, ed. The Forgotten Arts, Bk. 4. LC 75-10770. (Forgotten Arts Ser.). (Illus.). 64p. (Orig.). 1979. pap. 4.95 (ISBN 0-911658-95-5). Yankee Bks.
Davies, Owen L., ed. The Design & Analysis of Industrial Experiments. 2nd ed. LC 77-12563. pap. 160.00 (ISBN 0-317-27871-1, 2025259). Bks Demand UMI.
DiPaul, H. Bert. Focusing Industrial Arts on Career Education. LC 79-53500. (Illus.). 143p. (Orig.). 1979. pap. 2.95x (ISBN 0-9605418-0-2). DiPaul.
Feirer, John L. Industrial Arts Woodworking. 1977. wkbk 5.32 (ISBN 0-02-664650-1); tchr's. ed. 4.24 (ISBN 0-02-664680-3). Bennett IL.
Feirer, John L. & Lindbeck. Drawing & Planning for the Industrial Arts. new ed. (Illus.). 1975. text ed. 14.48 (ISBN 0-02-663480-5); tchr's guide, charts & worksheets 7.72 (ISBN 0-02-663490-2). Bennett IL.
Gerbracht, Carl & Robinson, Frank E. Understanding America's Industries. 1971. text ed. 18.64 (ISBN 0-87345-499-5). McKnight.
Henriksen, Erik K. Jig & Fixture Design Manual. LC 73-8810. (Illus.). 308p. 1973. 37.50 (ISBN 0-8311-1098-8). Indus Pr.
Holtzapffel, John J. The Principles & Practice of Ornamental & Complex Turning. (Illus.). 656p. 1973. Repr. of 1894 ed. 19.95 (ISBN 0-486-22965-3). Dover.
Industrial Crafts. Vorndran, Richard A., ed. LC 77-73248. 64p. 1978. pap. text ed. 4.00 (ISBN 0-02-820450-6). Glencoe.
Jorgensen, Eric, ed. BMW 320i: 1977-1982 Shop Manual. 1982p. (Orig.). pap. text ed. 13.95 (ISBN 0-89287-326-4, A139). Clymer Pubns.
--Chevy, Malibu, Chevelle, Monte Carlo: 1970-1984 Shop Manual. (Illus.). pap. text ed. 12.95 (ISBN 0-89287-319-1, A246). Clymer Pubns.
--Honda Twinstar 1978-1981: Service, Repair, Maintenance. (Illus.). pap. text ed. 13.95 (ISBN 0-89287-325-6, M324). Clymer Pubns.
--Kawasaki 900 & 1000cc Four, 1973-1980: Includes Shaft Drive Service Repair Performance. (Illus., Orig.). pap. text ed. 13.95 (ISBN 0-89287-321-3, M359). Clymer Pubns.
--Oldsmobile Cutlass: (Reardrive0 1970-1984 Manual. (Illus.). 342p. (Orig.). pap. text ed. 12.95 (ISBN 0-89287-324-8, A285). Clymer Pubns.
--Yamaha YZ100-490 Monoshock Singles 1975-1983: Service, Repair, Performance. (Illus.). 293p. (Orig.). pap. text ed. 13.95 (ISBN 0-89287-329-9, M413). Clymer Pubns.
Jorqgensen, Eric, ed. Datsun 210: 1979-1982 Shop Manual. (Illus.). pap. text ed. 12.95 (ISBN 0-89287-322-1, A 203). Clymer Pubns.
Lindbeck, John R. & Lathrop, Irving T. General Industry. (Illus.). 1977. 23.12 (ISBN 0-02-664230-1). student guide 6.64 (ISBN 0-02-664240-9). answer sheet 2.00 (ISBN 0-02-664250-6). Bennett IL.
Olson, D. Industrial Arts for the General Shop. 4th ed. 1973. text ed. 21.12 (ISBN 0-13-459131-3). P-H.
Scott, William R. & Cunnison, J. Industries of the Clyde Valley During the War. (Economic & Social History of the World War Ser.). 1924. 65.00x (ISBN 0-686-83583-2). Elliots Bks.
Veblen, Thorstein B. Instinct of Workmanship. rev. ed. LC 63-23515. Repr. of 1918 ed. 29.50x (ISBN 0-678-00051-4). Kelley.
Wells, H. G. Work, Wealth & Happiness of Mankind, 2 Vols. LC 69-10170. (Illus.). 1968. Repr. of 1931 ed. Set. lib. bdg. 49.75x (ISBN 0-8371-0263-4, WEHM). Greenwood.

INDUSTRIAL ARTS-BIBLIOGRAPHY
see also Inventors
Bolton, Henry C. Catalogue of Scientific & Technical Periodicals. 1665-1895. 2nd ed. Repr. of 1897 ed. 72.00 (ISBN 0-384-04985-0). Johnson Repr.
John Crerar Library. List of Books on the History of Industry & the Industrial Arts. LC 67-14030. 1966. Repr. of 1915 ed. 46.00x (ISBN 0-8103-3104-7). Gale.

INDUSTRIAL ARTS-BIOGRAPHY
Glenister, S. H. Stories of Great Craftsmen. facs. ed. LC 75-128247. (Essay Index Reprint Ser). 1939. 19.00 (ISBN 0-8369-1831-2). Ayer Co Pubs.

INDUSTRIAL ARTS-DICTIONARIES
Ernst, R. German-English, English-German Dictionary of Industrial Technics, 2 vols. 4th, rev., enl. ed. (Ger. & Eng.). Set. 150.00 (ISBN 0-686-77968-1). German-english (ISBN 3-87097-096-0). English-german (ISBN 3-87097-068-5). Heinman.
Franklin, Alfred L. Dictionnaire Historique Des Arts, Metiers & Professions Exerces Dans Paris Depuis Le Treizieme Siecle. (Biblio. & Ref. Ser.: No. 198). (Fr.). 1968. Repr. of 1906 ed. 49.00 (ISBN 0-8337-1231-4); 40.00 (ISBN 0-685-06747-5). B Franklin.

INDUSTRIAL ARTS-EXAMINATIONS, QUESTIONS, ETC.
Rudman, Jack. General Industrial Training Supervisor. (Career Examination Ser.: C-2893). (Cloth bdg. avail. on request). pap. 14.00 (ISBN 0-8373-2893-4). Natl Learning.
--Industrial Arts Education. (National Teachers Examination Ser.: NT-5). (Cloth bdg. avail. on request). pap. 11.95 (ISBN 0-8373-8415-X). Natl Learning.
--Industrial Arts: Junior High School. (Teachers License Examination Ser.: T-30). (Cloth bdg. avail. on request). pap. 13.95 (ISBN 0-8373-8030-8). Natl Learning.
--Industrial Arts: Senior High School. (Teachers License Examination Ser.: T-31). (Cloth bdg. avail on request). pap. 13.95 (ISBN 0-8373-8031-6). Natl Learning.
--Shop Subjects. (Teachers License Examination Ser.: T-53). (Cloth bdg. avail. on request). pap. 13.95 (ISBN 0-8373-8053-7). Natl Learning.

INDUSTRIAL ARTS-EXHIBITIONS
see Exhibitions

INDUSTRIAL ARTS-HISTORY
see also Inventions
Bremner, David. Industries of Scotland. LC 69-11242. Repr. of 1869 ed. 45.00x (ISBN 0-678-05583-1). Kelley.
Clow, Archibald & Clow, Nan L. Chemical Revolution. facs. ed. (Essay Index Reprint Ser). 1952. 42.00 (ISBN 0-8369-1909-2). Ayer Co Pubs.
De Baye, J. The Industrial Arts of the Anglo-Saxons. 1980. Repr. of 1893 ed. lib. bdg. 40.00 (ISBN 0-89341-380-1). Longwood Pub Group.
Giedion, Siegfried. Mechanization Takes Command. (Illus.). 1969. pap. 13.95 (ISBN 0-393-00489-9, Norton Lib). Norton.
Hodges, Henry. Artifacts: An Introduction to Early Materials & Technology. rev. ed. (Illus., Orig.). 1981. pap. text ed. 16.50x (ISBN 0-391-02246-6). Humanities.
Hudson, Kenneth. Industrial Archaeology of Southern England. LC 68-23822. (Illus.). 1968. 24.95x (ISBN 0-678-05606-4). Kelley.
Karmarsch, Karl. Geschichte Der Technologie Seit Der Mitte Des 18. Jahrhunderts. 1872. 55.00 (ISBN 0-384-28630-5). Johnson Repr.
McWhirr, Alan. Roman Crafts & Industries. (Shire Archaeology Ser.: No. 24). (Illus.). 64p. 1982. pap. 5.95 (ISBN 0-85263-594-X, Pub. by Shire Pubns England). Seven Hills Bks.
Miller, Walter. Daedalus & Thespis: Volume II: Sculpture, Pts. 1 & 2. 280p. 1970. Repr. of 1931 ed. 18.00x (ISBN 0-8262-0590-9). U of Mo Pr.
Mumford, Lewis. Technics & Civilization. LC 63-19641. (Illus.). 1963. pap. 8.95 (ISBN 0-15-688254-X, Harv). HarBraceJ.
Richardson, Albert E. Georgian England: A Survey of Social Life, Trades, Industries & Art from 1700 to 1820. facs. ed. LC 67-23265. (Essay Index Reprint Ser). 1931. 31.00 (ISBN 0-8369-0823-6). Ayer Co Pubs.
Smiles, Samuel. Industrial Biography: Iron-Workers & Tool Makers. LC 67-114712. (Illus.). Repr. of 1863 ed. 35.00x (ISBN 0-678-05727-3). Kelley.
Wolf, A. A History of Science, Technology & Philosophy in the Sixteenth & Seventeenth Centuries, 2 vols. (Illus.). 30.00 (ISBN 0-8446-1483-1). Peter Smith.

INDUSTRIAL ARTS-MUSEUMS
see Industrial Museums

INDUSTRIAL ARTS-STUDY AND TEACHING
Baird, Ronald J. Contemporary Industrial Teaching. LC 78-185957. (Illus.). 200p. 1972. text ed. 10.64 (ISBN 0-87006-130-5). Goodheart.
Butler, F. Coit. Instructional Systems Development for Vocational & Technical Training. LC 70-168490. 384p. 1972. 28.95 (ISBN 0-87778-027-7). Educ Tech Pubns.
Giachino, J. W. & Gallington, R. O. Course Construction in Industrial Arts, Vocational & Technical Education. 4th ed. 1977. text ed. 18.95 (ISBN 0-8269-4065-X). Am Technical.
Gropius, Walter. New Architecture & the Bauhaus. (Illus.). 1965. pap. 5.95 (ISBN 0-262-57006-8). MIT Pr.
Gunther, Theresa C. Manipulative Participation in the Study of Elementary Industrial Arts. LC 70-176825. (Columbia University. Teachers College. Contributions to Education: No. 490). Repr. of 1931 ed. 22.50 (ISBN 0-404-55490-3). AMS Pr.
Romano, Louis A. Manual & Industrial Education at Girard College 1831-1965: An Era in American Educational Experimentation. Cordasco, Fransecso, ed. LC 80-1075. (American Ethnic Groups Ser.). 1981. lib. bdg. 43.00x (ISBN 0-405-13450-9). Ayer Co Pubs.
Willmott, John N. High School Boys Electing Industrial Arts. LC 75-177636. (Columbia University. Teachers College. Contributions to Education Ser.: No. 836). Repr. of 1941 ed. 17.50 (ISBN 0-404-55836-4). AMS Pr.

INDUSTRIAL BUILDINGS
see also Factories
Anderson, M. & Lee, R. Efficiency in Lighting. Gyftopoulos, Elias P. & Cohen, Karen C., eds. (Industrial Energy-Conservation Manuals: No. 10). (Illus.). 104p. 1982. loose-leaf 20.00x (ISBN 0-262-01066-6). MIT Pr.
Buildings for Industry. LC 72-142926. (An Architectural Record Book). (Illus.). ix, 309p. Repr. of 1957 ed. lib. bdg. 31.75x (ISBN 0-8371-5928-8, ARBI). Greenwood.
Dietz, Albert G. & Cutler, Laurence S., eds. Industrialized Building Systems for Housing. 1971. 37.50x (ISBN 0-262-04034-4). MIT Pr.
Hudson, Kenneth. Industrial Archaeology of Southern England. LC 68-23822. (Illus.). 1968. 24.95x (ISBN 0-678-05606-4). Kelley.
Muter, W. Grant. The Buildings of an Industrial Community: Coalbrookdale & Ironbridge. 1979. 40.00x (ISBN 0-85033-342-3, Pub. by Phillimore England). State Mutual Bk.
Tandy, Clifford. The Landscape of Industry. LC 75-28033. 314p. 1975. 78.95x (ISBN 0-470-84440-X). Halsted Pr.

INDUSTRIAL CHEMISTRY
see Chemical Engineering; Chemistry, Technical

INDUSTRIAL DESIGN
see Design, Industrial

INDUSTRIAL DESIGN COORDINATION
Burcaw, George E. The Saxon House. LC 79-65600. (GEM Books Ser.). (Illus.). 122p. (Orig.). 1980. pap. 7.95 (ISBN 0-89301-065-0). U Pr of Idaho.
Greene, Anne Marie, ed. Designs & Utility Models Throughout the World. LC 82-20738. 1983. looseleaf 85.00 (ISBN 0-87632-378-6). Boardman.
Wolfendale, E., ed. Computer-Aided Design Techniques. (Illus.). 1971. 18.00 (ISBN 0-8088-0042-6). Davey.

A First Guide to Loss Prevention. 34p. 1981. 25.00x (ISBN 0-85295-106-X, Pub. by IChemE). State Mutual Bk.
Foster, Joseph W., 3rd, et al. Reliability, Availability & Maintainability: RAM. LC 80-81873. 272p. 1982. Repr. of 1981 ed. 39.95 (ISBN 0-930206-05-3). M-A Pr.
Gillies, M. T., ed. Water-Based Industrial Finishes: Recent Developments. LC 80-17520. (Chemical Technology Review Ser.: No. 167). 435p. 1980. 48.00 (ISBN 0-8155-0812-3). Noyes.
Hudson, Kenneth. Industrial Archaeology of Southern England. LC 68-23822. (Illus.). 1968. 24.95x (ISBN 0-678-05606-4). Kelley.
Human Engineering Guide to Equipment Design (JANAF) (Selected Government Publications Ser.: 1-698). 752p. 1972. 43.95x (ISBN 0-471-80011-2, Pub. by Wiley-Interscience). Wiley.
Industrial Furnaces - Design, Location & Equipment. (Eighty-Ninety Ser). 108p. 1974. pap. 3.75 (ISBN 0-685-44134-2, 86B). Natl Fire Prot.
Industrial Furnaces Using Special Processing Atmosphere. (Eighty-Ninety Ser). 148p. 1974. pap. 4.00 (ISBN 0-685-44135-0, 86C). Natl Fire Prot.
Industrial Heating Equipment Association Staff. The Directory of Industrial Heat Processing & Combustion Equipment, 1984. 150p. 1984. 25.00 (ISBN 0-915586-80-0). Van Nos Reinhold.
Industrial Robots Market. 310p. 1983. 1600.00 (ISBN 0-86621-526-3). Frost & Sullivan.
Industrial Safety Equipment Testing Products Market. 289p. 1983. 1300.00 (ISBN 0-86621-118-7, A1173). Frost & Sullivan.
Industrial Vision Systems Market. 246p. 1983. 1300.00 (ISBN 0-86621-156-X). Frost & Sullivan.
Industrial Workwear Market. 376p. 1984. 1675.00 (ISBN 0-86621-581-6, E663). Frost & Sullivan.
International Labour Office, Geneva. Audiovisual, Draughting, Office, Reproduction & Other Ancillary Equipment & Supplies: Equipment Planning Guide for Vocational & Technical Training & Education Programmes. (No. 15). (Illus.). 279p. (Orig.). 1982. pap. 22.80 (ISBN 92-2-102112-2). Intl Labour Office.
Kron, Joan & Slesin, Suzanne. High-Tech: The Industrial-Style Source Book for the Home. (Illus.). 1978. 29.95 (ISBN 0-517-53262-X, C N Potter Bks). Crown.
Lagadec, P. Major Technological Risk: An Assessment of Industrial Disasters. (Illus.). 536p. 1982. 66.00 (ISBN 0-08-028913-4). Pergamon.
Mayeux, Mansel M. Retailing Farm & Light Industrial Equipment. 2nd ed. (Illus.). 1983. lib. bdg. 26.50 (ISBN 0-87055-414-X). AVI.
Nairn, Alan E. & Stehli, Francis G., eds. The Ocean Basins & Margins, Vol. 6: The Indian Ocean. LC 72-83046. 794p. 1982. 95.00x (ISBN 0-306-37776-4, Plenum Pr). PLenum Pub.
Network Editors, ed. ATE for Equipment Production & Maintenance. 1982. 60.00x (ISBN 0-904999-61-0, Pub. by Network). State Mutual Bk.
Othwell, Roy R. & Zegveld, Walter. Reindustrialization & Technology. 300p. (Orig.). 1985. 30.00 (ISBN 0-87332-330-0); pap. 14.95 (ISBN 0-87332-331-9). M E Sharpe.
Page, John S. Estimator's Equipment Installation Man-Hour Manual. 2nd ed. LC 78-53193. (Estimator's Man-Hour Library). 280p. 1978. 39.95x (ISBN 0-87201-276-X). Gulf Pub.
Paruit, Bernard. Illustrated Glossary of Process Equipment: English-French-Chinese Edition. LC 83-1711. (Illus.). 324p. 1984. 39.95x (ISBN 0-87201-692-7). Gulf Pub.
Phatia, Mahesh, ed. Transfer Operations in Process Industries: Design & Equipment. LC 83-50699. (Process Equipment Ser.: Vol. 5). 373p. 1983. 35.00 (ISBN 0-87762-334-1). Technomic.
Rudman, Jack. Equipment Specialist. (Career Examination Ser.: C-971). (Cloth bdg. avail. on request). pap. 12.00 (ISBN 0-8373-0971-9). Natl Learning.
Welch, W. J. & Wilson, P. A. Facsimile Equipment: A Practical Evaluation Guide. 110p. 1982. pap. 14.20 (ISBN 0-471-89452-4). Wiley.
--Facsimile Equipment: A Practical Evaluation Guide. 2nd ed. 122p. 1985. pap. write for info. (ISBN 0-471-87896-0). Wiley.
Woods, Donald R. Selecting Process Equipment. 1984. text ed. 29.95 (ISBN 0-8359-6899-5). Reston.
Workholding. LC 82-61237. (Productivity Equipment Ser.). 640p. 1982. 44.50 (ISBN 0-87263-090-0). SME.

INDUSTRIAL EQUIPMENT–MAINTENANCE AND REPAIR
see Plant Maintenance

INDUSTRIAL EXHIBITIONS
see Exhibitions

INDUSTRIAL HOUSEKEEPING
Cralley, Lewis & Cralley, Lester. Industrial Hygiene of Plant Operations: Unit Operations & Product Fabrication, Vol. 2. LC 82-80255. (Industrial Hygiene of Plant Operations Ser.). 1984. 65.00 (ISBN 0-02-949360-9). Macmillan.
Feldman, Edwin B. Housekeeping Handbook for Institutions, Business & Industry. rev. ed. LC 75-83312. 502p. 1979. 29.95 (ISBN 0-8119-0072-X). Fell.
Sack, Thomas. Complete Guide to Building & Plant Maintenance. 2nd ed. LC 71-126828. (Illus.). 672p. 1971. 49.95 (ISBN 0-13-160101-6). P-H.

INDUSTRIAL MAINTENANCE
see Plant Maintenance

INDUSTRIAL MATERIALS
see Materials

INDUSTRIAL MICROBIOLOGY
see also Microbiological Synthesis
Ball, Christopher, ed. Genetics & Breeding of Industrial Microorganisms. 240p. 1984. 72.00 (ISBN 0-8493-5672-5). CRC Pr.
Bull, M. J., ed. Progress in Industrial Microbiology, Vol. 14. 294p. 1978. 68.00 (ISBN 0-444-41665-X). Elsevier.
--Progress in Industrial Microbiology, Vol. 15. 1979. 68.00 (ISBN 0-444-41815-6). Elsevier.
--Progress in Industrial Microbiology, Vol. 16. 350p. 1982. 78.75 (ISBN 0-444-42037-1). Elsevier.
Bushell, M. E., ed. Progress in Industrial Microbiology, Vol. 17: Industrial Microbiology, Spectroscopy & Pharmaceuticals. 232p. 1983. 64.00 (ISBN 0-444-42128-9). Elsevier.
Crueger, Wulf & Crueger, Anneliese. Biotechnology: A Textbook of Industrial Microbiology. Science Tech Inc., tr. from Ger. LC 84-1340. Tr. of Lehrbuch der Angewandten Mikrobiologie. (Illus.). 350p. 1984. text ed. 30.00x (ISBN 0-87893-126-0). Sinauer Assoc.
Developments in Industrial Microbiology, Vols. 16 & 17. 1975-76. Vol. 16. 25.00 (ISBN 0-934454-92-2); Vol. 17. 25.00 (ISBN 0-686-21617-2). Vol.18. 29.95 (ISBN 0-934454-83-3). Lubrecht & Cramer.
Hahn, Peter. Guide to the Literature for the Industrial Microbiologist. LC 73-19782. 206p. 1973. 35.00x (ISBN 0-306-68431-4, IFI Plenum). Plenum Pub.
Hockenhull, D. J. Progress in Industrial Microbiology, Vols. 4 & 5. Incl. Vol. 4. 214p. 56.75x (ISBN 0-677-10150-3); Vol. 5. 328p. 86.75x (ISBN 0-677-10160-0). 1969. Gordon.
Kirsop, B. E. The Stability of Industrial Organisms: UK Federation for Culture collections Symposium held at the University of Newcastle-upon-Tyne 20th July 1979. 57p. 1980. 32.00x (ISBN 0-85198-470-3, Pub. by CAB Bks England). State Mutual Bk.
Koda, Chester, ed. Developments in Industrial Microbiology, Vol. 3. LC 60-13953. 398p. 1962. 35.00x (ISBN 0-306-37033-6, Plenum Pr). Plenum Pub.
Peppler, Henry J., ed. Microbial Technology. LC 77-796. (Illus.). 464p. 1977. Repr. of 1967 ed. lib. bdg. 27.00 (ISBN 0-88275-538-2). Krieger.
Rich, Saul, ed. Developments in Industrial Microbiology, Vol. 2. LC 60-13953. 306p. 1961. 35.00x (ISBN 0-306-37032-8, Plenum Pr). Plenum Pub.
Schlessinger, David, ed. Microbiology 1976. LC 74-33538. 1976. 28.00 (ISBN 0-914826-11-5). Am Soc Microbio.
Society for Industrial Microbiology. Developments in Industrial Microbiology, 11 vols. LC 60-13953. Vols. 5-15. 25.00 ea. Lubrecht & Cramer.
Thoma, R. W., ed. Industrial Microbiology. (Benchmark Papers in Microbiology: Vol. 12). 1977. 57.95 (ISBN 0-87933-251-4). Van Nos Reinhold.
Underkofler, Leland A., ed. Developments in Industrial Microbiology: Proceedings of the Society for Industrial Microbiology, 41st General Meeting, Fort Collins, Colorado, August 1984, 38 papers, Vol. XXVI. 850p. 1985. 38.95 (ISBN 0-318-04035-2). Soc Indus Micro.
Underkofler, Leland A. & Nash, Claude H., eds. Developments in Industrial Microbiology: Proceedings of 1983 Annual Meeting, Vol. 25. 800p. 1984. 38.95 (ISBN 0-318-01836-5). Soc Indus Micro.
Wiseman, Alan, ed. Principles of Biotechnology. 192p. 1983. pap. 23.95 (ISBN 0-412-00261-2, NO. 5029). Methuen Inc.

INDUSTRIAL MUSEUMS
Clifford, Howard. Western Rail Guide. (Illus.). 168p. 1983. pap. 9.95 (ISBN 0-87564-540-2). Superior Pub.
Wamsley, James S. American Ingenuity: Henry Ford Museum & Greenfield Village. (Illus.). 224p. 1985. 37.50 (ISBN 0-8109-0961-8). Abrams.

INDUSTRIAL NOISE
Bell. Industrial Noise Control. (Mechanical Engineering Ser.). 536p. 1982. 49.50 (ISBN 0-8247-1787-2). Dekker.
Cheremisinoff. Guide for Industrial Noise Control. 190p. 1982. softcover 29.95 (ISBN 0-250-40536-9). Butterworth.
Fader, Bruce. Industrial Noise Control. LC 81-2158. 251p. 1981. 35.95x (ISBN 0-471-06007-0, Pub. by Wiley-Interscience). Wiley.
Faulkner, Lynn L., ed. Handbook of Industrial Noise Control. LC 75-41315. (Illus.). 608p. 1976. 47.50 (ISBN 0-8311-1110-0). Indus Pr.
Irwin, J. David & Graf, Edward R. Industrial Noise & Vibration Control. LC 78-7786. (Illus.). 1979. ref. 43.95 (ISBN 0-13-461574-3). P-H.
Miller, Richard. Noise Control Solutions for the Stone Industry. (Illus.). 90p. pap. text ed. 45.00 (ISBN 0-89671-028-9). SEAI Tech Pubns.
Miller, Richard K. Industrial Noise Update. (Illus.). 87p. 1981. pap. text ed. 30.00 (ISBN 0-89671-025-4). SEAI Tech Pubns.
--Noise Control for Construction. (Illus.). 140p. text ed. 55.00 (ISBN 0-89671-023-8). SEAI Tech Pubns.
--Noise Control Solutions for Printing & Publishing. (Illus.). 77p. 1981. pap. text ed. 45.00 (ISBN 0-89671-026-2). SEAI Tech Pubns.
--Noise Control Solutions for the Chemical & Petroleum Industries. new ed. 1981. text ed. 45.00x (ISBN 0-89671-036-X). SEAI Tech Pubns.
--Noise Control Solutions for the Food Industry. (Illus.). 110p. text ed. 45.00 (ISBN 0-89671-034-3). SEAI Tech Pubns.
--Noise Control Solutions for the Food Industry, Vol. II. (Illus.). 120p. 1981. pap. text ed. 45.00 (ISBN 0-89671-024-6). SEAI Tech Pubns.
--Noise Control Solutions for the Footwear Industry. 90p. pap. text ed. 45.00 (ISBN 0-89671-027-0). SEAI Tech Pubns.
--Noise Control Solutions for the Glass Industry. 120p. pap. text ed. 90.00 (ISBN 0-89671-016-5). SEAI Tech Pubns.
--Noise Control Solutions for the Metal Products Industry. (Illus.). 120p. text ed. 45.00 (ISBN 0-89671-031-9). SEAI Tech Pubns.
--Noise Control Solutions for the Metal Products Industry, Vol. II. (Illus.). 120p. pap. text ed. 45.00 (ISBN 0-89671-021-1). SEAI Tech Pubns.
--Noise Control Solutions for the Paper Industry. (Illus.). 80p. text ed. 45.00 (ISBN 0-89671-033-5). SEAI Tech Pubns.
--Noise Control Solutions for the Rubber & Plastics Industry. new ed. (Illus.). 1981. text ed. 45.00x (ISBN 0-89671-037-8). SEAI Tech Pubns.
--Noise Control Solutions for the Textile Industry. (Illus.). 90p. text ed. 45.00 (ISBN 0-89671-035-1). SEAI Tech Pubns.
--Noise Control Solutions for the Wire Industry. new ed. (Illus.). 1979. pap. text ed. 35.00x (ISBN 0-89671-006-8). SEAI Tech Pubns.
--Noise Control Solutions for the Wood Products Industry. 80p. text ed. 45.00 (ISBN 0-89671-032-7). SEAI Tech Pubns.
--Power Plant Noise Control. (Illus.). 130p. pap. text ed. 65.00 (ISBN 0-89671-019-X). SEAI Tech Pubns.
Yang, S. J. & Ellison, A. J. Machinery Noise Measurement. (Monographs in Electrical & Electronic Engineering). (Illus.). 224p. 1985. 35.00 (ISBN 0-19-859333-3). Oxford U Pr.

INDUSTRIAL PAINTING
see Painting, Industrial

INDUSTRIAL PLANTS
see Factories

INDUSTRIAL POISONS
see Industrial Toxicology

INDUSTRIAL PROCESS CONTROL
see Process Control

INDUSTRIAL PROCESSING
see Manufacturing Processes

INDUSTRIAL PROCUREMENT–DATA PROCESSING
National Computing Centre Ltd., ed. Production Control Packages. LC 72-97122. (Factfinder Ser: No. 13). 100p. 1976. pap. 15.00x (ISBN 0-85012-160-4). Intl Pubns Serv.

INDUSTRIAL RESEARCH
see Research, Industrial

INDUSTRIAL SAFETY
see also Clothing, Protective
also subdivisions Safety Appliances and Safety Measures under subjects, e.g. Factories–Safety Appliances
Aitio, Antero, et al, eds. Biological Monitoring & Surveillance of Workers Exposed to Chemicals. LC 82-2946. (Illus.). 403p. 1983. text ed. 64.50 (ISBN 0-89116-253-4). Hemisphere Pub.
American Water Works Association. Safety Practice for Water Utilities - M3. (AWWA Manuals). (Illus.). 128p. 1977. pap. text ed. 16.20 (ISBN 0-89867-061-6). Am Water Wks Assn.
Anton, Thomas. Occupational Safety & Health Management. 1979. text ed. 34.00 (ISBN 0-07-002106-6). McGraw.
Asfahl, Ray. Industrial Safety & Health Management. rev. ed. (Illus.). 416p. 1984. text ed. 35.95 (ISBN 0-13-463141-2). P-H.
Ashford, Nicholas A. Crisis in the Workplace: Occupational Disease & Injury - (A Report to the Ford Foundation) LC 75-28424. 1976. 35.00x (ISBN 0-262-01045-3). MIT Pr.
Beaulieu, Harry J. & Buchan, Roy M. Quantitative Industrial Hygiene. 1981. lib. bdg. 19.00 (ISBN 0-8240-7180-8). Garland Pub.
Blake, Roland P. Industrial Safety. 3rd ed. 1963. ref. ed. 24.95 (ISBN 0-13-463133-1). P-H.
Blockley, D. I. The Nature of Structure-Design & Safety. 365p. 1980. 99.95x (ISBN 0-470-27047-0). Halsted Pr.
BNA's Environmental & Safety Information Services. Job Safety & Health. (Policy & Practice Ser.). write for info. BNA.
--Mine Safety & Health Reporter. write for info. BNA.
--Occupational Safety & Health Reporter. write for info. BNA.
Bodurtha, Frank T. Industrial Explosion Prevention & Protection. (Illus.). 1980. 31.50 (ISBN 0-07-006359-1). McGraw.
Brown, D. Systems Analysis & Design for Safety. 399p. 1976. text ed. 31.95 (ISBN 0-13-881177-6). P-H.
Browning. The Loss Rate Concept in Safety Engineering. (Occupational Safety & Health Ser.: Vol. 6). 176p. 1980. 29.75 (ISBN 0-8247-1249-8). Dekker.
Building Work: A Compendium of Occupational Safety & Health Practice. (Occupational Safety & Health Ser.: No. 42). 261p. 1981. pap. 14.25 (ISBN 92-2-101907-1, ILO161, ILO). Unipub.
Chemical Engineering Magazine. Safe & Efficient Plant Operation & Maintenance. LC 80-14762. (Chemical Engineering Ser.). 400p. 1980. 37.50 (ISBN 0-07-010707-6). McGraw.
Cheremisinoff, Paul N. Management of Hazardous Occupational Environments: Analysis Revised. LC 84-51008. 202p. 1984. pap. 24.95 (ISBN 0-317-17391-X). Technomic.
Chicken, John C. Hazard Control Policy in Britain. LC 75-12900. 204p. 1975. text ed. 32.00 (ISBN 0-08-019739-6). Pergamon.
Chissick, S. S. & Derricott, R. Occupational Health & Safety Management: Property of Materials: Safety & Environmental Factors. LC 79-41218. 705p. 1981. 106.95 (ISBN 0-471-27646-4, Pub. by Wiley-Interscience). Wiley.
Clayton, George D. & Clayton, Florence E., eds. Patty's Industrial Hygiene & Toxicology, 5 pts. 3rd ed. 1983. Set. 515.00 (ISBN 0-471-87350-0). Wiley.
Cralley, Lewis J. & Cralley, Lester V. Patty's Industrial Hygiene Toxicology: The Work Environment, Vol. 3A. 2nd ed. 832p. 1985. 95.00 (ISBN 0-471-86137-5). Wiley.
Culbertson, Charles V. Managing Your Safety Manager. 48p. 1981. 5.50 (ISBN 0-937802-01-8). Risk Mgmt Soc.
Dalton, Thomas F. The Effects of Heat & Stress on Cleanup Personnel Working with Hazardous Materials. 1984. 25.00 (ISBN 0-318-01766-0). Spill Control Assn.
Denton, K. Safety Management. 416p. 1982. 40.00x (ISBN 0-07-016410-X). McGraw.
DeReamer, Russell. Modern Safety & Health Technology. LC 79-17487. 615p. 1980. 49.95x (ISBN 0-471-05729-0, Pub. by Wiley-Interscience). Wiley.
Dewis, Malcolm, ed. Tolley's Health & Safety at Work Handbook. 1982. 95.00x (ISBN 0-85459-029-3, Pub. by Tolley Pub England). State Mutual Bk.
Encyclopedia of Occupational Health & Safety 1983, 2 vols. 3rd ed. 2400p. 1983. 155.00 (ISBN 92-2-103289-2). Taylor & Francis.
European Convention of Constructional Steelwork. European Recommendations for the Fire Safety of Steel Structures. 106p. 1983. 70.25 (ISBN 0-444-42120-3). Elsevier.
Feldman, Alan S. & Grimes, Charles I. Hearing Conservation in Industry. 352p. 1985. 35.00 (ISBN 0-683-03112-0). Williams & Wilkins.
Ferry, Ted S. Safety Program Administration for Engineers & Managers: A Resource Guide for Establishing & Evaluating Safety Programs. (Illus.). 306p. 1984. 30.50x (ISBN 0-398-05000-7). C C Thomas.
Fife, Ian & Machin, E. Anthony. Health & Safety at Work. LC 81-182916. Date not set. cancelled (ISBN 0-406-20054-8). Butterworth.
Gardner, James E. Safety Training for the Supervisor. 3rd ed. LC 78-52505. 1979. pap. text ed. 9.95 (ISBN 0-201-03090-X). Addison-Wesley.
Germain, George L. Effective Safe Behavior Reinforcement. (The Effective Series Training Program for Supervisors). (Illus.). 37p. 1975. 3-ring binder 57.50 (ISBN 0-88061-025-5). Inst Pub GA.

Hutzinger, O., ed. Reactions & Processes. (The Handbook of Environmental Chemistry Ser.: Vol. 2, Pt. C). 180p. 1985. 38.00 (ISBN 0-387-13819-6). Springer-Verlag.

ILO-WHO Committee on Occupational Health. Geneva, 1968, 6th. Permissible Levels of Occupational Exposure to Airborne Toxic Substances: Report. (Technical Report Ser.: No. 415). (Also avail. in French & Spanish). 1969. pap. 1.20 (ISBN 92-4-120415-X). World Health.

LaGrega, Michael D. & Long, David A., eds. Toxic & Hazardous Wastes: Proceedings of the Sixteenth Mid-Atlantic Industrial Waste Conference. LC 84-51326. 587p. 1984. pap. 45.00 (ISBN 0-87762-363-5). Technomic.

Miller, Marshall L., ed. Toxic Control, Volume IV: Toxic Control in the Eighties. LC 80-80472. (Illus.). 210p. 1980. pap. text ed. 25.00 (ISBN 0-86587-053-5). Gov Insts.

Occupational Exposure to Airborne Substances Harmful to Health. (Codes Of Practice Ser.). viii, 44p. 1980. pap. 5.70 (ISBN 92-2-102442-3, ILO152, ILO). Unipub.

Plunkett, E. R. Handbook of Industrial Toxicology. 2nd ed. 1976. 40.00 (ISBN 0-8206-0201-9). Chem Pub.

Toxic Chemical & Explosives Facilities: Safety & Engineering Design. LC 79-9760. (Symposium Ser.: No. 96). 1979. 39.95 (ISBN 0-8412-0481-0). Am Chemical.

Toxic Substances Litigation 1982. (Litigation & Administrative Practice, Course Handbook Ser. 1981-1982). 563p. 1982. 30.00 (ISBN 0-686-80260-8, H4-4872). PLI.

Toxics: A Case Study, 1979. 1982. 3.25 (ISBN 0-686-33163-X). Ctr Analysis Public Issues.

Tsubaki, T. & Irukayama, K., eds. Minamata Disease: Methylmercury Poisoning in Minamata & Nigata, Japan. 1977. 85.75 (ISBN 0-444-99816-0). Elsevier.

INDUSTRIAL VACUUM
see Vacuum Technology

INDUSTRIAL WASTES
see Factory and Trade Waste

INDUSTRIAL WATER SUPPLY
see Water-Supply, Industrial

INDUSTRIALISTS

Fraser, Colin. Tractor Pioneer: The Life of Harry Ferguson. LC 73-85451. (Illus.). vi, 294p. 1973. 15.00x (ISBN 0-8214-0134-3, 82-81370). Ohio U Pr.

Minnigerode, Meade. Certain Rich Men. LC 71-121489. (Essay Index Reprint Ser). 1927. 18.00 (ISBN 0-8369-1714-6). Ayer Co Pubs.

Moore, Joseph A. Famous Leaders of Industry: Life Stories of Men Who Have Succeeded, Fifth Series. facsimile ed. LC 68-8505. (Essay Index Reprints - Famous Leaders Ser.). Repr. of 1945 ed. 25.50 (ISBN 0-8369-2326-X). Ayer Co Pubs.

Shumway, Harry I. Famous Leaders of Industry, Fourth Series. facsimile ed. LC 76-167417. (Essay Index Reprint Ser). Repr. of 1936 ed. 26.00 (ISBN 0-8369-2441-X). Ayer Co Pubs.

White, Trentwell M. Famous Leaders of Industry, Third Series. facsimile ed. LC 68-8505. (Essay Index Reprint Ser: Famous Leaders Ser). Repr. of 1931 ed. 25.50 (ISBN 0-8369-2259-X). Ayer Co Pubs.

INDUSTRIES
see Industrial Arts
also subdivision Industries under names of countries, etc. e.g. United States–Industries; names of particular industries

INDUSTRIES, CHEMICAL
see Chemical Industries

INDUSTRIES, ELECTRIC
see Electric Industries

INDUSTRY–DATA PROCESSING

Flora, Philip C. International Industrial Sensor Directory. (Illus.). 280p. (Orig.). Date not set. pap. text ed. 35.00 (ISBN 0-910747-19-9). Tech Data TX.

Halligan, Joseph. Manufacturing - Software. Winther, Richard, ed. (Software Directories Ser.: Vol. 1). (Orig.). 1985. 49.95 (ISBN 0-918451-89-2). Moore Data.

Harrison, Thomas J., ed. Minicomputers in Industrial Control. LC 77-93080. (Illus.). 356p. 1978. text ed. 36.00x (ISBN 0-87664-372-1). Instru Soc.

Hordeski, Michael F. Microprocessors in Industry. 1984. 49.50 (ISBN 0-442-23207-1). Van Nos Reinhold.

International Computer Programs Inc. ICP Software Directory, Vol. 6: Specialized Industry Systems. Hamilton, Dennis L., ed. 1984. pap. 95.00 (ISBN 0-88094-030-1). Intl Computer.

International Computer Programs Staff. ICP Software Directory, Vol. 6: Specialized Industry Systems. Hamilton, Dennis L., ed. 1985. pap. 95.00 (ISBN 0-88094-047-6). Intl Computer.

Kleinpeter, Joseph & Hawkey, Earl W. Computerized Management of Physical Plant Services. 125p. 17.50 (ISBN 0-317-33656-8); 12.50, members (ISBN 0-317-33657-6). Assn Phys Plant Admin.

Kompass, Edward J. & Williams, Theodore J., eds. Computer Software for Industrial Control: Proceedings of the 7th Annual Advanced Control Conference. 180p. 1983. Repr. of 1981 ed. Conference Papers 20.50 (ISBN 0-914331-06-X). Control Eng.

--Industrial Computing Control after 25 Years: Micros to Hierarchies (Proceedings of the 10th Annual Advanced Control Conference) 276p. 1984. Conference papers 37.50 (ISBN 0-914331-09-4). Control Eng.

Roberts, Steven K. Industrial Design with Microcomputers. (Illus.). 416p. 1982. 33.95 (ISBN 0-13-459461-4). P-H.

INDUSTRY–ENERGY CONSERVATION

Association of Energy Engineers Staff. Strategic Planning for Cogeneration & Energy Management. 600p. 1985. 45.00; pap. 30.00. Van Nos Reinhold.

Balassa, Bela. The Newly Industrializing Developing Countries after the Oil Crisis. (Working Paper: No. 437). 57p. 1980. pap. 3.00 (ISBN 0-686-39744-4, WP-0437). World Bank.

Brown, Harry L., ed. Energy Analysis of One Hundred Eight Industrial Processes. LC 84-48572. (Illus.). 313p. 1985. 39.00 (ISBN 0-915586-93-2). Fairmont Pr.

Bryant, Raymond C. & McGorray, J. J., eds. Managing Energy for Industry. (Illus.). 277p. 1983. 38.00 (ISBN 0-86587-108-6). Gov Insts.

Burt Hill Kosar Rittelmann Associates. Small Office Building Handbook: Design for Reducing First Costs & Utility Costs. (Illus.). 400p. 1984. 40.00 (ISBN 0-442-21126-0). Van Nos Reinhold.

Cho, Chun H. Computer Based Energy Management Systems: Technology & Applications (Monograph) (Energy Science & Engineering Ser.). 1984. 45.00 (ISBN 0-12-173380-7). Acad Pr.

De Renzo, D. J., ed. Industrial Energy Conservation Technologies & Research Opportunities. LC 83-3944. (Energy Tech. Rev. 82). (Illus.). 704p. (Orig.). 1983. 64.00 (ISBN 0-8155-0941-3). Noyes.

Energy-Conscious Iron & Steelmaking. 1981. 70.00x (ISBN 0-904357-32-5, Metals Soc). Brookfield Pub Co.

Energyworks, Inc. Staff. Energy-Efficient Products & Systems: A Comparative Catalog for Architects & Engineers. 860p. 1983. incl. three 6 month updates 135.00 (ISBN 0-471-87336-5, Pub. by Wiley-Interscience); pap. Jan. 1983 update (ISBN 0-471-88223-2); pap. 1.00 2nd supplement (ISBN 0-471-87887-1); pap. Jan. 1984 update (ISBN 0-471-80697-8). Wiley.

Fahey, Liam. Energy Management in Industrial Firms. LC 79-7939. (Outstanding Dissertations in Economics Ser.). 350p. 1984. lib. bdg. 36.00 (ISBN 0-8240-4187-9). Garland Pub.

Furgerson, W. F. Conserving Energy in Refrigeration. Gyftopoulos, Elias P. & Cohen, Karen C., eds. (Industrial Energy-Conservation Manuals: No. 12). 144p. 1982. loose-leaf 20.00x (ISBN 0-262-06080-9). MIT Pr.

Harrison, Michael R. Thermal Insulation. Gyftopoulos, Elias P. & Cohen, Karen C., eds. (Industrial Energy-Conservation Manuals: No. 11). 112p. 1982. loose-leaf 20.00x (ISBN 0-262-08112-1). MIT Pr.

IMR Corporation. Reducing Energy Costs in Small Businesses. 1983. text ed. 22.95 (ISBN 0-8359-6615-1). Reston.

Institution of Chemical Engineers & Linhoff, B. User Guide on Process Integration for the Efficient Use of Energy. (Illus.). 252p. 1983. 25.00 (ISBN 0-08-030245-9). Pergamon.

Kennedy, William J., Jr. & Turner, Wayne C. Energy Management. (Illus.). 304p. 1984. pap. text ed. 31.95 (ISBN 0-13-277674-X). P-H.

Kershner, Thomas R. & Kenney, James M. The Industrial Demand for Electricity. LC 81-48332. 1984. write for info. (ISBN 0-669-05332-5). Lexington Bks.

Lev, Benjamin, ed. Energy Models & Studies. (Studies in Management Science & Systems: Vol. 9). 600p. 1983. 89.50 (ISBN 0-444-86601-9, North Holland). Elsevier.

Lewtya, John, ed. Paper Machine Energy Factors. 24p. 1983. 11.95 (ISBN 0-89852-413-X); TAPPI members 8.00. TAPPI.

Mix, T. W. & Dweck, J. S. Conserving Energy in Distillation. Gyftopoulos, Elias P. & Cohen, Karen C., eds. (Industrial Energy-Conservation Manuals: No. 13). (Illus.). 112p. 1982. loose-leaf 20.00x (ISBN 0-262-13172-2). MIT Pr.

Monroe, Elmer S., Jr. Saving Fuel with Furnaces. Gyftopoulos, Elias P. & Cohen, Karen C., eds. (Industrial Energy-Conservation Manuals: No. 6). 56p. 1982. loose-leaf 20.00x (ISBN 0-262-13171-4). MIT Pr.

Payne, F. William, ed. Advanced Technologies: Improving Industrial Efficiency. LC 84-48433. 300p. 1985. 32.00 (ISBN 0-88173-001-7). Fairmont Pr.

Payne, Gordon A. Managing Energy in Commerce & Industry. (Illus.). 256p. 1984. text ed. 49.95 (ISBN 0-408-01168-8). Butterworth.

Reis, A., ed. Economics & Management of Energy in Industry: Proceedings of the European Congress, Algarve, Portugal, 2-5 April 1984, 2 Vols. 700p. 1984. Set. 105.00 (ISBN 0-08-030561-X, 310884). Pergamon.

Reiter, Sydney. Industrial & Commercial Heat Recovery Systems. 256p. 1983. 27.50 (ISBN 0-442-27943-4). Van Nos Reinhold.

Schmidt, Philip S. Electricity & Industrial Productivity: A Technical & Economic Perspective. (Illus.). 416p. 1984. pap. 75.00 (ISBN 0-08-031948-3). Pergamon.

Stephanopoulos, G. Synthesizing Networks of Heat Exchangers. Gyftopoulos, Elias P. & Cohen, Karen C., eds. (Industrial Energy-Conservation Manuals: No. 4). (Illus.). 128p. 1982. 3-ring binder pages 20.00x (ISBN 0-262-19203-9). MIT Pr.

Strategy for Energy Use in the Iron & Steel Industry. (Economic Commission for Europe Ser.: No. 41). (Illus.). 171p. 1985. pap. 21.00 (UN83/2E22, UN). Unipub.

Thumann, Albert. Energy Management Systems Sourcebook. LC 84-4877. 208p. 1984. 32.00 (ISBN 0-915586-52-5). Fairmont Pr.

Tunnah, Barry G. Industrial Energy Management. (Energy Management Training Program Monograph Ser.). 140p. Date not set. pap. 17.50x (ISBN 0-86531-765-8). Westview.

Twenty Ways to Conserve Energy in Office Buildings, Shopping Centers, & Other Commercial Properties. 50 copies 11.00 (ISBN 0-686-46419-2). Inst Real Estate.

Welding Institute of Canada, ed. Welding in Energy-Related Projects: Proceedings of the International Conference on Welding in Energy-Related Projects; Toronto, Canada, September 20-21, 1983. (Illus.). 502p. 1984. 80.00x (ISBN 0-08-025412-8). Pergamon.

Wyman, Harold E. & Ketz, J. Edward. Managing Corporate Energy Needs: The Role of Management Accounting. 116p. pap. 15.95 (ISBN 0-86641-058-8, 82136). Natl Assn Accts.

INEQUALITIES (MATHEMATICS)

Beckenbach, E. F. & Bellman, R. Inequalities. LC 62-4593. (Ergebnisse der Mathematik und Ihrer Grenzgebiete: Vol. 30). (Illus.). 1971. 29.50 (ISBN 0-387-03283-5). Springer-Verlag.

--An Introduction to Inequalities. LC 61-6228. (New Mathematical Library: No. 3). 135p. 1975. pap. 8.75 (ISBN 0-88385-603-4). Math Assn.

Beckenbach, Edwin, ed. General Inequalities II. (International Ser. of Numerical Mathematics: No. 47). 505p. 1980. pap. 45.95x (ISBN 0-8176-1056-1). Birkhauser.

Bensoussan, A. & Lions, J. L. Applications of Variational Inequalities in Stochastic Control. (Studies in Mathematics & Its Applications: Vol. 12). Orig. Title: Applications des Inequations Variationnelles en Controle Stochastique. 564p. 1982. 74.50 (ISBN 0-444-86358-3, North-Holland). Elsevier.

Duvant, G. & Lions, J. L. Inequalities in Mechanics & Physics. John, C., tr. from Fr. (Die Grundlehren der Mathematischen Wissenschaften: Vol. 219). (Illus.). 400p. 1976. 60.00 (ISBN 0-387-07327-2). Springer-Verlag.

Essen, M. R. The Cosine Pi Lambda Theorem. LC 75-17547. (Lecture Notes in Mathematics Ser.: Vol. 467). 112p. (Orig.). 1975. pap. 13.00 (ISBN 0-387-07176-8). Springer-Verlag.

Friedland, Shmuel. Nonoscillation, Disconjugacy & Integral Inequalities. LC 76-25246. 1976. 13.00 (ISBN 0-8218-2176-8, MEMO-176). Am Math.

Garcia-Cuerva & Rubio De Francia, J. L. Weighted Norm Inequalities & Related Topics. (Mathematics Studies: Vol. 116). 604p. 1985. 65.00 (ISBN 0-444-87804-1, North-Holland). Elsevier.

Glowinski, R., et al. Numerical Analysis of Variational Inequations. (Studies in Mathematics & Its Applications: Vol. 8). 776p. 1981. 95.75 (ISBN 0-444-86199-8, North-Holland). Elsevier.

Kazarinoff, N. D. Geometric Inequalities. LC 61-6229. (New Mathematical Library: No. 4). 132p. 1975. pap. 8.75 (ISBN 0-88385-604-2). Math Assn.

Kinderlehrer, David & Stampacchia, Guido. An Introduction to Variational Inequalities & Their Applications. LC 79-52793. (Pure & Applied Mathematics Ser.). 1980. 59.50 (ISBN 0-12-407350-6). Acad Pr.

Lakshmikantham, V. & Leela, S. Differential & Integral Inequalities: Theory & Application, 2 vols. Incl. Vol. 1. Ordinary Differential Equations. 1969. 80.00 (ISBN 0-12-434101-2); Vol. 2. Functional, Partial, Abstract & Complex Differential Equations. 80.00 (ISBN 0-12-434102-0). LC 68-8425. (Mathematics in Science & Engineering Ser.: Vol. 55). 1969. Acad Pr.

Marshall, Albert & Olkin, Ingram. Inequalities: Theory of Majorization & Its Applications. LC 79-50218. (Mathematics in Science & Engineering Ser.). 1979. 70.00 (ISBN 0-12-473750-1). Acad Pr.

Mikhlin, Solomon G. Constants in Some Inequalities of Analysis. LC 84-13108. 1985. 21.95 (ISBN 0-471-90559-3). Wiley.

Mitrinovic, D. S. & Vasic, P. M. Analytic Inequalities. LC 76-116492. (Grundlehren der Mathematischen Wissenschaften: Vol. 165). (Illus.). 1970. 47.00 (ISBN 0-387-04837-5). Springer-Verlag.

Polya, G. & Szego, G. Isoperimetric Inequalities in Mathematical Physics. (Annals of Math Studies). 1951. 24.00 (ISBN 0-527-02743-X). Kraus Repr.

Schroder, Johann. Operator Inequalities. LC 79-28754. (Mathematics in Science & Engineering Ser.). 1980. 59.50 (ISBN 0-12-629750-9). Acad Pr.

Shisha, Oved, ed. Inequalities: Proceedings, 3 vols. Vol. 1, 1967. 49.50 (ISBN 0-12-640350-3); Vol. 2, 1970. 86.50 (ISBN 0-12-640302-3); Vol. 3, 1972. 75.00 (ISBN 0-12-640303-1). Acad Pr.

Solodovnikov, A. S. Systems of Linear Inequalities. 123p. 1979. pap. 3.95 (ISBN 0-8285-1515-8, Pub. by Mir Pubs USSR). Imported Pubns.

Walter, Wolfgang. Differential & Integral Inequalities. rev. ed. Rosenblatt, L. & Shampine, L., trs. from Ger. LC 72-103330. (Ergebnisse der Mathematik und Ihrer Grenzgebiete: Vol. 55). (Illus.). 1970. 48.00 (ISBN 0-387-05088-4). Springer-Verlag.

Wilf, H. S. Finite Sections of Some Classical Inequalities. LC 75-105700. (Ergebnisse der Mathematik und Ihrer Grenzgebiete: Vol. 52). (Illus.). 1970. 25.00 (ISBN 0-387-04809-X). Springer-Verlag.

INERT ELEMENTS
see Gases, Rare

INERTIAL GUIDANCE
see Inertial Navigation Systems

INERTIAL NAVIGATION (AERONAUTICS)

Farrell, James L., ed. Integrated Aircraft Navigation. 1976. 59.00 (ISBN 0-12-249750-3). Acad Pr.

INERTIAL NAVIGATION SYSTEMS

Britting, Kenneth R. Inertial Navigation Systems Analysis. LC 70-168635. 249p. 1971. 42.95 (ISBN 0-471-10485-X, Pub. by Wiley-Interscience). Wiley.

INFANCY OF ANIMALS
see Animals, Infancy of

INFINITE PROCESSES
see Processes, Infinite

INFINITE SERIES
see Series, Infinite

INFINITESIMAL CALCULUS
see Calculus

INFINITESIMAL TRANSFORMATIONS
see Transformations, Infinitesimal

INFLAMMABLE MATERIALS

Backer, S., et al. Textile Fabric Flammability. LC 75-23061. 400p. 1976. text ed. 32.50x (ISBN 0-262-02117-X). MIT Pr.

Basic Classification of Flammable & Combustible Liquids. (Thirty Ser). 1973. pap. 2.00 (ISBN 0-685-58111-X, 321). Natl Fire Prot.

Carroll-Porczynski, C. Z. Flammability of Composite Fabrics. (Illus.). 1976. 45.00 (ISBN 0-8206-0246-9). Chem Pub.

Classification of the Flammability of Wearing Apparel. (Seven Hundred Ser.). 1968. pap. 2.00 (ISBN 0-685-58211-6, 702). Natl Fire Prot.

Cleaning or Safeguarding Small Tanks & Containers. (Thirty Ser). 1970. pap. 2.00 (ISBN 0-685-58110-1, 327). Natl Fire Prot.

Code for Explosive Materials. (Forty Ser.). 76p. 1973. pap. 2.00 (ISBN 0-685-44171-7, 495). Natl Fire Prot.

Code for Storage of Gaseous Oxidizing Materials. 1974. pap. 2.00 (ISBN 0-685-58202-7, 43C-T). Natl Fire Prot.

Critser, James R., Jr. Flame Retardants for Plastics, Rubber & Textiles (July 1971-June 1972) (Ser. 2-7172). 107p. 1972. 110.00 (ISBN 0-914428-11-X). Lexington Data Inc.

--Flame Retardants for Plastics, Rubber, Textiles & Paper (July 1973-June 1974) (Ser. 2-7374). 1974. 123.00 (ISBN 0-914428-22-5). Lexington Data.

Dip Tanks Containing Flammable or Combustible Liquids. (Thirty Ser). 1974. pap. 2.50 (ISBN 0-685-58108-X, 34). Natl Fire Prot.

Fire Hazard Properties of Flammable Liquids, Gases, Volatile Solids. (Thirty Ser.). 139p. 1969. pap. 3.00 (ISBN 0-685-46063-0, 325M). Natl Fire Prot.

Flammability of Cellular Plastics, Part 2. (Fire & Flammability Ser.: Vol. 19). 154p. 1981. pap. 25.00 (ISBN 0-87762-298-1). Technomic.

Flammability of Solid Plastics, Part 2. (Family & Flammability Ser.: Vol. 17). 208p. 1981. 25.00 (ISBN 0-87762-296-5). Technomic.

Flammable & Combustible Liquids & Gases in Manholes & Sewers. (Thirty Ser.). 1970. pap. 2.00 (ISBN 0-685-58109-8, 328). Natl Fire Prot.
Flammable & Combustible Liquids Code. (Thirty Ser.). 116p. 1973. pap. 2.00 (ISBN 0-685-44165-2, NO. 30). Natl Fire Prot.
Harris, Judith C., et al. Combustion of Hazardous Wastes: Sampling & Analysis Methods. LC 84-22690. (Pollution Technology Review Ser.: No. 117). (Illus.). 419p. 1985. 42.00 (ISBN 0-8155-1019-5). Noyes.
Henry, Martin, ed. The Flammable & Combustible Liquids Code Handbook. LC 79-56909. (Illus.). 256p. 1981. 16.50 (ISBN 0-87765-174-4). Natl Fire Prot.
Hilado, Carlos J. Flammability Handbook for Electrical Insulation. 145p. 1982. 40.00 (ISBN 0-87762-316-3). Technomic.
--Flammability Handbook for Thermal Insulation. LC 83-50455. 128p. 1983. 40.00 (ISBN 0-87762-329-5). Technomic.
International Symposium on Flammability & Fire Retardants, 1977. Fire Retardants: Proceedings. Bhatnagar, Vijay M., ed. LC 77-90574. (Illus.). 1977. pap. 14.95x (ISBN 0-87762-246-9). Technomic.
Johnson, Donald M. New Developments in Bulk Storage of Flammable Liquids. 1981. 2.50 (ISBN 0-686-31893-5, TR 81-1). Society Fire Protect.
Landrock, Arthur H. Handbook of Plastics Flammability & Combustion Toxicology: Principles, Materials, Testing, Safety & Smoke Inhalation Effects. LC 83-2342. (Illus.). 308p. (Orig.). 1983. 36.00 (ISBN 0-8155-0940-5, Noyes Pubns). Noyes.
Lewin, Menachem, et al, eds. Flame-Retardant Polymeric Materials, Vol. 2. LC 75-26781. (Illus.). 345p. 1978. 59.50x (ISBN 0-306-32212-9, Plenum Pr). Plenum Pub.
Meidl, James. Hazardous Materials Handbook. (Fire Science Ser). 1972. pap. text ed. write for info. (ISBN 0-02-476370-5, 47637). Macmillan.
Meidl, James H. Flammable Hazardous Materials. 2nd ed. 1978. text ed. write for info. (ISBN 0-02-476570-8). Macmillan.
Nadeau, Herbert G., ed. Fire Property Data-Cellular Plastics. 167p. 1981. pap. 25.00 (ISBN 0-87762-293-0). Technomic.
National Academy of Sciences, ed. Fire Dynamics & Scenarios, Vol. 4. LC 77-79218. (Fire Safety Aspects of Polymeric Materials). 1978. 15.00x (ISBN 0-87762-225-6). Technomic.
National Fire Protection Association. Flammable & Combustible Liquids Code: 1981. 1981. 10.00 (ISBN 0-317-07372-9, NFPA 30). Natl Fire Prot.
Portable Shipping Tanks. (Thirty Ser.). 1974. pap. 2.00 (ISBN 0-685-58105-5, 386). Natl Fire Prot.
Schreier, Peter, ed. Analysis of Volatiles. Methods-Applications: Proceedings-International Workshop. LC 84-1721. xi, 469p. 1984. 87.00x (ISBN 3-11-009805-9). De Gruyter.
Spray Application Using Flammable & Combustible Liquids. (Thirty Ser.). 56p. 1973. pap. 2.00 (ISBN 0-685-44167-9, 33). Natl Fire Prot.
Storage of Flammable & Combustible Liquids on Farms & Isolated Construction Projects. (Thirty Ser). 1972. pap. 2.00 (ISBN 0-685-58103-9, 395). Natl Fire Prot.
Tank Vehicles for Flammable & Combustible Liquids. (Thirty Ser). 1974. pap. 2.50 (ISBN 0-685-58035-0, 385). Natl Fire Prot.
Underground Leakage of Flammable & Combustible Liquids. (Thirty Ser.). 56p. 1972. pap. 2.00 (ISBN 0-685-46064-9, 329). Natl Fire Prot.

INFLAMMATION

Allen, Robert C., et al, eds. Marker Proteins in Inflammation: Proceedings of the Symposium; Lyon, France, April 22-25, 1981. Suskind, Robert M. (Illus.). 608p. 1982. 74.00 (ISBN 3-11-008625-5). De Gruyter.
Bekemeier, H., ed. Trends in Inflammation Research Two. Hirschelmann, R. (Agents & Actions Supplements: Vol. 10). 315p. 1982. text ed. 39.95 (ISBN 0-8176-1344-7). Birkhauser.
Bonta, I. L., et al, eds. Inflammation Mechanisms & Their Impact on Therapy. (Agents & Actions Supplements: No. 3). (Illus.). 192p. 1977. pap. text ed. 69.95x (ISBN 0-8176-0913-X). Birkhauser.
Brune, K. & Baggiolini, M., eds. Arachidonic Acid Metabolism in Inflammation & Thrombosis: Proceedings of the First European Workshop on Inflammation, Basel, 1979. (Agents & Actions Supplements: No. 4). (Illus.). 300p. 1979. text ed. 43.95x (ISBN 0-8176-1095-2). Birkhauser.
Glynn, L. E., ed. Tissue Repair & Regeneration. (Handbook of Inflammation: Vol. 3). 598p. 1981. 128.50 (ISBN 0-444-80278-9, Biomedical Pr). Elsevier.
Lewis, G. P. The Role of Prostaglandins in Inflammation. 179p. 1976. 60.00 (ISBN 3-456-80270-6, Pub. by Holdan Bk Ltd UK). State Mutual Bk.
Messmer, K. & Hammersen, F., eds. White Cell Rheology & Inflammation. (Mikrozirkulation in Forschung und Klinik; Progress in Applied Microcirculation Ser.: Vol. 7). (Illus.). x, 124p. 1985. pap. 28.75 (ISBN 3-8055-4040-X). S Karger.
Movat, H. Z., ed. Inflammatory Reaction. (Current Topics in Pathology Ser.: Vol. 68). (Illus.). 1979. 57.00 (ISBN 0-387-09394-X). Springer-Verlag.
Oppenheim, J. J., et al. Cellular Functions in Immunity & Inflammation. 1984. pap. 35.00 (ISBN 0-444-00951-5). Elsevier.
Scherrer, Robert A. & Whitehouse, Michael W., eds. Anti-Inflamatory Agents: Chemistry & Pharmacology, Vols. 1 & 2. 1974. Vol. 1. 80.50 (ISBN 0-12-623901-0); Vol. 2. 80.50 (ISBN 0-12-623902-9). Acad Pr.
Singh, Charlene P. Inflammation & Health Sciences: Medical Analysis Index with Research Bibliography. LC 85-47587. 150p. 1985. 29.95 (ISBN 0-88164-348-3); pap. 21.95 (ISBN 0-88164-349-1). ABBE Pubs Assn.
Velo, G. P., ed. Trends in Inflammation Research One. (Agents & Actions Supplement Ser.: Vol. 7). 362p. 1980. text ed. 93.95x (ISBN 0-8176-1177-0). Birkhauser.
Weissmann, Gerald, ed. Advances in Inflammation Research, Vol. 2. 228p. 1981. 35.50 (ISBN 0-89004-582-8). Raven.
--Advances in Inflammation Research, Vol. 4. 208p. 1982. text ed. 30.50 (ISBN 0-89004-669-7). Raven.
--Mediators of Inflammation. LC 74-20786. 216p. 1974. 25.00 (ISBN 0-306-30815-0, Plenum Pr). Plenum Pub.
Willoughby, D. A. & Giroud, J. P., eds. Inflammation: Mechanisms & Treatment. 1018p. 1981. text ed. 75.00 (ISBN 0-8391-1649-7). Univ Park.

INFLATABLE STRUCTURES

see Air-Supported Structures

INFLUENCE LINES

Molkenthin, A. Influence Surfaces of Two-Span Continuous Plates with Free Longitudinal Edges. dual language ed. (Eng, Ger., Illus.). 220p. 1971. 75.60 (ISBN 0-387-05212-7). Springer Verlag.

INFORMATION DISPLAY SYSTEMS

see also Cathode Ray Tubes

Advances in Display Technology I: Proceedings of the SPIE Annual Technical Symposium, 23rd, San Diego, 1979. (SPIE Seminar Proceedings: Vol. 199). 206p. 38.00 (ISBN 0-89252-227-5); 30.00, members (ISBN 0-317-34580-X). SPIE.
Advances in Display Technology IV, Vol. 457. 1984. 43.00 (ISBN 0-89252-492-8). Photo-Optical.
Aiyer, Arjun, et al. Bibliographic Specifications for Display: University of California Union Catalog. rev. ed. (Working Paper: No. 1). 1979. 5.00 (ISBN 0-686-87236-3). UCDLA.
Automated Education Center. Data Display Programming. LC 77-118118. 275p. 29.00 (ISBN 0-403-04461-8). Scholarly.
Bennett, John, et al, eds. Visual Display Terminal: Usability Issues & Health Concerns. 1984. 28.00 (ISBN 0-13-942482-2). P-H.
Biberman, L. M., ed. Perception of Displayed Information. LC 72-97695. (Optical Physics & Engineering Ser.). (Illus.). 345p. 1973. 55.00 (ISBN 0-306-30724-3, Plenum Pr). Plenum Pub.
Cakir, A., et al. Visual Display Terminals: A Manual Covering Ergonomics, Workplace Design, Health & Safety, Task Organization. LC 80-40070. 307p. 1980. 59.95x (ISBN 0-471-27793-2, Pub. by Wiley-Interscience). Wiley.
Cousins, Basil. Data Independence & Data Flow Systems. 20p. 1983. pap. 7.75x (ISBN 0-471-87934-7). Wiley.
Debry, R. K. Communicating with Display Terminals. 256p. 1985. 36.95 (ISBN 0-07-016185-2). McGraw.
Delobel, C. & Adiba, M. Relational Database Systems. Hollett, M. L., tr. 470p. 1985. 65.00 (ISBN 0-444-87718-5, North-Holland). Elsevier.
Display Technology II: Proceedings of the SPIE Technical Symposium, Los Angeles, 1981. (SPIE Seminar Proceedings: Vol. 271). 134p. 38.00 (ISBN 0-89252-303-4); 32.00, members (ISBN 0-317-34629-6). SPIE.
Fadok, George T. Effective Design of Codasyl Data Base. 400p. 1984. pap. text ed. 29.95. Macmillan.
Galbraith, Richard. Professional Programming Techniques: Starting with the BASICs. (Illus.). 308p. 1982. 17.95 (ISBN 0-8306-2428-7); pap. 10.95 (ISBN 0-8306-0128-7, 1428). TAB Bks.
Galitz, Wilbert O. Handbook of Screen Format Design. LC 84-62223. 235p. (Orig.). 1985. pap. 34.50 (ISBN 0-89435-119-2, SD1192). QED Info Sci.
Grandjean, Etienne & Vigliani, E., eds. Ergonomic Aspects of Visual Display Terminals: Proceedings of the International Workshop, Milan, March 1980. (Illus.). 300p. 1980. 55.00x (ISBN 0-85066-211-7). Taylor & Francis.
Grosswald, Blanche. Statistical Summary Report of the 1979 University of California Union Catalog Data Base. (Working Paper: No. 10). 1980. 5.00 (ISBN 0-686-87251-7). UCDLA.
Harper, William L. & Pollard, Robert C. Data Communications Desk Book: A Systems Analysis Approach. LC 81-17794. 352p. 1982. 59.95 (ISBN 0-13-196378-3). P-H.
Harris, Christopher J. & Valencia, J. M., eds. The Stability of Input-Output Dynamical Systems. (Mathematics Science Engineering Ser.). 1983. 49.00 (ISBN 0-12-327680-2). Acad Pr.
Lancaster, Don. Cheap Video Cookbook. LC 78-51584. 256p. 1978. pap. 8.95 (ISBN 0-672-21524-1, 21524). Sams.
--TV Typewriter Cookbook. LC 75-46215. 256p. 1976. pap. 12.95 (ISBN 0-672-21313-3, 21313). Sams.
Lee, Kaiman. Evaluation of Computer Graphic Terminals. 2nd ed. LC 74-184824. 92p. 1975. 12.00x (ISBN 0-915250-11-X). Environ Design.
Leondes, C. T., ed. Advances in Control & Dynamic Systems, Vol. 19. (Serial Publication Ser.). 1983. 39.50 (ISBN 0-12-012719-9). Acad Pr.
--Advances in Control & Dynamic Systems: Theory & Application, Vol. 17. (Serial Publication Ser.). 1981. 49.00 (ISBN 0-12-012717-2). Acad Pr.
--Control & Dynamic Systems: Advances in Theory & Applications, Vol. 20. (Serial Publication Ser.). 1983. 49.50 (ISBN 0-12-012720-2); Pt. 2. Nonlinear & Kalman Filtering Techniques. Acad Pr.
McKenzie, J., et al, eds. Interactive Computer Graphics in Science Teaching. LC 78-40598. (Computers & Their Applications Ser.). 247p. 1978. 42.95x (ISBN 0-470-26419-5). Halsted Pr.
Minicomputers & Microprocessors in Optical Systems: Proceedings of the SPIE Technical Symposium East, Washington, D.C., 1980. (SPIE Seminar Proceedings: Vol. 230). 216p. 37.00 (ISBN 0-89252-259-3); members 30.00 (ISBN 0-317-34690-3). SPIE.
Morison, Jacquelyne. Pocket Guide: The IBM Displaywriter. (Pitman Word Processing Pocket Guides Ser.). (Orig.). 1984. pap. 6.95 (ISBN 0-273-01994-5). Pitman Pub MA.
Network Editors. Device Technology. 1982. 80.00x (ISBN 0-904999-75-0, Pub. by Network). State Mutual Bk.
Network Editors, ed. Applications & Human Factors. 1982. 50.00x (ISBN 0-904999-57-2, Pub. by Network). State Mutual Bk.
--Communication Techniques & Systems. 1982. 60.00x (ISBN 0-904999-30-0, Pub. by Network). State Mutual Bk.
--Communication with Machine & Systems: Man-Machine Interfaces. 1982. 50.00x (ISBN 0-904999-63-7, Pub. by Network). State Mutual Bk.
--Computer Graphic Display Devices & Systems, 2 Vols. 1982. Vol. 1. 55.00 ea. (ISBN 0-904999-70-X, Pub. by Network). Vol. 2 (ISBN 0-904999-69-6). State Mutual Bk.
--Computer Graphics & Interactive Devices. 1982. 90.00x (ISBN 0-904999-54-8, Pub. by Network). State Mutual Bk.
--Display Applications & Future Techniques. 1982. 60.00x (ISBN 0-904999-55-6, Pub. by Network). State Mutual Bk.
--Display Components. 1982. 50.00x (ISBN 0-904999-66-1, Pub. by Network). State Mutual Bk.
--Display Components & Technology. 1982. 50.00x (ISBN 0-904999-56-4, Pub. by Network). State Mutual Bk.
--Display in Avionics & Defence. 1982. 70.00x (ISBN 0-904999-67-X, Pub. by Network). State Mutual Bk.
--Display Systems Including Use of Microprocessors. 1982. 80.00x (ISBN 0-904999-77-7, Pub. by Network). State Mutual Bk.
--Display Techniques. 1982. 75.00x (ISBN 0-904999-64-5, Pub. by Network). State Mutual Bk.
--Display Techniques & Components. 1982. 60.00x (ISBN 0-904999-52-1, Pub. by Network). State Mutual Bk.
--Future Developments. 1982. 50.00x (ISBN 0-904999-68-8, Pub. by Network Editors). State Mutual Bk.
--Graphics & Interactive Display. 1982. 50.00x (ISBN 0-904999-65-3, Pub. by Network). State Mutual Bk.
--Human Factors. 1982. 60.00 (ISBN 0-904999-53-X, Pub. by Network). State Mutual Bk.
--Human Factors & Interactive Displays. 1982. 80.00 (ISBN 0-904999-76-9, Pub. by Network). State Mutual Bk.
--Software for Computer Display Systems, Vol. 3. 1982. 79.00x (ISBN 0-904999-71-8, Pub. by Network). State Mutual Bk.
Online Conference, London, 1981. Viewdata '81. 688p. (Orig.). 1981. pap. text ed. 115.00 (ISBN 0-903796-85-6, Pub. by Online Conferences England). Online.
Pearce, B. G., ed. Health Hazards of VDUs? LC 82-21841. (Wiley Information Processing Ser.: 1-506). 244p. 1984. 29.95x (ISBN 0-471-90065-6, Pub. by Wiley Interscence). Wiley.
Refioglu, I. Electronic Displays. 467p. 1983. 54.50X (ISBN 0-471-88175-9, Pub. by Wiley-Interscience). Wiley.
Ross, P. J. A Simple Microprocessor System for Field Data Acquisition & Display. 1980. 20.00x (ISBN 0-643-02487-5, Pub. by CSJRO Australia). State Mutual Bk.
Saha, D. C. & Rao, G. P. Identification of Continuous Dynamical Systems. (Lecture Notes in Control & Information Sciences Ser.: Vol. 56). 158p. 1983. pap. 11.00 (ISBN 0-387-12759-3). Springer-Verlag.
Saperstone, S. H. Semidynamical Systems in Infinite Dimensional Spaces. (Applied Mathematical Sciences Ser.: Vol. 37). 474p. 1981. pap. 33.95 (ISBN 0-387-90643-6). Springer-Verlag.
Sippl, Charles J. & Dahl, Fred. Video Computers: How to Select, Mix, & Operate Personal Computers & Home Video Equipment. (Illus.). 256p. 1981. 15.95 (ISBN 0-13-941856-3, Spec); pap. 7.95 (ISBN 0-13-941849-0). P-H.
Tracton, Ken. Display Electronics. (Illus.). 1977. pap. 6.95 (ISBN 0-8306-6861-6, 861). TAB Bks.
Videotex & the Press. 1983. 30.00. Learned Info.
Videotex in Europe: Proceedings of Videotex in Europe Conference, Luxembourg, July 1980. 1983. 90.00 (ISBN 0-317-01040-9). Learned Info.
Weston, G. F. & Bittleston, R. Alphanumeric Displays: Devices, Drive Circuits & Applications. 208p. 1983. 32.50i (ISBN 0-07-069468-0). McGraw.

INFORMATION MEASUREMENT

see also Signal Processing

Beauchamp, K. G. & Yuen, C. K. Digital Methods for Signal Analysis. (Illus.). 1979. text ed. 50.00x (ISBN 0-04-621027-X). Allen Unwin.
Bowen, B. A. & Brown, W. R. VLSI Systems Design for Digital Signal Processing, Vol. 1: Signal Processing & Signal Processors. (Illus.). 256p. 1982. text ed. 39.95 (ISBN 0-13-942706-6). P-H.
Crochiere, Ronald E. & Rabiner, Lawrence R. Multirate Digital Signal Processing. (Illus.). 336p. 1983. 33.95 (ISBN 0-13-605162-6). P-H.
Feltham, Gerald A. Information Evaluation, Vol. 5. (Studies in Accounting Research). 149p. 1972. 6.00 (ISBN 0-86539-017-7). Am Accounting.
Gabel. Signals & Linear Systems. 3rd ed. 1986. price not set (ISBN 0-471-82513-1). Wiley.
Kung, S. Y., et al. VLSI & Modern Signal Processing. (Illus.). 448p. 1985. text ed. 43.95 (ISBN 0-13-942699-X). P-H.
Papoulis, Athanasios. Signal Analysis. 1977. text ed. 45.00 (ISBN 0-07-048460-0). McGraw.
Pick, H. L., Jr. & Saltzman, E., eds. Modes of Perceiving & Processing Information. 240p. 1978. text ed. 29.95x (ISBN 0-89859-354-9). L Erlbaum Assocs.
Striker, G., et al, eds. Measurement for Progress in Science & Technology: Acta Imeko, 1979, 3 vols. 213p. 1980. Set. 223.50 (ISBN 0-444-85477-0, North-Holland). Elsevier.
Taylor. Digital Filter Design Handbook. (Electrical Engineering & Electronics Ser.: Vol. 12). 1983. 64.75 (ISBN 0-8247-1357-5). Dekker.

INFORMATION NETWORKS

see also Computer Networks; Library Information Networks

Arbenz, K. & Martin, J. C. Mathematical Methods for Information Transmission. Orig. Title: Transmission de l'iformation Methodes Mathematiques. 1985. text ed. 50.00 (ISBN 0-89006-165-3). Artech Hse.
Ariav, Gadi & Clifford, James. New Directions in Database Systems. Ginzberg, Michael, ed. (Computer-Based Systems in Information Management Ser.). 304p. 1985. text ed. 35.00 (ISBN 0-89391-344-8). Ablex Pub.
Barber, Derek, ed. Data Networks: Development & Uses. 690p. 1980. pap. text ed. 168.00x (ISBN 0-903796-59-7, Pub. by Online Conferences England). Brookfield Pub Co.
Bartee, Thomas, ed. Data Communications Network & Systems. LC 84-51868. 39.95 (ISBN 0-672-22235-3, 22235). Sams.
Becker, Hal B. Functional Analysis of Information Networks: A Structured Approach to the Data Communication Environment. LC 80-15347. 294p. 1981. Repr. of 1973 ed. 29.50 (ISBN 0-89874-028-2). Krieger.
Blackwell, William A. & Grigsby, Leonard L. Introductory Network Theory. 1985. text ed. write for info. (ISBN 0-534-03771-2, 22R2100, Pub. by PWS Engineering). PWS Pubs.

Brown, Stanley E. The Directory of Office Information Systems. 3rd ed. 336p. 1984. pap. 49.95 (ISBN 0-935220-12-7). Knowledge Indus.

Ceri, S. & Pelagatti, G. Distributed Databases: Principles & Systems. 1984. 37.50 (ISBN 0-07-010829-3). McGraw.

Chantico-QED. Strategic & Operational Planning for Information System. LC 85-60179. (The Chantico Technical Management Ser.). (Illus.). 200p. (Orig.). Date not set. pap. 29.50 (ISBN 0-89435-151-6, CP 1516). QED Info Sci.

Cohen, Burton J. Cost-Effective Information Systems. LC 78-152375. pap. 20.00 (ISBN 0-317-10661-9, 2050389). Bks Demand UMI.

Conrad, James W. Standard & Protocols For Communications Network. 397p. 1982. 59.95 (ISBN 0-935506-03-9). Carnegie Pr.

Freeman, Harvey A. & Thurber, Kenneth J., eds. Local Network Equipment. LC 85-60466. (Tutorial Text Ser.). 370p. (Orig.). 1985. 36.00 (ISBN 0-8186-0605-3, 605); microfiche 36.00 (ISBN 0-8186-4605-5). IEEE Comp Soc.

Fuhrmann, P. A., ed. Mathematical Theory of Networks & Systems: Proceedings of the International Symposium Beer Sheva, Israel, June 20-24,2983. (Lectures Notes in Control & Information Science Ser.: Vol. 58). x, 906p. 1984. pap. 48.00 (ISBN 0-387-13168-X). Springer-Verlag.

Gault, D. & Nagy, Thomas. Building Your First Expert Systems. 1985. pap. 29.95 incl. disk (ISBN 0-912677-53-8). Ashton-Tate Bks.

Heany, Donald F. Development of Information Systems: What Managment Needs to Know. LC 68-30891. (Illus.). pap. 81.60 (ISBN 0-317-10041-6, 2012413). Bks Demand UMI.

Held, Gilbert. Data Communications Procurement Manual. LC 79-18075. (Illus.). 150p. 1979. text ed. 39.95 (ISBN 0-07-027952-7). McGraw.

Kay, Peg & Powell, Patricia, eds. Future Information Technology: Nineteen Eighty-Four Telecommunications. 2nd ed. (National Bureau of Standards Special Publications 500-119. Computer Science & Technology Ser.). 347p. (Orig.). pap. 9.50 (ISBN 0-318-11722-3). Gov Printing Office.

Kitahara, Yasusada. Information Network Systems: Telecommunications in the 21st Century. (Illus.). 160p. 1983. Heinemann Ed.

Kroeber, Watson. Computer-Based Information Systems: A Management Approach. 2nd ed. 640p. 1986. text ed. price not set (ISBN 0-02-366870-9). Macmillan.

McLean, Mick, ed. The Information Explosion: The New Electronic Media in Japan & Europe. LC 85-12666. (Emerging Patterns of Work & Communications in an Information Age Ser.: No. 3). 136p. 1985. lib. bdg. 27.95 (ISBN 0-313-25091-X, MIX/). Greenwood.

Marney-Petix, Victoria. Networking & Data Communications. 1985. text ed. 27.95 (ISBN 0-8359-4874-9). Reston.

National Computer Centre. Introducing Relational Database. 200p. 1983. pap. 21.55 (ISBN 0-471-87933-9). Wiley.

National Users Group. Multi-State Information System - Theoretical & Practical Issues: Proceedings of the Fourth Annual National Users Group Conference. King, James A., ed. 206p. 1980. pap. 10.00 (ISBN 0-936934-00-X). N S Kline Inst.

NFAIS Conference. Information Transfer: Incentives for Innovation; Proceedings of the 25th Annual Conference of NFAIS. 1984. 35.00 (ISBN 0-942308-17-4). NFAIS.

Olle, T. W., et al, eds. Information Systems Design Methodologies: A Comparative Review. 648p. 1982. 72.50 (ISBN 0-444-86407-5, I-301-82, North-Holland). Elsevier.

Ostle, Jud. Information Systems Analysis & Design. 500p. 1985. text ed. write for info. (ISBN 0-8087-6401-2). Burgess.

Rosenbloom, Richard S. & Wolek, Francis W. Technology & Information Transfer: A Survey of Practice in Industrial Organizations. LC 70-119550. pap. 47.50 (ISBN 0-317-10820-4, 2002225). Bks Demand UMI.

Rutkowski, Anthony. Integrated Services Digital Networks. 300p. 1985. text ed. 45.00. Artech Hse.

Schneider, H. J. & Wasserman, A. I., eds. Automated Tools for Information Systems Design: Proceedings IFIP WG Working Conference on Automated Tools for Information Systems Design & Development, 8.1, New Orleans, January 26-28, 1982. 262p. 1982. 42.75 (ISBN 0-444-86338-9, North-Holland). Elsevier.

Schwartz, M. Computer Communications Network Design & Analysis. 1977. sol. manual 4.00 (ISBN 0-13-165159-5). P-H.

Sherrod, John, ed. Information Systems & Networks: Eleventh Annual Symposium. LC 74-11941. 200p. 1975. lib. bdg. 29.95x (ISBN 0-8371-7717-0, ISN/). Greenwood.

Siegel, Efrem, et al. The Future of Videotext: Worldwide Perspectives for Home-Office Electronic Information Services. LC 83-17689. 195p. 1984. 22.95 (ISBN 0-13-345777-X); pap. 9.95 (ISBN 0-13-345769-9). P-H.

Siegel, Howard J. Interconnection Networks for Large-Scale Parallel Processing: Theory & Case Studies. LC 79-6015. 288p. 1985. 39.00x (ISBN 0-669-03594-7). Lexington Bks.

Sieghart, Paul, ed. Micro-Chips with Everything: The Consequences of Information Technology. (Illus.). 1983. 15.00 (ISBN 0-906890-33-0, Dist. by Scribner); pap. 6.95 (ISBN 0-906890-32-2). M Boyars.

Strassman, Paul A. Information Payoff: The Transformation of Work in the Electronic Age. (Illus.). 234p. 1985. 19.95x (ISBN 0-02-931720-7). Free Pr.

Szperski, N. & Grochla, E., eds. Design & Implementation of Computer-Based Information Systems, No. 1. (Information Systems Ser.). 383p. 1979. 47.50x (ISBN 90-286-0519-3). Sijthoff & Noordhoff.

Trute, Barry. Human Service Information Systems: How to Design & Implement Them. LC 84-27360. (Studies in Health & Human Services: Vol. 3). 224p. 1985. 49.95x (ISBN 0-88946-128-7). E Mellen.

INFORMATION NETWORKS, LIBRARY

see Library Information Networks

INFORMATION SCIENCE

see also Electronic Data Processing; Information Services; Information Storage and Retrieval Systems

A. C. Nielsen Co. The Business of Information, 1983, 2 vols. 1983. 300.00 (ISBN 0-942774-12-4). Info Indus.

Ackermann, J., ed. Uncertainty & Control. (Lecture Notes in Control & Information Sciences Ser.: Vol. 70). iv, 236p. 1985. pap. 16.00 (ISBN 0-387-15533-3). Springer-Verlag.

Anderson, Leslie. Industrial Information Systems. 1980. 69.00x (ISBN 0-86176-034-4, Pub. by MCB Pubns). State Mutual Bk.

Andriole, Stephen J., ed. The Future of Information Processing Technology: A Source Book. 1985. 29.95 (ISBN 0-89433-263-5). Petrocelli.

Arny, Linda Ray. The Search for Data in the Physical & Chemical Sciences. LC 83-20376. 160p. 1984. pap. 17.00 (ISBN 0-87111-308-2). SLA.

ASIS Annual Meeting, 43rd, 1980. Communicating Information: Proceedings of the 43rd ASIS Annual Meeting, Vol. 17. Benenfeld, Alan R., ed. LC 64-8303. (Illus.). 417p. 1980. professional ed. 19.50x (ISBN 0-914236-73-3, 319-BW). Knowledge Indus.

Austrian, Geoffrey D. Herman Hollerith: Forgotten Giant of Information Processing. LC 81-7752. 418p. 1985. pap. 12.95 (ISBN 0-231-05147-6). Columbia U Pr.

Automated Informatics Documentation System: A Thesaurus for Informatics. (Illus.). 167p. 1982. pap. 35.00 (ISBN 0-686-87240-1, IB100, UPB). Unipub.

Bakewell, K. G. How to Organise Information: A Manager's Guide to Techniques & Sources with a Checklist for Secretaries & Assistants. LC 84-10223. 225p. 1984. text ed. 33.95x (ISBN 0-566-02397-0). Gower Pub Co.

Bannon, Liam & Barry, Ursala, eds. Information Technology: Impact on the Way of Life. (Information & Technology Development Ser.: Vol. 1). 381p. 1983. 55.00 (ISBN 0-907567-34-7, TYP114, TYP); pap. 30.00 (ISBN 0-907567-35-5, TYP112). Unipub.

Barta, B. J. & Raab, B. H., eds. The Impact of Informatics on Vocational & Continuing Education: Proceedings of the IFIP WG 3.4 Working Conference, Jerusalem, Israel, 14-18 May, 1986. 240p. 1985. 35.25 (ISBN 0-444-87663-4, North-Holland). Elsevier.

Bennett, J. M. & Pearcey, T., eds. The New World of the Information Society: Proceedings of the 7th International Conference on Computer Communication Sydney, Australia, 30 Oct. - 2 Nov., 1984. 886p. 1985. 60.00 (ISBN 0-444-87649-9, North Holland). Elsevier.

Bjorn-Anderson, N., et al, eds. Information Society: For Richer, for Poorer. 320p. 1982. 47.00 (ISBN 0-444-86422-9, North-Holland). Elsevier.

Bjorn-Anderson, Neils, ed. Human Side of Information Processing. 230p. 1980. 42.75 (ISBN 0-444-85415-0, North-Holland). Elsevier.

Blissmer, Robert H. Computer Annual: An Introduction to Information Systems 1985-1986. (Wiley Series in Computers & Information Processing Systems for Business). 487p. 1985. pap. text ed. 18.95 (ISBN 0-471-81106-8); tchr's ed. avail. (ISBN 0-471-81105-X); tests avail. (ISBN 0-471-81916-6). Wiley.

Blum, E. K., et al, eds. Mathematical Studies of Information Processing: Proceedings, International Conference, Kyoto, Japan, August 23-26, 1978. (Lecture Notes in Computer Science Ser.: Vol. 75). 1979. pap. 37.00 (ISBN 0-387-09541-1). Springer-Verlag.

Brown, K. R., ed. The Challenge of Information Technology: Proceedings of the 41st FID Congress, Hong-Kong, September 13-16, 1982. xii, 356p. 1983. 51.00 (ISBN 0-444-86646-9, North-Holland). Elsevier.

Bubenko, Janis. Conceptual Information Modelling: Papers from the Nordic Research Course on "Conceptual Information Modelling for Data Bases", August 1979 in Ystad, Sweden. 687p. (Orig.). 1983. 36.95 (ISBN 0-86238-006-5, Pub. by Chartwell-Bratt England). Brookfield Pub Co.

Chase, Leslie R. & Henderson, Faye, eds. Information Sources, 1985. 1984. 59.75 (ISBN 0-317-16325-6). Info Indus.

Chase, Leslie R. & Tuttle, Patti, eds. Information Sources, 1986. 1985. pap. price not set (ISBN 0-942774-22-1). Info Indus.

Cherry, Colin. The Age of Access: Information Technology & Social Revolution. Edmondson, William, ed. (New Information Technology Ser.). 176p. 1985. 29.00 (ISBN 0-7099-3458-0, Pub. by Croom Helm Ltd). Longwood Pub Group.

Childers, Thomas. Information & Referral: Libraries & Information Science. LC 83-21492. (Libraries & Information Science Ser.). 384p. (Orig.). 1984. text ed. 39.50. Ablex Pub.

CISM (International Center for Mechanical Sciences), Dept of Automation & Information. Quantitative-Qualitative Measure of Information. Longo, G., ed. (CISM Pubns. Ser.: No. 138). (Illus.). 51p. 1973. pap. 8.80 (ISBN 0-387-81182-6). Springer-Verlag.

Clarkson, Albert. Toward Effective Strategic Analysis: New Applications of Information Technology. LC 81-69202. (Special Studies in National Security & Defense Policy). 179p. 1981. lib. bdg. 25.00x (ISBN 0-86531-243-5). Westview.

Courtney, James F., Jr. & Jensen, Ronald. The Systems Laboratory for Information Management. 1981. pap. 7.95x (ISBN 0-256-02574-6). Business Pubns.

Cuadra, Carlos, et al, eds. Annual Review of Information Science & Technology, Vol. 10. LC 66-25096. 1975. 27.50 (ISBN 0-87715-210-1). Am Soc Info Sci.

Cuadra, Carlos A., ed. The Annual Review of Information Science & Technology, 1968, Vol. 3. LC 66-25096. (Illus.). 457p. 1968. 45.00 (ISBN 0-685-94669-X, 315-BW). Knowledge Indus.

Cuadra, Carlos A. & Luke, Ann W., eds. The Annual Review of Information Science & Technology, 1969, Vol. 4. LC 66-25096. 547p. 1969. 45.00 (ISBN 0-85229-147-7, 314-BW). Knowledge Indus.

--The Annual Review of Information Science & Technology, 1970, Vol. 5. LC 66-25096. 468p. 1970. 45.00 (ISBN 0-85229-156-6, 313-BW). Knowledge Indus.

--The Annual Review of Information Science & Technology, 1972, Vol. 7. LC 66-25096. (Illus.). 606p. 1972. 45.00 (ISBN 0-87715-206-3, 312-BW). Knowledge Indus.

--The Annual Review of Information Science & Technology, 1973, Vol. 8. LC 66-25096. 411p. 1973. 45.00 (ISBN 0-87715-208-X, 311-BW). Knowledge Indus.

--The Annual Review of Information Science & Technology, 1974, Vol. 9. LC 66-25096. (Illus.). 457p. 1974. 45.00 (ISBN 0-87715-209-8, 310-BW). Knowledge Indus.

--The Annual Review of Information Science & Technology, 1975, Vol. 10. LC 66-25096. 476p. 1975. 45.00 (ISBN 0-87715-210-1, 309-BW). Knowledge Indus.

Daggett, et al. Computer & Information Technology. 1986. 14.95 (ISBN 0-538-04550-7, D55). SW Pub.

Davis, Charles H. & Rush, James E. Guide to Information Science. LC 78-75240. (Illus.). 1979. lib. bdg. 35.00 (ISBN 0-313-20982-0, DGI/). Greenwood.

--Guide to Information Science. LC 78-75240. xvii, 305p. 1980. pap. text ed. 9.95 (ISBN 0-313-22603-2, DGI:). Greenwood.

Davis, William S. & McCormack, Allison. Information Age. LC 78-55817. 1979. text ed. 23.95 (ISBN 0-201-01101-8); manual 2.95 (ISBN 0-201-01102-6). Addison-Wesley.

Debons, Anthony, et al. Information Science: An Introduction. (Professional Librarian Ser.). 150p. 1985. 36.50 (ISBN 0-86729-153-2); pap. 27.50 (ISBN 0-86729-152-4). Knowledge Indus.

--Information Science: An Introduction. 150p. 1985. 36.50 (ISBN 0-86729-153-2); pap. 27.50 (ISBN 0-86729-152-4). Knowledge Indus.

Deighton, Suzan, et al, eds. Computers & Information Processing World Index. 626p. 1984. lib. bdg. 85.00 (ISBN 0-89774-116-1, Co-Pub. with Gower Pub. Co). Oryx Pr.

Dervin, Brenda. Progress in Communication Sciences, Vol. 3. Voigt, Melvin J., ed. (Communication & Information Sciences Ser.). 350p. 1982. text ed. 39.50 (ISBN 0-89391-081-3). Ablex Pub.

Dictionary of Abbreviations in Information Science. 406p. 1976. 50.00x (ISBN 0-686-44776-X, Pub. by Collets). State Mutual Bk.

Dietschmann, Hans J., ed. Representation & Exchange of Knowledge As a Basis of Information Processes: Proceedings of the 5th International Research Forum in Information Science (IRFIS 5) Heidelberg, 5-7 Sept., 1983. 434p. 1984. 55.75 (ISBN 0-444-87563-8, I-302-84, North Holland). Elsevier.

Division of Science Information, National Science Foundation. Current Research on Scientific & Technical Information Transfer. LC 77-9216. (Micropapers Editions Ser). 1977. 12.95x (ISBN 0-88432-007-3). J Norton Pubs.

Edelstein, Alex S., et al, eds. Information Societies: Comparing the Japanese & American Experiences. LC 78-71366. (Illus.). 1978. pap. 10.95 (ISBN 0-933236-00-X). Intl Comm Ctr.

El-Hadidy, B. & Horne, E. E., eds. The Infrastructure of an Information Society: Proceedings of the 1st International Conference in Cairo, Egypt, 13-15 Dec. 1982. 644p. 1984. 69.00 (ISBN 0-444-87549-2, I-303-84, North Holland). Elsevier.

Fang, Josephine Riss & Nauta, Paul, eds. International Guide to Library & Information Science Education: A Reference Source for Educational Programs in the Information Fields World-Wide. (IFLA Publication Ser.: Vol. 32). 536p. 1985. lib. bdg. 46.00 (ISBN 3-598-20396-9). K G Saur.

Forester, Tom, ed. The Information Technology Revolution. 678p. (Orig.). 1985. text ed. 30.00x (ISBN 0-262-06095-7); pap. 14.95 (ISBN 0-262-56033-X). MIT Pr.

Fox, Christopher J. Information & Misinformation: An Investigation of the Notions of Information, Misinformation, Informing & Misinforming. LC 83-5545. (Contributions in Librarianship & Information Science Ser.: No. 45). xii, 223p. 1983. lib. bdg. 29.95 (ISBN 0-313-23928-2, FOI/). Greenwood.

Fuori, William M. & Tedesco, Dominick. Introduction to Information Processing. (Illus.). 352p. 1983. pap. text ed. 9.95 (ISBN 0-13-484634-6); text ed. 26.95 (ISBN -13-484601-X). P-H.

Garfield, Eugene. The Awards of Science & Other Essays. (Essays of an Information Scientist Ser.: Vol. 7). 673p. 1985. 30.00 (ISBN 0-317-20208-1). ISI Pr.

--Essays of an Information Scientist, Vol. 1 (1962-1973). (Illus.). 544p. 1977. 25.00 (ISBN 0-89495-001-0). ISI Pr.

--Essays of an Information Scientist, Vol. 2 (1974-1976). (Illus.). 708p. 1977. 25.00 (ISBN 0-89495-002-9). ISI Pr.

--Essays of an Information Scientist, Vol. 3 (1977-1978). (Illus.). 892p. 1980. 25.00 (ISBN 0-89495-009-6). ISI Pr.

--Essays of an Information Scientist, Vol. 4 (1979-1980). (Illus.). 780p. 1981. 25.00 (ISBN 0-89495-012-6). ISI Pr.

--Essays of an Information Scientist, Vol. 5 (1981-1982). (Illus.). 849p. 1983. 25.00 (ISBN 0-89495-023-1). ISI Pr.

Garvey, William D. Communication: The Essence of Science Facilitating Information Exchange Among Librarians, Scientists, Engineers, & Students. 1979. pap. text ed. 19.50 (ISBN 0-08-023344-9). Pergamon.

Goldberg, Robert & Lorin, Harold. The Economics of Information Processing: Vol. 1, Management Perspectives. LC 81-11429. 238p. 1982. 34.95 (ISBN 0-471-09206-1, Pub. by Wiley Interscience); member 28.75. Assn Inform & Image Mgmt.

--Economics of Information Processing: Vol. 2, Operation Programming & Software Models. LC 81-11429. 185p. 1982. 30.95 (ISBN 0-471-09767-5, Pub. by Wiley Interscience). Assn Inform & Image Mgmt.

Goldhaber, Gerald, et al. Information Strategies. Voigt, Mel, ed. LC 79-756. (Communication & Information Science Ser.). 368p. 1984. text ed. 35.00 (ISBN 0-89391-151-8). Ablex Pub.

Griffith, Belver C., ed. Key Papers in Information Science. LC 79-24288. (American Society for Information Sciences Ser.). 439p. 1980. 25.00x (ISBN 0-914236-50-4, 341-BW). Knowledge Indus.

Harman, Keith & McClure, Charles M. Strategic Planning for Sponsored Projects Administration: The Role of Information Management. LC 85-9881. (Emerging Patterns of Work & Communications in an Information Age Ser.: No. 1). (Illus.). 352p. 1985. lib. bdg. 45.00 (ISBN 0-313-24931-8, MST/). Greenwood.

Sieghart, Paul, ed. Chips with Everything: The Consequences of Information Technology. 1982. 39.00x (ISBN 0-906890-33-0, Pub. by Comedia England); pap. 26.00x (ISBN 0-906890-32-2). State Mutual Bk.

Slamecka, V. & Borka, H., eds. Planning & Organisation of National Research Programs in Information Science. (Illus.). 83p. 1982. pap. 66.00 (ISBN 0-08-026472-7). Pergamon.

Smith, Anthony. The Geopolitics of Information: How Western Culture Dominates the World. 1980. pap. 6.95 (ISBN 0-19-520274-0, GB 655). Oxford U Pr.

Smith, J. M. Documenting an Organization's Information Requirements. 240p. 1985. 24.95 (ISBN 0-471-81239-0). Wiley.

Smith, Linda C., ed. New Information Technologies-New Opportunities: Proceedings of the Clinic on Library Applications of Data Processing, 1981. LC 82-10947. 119p. 1982. 11.00 (ISBN 0-87845-066-1). U of Ill Lib Info Sci.

Spencer, Donald D. Principles of Information Processing. 250p. 1985. 17.95 (ISBN 0-675-20410-0). Additional supplements may be obtained from publisher. Merrill.

Sproull, Lee S. & Larkey, Patrick D., eds. Advances in Information Processing in Organizations, Vol. 2. 1985. 49.50 (ISBN 0-89232-425-2). Jai Pr.

Stamm, Keith R. Newspaper Use & Community Ties. Voigt, Melvin J., ed. (Communication & Information Science Ser.). 224p. 1985. text ed. 29.50 (ISBN 0-89391-136-4). Ablex Pub.

Stern, Robert A. & Stern, Nancy. An Introduction to Computers & Information Processing. LC 81-11428. 637p. 1982. 28.45 (ISBN 0-471-08723-8); tchrs.' ed 23.00 (ISBN 0-471-09941-4); tests 130.00 (ISBN 0-471-86212-6); study guide 13.45 (ISBN 0-471-09231-2). Wiley.

Stokes, Adrian. Concise Encyclopaedia of Information Technology. 2nd ed. 288p. 1985. text ed. 39.95 (ISBN 0-566-02531-0). Gower Pub Co.

Stover, William J. Information Technology in the Third World: Can It Lead to Humane National Development? 150p. 1983. softcover 16.50x (ISBN 0-86531-808-5). Westview.

Strategies & Policies on Informatics: IBI Background Documents Presented to the Intergovernmental Conference in Torremolinos, Spain, in Aug.-Sept. 1978. 284p. 1981. pap. 45.00 (ISBN 0-686-79511-3, UPB103, UPB). Unipub.

Stueart, Robert D., ed. Foundation in Library & Information Science: Contemporary Dimensions of Health Sciences Librarianship, Vol. 9. 1984. 40.00 (ISBN 0-89232-074-5). Jai Pr.

Sweeney, G. P., ed. Information & the Transformation of Society: Papers from the First Joint International Conference of the Institute of Information Scientists & the American Society for Information Science, St. Patrick's College, Dublin, Ireland, 28-30 June, 1982. (Contemporary Topics in Information Transfer Ser.: Vol. 2). 368p. 1983. 51.00 (ISBN 0-444-86505-5, I-494-82, North Holland). Elsevier.

Symposium, 4th, Marianske Lazne, Sept. 1-5, 1975. Mathematical Foundations of Computer Science. Becvar, J., ed. (Lecture Notes in Computer Science Ser.: Vol. 32). x, 476p. 1975. pap. 25.00 (ISBN 0-387-07389-2). Springer-Verlag.

Systems & Policy: The Function of Information in Improving Education Systems, National Case Studies of Argentina, Denmark, German Democratic Republic, Iraq & New Zealand. (IBEData Ser.). 82p. (Prepared for the International Bureau of Education). 1977. pap. 5.00 (ISBN 92-3-101522-2, U846, UNESCO). Unipub.

Tally, Roy D., ed. Information Choices & Policies: Proceedings of the 42nd ASIS Annual Meeting, Vol.16. LC 64-8303. 1979. 19.50x (ISBN 0-914236-47-4, 320-BW). Knowledge Indus.

Tou, Julius T., ed. Advances in Information Systems Science. Incl. Vol. 1. 318p. 1969. 49.50x (ISBN 0-306-39401-4); Vol. 2. 366p. 1969. 49.50x (ISBN 0-306-39402-2); Vol. 3. 368p. 1970. 49.50x (ISBN 0-306-39403-0); Vol. 4. 344p. 1972. 49.50x (ISBN 0-306-39404-9); Vol. 5. 357p. 1974. 49.50x (ISBN 0-306-39405-7); Vol. 6. 223p. 1976. 45.00 (ISBN 0-306-39406-5); Vol. 7. 327p. 1978. 49.50x (ISBN 0-306-39407-3). LC 69-12544. (Illus., Plenum Pr). Plenum Pub.

--Advances in information Systems Science, Vol. 9. 356p. 1985. 52.50x (ISBN 0-306-41644-1, Plenum). Plenum Pub.

Trute, Barry. Human Service Information Systems: How to Design & Implement Them. LC 84-27360. (Studies in Health & Human Services: Vol. 3). 224p. 1985. 49.95x (ISBN 0-88946-128-7). E Mellen.

User Education in Schools: A Survey of the Literature on Education for Information Use in Schools. 1981. 15.00x (ISBN 0-686-72513-1, Pub. by Brit Lib England). State Mutual Bk.

Vaillancourt, Pauline M. International Directory of Acronyms in Library, Information & Computer Sciences. LC 80-18352. xi, 518p. 1980. 50.00 (ISBN 0-8352-1152-5). Bowker.

Wiio, Osmo. Information & Communication Systems: An Introduction to the Concepts of Information, Communication, & Communication Research. (Communication & Information Science Ser.). Date not set. price not set (ISBN 0-89391-070-8). Ablex Pub.

Williams, James G & Pope, Elspeth. Simulation Activities in Library Communication & Information Science. (Communication Science & Technology Ser.: Vol. 6). 1976. 55.00 (ISBN 0-8247-6376-9). Dekker.

Williams, M. B., ed. Pathways to the Information Society: Proceedings of the Sixth International Conference on Computer Communication, London, 1982. 1018p. 1980. 55.00 (ISBN 0-444-86464-4, North Holland). Elsevier.

Williams, Martha E., ed. Annual Review of Information Science & Technology, Vol. 11. LC 66-25096. 1976. 35.00 (ISBN 0-87715-212-8). Am Soc Info Sci.

--Annual Review of Information Science & Technology, Vol. 20. (American Society for Information Science Ser.). 400p. 1985. 52.50 (ISBN 0-317-26894-5). Knowledge Indus.

--The Annual Review of Information Science & Technology, 1976, Vol. 11. LC 66-25096. (Illus.). 457p. 1976. 45.00 (ISBN 0-87715-212-8, 308-BW). Knowledge Indus.

--Annual Review of Information Science & Technology, 1977, Vol. 12. LC 66-25096. 361p. 1977. 45.00 (ISBN 0-914236-11-3, 307-BW). Knowledge Indus.

--Annual Review of Information Science & Technology, 1978, Vol. 13. LC 66-25096. 386p. 1978. 45.00 (ISBN 0-914236-21-0, 306-BW). Knowledge Indus.

--Annual Review of Information Science & Techology, 1979, Vol. 14. LC 66-25096. 375p. 1979. 45.00 (ISBN 0-914236-44-X, 305-BW). Knowledge Indus.

--Annual Review of Information Science & Technology, 1980, Vol. 15. LC 66-25096. 413p. 1980. 45.00 (ISBN 0-914236-65-2, 304-BW). Knowledge Indus.

--Annual Review of Information Science & Technology, 1981, Vol. 16. LC 66-25096. 422p. 1981. 45.00x (ISBN 0-914236-90-3, 303-BW). Knowledge Indus.

--Annual Review of Information Science & Technology, 1982, Vol. 17. LC 66-25096. 367p. 1982. 45.00x (ISBN 0-86729-032-3, 302-BW). Knowledge Indus.

--The Annual Review of Information Science & Technology, 1983, Vol. 18. LC 66-25096. 447p. 1983. 45.00x (ISBN 0-86729-050-1, 301-BW). Knowledge Indus.

--Annual Review of Information Science & Technology, 1984, Vol. 19. LC 66-25096. 417p. 1984. 50.00x (ISBN 0-86729-093-5, 346-BW). Knowledge Indus.

Wilson, John H., Jr., ed. A World of Information: Proceedings of the 35th Annual ASIS Meeting, Vol. 9, 1972. LC 64-8303. 295p. 1972. professional 15.00 (ISBN 0-87715-409-0, 324-BW). Knowledge Indus.

Wilson, Kenneth D. & Goldhurst, Richard. Pathways to Prosperity: Choices for Success in the Information Age. 160p. 1983. 23.95 (ISBN 0-03-069538-4). Praeger.

World Guide to Technological Information & Documentation Services. 1970. pap. 11.00 (U725, UNESCO). Unipub.

Zlotnick, Barbara B. Ready for Reference: Media Skills for Intermediate Students. (Teaching Library, Media, Research & Information Skills). 202p. 1984. pap. text ed. 19.50 (ISBN 0-87287-411-7). Libs Unl.

Zorkoczy, Peter. Information Technology. LC 82-23879. (Illus.). 152p. 1984. pap. 15.95 (ISBN 0-442-29391-7). Van Nos Reinhold.

--Information Technology: An Introduction. LC 82-10115. 137p. 1983. 29.95 (ISBN 0-86729-037-4, 412-BW). Knowledge Indus.

Zorkoczy, Peter, ed. Oxford Surveys in Information Technology, Vol. I. (Illus.). 400p. 1985. 50.00 (ISBN 0-19-859003-2). Oxford U Pr.

INFORMATION SCIENCE–STUDY AND TEACHING

Griffiths, M. & Tagg, E. D., eds. Role of Programming in Teaching Informatics: Proceedings of the IFIP TC3 Working Conference on Teaching Programming, Paris, France, 7-9 May, 1984. 212p. 1985. 37.00 (ISBN 0-444-87664-2, North-Holland). Elsevier.

Lovis, F. B & Tagg, E. D., eds. Informatics & Teacher Training. (Proceedings of the IFIP WG 3.1 Working Conference on Informatics & Teacher Training, Birmingham, UK, 16-20 July, 1984). 254p. 1984. 31.50 (ISBN 0-444-87639-1, North-Holland). Elsevier.

INFORMATION SERVICES

see also Electronic Publishing; Information Storage and Retrieval Systems; Research

Back to the Books: BI & the Theory of Information Sources. 76p. 1983. 15.00 (ISBN 0-8389-6587-3). Assn Coll & Res Libs.

Bakewell, K. G. How to Organise Information: A Manager's Guide to Techniques & Sources with a Checklist for Secretaries & Assistants. LC 84-10223. 225p. 1984. text ed. 33.95x (ISBN 0-566-02397-0). Gower Pub Co.

Chartrand, Robert L. & Morentz, James W. Information Technology Serving Society. (Illus.). 1979. 42.00 (ISBN 0-08-021979-9). Pergamon.

Ching-hih Chen & Hernon, Peter. Information Seeking: Assessing & Anticipating User Needs. 222p. 1982. 27.00 (ISBN 0-918212-50-2). Neal-Schuman.

Clark, D. & Unwin, K. Information Services in Rural Areas: Prospects for Telecommunications Access. 122p. 1980. 25.00x (ISBN 0-86094-058-6, Pub. by GEO Abstracts England). State Mutual Bk.

Darnay, Brigitte T., ed. Directory of Special Libraries & Information Centers, Vol. 1: Special Libraries & Information Centers in the United States & Canada, 2 vols. 9th ed. LC 82-6068. 1700p. 1985. Set. 320.00x (ISBN 0-8103-1888-1). Gale.

Doyle, Lauren. Information Retrieval & Processing. LC 75-1179. (Information Science Ser.). 410p. 1975. 49.95 (ISBN 0-471-22151-1, Pub. by Wiley-Interscience). Wiley.

Durrance, Joan. Armed for Action: Library Response to Citizen Information Needs. 190p. 1984. 29.95 (ISBN 0-918212-71-5). Neal Schuman.

Elin-Dor & Jones, C. R. Information Systems Management: Analytical Tools & Techniques. 222p. 1985. 29.95 (ISBN 0-444-00956-6, North-Holland). Elsevier.

Englefield, Dermot & Drewry, Gavin, eds. Information Sources in Politics & Political Science: A Survey Worldwide. LC 84-2819. (Guides to Information Sources Ser.). 528p. 1984. text ed. 69.95 (ISBN 0-408-11470-3). Butterworth.

Fang, Josephine Riss & Nauta, Paul, eds. International Guide to Library & Information Science Education: A Reference Source for Educational Programs in the Information Fields World-Wide. (IFLA Publication Ser.: Vol. 32). 536p. 1985. lib. bdg. 46.00 (ISBN 3-598-20396-9). K G Saur.

Firnberg, D. The Information Centre. (Computer State of the Art Report Ser.: Series No. 12, No. 2). (Illus.). 275p. 1984. 460.00 (ISBN 0-08-028586-4). Pergamon.

Giuliano, Vincent, et al. Into the Information Age: A Perspective for Federal Action on Information. 142p. 1979. pap. text ed. 9.00x (ISBN 0-8389-0283-9). ALA.

Grant, Mary M. & Berleant-Schiller, Riva, eds. Directory of Business & Financial Services. 8th ed. LC 83-20300. 200p. 1984. 35.00 (ISBN 0-87111-287-6). SLA.

Heilprin, Laurence B., ed. Toward Foundations of Information Science. LC 85-12612. 150p. 1985. 34.95 (ISBN 0-86729-149-4, 350-BW). Knowledge Indus.

Herner, Saul & Vellucci, Matthew J., eds. Selected Federal Computer-Based Information Systems. LC 72-85016. (Illus.). ix, 215p. 1972. text ed. 15.00 (ISBN 0-87815-007-2). Info Resources.

Hoffmann, Christa & Kenney, Brigitte. Changing Information Concepts & Technologies: A Reader for the Professional Librarian. LC 82-166. (Professional Librarian Ser.). 179p. 1982. professional 34.50 (ISBN 0-86729-028-5, 206-BW); pap. 27.50 professional (ISBN 0-86729-027-7). Knowledge Indus.

Hussain, Donna & Hussain, K. M. Information Resource Management. 1984. 29.95x (ISBN 0-256-02990-3). Irwin.

Information Processing Supplies (U. S.) 1985. write for info. (ISBN 0-86621-252-3). Frost & Sullivan.

Information Resources Management. 1979. 15.00 (ISBN 0-686-25588-7). Assn Syst Mgmt.

Instrumentation & Control Equipment Market in the Power Industry. 400p. 1984. 1500.00 (ISBN 0-86621-205-1, A1271). Frost & Sullivan.

Kibirige, Harry M. The Information Dilemma: A Critical Analysis of Information Pricing & the Fees Controversy. LC 83-5570. (New Directions in Librarianship Ser.: No. 4). (Illus.). xiv, 195p. 1983. lib. bdg. 29.95 (ISBN 0-313-23381-0, KII/). Greenwood.

Koenig, Michael E. Budgeting Techniques for Libraries & Information Centers. LC 80-27698. (Professional Development Ser.: Vol. 1). (Illus.). pap. 20.00 (ISBN 0-317-09538-2, 2020935). Bks Demand UMI.

Lambert, Steve. Online: A Guide to America's Leading Information Services. LC 84-27159. 319p. 1985. pap. 19.95 (ISBN 0-914845-35-7). Microsoft.

Lord, Kenniston W. The Data Center Disaster Consultant. 2nd ed. (Q.E.D. Information Services, Inc. Ser.). 224p. 1983. text ed. 57.50 (ISBN 0-13-196239-6). P-H.

Meltzer, Morton F. Information, the Ultimate Management Resource: How to Find, Use, & Manage It. LC 81-66222. pap. 55.80 (ISBN 0-317-28149-6, 2055749). Bks Demand UMI.

Mount, Ellis, ed. Training of Sci-Tech Librarians & Library Users. LC 81-6975. (Science & Technology Libraries: Vol. 1, No. 3). 72p. 1981. pap. text ed. 15.00 (ISBN 0-917724-75-5, B75). Haworth Pr.

Piercy, Nigel, ed. Management Implications of New Information Technology. 320p. 1984. 31.50 (ISBN 0-89397-201-0). Nichols Pub.

Rudman, Jack. Magnetic Tape Librarian. (Career Examination Ser.: C-2872). (Cloth bdg. avail. on request). pap. 10.00 (ISBN 0-8373-2872-1). Natl Learning.

Schmittroth, John, Jr., ed. Encyclopedia of Information Systems & Services: International. 6th ed. 600p. 1985. 175.00x (ISBN 0-8103-1538-6). Gale.

--Encyclopedia of Information Systems & Services: U. S. 6th ed. 1200p. 1985. 200.00x (ISBN 0-8103-1541-6). Gale.

--New Information Systems & Services. 6th ed. 400p. 1985. pap. text ed. 250.00x (ISBN 0-8103-0941-6). Gale.

Schneider, H. J. & Wasserman, A. I., eds. Automated Tools for Information Systems Design: Proceedings IFIP WG Working Conference on Automated Tools for Information Systems Design & Development, 8.1, New Orleans, January 26-28, 1982. 262p. 1982. 42.75 (ISBN 0-444-86338-9, North-Holland). Elsevier.

Selective Inventory of Information Services. (World Social Science Information Services: No. 3). 140p. 1981. pap. 11.25 (ISBN 92-3-001848-1, U1135, UNESCO). Unipub.

Smith, David. Systems Thinking in Library & Information Management. 206p. 1981. 15.00 (ISBN 0-85157-305-3, Pub. by Bingley England). Shoe String.

Stern, B. T., ed. Information & Innovation: Proceedings of a Seminar of ICSU-AB on the Role of Information in the Innovative Process, Amsterdam, The Netherlands, 1982. (Contemporary Topics in Information Transfer Ser.: Vol. 1). 192p. 1983. 38.50 (ISBN 0-444-86496-2, I-497-82, North Holland). Elsevier.

Stone, M. David. Getting On-Line: A Guide to Assessing Computer Information Services. 224p. 1984. 21.95 (ISBN 0-13-354416-8); pap. 14.95 (ISBN 0-13-354408-7). P-H.

Sturtz & Williams. Using Computer Information Services. LC 83-50165. 240p. 1983. pap. 12.95 (ISBN 0-672-21997-2, 21997). Sams.

Tedd, L. A. Case Studies in Computer-Based Bibliographic Information Services. 1979. 40.00x (ISBN 0-905984-30-7, Pub. by Brit Lib England). State Mutual Bk.

Van Der Haan, A. & Winters, A. A., eds. The Use of Information in a Changing World: Proceedings of the FID Congress, 42nd, the Hague, Netherlands, Sept. 24-27, 1984. 470p. 1984. 52.00 (ISBN 0-444-87554-9, I-301-84, North Holland). Elsevier.

Van Houten, H., ed. The Competitive Strength of the Information & Communication Industry in Europe. 1983. lib. bdg. 32.50 (ISBN 90-247-2860-6, Pub. by Martinus Nijhoff Netherlands). Kluwer Academic.

White, Herbert S. Managing the Special Library: Strategies for Success Within the Larger Organization. LC 83-24390. (Professional Librarian Ser.). 152p. 1984. professional 36.50 (ISBN 0-86729-088-9, 231-BW); pap. 27.50 professional (ISBN 0-86729-087-0). Knowledge Indus.

Williams, F. Profiting from Computer Information Services. 1984. cancelled (ISBN 0-317-05712-X). SYBEX.

Wilson, T. D. Office Automation & Information Services: Final Report on a Study of Current Development. (LIR Report 31). (Orig.). 1985. pap. 16.50 (ISBN 0-7123-3045-3, Pub. by British Lib). Longwood Pub Group.

Wilson, T. D. & Stephenson, J. Dissemination of Information. 2nd ed. (Examination Guide Ser.). 86p. 1969. 12.00 (ISBN 0-208-00862-4, Archon). Shoe String.

Woods, Lawrence A. & Pope, Nolan F. The Librarian's Guide to Microcomputer Technology & Applications. LC 83-13548. (American Society for Information Science Ser.). 209p. 1983. professional o.s.i. 34.50x (ISBN 0-86729-045-5); pap. 27.50x professional (ISBN 0-86729-044-7, 344-BW). Knowledge Indus.

INFORMATION STORAGE AND RETRIEVAL SYSTEMS

see also Automatic Indexing; Computers; Data Base Management; Data Tapes; Electronic Data Processing; Information Networks; Libraries–Automation; Machine-Readable Data Files

INIS: Authority List for Journal Titles. (INIS Reference Ser.: No. 11). pap. 7.75 (IN11/R6, IAEA). Unipub.
INIS: Description of Computer Programs. (INIS Reference Ser.: No. 14). pap. 5.75 (ISBN 92-0-178675-1, IN14/R1, IAEA). Unipub.
INIS: Descriptive Cataloging Samples. (INIS Reference Ser.: No. 2). pap. 2.25 (IN2/R2, IAEA). Unipub.
INIS: Descriptive Cataloguing Rules. (INIS Reference Ser.: No. 1). pap. 2.25 (IN1/R2, IAEA). Unipub.
INIS: Descriptive Cataloguing Samples. (INIS Reference Ser.: No. 2). 1978. pap. 5.50 (ISBN 92-0-178278-0, IN2/R3, IAEA). Unipub.
INIS: Instructions for Submitting Abstracts. (INIS Reference Ser.: No. 4). pap. 5.50 (ISBN 92-0-178171-7, IN4/R1, IAEA). Unipub.
INIS: Manual for Index. (INIS Reference Ser.: No. 12). 108p. 1974. pap. 5.50 (ISBN 92-0-178074-5, IN12/R2, IAEA). Unipub.
INIS: Multilingual Dictionary - English-French-German-Russian, No. 1. (INIS Reference Ser.: 20). 1983. pap. 23.25 (ISBN 9-2017-8283-7, IN20/R0, IAEA). Unipub.
INIS: Self-Teaching Manual. (INIS Reference Ser.: No. 15). 1972. pap. 8.75 (ISBN 92-0-178772-3, IN15/R0, IAEA). Unipub.
INIS: Subject Categories & Scope Descriptions. (INIS Reference Ser.: No. 3). pap. 3.75 (IN3/R4, IAEA). Unipub.
INIS: Subject Indexing Samples. (INIS Reference Ser.: No. 16). pap. 7.00 (ISBN 92-0-178775-8, IN16/R0, IAEA). Unipub.
INIS: Terminology & Codes for Countries & International Organizations. (INIS Reference Ser.: 5). 14p. pap. 5.50 (ISBN 92-0-178375-2, IN5/R3, IAEA). Unipub.
Inose, Hiroshi & Pierce, John R. Information Technology & Civilization. LC 83-20721. (Illus.). 263p. 1984. 19.95 (ISBN 0-7167-1514-7); pap. 9.95 (ISBN 0-7167-1515-5). W H Freeman.
Insull, Robert & Sumner, Jeanne, eds. Multi-State Information System: Proceedings of the Seventh Annual National Users Group Conference. 280p. 1982. pap. 10.00 (ISBN 0-936934-03-4). N S Kline Inst.
International Cooperative Information Systems: Proceedings of a Seminar Held in Vienna, Austria, 9-13 July 1979. 111p. 1980. pap. 10.00 (ISBN 0-88936-252-1, IDRC156, IDRC). Unipub.
International Global Data-Processing System Plan to Support the First GARP Global Experiment: Annexes. 22p. 1979. pap. 18.00 (ISBN 0-686-86845-5, W449, WMO). Unipub.
ISIS - A General Description of an Approach to Computerized Bibliographical Control. pap. 4.75 (ILO37, ILO). Unipub.
J. J. Keller & Associates, Inc., ed. Data Systems Source Guide-Transportation & Traffic. LC 81-86199. (20M). 250p. 1985. 3-ring binder 65.00 (ISBN 0-934674-41-8). J J Keller.
Jones, Elizabeth, ed. Declassified Documents Reference System Retrospective Collection. LC 76-39673. 1977. 335.00 (ISBN 0-8408-0029-0). Res Pubns Conn.
Kahn, Michael, et al. Micro: Information Retrieval System Version 5.0, Reference Manual. 236p. 1977. pap. 15.00 (ISBN 0-87736-335-8). U of Mich Inst Labor.
Katzan, Harry. Distributed Information Systems. 1979. 20.00 (ISBN 0-89433-104-3). Petrocelli.
Kent, Allen. Information Analysis & Retrieval. LC 70-155120. (Information Science Ser.). 367p. 1971. 49.95x (ISBN 0-471-46995-5). Wiley.
Kent, Allen, ed. Encyclopedia of Library & Information Science, Vol. 18. 1976. 65.00 (ISBN 0-8247-2118-7). Dekker.
Kiewitt, Eva L. Evaluating Information Retrieval Systems: The PROBE Program. LC 78-55322. 1978. lib. bdg. 29.95 (ISBN 0-313-20521-3, KPC/). Greenwood.
Kim, W., et al, eds. Query Processing in Database Systems. (Topics in Information Systems Ser.). (Illus.). 352p. 1985. 32.50 (ISBN 0-387-13831-5). Springer-Verlag.
King, Donald W. & Bryant, Edward C. The Evaluation of Information Services & Products. LC 76-141595. (Illus.). vii, 306p. 1971. text ed. 27.50 (ISBN 0-87815-003-X). Info Resources.
King, Donald W., ed. Key Papers in the Design & Evaluation of Information Systems. LC 78-23449. (American Society for Information Science Ser.). (Illus.). 405p. 1978. professional 25.00x (ISBN 0-914236-31-8, 339-BW). Knowledge Indus.
Kline, Linda J. & Carhart, Jane M., eds. Multi-State Information System: Proceedings of the Sixth Annual National Users Group Conference, May 4-6, 1981, Orangeburg, N.Y. 225p. (Orig.). 1982. pap. 10.00 (ISBN 0-936934-02-6). N S Kline Inst.
Kochen, Manfred. The Growth of Knowledge: Readings on Organization & Retrieval of Knowledge. LC 67-13526. 394p. 1967. text ed. 23.50 (ISBN 0-471-49695-2, Pub. by Wiley). Krieger.
Kohonen, T. Content-Addressable Memories. (Springer Ser. in Information Sciences: Vol. 1). (Illus.). 400p. 1980. 46.00 (ISBN 0-387-09823-2). Springer-Verlag.
Kraemer, Kenneth L., et al. The Management of Information Systems. 416p. 1980. 35.00x (ISBN 0-231-04886-6). Columbia U Pr.
Lancaster, F. W. Toward Paperless Information Systems. (Library & Information Science Ser.). (192). 1978. 33.00 (ISBN 0-12-436050-5). Acad Pr.
--Vocabulary Control for Information Retrieval. 2nd ed. LC 84-82260. (Illus.). 250p. 1985. text ed. 27.50 (ISBN 0-87815-053-6). Info Resources.
Lancaster, F. W. & Fayen, E. G. Information Retrieval On-Line. LC 73-9697. (Information Sciences Ser.). pap. 116.50 (ISBN 0-8357-9911-5, 2015840). Bks Demand UMI.
Lancaster, F. Wilfrid. Information Retrieval Systems: Characteristics, Testing & Evaluation. 2nd ed. LC 78-11078. (Information Sciences Ser.). 381p. 1979. 42.95x (ISBN 0-471-04673-6, Pub. by Wiley-Interscience). Wiley.
--Vocabulary Control for Information Retrieval. LC 78-186528. (Illus.). xiv, 233p. 1972. text ed. 27.50 (ISBN 0-87815-006-4). Info Resources.
Lane, J. E. Microprocessors & Information Handling. (Computing in the Eighties Ser.). 67p. 1981. pap. 15.00x (ISBN 0-85012-334-8). Intl Pubns Serv.
Leben, J. & Arnold, J. IBM CPU & Storage Architecture: System-370-Mode & 370-XA Mode. (Data Processing Training Ser.). 256p. 1984. pap. 49.95 (ISBN 0-471-80142-9). Wiley.
Lichtig. Case Mix Information Systems. 1986. price not set (ISBN 0-471-82384-8). Wiley.
Licklider, J. C. Libraries of the Future. 1965. 22.50x (ISBN 0-262-12016-X). MIT Pr.
Lomax, J. D. Data Dictionary Systems. (Illus.). 1977. pap. 45.00x (ISBN 0-85012-191-4). Intl Pubns Serv.
Lord, Kenniston W. The Data Center Disaster Consultant. 2nd ed. (Q.E.D. Information Services, Inc. Ser.). 224p. 1983. text ed. 57.50 (ISBN 0-13-196239-6). P-H.
Lucas, H. C. Anlysis, Design, & Implementation of Information Systems. 3rd ed. 448p. 1985. 35.95 (ISBN 0-07-038929-2). McGraw.
Lucas, H. C., et al, eds. Information Systems Environment. 346p. 1980. 47.00 (ISBN 0-444-86036-3, North-Holland). Elsevier.
Lucas, Henry C. The Analysis, Design & Implementation of Information Systems. rev. ed. (Management Information Systems Ser.). (Illus.). 416p. 1980. text ed. 36.95 (ISBN 0-07-038927-6). McGraw.
--Why Information Systems Fail. LC 74-18395. (Illus.). pap. 35.30 (ISBN 0-317-10726-7, 2021970). Bks Demand UMI.
Lucey, T. Management Information Systems. 1980. 10.00x (ISBN 0-905435-11-7, Pub. by DP Pubns). State Mutual Bk.
McCrank, Lawrence J., ed. Automating the Archives: Issues & Problems in Computer Applications. LC 81-11732. (Professional Librarian Ser.). 363p. 1981. 34.50x (ISBN 0-914236-95-4, 329-BW); pap. 27.50x (ISBN 0-914236-86-5). Knowledge Indus.
Maedke, Wilmer O., et al. Information & Records Management. LC 73-7362. (Illus.). 480p. 1981. 21.28x (ISBN 0-02-470800-3). Glencoe.
Manual on the Global Data-Processing System: Regional Aspects, Vol. 2. (Illus.). 72p. 1980. pap. 25.00 (ISBN 0-685-09233-X, W485, WMO). Unipub.
Manual on the Global Data-Processing System: Regional Aspects, Vol. 2. 74p. 1981. pap. 7.00 (ISBN 0-686-69635-2, W475, WMO). Unipub.
Marble, Duane F., et al. Basic Readings in Geographic Information Systems. 250p. 1984. looseleaf 30.95x (ISBN 0-913913-00-6). Spad Sys.
Martin, Edley W. & Perkins, William C. Computers & Information Systems: An Introduction. LC 72-95392. (Irwin-Dorsey Information Processing Ser.). pap. 160.00 (ISBN 0-317-29612-4, 2021665). Bks Demand UMI.
Martin, James. An Information Systems Manifesto. (Illus.). 352p. 1984. text ed. 45.00 (ISBN 0-13-464769-6). P-H.
--Systems Design from Provably Correct Constructs. (Illus.). 480p. 1985. text ed. 37.50 (ISBN 0-13-881483-X). P-H.
Mathies, M. Lorraine & Watson, Peter G. Computer Based Reference Services. LC 73-9967. 212p. 1973. pap. text ed. 15.00x (ISBN 0-8389-0156-5). ALA.
Mattelart, Armand & Schmucler, Hector. Communication & Information Technologies. Voigt, Melvin J., ed. Buxton, David, tr. from Fr. (Communication & Information Science Ser.). 200p. 1985. text ed. 24.50 (ISBN 0-89391-214-X). Ablex Pub.
Methlie, Laif B. Information Systems Development. 1978. 22.00x (ISBN 82-00-05216-8). Universitet.
Michie, Donald. Expert Systems in a Microelectronic Age. 287p. 1980. 30.00x (ISBN 0-85224-381-2, Pub by Edinburgh U Pr Scotland). Columbia U Pr.
Miller, Arthur R. Assault on Privacy: Computers, Data Banks, & Dossiers. LC 70-142588. 1971. 12.95 (ISBN 0-472-65500-0). U of Mich Pr.
Model Curriculum for Computer Information Systems. 67p. members PAP 4.00 (ISBN 0-318-17044-2); non/members(EF1) 4.00 (ISBN 0-318-17045-0). Data Process Mgmt.
Murray, John P. Managing Information Systems as a Corporate Resource. LC 83-70876. 200p. 1984. 25.00 (ISBN 0-87094-428-2). Dow Jones-Irwin.
Myer, Theodore H. Global Communications: A Computer-Based Message Systems Approach. 350p. 1986. pap. text ed. price not set (ISBN 0-02-949590-3). Macmillan.
Neibauer, Alan R. Applications in Word & Information Processing. LC 84-17533. 352p. 1984. pap. text ed. 20.80 (ISBN 0-8273-2400-6); instr's. guide 7.00 (ISBN 0-8273-2401-4). Delmar.
Oddy, et al. Information Retrieval Research. 1981. text ed. 69.95 (ISBN 0-408-10775-8). Butterworth.
Omlor, J. Dennis. Efficiency Analysis of File Organization & Information Retrieval. Stone, Harold S., ed. LC 81-11693. (Computer Science: Distributed Database Systems Ser.: No. 10). 124p. 1981. 29.95 (ISBN 0-8357-1226-5). UMI Res Pr.
Orientation Manual for INIS & AGRIS (OMINAS) - 1979. (INIS Reference Ser.: No. 18). 190p. 1979. pap. 11.25 (ISBN 9-2017-8279-9, IN18/R0, IAEA). Unipub.
Ostle, Jud. Information Systems Analysis & Design. 500p. 1985. text ed. write for info. (ISBN 0-8087-6401-2). Burgess.
Paice, C. B. Information Retrieval & the Computer. (Vol.26). 218p. 1977. 32.50 (ISBN 0-444-19494-0). Elsevier.
Palmer, Richards P. Integrated Information Management: A Systems Approach. (Applications in Information Management & Technolgy Ser.). 250p. 1986. pap. text ed. 35.00 (ISBN 0-918212-91-X). Neal-Schuman.
Payne, Eugene E., et al. The Scope of Management Information Systems: Computer & Information Systems Ser. 1983. 13.00 (ISBN 0-89806-014-1). Inst Indus Eng.
Petrarca, Anthony E., et al, eds. Information Interaction: Proceedings of the 45th Annual ASIS Meeting, Vol. 19, 1982. LC 64-8303. (American Society for Information Science Ser.). 431p. 1982. pap. 19.50x Professional (ISBN 0-86729-038-2, 317-BW). Knowledge Indus.
Plander, I., ed. Artificial Intelligence & Information-Control Systems of Robots: Proceedings of the International Conference on Artificial Intelligence & Information-Control Systems of Robots, Smolenice, 3rd, Czechoslovakia, June 11-15, 1984. 402p. 1984. 55.75 (ISBN 0-444-87533-6, Pub. by North Holland). Elsevier.
Popyk, M. K. Word Processing & Information Systems: A Practical Approach to Concepts. LC 82-25902. 352p. 1983. 24.50 (ISBN 0-07-050574-8). McGraw.
Powers, Michael J., et al. Computer Information Systems Development: Analysis & Design. 1984. text ed. 21.95 (ISBN 0-538-10820-7, J82). SW Pub.
Poynter, Dan. Word Processors & Information Processing. 172p. 1983. 16.95 (ISBN 0-13-963553-X); pap. 11.95 (ISBN 0-13-963546-7). P-H.
--Word Processors & Information Processing: What They Are & How to Buy. 2nd ed. LC 81-11128. (Illus.). 172p. (Orig.). 1982. 11.95 (ISBN 0-915516-31-4). Para Pub.
Prothro, Vivian C. Information Management Systems: A Data Base Primer. (Computer Science Ser.). 1976. 23.95 (ISBN 0-442-80336-2). Van Nos Reinhold.
Rademacher, Robert & Gibson, Harry. An Introduction to Computers & Information Systems. 1983. text ed. 21.95 (ISBN 0-538-10250-0, J25). SW Pub.
Radford, K. J. Information Systems for Strategic Decisions. (Illus.). 1978. ref. ed. 23.95 (ISBN 0-87909-389-7). Reston.
Rank Xerox (UK) Ltd, Uxbridge, UK, ed. Brave New World? Living with Information Technology. 188p. 1983. 15.90 (ISBN 0-08-025847-6). Pergamon.
Recommended Methods for Development-Information Systems: Manual for the Preparation of Records in Development-Information Systems, Vol. 1. 272p. 1983. pap. 20.00 (ISBN 0-88936-354-4, IDRCTS40, IDRC). Unipub.
Research & Education Association Staff. Handbook of Computers & Data Processing. LC 83-61837. (Illus.). 480p. 1983. 19.85 (ISBN 0-87891-546-X). Res & Educ.
Rivers, James E. & McCoy, Clyde B. Computerized Information Systems for Effective Organizational Management. LC 82-49089. 1984. write for info. (ISBN 0-669-06091-7). Lexington Bks.
Robinson, Dexter E. Selling Information Systems. (Reference Ser.). (Illus.). 142p. (Orig.). 1984. pap. 35.00 (ISBN 0-89258-083-6, R022). Assn Inform & Image Mgmt.
Rosenau, Fred S. & Chase, Leslie, eds. Proven Techniques for Increasing Database Use. LC 83-80073. 1983. 49.95 (ISBN 0-942774-09-4). Info Indus.
Rosenau, Fred S. & Chase, Leslie R., eds. How to Succeed in the Electronic Information Marketplace. 1984. pap. 59.95 (ISBN 0-942774-16-7). Info Indus.
Rosenfeld, J. L., ed. Information Processing Seventy-Four. LC 74-76063. 1107p. 1975. 106.50 (ISBN 0-444-10683-8, North-Holland). Elsevier.
Rule & McAdam. Politics of Privacy: Planning for Pesonal Data Systems As Powerful Technologies. 25.00 (ISBN 0-444-99074-7, RPP/, Pub. by Elsevier). Greenwood.
Sagiv, Yehoshua C. Optimization of Queries in Relational Databases. Stone, Harold, ed. LC 81-13079. (Computer Science: Distributed Database Systems Ser.: No. 12). 126p. 1981. 34.95 (ISBN 0-8357-1244-3). UMI Res Pr.
Salton, Gerard & McGill, Michael J. Introduction to Modern Information Retrieval. (Computer Science Ser.). 400p. 1983. 39.95 (ISBN 0-07-054484-0). McGraw.
Schmidt, J. W. & Brodie, M. L., eds. Relational Database Systems: Analysis & Comparison. 618p. 1983. 24.50 (ISBN 0-387-12032-7). Springer-Verlag.
Schmittroth, John, Jr., ed. New Information Systems & Services. 6th ed. 400p. 1985. pap. text ed. 250.00x (ISBN 0-8103-0941-6). Gale.
Schneider, H. J., ed. Formal Models & Practical Tools for Information Systems & Design. LC 79-19860. 296p. 1980. 47.00 (ISBN 0-444-85394-4, North Holland). Elsevier.
Schrapp, Michael. One-Pass Top Down Update Schemes for Search Trees. Design, Analysis & Application. (Reihe 10 Ser.: No. 38). 106p. 1984. pap. 28.00 (ISBN 3-18-148605-1, Pub. by VDI Verlag Germany). Brookfield Pub Co.
Schumacher, Robert. Information Resource Management: A Guide to Needs Analysis. 1985. text ed. 27.95 (ISBN 0-8359-3178-1). Reston.
Scientific American Editors. Information: A Scientific American Book. LC 66-29386. (Illus.). 218p. 1966. 18.95x (ISBN 0-7167-0967-8); pap. text ed. 10.95x (ISBN 0-7167-0966-X). W H Freeman.
Semprevivo, Philip C. Teams in Information Systems Development. LC 80-50608. 144p. (Orig.). 1980. pap. 19.50 (ISBN 0-917072-20-0). Yourdon.
Sernadas, A., et al, eds. Information Systems: Theoretical & Formal Aspects. 1985. 35.25 (ISBN 0-444-87706-1). Elsevier.
Sharp, John r. Some Fundamentals of Information Retrieval. 224p. 1965. 14.00x (ISBN 0-233-95712-X, 05820-3, Pub. by Gower Pub Co England). Lexington Bks.
Sheehan, Bernard S., ed. Information Technology: Advances & Applications. LC 81-48575. (Institutional Research Ser.: No. 35). 1982. pap. text ed. 8.95x (ISBN 0-87589-905-6). Jossey-Bass.
Sherrod, John, ed. Information Systems & Networks: Eleventh Annual Symposium. LC 74-11941. 200p. 1975. lib. bdg. 29.95x (ISBN 0-8371-7717-0, ISN/). Greenwood.
Skeans, Carolou & Hern, Ann. Advanced Information Processing Applications. 1984. pap. text ed. 15.95 (ISBN 0-8359-0069-X); instr's manual avail. (ISBN 0-8359-0076-2). Reston.
Smith & Medley. Computer Information Systems: Information Resource Management. 1986. text ed. price not set (ISBN 0-538-10190-3, J18). SW Pub.
Smith, Linda C., ed. New Information Technologies-New Opportunities: Proceedings of the Clinic on Library Applications of Data Processing, 1981. LC 82-10947. 119p. 1982. 11.00 (ISBN 0-87845-066-1). U of Ill Lib Info Sci.
Smith, William A., Jr. & Wechsler, Ben L. Planning Guide for Information System Evaluation Studies. 1983. 13.00 (ISBN 0-89806-016-8, 108). Inst Indus Eng.
Soergel, Dagobert. Information Storage & Retrieval: A Systems Approach. LC 83-15741. (Library Information Science). Date not set. 49.50 (ISBN 0-12-654260-0); pap. 24.95 (ISBN 0-12-654261-9). Acad Pr.
Solso, R. L., ed. Information Processing & Cognition: The Loyola Symposium. 386p. 1975. 36.00 (ISBN 0-89859-418-9). L Erlbaum Assocs.
Spark-Jones, K. Information Retrieval Experiment. 360p. 1981. 79.95 (ISBN 0-408-10648-4). Butterworth.

Kallman, Ernest A. & Reinharth, Leon. Information Systems for Planning & Decision Making. 360p. 1984. 36.95 (ISBN 0-442-25628-0). Van Nos Reinhold.

Kanter, Jerome. Management Information Systems. 3rd ed. (Illus.). 432p. 1984. text ed. 28.95 (ISBN 0-13-549543-1). P-H.

Kroenke, David M. Business Computer Systems: An Introduction. 1st ed. LC 80-84140. (Illus.). 576p. 1981. cancelled (ISBN 0-938188-00-3). Mitchell Pub.

--Business Computer Systems: An Introduction. 2nd ed. LC 83-17381. (Illus.). 689p. 1984. text ed. 25.95 (ISBN 0-938188-07-0); study guide-casebook 7.95 (ISBN 0-938188-12-7); COBOL manual 5.95 (ISBN 0-938188-03-8); tutorial diskette avail. Mitchell Pub.

Kuhn, Sarah. Computer Manufacturing in New England. (Illus.). 187p. 1982. pap. 12.00 (ISBN 0-943142-03-2). St Local Inter.

Leitch, Robert A. & Davis, K. Roscoe. Accounting Information Systems. (Illus.). 720p. 1983. 37.95 (ISBN 0-13-002949-1). P-H.

Li, David H. Accounting Information Systems: A Control Emphasis. 1983. 31.95x (ISBN 0-256-02909-1). Irwin.

Lindhe, Richard & Grossman, Steven D. Accounting Information Systems. 500p. 1980. text ed. 31.95x (ISBN 0-931920-23-X). Dame Pubns.

Lucas, Henry C., Jr. Implementation: The Key to Successful Information Systems. LC 80-27009. 224p. 1981. 37.00x (ISBN 0-231-04434-8). Columbia U Pr.

McCosh, Andrew, et al. Developing Managerial Information Systems. LC 80-14760. 387p. 1981. 37.95x (ISBN 0-470-26913-8). Halsted Pr.

McFarlan, F. Warren & McKenney, James L. Corporate Information Systems: The Issues Facing Senior Executives. 1983. pap. 13.50x (ISBN 0-256-02911-3). Irwin.

McLeod, Raymond & Forkner, Irvine. Computerized Business Information Systems: An Introduction to Data Processing. 2nd ed. LC 81-10471. 583p. 1982. text ed. 33.50 (ISBN 0-471-02575-5); tchr's ed. avail. (ISBN 0-471-02576-3); tests avail. (ISBN 0-471-86775-6); pap. 15.95 wkbk. (ISBN 0-471-86211-8). Wiley.

McLeod, Raymond, Jr. Management Information Systems. 2nd ed. 592p. 1983. 31.95 (ISBN 0-574-21410-0, 13-4410); casebook 10.95 (ISBN 0-574-21412-7, 13-4412); instructors guide avail. (ISBN 0-574-21411-9, 13-4411). SRA.

McNichols, Charles. Micro-Based Business Systems: Analysis, Design & Implementation with dBASE II. 300p. 1984. pap. cancelled (ISBN 0-912677-13-9). Ashton-Tate Bks.

Management's Guide to Computer Integrated Manufacturing. 93.00 (ISBN 0-686-31443-3). C I M Systems.

Martinez, M. R. & Lev, M. C., eds. Computer Integrated Manufacturing. (PED Ser.: Vol. 8). 148p. 1983. pap. text ed. 30.00 (ISBN 0-317-02557-0, H00288). ASME.

Mayros, Van & Werner, D. Michael. Data Bases for Business: Profiles & Applications. LC 82-70653. 178p. 1982. pap. 19.95 (ISBN 0-8019-7256-6). Chilton.

Moscove, Stephen A. & Simkin, Mark G. Accounting Information Systems: Concepts & Practice for Effective Decision Making. 2nd ed. LC 83-16842. 721p. 1984. 35.45 (ISBN 0-471-88354-9); tchr's manual avail. (ISBN 0-471-88124-4); test bank avail. (ISBN 0-471-81098-3). Wiley.

Murdick, Robert, et al. Accounting Information Systems. (Illus.). 1978. ref. ed. 36.95 (ISBN 0-13-002014-1). P-H.

Murdick, Robert G., et al. Information Systems for Modern Management. 3rd ed. (Illus.). 432p. 1984. text ed. 30.95 (ISBN 0-13-464736-X). P-H.

Naffah, N. Office Information Systems. 656p. 1982. 76.75 (ISBN 0-444-86398-2, North-Holland). Elsevier.

Nash, John F. & Roberts, Martin B. Accounting Information Systems. 704p. 1984. text ed. write for info. (ISBN 0-02-386050-2). Macmillan.

Naylor, Thomas H. & Mann, Michele H., eds. Computer Based Planning Systems. 199p. 1982. pap. 20.00 (ISBN 0-912841-05-2, 01). Planning Forum.

OECD. Microelectronic, Productivity & Employment. (Information Computer Communications Policy Ser.: No. 5). 290p. (Orig.). 1981. pap. 18.00x (ISBN 92-64-12162-5). OECD.

The Orbit I Study. (Illus.). 103p. 1983. binder 400.00 (ISBN 0-923426-05-1, ORBIT). Cross Info.

Page & Hooper. Accounting & Information Systems. 2nd ed. 1982. text ed. 30.95 (ISBN 0-8359-0090-8); practice case 8.95 (ISBN 0-8359-0092-4); instr's. manual free (ISBN 0-8359-0091-6). Reston.

Pappenheim. Business Information Systems. (Infotech Computer State of the Art Reports). (Illus.). 443p. 1981. 405.00 (ISBN 0-08-028560-0). Pergamon.

Perry, William E. The Accountants' Guide to Computer Systems. (Modern Accounting Perspectives & Practice Ser.). 286p. 1982. text ed. 45.00x (ISBN 0-471-08992-3, Pub. by Ronald Pr). Wiley.

Personal Productivity Management for Information Systems: Chantico-QED. 1985. pap. write for info. (ISBN 0-89435-162-1). Qed Info Sci.

Recommended Methods for Development-Information Systems: Manual for the Preparation of Records in Development-Information Systems, Vol. 1. 272p. 1983. pap. 20.00 (ISBN 0-88936-354-4, IDRCTS40, IDRC). Unipub.

Robinson, Leonard A., et al. Accounting Information Systems: A Cycle Approach. 584p. 1982. text ed. 33.95 scp (ISBN 0-06-045509-8, HarpC); resource manual avail. (ISBN 0-06-365514-4). Har-Row.

Romney, Marshall B., et al. Casebook in Accounting Information Systems. 112p. pap. text ed. 10.95x (ISBN 0-471-81445-8); solutions manual avail. Wiley.

Ross, Ronald G. Data Dictionaries & Data Administration: Concepts & Practices for Data Resource Management. 384p. 1981. 29.95 (ISBN 0-8144-5596-4). AMACOM.

Saffady, William. The Automated Office: An Introduction to the Technology. Plunka, Gene A., ed. (Reference Ser.). 241p. 1981. 17.75 (ISBN 0-89258-072-0, R017); member 13.25. Assn Inform & Image Mgmt.

Schewe, Charles D., ed. Marketing Information Systems: Selected Readings. LC 76-3791. pap. 48.30 (ISBN 0-317-29627-2, 2021522). Bks Demand UMI.

Schmitz, Homer. Hospital Information Systems. LC 79-15421. 188p. 1979. 34.00 (ISBN 0-89443-156-0). Aspen Systems.

Scott Morton, Michael. Management Decision Systems: Computer-Based Support for Decision Making. LC 72-132152. (Illus.). 216p. 1971. 14.95x (ISBN 0-87584-090-6). Harvard Busn.

Sharifi, Mohsen & Farah, Badie. Integrated Case Studies in Accounting Information Systems. 1985. pap. text ed. 16.95 (ISBN 0-8359-3205-2); tchr's. manual avail. (ISBN 0-8359-3206-0). Reston.

Smith, Bernard T. Focus Forecasting: Computer Techniques for Inventory Control. 260p. 1984. 35.00 (ISBN 0-939246-02-3). O W Ltd.

Teglovic, Steve & Lynch, Robert, eds. Topics in Management Information Systems. LC 73-3315. 295p. 1973. text ed. 29.50x (ISBN 0-8422-5092-1); pap. text ed. 8.50x (ISBN 0-8422-0277-3). Irvington.

Wang, Peter C., et al, eds. Information Linkage Between Applied Mathematics & Industry. 1979. 59.50 (ISBN 0-12-734250-8). Acad Pr.

Warner-Eddison Associates. Words That Mean Business: Three Thousand Terms for Access to Business Information. 235p. 1981. 49.95 (ISBN 0-918212-55-3). Neal-Schuman.

Weaver, Barbara N. & Bishop, Wiley L. The Corporate Memory: A Profitable & Practical Approach to Information Management & Retention Systems. LC 80-20187. 282p. 1981. Repr. of 1974 ed. text ed. 22.50 (ISBN 0-89874-245-5). Krieger.

Weis, Stephen, ed. Computer Systems Guide for Accountants. 1984. text ed. 29.95 (ISBN 0-8359-0851-8); pap. text ed. 17.95 (ISBN 0-8359-0850-X). Reston.

Wilkinson, Joseph W. Accounting & Information Systems. LC 81-13153. (Wiley Series in Accounting & Information Systems). 845p. 1982. text ed. 37.50 (ISBN 0-471-04986-7); tchr's manual avail. (ISBN 0-471-04987-5). Wiley.

Wilson, John L. Business System Options. 1978. 7.95 (ISBN 0-686-98070-0). Telecom Lib.

Wiseman, Charles. Strategy & Computers: Information Systems As Competitive Weapons. LC 85-70567. 1985. 25.00 (ISBN 0-87094-590-4). Dow Jones-Irwin.

Woodwell, Donald R. Automating Your Financial Portfolio: An Investor's Guide to Personal Computers. LC 82-73637. 220p. 1983. 19.95 (ISBN 0-87094-399-5). Dow Jones-Irwin.

Wu, Frederick H. Accounting Information Systems: Theory & Practice. (Illus.). 608p. 1983. text ed. 34.95 (ISBN 0-07-072121-1). McGraw.

INFORMATION STORAGE AND RETRIEVAL SYSTEMS–CHEMISTRY

Antony, Arthur. Guide to Basic Information Sources in Chemistry. LC 79-330. (Information Resources Ser.). 219p. 1979. 24.95x (ISBN 0-470-26587-6). Halsted Pr.

Arnett, Edward M. & Kent, Allen, eds. Computer Based Chemical Information. (Bks. in Library & Information Science: Vol. 4). 232p. 1973. 49.75 (ISBN 0-8247-6045-X). Dekker.

Ash, et al. Communication Storage & Retrieval of Chemical Information. 1985. 45.00 (ISBN 0-470-20145-2). Wiley.

Christoffersen, Ralph E. & Olson, Edward C., eds. Computer-Assisted Drug Design. LC 79-21038. (ACS Symposium Ser.: No. 112). 1979. 59.95 (ISBN 0-8412-0521-3). Am Chemical.

Davis, Charles H. & Rush, James E. Information Retrieval & Documentation in Chemistry. LC 72-791. (Contributions in Librarianship & Information Science: No. 8). 1974. lib. bdg. 25.00 (ISBN 0-8371-6364-1, DAI/). Greenwood.

Grayson, M. Information Retrieval in Chemistry & Chemical Patent Law. LC 82-24727. 116p. 1983. 24.95x (ISBN 0-471-89057-X, Pub. by Wiley-Interscience). Wiley.

Howe, W. Jeffrey, et al, eds. Retrieval of Medicinal Chemical Information. LC 78-21611. (ACS Symposium Ser.: No. 84). 1978. 26.95 (ISBN 0-8412-0465-9). Am Chemical.

Ohno, K. & Morokuma, K. Quantum Chemistry Literature Data Base: Bibliography of AB Initio Calculations for 1978-80. (Physical Sciences Data Ser.: Vol. 12). 460p. 1982. 95.75 (ISBN 0-444-42074-6). Elsevier.

Selover, Theodore R., Jr. & Klein, Max. Awareness of Information Sources. LC 84-18598. (Alche Symposium Ser.: Vol. 80, No. 237). 132p. 1984. pap. 30.00 (ISBN 0-8169-0326-3). Am Inst Chem Eng.

Zorena, P. Basic User's Guide to Full-Text Chemical Databases: How to Search ACS Journals & the Kirk-Othmer Encyclopedia Online. (On Line Chemical Information Ser.). 1985. pap. 20.00 (ISBN 0-471-82806-8). Wiley.

INFORMATION STORAGE AND RETRIEVAL SYSTEMS–CITIES AND TOWNS–PLANNING

Norris, G. & Ewart, W. Choosing & Managing Information Systems for Public Administration. 118p. 1979. text ed. 32.95x (ISBN 0-566-00244-2). Gower Pub Co.

INFORMATION STORAGE AND RETRIEVAL SYSTEMS–EDUCATION

Baker, Frank B. Computer Managed Instruction: Theory & Practice. LC 77-24006. (Illus.). 440p. 1978. 28.95 (ISBN 0-87778-099-4). Educ Tech Pubns.

Bliss, Joan, et al. Qualitative Data Analysis for Educational Research: A Guide to Uses of Systemic Networks. (Illus.). 224p. 1983. 29.00 (ISBN 0-7099-0698-6, Pub. by Croom Helm Ltd). Longwood Pub Group.

Buckingham, Richard A., ed. Education & Large Information Systems: Proceedings of the IFIP TC3-TC8 Working Conference, The Hague, The Netherlands, April 1977. 198p. 1978. 42.75 (ISBN 0-444-85047-3, North-Holland). Elsevier.

Burton, John, et al. Computers in Teaching Mathematics. (Computers in Education Ser.). 192p. 1983. pap. text ed. 15.95x (ISBN 0-201-10565-9). Addison-Wesley.

Chronicle Staff. C-LECT Professional Manual. 12p. (Orig.). 1983. write for info. (ISBN 0-912578-59-9). Chron Guide.

--C-LECT User Guide. (Orig.). 1983. pap. text ed. write for info. (ISBN 0-912578-60-2). Chron Guide.

De Land, E. C., ed. Information Technology in Health Science Education. LC 78-7201. 624p. 1978. 85.00x (ISBN 0-306-31113-5, Plenum Pr). Plenum Pub.

Hounsel, Dai, et al. Educational Information & the Teacher. 1980. 75.00x (ISBN 0-905984-52-8, Pub. by Brit Lib England). State Mutual Bk.

Jones, Ron, ed. Micros in the Primary Classroom. 128p. 1984. pap. text ed. 11.95 (ISBN 0-7131-0934-3). E Arnold.

Psacharopoulos, George, ed. Information: An Essential Factor in Educational Planning & Policy. (Illus.). 303p. 1980. pap. 18.75 (ISBN 92-3-101668-7, U1056, UNESCO). Unipub.

Taber, Florence. Microcomputers in Special Education: Selection & Decision Making Process. 112p. 1983. pap. 7.95 (ISBN 0-86586-135-8). Coun Exc Child.

Thomas, M. Angele, ed. Microcomputers in Special Education: Special Issue of Exceptional Children, October 1982. 96p. 1982. pap. 5.00 (ISBN 0-86586-139-0). Coun Exc Child.

User Education in Schools: A Survey of the Literature on Education for Information Use in Schools. 1981. 15.00x (ISBN 0-686-72513-1, Pub. by Brit Lib England). State Mutual Bk.

Vickery, B. C. The Use of On-line Search in Teaching: An Assessment of Projects Carried Out by U.K. Schools of Library & Information Studies. 1977. 30.00x (ISBN 0-905984-05-6, Pub. by Brit Lib England). State Mutual Bk.

INFORMATION STORAGE AND RETRIEVAL SYSTEMS–ENGINEERING

ASCE, Technical Council on Computer Practices, 1980. Computing in Civil Engineering 1980. Schelling, David R., ed. LC 80-66141. 739p. 1980. pap. 34.00x (ISBN 0-87262-246-0). Am Soc Civil Eng.

Atluri, Satya & Perrone, Nicholas, eds. Computer Methods for Nonlinear Solids & Structural Mechanics. 264p. 1983. pap. text ed. 50.00 (ISBN 0-317-02562-7, G00224). ASME.

Chang, Huan-Yang & Over, Ira Earl. Selected Numerical Methods & Computer Programs for Chemical Engineers. 235p. (Orig.). 1980. pap. text ed. 11.95 (ISBN 0-88408-131-1). Sterling Swift.

Chenevert, Martin & Roye, J. PIPECALC (TM) 1: Practical Pipeline Hydraulics. LC 84-9007. (Microcomputer Software for Pipeline Engineers Ser.). 1984. incl. disk 295.00x (ISBN 0-87201-741-9). Gulf Pub.

Nadler, Gerald, et al. Design Concepts for Information Systems. Rev. ed. 1983. 13.00 (ISBN 0-89806-015-X, 107). Inst Indus Eng.

National Approaches to the Acquisition of Technology. (Development & Transfer of Technology Ser.). pap. 9.50 (ISBN 0-686-93221-8, UN78/2B7, UN). Unipub.

Nobles, M. A. Using Computers to Solve Reservoir Engineering Problems. 2nd ed. LC 84-3759. 500p. 1984. 46.95x (ISBN 0-87201-899-7). Gulf Pub.

Perrone, Nicholas & Pilkey, Walter D., eds. Structural Mechanics Software Series, Vol. IV. (Illus.). 467p. 1982. 30.00x (ISBN 0-8139-0918-X). U Pr of Va.

Pilkey, Walter D. & Perrone, Nicholas, eds. Structural Mechanics Software Series, Vol. III. (Illus.). 344p. 1980. 30.00x (ISBN 0-8139-0857-4). U Pr of Va.

Report of the Seminar-cum-Study Tour on Load Dispatch Techniques & Application of Computer Technology to Power System Engineering Problems. pap. 5.00 (ISBN 0-686-94330-9, UN71/2F/14, UN). Unipub.

Savilescu, S., ed. Computer Operation of Power Systems: Proceedings of the International Symposium Brazil 1975. 1976. 64.00 (ISBN 0-444-41431-2). Elsevier.

Seireg, Ali A., ed. CIME (Computers in Mechanical Engineering Magazine) Research Supplement, Vol. 1. 79p. 1983. pap. text ed. 8.00 (ISBN 0-317-02556-2, G00234). ASME.

Symposium on Computers in Aerodynamics at the Aerodynamics Laboratories Polytechnic Institute of New York, 1979. Computers in Aerodynamics. Rubin, S. G. & Bloom, M. H., eds. 130p. 1980. 42.00 (ISBN 0-08-025426-8). Pergamon.

Winder, Alan A. & Loda, Charles J. Space Time Information Processing. (Illus.). 200p. 1980. Repr. of 1962 ed. 17.95 (ISBN 0-932146-04-X). Peninsula CA.

INFORMATION STORAGE AND RETRIEVAL SYSTEMS–LAW

A.A.L.L. Proceedings of the Annual Meeting, 1981. Legal Information for the 1980's: Meeting the Needs of the Legal Profession. (AALL Publication Ser.). 45.00 (ISBN 0-317-31413-0). Rothman.

American Law Institute-American Bar Association Joint Committee. Law & Computers in the Mid-Sixties: Course of Study Transcript. 399p. 1966. pap. 2.18 (ISBN 0-317-32232-X, B239). Am Law Inst.

Ciampi, C. Artificial Intelligence & Legal Information Systems. 476p. 1982. 57.50 (ISBN 0-444-86414-8, I-187-82, North-Holland). Elsevier.

Establishment of an Automated Data Base on Disarmament (UNIDIR) pap. 10.00 (UNEP203, UN). Unipub.

Hafner, Carole D. An Information Retrieval System Based on a Computer Model of Legal Knowledge. Stone, Harold, ed. LC 81-7484. (Computer Science Ser.: Artificial Intelligence: No. 1). 190p. 1981. 39.95 (ISBN 0-8357-1196-X, F3X). UMI Res Pr.

Kinney, E. Litigation Support Systems: 1980, 1 vol. LC 80-26267. 85.00 (ISBN 0-317-12023-9); Suppl., 1982. 20.00; Suppl., 1983. 24.00. Callaghan.

Kinsock, John E. Legal Databases Online: Lexis-Westlaw. (Advanced Online Searching Ser.). 1985. lib. bdg. 28.50 (ISBN 0-87287-404-4). Libs Unl.

Leonard, James. OCLC's Serials Control Subsystem: Its Suitability to Legal Serials & Continuations. Date not set. price not set. Am Assn Law Libs.

Marchand, Donald A. The Politics of Privacy, Computers, & Criminal Justice Records: Controlling the Social Costs of Technological Change. LC 80-80675. xvi, 433p. 1980. text ed. 34.95 (ISBN 0-87815-030-7). Info Resources.

Matthews, Elizabeth W. Access Points to the Law Library Card Catalog Interpretation. LC 82-80900. vi, 66p. 1982. lib. bdg. 22.50 (ISBN 0-89941-156-8). W S Hein.

Miskin, C. Library & Information Services for the Legal Profession. 1981. 45.00x (ISBN 0-905984-73-0, Pub. by Brit Lib England). State Mutual Bk.

--Library & Information Services for the Legal Profession. 72p. 1981. pap. 40.00x (ISBN 0-686-44635-6, Pub. by Brit Lib England). State Mutual Bk.

OECD Staff. An Exploration of Legal Issues in Information & Communication Technologies. (Info. Computer Communication Policy Ser.: No. 8). 136p. (Orig.). 1984. pap. 14.00x (ISBN 92-64-12527-2). OECD.

Stong, Kline D. Choosing & Using Computers: To Improve Your Law Practice. 158p. 1983. pap. 38.00 (ISBN 0-89707-100-X). Amer Bar Assn.

Strohofer, Jean & Wallce, Marie. The Private Law Library in the High-Tech Era. Practising Law Institute, ed. LC 83-220469. (Commercial Law & Practice Course Handbook Ser.: No. 308). (Illus.). 288p. 1983. 35.00. PLI.

Strong, Kline D. Retrieval Systems for Lawyers. LC 80-66349. (Illus.). 92p. (Orig.). 1980. pap. 22.00 (ISBN 0-89707-021-6, 5110057). Amer Bar Assn.

Tseng, Henry P. Complete Guide to Legal Materials in Microforms: 1978 Supplement. LC 76-15102. 1979. perfect bdg. 25.00 (ISBN 0-9602406-1-6). AMCO Intl.

INFORMATION STORAGE AND RETRIEVAL SYSTEMS–MEDICINE

Abell, Alphonse R. Recent Advances of Computers in Medicine: Guidebook for Research & Reference. LC 84-45003. 150p. 1984. 29.95 (ISBN 0-88164-166-9); pap. 21.95 (ISBN 0-88164-167-7). ABBE Pubs Assn.

Automated Hospital Information Systems: Getting the Most from the System You Select. LC 84-60126. 352p. 1984. pap. text ed. 49.00 (ISBN 0-914957-00-7). Pluribus Pr.

Automated Hospital Information Systems: How to Decide What You Want. LC 84-60127. 320p. 1984. pap. text ed. 45.00 (ISBN 0-914957-01-5). Pluribus Pr.

Bell, T., ed. Medical Information Systems for Prepaid Group Practice. 109p. 1978. pap. text ed. 10.00 (ISBN 0-936164-15-8). Group Health Assoc of Amer.

Blum, B. I., ed. Information Systems for Patient Care. (Computers & Medicine). (Illus.). 400p. 1984. 27.50 (ISBN 0-387-90912-5). Springer Verlag.

Blum, Bruce, ed. A Framework for Medical Information Science, Vol. 3, 4, & 9. 148p. 1984. pap. 39.00 (ISBN 0-85066-999-5). Taylor & Francis.

Computer Models & Application of the Sterile-Male Technique. (Panel Proceedings Ser.). (Illus.). 195p. (Orig.). 1973. pap. 18.00 (ISBN 92-0-111573-3, ISP340, IAEA). Unipub.

Current Procedural Terminology. 4th ed. 1970. pap. 12.00 (ISBN 0-89970-029-2, OP 041). AMA.

De Land, E. C., ed. Information Technology in Health Science Education. LC 78-7201. 624p. 1978. 85.00x (ISBN 0-306-31113-5, Plenum Pr). Plenum Pub.

Doyle, Owen, et al. Analysis Manual for Hospital Information Systems. LC 80-13875. (Illus.). 472p. (Orig.). 1980. pap. text ed. 42.50x (ISBN 0-914904-41-8). Health Admin Pr.

Duncan, Karen, ed. Information Technology & Health Care: The Critical Issues. 200p. 1980. 25.00 (ISBN 0-88283-031-7). AFIPS Pr.

Eisenfeld, J. & Delisi, C., eds. Mathematics & Computers in Biomedical Applications. 390p. 1985. 40.00 (ISBN 0-444-87678-2). Elsevier.

Grams, Ralph R. Medical Information Systems: The Laboratory Module. LC 78-71496. (Illus.). 430p. 1979. 59.50 (ISBN 0-89603-004-0). Humana.

Green, Lawrence & Kansler, Connie, eds. Professional & Scientific Literature on Patient Education: A Guide to Information Sources. (Health Affairs Information Guide Ser.: Vol. 5). 330p. 1980. 58.00x (ISBN 0-8103-1422-3). Gale.

Gremy, F., et al, eds. Medical Informatics Europe 1981: Proceedings. (Lecture Notes in Medical Informatics Ser.: Vol. 11). 975p. 1981. pap. 56.20 (ISBN 0-387-10568-9). Springer-Verlag.

Grobe, Susan J. Computer Primer & Resource for Nurses. (Illus.). 180p. 1984. pap. text ed. 9.75 (ISBN 0-397-54485-5, Lippincott Nursing). Lippincott.

Hodge, Melville H. Medical Information Systems: A Resource for Hospitals. LC 77-12739. 216p. 1978. 33.50 (ISBN 0-912862-47-5). Aspen Systems.

Howe, W. Jeffrey, et al, eds. Retrieval of Medicinal Chemical Information. LC 78-21611. (ACS Symposium Ser.: No. 84). 1978. 26.95 (ISBN 0-8412-0465-9). Am Chemical.

Irenshenko, Remona S. Guidebook of Subjects & References of Medical Computers. LC 84-45000. 150p. 1984. 29.95 (ISBN 0-88164-178-2); pap. 21.95 (ISBN 0-88164-179-0). ABBE Pubs Assn.

Johnsen, Jeffrey, ed. The Multi-State Information System: Proceedings of the Fifth Annual National Users Group Conference. 133p. 1981. pap. 10.00 (ISBN 0-936934-01-8). N S Kline Inst.

King, Jane. Searching Internal Database: A Comparative Evaluation of their Performance in Toxicology. 1982. 70.00 (ISBN 0-905984-80-3, Brit Lib England). State Mutual Bk.

Kupfer, David J., et al. Mental Health Information Systems: Design & Implementation. (Library & Information Science Ser.: Vol. 19). 1976. 39.75 (ISBN 0-8247-6445-5). Dekker.

Nair, Sreedhar, ed. Computers in Critical Care & Pulmonary Medicine, Vol. 1. LC 80-14503. 437p. 1980. 55.00x (ISBN 0-306-40449-4, Plenum Pr). Plenum Pub.

Pretschner, D. P. Personal Computing in Nuclear Medicine. (Lecture Notes in Medical Informatics: Vol. 18). 133p. 1982. pap. 13.50 (ISBN 0-387-11598-6). Springer-Verlag.

Schmitz, Homer. Hospital Information Systems. LC 79-15421. 188p. 1979. 34.00 (ISBN 0-89443-156-0). Aspen Systems.

Schneider, W. & Sagvall Hein, A. L., eds. Computational Linguistics in Medicine: Proceedings of the IFIP Working Conference on Computational Linguistics in Medicine. 182p. 1978. 47.00 (ISBN 0-444-85040-6, North-Holland). Elsevier.

Scholes, M., et al, eds. The Impact of Computers on Nursing: An International Review; Proceedings of the IFIP-IMIA Workshop on the Impact of Computers on Nursing, Church House, Westminster, London, 8-9 Sept., 1982, & Harrogate, England, 10-15 Sept., 1982. 590p. 1983. 60.00 (ISBN 0-444-86682-5, I-241-83, North Holland). Elsevier.

Speck, Pat K. Medical Management System Operator's Manual. Dossman, Sterly, ed. (Illus.). 354p. 1979. text ed. 100.00 (ISBN 0-912217-02-2); pap. 90.00 (ISBN 0-912217-03-0). Afton Oaks.

Ziegenfuss, James & Ziegenfuss, Donald, eds. Health Information Systems: A Bibliography. (IFI Date Base Library). 238p. 1984. 85.00x (ISBN 0-306-65208-0, IFI Plenum). Plenum Pub.

INFORMATION STORAGE AND RETRIEVAL SYSTEMS–METEOROLOGY

Craddock, J. M. Storage Cataloguing & Retrieval of Meteorological Information. (World Weather Watch Planning Reports: No. 34). xv, 234p. 1974. pap. 32.00 (ISBN 92-63-10366-6, W246, WMO). Unipub.

Further Planning of the Storage & Retrieval Service. (World Weather Watch Planning Reports: No. 32). 1970. pap. 16.00 (ISBN 0-685-02475-X, W244, WMO). Unipub.

Global Data-Processing System & Meteorological Service to Shipping. (World Weather Watch Planning Reports: No. 15). 26p. 1966. pap. 12.00 (ISBN 0-685-22305-1, W231, WMO). Unipub.

Satellite & Computer Applications to Synoptic Meteorology. (Illus.). 88p. (Orig.). 1971. pap. 15.00 (ISBN 0-685-02041-X, W96, WMO). Unipub.

INFORMATION STORAGE AND RETRIEVAL SYSTEMS–PHYSICS

Douglas, Shawhan. Physics with the Computer. (Orig.). 1981. tchr's ed. 24.95 (ISBN 0-87567-037-7); student's ed. 14.95; incl. diskettes 150.00. Entelek.

INFORMATION STORAGE AND RETRIEVAL SYSTEMS–SCIENCE

Arnett, Ross H., Jr. Entomological Information Storage & Retrieval. LC 70-140434. 1970. 7.95 (ISBN 0-916846-00-8). World Natural Hist.

Baillie, A. & Gilbert, R. J., eds. Automation, Mechanization & Data Handling in Microbiology. (Society for Applied Bacteriology Technical Ser.: No. 4). 1970. 41.50 (ISBN 0-12-073650-0). Acad Pr.

Beeler, J. R. Radiation Effects Computer Experiments. (Defects in Solids Ser.: Vol. 13). 882p. 1983. 168.00 (ISBN 0-444-86315-X, North Holland). Elsevier.

Coblans, H., et al. Science & Technology Policies Information Exchange System (SPINES) Feasibility Study. (Science Policy Studies & Documents: No. 33). (Illus.). 115p. (Orig.). 1974. pap. 6.00 (ISBN 92-3-101185-5, U571, UNESCO). Unipub.

Codlin, Ellen M. ASLIB Directory, Vol. 1: Information Sources in Science, Technology & Commerce. 634p. 1977. 90.00x (Pub. by Aslib England). State Mutual Bk.

Devsis Study Team. DEVSIS: The Preliminary Design of an International Information System for the Development Sciences. (Eng., Fr. & Span.). 247p. 1976. pap. 13.00 (ISBN 0-88936-084-7, IDRC65, IDRC). Unipub.

Evans, A. J., et al. Education & Training of Users of Scientific & Technical Information: UNISIST Guide for Teachers. (Illus.). 143p. (2nd Printing 1982). 1977. pap. 10.50 (ISBN 92-3-101452-8, U746, UNESCO). Unipub.

Goffman, William & Warren, Kenneth. Scientific Information Systems & the Principle of Selectivity. LC 80-49. 202p. 1980. 31.95 (ISBN 0-03-056081-0). Praeger.

Green, Lawrence & Kansler, Connie, eds. Professional & Scientific Literature on Patient Education: A Guide to Information Sources. (Health Affairs Information Guide Ser.: Vol. 5). 330p. 1980. 58.00x (ISBN 0-8103-1422-3). Gale.

Horsnell, V. Report of a Workshop on Multilingual Systems. 1976. 27.00x (ISBN 0-85350-137-8, Pub. by Brit Lib England). State Mutual Bk.

Lajeunesse, Marcel, ed. Repertoire des ecoles des sciences de l'information. (Fr.). 134p. 1979. ISSN 319-0709-2962. 6.00 (ISBN 0-318-13606-6). AUPELF.

Pritchard, Eileen & Scott, Paula R. Literature Searching in Science, Technology, & Agriculture. LC 83-18471. x, 174p. 1984. lib. bdg. 29.95 (ISBN 0-313-23710-7, PLR/). Greenwood.

Rudman, Jack. Manager Computer Operations. (Career Examination Ser.: C-2241). (Cloth bdg. avail. on request). pap. 12.00 (ISBN 0-8373-2241-3). Natl Learning.

UNISIST: Study Report on the Feasibility of a World Science Information System. (Illus.). 161p. (Orig.). 1971. pap. 6.75 (ISBN 92-3-100881-1, U704, UNESCO). Unipub.

Use of Analog & Digital Computers in Hydrology: Proceedings of the Tucson Symposium, 2 Vols. (Studies & Reports in Hydrology: No. 1). (Illus.). 1969. Set. 46.25 (ISBN 92-3-000734-X, U711, UNESCO). Vol. 1, 344p. Vol. 2, 411p. Unipub.

Whetstone, G. W. & Grigoriev, V. J., eds. Hydrologic Information Systems. (Studies & Reports in Hydrology: No. 14). 72p. (Orig., Co-published with WMO). 1972. pap. 9.25 (ISBN 92-3-100957-5, U289, UNESCO). Unipub.

Workshop on the Aquatic Sciences & Fisheries Information Systems (ASFIS) Cartagena, Colombia, 3-14 Dec. 1979. pap. 7.50 (F2109, FAO). Unipub.

INFORMATION STORAGE AND RETRIEVAL SYSTEMS–SOCIAL SCIENCES

Aiyepeku, Wilson O. International Socioeconomic Information Systems: An Evaluative Study of DEVSIS-Type Programs. 100p. 1983. pap. text ed. 8.00 (ISBN 0-88936-366-8, IDRCTS43, IDRC). Unipub.

Bloom, Martin, ed. Single-System Research Designs. (Journal of Social Service Research Ser.: Vol. 3, No. 1). 134p. 1979. pap. text ed. 10.00 (ISBN 0-917724-70-4, B70). Haworth Pr.

Cleary, Michael J. & Amsden, Robert T. A Data Analysis Handbook Using the SPSS System. (Illus., Orig.). 1979. pap. 9.95x (ISBN 0-89894-015-X). Advocate Pub Group.

Coats, R. B. & Parkin, A. Computer Models in the Social Sciences. (Orig.). 1977. pap. text ed. 17.95 (ISBN 0-316-14890-3). Little.

DARE Information Management System: A Condensed System Description (Computer Design Version 2) (Reports & Papers in the Social Sciences: No. 31). (Illus.). 23p. 1975. pap. 5.00 (ISBN 92-3-101256-8, U148, UNESCO). Unipub.

Devsis Study Team. DEVSIS: The Preliminary Design of an International Information System for the Development Sciences. (Eng., Fr. & Span.). 247p. 1976. pap. 13.00 (ISBN 0-88936-084-7, IDRC65, IDRC). Unipub.

Geyer, R. F. & Zouwen, J. van der, eds. Dependence & Inequality: A Systems Approach to the Problems of Mexico & Other Developing Countries. (Systems Science & World Order Library: Innovations in Systems Science). (Illus.). 336p. 1982. 39.00 (ISBN 0-08-027952-X). Pergamon.

Gillooly, William B. Literature Search: Document Retrieval in the Behavioral Sciences. (Illus., Orig.). 1969. pap. text ed. 1.25 (ISBN 0-685-16734-8). Mariner Pr.

Lawson, Harold, ed. Man & Society: Automated Information Processing. 188p. 1981. pap. text ed. 16.25x (ISBN 91-7082-252-2, Pub. by Almquist & Wiksell Sweden). Humanities.

Selective Inventory of Information Services. (World Social Science Information Services: No. 3). 140p. 1981. pap. 11.25 (ISBN 92-3-001848-1, U1135, UNESCO). Unipub.

INFORMATION STORAGE AND RETRIVAL SYSTEMS–TECHNOLOGY

Contemporary Problems in Technical Library & Information Center Management, 1974. 1974. 18.50 (ISBN 0-317-13875-8, 333-BW). Knowledge Indus.

Del Bigio, G. & Gottschalk, C. M. INIS: Descriptive Cataloguing Rules. Ruckenbacker, E., ed. (INIS Reference Ser.: No. 1, Rev. 6). 90p. 1985. pap. 7.50 (ISBN 92-0-178085-0, IN1R6, IAEA). Unipub.

INIS Atomindex: Five-Year Index: Report, Standard & Patent Numbers, May 1972 to June 1977. 296p. 1977. pap. 205.00 (ISBN 0-686-93138-6, IAEA). Unipub.

INIS: Authority List for Corporate Entries & Report Number Prefixes. 16th, Rev. ed. 554p. 1983. pap. text ed. 42.50 (ISBN 92-0-178383-3, IN6/R16, IAEA). Unipub.

INIS: Authority List for Corporate Entries. (INIS Reference Ser.: No. 6). pap. 13.25 (IN6/R9, IAEA). Unipub.

INIS: Authority List for Journal Titles. 10th Rev. ed. (INIS Reference Ser.: No. 11). 259p. 1982. pap. 18.00 (ISBN 92-0-178381-7, IN11/R10, IAEA). Unipub.

INIS: Authority List for Journal Titles. (INIS Reference Ser.: No. 11). pap. 6.75 (IN11/R5, IAEA). Unipub.

INIS: Character Set Representation & Coding Rules. (INIS Reference Ser.: No. 7, Rev. 2). (Illus.). 25p. 1983. pap. text ed. 5.00 (ISBN 92-0-178282-9, IN7/R2, IAEA). Unipub.

INIS: Description of Computer Programs. (INIS Reference Ser.: No. 14). pap. 5.75 (ISBN 92-0-178675-1, IN14/R1, IAEA). Unipub.

INIS: Descriptive Cataloging Samples. (INIS Reference Ser.: No. 2). pap. 2.25 (IN2/R2, IAEA). Unipub.

INIS: Descriptive Cataloguing Rules. (INIS Reference Ser.: No. 1). pap. 2.25 (IN1/R2, IAEA). Unipub.

INIS: Descriptive Cataloguing Samples. (INIS Reference Ser.: No. 2). 1978. pap. 5.50 (ISBN 92-0-178278-0, IN2/R3, IAEA). Unipub.

INIS: Instructions for Submitting Abstracts. (INIS Reference Ser.: No. 4). pap. 5.50 (ISBN 92-0-178171-7, IN4/R1, IAEA). Unipub.

INIS: Manual for Index. (INIS Reference Ser.: No. 12). 108p. 1974. pap. 5.50 (ISBN 92-0-178074-5, IN12/R2, IAEA). Unipub.

INIS: Multilingual Dictionary - English-French-German-Russian, No. 1. (INIS Reference Ser.: 20). 1983. pap. 23.25 (ISBN 9-2017-8283-7, IN20/R0, IAEA). Unipub.

INIS: Paper Tape Specifications & Record Format. Rev. ed. (INIS Reference Ser.: No. 8). 26p. 1971. pap. 5.50 (ISBN 92-0-178671-9, IN8/R1, IAEA). Unipub.

INIS: Self-Teaching Manual. (INIS Reference Ser.: No. 15). 1972. pap. 8.75 (ISBN 92-0-178772-3, IN15/R0, IAEA). Unipub.

INIS: Subject Categories & Scope Descriptions. (INIS Reference Ser.: No. 3). pap. 3.75 (IN3/R4, IAEA). Unipub.

INIS: Subject Indexing Samples. (INIS Reference Ser.: No. 16). pap. 7.00 (ISBN 92-0-178775-8, IN16/R0, IAEA). Unipub.

INIS: Terminology & Codes for Countries & International Organizations. 4th Rev. ed. (INIS Reference Ser.: No. 5). 15p. 1982. pap. 5.00 (ISBN 92-0-178481-3, IN5/R4, IAEA). Unipub.

INIS: Terminology & Codes for Countries & International Organizations. (INIS Reference Ser.: 5). 14p. pap. 5.50 (ISBN 92-0-178375-2, IN5/R3, IAEA). Unipub.

INIS: Transliteration Rules for Selected Non-Roman Characters. Rev. ed. (INIS Reference Ser.: No. 10). 8p. 1971. pap. write for info. (ISBN 92-0-178871-1, IN10/R1, IAEA). Unipub.

International Atomic Energy Agency. INIS Reference Series, 16 vols. (Illus.). 1100p. (Orig.). 1969-1974. pap. 72.25 (ISBN 0-685-02939-5, IAEA). Unipub.

Operating Experience with Nuclear Power Stations in Member States: Performance Anaysis Report 1976. (Illus.). 27p. 1978. pap. 6.25 (ISBN 92-0-159078-4, ISP481, IAEA). Unipub.

Thesaurus. (INIS Reference Ser.: Rev. 20). 756p. 1981. pap. 46.50 (ISBN 92-0-178081-8, IN13/R20, IAEA). Unipub.

INFORMATION THEORY

see also Automatic Control; Coding Theory; Data Transmission Systems; Error-Correcting Codes (Information Theory); Information Measurement; Machine Translating; Mathematical Linguistics; Modulation Theory; Punched Card Systems; Signal Theory (Telecommunication); Speech Processing Systems; Statistical Communication Theory; Switching Theory; Telecommunication

Aczel, J. & Daroczy, Z. On Measures of Information & Their Characterizations. (Mathematics in Science & Engineering Ser.). 1975. 49.50 (ISBN 0-12-043760-0). Acad Pr.

Anderson, Norman. Methods of Information Integration Theory, Vol. 2. 1982. 47.50 (ISBN 0-12-058102-7). Acad Pr.

Andronov, A. A., et al. Eleven Papers on Differential Equations & Two in Information Theory. LC 51-5559. (Translations, Ser.: No. 2, Vol. 33). 1963. 35.00 (ISBN 0-8218-1733-7, TRANS 2-33). Am Math.

Baccelli, F. & Fayolle, G., eds. Modelling & Performance Evaluation Methodology: Proceedings of the International Seminar, Paris, France, January 24-26, 1983. (Lecture Notes in Control & Information Sciences: Vol. 60). (Fr. & Eng., Illus.). vii, 653p. 1984. pap. 34.50 (ISBN 0-387-13288-0). Springer-Verlag.

Behara, M., et al, eds. Probability & Information Theory 2. LC 75-406171. (Lecture Notes in Mathematics: Vol. 296). v, 223p. 1973. pap. 14.00 (ISBN 0-387-06211-4). Springer-Verlag.

Bendat, Julius S. Principles & Applications of Random Noise Theory. rev. ed. LC 77-7225. 456p. 1977. Repr. of 1958 ed. lib. bdg. 26.00 (ISBN 0-88275-556-0). Krieger.

Calow, P. Biological Machines: A Cybernetic Approach to Life. LC 76-27603. 133p. 1976. pap. 14.95x (ISBN 0-8448-1005-3). Crane-Russak Co.

CISM (International Center for Mechanical Sciences), Dept. of Automation & Information, 1970. General Theory of Noiseless Channels. Katona, G., ed. (CISM International Center for Mechanical Sciences Ser.: No. 31). 69p. 1975. pap. 12.40 (ISBN 0-387-81167-2). Springer-Verlag.

CISM (International Center for Mechanical Sciences), Dept. of Automation & Informations, 1969. Selected Topics in Information Theory. Longo, G., ed. (CISM International Center for Mechanical Sciences Ser.: No. 18). (Illus.). 111p. 1974. pap. 15.70 (ISBN 0-387-81166-4). Springer-Verlag.

Clark, George C., Jr. & Cain, J. Bibb. Error-Correction Coding for Digital Communications. LC 81-1630. (Applications of Communications Theory Ser.). 436p. 1981. 45.00x (ISBN 0-306-40615-2, Plenum Pr). Plenum Pub.

Csiszar, I. & Elias, P. Topics in Information Theory. (Colloquia Mathematica Societatis Janos Bolyai Ser.: Vol. 16). 592p. 1977. 106.50 (ISBN 0-7204-0699-4, North Holland). Elsevier.

Findler, Nicholas V., ed. Associative Networks: The Representation & Use of Knowledge by Computers. LC 78-31318. 1979. 61.50 (ISBN 0-12-256380-8). Acad Pr.

Gallager, Robert G. Information Theory & Reliable Communication. LC 68-26850. 588p. 1968. 54.00x (ISBN 0-471-29048-3). Wiley.

Gallaire, H. & Minker, J., eds. Logic & Data Bases. LC 78-14032. 466p. 1978. 55.00x (ISBN 0-306-40060-X, Plenum Pr). Plenum Pub.

Gray, Robert M. & Davisson, Lee D., eds. Ergodic & Information Theory. (Benchmark Papers in Electrical Engineering & Computer Science: Vol. 19). 1977. 64.50 (ISBN 0-12-786590-X). Acad Pr.

Grusko, I. I., et al. Eleven Papers from the Fourth Prague Conference on Information Theory, Statistical Decision Functions, & Random Processes. LC 61-9803. (Selected Translations in Mathematical Statistics & Probability, Ser.: Vol. 8). 1970. 30.00 (ISBN 0-8218-1458-3, STAPRO-8). Am Math.

Guiasu, Silviu. Information Theory with New Applications. (Illus.). 1977. text ed. 65.00 (ISBN 0-07-025109-6). McGraw.

Hamming, Richard W. Coding & Information Theory. (Illus.). 1980. text ed. 36.95 (ISBN 0-13-139139-9). P-H.

--Coding & Information Theory. 2nd ed. (Illus.). 240p. 1986. text ed. 36.95 (ISBN 0-13-139072-4). P-H.

Harper, Nancy. Human Communication Theory: History of a Paradigm. 320p. 1979. pap. 11.25x (ISBN 0-8104-6091-2). Boynton Cook Pubs.

Harrison, William L. Computers & Information Processing: An Introduction. (Illus.). 650p. 1985. text ed. 26.95 (ISBN 0-314-85245-X). West Pub.

Hyvaerinen, L. P. Information Theory for Systems Engineers. LC 79-124608. (Econometrics & Operations Research: Vol. 17). (Illus.). 1971. 34.00 (ISBN 0-387-05224-0). Springer-Verlag.

IEEE Standard 171-1958: IEEE Standard Definitions of Terms for Information Theory. 1958. 5.00 (ISBN 0-317-03951-2, SHO1016). IEEE.

International Symposium on Probability & Information Theory, McMaster University, Canada, 1968. Proceedings. Behara, M., et al, eds. LC 76-80068. (Lecture Notes in Mathematics: Vol. 89). 1969. pap. 14.70 (ISBN 0-387-04608-9). Springer-Verlag.

Jagodzinski. The Theory & Practice of Cognitive Science. (Information Tecnology Ser.). 1984. write for info (ISBN 0-9901003-0-8, Pub. by Abacus England). Heyden.

Jones, D. S. Elementary Information Theory. (Oxford Applied Mathematics & Computing Science Ser.). (Illus.). 1979. 42.50x (ISBN 0-19-859636-7); pap. 15.95x (ISBN 0-19-859637-5). Oxford U Pr.

Kahout. Activity Structures: The Theory & Practice of Cognitive Science. (Information Technology Ser.). 1984. 31.00 (ISBN 0-9901002-8-6, Pub. by Abacus England). Heyden.

Kantor, Frederick W. Information Mechanics. LC 77-6747. 397p. 1977. 44.95x (ISBN 0-471-02968-8, Pub. by Wiley-Interscience). Wiley.

Khinchin, Alexander I. Mathematical Foundations of Information Theory. 1957. pap. text ed. 2.95 (ISBN 0-486-60434-9). Dover.

Kinneavy, James L. Theory of Discourse. 496p. 1980. pap. 9.95x (ISBN 0-393-00919-X). Norton.

Kozenik, Jaroslav. Conference on Informational Theory, Statistical Decision Functions, Random Processes: Transactions of the Ninth Prague Conference, Prague, from June 28th to July 2nd, 1982. 1983. Vol. A. lib. bdg. 50.00 (ISBN 90-277-1499-1, Pub. by Reidel Holland); Vol. B. lib. bdg. 50.00 (ISBN 90-277-1500-9, Pub. by Reidel Holland). Kluwer Academic.

Kozesnik, J., ed. Transactions. 1967. 95.00 (ISBN 0-12-423858-0). Acad Pr.

Kullbach, Solomon. Information Theory & Statistics. 14.50 (ISBN 0-8446-2412-8). Peter Smith.

Langefors, Borje & Samuelson, Kjell. Information & Data in Systems. 192p. 1976. 21.95 (ISBN 0-442-80349-4). Van Nos Reinhold.

Longo, G., ed. The Information Theory Approach to Communications. (CISM-Courses & Lectures: Vol. 229). (Illus.). 1978. pap. 49.60 (ISBN 0-387-81484-1). Springer-Verlag.

--Information Theory: New Trends & Open Problems. (International Centre for Mechanical Sciences, Courses & Lectures: No. 219). (Illus.). 1976. soft cover 35.00 (ISBN 3-211-81378-0). Springer-Verlag.

McEliece, Robert J. Encyclopedia of Mathematics & Its Applications: The Theory of Information & Coding: A Mathematical Framework for Communication, Vol. 3. (The Theory of Information & Coding Ser.). 1984. 32.50 (ISBN 0-521-30223-4). Cambridge U Pr.

MacKay, Donald M. Information, Mechanism & Meaning. 1970. pap. 5.95x (ISBN 0-262-63032-X). MIT Pr.

Meetham, A. R. Encyclopedia of Linguistics, Information & Control. 1969. 140.00 (ISBN 0-08-012337-6). Pergamon.

Nivat, M. & Perrin, D., eds. Automata on Infinite Words. (Lecture Notes in Computer Science: Vol. 192). (Fr. & Eng.). iii, 216p. 1985. pap. 14.60 (ISBN 0-387-15641-0). Springer Verlag.

Pierce, J. R. An Introduction to Information Theory: Symbols, Signals & Noise. 2nd, rev. ed. 320p. 1980. pap. 4.95 (ISBN 0-486-24061-4). Dover.

Pierce, John R. An Introduction to Information Theory: Symbols, Signals & Noise. 2nd rev. ed. 14.50 (ISBN 0-8446-5803-0). Peter Smith.

Renyi, A. Tagebuch ueber die Informationstheorie. (Wissenschalt & Kultur Ser.: No. 34). 174p. 1983. 19.95 (ISBN 0-8176-1006-5). Birkhauser.

Schweitzer, James A. Managing Information Security: A Program for the Electronic Information Age. 113p. 1982. 23.50 (ISBN 0-409-95055-6). Butterworth.

Shanmugam, K. Sam. Digital & Analog Communication Systems. LC 78-26191. 600p. 1979. text ed. 44.00 (ISBN 0-471-03090-2); tchr's manual avail. (ISBN 0-471-07832-8). Wiley.

--Digital & Analog Communication Systems. 600p. 1979. 32.95 (ISBN 0-686-98113-8). Telecom Lib.

Singh, Jagjit. Great Ideas in Information Theory, Language & Cibernetics. 15.25 (ISBN 0-8446-2946-4). Peter Smith.

Soroko, L. M. Holography & Coherent Optics. LC 78-4479. (Illus.). 834p. 1978. 99.50x (ISBN 0-306-40101-0, Plenum Pr). Plenum Pub.

Symposium, Brussels. Information & Prediction in Science: Proceedings. Dockx, S. & Bernays, P., eds. 1965. 63.00 (ISBN 0-12-219050-5). Acad Pr.

Usher, M. J. Information Theory for Information Technologists. (Computer Science Ser.). (Illus.). 235p. 1984. text ed. 39.50x (ISBN 0-333-36702-2); pap. text ed. 19.95x (ISBN 0-333-36703-0). Scholium Intl.

Wang, Georgette & Dissanayake, Wimal. Continuity & Change in Communication Systems. Voigt, Melvin J., ed. LC 84-2969. (Communication & Information Science Ser.). 268p. 1985. text ed. 39.50 (ISBN 0-89391-150-X). Ablex Pub.

Wiggert, Djimitri. Error-Control Coding & Applications. LC 78-23237. (Illus.). 1978. 25.00x (ISBN 0-89006-066-5). Artech Hse.

Yaglom, A. M. & Yaglom, I. M. Probability & Information. 1983. lib. bdg. 69.00 (ISBN 0-318-00432-1, Pub. by Reidel Holland). Kluwer Academic.

Yu, Francis T. Optics & Information Theory. LC 83-16273. 240p. 1984. Repr. of 1976 ed. lib. bdg. 29.95 (ISBN 0-89874-678-7). Krieger.

INFORMATION THEORY IN BIOLOGY

Gatlin, Lila L. Information Theory & the Living System. LC 76-187030. (Molecular Biology Ser.). (Illus.). 210p. 1972. 24.00x (ISBN 0-231-03634-5). Columbia U Pr.

Ramsey-Klee, Diane M., ed. Aids to Biological Communication: Prosthesis & Synthesis. 392p. 1970. 87.95 (ISBN 0-677-13410-X). Gordon.

Sampson, Jeffrey R. Biological Information Processing: Current Theory & Computer Simulation. 310p. 1984. 32.00 (ISBN 0-471-06281-2, Pub. by Wiley-Interscience). Wiley.

Varela, F. J. Principles of Biological Autonomy. (North Holland Ser. in General Systems Research: Vol. 2). 336p. 1979. 52.25 (ISBN 0-444-00321-5, North Holland). Elsevier.

Vassileva-Popova, J. G. & Jensen, E. V., eds. Biophysical & Biochemical Information Transfer in Recognition. LC 78-15876. 895p. 1978. 95.00x (ISBN 0-306-40036-7, Plenum Pr). Plenum Pub.

Vassileva-Popova, Julia G., ed. Physical & Chemical Bases of Biological Information Transfer. LC 75-30849. 475p. 1975. 59.50x (ISBN 0-306-30862-2, Plenum Pr). Plenum Pub.

INFOSTAR (COMPUTER PROGRAM)

Arca, Julie A. & Pirro, Charles F. InfoPower: Practical InfoStar Uses. 275p. 16.95 (ISBN 0-89599-108-X). SYBEX.

Lukers, Tom. The Illustrated InfoStar Book. Berliner, Thomas H., ed. (Illus.). 240p. 1985. pap. 16.95 (ISBN 0-915381-61-3). WordWare Pub.

INFRA-RED ASTRONOMY

Brancazio, Peter J. & Cameron, A. G., eds. Infrared Astronomy: Proceedings of a Conference Held at Goddard Space Center, 1968. LC 69-19544. (Illus.). 258p. 1968. 69.50 (ISBN 0-677-11980-1). Gordon.

Setti, Giancarlo, ed. Infrared Astronomy. (NATO Advanced Study Institutes Ser.: No. 38). 1978. lib. bdg. 42.00 (ISBN 90-277-0871-1, Pub. by Reidel Holland). Kluwer Academic.

INFRA-RED PHOTOGRAPHY

see Photography, Infra-Red

INFRA-RED RAYS

see also Infra-Red Astronomy; Infra-Red Technology

Bramson, M. A. Infrared Radiation: A Handbook for Applications. LC 66-26812. (Optical Physics & Engineering Ser.). 623p. 1968. 85.00x (ISBN 0-306-30274-8, Plenum Pr). Plenum Pub.

Button, Kenneth, ed. Infrared & Millimeter Waves: Systems & Components, Vol. 6. 1982. 67.50 (ISBN 0-12-147706-1). Acad Pr.

Button, Kenneth J. Infrared & Millimeter Waves: Millimeter Components & Techniques, Pt. III, Vol. 11. LC 79-6949. 1984. 75.00 (ISBN 0-12-147711-8). Acad Pr.

Button, Kenneth J., ed. Infrared & Millimeter Waves: Coherent Sources & Applications Pt. II, Vol. 7. 416p. 1983. 85.00 (ISBN 0-12-147707-X). Acad Pr.

--Infrared & Millimeter Waves: Instrumentation, Vol. II. LC 79-6949. 1979. 67.50 (ISBN 0-12-147702-9). Acad Pr.

--Infrared & Millimeter Waves: Sources of Radiation, Vol. 1. LC 79-6949. 1979. 65.00 (ISBN 0-12-147701-0). Acad Pr.

--Infrared & Millimeter Waves: Submillimeter Techniques, Vol. 3. 1980. 65.00 (ISBN 0-12-147703-7). Acad Pr.

--Infrared & Millimeter Waves, Vol. 13: Millimeter Components & Techniques, Pt. IV. Date not set. 85.00 (ISBN 0-12-147713-4). Acad Pr.

--Infrared Millimeter Waves, Vol. 14: Millimeter Components & Techniques, Pt. V. Date not set. 99.00 (ISBN 0-12-147714-2). Acad Pr.

Buttton, Kenneth J., et al, eds. Reviews of Infrared & Millimeter Waves: Vol. 2. Optically Pumped Far-Infrared Lasers. 492p. 1984. 69.50x (ISBN 0-306-41487-2, Plenum Pr). Plenum Pub.

CES Industries, Inc. Ed-Lab Eighty Experiment Manual: Infra-Red Sensor. (Illus., Orig.). 1983. write for info. (ISBN 0-86711-065-1). CES Industries.

Infrared Image Sensor Technology: Proceedings 1001 SPIE Technical Symposium East, Washington, D.C., 1980. (SPIE Seminar Proceedings: Vol. 225). 174p. 37.00 (ISBN 0-89252-254-2); members 30.00 (ISBN 0-317-34666-0). SPIE.

Infrared Imaging Systems Technology: Proceedings 1001 SPIE Technical Symposium East, Washington, D.C., 1980. (SPIE Seminar Proceedings: Vol. 226). 166p. 37.00 (ISBN 0-89252-255-0); members 30.00 (ISBN 0-317-34667-9). SPIE.

Moss, T. S. & Wolfe, W. L., eds. Infrared Physics. 1976. text ed. 55.00 (ISBN 0-08-020880-0). Pergamon.

Parker, Frank S. Applications of Infrared Spectroscopy in Biochemistry, Biology & Medicine. LC 70-131882. 600p. 1971. 65.00x (ISBN 0-306-30502-X, Plenum Pr). Plenum Pub.

INFRA-RED SPECTROMETRY

Alpert, Nelson L., et al. IR-Theory & Practice of Infrared Spectroscopy. rev. 2nd ed. LC 70-107535. 394p. 1970. 45.00 (ISBN 0-306-30399-X, Plenum Pr); pap. 8.95 (ISBN 0-306-20001-5, Plenum Pr). Plenum Pub.

--IR-Theory & Practice of Infrared Spectroscopy. LC 73-12968. 394p. 1973. pap. text ed. 8.95x (ISBN 0-306-20001-5, Rosetta). Plenum Pub.

Avram, Margareta & Mateescu, Gh. Infrared Spectroscopy: Applications in Organic Chemistry. LC 78-16322. 532p. 1978. Repr. of 1972 ed. lib. bdg. 33.00 (ISBN 0-88275-711-3). Krieger.

Brame, Edward & Graselli, Jeanette. Infrared & Raman Spectroscopy, Pt. A. (Practical Spectroscopy Ser.: Vol. 1). 1976. 65.00 (ISBN 0-8247-6392-0). Dekker.

Brame, Edward G. & Grasselli, Jeannette, eds. Infrared & Raman Spectroscopy, Pt. B. (Practical Spectroscopy Ser.: Vol. 1). 1977. 65.00 (ISBN 0-8247-6526-5). Dekker.

Chantry, G. W. Submillimetre Spectroscopy. 1972. 66.50 (ISBN 0-12-170550-1). Acad Pr.

Clark. Advances in Infared & Raman Spectroscopy, Vol. 9. 1982. 124.95 (ISBN 0-471-26215-3). Wiley.

--Advances in Infrared & Raman Spectroscopy, Vol. 8. 1981. 130.95 (ISBN 0-471-25640-4, Pub. by Wiley Heyden). Wiley.

Clark, R. J. & Hester, R. E. Advances In Infrared & Raman Spectroscopy, Vol. 10. 454p. 1983. 118.00 (ISBN 0-471-26216-1, Pub. by Wiley Heyden). Wiley.

Clark, R. J. & Hester, R. E., eds. Advances in Infrared & Raman Spectroscopy, 5 vols. Vol. 1. 1975 ed. 96.95 (ISBN 0-471-25631-5, Pub. by Wiley Heyden); Vol. 2. 1976 ed. 96.95 (ISBN 0-471-25632-3); Vol. 3. 1977 ed. o.p. 89.95 (ISBN 0-471-25633-1); Vol. 4. 1978 ed. o.p. 121.95 (ISBN 0-471-25634-X). Wiley.

--Advances in Infrared & Raman Spectroscopy, Vol. 5. 404p. 1978. casebound 130.95 (ISBN 0-471-25636-6, Pub. by Wiley Heyden). Wiley.

--Advances in Infrared & Raman Spectroscopy, Vol. 12. price not set (ISBN 0-471-90674-3). Wiley.

Cole, Howard, ed. Tables of Wavenumbers for the Calibration of Infrared Spectrometers, Vol. 9. 2nd ed. 1977. text ed. 44.00 (ISBN 0-08-021247-6). Pergamon.

Cook, B. W. & Jones, K. A Programmed Introduction to Infrared Spectroscopy. 207p. 1972. 43.95 (ISBN 0-471-25644-7, Wiley Heyden); pap. 35.95 (ISBN 0-471-25643-9). Wiley.

Cross, A. D. & Jones, R. A. Introduction to Practical Infra-Red Spectroscopy. 3rd ed. LC 69-20393. 87p. 1969. 22.50x (ISBN 0-306-30626-3, Plenum Pr). Plenum Pub.

Cross, A. D. & Jones, R. Alan. An Introduction to Practical Infra-Red Spectroscopy. 3rd ed. LC 69-20393. pap. 28.80 (ISBN 0-317-30341-4, 2024713). Bks Demand UMI.

Dolphin, David & Wick, Alexander. Tabulation of Infared Spectral Data. LC 76-48994. 566p. 1977. 31.50 (ISBN 0-471-21780-8). Krieger.

Ferraro, John R. Low-Frequency Vibrations in Inorganic & Coordination Compounds. LC 74-107528. 309p. 1971. 39.50x (ISBN 0-306-30453-8, Plenum Pr). Plenum Pub.

Ferraro, John R. & Basile, Louis J., eds. Fourier Transform Infrared Spectroscopy: Applications to Chemical Systems, Vol. 2. LC 78-26956. 1979. 55.00 (ISBN 0-12-254102-2). Acad Pr.

--Fourier Transform Infrared Spectroscopy, Vol. 4. 1985. 74.50 (ISBN 0-12-254104-9). Acad Pr.

Griffiths, Peter R. Chemical Infrared Fourier Transform Spectroscopy. LC 75-6505. (Chemical Analysis: A series of Monographs on Analytical Chemistry & Its Applications: Vol. 43). 340p. 1975. 58.00x (ISBN 0-471-32786-7, Pub by Wiley-Interscience). Wiley.

Hair, Michael L. Infrared Spectropscopy in Surface Chemistry. LC 67-17004. pap. 82.00 (ISBN 0-317-08343-0, 2017852). Bks Demand UMI.

Hallam, H. E., ed. Vibrational Spectroscopy of Trapped Species: Infrared & Raman Studies of Matrix-Isolated Molecules, Radicals & Ions. LC 72-8601. 430p. 1973. 114.95x (ISBN 0-471-34330-7, Pub. by Wiley-Interscience). Wiley.

Hallam, Harry E., ed. Vibrational Spectroscopy of Trapped Species: Infrared & Raman Studies of Matrix-Isolated Molecules, Radicals & Ions. LC 72-8601. pap. 110.50 (ISBN 0-317-26652-7, 2024035). Bks Demand UMI.

Mattson, James S., et al, eds. Infrared Correlation & Fourier Transform Spectroscopy. (Computers in Chemistry & Instrumentation Ser.: Vol. 7). 1976. 69.75 (ISBN 0-8247-6369-6). Dekker.

Miller, R. G. & Stace, B. C., eds. Laboratory Methods in Infrared Spectroscopy. 2nd ed. 396p. 1972. 69.95x (ISBN 0-471-25908-X, Wiley Heyden). Wiley.

Nakanishi, Koji & Solomon, Philippa H. Infrared Absorption Spectroscopy. 2nd ed. LC 76-27393. 1977. pap. 24.00x (ISBN 0-8162-6251-9). Holden-Day.

Paternite, Stephen & Paternite, David, eds. American Infrared Survey. LC 82-6160. (Illus.). 88p. 1982. 21.95 (ISBN 0-9609812-0-9). Photo Survey.

Waloff, Z. & Rainey, R. C. Field Studies on Factors Affecting the Displacement of Desert Locust Swarms in Eastern Africa. 1951. 35.00x (ISBN 0-85135-042-9, Pub. by Centre Overseas Research). State Mutual Bk.
Watson, Theo F., et al. Practical Insect Pest Management: A Self-Instructional Manual. (Illus.). 196p. 1976. pap. text ed. 11.95x (ISBN 0-7167-0558-3). W H Freeman.
Wilson, M. Curtis, et al. Practical Insect Pest Management: Fundamentals of Applied Entomology, No. 1. 2nd ed. LC 76-46901. (Illus.). 1977. 9.95x (ISBN 0-88133-031-0). Waveland Pr.
--Practical Insect Pest Management: Insects of Man's Household & Health, No. 5. LC 77-82251. (Illus.). 1977. 8.95x (ISBN 0-917974-07-7). Waveland Pr.
--Practical Insect Pest Management. 2nd ed. LC 79-57132. (Insects of Livestock & Agronomic Crops Ser.: No. 2). (Illus.). 208p. 1980. pap. text ed. 9.95x (ISBN 0-917974-39-5). Waveland Pr.
Wood, David, et al, eds. Control of Insect Behavior by Natural Products: Proceedings. LC 69-13486. 1970. 55.00 (ISBN 0-12-762650-6). Acad Pr.
Zak, Bill. Critters: Common Household & Garden Pests of Texas. 256p. 1984. 15.95 (ISBN 0-87833-384-3). Taylor Pub.

INSECT CONTROL–BIOLOGICAL CONTROL

Advances in Insect Population Control by the Sterile-Male Technique. (Technical Reports Ser.: No. 44). (Illus.). 79p. (Orig.). 1965. pap. 10.75 (ISBN 92-0-115065-2, IDC44, IAEA). Unipub.
Application of Induced Sterility for Control of Lepidopterous Populations. (Panel Proceedings Ser.). (Illus.). 169p. (Orig.). 1971. pap. 13.00 (ISBN 92-0-111271-8, ISP281, IAEA). Unipub.
Canada Department of Agriculture Staff Belleville, Ontario. Biological Control Programmes Against Insects & Weeds in Canada, 1959-1968. 266p. 1971. 35.00x (ISBN 0-85198-018-X, Pub. by CAB Bks England). State Mutual Bk.
Carson, Rachel. Silent Spring. (Illus.). 1962. 16.95 (ISBN 0-395-07506-8). HM.
Computer Models & Application of the Sterile-Male Technique. (Panel Proceedings Ser.). (Illus.). 195p. (Orig.). 1973. pap. 18.00 (ISBN 92-0-111573-3, ISP340, IAEA). Unipub.
Controlling Fruit Flies by the Sterile-Insect Technique. (Panel Proceedings Ser.). (Illus.). 175p. 1976. pap. 19.00 (ISBN 92-0-111575-X, ISP392, IAEA). Unipub.
Coppel, H. C. & Mertins, J. W. Biological Insect Press Suppression. LC 76-42188. (Advanced Series in Agricultural Sciences: Vol. 4). (Illus.). 1977. 43.00 (ISBN 3-540-07931-9). Springer-Verlag.
Davidson, G. Genetic Control of Insect Pests. 1974. 33.00 (ISBN 0-12-205750-3). Acad Pr.
DeBach, P. Biological Control by Natural Enemies. LC 73-90812. (Illus.). 325p. 1974. 49.50 (ISBN 0-521-20380-5); pap. 14.95 (ISBN 0-521-09835-1). Cambridge U Pr.
Howard, Leland O. & Fiske, William F. The Importation into the United States of the Parasites of the Gypsy Moth & the Brown-Tail Moth: Report of Progress of Previous & Concurrent Efforts of This Kind. Egerton, Frank N., 3rd, ed. LC 77-74230. (History of Ecology Ser.). (Illus.). 1978. Repr. of 1911 ed. lib. bdg. 32.00x (ISBN 0-405-10400-6). Ayer Co Pubs.
Hoy, Marjorie A. & Cunningham, Gary L. Biological Control of Pests by Mites: Proceedings of a Conference. LC 83-72136. (Illus.). 150p. (Orig.). 1983. pap. 15.00x (ISBN 0-931876-63-X, 3304). Ag & Nat Res.
Hurst, G. W. Meteorology & the Colorado Potato Beetle. (Technical Note Ser.: No. 137). (Illus.). x, 52p. 1975. pap. 15.00 (ISBN 92-63-10391-7, W162, WMO). Unipub.
Insect Ecology & the Sterile-Male Technique. (Panel Proceedings Ser.). (Illus.). 102p. (Orig.). 1969. pap. 9.25 (ISBN 92-0-011269-2, ISP223, IAEA). Unipub.
Laird, Marshall, ed. Blackflies: The Future for Biological Methods in Integrated Control. LC 81-66373. 1982. 59.50 (ISBN 0-12-434060-1). Acad Pr.
Lindguist, A. W., ed. Insect Population Control by the Sterile-Male Technique. (Technical Reports Ser.: No. 21). (Illus.). 60p. (Orig.). 1963. pap. 6.25 (ISBN 92-0-115063-6, IDC21, IAEA). Unipub.
Rabbinge, R. Biological Control of Fruit-Tree Red Spider Mite. (Simulation Monographs). 1976. pap. 30.00 (ISBN 90-220-0590-9, PDC18, PUDOC). Unipub.
Sabelis, M. W. Biological Control of Two-Spotted Spider Mites Using Phytoseiid Predators, Pt. 1. (Agricultural Research Reports: No. 910). 248p. 1981. pap. 24.50 (ISBN 90-220-0776-6, PDC233, PUDOC). Unipub.
Scruggs, C. G. The Peaceful Atom & the Deadly Fly. LC 75-28738. (Illus.). 311p. 1975. 12.95 (ISBN 0-8363-0135-8). Jenkins.
Shepard, Merle & Lawn, R. J. Insects on Grain Legumes in Northern Australia: A Survey of Potential Pests & Their Enemies. LC 82-13463. (Illus.). 89p. 1983. pap. 8.50 (ISBN 0-7022-1802-2). U of Queensland Pr.
Sokoloff, A. The Biology of Tribolium: With Special Emphasis on Genetic Aspects, Vol. 3. 1977. 125.00x (ISBN 0-19-857512-2). Oxford U Pr.
Steiner, William & Tabachnick, Walter, eds. Recent Development in the Genetics of Insect Disease Vectors. (Illus.). 665p. text ed. 26.00 (ISBN 0-87563-224-6). Stipes.
The Sterile-Insect Technique & Its Field Application. (Panel Proceedings Ser.). (Illus.). 138p. (Orig.). 1974. pap. 12.75 (ISBN 92-0-111374-9, ISP364, IAEA). Unipub.
Sterile Insect Technique & Radiation in Insect Control: Proceedings of a Symposium, Neuherberg, 29 June - 3 July 1981, Jointly Organized by IAEA & FAO. (Proceedings Ser.). (Illus.). 494p. 1982. pap. 64.00 (ISBN 92-0-010082-1, ISP595, IAEA). Unipub.
Sterile-Male Technique for Eradication or Control of Harmful Insects. (Panel Proceedings Ser.). 1969. pap. 9.75 (ISBN 92-0-111369-2, ISP224, IAEA). Unipub.
Sterility Principle for Insect Control: 1974. (Proceedings Ser.). (Illus.). 622p. 1975. pap. 62.00 (ISBN 92-0-010275-1, ISP377, IAEA). Unipub.
Wilson, F. A Review of the Biological Control of Insects & Weeds in Australia & Australian New Guinea. 104p. 1960. cloth 30.00x (ISBN 0-85198-065-1, Pub. by CAB Bks England). State Mutual Bk.

INSECT GALLS

see Galls (Botany)

INSECT METAMORPHOSIS

see Insects–Metamorphosis

INSECT-PLANT RELATIONSHIPS

Beattie, Andrew J. The Evolutionary Ecology of Ant-Plant Mutualisms. (Illus.). 176p. Date not set. price not set (ISBN 0-521-25281-4); pap. price not set (ISBN 0-521-27272-6). Cambridge U Pr.
Wheeler, Quentin & Blackwell, Meredith. Fungus-Insect Relationships: Perspectives in Ecology & Evolution. (Illus.). 464p. 1984. 62.50x (ISBN 0-231-05694-X). Columbia U Pr.

INSECT POPULATIONS

Ashall, C. & Ellis, P. E. Studies on Numbers & Mortality in Field Populations of the Desert Locust (Schistocerca Gregaria Forskal) 1962. 35.00x (ISBN 0-85135-004-6, Pub. by Centre Overseas Research). State Mutual Bk.
Clark, L. R., et al. The Ecology of Insect Populations in Theory & Practice. 1974. pap. 11.95 (ISBN 0-412-21170-X, NO.6059, Pub. by Chapman & Hall). Methuen Inc.
Dempster, J. P. The Population Dynamics of the Moroccan Locust (Dociostaurus Maroccanus Thunb) in Cyprus. 1957. 35.00x (ISBN 0-85135-011-9, Pub. by Centre Overseas Research). State Mutual Bk.
Insect Ecology & the Sterile-Male Technique. (Panel Proceedings Ser.). (Illus.). 102p. (Orig.). 1969. pap. 9.25 (ISBN 92-0-011269-2, ISP223, IAEA). Unipub.
Richards, O. W. & Waloff, N. Studies on the Biology & Population Dynamics of British Grasshoppers. 1954. 35.00x (ISBN 0-85135-034-8, Pub. by Centre Overseas Research). State Mutual Bk.
Varley, G. C., et al. Insect Population Ecology: An Analytic Approach. 1974. pap. 7.95x (ISBN 0-520-02667-5). U of Cal Pr.
Waloff, Z. The Upsurges & Recessions of the Desert Locust Plague: An Historical Survey. 1968. 35.00x (ISBN 0-85135-041-0, Pub. by Centre Overseas Research). State Mutual Bk.
Weese, Asa O. Animal Ecology of an Illinois Elm-Maple Forest. pap. 8.00 (ISBN 0-384-66400-8). Johnson Repr.

INSECT SOCIETIES

see also Ants; Bees; Insect Populations; Termites; Wasps

Breed, Michael D., ed. The Biology of Social Insects: Proceedings. 425p. 1982. softcover 30.00x (ISBN 0-86531-291-5). Westview.
Fabre, Jean H. Social Life in the Insect World. facsimile ed. Miall, Bernard, tr. LC 78-179517. (Select Bibliographies Reprint Ser). Repr. of 1912 ed. 23.50 (ISBN 0-8369-6646-5). Ayer Co Pubs.
Hermann, Henry. Social Insects, Vol. 3. 459p. 1982. 63.00 (ISBN 0-12-342203-5). Acad Pr.
Hermann, Henry R. Defensive Mechanisms in the Social Insects. LC 83-24798. 272p. 1984. 38.95x (ISBN 0-03-057002-6). Praeger.
--Social Insects, Vol. 2. 1981. 59.00 (ISBN 0-12-342202-7). Acad Pr.
--Social Insects, Vol. 4. 385p. 1982. 57.00 (ISBN 0-12-342204-3). Acad Pr.
Hermann, Henry R., ed. Social Insects, Vol. 1. LC 78-4871. 1979. 57.50 (ISBN 0-12-342201-9). Acad Pr.
International Congress of International Union for Study of Social Insects, Eighth, Wageningen, Netherlands, September 5-10, 1977: Proceedings. 1977. pap. 32.00 (ISBN 90-220-0640-9, PDC69, PUDOC). Unipub.
Oster, George F. & Wilson, Edward O. Caste & Ecology in the Social Insects. LC 78-51185. (Monographs in Population Biology: Vol. 12). (Illus.). 1978. 37.50 (ISBN 0-691-08210-3); pap. 13.50 (ISBN 0-691-02361-1). Princeton U Pr.
Watson, J. A., ed. Caste Differentiation in Social Insects. (Current Themes in Tropical Science Ser.: Vol. 3). (Illus.). 400p. 1985. 110.00 (ISBN 0-08-030783-3). Pergamon.
Wheeler, W. M. Social Life among the Insects: Being a Series of Lectures Delivered at the Lowell Institute in Boston in March, 1922. LC 23-12888. Repr. of 1923 ed. 34.00 (ISBN 0-384-67870-X). Johnson Repr.
Wilson, Edward O. Insect Societies. LC 74-148941. (Illus.). 1971. 25.00x (ISBN 0-674-45490-1, Belknap Pr); pap. 19.00 (ISBN 0-674-45495-2). Harvard U Pr.

INSECTICIDES

see also Insects, Injurious and Beneficial; Mothproofing; Spraying; also names of insecticides

Bennett, F. V. & Symmons, P. M. A Review of Estimates of the Effectiveness of Certain Control Techniques & Insecticides Against the Desert Locust. 1972. 35.00x (ISBN 0-85135-060-7, Pub. by Centre Overseas Research). State Mutual Bk.
Brooks, G. T. Chlorinated Insecticides, Vol. I. LC 83-13605. 260p. 1983. Repr. of 1974 ed. lib. bdg. 56.00 (ISBN 0-89874-664-7). Krieger.
--Chlorinated Insecticides, Vol. II. LC 83-13605. 208p. 1985. Repr. of 1974 ed. lib. bdg. 56.00 (ISBN 0-89874-663-9). Krieger.
Brown, A. W. & Pal, R. Insecticide Resistance in Arthropods. 2nd ed. (Monograph Ser: No. 38). (Illus.). 491p. 1971. pap. 16.40 (ISBN 92-4-140038-2, 943). World Health.
Busvine, J. R. A Critical Review of the Techniques for Testing Insecticides. 2nd ed. 345p. 1971. cloth 49.00x (ISBN 0-85198-030-9, Pub. by CAB Bks England). State Mutual Bk.
Casida, John E., ed. Pyrethrum: The Natural Insecticide. 1973. 59.50 (ISBN 0-12-162950-3). Acad Pr.
Coats, Joel. Insecticide Mode of Action. 472p. 1982. 59.50 (ISBN 0-12-177120-2). Acad Pr.
Control of Pesticides: A Survey of Existing Legislation. (International Digest of Health Legislation Ser: Vol. 20, No. 4). 150p. 1969. pap. 5.60 (ISBN 92-4-169204-9, 1020). World Health.
Elliott, Michael, ed. Synthetic Pyrethroids. LC 77-1810. (ACS Symposium Ser.: No. 42). 1977. 29.95 (ISBN 0-8412-0368-7). Am Chemical.
Getting the Bugs Out: A Guide to Sensible Pest Management in & Around the Home. (Illus.). 26p. 1981. pap. free (ISBN 0-930698-10-X). Natl Audubon.
Hall, Stanley A., ed. New Approaches to Pest Control & Eradication. LC 63-19396. (Advances in Chemistry Ser.: No. 41). 1963. pap. 8.95 (ISBN 0-8412-0042-4). Am Chemical.
Insecticides & Application Equipment for Tsetse Control: Prepared by the Centre for Overseas Pest Research, London, with the Support of the United Nations Development Programme. (Animal Production & Health Papers: No. 3). (Eng. & Fr.). 80p. 1977. pap. 9.00 (ISBN 92-5-100183-9, F723, FAO). Unipub.
International Conference on Alternative Insecticides for Vector Control, Atlanta, Feb. 1971. Proceedings. (Bulletin of WHO: Vol. 44, Nos. 1-3). 470p. 1971. pap. 14.40 (ISBN 0-686-09008-X, 922). World Health.
Jacobson, Martin. Insecticides of the Future. 104p. 1975. pap. 19.75 (ISBN 0-8247-6303-3). Dekker.
Jacobson, Martin & Crosby, Donald G., eds. Naturally Occurring Insecticides. 1970. 115.00 (ISBN 0-8247-1325-7). Dekker.
Kenaga, E. E. & Morgan, Robert W. Commercial & Experimental Organic Insecticides. 1978. 6.70 (ISBN 0-686-18862-4); members 4.00. Entomol Soc.
Kuhr, Ronald J. Carbamate Insecticides: Chemistry, Biochemistry & Toxicology. LC 74-25265. (Uniscience Ser.). 301p. 1976. 69.00 (ISBN 0-8493-5066-2). CRC Pr.
Lal, R., ed. Insecticide Microbiology. (Illus.). 270p. 1984. 47.00 (ISBN 0-387-13662-2). Springer-Verlag.
Maccuaig, R. D. & Yeates, M. N. Theoretical Studies on the Efficiency of Insecticidal Sprays for the Control of Flying Locust Swarms. 35.00x (ISBN 0-85135-057-7, Pub. by Centre Overseas Research). State Mutual Bk.
Maramorosch, Karl & Sherman, K. E., eds. Viral Insecticides for Biological Control. 1985. 69.50 (ISBN 0-12-470295-3). Acad Pr.
Matsumura, F., ed. Differential Toxicities of Insecticides & Halogenated Aromatics. (International Encyclopedia of Pharmacology & Therapeutics Ser.). (Illus.). 560p. 1983. 140.00 (ISBN 0-08-029826-5). Pergamon.
Matsumura, Fumio. Toxicology of Insecticides. LC 74-19258. (Illus.). 504p. 1975. 39.50x (ISBN 0-306-30787-1, Plenum Pr). Plenum Pub.
Measurements & Computations on the Behaviour of the Insecticides Azinphosmethyl & Dimethoate in Ditches. (Agricultural Research Reports: No. 884). 1979. pap. 28.00 (ISBN 90-220-0695-6, PDC118, PUDOC). Unipub.
Mullla, M. S., et al. Distribution, Transport, & Fate of the Insecticides: Malathion & Parathion in the Environment. Gunther, F. A., ed. (Residue Reviews Ser.: Vol. XXX). (Illus.). 172p. 1981. 24.00 (ISBN 0-387-90634-7). Springer-Verlag.
O'Brien, R. D. & Yamamoto, Izuru, eds. Biochemical Toxicology of Insecticides. 1970. 39.00 (ISBN 0-12-523935-1). Acad Pr.
Page, B. G. & Thompson, W. T. The Insecticide, Herbicide, Fungicide Quick Guide, 1985. 140p. pap. 12.00 (ISBN 0-913702-30-7). Thomson Pub CA.
Proceedings of the British Insecticide & Fungicide Conference, 8th, Vols. 1-3. 1975. Set. 100.00x (ISBN 0-901436-38-0, Pub. by BCPC Pubns England). State Mutual Bk.
Quraishi, M. Sayeed. Biochemical Insect Control: Its Impact on Economy, Environment & Natural Selection. LC 76-29701. 280p. 1977. 45.50x (ISBN 0-471-70275-7, Pub. by Wiley-Interscience). Wiley.
Ramulu, U. S. Chemistry of Insecticides & Fungicides. 342p. 1981. 25.00x (ISBN 0-686-72944-7, Pub. by Oxford & IBH India); 15.25x (ISBN 0-686-72945-5). State Mutual Bk.
Seventh British Insecticide & Fugicide Conference: Vol. 1, 2 & 3. 1973. Set. 100.00 (ISBN 0-901436-39-9, Pub. by BCPC Pubns England). State Mutual Bk.
Shepard, Merle, ed. Insect Pest Management. LC 73-9730. 1973. 36.50x (ISBN 0-8422-7114-7); pap. text ed. 19.50x (ISBN 0-8422-0296-X). Irvington.
Sixth British Insecticide & Fungicide Conference: Vol. 1, 2 & 3. 1971. Set. 100.00x (ISBN 0-901436-07-0, Pub. by BCPC Pubns England). State Mutual Bk.
T&F & Leahey. The Pyrethroid Insecticides. 1985. 44.00 (ISBN 0-85066-283-4). Taylor & Francis.
Thomson, W. T. Agricultural Chemicals, Book I: Insecticides. rev. ed. 260p. 1985. pap. 14.50 (ISBN 0-913702-31-5). Thomson Pub Ca.
Vector Control. (WHO Bulletin Supplement: Vol. 29). (Also avail. in French). 1963. pap. 4.80 (ISBN 92-4-068291-0). World Health.
Wegler, R., ed. Insecticides: Biochemical & Biological Methods, Natural Products. (Chemie der Pflanzenschutz und Schaedlingsbekaempfungsmittel). 500p. 1981. 152.30 (ISBN 0-387-10307-4). Springer-Verlag.
WHO Expert Committee on Insecticides, Geneva, 1970. Application & Dispersal of Pesticides: A Report. (Technical Report Ser: No. 465). 66p. 1971. pap. 2.00 (ISBN 92-4-120465-6, 931). World Health.
WHO Expert Committee on Insecticides, Geneva, 1968. Insecticide Resistance & Vector Control. (Technical Report Ser: No. 443). 279p. 1970. pap. 5.60 (ISBN 92-4-120443-5, 938). World Health.
Wilkinson, C. F., ed. Insecticide Biochemistry & Physiology. LC 76-10596. (Illus.). 790p. 1976. 69.50 (ISBN 0-306-30872-X, Plenum Pr). Plenum Pub.
--Insecticide Biochemistry & Physiology. 740p. 1976. 129.95 (ISBN 0-471-26086-X). Wiley.

INSECTIVOROUS PLANTS

Darwin, Charles R. Insectivorous Plants. 2nd rev. ed. LC 70-151602. Repr. of 1893 ed. 27.50 (ISBN 0-404-01928-5). AMS Pr.
--Insectivorous Plants, Vol. 12. LC 72-3897. (Illus.). x, 462p. 1972. 42.50 (ISBN 0-404-08412-5). AMS Pr.
Lloyd, Francis E. The Carnivorous Plants. (Illus.). 384p. 1976. pap. 7.95 (ISBN 0-486-23321-9). Dover.
--The Carnivorous Plants. 16.00 (ISBN 0-8446-5485-X). Peter Smith.
Schnell, Donald E. Carnivorous Plants of the United States & Canada. LC 76-26883. (Illus.). 126p. 1976. 19.95 (ISBN 0-910244-90-1). Blair.
Schwartz, Randall. Carnivorous Plants. 1975. pap. 1.25 (ISBN 0-380-00518-2, 26989). Avon.
Slack, Adrian. Carnivorous Plants. (Illus.). 240p. 1980. 30.00x (ISBN 0-262-19186-5); pap. 12.50 (ISBN 0-262-69089-6). MIT Pr.
--Carnivorous Plants. 176p. 1982. 37.00x (ISBN 0-85223-160-1, Pub. by Ebury Pr England). State Mutual Bk.

Dethier, Vincent G. To Know a Fly. LC 62-21838. (Illus.). 1963. pap. 7.95x (ISBN 0-8162-2240-1). Holden-Day.

Evans, Howard. Comparative Ethology & Evolution of the Sand Wasps. LC 66-18245. 1966. 32.50x (ISBN 0-674-15201-8). Harvard U Pr.

Evans, Howard E. Life on a Little-Known Planet. LC 84-86. (Illus.). 1984. pap. 9.95 (ISBN 0-226-22258-6). U of Chicago Pr.

Hunter-Jones, P. Laboratory Studies on the Inheritance of Phase Characters in Locusts. 1958. 35.00x (ISBN 0-85135-018-6, Pub. by Centre Overseas Research). State Mutual Bk.

Jermy, T., ed. The Host-Plant in Relation to Insect Behavior & Reproduction. LC 75-37209. 322p. 1976. 42.50x (ISBN 0-306-30909-2, Plenum Pr.). Plenum Pub.

Matthews, R. & Matthews, Robert W. Insect Behavior: A Sourcebook of Laboratory & Field Exercises. (Science Study Ser.). (Illus.). 290p. 1982. 22.00x (ISBN 0-86531-412-8). Westview.

Matthews, Robert W. & Matthews, Janice R. Insect Behavior. LC 78-7869. 507p. 1978. 42.95x (ISBN 0-471-57685-9, Pub. by Wiley-Interscience). Wiley.

Neider, Charles, ed. Fabulous Insects. facs. ed. LC 68-16960. (Essay Index Reprint Ser). 1954. 17.50 (ISBN 0-8369-0736-1). Ayer Co Pubs.

Pringle, J. W. Insect Flight. Head, J. J., ed. LC 78-53327. (Carolina Biology Readers Ser.). (Illus.). 16p. 1983. pap. 1.60 (ISBN 0-89278-252-8, 45-9652). Carolina Biological.

Rainey, R. C. Insect Flight. LC 75-22091. (Royal Entomological Society of London Symposium Ser.). 287p. 1976. 79.95x (ISBN 0-470-70550-7). Halsted Pr.

Rainey, R. C. & Waloff, Z. The Behavior of the Red Locust (Normadacris Septemfasciata Serville) in Relation to the Topography, Meteorology & Vegetatation of the Rukwa Rift Valley, Tanganyika. 1957. 35.00x (ISBN 0-85135-031-3, Pub. by Centre Overseas Research). State Mutual Bk.

Roeder, Kenneth D. Nerve Cells & Insect Behavior. rev. ed. LC 67-27092. (Books in Biology Ser: No. 4). 1967. 12.00x (ISBN 0-674-60800-3). Harvard U Pr.

Saunders, D. S. Insect Clocks. 2nd ed. LC 81-13815. (Illus.). 420p. 1982. 99.00 (ISBN 0-08-028848-0); pap. 48.00 (ISBN 0-08-028847-2). Pergamon.

Shorey, H. H. & McKelvey, John J., Jr. Chemical Control of Insect Behavior: Theory & Application. LC 76-46573. (Environmental Science & Technology Ser.). 414p. 1977. 48.50x (ISBN 0-471-78840-6, Pub. by Wiley-Interscience). Wiley.

Spieth, Herman T. Courtship Behavior of the Hawaiian Picture-Winged Drosophila. LC 83-24093. (Entomology Ser.: Vol. 103). 106p. 1984. lib. bdg. 9.50x (ISBN 0-520-09691-6). U of Cal Pr.

Stokes, Donald W. A Guide to Observing Insect Lives. (Stokes Nature Guides). 1983. 14.00i (ISBN 0-316-81724-4). Little.

--A Guide to Observing Insect Lives. 384p. 1984. pap. 8.70i (ISBN 0-316-81727-9). Little.

Stower, W. J. & Popov, G. B. Oviposition Behavior & Egg Mortality of the Desert Locust (Schistocerca Gregaria Forskal) on the Coast of Eritrea. 1958. 35.00x (ISBN 0-85135-037-2, Pub. by Centre Overseas Research). State Mutual Bk.

Thornhill, Randy & Alcock, John. The Evolution of Insect Mating Systems. 560p. 1985. pap. text ed. 19.95x. Harvard U Pr.

Von Frisch, Karl. Dance Language & Orientation of Bees. Chadwick, Leigh E., tr. LC 67-17321. (Illus., Ger). 1967. 30.00x (ISBN 0-674-19050-5, Belknap Pr). Harvard U Pr.

Watson, J. A., ed. Caste Differentiation in Social Insects. (Current Themes in Tropical Science Ser.: Vol. 3). (Illus.). 400p. 1985. 110.00 (ISBN 0-08-030783-3). Pergamon.

INSECTS–BIBLIOGRAPHY

Bonnet, Pierre. Bibliographia Araneorum: Analyse Methodique De Toute la Litterature Araneologique Jusqu'en 1939. LC 57-58745. 832p. 1968. Repr. 40.00 (ISBN 0-686-09299-6). Entomol Soc.

Parrella, M. P. & Robb, K. L. Economically Important Members of the Genus Liriomyza Mik: A Selected Bibliography. (Miscellaneous Publications of the E.S.A. Ser.: No. 59). 32p. 1985. 7.50 (ISBN 0-318-04408-0). Entomol Soc.

Robinson, G. S. Insects of the Falkland Islands: A Checklist & Bibliography. 38p. (Orig.). 1984. pap. text ed. 8.00x (ISBN 0-565-00955-9, Pub. by Brit Mus Nat Hist England). Sabbot-Natural Hist Bks.

INSECTS–BIOLOGICAL CONTROL

see Insect Control–Biological Control

INSECTS–COLLECTION AND PRESERVATION

see also Zoological Specimens–Collection and Preservation

Arnett, Ross H., Jr. & Arnett, Mary E., eds. The Naturalists' Directory of Insect Collectors & Identifiers, International, Pt. I. 44th ed. (The Naturalists' Directory (International) Ser.). 96p. (Orig.). 1985. pap. cancelled (ISBN 0-916846-15-6). Flora & Fauna.

Gordh, Gordon & Trjapitzin, V. Taxonomic Studies of the Encyrtidae with the Desriptions of New Species & a New Genus: Hymenoptera: Chalcidoidea. (Publications in Entomology: Vol. 93). 1982. pap. 10.00 (ISBN 0-520-09629-0). U of Cal Pr.

Hopkins, G. H. & Rothschild, M. An Illustrated Catalogue of the Rothschild Collection of Fleas, Vol. V: Leptopsyllidae & Ancistropsyllidae. 530p. 1971. 180.00x (ISBN 0-686-82366-4, Pub. by Brit Mus England). State Mutual Bk.

--An Illustrated Catalogue of the Rothschild Collection of Fleas, Vol. IV: Hystrichopsyllidae (Tenophthalminae, Dinopsyllinae & Listropsyllinae) 594p. 1966. 175.00x (ISBN 0-686-82367-2, Pub. by Brit Mus England). State Mutual Bk.

--An Illustrated Catalogue of the Rothschild Collection of Fleas, Vol. III: Hystrichopsyllidae (Acedestiinae, Anamiopsyllinae, Histrichopsyllinae, Neopsyllinae, Rhadinopsyllinae & Stenoponiinae) 559p. 1962. 125.00x (ISBN 0-686-82369-9, Pub. by Brit Mus England). State Mutual Bk.

--An Illustrated Catalogue of the Rothschild Collection of Fleas, Vol. II: Coptopsyllidae, Verminpsyllidae, Sephanociridae, Tschnopsyllidae, Hypsophthalmidae & Xiphiopsyllidae. 446p. 1956. 110.00x (ISBN 0-686-82370-2, Pub. by Brit Mus England). State Mutual Bk.

--An Illustrated Catalogue of the Rothschild Collection of Fleas, Vol. I: Tungidae & Pulicidae. 362p. 1953. 90.00x (ISBN 0-686-82372-9, Pub. by Brit Mus England). State Mutual Bk.

Mardon, D. K. An Illustrated Catalogue of the Rothschild Collection of Fleas, Vol. VI: Pygiopsyllidae. 298p. 1981. 200.00x (ISBN 0-686-82365-6, Pub. by Brit Mus England). State Mutual Bk.

Noonan, Gerald R. Type Specimens in the Insect Collections of the Milwaukee Public Museum. 14p. 1984. 2.75 (ISBN 0-89326-105-X). Milwaukee Pub Mus.

Peterson, Alvah. Entomological Techniques: How to Work with Insects. 10th ed. (Illus.). v, 435p. (Orig.). 1964. text ed. 29.95x (ISBN 0-911836-11-X). Entomological Repr.

INSECTS–CONTROL

see Insect Control

INSECTS–DEVELOPMENT

see also Insects–Metamorphosis; Larvae–Insects

Beermann, W., ed. Biochemical Differentiation in Insect Glands. LC 77-23423. (Results & Problems in Cell Differentiation: Vol. 8). (Illus.). 1977. 51.00 (ISBN 0-387-08286-7). Springer-Verlag.

Chen, P. S. Biochemical Aspects of Insect Development. (Monographs in Developmental Biology: Vol. 3). (Illus.). 1971. 30.75 (ISBN 3-8055-1265-1). S Karger.

Chu, H. F. How to Know the Immature Insects. 2nd ed. (Pictured Key Nature Ser.). 240p. 1983. wire coil write for info. (ISBN 0-697-04806-3); Wm C Brown.

Counce, S. J. & Waddington, C. H., eds. Developmental Systems: Insects. 1973. Vol. 1. 53.00 (ISBN 0-12-193301-6); Vol. 2. 97.50 (ISBN 0-12-193302-4). Acad Pr.

Jermy, T., ed. The Host-Plant in Relation to Insect Behavior & Reproduction. LC 75-37209. 322p. 1976. 42.50x (ISBN 0-306-30909-2, Plenum Pr.). Plenum Pub.

Lawrence, P. A. Insect Development. LC 76-8196. (Royal Entomological Society of London Symposium Ser.). 230p. 1976. 39.95x (ISBN 0-470-15098-X). Halsted Pr.

--Insect Development. LC 76-8196. 230p. 1979. 26.75 (ISBN 0-470-15098-X). Krieger.

Norris, M. J. Factors Affecting the Rate of Sexual Maturation of the Desert Locust (Schistocerca Gregaria Forskal) in the Laboratory. 1957. 40.00x (ISBN 0-85135-024-0, Pub. by Centre Overseas Research). State Mutual Bk.

Steinmann, H. & Zombari, L. An Atlas of Insect Morphology. 2nd ed. (Illus.). 250p. 1984. 33.00 (ISBN 9-6305-3883-0, Pub. by Kaido Hungary). Heyden.

Struble, D. L., et al. Pheromones: Current Research, 2 vols, Vol. 1. 176p. 1974. text ed. 28.50x (ISBN 0-8422-7211-9). Irvington.

Symposium on the Chemistry & Action of Insect Juvenile Hormones, Washington, D. C., 1971. Insect Juvenile Hormones: Chemistry & Action. Menn, Julius J. & Beroza, Morton, eds. 1972. 51.00 (ISBN 0-12-490950-7). Acad Pr.

INSECTS–DISEASES

see also Parasites–Insects

Cantwell, George, ed. Insect Diseases, Vol. 1. LC 73-90772. 326p. 1974. 59.75 (ISBN 0-8247-6117-0). Dekker.

--Insect Diseases, Vol. 2. 312p. 1974. 59.75 (ISBN 0-8247-6118-9). Dekker.

Carter, Walter. Insects in Relation to Plant Disease. 2nd ed. LC 73-4362. pap. 160.00 (ISBN 0-317-28102-X, 2055731). Bks Demand UMI.

Egerton, Frank N., ed. Ecological Studies on Insect Parasitism: An Original Anthology. LC 77-73820. (History of Ecology Ser.). 1978. lib. bdg. 24.50x (ISBN 0-405-10389-1). Ayer Co Pubs.

Laird, M., ed. Tsetse: The Future for Biological Methods in Integrated Control. (Illus.). 220p. 1977. pap. 10.00 (ISBN 0-88936-109-6, IDRC77, IDRC). Unipub.

Maramorosch, Karl, ed. Insect & Plant Viruses: An Atlas. 1978. 65.00 (ISBN 0-12-470275-9). Acad Pr.

Panda, N. Principles of Host-Plant Resistance to Insect Pests. LC 78-59169. (Illus.). 406p. 1980. text ed. 35.00x (ISBN 0-916672-93-X). Allanheld.

Poinar, G. O. & Thomas, G. M., eds. Diagnostic Manual for the Identification of Insect Pathogens. LC 77-15977. (Illus.). 230p. 1978. 22.50x (ISBN 0-306-31097-X, Plenum Pr). Plenum Pub.

Poinar, George O., Jr. & Thomas, Gerald M. Insect Pathogens & Parasites: Laboratory Guide. 408p. 1984. 49.50x (ISBN 0-306-41680-8, Plenum Pr). Plenum Pub.

Steinhaus, Edward A. Disease in a Minor Chord: Being a Semihistorical & Semibiographical Account of a Period in Science When One Could Be Happily Yet Seriously Concerned with the Diseases of Lowly Animals Without Backbones, Especially the Insects. LC 75-4527. 508p. 1975. 20.00x (ISBN 0-8142-0218-7). Ohio St U Pr.

Steinhaus, Edward A., ed. Insect Pathology: An Advanced Treatise, 2 Vols. 1963. 81.00 ea. Vol. 1 (ISBN 0-12-665801-3). Vol. 2 (ISBN 0-12-665802-1). Acad Pr.

INSECTS–EMBRYOLOGY

see Embryology–Insects

INSECTS–EVOLUTION

Ashburner, M., et al, eds. The Genetics of Drosphila, Vol. 3, Pt. A. Carson, H. L. 1981. 86.50 (ISBN 0-12-064945-4). Acad Pr.

Collins, Michael M. Genetics & Ecology of a Hybrid Zone in Hyalophora. LC 83-18019. (Entomology Ser.: Vol. 104). 112p. 1984. lib. bdg. 11.50x (ISBN 0-520-09953-2). U of Cal Pr.

Thornhill, Randy & Alcock, John. The Evolution of Insect Mating Systems. (Illus.). 576p. 1983. text ed. 35.00x (ISBN 0-674-27180-7). Harvard U Pr.

Weismann, August. Studies in the Theory of Descent, 2 vols. in 1. LC 72-1661. Repr. of 1882 ed. 57.50 (ISBN 0-404-08192-4). AMS Pr.

White, M. J., ed. Genetic Mechanisms of Speciation in Insects. LC 74-80531. 196p. 1974. lib. bdg. 26.00 (ISBN 90-277-0477-5, Pub. by Reidel Holland). Kluwer Academic.

INSECTS–EXTERMINATION

see Insect Control

INSECTS–GEOGRAPHICAL DISTRIBUTION

see also Insect Populations

Denno, R. F. & Dingle, H., eds. Insect Life History Patterns: Habitat & Geographic Variation. (Proceedings in Life Sciences Ser.). (Illus.). 225p. 1981. 36.00 (ISBN 0-387-90591-X). Springer-Verlag.

Insects of Eastern Larch, Cedar & Juniper. 99p. 1981. pap. 13.00 (ISBN 0-660-10421-0, SSC151, SSC). Unipub.

Metzler, Eric H. Annotated Checklist & Distribution Maps of the Royal Moths & Giant Silkworm Moths (Lepidoptera: Saturniidae) in Ohio. 1980. 2.50 (ISBN 0-86727-088-8). Ohio Bio Survey.

Powell, Jerry A. & Hogue, Charles L. California Insects. LC 78-62876. (California Natural History Guide Ser.). (Illus.). 1980. 15.95 (ISBN 0-520-03806-1); pap. 7.95 (ISBN 0-520-03782-0). U of Cal Pr.

Schreiber, Harold. Disperal Centres of Sphingidae (Lepidoptera) in the Neotropical Region. (Biogeographica Ser.: No. 10). (Illus.). 1978. lib. bdg. 34.00 (ISBN 90-6193-211-4, Pub. by Junk Pubs. Netherlands). Kluwer Academic.

Wheeler, George M. & Sterling, Keir B., eds. Reports Upon Insects Collected During Geographical & Geological Explorations & Surveys West of the One Hundredth Meridan, During the Years 1872, 1873, & 1874. LC 77-81109. (Biologists & Their World Ser.). (Illus.). 1978. Repr. of 1875 ed. lib. bdg. 22.00x (ISBN 0-405-10693-9). Ayer Co Pubs.

INSECTS–LARVAE

see Larvae–Insects

INSECTS–METAMORPHOSIS

Lubbock, John. On the Origin & Metamorphoses of Insects. 1978. Repr. of 1874 ed. lib. bdg. 20.00 (ISBN 0-8492-1586-2). R West.

Luscher, Martin, ed. Phase & Caste Determination in Insects - Endocrine Aspects: Proceedings of the International Congress of Entomology, 15th, Washington, D.C., 1976. text ed. 30.00 (ISBN 0-08-021256-5). Pergamon.

Tata, J. R. Metamorphosis. Head, J. J., ed. LC 78-52662. (Carolina Biology Readers Ser.). (Illus.). 16p. 1983. pap. 1.60 (ISBN 0-89278-246-3, 45-9646). Carolina Biological.

INSECTS–MIGRATION

Davey, J. T. & Johnston, H. B. The African Migratory Locust (Locusta Migratoria Migratorioides) R & FO in Nigeria. 91p. 1956. 35.00x (ISBN 0-85135-009-7, Pub. by Centre Overseas Research). State Mutual Bk.

Davies, D. E. Seasonal Breeding & Migrations of the Desert Locust (Schistocerca Gregaria Forskal) in North-Eastern Africa & the Middle East. 1952. 35.00x (ISBN 0-85135-010-0, Pub. by Centre Overseas Research). State Mutual Bk.

Fortescue-Foulkes, J. Seasonal Breeding & Migrations of the Desert Locust (Schistocerca Gregaria Forskal) in South-Western Asia. 1953. 35.00x (ISBN 0-85135-015-1, Pub. by Centre Overseas Research). State Mutual Bk.

INSECTS–PARASITES

see Parasites–Insects

INSECTS–PHYSIOLOGY

see also Insects, Effect of Radiation On

Bassler, U. Neural Basis of Elementary Behavior in Stick Insects. Strausfeld, C., tr. (Studies in Brain Function: Vol.10). (Illus.). 180p. 1983. 35.00 (ISBN 0-387-11918-3). Springer-Verlag.

Beament, J. W., et al, eds. Advances in Insect Physiology. Incl. Vol. 2. 1964. 70.00 (ISBN 0-12-024202-8); Vol. 3. 1966. 70.00 (ISBN 0-12-024203-6); Vol. 4. 1967. 75.00 (ISBN 0-12-024204-4); Vol. 5. 1968. 70.00 (ISBN 0-12-024205-2); Vol. 6, 1970. 60.00 (ISBN 0-12-024206-0); Vol. 7. 1970. 85.00 (ISBN 0-12-024207-9); Vol. 8. 1972. 75.00 (ISBN 0-12-024208-7); Vol. 9. Treherne, J. E. & Berridge, M. J., eds. 1972. 77.00 (ISBN 0-12-024209-5); Vol.10. 1974. 75.00 (ISBN 0-12-024210-9); Vol. 11. 1975. 75.00 (ISBN 0-12-024211-7); Vol. 12. 1977. 70.00 (ISBN 0-12-024212-5); Vol. 13. 1978. 75.00 (ISBN 0-12-024213-3). Acad Pr.

Berridge, M., ed. Advances in Insect Physiology, Vol. 18. Date not set. 79.50 (ISBN 0-12-024218-4). Acad Pr.

Berridge, M., et al, eds. Advances in Insect Physiology, Vol. 15. LC 63-14039. (Serial Publication). 1981. 96.00 (ISBN 0-12-024215-X). Acad Pr.

Berridge, M. J., et al. Advances in Insect Physiology, Vol. 17. (Serial Publication Ser.). 1984. 55.00 (ISBN 0-12-024217-6). Acad Pr.

Bhaskaran, Govindan, et al, eds. Current Topics in Insect Endocrinology & Nutrition. LC 80-24274. 368p. 1981. 49.50x (ISBN 0-306-40621-7, Plenum Pr). Plenum Pub.

Blum, M. S. Fundamentals of Insect Physiology. 640p. 40.00 (ISBN 0-471-05468-2). Wiley.

Bodenstein, Dietrich, ed. Milestones in Developmental Physiology of Insects: Papers in Development & Heredity. LC 70-133194. 231p. 1971. 25.00x (ISBN 0-306-50007-8, Plenum Pr). Plenum Pub.

Borkovec, A. B. & Kelly, T. J., eds. Insect Neurochemistry & Neurophysiology. 496p. 1984. 69.50x (ISBN 0-306-41511-9, Plenum Pr). Plenum Pub.

Bradley, T. J. & Miller, T. A., eds. Measurement of Ion Transport & Metabolic Rate in Insects. (Springer Series in Experimental Entomology). (Illus.). 290p. 1984. 41.00 (ISBN 0-387-90855-2). Springer-Verlag.

Bursell, F. Introduction to Insect Physiology. 1971. 55.00 (ISBN 0-12-146650-7). Acad Pr.

Gilmour, D. Biochemistry of Insects. 1961. 56.50 (ISBN 0-12-284050-X). Acad Pr.

Heinrich, Bernd. Insect Thermoregulation. LC 80-19452. 328p. 1981. 47.95 (ISBN 0-471-05144-6, Pub. by Wiley-Interscience). Wiley.

Hoffmann, K. H., ed. Environmental Physiology & Biochemistry of Insects. (Illus.). 280p. 1984. 34.50 (ISBN 0-387-13762-9). Springer-Verlag.

Horridge, G. A., ed. The Compound Eye & Vision of Insects. (Illus.). 1975. 79.00x (ISBN 0-19-857375-8). Oxford U Pr.

Jacobson, Martin. Insect Sex Pheromones. 1972. 71.50 (ISBN 0-12-379350-5). Acad Pr.

Jones, Jack C. The Circulatory System of Insects. (Illus.). 272p. 1977. 31.00x (ISBN 0-398-03636-5). C C Thomas.

Kennedy, J. S., ed. Symposia of the Royal Entomological Society of London: Insect Polymorphism. 115p. 1984. 35.00x (ISBN 0-317-07178-5, Pub. by FW Classey UK). State Mutual Bk.

Kerkut, G. A., ed. Comprehensive Insect Physiology, Biochemistry & Pharmacology, 13 vols. (Illus.). 8536p. 1985. Set. 2750.00 (ISBN 0-08-026850-1). Pergamon.

--Odonata: Vol. 2 - Agriidae & Gomphida. (Illus.). xxiv, 416p. 1977. Repr. of 1934 ed. 30.00 (ISBN 0-88065-087-7, Pub. by Messers Today & Tomorrows Printers & Publishers India). Scholarly Pubns.
--Odonata: Vol. 3 - Cordulegasteridae, Aeshnidae, Labellulidae. (Fauna of British India Ser.). (Illus.). xii, 472p. 1977. Repr. of 1936 ed. 30.00 (ISBN 0-88065-088-5, Pub. by Messers Today & Tomorrows Printers & Publishers India). Scholarly Pubns.
Hampson, G. F. Moths Lepidoptera, Vol. 2. iv, 609p. 30.00 (ISBN 0-88065-100-8, Pub. by Messers Today & Tomorrows Printers & Publishers India). Scholarly Pubns.
--Moths Lepidoptera: Subfam. Focillinae, Deltoidinae, Vol. 3. xxxiii, 546p. 1976. 25.00 (ISBN 0-88065-101-6, Pub. by Messers Today & Tomorrows Printers & Publishers India). Scholarly Pubns.
Kirby, W. F. Orthoptera - Acriidae. (Fauna of British India Ser.). x, 278p. 1973. Repr. of 1914 ed. 12.00 (ISBN 0-88065-147-4, Pub. by Messers Today & Tomorrows Printers & Publishers India). Scholarly Pubns.
Lefroy, H. Maxwell. Indian Insect Life: A Manual of the Insects of the Plains (Tropical India) xii, 786p. 1971. Repr. of 1909 ed. 100.00 (ISBN 0-88065-150-4, Pub. by Messers Today & Tomorrows Printers & Publishers India). Scholarly Pubns.
--Indian Insect Pests. xii, 318p. 1971. Repr. of 1906 ed. 15.00 (ISBN 0-88065-149-0, Pub. by Messers Today & Tomorrows Printers & Publishers India). Scholarly Pubns.
Lepidoptera: Butterflies, Vol. 2. 2nd ed. (Fauna of British India). (Illus.). 510p. 1978. Repr. of 1947 ed. 25.00 (ISBN 0-88065-215-2, Pub. by Messers Today & Tomorrows Printers & Publishers India). Scholarly Pubns.
Morley, C. B. Hymonoptera: Ichueumonidae: 1 Ichneumones Deltoidei, Vol. 3. (Illus.). xxxvi, 536p. 1973. Repr. of 1913 ed. 25.00 (ISBN 0-88065-162-8, Pub. by Messers Today & Tomorrows Printers & Publishers India). Scholarly Pubns.
Moths Lepidoptera, Vol. 4. (Fauna of British India). xxviii, 594p. 1976. 30.00 (ISBN 0-88065-102-4, Pub. by Messers Today & Tomorrows Printers & Publishers India). Scholarly Pubns.
Murthy, V. A. & Ananthakrishnan, T. N. Studies on Indian Chelonethi. (Oriental Insects Monograph: No. 4). 1977. 45.00x (ISBN 0-318-01587-0). Oriental Insects.
Talbot, G. Lepidoptera: Butterflies, Vol. I. 2nd ed. (Fauna of British India). (Illus.). xxx, 612p. 1978. Repr. of 1939 ed. 25.00 (ISBN 0-88065-199-7, Pub. by Messers Today & Tomorrows Printers & Publishers India). Scholarly Pubns.
White, R. S., et al. Diptera: Family Calliphoridae, Vol. 6. (Fauna of British India Ser.). (Illus.). xiv, 294p. 1977. Repr. of 1940 ed. 30.00 (ISBN 0-88065-210-1, Pub. by Messers Today & Tomorrows Printers & Publishers India). Scholarly Pubns.

INSECTS–NORTH AMERICA

Albrecht, Carl W. & Watkins, Reed A. Cross-Reference to Names of Ohio Skippers & Butterflies: Insecta, Lepidoptera, Hesperoidea & Papilionoidea. 1983. 4.00 (ISBN 0-86727-095-0). Ohio Bio Survey.
Arnett, Ross. American Insects: A Handbook of the Insects of America North of Mexico. (Illus.). 850p. 1985. 79.50 (ISBN 0-442-20866-9). Van Nos Reinhold.
Ashmead, W. H., et al. Insects, 2 pts. (Harriman Alaska Expedition, 1899). 1910. Pt. 1. pap. 24.00 (ISBN 0-527-38168-3); Pt. 2. pap. 24.00 (ISBN 0-527-38169-1). Kraus Repr.
Audubon Society & Milne, Lorus. The Audubon Society Field Guide to North American Insects & Spiders. LC 80-7620. (Illus.). 1008p. 1980. 13.50 (ISBN 0-394-50763-0). Knopf.
Bohart, R. M. & Menke, A. S. Sphecid Wasps of the World: A Generic Revision. 1976. 90.00x (ISBN 0-520-02318-8). U of Cal Pr.
Borror, Donald J. & White, Richard E. Field Guide to the Insects of America North of Mexico. (Peterson Field Guide Ser). 1970. 15.95 (ISBN 0-395-07436-3). HM.
--A Field Guide to the Insects of America North of Mexico. LC 70-80420. (Peterson Field Guide Ser.). 1974. pap. 10.95 (ISBN 0-395-18523-8). HM.
Caldwell, John S. The Jumping Plant-Lice of Ohio (Homoptera: Chermidae) 1938. 1.00 (ISBN 0-86727-033-0). Ohio Bio Survey.
Furth, David G. The Stink Bugs of Ohio (Hemiptera: Pentatomidae) 1974. 3.00 (ISBN 0-86727-069-1). Ohio Bio Survey.
Hall, Jack C. A Review of the North & Central American Species of Paravilla Painter (Diptera--Bombyliidae) (U. C. Publications in Entomology Ser.: Vol. 92). 192p. 1981. 15.00x (ISBN 0-520-09625-8). U of Cal Pr.
Hughes, Dave & Hafele, Rick. Western Hatches. (Illus.). 240p. (Orig.). 1981. pap. 18.95 (ISBN 0-936608-12-9). F Amato Pubns.
Johnson, Dorothy M. Leafhoppers of Ohio: Subfamily Typhlocybinae. 1935. 1.50 (ISBN 0-86727-030-6). Ohio Bio Survey.
Kosztarab, Michael. The Armored Scale Insects of Ohio. 1963. 3.50 (ISBN 0-86727-049-7). Ohio Bio Survey.
McCafferty, W. Patrick. Aquatic Entomology: The Fisherman's & Ecologists Illustrated Guide to Insects & Their Relatives. 448p. 1981. write for info. (ISBN 0-86720-000-6); pap. write for info. (ISBN 0-86720-017-0); write for info. Ltd. ed. (ISBN 0-86720-010-3). Jones & Bartlett.
Osborn, Herbert. The Fulgoridae of Ohio. 1938. 1.50 (ISBN 0-86727-034-9). Ohio Bio Survey.
--The Leafhoppers of Ohio. 1928. 2.00 (ISBN 0-86727-013-6). Ohio Bio Survey.
--The Membracidae of Ohio. 1940. 1.00 (ISBN 0-86727-036-5). Ohio Bio Survey.
Osborn, Herbert, et al. Recent Insect Invasions in Ohio. 1948. 1.00 (ISBN 0-86727-039-X). Ohio Bio Survey.
Richardson, John, et al. Fauna Boreali-Americana: Zoology of the Northern Parts of British America, Insecta, Pt. 4. Sterling, Keir B., ed. LC 77-81108. (Biologists & Their World Ser.). 1978. Repr. of 1837 ed. lib. bdg. 32.00x (ISBN 0-405-10692-0). Ayer Co Pubs.
Stone, Alan, et al, eds. A Catalog of the Diptera of America North of Mexico. 2nd printing ed. 1700p. 1983. Repr. of 1965 ed. text ed. 37.50x (ISBN 0-87474-890-9). Smithsonian.
Swan, Lester A. & Papp, Charles S. The Common Insects of North America. LC 75-138765. (Illus.). 752p. 1972. (HarpT); lib. bdg. 13.27i (ISBN 0-06-014179-4). Har-Row.
Watson, S. A. The Miridae of Ohio. 1928. 1.00 (ISBN 0-86727-015-2). Ohio Bio Survey.
West, Robert M. Review of the North American Eocene & Oligocene Apatemyidae (Mammalia: Insectivora) (Special Publications: No. 3). (Illus.). 42p. 1973. pap. 2.00 (ISBN 0-89672-028-4). Tex Tech Pr.
White, Richard E. The Anobiidae of Ohio. 1962. 2.50 (ISBN 0-86727-046-2). Ohio Bio Survey.

INSECTS–PHILIPPINE ISLANDS

Baltazar, Clare R. & Salazar, Nelia P. Philippine Insects: An Introduction. (Illus.). 1980. text ed. 17.00x (ISBN 0-8248-0675-1, Pub. by U of Philippines Pr); pap. text ed. 12.00x (ISBN 0-8248-0676-X). UH Pr.

INSECTS, AQUATIC

Frank, J. H., ed. Phytotelmata: Terrestrial Plants As Hosts of Aquatic Insect Communities. Lounibos, L. P. 304p. 1983. pap. text ed. 24.95 (ISBN 0-937548-05-7). Plexus Pub.
Lehmkuhl, Dennis M. How to Know the Aquatic Insects. (Pictured Key Nature Ser.). 275p. 1979. write for info.; wire coil (ISBN 0-697-04767-9). Wm C Brown.
Merritt, Ricard W. & Cummins, Kenneth W. An Introduction to the Aquatic Insects of North America. 3rd ed. (Illus.). 1983. text ed. 30.95 (ISBN 0-8403-3180-0, 40318001). Kendall-Hunt.
Needham, James G. & Needham, Paul R. Guide to the Study of Freshwater Biology. 5th ed. LC 62-20742. (Illus.). 1962. pap. 8.95x (ISBN 0-8162-6310-8). Holden-Day.
Resh, Vincent H. & Rosenberg, David M., eds. Ecology of Aquatic Insects. LC 83-21199. 638p. 1984. 49.95x (ISBN 0-03-059684-X). Praeger.
Usinger, Robert L., ed. Aquatic Insects of California, with Keys to North American Genera & California Species. (Illus.). 1956. 40.00x (ISBN 0-520-01293-3). U of Cal Pr.

INSECTS, DESTRUCTIVE AND USEFUL

see Insects, Injurious and Beneficial

INSECTS, EFFECT OF RADIATION ON

see also Insects–Physiology; Radiation–Physiological Effect

Isotopes & Radiation in Entomology. (Proceedings Ser.). (Eng., Fr., Rus. & Span., Illus.). 428p. (Orig.). 1968. pap. 30.75 (ISBN 92-0-010168-2, ISP166, IAEA). Unipub.
Radiation & Radioisotopes Applied to Insects of Agricultural Importance. (Proceedings Ser.). (Illus.). 508p. 1963. 25.25 (ISBN 92-0-010263-8, ISP74, IAEA). Unipub.
Sterility Principle For Insect Control Or Eradication 1970. (Proceedings Ser.). 1970. pap. 38.50 (ISBN 92-0-010171-2, ISP265, IAEA). Unipub.

INSECTS, FOSSIL

Bolton, H. The Insects of the British Coal Measures, Pts. 1-2. Repr. of 1922 ed. Set. 28.00 (ISBN 0-384-04980-X). Johnson Repr.
Kenward, H. K. The Analysis of Archaeological Insect Assemblages: A New Approach. (Archaeology of York-Principles & Methods Ser.: Vol. 19). 68p. 1978. pap. text ed. 15.45x (ISBN 0-900312-73-4, Pub. by Coun Brit Archaeology). Humanities.

INSECTS, INJURIOUS AND BENEFICIAL

see also Agricultural Pests; Galls (Botany); Household Pests; Insect Control; Insect-Plant Relationships; Insecticides; Insects As Carriers of Disease; Plants–Disease and Pest Resistance also subdivision Diseases and Pests under names of Crops, Plants, Trees, etc. e.g. Fruit–Diseases and Pests; also specific names of insect pests

Cavalloro, R., ed. Aphid Antagonists: Proceedings of a Meeting of the EC Experts' Group, Portici, Nov. 23-24, 1982. 152p. 1983. lib. bdg. 20.00 (ISBN 90-6191-505-8, Pub. by Balkema RSA). IPS.
Chandler, Asa C. & Read, C. P. Introduction to Parasitology: With Special References to the Parasites of Man. 10th ed. LC 61-5670. 822p. 1961. 45.45x (ISBN 0-471-14487-8). Wiley.
Dethier, V. G. Man's Plague? Insects & Agriculture. LC 75-15216. (Illus.). 237p. (Orig.). 1976. 9.95 (ISBN 0-87850-026-X). Darwin Pr.
FAO-WHO Meeting on Insect Viruses. Geneva, 1972. Use of Viruses for the Control of Insect Pests & Disease Vectors: Report. (Technical Report Ser.: No. 531). (Also avail. in French & Spanish). 1973. pap. 1.60 (ISBN 92-4-120531-8). World Health.
Fenemore, Peter G. Plant Pests & Their Control. (Illus.). 292p. 1983. pap. text ed. 29.95 (ISBN 0-409-60087-3). Butterworth.
Harris, Thaddeus W. Report on the Insects of Massachusetts Injurious to Vegetation. LC 70-125746. (American Environmental Studies). 1970. Repr. of 1841 ed. 27.00 (ISBN 0-405-02671-4). Ayer Co Pubs.
Insects of Eastern Spruces, Fir & Hemlock. 1979. pap. 9.00 (ISBN 0-660-01594-3, SSC130, SSC). Unipub.
Leftwich, A. W. A Dictionary of Entomology. LC 75-27143. 364p. 1976. 32.50x (ISBN 0-8448-0820-2). Crane-Russak Co.
Metcalf, Clell L., et al. Destructive & Useful Insects. 4th ed. (Agricultural Sciences Ser.). 1962. text ed. 62.95 (ISBN 0-07-041658-3). McGraw.
Nault, L. R. & Rodriguez, J. G. The Leafhoppers & Planthoppers. 576p. 1985. 50.00 (ISBN 0-471-80611-0). Wiley.
Novak, Vladimir, et al, eds. Atlas of Insects Harmful to Forest Trees. (Illus.). 126p. 1977. 85.00 (ISBN 0-444-99874-8). Elsevier.
Osborn, Herbert, et al. Recent Insect Invasions in Ohio. 1948. 1.00 (ISBN 0-86727-039-X). Ohio Bio Survey.
Panda, N. Principles of Host-Plant Resistance to Insect Pests. LC 78-59169. (Illus.). 406p. 1980. text ed. 35.00x (ISBN 0-916672-93-X). Allanheld.
Papp, Charles S. & Swan, Lester A. Ouch! A Guide to Biting & Stinging Insects & Other Arthropods. 2nd, rev. ed. (Illus.). 212p. (Orig.). 1983. pap. 8.95 (ISBN 0-9608404-0-0). Entomography.
Pyenson, Louis L. Fundamentals of Entomology & Plant Pathology. 2nd ed. (Illus.). 1980. text ed. 26.50 (ISBN 0-87055-334-8). AVI.
Riley, Charles V. Nine Annual Reports on the Noxious, Beneficial & Other Insects of the State of Missouri, 1869-1877: With a General Index & Supplement, 10 vols. in three. Sterling, Keir B., ed. LC 77-81105. (Biologists & Their World Ser.). 1978. Repr. of 1881 ed. lib. bdg. 132.50x (ISBN 0-405-10745-5). Ayer Co Pubs.
The Use of Viruses for the Control on Insect Pests & Disease Vectors. (Agricultural Planning Studies: No. 91). 48p. (Orig.). 1974. pap. 4.50 (ISBN 0-685-40246-0, F490, FAO). Unipub.
Vector Control. (WHO Bulletin Supplement: Vol. 29). (Also avail. in French). 1963. pap. 4.80 (ISBN 92-4-068291-0). World Health.
Westcott, Cynthia. The Gardener's Bug Book. LC 72-89822. 720p. 1973. 19.95 (ISBN 0-385-01525-9). Doubleday.
Williams, R. E., et al. Livestock Entomology. 336p. 1985. 41.95 (ISBN 0-471-81064-9). Wiley.
Wilson, M. C. & Schuder, D. L. Practical Insect Pest Management: Insects of Ornamental Plants, No. 4. 2nd ed. LC 85-50792. (Illus.). 150p. 1982. pap. text ed. 7.95x (ISBN 0-917974-93-X). Waveland Pr.
Zak, Bill. Critters: Common Household & Garden Pests of Texas. 256p. 1984. 15.95 (ISBN 0-87833-384-3). Taylor Pub.

INSECTS, INJURIOUS AND BENEFICIAL–BIOLOGICAL CONTROL

see Insect Control–Biological Control

INSECTS, INJURIOUS AND BENEFICIAL–CONTROL

see Insect Control

INSECTS, INJURIOUS AND BENEFICIAL–EXTERMINATION

see Insect Control

INSECTS, SOCIAL

see Insect Societies

INSECTS AS CARRIERS OF DISEASE

see also Mosquitoes; Tsetse-Flies; Virus Diseases of Plants

Brewer, J. W., et al. Readings in Insect-Plant Disease Relationships. new ed. LC 72-10029. (Illus.). 1973. pap. text ed. 13.25x (ISBN 0-8422-0264-1). Irvington.
Furman, Deane P. & Catts, Paul E. Manual of Medical Entomology. 4th ed. LC 81-10105. (Illus.). 224p. 1982. pap. 13.95 (ISBN 0-521-29920-9). Cambridge U Pr.
Kettle, D. S. Medical & Veterinary Entomology. 658p. 1984. 39.95. Wiley.
Orkin & Maibach. Cutaneous Infestations & Insect Bites. LC 84-22977. (Dermatology Ser.). 304p. 1985. 75.00 (ISBN 0-8247-7273-3). Dekker.
Vector Control in International Health. 144p. 1972. pap. 12.80 (ISBN 92-4-154016-8, 930). World Health.
Weber, Walter J. Fleas, Ticks & Cockroaches-Disease Transmitters. 70p. 1984. pap. 10.00 (ISBN 0-913702-27-7). Thomson Pub CA.
WHO Scientific Group. Geneva, 1972. Vector Ecology: Report. (Technical Report Ser.: No. 501). (Also avail. in French & Spanish). 1972. pap. 1.60 (ISBN 92-4-120501-6). World Health.

INSECTS AS CARRIERS OF DISEASE–CONTROL

see Insect Control

INSEMINATION, ARTIFICIAL

see Artificial Insemination

INSTINCT

see also Animal Intelligence

Ardrey, Robert. The Territorial Imperative: A Personal Inquiry into the Animal Origins of Property & Nations. LC 66-23572. (Illus.). 1966. 10.95 (ISBN 0-689-10015-9). Atheneum.
Darwin, Charles. Expression of the Emotions in Man & Animals. LC 65-17286. (Illus.). 1965. pap. 9.00x (ISBN 0-226-13656-6, P526, Phoen). U of Chicago Pr.
Darwin, Charles R. Expression of the Emotions in Man & Animals. Repr. of 1897 ed. 42.50 (ISBN 0-404-08410-9). AMS Pr.
--Expression of the Emotions in Man & Animals. LC 73-90703. Repr. of 1955 ed. lib. bdg. 22.50x (ISBN 0-8371-2291-0, DAEM). Greenwood.
Heller, Agnes. On Instincts. Fenyo, M., tr. from Hungarian. (Dialectic & Society: No. 5). 1979. pap. text ed. 11.00x (ISBN 90-232-1705-5). Humanities.
Menninger, Karl A. Love Against Hate. LC 42-50183. 1959. pap. 5.95 (ISBN 0-15-653892-X, Harv). HarBraceJ.
Romanes, George J. Mental Evolution in Animals: With a Posthumous Essay on Instinct by Charles Darwin. LC 71-96472. Repr. of 1884 ed. 28.00 (ISBN 0-404-05389-0). AMS Pr.
Schiller, Claire H., ed. Instinctive Behavior: The Development of a Modern Concept. LC 57-10590. (Illus.). 328p. 1964. text ed. 30.00 (ISBN 0-8236-2880-9); pap. text ed. 11.95 (ISBN 0-8236-8084-3, 22880). Intl Univs Pr.

INSTRUMENT FLYING

Campbell, Ron. Flying Training for the Private Pilot Licence: Instrument Flying, Radio Navigation & Instrument Approach Procedure. 1981. Instructor Manual, 308pp. pap. 18.00x (ISBN 0-246-11695-1, Pub. by Granada England); Student Manual, 200pp. pap. 18.00x (ISBN 0-246-11697-8). Sheridan.
Culver, Henry H., Jr. IFR Pocket Simulator Procedures. 3rd ed. LC 76-27149. (Illus.). 1982. spiral bdg. 19.95 (ISBN 0-9601062-1-9, Pub. by FIP). Aviation.
Instrument-Pilot-Airplane Flight Test Guide. (Pilot Training Ser.). 23p. 1976. pap. text ed. 3.75 (ISBN 0-89100-173-5, EA-AC61-56A). Aviation Maintenance.
Middlekauf, Dana & Horowitz, Milton. Instrument Rating Question Book Including Answers, Explanations, & References. rev. ed. (Pilot Training Ser.). 450p. 1984. pap. text ed. 12.95 (ISBN 0-89100-267-7, EA-FAA-T-8080-7C). Aviation Maintenance.
Professional Instrument Courses, Inc. & Dogan, Peter. Instrument Flight Training Manual. (Illus.). 208p. 1985. pap. 16.95t (ISBN 0-916413-02-0). Aviation.
Reithmaier, L. W. Instrument Pilot's Guide. 2nd ed. LC 74-30480. (Illus.). 206p. 1974. pap. 10.95 (ISBN 0-8168-7305-4). Aero.

INSTRUMENT INDUSTRY

see also Scientific Apparatus and Instruments

Curtis, Tony, ed. Instruments. (Illus.). 1978. 2.00 (ISBN 0-902921-39-8). Apollo.
Job Titles & Skills Used in the Instrumentation & Process Control Industries. LC 81-86194. 40p. 1981. pap. text ed. 10.00 (ISBN 0-87664-661-5). Instru Soc.
Liptak, Bela G., ed. Instrument Engineers Handbook: Process Control. rev. ed. LC 83-43297. 1136p. 1985. 75.00 (ISBN 0-8019-7290-6). Chilton.
Market Intelligence Research Company Staff. Analytical Instrument World Markets, 1980-1990. pap. text ed. 695.00x (ISBN 0-317-19558-1). Market Res Co.

INSTRUMENT MANUFACTURE

Instrument Fitting. 1982. 50.00x (ISBN 0-85083-069-9, Pub. by Engineering Ind). State Mutual Bk.

Trade & Technical Pr. Ltd., ed. Handbook of Instruments & Instrumentation. 650p. 1981. 169.00x (ISBN 0-85461-064-2, Pub. by Trade & Tech). State Mutual Bk.

INSTRUMENTAL ANALYSIS

Bastiansen, William. Instrumental Analysis. 1979. pap. text ed. 8.50 (ISBN 0-89669-016-4). Collegium Bk Pubs.

Bauer, Henry H., et al. Instrumental Analysis. 1978. text ed. 45.00 (ISBN 0-205-05922-8, 685922). Allyn.

Gouw, T. H. Guide to Modern Methods of Instrumental Analysis. LC 79-171913. 510p. 1972. 38.00 (ISBN 0-471-31925-2). Krieger.

Huskins, D. J. Quality Measuring Instruments in On-Line Process Analysis. 455p. 1982. 119.00x (ISBN 0-470-27521-9). Halsted Pr.

Robinson. Undergraduate Instrumental Analysis. 3rd ed. 456p. 1982. 28.75 (ISBN 0-8247-1530-6). Dekker.

--Undergraduate Instrumental Analysis. 4th, rev. & enl. ed. 1986. price not set (ISBN 0-8247-7406-X). Dekker.

Skoog, Douglas A. & West, Donald M. Principles of Instrumental Analysis. 3rd ed. 1985. text ed. 40.95x (ISBN 0-03-001229-5, CBS C); solns. manual 11.95 (ISBN 0-03-001232-5). SCP.

Strobel, H. A. Chemical Instrumentation. 2nd ed. 1973. 38.95 (ISBN 0-201-07301-3). Addison-Wesley.

Walton, Harold F. & Reyes, Jorge. Modern Chemical Analysis & Instrumentation. (Undergraduate Chemistry Ser.: Vol. 2). 368p. 1973. 34.75 (ISBN 0-8247-6033-6). Dekker.

Welcher, Frank J., ed. Standard Methods of Chemical Analysis: Instrumental Methods, Vol. IIIA. 6th ed. LC 74-23465. 996p. 1975. Repr. of 1966 ed. 70.00 (ISBN 0-88275-342-8). Krieger.

--Standard Methods of Chemical Analysis: Vol. IIIB, Instrumental Methods. 6th ed. LC 74-23465. 1060p. 1975. Repr. of 1966 ed. 74.00 (ISBN 0-88275-253-7). Krieger.

Willard. Instrumental Methods Analysis. 6th ed. write for info. Watts.

INSTRUMENTS, AERONAUTICAL
see Aeronautical Instruments

INSTRUMENTS, ASTRONOMICAL
see Astronomical Instruments

INSTRUMENTS, ELECTRIC
see Electric Apparatus and Appliances

INSTRUMENTS, ELECTRONIC
see Electronic Instruments

INSTRUMENTS, ENGINEERING
see Engineering Instruments

INSTRUMENTS, MATHEMATICAL
see Mathematical Instruments

INSTRUMENTS, MEASURING
see Measuring Instruments

INSTRUMENTS, METEOROLOGICAL
see Meteorological Instruments

INSTRUMENTS, NAUTICAL
see Nautical Instruments

INSTRUMENTS, OCEANOGRAPHIC
see Oceanographic Instruments

INSTRUMENTS, OPTICAL
see Optical Instruments

INSTRUMENTS, PHYSICAL
see Physical Instruments

INSTRUMENTS, SCIENTIFIC
see Scientific Apparatus and Instruments

INSTRUMENTS, SURVEYING
see Surveying–Instruments

INSTRUMENTS OF WAR
see Munitions

INSULAR FLORA AND FAUNA
see Island Flora and Fauna

INSULATING MATERIALS
see also Electric Insulators and Insulation

Business Communications Staff. Substitutes for Asbestos: What-Who-How Much. 1981. 850.00 (ISBN 0-89336-277-8, GB-061). BCC.

Clark, Frank M. Insulating Materials for Design & Engineering Practice. LC 62-17460. pap. 160.00 (ISBN 0-317-10029-7, 2051339). Bks Demand UMI.

Govan, F. A., et al, eds. Thermal Insulations Materials, & Systems for Energy Conservation in the '80s - STP 789. LC 82-70616. 890p. 1983. text ed. 68.00 (ISBN 0-8031-0230-5, 04-789000-10). ASTM.

Hess, L. Y., ed. Insulation Guide for Buildings & Industrial Processes. LC 79-84430. (Energy Technology Review Ser.: No. 43). (Illus.). 1979. 24.00 (ISBN 0-8155-0752-6). Noyes.

Insulation - Materials & Processes for Aerospace & Hydrospace Applications: Proceedings, Symposium, San Francisco, 25-28 May 1965. (Science of Advanced Materials & Process Engineering Ser., Vol. 8). pap. 8.00 (ISBN 0-938994-08-5). Soc Adv Material.

Mott, Nevill. Metal-Insulator Transitions. 294p. 1974. 33.00x (ISBN 0-85066-079-3). Taylor & Francis.

NAHB Research Foundation. Insulation Manual: Homes & Apartments. 2nd. ed. 149p. 1979. pap. 13.50 (ISBN 0-86718-061-7); pap. 10.00 members. Natl Assn Home.

Shepherd, James M. Super Insulation. (Illus.). 36p. 1983. pap. 3.95 (ISBN 0-9607308-1-8). Shepherd Pubs VA.

Society of Plastics Engineers. New Thermoset Developments for Wire & Cable Insulation: Regional Technical Conference, Society of Plastics Engineers, June 19-20,1979. pap. 37.00 (ISBN 0-317-08159-4, 2011386). Bks Demand UMI.

INSULATION (ELECTRIC)
see Electric Insulators and Insulation

INSULATION (HEAT)

American Society for Testing & Materials. Thermal Transmission Measurements of Insulation - STP 660. 458p. 1979. 39.50x (ISBN 0-8031-0589-4, 04-660000-10). ASTM.

Bauer, Paul E. & Collicott, Howard E. Entry Vehicle Heating & Thermal Protection Systems: Space Shuttle, Solar Starprobe, Jupiter Galileo Probe. 45.00 (ISBN 0-915928-74-4). AIAA.

Booth, Don, et al. Sun-Earth Buffering & Superinsulation. Wolf, Ray, ed. (Illus.). 232p. 1984. pap. 12.95 (ISBN 0-9604422-3-5). Rodale Pr Inc.

Burberry, Peter. Building for Energy Conservation. LC 77-17943. 60p. 1978. 24.95x (ISBN 0-470-99350-2). Halsted Pr.

Business Communications Staff. Insulation: A Resurging Business: E-035. 1981. 750.00 (ISBN 0-89336-293-X). BCC.

Croy, D. E. & Dougherty, D. A. Handbook of Thermal Insulation Applications. LC 83-22118. (Energy Technology Review Ser.: No.89). (Illus.). 392p. 1984. 45.00 (ISBN 0-8155-0968-5). Noyes.

Derricott, Robert & Chissick, Seymour. Energy Conservation & Thermal Insulation: Properties of Materials. LC 80-41587. (Safety & Environmental Factors Ser.). 785p. 1981. 100.00x (ISBN 0-471-27930-7, Pub. by Wiley-Interscience). Wiley.

Hardenbrook, Harry. Walker's Insulation Techniques & Estimating Handbook. (Illus.). 128p. pap. 12.95 (ISBN 0-911592-51-2, ScribT). Scribner.

Harrison, Michael R. Thermal Insulation. Gyftopoulos, Elias P. & Cohen, Karen C., eds. (Industrial Energy-Conservation Manuals: No. 11). 112p. 1982. loose-leaf 20.00x (ISBN 0-262-08112-1). MIT Pr.

Heat Transmission Measurements in Thermal Insulations, STP 544. 319p. 1974. 30.75 (ISBN 0-8031-0372-7, 04-544000-10). ASTM.

Hilado, Carlos J. Flammability Handbook for Thermal Insulation. LC 83-50455. 128p. 1983. 40.00 (ISBN 0-87762-329-5). Technomic.

Insulation Specifications, Vol. 2. (Research Report Ser.). 54p. 1981. pap. 5.50 (ISBN 0-86718-115-X); pap. 4.00 members. Natl Assn Home.

Jones, R. Framing, Sheathing & Insulation. LC 73-1847. 227p. 1973. pap. 12.40 (ISBN 0-8273-0096-4); answer book 3.00 (ISBN 0-8273-0097-2). Delmar.

Kovach, E. G., ed. Thermal Energy Storage. LC 77-71233. 1977. pap. text ed. 11.25 (ISBN 0-08-021724-9). Pergamon.

McElroy & Tye, eds. Thermal Insulation Performance - STP 718. 566p. 1980. 43.00 (ISBN 0-8031-0794-3, 04-718000-10). ASTM.

McGrath, Ed. The Superinsulated House: A Working Guide for Owner-Builders & Architects. (Illus.). 128p. 1982. pap. 11.95 (ISBN 0-918270-12-X). That New Pub.

Makram-Ebeid, S. & Tuck, B., eds. Semi-Insulating Three-Four Materials: Evian 1982. 420p. 1982. text ed. 62.95x (ISBN 0-906812-22-4, Pub. by Shiva Pub Ltd.). Birkhauser.

Midwest Plan Service Staff. Insulation & Heat Loss. rev. ed. (Illus.). 12p. 1985. 1.50 (ISBN 0-89373-065-3, AED-13). Midwest Plan Serv.

Nielsen, Sally E., ed. Insulating the Old House: A Handbook for the Owner. (Illus.). 1979. pap. 1.95 (ISBN 0-9600612-7-4). Greater Portland.

Probert, S. D. Thermal Insulation. (Illus.). 121p. 1968. 26.00 (ISBN 0-444-20025-8, Pub. by Elsevier Applied Sci England). Elsevier.

Probert, S. D. & Hub, D. R., eds. Thermal Insulation. (Illus.). 1968. text ed. 26.00x (Pub. by Applied Science). Burgess-Intl Ideas.

Schwartz, Kenneth J. Effects of Thermal Insulation on Fire Resistive Assemblies. 1981. 4.00 (ISBN 0-686-31892-7, TR 81-7). Society Fire Protect.

Shurcliff, William. Superinsulated Houses. (Illus.). 100p. 1982. pap. 7.95 (ISBN 0-931790-25-5). Brick Hse Pub.

Sunset Editors. Insulation & Weatherstripping. LC 77-90718. (Illus.). 80p. 1978. pap. 3.95 (ISBN 0-376-01262-5, Sunset Bks). Sunset-Lane.

Turner, William C. & Malloy, John F. Handbook of Thermal Insulation Design Economics for Pipes & Equipment. LC 77-10997. 376p. 1980. lib. bdg. 59.50 (ISBN 0-88275-837-3). Krieger.

--Thermal Insulation Handbook. LC 76-52962. 640p. 1981. lib. bdg. 69.50 (ISBN 0-88275-510-2). Krieger.

--Thermal Insulation Handbook. 624p. 1981. 72.50 (ISBN 0-07-039805-4). McGraw.

Turner, William C., III & Turner, William C., IV. Thermal Insulation for Residences & Buildings: Economic Design for Comfort & Safety in Homes & Buildings. LC 82-16232. 1985. price not set (ISBN 0-88275-985-X). Krieger.

United States Department of Housing & Urban Development. How to Insulate Your Home & Save Fuel. 11.75 (ISBN 0-8446-5619-4). Peter Smith.

INSULATION (SOUND)
see Soundproofing

INSURANCE–DATA PROCESSING

Anderson, Ronald T. Automating Your Agency Book. LC 82-60877. 288p. 1982. text ed. 16.35 (ISBN 0-87218-321-1). Natl Underwriter.

Cissley, Charles H. Systems & Data Processing in Insurance Companies. rev. ed. LC 82-80670. (FLMI Insurance Education Program Ser.). 287p. 1982. text ed. 12.00 (ISBN 0-915322-55-2); pap. 5.00 wkbk. (ISBN 0-915322-56-0); student guide avail. LOMA.

Computer Strategies. The Insurance Agency Computer Handbook. 150p. 1983. looseleaf 45.00x (ISBN 0-913505-11-0). Computer Strat.

Curran, Susan. New Technology & Insurance. 1981. 50.00x (ISBN 0-686-97106-X, Pub. by Fourmat England). State Mutual Bk.

Gantt, Michael D. & Gatza, James. Computers in Insurance. LC 80-67525. 150p. 1980. pap. 8.00 (ISBN 0-89463-029-6). Am Inst Property.

Insurance Company Automation (U. S.) 1985. write for info. (ISBN 0-86621-150-0). Frost & Sullivan.

Insurance Computer Application Software Market. 219p. 1984. 1550.00 (ISBN 0-86621-055-5, A1035). Frost & Sullivan.

Insurance-SOFTWHERE. Halligan, Joseph. (SOFTWHERE Software Directories Ser.: Vol. 1). (Orig.). 1984. pap. 29.95 (ISBN 0-918451-50-7). Moore Data.

International Computer Programs Staff. ICP Software Directory, Vol. 4: Banking, Insurance & Finance Systems. Hamilton, Dennis, ed. 1985. pap. 95.00 (ISBN 0-88094-045-X). Intl Computer.

McClung, Christina J. & Guerrieri, John A. Microcomputers for Insurance Professionals. LC 83-5761. (1-999). 127p. 1984. pap. 14.95 (ISBN 0-471-89721-3, Pub by Wiley Pr). Wiley.

Matthews, et al. Palmetto Insurance Company: A Computerized Office Simulation. 1984. 6.20 (ISBN 0-538-26700-3, Z70). SW Pub.

Readings for the Information Systems Specialty. (FLMI Insurance Education Program Ser.). 186p. 1980. pap. text ed. 10.00 (ISBN 0-915322-39-0). LOMA.

INSURANCE–MATHEMATICS

Beard, E., et al. Risk Theory: The Stochastic Basis of Insurance. 2nd ed. (Monographs on Applied Probability & Statistics). 1977. 17.50x (ISBN 0-412-15100-6, NO.6031, Pub. by Chapman & Hall). Methuen Inc.

Hogg, Robert V. & Klugman, Stuart A. Loss Distributions. LC 83-19663. (Probability & Mathematical Statistics-Applied Probability & Statistics Ser.: 1-346). 235p. 1984. 29.95x (ISBN 0-471-87929-0, 1-346, Pub. by Wiley-Interscience). Wiley.

Rudman, Jack. Actuary. (Career Examination Ser.: C-7). (Cloth bdg. avail. on request). pap. 12.00 (ISBN 0-8373-0007-X). Natl Learning.

--Assistant Actuary. (Career Examination Ser.: C-22). (Cloth bdg. avail. on request). pap. 12.00 (ISBN 0-8373-0022-3). Natl Learning.

Society of Actuaries. Transactions of the Society of Actuaries. Vol. XXXIII. 40.00 (ISBN 0-318-01767-9); Vol. XXXIV. 40.00 (ISBN 0-318-01768-7). Soc Actuaries.

INTEGER PROGRAMMING
see also Programming (Electronic Computers)

Conley, William. Computer Optimization Techniques. 1980. 25.00 (ISBN 0-89433-111-6). Petrocelli.

Garfinkel, Robert & Nemhauser, George L. Integer Programming. LC 72-3881. (Decision & Control Ser.). 528p. 1972. 46.95x (ISBN 0-471-29195-1, Pub. by Wiley-Interscience). Wiley.

Glover, Fred. A Fresh Look at Heuristic Principles for Integer Progamming. 1977. 2.50 (ISBN 0-686-64187-6). U CO Busn Res Div.

Greenberg, Harold. Integer Programming. (Mathematics in Science & Engineering Ser.: Vol. 76). 1971. 47.50 (ISBN 0-12-299450-7). Acad Pr.

Institute of Operations Research, Sponsored by IBM, University of Bonn, Germany, Sept. 8-12, 1975. Studies in Integer Programming: Proceedings of a Workshop Held in Bonn. Hammer, P. L., ed. (Annals of Discrete Mathematics: Vol. 1). 562p. 1977. 95.75 (ISBN 0-7204-0765-6, North-Holland). Elsevier.

Johnson, E. L. Integer Programming. LC 79-93152. (CBMS-NSF Regional Conference Ser.: No. 32). vii, 68p. 1980. pap. text ed. 11.00 (ISBN 0-89871-162-2). Soc Indus-Appl Math.

Kastning, C., ed. Integer Programming & Related Areas. (Lecture Notes in Economics & Mathematical Systems: Vol. 128). 1976. soft cover 24.00 (ISBN 0-387-07788-X). Springer-Verlag.

NATO Advanced Study Institute, Versailles, France, September 2-13, 1974. Combinatorial Programming: Methods & Application, Proceedings. Roy, B., ed. (NATO Advanced Study Institutes: No. C19). 386p. 1975. 47.50 (ISBN 9-0277-0506-2, Pub. by Reidel Holland). Kluwer Academic.

Nauss, Robert M. Parametric Integer Programming. LC 77-20207. 144p. 1978. text ed. 19.00x (ISBN 0-8262-0250-0). U of Mo Pr.

Taha, Hamdy A. Integer Programming Theory. 1975. 55.00 (ISBN 0-12-682150-X). Acad Pr.

Von Randow, R., ed. Integer Programming & Related Areas: A Classified Bibliography 1978-1981. (Lecture Notes in Economics & Mathematical Systems Ser.: Vol. 197). 338p. 1982. pap. 29.00 (ISBN 0-387-11203-0). Springer-Verlag.

--Integer Programming & Related Areas. (Lecture Notes in Economics & Mathematical Systems: Vol. 243). 408p. 1985. pap. 29.20 (ISBN 0-387-15226-1). Springer-Verlag.

INTEGRAL CALCULUS
see Calculus, Integral

INTEGRAL EQUATIONS
see also Calculus, Operational; Functional Analysis; Integral Transforms

Advances in Differential & Integral Equations: Studies in Applied Mathematics 5. Nohel, John S., ed. xvi, 207p. 1969. text ed. 16.50 (ISBN 0-89871-037-5). Soc Indus-Appl Math.

Ahiezer, N. I., et al. Fifteen Papers on Real & Complex Functions, Series, Differential & Integral Equations. LC 51-5559. (Translations Ser.: No. 2, Vol. 86). 1970. 34.00 (ISBN 0-8218-1786-8, TRANS 2-86). Am Math.

Albrecht, Julius & Collatz, Lothar, eds. Numerical Treatment of Integral Equations. (International Ser. of Numerical Mathematics Ser.: No. 53). 283p. 1981. pap. 38.95x (ISBN 0-8176-1105-3). Birkhauser.

Anderson, R. S. & De Hoog, F. R., eds. Application & Numberical Solution of Intergral Equations. (Mechanics Analysis Ser.: No. 6). 265p. 1980. 27.50x (ISBN 90-286-0450-2). Sijthoff & Noordhoff.

Anselone, P. M. Nonlinear Integral Equations. LC 64-17771. (U. S. Army Mathematics Research Center Publication Ser.: No. 11). pap. 97.50 (ISBN 0-317-08601-4, 2010205). Bks Demand UMI.

Atkinson, Kendall E. A Survey of Numerical Methods for the Solution of Fredholm Integral Equations of the Second Kind. LC 75-28900. vii, 230p. (Orig.). 1976. pap. text ed. 27.00 (ISBN 0-89871-034-0). Soc Indus-Appl Math.

Baker, Christopher T. The Numerical Treatment of Integral Equations. (Monographs on Numerical Analysis). (Illus.). 1977. text ed. 69.00x (ISBN 0-19-853406-X). Oxford U Pr.

Bart, H., et al. Minimal Factorization of Matrix & Operator Functions. (Operator Theory: Advances & Applications Ser.: No. 1). 236p. 1979. pap. 20.95x (ISBN 0-8176-1139-8). Birkhauser.

Corduneanu, Constantin. Principles of Differential & Integral Equations. 2nd ed. LC 77-2962. 1977. text ed. 14.95 (ISBN 0-8284-0295-7). Chelsea Pub.

Delves, L. M. & Mohamed, J. L. Computational Methods for Integral Equations. 350p. Date not set. price not set (ISBN 0-521-26629-7). Cambridge U Pr.

Delves, L. M. & Walsh, J., eds. Numerical Solution of Integral Equations. (Illus.). 1974. 39.95x (ISBN 0-19-853342-X). Oxford U Pr.

Deuflhard, Peter & Hairer, Ernst. Workshop on Numerical Treatment of Inverse Problems in Differential & Integral Equations. (Progress in Scientific Computing: Vol. 2). 372p. 1983. 27.50x (ISBN 0-8176-3125-9). Birkhauser.

Gohberg, I. C. & Fel'dman, I. A. Convolution Equations & Projection Methods for Their Solution. LC 73-22275. (Translations of Mathematical Monographs: Vol. 41). 262p. 1974. 56.00 (ISBN 0-8218-1591-1, MMONO-41). Am Math.

Goldberg, M. A., ed. Solution Methods for Integral Equations. LC 79-17900. (Mathematical Concepts & Methods in Science & Engineering Ser.: Vol. 18). 360p. 1979. 42.50x (ISBN 0-306-40254-8, Plenum Pr). Plenum Pub.

Graef, John R. Stability of Dynamical Systems: Theory & Application. (Lecture Notes in Pure & Applied Mathematics: Vol. 28). 1977. 55.00 (ISBN 0-8247-6410-2). Dekker.

Groetsch, C. W. The Theory of Tikhonov Regularization for Fredholm Equations of the First Kind. (Research Notes in Mathematics Ser.: No. 105). 128p. 1984. pap. text ed. 16.95 (ISBN 0-273-08642-1). Pitman Pub MA.

Hermann, R. Topics in the Geometric Theory of Integrable Systems. (Interdisciplinary Mathematics Ser.: Vol. XXIII). 347p. 1984. 65.00 (ISBN 0-915692-36-8, 991600169). Math Sci Pr.

Hochstadt, Harry. Integral Equations. LC 73-4230. (Pure & Applied Mathematics Ser.). 282p. 1973. 44.95x (ISBN 0-471-40165-X, Pub. by Wiley-Interscience). Wiley.

Hoheisel, Guido. Integral Equations. Tropper, A. Mary, tr. LC 68-15581. 1968. 8.50 (ISBN 0-8044-4405-6). Ungar.

Jerri. Introduction to Integral Equations with Applications. (Pure & Applied Mathematics Ser.). 384p. 1985. 39.75 (ISBN 0-8247-7293-8). Dekker.

Kanwal, Ram P. Linear Integral Equations: Theory & Techniques. 1971. 67.50 (ISBN 0-12-396550-0). Acad Pr.

Lakshmikantham, V. & Leela, S. Differential & Integral Inequalities: Theory & Application, 2 vols. Incl. Vol. 1. Ordinary Differential Equations. 1969. 80.00 (ISBN 0-12-434101-2); Vol. 2. Functional, Partial, Abstract & Complex Differential Equations. 80.00 (ISBN 0-12-434102-0). LC 68-8425. (Mathematics in Science & Engineering Ser.: Vol. 55). 1969. Acad Pr.

LaSalle, J. P. The Stability of Dynamical Systems. (CBMS-NSF Regional Conference Ser.: No. 25). v, 76p. (Orig.). 1976. pap. text ed. 14.00 (ISBN 0-89871-022-7). Soc Indus-Appl Math.

Levinson, Norman. Gap & Density Theorems. LC 41-6147. (Colloquium, Pbns. Ser.: Vol. 26). 246p. 1963. Repr. of 1940 ed. 23.00 (ISBN 0-8218-1026-X, COLL-26). Am Math.

Londen, S. O. & Staffan, O. J., eds. Volterra Equations: Proceedings, Helsinki Symposium, Finland, August 11-14, 1978. (Lecture Notes in Mathematics: Vol. 737). 1979. pap. 20.00 (ISBN 0-387-09534-9). Springer-Verlag.

Mikhlin, S. G. Linear Integral Equations. (Russian Monographs & Texts on the Physical Sciences). 240p. 1961. 45.25x (ISBN 0-677-20320-9). Gordon.

Miller, Richard K. & Sell, George R. Volterra Integral Equations & Topological Dynamics. LC 52-42839. (Memoirs: No. 102). 1979. pap. 12.00 (ISBN 0-8218-1802-3, MEMO-102). Am Math.

Niyogi, P. Integral Equation Method in Transonic Flow. (Lecture Notes in Physics: Vol. 157). 189p. 1982. pap. 14.00 (ISBN 0-387-11499-8). Springer-Verlag.

Paley, Raymond E. & Wiener, Norbert. Fourier Transforms in the Complex Domain. LC 35-3273. (Colloquium, Pbns. Ser.: Vol. 19). 183p. 1982. pap. 33.00 (ISBN 0-8218-1019-7, COLL-19). Am Math.

Petrovskii, Ivan G. Lectures on the Theory of Integral Equations. LC 57-3179. (Illus.). 1957. 9.00x (ISBN 0-910670-09-9). Graylock.

Ramm, A. Theory & Applications of Some New Classes of Integral Equations. 344p. 1980. pap. 26.00 (ISBN 0-387-90540-5). Springer-Verlag.

Schwabik, Stefan, et al. Differential & Integral Equations: Boundry Value Problems & Adjoints. 1979. 39.50 (ISBN 90-277-0802-9, Pub. by Reidel Holland). Kluwer Academic.

Srivastava, H. M. & Buschman, R. G. Convolution Integral Equations with Special Function Kernals. LC 76-52979. 164p. 1977. 18.95x (ISBN 0-470-99050-3). Halsted Pr.

Steklov Institute of Mathematics, Academy of Sciences, U S S R, No. 97. Milne Problem with Anisotropic Scattering: Proceedings. Maslennikov, M. Y., ed. (Proceedings of the Steklov Institute of Mathematics: No. 97). 1969. 43.00 (ISBN 0-8218-1897-X, STEKLO-97). Am Math.

Symposium in Pure Mathematics - Chicago - 1966. Singular Integrals: Proceedings. Calderon, A. P., ed. LC 67-16553. (Proceedings of Symposia in Pure Mathematics: Vol. 10). 384p. 1982. pap. 37.00 (ISBN 0-8218-1410-9, PSPUM-10). Am Math.

Symposium on the Numerical Treatment of O.D.E. Integral & Integro-Differential Equations. Rome 1960. 680p. 1961. 36.95x (ISBN 0-8176-0378-6). Birkhauser.

Tricomi, F. G. Integral Equations. (Mathematics Ser.). 238p. 1985. pap. 6.00 (ISBN 0-486-64828-1). Dover.

Tsokos, Chris P. & Padgett, W. J. Random Integral Equations with Applications to Life Sciences & Engineering. 1974. 70.00 (ISBN 0-12-702150-7). Acad Pr.

Vekua, N. P. Systems of Singular Integral Equations. 216p. 1967. 57.75x (ISBN 0-677-61340-7). Gordon.

Walter, Wolfgang. Differential & Integral Inequalities. rev. ed. Rosenblatt, L. & Shampine, L., trs. from Ger. LC 72-103330. (Ergebnisse der Mathematik und Ihrer Grenzgebiete: Vol. 55). (Illus.). 1970. 48.00 (ISBN 0-387-05088-4). Springer-Verlag.

Yano, Kentaro. Integral Formulas in Riemannian Geometry. LC 74-121180. (Pure & Applied Mathematics Ser.: No. 1). pap. 41.30 (ISBN 0-317-08364-3, 2055285). Bks Demand UMI.

Yoshida, Kosaku. Lectures in Differential & Integral Equations. LC 60-53007. (Pure & Applied Mathematics Ser.: Vol. 10). pap. 57.50 (ISBN 0-317-08522-0, 2007077). Bks Demand UMI.

INTEGRAL ERROR FUNCTION

see Error Functions

INTEGRAL FUNCTIONS

see Functions, Entire

INTEGRAL TRANSFORMS

Ablowitz, M. J. & Segur, H. Solitons & the Inverse Scattering Transform. LC 81-50600. (SIAM Studies in Applied Mathematics: No. 4). x, 425p. 1981. text ed. 57.00 (ISBN 0-89871-174-6). Soc Indus-Appl Math.

Colton, D. L. Solution of Boundary Value Problems by the Method of Integral Operators. (Research Notes in Mathematics Ser.: No. 6). 148p. (Orig.). 1976. pap. text ed. 21.95 (ISBN 0-273-00307-0). Pitman Pub MA.

Giffin, Walter C. Transform Techniques for Probability Modeling. (Operation Research Industrial Engineering Ser.). 1975. 59.50 (ISBN 0-12-282750-3). Acad Pr.

Katz, M. B. Questions of Uniqueness & Resolution in Reconstruction of 2-D & 3-D Objects from Their Projections. (Lecture Notes in Biomathematics: Vol. 26). 1978. pap. 15.00 (ISBN 0-387-09087-8). Springer-Verlag.

Oberhettinger, F. Tables of Bessel Transforms. LC 72-88727. 289p. 1972. pap. 17.00 (ISBN 0-387-05997-0). Springer-Verlag.

Wolf, K. B. Integral Transforms in Science & Engineering. LC 78-12482. (Mathematical Concepts & Methods in Science & Engineering Ser.: Vol. 11). 502p. 1979. 49.50x (ISBN 0-306-39251-8, Plenum Pr). Plenum Pub.

INTEGRALS

see also Bernstein Polynomials

Alfsen, E. M. Compact Convex Sets & Boundary Integrals. LC 72-136352. (Ergebnisse der Mathematik und Ihrer Grenzgebiete: Vol. 57). (Illus.). 1971. 31.00 (ISBN 0-387-05090-6). Springer-Verlag.

Babenko, K. I., et al. Twelve Papers on Approximations & Integrals. LC 51-5559. (Translations Ser.: No. 2, Vol. 44). 1966. Repr. of 1965 ed. 24.00 (ISBN 0-8218-1744-2, TRANS 2-44). Am Math.

Baker, Christopher T. & Miller, Geoffrey F. Treatment of Integral Equations by Numerical Methods. 1983. 45.00 (ISBN 0-12-074120-2). Acad Pr.

Bochner, Salomon. Fouriersche Integrale. LC 49-22695. (Ger). 10.50 (ISBN 0-8284-0042-3). Chelsea Pub.

Butzer, P. L. & Berens, H. Semi-Groups of Operators & Approximation. LC 68-11980. (Grundlehren der Mathematischen Wissenschaften: Vol. 145). 1967. 39.00 (ISBN 0-387-03832-9). Springer-Verlag.

Chakravarti, P. C. Integrals & Sums. 89p. 1970. 39.50 (ISBN 0-485-11114-4, Pub. by Athlone Pr Ltd). Longwood Pub Group.

Copson, Edward T. Asymptotic Expansions. (Cambridge Tracts in Mathematics & Mathematical Physics). 1965. 29.95 (ISBN 0-521-04721-8). Cambridge U Pr.

Craven, Bruce D. Lebesque Measure & Integral. LC 81-12151. 224p. 1982. text ed. 39.95 (ISBN 0-273-01754-3). Pitman Pub MA.

Dwight, Herbert B. Tables of Integrals & Other Mathematical Data. 4th ed. 1961. write for info. (ISBN 0-02-331170-3, 33117). Macmillan.

Ferguson, LeBaron O. Approximation by Polynomials with Integral Coefficients. LC 79-20331. (Mathematical Surveys: Vol. 17). 160p. 1980. 34.00 (ISBN 0-8218-1517-2). Am Math.

Gohberg, Israel, et al. Einfuehrung in die Theorie der Eindimensionalen Singularen Integraloperatoren. (Mathematische Reihe: No. 63). (Ger., Illus.). 379p. 1979. 68.95x (ISBN 0-8176-1020-0). Birkhauser.

Gradshteyn, I. S., et al. Tables of Integrals, Series & Products. 1980. 25.00 (ISBN 0-12-294760-6). Acad Pr.

Jacobs, Konrad. Measure & Integral. (Probability & Mathematical Statistics). 1978. 79.50 (ISBN 0-12-378550-2). Acad Pr.

Konrod, Aleksandr S. Nodes & Weights of Quadrature Formulas. LC 65-15002. 143p. 1965. 47.50x (ISBN 0-306-65111-4, IFI Plenum). Plenum Pub.

Kral, J. Integral Operators in Potential Theory. (Lecture Notes in Mathematics Ser.: Vol. 823). 171p. 1980. pap. 15.00 (ISBN 0-387-10227-2). Springer-Verlag.

McShane, E. J. Unified Integration. LC 82-16266. (Pure & Applied Mathematics Ser.). 1983. 60.00 (ISBN 0-12-486260-8). Acad Pr.

Nielsen. Direct Integral Theory. (Lecture Notes in Pure & Applied Mathematics Ser.: Vol. 61). 184p. 1980. 37.50 (ISBN 0-8247-6971-6). Dekker.

Pearcey, T. Table of the Fresnal Integral to Six Decimal Places. 1982. 30.00x (ISBN 0-686-97895-1, Pub. by CSIRO Australia). State Mutual Bk.

Petit Bois, G. Tables of Indefinite Integrals. 1906. pap. text ed. 6.50 (ISBN 0-486-60225-7). Dover.

Sadowsky, Cora. Interpolation of Operators & Singular Integrals. (Pure & Applied Math Ser.: Vol. 53). 1979. 65.00 (ISBN 0-8247-6883-3). Dekker.

Schochetman, Irwin E. Integral Operators in the Theory of Induced Banach Representations. LC 78-15819. (Memoirs Ser.: No. 207). 53p. 1978. pap. 12.00 (ISBN 0-8218-2207-1). Am Math.

Segal, I. E. & Kunze, R. A. Integrals & Operators. 2nd rev ed. LC 77-16682. (Grundlehren der Mathematischen Wissenschaften: Vol. 228). 1978. Repr. 44.00 (ISBN 0-387-08323-5). Springer-Verlag.

Shilov, G. E. & Gurevich, B. L. Integral, Measure & Derivative: A Unified Approach. Silverman, Richard, tr. 1977. pap. text ed. 5.95 (ISBN 0-486-63519-8). Dover.

Spiegel, Murray R. Real Variables. 1969. pap. 9.95 (ISBN 0-07-060221-2). McGraw.

Symposium in Pure Mathematics - Chicago - 1966. Singular Integrals: Proceedings. Calderon, A. P., ed. LC 67-16553. (Proceedings of Symposia in Pure Mathematics: Vol. 10). 384p. 1982. pap. 37.00 (ISBN 0-8218-1410-9, PSPUM-10). Am Math.

Wheeden, Richard & Zygmund, Antoni. Measure & Integral. (Monographs & Textbooks in Pure & Applied Mathematics). 1977. 33.75 (ISBN 0-8247-6499-4). Dekker.

INTEGRALS, DEFINITE

see also Error Functions; Numerical Integration

Apelblat, A. Tables of Definite & Infinite Integrals. (Physical Sciences Data Ser.: Vol. 13). 458p. 1983. 106.50 (ISBN 0-444-42151-3, I-470-82). Elsevier.

Carslaw, Horatio S. Introduction to the Theory of Fourier's Series & Integrals. 3rd ed. (Illus.). 1952. pap. 7.50 (ISBN 0-486-60048-3). Dover.

Fichtenholz, G. M. The Definite Integral. Silverman, R. A., tr. from Rus. LC 78-149513. (Pocket Mathematical Library Ser.). (Illus.). 98p. 1973. 30.25 (ISBN 0-677-21090-6). Gordon.

--The Indefinite Integral. Schwartz, Jacob D., ed. Silverman, Richard A., tr. from Rus. LC 76-135120. (Pocket Mathematical Library). (Illus.). 148p. 1971. 45.25 (ISBN 0-677-21030-2). Gordon.

INTEGRALS, DOUBLE

see Integrals, Multiple

INTEGRALS, ELLIPTIC

see Functions, Elliptic

INTEGRALS, GENERALIZED

see also Measure Theory

Berberian, Sterling K. Measure & Integration. LC 74-128871. 1970. Repr. of 1965 ed. text ed. 14.95 (ISBN 0-8284-0241-8). Chelsea Pub.

Bishop, Errett & Cheng, Henry. Constructive Measure Theory. LC 52-42839. (Memoirs: No. 116). 85p. 1972. pap. 9.00 (ISBN 0-8218-1816-3, MEMO-116). Am Math.

Burkill, John C. Lebesgue Integral. (Cambridge Tracts in Mathematics & Mathematical Physics). 1951. 16.95 (ISBN 0-521-04382-4). Cambridge U Pr.

George, C. Exercises in Integration. (Problem Bks. in Mathematics). (Illus.). 560p. 1984. 38.00 (ISBN 0-387-96060-0). Springer-Verlag.

Gunther, N. Integrales De Stieltjes. LC 50-1366. (Fr). 19.95 (ISBN 0-8284-0063-6). Chelsea Pub.

Guzman, M. De. Differentiation of Integrals in R to the nth Power. (Lecture Notes in Mathematics: Vol. 481). xii, 226p. 1975. pap. 16.00 (ISBN 0-387-07399-X). Springer-Verlag.

Kingman, John F. & Taylor, S. J. Introduction to Measure & Probability. 1966. 59.50 (ISBN 0-521-05888-0). Cambridge U Pr.

McBride, Adam C. Fractional Calculus & Integral Transforms of Generalized Functions. (Research in Mathematics Ser.: No. 31). 179p. (Orig.). 1979. pap. text ed. 22.50 (ISBN 0-273-08415-1). Pitman Pub MA.

McLeod, R. M. The Generalized Riemann Integral. LC 80-81043. (Carus Mathematical Monograph: No. 20). 275p. 1980. 21.00 (ISBN 0-88385-021-4). Math Assn.

Nielsen, Niels. Die Gammafunktion, 2 vols. in 1. Incl. Integrallogarithmus. LC 64-13785. (Ger.). 1965. 19.50 (ISBN 0-8284-0188-8). Chelsea Pub.

Pesin, Ivan N. Classical & Modern Integration Theories. (Probability & Mathematical Statistics Ser.: Vol. 8). (Rus). 1970. 49.50 (ISBN 0-12-552550-8). Acad Pr.

Pfeffer, Washek F. Integrals & Measures. (Monographs in Pure & Applied Mathematics: Vol. 42). 1977. 45.00 (ISBN 0-8247-6530-3). Dekker.

Phillips, Esther R., ed. An Introduction to Analysis & Integration Theory. 480p. 1984. pap. 10.95 (ISBN 0-486-64747-1). Dover.

Weir, A. J. General Integration & Measure. LC 73-91620. (Illus.). 344p. 1974. pap. 16.95 (ISBN 0-521-29715-X). Cambridge U Pr.

INTEGRALS, MULTIPLE

Budak, B. M. & Fomin, S. V. Multiple Integrals, Field Theory & Series. 640p. 1978. 18.00 (ISBN 0-8285-2096-8, Pub. by Mir Pubs USSR). Imported Pubns.

Bugrov, Y. S. & Nikolsky, S. M. Differential Equations, Multiple Integrals. (Theory of Functions of a Complex Variable Ser.). 475p. 1983. 9.95 (ISBN 0-8285-2657-5, Pub. by Mir Pubs USSR). Imported Pubns.

Major, P. Multiple Wiener-Ito Integrals. (Lecture Notes in Mathematics Ser.: Vol. 849). 127p. 1981. pap. 12.00 (ISBN 0-387-10575-1). Springer-Verlag.

Morrey, Charles B. Multiple Integrals in the Calculus of Variations. (Grundlehren der Mathematischen Wissenschaften: Vol. 130). 1966. 51.00 (ISBN 0-387-03524-9). Springer-Verlag.

INTEGRALS, STOCHASTIC

Bharucha-Reid, A. T. Random Integral Equations. (Mathematics in Science & Engineering Ser.: Vol. 96). 1972. 70.00 (ISBN 0-12-095750-7). Acad Pr.

Chung, K. L. & Williams, Ruth. An Introduction to Stochastic Integration. (Progress in Probability & Statistics Ser.: Vol. 4). 217p. 1983. text ed. 19.95 (ISBN 0-8176-3117-8). Birkhauser.

Engel, David D. The Multiple Stochastic Integral. (Memoirs of the American Mathematical Society: Vol. 265). 83p. 1982. pap. 9.00 (ISBN 0-8218-2265-9, MEMO-265). Am Math.

Krishnan, Venkatarama. Nonlinear Filtering & Smoothing: Introductionto Martingales, Stochastic Integrals & Estimation. LC 83-16712. 314p. 1984. 37.50x (ISBN 0-471-89840-6, Pub. by Wiley-Interscience). Wiley.

McKean, H. P., Jr. Stochastic Integrals. (Probability & Mathematical Statistics Ser,: Vol. 5). 1969. 39.50 (ISBN 0-12-483450-7). Acad Pr.

Tsokos, C. P. & Padgett, W. J. Random Integral Equations with Applications to Stochastic Systems. (Lecture Notes in Mathematics: Vol. 233). 174p. 1971. pap. 10.00 (ISBN 0-387-05660-2). Springer-Verlag.

INTEGRATED CIRCUITS

Adams, Charles K. Basic Integrated Circuit Theory & Projects. (Illus.). 266p. (Orig.). 1984. 19.95 (ISBN 0-8306-0699-8); pap. 11.95 (ISBN 0-8306-1699-3, 1699). TAB Bks.

American Micro Systems. Mos Integrated Circuits: Theory, Fabrication, Design & Systems Applications of MOS LSI. Penny, William M. & Lau, Lillian, eds. LC 79-1039. 494p. 1979. Repr. of 1972 ed. 27.50 (ISBN 0-88275-897-7). Krieger.

Antognetti, P. Power-Integrated Circuits: Physics, Design & Applications. 576p. 1985. price not set (ISBN 0-07-002129-5). McGraw.

Augarten, Stan. State of the Art: A Photographic History of the Integrated Circuit. LC 83-669. (Illus.). 90p. 1983. 17.95 (ISBN 0-89919-206-8); pap. 9.95 (ISBN 0-89919-195-9). Ticknor & Fields.

Barna, A. A. VHSIC (Very High Speed Integrated Circuits) Technologies & Tradeoffs. LC 81-4356. 114p. 1981. 24.95x (ISBN 0-471-09463-3, Pub. by Wiley-Interscience). Wiley.

Barna, Arpad & Porat, Dan I. Integrated Circuits in Digital Electronics. LC 73-6709. 483p. 1973. 49.95x (ISBN 0-471-05050-4, Pub. by Wiley-Interscience). Wiley.

Beadle, W. E., et al. Quick Reference Manual for Silicon Integrated Circuit Technology. 736p. 1985. 65.00 (ISBN 0-471-81588-8). Wiley.

Becher, William D. Logical Design Using Integrated Circuits. 1977. text ed. 21.50x (ISBN 0-8104-5859-4). Hayden.

Bell, David. Linear Integrated Circuits: Design & Applications. 1982. text ed. 21.95 (ISBN 0-8359-4074-8); solutions manual avail. (ISBN 0-8359-4075-6). Reston.

Berlin, Howard M. Design of Phase-Locked Loop Circuits, with Experiments. LC 78-57203. 256p. 1978. pap. 11.95 (ISBN 0-672-21545-4). Sams.

Bogart, Theodore F. Linear Integrated Circuits: Applications & Experiments. 245p. 1983. pap. text ed. 14.95x (ISBN 0-471-87512-0). Wiley.

Buchsbaum, Walter H. Encyclopedia of Integrated Circuits: A Handbook of Essential Reference Data. LC 80-21596. 384p. 1981. 24.95 (ISBN 0-13-275875-X). P-H.

Camenzind, Hans R. Electronic Integrated Systems Design. LC 78-12195. (Illus.). 342p. 1980. Repr. of 1972 ed. lib. bdg. 22.50 (ISBN 0-88275-763-6). Krieger.

Carr, Joseph J. Linear IC-OP Amp Handbook. 2nd ed. (Illus.). 350p. (Orig.). 1983. 21.95 (ISBN 0-8306-0150-3, 1550); pap. 13.95 (ISBN 0-8306-1550-4). TAB Bks.

Carr, William N. & Mize, Jack P. MOS-LSI Design & Application. LC 72-7407. (Texas Instruments Electronics Ser.). (Illus.). 320p. 1972. 54.50 (ISBN 0-07-010081-0). McGraw.

INTEGRATED CIRCUITS–VERY LARGE SCALE INTEGRATION

Drongowski, Paul J. A Graphical Engineering Aid for VLSI Systems. Stone, Harold, ed. LC 85-1041. (Computer Science Series: Computer Architecture & Design: No. 4). 226p. 1985. 44.95 (ISBN 0-8357-1656-2). UMI Res Pr.
Einspruch, N. VLSI Electronics: Microstructure Science, Vol. 7. 1983. 59.50 (ISBN 0-12-234107-4). Acad Pr.
Einspruch, Norman, ed. VLSI Electronics: Microstructure Science. 1982. Vol. 4. 53.00 (ISBN 0-12-234104-X); Vol. 6. suppl. material 79.00 (ISBN 0-12-234106-6). Acad Pr.
Einspruch, Norman & Huff, Howard, eds. VLSI Electronics: Microstructure Science, Vol. 12. Date not set. 75.00 (ISBN 0-12-234112-0). Acad Pr.
Einspruch, Norman G., ed. Surface & Interface Effects in VLSI, Vol. 10. (VLSI Electronics: Micro Structure Science Ser.). 1985. 65.00 (ISBN 0-12-234110-4). Acad Pr.
--VLSI Electronics: Microstructure Science, Vol. 3. LC 81-2877. 1982. 56.00 (ISBN 0-12-234103-1). Acad Pr.
--VLSI Electronics Microstructure Science, Vol. 5. 1982. 59.00 (ISBN 0-12-234105-8). Acad Pr.
--VLSI Electronics: Microstructure Science, Vol. 9. 1985. 72.00 (ISBN 0-12-234109-0). Acad Pr.
--VLSI Electronics: Microstructure Science Vol. 8: Plasma Processing for VLSI. LC 83-22351. 1984. 69.00 (ISBN 0-12-234108-2). Acad Pr.
Einspruch, Norman G. & Wisseman, William R., eds. VLSI Electronics, Vol. 11. (Serial Publication Ser.). 1985. 68.50 (ISBN 0-12-234111-2). Acad Pr.
Electronics Magazine. Large Scale Integration. 1976. 5.00 (ISBN 0-07-019187-5). McGraw.
Elmasry, M. I., ed. Digital VLSI Systems. LC 85-10724. (Reprint Ser.). 1985. 73.50 (ISBN 0-87942-190-8, PCO1842). Inst Electrical.
Florida Real Estate. 87.50 (ISBN 0-318-11930-7); Suppl. 1984. 28.00 (ISBN 0-318-11931-5); Suppl. 1983. 24.00 (ISBN 0-318-11932-3). Lawyers Co-Op.
Folberth, D. G. & Grobman, W. D., eds. VLSI-Technology & Design. LC 84-15848. 1984. 41.95 (ISBN 0-87942-180-0, PC01743). Inst Electrical.
Fu, K. S., ed. VLSI for Pattern Recognition & Image Processing. (Springer Series in Information Sciences: Vol. 13). (Illus.). 255p. 1984. 23.00 (ISBN 0-387-13268-6). Springer-Verlag.
Fuchs, Henry. Selected Reprints on VLSI Technologies & Computer Graphics. 490p. 1983. 36.00 (ISBN 0-8186-0491-3). IEEE Comp Soc.
Ghandhi, Sorab K. VLSI Fabrication Principles: Silicon & Gallium Arsenide. LC 82-10842. 665p. 1983. 56.50 (ISBN 0-471-86833-7, Pub. by Wiley-Interscience). Wiley.
Glaser, Lance A. & Dobberpuhl, Daniel W. The Design & Analysis of VLSI Circuits. 556p. 1985. text ed. 39.95 (ISBN 0-201-12580-3); write for info. solution manual (ISBN 0-201-12581-1). Addison-Wesley.
Gray, John, ed. VLSI Eighty-One: Very Large Scale Integration. LC 81-68035. 1981. 39.50 (ISBN 0-12-296860-3). Acad Pr.
Howes, M. J. & Morgan, D. V. Large Scale Integration: Devices, Circuits & Systems. LC 80-42016. (Wiley Ser. in Solid State Devices & Circuits). 346p. 1981. 44.95x (ISBN 0-471-27988-9, Pub. by Wiley-Interscience). Wiley.
Hu, T. C. & Kuh, E. S., eds. VLSI: Circuit Layout Theory. (Reprint Ser.). 300p. 1985. write for info. (ISBN 0-87942-193-2). Inst Electrical.
Knights, John C., ed. The Physics of VLSI: AIP Conference Proceedings No. 122. LC 84-72729. 292p. 1984. lib. bdg. 39.75 (ISBN 0-88318-321-8). Am Inst Physics.
Kung, H. T., et al, eds. VLSI Systems & Computations. 415p. 1981. text ed. 39.95 (ISBN 0-914894-35-8). Computer Sci.
Kung, S. Y., et al. VLSI & Modern Signal Processing. (Illus.). 448p. 1985. text ed. 43.95 (ISBN 0-13-942699-X). P-H.
Kunii, T. L., ed. VLSI Engineering: Beyond Software Engineering. (Lecture Notes in Computer Science Ser.: Vol. 163). viii, 308p. 1984. pap. 14.00 (ISBN 0-387-70002-1). Springer-Verlag.
Leighton, F. Thompson. Complexity Issues in VLSI: Optimal Layouts for the Shuffle-Exchange Graph & Other Networks. (Illus.). 112p. 1983. text ed. 25.00x (ISBN 0-262-12104-2). MIT Pr.
Leiserson, Charles E. Area-Efficient VLSI Computation. (Association for Computing Machinery Doctoral Dissertation Award Ser.). (Illus.). 152p. 1983. 25.00x (ISBN 0-262-12102-6). MIT Pr.
McGreivy, Denis J. & Pickar, Kenneth A. VLSI Technologies: Through the Eighties & Beyond. (Tutorial Texts Ser.). 343p. 1982. 30.00 (ISBN 0-8186-0424-7, Q424). IEEE Comp Soc.
Marcus, R B. & Sheng, T T. Transmission Electron Microscopy of Silicon VLSI Circuits & Structure. LC 83-3469. 217p. 1983. 48.50x (ISBN 0-471-09251-7, Pub. by Wiley-Interscience). Wiley.
Mead, Carver & Conway, Lynn. Introduction to VLSI Systems. LC 78-74688. 1979. text ed. 41.95 (ISBN 0-201-04358-0). Addison-Wesley.
Murarka, S. P, ed. Silicides for VLSI Applications. 1983. 21.50 (ISBN 0-12-511220-3). Acad Pr.
Muroga, S. VLSI System Design: When & How to Design Very Large Scale Integrated Circuits. 300p. 1984. pap. 19.00 (ISBN 0-471-88697-1, EE25, Pub. by Wiley Interscience). Wiley.
Muroga, Saburo. VLSI Systems Design: When & How to Design Very Large Scale Integrated Circuits. LC 82-8598. 496p. 1982. 39.95x (ISBN 0-471-86090-5). Wiley.
Nazemetz, John W., et al, eds. Computer Integrated Manufacturing System. 1985. write for info. (ISBN 0-89806-066-4). Inst Indus Eng.
Newkirk, John A. & Mathews, Robert G. The VLSI Designer's Library. (VLSI Systems Ser.). (Illus.). 200p. 1983. pap. 32.95 (ISBN 0-201-05444-2). Addison-Wesley.
Penfield, Paul, Jr. Proceedings, Conference on Advanced Research in VLSI, 1984. 200p. 1984. pap. text ed. 39.00 (ISBN 0-89006-136-X). Artech Hse.
PF474 Product Data Book. 148p. (Orig.). 1984. pap. write for info. (ISBN 0-926390-00-7). Proximity Tech.
Preparata, Franco P., ed. VLSI Theory. (Advances in Computing Research Ser.: Vol. 2). 275p. 1985. 57.50 (ISBN 0-89232-461-9). Jai Pr.
Proceedings of the Third Caltech Conference on VLSI. 39.95 (ISBN 0-914894-86-2). Computer Sci.
Pucknell, D. & Eshraghian, K. Basic VLSI Design: Principles & Applications. (Illus.). 352p. 1985. text ed. 39.95 (ISBN 0-13-067851-1). P-H.
Rabbat, Guy. Hardware & Software Concepts in VLSI. Rabbat, Guy, ed. (Van Nostrand Electrical-Computer Science & Engineering Ser.). (Illus.). 512p. 1983. 42.50 (ISBN 0-442-22538-5). Van Nos Reinhold.
Reghbati, Hassan. VLSI Testing & Validation Techniques. 450p. 1985. 39.00 (ISBN 0-8186-0668-1); prepub. 29.00. IEEE Comp Soc.
Rice, Rex. VLSI--the Coming Revolution in Applications & Design. (Tutorial Texts Ser.). 315p. 1980. 30.00 (ISBN 0-8186-0288-0, Q288). IEEE Comp Soc.
--VLSI Support Technologies: Computer-Aided Design, Testing, & Packaging. (Tutorial Texts Ser.). 450p. 1982. 30.00 (ISBN 0-8186-0386-0, Q386). IEEE Comp Soc.
Sugano, T. & Kim, H. Applications of Plasma Processes to VLSI Technology. 416p. 1985. 42.95 (ISBN 0-471-86960-0). Wiley.
Sze, Simon M., ed. VLSI Technology. (Illus.). 608p. 1983. 41.95 (ISBN 0-07-062686-3). McGraw.
Tsividis, Yannis & Antognetti, Paolo, eds. Design of MOS VLSI Circuits for Telecommunications. (Illus.). 640p. 1985. text ed. 34.95 (ISBN 0-13-200643-X). P-H.
Ullman, Jeffrey D. Computational Aspects of VLSI. LC 83-7529. 505p. 1984. text ed. 34.95 (ISBN 0-914894-95-1). Computer Sci.
VLSI Technical Committee Staff. VLSI-Signal Processing. LC 84-82077. 1984. 37.50 (ISBN 0-87942-186-X, PC01800). Inst Electrical.
Weste, Neil & Eshraghian, Karman. Principles of CMOS VLSI: A Systems Perspective. LC 84-16738. 1985. text ed. 39.95 (ISBN 0-201-08222-5). Addison-Wesley.

INTEGRATED DATA PROCESSING
see Electronic Data Processing

INTEGRATION, NUMERICAL
see Numerical Integration

INTEL 286 (MICROPROCESSOR)

INTEL. An Introduction to the iAPX 286: Concepts & Architecture. 1984. pap. text ed. 19.95 (ISBN 0-8359-3219-2). Reston.
Intel Corporation. IAPX 286 Programmer's Reference Manual Numeric Supplement. 16.95 (ISBN 0-8359-3054-8). Reston.
Intel Staff. IAPX 286 Architecture Extension Kernal K286 User's Guide. 180p. (Orig.). pap. 29.00 (ISBN 0-917017-08-0, 121961-001). Intel Corp.
--IAPX 286 Hardware Reference Manual. rev. ed. 500p. 1984. pap. 15.00 (ISBN 0-917017-12-9). Intel Corp.
--IAPX 286 Operating Systens Writer's Guide. 256p. (Orig.). 1984. pap. 15.00 (ISBN 0-917017-07-2, 121960-001). Intel Corp.
--IAPX 286 Programmer's Reference Manual Including the IAPX 286 Numeric Supplement. rev. ed. 576p. 1984. pap. 14.95 (ISBN 0-917017-11-0, 210498-002). Intel Corp.
--An Introduction to the Intel 286 Concepts & Architecture. 560p. (Orig.). 1985. pap. 16.95 (ISBN 0-917017-23-4, 230980-001). Intel Corp.

INTEL 432 (MICROPROCESSOR)

Hunter, Colin & Ready, Jim. Introduction to the Intel IAPX 432. text ed. cancelled (ISBN 0-8359-3223-0). Reston.
Hunter, Colin, et al. Introduction to the Intel IAPX 432 Microprocessor Architecture. 1985. pap. text ed. 22.95 (ISBN 0-8359-3222-2). Reston.
Organick, E. I. A Programmer's View of the Intel 432 System. 432p. 1983. 34.95 (ISBN 0-07-047719-1). McGraw.

INTEL 8080 (MICROCOMPUTER)

Coffron, James W. Getting Started with 8080, 8085, Z80, & 6800 Microprocessor Systems. (Illus.). 352p. 1984. pap. 14.95 (ISBN 0-13-354663-2). P-H.
Fernandez, Judi & Ashley, Ruth. Introduction to 8080-8085 Assembly Language Programming. LC 80-39650. (Wiley Self Teaching Guide Ser.: No. 1-581). 303p. 1981. pap. text ed. 12.95 (ISBN 0-471-08009-8, Pub. by Wiley Pr). Wiley.
Findley, Robert & Edwards, Raymond. Eighty-Eighty Software Gourmet Guide & Cookbook. pap. 13.95 (ISBN 0-8104-6280-X, 6280). Hayden.
Gaonkar, Ramesh. Microprocessor Architecture, Programming, & Applications with 8085-8080A. 672p. 1984. Additional supplements may be obtained from publisher. text ed. 32.95 (ISBN 0-675-20159-4). Merrill.
Intel Marketing Communications. The Eighty Eighty, Eighty Eighty-Five Microprocessor Book. LC 78-16936. (Intel Ser.: No. 1-402). 603p. 1980. 34.95x (ISBN 0-471-03568-8, Pub. by Wiley-Interscience). Wiley.
Intel Staff. Assembly Language Programming 8080-8085. 224p. (Orig.). 1980. pap. 13.00 (ISBN 0-917017-26-9, 980940-001). Intel Corp.
Larson, David, et al. Eighty-Eighty, Eighty-Eighty-Five, Software Design, Bk. 1. LC 78-57207. 336p. 1978. pap. 13.95 (ISBN 0-672-21541-1, 21697). Sams.
Leventhal, Lance A. & Saville, Winthrop. Assembly Language Subroutines: 8080-8085. 500p. (Orig.). 1984. pap. 18.95 (ISBN 0-931988-58-6, 58-6). Osborne-McGraw.
--Eighty Eighty, Eighty Eighty-Five: Assembly Language Subroutines. 500p. 1983. 17.95 (ISBN 0-07-931058-3). McGraw.
Miller, Alan R. Eighty-Eighty & 280 Assembly Language: Techniques for Improved Programming. LC 80-21492. 318p. 1981. pap. text ed. 12.95 (ISBN 0-471-08124-8). Wiley.
Spracklen, Kathe. Z-Eighty & Eighty-Eighty Assembly Language Programming. (Computer Programming Ser.). 192p. 1979. pap. 12.95 (ISBN 0-8104-5167-0). Hayden.
Titus, Christopher A. TEA: 8080-8085 Co-Resident Editor-Assembler. LC 79-65751. 256p. 1979. pap. 11.95 (ISBN 0-672-21628-0, 21628). Sams.
Titus, Christopher A., et al. Eighty-Eighty Eighty-Eighty-Five Software Design, Bk. 2. LC 78-57207. 352p. 1979. pap. 12.95 (ISBN 0-672-21615-9, 21615). Sams.
Uffenbeck, John. Microcomputers & Microprocessors: The 8080, 8085, & Z-80 Interfacing, Programming, & Troubleshooting. (Illus.). 704p. 1985. text ed. 37.95 (ISBN 0-13-580309-8). P-H.

INTEL 8085 (MICROPROCESSOR)

Coffron, James W. Getting Started with 8080, 8085, Z80, & 6800 Microprocessor Systems. (Illus.). 352p. 1984. pap. 14.95 (ISBN 0-13-354663-2). P-H.
--Practical Hardware Details for 8080, 8085, Z80, & 6800 Microprocessor Systems. (Illus.). 352p. 1981. text ed. 29.95 (ISBN 0-13-691089-0). P-H.
Fernandez, Judi & Ashley, Ruth. Introduction to 8080-8085 Assembly Language Programming. LC 80-39650. (Wiley Self Teaching Guide Ser.: No. 1-581). 303p. 1981. pap. text ed. 12.95 (ISBN 0-471-08009-8, Pub. by Wiley Pr). Wiley.
Gaonkar, Ramesh. Microprocessor Architecture, Programming, & Applications with 8085-8080A. 672p. 1984. Additional supplements may be obtained from publisher. text ed. 32.95 (ISBN 0-675-20159-4). Merrill.
INTEL. IAPX 86, 88, 186, User's Manual. 1984. pap. text ed. 20.95 (ISBN 0-8359-3033-5). Reston.
Intel Marketing Communications. The Eighty Eighty, Eighty Eighty-Five Microprocessor Book. LC 78-16936. (Intel Ser.: No. 1-402). 603p. 1980. 34.95x (ISBN 0-471-03568-8, Pub. by Wiley-Interscience). Wiley.
Intel Staff. Assembly Language Programming 8080-8085. 224p. (Orig.). 1980. pap. 13.00 (ISBN 0-917017-26-9, 980940-001). Intel Corp.
--MCS-80-85 Family User's Manual. rev. ed. 208p. 1983. pap. 10.00 (ISBN 0-917017-31-5, 205775-002). Intel Corp.
Larson, David, et al. Eighty-Eighty, Eighty-Eighty-Five, Software Design, Bk. 1. LC 78-57207. 336p. 1978. pap. 13.95 (ISBN 0-672-21541-1, 21697). Sams.
Leventhal, Lance A. & Saville, Winthrop. Assembly Language Subroutines: 8080-8085. 500p. (Orig.). 1984. pap. 18.95 (ISBN 0-931988-58-6, 58-6). Osborne-McGraw.
--Eighty Eighty, Eighty Eighty-Five: Assembly Language Subroutines. 500p. 1983. 17.95 (ISBN 0-07-931058-3). McGraw.
Morris, Norl. Pocket Guide: Assembly Language for the 8085. (Pitman Programming Pocket Guides Ser.). 64p. (Orig.). 1984. pap. 6.95 (ISBN 0-273-02123-0). Pitman Pub MA.
Titus, Christopher A. TEA: 8080-8085 Co-Resident Editor-Assembler. LC 79-65751. 256p. 1979. pap. 11.95 (ISBN 0-672-21628-0, 21628). Sams.
Titus, Christopher A., et al. Eighty-Eighty Eighty-Eighty-Five Software Design, Bk. 2. LC 78-57207. 352p. 1979. pap. 12.95 (ISBN 0-672-21615-9, 21615). Sams.
Uffenbeck, John. Microcomputers & Microprocessors: The 8080, 8085, & Z-80 Interfacing, Programming, & Troubleshooting. (Illus.). 704p. 1985. text ed. 37.95 (ISBN 0-13-580309-8). P-H.

INTEL 8086 (MICROPROCESSOR)

Coffron, James W. Eighty Eighty-Six Applications. 250p. 1984. pap. cancelled (ISBN 0-89588-191-8). SYBEX.
--Programming the 8086-8088. LC 83-50228. (Illus.). 311p. 1983. pap. 15.95 (ISBN 0-89588-120-9). SYBEX.
The Eighty Eighty-Six & Eighty Eighty-Eight Primer. 10.95 (ISBN 0-317-06046-5). Green Pub Inc.
IAPX 86-88, 186-188 User's Manual Programmer's Reference. 1983. pap. text ed. 18.95 (ISBN 0-8359-3035-1). Reston.
INTEL. IAPX 86, 88, 186, User's Manual. 1984. pap. text ed. 20.95 (ISBN 0-8359-3033-5). Reston.
Intel Staff. ASM86 Macro Assembler Operating Instructions for 8086-Based Systems Manual. rev. ed. 100p. 1983. pap. 13.00 (ISBN 0-917017-28-5, 121628-003). Intel Corp.
--IAPX 86-, 186-188 User's Manual Programmer's Reference. 448p. (Orig.). 1984. pap. 20.95 (ISBN 0-917017-32-3, 210912-001). Intel Corp.
--IAPX 86, 88 Family Utilities User's Guide. rev. ed. 280p. 1983. pap. 23.00 (ISBN 0-917017-01-3, 121616-004). Intel Corp.
--IAPX 86-88, 186-188 User's Manual Programmer's Reference, 2 Vols. 560p. (Orig.). 1984. pap. 16.95 (ISBN 0-917017-14-5, 210911-001). Intel Corp.
Morgan, Chris & Waite, Mitch. Eighty Eighty-Six & Eighty Eighty-Eight 16-Bit Microprocessor Primer. 224p. 1983. pap. 21.95 (ISBN 0-07-043109-4, BYTE Bks). McGraw.
Morse. The Eighty Eighty-Six & Eighty Eighty-Eight Primer: An Introduction to Their Architecture, System Design, & Programming. 2nd ed. 1983. 11.95 (ISBN 0-8104-6255-9, 6255). Hayden.
Morse, Stephen P. The Eighty Eighty-Six Primer: An Introduction to Its Architecture, System Design & Programming. 224p. 1980. pap. 10.95 (ISBN 0-8104-5165-4). Hayden.
Rector, Russell & Alexy, George. The Eighty Eighty-Six Book. 624p. 1980. pap. 18.95 (ISBN 0-07-931029-X, 29-X). Osborne-McGraw.
Scanlon, L. J. Eighty Eighty-Six, Eighty Eighty-Eight Assembly Language Programming. (Illus.). 224p. 1984. pap. 15.95 (ISBN 0-89303-424-X). Brady Comm.
Skinner, Thomas P. An Introduction to Assembly Language Programming for the 8086 Family: A Self-Teaching Guide. 1985. pap. 17.95 (ISBN 0-471-80825-3). Wiley.
Templeton, Harley & Berliner, Thomas H. From BASIC to 8086-8088 Assembly Language. LC 84-19644. (Illus.). 240p. 1984. pap. 19.95 (ISBN 0-915381-51-6). WordWare Pub.
Templeton, Harley & Wordware, Inc. From BASIC to 8086-8088 Assembly Language. 175p. 1985. pap. 19.95 (ISBN 0-13-331364-6). P H.
Yeung, B. C. Eighty-Eighty Six - Eighty-Eighty Eight Assembly Language Programming. 265p. 1984. pap. 19.95 (ISBN 0-471-90463-5). Wiley.

INTEL 8088 (MICROPROCESSOR)

Coffron, James W. Programming the 8086-8088. LC 83-50228. (Illus.). 311p. 1983. pap. 15.95 (ISBN 0-89588-120-9). SYBEX.
The Eighty Eighty-Six & Eighty Eighty-Eight Primer. 10.95 (ISBN 0-317-06046-5). Green Pub Inc.
Haskell, Richard. IBM PC Assembly Language Tutor. 240p. 1985. pap. cancelled (ISBN 0-13-448662-5). P-H.
IAPX 86-88, 186-188 User's Manual Programmer's Reference. 1983. pap. text ed. 18.95 (ISBN 0-8359-3035-1). Reston.

Kaplan, S. A. & Pikelner, S. B. Interstellar Medium. LC 70-85076. (Illus.). 1970. 30.00x (ISBN 0-674-46075-8). Harvard U Pr.

Lynds, Beverly T., ed. Dark Nebulae, Globules, & Protostars. LC 73-152040. (Illus.). 150p. 1971. 12.50x (ISBN 0-8165-0300-1). U of Ariz Pr.

Martin, P. G. Cosmic Dust. (Studies in Physics). (Illus.). 1978. 34.50x (ISBN 0-19-851458-1). Oxford U Pr.

NATO Advanced Study Institute, Schliersee, Germany, April, 1973. Interstellar Medium: Proceedings. Pinkau, K., ed. LC 73-91208. (NATO Advanced Study Institutes: No. C-6). 1973. lib. bdg. 37.00 (ISBN 90-277-0417-1, Pub. by Reidel Holland). Kluwer Academic.

Randall, Charles A., Jr., ed. Extra-Terrestrial Matter. LC 69-15447. (Illus.). 331p. 1969. 15.00 (ISBN 0-87580-009-2). N Ill U Pr.

Skobel'tsyn, D. V., ed. Methods in Stellar Atmosphere & Interplanetary Plasma Research. LC 74-26541. (P. N. Lebedev Physics Institute Ser.: Vol. 62). (Illus.). 202p. 1974. 55.00 (ISBN 0-306-10905-0, Consultants). Plenum Pub.

Solomon, P. M. & Edmunds, M. G. Giant Molecular Clouds in the Galaxy. (Illus.). 348p. 1980. 57.00 (ISBN 0-08-023068-7). Pergamon.

Spitzer, Lyman, Jr. Physical Processes in the Interstellar Medium. LC 77-14273. 318p. 1978. 34.95 (ISBN 0-471-02232-2, Pub. by Wiley-Interscience). Wiley.

Symposium on Cosmical Gas Dynamics,6th, et al. Interstellar Gas Dynamics: Proceedings. Habing, H. J., ed. LC 78-124849. (IAU Symposia: No.39). 388p. 1970. lib. bdg. 42.00 (ISBN 90-277-0172-5, Pub. by Reidel Holland). Kluwer Academic.

Symposium Organized by the International Astronomical Union, 52nd, the State Univ. of N.Y. at Albany, May-June, 1972. Interstellar Dust & Related Topics: Proceedings. Greenberg, J. M. & Van de Hulst, H. C., eds. LC 73-88590. 500p. 1973. lib. bdg. 84.00 (ISBN 90-277-0396-5, Pub. by Reidel Holland); pap. text ed. 50.00 (ISBN 90-277-0397-3, Pub. by Reidel Holland). Kluwer Academic.

Van Woerden, H., ed. Topics in Interstellar Matter. (Astrophysics & Space Science Library: No. 70). 1977. lib. bdg. 39.50 (ISBN 90-277-0835-5, Pub. by Reidel Holland). Kluwer Academic.

INTESTINES

Alexander-Williams, J. BIMR Gastroenterology Vol. 3: Large Intestine. new ed. 1983. text ed. 59.95 (ISBN 0-407-02289-9). Butterworth.

Csaky, T. Z., ed. Pharmacology of Intestinal Permeation I. (Handbook of Experimental Pharmacology Ser.: Vol. 70, Pt. 1). (Illus.). 800p. 1984. 217.00 (ISBN 0-387-13100-0). Springer-Verlag.

--Pharmacology of Intestinal Permeation 2. (Handbook of Experimental Pharmacology Ser.: Vol. 70, Pt. 2). (Illus.). 640p. 1984. 188.00 (ISBN 0-387-13101-9). Springer Verlag.

Donowitz, Mark & Sharp, Geoffrey W. Mechanisms of Intestinal Electrolyte Transport & Regulation by Calcium: Proceedings of Kroc Foundation Conference, Santa Ynez Valley, California, September 26-30, 1983. LC 84-17127. (Kroc Foundation Ser.: Vol. 17). 388p. 1984. 78.00 (ISBN 0-8451-0307-5). A R Liss.

Friedman. Functions of the Stomach & Intestine. 48.00 (ISBN 0-85602-048-6). Wiley.

Friedman, M. H. Functions of the Stomach & Intestine: Proceedings of the Thomas (J. Earl) Memorial Symposium, 1973. LC 75-9755. pap. 119.00 (ISBN 0-317-26194-0, 2052072). Bks Demand UMI.

Gilles-Baillien, M. & Gilles, R., eds. Intestinal Transport: Fundamental & Comparative Aspects. (Proceedings in Life Sciences Ser.). (Illus.). 210p. 1983. 44.50 (ISBN 0-387-12430-6). Springer-Verlag.

Kenny, Alexander D., ed. Intestinal Calcium Absorption & Its Regulation. 176p. 1981. 56.00 (ISBN 0-8493-5701-2). CRC Pr.

Robinson, J. W. & Dowling, R. H. Intestinal Adaptation & Its Mechanisms. (Illus.). 646p. 1982. text ed. 75.00 (ISBN 0-85200-442-7, Pub. by MTP Pr England). Kluwer Academic.

Wrong, O. M., et al. Large Intestine: Its Role in Mammalian Nutrition & Homeostasis. LC 81-4915. 217p. 1981. 26.95x (ISBN 0-470-27167-1). Halsted Pr.

INTESTINES–RADIOGRAPHY

Bennett, John R. Therapeutic Endoscopy & Radiology of the Gut. 1981. 72.50 (ISBN 0-8151-0674-2). Year Bk Med.

Nelson, R. S. Radioactive Phosphorus in the Diagnosis of Gastrointestinal Cancer. (Recent Results in Cancer Research: Vol. 10). (Illus.). 1967. 15.00 (ISBN 0-387-03958-9). Springer-Verlag.

Sellink, J. L. & Miller, R. E. Radiology of the Small Bowel. 1983. 98.00 (ISBN 90-247-2460-0, Pub. by Martinus Nijhoff Netherlands). Kluwer Academic.

--Radiology of the Small Bowel, Modern Enteroclysis Technique & Atlas. 1982. text ed. 98.00 (ISBN 90-247-2460-0, Pub. by Martinus Nijhoff Netherlands). Kluwer Academic.

INTRACOASTAL NAVIGATION

see Intracoastal Waterways

INTRACOASTAL WATERWAYS

see also Canals; Inland Navigation

Fagan, Brian. California Coastal Passages. Young, Noel, ed. LC 80-25968. (Illus.). 168p. (Orig.). 1981. pap. 16.95 (ISBN 0-88496-161-3, Co-Pub by ChartGuide). Capra Pr.

Federal Writers' Project. Intracoastal Waterway. LC 73-19778. (American Guidebook Ser.). 1981. Repr. of 1939 ed. 39.00x (ISBN 0-403-02213-4). Somerset Pub.

Garrity, Richard. Canal Boatman: My Life on Upstate Waterways. LC 77-21909. (York State Bks.). (Illus.). 240p. 1984. pap. 12.95 (ISBN 0-8156-0191-3). Syracuse U Pr.

Inland & Maritime Waterways & Ports: Proceedings of the XXV Congress of the Permanent International Association of Navigation Congresses, (PIANC) Edinburgh, Scotland, 11 vols. Incl. Section 1: Inland Waterways & Ports. 190.00 (ISBN 0-08-026753-X); Section 2: Maritime Ports & Seaways. 190.00 (ISBN 0-08-027278-9). (Illus.). 2750p. 1981. 400.00 (ISBN 0-08-026750-5). Pergamon.

Priestley, Joseph. Priestley's Navigable Rivers & Canals, 1831. (Illus.). 702p. 1969. 7.50 (ISBN 0-7153-4395-5). David & Charles.

INTRODUCTION OF ANIMALS

see Animal Introduction

INTRODUCTION OF PLANTS

see Plant Introduction

INTRUSIONS (GEOLOGY)

Gilbert, Grove K. Report of the Geology of the Henry Mountains: U.S. Geographical & Geological Survey of the Rocky Mounntain Region. Albritton, Claude C., Jr., ed. LC 77-6519. (History of Geology Ser.). (Illus.). 1978. Repr. of 1877 ed. lib. bdg. 21.00x (ISBN 0-405-10441-3). Ayer Co Pubs.

INTUITIONISTIC MATHEMATICS

Croft, H. & Guy, R. K. Unsolved Problems in Intuitive Mathematics: Unsolved Problems in Number Theory, Vol. 1. (Problem Books in Mathematics Ser.). (Illus.). 160p. 1981. 22.00 (ISBN 0-387-90593-6). Springer Verlag.

Dummett, Michael & Minio, Robert. Elements of Intuitionism. (Oxford Logic Guides Ser.). 1977. text ed. 39.95x (ISBN 0-19-853158-3). Oxford U Pr.

Luckhardt, H. Extensional Goedel Functional Interpretation: A Consistency Proof of Classical Analysis. LC 72-96046. (Lecture Notes in Mathematics: Vol. 306). 161p. 1973. pap. 12.00 (ISBN 0-387-06119-3). Springer-Verlag.

Troelstra, A. S. Choice Sequences: A Chapter of Intuitionistic Mathematics. (Oxford Logic Guides). 1977. 19.95x (ISBN 0-19-853163-X). Oxford U Pr.

--Metamathematical Investigations of Intuitionistic Arithmetic & Analysis. (Lecture Notes in Mathematics: Vol. 344). 1973. pap. 23.00 (ISBN 0-387-06491-5). Springer-Verlag.

Van Dalen, D., ed. Brouwer's Cambridge Lectures on Intuitionism. LC 80-41239. 100p. 1981. 29.95 (ISBN 0-521-23441-7). Cambridge U Pr.

INVARIANT IMBEDDING

Angel, Edward & Bellman, Richard. Dynamic Programming & Partial Differential Equations. (Mathematics in Science & Engineering Ser: Vol. 88). 1972. 60.00 (ISBN 0-12-057950-2). Acad Pr.

Bellman, Richard E. Invariant Imbedding & Time-Dependent Transport Processes. LC 64-9242. (Modern Analytic & Computational Methods in Science & Mathematics Ser.: Vol. 2). pap. 68.80 (ISBN 0-317-08610-3, 2007641). Bks Demand UMI.

Lee, E. Stanley. Quasilinearization & Invariant Imbedding. (Mathematics in Science & Engineering Ser.,: Vol. 41). 1968. 70.00 (ISBN 0-12-440250-X). Acad Pr.

Meyer, Gunther H. Initial Value Methods for Boundary Value Problems: Theory & Applications of Invariant Imbedding. (Mathematics in Science & Engineering Ser.). 1973. 55.00 (ISBN 0-12-492950-8). Acad Pr.

Shimizu, Akinao & Aoki, Katsutada. Application of Invariant Imbedding to Reactor Physics. (Nuclear Science & Technology Ser). 1972. 55.00 (ISBN 0-12-640150-0). Acad Pr.

INVARIANTS

see also Invariant Imbedding

Conley, C. Isolated Invariant Sets & the Morse Index. LC 78-1577. (Conference Board of the Mathematical Sciences Ser.: No. 38). 89p. 1982. pap. 15.00 (ISBN 0-8218-1688-8, CBMS 38). Am Math.

Dieudonne, J. A. & Carrell, James B. Invariant Theory: Old & New. 1971. 23.00 (ISBN 0-12-215540-8). Acad Pr.

Franzoni, T. & Vesentini, E. Holomorphic Maps & Invariant Distances. (Mathematics Studies: Vol. 40). 226p. 1980. 42.75 (ISBN 0-444-85436-3, North Holland). Elsevier.

Gherardelli, F., ed. Invariant Theory. (Lecture Notes in Mathematics Ser.: Vol.996). 159p. 1983. pap. 12.00 (ISBN 0-387-12319-9). Springer Verlag.

Grace, John A. & Young, Alfred. The Algebra of Invariants. LC 65-11860. 1965. 16.95 (ISBN 0-8284-0180-2). Chelsea Pub.

Hauptman, H. Crystal Structure Determination: The Role of Cosine Semivariants. LC 72-80574. 407p. 1972. 55.00x (ISBN 0-306-30703-0, Plenum Pr). Plenum Pub.

Hilbert, D., et al. Hilbert's Papers on Invariant Theory. LC 78-17596. (LIE Groups: History Frontiers & Applications Ser.: No. 8). 336p. 1978. 44.00 (ISBN 0-915692-26-0, 991600096). Math Sci Pr.

Kung, Joseph P., ed. Young Tableaux in Combinatorics, Invariant Theory, & Algebra: An Anthology of Recent Work. LC 82-11330. 347p. 1982. 32.00 (ISBN 0-12-428780-8). Acad Pr.

Logan, John D., ed. Invariant Variational Principles. 1977. 49.50 (ISBN 0-12-454750-8). Acad Pr.

Olum, Paul. Invariants for Effective Homotopy Classification & Extension of Mappings. LC 52-42839. (Memoirs: No. 37). 1978. pap. 14.00 (ISBN 0-8218-1237-8, MEMO-37). Am Math.

Sanders, Gerald A. Invariant Ordering. (Janua Linguarum Series Minor: No. 198). 156p. (Orig.). 1975. pap. text ed. 17.60x (ISBN 0-686-22607-0). Mouton.

Smith, Tony E. On the Transformational Invariance of Maximum-Likelihood Estimators. (Discussion Paper Ser.: No. 56). 1972. pap. 4.50 (ISBN 0-686-32223-1). Regional Sci Res Inst.

Springer, T. A. Invariant Theory. LC 77-5890. (Lecture Notes in Mathematics: Vol. 585). 1977. pap. 13.00 (ISBN 0-387-08242-5). Springer-Verlag.

INVARIANTS, DIFFERENTIAL

see Differential Invariants

INVENTIONS

see also Inventors; Patents; Research, Industrial; Technological Innovations; Technology Transfer

Baker, Henry E. Colored Inventor: A Record of Fifty Years. LC 71-75851. (American Negro: His History & Literature, Ser. No. 2). 1969. pap. 1.00 (ISBN 0-405-01943-2). Ayer Co Pubs.

Beard, Charles A., ed. Century of Progress. facs. ed. LC 79-128205. (Essay Index Reprint Ser). 1932. 27.50 (ISBN 0-8369-1903-3). Ayer Co Pubs.

Benner, Reuven. Betting on Ideas: Wars, Invention, Inflation. LC 85-8750. (Illus.). 227p. 1986. lib. bdg. price not set (ISBN 0-226-07400-5). U of Chicago Pr.

Burlingame, Roger. Engines of Democracy: Inventions & Society in Mature America. LC 75-22804. (America in Two Centuries Ser). (Illus.). 1976. Repr. of 1940 ed. 48.50x (ISBN 0-405-07676-2). Ayer Co Pubs.

--March of the Iron Men: A Social History of Union Through Invention. LC 75-22805. (America in Two Centuries Ser). (Illus.). 1976. Repr. of 1938 ed. 42.00x (ISBN 0-405-07677-0). Ayer Co Pubs.

Burt, Forrest D. & Want, Cleve E., eds. Invention & Design. 4th ed. 1985. pap. text ed. 11.95 (ISBN 0-394-33275-X, RanC). Random.

Calvert, Robert, ed. The Encyclopedia of Patent Practice & Invention Management. LC 74-1028. 880p. 1974. Repr. of 1964 ed. 49.50 (ISBN 0-88275-181-6). Krieger.

Carter, E. F. Dictionary of Inventions & Discoveries. rev. 2nd ed. LC 75-37058. 208p. 1976. 14.50x (ISBN 0-8448-0867-9). Crane-Russak Co.

Clarke, Athur C. Profiles of the Future: An Inquiry into the Limits of the Possible. rev. ed. 1984. 15.95 (ISBN 0-03-069783-2). HR&W.

Clarke, Donald. Enciclopedia De los Inventos. 2nd ed. (Espn.). 128p. 1978. 25.50 (ISBN 84-7091-134-1, S-50483). French & Eur.

--How It Works: The Illustrated Science & Invention Encyclopedia. 3rd ed. (Illus.). 3440p. 1983. lib. bdg. 324.95x (ISBN 0-686-39381-3). M Cavendish Corp.

Cohen, Randy & Anderson, Alexandra. Why Didn't I Think of That. (Illus.). 1980. pap. 5.95 (ISBN 0-449-90037-1, Columbine). Fawcett.

Constant, James N. Invention Secrecy Score: Government 30,000-Inventors 0. 97p. (Orig.). 1984. pap. 15.00 ltd. ed. (ISBN 0-930293-00-2). RCS Assocs.

Cook, Chester L. Inventor's Guide in a Series of Four Parts: How to Protect, Search, Compile Facts & Sell Your Invention. rev. ed. (Illus.). 52p. 1981. Repr. of 1979 ed. saddle stitch 11.95 (ISBN 0-9604670-1-7). C L Cook.

Cooper, Grace R. The Sewing Machine: Its Invention & Development. LC 75-619415. (Illus.). 238p. 1977. 27.50x (ISBN 0-87474-330-3). Smithsonian.

Dionne, Narcisse E. Inventaire chronologique des livres, 5 pts. in 1 vol. LC 70-164837. Repr. of 1912 ed. 45.00 (ISBN 0-404-02138-7). AMS Pr.

Fenner, T. W. & Everett, J. L. Inventor's Handbook. 1968. 17.00 (ISBN 0-8206-0070-9). Chem Pub.

Flumiani, C. M. The Theory of Inventiveness. LC 68-23100. (Illus.). 32p. 1972. 49.45 (ISBN 0-913314-15-3). Am Classical Coll Pr.

Fuller, R. Buckminster. Inventions: The Complete Patented Works of R. Buckminster Fuller. LC 83-9797. (Illus.). 356p. 1983. 40.00 (ISBN 0-312-43477-4); deluxe ed. 150.00 (ISBN 0-312-43478-2). St Martin.

--Inventions: The Patented Works of R. Buckminster Fuller. (Illus.). 356p. 1985. pap. 18.95 (ISBN 0-312-43479-0). St Martin.

Gilfillan, S. C. Sociology of Invention. 1970. pap. 4.95x (ISBN 0-262-57020-3). MIT Pr.

Giscard d'Estaing, Valerie-Anne. The World Almanac Book of Inventions. (Illus.). 384p. 1985. pap. 9.95 (ISBN 0-345-32661-X). World Almanac.

Goff, Harry. Inventions Wanted! LC 79-56695. (Illus.). 160p. (Orig.). 1980. pap. 5.95 (ISBN 0-914960-24-5). Academy Bks.

Greene, Orville & Durr, Frank. The Practical Inventor's Handbook. LC 78-26666. (Illus.). 1979. 39.95 (ISBN 0-07-024320-4). McGraw.

Hadamard, Jacques. Psychology of Invention in the Mathematical Field. 1945. pap. text ed. 3.50 (ISBN 0-486-20107-4). Dover.

His Majesties Gracious Grant & Privilege to William Braithwaite, for the Sole Printing & Publishing Musicke, His Way. LC 73-6105. (English Experience Ser.: No. 573). 1973. Repr. of 1636 ed. 3.50 (ISBN 90-221-0573-3). Walter J Johnson.

Illustrated Science & Invention Encyclopedia: How It Works, 23 vols. 1982. 183.54 (ISBN 0-87475-801-7). Stuttman.

Inventions, 2 vols. (British Parliamentary Papers Ser.). 1971. Set. 189.00x (ISBN 0-7165-1450-8, Pub. by Irish Academic Pr Ireland). Biblio Dist.

Inventions. 224p. 1983. pap. 1.95 (ISBN 0-911605-01-0). Avalon Hill.

Jones, David E. The Inventions of Daedalus: A Compendium of Plausible Schemes. LC 81-19605. (Illus.). 204p. 1982. 22.95 (ISBN 0-7167-1412-4); pap. 15.95 (ISBN 0-7167-1413-2). W H Freeman.

Jouffroy, A. Dictionnaire des Inventions et Decouvertes Anciennes et Modernes, 2 vols. Migne, J. P., ed. (Nouvelle Encyclopedie Theologique Ser.: Vols. 35-36). (Fr.). 1424p. Repr. of 1860 ed. lib. bdg. 181.00x (ISBN 0-89241-277-1). Caratzas.

Kivenson, Gilbert. The Art & Science of Inventing. 2nd ed. 256p. 1982. 17.95 (ISBN 0-442-24583-1). Van Nos Reinhold.

Meinhardt, Peter. Inventions, Patents & Trade Marks in Great Britain. 1971 ed. 397p. 25.00 (ISBN 0-686-37380-4). Beekman Pubs.

Model Law for Developing Countries on Inventions. 1965. pap. 7.50 (ISBN 0-686-53017-9, WIPO46, WIPO). Unipub.

Morison, Elting E. Men, Machines, & Modern Times. 1966. 15.00x (ISBN 0-262-13025-4); pap. 6.95x (ISBN 0-262-63018-4). MIT Pr.

Muncheryan, Hrand M. Patent It Yourself. (Illus.). 180p. (Orig.). 1982. 14.95 (ISBN 0-8306-2429-5, 1429); pap. 8.95 (ISBN 0-8306-1429-X). TAB Bks.

National Academy Of Engineering. Process of Technological Innovation. LC 72-601240. (Illus., Orig.). 1969. pap. 5.75 (ISBN 0-309-01726-2). Natl Acad Pr.

National Geographic Society. Those Inventive Americans. LC 75-125340. (Special Publications Ser.). (Illus.). 1971. avail. only from Natl. Geog. 6.95 (ISBN 0-87044-089-6). Natl Geog.

New & Improved... Inventors & Inventions That Have Changed the Modern World. 1981. 40.00x (ISBN 0-686-77432-9, Pub. by Brit Lib England). State Mutual Bk.

Newman, Joseph W. The Energy Machine of Joseph Newman: An Invention Whose Time Has Come. Soule, Evan R., Jr., ed. (Illus.). 287p. 1985. 38.45 (ISBN 0-9613835-1-8). J Newman Pub.

Phillips, Jeremy, ed. Employees' Inventions. 212p. 1981. 32.00 (ISBN 0-317-04164-9). Mansell.

Schmookler, Jacob. Invention & Economic Growth. LC 66-14453. 1966. 20.00x (ISBN 0-674-46400-1). Harvard U Pr.

--Patents, Inventions & Economic Change: Data & Selected Essays. Griliches, Zvi & Hurwicz, Leonid, eds. LC 74-188355. (Illus.). 320p. 1972. 17.50x (ISBN 0-674-65770-5). Harvard U Pr.

Schwenck, James E. & McNair, Eric P. How to Become a Successful Inventor: Design a Gadget in Your Spare Time & Strike It Rich! 1974. 7.95 (ISBN 0-8038-3031-9). Hastings.

Shuldner, Herbert. The Popular Science Book of Gadgets: Ingenious Devices for the Home. Michaelman, Herbert, ed. 1980. 7.98 (ISBN 0-517-54280-3, Michelman Books); pap. 3.98 Outlet (ISBN 0-517-54443-1, Michelman Books). Crown.

Tesla, Nilola & Valic, B. Nikola Tesla: My Inventions. (Illus.). 1977. 30.00x (ISBN 0-89918-777-3, Y-777). Vanous.

Ullrich, Hanns. Standards of Patentability for European Inventions. (IIC Studies: Vol. 1). 137p. 1977. pap. 34.20x (ISBN 3-527-25695-4). VCH Pubs.

Whitehurst, Bert W. Franchise Your Inventions. (Illus.). 70p. 1982. lib. bdg. 15.00x (ISBN 0-686-78701-3); pap. text ed. 10.00x (ISBN 0-686-78702-1). Galleon-Whitehurst.

The World Almanac of Inventions, Campagnie 12. 384p. (Orig.). 1985. pap. 9.95 (ISBN 0-911818-57-X). World Almanac.

Yerkes, Robert M., ed. New World of Science. facs. ed. LC 68-58818. (Essay Index Reprint Ser). 1920. 27.50 (ISBN 0-8369-1166-0). Ayer Co Pubs.

INVENTIONS–HISTORY

Daumas, Maurice, ed. The History of Technology & Invention, Vol. 3. (Illus.). 1978. 30.00 (ISBN 0-517-52037-0). Crown.

--History of Technology & Invention: Progress Through the Ages, 2 vols. Incl. Vol. 1. The Origins of Technological Civilization (ISBN 0-517-50727-7); Vol. 2. The First Stages of Mechanization (ISBN 0-517-50728-5). (Illus.). 1969. 30.00 ea. Crown.

--A History of Technology & Invention Progress Through the Ages, Vol. 1: The Origins of Technological Civilization to 1450. 520p. 1980. 60.00x (ISBN 0-7195-3730-4, Pub. by Murray Pubs England). State Mutual Bk.

--History of Technology & Invention Process Through the Ages, Vol. 2: The First Stages of Mechanization 1450-1725. 694p. 1980. 60.00x (ISBN 0-7195-3731-2, Pub. by Murray Pubs England). State Mutual Bk.

--A History of Technology & Invention Progress Through the Ages, Vol. 3: The Expansion of Mechanization 1725-1860. 700p. 1980. 60.00x (ISBN 0-7195-3732-0, Pub. by Murray Pubs England). State Mutual Bk.

Dutton, H. I. The Patent System & Inventive Activity During the Industrial Revolution, 1750-1852. LC 83-18803. 232p. 1984. 32.50 (ISBN 0-7190-0997-9, Pub. by Manchester Univ Pr). Longwood Pub Group.

Giedion, Siegfried. Mechanization Takes Command. (Illus.). 1969. pap. 13.95 (ISBN 0-393-00489-9, Norton Lib). Norton.

Hatfield, Stafford H. The Conquest of Thought by Invention in the Mechanical State of the Future. 1979. Repr. of 1929 ed. lib. bdg. 15.00 (ISBN 0-8495-2289-7). Arden Lib.

Hathaway, Esse V. Partners in Progress. facs. ed. LC 68-29213. (Essay Index Reprint Ser.). 1968. Repr. of 1935 ed. 18.00 (ISBN 0-8369-0518-0). Ayer Co Pubs.

Heher, J. M., ed. Great Sciencitific Adventures One As Reported in the New York Times: Program Guide. 155p. 1981. pap. text ed. 7.95 (ISBN 0-667-00594-3). Microfilming Corp.

Kaempffert, Waldemar B., ed. A Popular History of American Invention, 2 vols. LC 74-9385. (Illus.). Repr. of 1924 ed. Set. 125.00 (ISBN 0-404-11921-2); Vol. 1. (ISBN 0-404-11922-0); Vol. 2. (ISBN 0-404-11923-9). AMS Pr.

McCloy, Shelby T. French Inventions of the Eighteenth Century. LC 52-5903. pap. 63.80 (ISBN 0-317-10751-8, 2000284). Bks Demand UMI.

Rickards, Maurice, ed. New Inventions. 1969. 3.50 (ISBN 0-8038-5012-3). Hastings.

Saltz, Elizabeth. Growth of American Culture & Inventions. 64p. 1981. pap. 6.95 (ISBN 0-89962-228-3). Todd & Honeywell.

The Smithsonian Book of Invention. LC 78-62960. (Illus.). 256p. 1978. 19.95 (ISBN 0-89599-002-4, Dist. by Norton). Smithsonian Bks.

Swanson, James M. Scientific Discoveries & Soviet Law: A Sociohistorical Analysis. LC 84-12020. (University of Florida Social Sciences Monographs: No. 70). viii, 150p. 1985. pap. 11.00 (ISBN 0-8130-0805-0). U Presses Fla.

Usher, Abbott P. A History of Mechanical Inventions. rev. ed. LC 52-10758. pap. 115.80 (ISBN 0-317-10785-2, 2001620). Bks Demand UMI.

INVENTORS

see also Engineers

Baker, Henry E. Colored Inventor: A Record of Fifty Years. LC 71-75851. (American Negro: His History & Literature, Ser. No. 2). 1969. pap. 1.00 (ISBN 0-405-01943-2). Ayer Co Pubs.

British Library Science Reference Library Staff. A Who's Who of Invention, 1617-1980. 1985. diazo microfiche 450.00 (ISBN 0-317-26889-9, Pub. by British Lib). Longwood Pub Group.

British Library's Science Reference Library Staff. A Who's Who of Invention, 1617-1980: Nineteen Hundred to Nineteen Hundred-Eighty. 1985. microfiche 360.00 (ISBN 0-317-26888-0, Pub. by British Lib). Longwood Pub Group.

Burt, McKinley, Jr. Black Inventors of America. 1969. pap. 7.85 (ISBN 0-89420-095-X, 296959). Natl Book.

Constant, James N. Invention Secrecy Score: Government 30,000-Inventors 0. 97p. (Orig.). 1984. pap. 15.00 ltd. ed. (ISBN 0-930293-00-2). RCS Assocs.

Emanuels, George. John Muir Inventor. LC 85-60102. (Illus.). 1985. 16.50 (ISBN 0-914330-74-8); deluxe ed. 22.50. Diablo Bks.

Evans, David. The Ingenious Mr. Pedersen. 132p. 1979. Repr. of 1978 ed. text ed. 10.75x (ISBN 0-904387-29-1, Pub. by Alan Sutton England). Humanities.

Feldman, Anthony & Ford, Peter. Scientists & Inventors. (Horizons of Knowledge Ser.). (Illus.). 1979. 24.95 (ISBN 0-87196-410-4). Facts on File.

Freeland, Al. Uncle Al: The Life & Times of Inventor-Marksman Albin Freeland. (Illus.). 304p. 1982. 8.95 (ISBN 0-940286-51-3). Quest Pub IL.

Hathaway, Esse V. Partners in Progress. facs. ed. LC 68-29213. (Essay Index Reprint Ser.). 1968. Repr. of 1935 ed. 18.00 (ISBN 0-8369-0518-0). Ayer Co Pubs.

Iles, George. Leading American Inventors. facs. ed. LC 68-8472. (Essay Index Reprint Ser). 1968. Repr. of 1912 ed. 26.50 (ISBN 0-8369-0557-1). Ayer Co Pubs.

The Indefatigable Mr. Woodcroft' The Legacy of Invention. 1981. pap. 10.00x (ISBN 0-902914-53-7, Pub. by Brit Lib England). State Mutual Bk.

Johnson, F. Roy & Stephenson, Frank, Jr. The Gatling Gun & Flying Machine of Richard & Henry Gatling. (Illus.). 1979. 9.50 (ISBN 0-930230-37-X). Johnson NC.

Kirby, Richard S., ed. Inventors & Engineers of Old New Haven. facs. ed. LC 78-86765. (Essay Index Reprint Ser). 1939. 15.00 (ISBN 0-8369-1144-X). Ayer Co Pubs.

Kurylo, Friedrich & Susskind, Charles. Ferdinand Braun: A Life of the Nobel Prize Winner & Inventor of the Cathode-Ray Oscilloscope. (Illus.). 304p. 1981. 42.50x (ISBN 0-262-11077-6). MIT Pr.

Lectures for Inventors, Delivered at the Public Library December 1981-June 1982. 1983. pap. 7.00 (ISBN 0-89073-072-5). Boston Public Lib.

McGran, Philip. The Individual Inventor: What He Should Know about the U. S. Patent System. 24p. 1982. 5.00 (ISBN 0-682-49905-6). Exposition Pr FL.

National Geographic Society. Those Inventive Americans. LC 75-125340. (Special Publications Ser.). (Illus.). 1971. avail. only from Natl. Geog. 6.95 (ISBN 0-87044-089-6). Natl Geog.

Neumeyer, Fredrik & Stedman, John C. Employed Inventor in the United States. 1971. 42.50x (ISBN 0-262-14006-3). MIT Pr.

New & Improved... Inventors & Inventions That Have Changed the Modern World. 1981. 40.00x (ISBN 0-686-77432-9, Pub. by Brit Lib England). State Mutual Bk.

Oppenheimer, Francis J. Ezekiel to Einstein: Israel's Gifts to Science & Invention. facsimile ed. LC 70-167398. (Essay Index Reprint Ser). Repr. of 1940 ed. 9.75 (ISBN 0-8369-2438-X). Ayer Co Pubs.

Santos, Nelly E. Espanol Comercial. (Illus.). 410p. 1981. text ed. 21.95 scp (ISBN 0-06-045725-2, HarpC); instr's. manual avail. (ISBN 0-06-365825-9). Har-Row.

Sherlock, V. M. The Fever Man: A Biography of Dr. John Gorrie. LC 82-81065. 152p. 17.00 (ISBN 0-9610620-0-2). Medallion Pr.

Strickland, Mary. Memoir of the Life, Writings & Mechanical Inventions of Edmund Cartwright. LC 70-149329. (Documents of Social History). Repr. of 1843 ed. lib. bdg. 37.50x (ISBN 0-678-07769-X). Kelley.

Tesla, Nikola. Inventions, Researchs, & Writings. Repr. of 1894 ed. 14.00 (ISBN 0-913022-23-3). Angriff Pr.

Tesla, Nilola & Valic, B. Nikola Tesla: My Inventions. (Illus.). 1977. 30.00x (ISBN 0-89918-777-3, Y-777). Vanous.

Tomlinson, Norman. Louis Brennan C. B. Inventor Extraordinaire. 1981. 35.00x (ISBN 0-905540-18-2, Pub. by Hollewell Pubns). State Mutual Bk.

Wile, Frederic W. Emile Berliner: Maker of the Microphone. LC 74-4699. (Telecommunications Ser). (Illus.). 380p. 1974. Repr. of 1926 ed. 29.00x (ISBN 0-405-06062-9). Ayer Co Pubs.

Williams, James C. At Last Recognition in America, Vol. 1. LC 78-3007. (Illus.). 1978. 18.50 (ISBN 0-931564-00-X). BCA Pub.

INVERSE FUNCTIONS

see Functions, Inverse

INVERSIONS (GEOMETRY)

see also Involutes (Mathematics)

Bakelman, I. Ya. Inversions. Teller, Joan W. & Williams, Susan, trs. from Rus. LC 74-5727. (Popular Lectures in Mathematics Ser). 82p. 1975. pap. text ed. 4.50x (ISBN 0-226-03499-2). U of Chicago Pr.

Brichant, Francis. Force-Commutated Inverters: Design & Industrial Applications. Griffin, E., tr. from Fr. (Illus.). 200p. 1984. 34.95x (ISBN 0-02-948680-7). Macmillan.

Kim, Scott. Inversions: A Catalog of Calligraphic Cartwheels. 125p. 1985. pap. 9.95 (ISBN 0-262-61041-8, 00277216, Pub. by Bradford). MIT Pr.

Twomey, S. Introduction to the Mathematics of Inversion in Remote Sensing & Indirect Measurements. (Developments in Geomathematics Ser.: Vol. 3). 244p. 1977. 85.00 (ISBN 0-444-41547-5, North Holland). Elsevier.

INVERTEBRATES

see also Arachnida; Arthropoda; Brachiopoda; Coelenterata; Crustacea; Echinodermata; Insects; Mollusks; Myriapoda; Nervous System–Invertebrates; Polyzoa; Protozoa; Sponges; Worms

Acton, Ronald T., et al. Invertebrate Immune Defense Mechanisms. 1973. 23.50x (ISBN 0-8422-7054-X). Irvington.

Adiyodi, K. G. & Adiyodi, R. G. Reproductive Biology of Invertebrates: Spermatogenesis & Sperm Function, Vol. 2. 692p. 1983. 94.00 (ISBN 0-471-90071-0). Wiley.

Adiyodi, K. G. & Adiyodi, Rita G. Reproductive Biology of Invertebrates, Oogenesis, Oviposition & Oosorption, Vol. 1. LC 81-16355. 770p. 1983. 117.95 (ISBN 0-471-10128-1, Pub. by Wiley-Interscience). Wiley.

Alexander, R. McNeill. The Invertebrates. LC 78-6275. (Illus.). 1979. 82.00 (ISBN 0-521-22120-X); pap. 24.95 (ISBN 0-521-29361-8). Cambridge U Pr.

Allen, Richard K. Common Intertidal Invertebrates of Southern California. 1976. 11.95 (ISBN 0-917962-10-9). Peek Pubns.

Autrum, H., ed. Comparative Physiology & Evolution of Vision in Invertebrates: A: Invertebrate Photoreceptors. LC 78-21470. (Handbook of Sensory Physiology: Vol. 7, Pt. 6A). (Illus.). 1979. 187.00 (ISBN 0-387-08837-7). Springer-Verlag.

--Comparative Physiology & Evolution of Vision in Invertebrates B: Invertebrate Visual Centers & Behavior I. (Handbook of Sensory Physiology: Vol. VII, Pt. 6B). (Illus.). 650p. 1980. 161.00 (ISBN 0-387-08703-6). Springer-Verlag.

--Comparative Physiology & Evolution of Vision in Invertebrates C: Invertebrate Visual Centers & Behavior II. (Handbook of Sensory Physiology Ser.: Vol. VII-6c). (Illus.). 660p. 1981. 161.00 (ISBN 0-387-10422-4). Springer-Verlag.

Baker, C. F. Invertebrata Pacifica. 197p. 1969. Repr. of 1907 ed. 40.00x (ISBN 0-317-07103-3, Pub. by EW Classey UK). State Mutual Bk.

Barnes, Robert D. Invertebrate Zoology. 4th ed. 1980. text ed. 39.95 (ISBN 0-03-056747-5, CBS C). SCP.

Barrington, E. J. Intervertebrate Structure & Function. 2nd ed. 765p. 1979. pap. 24.95x (ISBN 0-470-26503-5). Halsted Pr.

Barth, Robert H. & Broshears, Robert. The Invertebrate World. 1982. text ed. 37.95 (ISBN 0-03-013276-2, CBS C). SCP.

Beck, D Elden & Braithwaite, Lee F. Invertebrate Zoology: Laboratory Workbook. 3rd ed. (Illus.). 1968. spiral bdg. 16.95x (ISBN 0-8087-0211-4). Burgess.

Beklemishev, V. N. Principles of Comparative Anatomy of Invertebrates, 2 Vols. Kabata, Z., ed. McLennan, J. M., tr. LC 70-97749. 1970. Set. 60.00x (ISBN 0-226-04175-1). U of Chicago Pr.

Borradaile, L. A. & Potts, F. A. Invertebrata. 4th ed. 1961. text ed. 44.50 (ISBN 0-521-04285-2). Cambridge U Pr.

Brusca, Richard C. Common Intertidal Invertebrates of the Gulf of California. rev. ed. LC 79-19894. (Illus.). 513p. 1980. pap. 26.95x (ISBN 0-8165-0682-5). U of Ariz Pr.

Buchsbaum, Mildred & Buchsbaum, John. Living Invertebrates. (Illus.). 800p. 1985. text ed. 35.00 (ISBN 0-86542-312-1). Blackwell Pubns.

Buchsbaum, Ralph. Animals Without Backbones. rev., 2nd ed. LC 48-9508. (Illus.). 405p. 1975. pap. 14.00x (ISBN 0-226-07870-1). U of Chicago Pr.

Buikema, Jr. & Cairns, Jr., eds. Aquatic Invertebrate Bioassays- STP 715. 218p. 1980. 24.00 (ISBN 0-8031-0802-8, 04-715000-16). ASTM.

Buttner-Kolisko, Agnes. Plankton Rotifers: Biology & Taxonomy. Kolisko, G., tr. from German. (Die Binnengewaesser). (Illus.). 146p. 1974. pap. text ed. 19.25x (ISBN 0-318-00462-3). Lubrecht & Cramer.

Calow, P. Invertebrate Biology: A Functional Approach. LC 81-6162. 224p. 1981. pap. 23.95x (ISBN 0-470-27238-4). Halsted Pr.

Carter, G. S. A General Zoology of the Invertebrates. (Illus.). 1965. text ed. 17.95 (ISBN 0-8464-1166-0). Beekman Pubs.

Chatton, E. Les Peridiniens Parasites. 1975. Repr. lib. bdg. 63.00x (ISBN 3-87429-100-6). Lubrecht & Cramer.

Cheng, Thomas C., ed. Pathogens of Invertebrates: Application in Biological Control & Transmission Mechanisms. (Comparative Pathobiology Ser.: Vol. 7). 268p. 1984. 49.50x (ISBN 0-306-41700-6, Plenum Pr). Plenum Pub.

Clark, Robert B. Dynamics in Metazoan Evolution: The Origin of the Coelom & Segments. 1964. 45.00x (ISBN 0-19-854353-0). Oxford U Pr.

Clark, W. H. & Adams, T. S., eds. Advances in Invertebrate Reproduction. (Developments in Endocrinology Ser.: Vol. 11). 400p. 1981. 68.50 (ISBN 0-444-00594-3, Biomedical Pr). Elsevier.

Clyne, Densey. The Garden Jungle. 184p. 1980. 27.95 (ISBN 0-00-216411-6, Pub. by W Collins Australia). Intl Spec Bk.

Cohen, Elias. Recognition Proteins, Receptors, & Probes: Invertebrates. LC 84-7878. (Progress in Clinical & Biological Research Ser.: Vol. 157). 228p. 1984. 38.00 (ISBN 0-8451-5007-3). A R Liss.

Cooper, Edwin L., ed. Contemporary Topics in Immunobiology, Vol. 4: Invertebrate Immunology. LC 78-165398. (Illus.). 316p. 1974. 32.50x (ISBN 0-306-37804-3, Plenum Pr). Plenum Pub.

Corning, W. C., et al. Invertebrate Learning. Incl. Vol. 1, Protozoans Through Annelids. 313p 1973. 37.50x (ISBN 0-306-37671-7); Vol. 2, Arthropods & Gastropod Mollusks. 296p. 1973. 37.50x (ISBN 0-306-37672-5); Vol. 3, Cephalopods & Echinoderms. 231p. 1975. 35.00x (ISBN 0-306-37673-3). LC 72-90335. (Illus., Plenum Pr). Plenum Pub.

Crawford, Clifford C. Biology of Desert Invertebrates. (Illus.). 314p. 1981. 42.00 (ISBN 0-387-10807-6). Springer Verlag.

Dales, R. P. Practical Invertebrate Zoology: A Laboratory Manual for the Study of the Major Groups of Invertebrates, Excluding Protochordates. 2nd ed. LC 81-6570. 356p. 1981. 31.95x (ISBN 0-470-27226-0); pap. 34.95. Halsted Pr.

Davidson, Elizabeth W., ed. Pathogenesis of Invertebrate Microbial Diseases. LC 81-65007. 576p. 1981. text ed. 42.50x (ISBN 0-86598-014-4). Allanheld.

Elliott, J. M. Some Methods for the Statistical Analysis of Samples of Benthic Invertebrates. 2nd ed. 1977. 25.00x (ISBN 0-900386-29-0, Pub. by Freshwater Bio). State Mutual Bk.

Engels, W. Advances in Invertebrate Reproduction. 1984. 92.50 (ISBN 0-444-80568-0, I-183-84). Elsevier.

Engemann, Joseph G. & Hegner, Robert W. Invertebrate Zoology. 3rd ed. 1981. text ed. write for info. (ISBN 0-02-333780-X). Macmillan.

Feder & Paul. Distribution & Abundance of Some Epibenthic Invertebrates of Cook Inlet, Alaska. (IMS Report Ser.: No. R80-3). 167p. 12.00 (ISBN 0-914500-11-2). U of AK Inst Marine.

Feder, et al. The Infaunal Invertebrates of the Southeastern Bering Sea. (IMS Report Ser.: No. R78-6). 346p. 22.85 (ISBN 0-914500-13-9). U of AK Inst Marine.

Freeman, W. H. & Bracegirdle, Brian. An Atlas of Invertebrate Structure. (Heinemann Biology Atlases Ser.). 1971. 12.50x (ISBN 0-435-60319-1). Heinemann Ed.

Fretter, V. & Graham, A. A Functional Anatomy of Invertebrates: Excluding Land Anthropods. 1976. 69.50 (ISBN 0-12-267550-9). Acad Pr.

Fretter, Vera & Peake, J., eds. Pulmonates: Vol. 2A, Systematics, Evolution & Ecology. 1979. 72.00 (ISBN 0-12-267502-9). Acad Pr.

--Pulmonates: Vol. 2b, Economic Malacology with Particular Reference to Achatina Fulica. 1979. 39.50 (ISBN 0-12-267541-X). Acad Pr.

George, J. David & George, Jennifer. Marine Life: An Illustrated Encyclopedia of Invertebrates in the Sea. LC 79-10976. 288p. 1979. 69.95 (ISBN 0-471-05675-8, Pub. by Wiley-Interscience). Wiley.

Gosner, K. L. Guide to Identification of Marine & Estuarine Invertebates: Cape Hatteras to the Bay of Fundy. 693p. 1974. 35.50x (ISBN 0-471-31901-5). Wiley.

Greenberg, Idaz. Field Guide to Marine Invertebrates. (Illus.). 1980. plastic card 3.95x (ISBN 0-913008-11-7). Seahawk Pr.

Harrison, Frederick W. & Cowden, Ronald R., eds. Developmental Biology or Freshwater Invertebrates. LC 82-14964. 608p. 1982. 72.00 (ISBN 0-8451-0222-2). A R Liss.
Hart, C. W. & Fuller, Samuel L. H., eds. Pollution Ecology of Estuarine Invertebrates. LC 79-18151. (Water Pollution Ser.). 1979. 55.00 (ISBN 0-12-328440-6). Acad Pr.
Hickman, Cleveland P. Biology of the Invertebrates. 2nd ed. LC 72-83970. (Illus.). 757p. 1973. text ed. 19.95 (ISBN 0-8016-2170-4). Mosby.
Hoffmann, J. & Porchet, M., eds. Biosynthesis, Metabolism & Mode of Action of Inverterbrate Hormones. (Proceedings in Life Sciences Ser.). (Illus.). 570p. 1984. 59.00 (ISBN 0-387-13667-3). Springer-Verlag.
House, M. R. The Origin of Major Invertebrate Groups. (Systematics Association Ser.: No. 12). 1979. 95.00 (ISBN 0-12-357450-1). Acad Pr.
Hoyle, Graham, ed. Identified Neurons & Behavior of Arthropods. LC 77-21603. (Illus.). 608p. 1977. 59.50x (ISBN 0-306-31001-5, Plenum Pr). Plenum Pub.
Kaestner, Alfred. Invertebrate Zoology: Vol. 1, Porifera, Cnidaria, Platyhelminthes, Aschelminthes, Mollusca, Annelida & Related Phyla. LC 67-13947. 597p. 1967. 32.50 (ISBN 0-470-45415-6). Krieger.
--Invertebrate Zoology: Vol. 2 Anachnids & Myriapods. Levi, Herbert W., tr. 482p. 1980. Repr. of 1968 ed. lib. bdg. 27.50 (ISBN 0-88275-692-3). Krieger.
Kummel, Bernhard & Gould, Stephen J., eds. Status of Invertebrate Paleontology, 1953, Vol. 112, No. 3. LC 79-8351. (The History of Paleontology Ser.). (Illus.). 1980. Repr. of 1954 ed. lib. bdg. 19.00x (ISBN 0-405-12715-4). Ayer Co Pubs.
Kurstak, E., et al, eds. Invertebrate Systems in Vitro. 598p. 1980. 133.25 (ISBN 0-444-80181-2, Biomedical Pr). Elsevier.
Kurstak, Edouard & Marqmorosch, Karl, eds. Invertebrate Tissue Culture: Applications in Medicine, Biology & Agriculture. 1976. 55.00 (ISBN 0-12-429740-4). Acad Pr.
Lamy. Invertebrate Oxygen-Binding Proteins. 864p. 1981. 115.00 (ISBN 0-8247-1243-9). Dekker.
Lewis, S. M. & Coster, J., eds. Quality Control in Haematology. 1976. 41.00 (ISBN 0-12-446850-0). Acad Pr.
Light, S. F. Light's Manual: Intertidal Invertebrates of the Central California Coast. 3rd, rev. ed. Smith, Ralph I. & Carlton, James T., eds. (S. F. Light's Laboratory & Field Text in Invertebrate Zoology Ser.). 1975. 37.50x (ISBN 0-520-02113-4). U of Cal Pr.
Lincoln, R. J. & Sheals, J. G. Collecting Invertebrate Animals. LC 79-14530. (Illus.). 1980. 32.50 (ISBN 0-521-22851-4). Cambridge U Pr.
Lindberg, David R. Acmaeidae: Invertebrates of the San Francisco Bay Estuary System, Vol. 2. Lee, Welton, ed. (Illus.). 1981. text ed. 12.50x (ISBN 0-910286-72-8). Boxwood.
Ludwig, William B. & Roach, Lee S. Studies on the Animal Ecology of the Hocking River Basin: The Bottom Invertebrates of the Hocking River & The Plankton of the Hocking River. 1932. 2.00 (ISBN 0-86727-025-X). Ohio Bio Survey.
Lutz, H., ed. Invertebrate Organ Cultures. (Documents in Biology Ser.: Vol. 2). 264p. 1970. 69.50x (ISBN 0-677-30100-6). Gordon.
Maramorosch, Karl, ed. Invertebrate Immunity: Mechanisms of Invertebrate Vector-Parasite Relations. 1975. 55.00 (ISBN 0-12-470265-1). Acad Pr.
Maramorosch, Karl & Mitsuhashi, Jun, eds. Invertebrate Cell Culture Applications. 245p. 1982. 29.50 (ISBN 0-12-470290-2). Acad Pr.
Meglitsch, Paul A. Invertebrate Zoology. 2nd ed. (Illus.). 1972. text ed. 28.95x (ISBN 0-19-501522-3). Oxford U Pr.
Mitchell, D. H. & Johnson, T. E. Invertebrate Models in Aging Research. 208p. 1984. 69.00 (ISBN 0-8493-5823-X). CRC Pr.
Morris, Robert H., et al. Intertidal Invertebrates of California. LC 77-92946. (Illus.). 904p. 1980. 48.75x (ISBN 0-8047-1045-7). Stanford U Pr.
Morris, S. Conway, et al, eds. The Origins & Relationships of Lower Invertebrates. (Illus.). 400p. 1985. 59.00x (ISBN 0-19-857181-X). Oxford U Pr.
Olive, John H. & Smith, Kenneth R. Benthic Macroinvertebrates As Indexes of Water Quality in the Scioto River Basin, Ohio. 1975. 8.00 (ISBN 0-86727-077-2). Ohio Bio Survey.
Pechenik, Jan A. Biology of the Invertebrates. 1985. text ed. write for info. (ISBN 0-87150-450-2, 40N4621, Prindle). PWS Pubs.
Prasad, S. N. Life of Invertebrates. 990p. 1980. text ed. 50.00 (ISBN 0-7069-1042-7, Pub. by Vikas India). Advent NY.
Ramsay, James A. Physiological Approach to the Lower Animals. 2nd ed. LC 68-21398. (Illus.). 1968. pap. 12.95x (ISBN 0-521-09537-9). Cambridge U Pr.
Ratcliffe, N. A. & Rowley, A. F., eds. Invertebrate Blood Cells: General Aspects, Animals Without True Circulatory Systems to Cephalopods, Vol. 1. LC 80-41248. 1981. 79.50 (ISBN 0-12-582101-8). Acad Pr.
Richards, K. S., ed. Biology of the Integument: Invertebrates, Vol. 1. (Illus.). 800p. 1984. 130.00 (ISBN 0-387-13062-4). Springer-Verlag.
Robison, R. A., ed. Treatise on Invertebrate Paleontology, Pt. W, Suppl. 2: Conodonta. LC 53-12913. (Illus.). 1981. 18.00 (ISBN 0-8137-3028-7). Geol Soc.
Rozsa, K. S., ed. Neurotransmitters in Invertebrates: Proceedings of a Satellite Symposium of the 28th International Congress of Physiological Sciences, Veszprem, Hungary, 1980. LC 80-42251. (Advances in Physiological Sciences: Vol. 22). (Illus.). 400p. 1981. 55.00 (ISBN 0-08-027343-2). Pergamon.
Russell-Hunter, W. D. A Life of Invertebrates. 1979. text ed. write for info. (ISBN 0-02-404620-5). Macmillan.
Salanki. Neurobiology of Invertebrates: Gastropoda Brain. 1976. 47.00 (ISBN 0-9960001-3-5, Pub. by Akademiai Kaido Hungary). Heyden.
Salanki, J., ed. Neurobiology Invertebrates: Proceedings of a Satellite Symposium of the 28th International Congress of Physiological Sciences, Tihany, Hungary, 1980, Vol. 23. LC 80-42252. (Illus.). 400p. 1981. 55.00 (ISBN 0-08-027344-0). Pergamon.
--Neurobiology of Invertebrates: Mechanism & Rhythm Regulation. 1973. 47.00 (ISBN 0-9960001-3-5, Pub. by Akademiai Kaido Hungary). Heyden.
Sawyer, Roger H. & Showman, Richard M., eds. The Cellular & Molecular Biology of Invertebrate Development. (Belle W. Baruch Library in Marine Science: Vol. 15). 1985. 39.95 (ISBN 0-87249-464-0). U of SC Pr.
Shelton, G. A., ed. Electrical Conduction & Behavior in "Simple" Invertebrates. (Illus.). 1982. 98.00x (ISBN 0-19-857171-2). Oxford U Pr.
Sherman, Irwin W. & Sherman, Vilia G. The Invertebrates: Function & Form: A Laboratory Guide. 2nd ed. (Illus.). 352p. 1976. pap. text ed. write for info. (ISBN 0-02-409840-X). Macmillan.
Smith, R. I., et al. Keys to Marine Invertebrates of the Woods Hole Region. (Illus.). 1964. pap. 6.50x (ISBN 0-912544-01-5). Marine Bio.
Sparks, Albert K. Invertebrate Pathology: Noncommunicable Diseases. 1972. 67.00 (ISBN 0-12-656450-7). Acad Pr.
Spotte, Stephen. Fish & Invertebrate Culture: Water Management in Closed Systems. 2nd ed. LC 78-10276. 179p. 1979. 23.50x (ISBN 0-471-02306-X, Pub. by Wiley-Interscience). Wiley.
Stancyk, Stephen E., ed. Reproductive Ecology of Marine Invertebrates. LC 79-13841. (Belle W. Baruch Library in Marine Science Ser.). xvi, 284p. 1979. lib. bdg. 39.95x (ISBN 0-87249-379-2). U of SC Pr.
Vago, C. Invertebrate Tissue Culture. 1971-72. Vol. 1. 68.00 (ISBN 0-12-709901-8); Vol. 2. 68.00 (ISBN 0-12-709902-6). Acad Pr.
Wagstaffe, Reginald & Fidler, J. Havelock. Preservation of Natural History Specimens. Incl. Vol. 1. Invertebrates. (Illus.). 220p. (ISBN 0-8464-0749-3); Vol. 2. Vertebrates, Geology, & Botany. (Illus.). 420p. (ISBN 0-8464-0750-7). 1971. 49.00x set (ISBN 0-8464-0751-5). Beekman Pubs.
Wesenberg-Lund, C. Biologie der Suesswassertiere: Wirbellose Tiere. (Illus.). 1967. 56.00 (ISBN 3-7682-0426-X). Lubrecht & Cramer.
Wessells, Norman K., intro. by. Vertebrate Structures & Functions: Readings from Scientific American. LC 73-17004. (Illus.). 440p. 1974. text ed. 25.95x (ISBN 0-7167-0890-6); pap. text ed. 13.95x (ISBN 0-7167-0889-2). W H Freeman.
Wolken, Jerome J. Invertebrate Photoreceptors: A Comparative Analysis. 1971. 36.00 (ISBN 0-12-762350-7). Acad Pr.
Zoological Society Of London - 23rd Symposium. Invertebrate Receptors. Newall, ed. 1968. 54.00 (ISBN 0-12-613323-9). Acad Pr.

INVERTEBRATES, FOSSIL

see also names of individual fossil phyla, classes, orders, etc. e.g. Mollusks, Fossil

Boardman, Richard S., et al, eds. Fossil Invertebrates. (Illus.). 956p. 1985. pap. text ed. 40.00x (ISBN 0-86542-302-4). Blackwell Sci.
Dacque, Edgar. Vergleichende Biologische Formenkunde der Fossilen Niederen Tiere: Biological Comparative Morphology of Lower Fossil Animals. Gould, Stephen J., ed. LC 79-8329. (The History of Paleontology Ser.). (Ger., Illus.). 1980. Repr. of 1921 ed. lib. bdg. 74.50x (ISBN 0-405-12710-3). Ayer Co Pubs.
Hartzschel, Walter. Treatise on Invertebrate Paleontology, Pt. W., Suppl. 1: Miscellanea, (Trace Fossils & Problematica) 2nd. rev. & enl. ed. LC 53-12913. (Illus.). 1975. 20.00 (ISBN 0-8137-3027-9). Geol Soc.
Lehman, Urich & Hillmer, G. Fossil Invertebrates. Lettau, J., tr. LC 82-9419. (Cambridge Earth Science Ser.). (Illus.). 240p. 1983. 42.50 (ISBN 0-521-24856-6); pap. 14.95 (ISBN 0-521-27028-6). Cambridge U Pr.
Moore, Raymond C. Treatise on Invertebrate Paleontology, Pt. U: Echinodermata 3, 2 vols. LC 53-12913. (Illus.). 1966. 27.50 (ISBN 0-8137-3022-8). Geol Soc.
Moore, Raymond C., ed. Treatise on Invertebrate Paleontology, Pt. C: Protista 2 (Foraminiferida, et, 2 vols. LC 53-12913. 1964. 37.00 (ISBN 0-8137-3003-1). Geol Soc.
--Treatise on Invertebrate Paleontology, Pt. D: Protista 3 (Radiolaria, Tintinnina) LC 53-12913. (Illus.). 1954. 16.00 (ISBN 0-8137-3004-X). Geol Soc.
--Treatise on Invertebrate Paleontology, Pt. F: Coelenterata. LC 53-12913. (Illus.). 1956. 23.50 (ISBN 0-8137-3006-6). Geol Soc.
--Treatise on Invertebrate Paleontology, Part G: Bryozoa. LC 53-12913. 1953. 16.00 (ISBN 0-8137-3007-4). Geol Soc.
--Treatise on Invertebrate Paleontology, Pt. H: Brachiopoda, 2 vols. LC 53-12913. (Illus.). 1965. 37.50 (ISBN 0-8137-3008-2). Geol Soc.
--Treatise on Invertebrate Paleontology, Pt. I: Mollusca 1. LC 53-12913. (Illus.). 1960. 26.00 (ISBN 0-8137-3009-0). Geol Soc.
--Treatise on Invertebrate Paleontology, Pt. K: Mollusca 3. LC 53-12913. (Illus.). 1964. 23.75 (ISBN 0-8137-3011-2). Geol Soc.
--Treatise on Invertebrate Paleontology, Pt. N: Mollusca 6 (Bivalvia, Vols. 1-2. LC 53-12913. (Illus.). 1969. 38.25 (ISBN 0-8137-3014-7). Geol Soc.
--Treatise on Invertebrate Paleontology, Pt. O: Arthropoda 1. LC 53-12913. (Illus.). 1959. 23.50 (ISBN 0-8137-3015-5). Geol Soc.
--Treatise on Invertebrate Paleontology, Pt. P: Arthropoda 2. LC 53-12913. (Illus.). 1955. 14.00 (ISBN 0-8137-3016-3). Geol Soc.
--Treatise on Invertebrate Paleontology, Pt. Q: Arthropoda 3. LC 53-12913. (Illus.). 1961. 22.75 (ISBN 0-8137-3017-1). Geol Soc.
--Treatise on Invertebrate Paleontology, Pt. R. Arthropoda 4, Vols. 1-2. LC 53-12913. (Illus.). 1969. 26.00 (ISBN 0-8137-3018-X). Geol Soc.
--Treatise on Invertebrate Paleontology, Pt. S: Echinodermata 1, 2 vols. LC 53-12913. (Illus.). 1968. 26.00 (ISBN 0-8137-3020-1). Geol Soc.
--Treatise on Invertebrate Paleontology, Pt. W: Miscellanea. LC 53-12913. (Illus.). 1962. 14.00 (ISBN 0-8137-3024-4). Geol Soc.
Moore, Raymond C. & Teichert, Curt, eds. Treatise on Invertebrate Paleontology: Part T: Echinodermata 2 (Crinoidea, 3 vols. LC 53-12913. (Illus.). 1978. Set. 55.00 (ISBN 0-8137-3021-X); Vol. 1. 27.00 (ISBN 0-686-82905-0); Vol. 2. 26.00 (ISBN 0-686-82906-9); Vol. 3. 13.00 (ISBN 0-686-82907-7). Geol Soc.
Moore, Raymond C., et al. Invertebrate Fossils. 1952. text ed. 56.95 (ISBN 0-07-043020-9). McGraw.
Murray, J. Atlas of Invertebrate Macrofossils. 235p. 1985. 24.95 (ISBN 0-470-20084-7). Halsted Pr.
Richards, Horace G. Catalogue of Invertebrate Fossil Types at the Academy of Natural Sciences of Philadelphia. (Special Publication: No. 8). 222p. (Orig.). 1968. pap. 13.00 (ISBN 0-910006-36-9). Acad Nat Sci Phila.
Robison, R. A., ed. Treatise on Invertebrate Paleontology, Part G: Bryoza, Vol. 1. rev. ed. 1983. 48.00 (ISBN 0-8137-3107-0). Geol Soc.
Robison, Richard A. & Tiechert, Curt, eds. Treatise on Invertebrate Paleontology, Pt. A: Introduction (Fossilization, Biogeography & Biostratigraphy) LC 53-12913. 1979. 25.00 (ISBN 0-8137-3001-5). Geol Soc.
Shimer, Harvey W. & Shrock, Robert R. Index Fossils of North America. (Illus.). 1944. 75.00x (ISBN 0-262-19001-X). MIT Pr.
Tasch, Paul. Paleobiology of the Invertebrates: Data Retrieval from the Fossil Record. 2nd ed. LC 79-14929. 975p. 1980. text ed. 52.95 (ISBN 0-471-05272-8). Wiley.

INVESTMENTS–DATA PROCESSING

Adams, N. Douglas. PC Wizardry on Wall Street: How to Use Your IBM & Compatibles to Invest in the Stock Market. 224p. 1985. 21.95 (ISBN 0-13-655010-X); pap. 14.95 (ISBN 0-13-655002-9). P-H.
Advanced Investment Strategies Inc. Investment Tax Analyst: IBM PC Visicalc. (Wiley Professional Software Ser.). 60p. 1983. incl. disc 150.00x (ISBN 0-471-88953-9). Wiley.
Arnold, Curtis M. Your Personal Computer Can Make You Rich in Stocks & Commodities. LC 83-51498. (Illus.). 300p. 34.95 (ISBN 0-9613048-0-4). M D Weiss Pub.
Bookbinder, Albert I. Computer-Assisted Investment Handbook. LC 82-61048. (Illus.). 220p. 1983. pap. text ed. 19.95 (ISBN 0-916106-03-9). Prog Pr.
Bookstaber, Richard. The Complete Investment Book: Trading Stocks, Bonds & Options with Computer Applications. 416p. 1985. pap. 19.95 (ISBN 0-673-15952-3). Scott F.
Brooks, Herb. Investing with a Computer: A Time-Series Analysis Approach. 1984. 19.95 (ISBN 0-89433-194-9). Petrocelli.
--Investing with a Computer: A Time-Series Analysis Approach. (A Petrocelli Bk.). 1984. 19.95. Van Nos Reinhold.
Computer Strategies. The Law Office Computer Handbook. 150p. 1983. looseleaf 45.00x (ISBN 0-913505-12-9). Computer Strat.
Davis, Jane. The Dynamics of Prostar. 300p. 1985. pap. 19.95 (ISBN 0-87094-669-2). Dow Jones-Irwin.
Dorf, Richard C. Investment Management with Microcomputers. 1984. 16.95 (ISBN 0-8359-3301-6). Reston.
--Investment Management with Your Personal Computer. Compute Editors, ed. (Orig.). 1985. pap. 14.95 (ISBN 0-87455-005-X). Compute Pubns.
Felsen, Jerry. Low-Cost, Personal-Computer-Based Investment Decision Systems. LC 77-83508. 1977. pap. 20.00 (ISBN 0-916376-03-6). CDS Pub.
Levin, Burgess A. The Apple User's Guide to Beating the Stock Market. (Illus.). 192p. 1984. pap. 14.95 (ISBN 0-8359-0137-8). Reston.
Mole. Basic Investment Appraisal. (Illus.). 160p. 1986. pap. 17.95. Butterworth.
Nicholson, Norm. Individual Investor's Microcomputer Resource Guide. (American Association of Individual Investors Financial Planning Library). 196p. 1984. pap. 11.95 (ISBN 0-930369-01-7). Invest Info.
Riley, W. B. & Montgomery, A. Guide to Computer Assisted Investment Analysis. 1982. 21.95 (ISBN 0-07-052916-7); pap. 16.95 (ISBN 0-07-052917-5). McGraw.
Schmeltz, L. R. Playing the Stock & Bond Markets with Your Personal Computer. 308p. 1981. 16.95 (ISBN 0-8306-9647-4); pap. 10.25 (ISBN 0-8306-1251-3, 1251). TAB Bks.
Seiter, Charles & Nichols, Steven. Advanced Money: Planning Investments on Your Computer. 160p. 1985. pap. 9.95 (ISBN 0-201-06598-3). Addison-Wesley.
Stock Market & Investment Software Guide. 244p. 1984. 19.95 (ISBN 0-317-04405-2). Micro Info.
Zomderman, Jon. The Personal Computer Investment Handbook. (Illus.). 160p. (Orig.). 1984. 17.95 (ISBN 0-8306-0807-9); pap. 11.95 (ISBN 0-8306-1807-4, 1807). TAB Bks.

INVOLUTES (MATHEMATICS)

Boltianski, V. G. La Envolvente. (Span.). 88p. 1977. pap. 1.95 (ISBN 0-8285-1452-6, Pub. by Mir Pubs USSR). Imported Pubns.
Khiralla, T. W. On the Geometry of External Involute Spur Gears. LC 76-49243. (Illus.). 1976. 25.00 (ISBN 0-9601752-1-0). T W Khiralla.

IODINE

Control of Iodine in the Nuclear Industry. (Technical Reports Ser.: No. 148). (Illus.). 101p. (Orig.). 1973. pap. 11.50 (ISBN 92-0-025073-4, IDC148, IAEA). Unipub.

IODINE–ISOTOPES

Iodine One Twenty-Nine: Evaluation of Release from Nuclear Power Generation. (NCRP Report Ser.: No. 75). 1984. 10.00 (ISBN 0-913392-65-0). NCRP Pubns.

ION BOMBARDMENT

see also Ion Implantation

Appleton, Zuhr R. Ion Beam & Surface Analysis in Plasma Edge Studies. (Nuclear Science Applications Ser.: Section B). 60p. 1984. 21.00 (ISBN 3-7186-0200-8). Harwood Academic.
Applications of Ion Beams to Materials: 1975. (Institute of Physics Conference Ser.: No. 28). 1975. 67.50 (ISBN 0-9960030-7-X, Pub. by Inst Physics England). Heyden.
Auciello, O. & Kelly, R., eds. Ion Bombardment Modification of Surfaces: Fundamentals & Applications. (Beam Modification of Materials Ser.: No. 1). 468p. 1984. 94.50 (ISBN 0-444-42365-6, I-308-84). Elsevier.
Centre National de la Recherche Scientifique. Ionic Bombardment: Theory & Applications. (Illus.). 360p. 1964. 93.75 (ISBN 0-677-10040-X). Gordon.
Grant, W. A., ed. Low Energy Ion Beams: Proceedings of the Third LEIB Conference, Loughborough, UK, 28-31 March 1983. 120p. 1983. pap. 27.50 (ISBN 0-08-030553-9). Pergamon.
Low-Energy Ion Beams 1977: Salford. (Institute of Physics Conference Ser.: No. 38). 1978. 75.00 (ISBN 0-9960031-8-5, Pub. by Inst Physics England). Heyden.
Mayer, J. W., et al. Ion Implantation. 1970. 59.50 (ISBN 0-12-480850-6). Acad Pr.

Meyer, Otto & Kappeler, Franz, eds. Ion Beam Surface Layer Analysis, 2 vols. Incl. Vol. 1. 494p. 75.00 (ISBN 0-306-35045-9); Vol. 2. 491p (ISBN 0-306-35046-7). 75.00. LC 76-2606. 1976. Set. 138.00x (Plenum Pr). Plenum Pub.

Wilson, I. H., ed. Low-Energy Ion Beams 1980. (Institute of Physics Conference Ser.: No. 54). 1981. 85.00 (ISBN 0-9960033-4-7, Pub. by Inst Physics England). Heyden.

Ziegler, J. F., et al, eds. The Stopping & Range of Ions in Solids. (Stopping & Range of Ions in Matter Ser.: Vol. 1). (Illus.). 150p. 1985. 60.00 (ISBN 0-08-021603-X, Pub. by Aberdeen Scotland). Pergamon.

Ziegler, James F., ed. New Uses of Ion Accelerators. LC 75-16315. 482p. 1975. 65.00x (ISBN 0-306-30853-3, Plenum Pr.). Plenum Pub.

ION EXCHANGE

Anderson, W. P., ed. Ion Transport in Plants. 1973. 97.00 (ISBN 0-12-058250-3). Acad Pr.

Bittar, E. Edward, ed. Membranes & Ion Transport, Vol. 1. pap. 123.50 (ISBN 0-317-29868-2, 2016176). Bks Demand UMI.

Braquet, P., et al, eds. Prostaglandins & Membrane Ion Transport. (Advances in Ion Transport Regulation Ser.). (Illus.). 430p. 1985. text ed. 59.50 (ISBN 0-88167-052-9). Raven.

Brice, David K. Ion Implantation Range & Energy Deposition Distributions, Vol. 1: High Incident Ion Energies. LC 74-34119. 602p. 1975. 95.00x (ISBN 0-306-67401-7, IFI Plenum). Plenum Pub.

Brouillard, F., ed. Physics of Ion-Ion & Electron-Ion Collisions. (NATO ASI Series B, Physics: Vol. 83). 550p. 1983. 79.50 (ISBN 0-306-41105-9, Plenum Pr). Plenum Pub.

Calmon, C. & Gold, H. Ion Exchange for Pollution Control, 2 vols. 1979. Vol. 1, 272p. 76.50 (ISBN 0-8493-5153-7); Vol. 2, 288p. 81.50 (ISBN 0-8493-5154-5). CRC Pr.

Clarkson, D. Ion Transport & Cell Structure in Plants. LC 74-7132. 350p. 1974. text ed. 42.95x (ISBN 0-470-15985-5). Halsted Pr.

Critser, James R., Jr. Ion Exchange-Chromatography: Processes & Equipment, 1973. (Ser. 7-73). 1974. 115.00 (ISBN 0-914428-23-3). Lexington Data.

Eberhard, K. A. Resonances in Heavy Ion Reactions: Bad Honnef, West Germany, 1981 Proceedings. (Lecture Notes in Physics Ser.: Vol. 156). 448p. 1982. 30.00 (ISBN 0-387-11487-4). Springer-Verlag.

Emelity, L. A. Operation & Control of Ion-Exchange Processes for Treatment of Radioactive Wastes. (Technical Reports Ser.: No. 78). (Illus.). 145p. 1967. pap. 10.00 (ISBN 92-0-125067-3, IDC78, IAEA). Unipub.

Flank, William H., ed. Adsorption & Ion Exchange with Synthetic Zeolites. LC 80-18916. (ACS Symposium Ser.: No. 135). 1980. 34.95 (ISBN 0-8412-0582-5). Am Chemical.

Flett, D. S., ed. Ion Exchange Membranes. LC 83-4343. 210p. 1983. 52.95 (ISBN 0-470-27452-2). Halsted Pr.

Hearn. Ion Pair Chromatography. (Chromatographic Science Ser.). 304p. 1985. 65.00 (ISBN 0-8247-7272-5). Dekker.

Helfferich, Friedrich. Ion Exchange. LC 61-15453. (McGraw-Hill Series in Advanced Chemistry). pap. 158.50 (ISBN 0-317-08944-7, 2003414). Bks Demand UMI.

Jacob, M. & Satz, H., eds. Quark Matter Formation & Heavy Ion Collisions: Proceedings of the Bielefeld Workshop, May 10-14, 1982. v, 586p. 1982. 60.00x (ISBN 9971-950-46-4, Pub. by World Sci Singapore); pap. 26.00x (ISBN 9971-950-47-2, Pub. by World Sci Singpore). Taylor & Francis.

Ma, T. S. & Hassan, S. S. Organic Analysis Using Ion-Selective Electrodes. (Analysis of Organic Materials Ser.). 1982. Vol. 1. 45.00 (ISBN 0-12-462901-6); Vol. 2. 59.50 (ISBN 0-12-462902-4). Acad Pr.

Ma, Y. H. & Ausikaitis, J. P., eds. Recent Advances in Adsorption & Ion Exchange. LC 82-24424. (AIChE Symposium). pap. 34.00 (ISBN 0-8169-0243-7, S-219); pap. 17.00 members (ISBN 0-686-47551-8). Am Inst Chem Eng.

Ma, Y. H., et al, eds. Adsorption & Ion Exchange, 1983. (AIChE Symposium Ser.: Vol. 79, No. 230). 85p. 1983. 30.00 (ISBN 0-8169-0267-4). Am Inst Chem Eng.

Marinsky, Jacob A., ed. Ion Exchange, Vol 2. LC 66-29027. pap. 64.00 (ISBN 0-317-08361-9, 2055055). Bks Demand UMI.

--Ion Exchange & Solvent Extraction, Vol. 8. Marcus, Yizhok. 456p. 1981. 65.00 (ISBN 0-8247-1333-8). Dekker.

Marinsky, Jacob A. & Marcus, Yizhok, eds. Ion Exchange & Solvent Extraction, Vol. 5. 294p. 1973. 65.00 (ISBN 0-8247-6061-1). Dekker.

--Ion Exchange & Solvent Extraction, Vol. 7. 1977. 65.00 (ISBN 0-8247-6571-0). Dekker.

Naden, D. & Streat, N., eds. Ion Exchange Technology. LC 84-10145. (Ellis Horwood Series of the Society of Chemical Industry). 742p. 1984. 110.00x (ISBN 0-470-20089-8). Wiley.

Nicolet, M. A. & Picraux, S. T. Ion Mixing & Surface Layer Alloying: Recent Advances. LC 84-14773. (Illus.). 162p. 1985. 32.00 (ISBN 0-8155-1006-3). Noyes.

Palmieri, F., et al, eds. Vectoral Reactions in Electron & Ion Transport in Michondria & Bacteria. (Developments in Bioenergetics & Biomembranes Ser.: Vol. 5). 430p. 1981. 73.75 (ISBN 0-444-80372-6, Biomedical Pr). Elsevier.

Paterson, Russell. An Introduction to Ion Exchange. LC 75-104789. pap. 29.30 (ISBN 0-317-09893-4, 2022545). Bks Demand UMI.

PTC 31-1973. 1974: Ion Exchange Equipment. 1979. pap. text ed. 8.00 (ISBN 0-685-41933-9, C00016). ASME.

Research in Ion Exchange Chromatography. 183p. 1958. 39.50x (ISBN 0-306-10546-2, Consultants). Plenum Pub.

Shatenshtein, A. I. Isotopic Exchange & the Replacement of Hydrogen in Organic Compounds. LC 62-12859. 308p. 1962. 35.00x (ISBN 0-306-10547-0, Consultants). Plenum Pub.

Sherman, John, ed. Adsorption & Ion Exchange-Progress & Future Prospects. LC 84-11020. (AIChE Symposium Ser.: Vol 80, No. 233). 124p. 1984. pap. 36.00 (ISBN 0-8169-0318-2). Am Inst Chem Eng.

Svehla, G. & Wilson, C., eds. Comprehensive Analytical Chemistry: Ion Exchangers in Analytical Chemistry, Vol. 14. 586p. 1982. 123.50 (ISBN 0-444-99717-2). Elsevier.

Sykova, Eva, et al, eds. Ion-Selective Microelectrodes & Their Use in Excitable Tissues. LC 81-1625. 380p. 1981. 39.50x (ISBN 0-306-40723-X, Plenum Pr). Plenum Pub.

Walton, H. F., ed. Ion-Exchange Chromatography. LC 75-31610. (Benchmark Papers in Analytical Chemistry Ser.: Vol. 1). 400p. 1976. 70.00 (ISBN 0-12-787725-8). Acad Pr.

ION EXCHANGE RESINS

see also Gums and Resins

Clearfield, A. Inorganic Ion Exchange Materials. 304p. 1982. 84.50 (ISBN 0-8493-5930-9). CRC Pr.

Kunin, Robert. Ion Exchange Resins. LC 58-6078. 518p. 1972. Repr. of 1958 ed. 32.50 (ISBN 0-88275-065-8). Krieger.

ION FLOW DYNAMICS

see also Magnetohydrodynamics; Plasma (Ionized Gases)

AGARD-NATO. Instrumentation for High Speed Plasma Flow. (Agardographs Ser.: No. 96). 196p. 1966. 69.50 (ISBN 0-677-11020-0). Gordon.

Bock, R., ed. Heavy Ion Collisions, Vol. 3. 674p. 1983. 140.50 (ISBN 0-444-85352-9, North-Holland). Elsevier.

--Heavy Ion Collisions: Heavy Ion Reactors & Microscopic Properties of Nuclear States, Vol. 2. 472p. 1980. 102.25 (ISBN 0-444-85295-6, North-Holland). Elsevier.

Bonnemann, K. H., et al, eds. Ionic Liquids, Molten Salts, & Polyelectrolytes: Berlin (West), 1982 Proceedings. (Lecture Notes in Physics: Vol. 172). 253p. 1982. pap. 17.00 (ISBN 0-387-11952-3). Springer-Verlag.

Broglia, R. A. & Ricci, R. A. Nuclear Structure & Heavy Ion Collisions. (Enrico Fermi Summer School Ser.: Vol. 77). 724p. 1982. 153.25 (ISBN 0-444-85462-2, North-Holland). Elsevier.

Hubler, G. K., et al, eds. Ion Implantation & Ion Beam Processing of Materials: Proceedings of the 3rd Symposium on Ion Implantation & Ion Beam Processing of Materials, Boston, MA, Nov. 1983. (Materials Research Society Symposia Ser.: Vol. 27). 800p. 1984. 95.00 (ISBN 0-444-00869-1, North Holland). Elsevier.

Sakmann, Bert, et al, eds. Single-Channel Recording. 526p. 1983. 50.00x (ISBN 0-306-41419-8, Plenum Pr). Plenum Pub.

Samaras, Demetrios G. Theory of Ion Flow Dynamics. LC 78-153896. 1971. pap. text ed. 8.50 (ISBN 0-486-60309-1). Dover.

Schultz, Stanley, ed. Ion Transport by Epithelia. (Society of General Physiologists Ser.: Vol. 36). 288p. 1981. text ed. 46.00 (ISBN 0-89004-610-7). Raven.

ION IMPLANTATION

Agajanian, A. H., ed. Ion Implantation in Microelectronics: A Comprehensive Bibliography. LC 81-10753. (Computer Science Information Guides Ser.: Vol. 1). 266p. 1981. lib. bdg. 85.00x (ISBN 0-306-65198-X, IFI Plenum). Plenum Pub.

Ashworth, V. & Grant, W. A., eds. Ion Implantation into Metals: Proceedings of the 3rd International Conference on Modification of Surface Properties of Metals by Ion Implantation, Held UMIST, Manchester, UK, June 23-26, 1981. LC 82-5293. 383p. 1982. 77.00 (ISBN 0-08-027625-3). Pergamon.

Chernow, Fred, et al, eds. Ion Implantation in Semiconductors 1976. Brice, David K. LC 77-2980. 754p. 1977. 95.00x (ISBN 0-306-36256-2, Plenum Pr). Plenum Pub.

Crowder, Billy L., ed. Ion Implantation in Semiconductors & Other Materials. LC 73-14789. (IBM Research Symposia Ser.). 654p. 1973. 85.00x (ISBN 0-306-30756-1, Plenum Pr). Plenum Pub.

Eisen, Fred H. & Chadderton, Lewis T., eds. Ion Implantation. LC 71-153515. (Illus.). 480p. 1971. 132.95 (ISBN 0-677-15000-8). Gordon.

Herman, H., ed. Treatise on Materials Science & Technology, Vol. 18: Ion Implantation. 1980. 75.00 (ISBN 0-12-341818-6). Acad Pr.

Hubler, G. K., et al, eds. Ion Implantation & Ion Beam Processing of Materials: Proceedings of the 3rd Symposium on Ion Implantation & Ion Beam Processing of Materials, Boston, MA, Nov. 1983. (Materials Research Society Symposia Ser.: Vol. 27). 800p. 1984. 95.00 (ISBN 0-444-00869-1, North Holland). Elsevier.

Metallurgical Society of AIME. Ion Implantation Metallurgy: Proceedings of a Symposium Held as Part of the Annual Meeting of the Materials Research Society, Cambridge, 1979. Preece, C. M. & Hirvonen, J. K., eds. LC 80-82278. pap. 50.80 (ISBN 0-317-27623-9, 2025064). Bks Demand UMI.

Namba, Susumu, ed. Ion Implantation in Semiconductors: Science & Technology. LC 75-8985. 742p. 1975. 95.00x (ISBN 0-306-30841-X, Plenum Pr). Plenum Pub.

Picraux & Choyke. Metastable Materials Formation by Ion Implantation. (Materials Research Society Symposia Ser.: Vol. 7). 446p. 1982. 83.00 (ISBN 0-444-00692-3, North-Holland). Elsevier.

Ryssel, H. & Glawischnig, H. Ion Implantation Techniques, Berchtesgaden, FRG, 1982. (Springer Series in Electrophysics: Vol. 10). (Illus.). 372p. 1982. 34.00 (ISBN 0-387-11878-0). Springer-Verlag.

Ryssel, H. & Ingolf, R. Ion Implantation. 398p. 1985. 59.95 (ISBN 0-471-10311-X). Wiley.

Ryssell, H. & Glawischnig, H., eds. Ion Implantation-Equipment & Techniques: Proceedings, Berchtesgaden, FRG, 1982. (Springer Series in Electrophysics: Vol. 11). (Illus.). 556p. 1983. 43.00 (ISBN 0-387-12491-8). Springer-Verlag.

Scully, J. C., ed. Ion Implantation & Ion Beam Analysis Techniques in Corrosion Studies. 1977. pap. text ed. 17.50 (ISBN 0-08-021420-7). Pergamon.

Smidt, F. A., ed. Ion Implantation for Materials Processing. LC 83-13147. (Chemical Technology Review: No. 224). (Illus.). 244p. 1984. 32.00 (ISBN 0-8155-0961-8). Noyes.

Vashishta, P., et al, eds. Fast Ion Transport in Solids, Electrodes & Electrolytes. LC 79-18065. 800p. 1979. 106.00 (ISBN 0-444-00353-3, North Holland). Elsevier.

Williams, James S. & Poate, John M., eds. Ion Implantation & Beam Processing. LC 83-71159. 1984. 59.50 (ISBN 0-12-756980-4). Acad Pr.

Wilson, Robert. G. & Brewer, George R. Ion Beams: With Applications to Ion Implantation. LC 79-1345. 512p. 1979. Repr. of 1973 ed. lib. bdg. 31.50 (ISBN 0-88275-899-3). Krieger.

Winterbon, K. Bruce. Ion Implantation Range & Energy Deposition Distributions: Low Incident Ion Energies, Vol. 2. LC 74-34119. 350p. 1975. 75.00x (ISBN 0-306-67402-5, Plenum Pr). Plenum Pub.

Ziegler, James F., ed. Ion Implantation: Science & Technology. 1984. 55.00 (ISBN 0-12-780620-2). Acad Pr.

ION MICROSCOPE

see Field-Ion Microscope

ION ROCKETS

AGARD-NATO. Physics & Technology of Ion Motors. (Agardographs Ser.: No. 88). (Illus.). 438p. 1966. 119.25 (ISBN 0-677-10570-3). Gordon.

Brewer, G. R. Ion Propulsion, Technology & Applications. 550p. 1970. 145.75 (ISBN 0-677-02600-5). Gordon.

IONIC BOMBARDMENT

see Ion Bombardment

IONIC CRYSTALS

see also Polarons

Devreese, J. T., ed. Polarons in Ionic Crystals & Polar Semiconductors: Proceedings of the 1971 Antwerp Advanced Study Institute. 1976. 76.75 (ISBN 0-444-10409-7, North-Holland). Elsevier.

Farge, Y. & Fontana, M. P. Electronic & Vibrational Properties of Point Defects in Ionic Crystals. (Defects in Crystalline Solids Ser.: Vol. 11). 271p. 1979. 68.00 (ISBN 0-444-85272-7, North Holland). Elsevier.

Skobel'tsyn, D. V., ed. Surface Properties of Semiconductors & Dynamics of Ionic Crystals. LC 77-136983. (P. N. Lebedev Physics Institute Ser.: Vol. 48). 148p. 1971. 27.50x (ISBN 0-306-10854-2, Consultants). Plenum Pub.

Sprackling, M. T. The Plastic Deformation of Simple Ionic Crystals. 1977. 47.00 (ISBN 0-12-657850-8). Acad Pr.

IONIC EQUILIBRIUM

Butler, James N. Solubility & Ph Calculations. LC 64-15563. (Chemistry Ser). (Orig.). 1964. pap. 6.95 (ISBN 0-201-00733-9). Addison-Wesley.

Massey, H. S., et al. Electronic & Ionic Impact Phenomena: Slow Collisions of Heavy Particles, Vol. 3. 2nd ed. 1971. 85.00x (ISBN 0-19-851252-X). Oxford U Pr.

Russotti, H. The Study of Ionic Equilibria: An Introduction. (Illus.). 1978. pap. text ed. 16.50x (ISBN 0-582-44175-7). Longman.

Schenk, George H. & Ebbing, Darell D. Qualitative Analysis & Ionic Equilibrium. LC 84-81935. 256p. 1984. pap. text ed. 7.95 (ISBN 0-395-36517-1). HM.

IONIC FLOWS

see Ion Flow Dynamics

IONIC PROPULSION

see Ion Rockets

IONIC SOLUTIONS

Kursanov, et al. Ionic Hydrogenation & Related Reactions. (Chemistry Reviews Supplement Ser.: Soviet Scientific Reviews, Section B, Vol. 1). 230p. 1984. text ed. 112.00 (ISBN 3-7186-0145-1). Harwood Academic.

Smedley, Stuart I. The Interpretation of Ionic Conductivity in Liquids. LC 80-17941. 211p. 1980. 35.00x (ISBN 0-306-40529-6, Plenum Pr). Plenum Pub.

IONIZATION

see also Auger Effect; Chemical Equilibrium; Collisions (Nuclear Physics); Hydrogen-Ion Concentration; Ion Exchange; Ionic Equilibrium; Scintillation Counters

Ahrens, L. H. Ionization Potentials: Some Variations, Implications & Applications. (Illus.). 100p. 1983. 32.00 (ISBN 0-08-025274-5). Pergamon.

Albert, A. & Serjeant, E. P. The Determination of Ionization Constants: A Laboratory Manual. 3rd ed. (Illus.). 150p. 1984. 33.00x (ISBN 0-412-24290-7, NO. 6848, Pub. by Chapman & Hall). Methuen Inc.

Bock, R., ed. Heavy Ion Collisions: Heavy Ion Reactors & Microscopic Properties of Nuclear States, Vol. 1. 676p. 1979. 121.50 (ISBN 0-7204-0738-9, North Holland). Elsevier.

Chin, S. L. & Lambropoulos, Peter. Multiphoton Ionization of Atoms: Quantum Electronics; Principles & Applications. LC 83-98663. 1984. 59.50 (ISBN 0-12-172780-7). Acad Pr.

Duncan, A. B. Rydberg Series in Atoms & Molecules. (Physical Chemistry Ser, Vol. 23). 1971. 45.00 (ISBN 0-12-223950-4). Acad Pr.

Effects of Ionizing Radiation on Aquatic Organisms & Ecosystems. (Technical Reports Ser.: No. 172). (Illus.). 131p. 1976. pap. 16.25 (ISBN 92-0-125076-2, IDC172, IAEA). Unipub.

Gomer, Robert. Field Emission & Field Ionization. LC 60-15237. (Harvard Monographs in Applied Science: No. 9). (Illus.). pap. 51.80 (ISBN 0-317-09155-7, 2002823). Bks Demand UMI.

Harrison, Alex G., ed. Chemical Ionization Mass Spectrometry. 168p. 1983. 60.00 (ISBN 0-8493-5616-4). CRC Pr.

Ionization Conductivity. 1970. 33.00 (ISBN 0-85066-027-0). Taylor & Francis.

Jones, J. R. The Ionization of Carbon Acids. 1974. 39.50 (ISBN 0-12-389750-5). Acad Pr.

Kaufman, Harold R. Fundamentals of Ion-Source Operation. (Illus.). 94p. (Orig.). 1984. pap. 18.00 (ISBN 0-930787-01-3). Commonwealth Sci.

Maerk, T. D. & Dunn, G. H., eds. Electron Impact Ionization. (Illus.). 400p. 1985. 58.50 (ISBN 0-387-81778-6). Springer-Verlag.

Morris. Soft Ionization Biological Mass Spectrometry. 152p. 1982. 49.95x (ISBN 0-471-26188-2, Wiley Heyden). Wiley.

Peterkops, Raimonds. Theory of Ionization of Atoms By Electron Impact. Hummer, D. G., ed. Aronson, Elliot, tr. LC 77-81310. (Illus.). pap. 68.30 (ISBN 0-317-09233-2, 2012203). Bks Demand UMI.

Pungor, E. & Buzas, I., eds. Ion-Selective Electrodes: Proceedings of the 3rd Symposium in 1981. (Analytical Chemistry Symposia Ser.: Vol. 8). 428p. 1982. 95.75 (ISBN 0-444-99714-8). Elsevier.

Serjeant, E. P. & Dempsey, B., eds. Ionization Constants of Organic Acids in Aqueous Solution. (Chemical Data Ser.: Vol. 23). (Illus.). 1979. text ed. 200.00 (ISBN 0-08-022339-7). Pergamon.

Smirnov, B. M. Physics of Weakly Ionized Gas. 428p. 1981. 12.00 (ISBN 0-8285-2197-2, Pub. by Mir Pubs USSR). Imported Pubns.

Sulman, Felix G. The Effect of Air Ionization, Electric Fields, Atmospherics & Other Electric Phenomena on Man & Animal. (Illus.). 424p. 1980. photocopy ed. spiral 40.50x (ISBN 0-398-03930-5). C C Thomas.

Weissmantel, C. & Gautherin, G. Ion Beam Etching, Sputtering & Plating. Date not set. price not set. Elsevier.

IONIZATION OF GASES

see also Air, Ionized; Photoionization of Gases

Almoster Ferreira, M. A., ed. Ionic Processes in the Gas Phase. lib. bdg. 46.50 (ISBN 0-318-00435-6, Pub. by Reidel Holland). Kluwer Academic.

Bowers, Michael T. Gas Phase Ion Chemistry: Vol. 3: Ions & Light. 1984. 75.00 (ISBN 0-12-120803-6). Acad Pr.

Cherrington, B. E. Gaseous Electronics & Gas Lasers. 1979. text ed. 57.00 (ISBN 0-08-020622-0). Pergamon.

Danilov, A. D. Chemistry of the Ionosphere. LC 68-31236. (Monographs in Geoscience Ser.). 296p. 1970. 32.50x (ISBN 0-306-30357-4, Plenum Pr). Plenum Pub.

Lighthill, M. J., et al, eds. Dynamics of Ionized Gases. 1973. 37.90x (ISBN 0-86008-079-X, Pub. by U of Tokyo Japan). Columbia U Pr.

Lindinger, W., et al, eds. Swarms of Ions & Electrons in Gases. (Illus.). 320p. 1984. 35.00 (ISBN 0-387-81823-5). Springer-Verlag.

McDaniel, Earl W. & Mason, Edward A. The Mobility & Diffusion of Ions in Gases. LC 72-13414. 372p. 1973. 37.50 (ISBN 0-471-58387-1, Pub. by Wiley). Krieger.

McIntosh, Robert L. Dielectric Behavior of Physically Absorbed Gases. LC 67-82258. pap. 43.00 (ISBN 0-317-08353-8, 2055411). Bks Demand UMI.

Nasser, Essam. Fundamentals of Gaseous Ionization & Plasma Electronics. LC 77-125275. (Wiley Series in Plasma Physics). pap. 89.30 (ISBN 0-317-08904-8, 2055184). Bks Demand UMI.

Pfotzer, G., et al. Time Pattern of Ionizing Radiation in Balloon Altitudes in High Latitudes, 2 Pts in 1. 1962. pap. 8.90 (ISBN 0-387-02880-3). Springer-Verlag.

Shuler, K. E. & Fenn, J. B., eds. Ionization in High-Temperature Gases. LC 63-23423. (Illus.). 409p. 1963. 30.00 (ISBN 0-317-36824-9); members 15.00 (ISBN 0-317-36825-7). AIAA.

Spitzer, L. Physics of Fully Ionized Gases. 2nd ed. (Interscience Tracts on Physics & Astronomy Ser.). 170p. 1962. 32.50 (ISBN 0-470-81723-2). Wiley.

A Survey of Phenomena in Ionized Gases: Invited Papers. (Proceedings Ser.). (Eng., Fr., Rus. & Ger., Illus.). 1968. pap. 48.50 (ISBN 92-0-030068-5, ISP178, IAEA). Unipub.

IONIZED AIR

see Air, Ionized

IONIZING RADIATION

see also Beta Rays; Cosmic Rays; Gamma Rays; Ultra-Violet Rays; X-Rays

British Nuclear Energy Society, ed. The Applications of Ionizing Radiation in the Chemical & Allied Industries. 74p. 1968. 40.00x (ISBN 0-901948-95-0, Pub. by Brit Nuclear England). State Mutual Bk.

ICRP. Protection Against Ionizing Radiation from External Sources Used in Medicine. (ICRP Publication: No. 33). 74p. 1982. 25.00 (ISBN 0-08-029779-X). Pergamon.

--Protection Against Ionizing Radiation in the Teaching of Science. International Commission on Radiological Protection & Sowby, F. D., eds. (ICRP Publications: No. 36). 14p. 1983. pap. 10.00 (ISBN 0-08-029818-4). Pergamon.

International Commission on Radiation Units. Determination of Dose Equivalents Resulting from External Radiation Sources. LC 84-23053. (ICRU Report Ser.: No. 39). 10p. 1985. pap. text ed. 10.00 (ISBN 0-913394-33-5). Intl Comm Rad Meas.

Ionizing Radiation: Levels & Effects, 2 vol. set. 448p. 1982. pap. 12.50 (ISBN 0-8002-3321-2). Taylor & Francis.

Ionizing Radiation: Sources & Biological Effects. 773p. 1982. 63.00 (ISBN 0-8002-3313-1). Taylor & Francis.

Kathren, Ronald L. & Sanders, Charles L. Ionizing Radiation: Tumorigenic & Tumoricidal Effects. 335p. 1983. 49.95 (ISBN 0-935470-17-4). Battelle.

Mettler, Fred A., Jr. & Moseley, Robert D., eds. Medical Effects of Ionizing Radiation. 304p. 1985. 59.50 (ISBN 0-8089-1704-8, 792896). Grune.

Mladjenovic, M. Radioisotope & Radiation Physics: An Introduction. 1973. 60.00 (ISBN 0-12-502350-2). Acad Pr.

National Research Council Assembly of Life Sciences. Federal Research on the Biological & Health Effects of Ionizing Radiation. 169p. 1981. pap. text ed. 12.50 (ISBN 0-309-03190-7). Natl Acad Pr.

Sources & Effects of Ionizing Radiation. pap. 33.00 (ISBN 0-686-94283-3, UN77/9/1, UN). Unipub.

Tait, W. H. Radiation Detection. LC 80-40240. 1980. text ed. 75.00 (ISBN 0-408-10645-X). Butterworth.

Wasserman, Harvey, et al. Killing Our Own: The Disaster of America's Experience with Atomic Radiation. 1982. 19.95 (ISBN 0-385-28537-X). Delacorte.

Woodhead, A. D., et al, eds. Assessment of Risk from Low-Level Exposure to Radiation & Chemicals: A Critical Overview. (Basic Life Sciences Ser.: Vol. 33). 542p. 1985. 65.00x (ISBN 0-306-42003-1, Plenum Pr). Plenum Pub.

IONOSPHERE

Al'pert, Y. L. Radio Wave Propagation & the Ionosphere, Vol. 1: The Ionosphere. 2nd ed. LC 75-167674. (Illus.). 430p. 1973. 45.00x (ISBN 0-306-17141-4, Consultants). Plenum Pub.

Anastassiades, M. A., ed. Solar Eclipses & the Ionosphere. LC 71-119056. 309p. 1970. 34.50x (ISBN 0-306-30480-5, Plenum Pr). Plenum Pub.

Danilov, A. D. Chemistry of the Ionosphere. LC 68-31236. (Monographs in Geoscience Ser.). 296p. 1970. 32.50x (ISBN 0-306-30357-4, Plenum Pr). Plenum Pub.

Giraud, A. & Petit, M. Ionospheric Techniques & Phenomena. (Geophysics & Astrophysics Monographs: No. 13). 1978. 45.00 (ISBN 90-277-0499-6, Pub. by Reidel Holland); pap. write for info. (ISBN 90-277-0500-3, Pub. by Reidel Holland). Kluwer Academic.

Manning, Laurence A. Bibliography of the Ionosphere: An Annotated Survey Through 1960. 1962. 45.00x (ISBN 0-8047-0125-3). Stanford U Pr.

Ratcliffe, J. A. An Introduction to the Ionosphere & Magnetosphere. LC 74-171680. (Illus.). 200p. 1972. 37.50 (ISBN 0-521-08341-9). Cambridge U Pr.

Rawer, Karl. Ionosphere: Its Significance for Geophysics & Radio Communication. Katz, Ludwig, tr. LC 57-6113. 1957. 11.50 (ISBN 0-8044-4788-8). Ungar.

Risbeth, Henry & Garriott, O. K. Introduction to Ionospheric Physics. (International Geophysics Ser.: Vol. 14). 1969. 49.50 (ISBN 0-12-588940-2). Acad Pr.

Skovli, G., ed. Polar Ionosphere & Magnetospheric Processes. 358p. 1970. 93.75x (ISBN 0-677-13930-6). Gordon.

Symposium On Ionospheric Physics - Alpbach - 1964. High Latitude Particles & the Ionosphere: Proceedings. Maehlum, B., ed. 1965. 65.00 (ISBN 0-12-465550-5). Acad Pr.

IONOSPHERIC RADIO WAVE PROPAGATION

see also Magneto-Ionic Theory

Al'pert, I. L. Radio Wave Propagation & the Ionosphere. LC 61-17727. pap. 101.00 (ISBN 0-317-09200-6, 2020656). Bks Demand UMI.

Al'pert, Y. L. Radio Wave Propagation & the Ionosphere, Vol. 1: The Ionosphere. 2nd ed. LC 75-167674. (Illus.). 430p. 1973. 45.00x (ISBN 0-306-17141-4, Consultants). Plenum Pub.

Al'pert, Y. L. & Fligel', D. S. Propagation of ELF & VLF Waves Near the Earth. LC 75-167674. (Illus.). 280p. 1974. 42.50x (ISBN 0-306-17142-2, Consultants). Plenum Pub.

Alpert, Yakov L., ed. Radio Wave Propagation & the Ionosphere: Propagation of Electromagnetic Waves Near the Earth, Vol. 2. 2nd ed. LC 75-167674. 268p. 1974. 42.50x (ISBN 0-306-17142-2, Plenum Pr). Plenum Pub.

ESRIN-ESLAB Symposium, 2nd Frascati, Italy 23-27, September, 1968. Low-Frequency Waves & Irregularities in the Ionosphere: Proceedings. D'Angelo, N., ed. (Astrophysics & Space Science Library: No.14). 218p. 1969. lib. bdg. 37.00 (ISBN 90-277-0114-8, Pub. by Reidel Holland). Kluwer Academic.

Folkestad, K., ed. Ionospheric Radio Communications. LC 68-20271. 468p. 1968. 42.50x (ISBN 0-306-30336-1, Plenum Pr). Plenum Pub.

Gurevich, A. Nonlinear Phenomena in the Ionosphere. (Physics & Chemistry in Space Ser.: Vol. 10). (Illus.). 1978. 65.00 (ISBN 0-387-08605-6). Springer-Verlag.

Gurevich, A. V. & Tsedilina, E. E. Long Distance Propagation of HF Radio Waves. (Physics & Chemistry in Space: Vol. 12). (Illus.). 350p. 1985. 79.00 (ISBN 0-387-15139-7). Springer-Verlag.

Kasha, Michael A. Ionosphere & Its Interaction with Satellites. (Illus.). 172p. 1969. 57.75 (ISBN 0-677-02090-2). Gordon.

Whale, H. A. Effects of Ionospheric Scattering on Very-Long Distance Radio Communication. LC 76-84765. 179p. 1969. 29.50x (ISBN 0-306-30420-1, Plenum Pr). Plenum Pub.

Yeh, K. C. & Liv, C. H. Theory of Ionospheric Waves. (International Geophysics Ser., Vol. 17). 1972. 70.00 (ISBN 0-12-770450-7). Acad Pr.

IONOSPHERIC RESEARCH

Grandal, Bjorn & Holtet, Jan A., eds. Dynamical & Chemical Coupling of the Neutral & Ionized Atmosphere. (Nato Advanced Study Institute Ser. C: No. 35). 1977. lib. bdg. 47.50 (ISBN 90-277-0840-1, Pub. by Reidel Holland). Kluwer Academic.

Johnson, R. G., ed. Energetic Ion Composition in the Earth's Magnetosphere. 1983. lib. bdg. 93.50 (ISBN 90-2771-562-9, Pub. by Reidel Holland). Kluwer Academic.

IONS

see also Activity Coefficients; Anions; Cations; Complex Ions; Electric Discharges through Gases; Electrolysis; Electrons; Ion Bombardment; Ion Rockets; Ionic Solutions; Metal Ions; Particle Accelerators; Plasma (Ionized Gases); Thermionic Emission

Acrivos, J. V., ed. Physics & Chemistry of Electrons & Ionsin Condensed Matter. 768p. 1984. 99.00 (ISBN 90-277-1799-0, Pub. by Reidel Holland). Kluwer Academic.

Andersen, Hans H., ed. Bibliography & Index of Experimental Range & Stopping Power Data. LC 77-22415. 1978. text ed. 57.00 (ISBN 0-08-021604-8). Pergamon.

Ausloos, P., ed. Kinetics of Ion-Molecule Reactions. LC 79-367. (NATO ASI Ser. B, Physics: Vol. 40). 516p. 1979. 75.00x (ISBN 0-306-40153-3, Plenum Pr). Plenum Pub.

Ausloos, Pierre, ed. Interactions Between Ions & Molecules. LC 74-31389. (NATO ASI Series B; Physics: Vol. 6). 690p. 1975. 95.00x (ISBN 0-306-35706-2, Plenum Pr). Plenum Pub.

Benninghoven, A., ed. Ion Formation from Organic Solids: Proceedings, Muenster, FRG, 1982. (Springer Series in Chemical Physics: Vol. 25). (Illus.). 269p. 1983. 33.00 (ISBN 0-387-12244-3). Springer-Verlag.

Berkowitz, Joseph & Groeneveld, Karl-Ontjes, eds. Molecular Ions: Geometric & Electronic Structures. (NATO ASI Series B, Physics: Vol. 90). 606p. 1983. 89.50x (ISBN 0-306-41264-0, Plenum Pr). Plenum Pub.

Bird, J. R., et al. Ion Beam Techniques in Archaeology & the Arts. 172p. 1984. 26.00 (ISBN 3-7186-0188-5). Harwood Academic.

Brown, H. C., ed. The Nonclassical Ion Problem. LC 76-45175. (Illus.). 301p. 1977. 39.50x (ISBN 0-306-30950-5, Plenum Pr). Plenum Pub.

Christophorou, Loucas G., ed. Electron & Ion Swarms: Proceedings of the Second International Swarm Seminar. (Illus.). 279p. 1981. 25.00 (ISBN 0-08-028084-6). Pergamon.

Copeland, J. L. Transport Properties of Ionic Liquids. 84p. 1974. 28.95 (ISBN 0-677-02830-X). Gordon.

Di Bartolo, Baldassare, ed. Optical Properties of Ions in Solids. LC 75-1190. (NATO ASI Series B, Physics: Vol. 8). 490p. 1975. 75.00x (ISBN 0-306-35708-9, Plenum Pr). Plenum Pub.

Dobler, Max. Ionophores & Their Structures. LC 81-4373. 379p. 1981. 81.50 (ISBN 0-471-05270-1, Pub. by Wiley-Interscience). Wiley.

Eisen, F. H, et al, eds. Ion Beam Processing in Advanced Electronic Materials & Device Technology, Vol. 45. 1985. text ed. 42.00 (ISBN 0-931837-10-3). Materials Res.

Eisenberg, Adi, ed. Ions in Polymers. LC 80-19321. (Advances in Chemistry Ser.: No. 187). 1980. 54.95 (ISBN 0-8412-0482-9). Am Chemical.

Franklin, J. L., ed. Ion-Molecule Reactions, 2 vols. LC 77-179758. 393p. 1972. Vol. 1, 362p. 59.50x (ISBN 0-306-30551-8, Plenum Pr); Vol. 2. 59.50x (ISBN 0-306-30552-6). Plenum Pub.

International Conference on Electron & Ion Beam Science & Technology (8th: 1978: Seattle) Electron & Ion Beam Science & Technology: Eighth International Conference. Bakish, Robert, ed. LC 71-120300. (Illus.). pap. 160.00 (ISBN 0-317-09143-3, 2051539). Bks Demand UMI.

International Conference on Electron & Ion Beam Science & Technology (4th: 1970: Los Angeles) Electron & Ion Beam Science & Technology: Fourth International Conference. Bakish, Robert, ed. LC 71-120300. pap. 160.00 (ISBN 0-317-09158-1, 2051709). Bks Demand UMI.

International Conference on Electron & Ion Beam Science & Technology (6th: 1974: San Francisco) Electron & Ion Beam Science & Technology: Sixth International Conference. Bakish, Robert, ed. LC 71-120300. (Illus.). pap. 151.50 (ISBN 0-317-09166-2, 2051357). Bks Demand UMI.

International Conference on Electron & Ion Beam Science & Technology (7th: 1976: San Francisco) Electron & Ion Beam Science & Technology: 7th International Conference, Proceedings of the Symposium. Bakish, Robert, ed. LC 71-120300. pap. 158.00 (ISBN 0-317-09048-8, 2051977). Bks Demand UMI.

Ions & Ion Pairs & Their Role in Chemical Reactions: International Symposium on Ions & Ion Pairs & Their Role in Chemical Reactions, Syracuse, New York, 1978. 30.00 (ISBN 0-08-022355-9). Pergamon.

Ions Can Do Strange Things. cancelled (ISBN 0-686-13627-6). Twen Fir Cent.

Janev, R. K., et al. Physics of Highly Charged Ions. (Springer Series in Electrophysics: Vol. 13). (Illus.). 350p. 1985. 52.00 (ISBN 0-387-12559-0). Springer-Verlag.

Kessler, M., et al, eds. Ion Measurement in Physiology & Medicine. (Illus.). 290p. 1985. pap. 42.00 (ISBN 0-387-15468-X). Springer-Verlag.

Koryta, Jiri. Ions, Electrodes & Membranes. LC 81-14762. 197p. 1982. 44.95x (ISBN 0-471-10007-2, Pub. by Wiley-Interscience); pap. 22.95x (ISBN 0-471-10008-0, Pub. by Wiley-Interscience). Wiley.

Koryta, Jiri & Stulik, Karel. Ion-Selective Electrodes. 2nd ed. LC 82-25297. 200p. 1984. 49.50 (ISBN 0-521-23873-0). Cambridge U Pr.

Kunin, Robert. Ion Exchange Resins. 2nd ed. LC 84-28886. 526p. 1985. Repr. of 1972 ed. lib. bdg. 32.50 (ISBN 0-89874-837-2). Krieger.

Leffert, H. L., ed. Growth Regulation by Ion Fluxes. LC 80-13986. (Annals of the New York Academy of Sciences: Vol. 339). 335p. pap. 62.00x (ISBN 0-89766-049-8). NY Acad Sci.

Limiting Steps in Ion Uptake by Plants from Soil. (Technical Reports Ser.: No. 65). (Illus.). 154p. 1966. pap. 12.50 (ISBN 92-0-115566-2, IDC65, IAEA). Unipub.

Littmark, U. & Ziegler, J. F. Handbook of Range Distributions for Energetic Ions in All Elements. LC 79-27825. (The Stopping & Ranges of Ions in Matter Ser.: Vol. 6). 490p. 1980. 85.00 (ISBN 0-08-023879-3). Pergamon.

Low-Energy Ion Beams 1977: Salford. (Institute of Physics Conference Ser.: No. 38). 1978. 75.00 (ISBN 0-9960031-8-5, Pub. by Inst Physics England). Heyden.

Luebbers, D. W., et al, eds. Progress in Enzyme & Ion-Selective Electrodes. (Illus.). 240p. 1981. pap. 27.70 (ISBN 0-387-10499-2). Springer-Verlag.

McDaniel, Earl W., et al. Ion-Molecule Reactions. LC 70-91647. 374p. 1970. 36.00 (ISBN 0-471-58386-3, Pub. by Wiley). Krieger.

McDonald, Hugh J. & Lappe, Robert J. Ionography: Electrophoresis in Stabilized Media. pap. 69.50 (ISBN 0-317-08649-9, 2011928). Bks Demand UMI.

McLafferty, F. W., ed. Mass Spectrometry of Organic Ions. 1963. 98.50 (ISBN 0-12-483650-X). Acad Pr.

Mc Manus, Samuel P., ed. Organic Reactive Intermediates. (Organic Chemistry Ser.). 1973. 67.00 (ISBN 0-12-485450-8). Acad Pr.

Marinsky, Jacob A. & Marcus, Yizhok, eds. Ion Exchange & Solvent Extraction, Vol. 6. 312p. 1974. 65.00 (ISBN 0-8247-6047-6). Dekker.

Massey, H. S. Electronic & Ionic Impact Phenomena, 2 vols. Incl. Vol. 1. Collision of Electrons with Atoms. 2nd ed. Massey, H. S. & Burhop, E. H. 85.00x (ISBN 0-19-851247-3); Vol. 2. Electron Collisions with Molecules & Photoionization. Massey, H. S. 85.00x (ISBN 0-19-851249-X). 1969. Oxford U Pr.

Massey, Harrie. Negative Ions. 3rd ed. LC 74-31792. (Cambridge Monographs on Physics). (Illus.). 600p. 1976. 160.00 (ISBN 0-521-20775-4). Cambridge U Pr.

Mullins, L. J. Ion Transport in Heart. 144p. 1981. 24.00 (ISBN 0-89004-645-X). Raven.

Munzinger, Peter B., ed. Nuclear Physics with Heavy Ions, Vol. 6. (Nuclear Science Research Conference Ser.). 492p. 1984. text ed. 108.00 (ISBN 3-7186-0196-6). Harwood Academic.

Neel, L., ed. Nonlinear Behaviour of Molecules, Atoms & Ions in Electric, Magnetic or Electromagnetic Fields. 516p. 1979. 100.00 (ISBN 0-444-41790-7). Elsevier.

Olah, George A. Halonium Ions. 206p. 1975. 22.50 (ISBN 0-471-65329-2). Krieger.

Papa, S., et al, eds. HPlus-ATPase Synthase: Structure, Function & Biosynthesis. 1984. 35.00 (ISBN 0-930357-00-0). ICSU Pr.

Picraux, S. T., et al, eds. Applications of Ion Beams to Metals. LC 74-4395. 706p. 1974. 89.50x (ISBN 0-306-30781-2, Plenum Pr). Plenum Pub.

Popouych. Tetraphenylborates. (IUPAC Solubility Data Ser.). 260p. 1981. 100.00 (ISBN 0-08-023928-5). Pergamon.

Pullamn, Alberte, et al, eds. Water & Ions in Biological Systems. 801p. 1985. 110.00x (ISBN 0-306-41921-1, Plenum Pr). Plenum Pub.

Roy, G. & Schmor, P., eds. Polarized Proton Ion Sources: Conference Proceedings, TRIUMF, Vancouver, 1983. LC 84-71235. (AIP Conference Proceedings Ser.: No. 117). 209p. 1984. lib. bdg. 37.00 (ISBN 0-88318-316-1). Am Inst Physics.

Scully, J. C., ed. Ion Implementation & Ion Beam Analysis Techniques in Corrosion: Selected Papers Presented at the Conference at the Corrosion & Protection Centre, UMIST, Manchester, 28-30 June 1978. 148p. 1981. 17.50 (ISBN 0-08-026135-3). Pergamon.

Sellin, A., ed. Structure & Collisions of Ions & Atoms. (Topics in Current Physics: Vol 5). (Illus.). 1978. 48.00 (ISBN 0-387-08576-9). Springer-Verlag.

Sigel, Helmut, ed. Inorganic Drugs in Deficiency & Disease. (Metal Ions in Biological Systems Ser.: Vol. 14). 416p. 1982. 75.00 (ISBN 0-8247-1569-1). Dekker.

Spach, G., et al, eds. Physical Chemistry of Transmembrane Ion Motions: Proceedings of the International Meeting of the Societe de Chimie Physiquie, 36th, Paris, Sept. 27-Oct. 1, 1982. (Studies in Physical & Theoretical Chemistry: Vol. 24). 856p. 1983. 138.50 (ISBN 0-444-42176-9). Elsevier.

Szwarc, Michael, ed. Ions & Ion Pairs in Organic Reactions: Vol. I. LC 71-170685. 411p. 1972. 29.50 (ISBN 0-471-84307-5). Krieger.

--Ions & Ion Pairs in Organic Reactions: Vol. II: Role of Ions & Ion Pairs in Chemical Reactions. LC 71-170685. 582p. 1974. 44.50 (ISBN 0-471-84308-3). Krieger.

Thomas, J. P. & Cachard, A., eds. Material Characterization Using Ion Beams. LC 77-13269. (NATO ASI Ser. B, Physics: Vol. 28). 535p. 1977. 75.00x (ISBN 0-306-35728-3, Plenum Pr). Plenum Pub.

Valyi, L. Atom & Ion Sources. LC 76-44880. 429p. 1978. 122.95x (ISBN 0-471-99463-4, Pub. by Wiley-Interscience). Wiley.

Vesely, J., et al. Analysis with Ion-Selective Electrodes. 245p. 1978. 94.95x (ISBN 0-470-26296-6). Halsted Pr.

Wilhelmi, Z. & Sikora, B. Heavy Ions & Nuclear Structure. (Nuclear Science Research Conference Ser.: Vol. 5). 483p. 1983. 98.50 (ISBN 3-7186-0164-8). Harwood Academic.

Wilson, I. H., ed. Low-Energy Ion Beams 1980. (Institute of Physics Conference Ser.: No. 54). 1981. 85.00 (ISBN 0-9960033-4-7, Pub. by Inst Physics England). Heyden.

IONS–SPECTRA

Cooks, R. G., et al. Metastable Ions. LC 72-97419. 296p. 1973. 68.00 (ISBN 0-444-41119-4). Elsevier.

Fiermans, L., et al, eds. Electron & Ion Spectroscopy of Solids. LC 78-6171. (NATO ASI Series B, Physics: Vol. 32). 487p. 1978. 75.00x (ISBN 0-306-35732-1, Plenum Pr). Plenum Pub.

Hartmann, H. & Wanczek, K. P. Ion Cyclotron Resonance Spectrometry. (Lecture Notes in Chemistry: Vol. 7). (Illus.). 1978. pap. 19.00 (ISBN 0-387-08760-5). Springer-Verlag.

Herzberg, Gerhard. Spectra & Structures of Simple Free Radicals: An Introduction to Molecular Spectroscopy. LC 70-124722. (Baker Non-Resident Lectureships in Chemistry Ser.). 240p. 1971. 35.00x (ISBN 0-8014-0584-X). Cornell U Pr.

International Conference on Secondary Ion Mass Spectrometry, 4th, Minoo-Kanko Hotel, Osaka, Japan, November 13-19, 1984. Secondary Ion Mass Spectrometry SIMS IV: Proceedings. Benninghoven, A., et al, eds. (Springer Series in Chemical Physics: Vol. 36). (Illus.). 495p. 1984. 38.50 (ISBN 0-318-03104-3). Springer Verlag.

Smith, Frank C. & Chang, Richard C. The Practice of Ion Chromatography. LC 82-23914. 218p. 1983. 60.00x (ISBN 0-471-05517-4, Pub. by Wiley-Interscience). Wiley.

IQSY

see International Years of the Quiet Sun, 1964-1965

IRIS (PLANT)

American Iris Society. Basic Iris Culture. (Illus.). 1982. 1.25 (ISBN 0-9601242-3-3). Am Iris.

Cassidy, G. E. & Linnegar, S. Growing Irises. (Illus.). 160p. 1982. 16.95 (ISBN 0-917304-42-X). Timber.

Dykes, William R. The Genus Iris. 1975. Repr. of 1913 ed. 30.00 (ISBN 0-486-23037-6). Dover.

--A Handbook of Garden Irises. LC 75-42381. (Illus.). 1976. Repr. of 1924 ed. write for info (ISBN 0-685-78307-3). Theophrastus.

Mathew, Brian. Crocus. (Illus.). 224p. 1982. 50.00 (ISBN 0-917304-23-3). Timber.

--The Iris. LC 81-40493. (Illus.). 176p. 1981. 40.00x (ISBN 0-87663-372-6). Universe.

Price, Molly. The Iris Book. (Illus.). 224p. 1973. pap. 5.95 (ISBN 0-486-21522-9). Dover.

--The Iris Book. 1983. 13.50 (ISBN 0-8446-6024-8). Peter Smith.

Warburton, Bee, ed. The World of Irises. LC 77-73698. (Illus.). 1978. 15.00 (ISBN 0-9601242-1-7). Am Iris.

Waters, W. George. Irises for Everyone. (Illus.). 1982. 3.00 (ISBN 0-9601242-4-1). Am Iris.

IRISH SETTERS

see Dogs–Breeds–Irish Setters

IRISH WOLF HOUND

see Dogs–Breeds–Irish Wolf Hounds

IRON

see also Building, Iron and Steel; Cast Iron; Iron Ores; Ironwork; Steel; Taconite; Wrought-Iron

CNRS. New Physical, Mechanical & Chemical Properties of Very High Purity Iron. 438p. 119.25 (ISBN 0-677-30730-6). Gordon.

Cordero, Raymond & Serjeantson, Richard, eds. Iron & Steel Works of the World 1978. 7th ed. LC 75-314459. 1978. 100.00x (ISBN 0-900542-21-7). Intl Pubns Serv.

Desulfurization of Iron & Steel & Sulfide Shape Control. 161p. 1980. 40.00 (ISBN 0-89520-151-8). Iron & Steel.

Din Steel & Iron: Quality Standards DIN Handbook 155, Pt. II. 77.50 (ISBN 0-01-112512-8). Heyden.

Din Steel & Iron: Quality Standards DIN Handbook 4, Pt. I. 77.50 (ISBN 0-686-28162-4, 11440-1). Heyden.

Direct Reduced Iron: Technology & Economics of Production & Use. 243p. 1980. 62.00 (ISBN 0-89520-150-X). Iron & Steel.

Dunford, H. B. & Dolphin, D. The Biological Chemistry of Iron. 1982. 59.50 (ISBN 90-277-1444-4, Pub. by Reidel Holland). Kluwer Academic.

Lepp, Henry, ed. Geochemistry of Iron. LC 74-23287. (Benchmark Papers in Geology Ser). 439p. 1975. 71.50 (ISBN 0-12-786939-5). Acad Pr.

Lovenberg, Walter, ed. Iron-Sulfur Proteins, 3 vols. Incl. Biological Properties. Vol. 1, 1973. 78.00 (ISBN 0-12-456001-6); Molecular Properties. Vol. 2, 1974. 72.00 (ISBN 0-12-456002-4); Vol. 3. 1977. 81.00 (ISBN 0-12-456003-2). 1973. Acad Pr.

Specification for Iron, Steel, & Oxyfuel Gas Welding Rods: A5.2. 8p. 1980. 10.00 (ISBN 0-87171-200-8); member 7.50. Am Welding.

Spencer, C. W. & Werner, F. E., eds. Iron & Its Dilute Solid Solutions. LC 63-13593. pap. 86.80 (ISBN 0-317-10963-4, 2000681). Bks Demand UMI.

Tatsch, J. H. Iron Deposits: Origin, Evolution & Present Characteristics. LC 76-28095. (Illus.). 650p. Date not set. 216.00 (ISBN 0-912890-12-6); prepub. 180.00. Tatsch.

Transactions of the Iron & Steel Society, Vol. III. LC 83-122618. 134p. 1983. 52.00 (ISBN 0-911277-02-1). ISS Found.

Trendall, A. F. & Morris, R. C., eds. Iron-Formation: Facts & Problems, Vol 6. 558p. 1983. 106.00 (ISBN 0-444-42144-0, I-387-83). Elsevier.

Van der Merwe, Nikolas J. The Carbon-Fourteen Dating of Iron. LC 75-76206. pap. 37.30 (ISBN 0-317-08213-2, 2020171). Bks Demand UMI.

Von Gustorf, Ernest A., ed. The Organic Chemistry of Iron, Vol. 2. (Organometallic Chemistry Ser.). 1981. 55.00 (ISBN 0-12-417102-8). Acad Pr.

IRON–BIBLIOGRAPHY

Worldwide Guide to Equivalent Irons & Steels. 1979. 112.00 (ISBN 0-87170-088-3). ASM.

IRON–DICTIONARIES

Abd-El-Wahed, A. M. Iron & Steel Industry Dictionary. (Eng., Fr., Ger. & Arabic.). 441p. 1974. 45.00 (ISBN 0-686-92487-8, M-9760). French & Eur.

Freeman, H. Taschenwoerterbuch Eisen und Stahl. (Ger. & Eng.). 600p. (Dictionary of Iron and Steel). 1966. 12.50 (ISBN 3-19-006215-3, M-7634, Pub. by M. Hueber). French & Eur.

Verlag Stahleisen, ed. Iron & Steel Dictionary. 1983. 21.00 (ISBN 0-9906000-2-5, Pub. by Verlag Stahleisen W Germany). Heyden.

IRON–METALLURGY

see also Sintering

American Society for Metals Staff. Source Book on Ductile Iron: A Discriminative Selection of Outstanding Articles from the Periodical & Reference Literature. Rauch, A. H., ed. LC 77-9278. (ASM Engineering Bookshelf Ser.). pap. 100.00 (ISBN 0-317-27679-4, 2019500). Bks Demand UMI.

Davis, Edward W. Pioneering with Taconite. LC 64-64494. (Illus.). 246p. 1964. 8.50 (ISBN 0-87351-023-2). Minn Hist.

Dennis, W. H. Foundations of Iron & Steel Metallurgy. (Illus.). 246p. 1967. 15.00 (ISBN 0-444-20006-1, Pub. by Elsevier Applied Sci England). Elsevier.

Direct Reduction of Iron Ore: A Bibliographical Survey. 644p. (Orig.). 1979. pap. text ed. 10.00x (ISBN 0-904357-26-0, Metals). Brookfield Pub Co.

Hausner, Henry H., et al, eds. Iron Powder Metallurgy. LC 67-17375. (Perspectives in Powder Metallurgy: Fundamentals, Methods, & Applications: Vol. 13). pap. 96.80 (ISBN 0-317-10417-9, 2019459). Bks Demand UMI.

Mechanical Working & Steel Processing Conference Proceedings, 24th. LC 75-17963. 570p. 60.00 (ISBN 0-89520-153-4). Iron & Steel.

Minkoff, I. The Physical Metallurgy of Cast Iron. LC 82-21984. 305p. 1983. 53.95x (ISBN 0-471-90006-0, Pub. by Wiley-Interscience). Wiley.

Strassburger, J. H., ed. Blast Furnace: Theory & Practice, 2 Vols. 1062p. 1969. Set. 255.50x (ISBN 0-677-10420-0). Gordon.

Transactions of the Iron & Steel Society, Vol. II. LC 83-122618. 130p. 1983. 52.00 (ISBN 0-911277-01-3). ISS Found.

Uys, J. M. & Bishop, H. L., eds. Process Simulation & Control in Iron & Steelmaking. LC 65-27847. (Metallurgical Society Conferences Ser.: Vol. 32). pap. 87.50 (ISBN 0-317-10476-4, 2001520). Bks Demand UMI.

IRON, WROUGHT

see Wrought-Iron

IRON AGE

see also Archaeology

Forde-Johnston, J. Hillforts of the Iron Age in England & Wales: A Survey of the Surface Evidence. (Illus.). 331p. 1976. 55.00x (ISBN 0-87471-802-3). Rowman.

Glob, P. V. The Bog People: Iron-Age Man Preserved. Bruce-Mitford, R. L., tr. LC 69-20391. (Illus.). 200p. 1969. 27.50 (ISBN 0-8014-0492-4). Cornell U Pr.

Harding, D., ed. Hillforts: Later Prehistoric Earthworks in Britain & Ireland. 1977. 90.00 (ISBN 0-12-324750-0). Acad Pr.

Oliver, Roland & Fagan, B. M. Africa in the Iron Age. LC 74-25639. (Illus.). 300p. 1975. 37.50 (ISBN 0-521-20598-0); pap. 11.95x (ISBN 0-521-09900-5). Cambridge U Pr.

Wells, Peter S. The Emergence of an Iron Age Economy: The Mecklenburg Grave Groups from Hallstatt & Sticna: Mecklenburg Collection Ser. Pt 3. LC 81-81958. (American School of Prehistoric Research Bulletins: Pt. III). (Illus.). 256p. (Orig.). 1981. pap. 30.00x (ISBN 0-87365-536-2). Peabody Harvard.

--Farms, Villages, & Cities: Commerce & Urban Origins in Late Prehistoric Europe. LC 84-45142. (Illus.). 352p. 1984. 32.50x (ISBN 0-8014-1554-3); pap. 14.95x (ISBN 0-8014-9298-X). Cornell U Pr.

Widgren, Mats. Settlement & Farming Systems in the Early Iron Age. (Stockholm Studies in Human Geography: No. 3). 132p. 1983. pap. text ed. 16.50x (ISBN 91-22-00602-8, Pub. by Almqvist & Wiksell Sweden). Humanities.

IRON ALLOYS

Lampman & Peters, eds. Ferroalloys & Other Additives to Liquid Iron & Steel- STP 739. 216p. 1981. 24.75 (ISBN 0-8031-0744-7, 04-739000-01). ASTM.

Touloukian, Y. S. & Ho, C. Y. Properties of Selected Ferrous Alloying Elements, Vol. III. (M-H-CINDAS Data Series on Material Properties). 288p. 1981. text ed. 56.00 (ISBN 0-07-065034-9). McGraw.

IRON AND STEEL BUILDING

see Building, Iron and Steel

IRON AND STEEL SHIPS

see Ships, Iron and Steel

IRON-FOUNDING

see also Cast Iron; Founding; Pattern-Making

Ammen, C. W. Casting Iron. (Illus.). 196p. 1984. o.p 15.95 (ISBN 0-8306-0210-0, 1610); pap. 10.25 (ISBN 0-8306-0610-6). TAB Bks.

Continuous Casting, Vol. I. LC 83-81654. 163p. 1983. 40.00 (ISBN 0-89520-157-7). Iron & Steel.

Continuous Casting: Fourth International Iron & Steel Congress, London 1982. 606p. 1984. text ed. 45.00x (ISBN 0-904357-47-3, Pub. by Metals Soc). Brookfield Pub Co.

IRON INDUSTRY AND TRADE

see also Cast Iron; Hardware; Iron-Founding; Ironwork; Steel Industry and Trade; Wrought-Iron

ASTM Specifications for Ferroalloys. 51p. 1980. pap. 5.25 (ISBN 0-8031-0834-6, 03-109080-01). ASTM.

Bining, Arthur C. Pennsylvania Iron Manufacture in the Eighteenth Century. rev. ed. LC 73-623131. (Illus.). 215p. 1973. 9.75 (ISBN 0-911124-72-1); pap. 5.75 (ISBN 0-911124-71-3). Pa Hist & Mus.

Bruce, Kathleen. Virginia Iron Manufacture in the Slave Era. LC 67-30856. Repr. of 1930 ed. 37.50x (ISBN 0-678-00414-5). Kelley.

Bugayev, K., et al. Iron & Steel Production. Savin, Ivan V., tr. from Rus. (Illus.). 246p. 1971. 12.00x (ISBN 0-8464-0533-4). Beekman Pubs.

Energy-Conscious Iron & Steelmaking. 1981. 70.00x (ISBN 0-904357-32-5, Metals Soc). Brookfield Pub Co.

Environmental Aspects of Iron & Steel Industry: A Workshop. (Industry Overviews: Vol. 8). pap. 5.00 (UNEP011, UNEP). Unipub.

Environmental Aspects of the Iron & Steel Industry: A Workshop. (Industry Overviews: Vol. 8). pap. 5.00 (UNEP011, UNEP). Unipub.

The Establishment of Iron & Steel Industries in Developing Countries & Its Impact on Training & the Development of Skills: Report II. ii, 48p. 1981. pap. 7.15 (ISBN 92-2-102687-6). Intl Labour Office.

French, Benjamin F. History of the Rise & Progress of the Iron Trade of the United States, 1621-1857. LC 68-55712. Repr. of 1858 ed. 25.00x (ISBN 0-678-00963-5). Kelley.

Harrison, T. S. Handbook of Analytical Control of Iron & Steel Production. LC 78-41222. (Ellis Horwood Series in Analytical Chemistry). 602p. 1979. 124.95 (ISBN 0-470-26538-8). Halsted Pr.

Hartley, Edward N. Ironworks on the Saugus: The Lynn & Braintree Ventures of the Company of Undertakers of the Ironworks in New England. (Illus.). 1971. 18.50x (ISBN 0-8061-0366-3). U of Okla Pr.

International Iron & Steel Congress. International Iron & Steel Congress: Proceedings of the 3rd, 16-20 April, Chicago, Illinois. LC 79-4097. pap. 160.00 (ISBN 0-317-27693-X, 2019494). Bks Demand UMI.

International Labour Office, Iron & Steel Committee, 10th Session, Geneva, 1981. The Improvement of Working Conditions & Working Environments in the Iron & Steel Industry: Report III. v, 86p. (Orig.). 1981. pap. 8.55 (ISBN 92-2-102688-4). Intl Labour Office.

Iron & Steel Scrap: The Significance & Influence on further Developments in the Iron & Steel Industries. pap. 12.00 (ISBN 0-686-94494-1, UN79/2E3, UN). Unipub.

The Iron Steel Industry in the Developing Countries. pap. 7.00 (ISBN 0-686-94496-8, UN74/2B/15, UN). Unipub.

Ironmaking Conference Participants. Ironmaking Conference: Proceedings of the Forty-Third Conference. 524p. 1984. 60.00 (ISBN 0-89520-163-1). Iron & Steel.

Ironmaking Conference: Proceedings of the Forty-Second Conference. LC 77-613444. 728p. 1983. 60.00 (ISBN 0-89520-156-9). Iron & Steel.

Ironmaking Conference, 44th Conference: Proceedings. 628p. 1985. 60.00 (ISBN 0-932897-04-5). Iron & Steel.

LaFayette, Kenneth D. Flaming Brands: Fifty Years of Iron Making in the Upper Peninsula of Michigan, 1848-1898. LC 77-72800. (Illus.). 1977. 4.75 (ISBN 0-918616-01-8). Northern Mich.

Low-Waste & Non-Waste Technology in the Iron & Steel Industry. 191p. 1981. pap. 15.00 (ISBN 0-686-78452-9, UN812E4, UN). Unipub.

The Maritime Transport of Iron Ore. pap. 6.00 (ISBN 0-686-94518-2, UN74/2D/4, UN). Unipub.

Occupational Safety & Health in the Iron & Steel Industry. 341p. 1983. pap. text ed. 12.85 (ISBN 92-2-103471-2, ILO273, ILO). Unipub.

Pearse, John B. A Concise History of the Iron Manufacture of the American Colonies up to the Revolution & of Pennsylvania Until the Present Time. (Illus.). 1876. 22.50 (ISBN 0-8337-2698-6). B Franklin.

Peters, A. T. Ferrous Production Metallurgy. LC 81-11710. 299p. 1982. 59.95x (ISBN 0-471-08597-9, Pub. by Wiley-Interscience). Wiley.

Pierce, Arthur D. Iron in the Pines: The Story of New Jersey's Ghost Towns & Bog Iron. (Illus.). 1966. pap. 9.95x (ISBN 0-8135-0514-3). Rutgers U Pr.

Pounds, Norman J. Geography of Iron & Steel. 4th rev. ed. (Orig.). 1968. pap. text ed. 6.00x (ISBN 0-09-106261-6, Hutchinson U Lib). Humanities.

Proceedings: Fortieth Electric Furnace Conference. LC 46-22879. 450p. 1983. 60.00 (ISBN 0-89520-154-2). Iron & Steel.

Process Technology Division (PTD) Conference Proceedings, Vol. 5: Measurement & Control Instrumentation in the Steel & Iron Industry. 254p. 1985. 60.00 (ISBN 0-932897-05-3). Iron & Steel.

Scrivenor, Harry. History of the Iron Trade: From the Earliest Records to the Present Period. 327p. 1967. Repr. of 1854 ed. 35.00x (ISBN 0-7146-1150-6, F Cass Co). Biblio Dist.

Smiles, Samuel. Industrial Biography: Iron-Workers & Tool Makers. LC 67-114712. (Illus.). Repr. of 1863 ed. 35.00x (ISBN 0-678-05727-3). Kelley.

Steel & Iron-Quality Standards One. (Din Handbook: No. 4). 1982. 77.50 (ISBN 0-686-39806-8, 11441-1, Pub. by DIN Germany). Heyden.

Strategy for Energy Use in the Iron & Steel Industry. (Economic Commission for Europe Ser.: No. 41). (Illus.). 171p. 1985. pap. 21.00 (UN83/2E22, UN). Unipub.

Swank, James H. History of the Manufacture of Iron in All Ages. 2nd ed. 1965. Repr. of 1892 ed. 22.50 (ISBN 0-8337-3463-6). B Franklin.

Technology Profiles of the Iron & Steel Industry. (Transfer & Development of Technology Ser.: No. 11). 44p. 1982. pap. 8.50 (ISBN 0-686-96627-9, UPB111, UNIDO). Unipub.

Tedesco, Paul H. Patriotism, Protection & Prosperity: James Moore Swank, the American Iron & Steel Association & the Tariff, 1873-1913. Bruchey, Stuart, ed. LC 84-48315. (American Economic History Ser.). 325p. 1985. lib. bdg. 40.00 (ISBN 0-8240-6663-4). Garland Pub.

Transactions of the Iron & Steel Society, Vol. I. LC 83-122618. 130p. 1982. 52.00 (ISBN 0-911277-00-5). ISS Found.
Transactions of the Iron & Steel Society, Vol. IV. 112p. 1984. 52.00 (ISBN 0-911277-03-X). ISS Found.
Walsh, William D. The Diffusion of Technological Change in the Pennsylvania Pig Iron Industry: 1850-1870. LC 75-2601. (Dissertations in American Economic History). (Illus.). 1975. 27.50x (ISBN 0-405-07222-8). Ayer Co Pubs.
Williams, R. V. Control & Analysis in Iron & Steel Making. (Monographs in Materials). 256p. 1983. text ed. 59.95 (ISBN 0-408-10713-8). Butterworth.

IRON INDUSTRY AND TRADE–VOCATIONAL GUIDANCE

I.L.O. Training & Retraining of Men & Women Wokers in the Metal Trades, with Special Reference to Technological Changes: Report III, Metal Trades Committee, 11th Session, Geneva, 1983. 73p. 1983. pap. 7.15 (ISBN 92-2-103362-7). Intl Labour Office.
Rudman, Jack. Foreman (Structures - Group C) (Iron Work) (Career Examination Ser.: C-1324). (Cloth bdg. avail. on request). pap. 12.00 (ISBN 0-8373-1324-4). Natl Learning.

IRON METABOLISM

Bezkorovainy, Anatoly. Biochemistry of Nonheme Iron. LC 80-16477. (Biochemistry of the Elments Ser.: Vol. 1). 455p. 1981. 52.50x (ISBN 0-306-40501-6, Plenum Pr). Plenum Pub.
Ciba Foundation. Iron Metabolism. LC 77-24153. (Ciba Foundation Symposium, New Ser.: 51). pap. 100.30 (ISBN 0-317-29777-5, 2022176). Bks Demand UMI.
Kies, Constance, ed. Nutritional Bioavailability of Iron. LC 82-16391. (ACS Symposium Ser.: No. 203). 204p. 1983. lib. bdg. 34.95 (ISBN 0-8412-0746-1). Am Chemical.
Siderophores from Microorganisms & Plants. (Structure & Bonding Ser.: Vol. 58). (Illus.). 160p. 1984. 30.00 (ISBN 0-387-13649-5). Springer-Verlag.

IRON MINES AND MINING

Hochschild, Harold K. Macintyre Mine: From Failure to Fortune. (Illus.). 27p. 1962. pap. 3.95 (ISBN 0-8156-8024-4, Pub. by Adirondack Museum). Syracuse U Pr.

IRON ORES

Agglomeration: Papers of the Symposium, 4th, Held in Toronto, Canada, 1985. 1985. 100.00 (ISBN 0-932897-00-2). Iron & Steel.
Ball, Derrick F., et al. Agglomeration of Iron Ores. LC 74-168614. pap. 102.00 (ISBN 0-317-10267-2, 2050890). Bks Demand UMI.
Direct Reduction of Iron Ore: A Bibliographical Survey. 644p. (Orig.). 1979. pap. text ed. 10.00x (ISBN 0-904357-26-0, Metals). Brookfield Pub Co.
Grout, Frank F. & Wolff, J. Fred. Geology of the Cuyuna District, Minnesota: A Progress Report. LC 55-9000. (Bulletin: No. 36). (Illus.). 1955. 3.00x (ISBN 0-8166-0106-2). Minn Geol Survey.
Melnik, Y. P., ed. Precambrian Banded Iron Formations: Physicochemical Conditions of Formations. (Developments in Precambrian Geology Ser.: Vol. 5). 310p. 1982. 72.50 (ISBN 0-444-41934-9). Elsevier.

IRON ORGANIC COMPOUNDS

see Organoiron Compounds

IRON-WORKS

Badger, Carl B. Badger's Illustrated Catalogue of Cast-Iron Architecture. 1982. pap. 9.95 (ISBN 0-486-24223-4). Dover.
Gale, W. K. Ironworking. (Shire Album Ser.: No. 64). (Illus.). 32p. 1981. pap. 3.50 (ISBN 0-85263-546-X, Pub. by Shire Pubns England). Seven Hills Bks.

IRONING

see Laundry and Laundry Industry

IRONWORK

see also Architectural Ironwork; Blacksmithing; Forging; Welding; Wrought-Iron

Cupola Practice & Mixing Iron. 1983. pap. 7.50 (ISBN 0-917914-12-0). Lindsay Pubns.

IRRADIATION

see also Radioactivation Analysis

Berdjis, Charles C. Pathology of Irradiation. LC 71-110278. 722p. 1970. 52.50 (ISBN 0-683-00601-0, Pub. by Williams & Wilkins). Krieger.
Biological Effects of Neutron & Proton Irradiation, 2 Vols. (Illus.). 879p. (Orig., Vol. 1, 433p; Vol. 2, 446p). 1964. 24.25 ea. (IAEA). Vol. 1 (ISBN 92-0-010064-3, ISP80-1). Vol. 2 (ISBN 92-0-010164-X, ISP80-2). Unipub.
British Nuclear Energy Society, ed. Post-Irradiation Examination. 366p. 1981. 100.00x (ISBN 0-7277-0111-8, Pub. by Brit Nuclear England). State Mutual Bk.
--Post-Irradiation Examination Techniques. 250p. 1972. 75.00x (ISBN 0-901948-78-0, Pub. by Brit Nuclear England). State Mutual Bk.
--Voids Formed by Irradiation of Reaction Materials. 376p. 1971. 60.00x (ISBN 0-901948-85-3, Pub. by Brit Nuclear England). State Mutual Bk.
Combination Processes in Food Irradiation. (Proceedings Ser.). (Illus.). 467p. 1981. pap. 64.50 (ISBN 92-0-110081-7, ISP568, IAEA). Unipub.
Elimination of Harmful Organisms from Food & Feed by Irradiation. (Panel Proceedings Ser.). (Illus.). 118p. 1968. pap. 8.00 (ISBN 92-0-111568-7, ISP200, IAEA). Unipub.
Ganmaster. Food Irradiation Now. 1982. 22.00 (ISBN 90-247-2763-4, Pub. by Martinus Nijhoff Netherlands). Kluwer Academic.
Gittus, J. Irradiation Effects in Crystalline Solids. (Illus.). 523p. 1978. 81.50 (ISBN 0-85334-778-6, Pub. by Elsevier Applied Sci England). Elsevier.
Improvement of Food Quality by Irradiation. (Panel Proceedings Ser.). (Illus.). 188p. (Orig.). 1974. pap. 16.25 (ISBN 92-0-011174-2, ISP370, IAEA). Unipub.
Inactivation of Peroxidase, Pectinesterase & Alkaline Phosphatase in Polymers as a Model for Irradiation of Dried Foodstuffs. (Agricultural Research Reports: No. 113). 1972. pap. 4.00 (ISBN 90-220-0383-3, PDC188, PUDOC). Unipub.
Irradiation Facilities for Research Reactors. (Proceedings Ser.). (Eng. & Fr., Illus.). 478p. (Orig.). 1973. pap. 41.25 (ISBN 92-0-050073-0, ISP316, IAEA). Unipub.
Kreuzer, Rudolf, ed. Freezing & Irradiation of Fish. (Illus.). 548p. 56.25 (ISBN 0-85238-008-9, FN50, FNB). Unipub.
Manual of Food Irradiation Dosimetry. (Technical Reports Ser.: No. 178). (Illus.). 161p. 1978. pap. 19.25 (ISBN 92-0-115277-9, IDC178, IAEA). Unipub.
Nonaqueous Reprocessing of Irradiated Fuels. (Bibliographical Ser.: No. 264). 2364p. 1976. pap. write for info. (ISBN 92-0-044167-X, STI/PUB/21/26, IAEA). Unipub.
Odum, Howard T. & Pigeon, Robert F., eds. A Tropical Rain Forest: A Study of Irradiation & Ecology at El Verde, Puerto Rico, 3 Vols. AEC Technical Information Center. LC 70-606844. 1652p. 1970. Set. pap. 49.25 (ISBN 0-87079-230-X, TID-24270); microfiche 4.50 (ISBN 0-87079-340-3, TID-24270). DOE.
Panel, Vienna, March 18-22, 1974. Requirements for the Irradiaton of Food on a Commercial Scale: Proceedings. (Illus.). 219p. 1975. pap. 22.75 (ISBN 92-0-111275-0, ISP394, IAEA). Unipub.
Russell, K. C. Phase Stability under Irradiation. (Illus.). 206p. 1985. pap. 75.00 (ISBN 0-08-032722-2, Pub. by Aberdeen Scotland). Pergamon.
Training Manual on Food Irradiation Technology & Techniques. (Technical Reports Ser.: No. 114). (Illus.). 220p. 1982. pap. 30.50 (ISBN 92-0-115082-2, IDC114/2, IAEA). Unipub.
Wholesomeness of Irradiated Food. (Food & Nutrition Papers: No. 6). 44p. 1977. pap. 6.25 (ISBN 92-5-100282-7, F495, FAO). Unipub.

IRRATIONAL NUMBERS

see Numbers, Irrational

IRREVERSIBLE PROCESSES

Accardi, L. & Frigerio, A., eds. Quantum Probability & Applications to the Quantum Theory of Irreversible Processes: Proceedings of the International Workshop Held at Villa Mondragone, Italy, Sept. 6-11, 1982. (Lecture Notes in Mathematics Ser.: Vol. 1055). vi, 411p. 1984. 21.50 (ISBN 0-387-12915-4). Springer-Verlag.
Day, W. A. The Thermodynamics of Simple Materials with Fading Memory. LC 77-183992. (Springer Tracts in Natural Philosophy: Vol. 22). (Illus.). 152p. 1972. 23.00 (ISBN 0-387-05704-8). Springer-Verlag.
Garrido, L. M., et al, eds. Irreversibility in the Many-Body Problem. LC 72-87519. 470p. 1972. 65.00x (ISBN 0-306-30711-1, Plenum Pr). Plenum Pub.
IUPAP Conference. Statistical Mechanics of Irreversible Change: Proceedings of the 6th IUPAP Conference on Statistical Mechanics, 1971. LC 55-8426. pap. 35.00 (ISBN 0-317-08501-8, 2010184). Bks Demand UMI.
Prigogine, Ilya. From Being to Becoming: Time & Complexity in the Physical Sciences. LC 79-26774. (Illus.). 272p. 1980. pap. text ed. 15.95x (ISBN 0-7167-1108-7). W H Freeman.
Ullmaier, H. Irreversible Properties of Type Two Superconductors. (Springer Tracts in Modern Physics Ser.: Vol. 76). (Illus.). 180p. 1975. 36.00 (ISBN 0-387-07424-4). Springer-Verlag.
Yourgrau, Wolfgang, et al. Treatise on Irreversible & Statistical Thermophysics: An Introduction to Nonclassical Thermodynamics. (Illus.). xx, 268p. 1982. pap. 6.50 (ISBN 0-486-64313-1). Dover.

IRRIGATION

see also Arid Regions; Dams; Irrigation Farming; Reservoirs; Saline Irrigation; Windmills

Aboukhaled, A. & Alfaro, A. Lysimeters. (Irrigation & Drainage Papers: No. 39). 74p. (2nd Printing 1983). 1982. pap. 7.50 (ISBN 92-5-101186-9, F2330, FAO). Unipub.
Alston, Richard M. Commercial Irrigation Enterprise: The Fear of Water Monopoly & the Genesis of Market Distortion in the Nineteenth Century American West. LC 77-14752. (Dissertations in American Economic History Ser.). 1978. 27.50 (ISBN 0-405-11025-1). Ayer Co Pubs.
American Society of Civil Engineers, Irrigation & Drainage Division. Age of Changing Priorities for Land & Water: Irrigation & Drainage Division Specialty Conference, Spokane, Washington, September 26-28, 1972. LC 73-155132. pap. 123.00 (ISBN 0-317-10781-X, 2007866). Bks Demand UMI.
American Society of Civil Engineers. Agricultural & Urban Considerations in Irrigation & Drainage: Selected Papers from Specialty Conference, Fort Collins, Colorado, April 22-24. pap. 160.00 (ISBN 0-317-10872-7, 2022520). Bks Demand UMI.
American Society of Civil Engineers, compiled By. Consumptive Use of Water & Irrigation Water Requirements. 227p. 1974. pap. 10.75x (ISBN 0-87262-068-9). Am Soc Civil Eng.
--Contribution of Irrigation & Drainage to the World Food Supply. 430p. 1975. pap. 22.00x (ISBN 0-87262-114-6). Am Soc Civil Eng.
American Society of Civil Engineers, Irrigation & Drainage Division. Environmental Aspects of Irrigation & Drainage: Proceedings of Specialty Conference, July 21-23, 1976. pap. 160.00 (ISBN 0-317-10817-4, 2016457). Bks Demand UMI.
American Society of Civil Engineers, Special Committee on Irrigation. Letter Symbols & Glossary for Hydraulics: With Special Reference to Irrigation. LC 42-233. (American Society of Civil Engineers, Manuals of Engineering Practice: No. 11). pap. 20.00 (ISBN 0-317-29810-0, 2052000). Bks Demand UMI.
American Society of Civil Engineers Staff. Social & Ecological Aspects of Irrigation & Drainage: Selected Papers. LC 75-30807. pap. 95.30 (ISBN 0-317-10978-2, 2007865). Bks Demand UMI.
ASCE Conference, Irrigation & Drainage Division, 1980. Irrigation & Drainage-Today's Challenges. Eggleston, Jerry, ed. LC 80-66950. 502p. 1980. pap. 38.50x (ISBN 0-87262-251-7). Am Soc Civil Eng.
Booher, L. J. Surface Irrigation. (Land & Water Development Documents: No. 3). (Illus.). 160p. (Orig.). 1974. pap. 8.00 (ISBN 92-5-100081-6, F455, FAO). Unipub.
Borrelli, John, et al, eds. Advances in Irrigation & Drainage: Surviving External Pressures. LC 83-71586. 568p. 1983. pap. 44.00x (ISBN 0-87262-370-X). Am Soc Civil Eng.
Bromley, Daniel W. Improving Irrigated Agriculture: Institutional Reform & the Small Farmer. (Working Paper: No. 531). 96p. 1982. pap. 3.00 (ISBN 0-8213-0064-4). World Bank.
Brough, Charles H. Irrigation in Utah. LC 78-64265. (Johns Hopkins University. Studies in the Social Sciences. Extra Volumes: 19). Repr. of 1898 ed. 21.50 (ISBN 0-404-61367-5). AMS Pr.
Bumli, George R., ed. Principles of Project Formulation for Irrigation & Drainage Projects. LC 82-73505. 144p. 1982. pap. 15.75x (ISBN 0-87262-345-9). Am Soc Civil Eng.
Carruthers, Ian, ed. Social & Economic Perspectives on Irrigation. 100p. 1981. pap. 24.00 (ISBN 0-08-026780-7). Pergamon.
Dregne, H. E. & Willis, W. O., eds. Dryland Agriculture. (Illus.). 1983. 35.00 (ISBN 0-89118-075-3). Am Soc Agron.
Finkel, Herman J., ed. CRC Handbook of Irrigation Technology, Vol. I. 369p. 1982. 66.00 (ISBN 0-8493-3231-1). CRC Pr.
Fukuda, Hitoshi, ed. Irrigation in the World: Comparative Development. 329p. 1976. 42.50x (ISBN 0-86008-174-5, Pub. by U of Tokyo Japan). Columbia U Pr.
Glysson, E. A., et al, eds. Innovations in the Water & Wastewater Fields. (Illus.). 240p. 1984. text ed. 34.95 (ISBN 0-250-40645-4). Butterworth.
Green, Donald E. Land of the Underground Rain: Irrigation on the Texas High Plains, 1910-1970. LC 72-7589. (Illus.). 328p. 1973. pap. 8.95 (ISBN 0-292-74629-6). U of Tex Pr.
Gupta, I. C. Use of Saline Water in Agriculture. 210p. 1981. 50.00x (ISBN 0-686-76671-7, Pub. by Oxford & IBH India). State Mutual Bk.
Hagen, R. M., et al, eds. Irrigation of Agricultural Lands. (Illus.). 1967. 22.50 (ISBN 0-89118-012-5). Am Soc Agron.
Hall, A. Drought & Irrigation in North-East Brazil. LC 77-82497. (Latin American Studies: No. 29). (Illus.). 1978. 34.50 (ISBN 0-521-21811-X). Cambridge U Pr.
Hanks, R. J. & Hill, R. W. Modeling Crop Responses to Irrigation in Relation to Soils, Climate & Salinity. (IIIC Publication: No. 4). 71p. 1981. 17.25 (ISBN 0-08-030762-0). Pergamon.
Hansen, V. E. & Israelsen, O. W. Irrigation Principles & Practices. 4th ed. 417p. 1980. 47.50 (ISBN 0-471-03058-9). Wiley.
Hansen, Vaughn E., et al. Irrigation Principles & Practices. 4th ed. (Arabic.). 450p. 1983. pap. 14.00 (ISBN 0-471-86941-4). Wiley.
Hexem, Roger W. & Heady, Earl O. Water Production Functions for Irrigated Agriculture. 1978. text ed. 11.50x (ISBN 0-8138-1785-4). Iowa St U Pr.
Hillel, Daniel, ed. Advances in Irrigation, Vol. I. 302p. 1982. 55.00 (ISBN 0-12-024301-6). Acad Pr.
--Advances in Irrigation, Vol. 2. 1983. 65.00 (ISBN 0-12-024302-4). Acad Pr.
Huston, Harvey. The Right of Appropriation & the Colorado System of Laws in Regard to Irrigation. 334p. 1983. Repr. of 1893 ed. lib. bdg. 27.50x (ISBN 0-8377-0649-1). Rothman.
International Irrigation Information Center, Bet Dagan, Israel, ed. Irrigation Equipment Manufacturers Directory. 2nd ed. LC 79-42940. (IIIC Publications: No. 5). 312p. 1980. 68.00 (ISBN 0-08-025512-4). Pergamon.
International Irrigation Information Center Bet Dagan, Israel, ed. Irrigation: International Guide to Organizations & Institutions. LC 80-49935. 165p. 1980. 54.00 (ISBN 0-08-026363-1). Pergamon.
Irrigation & Drainage in the Nineteen Eighties. 447p. 1979. pap. 27.00x (ISBN 0-87262-181-2). Am Soc Civil Eng.
Irrigation & Drainage Specialty Conference, Lincoln, Neb., 1971. Optimization of Irrigation & Drainage Systems: Proceedings. LC 73-158127. pap. 158.50 (ISBN 0-317-10762-3, 2004906). Bks Demand UMI.
Irrigation Association Membership Directory & Buyers Guide 1984. Date not set. 50.00 (ISBN 0-935030-06-9). Irrigation.
Irrigation Technical Conference Proceedings 1983. LC 76-12209. (Illus.). 14.00 (ISBN 0-935030-04-2). Irrigation.
James, D. W., et al. Modern Irrigated Soils. LC 82-2841. 235p. 1982. 32.50x (ISBN 0-471-06351-7, Pub. by Wiley-Interscience). Wiley.
Jarrett, A. R. Golf Course & Grounds Irrigation & Drainage. 1984. text ed. 29.95 (ISBN 0-8359-2563-3). Reston.
Kay, Melvyn. Sprinkler Irrigation. (Illus.). 96p. (Orig.). 1983. pap. 16.95 (ISBN 0-7134-1229-1, Pub. by Batsford England). David & Charles.
--Surface Irrigation. (Illus.). 144p. 1986. pap. 16.95 (ISBN 0-7134-1693-9, Pub. by Batsford England). David & Charles.
Kraatz, D. B. Irrigation Canal Lining. (Land & Water Development Documents: No. 1). 199p. 1977. pap. 14.25 (ISBN 92-5-100165-0, F1332, FAO). Unipub.
Lampen, Dorothy. Economic & Social Aspects of Federal Reclamation. Bruchey, Stuart, ed. LC 78-56686. (Management of Public Lands in the U. S. Ser.). (Illus.). 1979. Repr. of 1930 ed. lib. bdg. 12.00x (ISBN 0-405-11338-2). Ayer Co Pubs.
Legal, Institutional, & Social Aspects of Irrigation & Drainage & Water Resources Planning & Management. 909p. 1979. pap. 49.50x (ISBN 0-87262-140-5). Am Soc Civil Eng.
Majumdar, S. K. Irrigation Engineering. 350p. 1984. 4.00 (ISBN 0-07-451756-2). McGraw.
Mead, Elwood. Irrigation Institutions: A Discussion of the Economic & Legal Questions Created by the Growth of Irrigated Agriculture in the West. LC 72-2856. (Use & Abuse of America's Natural Resources Ser.). 406p. 1972. Repr. of 1903 ed. 25.50 (ISBN 0-405-04520-4). Ayer Co Pubs.
--Irrigation Institutions: A Discussion of the Economic & Legal Questions Created by the Growth of Irrigated Agriculture in the West. Repr. of 1903 ed. 30.00 (ISBN 0-384-37880-3). Johnson Repr.
Michael, A. M. Irrigation: Theory & Practice. 801p. 1982. 75.00x (ISBN 0-7069-1513-5). State Mutual Bk.
Multilingual Technical Dictionary on Irrigation & Drainage. (Eng. & Fr.). 40.00 (ISBN 0-318-18084-7); members 30.00 (ISBN 0-318-18085-5). US Comm Irrigation.
Multilingual Technical Dictionary on Irrigation & Drainage. (Sp. & Eng.). 1977. avail. US Comm Irrigation.
Multilingual Technical Dictionary on Irrigation & Drainage. (Rus. & Eng.). 1978. avail. US Comm Irrigation.
O'Brien, Michael J., et al. A Late Formative Irrigation Settlement below Monte Alban: Survey & Excavation on the Xoxocotlan Piedmont, Oaxaca, Mexico. (Institute of Latin American Studies Special Publications). (Illus.). 254p. 1982. text ed. 25.00x (ISBN 0-292-74628-8). U of Tex Pr.
OECD. Aid for the Development of Irrigation. Carruthers, Ian D., ed. 166p. 1984. pap. 11.00x (ISBN 92-64-12539-6). OECD.

also subdivision Isotopes under names of elements, e.g. Carbon–Isotopes

Advisory Group Meeting, Vienna, Jan. 27-31, 1975. Interpretation of Environmental Isotope & Hydrochemical Data in Groundwater Hydrology: Proceedings. (Panel Proceedings Ser.). (Illus.). 228p. (Orig.). 1976. pap. 25.25 (ISBN 92-0-141076-X, ISP429, IAEA). Unipub.

Audouze, Jean, ed. CNO Isotopes in Astrophysics. (Astrophysics & Space Science Lib. Ser.: No. 67). 1977. lib. bdg. 29.00 (ISBN 90-277-0807-X, Pub. by Reidel Holland). Kluwer Academic.

Barbier, E., ed. The Application of Nuclear Techniques to Geothermal Studies: Proceedings. 1978. pap. text ed. 85.00 (ISBN 0-08-021670-6). Pergamon.

Buncel, E. Carbanions: Mechanistic & Isotopic Aspects. (Reaction Mechanisms in Organic Chemistry Ser.: Vol. 9). 1974. 59.75 (ISBN 0-444-41190-9). Elsevier.

Buncel, E. & Lee. Isotopes in Cationic Reactions. (Isotopes in Organic Chemistry Ser.: Vol. 5). 234p. 1980. 70.25 (ISBN 0-444-41927-6). Elsevier.

Buncel, E. & Lee, C. C., eds. Isotopes in Hydrogen Transfer Processes. (Isotopes in Organic Chemistry: Vol. 2). 318p. 1976. 70.25 (ISBN 0-444-41352-9). Elsevier.

--Isotopes in Molecular Rearrangements. (Isotopes in Organic Chemistry Ser.: Vol. 1). 320p. 1975. 70.25 (ISBN 0-444-41223-9). Elsevier.

--Isotopes in Organic Chemistry: Isotopic Effects - Recent Developments in Theory & Experiment, Vol. 6. 266p. 1984. 85.25 (ISBN 0-444-42368-0, I-236-84). Elsevier.

Chapman, J. M. & Ayrey, G. The Use of Radioactive Isotopes in the Life Sciences. (Illus.). 148p. 1981. text ed. 28.50x (ISBN 0-04-570011-7); pap. text ed. 9.95x (ISBN 0-04-570012-5). Allen Unwin.

Consultants Bureau. Production of Isotopes: A Portion of the Proceedings of the All-Union Scientific & Technical Conference on Applications of Radioactive Isotopes. LC 59-14487. pap. 34.80 (ISBN 0-317-09120-4, 2020655). Bks Demand UMI.

Environmental Isotope Data: Part 1: World Survey of Isotope Concentration in Precipitation (1953-1963) (Technical Reports Ser.: No. 96). (Orig.). 1969. pap. 25.75 (ISBN 92-0-145069-9, IDC96, IAEA). Unipub.

Environmental Isotope Data: Part 5: World Survey of Isotope Concentration in Precipitation (1970-1971) (Technical Reports Ser.: No. 165). (Illus.). 309p. 1975. pap. 24.75 (ISBN 92-0-145075-3, IDC165, IAEA). Unipub.

Environmental Isotope Data: Part 6: World Survey of Isotope Concentration in Precipitation (1972-1975, Vol. 6. (Technical Reports Ser.: No. 192). (Illus.). 188p. 1979. pap. 23.50 (ISBN 92-0-145179-2, IDC192, IAEA). Unipub.

Faure, Gunter. Principles of Isotope Geology. LC 77-4479. (Intermediate Geology Ser.). 464p. 1977. text ed. 48.50 (ISBN 0-471-25665-X). Wiley.

Ferronsky, V. I. & Polyakov, V. A. Environmental Isotopes in the Hydrosphere. 466p. 1982. 79.95x (ISBN 0-471-10114-1, Pub. by Wiley-Interscience). Wiley.

Fritz, P. Handbook of Environmental Isotope Geochemistry, Vol. 2: The Terrestrial Environment, B. Date not set. write for info. (ISBN 0-444-42225-0). Elsevier.

Galimov, Eric M. The Biological Fractionation of Isotopes: Monograph. Vitaliano, Dorothy B., tr. 1985. 49.50 (ISBN 0-12-273970-1). Acad Pr.

International Union of Pure & Applied Chemistry. Isotope Mass Effects in Chemistry & Biology: Proceedings of a Symposium, Vienna, 1963. 346p. 1976. 33.00 (ISBN 0-08-020778-2). Pergamon.

Isotope Studies on Wheat Fertilization. (Technical Reports Ser.: No. 157). (Illus.). 99p. (Orig.). 1975. pap. 11.50 (ISBN 92-0-115074-1, IDC157, IAEA). Unipub.

Isotopes & Radiation in Soil Organic-Matter Studies. (Proceedings Ser.). (Eng., Fr., Rus. & Span., Illus.). 584p. (Orig.). 1968. pap. 36.00 (ISBN 92-0-010368-5, ISP190, IAEA). Unipub.

Isotopes in Lake Studies. (Panel Proceedings Ser.). (Illus.). 290p. 1980. pap. 37.00 (ISBN 92-0-141179-0, ISP511, IAEA). Unipub.

Klein, E. Roseland & Klein, Peter D., eds. Stable Isotopes: Proceedings of the Third International Conference. 1979. 58.00 (ISBN 0-12-413650-8). Acad Pr.

L'Annunziata, Michael F. & Legg, Joe. Isotopes & Radiation in Agricultural Sciences: Soil-Plant-Water Relationships, Vol. 1. 1984. 65.00 (ISBN 0-12-436601-5). Acad Pr.

L'Annuziata, Michael F. & Legg, Joe, eds. Isotopes & Radiation in Agricultural Sciences: Animals, Plants, Food & the Environment, Vol. 2. 1984. 75.00 (ISBN 0-12-436602-3). Acad Pr.

Lawrence, John H. & Hamilton, J. G., eds. Advances in Biological & Medical Physics, 17 vols. Incl. Vol. 1. 1948 (ISBN 0-12-005201-6); Vol. 2. 1951 (ISBN 0-12-005202-4); Vol. 3. Lawrence, John H. & Tobias, Cornelius, eds. 1953 (ISBN 0-12-005203-2); Vol. 4. 1956 (ISBN 0-12-005204-0); Vol. 5. 1957 (ISBN 0-12-005205-9); Vol. 6. Tobias, Cornelius A. & Lawrence, John H., eds. 1958 (ISBN 0-12-005206-7); Vol. 7. 1960 (ISBN 0-12-005207-5); Vol. 8. 1963 (ISBN 0-12-005208-3); Vol. 9. Lawrence, John H. & Gofman, John W., eds. 1964 (ISBN 0-12-005209-1); Vol. 10. 1965 (ISBN 0-12-005210-5); Vol. 11. 1967. (ISBN 0-12-005211-3); Vol. 12. 1968 (ISBN 0-12-005212-1); Vol. 13. 1971 (ISBN 0-12-005213-X); Vol. 14. 1973 (ISBN 0-12-005214-8); Vol. 15. 1974 (ISBN 0-12-005215-6); Vol. 16. 1978. 85.00 (ISBN 0-12-005216-4); Vol. 17. 1980. 80.00 (ISBN 0-12-005217-2). Vols. 1-16. 85.00 ea. Acad Pr.

Lederer, C. Michael & Shirley, V. S., eds. Table of Isotopes. 7th ed. LC 78-14938. 1600p. 1978. pap. 48.50X (ISBN 0-471-04180-7, Pub. by Wiley-Interscience). Wiley.

McLean, F. C. & Budy, A. M. Radiation, Isotopes, & Bone. (Atomic Energy Commission Monographs). 1964. 14.50 (ISBN 0-12-484950-4). Acad Pr.

Melander, Lars & Saunders, William H., Jr. Reaction Rates of Isotopic Molecules. LC 79-12363. 331p. 1980. 50.95 (ISBN 0-471-04396-6, Pub. by Wiley-Interscience). Wiley.

Ott, D. G. Syntheses with Stable Isotopes of Carbon, Nitrogen, & Oxygen. LC 80-19076. 224p. 1981. 37.95 (ISBN 0-471-04922-0, Pub. by Wiley-Interscience). Wiley.

Palaeoclimates & Palaeowaters: A Collection of Environmental Isotope Studies. (Panel Proceedings Ser.). (Illus.). 207p. 1983. pap. text ed. 33.00 (ISBN 92-0-141083-2, ISP621, IAEA). Unipub.

Rabinovich, Izrail' B. Influence of Isotopy on the Physicochemical Properties of Liquids. LC 69-17695. (Illus.). pap. 79.00 (ISBN 0-317-09392-4, 2020681). Bks Demand UMI.

Romer, Alfred, ed. Radiochemistry & the Discovery of Isotopes. LC 74-91273. 1970. lib. bdg. 10.50x (ISBN 0-88307-628-4). Gannon.

Schmidt, H. L., et al, eds. Stable Isotopes: Proceedings of the 4th International Conference, Julich, Mar. 23-26, 1981. (Analytical Chemistry Symposia Ser.: No. 11). 758p. 1982. 127.75 (ISBN 0-444-42076-2). Elsevier.

Stable Isotopes in the Life Sciences. (Panel Proceedings Ser.). 456p. 1977. pap. 53.75 (ISBN 92-0-011077-0, ISP442, IAEA). Unipub.

Statistical Treatment of Environmental Isotope Data in Precipitation. (Technical Reports Ser.: No. 206). (Illus.). 276p. 1981. pap. 32.50 (ISBN 92-0-145081-8, IDC206, IAEA). Unipub.

Talwar, G. P., ed. Non-Isotopic Immunoassays & Their Applications. (Workshop & Symposia Series, National Institute of Immunology, New Delhi: No. 1). (Illus.). xv, 436p. 1983. text ed. 45.00 (ISBN 0-7069-1900-9, Pub. by Vikas India). Advent NY.

Turnlund, Judith R. & Johnson, Phyllis E. Stable Isotopes in Nutrition. LC 84-12430. (Symposium Ser.: No. 258). 230p. 1984. 39.95x (ISBN 0-8412-0855-7). Am Chemical.

Zanchetti. Isotopin. (International Congress Ser.: Vol. 543). Date not set. price not set (ISBN 0-444-90190-6). Elsevier.

ISOTOPIC CESIUM

see Cesium–Isotopes

ISOTOPIC INDICATORS

see Radioactive Tracers

ISOZYMES

see Isoenzymes

ITERATIVE METHODS (MATHEMATICS)

Ansorge, R., et al, eds. Iterative Solution of Nonlinear Systems of Equations, Oberwolfach, FRG, 1982: Proceedings. (Lecture Notes in Mathematics: Vol. 953). 202p. 1982. pap. 14.00 (ISBN 0-387-11602-8). Springer-Verlag.

Hageman, L. A. & Young, D. M. Applied Interactive Methods. LC 80-29546. (Computer Science & Applied Mathematics Ser.). 1981. 55.00 (ISBN 0-12-313340-8). Acad Pr.

Hain, Richard M. Iterated Integrals & Homotopy Periods. LC 83-22416. (Memoirs Ser.: No. 291). 100p. 1984. pap. 10.00 (ISBN 0-8218-2291-8). Am Math.

Ortega, James M. & Rheinboldt, Werner C. Iterative Solution of Nonlinear Equations in Several Variables. (Computer Science & Applied Mathematics Ser). 1970. 70.00 (ISBN 0-12-528550-7). Acad Pr.

Patterson, W. M. Iterative Methods for the Solution of a Linear Operator Equation in Hilbert Space: A Survey. (Lecture Notes in Mathematics: Vol. 394). 183p. 1974. pap. 14.00 (ISBN 0-387-06805-8). Springer-Verlag.

Rall, Louis B. Computational Solution of Nonlinear Operator Equations. LC 78-2378. 236p. (Orig.). 1979. Repr. of 1969 ed. 13.50 (ISBN 0-88275-667-2). Krieger.

Traub, Joseph F. Iterative Methods for the Solution of Equations. 2nd ed. LC 81-66999. 328p. 1981. text ed. 17.95 (ISBN 0-8284-0312-0). Chelsea Pub.

Young, David M. Iterative Solution of Large Linear Systems. 1971. 75.00 (ISBN 0-12-773050-8). Acad Pr.

IVORY-STAINING

see Stains and Staining

IXODIDAE

see Ticks

J

J U 87 (BOMBERS)

see Stuka (Bombers)

JACK-RABBITS

see Hares; Rabbits

JACOBI POLYNOMIALS

see Functions, Orthogonal

JADE

Anderson, Eskil. Asbestos & Jade in the Kobuk River Region of Alaska. facs. ed. (Shorey Prospecting Ser.). 26p. pap. 3.95 (ISBN 0-8466-0037-4, S37). Shorey.

Chinese Jade Throughout the Ages. (Illus.). 1975. 50.00x (ISBN 0-686-31469-7, Pub. by Sotheby Pubns England). Biblio Dist.

Gump, Richard. Jade: Stone of Heaven. LC 62-12100. (Illus.). 1962. 14.95 (ISBN 0-385-01705-7). Doubleday.

Hartman, Joan M. Chinese Jade of Five Centuries. LC 69-12077. (Illus.). 1969. 27.50 (ISBN 0-8048-0099-5). C E Tuttle.

Hemrich, G. Handbook of Jade. pap. 2.50 (ISBN 0-910652-08-2). Gembooks.

Nott, Stanley C. Chinese Jade Throughout the Ages: A Review of Its Characteristics, Decoration, Folklore & Symbolism. LC 62-8839. (Illus.). 1962. 47.50 (ISBN 0-8048-0100-2). C E Tuttle.

Watt, James C. Chinese Jades from Han to Ch'ing. LC 80-20115. (Illus.). 236p. 1980. 22.50 (ISBN 0-87848-057-9). Asia Soc.

Wills, Geoffrey. Jade of the East. LC 72-78589. (Illus.). 200p. 1972. 38.50 (ISBN 0-8348-1854-X). Weatherhill.

JAGUAR (AUTOMOBILE)

see Automobiles, Foreign–Types–Jaguar

JAMMING (RADIO)

see Radio–Interference

JAPANESE BEETLE

Bourke, P. Climatic Aspects of the Possible Establishment of the Japanese Beetle in Europe. (Technical Note Ser.: No. 41). 9p. 1961. pap. 11.00 (ISBN 0-685-57275-7, W16, WMO). Unipub.

JAPANESE QUAIL

Fitzgerald, Theodore C. The Coturnix Quail: Anatomy & Histology. (Illus.). 1970. 12.95x (ISBN 0-8138-0356-X). Iowa St U Pr.

JAPANESE SCIENCE

see Science, Japanese

JAPANESE SWORDS

see Swords

JAYS

Bancroft, G. Thomas & Woolfenden, Glen E. Molt of Scrub Jays & Blue Jays in Florida. 51p. 1982. 8.00 (ISBN 0-943610-29-X). Am Ornithologists.

Wilmore, Sylvia B. Crows, Jays, Ravens & Their Relatives. LC 77-79245. (Illus.). 1977. 12.95 (ISBN 0-8397-1894-2). Eriksson.

--Crows, Jays, Ravens (& Their Relatives) (Illus.). 1979. pap. 9.95 (ISBN 0-87666-878-3, PS-779). TFH Pubns.

JAZZ (COMPUTER PROGRAM)

Barton, Taylor J. The Illustrated JAZZ Book. (Illustrated Ser.). (Illus.). 300p. (Orig.). 1985. pap. 16.98 (ISBN 0-915381-77-X). Wordware Pub.

Schussler, Terry. Using Jazz. LC 85-60690. 1985. pap. 19.95 (ISBN 0-88022-158-5, 144). Que Corp.

JCL (COMPUTER PROGRAM LANGUAGE)

see Job Control Language (Computer Program Language)

JEEP VEHICLE

see Automobiles–Types–Jeep

JELLYFISH

see Medusae

JERBOAS

Kirmiz, John P. Adaptation to Desert Environment: A Study of the Jerboa, Rat & Man. 168p. 1962. 24.50x (ISBN 0-306-30658-1, Plenum Pr). Plenum Pub.

JET FLOW

see Jets–Fluid Dynamics

JET FUEL

see Jet Planes–Fuel

JET PLANES

see also Jet Transports; Heinkel (Fighter Planes)

Boyne, Walter J. & Lopez, Donald S., eds. The Jet Age: Forty Years of Jet Aviation. LC 79-20216. (Illus.). 190p. 1979. 19.95 (ISBN 0-87474-248-X); pap. 10.95 (ISBN 0-87474-247-1). Smithsonian.

Calvert, Brian. Flying Concorde. LC 81-16745. (Illus.). 256p. 1982. 13.95 (ISBN 0-312-29685-1). St Martin.

Chen, C. J. Vertical Turbulent Buoyant Jets: A Review of Experimental Data. (Heat & Mass Transfer: Vol. 4). (Illus.). 94p. 1979. 33.00 (ISBN 0-08-024772-5). Pergamon.

Davies, David P. Handling the Big Jets. 3rd ed. (Illus.). 324p. 1973. 34.95 (ISBN 0-903083-01-9). Pan Am Nav.

Green, William & Cross, Roy. The Jet Aircraft of the World. Gilbert, James, ed. LC 79-7263. (Flight: Its First Seventy-Five Years Ser.). (Illus.). 1979. Repr. of 1956 ed. lib. bdg. 30.50x (ISBN 0-405-12173-3). Ayer Co Pubs.

Ingells, Douglas J. Seven Forty-Seven Boeing Superjet. LC 78-135055. (Illus.). 1970. pap. 14.95 (ISBN 0-8168-8704-7). Aero.

Jet Planes of the Third Reich. LC 81-84360. 1982. 49.95 (ISBN 0-914144-27-8). Monogram Aviation.

McAllister, Chris. Jet Liners. (Illus.). 64p. 1982. pap. 5.50 (ISBN 0-7134-4162-3, Pub. by Batsford England). David & Charles.

Masters, David. German Jet Genesis. (Illus.). 160p. 1982. 19.95 (ISBN 0-86720-622-5). Jane's Pub Inc.

Rodi, W., ed. Turbulent Buoyant Jets & Plumes, Vol. 6. (HMT Ser.). 192p. 1982. 39.00 (ISBN 0-08-026492-1). Pergamon.

Seddon, J. & Goldsmith, E. L. Intake Aerodynamics. 256p. 1985. 60.00x (ISBN 0-00-383048-9, Pub. by Collins England). Sheridan.

Serling, Robert J. The Jet Age. (Epic of Flight Ser.). 1982. lib. bdg. 21.27 (ISBN 0-8094-3301-X, Pub. by Time-Life). Silver.

Stevenson, James. Grumman F-14 "Tomcat". LC 75-7465. (Aero Ser.: Vol. 25). 104p. 1975. pap. 7.95 (ISBN 0-8168-0592-X). Aero.

Stewart, Stanley. Flying the Big Jets. (Illus.). 288p. 1985. 16.95 (ISBN 0-668-06346-7). Arco.

Wooldridge, E. T., Jr. The P-80 Shooting Star. Evolution of a Jet Fighter. LC 79-17648. (Famous Aircraft of the National Air & Space Museum Ser.: Bk. 3). (Illus.). 110p. 1979. pap. 6.95 (ISBN 0-87474-965-4). Smithsonian.

JET PLANES–FLIGHT TESTING

Penrose, Harald. No Echo in the Sky. LC 78-169433. (Literature & History of Aviation Ser.). 1971. Repr. of 1958 ed. 32.00 (ISBN 0-405-03776-7). Ayer Co Pubs.

JET PLANES–FUEL

Factors in Using Kerosine Jet Fuel of Reduced Flash Point, STP 688. 113p. 1979. soft cover 15.00x (ISBN 0-8031-0340-9, 04-688000-13). ASTM.

JET PLANES–MOTORS

see Airplanes–Jet Propulsion; Airplanes–Turbojet Engines

JET PLANES, MILITARY

see also B-Fifty-Two Bomber

Berliner, Don. World War Two Jet Fighters. Angle, Burr, ed. (Illus.). 72p. (Orig.). 1982. pap. 8.50 (ISBN 0-89024-041-8). Kalmbach.

Feuchtwanger, E. J. & Mason, R. A. Air Power in the Next Generation. 1979. text ed. 26.50x (ISBN 0-333-23609-2). Humanities.

Holder, William G. Convair F-106 Delta Dart. LC 75-15272. (Aero Ser.: Vol. 27). 104p. 1977. pap. 7.95 (ISBN 0-8168-0600-4). Aero.

JET PROPELLANTS

see Jet Planes–Fuel

JET PROPELLED AIRPLANES

see Airplanes–Jet Propulsion; Jet Planes

JET PROPULSION

see also Airplanes–Jet Propulsion; Rockets (Aeronautics); Rockets (Ordnance)

Koppes, Clayton R. JPL & the American Space Program: A History of the Jet Propulsion Laboratory 1936-1976. LC 82-40162. (Illus.). 320p. 1982. 23.50x (ISBN 0-300-02408-8). Yale U Pr.

Lewis, Alexander D. Gas Power Dynamics. LC 77-15095. 544p. 1978. Repr. of 1962 ed. lib. bdg. 34.00 (ISBN 0-88275-629-X). Krieger.

Lin, Chia-Ch'iao, ed. Turbulent Flows & Heat Transfer. LC 58-50928. (High Speed Aerodynamics & Jet Propulsion: Vol. 5). pap. 142.30 (ISBN 0-317-09274-X, 2001132). Bks Demand UMI.

JET STREAM

Reiter, Elmar R. Jet-Stream Meteorology. LC 63-13074. pap. 132.30 (ISBN 0-317-08097-0, 2020153). Bks Demand UMI.

--Jet Streams: How Do They Affect Our Weather? LC 78-25793. (Illus.). 1979. Repr. of 1967 ed. lib. bdg. 27.50x (ISBN 0-313-20782-8, REJS). Greenwood.

JUTE

Impact of Synthetics on Jute & Allied Fibers. (Commodity Bulletins: No. 46). 114p. (Orig.). 1969. pap. 10.00 (ISBN 92-5-101717-4, F239, FAO). Unipub.

Ranjam, T. C. Hanbook on Jute, Vols. 1-3. 1981. 40.00x (ISBN 0-686-76644-X, Pub. by Oxford & IBH India). State Mutual Bk.

The Retting of Jute. (Agricultural Services Bulletins: No. 60). 54p. 1985. pap. 7.50 (ISBN 92-5-101415-9, F2736, FAO). Unipub.

K

K-MESONS

see Mesons

K-THEORY

Bak, A. K-Theory of Forms. LC 80-7847. (Annals of Mathematics Studies: No. 98). 220p. 1981. 26.00x (ISBN 0-691-08274-X); pap. 10.50 (ISBN 0-691-08275-8). Princeton U Pr.

Bass, Hyman. Introduction to Some Methods of Algebraic K-Theory. LC 73-19925. (CBMS Regional Conference Series in Mathematics: No. 20). 68p. 1982. pap. 16.00 (ISBN 0-8218-1670-5, CBMS-20). Am Math.

Dennis, R. K. Algebraic K-Theory: Proccedings, Oberwolfach, FRG 1980, Vol. 1. (Lecture Notes in Mathematics Ser.: Vol. 966). 407p. 1982. pap. 22.00 (ISBN 0-387-11965-5). Springer-Verlag.

Dennis, R. K., ed. Algebraic K-Theory: Proceedings, Oberwolfach, FRG, 1980, Vol. II. (Lecture Notes in Mathematics: Vol. 967). 409p. 1982. pap. 22.00 (ISBN 0-387-11966-3). Springer-Verlag.

Friedlander, E. M. & Stein, M. R., eds. Algebraic K-Theory: Proceedings. (Lecture Notes in Mathematics Ser.: Vol. 854). 517p. 1981. pap. 29.00 (ISBN 0-387-10698-7). Springer-Verlag.

Hodgkin, L. H. Topics in K-Theory: Two Independent Contributions. LC 75-41435. (Lecture Notes in Mathematics: Vol. 496). 1975. pap. 19.00 (ISBN 0-387-07536-4). Springer-Verlag.

International Conference, Bielefeld, West Germany, July 26-30, 1982. Algebraic K-Theory, Number Theory, Geometry & Analysis: Proceedings. Bak, A., ed. (Lecture Notes in Mathematics Ser.: Vol. 1046). ix, 464p. 1984. pap. 24.00 (ISBN 0-387-12891-3). Springer-Verlag.

Karoubi, M. K-Theory: An Introduction. LC 77-23162. (Gsundlehsen Des Mathematischen Wissenschaften: Band 226). (Illus.). 1978. 51.00 (ISBN 0-387-08090-2). Springer-Verlag.

Mahammed, N. & Piccininni, R. Some Applications of Topological K-Theory. (Mathematical Ser.: Vol. 45). 318p. 1980. 47.00 (ISBN 0-444-86113-0, North Holland). Elsevier.

Moss, R. M. & Thomas, C. B. Algebraic K-Theory & Its Geometric Applications. LC 74-97991. (Lecture Notes in Mathematics Ser.). 1969. pap. 10.70 (ISBN 0-387-04627-5). Springer-Verlag.

Silvester, John R. Introduction to Algebraic K-Theory. 250p. 1981. 29.95x (ISBN 0-412-22700-2, NO. 6601, Pub by Chapman & Hall England); pap. 15.95x (ISBN 0-412-23740-7, NO. 6602). Methuen Inc.

Snaith, V. P. Algebraic Cobordism & K-Theory. LC 79-17981. (Memoirs Ser.: No. 221). 152p. 1979. pap. 12.00 (ISBN 0-8218-2221-7). Am Math.

--Algebraic K-Theory & Localized Stable Homotopy Theory. LC 83-3726. (Memoirs of the American Mathematical Society Ser.: No. 280). 108p. 1983. pap. 12.00 (ISBN 0-8218-2280-2). Am Math.

KANGAROO RATS

Nader, Iyad A. Kangaroo Rats: Intraspecific Variation in Dipodomys Spectabilis Merriam & Dipodomys Deserti Stephens. LC 78-9317. (Illinois Biological Monographs: No. 49). pap. 24.40 (ISBN 0-8357-9686-8, 2019004). Bks Demand UMI.

Setzer, Henry W. Subspeciation in the Kangaroo Rat: Dipodomys Ordii. (Museum Ser.: Vol. 1, No. 23). 101p. 1949. 5.25 (ISBN 0-317-04932-1). U of KS Mus Nat Hist.

KAONS

see Mesons

KARST

Dougherty, Percy H., ed. Environmental Karst. LC 84-80188. (Illus.). 178p. (Orig.). 1984. text ed. 7.95 (ISBN 0-9613107-0-7). Geo Speleo Pubns.

Herak, M. & Stringfield, V. T., eds. Important Karst Regions of the Northern Hemisphere. LC 74-151736. (Illus.). 565p. 1972. 117.00 (ISBN 0-444-40849-5). Elsevier.

Sweeting, Marjorie M. Karst Landforms. LC 72-172813. (Illus.). 380p. 1973. 55.00x (ISBN 0-231-03623-X). Columbia U Pr.

Trudgill, Stephen. Limestone Geomorphology. (Geomorphology Texts Ser.). (Illus.). 231p. 1985. pap. text ed. 19.95 (ISBN 0-582-30011-8). Longman.

KARYOKINESIS

see also Chromosomes; Meiosis

Guern, J. & Peaud-Lenoel, C., eds. Metabolism & Molecular Activities of Cytokinins: Proceedings. (Proceedings in Life Sciences Ser.). (Illus.). 370p. 1981. 61.00 (ISBN 0-387-10711-8). Springer-Verlag.

Hsu, T. C. & Benirschke, K. Atlas of Mammalian Chromosomes, Vols. 1-6. LC 67-19307. (Illus.). 1967-71. Vol. 1. loose-leaf boxed 27.00 (ISBN 0-387-03878-7); Vol. 3. loose-leaf boxed 26.00 (ISBN 0-387-04563-5); Vol. 4. loose-leaf boxed 34.00 (ISBN 0-387-04882-0); Vol. 5. loose-leaf boxed 37.00 (ISBN 0-387-05280-1); Vol. 6. 35.00 (ISBN 0-387-05590-8). Springer-Verlag.

Oppenheim, Joost J. & Cohen, Stanley, eds. Interleukins, Lymphokines & Cytokines (Symposium) 1983. 63.00 (ISBN 0-12-527540-4). Acad Pr.

Symposium on the Cell in Mitosis. Proceedings. Levine, Lawrence, ed. 1963. 49.00 (ISBN 0-12-444950-6). Acad Pr.

KARYOTYPES

see also Chromosome Abnormalities

Benirschke, K. & Hsu, T. C., eds. Chromosome Atlas: Fish, Amphibians, Reptiles & Birds, Vol. 1. LC 73-166079. (Illus.). 225p. 1972. loose leaf 25.00 (ISBN 0-387-05507-X). Springer-Verlag.

Buckton, K. E. & Evans, H. J. Methods for the Analysis of Human Chromosome Aberrations. (Also avail. in French & Russian). 1973. 4.80 (ISBN 92-4-154031-1). World Health.

International Conference on Comparative Mammalian Cytogenetics, Dartmouth Medical School, 1968. Proceedings. Benirschke, K., ed. (Illus.). 1969. 66.00 (ISBN 0-387-04442-6). Springer-Verlag.

Kaplan, Barbara. Preparation of the Normal Karyotype. LC 78-720409. (Illus.). 1979. 55.00 (ISBN 0-89189-057-2, 21-9-015-00); student ed. 9.00 (ISBN 0-89189-071-8, 21-9-015-20). Am Soc Clinical.

Kaplan, Barbara J. Preparation of the Normal Giemsa-Trypsin-Banded Karyotype: A Monograph. Evans, Leonard A., ed. LC 81-720284. (Illus.). 56p. 1982. tchrs. ed. 85.00 (ISBN 0-89189-148-X, 21-9-016-00); monograph 18.00 (ISBN 0-89189-149-8, 21-9-016-20). Am Soc Clinical.

Nagley, P., et al, eds. Manipulation & Expression of Genes in Eukaryotes. 1983. 44.50 (ISBN 0-12-513780-X). Acad Pr.

KAWASAKI MOTORCYCLE

Jorgensen, Eric, ed. Kawasaki KZ650 Fours 1977-1983 Service, Repair & Performance. (Illus.). pap. 13.95 (ISBN 0-89287-296-9, M358). Clymer Pubns.

Kawasaki KZ200 & 250 Singles 1978-1983 Service Repair Performance. (Illus., Orig.). 1981. pap. 13.95 (ISBN 0-89287-341-8, M448). Clymer Pubns.

Meek, Frank. Kawasaki 250, 350 & 400 (3-cyl) Models '72 - '79. (Owners Workshop Manuals Ser.: No. 134). 1979. 10.50 (ISBN 0-85696-134-5, Pub. by J H Haynes England). Haynes Pubns.

Robinson, Jeff, ed. Kawasaki Service - Repair Handbook: 250 & 350cc Twins, All Years. (Illus.). pap. text ed. 13.95 (ISBN 0-89287-016-8, M352). Clymer Pubns.

--Kawasaki Service--Repair Handbook: 80-350cc Rotary Valve Singles, 1966-1980. (Illus.). pap. 13.95 (ISBN 0-89287-152-0, M350). Clymer Pubns.

--Kawasaki Service & Repair Handbook: KZ400 & 440 Twins, 1974- 1983. (Illus.). pap. 13.95 (ISBN 0-89287-138-5, M355). Clymer Pubns.

Shoemark, P. Kawasaki 900 '73 - '79. (Owners Workshop Manuals Ser.: No. 222). 1979. 10.50 (ISBN 0-85696-222-8, Pub. by J H Haynes England). Haynes Pubns.

Shoemark, Pete. Kawasaki KZ400 & 440 Twins '75 - '81. (Owners Workshop Manuals Ser.: No. 281). 1982. 10.50 (ISBN 0-85696-711-4, Pub. by J H Haynes England). Haynes Pubns.

Vesely, Anton. Kawasaki KDX 80-420 Singles 1979-1981. Jorgensen, Eric, ed. (Illus., Orig.). 1981. pap. 13.95 (ISBN 0-89287-338-8, M446). Clymer Pubns.

--Kawasaki KX 80-450 Piston Port 1974-1981. Jorgensen, Eric, ed. (Illus., Orig.). 1981. pap. text ed. 13.95·(ISBN 0-89287-337-X, M445). Clymer Pubns.

--Kawasaki KZ500 & 550 Fours 1979-1983 Service Repair Performance. Wauson, Sydnie A., ed. (Illus., Orig.). 1982. pap. 13.95 (ISBN 0-89287-363-9). Clymer Pubns.

Vesely, Anton & Wauson, Sydnie. Kawasaki Jet Ski 1976-1983 Service-Repair-Maintenance. (Illus., Orig.). 1982. pap. 13.95 (ISBN 0-89287-354-X, X956). Clymer Pubns.

Vesley, Anton. Kawasaki KZ, Z, & ZX750: 1980-1983 Service Repair Performance. Wauson, Sydnie A., ed. (Illus., Orig.). 1982. text ed. 13.95 (ISBN 0-89287-356-6, M450). Clymer Pubns.

Wilkins, Stewart. Kawasaki 500 & 750 (3-cyl) Models '69 - '76. (Owners Workshop Manuals Ser.: No. 325). 1979. 10.50 (ISBN 0-85696-325-9, Pub. by J H Haynes England). Haynes Pubns.

KAYAKS

see Canoes and Canoeing

KAYPRO 10 (COMPUTER)

Frankel, Steven. The Complete Kaypro: Kaypro II, IV, & 10. 1983. pap. text ed. 16.95 (ISBN 0-8359-0802-X). Reston.

Human Connection. Using CP-M on Your Kaypro 10. (Illus.). 128p. 1984. pap. 19.50 (ISBN 0-8306-1774-4). TAB Bks.

KAYPRO II (COMPUTER)

Bennett, M. A. The Instant Expert's Guide to the Kaypro II. Dvorak, John C., ed. (Dvorak's Instant Expert Ser.). (Illus.). 192p. (Orig.). 1984. 7.95 (ISBN 0-440-54462-9, Dell Trade Paperback). Dell.

Frankel, Steven. The Complete Kaypro: Kaypro II, IV, & 10. 1983. pap. text ed. 16.95 (ISBN 0-8359-0802-X). Reston.

Lord, Kenniston W., Jr. Using the Kaypro II Personal Computer. LC 84-7402. 272p. 1984. 24.45 (ISBN 0-442-26038-5); pap. 15.45 (ISBN 0-442-26037-7). Van Nos Reinhold.

Platt, T. Gregory & Van Meter, Roz. The Perfect Manual for the Kaypro II. 2nd. ed. (PeopleTalk Ser.). (Illus.). 1983. pap. 17.95 (ISBN 0-915907-01-1). Peopletalk.

Platt, T. Gregory, et al. WordStar & Friends for the Kaypro II & 4. (PeopleTalk Ser.). (Illus.). 296p. 1983. pap. 21.95 (ISBN 0-915907-03-8). Peopletalk.

Ried, Andrea & Diedrichs, Gary. Your Kaypro II, 4 & 10. 250p. 14.95 (ISBN 0-89588-166-7). SYBEX.

KAYPRO IV (COMPUTER)

Frankel, Steven. The Complete Kaypro: Kaypro II, IV, & 10. 1983. pap. text ed. 16.95 (ISBN 0-8359-0802-X). Reston.

Platt, T. Gregory & Van Meter, Roz. The Perfect Manual for the Kaypro 4. (PeopleTalk Ser.). (Illus.). 256p. 1983. pap. 17.95 (ISBN 0-915907-02-X). Peopletalk.

Platt, T. Gregory, et al. WordStar & Friends for the Kaypro II & 4. (PeopleTalk Ser.). (Illus.). 296p. 1983. pap. 21.95 (ISBN 0-915907-03-8). Peopletalk.

KAYPRO COMPUTERS

Bromley, Dudley. Guide to Kaypro Computers. 1984. 13.95 (ISBN 0-317-05698-0). S&S.

Darnell, W. H. & Barton, P. J. BASIC Kaypro for Kids. (Illus.). 215p. 1984. pap. 16.95 (ISBN 0-8359-0393-1). Reston.

Houze, Bill & Lenfest, Dave. The Kaypro: Plain & Simple. LC 84-8532. (Illus.). 192p. (Orig.). 1984. 19.95 (ISBN 0-8306-0802-8); pap. 12.95 (ISBN 0-8306-1802-3, 1802). TAB Bks.

Kalb, Ken. The Kaypro: An Applications Guide. (Illus.). 224p. (Orig.). 1984. pap. 12.95 (ISBN 0-916688-70-4, 70-4). Creative Comp.

The Kaypro Software Directory. 25.00 (ISBN 0-318-03641-X). Kaypro.

Lenfest, Dave & Houze, Bill. Kaypro Word Processing: Plain & Simple. LC 84-8720. (Illus.). 192p. (Orig.). 1984. 21.95 (ISBN 0-8306-0812-5); pap. 13.95 (ISBN 0-8306-1812-0, 1812). TAB Bks.

McWilliams, Peter A. Word Processing on the Kaypro. 224p. 1983. pap. 9.95 (ISBN 0-345-31529-4). Ballantine.

Rensin, Joseph K. & Goldstein, Larry J. BASICally Kaypro: Programming the 2, 4 & 10. (Illus.). 288p. 1984. 16.95 (ISBN 0-89303-360-X). Brady Comm.

Ryan, Lee F. & Townsend, Andrew. The Kaypro Connection-Selecting, Installing & Using Peripherals: Selecting, Installing & Using Peripherals. (Illus.). 256p. (Orig.). 1985. 19.95 (ISBN 0-8306-0880-X, 1880); pap. 14.95 (ISBN 0-8306-1880-5). TAB Bks.

Tymes, Elna R. Businessman's Guide to the Kaypro. (Illus.). 200p. 1984. 16.95 (ISBN 0-8359-0601-9). Reston.

Uston, Ken. Ken Uston's Illustrated Guide to the Kaypro. (Illustrated Guides Ser.). (Illus.). 1984. 12.95 (ISBN 0-13-514795-6). P-H.

Weber Systems Inc. Staff. Kaypro Business Software in BASIC. (Applications Software Ser.). 330p. 1985. pap. 17.95 (ISBN 0-938862-51-0); diskette & bk 20.00 (ISBN 0-938862-52-9). Weber Systems.

Weber Systems, Inc. Staff. Kaypro User's Handbook. 312p. 1984. pap. 9.95 (ISBN 0-345-31595-2). Ballantine.

Williams, Gene B. Chilton's Guide to Kaypro Repair & Maintenance. LC 85-47833. 224p. 1985. pap. 12.50 (ISBN 0-8019-7626-X). Chilton.

Wolenik, Robert. Instant Wordstar for Kaypro. 1984. pap. text ed. 16.95 (ISBN 0-8359-3090-4). Reston.

--Instant Wordstar for the Kaypro. (Illus.). 224p. 15.95 (ISBN 0-317-13068-4). P-H.

KEESHOND

see Dogs–Breeds–Keeshond

KELP

Lee, William R. Kelp, Dulse & Other Supplements from the Sea. (Good Health Guide Ser.). 1983. pap. text ed. 1.45 (ISBN 0-87983-313-0). Keats.

Powell, Eric F. Kelp the Health Giver. 1980. 2.25 (ISBN 0-8464-1028-1). Beekman Pubs.

Thomson, William P. Kelp-Making in Orkney. 144p. 39.00x (ISBN 0-907618-02-2, Pub. by Orkney Pr Uk). State Mutual Bk.

KELVIN, WILLIAM THOMSON, BARON, 1824-1907

Sharlin, Harold & Sharlin, Tiby. Lord Kelvin: The Dynamic Victorian. LC 78-50771. (Illus.). 1979. 27.50 (ISBN 0-271-00203-4). Pa St U Pr.

Thompson, Silvanus P. The Life of Lord Kelvin, 2 vols. 2nd ed. LC 75-45133. (Illus.). 1977. text ed. 39.50 set (ISBN 0-8284-0292-2). Chelsea Pub.

KENNELLY-HEAVISIDE LAYER

see Ionosphere

KEPLER, JOHANNES, 1571-1630

Dow, T. W. Repeal Kepler's Laws. LC 60-13372. 1960. 5.00 (ISBN 0-910340-02-1). Celestial Pr.

Jardine, Nicholas. The Birth of History & Philosophy of Science: Kepler's "A Defence of Tycho Against Ursus" with Essays on Its Provenance & Significance. LC 83-14186. (Illus.). 288p. 1984. 62.50 (ISBN 0-521-25226-1). Cambridge U Pr.

Koestler, Arthur. The Watershed: A Biography of Johannes Kepler. Durston, John, frwd. by. LC 84-19690. (Illus.). 288p. 1985. pap. text ed. 12.00 (ISBN 0-8191-4339-1). U Pr of Amer.

Palter, Robert, compiled by. Johannes Kepler, 1571-1630: An Exhibit of Books, Manuscripts, & Related Materials. LC 70-180652. (Illus.). 1971. pap. 6.00 (ISBN 0-87959-014-9). U of Tex H Ransom Ctr.

KEPLER'S LAWS

see Orbits

KERAMICS

see Ceramics

KERATIN

Fraser, R. D., et al. Keratins: Their Composition, Structure & Biosynthesis. (Illus.). 320p. 1972. 24.75 (ISBN 0-398-02283-6). C C Thomas.

Leon, N. H. Chemical Reactivity & Modification of Keratin Fibres. 81p. 1975. 70.00x (ISBN 0-686-63750-X). State Mutual Bk.

Parakkal, P. F. & Alexander, Nancy J. Keratinization - a Survey of Vertebrate Epithelia. (Monographs on the Ultrastructure of Cells & Organisms). 1972. 27.50 (ISBN 0-12-454140-2). Acad Pr.

KERRY BLUE TERRIERS

see Dogs–Breeds–Kerry Blue Terriers

KETONES

Preston, Seaton T., Jr. & Pankratz, Ronald. A Guide to the Analysis of Ketones by Gas Chromatography. 2nd rev. ed. 1975. spiral 25.00 (ISBN 0-913106-07-0). PolyScience.

KEY DEER

see White-Tailed Deer

KEYBOARDS (ELECTRONICS)

Baumann, M. A. & Bahntge, M. A. Legal Keyboarding: Typewriters, Electric Typewriters, Word Processors. 286p. 1985. pap. 14.95 (ISBN 0-471-88590-8). Wiley.

Crawford, et al. Microcomputer Keyboarding-Formatting Applications. 1985. text ed. price not set wkbk. & diskettes (ISBN 0-538-26100-5, Z10). SW Pub.

--Microcomputer Keyboarding-Formatting Applications. 1986. pap. text ed. price not set (ISBN 0-538-21100-8, U10). SW Pub.

Farmer, G. M., et al. Keyboarding: An Introductory Course. 96p. 1985. 7.25 (ISBN 0-7715-0926-X). Forkner.

Novello, John A. The Contemporary Keyboardist. (Illus.). 475p. (Orig.). 1985. pap. 50.00 (ISBN 0-9614966-0-6). Source Prods.

KEYS

see Locks and Keys

KIDNEYS

Angieski, S. Biochemical Aspects of Renal Function. Dubach, C., ed. 242p. 1975. 75.00 (ISBN 3-456-80208-0, Pub. by Holdan Bk Ltd UK). State Mutual Bk.

Berlyne, G. H., ed. Reprinted Selected Top Articles Published 1976 - 1977. (Karger Highlights, Nephrology One). (Illus.). 1978. pap. 6.50 (ISBN 3-8055-2938-4). S Karger.

Bianchi, C., ed. Kidney, Small Proteins & Drugs. (Contributions to Nephrology: Vol. 42). (Illus.). x, 262p. 1984. 53.25 (ISBN 3-8055-3913-4). S Karger.

Brenner, Barry M. & Rector, Floyd C., eds. The Kidney, 2 vols. 2nd ed. LC 74-25474. (Illus.). 2708p. 1981. Set. text ed. 173.00 (ISBN 0-7216-1969-X); Vol. 1. text ed. 89.00 (ISBN 0-7216-1967-3); Vol. 2. text ed. 89.00 (ISBN 0-7216-1968-1). Saunders.

Brenner, Barry M. & Stein, Jay H., eds. Hormonal Function & the Kidney. (Contemporary Issues in Nephrology: Vol. 4). (Illus.). 1979. text ed. 40.00 (ISBN 0-443-08039-9). Churchill.

Chasis, Herbert & Goldring, William, eds. Homer William Smith, Sc. D. His Scientific & Literary Achievements. LC 65-10765. pap. 58.60 (ISBN 0-8357-9478-4, 2010289). Bks Demand UMI.

Coburn, J. W. & Massry, S. G., eds. Uses & Actions of 1,25 Dihyroxyvitamin D3 in Uremia. (Contributions to Nephrology: Vol. 18). (Illus.). x, 218p. 1980. 34.50 (ISBN 3-8055-3064-1). S Karger.

Dalton, A. J. & Haguenau, Francis. Ultrastructure of the Kidney. (Ultrastructure in Biological Systems). 1967. 51.00 (ISBN 0-12-200956-8). Acad Pr.

Deetjen, P., et al. Physiology of the Kidney & of Water Balance. LC 72-85949. (Illus.). 145p. 1975. pap. 18.00 (ISBN 0-387-90048-9). Springer-Verlag.

Dunn, Michael J. & Patrono, Carlo, eds. Prostaglandins & the Kidney: Biochemistry, Physiology, Pharmacology, & Clinical Applications. 438p. 1983. 49.50 (ISBN 0-306-41054-0, Plenum Med Bk). Plenum Pub.

Eisenbach, G. M. & Brod, Jan, eds. Non-Vasoactive Renal Hormones. (Contributions to Nephrology: Vol. 13). (Illus.). 1978. pap. 29.00 (ISBN 3-8055-2895-7). S Karger.

Finlayson, Birdwell & Thomas, William C., Jr., eds. Colloquium on Renal Lithiasis. LC 77-7779. (Illus.). 1976. 25.00 (ISBN 0-8130-0566-3). U Presses Fla.

Fleisch, H., et al, eds. Urolithiasis Research. LC 76-47019. 598p. 1976. 75.00x (ISBN 0-306-30988-2, Plenum Pr). Plenum Pub.

Friedman, E. A., ed. The John P. Merrill Festschrift: Nephrological Research Papers by Past & Present Members of the Merrill School of Nephrology. (Nephron: Vol. 22, Nos. 1-3). (Illus.). 1978. pap. 27.75 (ISBN 3-8055-2981-3). S Karger.

Gerrick, David J. Anatomy of the Sheep Kidney: Clinical Implications. (Illus.). 1978. 20.00 (ISBN 0-916750-04-3). Dayton Labs.

Hamburger, Jean, et al, eds. Advances in Nephrology, Vol 6. (Illus.). 1976. 59.95 (ISBN 0-8151-4115-7). Year Bk Med.

Harrington, Avery R. & Zimmerman, Stephen W. Pathophysiology of Renal. LC 81-7454. (Wiley Series in Pathophysiology). 258p. 1982. 19.50 (ISBN 0-471-07815-8, Pub. by Wiley Med). Wiley.

Horton, R. & Dunn, M. J., eds. Prostaglandins & the Kidney. (Journal: Mineral & Electrolyte Metabolism: Vol. 6, No. 1-2). (Illus.). 104p. 1981. pap. 30.00 (ISBN 3-8055-3406-X). S Karger.

International Congress of Nephrology, 7th, Montreal, June 18-23, 1978. Proceedings. Bergerson, Michael, ed. 1978. 63.50 (ISBN 3-8055-2915-5). S Karger.

International Congress, 6th, Florence, June 1975. Advances in Nephrology: Proceedings. Giovannetti, S. & Bonomini, V., eds. (Illus.). 800p. 1976. 26.25 (ISBN 3-8055-2287-8). S Karger.

International Symposium on the Glomerular Basement Membrane, 1st, Vienna, Sept. 1980. Proceedings. Lubec, G., ed. (Renal Physiology Journal: Vol. 4, No. 2-3). (Illus.). 100p. 1981. pap. 13.25 (ISBN 3-8055-3491-4). S Karger.

International Symposium on Unilateral Renal Function Studies, 1st, Montecatini Terme, May 1977, et al. Unilateral Renal Function Studies: Proceedings. Giovannetti, S. & Thomas, S., eds. (Contrubutions to Nephrology: Vol. 11). (Illus.). 1978. 33.25 (ISBN 3-8055-2858-2). S Karger.

Kaissling, B. & Kriz, W. Structural Analysis of the Rabbit Kidney. (Advances in Anatomy, Embryology & Cell Biology: Vol. 56). (Illus.). 1979. pap. 33.00 (ISBN 0-387-09145-9). Springer-Verlag.

Kidney & Body Fluids. (Advances in Physiological Sciences Ser.: Vol. 11). 70.00x (ISBN 0-08-026825-0). Pergamon.

Kinne, R. K., ed. Renal Biochemistry: Cells, Membranes, Molecules. 476p. 1985. 125.75 (ISBN 0-444-80627-X). Elsevier.

Klahr, Saulo, ed. The Kidney & Body Fluids in Health & Disease. 616p. 1984. pap. 29.50x (ISBN 0-306-41660-3, Plenum Med Bk). Plenum Pub.

Koushanpour, Esmail. Renal Physiology: Principles & Functions. LC 75-12489. (Illus.). Repr. of 1976 ed. 112.00 (ISBN 0-8357-9558-6, 2012275). Bks Demand UMI.

Kugler, P. On Angiotensin-Degrading Aminopeptidases in the Rat Kidney. Telger, Terry, tr. (Advances in Anatomy, Embryology & Cell Biology: Vol. 76). (Illus.). 86p. 1982. pap. 25.00 (ISBN 0-387-11452-1). Springer-Verlag.

Lote, Christopher J. Principles of Renal Physiology. (Illus.). 180p. 1982. text ed. 28.00x (ISBN 0-7099-0078-3). Sheridan.

--Principles of Renal Physiology. (Illus.). 179p. 1982. pap. text ed. 15.50x (ISBN 0-7099-0079-1, Pub. by Croom Helm England). Sheridan.

Maeda, K., et al, eds. Recent Advances in Renal Research: Contributions from Japan. (Contributions to Nephrology: Vol. 9). (Illus.). 1978. 21.00 (ISBN 3-8055-2826-4). S Karger.

Mandal, Anil K. & Bohman, Sven-Olof, eds. The Renal Papilla & Hypertension. LC 80-15989. (Illus.). 261p. 1980. 34.50x (ISBN 0-306-40506-7, Plenum Med Bk). Plenum Pub.

Marsh, Donald J. Renal Physiology. (Illus.). 164p. 1983. p. 19.50_o. (ISBN 0-89004-465-1); pap. 12.50 (ISBN 0-89004-992-0). Raven.

Massry, Shaul G. & Fleisch, Herbert, eds. Renal Handling of Phosphate. LC 79-18651. (Illus.). 400p. 1980. 45.00x (ISBN 0-306-40368-4, Plenum Med Bk). Plenum Pub.

Moffat, D. B. The Control of Water Balance by the Kidney. rev. ed. Head, J. J., ed. LC 76-62967. (Carolina Biology Readers Ser.). (Illus.). 16p. 1978. pap. 1.60 (ISBN 0-89278-214-5, 45-9614). Carolina Biological.

Morel, F., ed. Biochemistry of Kidney Functions. (INSERM Symposia Ser.: Vol. 21). 462p. 1982. 81.00 (ISBN 0-444-80417-X, Biomedical Pr). Elsevier.

Ono, J., et al, eds. Vitamin D & Calcium Metabolism in the Renal Diseases. (Contributions to Nephrology: Vol. 22). (Illus.). vi, 122p. 1980. soft cover 30.00 (ISBN 3-8055-0389-X). S Karger.

Peters, G., ed. Renal Adaptation to Nephron Loss. (Yale Journal of Biology & Medicine: Vol. 51, No. 3). (Illus.). 1979. pap. 16.75 (ISBN 3-8055-3024-2). S Karger.

Pitts, Robert F. Physiology of the Kidney & Body Fluids. 3rd ed. (Illus.). 307p. 1974. pap. 15.95 (ISBN 0-8151-6703-2). Year Bk Med.

Porter, George, ed. Nephrotoxic Mechanisms of Drugs & Environmental Toxins. LC 82-13156. 486p. 1982. 49.50x (ISBN 0-306-40977-1, Plenum Med Bk). Plenum Pub.

Riegel, J. A. Comparative Physiology of Renal Excretion. (University Reviews in Biology Ser.). (Illus.). 1972. pap. 8.95x (ISBN 0-02-850920-X). Hafner.

Robinson, Brian. Dialysis, Transplantation, Nephrology: Proceedings, European Dialysis & Transplant Asso., Volume 14. (Illus.). 1978. 49.95x (ISBN 0-8464-0329-3). Beekman Pubs.

Robinson, Brian, ed. Dialysis, Transplantation, Nephrology: Proceedings European Dialysis & Transplant Assoc. Volume 13. (Illus.). 1977. 59.95x (ISBN 0-8464-0328-5). Beekman Pubs.

Ross, D. B. & Guder, W. G., eds. Biochemical Aspects of Renal Function: Proceedings of a Symposium Held in Honour of Professor Sir Hans Krebs FRS, at Merton College, Oxford, 16-19 September 1979. (Illus.). 340p. 1980. pap. 61.00 (ISBN 0-08-025517-5). Pergamon.

Rossi, E. & Oetliker, O., eds. Nephrologie im Kindesalter III. (Paediatrische Fortbildungskurse fuer die Praxis: Bd. 45). (Ger., Illus.). 1978. 22.75 (ISBN 3-8055-2825-6). S Karger.

Sies, H. & Wendel, A., eds. Functions of Glutathione in Liver & Kidney. (Proceedings in Life Sciences Ser.). (Illus.). 1978. 39.00 (ISBN 0-387-09127-0). Springer-Verlag.

Silbernagel, S., ed. Abstracts of the International Conference on Renal Transport of Organic Substances Held in Innsbruck, July, 1980. (Journal: Renal Physiology: Vol. 2, No. 3). (Illus.). 66p. 1980. pap. 12.00 (ISBN 3-8055-1641-X). S Karger.

Smith, Homer W. Kidney: Structure & Functions in Health & Disease. (Illus.). 1951. 52.50x (ISBN 0-19-501140-6). Oxford U Pr.

Stokes, G. S. & Mahony, J. H., eds. Hormones & the Kidney. (Progress in Biochemical Pharmacology: Vol. 17). (Illus.). viii, 268p. 1981. 70.00 (ISBN 3-8055-1090-X). S Karger.

Strauss, Jose, ed. Neonatal Kidney & Fluid-Electrolytes. 1983. lib. bdg. 46.00 (ISBN 0-89838-575-X, Pub. by Martinus Nijhoff Netherlands). Kluwer Academic.

Sullivan, Lawrence P. & Grantham, Jared J. Physiology of the Kidney. 2nd ed. LC 81-18569. (Illus.). 236p. 1982. pap. 14.50 (ISBN 0-8121-0839-6). Lea & Febiger.

Symposium, Montreal, June 17, 1978. A New Class of Renally Active Compounds with Antihypertensive, Diuretic, Uricosuric Properties. Lemieux, G. & Steele, T. H., eds. (Nephron: Vol. 23 Suppl. 1). (Illus.). 1979. pap. 15.75 (ISBN 3-8055-3002-1). S Karger.

Thurau, K. Kidney & Urinary Tract Physiology, Vol. III. text ed. cancelled (ISBN 0-8391-1724-8). Univ Park.

KILNS

see also Drying Apparatus; Furnaces

Bachrich, Jack L. Dry Kiln Handbook. (Illus.). 373p. 1980. 50.00 (ISBN 0-87930-087-6, Pub. by H A Simons Intl Canada). Miller Freeman.

Brodie, Regis. The Energy-Efficient Potter: How to Save Money for Building Your Own Fuel-Efficient Kiln & Firing It Economically. (Illus.). 208p. (Orig.). 1982. pap. 12.95 (ISBN 0-8230-1614-5). Watson-Guptill.

Karp, Richard A. Proving Operating Systems Correct. Stone, Harold, ed. LC 82-13378. (Computer Science: System Programming Ser.: No. 16). 172p. 1983. 34.95 (ISBN 0-8357-1365-2). UMI Res Pr.

Olsen, Frederick. The Kiln Book. 2nd ed. 276p. 1983. 24.95 (ISBN 0-8019-7071-7). Chilton.

Peray, K. Rotary Cement Kiln. 2nd, rev. & enl. ed. (Illus.). 1985. 52.50 (ISBN 0-8206-0314-7). Chem Pub.

Rhodes, Daniel. Kilns, Design, Construction, & Operation. 2nd ed. LC 80-70262. 256p. 25.00 (ISBN 0-8019-7064-4). Chilton.

Ritchie, Ralph W. How to Get the Most Heat from Your Fuel, No. 1. LC 81-90069. (Energy Conservation in the Crafts - a Craft Monograph). (Illus.). 39p. (Orig.). 1979. pap. 4.50 (ISBN 0-939656-00-0). Studios West.

--How to Recover & Re-Use Heat from Kilns & Furnaces. LC 81-90073. (Energy Conservation in the Crafts - a Craft Monograph: No. 5). (Illus.). 52p. (Orig.). 1981. pap. 4.50 (ISBN 0-939656-04-3). Studios West.

--Kiln & Furnace Stacks, No. 2. LC 81-90070. (Energy Conservation in the Crafts - a Craft Monograph). (Illus.). 46p. (Orig.). 1980. pap. 4.00 (ISBN 0-939656-01-9). Studios West.

--Understanding & Using Burners. LC 81-90072. (Energy Conservation in the Crafts - a Craft Monograph: No. 4). (Illus.). 60p. (Orig.). 1981. pap. 4.50 (ISBN 0-939656-03-5). Studios West.

--User's Fuel Handbook. LC 81-90075. (Energy Conservation in the Crafts - a Craft Monograph: No. 7). (Illus., Orig.). 1981. pap. 4.50 (ISBN 0-939656-06-X). Studios West.

Ritchie, Ralph W. & Ritchie, Fern J. Electric Kiln Handbook, Vol. 6. LC 81-90074. (Energy Conservation in the Crafts-a Craft Monograph). (Illus.). 60p. (Orig.). 1981. pap. 5.00 (ISBN 0-939656-05-1). Studios West.

Roos, Werner & Rojczyk, Ursula. Construction of Simple Kiln Systems. 34p. 1984. pap. 3.50 (ISBN 3-528-02012-1, 990400387, Pub. by Vieweg & Sohn Germany). Heyden.

KINEMATICS

see also Hodograph; Mechanical Movements; Mechanics; Motion; Quaternions; Relativistic Kinematics; Screws, Theory of

Angeles, J. Spatial Kinematics Chains: Analysis - Synthesis - Optimization. (Illus.). 369p. 1982. 38.00 (ISBN 0-387-11398-3). Springer-Verlag.

Beggs, Joseph S. Kinematics. LC 82-15835. (Illus.). 223p. 1983. text ed. 24.50 (ISBN 0-89116-355-7). Hemisphere Pub.

Bottema, O. & Roth, B. Theoretical Kinematics. (Applied Mathematics & Mechanics: Vol. 24). 558p. 1979. 110.75 (ISBN 0-444-85124-0, North-Holland). Elsevier.

Clagett, Marshall, tr. Nicole Oresme & the Medieval Geometry of Qualities & Motions. (Medieval Science Pubns., No. 12). (Illus.). 728p. 1968. 50.00x (ISBN 0-299-04880-2). U of Wis Pr.

Endrenyi, Laszlo, ed. Kinetic Data Analysis: Design & Analysis of Enzyme & Pharmacokinetic Experiments. LC 81-120. 438p. 1981. 69.50x (ISBN 0-306-40724-8, Plenum Pr). Plenum Pub.

Fukuda, Tadashi. Statokinetic Reflexes in Equilibrium & Movement. Okhubo, Hitoshi & Ushio, Shinya, trs. 311p. 1984. 55.00x (ISBN 0-86008-343-8, Pub. by U of Tokyo Japan). Columbia U Pr.

Genta, G. Kinetic Energy Storage. (Illus.). 1985. text ed. 84.95 (ISBN 0-408-01396-6). Butterworth.

Karger, A. & Novak, J. Space Kinematics & Lie Groups. 438p. 1985. text ed. 88.00 (ISBN 2-88124-023-2). Gordon.

Kepler, Harold B. Basic Graphical Kinematics. 2nd ed. (Illus.). 384p. 1973. text ed. 35.50 (ISBN 0-07-034171-0). McGraw.

Kopilov, G. Elementary Kinematics of Elementary Particles. 270p. 1983. pap. 4.95 (ISBN 0-8285-2712-1, Pub. by Mir Pubs USSR). Imported Pubns.

Patton, William J. Kinematics. (Illus.). 1979. text ed. 25.95 (ISBN 0-8359-3693-7); students manual avail. (ISBN 0-8359-3694-5). Reston.

Pimenov, R. I. Kinematic Spaces. LC 69-20126. (Seminars in Mathematics Ser.: Vol. 6). 185p. 1970. 27.50x (ISBN 0-306-18806-6, Consultants). Plenum Pub.

KINEMATICS OF MACHINERY

see Machinery, Kinematics of

KINESIOLOGY

Garner, Clifford S. Special Techniques of Applied Kinesiology. (Illus.). viii, 55p. (Orig.). 1983. pap. 11.95 (ISBN 0-9612808-0-8). C S Garner.

Groves, Richard & Camaione, David N. Concepts in Kinesiology. 2nd ed. pap. text ed. 18.95 (ISBN 0-03-062372-3, CBS C). SCP.

Luttgens, Kathryn & Wells, Katherine. Kinesiology. 1982. text ed. 32.95 (ISBN 0-03-058358-6, CBS C). SCP.

KINETIC THEORY OF GASES

see Gases, Kinetic Theory of

KINETIC THEORY OF LIQUIDS

see Liquids, Kinetic Theory of

KINETICS

see Dynamics; Mechanics, Analytic; Motion

KINETICS, CHEMICAL

see Chemical Reaction, Rate Of

KINETOSCOPE

Dickson, W. K. & Dickson, Antonia. History of the Kinetograph, Kinetoscope & Kinetophonograph. LC 79-124005. (Literature of Cinema, Ser. 1). Repr. of 1895 ed. 11.95 (ISBN 0-405-01611-5). Ayer Co Pubs.

KINSEY, ALFRED CHARLES, 1894-1956

Pomeroy, Wardell B. Dr. Kinsey & the Institute for Sex Research. LC 82-4924. 496p. 1982. text ed. 36.00x (ISBN 0-300-02916-0); pap. 12.95 (ISBN 0-300-02801-6, Y-442). Yale U Pr.

KIRLIAN PHOTOGRAPHY

Dakin, H. S. High-Voltage Photography. 3rd ed. LC 74-77233. 1978. pap. 4.95 (ISBN 0-685-82476-4). H S Dakin.

Gennaro, L. & Guzzon, F. Kirlian Photography: Research & Prospects. (Illus.). 152p. 1982. 14.95 (ISBN 0-85692-045-2, Pub. by Salem Hse Ltd). Merrimack Pub Cir.

Kirlian Electrophotography: Data Package A. (Illus.). 97p. 1974. pap. 3.95 (ISBN 0-917200-06-3). ESPress.

Krippner, Stanley & Rubin, Daniel, eds. Galaxies of Life: The Human Aura in Acupuncture & Kirlian Photography. (Social Change Ser.). 210p. 1973. 33.75 (ISBN 0-677-15480-1). Gordon.

KITCHEN UTENSILS

Heckmann, Manfred. Corkscrews: An Introduction to Their Appreciation. Sullivan, Maurice, ed. (Illus.). 124p. 1981. 12.95 (ISBN 0-686-69566-6). Wine Appreciation.

Saks, Mark. The Calculator Cookbook: Maximizing the Computational Power of Your Hand-Held Calculator. 286p. 1983. 22.95 (ISBN 0-13-110395-4); pap. 10.95 (ISBN 0-13-110387-3). P-H.

Vapor Removal from Cooking Equipment. (Eighty-Ninety Ser). 1973. pap. 6.00 (ISBN 0-685-58163-2, 96). Natl Fire Prot.

KITCHENS

Better Homes & Gardens Editors. Better Homes & Gardens All About Your House: Your Kitchen. (All About your House Ser.). 160p. 1983. 9.95 (ISBN 0-696-02161-7). BH&G.

Brett, James. The Kitchen: One Hundred Solutions to Design Problems. 2nd ed. (Illus.). 208p. 1983. 32.50 (ISBN 0-8230-7327-0, Whitney Lib). Watson-Guptill.

Data Notes Publishing Staff. Kitchen Recycling: Data Notes. LC 83-90733. 35p. 1983. pap. text ed. 9.95 (ISBN 0-911569-51-0, Pub. by Data Notes). Prosperity & Profits.

Deacon, Gene E. Kid Tested Menus with Kitchen & Lunchroom Techniques for Day Care Centers. LC 81-90547. (Illus.). 120p. (Orig.). 1981. pap. 10.00 (ISBN 0-941790-01-0). Gold Crest.

Goldbeck, David. Designing the Convenient Kitchen. (Illus.). 100p. (Orig.). 1985. pap. 12.95x (ISBN 0-9606138-1-1). Ceres Pr.

Sumichrast, Michael J., et al. Kitchen Appliances & Other Equipment in New Homes. (Illus.). 86p. 1979. pap. 20.00 (ISBN 0-86718-063-3); pap. 15.00 members. Natl Assn Home.

Time-Life Books, ed. Kitchens & Bathrooms. (Home Repair Ser.). (Illus.). 1977. 11.95 (ISBN 0-8094-2386-3). Time-Life.

Walker, Jenepher. How to Design & Remodel Kitchens. ORTHO Books Editorial Staff, ed. LC 81-86179. (Illus.). 96p. 1982. pap. 5.95 (ISBN 0-917102-98-3). Ortho.

KITTYHAWK (FIGHTER PLANES)

see P-Forty (Fighter Planes)

KLYSTRONS

Hamilton, Donald R., et al. Klystrons & Microwave Triodes. (Illus.). 10.25 (ISBN 0-8446-2195-1). Peter Smith.

Hamilton, Donald R., et al, eds. Klystrons & Microwave Triodes. (Illus.). 1966. pap. text ed. 6.95 (ISBN 0-486-61558-8). Dover.

KNEADING MACHINERY

see Mixing Machinery

KNIT GOODS INDUSTRY

Burnip, M. S. & Thomas, J. H. The Production & Properties of Knitted & Woven Fabrics. 139p. 1969. 70.00x (ISBN 0-686-63783-6). State Mutual Bk.

Gottlieb, N. The Production & Properties of Warp-Knitted Fabrics. 100p. 1975. 70.00x (ISBN 0-686-63786-0). State Mutual Bk.

Henson, Gravenor. History of the Framework Knitters, Vol. 1. LC 70-97974. Repr. of 1831 ed. lib. bdg. 37.50x (ISBN 0-678-05671-4). Kelley.

Herbert, R. W. The Organization of a Seasonal Range of Knitted Fabrics. 1979. 60.00x (ISBN 0-686-63779-8). State Mutual Bk.

Smirfitt, J. A. The Production & Properties of Weft-Knitted Fabrics. 113p. 1973. 70.00x (ISBN 0-686-63787-9). State Mutual Bk.

Turner, J. D. The Production & Properties of Knitted Fabrics. 159p. 1971. 70.00x (ISBN 0-686-63782-8). State Mutual Bk.

KNITTING

American School of Needlework. The Great Afghan Book. Thomas, Mary, ed. LC 80-68389. (Illus.). 160p. 1981. 17.95 (ISBN 0-8069-5444-2, Columbia Hse). Sterling.

Burnham, Nellie. Knitted Toys & Dolls: Complete Instructions for 17 Easy-to-Do Projects. (Illus.). 32p. (Orig.). 1982. pap. 1.95 (ISBN 0-486-24148-3). Dover.

Cavendish, Marshall, ed. Step by Step to Better Knitting & Crochet. LC 81-67434. (Illus.). 288p. 1982. 19.95 (ISBN 0-668-05343-7, 5343). Arco.

Drysdale, R. Fair Isle Designs for Knitting. 1984. cancelled (ISBN 0-442-25175-0). Van Nos Reinhold.

Drysdale, Rosemary. Miniature Crocheting & Knitting for Dollhouses. (Illus.). 50p. 1982. pap. 2.25 (ISBN 0-486-23964-0). Dover.

Duncan, Ida R. Complete Book of Progressive Knitting. rev. ed. LC 70-149630. 1971. pap. 9.95 (ISBN 0-87140-243-2). Liveright.

Holbourne, David. The Book of Machine Knitting. (Illus.). 120p. 1983. pap. 9.95 (ISBN 0-7134-0543-0, Pub. by Batsford England). David & Charles.

Knitting. (Training for Industry Ser.). pap. 2.00 (ISBN 0-686-93255-2, UN70/2B6/3, UN). Unipub.

Meyers, Belle. Knitting Know-How: An Illustrated Encyclopedia. LC 80-7857. (Illus.). 208p. 1981. 14.95i (ISBN 0-06-014905-1, HarpT). Har-Row.

Neighbors, Jane. Reversible Two-Color Knitting. (Illus.). 224p. 1982. pap. 12.95 (ISBN 0-684-17647-5, ScribT). Scribner.

Weiss, Rita. Practical Modern Knitting. 1986. pap. cancelled (ISBN 0-442-29265-1). Van Nos Reinhold.

Workbasket Magazine Staff, ed. Aunt Ellen's Knitting Handbook: A Treasury of Techniques & Projects. LC 81-82242. (Illus.). 64p. (Orig.). 1981. pap. 2.95 (ISBN 0-86675-326-5, 3265). Mod Handcraft.

Zimmerman, Elizabeth. Elizabeth Zimmerman's Knitter's Almanac: Projects for Each Month of the Year. (Illus.). 152p. 1981. pap. 2.95 (ISBN 0-486-24178-5). Dover.

KNITTING, MACHINE

Critser, James R., Jr. Knitting Machinery (1975) (Ser. 9-75). 1976. 75.00 (ISBN 0-914428-39-X). Lexington Data.

Gartshore, Linda. The Machine Knitter's Dictionary. LC 83-60726. (Illus.). 192p. 1983. pap. 9.95 (ISBN 0-312-50221-4). St Martin.

Kinder, Kathleen. Techniques in Machine Knitting. (Illus.). 144p. 1985. 14.95 (ISBN 0-668-06285-1). Arco.

Smirfitt, J. A. An Introduction to Weft Knitting. 95p. 1975. 39.00x (ISBN 0-900541-73-3, Pub. by Meadowfield Pr England). State Mutual Bk.

Spencer, D. J. Knitting Technology: A Comprehensive Handbook & Practical Guide to Modern Day Principles & Practices. (Illus.). 300p. 1983. 40.00 (ISBN 0-08-024762-8); pap. 17.50 (ISBN 0-08-024763-6). Pergamon.

Thomas, D. G. An Introduction to Warp Knitting. 80p. 1976. 39.00x (ISBN 0-900541-06-7, Pub. by Meadowfield Pr England). State Mutual Bk.

KNIVES

Barney, Richard & Loveless, Bob. How to Make Knives. 5th ed. (Illus.). 182p. Repr. of 1977 ed. 16.95 (ISBN 0-911881-00-X). Am Blade Bk Serv.

Buerlein, Robert A. Allied Military Fighting Knives & the Men Who Made Them Famous. 2nd ed. LC 85-70203. (Illus.). 194p. (Orig.). 1985. 24.95 (ISBN 0-933489-00-5); pap. 17.95 (ISBN 0-933489-01-3); deluxe ed. write for info. ltd. ed. (ISBN 0-933489-02-1). Amer Hist Found.

Cassidy, William L. Knife Digest: Second Edition. 2nd ed. (Illus.). 178p. 1976. pap. 12.95 (ISBN 0-87364-059-4). Paladin Pr.

Combs, Roger & Lewis, Jack, eds. Gun Digest Book of Knives. 2nd ed. LC 73-83465. 288p. 1982. 10.95 (ISBN 0-910676-37-2). DBI.

Hardin, Albert N., Jr. & Hedden, Robert W. Light but Efficient: A Study of the M1880 Hunting & M1890 Intrenching Knives & Scabbards. LC 73-90405. (Illus.). 1973. 7.95 (ISBN 0-9601778-0-9). Hardin.

Hughes, B. R. Modern Handmade Knives. 1982. 9.95 (ISBN 0-913150-44-4). Pioneer Pr.

Kelley, Ben, Jr. Complete Book of Pocketknife Repair: A Cutlers Manual. Voyles, J. Bruce, ed. (Illus.). 129p. (Orig.). 1982. pap. 9.95 (ISBN 0-911881-01-8). Am Blade Bk Serv.

Latham, Sid. Knifecraft. LC 78-16825. (Illus.). 240p. 1978. 24.95 (ISBN 0-8117-0927-2). Stackpole.

--Knives & Knifemakers. (Illus.). 160p. 1974. pap. 10.95 (ISBN 0-02-011750-7, Collier). Macmillan.

McCreight, Tim. Custom Knifemaking: Ten Projects from a Master Craftsman. Senko, Peggy, ed. (Illus.). 234p. (Orig.). 1985. pap. 14.95 (ISBN 0-8117-2175-2). Stackpole.

Mayes, Jim. How to Make Your Own Knives. LC 78-57407. (Illus.). 1982. (An Everest House Book); pap. 9.95 (ISBN 0-89696-146-X). Dodd.

Stephens, Frederick J. Fighting Knives. (Illus.). 144p. 1985. pap. 11.95 (ISBN 0-668-06463-3). Arco.

Warner, Ken. The Practical Book of Knives. (Illus.). 192p. pap. 9.95 (ISBN 0-88317-025-6). Stoeger Pub Co.

KNOT THEORY

Birman, Joan S. Braids, Links & Mapping Class Groups. LC 74-2961. (Annals of Mathematics Studies: No. 82). 300p. 1974. 27.00x (ISBN 0-691-08149-2). Princeton U Pr.

Crowell, H. R. & Fox, H. R. Introduction to Know Theory. 4th ed. LC 77-22776. (Graduate Texts in Mathematics: Vol. 57). (Illus.). 1977. Repr. of 1963 ed. 29.80 (ISBN 0-387-90272-4). Springer-Verlag.

Hausman, J. C., ed. Knot Theory: Proceedings, Plans-Sur-Bex, Switzerland 1977. (Lecture Note in Mathematics Ser.: Vol. 685). 1979. 22.00 (ISBN 0-387-08952-7). Springer-Verlag.

Kauffman, Louis H. Formal Knot Theory. LC 83-42594. (Mathematical Notes: No. 30). 165p. 1983. pap. text ed. 12.00x (ISBN 0-691-08336-3). Princeton U Pr.

Levine, J. P. Algebraic Structure of Knot Modules. (Lecture Notes in Mathematics: Vol. 772). 104p. 1980. pap. 13.00 (ISBN 0-387-09739-2). Springer-Verlag.

Moran, S., ed. The Mathematical Theory of Knots & Braids: An Introduction. (Mathematical Studies: Vol. 82). 296p. 1983. 42.75 (ISBN 0-444-86714-7, I-274-83, North-Holland). Elsevier.

Murasugi, Kunio. On Closed Three Braids. LC 74-17176. (Memoirs: No. 151). 1974. pap. 11.00 (ISBN 0-8218-1851-1, MEMO-151). Am Math.

Neuwirth, L. P., ed. Knots, Groups, & 3-Manifolds: Papers Dedicated to the Memory of R. H. Fox. LC 75-5619. (Annals of Mathematics Studies: No. 84). 345p. 1975. 35.00 (ISBN 0-691-08170-0); pap. 13.50 (ISBN 0-691-08167-0). Princeton U Pr.

Ocken, Stanley. Parametrized Knot Theory. LC 76-3641. (Memoirs: No. 170). 114p. 1976. pap. 14.00 (ISBN 0-8218-1870-8, MEMO-170). Am Math.

Reidemeister, Kurt. Knot Theory. Boron, Leo F. & Christenson, Charles O., trs. from Ger. LC 83-72870. Orig. Title: Knotentheorie. (Illus.). 143p. 1983. pap. text ed. 14.95 (ISBN 0-914351-00-1). BCS Assocs.

Rolfsen, Dale. Knots & Links. LC 76-15514. (Mathematics Lecture Ser: No. 7). (Illus.). 439p. 1976. pap. text ed. 20.00 (ISBN 0-914098-16-0). Publish or Perish.

Stoltzfus, N. Unraveling the Integral Knot Concordance Group. LC 77-10133. (Memoirs Ser.: No. 192). 91p. 1977. pap. 13.00 (ISBN 0-8218-2192-X, MEMO 192). Am Math.

Takahashi, Moto-O. Two-Bridge Knotts Have Property P. LC 80-26113. (MEMO: No. 239). 104p. 1981. pap. 9.00 (ISBN 0-8218-2239-X). Am Math.

KNOTS (TOPOLOGY)

see Knot Theory

KNOTS AND SPLICES

Ashley, Clifford W. Ashley Book of Knots. (Illus.). 1944. 24.95 (ISBN 0-385-04025-3). Doubleday.

Belash, Constantine A. Braiding & Knotting: Techniques & Projects. (Illus.). 13.50 (ISBN 0-8446-5002-1). Peter Smith.

Berthier, Marc P. G. The Art of Knots. 1977. 6.95 (ISBN 0-385-11464-8). Doubleday.

Bigon, Mario & Regazzoni, Guido. Morrow's Guide to Knots: For Sailing Fishing, Camping & Climbing. Lyman, Kennie, ed. Piotrowska, Maria, tr. from Ital. LC 82-6308. (Illus.). 258p. 1982. 15.00 (ISBN 0-688-01225-6); pap. 9.70 (ISBN 0-688-01226-4). Morrow.

Blandford, Percy W. Practical Knots & Ropework. (Illus., Orig.). 1980. 14.95o.p (ISBN 0-8306-9956-2); pap. 9.95 (ISBN 0-8306-1237-8, 1237). TAB Bks.

Cassidy, John. Knots: For Squares & Others. (Illus.). 12p. (Orig.). 1985. pap. 6.95 (ISBN 0-932592-10-4). Klutz Pr.

Day, Cyrus L. Art of Knotting & Splicing. 3rd rev. ed. LC 55-10028. (Illus.). 225p. 1970. 18.95 (ISBN 0-87021-083-1). Naval Inst Pr.

--Knot & Splices. 1983. pap. 3.50 (ISBN 0-8286-0094-5). J De Graff.

Fiber: A Bibliography (Knotting, Stitchery & Surface Design) 1979. 5.70 (ISBN 0-88321-039-8). Am Craft.

Grainger, Stuart E. Creative Ropecraft. (Illus.). 1977. 12.95 (ISBN 0-393-08746-8). Norton.

Graumont, Raoul. Handbook of Knots. LC 45-11362. (Illus.). 208p. 1945. pap. 4.00 (ISBN 0-87033-030-6). Cornell Maritime.

Graumont, Raoul & Hensel, John. Encyclopedia of Knots & Fancy Rope Work. 4th ed. (Illus.). 706p. 1952. 25.00 (ISBN 0-87033-021-7). Cornell Maritime.

--Splicing Wire & Fiber Rope. LC 45-3379. (Illus.). 128p. 1945. pap. 5.00 (ISBN 0-87033-118-3). Cornell Maritime.

Graumont, Raoul & Wenstrom, Elmer. Fisherman's Knots & Nets. LC 48-423. (Illus.). 218p. 1948. pap. 6.95 (ISBN 0-87033-024-1). Cornell Maritime.

Harrison, P. P. The Harrison Book of Knots. 1981. 25.00x (ISBN 0-85174-346-3, Pub. by Nautical England). State Mutual Bk.

Jarman, Colin & Beavis, Bill. Modern Rope Seamanship. LC 76-20290. (Illus.). 1979. 16.95 (ISBN 0-87742-074-2). Intl Marine.

McNally, Tom. Complete Book of Fisherman's Knots. (Illus.). 1975. 7.95 (ISBN 0-89149-024-8); pap. 4.95 (ISBN 0-89149-020-5). Jolex.

Russell, John. The Arco Book of Useful Knots. LC 81-10977. (Illus.). 96p. 1982. pap. 4.95 (ISBN 0-668-05372-0, 5372). Arco.

Shaw, George R. Knots: Useful & Ornamental. 3rd ed. (Illus.). 1972. pap. 6.95 (ISBN 0-02-082030-5, Collier). Macmillan.

Smith, Hervey G. Marlinspike Sailor. rev. ed. LC 77-143856. (Illus.). 1971. 12.50 (ISBN 0-8286-0044-9). J De Graff.

Snyder, Paul & Snyder, Arthur. Knots & Lines Illustrated. LC 73-107462. 1970. 9.95 (ISBN 0-8286-0046-5). J De Graff.

Svensson, Sam. Handbook of Seaman's Ropework. LC 74-173886. (Illus.). 190p. 1972. 9.95 (ISBN 0-396-06475-2). Dodd.

Wheelock, Walt. Ropes, Knots & Slings for Climbers. rev. ed. (Illus.). 1982. wrappers 1.50 (ISBN 0-910856-00-1). La Siesta.

Winch, Quinton. Nets & Knots for Fishermen & Others. (Illus.). 72p. 1972. pap. 4.00 (Pub. by Batsford England). David & Charles.

KNOWLEDGE, THEORY OF

see also Perception; Sense Data; Senses and Sensation; Uniformity of Nature

Berkeley, George. A Treatise Concerning the Principles of Human Knowledge: Three Dialogues Between Hylas & Philonous. 288p. 1985. pap. 6.95 (ISBN 0-87548-446-8). Open Court.

Bronowski, Jacob. The Origins of Knowledge & Imagination. LC 77-13209. (Silliman Lectures Ser.). 1978. 17.50x (ISBN 0-300-02192-5); pap. 5.95x (ISBN 0-300-02409-6). Yale U Pr.

Churchland, P. M. Scientific Realism & the Plasticity of Mind. LC 78-73240. (Cambridge Studies in Philosophy). (Illus.). 1979. 29.95 (ISBN 0-521-22632-5). Cambridge U Pr.

Cohen, Robert S. & Wartofsky, Marx. Epistemology, Methodology, & the Social Sciences. 1983. lib. bdg. 48.00 (ISBN 90-277-1454-1, Pub. by Reidel Holland). Kluwer Academic.

Crosson, Frederick J., ed. Human & Artificial Intelligence. LC 78-131431. (Orig.). 1970. pap. text ed. 7.95x (ISBN 0-89197-220-X). Irvington.

Delbruck, Max. Mind from Matter: An Essay on Evolutionary Epistemology. Stent, Gunther & Presti, David, eds. (Illus.). 316p. 1985. pap. 14.95 (ISBN 0-86542-311-3). Blackwell Pubns.

Dietzgen, Joseph. The Nature of Human Brain Work: An Introduction to Dialectics. 127p. 1984. Repr. of 1906 ed. lib. bdg. 19.95 (ISBN 0-88286-105-0). C H Kerr.

Fernandez, Sergio L. Foundations of Objective Knowledge. 1985. lib. bdg. 39.50 (ISBN 90-277-1809-1, Pub. by Reidel Holland). Kluwer Academic.

Fetzer, James S. Sociobiology & Epistemology. 1985. lib. bdg. 39.50 (ISBN 90-277-2005-3, Pub. by Reidel Holland); pap. text ed. 14.95 (ISBN 90-277-2006-1). Kluwer Academic.

Frey, Gerhard, ed. Bela Juhos: Selected Papers. Foulkes, Paul, tr. LC 76-17019. (Vienna Circle Collection Ser: No. 7). 1976. lib. bdg. 55.00 (ISBN 90-277-0686-7, Pub. by Reidel Holland); pap. 28.95 (ISBN 90-277-0687-5). Kluwer Academic.

George & Johnson. Introductory Reading in Knowledge Representation. (Information Technology Ser.). 1984. write for info (ISBN 0-9901003-1-6, Pub. by Abacus England). Heyden.

Gopnik, I. & Gopnik, Myrna. From Models to Modules. Pylyshyn, Zenon, ed. (Theoretical Issues in Cognitive Science Ser.). 288p. 1986. text ed. 32.50 (ISBN 0-89391-355-3). Ablex Pub.

Handy, Rollo & Harwood, E. C. Useful Procedures of Inquiry. LC 72-93865. (Orig.). 1973. 12.50x (ISBN 0-913610-00-3). Behavioral Mass.

Horstmann, Rolf-Peter, et al, eds. Transcendental Arguments & Science. (Synthese Library: No. 133). 1979. lib. bdg. 34.00 (ISBN 90-277-0963-7, Pub. by Reidel Holland); pap. 16.00 (ISBN 90-277-0964-5). Kluwer Academic.

Johnson. The Theory of Knowledge & Artificial Intelligence. (Information Tecnology Ser.). 1984. write for info (ISBN 0-9901003-4-0, Pub. by Abacus England). Heyden.

Joske, W. D. Material Objects. 1967. 22.50 (ISBN 0-312-52150-2). St Martin.

Kant, Immanuel. Metaphysical Knowledge & Transcendental Problems. (Illus.). 167p. 1985. Repr. 89.55 (ISBN 0-89901-200-0). Found Class Reprints.

Kornblith, Hilary, ed. Naturalizing Epistemology. (Illus.). 320p. 1985. text ed. 22.50x (ISBN 0-262-11099-7, Pub. by Bradford). MIT Pr.

Lakatos, Imre. Philosophical Papers: Mathematics, Science & Epistemology, Vol. 2. Worrall, J. & Currie, G., eds. LC 77-14374. 295p. 1980. pap. 15.95 (ISBN 0-521-28030-3). Cambridge U Pr.

--Philosophical Papers: Mathematics, Science & Epistemology, Vol. 2. Worrall, J. & Currie, G., eds. LC 77-71415. 1978. 44.50 (ISBN 0-521-21769-5). Cambridge U Pr.

Lenzen, Victor F. Procedures of Empirical Science. LC 71-131570. (Foundations of the Unity of Science Ser: Vol. 1, No. 5). 1938. pap. 1.95x (ISBN 0-226-57580-2, P404, Phoen). U of Chicago Pr.

Levi, Isaac. The Enterprise of Knowledge: An Essay on Knowledge, Credal Probability, & Chance. 1980. text ed. 40.00x (ISBN 0-262-12082-8). MIT Pr.

MacKay, Donald M. Science & the Quest for Meaning. LC 81-17504. pap. 21.80 (ISBN 0-317-30150-0, 2025333). Bks Demand UMI.

Mattessich, Richard. Instrumental Reasoning & Systems Methodology. (Theory & Decision Library: No. 15). 1978. lib. bdg. 45.00 (ISBN 90-277-0837-1, Pub. by Reidel Holland); pap. 20.00 (ISBN 0-686-28628-6, Pub. by Reidel Holland). Kluwer Academic.

Mill, J. S. John Stuart Mill's Philosophy of Scientific Method. (Library of Classics Ser.: No. 12). 1950. pap. text ed. 8.95x (ISBN 0-02-849250-1). Hafner.

Morris, Charles R. Idealistic Logic. LC 76-102578. 1970. Repr. of 1933 ed. 24.50x (ISBN 0-8046-0738-9, Pub. by Kennikat). Assoc Faculty Pr.

Nelson, Alvin F. Inquiry & Reality: A Discourse in Pragmatic Synthesis. LC 75-46077. pap. 48.00 (ISBN 0-317-09210-3, 2021573). Bks Demand UMI.

Niiniluoto, Ilkka. Is Science Progressive? 1984. lib. bdg. 39.50 (ISBN 0-318-03669-X, Pub. by Reidel Holland). Kluwer Academic.

Polanyi, Michael. Knowing & Being. Grene, Marjorie, ed. LC 76-77151. 1969. pap. 8.50x (ISBN 0-226-67285-9). U of Chicago Pr.

--Study of Man. LC 59-4021. 1963. pap. 9.00 (ISBN 0-226-67292-1, P128, Phoen). U of Chicago Pr.

Popper, Karl R. Conjectures & Refutations: The Growth of Scientific Knowledge. 1968. pap. 8.95xi (ISBN 0-06-131376-9, TB1376, Torch). Har-Row.

Riedl, Rupert. Biology of Knowledge: The Evolutionary Basis of Reason. 252p. 1984. 47.95x (ISBN 0-471-10309-8, Pub. by Wiley-Interscience). Wiley.

Roth, Michael D. & Galis, Leon, eds. Knowing: Essays in the Analysis of Knowledge. 246p. 1984. pap. text ed. 10.25 (ISBN 0-8191-4262-X). U Pr of Amer.

Schlesinger, G. The Range of Epistemic Logic. (Scots Philosophical Monographs). 176p. 1985. text ed. 26.75x (ISBN 0-08-032416-9, Pub. by Aberdeen U Scotland); pap. text ed. 18.50x (ISBN 0-08-032417-7, Pub. by Aberdeen U Scotland). Humanities.

Schlick, Moritz. General Theory of Knowledge. LC 85-5018. 432p. 1985. pap. 12.95 (ISBN 0-87548-442-5). Open Court.

Seltman, Muriel & Seltman, Peter. Piaget's Logic: A Critique of Genetic Epistemology. 420p. 1985. text ed. 40.00x (ISBN 0-04-370154-X). Allen Unwin.

Shlechtor, Theodore & Toglia, Michael. New Directions in Cognitive Science. 306p. 1985. text ed. 45.00 (ISBN 0-89391-230-1). Ablex Pub.

Simms, James R. Measure of Knowledge. LC 71-118312. 1970. 8.75 (ISBN 0-8022-2347-8). Philos Lib.

Stemmer, Nathan. The Roots of Knowledge. LC 83-8617. 200p. 1983. 25.00 (ISBN 0-312-69308-7). St Martin.

Whitehead, Alfred N. Concept of Nature. pap. 11.95 (ISBN 0-521-09245-0). Cambridge U Pr.

Windelband, Wilhelm. Theories in Logic. LC 61-15253. 1962. 2.75 (ISBN 0-8022-1899-7). Philos Lib.

Wuketits, Franz M., ed. Concepts & Approaches in Evolutionary Epistemology. 1983. lib. bdg. 52.00 (ISBN 90-277-1577-7, Pub. by Reidel Holland). Kluwer Academic.

Ziff, Paul. Epistemic Analysis. 220p. 1984. lib. bdg. 32.50 (ISBN 90-277-1751-6, Pub. by Reidel Holland). Kluwer Academic.

KODAK CAMERA

see Cameras–Types–Kodak

Shifrine, Moshe & Wilson, Floyd D., eds. The Canine as a Biomedical Research Model: Immunological, Hematological & Oncological Aspects. DOE Technical Information Center. LC 80-24174. 435p. 1980. 19.00 (ISBN 0-87079-122-2, DOE/TIC-10191); microfiche 4.50 (ISBN 0-87079-457-4, DOE/TIC-10191). DOE.

Silverman, Paul. Animal Behavior in the Laboratory. LC 77-8842. (Illus.). 1978. text ed. 35.00x (ISBN 0-87663-727-6, Pica Pr). Universe.

Smyth, D. H. Alternatives to Animal Experiments. 1978. pap. 5.95 (ISBN 0-85967-396-0). Scolar.

Solberg, Victoria B. Laboratory Manual for Animal Technicians. (Illus.). 116p. (Orig.). 1985. pap. text ed. 10.50x (ISBN 0-8138-1066-3). Iowa St U Pr.

Sperlinger, David. Animals in Research: New Perspectives in Animal Experimentation. LC 80-49974. 373p. 1981. 59.95 (ISBN 0-471-27843-2, Pub. by Wiley-Interscience). Wiley.

Stolte, H. & Alt, Jeannette. Research Animals & Experimental Design in Nephrology. (Contributions to Nephrology: Vol. 19). (Illus.). x, 250p. 1980. soft cover 35.00 (ISBN 3-8055-3075-7). S Karger.

Symposium on the Syrian Hamster in Toxicology & Carcinogenesis Research, Boston, November 30-December 2, 1977. The Syrian Hamster in Toxicology & Carcinogenesis: Proceedings. Homburger, F., ed. (Progress in Experimental Tumor Research: Vol. 24). (Illus.). 1979. 69.50 (ISBN 3-8055-2890-6). S Karger.

A Systematic Comparison of Chemically Induced Eye Injury in the Albino Rabbit & Rhesus Monkey. 150.00 (ISBN 0-9601394-1-9). Soap & Detergent.

Universities Federation for Animal Welfare. Handbook on the Care & Management of Laboratory Animals. 5th ed. (Illus.). 1976. text ed. 52.50 (ISBN 0-443-01404-3). Churchill.

Van Zwieten, Matthew J. The Rat As an Animal Model in Breast Cancer Research. (Developments in Oncology Ser.). 300p. 1984. text ed. 52.00 (ISBN 0-89838-624-1, Pub. by Martinus Nijhoff Netherlands). Kluwer Academic.

Watterson, Ray L. & Schoenwolf, Gary C. Laboratory Studies of Chick, Pig, & Frog Embryos: Guide & Atlas of Vertebrate Embryology. 5th ed. (Illus.). 203p. write for info. (ISBN 0-8087-3761-9). Burgess.

Weisbroth, Stephen H., et al, eds. The Biology of the Laboratory Rabbit. 1974. 85.00 (ISBN 0-12-742150-5). Acad Pr.

LABORATORY TECHNICIANS

see also Medical Technologists

Casciero, Albert J. & Roney, Raymond G. Introduction to AV for Technical Assistants. LC 81-13690. (Library Science Text). (Illus.). 250p. 1981. lib. bdg. 28.00 (ISBN 0-87287-232-7); 20.00 (ISBN 0-87287-281-5). Libs Unl.

Hawkins, M. D. Technician Safety & Laboratory Practice. 256p. 1980. 30.00x (ISBN 0-304-30550-2, Pub. by Cassell England). State Mutual Bk.

Morgan, Seth A. Manual for the Laboratory Assistant. pap. 4.95x (ISBN 0-89741-007-6). Roadrunner Tech.

Oppenheim, Irwin A. Textbook for Laboratory Assistants. 3rd ed. LC 80-26455. (Illus.). 187p. 1981. pap. text ed. 14.50 (ISBN 0-8016-3722-8). Mosby.

Rudman, Jack. Certified Laboratory Assistant. (Career Examination Ser.: C-179). (Cloth bdg. avail. on request). pap. 12.00 (ISBN 0-8373-0179-3). Natl Learning.

--Instrumentation Technician. (Career Examination Ser.: C-2366). (Cloth bdg. avail. on request). pap. 10.00 (ISBN 0-685-60428-4). Natl Learning.

--Labor Technician. (Career Examination Ser.: C-1587). (Cloth bdg. avail. on request). pap. 10.00 (ISBN 0-686-53357-7). Natl Learning.

--Laboratory Aide. (Career Examination Ser.: C-430). (Cloth bdg. avail. on request). pap. 10.00 (ISBN 0-8373-0430-X). Natl Learning.

--Laboratory Assistant. (Career Examination Ser.: C-1879). (Cloth bdg. avail. on request). 1977. pap. 10.00 (ISBN 0-8373-1879-3). Natl Learning.

--Laboratory Equipment Specialist. (Career Examination Ser.: C-2297). (Cloth bdg. avail. on request). 1977. pap. 10.00 (ISBN 0-8373-2297-9). Natl Learning.

--Laboratory Helper (Man) (Career Examination Ser.: C-446). (Cloth bdg. avail. on request). pap. 8.00 (ISBN 0-8373-0446-6). Natl Learning.

--Laboratory Helper (Women) (Career Examination Ser.: C-447). (Cloth bdg. avail. on request). pap. 8.00 (ISBN 0-8373-0447-4). Natl Learning.

--Laboratory Technician. (Career Examination Ser.: C-1734). (Cloth bdg. avail. on request). pap. 10.00 (ISBN 0-8373-1734-7). Natl Learning.

--Laboratory Technician - Secondary Schools. (Teachers License Examination Ser.: T-36). (Cloth bdg. avail. on request). pap. 13.95- (ISBN 0-8373-8036-7). Natl Learning.

--Laboratory Technician Trainee. (Career Examination Ser.: C-2909). (Cloth bdg. avail on request). pap. 10.00 (ISBN 0-8373-2909-4). Natl Learning.

--Registered Technologist - R.T.(AR-RT) (Career Examination Ser.: C-680). (Cloth bdg. avail. on request). pap. 10.00 (ISBN 0-8373-0680-9). Natl Learning.

Schapiro, Melvin & Kuritsky, Joel. The Gastroenterology Assistant: A Laboratory Manual. 2nd ed. LC 81-50268. (Illus.). 150p. 1981. 25.00 (ISBN 0-9605718-3-3). Valley Presbyterian.

Taub, Howard. Basic Laboratory Skills for Laboratory Assistants: Measurements, Inventory of Supplies, Collecting Specimens, Specimen Processing, Media Preparation. (Illus.). 612p. 1980. spiral 39.00x (ISBN 0-398-04132-6). C C Thomas.

LABOULBENIACEAE

Benjamin, Richard K. Introduction & Supplement to Thaxter's Contribution Towards a Monograph of the Laboulbeniacea. 1971. 11.20 (ISBN 3-7682-0708-0). Lubrecht & Cramer.

Thaxter, R. Contribution Towards a Monograph of the Laboulbeniaceae. (Illus.). 1971. 140.00 (ISBN 3-7682-0708-0). Lubrecht & Cramer.

LABRADOR DOGS

see Dogs–Breeds–Labrador Dogs

LABRADOR RETRIEVERS

see Dogs–Breeds–Labrador Dogs

LABYRINTH (EAR)

Hammer, Gunnar. A Quantitative Cytochemical Study of Shock Wave Effects on Spiral Ganglion Cells. 1956. 12.00 (ISBN 0-384-21250-6). Johnson Repr.

Lombard, R. E. Comparative Morphology of the Inner Ear in Salamanders: Caudata-Amphibia. (Contributions to Vertebrate Evolution: Vol. 2). 1977. 32.00 (ISBN 3-8055-2408-0). S Karger.

Wersall, Jan. Studies in the Structure & Innervation of the Sensory Epithelium of the Cristae Ampullares in the Guinea Pig. Repr. of 1956 ed. 12.00 (ISBN 0-384-66900-X). Johnson Repr.

LACE AND LACE MAKING

Brooke, Margaret L. Lace in the Making. 1975. Repr. of 1923 ed. 11.95 (ISBN 0-686-11142-7). Robin & Russ.

Buck, Anne. Thomas Lester: His Lace & the East Midlands Industry. 29.95 (ISBN 0-903585-09-X). Robin & Russ.

Bullock, Alice-May. Lace & Lacemaking. LC 81-81037. (Illus.). 168p. 1981. 19.95 (ISBN 0-88332-261-7, 8193). Larousse.

Clifford, C. R., ed. Lace Dictionary: Including Historic & Commercial Terms, Technical Terms, Native & Foreign. (Illus.). 156p. 1981. Repr. of 1913 ed. 35.00x (ISBN 0-8103-4311-8). Gale.

Cook, Bridget M. & Stott, Geraldine. The Book of Bobbin Lace Stitches. (Illus.). 144p. 1980. 18.50 (ISBN 0-8231-5057-7). Branford.

Gubser, Elsie. Bobbin Lace. (Illus.). 6.00 (ISBN 0-686-09828-5). Robin & Russ.

Guide to Lace-Making. Repr. 4.95 (ISBN 0-686-09833-1). Robin & Russ.

Jackson, Emily. The History of Hand Made Lace: Dealing with the Origin of Lace, the Growth of the Great Lace Centres, Etc. LC 70-136558. (Tower Bks.). (Illus.). xiv, 245p. 1972. Repr. of 1900 ed. 53.00x (ISBN 0-8103-3935-8). Gale.

Jourdain, M. Old Lace: A Handbook for Collectors; an Account of the Different Styles of Lace, Their History, Characteristics & Manufacture. (Illus.). 121p. 1981. Repr. of 1908 ed. 35.00x (ISBN 0-8103-4310-X). Gale.

Kliot, Jules & Kliot, Kaethe, eds. Needle Laces: Battenberg, Point & Reticella. (Illus.). 1981. pap. 5.95 (ISBN 0-916896-18-8). Lacis Pubns.

Kliot, Kaethe & Kliot, Jules. Bobbin Lace: Form by the Twisting of Cords. (Arts & Crafts Ser.). (Illus.). 264p. 1973. pap. 4.95 (ISBN 0-517-50593-2). Crown.

Die Kloppelspitzen. (Second Ser.). (Ger., Illus.). 1981. 50.00x (ISBN 0-8103-4313-4). Gale.

Knight, Pauline. The Technique of Filet Lace. (Illus.). 144p. 1980. 22.50 (ISBN 0-7134-1698-X, Pub. by Batsford England). David & Charles.

Luxton, Elsie. The Technique of Honiton Lace. (Illus.). 168p. 1979. 13.50 (ISBN 0-8231-5051-8). Branford.

May, Florence L. Hispanic Lace & Lacemaking. 1980. 12.00 (ISBN 0-87535-048-8). Hispanic Soc.

Milroy, M. E., ed. Church Lace: Being Eight Ecclesiastical Patterns in Pillow Lace. (Illus.). 121p. 1981. Repr. of 1920 ed. 42.00x (ISBN 0-8103-3014-8). Gale.

Mincoff, Elizabeth & Marriage, Margaret S. Pillow Lace: A Practical Handbook. 22.95 (ISBN 0-903585-10-3). Robin & Russ.

Moody, Penderel, ed. Devon Pillow Lace: Its History & How to Make It. (Illus.). 160p. 1981. Repr. of 1907 ed. 42.00x (ISBN 0-8103-3031-8). Gale.

Nass, Ulla. Harness Lace. (Illus.). 52p. 1977. pap. 8.95 (ISBN 0-9606468-0-9). Nass.

Nottingham, Pamela. Bobbin Lace Making. LC 83-80572. (Illus., Orig.). 1983. pap. 12.95 (ISBN 0-88332-320-6, 8053). Larousse.

--The Technique of Bucks Point Lace. (Illus.). 168p. 1982. 19.95 (ISBN 0-88332-288-9, 8197). Larousse.

Ondori Publishing Company Staff. White Crochet Lace. (Illus.). 96p. 1982. pap. 6.50 (ISBN 0-87040-521-7). Japan Pubns USA.

Powys, Marian. Lace & Lace Making. (Illus.). 219p. 1981. Repr. of 1955 ed. 48.00x (ISBN 0-8103-4312-6). Gale.

Stillwell, Alexandra. The Technique of Teneriffe Lace. (Illus.). 144p. 1980. 16.95 (ISBN 0-8231-5053-4). Branford.

Wright, Doreen. Bobbin Lace Making. (Illus.). 1971. 10.75 (ISBN 0-8231-5033-X). Branford.

LACERTIDAE

Boulenger, George A. Monograph of the Lacertidae, 2 Vols. (Illus.). 1920-1921. Set. 75.00 (ISBN 0-384-05305-X). Johnson Repr.

LACERTILIA

see Lizards

LACQUER AND LACQUERING

see also Metals–Finishing; Varnish and Varnishing

Hearns, E. J. Brittle Lacquers for Strain Measurement. 68p. 1971. 39.00x (ISBN 0-900541-36-9, Pub. by Meadowfield Pr England). State Mutual Bk.

Lacquer: An International History & Illustrated Survey. (Illus.). 288p. 1984. 75.00 (ISBN 0-8109-1279-1). Abrams.

Recent Developments in Cellulose: Ester Lacquers. 64p. 1976. 50.00x (ISBN 0-686-44699-2, Pub. by Chandler England). State Mutual Bk.

LACTARIA

Hesler, L. R. & Smith, Alexander H. North American Species of Lactarius. (Illus.). 856p. 1979. text ed. 25.00x (ISBN 0-472-08440-2). U of Mich Pr.

LACTONES

Yoshioka, Hirosuke, et al, eds. Sesquiterpene Lactones: Chemistry, NMR & Plant Distribution. 544p. 1973. 60.00x (ISBN 0-86008-075-7, Pub. by U of Tokyo Japan). Columbia U Pr.

LADYBIRDS

Ali, Mohamed. Ecological & Physiological Studies on the Alfalfa Ladybird. 1981. 50.00x (ISBN 0-569-08553-5, Pub. by Collet's). State Mutual Bk.

Gage, John H. The Larvae of the Coccinellidae. (Illinois Biological Monographs: Vol. 6, No. 4). pap. 8.00 (ISBN 0-384-17550-3). Johnson Repr.

LADYFISH

see Bonefish

LAGRANGE EQUATIONS

Kilmister, C. W. Lagrangian Dynamics: An Introduction for Students. LC 68-28883. 136p. 1968. 22.50x (ISBN 0-306-30368-X, Plenum Pr). Plenum Pub.

Wells, Dare A. Lagrangian Dynamics. (Schaum's Outline Ser). (Orig.). 1967. pap. 9.95 (ISBN 0-07-069258-0). McGraw.

LAGRANGIAN FUNCTIONS

Bertsekas, Dimitri P. Constrained Optimization & Lagrange Multipler Methods. (Computer Science & Applied Mathematics Ser.). 1982. 65.00 (ISBN 0-12-093480-9). Acad Pr.

Dittrich, W. & Reuter, M. Effective Lagrangians in Quantum Electrodynamics. (Lecture Notes in Physics: Vol. 220). v, 244p. 1985. pap. 14.60 (ISBN 0-387-15182-6). Springer-Verlag.

Edelen, D. G. Lagrangian Mechanics of Nonconservative Nonholomic Systems. (Mechanics: Dynamical Systems Ser.: No. 2). 314p. 1977. 30.00x (ISBN 90-286-0077-9). Sijthoff & Noordhoff.

Leray, Jean. Lagrangian Analysis & Quantum Mechanics: A Mathematical Structure Related to Asymptotic Expansions & the Maslov Index. Schroeder, Carolyn, tr. 1982. 40.00x (ISBN 0-262-12087-9). MIT Pr.

LAKELAND TERRIERS

see Dogs–Breeds–Lakeland Terrier

LAKES

see also Limnology; Thermal Pollution of Rivers, Lakes, etc.;

also names of lakes e.g. Superior Lake

Ackermann, William C., et al, eds. Man-Made Lakes: Their Problems & Environmental Effects. LC 73-86486. (Geophysical Monographs: Vol. 17). (Illus.). 847p. 1973. 35.00 (ISBN 0-87590-017-8). Am Geophysical.

Bloomfield, J. A., ed. The Lakes of New York State, 2 vols. Incl. Vol. 1. Ecology of the Finger Lakes. 47.50 (ISBN 0-12-107301-7); Vol. 2. The Lakes of Western New York. 43.00 (ISBN 0-12-107302-5). 1978. Acad Pr.

Bloomfield, Jay A., ed. Lakes of New York State, Vol. 3: Ecology of the Lakes of East-Central New York. 1980. 39.50 (ISBN 0-12-107303-3). Acad Pr.

Britt, N. Wilson, et al. Limmological Studies of the Island Area of Western Lake Erie. 1973. 3.00 (ISBN 0-86727-062-4). Ohio Bio Survey.

Dokulil, M., et al, eds. Shallow Lakes: Contributions to Their Limnology. (Developmrnts in Hydrobiology Ser.: No. 3). 218p. 1981. PLB 59.50 (ISBN 0-686-28842-4, Pub. by Junk Pubs Netherlands). Kluwer Academic.

Dussart, Bernard H., et al. Man-Made Lakes As Modified Ecosystems. (SCOPE Ser. (Scientific Committee on Problems of the Environment): Scope Report 2). 76p. 1972. pap. 11.95 (ISBN 0-471-99595-9, Pub. by Wiley-Interscience). Wiley.

Forel, Francois A. Handbuch der Seenkunde, Allgemeine Limnologie: Handbook of Lake Studies. Egerton, Frank N., 3rd, ed. LC 77-74225. (History of Ecology Ser.). 1978. Repr. of 1901 ed. lib. bdg. 21.00x (ISBN 0-405-10395-6). Ayer Co Pubs.

Gaines, David. Mono Lake Guidebook. LC 81-82402. (Illus.). 120p. (Orig.). 1981. pap. 5.95 (ISBN 0-939716-00-3). Mono Lake Comm.

Gibbs, R. J. & Shaw, R. P., eds. Transport Processes in Lakes & Oceans. LC 77-11099. (Marine Science Ser.: Vol. 7). 296p. 1977. 49.50x (ISBN 0-306-35507-8, Plenum Pr). Plenum Pub.

Graf, W. H. & Mortimer, C. H., eds. Hydrodynamics of Lakes: Proceeding of the Symposium, Switzerland, Oct. 1978. LC 79-17492. (Developments in Water Science Ser.: Vol. 11). 360p. 1979. 72.50 (ISBN 0-444-41827-X). Elsevier.

Hakanson, L. & Jansson, M. Principles of Lake Sedimentology. (Illus.). 320p. 1983. 41.00 (ISBN 0-387-12645-7). Springer-Verlag.

Hakanson, Lars. A Manual of Lake Morphometry. (Illus.). 78p. 1981. pap. 16.90 (ISBN 0-387-10480-1). Springer-Verlag.

Henderson-Sellers, B. Engineering Limnology. LC 84-1765. 500p. 1984. text ed. 65.95 (ISBN 0-273-08539-5). Pitman Pub MA.

Hutter, K., ed. Hydrodynamics of Lakes. (CISM: International Centre for Mechanical Sciences Courses & Lectures Ser.: No. 286). (Illus.). viii, 341p. 1984. 23.70 (ISBN 0-387-81812-X). Springer-Verlag.

Ilmavirta, V. & Jones, R. I. Lakes & Water Management. 1982. 54.50 (ISBN 90-6193-758-2, Pub. by Junk Pubs Netherlands). Kluwer Academic.

Jenkins, S. H., ed. Eutrophication of Deep Lakes: Proceedings of Seminar Held in Oslo, Norway June 1978. (Progress in Water Technology Ser.: Vol. 12, No. 2). (Illus.). 208p. 1980. pap. 52.00 (ISBN 0-08-026024-1). Pergamon.

Johnson, Daniel M., et al. Atlas of Oregon Lakes. LC 84-675319. (Illus.). 328p. 1985. text ed. 30.00 (ISBN 0-87071-342-6); pap. 17.95 (ISBN 0-87071-343-4). Oreg St U Pr.

Jorgensen, S. E, ed. Lake Management. (Water Development, Supply & Management). 1980. 50.00 (ISBN 0-08-022432-6). Pergamon.

Kabisch, Klaus & Hemmerling, Joachim. Ponds & Pools: Oases in the Landscape. (Illus.). 261p. 1983. 14.95 (ISBN 0-668-05674-6, 5674). Arco.

Maitland, P. S. The Ecology of Scotland's Largest Lochs. (Monographiae Biologicae: No. 44). 304p. 1981. 67.00 (ISBN 90-6193-097-9, Pub. by Junk Pubs Netherlands). Kluwer Academic.

Murray, John & Pullar, Laurence. Bathymetrical Survey of the Scottish Fresh Water Lochs, Vol. 1. Egerton, Frank N., 3rd, ed. LC 77-74243. (History of Ecology Ser.). (Illus.). 1978. Repr. of 1910 ed. lib. bdg. 65.00x (ISBN 0-405-10412-X). Ayer Co Pubs.

Neal, James T., ed. Playas & Dried Lakes: Occurrence & Development. LC 74-31134. (Benchmark Papers in Geology Ser: No. 20). 411p. 1975. 69.00 (ISBN 0-12-787110-1). Acad Pr.

Nute, Grace L. Voyageur's Highway: Minnesota's Border Lake Land. LC 65-63529. (Illus.). 113p. 1941. pap. 5.50 (ISBN 0-87351-006-2, X1941). Minn Hist.

Preston, William L. Vanishing Landscapes: Land & Life in the Tulare Lake Basin. LC 80-6055. (Illus.). 290p. 1981. 25.00 (ISBN 0-520-04053-8). U of Cal Pr.

Ramsbottom, A. E. Depth Charts of the Cumbrian Lakes. 1976. 20.00x (ISBN 0-900386-25-8, Pub. by Freshwater Bio). State Mutual Bk.

Rivers & Lakes. LC 84-24463. (Planet Earth Ser.). 1985. lib. bdg. 19.94 (ISBN 0-8094-4509-3, Pub. by Time-Life). Silver.

Serruya, Colette. Lake Kinneret: Lake of Tiberias, Sea of Galilee. (Monographiae Biologicae: No.32). 1978. lib. bdg. 68.50 (ISBN 90-619-3085-5, Pub. by Junk Pubs Netherlands). Kluwer Academic.

LANDING OPERATIONS

Here are entered general works on the landing of waterborne or airborne troops on hostile territory, including the tactics of transporting, landing and establishing such troops and their supplies, and combat during the landing phase. Works on the joint operation of air, land and sea forces to establish troops on shore, as developed in World War II, are entered under Amphibious Warfare.

U. S. Navy Department. Allied Landing Craft & Ships. (Illus.). 200p. 1985. 11.95 (ISBN 0-87021-064-5). Naval Inst Pr.

LANDSLIDES

Coates, Donald R., ed. Reviews in Engineering Geology, Vol. 3: Landslides. LC 62-51690. (Illus.). 1977. pap. 27.00 (ISBN 0-8137-4103-3). Geol Soc.

Reeves, R. B., ed. Application of Walls to Landslide Control Problems. LC 82-70668. 133p. 1982. pap. 14.00x (ISBN 0-87262-302-5). Am Soc Civil Eng.

Sutter, John H. & Hecht, MervynL. Landslide & Subsidence Liability. LC 73-620016. 240p. 1974. 40.00 (ISBN 0-88124-033-8). Cal Cont Ed Bar.

Veder, C. & Hilbert, F. Landslides & Their Stabilization. (Illus.). 247p. 1981. 59.50 (ISBN 0-387-81627-5). Springer-Verlag.

Voight, B. Rockslides & Avalanches, Pt. 1: Natural Phenomena. (Development in Geotechnical Engineering Ser.: Vol. 14A). 834p. 1978. 119.25 (ISBN 0-444-41507-6). Elsevier.

--Rockslides & Avalanches, Pt. 2: Engineering Sites. (Developments in Geotechnical Engineering Ser.: Vol. 14B). 850p. 1980. 119.25 (ISBN 0-444-41508-4). Elsevier.

Zaruba, Q. Landslides & Their Control. 2nd ed. (Developments in Geotechnical Engineering Ser.: Vol. 31). 324p. 1982. 64.00 (ISBN 0-444-99700-8). Elsevier.

LANGLEY, SAMUEL PIERPONT, 1834-1906

Vaeth, J. Gordon. Langley: Man of Science & Flight. LC 66-29472. Repr. of 1966 ed. 24.20 (ISBN 0-8357-9920-4, 2012371). Bks Demand UMI.

LANGUAGE DATA PROCESSING

see Linguistics–Data Processing

LANTERN SLIDES

see Slides (Photography)

LAPIDARY ART

see Gem Cutting

LAPLACE, PIERRE SIMON, MARQUIS DE, 1749-1827

Hahn, Roger, compiled by. Calendar of the Correspondence of Pierre Simon Laplace. LC 81-51031. (Berkeley Papers in History of Science: No. 8). 100p. (Orig.). 1982. pap. 7.00x (ISBN 0-918102-07-3). U Cal Hist Sci Tech.

LAPLACE TRANSFORMATION

Bellman, R. & Roth, R. The Laplace Transform. (Series in Modern Applied Mathematics: Vol. 3). 176p. 1984. 21.00 (ISBN 9971-966-73-5, Pub. by World Sci Singapore). Taylor & Francis.

Beltrami, E. J. & Wohlers, M. R. Distributions & the Boundary Values of Analytic Functions. 1966. 29.00 (ISBN 0-12-085550-X). Acad Pr.

Bogart, T. F. Laplace Transforms: Theory & Experiments. 160p. 1983. pap. 14.95 (ISBN 0-471-87509-0). Wiley.

Carslaw, Horatio S. & Jaeger, J. C. Conduction of Heat in Solids. 2nd ed. (Illus.). 1959. 45.00x (ISBN 0-19-853303-9). Oxford U Pr.

Doetsch, G. Introduction to the Theory & Application of the Laplace Transformation. Nader, W., ed. & tr. LC 73-10661. (Illus.). 340p. 1974. 45.00 (ISBN 0-387-06407-9). Springer-Verlag.

Donaldson, Thomas. A Laplace Transform Calculus for Partial Differential Operators. LC 74-7370. (Memoirs: No. 143). 166p. 1974. pap. 11.00 (ISBN 0-8218-1843-0, MEMO-143). Am Math.

Holl, Dio L., et al. Introduction to the La Place Transform. LC 59-7720. (Century Mathematics Ser.). (Illus.). 1959. 39.50x (ISBN 0-89197-247-1). Irvington.

Kuhfittig, P. K. Introduction to the LaPlace Transform. LC 77-29017. (Mathematical Concepts & Methods in Science & Engineering Ser.: Vol. 8). (Illus.). 215p. 1978. 32.50x (ISBN 0-306-31060-0, Plenum Pr). Plenum Pub.

LePage, Wilbur R. Complex Variables & the Laplace Transform for Engineers. (Illus.). 1980. pap. text ed. 7.95 (ISBN 0-486-63926-6). Dover.

Levy, Ezra C. New Table of Laplace Transformation Pairs. 3rd ed. 1982. pap. 5.95 (ISBN 0-910266-11-5). Bk Page.

Muth, Eginhard J. Transform Methods with Applications to Engineering & Operations Research. (Illus.). 1977. ref. ed. O.P. 29.95 (ISBN 0-13-928861-9). P-H.

Oberhettinger, F. & Badii, L. Tables of Laplace Transforms. LC 73-81328. vii, 428p. 1973. pap. 34.90 (ISBN 0-387-06350-1). Springer-Verlag.

Reynolds, James A. Applied Transformed Circuit Theory for Technology. LC 84-7525. 335p. 1985. 34.95 (ISBN 0-471-09819-1). Wiley.

Spiegel, Murray R. Laplace Transforms. (Orig.). 1965. pap. 9.95 (ISBN 0-07-060231-X). McGraw.

Watson, E. LaPlace Transforms & Applications. 1981. 24.50 (ISBN 0-442-30176-6). Van Nos Reinhold.

LAPLACE TRANSFORMATION–PROGRAMMED INSTRUCTION

Strum, Robert D. & Ward, John R. Laplace Transform Solution of Differential Equations. (Orig., Prog. Bk.). 1968. pap. 25.95 ref. ed. (ISBN 0-13-522805-0). P-H.

LAPLACE'S EQUATIONS

see Harmonic Functions

LAPPING

see Grinding and Polishing

LARAMIE FORMATION

see Geology, Stratigraphic–Cretaceous

LARGE NUMBERS, LAW OF

see Law of Large Numbers

LARKSPUR

see Delphinium

LARVAE

see also Caterpillars

Chia, F. & Rice, M. E., eds. Settlement & Metamorphosis of Marine Invertebrate Larvae: Proceedings of a Symposium Held at Toronto, Canada, Dec. 27-28, 1977. 290p. 1979. 45.50 (ISBN 0-444-00277-4, Biomedical Pr). Elsevier.

Garrison, Rosser W. Revision of the Genus Bnahagma of the U. S. West of the Rocky Mountains & Identification of Certain Larvae by Discriminand Analysis: Publications in Entomology. (Vol. 105). 1985. 11.00x (ISBN 0-520-09954-0). U of Cal Pr.

Gastang, Walter. Larval Forms & Other Zoological Verses. LC 85-14114. (Illus.). 106p. 1985. pap. 5.95 (ISBN 0-226-28423-9). U of Chicago Pr.

Leis, J. M. & Rennis, D. S. The Larvae of Indo-Pacific Coral Reef Fishes: A Guide to Identification. (Illus.). 280p. 1983. text ed. 25.00X (ISBN 0-8248-0910-6). UH Pr.

Smith, DeBoyd L. A Guide to Marine Coastal Plankton & Marine Invertebrate Larvae. LC 76-62564. (Illus.). 1978. pap. text ed. 9.95 (ISBN 0-8403-1672-0). Kendall-Hunt.

LARVAE–INSECTS

see also Caterpillars; Insects–Development

Chu, H. F. How to Know the Immature Insects. 2nd ed. (Pictured Key Nature Ser.). 240p. 1983. wire coil write for info. (ISBN 0-697-04806-3); Wm C Brown.

Fracker, Stanley B. The Classification of Lepidopterous Larvae. (Illus.). Repr. of 1915 ed. 15.00 (ISBN 0-384-16670-9). Johnson Repr.

Gage, John H. The Larvae of the Coccinellidae. (Illinois Biological Monographs: Vol. 6, No. 4). pap. 8.00 (ISBN 0-384-17550-3). Johnson Repr.

Growth in Bupalus Piniarius in Relation to Larval Density. (Agricultural Research Reports: No. 742). 1970. pap. 12.25 (ISBN 90-220-0298-5, PDC181, PUDOC). Unipub.

Hickin, Norman E. Caddis Larvae: Larvae of the British Trichoptera. LC 68-58408. (Illus.). 480p. 1968. 30.00 (ISBN 0-8386-6945-X). Fairleigh Dickinson.

Hinton, H. E. Biology of Insect Eggs, 3 vols. LC 77-30390. (Illus.). 1500p. 1981. Set. 440.00 (ISBN 0-08-021539-4). Pergamon.

Johannsen, Oskar A. Aquatic Diptera. LC 78-7782. (Illus.). 370p. 1969. 17.50 (ISBN 0-911836-01-2). Entomological Repr.

McGinley, Ronald J. Systematics of the Colletidae Based on Mature Larvae with Phenetic Analysis of Apoid Larvae (Hymenoptera, Apoidea) (U. C. Publications in Entomology Ser.: Vol. 91). 332p. 1981. 18.50x (ISBN 0-520-09623-1). U of Cal Pr.

Ritcher, Paul O. White Grubs & Their Allies. LC 66-63008. (Studies in Entomology Ser: No. 4). (Illus.). 216p. 1966. 19.95x (ISBN 0-87071-054-0). Oreg St U Pr.

Yuasa, Hachiro. A Classification of the Larvae of the Tenthredinoidea. (Illinois Biological Monographs: Vol. 7, No. 4). 15.00 (ISBN 0-384-70500-6). Johnson Repr.

LASER COAGULATION

Skobel'tsyn, D. V., ed. Spectroscopy of Laser Crystals with Ionic Structure. LC 73-83902. (P. N. Lebedev Physics Institute Ser.: Vol. 60). (Illus.). 153p. 1974. 42.50 (ISBN 0-306-10898-4, Consultants). Plenum Pub.

LASER PHOTOGRAPHY

see Holography

LASER SPECTROSCOPY

Alfano, R. R. Semiconductors Probed by Ultrafast Laser Spectroscopy, Vol. 1. 1985. 79.50 (ISBN 0-12-049901-0). Acad Pr.

--Semiconductors Probed by Ultrafast Laser Spectroscopy, Vol. 2. 1985. 85.00 (ISBN 0-12-049902-9). Acad Pr.

American Society for Testing & Materials. Laser Induced Damage in Optical Materials, 1976: Proceedings of a Symposium. Glass, Alexander J. & Guenther, Arthur H., eds. LC 76-600074. pap. 103.00 (ISBN 0-317-27764-2, 2015510). Bks Demand UMI.

Demtroeder, W. Laser Spectroscopy: Basic Concepts & Instrumentation. (Springer Series in Chemical Physics: Vol. 5). (Illus.). 694p. 1981. 39.00 (ISBN 0-387-10343-0). Springer-Verlag.

Eisenthal, K. B., et al, eds. Picosecond Phenomena III, Garmisch Partenkirchen, FRG, 1982: Proceedings. (Springer Series in Chemical Physics: Vol. 23). (Illus.). 401p. 1982. 33.00 (ISBN 0-387-11912-4). Springer-Verlag.

Freeman, Stanley K. Application of Laser Raman Spectroscopy. LC 73-12688. 350p. 1974. 25.00 (ISBN 0-471-27788-6). Krieger.

Garetz, Bruce A. & Lombardi, John R. Advances in Laser Spectroscopy, Vol. I. 245p. 1982. 54.95x (ISBN 0-471-26185-8, Pub. by Wiley Heyden). Wiley.

Garetz, Bruce A. & Lombardi, John R., eds. Advances in Laser Spectroscopy, Vol. 2. 261p. 1983. 48.95x (ISBN 0-471-26281-1, Pub. by Wiley-Interscience). Wiley.

Lambropoulos, P. & Smith, S. J., eds. Multiphoton Processes. (Springer Series on Atoms & Plasmas: Vol. 2). (Illus.). 220p. 1984. 26.00 (ISBN 0-387-15068-4). Springer-Verlag.

Letokhov, V. S. & Chebotayev, V. P. Nonlinear Laser Spectroscopy. (Springer Optical Sciences Ser.: Vol. 4). (Illus.). 1977. 44.00 (ISBN 0-387-08044-9). Springer-Verlag.

Levenson, Marc. Introduction to Nonlinear Laser Spectroscopy. LC 81-17608. (Quantum Electronics: Principles & Applications Ser.). 1982. 34.50 (ISBN 0-12-444720-1). Acad Pr.

McKellar, A. R., et al, eds. Laser Spectroscopy Five: Proceedings. (Springer Series in Optical Sciences: Vol. 30). (Illus.). 495p. 1981. 33.00 (ISBN 0-387-10914-5). Springer-Verlag.

Martellucci, S. & Chester, A. N., eds. Analytical Laser Spectroscopy. (NATO ASI Series B, Physics: Vol. 119). 298p. 1985. 52.50x (ISBN 0-306-41897-5, Plenum Pr). Plenum Pub.

Omenetto, N. Analytical Laser Spectroscopy, Vol. 50. LC 78-7977. (Chemical Analysis Ser.). 550p. 1979. 92.00x (ISBN 0-471-65371-3, 1-075). Wiley.

Stenholm, Stig. Foundations of Laser Spectroscopy. LC 83-14499. (Pure & Applied Optics ser.: 1-349). 268p. 1984. 38.95x (ISBN 0-471-05999-4, Pub. by Wiley-Interscience). Wiley.

Tobin, Marvin C. Laser Raman Spectroscopy. LC 80-11511. 184p. 1982. Repr. of 1971 ed. lib. bdg. 25.50 (ISBN 0-89874-159-9). Krieger.

Walter, H., ed. Laser Spectroscopy of Atoms & Molecules. (Topics in Applied Physics Ser.: Vol. 2). (Illus.). 340p. 1976. 60.00 (ISBN 0-387-07324-8). Springer-Verlag.

Walther, H. & Rothe, K. W., eds. Laser Spectroscopy Four. (Springer Ser. in Optical Sciences: Vol. 21). (Illus.). 1979. 52.00 (ISBN 0-387-09766-X). Springer-Verlag.

Weber, H. P. & Luthy, W. Laser Spectroscopy, VI. (Springer Series in Optical Sciences: Vol. 40). (Illus.). 442p. 1983. 32.00 (ISBN 0-387-12957-X). Springer-Verlag.

Yen, W. M. & Selzer, P. M., eds. Laser Spectroscopy of Solids. (Topics in Applied Physics Ser.: Vol. 49). (Illus.). 310p. 1981. 63.00 (ISBN 0-387-10638-3). Springer-Verlag.

LASERS

see also Nonlinear Optics

AIP Conference Proceedings No. 90 Boulder, 1982. Laser Techniques for Extreme Ultraviolet Spectroscopy. McIlrath, T. J. & Freeman, R. R., eds. LC 82-73205. 497p. 1982. lib. bdg. 37.00 (ISBN 0-88318-189-4). Am Inst Physics.

AIP Conference Proceedings No. 90. Los Alamos, 1982. Laser Acceleration of Particles. Channell, Paul J., ed. LC 82-73361. 276p. 1982. lib. bdg. 32.00 (ISBN 0-88318-190-8). Am Inst Physics.

Anderson, John D. Gasdynamic Lasers: An Introduction. (Quantum Electronic Ser.). 1976. 44.00 (ISBN 0-12-056950-7). Acad Pr.

Appleton, B. R. & Cellar, G. K., eds. Laser & Electron-Beam Interactions with Solids. (Materials Research Society Symposia Ser.: Vol. 4). 812p. 1982. 109.00 (ISBN 0-444-00693-1). Elsevier.

Arecchi, F. T. & Schulz-Dubois, E. D., eds. Laser Handbook, 2 vols. LC 73-146191. 1947p. 1973. Set. 213.00 (ISBN 0-444-10379-1, North-Holland). Elsevier.

Aussenegg, F. R., et al, eds. Surface Studies with Lasers. (Springer Series in Chemical Physics: Vol. 33). (Illus.). 270p. 1983. 29.00 (ISBN 0-387-12598-1). Springer-Verlag.

Auston, D. H. & Eisenthal, K. B., eds. Ultrafast Phenomena IV. (Chemical Physics Ser.: Vol. 38). (Illus.). xvi, 509p. 1984. 29.00 (ISBN 0-387-13834-X). Springer-Verlag.

Baeuerle, D., ed. Laser Processing & Diagnostics. (Springer Series in Chemical Physics: Vol. 39). (Illus.). 560p. 1984. 34.00 (ISBN 0-387-13843-9). Springer-Verlag.

Bagratashvili, V. N., et al. Multiple Photon Infrared Laser Photophysics & Photochemistry. 530p. 1985. text ed. 65.00 (ISBN 3-7186-0269-5). Harwood Academic.

Basov, N. G. Lasers & Holographic Data Processing. 142p. 1985. pap. 4.95 (ISBN 0-8285-2883-7, Pub by Mir Pubns USSR). Imported Pubns.

Basov, N. G., ed. High-Power Lasers & Laser Plasmas. LC 78-794. (P. N. Lebedev Physics Institute Ser.: Vol. 85). (Illus.). 249p. 1978. 65.00 (ISBN 0-306-10943-3, Consultants). Plenum Pub.

--Lasers & Their Applications. LC 76-26590. (P. N. Lebedev Physics Institute Ser.: Vol. 76). (Illus.). 223p. 1976. 65.00x (ISBN 0-306-10927-1, Consultants). Plenum Pub.

--Lasers & Their Applications in Physical Research. LC 78-13582. (P. N. Lebedev Physics Institute Ser.: Vol. 91). (Illus.). 234p. 1979. 65.00x (ISBN 0-306-10949-2, Consultants). Plenum Pub.

--Pulse Gas-Discharge Atomic & Molecular Lasers. LC 76-57191. (P. N. Lebedev Physics Institute Ser.: Vol. 81). (Illus.). 186p. 1976. 65.00x (ISBN 0-306-10931-X, Consultants). Plenum Pub.

--Research in Molecular Laser Plasmas. LC 76-25553. (P. N. Lebedev Physics Institute Ser.: Vol. 78). (Illus.). 115p. 1976. 59.50x (ISBN 0-306-10928-X, Consultants). Plenum Pub.

--Temporal Characteristics of Laser Pulses & Interaction of Laser Radiation with Matter. LC 77-13406. (P. N. Lebedev Physics Institute Ser.: Vol. 84). (Illus.). 208p. 1978. 65.00 (ISBN 0-306-10942-5, Consultants). Plenum Pub.

--Theoretical Problems in Spectroscopy & Gas Dynamics of Lasers. LC 79-17616. (P. N. Lebedev Physics Institute Ser.: Vol. 83). (Illus.). 232p. 1978. 65.00 (ISBN 0-306-10938-7, Consultants). Plenum Pub.

Bass, M., ed. Laser Materials Processing. (Material Processing Theory & Practice: Vol. 3). 475p. 1983. 97.75 (ISBN 0-686-46005-7, North Holland). Elsevier.

Bass, Michael, ed. Materials Processing Symposium ICALEO '82: Proceedings, Vol. 31. 165p. 1983. pap. 55.00 (ISBN 0-912035-00-5). Laser Inst.

Beesley, M. J. Lasers & their Applications. 2nd ed. 270p. 1978. cancelled (ISBN 0-85066-045-9). Taylor & Francis.

Beiser, L., ed. Advances in Laser Scanning & Recording, Vol. 396. 224p. 42.00 (ISBN 0-89252-431-6). Photo-Optical.

Belforte, David. International Laser Processing Conference: Proceedings, Vol.30. 448p. 1981. 30.00 (ISBN 0-912035-05-6). Laser Inst.

Bennett, W. R., ed. The Physics of Gas Lasers. (Documents on Modern Physics Ser.). 224p. 1977. 46.25 (ISBN 0-677-03320-6). Gordon.

Bennett, W. R., Jr. Atomic Gas Laser Transition Data: A Critical Evaluation. LC 79-22073. 300p. 1979. 95.00x (ISBN 0-306-65187-4, IFI Plenum). Plenum Pub.

Ben-Shaul, A., et al. Lasers & Chemical Change. (Springer Ser. in Chemical Physics: Vol. 10). (Illus.). 497p. 1981. 49.00 (ISBN 0-387-10379-1). Springer-Verlag.

Bertolotti, M. Masers & Lasers: An Historical Approach. 1983. 29.00 (ISBN 0-9960024-3-X, Pub. by A Hilger England). Heyden.

Bertolotti, M., ed. Physical Processes in Laser-Materials Interactions. (NATO ASI Series B, Physics: Vol. 84). 534p. 1983. 75.00 (ISBN 0-306-41107-5, Plenum Pr). Plenum Pub.

Bloom, Arnold L. Gas Lasers. LC 77-28278. 184p. 1978. Repr. of 1968 ed. lib. bdg. 14.50 (ISBN 0-88275-659-1). Krieger.

Bowen, J. R., et al. Flames, Lasers & Reactive Systems. 45.00 (ISBN 0-915928-77-9). AIAA.

Bradley, D. J., et al. Ultra-Short Laser Pulses. (Phil. Strans. Ser. A: Vol. 298). (Illus.). 204p. 1981. text ed. 60.00x (ISBN 0-85403-147-2, Pub. by Royal Soc London). Scholium Intl.

Brederlow, G., et al. The High-Power Iodine Laser. (Springer Ser. in Optical Sciences: Vol. 34). (Illus.). 182p. 1983. 38.00 (ISBN 0-387-11792-X). Springer-Verlag.

Brewer, Richard G. & Mooradian, Aram, eds. Laser Spectroscopy. LC 74-12090. 671p. 1974. 69.50x (ISBN 0-306-30802-9, Plenum Pr). Plenum Pub.

Brown, Ronald. Lasers: Tools of Modern Technology. LC 68-18081. (Doubleday Science Ser.). (Illus.). pap. 48.00 (ISBN 0-317-08831-9, 2011716). Bks Demand UMI.

Business Communications Staff. Laser. 1985. pap. 1750.00 (ISBN 0-89336-453-3, GB050N). BCC.

Butler, J. K. Semiconductor Injection Lasers. LC 79-91615. 395p. 1980. 44.95x (ISBN 0-471-08156-6, Pub. by Wiley Interscience); pap. 29.50x (ISBN 0-471-08157-4). Wiley.

Motz, H. The Physics of Laser Fusion. 1979. 56.50 (ISBN 0-12-509350-0). Acad Pr.

Mukherjee, Kali & Majumder, J., eds. Lasers in Metallurgy. 301p. 1981. 36.00 (ISBN 0-317-37206-8); 24.00 (ISBN 0-317-37207-6); students 12.00 (ISBN 0-317-37208-4). Metal Soc.

Mumola, Peter, ed. Lasers & Electro-Optics Symposium ICALEO '82: Proceedings, Vol. 34. 92p. 1983. pap. 40.00 (ISBN 0-912035-03-X). Laser Inst.

Muncheryan, Hrand M. Principles & Practice of Laser Technology. (Illus.). 294p. 1983. pap. 14.50 (ISBN 0-8306-1529-6, 1529). TAB Bks.

Narayan, J. & Brown, W. L., eds. Laser-Solid Interactions & Transient Thermal Processing of Materials. 782p. 1983. 104.50 (ISBN 0-444-00788-1, North Holland). Elsevier.

Onorato, Michele. Gas Flow & Chemical Lasers. 774p. 1985. 115.00x (ISBN 0-306-41478-3, Plenum Pr). Plenum Pub.

O'Shea, Donald C., et al. Introduction to Lasers & Their Applications. (Physics Ser.). 1977. text ed. 34.95 (ISBN 0-201-05509-0). Addison-Wesley.

Payne, Keith B., ed. Laser Weapons in Space: Policy & Doctrine Issues. LC 82-20045. (Replica). 230p. 1983. softcover 22.00x (ISBN 0-86531-937-5). Westview.

Pressley, Robert J. Handbook of Lasers, CRC: With Selected Data on Optical Technology. LC 72-163066. (Handbook Ser.). (Illus.). 631p. 1971. 49.95 (ISBN 0-87819-381-2). CRC Pr.

Proceedings of an International Conference on Lasers, May, 1980--Shanghai & Beijing. LC 83-3473. 909p. 1983. 110.95 (ISBN 0-471-87093-5, Pub. by Wiley-Interscience). Wiley.

Rahman, N. K. & Guidotti, C., eds. Collisions & Half-Collisions with Lasers. 443p. 1984. 72.00 (ISBN 3-7186-0192-3). Harwood Academic.

Raizer, Y. P., ed. Laser-Induced Discharge Phenomena. LC 77-21738. (Illus.). 380p. 1977. 55.00x (ISBN 0-306-10923-9, Consultants). Plenum Pub.

Ratner, A. M. Spectral, Spatial, & Temporal Properties of Lasers. LC 76-167677. (Optical Physics & Engineering Ser.). 220p. 1972. 42.50x (ISBN 0-306-30542-9, Plenum Pr). Plenum Pub.

Ready, John, ed. Lasers in Modern Industry. LC 79-66705. (Manufacturing Update Ser.). (Illus.). 1979. 32.00 (ISBN 0-87263-052-8). SME.

Ready, John F. Effects of High-Power Laser Radiation. 1971. 65.00 (ISBN 0-12-583950-2). Acad Pr.

Rhodes, C. K. & Egger, N., eds. Excimer Lasers, Nineteen Eighty-Three: OSA, Lake Tahoe, Nevada. LC 83-71437. (AIP Conference Proceedings No. 100, Subseries on Optical Science & Engineering No. 3). 354p. 1983. lib. bdg. 36.50 (ISBN 0-88318-199-1). Am Inst Physics.

Ross, Monte. Laser Applications, Vol. 5. (Serial Publication). 1984. 62.00 (ISBN 0-12-431905-X). Acad Pr.

Ross, Monte, ed. Laser Applications, 3 vols. Vol. 1, 1971. 75.00 (ISBN 0-12-431901-7); Vol. 2, 1974. 75.00 (ISBN 0-12-431902-5); Vol. 3, 1977. 70.00 (ISBN 0-12-431903-3). Acad Pr.

Rykalin, N., et al. Laser Machining & Welding. (Illus.). 1979. 57.00 (ISBN 0-08-022724-4). Pergamon.

Safford, Edward L., Jr. The Fiberoptics & Laser Handbook. (Illus.). 364p. (Orig.). 1984. 21.95 (ISBN 0-8306-0671-8); pap. 16.95 (ISBN 0-8306-1671-3, 1671). TAB Bks.

Schaefer, F. P., ed. Dye Lasers. 2nd.rev ed. (Topics in Applied Physics: Vol.1p). (Illus.). xi, 285p. 1977. pap. 28.00 (ISBN 0-387-08470-3). Springer-Verlag.

Selected Bibliography: Laser Applications in the Graphic Arts, Vol. 1. 19p. 1976. pap. 20.00 (ISBN 0-317-14989-X). Tech & Ed Ctr Graph Arts RIT.

Selected Bibliography: Laser Applications in the Grapic Arts, Vol. 2. 46p. 1981. pap. 20.00 (ISBN 0-317-14990-3). Tech & Ed Ctr Graph Arts RIT.

Shimoda, K. Introduction to Laser Physics. (Springer Series in Optical Sciences: Vol. 44). (Illus.). 230p. 1984. 28.00 (ISBN 0-387-13430-1). Springer-Verlag.

Siegman, Anthony E. Lasers. LC 81-51269. (Illus.). 575p. 1986. 42.00x (ISBN 0-935702-11-3). Univ Sci Bks.

Skobel'tsyn, D. V. Physical Processes in Lasers. LC 72-94826. (P. N. Lebedev Physics Institute Ser.: Vol. 56). (Illus.). 181p. 1973. 45.00 (ISBN 0-306-10884-4, Consultants). Plenum Pub.

Skobel'tsyn, D. V., ed. Quantum Electronics in Lasers & Masers, Pt. 1. LC 68-13059. (P. N. Lebedev Physics Institute Ser.: Vol. 31). (Illus.). 161p. 1968. 32.50x (ISBN 0-306-10800-3, Consultants). Plenum Pub.

Smith, Kenneth & Thompson, R. M. Computer Modeling of Gas Lasers. LC 77-29106. (Optical Physics & Engineering Ser.). (Illus.). 432p. 1978. 69.50x (ISBN 0-306-31099-6, Plenum Pr). Plenum Pub.

Smith, William V. Laser Applications. LC 71-119912. (Modern Frontiers in Applied Science). (Illus.). 200p. 1970. 12.00 (ISBN 0-89006-001-0). Artech Hse.

Society of Photo-Optical Instrumentation Engineers, Seminar. Impact of Lasers in Spectroscopy I: Proceedings. 164p. 1975. 11.00 (ISBN 0-89252-061-2). Photo-Optical.

Sona. Lasers & Their Applications. 644p. 1976. 103.95x (ISBN 0-677-15030-X). Gordon.

Steinfeld, J. I., ed. Laser & Coherence Spectroscopy. LC 77-11119. (Illus.). 548p. 1978. 72.50x (ISBN 0-306-31027-9, Plenum Pr). Plenum Pub.

Steinfeld, Jeffrey I., ed. Electronic Transition Lasers. LC 76-4504. 300p. 1976. text ed. 32.50x (ISBN 0-262-19146-6). MIT Pr.

--Laser-Induced Chemical Processes. LC 80-20478. 288p. 1981. 42.50x (ISBN 0-306-40587-3, Plenum Pr). Plenum Pub.

Stitch, M. L., ed. Laser Handbook, Vol. 3. 846p. 1979. 168.00 (ISBN 0-444-85271-9, North Holland). Elsevier.

Strohbehn, J. W., ed. Laser Beam Propagation in the Atmosphere. (Topics in Applied Physics: Vol. 25). (Illus.). 1978. 67.00 (ISBN 0-387-08812-1). Springer-Verlag.

Svelto, Orazio. Principles of Lasers. 2nd ed. Hanna, David C., tr. from Ital. LC 82-484. 392p. 1982. 29.50x (ISBN 0-306-40862-7, Plenum Pr). Plenum Pub.

Tarasov, L. V. Laser Age in Optics. 206p. 1985. 6.95 (ISBN 0-8285-2075-5, Pub. by Mir Pubs USSR). Imported Pubns.

--Laser Physics. 208p. 1983. 10.95 (ISBN 0-8285-2570-6, Pub. by Mir Pubs USSR). Imported Pubns.

Tech Tran Corporation Staff. Lasers in Metalworking: A Summary & Forecast. (Illus.). 165p. 1983. spiral bdg. 50.00 (ISBN 0-918989-03-5). Tech Tran Consult.

Thompson, G. H. B. Physics of Semiconductor Laser Devices. 549p. 1980. 84.95 (ISBN 0-471-27685-5). Wiley.

Thompson, H. Doyle & Stevenson, Warren H., eds. Laser Velocimetry & Particle Sizing: Proceedings. LC 79-59. (Illus.). 566p. 1979. text ed. 74.50 (ISBN 0-89116-150-3). Hemisphere Pub.

Thomson, J., et al. Frequency Conversion. (Wykeham Technology Ser.: No. 1). 216p. 1969. 9.95x (ISBN 0-8448-1172-6). Crane Russak Co.

Thyagarajan, K. & Ghatak, A. K. Lasers: Theory & Applications. LC 81-12176. (Optical Physics & Engineering Ser.). 444p. 1981. 59.50x (ISBN 0-306-40598-9, Plenum Pr). Plenum Pub.

Tillman, Dick & Powlison, Dave. The New Laser Sailing. (Illus.). 160p. 1983. 15.95 (ISBN 0-914814-32-X). Sail Bks.

Townes, C. H. & Miles, P. A., eds. Quantum Electronics & Coherent Light. (Italian Physical Society Ser.: Course 31). 1965. 80.00 (ISBN 0-12-368831-0). Acad Pr.

The U. S. Military Laser Market. (Defense & Aerospace-U. S. Industry Reports). 1981. 1100.00 (ISBN 0-86621-036-9, A866). Frost & Sullivan.

Use of Lasers in Materials Processing Applications, Vol. 26. 90p. 1980. 30.00 (ISBN 0-912035-09-9). Laser Inst.

Vanier, Jacques. Basic Theory of Lasers & Masers: A Density Matrix Approach. Montroll, E. W., et al, eds. (Documents on Modern Physics Ser.). (Illus.). 128p. 1971. 37.25x (ISBN 0-677-30340-8). Gordon.

Velikhov, E. P. Molecular Gas Lasers. 266p. 1981. pap. 8.00 (ISBN 0-8285-2280-4, Pub. by Mir Pubs USSR). Imported Pubns.

Verdeyen, Joseph T. Laser Electronics. (Illus.). 480p. 1981. 40.95 (ISBN 0-13-485201-X). P-H.

Weber, Joseph, ed. Lasers, 2 Vols. (International Science Review Ser). 1968. Vol. 1, 832p. 149.25 (ISBN 0-677-00880-5); Vol. 2, 760p. 149.25 (ISBN 0-677-00890-2). Gordon.

Weber, Marvin J., ed. CRC Handbook of Laser Science & Technology, Vols. I & II. Incl. (Lasers & Masers Ser.). 568p. Vol. I. 105.00 (ISBN 0-8493-3501-9); (Gas Lasers Ser.). 584p. Vol. II. 105.00 (ISBN 0-8493-3502-7). 1982. CRC Pr.

Wendt, John F, ed. Gas-Flow & Chemical Lasers. LC 79-12779. (Von Karman Inst Bk.). (Illus.). 608p. 1979. text ed. 92.00 (ISBN 0-89116-147-3). Hemisphere Pub.

West, Michael A., ed. Lasers in Chemistry. 438p. (Proceedings). 1977. 85.00 (ISBN 0-444-41630-7). Elsevier.

Wherrett, B. S., ed. Laser Advances & Applications Proceedings: Proceedings of the National Quantum Electronics Conference, 4th, Heriot-Watt University, Edinburgh, 1979. LC 80-40119. 278p. 1980. 62.95 (ISBN 0-471-27792-4). Wiley.

White, C. W. & Peercy, P. S., eds. Laser & Electron Beam Processing of Materials. 1980. 60.00 (ISBN 0-12-746850-1). Acad Pr.

Wilson, Leroy E., et al, eds. Electronic Transition Lasers II. LC 77-688. 1977. text ed. 27.50x (ISBN 0-262-23084-4). MIT Pr.

Winburn. Laser Safety: A Practical Approach. (Occupational Safety & Health Ser.). 264p. 1985. 39.75 (ISBN 0-8247-7348-9). Dekker.

Wolbarsht, Myron L., ed. Laser Applications in Medicine & Biology. Incl. Vol. 1. 288p. 1971. 45.00x (ISBN 0-306-37161-8); Vol. 2. 404p. 1974. 59.50x (ISBN 0-306-37162-6); Vol. 3. 348p. 1977. 55.00x (ISBN 0-306-37163-4). LC 77-128514. (Illus., Plenum Pr). Plenum Pub.

Yariv, Amnon. Introduction to Optical Electronics. 2nd ed. LC 76-11773. 1976. text ed. 39.95 (ISBN 0-03-089892-7, HoltC). HR&W.

Zewail, ed. Advances in Laser Chemistry: Proceedings of the Conference on Advances in Laser Chemistry, California Institute of Technology, Pasadena, USA, March 20-22, 1978. (Springer Series in Chemical Physics: Vol. 3). (Illus.). 1978. 36.00 (ISBN 0-387-08997-7). Springer-Verlag.

Zuev, V. E. Laser Beams in the Atmosphere. Wood, James S., tr. from Rus. LC 81-19508. 515p. 1982. 85.00x (ISBN 0-306-10967-0, Consultants). Plenum Pub.

LASERS–BIBLIOGRAPHY

Belforte, David A., ed. Industrial Laser Materials Processing Bibliography, 5 vols. 4th ed. 500p. 1985. pap. text ed. 145.00 (ISBN 0-916389-05-7). Belforte Assoc.

Tomiyasu, Kiyo. Laser Literature: An Annotated Guide. LC 68-21474. 172p. 1968. 27.50x (ISBN 0-306-30335-3, Plenum Pr). Plenum Pub.

LASERS IN MEDICINE

Arndt, K. A., et al. Cutaneous Laser Therapy: Principles & Methods. LC 82-17379. 241p. 1983. 47.00 (ISBN 0-471-87751-4, Pub. by Wiley Med). Wiley.

Aron-Rosa, Daniele, ed. Pulsed Yag Laser Surgery. LC 83-60475. 224p. 1983. 49.50 (ISBN 0-943432-03-0, 278). Slack Inc.

Atsumi, K., ed. New Frontiers in Laser Medicine & Surgery. (International Congress Ser.: No. 609). 528p. 1983. 100.00 (ISBN 0-444-90305-4, I-205-83, Excerpta Medica). Elsevier.

Baggish, Michael S. Basic & Advanced Laser Surgery in Gynecology. 448p. 1985. write for info. (ISBN 0-8385-0520-1). ACC.

Balian, R. & Adam, J. G. Laser-Plasma Interactions. (Les Houches Summer School Ser.: Vol. 34). 808p. 1982. 159.75 (ISBN 0-444-86215-3, I-183-82). Elsevier.

Bellina, Joseph H. & Bandieramonte, Gaetano. Principles & Practice of Gynecologic Laser Surgery. 308p. 1984. 39.50x (ISBN 0-306-41543-7, Plenum Pr). Plenum Pub.

Berns, Michael W. & Mirhoseini, Mahmood. Laser Application to Occlusive Vascular Disease. LC 85-4608. 154p. 1985. 28.00 (ISBN 0-8451-0246-X). A R Liss.

Birngruber, R. & Gabel, V. P., eds. Laser Treatment & Photocoagulation of the Eye. (Documenta Ophthalmologica Proceedings Ser.). 1983. lib. bdg. 67.00 (ISBN 90-619-3732-9, Pub. by Junk Pubs Netherlands). Kluwer Academic.

Brown, D. C. High Peak Power Nd: Class Laser Systems. (Springer Series in Optical Sciences: Vol. 25). (Illus.). 276p. 1981. 47.00 (ISBN 0-387-10516-6). Springer-Verlag.

Dixon, J. A. Surgical Application of the Laser. (Illus.). 1983. 44.95 (ISBN 0-8151-2514-3). Year Bk Med.

Fleischer, D., et al, eds. Therapeutic Laser Endoscopy in Gastrointestinal Disease. 1983. lib. bdg. 43.50 (ISBN 0-89838-577-6, Pub. by Martinus Nijhoff Netherlands). Kluwer Academic.

Goldman, L., ed. The Biomedical Laser: Technology & Clinical Applications. (Illus.). 350p. 1981. 42.00 (ISBN 0-387-90571-5). Springer-Verlag.

Goldman, Leon. Laser Cancer Research. (Recent Results in Cancer Research: Vol. 4). (Illus.). 1966. 15.00 (ISBN 0-387-03643-1). Springer-Verlag.

Hieftje, Gary M., et al, eds. Lasers in Chemical Analysis. LC 80-84082. (Contemporary Instrumentation & Analysis). (Illus.). 352p. 1981. 49.50 (ISBN 0-89603-027-X). Humana.

Hillenkamp, F., et al, eds. Lasers in Biology & Medicine. LC 80-18895. (NATO ASI Series A, Life Sciences: Vol. 34). 474p. 1981. 69.50x (ISBN 0-306-40470-2, Plenum Pr). Plenum Pub.

Joffe, S. N., et al, eds. Neodymium: YAG Laser in Medicine & Surgery. 1983. 55.00 (ISBN 0-444-00821-7, Biomedcal Pr). Elsevier.

Kaplan, I. & Giler, S. CO-Two Laser Surgery. (Illus.). 220p. 1984. 79.00 (ISBN 0-387-13012-8). Springer-Verlag.

Keates, Richard & Fry, S. M. Ophthalmic Neodymuim: Yag Lasers. LC 83-60644. 96p. 1983. 19.50 (ISBN 0-943432-04-9). Slack Inc.

Koebner, Hans K. Lasers in Medicine, Vol. 1. LC 79-40525. 274p. 1980. 133.95x (ISBN 0-471-27602-2, Pub. by Wiley-Interscience). Wiley.

L'Esperance. Ophthalmic Lasers: Photocoagulation, Photoradiation & Surgery. 2nd ed. 1983. 81.50 (ISBN 0-8016-2823-7). Mosby.

Lobraico, Rocco, ed. ICALEO Medicine & Biology Symposium Eighty-Three, Vol. 37. 1984. 40.00 (ISBN 0-912035-18-8). Laser Inst.

Macardle, Melanie T. Lasers in Medicine, Science & Biology: Research & Reference Guidebook. LC 84-45167. 150p. 1984. 29.95 (ISBN 0-88164-168-5); pap. 21.95 (ISBN 0-88164-169-3). ABBE Pubs Assn.

McGuff, Paul E. Surgical Applications of Laser. (Illus.). 224p. 1966. photocopy ed. 21.50x (ISBN 0-398-01259-8). C C Thomas.

Mackety, C. J. Perioperative Laser Nursing. LC 83-51728. 250p. 1984. 19.50 (ISBN 0-943432-21-9). Slack Inc.

March, Wayne F. Ophthalmic Lasers: Current Clinical Uses. LC 83-51651. 352p. 1984. 60.00 (ISBN 0-943432-25-1). Slack Inc.

Market Intelligence Research Company Staff. World Markets for Surgical Lasers. 145p. pap. text ed. 595.00 (ISBN 0-317-19571-9). Market Res Co.

Pfister, Judith & Kneedler, Julia A. A Guide to Lasers in the OR. (Illus.). 1983. write for info. (ISBN 0-9613138-0-3). Educ Des Edit Cons.

Pratesi, R. & Sacchi, C. A., eds. Lasers in Photomedicine & Photobiology: Proceedings. (Springer Series in Optical Sciences: Vol. 22). (Illus.). 235p. 1980. 35.00 (ISBN 0-387-10178-0). Springer-Verlag.

Robin. Lasers in Ophthalmology. 1985. 75.00 (ISBN 0-8151-7311-3). Year Bk Med.

Satelle, D. B., et al, eds. Biomedical Applications of Laser Light Scattering: Proceedings, Workshop Meeting, Cambridge, U. K., 1981. 428p. 1982. 85.00 (ISBN 0-444-80456-0, Biomedical Pr). Elsevier.

Schwarz, H. J., et al, eds. Laser Interaction & Related Plasma Phenomena, Vol. 5. LC 79-135851. 863p. 1981. 95.00x (ISBN 0-306-40545-8, Plenum Pr). Plenum Pub.

Schwarz, Helmut J. & Hora, Heinrich, eds. Laser Interaction & Related Plasma Phenomena. Incl. Vol. 1. 523p. 1970. 75.00x (ISBN 0-306-37141-3); Vol. 2. 597p. 1972. 75.00x (ISBN 0-306-37142-1); Vol. 3A. 458p. 1974. 75.00x (ISBN 0-306-37143-X); Vol. 3B. 561p. 1974. 75.00x (ISBN 0-306-37150-2); Vol. 4A. 677p. 1977. 85.00x (ISBN 0-306-37144-8); Vol. 4B. 575p. 1977. 75.00x (ISBN 0-306-37154-5). LC 79-135851. (Illus., Plenum Pr). Plenum Pub.

Sliney, David & Wolbarsht, Myron. Safety with Lasers & Other Optical Sources: A Comprehensive Handbook. LC 80-16591. 1060p. 1980. 65.00x (ISBN 0-306-40434-6, Plenum Pr). Plenum Pub.

Spaeth, George L. & Schwartz, Louis. Laser Therapy of the Anterior Segment: A Practical Approach. LC 83-50367. 176p. 1984. 49.50 (ISBN 0-943432-14-6). Slack Inc.

Trokel, Stephen, ed. YAG Laser Ophthalmic Microsurgery. (Illus.). 221p. 1983. 55.00 (ISBN 0-8385-9929-X). ACC.

Wolbarsht, Myron L., ed. Laser Applications in Medicine & Biology. Incl. Vol. 1. 288p. 1971. 45.00x (ISBN 0-306-37161-8); Vol. 2. 404p. 1974. 59.50x (ISBN 0-306-37162-6); Vol. 3. 348p. 1977. 55.00x (ISBN 0-306-37163-4). LC 77-128514. (Illus., Plenum Pr). Plenum Pub.

LASTS (SHOES)

see Boots and Shoes

LATENT STRUCTURE ANALYSIS

Goodman, Leo A. Analyzing Qualitative-Categorical Date: Log-Linear Models & Latent Structure Analysis. Magidson, Jay & Davis, James A., eds. 484p. 1984. Repr. of 1978 ed. lib. bdg. 32.50 (ISBN 0-8191-4105-4). U Pr of Amer.

--Analyzing Qualitative-Categorical Data: Log-Linear Models & Latent Structure Analysis. Magidson, Jay, ed. 484p. 1985. pap. text ed. 22.75 (ISBN 0-8191-4686-2). U Pr of Amer.

Weiss, David J. New Horizons in Testing: Latent Trait Test & Computerized Adaptive Testing. 1983. 38.00 (ISBN 0-12-742780-5). Acad Pr.

LATERITE

Evans, D. J., et al, eds. International Laterite Symposium. LC 78-73974. (Illus.). 1979. text ed. 33.00x (ISBN 0-89520-255-7). Soc Mining Eng.

McFarlane, J. M. Laterite & Landscape. 1977. 33.00 (ISBN 0-12-484450-2). Acad Pr.

Persons, Benjamin S. Laterite: Genesis, Location, Use. LC 73-107541. 103p. 1970. 29.50x (ISBN 0-306-30450-3, Plenum Pr). Plenum Pub.

LATEX

Floor Coverings, Latex, Carbon Black & Foams: Testing Standards for Chemical Analyses. (DIN Standards Ser.). 464.00 (ISBN 0-686-31848-X, 11199-2-131). Wiley.

LATHES

see also Turning

Bradley, Ian. Myford Series 7 Lathe Manual. 326p. 1985. pap. 13.95 (ISBN 0-85242-775-1, Pub. by Argus). Aztex.
--Shaping Machine & Lathe Tools. (Illus.). 80p. 1985. pap. 4.40 (ISBN 0-85242-485-X, Pub. by Argus). Aztex.
Cain, Tubal. Milling Operations in the Lathe. (Workshop Practice Ser.: No. 5). (Illus.). 128p. (Orig.). 1984. pap. 9.95 (ISBN 0-85242-840-5, Pub. by Argus). Aztex.
Cleeve, Martin. Screwcutting in the Lathe. (Workshop Practice Ser.: No. 3). (Illus.). 128p. 1985. pap. 9.95 (ISBN 0-85242-838-3, Pub. by Argus). Aztex.
Engineering Industry Training Board, ed. Training for Capstan, Turret, & Sequence Controlled Lathe Setters & Operators, 21 vols. (Illus.). 1973. Set. 89.95x (ISBN 0-89563-023-0). Intl Ideas.
--Training for Fixed Headstock Single Spindle Automatic Lathe Setters & Operators, 30 vols. (Illus.). 1978. folder 89.95x (ISBN 0-85083-425-2). Intl Ideas.
--Training for Multi-Spindle Automatic Lathe Setters & Operators, 31 vols. (Illus.). 1979. Set. folder 89.95x (ISBN 0-85083-463-5). Intl Ideas.
--Training for Sliding Headstock Single Spindle Automatic Lathe (Swiss Auto) Setters & Operators, 26 vols. (Illus.). 1978. Set. folder 79.95x (ISBN 0-85083-426-0). Intl Ideas.
Kibbe, Richard R. Lathe Operations. LC 84-11797. 236p. 1985. pap. 17.95 (ISBN 0-471-89023-5). Wiley.
Know Your Lathe. (Illus.). 104p. 1979. pap. 7.95 (ISBN 0-85242-557-0). Aztex.
Krar, S. F. & Oswald, J. W. Turning Technology: Engine & Turret Lathes. LC 78-153723. 1971. pap. text ed. 14.80 (ISBN 0-8273-0206-1); instructor's guide o.p. 3.60 (ISBN 0-8273-0207-X). Delmar.
Perrigo, O. E. Lathe Design-Construction & Operation. 1984. pap. 12.95 (ISBN 0-917914-18-X). Lindsay Pubns.
Sparey, L. H. The Amateur's Lathe. rev. ed. (Illus.). 224p. 1983. pap. 10.95 (ISBN 0-85344-143-X). Aztex.
Westbury, E. T. Metal Turning Lathes. (Illus.). 154p. 1979. pap. 8.95 (ISBN 0-317-00059-4). Aztex.
Westbury, E. T., et al. Lathe Accessories. (Illus.). 109p. 1981. pap. 6.50 (ISBN 0-85344-100-6). Aztex.

LATHYRUS

Hitchcock, C. Leo. Revision of the North American Species of Lathyrus. LC 53-9615. (Publications in Biology Ser.: No. 15). (Illus.). 104p. 1952. pap. 10.00x (ISBN 0-295-73913-4). U of Wash Pr.

LATITUDE VARIATION

Klein, Felix. Ueber Die Theorie Des Kreisels. 1965. 60.00 (ISBN 0-384-29720-X). Johnson Repr.

LATTICE THEORY

see also Crystal Lattices; Crystallography, Mathematical

Balbes, Raymond & Dwinger, Philip. Distributive Lattices. LC 73-94309. 320p. 1975. 25.00x (ISBN 0-8262-0163-6). U of Mo Pr.
Banaschewski, B. & Hoffmann, R. E., eds. Continuous Lattices: Proceedings. (Lecture Notes in Mathematics: Vol. 871). 413p. 1981. pap. 24.00 (ISBN 0-387-10848-3). Springer-Verlag.
Bhatt, P. Problems in Structural Analysis by Matrix Methods. (Illus.). 465p. 1981. pap. 22.50x (ISBN 0-86095-881-7). Longman.
Bilz, H. & Kress, W. Phonon Dispersion Relations in Insulators. (Springer Ser. in Solid-State Sciences: Vol. 10). (Illus.). 1979. 48.00 (ISBN 0-387-09399-0). Springer-Verlag.
Birkhoff, Garrett D. Lattice Theory. rev. ed. LC 66-23707. (Colloquium Pubns. Ser.: Vol. 25). 418p. 1979. pap. 39.00 (ISBN 0-8218-1025-1, COLL-25). Am Math.
Blumenthal, Leonard M. & Menger, Karl. Studies in Geometry. LC 74-75624. (Illus.). 512p. 1970. text ed. 31.95 (ISBN 0-7167-0437-4). W H Freeman.
Boggs, Robert G. Elementary Structural Analysis. 1984. text ed. 38.95 (ISBN 0-03-063933-6). HR&W.
Brohn, David. Understanding Structural Analysis. (Illus.). 224p. 1984. pap. text ed. 23.50x (ISBN 0-246-12238-2, Pub. by Granada England). Sheridan.
Cartwright, Donald. Extensions of Positive Operators Between Banach Lattices. LC 75-19496. (Memoirs: No. 164). 48p. 1975. pap. 12.00 (ISBN 0-8218-1864-3, MEMO-164). Am Math.
Cassie, W. F. Structural Analysis: The Solution of Statically Indeterminate Structures. 3rd ed. LC 67-72611. pap. 73.80 (ISBN 0-317-11039-X, 2004914). Bks Demand UMI.
Chajes, Alexander. Structural Analysis. (Illus.). 384p. 1983. 35.95 (ISBN 0-13-853408-X). P-H.
Chu-Kia Wang & Salmon, Charles G. Introductory Structural Analysis. (Illus.). 656p. 1983. 37.95 (ISBN 0-13-501569-3). P-H.
Classical Methods of Structural Analysis: Arabic Edition PPR. 1986. pap. price not set (ISBN 0-471-82571-9). Wiley.
Coates, R., et al. Sructural Analysis. 2nd ed. 1980. pap. 35.95 (ISBN 0-442-30757-8). Van Nos Reinhold.
Creutz, Michael. Quarks, Gluons & Lattices. (Monographs on Mathematical Physics). (Illus.). 175p. 1985. pap. 12.95 (ISBN 0-521-31535-2). Cambridge U Pr.
Cruse, Thomas A. & Griffin, Donald S., eds. Three-Dimensional Continuum Computer Programs for Structural Analysis: Presented at the Winter Annual Meeting of the American Society of Mechanical Engineers, New York, NY, November 26-30, 1972. LC 72-92593. pap. 20.00 (ISBN 0-317-10641-4, 2022061). Bks Demand UMI.
Dawe, D. J. Matrix & Finite Element Analysis of Structures. (Illus.). 1984. 49.00x (ISBN 0-19-856211-X). Oxford U Pr.
Devreese, J. T. & Van Doren, V. E., eds. Ab Initio Calculation of Phonon Spectra. 312p. 1983. 42.50x (ISBN 0-306-41119-9, Plenum Pr). Plenum Pub.
Domokos, G. & Kovesi-Domokos, S. Lattice Gauge Theory-Supersymmetry & Grand Unification: Proceedings of the 7th Johns Hopkins Workshop on Current Problems in Particle Theory, Bad Honnef-Bonn, June 21-23, 1983. 350p. 1983. 40.00x (ISBN 9971-950-63-4, Pub. by World Sci Singapore); pap. 21.00x (ISBN 9971-950-62-6, Pub. by World Sci Singapore). Taylor & Francis.
Dorner, B. Coherent Inelastic Neutron Scattering in Lattices Dynamics. (Springer Tracts in Modern Physics Ser.: Vol. 93). (Illus.). 120p. 1982. 24.00 (ISBN 0-387-11049-6). Springer-Verlag.
Elms, D. An Introduction to Modern Structural Analysis. 230p. 1971. 69.50 (ISBN 0-677-62030-6). Gordon.
Freese, R. S. The Structure of Modular Lattices of Width Four with Applications to Varieties of Lattices. LC 76-49468. (Memoirs: No. 181). 91p. 1977. pap. 13.00 (ISBN 0-8218-2181-4, MEMO-181). Am Math.
Fricker, Francois. Einfuhrung in die Gitterpunktlehre. (Mathematical Ser.: Vol. 73). (Ger.). 256p. 1981. text ed. 51.95x (ISBN 0-8176-1236-X). Birkhauser.
Garcia, O. C. & Taylor, W. The Lattice of Interpretability Types of Varieties. LC 84-10997. (Memoirs of the American Mathematical Society: Vol. 305). 126p. 1984. pap. 12.00 (ISBN 0-8218-2308-6). Am Math.
Ghali, A. & Neville, A. M. Structural Analysis: A Unified Classical & Matrix Approach. 2nd ed. 1978. pap. 29.95x (ISBN 0-412-14990-7, 6122, Pub. by Chapman & Hall). Methuen Inc.
Gierz, G., et al. A Compendium of Continuous Lattices. 380p. 1980. 24.00 (ISBN 0-387-10111-X). Springer-Verlag.
Gratzer, G. H. Lattice Theory: First Concepts & Distributive Lattices. LC 75-151136. (Mathematics Ser). (Illus.). 212p. 1971. text ed. 35.95 (ISBN 0-7167-0442-0). W H Freeman.
Gruber, C., et al. Group Analysis of Classical Lattice Systems. LC 77-2821. (Lecture Notes in Physics: Vol. 60). 1977. pap. 21.00 (ISBN 0-387-08137-2). Springer-Verlag.
Gutkowski, Richard M. Structures: Fundamental Theory & Behavior. 592p. 1980. 36.50 (ISBN 0-442-22983-6). Van Nos Reinhold.
Hammer, Joseph. Unsolved Problems Concerning Lattice Points. LC 72-95013. (Research Notes in Mathematics Ser.: No. 15). 1978. pap. text ed. 16.95 (ISBN 0-273-01103-0). Pitman Pub MA.
Hardy, J. R. & Karo, A. M. The Lattice Dynamics & Statistics of Alkali Halide Crystals. LC 79-339. 324p. 1979. 49.50x (ISBN 0-306-40221-1, Plenum Pr). Plenum Pub.
Hermann, Robert. Toda Lattices, Cosymplectic Manifolds, Baecklund Transformations & Kinks, Pt. B. (Interdisciplinary Mathematics Ser.: No. 18). 145p. 1977. 20.00 (ISBN 0-915692-25-2, 991600312). Math Sci Pr.
Hibbeler, Russell C. Structural Analysis. 512p. 1985. text ed. write for info. (ISBN 0-02-354460-0). Macmillan.
Hoffman. Continuous Lattices & Their Applications. (Lecture Notes in Pure & Applied Mathematics Ser.). 352p. 1985. write for info. (ISBN 0-8247-7331-4). Dekker.
Horton, G. K. & Yamada, Y. Lattice Dynamical Properties of Solids, Vol. 5. Date not set. write for info. (ISBN 0-444-86780-5). Elsevier.
Huhn, A. P. & Schmidt, E. T. Lattice Theory. (Colloquia Mathematic Societatis Ser.: Vol.14). 462p. 1977. 85.00 (ISBN 0-7204-0498-3, North-Holland). Elsevier.
Huhn, A. P. & Schmidt, E. T., eds. Contributions to Lattice Theory. (Colloquia Mathematica Societatis Janos Bolyai Ser.: Vol. 33). 1984. 92.50 (ISBN 0-444-86507-1, I-447-83). Elsevier.
Hult, J. & Lemaitre, J., eds. Physical Non-Linearities in Structural Analysis Symposium. (IUTAM Ser.). (Illus.). 287p. 1981. 37.00 (ISBN 0-387-10544-1). Springer-Verlag.
Israel, Robert B. Convexity in the Theory of Lattice Gasses. LC 78-51171. (Physic Ser). 1979. 27.00 (ISBN 0-691-08209-X); pap. 13.50 (ISBN 0-691-08216-2). Princeton U Pr.
Jawad, Maan H. & Farr, James R. Structural Analysis & Design of Process Equipment. LC 83-12475. 704p. 1984. 69.95x (ISBN 0-471-09207-X, Pub. by Wiley-Interscience). Wiley.
Kalmbach, G. Orthomodular Lattices. (London Mathematical Society Monograph Ser.: No. 18). 1983. 65.00 (ISBN 0-12-394580-1). Acad Pr.
Keimel, K. & Hofmann, K. H. General Character Theory for Partially Ordered Sets & Lattices. LC 52-42839. (Memoirs: No. 122). 121p. 1972. pap. 9.00 (ISBN 0-8218-1822-8, MEMO-122). Am Math.
Keller, Robert. The Practice of Structured Analysis: Exploding Myths. LC 83-62140. (Illus.). 136p. 1983. pap. 18.50 (ISBN 0-917072-31-6). Yourdon.
Lefkowitz, I., et al. International Conference on Low Lying Lattice Vibrational Modes & Their Relationship to Superconductivity & Ferroelectricity: Proceedings, Puerto Rico, 1975, 2 vols. 472p. 1977. Set. pap. 321.25x (ISBN 0-677-15535-2). Gordon.
Light Water Lattices. (Technical Reports Ser.: No. 12). (Illus.). 363p. 1962. pap. 19.25 (ISBN 92-0-055062-2, IDC12, IAEA). Unipub.
Livesley, R. K. Matrix Methods of Structural Analysis. 2nd ed. 208p. 1975. text ed. 33.00 (ISBN 0-08-018888-5); pap. text ed. 15.00 (ISBN 0-08-018887-7). Pergamon.
Loomis, Lynn H. Lattice Theoretic Background of the Dimension Theory of Operator Algebras. LC 52-42839. (Memoirs: No. 18). 36p. 1972. Repr. of 1955 ed. 10.00 (ISBN 0-8218-1218-1, MEMO-18). Am Math.
Ludwig, W. Recent Developments in Lattice Theory. (Springer Tracts in Modern Physics: Vol. 43). (Illus.). 1967. 69.70 (ISBN 0-387-03982-1). Springer-Verlag.
McCormac, Jack C. Structural Analysis. 4th ed. 640p. 1984. text ed. 33.95 scp (ISBN 0-06-044342-1, HarpC); avail. sol. manual (ISBN 0-06-364116-X). Har-Row.
Maeda, F. & Maeda, S. Theory of Symmetric Lattices. LC 73-128138. (Grundlehren der Mathematischen Wissenschaften: Vol. 173). (Illus.). 1971. 36.00 (ISBN 0-387-05118-X). Springer-Verlag.
Mantell, Murray I. & Marron, John. Structural Analysis. LC 62-9753. (Illus.). pap. cancelled (ISBN 0-317-10794-1, 2012356). Bks Demand UMI.
Messing, W. The Crystals Associated to Barsotti-Tate Groups: With Applications to Abelian Schemes. LC 72-79007. (Lecture Notes in Mathematics: Vol. 264). 193p. 1972. pap. 10.00 (ISBN 0-387-05840-0). Springer-Verlag.
Mohanty, Gopal. Lattice Path Counting & Applications. LC 79-23524. (Probability & Mathematical Ser.). 1979. 39.50 (ISBN 0-12-504050-4). Acad Pr.
Narayana, T. V. Lattice Path Combinatorics with Statistical Applications. LC 78-6710. (Mathematical Expositions Ser.). 1979. 20.00x (ISBN 0-8020-5405-6). U of Toronto Pr.
Neal, B. G. The Plastic Methods of Structural Analysis: SI Version. 3rd ed. 1977. 15.95x (ISBN 0-412-21450-4, NO. 6208, Pub. by Chapman & Hall). Methuen Inc.
Nikodym, Otton M. Mathematical Apparatus for Quantum-Theories. (Grundlehren der Mathematischen Wissenschaften: Vol. 129). 1966. 95.00 (ISBN 0-387-03523-0). Springer-Verlag.
Noor, A. K. & McComb, H. G., Jr. Trends in Computerized Structural Analysis & Synthesis, Vol. 10, no. 1-2. 83.00 (ISBN 0-08-028707-7); pap. 75.00 o. p. (ISBN 0-08-023261-2). Pergamon.
Pandit, G. S. & Gupta, S. P. Structural Analysis: A Matrix Approach. 592p. 1983. 11.00 (ISBN 0-07-096554-4). McGraw.
Pierce, Richard S. Translation Lattices. LC 52-42839. (Memoirs: No. 32). 66p. 1978. pap. 14.00 (ISBN 0-8218-1232-7, MEMO-32). Am Math.
Roggenkamp, K. W. Lattices Over Orders 2. new ed. LC 71-108334. (Lecture Notes in Mathematics: Vol. 142). 1970. pap. 18.30 (ISBN 0-387-04931-2). Springer-Verlag.
Roggenkamp, K. W. & Huber-Dyson, V. Lattices Over Orders 1. (Lecture Notes in Mathematics: Vol. 115). 1970. pap. 18.30 (ISBN 0-387-04904-5). Springer-Verlag.
Rose, Henry. Nonmodular Lattice Varieties. LC 83-22449. (Memoirs: No. 292). 78p. 1984. 9.00 (ISBN 0-8218-2292-6, MEMO 292). Am Math.
Schaefer, H. H. Branach Lattices & Positive Operators. (Die Grundlehren der Mathematischen Wissenschaften Ser.: Vol. 215). xi, 376p. 1974. 57.00 (ISBN 0-387-06936-4). Springer-Verlag.
Skonjakov, L. A. Elements of Lattice Theorgy. 1978. 49.00 (ISBN 0-9960018-6-7, Pub. by A Hilger England). Heyden.
Smolira, M. Analysis of Structures by the Force-Displacement Method. 389p. 1980. 61.00 (ISBN 0-85334-814-6, Pub. by Elsevier Applied Sci England). Elsevier.
Symposium in Pure Mathematics. Monterey, Calif. 1959. Lattice Theory: Proceedings. Dilworth, R. P., ed. LC 50-1183. (Proceedings of Symposia in Pure Mathematics: Vol. 2). 1961. 24.00 (ISBN 0-8218-1402-8, PSPUM-2). Am Math.
Teague, Lavette C., Jr. & Pidgeon, Christopher W. Structured Analysis Methods for Computer Information Systems. 400p. 1984. pap. text ed. 24.95 (ISBN 0-574-21495-X, 13-4495); instr's guide avail. (ISBN 0-574-21496-8, 13-3496). SRA.
Thelliez, S. Introduction a l'Etude des Structures Ternaires de Commutation. (Theorie des Systemes Ser.). 204p. 1973. 64.95x (ISBN 0-677-50330-X). Gordon.
Thompson, Richard L. Equilibrium States on Thin Energy Shells. LC 74-14723. (Memoirs Ser.: No. 150). 110p. 1974. pap. 11.00 (ISBN 0-8218-1850-3, MEMO-150). Am Math.
Toda, M. Theory of Nonlinear Lattices. (Springer Series in Solid-State Sciences: Vol. 20). (Illus.). 220p. 1981. 38.00 (ISBN 0-387-10224-8). Springer-Verlag.
Tuma, J. J. Advanced Structural Analysis. (Schaum's Outline Ser.). pap. 10.95 (ISBN 0-07-065426-3). McGraw.
Valid, N. Mechanics of Continuous Media & Analysis of Structures. (Series in Applied Mathematics & Mechanics: Vol. 26). 358p. 1981. 64.00 (ISBN 0-444-86150-5, North-Holland). Elsevier.
Vulikh, B. Z. Introduction to the Theory of Partially Ordered Spaces. 404p. 1967. 106.50x (ISBN 0-677-61330-X). Gordon.
West, H. H. Analysis of Structures: An Intergration of Classical & Modern Methods. 689p. 1980. text ed. 46.95 (ISBN 0-471-02036-2). Wiley.

LAUGHING GAS

see Nitrous Oxide

LAUNDRY AND LAUNDRY INDUSTRY

Rudman, Jack. Laundry Foreman. (Career Examination Ser.: C-2244). (Cloth bdg. avail. on request). pap. 10.00 (ISBN 0-8373-2244-8). Natl Learning.
--Laundry Supervisor. (Career Examination Ser.: C-1339). (Cloth bdg. avail. on request). pap. 10.00 (ISBN 0-8373-1339-2). Natl Learning.
--Laundry Washman. (Career Examination Ser.: C-1340). (Cloth bdg. avail. on request). pap. 8.00 (ISBN 0-8373-1340-6). Natl Learning.
--Laundry Worker. (Career Examination Ser.: C-435). (Cloth bdg. avail. on request). pap. 8.00 (ISBN 0-8373-0435-0). Natl Learning.
--Senior Laundry Supervisor. (Career Examination Ser.: C-2220). (Cloth bdg. avail. on request). pap. 12.00 (ISBN 0-8373-2220-0). Natl Learning.
--Senior Laundry Worker. (Career Examination Ser.: C-719). (Cloth bdg. avail. on request). pap. 12.00 (ISBN 0-8373-0719-8). Natl Learning.

LAURACEAE

Mez, Carl. Lauraceae Americaneae Monographice Descrips. 1963. Repr. of 1889 ed. 28.00 (ISBN 3-7682-0171-6). Lubrecht & Cramer.

LAVOISIER, ANTOINE LAURENT, 1743-1794

Aykroyd, Wallace R. Three Philosophers: Lavoisier, Priestley & Cavendish. LC 77-98808. Repr. of 1935 ed. lib. bdg. 18.75 (ISBN 0-8371-2890-0, AYTB). Greenwood.
Duveen, Dennis I. Supplementary Volume to a Bibliography of the Works of Antoine Lavoisier: 1753-1794. 173p. 1965. 26.50x (ISBN 0-8464-0900-3). Beekman Pubs.
Duveen, Dennis I. & Klickstein, H. S. Bibliography of the Works of Antoine Lavoisier: Bibliography of the Works of Antoine Lavoisier: Seventeen Forty-Three to Seventeen Ninety-Four. (Illus.). 491p. 1954. 37.50x (ISBN 0-8464-0192-4). Beekman Pubs.
Grimaux, Edouard. Lavoisier: Seventeen Forty-Three to Seventeen Ninety-Four. Cohen, I. Bernard, ed. LC 80-2124. (Development of Science Ser.). (Illus.). 1981. lib. bdg. 35.00x (ISBN 0-405-13963-2). Ayer Co Pubs.
Holmes, Frederic L. Lavoisier & the Chemistry of Life: An Exploration of Scientific Creativity. LC 84-40152. (Wisconsin Publications in the History of Science & Medicine Ser.: No. 4). (Illus.). 608p. 1984. text ed. 37.50x (ISBN 0-299-09980-6). U of Wis Pr.

Lavoisier, A. L. & Laplace, P. S. Memoir on Heat. Guerlac, Henry, ed. Tr. of Memoire sur la Chaleur. 1981. 14.95 (ISBN 0-88202-195-8). Watson Pub Intl.

LAW–DATA PROCESSING

A Boon to Legal Research-Computers. 5p. pap. 2.00 (ISBN 0-317-30763-0). Amer Bar Assn.

Boxerman, Lawerence A., intro. by. Computer Applications in Juvenile Court. 78p. 1974. 3.00 (ISBN 0-318-15763-2, T900). Natl Juv & Family Ct Judges.

Congressional Information Service, Inc. Staff. CIS Online User Guide & Thesaurus. 400p. 1982. loose-leaf guide 75.00 (ISBN 0-912380-98-5). Thesaurus (ISBN 0-912380-99-3). Cong Info.

Council of Europe. Harmonisation Measures in the Field of Legal Data Processing in the Member States of the Council of Europe. 25p. 1982. 5.00 (ISBN 92-871-0036-5, Council of Europe). Unipub.

--Harmonisation of Laws Relating to the Requirement of Written Proof & the Admissibility of Reproductions of Documents & Recordings on Computers. 21p. 1982. 6.00 (ISBN 92-871-0044-6, Council of Europe). Unipub.

Cwiklo, William E., ed. Computers in Litigation Support. 353p. Repr. text ed. 25.00 (ISBN 0-89433-086-1). Petrocelli.

Delaplain, Richard W., et al. Computer-Aided Transcription in the Courts. (Illus.). 259p. (Orig.). 1981. pap. 12.50 (ISBN 0-89656-051-1, R0057). Natl Ctr St Courts.

Edge, C. T. Small Computer Systems for Solicitors, 2 Pts. 152p. (Orig.). 1983. pap. text ed. 38.50x (ISBN 0-566-03442-5). Gower Pub Co.

Eres, Beth K. Legal & Legislative Information Processing. LC 79-7063. (Illus.). xvi, 299p. 1980. lib. bdg. 35.00 (ISBN 0-313-21343-7, ERL/). Greenwood.

Gonzales, Laurence. Computers for Lawyers. LC 99-943923. 1984. pap. 6.95 (ISBN 0-345-31479-4). Ballantine.

Good, Phillip I. A Critical Guide to Software for the IBM PC & PC Compatible Computers: Computers for Professionals in Business, Agriculture, Law & Health. LC 83-17148. (Illus.). 284p. 1983. pap. 12.95 (ISBN 0-8019-7413-5). Chilton.

Halligan, Joseph. Legal-SOFTWHERE. Winther, Richard P., ed. (SOFTWHERE Software Directories Ser.: Vol. 1). (Orig.). 1984. pap. 29.95 (ISBN 0-918451-60-4). Moore Data.

Index of Computer Hardware & Software in Use in North Carolina Local Governments. 209p. 1984. 8.00 (ISBN 0-686-39424-0). U of NC Inst Gov.

Kelman, Alistair & Sizer, Richard. The Computer in Court. 112p. 1982. text ed. 35.50x (ISBN 0-566-03419-0). Gower Pub Co.

Kinsock, John E. Legal Databases Online: Lexis-Westlaw. (Advanced Online Searching Ser.). 1985. lib. bdg. 28.50 (ISBN 0-87287-404-4). Libs Unl.

Lawyers' Microcomputing Sourcebook 1985. 500p. Date not set. pap. cancelled (ISBN 0-8352-1921-6). Bowker.

Legal & Professional Time Billing Software Guide. 288p. 1984. 19.95 (ISBN 0-317-04400-1). Micro Info.

Leonard, James. OCLC's Serials Control Subsystem: Its Suitability to Legal Serials & Continuations. Date not set. price not set. Am Assn Law Libs.

Levy, Charlotte L. Computer-Assisted Litigation Support: An Annotated Bibliography. LC 84-1756. (CompuBibs Ser.: No. 4). 31p. 1984. pap. 10.00x (ISBN 0-914791-02-8). Vantage Info.

Locate: A Directory of Law Office Computer Software. 200p. 1984. 28.00 (ISBN 0-89707-148-4). Amer Bar Assn.

McClung, Christina J., et al. Microcomputers for Legal Professionals. LC 83-5730. (Personal Computers for Professionals Ser.: 1-999). 141p. 1984. pap. 14.95 (ISBN 0-471-89723-X, 1-999, Pub by Wiley Pr). Wiley.

McDonald, Ann L. Communicating with Legal Databases. 350p. 1985. lib. bdg. write for info. (ISBN 0-918212-95-2). Neal-Schuman.

Martino, A. A. Deontic Logic, Computational Linguistics & Legal Information Systems. 518p. 1982. 66.00 (ISBN 0-444-86415-6, North-Holland). Elsevier.

Mason, Mary Ann. An Introduction to the Use of Computers in Law. LC 83-27743. 223p. 1984. pap. text ed. 10.95 (ISBN 0-314-80352-1). West Pub.

Morneau, Robert H., Jr. Computer Programs for Traffic Accident Investigation. LC 83-40339. 160p. 1984. spiral 19.75x (ISBN 0-398-04958-0). C C Thomas.

National Center for State Courts & Bureau Justice of Statistics, eds. Word Processing in the Courts. LC 84-14860. 64p. (Orig.). 1984. pap. text ed. 10.00 (ISBN 0-89656-077-5, R-091). Natl Ctr St Courts.

Park, Roger C. Computer-Aided Exercises in Civil Procedure. 2nd ed. LC 83-16815. (Misc. Ser.). 167p. 1983. pap. text ed. 9.95 (ISBN 0-314-76495-X). West Pub.

Planning for Computers: Evaluating Data Processing Needs for Medium & Large Law Firms. LC 81-68751. 133p. 1981. pap. 25.00 (ISBN 0-89707-051-8). Amer Bar Assn.

Stong, Kline D. Choosing & Using Computers: To Improve Your Law Practice. 158p. 1983. pap. 38.00 (ISBN 0-89707-100-X). Amer Bar Assn.

Trew, A. J. & Armstron, H. The Good Computer Guide for Lawyers: A Systems Review. (Legal Technology Library). 192p. 1985. pap. 13.00 (ISBN 0-08-039238-5, Pub. by Waterlow). Pergamon.

Use of Computers in Litigation. LC 79-88511. 512p. 1979. 25.00 (ISBN 0-89707-007-0). Amer Bar Assn.

Waldron, Joseph A. Computers in Criminal Justice: An Introduction to Small Computers. 73p. 1983. pap. 8.95 (ISBN 0-932930-58-1). Pilgrimage Inc.

Wilkins, Robert P. The Lawyer's PC, Vol. I. 400p. 1984. 34.95 (ISBN 0-9608450-3-8). R P W Pub.

--What a Lawyer Needs to Know to Buy & Use a Computer. 14.95 (ISBN 0-9608450-2-X). R P W Pub.

Williams. Computer-Readable Databases, a Directory & Data Source Book: Business, Law, Humanities & Social Sciences. 4th ed. Date not set. write for info. (ISBN 0-444-87614-6). Elsevier.

LAW OF LARGE NUMBERS

Davis, P. J. The Lore of Large Numbers. LC 61-13842. (New Mathematical Library: No. 6). 165p. 1975. pap. 10.00 (ISBN 0-88385-606-9). Math Assn.

Padgett, W. J. & Taylor, R. L. Laws of Large Numbers for Normed Linear Spaces & Certain Frechet Spaces. (Lecture Notes in Mathematics: Vol. 360). 111p. 1973. pap. 12.00 (ISBN 0-387-06585-7). Springer-Verlag.

LAW OFFICES

Computer Strategies. The Law Office Computer Handbook. 150p. 1983. looseleaf 45.00x (ISBN 0-913505-12-9). Computer Strat.

Hoffman, Paul S., et al. Telephone Equipment for the Law Office: A Lawyer's Guide to Communications Systems. LC 83-70281. (Monograph Series Section of Economics of Law Practice, American Bar Association). (Illus.). x, 76p. 1983. 25.00 (ISBN 0-89707-098-4, 511-0077). Amer Bar Assn.

Locate: A Directory of Law Office Computer Software. 200p. 1984. 28.00 (ISBN 0-89707-148-4). Amer Bar Assn.

Luedtke, Peter & Luedtke, Rainer. Computers for Law Offices. LC 84-4488. (Computer Selection Books for Professionals Ser.). 1984. 19.95 (ISBN 0-15-600288-4, BFP). HarBraceJ.

Piovia, Sara. A Commonsense Guide to Law Office Automation. 240p. 1984. 19.95 (ISBN 0-13-152836-X); pap. 12.95 (ISBN 0-13-152802-5). P-H.

The Practical Lawyer's Manual for Automatic Law Office Typing & Word Processing. 116p. 1979. pap. 7.50 (ISBN 0-317-30702-9, F113). Am Law Inst.

Remer, Daniel. Computer Power for Your Law Office. LC 83-61382. (Illus.). 142p. 1983. pap. 19.95 (ISBN 0-89588-109-8). SYBEX.

Rhoads, F. D. & Edwards, J. Law Office Guide to Small Computers. (General Publications). (Illus.). 448p. 1984. 70.00 (ISBN 0-07-052091-7, Shepards-McGraw). McGraw.

LAWNS

see also Grasses

Baudendistel, Robert F. Lawn & Garden Construction. 1983. text ed. 22.95 (ISBN 0-8359-3952-9). Reston.

Beard, James B., et al, eds. Turfgrass Bibliography from 1672-1972. 730p. 1977. 35.00x (ISBN 0-87013-195-8). Mich St U Pr.

Duble, Richard & Kell, J. Carroll. Southern Lawns & Groundcovers. LC 77-73533. (Illus.). 96p. (Orig.). 1977. pap. 6.95x (ISBN 0-88415-426-2, Pub. by Pacesetter Pr). Gulf Pub.

Hawthorne, R. Dawson's Practical Lawncraft. (Illus.). 313p. 1977. 24.95x (ISBN 0-8464-1085-0). Beekman Pubs.

The Home Lawn Handbook. 2.25 (ISBN 0-686-21163-4). Bklyn Botanic.

MacCaskey, Michael R. All about Lawns. Ortho Books Editorial Staff, ed. LC 79-52995. (Illus.). 96p. 1980. pap. 5.95 ea. Midwest-Northeast Ed (ISBN 0-917102-83-5). Southern Ed (ISBN 0-917102-84-3). Western Ed (ISBN 0-917102-77-0). Ortho.

Schery, Robert W. Lawn Keeping. 1976. (Spec); pap. 5.95 (ISBN 0-13-526863-X). P-H.

Sunset Editors. Lawns & Ground Covers. LC 78-70267. (Illus.). 96p. 1979. pap. 4.95 (ISBN 0-376-03507-2, Sunset Bks.). Sunset-Lane.

Vengris, Jonas. Lawns. Rev. ed. LC 82-82822. (Illus.). 250p. 1982. pap. 15.50 (ISBN 0-913702-19-6). Thomson Pub CA.

LAYOUT

see Printing–Layout and Typography

LAYOUT, FACTORY

see Factories–Design and Construction

LEAD

Boggess, W. R. & Wixson, B. G., eds. Lead in the Environment. (Illus.). 272p. 1979. text ed. 43.00 (ISBN 0-7194-0024-4, Pub. by Castle Hse England). J K Burgess.

Doe, Bruce R. Lead Isotopes. LC 70-124067. (Minerals, Rocks & Inorganic Materials: Vol. 3). (Illus.). 1970. 26.00 (ISBN 0-387-05205-4). Springer-Verlag.

Harrison, R. M. & Laxen, D. P. Lead Pollution: Causes & Control. 168p. 1981. 23.00x (ISBN 0-412-16360-8, NO. 6570, Pub. by Chapman & Hall). Methuen Inc.

Hayward, P. L. & Harrison, D. A. Batch Lead Refining: A Case Study for Process Modelling, 1979. 1981. 70.00x (ISBN 0-686-97039-X, Pub. by W Spring England). State Mutual Bk.

Hehner, Nels E. & Ritchie, Everett J. Lead Oxides: Chemistry, Technology, Battery Manufacturing Uses, History. 1974. 15.00 (ISBN 0-685-56653-6). IBMA Pubns.

Hepple, P., ed. Lead in the Environment. (Illus.). 82p. 1973. 18.50 (ISBN 0-85334-485-X, Pub. by Elsevier Applied Sci England). Elsevier.

International Experts Discussion on Lead Occurrence, Fate & Pollution in the Marine Environment, Rovinj, Yugoslavia, 18-22 October 1977. Lead in the Marine Environment: Proceedings. Konrad, Z. & Branica, M., eds. LC 80-40023. (Illus.). 364p. 1980. pap. 81.00 (ISBN 0-08-022960-3). Pergamon.

Kuhn, A. T., ed. The Electrochemistry of Lead. 1979. 78.50 (ISBN 0-12-428350-0). Acad Pr.

Lynam, Donald R. & Piantanida, Lillian, eds. Environmental Lead: The Proceedings of the 2nd International Symposium on Environmental Lead Research. (Ecotoxicology & Environmental Quality Ser.). 1981. 48.50 (ISBN 0-12-460520-6). Acad Pr.

Measurement of Lead in the Atmosphere; Sampling Stacks for Particulates; & Determination of Oxides of Nitrogen in Combustion Products- DS 55-S5, S6, S8. 343p. 1975. pap. 18.00 (ISBN 0-8031-0387-5, 05-0550990-17). ASTM.

Measurement to Lead in the Atmosphere: Sampling Stacks for Particulates; & Determination of Oxides of Nitrogen in Combustion Products, DS 55. 343p. (Supplements S5, S6, S8 are also available). 1975. pap. 18.00 (ISBN 0-8031-0387-5, 05-055099-17). ASTM.

Mills, J. W. Zinc & Lead Ore Deposits in Carbonate Rocks, Stevens County, Washington. (Bulletin Ser.: No. 70). (Illus.). 171p. 1977. 3.00 (ISBN 0-686-34719-6). Geologic Pubns.

Needleman, Herbert L., ed. Low Level Lead Exposure: The Clinical Implications of Current Research. 336p. 1980. text ed. 52.50 (ISBN 0-89004-455-4). Raven.

Nriagu, J. O., ed. The Biogeochemistry of Lead in the Environment, 2 pts. (Topics in Environmental Health Ser.: Vol. 1). 1978. Pt. A, Ecological Cycles. 105.75 (ISBN 0-444-41599-8, Biomedical Pr); Pt. B, Biological Effects. 101.50 (ISBN 0-444-80050-6); 125.75. Elsevier.

Rowe, D. J. Lead Manufacturing in Britain: A History. (Illus.). 427p. 1983. 29.95 (ISBN 0-7099-2250-7, Pub. by Croom Helm). Longwood Pub Group.

Singhal, Radhey L. & Thomas, John A., eds. Lead Toxicity. LC 79-16784. (Illus.). 524p. 1980. text ed. 45.00 (ISBN 0-8067-1801-3). Urban & S.

Weaver, Lawrence. English Leadwork: Its Art & History. LC 68-57195. (Illus.). 1969. Repr. of 1909 ed. lib. bdg. 26.00 (ISBN 0-405-09057-9, Pub. by Blom). Ayer Co Pubs.

Willies, Lynn. Lead & Leadmining. (Shire Album Ser.: No. 85). (Illus.). 32p. (Orig.). 1982. pap. 2.95 (ISBN 0-85263-596-6, Pub. by Shire Pubns England). Seven Hills Bks.

LEAD MINES AND MINING

AIME International Symposium: Mining & Metallurgy of Lead & Zinc. LC 78-132404. 1970. 50.00x (ISBN 0-89520-040-6). Soc Mining Eng.

Brown, John S., ed. Genesis of Stratiform Lead, Zinc, Barite, Fluorite Deposits in Carbonate Rocks (The So-called Mississipi Valley Type Deposits) A Symposium. (Economic Geology, Monograph Ser.: No. 3). pap. 113.30 (ISBN 0-317-27600-X, 2014765). Bks Demand UMI.

Gibson, Arrell M. Wilderness Bonanza: The Tri-State Mining District of Missouri, Kansas & Oklahoma. LC 77-177335. (Illus.). 350p. 1972. 19.95 (ISBN 0-8061-0990-4); pap. 9.95 (ISBN 0-8061-1033-3). U of Okla Pr.

Hunt, Christopher J. Lead Miners of the Northern Pennines in the 18th & 19th Centuries. LC 77-103011. (Illus.). 1970. lib. bdg. 27.50x (ISBN 0-678-06779-1). Kelley.

Rausch, D. O., et al, eds. Lead-Zinc Update. LC 77-83619. (Illus.). 1977. text ed. 25.00x (ISBN 0-89520-250-6). Soc Mining Eng.

Schoolcraft, Henry R. A View of the Lead Mines of Missouri: Including Some Observations on the Mineralogy, Geology, Geography, Antiquities, Soil, Climate, Population & Productions of Missouri & Arkansas, & Other Sections of the Western Country. LC 72-2867. (Use & Abuse of America's Natural Resources Ser). (Illus.). 302p. 1972. Repr. of 1819 ed. 21.00 (ISBN 0-405-04534-4). Ayer Co Pubs.

LEAD ORGANIC COMPOUNDS

see Organolead Compounds

LEAD-POISONING

Chisolm, J. J. & O'Hara, D. M. Lead Absorption in Children: Management, Clinical & Environmental Aspects. LC 81-16306. (Illus.). 240p. 1982. 32.50 (ISBN 0-8067-0331-8). Urban & S.

Committee on Biological Effects of Atmospheric Pollutants. Lead: Airborne Lead in Perspective. LC 71-186214. (Biological Effects of Atmospheric Pollutants Ser.). (Illus.). 1972. pap. 10.95 (ISBN 0-309-01941-9). Natl Acad Pr.

Jernigan, E., et al. Lead Poisoning in Man & the Environment. 1973. text ed. 34.50x (ISBN 0-8422-7105-8). Irvington.

Lead in the Human Environment. 1980. 13.95 (ISBN 0-309-03021-8). Natl Acad Pr.

Needleman, Herbert L., ed. Low Level Lead Exposure: The Clinical Implications of Current Research. 336p. 1980. text ed. 52.50 (ISBN 0-89004-455-4). Raven.

Rutter, Michael & Jones, Robin R. Lead Versus Health: Sources & Effects of Low Level Lead Exposure. LC 82-16000. 379p. 1983. 42.95 (ISBN 0-471-90028-1, Pub. by Wiley-Interscience). Wiley.

Wedeen, Richard P. Poison in the Pot: The Legacy of Lead. 1984. 24.95 (ISBN 0-317-18487-3). S Ill U Pr.

LEARNED INSTITUTIONS AND SOCIETIES

Brown, Harcourt. Scientific Organizations in Seventeenth Century France, 1620-1680. LC 66-27046. 1967. Repr. of 1934 ed. 8.50x (ISBN 0-8462-0974-8). Russell.

Edelstein, Alex S., et al. Information Societies: Comparing the Japanese & American Experiences. LC 78-71366. 314p. (Orig.). 1979. pap. 15.00x (ISBN 0-295-95667-4, Pub. by Intl Communication Ctr). U of Wash Pr.

Hole, James. Essay on the History & Management of Literary, Scientific & Mechanics' Institutes. 186p. 1970. Repr. of 1853 ed. 27.50x (ISBN 0-7146-2410-1, F Cass Co). Biblio Dist.

Oleson, Alexandra & Brown, Sanborn C., eds. The Pursuit of Knowledge in the Early American Republic: American Scientific & Learned Societies from Colonial Times to the Civil War. LC 75-36941. (Illus.). 398p. 1976. 33.50x (ISBN 0-8018-1679-3). Johns Hopkins.

Reuss, Jeremias D. Repertorium Commentationuma Societatibus Litterariis Editarum Secundum Disciplinarum Ordinem, 16 vols. 1962. 550.00 (ISBN 0-8337-2966-7). B Franklin.

Verrel, Barbara & Opitz, Helmut, eds. World Guide to Scientific Associations & Learned Societies. 947p. 1984. lib. bdg. 112.00 (ISBN 3-598-20522-8). K G Saur.

LEARNING, PSYCHOLOGY OF–MATHEMATICAL MODELS

Iosifescu, Marius & Theodorescu, Radu. Random Processes & Learning. LC 68-54828. (Grundlehren der Mathematischen Wissenschaften: Vol. 150). 1969. 48.00 (ISBN 0-387-04504-X). Springer-Verlag.

Norman, M. Frank. Markov Processes & Learning Models. (Mathematics in Science & Engineering Ser.: Vol. 84). 1972. 60.00 (ISBN 0-12-521450-2). Acad Pr.

Spada, H. & Kempf, W. Structual Models of Thinking & Learning. 452p. 1977. 65.00 (ISBN 3-456-80367-2, Pub. by Holdan Bk Ltd UK). State Mutual Bk.

Tsypkin, Ya Z. Foundations of the Theory of Learning Systems. (Mathematics in Science & Engineering Ser.). 1973. 60.00 (ISBN 0-12-702060-8). Acad Pr.

LEAST SQUARES

see also Correlation (Statistics); Estimation Theory; Graphic Methods; Probabilities

Bernstein, Serge & Poussin, Charles D. Approximation, 2 Vols. in 1. LC 69-16996. (Fr). 15.95 (ISBN 0-8284-0198-5). Chelsea Pub.

Bevington, Philip R. Data Reduction & Error Analysis for the Physical Sciences. LC 69-16942. 1969. pap. text ed. 26.95 (ISBN 0-07-005135-6). McGraw.

Forthofer, Ronald H. & Lehnen, Robert G. Public Program Analysis: A New Approach to Categorical Data. 294p. 1981. 31.95 (ISBN 0-534-97974-2). Van Nos Reinhold.

Giordano, Arthur A. & Hsu, Frank M. Least Square Estimation with Applications to Digital Signal Processing. 416p. 1985. 44.90 (ISBN 0-471-87857-X, Pub. by Wiley-Interscience). Wiley.

Hirvonen, R. A. Adjustment by Least Squares in Geodesy & Photogrammetry. LC 71-158408. 261p. 20.00 (ISBN 0-8044-4397-1). Ungar.

Longley, James W. Least Squares Computations. LC 84-14939. (Lecture Notes in Pure & Applied Mathematics). 288p. 1984. 39.75 (ISBN 0-8247-7232-6). Dekker.

Mikhail, Edward M. Observations & Least Squares. LC 81-43906. 510p. 1982. pap. text ed. 19.50 (ISBN 0-8191-2397-8). U Pr of Amer.

Slater, P., ed. The Measurement of Intrapersonal Space by Grid Techniques: Explorations of Intrapersonal Space, Vol. 1. LC 76-8908. 258p. 1976. 63.95x (ISBN 0-471-01360-9, Pub. by Wiley-Interscience). Wiley.

Sumar Corporation. LSF: The Least Squares Curve Fitter. (Illus.). 64p. 1983. 39.95 (ISBN 0-13-541227-7). P-H.

LEATHER

see also Tanning

Acceptable Quality Levels in Leathers. pap. 3.00 (ISBN 0-686-94803-3, UN76/2B6, UN). Unipub.

Information Sources on Leather & Leather Products Industries. (UNIDO Guides to Information Sources: No. 3). 85p. 1980. pap. 4.00 (ISBN 0-686-70130-5, UNID 226, UN). Unipub.

McDowell, Kendall. The Art of Making Skins. 2nd ed. Kramer, J. Thomas, frwd. by. LC 81-82213. (Illus.). 98p. 1981. pap. 4.95 (ISBN 0-939964-03-1). GRF Ltd.

Thomas, Bill & Stebel, Sid. Shoe Leather Treatment... LC 79-56300. (Illus.). 350p. 1980. 11.95 (ISBN 0-87477-126-9). J P Tarcher.

LEATHER GARMENTS

The Leather Jacket Soldier. 10.00 (ISBN 0-686-74361-X). Westernlore.

LEATHER INDUSTRY AND TRADE

see also Bookbinding; Boots and Shoes; Harness Making and Trade

Acceptable Quality Levels in Leathers. pap. 3.00 (ISBN 0-686-94803-3, UN76/2B6, UN). Unipub.

A Discourse, Tendered to the High Court of Parliament. LC 74-28870. (English Experience Ser.: No. 749). 1975. Repr. of 1629 ed. 3.50 (ISBN 90-221-0749-3). Walter J Johnson.

European Leather Guide & Tanners of the World. 1985. 175.00x (ISBN 0-685-79495-4). State Mutual Bk.

Information Sources on Leather & Leather Products Industries. (UNIDO Guides to Information Sources: No. 3). 85p. 1980. pap. 4.00 (ISBN 0-686-70130-5, UNID 226, UN). Unipub.

The Interrelationship Between Parameters of the Leather Industry. pap. 1.50 (ISBN 0-686-94741-X, UN73/2B/2, UN). Unipub.

Moseley, G. C. Leather Goods Manufacture: Methods & Processes. 340p. 1984. pap. text ed. 25.00 (ISBN 0-87556-389-9). Saifer.

O'Flaherty, Fred, et al, eds. The Chemistry & Technology of Leather, 4 vols. LC 76-50622. (ACS Monographs). 1978. Repr. of 1956 ed. Vol. 1 510p. 34.00 (ISBN 0-88275-474-2); Vol. 2 568p. Repr. of 1958 ed. 38.50 (ISBN 0-88275-886-1); Vol. 3 528p. Repr. of 1962 ed. 35.50 (ISBN 0-88275-887-X); Vol. 4 448p. Repr. of 1965 ed. 31.00 (ISBN 0-88275-888-8); Set. 124.75 (ISBN 0-89874-381-8). Krieger.

Thorstensen, Thomas C. Practical Leather Technology. 3rd ed. LC 83-19557. 340p. 1985. lib. bdg. 26.50 (ISBN 0-89874-692-2). Krieger.

LEAVES

Baker, N. K., et al. Control of Leaf Growth. (Society for Experimental Biology Seminar Ser.: No. 27). 300p. Date not set. price not set (ISBN 0-521-30480-6). Cambridge U Pr.

Camacho. Geometric Theory of Foliations. 1985. text ed. 24.95 (ISBN 0-8176-3139-9). Birkhauser.

Control of Bitter Pit & Breakdown by Calcium in the Apples Cox's Orange Pippin & Jonathan. (Agricultural Research Reports: No. 711). 43p. 1968. pap. 4.00 (ISBN 0-686-71855-0, PDC173, PUDOC). Unipub.

Dale, John E. & Milthorpe, Frederick L., eds. The Growth & Functioning of Leaves. LC 82-4377. (Illus.). 550p. 1983. 89.50 (ISBN 0-521-23761-0). Cambridge U Pr.

Prance, Ghillean T. Leaves: The Formation, Characteristics, & Uses of Hundreds of Leaves Found in All Parts of the World. LC 83-14336. (Illus.). 244p. 1985. 35.00 (ISBN 0-517-55152-7). Crown.

Roth, I. Stratification of Tropical Forests as seen in Leaf Structure. (Task for Vegetation Science). 1984. lib. bdg. 115.00 (ISBN 90-6193-946-1, Pub. by Junk Pubs Netherlands). Kluwer Academic.

Telek, Lehel & Graham, Horace D. Leaf Protein Concentrates. (Illus.). 1983. lib. bdg. 115.00 (ISBN 0-87055-412-3). AVI.

Williams, R. F. The Shoot Apex & Leaf Growth. (Illus.). 280p. 1975. 44.50 (ISBN 0-521-20453-4). Cambridge U Pr.

LEAVES–ANATOMY

see also Stomata

Maksymowych, R. Analysis of Leaf Development. LC 72-83585. (Developmental & Cell Biology Monographs: No. 1). (Illus.). 112p. 1973. 37.50 (ISBN 0-521-20017-2). Cambridge U Pr.

LEBESGUE MEASURE

see Measure Theory

LECIDEA

Hertel, Hannes. Revision Einiger Calciphiler Formenkreise der Flechtengattung Lecidea. (Illus.). 1967. pap. 21.00 (ISBN 3-7682-5424-0). Lubrecht & Cramer.

LECYTHI

Prance, Ghillean T. & Mori, Scott A. Lecythidaceae-Part One the Actinomonophic-Flowered New World Lecythidaceae: Asteranthos, Gustavia, Grias, Allantoma & Cariniana. LC 79-4659. (Flora Neotropica Ser.: Vol. 21). 1979. pap. 28.00x (ISBN 0-89327-193-4). NY Botanical.

LEECHES

Bennike, S. Boisen. Contributions to the Ecology & Biology of the Danish Fresh-Water Leeches. Repr. of 1943 ed. 21.00 (ISBN 0-384-03905-7). Johnson Repr.

Elliott, J. M. & Mann, K. H. A Key to the British Freshwater Leeches. 1979. 25.00x (ISBN 0-900386-38-X, Pub. by Freshwater Bio). State Mutual Bk.

Sawyer, Roy T. Leech Biology & Behavior, 3 vols. (Illus.). 500p. 1984. Set. 89.00x; Vol. 1; Anatomy, Physiology & Behavior. 45.00 (ISBN 0-19-857377-4); Vol. 2; Feeding Biology, Ecology & Systematics. 45.00 (ISBN 0-19-857622-6); Vol. 3; Bibliography. 19.95 (ISBN 0-19-857623-4). Oxford U Pr.

LEEUWENHOEK, ANTHONY VAN, 1632-1723

Leeuwenhoek, Anthony Van. Anthony Van Leeuwenhoek & His Little Animals. pap. 7.50 (ISBN 0-486-60594-9). Dover.

LEGAL RESEARCH–DATA PROCESSING

A Boon to Legal Research-Computers. 5p. pap. 2.00 (ISBN 0-317-30763-0). Amer Bar Assn.

Sprowl, James A. Computer-Assisted Legal Research: An Analysis of Full-Text Document Retrieval Systems, Particularly the LEXIS System. 52p. (Reprinted from 1976 ABF Res. J., No. 1). 1976. 2.50 (ISBN 0-317-33323-2). Am Bar Foun.

--A Manual for Computer-Assisted Legal Research. LC 76-45588. pap. 31.50 (ISBN 0-317-26201-7, 2052130). Bks Demand UMI.

LEGUMES

Here are entered works on those plants belonging to the family Leguminosae, the pods or seeds of which are edible for man or domestic animals, e.g. peas, beans, lentils, etc., treated collectively.

see also names of luguminous plants

Allen, O. N. & Allen, Ethel K. The Leguminosae: A Source Book of Characteristics, Uses & Nodulation. LC 80-5104. (Illus.). 878p. 1981. 65.00x (ISBN 0-299-08400-0). U of Wis Pr.

Alpha Pyramis Research Division Staff. Carob: A Bibliography. 1984. pap. 3.50 (Pub. by Alpha Pyramis). Prosperity & Profits.

Andrew, C. S. & Kamprath, E. J. Mineral Nutrition of Legumes in Tropical & Subtropical Soils. 415p. 1978. 36.00 (ISBN 0-643-00311-8, C014, CSIRO). Unipub.

Andrew, C. S. & Kamprath, E. J., eds. Mineral Nutrition of Legumes in Tropical & Subtropical Soils. 1979. 28.00x (ISBN 0-643-00311-8, Pub. by CSIRO). Intl Spec Bk.

Andrews, C. S. & Kamprath, E. J. Mineral Nutrition of Legumes in Tropical & Subtropical Soils. 415p. 1982. 60.00x (Pub. by CSIRO Australia). State Mutual Bk.

Arora, S. K. Chemistry & Biochemistry of Legumes. 400p. 1983. text ed. 49.50 (ISBN 0-7131-2854-2). E Arnold.

Aykroyd, W. R. & Doughty, Joyce. Legumes in Human Nutrition. 2nd ed. (Food & Nutrition Papers: No. 20). (Eng., Fr. & Span.). 160p. 1982. pap. 11.75 (ISBN 92-5-101181-8, F2329, FAO). Unipub.

Aykroyo, W. R. & Doughty, J. Legumes in Human Nutrition. (Nutritional Studies: No. 19). 138p. (5th Printing 1977). 1964. pap. 7.25 (ISBN 92-5-100440-4, F257, FAO). Unipub.

Bergersen, F. J. Root Nodules of Legumes: Structure & Functions. LC 83-185046. (Botanical Research Studies Press). 164p. 1982. 37.95x (ISBN 0-471-10456-6, Pub. by Res Stud Pr). Wiley.

Bird, Julio & Maramorosch, Karl, eds. Tropical Diseases of Legumes: Papers Presented at the Rio Piedras Agricultural Experiment Station of the University of Puerto Rico, Mayaguez Campus, June, 1974. 1975. 39.50 (ISBN 0-12-099950-1). Acad Pr.

Bland, Brian F. Crop Production: Cereals & Legumes. 1971. 73.50 (ISBN 0-12-104050-X). Acad Pr.

Bond, D. A., ed. Vicia Faba: Feeding Value, Processing & Viruses. (World Crops: Production, Utilization, & Description: Vol. 3). x, 424p. 1980. lib. bdg. 50.00 (ISBN 9-0247-2362-0, Pub. by Martinus Nijhoff Netherlands). Kluwer Academic.

Candolle, A. De. Memoires sur la Famille des Legumineuses. (Illus.). 1966. Repr. of 1825 ed. 78.40 (ISBN 3-7682-0299-2). Lubrecht & Cramer.

Competition Between Legumes & Grasses. (Agricultural Research Reports: No. 687). 1966. pap. 4.00 (PDC166, PUDOC). Unipub.

Cummins, George B. Rust Fungi on Legumes & Composites in North America. LC 78-60541. 426p. 1978. pap. 14.95x (ISBN 0-8165-0653-1). U of Ariz Pr.

Dovlo, F. E. & Williams, C. E. Cowpeas: Home Preparation & Its Use in West Africa. 96p. 1976. pap. 6.00 (ISBN 0-88936-071-5, IDRC55, IDRC). Unipub.

Duke, James A. Handbook of Legumes of World Economic Importance. LC 80-16421. (Illus.). 356p. 1981. 55.00x (ISBN 0-306-40406-0, Plenum Pr). Plenum Pub.

Elementary Science Study. Life of Beans & Peas. 2nd ed. 1975. 9.16 (ISBN 0-07-018581-6). McGraw.

Grear, John W. A Revision of the New World Species of Rhynchosia (Leguminosae-Faboideae) LC 78-17663. (Memoirs Ser.: Vol. 31, No. 1). 1978. pap. 15.00x (ISBN 0-89327-208-6). NY Botanical.

Harbourne, J. B., et al, eds. Chemotaxonomy of Leguminosae. 1971. 96.00 (ISBN 0-12-324652-0). Acad Pr.

Hawtin, G. C. & Chancellor, G. J., eds. Food Legume Improvement & Development: Proceedings of a Workshop Held at the University of Aleppo, Syria, 2-7 May 1978. 216p. 1979. pap. 15.00 (ISBN 0-88936-202-5, IDRC126, IDRC). Unipub.

Hebblethwaite, Paul D. The Faba Bean: A Basis for Improvement. (Illus.). 512p. 1983. text ed. 140.00 (ISBN 0-408-10695-6). Butterworth.

Heywood, V. H., ed. Botanical Systematics, Vol. 1. 1976. 70.50 (ISBN 0-12-346901-5). Acad Pr.

Hunter, Peter J. Peter Hunter's Guide to Grasses, Clovers, & Weeds. (Illus.). 80p. pap. 7.50 (ISBN 0-938670-02-6). By Hand & Foot.

Isely, Duane. Leguminosae of the United States Pt. III: Subfamily Papilionoideae-Tribes Sophoreae, Podalyreae, Loteae. (Memoirs of the New York Botanical Garden Ser.: Vol. 25, No. 3). (Illus.). 1981. pap. 35.00x (ISBN 0-89327-232-9). NY Botanical.

--Leguminosae of the United States: Subfamily Caesalpinioideae. LC 66-6394. (Memoirs of the New York Botanical Garden: Vol. 25, No. 2). (Illus.). 1975. pap. 12.00x (ISBN 0-89327-054-7). NY Botanical.

--Leguminosae of the United States: Subfamily Mimosoideae. LC 66-6394. (Memoirs of the New York Botanical Garden: Vol. 25, No. 1). (Illus.). 1975. pap. 10.00x (ISBN 0-89327-053-9). NY Botanical.

Iswaran, V. A Manual for the Proper Use of Inoculants & Pelleting for Legumes. (Illus.). 195p. 1983. 15.00 (ISBN 0-88065-239-X, Pub. by Messers Today & Tomorrow Printers & Publishers India). Scholarly Pubns.

Jones, D. G. & Davies, D. R., eds. Temperate Legumes: Physiology, Genetics & Nodulation. 448p. 1983. text ed. 26.95 (ISBN 0-273-08601-4). Pitman Pub MA.

Labeyrie, V., ed. The Ecology of Bruchids Attacking Legumes: Proceedings of the International Symposium Held at Tours, 1980. (Series Entomologica: No. 19). 1981. lib. bdg. 63.00 (ISBN 90-6193-883-X, Pub. by Junk Pubs Netherlands). Kluwer Academic.

Legume Inoculants & Their Use. (Illus.). 63p. 1985. pap. 12.50 (ISBN 92-5-101441-8, F2701 5071, FAO). Unipub.

Polhill, R. M. & Raven, P. H., eds. Advances in Legume Systematics, 2 Pts. (Illus.). 1981. pap. 70.00x (ISBN 0-85521-224-1, Pub. by Brit Mus Nat Hist England). Sabbot-Natural Hist Bks.

Report of the First FAO-DANIDA Training Course on Improvement & Production of Food Legumes for Africa & the Near East: University of Teheran, May 3 - August 30, 1975. (Danish Funds-in-Trust Ser.). 24p. 1976. pap. 7.50 (ISBN 0-685-66333-7, F1095, FAO). Unipub.

Salunkhe, D. K., et al, eds. Postharvest Biotechnology of Cereals. 224p. 1985. 67.00 (ISBN 0-8493-6288-1). CRC Pr.

Shepard, Merle & Lawn, R. J. Insects on Grain Legumes in Northern Australia: A Survey of Potential Pests & Their Enemies. LC 82-13463. (Illus.). 89p. 1983. pap. 8.50 (ISBN 0-7022-1802-2). U of Queensland Pr.

Spedding, C. R. & Diekmahns, E. C., eds. Grasses & Legumes in British Agriculture. 511p. 1972. 89.00x (ISBN 0-85198-016-3, Pub. by CAB Bks England). State Mutual Bk.

Summerfield, R. J. & Bunting, A. H., eds. Advances in Legume Science, Vol. 1. (Illus.). xvi, 667p. 1980. pap. 35.00x (ISBN 0-85521-223-3, Pub by Brit Mus Nat Hist England). Sabbot-Natural Hist Bks.

Summerfield, R. J. & Roberts, E. H., eds. Grain Legume Crops. 600p. 1985. text ed. 85.00x (ISBN 0-00-383037-3, Pub. by Collins England). Sheridan.

Vincent, J. M. Nitrogen Fixation in Legumes. 1982. 35.00 (ISBN 0-12-721980-3). Acad Pr.

Whistler, Roy L. & Hymowitz, Theodore. Guar: Agronomy, Production, Industrial Use, & Nutrition. LC 78-58137. (Illus.). 136p. 1979. 9.95 (ISBN 0-911198-51-2). Purdue U Pr.

Whyte, R. O., et al. Legumes in Agriculture. (Agricultural Planning Studies: No. 21). (Orig.). 1973. pap. 13.25 (ISBN 0-685-02453-9, F255, FAO). Unipub.

Wilson, John R. Plant Relations in Pastures. 425p. 1978. pap. 45.00 (ISBN 0-643-00264-2, C005, CSIRO). Unipub.

LEIBNIZ, GOTTFRIED WILHELM, FREIHERR VON, 1646-1716

Axelos, Christos. Die Ontologischen Grundlagen der Freiheitstheorie von Leibniz. LC 72-81544. 385p. 1973. 28.40x (ISBN 3-11-002221-4). De Gruyter.

Barber, W. H. Leibniz in France-From Arnauld to Voltaire: A Study in French Reactions to Leibnizianism, 1670-1760. Sleigh, R. C., Jr., ed. LC 84-48416. (The Philosophy of Leibniz Ser.). 276p. 1985. lib. bdg. 40.00 (ISBN 0-8240-6529-8). Garland Pub.

Broad, C. D. & Lewy, C. Leibniz: An Introduction. LC 74-31784. 192p. 1975. 32.50 (ISBN 0-521-20691-X); pap. 10.95 (ISBN 0-521-09925-0). Cambridge U Pr.

Grua, Gaston. Jurisprudence Universelle et Theodicee Selon Leibniz. Sleigh, R. C., Jr., ed. LC 84-48417. (The Philosophy of Leibniz Ser.). 415p. 1985. lib. bdg. 65.00 (ISBN 0-8240-6530-1). Garland Pub.

--La Justice Humaine Selon Leibniz. Sleigh, R. C., Jr., ed. LC 84-48418. (The Philosophy of Leibniz Ser.). 548p. 1985. lib. bdg. 80.00 (ISBN 0-8240-6531-X). Garland Pub.

Jalabert, Jacques. Le Dieu de Leibniz. Sleigh, R. C., Jr., ed. LC 84-48419. (The Philosophy of Leibniz Ser.). 224p. 1985. lib. bdg. 35.00 (ISBN 0-8240-6532-8). Garland Pub.

--La Theorie Leibnizienne de la Sustance. Sleigh, R. C., Jr., ed. LC 84-48420. (The Philosophy of Lebniz Ser.). 282p. 1985. lib. bdg. 45.00 (ISBN 0-8240-6533-6). Garland Pub.

Kauppi, Raili. Uber die Leibnizsche Logik Mit Besonderer Berucksictigung des Problems der Intension und der Extension. Sleigh, R. C., Jr., ed. LC 84-48421. (The Philosophy of Leibniz Ser.). 279p. 1985. lib. bdg. 35.00 (ISBN 0-317-14539-8). Garland Pub.

Leibniz, G. W. The Leibniz-Arnauld Correspondence: Edited & Translated by H. T. Mason, with an Introduction by G. H. R. Parkinson. Sleigh, R. C., Jr., ed. LC 84-49422. (The Philosophy of Leibniz Ser.). 180p. 1985. lib. bdg. 30.00 (ISBN 0-8240-6535-2). Garland Pub.

--Lettres de Leibniz a Arnauld D'Apres un Manuscrit Inedit. Sleigh, R. C., Jr., ed. LC 84-48423. (The Philosophy of Leibniz Ser.). 111p. 1985. lib. bdg. 30.00 (ISBN 0-8240-6536-0). Garland Pub.

--The Monadology & Other Philosophical Writings. Sleigh, R. C., ed. LC 84-48424. (The Philosophy of Leibniz Ser.). 437p. 1985. lib. bdg. 55.00 (ISBN 0-8240-6537-9). Garland Pub.

--Textes Inedits d'apres les Manuscrits de la Biblioteque Provinciale de Hanovre, 2 vols. Sleigh, R. C., Jr., ed. LC 84-48425. (The Philosophy of Leibniz Ser.). 936p. 1985. Set. lib. bdg. 150.00 (ISBN 0-8240-6538-7). Garland Pub.

Leibniz, Gottfried W. The Preface to Leibniz' Novissima Sinice. Lach, Donald F., tr. LC 57-14876. pap. 29.00 (ISBN 0-317-08437-2, 2001168). Bks Demand UMI.

Martin, Gottfried. Leibniz: Logic & Metaphysics. Sleigh, R. C., Jr., ed. LC 84-48426. (The Philosophy of Leibniz Ser.). 195p. 1985. lib. bdg. 30.00 (ISBN 0-8240-6539-5). Garland Pub.

Merz, John T. Leibniz. 1978. Repr. of 1901 ed. lib. bdg. 35.00 (ISBN 0-8495-3823-8). Arden Lib.

Meyer, R. W. Leibniz & the Seventeenth Century Revolution. Sleigh, R. C., Jr., ed. LC 84-48427. (The Philosophy of Leibniz Ser.). 277p. 1985. lib. bdg. 35.00 (ISBN 0-8240-6540-9). Garland Pub.

Ortega y Gasset, Jose. Idea of Principle in Leibnitz & the Evolution of Deductive Theory. LC 66-18068. 1971. 10.00x (ISBN 0-393-01086-4). Norton.

Parkinson, G. H. Logic & Reality in Leibniz's Metaphysics. Sleigh, R. C., Jr., ed. LC 84-48428. (The Philosophy of Leibniz Ser.). 196p. 1985. lib. bdg. 30.00 (ISBN 0-8240-6541-7). Garland Pub.

Rescher, Nicholas. Leibniz: An Introduction to His Philosophy. (American Philosophical Quarterly Library of Philosophy). (Illus.). 167p. 1979. 20.00x (ISBN 0-8476-6110-5). Rowman.

Woolhouse, R. S., ed. Leibniz: Metaphysics & Philosophy of Science. (Oxford Readings in Philosophy Ser.). 1981. pap. 7.95x (ISBN 0-19-875050-1). Oxford U Pr.

Yost, R. M., Jr. Leibniz & Philosophical Analysis. Sleigh, R. C., Jr., ed. LC 84-48429. (The Philosophy of Leibniz Ser.). 207p. 1985. lib. bdg. 30.00 (ISBN 0-8240-6542-5). Garland Pub.

LEICA CAMERAS

see Cameras–Types–Leica

LEJEUNEACEAE

Schuster, R. M. An Annotated Synopsis of the Genera & Subgenera of Lejeuneacea, 1: Introduction, Annotated Keys to Subfamilies & Genera. 1963. 31.00 (ISBN 3-7682-5409-7). Lubrecht & Cramer.

LELAND, HENRY M., b. 1843

Leland, Ottilie & Millbrook, Minie D. Master of Precision: Henry M. Leland. LC 73-15315. (Illus.). 296p. 1975. Repr. of 1966 ed. lib. bdg. 24.75x (ISBN 0-8371-7192-X, LEMP). Greenwood.

LEMMINGS

Elton, Charles. Voles, Mice & Lemmings. 1971. Repr. of 1942 ed. 33.10 (ISBN 3-7682-0275-5). Lubrecht & Cramer.

Jones, J. Knox, Jr. A New Bog Lemming (Genus Synaptomys) from Nebraska. (Museum Ser.: Vol. 9, No. 13). 4p. 1958. pap. 1.25 (ISBN 0-317-04834-1). U of KS Mus Nat Hist.

Krebs, Charles J. The Lemming Cycle at Baker Lake: Northwest Territories During 1959-1962. Repr. of 1964 ed. 13.00 (ISBN 0-384-30423-0). Johnson Repr.

LEMON

Sinclair, Walton B. The Biochemistry & Physiology of the Lemon & Other Citrus Fruits. LC 83-72137. (Illus.). 1000p. (Orig.). 1983. 55.00x (ISBN 0-931876-64-8, 3306). Ag & Nat Res.

Tobias, Doris & Merris, Mary. The Golden Lemon: A Collection of Special Recipes. LC 77-88908. viii, 210p. 1981. pap. 6.95 (ISBN 0-689-70609-X, 268). Atheneum.

LEMURS

see also Monkeys

Lamberton, Charles. Selected Papers on the Subfossil Lemurs of Madagascar: 1934-1956. LC 78-72726. 67.50 (ISBN 0-404-18297-6). AMS Pr.

Tattersall, Ian. The Primates of Madagascar. LC 81-15477. 448p. 1982. 50.00x (ISBN 0-231-04704-5). Columbia U Pr.

Tattersall, Ian T. & Sussman, Robert W., eds. Lemur Biology. LC 74-28112. (Illus.). 378p. 1975. 45.00x (ISBN 0-306-30817-7, Plenum Pr). Plenum Pub.

LENS, CRYSTALLINE

see Crystalline Lens

LENSES

see also Contact Lenses

Clayman, Henry M., et al. Intraocular Lens Implantation: Techniques & Complications. LC 82-8267. (Illus.). 300p. 1983. text ed. 64.95 (ISBN 0-8016-1080-X). Mosby.

Emsley, H. H. Opthalmic Lenses. (Illus.). 340p. 1984. pap. 25.00x (ISBN 0-87556-375-9). Saifer.

Fechner, Paul & Alpar, John J. Intraocular Lenses. (Illus.). 304p. 1985. text ed. 48.00 (ISBN 0-86577-123-5). Thieme-Stratton.

Harting, E. & Read, F. H. Electrostatic Lenses. 322p. 1976. 76.75 (ISBN 0-444-41319-7). Elsevier.

Hawkes, P. W. Properties of Magnetic Electron Lenses. (Topics in Current Physics Ser.: Vol. 18). (Illus.). 470p. 1982. 48.00 (ISBN 0-387-10296-5). Springer-Verlag.

Horne, D. F. Lens Mechanism Technology. 1975. 70.00 (ISBN 0-9960026-2-6, Pub. by A Hilger England). Heyden.

Jalie, M. The Principles of Ophthalmic Lenses. 1981. 79.00x (ISBN 0-686-45410-3, Pub. by Assn Disp Opt England). State Mutual Bk.

Janney, G. D. & Tunnacliffe, A. H. Worked Problems in Ophthalmic Lenses. 1981. 40.00x (ISBN 0-686-45414-6, Pub. by Assn Disp Opt England). State Mutual Bk.

Maisel. The Ocular Lens. 504p. 1985. 85.00 (ISBN 0-8247-7297-0). Dekker.

Ogle, Kenneth N. Optics: An Introduction for Ophthalmologists. 2nd ed. (Illus.). 288p. 1979. photocopy 30.50 (ISBN 0-398-01417-5). C C Thomas.

Olmos, Edwin, et al. Intraocular Lenses. LC 80-21860. 270p. 1981. 45.95 (ISBN 0-03-058033-1). Praeger.

Schachar, Ronald A. Intraocular Lenses. (Illus.). 144p. 1979. 18.50x (ISBN 0-398-03800-7). C C Thomas.

LENSES, PHOTOGRAPHIC

Bancroft, Keith. Amphoto Guide to Lenses. (Illus.). 169p. 1981. (Amphoto); pap. 7.95 (ISBN 0-8174-3527-1). Watson-Guptill.

Brooks, David. Lenses & Lens Accessories. (Illus.). 128p. 1982. pap. 14.95 (ISBN 0-930764-34-X). Curtin & London.

Eastman Kodak Company. Filters & Lens Attachments for Black-&-White & Color Pictures. 1975. pap. 2.95 (ISBN 0-87985-254-2, AB-1). Eastman Kodak.

Eastman Kodak Company, ed. KW-Eighteen, Lenses for 35mm Cameras. (Kodak Workshop Ser.). (Illus.). 96p. (Orig.). Date not set. pap. 8.95 (ISBN 0-87985-303-4). Eastman Kodak.

Ericksenn, Lief. The Long Lens Book: All about Zoom Tele & Supertele Lenses & Pro Techniques of Using Them. (Illus.). 144p. 1983. 24.95 (ISBN 0-8174-4241-3, Amphoto); pap. 16.95 (ISBN 0-8174-4240-5). Watson-Guptill.

Gaunt, Leonard. Zoom & Special Lenses. LC 80-41245. (Camera Books). (Illus.). 128p. 1981. pap. 9.95 (ISBN 0-240-51069-0). Focal Pr.

Hawken, William. Zoom Lens Photography. (Illus., Orig.). 1981. pap. 10.95 (ISBN 0-930764-29-3). Curtin & London.

How to Use Interchangeable Lenses. 1981. 2.50 (ISBN 0-88284-141-6). Alfred Pub.

Lahue, Kalton C. Photo Filters & Lens Attachments. (Petersen's Photographic Library: Vol. 5). (Illus.). 160p. 1981. pap. 8.95 (ISBN 0-8227-4044-3). Petersen Pub.

--Wide Angle Photography. LC 77-74100. (Photography How-to Ser.). (Illus.). 1977. pap. 3.95 (ISBN 0-8227-4014-1). Petersen Pub.

Photographic Lenses. (Petersen's Photographic Library: Vol. 8). (Illus.). 160p. (Orig.). 1982. pap. text ed. 9.95 (ISBN 0-8227-4054-0). Petersen Pub.

Ray, Sidney F. The Lens & All Its Jobs. (Media Manuals Ser.). 1979. pap. 8.95 (ISBN 0-8038-4299-6). Hastings.

Reynolds, Clyde. Lenses. (Photographer's Library). (Illus.). 144p. (Orig.). 1984. pap. 15.95 (ISBN 0-240-51120-4). Focal Pr.

Taylor, Herb, ed. What Your Lenses Can Do. LC 81-71225. (Illus.). 120p. 1982. pap. 7.95 (ISBN 0-385-18146-9). Doubleday.

Taylor, Herb, et al. What Your Lenses Can Do. LC 81-71225. (Modern Photo Guides). (Illus.). 120p. (Orig.). 1982. pap. 7.95 (ISBN 0-385-18146-9). Avalon Comm.

Werner, Donald L., ed. Light & Lens: Methods of Photography. LC 73-84659. (Illus.). 80p. 1973. pap. 8.00 (ISBN 0-87100-043-1, Pub. by Hudson River Mus). Pub Ctr Cult Res.

LENSLESS PHOTOGRAPHY

see Holography

LEONARDO DA VINCI, 1452-1519

Amey, Peter, et al. Leonardo Da Vinci. Yapp, Malcolm, et al, eds. (World History Ser.). (Illus.). 1980. lib. bdg. 6.95 (ISBN 0-89908-041-3); pap. text ed. 2.45 (ISBN 0-89908-016-2). Greenhaven.

Bax, Clifford. Leonardo Da Vinci. 160p. 1980. Repr. of 1932 ed. lib. bdg. 27.50 (ISBN 0-8495-0464-3). Arden Lib.

Clark, Kenneth. Leonardo Da Vinci. 256p. 1976. pap. 4.95 (ISBN 0-14-020430-X, Pelican). Penguin.

Davinci, Ladislao, tr. from Italian. The Madrid Codices of Leonardo Da Vinci. LC 73-23091. 1974. 400.00 (ISBN 0-07-037194-6). McGraw.

Da Vinci, Leonardo. Drawings of Da Vinci. Belt, Elmer, ed. (Master Draughtsman Ser). (Illus., Orig.). treasure trove bdg. 9.95x (ISBN 0-87505-004-2); pap. 4.95 (ISBN 0-87505-157-X). Borden.

--Leonardo da Vinci: Codex Trivulzianus. until October 1, 1984 thereafter 345.00 295.00 (ISBN 0-384-32296-4). Johnson Repr.

--Leonardo da Vinci Drawings. (Illus.). 1983. pap. 2.75 (ISBN 0-486-23951-9). Dover.

--The Notebooks of Leonardo Da Vinci. Richter, Irma A., ed. (World's Classics Ser.). (Illus.). 1982. pap. 4.95 (ISBN 0-19-281538-5). Oxford U Pr.

Eissler, Kurt R. Leonardo Da Vinci: Psychoanalytic Notes on the Enigma. LC 61-11610. (Illus.). 379p. 1961. text ed. 35.00 (ISBN 0-8236-3000-5). Intl Univs Pr.

Freud, Sigmund. Leonardo Da Vinci: A Study in Psychosexuality. 1966. pap. 2.95 (ISBN 0-394-70132-1, V132, Vin). Random.

Hart, Ivor B. The Mechanical Investigations of Leonardo da Vinci. LC 82-2967. (Illus.). xiv, 240p. 1982. Repr. of 1963 ed. lib. bdg. 42.50x (ISBN 0-313-23489-2, HAMEC). Greenwood.

Keele, Kenneth & Roberts, Jane. Leonardo Da Vinci: Anatomical Drawings from the Royal Library, Windsor Castle. (Illus.). 168p. 1983. 35.00 (ISBN 0-87099-362-3); pap. 19.95. Metro Mus Art.

Keele, Kenneth D. Leonardo da Vinci's Elements of the Science of Man: Monograph. 1983. 90.00 (ISBN 0-12-403980-4). Acad Pr.

Kemp, Martin. Leonardo da Vinci: The Marvelous Works of Nature & Man. LC 81-279. (Illus.). 384p. 1981. 30.00 (ISBN 0-674-52460-8). Harvard U Pr.

--Leonardo da Vinci: The Marvelous Works of Nature & Man. 368p. 1981. 70.00x (ISBN 0-460-04354-4, Pub. by Dent Australia). State Mutual Bk.

MacCurdy, Edward, tr. The Notebooks of Leonardo Da Vinci, 2 vols. 1176p. 1978. 39.95 (ISBN 0-224-01279-7, Pub. by Jonathan Cape). Merrimack Pub Cir.

Panofsky, Erwin. The Codex Huygens & Leonardo Da Vinci's Art Theory: The Pierpoint Morgan Library Codex M. A. 1139. (Warburg Institute Studies: Vol. 13). Repr. of 1940 ed. 32.00 (ISBN 0-317-15640-3). Kraus Repr.

Pedretti, Carlo. Catalogue of the Newly Restored Sheets of the Leonardo Da Vinci Codex Atlanticus. 1978. leather bdg. 100.00 (ISBN 0-384-32305-7); cloth bdg. 60.00 (ISBN 0-384-32304-9). Johnson Repr.

--Leonardo, Architect. LC 85-45954. (Illus.). 363p. 1985. 75.00 (ISBN 0-8478-0646-4). Rizzoli Intl.

--Leonardo da Vinci: Nature Studies from the Royal Library at Windsor Castle. LC 81-84558. (Illus.). 96p. (Orig.). 1981. pap. 17.50 (ISBN 0-295-96064-7). U of Wash Pr.

--Leonardo Da Vinci: The Royal Palace at Romorantin. LC 76-102673. 1972. 40.00x (ISBN 0-674-52455-1, Belknap Pr). Harvard U Pr.

Ponting, Kenneth G. & Litt, M. Leonardo da Vinci: Drawings of Textile Machines. (Illus.). 1979. text ed. 26.50x (ISBN 0-239-00193-1). Humanities.

Popham, A. E. The Drawings of Leonardo da Vinci. (Illus.). 320p. 1981. (Pub. by Jonathan Cape); pap. 8.95 (ISBN 0-224-60462-7, Pub. by Jonathan Cape). Merrimack Pub Cir.

Strong, Donald S. Leonardo on the Eye: An English Translation & Critical Commentary of MS.D in the Bibliotheque Nationale, Paris, with Studies on Leonardo's Methodology & Theories on Optics. LC 78-74382. (Fine Arts Dissertations, Fourth Ser.). (Illus.). 1980. lib. bdg. 53.00 (ISBN 0-8240-3968-8). Garland Pub.

Taylor, Pamela, ed. Notebooks of Leonardo Da Vinci. pap. 5.95 (ISBN 0-452-25283-0, Z5283, Plume). NAL.

Taylor, Rachel A. Leonardo the Florentine. 1973. Repr. of 1928 ed. 40.00 (ISBN 0-8274-1615-6). R West.

Zubov, V. P. Leonardo Da Vinci. Kraus, David, tr. LC 67-27096. (Illus.). Repr. of 1968 ed. 88.80 (ISBN 0-8357-9164-5, 2017264). Bks Demand UMI.

LEONARDO DA VINCI, 1452-1519–BIBLIOGRAPHY

Verga, Ettore. Bibliografia Vinciana 1493-1930, 2 Vols. 1967. Repr. of 1931 ed. 50.50 (ISBN 0-8337-3634-5). B Franklin.

LEOPARDS

Adamson, Joy. Queen of Shaba: The Story of an African Leopard. LC 80-7931. (A Helen & Kurt Wolff Bk.). (Illus.). 256p. 1980. 14.95 (ISBN 0-15-175651-1). HarBraceJ.

Myers, Norman. The Leopard (Panthera Pardus) in Africa. (Illus.). 79p. 1976. pap. 12.00 (ISBN 2-88032-017-8, IUCN24, IUCN). Unipub.

LEPADIDAE

Darwin, Charles. The Fossil Lepadidae. 1851. pap. 14.00 (ISBN 0-384-10860-1). Johnson Repr.

LEPIDOPTERA

Albrecht, Carl W. & Watkins, Reed A. Cross-Reference to Names of Ohio Skippers & Butterflies: Insecta, Lepidoptera, Hesperoidea & Papilionoidea. 1983. 4.00 (ISBN 0-86727-095-0). Ohio Bio Survey.

Application of Induced Sterility for Control of Lepidopterous Populations. (Panel Proceedings Ser.). (Illus.). 169p. (Orig.). 1971. pap. 13.00 (ISBN 92-0-111271-8, ISP281, IAEA). Unipub.

Arnold, Richard A. Ecological Studies of Six Endangered Butterflies, (Lepidoptera, Lycaenidae) Island Biogeography, Patch Dynamics & the Design of Habitat Preserves. (University of California Publications in Entomology: Vol. 99). 1983. pap. 15.00x (ISBN 0-520-09671-1). U of Cal Pr.

Bell, R. D. & Scott, F. B. Moths Lepidoptera: Sphingidae, Vol. 5. (Fauna of British India Ser.). (Illus.). xviii, 537p. 1976. Repr. 40.00 (ISBN 0-88065-056-7, Pub. by Messers Today & Tomorrows Printers & Publishers India). Scholarly Pubns.

Carter, David J. Pest Lepidopters of Europe. (Entomologica Ser.). 1984. lib. bdg. 89.50 (ISBN 90-6193-504-0, Pub. by Junk Pubs Netherlands). Kluwer Academic.

Dickson, R. A Lepidopterist's Handbook. 136p. 1976. 40.00x (ISBN 0-686-75579-0, Pub. by Amateur Entomol Soc). State Mutual Bk.

Fletcher, D. S. A Revision of the Old World Genus Zamarada: (Lepidoptera: Geometridae) (Bulletin of the British Museum Natural History Ser.: Supplement No. 2). (Illus.). 1974. pap. text ed. 85.00x (ISBN 0-8277-4358-0, Pub. by Brit Mus Nat Hist). Sabbot-Natural Hist Bks.

Fox, R. M. & Real, H. G. A Monograph of the Ithomiidae: Napeogenini, Pt. 4. (Memoirs Ser: No. 15). (Illus.). 368p. 1971. 30.00x (ISBN 0-686-01270-4). Am Entom Inst.

Fracker, Stanley B. The Classification of Lepidopterous Larvae. (Illus.). Repr. of 1915 ed. 15.00 (ISBN 0-384-16670-9). Johnson Repr.

Hampson, G. F. Moths Lepidoptera, Vol. 1. vii, 527p. 25.00 (ISBN 0-88065-099-0, Pub. by Messers Today & Tomorrows Printers & Publishers India). Scholarly Pubns.

--Moths Lepidoptera, Vol. 2. iv, 609p. 30.00 (ISBN 0-88065-100-8, Pub. by Messers Today & Tomorrows Printers & Publishers India). Scholarly Pubns.

--Moths Lepidoptera: Subfam. Focillinae, Deltoidinae, Vol. 3. xxxiii, 546p. 1976. 25.00 (ISBN 0-88065-101-6, Pub. by Messers Today & Tomorrows Printers & Publishers India). Scholarly Pubns.

Heppner, J. B. Catalog of the Lepidoptera of the World: Families 2, 3, 5, 6, 7, 8, 9, 10, 11, 13, 18, 44, 45, 52, 60 & 62. (Lepidopterorum Catalogus (New Series)). 56p. 1985. pap. price not set (ISBN 0-916846-23-7). Flora & Fauna.

Heppner, J. B., ed. Catalog of the Lepidoptera of the World, 30 vols. (Lepidopterorum Catalogus (New Series)). 6000p. Date not set. Set. pap. price not set (ISBN 0-916846-22-9). Flora & Fauna.

Heppner, John B., ed. Atlas of Neotropical Lepidotera. (AONL Ser.). 1984. lib. bdg. 39.00 (ISBN 90-6193-038-3, Pub. by Junk Pubs Netherlands). Kluwer-Academic.

Holloway, J. D. The Lepidoptera of Norfolk Island. (Series Entomologica: No. 13). (Illus.). 1977. lib. bdg. 45.00 (ISBN 90-6193-123-1, Pub. by Junk Pubs Netherlands). Kluwer Academic.

Lepidoptera: Butterflies, Vol. 2. 2nd ed. (Fauna of British India). (Illus.). 510p. 1978. Repr. of 1947 ed. 25.00 (ISBN 0-88065-215-2, Pub. by Messers Today & Tomorrows Printers & Publishers India). Scholarly Pubns.

Moths Lepidoptera, Vol. 4. (Fauna of British India). xxviii, 594p. 1976. 30.00 (ISBN 0-88065-102-4, Pub. by Messers Today & Tomorrows Printers & Publishers India). Scholarly Pubns.

Odiyo, P. O. Seasonal Distribution & Migrations of Agrotis Ipsilon (Hufnagel) Leipidoptera, Noctuidae. 1975. 35.00x (ISBN 0-85135-070-4, Pub. by Centre Overseas Research). State Mutual Bk.

Schmid, Michael & Endicott, Bradford M. Mariposas De Venezuela. (Span & Eng., Illus.). xi, 67p. (Orig.). 1968. 9.95x (ISBN 0-911836-15-2). Entomological Repr.

Schreiber, Harold. Disperal Centres of Sphingidae (Lepidoptera) in the Neotropical Region. (Biogeographica Ser.: No. 10). (Illus.). 1978. lib. bdg. 34.00 (ISBN 90-6193-211-4, Pub. by Junk Pubs. Netherlands). Kluwer Academic.

Selman, Charles L. A Pictorial Key to the Hawkmoths (Lepidotera: Sphingidae) of Eastern United States (Except Florida) 1975. 1.50 (ISBN 0-86727-079-9). Ohio Bio Survey.

Sokoloff, P. A. Practical Hints for Collecting & Studying the Microlepidoptera. 40p. 21.00x (ISBN 0-686-75581-2, Pub. by Amateur Entomol Soc). State Mutual Bk.

Talbot, G. Lepidoptera: Butterflies, Vol I. 2nd ed. (Fauna of British India). (Illus.). xxx, 612p. 1978. Repr. of 1939 ed. 25.00 (ISBN 0-88065-199-7, Pub. by Messers Today & Tomorrows Printers & Publishers India). Scholarly Pubns.

Tietz, Harrison M. An Index to the Described Life Histories, Early Stages & Hosts of the Macrolepidoptera of the Continental United States & Canada, 2 vols. iv, 1041p. (Orig.). 1972. text ed. 25.00x (ISBN 0-913492-01-9). Entomological Repr.

Vane-Wright, Richard I. & Ackery, Phillip R. The Biology of Butterflies: Symposium. (Royal Entomological Society Ser.). 1984. 60.00 (ISBN 0-12-713750-5). Acad Pr.

Varley, G. C. A Plea for a New Look at Lepidoptera: Special Reference to the Scent Distributing Organs of Male Moths. 1962. write for info. (Pub. by FW Classey UK). State Mutual Bk.

Weismann, August. Studies in the Theory of Descent, 2 vols. in 1. LC 72-1661. Repr. of 1882 ed. 57.50 (ISBN 0-404-08192-4). AMS Pr.

Young, Allen M. & Stein, Daniel. Studies on the Evolutionary Biology of the Neotropical Nymphalid Butterfly Anartia Fatima in Costa Rica. 1976. 2.00 (ISBN 0-89326-019-3). Milwaukee Pub Mus.

LEPTOME

see Phloem

LEPTONS (NUCLEAR PHYSICS)

see also Electrons; Fermions; Muons; Neutrinos; Positrons

Association of Research Libraries, Systems & Procedures Exchange Center. Integrated Library Information Systems. (SPEC Kit & Flyer Ser.: No. 90). 88p. 1983. (10.00 for ARL members) 20.00 (ISBN 0-318-03465-4). Assn Res Lib.

Becker, Jorg. Information Technology & a New International Order. (Information & Society Ser.). 141p. 1984. pap. text ed. 19.95x (ISBN 0-86238-043-X, Pub. by Chartwell-Bratt England). Brookfield Pub Co.

Biscoe, Eleanor, ed. Planning for Statewide Continuing Education for Library-Information-Media Personnel. 1980. 5.00 (ISBN 0-686-39877-7); 4.25 (ISBN 0-686-39878-5). Clene Pubns.

Brophy, Peter. Management Information Systems in Libraries. 200p. 1985. text ed. price not set (ISBN 0-566-03551-0). Gower Pub Co.

Chartrand, Robert Lee & Morentz, James W., Jr., eds. Information Technology Serving Society. 1979. 25.00 (ISBN 0-08-021979-9). Chartrand.

Ching-hih Chen & Hernon, Peter. Information Seeking: Assessing & Anticipating User Needs. 222p. 1982. 27.00 (ISBN 0-918212-50-2). Neal-Schuman.

Cibbarelli, Pamela & Kazlauskas, Edward, eds. Directory of Information Management Software for Libraries, Information Centers, Record Centers, 1985-1986. 239p. 1985. pap. 49.00 (ISBN 0-913203-14-9). Pacific Info.

Collier, Mel. Local Area Networks: The Implications for Library & Information Science. (LIR Report Ser.: No. 19). 53p. (Orig.). 1984. pap. 14.25 (ISBN 0-7123-3028-3, Pub. by British Lib). Longwood Pub Group.

Culotta, W., et al, eds. Local Area Networks: Proceedings of the LACASIS Seminar, Los Angeles, 1984. (Illus.). 174p. 1985. pap. text ed. 28.50x (ISBN 0-913203-12-2). Pacific Info.

Duffy, Michelle. Self-Instructional Introduction to Searching the OCLC on-Line Union Catalog. 2nd ed. (Amigos Training Ser.: No. 2). 53p. pap. 7.50 (ISBN 0-938288-01-6). AMIGOS Biblio.

Fang, Josephine R. & Songe, Alice H. International Guide to Library, Archival, & Information Science Associations. 2nd ed. 448p. 1980. 32.50 (ISBN 0-8352-1285-8). Bowker.

Genaway, David C. Integrated Online Library Systems: Principles, Planning & Implementation. LC 84-15406. (Professional Librarian). 151p. 1984. professional 36.50 (ISBN 0-86729-092-7, 234-BW); pap. 28.50 (ISBN 0-86729-091-9). Knowledge Indus.

Genaway, David C., ed. Conference on Integrated Online Library Systems, September 26 & 27, 1983. Columbus Ohio, Proceedings. vi, 281p. 1983. pap. 39.95 (ISBN 0-943970-02-4). Genaway.

Glaeser, P. S., ed. Data for Science & Technology: Proceedings of the International CODATA Conference, Eighth, Jachranka, Poland, 4-7 Oct., 1982. 350p. 1983. 49.00 (ISBN 0-444-86668-X, I-460-83, North Holland). Elsevier.

Hayes, Robert M. Universities, Information Technology, & Academic Libraries. (Libraries & Information Science Ser.). 196p. 1986. text ed. 29.50 (ISBN 0-89391-266-2). Ablex Pub.

Hoover, Ryan E., ed. Library & Information Manager's Guide to Online Services. LC 80-21602. (Professional Librarian Ser.). (Illus.). 270p. 1980. professional 34.50 (ISBN 0-914236-60-1, 215-BW). Knowledge Indus.

Information Roundup, Microform & Data Processing for the Library & Information Center: Proceedings of the 4th ASIS Mid-Year Meeting, 1975. 1975. 14.00 (ISBN 0-317-13872-3, 337-BW). Knowledge Indus.

Jones, Clara S., ed. Public Library Information & Referral Service. 265p. 1981. pap. 14.50x (ISBN 0-915794-06-3, Lib Prof Pubns). Shoe String.

Keenan, Stella. How to go On-Line: Guidelines for the Establishment of On-Line Services in Public Libraries. 1980. 30.00x (ISBN 0-905984-57-9, Pub. by Brit Lib England). State Mutual Bk.

Kent & Galvin, eds. The Structure & Governance of Library Networks, Vol. 27. (Bks. in Library & Information Science). 1979. 65.00 (ISBN 0-8247-6866-3). Dekker.

Lengenfelder, Helga. Libraries, Information Centers & Databases in Science & Technology: A World Guide. 561p. 1985. 100.00x (ISBN 3-598-10533-9). K G Saur.

Leong, Carol. Dictionary of Library & Information Sciences, English-Chinese, Chinese-English. 328p. 1984. lib. bdg. 41.00 (ISBN 3-598-10532-0). K G Saur.

Luquire, Wilson, ed. Experiences of Library Network Administrators. LC 84-22428. (Resource Sharing & Information Networks Ser.: Vol. 2, Nos. 1-2). 144p. 1985. text ed. 22.95 (ISBN 0-86656-388-1). Haworth Pr.

--Library Networking: Current Problems & Future Prospects. LC 83-18474. (Resource Sharing & Information Networks Ser.: Vol. 1, Nos. 1&2). 140p. 1983. text ed. 22.95 (ISBN 0-86656-270-2, B270). Haworth Pr.

Markuson, Barbara & Woolls, Blanche, eds. Networks for Networkers: Critical Issues in Cooperative Library Development. LC 79-24054. 444p. 1980. 27.95 (ISBN 0-918212-22-7). Neal-Schuman.

Martin, Susan K. Library Networks: 1981-1982. LC 80-26710. (Professional Librarian Ser.). 160p. 1981. professional 29.50 (ISBN 0-914236-55-5, 218-BW); pap. 24.50 professional (ISBN 0-914236-66-0). Knowledge Indus.

Matthews, Joseph R. Directory of Automated Library Systems. 217p. (Orig.). 1985. pap. text ed. 34.95 (ISBN 0-918212-82-0). Neal-Schuman.

Online Bibliographic Database Searching in College Libraries: Clip Note 4-83. 132p. 1983. 19.00 (ISBN 0-8389-6624-1). Assn Coll & Res Libs.

Palmer, Richard P. Case Studies in Library Computer Systems. LC 73-17008. (Bowker Series in Problem-Centered Approaches to Librarianship). pap. 57.50 (ISBN 0-317-19842-4, 2023052). Bks Demand UMI.

Patrick, Ruth J., et al. A Study of Library Cooperatives, Networks & Demonstration Projects, 2 vols. in 1. 280p. 1980. Set. 42.50 (ISBN 0-208-01942-1, Linnet). Vol. 1: Findings & Recomendations. Vol. 2: Case Study Reports. Shoe String.

Public Library Association Staff. Job & Career Information Centers for Public Libraries. LC 85-13519. (Public Library Reporter Ser.: No. 21). 50p. 1985. pap. text ed. 5.95 (ISBN 0-8389-3322-X). ALA.

Rouse, William B. & Rouse, Sandra H. Management of Library Networks: Policy Analysis, Implementation, & Control. LC 80-12644. (Information Sciences Ser.). 288p. 1980. 45.95 (ISBN 0-471-05534-4, Pub. by Wiley Interscience). Wiley.

Rush, James E., ed. Interlibrary Loan, Vol. 6. LC 83-9584. (Library Systems Evaluation Guides). (Illus.). 248p. 1985. velo bound 59.50 (ISBN 0-912803-06-1). Rush Assoc.

Shaw, Debra & Prentice, Ann E., eds. Public Library Networking & Inter-Library Co-Operation. (Public Library Quarterly: Vol. 2, Nos. 3-4). 113p. 1982. pap. text ed. 20.00 (ISBN 0-86656-116-1, B116). Haworth Pr.

Special Libraries Association. The Special Library Role in Networks: A Conference Held at the General Motors Research Laboratories, Warren, Michigan, May 5-6, 1980. Gibson, Robert W., Jr., ed. LC 81-140531. pap. 76.50 (ISBN 0-317-30408-9, 2024959). Bks Demand UMI.

Special Libraries Association, Networking Committee. Getting into Networking: Guidelines for Special Libraries. LC 76-58875. (SLA State-of-the-Art Review Ser.: No. 5). pap. 20.00 (ISBN 0-317-30404-6, 2024961). Bks Demand UMI.

Swihart, Stanley J. & Hefley, Beryl F. Computer Systems in the Library: A Handbook for Managers & Designers. LC 73-603. (Information Sciences Ser.). pap. 88.00 (ISBN 0-317-10536-1, 2055607). Bks Demand UMI.

Varlejs, Jana. Communication, Information, Libraries: A New Alliance. LC 84-29706. 96p. 1985. pap. 9.95 (ISBN 0-89950-146-X). McFarland & Co.

Vulton, A. J. & Pearce, A. On-Line Experiments in Public Libraries. 1980. 30.00x (ISBN 0-905984-56-0, Pub. by Brit Lib England). State Mutual Bk.

Walton, Robert A. Microcomputers: A Planning & Implementation Guide for Librarians & Information Professionals. LC 82-42934. (Illus.). 104p. 1983. pap. 24.95 (ISBN 0-89774-097-1). Oryx Pr.

Wedgeworth, Robert, ed. ALA Yearbook of Library & Information Services, 1984. 382p. 1984. lib. bdg. 65.00x (ISBN 0-8389-0413-0). ALA.

--ALA Yearbook of Library & Information Services, 1985. 400p. 1985. text ed. 65.00x (ISBN 0-8389-0434-3). ALA.

Yeates, R. Prestel in the Public Library: Reactions to the General Public to Prestel & its Potential for Conveying Local Information. 1982. 55.00x (ISBN 0-905984-79-X, Pub. by Brit Lib England). State Mutual Bk.

LIBRARY NETWORKS

see Library Information Networks

LIBRARY SCIENCE–DATA PROCESSING

American Library Association Committee on Cataloging Staff. Guidelines for Using AACR2 Chapter Nine for Cataloging Microcomputer Software. LC 84-11168. 34p. 1984. pap. text ed. 4.50x (ISBN 0-8389-5651-3). ALA.

Aveney, Brian & Butler, Brett, eds. Online Catalogs, Online Reference: Converging Trends. LC 84-11023. (Library & Information Technology Ser.: No. 2). 212p. 1984. pap. text ed. 20.00x (ISBN 0-8389-3308-4). ALA.

Bewsey, Julia J. Microcomputers & Libraries: An Annotated Bibliography. (CompuBibs Ser.: No.8). 63p. 1985. pap. 15.00x (ISBN 0-914791-07-9). Vantage Info.

Broadbent, K. P. Dissemination of Scientific Information in the People's Republic of China. (Illus.). 60p. 1980. pap. 8.00 (ISBN 0-88936-238-6, IDRC148, IDRC). Unipub.

Burton, Paul. Bibliography of Micros in Libraries. 70p. 1985. text ed. write for info. (ISBN 0-566-03540-5). Gower Pub Co.

Burton, Paul F. Microcomputer Applications in Academic Libraries. (LIR Reports Ser.). 133p. (Orig.). 1983. pap. 17.50 (ISBN 0-7123-3021-6, Pub. by British Lib). Longwood Pub Group.

Chen, Ching-chih & Bressler, Stacey E. Microcomputers in Libraries. (Applications in Information Management & Technology Ser.). (Illus.). 259p. (Orig.). 1982. pap. text ed. 27.95 (ISBN 0-918212-61-8). Neal-Schuman.

Chen, Ching-Chih & De Young, Barbara. Integrating Micro-Based IBMs Libraries. 107p. pap. 14.95 (ISBN 0-931555-10-8). Microuse Info.

Chen, Ching-Chin & De Young, Barbara. The dBASE Workbook for Librarians. 69p. pap. 9.95 (ISBN 0-931555-11-6). Microuse Info.

Clark, Philip M. Microcomputer Spreadsheet Models for Libraries: Preparing Documents, Budgets, & Statistical Reports. LC 84-20470. 134p. 1985. pap. text ed. 24.95x (ISBN 0-8389-0403-3). ALA.

Clinic on Library Applications of Data Processing, 1968. Proceedings. Carroll, Dewey E., ed. LC 65-1841. 235p. 1969. 7.00x (ISBN 0-87845-017-3). U of Ill Lib Info Sci.

Clinic on Library Applications of Data Processing, 1969. Proceedings. Carroll, Dewey E., ed. LC 65-1841. 149p. 1970. 7.00x (ISBN 0-87845-018-1). U of Ill Lib Info Sci.

Costa, Betty & Costa, Marie. A Micro Handbook for Small Libraries & Media Centers. 220p. 1983. lib. bdg. 19.50 (ISBN 0-87287-354-4). Libs Unl.

Davis, Charles H. & Lundeen, Gerald W. Illustrative Computer Programming for Libraries: Selected Examples for Information Specialists. 2nd ed. LC 81-1128. (Contributions in Librarianship & Information Science Ser.: No. 39). (Illus.). 120p. 1981. lib. bdg. 17.50 (ISBN 0-313-22151-0, DAD/). Greenwood.

Dowlin, Kenneth E. The Electronic Library: The Promise & the Process. (Applications in Information Management & Technology Ser.). (Illus.). 199p. 1984. pap. 27.95 (ISBN 0-918212-75-8). Neal-Schuman.

Gates, Hilary. Directory of Library & Information Retrieval Software for Microcomputers. LC 84-24738. 59p. 1985. pap. text ed. 17.95 (ISBN 0-566-03531-6). Gower Pub Co.

Gellatly, Peter, ed. The Management of Serials Automation: Current Technology & Strategies for Future Planning. LC 82-6166. (The Supplement to Serials Librarian Ser.: Vol. 6). 293p. 1982. 45.00 (ISBN 0-917724-37-2, B37); pap. 24.95 (ISBN 0-86656-310-5). Haworth Pr.

Genaway, David C., ed. Conference on Integrated Online Library Systems, 1st, September 26th & 27th, 1983, Columbus, Ohio: Proceedings. 2nd, enl., rev. ed. (Orig.). 1983. pap. 39.95 (ISBN 0-317-04899-6). Genaway.

--Conference on Integrated Online Library Systems, 2nd, September 13th & 14th, 1984, Atlanta, Georgia: Proceedings. 1984. pap. 39.95 (ISBN 0-943970-04-0). Genaway.

Gough, Chet & Srikantaiah, Taverekere. Systems Analysis in Libraries: A Question & Answer Approach. (Illus.). 1978. 16.00 (ISBN 0-208-01753-4, Linnet). Shoe String.

Hayes, Robert M. & Becker, Joseph. Handbook of Data Processing for Libraries. 2nd ed. LC 74-9690. (Information Sciences Ser). 688p. 1974. 63.50 (ISBN 0-471-36483-5, Pub. by Wiley-Interscience). Wiley.

Hoover, Ryan E., ed. Library & Information Manager's Guide to Online Services. LC 80-21602. (Professional Librarian Ser.). (Illus.). 270p. 1980. professional 34.50 (ISBN 0-914236-60-1, 215-BW). Knowledge Indus.

Hunter, Eric J. The ABC of BASIC: An Introduction to Programming for Librarians. 116p. 1982. 16.00 (ISBN 0-85157-355-X, Pub. by Bingley England). Shoe String.

Information Roundup, Microform & Data Processing for the Library & Information Center: Proceedings of the 4th ASIS Mid-Year Meeting, 1975. 1975. 14.00 (ISBN 0-317-13872-3, 337-BW). Knowledge Indus.

Juergens, Bonnie. Self Instructional Introduction to the OCLC Models 100 & 105 Terminals, No. 1. rev., 2nd ed. Duffy, Michelle, ed. (AMIGOS Training Series: No. 1). 40p. 1981. 3 hole punch, stapled 12.50 (ISBN 0-938288-00-8). AMIGOS Biblio.

Kazlauskas, Edward J. Systems Analysis for Library Microcomputer Applications. (Professional Skills Ser.). (Illus.). 104p. 1985. pap. text ed. 24.50 (ISBN 0-913203-11-4). Pacific Info.

Keenan, Stella. How to go On-Line: Guidelines for the Establishment of On-Line Services in Public Libraries. 1980. 30.00x (ISBN 0-905984-57-9, Pub. by Brit Lib England). State Mutual Bk.

Kent & Galvin. The On Line Revolution in Libraries. (Library Science Ser.: Vol. 23). 1978. 65.00 (ISBN 0-8247-6754-3). Dekker.

Keren, C. & Perlmutter, L., eds. The Application of Mini- & Micro-Computers in Information, Documentation & Libraries: Proceeding of the International Conference, Tel-Aviv, Israel, 13-18 March 1983. 802p. 1984. 74.00 (ISBN 0-444-86767-8). Elsevier.

Kesner, Richard M. & Jones, Clifton H. Microcomputer Applications in Libraries: A Management Tool for the 1980s & Beyond. LC 83-22566. (New Directions in Librarianship Ser.: No. 5). xvii, 250p. 1984. lib. bdg. 29.95 (ISBN 0-313-22939-2, KMI/). Greenwood.

Kids, Libraries & Microcomputers: A Formula for Success. 1983. pap. write for info. Contemp Issues.

Lancaster, F. W., ed. Problems & Failures in Library Automation: Proceedings of the Clinic on Library Applications of Data Processing, 1978. LC 78-31801. 109p. 1979. 9.00 (ISBN 0-87845-050-5). U of Ill Lib Info Sci.

--The Role of the Library in an Electronic Society: Proceedings of the Clinic on Library Applications of Data Processing 1979. LC 79-19449. 200p. 1980. 9.00 (ISBN 0-87845-053-X). U of Ill Lib Info Sci.

Lancaster, F. Wilfrid, ed. Clinic on Library Applications of Data Processing, Proceedings, 1979: The Role of the Library in an Electronic Society. LC 79-19449. 200p. 1980. 9.00x (ISBN 0-87845-053-X). U of Ill Lib Info Sci.

Martyn, John & Lancaster, F. Wilfrid. Investigative Methods in Library & Information Science: An Introduction. LC 81-80538. (Illus.). v, 260p. 1981. text ed. 30.50 (ISBN 0-87815-035-8). Info Resources.

Mott, Thomas H., Jr., et al. Introduction to PL-1 Programming for Library & Information Science. (Library & Information Science Ser.). 239p. 1972. text ed. 37.50 (ISBN 0-12-508750-0). Acad Pr.

Norman, Adrian. Electronic Document Delivery: The Artemis Concept. LC 81-20774. (Communications Library). 226p. 1982. text ed. 45.00 professional (ISBN 0-86729-011-0, 407-BW). Knowledge Indus.

Oboler, Eli M. To Free the Mind: Libraries, Technology, & Intellectual Freedom. 135p. 1983. 15.00 (ISBN 0-87287-325-0). Libs Unl.

Palmer, Richard P. Case Studies in Library Computer Systems. LC 73-17008. (Bowker Series in Problem-Centered Approaches to Librarianship). pap. 57.50 (ISBN 0-317-19842-4, 2023052). Bks Demand UMI.

Patrick, Ruth J., et al. A Study of Library Cooperatives, Networks & Demonstration Projects, 2 vols. in 1. 280p. 1980. Set. 42.50 (ISBN 0-208-01942-1, Linnet). Vol. 1: Findings & Recomendations. Vol. 2: Case Study Reports. Shoe String.

Public Access to Library Automation: Proceedings of the Clinic on Library Applications of Data Processing,1980. LC 81-11685. 128p. 1981. 10.00 (ISBN 0-87845-065-3). U of Ill Lib Info Sci.

Rowley, Jennifer E. Mechanized In-House Information Systems. 208p. 1979. 20.50 (ISBN 0-85157-259-6, Pub. by Bingley England). Shoe String.

Rush, James E., ed. Public Service, Vol. 3. LC 83-9584. (Library Systems Evaluation Guides Ser.). (Illus.). 267p. 1983. velo bound 59.50 (ISBN 0-912803-03-7). Rush Assoc.

--System Integration, Vol. 8. LC 83-9584. (Library Systems Evaluation Guides). (Illus.). 240p. 1985. velo bd. 59.50 (ISBN 0-912803-08-8). Rush Assoc.

Simonton, Wesley & McClaskey, Marilyn J. AACR Two & the Catalog: Theory-Structure-Changes. LC 81-11757. 78p. 1981. pap. 9.50 (ISBN 0-87287-267-X). Libs Unl.

Swihart, Stanley J. & Hefley, Beryl F. Computer Systems in the Library: A Handbook for Managers & Designers. LC 73-603. (Information Sciences Ser.). pap. 88.00 (ISBN 0-317-10536-1, 2055607). Bks Demand UMI.

Vaillancourt, Pauline M. International Directory of Acronyms in Library, Information & Computer Sciences. LC 80-18352. xi, 518p. 1980. 50.00 (ISBN 0-8352-1152-5). Bowker.

Walton, Robert A. Microcomputers: A Planning & Implementation Guide for Librarians & Information Professionals. LC 82-42934. (Illus.). 104p. 1983. pap. 24.95 (ISBN 0-89774-097-1). Oryx Pr.

Santilli, R. M. Applications of Lie-Admissible Algebras in Physics, Vol. 3. 402p. 1983. pap. text ed. 50.00x (ISBN 0-911767-08-8). Hadronic Pr Inc.

Seligman, G. B. Modular Lie Algebras. LC 67-28452. (Ergebnisse der Mathematik & Ihrer Grenzgebiete: Vol. 40). 1967. 34.00 (ISBN 0-387-03782-9). Springer-Verlag.

Seligman, George. Rational Methods in Lie Algebras. (Lecture Notes in Pure and Applied Mathematics Ser: Vol. 17). 1976. 56.50 (ISBN 0-8247-6480-3). Dekker.

Slodowy, P. Simple Singularities & Simple Algebraic Groups. (Lecture Notes in Mathematics: Vol. 815). 175p. 1980. pap. 15.00 (ISBN 0-387-10026-1). Springer-Verlag.

Stewart, I. Lie Algebra Generated by Finite-Dimensional Ideals. (Research Notes in Mathematics Ser.: No. 2). 154p. 1975. text ed. 20.50 (ISBN 0-273-00142-6). Pitman Pub MA.

Stewart, I. N. Lie Algebras. LC 73-117720. (Lecture Notes in Mathematics: Vol. 127). 1970. pap. 10.70 (ISBN 0-387-04916-9). Springer-Verlag.

Tsujishita, Toru. Continuous Cohomology of the Lie Algebra of Vector Fields. LC 81-16519. (Memoirs of the American Mathematical Society: No. 253). 155p. 1981. pap. 11.00 (ISBN 0-8218-2253-5). Am Math.

Van Der Kallen, W. L. Infinitesimally Central Extensions of Chevalley Groups. (Lecture Notes in Mathematics: Vol. 356). 147p. 1973. pap. 12.00 (ISBN 0-387-06559-8). Springer-Verlag.

Varadarajan, V. S. Lie Groups, Lie Algebras & Their Representations. (Graduate Texts in Mathematics: Vol. 102). 430p. 1984. Repr. of 1974 ed. 29.80 (ISBN 0-387-90969-9). Springer Verlag.

Wan-Z-Xian. Lie Algebras. LC 74-13832. 244p. 1975. text ed. 44.00 (ISBN 0-08-017952-5). Pergamon.

Winter, D., ed. Lie Algebras & Related Topics, New Brunswick, New Jersey 1981: Proceedings. (Lecture Notes in Mathematics: Vol. 933). 236p. 1982. pap. 13.00 (ISBN 0-387-11563-3). Springer-Verlag.

Winter, David J. Abstract Lie Algebras. 1972. 30.00x (ISBN 0-262-23051-8). MIT Pr.

LIE DETECTORS AND DETECTION

Abrams, Stanley. Polygraph Handbook for Attorneys. LC 77-6074. (Illus.). 1977. 27.00x (ISBN 0-669-01598-9). Lexington Bks.

Academy for Scientific Interrogation. Academy Lectures on Lie Detection, Vol. I. 112p. 1957. 13.75x (ISBN 0-398-00005-0). C C Thomas.

--Academy Lectures on Lie Detection, Vol. II. 168p. 1958. 19.75x (ISBN 0-398-04182-2). C C Thomas.

Bailey, F. Lee & Marcy, Lynn P. What You Should Know about the Lie Detector. 200p. 1984. cancelled (ISBN 0-910287-03-1). TelShare Pub Co.

Ferguson, Robert J., et al. Preemployment Polygraphy. 184p. 1984. 24.75x (ISBN 0-398-05011-2). C C Thomas.

Ferguson, Robert J., Jr. The Polygraph in Private Industry. (Illus.). 352p. 1966. 28.75x (ISBN 0-398-00557-5). C C Thomas.

Ferguson, Robert J., Jr. & Miller, Allan L. Polygraph for the Defense. 312p. 1974. 25.50x (ISBN 0-398-02877-X). C C Thomas.

--The Polygraph in Court. (Illus.). 372p. 1973. photocopy ed. 28.75x (ISBN 0-398-02679-3). C C Thomas.

Keeler, Eloise. Lie Detector Man. 200p. 1984. 12.95 (ISBN 0-910287-02-3). TelShare Pub Co.

Lykken, David T. A Tremor in the Blood: Uses & Abuses of the Lie Detector. LC 80-10697. 320p. 1980. 22.95 (ISBN 0-07-039210-2). McGraw.

Matte, James A. The Art & Science of the Polygraph Technique. (Illus.). 296p. 1980. photocopy ed. 29.50x (ISBN 0-398-04044-3). C C Thomas.

LIE GROUPS

see also Lie Algebras

Ackerman, M. & Hermann, Robert. Sophus Lie's Eighteen Eighty Transformation Group Paper. LC 75-17416. (Lie Groups: History, Frontiers on Applications Ser.: No. 1). 1975. 55.00 (ISBN 0-915692-10-4). Math Sci Pr.

Adams, J. Frank. Lectures on Lie Groups. LC 82-51014. (Midway Reprints Ser.). 168p. 1983. pap. text ed. 11.00x (ISBN 0-226-00530-5). U of Chicago Pr.

Ash, A., et al. Smooth Compactification of Locally Symmetric Varieties. LC 75-38142. (Lie Groups: History, Frontiers & Applications Ser.: No. 4). 340p. 1975. 19.00 (ISBN 0-915692-12-0, 991600061). Math Sci Pr.

Atiyah, M. F. Elliptic Operators & Compact Groups. (Lecture Notes in Mathematics Ser.: Vol. 401). v, 93p. 1974. pap. 13.00 (ISBN 3-540-06855-4). Springer-Verlag.

Atiyah, M. F., et al. Representation Theory of Lie Groups. LC 78-73820. (London Mathematical Society Lecture Note: No. 34). 1980. pap. 37.50 (ISBN 0-521-22636-8). Cambridge U Pr.

Auslander, L. & Tolimieri, R. Abelian Harmonic Analysis, Theta Functions & Functional Analysis on a Nilmanifold. (Lecture Notes in Mathematics Ser.: Vol. 436). v, 99p. 1975. pap. 13.00 (ISBN 0-387-07134-2). Springer-Verlag.

Azencott, R. & Wilson, E. N. Homogenous Manifolds with Negative Curvature II. LC 76-44403. (Memoirs: No. 178). 102p. 1976. pap. 13.00 (ISBN 0-8218-2178-4, MEMO178). Am Math.

Belinfante, J. G. F. & Kolman, B. A Survey of Lie Groups & Lie Algebras. LC 72-77081. ix, 164p. 1972. 19.50 (ISBN 0-89871-044-8). Soc Indus-Appl Math.

Borel, Armand, et al. Lie Algebras & Lie Groups. LC 52-42839. (Memoirs: No. 14). 54p. 1972. pap. 10.00 (ISBN 0-8218-1214-9, MEMO-14). Am Math.

Bredon, Glen E. Introduction to Compact Transformation Groups. (Pure & Applied Mathematics Ser). 1972. 77.00 (ISBN 0-12-128850-1). Acad Pr.

Brocker, T. & Dieck, Tom T. Representations of Compact Lie Groups. (Graduate Texts in Mathematics Ser.: Vol. 98). (Illus.). x, 313p. 1985. 39.00 (ISBN 0-387-13678-9). Springer-Verlag.

Carmona, J. & Vergne, M., eds. Non Commutative Harmonic Analysis & Lie Groups. (Lecture Notes in Mathematics Ser.: 1020). 187p. 1983. pap. 12.00 (ISBN 0-387-12717-8). Springer-Verlag.

Carter, Roger. Simple Groups of Lie Type. LC 72-39228. (Pure & Applied Mathematics Ser.: Vol. 28). pap. 85.80 (ISBN 0-317-26151-7, 2024274). Bks Demand UMI.

Carter, Roger W. Finite Groups of LIE Type Conjugacy Classes & Complex Characters. LC 84-13077. (Pure & Applied Mathematics Ser.: Vol. V). 1985. 69.95 (ISBN 0-471-90554-2, Pub. by Wiley-Interscience). Wiley.

D'Atri, J. E. & Ziller, W. Naturally Reductive Metrics & Einstein Metrics on Compact Lie Groups. LC 79-7. (Memoirs Ser.: No. 215). 72p. 1982. pap. 13.00 (ISBN 0-8218-2215-2). Am Math.

De la Harpe, P. Classical Banach-Lie Algebras & Banach-Lie Groups of Operators in Hilbert Space. LC 72-88729. (Lecture Notes in Mathematics: Vol. 285). 160p. 1972. pap. 9.00 (ISBN 0-387-05984-9). Springer-Verlag.

Dieudonne, J. Introduction to the Theory of Formal Groups. (Pure & Applied Mathematics Ser: Vol. 20). 288p. 1973. 55.00 (ISBN 0-8247-6011-5). Dekker.

Dieudonne, Jean. Special Functions & Linear Representations of Lie Groups. LC 79-22180. (CBMS Regional Conference Ser. in Mathematics: No. 42). 59p. 1982. pap. 11.00 (ISBN 0-8218-1692-6, CBMS-42). Am Math.

Enright, T. J. Lectures on Representations of Complex Semi-Simple Lie Groups. (Tata Institute Lectures on Mathematics Ser.). 91p. 1981. pap. 10.50 (ISBN 0-387-10829-7). Springer-Verlag.

Erven, J. & Falkowski, B. J. Low Order Cohomology & Applications. (Lecture Notes in Mathematics Ser.: Vol. 877). 126p. 1981. pap. 12.00 (ISBN 0-387-10864-5). Springer-Verlag.

Gaal, S. A. Linear Analysis & Representation Theory. LC 72-95686. (Die Grundlehren der Mathematischen Wissenschaften: Vol. 198). ix, 688p. 1973. 71.00 (ISBN 0-387-06195-9). Springer-Verlag.

Gilmore, Robert. Lie Groups, Lie Algebras & Some of Their Applications. LC 73-10030. 587p. 1974. 56.95x (ISBN 0-471-30179-5, Pub. by Wiley-Interscience). Wiley.

Glasner, M. S. Proximal Flows. (Lecture Notes in Mathematics: Vol. 517). 1976. pap. 13.00 (ISBN 0-387-07689-1). Springer-Verlag.

Hano, Jun-Ichi, ed. Manifolds & Lie Groups: Papers in Honor of Yozo Matsushima. (Progress in Mathematics Ser.: 14). 608p. 1981. text ed. 35.00x (ISBN 0-8176-3053-8). Birkhauser.

Hausner, Melvin & Schwartz, Jacob T. Lie Groups, Lie Algebras. LC 66-28064. (Notes on Mathematics & Its Application Ser.). 240p. 1968. 40.50 (ISBN 0-677-00280-7). Gordon.

Helgason, Sigurdur. Analysis on Lie Groups & Homogeneous Spaces. LC 72-10153. (CBMS Regional Conference Series in Mathematics: Vol. 14). 64p. 1982. pap. text ed. 14.00 (ISBN 0-686-93290-0). Am Math.

--Differential Geometry, Lie Groups & Symmetric Spaces. (Pure & Applied Mathematics Ser.). 1978. 29.50 (ISBN 0-12-338460-5). Acad Pr.

Herb, R., et al, eds. Lie Group Representations III. (Lecture Notes in Mathematics Ser.: Vol. 1077). xi, 454p. 1984. pap. 25.00 (ISBN 0-387-13385-2). Springer-Verlag.

--Lie Group Representations II. (Lecture Notes in Mathematics: Vol. 1041). 340p. 1984. pap. 18.00 (ISBN 0-387-12715-1). Springer Verlag.

--Lie Group Presentations, I. (Lecture Notes in Mathematics Ser.: Vol. 1024). 369p. 1983. pap. 19.00 (ISBN 0-387-12725-9). Springer-Verlag.

Hermann, Robert & Ackerman, M. Sophus Lie's 1884 Differential Invariants Paper. LC 75-43189. (Lie Groups: History Frontiers & Applications Ser.: No. 3). 273p. 1975. 36.00 (ISBN 0-915692-13-9, 991600053). Math Sci Pr.

Humphreys, J. E. Algebraic Groups & Modular Lie Algebras. (Memoirs: No. 71). 76p. 1967. pap. 9.00 (ISBN 0-8218-1271-8, MEMO-71). Am Math.

Jensen, G. Higher Order Contact of Submanifolds of Homogeneous Spaces. LC 77-14394. (Lecture Notes in Mathematics Ser.: Vol. 610). 1977. pap. text ed. 14.00 (ISBN 0-387-08433-9). Springer-Verlag.

Kaplansky, Irving. Lie Algebras & Locally Compact Groups. LC 76-136207. (Chicago Lectures in Mathematics Ser.). 1971. pap. 7.00x (ISBN 0-226-42453-7). U of Chicago Pr.

Kumpera, Antonio & Spenser, Donald. Lie Equations: General Theory. LC 77-39055. (Annals of Mathematics Studies: No. 73). 300p. 1972. 25.00 (ISBN 0-691-08111-5). Princeton U Pr.

Lazarov, Conner & Wasserman, Arthur. Complex Actions of Lie Groups. LC 73-18039. (Memoirs: No. 137). 82p. 1973. pap. 10.00 (ISBN 0-8218-1837-6, MEMO-137). Am Math.

Magid, Andy R. Module Categories of Analytic Groups. LC 81-10215. (Cambridge Tracts in Mathematics: No. 81). 130p. 1982. 32.50 (ISBN 0-521-24200-2). Cambridge U Pr.

Magus, Alfred. Non-Spherical Principal Series Representations of a Semisimple Lie Group. LC 79-10157. (Memoirs Ser.: No. 216). 52p. 1979. pap. 10.00 (ISBN 0-8218-2216-0). Am Math.

Miller, Willard, Jr. Symmetry Groups & Their Applications. (Pure & Applied Mathematics Ser.: Vol. 50). 1972. 79.50 (ISBN 0-12-497460-0). Acad Pr.

Normand, J. M. A Lie Group: Rotation in Quantum Mechanics. 486p. 1981. 72.50 (ISBN 0-444-86125-4, North-Holland). Elsevier.

Omori, H. Infinite Dimensional Lie Transformation Groups. LC 74-23625. (Lecture Notes in Mathematics: Vol. 427). xi, 149p. 1974. pap. 14.00 (ISBN 0-387-07013-3). Springer-Verlag.

Price, John F. Lie Groups & Compact Groups. LC 76-14034. (London Mathematical Society Lecture Notes Ser.: No. 25). 1977. pap. 21.95x (ISBN 0-521-21340-1). Cambridge U Pr.

Stein, Elias M. Analytic Continuation of Group Representatives. LC 73-151591. (Yale Mathematical Monographs: No. 2). Repr. of 1971 ed. 15.00 (ISBN 0-8357-1679-1, 2016791). Bks Demand UMI.

--Topics in Harmonic Analysis Related to the Littlewood-Paley Theory. LC 72-83688. (Annals of Mathematics Studies: No. 63). 1969. 22.00x (ISBN 0-691-08067-4). Princeton U Pr.

Symposia in Pure Mathematics, Vol. 26. Harmonic Analysis on Homogeneous Spaces: Proceedings. Moore, Calvin C., ed. LC 73-10456. (Proceedings of Symposia in Pure Mathematics: Vol. 26). 480p. 1978. pap. 42.00 (ISBN 0-8218-1426-5, PSPUM-26). Am Math.

Tondeur, Philippe. Introduction to Lie Groups & Transformation Groups. 2nd ed. LC 78-99012. (Lecture Notes in Mathematics: Vol. 7). 1969. pap. 10.70 (ISBN 0-387-04599-6). Springer-Verlag.

Varadarajan, V. S. Lie Groups, Lie Algebras & Their Representations. (Graduate Texts in Mathematics: Vol. 102). 430p. 1984. Repr. of 1974 ed. 29.80 (ISBN 0-387-90969-9). Springer Verlag.

Warner, F. W. Foundations of Differentiable Manifolds & Lie Groups. (Graduate Texts in Mathematics Ser.: Vol. 94). (Illus.). 270p. 1983. 22.00 (ISBN 0-387-90894-3). Springer Verlag.

Warner, G. Harmonic Analysis on Semi-Simple Lie Groups, Pt. 1. LC 70-160590. (Die Grundlehren der Mathematischen Wissenschaften: Vol. 188). (Illus.). 600p. 1972. 51.00 (ISBN 0-387-05468-5). Springer-Verlag.

--Harmonic Analysis on Semi-Simple Lie Groups, Pt. 2. (Die Grundlehren der Mathematischen Wissenschaften: Vol. 189). 600p. 1972. 49.00 (ISBN 0-387-05469-3). Springer-Verlag.

Wolf, J. A. Unitary Representations of Maximal Parabolic Subgroups of the Classical Groups. LC 76-44397. (Memoirs: No. 180). 193p. 1976. pap. 15.00 (ISBN 0-8218-2180-6, MEMO-180). Am Math.

Wolf, J. A., et al, eds. Harmonic Analysis & Representations of Semi-Simple Lie Groups. (Mathematical Physics & Applied Mathematics: No. 5). 508p. 1980. lib. bdg. 66.00 (ISBN 90-277-1042-2, Pub. by Reidel Holland). Kluwer Academic.

Wolf, Joseph A. Unitary Representations on Partially Holomorphic Cohomology Spaces. LC 73-21505. (Memoirs: No. 138). 156p. 1974. pap. 11.00 (ISBN 0-8218-1838-4, MEMO-138). Am Math.

Zelobenko, D. P. Compact Lie Groups & Their Representations. LC 73-17185. (Translations of Mathematical Monographs: Vol. 40). 448p. 1983. pap. 45.00 (ISBN 0-8218-1590-3, MMONO-40). Am Math.

LIFE–ORIGIN

see also Man–Origin; Spontaneous Generation

Abel, Ernest L. Ancient Views on the Origins of Life. LC 72-656. 93p. 1973. 15.00 (ISBN 0-8386-1198-2). Fairleigh Dickinson.

Anbar, Michael. The Genesis of Life. 400p. 1986. text ed. 34.00 (ISBN 0-02-949030-8). Macmillan.

Blechschmidt, E. The Beginnings of Human Life. Transemantics, Inc., tr. from Ger. LC 77-16658. (Heidelberg Science Library). (Illus.). 1977. pap. 17.00 (ISBN 0-387-90249-X). Springer-Verlag.

Bliss, Richard B. & Parker, Gary E. Origin of Life. LC 78-58477. (Illus.). 1978. pap. 4.95 (ISBN 0-89051-053-9). Master Bks.

Brooks, J. & Shaw, G. Origin & Development of Living Systems. 1973. 61.00 (ISBN 0-12-135740-6). Acad Pr.

Buvet, R. & Ponnamperuma, C., eds. Chemical Evolution & the Origin of Life. LC 75-146189. (Molecular Evolution Ser.: Vol. 1). (Illus.). 571p. 1971. 34.00 (ISBN 0-444-10093-8, North-Holland). Elsevier.

Cairns-Smith, A. G. Genetic Takeover & the Mineral Origins of Life. LC 81-17070. (Illus.). 1982. 34.50 (ISBN 0-521-23312-7). Cambridge U Pr.

--Seven Clues to the Origin of Life: A Scientific Detective Story. 154p. 1985. 17.95 (ISBN 0-521-27522-9). Cambridge U Pr.

Crile, George. The Phenomena of Life: A Radio-Electric Interpretation. Rowland, Amy, ed. 377p. Repr. of 1936 ed. lib. bdg. 60.00 (ISBN 0-89984-026-4). Century Bookbindery.

Day, William. Genesis on Planet Earth: The Search for Life's Beginning. 2nd ed. LC 83-21900. 320p. 1984. 36.00x (ISBN 0-300-02954-3); pap. 12.95x (ISBN 0-300-03202-1, Y-494). Yale U Pr.

Dillon, L. S. The Genetic Mechanism & the Origin of Life. LC 78-4478. (Illus.). 573p. 1978. 55.00 (ISBN 0-306-31090-2, Plenum Pr). Plenum Pub.

Dose, K., et al, eds. The Origin of Life & Evolutionary Biochemistry. LC 74-10703. 484p. 1974. 59.50x (ISBN 0-306-30811-8, Plenum Pr). Plenum Pub.

--Origins of Life: Proceedings of the Seventh International Conference, Mainz, July 10-15, 1983 (A Special Issue of a Journal) 1984. lib. bdg. 109.00 (ISBN 90-277-1694-3, Pub. by Reidel Holland). Kluwer Academic.

Drummond, Henry. The Treatise on Biogenesis by Henry Drummond. (Illus.). 129p. 1982. Repr. of 1886 ed. 79.95 (ISBN 0-89901-069-5). Found Class Reprints.

Eccles, Sir John. The Human Mystery. LC 78-12095. (Illus.). 1978. 25.00 (ISBN 0-387-09016-9). Springer-Verlag.

Firsoff, V. A. At the Crossroads of Knowledge: The Origins of Life on This Planet & Elsewhere in the Universe. 1981. 16.95x (ISBN 0-86025-812-2). Intl Ideas.

Fleischer, Sidney, ed. Methods in Enzymology: Biomembranes: Membrane Biogenesis: Assembly & Targeting (General Methods Eukaryotes, Vol. 96, Pt. J. Fleischer, Becca. 1983. 79.00 (ISBN 0-12-181996-5). Acad Pr.

Fourth International Conference on the Origin of Life, 1973, Invited Papers & Contributed Papers, et al. Cosmochemical Evolution & the Origins of Life, 2 vols. Oro, J. & Miller, S. L., eds. LC 74-77967. vii, 755p. 1974. Vol. 1. lib. bdg. 59.00 (ISBN 90-277-0519-4, Pub. by Reidel Holland); Vol. 2. lib. bdg. 36.00 (ISBN 9-0277-0518-6). Kluwer Academic.

Fox, Sidney W. & Dose, Klaus. Molecular Evolution & the Origins of Life. 2nd expanded ed. LC 77-21434. (Biology-a Series of Textbooks: Vol. 2). 1977. 49.75 (ISBN 0-8247-6619-9). Dekker.

Gish, Duane T. Speculations & Experiments Related to the Origin of Life: A Critique. (ICR Technical Monograph: No. 1). (Illus.). 41p. 1972. pap. 5.95 (ISBN 0-89051-010-5). Master Bks.

Goldsmith, Donald. The Quest for Extraterrestrial Life: A Book of Readings. LC 79-57423. (Illus.). 308p. 1980. 20.00x (ISBN 0-935702-08-3); pap. text ed. 13.50x (ISBN 0-935702-02-4). Univ Sci Bks.

Hakanson, Rolf & Thorell, Jan, eds. Biogenetics of Neurohormonal Peptides. 1985. 42.00 (ISBN 0-12-317450-3). Acad Pr.

Hocking, Brian. Biology or Oblivion: Lessons from the Ultimate Science. rev ed. 150p. 1972. 5.50 (ISBN 0-87073-802-X); pap. text ed. 3.50 (ISBN 0-87073-803-8). Schenkman Bks Inc.

Lygre, David G. Life Manipulation. 177p. 1980. pap. 7.95 (ISBN 0-8027-7162-9). Walker & Co.
McGraw-Hill Editors. Dictionary of the Life Sciences. (Illus.). 1976. 36.00 (ISBN 0-07-045262-8). McGraw.
Mader, Sylvia S. Inquiry into Life. 3rd ed. 816p. 1982. text ed. write for info. (ISBN 0-697-04711-3); instrs.' manual avail. (ISBN 0-697-04718-0); study guide avail. (ISBN 0-697-04719-9); lab manual avail. (ISBN 0-697-04720-2); transparencies avail. (ISBN 0-697-04728-8). Wm C Brown.
Magner. A History of the Life Sciences. 496p. 1979. 34.50 (ISBN 0-8247-6824-8). Dekker.
Martin, E. A. A Dictionary of Life Sciences. 2nd rev. ed. LC 83-13253. (Illus.). 416p. 1984. 25.00x (ISBN 0-87663-740-3, Pica Pr). Universe.
Matthews, D. E., ed. Mathematics & the Life Sciences: Selected Lectures, Canadian Mathematical Congress, Aug.1975. LC 77-11151. (Lect. Notes in Biomathematics Ser.: Vol. 18). 1977. pap. text ed. 22.00 (ISBN 0-387-08351-0). Springer-Verlag.
Milton, J. Susan & Tsokos, Janice O. Statistical Methods in the Biological & Health Sciences. (Illus.). 512p. 1983. 36.95 (ISBN 0-07-042359-8). McGraw.
Olinick, Michael. Introduction to Mathematical Models in the Social & Life Sciences. LC 77-77758. (Illus.). 1978. text ed. 26.95 (ISBN 0-201-05448-5). Addison-Wesley.
Oparin, Alexander I. The Chemical Origin of Life. (Illus.). 152p. 1964. photocopy ed. 14.75x (ISBN 0-398-01426-4). C C Thomas.
Poti, S. J. Quantitive Studies in Life Science. 250p. 1983. text ed. 55.00x (ISBN 0-7069-1247-0, Pub by Vikas India). Advent NY.
Smith, Roger C., et al. Smith's Guide to the Literature of the Life Sciences. 9th ed. LC 79-55580. 1980. pap. 15.95x (ISBN 0-8087-3576-4). Burgess.
Stable Isotopes in the Life Sciences. (Panel Proceedings Ser.). 456p. 1977. pap. 53.75 (ISBN 92-0-011077-0, ISP442, IAEA). Unipub.
Ulleck, Ronald B., ed. Life Sciences Jobs Handbook. rev. ed. 1982. pap. 14.95 (ISBN 0-937562-12-2). Prospect Pr.
Wilson, Samuel & Roe, Richard, eds. Biology Anthology: Readings in the Life Sciences. LC 74-2810. 320p. 1974. pap. text ed. 13.50 (ISBN 0-8299-0019-5). West Pub.
Winchester, A. M. & Jaques, H. E. How to Know the Living Things. 2nd ed. 192p. 1981. write for info. wire coil (ISBN 0-697-04780-6). Wm C Brown.
Wong & Bernstein. Ideas & Investigations in Science: Life Science. 2nd ed. 1977. 21.84 (ISBN 0-13-449991-3). lab data bk. o.p. 4.72 (ISBN 0-685-78778-8). P-H.

LIFE SUPPORT SYSTEMS (SPACE ENVIRONMENT)
see also Project Apollo; Space Ships
Phillips, Charles. Basic Life Support Skills. 2nd ed. (Illus.). 224p. 1985. pap. text ed. 14.95 (ISBN 0-89303-253-0). Brady Comm.

LIFT STATIONS
see Pumping Stations

LIFTS
see Elevators; Hoisting Machinery

LIGAND FIELD THEORY
Busch, Daryl H. Reactions of Coordinated Ligands & Homogeneous Catalysis: A Symposium Sponsored by the American Chemical Society, Washington, D.C., March 22-24, 1962. LC 63-13314. (American Chemical Society Advances in Chemistry Ser.: No. 37). pap. 65.80 (ISBN 0-317-09028-3, 2051256). Bks Demand UMI.
Figgis, B. N. Introduction to Ligand Fields. LC 84-23371. 362p. 1985. Repr. of 1966 ed. lib. bdg. price not set (ISBN 0-89874-819-4). Krieger.
Gerloch, M. Magnetism & Ligand-Field Analysis. LC 83-1820. (Illus.). 650p. 1984. 110.00 (ISBN 0-521-24939-2). Cambridge U Pr.
Konig, E. & Kremer, S. Ligand Field Energy Diagrams. LC 76-45670. (Illus.). 454p. 1977. 65.00x (ISBN 0-306-30946-7, Plenum Pr). Plenum Pub.
Kragten, J. Atlas of Metal-Ligand Equilibria in Aqueous Solution. LC 77-12168. 781p. 1978. 174.95x (ISBN 0-470-99309-X). Halsted Pr.
Kricka. Ligand-Binder Assays: Labels & Analytical Strategies. (Clinical & Biochemical Analysis Ser.). 368p. 1985. 65.00 (ISBN 0-8247-7420-5). Dekker.
Radioassays & Non-Isotopic Ligand Assays Product Guide, Vol. 29, No. 5. 986p. 1983. 10.00 (ISBN 0-317-02266-0). Am Assn Clinical Chem.
Sugano, Satoru, et al. Multiplets of Transition-Metal Ions in Crystals. (Pure & Applied Physics Ser.: Vol. 33). 1970. 76.00 (ISBN 0-12-676050-0). Acad Pr.
Travis, Jeffrey C. Fundamentals of RIA & Other Ligand Assays: A Programmed Text. (Illus.). 1977. 22.50 (ISBN 0-930914-05-8). Sci Newsletters.
Triggle, D. J., et al, eds. Cholinergic Ligand Interactions. 1971. 43.50 (ISBN 0-12-700450-5). Acad Pr.

LIGHT
see also Color; Doppler Effect; Electroluminescence; Interference (Light); Lasers; Light Filters; Luminescence; Optics; Photobiology; Photometry; Photons; Polarization (Light); Radiation; Radioactivity; Reflection (Optics); Refraction; Spectrum Analysis; X-Rays
Adorno, Theodor W. Prisms. Weber, Samuel & Weber, Shierry, trs. from Ger. 272p. 1982. pap. 6.95 (ISBN 0-262-51025-1). MIT Pr.
Babbitt, Edwin D. Principles of Light & Color. (Illus.). 578p. Date not set. 27.00 (ISBN 0-89540-060-X, SB-060). Sun Pub.
Babbitt, Edwin S. The Principles of Light & Color. 1980. pap. text ed. 7.95 (ISBN 0-8065-0748-9). Citadel Pr.
Bohren, Craig F. & Huffman, Donald R. Absorption & Scattering of Light by Small Particles. 530p. 1983. 51.95 (ISBN 0-471-05772-X, Pub. by Wiley-Interscience). Wiley.
De Waters, Lillian. Light. (Atomic Ser). pap. 0.95 (ISBN 0-686-05724-4). L De Waters.
Ditchburn, R. W. Light, 3 vols. 3rd. ed. 1977. Vol. 2, 1976. pap. 33.00 (ISBN 0-12-218102-6); Vol. 3. 70.00 (ISBN 0-12-218150-6). Acad Pr.
Elementary Science Study. Light & Shadows. 2nd ed. 1975. tchr's. guide 11.32 (ISBN 0-07-018582-4). McGraw.
Evans, G. C., et al, eds. Light As an Ecological Factor II: The 16th Symposium of the British Ecological Society, March 26-28, 1974. LC 76-921. (British Ecological Society Symposia Ser.). 616p. 1976. 73.95x (ISBN 0-470-15043-2). Halsted Pr.
Graf, Calvin R. Exploring Light, Radio & Sound Energy: With Projects. (Illus.). 240p. (Orig.). 1985. 17.95 (ISBN 0-8306-0758-7, 1758); pap. 10.95 (ISBN 0-8306-1758-2). TAB Bks.
Grosslight, Jane. Light: Effective Use of Daylight & Electrical Lighting in Residential & Commercial Spaces. (Illus.). 208p. 1984. 24.95 (ISBN 0-13-536300-4); pap. 14.95 (ISBN 0-13-536292-X). P-H.
Guillet, James. Polymer Photophysics & Photochemistry: An Introduction to the Study of Photoprocesses in Macromolecules. 391p. 1985. 79.50 (ISBN 0-521-23506-5). Cambridge U Pr.
Henderson, S. T. Daylight & Its Spectrum. 2nd ed. LC 77-88254. 349p. 1978. 58.95x (ISBN 0-470-99328-6). Halsted Pr.
Henry, Dennis C., et al. Experiments in Light, Electricity, & Modern Physics, Laboratory Manual. 1978. pap. text ed. 7.95 (ISBN 0-8403-1889-8). Kendall-Hunt.
Jaffe, Bernard. Michelson & the Speed of Light. LC 78-25969. (Illus.). 1979. Repr. of 1960 ed. lib. bdg. 24.75x (ISBN 0-313-20777-1, JAMI). Greenwood.
Kantor, Wallace. Relativistic Propagation of Light. 1976. 10.00x (ISBN 0-87291-084-9); pap. 6.95x (ISBN 0-685-74222-9). Coronado Pr.
Light & Color: Images from New Mexico. (Illus.). 1980. pap. 8.95 (ISBN 0-89013-134-1). Museum NM Pr.
Marcuse, Dietrich. Light Transmission Optics. 2nd ed. 500p. 1982. 34.50 (ISBN 0-442-26309-0). Van Nos Reinhold.
Minnaert, M. Nature of Light & Colour in the Open Air. 1948. pap. text ed. 6.00 (ISBN 0-486-20196-1). Dover.
--The Nature of Light & Colour in the Open Air. LC 54-10021. 1954. lib. bdg. 13.50x (ISBN 0-88307-651-9). Gannon.
Newton, Isaac. Opticks, or a Treatise of the Reflections, Refractions, Inflections & Colours of Light. 16.00 (ISBN 0-8446-5799-9). Peter Smith.
Northcutt, Glenn & Davis, Roger, eds. Fish Neurobiology, Vol. 1: Brain Stem & Sense Organs. (Illus.). 368p. 1983. text ed. 45.00x (ISBN 0-472-10005-X). U of Mich Pr.
Overheim, R. Daniel & Wagner, David L. Light & Color. LC 81-21955. 269p. 1982. 26.95 (ISBN 0-471-08348-8); tchr's manual avail. (ISBN 0-471-86517-6). Wiley.
Perina, Jan. Coherence of Light. LC 77-141981. 318p. (Orig.). 1972. 24.50. Krieger.
Priestley, Joseph. History & Present State of Discoveries Relating to Vision, Light, & Colours. Cohen, I. Bernard, ed. LC 80-2142. (Development of Science Ser.). (Illus.). 1981. lib. bdg. 70.00x (ISBN 0-405-13897-0). Ayer Co Pubs.
Rabek, J. F. Experimental Methods in Photochemistry & Photophysics. 1098p. 1982. 260.00 (ISBN 0-471-10090-0). Wiley.
Ruechardt, Eduard. Light, Visible & Invisible. LC 58-5904. (Ann Arbor Science Library). pap. 50.30 (ISBN 0-317-12982-1, 2055643). Bks Demand UMI.
Sabra, A. I. Theories of Light from Descartes to Newton. LC 81-6108. (Illus.). 380p. 1981. 44.50 (ISBN 0-521-24094-8); pap. 13.95 (ISBN 0-521-28436-8). Cambridge U Pr.
Sanders, J. M. The Velocity of Light. 1965. 18.00 (ISBN 0-08-011315-X); pap. 8.25 (ISBN 0-08-011314-1). Pergamon.
Seliger, Howard H. & McElroy, W. D. Light: Physical & Biological Action. (U. S. Atomic Energy Commission Monographs). 1965. 23.50 (ISBN 0-12-635850-8). Acad Pr.
Simmons, Joseph W. & Guttmann, Mark J. States, Waves & Photons: A Modern Introduction to Light. LC 73-102998. (Addison-Wesley Series in Physics). pap. 72.80 (ISBN 0-317-08759-2, 2051972). Bks Demand UMI.
Skobel'tsyn, D. V., ed. Physical Acoustics & Optics: Molecular Scattering of Light; Propagation of Hypersound; Metal Optics. LC 75-33201. (P. N. Lebedev Physics Institute Ser.: Vol. 72). (Illus.). 210p. 1975. 65.00x (ISBN 0-306-10918-2, Consultants). Plenum Pub.
Tarasov, L. V. & Tarasov, A. N. Discussions on Refraction of Light. 239p. 1985. pap. 3.95 (ISBN 0-8285-2885-3, Pub. by Mir Pubs USSR). Imported Pubns.
Tyler, John E., ed. Light in the Sea. (Benchmark Paper in Optics Ser.: Vol. 3). 1977. 61.50 (ISBN 0-12-787595-6). Acad Pr.
Tyndall, John. Lectures on Light: Delivered in the United States in Eighteen Seventy-Two to Eighteen Seventy-Three. Cohen, I. Bernard, ed. LC 79-8003. (Three Centuries of Science in America Ser.). (Illus.). 1980. Repr. of 1873 ed. lib. bdg. 16.00x (ISBN 0-405-12592-5). Ayer Co Pubs.
Walker, Jearl, intro. by. Light & Its Uses: Making & Using Lasers, Holograms, Interferometers & Instruments of Dispersion - Readings from Scientific American. LC 79-27551. (Illus.). 147p. 1980. text ed. 19.95xp. (ISBN 0-7167-1184-2); pap. text ed. 11.95x (ISBN 0-7167-1185-0). W H Freeman.
Warren, Eugene. Geometries of Light. LC 81-2067. (The Wheaton Literary Ser.). 103p. 1981. pap. 4.95 (ISBN 0-87788-300-9). Shaw Pubs.

LIGHT–CHEMICAL ACTION
see Photochemistry

LIGHT–PHYSIOLOGICAL EFFECT
see also Color–Physiological Effect; Photoperiodism; Plants, Effect of Light On
Allen, Mary B., ed. Comparative Biochemistry of Photoreactive Systems. 1960. 71.50 (ISBN 0-12-051750-7). Acad Pr.
Bensasson, R. V., et al, eds. Primary Photo-Processes in Biology & Medicine. (NATO ASI Series A, Life Sciences: Vol. 8). 528p. 1985. 85.00x (ISBN 0-306-41930-0). Plenum Pub.
Giese, A. C., ed. Photophysiology. Incl. Vol. 1. General Principles - Action of Light on Plants. 1964. 67.50 (ISBN 0-12-282601-9); Vol. 2. Action of Light on Animals & Microorganisms, Photobiochemical Mechanisms, Bioluminescence. 1964. 67.50 (ISBN 0-12-282602-7); Vols. 3 & 4. Current Topics. 1968; Vols. 5-7. Current Topics in Photobiology & Photochemistry. Vol. 5, 1970. 64.50 (ISBN 0-12-282605-1); Vol. 6, 1971. 67.50 (ISBN 0-12-282606-X); Vol. 7, 1972. 67.50 (ISBN 0-12-282607-8); Vol. 8. 1973. 67.50 (ISBN 0-12-282608-6). Acad Pr.
Hollwich, F. The Influence of Ocular Light Perception on Metabolism in Man & Animal. LC 78-17076. (Topics in Environmental Physiology & Medicine Ser.). (Illus.). 1979. 52.00 (ISBN 0-387-90315-1). Springer-Verlag.
Ott, John N. Health & Light. (Illus.). 225p. 1973. Devin.
--My Ivory Cellar. (Illus.). 8.50 (ISBN 0-8159-6217-7). Devin.
Smith, Kendric C., ed. Topics in Photomedicine. 412p. 1984. 65.00x (ISBN 0-306-41510-0, Plenum Pr). Plenum Pub.
Waldman, Gary. Introduction to Light: The Physics of Light, Vision, & Color. (Illus.). 240p. 1983. prof. ref. 25.95 (ISBN 0-13-486027-6). P-H.
Williams, Theodore P. & Baker, B. N., eds. The Effect of Constant Light on Visual Processes. LC 79-26293. 465p. 1980. 59.50 (ISBN 0-306-40328-5, Plenum Pr). Plenum Pub.

LIGHT–SCATTERING
Barron, Lawrence D. Molecular Light Scattering & Optical Activity. 425p. 1983. 72.50 (ISBN 0-521-24602-4). Cambridge U Pr.
Bendow, Bernard, et al, eds. Theory of Light Scattering in Condensed Matter. LC 76-47492. 540p. 1976. 79.50x (ISBN 0-306-30993-9, Plenum Pr). Plenum Pub.
Bergman, Werner & Heller, Wilfried. Angular Light Scattering Maxima & Minima in Monodisperse & Heterodisperse Systems of Spheres. LC 77-6931. (Illus.). pap. 68.80 (ISBN 0-8357-9828-3, 2013660). Bks Demand UMI.
Berne, Bruce J. & Pecora, Robert. Dynamic Light Scattering: With Applications to Chemistry, Biology & Physics. LC 75-19140. 376p. 1976. 54.95 (ISBN 0-471-07100-5, Pub. by Wiley-Interscience). Wiley.
Birman, J. L., et al, eds. Light Scattering in Solids. LC 79-21683. 557p. 1980. 85.00x (ISBN 0-306-40313-7, Plenum Pr). Plenum Pub.
Bohren, Craig F. & Huffman, Donald R. Absorption & Scattering of Light by Small Particles. 530p. 1983. 51.95 (ISBN 0-471-05772-X, Pub. by Wiley-Interscience). Wiley.
Boll, Richard Henry. Tables of Light-Scattering Functions: Relative Indices of Less Than Unity & Infinity. LC 57-7175. pap. 93.00 (ISBN 0-317-08493-3, 2011234). Bks Demand UMI.
Buckingham, A. D., et al. Light Scattering in Physics, Chemistry & Biology. (Royal Society Ser.). (Illus.). 261p. 1980. Repr. of 1979 ed. text ed. 71.00x (ISBN 0-85403-127-8, Pub. by Royal Society London). Scholium Intl.
Cantow, H. J., et al. Light Scattering from Polymers. (Advances in Polymer Science Ser.: Vol. 48). (Illus.). 167p. 1983. 41.50 (ISBN 0-387-12030-0). Springer-Verlag.
Cardona, M. & Guentherodt, G., eds. Light Scattering in Solids II: Basic Concept & Instrumentation. (Topics in Applied Physics Ser.: Vol. 50). (Illus.). 251p. 1982. 48.00 (ISBN 0-387-11380-0). Springer-Verlag.
Cardona, M. & Guntherodt, G., eds. Light Scattering in Solids IV: Electronic Scattering, Spin Effects, SERS & Morphic Effects. LC 83-13095. (Topics in Applied Physics: Vol. 54). (Illus.). 560p. 1984. 47.50 (ISBN 0-387-11942-6). Springer-Verlag.
Crosignani, Bruno & Di Porto, Paolo. Statistical Properties of Scattered Light. (Quantum Electronics Ser.). 1975. 59.50 (ISBN 0-12-199050-8). Acad Pr.
Cummins, H. Z. & Levanyuk, A. P., eds. Light Scattering Near Phase Transitions. (Modern Problems in Condensed Matter Science Ser.: Vol. 5). 660p. 1984. 129.00 (ISBN 0-444-86466-0, North-Holland). Elsevier.
Dahneke, Barton E. Measurement of Suspended Particles by Quasi-Elastic Light Scattering. 570p. 1983. 48.50 (ISBN 0-471-87289-X, Pub. by Wiley-Interscience). Wiley.
Degiorgio, V., et al, eds. Light Scattering in Liquids & Macromolecular Solutions. LC 80-20472. 305p. 1980. 49.50x (ISBN 0-306-40558-X, Plenum Pr). Plenum Pub.
Fabelinskii, I. L. Molecular Scattering of Light. LC 67-10534. 622p. 1968. 69.50x (ISBN 0-306-30308-6, Plenum Pr). Plenum Pub.
Feigelson, E. M. & Malkevich, M. S. Calculation of the Brightness of Light in the Case of Anisotropic Scattering. LC 60-8720. (Transactions (Trudy) of the Institute of Atmospheric Physics Ser.: Pt. 1). pap. 27.50 (ISBN 0-317-08290-6, 2020687). Bks Demand UMI.
Hayes, William & Loudon, Rodney. Scattering of Light by Crystals. LC 78-9008. 360p. 1978. 54.50 (ISBN 0-471-03191-7, Pub. by Wiley-Interscience). Wiley.
Heller, Wilfried. Light Scattering Functions of Flow-Oriented Spheroids. LC 77-156067. 1124p. 1974. 50.00 (ISBN 0-8143-1537-2). Wayne St U Pr.
Heller, Wilfried & Bergman, Werner. Angular Light Scattering Maxima & Minima in Monodisperse & Heterodisperse Systems of Spheres. 1977. write for info. (ISBN 0-8143-1584-4). Wayne St U Pr.
Heller, Wilfried, et al. Depolarization & Related Ratios of Light Scattering by Spheroids. LC 74-13816. 105p. 1974. 12.00 (ISBN 0-8143-1527-5). Wayne St U Pr.
International Conference on Light Scattering Spectra of Solids, New York University, New York, 1968. Proceedings. Wright, G. B., ed. (Illus.). 1969. 135.00 (ISBN 0-387-04645-3). Springer-Verlag.
Kerker, Milton. Scattering of Light & Other Electromagnetic Radiation. (Physical Chemistry Ser.: Vol. 16). 1969. 94.50 (ISBN 0-12-404550-2). Acad Pr.
McCartney, Earl J. Optics of the Atmosphere: Scattering by Molecules & Particles. LC 76-10941. (Pure & Applied Optics Ser). 408p. 1976. 60.95x (ISBN 0-471-01526-1, Pub. by Wiley-Interscience). Wiley.
McIntyre, Donald & Gornick, F., eds. Light-Scattering from Dilute Polymer Solutions. (International Science Review Ser.). (Illus.). 332p. 1964. 62.50 (ISBN 0-677-00510-5). Gordon.
Schuerman, D. W., ed. Light Scattering by Irregularly Shaped Particles. LC 79-27691. 345p. 1980. 52.50x (ISBN 0-306-40421-4, Plenum Pr). Plenum Pub.
Sobolev, V. V. Light Scattering in Planetary Atmospheres. Irvine, W. M., tr. 1975. text ed. 54.00 (ISBN 0-08-017934-7). Pergamon.

Tarasov, L. V. & Tarasov, A. N. Discussions on Refraction of Light. 239p. 1985. pap. 3.95 (ISBN 0-8285-2885-3, Pub. by Mir Pubs USSR). Imported Pubns.
U. S.-Japan Seminar on Inelastic Light Scattering, Santa Monica, California. January 22-25, 1979. Inelastic Light Scattering: Proceedings. Burstein, E. & Kawamura, H., eds. 124p. 1980. 31.00 (ISBN 0-08-025425-X). Pergamon.
Van de Hulst, H. C. Light Scattering by Small Particles. x, 470p. 1982. pap. 7.50 (ISBN 0-486-64228-3). Dover.
--Light Scattering by Small Particles. 16.50 (ISBN 0-8446-5917-7). Peter Smith.

LIGHT-TABLES, ETC.
see Optics-Tables, etc.

LIGHT, COLORED
see Light-Physiological Effect

LIGHT, ELECTRIC
see Electric Lighting; Photometry

LIGHT, ELECTROMAGNETIC THEORY OF
see Electromagnetic Theory

LIGHT, INVISIBLE
see Spectrum, Infra-Red; Spectrum, Ultra-Violet

LIGHT, WAVE THEORY OF
see also Electromagnetic Theory; Optics, Physical

Chapple, M. A Level Physics: Wave Motion-Sound & Light, Vol. 2. 2nd ed. (Illus.). 240p. (Orig.). 1979. pap. text ed. 14.95x (ISBN 0-7121-0155-1, Pub. by Macdonald & Evans England). Trans-Atlantic.
Fresnel, Augustin J. Oeuvres Completes, 3 vols. (Lat.). Repr. of 1866 ed. 160.00 (ISBN 0-384-16770-5). Johnson Repr.
Frish, S. Problems of Wave Optics. 69p. 1976. pap. 1.95 (ISBN 0-8285-0831-3, Pub. by Mir Pubs USSR). Imported Pubns.
Home, Roderick W. The Effluvial Theory of Light. Cohen, I. Bernard, ed. LC 80-2317. (Development of Science Ser.). (Illus.). 1981. lib. bdg. 26.00x (ISBN 0-405-13965-9). Ayer Co Pubs.
Simmons, Joseph W. & Guttmann, Mark J. States, Waves & Photons: A Modern Introduction to Light. LC 73-102998. (Addison-Wesley Series in Physics). pap. 72.80 (ISBN 0-317-08759-2, 2051972). Bks Demand UMI.

LIGHT AMPLIFICATION BY STIMULATED EMISSION OF RADIATION
see Lasers

LIGHT FILTERS
see also Light; Optics; Photographic Optics

Eastman Kodak Company. Filters & Lens Attachments for Black-&-White & Color Pictures. 1975. pap. 2.95 (ISBN 0-87985-254-2, AB-1). Eastman Kodak.
How to Use Filters. 1981. 2.50 (ISBN 0-88284-143-2). Alfred Pub.
Smith, Robb. Amphoto Guide to Filters. (Illus.). 200p. 1979. (Amphoto); pap. 7.95 (ISBN 0-8174-2132-7). Watson-Guptill.

LIGHT METALS
see also Alkali Metals; Alkaline Earth Metals; Aluminum; Aluminum Alloys; Magnesium

McGeer, J. P., ed. Light Metals 1984: Proceedings, AIME Annual Meeting, Los Angeles, 1984. LC 72-623660. (Illus.). 1749p. 1984. 55.00 (ISBN 0-89520-470-3). Metal Soc.
Polmear, I. J. Light Alloys Metallurgy of the Light Metals. 224p. 1981. 45.00x (Pub. by E Arnold England). State Mutual Bk.

LIGHT PRODUCTION IN ANIMALS AND PLANTS
see Bioluminescence

LIGHT QUANTUM
see Photons

LIGHTER THAN AIR CRAFT
see Air-Ships

LIGHTHOUSES

Beaver, Patrick. A History of Lighthouses. (Illus.). 182p. 1973. 7.95 (ISBN 0-8065-0368-8). Citadel Pr.
--A History of Lighthouses. (Illus.). 158p. 1976. pap. 4.95 (ISBN 0-8065-0256-8). Citadel Pr.
Gibbs, James A. Sentinels of the North Pacific. (Illus.). 1955. 8.95 (ISBN 0-8323-0011-X). Binford.
Parker, Tony. Lighthouse. LC 76-11056. 1976. 8.95 (ISBN 0-8008-4853-5). Taplinger.
Shattuck, Clifford. The Nubble: Cape Neddick Lightstation, York, Maine. LC 79-53507. (Illus.). 1979. pap. 5.95 (ISBN 0-87027-195-4). Cumberland Pr.

LIGHTING
see also Acetylene; Candles; Electric Lighting; Lamps; Lighting, Architectural and Decorative; Stage Lighting

Acceptability of a Luminaire from VCP Standpoint. (Measurement & Testing Guides Ser.). 1972. member 2.25 (ISBN 0-686-96274-5, LM-38); non-member 4.50 (ISBN 0-686-99752-2). Illum Eng.
Addendum. 2.00 (CP-934A). Illum Eng.
Advanced Lighting Problems Course. (Lighting Education Ser.). 1971. 14.00 (ISBN 0-686-96081-5, ED-4); 9.00 (ISBN 0-686-99698-4); instr's. manual avail. Illum Eng.
Advanced Lighting Problems Course. 14.00 (ISBN 0-686-47872-X, 3D-4). Illum Eng.
Aircraft-Airline Industries. (IES Committee Reports Ser.). 1975. 5.50 (ISBN 0-686-96209-5, CP-40); members 2.75 (ISBN 0-686-99733-6). Illum Eng.
Lighting for the Aircraft Airline Industries. 5.50 (ISBN 0-686-47878-9). Illum Eng.
American National Standard Practice for Industrial Lighting. rev. ed. (Illus.). 52p. 1984. 14.00 (ISBN 0-87995-001-3, RP7); member 5.00. Illum Eng.
Anderson, M. & Lee, R. Efficiency in Lighting. Gyftopoulos, Elias P. & Cohen, Karen C., eds. (Industrial Energy-Conservation Manuals: No. 10). (Illus.). 104p. 1982. loose-leaf 20.00x (ISBN 0-262-01066-6). MIT Pr.
Boyce, P. R. Human Factors in Lighting. (Illus.). xiii, 420p. 1981. 52.00x (ISBN 0-686-28903-X). Burgess-Intl Ideas.
--Human Factors in Lighting. (Illus.). 421p. 1981. text ed. 45.00x (ISBN 0-02-949250-5). Macmillan.
Calculating Maintained Illumination. (Measurement & Testing Guides Ser.). 1970. 4.50 (ISBN 0-686-96264-8, LM-34). Illum Eng.
Calibration of Photoelectric Control Devices. (Measurement & Testing Guides Ser.). 1974. 4.50 (ISBN 0-686-96314-8, LM-48). Illum Eng.
Cayless, M. A. & Marsden, A. M. Lamps & Lighting. 3rd ed. 640p. 1984. text ed. 49.50 (ISBN 0-7131-3487-9). E Arnold.
Committee on Interior Lighting for Public Conveyances of the IES. Public Conveyances: Road-Rail Interior Lighting. new ed. (Illus.). 20p. 1974. tech. manual 6.50 (ISBN 0-87995-004-8, IES CP-12); member 3.25. Illum Eng.
Daylighting. (ANSI & IES Recommended Lighting Practices Ser.). 1979. member 9.00 (ISBN 0-686-96134-X, RP-5). Illum Eng.
Design of Light Control. (Measurement & Testing Guides Ser.). 1970. Repr. of 1958 ed. 8.00 (ISBN 0-686-96242-7, LM-17); members 4.00 (ISBN 0-686-99743-3). Illum Eng.
Determining the Acceptability of a Luminaire from the VCP Standpoint. 4.50 (ISBN 0-686-47889-4, LM-38). Illum Eng.
Early Lighting: A Pictorial Guide. 2nd ed. LC 78-68597. 140p. 1979. 18.75 (ISBN 0-917422-03-1). Rushlight Club.
ESI Specification in Interior Spaces. (ANSI & IES Recommended Lighting Practices Ser.). 1977. member 4.50 (ISBN 0-686-96169-2, RP-18); non-member 9.00 (ISBN 0-686-99717-4). Illum Eng.
Evaluating Visual Effectiveness: Lighting Systems. (Measurement & Testing Guides Ser.). 1970. member 2.25 (ISBN 0-686-96259-1, LM-33); non-member 4.50 (ISBN 0-686-99748-4). Illum Eng.
General Procedure for Calculating Maintained Illumination. 4.50 (ISBN 0-686-47887-8, LM-34). Illum Eng.
Graf, Rudolf F. & Graf, Calvin R. Emergency Lighting & Power Projects. LC 84-8865. (Illus.). 304p. (Orig.). 1985. 18.95 (ISBN 0-8306-0788-9); pap. cancelled (1788). TAB Bks.
Grosslight, Jane. Light: Effective Use of Daylight & Electrical Lighting in Residential & Commercial Spaces. (Illus.). 208p. 1984. 24.95 (ISBN 0-13-536300-4); pap. 14.95 (ISBN 0-13-536292-X). P-H.
Guide for Photometric Measurement of Roadway Lighting Installations. (Measurement & Testing Guides Ser.). 1975. member 2.00 (ISBN 0-686-96320-2, LM-50); non-member 4.00 (ISBN 0-686-99764-6). Illum Eng.
Hayward, Arthur H. Colonial & Early American Lighting. 3rd ed. 1962. pap. 5.95 (ISBN 0-486-20975-X). Dover.
--Colonial & Early American Lighting. 3rd enl. ed. (Illus.). 15.25 (ISBN 0-8446-2224-9). Peter Smith.
Helms, R. Illumination Engineering for Energy Efficient Luminous Environments. 1980. 47.95 (ISBN 0-13-450809-2). P-H.
Hopkinson, R. G. & Kay, J. D. The Lighting of Buildings. 318p. 1972. 16.95 (ISBN 0-571-04770-X). Faber & Faber.
IES Approved Method for Electrical & Photometric Measurements of General Service Incandescent Filament Lamps. 5.50 (ISBN 0-686-47895-9, LM-45). Illum Eng.
IES Approved Method for Photoelectric Measurements for HID Lamps. 4.50 (ISBN 0-686-47902-5, LM-51). Illum Eng.
IES Approved Method for Photometric Measuring & Reporting Tests on Reflector Type Lamps. 6.50 (ISBN 0-686-47883-5, LM-20). Illum Eng.
IES Approved Method for Photometric Testing of Indoor Luminaires Using HID Lamps. 4.50 (ISBN 0-686-47896-7, LM-46). Illum Eng.
IES Approved Method for Photometric Testing of Outdoor Luminaires. 5.50 (ISBN 0-686-47880-0, LM-10). Illum Eng.
IES Approved Method of Reflectometry. 4.50 (LM-44). Illum Eng.
IES Energy Management Committee. IES Recommended Procedure for Lighting Power Limit Determination. (Lighting Energy Management Ser.). (Illus., Orig.). 12.00 (ISBN 0-87995-012-9, IES LEM-1); 7.00 (ISBN 0-686-46680-2). Illum Eng.
IES Guide to Design of Light Control. 8.00 (ISBN 0-686-47882-7, LM-17). Illum Eng.
IES Lighting Handbooks: Nineteen Eighty-One Reference & Application Volumes, 2 vols. Set. 107.00 (ISBN 0-686-47912-2); Reference vol. 87.00 (ISBN 0-686-47913-0); Application vol. 58.50 ea. (ISBN 0-686-47914-9); members 48.50 ea. Illum Eng.
IES Lighting Survey Form A. 4.50 (ISBN 0-686-47884-3, LM-21). Illum Eng.
IES Recommended Procedure for Calculating Coefficients of Utilization, Wall & Ceiling Cavity Exitance. 6.00 (ISBN 0-686-47906-8, LM-57). Illum Eng.
IES Roadway Lighting Committee. American National Standard Practice for Roadway Lighting. 1983. 14.00 (ISBN 0-87995-013-7, RP-8). Illum Eng.
Industrial Lighting. 1984. 14.00 (ISBN 0-686-47866-5, RP-7); members 5.00. Illum Eng.
An Informational Guide for Roadway Lighting. rev. & updated ed. 1984. pap. 3.00 (ISBN 0-686-32361-0, GL-5). AASHTO.
Interior Lighting of Public Conveyances: Road & Rail. 6.50 (ISBN 0-686-47874-6, CP-12). Illum Eng.
Kalff, L. C. Creative Light. LC 76-169174. 148p. 1971. 19.95 (ISBN -686-78298-4). Krieger.
Kaufman, John E., ed. IES Lighting Handbook: Student Reference. abr. ed. (Illus.). 125p. 1982. pap. 15.00 (ISBN 0-87995-010-2). Illum Eng.
Kaufman, John E. & Christensen, Jack F., eds. Lighting Handbook. 6th ed. LC 77-186864. (Illus.). 770p. 1981. 58.50 (ISBN 0-87995-000-5); members 47.50 (ISBN 0-685-23764-8). Illum Eng.
Library Lighting. (ANSI & IES Recommended Lighting Practices Ser.). 1974. 6.50 (ISBN 0-686-96131-5, RP-4); members 3.25 (ISBN 0-686-99706-9). Illum Eng.
Life Performance Testing of Fluorescent Lamps. (Measurement & Testing Guides Ser.). 1982. 5.00 (ISBN 0-686-96283-4, LM-40); members 3.00 (ISBN 0-686-99754-9). Illum Eng.
Life-Testing HID Lamps. (Measurement & Testing Guides Ser.). 1982. member 3.00 (ISBN 0-686-96308-3, LM-47); non-member 5.00 (ISBN 0-686-99761-1). Illum Eng.
Lighting for Dairy Farms. (IES Committee Reports Ser.). 1965. 4.50 (ISBN 0-686-96191-9, CP-33); members 2.00 (ISBN 0-686-99726-3). Illum Eng.
Lighting for Health Care Facilities. (IES Committee Reports Ser.). 1978. member 6.00 (ISBN 0-686-96186-2, CP-29); non-member 10.00 (ISBN 0-686-99724-7). Illum Eng.
Lighting for Manufacturing Rubber Tires. 4.50 (ISBN 0-686-47876-2, CP-35). Illum Eng.
Lighting for Proscenium Stages. (IES Committee Reports Ser.). 1968. member 2.25 (ISBN 0-686-96193-5, CP-34); non-member 4.50 (ISBN 0-686-99727-1). Illum Eng.
Lighting for the Poultry Industry. 4.50 (ISBN 0-686-47877-0). Illum Eng.
Lighting Fundamentals Course. (Lighting Education Ser.). 1976. 10.00 (ISBN 0-686-96067-X, ED-2); members 6.50 (ISBN 0-686-99695-X). Illum Eng.
Lighting Merchandise Areas. (ANSI & RES Recommended Lighting Practices Ser.). 1976. 10.00 (ISBN 0-686-96124-2, RP-2); members 5.00 (ISBN 0-686-99704-2). Illum Eng.
Lighting System Noise Criterion (LS-NC) Ratings. 1980. 5.00 (ISBN 0-318-18023-5, LE 2-1974). Natl Elec Mfrs.
Lynes, J. A. & Pritchard, D. C., eds. Developments in Lighting, Vols. 1 & 2. Vol. 1, 1978. 46.25 (ISBN 0-85334-774-3, Pub. by Elsevier Applied Sci England); Vol. 2, 1982. 50.00 (ISBN 0-85334-985-1). Elsevier.
Lyone, Stanley. Management Guide to Modern Industrial Lighting. 2nd ed. 176p. 1983. text ed. 39.95 (ISBN 0-408-01147-5). Butterworth.
Lyons. Handbook of Industrial Lighting. 1981. text ed. 49.95 (ISBN 0-408-00525-4). Butterworth.
Method for Electrical & Photometric Measurements of General Service Incandescent Filament Lamps. (Measurement & Testing Guides Ser.). 1981. 5.50 (ISBN 0-686-96301-6, LM-45); members 3.00 (ISBN 0-686-99759-X). Illum Eng.
Method for Photometric Testing of Indoor Luminaires Using HID Lamps. (Measurement & Testing Guides Ser.). 1974. 4.50 (ISBN 0-686-96305-9, LM-46); members 2.20 (ISBN 0-686-99760-3). Illum Eng.
Method for the Electrical & Photometric Measurements of Fluorescent Lamps. (Measurement & Testing Guides Ser.). 1982. 6.50 (ISBN 0-686-96228-1, LM-9); members 3.75 (ISBN 0-686-99739-5). Illum Eng.
Murdoch, Joseph B. Illumination Engineering: From Edison's Lamp to the Laser. 480p. 1985. text ed. 44.50 (ISBN 0-317-06092-9). Macmillan.
National Academy Of Sciences. Plastics in Building Illumination. 1958. pap. 3.00. Natl Acad Pr.
Natural Lighting. (Illus.). 1982. pap. 9.95 (ISBN 0-918984-05-X). SolarVision.
Norman, L. D. & Frost, J. W. Lighting for Engineers & Designers. 256p. 1986. 24.00x (ISBN 0-246-12081-9, Pub. by Granada England). Sheridan.
Office Lighting. 1982. 13.50 (ISBN 0-686-47863-0, RP-1). Illum Eng.
Practical Guide to Colorimetry of Light Sources. 4.50 (ISBN 0-686-47881-9). Illum Eng.
Predetermination of Contrast Rendition Factors for the Calculation of ESI. 9.00 (ISBN 0-686-47890-8, LM-39). Illum Eng.
Roadway Lighting Fundamentals Course. (Lighting Education Ser.). 1981. 13.50 (ISBN 0-686-96075-0, ED-3); members 8.00 (ISBN 0-686-99697-6). Illum Eng.
Roadway Sign Lighting. 1983. 6.00 (ISBN 0-686-47868-1). Illum Eng.
Rudman, Jack. Assistant Supervisor (Lighting) (Career Examination Ser.: C-2006). (Cloth bdg. avail. on request). pap. 12.00 (ISBN 0-8373-2006-2). Natl Learning.
--Foreman of Lighting. (Career Examination Ser.: C-271). (Cloth bdg. avail. on request). pap. 10.00 (ISBN 0-8373-0271-4). Natl Learning.
--Lighting Inspector. (Career Examination Ser.: C-2134). (Cloth bdg. avail. on request). 1977. pap. 10.00 (ISBN 0-8373-2134-4). Natl Learning.
Samuelson, David. Motion Picture Camera & Lighting Equipment. (Media Manuals Ser.). 1977. pap. 8.95 (ISBN 0-8038-4685-1). Hastings.
School Lighting. (ANSI & RES Recommended Lighting Practices Ser.). 1979. member 6.00 (ISBN 0-686-96127-7, RP-3); non-member 10.00 (ISBN 0-686-99705-0). Illum Eng.
Selection of Illuminance Values for Interior Lighting Design. (ANSI & IES Recommended Lighting Practices Ser.). 1980. 5.00 (ISBN 0-686-96165-X, RP-15A); members 2.50 (ISBN 0-686-99714-X). Illum Eng.
Sorcar, Prafulla C. Rapid Lighting Design & Cost Estimating. LC 79-4690. (Illus.). 1979. 45.00 (ISBN 0-07-059651-4). McGraw.
The Specification of an ESI Rating in Interior Spaces When Specific Task Locations Are Unknown. 1977. 9.50 (ISBN 0-686-47867-3, RP-18). Illum Eng.
Sports Lighting. (ANSI & IES Recommended Lighting Practices). 1969. 8.00 (ISBN 0-686-96138-2, RP-6); member 5.00 (ISBN 0-686-99708-5). Illum Eng.
Trotter, D. A. The Lighting of Underground Mines. 1982. 48.00x (ISBN 0-87849-041-8). Trans Tech.
Wilson, William H. How to Design & Install Outdoor Lighting. Smith, Michael D., ed. LC 83-62652. (Illus.). 96p. 1984. pap. 5.95 (ISBN 0-89721-026-3). Ortho.
Zimmermann, Ralf. Dictionary of Lighting. 362p. 1980. 70.00x (ISBN 0-569-08526-8, Pub. by Collet's). State Mutual Bk.

LIGHTING, ARCHITECTURAL AND DECORATIVE

Egan, M. David. Concepts in Lighting for Architecture. LC 82-20832. (Illus.). 272p. 1983. 38.00 (ISBN 0-07-019054-2). McGraw.
Evans, Benjamin. Daylight in Architecture. LC 80-26066. (Illus.). 204p. 1982. 42.50x (ISBN 0-07-019768-7). McGraw.
Lambeth, et al. Solar Four. 96p. 1981. softcover 14.95 (ISBN 0-9601678-7-0). Lambeth.
Moore, Fuller. Concepts & Practices of Architectural Daylighting. LC 84-29929. (Illus.). 304p. 1985. 39.95 (ISBN 0-442-26439-9). Van Nos Reinhold.
Nuckolls, James L. Interior Lighting for Environmental Designers. 2nd ed. LC 83-1382. 407p. 1983. 42.95x (ISBN 0-471-87381-0, Pub. by Wiley-Interscience). Wiley.
Ramsey, Dan. Effective Lighting for Home & Business. (Illus.). 224p. 1984. 18.95 (ISBN 0-8306-0658-0); pap. 13.50 (ISBN 0-8306-1658-6, 1658). TAB Bks.
Residence Lighting Committee. Design Criteria for Lighting Interior Living Spaces. rev. ed. (Illus.). 52p. 1980. 13.50 (ISBN 0-87995-006-4, RP-11); 8.00. Illum Eng.
Sunset Editors. Home Lighting. LC 82-81371. (Illus.). 96p. (Orig.). 1982. pap. 4.95 (ISBN 0-376-01312-5, Sunset Bks). Sunset-Lane.
Traister, John E. Practical Lighting Applications for Building Construction. 200p. 1981. 21.95 (ISBN 0-442-24727-3). Van Nos Reinhold.

LIGHTNING
see also Atmospheric Electricity; Transients (Electricity)

Barry, James D. Ball Lightning & Bead Lightning: Extreme Forms of Atmospheric Electricity. LC 79-19017. (Illus.). 308p. 1980. 35.00x (ISBN 0-306-40272-6, Plenum Pr). Plenum Pub.

Corliss, William R. Lightning, Auroras, Nocturnal Lights & Related Luminous Phenomena. LC 82-99902. (A Catalog of Geophysical Anomalies Ser.). (Illus.). 248p. 1982. 11.95 (ISBN 0-915554-09-7). Sourcebook.

Hart, William C. & Malone, Edgar W. Lightning & Lightning Protection. White, Donald R., ed. LC 79-65691. (Illus.). 181p. 1979. text ed. 42.00 (ISBN 0-932263-14-3). White Consult.

Harward, Simon. A Discourse of Lightnings. LC 75-171762. (English Experience Ser.: No. 385). 24p. 1971. Repr. of 1607 ed. 7.00 (ISBN 90-221-0385-4). Walter J Johnson.

Lightning Protection Code. (Seventy Ser.). 59p. 1968. pap. 2.00 (ISBN 0-685-46076-2, 78). Natl Fire Prot.

Ritchie, Donald J. Ball Lightning. LC 61-15177. 70p. 1961. 17.50x (ISBN 0-306-10509-8, Consultants). Plenum Pub.

Salanave, Leon E. Lightning & Its Spectrum: An Atlas of Photographs. LC 80-18882. (Illus.). 136p. 1980. 30.00 (ISBN 0-8165-0374-5). U of Ariz Pr.

Singer, Stanley. The Nature of Ball Lightning. LC 70-128512. 169p. 1971. 35.00x (ISBN 0-306-30494-5, Plenum Pr). Plenum Pub.

Uman, Martin A. Lightning. (Physics Ser.). 320p. 1984. pap. 7.95 (ISBN 0-486-64575-4). Dover.

Viemeister, Peter E. The Lightning Book. (Illus.). 316p. 1972. pap. 5.95 (ISBN 0-262-72004-3). MIT Pr.

LIGHTNING (FIGHTER PLANES)

Gurney, Gene. P-38 Lightning. LC 70-76218. (Famous Aircraft Ser). (Illus., Orig.). 1969. pap. 4.95 (ISBN 0-668-02015-6). Arco.

LIGHTNING ARRESTERS

Lightning Protection Code. (Seventy Ser.). 59p. 1968. pap. 2.00 (ISBN 0-685-46076-2, 78). Natl Fire Prot.

LIGNIN

see also Wood–Chemistry

Brauns, Friedrich E. & Brauns, Dorothy A. Chemistry of Lignin: Supplementary Volume Covering Literature for 1949-58. 1960. 90.00 (ISBN 0-12-127861-1). Acad Pr.

Crawford, Ronald L. Lignin Biodegradation & Transformation. LC 80-39557. 154p. 1981. 37.50x (ISBN 0-471-05743-6, Pub. by Wiley-Interscience). Wiley.

Kirk, T. Kent, et al. Lignin Biodegradation: Microbiology, Chemistry & Potential Applications, 2 vols. 1980. Vol. 1, 256 Pgs. 73.00 (ISBN 0-8493-5459-5); Vol. 2, 272 Pgs. 76.50 (ISBN 0-8493-5460-9). CRC Pr.

Sarkanen, K. V. & Ludwig, Charles H. Lignins: Occurrence, Formation, Structure & Reactions. LC 79-148456. (Illus.). 916p. 1971. 125.00 (ISBN 0-471-75422-6, Pub. by Wiley-Interscience). Wiley.

Schubert, Walter J. Lignin Biochemistry. 1965. 37.50 (ISBN 0-12-630950-7). Acad Pr.

LIGNITE

see also Coal

Kaiser, W. R. Texas Lignite: Near-Surface & Deep-Basin Resources. (Report of Investigations Ser.: RI 79). (Illus.). 70p. 1979. Repr. of 1974 ed. 3.00 (ISBN 0-318-03203-1). Bur Econ Geology.

Kaiser, W. R., et al. Lignite Resources in Texas. (Report of Investigations: RI 104). (Illus.). 52p. 1980. 2.00 (ISBN 0-318-03244-9). Bur Econ Geology.

Nowacki, Perry, ed. Lignite Technology. LC 79-26051. (Energy Technology Review Ser. No. 53; Chemical Technology Review Ser.: No. 146). (Illus.). 228p. 1980. 42.00 (ISBN 0-8155-0783-6). Noyes.

Tewalt, Susan J., et al. Detailed Evaluation of Two Texas Lignite Deposits of Deltaic & Fluvial Origins. (Geological Circular Ser.: GC 82-2). (Illus.). 12p. 1982. Repr. 1.00 (ISBN 0-686-37546-7). Bur Econ Geology.

LILIES

Jekyll, Gertrude. Lilies for English Gardens. (Illus.). 156p. 1982. 29.50 (ISBN 0-907462-28-6). Antique Collect.

Redoute, Pierre. Lilies & Related Flowers. LC 81-11021. (Illus.). 240p. 1982. 60.00 (ISBN 0-87951-135-4). Overlook Pr.

Synge, Patrick M. Lillies. 1981. 90.00x (ISBN 0-686-78780-3, Pub. by RHS Ent England). State Mutual Bk.

Synge, Patrick M., compiled by. Lilies: A Revision of Elwes' Monograph of the Genus Lilium & Its Supplements. LC 79-9682. (Illus.). 280p. 1980. 65.00x (ISBN 0-87663-340-8). Universe.

LIMBIC SYSTEM

Girgis, Makram. Neural Substrates of Limbic Epilepsy. (Illus.). 200p. 1981. 42.50 (ISBN 0-87527-238-X). Green.

Hamilton, Leonard W., ed. Basic Limbic System Anatomy of the Rat. LC 76-46401. (Illus.). 167p. 1976. 25.00x (ISBN 0-306-30925-4, Plenum Pr). Plenum Pub.

Hockman, Charles H., ed. Limbic System Mechanisms & Autonomic Function. (Illus.). 312p. 1972. photocopy ed. 39.75x (ISBN 0-398-02315-8). C C Thomas.

Isaacson, Robert L. The Limbic System. LC 74-8298. (Illus.). 292p. 1974. 22.50x (ISBN 0-306-30773-1, Plenum Pr). Plenum Pub.

--The Limbic System. 2nd ed. (Illus.). 342p. 1982. 27.50x (ISBN 0-306-40874-0, Plenum Pr). Plenum Pub.

Kelly, Desmond. Anxiety & Emotions: Physiological Basis & Treatment. (Illus.). 424p. 1980. 24.75x (ISBN 0-398-03893-7). C C Thomas.

Livingston, K. E. & Hornykiewicz, O., eds. Limbic Mechanisms: The Continuing Evolution of the Limbic System Concept. LC 78-1542. 558p. 1978. 55.00x (ISBN 0-306-31135-6, Plenum Pr). Plenum Pub.

Reep, R., ed. Relationship Between Prefrontal & Limbic Cortex: A Comparative Anatomical Review. (Journal: Brain, Behavioral & Evolution: Vol. 25, Nos. 1-2). (Illus.). 80p. 1985. pap. 23.50 (ISBN 3-8055-4033-7). S Karger.

LIME

see also Cement

Boynton, Robert S. Chemistry & Technology of Lime & Limestone. 2nd ed. LC 79-16140. 578p. 1980. 90.00 (ISBN 0-471-02771-5, Pub. by Wiley-Interscience). Wiley.

Fitz, J., ed. Limes: Proceedings 11th Intl. Lime Congress. 1977. 55.00 (ISBN 0-9960002-8-3, Pub. by Akademiai Kaido Hungary). Heyden.

LIMESTONE

Boynton, Robert S. Chemistry & Technology of Lime & Limestone. 2nd ed. LC 79-16140. 578p. 1980. 90.00 (ISBN 0-471-02771-5, Pub. by Wiley-Interscience). Wiley.

Cayeux, L. Carbonate Rocks, Limestone & Dolmites, Sedimentary Rocks of France. Carozzi, A. V., tr. (Illus.). 1969. Repr. 53.95x (ISBN 0-02-842660-6). Hafner.

Danner, Wilbert R. Limestone Resources of Western Washington. (Bulletin Ser.: No. 52). (Illus.). 474p. 1966. 4.50 (ISBN 0-686-34705-6). Geologic Pubns.

Fischer, Alfred G., et al. Electron Micrographs of Limestones & Their Nannofossils. (Monographs in Geology & Paleontology Ser). (Illus.). 1967. 20.00 (ISBN 0-691-07953-6); pap. 9.95 (ISBN 0-691-07954-4). Princeton U Pr.

Fluegel, Erik. Microfacies Analysis of Limestones. (Illus.). 550p. 1982. 69.50 (ISBN 0-387-11269-3). Springer-Verlag.

Ford, Trevor D. Limestone & Caves of the Peak District. 469p. 1981. 50.00x (ISBN 0-86094-005-5, Pub. by GEO Abstracts England). State Mutual Bk.

Johnson, J. Harlan. Limestone-Building Algae & Algal Limestones. 297p. 1961. 2.70 (ISBN 0-918062-11-X). Colo Sch Mines.

Lozo, F. E. Symposium on Edwards Limestone in Central Texas. (Illus.). 235p. 1959. 5.00 (ISBN 0-318-03309-7, PUB 5905). Bur Econ Geology.

Matti, Jonathan C., et al. Silurian & Lower Denonian Basin & Basin-Slope Limestones. LC 74-19734. (Geological Society of America Ser.: No. 159). pap. 20.00 (ISBN 0-317-28377-4, 2025458). Bks Demand UMI.

Mills, Joseph W. High-Calcium Limestones of Eastern Washington. (Bulletin Ser.: No. 48). (Illus.). 268p. 1962. 4.00 (ISBN 0-686-34701-3). Geologic Pubns.

Pray, Lloyd C. & Murray, Raymond C., eds. Dolomitization & Limestone Diagenesis: A Symposium. LC 73-15328. (Society of Economic Paleontologists & Mineralogists, Special Publication: No. 13). pap. 47.50 (ISBN 0-317-27156-3, 2024739). Bks Demand UMI.

Raese, Jon & Goldberg, J. H., eds. Algal Limestones Within the Minturn Formation, Meeker to Dotsero Area, Western Colorado. (Colorado School of Mines Quarterly Ser.: Vol. 78, No. 2). (Illus.). 14p. 1983. pap. 10.00 (ISBN 0-686-45171-6). Colo Sch Mines.

Rodda, P. U., et al. Limestone & Dolomite Resources, Lower Cretaceous Rocks, Texas. (Report of Investigations: RI 56). (Illus.). 286p. 1966. Repr. 4.50 (ISBN 0-686-29338-X). Bur Econ Geology.

Salanki, J. & Ponyi, E., eds. Limnology of Shallow Waters. 1977. 22.00 (ISBN 0-9960001-1-9, Pub. by Akademiai Kaido Hungary). Heyden.

Sanders, Scott R. Stone Country. LC 84-43154. (Illus.). 256p. 1985. 24.95 (ISBN 0-253-18515-7). Ind U Pr.

Trudgill, Stephen. Limestone Geomorphology. (Geomorphology Texts Ser.). (Illus.). 231p. 1985. pap. text ed. 19.95 (ISBN 0-582-30011-8). Longman.

LIMIT ANALYSIS (THEORY OF STRUCTURES)

see Plastic Analysis (Theory of Structures)

LIMITED ACCESS HIGHWAYS

see Express Highways

LIMITS (MATHEMATICS)

see Calculus

LIMNOLOGY

see also Fresh-Water Biology; Paleolimnology; ; Water Chemistry

Allanson, B. R., ed. Lake Sibaya. (Monographiae Biologicae: No. 36). 1980. lib. bdg. 68.50 (ISBN 90-6193-088-X, Pub. by Junk Pubs Netherlands). Kluwer Academic.

Britt, N. Wilson, et al. Limmological Studies of the Island Area of Western Lake Erie. 1973. 3.00 (ISBN 0-86727-062-4). Ohio Bio Survey.

Cole, Gerald A. Textbook of Limnology. 3rd ed. LC 82-10607. (Illus.). 401p. 1983. text ed. 24.95 (ISBN 0-8016-1004-4). Mosby.

Deevey, Edward S., Jr. Limnologic Studies in Middle America with a Chapter on Aztec Limnology. (Connecticut Academy of Arts & Sciences Transactions Ser.: Vol. 39). 1957. 15.00 (ISBN 0-317-03799-4). Shoe String.

Dumont, H. J., et al, eds. Limnology & Marine Biology in the Sudan. (Developments in Hydrobiology Ser.). 1984. lib. bdg. 84.00 (ISBN 90-6193-772-8, Pub. by Junk Pubs Netherlands). Kluwer Academic.

Egerton, Frank N., 3rd, ed. Limnology in Wisconsin: An Original Anthology. LC 77-74203. (History of Ecology Ser.). (Illus.). 1978. lib. bdg. 57.50x (ISBN 0-405-10373-5). Ayer Co Pubs.

Fraser, J. C. Determining Discharges for Fluvial Resources. (Fisheries Technical Papers: No. 143). (Illus.). 102p. 1975. pap. 7.50 (ISBN 92-5-101909-6, F873, FAO). Unipub.

Goldman, Charles & Horne, Alexander. Limnology. (Illus.). 633p. 1982. text ed. 39.95 (ISBN 0-07-023651-8). McGraw.

Henderson-Sellers, B. Engineering Limnology. LC 84-1765. 500p. 1984. text ed. 65.95 (ISBN 0-273-08539-5). Pitman Pub MA.

Hobbie, J. E., ed. Limnology of Tundra Ponds: Barrow, Alaska. LC 80-26373. (US-IBP Synthesis Ser.: Vol. 13). 514p. 1980. 38.50 (ISBN 0-87933-386-3). Van Nos Reinhold.

Horie, S. Lake Biwa. (Monographiae Biologicae). 1985. lib. bdg. 145.00 (ISBN 90-6193-095-2, Pub. by Junk Pubs Netherland). Kluwer Academic.

Hutchinson, G. Evelyn. A Treatise on Liminology, 3 vols. Incl. Vol. 1, 2 pts. 1957. Set. pap. 48.50 (ISBN 0-471-42567-2); Pt. 1. Geography & Physics of Lakes. 672p. 1957. 26.95 (ISBN 0-471-42568-0); Vol. 1, Pt. 2. Chemistry of Lakes. 474p. 1957. pap. 24.95x (ISBN 0-471-42569-9); Vol. 2. Introduction to Lake Biology & the Limnoplankton. 1957. 99.95x (ISBN 0-471-42572-9); Vol. 3. Limnological Biology. 660p. 1975. 54.50x (ISBN 0-471-42574-5). LC 57-8888 (Pub. by Wiley-Interscience). Wiley.

Hutter, K., ed. Hydrodynamics of Lakes. (CISM: International Centre for Mechanical Sciences Courses & Lectures Ser.: No. 286). (Illus.). viii, 341p. 1984. 23.70 (ISBN 0-387-81812-X). Springer-Verlag.

Hutzinger, O., ed. The Natural Environment & the Biogeochemical Cycles. (The Handbook of Environmental Chemistry Ser.: Vol. 1, Pt. D). (Illus.). 260p. 1985. 59.00 (ISBN 0-387-15000-5). Springer-Verlag.

Lind, Owen T. Handbook of Common Methods in Limnology. 2nd ed. LC 78-21173. (Illus.). 200p. 1979. pap. text ed. 14.95 (ISBN 0-8016-3019-3). Mosby.

Loffler, H., ed. Neusiedlersee: The Limnology of a Shallow Lake in Central Europe. (Monographiae Biologicae Ser.: No. 37). (Illus.). x, 559p. 1980. lib. bdg. 103.00 (ISBN 90-6193-089-8, Pub. by Junk Pubs Netherlands). Kluwer Academic.

Mackereth, F. J., et al. Water Analysis: Some Revised Methods for Limnologists. 1978. 25.00x (ISBN 0-900386-31-2, Pub. by Freshwater Bio). State Mutual Bk.

McLusky, Donald S. Ecology of Estuaries. (Scholarship Ser. in Biology). 1971. text ed. 9.50x (ISBN 0-435-61600-5). Heinemann Ed.

--Estuarine Ecosystem. LC 80-28199. (Tertiary Level Biology Ser.). 150p. 1981. 32.95x (ISBN 0-470-27127-2). Halsted Pr.

Murray, John & Pullar, Laurence. Bathymetrical Survey of the Scottish Fresh Water Lochs, Vol. 1. Egerton, Frank N., 3rd, ed. LC 77-74243. (History of Ecology Ser.). (Illus.). 1978. Repr. of 1910 ed. lib. bdg. 65.00x (ISBN 0-405-10412-X). Ayer Co Pubs.

Patrick, R., et al. The Catherwood Foundation Peruvian-Amazon Expedition: Limnological & Systematic Studies. (Monograph: No. 14). (Illus.). 495p. (Orig.). 1966. pap. 23.00 (ISBN 0-910006-22-9). Acad Nat Sci Phila.

Russell-Hunter, W. D. Aquatic Productivity: An Introduction to Some Basic Aspects of Biological Oceanography & Limnology. (Illus.). 1970. text ed. 12.95x (ISBN 0-685-04258-8). Macmillan.

Rzoska, Julian. On the Nature of Rivers: With Case Stories of the Nile, Zaire, & Amazon. 1978. pap. 10.50 (ISBN 90-6193-589-X, Pub. by Junk Pubs Netherlands). Kluwer Academic.

Serruya, Colette & Pollingher, Utsa. Lakes of the Warm Belt. LC 82-19857. (Illus.). 500p. 1983. 95.00 (ISBN 0-521-23357-7). Cambridge U Pr.

Wetzel, Robert G. Limnology. 2nd ed. 1983. text ed. 39.95 (ISBN 0-03-057913-9, CBS C). SCP.

Wetzel, Robert G. & Likens, Gene E. Limnological Analyses. 1979. pap. text ed. 24.95 (ISBN 0-7216-9243-5, CBS C). SCP.

LIMU

see Algae; Mosses

LINE GEOMETRY

see also Algebras, Linear; Complexes

Jessop, Charles H. Treatise on the Line Complex. LC 68-55945. 1969. Repr. of 1903 ed. 14.95 (ISBN 0-8284-0223-X). Chelsea Pub.

Timerding, H. Emil. Geometrie der Krafte. (Bibliotheca Mathematica Teubneriana: No. 33). (Ger). Repr. of 1908 ed. 28.00 (ISBN 0-384-60640-7). Johnson Repr.

Vasilyev, N. & Gutenmacher, V. Straight Lines & Curves. 1980. 5.45 (ISBN 0-8285-1792-4, Pub. by Mir Pubs USSR). Imported Pubns.

LINEAR ACCELERATORS

Radiological Safety Aspects of the Operation of Electron Linear Accelerators. (Technical Reports Ser.: No. 188). (Illus.). 327p. 1979. pap. 49.25 (ISBN 92-0-125179-3, IDC188, IAEA). Unipub.

LINEAR ALGEBRAS

see Algebras, Linear

LINEAR COMPLEXES

see Complexes

LINEAR DIFFERENTIAL EQUATIONS

see Differential Equations, Linear

LINEAR DIGITAL FILTERS (MATHEMATICS)

see Digital Filters (Mathematics)

LINEAR ELLIPTIC DIFFERENTIAL EQUATIONS

see Differential Equations, Elliptic

LINEAR FREE ENERGY RELATIONSHIP

Chapman, N. B. & Shorter, J., eds. Advances in Linear Free-Energy Relationships. LC 78-161305. 448p. 1972. 65.00x (ISBN 0-306-30566-6, Plenum Pr). Plenum Pub.

Johnson, C. D. The Hammett Equation. LC 72-93140. (Chemistry Texts Ser). (Illus.). 180p. 1973. 34.50 (ISBN 0-521-20138-1). Cambridge U Pr.

LINEAR INPUT LOGIC

see Threshold Logic

LINEAR MAPS

see Linear Operators

LINEAR NORMED SPACES

see Normed Linear Spaces

LINEAR OPERATORS

Akheizer, N. I. Theory of Linear Operators in Hilbert Space, Vol. 1. Everitt, N., ed. Dawson, E. R., tr. (Monographs & Studies: No. 9). 320p. 1980. text ed. 89.95 (ISBN 0-273-08495-X). Pitman Pub MA.

Akheizer, N. I. & Glazman, I. M. Theory of Linear Operators in Hilbert Space, Vol. 2. Everitt, N., ed. Dawson, E. R., tr. (Monographs & Studies: No. 10). 280p. 1980. text ed. 84.50 (ISBN 0-273-08496-8). Pitman Pub MA.

Arsene, et al. Spectral Theory of Linear Operators & Related Topics. (Operator Theory Ser.: No. 14). 1985. text ed. 39.95x (ISBN 0-317-18422-9). Birkhauser.

Beals, Richard. Topics in Operator Theory. LC 70-147095. (Chicago Lectures in Mathematics Ser). (Orig.). 1971. pap. 6.00x (ISBN 0-226-03985-4). U of Chicago Pr.

Boumans, P. W., ed. Line Coincidence Tables for Inductively Coupled Plasma Atomic Emission Spectrometry, 2 vols. (Fr., Illus.). 941p. 1981. 250.00 (ISBN 0-08-026269-4). Pergamon.

--Line Coincidence Tables for Inductively Coupled Plasma Atomic Emission Spectrometry, 2 vols. (Span., Illus.). 941p. 1981. 250.00 (ISBN 0-08-026270-8). Pergamon.

Brodskii, M. S. Triangular & Jordan Representations of Linear Operators. LC 74-162998. (Translations of Mathematical Monographs: Vol. 32). 1972. 34.00 (ISBN 0-8218-1582-2, MMONO-32). Am Math.

Chatelin, Francoise. Spectral Approximation of Linear Operators. (Computer Science & Applied Mathematics Ser.). 1983. 69.50 (ISBN 0-12-170620-6). Acad Pr.

Coddington, Earl A. Extension Theory of Formally Normal & Symmetric Subspaces. LC 73-7870. (Memoirs: No. 134). 80p. 1973. pap. 10.00 (ISBN 0-8218-1834-1, MEMO-134). Am Math.

De Vore, R. A. The Approximation of Continuous Functions by Positive Linear Operators. LC 72-91891. (Lecture Notes in Mathematics: Vol. 293). viii, 289p. 1972. pap. 13.00 (ISBN 0-387-06038-3). Springer-Verlag.

Diestel, J. & Uhl, J. J. Vector Measures. LC 77-9625. (Mathematical Surveys Ser.: No. 15). 322p. 1979. pap. 36.00 (ISBN 0-8218-1515-6, SURV15). Am Math.

LINEAR SYSTEM THEORY
see System Analysis
LINEAR TOPOLOGICAL SPACES
see also Distributions, Theory of (Functional Analysis); Topological Algebras
Adasch, N., et al. Topological Vector Spaces: The Theory Without Convexity Conditions. (Lecture Notes in Mathematics: Vol. 639). 1978. pap. 14.00 (ISBN 0-387-08662-5). Springer-Verlag.
Cristescu, R. Ordered Vector Spaces & Linear Operations. 1976. 42.00 (ISBN 0-9961002-5-3, Pub. by Abacus England). Heyden.
Engelking, R. Dimension Theory. (Mathematical Library Ser.: Vol. 19). 314p. 1979. 64.00 (ISBN 0-444-85176-3, North Holland). Elsevier.
Froelicher, A. & Bucher, W. Calculus in Vector Spaces Without Norm. (Lecture Notes in Mathematics). (Orig.). 1966. pap. 10.70 (ISBN 0-387-03612-1). Springer-Verlag.
Gierz, G. Bundles of Topological Vector Spaces & Their Duality. (Lecture Notes in Mathematics: Vol. 955). 296p. 1982. pap. 16.00 (ISBN 0-387-11610-9). Springer-Verlag.
Graves, William H., ed. Conference on Integration, Topology & Geometry in Linear Spaces: Proceedings. LC 80-25417. (Contemporary Mathematics Ser.: Vol. 2). 269p. 1980. pap. 19.00 (ISBN 0-8218-5002-4, CONM-2). Am Math.
Hirsch, Morris W. & Mazur, Barry. Smoothings of Piecewise Linear Manifolds. LC 74-2967. (Annals of Mathematics Studies: No. 80). 165p. 1974. 16.50x (ISBN 0-691-08145-X). Princeton U Pr.
Husain, T. & Khaleelulla, S. M. Barrelledness in Topological & Ordered Vector Spaces. (Lecture Notes in Mathematics: Vol. 692). 1978. pap. 20.00 (ISBN 0-387-09096-7). Springer-Verlag.
Husain, Taqdir. The Open Mapping & Closed Graph Theorems in Topological Vector Spaces. LC 76-10334. 118p. 1976. Repr. of 1965 ed. 8.95 (ISBN 0-88275-412-2). Krieger.
Khaleolulla, S. M. Counterexamples in Topological Vector Spaces. (Lecture Notes in Mathematics Ser.: Vol. 936). 179p. 1982. pap. 13.00 (ISBN 0-387-11565-X). Springer-Verlag.
Klein, Erwin & Thompson, Anthony C. Theory of Correspondences: Including Applications to Mathematical Economics. Kaplan, David B., ed. LC 84-2407. (Canadian Mathematical Society Series of Monographs & Advanced Texts: 1-590). 256p. 1984. text ed. 39.95x (ISBN 0-471-88016-7, Wiley-Interscience). Wiley.
Koethe, G. Topological Vector Space Two. LC 78-84831. (Grundlehren der Mathematischen Wissenschaften: Vol. 237). 1979. 55.00 (ISBN 0-387-90400-X). Springer-Verlag.
--Topological Vector Spaces One. Garling, D. J. H., tr. (Grundlehren der Mathematischen Wissenshaften: Vol. 159). 456p. (Second Revised Printing). 1969. 48.00 (ISBN 0-387-04509-0). Springer-Verlag.
Larsen, Ronald. Multiplier Problem. LC 74-97959. (Lecture Notes in Mathematics: Vol. 105). 1969. pap. 14.70 (ISBN 0-387-04624-0). Springer-Verlag.
Marti, J. T. Introduction to the Theory of Bases. LC 73-83680. (Springer Tracts in Natural Philosophy: Vol. 18). 1969. 25.00 (ISBN 0-387-04716-6). Springer-Verlag.
Nachbin, L. Topology in Spaces of Holomorphic Mappings. LC 68-29710. (Ergebnisse der Mathematik, und Ihrer Grenzgebiete: Vol. 47). 1969. 19.00 (ISBN 0-387-04470-1). Springer-Verlag.
Nachbin, Leopoldo. Elements of Approximation Theory. LC 76-48. 132p. 1976. Repr. of 1967 ed. 11.50 (ISBN 0-88275-388-6). Krieger.
Namioka, Isaac. Partially Ordered Linear Topological Spaces. LC 52-42389. (Memoirs: No. 24). 50p. 1974. pap. 14.00 (ISBN 0-8218-1224-6, MEMO-24). Am Math.
Narici & Beckenstein. Topological Vector Spaces. (Monographs & Textbooks in Pure & Applied Mathematics). 400p. 1985. 69.75 (ISBN 0-8247-7315-2). Dekker.
Noverraz, Ph. Pseudo-Convexite, Convexite Polynomiale et Domaines D'holomorphie En Dimension Infinie. (Mathematics Studies: Vol. 3). 1975. pap. 17.00 (ISBN 0-444-10692-8, North-Holland). Elsevier.
Parthasarathy, T. Selection Theorems & Their Applications. LC 72-78192. (Lecture Notes in Mathematics: Vol. 263). 108p. 1972. pap. 9.00 (ISBN 0-387-05818-4). Springer-Verlag.
Pietsch, A. Nuclear Locally Convex Spaces. Ruckle, U. H., tr. from Ger. LC 78-178753. (Ergebnisse der Mathematik und Ihrer Grenzgebiete: Vol. 66). 205p. 1972. 27.00 (ISBN 0-387-05644-0). Springer-Verlag.
Robertson, A. P. & Robertson, Wendy. Topological Vector Spaces. 2nd ed. LC 72-89805. (Cambridge Tracts in Mathematics Ser: No. 53). 1980. pap. 13.95 (ISBN 0-521-29882-2). Cambridge U Pr.
Rourke, C. P. & Sanderson, B. J. Introduction to Piecewise-Linear Topology. (Springer Study Edition Ser.). (Illus.). 130p. 1982. pap. 13.00 (ISBN 0-387-11102-6). Springer-Verlag.
Schaefer, H. H. Branach Lattices & Positive Operators. (Die Grundlehren der Mathematischen Wissenschaften Ser.: Vol. 215). xi, 376p. 1974. 57.00 (ISBN 0-387-06936-4). Springer-Verlag.
--Topological Vector Spaces. LC 65-24692. (Graduate Texts in Mathematics: Vol. 3). 1971. text ed. 29.50 (ISBN 0-387-90026-8). Springer-Verlag.
Summer School on Topological Vector Spaces. Proceedings. Waelbroeck, L., ed. LC 73-83244. (Lecture Notes in Mathematics: Vol. 331). vi, 226p. (2 contributions in French). 1973. pap. 16.00 (ISBN 0-387-06367-6). Springer-Verlag.
Treves, Francois. Topological Vector Spaces, Distributions & Kernels. 1967. 79.50 (ISBN 0-12-699450-1). Acad Pr.
Treves, Franxois. Locally Convex Spaces & Linear Partial Differential Equations. LC 67-25286. (Grundlehren der Mathematischen Wissenschaften: Vol. 146). 1967. 28.00 (ISBN 0-387-03833-7). Springer-Verlag.
Vulikh, B. Z. Introduction to the Theory of Partially Ordered Spaces. 404p. 1967. 106.50x (ISBN 0-677-61330-X). Gordon.
Waelbroeck, L. Topological Vector Spaces & Algebras. (Lecture Notes in Mathematics: Vol. 230). 158p. 1971. pap. 11.00 (ISBN 0-387-05650-5). Springer-Verlag.
Wilansky, Albert. Modern Methods in Topological Vector Spaces. 1978. text ed. 48.95 (ISBN 0-07-070180-6). McGraw.
LINEAR VECTOR SPACES
see Vector Spaces
LINGUISTICS–DATA PROCESSING
see also Computer Prose; Machine Translating; Mathematical Linguistics; Speech Processing Systems
Aarts, J. & Maijs, W., eds. Corpus Linguistics. (Costerus New Ser.: No. 45). 229p. 1984. pap. text ed. 23.50x (ISBN 90-6203-696-1, Pub. by Rodopi Holland). Humanities.
Abramson, Harvey. Theory & Application of a Bottom-up Syntax-Directed Translator. (ACM Monograph Ser.). 1973. 37.00 (ISBN 0-12-042650-1). Acad Pr.
Advanced Techniques in Neuro-Linguistic Programming, Bk. I. (NLP Skill Builder Ser.). (Illus.). 167p. 1985. 18.00 (ISBN 0-943920-07-8); pap. 10.00 (ISBN 0-943920-08-6). Metamorphous Pr.
Ahmad, K., et al. Computers, Language Learning & Language Teaching. (New Directions in Language Teaching Ser.). (Illus.). 128p. Date not set. price not set (ISBN 0-521-26569-X); pap. price not set (ISBN 0-521-31957-9). Cambridge U Pr.
Allen, Sture & Petofi, Janos S., eds. Aspects of Automatized Text Processing, Vol. 17. (Paper in Textlinguistics Ser.). 194p. (Orig.). 1979. pap. text ed. 14.00x (ISBN 3-87118-363-6, Pub. by Helmut Buske Verlag Hamburg). Benjamins North Am.
Automated Education Center. Automatic Language Processing. 19.50 (ISBN 0-403-04455-3). Scholarly.
Balajthy, Ernest. Microcomputers in Reading & Language Arts. (Illus.). 304p. 1986. pap. text ed. 16.95 (ISBN 0-13-580473-6). P-H.
Bara, B. G. & Guida, G. Computational Models of Natural Language Processing. (Fundamental Studies in Computer Science: Vol. 9). 1984. 50.00 (ISBN 0-444-87598-0). Elsevier.
Bolc, Leonhard, ed. Speech Communication with Computers. 1978. pap. 29.00x (ISBN 3-4461-2650-3). Adlers Foreign Bks.
Borko, Harold. Automated Language Processing. LC 66-26735. 386p. 1967. 23.50 (ISBN 0-471-08950-8, Pub. by Wiley). Krieger.
Carvell, H. T. & Svartvik, J. Computational Experiments in Grammatical Classification. LC 68-23805. (Janua Linguarum, Ser. Minor: No. 61). (Orig.). 1969. pap. text ed. 23.20x (ISBN 90-2790-682-3). Mouton.
Davey, Anthony. Discourse Production: A Computer Model of Some Aspects of a Speaker. 168p. 1979. 24.00x (ISBN 0-85224-339-1, Pub. by Edinburgh U Pr Scotland). Columbia U Pr.
De Mori, Renato. Computer Models of Speech Using Fuzzy Algorithms. (Advanced Applications in Pattern Recognition Ser.). 508p. 1983. 59.50x (ISBN 0-306-41381-7, Plenum Pr). Plenum Pub.
Findler, Nicholas V., ed. Associative Networks: The Representation & Use of Knowledge by Computers. LC 78-31318. 1979. 61.50 (ISBN 0-12-256380-8). Acad Pr.
Fosdick, Howard. Structured PL-I Programming: For Textual & Library Processing. 350p. 1982. lib. bdg. 25.00 (ISBN 0-87287-328-5). Libs Unl.
Fu, King Sun. Syntactic Pattern Recognition & Applications. (Advances in Computing Science & Technology Ser.). (Illus.). 640p. 1982. text ed. 52.00 (ISBN 0-13-880120-7). P-H.
Garvin, Paul L. & Spolsky, Bernard, eds. Computation in Linguistics: A Case Book. LC 66-12755. (Indiana University Studies in the History & Theory of Linguistics). (Illus.). Repr. of 1966 ed. cancelled (ISBN 0-8357-9200-5, 2015818). Bks Demand UMI.
Haton, J. P., ed. Fundamentals in Man-Machine Communication: Speech, Vision & Natural Language. (CREST Advanced Course Ser.). 400p. Date not set. price not set (ISBN 0-521-30983-2). Cambridge U Pr.
Kelly, E. & Stone, P., eds. Computer Recognition of English Word Senses. (Linguistic Ser.: Vol. 13). 269p. 1975. pap. 32.00 (ISBN 0-444-10831-9, North-Holland). Elsevier.
Kolers, Paul A., et al, eds. Processing of Visible Language, Vol. 2. LC 80-22602. 633p. 1980. 69.50 (ISBN 0-306-40576-8, Plenum Pr). Plenum Pub.
Kummel, P. Formalization of Natural Languages. LC 77-6812. (Communication & Cybernetics Ser: Vol. 15). 1979. 48.00 (ISBN 0-387-08271-9). Springer-Verlag.
Leonard, R. Interpretation of English Noun Sequences on the Computer. (Linguistic Ser.: Vol. 51). 436p. 1984. 55.75 (ISBN 0-444-87658-8, North-Holland). Elsevier.
Lewis, Harry R. & Papadimitriou, Christos H. Elements of the Theory of Computation. (Software Ser.). (Illus.). 496p. 1981. text ed. 29.95 (ISBN 0-13-273417-6). P-H.
Litwiller, Bonnie & Duncan, David. Activities for the Maintenance of Computational Skills & the Discovery of Patterns. LC 80-19773. (Illus.). 96p. 1980. pap. 4.50 (ISBN 0-87353-169-8). NCTM.
McKeown, Kathleen R. Text Generation: Using Discourse Strategies & Focus Constraints to Generate Natural Language Text. (Studies in Natural Language Processing). (Illus.). 248p. 1985. 29.95 (ISBN 0-521-30116-5). Cambridge U Pr.
Martino, A. A. Deontic Logic, Computational Linguistics & Legal Information Systems. 518p. 1982. 66.00 (ISBN 0-444-86415-6, North-Holland). Elsevier.
Minsky, Marvin L., ed. Semantic Information Processing. LC 68-18239. 440p. 1969. 35.00x (ISBN 0-262-13044-0). MIT Pr.
Nijholt, A. Context-Free Grammars: Covers, Normal Forms, & Parsing. (Lecture Notes in Computer Science Ser.: Vol. 93). 253p. 1980. pap. 20.00 (ISBN 0-387-10245-0). Springer-Verlag.
Papp, Ferenc & Szepe, Gyorgy, eds. Papers in Computational Linguistics. (Janua Linguarum, Ser. Major: No. 91). 585p. text ed. 76.80x (ISBN 90-279-3285-9). Mouton.
Ritchie, Graeme D. Computational Grammar: An Artificial Intelligence Approach to Linguistic Description. (Harvester Studies in Cognitive Science: No. 15). 254p. 1980. 27.50x (ISBN 0-389-20048-4). B&N Imports.
Sager, Naomi. Natural Language Information Processing: A Computer Grammmar of English & Its Applications. 1980. text ed. 43.95 (ISBN 0-201-06769-2). Addison-Wesley.
Sedelow, Walter A., Jr. & Sedelow, Sally Y., eds. Computers in Language Research. (Trends in Linguistic Ser.). 1979. pap. text ed. 27.20x (ISBN 90-279-7846-8). Mouton.
--Computers in Language Research 2. 2 ed. LC 83-11476. (Trends in Linguistics Studies & Monographs: No. 19). viii, 301p. 1983. 50.40x (ISBN 90-279-3009-0). Mouton.
Stindlova, Jitka, ed. Machines Dans La Linguistique. (Janua Linguarum, Series Major: No. 30). 1968. text ed. 40.80x (ISBN 90-2790-617-3). Mouton.
Tucker, Allen B., Jr. Text Processing: Algorithms, Languages, & Applications. LC 79-23130. (Computer Science & Applied Mathematics Ser.). 1979. 25.00 (ISBN 0-12-702550-2). Acad Pr.
Wang, William S. Language, Script & the Computer: Readings from Scientific American. (Scientific American Reader Ser.). 150p. 1985. pap. 12.95 (ISBN 0-7167-1756-5). W H Freeman.
Webber, Bonnie L. A Formal Approach to Discourse Anaphora. Hankamer, Jorge, ed. LC 78-67737. (Outstanding Dissertations in Linguistics Ser.). 1985. lib. bdg. 29.00 (ISBN 0-8240-9670-3). Garland Pub.
Wheatley, Jon. Language & Rules. LC 70-95011. (Janua Linguarum, Ser. Minor: No. 80). (Orig.). 1970. pap. text ed. 5.60x (ISBN 0-686-22416-7). Mouton.
Zarrella, John. Language Translators. LC 82-48049. (Microprocessor Software Engineering Concepts Ser.). 200p. (Orig.). 1982. pap. 16.95 (ISBN 0-935230-06-8). Microcomputer Appns.
LINKAGE (GENETICS)
see also Chromosomes
Ott, Jurg. Analysis of Human Genetic Linkage. LC 84-21295. (Contemporary Medicine & Public Health Ser.). 240p. 1985. 35.00x (ISBN 0-8018-2485-0). Johns Hopkins.
LINKS AND LINK-MOTION
Auchincloss, William S. Slide Value & Link Motions. 1983. pap. 9.95 (ISBN 0-917914-13-9). Lindsay Pubns.
Chironis, Nicholas P. Mechanisms, Linkages, & Mechanical Controls. 1965. 57.75 (ISBN 0-07-010775-0). McGraw.
Korein, James U. A Geometric Investigation of Reach. (Association for Computing Machinery Distinguished Dissertation Award Ser.). (Illus.). 210p. 1985. text ed. 30.00x (ISBN 0-262-11104-7). MIT Pr.
LINNE, CARL VON, 1707-1778
Broberg, Gunnar, ed. Linnaeus: Progress & Prospects in Linnaean Research. (Illus.). 318p. 1980. 49.50x (ISBN 0-913196-31-2). Hunt Inst Botanical.
Larson, James L. Reason & Experience: The Representation of Natural Order in the Work of Carl von Linne. LC 70-632164. 1971. 28.50x (ISBN 0-520-01834-6). U of Cal Pr.
Lindroth, Stan, et al. Linnaeus: The Man & His Work. Frangsmyr, Tore, ed. Srigley, Michael & Vowles, Bernard, trs. from Swedish. LC 82-2044. (Illus.). 288p. 1983. text ed. 27.50x (ISBN 0-520-04568-8). U of Cal Pr.
Stearn, W. T. Three Prefaces on Linnaeus & Robert Brown. (Illus.). 1962. pap. 7.20 (ISBN 3-7682-0099-X). Lubrecht & Cramer.
LINOTYPE
Barnett, George E. Chapters on Machinery & Labor. LC 68-25563. (Masterworks in Industrial Relations Ser.). 191p. 1969. Repr. of 1926 ed. 6.95x (ISBN 0-8093-0397-3). S Ill U Pr.
Thompson, John S. The Mechanism of the Linotype. Bidwell, John, ed. Bd. with History of Composing Machines. LC 78-74413. (Nineteenth Century Book Arts & Printing History Ser.: Vol. 23). (Illus.). 1980. lib. bdg. 46.00 (ISBN 0-8240-3897-5). Garland Pub.
LIONS
Schaller, George B. The Serengeti Lion: A Study of Predator-Prey Relations. LC 78-180043. (Wildlife Behavior & Ecology Ser.). (Illus.). 472p. 1976. pap. 12.95 (ISBN 0-226-73640-7, P661, Phoen). U of Chicago Pr.
LIPID METABOLISM
Bazan, Nicolas G., et al. New Trends in Nutrition, Lipid Research, & Cardiovascular Diseases. LC 81-15650. (Current Topics in Nutrition & Disease: Vol. 5). 332p. 1981. 30.00 (ISBN 0-8451-1604-5). A R Liss.
Brisson, Germain J. Lipids in Human Nutrition. LC 81-17013. (Illus.). 200p. 1981. text ed. 22.50 (ISBN 0-937218-12-X). J K Burgess.
Ferrari, R., et al, eds. Myocardial Ischemia & Lipid Metabolism. 328p. 1984. 49.50x (ISBN 0-306-41832-0, Plenum Pr). Plenum Pub.
Halpern, M. J., ed. Lipid Metabolism & Its Pathology. 239p. 1984. 49.50x (ISBN 0-306-41899-1, Plenum Pr). Plenum Pub.
King, H. K. The Chemistry of Lipids in Health & Disease: A Review of Our Present Knowledge of Lipids; Their Chemical Structure; Their Breakdown & Synthesis in Living Organisms; Their Place in Human Nutrition; & Their Abnormalities of Metabolism in Disease. (Illus.). 120p. 1960. 13.50x (ISBN 0-398-04310-8). C C Thomas.
Kritchevsky, David & Gibney, Michael J., eds. Animal & Vegetable Proteins in Lipid Metabolism & Atherosclerosis. LC 82-23961. (Current Topics in Nutrition & Disease Ser.: Vol. 8). 190p. 1983. 32.00 (ISBN 0-8451-1607-X). A R Liss.
Paoletti, Rodolfo, ed. Lipid Pharmacology. (Medicinal Chemistry: Vol. 2). 1964. 75.00 (ISBN 0-12-544950-X). Acad Pr.
Snyder, Fred, ed. Lipid Metabolism in Mammals, 2 vols. Incl. Vol. 1. 420p (ISBN 0-306-35802-6); Vol. 2. 408p (ISBN 0-306-35803-4). LC 77-913. (Monographs in Lipid Research). (Illus.). 1977. 49.50x ea. (Plenum Pr). Plenum Pub.
Wakil, Salih J., ed. Lipid Metabolism, Vol. 1. 1970. 79.50 (ISBN 0-12-730950-0). Acad Pr.
LIPIDS
see also Lipid Metabolism; Lipoproteins; Steroids
Anderson, Laurens & Unger, Frank M., eds. Bacterial Lipopolysaccharides: Structure, Synthesis, & Biological Activities. LC 83-158282. (ACS Symposium Ser.: No. 231). 325p. 1983. lib. bdg. 44.95x (ISBN 0-8412-0800-X). Am Chemical.
Bazan, N. G., et al, eds. Function & Biosynthesis of Lipids. LC 77-6831. (Advances in Experimental Medicine & Biology Ser.: Vol. 83). 658p. 1977. 79.50x (ISBN 0-306-39083-3, Plenum Pr). Plenum Pub.
Bergmeyer, H. U. Lipids, Amino Acids & Related Compounds, Vol. 8. 3rd ed. LC 84-105641. (Methods of Enzymatic Analysis). (Illus.). 600p. 1985. lib. bdg. 135.00 (ISBN 0-89573-238-6). VCH Pubs.

Properties of Materials for Liquified Natural Gas Tankage - STP 579. 424p. 1975. 39.75 (ISBN 0-8031-0538-X, 04-579000-30). ASTM.

LIQUEFIED PETROLEUM GAS

Huges, John R. The Storage & Handling of Petroleum Liquids. 2nd ed. (Illus.). 331p. 1978. pap. text ed. 42.95x (ISBN 0-85264-251-2, Pub. by Charles Griffin & Co Ltd England). Lubrecht & Cramer.

Institute of Petroleum. Liquified Petroleum Gas Safety Code. 1971. 16.75 (ISBN 0-444-39970-4, Pub. by Elsevier Applied Sci England). Elsevier.

Liquefied Petroleum Gases at Utility Gas Plants. (Fifty Ser.). 53p. 1974. pap. 3.00 (ISBN 0-685-46071-1, 59). Natl Fire Prot.

Liquefied Petroleum Gases, Storage & Handling. (Fifty Ser.). 53p. 1974. pap. 4.00 (ISBN 0-685-46070-3, 58). Natl Fire Prot.

LP-Gas Engine Fuels- STP 525. 140p. 1973. 4.75 (ISBN 0-8031-0104-X, 04 525000 12). ASTM.

Williams, A. F. & Lom, W. L. Liquefied Petroleum Gases: Guide to Properties, Aplications & Uses. 2nd rev. & extended ed. 522p. 1982. 116.95 (ISBN 0-470-27275-9). Halsted Pr.

Woolcott, T. W. Liquified Petroleum Gas Tanker Practice. (Illus.). 1977. 35.00 (ISBN 0-85174-295-5). Heinman.

LIQUID AMMONIA

Nicholls, D. Inorganic Chemistry in Liquid Ammonia. (Topics in Inorganic & General Chemistry Ser.: Vol. 17). 238p. 1979. 55.50 (ISBN 0-444-41774-5). Elsevier.

LIQUID CHROMATOGRAPHY

Balke, S. T. Quantitative Column Liquid Chromatography: A Survey of Chemometric Methods. (Journal of Chromatography Library: Vol. 29). 1984. 61.00 (ISBN 0-444-42393-1). Elsevier.

Bristow, P. A. Liquid Chromatography in Practice. 28.00 (ISBN 0-9504833-1-1); pap. 20.00 (ISBN 0-9504833-0-3); microfiche 10.00 (ISBN 0-9504833-2-X). Lab Data Control.

Brown, Phyllis R. High Pressure Liquid Chromatography: Biochemical & Biomedical Applications. 1973. 33.00 (ISBN 0-12-136950-1). Acad Pr.

Cazes. Liquid Chromatography of Polymers & Related Materials, Part III. (Chromatographic Science Ser., Vol. 19). 232p. 1981. 40.00 (ISBN 0-8247-1514-4). Dekker.

Cazes & De La Marre. Liquid Chromatography of Polymers & Related Materials Part II. (Chromatographic Science Ser.: Vol. 13). 232p. 1980. 44.50 (ISBN 0-8247-6985-6). Dekker.

Cazes, J. Liquid Chromatography of Polymers & Related Materials, Pt. I. (Chromatgraphic Science Ser.: Vol. 8). 1977. 45.00 (ISBN 0-8247-6592-3). Dekker.

Colin, Henri & Excoffier, Jean-Louis. A Guide to the HPLC Literature 1980-1981, Vol. 2. LC 84-11967. 922p. 1984. text ed. 110.00 (ISBN 0-471-87992-4). Wiley.

--A Guide to the HPLC Literature 1982, Vol. 3. 532p. 1984. text ed. 60.00 (ISBN 0-471-80687-0); Three-Volume Set. text ed. write for info. (ISBN 0-471-82056-3). Wiley.

Colin, Henri, et al. A Guide to the HPLC Literature: 1966-1979, Vol. 1. 900p. 1984. text ed. 125.00 (ISBN 0-471-87993-2, Pub. by Wiley-Interscience). Wiley.

Crippen, Raymond C. GC-LC, Instruments, Derivatives in Identifying Pollutants & Unknowns. (Illus.). 452p. 1983. 83.00 (ISBN 0-08-027185-5). Pergamon.

Desiderio, D. M. Analysis of Neuropeptides by Liquid Chromatography & Mass Spectrometry. (Techniques & Instrumentation in Analytical Chemistry Ser.: No. 6). 236p. 1984. 61.00 (ISBN 0-444-42418-0). Elsevier.

Deyl, Z., et al, eds. Liquid Column Chromatography: A Survey of Modern Techniques & Applications. (Journal of Chromatography Library: Vol. 3). 1176p. 1975. 149.00 (ISBN 0-444-41156-9). Elsevier.

Dixon, P. F., et al, eds. High Pressure Liquid Chromatography in Clinical Chemistry. 1976. 42.00 (ISBN 0-12-218450-5). Acad Pr.

Eksborg, S., et al, eds. Liquid Chromatography in the Biomedical Sciences: Invited Papers from the 15th International Symposium Held in Ronneby, Sweden, 18-21 June 1984. 200p. 1985. pap. 25.00 (ISBN 0-08-032600-5). Pergamon.

Engelhardt, H. High Performance Liquid Chromatography. Gutnikov, G., tr. from Ger. LC 78-22002. (Chemical Laboratory Practice Ser.). (Illus.). 1978. 34.00 (ISBN 0-387-09005-3). Springer-Verlag.

Hamilton, R. J. & Sewell, P. A. Introduction to High Performance Liquid Chromatography. LC 81-16840. (Illus.). 224p. 1982. 29.95 (ISBN 0-412-23430-0, NO. 6629, Pub. by Chapman & Hall England). Methuen Inc.

Hancock. High Performance Liquid Chromatography in Biotechnology. 1985. price not set (ISBN 0-471-82584-0). Wiley.

Hawk. Biological-Biomedical Applications of Liquid Chromatography. (Chromatographic Science Ser.: Vol. 10). 1979. 85.00 (ISBN 0-8247-6784-5). Dekker.

--Biological-Biomedical Applications of Liquid Chromatography, II. (Chromatographic Science Ser.: Vol. 12). 1979. 85.00 (ISBN 0-8247-6915-5). Dekker.

Hawk, Gerald L., ed. Biological-Biomedical Applications of Liquid Chromatography III. (Chromatographic Science Ser.: Vol. 15). (Illus.). 440p. 1981. 85.00 (ISBN 0-8247-1297-8). Dekker.

Hearn, Milton & T. W. Hearn, Etal, eds. High Performance Liquid Chromatography of Proteins & Peptides: Proceedings of First International Symposium. 1983. 35.00 (ISBN 0-12-335780-2). Acad Pr.

Horvath, Csaba, ed. High-Performance Liquid Chromatography: Advances & Perspectives, Vol. 1. (Serial Publication). 1980. 55.00 (ISBN 0-12-312201-5). Acad Pr.

--High Performance Liquid Chromatography: Advances & Perspectives, Vol. 2. 1980. 59.50 (ISBN 0-12-312202-3). Acad Pr.

Huber, J., ed. Instrumentation for High Performance Liquid Chromatography. (Journal of Chromatography Library: Vol. 13). 204p. 1978. 42.75 (ISBN 0-444-41648-X). Elsevier.

Hupe, K. P., ed. High Performance Liquid Chromatography in Biochemistry. 564p. 1985. text ed. 88.00 (ISBN 0-89573-066-9). VCH Pubs.

International Resource Development Inc. High Performance Liquid Chromotography. 142p. 1984. 985.00x (ISBN 0-88694-605-0). Intl Res Dev.

Jandera, P. Gradient Elution in Column Liquid Chromatography. (Journal of Chromatography Library: Vol. 31). 510p. 1985. 90.75 (ISBN 0-444-42124-6). Elsevier.

Kabra, Pokar & Marton, Laurence J., eds. Liquid Chromatography in Clinical Analysis. LC 80-84083. (Biological Methods Ser.). 496p. 1981. 65.00 (ISBN 0-89603-026-1). Humana.

Kabra, Pokar M. & Marton, Laurence J., eds. Clinical Liquid Chromatography, Vol. I. 232p. 1984. 63.00 (ISBN 0-8493-6637-2). CRC Pr.

--Clinical Liquid Chromatography, Vol. II. 240p. 1984. 72.00 (ISBN 0-8493-6638-0). CRC Pr.

Kalasz, H., ed. New Approaches in Liquid Chromatography: Proceedings of the 2nd Annual American-Eastern European Symposium on Advances in Liquid Chematography, Szeged, Hungary, June 16-18, 1982. (Analytical Chemistry Symposia Ser.: No. 16). 300p. 1984. 67.50 (ISBN 0-444-99642-7, I-143-84). Elsevier.

Knapman, C. E. & Maggs, R. J., eds. Gas & Liquid Chromatography Abstacts, 1970. LC 62-22896. pap. 93.00 (ISBN 0-317-27252-7, 2023707). Bks Demand UMI.

Knapman, C. E. H., ed. Gas & Liquid Chromatography Abstracts: Cumulative Indexes 1969-73. 381p. 1976. 70.50 (ISBN 0-85334-643-7, Pub. by Elsevier Applied Sci England). Elsevier.

Knox, John H. High Performance Liquid Chromatography. 205p. 1981. pap. 18.50x (ISBN 0-85224-383-9, Pub. by Edinburgh U Pr Scotland). Columbia U Pr.

Krstulovic, Ante M. & Brown, Phyllis R. Reversed-Phase High Performance Liquid Chromatography: Theory, Practice, & Biomedical Applications. LC 81-15944. 296p. 1982. 46.00x (ISBN 0-471-05369-4, Pub. by Wiley Interscience). Wiley.

Kucera, P., ed. Microcolumn High-Performance Liquid Chromatography. (Journal of Chromatography Library: Vol. 28). 302p. 1984. 63.50 (ISBN 0-444-42290-0, I-042-84). Elsevier.

Lawrence, J. F. & Frei, R. W. Chemical Derivatization in Liquid Chromatography. (Journal of Chromatography Library: Vol. 7). 214p. 1976. 55.50 (ISBN 0-444-41429-0). Elsevier.

Lawrence, James F. Organic Trace Analysis by Liquid Chromatography. LC 81-3464. 1981. 44.00 (ISBN 0-12-439150-8). Acad Pr.

Liquid Chromatographic Data Compilation AMD 41. 196p. 1975. pap. 15.00 (ISBN 0-8031-0292-5, 10-041000-39). ASTM.

OAS General Secretariat. Cromatografia Liquida Alta Presion: Monografia, No. 10. (Serie de Quimica). (Span., Illus.). 72p. 1980. pap. 3.50 (ISBN 0-8270-1229-2). OAS.

Parris, N. A. Instrumental Liquid Chromatography. (Journal of Chromatography Library: Vol. 5). 330p. 1976. 63.75 (ISBN 0-444-41427-4). Elsevier.

--Instrumental Liquid Chromatography: A Practical Manual on High-Performance Liquid Chromatography Methods. 2nd, rev. ed. (Journal of Chromatography Ser.: Vol. 27). 1984. 86.75 (ISBN 0-444-42061-4). Elsevier.

Pattison, J. B. A Programmed Introduction to Gas-Liquid Chromatography. 136p. 1977. 36.95x (ISBN 0-471-25950-0, Wiley Heyden). Wiley.

Runser, Dennis J. Maintaining & Troubleshooting HPLC Systems: A Users Guide. LC 80-25444. 163p. 1981. 40.00 (ISBN 0-471-06479-3, Pub. by Wiley-Interscience). Wiley.

Scott, Raymond P. W., ed. Small Bore Liquid Chromatography Columns: Their Properties & Uses. LC 84-2393. (Chemical Analysis: A Series of Monographs on Analytical Chemistry & its Applications: 1-075). 271p. 1984. text ed. 48.50x (ISBN 0-471-80052-X). Wiley.

Simpson, C. F. Techniques of Liquid Chromatography. LC 82-17512. 464p. 1982. 58.95x (ISBN 0-471-26220-X, Pub. by Wiley Heyden). Wiley.

Simpson, Colin F., ed. Practical High Performance Liquid Chromatography. pap. 81.80 (ISBN 0-317-28972-1, 2052065). Bks Demand UMI.

Snyder, L. R. & Kirkland, J. J. Introduction to Modern Liquid Chromatography. 2nd ed. LC 79-4537. 863p. 1979. 55.00x (ISBN 0-471-03822-9, Pub. by Wiley-Interscience). Wiley.

Snyder, Lloyd R. Principles of Adsorption Chromatography: The Separation of Nonionic Organic Compounds. LC 68-17426. (Chromatographic Science: Vol. 3). (Illus.). pap. 107.30 (ISBN 0-317-08018-0, 2017858). Bks Demand UMI.

Vickrey. Liquid Chromatograph Detectors. LC 83-7428. (Chromatographic Science Ser.). 376p. 1983. 65.00 (ISBN 0-8247-1916-6). Dekker.

Wehr. HPLC of Peptides & Proteins. 1985. write for info. (ISBN 0-471-26107-6). Wiley.

Yau, W. W., et al. Modern Size-Exclusion Liquid Chromatography: Practice of Gel Permeation & Gel Filtration Chromatography. LC 79-12739. 476p. 1979. 59.00x (ISBN 0-471-03387-1, Pub. by Wiley-Interscience). Wiley.

LIQUID CRYSTALS

Adler, G., ed. Molecular Crystals & Liquid Crystals Special Topics: Proceedings of the Fifth International Symposium on Organic Solid State Chemistry, Brandeis University, June 1978, 2 pts. 632p. 1979. 531.50 (ISBN 0-677-40265-1). Gordon.

Bahadur, Birendra. Liquid Crystal Displays. (Molecular Crystals & Liquid Crystals Ser.). 104p. 1984. pap. 39.00 (ISBN 0-677-06675-9). Gordon.

Bata, L., ed. Advances in Liquid Crystal Research & Applications: Proceedings of the Third Liquid Crystal Conference of the Socialist Countries, Budapest, 27-31 August 1979. 1000p. 1981. 215.00 (ISBN 0-08-026191-4). Pergamon.

Beguin, A., et al. Sources of Thermodynamic Data on Mesogens: A Special Issue of the Journal of Molecular Crystals & Liquid Crystals. 340p. 1984. pap. text ed. 94.00 (ISBN 0-677-16575-7). Gordon.

Blinov, Lev M. Electro-Optical & Magneto-Optical Properties of Liquid Crystals. LC 82-24800. 341p. 1984. 74.95x (ISBN 0-471-10231-8, Pub. by Wiley-Interscience). Wiley.

Blumstein, Alexandre, ed. Mesomorphic Order in Polymers & Polymerization in Liquid Crystalline Media. LC 78-9470. (ACS Symposium Ser.: No. 74). 1978. 30.95 (ISBN 0-8412-0419-5). Am Chemical.

--Polymeric Liquid Crystals. 449p. 1985. 75.00x (ISBN 0-306-41814-2, Plenum Pr). Plenum Pub.

Brown, Glen H. & Labes, M. M., eds. Liquid Crystals Three: Proceedings, 2 pts. 1198p. 1972. Set. 321.25 (ISBN 0-677-15010-5). Gordon.

Brown, Glen H., et al, eds. Liquid Crystals One: Proceedings. 494p. 1967. 132.95 (ISBN 0-677-11840-6). Gordon.

--Liquid Crystals Two: Proceedings, 2 pts. 910p. 1969. Pt. 1, 252p. 69.50 (ISBN 0-677-13830-X); Pt. 2, 910p. 236.95x (ISBN 0-677-13840-7). Gordon.

Brown, Glenn H. & Wolken, Jerome J. Liquid Crystals & Biological Structures. LC 78-67873. 1979. 37.50 (ISBN 0-12-136850-5). Acad Pr.

Brown, Glenn H., ed. Advances in Liquid Crystals, 3 vols. Incl. Vol. 1. 1975. 85.00 (ISBN 0-12-025001-2); Vol. 2. 1976. 90.00 (ISBN 0-12-025002-0); Vol. 3. 1978. 70.00 (ISBN 0-12-025003-9). LC 74-17973. Acad Pr.

--Advances in Liquid Crystals, Vol. 4. (Serial Publication Ser.). 1979. 50.00 (ISBN 0-12-025004-7). Acad Pr.

--Advances in Liquid Crystals, Vol. 5. 1983. 50.00 (ISBN 0-12-025005-5). Acad Pr.

--Advances in Liquid Crystals, Vol. 6. (Serial Publication Ser.). 1983. 80.00 (ISBN 0-12-025006-3). Acad Pr.

Chandrasekhar, S. Liquid Crystals. LC 75-32913. (Cambridge Monographs in Physics). (Illus.). 1977. 90.00 (ISBN 0-521-21149-2). Cambridge U Pr.

--Liquid Crystals. (Cambridge Monographs in Physics). (Illus.). 352p. 1980. pap. 29.95 (ISBN 0-521-29841-5). Cambridge U Pr.

Chapoy, L. L., ed. Recent Advances in Liquid Crystalline Polymers: Proceedings of the European Science Foundation Sixth Polymer Workshop, Lyngby, Denmark, 12-14 September 1983. (Illus.). 352p. 1985. 60.00 (ISBN 0-85334-313-6, Pub. by Elsevier Applied Sci England). Elsevier.

Cognard, Jacques. Alignment of Nematic Liquid Crystals & Their Mixtures. (Molecular Crystals & Liquid Crystals Supplement Ser.). 78p. 1982. 28.50 (ISBN 0-677-05905-1). Gordon.

De Jeu, W. H. Physical Properties of Liquid Crystalline Materials. 140p. 1980. 45.25 (ISBN 0-677-04040-7). Gordon.

Demus, D. & Richter, L. Textures of Liquid Crystals. (Illus.). 228p. 1978. 108.90x (ISBN 0-89573-015-4). VCH Pubs.

Emsley, James W. Nuclear Magnetic Resonance of Liquid Crystals. 1984. lib. bdg. 76.00 (ISBN 90-277-1878-4, Pub. by Reidel Holland). Kluwer Academic.

Frank, Charles. Liquid Crystals: Their Physics, Chemistry & Applications. (Series A: Vol. 309). (Illus.). 169p. 1983. text ed. 55.00x (ISBN 0-85403-210-X, Pub. by Royal Soc London). Scholium Intl.

Goodby, J. W. & Gray, G. W. Smectic Liquid Crystals: Textures & Structures. 200p. 1984. write for info. (ISBN 0-9914000-0-3, Pub. by Blackie & Son UK). Heyden.

Gordon, M., ed. Liquid Crystal Polymers I. (Advances in Polymer Science, Fortschritte der Hochpolymerenforschung: Vol. 59). (Illus.). 180p. 1984. 41.00 (ISBN 0-387-12818-2). Springer Verlag.

Gordon, M. & Plate, N. A., eds. Liquid Crystal Polymers II-III. (Advances in Polymer Science Ser.: Vol. 60-61). (Illus.). 1984. 54.00 (ISBN 0-387-12994-4). Springer-Verlag.

Gray, G. W. & Winsor, P. A., eds. Liquid Crystals & Plastic Crystals: Preparation, Constitution & Applications, Vol. 1. LC 73-11504. (Illus.). 383p. 1974. 74.95 (ISBN 0-470-32339-6). Halsted Pr.

--Liquid Crystals & Plastic Crystals: Physico-Chemical Properties & Methods of Investigation, Vol. 2. LC 73-11505. (Illus.). 314p. 1974. 79.95 (ISBN 0-470-32340-X). Halsted Pr.

Griffin, Anselm C. & Johnson, Julian F., eds. Liquid Crystals & Ordered Fields, Vol. 4. 1162p. 1984. 135.00x (ISBN 0-306-41394-9, Plenum Pr). Plenum Pub.

Helfreich, W. & Heppke, G. Liquid Crystals of One & Two Dimensional Order: Proceedings. (Springer Series in Chemical Physics: Vol. 11). (Illus.). 416p. 1980. 48.00 (ISBN 0-387-10399-6). Springer-Verlag.

Johnson, Julian & Porter, Roger, eds. Liquid Crystals & Ordered Fluids. Incl. Vol. 1. LC 76-110760. 494p. 1970. 75.00x (ISBN 0-306-30466-X); Vol. 2. LC 74-1269. 783p. 1974. 95.00x (ISBN 0-306-35182-X); Vol. 3. LC 74-1269. 559p. 1978. 85.00x (ISBN 0-306-35183-8). Plenum Pr). Plenum Pub.

Kapustina, O. A. & Andreev, N. N. Acoustooptical Phenomena in Liquid Crystals. (Molecular Crystals & Liquid Crystals Ser.). 172p. 1984. pap. text ed. 65.00 (ISBN 0-677-06605-8). Gordon.

Kelker, H. & Hatz, R. Handbook of Liquid Crystals. (Illus.). 917p. 1980. 262.50x (ISBN 0-89573-008-1). VCH Pubs.

Khetrapal, C. L. Lyotropic Liquid Crystals. (NMR (Nuclear Magnetic Resonance) Ser.). (Illus.). 180p. 1975. 25.00 (ISBN 0-387-07303-5). Springer-Verlag.

Liquid Crystal Compounds & Mixtures. 1984. 3 ring bdg. 80.00 (ISBN 0-317-20431-9). Optosonic Pr.

Luckhurst, G. R. & Gray, G. W., eds. The Molecular Physics of Liquid Crystals. 1979. 58.00 (ISBN 0-12-458950-2). Acad Pr.

March, Norman & Tosi, Mario, eds. Polymers, Liquid Crystals & Low-Dimensional Solids. (Physics of Solids & Liquids Ser.). 622p. 1984. 89.50x (ISBN 0-306-41641-7, Plenum Pr). Plenum Pub.

Molecular Crystals & Liquid Crystals, Special Topics: Proceedings of the Sixth International Liquid Crystal Conference, Kent State Univ., Aug. 1976, 4 pts. 1312p. 1976. Set. pap. 582.25x (ISBN 0-677-40275-9). Gordon.

Molecular Crystals & Liquid Crystals Special Topics: Proceedings of the Eighth International Liquid Crystals Conference, Kyoto, Japan, June 30-July 4, 1980, 6 vols. 1955p. 1981. pap. 698.95x (ISBN 0-677-40295-3). Gordon.

Priestly, E. B., et al. Introduction to Liquid Crystals. LC 75-34195. 356p. 1975. 35.00x (ISBN 0-306-30858-4, Plenum Pr). Plenum Pub.

Sprokel, Gerald J., ed. The Physics & Chemistry of Liquid Crystal Devices. LC 80-12097. (IBM Research Symposia Ser.). 362p. 1980. 55.00 (ISBN 0-306-40440-0, Plenum Pr). Plenum Pub.

Takeda, Masatmi & Kobayashi, Shunshuke. Applied Liquid Crystal Research. (Molecular Crystals & Liquid Crystals Ser.). 239p. 1984. pap. text ed. 280.00 (ISBN 0-677-06295-8). Gordon.

LIQUID FUEL ROCKETS

see Liquid Propellant Rockets

LIQUID FUELS

see also Coal Liquefaction; Gasoline; Liquefied Petroleum Gas; Petroleum As Fuel; Petroleum Products

Black, J. Liquid Fuels in Australia: A Social Science Research Perspective. 280p. 1983. 37.50 (ISBN 0-08-024834-9); 21.00 (ISBN 0-08-024833-0). Pergamon.

Campbell, Ian. Biomass, Catalysts, & Liquid Fuels. 169p. 1983. 36.00 (ISBN 0-87762-331-7). Technomic.

Ellington, R. T., ed. Liquid Fuels from Coal. 1977. 42.50 (ISBN 0-12-237250-6). Acad Pr.

Liquid Gas Carrier Register, 1982. LC 75-644549. (Illus.). 155p. 1982. 135.00x (ISBN 0-900291-32-X). Intl Pubns Serv.

Liquid Gas Carrier Register, 1984. write for info. Intl Pubns Serv.

Steele, Henry B. Economic Potentialities of Synthetic Liquid Fuels from Oil Shale. Bruchey, Stuart, ed. LC 78-22751. (Energy in the American Economy Ser.). (Illus.). 1979. lib. bdg. 40.00x (ISBN 0-405-12015-X). Ayer Co Pubs.

Stewart, G. A. & Gartside, G. The Potential for Liquid Fuels from Agriculture & Forestry in Australia. 147p. 1979. pap. 9.00 (ISBN 0-643-00353-3, C025, CSIRO). Unipub.

Stewart, G. A., et al. The Potential for Liquid Fuels from Agriculture & Forestry in Australia. 147p. 1980. pap. 8.00x (ISBN 0-643-00353-3, Pub. by CSIRO Australia). Intl Spec Bk.

Wise, Donald L. Liquid Fuel Developments. 224p. 1983. 71.00 (ISBN 0-8493-6094-3). CRC Pr.

Wise, Donald L., ed. Liquid Fuel Systems. 224p. 1983. 70.00 (ISBN 0-8493-6093-5). CRC Pr.

LIQUID HELIUM

see also Superfluidity

Careri, G., ed. Liquid Helium. (Italian Physical Society: Course 21). 1964. 85.00 (ISBN 0-12-368821-3). Acad Pr.

Keller, William E. Helium-Three & Helium-Four. LC 68-25382. (International Cryogenics Monographs). (Illus.). 431p. 1969. 59.50x (ISBN 0-306-30346-9, Plenum Pr). Plenum Pub.

Wilks, John. Properties of Liquid & Solid Helium. (International Series of Monographs on Physics). 1967. 79.00x (ISBN 0-19-851245-7). Oxford U Pr.

LIQUID HYDROGEN

Liquified Hydrogen Systems at Consumer Sites. (Fifty Ser). 1973. pap. 2.00 (ISBN 0-685-58092-X, 50B). Natl Fire Prot.

LIQUID METALS

see also Mercury; Metallic Glasses

Borgstedt, H. V., ed. Material Behavior & Physical Chemistry in Liquid Metal Systems. LC 82-3680. 562p. 1982. 79.50x (ISBN 0-306-40917-8, Plenum Pr). Plenum Pub.

Branover, H., et al, eds. Liquid-Metal & Magnetohydrodynamics. 45.00 (ISBN 0-915928-70-1). AIAA.

Chen, John C. & Bishop, A. A., eds. Liquid-Metal Heat Transfer & Fluid Dynamics: Presented at the Annual Winter Meeting of ASME, New York,N. Y., November 30, 1970. LC 76-141816. pap. 46.30 (ISBN 0-317-09992-2). Bks Demand UMI.

Chow, Brian G. The Liquid Metal Fast Breeder Reactor: An Economic Analysis. LC 75-39899. 1975. pap. 4.25 (ISBN 0-8447-3192-7). Am Enterprise.

Draley, J. E. & Weeks, J. R. Corrosion by Liquid Metals. LC 75-119057. 615p. 1970. 49.50x (ISBN 0-306-30482-1, Plenum Pr). Plenum Pub.

Dwyer, O. E. Boiling Liquid-Metal Heat Transfer. LC 75-11012. (Nuclear Science Technology Ser.). (Illus.). 1976. text ed. 37.95 (ISBN 0-89448-000-6, 300008). Am Nuclear Soc.

Gubanov, Alexsandr I. Quantum Electron Theory of Amorphous Conductors. LC 65-10526. 277p. 1965. 35.00x (ISBN 0-306-10703-1, Consultants). Plenum Pub.

Kirko, Igor M. Magnetohydrodynamics of Liquid Metals. LC 65-17789. 80p. 1965. 25.00x (ISBN 0-306-10732-5, Consultants). Plenum Pub.

Liquid-Metal Flows & Magnetohydrodynamics. LC 83-2610. (Illus.). 454p. 1983. 55.00 (ISBN 0-317-36804-4); members 35.00 (ISBN 0-317-36805-2). AIAA.

Liquid Metals 1976: Bristol. (Institute of Physics Conference Ser.: No. 30). 1977. 87.50 (ISBN 0-9960030-9-6, Pub. by Inst Physics England). Heyden.

Luscher, E. & Coufal, H., eds. Liquid & Amorphous Metals: Mechanics of Plastic Solids. (NATO-Advanced Study Institute Ser.). 672p. 1980. 75.00x (ISBN 9-0286-0680-7). Sijthoff & Noordhoff.

LIQUID PROPELLANT ROCKETS

Sakae, Takeuchi, ed. The Properties of Liquid Metals. 670p. 1973. cancelled (ISBN 0-85066-065-3). Taylor & Francis.

LIQUID-VAPOR EQUILIBRIUM

see Vapor-Liquid Equilibrium

LIQUIDS

see also Brownian Movements; Hydraulics; Hydrodynamics; Hydrostatics; Liquid Metals; Permeability; Quantum Liquids; Surface Tension

Barnes, A. J., et al, eds. Molecular Liquids: Dynamics & Interactions. 1984. lib. bdg. 79.50 (ISBN 90-277-1817-2, Pub. by Reidel Holland). Kluwer Academic.

Bax, Ad. Two-Dimensional Nuclear Magnetic Resonance in Liquids. 1982. 29.50 (ISBN 90-277-1412-6, Pub. by Reidel Holland). Kluwer Academic.

Baym. Landav Fermi: Liquid Theory & Low Temperature Properties of Normal Liquid Helium. 1985. price not set (ISBN 0-471-82418-6). Wiley.

Benedek, Paul & Otti, Ferenc. Computer Aided Chemical Thermodynamics of Gases & Liquids: Theory, Models & Programs. 832p. 1985. write for info. (ISBN 0-471-87825-1). Wiley.

Bienenstock, Arthur, ed. Liquids & Amorphous Materials. (Transactions of the American Crystallographic Association Ser.: Vol. 10). 84p. 1974. pap. 15.00 (ISBN 0-686-60381-8). Polycrystal Bk Serv.

Buckingham, A. D., et al. Organic Liquids: Structure, Dynamics & Chemical Properties. LC 78-8462. 352p. 1978. 87.95 (ISBN 0-471-99673-4, Pub. by Wiley-Interscience). Wiley.

Cho, Chun H. Measurement & Control of Liquid Level: An Independent Learning Module of the Instrument Society of America. LC 82-48156. 288p. 1982. text ed. 39.95x (ISBN 0-87664-625-9). Instru Soc.

Croxton, Clive A. Statistical Mechanics of the Liquid Surface. LC 79-40819. 345p. 1980. 89.95 (ISBN 0-471-27663-4, Pub. by Wiley-Interscience). Wiley.

D'Ans, J., et al. Densities of Binary Aqueous Systems & Heat Capacities of Liquid Systems. LC 62-53136. (Landolt-Boernstein Group IV: Vol. 1, Pt. B). (Illus.). 1977. 134.40 (ISBN 0-387-08272-7). Springer-Verlag.

Dupuy, J. & Dianioux, A. J., eds. Microscopic Structure & Dynamics of Liquids. LC 78-4197. (NATO ASI Series B, Physics: Vol. 33). 534p. 1978. 79.50x (ISBN 0-306-35733-X, Plenum Pr). Plenum Pub.

Fisher, Iosif Z. Statistical Theory of Liquids. Switz, Theodore M., tr. LC 64-22249. pap. 86.80 suppl. (ISBN 0-317-08823-8, 2020284). Bks Demand UMI.

Gerrard, W. Solubility of Gases & Liquids: A Graphic Approach. LC 76-10676. (Illus.). 275p. 1976. 49.50x (ISBN 0-306-30866-5, Plenum Pr). Plenum Pub.

Goodwin, B. M., ed. Properties of Pure Liquids. LC 80-25560. (AIChEMI Modular Instruction D. Ser.: Vol. 2). 70p. 1981. pap. 30.00 (ISBN 0-8169-0179-1, J-10); pap. 15.00 members (ISBN 0-317-03843-5). Am Inst Chem Eng.

Gregory, J. Solid-Liquid Separation. 363p. 1984. 87.95 (ISBN 0-470-20021-9). Halsted Pr.

Halley, J. W., ed. Correlation Functions & Quasiparticle Interactions in Condensed Matter. LC 78-18837. (NATO ASI Series B, Physics: Vol. 35). 676p. 1978. 95.00x (ISBN 0-306-40018-9, Plenum Pr). Plenum Pub.

Hansen, J. P. & McDonald, I. R. The Theory of Simple Liquids. 1977. 68.00 (ISBN 0-12-323850-1). Acad Pr.

Harrison, G. Dynamic Properties of Super-Cooled Liquids. 1976. 37.00 (ISBN 0-12-328150-4). Acad Pr.

Hildebrand, Joel, et al. Regular & Related Solutions: The Solubility of Gases, Liquids & Solids. LC 79-122670. 238p. 1970. 15.95 (ISBN 0-442-15665-0). Krieger.

Holland, F. A. & Chapman, F. S. Pumping of Liquids. LC 66-29034. 414p. 1966. 23.50 (ISBN 0-442-15118-7). Krieger.

Kirkwood, John G. Theory of Liquids. Alder, B., ed. (Documents on Modern Physics Ser.). (Illus.). 166p. (Orig.). 1968. 40.50 (ISBN 0-677-00350-1). Gordon.

Kobayashi, Yutaka & Maudsley, David V. Biological Applications of Liquid Scintillation Counting. 1974. 44.00 (ISBN 0-12-417250-4). Acad Pr.

Kohler, Friedrich. The Liquid State. LC 75-185277. (Monographs in Modern Chemistry: Vol. 1). (Illus.). 256p. 1972. 49.50x (ISBN 3-527-25390-4). VCH Pubs.

Kruus, Peeter. Liquids & Solutions: Structure & Dynamics. 1977. 99.75 (ISBN 0-8247-6427-7). Dekker.

Murrell, J. N. & Boucher, E. A. Properties of Liquids & Solutions. LC 81-21921. 288p. 1982. 53.95 (ISBN 0-471-10201-6, Pub. by Wiley-Interscience); pap. text ed. 24.95 (ISBN 0-471-10202-4, Pub. by Wiley-Interscience). Wiley.

Muus, L. T. & Atkins, P. W., eds. Electron Spin Relaxation in Liquids. LC 72-76022. 537p. 1972. 75.00x (ISBN 0-306-30588-7, Plenum Pr). Plenum Pub.

National Fire Protection Association. Flammable & Combustible Liquids Code: 1981. 1981. 10.00 (ISBN 0-317-07372-9, NFPA 30). Natl Fire Prot.

Noakes, G. R., ed. Sources of Physics Teaching: Gravity. Liquids. Gases, Vol. 5. 1970. pap. text ed. 18.50x (ISBN 0-85066-040-8). Intl Ideas.

Nyvlt, J. Solid-Liquid Phase Equilibria. 248p. 1977. 61.75 (ISBN 0-444-99850-0). Elsevier.

Oldshue, James Y. Fluid Mixing Technology. (Chemical Engineering Ser.). 400p. 1983. 41.00x (ISBN 0-07-047685-3). McGraw.

Parfitt, Geoffrey D. & Rochester, Colin H., eds. Absorption From Solution at the Solid Liquid Interface. 1983. 79.50 (ISBN 0-12-544980-1). Acad Pr.

Platten, J. K. & Legros, J. C. Convection in Liquids. (Illus.). 700p. 1983. 76.00 (ISBN 0-387-12637-6). Springer-Verlag.

Rabinovich, Izrail' B. Influence of Isotopy on the Physicochemical Properties of Liquids. LC 69-17695. (Illus.). pap. 79.00 (ISBN 0-317-09392-4, 2020681). Bks Demand UMI.

Rabinovich, Viktor Abramovich. Thermophysical Properties of Gases & Liquids. (Physical Constants & Properties of Substances No.1). pap. 53.80 (ISBN 0-317-08438-0, 2004605). Bks Demand UMI.

Reintjes, John F. Nonlinear Optical Parametric Processes in Liquids & Gases. LC 82-11603. 1984. 67.00 (ISBN 0-12-585980-5). Acad Pr.

Rothschild, Walter G. Dynamics of Molecular Liquids. LC 83-10203. 415p. 1984. 51.95x (ISBN 0-471-73971-5, Pub. by Wiley-Interscience). Wiley.

Rowlinson, J. & Swinton, F. L. Liquids & Liquid Mixtures. 3rd ed. 320p. 1982. pap. text ed. 34.95 (ISBN 0-408-24193-4). Butterworth.

Rowlinson, J. S. Liquids & Liquid Mixtures. 2nd ed. LC 79-75522. 371p. 1969. 37.50x (ISBN 0-306-30694-8, Plenum Pr). Plenum Pub.

Schwentner, N., et al. Electronic Excitations in Condensed Rare Gases. (Tracts in Modern Physics Ser.: Vol. 107). (Illus.). 250p. 1985. 34.00 (ISBN 0-387-15382-9). Springer Verlag.

Societe De Chimie Physique, 24th, Paris-Orsay, July 2-6, 1973. Molecular Motions of Liquids: Proceedings. Lascombe, J., ed. LC 73-91947. 1974. lib. bdg. 105.00 (ISBN 90-277-0431-7, Pub. by Reidel Holland). Kluwer Academic.

Sprackling, Michael. Liquids & Solids. (Student Physics Ser.). (Illus.). 224p. (Orig.). 1985. pap. 9.95x (ISBN 0-7102-0484-1). Routledge & Kegan.

Symposium on Liquid Scintillation Counting. Liquid Scintillation Counting: Proceedings of a Symposium on Liquid Scintillation Counting, Brighton, England, Sept. 3-6, 1973, Vol. 3. Crook, M. A. & Johnson, P., eds. LC 70-156826. pap. 80.30 (ISBN 0-317-29707-4). Bks Demand UMI.

--Liquid Scintillation Counting: Proceedings of a Symposium on Liquid Scintillation Counting, Bath, England, Sept. 16-19, 1975, Vol. 4. Crook, M. A. & Johnson, P., eds. LC 70-156826. pap. 69.80 (ISBN 0-317-29709-0, 2024010). Bks Demand UMI.

--Liquid Scintillation Counting: Proceedings of a Symposium on Liquid Scintillation Counting, Bath, England, September 13-16, 1977, Vol. 5. Crook, M. A. & Johnson, P., eds. pap. 29.00 (ISBN 0-317-29406-7, 2024011). Bks Demand UMI.

Tabor, D. Gases, Liquids & Solids. 2nd ed. LC 78-26451. (Illus.). 1980. 59.50 (ISBN 0-521-22383-0); pap. 19.95 (ISBN 0-521-29466-5). Cambridge U Pr.

Tank Vehicles for Flammable & Combustible Liquids. (Thirty Ser). 1974. pap. 2.50 (ISBN 0-685-58035-0, 385). Natl Fire Prot.

Temperley, H. N. & Trevena, D. H. Liquids & Their Properties: A Molecular & Microscopic Treatise. LC 77-8177. 169p. 1978. 74.95x (ISBN 0-470-99203-4). Halsted Pr.

Toglia, Joseph U. Electronystagmography: Technical Aspects & Atlas. (Illus.). 168p. 1976. photocopy ed. 23.50x (ISBN 0-398-03537-7). C C Thomas.

Trevena, D. H. The Liquid Phase. (The Wykeham Science Ser.: No. 37). 122p. pap. cancelled (ISBN 0-85109-031-1). Taylor & Francis.

Trevena, D. H. & Cooke, R. J. The Liquid Phase. LC 75-19034. (Wykeham Science Ser.: No. 37). 122p. 1975. 9.95x (ISBN 0-8448-1164-5). Crane-Russak Co.

Vargaftik, N. B. Handbook of Physical Properties of Liquids & Gases: Pure Substances & Mixtures. 2nd ed. LC 82-25857. 758p. 1983. text ed. 69.50 (ISBN 0-89116-356-5). Hemisphere Pub.

Weber, A., ed. Raman Spectroscopy of Gases & Liquids. (Topics in Current Physics Ser.: Vol. 11). (Illus.). 1979. 37.00 (ISBN 0-387-09036-3). Springer-Verlag.

Wilson, A. C. Insulating Liquids: Their Uses, Manufacture & Properties. (IEE Electrical & Electronics Materials & Devices). (Illus.). 1980. 48.00 (ISBN 0-906048-23-0). Inst Elect Eng.

Wisniak, J. & Tamir, A. Liquid-Liquid Equilibrium & Extraction: A Literature Source Book, 2 Pts. (Physical Science Data Ser.: Vol. 7). 1980-81. Pt. A, 1252p. 170.25 (ISBN 0-444-41909-8); Pt. B, 1438p. 202.25 (ISBN 0-444-42023-1). Elsevier.

LIQUIDS–COMPRESSIBILITY

see Compressibility

LIQUIDS–DIFFUSION

see Diffusion

LIQUIDS–VISCOSITY

see Viscosity

LIQUIDS, KINETIC THEORY OF

Babuel-Peyrissac, Jean-Paul. Equations Cinetiques des Fluides & des Plasmas. (Cours & Documents de Mathematiques & de Physique Ser.). 306p. 1975. 129.50 (ISBN 0-677-50630-9). Gordon.

Liboff, Richard L. Introduction to the Theory of Kinetic Equations. corr. ed. LC 76-30383. (Illus.). 410p. 1979. Repr. of 1969 ed. lib. bdg. 24.00 (ISBN 0-88275-496-3). Krieger.

Nozdrev, V. F. Application of Ultrasonics to Molecular Physics. (Russian Monographs). (Illus.). 542p. 1963. 132.95 (ISBN 0-677-20360-8). Gordon.

Resibois, P. & De Leener, M. F. Classical Kinetic Theory of Fluids. LC 76-58852. 412p. 1977. 63.50 (ISBN 0-471-71694-4, Pub. by Wiley-Interscience). Wiley.

LIQUEFACTION OF COAL

see Coal Liquefaction

LIQUORS

see also Brewing; Distillation

also names of liquors, e.g. Brandy

Erdos, Richard. One Thousand Remarkable Facts About Booze. 192p. 1981. pap. 5.95 (ISBN 0-8317-0958-8, Rutledge Pr). Smith Pubs.

Hogg, Anthony. Cocktails & Mixed Drinks. (Illus.). 128p. 1981. 7.95 (ISBN 0-600-32028-6, 8179). Larousse.

Stewart, Hilary. Wild Teas, Coffees, & Cordials. (Illus.). 128p. 1981. pap. 8.95 (ISBN 0-295-95804-9). U of Wash Pr.

LISA (COMPUTER)

Coleman, Joseph. Apple Lisa: A User-Friendly Handbook. (Illus.). 320p. (Orig.). 1984. 24.95 (ISBN 0-8306-0691-2, 1691); pap. text ed. 16.95 (ISBN 0-8306-1691-8). TAB Bks.

Lisa Owners Guide. (Lisa Reference Manuals). Date not set. 45.00 (ISBN 0-317-04435-4, A6L0103). Apple Comp.

Mesa Research. The Lisa Connection. 1984. pap. 19.95 (ISBN 0-8359-4088-8). Reston.

Naiman, Arthur. Introduction to the Lisa. 957p. 1984. pap. 9.95 (ISBN 0-201-15895-7). Addison-Wesley.

Schmucker, Kurt J. The Complete Book of Lisa. Makower, Joel, ed. (Hands On! Computer Bks.). (Illus.). 224p. (Orig.). 1984. pap. 17.95 (ISBN 0-06-669008-0). Har Row.

Weber Systems, Inc. Staff. Apple Lisa User's Handbook. (WSI's User's Handbook to Personal Computers Ser.). 350p. (Orig.). pap. cancelled (ISBN 0-938862-23-5). Weber Systems.

LISP (COMPUTER PROGRAM LANGUAGE)

Allen, J. Anatomy of LISP. (Computer Science Ser.). (Illus.). 1978. 42.50 (ISBN 0-07-001115-X). McGraw.

Friedman, Daniel P. The Little LISPer. LC 73-91284. 58p. 1974. pap. text ed. 7.50 (ISBN 0-574-19165-8, 13-2165). SRA.

Gloess, Paul Y. Understanding LISP. (Handy Guide). 64p. (Orig.). 1983. pap. 3.50 (ISBN 0-88284-219-6). Alfred Pub.

Gnosis, Inc. Learning LISP. 192p. 1983. 21.95 (ISBN 0-13-527821-X); disk 14.95 (ISBN 0-13-527813-9); book & disk 29.95 (ISBN 0-13-527839-2). P-H.

Hasemer, Tony. A Beginner's Guide to LISP. 208p. 1984. write for info. (ISBN 0-201-14634-7). Benjamin-Cummings.

--Looking at LISP. 288p. 1983. pap. 16.95 (ISBN 0-201-12080-1). Addison-Wesley.

LISP. (Alfred's Language Bks.). 1981. pap. 3.50 (ISBN 0-317-04678-0). Alfred Pub.

McCarthy, John. LISP One-Point-Five Programmer's Manual. 1962. 7.95x (ISBN 0-262-13011-4). MIT Pr.

Meehan, James R., ed. The New UCI LISP Manual. (Artificial Intelligence Ser.). 336p. 1979. pap. text ed. 14.95x (ISBN 0-89859-012-4). L Erlbaum Assocs.

Siklossy, Laurent. Let's Talk Lisp. ref. ed. 456p. 1976. 23.95 (ISBN 0-13-532762-8). P-H.

Touretzky, David. LISP: A Gentle Introduction to Symbolic Computation. 240p. 1984. pap. text ed. 18.22i (ISBN 0-06-046657-X, HarpC). Har-Row.

Tracton, Ken. Programmer's Guide to LISP. (Illus.). 1979. 13.95 (ISBN 0-8306-9761-6); pap. 11.95 (ISBN 0-8306-1045-6, 1045). TAB Bks.

Wilensky, Robert. LISPcraft. 1984. text ed. 19.95x (ISBN 0-393-95442-0); tchrs. manual avail. (ISBN 0-393-95455-2). Norton.

LIST PROCESSING (ELECTRONIC COMPUTERS)

Bowen & Behr. The Logical Design of Multiple Microprocessor Systems. (Illus.). 272p. 1980. text ed. 37.50 (ISBN 0-13-539908-4). P-H.

LITERATURE AND SCIENCE

Barber, Otto. H. G. Wells' Verhaltnis Zum Darwinismus. pap. 8.00 (ISBN 0-384-03380-6). Johnson Repr.

Brier, Bob & Digby, Joan. Permutations: Reading in Science & Literature. 1985. pap. 12.95 (ISBN 0-688-01945-5, Quill). Morrow.

Cosslett, Tess. The Scientific Movement & Victorian Literature. LC 82-10284. 1983. 22.50x (ISBN 0-312-70298-1). St Martin.

Dudley, Fred A., ed. The Relations of Literature & Science: A Selected Bibliography, 1930-1949. LC 50-4895. pap. 36.50 (ISBN 0-317-10401-2, 2000294). Bks Demand UMI.

Hayles, N. Katherine. The Cosmic Web: Scientific Field Models & Literary Strategies in the Twentieth Century. LC 84-45141. 232p. 1984. 19.95x (ISBN 0-8014-1742-2). Cornell U Pr.

Morton, Peter. The Vital Science: Biology & the Literary Imagination 1860-1900. LC 84-10991. 240p. 1984. text ed. 29.95x (ISBN 0-04-800025-6). Allen Unwin.

Motte, Warren F. Oulipo: A Primer of Potential Literature. LC 85-8724. 240p. (Orig.). 1986. 22.95x (ISBN 0-8032-3096-6). U of Nebr Pr.

--Oulipo: A Primer of Potential Literature. LC 85-8724. 240p. (Orig.). 1986. pap. 9.95 (ISBN 0-8032-8131-5, BB944, Pub. by Bison). U of Nebr Pr.

Nicholl, Charles. The Chemical Theatre. 272p. 1980. 36.95 (ISBN 0-7100-0515-6). Routledge & Kegan.

Nicholson, Marjorie H. Newton Demands the Muse: Newton's "Opticks" & the Eighteenth Century Poets. LC 78-13146. 1979. Repr. of 1966 ed. lib. bdg. 24.75x (ISBN 0-313-21044-6, NIND). Greenwood.

Sussman, Herbert L. Victorians & the Machine: Literary Response to Technology. LC 68-14274. (Illus.). Repr. of 1968 ed. 51.90 (ISBN 0-8357-9184-X, 2016540). Bks Demand UMI.

LITHIUM

Bach, Ricardo, ed. Lithium: Current Applications in Science, Medicine & Technology. 448p. 1985. 80.00 (ISBN 0-471-80073-2). Wiley.

Berner, P., et al, eds. Current Perspectives in Lithium Prophylaxis. (Bibliotheca Psychiatrica: Vol. 161). (Illus.). viii, 248p. 1981. pap. 37.50 (ISBN 3-8055-1753-X). S Karger.

Dubrova, Sara K. Vitreous Lithium Silicates: Their Properties & Field of Application. 46p. 1964. 20.00x (ISBN 0-306-10679-5, Consultants). Plenum Pub.

Emrich, H. M. & Aldenhoff, J. B., eds. Basic Mechanisms in the Action of Lithium: Proceedings of a Symposium at Schloss Ringberg, Bavaria, Germany, October 4-6, 1981. (International Congress Ser.: No. 572). 272p. 1982. 74.50 (ISBN 0-444-90249-X, Excerpta Medica). Elsevier.

Fox, Ira L. Ins & Outs of Ups & Downs. LC 82-90730. 1983. 10.95 (ISBN 0-87212-170-4). Libra.

Gershon, Samuel & Shopsin, Baron, eds. Lithium: Its Role in Psychiatric Research & Treatment. LC 72-91021. (Illus.). 369p. 1973. 35.00x (ISBN 0-306-30720-0, Plenum Pr). Plenum Pub.

Gorsini, G. U., ed. Current Trends in Lithium & Rubidium. 1984. lib. bdg. 49.50 (ISBN 0-85200-782-5, Pub. by MTP Pr England). Kluwer Academic.

Jefferson, James W., et al. Lithium Encyclopedia for Clinical Practice. LC 83-2798. (Illus.). 340p. 1983. spiral bdg. 19.50x (ISBN 0-88048-011-4, 48-011-4). Am Psychiatric.

Johnson, F. Neil. Handbook of Lithium Therapy. (Illus.). 476p. 1980. text ed. 42.50 (ISBN 0-8391-1478-8). Univ Park.

Penner, S. S. Lithium: Needs & Resources. 1979. 26.00 (ISBN 0-08-022733-3). Pergamon.

Rossof, Arthur H. & Robinson, William A., eds. Lithium Effects of Granulopoiesis & Immune Function. LC 80-116. (Advances in Experimental Medicine & Biology Ser.: Vol. 127). 489p. 1980. 65.00x (ISBN 0-306-40359-5, Plenum Pr). Plenum Pub.

Schou, M. Lithium Treatment of Manic-Depressive Illness. 2nd, rev. ed. (Illus.). x, 50p. 1983. pap. 6.50 (ISBN 3-8055-3678-X). S Karger.

Smith, Donald F. Lithium & Animal Behavior. Horrobin, D. F., ed. (Lithium Research Review Ser.: Vol. I). 66p. 1980. Repr. of 1977 ed. 12.95 (ISBN 0-87705-961-6). Human Sci Pr.

Smith, Donald F. & Horrobin, D. F. Lithium & Animal Behavior. LC 81-13321. (Lithium Research Review Ser.: Vol. II). 134p. 1982. 16.95 (ISBN 0-89885-075-4). Human Sci Pr.

Starke, E. A., Jr. & Sanders, T. H., Jr., eds. Aluminum-Lithium Alloys II: Proceedings, Monterey, California, 1983. (Illus.). 692p. 1984. 62.00; members 32.00; student members 17.00. Metal Soc.

LITHOGRAPHY

see also Chromolithography; Color-Printing; Offset Printing; Photolithography

Moreau, Wayne M. Semiconductor Lithography. (Illus.). 1500p. cancelled (ISBN 0-913811-02-5). Northeast A S.

Thompson, L. F. & Wilson, C. G., eds. An Introduction to Microlithography. LC 83-5968. (ACS Symposium Ser.: No. 219). 363p. 1983. lib. bdg. 49.95x (ISBN 0-8412-0775-5). Am Chemical.

Thompson, L. F., et al, eds. Materials for Microlithography: Radiation-Sensitive Polymers. LC 84-21744. (ACS Symposium Ser.: No. 266). 496p. 1984. lib. bdg. 54.95x (ISBN 0-8412-0871-9). Am Chemical.

LITHOLOGY

see Petrology

LITHOPHYTES

see Corals

LITTORAL FLORA

see Coastal Flora

LIVER

Arias, I. M. & Frenkel, M., eds. The Liver Annual, Vol. 2, 1982. (Liver Ser.: Vol. 2). 474p. 1982. 81.00 (ISBN 0-444-90241-4). Elsevier.

Arias, I. M., et al, eds. The Liver Annual, 1984, Vol. 4. 520p. 1984. 70.00 (ISBN 0-444-90346-1, I-275-84). Elsevier.

Becker, Frederick F., ed. The Liver: Normal & Abnormal Functions, 2 pts. (Biochemistry of Disease Ser.: Vol. 5). 592p. 1975. Part A. 85.00 (ISBN 0-8247-6205-3); Part B. 75.00 (ISBN 0-8247-6214-2). Dekker.

Davis, M., et al, eds. Drug Reactions & the Liver. 300p. 1981. text ed. 62.00x (ISBN 0-8464-1220-9). Beekman Pubs.

Fausto, Nelson, et al. Liver Regeneration, No. 2. LC 72-13504. (Illus.). 220p. 1973. text ed. 24.00x (ISBN 0-8422-7080-9). Irvington.

Gastaad Symposium, 1st International, Swiss Society for Gastroenlerology. The Liver: Quantitative Aspects of Structure & Function, Proceedings. Preisig, R. & Paumgartener, G., eds. (Illus.). 1973. 27.75 (ISBN 3-8055-1603-7). S Karger.

Glaumann, Hans, et al, eds. Plasma Protein Secretion by the Liver. 1984. 75.00 (ISBN 0-12-286180-9). Acad Pr.

Gram, T. E., ed. Extrahepatic Metabolism of Drugs & Other Foreign Compounds. (Monographs in Pharmacology & Physiology: Vol. 5). (Illus.). 470p. 1980. 60.00 (ISBN 0-89335-095-8). SP Med & Sci Bks.

Herlinger, Hans. Clinical Radiology of the Liver, Pts. A & B. (Diagnostic Radiology Ser.: Vol. 1). (Illus.). 1224p. 1983. 295.00 set (ISBN 0-8247-1069-X). Vol. A. 542 p. Vol. B 656 p. Dekker.

Hue, L. & Van de Werve, G., eds. Short Term Regulation of Liver Metabolism. 464p. 1982. 119.75 (ISBN 0-444-80333-5, Biomedical Pr). Elsevier.

International Symposium on: HBsAg Containing Immune Complexes: Renal & Other Extra-Hepatic Manifestations: Italy, Sept. 1979, et al. Systematic Effects of HBsAg Immune Complexes: Proceedings. Bartoli, E. & Chiandussi, L., eds. 308p. 1981. text ed. 33.00 (ISBN 0-686-31134-5, Pub. by Piccin Italy). J K Burgess.

Langer, Maria. The Endocrine & the Liver: Proceedings of the Serono Symposia, No. 51. 1983. 70.00 (ISBN 0-12-436580-9). Acad Pr.

Lesch, R., et al. Liver. Eichler, O., ed. (Handbook of Experimental Pharmacology: Bund 16). 1976. 142.00 (ISBN 0-387-07647-6). Springer-Verlag.

Malkin, Leonard I., et al. Liver Regeneration, No. 1. (Illus.). 200p. 1973. text ed. 24.00x (ISBN 0-8422-7079-5). Irvington.

Motta, Pietro, et al. The Liver: An Atlas of Scanning Electron Microscopy. LC 77-95454. (Illus.). 174p. 1978. 46.00 (ISBN 0-89640-026-3). Igaku-Shoin.

Plaa, G. L. & Hewitt, W. R., eds. Toxicology of the Liver. (Target Organ Toxicology Ser.). 350p. 1982. text ed. 59.00 (ISBN 0-89004-584-4). Raven.

Popper, Hans & Reutter, Werner, eds. Structural Carbohydrates in the Liver: Falk Symposium, No 34. 600p. 1983. text ed. write for info. (ISBN 0-85200-711-6, Pub. by MTP Pr England). Kluwer Academic.

Powell, L. Metals & the Liver. (Liver; Normal Function & Disease Ser.: Vol. 1). 1978. 69.75 (ISBN 0-8247-6740-3). Dekker.

Serafani, Aldo N. & Guter, Marvin. Medical Imaging of the Liver & Spleen. 1983. 55.00 (ISBN 0-8385-6224-8). ACC.

Sherlock, S. V. The Human Liver. Head, J. J., ed. LC 76-50844. (Carolina Biology Readers Ser.). (Illus.). 16p. 1978. pap. 1.60 (ISBN 0-89278-283-8, 45-9683). Carolina Biological.

Sies, H. & Wendel, A., eds. Functions of Glutathione in Liver & Kidney. (Proceedings in Life Sciences Ser.). (Illus.). 1978. 39.00 (ISBN 0-387-09127-0). Springer-Verlag.

Taylor, W., ed. The Hepatobiliary System: Fundamental & Pathological Mechanisms. LC 76-2486. (NATO ASI Series A, Life Sciences: Vol. 7). 671p. 1976. 79.50x (ISBN 0-306-35607-4, Plenum Pr). Plenum Pub.

LIVERPOOL AND MANCHESTER RAILWAY

Booth, Henry. Account of the Liverpool & Manchester Railway. (Illus.). 104p. 1969. Repr. of 1830 ed. 25.00x (ISBN 0-7146-1433-5, F Cass Co). Biblio Dist.

Thomas, R. H. The Liverpool & Manchester Railway. LC 79-57313. (Illus.). 264p. 1980. 45.00 (ISBN 0-7134-0537-6, Pub. by Batsford England). David & Charles.

LIVERWORTS

Bonner, C. E. Index Hepaticarum: An Index to the Liverworts of the World. Incl. Pt. 2. Achiton to Balantiopsis. 26.25 (ISBN 3-7682-0092-2); Pt. 3. Barbilophozia to Ceranthus. 26.25 (ISBN 3-7682-0093-0); Pt. 4. Ceratolejeunea to Crystolejeunea. 26.25 (ISBN 3-7682-0094-9); Pt. 5. Delavayella to Geothallus. 35.00 (ISBN 3-7682-0095-7); Pt. 6. Goebelliella to Jubula. 26.25 (ISBN 3-7682-0096-5). 1963-66. Lubrecht & Cramer.

--Index Hepaticarum, Index to the Liverworts of the World Part 7A: Supplement, Additions & Corrections to Parts 2-4. 1977. pap. text ed. 21.00 (ISBN 3-7682-0097-3). Lubrecht & Cramer.

--Index Hepaticarum. Index to the Liverworts of the World Part 8: Jungermannia. 1976. pap. text ed. 42.00. Lubrecht & Cramer.

--Index Hepaticarum. Part 9: Jungermanniopsis-Lejeunea. 1978. pap. 35.00x. Lubrecht & Cramer.

Conard, Henry S. & Redfearn, Paul L., Jr. How to Know the Mosses & Liverworts. 2nd ed. (Pict. Key Nature Ser.). 320p. 1979. wire coil write for info. (ISBN 0-697-04768-7). Wm C Brown.

Crandall, B. J. Morphology & Development of Branches in the Leafy Hepaticae. (Illus.). 1970. 28.00 (ISBN 3-7682-5430-5). Lubrecht & Cramer.

Gottsche, K. M., et al. Synopsis Hepaticarum. 1967. Repr. of 1844 ed. 56.00 (ISBN 3-7682-0516-9). Lubrecht & Cramer.

Husnot, P. T. Hepatologia Gallica. 2nd ed. (Illus.). 1968. Repr. of 1922 ed. 15.00 (ISBN 90-6123-081-0). Lubrecht & Cramer.

Schuster, R. M. Boreal Hepaticae, a Manual of Liverworts of Minnesota & Adjacent Regions. (Bryophytorum Bibliotheca Ser.: No. 11). (Illus.). 1977. lib. bdg. 35.00x (ISBN 3-7682-1150-9). Lubrecht & Cramer.

Schuster, Rudolf M. Hepaticae & Anthocerotae of North America East of the Hundredth Meridian, 4 vols. LC 66-14791. 1966-74. 100.00x ea. Vol. 1 (ISBN 0-231-08981-3). Vol. 2 (ISBN 0-231-08982-1). Vol. 3 (ISBN 0-231-03567-5). Vol. 4. 120.00 (ISBN 0-231-04608-1). Columbia U Pr.

Steere, William C. Liverworts of Southern Michigan. LC 40-10272. (Bulletin Ser.: No. 17). (Illus.). 97p. (Orig.). 1940. pap. 3.00x (ISBN 0-87737-004-4, 17). Cranbrook.

Watson, E. Vernon. British Mosses & Liverworts. 3rd ed. LC 81-10081. (Illus.). 512p. 1982. 59.50 (ISBN 0-521-24004-2). Cambridge U Pr.

LIVESTOCK

see also Cattle; Donkeys; Goats; Horses; Mules; Pastures; Range Management; Sheep

also headings beginning with the word Livestock

Acker, Duane. Animal Science & Industry. x ed. (Illus.). 720p. 1983. 33.95 (ISBN 0-13-037416-4). P-H.

Animal Husbandry: Animal Diseases, How Animals Reproduce. Rev. ed. (Economic & Social Development Papers: No. 3). (Illus.). 33p. 1976. pap. 5.50 (ISBN 92-5-100148-0, F67, FAO). Unipub.

Animal Husbandry: Feeding & Care of Animals. (Better Farming Ser.: No. 8). (Illus.). 38p. 1976. pap. 7.50 (ISBN 92-5-100147-2, F66, FAO). Unipub.

Banerjee, G. C. A Textbook of Animal Husbandry. 4th ed. 1981. 35.00x (ISBN 0-686-72968-4, Pub. by Oxford & IBH India). State Mutual Bk.

Bearden, H. Joe & Fuquay, John. Applied Animal Reproduction. 2nd. ed. 1984. text ed. 23.95 (ISBN 0-8359-0106-8); instr's manual avail. (ISBN 0-8359-0107-6). Reston.

Belanger, Jerome. The Homesteader's Handbook to Raising Small Livestock. Stoner, Carol, ed. LC 73-88254. (Illus.). 256p. 1974. 12.95 (ISBN 0-87857-075-6). Rodale Pr Inc.

Berleant-Schiller, Riva & Shanklin, Eugenia, eds. The Keeping of Animals: Adaptation & Social Relations in Livestock Producing Communities. LC 81-65015. (Illus.). 208p. 1982. text ed. 25.95x (ISBN 0-86598-033-0). Allanheld.

Blakely, James & Bade, David. The Science of Animal Husbandry. 4th ed. 1985. text ed. 24.95 (ISBN 0-8359-6897-9); instr's manual avail. (ISBN 0-8359-6898-7). Reston.

Boatfield, Graham. Farm Livestock. 2nd ed. (Illus.). 144p. 1983. pap. 13.95 (ISBN 0-85236-130-0, Pub. by Farming Pr UK). Diamond Farm Bk.

Boggs, Donald L. & Merkel, Robert A. Live Animal Carcass Evaluation & Selection Manual. 208p. (Orig.). 1984. pap. text ed. 12.95 (ISBN 0-8403-3331-5, 40333101). Kendall-Hunt.

Briggs, Hilton M. & Briggs, Dinus M. Modern Breeds of Livestock. 4th ed. (Illus.). 1980. text ed. write for info. (ISBN 0-02-314730-X). Macmillan.

Brown, T. Freeze Branding. (Orig.). 1982. pap. 5.00 (ISBN 0-911217-00-2). SW Amer Pub Co.

Buckett, M. Introduction to Livestock Husbandry. 2nd ed. 1977. 28.00 (ISBN 0-08-021180-1); pap. 10.25 (ISBN 0-08-021179-8). Pergamon.

Bundy, Clarence E., et al. Livestock & Poultry Production. 4th ed. 1975. text ed. 31.52 (ISBN 0-13-538579-2). P-H.

Business Communications Staff. Livestock & Bio-Technology. 1984. 1750.00 (ISBN 0-89336-361-8, GA-054). BCC.

CAB Books, ed. Livestock Management in the Arid Zone: V Squires. 271p. 1981. 90.00x (ISBN 0-909605-23-8, Pub. by CAB Bks England). State Mutual Bk.

Campbell, John R. & Lasley, John F. The Science of Animals That Serve Mankind. 2nd ed. (Agricultural Science Ser.). (Illus.). 736p. 1975. text ed. 39.95 (ISBN 0-07-009696-1). McGraw.

Clemen, Rudolf A. The American Livestock & Meat Industry. abr. ed. (Illus.). 1923. 35.00 (ISBN 0-384-09305-1). Johnson Repr.

Cole, H. H., ed. Introduction to Livestock Production: Including Dairy & Poultry. 2nd ed. LC 66-16377. (Illus.). 827p. 1966. 35.95 (ISBN 0-7167-0812-4). W H Freeman.

Cole, H. H. & Garrett, W. N., eds. Animal Agriculture: The Biology, Husbandry, & Use of Domestic Animals. 2nd ed. LC 79-18984. (Animal Science Ser.). (Illus.). 739p. 1980. text ed. 28.95 (ISBN 0-7167-1099-4). W H Freeman.

Coop, J. E. Sheep & Goat Production. (World Animal Science Ser.: Vol. 1C). 492p. 1982. 121.50 (ISBN 0-444-41989-6). Elsevier.

DeVos, Antoon. Deer Farming. (Animal Production & Health Papers: No. 27). 60p. 1982. pap. 7.50 (ISBN 92-5-101137-0, F2362, FAO). Unipub.

Dickinson, Darol. Photographing Livestock: The Complete Guide. LC 79-88468. (Illus.). pap. 7.95 (ISBN 0-87358-200-4). Northland.

Eldridge, Franklin E. Cytogenetics of Livestock. (Illus.). 1985. text ed. 49.50 (ISBN 0-87055-483-2). AVI.

Fraser, Alistair & Thear, Katie, eds. Small Farmer's Guide to Raising Livestock & Poultry. (Illus.). 240p. 1981. 14.95 (ISBN 0-668-04687-2). Arco.

Guide to Statistics of Livestock & Livestock Products. 98p. 1976. pap. 11.75 (ISBN 0-685-68956-5, F928, FAO). Unipub.

Hafez, E. S., ed. Reproduction in Farm Animals. 4th ed. LC 80-10489. (Illus.). 627p. 1980. text ed. 31.00 (ISBN 0-8121-0697-0). Lea & Febiger.

Haynes, N. Bruce. Keeping Livestock Healthy: A Veterinary Guide. LC 78-8025. (Illus.). 1978. pap. 12.95 (ISBN 0-88266-134-5). Garden Way Pub.

Heady, Earl O. & Bhide, Shashanka, eds. Livestock Response Functions. (Illus.). 332p. 1984. 29.95x (ISBN 0-8138-1091-4). Iowa St U Pr.

Hormones in Animal Production: Selected Papers Presented to the Joint FAO-WHO Expert Committee on Food Additives, Geneva, 23 March-1 April 1981. (Animal Production & Health Papers: No. 31). 62p. 1982. pap. 7.50 (ISBN 92-5-101213-X, F2342, FAO). Unipub.

Hoveland, Carl S., ed. The Biological Nitrogen Fixation in Foreign-Livestock Systems. 1976. pap. 6.25 (ISBN 0-89118-046-X). Am Soc Agron.

Intensive Sheep Production in the Near East. (Animal Production & Health Paper: No. 40). 67p. 1984. pap. text ed. 7.50 (ISBN 92-5-101399-3, F2530, FAO). Unipub.

IPC Business Press, ed. British Farmer & Stockbreeder Year Book & Farm Diary. 1981. 25.00x (ISBN 0-617-00214-2, Pub. by IPC Busn England). State Mutual Bk.

Kamstra, Leslie D. Livestock Nutrition. (Illus.). 223p. 1982. pap. text ed. 9.95x (ISBN 0-89641-081-1). American Pr.

Kempster, A. J. & Cuthbertson, A., eds. Carcase Evaluation in Livestone Breeding, Production & Marketing. 250p. 1982. 43.00x (ISBN 0-86531-531-0). Westview.

Kilgour, Ron & Dalton, Clive. Livestock Behavior: A Practical Guide. 256p. 1983. 24.00x (ISBN 0-86531-576-0, Pub. by Granada Ltd. England). Westview.

Lane, Ron & Cross, Tim. Database Applications for Livestock Recordkeeping. 1985. text ed. 29.95 (ISBN 0-8359-1239-6); pap. text ed. 19.95 (ISBN 0-8359-1238-8). Reston.

Lasley, John F. Genetics of Livestock Improvement. 3rd ed. LC 77-22807. (Illus.). 1978. ref. ed. 37.95 (ISBN 0-13-351106-5). P-H.

Latham, Hiram. Trans-Missouri Stock Raising. Dykes, J. C., ed. 1962. Repr. of 1871 ed. 12.50 (ISBN 0-912094-02-8). Old West.

Lerner, I. M. & Donald, H. P. Modern Developments in Animal Breeding. 1966. 59.00 (ISBN 0-12-444350-8). Acad Pr.

Lerner, I. Michael. The Genetic Basis of Selection. LC 73-19295. (Illus.). 298p. 1974. Repr. of 1958 ed. lib. bdg. 24.75x (ISBN 0-8371-7315-9, LEGB). Greenwood.

Livestock Environment II. LC 82-72456. 624p. 1982. text ed. 36.50 (ISBN 0-916150-45-3). Am Soc Ag Eng.

Lush, Jay L. Animal Breeding Plans. facs. ed. (Illus.). 1945. pap. 18.50x (ISBN 0-8138-2345-5). Iowa St U Pr.

McCoy, John H. Livestock & Meat Marketing. 2nd ed. (Illus.). 1979. text ed. 29.50 (ISBN 0-87055-321-6). AVI.

McNitt, J. I. Livestock Husbandry Techniques. (Illus.). 256p. (Orig.). 1982. pap. text ed. 12.25x (ISBN 0-246-11871-7, Pub. by Granada England). Brookfield Pub Co.

--Livestock Husbandry Techniques. 280p. 1983. pap. 13.50x (ISBN 0-246-11871-7, Pub. by Granada England). Sheridan.

Mason, I. L. A Dictionary of Livestock Breeds. 268p. 1969. cloth 50.00x (ISBN 0-85198-007-4, Pub. by CAB Bks England). State Mutual Bk.

Mason, I. L. & Buvanendran, V. Breeding Plans For Ruminant Livestock in the Tropics. (Animal Production & Health Papers: No. 34). 89p. 1982. pap. text ed. 7.50 (ISBN 92-5-101247-4, F2381, FAO). Unipub.

Merkel, James A. Managing Livestock Wastes. (Illus.). 1981. text ed. 29.50 (ISBN 0-87055-373-9). AVI.

Mettler, John J. Basic Butchering of Livestock & Game. LC 85-70195. (Illus.). 160p. 1985. pap. 9.95 (ISBN 0-88266-391-7). Garden Way Pub.

Midwest Plan Service Engineers. Livestock Waste Facilities Handbook. 2nd ed. Midwest Plan Service Staff, ed. LC 84-9687. (Illus.). 112p. 1985. pap. 6.00 (ISBN 0-89373-063-7, MWPS-18). Midwest Plan Serv.

Moss, R., ed. Transport of Animals Intended for Breeding, Production & Slaughter. 1982. lib. bdg. 34.50 (ISBN 90-247-2679-4, Pub. by Martinus Nijhoff Netherlands). Kluwer Academic.

Nelson, R. H. An Introduction to Feeding Farm Livestock. 2nd ed. 1979. pap. text ed. 9.75 (ISBN 0-08-023756-8). Pergamon.

Overcash, Michael R. & Humenik, Frank J. Livestock Waste Management, 2 vols. 512p. 1983. 67.00 ea. Vol. I (ISBN 0-8493-5595-8). Vol. II. CRC Pr.

Park, R. D., et al. Animal Husbandry. 2nd ed. (Illus.). 1970. pap. 16.95x (ISBN 0-19-859422-4). Oxford U Pr.

Parks, J. R. A Theory of Feeding & Growth of Animals. (Advanced Series in Agriculture: Vol. 11). (Illus.). 322p. 1982. 57.00 (ISBN 0-387-11122-0). Springer-Verlag.

Peterson, Paul, et al. Working in Animal Science. Amberson, Max, ed. (Illus.). 1978. pap. text ed. 13.72 (ISBN 0-07-000839-6). McGraw.

Politiek, R. D. & Bakker, J. J., eds. Livestock Production in Europe: Perspectives & Prospects. (Developments in Animal & Veterinary Sciences Ser.: No. 8). 354p. 1982. 53.25 (ISBN 0-444-42105-X). Elsevier.

Price, C. J. & Reed, C. J. Practical Parasitology: General Laboratory Techniques & Parasitic Protozoa Notes for Students of Animal Husbandry. 112p. 1970. pap. 3.00 (ISBN 92-5-101581-3, F330, FAO). Unipub.

Raikes, Philip L. Livestock Development & Policy in East Africa. (Centre for Development Research Ser.: No. 6). (Illus.). 254p. 1983. pap. text ed. 12.50x (ISBN 0-8419-9761-6, Africana). Holmes & Meier.

Report of Working Party on Crop & Livestock Insurance: Bangkok, 1956. 44p. 1957. pap. 4.50 (ISBN 0-686-93273-0, F389, FAO). Unipub.

Ritchie, Harland D. Livestock Judging & Evaluation Manual. (Illus.). x, 205p. 1969. pap. 6.50 (ISBN 0-87013-152-4). Mich St U Pr.

Sainsbury, David. Animal Health: Health, Disease & Welfare of Farm Livestock. 240p. 1983. softcover 25.00x (ISBN 0-86531-580-9, Pub. by Granada, England Ltd.). Westview.

--Animal Health: Health, Disease & Welfare of Farm Livestock. 240p. 1983. pap. 20.00x (ISBN 0-246-11625-0, Pub. by Granada England). Sheridan.

Sennholz, Lyn M., et al. Livestock Hedging Course. 160p. (Orig.). 1984. wkbk. 65.00 (ISBN 0-915513-05-6). Ctr Futures Ed.

Shepherd, William. Prairie Experiences in Handling Cattle & Sheep. facsimile ed. LC 70-165807. (Select Bibliographies Reprint Ser.). Repr. of 1885 ed. 18.00 (ISBN 0-8369-5964-7). Ayer Co Pubs.

Sims, John A. & Johnson, Leslie E. Animals in the American Economy. (Illus.). 228p. 1972. text ed. 11.95x (ISBN 0-8138-0245-8). Iowa St U Pr.

Sorensen, Anton M., Jr. Animal Reproduction: Principles & Practice. Zappa, C. Robert, ed. (Agricultural Sciences Ser.). (Illus.). 1979. text ed. 42.95 (ISBN 0-07-059670-0). McGraw.

Stufflebeam, Charles E. Principles of Animal Agriculture. (Illus.). 464p. 1983. 28.95 (ISBN 0-13-700948-8). P-H.

Swatland, H. J. Structure & Development of Meat Animals. (Illus.). 512p. 1984. 41.95 (ISBN 0-13-854398-4). P-H.

Swithi, G. R. & Chatrath, M. S. Improving Crop & Animal Productivity. 629p. 1981. 120.00x (ISBN 0-686-76645-8, Pub by Oxford & IBH India). State Mutual Bk.

Teutsch, Gotthard M. & Von Loeper, Eisenhart, eds. Intensivhaltung von Nutztieren aus ethischer, rechtlicher und ethologischer Sicht. (Tierhaltung-Animal Management: No. 8). (Ger.). 228p. 1979. pap. 20.95x (ISBN 0-8176-1119-3). Birkhauser.

Thear, Katie & Fraser, Alistair, eds. Raising Livestock & Poultry: A Smallholder's Guide. 240p. 1981. 25.00 (ISBN 0-906348-11-0, Pub. by Dunitz). State Mutual Bk.

Warwick, E. J. & Legates, J. E. Breeding & Improving of Farm Animals. 7th ed. (Agricultural Sciences Ser). (Illus.). 1979. text ed. 44.95 (ISBN 0-07-068375-1). McGraw.

Wilkinson, J. M. Milk & Meat from Grass. (Illus.). 224p. 1984. pap. 20.00x (ISBN 0-246-12290-0, Pub. by Granada England). Sheridan.

Yagil, R. Camels & Camel Milk. (Animal Production & Health Papers: No. 26). 72p. 1982. pap. 7.50 (ISBN 92-5-101169-9, F2310, FAO). Unipub.

Yousef, M. K., ed. Stress Physiology in Livestock, Vol. I. LC 83-26321. 240p. 1984. 72.00 (ISBN 0-8493-5667-9). CRC Pr.

LIVESTOCK–HOUSING

see also Farm Buildings; Stables

Clark, J. A. Environmental Aspects of Housing for Animal Production. 1981. text ed. 130.00 (ISBN 0-408-10688-3). Butterworth.

Curtis, Stanley E. Environmental Management in Animal Agriculture. (Illus.). 410p. 1983. pap. text ed. 43.25x (ISBN 0-8138-0556-2). Iowa St U Pr.

Midwest Plan Service Engineers. Swine Housing & Equipment Handbook. 4th ed. Midwest Plan Service Staff, ed. LC 82-2292. (Illus.). 112p. 1983. pap. 6.00 (ISBN 0-89373-054-8, MWPS-8). Midwest Plan Serv.

Midwest Plan Service Personnel. Horse Housing & Equipment Handbook. 1st ed. (Illus.). 60p. 1971. pap. 5.00 (ISBN 0-89373-009-2, MWPS-15). Midwest Plan Serv.

Midwest Plan Service Staff. Solar Livestock Housing Handbook. LC 82-20889. (Illus.). 88p. (Orig.). 1983. pap. 6.00 (ISBN 0-89373-056-4, MWPS-23). Midwest Plan Serv.

Pelley, Lee. In One Barn: Efficient Livestock Housing & Management Under One Roof. (Illus.). 166p. (Orig.). 1984. pap. 11.95 (ISBN 0-88150-006-2). Countryman.

Smith, C. V. Some Environmental Problems of Livestock Housing. (Technical Note Ser.: No. 122). (Illus.). 98p. (Orig.). 1972. pap. 15.00 (ISBN 0-685-34862-8, W120, WMO). Unipub.

LIVESTOCK–STUDY AND TEACHING

Commission on Education in Agriculture & Natural Resources. Undergraduate Teaching in the Animal Sciences. 1967. pap. 5.25 (ISBN 0-309-01486-7). Natl Acad Pr.

LIVESTOCK–CHINA

Taylor, George E. The Livestock of China. LC 78-74304. (The Modern Chinese Economy Ser.). 174p. 1980. lib. bdg. 26.00 (ISBN 0-8240-4286-7). Garland Pub.

LIVESTOCK–GREAT BRITAIN

Alderson, Lawrence. Rare Breeds. (Shire Album Ser.: No. 118). (Illus.). 32p. (Orig.). 1984. pap. 2.95 (ISBN 0-85263-677-6, Pub. by Shire Pubns England). Seven Hills Bks.

LIVESTOCK–INDIA

Ranjhan, S. K. Animal Nutrition & Feeding Practices in India. (Illus.). 339p. 1977. 11.00x (ISBN 0-7069-0509-1, Pub. by Vikas India). Advent NY.

LIVESTOCK–TROPICS

Ranjhan, S. K. Animal Nutrition in Tropics. 2nd ed. 480p. 1982. 50.00x (ISBN 0-7069-1374-4, Pub. by Garlandfold England); pap. 40.00x (ISBN 0-7069-1375-2). State Mutual Bk.

Williamson, G. & Payne, W. J. An Introduction to Animal Husbandry in the Tropics. 3rd ed. (Tropical Agriculture Ser.). (Illus.). 1978. text ed. 31.00x (ISBN 0-582-46813-2). Longman.

LIVESTOCK BUILDINGS

see Livestock–Housing

LIVESTOCK EXHIBITIONS

Minish, Gary, et al. Livestock Judging. 1985. pap. text ed. 18.95 (ISBN 0-8359-4089-6). Reston.

Winogrand, Garry & Tyler, Ron. Stock Photographs: The Fort Worth Fat Stock Show & Rodeo. (Illus.). 128p. 1980. 19.95 (ISBN 0-292-72433-0). U of Tex Pr.

LIVING FOSSILS

see also names of living fossils, e.g Platypus

Eldredge, N. & Stanley, S. M., eds. Living Fossils. (Casebooks in Earth Sciences). (Illus.). 305p. 1984. 45.00 (ISBN 0-387-90957-5). Springer-Verlag.

LIZARDS

see also Chameleons

Boulenger, G. A. Catalogue of the Lizards in the British Museum, 3 vols. in 2. (Illus.). 1964. 168.00 (ISBN 3-7682-0239-9). Lubrecht & Cramer.

Burghardt, Gordon M., ed. Iguanas of the World: Their Behavior, Ecology & Conservation. Rand, A. Stanley. LC 82-7932. (Animal Behavior, Ecology, Conservation & Management Ser.). (Illus.). 472p. 1983. 55.00 (ISBN 0-8155-0917-0). Noyes.

Carpenter, Charles C. Comparative Display Behavior in the Genus Sceloporus (Iguanidae) 71p. 1978. 4.50 (ISBN 0-89326-032-0). Milwaukee Pub Mus.

Cei, Jose M. A New Species of Liolaemus (Sauria: Iguanidae) from the Andean Mountains of the Southern Mendoza Volcanic Region of Argentina. (Occasional Papers: Vol. 76). 6p. 1978. 1.25 (ISBN 0-317-04841-4). U of KS Mus Nat Hist.

--A New Species of Tropidurus (Sauria, Iguanidae) from the Arid Chacoan & Western Regions of Argentina. (Occasional Papers: No. 97). 10p. 1982. 1.75 (ISBN 0-317-04843-0). U of KS Mus Nat Hist.

Dixon, James R. A Systematic Review of the Teiid Lizards, Genus Bachia, with Remarks on Heterodactlus & Anotosaura. (Miscellaneous Publications: No. 57). 47p. 1973. pap. 2.50 (ISBN 0-686-79839-2). U of KS Mus Nat Hist.

Duellman, William E. A New Subspecies of Lizard, Cnemidophorus Sacki, from Michoacan, Mexico. (Museum Series: Vol. 10, No. 9). 12p. 1960. 1.25 (ISBN 0-317-04846-5). U of KS Mus Nat Hist.

Echteracht, Arthur C. Middle American Lizards of the Genus Ameiva (Teidae) with Emphasis on Geographic Variation. (Miscellaneous Publications Ser.: No. 55). 86p. 1971. pap. 4.50 (ISBN 0-686-80353-1). U of KS Mus Nat Hist.

Fitch, Henry S. Population Structure & Survivorship in Some Costa Rican Lizards. (Occasional Papers: No. 18). 41p. 1973. pap. 2.25 (ISBN 0-686-80356-6). U of KS Mus Nat Hist.

--Sexual Size Differences in the Mainland Anoles. (Occasional Papers: No. 50). 21p. 1976. pap. 1.25 (ISBN 0-686-80357-4). U of KS Mus Nat Hist.

Fitch, Henry S., et al. Variation in the Central American Iguanid Lizard, Anolis Cupreus, with the Description of a New Subspecies. (Occasional Papers: No. 8). 20p. 1972. 1.25 (ISBN 0-317-04857-0). U of KS Mus Nat Hist.

Fritts, Thomas H. New Species of Lizards of the Genus Stenocercus from Peru: (Sauria: Iguanidae) (Occasional Papers: Vol. 10). 21p. 1972. 1.25 (ISBN 0-317-04864-3). U of KS Mus Nat Hist.

Huey, Raymond B., et al, eds. Lizard Ecology: Studies of a Model Organism. (Illus.). 720p. 1983. text ed. 35.00x (ISBN 0-674-53673-8). Harvard U Pr.

Milstead, William W., ed. Lizard Ecology: A Symposium. LC 66-17955. 312p. 1967. 20.00x (ISBN 0-8262-0058-3). U of Mo Pr.

Rieppel, Oliver. The Phylogeny of Anguinomorph Lizards. 88p. 1980. pap. text ed. 43.95 (ISBN 0-8176-1224-6). Birkhauser.

Roberts, Mervin F. All about Chameleons & 'Anoles' (Illus.). 1977. 4.95 (ISBN 0-87666-772-8, PS-310). TFH Pubns.

Roberts, Mervin F. & Roberts, Martha D. All about Iguanas. (Orig.). 1976. 4.95 (ISBN 0-87666-774-4, PS-311). TFH Pubns.

Schwaner, Terry D. Reproductive Biology of Lizards on the American Samoan Islands. (Occasional Papers: No. 86). 53p. 1980. 3.00 (ISBN 0-317-04887-2). U of KS Mus Nat Hist.

Schwartz, Albert. Variation in Hispaniolan Anolis Olssoni Schmidt: Reptilia Sauria Iguanidae, No. 47. 21p. 1981. 3.00 (ISBN 0-89326-077-0). Milwaukee Pub Mus.

Schwartz, Albert & Henderson, Robert W. Anolis Cybotes (Reptilia, Iguanidae) The Eastern Hispaniolan Populations. 1982. 2.50 (ISBN 0-89326-079-7). Milwaukee Pub Mus.

Smith, Hobart M. Handbook of Lizards: Lizards of the United States & Canada. (HANH Ser.). (Illus.). 578p. 1946. 37.50x (ISBN 0-8014-0393-6). Comstock.

Smith, Malcolm. The Fauna of British India, Including Ceylon & Burma: Reptilia & Amphibia, 2 vols. Incl. Vol. 1. Loricata, Testudines. 189p. Repr. of 1931 ed. Vol. 1. 15.00 (ISBN 0-88359-005-0); Vol. 2. Sauria. Repr. of 1935 ed. Vol. 2. 22.50 (ISBN 0-88359-006-9). (Illus.). 1973. Set. 35.00 (ISBN 0-88359-007-7). R Curtis Bks.

Storr, G. M. & Smith, L. A. Lizards of Western Australia: Skinks, Vol. 1. (Illus.). xii, 200p. 1982. pap. 23.00 (ISBN 0-85564-195-9, Pub. by U of W Austral Pr). Intl Spec Bk.

Wynne, Richard H. Lizards in Captivity. (Illus.). 192p. 1981. 7.95 (ISBN 0-87666-921-6, PS-769). TFH Pubns.

LLAMAS

Tillman, Andy. Silent Brother: The History & Care of Llamas. 132p. (Orig.). 1981. pap. text ed. 12.95 (ISBN 0-941984-00-1). Early Winters.

LNG

see Liquefied Natural Gas

LOAD (ELECTRIC POWER)

see Electric Power-Plants–Load

LOADING AND UNLOADING

see also Bulk Solids Handling; Cargo Handling

Cross, Framk L., Jr. & Forehand, David, eds. Air Pollution Emissions from Bulk Loading Facilities. LC 75-26079. (Environmental Monograph: Vol. 6). (Illus.). 22p. 1976. 3.95 (ISBN 0-87762-179-9). Technomic.

Slater, Alan. Vehicle Load Planning. 1979. 90.00x (ISBN 0-86176-032-8, Pub. by MCB Pubns). State Mutual Bk.

LOBACHEVSKI GEOMETRY

see Geometry, Hyperbolic

LOBSTER FISHERIES

Herrick, Francis H. Natural History of the American Lobster. Egerton, Frank N., 3rd, ed. LC 77-74228. (History of Ecology Ser.). (Illus.). 1978. Repr. of 1911 ed. lib. bdg. 23.50x (ISBN 0-405-10398-0). Ayer Co Pubs.

Stewart, Robert. A Living from Lobsters. 1978. 25.00x (ISBN 0-685-63431-0). State Mutual Bk.

LOBSTERS

Bliss, Dorothy. Shrimps, Lobster, & Crabs: Their Fascinating Life Story. LC 82-7853. (Illus.). 256p. 1982. 14.95 (ISBN 0-8329-0124-5). New Century.

Cobb, Stanley J. The American Lobster: The Biology of Homarus Americanus. (Marine Technical Report Ser: No. 49). 1976. pap. 2.00 (ISBN 0-938412-01-9). URI MAS.

Farmer, A. S. Synopsis of Biological Data on the Norway Lobster: Nephrops Norvegicus (Linnaeus, 1758) (Fisheries Synopses: No. 112). (Illus.). 97p. 1975. pap. 7.50 (ISBN 92-5-101906-1, F845, FAO). Unipub.

Headstrom, Richard. All about Lobsters, Crabs, Shrimps, & Their Relatives. (Nature Ser.). 144p. 1985. pap. 3.95 (ISBN 0-486-24795-3). Dover.

Merriam, Kendall A. Illustrated Dictionary of Lobstering. LC 78-61525. (Illus., Orig.). 1978. pap. 6.95 (ISBN 0-87027-192-X). Cumberland Pr.

Philipps, B. F. & Morgan, G. R. Synopsis of Biological Data on the Western Rock Lobster: Panulirus cygnus (George, 1962) (Fisheries Synopses: No.128). 69p. 1980. pap. 7.50 (ISBN 92-5-101025-0, F2166, FAO). Unipub.

Philips, B. F. & Cobb, J. S. Workshop on Lobster & Rock Lobster Ecology & Physiology. 300p. 1982. 95.00x (ISBN 0-643-00243-X, Pub. by CSIRO Australia). State Mutual Bk.

Prudden, T. M. About Lobsters. LC 62-21299. (Illus.). 1973. pap. 6.95 (ISBN 0-87027-127-X). Cumberland Pr.

Stewart, Robert. A Living from Lobsters. 2nd ed. (Illus.). 70p. 12.00 (ISBN 0-85238-099-2, FN56, FNB). Unipub.

Williams, Austin B. Shrimps, Lobsters, & Crabs of the Atlantic Coast. rev. ed. LC 83-600095. (Illus.). 568p. 1984. text ed. 40.00x (ISBN 0-87474-960-3). Smithsonian.

LOCAL GOVERNMENT–DATA PROCESSING

ATA Handbook of Data Processing in the Motor Carrier Industry. 1983. text ed. 100.00 (ISBN 0-88711-027-4). Am Trucking Assns.

Griesemer, James R. Microcomputers in Local Government. LC 83-18367. (Practical Management Ser.). 150p. (Orig.). 1983. 19.95 (ISBN 0-87326-040-6). Intl City Mgt.

J. J. Keller & Associates, Inc., ed. Data Systems Source Guide-Transportation & Traffic. LC 81-86199. (20M). 250p. 1985. 3-ring binder 65.00 (ISBN 0-934674-41-8). J J Keller.

McKean, Roland N. Efficiency in Government Through Systems Analysis. LC 58-7902. Repr. of 1958 ed. 86.50 (ISBN 0-8357-9878-X, 2012597). Bks Demand UMI.

Research Directions in Computer Control of Urban Traffic Systems. 393p. 1979. pap. 20.00x (ISBN 0-87262-179-0). Am Soc Civil Eng.

Schoech, Dick J. Computer Use in Human Services: A Guide to Information Management. LC 81-6407. 312p. 1982. 34.95 (ISBN 0-87705-502-5). Human Sci Pr.

LOCAL TRANSIT

see also Subways

Burke, Catherine G. Innovation & Public Policy: The Case of Personal Rapid Transit. LC 79-2410. (Illus.). 416p. 1979. 28.50x (ISBN 0-669-03167-4). Lexington Bks.

Carson, Robert B. Whatever Happened to the Trolley? 1977. pap. text ed. 9.50 (ISBN 0-8191-0330-6). U Pr of Amer.

Cheape, Charles W. Moving the Masses: Urban Public Transit in New York, Boston, & Philadelphia, 1880 to 1912. LC 79-15875. (Harvard Studies in Business History: No. 31). (Illus.). 1980. text ed. 18.50x (ISBN 0-674-58827-4). Harvard U Pr.

Gray, G. & Hoel, L. Public Transportation: Planning, Operations & Management. 1979. 47.95 (ISBN 0-13-739169-2). P-H.

Hamer, Andrew, ed. Out of Cars - into Transit: Urban Transportation Planning Crisis. LC 76-7900. (Research Monograph: No. 65). 196p. 1976. pap. 15.95 (ISBN 0-88406-097-7). Ga St U Busn Pub.

Hillman, Mayer, et al. Transport Realities & Planning Policy: Studies of Friction & Freedom in Daily Travel. 200p. 1976. 29.00x (ISBN 0-686-87344-0, Pub. by Policy Studies). State Mutual Bk.

Jansen, G. R., et al, eds. New Developments in Modelling Travel Demand & Urban Systems. 420p. 1979. 45.75x (ISBN 0-566-00269-8). Gower Pub Co.

McCaleb, Charles S. Tracks, Tires & Wires: Public Transportation in California's Santa Clara Valley. Sebree, Mac, ed. LC 81-13712. (Interurbans Special Ser.: No. 78). (Illus.). 192p. 1981. 27.95 (ISBN 0-916374-48-3). Interurban.

McGuire, William & Teed, Charles. Fruit Belt Route: The Railways of Grand Junction, Colorado. (Illus.). 56p. (Orig.). 1981. pap. 5.95 (ISBN 0-939646-00-5). Natl Rail Rio Grande.

McKane, John & Perles, Anthony. Inside Muni. Walker, Jim, ed. LC 82-80115. (Interurbans Special Ser.: No. 79). (Illus.). 272p. 1982. 35.95 (ISBN 0-916374-49-1). Interurban.

Meyer, John R., et al. Urban Transportation Problem. LC 65-13848. (Rand Corporation Research Studies Ser.). (Illus.). 1965. 25.00x (ISBN 0-674-93120-3); pap. 8.95x (ISBN 0-674-93121-1). Harvard U Pr.

OECD, ed. Urban Public Transport: Evaluation of Performance. (Road Research Ser.). (Illus.). 76p. 1980. pap. 5.50x (ISBN 9-2641-2127-7, 77-80-04-1). OECD.

Pederson, E. O. Transportation in Cities. 1981. 13.75 (ISBN 0-08-024666-4). Pergamon.

Perry, James L. & Angle, Harold L. Labor-Management Relations & Public Agency Effectiveness: A Study of Urban Mass Transit. LC 80-10746. (Pergamon Policy Studies on Business). 208p. 1980. 29.00 (ISBN 0-08-025953-7). Pergamon.

Priest, Donald E. & Black, J. Thomas. Joint Development: Making the Real Estate-Transit Connection. LC 79-66189. (Illus.). 216p. 1979. pap. 32.00 (ISBN 0-87420-588-3, L57); pap. 24.00 members. Urban Land.

Trzyna, Thomas N. & Beck, Joseph R. Urban Mass Transit: A Guide to Organizations & Information Resources. LC 78-12497. (Who's Doing What Ser.: No. 5). 1979. pap. 25.00x (ISBN 0-912102-38-1). Cal Inst Public.

Vuchic, Vukan. Urban Public Transportation. (Illus.). 672p. 1981. text ed. 46.95 (ISBN 0-13-939496-6). P-H.

Willson, Beckles. The Story of Rapid Transit. (Illus.). 1979. Repr. of 1904 ed. lib. bdg. 20.00 (ISBN 0-8495-5809-3). Arden Lib.

Wingo, Lowdon, Jr. Transportation & Urban Land. LC 77-86416. (Resources for the Future Ser.). 144p. Repr. of 1961 ed. 25.00 (ISBN 0-404-60346-7). AMS Pr.

Wren, A., ed. Computer Scheduling of Public Transportation: Urban Passenger Vehicle & Crew Scheduling. 360p. 1981. 57.50 (ISBN 0-444-86170-X, North-Holland). Elsevier.

Yago, Glenn. The Decline of Transit: Urban Transportation in German & U.S. Cities, 1900-1970. LC 83-7297. 272p. 1984. 29.95 (ISBN 0-521-25633-X). Cambridge U Pr.

LOCALLY COMPACT GROUPS

Argabright, Loren & De Lamadrid, Jesus G. Fourier Analysis of Unbounded Measures on Locally Compact Abelian Groups. LC 74-6499. (Memoirs: No. 145). 53p. 1974. pap. 10.00 (ISBN 0-8218-1845-7, MEMO-145). Am Math.

Berg, C. & Forst, G. Potential Theory on Locally Compact Abelian Groups. (Ergebnisse der Mathematik und Ihrer Grenzgebiete Ser.: Vol. 87). 240p. 1975. 37.00 (ISBN 0-387-07249-7). Springer-Verlag.

Gaal, S. A. Linear Analysis & Representation Theory. LC 72-95686. (Die Grundlehren der Mathematischen Wissenschaften: Vol. 198). ix, 688p. 1973. 71.00 (ISBN 0-387-06195-9). Springer-Verlag.

Morris, S. A. Pontryagin Duality & the Structure of Locally Compact Abelian Groups. LC 76-53519. (London Mathematical Society Lecture Note Ser.: No. 29). 1977. 22.95x (ISBN 0-521-21543-9). Cambridge U Pr.

Parthasarathy, K. R. Multipliers on Locally Compact Groups. LC 71-84142. (Lecture Notes in Mathematics: Vol. 93). (Orig.). 1969. pap. 10.70 (ISBN 0-387-04612-7). Springer-Verlag.

Pier, Jean-Paul. Amenable Locally Compact Groups. LC 84-7366. (Pure & Applied Mathematics Ser.: 1237). 418p. 1984. text ed. 44.95x (ISBN 0-471-89390-0, Pub. by Wiley-Interscience). Wiley.

Reiter, H. L-Prime Algebras & Segal Algebras. LC 76-178758. (Lecture Notes in Mathematics: Vol. 231). 113p. 1971. pap. 11.00 (ISBN 0-387-05651-3). Springer-Verlag.

Robert, Alain. Introduction to the Representation Theory of Compact & Locally Compact Groups. LC 82-19730. (London Mathematical Society Lecture Note Ser.: Note 80). 220p. 1983. pap. 24.95 (ISBN 0-521-28975-0). Cambridge U Pr.

Stratila, S. V. & Voiculescu, D. V. Representations of AF-Algebras & of the Group U (Infinity) (Lecture Notes in Mathematics: Vol. 486). ix, 169p. 1975. pap. 14.00 (ISBN 0-387-07403-1). Springer-Verlag.

Symposia in Pure Mathematics, Vol. 26. Harmonic Analysis on Homogeneous Spaces: Proceedings. Moore, Calvin C., ed. LC 73-10456. (Proceedings of Symposia in Pure Mathematics: Vol. 26). 480p. 1978. pap. 42.00 (ISBN 0-8218-1426-5, PSPUM-26). Am Math.

LOCKHEED AIRPLANES

Bowers, P. Lockheed P-3 Variants: Minigraph 11. write for info (ISBN 0-942548-16-7). Aerofax.

Francillon, Rene J. Lockheed Aircraft since 1913. (Illus.). 512p. 1982. 39.95 (ISBN 0-370-30329-6, Pub. by the Bodley Head). Merrimack Pub Cir.

Lockheed Aircraft Corporation. Of Men & Stars: A History of Lockheed Aircraft Corporation. Gilbert, James, ed. LC 79-7280. (Flight: Its First Seventy-Five Years Ser.). (Illus.). 1979. Repr. of 1957 ed. lib. bdg. 24.50x (ISBN 0-405-12189-X). Ayer Co Pubs.

Maloney, Edward T. Lockheed P-38. LC 68-31778. (Aero Ser.: Vol. 19). (Illus.). 1968. pap. 3.95 (ISBN 0-8168-0572-5). Aero.

Miller, J. Lockheed SR-71 (A-12 YF-12 D-21) Minigraph 1. rev. ed. write for info. (ISBN 0-942548-26-4). Aerofax.

Miller, Jay. Aerograph 3: Lockheed U-2. (Aerograph Ser.). (Illus.). 124p. 1983. pap. 18.95 (ISBN 0-942548-05-1). Aerofax.

--Lockheed SR-71, Minigraph I. (Minigraph Ser.). (Illus.). 17p. 1983. pap. 3.95 (ISBN 0-317-17911-X, Pub. by Argus Bks. Ltd. (England)). Motorbooks Intl.

LOCKS AND KEYS

Allen, Sam. Locks & Alarms. (Illus.). 352p. (Orig.). 1984. 21.95 (ISBN 0-8306-0359-X); pap. 15.95 (ISBN 0-8306-0259-3, 1559). TAB Bks.

Alth, Max. All about Locks & Locksmithing. (Illus.). 1972. pap. 4.50 (ISBN 0-8015-0151-2, Hawthorn). Dutton.

Butter, F. J. Locks & Lockmaking. (Illus.). 135p. 1984. pap. text ed. 15.00 (ISBN 0-87556-392-9). Saifer.

Eddie The Wire. The Complete Guide to Lock Picking. 1981. pap. 9.95 (ISBN 0-686-30630-9). Loompanics.

--How to Make Your Own Professional Lock Tools. 1980. pap. 5.95 (ISBN 0-686-30628-7). Loompanics.

--How to Make Your Own Professional Lock Tools, Vol. 2. 1981. pap. 5.95 (ISBN 0-686-30629-5). Loompanics.

Hobbs, A. C. Construction of Locks & Safes. Tomlinson, Charles, ed. (Illus.). vi, 212p. 1982. Repr. of 1868 ed. 20.00 (ISBN 0-87556-126-8); stiff wrappers 15.00 (ISBN 0-686-82966-2). Saifer.

Tobias, Marc W. Locks, Safes, & Security: A Handbook for Law Enforcement Personnel. (Illus.). 352p. 1971. photocopy ed. 35.50x (ISBN 0-398-02155-4). C C Thomas.

LOCKSMITHING

Alth, Max. All about Locks & Locksmithing. (Illus.). 1972. pap. 4.50 (ISBN 0-8015-0151-2, Hawthorn). Dutton.

Butter, F. J. Locks & Lockmaking. (Illus.). 135p. 1984. pap. text ed. 15.00 (ISBN 0-87556-392-9). Saifer.

Crichton, Whitcomb. Practical Course in Modern Locksmithing. 222p. 1943. 16.95 (ISBN 0-911012-06-0). Nelson-Hall.

Eddie The Wire. How to Make Your Own Professional Lock Tools. 1980. pap. 5.95 (ISBN 0-686-30628-7). Loompanics.

--How to Make Your Own Professional Lock Tools, Vol. 2. 1981. pap. 5.95 (ISBN 0-686-30629-5). Loompanics.

Lock Pick Design Manual. (Illus.). 24p. 1973. pap. 6.00 (ISBN 0-87364-081-0). Paladin Pr.

Mayers, Keith. A Dictionary of Locksmithing. 1980. pap. 6.50 (ISBN 0-9604860-0-3). Mayers-Joseph.

Robinson, Robert L. Complete Course in Professional Locksmithing. LC 73-174584. (Illus.). 414p. 1973. 54.95x (ISBN 0-911012-15-X). Nelson-Hall.

Roper, C. A. The Complete Book of Locks & Locksmithing. 2nd ed. (Illus.). 352p. 1983. pap. 15.95 (ISBN 0-8306-1530-X). TAB Bks.

Rudman, Jack. Foreman Locksmith. (Career Examination Ser.: C-2223). (Cloth bdg. avail. on request). pap. 10.00 (ISBN 0-8373-2223-5). Natl Learning.

--Locksmith. (Career Examination Ser.: C-1348). (Cloth bdg. avail. on request). pap. 10.00 (ISBN 0-8373-1348-1). Natl Learning.

--Maintenance Locksmith. (Career Examination Ser.: C-1353). (Cloth bdg. avail. on request). pap. 10.00 (ISBN 0-8373-1353-8). Natl Learning.

Steed. Locksmithing. (Illus.). 182p. 1982. 13.95 (ISBN 0-8306-0073-6); pap. 8.95 (ISBN 0-8306-1403-6, 1403). TAB Bks.

LOCOMOTION

see also Animal Locomotion; Automobiles; Boats and Boating; Coaching; Flight; Navigation; Transportation

Dagg, A. I. & James, A. Running, Walking & Jumping: The Science of Locomotion. LC 77-15301. (Wykeham Science Ser.: No. 42). 143p. 1977. 14.95x (ISBN 0-8448-1169-6). Crane-Russak Co.

Jenkins, Farish A., ed. Primate Locomotion. 1974. 67.50 (ISBN 0-12-384050-3). Acad Pr.

Lowe, John C. & Moryadas, S. The Geography of Movement. (Illus.). 333p. 1984. Repr. of 1975 ed. text ed. 24.95x (ISBN 0-88133-100-7). Waveland Pr.

Pauwels, F. Biomechanics of the Locomotor Apparatus. (Illus.). 520p. 1980. 191.00 (ISBN 0-387-09131-9). Springer-Verlag.

LOCOMOTIVE DIESELS

see Diesel Locomotives

LOCOMOTIVE ENGINEERS

Abdill, George. Locomotive Engineer Album. (Encore Ed.). (Illus.). 9.95 (ISBN 0-87564-534-8). Superior Pub.

Kaplan, Michael. Otto Mears: Paradoxical Pathfinder. Nossaman, Allen, ed. 296p. 1982. pap. 9.95 (ISBN 0-9608000-2-6). San Juan County.

Reed, Brian. Crewe Locomotive Works. (Illus.). 240p. 1982. 27.50 (ISBN 0-7153-8228-4). David & Charles.

LOCOMOTIVES

see also Diesel Locomotives; Electric Locomotives

American Locomotive Company: Rotary Snow Plows 1909. (Illus.). 1973. pap. 2.50 (ISBN 0-913556-05-X). Spec Pr NJ.

American Locomotive Company: USRA Locomotive 1919. LC 78-82227. (Illus.). 1973. pap. 3.00 (ISBN 0-913556-04-1). Spec Pr NJ.

Anderson, Norman E. & Macdermot, C. G. PA-Four Locomotive. LC 78-51249. (Illus.). 128p. 1978. 25.00 (ISBN 0-89685-035-8). Chatham Pub CA.

Baldwin Locomotive Works (BALDWIN) General Catalogue 1915. LC 72-96486. (Illus.). 1972. 9.00 (ISBN 0-913556-02-5); pap. 6.00 (ISBN 0-913556-03-3). Spec Pr NJ.

BALDWIN Logging Locomotives 1913. LC 73-84950. (Illus.). 1973. pap. 4.00 (ISBN 0-913556-09-2). Spec Pr NJ.

BALDWIN Narrow-Gauge Locomotives 1872-1876. LC 73-82229. (Illus.). 1973. 6.00 (ISBN 0-913556-35-1); pap. 4.00 (ISBN 0-913556-31-9). Spec Pr NJ.

Basic Steam Locomotive Maintenance. 18.95 (ISBN 0-686-75182-5). Chatham Pub CA.

Bradley, D. L. Drummond Greyhounds of the LSWR. 1977. 15.95 (ISBN 0-7153-7329-3). David & Charles.

Casserly, H. C. British Locomotive Names of the 20th Century. 25.00x (ISBN 0-392-07681-0, SpS). Sportshelf.

Cook, Richard J. Super Power Steam Locomotives. LC 66-29787. (Illus.). 144p. 1966. 20.95 (ISBN 0-87095-010-X). Golden West.

Eatwell, David. Steam Locomotives. (Illus.). 64p. 1983. pap. 5.50 (ISBN 0-7134-1835-4, Pub. by Batsford England). David & Charles.

Halcroft, H. Locomotive Adventure, Vol. 2. 17.75x (ISBN 0-392-08040-0, SpS). Sportshelf.

Hauff, Steve & Gertz, Jim. Willamette Locomotive. LC 76-24498. 1977. 15.00 (ISBN 0-8323-0274-0). Binford.

Jenkinson, David. The Power of the Royal Scots. 128p. pap. text ed. 35.00 (ISBN 0-86093-175-7, ORPC Ltd UK). State Mutual Bk.

Locomotives of the Rio Grande. pap. 9.95 soft cover (ISBN 0-686-75188-4). Chatham Pub CA.

McDonald, Charles. Diesel Locomotive Rosters: United States, Canada & Mexico. Hayden, Bob, ed. (Illus.). 124p. (Orig.). 1982. pap. 7.50 (ISBN 0-89024-043-4). Kalmbach.

Motive Power of the Union Pacific. 39.50 (ISBN 0-686-75190-6). Chatham Pub CA.

North British Locomotive Co. Catalogue of Narrow Gauge Locomotives. LC 70-99262. (Illus.). Repr. of 1912 ed. 17.95x (ISBN 0-678-05666-8). Kelley.

Shays & Other Geared Locomotives from Catalogs & Cyclopedias. (Train Shed Cyclopedia Ser: No. 34). (Illus.). 64p. 1975. pap. 4.50 (ISBN 0-912318-65-1). N K Gregg.

Simmons-Boardman Publishing Corp. Car & Locomotive Cyclopedia, 1984. 5th ed. LC 84-50897. (The Car & Locomotive Cyclopedia of American Practices Ser.). 1000p. 1984. 69.95 (ISBN 0-911382-01-1). Simmons Boardman.

Southern Pacific Motive Power Annual, 1974-1976. (Illus.). 1976. 15.00 (ISBN 0-89685-008-0). Chatham Pub CA.

Southern Pacific Motive Power Annual, 1971. (Illus.). 1971. 12.50 (ISBN 0-89685-005-6). Chatham Pub CA.

Southern Pacific Motive Power Annual, 1972. (Illus.). 1973. 12.50 (ISBN 0-89685-006-4). Chatham Pub CA.

Southern Pacific Motive Power Annual, 1973. (Illus.). 1974. 12.50 (ISBN 0-89685-007-2). Chatham Pub CA.

The Sp 4300 4-8-2's. 30.00 (ISBN 0-686-75209-0). Chatham Pub CA.

Summers, A. W. Engines Good & Bad. 96p. 29.00x (ISBN 0-86093-326-1, Pub. by ORPC Ltd UK). State Mutual Bk.

Tuplin, W. A. The Steam Locomotive. 1974. 10.00 (ISBN 0-684-13749-6, ScribT). Scribner.

Union Pacific Motive Power Review. 11.95 (ISBN 0-686-75211-2). Chatham Pub CA.

Vaughan, J. A. M. & Marsden, C. J. The Power of the 56's. 128p. 30.00x (ISBN 0-86093-150-1, Pub. by ORPC Ltd UK). State Mutual Bk.

Vaughn, John A. The Power of the H. S. T.'s. 120p. 30.00x (ISBN 0-86093-186-2, Pub. by ORPC Ltd UK). State Mutual Bk.

Warren, Alan M. Rescued from Barry: Locomotive Restoration. (Illus.). 192p. 1983. 19.95 (ISBN 0-7153-8260-8). David & Charles.

Western Pacific Steam Locomotives. 38.50 (ISBN 0-686-75214-7). Chatham Pub CA.

Whitely, J. S. & Marrison, G. W. Power of the A1s, A2s, & A3s. 112p. 35.00 (ISBN 0-86093-133-1, Pub. by ORPC Ltd UK). State Mutual Bk.

Whitely, J. S. & Morrison, G. W. The Power of the BR Standard Pacifics. 112p. 35.00x (ISBN 0-86093-067-X, Pub. by ORPC Ltd UK). State Mutual Bk.

Why You Can Haul at Least Thirty per Cent More per Ton of Locomotive with the Modern Heisler. 1975. Repr. 3.00 (ISBN 0-87012-212-6). McClain.

Wright, Roy V., ed. Famous Passenger Trains from the 1943 Car Builder's Cyclopedia. (Train Shed Cyclopedia Ser., No. 16). (Illus.). 1974. pap. 3.95 (ISBN 0-912318-45-7). N K Gregg.

--Four-Eight-Four's & Other Heavy Passenger Locos, 1927-1941. (Train Shed Cyclopedia Ser., No. 14). (Illus.). 1973. pap. 3.95 (ISBN 0-912318-43-0). N K Gregg.

--Heavy Traction, 1922-1941. (Train Shed Cyclopedia Ser., No. 15). (Illus.). 1974. pap. 4.95 (ISBN 0-912318-44-9). N K Gregg.

--Industrial & Foreign Locomotives from the Nineteen Thirty Locomotive Cyclopedia. (Train Shed Cyclopedia Ser: No. 37). (Illus.). 72p. 1975. pap. 4.95 (ISBN 0-912318-68-6). N K Gregg.

--Locomotive Cabs & Fittings from the 1927 Locomotive Cyclopedia, Pt. 1. (Train Shed Cyclopedia Ser: No. 40). (Illus.). 40p. 1975. pap. 3.00 (ISBN 0-912318-71-6). N K Gregg.

--Locomotive Cabs & Fittings from the 1927 Locomotive Cyclopedia, Pt. 2. (Train Shed Cyclopedia Ser: No. 41). (Illus.). 40p. 1975. pap. 3.00 (ISBN 0-912318-72-4). N K Gregg.

--Locomotive Drawings & Boilers: Part 2. (Train Shed Ser.: No. 68). (Illus.). 1978. pap. 4.50 (ISBN 0-87962-074-9). N K Gregg.

--Locomotives from the Nineteen Sixteen Locomotive Dictionary. (Train Shed Cyclopedia Ser., No. 18). (Illus.). 1974. pap. 4.95 (ISBN 0-912318-47-3). N K Gregg.

--Locomotives from the Nineteen Twenty-Seven Locomotive Cyclopedia, Pt. 1, Pt. 1. (Train Shed Cyclopedia Ser: No. 31). (Illus.). 80p. 1975. pap. 5.50 (ISBN 0-912318-62-7). N K Gregg.

--Locomotives, Tenders & Trucks from the 1927 Locomotive Cyclopedia, Pt. 2. (Train Shed Cyclopedia Ser: No. 32). (Illus.). 80p. 1975. pap. 5.50 (ISBN 0-912318-63-5). N K Gregg.

--Steam Locomotives & Tenders from the 1938 Locomotive Cyclopedia: Part 2. 10th ed. (Train Shed Cyclopedia Ser., No. 23). (Illus.). 1974. pap. 4.50 (ISBN 0-912318-53-8). N K Gregg.

--Steam Locomotives from the 1919 Locomotive Dictionary & Cyclopedia, No. 52. (Train Shed Ser.). (Illus.). 1976. pap. 4.50 (ISBN 0-912318-84-8). N K Gregg.

--Steam Locomotives from the 1919 Locomotive Dictionary & Cyclopedia: Part 2, No. 53. (Train Shed Ser.). (Illus.). 1977. pap. 4.50 (ISBN 0-912318-85-6). N K Gregg.

--Steam Locomotives from the 1938 Locomotive Cyclopedia: Part 1. 10th ed. (Train Shed Cyclopedia Ser., No. 22). (Illus.). 1974. pap. 4.50 (ISBN 0-912318-52-X). N K Gregg.

LOCOMOTIVES–HISTORY

Allan, Cecil J. Nineteen Forty-Eight British Railway Locomotives, Comb. Vol. 10.00x (ISBN 0-392-08815-0, SpS). Sportshelf.

Articulated Steam Locomotives of North America. 45.00 (ISBN 0-686-70715-X). Chatham Pub CA.

BALDWIN Narrow-Gauge Locomotives 1872-1876. LC 73-82229. (Illus.). 1973. 6.00 (ISBN 0-913556-35-1); pap. 4.00 (ISBN 0-913556-31-9). Spec Pr NJ.

Cockman, F. G. British Railways' Steam Locomotives. (History in Camera Ser.). (Illus.). 64p. (Orig.). 1980. pap. 6.95 (ISBN 0-85263-531-1, Pub. by Shire Pubns England). Seven Hills Bks.

Cotton Belt Locomotives. (Illus.). 25.00 (ISBN 0-686-64894-3). Chatham Pub CA.

Crump, Spencer. Rail Car, Locomotive & Trolley Builders: An All-Time Directory. Date not set. write for info. (ISBN 0-87046-032-3, Pub. by Trans-Anglo). Interurban.

Duke, Donald. Southern Pacific Steam Locomotives. LC 62-6982. (Illus.). 88p. 13.95 (ISBN 0-87095-012-6). Golden West.

Durrant, A. E. The Garratt Locomotive. LC 80-70298. (Illus.). 176p. 1981. 28.00 (ISBN 0-7153-7641-1). David & Charles.

Fowler, George L., ed. Locomotive Dictionary. (Illus.). 684p. 1972. Repr. of 1906 ed. lib. bdg. 24.95 buckram (ISBN 0-912318-20-1). N K Gregg.

Glover, G. French Steam Locomotives, 1840-1950. 96p. 1974. 35.00x (ISBN 0-85992-011-9, Pub. by B Rose Pub). State Mutual Bk.

Hewison, C. H. Locomotive Boiler Explosions. (Illus.). 144p. 1983. 16.50 (ISBN 0-7153-8305-1). David & Charles.

Hilton, George W. Monon Route. 2nd ed. LC 78-52512. (Illus.). 468p. 1978. Repr. of 1978 ed. 30.00 (ISBN 0-8310-7115-X). Howell-North.

Kennedy, Rex. Diesels & Electrics on Shed: Eastern Region, Vol. 2. 96p. 30.00x (ISBN 0-86093-036-X, Pub. by ORPC Ltd UK). State Mutual Bk.

--Diesels & Electrics on Shed: Scottish Region, Vol. 4. 112p. 30.00x (ISBN 0-86093-043-2, Pub. by ORPC Ltd UK). State Mutual Bk.

Koenig, Karl R. Virginia & Truckee Locomotives. LC 80-67819. (Illus.). 88p. 1980. pap. 14.00 (ISBN 0-89685-102-8). Chatham Pub CA.

Locomotives of the Rio Grande: Colorado Railroad Museum. LC 80-24685. (Illus.). 96p. 1981. 9.95 (ISBN 0-918654-25-4). Co RR Mus.

Locos of the Forties & Fifties New Formulas: Electrics & Turbines, Part 10. (Train Shed Ser.: No. 66). (Illus.). 1978. pap. 4.50 (ISBN 0-87962-068-4). N K Gregg.

Maskelyne, J. N. Locomotives I Have Known. 216p. 1982. 24.95 (ISBN 0-85242-636-4, Pub. by Argus). Aztex.

Mohawk That Refused to Abdicate. 25.00 (ISBN 0-685-83356-9). Chatham Pub CA.

Nock, O. S. The Gresley Pacifics: Combined Volume. (Illus.). 280p. 1982. 28.95 (ISBN 0-7153-8388-4). David & Charles.

Nock, Oswald S. Caledonian Dunalastairs & Associated Classes. LC 68-23835. (Illus.). 1968. 17.95x (ISBN 0-678-05619-6). Kelley.

--LNER Steam. LC 68-26165. (Illus.). 1969. 22.95x (ISBN 0-678-05520-3). Kelley.

Olmsted, Robert. The Diesel Years. LC 75-17721. (Illus.). 170p. 1975. 20.95 (ISBN 0-87095-054-1). Golden West.

Pacific Coast Shay. 16.95 (ISBN 0-685-83366-6). Chatham Pub CA.

Ramsey, Dirk & Lawrence, George. Locomotive Three Hundred Forty-Six: The First Hundred Years. LC 81-7755. (Illus.). 40p. 1981. 3.95 (ISBN 0-918654-30-0). Co RR Mus.

Ransome-Wallis, P. The Last Steam Locomotive of British Railways. 27.50x (ISBN 0-392-15392-0, SpS). Sportshelf.

Reisdorff, James J. Locomotive Sixty-Nine: From Alaska to Nebraska. (Illus.). 28p. 1984. pap. 3.00 (ISBN 0-9609568-2-4). South Platte.

Stagner, Lloyd E. Steam Locomotives of the Frisco Line. LC 76-22529. (Illus.). 160p. 1976. 13.95 (ISBN 0-87108-588-7). Pruett.

Talbot, E. A Pictorial Record of British Railway Standard Steam Locomotives. 160p. 45.00x (ISBN 0-86093-158-7, Pub. by ORPC Ltd Uk). State Mutual Bk.

Tufnell, Robert. Prototype Locomotives. (Illus.). 96p. 1985. 16.95 (ISBN 0-7153-8397-3). David & Charles.

Tuplin, W. A. The Steam Locomotive. 1980. text ed. 21.25x (ISBN 0-239-00198-2). Humanities.

Tuplin, William A. British Steam since Nineteen Hundred. LC 69-12249. (Illus.). 1968. 17.95x (ISBN 0-678-05637-4). Kelley.

Webb, Brian. Deltic Locomotives of British Rail. LC 81-67013. (Illus.). 96p. 1982. 17.50 (ISBN 0-7153-8110-5). David & Charles.

Westwood, J. N. Locomotive Designers in the Age of Steam. LC 77-90502. 285p. 1978. 25.00 (ISBN 0-8386-2220-8). Fairleigh Dickinson.

--Soviet Locomotive Technology During Industrialization 1928-1952. (Studies in Soviet History & Society). 240p. 1982. text ed. 32.00x (ISBN 0-333-27516-0, Pub. by Macmillan England). Humanities.

White, John H., Jr. A History of the American Locomotive: Its Development, 1830-1880. (Illus.). 1980. pap. 12.00 (ISBN 0-486-23818-0). Dover.

--A History of the American Locomotive, Its Development: 1830-1880. 21.00 (ISBN 0-8446-5828-6). Peter Smith.

White, John H., Jr., ed. Early American Locomotives. (Illus.). 10.00 (ISBN 0-8446-4838-8). Peter Smith.

Wright, Roy V., ed. Box Stock & Refrigerator Cars from the 1931 Car Builders' Cyclopedia of American Practice. 13th ed. (Train Shed Cyclopedia Ser., No. 3). (Illus.). 1972. pap. 4.50 (ISBN 0-912318-27-9). N K Gregg.

--Gondolas & Hoppers from the Nineteen Forty Car Builders' Cyclopedia of American Practice. 15th ed. (Train Shed Cyclopedia Ser, No. 5). (Illus.). 1973. pap. 4.50 (ISBN 0-912318-29-5). N K Gregg.

--Locos of the Forties & Fifties from the 1941 Locomotive Cyclopedia of American Practice: Diesels Part 7, No. 58. (Train Shed Ser.). (Illus.). 1977. pap. 4.50 (ISBN 0-912318-93-7). N K Gregg.

--Locos of the Forties & Fifties New Formula from the Nineteen Forty-One Locomotive Cyclopedia of American Practice: Steam Part 1, No. 45. (Train Shed Ser.). (Illus.). 1976. pap. 4.50 (ISBN 0-912318-77-5). N K Gregg.

--Locos of the Forties & Fifties New Formula from the Nineteen Forty-One Locomotive Cyclopedia of American Practice: Steam Part 2, No. 47. (Train Shed Ser.). (Illus.). 1976. pap. 4.50 (ISBN 0-912318-79-1). N K Gregg.

--Locos of the Forties & Fifties New Formula from The Nineteen Forty-One Locomotive Cyclopedia of American Practice: Steam Part 3, No. 49. (Train Shed Ser.). (Illus.). 1976. pap. 4.50 (ISBN 0-912318-81-3). N K Gregg.

--Locos of the Forties & Fifties New Formula from the Nineteen Forty-One Locomotive Cyclopedia of American Practice: Steam Part 4, No. 50. (Train Shed Ser.). (Illus.). 1976. pap. 4.50 (ISBN 0-912318-82-1). N K Gregg.

--Locos of the Forties & Fifties New Formula from the Nineteen Forty-One Locomotive Cyclopedia of Amerian Practice: Steam Part 5, No. 51. (Train Shed Ser.). (Illus.). 1976. pap. 4.50 (ISBN 0-912318-83-X). N K Gregg.

--Locos of the Forties & Fifties New Formula from the Nineteen Forty-One Locomotive Cyclopedia of American Practice: Diesels Part 8, No. 60. (Train Shed Ser.). (Illus.). 1977. pap. 4.50 (ISBN 0-912318-95-3). N K Gregg.

--Locos of the Forties & Fifties New Formula from the 1941 Locomotive Cyclopedia of American Practice: Steam Part 6, No. 56. (Train Shed Ser.). (Illus.). 1977. pap. 4.50 (ISBN 0-685-78540-8). N K Gregg.

--Locos of the Forties & Fifties Still More Diesels: Part 9. (Train Shed Ser.: No. 64). (Illus.). 1977. pap. 4.50 (ISBN 0-912318-99-6). N K Gregg.

--Rail Motor Cars of the Nineteen Thirty's from the 1931 & 1937 Car Builders' Cyclopedias. (Train Shed Cyclopedia Ser, No. 10). (Illus.). 1973. pap. 4.50 (ISBN 0-912318-34-1). N K Gregg.

--War & Standard Locomotives & Cars. (Train Shed Cyclopedia Ser, No. 9). (Illus.). 1973. pap. 4.50 (ISBN 0-912318-33-3). N K Gregg.

LOCOMOTIVES–MODELS

Evans, Martin. Model Locomotive Boilers. (Illus.). 144p. 1977. pap. 8.95 (ISBN 0-85242-483-3). Aztex.

--Model Locomotive Valve Gears. (Illus.). 102p. 1985. pap. 8.95 (ISBN 0-85242-162-1, Pub. by Argus). Aztex.

Heisler Locomotive: Eighteen Ninety-One to Nineteen Forty-One. (Illus.). 20.00 (ISBN 0-686-91942-4). Chatham Pub CA.

Pocket Diesel & Electric Guide: A Quick Reference Handbook to Locomotives in Service. LC 74-80803. (Illus.). 1974. wirebound 5.00 (ISBN 0-913556-11-4); pap. 4.00 (ISBN 0-913556-12-2). Spec Pr NJ.

Simple Model Locomotive Building: Introducing LBSC's Tich. (Illus.). 268p. 1985. pap. 13.95 (ISBN 0-85242-786-7, Pub. by Argus). Aztex.

LOCOMOTIVES–PICTORIAL WORKS

Collias, Joe G. The Last of Steam. LC 60-14067. (Illus.). 1960. 25.00 (ISBN 0-8310-7018-8). Howell-North.

--The Search for Steam. LC 72-86957. (Illus.). 1972. 25.00 (ISBN 0-8310-7092-7). Howell-North.

Fitt, William C., ed. Union Pacific FEF-3 Class 4-8-4 Locomotive Drawings. LC 75-27822. (Illus.). 54p. 1975. pap. 15.50 (ISBN 0-914104-02-0). Wildwood Pubns MI.

Last of Steam. 25.00 (ISBN 0-685-83344-5). Chatham Pub CA.

LeMassena, Robert A. Articulated Steam Locomotives of North America: A Catalogue of "Giant Steam". (Illus.). 416p. 1979. 49.00 (ISBN 0-913582-26-3). Sundance.

Russell, J. H. A Pictorial Record of Great Western Absorbed Engines. 288p. 60.00x (ISBN 0-902888-74-9, Pub. by ORPC Ltd UK). State Mutual Bk.

White, John H., Jr. Early American Locomotives. LC 79-188951. (Illus.). 142p. (Orig.). 1972. pap. 6.95 (ISBN 0-486-22772-3). Dover.

LOCUSTS

Albrecht, F. O. The Anatomy of the Red Locust (Nomadacris Septemfasciate Serville) 1956. 35.00x (ISBN 0-85135-067-4, Pub. by Centre Overseas Research). State Mutual Bk.

Application of Remote Sensing Techniques for Improving Desert Locust Survey & Control. (Illus.). 92p. 1977. pap. 10.50 (ISBN 92-5-100112-X, F721, FAO). Unipub.

Ashall, C. & Ellis, P. E. Studies on Numbers & Mortality in Field Populations of the Desert Locust (Schistocerca Gregaria Forskal) 1962. 35.00x (ISBN 0-85135-004-6, Pub. by Centre Overseas Research). State Mutual Bk.

Bennett, F. V. & Symmons, P. M. A Review of Estimates of the Effectiveness of Certain Control Techniques & Insecticides Against the Desert Locust. 1972. 35.00x (ISBN 0-85135-060-7, Pub. by Centre Overseas Research). State Mutual Bk.

Betts, E. Outbreaks of the African Migratory Locust (Locusta Migratoria Migratoriodes R & F) Since 1871. 1961. 35.00x (ISBN 0-85135-005-4, Pub. by Centre Overseas Research). State Mutual Bk.

Bullen, F. T. The Distribution of the Damage Potential of the Desert Locust (Schistocerca Gregaria Forskal) 1969. 35.00x (ISBN 0-85135-045-3, Pub. by Centre Overseas Research). State Mutual Bk.

Burnett, G. F. Field Observations on the Behavior of the Red Locust (Nomadacris Septemfasciata Serville) in the Solitary Phase. 1951. 40.00x (ISBN 0-85135-006-2, Pub. by Centre Overseas Research). State Mutual Bk.

Casimir, M. & Bament, R. C. An Outbreak of the Australian Plague Locust, (Hortoicetes Terminiferal Walk.), During 1966-67 & the Influence of Weather on Swarm Flight. 1974. 35.00x (ISBN 0-85135-062-3, Pub. by Centre Overseas Research). State Mutual Bk.

Chapman, R. F. A Laboratory Study of Roosting Behavior in Hoppers of the African Migratory Locust (Locusta Migratoria Migratorioides R & F) 1955. 35.00x (ISBN 0-85135-007-0, Pub. by Centre Overseas Research). State Mutual Bk.

Davey, J. T. & Johnston, H. B. The African Migratory Locust (Locusta Migratoria Migratorioides) R & FO in Nigeria. 91p. 1956. 35.00x (ISBN 0-85135-009-7, Pub. by Centre Overseas Research). State Mutual Bk.

Davies, D. E. Seasonal Breeding & Migrations of the Desert Locust (Schistocerca Gregaria Forskal) in North-Eastern Africa & the Middle East. 1952. 35.00x (ISBN 0-85135-010-0, Pub. by Centre Overseas Research). State Mutual Bk.

Dempster, J. P. The Population Dynamics of the Moroccan Locust (Dociostaurus Maroccanus Thunb) in Cyprus. 1957. 35.00x (ISBN 0-85135-011-9, Pub. by Centre Overseas Research). State Mutual Bk.

The Desert Locust Pocket Book. 1978p. 37.00x (ISBN 0-85135-083-6, Pub. by Centre Overseas Research). State Mutual Bk.

Desert Locust Project: Final Report of the Food & Agriculture Organization. (Orig.). 1968. pap. 16.50 (ISBN 0-685-09377-8, F114, FAO). Unipub.

Dirsh, V. A. Morphometrical Studies on Phases of the Desert Locust (Schistocerca Gregaria Forskal) 1953. 35.00x (ISBN 0-85135-066-6, Pub. by Centre Overseas Research). State Mutual Bk.

Dirsh, V. M. The African Genera of Acridoidea. 579p. 1965. 60.00x (ISBN 0-521-04837-0, Pub. by Centre Overseas Research). State Mutual Bk.

Field Observations of the Behavior of Hoppers of the Red Locust (Nomadacris Septemfasciata Serville) 1959. 40.00x (ISBN 0-85135-043-7, Pub. by Centre Overseas Research). State Mutual Bk.

Fortescue-Foulkes, J. Seasonal Breeding & Migrations of the Desert Locust (Schistocerca Gregaria Forskal) in South-Western Asia. 1953. 35.00x (ISBN 0-85135-015-1, Pub. by Centre Overseas Research). State Mutual Bk.

Hemming, C. F. & Symmons, P. M. The Germination & Growth of Schouwia Purpurea (Forskal) Schweinf & Its Role as a Habitat of the Desert Locust. 1969. 35.00x (ISBN 0-85135-054-2, Pub. by Centre Overseas Research). State Mutual Bk.

Hemming, C. F. & Taylor, T. H., eds. Proceedings of the International Study Conference on the Current & Future Problems of Acridology, London, 1970. 1972. 50.00x (ISBN 0-686-82422-9, Pub. by Centre Overseas Research). State Mutual BK.

Hunter-Jones, P. Laboratory Studies on the Inheritance of Phase Characters in Locusts. 1958. 35.00x (ISBN 0-85135-018-6, Pub. by Centre Overseas Research). State Mutual Bk.

Johnston, D. R., ed. Factors Affecting Aerial Application of Microencapsulated Pheromone Formulation for Control of Pectinophora Gossypiella (Saunders) by Communication Disruption on Cotton in Egypt. 1982. 35.00x (ISBN 0-686-82424-5, Pub. by Centre Overseas Research). State Mutual Bk.

Johnston, H. B. Annotated Catalogue of African Grasshoppers. 834p. 1956. 75.00x (ISBN 0-521-05442-7, Pub. by Centre Overseas Research). State Mutual Bk.

--Annotated Catalogue of African Grasshoppers: Supplement. 1968. 45.00x (ISBN 0-521-05443-5, Pub. by Centre Overseas Research). State Mutual Bk.

Johnston, H. B. & Buxton, D. R. Field Observations on Locusts in Eastern Africa. 1949. 35.00x (ISBN 0-85135-008-9, Pub. by Centre Overseas Research). State Mutual Bk.

Jones, Jack C. The Anatomy of the Grasshopper: Romalea Microptera. (Illus.). 292p. 1981. spiral, photocopy ed. 30.75x (ISBN 0-398-04126-1). C C Thomas.

Joyce, R. J. The Ecology of Grasshoppers in Cast Central Sudan. 1952. 40.00x (ISBN 0-85135-019-4, Pub. by Centre Overseas Research). State Mutual Bk.

Lloyd, J. H. Operational Research on Preventive Control of the Red Locust (Nomadacris Septemfasciata Serville) 1959. 35.00x (ISBN 0-85135-020-8, Pub. by Centre Overseas Research). State Mutual Bk.

Locust & Grasshopper Agricultural Manual. 1982. 195.00 (ISBN 0-85135-120-4, Pub. by Centre Overseas Research). State Mutual BK.

The Locust Handbook. 1966. 35.00 (ISBN 0-85135-053-4, Pub. by Centre Overseas Research). State Mutual Bk.

Maccuaig, R. D. & Yeates, M. N. Theoretical Studies on the Efficiency of Insecticidal Sprays for the Control of Flying Locust Swarms. 35.00x (ISBN 0-85135-057-7, Pub. by Centre Overseas Research). State Mutual Bk.

Magor, J. T. Outbreaks of the Australian Plague Locust (Hortoicetes Terminifera Walk.) During the Seasons 1937 to 1962, with Particular Reference to Rainfall. 1970. 40.00x (ISBN 0-85135-002-X, Pub. by Centre Overseas Research). State Mutual Bk.

Magor, J. T. & Ward, P. Illustrated Descriptions, Distribution Maps & Bibliography of the Species of Quelea (Weaverbirds; Ploceidae) (Illus.). 1972. 35.00x (ISBN 0-85135-058-5, Pub. by Centre Overseas Research). State Mutual Bk.

Merton, L. F. The Moroccan Locust (Dociostaurus Maroccanus Thunberg) 1961. 35.00X (ISBN 0-85135-021-6, Pub. by Centre Overseas Research). State Mutual Bk.

Nickerson, N. Pigmentation of Hoppers of the Desert Locust (Schistocerca Gregaria Forskal) in Relation to Phase Coloration. 1956. 35.00x (ISBN 0-85135-023-2, Pub. by Centre Overseas Research). State Mutual Bk.

Norris, M. J. Factors Affecting the Rate of Sexual Maturation of the Desert Locust (Schistocerca Gregaria Forskal) in the Laboratory. 1957. 40.00x (ISBN 0-85135-024-0, Pub. by Centre Overseas Research). State Mutual Bk.

--Laboratory Experiments on Aviposition Responses of the Desert Locust (Schistocerca Gregaria Forskal) 1968. 35.00x (ISBN 0-686-82420-2, Pub. by Centre Overseas Research). State Mutual Bk.

--Reproduction in the Red Locust (Nomadacris Septemfasciata Serville) in the Laboratory. 1959. 35.00x (ISBN 0-85135-027-5, Pub. by Centre Overseas Research). State Mutual Bk.

--Reproduction in the Sert Locust (Schistocerca Gregaria Forskal) 1952. 35.00x (ISBN 0-85135-026-7, Pub. by Centre Overseas Research). State Mutual Bk.

Observations on the Population Dynamics of the Red Locust, Noma Dacris Septemfasciata, & Its Outbreak Areas. (Agricultural Research Reports: No. 694). 1967. pap. 12.75 (ISBN 90-220-0155-5, PDC168, PUDOC). Unipub.

Odiyo, P. O. Seasonal Distribution & Migrations of Agrotis Ipsilon (Hufnagel) Leipidoptera, Noctuidae. 1975. 35.00x (ISBN 0-85135-070-4, Pub. by Centre Overseas Research). State Mutual Bk.

Otte, Daniel. The North American Grasshoppers: Acrididae - Gomphocerinae & Acridinae, Vol. 1. (Illus.). 368p. 1981. text ed. 45.00x (ISBN 0-674-62660-5). Harvard U Pr.

--The North American Grasshoppers: Acrididae, Oedipodinae, Vol. 2. (Illus.). 352p. 1984. text ed. 60.00x (ISBN 0-674-62661-3). Harvard U Pr.

Popov, G. & Ratcliffe, M. The Sahelian Tree Locust Anacridium Melanorhodon Walker. 1968. 35.00x (ISBN 0-85135-044-5, Pub. by Centre Overseas Research). State Mutual Bk.

Popov, G. B. Ecological Studies on Oviposition by Swarms of the Desert Locust (Schistocerca Gregaria Forskal) in Eastern Africa. 1958. 35.00x (ISBN 0-85135-029-1, Pub. by Centre Overseas Research). State Mutual Bk.

--Studies on Oviposition, Egg Development & Mortality in Oedaleus Senegalenis: Krauss, Orthoptera, Acridoidea in the Sahel. 1980. 35.00x (ISBN 0-85135-111-5, Pub. by Centre Overseas Research). State Mutual Bk.

Rainey, R. C. Meteorology & the Migration of Desert Locusts: Applications of Synoptic Meteorology in Locust Control. 1963. 35.00 (ISBN 0-686-82414-8, Pub. by Centre Overseas Research). State Mutual Bk.

Rainey, R. C. & Aspilden, C. Meteorology & the Migration of Desert Locusts. (Technical Note Ser.). 1963. pap. 25.00 (ISBN 0-685-22324-8, W25, WMO). Unipub.

Rainey, R. C. & Waloff, Z. The Behavior of the Red Locust (Normadacris Septemfasciata Serville) in Relation to the Topography, Meteorology & Vegetatation of the Rukwa Rift Valley, Tanganyika. 1957. 35.00x (ISBN 0-85135-031-3, Pub. by Centre Overseas Research). State Mutual Bk.

Rehn, James A. & Grant, Harold J., Jr. A Monograph of the Orthoptera of North America (North of Mexico, Vol. 1. (Monograph: No. 12). (Illus.). 257p. (Orig.). 1961. pap. 18.00 (ISBN 0-910006-18-0). Acad Nat Sci Phila.

Report for Controlling the Desert Locust in the Eastern Region of Southwest Asia: Commission Meeting, 12th Session. 28p. 1978. pap. 7.50 (ISBN 0-685-20385-9, F1266, FAO). Unipub.

Report of the FAO Desert Locust Control Committee: 19th Session, Rome, 1975. 32p. 1976. pap. 7.50 (ISBN 0-685-66347-7, F1127, FAO). Unipub.

Report of the Seventh Session of the Commission for Controlling the Desert Locust in the Near East. 24p. 1977. pap. 7.50 (ISBN 92-5-100198-7, F1108, FAO). Unipub.

Report of the Twentieth Session of the FAO Desert Locust Control Committee. 41p. 1977. pap. 7.50 (ISBN 92-5-100191-X, F1128, FAO). Unipub.

Report of the Twenty-First Session of the FAO Desert Locust Control Committee. 41p. 1978. pap. 7.50 (ISBN 92-5-100492-7, F1344, FAO). Unipub.

Richards, O. W. The Study of the Numbers of the Red Locust (Nomadacris Septemfasciata Serville) 1953. 35.00x (ISBN 0-85135-032-1, Pub. by Centre Overseas Research). State Mutual Bk.

Richards, O. W. & Waloff, N. Studies on the Biology & Population Dynamics of British Grasshoppers. 1954. 35.00x (ISBN 0-85135-034-8, Pub. by Centre Overseas Research). State Mutual Bk.

Riley, J. R. & Reynolds, D. R. Radar Observations of Spodoptera Exempta Kenya: March-April 1979. 1981. 35.00x (ISBN 0-85135-115-8, Pub. by Centre Overseas Research). State Mutual Bk.

Roffey, J. Locusts & Grasshoppers of Economic Importance in Thailand. 1979. 75.00x (ISBN 0-686-82431-8, Pub. by Centre Overseas Research). State Mutual Bk.

--Observations on Night Flight on the Desert Locust (Schistocerca Gregaria Forskal) 1963. 35.00x (ISBN 0-85135-033-X, Pub. by Centre Overseas Research). State Mutual Bk.

Shulov, A. The Development of Eggs of the Red Locust, Nomandacris Septemfasciata (Serville) & the African Migratory Locust, Locusta Migratoria Migratorioides (R&F), & Its Interruption under Particular Conditions of Humidity. 1970. 35.00x (ISBN 0-85135-001-1, Pub. by Centre Overseas Research). State Mutual Bk.

Shulov, A. & Pener, M. P. Studies on the Development of Eggs of the Desert Locust (Schistocerca Gregaria Forskal) & Its Interruption under Particular Conditions of Humidity. 1963. 35.00x (ISBN 0-85135-035-6, Pub. by Centre Overseas Research). State Mutual Bk.

Stower, W. J. The Colour Patterns of Hoppers of the Desert Locust (Schistocerca Gregaria Forskal) 1959. 35.00x (ISBN 0-85135-036-4, Pub. by Centre Overseas Research). State Mutual Bk.

Stower, W. J. & Popov, G. B. Oviposition Behavior & Egg Mortality of the Desert Locust (Schistocerca Gregaria Forskal) on the Coast of Eritrea. 1958. 35.00x (ISBN 0-85135-037-2, Pub. by Centre Overseas Research). State Mutual Bk.

Uvarov, B. P. Grasshoppers & Locusts, 3 vols. 481p. 1982. 100.00x set (Pub. by Centre Overseas Research). State Mutual Bk.

--Grasshoppers & Locusts: A Handbook of General Acridology, 2 Vols. Vol. 1, 1966. 50.00x (ISBN 0-521-06669-7, Pub. by Centre Overseas Research); Vol. 2, 1977. 70.00x (ISBN 0-85135-072-0, Pub. by Centre Overseas Research). State Mutual Bk.

Uvarov, B. P. & Chapman, E. Observations on the Moroccan Locust (Dociostaurus Maroccanus Thunberg) in Cyprus, 1950. 1951. 35.00x (ISBN 0-85135-039-9, Pub. by Centre Overseas Research). State Mutual Bk.

Versey-Fitzgerald, D. F. The Vegetation of the Outbreak Areas of the Red Locust (Nomadacris Septemfasciata Serville in Tanganyika & Northern Rhodesia) 1955. 35.00x (ISBN 0-85135-014-3, Pub by Centre Overseas Research). State Mutual Bk.

Waloff, Z. Some Temporal Characteristics of Desert Locust Plagues. 1976. 35.00x (ISBN 0-85135-075-5, Pub. by Centre Overseas Research). State Mutual Bk.

--The Upsurges & Recessions of the Desert Locust Plague: An Historical Survey. 1968. 35.00x (ISBN 0-85135-041-0, Pub. by Centre Overseas Research). State Mutual Bk.

Waloff, Z. & Rainey, R. C. Field Studies on Factors Affecting the Displacement of Desert Locust Swarms in Eastern Africa. 1951. 35.00x (ISBN 0-85135-042-9, Pub. by Centre Overseas Research). State Mutual Bk.

Wardhaugh, K. & Ashour, Y. Experiments on the Incubation & Hopper Development Periods of the Desert Locust (Schistocerca Gregaria Forskal) in Saudi Arabia. 1969. 35.00x (ISBN 0-85135-048-8, Pub. by Centre Overseas Research). State Mutual Bk.

LOESS

Pecsi, M., ed. Studies on Loess. 555p. 1980. pap. text ed. 52.50x (ISBN 963-05-2871-1, 41212, Pub. by Kultura Pr Hungary). Humanities.

Smalley, I. J. Loess: A Partial Bibliography. 103p. 1980. 25.00x (ISBN 0-86094-036-5, Pub. by GEO Abstracts England). State Mutual Bk.

Smalley, I. J., ed. Loess: Lithology & Genesis. LC 75-30690. (Benchmark Papers in Geology: Vol. 26). 448p. 1975. 67.50 (ISBN 0-12-787472-0). Acad Pr.

LOG SCALING

see Forests and Forestry–Mensuration

LOGARITHMS

see also Functions, Exponential; Mathematics–Tables, etc.; Slide-Rule

Ball, W. Rouse, et al, eds. String Figures & Other Monographs, 4 vols in 1. Incl. String Figures. Ball, W. R; History of the Slide Rule. Cajori, F; Non Euclidean Geometry. Carslaw, Horatio S; Methods Geometrical Construction. Petersen, Julius. LC 59-11780. 15.95 (ISBN 0-8284-0130-6). Chelsea Pub.

Bateman, Richard M. Log Quality Control. (Illus.). 416p. 1984. 52.00 (ISBN 0-934634-89-0). Intl Human Res.

Bauschinger, J. & Peters, J. Logarithmic Trigonometrical Tables to 8 Decimal Places or Numbers 1-200,000 & Trigon: Functions for Sexagesmil Second of the Quadrant, 2vols. 3rd ed. 1971. 45.00 (ISBN 0-934454-57-4). Lubrecht & Cramer.

Bruhns. New Manual of Logarithms. 634p. 1941. 25.00 (ISBN 0-442-01145-8, Pub. by Van Nos Reinhold). Krieger.

Davis, Harold T. & Nelson, William F. Elements of Statistics with Application to Economic Data. rev. & enl. 2nd ed. LC 78-163681. Repr. of 1937 ed. 28.50 (ISBN 0-404-01994-3). AMS Pr.

Evans, Griffith C. Logarithmic Potential, 2 vols. in 1. 2nd ed. Incl. Fundamental Existence Theorems. Bliss, Gilbert A. Repr. of 1927 ed. 19.50 (ISBN 0-8284-0305-8). Chelsea Pub.

Fienberg, Stephen. The Analysis of Cross-Classified Categorical Data. 2nd ed. 1980. text ed. 18.50x (ISBN 0-262-06071-X). MIT Pr.

Glover, James W. & Carver, Henry C. Tables of Compound Interest Functions & Logarithms of Compound Interest Functions. 1921. 3.00x (ISBN 0-685-21808-2). Wahr.

Hughes, Richard S. Logarithmic Video Amplifiers. LC 70-178294. pap. 47.50 (ISBN 0-317-27670-0, 2025057). Bks Demand UMI.

Kells, Lyman M., et al. Log & Trig Tables. 1955. pap. 2.95 (ISBN 0-07-033601-6). McGraw.

Lewin, Leonard. Polylogarithms & Associated Functions. 360p. 1981. 71.00 (ISBN 0-444-00550-1, North-Holland). Elsevier.

Markushevich, A. I. Areas & Logarithms. 70p. 1981. pap. 2.00 (ISBN 0-8285-2054-2, Pub. by Mir Pubs USSR). Imported Pubns.

Merrill, Arthur A. Log Scale Construction. 29p. pap. 4.00 (ISBN 0-911894-31-4). Analysis.

Napier, John. A Description of the Admirable Table of Logarithmes. Wright, tr. LC 79-25885. (English Experience Ser.: No. 211). 1969. Repr. of 1616 ed. 16.00 (ISBN 90-221-0211-4). Walter J Johnson.

Norwood, Richard. Trigonometrie, or the Doctrine of Triangles, 2 pts. LC 78-171779. (English Experience Ser.: No. 404). 362p. 1971. Repr. of 1631 ed. 53.00 (ISBN 90-221-0404-4). Walter J Johnson.

Peters, J., et al. Ten-Place Logarithm Tables, 3 vols. Hyman, Charles J., tr. Incl. German Text with English Translations. LC 57-6794. Set. 60.00 (ISBN 0-8044-4748-9); German Text Only. LC 57-6795. Set. 45.00 (ISBN 0-8044-4752-7). Ungar.

Smoley, C. K. Five Decimal Logarithmic-Trigonometric Tables. rev. ed. Smoley, E. R. & Smoley, N. G., eds. 1971. pap. 5.00 (ISBN 0-911390-06-5). Smoley.

--Parallel Tables of Logarithms & Squares. rev. ed. Smoley, E. R. & Smoley, N. G., eds. 1974. fabricoid 27.50 (ISBN 0-911390-02-2). Smoley.

--Segmental Functions, Text & Tables. rev. ed. Smoley, E. R. & Smoley, N. G., eds. 1974. fabricoid 27.50 (ISBN 0-911390-04-9). Smoley.

Spenceley, George W., et al. Smithsonian Logarithmic Tables: To Base e & Base Ten. LC 52-60707. 402p. 1960. 15.00x (ISBN 0-87474-004-5). Smithsonian.

Uhler, Horace S. Original Tables to One Hundred & Thirty-Seven Decimal Places of Natural Logarithms for Factors of the Form One Plus N Ten Minus P Enhanced by Auxiliary Tables of Logarithms of Small Integers. 1942. pap. 39.50x (ISBN 0-685-89769-9). Elliots Bks.

LOGGING

see Lumbering

LOGGING RAILROADS

BALDWIN Logging Locomotives 1913. LC 73-84950. (Illus.). 1973. pap. 4.00 (ISBN 0-913556-09-2). Spec Pr NJ.

King, Frank. Minnesota Logging Railroads. LC 81-6940. (Illus.). 224p. 34.95 (ISBN 0-87095-076-2). Golden West.

Labbe, John T. & Goe, Vernon. Railroads in the Woods. LC 61-11373. (Illus.). 1961. 15.00 (ISBN 0-8310-7023-4). Howell-North.

Last of the Three-Foot Loggers. 15.95 (ISBN 0-686-70721-4). Chatham Pub CA.

Spencer, James. The Northwest Loggers: Rayonier, Vol. 1. (Illus.). 160p. 1982. 29.95 (ISBN 0-933506-07-4). Darwin Pubns.

Steam & Thunder in the Timber. 60.00 (ISBN 0-686-75206-6). Chatham Pub CA.

They Felled the Redwoods. (Illus.). 19.95 (ISBN 0-686-70734-6). Chatham Pub CA.

LOGIC

see also Abstraction; Induction (Logic); Knowledge, Theory Of; Logic Machines; Probabilities; Reasoning; Uniformity of Nature

Abramov, L. M., et al. Fourteen Papers on Logic, Algebra, Complex Variables & Topology. LC 51-5559. (Translations Ser.: No. 2, Vol. 48). 1965. 32.00 (ISBN 0-8218-1748-5, TRANS 2-48). Am Math.

Acock. Informal Logic Examples. 288p. 1985. write for info. (ISBN 0-534-04494-8). Wadsworth Pub.

Adams, E. The Logic of Conditionals: An Application of Probability to Deductive Logic. LC 75-20306. (Synthese Library: No. 86). 140p. 1975. lib. bdg. 29.00 (ISBN 90-277-0631-X, Pub. by Reidel Holland). Kluwer Academic.

Adian, S. T. & Higman, C. World Problems-Two. (Studies in Logic: Vol. 95). x, 578p. 1980. 93.75 (ISBN 0-444-85343-X). Elsevier.

Agostini, Franco. Math & Logic Games: A Book of Puzzles & Problems. Foulkes, Paul, tr. LC 83-1542. (Illus.). 184p. 1984. 18.95 (ISBN 0-87196-212-8). Facts on File.

Albury, W. R. Condillac: Loqique. Bonnot de Condillac, Etienne, tr. LC 77-86228. 1980. 20.00 (ISBN 0-913870-38-2). Abaris Bks.

Al-Hibri, Azizah. Deontic Logic: A Comprehensive Appraisal & a View Proposal. LC 78-66422. 1978. pap. text ed. 11.00 (ISBN 0-8191-0303-9). U Pr of Amer.

Andree, Josephine & Andree, Richard. Logic Unlocks. 1979. pap. 2.00 (ISBN 0-686-28235-3); tchr's ed. 2.00. Mu Alpha Theta.

Angell, Richard B. Reasoning & Logic. LC 63-16209. (Century Philosophy Ser.). (Illus.). 1964. 39.50x (ISBN 0-89197-375-3); pap. text ed. 19.95x (ISBN 0-89197-376-1). Irvington.

Annemann, Theodore. Practical Mental Logic. (Illus.). 310p. (Orig.). 1983. pap. 5.95 (ISBN 0-486-24426-1). Dover.

Aristotelian Society For The Systematic Study of Philosophy. Relativity, Logic & Mysticism: Proceedings, Supplementary Vol. 3. 14.00 (ISBN 0-384-50269-5); pap. 9.00 (ISBN 0-384-48086-1). Johnson Repr.

Bacon, Francis. The Advancement of Learning. Kitchin, G. W., ed. (Rowman & Littlefield University Library). 246p. 1973. 13.00x (ISBN 0-87471-664-0); pap. 7.50x (ISBN 0-87471-665-9). Rowman.

Baldwin, James M. Thought & Things: Study of the Development & Meaning of Thought or Genetic Logic, 4 vols. in 2. LC 74-21397. (Classics in Child Development Ser). 1975. Repr. 94.00x (ISBN 0-405-06451-9). Ayer Co Pubs.

Barker, S. F. Elements of Logic. 4th ed. 416p. 1985. 26.95 (ISBN 0-07-003726-4); Written Cavalier & Dreisbach, 168p. study guide 9.95 (ISBN 0-07-003728-0). McGraw.

Barnett, Peter. Tools of Thought: The Practical Foundations of Formal Reasoning. 310p. 1981. 18.95x (ISBN 0-87073-655-8); pap. text ed. 9.95x (ISBN 0-87073-656-6). Schenkman Bks Inc.

Barry, Vincent E. Practical Logic. 2nd ed. LC 80-21202. 1981. text ed. 24.95 (ISBN 0-03-056836-6, HoltC). HR&W.

Barwise, J., et al, eds. Kleene Symposium. (Studies in Logic: Vol. 101). 426p. 1980. 70.25 (ISBN 0-444-85345-6). Elsevier.

Basseches, Michael. Dialectical Thinking & Adult Development. Broughton, John, et al, eds. LC 84-2935. (Path Ser.). 436p. 1985. inst. ed. 49.50 (ISBN 0-89391-017-1); pers. ed. 36.50. Ablex Pub.

Baum, Robert J. Logic. 2nd ed. LC 80-11084. 608p. 1980. text ed. 29.95 (ISBN 0-03-046396-3, HoltC); answer key 20.00 (ISBN 0-03-056878-1). HR&W.

Baynes, Thomas S. Essay on the New Analytic of Logical Forms. LC 73-168274. (Research & Source Works Ser.: No. 897). 170p. (Philosophy Monographs, No. 88). 1972. Repr. of 1850 ed. lib. bdg. 21.00 (ISBN 0-8337-0197-5). B Franklin.

Bealer, George. Quality & Concept. (Clarendon Library of Logic & Philosophy). (Illus.). 1982. 29.95x (ISBN 0-19-824428-2). Oxford U Pr.

Beardsley, Monroe. Practical Logic. 1950. text ed. 22.95 (ISBN 0-13-692111-6). P-H.

Belnap, Nuel D. & Steel, Thomas B., Jr. The Logic of Questions & Answers. LC 75-27761. 1976. 22.50x (ISBN 0-300-01962-9). Yale U Pr.

Bennett, John B. Rational Thinking: A Study in Basic Logic. 1980. 22.95x (ISBN 0-88229-285-4); pap. 10.95x (ISBN 0-88229-739-2). Nelson-Hall.

Beonio-Brocchieri Fumagalli, M. T. The Logic of Abelard. Pleasance, Simon, tr. from It. (Synthese Library: No. 1). 101p. 1969. lib. bdg. 18.50 (ISBN 90-277-0068-0, Pub. by Reidel Holland). Kluwer Academic.

Bergmann, Merrie, et al. The Logic Book. 608p. 1980. text ed. 27.00 (ISBN 0-394-32679-2, KnopfC). Knopf.

Beth, E. W. Aspects of Modern Logic. De Jongh, D. M. & De Jongh-Kearl, Susan, trs. from Dutch. LC 79-135102. (Synthese Library: No. 32). 176p. 1971. 26.00 (ISBN 90-277-0173-3, Pub. by Reidel Holland). Kluwer Academic.

Bishop, E. & Bridges, D. Contructive Analysis. (Grundlehren der Mathematischen Wissenschaften: Vol. 279). 500p. 1985. 48.00 (ISBN 0-387-15066-8). Springer-Verlag.

Biswas, Nripendra U. Introduction to Logic & Switching Theory. 358p. 1975. 67.25x (ISBN 0-677-02860-1). Gordon.

Bittinger, M. L. Logic, Proof, & Sets. 2nd ed. LC 81-14913. 144p. 1982. pap. text ed. 8.95 (ISBN 0-201-10384-2). Addison-Wesley.

Black, Max. Caveats & Critiques: Philosophical Essays in Language, Logic, & Art. LC 74-25365. (Illus.). 280p. 1975. 25.00x (ISBN 0-8014-0958-6). Cornell U Pr.

--Critical Thinking. 2nd ed. 1952. text ed. 22.95 (ISBN 0-13-194092-9). P-H.

Bogoslovsky, B. B. The Technique of Controversy: Principles of Dynamic Logic. 1977. lib. bdg. 59.95 (ISBN 0-8490-1180-9). Gordon Pr.

Bohnert, Herbert G. Logic: Its Use & Basis. 1977. pap. text ed. 13.75 (ISBN 0-8191-0265-2). U Pr of Amer.

Bolzano, Bernhard. The Theory of Science, (Die Wissenschaftslehre Oder Versuch Einer Neuen Darstellung der Logik) George, Rolf, ed. & tr. LC 71-126765. 1972. 48.50x (ISBN 0-520-01787-0). U of Cal Pr.

Lambert, K., ed. Philosophical Problems in Logic: Some Recent Developments. (Synthese Library: No. 29). 176p. 1970. lib. bdg. 25.00 (ISBN 90-277-0079-6, Pub. by Reidel Holland). Kluwer Academic.
Lamm, Zvi. Conflicting Theories of Instruction: Conceptual Dimensions. LC 76-9238. 1976. 24.00x (ISBN 0-8211-1112-4); text ed. 21.50x 10 or more copies (ISBN 0-685-73826-4). McCutchan.
Langer, Jonas. The Origin of Logic: From Six to Twelve Months. LC 79-23266. (Developmental Psychology Ser.). 1980. 47.50 (ISBN 0-12-436150-1). Acad Pr.
Lemmon, E. J. Beginning Logic. LC 78-51926. 217p. 1979. 15.00 (ISBN 0-915144-66-2); pap. text ed. 9.50x (ISBN 0-915144-50-6). Hackett Pub.
Lemmon, E. J. & Schumm, George. Beginning Logic: Teaching Companion. LC 78-51926. 108p. (Orig.). 1979. pap. text ed. 3.95 (ISBN 0-915144-65-4). Hackett Pub.
Levin, Gerald. Writing & Logic. 276p. 1982. pap. text ed. 9.95 (ISBN 0-15-597788-1, HC); instr's manual (ISBN 0-15-597789-X). HarBraceJ.
Levin, Harold. Categorial Grammar & the Logical Form of Quantification. (Indices-Monographs in Philosophical Logic & Formal Linguistics). 151p. 1982. text ed. 30.45x (ISBN 8-87088-048-6, Pub. by Bibliopolis); pap. text ed. 15.45x (ISBN 8-87088-058-3). Humanities.
Lewis, David. Counterfactuals. LC 72-78430. 1973. 10.00 (ISBN 0-674-17540-9). Harvard U Pr.
Longley, Peter. Contemporary Logic. LC 80-1443. 178p. (Orig.). 1981. pap. text ed. 10.50 (ISBN 0-8191-1458-8). U Pr of Amer.
Lorenzen, P. Formal Logic. Crosson, Frederick J., tr. from Ger. (Synthese Library: Vol. 9). 123p. 1965. lib. bdg. 18.50 (ISBN 90-277-0080-X, Pub. by Reidel Holland). Kluwer Academic.
Lorenzen, Paul. Formale Logik. 4th ed. (Sammlung Goeschen, Vol. 1176-1176a). (Ger). 1970. 4.30 (ISBN 3-11-002772-0). De Gruyter.
Lotze, Hermann. Logic, 2 vols. Natanson, Maurice, ed. LC 78-66738. (Phenomenology Background, Foreground & Influences Ser.: Vol. 8). 1980. Set. lib. bdg. 94.00 (ISBN 0-8240-9562-6). Garland Pub.
McArthur, Robert P. Tense Logic. 1976. lib. bdg. 21.00 (ISBN 90-277-0697-2, Pub. by Reidel Holland). Kluwer Academic.
McCurdy, Lyle B. & McHenry, Albert L. Digital Logic Design & Applications: An Experimental Approach. (Illus.). 144p. 1981. pap. text ed. 14.95 (ISBN 0-13-212381-9). P-H.
Machina, Kenton. Basic Applied Logic. 1982. text ed. 22.75x (ISBN 0-673-15359-2). Scott F.
McTaggart, John M. Commentary on Hegel's Logic. LC 64-10391. 1964. Repr. of 1910 ed. 18.00x (ISBN 0-8462-0425-8). Russell.
Makinson, D. C. Topics in Modern Logic. (University Paperback Ser.). 107p. 1973. pap. 4.95x (ISBN 0-416-78100-4, NO. 2309). Methuen Inc.
Mally, E. Logische Schriften: Grosses Logikfragment, Grundgesetze des Sollens. LC 73-135106. (Synthese Historical Library: No. 3). (Ger.). 347p. 1971. lib. bdg. 45.00 (ISBN 90-277-0174-1, Pub. by Reidel Holland). Kluwer Academic.
Martin, Richard. Primordiality, Science, & Value. LC 80-14724. 336p. 1980. 44.50x (ISBN 0-87395-418-1); pap. 16.95. State U NY Pr.
Meiland, Jack W. Talking about Particulars. (International Library of Philosophy & Scientific Method). 1970. text ed. 15.50x (ISBN 0-391-00056-X). Humanities.
Menne, A., ed. Logico-Philosophical Studies. Glover, Horace S., tr. 136p. 1962. lib. bdg. 21.00 (ISBN 90-277-0082-6, Pub. by Reidel Holland). Kluwer Academic.
Mill, J. S. John Stuart Mill's Philosophy of Scientific Method. (Library of Classics Ser.: No. 12). 1950. pap. text ed. 8.95x (ISBN 0-02-849250-1). Hafner.
Mill, John S. System of Logic: Ratiocinative & Inductive, 2 vols. Robson, J. M., ed. LC 73-78926. (Collected Works of John Stuart Mill). 1974. Set. 85.00x (ISBN 0-8020-1875-0). U of Toronto Pr.
Miller, Harlan. Arguments, Arrows, Trees & Truth: A First Book in Logic & Language. 2nd ed. 242p. 1980. pap. text ed. 8.65x (ISBN 0-89894-036-2). Advocate Pub Group.
Minto, William. Logic, Inductive & Deductive. 16.75 (ISBN 0-8369-6997-9, 7814). Ayer Co Pubs.
Mitchell, David. Introduction to Logic. 1967. text ed. 9.00x o. p. (ISBN 0-09-064633-9, Hutchinson U Lib); pap. text ed. 7.00x (ISBN 0-09-064634-7, Hutchinson U Lib). Humanities.
Mohanty, J. N., ed. Readings on Edmund Husserl's Logical Investigations. 1977. lib. bdg. 28.00 (ISBN 90-247-1928-3, Pub. by Martinus Nijhoff Netherlands). Kluwer Academic.
Monnich, Uwe, ed. Aspects of Philosophical Logic. 296p. 1981. 52.50 (ISBN 90-277-1201-8, Pub. by Reidel Holland). Kluwer Academic.
Moody, Ernest A. Logic of William of Ockham. LC 65-17914. 1965. Repr. of 1935 ed. 20.00x (ISBN 0-8462-0666-8). Russell.
Moore, Rosalind, ed. The Dell Book of Logic Problems. (Orig.). 1984. pap. 7.95 (ISBN 0-440-51891-1, Dell Trade Pbks). Dell.
Morris, Charles R. Idealistic Logic. LC 76-102578. 1970. Repr. of 1933 ed. 24.50x (ISBN 0-8046-0738-9, Pub. by Kennikat). Assoc Faculty Pr.
Needham, Charles W. Cerebral Logic: Solving the Problem of Mind & Brain. (Illus.). 232p. 1978. 23.50x (ISBN 0-398-03754-X). C C Thomas.
Nelson, R. J. The Logic of Mind. 1982. 59.50 (ISBN 90-277-1399-5, Pub. by Reidel Holland). Kluwer Academic.
Norman, Edward & Barr, Murray. Logic, Proof, & Mathematical Structures. cancelled (ISBN 0-8130-0739-9). U Presses Fla.
Northrop, F. S. The Logic of the Sciences & the Humanities. LC 83-60576. xiv, 402p. 1983. pap. text ed. 17.00 (ISBN 0-918024-31-5). Ox Bow.
Northrop, Filmer S. The Logic of the Sciences & the Humanities. LC 78-21524. 1979. Repr. of 1959 ed. lib. bdg. 32.50x (ISBN 0-313-21161-2, NOLS). Greenwood.
Novack, George. Introduction to the Logic of Marxism. rev. 5th ed. LC 76-87909. 1969. 16.00 (ISBN 0-87348-019-8); pap. 3.95 (ISBN 0-87348-018-X). Path Pr NY.
Nute, Donald. Topics in Conditional Logic. (Philosophical Studies Series in Philosophy: No. 20). 168p. 1980. lib. bdg. 31.50 (ISBN 90-277-1049-X, Pub. by Reidel Holland). Kluwer Academic.
Nyasani, Joseph M. An Introduction to Traditional Logic. (European University Studies, Series 20, Philosophy: Vol. 88). 174p. 1981. 13.10 (ISBN 3-8204-5725-9). P Lang Pubs.
Oesterle, John A. Logic: The Art of Defining & Reasoning. 2nd ed. 1963. pap. text ed. 19.95 (ISBN 0-13-539999-8). P-H.
Ortega y Gasset, Jose. Idea of Principle in Leibnitz & the Evolution of Deductive Theory. LC 66-18068. 1971. 10.00x (ISBN 0-393-01086-4). Norton.
Osherson, D. N. Logical Inference: Underlying Operations. (Vol. 2). 192p. 1974. text ed. 24.95x (ISBN 0-89859-502-9). L Erlbaum Assocs.
Otto, Herbert R. The Linguistic Basis of Logic Translation. LC 78-63261. 1978. pap. text ed. 11.75 (ISBN 0-8191-0617-8). U Pr of Amer.
Owen, G. E. Logic, Science & Dialectic: Collected Papers in Greek Philosophy. Nussbaum, Martha C., ed. 320p. 1984. 37.50x (ISBN 0-8014-1726-0). Cornell U Pr.
Palmer, Humphrey. Presupposition & Transcendental Inference. LC 84-18050. 108p. 1984. 27.50 (ISBN 0-312-69613-2). St Martin.
Panfilov, V. Z. Grammar & Logic. LC 68-15535. (Janua Linguarum, Ser. Minor: No. 63). (Orig.). 1968. pap. text ed. 11.20x (ISBN 90-2790-591-6). Mouton.
Peirce, Charles S. Chance, Love & Logic. 317p. 1980. Repr. of 1923 ed. lib. bdg. 50.00 (ISBN 0-89984-386-7). Century Bookbindery.
Piaget, Jean. Logique & Connaissance Scientifique. (Methodique Ser.). 1360p. 55.95 (ISBN 0-686-56429-4). French & Eur.
Popper, Karl R. Logic of Scientific Discovery. rev. ed. pap. 9.50xi (ISBN 0-06-130576-6, TB576, Torch). Har-Row.
Pospesel, Howard & Marans, David. Arguments: Deductive Logic Exercises. 2nd ed. (Illus.). 1978. pap. text ed. 14.95 (ISBN 0-13-045880-5). P-H.
Prazak, Milos. Language & Logic. LC 76-141264. 154p. 1972. Repr. of 1963 ed. lib. bdg. 15.00x (ISBN 0-8371-5860-5, PRLL). Greenwood.
Prior, Arthur N. Formal Logic. 2nd ed. 1962. 36.95x (ISBN 0-19-824156-9). Oxford U Pr.
--Objects of Thought. Geach, P., ed. 1971. 31.50x (ISBN 0-19-824354-5). Oxford U Pr.
--Papers in Logic & Ethics. Geach, P. T. & Kenny, A. J., eds. LC 76-9376. 238p. 1976. 13.50x (ISBN 0-87023-213-4). U of Mass Pr.
Przexecki, Marian & Wojcicki, Ryszard, eds. Twenty-Five Years of Logical Methodology in Poland. LC 76-7064. (Synthese Library Set: No. 87). 1976. lib. bdg. 71.00 (ISBN 90-277-0601-8, Pub by Reidel Holland). Kluwer Academic.
Quine, W. V. Elementary Logic. rev. ed. LC 80-81978. 144p. 1981. text ed. 8.95x (ISBN 0-674-24450-8); pap. text ed. 4.95x (ISBN 0-674-24451-6). Harvard U Pr.
--Methods of Logic. 4th ed. (Illus.). 320p. 1982. text ed. 25.00x (ISBN 0-674-57175-4); pap. text ed. 9.95x (ISBN 0-674-57176-2). Harvard U Pr.
--Philosophy of Logic. 1970. pap. 13.95 ref. ed. (ISBN 0-13-663625-X). P-H.
Reichenbach, Hans. Elements of Symbolic Logic. 444p. 1980. pap. 7.95 (ISBN 0-486-24004-5). Dover.
Rescher, N. Topics in Philosophical Logic. (Synthese Library: No. 17). 347p. 1968. lib. bdg. 42.00 (ISBN 90-277-0084-2, Pub. by Reidel Holland). Kluwer Academic.
Rhodes, Charles M. Mastering the Decisive Power of Logical Thinking. (Illus.). 1980. deluxe ed. 49.75 (ISBN 0-89266-223-9). Am Classical Coll Pr.
Rodman, Alexius. An Introduction to Logic: Mastering the Powers of Logical Thinking. (Illus.). 1980. deluxe ed. 57.75 (ISBN 0-89266-228-X). Am Classical Coll Pr.
Rosser, J. Barkley & Turquette, Atwell R. Many-Valued Logics. LC 77-405. (Studies in Logic & the Foundations of Mathematics). 1977. Repr. of 1952 ed. lib. bdg. 24.75x (ISBN 0-8371-9449-0, ROMV). Greenwood.
Royce, Josiah. Principles of Logic. (Orig.). pap. 0.95 (ISBN 0-685-19411-6, 114, WL). Citadel Pr.
Rubin, Ronald & Young, Charles M. Logic Made Simple. Rev., 2nd ed. LC 83-71617. 160p. 1983. pap. text ed. 13.95 (ISBN 0-941736-01-6). Arete Pr.
Runes, Dagobert D., ed. Classics in Logic. LC 62-15033. 1962. 10.00 (ISBN 0-8022-1426-6). Philos Lib.
Runkle, Gerald. Good Thinking: An Introduction to Logic. 2nd ed. LC 80-29326. 1981. text ed. 20.95 (ISBN 0-03-058161-3, HoltC). HR&W.
Russell, Bertrand. Mysticism & Logic & Other Essays. 2nd ed. LC 81-119829. 168p. 1981. pap. 8.95x (ISBN 0-389-20135-9, 06657). B&N Imports.
Sartre, Jean-Paul. Critique of Dialectical Reason. (Illus.). 840p. 1983. 39.95 (ISBN 0-8052-7013-2, Pub. by NLB); pap. 14.50 (ISBN 0-8052-7137-6). Schocken.
Schiller, Ferdinand C. Formal Logic, a Scientific & Social Problem. LC 75-3345. Repr. of 1912 ed. 31.50 (ISBN 0-404-59344-5). AMS Pr.
Searles, Herbert L. Logic & Scientific Methods: An Introductory Course. 3rd ed. LC 68-13474. (Illus.). Repr. of 1968 ed. 93.50 (ISBN 0-8357-9924-7, 2013408). Bks Demand UMI.
Secor, Marie & Fahnestock, Jeanne. A Rhetoric for Argument. 416p. 1982. text ed. 13.95 (ISBN 0-394-32416-1, RanC). Random.
Seltman, Muriel & Seltman, Peter. Piaget's Logic: A Critique of Genetic Epistemology. 420p. 1985. text ed. 40.00x (ISBN 0-04-370154-X). Allen Unwin.
Semenenko, M. I., et al. Twelve Papers in Logic & Algebra. Silver, Ben, ed. LC 79-9994. (American Mathematical Society Translations Ser. 2: Vol. 113). 1979. 35.00 (ISBN 0-8218-3063-5, TRANS 2-113). Am Math.
Simco, Nancy D. & James, Gene G. Elementary Logic. 2nd ed. 336p. 1982. text ed. write for info. (ISBN 0-534-01363-5). Wadsworth Pub.
Simonds, Roger T. Beginning Philosophical Logic. 1977. pap. text ed. 11.25 (ISBN 0-8191-0262-8). U Pr of Amer.
Smiley, T. J. & Shoesmith, D. J. Multiple-Conclusion Logic. LC 77-84003. (Illus.). 1978. 67.50 (ISBN 0-521-21765-2). Cambridge U Pr.
Smullyan, Raymond. Five Thousand B.C. & Other Philosophical Fantasies. 192p. 1984. pap. 5.95 (ISBN 0-312-29517-0). St Martin.
--What Is the Name of This Book? The Riddle of Dracula & Other Logical Puzzles. LC 77-18692. 1978. 8.95 (ISBN 0-13-955088-7); pap. 4.95 (ISBN 0-13-955062-3). P-H.
Strawson, P. F. Introduction to Logical Theory. 1963. pap. 11.95x (ISBN 0-416-68220-0, NO. 2536). Methuen Inc.
Strawson, P. F., ed. Philosophical Logic. (Oxford Readings in Philosophy Ser). (Orig.). 1967. pap. 8.95x (ISBN 0-19-500375-6). Oxford U Pr.
Sullivan, D. J. Fundamentals of Logic. 1963. text ed. 29.95 (ISBN 0-07-062338-4). McGraw.
Swain, M., ed. Induction, Acceptance, & Rational Belief. (Synthese Library: No. 26). 232p. 1970. lib. bdg. 26.00 (ISBN 90-277-0086-9, Pub. by Reidel Holland). Kluwer Academic.
Tammelo, I. Modern Logic in the Service of Law. 1978. pap. 20.00 (ISBN 0-387-81486-8). Springer-Verlag.
Tarski, Alfred. Logic, Semantics, Metamathematics. 2nd ed. Corcoran, John, ed. Woodger, J. H., tr. 520p. 1983. lib. bdg. 50.00 (ISBN 0-915144-75-1); pap. text ed. 29.50 (ISBN 0-915144-76-X). Hackett Pub.
Topoi: The Categorical Analysis of Logic. 2nd, rev. ed. (Studies in Logic & the Foundation of Mathematics: Vol. 98). 1984. 76.75 (ISBN 0-444-86711-2, I-499-83, North-Holland). Elsevier.
Toulmin, Stephen. Uses of Argument. 1958-1964. pap. 11.95 (ISBN 0-521-09230-2). Cambridge U Pr.
Udolf, Roy. Logic Design for Behavioral Scientists. LC 73-75622. 285p. 1973. 23.95x (ISBN 0-911012-54-0). Nelson-Hall.
Venetus, Paulus. Logica Parva: A Translation of the 1472 Edition with Introduction & Notes. Perreiah, Alan R., tr. from Latin. LC 83-2023. (Illus.). 372p. 1984. 59.95x (ISBN 0-8132-0587-5). Cath U Pr.
Venn, John. Principles of Empirical or Inductive Logic. 2nd ed. LC 77-165344. 604p. 1973. Repr. of 1907 ed. 33.50 (ISBN 0-8337-3625-6). B Franklin.
--The Principles of Inductive Logic. 2nd ed. LC 72-119162. Orig. Title: The Principles of Empirical, or Inductive Logic. 624p. 1973. 19.50 (ISBN 0-8284-0265-5). Chelsea Pub.
Vidyabhusana, Satis Chandra. History of the Medieval School of Indian Logic. 2nd ed. LC 77-913386. 1977. 12.50x (ISBN 0-89684-407-2). Orient Bk Dist.
Wald, Henri. Introduction to Dialectical Logic. (Philosophical Currents Ser: No. 14). 240p. 1975. pap. text ed. 34.75x (ISBN 90-6032-040-9). Humanities.
Wallace, William. The Logic of Hegel: Translated from the Encyclopedia of the Philosophical Sciences, with Prolegomena. 1979. Repr. of 1874 ed. lib. bdg. 100.00 (ISBN 0-8495-5718-6). Arden Lib.
Waters, Anthony. An Introduction to Deductive Argument Analysis. LC 81-40311. (Illus.). 286p. (Orig.). 1982. lib. bdg. 26.00 (ISBN 0-8191-2095-2); pap. text ed. 13.00 (ISBN 0-8191-2096-0). U Pr of Amer.
Wells, D. G. Recreations in Logic. LC 79-51882. (Illus., Orig.). 1980. pap. 1.75 (ISBN 0-486-23895-4). Dover.
Whately, Richard. Elements of Logic. LC 75-17581. 360p. 1975. lib. bdg. 50.00x (ISBN 0-8201-1157-0). Schol Facsimiles.
Windelband, Wilhelm. Theories in Logic. LC 61-15253. 1962. 2.75 (ISBN 0-8022-1899-7). Philos Lib.
Wright, Georg H. Von. Handlung,Norm und Intension: Untersuchungen Zur Deontischen Logik. Poser, Hans, ed. (De Gruyter Studienbuch). 1977. 12.80x (ISBN 3-11-004930-9). De Gruyter.
Yourgrau, Wolfgang & Breck, Allen D., eds. Physics, Logic, & History. LC 68-32135. 336p. 1970. 39.50x (ISBN 0-306-30360-4, Plenum Pr). Plenum Pub.
Ziehen, Theodor. Lehrbuch der Logik: Auf positivistischer Grundlage mit Beruecksichtigung der Geschichte der Logik. viii, 866p. 1974. Repr. of 1920 ed. 90.00x (ISBN 3-11-003305-4). De Gruyter.
Ziembinski, Zygmunt. Practical Logic: With the Appendix on Deontic Logic. Ter-Oganian, Leon, tr. LC 75-45254. 1976. lib. bdg. 43.00 (ISBN 90-277-0557-7, Pub. by Reidel Holland). Kluwer Academic.
Zierer, Ernesto. Formal Logic & Linguistics. LC 78-134547. (Janua Linguarum, Ser. Minor: No. 102). 92p. (Orig.). 1972. pap. text ed. 8.80x (ISBN 90-2792-009-5). Mouton.
Zinoviev, A. A. Logical Physics. 1983. lib. bdg. 59.00 (ISBN 90-277-0734-0, Pub. by Reidel Holland). Kluwer Academic.
Zinoviev, A. A., et al. Philosophical Problems of Many-Valued Logic. rev. ed. Kung, Guido & Comey, David, eds. Kung, Guido & Comey, David, trs. from Rus. (Synthese Library: No. 7). 155p. 1963. lib. bdg. 24.00 (ISBN 90-277-0091-5, Pub. by Reidel Holland). Kluwer Academic.

LOGIC, SYMBOLIC AND MATHEMATICAL

see also Algebra, Abstract; Algebra, Boolean; Axiomatic Set Theory; Categories (Mathematics); Constructive Mathematics; Goedel's Theorem; Logic Machines; Machine Theory; Metamathematics; Model Theory; Probabilities; Reasoning; Recursive Functions; Science–Methodology; Set Theory; Switching Theory; Threshold Logic

Abramov, L. M., et al. Fifteen Papers on Topology & Logic. LC 51-5559. (Translations Ser.: No. 2, Vol. 39). 1964. 25.00 (ISBN 0-8218-1739-6, TRANS 2-39). Am Math.
--Fourteen Papers on Logic, Algebra, Complex Variables & Topology. LC 51-5559. (Translations Ser.: No. 2, Vol. 48). 1965. 32.00 (ISBN 0-8218-1748-5, TRANS 2-48). Am Math.
Addison, J. W., et al, eds. The Theory of Models: Proceedings of the International Symposium at Berkeley, 1963. (Studies in Logic & the Foundations of Mathematics). xvi, 494p. 1965. 85.00 (ISBN 0-7204-2233-7, North-Holland). Elsevier.
Adjan, S. I., ed. Mathematical Logic, the Theory of Algorithms & the Theory of Sets: Dedicated to Academician Petr Sergeevic Novikov. LC 77-3359. (Proceedings of the Steklov Institute of Mathematics Ser.: No. 133). 1977. 66.00 (ISBN 0-8218-3033-3, STEKLO 133). Am Math.
Aiserman, Mark A., et al. Logic, Automata & Algorithms. (Mathematics in Science & Engineering Ser). (Rus). 1971. 80.50 (ISBN 0-12-046350-4). Acad Pr.

Langer, Susanne K. Introduction to Symbolic Logic. 3rd ed. 1953. pap. text ed. 6.50 (ISBN 0-486-60164-1). Dover.
Leisenring, A. C. Mathematical Logic & Hilbert's E-Symbol. 152p. 1969. 48.75x (ISBN 0-677-61790-9). Gordon.
Lerman, M. Degrees of Unsolvability: Local & Global Theory. (Perspectives in Mathematical Logic Ser.). (Illus.). 307p. 1983. 51.00 (ISBN 0-387-12155-2). Springer-Verlag.
Lerman, M., et al, eds. Logic Year 1979-1980. (Lecture Notes in Mathematics Ser.: Vol. 859). 326p. 1981. pap. 20.00 (ISBN 0-387-10708-8). Springer-Verlag.
Levy, Robert J. Introductory Logic. 110p. (Orig.). 1984. pap. text ed. 8.75 (ISBN 0-8191-4179-8). U Pr of Amer.
Lewis, Harry R. & Papadimitriou, Christos H. Elements of the Theory of Computation. (Software Ser.). (Illus.). 496p. 1981. text ed. 29.95 (ISBN 0-13-273417-6). P-H.
Lieber, Hugh G. & Lieber, Lillian R. The Education of T. C. Mits. (Illus.). pap. 5.95 1978 (ISBN 0-393-00906-8). Norton.
Lightstone, A. H. Mathematical Logic: An Introduction to Model Theory. LC 77-17838. (Mathematical Concepts & Methods in Science & Engineering Ser.: Vol. 9). (Illus.). 352p. 1978. 29.50x (ISBN 0-306-30894-0, Plenum Pr). Plenum Pub.
Lloyd, J. W. Foundations of Logic Programming. (Symbolic Computation, Artificial Intelligence Ser.). x, 124p. 1984. 17.00 (ISBN 0-387-13299-6). Springer-Verlag.
Logic, Conference, Kiel, 1974. Proceedings. Muller, G. H., et al, eds. LC 75-40481. (Lecture Notes in Mathematics: Vol. 499). 1975. pap. 31.00 (ISBN 0-387-07534-8). Springer-Verlag.
Lolli, G., et al, eds. Logic Colloquim '82: Proceedings of the Colloquium Held in Florence, 23-28, Aug. 1982. (Studies in Logic & the Foundations of Mathematics: Vol. 112). 358p. 1984. 52.00 (ISBN 0-444-86876-3). Elsevier.
MacIntyre, A. & Pacholsk, I. L. Logic Colloquium 1977. (Studies in Logic & the Foundations of Mathematics: Vol. 96). 312p. 1978. 59.75 (ISBN 0-444-85178-X, North Holland). Elsevier.
McShane, Philip. Randomness, Statistics & Emergence. LC 78-122619. 1970. 22.95x (ISBN 0-268-00436-6). U of Notre Dame Pr.
Malitz, J. Introduction to Mathematical Logic: Set Theory-Computable Functions-Model Theory. (Undergraduate Texts in Mathematics). (Illus.). 1979. 20.00 (ISBN 0-387-90346-1). Springer-Verlag.
Manin, Y. I. A Course in Mathematical Logic. Koblitz, N., tr. from Russian. LC 77-1838. (Graduate Texts in Mathematics: Vol. 53). 1977. pap. text ed. 29.80 (ISBN 0-387-90243-0). Springer-Verlag.
Manna, Z., et al. Studies in Automatic Programming Logic. (Artificial Intelligence Ser.: Vol. 4). 192p. 1977. 32.50 (ISBN 0-444-00224-3, North Holland); pap. text ed. 18.25 (ISBN 0-444-00225-1). Elsevier.
Marek, Wiktor. Elements of Logic & Foundations of Mathematics in Problems. 1982. 39.50 (ISBN 90-277-1084-8, Pub. by Reidel Holland). Kluwer Academic.
Martin-Lof, P. Intuitionistic Type Theory. (Studies in Proof Theory). 110p. 1984. pap. text ed. 15.45x (ISBN 88-7088-105-9, Pub. by Bibliopolis Italy). Humanities.
Mendelson, Elliott. Introduction to Mathematical Logic. 2nd ed. LC 78-65959. 328p. 1979. write for info. (ISBN 0-442-25307-9). Van Nos Reinhold.
Miller, Charles F., 3rd. On Group-Theoretic Decision Problems & Their Classification. (Annals of Mathematics Studies: No. 68). 1971. 17.50x (ISBN 0-691-08091-7). Princeton U Pr.
Monk, J. D. Mathematical Logic. LC 75-42416. (Graduate Texts in Mathematics Ser.: Vol. 37). 1976. 30.95 (ISBN 0-387-90170-1). Springer-Verlag.
Mostowski, A. Foundational Studies: Selected Works, Vols. 1 & 2. LC 77-18025. (Studies in Logic: Vol. 93). 1242p. 1980. Set. 138.50 (ISBN 0-444-85104-6, North Holland). Elsevier.
Mueller, G. H., et al, eds. Logic Symposia, Hakone, 1979, 1980: Proceedings. (Lecture Notes in Mathematics Ser.: Vol. 891). 394p. 1981. pap. 24.00 (ISBN 0-387-11161-1). Springer-Verlag.
Oglesby, Francis C. Examination of a Decision Procedure. LC 52-42839. (Memoirs: No. 44). 148p. 1971. pap. 11.00 (ISBN 0-8218-1244-0, MEMO-44). Am Math.
Pillay, Anand. An Introduction to Stability Theory. (Oxford Logic Guides Ser.). 1983. 29.95x (ISBN 0-19-853186-9). Oxford U Pr.
Pinkava. Logic for System Modelling. (Information Technology Ser.). 1984. 25.00 (ISBN 0-9901003-2-4, Pub. by Abacus England). Heyden.
Polya, Gyorgy. Mathematics & Plausible Reasoning, 2 vols. Incl. Vol. 1. Induction & Analogy in Mathematics. 1954. 27.50 (ISBN 0-691-08005-4); Vol. 2. Patterns of Plausible Inference. rev. ed. 1969. 27.50 (ISBN 0-691-08006-2). Set. 45.00 (ISBN 0-685-23091-0). Princeton U Pr.
Ponasse, Daniel. Mathematical Logic. LC 72-136738. (Notes on Mathematics & Its Applications Ser.). Orig. Title: Logique Mathematique. 136p. 1973. 32.50x (ISBN 0-677-30390-4). Gordon.
Popper, Karl R. The Subtle Connection Between the Theory of Experience & the Logic of Science, 2 vols. (Illus.). 187p. 1985. Set. 167.50 (ISBN 0-89901-227-2). Found Class Reprints.
Pospesel, Howard. Introduction to Logic: Predicate Logic. (Illus.). 224p. 1976. text ed. 18.95 (ISBN 0-13-486225-2). P-H.
Prior, Arthur N. Past, Present & Future. 1967. 39.95x (ISBN 0-19-824311-1). Oxford U Pr.
Quine, Willard V. Mathematical Logic. rev ed. LC 51-7541. 1951. 20.00x (ISBN 0-674-55450-7); pap. 8.95x (ISBN 0-674-55451-5). Harvard U Pr.
--Set Theory & Its Logic. rev. ed. LC 68-14271. 1969. 8.95 (ISBN 0-674-80207-1, Belknap Pr). Harvard U Pr.
--Word & Object. 1960. pap. 8.95 (ISBN 0-262-67001-1). MIT Pr.
Rescher, N. & Urquhart, A. J. Temporal Logic. LC 74-141565. (Library of Exact Philosophy: Vol. 3). (Illus.). 1971. 39.00 (ISBN 0-387-80995-3). Springer-Verlag.
Rescher, Nicholas. Studies in the History of Arabic Logic. LC 63-17521. pap. 27.00 (ISBN 0-317-08256-6, 2010499). Bks Demand UMI.
Richter, M. M., et al, eds. Computation & Proof Theory, Pt. 2. (Lecture Notes in Mathematics Ser.: Vol. 1104). viii, 475p. 1984. pap. 25.00 (ISBN 0-387-13901-X). Springer-Verlag.
Rine, D. C., ed. Computer Science & Multiple Valued Logic: Theory & Applications. rev. ed. 642p. 1984. 65.00 (ISBN 0-444-86882-8, North Holland). Elsevier.
Roethel, Louis & Weinstein, Abraham. Logic, Sets, & Numbers: A Positive Approach to Math. 2nd ed. 1976. write for info. (ISBN 0-534-00491-1). Wadsworth Pub.
Rood, Harold J. Logic & Structured Design for Computer Programmers. 1985. pap. text ed. write for info. (ISBN 0-87150-869-9, 37L8800, Prindle). PWS Pubs.
Rosser, John B. Logic for Mathematicians. 2nd ed. LC 77-7663. 1978. text ed. 19.95 (ISBN 0-8284-0294-9). Chelsea Pub.
Roth, Charles H., Jr. Fundamentals of Logic Design. 3rd ed. (Illus.). 650p. 1985. text ed. 30.95 (ISBN 0-314-85292-1). West Pub.
Runnggaldier, Edmund. Zeichen und Bezeichnetes: Sprachphilosophische Untersuchungen zum Problem der Referenz. (Grundlagen der Kommunikation - Bibliothekausgabe Ser.). (Ger.). xii, 363p. 1985. 43.20x (ISBN 3-11-010107-6). De Gruyter.
Salwicki, A. Logics of Programs & Their Applications: Proceedings 1980, Poznan, Poland. (Lecture Notes in Computer Science: Vol. 148). 324p. 1983. pap. 16.50 (ISBN 0-387-11981-7). Springer-Verlag.
Schagrin, M. & Rapaport, W. Logic: A Computer Approach. 368p. 1985. 19.95 (ISBN 0-07-055131-6). McGraw.
Schroeder, Ernst. Algebra der Logik, 5 vols. in 3. 2nd ed. LC 63-11315. (Ger.). 2192p. 1980. Set. 85.00 (ISBN 0-8284-0171-3). Chelsea Pub.
Shapiro, S., ed. Intensional Mathematics. (Studies in Logic & the Foundations of Mathematics: Vol. 113). 230p. 1985. 37.00 (ISBN 0-444-87632-4, North-Holland). Elsevier.
Shearman, A. T. The Development of Symbolic Logic. (Reprints in Philosophy Ser.). Repr. of 1906 ed. lib. bdg. 34.50x (ISBN 0-697-00048-6). Irvington.
Slisenko, A. O., ed. Studies in Constructive Mathematics & Mathematical Logic. LC 69-12507. (Seminars in Mathematics Ser.: Vol. 4, Pt. 1). pap. 24.00 (ISBN 0-317-08580-8, 2020696). Bks Demand UMI.
--Studies in Constructive Mathematics & Mathematical Logic, Part 1. LC 69-12507. (Seminars in Mathematics Ser.: Vol. 4). 88p. 1969. 25.00x (ISBN 0-306-18804-X, Consultants). Plenum Pub.
Smith, J. E., ed. Integrated Injection Logic. LC 80-18841. 1980. 44.65 (ISBN 0-87942-137-1, PC1305). Inst Electrical.
Steen, S. W. Mathematical Logic with Special Reference to the Natural Numbers. 1971. 95.00 (ISBN 0-521-08053-3). Cambridge U Pr.
Steklov Institute of Mathematics, Academy of Sciences, U S S R. Calculi of Symbolic Logic: Proceedings I. Orevkov, V. P., ed. (Proceedings of the Steklov Institute of Mathematics: No. 98). 1971. 46.00 (ISBN 0-8218-1898-8, STEKLO-98). Am Math.
Steklov Institute of Mathematics, Academy of Sciences, USSR, No. 121. Logical & Logico-Mathematical Calculi, 2: Proceedings. Orevkov, V. P., ed. LC 74-8854. 1974. text ed. 47.00 (ISBN 0-8218-3021-X, STEKLO-121). Am Math.
Stenius, Erik. Wittgenstein's Tractatus: A Critical Exposition of Its Main Lines on Thought. LC 81-13222. xi, 241p. 1982. Repr. of 1964 ed. lib. bdg. 25.00x (ISBN 0-313-23246-6, STWI). Greenwood.
Stoll, Robert R. Sets, Logic, & Axiomatic Theories. 2nd ed. LC 74-8932. pap. 61.00 (ISBN 0-317-08628-6, 2055554). Bks Demand UMI.
Stolyar, A. A. Introduction to Elementary Mathematical Logic. (Mathematics Ser.). 209p. 1984. pap. 5.00 (ISBN 0-486-64561-4). Dover.
Symposium on Logic, Boston, 1972-73. Logic Colloquium. Parikh, R., ed. (Lecture Notes in Mathematics Ser.: Vol. 453). iv, 251p. (Orig.). 1975. pap. 17.00 (ISBN 0-387-07155-5). Springer-Verlag.
Takeuti, Gaisi. Two Applications of Logic to Mathematics. (Publications of the Mathematical Society of Japan Ser.: No. 13). 1978. 23.50x (ISBN 0-691-08212-X). Princeton U Pr.
Tapscott, Bangs L. Elementary Applied Symbolic Logic. (Illus.). 512p. 1976. text ed. 23.95 (ISBN 0-13-252940-8). P-H.
Tennant, N. Natural Logic. 196p. 1979. 18.00x (ISBN 0-85224-347-2, Pub. by Edinburgh U Pr Scotland). Columbia U Pr.
Thomas, James A. Symbolic Logic. (Philosophy Ser.). 1977. text ed. 17.50 (ISBN 0-675-08558-6). Merrill.
Thomas, R., ed. Kinetic Logic. (Lecture Notes in Biomathematics: Vol. 29). 507p. 1979. pap. 32.00 (ISBN 0-387-09556-X). Springer-Verlag.
Thomason, Richmond H. Symbolic Logic: An Introduction. (Illus.). 1970. text ed. write for info. (ISBN 0-02-420210-X). Macmillan.
Troelstra, A. S. Principles of Intuitionism. LC 74-88182. (Lecture Notes in Mathematics: Vol. 95). 1969. pap. 10.70 (ISBN 0-387-04614-3). Springer-Verlag.
Van Heijenoort, Jean. Frege & Godel: Two Fundamental Texts in Mathematical Logic. abr. ed. LC 71-116736. 1970. 10.00x (ISBN 0-674-31844-7); pap. 7.95x (ISBN 0-674-31845-5). Harvard U Pr.
Van Heijenoort, Jean, ed. From Frege to Godel: A Source Book in Mathematical Logic, 1879-1931. LC 67-10905. (Source Books in the History of the Sciences Ser). 1967. 35.00x (ISBN 0-674-32450-1); pap. 15.00x (ISBN 0-674-32449-8). Harvard U Pr.
Venn, John. Symbolic Logic. LC 70-165345. (Research & Source Works Ser.: No. 778). 1971. Repr. of 1894 ed. lib. bdg. 32.00 (ISBN 0-8337-3626-4). B Franklin.
--Symbolic Logic. 2nd ed. LC 79-119161. 1971. text ed. 19.50 (ISBN 0-8284-0251-5). Chelsea Pub.
Von Wright, Georg H. The Logical Problem of Induction. 2nd ed. LC 78-24370. 1979. Repr. of 1957 ed. lib. bdg. 24.75x (ISBN 0-313-20830-1, WRLP). Greenwood.
Wallace-Garden, R. Modern Logic & Quantum Mechanics. 178p. 1983. 35.00 (ISBN 0-9960027-3-1, Pub. by A. Hilger England). Heyden.
Wang, Hao. From Mathematics to Philosophy. (International Library of Philosophy & Scientific Method). 420p. 1973. text ed. 29.75x (ISBN 0-391-00335-6). Humanities.
--Logic, Computers & Sets. LC 70-113155. Orig. Title: Survey of Mathematical Logic. 1970. Repr. of 1962 ed. text ed. 24.95 (ISBN 0-8284-0245-0). Chelsea Pub.
--Popular Lectures on Mathematical Logic. 286p. 1981. text ed. 34.95 (ISBN 0-442-23109-1). Van Nos Reinhold.
Warring, R. H. Logic Made Easy. (Illus.). 112p. 1985. pap. 7.95 (ISBN 0-8306-1853-8, 1853). Tab Bks.
Whitehead, Alfred N. & Russell, Bertrand. Principia Mathematica, 3 Vols. Set. 350.00 (ISBN 0-521-06791-X). Cambridge U Pr.
--Principia Mathematica to Fifty-Six. 2nd ed. 1925-27. pap. 29.95 (ISBN 0-521-09187-X). Cambridge U Pr.
Wiatrowski, Claude A. & House, Charles H. Logic Circuits & Microcomputer Systems. Cerra, Frank J., ed. (McGraw-Hill Series in Electrical Engineering: Computer Engineering & Switching Theory-Electronics & Electronic Circuits). (Illus.). 512p. 1980. text ed. 42.00 (ISBN 0-07-070090-7). McGraw.
Wittgenstein, Ludwig. Philosophical Grammar. Kenny, A. J., tr. 1974. 38.50x (ISBN 0-520-02664-0); pap. 9.95 (ISBN 0-520-03725-1). U of Cal Pr.
--Tractatus Logico-Philosophicus: German-English Text. (Inter. Library of Philosophy & Scientific Method). 1922. pap. text ed. 6.25x (ISBN 0-7100-7923-0). Humanities.
Woodger, Joseph H. Technique of Theory Construction. (Foundations of the Unity of Science Ser: Vol. 2, No. 5). 1939. pap. 1.95x (ISBN 0-226-57595-0, P414, Phoen). U of Chicago Pr.
Zissos, D. Problems & Solutions in Logic Design. 2nd ed. (Illus.). 1979. 37.50x (ISBN 0-19-859362-7). Oxford U Pr.

LOGIC CIRCUITS

Almaini, A. E. Electronic Logic Systems. (Illus.). 448p. 1986. text ed. 36.95 (ISBN 0-13-251752-3). P-H.
Mano, M. Digital Logic & Computer Design. 1979. 39.95 (ISBN 0-13-214510-3). P-H.
Parr, E. A. The Logic Designer's Guidebook. 480p. 42.50 (ISBN 0-07-048492-9). McGraw.

LOGIC MACHINES

see also Artificial Intelligence

Beth, E. W. & Piaget, J. Mathematical Epistemology & Psychology. 348p. 1966. 73.00 (ISBN 0-677-01290-X). Gordon.
Blakeslee, Thomas R. Digital Design with Standard MSI & LSI: Design Techniques for the Microcomputer Age. 2nd ed. LC 78-24201. 384p. 1979. 28.95 (ISBN 0-471-05222-1, Pub. by Wiley-Interscience). Wiley.
Boyce, Jefferson. Digital Logic: Operation & Analysis. 2nd ed. (Illus.). 464p. 1982. 32.95 (ISBN 0-13-214619-3). P-H.
Floyd, Thomas L. Digital Fundamentals. 2nd ed. Orig. Title: Digital Logic Fundamentals. 624p. 1982. text ed. 29.95 (ISBN 0-675-09876-9). Additional Supplements May Be Obtained From Publisher. Merrill.
Gardner, Martin. Logic Machines & Diagrams. 2nd ed. LC 82-11157. xiv, 162p. 1983. lib. bdg. 16.00x (ISBN 0-226-28243-0); pap. 5.95 (ISBN 0-226-28244-9). U of Chicago Pr.
Hope, Gordon S. Integrated Devices in Digital Circuit Design. LC 80-17172. 368p. 1981. 43.95x (ISBN 0-471-07920-0, Pub. by Wiley-Interscience). Wiley.
Krutz, Ronald L. Microprocessors & Logic Design. LC 79-17874. 467p. 1980. text ed. 44.95x (ISBN 0-471-02083-4). Wiley.
Mandl, Matthew. Introduction to Digital Logic Techniques & Systems. LC 82-13337. (Illus.). 201p. 1983. 31.95 (ISBN 0-8359-3175-7). Reston.
Mano, M. Digital Logic & Computer Design. 1979. 39.95 (ISBN 0-13-214510-3). P-H.
Michie, Donald. Machine Intelligence & Related Topics. 328p. 1982. 57.75 (ISBN 0-677-05560-9). Gordon.
Middleton, Robert G. Digital Logic Circuits: Tests & Analysis. LC 81-86555. 224p. 1983. pap. 16.95 (ISBN 0-672-21799-6). Sams.
Myers, Glenford J. Digital System Design with LSI Bit-Slice Logic. 338p. 1980. 44.95x (ISBN 0-471-05376-7, Pub. by Wiley-Interscience). Wiley.
Oberman, R. M. Digital Circuits for Binary Arithmetic. 340p. 1979. 59.95x (ISBN 0-470-26373-3). Halsted Pr.
Roth, J. Paul. Computer Logic, Testing & Verification. LC 79-27230. (Digital System Design Ser.). (Illus.). 1980. text ed. 37.95 (ISBN 0-914894-62-5). Computer Sci.
Scott, John. Basic Computer Logic. LC 80-5074. (The Lexington Books Series in Computer Science). 256p. 1981. 26.50x (ISBN 0-669-03706-0). Lexington Bks.
Shelly, Gary B. & Cashman, Thomas J. Introduction to Flowcharting & Computer Programming Logic. LC 72-95674. (Illus.). 251p. 1972. pap. text ed. 21.95 (ISBN 0-88236-345-X). Anaheim Pub Co.
Shostak, R. E., ed. Seventh International Conference on Automated Deduction: Proceedings, Napa, California, May 14-16, 1984. (Lecture Notes in Computer Science Ser.: Vol. 170). iv, 508p. 1984. pap. 25.50 (ISBN 0-387-96022-8). Springer-Verlag.
Turner, Raymond. Non-Standard Logic. (Artificial Intelligence Ser.). 160p. 1984. 29.95 (ISBN 0-470-20123-1). Wiley.
Zissos, D. Problems & Solutions in Logic Design. 2nd ed. (Illus.). 1979. 37.50x (ISBN 0-19-859362-7). Oxford U Pr.

LOGIC OF MATHEMATICS

see Mathematics–Philosophy

LOGIC STRUCTURE TABLES

see Decision Logic Tables

LOGO (COMPUTER PROGRAM LANGUAGE)

Abelson, Hal. Apple LOGO. (Illus.). 256p. 1982. pap. 18.95 (ISBN 0-07-000425-0, BYTE Bks). McGraw.
--LOGO for the Apple II. 1982. 18.95 (ISBN 0-07-000426-9, BYTE Bks). McGraw.
--TI LOGO. (Illus.). 1984. pap. 17.95 (ISBN 0-07-038459-2, BYTE Bks). McGraw.
Adams, Tony, et al. Learning LOGO on the TRS-80 Color Computer. (Illus.). 174p. 1984. pap. 12.95 (ISBN 0-13-527961-5). P-H.
Allan, Boris. Pocket Guide: LOGO. (Pitman Programming Pocket Guides Ser.). 64p. (Orig.). 1984. pap. 6.95 (ISBN 0-273-02109-5). Pitman Pub MA.

Kwatinetz, Michael, et al. Everything You Need to Know to Do Your Taxes with Lotus 1-2-3. 224p. 1985. pap. 14.95 (ISBN 0-8069-7928-3). Sterling.

Laric, Michael V. & Stiff, M. Ronald. Lotus 1-2-3 for Marketing & Sales. 256p. 1984. pap. 24.95; incl. disk 39.95 (ISBN 0-13-540956-X). P-H.

Latif, Rebecca C. Using Lotus 1-2-3: A Guide for Non-Programmers. 1985. pap. text ed. 19.95 (ISBN 0-8359-8165-7). Reston.

McMullen, John & McMullen, Barbara. One-Two-Three User's Guide for the IBM PC. cancelled 18.95 (ISBN 0-89303-740-0). Brady Comm.

Maffei, Nick. Money Management Worksheets for 1-2-3 Symphony. (Illus.). 192p. (Orig.). 1985. 21.95 (ISBN 0-8306-0968-7, 1968); pap. 14.95 (ISBN 0-8306-1968-2). TAB Bks.

Molloy, James F. & Curtin, Dennis P. Business Problem Solving: A 1-2-3 Business User's Guide. (Illus.). 176p. 1984. pap. 19.50 (ISBN 0-930764-85-4); software on floppy disk o.p. 29.95. Van Nos Reinhold.

Nitz, Lawrence H. Business Analysis & Graphics with Lotus 1-2-3. (Illus.). 176p. 1985. pap. 17.95 (ISBN 0-13-091604-8). P-H.

Ochi, Kaz & Hughes, Pat. Accounting with Lotus 1-2-3. 200p. 1983. pap. write for info (ISBN 0-534-03038-6). Wadsworth Pub.

O'Keeffe, Linda. Integrated Spreadsheet Software: Lotus 1-2-3 & Context MBA. Seybold, Patricia B., ed. (Seybold Series on Professional Computing). (Illus.). 183p. 1984. pap. 15.96 (ISBN 0-07-056321-7, BYTE Bks). McGraw.

Osgood, William & Curtin, Dennis. Preparing Your Business Plan with Lotus 1-2-3. (Illus.). 176p. 1985. pap. 21.95 (ISBN 0-13-698424-X); incl. disk 38.95 (ISBN 0-13-698432-0). P-H.

Osgood, William R. & Molloy, James F., Jr. Business Decision Making for Higher Profits: A 1-2-3 Business User's Guide. (Illus.). 192p. 1984. pap. 18.95 (ISBN 0-930764-89-7); software on floppy disk 32.50 (ISBN 0-88703-001-7). Van Nos Reinhold.

Pirisino, Jim, ed. Minute Manual for Lotus 1-2-3. (Orig.). Date not set. pap. price not set (ISBN 0-913131-05-9). Minuteware.

Psulkowski, Raymond. Lotus: The Elan, Cortina, & Europa. (Illus.). 128p. 1985. 19.95 (ISBN 0-8306-2106-7, 2106). TAB Bks.

Ridington, Richard W., Jr. & Williams, Mark. The Hidden Power of Lotus 1-2-3: Using Macros. 288p. 1985. pap. 18.95 (ISBN 0-89303-517-3); diskette 30.00 (ISBN 0-89303-519-X); book & diskette 49.95 (ISBN 0-89303-518-1). Brady Comm.

Savarese, Edward & Sondak, Mornam. Using Lotus 1-2-3. 1984. cancelled (ISBN 0-89303-920-9). Brady Comm.

Schware, Robert & Trembour, Alice. All about 1-2-3. (Illus.). 160p. 1983. pap. 9.95 (ISBN 0-88056-129-7). Dilithium Pr.

Shaffer, Dan. One-Two-Three Revealed. pap. 16.95 (ISBN 0-317-06055-4). P-H.

--One-Two-Three Revealed. 1984. 21.95 (ISBN 0-8359-5238-X); pap. 16.95 (ISBN 0-8359-5236-3). Reston.

Simpson, Alan. The Best Book of Lotus 1-2-3. LC 83-51529. 272p. 1984. pap. 12.95 (ISBN 0-672-22307-4, 22307). Sams.

Startz, Richard. Working with One-Two-Three on the IBM PC & Compatibles. 132p. 1984. pap. text ed. 18.70 scp (ISBN 0-06-046426-7, HarpC). Har-Row.

Sueltz, Daniel & Kinder, Bruce. Unleashing 1-2-3. 14.95 (ISBN 0-13-937236-9). P-H.

Urschel, William. Ready to Run Accounting with Lotus 1-2-3 & Symphony. 225p. 1984. incl. disk 44.95 (ISBN 0-88284-330-3). Alfred Pub.

Weber Systems Inc. Staff. Lotus 1-2-3 Business Models. (Applications Software Models Ser.). 300p. pap. cancelled. Weber Systems.

Weber Systems Staff. Lotus 1-2-3 User's Handbook. (User's Handbook Ser.). 304p. (Orig.). 1985. pap. 14.95 (ISBN 0-345-32939-2). Ballantine.

Weyandt, Palmer. Your Income Tax in 1-2-3. Berliner, Thomas H., ed. 1984. pap. 29.95 (ISBN 0-915381-68-0). WordWare Pub.

William, Robert E. Financial Calculations for Lotus 1-2-3. 175p. 14.95 (ISBN 0-943518-10-5). Mgmt Info Inc.

Williams, Andrew T. Lotus 1-2-3 from A to Z with Bridges to Symphony. 224p. 1984. pap. 16.95 (ISBN 0-471-87919-3, Pub by Wiley Pr). Wiley.

Williams, Robert. Power of Financial Calculations for Lotus 1-2-3. 150p. 1984. pap. 14.95 (ISBN 0-13-687690-0); incl. disk 28.95 (ISBN 0-13-687732-X). P-H.

--Power of Lotus 1-2-3. (Power of Ser.). 150p. 1984. pap. 14.95 (ISBN 0-13-687525-4); incl. disk 28.95 (ISBN 0-13-687757-5). P-H.

Williams, Robert E. The Power of: Lotus 1-2-3. (Illus.). 178p. 1983. pap. 14.95 (ISBN 0-943518-08-3); pap. 28.95, incl. diskette. Mgmt Info Inc.

Willmott, Thomas. Software Solutions for the IBM PC: A Practical Guide to dBASE, Lotus 1-2-3, VisiCalc, WordStar & More. 230p. 1983. 21.95 (ISBN 0-13-822395-5); pap. 14.95 (ISBN 0-13-822387-4). P-H.

LOUD-SPEAKERS

Colloms, M. High Performance Loudspeakers. 3rd ed. 1985. 29.95 (ISBN 0-470-20107-X). Halsted Pr.

Colloms, Martin. High Performance Loudspeakers. 2nd ed. LC 79-21318. 245p. 1979. 29.95x (ISBN 0-470-26875-1). Halsted Pr.

Gayford, M. L. Electroacoustics. 289p. 1971. 37.75 (ISBN 0-444-19649-8). Elsevier.

LOUSE

see Lice

LOW TEMPERATURE BIOLOGY

see Cryobiology

LOW TEMPERATURE ENGINEERING

see also Gases–Liquefaction; Materials at Low Temperatures; Refrigeration and Refrigerating Machinery

Advances in Cryogenic Engineering, Vol. 24. (Illus.). 598p. 1978. 75.00x (ISBN 0-306-38024-2, Plenum Pr). Plenum Pub.

Arkharov, A. Theory & Design of Cryogenic Systems. 430p. 1981. 11.60 (ISBN 0-8285-1974-9, Pub. by Mir Pubs USSR). Imported Pubns.

Bailey, C. A. Advanced Cryogenics. LC 77-119158. (International Cryogenics Monographs Ser.). 527p. 1971. 65.00x (ISBN 0-306-30458-9, Plenum Pr). Plenum Pub.

Boenig, Herman V., ed. Advances in Low-Temperature Plasma Chemistry, Technology, Applications, Vol. 1. LC 84-51635. 377p. 1984. 55.00 (ISBN 0-87762-373-2). Technomic.

Booth, Sterling & Vance, Robert W., eds. Applications of Cryogenic Technology, Vol. 8. LC 68-57815. (Cryogenic Society of America Applications of Cryogenic Technology Ser.). (Illus.). 1976. text ed. 30.00x (ISBN 0-87936-010-0). Scholium Intl.

Breurr, D. F., ed. Progress in Low Temperature Physics, Vol. 9. Date not set. price not set (North-Holland). Elsevier.

Chung, J. S. & Lunardini, V. J., eds. Offshore Mechanics & Arctic Engineering Symposium, 2nd International: Proceedings. 812p. 1983. pap. text ed. 100.00 (ISBN 0-317-02642-9, I00156). ASME.

Clark, A. F. & Reed, R. P., eds. Advances in Cryogenic Engineering, Vol. 26. LC 57-35598. 717p. 1981. 89.50x (ISBN 0-306-40531-8, Plenum Pr). Plenum Pub.

Conference of the Cryogenic Society of America, 5th, 1972. Application of Cryogenic Technology: Proceedings, Vol. 5. Carr, Robert H., ed. LC 68-57815. 352p. 1973. text ed. 30.00x (ISBN 0-87936-001-1). Scholium Intl.

Conference of the Cryogenic Society of America, 1973. Applications of Cryogenic Technology: Proceedings, Vol. 6. Vance, Robert H. & Booth, Sterling H., eds. LC 68-57815. (Illus.). 290p. 1974. text ed. 30.00x (ISBN 0-87936-003-8). Scholium Intl.

Cryogenic Society of America, LNG Terminals & Safety Symposium. Applications of Cryogenic Technology: Proceedings, Vol. 9. Petsinger, Robert E. & Vance, Robert W., eds. LC 68-57815. 1979. 45.00x (ISBN 0-87936-014-3). Scholium Intl.

Douzou, P. Cryobiochemistry: An Introduction. 1977. 49.50 (ISBN 0-12-221050-6). Acad Pr.

Fast, R. W., ed. Advances in Cryogenic Engineering, Vol. 27. LC 57-35598. 1252p. 1982. 105.00x (ISBN 0-306-41103-2, Plenum Pr). Plenum Pub.

Frechette, V. D., et al, eds. Quality Assurance in Ceramic Industries. LC 79-14166. 275p. 1979. 49.50 (ISBN 0-306-40183-5, Plenum Pr). Plenum Pub.

Frederking, T. H., et al, eds. Cryogenic Processes & Equipment, Nineteen Eighty-Two. LC 83-11414. (AIChE Symposium: Vol. 79). 143p. 1983. pap. 40.00 (ISBN 0-8169-0249-6); pap. 20.00 members (ISBN 0-317-03720-X). Am Inst Chem Eng.

Gottzman, C. F. Cryogenic Processes & Equipment in Energy Systems. 200p. 1980. 40.00 (ISBN 0-686-69847-9, H00164). ASME.

Hasselman, D. P. & Heller, R. A., eds. Thermal Stresses in Severe Environments. LC 80-17767. 750p. 1980. 95.00x (ISBN 0-306-40544-X, Plenum Pr). Plenum Pub.

Hill, A. W., et al. Handbook on BS 5337, 1976: Incorporating Amendment No. 1 & No. 2. 2nd ed. (Viewpoint Publication Ser.). (Illus.). 64p. 1983. text ed. 30.00x (ISBN 0-86310-009-0, Pub. by C&CA London). Scholium Intl.

International Conference, Newcastle upon Tyne 1st, 1981. Cryogenic Concrete: Proceedings. Concrete Society, ed. (Illus.). 352p. 1983. text ed. 58.00 (ISBN 0-86095-705-5). Longman.

International Conference on Low Temperature Physics. Proceedings of the VIIth International Conference on Low Temperature Physics, University of Toronto, Canada, 29th August-3rd September, 1960. Graham, G. M. & Hallett, Hollis A., eds. pap. 160.00 (ISBN 0-317-27638-7, 2014223). Bks Demand UMI.

International Offshore Mechanics & Arctic Engineering Symposium, 3rd: Proceedings. 1983. pap. text ed. write for info (IX0161). ASME.

Reed, R. P. & Clark, A. F., eds. Advances in Cryogenic Engineering, Vol. 28. LC 57-35598. 943p. 1982. 95.00x (ISBN 0-306-41104-0, Plenum Pr). Plenum Pub.

Reed, R. P. & Horiuchi, T., eds. Austenitic Steels at Low Temperature. (Cryogenic Materials Ser.). 400p. 1983. 62.50x (ISBN 0-306-41371-X, Plenum Pr). Plenum Pub.

Timmerhaus, K. D. Advances in Cryogenic Engineering, Vol. 19. (Illus.). 524p. 1974. 65.00x (ISBN 0-306-38019-6, Plenum Pr). Plenum Pub.

Timmerhaus, K. D., ed. Advances in Cryogenic Engineering, Vol. 20. LC 57-35598. (Illus.). 550p. 1975. 65.00x (Plenum Pr). Plenum Pub.

--Advances in Cryogenic Engineering, Vol. 23. LC 57-35598. 765p. 1978. 75.00x (ISBN 0-306-38023-4, Plenum Pr). Plenum Pub.

Timmerhaus, K. D. & Snyder, H. A., eds. Advances in Cryogenic Engineering, Vol. 25. LC 57-35598. (Illus.). 868p. 1980. 85.00x (ISBN 0-306-40504-0, Plenum Pr). Plenum Pub.

Vance, Robert W. & Weinstock, Harold, eds. Applications of Cryogenic Technology. LC 68-57815. (Illus.). 1969. 16.95 (ISBN 0-87252-011-0). Tinnon-Brown.

Walker, Graham. Cryocoolers, Part 1: Fundamentals. (The International Cryogenics Monograph). 355p. 1983. 55.50x (ISBN 0-306-40715-9, Plenum Press). Plenum Pub.

Zabetakis, M. G. Safety with Cryogenic Fluids. LC 66-12628. (International Cryogenics Monographs Ser.). 156p. 1967. 32.50x (ISBN 0-306-30285-3, Plenum Pr). Plenum Pub.

LOW TEMPERATURE MATERIALS

see Materials at Low Temperatures

LOW TEMPERATURE METALS

see Metals at Low Temperatures

LOW TEMPERATURE RESEARCH

see also Cold; Gases–Liquefaction; Thermomagnetism

Ashwood, M. J. & Farrant, Smith J. Low Temperature Preservation in Medicine & Biology. 336p. 1980. text ed. 42.00 (ISBN 0-8391-1492-3). Univ Park.

Frederking, T. H., et al, eds. Cryogenic Processes & Equipment, Nineteen Eighty-Two. LC 83-11414. (AIChE Symposium: Vol. 79). 143p. 1983. pap. 40.00 (ISBN 0-8169-0249-6); pap. 20.00 members (ISBN 0-317-03720-X). Am Inst Chem Eng.

Garrett, Charles G. Magnetic Cooling. LC 53-10474. (Harvard Monographs in Applied Science: No. 4). pap. 31.00 (ISBN 0-317-09162-X, 2001562). Bks Demand UMI.

Louasmaa, O. V. Experimental Principles & Methods Below 1k. 1974. 66.00 (ISBN 0-12-455950-6). Acad Pr.

Zabetakis, Michael G. Safety with Cryogenic Fluids. LC 66-12628. (International Cryogenics Monograph Ser.). pap. 42.80 (ISBN 0-317-27805-3, 2055952). Bks Demand UMI.

LOW TEMPERATURES

see also Cold; Cryobiology; Low Temperature Engineering; Low Temperature Research; Materials at Low Temperatures; Quantum Liquids; Solid Helium; Superfluidity

Bailey, C. A. Advanced Cryogenics. LC 77-119158. (International Cryogenics Monographs Ser.). 527p. 1971. 65.00x (ISBN 0-306-30458-9, Plenum Pr). Plenum Pub.

Brewer, D. F., ed. Progress in Low Temperature Physics, 2 vols, Vol. 7. 1979. Set. o.p 114.75 (ISBN 0-444-85210-7, North Holland); Vol. 7b. 85.00 (ISBN 0-444-85209-3). Elsevier.

Croft, A. J. Cryogenic Laboratory Equipment. LC 65-11337. (International Cryogenics Monographs Ser.). 182p. 1969. 39.50x (ISBN 0-306-30253-5, Plenum Pr). Plenum Pub.

Frederking, T. H., et al, eds. Cryogenic Processes & Equipment, Nineteen Eighty-Two. LC 83-11414. (AIChE Symposium: Vol. 79). 143p. 1983. pap. 40.00 (ISBN 0-8169-0249-6); pap. 20.00 members (ISBN 0-317-03720-X). Am Inst Chem Eng.

Gopal, Erode S. Specific Heats at Low Temperatures. LC 65-11339. (International Cyrogenics Monographs). 240p. 1966. 45.00x (ISBN 0-306-30222-5, Plenum Pr). Plenum Pub.

International Conference on Low Temperature Physics (9th: 1964: Columbus, Ohio) Low Temperature Physics: LT9, 2 Pts. Daunt, J. G. & Edwards, D. O., eds. LC 65-14085. Pt. A. pap. 160.00 (ISBN 0-317-11126-4, 2019403); Pt. B. pap. 160.00 (ISBN 0-317-11127-2). Bks Demand UMI.

Louasmaa, O. V. Experimental Principles & Methods Below 1k. 1974. 66.00 (ISBN 0-12-455950-6). Acad Pr.

Timmerhaus, K. D., et al, eds. Low Temperature Physics - LT-13, 4 vols. Incl. Vol. 1. Quantum Fluids. 669p. 95.00x (ISBN 0-306-35121-8); Vol. 2. Quantum Crystals & Magnetism. 668p. 95.00x (ISBN 0-306-35122-6); Vol. 3. Superconductivity. 834p. 105.00x (ISBN 0-306-35123-4); Vol. 4. Electronic Properties, Instrumentation, & Measurement. 684p. 95.00x (ISBN 0-306-35124-2). LC 73-81092. (Illus.). 1974 (Plenum Pr). Plenum Pub.

Turner, F. H. Concrete & Cryogenics. (Viewpoint Publication Ser.). (Illus.). 125p. 1979. pap. text ed. 35.00x (ISBN 0-7210-1124-1, Pub by C&CA London). Scholium Intl.

White, Guy K. Experimental Techniques in Low-Temperature Physics. 3rd ed. (Monographs on the Physics & Chemistry of Materials). (Illus.). 1979. 59.00x (ISBN 0-19-851359-3). Oxford U Pr.

Zemansky, Mark W. Temperatures Very Low & Very High. 144p. 1981. pap. 4.50 (ISBN 0-486-24072-X). Dover.

LOWER SILURIAN PERIOD

see Geology, Stratigraphic–Ordovician

LPG

see Liquefied Petroleum Gas

LSI II (COMPUTER)

Desautels, Edouard J. Assembly Language Programming for PDP-11 & LSI-11 Computers: An Introduction to Computer Organization. 574p. 1982. pap. 23.95 (ISBN 0-697-08164-8); solutions manual avail. (ISBN 0-697-08165-6). Wm C Brown.

LUBRICATION AND LUBRICANTS

see also Bearings (Machinery); Fluid Film Bearings; Metal-Working Lubricants; Oils and Fats; Petroleum Products; also names of lubricants

Additives for Fuels & Lubricants: An Important & Growing Market. 1983. 1250.00 (ISBN 0-89336-239-5, C-027). BCC.

ASTM & Other Specifications for Petroleum Products & Lubricants, 1984. 4th ed. 350p. 1984. 40.00 (ISBN 0-8031-0835-4, 03-402384-12). ASTM.

Billett, M. G. A Handbook of Industrial Lubrication. 1979. 33.00 (ISBN 0-08-024232-4). Pergamon.

Boner, C. J. Modern Lubricating Greases. LC 75-18294. (Illus.). 250p. 1976. ref. ed. 40.00x (ISBN 0-87936-002-X). Scholium Intl.

Booser, E. R., ed. CRC Handbook of Lubrication: Theory & Practice of Tribology, Vol. II. 704p. 1984. 115.00 (ISBN 0-8493-3902-2). CRC Pr.

Business Communications Staff. Fuel & Lubricant Additives. 1983. 1250.00 (ISBN 0-89336-239-5, C-027). BCC.

Cameron, A. & Ettles, C. M. Basic Lubrication Theory. 3rd ed. (Engineering Science Ser.). 256p. 1983. pap. 34.95 (ISBN 0-470-27554-5). Halsted Pr.

Cameron, Alastair. The Principles of Lubrication. LC 67-70366. pap. 156.30 (ISBN 0-317-29446-6, 2055943). Bks Demand UMI.

Cheng, H. S. & Keer, L. M., eds. Solid Contact & Lubrication. (AMD: Vol. 39). 248p. 1980. 30.00 (ISBN 0-686-69861-4, G00172). ASME.

Clauss, Francis J. Solid Lubricants & Self-Lubricating Solids. 1972. 61.50 (ISBN 0-12-176150-9). Acad Pr.

Davenport, T. C., ed. Rheology of Lubricants. (Illus.). 148p. 1973. 22.25 (ISBN 0-85334-473-6, Pub. by Elsevier Applied Sci England). Elsevier.

Erlich, Melville, ed. Lubricating Grease Guide. LC 84-61641. (Illus.). 140p. (Orig.). 1984. pap. 10.00 (ISBN 0-9613935-0-5). Natl Lubrica Grease.

Fuels & Lubricants Technology: An Overview. 1985. 25.00 (ISBN 0-89883-825-8, SP603). Soc Auto Engineers.

Fuller, Dudely D., et al. Theory & Practice of Lubrication for Engineers. 2nd ed. LC 83-27394. 682p. 1984. text ed. 64.95x (ISBN 0-471-04703-1, Pub. by Wiley-Interscience). Wiley.

Gross, William A., et al. Fluid Film Lubrication. LC 80-36889. 773p. 1980. 57.95x (ISBN 0-471-08357-7). Wiley.

Hersey, Mayo D. Theory & Research in Lubrication: Foundations for Future Developments. LC 66-21058. 488p. 1966. text ed. 28.50 (ISBN 0-471-37346-X, Pub. by Wiley). Krieger.

Institute of Marine Engineers, Ministry of Defense. Lubrication: Successes & Failures. (Illus.). 70p. 1973. limp bdg. 10.55x (ISBN 0-900976-12-8, Pub. by Inst Marine Eng). Intl Spec Bk.

Institute of Petroleum. Gear Lubrication. (Illus.). 345p. 1966. 55.50 (ISBN 0-444-39972-0, Pub. by Elsevier Applied Sci England). Elsevier.

Institute of Petroleum (Great Britain) Staff. Gear Lubrication: Proceedings. LC 67-76475. pap. 79.00 (ISBN 0-317-28913-6, 2023691). Bks Demand UMI.

LUNAR EXPLORATION

see Moon–Exploration

LUNAR GEOLOGY

Chamberlain, Joseph, ed. Reviews of Lunar Sciences. (Illus.). 540p. 1977. pap. 5.00 (ISBN 0-87590-220-0). Am Geophysical.

Green, Jack, ed. Geological Problems in Lunar & Planetary Research. (Science & Technology Ser.: Vol. 25). (Illus.). 1971. lib. bdg. 45.00x (ISBN 0-87703-056-1, Pub. by Am Astronaut). Univelt Inc.

--Interpretation of Lunar Probe Data. (Science & Technology Ser.: Vol. 14). 1967. 25.00x (ISBN 0-87703-042-1, Pub. by Am Astronaut). Univelt Inc.

Guest, J. E. & Greeley, R. Geology on the Moon. LC 77-371984. (Wykeham Science Ser.: No. 43). 235p. 1977. 17.95x (ISBN 0-8448-1170-X); pap. 12.50x (ISBN 0-8448-1346-X). Crane-Russak Co.

--Geology on the Moon. (Wykeham Science Ser.: No. 43). 220p. 1977. cancelled (ISBN 0-85109-580-1); pap. cancelled (ISBN 0-85109-540-2). Taylor & Francis.

Karr, Clarence, ed. Infrared & Raman Spectroscopy of Lunar & Terrestrial Minerals. 1975. 78.00 (ISBN 0-12-399950-2). Acad Pr.

Kopal, Z. & Goudas, C. L. Measure of the Moon. 498p. 1967. 123.75 (ISBN 0-677-11850-3). Gordon.

Levinson, A. A. & Taylor, Ross. Moon Rocks & Minerals. 240p. 1972. text ed. 33.00 (ISBN 0-08-016669-5). Pergamon.

Lunar & Planetary Institute. Proceedings of the Conference on the Lunar Highlands Crust: Houston, Texas, USA, 14-16 November 1979. 550p. 1980. 57.00 (ISBN 0-08-026304-6). Pergamon.

Lunar & Planetary Institute, Houston, Texas, U. S. A., ed. Proceedings of the Conference on Multi-Ring Basins. 300p. 1981. 39.00 (ISBN 0-08-028045-5). Pergamon.

Lunar & Planetary Science Conference, 9th, Houston, 1978. Proceedings, 3 vols. Lunar & Planetary Institute, Houston, Texas, compiled by. (Geochimica et Cosmochimicha Acta: Suppl. 10). 1979. Set. 270.00 (ISBN 0-08-022966-2). Pergamon.

Mason, Brian H. & Melson, William G. The Lunar Rocks. LC 73-129659. pap. 46.30 (ISBN 0-317-08373-2, 2055128). Bks Demand UMI.

Mutch, Thomas A. Geology of the Moon: A Stratigraphic View. rev. ed. LC 79-83687. 1973. 60.00x (ISBN 0-691-08110-7). Princeton U Pr.

Randall, Charles A., Jr., ed. Extra-Terrestrial Matter. LC 69-15447. (Illus.). 331p. 1969. 15.00 (ISBN 0-87580-009-2). N Ill U Pr.

LUNAR PROBES

Green, Jack, ed. Interpretation of Lunar Probe Data. (Science & Technology Ser.: Vol. 14). 1967. 25.00x (ISBN 0-87703-042-1, Pub. by Am Astronaut). Univelt Inc.

LUNAR THEORY

see Moon, Theory Of

LUNGS

see also Respiration

Abramson, Joan. Practical Application of the Gas Laws to Pulmonary Physiology. 97p. (Orig.). 1981. pap. text ed. 8.95x (ISBN 0-89787-107-3). Gorsuch Scarisbrick.

Atkins, Harold L. Pulmonary Nuclear Medicine. (Lung Biology in Health & Diseases Ser.). 344p. 1984. 69.75 (ISBN 0-8247-7233-4). Dekker.

Berti, F., et al, eds. Cyclooxygenase & Lipoxygenase Modulators in Lung Reactivity. (Progress in Biochemical Pharmacology: Vol. 20). (Illus.). x, 146p. 1985. 56.75 (ISBN 3-8055-3974-6). S Karger.

Bonsignore, G. & Cumming, G., eds. The Lung in Its Environment. LC 81-12004. (Ettore Majorana International Science Ser., Life Sciences: Vol. 6). 526p. 1981. 69.50x (ISBN 0-306-40742-6, Plenum Pr). Plenum Pub.

Carlon & Howland. High Frequency Ventilation. (Lung & Biology Ser.). 328p. 1985. 57.50 (ISBN 0-8247-7364-0). Dekker.

Cumming, G. & Bonsignore, G., eds. Smoking & the Lung. (Ettore Majorana International Science Series, Life Sciences: Vol. 17). 520p. 1985. 82.50x (ISBN 0-306-41828-2, Plenum Pr). Plenum Pub.

Cumming, Gordon & Bonsignore, Giovanni, eds. Cellular Biology of the Lung. LC 81-23407. (Ettore Majorana International Science Ser., Life Sciences: Vol. 10). 496p. 1982. text ed. 65.00 (ISBN 0-306-40910-0, Plenum Pr). Plenum Pub.

Dempsey, Jerome A. & Reed, Charles E., eds. Muscular Exercise & the Lung. (Illus.). 416p. 1977. 50.00x (ISBN 0-299-07220-7). U of Wis Pr.

Edge, J. R., et al. The Aging Lung: Normal Function. LC 73-1458. 1974. 19.00x (ISBN 0-8422-7165-1). Irvington.

Engel, L. A. Gas Mixing & Distribution in the Lung. (Lung Biology in Health & Disease Ser.). 440p. 1985. 75.00 (ISBN 0-8247-7284-9). Dekker.

Esenwein, Mark. Pulmonary Function Technology: The Basics. (Illus.). 900p. 1985. pap. text ed. 155.00 (ISBN 0-933195-09-5). Cal College Pr.

Farrell, Philip, ed. Lung Development: Biological & Clinical Perspectives, 2 vols. LC 82-1616. 1982. Vol. 1: Biochemistry & Physiology. 55.00 (ISBN 0-12-249701-5); Vol. 2: Neonatal Respiratory Distress. 44.00 (ISBN 0-12-249702-3). Acad Pr.

Fraser, Robert G. & Pave, J. A. Organ Physiology: Structure & Function of the Lung. 2nd ed. LC 76-20933. pap. 59.50 (ISBN 0-317-26430-3, 2024986). Bks Demand UMI.

Freundlich, I. Pulmonary Masses, Cysts & Cavities: A Radiologic Approach. 1981. 39.95 (ISBN 0-8151-3330-8). Year Bk Med.

Hodson, W. A. Development of the Lung. (Lung Biology in Health & Disease: Vol. 6). 1977. 95.00 (ISBN 0-8247-6377-7). Dekker.

Hornbein. Regulation of Breathing, 2 pts. (Lung Biology in Health & Disease Ser.: Vol. 17). 1981. Pt. 1. 85.00 (ISBN 0-8247-6607-5); Pt. 2. 99.50 (ISBN 0-8247-1013-4). Dekker.

Hughes, G. M. The Vertebrate Lung. rev. ed. Head, J. J., ed. LC 77-75590. (Carolina Biology Readers Ser.). (Illus.). 16p. 1979. pap. 1.60 (ISBN 0-89278-259-5, 45-9659). Carolina Biological.

Ingwersen, Ulla. Respiratory Physical Therapy & Pulmonary Care. LC 76-27094. pap. 44.00 (ISBN 0-317-07783-X, 2017410). Bks Demand UMI.

Lim, Thomas P. Physiology of the Lung. (Illus.). 196p. 1983. pap. 16.75x spiral (ISBN 0-398-04727-8). C C Thomas.

Mandell, Charles H. Scintillation Camera Lung Imaging: An Anatomic Atlas & Guide. LC 76-16057. 208p. 1976. 70.50 (ISBN 0-8089-0960-6, 792660). Grune.

Nelson. Pulmonary Development: Transition from Intrauterine to Extrauterine Life. (Lung Biology Ser.). 544p. 1985. 75.00 (ISBN 0-8247-7316-0). Dekker.

Pickrell, John A., ed. Lung Connective Tissue: Location, Metabolism, & Response to Injury. 224p. 1981. 66.00 (ISBN 0-8493-5749-7). CRC Pr.

Randall, D. J., et al. The Evolution of Air Breathing in Vertebrates. LC 80-462. (Illus.). 176p. 1981. 34.50 (ISBN 0-521-22259-1). Cambridge U Pr.

Rhyne, Theodore L. Acoustic Instrumentation & Characterisation of Lung Tissue. LC 77-21979. (Ultrasound in Biomedicine Ser.). 109p. 1977. pap. 43.95 (ISBN 0-471-27884-X, Pub. by Wiley-Interscience). Wiley.

Saunders & Sullivan. Sleep & Breathing. (Lung Biology in Health & Disease Ser.). 640p. 1984. 75.00 (ISBN 0-8247-7064-1). Dekker.

Snider, Gordon L. Clinical Pulmonary Medicine. 1981. 34.50 (ISBN 0-316-80218-2). Little.

Staub, Norman C., ed. Lung Water & Solute Exchange. (Lung Biology in Health & Disease Ser.: Vol. 7). 1978. 85.00 (ISBN 0-8247-6379-3). Dekker.

LYAPUNOV FUNCTIONS

see Liapunov Functions

LYCOPERDON

see Puffballs

LYCOPDIUM

see Club-Mosses

LYELL, CHARLES, SIR, 1797-1875

Lyell, Charles. Travels in North America, the Years, 1841-2: Geological Observations on the United States, Canada & Nova Scotia, 2 vols. in one. Albritton, Claude C., Jr., ed. LC 77-6525. (History of Geology Ser.). (Illus.). 1978. Repr. of 1845 ed. lib. bdg. 40.00x (ISBN 0-405-10447-2). Ayer Co Pubs.

Wilson, Leonard G. Charles Lyell, the Years to Eighteen Forty One: The Revolution in Geology. LC 72-75212. (Illus.). Repr. of 1972 ed. 107.80 (ISBN 0-8357-9105-X, 2016785). Bks Demand UMI.

LYGAEIDAE

Usinger, R. L. Genus Nysius & Its Allies in the Hawaiian Islands. (BMB). Repr. of 1942 ed. 22.00 (ISBN 0-527-02281-0). Kraus Repr.

LYMPHOCYTES

Aiuti, F. & Wigzell, H., eds. Thymus, Thymic Hormones & T Lymphocytes. (Serono Symposia Ser.: No. 38). 1980. 60.00 (ISBN 0-12-046450-0). Acad Pr.

Arber, W., et al, eds. Current Topics in Microbiology & Immunology, Vols. 86-87. (Illus.). 1980. Vol. 86. 45.00 (ISBN 0-387-09432-6); Vol. 87. 42.00 (ISBN 0-387-09433-4). Springer-Verlag.

Bona, Constantin. Idiotypes & Lymphocytes. LC 81-10759. (Immunology: An International Series of Monographs & Treatise). 1981. 35.00 (ISBN 0-12-112950-0). Acad Pr.

Castellani, Amleto, ed. Lymphocyte Stimulation: Differential Sensitivity to Radiation, Biochemical & Immunological Processes. LC 80-19883. 196p. 1980. 35.00x (ISBN 0-306-40475-3, Plenum Pr). Plenum Pub.

Cold Spring Harbor Symposia on Quantitative Biology: Origins of Lymphocyte Diversity, 2 bks, Vol. 41. LC 34-8174. (Illus.). 1024p. 1977. Set. 107.50 (ISBN 0-87969-040-2). Cold Spring Harbor.

De Sousa, Maria. Lymphocyte Circulation: Experimental & Clinical Aspects. LC 80-40848. 259p. 1981. 69.95x (ISBN 0-471-27854-8, Pub. by Wiley-Interscience). Wiley.

Elves, Michael W. The Lymphocytes. 604p. 1972. 40.00x (ISBN 0-686-80812-6, Pub. by Lloyd-Luke England). State Mutual Bk.

Epstein, M. A. & Achong, B. G., eds. The Epstein-Barr Virus. (Illus.). 1979. 77.00 (ISBN 0-387-09272-2). Springer-Verlag.

Escobar, M. R. & Friedman, H., eds. Macrophages & Lymphocytes: Nature, Functions & Interaction, Pt. B. (Advances in Experimental Medicine & Biology Ser.: Vol. 121B). 625p. 1980. 75.00x (ISBN 0-306-40286-6, Plenum Pr). Plenum Pub.

Fathman, C. Garrison, ed. Isolation, Characterization & Utilization of T Lymphocyte Clones. 1982. 65.00 (ISBN 0-12-249920-4). Acad Pr.

Fauci, Anthony S. & Ballieux, Rudy, eds. Human B-Lymphocyte Function: Activation & Immunoregulation. 352p. 1982. text ed. 71.50 (ISBN 0-89004-620-4). Raven.

Feldman, Michael & Globerson, Amiela, eds. Immune Reactivity of Lymphocytes: Development, Expression, & Control. LC 75-42123. (Advances in Experimental Medicine & Biology Ser.: Vol. 66). 751p. 1976. 79.50x (ISBN 0-306-39066-3, Plenum Pr). Plenum Pub.

Garland, P. B. & Crumpton, M. J., eds. The Lymphocyte Cell Surface. (Symposia Ser.: No. 45). 124p. 1981. 60.00x (ISBN 0-904498-10-7, Pub. by Biochemical England). State Mutual Bk.

Haas, W. & Von Boehmer, H. Techniques for Separation & Selection of Specific Lymphocytes. (Current Topics in Microbiology & Immunology Ser.: Vol. 84). (Illus.). 1978. 35.00 (ISBN 0-387-09029-0). Springer-Verlag.

ICN-UCLA Symposia on Molecular & Cellular Biology, 1979. T & B Lymphocytes: Recognition & Function: Symposium, Vol. XVI. Bach, Fritz H., et al, eds. LC 79-26438. 1979. 70.00 (ISBN 0-12-069850-1). Acad Pr.

Inglis. B Lymphocytes Today. 1983. 14.95 (ISBN 0-444-80454-4). Elsevier.

Katz, D. H. Lymphocyte Differentiation, Recognition & Regulation. 1977. 85.00 (ISBN 0-12-401640-5). Acad Pr.

Klinman, et al. B Lymphocytes in the Immune Response. (Developments in Immunology Ser.: Vol. 15). 540p. 1981. 96.00 (ISBN 0-444-00611-7, Biomedical Pr). Elsevier.

Lehmann-Grube, F., ed. Lymphocytic Choriomeningitis Virus & Other Arenaviruses. LC 73-10673. xiii, 339p. 1973. pap. 39.00 (ISBN 0-387-06403-6). Springer-Verlag.

Loor, F. & Roelants, G. E., eds. B & T Cells in Immune Recognition. LC 76-26913. 504p. 1977. 97.95x (ISBN 0-471-99438-3, Pub. by Wiley-Interscience). Wiley.

Lucas, D. O., ed. Regulatory Mechanism in Lymphocyte Activation. 1977. 82.50 (ISBN 0-12-458050-5). Acad Pr.

Marchalonis, John J., ed. The Lymphocyte: Structure & Function, Pt. 1. (Immunology Ser.: Vol. 5). 1977. 75.00 (ISBN 0-8247-6418-8). Dekker.

--The Lymphocyte: Structure & Function, Pt. 2. (Immunology Ser.: Vol. 5). 1977. 75.00 (ISBN 0-8247-6419-6). Dekker.

Mathe, G., et al, eds. Lymphocytes, Macrophages, & Cancer. LC 76-26538. (Recent Results in Cancer Research Ser.: Vol. 56). 1976. 35.00 (ISBN 3-540-07902-5). Springer-Verlag.

Melchers, F., et al, eds. Lymphocyte Hybridomas: Second Workshop. (Illus.). 1979. 21.00 (ISBN 0-387-09670-1). Springer-Verlag.

Oppenheim, Joost J. & Cohen, Stanley, eds. Interleukins, Lymphokines & Cytokines (Symposium) 1983. 63.00 (ISBN 0-12-527540-4). Acad Pr.

Pernis, Benvenuto & Vogel, Henry J., eds. Regulatory T Lymphocytes. (P & S Biomedical Science Ser.). 1980. 65.00 (ISBN 0-12-551860-9). Acad Pr.

Pick, Edgar, ed. Lymphokine Reports: A Forum for Nonantibody Lymphocyte Products, Vol. 1. 1980. 39.50 (ISBN 0-12-432001-5). Acad Pr.

Wecker, E. & Horack, I., eds. Retrovirus Genes in Lymphocyte Function & Growth. (Current Topics in Microbiology & Immunology Ser.: Vol. 98). (Illus.). 180p. 1982. 32.00 (ISBN 0-387-11225-1). Springer-Verlag.

Williams, Ralph C., Jr., ed. Lymphocytes & Their Interactions. 240p. 1975. text ed. 26.50 (ISBN 0-89004-052-4). Raven.

LYSENKO, TROFIM DENISOVICH, 1898-

Huxley, Julian S. Heredity, East & West: Lysenko & World Science. LC 49-50254. 1969. Repr. of 1949 ed. 16.00 (ISBN 0-527-43810-3). Kraus Repr.

Lecourt, Dominique. Proletarian Science? The Case of Lysenko. 1978. 14.00 (ISBN 0-8052-7006-X, Pub by NLB). Schocken.

Medvedev, Zhores. The Rise & Fall of T. D. Lysenko. Lawrence, Lucy G., ed. Lerner, I. Michael, tr. LC 79-77519. pap. 76.00 (ISBN 0-317-26082-0, 2023770). Bks Demand UMI.

LYSOSOMES

Allison, A. C. Lysosomes. rev. ed. Head, J. J., ed. LC 76-29372. (Carolina Biology Readers Ser.). (Illus.). 16p. 1977. pap. 1.60 (ISBN 0-89278-258-7, 45-9658). Carolina Biological.

Barranger, John A. & Brady, Roscoe O., eds. Molecular Basis of Lysosomal Storage Disorders. 1984. 45.00 (ISBN 0-12-079280-X). Acad Pr.

Callahan, John W. & Lowden, J. Alexander, eds. Lysosomes & Lysosomal Storage Diseases. 455p. 1981. text ed. 71.50 (ISBN 0-89004-476-7). Raven.

Daems, W. T., et al, eds. Cell Biological Aspects of Disease: The Plasma Membrane & Lysosomes. (Boerhaave Series for Postgraduate Medical Education: No. 19). 330p. 1981. PLB 68.50 (ISBN 90-6021-466-8, Pub. by Leiden Univ Netherlands). Kluwer Academic.

Dingle, J. T., ed. Lysosomes: A Laboratory Handbook. 2nd ed. 324p. 1977. 85.00 (ISBN 0-7204-0627-7, Biomedical Pr). Elsevier.

Dingle, J. T & Fell, H. B., eds. Lysosomes in Biology & Pathology, Vols. 1-6. (Frontiers in Biology Ser.: Vols. 14, 29, 43, 45, 48). 1969-77. Repr. Vol. 1. 128.50 (ISBN 0-444-10501-8, Biomedical Pr); Vol. 2. 146.00 (ISBN 0-444-10502-6); Vol. 3. 122.75 (ISBN 0-444-10405-4); Vol. 4. 155.50 (ISBN 0-444-10810-6); Vol. 5. 113.75 (ISBN 0-444-11204-9); Vol. 6. 146.00 (ISBN 0-7204-0668-4). Elsevier.

Dingle, J. T., et al. Lysosomes in Biology & Pathology, Vol. 7. 1984. 125.00 (ISBN 0-444-80523-0, I-174-84). Elsevier.

Hers, H. G. & Van Hoof, F., eds. Lysosomes & Storage Diseases. 1973. 97.50 (ISBN 0-12-342850-5). Acad Pr.

Holtzman, E. Lysosomes: A Survey. (Cell Biology Monographs: Vol. 3). (Illus.). 300p. 1976. 79.00 (ISBN 0-387-81316-0). Springer-Verlag.

Matile, P. The Lytic Compartment of Plant Cells. LC 75-5931. (Cell Biology Monographs: Vol. 1). (Illus.). xiii, 183p. 1975. 55.00 (ISBN 0-387-81296-2). Springer-Verlag.

Osserman, Elliot F., et al. Lysosome. 1974. 94.00 (ISBN 0-12-528950-2). Acad Pr.

M

M. G. AUTOMOBILE

see Automobiles, Foreign–Types–M. G.

MACAQUES

Albrecht, Gene H. The Craniofacial Morphology of the Sulawesi Macaques: Multivariate Analysis As a Tool in Systematics. (Contributions to Primatology: Vol. 13). (Illus.). 1977. 31.50 (ISBN 3-8055-2694-6). S Karger.

Chevalier-Skolnikoff, Suzanne. The Ontogeny of Communication in the Stumptail Macaque. (Contributions to Primatology: Vol. 2). (Illus.). 174p. 1974. 31.50 (ISBN 3-8055-1647-9). S Karger.

Fa, John E., ed. The Barbary Macaque: A Case Study in Conservation. LC 84-11618. 388p. 1984. 49.50x (ISBN 0-306-41733-2, Plenum Pr). Plenum Pub.

Fedigan, L. M. A Study of Roles in the Arashiyama West Troop of Japanese Monkeys (Macaca Fuscata) Szalay, F. S., ed. (Contributions to Primatology: Vol. 9). (Illus.). 116p. 1976. 21.00 (ISBN 3-8055-2334-3). S Karger.

Lindburg, Donald G. The Macaques: Studies in Ecology, Behavior & Evolution. (Primate Behavior & Development Ser.). 400p. 1980. text ed. 26.50 (ISBN 0-442-24817-2). Van Nos Reinhold.

Winters, W. D., et al. A Stereotaxic Brain Atlas for Macaca Nemestrina. LC 69-16743. (Illus.). 1969. 70.00x (ISBN 0-520-01445-6). U of Cal Pr.

MACARONI WHEAT

see Wheat

MCCORMICK, CYRUS HALL, 1809-1884

Casson, Herbert N. Cyrus Hall McCormick: His Life & Work. LC 74-152977. (Select Bibliographies Reprint Ser.). 1972. Repr. of 1909 ed. 24.50 (ISBN 0-8369-5729-6). Ayer Co Pubs.

Schwefel, Hans-Paul. Numerical Optimization of Computer Models. LC 81-173223. 389p. 1981. 42.95 (ISBN 0-471-09988-0, Pub. by Wiley-Interscience). Wiley.

Starke, P. H. Abstract Automata. 1972. 36.25 (ISBN 0-444-10349-X, North-Holland); pap. 23.50 (ISBN 0-444-10354-6, North Holland). Elsevier.

Tou, Julius T., ed. Applied Automata Theory. LC 68-26634. (Electrical Science Ser.). 1969. 80.00 (ISBN 0-12-696230-8). Acad Pr.

Tsetlin, M. L. Automata Theory & Modeling of Biological Systems. (Mathematics in Science & Engineering Ser.). 1973. 70.00 (ISBN 0-12-701650-3). Acad Pr.

Usher, M. B. & Ocloo, J. K. The Natural Resistance of Eighty-Five West African Hardwood Timbers to Attack by Termites & Micro-Organisms. 1979. 35.00x (ISBN 0-85135-103-4, Pub. by Centre Overseas Research). State Mutual Bk.

Wang, Hao. Logic, Computers & Sets. LC 70-113155. Orig. Title: Survey of Mathematical Logic. 1970. Repr. of 1962 ed. text ed. 24.95 (ISBN 0-8284-0245-0). Chelsea Pub.

Weihrauch, K., ed. Theoretical Computer Science: GI Conference, 4th Conference, Aachen, March 26-28, 1979. (Lecture Notes in Computer Science: Vol. 67). 1979. pap. 20.00 (ISBN 0-387-09118-1). Springer-Verlag.

Wilson, Charles E., et al. Kinematics & Dynamics of Machinery. 816p. 1983. text ed. 38.95 scp (ISBN 0-06-044437-1, HarpC); solutions manual avail. (ISBN 0-06-364577-7). Har-Row.

MACHINE-TOOLS
see also Jigs and Fixtures; Manufacturing Processes; Tool-Steel;
also specific machine tools, e.g. Planning Machines

American Machinist Magazine. Tools of Our Trade. LC 82-7773. 1982. 35.50 (ISBN 0-07-001547-3). McGraw.

Anderson, James & Tatro, Earl E. Shop Theory. 6th ed. (Illus.). 576p. 1974. text ed. 25.40 (ISBN 0-07-001612-7). McGraw.

Brothwell, C., et al, eds. Maintenance of Numerically Controlled Machine Tools, 2 vols. 2nd ed. (Engineering Craftsmen Ser.: No. J27). (Illus.). 1973. Set. sprial bdg. 75.00x (ISBN 0-85083-155-5). Intl Ideas.

Dixon, Robert G. Benchwork. LC 80-66607. (Machine Trades-Machine Shop Ser.). (Illus.). 211p. 1981. pap. text ed. 11.60 (ISBN 0-8273-1743-3); instr's. guide 2.85 (ISBN 0-8273-1744-1). Delmar.

Effective Use of Machine Tools & Related Aspects of Managements in Developing Countries. pap. 3.00 (ISBN 0-686-94606-5, UN72/2B6, UN). Unipub.

Floud, Roderick. The British Machine-Tool Industry, 1850-1914. LC 75-46205. (Illus.). 180p. 1976. 34.50 (ISBN 0-521-21203-0). Cambridge U Pr.

Gross, Hans, ed. Electrical Feed-Drives for Machine Tools. 363p. 1983. 54.95x (ISBN 0-471-26273-0). Wiley.

Heineman, Stephen S. & Genevro, George W. Machine Tools: Processes & Applications. 1979. text ed. 28.50 scp (ISBN 0-06-453305-0, HarpC); scp instr's manual 4.50 (ISBN 0-06-453307-7). Har-Row.

Heritage, P., et al, eds. Machining for Toolmaking & Experimental Work, 3 vols. 2nd ed. (Engineering Craftsmen: No. H1). (Illus.). 1977. Set. spiral bdg. 75.00x (ISBN 0-85083-024-9). Intl Ideas.

Hine, Charles R. Machine Tools & Processes for Engineers. LC 81-14246. 634p. 1982. Repr. of 1971 ed. lib. bdg. 36.50 (ISBN 0-89874-354-0). Krieger.

Hutton, F. R. Illustrated Machine Tools of 1885. Orig. Title: Report on Machine-Tools & Woodworking Machinery. 118p. 1981. pap. 8.95 (ISBN 0-917914-00-7). Lindsay Pubns.

Kibbe, Richard R. & Neely, John E. Machine Tool Practices. 2nd ed. LC 81-7606. 806p. 1982. 32.95 (ISBN 0-471-05788-6); student wkbk. 9.95 (ISBN 0-471-86652-0); solutions manual. Wiley.

Koenigsberger, F. & Tlusty, J. Machine Tool Structures, Vol. 1. LC 79-84073. 1970. 110.00 (ISBN 0-08-013405-X). Pergamon.

Koenigsberger, T. & Tobias, S. A., eds. Proceedings of the Sixteenth Machine Tool Design & Research Conference. LC 76-5219. (International Machine Tool Design & Research Conference Ser.). 599p. 1976. text ed. 139.95x (ISBN 0-470-15100-5). Halsted Pr.

Krar, S. F. & Oswald, J. W. Machine Tool Operations Visutext. 208p. 1983. text ed. 17.50 (ISBN 0-07-035431-6). McGraw.

--Turning Technology: Engine & Turret Lathes. LC 78-153723. 1971. pap. text ed. 14.80 (ISBN 0-8273-0206-1); instructor's guide o.p. 3.60 (ISBN 0-8273-0207-X). Delmar.

Krar, S. F., et al. Technology of Machine Tools. 3rd ed. 672p. 31.00 (ISBN 0-07-035425-1); wkbk. 13.15 (ISBN 0-07-022128-6). McGraw.

Krar, Stephen F., et al. Technology of Machine Tools. 2nd ed. LC 77-3663. (Illus.). 1977. text ed. 31.00 (ISBN 0-07-035383-2). McGraw.

Krar, Steve F. Machine Tool Operations. LC 81-185871. (Illus.). 416p. 1983. 25.15 (ISBN 0-07-035430-8). McGraw.

Lane, K. A., ed. Machine Tools, 1984: Proceedings of the International Conference, Birmingham, UK, 26-28 June 1984. 650p. 1984. 87.00 (ISBN 0-444-87542-5, North Holland). Elsevier.

Linsley, Horace E. Machine Tools, What They Are & How They Work: An Introduction to the Fundamentals of Mass Production. Hall, Herbert D., ed. LC 57-7456. pap. 112.00 (ISBN 0-317-10939-1, 2001907). Bks Demand UMI.

Machine Tool & Design Research International Conference, 14th & Koenigsberger, F. Proceedings. Tobias, S. A., ed. 841p. 1974. 149.95 (ISBN 0-470-49746-7). Halsted Pr.

Machine Tool Industry. (UNIDO Guides to Information Sources: No. 22). pap. 4.00 (ISBN 0-686-93237-4, UNID168, UN). Unipub.

Machine Tools in Asia & the Pacific. pap. 3.50 (ISBN 0-686-94560-3, UN75/2B/4, UN). Unipub.

Machine Tools in Latin America. pap. 3.00 (ISBN 0-686-94594-8, UN73/2B/11, UN). Unipub.

Machining for Toolmaking & Experimental Work, 3 vols. 50.00x (ISBN 0-85083-024-9, Pub. by Engineering Ind). State Mutual Bk.

Maintenance of Numerically Controlled Machine Tools, 2 vols. 1983. 52.00x (ISBN 0-85083-155-5, Pub. by Engineering Ind). State Mutual Bk.

Matt, Stephen R. Machine Tool Operation: An Introduction. 1985. text ed. write for info. (ISBN 0-534-01039-3, Breton Pubs). Wadsworth Pub.

National Machine Tool Builder's Association (NMTBA) Shop Theory: Special Edition. 176p. 1984. pap. 9.95 (ISBN 0-471-89019-7). Wiley.

Oliver, Clifford. Operations Manual for Machine Tool Technology. 272p. 1982. pap. 19.95 (ISBN 0-471-04744-9). Wiley.

Olivo, C. Thomas. Advanced Machine Technology. 1982. text ed. write for info. (ISBN 0-534-01040-7, Breton Pubs). Wadsworth Pub.

Regional Seminar on Machine Tools in Developing Countries of Europe & the Middle East. pap. 3.00 (ISBN 0-686-94457-7, UN72/2B/22, UN). Unipub.

Ryder, G. H. Jigs, Fixtures, Tools & Gauges. 6th ed. Orig. Title: Jigs, Tools & Fixtures. (Illus.). 176p. 1973. text ed. 15.50x (ISBN 0-291-39432-9). Scholium Intl.

Schlesinger, G. Testing Machine Tools: For the Use of Machine Tool Makers, Users Inspectors & Plant Engineers. 8th ed. 1978. text ed. 21.00 (ISBN 0-08-021685-4). Pergamon.

Sigmon, D. L. A Framing Guide & Steel Square Book. rev. ed. 312p. 1958. 12.95 (ISBN 0-914760-01-7). Cline-Sigmon.

Steffy, Wilbert. Economics of Machine Tool Procurement. LC 77-90986. (Manufacturing Data Ser.). 1978. 12.75 (ISBN 0-87263-041-2). SME.

Technical Publications Staff. Chain Saw Service Manual. 7th ed. 336p. (Orig.). 1985. pap. 10.95 (ISBN 0-87288-001-X, CSS-7). Tech Pubns.

Thompson, Robert W., ed. The Machinability of Engineering Materials. 1983. 64.00 (ISBN 0-87170-160-X). ASM.

Tobias, S. A. & Koenigsberger, F., eds. Proceedings of the Thirteenth International Machine Tool Design & Research Conference. LC 73-2955. 573p. 1973. 139.95x (ISBN 0-470-87529-1). Halsted Pr.

Weck, M. Machine Tools: Automation & Controls, Vol. 3. 400p. 1983. write for info. (ISBN 0-471-26224-2). Wiley.

--Machine Tools: Types of Machines, Forms of Construction & Applications, Vol. 1. 400p. 1983. write for info. (ISBN 0-471-26222-6). Wiley.

Weck, Manfred. Handbook of Machine Tools, 4 vols. 1192p. 1984. 185.00x set (ISBN 0-471-26226-9, Pub. by Wiley Heyden). Wiley.

--Machine Tools: Construction & Mathematical Analysis, Vol. 2. 400p. 1983. write for info. (ISBN 0-471-26223-4, Pub. by Wiley Heyden). Wiley.

--Machine Tools: Metrological Analysis & Performance Tests, Vol. 4. 400p. 1984. Set. write for info. (ISBN 0-471-26225-0, Pub. by Wiley Heyden). Wiley.

Woodbury, Robert S. Studies in the History of Machine Tools. (History of Science & Technology Ser). 625p. 1973. pap. 12.50x (ISBN 0-262-73033-2). MIT Pr.

MACHINE-TOOLS–DESIGN

Donaldson, Cyril & Le Cain, George. Tool Design. 3rd ed. (Illus.). 840p. 1973. text ed. 37.55 (ISBN 0-07-017531-4). McGraw.

Machine Tool Design & Research International Conference, 12th, et al. Proceedings. Tobias, S. A., ed. LC 72-6276. 582p. 1972. 139.95x (ISBN 0-470-49745-9). Halsted Pr.

Parkinson, S. T. New Product Development in Engineering: A Comparison of the British & West German Machine Tool Industries. LC 83-20855. (Management & Industrial Relations Ser.: No. 6). 150p. 1984. 29.95 (ISBN 0-521-25796-4). Cambridge U Pr.

Welbourn, D. B. & Smith, J. D. Machine-tool Dynamics: An Introduction. LC 71-101447. pap. 38.00 (ISBN 0-317-27088-5, 2024558). Bks Demand UMI.

MACHINE TOOLS–DICTIONARIES

Freeman, Henry G. Fachwoerterbuch Spanende Werkzeugmaschinen. (Ger. & Eng.). 527p. (Dictionary of Machine Tools). 1965. leatherette 72.00 (ISBN 3-7736-5090-6, M-7403, Pub. by Verlag W. Gerardet). French & Eur.

--Spanende Werkzeugmaschinen, Deutsch-Englische Begriffserlauterungen und Kommentare. (Ger. & Eng.). 617p. (Machine Tools, German-English Explanations and Comments). 1973. 75.00 (ISBN 3-7736-5082-5, M-7624, Pub. by Verlag W. Girardet). French & Eur.

Lexicue Trilingue des Termes d'usage Courant En Machines Outils; les Tours, Pt. 1. (Fr.). 74p. (Trilingual Lexicon of Common Terms in Machine Tools; Wheels). 1961. pap. 12.50 (ISBN 0-686-56791-9, M-6374). French & Eur.

Lexique Trilinque des Termes d'Usage Courant En Machines Outils, les Perceuses, Pt. 2. (Fr.). 96p. (Trilingual Lexicon of Commonly Used Terms in Machine Tools; Drilling Tools). pap. 12.50 (ISBN 0-686-56792-7, M-6375). French & Eur.

MACHINE TOOLS–NUMERICAL CONTROL

American Society of Tool & Manufacturing Engineers Staff. Fundamentals of Tool Design. (Illus.). 1962. text ed. 32.95 (ISBN 0-13-344861-4). P-H.

Barron, C. H. Numerical Control for Machine Tools. 1971. 32.00 (ISBN 0-07-003824-4). McGraw.

Bezier, P. Numerical Control: Mathematics & Applications. LC 70-39230. (Wiley Series in Computing). Repr. of 1972 ed. 48.70 (ISBN 0-8357-9944-1, 2014900). Bks Demand UMI.

Brewer, R. G., et al, eds. NC-CNC Machining II. (E.I.T.B. Training Manuals Ser.). (Illus.). 230p. 1982. 42.50x (ISBN 0-85083-539-9). Intl Ideas.

Chambers, H. & Chacey, C. Drafting & Manual Programming for Numerical Control. 1980. 32.95 (ISBN 0-13-219113-X). P-H.

Childs, James J. Numerical Control Part Programming. LC 73-9766. (Illus.). 340p. 1973. 24.95 (ISBN 0-8311-1099-6). Indus Pr.

--Principles of Numerical Control. 3rd ed. LC 81-20296. (Illus.). 316p. 1982. 24.95 (ISBN 0-8311-1135-6). Indus Pr.

Hatvany, J., ed. Computer Languages for Numerical Control. 152p. (Proceedings). 1973. 41.00 (ISBN 0-444-10572-7, Biomedical Pr). Elsevier.

International High Technology Machine Tool & Production Engineering Conference, 1st. MACH-TECH: Papers, 13 papers. 1983. Set. 45.50 (ISBN 0-317-06842-3, 809). SME.

Koren, Yoram. Computer Control of Manufacturing Systems. (Illus.). 352p. 1983. text ed. 42.00 (ISBN 0-07-035341-7). McGraw.

Moorhead, Jack, ed. Numerical Control Applications. LC 80-52613. (Manufacturing Update Ser.). (Illus.). 260p. 1980. 32.00 (ISBN 0-87263-058-7). SME.

Parsons, Noel R., ed. N-C Machinability Data Systems. LC 74-153852. (Society of Manufacturing Engineers Numerical Control Ser.). pap. 54.80 (ISBN 0-317-09442-4, 2015999). Bks Demand UMI.

--NC Machinability Data Systems. LC 74-153852. (Numerical Control Ser). 1971. text ed. 13.60x (ISBN 0-87263-029-3). SME.

Popowski, John D. Mathematical Tools for Machine Technology. 1982. text ed. write for info. (ISBN 0-534-01096-2, Breton Pubs). Wadsworth Pub.

Prather, Ronald E. Discrete Mathematical Structures for Computer Science. LC 75-25014. (Illus.). 680p. 1976. text ed. 34.50 (ISBN 0-395-20622-7); solutions manual 3.50 (ISBN 0-395-20623-5). HM.

Roberts, Arthur & Prentice, Richard. Programming for Numerical Control Machines. 2nd ed. (Illus.). 1978. text ed. 30.95x (ISBN 0-07-053156-0). McGraw.

Sava, Michael & Pusztai, Joseph. Computer Numerical Control. 1983. text ed. 28.95 (ISBN 0-8359-0924-7). Reston.

Smith, Donald N., ed. Numerical Control for Tomorrow. Peelle, David M. (Illus.). 181p. 1969. 12.00 (ISBN 0-938654-04-7, NC TOM). Indus Dev Inst Sci.

MACHINE-TOOLS, AUTOMATIC
see Machine-Tools

MACHINE-TRACTOR STATIONS

Miller, Robert F. One Hundred Thousand Tractors: The MTS & the Development of Controls in Soviet Agriculture. LC 70-95929. (Russian Research Center Studies: No. 60). 1970. 25.00x (ISBN 0-674-63875-1). Harvard U Pr.

MACHINE TRADE
see Machinery–Trade and Manufacture

MACHINE TRANSLATING
see also Translating Machines

Akhmanova, O. S., et al. Exact Methods in Linguistic Research. Haynes, David G. & Mohr, Dolores V., trs. LC 63-19957. 1963. 44.00x (ISBN 0-520-00542-2). U of Cal Pr.

Allen, Sture & Petofi, Janos S., eds. Aspects of Automatized Text Processing, Vol. 17. (Paper in Textlinguistics Ser.). 194p. (Orig.). 1979. pap. text ed. 14.00x (ISBN 3-87118-363-6, Pub. by Helmut Buske Verlag Hamburg). Benjamins North Am.

Ceccato, Silvio, ed. Linguistic Analysis & Programming for Mechanical Translation. (Illus.). 246p. 1961. 46.25 (ISBN 0-677-00110-X). Gordon.

Garvin, Paul L. On Machine Translation. LC 79-182469. (Janua Linguarum Ser. Minor: No. 128). 142p. (Orig.). 1972. pap. text ed. 13.60x (ISBN 90-2792-004-4). Mouton.

Henisz-Dostert, Bozena, et al. Machine Translation. (Trends in Linguistics, Studies, & Monographs: No. 16). 1979. text ed. 30.00x (ISBN 90-279-7836-0). Mouton.

Ingerman, Peter Z. Syntax Oriented Translator. 1966. 16.00 (ISBN 0-12-370850-8). Acad Pr.

Lawson, V. Practical Experience of Machine Translation. 200p. 1982. 42.75 (ISBN 0-444-86381-8, North-Holland). Elsevier.

Locke, William N. & Booth, E. Donald, eds. Machine Translation of Languages: Fourteen Essays. LC 75-29339. 243p. 1976. Repr. of 1955 ed. lib. bdg. 19.75x (ISBN 0-8371-8434-7, LOMT). Greenwood.

MACHINERY
see also Bearings (Machinery); Construction Equipment; Electric Engineering; Electric Machinery; Engines; Friction; Gearing; Hydraulic Machinery; Inventions; Locomotives; Lubrication and Lubricants; Machine-Tools; Mechanical Drawing; Mechanical Engineering; Mechanics; Patents; Power Transmission; Sealing (Technology); Shafting; Steam-Engines; Turning; Windmills
also machinery used in particular industries or for special purposes, e.g. Agricultural Machinery; Calculating Machines

American Society for Metals. Influence of Metallurgy on Machinability: An International Symposium, Proceedings. Tipnis, Vijay A., compiled by. LC 75-29683. (Materials-Metalworking Technology Ser.: No. 7). (Illus.). pap. 120.00 (ISBN 0-317-09746-6, 2019477). Bks Demand UMI.

American Society of Mechanical Engineers, Lubrication Division. Diagnosing Machinery Health: Presented at the Winter Annual Meeting of the American Society of Mechanical Engineers, San Francisco, California, December 10-15, 1978. Dill, J. F. & Petrovic, W. K., eds. LC 78-59891. pap. 20.00 (ISBN 0-317-11179-5, 2015394). Bks Demand UMI.

Appraisal of Machinery & Equipment. LC 73-97948. (ASA Monograph: No. 2). 1969. 5.00 (ISBN 0-937828-11-4). Am Soc Appraisers.

Barnett, George E. Chapters on Machinery & Labor. LC 68-25563. (Arcturus Books Paperbacks Ser.). 191p. 1969. pap. 2.25x (ISBN 0-8093-0398-1). S Ill U Pr.

Barron, D. Assemblers & Loaders. 3rd ed. 120p. 1978. 24.75 (ISBN 0-444-19462-2). Elsevier.

The Book of Knowledge of Ingenious Mechanical Devices: Kitab Ft Ma 'rifat Al-Hiyal Al-Handasiyya. LC 72-92529. 286p. 1974. lib. bdg. 126.00 (ISBN 90-277-0329-9, Pub. by Reidel Holland). Kluwer Academic.

Buck, Gordon S. Machinery Alignment Tables: Face-OD & Reverse Indicator Methods. LC 83-22692. 320p. (Orig.). 1984. pap. 18.95x spiral bound (ISBN 0-87201-015-5). Gulf Pub.

Burroughs, William S. The Soft Machine. Bd. with Nova Express; The Wild Boys: Three Novels. LC 80-8062. 544p. (Orig.). 1981. pap. 5.95 (ISBN 0-394-17749-5, B446, BC). Grove.

Collett, Ritter. Men of the Machine. (Illus.). 254p. 1977. 8.95 (ISBN 0-913428-28-0). Landfall Pr.

Cooper, Grace R. The Sewing Machine: Its Invention & Development. LC 75-619415. (Illus.). 238p. 1977. 27.50x (ISBN 0-87474-330-3). Smithsonian.

Darack, Arthur. Outdoor Power Equipment: How It Works, How to Fix It. LC 77-70404. 1977. pap. 4.95 (ISBN 0-8128-2276-5). Stein & Day.

Echaore & Wentz. Machines. (Science in Action Ser.). (Illus.). 48p. 1984. pap. text ed. 2.85 (ISBN 0-88102-021-4); tchr's guide avail. Janus Bks.

Cooper, C. A. & Clark, J. A., eds. Employment, Economics & Technology: The Impact of Technological Change on the Labor Market. LC 82-42543. 180p. 1982. 25.00x (ISBN 0-312-24459-2). St Martin.

Dahlberg, Arthur A. Jobs, Machines & Capitalism. LC 70-91296. (BCL Ser. I). Repr. of 1932 ed. 16.50 (ISBN 0-404-01917-X). AMS Pr.

Dodd, William. Labouring Classes of England. LC 68-55703. Repr. of 1847 ed. 22.50x (ISBN 0-678-00961-9). Kelley.

Fassbender, A. G., et al. Energy Efficient Industrial Technology in Europe & Japan. LC 83-13065. (Energy Technology Review No. 85). (Illus.). 416p. 1984. 45.00 (ISBN 0-8155-0958-8). Noyes.

Game, Ann & Pringle, Rosemary. Gender at Work. 180p. 1983. pap. text ed. 9.95 (ISBN 0-86861-261-8). Allen Unwin.

Gaskell, Peter. Artisans & Machinery. LC 68-28259. Repr. of 1836 ed. 39.50x (ISBN 0-678-05047-3). Kelley.

Gillespie, Laroux K., ed. Deburring Capabilities & Limitations. LC 76-47179. (Illus.). text ed. 15.95 (ISBN 0-87263-038-2). SME.

Hirschhorn, Larry. Beyond Mechanization: Work & Technology in a Post-Industrial Age. LC 84-947. (Illus.). 216p. 1984. text ed. 17.50x (ISBN 0-262-08142-3). MIT Pr.

Holloman, J. Herbert. Technical Change & American Enterprise. LC 74-19049. 52p. 1974. 1.50 (ISBN 0-89068-013-2). Natl Planning.

Jones, Barry. Sleepers, Wake! Technology & the Future of Work. 2nd ed. (Illus.). 302p. 1985. pap. 9.95 (ISBN 0-19-554453-6). Oxford U Pr.

Knowles, Lillian C. Industrial & Commercial Revolutions in Great Britain During the Nineteenth Century. 4th ed. LC 67-27704. Repr. of 1961 ed. 35.00x (ISBN 0-678-06518-7). Kelley.

Machinability Data Center Technical Staff, ed. Machining Data Handbook, 2 vols. 3rd ed. LC 80-81480. (Illus.). 1980. Set. 150.00x (ISBN 0-936974-00-1). Metcut Res Assocs.

North-South Technology Transfer: The Adjustment Ahead. (Analytical Studies). 222p. (Orig.). 1982. pap. text ed. 20.00x (ISBN 92-64-12265-6). OECD.

Powell, James. Investing in High Tech Industries: Picking Tomorrow's Winners Today. 1985. 35.00 (ISBN 0-87094-596-3). Dow Jones-Irwin.

Smith, Elliot D. & Nyman, Richmond C. Technology & Labor: Study of the Human Problems of Labor Saving. Stein, Leon, ed. LC 77-70533. (Work Ser.). 1977. Repr. of 1939 ed. lib. bdg. 24.50x (ISBN 0-405-10201-1). Ayer Co Pubs.

Soule, George. What Automation Does to Human Beings. Stein, Leon, ed. LC 77-70534. (Work Ser.). 1977. Repr. of 1956 ed. lib. bdg. 20.00x (ISBN 0-405-10202-X). Ayer Co Pubs.

Tozer, John. Mathematical Investigation of the Effect of Machinery on the Wealth of a Community & On the Effect Of the Non-Residence of Landlords On the Wealth of a Community. LC 66-21696. 1968. 15.00x (ISBN 0-678-00300-9). Kelley.

Walker, Charles R. Toward the Automatic Factory: A Case Study of Men & Machines. LC 76-45083. (Illus.). 1977. Repr. of 1957 ed. lib. bdg. 22.50x (ISBN 0-8371-9301-X, WATA). Greenwood.

Warner, Malcolm, ed. Microprocessors, Manpower & Society. LC 83-40148. 390p. 1984. 39.95 (ISBN 0-312-53187-7). St Martin.

Wedderburn, Dorothy & Crompton, Rosemary. Worker's Attitudes & Technology. LC 70-183225. (Cambridge Papers in Sociology: No. 2). (Illus.). 143p. 1972. pap. 10.95 (ISBN 0-521-09711-8). Cambridge U Pr.

Yellowitz, Irwin. Industrialization & the American Labor Movement, 1850-1900. 1976. 18.50x (ISBN 0-8046-9150-9, Pub. by Kennikat). Assoc Faculty Pr.

MACHINES
see Machinery

MACHINES, LOGIC
see Logic Machines

MACHINING OF METALS
see Metal-Work

MACHINISTS

American Machinist Magazine Staff. Best of American Machinist Magazine, Jan-Jun 1909. 1985. pap. 9.95 (ISBN 0-917914-26-0). Lindsay Pubns.

Blueprint Reading for Machinists-Advanced. LC 75-138355. 86p. 1972. 12.80 (ISBN 0-8273-0087-5); instructor's guide o.p. 2.75 (ISBN 0-8273-0088-3). Delmar.

Educational Research Council of America. Machinist. rev. ed. Kunze, Linda J. & Marchak, John P., eds. (Real People at Work Ser.). (Illus.). 36p. 1976. pap. text ed. 2.70 (ISBN 0-89247-057-7, 9337). Changing Times.

Lehrling, George. Machinist: Basic Skill Development. LC 77-73238. pap. 64.00 (ISBN 0-317-11103-5, 2011575). Bks Demand UMI.

Marshall, Oscar S. Journeyman Machinist En Route to the Stars. Douglas, Eva M., ed. LC 78-64614. (Illus.). 1979. 12.00 (ISBN 0-88492-025-9). W S Sullwold.

Rudman, Jack. Foreman Machinist. (Career Examination Ser.: C-1414). (Cloth bdg. avail. on request). pap. 10.00 (ISBN 0-8373-1414-3). Natl Learning.

--Machinist. (Career Examination Ser.: C-460). (Cloth bdg. avail. on request). pap. 10.00 (ISBN 0-8373-0460-1). Natl Learning.

--Maintenance Machinist. (Career Examination Ser.: C-1354). (Cloth bdg. avail. on request). pap. 10.00 (ISBN 0-8373-1354-6). Natl Learning.

MACINTOSH (COMPUTER)

Aker, Sharon Z. Microsoft BASIC Programming for the Mac. 1985. pap. 17.95 (ISBN 0-673-18167-7). Scott F.

Aldridge, Adele & Davis, Frederic E. MacArt for the Macintosh: The Marriage of Art & Science. (Micropower Ser.). 224p. 1985. deluxe ed. 29.95 incl. diskette (ISBN 0-697-00735-9); pap. 16.95 (ISBN 0-697-00708-1). Wm C Brown.

Allswang, John M. Macintosh: The Definitive User's Guide. LC 84-24226. (Illus.). 256p. 1985. pap. 15.95 (ISBN 0-89303-649-8). Brady Comm.

Anderson, John J. The Insider's Guide to the Macintosh: Tips, Shortcuts & Helpful Hints from the Professionals. (Illus.). 240p. (Orig.). pap. cancelled (ISBN 0-916688-93-3, 933). Creative Comp.

The Apple Macintosh Microcomputer. (Nanos Reference Cards Ser.). Date not set. price not set (ISBN 0-915069-27-X). Nanos Sys.

The Apple Macintosh User's Encyclopedia. 1984. 19.95 (ISBN 0-912003-34-0). Bk Co.

Arden Group Staff & Martin, James. A Breakthrough in Making Computers Friendly: The Macintosh Computer. (Illus.). 320p. 1986. text ed. 30.00 (ISBN 0-13-081589-6); pap. 19.95 (ISBN 0-317-29660-4). P-H.

Beekman, George. The Macintosh Home Companion. (Home Companion Ser.). (Illus., Orig.). Date not set. pap. 19.95 (ISBN 0-88190-385-X, BO385). Datamost.

Behrendt, Bill L. Conquering the Macintosh Kingdom: Twenty-Five Original Games in Dazzling Sight & Sound. (Illus.). 200p. 1985. pap. 15.95 (ISBN 0-13-167974-0). P-H.

--Music & Sound for the Macintosh. price not set. P-H.

--Music & Sound for the Macintosh. (Illus.). 200p. 1985. pap. 15.95 (ISBN 0-13-607185-6). P-H.

Berentes, Drew. MacPascal Programming. 1985. 22.95 (ISBN 0-8306-0891-5, 1891); pap. 16.95 (ISBN 0-8306-1891-0). TAB Bks.

BIS Applied Systems & MacKintosh International. The Local Area Network Reference Guide. Brooks, Tom, ed. (Illus.). 288p. 1985. text ed. 70.00 (ISBN 0-13-539586-0). P-H.

Brecher, J. & Cherry, G. Macintosh Pascal. 1985. 17.95 (ISBN 0-8359-4174-4). Reston.

Brecher, Jerry & Cherry, George. Macintosh Pascal. (Illus.). 360p. 17.95 (ISBN 0-317-13084-6). P-H.

Burns, Diane K. & Venit, Sharyn D. Mac at Work: Macintosh Windows on Business. 224p. 1985. pap. 17.95 (ISBN 0-471-82050-4); Book with program disk. 39.95 (ISBN 0-471-82737-1). Wiley.

Caggiano, J. The Complete Guide to Your Macintosh. 1984. 19.95 (ISBN 0-317-05711-1). SYBEX.

Caggiano, Joseph. The Macintosh: A Practical Guide. (Illus.). 280p. 1984. pap. 12.95 (ISBN 0-89588-216-7). SYBEX.

Campbell, John. The Macintosh Connection. 1985. 17.95 (ISBN 0-8359-4172-8). Reston.

Carmony, Lowell A. & Holliday, Robert. Pascal on the Macintosh. LC 84-19895. 370p. text ed. cancelled (ISBN 0-88175-032-8, Dist. by Har-Row). Computer Sci.

Carmony, Lowell A. & Holliday, Robert L. Macintosh BASIC. LC 84-23051. (Illus.). Date not set. pap. 19.95 (ISBN 0-88175-082-4). Computer Sci.

--Macintosh Pascal. LC 84-19901. (Illus.). 315p. 1985. pap. 19.95 (ISBN 0-88175-081-6); student's diskette 20.00 (ISBN 0-88175-088-3); solutions diskette 15.00 (ISBN 0-88175-089-1). Computer Sci.

Chaya, Ruth K. & Miller, Joan M. More BASIC Programming for the Classroom & Home Teacher (IBM PC, IBM PCjr, Commodore, Apple, Macintosh) 262p. (Orig.). 1985. pap. text ed. 17.95X (ISBN 0-8077-2780-6). Tchrs Coll.

Chernicoff. Mac Revealed: Programming with the Macintosh Toolbox. 256p. 1984. 19.95 (ISBN 0-317-06578-5, 6551). Hayden.

--Macintosh Pascal. Date not set. price not set. Hayden.

--Macintosh Revealed: Programming the Macintosh Toolbox. 1985. 24.95 (ISBN 0-8104-6551-5). Hayden.

Chernicott. Macintosh Revealed: Programming with the Macintosh Toolbox. (Mac Library). 256p. 1984. 19.95 (ISBN 0-317-05879-7). Hayden.

Coan & Coan. Microsoft BASIC for the Macintosh. 1985. 18.95 (ISBN 0-8104-6558-2). Hayden.

Compute Editors. MacOffice: Using the Macintosh for Everything. (Orig.). 1985. pap. 18.95 (ISBN 0-87455-006-8). Compute Pubns.

Connolly, Edward S. & Lieberman, Philip. Introducing the Apple Macintosh. LC 84-50035. 192p. 1984. 12.95 (ISBN 0-672-22361-9). Sams.

Crissman, Susan & Weintraut, Steven. Collegiate Guide to the Macintosh. trade ed. (Micropower Ser.). 208p. 1985. pap. cancelled (ISBN 0-697-00740-5). Wm C Brown.

Dayton, Rick. Macintosh Microsoft BASIC. price not set. P-H.

--Understanding the Macintosh. 1984. pap. text ed. 18.95 (ISBN 0-8359-8054-5). Reston.

DiElsie, et al. Programming Macintosh BASIC. 350p. 1985. pap. text ed. write for info. (ISBN 0-8087-6404-7). Burgess.

Duff, C. Introducing the Macintosh. 1984. pap. 14.95 (ISBN 0-07-018024-5, BYTE Bks). McGraw.

Ettlin, Walter A. Multiplan Made Easy. 14.95 (ISBN 0-07-881135-X, 135-X). Osborne-McGraw.

Ettlin, Walter A. & Solberg, Gregory. The Microsoft BASIC Book! Macintosh Edition. 464p. (Orig.). 1985. pap. 18.95 (ISBN 0-07-881169-4, 169-4). Osborne McGraw.

Expert Systems. Personal Financial Advertising for the Macintosh. 1985. 49.95 (ISBN 0-8104-7560-X). Hayden.

Flast, Robert & Flast, Lauren. Macintosh Spreadsheets: Using Microsoft Multiplan, Chart, & File. 200p. (Orig.). 1985. pap. 16.95 (ISBN 0-07-881187-2). Osborne-McGraw.

Flock, Emil & Flock, Miriam. BASIC Primer for the Macintosh. 1985. pap. 17.95 (ISBN 0-452-25639-9, Plume). NAL.

Gader, Bertram & Nodar, Manuel V. Mac Software for Pennies. 1986. pap. 12.95 (ISBN 0-446-38285-X). Warner Bks.

Glau, Gregory R. Business Graphics for the Macintosh. 250p. 1985. pap. 19.95 (ISBN 0-87094-693-5). Dow Jones-Irwin.

Goldstein, Larry J. & Schneider, David. Microsoft BASIC for the Macintosh. (Illus.). 576p. 1984. pap. 21.95 (ISBN 0-89303-662-5). Brady Comm.

Good, Phillip I. & Good, Kathryn. Managing Your Office with Macintosh. LC 84-45689. 176p. (Orig.). 1985. pap. 16.95 (ISBN 0-8019-7543-3). Chilton.

Goodman, Danny. Supermac. 250p. 1985. pap. 12.95 (ISBN 0-671-49256-X, Pub. by Computer Bks). S&S.

Grams, Marilyn. How to Make Money Writing with Your Macintosh & Get Published Instantly with a Laser Printer. LC 85-71821. (Illus.). 192p. 1985. pap. 14.95 (ISBN 0-932707-15-7). Achievement Pr.

Green, Kenneth C. & Van Dam, Rika. The Joy of Macintosh: Recipes for Using Your Mac Productively. 1986. pap. 18.95 (ISBN 0-673-18329-7). Scott F.

--The Macintosh Apple: A Comprehensive Reference Guide. (Illus.). 256p. pap. 14.95 (ISBN 0-88056-332-X). Dilithium Pr.

Grillo, John P. & Robertson, J. Douglas. Graphics for the Macintosh: An Idea Book. 1985. 17.95 (ISBN 0-03-000477-2). CBS Ed.

Guzelimian, Vahe. Becoming a MacArtist. Compute!, ed. (Orig.). 1985. pap. 17.95 (ISBN 0-942386-80-9). Compute Pubns.

Hartnell, Tim & Cook, W. Getting Started on Your Mac If You've Never Used a Computer Before. 1985. pap. 12.95 (ISBN 0-345-32244-4). Ballantine.

Heid, James. Programming in Macintosh BASIC. 1985. pap. 24.95 (ISBN 0-912677-48-1). Ashton-Tate Bks.

Hoenig, Alan. Microsoft Word for the Macintosh: Word Processing & the Professional. (Micropower Ser.). 208p. 1985. pap. 14.95 (ISBN 0-697-00879-7). WM C Brown.

Hoffman, Paul. Microsoft Word Made Easy. 250p. (Orig.). pap. 14.95 (ISBN 0-07-881144-9, 144-9). Osborne-McGraw.

Hogan, Thom. Inside the Macintosh. 15.95 (ISBN 0-89303-553-X). Brady Comm.

Holtz, Frederick. Using & Programming the Macintosh, with 32 Ready-to-Run Programs. (Illus.). 256p. (Orig.). 16.95 (ISBN 0-8306-0840-0, 1840); pap. 12.50 (ISBN 0-8306-1840-6). TAB Bks.

Houlberg, Michael. Macintosh Typefaces: A Reference Guide to Shapes, Sizes & Styles. 113p. 1984. pap. 14.95 (ISBN 0-932287-00-X). Houlberg Dev.

Kamins, Scott. Introduction to Macintosh BASIC. 1984. pap. 18.95 (ISBN 0-317-13953-3, 6550-7). Hayden.

Kater, David. Macintosh Graphics & Sound. 350p. (Orig.). 1985. pap. 17.95 (ISBN 0-07-881177-5, 177-5). Osborne-McGraw.

Kater, David A. & Kater, Richard L. The Printed Word: The Microsoft Guide to Advanced Word Processing on the Apple Macintosh. (Illus.). 336p. 1985. pap. 17.95 (ISBN 0-914845-53-5). Microsoft.

Kepner, Terry & Robinson, Mark. Fifty-Eight Business Programs for the Macintosh. 1985. pap. 18.95 (ISBN 0-673-18284-3). Scott F.

Kronick, Scott. Macintosh Pascal Illustrated. LC 85-3907. 1985. 16.95 (ISBN 0-201-11675-8). Addison-Wesley.

Lambert, Steve. Presentation Graphics on the Apple Macintosh: How to Use Microsoft Chart to Create Dazzling Graphics for Professional & Corporate Applications. 288p. 1984. pap. 18.95 (ISBN 0-914845-11-X). Microsoft.

Laris, Michael V. & Stiff, M. Ronald. Multiplan for the Macintosh with Microsoft Chart. (Microcomputer Power Ser.). 180p. 1984. pap. 16.95 (ISBN 0-697-00456-2); incl. disk 26.95 (ISBN 0-697-00462-7). Wm C Brown.

Ledgard, Henry & Singer, Andrew. Pascal for the Macintosh. LC 84-24503. 456p. 1985. pap. text ed. 18.95 (ISBN 0-201-11772-X). Addison-Wesley.

Leemon, Sheldon & Levitan, Arlan. MacTalk: Telecomputing on the Macintosh. Compute!, ed. (Orig.). 1985. pap. 14.95 (ISBN 0-942386-85-X). Compute Pubns.

Lewis, Gerard. Macintosh Pascal: Learning to Program Right the First Time. 312p. 1984. pap. cancelled (ISBN 0-88693-165-7). Banbury Bks.

--Macintosh: The Appliance of the Future. 288p. 1984. pap. 14.95 (ISBN 0-88693-031-6). Banbury Bks.

Lien, David A. Learning Microsoft BASIC for the Macintosh: New Microsoft 2.0 Version. LC 85-71339. (Illus.). 458p. (Orig.). 1985. pap. 19.95 (ISBN 0-932760-34-1). Compusoft.

Louden, Robert K. Beginning BASIC on the Apple Macintosh. 128p. 1984. incl. disk 23.95 (ISBN 0-88284-307-9). Alfred Pub.

Luehrmann, Arthur & Peckham, Herbert. Macintosh BASIC. 1985. 16.95 (ISBN 0-03-004219-4). CBS Ed.

McComb, Gordon. Macintosh User's Guide. LC 84-51097. 440p. 1984. 16.95 (ISBN 0-672-22328-7, 22328). Sams.

Macintosh Magic. (Illus.). 250p. 1984. pap. 12.95 (ISBN 0-525-48122-2, 01258-370). Dutton.

Mackie, Peter H. & Griffin, John R. PC to Mac & Back: A File Transfer Utility for the IBM-PC & Macintosh. (Illus.). 165p. incl. disk 49.95 (ISBN 0-88056-224-2). Dilithium Pr.

Malitz, Isaac. The Super Computer Snooper for the Apple Macintosh. (Super Computer Snooper Ser.). Date not set. 14.95 (ISBN 0-88190-424-4, BO424). Datamost.

Maran, Richard. The Graphic Macintosh Book. 1985. FPT 11.95 (ISBN 0-03-928875-7). CBS Ed.

Markoff, John, et al. The Instant Expert's Guide to the Apple Macintosh. (Dvorak's Instant Expert Ser.). (Orig.). 1985. pap. 9.95 (ISBN 0-440-54063-1). Dell.

Mathews, Keith. Assembly Language Primer for the Macintosh. (Illus.). 1985. pap. 24.95 (ISBN 0-452-25642-9, Plume). NAL.

Mellin, Michael, et al, eds. The Book of Apple Macintosh Software 1985. 200p. 1985. pap. 19.95 (ISBN 0-912003-20-0). Bk Co.

Microtrend, Inc. Microsoft Windows on the IBM PC. (Microtrend Ser.). 1984. cancelled (ISBN 0-13-581661-0). P-H.

Microtrend, Inc. Editors. MacGuide: The Complete Handbook to the Macintosh. 1985. 14.95 (ISBN 0-452-25569-4, Plume). NAL.

Miller, David. Macintosh Data Files. 1984. 16.95 (ISBN 0-8359-4173-6). Reston.

--Macintosh Data Files. (Illus.). 232p. 14.95. P-H.

Miller, Merl & Knecht, Ken. Microsoft BASIC 2.0 for the Apple Macintosh. LC 85-60684. (Illus.). 336p. (Orig.). 1985. pap. 16.95x (ISBN 0-933557-00-0). Merl Miller Assoc.

Miller, Merl & Myers, Mary. Presenting the Macintosh. 129p. 1984. pap. 5.95 (ISBN 0-88056-305-2). Dilithium Pr.

Moll, Robert & Folsom, Rachel. Macintosh Pascal. LC 84-81937. 494p. pap. 23.95 (ISBN 0-395-37574-6); solutions manual 2.00 (ISBN 0-395-37575-4). HM.

Morgan, Christopher. Hidden Powers of the Macintosh. (Illus.). 1985. pap. 21.95 (ISBN 0-452-25643-7, Plume). NAL.

Mortimore, Eugene. Macintosh Applications for Engineers. Date not set. price not set. P-H.

--Macintosh MacDraw & MacWrite for Engineers, Vol. II. 1985. text ed. 21.95 (ISBN 0-8359-4150-7); pap. 17.95 (ISBN 0-8359-4149-3). Reston.

--Macintosh MacDraw & MacWrite for Engineers. 1985. text ed. 21.95 (ISBN 0-8359-4155-8); pap. 17.95 (ISBN 0-8359-4153-1). Reston.

Pethig, Ronald. Dielectric & Electronic Properties of Biological Materials. LC 78-13694. 376p. 1979. 71.95 (ISBN 0-471-99728-5, Pub. by Wiley-Interscience). Wiley.

Poland, D. & Scheraga, H. A. Theory of Helix Coil Transitions in Biopolymers. (Molecular Biology). 1970. 75.00 (ISBN 0-12-559550-6). Acad Pr.

Randall, James C., ed. NMR & Macromolecules: Sequence, Dynamic, & Domain Structure. LC 84-366. (ACS Symposium Ser.: No. 247). 280p. 1984. lib. bdg. 34.95x (ISBN 0-8412-0829-8). Am Chemical.

Reinisch, R. F., ed. Photochemistry of Macromolecules. LC 70-127936. 229p. 1970. 39.50x (ISBN 0-306-30499-6, Plenum Pr). Plenum Pub.

Roberts, Richard B., ed. Studies in Macromolecular Biosynthesis. (Illus.). 702p. 1964. 29.00 (ISBN 0-87279-635-3, 624). Carnegie Inst.

Saltman, P. & Hegenuer, J., eds. The Biochemistry & Physiology of Iron: Proceedings of the 5th International Conference on Problems of Iron Storage & Transport, University of California, San Diego, Aug. 24-26, 1981. 836p. 1982. 106.00 (ISBN 0-444-00688-5, Biomedical Pr). Elsevier.

Salvatore, F., et al, eds. Macromolecules in the Functioning Cell. LC 78-27547. 351p. 1979. 45.00x (ISBN 0-306-40146-0, Plenum Pr). Plenum Pub.

Sedacek, B. & Overberger, C. G. Microcalorimetry of Macromolecules. 112p. 1981. pap. 20.95 (ISBN 0-471-86313-0, Pub. by Wiley-Interscience). Wiley.

Seymour, Raymond & Stahl, G. Allan, eds. Macromolecular Solutions: Solvent-Property Relationships in Polymers. (Illus.). 245p. 1982. 47.00 (ISBN 0-08-026337-2). Pergamon.

Silverstein, S. C., ed. Transport of Macromolecules in Cellular Systems, LSRR 11. (Dahlem Workshop Reports Ser.: L.S.R.R. No. 11). 1978. pap. 42.40x (ISBN 0-89573-095-2). VCH Pubs.

Societe de Chimie Physique, 23rd. Dynamic Aspects of Conformation Changes in Biological Macromolecules: Proceedings. Sadron, C., ed. LC 72-97962. 400p. 1973. lib. bdg. 79.00 (ISBN 90-277-0334-5, Pub. by Reidel Holland). Kluwer Academic.

Society for the Study of Development & Growth - Symposium. Cytodifferentiation & Macromolecular Synthesis: Proceedings. Locke, M., ed. 1963. 51.00 (ISBN 0-12-454156-9). Acad Pr.

Spragg, S. P. The Physical Behavior of Macromolecules with Biological Functions. LC 80-40280. (Molecular Biophysics & Biochemistry Monographs). 202p. 1980. 51.95 (ISBN 0-471-27784-3, Pub. by Wiley-Interscience). Wiley.

Tanford, Charles. Physical Chemistry of Macromolecules. LC 61-11511. 710p. 1961. 54.50x (ISBN 0-471-84447-0, Wiley-Interscience). Wiley.

Tsuchida, E. & Abe, K. Interactions Between Macromolecules in Solution & Intermacromolecular Complexes. (Advances in Polymer Science Ser.: Vol. 45). (Illus.). 150p. 1982. 41.00 (ISBN 0-387-11624-9). Springer-Verlag.

Venkataraghavan, Babu, intro. by. Macromolecular Structure & Specificity: Computer-Assisted Modeling & Applications. (Annals of The New York Academy of Sciences Ser.: Vol. 439). 209p. 1984. lib. bdg. 48.00x (ISBN 0-89766-272-5); pap. 48.00x (ISBN 0-89766-273-3). NY Acad Sci.

Williams, J. W. Ultracentrifugation of Macromolecules: Modern Topics. 1973. 33.00 (ISBN 0-12-755160-3). Acad Pr.

Wilson, A. D. & Crisp, S. Organolithic Macromolecular Materials. (Illus.). 298p. 1977. 37.00 (ISBN 0-85334-699-2, Pub. by Elsevier Applied Sci England). Elsevier.

Wunderlich, Berhard. Macromolecular Physics: Crystals, Structure, Morphology & Defects, 2 vols. 1973. Vol. 1, 1973. 73.00 (ISBN 0-12-765601-4); Vol. 2, 1976. 86.50 (ISBN 0-12-765602-2). Acad Pr.

Wunderlich, Bernhard. Macromolecular Physics: Vol. 3, Crystal Melting. LC 72-82632. 1980. 55.00 (ISBN 0-12-765603-0). Acad Pr.

MACROPHAGES

Chirigos, Michael A., et al, eds. Mediation of Cellular Immunity in Cancer by Immune Modifiers. (Progress in Cancer Research & Therapy Ser.: Vol. 19). 288p. 1981. text ed. 45.50 (ISBN 0-89004-628-X). Raven.

Escobar, M. R. & Friedman, H., eds. Macrophages & Lymphocytes: Nature, Functions & Interaction, Pt. B. (Advances in Experimental Medicine & Biology Ser.: Vol. 121B). 625p. 1980. 75.00x (ISBN 0-306-40286-6, Plenum Pr). Plenum Pub.

Herscowitz, H. B. Manual of Macrophage Methodology. (Immunology Ser.: Vol. 13). 1981. 69.75 (ISBN 0-8247-1222-6). Dekker.

Koren. Macrophage-Mediated Antibody. (Immunology Ser.). 384p. 1983. 55.00 (ISBN 0-8247-7011-0). Dekker.

Mathe, G., et al, eds. Lymphocytes, Macrophages, & Cancer. LC 76-26538. (Recent Results in Cancer Research Ser.: Vol. 56). 1976. 35.00 (ISBN 3-540-07902-5). Springer-Verlag.

Midwest Autumn Immunology Conference, 7th Meeting, Michigan, Nov. 1978. Immunologic Tolerance & Macrophage Function: Proceedings. Baram, R., et al, eds. LC 79-243. (Developments in Immunology Ser.: Vol. 4). 266p. 1979. 65.00 (ISBN 0-444-00316-9, Biomedical Pr). Elsevier.

Normann, Sigurd J. & Sorkin, Ernst, eds. Macrophages & Natural Killer Cells. (Advances in Experimental Medicine & Biology: Vol. 155). 874p. 1982. 95.00x (ISBN 0-306-41180-6, Plenum Pr). PLenum Pub.

Pearsall, Nancy N. & Weiser, Russell S. The Macrophage. LC 77-85844. (Illus.). Repr. of 1970 ed. 40.70 (ISBN 0-8357-9410-5, 2014576). Bks Demand UMI.

Unanue, Emil R. & Rosenthal, Alan S., eds. Macrophage Regulation of Immunity. LC 79-24609. 1980. 45.00 (ISBN 0-12-708550-5). Acad Pr.

Vernon-Roberts, B. The Macrophage. LC 72-184141. (Biological Structure & Function: 2). pap. 62.50 (ISBN 0-317-27095-8, 2024552). Bks Demand UMI.

MACROPHOTOGRAPHY

see also Photomicrography

Druyt, W. Macrophotography. (Photo Tips Ser.). (Illus.). 96p. (Orig.). 1980. pap. 4.95 (ISBN 0-85242-624-0, 3624). Morgan.

Hawken, William R. Close-up Photography. (Illus.). 132p. (Orig.). 1982. pap. 10.95 (ISBN 0-930764-33-1). Curtin & London.

White, William, Jr. Photomacrography. (Illus.). 352p. 1985. 49.95x (ISBN 0-240-51189-1). Focal Pr.

MACWRITE (COMPUTER PROGRAM)

Busch, David. Secrets of MacWrite, MacPaint, & MacDraw. (Microcomputer Bookshelf Ser.). 256p. (Orig.). 1985. pap. 13.95 (ISBN 0-317-18227-7). Little.

MAGELLAN, STRAIT OF

Sarmiento De Gamboa, Pedro. Narratives of the Voyages of Pedro Sarmiento De Gamboa to the Straits of Magellan. Markham, Clements R., ed. & tr. LC 74-136043. (Hakluyt Society First Ser: No. 91). 1970. lib. bdg. 32.00 (ISBN 0-8337-2239-5). B Franklin.

MAGELLANIC CLOUDS

Hodge, Paul W. & Wright, Frances W. The Small Magellanic Cloud. LC 76-49159. (Illus.). 80p. 1978. 65.00x (ISBN 0-295-95387-X). U of Wash Pr.

Philip, A. Davis & Senduleak, N., eds. A Deep Objective Prism Survey of the Large Magellanic Cloud for OB & Supergiant Stars, Part 1. 30p. 1983. 12.00 (ISBN 0-9607902-3-3). Davis Pr.

Symposium on the Magellanic Clouds, Santiago De Chile, March 1969. The Magellanic Clouds. Muller, A. B., ed. LC 73-154743. (Astrophysics & Space Science Library: No.23). 189p. 1971. lib. bdg. 26.00 (ISBN 90-277-0205-5, Pub. by Reidel Holland). Kluwer Academic.

MAGIC SQUARES

see also Mathematical Recreations

Ollerenshaw, Kathleen & Bondi, Herman. Magic Squares of Order Four. (Phil. Trans. Royal Society Series A: Vol. 306). (Illus.). 99p. (Orig.). 1983. pap. text ed. 26.00x (ISBN 0-85403-201-0, Pub. by Royal Soc London). Scholium Intl.

MAGNESIUM

Aikawa, Jerry K. Magnesium: It's Biologic Significance. 144p. 1981. 52.00 (ISBN 0-8493-5871-X). CRC Pr.

--Relationship of Magnesium to Disease in Domestic Animals & in Humans. (Illus.). 160p. 1971. 16.75x (ISBN 0-398-02215-1). C C Thomas.

Bennett, W. A. Character & Tonnage of the Turk Magnesite Deposit. (Reports of Investigations Ser.: No. 7). (Illus.). 1943. 0.25 (ISBN 0-686-38465-2). Geologic Pubns.

Brace, Arthur William & Allen, F. A. Magnesium Casting Technology. LC 58-821. (Illus.). pap. 43.50 (ISBN 0-317-11125-6, 2051325). Bks Demand UMI.

Interrelationships Between Potassium & Magnesium Absorption by Oats. (Agricultural Reseach Reports: No. 642). 1964. pap. 7.25 (ISBN 90-220-0103-2, PDC163, PUDOC). Unipub.

Magnesium Storage, Handling & Processing. (Forty Ser). 1974. pap. 2.50 (ISBN 0-685-58155-1, 48). Natl Fire Prot.

Seelig, Mildred S., ed. Magnesium Deficiency in the Pathogenesis of Disease. LC 78-27742. (Topics in Bone & Mineral Disorders Ser.). 500p. 1980. 55.00x (ISBN 0-306-40202-5, Plenum Pr). Plenum Pub.

Specification for Magnesium-Alloy Welding Rods & Bare Electrodes: A5.19. 18p. 1980. 10.00 (ISBN 0-87171-207-5); member 7.50. Am Welding.

Standard for the Manufacture of Aluminum or Magnesium Powder. (Sixty Ser.). 1974. pap. 2.00 (ISBN 0-685-58073-3, 651). Natl Fire Prot.

Wacker, Warren E. Magnesium & Man. LC 80-14189. (Commonwealth Fund Ser.). 1980. text ed. 17.50x (ISBN 0-674-54225-8). Harvard U Pr.

MAGNESIUM METABOLISM

see also Grass Tetany

Altura, B. M. & Altura, Bella T., eds. Dietary Minerals & Cardiovascular Disease. (Journal: Magnesium: Vol. 1, No. 3-6). (Illus.). vi, 188p. 1983. pap. 55.50 (ISBN 3-8055-3682-8). S Karger.

Cantin, Marc & Seelig, Mildred S., eds. Magnesium in Health & Disease. LC 78-13181. (Monographs of the Am College of Nutrition: Vol. 4). (Illus.). 1154p. 1980. 225.00 (ISBN 0-89335-055-9). SP Med & Sci Bks.

Durlach, J. & Altura, B. M., eds. Magnesium, Diabetes & Carbohydrate Metabolism: Journal - Magnesium. (Vol. 2, Nos. 4-6). (Illus.). iv, 172p. 1984. pap. 41.75 (ISBN 3-8055-3865-0). S Karger.

Halpern, M. J. & Durlach, J., eds. Magnesium Deficiency. (Illus.). viii, 248p. 1985. 79.75 (ISBN 3-8055-3979-7). S Karger.

MAGNETIC AMPLIFIERS

Transducer Market. 240p. 1984. 1500.00 (ISBN 0-86621-320-1). Frost & Sullivan.

MAGNETIC DISKS

Optical & Magnetic Disc Media. (Reports Ser.: No. 502). 181p. 1982. 1285.00x (ISBN 0-88694-502-X). Intl Res Dev.

MAGNETIC DOMAIN

see Domain Structure

MAGNETIC FIELDS

see also Electromagnetic Fields; Galvanomagnetic Effects; Hyperfine Interactions; Magnetic Resonance

Barnes, Thomas. Origin & Destiny of the Earth's Magnetic Field. LC 73-79065. (ICR Technical Monograph: No. 4). (Illus.). 64p. 1973. pap. 7.95 (ISBN 0-89051-013-X). Master Bks.

Barnothy, Madeline F., ed. Biological Effects of Magnetic Fields. Incl. Vol. 1. 335p. 1964. 39.50x (ISBN 0-306-37601-6); Vol. 2. 327p. 1969. 39.50x (ISBN 0-306-37602-4). LC 64-13146 (Plenum Pr). Plenum Pub.

Canuto, V., ed. Role of Magnetic Fields in Physics & Astrophysics, Vol. 257. (Annals of the New York Academy of Sciences). 226p. 1975. 38.00x (ISBN 0-89072-012-6). NY Acad Sci.

Chari, M. V. & Silvester, P., eds. Finite Elements in Electrical & Magnetic Field Problems. LC 79-1037. (Wiley Series in Numerical Methods in Engineering). 219p. 1980. 53.95 (ISBN 0-471-27578-6, Pub. by Wiley-Interscience). Wiley.

Davis, Albert R. & Rawls, Walter C., Jr. Magnetism & Its Effects on the Living System. LC 74-84423. (Illus.). 1974. 9.50 (ISBN 0-682-48087-8, University). Exposition Pr FL.

Gerloch, M. Magnetism & Ligand-Field Analysis. LC 83-1820. (Illus.). 650p. 1984. 110.00 (ISBN 0-521-24939-2). Cambridge U Pr.

Herlach, F., ed. Strong & Ultrastrong Magnetic Fields. (Topics in Applied Physics Ser.: Vol. 57). (Illus.). 375p. 1985. 48.50 (ISBN 0-387-13504-9). Springer-Verlag.

Howard, Robert & Bumba, V. Atlas of Solar Magnetic Fields. 1967. 10.00 (ISBN 0-87279-637-X). Carnegie Inst.

Lockheed Symposium on Magnetohydrodynamics. The Plasma in a Magnetic Field: A Symposium on Magnetohydrodynamics, 2nd, 1957, Palo Alto. LC 58-11698. pap. 34.80 (ISBN 0-317-07849-6, 2000317). Bks Demand UMI.

Loewinsohn, Ron. Magnetic Field(s) LC 82-48879. 1983. 12.95 (ISBN 0-394-53105-1). Knopf.

--Magnetic Field(s) 192p. 1984. pap. 5.95 (ISBN 0-553-34117-0). Bantam.

Miura, N. & Chikazumi, S., eds. Physics in High Magnetic Fields: Proceedings. (Springer Ser. in Solid-State Sciences: Vol. 24). (Illus.). 358p. 1981. 47.00 (ISBN 0-387-10587-5). Springer-Verlag.

Parkinson, David & Mulhall, Brian E. The Generation of High Magnetic Fields. LC 67-13568. (International Cryogenics Monographs Ser.). 165p. 1967. 35.00x (ISBN 0-306-30250-0, Plenum Pr). Plenum Pub.

Parkinson, David H. & Mulhall, Brian E. The Generation of High Magnetic Fields. LC 67-13568. (International Cryogenics Monograph Ser.). pap. 44.30 (ISBN 0-317-27895-9, 2055789). Bks Demand UMI.

Siemens Programmed Instruction "PI" Self-Study Books. (Magnetic Field: No. 3). 1978. 2.00 (ISBN 0-471-25968-3, Wiley Heyden). Wiley.

Siemens Programmed Instruction "PI" Study Books. (Magnetic Circuit: No. 4). 72p. 1978. 2.95 (ISBN 0-471-25971-3, Wiley Heyden). Wiley.

Skobel'tsyn, D. V., ed. Physical Investigations in Strong Magnetic Fields. LC 74-23793. (P. N. Lebedev Physics Institute Ser.: Vol. 67). (Illus.). 167p. 1974. 55.00 (ISBN 0-306-10906-9, Consultants). Plenum Pub.

Tenforde, T. S., ed. Magnetic Field Effects on Biological Systems. LC 79-20739. 108p. 1979. 27.50x (ISBN 0-306-40312-9, Plenum Pr). Plenum Pub.

MAGNETIC FIELDS–PHYSIOLOGICAL EFFECTS

Weinberg, H., ed. Biomagnetism: Application & Theory: Proceedings of the Fifth World Conference on Biomagnetism, Vancouver, Canada, August 1984. (Illus.). 450p. 1985. pap. 90.00 (ISBN 0-08-031971-8). Pergamon.

MAGNETIC FIELDS (COSMIC PHYSICS)

see also Magnetism, Terrestrial; Magnetohydrodynamics

Advanced Study Institute, Bergen, Norway, 1965. Radiation Trapped in the Earth's Magnetic Field: Proceedings. McCormac, B. M., ed. (Astrophysics & Space Library: No. 5). 901p. 1966. lib. bdg. 79.00 (ISBN 90-277-0130-X, Pub. by Reidel Holland). Kluwer Academic.

Advanced Summer Institute, Sheffield, England, 13-12 August, 1973. Magnetospheric Physics: Proceedings. McCormac, B. M., ed. LC 74-76472. (Astrophysics & Space Science Library: No. 44). 370p. 1974. lib. bdg. 66.00 (ISBN 90-277-0454-6, Pub. by Reidel Holland). Kluwer Academic.

I.A.U. Symposium, No. 43, College de France, Paris, August 31-September 4, 1970. Solar Magnetic Fields: Proceedings. Howard, R., ed. LC 78-159656. (I.A.U. Symposia). 361p. 1971. lib. bdg. 76.00 (ISBN 90-277-0201-2, Pub. by Reidel Holland). Kluwer Academic.

Jacobs. Reversals of the Earth's Magnetic Field. 276p. 1984. 35.00 (ISBN 0-9903000-2-1, Pub. by A Hilger England). Heyden.

Knott, K., ed. Physics of Planetary Magnetospheres, Vol. 1, Pt. 1. (Illus.). 390p. 1981. pap. 51.00 (ISBN 0-08-027151-0). Pergamon.

Merrill, Ronald T. The Earth's Magnetic Field: Its History Origin & Planetary Perspective. McElhinny, Michael W., ed. (International Geophysics Ser.). 1984. 67.50 (ISBN 0-12-491240-0); pap. 30.00 (ISBN 0-12-491242-7). Acad Pr.

Parker, E. N. Cosmical Magnetic Fields: Their Origin & Their Activity. (International Series of Monographs on Physics). (Illus.). 1979. 98.00x (ISBN 0-19-851290-2). Oxford U Pr.

Southwood, D. J. ULF Pulsations in the Magnetosphere. 1981. 29.50 (ISBN 90-277-1232-8, Pub. by Reidel Holland). Kluwer Academic.

MAGNETIC FLUIDS

International Advanced Course & Workshop on Thermomechanics of Magnetic Fluids, Udine, Italy, Oct. 3-7, 1977. Thermomechanics of Magnetic Fluids: Theory & Applications, Proceedings. new ed. Berkovsky, Boris, ed. LC 78-15126. 318p. 1978. text ed. 85.95 (ISBN 0-89116-143-0). Hemisphere Pub.

Rosensweig, Ronald E. Ferrohydrodynamics. (Cambridge Monographs in Mechanics & Applied Mathematics). (Illus.). 352p. Date not set. price not set (ISBN 0-521-25624-0). Cambridge U Pr.

MAGNETIC MATERIALS

see also Ferrites (Magnetic Materials); Magnets

AIP Conference. Magnetism & Magnetic Materials: Proceedings, 1973, 2 pts. Graham, C. D., Jr. & Rhyne, J. J., eds. LC 52-2468. (AIP Conference Proceedings: No. 18). 1974. 25.00x (ISBN 0-88318-117-7). Am Inst Physics.

AIP Conference, Chicago, 1971. Magnetism & Magnetic Materials: Proceedings, 1971, 2 pts. Graham, C. D., Jr. & Rhyne, J. J., eds. LC 59-2468. (AIP Conference Proceedings: No. 5). 1573p. 1972. 22.00 (ISBN 0-88318-104-5). Am Inst Physics.

AIP Conference, Denver, 1972. Magnetism & Magnetic Materials: Proceedings, 1972, 2 pts. Graham, C. D., Jr. & Rhyne, J. J., eds. LC 72-623469. (AIP Conference Proceedings: No. 10). 1714p. 1973. 24.00x (ISBN 0-88318-109-6). Am Inst Physics.

Annual Conference on Magnetic Materials, 22nd, Pittsburgh, June 15-18, 1976. Magnetism & Magnetic Materials: Proceedings, 1976. LC 76-47106. (AIP Conference Proceedings: No. 34). 1976. 19.50 (ISBN 0-88318-133-9). Am Inst Physics.

Becker, J. J., et al, eds. Magnetism & Magnetic Materials: Proceedings, 1975. LC 76-10931. (AIP Conference Proceedings: No. 29). 693p. 1976. 30.00 (ISBN 0-88318-128-2). Am Inst Physics.

Boll, R. Soft Magnetic Materials. 348p. 1979. 49.95 (ISBN 0-471-25600-5, Pub. by Wiley Heyden). Wiley.

Magnetism & Magnetic Materials Digest. Incl. 1965. White, R. L. & Wickersheim, K. A., eds. 1965. 47.00 (ISBN 0-12-747150-2); 1966. Haas, Warren C. & Jarrett, H. S., eds. 1968. 54.00 (ISBN 0-12-312750-5); 1967. Doyle, W. D. & Harris, A. B., eds. 1967. 65.00 (ISBN 0-12-221550-8); 1968. Chang, H. & McGuire, T. R., eds. 1968. 68.50 (ISBN 0-12-170450-5). Acad Pr.

Marson, Ron. Magnetism Thirty-Three. LC 81-90445. (Science with Simple Things Ser.: No. 33). (Illus.). 78p. 1983. pap. 13.95 tchr's ed (ISBN 0-941008-33-9). Tops Learning.

Mattis, D. C. The Theory of Magnetism II. (Springer Series in Solid-State Sciences: Vol. 55). (Illus.). 190p. 1985. 29.50 (ISBN 0-387-15025-0). Springer-Verlag.

Maxwell, James C. Electricity & Magnetism, 2 Vols. (Illus.). 1891. pap. text ed. 8.50 ea.; Vol. 1. pap. text ed. (ISBN 0-486-60636-8); Vol. 2. pap. text ed. (ISBN 0-486-60637-6). Dover.

Mintz, Stephan & Perlmutter, Arnold, eds. New Pathways in High Energy Physics, Pt. 1: Magnetic Charge & Other Fundamental Approaches. LC 76-20476. (Studies in the Natural Sciences Ser.: Vol. 10). 415p. 1976. 65.00x (ISBN 0-306-36910-9, Plenum Pr). Plenum Pub.

Moriya, T. Spin Fluctuations in Itinerant Electron Magnetism. (Solid-State Sciences Ser.: Vol. 56). (Illus.). 260p. 1985. 35.00 (ISBN 0-387-15422-1). Springer-Verlag.

Morrish, Allan H. The Physical Principles of Magnetism. LC 78-2480. 696p. 1980. Repr. of 1965 ed. lib. bdg. 38.00 (ISBN 0-88275-670-2). Krieger.

Mottelay, Paul F., ed. Bibliographical History of Electricity & Magnetism. LC 74-26277. (History, Philosophy & Sociology of Science Ser.). (Illus.). 1975. Repr. 48.00x (ISBN 0-405-06605-8). Ayer Co Pubs.

Nayfeh, Munir H. & Brussel, Morton K. Electricity & Magnetism. LC 84-19478. 688p. 1985. text ed. 31.95x (ISBN 0-471-87681-X). Wiley.

O'Dell, T. H. Magnetic Bubbles. LC 74-12048. 159p. 1974. 24.95x (ISBN 0-470-65259-4). Halsted Pr.

Purcell, E. M. Berkeley Physics Course: Electricity & Magnetism, Vol. 2. 2nd ed. 33.95 (ISBN 0-07-004908-4). McGraw.

Rado, George T. & Suhl, H., eds. Magnetism: A Treatise on Modern Theory & Materials, 5 vols. 1963-1973. Vol. 1, 1963. 86.50 (ISBN 0-12-575301-2); Vol. 2A, 1965. 76.50 (ISBN 0-12-575302-0); Vol. 2B, 1967. 76.50 (ISBN 0-12-575342-X); Vol. 3, 1963. 77.00 (ISBN 0-12-575303-9); Vol. 5. o.p 78.00 (ISBN 0-12-575305-5). Acad Pr.

Rawls, Walter, Jr. & Davis, Albert R. Magnetism & Its Effect on the Living System. 9.50x (ISBN 0-682-48087-8). Cancer Control Soc.

Sakura, Y. Recent Magnetics of Electronics, 1983. 1984. 95.00 (ISBN 0-444-86656-6, I-164-83). Elsevier.

Scott, William T. The Physics of Electricity & Magnetism. 2nd ed. LC 75-42235. 722p. 1977. Repr. of 1966 ed. 34.50 (ISBN 0-88275-375-4). Krieger.

Sears, Francis W. Electricity & Magnetism. (Illus.). 1951. 23.95 (ISBN 0-201-06900-8). Addison-Wesley.

Smith, S. & Wunkery, Quatt. Magnetic Components: Design & Applications. 1985. 39.95 (ISBN 0-442-20397-7). Van Nos Reinhold.

Sprott, Julien C. Introduction to Modern Electronics. LC 80-25366. 349p. 1981. 34.50 (ISBN 0-471-05840-8); 10.50 (ISBN 0-471-86375-0). Wiley.

Stacey, F. D. & Banerjee, S. K. Physical Principles of Rock Magnetism. LC 72-87965. (Developments in Solid Earth Geophysics Ser.: Vol. 5). 224p. 1974. 59.75 (ISBN 0-444-41084-8, X1973). Elsevier.

Suematsu, Y., ed. Optical Devices & Fibers, 1984. (Japan Annual Reviews in Electronics, Computers & Telecommunications Ser.: Vol. 11). 330p. 1984. 95.00 (ISBN 0-444-87502-6, I-267-84, North Holland). Elsevier.

The Theory of Magnetism One: Statistics & Dynamics. (Springer Series in Solid-State Sciences: Vol. 17). (Illus.). 320p. 1981. 37.00 (ISBN 0-387-10611-1). Springer-Verlag.

Tyablikov, S. V. Methods in the Quantum Theory of Magnetism. LC 65-27345. 354p. 1967. 37.50x (ISBN 0-306-30263-2, Plenum Pr). Plenum Pub.

Van Vleck, John H. Theory of Electric & Magnetic Susceptibilities. (International Series of Monographs on Physics). (Illus.). 1932. pap. 42.50x (ISBN 0-19-851243-0). Oxford U Pr.

Vigoreaux. Units & Standards of Electrimagnetism. (The Wykeham Science Ser.: No. 15). 82p. 1971. pap. cancelled (ISBN 0-85109-190-3). Taylor & Francis.

Vonsovsky, S. V. Magnetism of Elementary Particles. 295p. 1975. 6.45 (ISBN 0-8285-0792-9, Pub. by Mir Pubs USSR). Imported Pubns.

Wagner, D. Introduction to the Theory of Magnetism. 290p. 1972. text ed. 33.00 (ISBN 0-08-016595-8). Pergamon.

Weltner, W. Magnetic Atoms & Molecules. 1983. 42.50 (ISBN 0-442-29206-6). Van Nos Reinhold.

Williamson, Samuel J., et al, eds. Biomagnetism: An Interdisciplinary Approach. (NATO ASI Series A, Life Sciences: Vol. 66). 726p. 1983. 95.00x (ISBN 0-306-41369-8, Plenum Pr). Plenum Pub.

Winkler, G. Magnetic Garnets. (Vieweg Tracts in Pure & Applied Physics Ser.: Vol. 5). 1981. 82.00 (ISBN 0-9940013-3-9, Pub. by Vieweg & Sohn Germany). Heyden.

Winkler, G. & Hansen, P., eds. Intermag 84: Digest of the International Magnetics Conference, Hamburg, April 10-13, 1984. 546p. 1984. 70.00 (ISBN 0-444-87510-7). Elsevier.

Yarwood, John. Electricity & Magnetism. 1981. 25.00x (ISBN 0-7231-0808-0, Pub. by Univ Tutorial England). State Mutual Bk.

Yoder, H. S., Jr. Generation of Basaltic Magma. LC 76-29672. 1976. pap. text ed. 9.50 (ISBN 0-309-02504-4). Natl Acad Pr.

MAGNETISM–EARLY WORKS T0 1800

Barlow, William. A Briefe Discovery of the Idle Animadversions of Mark Ridley, Doctor of Phisicke. LC 71-38149. (English Experience Ser.: No. 429). 16p. 1972. Repr. of 1618 ed. 7.00 (ISBN 90-221-0429-X). Walter J Johnson.

—Magnetical Advertisements. LC 68-54616. (English Experience Ser.: No. 47). Repr. of 1616 ed. 14.00 (ISBN 90-221-0047-2). Walter J Johnson.

Home, R. W. Aepinus's Essay on the Theory of Electricity & Magnetism. Connor, P. J., tr. LC 78-10105. 1979. 53.00x (ISBN 0-691-08222-7). Princeton U Pr.

Norman, Robert. The Newe Attractive, Containing a Short Discourse of the Magnes or Lodestone, Etc. LC 73-6153. (English Experience Ser.: No. 616). (Illus.). 76p. 1973. Repr. of 1581 ed. 21.00 (ISBN 90-221-0616-0). Walter J Johnson.

MAGNETISM, TERRESTRIAL

Creer, K. M., et al, eds. Geomagnetism of Baked Clays & Recent Sediments. 324p. 1983. 53.25 (ISBN 0-444-42231-5, I-268-83). Elsevier.

Dessler, Alexander J., ed. Physics of the Jovian Magnetosphere. (Cambridge Planetary Science 3). (Illus.). 400p. 1983. 32.50 (ISBN 0-521-24558-3). Cambridge U Pr.

Dubrov, A. P. The Geomagnetic Field & Life: Geomagnetobiology. LC 78-1705. (Illus.). 335p. 1978. 55.00x (ISBN 0-306-31072-4, Plenum Pr). Plenum Pub.

European Geophysical Symposium, August 1980, Budapest. Geomagnetic Pulsations. Orr, D., ed. 100p. 1983. pap. 27.50 (ISBN 0-08-026508-1). Pergamon.

Fuller, M., et al, eds. Tectomagnetics & Local Geomagnetic Field Variations. (Advances in Earth & Planetary Sciences Ser.: No. 5). 140p. 1979. 22.50x (ISBN 0-89955-212-9, Pub. by Japan Sci Soc Japan). Intl Spec Bk.

Jacobs, J. A. Geomagnetic Micropulsations. LC 70-107315. (Physics & Chemistry in Space: Vol. 1). (Illus.). 1970. 29.00 (ISBN 0-387-04986-X). Springer-Verlag.

Knott, K., et al, eds. Advances in Magnetospheric Physics with GEOS-1 & ISEE. 1979. lib. bdg. 68.50 (ISBN 0-686-25183-0, Pub. by Reidel Holland). Kluwer Academic.

Matsushita, S. & Campbell, W. H., eds. Physics of Geomagnetic Phenomena, 2 Vols. (International Geophysics Ser.: Vol. 11). 1967. Vol. 1. 85.00 (ISBN 0-12-480301-6); Vol. 2, 1968. 89.50 (ISBN 0-12-480302-4). Acad Pr.

Nishida, A. Geomagnetic Diagnosis of the Magnetosphere. (Physics & Chemistry in Space Ser.: Vol. 9). (Illus.). 1978. 55.00 (ISBN 0-387-08297-2). Springer-Verlag.

Schmucker, Ulrich. Anomalies of Geomagnetic Variations in the Southwestern United States. LC 74-627675. (University of California. Scripps Institution of Oceanography, Bulletin: Vol. 13). pap. 44.50 (ISBN 0-317-08781-9, 2021289). Bks Demand UMI.

Shea, James H., ed. Plate Tectonics. (Benchmark Papers in Geology: Vol. 89). (Illus.). 368p. 1985. 49.50 (ISBN 0-442-27661-3). Van Nos Reinhold.

Stuart, W. F., ed. Geomagnetic Observatory & Survey Practice: Reprinted from the Journal Gemophysical Surveys, Vol 6, Nos. 3 & 4. 1985. 39.00 (ISBN 90-277-1908-X, Pub. by Reidel Holland). Kluwer Academic.

Thompson, Roy & Oldfield, Frank. Environmental Magnetism. (Illus.). 256p. 1985. text ed. 39.95x (ISBN 0-04-538003-1). Allen Unwin.

Waynick, A. H., ed. Geomagnetism & Aeronomy. LC 65-60042. (Antarctic Research Ser.: Vol. 4). (Illus.). 236p. 1965. 13.00 (ISBN 0-87590-104-2). Am Geophysical.

Wienert, Karl A. Notes on Geomagnetic Observatory & Survey Practice. (Earth Sciences Ser.: No. 5). (Illus.). 217p. 1970. pap. 17.00 (ISBN 92-3-100816-1, U432, UNESCO). Unipub.

MAGNETOHYDRODYNAMIC GENERATORS

see also Plasma Rockets

Caldirola, P. & Knoepfel, H., eds. Physics of High Energy Density. (Italian Physical Society: Course 48). 1971. 80.00 (ISBN 0-12-368848-5). Acad Pr.

MAGNETOHYDRODYNAMICS

see also Cosmic Electrodynamics; Ion Flow Dynamics; Magnetohydrodynamic Generators; Plasma Dynamics; Plasma Instabilities; Rockets (Aeronautics); Van Allen Radiation Belts

Bateman, Glenn. MHD Instabilities. 1978. text ed. 34.50x (ISBN 0-262-02131-5). MIT Pr.

Branover, H., et al, eds. Liquid-Metal & Magnetohydrodynamics. 45.00 (ISBN 0-915928-70-1). AIAA.

Cabannes, Henri. Theoretical Magnetofluid-Dynamics. LC 75-117095. (Applied Mathematics & Mechanics Ser.: Vol. 13). 1970. 70.00 (ISBN 0-12-153750-1). Acad Pr.

Chandrasekhar, S. Hydrodynamic & Hydromagnetic Stability. (Illus.). 704p. pap. 11.95 (ISBN 0-486-64071-X). Dover.

Cowling, T. G. Magnetohydrodynamics. Meadows, A. J., ed. (Mas 2). 1976. 32.00 (ISBN 0-9960026-5-0, Pub. by A Hilger England). Heyden.

Dragos, L. Magneto-Fluid Dynamics. 1975. 43.00 (ISBN 0-9961001-6-4, Pub. by Abacus England). Heyden.

Electricity from Magnetohydrodynamics, 1968: Warsaw. Vol. 1. pap. 34.25 (ISBN 92-0-030468-0, ISP191-1, IAEA); Vol. 2. pap. 34.25 (ISBN 92-0-030568-7, ISP191-2); Vol. 3. pap. 34.25 (ISBN 92-0-030668-3, ISP191-3); Vol. 4. pap. 34.25 (ISBN 92-0-030768-X, ISP191-4); Vol. 5. pap. 34.25 (ISBN 92-0-030868-6, ISP191-5); Vol. 6. pap. 34.25 (ISBN 92-0-030968-2, ISP191-6). Unipub.

Frieser, R. G. & Mogab, C. J., eds. Plasma Processing: Symposium on Plasma Etchins & Deposition, Proceedings. LC 81-65237. (Electrochemical Society Proceedings Ser.: Vol. 81-1). (Illus.). pap. 87.00 (ISBN 0-317-09584-6, 2051749). Bks Demand UMI.

Gruber, R. & Rappaz, J. Finite Element Methods in Linear Ideal Magnetohydrodynamics. (Computational Physics Ser.). (Illus.). 200p. 1985. 34.00 (ISBN 0-387-13398-4). Springer Verlag.

Gundersen, Roy M. Linearized Analysis of One-Dimensional Magnetohydrodynamic Flows. (Springer Tracts in Natural Philosophy: Vol. 1). (Illus.). 1964. 19.50 (ISBN 0-387-03216-9). Springer-Verlag.

Hesaaraki, Mahmud. Structure of Shock Waves in Magnetohydrodynamics. LC 84-3085. (Memoirs: No. 302). 98p. 1984. pap. 10.00 (ISBN 0-8218-2303-5). Am Math.

Jeffrey, Alan & Taniuti, T., eds. M H D Stability & Thermonuclear Containment. (Perspectives in Physics Ser.). 1966. 49.50 (ISBN 0-12-382550-4). Acad Pr.

Kirko, Igor M. Magnetohydrodynamics of Liquid Metals. LC 65-17789. 80p. 1965. 25.00x (ISBN 0-306-10732-5, Consultants). Plenum Pub.

Kolm, Henry, et al, eds. High Magnetic Fields. 1961. 50.00x (ISBN 0-262-11008-3). MIT Pr.

Krause, F. & Radler, K-H. Mean-Field Magnetohydrodynamics & Dynamo Theory. (Illus.). 270p. 1981. 40.00 (ISBN 0-08-025041-6). Pergamon.

Lockheed Symposium on Magnetohydrodynamics, (5th: 1960: Palo Alto) Radiation & Waves in Plasmas. Mitchner, Morton, ed. LC 61-14651. pap. 41.80 (ISBN 0-317-07864-X, 2000319). Bks Demand UMI.

Mather, N. W. & Sutton, G. W. Engineering Aspects of Magnetohydrodynamics. 688p. 1964. 163.25 (ISBN 0-677-10320-4). Gordon.

Moffatt, H. K., et al, eds. Metallurgical Applications of Magnetohydrodynamics. 344p. 1984. pap. text ed. 70.00x (ISBN 0-904357-60-0, Metals Soc). Brookfield Pub Co.

Nishida, A., ed. Magnetospheric Plasma Physics. 364p. 1982. 49.50 (ISBN 90-277-1345-6, Pub. by Reidel Holland). Kluwer Academic.

Northwestern University, Evanston, Ill. Magnetohydrodynamics: Proceedings. Cambel, Ali B. & Anderson, Thomas P., eds. pap. 100.80 (ISBN 0-317-10112-9, 2006374). Bks Demand UMI.

Pai Shih-I. Magnetogasdynamics & Plasma Dynamics. (Illus.). 1962. 29.00 (ISBN 0-387-80608-3). Springer-Verlag.

Priest, E. Solar Magnetohydrodynamics. 1982. lib. bdg. 99.00 (ISBN 90-277-1374-X, Pub. by Reidel Holland). Kluwer Academic.

Roberts, Paul H. An Introduction to Magnetohydrodynamics. LC 67-88253. pap. 68.50 (ISBN 0-317-08669-3, 2055320). Bks Demand UMI.

Roederer, J. G. Dynamics of Geomagnetically Trapped Radiation. LC 73-109668. (Physics & Chemistry in Space: Vol. 2). (Illus.). 1970. 24.00 (ISBN 0-387-04987-8). Springer-Verlag.

Shercliff, J. A. A Textbook of Magnetohydrodynamics. Pergamon.

Sturrock, P. A., ed. Plasma Astrophysics. (Italian Physical Society: Course 39). 1967. 70.00 (ISBN 0-12-368839-6). Acad Pr.

Symposia in Applied Mathematics - New York - 1965. Magneto-Fluid & Plasma Dynamics: Proceedings. Grad, H., ed. LC 66-20436. (Proceedings of Symposia in Applied Mathematics: Vol. 18). 1967. 23.00 (ISBN 0-8218-1318-8, PSAPM-18). Am Math.

MAGNETOHYDRODYNAMICS–BIBLIOGRAPHY

Bethmann, Johannes. Untersuchungen Uber Die Mhd. 18.00 (ISBN 0-384-04083-7); pap. 13.00 (ISBN 0-685-02222-6). Johnson Repr.

MAGNETO-IONIC THEORY

see also Ionospheric Radio Wave Propagation

Budden, K. G. Lectures on Magnetoionic Theory. (Documents on Modern Physics Ser.). 96p. 1964. 30.25 (ISBN 0-677-00100-2). Gordon.

Ratcliffe, John A. The Magneto-Ionic Theory & Its Applications to the Ionosphere: A Monograph. LC 59-896. pap. 54.00 (ISBN 0-317-11075-6, 2050747). Bks Demand UMI.

MAGNETOMETER

Dalton, Murphy L., Jr. Searching with 1 & 2 Sensor-Location Magnetometers. rev. ed. (One Hundred Forty-Eight Ser.). (Illus.). 144p. pap. text ed. 19.00 (ISBN 0-317-19114-4). M L Dalton Res.

MAGNETO-OPTICS

see also Electromagnetic Theory; Electrons; Polarization (Light)

Devreese, J. T., ed. Theoretical Aspects & the New Developments in Magneto-Optics. LC 80-18871. (NATO ASI Series B, Physics: Vol. 60). 635p. 1981. 89.50x (ISBN 0-306-40555-5, Plenum Pr). Plenum Pub.

Wachter, P., ed. Magneto-Optics. (Journal Physica Ser.: Vol. 89). 1977. 46.50 (ISBN 0-7204-0737-0, North Holland). Elsevier.

MAGNETOSTATICS

see also Magnetic Fields

Akasofu, S. I., ed. Dynamics of the Magnetosphere. (Astrophysics & Space Science Library: No. 78). 1980. lib. bdg. 79.00 (ISBN 90-277-1052-X, Pub. by Reidel Holland). Kluwer Academic.

Brown, William F., Jr. Magnetoelastic Interactions. (Springer Tracts in Natural Philosophy: Vol. 9). (Illus.). 1966. 39.00 (ISBN 0-387-03674-1). Springer-Verlag.

MAGNETS

see also Solenoids

Brechna, H. Superconducting Magnet Systems. LC 72-96051. (Technische Physik in Einveldarstellungen: Vol. 18). (Illus.). 480p. 1973. 110.00 (ISBN 0-387-06103-7). Springer-Verlag.

McCaig, M. Permanent Magnets in Theory & Practice. LC 77-23949. 374p. 1977. 54.95x (ISBN 0-470-99269-7). Halsted Pr.

Nesbitt, E. A. & Wernick, J. A. Rare Earth Permanent Magnets. (Materials Science Ser). 1973. 30.00 (ISBN 0-12-515450-X). Acad Pr.

Parker, Rollin J. & Studders, R. J. Permanent Magnets & Their Applications. LC 62-10930. 406p. 1962. 64.50x (ISBN 0-471-66264-X, Pub. by Wiley-Interscience). Wiley.

Thome, Richard J. & Tarrh, John M. MHD & Fusion Magnets: Field & Force Design Concepts. LC 81-19666. 347p. 1982. 44.95x (ISBN 0-471-09317-3, Pub. by Wiley-Interscience). Wiley.

MAGNOLIA

Treseder, N. G. Magnolias. 1981. 90.00x (ISBN 0-686-78781-1, Pub. by RHS Ent England). State Mutual Bk.

Treseder, Neil. Magnolias. (Illus.). 220p. 1978. 65.00 (ISBN 0-571-09619-0). Faber & Faber.

MAHAKA

see Tobacco

MAIL PLANES

see Transport Planes

MAIL PREPARATIONS

Davis, Steve, et al. The Electric Mailbox: A User's Guide to Electronic Mail Services. LC 84-91756. 260p. 1985. pap. 19.95 (ISBN 0-911061-14-2). S Davis Pub.

Paper-Based Electronic Mail. (Reports Ser.: No. 504). 206p. 1982. 1285.00x (ISBN 0-88694-504-6). Intl Res Dev.

MAILMERGE (COMPUTER PROGRAM)

Maas, Wolfgang & Fath, Irene. Soft Quick Mailmerge. 1985. pap. 9.95 (ISBN 0-8224-6418-7). Pitman Learning.

MAINTAINABILITY (ENGINEERING)

see also Reliability (Engineering)

Dhillon, Balbir S. & Reiche, Hans. Reliability & Maintainability Management. (Illus.). 288p. 1985. 36.95 (ISBN 0-442-27637-0). Van Nos Reinhold.

Lillegraven, Jason A., et al, eds. Mesozoic Mammals: The First Two-Thirds of Mammalian History. 1980. 50.00x (ISBN 0-520-03582-8); pap. 12.95x (ISBN 0-520-03951-3, CAMPUS NO. 234). U of Cal Pr.
Line, Les & Ricciuti, Edward R. The Audubon Society Book of Wild Animals. LC 77-9159. (Audubon Society Ser.). (Illus.). 1977. 50.00 (ISBN 0-8109-0670-8). Abrams.
Loates, G. & Peterson, R. Mammals of the Eastern Region. 1980. 29.95 (ISBN 0-13-548081-7). P-H.
Lodge, G. A. & Lamming, G. E., eds. Growth & Development of Mammals. LC 68-28665. 528p. 1968. 65.00x (ISBN 0-306-30690-5, Plenum Pr). Plenum Pub.
Lowery, George H., Jr. The Mammals of Louisiana & Its Adjacent Waters. LC 73-89662. (Illus.). 565p. 1974. 27.50 (ISBN 0-8071-0609-7). La State U Pr.
Lyman, Charles, et al. Hibernation & Torpor in Mammals & Birds. (Physiological Ecology Ser.). 317p. 1982. 43.50 (ISBN 0-12-460420-X). Acad Pr.
McCullough, Dale R. The George Reserve Deer Herd: Population Ecology of a K-Selected Species. (Illus.). 1979. lib. bdg. 16.00x (ISBN 0-472-08611-1, 08611). U of Mich Pr.
McLaren, Anne. Mammalian Chimaeras. LC 75-40988. (Developmental and Cell Biology Ser.: No. 4). (Illus.). 160p. 1976. 39.50 (ISBN 0-521-21183-2). Cambridge U Pr.
McLaughlin, Charles A. Mammals of Los Angeles County, California. (Science Ser.: No. 21). (Illus.). 34p. 1959. pap. 1.50 (ISBN 0-938644-02-5). Nat Hist Mus.
Maple, Terry L. Orang-Utan Behavior. (Van Nostrand Reinhold Primate Behavior & Development Ser.). 272p. 1980. text ed. 34.50 (ISBN 0-442-25154-8). Van Nos Reinhold.
Martin, R. E. & Chapman, B. R., eds. Contributions in Mammalogy in Honor of Robert L. Packard. (Special Publications of the Museum Ser.: No. 22). 234p. 1984. 50.00 (ISBN 0-89672-124-8); pap. 25.00 (ISBN 0-89672-123-X). Tex Tech Pr.
Miller, Gerrit S. Catalogue of the Mammals of Western Europe in the British Museum. (Illus.). Repr. of 1912 ed. 65.00 (ISBN 0-384-38940-6). Johnson Repr.
Miller, Linus W. Notes of an Exile to Van Dieman's Land. Repr. of 1846 ed. 30.00 (ISBN 0-384-38970-8). Johnson Repr.
Murie, Adolph. Mammals of Denali. (Illus.). 64p. 1983. pap. 4.50 (ISBN 0-9602876-6-3). Alaska Natural.
Murray, Andrew. The Geographical Distribution of Mammals. Sterling, Keir B., ed. LC 77-81073. (Biologists & Their World Ser.). (Illus.). 1978. Repr. of 1866 ed. lib. bdg. 54.00x (ISBN 0-405-10642-4). Ayer Co Pubs.
Nowak, Ronald M. & Paradiso, John L., eds. Walker's Mammals of the World, 2 vols. 4th ed. LC 82-49056. (Illus.). 1472p. 1983. 65.00 set (ISBN 0-8018-2525-3). Johns Hopkins.
Orci, L. & Perrelet, A. Freeze-Etch Histology: A Comparison Between Thin Sections & Freeze-Etch Replicas. LC 74-22379. (Illus.). 184p. 1975. 87.00 (ISBN 0-387-07043-5). Springer-Verlag.
Osman, William C. Evolutionary Biology of the Primates. 1973. 37.00 (ISBN 0-12-528750-X). Acad Pr.
Palmer, T. S. Index Generum Mammalium: A List of the Genera & Families of Mammals. 1968. Repr. of 1904 ed. 70.00 (ISBN 3-7682-0535-5). Lubrecht & Cramer.
Paul, John R. Mammalia. (Inventory of the Collections Ser.: Pt. 1). 11p. Ill St Museum.
Peshev, Tsolo C., et al. The International History of Mammalogy. Sterling, Keir B., ed. (Eastern Europe & Fennoscandia Ser.: Vol. I). (Illus.). 200p. 1985. 25.00 (ISBN 0-910485-00-3); pap. 20.00 (ISBN 0-910485-01-1). One World Pr.
Poole, Trevor B. Social Behaviour in Mammals. (Tertiary Level Biology Ser.). 256p. 1982. (Pub. by Chapman & Hall); pap. text ed. 22.50 (ISBN 0-412-00111-X, NO. 5016, Pub. by Chapman & Hall). Methuen Inc.
Ray, John. Synopsis Methodica Animalium Quadrupedum et Serpentini Generis. Sterling, Keir B., ed. LC 77-81111. (Biologists & Their World Ser.). (Latin.). 1978. Repr. of 1693 ed. lib. bdg. 29.00x (ISBN 0-405-10694-7). Ayer Co Pubs.
Report of the IUCN Workshop on Marine Mammals-Fishery Interactions. 68p. 1980. pap. 10.00 (IUCN123, IUCN). Unipub.
Riney, Thane. Study & Management of Large Mammals. LC 81-11519. 552p. 1982. 69.95 (ISBN 0-471-10062-5, Pub. by Wiley-Interscience). Wiley.
Russell, L. B., ed. Genetic Mosaics & Chimeras in Mammals. LC 78-23172. (Basic Life Sciences Ser.: Vol. 12). 499p. 1978. 59.50x (ISBN 0-306-40065-0, Plenum Pr). Plenum Pub.
Schaller, George B. Mountain Monarchs: Wild Sheep & Goats of the Himalaya. LC 77-1336. (Wildlife Behavior & Ecology Ser.). 1977. pap. 12.50x (ISBN 0-226-73642-3). U of Chicago Pr.
Sclater, William L. & Sclater, Philip L. The Geography of Mammals. Sterling, Keir B., ed. LC 77-81080. (Biologists & Their World Ser.). (Illus.). 1978. Repr. of 1899 ed. lib. bdg. 32.00x (ISBN 0-405-10647-5). Ayer Co Pubs.
Searle, Anthony G. Comparative Genetics of Coat Colour in Mammals. 1968. 64.50 (ISBN 0-12-633450-1). Acad Pr.
Segal, Sheldon J., et al. The Regulation of Mammalian Reproduction. (Illus.). 614p. 1973. photocopy ed. 59.75x (ISBN 0-398-02405-7). C C Thomas.
Seton, Ernest S. Life-Histories of the Northern Animals: An Account of the Mammals of Manitoba, 2. LC 73-17845. (Natural Sciences in America Ser.). (Illus.). 1514p. 1974. Repr. Set. 103.50x (ISBN 0-405-05767-9); Vol. 1. 52.00x (ISBN 0-405-05768-7); Vol. 2. 52.00x (ISBN 0-405-05769-5). Ayer Co Pubs.
Somien, George. Sensory Coding in the Mammalian Nervous System. LC 75-31519. pap. 100.80 (ISBN 0-317-26288-2, 2155694). Bks Demand UMI.
Stehlin, Hans G. Die Saugethiere des schweizerischen Eocaens. LC 78-72723. Repr. of 1912 ed. 67.50 (ISBN 0-404-18300-X). AMS Pr.
Stoddart, D. M., ed. Ecology of Small Mammals. 386p. 1979. 46.00 (ISBN 0-412-14790-4, NO.6277, Pub. by Chapman & Hall England). Methuen Inc.
Stone, Jonathan, et al. Development of Visual Pathways in Mammals. LC 84-10022. (Neurology & Neurobiology Ser.: Vol. 9). 508p. 1984. 68.00 (ISBN 0-8451-2710-1). A R Liss.
Strahan, Ronald, ed. The Complete Book Of Australian Mammals: The National Photographic Index of Australian Wildlife. (Illus.). 532p. 1984. 50.00 (ISBN 0-207-14454-0, Pub. by Salem Hse Ltd). Merrimack Pub Cir.
Thorburns's Mammals. (Illus.). 128p. 1985. pap. 12.95 (ISBN 0-7181-2253-4, Pub. by Michael Joseph). Merrimack Pub Cir.
Topsell, Edward. The Historie of Foure-Footed Beastes, Collected Out of All Volumes of C. Gesner, & All Other Writers to This Present Day. LC 72-6034. (English Experience Ser.: No. 561). 816p. 1973. Repr. of 1607 ed. 104.00 (ISBN 90-221-0561-X). Walter J Johnson.
Turner, Dennis C. The Vampire Bat: A Field Study in Behavior & Ecology. LC 74-24396. (Illus.). 160p. 1975. 17.50x (ISBN 0-8018-1680-7). Johns Hopkins.
Vandenbergh, John G., ed. Pheromones & Reproduction in Mammals. LC 82-22776. 1983. 41.50 (ISBN 0-12-710780-0). Acad Pr.
Van Gelder, Richard G. Mammals of the National Parks. LC 81-17162. (Illus.). 336p. 1982. 26.50x (ISBN 0-8018-2688-8); pap. 8.95 (ISBN 0-8018-2689-6). Johns Hopkins.
Vaughan, Terry A. Mammalogy. 3rd ed. LC 77-2111. 1986. text ed. 28.95 (ISBN 0-03-058474-4, CBS C). SCP.
Waterhouse, George R. A Natural History of the Mammalia. Sterling, Keir B., ed. LC 77-83843. (Biologists & Their World Ser.). (Illus.). 1978. Repr. of 1848 ed. lib. bdg. 85.00x (ISBN 0-405-10739-0). Ayer Co Pubs.
Weber, G. Metabolic Regulation of Mammalian Systems. Date not set. price not set (ISBN 0-08-017706-9). Pergamon.
West, Robert M. The North American Phenacondonidae (Mammalia, Condylarthra) 78p. 1976. 3.25 (ISBN 0-89326-017-7). Milwaukee Pub Mus.
Young, John Z. & Hobbs, M. J. The Life of Mammals: Their Anatomy & Physiology. 2nd ed. (Illus.). 1975. text ed. 39.00x (ISBN 0-19-857156-9). Oxford U Pr.
Zoological Society of London - 26th Symposium. Variation in Mammalian Populations. Berry, R. J. & Southern, H. N., eds. 1971. 63.50 (ISBN 0-12-613326-3). Acad Pr.

MAMMALS–EMBRYOLOGY

see Embryology–Mammals

MAMMALS–PHYSIOLOGY

Agar, N. S. & Board, P. G., eds. Red Blood Cells of Domestic Animals. xviii, 420p. 1983. 130.75 (ISBN 0-444-80455-2). Elsevier.
Albone, Eric S. Mammalian Semiochemistry: The Investigation of Chemical Signals Between Mammals. LC 83-10231. 360p. 1984. 57.00x (ISBN 0-471-10253-9, Pub. by Wiley-Interscience). Wiley.
Allen, Phyllis A. Mammalian Physiology Level II. (Illus.). 144p. 1981. pap. text ed. 17.95x (ISBN 0-7121-1283-9). Trans-Atlantic.
Anderson, Paul D. Laboratory Manual & Study Guide for Clinical Anatomy & Physiology for Allied Health Sciences. LC 75-21143. (Illus.). Repr. of 1976 ed. 43.40 (ISBN 0-8357-9549-7, 2016689). Bks Demand UMI.
Bennett, Geoffrey W. & Whitehead, Saffron A. Mammalian Neuroendocrinology. (Illus.). 1983. pap. 19.95x (ISBN 0-19-520416-6). Oxford U Pr.
Biology of Reproduction in Mammals. 540p. 1969. 39.00x (ISBN 0-686-45134-1, Pub. by Biochemical England). State Mutual Bk.
Ciba Foundation. Development of Mammalian Absorptive Processes. LC 79-20804. (Ciba Foundation Symposium, New Ser.: 70). pap. 87.50 (ISBN 0-317-29760-0, 2022189). Bks Demand UMI.
Doty, Richard L., ed. Mammalian Olfaction: Reproducive Processes, & Behavior. 1976. 55.00 (ISBN 0-12-221250-9). Acad Pr.
The Environment & Reproduction in Mammals & Birds. 628p. 1973. 60.00x (ISBN 0-686-45143-0, Pub. by Biochemical England). State Mutual Bk.
Gesellschaft Fuer Biologische Chemie, 21st Colloquium, Mossbach-Baden, 1970. Mammalian Reproduction: Proceedings. Gibian, H. & Plotz, J., eds. LC 77-140558. (Illus.). 1970. 46.00 (ISBN 0-387-05066-3). Springer-Verlag.
Gessaman, James A. Ecological Energetics of Homeotherms. LC 72-80316. 155p. 1973. pap. 7.50 (ISBN 0-87421-053-4). Utah St U Pr.
Girardier, Lucien & Stock, Michael J., eds. Mammalian Thermogenesis. LC 83-1929. (Illus.). 359p. 1983. 80.00 (ISBN 0-412-23550-1, NO. 6822, Pub. by Chapman & Hall). Methuen Inc.
Guraya, S. S. Biology of Ovarian Follicles in Mammals. (Illus.). 340p. 1985. 69.50 (ISBN 0-387-15022-6). Springer-Verlag.
Gwatkin, Ralph B. Fertilization Mechanisms in Man & Mammals. LC 77-1189. (Illus.). 171p. 1977. 29.50x (ISBN 0-306-31009-0, Plenum Pr). Plenum Pub.
Hogarth, Peter J. Immunological Aspects of Mammalian Reproduction. LC 81-86329. 204p. 1982. 43.95 (ISBN 0-03-061903-3). Praeger.
Kaufman, Matthew H. Early Mammalian Development: Parthenogenetic Studies. LC 83-1823. (Developmental & Cell Biology Ser.: No. 14). 200p. 1984. 64.50 (ISBN 0-521-25449-3). Cambridge U Pr.
Kempczinski, R. F., et al. Organ & Tissue Regeneration in Mammals II. new ed. LC 72-13503. 157p. 1973. text ed. 25.50x (ISBN 0-8422-7059-0). Irvington.
Kerkut, G. A. & Wheal, H. V., eds. Electrophysiology of Isolated Mammalian CNS Preparations. LC 80-42081. 408p. 1981. 67.00 (ISBN 0-12-404680-0). Acad Pr.
Madge, David S. The Mammalian Alimentary System: A Functional Approach. LC 75-34543. (Special Topics in Biology Ser). 195p. 1976. pap. 14.50x (ISBN 0-8448-0850-4). Crane-Russak Co.
Marshall, Patricia T. & Hughes, George M. Physiology of Mammals & Other Vertebrates. 2nd ed. LC 78-73810. (Illus.). 1981. 49.50 (ISBN 0-521-22633-3); pap. 21.95 (ISBN 0-521-29586-6). Cambridge U Pr.
Mayer, William V. & Van Gelder, R. G., eds. Physiological Mammalogy, 2 vols. Incl. Vol. 1 (ISBN 0-12-481001-2); Vol. 2 (ISBN 0-12-481002-0). 1964. 63.00 ea. Acad Pr.
Moore, W. J. The Mammalian Skull. (Biological Structure & Function Ser.: No. 8). (Illus.). 400p. 1981. 99.50 (ISBN 0-521-23318-6). Cambridge U Pr.
Motta, P. M. & Hafez, E. S., eds. Biology of the Ovary. (Developments in Obstetrics & Gynecology Ser.: No. 2). 345p. 1980. lib. bdg. 87.00 (ISBN 90-247-2316-7, Pub. by Martinus Nijhoff Netherlands). Kluwer Academic.
Nettesheim, P., et al. Organ & Tissue Regeneration in Mammals I. LC 72-13503. 167p. 1972. text ed. 27.50x (ISBN 0-8422-7048-5). Irvington.
Papageorgiou, Nikolaos. Population Energy Relationships of the Agrimi (Capra Aegagrus Cretica) on Theodorou Island, Greece. (Mammalia Depicta Ser.: Vol. 11). (Illus.). 56p. (Orig.). pap. text ed. 14.10 (ISBN 3-490-21518-4). Parey Sci Pubs.
Peters, Hannah & McNatty, Kenneth P. The Ovary: A Correlation of Structure & Function in Mammals. LC 79-6741. 1980. 44.50x (ISBN 0-520-04124-0). U of Cal Pr.
Scheline, R. R. Mammalian Metabolism of Plant Xenobiotics. 1979. 82.00 (ISBN 0-12-623350-0). Acad Pr.
Sies, H. & Haussinger, D., eds. Glutamine Metabolism in Mammalian Tissues. (Illus.). 295p. 1984. 44.00 (ISBN 0-387-13454-9). Springer Verlag.
Smith, Michael H. & Joule, James, eds. Mammalian Population Genetics. LC 80-24667. 392p. 1980. 28.00x (ISBN 0-8203-0547-2). U of Ga Pr.
Sokolov, V. E. Mammal Skin. LC 75-46042. (Illus.). 704p. 1981. 72.50x (ISBN 0-520-03198-9). U of Cal Pr.
Stoddart, D. M. & Stoddart, D. M., eds. Olfaction in Mammals. (Symposia of the Zoological Society of London: No. 45). 1980. 66.00 (ISBN 0-12-613345-X). Acad Pr.

MAMMALS–AFRICA

Altmann, Jeanne. Baboon Mothers & Infants. LC 79-21568. (Illus.). 1980. text ed. 18.50x (ISBN 0-674-05856-9); pap. text ed. 8.95x (ISBN 0-674-05857-7). Harvard U Pr.
Dorst & Dandelot. A Field Guide to the Larger Mammals of Africa. 24.95 (ISBN 0-00-219294-2, Collins Pub England). Greene.
Eltringham, S. K. The Ecology & Conservation of Large African Mammals. (Illus.). 304p. 1980. text ed. 49.95 (ISBN 0-8391-1493-1). Univ Park.
Haltenorth & Diller. A Field Guide to the Mammals of Africa. 34.95 (ISBN 0-00-219778-2, Collins Pub England). Greene.
Hufnagl, Ernst. Libyan Mammals. (Libya Past & Present Ser.: Vol. 3). (Illus.). 16.00 (ISBN 0-902675-08-7). Oleander Pr.
Kingdon, J., ed. East African Mammals, Vol. 3, Pt. D. 1982. 98.00 (ISBN 0-12-408345-5). Acad Pr.
Kingdon, Jonathan. East African Mammals: An Atlas of Evolution in Africa. Vol. 1, 1971. 79.50 (ISBN 0-12-408301-3); Vol. 2, 2 Pts. 79.50 ea. Pt. A (ISBN 0-12-408302-1). Pt. B. (ISBN 0-12-408342-0); Vol. 3, Pt. A, 1978. 99.50 (ISBN 0-12-408303-X); Vol. 3b. 132.00 (ISBN 0-12-408343-9). Acad Pr.
--East African Mammals: An Atlas of Evolution in Africa, Vol. I. LC 83-24174. (Illus.). 456p. 1984. pap. 25.00 (ISBN 0-226-43718-3). U of Chicago Pr.
--East African Mammals: An Atlas of Evolution in Africa. Vol. II, Pt. A: Insectivores & Bats. LC 83-24174. (Illus.). 404p. 1984. pap. 25.00 (ISBN 0-226-43719-1). U of Chicago Pr.
--East African Mammals: An Atlas of Evolution in Africa. Vol. II, Pt. B: Hares & Rodents. LC 83-24174. (Illus.). 428p. 1984. pap. 25.00 (ISBN 0-226-43720-5). U of Chicago Pr.
Leuthold, W. African Ungulates: A Comparative Review of Their Ethology & Behavioral Ecology. Farner, D. S., ed. LC 76-44535. (Zoophysiology & Ecology Ser.: Vol. 8). (Illus.). 1977. 46.00 (ISBN 0-387-07951-3). Springer-Verlag.
Maglio, Vincent J. & Cooke, H. B., eds. Evolution of African Mammals. LC 77-19318. (Illus.). 1978. 60.00x (ISBN 0-674-27075-4). Harvard U Pr.
Meester, J. & Setzer, H. W., eds. The Mammals of Africa: An Identification Manual. LC 70-169904. 1971. three-ring binder 45.00x (ISBN 0-87474-116-5). Smithsonian.
Moss, Cynthia. Portraits in the Wild: Animal Behavior in East Africa. 2nd ed. LC 81-23092. (Illus.). 1982. 28.00x (ISBN 0-226-54232-7); pap. 11.95 (ISBN 0-226-54233-5). U of Chicago Pr.
Sinclair, A. R. E. The African Buffalo: A Study of Resource Limitations of Populations. LC 76-22955. (Wildlife Behavior & Ecology Ser.). (Illus.). 1977. 20.00x (ISBN 0-226-76030-8). U of Chicago Pr.
Wesselman, H. B. The Omo Micromammals: Systematics & Paleoecology of Early Man Sites from Ethiopia. (Contributions to Vertebrate Evolution: Vol. 7). (Illus.). x, 222p. 1984. 41.75 (ISBN 3-8055-3935-5). S Karger.

MAMMALS–ARABIA

Harrison, David L. Mammals of the Arabian Gulf. (The Natural History of the Arabian Gulf Ser.). (Illus.). 88p. 1981. text ed. 19.50x (ISBN 0-04-599007-7). Allen Unwin.

MAMMALS–AUSTRALIA

Ride, W. D. Guide to the Native Mammals of Australia. (Illus.). 1970. 46.00x (ISBN 0-19-550252-3). Oxford U Pr.

MAMMALS–EUROPE

Corbet, G. B. Terrestrial Mammals of Western Europe. LC 66-23640. (Illus.). 1966. 14.95 (ISBN 0-8023-1030-3). Dufour.
Corbett & Ovenden. The Mammals of Britain & Europe. pap. 15.95 (ISBN 0-00-219774-X, Collins Pub England). Greene.
Haltenorth, Theodore. Mammals, Amphibians & Reptiles. (Nature Guides Ser.). (Illus.). 144p. 1979. pap. 5.95 (ISBN 0-7011-2364-8, Pub. by Chatto & Windus). Merrimack Pub Cir.

MAMMALS–GREAT BRITAIN

Corbett & Ovenden. The Mammals of Britain & Europe. pap. 15.95 (ISBN 0-00-219774-X, Collins Pub England). Greene.

MAMMALS–INDIA

Hrdy, Sarah B. The Langurs of Abu: Female & Male Strategies of Reproduction. (Illus.). 1977. 22.50x (ISBN 0-674-51057-7); pap. 8.95x (ISBN 0-674-51058-5). Harvard U Pr.

MAMMALS–MALAYA

Harrison, John. An Introduction of Mammals of Singapore & Malaya. 352p. 1974. 49.00x (ISBN 0-317-07099-1, Pub. by EW Classey UK). State Mutual Bk.

West, Robert M. Review of the North American Eocene & Oligocene Apatemyidae (Mammalia: Insectivora) (Special Publications: No. 3). (Illus.). 42p. 1973. pap. 2.00 (ISBN 0-89672-028-4). Tex Tech Pr.

MAMMALS–SOUTH AMERICA

Hershkovitz, Philip. Living New World Monkeys (Platyrrhini) With an Introduction to Primates, Vol. 1. LC 75-9059. (Illus.). 1978. 110.00 (ISBN 0-226-32788-4). U of Chicago Pr.

Myers, Philip. Patterns of Reproduction of Four Species of Vespertiliohia Bats in Paraguay. (Publ. in Zoology Ser: Vol. 107). 1977. pap. 17.50x (ISBN 0-520-09554-5). U of Cal Pr.

Simpson, George G. Splendid Isolation: The Curious History of South American Mannals. LC 79-17630. (Illus.). 1980. 26.00x (ISBN 0-300-02434-7). Yale U Pr.

MAMMALS, FOSSIL

see also Vertebrates, Fossil

Broadhead, T. W., ed. Mammals: Notes for a Short Course Organized by P. D. Gingerich & C. E. Badgley. (Studies in Geology). (Illus.). 234p. 1984. pap. 9.00 (ISBN 0-910249-07-5). U Of Tenn Geo.

Clemens, William A., Jr. Records of the Fossil Mammal Sinclairella, Family Apatemyidae, from the Chadronian & Orellan. (Museum Ser.: Vol. 14, No. 17). 9p. 1964. pap. 1.25 (ISBN 0-317-04964-X). U of KS Mus Nat Hist.

Kurten, Bjorn. The Age of Mammals. LC 79-177479. (Illus.). 250p. 1972. 30.00x (ISBN 0-231-03624-8); pap. 13.00x (ISBN 0-231-03647-7). Columbia U Pr.

Lawrence, Barbara. Mammals Found at the Awatovi Site. (HU PMP Ser.). (Illus.). 1951. pap. 15.00 (ISBN 0-527-01290-4). Kraus Repr.

Leidy, Joseph. The Extinct Mammalian Fauna of Dakota & Nebraska, & a Account of Some Allied Forms from Other Localities: Synopsis of the Mammalian Remains of North America. 2nd ed. LC 73-17828. (Natural Sciences in America Ser.: Vol. 3). (Illus.). 536p. 1974. Repr. 37.50x (ISBN 0-405-05746-6). Ayer Co Pubs.

Olsen, Stanley J. An Osteology of Some Maya Mammals. (Peabody Museum Papers: No. 73). (Illus.). 110p. (Orig.). 1982. pap. 13.50x (ISBN 0-87365-199-5). Peabody Harvard.

Savage, Donald E. & Russell, Donald E. Mammalian Paleofaunas of the World. LC 82-13764. (Evolutionary Biology Ser.). (Illus.). 432p. 1983. 85.95 (ISBN 0-201-06494-4). Addison-Wesley.

Simpson, George G. A Catalogue of the Mesozoic Mammalia in the Geological Department of the British Museum & American Mesozoic Mammalia: Memoirs of the Peabody Museum of Yale University, Vol. Iii, Pt. 1, 2vols. In 1. Gould, Stephen J., ed. LC 79-8350. (History of Paleontology Ser.). (Illus.). 1980. Repr. of 1928 ed. lib. bdg. 66.50x (ISBN 0-405-12743-X). Ayer Co Pubs.

--Discoverers of the Lost World: An Account of Some of Those Who Brought Back to Life South American Mammals Long Buried in the Abyss of Time. LC 84-2243. (Illus.). 240p. 1984. 25.00x (ISBN 0-300-03188-2). Yale U Pr.

MAMMARY GLANDS

see also Udder

Gallager, H. Stephen, et al, eds. The Breast. LC 78-14811. (Illus.). 564p. 1978. text ed. 79.50 (ISBN 0-8016-1727-8). Mosby.

Hollmann, K. H. & Verley, J. M., eds. New Frontiers in Mammary Pathology, Vol. 2. 450p. 1983. 55.00x (ISBN 0-306-41178-4, Plenum Pr). Plenum Pub.

NCRP. Mammography. LC 80-82437. (NCRP Reports Ser.: No. 66). 1980. 9.00 (ISBN 0-913392-51-0). NCRP Pubns.

MAMMILARIA

Craig, Robert T. The Mammillaria Handbook. (Illus.). 1945. 30.00 (ISBN 0-384-10090-2). Johnson Repr.

Pilbeam, John. Mammillaria: A Collector's Guide. LC 81-2956. (Illus.). 200p. 1981. text ed. 40.00x (ISBN 0-87663-360-2). Universe.

MAMMOTH

Anderson, Netta C. & Udden, Johan A. Fossil Mastodon & Mammoth Remains in Illinois & Iowa, & Proboscidian Fossils of the Pleistocene Deposits in Illinois & Iowa. LC 6-20234. (Augustana College Library Publication Ser.: No. 5). 57p. 1905. pap. 1.00 (ISBN 0-910182-03-5). Augustana Coll.

Howorth, Henry H. The Mammoth & the Flood. 496p. 1984. Repr. of 1887 ed. photocopy 19.95 (ISBN 0-915554-14-3). Sourcebook.

MAN

see also Anthropology; Anthropometry; Craniology; Creation; Heredity; Human Biology

Adams, Mary, ed. Science in the Changing World. facs. ed. LC 68-29188. (Essay Index Reprint Ser). 1968. Repr. of 1933 ed. 18.00 (ISBN 0-8369-0136-3). Ayer Co Pubs.

Alexander, Jason. In Praise of the Common Man. LC 80-54489. 86p. (Orig.). 1980. pap. 9.95 (ISBN 0-931826-02-0). Sitnalta Pr.

Alland, Alexander, Jr. The Human Imperative. LC 77-183227. 185p. 1972. 21.00x (ISBN 0-231-03228-5); pap. 10.00x (ISBN 0-231-08301-7). Columbia U Pr.

Arguelles, Jose. Earth Ascending: An Illustrated Treatise on the Law Governing Whole Systems. LC 83-20052. (Illus.). 150p. 1984. pap. 12.95 (ISBN 0-87773-263-9, 72330-9). Shambhala Pubns.

Ashley Montagu. The Biosocial Nature of Man. LC 72-11331. 123p. 1973. Repr. of 1956 ed. lib. bdg. 15.00 (ISBN 0-8371-6658-6, MOBN). Greenwood.

Bates, Marston. Gluttons & Libertines: Human Problems of Being Natural. LC 66-11978. 1971. pap. 2.95 (ISBN 0-394-71267-6, V-267, Vin). Random.

Benjamin, Elsie. Man at Home in the Universe: A Study of the Great Evolutionary Cycle: the "Globes", the "Rounds", "Races", "Root-Races" & "Sub-Races". (Study Ser.: No. 8). 36p. 1981. pap. 3.00 (ISBN 0-913004-43-X). Point Loma Pub.

Boevey, James. The Art of Building a Man. 1966. 20.00x (ISBN 0-900008-11-3, Pub. by U of London England). State Mutual Bk.

Bronowski, J. Identity of Man. rev. ed. LC 71-188042. 1971 (AMS). pap. 3.50 (ISBN 0-385-00171-1, AMS). Natural Hist.

Burr, Harold S. The Nature of Man & the Meaning of Existence. 108p. 1962. 11.75x (ISBN 0-398-04225-X). C C Thomas.

Cabanis, Pierre J. On the Relations Between the Physical & Moral Aspects of Man, Vol. I. Saidi, Margaret D., tr. LC 80-21694. pap. 112.00 (ISBN 0-317-08229-9, 2019949). Bks Demand UMI.

Collins, Gary. Hombre En Transicion. Ingledew, Roberto, tr. from Eng. Tr. of Man in Transition. (Span.). 220p. 1978. pap. 4.95 (ISBN 0-89922-124-6). Edit Caribe.

Constant, Benjamin. De la Perfectibilite de l'Espece Humaine. 1967. 7.95 (ISBN 0-686-54608-3). French & Eur.

Corner, George W. Ourselves Unborn: An Embryologist's Essay on Man. LC 71-143884. 188p. 1972. Repr. of 1944 ed. 16.50 (ISBN 0-685-02973-5, Archon). Shoe String.

Cox, Jan. Magnus Machina: The Great Machine. 1970. 7.95 (ISBN 0-87707-092-X); pap. 5.95 (ISBN 0-686-65960-0). Chan Shal Imi.

Daires, John L. Man & His Universe. 1937. 15.00 (ISBN 0-686-17421-6). Ridgeway Bks.

Darwin, Charles R. The Descent of Man. 1902. 30.00 (ISBN 0-8274-2165-6). R West.

Dubos, Rene. Celebrations of Life. 1981. 12.95 (ISBN 0-07-017893-3). McGraw.

Eiseley, Loren. The Invisible Pyramid. 1983. 14.25 (ISBN 0-8446-5980-0). Peter Smith.

Frankel, Charles. Case for Modern Man. facsimile ed. LC 71-167342. (Essay Index Reprint Ser). Repr. of 1956 ed. 16.00 (ISBN 0-8369-2648-X). Ayer Co Pubs.

Haddon, Alfred. The Study of Man. (Classics of Anthropology Ser.). 74.00 (ISBN 0-8240-9647-9). Garland Pub.

Haughton, Rosemary. Transformation of Man. rev. ed. 1980. pap. 6.95 (ISBN 0-87243-102-9). Templegate.

Hess, Wilford, et al. The Appearance of Man: Replenishment of the Earth, Vol. 2. 1979. perfect bdg. 8.95 (ISBN 0-88252-094-6). Paladin Hse.

Hollis, Martin. Models of Man. LC 76-49902. (Illus.). 1977. 37.50 (ISBN 0-521-21546-3); pap. 10.95x (ISBN 0-521-29181-X). Cambridge U Pr.

Huxley, Julian S. Man Stands Alone. LC 72-128265. (Essay Index Reprint Ser.). 1941. 22.00 (ISBN 0-8369-1961-0). Ayer Co Pubs.

Jacob, Stanley W., et al. Structure & Function in Man. 5th ed. LC 77-84673. (Illus.). 1982. text ed. 28.95 (ISBN 0-7216-5094-5); 13.95 (ISBN 0-7216-5093-7); transparencies avail. Saunders.

Jantsch, Erich. Design for Evolution: Self-Organization & Planning in the Life of Human Systems. Laszlo, Ervin, ed. LC 74-77525. (International Library of Systems Theory & Philosophy Ser). 320p. 1975. 9.95 (ISBN 0-8076-0757-6). Braziller.

Jensen, Bernard. The Chemistry of Man. 1983. pap. write for info. B Jensen.

Kaelin, E. F., ed. Man & Value: Essays in Honor of William H. Werkmeister. 1981. 19.25 (ISBN 0-8130-0688-0). U Presses Fla.

Kirkpatrick, Edwin A. Sciences of Man in the Making. facsimile ed. LC 75-156672. (Essay Index Reprints - International Library of Psychology, Philosophy, & Scientific Method). Repr. of 1932 ed. 22.00 (ISBN 0-8369-2282-4). Ayer Co Pubs.

Korzybski, Alfred. Manhood of Humanity. 2nd ed. 326p. 1950. 9.00x (ISBN 0-937298-00-X). Inst Gen Seman.

La Barre, Weston. Human Animal. LC 54-12371. 1960. pap. 2.25 (ISBN 0-226-46706-6, P45, Phoen). U of Chicago Pr.

Lawrence, Roy. Motive & Intention: An Essay in the Appreciation of Action. LC 72-186548. (Publications in Analytical Philosophy Ser). Repr. of 1972 ed. 36.50 (ISBN 0-8357-9465-2, 2015301). Bks Demand UMI.

Lewis, John. Uniqueness of Man. 1974. pap. 7.95x (ISBN 0-8464-0948-8). Beekman Pubs.

Loos, Amandus W., ed. Nature of Man. facs. ed. LC 69-18930. (Essay Index Reprint Ser). 1950. 14.00 (ISBN 0-8369-1042-7). Ayer Co Pubs.

Mayer, Milton. The Nature of the Beast. Gustafson, W. Eric, ed. LC 74-21243. 376p. 1975. 15.00x (ISBN 0-87023-176-6). U of Mass Pr.

Mora, George, ed. On the Relations Between the Physical & Moral Aspects of Man, Vol. 2. Saidi, Margaret D., tr. LC 80-21694. pap. 109.50 (ISBN 0-317-08233-7, 2019949). Bks Demand UMI.

North, Gloria. Twentieth Century Man. 16p. 1979. pap. 1.00 (ISBN 0-686-27736-8). Samisdat.

Petacchi, Donald. Work for Being in the Machine Age. LC 80-82646. 80p. 1980. 12.95 (ISBN 0-8022-2376-1). Philos Lib.

Rensch, Bernhard. Homo Sapiens: From Man to DemiGod. LC 72-80482. 1972. 30.00x (ISBN 0-231-03683-3). Columbia U Pr.

Rhinelander, Philip H. Is Man Incomprehensible to Man? (Illus.). 117p. 1974. text ed. 13.95x (ISBN 0-7167-0765-9); pap. text ed. 8.95x (ISBN 0-7167-0764-0). W H Freeman.

Richards, Fred & Richards, Anne C. Homonovus: The New Man. LC 72-96551. 193p. 1973. pap. 4.25x (ISBN 0-88310-001-0). Publishers Consult.

Robinson, Lytle W. Edgar Cayce's Story of the Origin & Destiny of Man. 208p. 20.00x (ISBN 0-85435-311-9, Pub. by Spearman England). State Mutual Bk.

Sears, Robert R. & Feldman, S. Shirley, eds. The Seven Ages of Man: A Survey of Human Development. LC 73-12029. 155p. 1973. pap. 6.95x (ISBN 0-913232-06-8). W Kaufmann.

Shackley, Myra. Rocks & Man. (Illus.). 160p. 1982. pap. text ed. 9.95x (ISBN 0-04-913019-6). Allen Unwin.

Sheldon, William. Atlas of Men: A Guide for Somatotyping the Adult Male of All Ages. 1970. Repr. of 1954 ed. 27.95x (ISBN 0-02-852160-9). Hafner.

Smith, Grafton E. The Evolution of Man: Essays. 2nd ed. LC 77-86438. Repr. of 1927 ed. 18.50 (ISBN 0-404-16677-6). AMS Pr.

Spengler, Oswald. Man & Technics: A Contribution to a Philosophy of Life. Atkinson, Charles F., tr. from Ger. LC 76-7913. 1976. Repr. of 1932 ed. lib. bdg. 15.00 (ISBN 0-8371-8875-X, SPMT). Greenwood.

Steele, F. & Bourne, A., eds. The Man-Food Equation. 1976. 49.00 (ISBN 0-12-664850-6). Acad Pr.

Stein, Walter J. Man & His Place in History. 1980. pap. 4.25 (ISBN 0-906492-35-1, Pub. by Kolisko Archives). St George Bk Serv.

Tarneja, Sukh R. Nature, Spirituality & Science. 240p. 1980. text ed. 27.50x (ISBN 0-7069-1203-9, Pub by Vikas India). Advent NY.

Teilhard De Chardin, Pierre. Human Energy. LC 79-139231. Orig. Title: L' Energie Humaine. 191p. 1972. pap. 3.95 (ISBN 0-15-642300-6, HB234, Harv). HarBraceJ.

--Place De L'homme Dans la Nature. (Coll. le monde en 10-18). 1963. pap. 3.95 (ISBN 0-685-11497-X). French & Eur.

Trigg, Roger. The Shaping of Man: Philosophical Aspects of Sociobiology. LC 82-16868. 208p. 1983. 14.95 (ISBN 0-8052-3840-9). Schocken.

Zdravomyslov, A. G., et al, eds. Man & His Work. Dunn, Stephen P., tr. LC 72-77457. Orig. Title: Chelovek: Ego Rabota. Repr. of 1970 ed. 101.50 (ISBN 0-8357-9437-7, 2016135). Bks Demand UMI.

MAN–INFLUENCE OF ENVIRONMENT

see also Altitude, Influence of; Environmental Health; Genetic Psychology; Weightlessness

Altman, Irwin & Wohlwill, J. F., eds. Human Behavior & Environment, Vol. 1. (Illus.). 316p. 1976. 32.50x (ISBN 0-306-33301-5, Plenum Pr). Plenum Pub.

--Human Behavior & Environment, Vol. 2: Advances in Theory & Research. (Illus.). 358p. 1977. 32.50x (ISBN 0-306-33302-3, Plenum Pr). Plenum Pub.

Altman, Irwin, et al, eds. Human Behavior & Environment, Vol. 4: Environment & Culture. (Illus.). 368p. 1980. 32.50x (ISBN 0-306-40367-6, Plenum Pr). Plenum Pub.

--Human Behavior & Environment, Vol. 5: Transportation & Behavior. LC 76-382942. 301p. 1982. 32.50 (ISBN 0-306-40773-6, Plenum Pr). Plenum Pub.

American Academy of Political & Social Science, Annual Meeting, 83rd. The Environment & the Quality of Life: A World View: Proceedings. Wolfgang, Marvin E. & Ginsberg, Ralph B., eds. LC 79-50266. (Annals: No. 444). 1979. 15.00 (ISBN 0-87761-240-4); pap. 7.95 (ISBN 0-87761-241-2). Am Acad Pol Soc Sci.

American Environmental Studies, 42 Vols. 1971. Repr. Set. 725.00 (ISBN 0-405-02650-1). Ayer Co Pubs.

Baker, P. T., ed. The Biology of High-Altitude Peoples. LC 76-50311. (International Biological Programme Ser.: No. 14). (Illus.). 1978. 79.50 (ISBN 0-521-21523-4). Cambridge U Pr.

Barker, Roger G., et al. Habitats, Enviroments, & Human Behavior: Studies in Ecological Psychology & Eco-Behavioral Science. LC 77-82912. (Social & Behavioral Science Ser.). 1978. text ed. 27.95x (ISBN 0-87589-356-2). Jossey-Bass.

Barnes, Bernard. Man & the Changing Landscape. (Work Notes Ser.: No. 3). (Illus.). 144p. pap. text ed. 14.00x (ISBN 0-906367-12-3, Merseyside County Mus of Liverpool England). Smithsonian.

Bianchi, G., et al, eds. Man under Vibration: Suffering & Protection. (Studies in Environmental Science: Vol. 13). 438p. 1982. 83.00 (ISBN 0-444-99743-1). Elsevier.

Byrne, John M., et al, eds. Families & the Energy Transition. LC 85-17706. (Marriage & Family Review Ser.: Vol. 9, Nos. 1-2). 300p. 1985. text ed. 29.95 (ISBN 0-86656-451-9, B451); pap. 22.95 (ISBN 0-86656-494-2, B494). Haworth Pr.

Calabrese, Edward J. Pollutants & High Risk Groups: The Biological Basis of Increased Human Susceptibility to Environmental & Occupational Pollutants. LC 77-13957. (Environmental Science & Technology: Wiley-Interscience Series of Texts & Monographs). 266p. 1977. 58.95 (ISBN 0-471-02940-8, Pub. by Wiley-Inerscience). Wiley.

Capstick, Peter H. Maneaters. (Illus.). 200p. 1981. 17.95 (ISBN 0-8227-3023-5). Petersen Pub.

Coelho, George V., et al, eds. Uprooting & Development--Dilemmas of Coping with Modernization. LC 81-16539. (Current Topics in Mental Health Ser.). 566p. 1980. 37.50x (ISBN 0-306-40509-1, Plenum Pr). Plenum Pub.

Conklin, Edwin G. Heredity & Environment in the Development of Men. 6th rev. ed. (Illus.). 1930. 28.00 (ISBN 0-384-09755-3). Johnson Repr.

Cravens, Hamilton. Triumph of Evolution: American Scientists & the Heredity-Environment Controversy, 1900-1941. LC 77-20570. (Illus.). 1978. 26.00x (ISBN 0-8122-7744-9). U of Pa Pr.

Cronin, Ned J., ed. EIS Annual Review, Vol. 1. LC 78-73101. (Illus.). xii, 397p. 1978. text ed. 25.00 (ISBN 0-87815-024-2). Info Resources.

Da Silva, Armando. Tai Yu Shan: Traditional Ecological Adoptation in a South Chinese Island. (Asian Folklore & Social Life Monograph: No. 32). 1972. 14.00 (ISBN 0-89986-032-X). Oriental Bk Store.

Davidson, Norman. Crime & the Environment. 1981. 26.50x (ISBN 0-312-17198-6). St Martin.

Dubos, Rene. A God Within. LC 76-37224. 320p. 1972. text ed. 29.50x (ISBN 0-684-12768-7). Irvington.

--Man Adapting. enl. ed. LC 80-16492. (Silliman Lectures Ser.). (Illus.). 527p. 1980. 36.00x (ISBN 0-300-02580-7); pap. 9.95 (ISBN 0-300-02581-5, Y-197). Yale U Pr.

--So Human an Animal. LC 68-27794. (The Scribner Library of Contemporary Classics). 228p. 1984. pap. 7.95 (ISBN 0-684-71753-0, SL195, ScribT). Scribner.

Eisenbud, Merril. Environment, Technology & Health: Human Ecology in Historical Perspective. LC 78-55062. 1978. 32.50x (ISBN 0-8147-2154-0); pap. 17.50x (ISBN 0-8147-2160-5). NYU Pr.

Ekirch, Arthur A., Jr. Man & Nature in America. LC 63-14925. xvi, 231p. 1973. pap. 4.75 (ISBN 0-8032-5785-6, BB 574, Bison). U of Nebr Pr.

Environmental Physiology & Psychology in Arid Conditions: Review of Research. (Arid Zone Research Ser.: No. 22). 345p. 1963. 26.00 (ISBN 92-3-100531-6, U221, UNESCO); pap. write for info (ISBN 92-3-100532-4). Unipub.

Ewald, William R., Jr., ed. Environment for Man: The Next Fifty Years. LC 67-14215. (Midland Bks.: No. 102). (Illus.). Repr. of 1967 ed. 60.50 (ISBN 0-8357-9207-2, 2017619). Bks Demand UMI.

Farber, Seymour M. & Wilson, Roger H. The Air We Breathe: A Study of Man & His Environment. (Illus.). 432p. 1961. 35.50x (ISBN 0-398-00544-3). C C Thomas.

Flouride: The Cause of the Poisoning of America. 2.00 (ISBN 0-318-04608-3). Top-Ecol Pr.

BOOKS - SUBJECT INDEX

MAN–ORIGIN

Geller, E. Scott, et al. Preserving the Environment: New Strategies for Behavior Change. (Pergamon General Psychology Ser.: No. 102). (Illus.). 300p. 1982. 39.00 (ISBN 0-08-024615-X); pap. 12.95 (ISBN 0-08-024614-1). Pergamon.
Gerasimov, I. P., ed. Man, Society & the Environment. 340p. 1975. 5.45 (ISBN 0-8285-0432-6, Pub. by Progress Pubs USSR). Imported Pubns.
Gove, Walter R. & Carpenter, G. Russell. The Fundamental Connection Between Nature & Nurture: A Review of the Evidence. LC 80-8961. 320p. 1981. 31.50x (ISBN 0-669-04483-0). Lexington Bks.
Griffith, Jack S. Laboratory Manual for Man & His Environment. 128p. 1983. pap. 9.95 (ISBN 0-8403-3146-0). Kendall-Hunt.
Griffiths, John F. Climate & the Environment: The Atmospheric Impact on Man. LC 76-5801. (Environmental Studies Ser.: Vol. 2). 1976. pap. text ed. 12.00x (ISBN 0-236-40022-3). Westview.
Grossin, William. Les Temps de la Vie Quotidienne. (Interaction, l'Homme et Son Environment Social Ser.: No. 3). (Fr.). 416p. 1975. pap. text ed. 29.60x (ISBN 90-2797-785-2). Mouton.
Hadlow, Leonard. Climate, Vegetation & Man. 6.00 (ISBN 0-685-28346-1). Philos Lib.
Hiernaux, Jean. Man in the Heat, High Altitude, & Society. (Illus.). 130p. 1982. 24.75x (ISBN 0-398-04644-1). C C Thomas.
Jennings, Burgess H. & Murphy, John E. Interactions of Man & His Environment. LC 66-16371. 150p. 1966. 19.50x (ISBN 0-306-30234-9, Plenum Pr). Plenum Pub.
Lamb, H. H. Climate, History & the Modern World. (Illus.). 480p. 1982. 35.00x (ISBN 0-416-33430-X, NO. 3695); pap. 17.95 (ISBN 0-416-33440-7, NO. 3696). Methuen Inc.
LeBlanc, Jacques. Man in the Cold. (Illus.). 208p. 1975. 21.75x (ISBN 0-398-03429-X). C C Thomas.
Lovell, Alred C. Man's Relation to the Universe. LC 75-14096. pap. 31.00 (ISBN 0-317-07757-0, 2055542). Bks Demand UMI.
McEvoy, James & Dietz, Thomas. Handbook for Environmental Planning: The Social Consequences of Environmental Change. LC 76-57239. 354p. 1977. 32.00 (ISBN 0-471-58389-8). Krieger.
Marotz, Glen & McColl, Robert. Coping with Natural Environments. 144p. 1982. pap. text ed. 10.95 (ISBN 0-8403-2651-3). Kendall-Hunt.
Maximum Concentrations at the Workplace & Biological Tolerance Values for Working Materials, 1984. 94p. 1984. lab manual 10.50 (ISBN 0-89573-379-X). VCH Pubs.
Moser, Leo J. The Technology Trap. LC 78-26034. 288p. 1979. 23.95x (ISBN 0-88229-419-9); pap. 11.95 (ISBN 0-88229-669-8). Nelson-Hall.
Netting, Robert M. Balancing on an Alp: Ecological Change & Continuity in a Swiss Mountain Community. LC 81-358. (Illus.). 436p. 1981. 49.50 (ISBN 0-521-23743-2); pap. 17.95 (ISBN 0-521-28197-0). Cambridge U Pr.
Norwood, Christopher. At Highest Risk: Environmental Hazards to Young & Unborn Children. LC 79-20053. 1980. 10.95 (ISBN 0-07-047453-2). McGraw.
Oliver, John E. Climate & Man's Environment: An Introduction to Applied Climatology. LC 73-5707. 517p. 1973. text ed. 43.50x (ISBN 0-471-65338-1). Wiley.
Organization for Economic Cooperation & Development. Environment Policies for the 1980's. 110p. (Orig.). 1980. pap. text ed. 9.00x (ISBN 92-64-12049-1, 9780021). OECD.
Parry, M. L. Climatic Change, Agriculture, & Settlement. (Studies in Historical Geography). 214p. 1978. 18.50 (ISBN 0-208-01722-4, Archon). Shoe String.
Peate, I. C., ed. Studies in Regional Consciousness & Environment: Essays Presented to H. J. Fleure. facs. ed. LC 68-26478. (Essay Index Reprint Ser). (Illus.). 1968. Repr. of 1930 ed. 20.00 (ISBN 0-8369-0917-8). Ayer Co Pubs.
Poulton, E. C. Environment & Human Efficiency. (Illus.). 336p. 1972. 21.75x (ISBN 0-398-01515-5). C C Thomas.
Rees, A. R. & Purcell, H. J., eds. Disease & the Environment: Proceedings of the Inaugural Conference of the Society for Environmental Therapy Held in Oxford, March, 1981. 224p. 1982. 52.50 (ISBN 0-471-10203-2, Pub. by Wiley Med). Wiley.
Reno, Edward A., Jr., ed. The New York Times Cumulative Subject & Personal Name Index: Environment, 1965-1975. 778p. 1978. 75.00 (ISBN 0-667-00606-0). Microfilming Corp.
Seamon, David. A Geography of the Life World: Movement, Rest & Encounter. 1979. 27.50x (ISBN 0-312-32257-7). St Martin.
Shifrin, Norma. Changing Life on Earth: Study Guide. 1979. 12.95 (ISBN 0-8403-1977-0, 40197702). Kendall-Hunt.
Sloan, A. W. Man in Extreme Environments. (Illus.). 144p. 1979. 16.75x (ISBN 0-398-03941-0). C C Thomas.
Soyka, Fred & Edmonds, Alan. The Ion Effect. 1978. pap. 3.95 (ISBN 0-553-34232-0). Bantam.
Steyaert, Thomas A. Biology: A Contemporary View. (Illus.). 512p. 1975. text ed. 37.95 (ISBN 0-07-061346-X). McGraw.
Suedfeld, Peter & Russell, James A., eds. The Behavioral Basis of Design: Selected Papers, Bk. 1. LC 76-11594. (Community Development Ser.: Vol. 28). 1976. 34.50 (ISBN 0-87933-248-4). Van Nos Reinhold.
Suedfeld, Peter, et al, eds. The Behavioral Basis of Design: Bk. 2, Session Summaries & Papers. LC 76-11594. (Community Development Ser.: Vol. 36). (Illus.). 1977. 41.95 (ISBN 0-87933-293-X). Van Nos Reinhold.
Sulman, Felix G. The Effect of Air Ionization, Electric Fields, Atmospherics & Other Electric Phenomena on Man & Animal. (Illus.). 424p. 1980. photocopy ed. spiral 40.50x (ISBN 0-398-03930-5). C C Thomas.
Technical Meeting of the Institute of Environment Sciences, 25th Annual, Seattle, Washington, April 1979. Learning to Use Our Environment: Proceedings. (Illus.). 1979. pap. text ed. 25.00 (ISBN 0-915414-19-8). Inst Environ Sci.
Thirgood, J. V. Man & the Mediterranean Forest. LC 81-66368. 1981. 33.00 (ISBN 0-12-687250-3). Acad Pr.
Thoday, J. M. & Parkes, A. S., eds. Genetic & Environmental Influences on Behavior. LC 68-54003. (Eugenics Society Symposia Ser.: Vol. 4). 210p. 1969. 29.50x (ISBN 0-306-38704-2, Plenum Pr). Plenum Pub.
Timbrell, J. A. Principles of Biochemical Toxicology. 240p. 1985. 30.00x (ISBN 0-85066-221-4); pap. text ed. 18.00x (ISBN 0-85066-319-9). Taylor & Francis.
Viollet-Le-Duc, Eugene E. Habitations of Man in All Ages. Bucknall, Benjamin, tr. LC 74-146922. 1971. Repr. of 1876 ed. 65.00x (ISBN 0-8103-3787-8). Gale.
Ward, Robert D. Climate, Considered Especially in Relation to Man. 2nd rev. ed. LC 77-10242. 400p. 1983. Repr. of 1918 ed. 42.50 (ISBN 0-404-16220-7). AMS Pr.
White, Gilbert F. & Haas, J. Eugene. Assessment of Research on Natural Hazards. LC 75-2058. (Environmental Studies Ser.). (Illus.). 487p. 1975. 40.00x (ISBN 0-262-23071-2). MIT Pr.
Whyte, Anne. Guidelines for Field Studies in Environmental Perception. (MAB Technical Notes: No. 5). (Prepared in cooperation with SCOPE). 1977. pap. 9.25 (ISBN 92-3-101483-8, U783, UNESCO). Unipub.
Winkler, Franz E. Man: The Bridge Between Two Worlds. LC 80-82064. 268p. 1980. pap. 4.95 (ISBN 0-913098-32-9). Myrin Institute.
Winthrop, Henry, ed. Environment & Man: Some Traditional & Extended Meanings of Ecology. 1971. pap. text ed. 3.95x (ISBN 0-8422-0139-4). Irvington.
Wohlwill, J. F. & Weisman, G. D. The Physical Environment & Behavior: An Annotated Bibliography & Guide to the Literature. LC 81-4840. 484p. 1981. 50.00x (ISBN 0-306-40739-6, Plenum Pr). Plenum Pub.

MAN–INFLUENCE ON NATURE

see also Environmental Policy; Pollution

American Environmental Studies, 42 Vols. 1971. Repr. Set. 725.00 (ISBN 0-405-02650-1). Ayer Co Pubs.
Appleyard, R. T., ed. Man & His Environment: Octagon Lectures, 1969. 1970. pap. 6.50x (ISBN 0-85564-042-1, Pub. by U of W Austral Pr). Intl Spec Bk.
Arbib, Robert S., Jr. Lord's Woods. LC 73-139373. 1971. 6.95 (ISBN 0-393-08639-9). Norton.
Ashby, Eric. Reconciling Man with the Environment. LC 77-91909. 1978. 10.00x (ISBN 0-8047-0986-6); pap. 3.95 (ISBN 0-8047-1041-4, SP-155). Stanford U Pr.
Barnes, Bernard. Man & the Changing Landscape. (Work Notes Ser.: No. 3). (Illus.). 144p. pap. text ed. 14.00x (ISBN 0-906367-12-3, Merseyside County Mus of Liverpool England). Smithsonian.
Benarde, Melvin. Our Precarious Habitat. rev. ed. (Illus.). 384p. 1973. 8.25 (ISBN 0-393-06360-7); pap. 6.95x (ISBN 0-393-09372-7). Norton.
Bennett, Charles F., Jr. Man & Earth's Ecosystems: An Introduction to the Geography of Human Modification of the Earth. LC 75-22330. 331p. 1976. text ed. 33.95x (ISBN 0-471-06638-9). Wiley.
Beyer, Jan E. Aquatic Ecosystems: An Operational Research Approach. LC 79-57217. (Illus.). 328p. 1981. 22.50x (ISBN 0-295-95719-0). U of Wash Pr.
Borland, Hal. The History of Wildlife in America. Bourne, Russell & MacConomy, Alma D., eds. LC 75-15494. (Illus.). 208p. 1975. 14.95 (ISBN 0-912186-20-8). Natl Wildlife.
Disch, Robert, ed. Ecological Conscience: Values for Survival. LC 71-130009. 1970. pap. 2.45 (ISBN 0-13-222810-6, Spec). P-H.
Dolzer, Rudolf. Property & Environment: The Social Obligation Inherent in Ownership. (Environmental Policy & Law Papers: No. 12). 72p. 1976. pap. 10.00 (ISBN 2-88032-082-8, IUCN41, IUCN). Unipub.
Doughty, Robin W. Wildlife & Man in Texas: Environmental Change & Conservation. LC 83-45103. (Illus.). 256p. 1983. 16.95 (ISBN 0-89096-154-9). Tex A&M Univ Pr.
Drew, David. Man-Environment Processes. (Processes in Physical Geography Ser.: No. 6). (Illus.). 152p. 1983. pap. text ed. 9.95x (ISBN 0-04-551063-6). Allen Unwin.
The Ecology of Man in the Tropical Environment. (Illus.). 355p. 1964. pap. 20.00 (ISBN 2-88032-054-2, IUCN36, IUCN). Unipub.
Fleagle, Robert G., ed. Weather Modification: Science & Public Policy. LC 68-8511. (Public Policy Issues in Resource Management Ser.: Vol. 3). (Illus.). 158p. 1968. 20.00x (ISBN 0-295-78551-9). U of Wash Pr.
Goudie, Andrew. The Human Impact: Man's Role in Environmental Change. (Illus.). 328p. 1982. pap. text ed. 11.95x (ISBN 0-262-57058-0). MIT Pr.
Hancock, William K. Discovering Monaro: A Study of Man's Impact on His Environment. LC 78-178280. (Illus.). 256p. 1972. 37.50 (ISBN 0-521-08439-3). Cambridge U Pr.
Hay, John. The Undiscovered Country. (Illus.). 157p. 1982. 12.95 (ISBN 0-393-01571-8). Norton.
Holdgate, Martin W. & White, Gilbert F., eds. Environmental Issues-Scope Report 10. LC 77-2667. 224p. 1977. 39.95 (ISBN 0-471-99503-7, Pub. by Wiley-Interscience). Wiley.
Holzner, W. & Werger, M. J. Man's Impact on Vegetation. 1983. 98.00 (ISBN 90-6193-685-3, Pub. by Junk Pubs Netherlands). Kluwer Academic.
Human Activity & the Environment. 1979. pap. 5.25 (ISBN 0-685-90714-7, SSC113, SSC). Unipub.
Kabir, Humayun. Men & Rivers. 1981. 2.75x (ISBN 0-8364-0702-4, Pub. by Sargam India). South Asia Bks.
Leiss, William. The Domination of Nature. LC 74-6090. 252p. 1974. pap. 6.95x (ISBN 0-8070-4161-0, BP492). Beacon Pr.
--The Domination of Nature. LC 75-188358. 1972. 6.95 (ISBN 0-8076-0646-4). Braziller.
McHarg, Ian L. Design with Nature. LC 76-77344. 1971. pap. 12.95 (ISBN 0-385-05509-9). Natural Hist.
McKain, David W., ed. Whole Earth: Essays in Appreciation, Anger, & Hope. 384p. 1971. pap. text ed. 11.95 (ISBN 0-312-87045-0). St Martin.
Manners, I. A. & Mikesell, M. W., eds. Perspectives on Environment. LC 73-88849. (General Ser.: No. 13). 1974. pap. 3.95 (ISBN 0-89291-044-5). Assn Am Geographers.
Marsh, George P. Earth As Modified by Human Action. LC 74-106906. 1970. Repr. of 1878 ed. 32.00 (ISBN 0-403-00198-6). Scholarly.
--Man & Nature. Lowenthal, David, ed. LC 65-11591. (The John Harvard Library). pap. 8.95x (ISBN 0-674-54400-5). Harvard U Pr.
Matthews, William H., ed. Man's Impact on the Global Environment: Assessment & Recommendations for Action. (Study of Critical Environmental Problems). 1970. o. p. 27.50x (ISBN 0-262-19086-9); pap. 5.95x (ISBN 0-262-69027-6). MIT Pr.
Mediterranean Forest & Maquis: Ecology, Conservation & Management. (MAB Technical Notes: No. 2). (Illus.). 79p. 1977. pap. 5.25 (ISBN 92-3-101388-2, U378, UNESCO). Unipub.
Le Monde de la nature. (Illus.). 1978. text ed. 26.95x (ISBN 2-03-019112-4). Larousse.
Moscovici, Serge. Society Against Nature. Rabinowitz, Sacha, tr. from Fr. (European Ideas Ser.). 1976. text ed. 17.50x (ISBN 0-391-00523-5). Humanities.
Moser, Leo J. The Technology Trap. LC 78-26034. 288p. 1979. 23.95x (ISBN 0-88229-419-9); pap. 11.95 (ISBN 0-88229-669-8). Nelson-Hall.
National Geographic Society, ed. As We Live & Breathe: The Challenge of Our Environment. LC 74-151945. (Special Publications Ser.). (Illus.). 1971. 6.95, avail. only from Natl Geog (ISBN 0-87044-097-7). Natl Geog.
Newman, H. H., ed. Nature of the World & of Man. 562p. 1981. Repr. of 1926 ed. lib. bdg. 50.00 (ISBN 0-89984-004-3). Century Bookbindery.
Pewe, Troy L., ed. Desert Dust: Origin, Characteristics, & Effects on Man. (Special Paper: No. 186). (Illus.). 186p. 1981. 30.00 (ISBN 0-8137-2186-5). Geol Soc.
Poirot, Eugene M. Our Margin of Life. LC 78-52144. (Illus.). 139p. (Orig.). 1978. pap. 4.00 (ISBN 0-911311-06-8). Halycon Hse.
Reddy, A. K. Technology, Development & the Environment: A Re-Appraisal. (Studies Ser.: Vol. 1). 52p. 1979. pap. 5.00 (ISBN 92-807-1006-0, UNEP022, UNEP). Unipub.
Reno, Edward A., Jr., ed. The New York Times Cumulative Subject & Personal Name Index: Environment, 1965-1975. 778p. 1978. 75.00 (ISBN 0-667-00606-0). Microfilming Corp.
Rose, J., ed. Technological Injury: The Effect of Technological Advances on Environment Life & Society. 244p. 1969. pap. 37.25 (ISBN 0-677-13645-5). Gordon.
Sasson, Albert. Developpement et Environment: Fait et Perspectives dans les Pays Industrialises et en Voie de Developpement. LC 74-78190. (Fr.). 423p. 1975. pap. text ed. 26.40x (ISBN 90-2797-596-5). Mouton.
Schneider, Stephen H. & Morton, Lynne. The Primordial Bond: Exploring Connections Between Man & Nature Through the Humanities & Sciences. LC 80-20376. (Illus.). 336p. 1981. (full discount avail.) 15.95 (ISBN 0-306-40519-9, Plenum Pr). Plenum Pub.
Schueler, Donald G. Incident at Eagle Ranch: Man & Predator in the American West. LC 80-13588. 320p. 1980. 12.95 (ISBN 0-87156-230-8). Sierra.
Sheffield, Charles. Man on Earth: How Civilization & Technology Changed the Face of the World, A Survey from Space. LC 83-804. (Illus.). 160p. 1983. 29.95 (ISBN 0-02-610100-9). Macmillan.
Shepard, Paul. Nature & Madness. LC 82-3314. 288p. 1983. 15.95 (ISBN 0-87156-319-3). Sierra.
Singh, Indera P. & Tiwari, S. C., eds. Man & His Environment. (International Conference of Anthropological & Ethnological Sciences Ser.: No. 10). 299p. 1980. text ed. 19.50x (ISBN 0-391-02140-0). Humanities.
Slack, Walter H. The Surplus Species: Need Man Prevail? LC 81-40833. 172p. (Orig.). 1982. lib. bdg. 25.00 (ISBN 0-8191-2231-9); pap. text ed. 11.25 (ISBN 0-8191-2232-7). U Pr of Amer.
Spiro, Thomas G. & Stigliani, William. Environmental Issues in Chemical Perspective. 1980. 24.50x (ISBN 0-87395-427-0). State U NY Pr.
Strange, L. R. Human Influences in African Pastureland Environments: With Special Reference to the Arid & Semiarid Pastoral Regions of Eastern Africa. (Pasture & Fodder Crop Studies: No. 8). 102p. 1980. pap. 7.50 (ISBN 92-5-100874-4, F2076, FAO). Unipub.
Straub, Calvin C. The Man-Made Environment. 248p. 1982. pap. text ed. 15.95 (ISBN 0-8403-2903-2). Kendall-Hunt.
Thomas, Keith. Man & the Natural World: A History of Modern Sensibility. LC 82-14384. (Illus.). 432p. 1983. 19.45 (ISBN 0-394-49945-X). Pantheon.
Thomas, William L., Jr., ed. Man's Role in Changing the Face of the Earth, 2 Vols. LC 56-5865. (Illus.). 1971. Vol. 1. pap. 10.00x (ISBN 0-226-79604-3, P390, Phoen); Vol. 2. pap. 6.95X (ISBN 0-226-79605-1, P391). U of Chicago Pr.
Tivy, J. & O'Hare, G. Human Impact on the Ecosystem. LC 81-82809. (Conceptual Frameworks in Geography Ser.). (Illus.). 240p. (Orig.). 1982. text ed. 21.95x (ISBN 0-05-003203-8); 12.95x (ISBN 0-686-36898-3). Longman.
Von Baer, Carl E. & Coleman, William. Carl Ernst Von Baer on the Study of Man & Nature. LC 80-2105. (Illus.). 1981. lib. bdg. 55.00x (ISBN 0-405-13870-9). Ayer Co Pubs.
Walker, D. & West, R. G., eds. Studies in the Vegetation History of the British Isles. 89.50 (ISBN 0-521-07565-3). Cambridge U Pr.
Weapons of Mass Destruction & the Environment. 107p. 1977. 11.00x (ISBN 0-85066-132-3). Taylor & Francis.
White, George S. The Finer Forces of Nature in Diagnosis & Therapy. 231p. 1981. pap. 11.50 (ISBN 0-89540-080-4, SB-080). Sun Pub.
Wilson, Larry D. & Porras, Louis. The Ecological Impact of Man on the South Florida Herpetofauna. Collins, Joseph T., ed. (Special Publications Ser.: No. 9). 89p. (Orig.). 1983. pap. 7.00 (ISBN 0-89338-018-0). U of KS Mus Nat Hist.
Winkler, Franz E. Man: The Bridge Between Two Worlds. LC 80-82064. 268p. 1980. pap. 4.95 (ISBN 0-913098-32-9). Myrin Institute.
Witters, Weldon L. & Jones-Witters, Patricia. Environmental Biology: The Human Factor. 2nd ed. LC 75-35412. 1982. perfect bdg. 9.95 (ISBN 0-8403-2812-5). Kendall Hunt.
Yapp, W. B. & Smith, M. I. Production, Pollution, Protection. (Wykeham Science Ser.: No. 19). 196p. 1972. 9.95x (ISBN 0-8448-1121-1). Crane-Russak Co.

MAN–ORIGIN

see also Anatomy, Comparative; Evolution; Human Evolution; Life–Origin

Bonin, Gerhardt Von. The Evolution of the Human Brain. LC 63-13062. (Midway Reprint Ser.). 1975. pap. 6.95x (ISBN 0-226-06436-0). U of Chicago Pr.
Burgess, Robert F. Man: Twelve Thousand Years Under the Sea. LC 80-186. (Illus.). 448p. 1980. 12.95 (ISBN 0-396-07801-X). Dodd.
Cairns-Smith, A. G. Seven Clues to the Origin of Life: A Scientific Detective Story. 154p. 1985. 17.95 (ISBN 0-521-27522-9). Cambridge U Pr.
Chapman, A. J. & Jones, D. M., eds. Models of Man. 430p. 1981. pap. 19.95x (ISBN 0-901715-12-3). L Erlbaum Assocs.
Cold Spring Harbor Symposia on Quantitative Biology: Origin & Evolution of Man, Vol. 15. LC 34-8174. (Illus.). 437p. 1951. 38.00x (ISBN 0-87969-014-3). Cold Spring Harbor.
Dobzhansky, Theodosius. Mankind Evolving: The Evolution of the Human Species. (Silliman Memorial Lectures Ser.). (Illus.). 1962. 33.00x (ISBN 0-300-00427-3); pap. 8.95x 1964 (ISBN 0-300-00070-7, Y116). Yale U Pr.
Eiseley, Loren. Immense Journey. 1957. pap. 2.95 (ISBN 0-394-70157-7, Vin). Random.
Elliott, Scott F. Evolution & the Rediscovery of Prehistoric Man, 2 vols. (A Great Currents of History Library Bk.). (Illus.). 239p. 1985. Set. 189.75 (ISBN 0-89266-534-3). Am Classical Coll Pr.
Gaisford, ed. Atlas of Man. LC 78-4364. (Illus.). 1978. 25.00 (ISBN 0-312-05991-4). St Martin.
Goodman, Jeffrey. The Genesis Mystery: Explaining the Sudden Appearance of Modern Man. LC 82-40362. 320p. 1983. 16.60 (ISBN 0-8129-1039-7). Times Bks.
Gribbin, John. Genesis: The Origins of Man & the Universe. 352p. 1981. 35.00x (ISBN 0-460-04505-9, Pub. by Dent Australia). State Mutual Bk.
Hooton, Earnest A. Apes, Men & Morons. LC 76-134095. (Essay Index Reprint Ser). 1937. 21.50 (ISBN 0-8369-1956-4). Ayer Co Pubs.
Huxley, Thomas H. Evolution & Ethics, & Other Essays. LC 70-8391. 334p. 1897. Repr. 49.00x (ISBN 0-403-00041-6). Scholarly.
James, E. O. The Beginnings of Man. 1929. 17.50 (ISBN 0-8482-4654-3). Norwood Edns.
Keats, Brony S., et al. Source Book for Linkage in Man. LC 78-21207. 1979. 37.50x (ISBN 0-8018-2188-6). Johns Hopkins.
Keith, Arthur. The Antiquity of Man, 2 vols. Set. 250.00 (ISBN 0-87968-159-4). Gordon Pr.
Larsen, Clark S. & Matter, Robert M. Human Origins: The Fossil Record. (Illus.). 292p. (Orig.). 1985. pap. text ed. 12.95x (ISBN 0-88133-146-5). Waveland Pr.
Leakey, Richard & Lewin, Roger. Origins: What New Discoveries Reveal About the Emergence of Our Species & Its Possible Future. 1982. pap. 7.95 (ISBN 0-525-48013-7, 0772-230). Dutton.
Long, Barry. The Origins of Man & the Universe: The Myth That Came to Life. 256p. (Orig.). 1984. pap. 12.95 (ISBN 0-7102-0337-3). Routledge & Kegan.
Lyell, Charles. Geological Evidence of the Antiquity of Man. 4th ed. LC 72-1728. (Illus.). Repr. of 1873 ed. 35.00 (ISBN 0-404-08138-X). AMS Pr.
MacCurdy, George G., ed. Early Man. facs. ed. LC 77-86770. (Essay Index Reprint Ser). 1937. 27.50 (ISBN 0-8369-1184-9). Ayer Co Pubs.
Oakley, Kenneth P. Problem of Man's Antiquity. (Illus.). 1964. 15.00 (ISBN 0-384-42700-6); pap. 10.00 (ISBN 0-384-42701-4). Johnson Repr.
The Origin of Homo Sapiens. (Ecology & Conservation Ser.). (Illus.). 321p. 1972. 24.75 (ISBN 92-3-000948-2, U443, UNESCO). Unipub.
Robinson, Lytle W. Edgar Cayce's Story of the Origin & Destiny of Man. 208p. 20.00x (ISBN 0-85435-311-9, Pub. by Spearman England). State Mutual Bk.
Smith, Fred H. & Spencer, Frank. The Origins of Modern Humans: A World Survey of Fossil Evidence. LC 84-859. 612p. 1984. 70.00 (ISBN 0-8451-0233-8). A R Liss.
Smith, Grafton E., et al. Early Man: His Origin, Development & Culture. facs. ed. LC 67-28750. (Essay Index Reprint Ser). 1931. 18.00 (ISBN 0-8369-0398-6). Ayer Co Pubs.
Teilhard De Chardin, Pierre. Place De L'homme Dans la Nature. (Coll. le monde en 10-18). 1963. pap. 3.95 (ISBN 0-685-11497-X). French & Eur.
Thorpe, William H. Science, Man, & Morals. LC 76-14962. (Illus.). 1976. Repr. of 1965 ed. lib. bdg. 16.00x (ISBN 0-8371-8143-7, THSMM). Greenwood.
Tobin, Thomas H. The Creation of Man: Philo & the History of Interpretation. Vawter, Bruce, ed. LC 82-19891. (Catholic Biblical Quarterly Monographs: No. 14). viii, 199p. (Orig.). 1983. pap. 6.00x (ISBN 0-915170-13-2). Catholic Biblical.
Von Koenigswald, G. H. The Evolution of Man. rev. ed. Pomerans, Arnold J., tr. from Ger. LC 73-80572. (Ann Arbor Science Library). Tr. of Die Geschichte Des Menschen. (Illus.). 160p. 1976. 9.95 (ISBN 0-472-00120-5); pap. 4.95 (ISBN 0-472-05020-6, AA). U of Mich Pr.
Weidenreich, Franz. Apes, Giants & Man. (Illus.). 1946. 10.00x (ISBN 0-226-88147-4). U of Chicago Pr.

MAN, FOSSIL

see Fossil Man

MAN IN SPACE

see Life Support Systems (Space Environment)

MAN-MACHINE CONTROL SYSTEMS

see Man-Machine Systems

MAN-MACHINE SYSTEMS

Abbott, J. Man-Machine Interface Design. 180p. 1982. pap. 27.35 (ISBN 0-471-89409-5). Wiley.
Badre, Albert & Shneiderman, Ben, eds. Directions in Human-Computer Interaction. LC 82-11575. (Human-Computer Interaction Ser.: Vol. 1). 240p. 1982. text ed. 36.50 (ISBN 0-89391-144-5). Ablex Pub.
Budde, James F. Measuring Performance in Human Service Systems: Planning, Organization, & Control. LC 79-19551. pap. 55.30 (ISBN 0-317-26905-4, 2023557). Bks Demand UMI.
Chapanis, Alphonse. Man-Machine Engineering. LC 65-15099. (Behavioral Science in Industry Ser). (Orig.). 1966. pap. text ed. 7.25 pub net (ISBN 0-8185-0306-8). Brooks-Cole.
Computers, Ergonomics, & User Friendly System Design. cancelled. Report.
Coombs, M. J. & Alty, J. L. Computing Skills & the User Interface. LC 80-2768. (Computers & People Ser.). 1981. 49.50 (ISBN 0-12-186520-7). Acad Pr.
Cullen, T. R. The Ego & the Machine. 3rd ed. 2.00 (ISBN 0-930768-00-0). Gottlieb & Allen.
Dana, Richard T. The Human Machine in Industry. (Management History Ser.: No. 35). 326p. Repr. of 1927 ed. 22.50 (ISBN 0-87960-038-1). Hive Pub.
Demb, A. Computer Systems for Human Systems. LC 77-30730. (Illus.). 186p. 1979. 48.00 (ISBN 0-08-023029-6). Pergamon.
Grandjean, Etienne & Vigliani, E., eds. Ergonomic Aspects of Visual Display Terminals: Proceedings of the International Workshop, Milan, March 1980. (Illus.). 300p. 1980. 55.00x (ISBN 0-85066-211-7). Taylor & Francis.
Hatson, Rex. Advances in Human-Computer Interaction, Vol. 1. Shneiderman, Ben, ed. (Human-Computer Interaction Ser.). 300p. 1985. text ed. 35.00 (ISBN 0-89391-244-1). Ablex Pub.
Hirschhorn, Larry. Beyond Mechanization: Work & Technology in a Post-Industrial Age. LC 84-947. (Illus.). 216p. 1984. text ed. 17.50x (ISBN 0-262-08142-3). MIT Pr.
IFAC-IFIP-IEA-IFORS Symposium, Baden-Baden, BRD, Sept. 1982 & Johannsen, G. Analysis, Design, & Evaluation of Man-Machine Systems: Proceedings. Rijnsdorp, J. E., ed. (IFAC Proceedings Ser.). 434p. 1983. 108.00 (ISBN 0-08-029348-4). Pergamon.
International Conference on Man-Machine Systems, Manchester, UK, July 1982. Man-Machine Systems. (IEE Conference Publications: No. 212). 280p. 1982. pap. 70.00 (ISBN 0-85296-264-9). Inst Elect Eng.
Karp, Richard A. Proving Operating Systems Correct. Stone, Harold, ed. LC 82-13378. (Computer Science: System Programming Ser.: No. 16). 172p. 1983. 34.95 (ISBN 0-8357-1365-2). UMI Res Pr.
Kauffman, Draper, Jr. Systems I: An Introduction to Systems Thinking. DeWane, Michael L., ed. (The Future Systems Ser.). (Illus.). 44p. (Orig.). 1980. pap. text ed. 5.95 (ISBN 0-941506-00-2). Future Syst TLH.
Kent, Ernest W. The Brains of Men & Machines. 272p. 1980. 21.95 (ISBN 0-07-034123-0, BYTE Bks). McGraw.
Kompass, Edward J. & Williams, Theodore J., eds. Man-Machine Interfaces for Industrial Control: Proceedings of the 6th Annual Advanced Control Conference. 152p. 1983. Repr. of 1980 ed. 20.50 (ISBN 0-914331-05-1). Control Eng.
Lampson, Butler W. Research in Man-Machine Communications Using Time Shared Computer Systems. LC 77-131392. 73p. 1969. 19.00 (ISBN 0-403-04513-4). Scholarly.
Maloney, James J., ed. Online Searching Technique & Management. LC 83-11954. vii, 195p. 1983. pap. text ed. 25.00x (ISBN 0-8389-3285-1). ALA.
Martin, James. Design of Man-Computer Dialogues. (Illus.). 496p. 1973. ref. ed. 42.50 (ISBN 0-13-201251-0). P-H.
Moos, Rudolph H. The Human Context. LC 83-17562. 460p. 1985. Repr. of 1976 ed. lib. bdg. write for info. (ISBN 0-89874-679-5). Krieger.
Morecki, A., et al. Cybernetic Systems of Limb Movements in Man, Animals & Robots. LC 82-15717. 250p. 1984. 69.95x (ISBN 0-470-27374-7). Halsted Pr.
Murray, D. & Bevan, N., eds. Man Machine Integration: The Coming of Age. (Computer State of the Art Report, Series 13: No. 1). (Illus.). 300p. 1985. 569.50 (ISBN 0-08-028594-5, Pub. by Aberdeen Scotland). Pergamon.
Norman, Donald A. & Draper, Stephen. User Centered System Design. (New Perspectives on Human-Computer Interaction Ser.). 600p. 1986. text ed. price not set (ISBN 0-89859-781-1). L Erlbaum Assocs.
Oborne, David J. Ergonomics at Work. LC 81-14642. 321p. 1982. 35.95x (ISBN 0-471-10030-7, Pub. by Wiley-Interscience). Wiley.
Parsons, Henry McILvaine. Man-Machine System Experiments. LC 71-166483. (Illus.). 632p. 1972. 45.00x (ISBN 0-8018-1322-0). Johns Hopkins.
Petacchi, Donald. Work for Being in the Machine Age. LC 80-82646. 80p. 1980. 12.95 (ISBN 0-8022-2376-1). Philos Lib.
Pfaff, G. E., ed. User Interface Management Systems. (Eurographic Seminars Ser.). (Illus.). 240p. 1985. 34.50 (ISBN 0-387-13803-X). Springer-Verlag.
Rouse, William B., ed. Advances in Man-Machine Systems Research, Vol. 1. 1984. 45.00 (ISBN 0-89232-404-X). Jai Pr.
Sage, A. P., ed. Control Frontiers in Knowledge Based & Man-Machine Systems. 180p. 1983. pap. 34.75 (ISBN 0-08-031153-9). Pergamon.
Salvendy, G., ed. Human-Computer Interaction: Proceedings of the U. S. A.-Japan Conference on Human-Computer Interaction, 1st Honolulu, Hawaii, Aug. 18-20, 1984. (Advances in Human Factors-Ergonomics Ser.: Vol. 1). 1984. 74.50 (ISBN 0-444-42395-8). Elsevier.
Shackel. Man-Computer Communication, 2 vols. (Infotech Computer State of the Art Reports Ser.). 600p. 1979. Set. 145.00 (ISBN 0-08-028522-8). Pergamon.
Sheridan, T. B. & Johannsen, G., eds. Monitoring Behavior & Supervisory Control. LC 76-41687. (NATO Conference Series III, Human Factors: Volume 1). 537p. 1976. 59.50x (ISBN 0-306-32881-X, Plenum Pr). Plenum Pub.
Siegel, A. I. & Wolf, J. J. Man Machine Simulation Models: Psychosocial & Performance Interaction. LC 70-84967. Repr. of 1969 ed. 47.80 (ISBN 0-8357-9377-X, 2055131). Bks Demand UMI.
Singleton, W. T. & Fox, J. C., eds. Measurement of Man at Work: Papers. 268p. 1973. 33.00x (ISBN 0-85066-041-6). Taylor & Francis.
Smith, H. T. & Green, T. Human Interaction with Computers. LC 79-42930. 1980. 42.00 (ISBN 0-12-652850-0); pap. 23.00 (ISBN 0-12-652852-7). Acad Pr.

MAN-MADE LAKES

see Reservoirs

MAN ON OTHER PLANETS

see Life on Other Planets

MANAGEMENT

see also Computer Programming Management; Factory Management; Farm Management; Work Measurement

also subdivision management under specific subjects, e.g. Railroads–Management

Allen, Thomas J. Managing the Flow of Technology. 336p. 1977. pap. text ed. 12.50x (ISBN 0-262-51027-8). MIT Pr.
Anderson, David R., et al. An Introduction to Management Science: Quantitative Approaches to Decision Making. 4th ed. (Illus.). 752p. 1985. text ed. 30.95 (ISBN 0-314-85214-X). West Pub.
Ansoff, Igor, et al, eds. From Strategic Planning to Strategic Management. LC 74-20598. 259p. 1976. 57.95x (ISBN 0-471-03223-9, Pub. by Wiley-Interscience). Wiley.
Archibald, Russell D. Managing High-Technology Programs & Projects. LC 76-3789. 278p. 1976. 49.95x (ISBN 0-471-03308-1, Pub. by Wiley-Interscience). Wiley.
Argyris, Chris. Intervention Theory & Method: A Behavioral Science View. LC 79-114331. (Business Ser). 1970. text ed. 33.95 (ISBN 0-201-00342-2). Addison-Wesley.
Ashford, John. Statistics for Management. 2nd ed. (Illus.). 458p. (Orig.). 1980. pap. text ed. 25.00x (ISBN 0-85292-271-X). Intl Pubns Serv.
Austin, Larry M. & Burns, James R. Management Science. 608p. 1985. text ed. write for info. (ISBN 0-02-304840-9). Macmillan.
Badawy, Michael K. Developing Managerial Skills in Engineers & Scientists. (Managerial Skill Development in Engineering & Science Ser.). 480p. 1982. 31.50 (ISBN 0-442-20481-7). Van Nos Reinhold.
Baker, Kenneth R. & Kropp, Dean H. Management Science: An Introduction to Decision Models. 650p. 1985. text ed. 33.95 (ISBN 0-471-87766-2). Wiley.
Baughman, James P., et al. Environmental Analysis for Management. 1974. 31.95x (ISBN 0-256-01561-9). Irwin.
Baumgartner, J. S. Systems Management. 522p. 1979. 27.50 (ISBN 0-87179-297-4). BNA.
Bennett, Dudley. TA & the Manager. LC 76-20559. pap. cancelled (ISBN 0-317-10213-3, 2022624). Bks Demand UMI.
Bensoussan, A., et al, eds. Applied Stochastic Control in Econometrics & Management. (Contributions to Economic Analysis Ser.: Vol. 130). 304p. 1981. 64.00 (ISBN 0-444-85408-8, North-Holland). Elsevier.
Berry, William L., et al. Management Decision Sciences: Cases & Readings. 1980. 27.95x (ISBN 0-256-02219-4). Irwin.
Biggs, Charles L., et al. Managing the Systems Development Process. 1980. text ed. 39.95 (ISBN 0-13-550830-4). P-H.
Birchall, D. W. & Hammond, V. Tomorrow's Office Today: Managing Technological Change. 202p. 1981. 32.95x (ISBN 0-470-27236-8). Halsted Pr.
Black. Cost Engineering Management Techniques. (Cost Engineering Ser.). 264p. 1984. 35.00 (ISBN 0-8247-7088-9). Dekker.
Bowers, David. Systems of Organization: Management of the Human Resource. LC 75-31052. 1977. pap. text ed. 9.95x (ISBN 0-472-08173-X). U of Mich Pr.
Brightman, Harvey J. Problem-Solving: A Logical & Creative Approach. LC 80-25078. 1980. 18.95 (ISBN 0-88406-131-0). Ga St U Busn Pub.
Bronson, Gary J. & Bronson, R. Mathemathics for Management. 1977. text ed. 28.50 scp (ISBN 0-7002-2503-X, HarpC); scp solutions manual 9.50 (ISBN 0-7002-2505-6). Har-Row.
Brown, Warren B. & Moberg, Dennis G. Organization Theory & Management: A Macro Approach. LC 79-18709. (Wiley Series in Management). 685p. 1980. 38.45 (ISBN 0-471-02023-0). Wiley.
Brown, Wilfred & Jaques, Elliot. Glacier Project Papers: Some Essays on Organization & Management from the Glacier Project Research. (Glacier Project Ser.). 285p. 1965. 7.95x (ISBN 0-8093-0373-6). S Ill U Pr.
Buffa, Elwood S. Elements of Production Operations Management. LC 80-26666. 250p. 1981. pap. text ed. 20.95 (ISBN 0-471-08532-4). Wiley.
Bunn, Derek W. Analysis for Optimal Decisions. LC 81-19698. 275p. 1982. 44.95 (ISBN 0-471-10132-X, Pub. by Wiley-Interscience); pap. 24.95 (ISBN 0-471-10133-8, Pub. by Wiley-Interscience). Wiley.
Burghes, D. N. & Wood, A. D. Mathematical Models in the Social Management & Life Sciences. LC 79-40989. (Mathematics & Its Applications Ser.). 287p. 1980. pap. text ed. 28.95x (ISBN 0-470-27073-X). Halsted Pr.
Canada, John R. & White, John A., Jr. Capital Investment Decision Analysis for Management & Engineering. 1980. text ed. 34.95 (ISBN 0-13-113555-4). P-H.
Chambers, Harry T. The Management of Small Offset Print Departments. 2nd ed. 217p. 1979. text ed. 31.50x (ISBN 0-220-67007-2, Pub. by Busn Bks England). Brookfield Pub Co.
Christopher, Edward E. Behavioral Theory for Managers. 1977. pap. text ed. 12.25 (ISBN 0-8191-0352-7). U Pr of Amer.
Church, Alexander H. The Science & Practice of Management. LC 77-17901. (Management History Ser.: No. 24). 555p. Repr. of 1914 ed. 32.50 (ISBN 0-87960-037-3). Hive Pub.
Cooke, W. P. Quantitative Methods for Management Decisions. 704p. 1985. 33.95 (ISBN 0-07-012518-X); study guide 13.95 (ISBN 0-07-012519-8). McGraw.
Cortada, James W. Managing DP Hardware: Capacity Planning, Cost Justification, Availability & Energy Management. (Data Processing Management Ser.). (Illus.). 416p. 1983. text ed. 36.95 (ISBN 0-13-550392-2). P-H.
Couger, Daniel J. & Zawacki, Robert A. Motivating & Managing Computer Personnel. 232p. 1980. members 25.95 (ISBN 0-318-17053-1); (W4) 27.95 (ISBN 0-318-17054-X). Data Process Mgmt.
Coyle, John J. & Bardi, Edward. The Management of Business Logistics. 2nd ed. 500p. 1980. text ed. 24.95 (ISBN 0-8299-0325-9); instrs.' manual avail. (ISBN 0-8299-0472-7). West Pub.
Croft, David. Applied Statistics for Management Studies. 3rd ed. (Illus.). 304p. (Orig.). 1983. pap. text ed. 19.95x (ISBN 0-7121-0182-9, Pub. by Macdonald & Evans England). Trans-Atlantic.
Cummings, Thomas G. & Srivastva, Suresh. Management of Work: A Socio-Technical Systems Approach. LC 76-47659. 247p. 1977. pap. 14.95 (ISBN 0-88390-166-8). Univ Assocs.

Wheelwright, Steven C. & Makridakis, Spyros. Forecasting Methods for Management. 3rd ed. LC 79-23476. (Systems & Controls for Financial Management Ser.). 362p. 1980. 35.95 (ISBN 0-471-05630-8, Pub. by Ronald Pr). Wiley.

White, E. N. Maintenance Planning, Control & Documentation. 2nd ed. 232p. 1979. text ed. 49.50x (ISBN 0-566-02144-7). Gower Pub Co.

Whysler, R. O. Get Going! Tips on Managing Your Time & Increasing Your Effectiveness. (Illus.). 75p. (Orig.). 1982. pap. 13.00x looseleaf (ISBN 0-935402-11-X); lib. bdg. 12.00x (ISBN 0-935402-12-8). Intl Comm Serv.

Wild, Ray. Operations Management: A Policy Framework. (Illus.). 1979. 42.00 (ISBN 0-08-022504-7); pap. 16.50 (ISBN 0-08-022505-5). Pergamon.

Williams. Mathematics with Applications in the Management, Natural & Social Sciences. 1985. 31.52 (ISBN 0-205-07188-0, 567188); instr. manual 7.23 (ISBN 0-205-07189-9, 567189). Allyn.

Winger, Bernard J. Cases in Financial Management. LC 80-11532. (Finance Ser.). 211p. 1981. pap. 14.95 (ISBN 0-471-84209-5, Pub. by Grid). Wiley.

Wiseman, A. J., et al. Arable Management Nineteen Eighty. 240p. 1981. 35.00x (ISBN 0-7198-2538-5, Pub. by Northwood Bks). State Mutual Bk.

Wu, Nesa L. & Wu, Jack A. Introduction to Management Science. 1980. 31.95 (ISBN 0-395-30774-0). HM.

MANAGEMENT–ABBREVIATIONS

Pugh, Eric, compiled by. Pugh's Dictionary of Acronyms & Abbreviations. 348p. 1981. lib. bdg. 87.50x (ISBN 0-89774-012-2). Oryx Pr.

MANAGEMENT–BIBLIOGRAPHY

Bradley, Hugh E. The Operations Research & Management Science CumIndex, Vol. 10. 1979. 60.00 (ISBN 0-88274-009-1). R & D Pr.

Morrill, Chester, Jr., ed. Systems & Procedures Including Office Management Information Sources. LC 67-31261. (Management Information Ser.: No. 12). 1967. 60.00x (ISBN 0-8103-0812-6). Gale.

MANAGEMENT–DATA PROCESSING

Ahituv, Niv & Neumann, Seev. Principles of Information Systems for Management. 544p. 1982. write for info. (ISBN 0-697-08154-0); solutions manual avail. (ISBN 0-697-08155-9). Wm C Brown.

Anderson, R. G. Data Processing & Management Information Systems. 4th ed. (Illus.). 480p. 1983. pap. text ed. 15.95x (ISBN 0-7121-0431-3). Trans-Atlantic.

Atherton, Judith. Management of Professional Information Services. 1978. 90.00x (ISBN 0-905440-32-3, Pub. by MCB Pubns). State Mutual Bk.

Ayer, Steve J. & Patrinostro, Frank S. Software Development Planning & Management Documents. (Software Development Documentation Ser.: Vol. 1). (Illus., Orig.). 1985. pap. 49.50 (ISBN 0-9611694-2-7). Tech Comm Assoc.

Bocchino, William A. Management Information Systems: Tools & Techniques. LC 73-38416. (Illus.). 384p. 1972. ref. ed. O.P. 24.95 (ISBN 0-13-548693-9). P-H.

Boon. Management Information Systems. (Infotech Computer State of the Art Reports). 661p. 1974. 310.00s (ISBN 0-08-028554-6). Pergamon.

Bugg, Phillip W. Microcomputers in the Corporate Environment. (Illus.). 192p. 1986. text ed. 30.00 (ISBN 0-13-580234-2). P-H.

Burns & Austin. Management Science Models & the Microcomputer. 400p. 1985. pap. write for info. (ISBN 0-02-317300-9). Macmillan.

Carlson, E. D., et al. Display Generation & Management Systems (DGMS) for Interactive Business Applications. 15.00 (ISBN 0-9940013-8-X, Pub. by Vieweg & Sohn Germany). Heyden.

Chacko, George K. Management Information Systems. (Illus.). 454p. text ed. 29.95 (ISBN 0-89433-095-0). Petrocelli.

Champine, G. A. Computer Technology Impact on Management. 292p. 1978. 38.50 (ISBN 0-444-85179-8, North-Holland). Elsevier.

Chang, S. K. & Fu, K. S., eds. Pictorial Information Systems. (Lecture Notes in Computer Science: Vol. 80). 441p. 1980. pap. 28.00 (ISBN 0-387-09757-0). Springer-Verlag.

Chang, Shi-Kuo, ed. Management & Office Information Systems. 490p. 1984. 59.50x (ISBN 0-306-41447-3, Plenum Pr). Plenum Pub.

Cho, Chun H. Computer Based Energy Management Systems: Technology & Applications (Monograph) (Energy Science & Engineering Ser.). 1984. 45.00 (ISBN 0-12-173380-7). Acad Pr.

Chorafas, D. N. Management Workstations for Greater Productivity. 256p. 1986. 24.95 (ISBN 0-07-010859-5). McGraw.

Clowes, Kenneth W. The Impact of Computers on Managers. Dickson, Gary, ed. LC 82-4879. (Management Information Systems Ser.: No. 2). 206p. 1982. 39.95 (ISBN 0-8357-1337-7). UMI Res Pr.

Computerized Work Measurement: Unedited Collection. 1984. write for info. (ISBN 0-89806-063-X). Inst Indus Eng.

Connell, Stephen & Galbraith, Ian A. Electronic Mail: A Revolution in Business Communications. (Illus.). 152p. 1983. pap. 14.95 (ISBN 0-442-21691-2). Van Nos Reinhold.

Cooper, J. Microprocessor Background for Management Personnel. 208p. 1981. 23.95 (ISBN 0-13-580829-4). P-H.

Cornell, Joseph A. Computers in Hospital Pharmacy Management: Fundamentals & Applications. LC 82-24381. 228p. 1983. 32.00 (ISBN 0-89443-673-2). Aspen Systems.

Curtin, Dennis P. Manager's Guide to Framework: An Illustrated Short Course. 160p. 1985. pap. 18.95 (ISBN 0-13-550070-2). P-H.

Davis, Gordon B. Management Information Systems: Conceptual Foundations, Structure & Development. (Illus.). 480p. 1974. text ed. 35.95 (ISBN 0-07-015827-4). McGraw.

Dery, David. Computers in Welfare: The MIS-Match. LC 81-224. (Managing Information Ser.: Vol. 3). (Illus.). 264p. 1981. 25.00 (ISBN 0-8039-1610-8). Sage.

Dock, V. Thomas & Essick, Edward. Principles of Business Data Processing with MIS...including BASIC. 4th ed. 640p. 1981. text ed. 25.95 (ISBN 0-574-21305-8, 13-4305); instructor's guide avail. (ISBN 0-574-21301-5, 13-4301); study guide 10.95 (ISBN 0-574-21302-3, 13-4302). SRA.

Dock, V. Thomas, et al, eds. MIS: A Managerial Perspective. LC 77-7063. 1977. pap. text ed. 16.95 (ISBN 0-574-21050-4, 13-4050). SRA.

Ein-Dor, Phillip & Segev, Eli. A Paradigm for Management Information Systems. LC 81-1825. 304p. 1981. 39.95 (ISBN 0-03-058017-X). Praeger.

Fahey, Robert J., et al. Computers, Science & Management Dynamics. LC 72-102175. 1969. 12.00 (ISBN 0-910586-38-1). Finan Exec.

Federico, Pat A., et al. Management Information Systems & Organizational Behavior. Brun, Kim & McCalla, Douglas B., eds. LC 80-15174. 204p. 1980. 31.95 (ISBN 0-03-057021-2). Praeger.

Federico, Pat Anthony. Management Information Systems & Organization Behavior. 2nd ed. LC 85-6497. 240p. 1985. 37.95 (ISBN 0-03-003969-X). Praeger.

Fuhrman & Buck. Microcomputers for Management Decision Making. (Illus.). 400p. 1986. text ed. 26.95 (ISBN 0-13-580325-X). P-H.

Gant, Wanda & Casale, James F., eds. Making Business Systems Effective: The Papers & Proceedings of Syntopican XIII. 500p. (Orig.). 1985. pap. text ed. 30.00 (ISBN 0-935220-13-5). Assn Info Sys.

Goudas, C. L. & Pande, G. C., eds. Computers: Applications in Industry & Management. 450p. 1980. 59.75 (ISBN 0-444-86053-3, North Holland). Elsevier.

Gremillion, Lee L. Managing MIS Implementation. Dickson, Gary, ed. LC 82-4787. (Management Information Systems Ser.: No. 1). 198p. 1982. 39.95 (ISBN 0-8357-1321-0). UMI Res Pr.

Haider, Klaus. Managing Word Processing. 1985. 29.95 (ISBN 0-8359-4229-5); pap. text ed. 19.95 (ISBN 0-8359-4228-7). Reston.

Harrison, William. Management Information Systems: An Introduction for CETA Personnel. (Papers in Manpower Studies & Education: No. 2). 1975. 2.00x (ISBN 0-87071-328-0). Oreg St U Pr.

Hayhurst, G. Mathematical Programming for Management & Business. 1976. pap. 18.95x (ISBN 0-7131-3355-4). Intl Ideas.

Hernandez, Ernie, Jr. Management Strategies for Coping with Computers. (Illus.). 206p. 1985. pap. 26.95 (ISBN 0-910657-03-3). Frontline.

Hesse, Rick. Decision Making: A Management Science Guide for the IBM-PC. (IBM-PC Ser.: 1-646). 224p. 1984. pap. 16.95 (ISBN 0-471-89206-8, Wiley Professional Software); disk 29.95 (ISBN 0-471-89026-X); bk. & disk 46.90 (ISBN 0-471-89003-0). Wiley.

Hicks, James O. Management Information Systems. 316p. 1984. write for info. instr's manual with test bank (ISBN 0-314-77913-2). West Pub.

Hicks, James O., Jr. Management Information Systems. 625p. 1984. text ed. 29.95 (ISBN 0-314-77912-4); transparency masters avail. (ISBN 0-314-81473-6). West Pub.

--Management Information Systems (International Edition) 625p. 1984. 17.00 (ISBN 0-314-77914-0). West Pub.

Hillier, Frederick S. & Lieberman, Gerald J. Introduction to Operations Research. 3rd ed. LC 78-54193. 848p. 1980. text ed. 39.00x (ISBN 0-8162-3867-7); solutions manual 10.00x (ISBN 0-8162-4518-5); Study guide 10.00x. Holden-Day.

Hogan, Rex. Diagnostic Techniques for IMS Data Bases. 1985. pap. write for info. (ISBN 0-89435-174-5). Qed Info Sci.

Hopeman, Richard. Systems Analysis & Operations Management. LC 69-19269. 1969. text ed. 19.95 (ISBN 0-675-09514-X). Merrill.

House, William C., Jr. Interactive Decision Oriented Data Base Systems. 1977. 29.95 (ISBN 0-442-80339-7). Van Nos Reinhold.

Industrial Relations Counselors Symposium, 1965. Computer Technology: Concepts for Management. pap. 3.50 (ISBN 0-87330-015-7). Indus Rel.

Ingle, Marcus D., et al. Microcomputers in Development: A Manager's Guide. LC 83-19558. (K. P. Guideline Ser.). (Illus.). xi, 174p. (Orig.). 1983. pap. text ed. 12.75x (ISBN 0-931816-03-3). Kumarian Pr.

International Computer Programs Inc. ICP Software Directory, Vol. 3: Management & Administration Systems. Hamilton, Dennis L., ed. 1984. pap. 95.00 (ISBN 0-88094-027-1). Intl Computer.

International Computer Programs Staff. ICP Software Directory, Vol. 3: Management & Administration Systems. Hamilton, Dennis L., ed. 1985. pap. 95.00 (ISBN 0-88094-044-1). Intl Computer.

Jackson, Barbara B. Computer Models in Management. 1979. 27.95x (ISBN 0-256-02225-9). Irwin.

Jamieson, D. M., et al, eds. General Theory of Systems Applied to Management & Organization: Application, Vol. 2. (System Inquiry Ser.). 323p. 1980. pap. text ed. 14.75x (ISBN 0-914105-12-4). Intersystems Pubns.

Jenkins, A. Milton. MIS Design Variables & Decision Making Performance: A Simulation Experiment. Dickson, Gary, ed. LC 82-21858. (Management Information Systems Ser.: No. 3). 269p. 1983. 39.95 (ISBN 0-8357-1399-7). UMI Res Pr.

Jones, G. T. Data Capture in the Retail Environment. (Illus.). 1977. pap. 29.00x (ISBN 0-85012-168-X). Intl Pubns Serv.

Jones, W. S., et al. Micros for Managers. 192p. 1981. pap. 27.00 (ISBN 0-906048-60-5, NS010). Inst Elect Eng.

Kallman, E. Information System for Planning & Decision Making. 1984. 36.95 (ISBN 0-442-25628-0). Van Nos Reinhold.

Katzan, Harry, Jr. Multinational Computer Systems: An Introduction to Transnational Data Flow & Data Regulation. (Van Nostrand Reinhold International Series on Data Communications & Networks). 224p. 1980. 19.95 (ISBN 0-442-21573-8). Van Nos Reinhold.

Kenney, Donald P. Minicomputers: Low-Cost Computer Power for Management. rev. ed. LC 78-14413. 288p. 1981. pap. 7.95 (ISBN 0-8144-7560-4). Am Mgmt Assns.

--Minicomputers: Low-cost Computer Power for Management. LC 72-92752. pap. 51.80 (ISBN 0-317-20790-3, 2023915). Bks Demand UMI.

Kindred, Alton R. Data Systems & Management. 3rd ed. (Illus.). 432p. 1985. text ed. 26.95 (ISBN 0-13-196189-6). P-H.

Kirk, Francis G. Total System Development for Information Systems. LC 73-4359. (Business Data Processing: A Wiley Ser.). 284p. 1973. 49.95x (ISBN 0-471-48260-9, Pub. by Wiley-Interscience). Wiley.

Kleinschrod, Walter. Management's Guide to Word Processing. 1980. 75.50 (ISBN 0-85013-070-0). Dartnell Corp.

Kroeber, Donald W. Management Information Systems: A Handbook for Modern Managers. (Illus.). 288p. 1982. 17.95 (ISBN 0-02-917990-4). Free Pr.

Krukow, Ira. Project Management with the IBM PC. 128p. 1985. 11.95 (ISBN 0-89303-774-5). Brady Comm.

Langer, Steven, ed. Compensation in the MIS-dp Field. 346p. 1984. pap. 195.00 (ISBN 0-916506-00-2). Abbott Langer Assocs.

Lee, S. M., et al. Network Analysis for Management Decisions. (International Series in Management Science-Operational Research). 1981. lib. bdg. 30.00 (ISBN 0-89838-077-4). Kluwer Academic.

Leitch, Robert A. & Davis, K. Roscoe. Accounting Information Systems. (Illus.). 720p. 1983. 37.95 (ISBN 0-13-002949-1). P-H.

Levinson, Risha W. & Haynes, Karen S., eds. Accessing Human Services. LC 84-16012. 320p. 1985. 29.95 (ISBN 0-8039-2388-0); pap. 14.00 (ISBN 0-8039-2389-9). Sage.

Lewis, Colin. Managing with Micros: Management Uses of Microcomputers. 2nd ed. 208p. 1984. 24.95x (ISBN 0-631-13922-2); pap. 10.95x (ISBN 0-631-13642-8). Basil Blackwell.

Ligon, Helen H. Successful Management Information Systems. Dufey, Gunter, ed. LC 78-24565. (Research for Business Decisions Ser.: No. 9). 192p. 1978. 39.95 (ISBN 0-8357-0958-2). UMI Res Pr.

Lucas, Henry & Gibson, Cyrus F. Casebook for Management Information Systems. 2nd ed. (Management Information Systems Ser.). (Illus.). 480p. 1980. pap. text ed. 19.95 (ISBN 0-07-038939-X). McGraw.

Lucey, T. Management Information Systems: An Instructional Manual. 112p. 1981. 20.00x (ISBN 0-905435-01-X, Pub. by DP Pubns). State Mutual Bk.

McCosh, Andrew, et al. Developing Managerial Information Systems. LC 80-14760. 387p. 1981. 37.95x (ISBN 0-470-26913-8). Halsted Pr.

McFarlan, F. Warren, ed. The Information Systems Research Challenge: Proceedings. (Illus.). 320p. 1984. pap. 35.00 (ISBN 0-87584-161-9). Harvard Busn.

McLean, Ephraim R. & Soden, John V. Strategic Planning for MIS. LC 77-58483. 489p. 1977. 42.95x (ISBN 0-471-58562-9, Pub. by Wiley-Interscience). Wiley.

McNichols, Charles. Management & the Computer. 1985. pap. text ed. 17.95 (ISBN 0-8359-4170-1). Reston.

Managing by Computer: Making Your PC a Profit Center. 120p. 4.95 (ISBN 0-318-12059-3). Res Inst Am.

Marcotorchino, J. F., et al, eds. Data Analysis in Real Life Environment. (Advanced Series in Management: Vol. 8). 1985. 55.75 (ISBN 0-444-87692-8). Elsevier.

Matthews, Don Q. The Design of the Management Information System. 2nd ed. 238p. 1981. 18.95 (ISBN 0-86670-002-1). Moffat Pub.

Mautz, Robert K. & Merten, Alan G. Senior Management Control of Computer-Based Information Systems. LC 83-80636. 1983. lib. bdg. 8.00 (ISBN 0-910586-49-7). Finan Exec.

Moder, J., et al. Project Management with CPM, PERT & PRECEDENCE Diagramming. 3rd ed. 464p. 1983. 27.50 (ISBN 0-442-25415-6). Van Nos Reinhold.

Moen, Aaron N. & Moen, Ronald A. Computer Programs for Natural Resource Analysis & Management, Vol. I. 103p. (Orig.). 1985. pap. 15.00x (ISBN 0-913523-04-6). CornerBrook Pr.

Moul, Derek J. & Woolliams, Peter. Developing an Understanding of the Management of the Business: Using Micro-Computer Based Dynamic Management Exercises. 100p. 1984. 17.95 (ISBN 0-471-90359-0, Pub. by Wiley-Interscience); wkbk 9.95 (ISBN 0-471-90358-2). Wiley.

Murdick, Robert C. & Ross, Joel E. Introduction to Management Information Systems. (Illus.). 1977. 28.95 (ISBN 0-13-486233-3). P-H.

Murdick, Robert G. MIS: Concepts & Design. 1980. text ed. 29.95 (ISBN 0-13-585331-1). P-H.

Murdick, Robert G. & Ross, Joel E. Information Systems for Modern Management. 2nd ed. (Illus.). 640p. 1975. ref. ed. 29.95. P-H.

National Computing Centre. Guidelines for Computer Managers. 256p. 1981. 38.25 (ISBN 0-471-89455-9, DP00, Pub. by Wiley-Interscience). Wiley.

Novosad, John P. Systems, Modeling, & Decision Making. 280p. 1982. pap. text ed. 16.95 (ISBN 0-8403-2676-9). Kendall-Hunt.

Paker, Y. Minicomputers: A Reference Book for Engineers, Scientists & Managers. 1980. 59.00 (ISBN 0-9961005-0-4, 996100504, Pub. by Abacus England). Heyden.

Perry, William E. The Managers Survival Guide to Computer Systems. 1984. pap. 4.95 (ISBN 0-451-62340-1, Ment). NAL.

Philippakis, Andreas S. & Kazmier, Leonard J. Information Systems Through COBOL. 2nd ed. (Illus.). 1978. text ed. 33.95 (ISBN 0-07-049791-5). McGraw.

Philips, Sheldon W. & King, Brian L. GLAS: Payroll for SuperCalc. (Key-By-Key Ser.). (Illus.). 170p. 1983. write for info. (ISBN 0-534-02857-8); write for info. Wadsworth Pub.

Pidd, Michael. Computer Simulation in Management Science. LC 83-14489. 237p. 1984. 19.95x (ISBN 0-471-90281-0, Pub. by Wiley-Interscience). Wiley.

Riley, M. J., ed. Management Information Systems. 2nd ed. 425p. 1981. pap. text ed. 19.95x (ISBN 0-8162-7190-9). Holden-Day.

Rubicon Staff. Management & Computers: 1985. 1985. 49.95 (ISBN 0-938124-05-6). P R Lees-Haley.

Rudwick, Bernard. Solving Management Problems: A Systems Approach to Planning & Control. LC 78-23266. (Systems Engineering & Analysis Ser.). 496p. 1979. 53.50x (ISBN 0-471-04246-3, Pub. by Wiley-Interscience). Wiley.

Sanders, Norman. Computer-Aided Management. 288p. 1985. 25.00 (ISBN 0-89397-221-5). Nichols Pub.

The Solid Modeling Revolution: Today's Strategies for Selection & Implementation of Systems. (Illus.). 400p. 1985. 3-ring binder 290.00 (ISBN 0-932007-01-5). Mgmt Roundtable.

Sprague, Ralph H., Jr. & Carlson, Eric D. Building Effective Decision Support Systems. 304p. 1982. 29.95 (ISBN 0-13-086215-0). P-H.

Steiss, Alan W. Management Control in Government. LC 81-47027. (Illus.). 368p. 1982. 31.00x (ISBN 0-669-05375-9). Lexington Bks.

Stevens, John M. & McGowan, Robert P. Information Systems & Public Management. 302p. 1985. 38.95 (ISBN 0-03-004447-2). Praeger.

Stout, Russell, Jr. Organizations, Management, & Control: An Annotated Bibliography. LC 79-3639. 208p. 1980. 17.50x (ISBN 0-253-14448-5). Ind U Pr.

Taggart. Informations Systems: An Introduction to Computers in Organizations. 500p. 1980. text ed. 34.39 scp (ISBN 0-205-06908-8, 2069083); instrs' manual avail. (ISBN 0-205-06909-6). Allyn.

Teglovic, Steve & Lynch, Robert, eds. Topics in Management Information Systems. LC 73-3315. 295p. 1973. text ed. 29.50x (ISBN 0-8422-5092-1); pap. text ed. 8.50x (ISBN 0-8422-0277-3). Irvington.

Thierauf, Robert J. Distributed Processing Systems. (Illus.). 1978. 30.95 (ISBN 0-13-216507-4). P-H.

--Effective Management Information Systems. 576p. 1984. text ed. 29.95 (ISBN 0-675-20107-1). Additional supplements may be obtained from publisher. Merrill.

--Systems Analysis & Design of Real-Time Management Information Systems. LC 74-28368. (Illus.). 624p. 1975. ref. ed. 33.95 (ISBN 0-13-881219-5). P-H.

Tou, Julius T., ed. Information Systems (COINS IV) LC 74-4403. (Illus.). 506p. 1974. 69.50x (ISBN 0-306-35134-X, Plenum Pr). Plenum Pub.

Tricker, R. I. & Boland, Richard. Management Information & Control Systems. 2nd ed. LC 82-7056. 346p. 1982. 49.95x (ISBN 0-471-10450-7, Pub. by Wiley-Interscience); pap. text ed. 21.95x (ISBN 0-471-90020-6); pap. text ed. 20.00 members. Assn Inform & Image Mgmt

Walsh, Myles E. Realizing the Potential of Computer-Based Information Systems. 275p. 1984. pap. 26.95 (ISBN 0-02-949810-4). Macmillan.

Westin, Alan F., ed. Information Technology in a Democracy. LC 72-143233. (Studies in Technology & Society). 1971. 27.50x (ISBN 0-674-45435-9). Harvard U Pr.

Wysong, E. M. & De Lott, O. I. Information Systems Auditing. 1984. 29.00 (ISBN 0-444-86778-3, I-530-83). Elsevier.

MANAGEMENT OF FACTORIES

see Factory Management

MANATEES

Bertram, G. L. Conservation of Sirenia: Current Status & Perspectives for Action. 1974. pap. 7.50 (ISBN 2-88032-023-2, IUCN35, IUCN). Unipub.

Domning, Daryl. Sirenian Evolution in the North Pacific Ocean. (Publications in Geological Science Ser.: Vol. 118). 1978. 18.00x (ISBN 0-520-09581-2). U of Cal Pr.

Hartman, Daniel S. Ecology & Behavior of the Manatee (Trichechus Manatus) in Florida. (ASM Special Publication Ser.: No. 5). (Illus.). viii, 153p. 1979. 12.00 (ISBN 0-943612-04-7). Am Soc Mammalogists.

Kaiser, H. E. Morphology of the Sirenia. (Illus.). 1974. 10.25 (ISBN 3-8055-1609-6). S Karger.

MANGANESE

The Processing & Marketing of Manganese: Areas for International Co-operation. (Studies in the Processing, Marketing & Distribution of Commodities Ser.). 57p. 8.00 (ISBN 0-317-18701-5, E.84.II.D.18.). UN.

UNCTAD Secretariat. Studies in the Processing, Marketing & Distribution of Commodities: The Processing & Marketing of Manganese: Areas for International Cooperation. 57p. 1985. pap. 8.00 (UN84/2D18 5071, UN). Unipub.

MANGANESE MINES AND MINING, SUBMARINE

see also Hydraulic Mining

Analysis of Exploration & Mining Technology for Manganese Nodules. 1982. 300.00x (ISBN 0-86010-348-X, Pub. by Graham & Trotman England). State Mutual Bk.

Graham & Trotman Ltd. Assessment of Manganese Nodules Resources. 90p. 1982. 80.00x (ISBN 0-86010-347-1, Pub. by Graham & Trotman England). State Mutual Bk.

Graham & Trotman Ltd., ed. Seabed Minerals Series: Analysis of Exploration, Vol. 2. 120p. 1982. 50.00x (Pub. by Graham & Trotman England). State Mutual Bk.

--Seabed Minerals Series: Vol. 3, Analysis of Processing Technology for Manganese Nodules. 90p. 1982. 50.00x (ISBN 0-86010-349-8, Pub. by Graham & Trotman England). State Mutual Bk.

United Nations Editors, ed. Assessment of Manganese Nodule Resources, Vol. 1. (Seabed Minerals Ser.). 120p. 1983. 24.50x (ISBN 0-8448-1428-8). Crane-Russak Co.

United Nations Staff, ed. Analysis of Processing Technology for Manganese Nodules, Vol. 3. (Seabed Minerals Ser.). 90p. 1983. 24.50x (ISBN 0-8448-1431-8). Crane-Russak Co.

MANGANESE ORES

Arndt, Diether. Manganese Compounds As Oxidizing Agents in Organic Chemistry. Muller, Eugen, ed. Lee, Donald G., tr. from Ger. 368p. 1981. 45.00x (ISBN 0-87548-355-0). Open Court.

Bashkin, S. & Stoner, J. O., Jr. Atomic Energy-Level & Grotrian Diagrams, Vol. 4: Manganese I-XXV. 354p. 1983. 78.75 (ISBN 0-444-86463-6, I-517-82, North Holland). Elsevier.

Glasby, G. P., ed. Marine Manganese Deposits. LC 76-48895. (Oceanography Ser.: Vol. 15). 494p. 1977. 85.00 (ISBN 0-444-41524-6). Elsevier.

Josephson, Emanuel M. The Thymus, Myasthenia Gravis & Manganese. 1979. write for info. (ISBN 0-685-96470-1). Revisionist Pr.

Max Planck Society for the Advancement of Science, Gmelin Institute for Inorganic Chemistry. Manganese, Pt. C, The Compounds: Section 2, Manganate Compounds with Metals, from Li to U. (Gmelin Handbuch der Anorganischen Chemie, 8th Ed.). (Illus.). 302p. 1975. 204.60 (ISBN 0-387-93287-9). Springer-Verlag.

Roy, Supriya. Manganese Deposits. 1981. 65.00 (ISBN 0-12-601080-3). Acad Pr.

Sorem, R. K. & Fewkes, R. H. Manganese Nodules: Research Data & Methods of Investigation. LC 79-20057. 732p. 1979. 125.00x (ISBN 0-306-65186-6, IFI Plenum). Plenum Pub.

United Nations Ocean Economics & Technology Office. Manganese Nodules: Dimensions & Perspectives. (Natural Resources Forum Library). 1979. lib. bdg. 34.00 (ISBN 90-277-0500-3, Pub. by Reidel Holland); pap. 16.00 (ISBN 90-277-0902-5). Kluwer Academic.

MANGROVE

Chapman, V. J. Mangrove Vegetation. 1976. 52.50 (ISBN 3-7682-0926-1). Lubrecht & Cramer.

Lear, Richard & Turner, Tom. Mangroves of Australia. (Illus.). 1977. pap. 5.95x (ISBN 0-7022-1420-5). U of Queensland Pr.

Management & Utilization of Mangroves in Asia & the Pacific. (Environment Papers: No. 3). 181p. 1982. pap. 13.00 (ISBN 92-5-101221-0, F2364, FAO). Unipub.

Tomlinson, P. B. The Botany of Mangroves. (Cambridge Tropical Biology Ser.). (Illus.). 480p. Date not set. price not set (ISBN 0-521-25567-8). Cambridge U Pr.

MANIFOLDS (MATHEMATICS)

Abraham, R. & Marsden, J. E. Manifolds, Tensor Analysis, & Applications. LC 82-13737. 582p. 1983. text ed. 41.95 (ISBN 0-201-10168-8). Addison-Wesley.

Aliprantis, Charalambos D. & Burkinshaw, Owen. Locally Solid Riesz Spaces. (Pure & Applied Mathematics Ser.). 1978. 47.50 (ISBN 0-12-050250-X). Acad Pr.

Assadi, Amir H. Finite Group Actions on Simply-Connected Manifolds & CW Complexes. LC 81-19104. (Memoirs: No. 257). 117p. 1982. pap. 9.00 (ISBN 0-8218-2257-8, MEMO-257). Am Math.

Atiyah, M. F. Elliptic Operators & Compact Groups. (Lecture Notes in Mathematics Ser.: Vol. 401). v, 93p. 1974. pap. 13.00 (ISBN 3-540-06855-4). Springer-Verlag.

Aubin, T. Nonlinear Analysis on Manifolds: Monge-Ampere Equations. (Grundlehren der mathematischen Wiszenschaften: Vol. 252). 204p. 1983. 37.50 (ISBN 0-387-90704-1). Springer-Verlag.

Aulbach, B. Continuous & Discrete Dynamics near Manifolds of Equilibria. (Lecture Notes in Mathematics Ser.: Vol. 1058). ix, 142p. 1984. pap. 11.00 (ISBN 0-387-13329-1). Springer-Verlag.

Auslander, L. & Tolimieri, R. Abelian Harmonic Analysis, Theta Functions & Functional Analysis on a Nilmanifold. (Lecture Notes in Mathematics Ser.: Vol. 436). v, 99p. 1975. pap. 13.00 (ISBN 0-387-07134-2). Springer-Verlag.

Besse, A. L. Manifolds All of Whose Geodesics Are Closed. (Ergebnisse der Mathmatik und Ihrer Grenzbebiete: Vol. 93). (Illus.). 1978. 51.00 (ISBN 0-387-08158-5). Springer-Verlag.

Bing, R. H. The Geometric Topology of Three Manifolds. LC 83-14962. (Colloquium Publications Ser.: Vol. 40). 240p. 1983. 54.00 (ISBN 0-8218-1040-5). Am Math.

Bishop, Richard & Goldberg, Samuel. Tensor Analysis on Manifolds. (Illus.). 1980. pap. 5.95 (ISBN 0-486-64039-6). Dover.

Bombieri, Enrico. Seminar on Minimal Submanifolds. LC 82-61356. (Annals of Mathematics Studies: No. 103). 500p. 1983. 45.00 (ISBN 0-691-08324-X); pap. 15.00 (ISBN 0-691-08319-3). Princeton U Pr.

Borisovich, Y. G. & Gliklikh, Y. E., eds. Global Analysis Studies & Applications I. (Lecture Notes in Mathematics Ser.: Vol. 1108). v, 301p. 1984. pap. text ed. 16.00 (ISBN 0-387-13910-9). Springer-Verlag.

Browder, W. Surgery on Simply-Connected Manifolds. LC 70-175907. (Ergebnisse der Mathematik und Ihrer Grenzgebiete: Vol. 65). 140p. 1972. 21.00 (ISBN 0-387-05629-7). Springer-Verlag.

Burghelea, D. & Lashof, R. Groups of Automarphisms of Manifolds. (Lecture Notes in Mathematics Ser.: Vol. 473). 156p. 1975. pap. 13.00 (ISBN 0-387-07182-2). Springer-Verlag.

Carr, J. Applications of Centre Manifold Theory. (Applied Mathematical Sciences Ser.: Vol. 35). 160p. 1981. pap. 17.50 (ISBN 0-387-90577-4). Springer-Verlag.

Cartan, Elie. On Manifolds with Affine Connections & General Relativity. (Monographs & Textbooks in Physical Sciences). 150p. 1984. text ed. 45.50x (ISBN 88-7088-086-9, Pub. by Bibliopolis, Italy). Humanities.

Cecil, T. E. & Ryan, P. J. Tight & Taut Immersions of Manifolds. (Research Notes in Mathematics Ser.: No. 107). 300p. 1985. pap. text ed. 22.95 (ISBN 0-273-08631-6). Pitman Pub MA.

Centro Internationale Mathematico Estivo. Bifurcation Theory & Applications: Lectures Given at the Second Session of the Centro Internationale Mathematico Estivo held at Montecatini, Italy, June 24-July 2, 1983. Salvadori, L., ed. (Lecture Notes in Mathematics Ser.: Vol. 1057). vii, 223p. 1984. pap. 12.50 (ISBN 0-387-12931-6). Springer-Verlag.

Chapman, T. A. Lectures on Hilbert Cube Manifolds. LC 76-48316. (Conference Board of the Mathematical Sciences Ser.: No. 28). 1982. pap. 15.00 (ISBN 0-8218-1678-0, CBMS28). Am Math.

Choquet-Bruhat, Y., et al. Analysis, Manifolds & Physics. rev. ed. 630p. 1982. 29.50 (ISBN 0-444-86017-7, North-Holland). Elsevier.

Conference on Topological Methods in Algebraic Topology, SUNY, Binghamton, Oct. 1973. Algebraic & Geometrical Methods in Topology: Proceedings. McAuley, L. F., ed. (Lecture Notes in Mathematics Ser.: Vol. 428). xi, 280p. 1974. pap. 18.00 (ISBN 0-387-07019-2). Springer-Verlag.

De Medrano, Lopez. Involutions on Manifolds. LC 74-139952. (Ergebnisse der Mathematik und Ihrer Grenzgebiete: Vol. 59). (Illus.). 1971. 28.00 (ISBN 0-387-05092-2). Springer-Verlag.

Eberlein, Patrick. Surfaces of Nonpositive Curvature. LC 79-15112. (Memoirs: No. 218). 90p. 1979. pap. 10.00 (ISBN 0-8218-2218-7, MEMO-218). Am Math.

Elworthy, K. D. Stochastic Differential Equations on Manifolds. LC 82-4426. (London Mathematical Society Lecture Note Ser.: No. 70). 326p. 1982. pap. 32.50 (ISBN 0-521-28767-7). Cambridge U Pr.

Fenn, R., ed. Topology of Low-Dimensional Manifolds: Proceedings. (Lecture Notes in Mathematics: Vol. 722). 1979. pap. 14.00 (ISBN 0-387-09506-3). Springer-Verlag.

Field, M. J. Several Complex Variables & Complex Manifolds, Pt. II. LC 81-21590. (London Mathematical Society Lecture Note Ser.: No. 66). 220p. 1982. pap. 27.95 (ISBN 0-521-28888-6). Cambridge U Pr.

--Several Complex Variables & Computer Manifolds Part I. LC 81-21590. (London Mathematical Society Lecture Note Ser.: No. 65). 200p. 1982. pap. 22.95 (ISBN 0-521-28301-9). Cambridge U Pr.

Hall, Lowell H. Group Theory & Symmetry in Chemistry. LC 69-13607. pap. 96.00 (ISBN 0-317-08736-3, 2004355). Bks Demand UMI.

Hamilton, R. S. Harmonic Maps of Manifolds with Boundary. (Lecture Notes in Mathematics Ser.: Vol. 471). 168p. 1975. pap. 14.00 (ISBN 0-387-07185-7). Springer-Verlag.

Hempel, John. Intersection Calculus on Surfaces with Applications to 3-Manifolds. LC 83-3724. (Memoirs of the American Mathematical Society: No. 282). 50p. 1983. pap. 9.00 (ISBN 0-8218-2282-9). Am Math.

--Three-Manifolds. LC 76-3027. (Annals of Mathematics Studies: No. 86). 204p. 1976. 25.50x (ISBN 0-691-08178-6); pap. 13.50x (ISBN 0-691-08183-2). Princeton U Pr.

Herbert, Ralph J. Multiple Points of Immersed Manifolds. LC 81-12772. (Memoirs of the American Mathematical Society: No. 250). 61p. 1981. pap. 9.00 (ISBN 0-8218-2250-0). Am Math.

Hirsch, Morris W. & Mazur, Barry. Smoothings of Piecewise Linear Manifolds. LC 74-2967. (Annals of Mathematics Studies: No. 80). 165p. 1974. 16.50x (ISBN 0-691-08145-X). Princeton U Pr.

Hirzebruch, F., et al. Differentiable Manifolds & Quadratic Forms. LC 70-176304. (Lecture Notes in Pure & Applied Mathematics Ser.: Vol. 4). pap. 24.00 (ISBN 0-8357-9080-0, 2017692). Bks Demand UMI.

Iberkleid, W. & Petrie, T. Smooth S-One Manifolds. (Lecture Notes in Mathematics: Vol. 557). 1976. soft cover 13.00 (ISBN 0-387-08002-3). Springer-Verlag.

Jackson, R. J. Canonical Differential Operators & Lower-Order Symbols. LC 73-8760. (Memoirs: No. 135). 235p. 1973. pap. 12.00 (ISBN 0-8218-1835-X, MEMO-135). Am Math.

James, I. M. The Topology of Stiefel Manifolds. LC 76-9646. (London Mathematical Society Lecture Notes Ser.: No. 24). 1977. 16.95x (ISBN 0-521-21334-7). Cambridge U Pr.

Jensen, G. Higher Order Contact of Submanifolds of Homogeneous Spaces. LC 77-14394. (Lecture Notes in Mathematics Ser.: Vol. 610). 1977. pap. text ed. 14.00 (ISBN 0-387-08433-9). Springer-Verlag.

Johannson, K. Homotopy Equivalence of Three-Manifolds with Boundaries. (Lecture Notes in Mathematics: Vol. 761). 303p. 1979. pap. 23.00 (ISBN 0-387-09714-7). Springer-Verlag.

Kirby, Robion C. & Siebenmann, Laurence C. Foundational Essays on Topological Manifolds, Smoothing & Triangulations. LC 76-45918. (Annals of Mathematical Studies: No. 88). 352p. 1977. 35.00 (ISBN 0-691-08190-5); pap. 15.50x (ISBN 0-691-08191-3). Princeton U Pr.

Kobayashi, Shoshichi. Hyperbolic Manifolds & Holomorphic Mappings. LC 70-131390. (Pure & Applied Mathematics Ser.: No. 2). pap. 39.30 (ISBN 0-317-08025-3, 2017855). Bks Demand UMI.

Madsen, Ib & Milgram, R. James. The Classified Spaces for Surgery & Cobordism of Manifolds. LC 78-70311. (Annals of Mathematics Studies: No. 92). 1979. 33.00x (ISBN 0-691-08225-1); pap. 13.50 (ISBN 0-691-08226-X). Princeton U Pr.

Matsushima, Y. Differentiable Manifolds. LC 71-182215. (Pure & Applied Mathematics Ser.: Vol. 9). 1972. 55.00 (ISBN 0-8247-1445-8). Dekker.

Matsushima, Yozo. Holomorphic Vector Fields on Compact Kaehler Manifolds. LC 77-145641. (CBMS Regional Conference Series in Mathematics: No. 7). 38p. 1971. pap. 9.00 (ISBN 0-8218-1656-X, CBMS-7). Am Math.

Millett, K. C., ed. Algebraic & Geometric Topology: Proceedings of a Symposium Held at Santa Barbara in Honor of Raymond L. Wilder, July 25-29, 1977. LC 78-15091. (Lecture Notes in Mathematics: Vol. 664). 1978. pap. 16.00 (ISBN 0-387-08920-9). Springer-Verlag.

Moishezon, B. Complex Surfaces & Connected Sums of Complex Projective Planes. LC 77-22136. (Lecture Notes in Mathematics: Vol. 603). (Illus.). 1977. pap. text ed. 18.00 (ISBN 0-387-08355-3). Springer-Verlag.

Morgan, John W. & Bass, Hyman. The Smith Conjecture. LC 83-15846. (Pure & Applied Mathematics Ser.). 1984. 55.00 (ISBN 0-12-506980-4). Acad Pr.

Neuwirth, L. P., ed. Knots, Groups, & 3-Manifolds: Papers Dedicated to the Memory of R. H. Fox. LC 75-5619. (Annals of Mathematics Studies: No. 84). 345p. 1975. 35.00 (ISBN 0-691-08170-0); pap. 13.50 (ISBN 0-691-08167-0). Princeton U Pr.

Nottrot, R. Optimal Processes on Manifolds: An Application of Stokes' Theorem. (Lecture Notes on Mathematics: Vol. 963). 124p. 1982. pap. 10.00 (ISBN 0-387-11963-9). Springer-Verlag.

Poston, T. & Woodcock, A. E. A Geometrical Study of the Elementary Catastrophes. LC 73-22575. (Lectures Notes in Mathematics: Vol. 373). (Illus.). v, 257p. 1974. pap. 18.00 (ISBN 0-387-06681-0). Springer-Verlag.

Stallings, John R. Group Theory & Three-Dimensional Manifolds. LC 70-151590. (Yale Mathematical Monographs Ser.: Vol. 4). pap. 20.00 (ISBN 0-317-09475-0, 2016792). Bks Demand UMI.

Stoll, Wilhelm. Invariant Forms on Grassman Manifolds. LC 77-85946. (Annals of Mathematics Studies Ser.: No. 89). 128p. 1978. 20.00 (ISBN 0-691-08198-0); pap. 10.50 (ISBN 0-691-08199-9). Princeton U Pr.

Stone, D. A. Stratified Polyhedra. LC 77-187427. (Lecture Notes in Mathematics: Vol. 252). 193p. 1972. pap. 10.00 (ISBN 0-387-05726-9). Springer-Verlag.

--Processes & Materials of Manufacture. 3rd ed. 1983. text ed. 45.00 (ISBN 0-205-07888-5, 327888). Allyn.

Link, Albert N. Research & Development in U. S. Manufacturing. 144p. 1981. 27.95 (ISBN 0-03-057677-6). Praeger.

Livingston, K. C. & Graham, T. C., eds. Manufacturing Processes in Canada. LC 60-4680. (Illus.). pap. 77.00 (ISBN 0-317-11048-9, 2014301). Bks Demand UMI.

McCabe, Robert E., et al. Metering Pump Handbook. (Illus.). 300p. 1984. text ed. 29.95 (ISBN 0-8311-1157-7). Indus Pr.

McCarty, Frank, intro. by. AUTOFACT West Proceedings, Vol. 2. LC 80-53423. (Illus.). 842p. 1980. pap. 55.00 (ISBN 0-87263-066-8). SME.

Major Loss Prevention in the Process Industries: Proceedings, No. 34, Newcastle-Upon-Tyne, 1971. 258p. 1981. 72.00x (ISBN 0-85295-078-0, Pub. by Inst Chem Eng England). State Mutual Bk.

Management's Guide to Computer Integrated Manufacturing. 93.00 (ISBN 0-686-31443-3). C I M Systems.

Manufacturing-Processing Machine Setting. 1982. 50.00x (ISBN 0-85083-458-9, Pub. by Engineering Ind). State Mutual Bk.

Martin, T., ed. Design of Work in Automated Manufacturing Systems: Proceedings of the IFAC Workshop, Karlsruhe, FRG, 7-9 November 1983. (IFAC Proceedings Ser.). 188p. 1984. 46.00 (ISBN 0-08-031118-0). Pergamon.

Martinez, M. R. & Lev, M. C., eds. Computer Integrated Manufacturing. (PED Ser.: Vol. 8). 148p. 1983. pap. text ed. 30.00 (ISBN 0-317-02557-0, H00288). ASME.

Mayr, Otto & Post, Robert C., eds. Yankee Enterprise: The Rise of the American System of Manufacturers. LC 81-607315. (Illus.). 236p. (Orig.). 1982. text ed. 19.95x (ISBN 0-87474-634-5); pap. text ed. 9.95x (ISBN 0-87474-631-0). Smithsonian.

Meade, L. E., intro. by. Material & Process Advances '82. (National SAMPE Technical Conference Ser.). (Illus.). 1982. 60.00 (ISBN 0-938994-21-2). Soc Adv Material.

MiCon Seventy-Eight: Optimization of Processing, Properties & Service Performance Through Microstructural Control - STP 672. 677p. 1979. 59.50x (ISBN 0-8031-0517-7, 04-672000-28). ASTM.

Miller, Richard K. Artificial Intelligence Applications for Manufacturing. (Illus.). 200p. 1984. pap. text ed. 110.00 (ISBN 0-89671-062-9). SEAI Tech Pubns.

Miller, Richard S. Planning & Designing the Totally Automated Manufacturing Plant. (Illus.). 240p. 1984. pap. text ed. cancelled (ISBN 0-89671-059-9). SEAI Tech Pubns.

Millis, N. & Pittard, A. J., eds. The Applications of Microbial Physiology & Genetics to Industrial Processes. 250p. Date not set. write for info. (ISBN 0-12-497520-8). Acad Pr.

Nicks, J E. BASIC Programming Solutions for Manufacturing. (Illus.). 298p. 1982. 32.00 (ISBN 0-87263-076-5). SME.

Parsley, K. J. Manufacturing Technology. (Illus.). 256p. 1983. pap. text ed. 18.95x (ISBN 0-686-45512-6). Trans-Atlantic.

Phatia, Mahesh, ed. Transfer Operations in Process Industries: Design & Equipment. LC 83-50699. (Process Equipment Ser.: Vol. 5). 373p. 1983. 35.00 (ISBN 0-87762-334-1). Technomic.

Plossi, George. Manufacturing Control: The Last Frontier for Profits. LC 73-8965. 1973. 23.95 (ISBN 0-87909-483-4). Reston.

Proceedings of First International Conference in Simulation in Manufacturing. 1985. 85.00x (ISBN 0-903608-84-7, Pub. by IFS Pubns UK). Air Sci Co.

Rajbman, N. S. & Chadeev, V. M. Identification of Industrial Processes: The Application of Computers in Research & Production Control. 436p. 1980. 64.00 (ISBN 0-444-85181-X, North-Holland). Elsevier.

Rathmill, K., ed. Flexible Manufacturing Systems 2: Proceedings of the Second International Conference, London, UK, Oct. 1983. 700p. 1983. 86.75 (ISBN 0-444-86815-1, I-509-83, North-Holland). Elsevier.

Rathmill, Keith, ed. Robotic Assembly. 350p. 1985. 42.00x (ISBN 0-903608-71-5, Pub. by IFS Pubns UK). Air Sci Co.

Rembold, Ulrich, et al, eds. Computers in Manufacturing. (Manufacturing Engineering & Material Processing Ser.: Vol. 1). (Illus.). 592p. 1977. pap. 95.00 (ISBN 0-8247-1821-6). Dekker.

Schey, John A. Introduction to Manufacturing Processes. (Illus.). 1977. text ed. 42.00 (ISBN 0-07-055274-6). McGraw.

Schmitz, Hubert. Manufacturing in the Backyard: Case Studies on Accumulation & Employment in Small-Scale Brazilian Industry. LC 81-17604. (Illus.). 242p. 1982. 29.50x (ISBN 0-86598-076-4). Allanheld.

Schreiber, F. A. & Litwin, W., eds. Distributed Data Sharing Systems: Proceedings of the Third International Seminar Held in Parma, Italy, 28-30 March, 1984. 246p. 1985. 44.50 (ISBN 0-444-87637-5, North-Holland). Elsevier.

Smith, Donald, et al. CAD-CAM International Delphi Forecast. LC 80-53001. (Illus.). 181p. 1980. pap. 29.00 (ISBN 0-87263-062-5). SME.

Society of Manufacturing Engineers. Flexible Manufacturing Systems, 1985. 1985. 64.00 (ISBN 0-87263-182-6). SME.

--NAMRC 1985 XIII: Proceedings. 1985. 70.00 (ISBN 0-87263-186-9). SME.

Strassmann, Wolfgang P. Risk & Technological Innovation: American Manufacturing Methods During the Nineteenth Century. LC 81-4252. x, 249p. 1981. Repr. lib. bdg. 25.00x (ISBN 0-313-23083-8, STRIT). Greenwood.

Taraman, Khalil S., ed. CAD-CAM: Meeting Today's Productivity Challenge. LC 80-69006. (Manufacturing Update Ser.). (Illus.). 290p. 1980. 32.00 (ISBN 0-87263-063-3, 554). SME.

Technical Insights, Inc. Staff. The Handbook of Manufacturing Software: A Comprehensive Directory. LC 84-51894. 192p. 1985. 197.00 (ISBN 0-914993-04-6). Tech Insights.

Thode, Bradley R. Materials Processing. LC 80-70702. (Industrial Arts Ser.). (Illus.). 306p. 1982. text ed. 19.60 (ISBN 0-8273-1767-0); instr's. manual 3.60 (ISBN 0-8273-1768-9). Delmar.

Town, H. C. & Moore, H. Manufacturing Technology, Vol. 1. 1979. pap. 12.95 (ISBN 0-7134-1095-7, Pub. by Batsford England). David & Charles.

Warnecke, H. J., ed. Flexible Manufacturing Systems: Proceedings of the 3rd International Conference, Boeblingen, near Stuttgart, BRD, 11-13 September 1984. 500p. 1985. 111.00 (ISBN 0-444-87623-5, North-Holland). Elsevier.

Weyher, Douglas F. Adhesives in Modern Manufacturing. Bruno, E. J., ed. LC 79-93212. (Manufacturing Data Ser.). pap. 49.50 (ISBN 0-317-29881-X, 201600). Bks Demand UMI.

Wilson, B., et al, eds. Efficiency of Manufacturing Systems. (NATO Conference Series II: Systems Science: Vol. 14). 346p. 1983. 49.50x (ISBN 0-306-41256-X, Plenum Pr). Plenum Pub.

Wilson, R. C. & Henry, Robert A. Introduction to Group Technology in Manufacturing & Engineering. (Illus.). 70p. 1977. 12.00 (ISBN 0-938654-19-5, GROUP). Indus Dev Inst Sci.

World Petroleum Congress. Proceedings of the Eighth World Petroleum Congress: Manufacturing, Vol. 4. (Illus.). 433p. 1971. 105.50 (ISBN 0-85334-519-8, Pub. by Elsevier Applied Sci England). Elsevier.

Wright, R. T. & Jensen, T. R. Manufacturing Material Processing, Management, Careers. LC 76-5892. 336p. 16.80. Goodheart.

Yankee, Herbert W. Manufacturing Processes. LC 78-13059. (Illus.). 1978. 37.95 (ISBN 0-13-555557-4). P-H.

Zintak, Dennis, ed. Improving Production with Coolants & Lubricants. LC 82-80849. (Manfacturing Update Ser.). 260p. 1982. 32.00 (ISBN 0-87263-081-1). SME.

MANUFACTURING PROCESSES–DATA PROCESSING

Barnes, Marvin P. Computer-Assisted Mineral Appraisal & Feasibility. LC 79-52270. (Illus.). 167p. 1980. text ed. 33.00x (ISBN 0-89520-262-X). Soc Mining Eng.

Bertrand, J. W. & Wortmann, J. C. Production Control & Information Systems for Component Manufacturing Shops. (Studies in Production & Engineering Economics: Vol. 1). 104p. 1981. 74.50 (ISBN 0-444-41964-0). Elsevier.

Cassell, Douglas A. Introduction to Computer-Aided Manufacturing in Electronics. LC 73-177882. 248p. 1972. 21.50 (ISBN 0-471-14053-8, Pub. by Wiley). Krieger.

Dayasena, P. J., ed. Microprocessor Applications in Manufacturing Industry: Bibliography. 1981. 36.00 (ISBN 0-85296-227-4). Inst Elect Eng.

DeVries, W. R., ed. Computer Applications in Manufacturing Systems. (PED: Vol. 2). 101p. 1980. 18.00 (ISBN 0-317-06810-5, G00194). ASME.

Gardner, Leonard B., ed. Automated Manufacturing-STP 862. LC 85-1243. (Illus.). 255p. 1985. text ed. 38.00 (ISBN 0-8031-0422-7, 04-862000-32). ASTM.

Goudas, C. L. & Pande, G. C., eds. Computers: Applications in Industry & Management. 450p. 1980. 59.75 (ISBN 0-444-86053-3, North Holland). Elsevier.

Grady, Perry L. & Mock, Gary N. Microprocessors & Minicomputers in the Textile Industry. LC 80-82119. 488p. 1983. text ed. 59.95 (ISBN 0-87664-485-X, I485-X). Instru Soc.

Humphreys, Kenneth K. & Leonard, Joseph W., eds. Basic Mathematics & Computer Techniques for Coal Preparation & Mining. (Energy, Power, & Environment Ser.: Vol. 17). (Illus.). 248p. 1983. 45.00 (ISBN 0-8247-1884-4). Dekker.

Increasing Industrial Productivity Through Source Data Automation. 1978. pap. 2.00 (ISBN 0-918734-20-7). Reymont.

International Computer Programs Inc. ICP Software Directory, Vol. 5: Manufacturing & Engineering Systems. Hamilton, Dennis L., ed. 1984. pap. 95.00 (ISBN 0-88094-029-8). Intl Computer.

International Computer Programs Staff. ICP Software Directory, Vol. 5: Manufacturing & Engineering Systems. Hamilton, Dennis L., ed. 1985. pap. 95.00 (ISBN 0-88094-046-8). Intl Computer.

Kochar, A. K. & Burns, N. D. Microprocessors & Their Manufacturing Applications. 344p. 1983. text ed. 29.95 (ISBN 0-7131-3470-4). E Arnold.

Mermet, Jean P., ed. CAD in Medium Sized & Small Industries: Proceedings of the European Conference on Computer Aided Design, MICAD 80, Paris, France, September 1980. 664p. 1981. 85.00 (ISBN 0-444-86145-9, North-Holland). Elsevier.

Microprocessor-Based Measuring Instrumentation Market in W. European Manufacturing. 262p. 1983. 1200.00 (ISBN 0-86621-549-2, E625). Frost & Sullivan.

Micros in Manufacturing. 135p. 1980. 23.00x (ISBN 0-903796-66-X, Pub. by Online). Taylor & Francis.

Miller, Richard K., et al. The Handbook of Manufacturing Software, 1984. (Illus.). 300p. 1984. pap. text ed. 197.00 (ISBN 0-89671-058-0). SEAI Tech Pubns.

Nazemetz, John W., et al, eds. Computer Integrated Manufacturing System. 1985. write for info. (ISBN 0-89806-066-4). Inst Indus Eng.

Nicks, J E. BASIC Programming Solutions for Manufacturing. (Illus.). 298p. 1982. 32.00 (ISBN 0-87263-076-5). SME.

O'Neil, Thomas J., ed. Application of Computers & Operations Research in the Mineral Industry: 16th International Symposium. LC 79-52273. (Illus.). 651p. 1979. text ed. 33.00x (ISBN 0-89520-261-1). Soc Mining Eng.

Pantumsinchai, Pricha & Hassan, M. Zia. BASIC Programs for Production & Operations Management. (Illus.). 448p. 1983. pap. 18.95 (ISBN 0-686-38834-8). P H.

Pao, Y. C. Elements of Computer-Aided Design & Manufacturing. LC 84-5256. 498p. 1985. 33.95 (ISBN 0-471-88194-5); solution manual avail. (ISBN 0-471-80146-1). Wiley.

Pressman, R. S. & Williams, J. E. Numerical Control & Computer-Aided Manufacturing. LC 76-23218. 310p. 1977. text ed. 48.50x (ISBN 0-471-01555-5). Wiley.

Rembold, Ulrich & Armbruster, Karl. Interface Technology for Computer-Controlled Manufacturing Processes. (Manufacturing Engineering & Materials Processing Ser.: Vol. 9). (Illus.). 376p. 1983. 48.50 (ISBN 0-8247-1836-4). Dekker.

Rembold, Ulrich, et al, eds. Computers in Manufacturing. (Manufacturing Engineering & Material Processing Ser.: Vol. 1). (Illus.). 592p. 1977. pap. 95.00 (ISBN 0-8247-1821-6). Dekker.

Rhodes, D. J. Computers, Information & Manufacturing Systems. 160p. 1984. 29.95x (ISBN 0-03-071672-1). Praeger.

Society of Manufacturing Engineers. BASIC Programming Solutions for Manufacturing. 300p. 1982. 45.95 (ISBN 0-13-066332-8). P-H.

--CAPP Computer Aided Process Planning. 1985. 35.00 (ISBN 0-87263-187-7). SME.

Weiss, Alfred, ed. Computer Methods for the Eighties, in the Mineral Industry. LC 79-52274. (Illus.). 975p. 1979. text ed. 55.00x (ISBN 0-89520-257-3). Soc Mining Eng.

MANURES

see Fertilizers and Manures

MANUSCRIPTS–CONSERVATION AND RESTORATION

see also Books–Conservation and Restoration

Banks, Paul N. A Selective Bibliography on the Conservation of Research Library Materials. 150p. 1981. member 8.50 (ISBN 0-686-95761-X, 5003); non-member 10.00 (ISBN 0-686-99604-6). Soc Am Archivists.

Barrow, W. J. Manuscripts & Documents: Their Deterioration & Restoration. rev. ed. LC 72-89855. (Illus.). 84p. 1972. Repr. of 1976 ed. 9.95x (ISBN 0-8139-0408-0). U Pr of Va.

Gunner, Jean. Simple Repair & Preservation Techniques for Collection Curators, Librarians & Archivists. 3rd ed. (Illus.). 22p. 1984. pap. 3.00 (ISBN 0-913196-44-4). Hunt Inst Botanical.

Kane, Lucile M. Guide to the Care & Administration of Manuscripts. 2nd ed. (Illus.). 74p. 1966. pap. 6.00 (ISBN 0-910050-02-3). AASLH Pr.

MANY-BODY PROBLEM

see Problem of Many Bodies

MAP DRAWING

see also Cartography; Topographical Drawing

Ali, Jamil. Determination of the Coordinates of Positions for the Correction of Distances Between Cities. 1967. 24.95x (ISBN 0-8156-6007-3, Am U Beirut). Syracuse U Pr.

Keates, J. S. Cartographic Design & Production. LC 72-9251. 240p. 1973. pap. 42.95x (ISBN 0-470-15106-4). Halsted Pr.

Larsgaard, Mary L. Topographic Mapping of the Americas, Australia, & New Zealand. LC 84-3874. 230p. 1984. text ed. 45.00 (ISBN 0-87287-276-9). Libs Unl.

Sebert, Louis M. Mapping with Simple Instruments. (Illus., Orig.). 1985. pap. 8.00 (ISBN 0-947883-00-2). Pendragon Ltd.

MAP-PROJECTION

see also Cartography; Orthographic Projection; Surfaces, Representation Of

Deetz, Charles H. & Adams, Oscar S. Elements of Map Projection with Applications to Map & Chart Construction. 5th ed. LC 77-89015. Repr. of 1945 ed. lib. bdg. 32.25x (ISBN 0-8371-2268-6, DEMP). Greenwood.

Denes, Agnes. Isometric Systems in Isotropic Space, Map Projections from the Study of Distortions, 1973-1979. LC 79-66223. (Illus.). 100p. 1979. 75.00x (ISBN 0-89822-007-6). Visual Studies.

McDonnel. Introduction to Map Projections. 1979. 24.75 (ISBN 0-8247-6830-2). Dekker.

MAPPER (COMPUTER SYSTEM)

Katzan, Harry, Jr. Invitation to MAPPER: A Pragmatic Approach to End-User Computing. 256p. 1983. 24.95 (ISBN 0-89433-222-8). Petrocelli.

MAPPING, CONFORMAL

see Conformal Mapping

MAPS

see also Nautical Charts

American Geographical Society, Map Department, New York. Index to Maps in Books & Periodicals, First Supplement. 1971. lib. bdg. 110.00 (ISBN 0-8161-0806-4, Hall Library). G K Hall.

Barnette, David W. Map Coloring, Polyhedra & the Four-Color Problem. (Dolciani Mathematical Expositions Ser.: Vol. 8). 1984. 30.00 (ISBN 0-88385-309-4, 82062783). Math Assn.

Baues, H. J. Obstruction Theory on the Homotopy Classification of Maps. (Lecture Notes in Mathematics Ser: Vol. 628). 1977. pap. 22.00 (ISBN 0-387-08534-3). Springer-Verlag.

Bonacker, Wilhelm. Karten-Woerterbuch. (Ger.). 1970. 39.95 (ISBN 3-7812-0704-8, M-7493, Pub. by Kirschbaum). French & Eur.

Brown, Lloyd A. The Story of Maps. (Illus.). 16.00 (ISBN 0-8446-5739-5). Peter Smith.

--The Story of Maps. LC 79-52395. (Illus.). 417p. 1980. Repr. of 1949 ed. 11.95 (ISBN 0-938164-00-7). Vintage Bk Co.

Debruin, Richard. One-Hundred Topographic Maps. 128p. (Orig.). 1970. pap. text ed. 6.95 (ISBN 0-8331-1704-1). Hubbard Sci.

Feild, Lance. Map User's Sourcebook. LC 81-18941. 194p. 1982. lib. bdg. 17.50 (ISBN 0-379-20717-6). Oceana.

Fleming, June. Staying Found: The Complete Map & Compass Handbook. LC 81-52429. (Illus.). 192p. (Orig.). 1982. pap. 4.95 (ISBN 0-394-75152-3, Vin). Random.

Greenhood, David. Mapping. rev. ed. LC 63-20905. 1964. 20.00x (ISBN 0-226-30696-8); pap. 9.95 (ISBN 0-226-30697-6, P521, Phoen). U of Chicago Pr.

Iooss, G. Bifurcation of Maps & Applications. (Mathematics Studies: Vol. 36). 232p. 1979. 47.00 (ISBN 0-444-85304-9, North Holland). Elsevier.

Jennings, J. H. Elementary Map Interpretation. 1960. text ed. 7.95 (ISBN 0-521-20899-8). Cambridge U Pr.

Keates, J S. Understanding Maps. LC 81-6921. 139p. 1982. pap. 18.95x (ISBN 0-470-27271-6). Halsted Pr.

Kranich, Roger E. & Messec, Jerry L. Learning to Use Maps. (Illus.). 1978. text ed. write for info. (ISBN 0-88323-149-2, 236); 3.00x (ISBN 0-88323-150-6); teacher's answer key free (239). Richards Pub.

Lewis, Peter. Maps & Statistics. 1977. pap. 20.95x (ISBN 0-416-65380-4, NO. 6180). Methuen Inc.

Mariners Museum Library - Newport News - Virginia. Catalog of Maps, Ships' Papers & Logbooks. 1964. lib. bdg. 100.00 (ISBN 0-8161-0686-X, Hall Library). G K Hall.

Martinet, Jean. Singularities of Smooth Functions & Maps. Simon, C. P., tr. LC 81-18034. (London Mathematical Society Lecture Note Ser.: No. 58). 180p. 1982. pap. 22.95 (ISBN 0-521-23398-4). Cambridge U Pr.

Meyers Kontinente und Meere-Daten, Karten Die Enzyklopadie der Erde, 8 vols. (Ger.). 1973. 625.00 (ISBN 0-686-56633-5). French & Eur.

Monmonier, Mark S. Maps, Distortion, & Meaning. Natoli, Salvatore, ed. LC 76-44640. (Resource Papers for College Geography Ser). 48p. 1977. pap. text ed. 4.00 (ISBN 0-89291-120-4). Assn Am Geographers.

Muehrcke, Phillip C. Map Use: Reading, Analysis & Interpretation. rev. ed. LC 78-70573. (Illus.). xi, 469p. 1980. pap. text ed. 19.95x (ISBN 0-9602978-1-2). JP Pubns WI.

Preston, C. Iterates of Maps on an Interval. (Lecture notes in Mathematics: Vol. 999). 205p. 1983. pap. 13.00 (ISBN 0-387-12322-9). Springer-Verlag.

Robinson, Arthur H. & Petchenik, Barbara B. The Nature of Maps: Essays Toward Understanding Maps & Mapping. LC 75-36401. (Illus.). 1976. lib. bdg. 10.00x (ISBN 0-226-72281-3). U of Chicago Pr.

Sebert, Louis M. Mapping with Simple Instruments. (Illus., Orig.). 1985. pap. 8.00 (ISBN 0-947883-00-2). Pendragon Ltd.

Soil Map of Europe. 31p. 1965. 41.75 (ISBN 0-685-02466-0, F425, FAO). Unipub.

Tooley, R. V. Tooley's Dictionary of Mapmakers: Supplement, No. 1. LC 84-29759. 128p. 1985. 39.50 (ISBN 0-8451-1703-3). A R Liss.

Van Balen, John, compiled by. Index to Maps in Earth Science Publications, 1963-1983. LC 85-7978. v, 400p. 1985. lib. bdg. 49.95 (ISBN 0-313-24963-6, VBI/). Greenwood.

MAPS, GEOLOGICAL

see Geology–Maps

MAPS, LINEAR

see Linear Operators

MAPS, METEOROLOGICAL

see Meteorology–Charts, Diagrams, etc.

MAPS FOR THE VISUALLY HANDICAPPED

Wiedel, Joseph W., ed. First International Symposium on Maps & Graphics for the Visually Handicapped: Proceedings. LC 83-73096. 190p. 1983. pap. 9.00 (ISBN 0-317-01349-1). Assn Am Geographers.

MARBLE–STAINING

see Stains and Staining

MARGARINE

see Oleomargarine

MARIHUANA

Abel, Ernest L., compiled by. A Comprehensive Guide to the Cannabis Literature. LC 78-20014. 1979. lib. bdg. 55.00 (ISBN 0-313-20721-6, ACG/). Greenwood.

Abel, Ernest L., ed. The Scientific Study of Marihuana. LC 76-4508. 320p. 1976. 24.95x (ISBN 0-88229-144-0). Nelson-Hall.

American Health Research Institute, Ltd. Cannabis (Marijuana) & Cannabinoids: Medical Subject Research Directory with Bibliography. Bartone, John C., ed. LC 82-72018. 105p. 1982. 29.95 (ISBN 0-941864-52-9); pap. 21.95 (ISBN 0-941864-53-7). ABBE Pubs Assn.

Analysis of Drugs & Metabolites by Gas Chromatography - Mass Spectrometry: Natural, Pyrolytic & Metabolic Products of Tobacco & Marijuana, Vol. 7. 1980. 89.75 (ISBN 0-8247-6861-2). Dekker.

Blasinsky, Margaret & Russell, George K. Urine Testing for Marijuana Use: Implications for a Variety of Setting. 49p. (Orig.). 1981. pap. 2.50 (ISBN 0-942348-03-6). Am Council Drug Ed.

Cervantes, Jorge. Indoor Marijuana Horticulture. Bushwell, John & Greengenes, eds. (Illus.). 288p. 1984. pap. 14.95 (ISBN 0-932331-01-7). Interport U S A.

Clarke, Robert C. Marijuana Botany: An Advanced Study; the Propagation & Breeding of Distinctive Cannabis. LC 81-2478. (Illus.). 200p. 1981. pap. 10.95 (ISBN 0-915904-45-4). And-Or Pr.

Cohen, Mirian. Marijuana: Its Effects on Mind & Body. (Encyclopedia of Psychoactive Drugs Ser.). (Illus.). 1985. PLB 15.95x (ISBN 0-87754-754-8). Chelsea Hse.

Cohen, Sidney & Stillman, Richard C., eds. The Therapeutic Potential of Marihuana. LC 76-17106. 527p. 1976. 55.00x (ISBN 0-306-30955-6, Plenum Pr). Plenum Pub.

Daniels, Patrick. How to Grow Marijuana Hydroponically. (Illus.). 1978. perfect bdg. 5.95 (ISBN 0-686-25126-1). Pacific Pipeline.

Dews, Peter B., et al. Marijuana: Biochemical, Physiological, & Pathological Effects. (Illus.). 220p. 1973. text ed. 32.50x (ISBN 0-8422-7094-9). Irvington.

Drake, Bill. Marijuana Cultivation: A Handbook of Essential Techniques. 1984. 10.95 (ISBN 0-686-78527-4). Wingbow Pr.

Frank, Mel & Rosenthal, Ed. The Indoor-Outdoor Highest Quality Marijuana Grower's Guide. rev. ed. LC 81-10942. 96p. 1982. pap. 5.95 (ISBN 0-915904-59-4). And-Or Pr.

--Marijuana Grower's Guide. LC 77-82452. 1978. deluxe ed. 14.95 (ISBN 0-915904-26-8); spiral bdg. 17.95 (ISBN 0-915904-75-6). And-Or Pr.

Harvey, D. J. & Paton, Wiiliam, eds. Marihuana Nineteen Eighty-Four: Proceeedings of the Oxford Symposium on Cannabis, Third International Cannabis Symposium, Ninth International Congress of Pharmacology. (Illus.). 750p. 1985. text ed. 99.00 (ISBN 0-904147-95-9). IRL Pr.

Jones, Helen C. & Lovinger, Paul W. The Marijuana Question: Science's Search for an Answer. (Illus.). 560p. 1985. 24.95 (ISBN 0-396-08399-4). Dodd.

Lantner, Ingrid L. A Pediatrician's View of Marijuana. LC 82-198589. 48p. (Orig.). 1982. pap. 2.50 (ISBN 0-942348-06-0). Am Council Drug Ed.

Lewis, M. F., ed. Current Research in Marijuana. 1972. 37.50 (ISBN 0-12-447050-5). Acad Pr.

Nahas, G. G., ed. Marihuana: Chemistry, Biochemistry, & Cellular Efffects. 400p. 1976. 35.00 (ISBN 0-387-07554-2). Springer-Verlag.

Nahas, Gabriel G. Keep off the Grass: A Scientific Enquiry into the Biological Effects of Marijuana. (Illus.). 1979. 17.75 (ISBN 0-08-023779-7); pap. 7.50 (ISBN 0-08-023780-0). Pergamon.

Nahas, Gabriel G., et al. Marihuana in Science & Medicine. 324p. 1984. text ed. 53.00 (ISBN 0-88167-014-6). Raven.

National Research Council Institute of Medicine. Marijuana & Health. 208p. 1982. pap. text ed. 13.50 (ISBN 0-309-03236-9). Natl Acad Pr.

Roffman, Roger A. Marijuana As Medicine. LC 82-6584. 180p. 1982. 11.95 (ISBN 0-914842-71-4); pap. 8.95 (ISBN 0-914842-72-2). Madrona Pubs.

Russell, George K. Marihuana Today: A Complilation of Medical Findings for the Layman. rev. ed. LC 81-85323. (Illus.). 89p. 1983. pap. 3.00 (ISBN 0-913098-41-8). Myrin Institute.

Smith, Carol G. & Asch, Ricardo H. Marijuana & Reproduction. LC 82-244203. (Illus.). 31p. 1982. pap. 2.50 (ISBN 0-942348-07-9). Am Council Drug Ed.

Starks, Michael. Marijuana Potency. LC 77-82454. 1977. pap. 10.95 (ISBN 0-915904-27-6). And-Or Pr.

Tashkin, Donald P. & Cohen, Sidney. Marijuana Smoking & Its Effects on the Lungs. LC 81-215544. (Illus.). 56p. 1981. pap. 2.50 (ISBN 0-942348-00-1). Am Council Drug Ed.

Vinson, Joseph A., ed. Cannabinoid Analysis in Physiological Fluids. LC 79-10934. (ACS Symposium Ser.: No. 98). 1979. 29.95 (ISBN 0-8412-0488-8). Am Chemical.

Wilkerson, Don. Marijuana: Revised & Updated. 160p. 1983. pap. 5.95 (Power Bks.). Revell.

MARINAS

see also Docks; Piers; Shore Protection

Ecology of Small Boat Marinas. (Marine Technical Report: No. 5). 1973. pap. 1.00 (ISBN 0-938412-17-5). URI MAS.

Fire Protection Standard for Marinas & Boatyards. (Three Hundred Ser.). 1969. pap. 2.00 (ISBN 0-685-58056-3, 303). Natl Fire Prot.

Head, Derek. Residential Marinas & Yachting Amenities. (Marinas Ser.: No. 3). (Illus.). 84p. (Orig.). 1980. pap. text ed. 19.75x (ISBN 0-7210-1135-7, Pub. by C&CA London). Scholium Intl.

Operation of Marine Terminals. (Three Hundred Ser.). 1967. pap. 2.00 (ISBN 0-685-58058-X, 307). Natl Fire Prot.

MARINE ALGAE

Abbott, Isabella A. & Dawson, E. Yale. How to Know the Seaweeds. 2nd ed. (Pictured Key Nature Ser.). 200p. 1978. Wire Coil. write for info. (ISBN 0-697-04892-6). Wm C Brown.

Abbott, Isabella A. & Hollenberg, George J. Marine Algae of California. LC 74-82774. (Illus.). 1976. 30.00x (ISBN 0-8047-0867-3). Stanford U Pr.

Chapman, V. J., ed. The Marine Algae of New Zealand: Phaeophyceae, Vol.2. 1961. pap. 14.00 (ISBN 3-7682-0077-9). Lubrecht & Cramer.

Dawes, Clinton J. Marine Algae of the West Coast of Florida. LC 73-22107. (Illus.). 272p. 1974. 15.00x (ISBN 0-87024-258-X). U of Miami Pr.

Dawson, E. Y. Marine Red Algae of Pacific Mexico: Ceramiales, Dasyaceae, Rhodomelaceae, Part 8. (Illus.). 1963. pap. 8.00 (ISBN 3-7682-0209-7). Lubrecht & Cramer.

Farlow, W. C. The Marine Algae of New England & Adjacent Coast. (Illus.). 1969. Repr. of 1881 ed. 35.00 (ISBN 3-7682-0582-7). Lubrecht & Cramer.

Funk, Georg. Die Algenvegetation Des Golfes Von Neapel. (Pubbl. d. Stazione Zool. di Napoli). (Ger., Illus.). Repr. of 1927 ed. lib. bdg. 63.00 (ISBN 3-87429-142-1). Lubrecht & Cramer.

Harvey, W. H. Nereis Australis, or Algae of the Southern Ocean: 1847-49. (Illus.). 1965. 56.00 (ISBN 3-7682-0261-5). Lubrecht & Cramer.

--Nereis Boreali-Americana: 1852-1858, 3 parts in 1. (Illus.). 1976. 87.50 (ISBN 3-7682-1063-4). Lubrecht & Cramer.

Hillson, Charles J. Seaweeds: A Color-Coded, Illustrated Guide to Common Marine Plants of the East Coast of the United States. LC 76-42192. (Keystone Bks.). 1977. lib. bdg. 17.95x (ISBN 0-271-01239-0); pap. 9.75 (ISBN 0-271-01247-1). Pa St U Pr.

Hoppe, ed. Marine Algae in Pharmaceutical Science. 1979. 68.00 (ISBN 3-11-007375-7). De Gruyter.

Hoppe, Heinz A. & Levring, Tore, eds. Marine Algae in Pharmaceutical Science, Vol. 2. (Illus.). 309p. 1982. 56.00 (ISBN 3-11-008626-3). De Gruyter.

Humm, Harold J. The Marine Algae of Virginia. LC 78-16319. (Virginia Institute of Marine Science, Special Papers in Marine Science Ser.: No. 3). (Illus.). 263p. 1979. 16.95x (ISBN 0-8139-0701-2). U Pr of Va.

International Seaweed Symposium, 7th, Sappora, Japan, Aug. 1971. Proceedings. Science Council of Japan, ed. 607p. 1973. 72.95x (ISBN 0-470-77090-2). Halsted Pr.

Johnson, H. H. & Ferris, B. J. Tertiary & Pleistocene Coralline Algae from Lau, Fiji. (BMB). 1950. pap. 10.00 (ISBN 0-527-02309-4). Kraus Repr.

Kapraun, Donald F. An Illustrated Guide to Benthic Marine Algae of Coastal North Carolina: I. Rhodophyta. LC 79-21566. (Illus.). viii, 195p. 1980. pap. 9.95x (ISBN 0-8078-4063-7). U of NC Pr.

--An Illustrated Guide to the Benthic Marine Algae of Coastal North Carolina, II: Chlorophyta Phycologica. (Bibliotheca Phycologica Ser.: No. 58). (Illus.). 250p. 1984. lib. bdg. 17.50x (ISBN 3-7682-1326-9). Lubrecht & Cramer.

Kingsbury, John M. Seaweeds of Cape Cod & the Islands. LC 69-15903. (Illus.). 1969. 14.50 (ISBN 0-85699-009-4). Chatham Pr.

Lamb, I. Mackenzie & Zimmerman, Martin H. Benthic Marine Algae of the Antarctic Peninsula: Paper 4 in Biology of the Antarctic Seas V. Pawson, David L., ed. (Antarctic Research Ser.: Vol. 23). 104p. 1977. pap. 39.95 (ISBN 0-87590-128-X). Am Geophysical.

Lawson, G. W. & John, D. M. The Marine Algae & Coastal Environment of Tropical West Africa. (Nova Hedwigia Beiheft Ser.: No. 70). (Illus.). 450p. 1982. lib. bdg. 70.00x (ISBN 3-7682-5470-4). Lubrecht & Cramer.

Levring, Tore, et al. Marine Algae: A Survey of Research & Utilization. (Botanica Marina Handbks, Vol. 1). (Illus.). 421p. 1969. 67.20x (ISBN 3-11-005621-6). De Gruyter.

Mathieson, A. C. Morphological Studies of the Marine Brown Alga Taonia Lennebackerae Farlow Ex. J. Agardh L. (Illus.). 1966. pap. 4.00 (ISBN 3-7682-0439-1). Lubrecht & Cramer.

Mshigeni, K. E. Biology & Ecology of Benthic Marine Algae with Special Reference to Hypnea (Rhodophyta, Gigartinales: A Review of the Literature. (Bibliotheca Phycologica Ser.: No. 36). 1978. pap. 14.00x (ISBN 3-7682-1166-5). Lubrecht & Cramer.

Neal, M. C. Hawaiian Marine Algae. (BMB Ser.). Repr. of 1930 ed. 11.00 (ISBN 0-527-02173-3). Kraus Repr.

Nizamuddin, Mohammed. Contribution to the Marine Algae of Libya Dictyotales. (Bibliotheca Phycologica Ser.: No. 54). (Illus.). 120p. 1982. pap. text ed. 14.00x (ISBN 3-7682-1305-6). Lubrecht & Cramer.

North, W. J., ed. Biology of the Giant Kelp Beds (Macrocystis) in California. 1971. 70.00 (ISBN 3-7682-5432-1). Lubrecht & Cramer.

Schnetter, R. & Bula, G. Marine Algen der Pazifikkueste von Kolumbien (Algas Marinas del litoral pacifico de Colombia) Chlorophyceae, Phaeophyceae, Rodophyceae: Synoptic Edition-German & Spanish. (Bibliotheca Phycologica Ser.: No. 60). (Illus.). 288p. 1983. text ed. 35.00x (ISBN 3-7682-1347-1). Lubrecht & Cramer.

Setchell, W. A. & Gardener, N. L. The Marine Algae of the Pacific Coast of North America: 1919-29, 3 pts. in 1. (Bibl. Phyco.). 1967. 63.00 (ISBN 3-7682-0454-5). Lubrecht & Cramer.

Stephenson, W. A. Seaweed in Agriculture & Horticulture. 3rd ed. Bargyla & Rateaver, Gylver, eds. LC 74-12812. (Conservation Gardening & Farming Ser: Ser. C). 1974. pap. 7.00 (ISBN 0-9600698-3-6). Rateavers.

Taylor, W. R. The Marine Algae of Florida: With Special Reference to Dry Tortugas. (Bibl. Phyco. Ser.: Vol.2). 1967. Repr. of 1928 ed. 42.00 (ISBN 3-7682-0504-5). Lubrecht & Cramer.

Taylor, William R. Marine Algae of the Eastern Tropical & Sub-Tropical Coasts of the Americas. LC 59-9736. (Illus.). 1960. 39.50x (ISBN 0-472-08841-6). U of Mich Pr.

--Marine Algae of the Northeastern Coast of North America. 2nd rev. ed. LC 57-7103. (Illus.). 1957. 35.00x (ISBN 0-472-08840-8). U of Mich Pr.

MARINE AQUARIUMS

Axelrod, Herbert R. Breeding Aquarium Fishes, Bk. 2. 1971. 16.95 (ISBN 0-87666-007-3, H-941). TFH Pubns.

Axelrod, Herbert R. & Burgess, Lourdes. Breeding Aquarium Fishes, Bk. 3. 1973. 16.95 (ISBN 0-87666-025-1, H-946). TFH Pubns.

Axelrod, Herbert R. & Burgess, Warren. Saltwater Aquarium Fishes. 12.95 (ISBN 0-87666-138-X, H-914). TFH Pubns.

Axelrod, Herbert R., et al. Exotic Marine Fishes. (Illus.). 608p. 1973. 19.95 (ISBN 0-87666-102-9, H938); looseleaf bdg. 29.95 (ISBN 0-87666-103-7, H-938). TFH Pubns.

Barker, Craig. Starting a Marine Aquarium. 1972. 4.95 (ISBN 0-87666-751-5, PS-305). TFH Pubns.

Bower, Carol E. The Basic Marine Aquarium: A Simplified, Modern Approach to the Care of Saltwater Fishes. (Illus.). 290p. 1983. pap. 14.95 (ISBN 0-398-04736-7). C C Thomas.

Burgess, Warren E. Marine Aquaria. (Illus.). 96p. text ed. 4.95 (ISBN 0-87666-533-4, KW-088). TFH Pubns.

--The T.F.H. Book of Marine Aquariums. (Illus.). 96p. 1982. 6.95 (ISBN 0-87666-801-5, HP-006). TFH Pubns.

Emmens, Cliff W. The Marine Aquarium in Theory & Practice. (Illus.). 208p. 1975. 19.95 (ISBN 0-87666-446-X, PS-735). TFH Pubns.

Friese, U. Erich. Marine Invertebrates in the Home Aquarium. (Illus.). 240p. (Orig.). 1973. 14.95 (ISBN 0-87666-793-0, PS-658). TFH Pubns.

Hargreaves, Vincent B. Tropical Marine Aquarium. (Illus.). 160p. 1983. 18.95 (ISBN 0-7153-7636-5). David & Charles.

Moe, Martin A., Jr. The Marine Aquarium Handbook: Beginner to Breeder. LC 82-3400. 176p. (Orig.). 1982. pap. 9.95 (ISBN 0-939960-02-8). Norns Pub Co.

O'Connell, R. F. The Marine Aquarium for the Home Aquarist. 1975. pap. 5.95 (ISBN 0-686-77058-7). Great Outdoors.

Spotte, Stephen. Marine Aquarium Keeping: Science, Animals & Art. 1985. pap. 12.95 (ISBN 0-471-82591-3). Wiley.

--Marine Aquarium Keeping: The Science, Animals & Art. LC 73-4425. (Illus.). 171p. 1973. 19.50 (ISBN 0-471-81759-7, Pub. by Wiley-Interscience). Wiley.

Stevenson, Robert A. The Complete Book of Salt-Water Aquariums: How to Equip & Maintain Your Marine Aquarium & Understand Its Ecology. (Funk & W Bk.). 224p. 1974. 11.49i (ISBN 0-308-10090-5). T Y Crowell.

--The Complete Book of Saltwater Aquariums. LC 73-21528. (Funk & W Bk.). (Illus.). 1976. pap. 3.95i (ISBN 0-308-10232-0). T Y Crowell.

Straughan, Robert P. The Salt-Water Aquarium in the Home. (Illus.). 384p. 1959. 19.95 (ISBN 0-498-01531-9). A S Barnes.

Wickler, Wolfgang. The Marine Aquarium. Vevers, Gwynne, tr. from Ger. (Illus.). 178p. (Orig.). 1973. pap. 9.95 (ISBN 0-87666-098-7, PS-695). TFH Pubns.

MARINE ARCHAEOLOGY

see Underwater Archaeology

MARINE ARCHITECTURE

see Naval Architecture; Ship-Building

MARINE BIOLOGY

see also Marine Aquariums; Marine Ecology; Marine Fauna; Marine Flora; Marine Microbiology; Marine Resources; Marine Sediments; Ocean Bottom; Photography, Submarine; Seashore Biology; Sedimentation and Deposition; Shells

Agassiz, Elizabeth & Agassiz, Alexander. Seaside Studies in Natural History: Marine Animals of Massachusetts Bay. LC 75-125726. (American Environmental Studies). (Illus.). 1970. Repr. of 1865 ed. 23.50 (ISBN 0-405-02651-X). Ayer Co Pubs.

Andersen, Neil R. & Zahuranec, Bernard J., eds. Oceanic Sound Scattering Prediction. LC 77-3445. (Marine Science Ser.: Vol. 5). 859p. 1977. 110.00x (ISBN 0-306-35505-1, Plenum Pr). Plenum Pub.

Baiardi, John C. & Ruggieri, George D., eds. Aquatic Sciences. (Annals of the New York Academy of Sciences: Vol. 245). 70p. 1974. 17.00x (ISBN 0-89072-759-7). NY Acad Sci.

Barica, J. & Mur, L., eds. Hypertrophic Ecosystems. (Developments in Hydrobiology Ser.: No. 2). 330p. 1981. PLB 87.00 (ISBN 90-6193-752-3, Pub. by Junk Pubs. Netherlands). Kluwer Academic.

Barnes, H. Oceanography & Marine Biology. 1959. 10.75 (ISBN 0-08-026258-9). Pergamon.

Barnes, Harold, ed. Oceanography & Marine Biology: An Annual Review, Vol. 15. 1977. 75.00 (ISBN 0-900015-39-X). Taylor-Carlisle.

--Oceanography & Marine Biology: An Annual Review, Vol. 16. 1978. 80.00 (ISBN 0-900015-44-6). Taylor-Carlisle.

--Oceanography & Marine Biology: Annual Review, Vol. 14. 1976. 75.00 (ISBN 0-900015-37-3). Taylor-Carlisle.

--Proceedings of the Ninth European Marine Biology Symposium, Oban, 1974. 1976. 65.00x (ISBN 0-900015-34-9). Taylor-Carlisle.

Barnes, John A. & Von Bodungen, Bodo. The Bermuda Marine Environment, Vol. II. (Bermuda Biological Station Special Pubn Ser.: No. 17). (Illus.). 1978. pap. 6.50 (ISBN 0-917642-17-1). Bermuda Bio.

Barnes, M. Oceanography & Marine Biology: An Annual Review, Vol. 20. (Illus.). 778p. 1983. 82.80 (ISBN 0-08-028460-4). Pergamon.

Barnes, M., ed. Oceanography & Marine Biology: An Annual Review, Vol. 21. (Oceanography & Marine Biology Ser.). (Illus.). 590p. 1983. 82.80 (ISBN 0-08-030360-9). Pergamon.

Barnes, Margaret, ed. Oceanography & Marine Biology: An Annual Review. LC 64-1930. (Oceanography & Marine Biology Ser.: Vol. 22). (Illus.). 590p. 1984. 76.80 (ISBN 0-08-030392-7). Pergamon.

Barnes, Margaret & Barnes, Harold, eds. Oceanography & Marine Biology: An Annual Review, Vol. 18. (Illus.). 528p. 1980. 63.00 (ISBN 0-08-025732-1). Pergamon.

The Bay Bib: Rhode Island Marine Bibliography, 2 vols. (Marine Technical Reports: Nos. 70 & 71). Set. 5.00 (ISBN 0-686-34464-2); keyword in context index 2.00 (ISBN 0-938412-02-7). URI MAS.

Bayne, Brian L., ed. The Effects of Stress & Pollution on Marine Animals. LC 84-18145. 400p. 1984. 45.95x (ISBN 0-03-057019-0). Praeger.

Blaxter, J. H., ed. Advances in Marine Biology, Vol. 22. (Serial Publication Ser.). 1985. 57.00 (ISBN 0-12-026122-7). Acad Pr.

Blaxter, J. H., et al, eds. Advances in Marine Biology, Vol. 17. LC 63-14040. (Serial Publication Ser.). 1980. 85.00 (ISBN 0-12-026117-0). Acad Pr.

--Advances in Marine Biology, Vol. 19. (Serial Publication Ser.). 1982. 75.00 (ISBN 0-12-026119-7). Acad Pr.

--Advances in Marine Biology, Vol. 20. (Serial Publication Ser.). 1982. 75.00 (ISBN 0-12-026120-0). Acad Pr.

Bliss, Dorothy E. & Provenzano, Anthony J. Biology of Crustacea, Vol. 10. Date not set. 65.00 (ISBN 0-12-106410-7). Acad Pr.

Brusca, Gary J. & Brusca, Richard C. A Naturalist's Seashore Guide: Common Marine Life Along the Northern California Coast & Adjacent Shores. 215p. 1978. pap. 8.95x (ISBN 0-916422-12-7). Mad River.

Cabioch, L. & Glemare, M. Fluctuation & Succession in Marine Ecosystems. 224p. 1983. pap. 28.00 (ISBN 2-04-011898-5, Pub by Gauthier-Villars FR). Heyden.

Caljon, A. G. Brackish-Water Phytoplankton of the Flemish Lowland. (Developments in Hydrobiology Ser.). 1984. lib. bdg. 74.50 (ISBN 90-6193-769-8, Pub. by Junk Pubs Netherlands). Kluwer-Academic.

Carpenter, Edward J. & Capone, Douglas G., eds. Nitrogen in the Marine Environment. LC 83-2829. 1983. 59.00 (ISBN 0-12-160280-X). Acad Pr.

Cavanaugh, G. M., et al. Formulae & Methods. 1964. 6.00 (ISBN 0-685-52858-8). Marine Bio.

Coker, Robert E. This Great & Wide Sea: An Introduction to Oceanography & Marine Biology. (Illus.). pap. 4.95xi (ISBN 0-06-130551-0, TB551, Torch). Har-Row.

Colin, Patrick I. Caribbean Reef Invertebrates & Plants. (Illus.). 1978. 29.95 (ISBN 0-87666-460-5, H-971). TFH Pubns.

Colwell. Pathogens & Toxins in the Marine Environment. 1985. write for info. (ISBN 0-471-82593-X). Wiley.

Coppejans, E. Iconographie d'Algues Mediterraneennes: (Chlorophyta, Phaeophyta, Rhodophyta) (Bibliotheca Phycologica Ser.: No. 63). (Illus.). 1983. text ed. 73.50 (ISBN 3-7682-1357-9). Lubrecht & Cramer.

Coulombe, Deborah. The Seaside Naturalist: A Guide to Nature at the Seashore. 256p. 1984. 19.95 (ISBN 0-13-797259-8); pap. 12.95 (ISBN 0-13-797242-3). P-H.

Cousteau, Jacques. Jacques Cousteau: The Ocean World. (Illus.). 1979. 60.00 (ISBN 0-8109-0777-1). Abrams.

Cousteau, Jacques-Yves. Jacques Cousteau: The Ocean World. (Illus.). 446p. 1985. 24.95 (ISBN 0-8109-8068-1). Abrams.

Cousteau, Jacques-Yves & Dumas, Frederic. The Silent World. LC 52-5431. 1953. 15.00i (ISBN 0-06-010890-8, HarpT). Har-Row.

Cox, ed. Phytoflagellates. (Developments in Marine Biology Ser.: Vol. 2). 474p. 1980. 76.50 (ISBN 0-444-00363-0, Biomedical Pr). Elsevier.

Cracknell, Arthur P., ed. Remote Sensing Applications in Marine Science & Technology. 1983. lib. bdg. 78.00 (ISBN 90-2771-608-0, Pub. by Reidel Holland). Kluwer Academic.

Cribb, James & Cousteau, Jacques. Marine Life of the Caribbean. (Illus.). 1984. 15.95 (ISBN 0-19-540616-8). Skyline Press.

Crowder, William. Seashore Life Between the Tides. LC 75-16036. Orig. Title: Between the Tides. (Illus.). 512p. 1975. pap. 7.50 (ISBN 0-486-23221-2). Dover.

Davis, J. D. & Merriman, D., eds. Observations on the Ecology & Biology of Western Cape Cod Bay, Massachusetts. (Lecture Notes on Coastal & Estuarine Studies: Vol. 11). x, 289p. 1984. pap. 22.00 (ISBN 0-387-96084-8). Springer-Verlag.

Dawes, Clinton J. Marine Botany. LC 1-7527. 628p. 1981. 53.50 (ISBN 0-471-07844-1, Pub. by Wiley-Interscience). Wiley.

Douglas, Philip A. & Stroud, Richard H., eds. A Symposium on the Biological Significance of Estuaries. 1971. 4.00 (ISBN 0-686-21854-X). Sport Fishing.

Drew, E. A., et al, eds. Underwater Research. 1976. 68.00 (ISBN 0-12-221950-3). Acad Pr.

Dumont, H. J. & Green, J., eds. Rotatoria. (Developments in Hydrobiology Ser.: No. 1). 268p. 1980. lib. bdg. 79.00 (ISBN 90-6193-754-X, Pub. Junk Pubs Netherlands). Kluwer Academic.

Dumont, H. J., et al, eds. Limnology & Marine Biology in the Sudan. (Developments in Hydrobiology Ser.). 1984. lib. bdg. 84.00 (ISBN 90-6193-772-8, Pub. by Junk Pubs Netherlands). Kluwer Academic.

Eisler, ed. Trace Metal Concentrations in Marine Organisms. 3500p. 1981. 130.00 (ISBN 0-08-025975-8). Pergamon.

English-Japanese Marine Terms Dictionary. (Eng. & Japanese.). 542p. 95.00 (ISBN 0-686-92390-1, M-93491). French & Eur.

European Marine Biology Symposium Staff. Fourth European Marine Biology Symposium. Crisp, D. J., ed. LC 71-173829. pap. 152.50 (ISBN 0-317-28414-2, 2022442). Bks Demand UMI.

Falkowski, Paul G., ed. Primary Productivity in the Sea. LC 80-24664. (Environmental Science Research Ser.: Vol. 19). 542p. 1980. 67.50 (ISBN 0-306-40623-3, Plenum Pr). Plenum Pub.

Fincham, A. A. Basic Marine Biology. 157p. 1984. 37.50 (ISBN 0-521-26421-9); pap. 14.95 (ISBN 0-521-26966-0). Cambridge U Pr.

Fishelson, Lev. Mysteries of the Red Sea. (Illus.). 144p. 1984. 29.95 (ISBN 0-911378-53-7, Pub. by Massada). Sheridan.

Forbes, Edward & Godwin-Austen, Robert. The Natural History of the European Seas. Egerton, Frank N., 3rd, ed. LC 77-74221. (History of Ecology Ser.). 1978. Repr. of 1859 ed. lib. bdg. 24.50x (ISBN 0-405-10392-1). Ayer Co Pubs.

Freeland, Howard J., et al, eds. Fjord Oceanography. LC 80-12273. (NATO Conference Series IV, Marine Science: Vol. 4). 730p. 1980. 95.00x (ISBN 0-306-40439-7, Plenum Pr). Plenum Pub.

Friedrich, Hermann. Marine Biology: An Introduction to Its Problems & Results. LC 71-93028. (Biology Ser). (Illus.). 486p. 1970. 20.00x (ISBN 0-295-95011-0). U of Wash Pr.

Galbraith, Robert & Boehler, Ted. Subtidal Marine Biology of California. LC 74-11235. (Illus.). 128p. (Orig.). 1974. 11.95 (ISBN 0-87961-027-1); pap. 5.95 (ISBN 0-87961-026-3). Naturegraph.

George, J. David & George, Jennifer. Marine Life: An Illustrated Encyclopedia of Invertebrates in the Sea. LC 79-10976. 288p. 1979. 69.95 (ISBN 0-471-05675-8, Pub. by Wiley-Interscience). Wiley.

Gery, Jacques. Characoids of the World. (Illus.). 1978. 29.95 (ISBN 0-87666-458-3, H-961). TFH Pubns.

Gotshall, Daniel W. & Laurent, Laurence L. Pacific Coast Subtidal Marine Invertebrates, a Fishwatchers' Guide. LC 79-64128. 112p. 1979. pap. 12.95 (ISBN 0-930118-03-0). Sea Chall.

Gray, J. S. & Christianson, M. E. European Marine Biology, 18th Symposium: Marine Biology of the Polar Regions & Effects of Stress on Marine Organisms. 1985. 49.95 (ISBN 0-471-90465-1). Wiley.

Harvey, Hildebrande W. Chemistry & Fertility of Sea Waters. 2nd ed. 1957. 49.50 (ISBN 0-521-05225-4). Cambridge U Pr.

Hashimoto, Yoshiro. Marine Toxins & Other Bioactive Marine Metabolites. 1979. 46.00x (ISBN 0-89955-131-9, Pub. by Japan Sci Soc Japan). Intl Spec Bk.

Hedgpeth, Joel W., ed. Outer Shores One: Ed Ricketts & John Steinbeck Explore the Pacific Coast. 128p. 1978. pap. 8.95x (ISBN 0-916422-13-5). Mad River.

Hickson, Sydney J. The Story of Life in the Seas. 1978. Repr. of 1904 ed. lib. bdg. 20.00 (ISBN 0-8495-2324-9). Arden Lib.

Horner, Rita, ed. Sea Ice Biota. 240p. 1985. 76.00 (ISBN 0-8493-6578-3). CRC Pr.

Impacts of Radionuclide Releases into the Marine Environment: Proceedings of a Symposium Held in Vienna, October 6-10, 1980 Jointly Organized by IAEA & NEA (OECD) (Proceedings Ser.). (Illus.). 750p. 1981. pap. 103.00 (ISBN 92-0-020481-3, ISP565, IAEA). Unipub.

Jensen, Albert C. Wildlife of the Oceans. (Wldlife Habitat Ser.). (Illus.). 1979. 19.95 (ISBN 0-8109-1758-0). Abrams.

Johnstone, James. Conditions of Life in the Sea: Short Account of Quantitative Marine Biological Research. Egerton, Frank N., 3rd, ed. LC 77-74232. (History of Ecology Ser.). (Illus.). 1978. Repr. of 1908 ed. lib. bdg. 27.50x (ISBN 0-405-10401-4). Ayer Co Pubs.

Jones, N. V. & Wolff, W. J., eds. Feeding & Survival Strategies of Estuarine Organisms. LC 81-12005. (Marine Science Ser.: Vol. 15). 316p. 1981. 49.50x (ISBN 0-306-40813-9, Plenum Pr). Plenum Pub.

Jones, O. A. & Endean, R., eds. Biology & Geology of Coral Reefs, 4 vols. Incl. Vol. 1. Geology. 1973. 71.50 (ISBN 0-12-389601-0); Vol. 2. Biology - One. 1974. 83.50 (ISBN 0-12-389602-9); Vol. 3. Biology - Two. 1976. 95.50 (ISBN 0-12-389603-7); Vol. 4. 1977. 75.00 (ISBN 0-12-389604-5). Set. Acad Pr.

Kirsch, Catherine A. Things That Stings. (Illus.). 1978. 20.00 (ISBN 0-916750-66-3). Dayton Labs.

Kohlmeyer, Jan & Kohlmeyer, Ericka. Marine Mycology: The Higher Fungi. LC 79-14703. 1979. 76.50 (ISBN 0-12-418350-6). Acad Pr.

Lasker, Reuben. Marine Fish Larvae: Morphology, Ecology, & Relation to Fisheries. LC 81-13073. (Illus.). 132p. (Orig.). 1982. pap. 8.50x (ISBN 0-295-95883-9, Pub. by Wash Sea Grant). U of Wash Pr.

Lerman, Matthew. Marine Biology: Environment, Diversity, & Ecology. (Illus.). 450p. 1985. pap. 26.95x (ISBN 0-8053-6402-1); price not set instr's guide. Benjamin-Cummings.

Lippson, Alice J. & Lippson, Robert L. Life in the Chesapeake Bay. LC 83-11278. 240p. 1984. text ed. 22.95 (ISBN 0-8018-3012-5); pap. text ed. 12.95 (ISBN 0-8018-3013-3). Johns Hopkins.

Littler, Mark S. & Littler, Diane S. Handbook of Phycological Methods: Ecological Field Methods: Macroalgae. (Illus.). 624p. Date not set. price not set (ISBN 0-521-24915-5). Cambridge U Pr.

Long Term Observation of Plankton Fluctuation in the Central Adriatic. (General Fisheries Council of the Mediterranean (GFCM): Studies & Reviews: No. 41). (Eng. & Fr.). 39p. 1969. pap. 7.50 (ISBN 92-5-001960-2, F1801, FAO). Unipub.

McConnaughey, Bayard H. Introduction to Marine Biology. 3rd ed. LC 77-25826. (Illus.). 624p. 1978. text ed. 24.95 (ISBN 0-8016-3258-7). Mosby.

McConnaughey, Bayard H. & Zottoli, Robert. Introduction to Marine Biology. 4th ed. LC 82-12511. 638p. 1983. text ed. 27.95 (ISBN 0-8016-3259-5). Mosby.

Macdonald, A. G. Physiological Aspects of Deep Sea Biology. LC 73-90652. (Physiological Society Monographs: No. 31). (Illus.). 440p. 1975. 110.00 (ISBN 0-521-20397-X). Cambridge U Pr.

McLusky, Donald S. Ecology of Estuaries. (Scholarship Ser. in Biology). 1971. text ed. 9.50x (ISBN 0-435-61600-5). Heinemann Ed.

--Estuarine Ecosystem. LC 80-28199. (Tertiary Level Biology Ser.). 150p. 1981. 32.95x (ISBN 0-470-27127-2). Halsted Pr.

Malins, D. C. & Sargent, J. R. Biochemical & Biophysical Perspectives in Marine Biology. Vol. 1 1975. 62.00 (ISBN 0-12-466601-9); Vol. 2 1975. 62.00 (ISBN 0-12-466602-7); Vol. 3 1976. 73.00 (ISBN 0-12-466603-5). Acad Pr.

Malins, D. C. & Sargent, J. R., eds. Biochemical & Biophysical Perspectives in Marine Biology, Vol. 4. 1979. 50.00 (ISBN 0-12-466604-3). Acad Pr.

Marine Biological Laboratory. Serial Publications. 1983. 10.00 (ISBN 0-685-52862-6). Marine Bio.

Marine Biological Laboratory & Woods Hole Oceanographic Institution, Woods Hole, Massachusetts. Catalog of the Library of the Marine Biological Laboratory & the Woods Hole Oceanographic Institution, 12 vols. 1971. lib. bdg. 1185.00 set (ISBN 0-8161-0937-0, Hall Library); journal catalog o.p. 55.00 (ISBN 0-8161-0115-9). G K Hall.

Marine Biology. Incl. Vol. 2. Phytoplankiton. 2nd ed. Oppenheimer, C. H., ed. 370p. 1969. 72.75 (ISBN 0-677-65090-6); Vol. 3. Ecology of Invertebrates. 3rd ed. 314p. 1966. 63.95 (ISBN 0-677-65100-7); Vol. 4. Unresolved Problems in Marine Microbiology. 4th ed. 486p. 1968. 95.75 (ISBN 0-677-65110-4); Vol. 5. 5th ed. 622p. 1969. 123.25 (ISBN 0-677-13310-3). Gordon.

Mariscal, R. N. Experimental Marine Biology. 1974. 55.00 (ISBN 0-12-472450-7). Acad Pr.

Marshall, N. B. Aspects of Deep Sea Biology. 1977. lib. bdg. 105.00 (ISBN 0-8490-1458-1). Gordon Pr.

Meadows, P. S. & Campbell, J. I. An Introduction to Marine Science. LC 78-6738. (Tertiary Level Biology Ser.). 179p. 1978. pap. text ed. 28.95x (ISBN 0-470-26379-2). Halsted Pr.

Moe, Martin A., Jr. The Marine Aquarium Handbook: Beginner to Breeder. LC 82-3400. 176p. (Orig.). 1982. pap. 9.95 (ISBN 0-939960-02-8). Norns Pub Co.

Mordukhai-Boltovskoi, D., ed. The River Volga & Its Life. (Monographiae Biologicae: No. 33). 1979. lib. bdg. 74.00 (ISBN 90-6193-084-7, Pub. by Junk Pubs Netherlands). Kluwer Academic.

Newell, R. C. Biology of Intertidal Animals. 781p. 1979. 60.00x (ISBN 0-9506920-0-X). State Mutual Bk.

Niesen, Thomas M. The Marine Biology Coloring Book. (Illus.). 224p. (Orig.). 1982. pap. 9.57i (ISBN 0-06-460303-2, CO 303, COS). B&N NY.

North, Wheeler. Underwater California. LC 75-13153. (Natural History Guide Ser). (Illus.). 1976. pap. 5.95 (ISBN 0-520-03039-7). U of Cal Pr.

Nybakken, James W. Marine Biology: An Ecological Approach. 446p. 1982. text ed. 30.50 scp (ISBN 0-06-044849-0, HarpC); inst. manual avail. (ISBN 0-06-364800-8). Har-Row.

Oceanography & Marine Biology, Vol. 17. 65.00 (ISBN 0-08-023849-1). Pergamon.

Oceanography & Marine Biology: An Annual Review, Vol. 17. 1979. 85.00 (ISBN 0-08-023849-1). Taylor-Carlisle.

Oceanography & Marine Biology: An Annual Review, Vol. 18. 1980. 100.00 (ISBN 0-686-29371-1). Taylor Carlisle.

Oceanography & Marine Biology: An Annual Review, Vol.19. (Illus.). 655p. 1981. 93.50 (ISBN 0-08-028439-6). Pergamon.

Olausson, Eric & Cato, Ingemar. Chemistry & Biochemistry of Estuaries. LC 79-41211. 452p. 1980. 106.95x (ISBN 0-471-27679-0, Pub. by Wiley-Interscience). Wiley.

Oppenheimer, Carl H. Symposium on Marine Microbiology. 792p. 1963. photocopy ed. 78.50x (ISBN 0-398-01426-4). C C Thomas.

Parker, Henry S. Exploring the Oceans: An Introduction for the Traveler & Amateur Naturalist. (Illus.). 368p. 1985. pap. 15.95 (ISBN 0-13-297706-0). P-H.

Pickering, A. D., ed. Stress & Fish. LC 81-67907. 1981. 59.50 (ISBN 0-12-554550-9). Acad Pr.

Platt, T., et al. Mathematical Models in Biological Oceanography. (Monographs on Oceanographic Methodology: No. 7). (Illus.). 157p. 1982. pap. 18.75 (ISBN 92-3-101922-8, U1200, UNESCO). Unipub.

Por, F. D. & Dor, I., eds. Hydrobiology of the Mangal. (Developments in Hydrobiology). 1984. lib. bdg. 69.00 (ISBN 90-6193-771-X, Pub. by Junk Pubs Netherlands). Kluwer Academic.

A Preliminary Classification of Coastal & Marine Environments. 1975. pap. 7.50 (ISBN 0-686-53042-X, IUCN44, IUCN). Unipub.

Ragotzkie, Robert A., ed. Man & the Marine Environment. 200p. 1983. 66.00 (ISBN 0-8493-5759-4). CRC Pr.

Rheinheimer, G., ed. Microbial Ecology of a Brackish Water Environment. (Ecological Studies: Vol. 25). (Illus.). 1977. 52.00 (ISBN 0-387-08492-4). Springer-Verlag.

Rowe, Gilbert T. Deep Sea Biology: The Sea, Vol. 8. LC 62-18366. (Ideas & Observations on Progress in the Study of the Seas Ser.). 544p. 1983. 69.95x (ISBN 0-471-04402-4, 1-293, Pub. by Wiley-Interscience). Wiley.

Russell, F. S. Advances in Marine Biology, Vol. 21. (Serial Publication Ser.). 1984. 55.00 (ISBN 0-12-026121-9). Acad Pr.

Russell, F. S., ed. Advances in Marine Biology. Incl. Vol. 1. 1963. 75.00 (ISBN 0-12-026101-4); Vol. 2. 1964. 55.00 (ISBN 0-12-026102-2); Vol. 3. 1966; Vol. 4. 1966. 60.00 (ISBN 0-12-026104-9); Vol. 5. 1968. 70.00 (ISBN 0-12-026105-7); Vol. 6. Yonge, Maurice, ed. 1969. 70.00 (ISBN 0-12-026106-5); Vol. 7. 1969. 70.00 (ISBN 0-12-026107-3); Vol. 8. 1971. 70.00 (ISBN 0-12-026108-1); Vol. 9. 1971. 90.00 (ISBN 0-12-026109-X); Vol. 10. 1972. 85.00 (ISBN 0-12-026110-3); Vol. 11. 1973. 60.00 (ISBN 0-12-026111-1); Vol. 15. 1978. 91.00 (ISBN 0-12-026115-4). Acad Pr.

--Advances in Marine Biology. Incl. Vol. 12. 1975. 80.00 (ISBN 0-12-026112-X); Vol. 13. 1977. 80.00 (ISBN 0-12-026113-8); Vol. 14. Cushing, D. H., ed. 1976. 85.00 (ISBN 0-12-026114-6). (Serial Publication). Acad Pr.

--Advances in Marine Biology, Vol. 16. (Serial Publication). 1979. 104.00 (ISBN 0-12-026116-2). Acad Pr.

Russell, H. D. Notes on Methods for the Narcotization, Killing, Fixation, & Preservation of Marine Organisms. 1963. pap. 4.50x (ISBN 0-685-52861-8). Marine Bio.

Hulm, Peter. A Strategy for the Seas: The Regional Seas Programme Past & Future. 28p. 1984. 5.00 (UNEP090, UNEP). Unipub.

Hynes. The Ecology of Running Waters. 580p. 1982. 60.00x (ISBN 0-85323-100-1, Pub. by Liverpool Univ England). State Mutual Bk.

Institute of Petroleum. Marine Ecology & Oil Pollution. Baker, Jennifer M., ed. (Illus.). 566p. 1976. 77.75 (ISBN 0-85334-447-7, Pub. by Elsevier Applied Sci England). Elsevier.

International Symposium, Rotterdam, September 11-12, 1980. Disposal of Chemical Waste in the Marine Environment: Implications of International Dumping Conventions: Proceedings. Hueck-Van Der Plas, E. H., ed. 216p. 1981. pap. 17.50 (ISBN 0-08-026289-9). Pergamon.

Irby, Bobby N., et al. Diversity of Marine Animals. LC 83-19721. (Man & the Gulf Ser.: Vol. 3). 120p. 1984. pap. text ed. 6.00 (ISBN 0-87805-203-8). U Pr of Miss.

--Diversity of Marine Plants. LC 83-16994. (Man & the Gulf Ser.: Vol. 4). (Illus.). 120p. 1984. pap. text ed. 6.00 (ISBN 0-87805-204-6). U Pr of Miss.

Kennish, M. J. & Lutz, R. A., eds. Ecology of Barnegat Bay, New Jersey. (Lecture Notes on Coastal & Estuarine Studies: Vol. 6). (Illus.). 300p. 1984. pap. 36.00 (ISBN 0-387-90935-4). Springer-Verlag.

Kinne, O. Marine Ecology: A Comprehensive Integrated Treatise on Life in Oceans & Coastal Waters, Vols. 1-4. Incl. Vol. 1. Environmental Factors, 3 pts. 681p. 1970. Pt. 1. 94.95x (ISBN 0-471-48001-0); Vol. 2. Marine Ecology: Physiological Mechanisms, 2 pts. 449p. 1975. Pt. 1. 91.95x (ISBN 0-471-48004-5); Vol. 3. Cultivation, 3 pts. 1976. Pt. 1. 87.25 (ISBN 0-471-48005-3); Pt. 3. 74.95x (ISBN 0-471-48007-X); Vol. 4. Marine Ecology: Dynamics. Kinne, O. LC 79-121779. 746p. 1978. Pt. 1. 145.95x (ISBN 0-471-48008-8). LC 79-221779 (Pub. by Wiley-Interscience). Wiley.

Kinne, Otto. Marine Ecology: A Comprehensive, Integrated Treatise on Life in Oceans & Coastal Waters, Vol. 5. (Ocean Management Ser.: Pt. 2). 550p. 1984. 84.95x (ISBN 0-471-90159-8, 1174, Pub. by Wiley-Interscience). Wiley.

--Marine Ecology: A Comprehensive, Integrated Treatise on Life in Oceans & Coastal Waters, Vol. 5, Pt. 4: Ocean Management. (Marine Ecology Ser.: A Comprehensive, Integrated Treatise on Life in Oceans & Coastal Waters). 450p. 1984. 89.00 (ISBN 0-471-90217-9, 1-174, Pub. by Wiley-Interscience). Wiley.

Kinne, Otto, ed. Marine Ecology: A Comprehensive, Integrated Treatise on Life in Oceans & Coastal Waters, Vol. 5. LC 79-121779. (Ocean Management Ser.: Pt. 3). 527p. 1984. 100.00x (ISBN 0-471-90216-0, 1-174, Pub. by Wiley-Interscience). Wiley.

Kremer, J. & Nixon, S. W. A Coastal Marine Ecosystem: Simulation & Analysis. LC 77-22785. (Ecological Studies: Vol. 24). (Illus.). 1977. 46.00 (ISBN 0-387-08365-0). Springer-Verlag.

Laevastu, Taivo & Hayes, Murray L. Fisheries Oceanography & Ecology. 1981. 79.00x (ISBN 0-686-78648-3, Pub. by Fishing News England). State Mutual Bk.

L'association Europeenne Oceanique. Metallic Effluents of Industrial Origin in the Marine Environment. 204p. 1977. 79.00x (ISBN 0-86010-063-4, Pub. by Graham & Trotman England). State Mutual Bk.

Levinton, Jeffrey S. Marine Ecology. (Illus.). 1982. 39.95 (ISBN 0-13-556852-8). P-H.

Livingston, R. J., ed. Ecological Processes in Coastal & Marine Systems. LC 79-12388. (Marine Science Ser.: Vol. 10). 560p. 1979. 79.50x (ISBN 0-306-40318-8, Plenum Pr). Plenum Pub.

Longhurst, A. R., ed. Analysis of Marine Ecosystems. 1981. 95.00 (ISBN 0-12-455560-8). Acad Pr.

May, R. M., ed. Exploitation of Marine Communities. (Dahlem Workshop Reports Ser.: Vol. 32). (Illus.). 370p. 1984. 20.00 (ISBN 0-387-15028-5). Springer-Verlag.

Mediterranean Action Plan & the Final Act of the Conference of Plenipotentiaries of the Coastal States of the Mediterranean Region for the Protection of the Mediterranean Sea. 53p. 1978. pap. 7.50 (ISBN 0-686-93581-0, UNEP010, UNEP). Unipub.

Menzies, Robert J., et al. Abyssal Environment & Ecology of the World Oceans. LC 72-8780. 488p. 1973. 37.50 (ISBN 0-686-65289-4, Pub. by Wiley). Krieger.

Moraitou-Apostolopoulou, Maria & Kiortsis, Vassili. Mediterranean Marine Ecosystems. (NATO Conference Series I, Ecology: Vol. 8). 416p. 1985. 65.00x (ISBN 0-306-41910-6, Plenum Pr). Plenum Pub.

Nebert & Burrell. Marine Environmental Studies in Boca de Quadra & Smeaton Bay: Physical Oceanography, 1980. (IMS Report Ser.: No. R81-5). 59p. 5.25 (ISBN 0-914500-12-0). U of AK Inst Marine.

Nichols, David, ed. Monitoring the Marine Environment. LC 78-71806. 220p. 1979. 39.95 (ISBN 0-03-050746-4). Praeger.

North, W. J., ed. Biology of the Giant Kelp Beds (Macrocystis) in California. 1971. 70.00 (ISBN 3-7682-5432-1). Lubrecht & Cramer.

Olausson, Eric & Cato, Ingemar. Chemistry & Biochemistry of Estuaries. LC 79-41211. 452p. 1980. 106.95x (ISBN 0-471-27679-0, Pub. by Wiley-Interscience). Wiley.

Organism-Substrate Relationships in Lowland Streams. (Agricultural Research Reports: No. 907). 211p. 1981. pap. 34.25 (ISBN 90-220-0759-6, PDC222, PUDOC). Unipub.

Por, F. D. Lessepsian Migration: The Influx of Red Sea Biota into the Mediterranaen by Way of the Suez Canal. LC 77-24546. (Ecological Studies: Vol. 23). (Illus.). 1978. 41.00 (ISBN 0-387-08381-2). Springer-Verlag.

The Real Beneficiaries of Federal Dredging: A Legal, Political & Economic Assessment of the Fifty-Foot Channel for the Port of Baltimore. pap. 4.00 (ISBN 0-943676-00-2). MD Sea Grant Col.

Reise, K. Tidal Flat Ecology. (Ecological Studies: Vol. 54). (Illus.). 210p. 1985. 34.50 (ISBN 0-387-15447-7). Springer-Verlag.

Report of the IUCN Workshop on Marine Mammals-Fishery Interactions. 68p. 1980. pap. 10.00 (IUCN123, IUCN). Unipub.

Rohde, Klaus. Ecology of Marine Parasites. LC 81-12934. (Australian Ecology Ser.). (Illus.). 245p. 1982. text ed. 25.00 (ISBN 0-7022-1660-7); pap. text ed. 12.95 (ISBN 0-7022-1670-4). U of Queensland Pr.

Rudloe, Jack. Erotic Ocean: A Handbook for Beachcombers & Marine Naturalists. (Illus.). 464p. 1984. pap. 12.95 (ISBN 0-525-48127-3, 01258-370). Dutton.

Siegfried, W. R., et al, eds. Antarctic Nutrient Cycles & Food Webs. (Illus.). 700p. 1985. 59.00 (ISBN 0-387-13417-4). Springer-Verlag.

Spitsbergen, Judith M. Seacoast Life: An Ecological Guide to Natural Seashore Communities in North Carolina. LC 83-80687. (Illus.). 114p. 1983. pap. 5.95 (ISBN 0-8078-4109-9). U of NC Pr.

Steele, J. H., ed. Marine Food Chains: Proceedings of a Symposium Held at the University of Aarhus, Denmark, from 23rd to 26th July 1968. (Illus.). 1973. Repr. of 1970 ed. lib. bdg. 47.25x (ISBN 3-87429-047-6). Lubrecht & Cramer.

Steele, John H. The Structure of Marine Ecosystems. LC 73-82350. 144p. 1974. text ed. 8.95x (ISBN 0-674-84420-3); pap. 3.95x (ISBN 0-674-84421-1). Harvard U Pr.

Steeman, Nielson E. Marine Photosynthesis. LC 74-29691. (Oceanography Ser.: Vol. 13). 142p. 1975. 57.50 (ISBN 0-444-41320-0). Elsevier.

Stumm, Werner, ed. Chemical Processes in Lakes. (Enviromental Science & Technology: A Wiley-Interscience Series of Texts & Monographs: 1-121). 435p. 1985. text ed. 59.95x (ISBN 0-471-88261-5, Pub. by Wiley-Interscience). Wiley.

Tait, R. V. Elements of Marine Ecology. 3rd ed. (Illus.). 304p. 1981. pap. 29.95 (ISBN 0-408-71054-3). Butterworth.

Thorson, Gunner. Life in the Sea. LC 73-118405. (World University Library). (Illus., Orig.). 1971. pap. 3.95 (ISBN 0-07-064543-4). McGraw.

Valiela, I. Marine Ecological Processes. (Springer Advanced Texts in Life Sciences). (Illus.). 536p. 1984. 34.00 (ISBN 0-387-90929-X). Springer-Verlag.

Vernberg, F. J. & Vernberg, W. B., eds. Functional Adaptations of Marine Organisms. (Physiological Ecology Ser.). 1981. 43.50 (ISBN 0-12-718280-2). Acad Pr.

Ward, C. H., et al, eds. Offshore Ecology Investigation. (Rice University Studies: Vol. 65, Nos. 4 & 5). (Illus.). 600p. (Orig.). 1980. pap. 20.00x (ISBN 0-89263-243-7). Rice Univ.

Warner, Richard E., ed. California Riparian Systems: Proceedings of a Conference on Their Ecology, Conservation, & Productive Management. 1982. text ed. 57.50x (ISBN 0-520-05034-7); pap. 19.95x (ISBN 0-520-05035-5, CAL 682). U Of Cal Pr.

Whitton, B. A., ed. Ecology of European Rivers. (Illus.). 550p. 1984. text ed. 99.00x (ISBN 0-632-00816-4). Blackwell Pubns.

MARINE ENGINEERING

see also Electricity on Ships; Marine Engines; Nautical Instruments; Ship Propulsion; Steam-Boilers

Alexsandrov, Michail. On the Dynamics of Cables with Application to Marine Use. (University of Michigan Dept. of Naval Architecture & Marine Engineering Report Ser.: No. 76). pap. 20.00 (ISBN 0-317-28262-X, 2022630). Bks Demand UMI.

American Society of Civil Engineers. Coastal Engineering: Proceedings of 10th Conference, Tokyo, Japan, September, 1966, 2 vols, Vols. 1 & 2. pap. 160.00 ea. (2019545). Bks Demand UMI.

Bennett, J. V. Heat Engines: Questions & Answers. (Marine Engineering Ser.). 116p. 1975. pap. 9.95x (ISBN 0-540-07340-7). Sheridan.

Bernitsas, Michael M. & Kekridis, Nikos S. Nonlinear Simulation of Time Dependent Towing of Ocean Vehicles. (University of Michigan Dept. of Naval Architecture & Marine Engineering Ser.: No. 283). pap. 20.00 (ISBN 0-317-30470-4, 2024824). Bks Demand UMI.

Bernitsas, Michael M., et al. Parametric Analysis of Static 2-Dimensional Riser Behavior. (University of Michigan Dept. of Naval Achitecture & Marine Engineering, Report: No. 287). pap. 38.50 (ISBN 0-317-27122-9, 2024686). Bks Demand UMI.

Beyn, Edgar J. The Twelve Volt Doctor's Practical Handbook: For the Boat's Electric System. rev. ed. (Illus.). 1983. write for info. (ISBN 0-911551-07-7). SPA Creek.

Bhattacharya, Rameswar. Dynamics of Marine Vehicles. LC 78-950. (Ocean Engineering Ser.). 498p. 1978. text ed. 70.95x cloth (ISBN 0-471-07206-0, Pub. by Wiley-Interscience). Wiley.

Bishop, W. E., et al, eds. Aquatic Toxicology & Hazard Assessment: Sixth Symposium. LC 82-73772. (Special Technical Publications: No. 802). 560p. 1983. text ed. 59.00 (ISBN 0-8031-0255-0, 04-802000-16). ASTM.

Blakey, T. N., ed. English for Maritime Studies Book. (Materials for Language Practice (ESP)). 192p. 1982. pap. 8.50 (ISBN 0-08-028636-4). Pergamon.

Bolger, Philip C. Thirty-Odd Boats. LC 82-80403. (Illus.). 224p. 1982. 22.50 (ISBN 0-87742-152-8). Intl Marine.

Bowyer, Peter. Trouble Shooting & Maintenance of Boat Engines. (Illus.). 184p. 1983. 22.50 (ISBN 0-333-34556-8, Pub. by Nautical Bks England). Sheridan.

Brandon, Larry L. & Brandon, Kathleen M. The Brandon Maintenance Log. 356p. (Orig.). 1982. looseleaf 49.95 (ISBN 0-934114-38-2, BK-284). Marine Educ.

Brockett, W. A., et al. Elements of Applied Thermodynamics. 4th ed. LC 77-73341. (Illus.). 552p. 1978. text ed. 23.95x (ISBN 0-87021-169-2). Naval Inst Pr.

Bryan, George M. & Heirtzler, James R. Ocean Margin Drilling Program Atlases, Vol. 5. (Regional Atlas Ser.). 1984. write for info. spiral bdg (ISBN 0-86720-255-6, Marine Sci Intl). Jones & Bartlett.

Claviez, Wolfram. Seemaennisches Woerterbuch. (Ger.). 1973. 38.50 (ISBN 3-7688-0166-7, M-7620, Pub. by Delius, Klaving & Co.). French & Eur.

Coastal Lagoon Survey. (Technical Papers in Marine Science: No. 31). 280p. 1980. pap. 17.75 (ISBN 0-686-74026-2, U1085, UNESCO). Unipub.

Commission for Marine Meteorology: Albridged Final Report of the Seventh Session (1976) 119p. 1977. pap. 25.00 (ISBN 92-63-10462-X, W212, WMO). Unipub.

Curling, B. C. The History of the Institute of Marine Engineers. 242p. 1961. 3.00x (ISBN 0-900976-92-6, Pub. by Inst Marine Eng). Intl Spec Bk.

Duffett, John. Modern Marine Maintenance. 256p. 1973. 9.95 (ISBN 0-910990-15-8). Hearst Bks.

Europort Conference, 1973. Wear, Lubrication & Repair: Proceedings. 40p. 1973. limp bdg. 9.00 (ISBN 0-900976-36-5, Pub. by Inst Marine Eng). Intl Spec Bk.

Felger, Dan. Engineering for the OOD. LC 78-70964. (Illus.). 256p. 1979. 16.95x (ISBN 0-87021-172-2). Naval Inst Pr.

Fisher, W. A. Engineering for Nautical Students. 4th ed. 299p. 1973. 16.50x (ISBN 0-85174-090-1). Sheridan.

Flanagan, G. T. Feed Water Systems & Treatment. (Marine Engineering Ser.). 144p. 1978. pap. 9.95x (ISBN 0-540-07343-1). Sheridan.

--Marine Boilers: Questions & Answers. 2nd ed. (Marine Engineering Ser.). 102p. 1980. pap. 9.95x (ISBN 0-540-07348-2). Sheridan.

Ford, Louis R. Practical Marine Diesel Engineering. 4th ed. LC 43-4152. (Illus.). 1948. 7.00 (ISBN 0-911090-11-8). Pacific Bk Supply.

Frederick, S. H. & Capper, H., eds. Materials for Marine Machinery. 1977. 45.00x (ISBN 0-900976-42-X, Pub. by Inst Marine Eng). Intl Spec Bk.

Gerwick, Ben C., Jr., et al, eds. Arctic Engineering for the Twenty-First Century. (Proceedings of the First Spilhaus Symposium Ser.). 240p. 1985. text ed. 30.00 (ISBN 0-933957-00-9). Marine Tech Soc.

Gillie, Angelo C. & Pratt, Arden L. Marine Technology Programs: Where We Are & Where We're Going. LC 78-28301. pap. 20.00 (ISBN 0-317-10859-X, 2020570). Bks Demand UMI.

Goring, Loris. The Care & Repair of Marine Petrol Engines. (Illus.). 134p. (Orig.). 1985. pap. 14.50 (ISBN 0-229-11744-9, Pub. by Adlard Coles). Sheridan.

Grayson, Stan. Old Marine Engines: The World of the One Longer. LC 82-80402. (Illus.). 224p. 1982. 25.00 (ISBN 0-87742-155-2). Intl Marine.

Gritzen, Edward F. Introduction to Naval Engineering. LC 79-90773. 448p. 1980. text ed. 16.95x (ISBN 0-87021-319-9). Naval Inst Pr.

Hatch Covers - Design, Installation, Operation & Maintenance. 1981. 75.00x (ISBN 0-686-97080-2, Pub. by Marine Mgmt England). State Mutual Bk.

Health Monitoring of Ships' Machinery. 1981. 75.00x (ISBN 0-686-97082-9, Pub. by Marine Mgmt England). State Mutual Bk.

Heller, M. R., ed. Maritime Simulation. (Illus.). xii, 290p. 1985. 29.50 (ISBN 0-387-15620-8). Springer-Verlag.

Institute of Marine Engineers. Factors in the Selection of Marine Machinery & Plant with Particular Reference to Reliability, Maintenance & Cost. (Illus.). 104p. 1972. limp bdg. 15.00x (ISBN 0-900976-91-8, Pub. by Inst Marine Eng). Intl Spec Bk.

--Glossary of Marine Technology Terms. 178p. 1980. pap. 15.00x (ISBN 0-434-90840-1). Sheridan.

Institute of Marine Engineers, compiled by. Business Management: 1. Incl. The Functions of Management. Kenrick, K. G; An Introduction of Management Techniques. Boyes, J; Communication. Casson, J; Financial Aspects of Management. Turner, J. B; Financial Accounting. Philips, J; Some Aspects of Planning Control. Nelson, R. G. (Topics in Marine Engineering Ser.). 56p. 1973. pap. 3.50x (ISBN 0-900976-10-1, Pub. by Inst Marine Eng). Intl Spec BK.

Institute of Marine Engineers, International Marine & Shipping Conference, 1973. IMAS Seventy-Three: Proceedings. Incl. Boilers, Main Steam Turbines & Gearing. 76p. Group 1. 9.00x (ISBN 0-900976-16-0); Ship Operation & Management: Ship & Propulsion Systems. 60p. Group 2. 9.00x (ISBN 0-900976-17-9); Fuel, Lubrication & Fire. 22p. Group 3. 6.00x (ISBN 0-900976-18-7); Marine Pollution - Noise, Sewage & Oil. 66p. Group 4. 9.00x (ISBN 0-89955-399-0); Training & Manning. 30p. Group 5. 6.00x (ISBN 0-900976-20-9); Radio Communications & Navigational Aids. 34p. Group 6. 6.00x (ISBN 0-900976-21-7); Ocean Engineering. 16p. Group 7. 6.00x (ISBN 0-900976-22-5); Marine Diesel Engines. 66p. Group 8. 9.00x (ISBN 0-900976-23-3); Stern Gear, Shafting & Propellers. 70p. Group 9. 9.00x (ISBN 0-900976-24-1). 434p. 1973. Bound Volume. 36.00 (ISBN 0-900976-25-X, Pub. by Inst Marine Eng). Intl Spec Bk.

Institution of Civil Engineers Staff, ed. The Marine Environment & Oil Facilities. 168p. 1979. 27.75x (ISBN 0-7277-0075-8). Am Soc Civil Eng.

International Conference on Port & Ocean Engineering Under Arctic Conditions, Third, Fairbanks, Alaska, 11-15 August 1975. Assessment of the Arctic Marine Environment: Selected Topics. Hood, D. W. & Burrell, D. C., eds. LC 75-43209. (Occasional Publications Ser.: No. 4). (Illus.). 468p. 1976. 3.00 (ISBN 0-914500-07-4). U. of AK Inst Marine.

IPC Business Press. Marine Propulsion & Future Fuels. 1980. 55.00x (ISBN 0-686-79381-1, Pub. by IPC Busn England). State Mutual Bk.

IPC Business Press, ed. Directory of Shipowners, Shipbuilders & Marine Engineers. 70.00x (ISBN 0-617-00310-6, Pub. by IPC Busn England). State Mutual Bk.

Jolliff, James V. & Robertson, H. E. Naval Engineer's Guide. LC 78-188009. 336p. 1972. 8.50x (ISBN 0-87021-415-2). Naval Inst Pr.

Kirch, Patrick V. Marine Exploitation in Prehistoric Hawai'i: Archaeological Investigations at Kalahuipua'a, Hawai'i Island. LC 79-52731. (Pacific Anthropological Records: No. 29). 235p. 1979. pap. 11.00 (ISBN 0-910240-71-X). Bishop Mus.

Kokarakis, J. E. & Bernitsas, M. M. Static Analysis of Operating & Disconnected Risers with or Without Articulations. (University of Michigan, Dept. of Naval Architecture & Marine Engineering, University of Michigan, 1984: No. 286). pap. 29.80 (ISBN 0-317-27123-7, 2024685). Bks Demand UMI.

Kokkinis, Theodore & Bernitsas, M. M. Program FARSEP: A Program for Determination of the Far Postbuckling Section of the Secondary Equilibrium Path of Marine Risers. (University of Michigan, Dept. of Naval Architecture & Marine Engineering, Report: No. 278). pap. 20.00 (ISBN 0-317-27131-8, 2024683). Bks Demand UMI.

Latorre, Robert, et al. Linear Simulation of Time Dependent Towing of Ocean Vehicles. (University of Michigan Dept. of Naval Architecture & Marine Engineering Ser.: No. 268). pap. 20.50 (ISBN 0-317-30469-0, 2024825). Bks Demand UMI.

Laws, W. Electricity Applied to Marine Engineering. 4th ed. Tyrell, R., rev. by. 454p. 1966. pap. 12.00x (ISBN 0-900976-31-4, Pub. by Inst Marine Eng). Intl Spec Bk.

--Electricity Applied to Marine Engineering. 445p. 1981. 75.00x (ISBN 0-900976-31-4, Pub. by Marine Mgmt England). State Mutual Bk.

Links Between Producers & Users of Marine Technologies: Report of the Expert Group Meeting on Links between Producers & Users of Marine Technologies, United Nations Headquarters, 14-17 December 1981. 76p. 1983. pap. text ed. 10.00 (ISBN 0-686-46329-3, UN82/2A20, UN). Unipub.

Lloyd's Marine Equipment Guide. 1985. 71.00x (ISBN 0-317-19340-6). Intl Pubns Serv.

McCormick, Michael E., ed. Anchoring Systems. 1979. text ed. 33.00 (ISBN 0-08-022694-9). Pergamon.

McGeorge, H. D. General Engineering Knowledge. 2nd ed. (Marine Engineering Ser.). (Illus.). 122p. 1984. pap. text ed. 9.95x (ISBN 0-540-07359-8, Pub. by Stanford Maritime England). Sheridan.

Masuda, M., ed. Dictionary of Marine Engineering Terms: Japanese-English, English-Japanese. (Japanese & Eng.). 313p. 1980. 35.00 (ISBN 0-686-92525-4, M-9339). French & Eur.

Milton, J. H., et al. Running & Maintenance of Marine Machinery. 286p. 1981. 62.00x (ISBN 0-686-97120-5, Pub. by Marine Mgmt England). State Mutual Bk.

Ministry of Education. Scientific Terms Naval Architecture & Marine Engineering: Japanese-English, English-Japanese. (Japanese & Eng.). 526p. 1955. leatherette 24.95 (ISBN 0-686-92523-8, M-9337). French & Eur.

Norris, A. Commissioning & Sea Trials of Machinery in Ships. (Marine Engineering Practice Ser.: Vol. 2, Pt. 12). 1979. pap. 12.00x (ISBN 0-900976-60-8, Pub. by Inst Marine Eng). Intl Spec Bk.

--Operation of Machinery in Motorships: Main Diesels, Boilers & Auxiliary Plant. 164p. 1981. 59.00x (ISBN 0-686-97107-8, Pub. by Marine Mgmt England). State Mutual Bk.

--Operation of Machinery in Ships: Steam Turbines Boilers & Auxiliary Plant. (Practice Ser.: Vol. 2, Pt. 15). 1979. 9.00x (ISBN 0-900976-80-2, Pub. by Inst Marine Eng). Intl Spec Bk.

Ogilvie, T. Francis. Oscillating Pressure Fields on a Free Surface. (University of Michiagan, Dept. of Nval Architecture & Marine Engineering, Report: No. 30). pap. 20.00 (ISBN 0-317-27206-3, 2023868). Bks Demand UMI.

Osbourne, Alan & Neild, A. B., eds. Modern Marine Engineer's Manual, Vol. 1. 2nd ed. LC 65-18208. (Illus.). 1965. Vol. 1. 30.00x (ISBN 0-87033-063-2). Cornell Maritime.

Panel on Fates & Effects of Drilling Fluids & Cuttings in the Marine Environment, National Research Council. Drilling Discharges in the Marine Environment. 1983. pap. text ed. 14.75 (ISBN 0-309-03431-0). Natl Acad Pr.

Paterson, W. B. Marine Engine Room Blue Book. 3rd ed. LC 83-46035. (Illus.). 336p. 1984. pap. 15.00 (ISBN 0-87033-315-1). Cornell Maritime.

Petrie, George L. Simulation of the Maneuverability of Inland Waterway Tows. (University of Michigan, Dept. of Naval Architecture & Marine Engineering, Report: No. 186). pap. 23.30 (ISBN 0-317-27207-1, 2023871). Bks Demand UMI.

Practical Experience with Shipboard Automation: A Joint Conference Held on March 6, 1974. (Illus.). 58p. 1975. pap. 15.00x (ISBN 0-900976-40-3, Pub. by Inst Marine Eng). Intl Spec Bk.

Prescott, John. Directory of Shipowners, Shipbuilders & Marine Engineers, 1982. 80th ed. LC 35-4199. 1534p. 1982. 84.00x (ISBN 0-617-00277-0). Intl Pubns Serv.

Pretzer, Roger. Marine Metals Manual. LC 75-4341. (Illus.). pap. 20.00 (ISBN 0-8357-9257-9, 2011709). Bks Demand UMI.

Rose, Pat R. The Solar Boat Book. rev. ed. LC 83-70115. (Illus.). 266p. 1983. 14.95 (ISBN 0-89815-089-2); pap. 8.95 (ISBN 0-89815-086-8). Ten Speed Pr.

Roy, G. J. Notes on Instrumentation & Control. Rev. ed. (Marine Engineering Ser.). 144p. 1983. pap. 9.95x (ISBN 0-540-07344-X). Sheridan.

Royal Society of London. Marine Technology in the Nineteen Nineties: Proceedings of a Royal Society Discussion Meeting held on 17-18 March 1982. Charnock, H. & Adye, A. M., eds. (Illus.). 202p. 1983. text ed. 62.00x (ISBN 0-85403-197-9, Pub. by Royal Soc London). Scholium Intl.

Running & Maintenance of Marine Machinery. 5th ed. (Illus.). 286p. 1975. pap. 15.00x (ISBN 0-900976-02-0, Pub. by Inst Marine Eng). Intl Spec Bk.

Seminar on Mechanical Engineering in a Marine Environment. 45p. 1983. pap. text ed. 12.00x (ISBN 0-85825-192-2, Pub. by Inst Engineering Australia). Brookfield Pub Co.

Shannon, J. F. Marine Gearing. (Marine Engineering Design & Installation Ser.). (Illus.). 1978. pap. 19.50x (ISBN 0-900976-67-5, Pub. by Inst Marine Eng). Intl Spec Bk.

--Marine Gearing. 180p. 1981. 55.00x (ISBN 0-900976-67-5, Pub. by Marine Mgmt England). State Mutual Bk.

Shor, Alexander & Uchipi, Elazar. Ocean Margin Drilling Program Atlases, Vol. 2. (Regional Atlas Ser.). 1984. write for info. spiral bdg (ISBN 0-86720-252-1, Marine Sci Intl). Jones & Bartlett.

Shor, Alexander N. & Uchipi, Elazar. Ocean Margin Drilling Program Atlases, Vol. 3. (Regional Atlas Ser.). 1984. write for info. spiral bdg (ISBN 0-86720-253-X, Marine Sci Intl). Jones & Bartlett.

Simulator Training for Seagoing Engineers. 1981. 75.00x (ISBN 0-686-97128-0, Pub. by Marine Mgmt England). State Mutual Bk.

Smith, I. & Mulroney, R. A. Parallel Indexing Techniques. 1979. pap. 6.50x (ISBN 0-540-07353-9). Sheridan.

The Society of Naval Architects & Marine Engineers: Transactions, Vol. 87. 412p. 1980. text ed. 25.00 (ISBN 0-9603048-1-9). Soc Naval Arch.

Society of Naval Architects & Marine Engineers, Annual Meetings, 92nd, New York, Nov. 1984. Transactions, Vol. 92. (Illus.). 1985. write for info. (ISBN 0-9603048-6-X). Soc Naval Arch.

Society of Naval Architects & Marine Engineers. Transactions: Proceedings of the Society of Naval Architects & Marine Engineers Annual Meeting, 91st, New York, Nov. 1983. (Illus.). 412p. 1984. write for info. (ISBN 0-9603048-5-1). Soc Naval Arch.

Souchotte, E. Marine Auxiliary Machinery. 6th ed. 512p. 1983. text ed. 49.95 (ISBN 0-408-01123-8). Butterworth.

Sterling. Pumping Systems. 74p. 1981. 45.00x (ISBN 0-900976-43-8, Pub. by Marine Mgmt England). State Mutual Bk.

Taylor & Billis. Control Engineering for Marine Engineers. (Illus.). 320p. 1985. text ed. 49.95 (ISBN 0-408-01313-3). Butterworth.

Transactions: Proceedings of the Society of Naval Architects & Marine Engineers Annual Meeting, 90th, New York, Nov. 1982. (Illus.). 460p. 1983. write for info. (ISBN 0-9603048-4-3). Soc Naval Arch.

Use of Organic Fluids for Waste Heat Recovery in Ships & Industry. 1981. 125.00x (ISBN 0-686-97129-9, Pub. by Marine Mgmt England). State Mutual Bk.

Vandegrift, John F., Sr. Basic Math Handbook for Practical Marine Engineers. Block, Richard A., ed. 168p. (Orig.). 1985. pap. 18.00 (ISBN 0-934114-64-1, BK-458). Marine Educ.

Vibration & Noise Levels in Ships. 1981. 75.00x (ISBN 0-686-97133-7, Pub. by Marine Mgmt England). State Mutual Bk.

Ward, Robert J. Workboat Engineer & Oiler. rev. "A" ed. Block, Richard A., ed. (Illus.). 520p. (Orig.). 1983. pap. 34.00 (ISBN 0-934114-44-7, BK-107). Marine Educ.

Watson. Marine Electrical Practice. 5th ed. 1981. text ed. 57.50 (ISBN 0-408-00498-3). Butterworth.

Woodward, John B. Marine Shaft Alignment Calculations. (Michigan Marine Engineering Ser.). 60p. (Orig.). 1985. pap. text ed. 5.00 (ISBN 0-931781-00-0). Jenning Pr.

Yeandle, P. T. Mathematics: Questions & Answers. (Marine Engineering Ser.). 144p. 1979. pap. 9.95x (ISBN 0-540-07337-7). Sheridan.

MARINE ENGINEERING–BIBLIOGRAPHY

Bernardi, S. D. Bibliography of Schlicht Functions. LC 83-7958. 363p. 1983. 32.50 (ISBN 0-936166-09-6). Mariner Pub.

MARINE ENGINEERING–EXAMINATIONS, QUESTIONS, ETC.

Paterson, William B. Red Book of Marine Engineering Questions & Answers, Vol. 1: Third & Second Assistant Engineers. 4th ed. LC 76-153141. (Illus.). 1972. pap. 15.00x (ISBN 0-87033-088-8). Cornell Maritime.

--Red Book of Marine Engineering Questions & Answers, Vol. 2: First Assistant & Chief Engineer. 4th ed. LC 76-153141. (Illus.). 1973. pap. 11.00x (ISBN 0-87033-089-6). Cornell Maritime.

Rudman, Jack. Chief Marine Engineer. (Career Examination Ser.: C-1794). (Cloth bdg. avail. on request). pap. 14.00 (ISBN 0-8373-1794-0). Natl Learning.

--Marine Engineer. (Career Examination Ser.: C-1363). (Cloth bdg. avail. on request). pap. 10.00 (ISBN 0-8373-1363-5). Natl Learning.

MARINE ENGINES

see also Diesel Motor; Marine Diesel Motors; Marine Nuclear Reactor Plants; Steam-Boilers; Steam-Turbines

Bowyer, Peter. Trouble Shooting & Maintenance of Boat Engines. (Illus.). 184p. 1983. 22.50 (ISBN 0-333-34556-8, Pub. by Nautical Bks England). Sheridan.

Cundell, John & King, Jim. Introducing Model Marine Steam. (Illus.). 112p. (Orig.). 1983. pap. 11.95 (ISBN 0-85242-814-6, Pub. by Argus). Aztex.

Donald, K. M. Marine Steam Turbines. 146p. 1981. 52.00x (ISBN 0-900976-58-6, Pub. by Marine Mgmt England). State Mutual Bk.

Goring, Loris. The Care & Repair of Marine Petrol Engines. (Illus.). 134p. (Orig.). 1985. pap. 14.50 (ISBN 0-229-11744-9, Pub. by Adlard Coles). Sheridan.

Health Monitoring of Ships' Machinery. 1981. 75.00x (ISBN 0-686-97082-9, Pub. by Marine Mgmt England). State Mutual Bk.

McBirnie, S. C. & Fox, W. J. Marine Steam Engines & Turbines. 4th ed. (Illus.). 672p. 1980. text ed. 57.50 (ISBN 0-408-00387-1). Butterworth.

Milton, J. H., et al. Running & Maintenance of Marine Machinery. 286p. 1981. 62.00x (ISBN 0-686-97120-5, Pub. by Marine Mgmt England). State Mutual Bk.

Norris, A. Operation of Machinery in Motorships: Main Diesels, Boilers & Auxiliary Plant. 164p. 1981. 59.00x (ISBN 0-686-97107-8, Pub. by Marine Mgmt England). State Mutual Bk.

Paterson, W. B. Marine Engine Room Blue Book. 3rd ed. LC 83-46035. (Illus.). 336p. 1984. pap. 15.00 (ISBN 0-87033-315-1). Cornell Maritime.

Rayman, A. A. High Speed Marine Engines. 60p. 1985. pap. 2.50 (ISBN 0-85242-540-6, Pub. by Argus). Aztex.

Roy, Gordon. Steam Turbines & Gearing. (Marine Engineering Ser.). (Illus.). 113p. 1984. pap. text ed. 9.95x (ISBN 0-540-07358-X, Pub. by Stanford Maritime). Sheridan.

Wakefield, S. B., ed. Marine Propulsion Systems. 159p. 1981. 60.00x (ISBN 0-900976-35-7, Pub. by Marine Mgmt England). State Mutual Bk.

Witt, Glen L. & Hankinson, Ken. Inboard Motor Installations. 2nd rev. ed. LC 78-58127. (Illus.). 1978. text ed. 14.95 (ISBN 0-686-08739-9). Glen-L Marine.

MARINE FAUNA

see also Fishes; Marine Aquariums; Marine Mammals; Sea Monsters

Aleyev, Yu G. Nekton. (Illus.). 1977. lib. bdg. 63.00 (ISBN 90-6193-560-1, Pub. by Junk Pubs Netherlands). Kluwer Academic.

Arnold, Augusta F. Sea-Beach at Ebb-Tide. LC 68-20554. (Illus.). 1968. pap. 7.95 (ISBN 0-486-21949-6). Dover.

Aspects of Brackish Water Fish & Crustacean Culture in the Mediterranean. (General Fisheries Council of the Mediterranean (GFCM): Studies & Reviews: No. 57). (Eng. & Fr.). 135p. 1980. pap. 8.75 (ISBN 92-5-000964-X, F2103, FAO). Unipub.

Baker, Joseph T. & Murphy, Vreni. Compounds from Marine Organisms, Vol. 2. (Section B, Handbook of Marine Science). 240p. 1981. 56.00 (ISBN 0-8493-0214-5). CRC Pr.

Behrens, David W. Pacific Coast Nudibranchs. LC 80-51439. (Illus.). 112p. 1980. pap. 14.95 (ISBN 0-930118-05-7). Western Marine Ent.

Bolis, L., et al, eds. Toxins, Drugs & Pollutants in Marine Animals. (Proceedings in Life Sciences Ser.). (Illus.). vi, 200p. 1984. 34.00 (ISBN 0-387-13643-6). Springer-Verlag.

Bouthillette, Guy. Tidal Zones: A Guide to Plants & Animals Where the Sea Meets the Shore. Feller-Roth, Barbara, ed. (Maine Geographic Ser.). (Illus.). 48p. 1983. pap. 2.95 (ISBN 0-89933-053-3). DeLorme Pub.

Bullen, Frank T. Creatures of the Sea: Sea Birds, Beasts, & Fishes. 1977. lib. bdg. 69.95 (ISBN 0-8490-1682-7). Gordon Pr.

Burger, Joanna, et al, eds. Behavior of Marine Animals, Vol. 4: Marine Birds. LC 79-167675. 532p. 1980. 55.00x (ISBN 0-306-37574-5, Plenum Pr). Plenum Pub.

Clark, A. H. Ophiuroidea of the Hawaiian Islands. (BMB Ser.). Repr. of 1949 ed. 19.00 (ISBN 0-527-02303-5). Kraus Repr.

Data on Contaminants in Aquatic Organisms: Report of the FAO-UNEP Expert Consultation on Contaminent Monitoring, Rome, 1974. (Fisheries Reports: No. 161). 30p. 1976. pap. 7.50 (ISBN 0-685-67380-4, F804, FAO). Unipub.

Edmondson, C. H., et al. Marine Zoology of Tropical Central Pacific. (BMB Ser.). Repr. of 1925 ed. 19.00 (ISBN 0-527-02130-X). Kraus Repr.

Ely, C. A. Shallow-Water Asteroidea & Ophiuroidea of Hawaii. (BMB Ser.). Repr. of 1942 ed. 12.00 (ISBN 0-527-02284-5). Kraus Repr.

European Symposium on Marine Biology, 12th. Physiology & Behaviour of Marine Organisms: Proceedings. McLusky, D. S. & Berry, A. J., eds. LC 77-30559. 1978. text ed. 72.00 (ISBN 0-08-021548-3). Pergamon.

Fotheringham, Nick, et al. Beachcomber's Guide to Gulf Coast Marine Life. LC 80-10607. (Illus.). 124p. (Orig.). 1980. pap. 9.95x (ISBN 0-88415-062-3, Lone Star Bks). Gulf Pub.

Fowler, H. W. & Ball, S. C. Fishes of Hawaii, Johnston Island, & Wake Island. (BMB). pap. 8.00 (ISBN 0-527-02129-6). Kraus Repr.

Gotshall, Daniel W. Marine Animals of Baja California. LC 82-50492. (Illus.). 112p. 1982. ltd. ed. 29.95 (ISBN 0-930118-08-1, Dist. by Western Marine Enterprises); pap. 17.95 (ISBN 0-930030-24-9). Sea Chall.

Grant, P. T. & Mackie, A. M., eds. Chemoreception in Marine Organisms. 1974. 57.00 (ISBN 0-12-295650-8). Acad Pr.

Great Britain Challenger Office. Report on the Scientific Results of the Voyage of H. M. S. Challenger During the Years 1873-1876, 50 Vols. (Illus.). 1880-1895. Set. 5000.00 (ISBN 0-384-19750-7). Johnson Repr.

Green, J. Biology of Estuarine Animals. LC 68-21828. (Biology Ser.). (Illus.). 404p. 1968. 20.00x (ISBN 0-295-95122-2). U of Wash Pr.

Greenberg, Idaz & Greenberg, Jerry. Sharks & Other Dangerous Sea Creatures. (Illus.). 64p. 1981. pap. 4.95 (ISBN 0-913008-09-5, G-095). Banyan Bks.

--Sharks & Other Dangerous Sea Creatures. (Illus.). 1981. saddlestiched 4.95x (ISBN 0-913008-09-5). Seahawk Pr.

Gulland, John A. The Management of Marine Fisheries. LC 74-2473. (Illus.). 206p. 1974. 25.00x (ISBN 0-295-95335-7). U of Wash Pr.

Halstead, Bruce W. Poisonous & Venomous Marine Animals of the World. 2nd, rev. ed. LC 84-70414. (Illus.). 1500p. 1986. 200.00 (ISBN 0-87850-050-2). Darwin Pr.

Helm, Thomas. Dangerous Sea Creatures: A Complete Guide to Hazardous Marine Life. LC 75-25960. (Funk & W Bk.). (Illus.). 288p. 1976. pap. 4.95i (ISBN 0-308-10238-X). T Y Crowell.

Hobson, Edmund & Chave, Edith H. Hawaiian Reef Animals. LC 72-84060. (Illus.). 159p. 1979. pap. 15.95 (ISBN 0-8248-0653-0). UH Pr.

Holly, M. Polychaeta from Hawaii. (BMB). pap. 8.00 (ISBN 0-527-02235-7). Kraus Repr.

Humes, Arthur G. A Review of the Copepoda Associated with Sea Anemones. LC 81-71035. (Transactions Ser.: Vol. 72, Pt. 2). 1982. 12.00 (ISBN 0-87169-722-X). Am Philos.

Illies, Joachim, ed. Limnofauna Europaea: A Checklist of the Animals Inhabiting European Inland Waters, with Accounts of Their Distribution & Ecology (Except Protozoa) 532p. 1978. text ed. 120.00 (ISBN 90-265-0275-3, Pub. by Swets Pub Serv Holland). Swets North Am.

Irby, Bobby N., et al. Diversity of Marine Animals. LC 83-19721. (Man & the Gulf Ser.: Vol. 3). 120p. 1984. pap. text ed. 6.00 (ISBN 0-87805-203-8). U Pr of Miss.

Jones, N. V. & Wolff, W. J., eds. Feeding & Survival Strategies of Estuarine Organisms. LC 81-12005. (Marine Science Ser.: Vol. 15). 316p. 1981. 49.50x (ISBN 0-306-40813-9, Plenum Pr). Plenum Pub.

Khan, M. A., et al, eds. Pesticide & Xenobiotic Metabolism in Aquatic Organisms. LC 79-4598. (ACS Symposium Ser.: No. 99). 1979. 42.95 (ISBN 0-8412-0489-6). Am Chemical.

Line, Les & Reiger, George. The Audubon Society Book of Marine Wildlife. (Audobon Society Bks.). (Illus.). 1980. 50.00 (ISBN 0-8109-0672-4). Abrams.

Malins, D. C. & Sargent, J. R., eds. Biochemical & Biophysical Perspectives in Marine Biology, Vol. 4. 1979. 50.00 (ISBN 0-12-466604-3). Acad Pr.

Mammals in the Seas: Small Cetaceans, Seals, Sirenians & Otters, Vol. 4. (Fisheries Ser.: No. 5). 531p. 1982. text ed. 80.50 (ISBN 92-5-100514-1, F2386, FAO). Unipub.

Murray, John. Selections from the Report on the Scientific Results of the Voyage of H.M.S. Challenger During the Years 1872-76. Egerton, Frank N., 3rd, ed. LC 77-74242. (History of Ecology Ser.). (Illus.). 1978. Repr. of 1895 ed. lib. bdg. 19.00x (ISBN 0-405-10411-1). Ayer Co Pubs.

Names of Fishes, Shellfish & Marine Animals. (Terminology Bulletin: No. 38C). (Eng., Lat. & Chinese.). 142p. 1979. pap. 5.70 (ISBN 92-5-000788-4, FAO). Unipub.
Naylor, E. & Hartnoll, E. G., eds. Cyclic Phenomena in Marine Plants & Animals. 1979. 80.00 (ISBN 0-08-023217-5). Pergamon.
Newman, G. The Living Marine Resources of the Southeast Atlantic. (Fisheries Technical Papers: No. 178). (Eng., Fr. & Span.). 67p. 1977. pap. 7.50 (ISBN 92-5-100446-3, F1310, FAO). Unipub.
Ohsawa, Lima. Macrobiotic Cuisine. (Illus.). 224p. (Orig.). 1985. pap. 11.49 (ISBN 0-87040-600-0). Har-Row.
Pequegnat, Willis E. & Chace, Fenner A., Jr., eds. Contributions on the Biology of the Gulf of Mexico. LC 71-135998. (Texas A&M University Oceanographic Studies: Vol. 1). 270p. 1970. 29.95x (ISBN 0-87201-346-4). Gulf Pub.
Romashko, Sandra. Living Coral. 3rd ed. LC 76-12930. 1985. pap. 3.95 (ISBN 0-317-19733-9). Windward Pub.
Roux, Charles. Animals of the Seashore. LC 83-50222. (Nature's Hidden World Ser.). 48p. 1984. 12.68 (ISBN 0-382-06712-6). Silver.
Ruivo, Mario, ed. Marine Pollution & Sea Life. 1978. 59.00 (ISBN 0-685-63432-9). State Mutual Bk.
Scilla, Agostino. De Corporibus Marinis Lapidescentibus Quae Defossa Reperiuntur Addita Dissertatione Fabii Columnae Glossopetris: On Petrified Marine Bodies Discovered Buried, to Which Is Appended a Dissertation by Fabio Colonna on Tongue Stones. Gould, Stephen J., ed. LC 79-8349. (History of Paleontology Ser.). (Latin., Illus.). 1980. Repr. of 1747 ed. lib. bdg. 12.00x (ISBN 0-405-12742-1). Ayer Co Pubs.
Smith, R. I., et al. Keys to Marine Invertebrates of the Woods Hole Region. (Illus.). 1964. pap. 6.50x (ISBN 0-912544-01-5). Marine Bio.
Stancyk, Stephen E., ed. Reproductive Ecology of Marine Invertebrates. LC 79-13841. (Belle W. Baruch Library in Marine Science Ser.). xvi, 284p. 1979. lib. bdg. 39.95x (ISBN 0-87249-379-2). U of SC Pr.
Stubbings, H. G. Balanus Balanoides. 175p. 1975. 45.00x (ISBN 0-85323-233-4, Pub. by Liverpool Univ England). State Mutual Bk.
Styles, Bonnie W. Faunal Exploitation & Resource Selection. LC 80-27767. (Scientific Papers: No.3). (Illus.). 312p. 1981. pap. 12.00 (ISBN 0-942118-09-X, E78.13S85). Ctr Amer Arche.
Vernberg, F. J. & Vernberg, W. B., eds. Functional Adaptations of Marine Organisms. (Physiological Ecology Ser.). 1981. 43.50 (ISBN 0-12-718280-2). Acad Pr.
Whyte, Mal. North American Sealife Coloring Album. (Wildlife Ser.). (Illus.). 1973. pap. 3.95 (ISBN 0-8431-1713-3, 27-2). Troubador Pr.
Williams, Austin B. Shrimps, Lobsters, & Crabs of the Atlantic Coast. rev. ed. LC 83-600095. (Illus.). 568p. 1984. text ed. 40.00x (ISBN 0-87474-960-3). Smithsonian.
Winberg, G. G. Methods for the Estimation of Production of Aquatic Animals. 1971. 36.00 (ISBN 0-12-758350-5). Acad Pr.
Winn, H. E. & Olla, B. L. Behavior of Marine Animals, Vols. 1-3. Incl. Vol. 1. Invertebrates. 273p. 1972. 35.00 (ISBN 0-306-37571-0); Vol. 2. Vertebrates. 521p. 1972. 35.00 (ISBN 0-306-37572-9); Vol. 3. Cetaceans. 460p. 1978. 49.50 (ISBN 0-306-37573-7). LC 79-16775 (Plenum Pr). Plenum Pub.

MARINE FAUNA–ATLANTIC COAST

Fox, Richard S. & Ruppert, Edward E., eds. Shallow-Water Marine Benthic Macro-Invertebrates of South Carolina. (Belle W. Baruch Library in Marine Science: No. 14). 1985. 39.95x (ISBN 0-87249-473-X). U of SC Pr.
Newman, G. The Living Marine Resources of the Southeast Atlantic. (Fisheries Technical Papers: No. 178). (Eng., Fr. & Span.). 67p. 1977. pap. 7.50 (ISBN 92-5-100446-3, F1310, FAO). Unipub.
Roe, H. S. Progress in Oceanography, Vol. 13, Nos. 3-4. (Illus.). 276p. 1984. pap. 75.00 (ISBN 0-08-031735-9). Pergamon.

MARINE FAUNA–AUSTRALIA

Thompson, H. Pelagic Tunicates of Australia. 1982. 30.00x (ISBN 0-686-97903-6, Pub. by CSIRO Australia). State Mutual Bk.

MARINE FAUNA–BERMUDA ISLANDS

Sterrer, W. E. Marine Fauna & Flora of Bermuda: A Systematic Guide to the Identification of Marine Organisms. 1120p. 1985. 80.00 (ISBN 0-471-82336-8). Wiley.

MARINE FAUNA–GREAT BRITAIN

Newell, R. C. Biology of Intertidal Animals. 781p. 1979. 60.00x (ISBN 0-9506920-0-X). State Mutual Bk.

MARINE FAUNA–PACIFIC COAST

Angell, Tony & Balcolm, Kenneth C., III. Marine Birds & Mammals of Puget Sound. LC 82-10946. (A Puget Sound Bk.). (Illus.). 128p. (Orig.). 1982. pap. 14.50 (ISBN 0-295-95942-8, Pub. by Wash Sea Grant). U of Wash Pr.
Burgess, Warren E. & Axelrod, Herbert R. Pacific Marine Fishes, Bk. 3. (Illus.). 272p. 1973. 29.95 (ISBN 0-87666-125-8, PS-719). TFH Pubns.
Dewees, Christopher M. The Printer's Catch: An Artist's Guide to Pacific Coast Edible Marine Life. LC 83-51816. (Illus.). 128p. 1984. 26.95 (ISBN 0-930118-10-3). Sea Chall.
Gotshall, Daniel W. Marine Animals of Baja California. LC 82-50492. (Illus.). 112p. 1982. pap. 17.95 (ISBN 0-930030-24-9). Western Marine.
Kozloff, Eugene N. Seashore Life of the Northern Pacific Coast: An Illustrated Guide to Northern California, Oregon, Washington, & British Columbia. LC 83-1130. (Illus.). 378p. 1983. 40.00x (ISBN 0-295-96030-2); pap. 19.95 (ISBN 0-295-96084-1). U of Wash Pr.
Smith, Lynwood. Common Seashore Life of the Pacific Northwest. (Illus.). 66p. 1962. 10.95 (ISBN 0-911010-65-3). pap. 4.95 (ISBN 0-911010-64-5). Naturegraph.
Warr, Diana & Collier, Albert. Seashore Biology Notes: A New Guide to the Common Animals in the Northern Gulf of California Tidepools. (Illus., Orig.). 1982. 7.95 (ISBN 0-938372-02-5). Winter Pub Co.

MARINE FLORA

see also Coastal Flora; Marine Algae; Marine Aquariums; Phytoplankton; Primary Productivity (Biology)

Arnold, Augusta F. Sea-Beach at Ebb-Tide. LC 68-20554. (Illus.). 1968. pap. 7.95 (ISBN 0-486-21949-6). Dover.
Baker, Joseph T. & Murphy, Vreni. Compounds from Marine Organisms, Vol. 2. (Section B, Handbook of Marine Science). 240p. 1981. 56.00 (ISBN 0-8493-0214-5). CRC Pr.
Bouthillette, Guy. Tidal Zones: A Guide to Plants & Animals Where the Sea Meets the Shore. Feller-Roth, Barbara, ed. (Maine Geographic Ser.). (Illus.). 48p. 1983. pap. 2.95 (ISBN 0-89933-053-3). DeLorme Pub.
Dawes, Clinton J. Marine Botany. LC 1-7527. 628p. 1981. 53.50 (ISBN 0-471-07844-1, Pub. by Wiley-Interscience). Wiley.
Dawson, E. Yale. Seashore Plants of Northern California. (California Natural History Guides: No. 20). 1966. pap. 3.25 (ISBN 0-520-00301-2). U of Cal Pr.
--Seashore Plants of Southern California. (California Natural History Guides: No. 19). 1966. pap. 2.95 (ISBN 0-520-00300-4). U of Cal Pr.
European Symposium on Marine Biology, 12th. Physiology & Behaviour of Marine Organisms: Proceedings. McLusky, D. S. & Berry, A. J., eds. LC 77-30559. 1978. text ed. 72.00 (ISBN 0-08-021548-3). Pergamon.
Hillson, Charles J. Seaweeds: A Color-Coded, Illustrated Guide to Common Marine Plants of the East Coast of the United States. LC 76-42192. (Keystone Bks.). 1977. lib. bdg. 17.95x (ISBN 0-271-01239-0); pap. 9.75 (ISBN 0-271-01247-1). Pa St U Pr.
Humes, Arthur G. A Review of the Copepoda Associated with Sea Anemones. LC 81-71035. (Transactions Ser.: Vol. 72, Pt. 2). 1982. 12.00 (ISBN 0-87169-722-X). Am Philos.
Irby, Bobby N., et al. Diversity of Marine Plants. LC 83-16994. (Man & the Gulf Ser.: Vol. 4). (Illus.). 120p. 1984. pap. text ed. 6.00 (ISBN 0-87805-204-6). U Pr of Miss.
Krauss, Robert W., ed. The Marine Plant Biomass of the Pacific Northwest Coast: A Potential Economic Resource. (Illus.). 416p. 1978. text ed. 19.95x (ISBN 0-87071-447-3). Oreg St U Pr.
Kuznetsov, S. I. The Microflora of Lakes & Its Geochemical Activity. Oppenheimer, Carl H., ed. LC 73-21215. (Illus.). 503p. 1975. 27.50x (ISBN 0-292-75010-2). U of Tex Pr.
Naylor, E. & Hartnoll, E. G., eds. Cyclic Phenomena in Marine Plants & Animals. 1979. 80.00 (ISBN 0-08-023217-5). Pergamon.
Steeman, Nielson E. Marine Photosynthesis. LC 74-29691. (Oceanography Ser.: Vol. 13). 142p. 1975. 57.50 (ISBN 0-444-41320-0). Elsevier.
Sterrer, W. E. Marine Fauna & Flora of Bermuda: A Systematic Guide to the Identification of Marine Organisms. 1120p. 1985. 80.00 (ISBN 0-471-82336-8). Wiley.
Tolbert, N. E. & Osmond, C. B., eds. Photorespiration in Marine Plants. (Illus.). 139p. 1976. 7.50x (ISBN 0-643-00201-4). Sabbot-Natural Hist Bks.
Zaneveld, J. S. Iconography of Antartic & Sub-Antarctic Benthie Marine Algae: Chlorophycophyto & Chrysophycophyta, Part 1. 1969. pap. 14.00 (ISBN 3-7682-0631-9). Lubrecht & Cramer.

MARINE FUNGI

Anastasiou, C. J. Ascomycetes & Fungi Imperfecti from the Salton Sea. 1963. 6.40 (ISBN 3-7682-0210-0). Lubrecht & Cramer.
Ingold, C. T. An Illustrated Guide to Aquatic & Water Borne Hyphomycetes (Fungi Imperfecti) 1975. 20.00x (ISBN 0-900386-22-3, Pub. by Freshwater Bio). State Mutual Bk.
Johnson, T. W., Jr. & Sparrow, F. K., Jr. Fungi in Oceans & Estuaries. (Illus.). 1970. pap. 35.00 (ISBN 3-7682-0076-0). Lubrecht & Cramer.
Kirk, P. W. Morphogenesis & Microscopic Cytochemistry of Marine Pyrenomycete Ascospores. (Illus.). 1966. pap. 14.00 (ISBN 3-7682-5422-4). Lubrecht & Cramer.

MARINE GEOLOGY

see Submarine Geology

MARINE GEOTECHNIQUE

Gordon, R. & Spaulding, M. L. Numerical Models for Tidal Rivers, Estuaries & Coastal Waters: Bibliography. (Technical Report Ser.: No. 32). 55p. 1974. 2.00 (ISBN 0-938412-31-0, P376). URI MAS.
Richards, Adrian, ed. Marine Geotechnology: Marine Slope Stability Conference, Vol. 2. 392p. 1977. 45.00x (ISBN 0-8448-1352-4). Crane-Russak Co.
Richards, Adrian F., ed. Marine Geotechnique: Proceedings. LC 67-27773. (Illus.). Repr. of 1967 ed. 63.70 (ISBN 0-8357-9688-4, 2014936). Bks Demand UMI.
Rona, Peter A., et al, eds. Hydrothermal Processes at Seafloor Spreading Centers. (NATO Conference Series IV, Marine Sciences: Vol. 12). 792p. 1983. 110.00 (ISBN 0-306-41482-1, Plenum Pr). Plenum Pub.

MARINE INSTRUMENTS

see Nautical Instruments

MARINE INVERTEBRATES

Berg, Carl J., Jr., ed. Culture of Marine Invertebrates: Selected Readings. LC 83-61. 400p. 1983. 45.00 (ISBN 0-87933-105-4). Van Nos Reinhold.
Chia, F. & Rice, M. E., eds. Settlement & Metamorphosis of Marine Invertebrate Larvae: Proceedings of a Symposium Held at Toronto, Canada, Dec. 27-28, 1977. 290p. 1979. 45.50 (ISBN 0-444-00277-4, Biomedical Pr). Elsevier.
Cohen, William D. Blood Cells of Marine Invertebrates. LC 84-26174. (MBL Ser.: Vol. 6). 280p. 1985. 66.00 (ISBN 0-8451-2205-3). A R Liss.
DeLuca, Charles J. & DeLuca, Diana M. Pacific Marine Life: A Survey of Pacific Ocean Invertebrates. LC 76-12228. 1976. pap. 2.75 (ISBN 0-8048-1212-8). C E Tuttle.
Giese, Arthur C. & Pearse, John S., eds. Reproduction of Marine Invertebrates: Acoelomate & Psuedocollomate Metazoans, Vol. 1. 1974. 78.00 (ISBN 0-12-282501-2). Acad Pr.
--Reproduction of Marine Invertebrates: Molluscs: Pelecypods & Lesser Classes, Vol. 5. LC 72-84365. 1979. 70.00 (ISBN 0-12-282505-5). Acad Pr.
Giese, Pearse. Reproduction of Marine Invertebrates: Entoprocts: Lesser Callomates. 1975. Vol. 2. 80.50. Acad Pr.
Gotshall, Daniel W. & Laurent, Laurence L. Pacific Coast Subtidal Marine Invertebrates. LC 79-64128. (Illus.). 112p. pap. 12.95 (ISBN 0-930118-03-0). Western Marine Ent.
Hammen, Carl S. Marine Invertebrates: Comparative Physiology. LC 80-51505. (Illus.). 141p. 1980. text ed. 14.00x (ISBN 0-87451-188-7). U Pr of New Eng.
Lowry, James K. Soft Bottom Macrobenthic Community of Arthur Harbor, Antarctica: Paper 1 in Biology of the Antarctic Seas V. Pawson, David L., ed. LC 75-22056. (Antarctic Research Ser: Vol. 23). (Illus.). 20p. 1975. pap. 5.20 (ISBN 0-87590-123-9). Am Geophysical.
National Research Council Assembly of Life Sciences. Marine Invertebrates. 1981. pap. 19.25 (ISBN 0-309-03134-6). Natl Acad Pr.
Smith, Walter L. & Chanley, Matoira H., eds. Culture of Marine Invertebrate Animals. LC 74-11367. 346p. 1974. 45.00x (ISBN 0-306-30804-5, Plenum Pr). Plenum Pub.
Stancyk, Stephen E., ed. Reproductive Ecology of Marine Invertebrates. LC 79-13841. (Belle W. Baruch Library in Marine Science Ser.). xvi, 284p. 1979. lib. bdg. 39.95x (ISBN 0-87249-379-2). U of SC Pr.
Walls, Jerry G., ed. The Encyclopedia of Marine Invertebrates. (Illus.). 736p. 1982. 49.95 (ISBN 0-87666-495-8, H-951). TFH Pubns.

MARINE MAMMALS

Allen, Glover M. Extinct & Vanishing Mammals of the Western Hemisphere: With the Marine Species of All Oceans. LC 72-85661. xv, 620p. 1973. Repr. of 1942 ed. lib. bdg. 30.00 (ISBN 0-8154-0433-6). Cooper Sq.
Beverton, R. J. H., et al, eds. Marine Mammals & Fisheries. (Illus.). 350p. 1985. text ed. 55.00x (ISBN 0-04-639003-0). Allen Unwin.
Carnegie Institution Of Washington. Marine Mammals. Repr. of 1934 ed. 19.00 (ISBN 0-685-02195-5). Johnson Repr.
Fay, F. H., et al, eds. A Field Manual of Procedures for Postmortem Examination of Alaskan Marine Mammals. (IMS Report Ser.: No. R79-1). write for info. (ISBN 0-914500-09-0). U of AK Inst Marine.
Haley, Delphine. Marine Mammals. LC 78-16859. (Illus.). 256p. 1979. cloth 26.50 (ISBN 0-914718-35-5). Pacific Search.
Harrison, R. J. Deep Diving in Mammals. 57p. 1976. 39.00x (ISBN 0-900541-89-X, Pub. by Meadowfield Pr England). State Mutual Bk.
--Functional Anatomy of Marine Mammals, Vols. 2 & 3. Vol. 2, 1975. 60.00 (ISBN 0-12-328002-8). Vol. 3, 1978. 69.50 (ISBN 0-12-328003-6). Acad Pr.
Harrison, R. J., ed. Functional Anatomy of Marine Mammals, Vol. 1. 1973. 78.50 (ISBN 0-12-328001-X). Acad Pr.
Harrison, Richard J. & King, Judith E. Marine Mammals. (Repr. of 1965 ed.). 1968. pap. text ed. 13.00x (ISBN 0-09-074342-3, Hutchinson U Lib). Humanities.
Howard, Edwin B. Pathobiology of Marine Mammal Diseases, 2 Vols. 1983. Vol. I, 248p. 68.00 (ISBN 0-8493-6311-X); Vol. II, 240p. 68.00 (ISBN 0-317-03381-6). CRC Pr.
Howard, Edwin B., ed. Pathobiology of Marine Mammal Diseases, Vol. II. 240p. 1983. 68.00 (ISBN 0-8493-6312-8). CRC Pr.
Katona, Steve & Richardson, David. A Field Guide to the Whales, Porpoises, & Seals of the Gulf of Maine & Eastern Canada: Cape Cod to Labrador. (Illus.). 224p. 1983. 22.95 (ISBN 0-684-17901-6, ScribT); pap. 13.95 (ISBN 0-684-17902-4). Scribner.
Kooyman, Gerald L. Weddell Seal: Consummate Diver. LC 80-18794. (Illus.). 176p. 1981. 44.50 (ISBN 0-521-23657-6). Cambridge U Pr.
Marine Birds & Mammals. pap. 14.50 (ISBN 0-317-31646-X). U of Wash Pr.
Orr, Robert T. Marine Mammals of California. LC 78-165233. (California Natural History Guides Ser.: No. 29). 88p. 1972. pap. 4.95 (ISBN 0-520-02077-4). U of Cal Pr.
Report of the Advisory Committee of Marine Resources Research Working Party on Marine Mammals: With the Cooperation of the United Nations Environment Programme. (Fisheries Reports: No. 194). (Eng., Fr. & Span.). 52p. 1977. pap. 7.50 (ISBN 92-5-100447-1, F1313, FAO). Unipub.
Ridgeway, Sam H. & Harrison, Richard, eds. Handbook of Marine Mammals: Vol. 1, the Walrus, Sea Lions, Fur Seals & Sea Otter. LC 80-42010. 1981. 41.50 (ISBN 0-12-588501-6). Acad Pr.
--Handbook of Marine Mammals: Vol. 2, Seals. LC 80-42010. 1981. 48.50 (ISBN 0-12-588502-4). Acad Pr.
Ridgway, Sam H. & Harrison, Richard J., eds. Handbook of Marine Mammals, Vol. 3. Date not set. 64.50 (ISBN 0-12-588503-2). Acad Pr.
Scammon, Charles M. Marine Mammals & the American Whale Fishery. LC 68-56382. (Illus.). 1969. Repr. of 1874 ed. lib. bdg. 75.00x (ISBN 0-910950-02-4). Ransom Dist Co.
--Marine Mammals of the Northwestern Coast of North America. LC 68-54705. (Illus.). 1968. pap. 7.95 (ISBN 0-486-21976-3). Dover.
--The Marine Mammals of the Northwestern Coast of North America: Together with an Account of the American Whale-Fishery. (Illus.). 15.25 (ISBN 0-8446-0243-4). Peter Smith.
World Review of Interactions Between Marine Mammals & Fisheries. (Fisheries Technical Papers: No. 251). 190p. 1985. pap. 16.00 (ISBN 92-5-102145-7, F2709 5071, FAO). Unipub.

MARINE METEOROLOGY

see Meteorology, Maritime

MARINE MICROBIOLOGY

Droop, M. & Wood, F., eds. Advances in Microbiology of the Sea, Vol. 1. 1968. 50.00 (ISBN 0-12-027801-4). Acad Pr.
Droop, M. R. & Jannasch, H. W., eds. Advances in Aquatic Microbiology, Vol. 2. LC 76-5988. (Serial Publication Ser.). 1980. 60.00 (ISBN 0-12-003002-0). Acad Pr.
Haq, B. U. & Boersma, A. Introduction to Marine Micropaleontology. 376p. 1978. 32.75 (ISBN 0-444-00267-7). Elsevier.
Litchfield, C. D. Marine Microbiology. (Benchmark Papers in Microbiology: Vol. 11). 1976. 70.50 (ISBN 0-12-786975-1). Acad Pr.
Rheinheimer, G. Aquatic Microbiology. 2nd ed. LC 79-40645. 235p. 1980. 37.95 (ISBN 0-471-27643-X, Pub. by Wiley-Interscience). Wiley.
--Aquatic Microbiology. 3rd ed. 29.95 (ISBN 0-471-90657-3). Wiley.
Sieburth, John M. Sea Microbes. (Illus.). 1979. text ed. 70.00x (ISBN 0-19-502419-2). Oxford U Pr.
Skinner, F. A. & Shewan, M. J., eds. Aquatic Microbiology. (Society of Applied Bacteriology Symposia: No. 6). 1978. 62.00 (ISBN 0-12-648030-3). Acad Pr.

MARINE NUCLEAR REACTOR PLANTS

Crouch, Holmes F. Nuclear Ship Propulsion. LC 59-13449. (Illus.). 369p. 1960. 20.00x (ISBN 0-87033-071-3). Cornell Maritime.

Design Basis Flood for Nuclear Power Plants on River Sites: A Safety Guide. (Safety Ser.: No. 50-SG-S10A). 64p. 1983. pap. text ed. 13.75 (ISBN 92-0-123083-4, ISP602, IAEA). Unipub.

MARINE POLLUTION

see also Marine Resources Conservation; Oil Pollution of Rivers, Harbors, etc.

Aquatic Toxicology & Hazard Assessment (Fourth Conference)- STP 737. 466p. 1981. 43.00 (ISBN 0-8031-0799-4, 04-737000-16). ASTM.

Bates, J. H. U. K. Marine Pollution Law. 1984. 85.00 (ISBN 1-850-44028-X). Lloyds London Pr.

Bioassays & Toxicity Testing. 1979. pap. 16.25 (ISBN 0-685-96671-2, F1576, FAO). Unipub.

Bishop, Paul L. Marine Pollution & Its Control. (Water Resource Engineering Ser.). (Illus.). 384p. 1982. text ed. 45.00 (ISBN 0-07-005482-7). McGraw.

Center for Ocean Management Studies. Impact of Marine Pollution on Society. (Illus.). 320p. 1982. 29.95x (ISBN 0-686-86218-X). Bergin & Garvey.

Champ, Michael A. & Park, P. K. Global Marine Pollution Bibliography: Ocean Dumping of Municipal & Industrial Wastes. LC 82-28060. 424p. 1982. 75.00x (ISBN 0-306-65205-6, Consultants). Plenum Pub.

Charney, Jonathan I., ed. The New Nationalism & the Use of Common Spaces: Issues in Marine Pollution & the Exploitation of Antarctica. LC 81-65006. (Illus.). 358p. 1982. text ed. 39.50x (ISBN 0-86598-012-8). Allanheld.

A Comprehensive Plan for the Global Investigation in the Marine Environment & Baseline Study Guidelines. (Intergovernmental Oceanographic Commission Technical Ser.: No. 14). (Illus.). 42p. 1976. pap. 5.00 (ISBN 92-3-101430-7, U100, UNESCO). Unipub.

Coordinated Mediterranean Pollution Monitoring & Research Programme (MED POL) 64p. 1977. pap. 7.50 (ISBN 0-686-93203-X, F1263, FAO). Unipub.

Cormack, D. Response to Oil & Chemical Marine Pollution. (Illus.). 531p. 1983. 87.00 (ISBN 0-85334-182-6, Pub. by Elsevier Applied Sci England). Elsevier.

Cusine, Douglas J. & Grant, John P., eds. The Impact of Marine Pollution. LC 80-670. 324p. 1980. text ed. 32.50x (ISBN 0-916672-54-9). Allanheld.

Directory of Experts on Marine Pollution. (Fisheries Technical Papers: No. 99). 94p. 1973. pap. 7.50 (ISBN 0-686-93174-2, F1746, FAO). Unipub.

Directory of Mediterranean Marine Research Centres. 1979. pap. 40.00 (ISBN 0-686-59759-1, UNEP028, UNEP). Unipub.

Duedall, Iver. W., et al, eds. Biological Processes & Wastes in the Ocean. LC 84-29733. (Oceanic Processes in Marine Pollution Ser.: Vol. 1). 1985. lib. bdg. price not set (ISBN 0-89874-810-0). Krieger.

Duedall, Iver W., et al, eds. Physicochemical Processes & Wastes in the Ocean. LC 84-29746. (Oceanic Processes in Marine Pollution Ser.: Vol. 2). 1986. lib. bdg. price not set (ISBN 0-89874-811-9). Krieger.

--Scientific Considerations of Marine Waste Management. LC 84-29691. (Oceanic Processes in Marine Pollution Ser.: Vol. 3). 1985. lib. bdg. price not set (ISBN 0-89874-812-7). Krieger.

--Scientific Monitoring Strategies for Ocean Waste Disposal. LC 84-29701. (Oceanic Processes in Marine Pollution Ser.: Vol. 4). 1986. lib. bdg. price not set (ISBN 0-89874-813-5). Krieger.

Ellis, Derek V., ed. Marine Tailings Disposal. LC 82-73416. (Illus.). 368p. 1982. 59.95 (ISBN 0-250-40614-4). Butterworth.

Ferguson-Wood, E. & Johannes, R., eds. Tropical Marine Pollution. 192p. 1975. 64.00 (ISBN 0-444-41298-0). Elsevier.

Geyer, R. A., ed. Marine Environmental Pollution, Vol. 2: Dumping & Mining. (Oceanography Ser.: Vol. 27B). 574p. 1981. 110.75 (ISBN 0-444-41855-5). Elsevier.

Goldberg, Edward D. The Health of the Oceans. 172p. (Orig.). 1976. pap. 10.50 (ISBN 92-3-101356-4, U281, UNESCO). Unipub.

Hurford, N. Observations from a Helicopter of Insoluble Substances Discharged into a Ship's Wake, 1980. 1981. 40.00x (ISBN 0-686-97126-4, Pub. by W Spring England). State Mutual Bk.

--Residue Assessment Trials on Coastal Chemical Tankers, 1980. 1981. 30.00x (ISBN 0-686-97154-X, Pub. by W Spring England). State Mutual Bk.

International Experts Discussion on Lead Occurrence, Fate & Pollution in the Marine Environment, Rovinj, Yugoslavia, 18-22 October 1977. Lead in the Marine Environment: Proceedings. Konrad, Z. & Branica, M., eds. LC 80-40023. (Illus.). 364p. 1980. pap. 81.00 (ISBN 0-08-022960-3). Pergamon.

Johnston, R., ed. Marine Pollution. 1977. 95.00 (ISBN 0-12-387650-8). Acad Pr.

McNulty, J. Kneeland. Effects of Abatement of Domestic Sewage Pollution on the Benthos, Volumes of Zooplankton, & the Fouling Organisms of Biscayne Bay, Florida. LC 69-19867. (Studies in Tropical Oceanography Ser: No. 9). 1970. 6.95x (ISBN 0-87024-113-3). U Miami Marine.

Massin, Jean-Marie, ed. Remote Sensing for the Control of Marine Pollution. LC 84-9843. (NATO-Challenges of Modern Society Ser.: Vol. 6). 478p. 1984. 72.50 (ISBN 0-306-41734-0, Plenum Pr). Plenum Pub.

Moore, P. G. Marine Pollution. 66p. 1978. 39.00x (ISBN 0-686-97029-2, Pub. by Meadowfield England). State Mutual Bk.

Nash, A. E., et al. Oil Pollution & the Public Interest: A Study of the Santa Barbara Oil Spill. LC 72-5116. (Illus.). 157p. (Orig.). 1972. pap. 3.75x (ISBN 0-87772-085-1). Inst Gov Stud Berk.

Ocean Affairs Board. Assessing Potential Ocean Pollutants. 438p. 1975. pap. 10.75 (ISBN 0-309-02325-4). Natl Acad Pr.

Palmer, H. D. & Gross, M. G., eds. Ocean Dumping & Marine Pollution: Geological Aspects of Waste Disposal at Sea. 268p. 1979. 39.50 (ISBN 0-87933-343-X). Van Nos Reinhold.

Park, Kilho P., et al, eds. Wastes in the Ocean: Radioactive Wastes & the Ocean, Vol. 3. (Environmental Science & Technology Texts & Monographs: No. 1-121). 522p. 1983. 85.00 (ISBN 0-471-09770-5, Pub. by Wiley Interscience). Wiley.

Pearson, et al, eds. Aquatic Toxicology & Hazard Assessment (Fifth Conference)- STP 766. 414p. 1982. 44.50 (ISBN 0-8031-0796-X, 04-766000-16). ASTM.

Reduction of Pollution from Shipping. 1981. 80.00x (ISBN 0-686-97118-3, Pub. by Marine Mgmt England). State Mutual Bk.

Reed, Alexander W. Ocean Waste Disposal Practices. LC 75-15205. (Pollution Technology Review No. 23; Ocean Technology Review No. 4). (Illus.). 336p. 1976. 24.00 (ISBN 0-8155-0591-4). Noyes.

Report of the IMCO-FAO-UNESCO-WMO-WHO-IAEA-UN Joint Group of Experts on the Scientific Aspects of Marine Pollution. (GESAMP Reports & Studies: No. 4). 36p. 1976. pap. 7.50 (ISBN 92-5-100064-6, F1109, FAO). Unipub.

Royal Society. Assessment of Sublethal Effects of Pollutants in the Sea. Cole, H. A., ed. (Illus.). 1979. text ed. 55.00x (ISBN 0-85403-112-X, Pub. by Royal Soc. London). Scholium Intl.

Skinner, Brian J. & Turekian, Karl K. Man & the Ocean. (Foundations of Earth Science Ser.). (Illus.). 160p. 1973. pap. 13.95 (ISBN 0-13-550970-X). P-H.

Soule, Dorothy & Walsh, Don, eds. Waste Disposal in the Oceans: Minimizing Impact, Maximizing Benefits. 175p. 1983. 27.50x (ISBN 0-86531-966-9). Westview.

Timagenis. International Control of Marine Pollution, Vols. 1-2. LC 80-124574. 64p. 1979. 37.50 ea. Vol. 1 (ISBN 0-379-20685-4). Vol. 2 (ISBN 0-379-20686-2). Set. 75.00. Oceana.

Titow, W. V., ed. PVC Technology. 4th ed. 1264p. 1984. 165.00 (ISBN 0-85334-249-0, Pub. by Elsevier Applied Sci England). Elsevier.

Vernberg, John, et al, eds. Biological Monitoring of Marine Pollutants. 1981. 45.00 (ISBN 0-12-718450-3). Acad Pr.

Vernberg, Winona B., et al, eds. Physiological Mechanisms of Marine Pollutant Toxicity. 1982. 45.00 (ISBN 0-12-718460-0). Acad Pr.

MARINE RESOURCES

see also Amber; Continental Shelf; Fisheries; Fishery Products; Ocean Engineering; Salt; Sea-Water

ACMRR Working Party on FAO Regional Fisheries Councils & Commissions. Report of the Fifth Session of the Advisory Committee on Marine Resources Research: Rome, 1968. (Fisheries Reports: No. 56, Suppl. 2). 29p. 1968. pap. 7.50 (ISBN 0-686-92754-0, F1671, FAO). Unipub.

Al-Abdul-Razzak, Fatimah H. Marine Resources of Kuwait: Their Role in the Development of Non-Oil Resources. (Illus.). 300p. 1985. 55.00x (ISBN 0-7103-0069-7, Kegan Paul). Routledge & Kegan.

Aleem, A. A. Marine Resources of the United Arab Republic. (General Fisheries Council of the Mediterranean (GFCM): Studies & Reviews: No. 43). 22p. 1969. pap. 7.50 (ISBN 92-5-101962-2, F1803, FAO). Unipub.

Andrassy, Juraj. International Law & the Resources of the Sea. LC 76-130960. (International Legal Studies). (Illus.). 191p. 1970. 26.00x (ISBN 0-231-03409-1). Columbia U Pr.

Atlas of the Living Resources of the Seas. New ed. (Fisheries Ser.: No. 15). (Illus.). 23p. 1981. pap. 120.00 (ISBN 92-5-001000-1, F2267, FAO). Unipub.

Barton, Robert. Atlas of the Sea. LC 73-18541. (John Day Bk.). (Illus.). 128p. 1974. 10.95i (ISBN 0-381-98267-X). T Y Crowell.

Bibliography of Living Marine Resources. (Regional Fishery Survey & Development Project). 47p. 1977. pap. 7.50 (ISBN 92-5-100200-2, F727, FAO). Unipub.

Borgese, Elisabeth M. The Mines of Neptune: Minerals & Metals from the Sea. (Illus.). 1985. 35.00 (ISBN 0-8109-1322-4). Abrams.

Brin, Andre. Energy & the Oceans. 164p. 1981. 40.00x (ISBN 0-86103-024-9, Pub. by Westbury House). State Mutual Bk.

Brooks, Douglas L. America Looks to the Sea: Ocean Use & the National Interest. 266p. 1984. write for info. (ISBN 0-86720-250-5). Jones & Bartlett.

Brown, Gardner M., Jr. & Crutchfield, James, eds. Economics of Ocean Resources: A Research Agenda. LC 82-17471. 242p. (Orig.). 1983. pap. 12.00 (ISBN 0-295-95982-7, Pub. by Wash Sea Grant). U of Wash Pr.

Bunich, P. C. & Kharchev, K. Ocean & Its Resources. 149p. 1977. pap. 4.95 (ISBN 0-8285-1513-1, Pub. by Mir Pubs USSR). Imported Pubns.

Charlier, Roger H. Non-Living Ocean Resources. 1979. pap. 5.00 (ISBN 0-686-27713-9). Maple Mont.

Chong, Kee Chai & Smith, Ian R. Economics of the Philippine Milkfish Resource System. 66p. 1982. pap. 11.75 (ISBN 92-808-0346-8, TUNU182, UNU). Unipub.

Cronan, David S. Underwater Minerals. (Ocean Science Resources & Technology Ser.). 1980. 65.00 (ISBN 0-12-197480-4). Acad Pr.

Cuyvers, Luc. Ocean Uses & Their Regulation. LC 84-3587. 179p. 1984. 29.95x (ISBN 0-471-88676-9, Pub. by Wiley-Interscience); pap. text ed. 19.95x (ISBN 0-471-88675-0). Wiley.

Finn, Daniel P. Managing the Ocean Resources of the United States: The Role of the Federal Marine Sanctuary Program. (Lecture Notes in Coastal & Estuarine Studies: Vol. 2). (Illus.). 193p. 1982. pap. 18.00 (ISBN 0-387-11583-8). Springer-Verlag.

Fishing News Books Ltd., ed. Study of the Sea: The Development of Marine Research Under the Auspices of the International Council for the Exploration of the Sea. 272p. 1981. 90.00x (ISBN 0-85238-112-3, Pub. by Fishing News England). State Mutual Bk.

Friedheim, Robert L. Understanding the Debate on Ocean Resources. (Monograph Series in World Affairs: Vol. 6, 1968-69 Ser., Bk. 3). (Orig.). 1969. 4.95 (ISBN 0-87940-020-X). Monograph Series.

Gordon, Bernard L., ed. Energy from the Sea: Marine Resource Readings. new ed. (Illus.). 1977. pap. 12.50 (ISBN 0-910258-07-4). Book & Tackle.

Harvesting Ocean Energy. (Insights Ser.: No. 6). (Illus.). 192p. 1981. pap. 17.00 (ISBN 92-3-101873-6, U1144, UNESCO). Unipub.

Idyll, C. P. The Sea Against Hunger. new, rev. ed. LC 77-2655. (Apollo Eds.). (Illus.). 1978. pap. 6.95i (ISBN 0-8152-0422-1, A-422). T Y Crowell.

International Biological Programme Section PM (Productivity Marine) Bibliography on Methods of Studying the Marine Beaches. (Fisheries Technical Papers: No. 98). 102p. 1970. pap. 7.50 (ISBN 0-686-93103-3, F1745, FAO). Unipub.

Jones, Erin B. Law of the Sea: Oceanic Resources. LC 72-96510. xiv, 176p. 1972. 10.95 (ISBN 0-87074-134-9). SMU Press.

Lee, William W. L. Decisions in Marine Mining: The Role of Preferences & Tradeoffs. LC 79-648. 240p. 1979. prof ref 29.95x (ISBN 0-88410-369-2). Ballinger Pub.

Ling, Shao-Wen. Aquaculture in Southeast Asia: A Historical Overview. Mumaw, Laura, ed. LC 77-3828. (Washington Sea Hgrant Ser.). (Illus.). 108p. 1977. (Pub. by Washington Sea Grant); pap. 10.00x (ISBN 0-295-95563-5). U of Wash Pr.

Living Deep Water Resources of the Western Mediterranean & Their Exploitation. (General Fisheries Council of the Mediterranean (GFCM): Studies & Reviews: No. 44). 38p. 1970. pap. 7.50 (ISBN 92-5-101963-0, F1804, FAO). Unipub.

Mangone, Gerard J. The Future of Gas & Oil from the Sea. 240p. 1983. 35.00 (ISBN 0-442-26164-0). Van Nos Reinhold.

--Marine Policy for America. 382p. 1977. text ed. 9.50x. Lexington Bks.

Martin, Roy E., et al. Chemistry & Biochemistry of Marine Food Products. (Illus.). 1982. lib. bdg. 49.50 (ISBN 0-87055-408-5). AVI.

Marx, Wesley. The Oceans: Our Last Resource. LC 81-5332. (Illus.). 320p. 1981. 13.95 (ISBN 0-87156-291-X). Sierra.

Miles, Edward & Gibbs, Stephen. The Management of Marine Regions: The North Pacific. (Illus.). 700p. 1982. 50.00x (ISBN 0-520-04458-4). U of Cal Pr.

Neumeyer, Ken. Sailing the Farm: Independence on Thirty Feet-A Survival Guide to Homesteading the Ocean. LC 81-51896. 256p. (Orig.). 1981. 14.95 (ISBN 0-89815-085-X); pap. 7.95 (ISBN 0-89815-051-5). Ten Speed Pr.

Nixon, P. H. People & the Sea, 3 Vols. 1977. 2.00 ea. (ISBN 0-686-36988-2). URI MAS.

Ocean Energy Resources: Presented at the Energy Technology Conference, Houston, Texas, Sept. 18-23, 1977. LC 77-82206. (American Society of Mechanical Engineers. Ocean Engineering Division Ser.: Vol. 4). (Illus.). pap. 27.50 (ISBN 0-317-09776-8, 2016806). Bks Demand UMI.

Rapport de la Septieme session du Comite Concultatif de la Recherche sur les Ressources de la Mer: Fisheries Report Ser. (Fr.). pap. 8.25 (F1281, FAO). Unipub.

Reintjes, John W., ed. Improving Multiple Use of Coastal & Marine Resources. 96p. 1983. pap. 10.00 (ISBN 0-913235-01-6); 8.00. AM Fisheries Soc.

Report of Committee of Experts on Marine Resources Research: Selected Working Papers, 9th Session, Rome, 1978. (Fisheries Reports: No. 206, Suppl. 1). 36p. 1978. pap. 7.50 (ISBN 0-686-93092-4, F1515, FAO). Unipub.

Report of the Ninth Session of the Advisory Committee of Experts on Marine Resources Research: Supplement No. 1, Selected Working Papers, Rome, June 5-9, 1978. 2nd ed. (Fisheries Reports: No. 206). 61p. 1979. pap. 7.50 (ISBN 92-5-100646-6, F1523, FAO). Unipub.

Report of the Second Joint Meeting of the Working Party on Assessment of Fish Resources & the Working Party on Stock Assessment of Shrimp & Lobster Resources (WECAF) Mexico City, Mexico, 26-29 Nov. 1979. (Fisheries Reports: No. 235). (Eng. & Span.). 49p. 1981. pap. 7.50 (ISBN 92-5-101049-8, F2143, FAO). Unipub.

Report of the Third Session of the Committee on Resource Management of the General Fisheries Council for the Mediterranean: Rome, 17-19 June 1980. (Fisheries Reports: No. 240). (Eng. & Fr.). 20p. 1980. pap. 7.50 (ISBN 92-5-100966-X, F2087, FAO). Unipub.

Scheuer, Paul J., ed. Marine Natural Products: Chemical & Biological Perspectives, Vol. 2. (Marine Natural Products: Chemical & Biological Perspectives Ser.). 1978. 65.00 (ISBN 0-12-624002-7). Acad Pr.

--Marine Natural Products: Chemical & Biological Perspectives, Vol. 3. LC 77-10960. 1980. 44.00 (ISBN 0-12-624003-5). Acad Pr.

--Marine Natural Products: Chemical & Biological Perspectives, Vol. 5. 1983. 69.50 (ISBN 0-12-624005-1). Acad Pr.

The Sea: A Select Bibliography on the Legal, Political, Economic & Technological Aspects, 1978-1979. 46p. 1980. pap. 5.00 (ISBN 0-686-68970-4, UN8016, UN). Unipub.

The Sea: A Select Bibliography on the Legal, Political, Economic & Technological Aspects, 1975-1978. (Eng. & Fr.). pap. 5.00 (ISBN 0-686-94863-7, UN78/1/3, UN). Unipub.

The Sea: A Select Bibliography on the Legal, Political, Economic & Technological Aspects, 1975-1976. (Eng. & Fr.). pap. 3.00 (ISBN 0-686-94864-5, UN76/1/6, UN). Unipub.

Skinner, Brian J. & Turekian, Karl K. Man & the Ocean. (Foundations of Earth Science Ser.). (Illus.). 160p. 1973. pap. 13.95 (ISBN 0-13-550970-X). P-H.

Stevenson, David K. A Review of the Marine Resources of the Western Central Atlantic Fisheries Commission (WECAFC) Region. (Fisheries Technical Papers: No. 211). (Eng. & Span.). 142p. 1981. pap. 10.50 (ISBN 92-5-101153-2, F2286, FAO). Unipub.

Symposium on Investigations & Resources of the Caribbean Sea & Adjacent Regions: Preparatory to the Co-operative Investigations of the Caribbean & Adjacent Regions (CICAR) Organized Jointly by UNESCO & FAO, Willemstad, Curacao, Netherlands Antilles, 18-26 Nov. 1968. (Eng. & Span.). 545p. 1971. 26.25 (U649, UNESCO). Unipub.

Thorson, Gunner. Life in the Sea. LC 73-118405. (World University Library). (Illus., Orig.). 1971. pap. 3.95 (ISBN 0-07-064543-4). McGraw.

Troadec, J. P. & Garcia, S. The Fish Resources of the Eastern Central Atlantic: The Resources of the Gulf of Guinea from Angola to Mauritania, Pt. 1. (Fisheries Technical Papers: No. 186). (Eng. & Fr.). 171p. 1980. pap. 12.50 (ISBN 92-5-100851-5, F2028, FAO). Unipub.

Walsh, Don & Cappellari, Marjorie, eds. Energy & Sea Power - Challenge for the Decade. (Illus.). 206p. 1981. 28.00 (ISBN 0-08-028035-8). Pergamon.

World List of Aquatic Sciences & Fisheries Serial Titles. (Fisheries Technical Papers: No. 147, Suppl. 4). 128p. 1980. pap. 9.50 (ISBN 92-5-100904-X, F1946, FAO). Unipub.

World List of Aquatic Sciences & Fisheries Serial Titles. (Fisheries Technical Papers: No. 148, Suppl. 4). 128p. 1980. pap. 8.00 (ISBN 92-5-000882-1, F1947, FAO). Unipub.

MARINE RESOURCES AND STATE

Eckert, Ross D. The Enclosure of Ocean Resources: Economics & the Law of the Sea. LC 78-70388. (Publications Ser.: No. 210). (Illus.). 1979. 16.95x (ISBN 0-8179-7101-7). Hoover Inst Pr.

Friedheim, Robert L., et al. Japan & the New Ocean Regime. 350p. 1983. softcover 32.00x (ISBN 0-86531-687-2). Westview.

MARINE RESOURCES CONSERVATION

Craven, John P. The Management of Pacific Marine Resources: Present Problems & Future Trends. (Illus.). 96p. 1982. lib. bdg. 14.00x (ISBN 0-86531-424-1). Westview.

Lewis, Tracy R. Stochastic Modeling of Ocean Fisheries Resource Management. LC 81-51282. (Illus.). 118p. 1983. 30.00x (ISBN 0-295-95838-3). U of Wash Pr.

Padelford, Norman J. Public Policy for the Use of the Seas. rev. ed. 1970. pap. 13.00x (ISBN 0-262-66001-6). MIT Pr.

Shusterich, Kurt M. Resource Management & the Oceans: The Political Economy of Deep Seabed Mining. (A Westview Replicia Edition Ser.). (Illus.). 280p. 1982. softcover 26.00x (ISBN 0-86531-901-4). Westview.

Tomasevich, J. International Agreements on Conservation of Marine Resources, with Special Reference to the North Pacific. Repr. of 1943 ed. 17.00 (ISBN 0-527-90450-3). Kraus Repr.

Walsh, Don, ed. The Law of the Sea: Issues in Ocean Resource Management. LC 77-7823. (Praeger Special Studies). 284p. 1977. 43.95 (ISBN 0-03-022666-X). Praeger.

MARINE SEDIMENTS

Cline, R. M. & Hays, J. D., eds. Investigation of Late Quaternary Paleoceanography & Paleoclimatology. LC 75-40899. (Memoir: No. 145). (Illus.). 1976. 30.00 (ISBN 0-8137-1145-2). Geol Soc.

Ginsburg, R. N., et al. South Florida Carbonate Sediments. (Sedimenta II). (Illus.). 71p. (Orig.). 1972. pap. 6.00 (ISBN 0-932981-02-X). Univ Miami CSL.

Gray, J. S. The Ecology of Marine Sediments. (Cambridge Studies in Modern Biology: No. 2). (Illus.). 170p. 1981. 39.50 (ISBN 0-521-23553-7); pap. 18.95 (ISBN 0-521-28027-3). Cambridge U Pr.

Grimes, Judith A. & Rushforth, S. R. Diatoms of Recent Bottom Sediments of Utah Lake, Utah, USA. (Bibliotheca Phycologica Ser.: No. 55). (Illus.). 180p. 1982. text ed. 21.00x (ISBN 3-7682-1310-2). Lubrecht & Cramer.

Hakanson, L. & Jansson, M. Principles of Lake Sedimentology. (Illus.). 320p. 1983. 41.00 (ISBN 0-387-12645-7). Springer-Verlag.

Hampton, Lloyd. Physics of Sound in Marine Sediments. LC 74-8022. (Marine Science Ser.: Vol. 1). 569p. 1974. 79.50x (ISBN 0-306-35501-9, Plenum Pr). Plenum Pub.

Hardie, Lawrence A. Sedimentation of the Modern Carbonate Tidal Flats of Northwest Andros Island, Bahamas. LC 76-47389. (Johns Hopkins University Studies in Geology: No. 22). (Illus.). 232p. 1977. 28.00x (ISBN 0-8018-1895-8). Johns Hopkins.

Harris, P. M. Facies Anatomy & Diagenesis of a Bahamian Ooid Shoal. (Sedimenta VII). (Illus.). 163p. 1979. 7.00 (ISBN 0-932981-06-2). Univ Miami CSL.

Heezen, B. C. Influence of Abyssal Circulation on Sedimentary Accumulations in Space & Time. (Developments in Sedimentology Ser.: Vol. 23). 216p. 1977. 53.25 (ISBN 0-444-41569-6). Elsevier.

Inderbitzen, Anton L., ed. Deep-Sea Sediments: Physical & Mechanical Properties. LC 74-7140. (Marine Science Ser.: Vol. 2). 497p. 1974. 75.00x (ISBN 0-306-35502-7, Plenum Pr). Plenum Pub.

Influence of Denitrification in Aquatic Sediments on the Nitrogen Content of Natural Waters. (Agricultural Research Reports: 858). 1976. pap. 10.00 (ISBN 90-220-0620-4, PDC110, PUDOC). Unipub.

Kaplan, Isaac R., ed. Natural Gases in Marine Sediments. LC 74-11492. (Marine Science Ser.: Vol. 3). 324p. 1974. 49.50x (ISBN 0-306-35503-5, Plenum Pr). Plenum Pub.

Klein, G. deVries, ed. Holocene Tidal Sedimentation. (Benchmark Papers in Geology Ser.: Vol. 30). 432p. 1976. 70.50 (ISBN 0-12-786859-3). Acad Pr.

Komar, Paul D. Beach Processes & Sedimentation. (Illus.). 464p. 1976. 43.95 (ISBN 0-13-072595-1). P-H.

Molnia, Bruce F., ed. Glacial-Marine Sedimentation. 854p. 1984. 65.00x (ISBN 0-306-41497-X, Plenum Pr). Plenum Pub.

Palmer, H. D. & Gross, M. G., eds. Ocean Dumping & Marine Pollution: Geological Aspects of Waste Disposal at Sea. 268p. 1979. 39.50 (ISBN 0-87933-343-X). Van Nos Reinhold.

Perkins, Bob F. Deltaic Sedimentation on the Louisiana Coast. 1982. 10.00. SEPM.

Riedel, W. R. & Saito, T., eds. Marine Plankton & Sediments: Kiel Symposium. (Micropaleontology Special Publications Ser.: No. 3). 235p. 1980. 20.00 (ISBN 0-686-84254-5). Am Mus Natl Hist.

Rose, P. R. & Lidz, B. Diagnostic Foraminiferal Assemblages of Shallow-Water Modern Environments: South Florida & the Bahamas, No. VI. (Sedimenta Ser.). 55p. 1977. 6.00 (ISBN 0-932981-05-4). Univ Miami CSL.

Schopf, Thomas J. Paleoceanography. LC 79-12546. (Illus.). 1980. 25.00x (ISBN 0-674-65215-0). Harvard U Pr.

Schwarz, H. Subaqueous Slope Failures: Experiments & Modern Occurences. (Contributions to Sedimentology: No. 11). (Illus.). 116p. 1982. pap. text ed. 29.60x (ISBN 3-510-57011-1). Lubrecht & Cramer.

Silvester, R. Coastal Engineering, Vol. 2: Sedimentation, Estuaries, Tides, Effluents, Modelling. LC 72-97435. (Developments in Geotechnical Engineering Ser.: Vol. 4B). 338p. 1974. 68.00 (ISBN 0-444-41102-X). Elsevier.

Turney, W. Jack & Perkins, Bob F. Molluscan Distribution in Florida Bay. (Sedimenta III). (Illus.). 37p. 1972. pap. 4.00 (ISBN 0-932981-03-8). Univ Miami CSL.

Weaver, C. E. & Beck, K. C. Miocene of the South East United States: A Model for Chemical Sedimentation in a Peri-Marine Environment. (Developments in Sedimentology Ser.: Vol. 22). 234p. 1977. 57.50 (ISBN 0-444-41568-8). Elsevier.

MARINE SERVICE

see also Lighthouses; Navigation; Shipping; Signals and Signaling

Heitzman, William R. Opportunities in Marine & Maritime Careers. (VGM Career Bks.). (Illus.). 160p. 1983. 7.95 (ISBN 0-8442-6634-5, 6634-5, Passport Bks.); pap. 5.95 (ISBN 0-8442-6635-3, 6635-3). Natl Textbk.

Putz, George & Spectre, Peter H., eds. The Mariner's Catalog, Vol. 3. LC 73-88647. (Illus.). 192p. 1975. pap. 2.00 (ISBN 0-87742-058-0). Intl Marine.

Sell's Publications Ltd. Staff, ed. Sell's Marine Market. 656p. 1984. 120.00x (ISBN 0-85499-988-4, Pub. by Sells Pubns England). State Mutual Bk.

Voskuil, C. A. & Wade, J. A., eds. Hague-Zagreb Essays-Three. 329p. 1980. 32.50 (ISBN 90-286-0749-8). Sijthoff & Noordhoff.

MARINE SOIL MECHANICS

see Marine Geotechnique

MARINE STRUCTURES

see Offshore Structures

MARINE SURVEYING

see Hydrographic Surveying

MARINE TECHNOLOGY

see Marine Engineering

MARINE ZOOLOGY

see Marine Fauna

MARINER'S COMPASS

see Compass

MARITIME METEOROLOGY

see Meteorology, Maritime

MARITIME SURVEYING

see Hydrographic Surveying

MARKET GARDENING

see Truck Farming

MARKETING–DATA PROCESSING

Allen, Peter, ed. Artificial Intelligence: A Market Assessment. 200p. 1984. pap. 1250.00 (ISBN 0-931634-44-X). FIND-SVP.

Amstutz, Arnold E. Computer Simulation of Competitive Market Response. (Illus.). 1967. pap. 12.50x (ISBN 0-262-51009-X). MIT Pr.

Breyer, Ralph F. Quantitative Systemic Analysis & Control. Assael, Henry, ed. LC 78-250. (Century of Marketing Ser.). 1978. Repr. of 1949 ed. lib. bdg. 30.00x (ISBN 0-405-11164-9). Ayer Co Pubs.

Chase, Cochran, et al. Solving Marketing Problems with VisiCalc on Apple II, IIe Computers. 300p. (Orig.). 1984. pap. 29.95 incl. disc (ISBN 0-8019-7422-4). Chilton.

--Solving Marketing Problems with VisiCalc on the IBM PC. 300p. (Orig.). 1984. pap. 29.95 incl. disc (ISBN 0-8019-7542-5). Chilton.

Earle, Ted C. Financial Markets Data Base, 2 vols. 1129p. 1983. Set. 2400.00 (ISBN 0-9611670-0-9). Market Timing.

Eskin, Gerald & Montgomery, David. Computer Models in Marketing: Data Analysis. 128p. 1977. pap. 15.00 (ISBN 0-89426-002-2). Scientific Pr.

Fisher, Peg. Sucessful Telemarketing Manual. 300p. 1985. 91.50 (ISBN 0-85013-152-9). Dartnell Corp.

Hugo, I. S. Marketing & the Computer. 1967. pap. 13.25 (ISBN 0-08-012605-7). Pergamon.

Hunt, Daniel V. Industrial Robotics Handbook. (Illus.). 432p. 1983. 34.00 (ISBN 0-8311-1148-8). Indus Pr.

Kelleher, Robert F. Industrial Marketing & Sales Management in the Computer Age. 180p. 1982. 21.95 (ISBN 0-8436-0867-6). Van Nos Reinhold.

Laric, Michael V. & Stiff, M. Ronald. Lotus 1-2-3 for Marketing & Sales. 256p. 1984. pap. 24.95; incl. disk 39.95 (ISBN 0-13-540956-X). P-H.

--Multiplan for Marketing & Sales. 256p. 1984. pap. 14.95 (ISBN 0-13-605080-8); incl. disk 29.95 (ISBN 0-13-605098-0). P-H.

--VisiCalc for Marketing & Sales. 275p. 1984. pap. 12.95 (ISBN 0-13-938465-0); 39.95 (ISBN 0-13-938531-2). P-H.

Laric, Michael V. & Stiff, Ronald. Marketing & Business Planning with the IBM PCs: A Guide to the Productive Use of Personal Computers for Business & Marketing Professionals. (Illus.). 224p. 1985. pap. 16.95 (ISBN 0-13-557067-0). P H.

Mayros, Van & Werner, D. Michael. Marketing Information Systems: Design & Applications for Marketers. LC 81-69051. 320p. 35.00 (ISBN 0-8019-7133-0). Chilton.

Strauss, Lawrence. Electronic Marketing: Emerging TV & Computer Channels for Interactive Home Shopping. LC 83-185. (Communications Library). (Illus.). 154p. 1983. Professional 34.95 (ISBN 0-86729-023-4, 408-BW). Knowledge Indus.

Svigals, Terome. Planning for Future Market Events Using Data Processing Support: A Five Step Growth Plan. LC 82-48765. 1983. 27.95x (ISBN 0-02-949740-X). Macmillan.

Wight, Oliver W. Production & Inventory Management in the Computer Age. LC 74-7127. 300p. 1974. 22.50 (ISBN 0-442-29367-4). Van Nos Reinhold.

MARKOFF PROCESSES

see Markov Processes

MARKOV CHAINS

see Markov Processes

MARKOV PROCESSES

Bartos, Otomar J. Simple Models of Group Behavior. LC 67-21498. (Illus.). 345p. 1967. 36.00x (ISBN 0-231-02894-6); pap. 18.00x (ISBN 0-231-02893-8). Columbia U Pr.

Billingsley, Patrick. Statistical Inference for Markov Processes. LC 61-8646. (Midway Reprint Ser.). 84p. 1975. pap. text ed. 5.50x (ISBN 0-226-05077-7). U. of Chicago Pr.

Blumenthal, Robert M. Markov Processes & Potential Theory. LC 68-18659. (Pure & Applied Mathematics Ser.: Vol. 29). 1968. 68.50 (ISBN 0-12-107850-7). Acad Pr.

Chung, K. L. Lectures from Markov Processes to Brownian Motion. (Grundlehren der Mathematischen Wissenschaften). (Illus.). 256p. 1982. 39.50 (ISBN 0-387-90618-5). Springer-Verlag.

--Lectures on Boundary Theory for Markov Chains. (Annals of Mathematics Studies: No. 65). 1970. 15.50 (ISBN 0-691-08075-5). Princeton U Pr.

Chung Kai Lai. Markov Chains with Stationary Transition Probabilities. 2nd ed. (Die Grundlehren der Mathematischen Wissenschaten: Vol. 104). 1967. 44.00 (ISBN 0-387-03822-1). Springer-Verlag.

CISM (International Center for Mechanical Sciences), Dept. of Automation & Information, University of Trieste, 1971. Coding for Markov Sources. Longo, G., ed. (CISM Pubns. Ser.: No. 110). (Illus.). 99p. 1973. pap. 13.90 (ISBN 0-387-81154-0). Springer-Verlag.

Derman, Cyrus. Finite State Markovian Decision Processes. (Mathematics in Science & Engineering Ser.: Vol. 67). 1970. 49.50 (ISBN 0-12-209250-3). Acad Pr.

Dobryshin, R. L., et al, eds. Locally Interacting Systems & Their Application in Biology: Proceedings of the School - Seminar on Markov Interaction Processes in Biology, Held in Pushchino, Moscow Region, March, 1976. (Lecture Notes in Mathematics Ser.: Vol. 653). 1978. pap. 16.00 (ISBN 0-387-08450-9). Springer-Verlag.

Dynkin, E. B. Markov Processes & Related Problems of Analysis. LC 81-38438. (London Mathematical Society Lecture Note Ser.: No. 54). 300p. 1982. pap. 29.95 (ISBN 0-521-28512-7). Cambridge U Pr.

Dynkin, E. B. & Yushkevich, A. A. Markov Processes: Theorems & Problems. LC 69-12529. 237p. 1969. 27.50x (ISBN 0-306-30378-7, Plenum Pr). Plenum Pub.

Ethier, S. N. & Kurtz, T. G. Markov Processes: Characterization & Convergence. (Probability & Mathematical Statistics Ser.). 1985. 49.95 (ISBN 0-471-08186-8). Wiley.

Fleming, W. H. & Rishel, R. W. Deterministic & Stochastic Optimal Control. LC 75-28391. (Applications of Mathematics Ser.: Vol. 1). (Illus.). xi, 222p. 1975. 44.00 (ISBN 0-387-90155-8). Springer-Verlag.

Freedman, B. Markov Chains. (Illus.). 382p. 1983. Repr. of 1971 ed. 30.00 (ISBN 0-387-90808-0). Springer-Verlag.

Freedman, D. Approximating Countable Markov Chains. (Illus.). 140p. 1983. Repr. of 1972 ed. 24.00 (ISBN 0-387-90804-8). Springer-Verlag.

Freedman, David A. Approximating Countable Markov Chains. LC 76-142943. 140p. 1972. 38.00x (ISBN 0-8162-3034-X). Holden-Day.

Fukushima, M. Dirichlet Forms & Markov Processes. (North-Holland Mathematical Library: Vol. 23). 196p. 1980. 51.00 (ISBN 0-444-85421-5, North Holland). Elsevier.

--Functional Analysis in Markov Processes, Katata & Kyoto, Japan 1981 Proceedings. (Lecture Notes in Mathematics: Vol. 923). 307p. 1982. pap. 20.00 (ISBN 0-387-11484-X). Springer-Verlag.

Getoor, R. K. Markov Processes: Ray Processes & Right Processes, Vol. 440. (Lecture Notes in Mathematics Ser). v, 118p. 1975. pap. 13.00 (ISBN 0-387-07140-7). Springer-Verlag.

Hartley, R. Recent Developments in Markow Decision Process. (IMA Conference Ser.). 1981. 48.50 (ISBN 0-12-328460-0). Acad Pr.

Iosifescu, Marius. Finite Markov Processes & Applications. LC 79-42726. 295p. 1980. 48.95x (ISBN 0-471-27677-4). Wiley.

Isaacson, Dean L. & Madsen, Richard W. Markov Chains: Theory & Applications. LC 75-30646. (Probability & Mathematical Statistics Ser.). 1976. 43.50x (ISBN 0-471-42862-0, Pub. by Wiley-Interscience). Wiley.

--Markov Chains: Theory & Applications. LC 84-27792. 270p. 1985. Repr. of 1976 ed. lib. bdg. write for info. (ISBN 0-89874-834-8). Krieger.

Keilson, J. Markov Chain Models - Rarity & Exponentiality. (Applied Mathematical Sciences Ser.: Vol. 28). 1979. pap. 17.50 (ISBN 0-387-90405-0). Springer-Verlag.

Kindermann, Ross & Snell, J. Laurie. Markov Random Fields & Their Applications. LC 80-22764. (Contemporary Mathematics Ser.: Vol. 1). 142p. 1983. pap. 12.00 (ISBN 0-8218-5001-6, CONM 1). Am Math.

Kingman, John. Regenerative Phenomena. LC 70-39143. (Wiley Series in Probability & Mathematical Statistics). pap. 50.50 (ISBN 0-317-26124-X, 2024279). Bks Demand UMI.

Krein, M. G. & Nudel'Man, A. A. The Markov Moment Problem & Extremal Problems. LC 77-11716. (Translations of Mathematical Monographs: Vol. 50). 1977. 79.00 (ISBN 0-8218-4500-4, MMONO50). Am Math.

Kushner, Harold J. Stochastic Stability & Control. (Mathematics in Science & Engineering Ser.: Vol. 33). 1967. 39.50 (ISBN 0-12-430150-9). Acad Pr.

Lamperti, J. Stochastic Processes: A Survey of the Mathematical Theory. LC 77-24321. (Applied Mathematical Sciences Ser.: Vol. 23). 1977. pap. 26.50 (ISBN 0-387-90275-9). Springer-Verlag.

Lee, T. C., et al. Estimating Parameters of the Markov Probability Models. 2nd ed. (Contributions to Economic Analysis Ser.: Vol. 65). 260p. 1977. 46.75 (ISBN 0-7204-3163-8, North Holland). Elsevier.

Lowry, George G., ed. Markov Chains & Monto Carlo Calculations in Polymer Science. LC 70-84777. (Monographs in Macromolecular Chemistry). pap. 84.50 (ISBN 0-317-08367-8, 2055048). Bks Demand UMI.

Mandl, P. Analytical Treatment of One-Dimensional Markov Processes. LC 68-59694. (Die Grundlehren der Mathematischen Wissenschaften: Vol. 151). 1968. 31.00 (ISBN 0-387-04142-7). Springer-Verlag.

Marble, Duane F. Two Computer Programs for the Analysis of Simple Markov Chains. (Discussion Paper Ser.: No. 6). 1964. pap. 5.75 (ISBN 0-686-32174-X). Regional Sci Res Inst.

Martin, J. J. Bayesian Decision Problems & Makrov Chains. LC 74-32489. 216p. 1975. Repr. of 1967 ed. 15.00 (ISBN 0-88275-277-4). Krieger.

Norman, M. Frank. Markov Processes & Learning Models. (Mathematics in Science & Engineering Ser.: Vol. 84). 1972. 60.00 (ISBN 0-12-521450-2). Acad Pr.

Nummelin, Esa. General Irreducible Markov Chains & Non-Linear Operators. (Tracts in Mathematics Ser.: No. 83). 200p. 1984. 37.50 (ISBN 0-521-25005-6). Cambridge U Pr.

Paz, Azaria. Introduction to Probabilistic Automata. LC 74-137627. (Computer Science & Applied Mathematics Ser). 1971. 60.00 (ISBN 0-12-547650-7). Acad Pr.

Rapoport, Amnon, et al. Response Models for Detection of Change. (Theory & Decision Library: No. 18). 1979. lib. bdg. 30.00 (ISBN 90-277-0934-3, Pub. by Reidel Holland). Kluwer Academic.

Revuz, D. Markov Chains. LC 74-80112. (Mathematical Library: Vol. 11). 336p. 1975. 55.25 (ISBN 0-444-10752-5, North-Holland). Elsevier.

--Markov Chains. rev. ed. (Mathematical Library: Vol. 11). 1984. 57.75 (ISBN 0-444-86400-8, I-548-83, North-Holland). Elsevier.

Rozanov, Y. A. Markov Random Fields. Elson, C. M., tr. from Rus. (Illus.). 201p. 1982. 46.50 (ISBN 0-387-90708-4). Springer-Verlag.

Scott, Allen J. A Procedure for the Estimation of Markov Transition Probabilities. (Discussion Ser.: No. 8). 1965. pap. 5.75 (ISBN 0-686-32177-4). Regional Sci Res Inst.

Kicklighter, Clois E. Modern Masonry. LC 80-17966. (Illus.). 256p. 1980. text ed. 16.00 (ISBN 0-87006-296-4). Goodheart.

Kreh, R. T. Simplified Masonry Skills. 2nd ed. 336p. 1982. 21.95 (ISBN 0-442-25337-0). Van Nos Reinhold.

Kreh, Richard. Masonry Skills. 2nd ed. LC 80-70701. (Masonry Trades Ser.). 328p. 1982. text ed. 19.00 (ISBN 0-8273-2153-8); pap. text ed. 16.00 (ISBN 0-8273-1957-6); instr's. guide 4.80 (ISBN 0-8273-1768-9). Delmar.

Kreh, Richard T. Safety for Masons. LC 78-53663. 1979. pap. text ed. 7.40 (ISBN 0-8273-1668-2); instructor's guide 3.00 (ISBN 0-8273-1669-0). Delmar.

Kreh, Richard T., Sr. Advanced Masonry Skills. 2nd ed. LC 82-70523. (Illus.). 455p. 1983. pap. text ed. 17.80 (ISBN 0-8273-2148-1); instr's guide 5.25 (ISBN 0-8273-2149-X). Delmar.

Long, Charles. The Backyard Stonebuilder: Fourteen Projects for the Weekend Mason. (Illus.). 160p. (Orig.). 1985. pap. 9.95 (ISBN 0-920197-19-1, Pub. by Summerhill CN). Sterling.

McKee, Harley J. Introduction to Early American Masonry: Stone, Brick, Mortar & Plaster. LC 73-84522. (Illus.). 92p. 1973. pap. 7.95 (ISBN 0-89133-006-2). Preservation Pr.

McRaven, Charles. Building with Stone. (Illus.). 1980. 15.34i (ISBN 0-690-01879-7); pap. 9.95 (ISBN 0-690-01912-2). Har-Row.

Maguire, Byron W. Masonry & Concrete. (Illus.). 1978. ref. ed. 24.95 (ISBN 0-87909-521-0). Reston.

Masonry. (Home Repair & Improvement Ser.). (Illus.). 1976. 11.95 (ISBN 0-8094-2362-6). Time-Life.

Masonry: Equipment Planning Guides for Vocational & Technical Training & Education Programmes, Vol. 12. pap. 22.80 (ILO245, ILO). Unipub.

Masonry: Past & Present- STP 589. 295p. 1975. 30.00 (ISBN 0-8031-0507-X, 04-589000-07). ASTM.

National Association of Home Builders. Incentive Apprenticeship Training for Cement Masons. (Illus.). 371p. 3-ring binder (slide tapes avail.) 67.00 (ISBN 0-86718-079-X). Natl Assn Home.

--Incentive Apprenticeship Training for Plasterers. (Illus.). 345p. (slide tapes avail.) 67.00 (ISBN 0-86718-078-1). Natl Assn Home.

Nickey. Masonary Construction: The Trowel Worker's Bible. (Illus.). 256p. 1982. pap. 8.95 (ISBN 0-8306-1280-7, 1280). TAB Bks.

Nolan, Ken. Masonry & Concrete Construction. 224p. (Orig.). 1982. pap. 13.50 (ISBN 0-910460-92-2). Craftsman.

Randall, Frank A., Jr. & Panarese, William C. Concrete Masonry Handbook. Portland Cement Association, ed. (Illus.). 220p. 1976. 17.50 (ISBN 0-89312-001-4, EB008M). Portland Cement.

Research & Education Association. Handbook of Concrete Technology & Masonry Construction. LC 81-50761. (Illus.). 832p. (Orig.). 1981. 26.75x (ISBN 0-87891-528-1). Res & Educ.

Rudman, Jack. Cement Mason. (Career Examination Ser.: C-132). (Cloth bdg. avail. on request). pap. 12.00 (ISBN 0-8373-0132-7). Natl Learning.

--Foreman (Structures - Group B) (Masonry) (Career Examination Ser.: C-1323). (Cloth bdg. avail. on request). pap. 12.00 (ISBN 0-8373-1323-6). Natl Learning.

--Masonry. (Occupational Competency Examination Ser.: OCE-23). (Cloth bdg. avail. on request). pap. 13.95 (ISBN 0-8373-5723-3). Natl Learning.

Standards for Natural Stone Works & Concrete Stone Works. (DIN Standards Ser.). 334.00 (ISBN 0-686-31842-0, 1348-2/79). Heyden.

Sunset Editors. Basic Masonry Illustrated. LC 80-53484. (Illus.). 96p. (Orig.). 1981. pap. 4.95 (ISBN 0-376-01360-5, Sunset Bks.). Sunset-Lane.

--Walks, Walls, & Patio Floors. 3rd ed. LC 72-92521. (Illus.). 96p. 1973. pap. 5.95 (ISBN 0-376-01706-6, Sunset Bks.). Sunset-Lane.

U. S. Army. Concrete, Masonry & Brickwork: A Practical Handbook for the Homeowner & Small Builder. LC 75-12130. (Illus.). 204p. 1975. pap. 5.95 (ISBN 0-486-23203-4). Dover.

Yee, Min S., ed. Basic Masonry Techniques. (Illus.). 1985. 5.95 (ISBN 0-89721-045-X). Ortho.

MASONS (TRADE)

see Stone-Masons

MASS (CHEMISTRY)

see Atomic Mass

MASS (PHYSICS)

see also Atomic Mass; Mass Spectrometry; Mass Transfer

Cherimisinoff, et al. Biomass: Applications, Technology & Production, Vol. 5. (Energy Power & Environment Ser.). 232p. 1980. 45.00 (ISBN 0-8247-6933-3). Dekker.

Flaherty, F. J., ed. Asymptotic Behavior of Mass & Spacetime Geometry. (Lecture Notes in Physics Ser.: Vol. 202). 213p. 1984. pap. 13.50 (ISBN 0-387-13351-8). Springer-Verlag.

Geankoplis, Christie J. Transport Processes: Momentum, Heat & Mass. 350p. 1983. scp 39.21 (ISBN 0-205-07787-0, 327787). Allyn.

Soldano, B. A. Mass, Measurement & Motion Sequel Two: A New Look at Maxwell's Equations & the Permittivity of Free Space. Brantley, William H., ed. (Illus.). 50p. (Orig.). 1982. pap. 7.00 (ISBN 0-943410-00-2). Grenridge Pub.

MASS SPECTROMETRY

see also Molecular Spectra; Time-Of-Flight Mass Spectrometry

Ahearn, Arthur J., ed. Trace Analysis by Mass Spectrometry. 1972. 78.00 (ISBN 0-12-044650-2). Acad Pr.

Analysis of Drugs & Metabolites by Gas Chromatography - Mass Spectometry: Natural, Pyrolytic & Metabolic Products of Tobacco & Marijuana, Vol. 7. 1980. 89.75 (ISBN 0-8247-6861-2). Dekker.

Beckey, H. D. Principles of Field Ionization & Field Desorption Mass Spectrometry. LC 77-33014. 1971. 62.00 (ISBN 0-08-017557-0). Pergamon.

Benninghoven, A., et al, eds. Secondary Ion Mass Spectrometry SIMS III: Proceedings. (Springer Series in Chemical Physics: Vol. 19). (Illus.). 444p. 1982. 42.00 (ISBN 0-387-11372-X). Springer-Verlag.

--Secondary Ion Mass Spectrometry SIMS-II: Proceedings of the International Conference on Secondary Ion Mass Spectrometry. LC 79-23997. (Springer Ser. in Chemical Physics: Vol. 9). (Illus.). 298p. 1979. 42.00 (ISBN 3-540-09843-7). Springer-Verlag.

Beynon, J. H. & Williams, A. E. Mass & Abundance Tables for Use in Mass Spectrometry. 570p. 1963. 117.00 (ISBN 0-444-40044-3). Elsevier.

Beynon, J. H., et al. The Mass Spectra of Organic Molecules. (Illus.). 510p. 1968. 81.00 (ISBN 0-444-40046-X). Elsevier.

Broder, Lawrence E. & Carter, Stephen K. Meningeal Leukemia. LC 74-190394. pap. 35.00 (ISBN 0-317-07814-3, 2020706). Bks Demand UMI.

Budde, William L. & Eichelberger, James W., eds. Organics Analysis Using Gas Chromatography-Mass Spectrometry: A Techniques & Procedures Manual. LC 79-88484. (Illus.). 1979. 39.95 (ISBN 0-250-40318-8). Butterworth.

Budzikiewicz, Herbert & Djerassi, Carl. Interpretation of Mass Spectra of Organic Compounds. LC 64-14625. (Holden-Day Series in Physical Techniques in Chemistry). pap. 72.00 (ISBN 0-317-09615-X, 2051040). Bks Demand UMI.

--Mass Spectrometry of Organic Compounds. LC 67-26374. (Holden-Day Series in Physical Techinques in Chemistry). pap. 160.00 (ISBN 0-317-09621-4, 2051041). Bks Demand UMI.

Chapman, J. R. Computers in Mass Spectrometry. 1978. 49.50 (ISBN 0-12-168750-3). Acad Pr.

--Practical Organic Mass Spectrometry. 29.95 (ISBN 0-471-90696-4). Wiley.

Cooks, R. G., et al. Metastable Ions. LC 72-97419. 296p. 1973. 68.00 (ISBN 0-444-41119-4). Elsevier.

Daly, N. R., ed. Advances in Mass Spectrometry, Vol. 7 In 2 Parts. 1800p. 1978. 435.95 (ISBN 0-471-25657-9, Pub. by Wiley Heyden). Wiley.

Das, K. G. Organic Mass Spectrometry. 1981. 25.00x (ISBN 0-686-72958-7, Pub. by Oxford & IBH India). State Mutual Bk.

De Galan, L. Analytical Spectrometry. (Illus.). 1981. text ed. 37.50 (ISBN 0-9960017-1-9, Pub. by A Hilger England). Heyden.

De Leenheer, A. P. & Roncucci, R. R., eds. Quantitative Mass Spectrometry in Life Sciences, Vol. II. 502p. 1979. 89.50 (ISBN 0-444-41760-5). Elsevier.

Derrick. Field Ionization & Field Desorption Mass Spectrometry. 1978. write for info. (ISBN 0-685-84731-4). Elsevier.

Desiderio, D. M. Analysis of Neuropeptides by Liquid Chromatography & Mass Spectrometry. (Techniques & Instrumentation in Analytical Chemistry Ser.: No. 6). 236p. 1984. 61.00 (ISBN 0-444-42418-0). Elsevier.

Drewes, S. E. Chroman & Related Compounds. LC 73-84458. (Progress in Mass Spectrometry: Vol. 2). (Illus.). 145p. 1974. 48.80x (ISBN 3-527-25494-3). VCH Pubs.

Facchetti, S. Mass Spectrometry of Large Molecules. 1985. 85.25 (ISBN 0-444-42456-3). Elsevier.

Facchetti, S., ed. Applications of Mass Spectrometry to Trace Analysis: Lectures, Ispra, Italy, 1980. 322p. 1982. 78.75 (ISBN 0-444-42042-8). Elsevier.

Frigerio, A., ed. Chromatography & Mass Spectrometry in Biomedical Sciences, No. 2. (Analytical Chemistry Symposia Ser.: Vol. 14). 506p. 1983. 106.50 (ISBN 0-444-42154-8). Elsevier.

--Recent Developments in Mass Spectrometry in Biochemistry, Medicine & Environmental Research. (Analytical Chemistry Symposia Ser.: Vol. 7). 1981. 76.75 (ISBN 0-444-42029-0). Elsevier.

--Recent Developments in Mass Spectrometry in Biochemistry, Medicine & Environmental Research: Proc. of the 8th International Symposium, Venice, June 18-19, 1983. (Analytical Chemistry Symposia Ser.: Vol. 12). 346p. 1983. 81.00 (ISBN 0-444-42055-X). Elsevier.

Frigerio, A. & McCamish, M., eds. Recent Developments in Mass Spectrometry in Biochemistry & Medicine, Vol. 6. (Analytical Chemistry Symposia Ser.: Vol. 4). 554p. 1981. 85.00 (ISBN 0-444-41870-9). Elsevier.

Frigerio, Alberto & Ghisalberti, Emilio L., eds. Mass Spectrometry in Drug Metabolism. LC 76-53013. 544p. 1977. 65.00x (ISBN 0-306-31018-X, Plenum Pr). Plenum Pub.

Gross, Michael L., ed. High Performance Mass Spectrometry: Chemical Applications. LC 78-789. (ACS Symposium Ser.: No. 70). 1978. 39.95 (ISBN 0-8412-0422-5). Am Chemical.

Gudzinowicz, B. J. Analysis of Drugs & Metabolites by Gas Chromatography - Mass Spectometry: Antipsychotic, Antiemetic & Antidepressant Drugs, Vol. 3. 1977. 49.75 (ISBN 0-8247-6586-9). Dekker.

Gudzinowicz, B. J., et al. Fundamentals of Integrated Gc-Ms, Pt. I: Gas Chromatograpghy. (Chromatographic Science Ser.: Vol. 7). 1976. 95.00 (ISBN 0-8247-6365-3). Dekker.

Gudzinowicz, Michael J. & Gudzinowicz, Benjamin J. The Analysis of Drugs & Related Compounds by Gas Chromotography-Mass Spectometry: Respiratory Gases, Volatile Anesthetics, Ethyl Alcohol, & Related Toxicological Materials, Vol. 1. 1977. 89.75 (ISBN 0-8247-6576-1). Dekker.

Hamming, Mynard C. & Foster, Norman G. Interpretation of Mass Spectra of Organic Compounds. 1972. 95.00 (ISBN 0-12-322150-1). Acad Pr.

Haque, Rizwanel & Biros, Francis J., eds. Mass Spectrometry & NMR Spectroscopy in Pesticide Chemistry. LC 73-20005. (Environmental Science Research Ser.: Vol. 4). 348p. 1974. 49.50x (ISBN 0-306-36304-6, Plenum Pr). Plenum Pub.

Hites, Ronald, ed. Handbook of Mass Spectra of Environmental Contaminants. 432p. 1985. 69.50 (ISBN 0-8493-0537-3). CRC Pr.

Index on Mass Spectral Data. 632p. 1969. 50.00 (ISBN 0-8031-0807-9, 10-011000-39). ASTM.

Institute of Petroleum & Quayle, A., eds. Advances in Mass Spectrometry, Vol. 5. (Illus.). 736p. 1971. 89.00 (ISBN 0-85334-498-1, Pub. by Elsevier Applied Sci England). Elsevier.

Institute of Petroleum & West, A., eds. Advances in Mass Spectrometry, Vol. 6. (Illus.). 1091p. 1974. 137.00 (ISBN 0-85334-459-0, Pub. by Elsevier Applied Sci England). Elsevier.

International Symposium on Quantitative Mass Spectrometry in Life Sciences, 1st, State University of Ghent Belgium June 16-18 1976. Quantitative Mass Spectrometry in Life Sciences: Proceedings. DeLeenheer, A. P. & Roncucci, Romeo R, eds. LC 77-3404. 254p. 1977. 64.00 (ISBN 0-444-41557-2). Elsevier.

International Symposium, 3rd, Amsterdam, Sept. 1976. Analytical Pryolysis: Proceedings. Jones, C. E. & Cramers, C. A., eds. 424p. 1977. 83.00 (ISBN 0-444-41558-0). Elsevier.

Jayaram, R. Mass Spectrometry: Theory & Applications. LC 65-25239. 225p. 1966. 29.50x (ISBN 0-306-30237-3, Plenum Pr). Plenum Pub.

Johnstone, R. A. Mass Spectrometry, Vols. 1-4. Incl. Vol. 1. 1968-70 Literature. 1971. 34.00 (ISBN 0-85186-258-6); Vol. 2. 1970-72 Literature. 1973. 32.00 (ISBN 0-85186-268-3); Vol. 3. 1972-74 Literature. 1975. 43.00 (ISBN 0-85186-278-0); Vol. 4. 1974-76 Literature. 1977. 57.00 (ISBN 0-85186-288-8). Am Chemical.

Johnstone, R. A., ed. Mass Spectrometry, Vol. 7. 440p. 1985. 92.00 (ISBN 0-85186-318-3, 996104739, Pub. by Royal Soc Chem UK). Heyden.

Kendrick, E., ed. Advances in Mass Spectrometry: Proceedings of a Conference Held in Berlin, September, 1967, Vol. 4. pap. 160.00 (ISBN 0-317-26544-X, 2023994). Bks Demand UMI.

Kennett, B. H., et al. Mass Spectra of Organic Compounds: Pt. 1. 158p. 1981. 60.00x (ISBN 0-643-00272-3, Pub. by CSIRO Australia). State Mutual Bk.

--Mass Spectra of Organic Compounds: Pt. 2. 158p. 1981. 60.00x (ISBN 0-643-00273-1, Pub. by CSIRO Australia). State Mutual Bk.

--Mass Spectra of Organic Compounds: Pt. 3. 158p. 1981. 60.00x (ISBN 0-686-73075-5, Pub. by CSIRO Australia). State Mutual Bk.

--Mass Spectra of Organic Compounds: Pt. 4. 158p. 1981. 60.00x (ISBN 0-686-73076-3, Pub. by CSIRO Australia). State Mutual Bk.

--Mass Spectra of Organic Compounds: Pt. 5. 158p. 1981. 60.00x (ISBN 0-643-00276-6, Pub. by CSIRO Australia). State Mutual Bk.

--Mass Spectra of Organic Compounds: Pt. 6. 158p. 1981. 60.00x (ISBN 0-643-00277-4, Pub. by CSIRO Australia). State Mutual Bk.

--Mass Spectra of Organic Compounds: Pt. 7. 158p. 1981. 60.00x (ISBN 0-643-02588-X, Pub. by CSIRO Australia). State Mutual Bk.

--Mass Spectra of Organic Compounds: Pt. 8. 158p. 1981. 60.00x (ISBN 0-643-02589-8, Pub. by CSIRO Australia). State Mutual Bk.

Levsen, K. Fundamental Aspects of Organic Mass Spectrometry. (Progress in Mass Spectroscopy Ser.: Vol. 4). (Illus.). 312p. 1978. 60.00x (ISBN 0-89573-009-X). VCH Pubs.

Litzow, M. R. & Spalding, T. R. Mass Spectrometry of Inorganic & Organometallic Compounds. (Physical Inorganic Chemistry Monographs: Vol. 2). 620p. 1973. 117.00 (ISBN 0-444-41047-3). Elsevier.

MacColl, A. Current Topics in Mass Spectroscopy & Chemical Kinetics. 1982. 59.95 (ISBN 0-471-26197-1). Wiley.

McFadden, W. H. Techniques of Combined Gas Chromatography - Mass Spectrometry: Applications in Organic Analysis. LC 73-6916. 463p. 1973. 60.00x (ISBN 0-471-58388-X, Pub. by Wiley-Interscience). Wiley.

McLafferty, F. W. Tandem Mass Spectrometry. 506p. 1983. 50.00x (ISBN 0-471-86597-4, Pub. by Wiley-Interscience). Wiley.

McLafferty, F. W., ed. Mass Spectrometry of Organic Ions. 1963. 98.50 (ISBN 0-12-483650-X). Acad Pr.

McLafferty, Fred W. Interpretation of Mass Spectra. Turro, Nicholas J., ed. LC 80-51179. (Organic Chemistry Ser.). 303p. 1980. text ed. 15.00x (ISBN 0-935702-04-0). Univ Sci Bks.

--Mass Spectral Correlations. 2nd ed. LC 81-205644. (Advances in Chemistry Ser: No. 40). 1982. pap. 19.95 (ISBN 0-8412-0712-7); 29.95 (ISBN 0-8412-0702-X). Am Chemical.

Majer, J. R. The Mass Spectrometer. (The Wykeman Science Ser.: No. 44). 160p. 1977. cancelled (ISBN 0-85109-590-9); pap. write for info. (ISBN 0-85109-550-X). Taylor & Francis.

Majer, J. R. & Berry, M. The Mass Spectrometer. LC 77-15307. (Wykeham Science Ser.: No. 44). 159p. 1977. 16.95x (ISBN 0-8448-1171-8). Crane-Russak Co.

Mass Spectra of Organic Compounds, Pts. 1-8. 1982. Set. 480.00x (ISBN 0-686-97909-5, Pub. by CSIRO Australia). State Mutual Bk.

Mead, W. L., ed. Advances in Mass Spectrometry: Proceedings of a Conference Held in Paris, September, 1964, Vol. 3. pap. 160.00 (ISBN 0-317-26543-1, 2023993). Bks Demand UMI.

Mee, John M. Direct Mass Spectrometry of Body Metabolites: Quantitative Methodology & Clinical Appications. (Illus.). ix, 135p. 1984. pap. 15.00 (ISBN 0-318-04438-2). Brandon Lane Pr.

Merritt & McEwen. Mass Spectronomy, Pt. A. (Practical Spectroscopy Ser.: Vol. 3). 1979. 65.00 (ISBN 0-8247-6749-7). Dekker.

Meuzelaar, H. L. & Haverkamp, J. Pyrolysis Mass Spectrometry of Recent & Fossil Biomaterials. (Techniques & Instrumentation in Analytical Chemistry Ser.: Vol. 3). 294p. 1982. 61.75 (ISBN 0-444-42099-1). Elsevier.

Middleditch, Brian S., ed. Practical Mass Spectrometry: A Contemporary Introduction. LC 79-351. 404p. 1979. 35.00 (ISBN 0-306-40230-0, Plenum Pr). Plenum Pub.

Middleditch, Brian S., et al. Mass Spectrometry of Priority Pollutants. LC 80-14953. 320p. 1981. 45.00x (ISBN 0-306-40505-9, Plenum Pr). Plenum Pub.

Morris. Soft Ionization Biological Mass Spectrometry. 152p. 1982. 49.95x (ISBN 0-471-26188-2, Wiley Heyden). Wiley.

NATO Advanced Study Institute on Mass Spectrometry 2nd 1966. Modern Aspects of Mass Spectrometry. Reed, Rowland I., ed. LC 68-16994. pap. 100.30 (ISBN 0-317-08735-5, 2020703). Bks Demand UMI.

Payne, J. P., et al. The Medical & Biological Applications of Mass Spectroscopy. 1979. 39.00 (ISBN 0-12-547950-6). Acad Pr.

Pfleger, K., et al, eds. Mass Spectral & GC Data of Drugs, Poisons & Their Metabolites, 2 vols. 1985. Vol. 1, 208p. lib. bdg. 195.00 set (ISBN 0-317-30652-9). Vol. 2, 744p. VCH Pubs.

Porter, Quinton N. Mass Spectrometry of Heterocyclic Compounds. 2nd ed. LC 84-13167. (General Heterocyclic Chemistry Ser.). 1136p. 1985. 250.00 (ISBN 0-471-09901-5, Pub. by Wiley-Interscience). Wiley.

Price, D. Dynamic Mass Spectrometry, Vol. 6. Todd, J. F., ed. 384p. 1981. 114.95 (ISBN 0-471-26191-2, Pub. by Wiley Heyden). Wiley.

Price, D., ed. Dynamic Mass Spectrometry, Vol. 2. 279p. 1971. 88.95 (ISBN 0-471-25962-4, Pub. by Wiley Heyden). Wiley.

Bruggeman, Gordon & Weiss, Volker, eds. Innovations in Materials Processing. (Sagamore Army Materials Research Conference Proceedings Ser.: Vol. 30). 494p. 1985. 79.50x (ISBN 0-306-41839-8, Plenum Pr). Plenum Pub.

Budinski, Kenneth. Engineering Materials: Properties & Selection. 2nd ed. 1983. text ed. 30.95 (ISBN 0-8359-1692-8); instr's. manual free (ISBN 0-8359-1695-2). Reston.

Bunge, H. J. & Esling, C., eds. Quantitive Texture Analysis. 551p. 1981. 100.00 (ISBN 0-9911001-8-2). Heyden.

Bunge, Hans. Texture Analysis in Materials Science: Mathematical Methods. 2nd ed. Morris, Peter, tr. from Ger. LC 79-40054. 1982. text ed. 99.95 (ISBN 0-408-10642-5). Butterworth.

Business Communications Staff. Barrier Materials: Markets, Developments, Technologies. 1983. 1500.00 (ISBN 0-89336-364-2, P-071). BCC.

--Rapidly-Solidified Amorphous Materials. 184p. 1984. pap. 1500.00 (ISBN 0-89336-396-0, GB-079). BCC.

Callister, W. D. Materials Science & Engineering: An Introduction. 602p. 1985. 34.95 (ISBN 0-471-08145-0). Wiley.

Carlsson, J., ed. Mechanical Behaviour of Materials: Proceedings of the Fourth International Conference on Mechanical Behaviour of Materials, Stockholm, Sweden, August 15-19, 1983, 2 Vols, No. IV. (International Series on Strength & Fracture of Materials & Structures). (Illus.). 1175p. 1984. 225.00 (ISBN 0-08-029340-9). Pergamon.

Chalmers, B., ed. Progress in Materials Science, Vol. 23. 280p. 1980. 105.00 (ISBN 0-08-024846-2). Pergamon.

Chalmers, B., et al, eds. Progress in Materials Science, Vols. 15-21. Incl. Vol. 15, Pt. 1. 1971. pap. 15.50 (ISBN 0-08-015869-2); Vol. 15, Pt. 2. 1972. pap. 15.50 (ISBN 0-08-016824-8); Vol. 15, Pt. 3. 1972. pap. 15.50 (ISBN 0-08-016877-9); Vol. 15, Pt. 4. 1973. pap. 15.50 (ISBN 0-08-017132-X); Vol. 15, Complete. 85.00 (ISBN 0-08-017154-0); Vol. 16. 1972. 85.00 (ISBN 0-08-016866-3); Vol. 17. 1972. 31.00 (ISBN 0-08-017011-0); Vol. 18. 1974. 85.00 (ISBN 0-08-017155-9); Vol. 19. 1974. 85.00 (ISBN 0-08-017964-9); Vol. 20. 1977. 300.00 (ISBN 0-08-021143-7); Vol. 21, Pt. 1. 1975. pap. 12.00 (ISBN 0-08-018172-4); Vol. 21, Pt. 2. 1976. pap. 15.50 (ISBN 0-08-019831-7); Vol. 21, Pts. 3 & 4. pap. 33.00 (ISBN 0-08-019987-9); Vol. 21, Complete. 1977. 85.00 (ISBN 0-08-018171-6). pap. write for info. Pergamon.

--Progress in Materials Science, Vols. 6-10, 12-13. Incl. Vol. 6. 1956. 85.00 (ISBN 0-08-009035-4); Vol. 7. 1958; Vol. 8. 1959. 60.00 (ISBN 0-08-009294-2); Vol. 9, Pt. 1. 1961; Vol. 9, Pt. 2. 1962; Vol. 9, Pt. 3. Effects of Environment on Mechanical Properties of Metals. 1962; Vol. 9, Pt. 4. 1962; Vol. 9, Pt. 5. 1962; Vol. 10, Pt. 1. Alloy Phases of the Noble Metals. 1963. pap. 15.50 (ISBN 0-08-009618-2); Vol. 10, Complete. 1963. 67.50 (ISBN 0-08-010981-0); Vol. 12, Pt. 1. 1963; Vol. 12, Pt. 2. 1964. pap. 12.50 (ISBN 0-08-010035-X); Vol. 13, Pt. 1. write for info. Pergamon.

Chang, Leroy L. & Giessen, B. C., eds. Synthetic Modulated Structures. (Materials Science & Technology Ser.). Date not set. 87.00 (ISBN 0-12-170470-X). Acad Pr.

Charles, J. A. & Crane, F. A. Selection & Use of Engineering Materials. (Illus.). 328p. 1984. text ed. 49.95 (ISBN 0-408-10858-4); pap. text ed. 29.95 (ISBN 0-408-10859-2). Butterworth.

Chen, Wai-Fah & Saleeb, Atef F. Constitutive Equations for Engineering Materials: Elasticity & Modeling, Vol. 1. LC 81-16433. 580p. 1982. 78.95x (ISBN 0-471-09149-9, Pub. by Wiley-Interscience). Wiley.

Christian, J. W. & Haasen, P., eds. Progress in Materials Science, Vol. 27. (Illus.). 460p. 1983. 130.00 (ISBN 0-08-030029-4). Pergamon.

Christian, J. W., et al. Progress in Materials Science, Vol. 25. 110.00x (ISBN 0-08-029096-5). Pergamon.

Christian, J. W., et al, eds. Materials Science Progress: Supplement to Progress in Materials Science. (Illus.). 330p. 1981. 55.00 (ISBN 0-08-027147-2). Pergamon.

Clauser, H. R. Encyclopedia Handbook of Materials, Parts & Finishes. new rev. ed. LC 75-43010. 1976. 29.00 (ISBN 0-87762-189-6). Technomic.

Clauser, Henry. Industrial & Manufacturing Materials. (Illus.). 416p. 1975. text ed. 34.25 (ISBN 0-07-011285-1). McGraw.

Collieu, A. & Powney, Derek J. The Mechanical & Thermal Properties of Materials. LC 72-85498. 294p. 1973. 19.50x (ISBN 0-8448-0074-0). Crane-Russak Co.

Committee on Materials Specifications, Testing Methods & Standards, National Research Council. Materials & Process Specifications & Standards. LC 77-92433. (Illus.). 1977. pap. text ed. 9.95 (ISBN 0-309-02731-4). Natl Acad Pr.

Conference on Aircraft Structures & Materials Application: Meeting Held September 9-11, 1969, Seattle, Washington. (The National SAMPE Technical Conference Ser.: Vol. 1). 563p. 1983. 10.00 (ISBN 0-938994-00-X). Soc Adv Material.

Conference on Bicentennial of Materials: Meeting Held October 12-14, 1976, Seattle, Washington. (The National SAMPE Technical Conference Ser.: Vol. 8). 502p. 1983. 20.00 (ISBN 0-938994-03-4). Soc Adv Material.

Conference on Materials & Processes - In Service Performance: Meeting Held October 4-6, 1977, Atlanta, Georgia. (The National SAMPE Technical Conference Ser.: Vol. 9). 562p. 1983. 20.00 (ISBN 0-938994-04-2). Soc Adv Material.

Conference on Materials on the Move: Meeting Held October 8-10, 1974, Dayton, Ohio. (The National SAMPE Technical Conference Ser.: Vol. 6). 461p. 1983. 20.00 (ISBN 0-938994-01-8). Soc Adv Material.

Conference on Materials Review '75: Meeting Held October 14-16, 1975, Albuquerque, New Mexico. (The National SAMPE Technical Conference Ser.: Vol. 7). 532p. 1983. 20.00 (ISBN 0-938994-02-6). Soc Adv Material.

Conference on New Horizons - Materials & Processes for the Eighties: Meeting Held November 13-15, 1979, Boston, Massachusetts. (The National SAMPE Technical Conference Ser.: Vol. 11). 1051p. 1983. 50.00 (ISBN 0-938994-05-0). Soc Adv Material.

Cook, Nathan H. Mechanics & Materials for Design. LC 83-11337. (Illus.). 496p. 1984. text ed. 34.00x (ISBN 0-07-012486-8). McGraw.

Cook, Robert D. & Young, Warren C. Advanced Mechanics of Materials. 1985. text ed. write for info. (ISBN 0-02-324620-0). Macmillan.

Cordon, William A. Properties, Evaluation & Control of Engineering Materials. 1979. text ed. 45.00 (ISBN 0-07-013123-6). McGraw.

Crawford, J. H., Jr., et al, eds. Defect Properties & Processing of High-Technology Nonmetallic Materials: Proceedings of the Symposium on Defect Properties & Processing of High-Tecnology Nonmetalic Materials, Boston, MA, Nov. 14-17, 1983. (Materials Research Society Symposia Proceedings Ser.: Vol. 24). 494p. 1984. 80.00 (ISBN 0-444-00904-3, North Holland). Elsevier.

Creyke, W. E., et al. Design with Non-Ductile Materials. (Illus.). xix, 294p. 1982. 55.50 (ISBN 0-85334-149-4, I-359-82, Pub. by Elsevier Applied Sci England). Elsevier.

Crilly, Eugene R. Material & Process Applications: Land, Sea, Air, Space. (The Science of Advanced Materials & Process Engineering Ser.). 1981. 55.00 (ISBN 0-938994-18-2). Soc Adv Material.

Davis, H., et al. The Testing of Engineering Materials. 4th ed. 480p. 1982. 44.00x (ISBN 0-07-015656-5). McGraw.

DeGarmo, E. Paul & Kohser, Ronald A. Materials & Processes in Manufacturing. 6th ed. (Illus.). 1024p. 1984. text ed. write for info. (ISBN 0-02-328620-2). Macmillan.

Derucher, Kenneth & Heins, Conrad. Materials for Civil & Highway Engineers. (Illus.). 416p. 1981. text ed. 37.95 (ISBN 0-13-560490-7). P-H.

Desai, C. S. & Siriwardane, H. J. Constitution Laws for Engineering Materials with Emphasis on Geologic Materials. (Illus.). 464p. 1984. 40.95 (ISBN 0-13-167940-6). P-H.

Desai, C. S. & Gallagher, R. H., eds. Mechanics of Engineering Materials. (Numerical Methods in Engineering Ser.). 691p. 1984. 45.00 (ISBN 0-471-90276-4). Wiley.

DOE Technical Information Center. Engineering Materials: A Bibliography. 57p. 1982. pap. 10.00 (ISBN 0-87079-488-4, DOE/TIC-4628); microfiche 4.50 (ISBN 0-87079-489-2, DOE/TIC-4628). Doe.

Dvorak, G. J. & Shield, R. T. Mechanics of Material Behavior. (Studies in Applied Mechanics: Vol. 6). 1984. 94.25 (ISBN 0-444-42169-6, I-091-84). Elsevier.

Eisenstadt, Melvin M. Introduction to Mechanical Properties of Materials: An Ecological Approach. 1971. text ed. write for info. (ISBN 0-02-332140-7, 33214). Macmillan.

Electronic Properties of Materials: A Guide to the Literature, 3 vols. Incl. Vol. 1. Johnson, H. Thayne. 1681p. 1965. 195.00 (ISBN 0-306-68221-4); Vol. 2. Grigsby, Donald L., et al. 1800p. 1967. 195.00 (ISBN 0-306-68222-2); Vol. 3. Grigsby, Donald L. LC 65-12176. 1895p. 1971. 195.00 (ISBN 0-306-68223-0). IFI Plenum). Plenum Pub.

Energistic Materials Symposium: Proceedings, Chicago IL, 7-9 May 1968. (Science of Advanced Materials & Process Engineering Ser., Vol. 13). 20.00 (ISBN 0-938994-13-1). Soc Adv Material.

Ericsson, T., ed. Computers in Materials Technology: Proceedings of the Conference Held in Linkoping, June 1980. 200p. 1981. 39.00 (ISBN 0-08-027570-2). Pergamon.

Evans, Lee S. Chemical & Process Plant: A Guide to the Selection of Engineering Materials. 2nd ed. LC 80-20355. 190p. 1980. 44.95x (ISBN 0-470-27064-0). Halsted Pr.

Fan, J. C. & Johnson, N. M. Energy Beam-Solid Interactions & Transient Thermal Processing: Proceedings of the 6th Symposium on Energy Beam Solid Interactions & Transient Thermal Processing, Boston, MA, 1983. (Materials Research Society Symposia Ser.: Vol. 23). 788p. 1984. 95.00 (ISBN 0-444-00903-5, North Holland). Elsevier.

Farag, M. M. Materials & Process Selection in Engineering. (Illus.). 320p. 1979. 63.00 (ISBN 0-85334-824-3, Pub. by Elsevier Applied Sci England). Elsevier.

Feldman, Leonard, et al. Materials Analysis by Ion Channeling: Submicron Crystallography. 1982. 44.00 (ISBN 0-12-252680-5). Acad Pr.

Feltham, P. Deformation & Strength of Materials. 142p. 1966. 25.00x (ISBN 0-306-30648-4, Plenum Pr). Plenum Pub.

Finniston, H. M., ed. Structural Characteristics of Materials. (Illus.). 1971. 48.50x (Pub. by Applied Science). Burgess-Intl Ideas.

Fitzgerald, R. W. Mechanics of Materials. 2nd ed. LC 81-4737. 1982. 36.95 (ISBN 0-201-04073-5); avail. solutions manual 4.00 (ISBN 0-201-04573-7). Addison-Wesley.

Flinn, Richard A. & Trojan, Paul K. Engineering Materials & Their Applications. 2nd ed. (Illus.). 753p. 1981. text ed. 34.95 (ISBN 0-395-29645-5); solutions manual 7.50 (ISBN 0-395-29646-3). HM.

Francis, Philip H. & Lindholm, Ulric S. Advanced Experimental Techniques in the Mechanics of Materials. 462p. 1973. 101.25 (ISBN 0-677-12570-4). Gordon.

Fundamentals of Materials. rev. ed. 154p. 1981. Set. training materials 3400.00x (ISBN 0-87683-050-5); 60.00x (ISBN 0-87683-051-3); lesson plans 2250.00x (ISBN 0-87683-052-1); transparencies 750.00x (ISBN 0-87683-053-X); question bank 1175.00x (ISBN 0-87683-054-8). G P Courseware.

Gibbons, J. F., et al, eds. Laser & Electron Beam Solid Interactions & Materials Processing. (Materials Research Society Proceedings: Vol. 1). 630p. 1981. 90.00 (ISBN 0-444-00595-1, North-Holland). Elsevier.

Giess, E. A., et al, eds. Electronic Packaging Materials Science, Vol. 40. LC 85-4849. 1985. text ed. 36.00 (ISBN 0-931837-05-7). Materials Res.

Gillies, M. T. Nonwoven Materials-Recent Developments. LC 79-5445. (Chemical Technology Review: No. 141). (Illus.). 372p. 1980. 45.00 (ISBN 0-8155-0776-3). Noyes.

Gourd, L. M. Introduction to Engineering Materials. 192p. 1982. pap. text ed. 18.50x (ISBN 0-7131-3444-5). Intl Ideas.

Granet, Irving. Modern Materials Science. (Illus.). 1980. text ed. 25.95 (ISBN 0-8359-4569-3); solutions manual avail. (ISBN 0-8359-4570-7). Reston.

Guy, A. G. Essentials of Materials Science. 1976. text ed. 42.00 (ISBN 0-07-025351-X). McGraw.

Handbook of Industrial Materials. 600p. 1981. 175.00x (ISBN 0-686-86768-8, Pub. by Trade & Tech). State Mutual Bk.

Harris, Bryan & Bunsell, A. R. Structure & Properties of Engineering Materials. LC 76-41771. (Introductory Engineering Ser.). (Illus.). pap. 90.80 (ISBN 0-317-08294-9, 2019608). Bks Demand UMI.

Hartwig, Gunther & Evans, David, eds. Nonmetallic Materials & Composites at Low Temperatures Two. LC 82-367. (Cryogenic Materials Ser.). 410p. 1982. 59.50x (ISBN 0-306-40894-5, Plenum Pr). Plenum Pub.

Hausner, Henry, ed. Modern Materials: Advances in Development & Applications. Incl. Vol. 1. 1958; Vol. 2. 1960. 77.00 (ISBN 0-12-462202-X); Vol. 3. 1963. 77.00 (ISBN 0-12-462203-8); Vol. 4. Gonser, B. W. & Hausner, Henry H., eds. 1964. 77.00 (ISBN 0-12-462204-6); Vol. 5. Gonser, B. W., ed. 1965; Vol. 6. 1968; Vol. 7. 1970. 77.00 (ISBN 0-12-462207-0). Acad Pr.

Hayden, H. W. & Moffatt, W. G. The Structure & Properties of Materials: Mechanical Behavior, Vol. 3. 247p. 1965. pap. 21.95 (ISBN 0-471-36469-X). Wiley.

Henisch, H. K., et al, eds. Phase Transitions & Their Applications in Materials Science. LC 73-14411. 300p. 1974. text ed. 45.00 (ISBN 0-08-017955-X). Pergamon.

Herbst, John A. & Sastry, K. V., eds. On-Stream Characterization & Control of Particulate Processes. 308p. 1981. pap. 29.00x (ISBN 0-939204-02-9, 78-19). Eng Found.

Herman, H. & Tu, K. N., eds. Treatise on Materials Science & Technology, Vol. 24. 306p. 1982. 52.50 (ISBN 0-12-341824-0). Acad Pr.

Herman, Herbert. Treatise on Materials Science & Technology: Embrittlement of Engineering Alloys, Vol. 25. 1983. 89.00 (ISBN 0-12-341825-9). Acad Pr.

--Treatise on Materials Science & Technology, Vol. 19: Experimental Methods, Pt. A. LC 77-182672. 1980. 44.00 (ISBN 0-12-341819-4). Acad Pr.

Herman, Herbert & Frandin, F. Treatise on Materials Science & Technology: Vol. 21, Electronic Structure & Properties. LC 81-2457. 1981. 65.00 (ISBN 0-12-341821-6). Acad Pr.

Herman, Herbert, ed. Treatise on Materials Science, Vols. 1-12. Incl. Vol. 1. 1972. 67.50 (ISBN 0-12-341801-1); Vol. 2. 1973. 82.50 (ISBN 0-12-341802-X); Vol. 3. Ultrasonic Investigation of Mechanical Properties. Green, Robert E., Jr. 1973. 39.50 (ISBN 0-12-341803-8); Vol. 4, 1974. 76.00 (ISBN 0-12-341804-6); Vol. 5. 1974. 76.00 (ISBN 0-12-341805-4); Vol. 6. Plastic Deformation of Materials. 1975. 82.00 (ISBN 0-12-341806-2); Vol. 7. Microstructure of Irradiated Materials. 1975. 52.50 (ISBN 0-12-341807-0); Vol. 8. 1975. 67.50 (ISBN 0-12-341808-9); Vol. 9. Ceramic Fabrication Processes. Wang, F. F., ed. 1976. 80.00 (ISBN 0-12-341809-7); Vol. 10. Properties of Solid Polymeric Materials: Part A. Schulz, J. M., ed. 1977. 81.00 (ISBN 0-12-341810-0); Vol. 10. Properties of Solid Polymeric Materials: Part B. Schultz, J. M., ed. 1977. 82.00 (ISBN 0-12-341841-0); Vol. 11. Properties & Microstructure. MacCrone, R. K., ed. 1977. 85.00 (ISBN 0-12-341811-9); Vol. 12. Glass I: Interaction with Electromagnetic Radiation. Tomozawa, Minoru, ed. 1977. 80.00 (ISBN 0-12-341812-7). LC 78-27077. Acad Pr.

--Treatise on Materials Science & Technology: Glass IV, Vol. 26. 1985. 69.50 (ISBN 0-12-341826-7). Acad Pr.

--Treatise on Materials Science & Technology, Vol. 15: Neutron Scattering in Materials Science. (Treatise on Materials Science & Technology Ser.). 1979. 83.00 (ISBN 0-12-341815-1). Acad Pr.

Hi-Tech Review 1984. (National SAMPE Technical Conference Ser.). (Illus.). 60.00 (ISBN 0-938994-25-5). Soc Adv Material.

Higdon, Archie, et al. Mechanics of Materials. 4th ed. LC 84-7583. 744p. 1985. 37.95 (ISBN 0-471-89044-8). Wiley.

Honig, J. M. & Rao, C. N., eds. Preparation & Characterization of Materials. LC 81-20510. 1982. 49.50 (ISBN 0-12-355040-8). Acad Pr.

Hornsey, et al. Mechanics & Materials: An Individualized Approach - Reference Manual-Study Guide. LC 76-18470. (Illus.). 1977. pap. 32.50 (ISBN 0-395-24993-7); solutions manual 10.50 (ISBN 0-395-24994-5). HM.

Huggins, R. A., et al, eds. Annual Review of Materials Science, Vol. 13. LC 75-172108. (Illus.). 1983. text ed. 64.00 (ISBN 0-8243-1713-0). Annual Reviews.

Huggins, Robert A., et al, eds. Annual Review of Materials Science, Vol. 7. LC 75-172108. (Illus.). 1977. text ed. 20.00 (ISBN 0-8243-1707-6). Annual Reviews.

--Annual Review of Materials Science, Vol. 8. LC 75-172108. (Illus.). 1978. text ed. 20.00 (ISBN 0-8243-1708-4). Annual Reviews.

--Annual Review of Materials Science, Vol. 9. LC 75-172108. (Illus.). 1979. text ed. 20.00 (ISBN 0-8243-1709-2). Annual Reviews.

--Annual Review of Materials Science, Vol. 10. LC 75-172108. (Illus.). 1980. text ed. 20.00 (ISBN 0-8243-1710-6). Annual Reviews.

--Annual Review of Materials Science, Vol. 11. LC 75-172108. (Illus.). 1981. text ed. 20.00 (ISBN 0-8243-1711-4). Annual Reviews.

--Annual Review of Materials Science, Vol. 12. LC 75-172108. (Illus.). 1982. text ed. 22.00 (ISBN 0-8243-1712-2). Annual Reviews.

--Annual Review of Materials Science, Vol. 15. (Illus.). 500p. 1985. text ed. 64.00 (ISBN 0-8243-1715-7). Annual Reviews.

Institution of Chemical Engineers, Research Committee Working Party. Materials & Energy Resources. 68p. 1981. 42.00x (ISBN 0-85295-012-8, Pub. by Inst Chem Eng England). State Mutual Bk.

Interamerican Conference on Materials Technology (2nd: 1970: Mexico City, Mexico) An Interamerican Approach for the Seventies: Presented at the Second Interamerican Conference on Materials Technology, August 24-27, 1970, Unidad de Congresos, Mexico City, Mexico, 2 pts. Incl. Pt. 1. Materials Technology. 160.00 (ISBN 0-317-10705-4); Pt. 2. Materials Education. 34.80 (ISBN 0-317-10706-2). LC 68-25870. pap. write for info. (2016873). Bks Demand UMI.

Twenty-Twenty Vision in Materials for 2000. new ed. (National SAMPE Technical Conference Ser.). (Illus.). 1983. 60.00 (ISBN 0-938994-23-9). Soc Adv Material.

Van der Biest, O. Analysis of High Temperature Materials. (Illus.). 261p. 1983. 52.00 (ISBN 0-85334-172-9, I-464-82, Pub. by Elsevier Applied Sci England). Elsevier.

Van Vlack, Lawrence H. Elements of Material Science & Engineering. 5th ed. (Metallurgy & Materials Engineering Ser.). 550p. 1985. text ed. 38.95 (ISBN 0-201-08086-9); solution manual 2.50 (ISBN 0-201-08086-9). Addison-Wesley.

Wagner, Richard. Field-Ion Microscopy in Materials Science. (Crystals Ser.: Vol. 6). (Illus.). 120p. 1982. 40.00 (ISBN 0-387-11712-1). Springer-Verlag.

Walters, A. H., et al, eds. Biodeterioration of Materials, Vols. 1 & 2. 1968-72. Vol. 1: Microbiological & Allied Aspects. 92.50 (ISBN 0-85334-623-2, Pub. by Elsevier Applied Sci England); Vol.2: Biodynamic Effects of Messinian Salinity. 92.50 (ISBN 0-85334-538-4). Elsevier.

Waseda, Yoshio. The Structure of Non-Crystalline Materials. (Illus.). 304p. 1980. text ed. 66.95 (ISBN 0-07-068426-X). McGraw.

Weissmann, Sigmund, et al, eds. Application of X-Ray Topographic Methods to Materials Science. 550p. 1984. 75.00x (ISBN 0-306-41838-X, Plenum Pr). Plenum Pub.

Wenk, Hans Rudolf, ed. Preferred Orientation in Deformed Materials. 1985. 59.50 (ISBN 0-12-744020-8). Acad Pr.

Williams, David B. Practical Analytical Electron Microscopy in Materials Science. (Illus.). 180p. 1984. pap. 30.00 (ISBN 0-9612934-0-3). Electron Optics Pub Grp.

Winkler, G. & Hansen, P., eds. Intermag 84: Digest of the International Magnetics Conference, Hamburg, April 10-13, 1984. 546p. 1984. 70.00 (ISBN 0-444-87510-7). Elsevier.

Wright, John R. & Helsel, Larry D. Materials Processing. 1985. text ed. 27.95 (ISBN 0-8359-4333-X); solutions manual avail. (ISBN 0-8359-4334-8). Reston.

Wyatt, L. M. Materials of Construction for Steam Power Plant. (Illus.). 312p. 1976. 52.00 (ISBN 0-85334-661-5, Pub. by Elsevier Applied Sci England). Elsevier.

Wyskida, Richard M. & McDaniel, Don M. Modeling of Cushioning Systems. 336p. 1980. 59.25 (ISBN 0-677-05480-7). Gordon.

Zimmerman, O. T. & Lavine, Irvin. Handbook of Material Trade Names, with Supplement 4, 1953-1965. Supplements I, II, III. o.p.; Supplement 4. 43.10x; Handbook. Indus Res Serv.

MATERIALS–BRITTLENESS

see Brittleness

MATERIALS–CREEP

see also Concrete–Creep; Metals–Creep

Ashby, M. F. & Brown, L. M., eds. Perspectives in Creep Fracture. 180p. 1983. 35.00 (ISBN 0-08-030541-5). Pergamon.

Boyle, James T. & Spence, John. Stress Analysis for Creep. 307p. 1983. 59.95 (ISBN 0-408-01172-6). Butterworth.

CISM (International Center for Mechanical Sciences), Dept. for Mechanics of Deformable Bodies. Creep Transition in Cylinders. Seth, B. R., ed. (CISM Pubns. Ser.: No. 149). 29p. 1973. pap. 5.90 (ISBN 0-387-81170-2). Springer-Verlag.

Conway, J. B. Numerical Methods for Creep & Rupture Analysis. 212p. 1967. 57.75 (ISBN 0-677-01090-7). Gordon.

Conway, J. B. & Flagella, P. N. Creep-Rupture Data for the Refractory Metals to High Temperatures. 798p. 1971. 205.75 (ISBN 0-677-02660-9). Gordon.

Curran, R. M., ed. Creep-fatique Interaction, 1976 ASME-EPC Symposium: Presented at the Winter Meeting of the ASME, New York, N. Y. December 5-10, 1976. LC 76-28849. pap. 109.50 (ISBN 0-317-08007-5, 2016816). Bks Demand UMI.

Evans, H. E. Mechanisms of Creep Fracture. 328p. 1984. 57.00 (ISBN 0-85334-193-1, Pub. by Elsevier Applied Sci England). Elsevier.

Gittus, J. Creep, Viscoelasticity & Creep Fracture in Solids. (Illus.). 725p. 1975. 92.50 (ISBN 0-85334-597-X, Pub. by Elsevier Applied Sci England). Elsevier.

International Union of Theoretical & Applied Mechanics Colloquium, Stanford Univ, 1960. Creep in Structures. Hoff, N. J., ed. (Illus.). 1962. 74.40 (ISBN 0-387-02796-3). Springer-Verlag.

International Union of Theoretical & Applied Mechanics Symposium, 2nd, Gothenburg, Sweden, 1970. Creep in Structures, Nineteen Seventy. Holt, J., ed. LC 75-182441. (Illus.). 440p. 1972. 82.60 (ISBN 0-387-05601-7). Springer-Verlag.

Jetter, R. I., et al, eds. Metallic Bellows & Expansion Joints. (PVP Ser.: Vol. 51). 154p. 1981. 30.00 (ISBN 0-686-34510-X, H00187). ASME.

Kraus, Harry. Creep Analysis. LC 80-15242. 250p. 1980. 46.50x (ISBN 0-471-06255-3, Pub. by Wiley-Interscience). Wiley.

Larsson, L. H., ed. Subcritical Crack Growth Due to Fatigue, Stress Corrosion & Creep: Selected Proceedings of the Third Advanced Seminar on Fracture Mechanics (ASFM 3), Joint Research Centre, Ispra, Italy, 19-23 October 1981. (Illus.). 640p. 1985. 112.50 (ISBN 0-85334-289-X, Pub. by Elsevier Applied Sci England). Elsevier.

Mukherjee, S. Boundary Element Methods in Creep & Fracture. (Illus.). 224p. 1983. 33.50 (ISBN 0-85334-163-X, I-430-82, Pub. by Elsevier Applied Sci England). Elsevier.

Odgvist, Folke K. Mathematical Theory of Creep & Creep Ruptures. 2nd ed. LC 75-306213. (Oxford Mathematical Monographs). (Illus.). pap. 53.30 (ISBN 0-317-08339-2, 2051834). Bks Demand UMI.

Poirier, J. P. Creep of Crystals. (Cambridge Earth Science Ser.). (Illus.). 275p. 1985. 49.50 (ISBN 0-521-26177-5); pap. 22.95 (ISBN 0-521-27851-1). Cambridge U Pr.

Ponter, A. R. & Hayhurst, D. R., eds. Creep in Structures (Third IUTAM Symposium) Proceedings. (IUTAM-International Union of Theoretical & Applied Mechanics Ser.). 615p. 1981. 62.00 (ISBN 0-387-10596-4). Springer-Verlag.

Ruesch, H., et al. Creep & Shrinkage: Their Effect on the Behavior of Concrete Structures. (Illus.). 284p. 1983. 62.00 (ISBN 0-387-90669-X). Springer-Verlag.

TMS-AIME Fall Meeting, Milwaukee, Sept. 16-20, 1979. Creep-Fatigue-Environment Interactions. Stoloff, N. & Pelloux, R., eds. 179p. 26.00 (ISBN 0-89520-368-5, 188); members 16.00 (ISBN 0-317-37215-7); student members 10.00 (ISBN 0-317-37216-5). Metal Soc.

MATERIALS–DETERIORATION

see also Corrosion and Anti-Corrosives

American Society for Materials & Testing. Corrosion & Degradation of Implant Materials, STP 684. 369p. 1979. 37.75x (ISBN 0-8031-0313-1, 04-684000-27). ASTM.

Bogdanoff, John L. & Kozin, Frank. Probabilistic Models of Cumulative Damage. LC 84-11799. 341p. 1985. text ed. 53.50 (ISBN 0-471-88180-5, Pub. by Wiley Interscience). Wiley.

Erosion, Wear & Interfaces with Corrosion, STP 567. 343p. 1974. 35.00 (ISBN 0-8031-0335-2, 04-567000-29). ASTM.

Fraker, Anna C. & Griffin, Charles D., eds. Corrosion & Degradation of Implant Materials-STP 859: Second Symposium. LC 84-70337. (Illus.). 470p. 1985. text ed. 62.00 (ISBN 0-8031-0427-8, 04-859000-27). ASTM.

Glaeser, W. A., et al, eds. Wear of Materials. Incl. Wear of Materials, 1979. Ludema, K. C. et al., ed. 685p. 1979. 60.00 (H00143); Wear of Materials. Ludema, K. C., ed. 1983. pap. text ed. 85.00 (H00254). 585p. 1977. pap. text ed. 50.00 (ISBN 0-685-81976-0, H00100). ASME.

Norton, J. F., ed. High Temperature Materials Corrosion in Coal Gasification Atmospheres. 152p. 1984. 37.00 (ISBN 0-85334-241-5, I-522-83, Pub. by Elsevier Applied Sci England). Elsevier.

MATERIALS–DYNAMIC TESTING

see also Structural Dynamics

American Society for Testing & Materials. Symposium on Dynamic Behavior of Materials. LC 63-20729. (American Society for Testing & Materials. Special Technical Publication Ser.: No. 336). pap. 80.80 (ISBN 0-317-10854-9, 2000144). Bks Demand UMI.

--Symposium on Stress-Strain-Time-Temperature Relationships in Materials. LC 62-22248. (American Society for Testing & Materials: Special Publication, No. 325). pap. 33.80 (ISBN 0-317-10835-2, 2000133). Bks Demand UMI.

Burke, J. J. & Weiss, V., eds. Nondestructive Evaluation of Materials. LC 79-12538. (Sagamore Army Materials Research Conference Proceedings Ser.: Vol. 23). 542p. 1979. 79.50x (ISBN 0-306-40185-1, Plenum Pr). Plenum Pub.

Engel, Peter A. Impact Wear of Materials. (Tribology Ser.: Vol. 2). 340p. 1976. 76.75 (ISBN 0-444-41533-5). Elsevier.

Instrumented Impacted Testing- STP 563. 220p. 1974. 21.75 (ISBN 0-8031-0738-2, 04-563000-23). ASTM.

Mader, Charles L., et al, eds. Los Alamos: Explosives Performance Data. LC 82-40391. (Los Alamos Series on Dynamic Material Properties: Vol. 7). 824p. 1983. 48.50x (ISBN 0-520-04014-7). U of Cal Pr.

MATERIALS–FATIGUE

see also Fracture Mechanics; also subdivision Fatigue under specific subjects, e.g. Metals–Fatigue

Abelkis & Hudson, eds. Design of Fatigue & Fracture Resistant Structures - STP 761. 486p. 1982. 51.00 (ISBN 0-8031-0714-5, 04-761000-30). ASTM.

American Society for Testing & Materials, et al. Fatigue at Elevated Temperatures. Carden, A. E., ed. LC 73-76958. (American Society for Testing & Materials Special Technical Publications Ser.: 520). (Illus.). pap. 160.00 (ISBN 0-317-11056-X). Bks Demand UMI.

American Society for Testing & Materials. Fatigue Crack Propagation. LC 67-14532. (Special Technical Publication Ser.: No. 415). pap. 138.00 (ISBN 0-317-11250-3, 2001125). Bks Demand UMI.

--Manual on Low Cycle Fatigue Testing. LC 70-97730. (ASTM Special Technical Publication: No. 465). pap. 52.50 (ISBN 0-317-26536-9, 2023987). Bks Demand UMI.

--Symposium on Fatigue Tests of Aircraft Structures: Low-Cycle, Full-Scale, & Helicopters. LC 63-15793. (American Society for Testing & Materials. Special Technical Publication Ser.: No. 338). pap. 69.80 (ISBN 0-317-09223-5, 2000142). Bks Demand UMI.

Bibliography on the Fatigue of Materials, Components & Structures: Vol. 2, 1951-1960. Incl. 115.00 (ISBN 0-08-021713-3). Pergamon.

Bloom, J. M. & Ekvall, J. C., eds. Probabilistic Fracture Mechanics & Fatigue Methods: Applications for Structural Design & Maintenance - STP 798. LC 82-83518. 215p. 1983. text ed. 36.00 (ISBN 0-8031-0242-9, 04-798000-30). ASTM.

Bryan & Potter, eds. Effect of Load Variables on Fatigue Crack Initiation & Propagation - STP 714. 242p. 1980. 27.00 (ISBN 0-8031-0720-X, 04-714000-30). ASTM.

Burke, John J., et al, eds. Fatigue: An Interdisciplinary Approach. LC 64-21083. (Sagamore Army Materials Research Conference Ser.: Vol. 10). 414p. 1964. 35.00x (ISBN 0-306-34510-2, Plenum Pr). Plenum Pub.

Cruse, T. A., ed. Fatigue Life Technology, Bk No. H00096. Gallagher, J. P. pap. text ed. 18.00 (ISBN 0-685-79860-7). ASME.

Curran, R. M., ed. Creep-fatique Interaction, 1976 ASME-EPC Symposium: Presented at the Winter Meeting of the ASME, New York, N. Y. December 5-10, 1976. LC 76-28849. pap. 109.50 (ISBN 0-317-08007-5, 2016816). Bks Demand UMI.

Cyclic Stress-Strain Behavior: Analysis, Experimentation & Failure Prediction, STP 519. 289p. 1973. 28.00 (ISBN 0-8031-0078-7, 04-519000-30). ASTM.

Durability of Building Materials & Components, STP 691. 1034p. 1980. 74.95x (ISBN 0-8031-0325-5, 04-691000-10). ASTM.

Effects of Environment & Complex Load History on Fatigue Life, STP 462. 332p. 1970. 22.00 (ISBN 0-8031-0032-9, 04-462000-30). ASTM.

Fatigue Mechanisms- STP 675. 922p. 1979. 65.00x (ISBN 0-8031-0345-X, 04-675000-30). ASTM.

Fatigue of Fibrous Composite Materials STP 723. 311p. 1981. 30.00 (ISBN 0-8031-0719-6, 04-723000-33). ASTM.

Fatigue: Properties & Behavior. cancelled (ISBN 0-89883-832-0, SP611). Soc Auto Engineers.

Hertzberg, Richard W. Deformation & Fracture Mechanics of Engineering Materials. 2nd ed. LC 83-5881. 697p. 1983. 46.50 (ISBN 0-471-08609-6); write for info (ISBN 0-471-89367-6). Wiley.

Hertzberg, Richard W. & Manson, John A. Fatigue of Engineering Plastics. LC 79-6786. 1980. 42.00 (ISBN 0-12-343550-1). Acad Pr.

Jaffee, R. I., ed. Corrosion Fatigue of Steam Turbine Blade Materials: Workshop Proceedings, Palo Alto, CA, U. S. A., 21-24 September 1981. (Illus.). 732p. 1983. 65.00 (ISBN 0-08-030163-0). Pergamon.

Johnson, L. G. Statistical Treatment of Fatigue Experiments. 116p. 1964. 27.75 (ISBN 0-444-40322-1). Elsevier.

Lankford, J., et al. Fatigue Mechanisms: Advances in Quantitative Measurement of Physical Damage- STP 811. LC 82-73773. 498p. 1983. text ed. 50.00 (ISBN 0-8031-0250-X, 04-811000-30). ASTM.

Liebowitz, H., ed. Progress in Fatigue & Fracture, Vol. 8 No. 1. 1976. text ed. 66.00 (ISBN 0-08-020866-5). Pergamon.

Little, R. E. & Jebe, E. H. Statistical Design of Fatigue Experiments. (Illus.). 280p. 1975. 55.50 (ISBN 0-85334-587-2, Pub. by Elsevier Applied Sci England). Elsevier.

Mann, J. Y. Bibliography on the Fatigue of Materials, Components & Structures: Vol. 3-1961 to 1965, Vol. 3, 1961-1965. 510p. 1983. 99.00 (ISBN 0-08-025449-7). Pergamon.

Manson, S. S. Thermal Stress & Low-Cycle Fatigue. LC 80-29623. 416p. 1981. Repr. of 1966 ed. lib. bdg. 39.50 (ISBN 0-89874-279-X). Krieger.

Marsh, Thomas O. Roots of Crime: A Bio-Physical Approach to Crime Prevention & Rehabilitation. 208p. 1984. pap. text ed. 9.95 (ISBN 0-8290-1570-1). Irvington.

Mescall, John & Weiss, Volker, eds. Material Behavior Under High Stress & Ultrahigh Loading Rates. (Sagamore Army Materials Research Conference Ser.: Vol. 29). 336p. 1983. 49.50x (ISBN 0-306-41474-0, Plenum Pr). Plenum Pub.

Miller, K. J. & Brown, M. W., eds. Multiaxial Fatigue. LC 85-7376. (Special Technical Publications (STP) Ser.: No. 853). (Illus.). 750p. 1985. text ed. 88.00 (ISBN 0-8031-0444-8, 04-85300030). ASTM.

Mura, T., ed. Mechanics of Fatigue. (AMD Ser.: Vol. 47). 188p. 1981. 30.00 (ISBN 0-686-34479-0, H00197). ASME.

Osgood, Carl C. Fatigue Design. 2nd ed. (International Ser. on the Strength & Fracture of Materials & Structures). 500p. 1982. 61.00 (ISBN 0-08-026167-1); pap. 25.00 (ISBN 0-08-026166-3). Pergamon.

Parker, A. P. Mechanics of Fracture & Fatigue: An Introduction. 1981. 33.00x (ISBN 0-419-11460-2, NO. 6495, Pub. by E & FN Spon); pap. 16.95x (ISBN 0-419-11470-X, NO. 6494). Methuen Inc.

Part-Through Crack Fatigue Life Prediction - STP 687. 226p. 1979. 26.25x (ISBN 0-8031-0532-0, 04-687000-30). ASTM.

Probalistic Aspects of Fatigue - STP 511. 203p. 1972. 19.75 (ISBN 0-8031-0103-1, 04-511000-30). ASTM.

Puskar, A. & Golovin, S. A. Fatigue in Materials: Cumulative Damage Processes. (Materials Science Monographs: Vol. 24). 320p. 1984. 72.25 (ISBN 0-444-99597-8). Elsevier.

Sandor, Bela I. Fundamentals of Cyclic Stress & Strain. LC 70-176415. (Illus.). 184p. 1972. text ed. 22.50x (ISBN 0-299-06100-0). U of Wis Pr.

Service Fatigue Loads Monitoring, Simulation, Analysis- STP 671. 298p. 1979. 29.50x (ISBN 0-8031-0721-8, 04-671000-30). ASTM.

Shin, Y. S. & Au-Yang, M. K., eds. Random Fatigue Life Prediction. (PVP Ser.: Vol. 72). 148p. 1983. pap. text ed. 30.00 (ISBN 0-317-02643-7, H00258). ASME.

Skelton, R. P., ed. Fatigue at High Temperature. (Illus.). 409p. 1983. 81.50 (ISBN 0-85334-167-2, I-458-82, Pub. by Elsevier Applied Sci England). Elsevier.

Smith, Alrick L. Reliability of Engineering Materials. (Illus.). 160p. (Orig.). 1985. pap. text ed. 35.95 (ISBN 0-408-01507-1). Butterworth.

Society of Automotive Engineers. Fatigue Resistance: Forecasting & Testing. LC 79-66724. 88p. 1979. Five papers. pap. 15.00 (ISBN 0-89883-219-5, SP448). Soc Auto Engineers.

Stephens, Ralph I., ed. Fatigue at Low Temperatures-STP 857. LC 84-70334. (Illus.). 325p. 1985. text ed. 44.00 (ISBN 0-8031-0411-1, 04-857000-30). ASTM.

Sumner, G. & Livesey, V. B., eds. Techniques for High Temperature Fatigue Testing: Based on th Edited Proceedings of the Springfield Symposium, Preston, U. K., 13-14 September 1983. (Illus.). 224p. 1985. 39.00 (ISBN 0-85334-314-4, Pub. by Elsevier Applied Sci England). Elsevier.

Taske, C. E., et al, eds. Thermal & Environmental Effects in Fatigue: Research-Design Interface. (PVP Ser.: Vol. 71). 256p. 1983. pap. text ed. 50.00 (ISBN 0-317-02651-8, H00257). ASME.

Tourret, R. & Wright, E. P., eds. Symposium on Rolling Fatigue Performance: Testing of Lubricants. 324p. 1979. 88.95 (ISBN 0-471-25823-7). Wiley.

Verma, S. K. Materials Performance in Coal Gasification Environments. write for info. Metal Prop Coun.

Young, J. F., ed. Very High Strength Cement-Based Materials, Vol. 42. LC 85-5144. 1985. text ed. 36.00 (ISBN 0-931837-07-3). Materials Res.

MATERIALS–HANDLING AND TRANSPORTATION

see Materials Handling

MATERIALS–RADIOGRAPHY

see Radiography, Industrial

MATERIALS–RESEARCH

see Materials Research

MATERIALS–STRENGTHENING MECHANISMS

see Strengthening Mechanisms in Solids

MATERIALS–TESTING

see also Brittleness; Materials–Fatigue; Mechanical Wear; Moire Method

American Society for Materials & Testing. Computer Automation of Materials Testing, STP 710. (710). 235p. 1980. 21.75x (ISBN 0-8031-0267-4, 04-710000-32). ASTM.

American Society for Testing & Materials: Proceedings. 590p. 1983. 29.50 (ISBN 0-8031-0536-3, 07-000830-00). ASTM.

MATERIALS—THERMAL PROPERTIES

MATERIALS, EFFECT OF RADIATION ON

Fridman, Ya. B., ed. Strength & Deformation in Nonuniform Temperature Fields. LC 63-17641. 169p. 1964. 30.00x (ISBN 0-306-10688-4, Consultants). Plenum Pub.

Kircher, John F. & Bowman, Richard E. Effects of Radiation on Materials & Components. LC 64-16977. 702p. (Orig.). 1964. 38.50 (ISBN 0-686-81277-8). Krieger.

Kramer, et al, eds. Effects of Radiation on Materials- 10th International Symposium- STP 725: 10th International Symposium, STP 725. 765p. 1981. 60.00 (ISBN 0-8031-0755-2, 04-725000-35). ASTM.

Narayan, J. & Brown, W. L., eds. Laser-Solid Interactions & Transient Thermal Processing of Materials. 782p. 1983. 104.50 (ISBN 0-444-00788-1, North Holland). Elsevier.

Silverman, Joseph, ed. Advances in Radiation Processing: Transactions of the Second International Meeting on Radiation Processing Held at Miami, Florida 22-26 Oct. 1978, 2 vols, Vol. 14, No. 1-3 & 4-6. 948p. 1980. Set. 145.00 (ISBN 0-08-025025-4). Pergamon.

Steele, Lendell E., ed. Radiation Embrittlement & Surveillance of Nuclear Reactor Pressure Vessels: An International Study - STP 819. LC 83-70258. 218p. 1983. text ed. 34.00 (ISBN 0-8031-0263-1, 04-819000-35). ASTM.

MATERIALS, MAGNETIC

see Magnetic Materials

MATERIALS, RADIOACTIVE

see Radioactive Substances

MATERIALS, STRENGTH OF

see Strength of Materials

MATERIALS AT HIGH TEMPERATURES

see also Heat Resistant Materials; Metals at High Temperatures

Bahn, Gilbert S. Kinetics, Equilibria, & Performance of High Temperature Systems. 406p. 1963. 106.50 (ISBN 0-677-10030-2). Gordon.

Baylac, G., ed. Inelastic Analysis & Life Prediction In Elevated Temperature Design. (PVP Ser.: Vol. 59). 250p. 1982. 44.00 (H00216). ASME.

Belton, G. R. & Worrell, W. L., eds. Heterogeneous Kinetics at Elevated Temperatures. LC 70-128401. 532p. 1970. 75.00x (ISBN 0-306-30500-3, Plenum Pr). Plenum Pub.

British Ceramic Research Association Symposium. Special Ceramics: Proceedings, 3 vols. Popper, P., ed. Incl. Vol. 1. 1961. 55.00 (ISBN 0-12-561650-3); Vol. 2. 1963; Vol. 3. 1966. Acad Pr.

Chu, C. W. & Woolam, J. A., eds. High Pressure & Low-Temperature Physics. LC 78-7290. 614p. 1978. 89.50x (ISBN 0-306-40014-6, Plenum Pr). Plenum Pub.

Foroulis, Z. A., ed. High Temperature Metallic Corrosion of Sulfur & Its Compounds. LC 71-120299. pap. 68.80 (ISBN 0-317-08511-5, 2051581). Bks Demand UMI.

Ginzburg, V. L. & Kirzhnits, D. A., eds. High-Temperature Superconductivity. Agyei, A. K., tr. from Russian. LC 82-5295. 364p. 1982. 59.50x (ISBN 0-306-10970-0, AACR2, Consultants). Plenum Pub.

Gole, James L. & Stwalley, William C., eds. Metal Bonding & Interactions in High Temperature Systems with Emphasis on Alkali Metals. LC 81-20555. (ACS Symposium Ser.: No. 179). 1982. 59.95 (ISBN 0-8412-0689-9). Am Chemical.

International Union of Theoretical & Applied Mechanics Symposium, Glasgow, 1968. Thermoinelasticity: Proceedings. Boley, B. A., ed. LC 75-94050. (Illus.). 1970. 79.70 (ISBN 0-387-80961-9). Springer-Verlag.

Jortner, J., ed. Thermomechanical Behavior of High Temperature Composites. (AD-04 Ser.). 1982. 30.00 (H00248). ASME.

McLean, M. Directionally Solidified Materials for High Temperature Service. 345p. (Orig.). 1983. pap. text ed. 50.00x (ISBN 0-904357-51-1, Pub. by the MetalS Society). Brookfield Pub Co.

Norton, J. F., ed. High Temperature Materials Corrosion in Coal Gasification Atmospheres. 152p. 1984. 37.00 (ISBN 0-85334-241-5, I-522-83, Pub. by Elsevier Applied Sci England). Elsevier.

Schaefer, A. O., ed. Reports of Current Work on Behavior of Materials at Elevated Temperatures: November 18-21, 1974, New York, N. Y. Held as Part of the 1974 ASME Winter Annual Meeting. LC 74-22198. pap. 48.30 (ISBN 0-317-08567-0, 2016882). Bks Demand UMI.

Symposium on Thermophysical Properties, 3rd, 1965, Purdue University. Advances in Thermophysical Properties at Extreme Temperatures & Pressures: Papers Presented at Third Symposium on Thermophysical Properties. Gratch, Serge, ed. LC 59-1391. pap. 88.00 (ISBN 0-317-08326-0, 2015857). Bks Demand UMI.

Toropov, N. A. Structural Transformations in Glasses at High Temperatures. LC 58-44503. (The Structure of Glass Ser.: Vol. 5). 223p. 1965. 39.50 (ISBN 0-306-18305-6, Consultants). Plenum Pub.

Toropov, N. A., ed. Chemistry of High Temperature Materials. LC 74-79891. (Illus.). 237p. 1969. 35.00x (ISBN 0-306-10820-8, Consultants). Plenum Pub.

Yamada, Y. & Roche, R. L., eds. An International Dialogue of Experiences In Elevated Temperature Design: Benchmark Problem Studies & Piping System At Elevated Temperatures. (PVP Ser.: Vol. 66). 204p. 1982. 30.00 (H00223). ASME.

Yamada, Y & Roche, R. L., eds. An International Dialogue of Experiences In Elevated Temperature Design: Material Behavior at Elevated Temperatures & Components Analysis. (PVP Ser.: Vol. 60). 178p. 1982. 34.00 (H00217). ASME.

MATERIALS AT LOW TEMPERATURES

Chu, C. W. & Woolam, J. A., eds. High Pressure & Low-Temperature Physics. LC 78-7290. 614p. 1978. 89.50x (ISBN 0-306-40014-6, Plenum Pr). Plenum Pub.

Clark, A. F., et al, eds. Nonmetallic Materials & Composites at Low Temperatures One. LC 78-26576. (Cryogenic Materials Ser.). 456p. 1979. 69.50x (ISBN 0-306-40077-4, Plenum Pr). Plenum Pub.

Fracture Toughness Testing at Cryogenic Temperatures - STP 496. 82p. 1971. pap. 5.00 (ISBN 0-8031-0034-5, 04-496000-30). ASTM.

International Conference, Newcastle upon Tyne 1st, 1981. Cryogenic Concrete: Proceedings. Concrete Society, ed. (Illus.). 352p. 1983. text ed. 58.00 (ISBN 0-86095-705-5). Longman.

McClintock, P. V. & Meredith, D. J. Matter at Low Temperatures. 264p. 1984. pap. text ed. 29.95x (ISBN 0-471-81315-X, Pub. by Wiley-Interscience). Wiley.

Perepechko, I. I. Low-Temperature Properties of Polymers. 272p. 1981. 44.00 (ISBN 0-08-025301-6). Pergamon.

Reed, R. P. & Clark, A. F., eds. Materials at Low Temperatures. 1983. 116.00 (ISBN 0-87170-146-4). ASM.

Stephens, Ralph I., ed. Fatigue at Low Temperatures-STP 857. LC 84-70334. (Illus.). 325p. 1985. text ed. 44.00 (ISBN 0-8031-0411-1, 04-857000-30). ASTM.

White, Guy K. Experimental Techniques in Low-Temperature Physics. 3rd ed. (Monographs on the Physics & Chemistry of Materials). (Illus.). 1979. 59.00x (ISBN 0-19-851359-3). Oxford U Pr.

Wigley, D. A. Mechanical Properties of Materials at Low Temperatures. LC 72-159030. (International Cryogenics Monographs). 326p. 1971. 49.50x (ISBN 0-306-30514-3, Plenum Pr). Plenum Pub.

MATERIALS HANDLING

see also Bulk Solids Handling; Cargo Handling; Conveying Machinery; Hydraulic Conveying; Motor-Trucks; Pallets (Shipping, Storage, etc.)

Allegri, Theodore H. Materials Handling: Principles & Applications. (Illus.). 480p. 1984. 42.50 (ISBN 0-442-20985-1). Van Nos Reinhold.

American Society for Testing & Materials. Plane Strain Crack Toughness: Testing of High Strength Metallic Materials. LC 66-29517. (American Society for Testing & Materials, Special Technical Publication Ser.: No. 410). pap. 34.00 (ISBN 0-317-08331-7, 2051707). Bks Demand UMI.

Apple, J. M. Plant Layout & Materials Handling. 3rd ed. LC 77-75127. (Illus.). 600p. 1977. 40.95x (ISBN 0-471-07171-4). Wiley.

Apple, James M. Material Handling Systems Design. (Illus.). 656p. 1972. 51.50 (ISBN 0-471-06652-4, Pub. by Wiley-Interscience). Wiley.

ASTM Committee F-20, Division on Hazardous Materials Spill Response, ed. A Guide to the Safe Handling of Hazardous Materials Accidents- STP 825-A. LC 83-71801. 55p. 1983. pap. text ed. 15.00 (ISBN 0-8031-0261-5, 04-825000-31). ASTM.

ASTM Standards on Computerized Systems. LC 83-641658. (Annual Books of ASTM Standards, 1983). 102p. 1983. pap. 19.00 (ISBN 0-8031-0269-0, 03-53108-32). ASTM.

Automated Materials Handling: Proceedings of the 2nd International Conference. 1985. 80.00x (ISBN 0-903608-90-1, Pub. by IFS Pubns UK). Air Sci Co.

Automation in Warehousing: Proceedings of the Fifth International Conference, Atlanta, GA, U. S. A., December 1983. 80.00 (ISBN 0-903608-52-9, IFSPUBS). Scholium Intl.

Boresi, Arthur P., et al. Advanced Mechanics of Materials. 3rd ed. LC 77-28283. 696p. 1978. text ed. 44.50x (ISBN 0-471-08892-7). Wiley.

Chemical Engineering Magazine. Solids Handling. McNaughton, Kenneth, ed. (Illus.). 263p. 1981. 32.50 (ISBN 0-07-010781-5). McGraw.

Chen, M. M., et al, eds. Transport Phenomena in Materials Processing. (HTD Ser.: Vol. 10). 124p. 1983. pap. text ed. 30.00 (ISBN 0-317-02657-7, H00283). ASME.

Colijn, Hendrik. Weighing & Proportioning of Bulk Solids. 2nd ed. LC 74-77792. (Bulk Materials Handling Ser.). (Illus.). 362p. 1983. 60.00 (ISBN 0-87849-047-7). Trans Tech.

Cost, Patricia, ed. Selected Bibliography: Materials Handling. 1984. pap. 22.00 (ISBN 0-89938-020-4). Tech & Ed Ctr Graph Arts RIT.

Hollier, R. H., ed. Automated Materials Handling: Proceedings of the First International Conference, London, UK, April 1983. iv, 284p. 1983. 72.50 (ISBN 0-444-86666-3, I-279-83, North-Holland). Elsevier.

Kulwiecv, Raymond A., et al. Materials Handling Handbook. 2nd ed. American Society of Mechanical Engineering, ed. LC 84-10443. 1458p. 1985. 79.95x (ISBN 0-471-09782-9, Pub. by Wiley-Interscience); text ed. write for info. Wiley.

Leenders, Michael R., et al. Purchasing & Materials Management. 7th ed. 1980. 30.95x (ISBN 0-256-02374-3). Irwin.

Lindkvist, R. G. T. Handbook of Materials Handling. 1984. 69.95 (ISBN 0-470-20098-7). Halsted Pr.

Material Handling Equipment. 1983. 495.00 (ISBN 0-318-00498-4). Busn Trend.

Murphy, G. J. Transport & Distribution. 2nd ed. 300p. 1978. text ed. 36.75x (ISBN 0-220-66321-1, Pub. by Busn Bks England). Brookfield Pub Co.

--The Transport Operators Guide to Professional Competence. 314p. 1980. pap. 21.00x (ISBN 0-09-141591-8, Pub. by Busn Bks England). Brookfield Pub Co.

Road Haulage Companies. 1985. 200.00x (ISBN 0-317-14464-2, Pub. by Jordan & Sons UK). State Mutual Bk.

Wasp, Edward J., et al. Slurry Pipeline Transportation. new ed. (Bulk Materials Handling Ser.). (Illus.). 300p. 1977. text ed. 60.00 (ISBN 0-87849-016-7). Trans Tech.

Wireman, Terry. Plant Layout & Material Handling. 1984. text ed. 27.95 (ISBN 0-8359-5577-X). Reston.

Zajic, J. E. & Himmelman, W. A. Highly Hazardous Material Spills & Emergency Planning. (Hazardous & Toxic Substances Ser.: Vol. 1). 1978. pap. 55.00 (ISBN 0-8247-7228-8). Dekker.

MATERIALS MANAGEMENT

Brown, Robert G. Materials Management Systems: A Modular Library. LC 77-8281. 436p. 1977. 45.95x (ISBN 0-471-11182-1, Pub. by Ronald Pr). Wiley.

Cavinato, Joseph L. Purchasing & Materials Management: Integrative Strategies. (Illus.). 550p. 1984. text ed. 30.95 (ISBN 0-314-77869-1); instr's. manual avail. (ISBN 0-314-77870-5). West Pub.

Charles, J. A. & Crane, F. A. Selection & Use of Engineering Materials. (Illus.). 328p. 1984. text ed. 49.95 (ISBN 0-408-10858-4); pap. text ed. 29.95 (ISBN 0-408-10859-2). Butterworth.

Colton, Raymond R. & Rohrs, Walter F. Industrial Purchasing & Effective Materials Management. 1984. text ed. 23.95 (ISBN 0-8359-3096-3); instr's manual avail. (ISBN 0-8359-3097-1). Reston.

Compton, H. K. Supplies & Materials Management. 2nd ed. (Illus.). 512p. 1979. text ed. 37.50x (ISBN 0-7121-1964-7, Pub. by Macdonald & Evans England). Trans-Atlantic.

Gilmour, Peter & Miller, Jeffrey. Perspectives in Materials Management: A Case Study. 1979. 80.00x (ISBN 0-86176-003-4, Pub. by MCB Pubns). State Mutual Bk.

Heskett, J. L., et al. Case Problems in Business Logistics. 360p. 1973. pap. 25.95 (ISBN 0-471-06599-4). Wiley.

Leenders, Michael R., et al. Purchasing & Materials Management. 7th ed. 1980. 30.95x (ISBN 0-256-02374-3). Irwin.

Nair, N. K. Purchasing & Materials Management. 400p. 1984. pap. text ed. 18.95x (ISBN 0-7069-2719-2, Pub. by Vikas India). Advent NY.

National Materials Advisory Board. National Materials Policy. LC 74-23549. 1975. pap. 12.95 (ISBN 0-309-02247-9). Natl Acad Pr.

Niku-Lari, A. & Al-Hassani, S. T., eds. Shot Peening: Proceedings of the 1st International Conference, Paris, 14-17 September 1981. 528p. 1982. 110.00 (ISBN 0-08-027599-0). Pergamon.

Sanderson, Edward D. Effective Hospital Material Management. 332p. Date not set. price not set (ISBN 0-87189-098-4). Aspen Systems.

Smolik, Donald P. Material Requirements of Manufacturing. 320p. 1982. 24.95 (ISBN 0-442-25855-0). Van Nos Reinhold.

Tersine, R. J. & Campbell, J. H. Modern Materials Management. 282p. 1977. 33.50 (ISBN 0-444-00228-6, North Holland). Elsevier.

Zenz, Gary L. Purchasing & the Management of Materials. 5th ed. LC 80-21649. (Marketing Ser.). 514p. 1981. 37.50x (ISBN 0-471-06091-7). Wiley.

MATERIALS RESEARCH

Altenpohl, D. G., et al. Materials in World Perspective. (Materials Research & Engineering Ser.: Vol. 1). (Illus.). 208p. 1980. pap. 39.00 (ISBN 0-387-10037-7). Springer-Verlag.

Applications of Electron Microfractography to Materials Research - STP 493. 96p. 1971. pap. 8.25 (ISBN 0-8031-0746-3, 04-493000-30). ASTM.

Bewersdorff, A., ed. Materials Science in Space. (Advances in Space Research Ser.: Vol. 1, No. 5). (Illus.). 171p. 1981. pap. 23.00 (ISBN 0-08-027161-8). Pergamon.

Braun, J. D., et al. Microstructural Science, Vol. 5. 508p. 1977. 105.00 (ISBN 0-444-00204-9). Elsevier.

Burke, John J. & Weiss, Volker, eds. Risk & Failure Analysis for Improved Performance & Reliability. LC 80-12346. (Sagamore Army Materials Research Conference Proceedings Ser.: Vol. 24). 366p. 1980. 55.00x (ISBN 0-306-40446-X, Plenum Pr). Plenum Pub.

Christian, J. W. & Haasen, P., eds. Progress in Materials Science, Vol. 26. (Illus.). 420p. 1982. 130.00 (ISBN 0-08-029122-8). Pergamon.

Francis, Philip H. & Lindholm, Ulric S. Advanced Experimental Techniques in the Mechanics of Materials. 462p. 1973. 101.25 (ISBN 0-677-12570-4). Gordon.

Grogan, John C. & Conway, John T., eds. Masonry-STP 871: Research, Application & Problems. LC 85-3852. (Illus.). 253p. 1985. text ed. 36.00 (ISBN 0-8031-0402-2, 04-871000-07). ASTM.

Huggins, Robert A., et al, eds. Annual Review of Materials Science, Vol. 2. LC 75-172108. (Illus.). 1972. text ed. 20.00 (ISBN 0-8243-1702-5). Annual Reviews.

--Annual Review of Materials Science, Vol. 3. LC 75-172108. (Illus.). 1973. text ed. 20.00 (ISBN 0-8243-1703-3). Annual Reviews.

--Annual Review of Materials Science, Vol. 4. LC 75-172108. (Illus.). 1974. text ed. 20.00 (ISBN 0-8243-1704-1). Annual Reviews.

--Annual Review of Materials Science, Vol. 5. LC 75-172108. (Illus.). 1975. text ed. 20.00 (ISBN 0-8243-1705-X). Annual Reviews.

--Annual Review of Materials Science, Vol. 6. LC 75-172108. (Illus.). 1976. text ed. 20.00 (ISBN 0-8243-1706-8). Annual Reviews.

--Annual Review of Materials Science, Vol. 10. LC 75-172108. (Illus.). 1980. text ed. 20.00 (ISBN 0-8243-1710-6). Annual Reviews.

Kaldis, E., ed. Current Topics in Materials Science, Vol. 8. 494p. 1982. 113.00 (ISBN 0-444-86273-0, North-Holland). Elsevier.

Kanert, O. & Mehring, M. Static Quadrupole Effects in Disordered Cubic Solids. Diehl, P., ed. Bd. with Nuclear Magnetic Relaxation Spectroscopy. Noack, F. (NMR-Basic Principles & Progress: Vol. 3). (Illus.). 130p. 1971. 32.00 (ISBN 0-387-05392-1). Springer-Verlag.

Kriegel, W. W. & Palmour, H., 3rd, eds. Ceramics in Severe Environments. LC 63-17645. (Materials Science Research Ser.: Vol. 5). 628p. 1971. 89.50x (ISBN 0-306-38505-8, Plenum Pr). Plenum Pub.

Kumar, Dharmenora & Jain, S. K. Materials Science & Manufacturing Processes. Shargava, A. K., ed. 410p. 1983. text ed. 45.00x o. p. (ISBN 0-7069-2146-1, Pub. by Vikas India); pap. text ed. 15.95x (ISBN 0-7069-2146-1, Pub. by Vikas India). Advent NY.

Ludeke. Interfaces & Contacts. (Proceedings of Symposia of Materials Research Society Ser.: Vol. 18). 1983. 88.00 (ISBN 0-444-00820-9). Elsevier.

Materials Performance & the Deep Sea- STP 445. 146p. 1969. pap. 9.50 (ISBN 0-8031-0706-4, 04-445000-41). ASTM.

National Research Council, Commission on Sociotechnical Systems. Materials Technology in the Near-Term Energy Program. xiii, 122p. 1974. pap. 8.50 (ISBN 0-309-02322-X). Natl Acad Pr.

Research Needs Report: Design, Materials & Manufacturing Research. 1976. pap. text ed. 5.00 (ISBN 0-685-72347-X, H00089). ASME.

Roy, Rustum, ed. Materials Science & Engineering in the United States. LC 77-84670. (Illus.). 1970. 22.50x (ISBN 0-271-00101-1). Pa St U Pr.

Technical Insights, Inc. Advanced Materials Research: A Guide to R&D Centers. LC 84-51895. 285p. 1984. 270.00 (ISBN 0-914993-05-4). Tech Insights.

Thomas, J. P. & Cachard, A., eds. Material Characterization Using Ion Beams. LC 77-13269. (NATO ASI Ser. B, Physics: Vol. 28). 535p. 1977. 75.00x (ISBN 0-306-35728-3, Plenum Pr). Plenum Pub.

Duncan, John. The Elements of Complex Analysis. pap. 80.80 (ISBN 0-317-09164-6, 2016025). Bks Demand UMI.

Dunning-Davies, J. Mathematical Methods for Mathematicians, Physical Scientists & Engineers. 425p. 1982. 64.95x (ISBN 0-470-27322-4). Halsted Pr.

Dynkin, E. B., et al. Eleven Papers on Analysis, Probability & Topology. LC 51-5559. (Translations, Ser.: No. 2, Vol. 12). 1966. Repr. of 1959 ed. 27.00 (ISBN 0-8218-1712-4, TRANS 2-12). Am Math.

Eaves, Edgar D. & Carruth, J. H. Introductory Mathematical Analysis. 5th ed. 1978. text ed. 40.03 (ISBN 0-205-05991-0, 5659914); 40.01 (ISBN 0-205-08259-9, 568259); student study guide avail. (ISBN 0-205-05993-7). Allyn.

Eells, J., ed. Complex Analysis Trieste: Proceedings, 1981. (Lecture Notes in Mathematics Ser.: Vol. 950). 428p. 1982. pap. 23.00 (ISBN 0-387-11596-X). Springer-Verlag.

Ehrig, H. & Mahr, B. Fundamentals of Algebraic Specification I. (EATCS Monographs on Theoretical Computer Science: Vol. 6). 336p. 1985. 29.50 (ISBN 0-387-13718-1). Springer-Verlag.

Engel'son, Ja. L., et al. Seven Papers on Analysis. LC 51-5559. (Translations Ser.: No. 2, Vol. 60). 1967. 36.00 (ISBN 0-8218-1760-4, TRANS 2-60). Am Math.

Fedorjuk, M. V., et al. Eleven Papers on Analysis. LC 51-5559. (Translations, Ser.: No. 2, Vol. 34). 1963. 33.00 (ISBN 0-8218-1734-5, TRANS 2-34). Am Math.

Fiacco, A. V. & Kortanek, K. O., eds. Semi-Infinite Programming & Applications. (Lecture Notes in Economics & Mathematical Systems: Vol. 215). 322p. 1983. pap. 23.50 (ISBN 0-387-12304-0). Springer-Verlag.

Fikhtengol'ts, G. M. Fundamentals of Mathematical Analysis, 2 Vols. 1965. Vol. 1. pap. 18.75 (ISBN 0-08-013473-4). Pergamon.

Fischer, E. Intermediate Real Analysis. (Undergraduate Texts in Mathematics Ser.). (Illus.). 770p. 1983. 32.00 (ISBN 0-387-90721-1). Springer-Verlag.

Folland, Gerald B. Real Analysis: Modern Techniques & Their Applications. LC 84-10435. (Pure & Applied Mathematics Ser.: 1-237). 350p. 1984. text ed. 34.95 (ISBN 0-471-80958-6, Pub. by Wiley-Interscience). Wiley.

Fomin, S., et al. Nine Papers on Foundations, Measure Theory, & Analysis. (Translations Ser.: No. 2, Vol. 57). 1966. 37.00 (ISBN 0-8218-1757-4, TRANS 2-57). Am Math.

Freud, G. Orthogonale Polynome. (Mathematische Eihe Ser.: No. 33). (Ger., Illus.). 294p. 1969. 49.95x (ISBN 0-8176-0127-9). Birkhauser.

Friedman, Avner. Foundations of Modern Analysis. (Illus.). 250p. 1983. pap. 5.50 (ISBN 0-486-64062-0). Dover.

Fulton, W. Intersection Theory. (Ergbenisse der Mathematik und iher Grenzgebiete: 3. Folge, Vol. 2). 480p. 1983. 39.00 (ISBN 0-387-12176-5). Springer-Verlag.

Gagaev, B. M., et al. Thirteen Papers on Analysis. LC 51-5559. (Translations Ser.: No. 2, Vol. 10). 1963. Repr. of 1958 ed. 32.00 (ISBN 0-8218-1710-8, TRANS 2-10). Am Math.

Gahler, W. Grundstrukturen der Analysis, 2 vols. (Mathematische Reihe Ser.: Nos. 58 & 61). (Ger.). 1978. Vol. 1, 396p. 54.95x (ISBN 0-8176-0901-6); Vol. 2, 496p. 71.95x (ISBN 0-8176-0966-0). Birkhauser.

Garnir, H. G. Les Problemes aux Limites de la Physique Mathematique. (Mathematische Reihe Ser.: No. 23). (Fr., Illus.). 234p. 1958. 36.95x (ISBN 0-8176-0134-1). Birkhauser.

Garnir, H. G., et al. Analyse Fonctionnelle. 2nd ed. Incl. Vol. 1. Theorie Generale. 562p. 1968. 101.95 (ISBN 0-8176-0135-X); Vol. 2. Mesure et Integration dans l'Espace Euclidien. 288p. 1972. 61.95x (ISBN 0-8176-0545-2); Vol. 3. Espaces Fonctionnels Usuels. 375p. 1973. 81.95 (ISBN 0-8176-0546-0). (Mathematische Reihe Ser.: Vols. 36, 37 & 45). (Fr.). Birkhauser.

Gaughan, Edward D. Introduction to Analysis. 2nd ed. LC 75-16601. (Contemporary Undergraduate Mathematics Ser.). 1975. text ed. 23.25 pub net (ISBN 0-8185-0172-3). Brooks-Cole.

Gelbaum, B. R. Problems in Analysis. (Problem Books in Mathematics). (Illus.). 224p. 1982. 32.00 (ISBN 0-387-90692-4). Springer-Verlag.

Gohagan, John K. Quantitative Analysis for Public Policy. (Quantitative Methods for Management Ser.). (Illus.). 1980. text ed. 34.95x (ISBN 0-07-023570-8). McGraw.

Gohberg, I. Z. & Feldman, I. A. Faltungsgleichungen und Projektionsverfahren Zu Ihrer Losung. Prossdorf, S., ed. (Mathematische Reihe Ser.: No. 49). (Ger.). 288p. 1974. 39.95x (ISBN 0-8176-0722-6). Birkhauser.

Goldberg, Richard R. Methods of Real Analysis. 2nd ed. LC 75-30615. 402p. 1976. text ed. 41.00x (ISBN 0-471-31065-4). Wiley.

Goldstein, M. & Dillon, W. R. Discrete Discriminant Analysis. 190p. 1978. 34.50x (ISBN 0-471-04167-X, Pub. by Wiley-Interscience). Wiley.

Golinskii, B. L., et al. Thirteen Papers on Algebra & Analysis. LC 51-5559. (Translations Ser.: No. 2, Vol. 76). 1968. 35.00 (ISBN 0-8218-1776-0, TRANS 2-76). Am Math.

Greenberg, Harvey & Maybee, John, eds. Computer-Assisted Analysis & Model Simplification. LC 80-28509. 1981. 44.50 (ISBN 0-12-299680-1). Acad Pr.

Greub, Werner, et al. Connections, Curvature, & Cohomology, 3 vols. Incl. Vol. 1. De Rham Cohomology of Manifold & Vector Bundles. 1972. 69.50 (ISBN 0-12-302701-2); Vol. 2. Lie Groups, Principal Bundles & Characteristic Classes. 1973. 79.50 (ISBN 0-12-302702-0); Vol. 3. Cohomology of Principle Bundles & Homogeneous Spaces. 1976. 94.00 (ISBN 0-12-302703-9). (Pure & Applied Mathematics Ser.). Acad Pr.

Grossman. Applied Mathematical Analysis. 1985. text ed. write for info (ISBN 0-534-05766-7). Wadsworth Pub.

Gunning, R. C. Problems in Analysis: A Symposium in Honor of Salomon Bochner. (Mathematical Series, No. 31). 1970. 39.00 (ISBN 0-691-08076-3). Princeton U Pr.

Haack, W. & Wendland, W. Vorlesungen uber Partielle und pfaffsche Diggerentialgleichungen. (Mathematische Reihe Ser.: No. 3). (Ger., Illus.). 555p. 1969. 92.95x (ISBN 0-8176-0159-7). Birkhauser.

Henrici, P. Applied & Computational Complex Analysis: Discrete Fourier Analysis, Cauchy Integrals, Construction of Conformal Maps, Univalent Functions. (Pure & Applied Mathematics Ser.). 1985. write for info. (ISBN 0-471-08703-3). Wiley.

Henrici, Peter. Applied & Computational Complex Analysis: Power Series, Integration-Conformal Mapping-Location of Zeroes, Vol. 1. LC 73-19723. (Pure & Applied Mathematics Ser.). 682p. 1974. 59.95x (ISBN 0-471-37244-7, Pub. by Wiley-Interscience). Wiley.

Hille, Einar. Einar Hille: Selected Papers: Classical Analysis & Functional Analysis. Kallman, Robert R., ed. LC 74-18465. (MIT Press Mathematicians of Our Time Ser.: Vol. 2). 752p. 1975. 55.00x (ISBN 0-262-08080-X). MIT Pr.

Hinchey, Fred A. Introduction to Applicable Mathematics: Advanced Analysis, Vol. 2, Pt. 2. (Applied Mathematics Ser.: I-039). 730p. 1984. text ed. 29.95x (ISBN 0-470-20023-5). Halsted Pr.

Hirsch, M. W., et al. Invariant Manifolds. (Lecture Notes in Mathematics: Vol. 583). 1977. soft cover 13.00 (ISBN 0-387-08148-8). Springer-Verlag.

Hirschmann, I. I., Jr., ed. Studies in Real & Complex Analysis. LC 65-22403. (MAA Studies: No. 3). 213p. 1965. 16.50 (ISBN 0-88385-103-2). Math Assn.

Hope, K. Methods of Multivariate Analysis. 288p. 1978. 56.75 (ISBN 0-677-61360-1). Gordon.

Hubbard, John H. Sur les sections analytiques de la courbe universelle de Teichmuller. LC 75-41604. (Memoirs: No. 166). 137p. 1976. pap. 14.00 (ISBN 0-8218-1866-X, MEMO-166). Am Math.

Hurd, A. E. & Loeb, P. A. An Introduction to Nonstandard Real Analysis. (Pure & Applied Mathematics Ser.). Date not set. text ed. 35.00 (ISBN 0-12-362440-1). Acad Pr.

Hurd, A. E., ed. Nonstandard Analysis: Recent Developments. (Lecture Notes in Mathematics: Vol. 983). 213p. 1983. pap. 14.00 (ISBN 0-387-12279-6). Springer-Verlag.

Iverson, K. E. Elementary Analysis. (Illus., Orig.). 1976. pap. text ed. 7.25 (ISBN 0-917326-01-6). APL Pr.

Johnsonbaugh & Pfaffenberger, eds. Foundations of Mathematical Analysis. (Lecture Notes in Pure & Applied Mathematics: Vol. 62). 1981. 35.00 (ISBN 0-8247-6919-8). Dekker.

Kantenwein, Lee L. Diagrammatical Analysis. 98p. pap. 8.95 (ISBN 0-88469-150-0). BMH Bks.

Kasch, F. Modules & Rings: A Translation of Muduln und Ringe. (London Mathematical Society Monograph: Vol. 17). 1982. 70.00 (ISBN 0-12-400350-8). Acad Pr.

Khinchin, A. I. A Course of Mathematical Analysis. 680p. 1960. 131.95 (ISBN 0-677-20130-3). Gordon.

Klambauer. Problems & Propositions in Analysis. (Lecture Notes in Pure & Applied Mathematics Ser.: Vol. 49). 1979. 35.00 (ISBN 0-8247-6887-6). Dekker.

Klambauer, G. Mathematical Analysis. (Pure & Applied Mathematics Ser.: Vol. 31). 1975. 35.00 (ISBN 0-8247-6329-7). Dekker.

Kloetzler, R. Mehrdimensionale Variationsrechnung. (Mathematische Reihe Ser.: No. 44). (Ger., Illus.). 299p. 1970. 49.95x (ISBN 0-8176-0223-2). Birkhauser.

Krasnoselskiy, M. A., et al. Plane Vector Fields. 1966. 50.00 (ISBN 0-12-425950-2). Acad Pr.

Lachenbruch, Peter A. Discriminant Analysis. LC 74-11057. 1975. 14.95x (ISBN 0-02-848250-6). Hafner.

Lakshmikanthan, V., ed. Applied Nonlinear Analysis. LC 79-10237. 1979. 65.00 (ISBN 0-12-434180-2). Acad Pr.

Lang. Real Analysis. 1983. 34.95 (ISBN 0-201-14179-5). Addison Wesley.

Lang, S. Undergraduate Analysis. (Undergraduate Texts in Mathematics Ser.). (Illus.). 545p. 1983. Repr. of 1968 ed. 29.50 (ISBN 0-387-90800-5). Springer-Verlag.

Laufer, Henry B. Normal Two-Dimensional Singularities. LC 78-160261. (Annals of Mathematics Studies: No. 71). 1971. 21.50 (ISBN 0-691-08100-X). Princeton U Pr.

Lawrynowicz, J., ed. Analytic Functions Kozubnik 1979: Proceedings. (Lecture Notes in Mathematics: Vol. 798). 476p. 1980. pap. 31.00 (ISBN 0-387-09985-9). Springer-Verlag.

Le Corbeiller, Philippe. Dimensional Analysis. (Program bk). 1966. pap. text ed. 16.95x (ISBN 0-89197-126-2). Irvington.

Levitan, B. M., et al. Six Papers in Analysis. LC 73-15614. (Translations Ser.: No. 2, Vol. 101). 1973. 43.00 (ISBN 0-8218-3051-1, TRANS 2-101). Am Math.

Li, Ching C. Path Analysis: A Primer. 1975. pap. text ed. 11.95x (ISBN 0-910286-40-X). Boxwood.

McBrien, Vincent O. Introductory Analysis. LC 61-6044. (Century Mathematics Ser.). (Illus.). 1969. 37.00x (ISBN 0-89197-248-X); pap. text ed. 19.50x (ISBN 0-89197-804-6). Irvington.

Malik, S. C. Mathematical Analysis. 698p. 1984. 29.95x (ISBN 0-470-20025-1). Halsted Pr.

--Principles of Real Analysis. LC 82-20051. 379p. 1982. 21.95x (ISBN 0-470-27369-0). Halsted Pr.

Marsden, Jerrold E. Elementary Classical Analysis. LC 74-5764. (Illus.). 549p. 1974. text ed. 34.95x (ISBN 0-7167-0452-8). W H Freeman.

Marti, J. Konvexe Analysis. (Mathematische Reihe Ser.: No. 54). (Ger.). 286p. 1977. 57.95x (ISBN 0-8176-0839-7). Birkhauser.

Maurin, Krzysztof. Analysis, Part 1: Elements. Lepa, Eugene, tr. from Polish. LC 74-80525. 672p. 1976. lib. bdg. 55.00 (ISBN 90-277-0484-8, Pub. by Reidel Holland). Kluwer Academic.

Meir, A., ed. Spline Functions & Approximation Theory. Sharma, A. (International Series of Numerical Mathematics: No. 21). 386p. 1973. 54.95x (ISBN 0-8176-0670-X). Birkhauser.

Michlin, S. G. Approximation Auf Dem Kubischen Gitter. Lehmann, R., tr. from Rus. (Mathematische Reihe Ser.: No. 59). (Ger.). 204p. 1976. 32.95x (ISBN 0-8176-0873-7). Birkhauser.

Mickley, Harold S., et al. Applied Mathematics in Chemical Engineering. 2nd ed. (Chemical Engineering Ser.). (Illus.). 1957. text ed. 42.00 (ISBN 0-07-041800-4). McGraw.

Milnor, John. Introduction to Algebraic K-Theory. LC 74-161197. (Annals of Mathematics Studies: No. 72). 220p. 1971. 23.50 (ISBN 0-691-08101-8). Princeton U Pr.

Mitrinovic, D. S. & Vasic, P. M. Analytic Inequalities. LC 76-116492. (Grundlehren der Mathematischen Wissenschaften: Vol. 165). (Illus.). 1970. 47.00 (ISBN 0-387-04837-5). Springer-Verlag.

Moise, E. E. Introductory Problem Courses in Analysis & Topology. (Universitext Ser.). 94p. 1982. pap. 15.00 (ISBN 0-387-90701-7). Springer-Verlag.

Moore, R. E. Methods & Applications of Interval Analysis. LC 79-67191. (SIAM Studies in Applied Mathematics: No. 2). xi, 190p. 1979. text ed. 19.50 (ISBN 0-89871-161-4). Soc Indus-Appl Math.

Mozzochi, C. J. Foundations of Analysis: Landau Revisited. LC 75-46243. 1976. text ed. 7.50 (ISBN 0-682-48511-X, University). Exposition Pr FL.

Nachbin, Leopoldo, ed. Mathematical Analysis & Applications. (Advances in Mathematics Supplementary Studies: Vol. 7). 1981. Pt. A. 70.00 (ISBN 0-12-512801-0); Pt. B. 65.00 (ISBN 0-12-512802-9). Acad Pr.

Nevanlinna, F. & Nevanlinna, R. Absolute Analysis. Emig, P., tr. from Ger. LC 73-75652. (Die Grundlehren der Mathematischen Wissenschaften: Vol. 102). (Illus.). 280p. 1973. 58.00 (ISBN 0-387-05917-2). Springer-Verlag.

Nikolsky, S. M. Course of Mathematical Analysis, 2 vols. 901p. 1977. Set. 16.50 (ISBN 0-8285-0706-6, Pub. by Mir Pubs USSR); Vol. 1; 460 Pp. 8.50 (ISBN 0-8285-0709-0); Vol. 2; 441 Pp. 8.50 (ISBN 0-8285-0711-2). Imported Pubns.

Ostrowski, A. Aufgabensammlung zur Infinitesimalrechnung. Incl. Vol. 1. Funktionen Einer Variablen. 341p. 1967. 41.95x (ISBN 0-8176-0290-9); Vol. 2A. Differentialrechnung Auf Dem Gebiete Mehrerer Varíblen. Aufgaben und Hinweise. 300p. 1972. 41.95x (ISBN 0-8176-0534-7); Vol. 2B. Differentialrechnung Auf Dem Gebiete Mehrerer Variablen, Losungen. 233p. 1972. 41.95x (ISBN 0-8176-0572-X). (Mathematische Reihe Ser.: Vols. 28, 38, 47 & 56). (Ger.). Birkhauser.

Parzynski, William & Zipse, Philip. Introduction to Mathematical Analysis. (Illus.). 384p. 1982. text ed. 34.95x (ISBN 0-07-048845-2). McGraw.

Paul & Haessler. Introductory Mathematical Analysis. 4th ed. 1984. text ed. 31.95 (ISBN 0-8359-3274-5); solutions manual avail. (ISBN 0-8359-3275-3). Reston.

Perry, P. Scattering Theory by the Enss Method. (Mathematical Reports: Vol. 1, No. 1). 347p. 1984. 82.00 (ISBN 3-7186-0093-5). Harwood Academic.

Polya, G. & Szego, G. Problems & Theorems in Analysis, No. 1: Series, Integral Calculus, Theory of Functions. (Illus.). 1970. pap. 21.50 (ISBN 0-387-90224-4). Springer-Verlag.

Pothoven, K. & Mukherjea, A., eds. Real & Functional Analysis. LC 77-14282. (Mathematical Concepts & Methods in Science & Engineering Ser: Vol. 6). (Illus.). 539p. 1977. 49.50x (ISBN 0-306-31015-5, Plenum Pr). Plenum Pub.

Prossdorf, S. Einige Klassen Singularer Gleichungen. (Mathematische Reihe Ser.: No. 46). (Ger.). 366p. 1974. 64.95x (ISBN 0-8176-0724-2). Birkhauser.

Protter, M. H. & Morrey, C. B. A First Course in Real Analysis. LC 76-43978. (Undergraduate Texts in Mathematics Ser.). 1977. 29.50 (ISBN 0-387-90215-5). Springer-Verlag.

Protter, Murray H. & Morrey, Charles B., Jr. Modern Mathematical Analysis. 1964. 34.95 (ISBN 0-201-05995-9). Addison-Wesley.

Reid, William H., ed. Mathematical Problems in the Geophysical Sciences II: Inverse Problems, Dynamo Theory & Tides. LC 62-21481. (Lectures in Applied Mathematics Ser.: Vol. 14). 370p. 1971. 46.00 (ISBN 0-8218-1114-2, LAM-14). Am Math.

Reimann, H. M. & Rychener, T. Funktionen Beschrankter Mittlerer Oszillation. (Lecture Notes in Mathematics: Vol. 487). 141p. 1975. pap. 10.70 (ISBN 0-387-07404-X). Springer-Verlag.

Rheinbolt, W. C. Numerical Analysis of Parameterized Nonlinear Equations. (Lecture Notes in the Mathematical Sciences Ser.). 256p. 1985. pap. 29.50 (ISBN 0-471-88814-1). Wiley.

Riley, K. F. Mathematical Methods for the Physical Sciences. LC 73-89765. 512p. (Orig.). 1974. 69.50 (ISBN 0-521-20390-2); pap. 27.95x (ISBN 0-521-09839-4). Cambridge U Pr.

Rockafellar, R. Tyrrell. Convex Analysis. LC 68-56318. (Mathematical Ser.: No. 28). 1969. 40.00 (ISBN 0-691-08069-0). Princeton U Pr.

Rota, Gian-Carlo, ed. Studies in Analysis. (Advances in Mathematics Supplementary Studies Ser.: Vol. 4). 1979. 70.00 (ISBN 0-12-599150-9). Acad Pr.

Rudin, Walter. Lectures on the Edge-of-the-Wedge Theorem. LC 73-145640. (CBMS Regional Conference Series in Mathematics: No. 6). vi, 30p. 1971. 9.00 (ISBN 0-8218-1655-1, CBMS-6). Am Math.

--Principles of Mathematical Analysis. (International Series in Pure & Applied Mathematics). 1976. text ed. 42.95 (ISBN 0-07-054235-X). McGraw.

--Real & Complex Analysis. 2nd ed. (Higher Mathematics Ser.). 416p. 1973. text ed. 45.95 (ISBN 0-07-054233-3). McGraw.

Samoilenko, A. M. & Ronto, N. I. Numerical-Analytic Methods of Investigating Periodic Solutions. 183p. 1979. pap. 4.95 (ISBN 0-8285-1514-X, Pub. by Mir Pubs USSR). Imported Pubns.

Sanin, Nikolai A. Constructive Real Numbers & Function Spaces. LC 68-19437. (Translations of Mathematical Monographs: Vol. 21). 1968. 42.00 (ISBN 0-8218-1571-7, MMONO-21). Am Math.

Schulze, B. W. & Wildenhain, G. Methoden der Potential Theorie Fur Elliptische Differentialgleichungen Beliebiger Ordnung. (Mathematische Reihe Ser.: No. 60). (Ger.). 424p. 1977. 91.95x (ISBN 0-8176-0944-X). Birkhauser.

Seminaire Pierre Lelong (Analyse) Annee 1973-4. Proceedings. (Lecture Notes in Mathematics: Vol. 474). 182p. 1975. pap. 10.70 (ISBN 0-387-07189-X). Springer-Verlag.

Shilov, G. Y. Mathematical Analysis: A Special Course. 1965. pap. 24.20 (ISBN 0-08-013616-8). Pergamon.

Kohlas, Jurg. Stochastic Methods of Operations Research. LC 81-21574. 160p. 1982. 39.50 (ISBN 0-521-23899-4); pap. 14.95 (ISBN 0-521-28292-6). Cambridge U Pr.

Louden, Louise & Church, John. Mathematical Modeling. LC 77-88450. (Bibliographic Ser.: No. 278). 1977. pap. 45.00 (ISBN 0-87010-029-7). Inst Paper Chem.

Magid, A. R. Applied Matrix Models: A Second Course in Linear Algebra with Computer Applications. 240p. 1985. 32.95 (ISBN 0-471-88865-6). Wiley.

Maki, Daniel & Thompson, Maynard. Mathematical Models & Applications: With Emphasis on the Social, Life, & Management Sciences. (Illus.). 464p. 1973. ref. ed. 39.95 (ISBN 0-13-561670-0). P-H.

Marchuk, G. I. & Belykh, L. N., eds. Mathematical Modeling in Immunology & Medicine. 396p. 1983. 51.00 (ISBN 0-444-86588-8, I-36-83, North-Holland). Elsevier.

Mischke, Charles R. Mathematical Model Building: An introduction to Engineering. 2nd rev. ed. (Illus.). 1980. text ed. 21.50x (ISBN 0-8138-1005-1). Iowa St U Pr.

Nicholson, H., ed. Modelling of Dynamical Systems, Vol. 1. (IEE Control Engineering Ser.: No. 12). (Illus.). 256p. 1980. 82.00 (ISBN 0-906048-38-9, CE012). Inst Elect Eng.

--Modelling of Dynamical Systems, Vol. 2. (IEE Control Engineering Ser.: No. 13). (Illus.). 288p. 1981. 82.00 (ISBN 0-906048-45-1, CE013, Pub. by Peregrinus England). Inst Elect Eng.

Pollard, J. H. Mathematical Models for the Growth of Human Populations. LC 72-91957. 204p. 1973. 39.50 (ISBN 0-521-20111-X); pap. 12.95x (ISBN 0-521-29442-8). Cambridge U Pr.

Reismann, Herbert & Pawlik, Peter S. Elastokinetics. LC 74-4510. 512p. 1974. text ed. 44.95 (ISBN 0-8299-0016-0). West Pub.

Research & Education Association Staff, ed. Mathematical Modeling. LC 82-80745. (Illus.). 384p. (Orig.). 1982. pap. text ed. 13.30x (ISBN 0-87891-538-9). Res & Educ.

Roberts, F. S., ed. Energy: Mathematics & Models. LC 75-41915. (SIAM-SIMS Conference Ser.: No. 3). xxiv, 276p. 1976. pap. text ed. 24.00 (ISBN 0-89871-029-4). Soc Indus-Appl Math.

Rubinstein, Mashe F. Patterns of Problem Solving. LC 74-20721. (Illus.). 640p. 1975. text ed. 34.95 ref. ed. (ISBN 0-13-654251-4). P-H.

Saaty, Thomas L. & Alexander, Joyce M. Thinking with Models: Mathematical Models in the Physical, Biological & Social Sciences. (I S Modern Applied Mathematics & Computer Science: Vol. 2). (Illus.). 208p. 1981. 39.00 (ISBN 0-08-026475-1); pap. 16.50 (ISBN 0-08-026474-3). Pergamon.

Sinha, Naresh K. & Kuzsta, Boguslaw. Modeling & Identification of Dynamic Systems. 368p. 1983. 35.95 (ISBN 0-442-28162-5). Van Nos Reinhold.

Skala, Heinz J., et al, eds. Aspects of Vagueness. 1984. lib. bdg. 39.50 (ISBN 90-277-1692-7, Pub. by Reidel Holland). Kluwer Academic.

Smith, J. M. Mathematical Modeling & Digital Simulation for Engineers & Scientists. LC 76-52419. 332p. 1977. 40.50x (ISBN 0-471-80344-8, Pub. by Wiley-Interscience). Wiley.

West, Bruce J. Mathematical Models As a Tool for Social Sciences. 134p. 1980. 35.25 (ISBN 0-677-10390-5). Gordon.

West, Donna. Math Doins for High Achievers. (Illus.). 44p. 1979. pap. text ed. 3.95 (ISBN 0-914634-74-7). DOK Pubs.

Whiteman, Charles H. Linear Rational Expectations Models: A User's Guide. 130p. 1983. 19.50 (ISBN 0-8166-1181-5); pap. 9.95 (ISBN 0-8166-1179-3). U of Minn Pr.

Williams, H. P. Model Building in Mathematical Programming. LC 77-7380. 330p. 1978. pap. 37.95x (ISBN 0-471-99541-X, Pub. by Wiley-Interscience). Wiley.

--Model Building in Mathematical Programming. 1985. 39.95 (ISBN 0-471-90605-0); pap. 19.95 (ISBN 0-471-90606-9). Wiley.

Yaglom, I. M. Mathematical Structures & Mathematical Modeling. 1983. 80.50 (ISBN 0-677-06110-2). Gordon.

MATHEMATICAL NOTATION

see also Quaternions; Vector Analysis

Cajori, Florian. History of Mathematical Notations, 2 vols. Incl. Vol. 1. Notations in Elementary Mathematics. xvi, 467p. 1951. pap. 10.95 (ISBN 0-87548-154-X); Vol. 2. Notations Mainly in Higher Mathematics. xviii, 384p. 1952. 24.95 (ISBN 0-87548-172-8). (Illus.). Open Court.

MATHEMATICAL OPTIMIZATION

see also Decision-Making–Mathematical Models; Dynamic Programming; Experimental Design; Games of Strategy (Mathematics); Programming (Mathematics); System Analysis

Adby, P. R. & Dempster, M. A. Introduction to Optimization Methods. (Mathematics Ser.). 1974. pap. 15.95x (ISBN 0-412-11040-7, NO.6001, Pub. by Chapman & Hall). Methuen Inc.

Albrecht, F. Topics in Control Theory. (Lecture Notes in Mathematics: Vol. 63). 1968. pap. 10.70 (ISBN 0-387-04233-4). Springer-Verlag.

Aubin, J. P. Explicit Methods of Optimization. 300p. 1984. 44.00 (ISBN 0-9912000-0-4, Pub. by Gauthier-Villars FR). Heyden.

Aubin, J. P., et al, eds. Annals of the CEREMADE: Mathematical Techniques of Optimization, Control, & Decision. 223p. 1982. text ed. 27.00x (ISBN 0-8176-3032-5). Birkhauser.

Aubin, Jean-Pierre. Applied Abstract Analysis. LC 77-2382. (Pure & Applied Mathematics Ser.). 263p. 1977. 47.50x (ISBN 0-471-02146-6, Pub. by Wiley-Interscience). Wiley.

Auslender, A., et al, eds. Optimization & Optimal Control: Proceedings. (Lecture Notes in Control & Information Sciences Ser.: Vol. 30). 254p. 1981. pap. 18.00 (ISBN 0-387-10627-8). Springer-Verlag.

Bachem, A., et al, eds. Bonn Workshop on Combinatorial Optimization. (Mathematics Studies: Vol. 66). 312p. 1982. pap. 51.00 (ISBN 0-444-86366-4, I-320-82, North Holland). Elsevier.

Bagchi, A. & Jongen, H. T., eds. Systems & Optimization. (Lecture Notes in Control & Information Sciences Ser.: Vol. 66). x, 206p. 1985. pap. 13.00 (ISBN 0-387-15004-8). Springer-Verlag.

Balakrishna, A. V. & Neustadt, Lucien W., eds. Computing Methods in Optimization Problems: Proceedings. 1964. 55.00 (ISBN 0-12-076950-6). Acad Pr.

Balakrishnan, A. V. & Neustadt, L. W., eds. Techniques of Optimization. 1972. 65.00 (ISBN 0-12-076960-3). Acad Pr.

Bank, B. & Guddat, J., eds. Non-Linear Parametric Optimization. 224p. 1983. 29.95 (ISBN 0-8176-1375-7). Birkhauser.

Bazaraa, M. S. & Shetty, C. M. Foundations of Optimization. (Lecture Notes in Economics & Mathematical Systems: Vol. 122). 1976. pap. 13.00 (ISBN 0-387-07680-8). Springer-Verlag.

Beightler, Charles S., et al. Foundations of Optimization. 2nd ed. (International Ser. in Industrial & Systems Engineering). (Illus.). 1979. text ed. 35.95 (ISBN 0-13-330332-2). P-H.

Bell, D. J. & Jacobson, D. H. Singular Optimal Control Problems. (Mathematics in Science & Engineering Ser.). 1975. 39.50 (ISBN 0-12-085060-5). Acad Pr.

Beltrami, E. J. Algorithmic Approach to Nonlinear Analysis & Optimization. (Mathematics in Science & Engineering Ser.: Vol. 63). 1970. 55.00 (ISBN 0-12-085560-7). Acad Pr.

Bensoussan, A. & Lions, J. L., eds. Analysis & Optimization of Systems: Proceedings of the Sixth International Conference on Analysis & Optimization of Systems, Nice, June 19-22, 1983. (Lecture Notes in Control & Information Sciences,: Vol. 62, Pt. 1). (Illus.). xix, 591p. 1984. pap. 34.50 (ISBN 0-387-13551-0). Springer-Verlag.

--International Symposium on Systems Optimization & Analysis. (Lecture Notes in Control & Information Sciences: Vol. 14). (Illus.). 1979. pap. 20.00 (ISBN 0-387-09447-4). Springer-Verlag.

Bensoussan, E. & Lions, J. L., eds. Analysis & Optimization of Systems: Proceedings of the Sixth International Conference on Analysis & Optimization of Systems. Nice, June 19-22, 1983. (Lecture Notes in Control & Information Sciences: Vol. 63, Pt. 2). (Illus.). xix, 700p. 1984. pap. 34.50 (ISBN 0-387-13552-9). Springer-Verlag.

Bertsekas, Dimitri P. & Shreve, Steven E. Stochastic Optimal Control: The Discrete Time Case. (Mathematics in Science & Engineering Ser.). 1978. 70.00 (ISBN 0-12-093260-1). Acad Pr.

Biennial Seminar of the Canadian Mathematical Congress, 14th University of Western Ontario, August 1973. Optimal Control Theory & Its Applications: Proceedings, 2 pts. Kirby, B. J., ed. (Lecture Notes in Economics & Mathematical Systems Ser.). 1974. Pt. 2. pap. 22.00 (ISBN 0-387-07026-5). Springer-Verlag.

Boggs, Paul, et al, eds. Numerical Optimization Nineteen Eighty-Four. LC 85-50611. xi, 287p. 1985. text ed. 30.50 (ISBN 0-89871-054-5). Soc Indus-Appl Math.

Brosowski, Bruno & Martensen, Erich, eds. Approximation & Optimization in Mathematical Physics. 205p. 1983. pap. 25.80 (ISBN 3-8204-7631-8). P Lang Pubs.

Bunday, B. D. BASIC Optimization Methods. 192p. 1984. pap. 14.95 (ISBN 0-7131-3506-9). E Arnold.

Burstein, Joseph. Sequential Optimization. (Illus.). 90p. 1985. pap. 20.00 (ISBN 0-9607126-2-3). Metrics Pr.

Cea, J., ed. Optimization Techniques Modeling & Optimization in the Service of Man: Pt. 2. LC 76-9857. (Lecture Notes in Computer Science: Vol. 41). 1976. pap. 29.00 (ISBN 0-387-07623-9). Springer-Verlag.

--Optimization Techniques: Modeling & Optimization in the Service of Man, Pt. 1. LC 76-9857. (Lecture Notes in Computer Science Ser.: Vol. 40.). 1976. pap. 39.00 (ISBN 0-387-07622-0). Springer-Verlag.

Cecconi, J. P. & Zolezzi, T., eds. Mathematical Theories of Optimization: Proceedings, S. Margherita Ligure, Genova, Italy, 1981. (Lecture Notes in Mathematics: Vol. 979). 268p. 1983. pap. 17.00 (ISBN 0-387-11999-X). Springer-Verlag.

Cencov, N. N. Statistical Decision Rules & Optimal Inference. LC 81-15039. (Mathematical Monographs: Vol. 53). 88.00 (ISBN 0-8218-4502-0, MMONO). Am Math.

Cesari, Lamberto. Optimization Theory & Applications: Problems with Ordinary Differential Equations. (Applications of Mathematics: Vol. 17). (Illus.). 544p. 1983. 69.50 (ISBN 0-387-90676-2). Springer-Verlag.

Christofides, Nicos, et al, eds. Combinatorial Optimization. LC 78-11131. 425p. 1979. 84.95 (ISBN 0-471-99749-8, Pub. by Wiley-Interscience). Wiley.

CISM (International Center for Mechanical Sciences), Dept. of Automation & Information, 1972. Periodic Optimization, 2 vols. Marzollo, A., ed. (CISM Pubns. Ser.: No. 135). (Illus.). 532p. 1973. Set. pap. 50.70 (ISBN 0-387-81135-4). Springer-Verlag.

Clarke, F. H. Optimization & Nonsmooth Analysis. (Canadian Mathematical Society Ser.). 308p. 1983. 37.50 (ISBN 0-471-87504-X). Wiley.

Clements, D. J. & Anderson, B. D. Singular Optimal Control: The Linear-Quadratic Problem. (Lecture Notes in Control & Information Science: Vol. 5). 1978. pap. 12.00 (ISBN 0-387-08694-3). Springer-Verlag.

Coleman, T. F. Large Sparse Numerical Optimization. (Lecture Notes in Computer Science: Vol. 165). v, 105p. 1984. pap. 11.50 (ISBN 0-387-12914-6). Springer Verlag.

Collatz, L. & Wetterling, W. Optimization Problems. Hadsack, P. R., tr. from Ger. (Applied Mathematical Sciences Ser.: Vol. 17). (Illus.). 370p. (Orig.). 1975. pap. text ed. 22.00 (ISBN 0-387-90143-4). Springer-Verlag.

Collatz, L. & Meinardus, G., eds. Numerische Methoden bei Graphentheoretischen und Kombinatorischen Problemen, Vol. 1. (International Series of Numerical Mathematics: No. 29). (Ger., Illus.). 159p. 1975. 27.95x (ISBN 0-8176-0786-2). Birkhauser.

Collatz, L., et al, eds. Numerische Methoden bei Graphentheoretischen und Kombinatorishen Problemen: Vol. II. (International Series of Numerical Mathematics: No. 46). (Ger. & Eng., Illus.). 255p. 1979. pap. 37.95 (ISBN 0-8176-1078-2). Birkhauser.

Colloquium on Methods of Optimization, Novosibirsk USSR, 1968. Proceedings. Moiseev, N. N., ed. LC 77-106194. (Lecture Notes in Mathematics: Vol. 112). (Eng. & Fr.). 1970. pap. 14.70 (ISBN 0-387-04901-0). Springer-Verlag.

Conference Held at Oberwolfach, Nov. 17-23, 1974, et al. Optimization & Optimal Control: Proceedings. Bulirsch, R. & Oettli, W., eds. LC 75-23372. (Lecture Notes in Mathematics: Vol. 477). vii, 294p. 1975. pap. 18.00 (ISBN 0-387-07393-0). Springer-Verlag.

Conference on Optimization Techniques, 5th. Proceedings, Pt. 2. Ruberti, A., ed. (Lecture Notes in Computer Science: Vol. 4). (Illus.). 389p. 1973. pap. 21.00 (ISBN 0-387-06600-4). Springer-Verlag.

Conley, William. Optimization: A Simplified Approach. (Illus.). 272p. 1981. 20.00 (ISBN 0-89433-121-3). Petrocelli.

Conley, William C. Computer Optimization Techniques. rev. ed. (Illus.). 350p. 1984. text ed. 29.95 (ISBN 0-89433-213-9). Petrocelli.

Daniels, R. W. Introduction to Numerical Methods Optimization Techniques. 294p. 1978. 32.50 (ISBN 0-444-00263-4, North-Holland). Elsevier.

Dantzig, G. B. & Eaves, B. C., eds. Studies in Optimization. LC 74-21481. (MAA Studies: No. 10). 174p. 1977. 16.50 (ISBN 0-88385-110-5). Math Assn.

Dennis, John E. & Schnabel, Robert B. Numerical Methods for Unconstrained Optimization & Nonlinear Equations. (Illus.). 272p. 1983. text ed. 35.95 (ISBN 0-13-627216-9). P-H.

Dixon, L. C. & Szego, G. P., eds. Towards Global Optimisation, Vols. I & II. LC 74-28195. 1975-78. Vol. I. 68.00 (ISBN 0-444-10955-2, North-Holland); Vol. II. 68.00 (ISBN 0-444-85171-2). Elsevier.

Dixon, L. C., et al, eds. Nonlinear Optimization, Theory & Algorithms. 492p. 1980. 35.00x (ISBN 0-8176-3020-1). Birkhauser.

Dixon, L. W., ed. Optimization in Action: Proceedings. 1977. 76.50 (ISBN 0-12-218550-1). Acad Pr.

Dorny, C. Nelson. A Vector Space Approach to Models & Optimization. LC 80-12423. 620p. 1980. lib. bdg. 34.50 (ISBN 0-89874-210-2). Krieger.

Dyer, P. & McReynolds, S. R. Computation & Theory of Optimal Control. (Mathematics in Science & Engineering Ser., Vol. 65). 1970. 70.00 (ISBN 0-12-226250-6). Acad Pr.

Ekeland, Ivar & Turnbull, Thomas. Infinite-Dimensional Optmization & Convexity. LC 83-50048. (Chicago Lectures in Mathematics). (Illus.). viii, 166p. 1983. lib. bdg. 16.00x (ISBN 0-226-19987-8); pap. text ed. 8.00x (ISBN 0-226-19988-6). U of Chicago Pr.

Eschenauer, H. & Olhoff, N., eds. Optimization Methods in Structure Design. 460p. 1983. text ed. 24.95 (ISBN 3-411-01654-X, Pub. by Bibliographisches Institut). Birkhauser.

Fedorov, V. V. Theory of Optimal Experiments. (Probability & Mathematical Statistics Ser.). 1972. 67.00 (ISBN 0-12-250750-9). Acad Pr.

Fleming, W. H. & Rishel, R. W. Deterministic & Stochastic Optimal Control. LC 75-28391. (Applications of Mathematics Ser.: Vol. 1). (Illus.). xi, 222p. 1975. 44.00 (ISBN 0-387-90155-8). Springer-Verlag.

Fletcher, R. Practical Methods of Optimization: Constrained Optimization, Vol. 2. 224p. 1981. 37.95x (ISBN 0-471-27828-9, Pub. by Wiley Interscience). Wiley.

--Practical Methods of Optimization: Unconstrained Optimization, Vol. 1. LC 79-41486. 120p. 1980. 34.95x (ISBN 0-471-27711-8, Pub. by Wiley-Interscience). Wiley.

Foulds, L. Combinatorial Optimization. (Undergraduate Texts in Mathematics Ser.). (Illus.). 280p. 1984. 36.00 (ISBN 0-387-90977-X). Springer-Verlag.

Foulds, L. R. Optimization Techniques: An Introduction. (Undergraduate Text in Mathematics). (Illus.). 502p. 1981. 39.00 (ISBN 0-387-90586-3). Springer-Verlag.

Friedrich, Klaus. Friction & Wear of Polymer Composites. (Progress Report of the VDI-Z Series 18: No. 15). (Illus.). 102p. 1984. pap. 32.00 (ISBN 0-9907001-1-9, Pub. by VDI Verlag Gmbh Dusseldorf). Heyden.

Gabasov, R. & Kirillova, F. The Qualitative Theory of Optimal Processes. Casti, John L., tr. (Control & Systems Theory: Vol. 3). 1976. 110.00 (ISBN 0-8247-6545-1). Dekker.

Gabasov, R. & Kirillova, F. M., eds. Singular Optimal Controls. (Mathematical Concepts & Methods in Science & Engineering Ser.: Vol. 10). (Illus.). 262p. 1978. 29.50x (ISBN 0-306-39250-X, Plenum Pr). Plenum Pub.

Gamkrelidze, R. V. Principles of Optimal Control Theory. LC 77-10742. (Mathematical Concepts & Methods in Science & Engineering Ser.: Vol. 7). 185p. 1977. 32.50 (ISBN 0-306-30977-7, Plenum Pr). Plenum Pub.

Girsanov, I. V. Lectures on Mathematical Theory of Extremum Problems. Louvish, D., tr. from Rus. LC 72-80360. (Lecture Notes in Economics & Mathematical Systems: Vol. 67). (Illus.). 139p. 1972. pap. 11.00 (ISBN 0-387-05857-5). Springer-Verlag.

Glashoff, K. & Gustafson, S. A. Linear Optimization & Approximation: An Introduction to the Theoretical Analysis & Numerical Treatment of Semi-Infinite Programs. (Applied Mathematical Science Ser.: Vol. 45). (Illus.). 197p. 1983. pap. 21.50 (ISBN 0-387-90857-9). Springer-Verlag.

Gottfried, Byron S. & Weisman, Joel. Introduction to Optimization Theory. (Illus.). 592p. 1973. ref. ed. 34.95 (ISBN 0-13-491472-4). P-H.

Greig, D. M. Optimisation. LC 79-42892. (Longman Mathematical Texts). (Illus.). 179p. 1980. pap. text ed. 14.50x (ISBN 0-582-44186-2). Longman.

Hammer, P. L., et al. Discrete Optimization: I & II. (Annals of Discrete Mathematics: Vols. 4 & 5). 1979. I. 76.75 (ISBN 0-444-85322-7, North-Holland); II. 93.75 (ISBN 0-444-85323-5). Elsevier.

Haug, E. J., ed. Computer Aided Analysis & Optimization of Mechanical System Dynamics. (NATO ASI Ser., Series F - Computer & Systems Sciences: Vol. 9). xxii, 700p. 1984. 49.50 (ISBN 0-387-12887-5). Springer-Verlag.

Henn, R., et al, eds. Optimization & Operations Research: Proceedings of a Workshop Held at the University of Bonn, October 2-8, 1977. (Lecture Notes in Econometrics & Operations Research Ser.: Vol. 157). 1978. pap. 17.00 (ISBN 0-387-08842-3). Springer-Verlag.

Hestenes, M. Conjugate Direction Methods in Optimization. (Applications of Mathematics Ser.: Vol. 12). (Illus.). 325p. 1980. 37.00 (ISBN 0-387-90455-7). Springer-Verlag.

Hestenes, Magnus R. Calculus of Variations & Optimal Control Theory. LC 79-25451. 418p. 1980. Repr. of 1966 ed. lib. bdg. 26.50 (ISBN 0-89874-092-4). Krieger.

MATHEMATICAL PHYSICS

see also Boundary Value Problems; Dimensional Analysis; Elasticity; Electricity; Electronics-Mathematics; Engineering Mathematics; Ergodic Theory; Error Functions; Existence Theorems; Gases, Kinetic Theory of; Hydrodynamics; Invariant Imbedding; Magnetism; Nonlinear Theories; Optics, Physical; Perturbation (Mathematics); Potential, Theory of; Random Walks (Mathematics); Sound; Switching Theory; System Analysis; Thermodynamics; Transport Theory

Beiglbeeck, W., et al, eds. Feynman Path Integrals: Proceedings, International Colloquium, Marseilles May 1978. (Lecture Notes in Physics: Vol. 106). 1979. pap. 24.00 (ISBN 0-387-09532-2). Springer-Verlag.

Belinfante, F. J. Survey of Hidden Variables Theories. 376p. 1973. Pergamon.

Berezin, F. A. Method of Second Quantization. (Pure and Applied Physics Ser.: Vol. 24). 1966. 47.50 (ISBN 0-12-089450-5). Acad Pr.

Bhagavantam, S. & Venkatarayudu, T. Theory of Groups & Its Application to Physical Problems. 1969. 32.00 (ISBN 0-12-095460-5). Acad Pr.

Birman, M. S., ed. Topics in Mathematical Physics, 5 vols. Incl. Vol. 1. Spectral Theory & Wave Processes. LC 67-16365. 114p. 1967 (ISBN 0-306-18401-X); Vol. 2. Spectral Theory & Problems in Diffraction. LC 68-28089. 134p. 1968 (ISBN 0-306-18402-8); Vol. 3. Spectral Theory. LC 78-93768. 93p. 1969 (ISBN 0-306-18403-6); Vol. 4. Spectral Theory & Wave Processes. LC 68-28089. 121p. 1971 (ISBN 0-306-18404-4); Vol. 5. Spectral Theory. LC 68-28089. 112p. 1972 (ISBN 0-306-18405-2). 25.00x ea. (Consultants). Plenum Pub.

Bitsadze, A. V. Equations of Mathematical Physics. 1980. 8.95 (ISBN 0-8285-1809-2, Pub. by Mir Pubs USSR). Imported Pubns.

Bleuler, K., et al, eds. Differential Geometrical Methods in Mathematical Physics II: Proceedings, University of Bonn, July 13-16, 1977. (Lecture Notes in Mathematics Ser.: Vol. 676). 1978. pap. 37.00 (ISBN 0-387-08935-7). Springer-Verlag.

Bloom, C. O. & Kazarinoff, N. D. Short Wave Radiation Problems in Homogeneous Media: Asymptotic Solutions. (Lecture Notes in Mathematics: Vol. 522). 1976. 13.00 (ISBN 0-387-07698-0). Springer-Verlag.

Braaksma, B. L., et al, eds. Dynamical Systems & Bifurcations. (Lecture Notes in Mathematics: Vol. 1125). v, 129p. 1985. pap. 9.80 (ISBN 0-387-15233-4). Springer Verlag.

Buckmaster, John D., ed. The Mathematics of Combustion. LC 85-50339. (Frontiers in Applied Mathematics: No. 2). xii, 288p. 1985. 32.50 (ISBN 0-89871-053-7). Soc Indus-Appl Math.

Burke, William L. Applied Differential Geometry. (Illus.). 400p. 1985. 54.50 (ISBN 0-521-26317-4); pap. 19.95 (ISBN 0-521-26929-6). Cambridge U Pr.

Busse, W. & Zelazny, R., eds. Computing in Accelerator Design & Operation. (Lecture Notes in Physics Ser.: Vol. 215). xii, 574p. 1984. pap. 28.00 (ISBN 0-387-13909-5). Springer-Verlag.

Butkov, E. Mathematical Physics. 1968. 38.95 (ISBN 0-201-00727-4). Addison-Wesley.

Cahen, M. & Flato, M., eds. Differential Geometry & Relativity. new ed. (Mathematical Physics & Applied Mathematics Ser: No. 3). 1976. lib. bdg. 42.00 (ISBN 90-277-0745-6, Pub. by Reidel Holland). Kluwer Academic.

Choquet-Bruhat, Y., et al. Analysis, Manifolds & Physics. rev. ed. 630p. 1982. 29.50 (ISBN 0-444-86017-7, North-Holland). Elsevier.

Ciarlet, P. G. Lectures on Three-Dimensional Elasticity. (Tata Institute Lectures on Mathematics). 160p. 1983. pap. 7.90 (ISBN 0-387-12331-8). Springer-Verlag.

CISM (International Center for Mechanical Sciences), Dept. of Automation & Information. Mathematical Structure of Finite Random Cybernetic Systems. Quiasu, S., ed. (CISM Pubns. Ser.: No. 86). (Illus.). 215p. 1974. pap. 21.00 (ISBN 0-387-81174-5). Springer-Verlag.

Claro, F., ed. Nonlinear Phenomena in Physics. (Springer Proceedings in Physics: Vol. 3). (Illus.). ix, 441p. 1985. 35.00 (ISBN 0-387-15273-3). Springer-Verlag.

Courant, R. & Hilbert, D. Methods of Mathematical Physics, 2 vols. Set. 110.00x (ISBN 0-471-17990-6, Pub. by Wiley-Interscience); Vol. 1, 1953. 51.95x (ISBN 0-470-17952-X); Vol. 2, 1962. 70.95x (ISBN 0-470-17985-6). Wiley.

Creutz, Michael. Quarks, Gluons & Lattices. LC 83-2089. (Cambridge Monographs on Mathematical Physics). 175p. 1984. 34.50 (ISBN 0-521-24405-6). Cambridge U Pr.

Dehesa, J. S., et al, eds. Mathematical & Computational Methods in Nuclear Physics. (Lecture Notes in Physics Ser.: Vol. 209). vi, 276p. 1984. pap. 16.50 (ISBN 0-387-13392-5). Springer-Verlag.

Dell'Antonio, G., et al, eds. Mathematical Problems in Theoretical Physics: International Conference, Held in Rome, June 6-15, 1977. (Lecture Notes in Physics: Vol. 80). 1979. pap. 27.00 (ISBN 0-387-08853-9). Springer-Verlag.

De Witt, Bryce S. Supermanifolds. (Monographs on Mathematical Physics). 350p. 1984. 59.50 (ISBN 0-521-25850-2). Cambridge U Pr.

Diaz, J. B., ed. Alexander Weinstein Selecta. 629p. 1978. text ed. 53.95 (ISBN 0-273-08411-9). Pitman Pub MA.

Diaz, J. G. & Pai, S. I., eds. Fluid Dynamics & Applied Mathematics. (Illus.). 218p. 1962. 57.75 (ISBN 0-677-10110-4). Gordon.

Drazin, P. G. Solitons. LC 83-7170. (London Mathematical Society Lecture Note Ser. No. 85). 136p. 1983. pap. 16.95 (ISBN 0-521-27422-2). Cambridge U Pr.

Dreizler, Reiner M. & Da Providencia, Joo, eds. Density Functional Methods in Physics. (NATO ASI Series B Physics: Vol. 123). 542p. 1985. 85.00x (ISBN 0-306-41926-2, Plenum Pr). Plenum Pub.

Dyachenko, V. F. Basic Computational Math. 125p. 1979. pap. 4.95 (ISBN 0-8285-1593-X, Pub. by Mir Pubs USSR). Imported Pubns.

Eisberg, Robert M. Applied Mathematical Physics with Programmable Pocket Calculators. (Illus.). 1976. pap. text ed. 18.95 (ISBN 0-07-019109-3). McGraw.

Enz, C. P. & Mehra, J., eds. Physical Reality & Mathematical Description: Dedicated to Josef Maria Jauch on the Occasion of His Sixtieth Birthday. LC 74-81937. xxiii, 552p. 1974. lib. bdg. 66.00 (ISBN 90-277-0513-5, Pub. by Reidel Holland). Kluwer Academic.

Fluegge, S. Practical Quantum Mechanics. LC 74-23732. (Illus.). xiv, 623p. 1974. pap. 26.00 (ISBN 0-387-07050-8). Springer-Verlag.

--Practical Quantum Mechanics One. rev. ed. (Die Grundlehren der Mathematischen Wissenschaften: Vol. 177). 1971. 52.00 (ISBN 0-387-05276-3). Springer-Verlag.

--Practical Quantum Mechanics Two. rev. ed. (Grundlehren der Mathematischen Wissenschaften: Vol. 178). 1971. 49.60 (ISBN 0-387-05277-1). Springer-Verlag.

Garcia, P. L., et al, eds. Differential Geometrical Methods in Mathematical Physics: Proceedings. (Lecture Notes in Mathematics: Vol. 836). 538p. 1980. 32.00 (ISBN 0-387-10275-2). Springer-Verlag.

Geroch, Robert. Mathematical Physics. (Chicago Lectures in Physics Ser.). 310p. 1985. lib. bdg. price not set (ISBN 0-226-28861-7); pap. text ed. price not set (ISBN 0-226-28862-5). U of Chicago Pr.

Gilbert, Robert P. & Newton, Roger G. Analytic Methods in Mathematical Physics. 590p. 1970. 112.25 (ISBN 0-677-13560-2). Gordon.

Greenspan, Donald. Arithmetic Applied Mathematics. LC 80-40295. (Illus.). 172p. 1980. 34.00 (ISBN 0-08-025047-5); pap. 12.00 (ISBN 0-08-025046-7). Pergamon.

--Discrete Numerical Methods in Physics & Engineering. (Mathematics in Science & Engineering Ser.). 1974. 55.00 (ISBN 0-12-300350-4). Acad Pr.

Grodins, Fred S. Control Theory & Biological Systems. LC 63-10521. 205p. 1963. 32.00x (ISBN 0-231-02517-3). Columbia U Pr.

Guettinger, W. & Eikemeier, H., eds. Structural Stability in Physics: Proceedings of Two International Symposia. (Springer Ser. in Synergetics). (Illus.). 1979. 43.00 (ISBN 0-387-09463-6). Springer-Verlag.

Gurel, Okan, ed. Bifurcation Theory & Applications in Scientific Disciplines, Vol. 316. Rossler, Otto E. (Annals of the New York Academy of Sciences). 708p. (Orig.). 1979. pap. 87.00x (ISBN 0-89766-000-5). NY Acad Sci.

Hall, George G. Applied Group Theory. LC 67-73110. (Mathematical Physics Ser.). pap. 34.00 (ISBN 0-317-08613-8, 2004946). Bks Demand UMI.

Harman, P. M., ed. Wranglers & Physicists: Studies on Cambridge Mathematical Physics in the Nineteenth Century. LC 85-1485. 320p. 1985. 27.00 (ISBN 0-7190-1756-4, Pub. by Manchester Univ Pr). Longwood Pub Group.

Harper, P. G. & Weaire, Denis. Introduction to Physical Mathematics. (Illus.). 220p. 1985. 42.50 (ISBN 0-521-26278-X); pap. 14.95 (ISBN 0-521-26908-3). Cambridge U Pr.

Harris, Edward G. Introduction to Modern Theoretical Physics, 2 vols. Incl. Vol. 1. Classical Physics & Relativity. 392p. 46.50x (ISBN 0-471-35325-6); Vol. 2. Quantum Theory & Statistical Physics. 402p. LC 75-14497. 1975 (Pub. by Wiley-Interscience). Wiley.

Hermann, Robert. Energy Momentum Tensors. (Interdisciplinary Mathematics Ser.: No. 4). 153p. 1973. 14.00 (ISBN 0-915692-03-1, 99160024X). Math Sci Pr.

--Topics in General Relativity. (Interdisciplinary Mathematics Ser: No. 5). 161p. 1973. 15.00 (ISBN 0-915692-04-X, 991600223). Math Sci Pr.

--Topics in the Mathematics of Quantum Mechanics. (Interdisciplinary Mathematics Ser: No. 6). 250p. 1973. 21.00 (ISBN 0-915692-05-8, 991600231). Math Sci Pr.

--Vector Bundles in Mathematical Physics, Vol. 1. (Mathematical Physics Monographs: No. 14). 1970. pap. text ed. 15.95 (ISBN 0-8053-3945-0). Benjamin-Cummings.

--Vector Bundles in Mathematical Physics, Vol. 2. (Mathematical Physics Monographs: No. 16). 1970. pap. 15.95 (ISBN 0-8053-3949-3). Benjamin-Cummings.

Hestenes, David. Space-Time Algebra. (Documents on Modern Physics Ser.). 102p. (Orig.). 1966. 28.95x (ISBN 0-677-01390-6). Gordon.

Hughston, L. Twistors & Particles. (Lecture Notes in Physics Ser.: Vol. 97). 1979. pap. 14.00 (ISBN 0-387-09244-7). Springer-Verlag.

Iachello, F., ed. Interacting Bosons in Nuclear Physics. LC 79-13600. (Ettore Majorana International Science Series; Physical Sciences: Vol. 1). 201p. 1979. 42.50x (ISBN 0-306-40190-8, Plenum Pr). Plenum Pub.

Ibragimov, Nail H. Transformation Groups Applied to Mathematical Physics. 1985. lib. bdg. 69.00 (ISBN 90-277-1847-4, Pub. by Reidel Holland). Kluwer Academic.

Il'in, V. P., ed. Boundary Value Problems of Mathematical Physics & Related Aspects of Function Theory, Pt. 1. LC 69-12506. (Seminars in Mathematics Ser.: Vol. 5). 96p. 1969. 29.50x (ISBN 0-306-18805-8, Consultants). Plenum Pub.

International Symposium "Fifty Years Schroedinger Equation", Vienna, June 10-12, 1976. The Schroedinger Equation: Proceedings. Thirring, W. & Urban, P., eds. (Acta Physica Austriaca Supplementum: 17). (Illus.). 1977. 39.00 (ISBN 0-387-81437-X). Springer-Verlag.

International Symposium on Mathematical Problems, Kyoto University, Kyoto, Japan, Jan. 23-29, 1975. Proceedings. (Lecture Notes in Physics Ser.). 562p. 1975. pap. 28.00 (ISBN 0-387-07174-1). Springer-Verlag.

International University Courses on Nuclear Physics, 12th, Schladming, Austria, 1973. Recent Developments in Mathematical Physics: Proceedings. Urban, P., ed. LC 73-13322. (Acta Physica Austriaca: Suppl. 2). (Illus.). vi, 610p. 1973. 87.40 (ISBN 0-387-81190-7). Springer-Verlag.

Islam, J. N. Rotating Fields in General Relativity. 136p. 1985. 34.50 (ISBN 0-521-26082-5). Cambridge U Pr.

Jeffreys, Harold & Jeffreys, Bertha S. Methods of Mathematical Physics. 3rd ed. (Illus.). 1956. pap. 32.50 (ISBN 0-521-09723-1). Cambridge U Pr.

Jost, R. Local Quantum Theory. (Italian Physical Society: Course 45). 1970. 70.00 (ISBN 0-12-368845-0). Acad Pr.

Kaiser, G. & Marsden, J. E., eds. Geometric Methods in Mathematical Physics: Proceedings. (Lecture Notes in Mathematics Ser.: Vol. 775). 257p. 1980. pap. 20.00 (ISBN 0-387-09742-2). Springer-Verlag.

Kemmer, N. Vector Analysis. LC 75-36025. (Illus.). 230p. 1977. 59.50 (ISBN 0-521-21158-1); pap. 18.95x (ISBN 0-521-29064-3). Cambridge U Pr.

Kompaneyets, Alexander. Theoretical Physics. (Russian Monographs). (Illus.). 592p. 1964. 124.95 (ISBN 0-677-20150-8). Gordon.

Koonin, Steven E. Computational Physics. 1985. 31.95. Addison-Wesley.

Kraus, K. States, Effects & Operations. Boehm, A., et al, eds. (Lecture Notes in Physics Ser.: Vol. 190). 151p. 1983. pap. 10.00 (ISBN 0-387-12732-1). Springer Verlag.

Kraut, Edgar A. Fundamentals of Mathematical Physics. LC 79-4467. 480p. 1979. Repr. of 1967 ed. lib. bdg. 28.00 (ISBN 0-88275-918-3). Krieger.

Kreyszig, Erwin. Advanced Engineering Mathematics. 5th ed. 988p. 1983. 42.45 (ISBN 0-471-86251-7); tchrs.' manual avail. (ISBN 0-471-89855-4). Wiley.

Ladyzhenskaya, O. A., ed. Boundary Value Problems of Mathematical Physics & Related Aspects of Function Theory, Part 3. LC 69-12506. (Seminars in Mathematics Ser.: Vol. 11). 79p. 1970. 25.00x (ISBN 0-306-18811-2, Consultants). Plenum Pub.

--Boundary Value Problems of Mathematical Physics & Related Aspects of Function Theory. LC 69-12506. (Seminars in Mathematics Ser.: Vol. 14, Pt. 4). (Russian., Illus.). pap. 40.80 (ISBN 0-317-08603-0, 2020698). Bks Demand UMI.

Langer, Rudolph E., ed. Partial Differential Equations & Continuum Mechanics. (Mathematics Research Center Pubns., No. 5). (Illus.). 414p. 1961. 17.00x (ISBN 0-299-02350-8). U of Wis Pr.

Lattes, Robert. Methods of Resolution for Selected Boundary Problems in Mathematical Physics. (Documents on Modern Physics Ser.). 200p. 1969. 57.75x (ISBN 0-677-30060-3). Gordon.

--Quelques Methodes de Resolutions de Problemes aux Limites de la Physique Mathematiques. (Cours & Documents de Mathematiques & de Physique Ser.). 196p. (Orig.). 1967. 57.75x (ISBN 0-677-50060-2). Gordon.

Lavrentiev, M. M. Some Improperly Posed Problems of Mathematical Physics. Sacker, R. J., tr. (Springer Tracts in Natural Philosophy: Vol. 11). (Illus.). 1967. 20.00 (ISBN 0-387-03984-8). Springer-Verlag.

Lebedev, N. N. Special Functions & Their Applications. rev. ed. Silverman, Richard A., tr. from Rus. LC 72-86228. 320p. 1972. pap. 6.00 (ISBN 0-486-60624-4). Dover.

Levy, M. & Lurcat, F., eds. Cargese Lecture Notes, 1965: Application of Mathematics to Problems in Theoretical Physics. 516p. 1967. 132.95x (ISBN 0-677-11660-8). Gordon.

Liboff, Richard L. & Rostoker, Norman, eds. Kinetic Equations. LC 72-122848. (Illus.). 362p. 1971. 66.00 (ISBN 0-677-14080-0). Gordon.

Lieb, E. H., et al, eds. Studies in Mathematical Physics: Essays in Honor of Valentine Bargmann. LC 76-4057. (Princeton Series in Physics). (Illus.). 472p. 1976. 50.00x (ISBN 0-691-08180-8); pap. 15.50x (ISBN 0-691-08185-9). Princeton U Pr.

Liggett, T. M. Interacting Particle Systems. (Grundlehren der Mathematischen Wissenschaften Ser.: Vol. 276). (Illus.). 500p. 1985. 54.00 (ISBN 0-387-96069-4). Springer-Verlag.

Loebl, Ernest M., ed. Group Theory & Its Applications, 3 vols. LC 67-23166. Vol. 1 1968. 81.00 (ISBN 0-12-455150-5); Vol. 2 1971. 71.50 (ISBN 0-12-455152-1); 98.50 (ISBN 0-12-455153-X). Vol. 3, 1975. Acad Pr.

Lomont, John S. Applications of Finite Groups. 1959. 57.50 (ISBN 0-12-455550-0). Acad Pr.

Longair, Malcolm S. Theoretical Concepts in Physics: An Alternative View of Theoretical Reasoning in Physics. 320p. 1984. 52.50 (ISBN 0-521-25550-3); pap. 15.95 (ISBN 0-521-27553-9). Cambridge U Pr.

Mackey, George W. Mathematical Foundations of Quantum Mechanics. (Mathematical Physics Monographs: No. 1). 1963. 30.95 (ISBN 0-8053-6701-2). Benjamin-Cummings.

Mahanthappa, K. T. & Randa, James, eds. Quantum Flavordynamics, Quantum Chromodynamics & Unified Theories. LC 80-12289. (NATO ASI Series B, Physics: Vol. 54). 505p. 1980. 75.00 (ISBN 0-306-40436-2, Plenum Pr). Plenum Pub.

Marcus, Paul M. & Janak, J. F., eds. Computational Methods in Band Theory. LC 77-142039. (IBM Research Symposia Ser). 578p. 1971. 79.50x (ISBN 0-306-30520-8, Plenum Pr). Plenum Pub.

Margenau, Henry & Murphy, George M. The Mathematics of Physics & Chemistry. 2nd ed. LC 76-18724. 618p. 1976. Repr. of 1956 ed. text ed. 32.50 (ISBN 0-88275-423-8). Krieger.

Marsden, J. E. Lectures on Geometric Methods in Mathematical Physics. LC 80-54307. (CBMS-NSF Regional Conference Ser.: No. 37). v, 97p. 1981. pap. text ed. 14.00 (ISBN 0-89871-170-3). Soc Indus-Appl Math.

Marsden, Jerry. Applications of Global Analysis in Mathematical Physics. LC 74-75308. (Mathematics Lecture Ser., No. 2). 273p. 1974. pap. text ed. 18.00 (ISBN 0-914098-11-X). Publish or Perish.

Martin-Loef, A. Statistical Mechanics & the Foundations of Thermodynamics. (Lecture Notes in Physics Ser.: Vol. 101). 1979. pap. 13.00 (ISBN 0-387-09255-2). Springer-Verlag.

Mathews, Jon & Walker, Robert L. Mathematical Methods of Physics. 2nd ed. 1970. text ed. 38.95 (ISBN 0-8053-7002-1). Benjamin-Cummings.

Maurin, K. & Raczka, R., eds. Mathematical Physics & Physical Mathematics. LC 74-34289. (Mathematical Physics & Applied Mathematics Ser.: No. 2). 1976. lib. bdg. 55.00 (ISBN 90-277-0537-2, Pub. by Reidel Holland). Kluwer Academic.

Menzel, Donald H. Fundamental Formulas of Physics, 2 Vols. 2nd ed. (Illus.). 1960. Vol. 1. pap. text ed. 8.00 (ISBN 0-486-60595-7); Vol. 2. pap. text ed. 8.00 (ISBN 0-486-60596-5). Dover.

--Mathematical Physics. 1953. pap. text ed. 7.00 (ISBN 0-486-60056-4). Dover.

Mickley, Harold S., et al. Applied Mathematics in Chemical Engineering. 2nd ed. (Chemical Engineering Ser.). (Illus.). 1957. text ed. 42.00 (ISBN 0-07-041800-4). McGraw.

Mitter, H. & Pittner, L., eds. New Developments in Mathematical Physics: Proceedings. (Acta Physica Austriaca: Supplementum 23). (Illus.). 701p. 1981. 73.50 (ISBN 0-387-81676-3). Springer-Verlag.

Moon, P. & Spencer, D. E. Field Theory Handbook: Including Coordinate Systems, Differential Equations & Their Solutions. 2nd ed. LC 77-178288. (Illus.). viii, 236p. 1971. 57.90 (ISBN 0-387-02732-7). Springer-Verlag.

Moraal, H. Classical, Discrete Spin Models. (Lecture Notes in Physics Ser.: Vol. 214). vii, 251p. 1984. pap. 14.00 (ISBN 0-387-13896-X). Springer-Verlag.

Ward, Alan. Tricks with Science, Words & Numbers. (Illus.). 96p. 1983. 14.95 (ISBN 0-7134-3653-0, Pub. by Batsford England). David & Charles.

MATHEMATICAL RECREATIONS–DATA PROCESSING

Farrell, Patricia & Lundegren, Herberta M. The Process of Recreation Programming: Theory & Technique. 2nd ed. LC 82-17626. 296p. 1983. text ed. 27.45 (ISBN 0-471-86181-2). Wiley.

International Conference on Advances in Computer Chess, London, UK, April 1981. Advances in Computer Chess III: Proceedings. Clarke, M. R., ed. LC 78-309646. (Pergamon Chess Ser.). 182p. 1982. 25.00 (ISBN 0-08-026898-6). Pergamon.

Sage, Edwin R. Fun & Games with the Computer. 351p. 1975. pap. text ed. 14.95 (ISBN 0-87567-075-X). Entelek.

MATHEMATICAL RESEARCH

Bachmann, Heinz. Der Weg der Mathematischen Grundlagenforschung. (Ger.). 240p. 1983. 20.00 (ISBN 3-261-05089-6). P Lang Pubs.

Committee on an Assessment of Quality-Related Characteristics of Research-Doctorate Programs in the U. S., National Research Council. An Assessment of Research-Doctorate Programs in the U. S. Mathematical & Physical Sciences. 243p. 1982. pap. text ed. 11.50 (ISBN 0-309-03299-7). Natl Acad Pr.

Conway, John B. Subnormal Operators. LC 81-231. (Research Notes in Mathematics: No. 51). 400p. 1981. pap. text ed. 29.95 (ISBN 0-273-08520-4). Pitman Pub MA.

Driscoll, Mark J. Research Within Reach: Elementary School Mathematics. 141p. 1981. pap. 6.25 (ISBN 0-87353-194-9). NCTM.

El Tom, M. E., ed. Developing Mathematics in Third World Countries. (North Holland Mathematics Studies: Vol. 33). 208p. 1979. 47.00 (ISBN 0-444-85260-3, North Holland). Elsevier.

Fennema, Elizabeth, ed. Mathematics Education Research: Implications for the 80's. LC 81-67144. 182p. 1981. 6.75 (ISBN 0-87353-196-5). NCTM.

Jacobs, Judith E., ed. Perspectives on Women & Mathematics. 166p. 1978. pap. 6.75 (ISBN 0-686-79358-7). NCTM.

Keng, Hua L., et al. Second-Order Systems of Partial Differential Equations in the Plane. (Research Notes in Mathematics Ser.: No. 128). 250p. 1985. pap. text ed. 20.95 (ISBN 0-273-08645-6). Pitman Pub MA.

Lie, Sophus. Vorlesungen Uber Continuierliche Gruppen Mit Geometrischen und Anderen Anwendungen. 2nd ed. LC 66-12879. (Ger). 1971. text ed. 39.95 (ISBN 0-8284-0199-3). Chelsea Pub.

Mehrtens, H., ed. Social History of Mathematics. 320p. 1981. 29.95x (ISBN 0-8176-3033-3). Birkhauser.

Petrie, Chris J. Elongational Flows. (Research Notes in Mathematics Ser.: No. 29). 254p. (Orig.). 1979. pap. text ed. 27.50 (ISBN 0-273-08406-2). Pitman Pub MA.

Sylvester, James J. Collected Mathematical Papers, 4 Vols. LC 76-250188. 1973. Repr. of 1904 ed. text ed. 125.00 (ISBN 0-8284-0253-1). Chelsea Pub.

Symposium in Applied Mathematics. The Influence of Computing on Mathematical Research & Education. La Salle, Joseph P., ed. LC 74-5166. (Proceedings of Symposia in Applied Mathematics: Vol. 20). 1974. 38.00 (ISBN 0-8218-1326-9, PSAPM-20). Am Math.

Wilcox, Calvin H., ed. Asymptotic Solutions of Differential Equations & Their Applications: Proceedings of A Symposium Conducted by the Mathematics Research Center. LC 64-55696. (U. S. Army, University of Wisconsin, 1964: No. 13). pap. 73.50 (ISBN 0-317-28088-0, 2055726). Bks Demand UMI.

MATHEMATICAL SEQUENCES

see Sequences (Mathematics)

MATHEMATICAL SETS

see Set Theory

MATHEMATICAL STATISTICS

see also Biometry; Correlation (Statistics); Errors, Theory Of; Estimation Theory; Law of Large Numbers; Least Squares; Mathematical Linguistics; Multivariate Analysis; Nonparametric Statistics; Probabilities; Regression Analysis; Sampling (Statistics); Sequential Analysis; Statistical Astronomy; Statistical Hypothesis Testing; Statistics; Time-Series Analysis

Aickin, M. Linear Statistical Analysis of Discrete Data. (Probability & Mathematical Statistics Ser.). 358p. 1983. 38.95 (ISBN 0-471-09774-8). Wiley.

Aitchison, J. & Brown, J. A. Lognormal Distribution. (Cambridge Department of Applied Economic Monographs: No. 5). 1957. 37.50 (ISBN 0-521-04011-6). Cambridge U Pr.

Aivazjan, S. A., et al. Twenty-Two Papers on Statistics & Probability. LC 61-9803. (Selected Translations in Mathematical Statistics & Probability Ser.: Vol. 6). 1966. 35.00 (ISBN 0-8218-1456-7, STAPRO-6). Am Math.

Aleskjavicene, A., et al. Twenty-Two Papers on Statistics & Probability. (Selected Translations in Mathematical Statistics & Probability: Vol. 11). 1973. 33.00 (ISBN 0-8218-1461-3, STAPRO-11). Am Math.

Ambarcumjan, G. A., et al. Thirty-Five Papers on Statistics & Probability. LC 61-9803. (Selected Translations in Mathematical Statistics & Probability Ser.: Vol. 4). 1963. 32.00 (ISBN 0-8218-1454-0, STAPRO-4). Am Math.

Anosov, D. V., et al. Twenty-Four Papers on Statistics & Probability: Twenty-Four Papers Statistics & Probability. LC 61-9803. (Selected Translations in Mathematical Statistics & Probability: Vol. 14). 296p. 1978. 38.00 (ISBN 0-8218-1464-8, STAPRO-14); institutional members 28.50; individual members 19.00. Am Math.

Arato, M., et al. Twenty Papers on Statistics & Probability. (Selected Transactions in Mathematics Statistics & Probability Ser.: Vol. 13). 1973. 55.00 (ISBN 0-8218-1463-X, STAPRO 13). Am Math.

--Thirty-Two Papers on Statistics & Probability. LC 61-9803. (Selected Translations in Mathematical Statistics & Probability Ser.: Vol. 10). 1972. 36.00 (ISBN 0-8218-1460-5, STAPRO-10). Am Math.

Arthanari, Subramanvam & Dodge, Yadolah. Mathematical Programming in Statistics. LC 80-21637. (Probability & Math Statistics Ser.: Applied Probability & Statistics). 413p. 1981. 45.95x (ISBN 0-471-08073-X, Pub. by Wiley-Interscience). Wiley.

Athreya, K. B. & Ney, P. E. Branching Processes. LC 72-75819. (Die Grundlehren der Mathematischen Wissenshaften: Vol. 196). 300p. 1972. 39.00 (ISBN 0-387-05790-0). Springer-Verlag.

Baggaley, Andrew R. Mathematics for Introductory Statistics: A Programmed Review. LC 69-19103. pap. 46.30 (ISBN 0-317-09324-X, 2055271). Bks Demand UMI.

Bancroft, T. A. Topics in Intermediate Statistical Methods, Vol. 1. 1968. 7.50x (ISBN 0-8138-0842-1). Iowa St U Pr.

Bancroft, T. A. & Brown, Susan A., eds. Statistical Papers in Honor of George W. Snedecor. LC 79-106603. (Illus.). 1972. 14.50x (ISBN 0-8138-1585-1). Iowa St U Pr.

Barnett, V. Comparative Statistical Inference. LC 73-1833. (Probability & Mathematical Statistics Ser.: Probability Section). 287p. 1973. 49.95x (ISBN 0-471-05401-1, Pub. by Wiley-Interscience). Wiley.

Barra, J. R., et al, eds. Recent Developments in Statistics: European Meeting of Statisticians, Sept. 6-11, 1976, Grenoble, France. 808p. 1977. 95.75 (ISBN 0-7204-0751-6, North-Holland). Elsevier.

Bashaw, W. L. Mathematics for Statistics. LC 84-11228. 344p. 1984. Repr. of 1969 ed. lib. bdg. 23.50 (ISBN 0-89874-762-7). Krieger.

Bauer, Edward L. Statistical Manual for Chemists. 2nd ed. 1971. 39.00 (ISBN 0-12-082756-5). Acad Pr.

Bazigos, G. P. Mathematics for Fishery Statisticians. (Fisheries Technical Papers: No. 169). 193p. (2nd Printing 1978). 1977. pap. 14.00 (ISBN 92-5-100314-9, F1241, FAO). Unipub.

Becker, Richard A. & Chambers, John M. Extending the S System, Vol. II. LC 84-29933. (Statistics Ser.). 164p. 1985. pap. text ed. 14.95 (ISBN 0-534-05016-6). Brooks-Cole.

Bennett, Carl A., et al. Statistical Analysis in Chemistry & the Chemical Industry. LC 54-11428. (Wiley Publications in Statistics Ser.). pap. 160.00 (ISBN 0-317-09349-5, 2055153). Bks Demand UMI.

Bergstrom, Harald. Weak Convergence of Measures. (Probability & Mathematical Statistics Ser.). 1982. 49.50 (ISBN 0-12-091080-2). Acad Pr.

Berman, D. L., et al. Nineteen Papers on Statistics & Probability. LC 61-9803. (Selected Translations on Mathematical Statistics & Probability Ser: Vol. 5). 1965. 30.00 (ISBN 0-8218-1455-9, STAPRO-5). Am Math.

Bickel, P. J. & Doksum, K. A. Mathematical Statistics: Basic Ideas & Selected Topics. LC 76-8724. 1977. 40.00x (ISBN 0-8162-0784-4). Holden-Day.

Bickel, Peter J. & Doksum, Kjell, eds. A Festschrift for Erich L. Lehmann. (Wadsworth Statistics-Probability Ser.). 461p. 1982. write for info. (ISBN 0-534-98044-9). Wadsworth Pub.

Borovkov, A. A., et al. Nineteen Papers on Statistics & Probability. LC 61-9803. (Selected Translations on Mathematical Statistics & Probability Ser.: Vol. 2). 1962. 23.00 (ISBN 0-8218-1452-4, STAPRO-2). Am Math.

Bowley, Arthur L. F. Y. Edgeworth's Contributions to Mathematical Statistics. LC 68-24161. Repr. of 1928 ed. 19.50x (ISBN 0-678-00889-2). Kelley.

Box, George E. & Tiao, George C. Bayesian Inference in Statistical Analysis. LC 78-172804. 1973. text ed. 30.95 (ISBN 0-201-00622-7). Addison-Wesley.

Brooks, Charles E. & Carruthers, N. Handbook of Statistical Methods in Meteorology. LC 77-10222. Repr. of 1953 ed. 30.50 (ISBN 0-404-16202-9). AMS Pr.

Brunk, H. D. Introduction to Mathematical Statistics. 3rd ed. LC 74-82348. 400p. 1975. text ed. 38.50 (ISBN 0-471-00834-6). Wiley.

Buning, Herbert & Naeve, Peter, eds. Computational Statistics. 348p. 1981. text ed. 39.20 (ISBN 3-11-008419-8). De Gruyter.

Bunke, H. & Bunke, O., eds. Statistical Inference in Linear Models, Vol. 1. (Probability & Mathematical Statistics Applied Probability & Statistics Section Ser.: 1-345). 400p. 1985. 54.95x (ISBN 0-471-10334-9, Pub. by Wiley-Interscience). Wiley.

Cerkasov, I. D., et al. Eighteen Papers on Statistics & Probability. LC 61-9803. (Selected Translations on Mathematical Statistics & Probability Ser.: Vol. 3). 1963. 29.00 (ISBN 0-8218-1453-2, STAPRO-3). Am Math.

Ch'En Hsi-Ju, et al. Twenty Papers on Statistics & Probability. LC 61-9803. (Selected Translations in Mathematical Statistics & Probability Ser.: Vol. 12). 1973. 46.00 (ISBN 0-8218-1462-1, STAPRO-12). Am Math.

Choi, Sung C. Introductory Applied Statistics in Science. (Illus.). 1978. ref. ed. 26.95 (ISBN 0-13-501619-3). P-H.

Cook, R. D. & Weisberg, S. Residuals & Influence in Regression. 200p. 1982. 60.00x (ISBN 0-412-24280-X, Pub. by Chapman & Hall England). State Mutual Bk.

Couch, James. Fundamentals of Statistics for the Behavioral Sciences. LC 81-51854. 423p. 1982. text ed. 24.95 (ISBN 0-312-31195-8); study guide 6.95 (ISBN 0-312-31197-4); intr's. manual avail. St Martin.

Crabill, Delmar. Statistical Theory: An Introduction. 296p. (Orig.). 1984. pap. text ed. 12.00 (ISBN 0-8191-3796-0). U Pr of Amer.

Cramer, H. Mathematical Methods of Statistics. (Mathematical Ser.: Vol. 9). 1946. 39.00 (ISBN 0-691-08004-6). Princeton U Pr.

Csiszar, Imre & Korner, Janos. Information Theory: Coding Theorems for Discrete Memoryless Systems. (Probability and Mathematical Statistics Ser.). 1982. 64.00 (ISBN 0-12-198450-8). Acad Pr.

Csorgo, M. & Revesz, P. Strong Aproximations in Probability & Statistics. LC 79-57112. (Probability & Mathematical Statistics Ser.). 1981. 44.50 (ISBN 0-12-198540-7). Acad Pr.

Csorgo, Miklos. Quantile Processes with Statistical Applications. LC 83-60222. (CBMS-NSF Regional Conference Ser.: No. 42). xiii, 156p. 1983. pap. text ed. 17.50 (ISBN 0-89871-185-1). Soc Indus-Appl Math.

Culanovski, I. V., et al. Twenty-Five Papers on Statistics & Probability. LC 61-9803. (Selected Translations in Mathematical Statistics & Probability Ser.: Vol. 1). 1961. 37.00 (ISBN 0-8218-1451-6, STAPRO-1). Am Math.

Daniel, Wayne W. Introductory Statistics with Applications. LC 76-10897. (Illus.). 1977. text ed. 30.95 (ISBN 0-395-24430-7); study guide 12.95 (ISBN 0-395-24843-4). HM.

Davison, Mark L. Multidimensional Scaling. LC 82-17403. (Probability & Mathematical Statistics: Applied Probability & Statistic Section Ser.). 242p. 1983. 29.95 (ISBN 0-471-86417-X, Pub. by Wiley-Interscience). Wiley.

Degroot, Morris. Probability & Statistics. LC 74-19691. (Behavioral Science Quantitative Methods Ser). (Illus.). 624p. 1975. text ed. 27.95 (ISBN 0-201-01503-X); sol. manual 7.95 (ISBN 0-201-01509-9). Addison-Wesley.

Dudewicz, Edward J., ed. The Frontiers of Modern Statistical Inference Procedures: Proceedings & Discussions of the IPASRAS Conference (First International Conference on Inference Procedures Associated with Statistical Ranking & Selection, East-West Center, Honolulu, July 1982) LC 83-72590. (Series in Mathematical & Management Sciences: Vol. 10). 1985. for info. 79.95 (ISBN 0-935950-07-9). Am Sciences Pr.

Durran, J. H. Statistics & Probability. LC 70-96086. (School Mathematics Project Handbks). 1970. text ed. 27.95 (ISBN 0-521-06933-5). Cambridge U Pr.

Ehrenberg, A. S. Data Reduction: Analyzing & Interpreting Statistical Data. LC 74-3724. 391p. 1975. 64.95x (ISBN 0-471-23399-4, Pub. by Wiley-Interscience); pap. 24.95x (ISBN 0-471-23398-6). Wiley.

Ellis, L. E. Statistics & Probability (Draft Edition) (School Mathematics Project Further Mathematics Ser). (Illus.). 1971. text ed. 9.95 (ISBN 0-521-08026-6). Cambridge U Pr.

Experimental Statistics (NATRELLA) Selected Government Publications. (A Wiley Reprint Ser.: 1-698). 552p. 1966. 29.95x (ISBN 0-471-79999-8, Pub. by Wiley-Interscience). Wiley.

Fabian, Vaclav & Hannan, James. Introduction to Probability & Mathematical Statistics. LC 84-12998. (Wiley Series in Probability & Mathematical Statistics: 1-345). 448p. 1985. text ed. 42.95 (ISBN 0-471-25023-6, Pub. by Wiley Interscience). Wiley.

Fiacco, A. V., ed. Sensitivity, Stability & Parametric Analysis. (Mathematical Programming Studies: Vol. 21). 242p. 1985. pap. 24.00 (ISBN 0-444-87573-5, North-Holland). Elsevier.

Finney, D. J. Probit Analysis. 3rd ed. LC 78-134618. (Illus.). 1971. 70.00 (ISBN 0-521-08041-X). Cambridge U Pr.

--Statistics for Mathematicians: An Introduction. 1968. 8.85 (ISBN 0-934454-74-4). Lubrecht & Cramer.

Fisher, Ronald A. Statistical Methods & Scientific Inference. rev. ed. 1973. 14.95x (ISBN 0-02-844740-9). Hafner.

Fisz, Marek. Probability Theory & Mathematical Statistics. 3rd ed. LC 80-12455. 696p. 1980. Repr. of 1963 ed. lib. bdg. 39.50 (ISBN 0-89874-179-3). Krieger.

Fox, John. Linear Statistical Models & Related Methods: With Applications to Social Research. LC 83-23278. (Probability & Mathematical Statistics Ser.: 1-346). 496p. 1984. 39.95x (ISBN 0-471-09913-9, NO. 1-346, Pub. by Wiley-Interscience). Wiley.

Freund, John E. & Walpole, Ronald E. Mathematical Statistics. 3rd ed. 1980. text ed. 36.95 (ISBN 0-13-562066-X). P-H.

Furstenberg, H. Stationary Processes & Prediction Theory. (Annals of Mathematics Studies, Vol. 44). (Orig.). 1960. pap. 32.00x (ISBN 0-691-08041-0). Princeton U Pr.

Galambos, Janos. The Asymptotic Theory of Extreme Order Statistics. LC 78-1916. (Probability & Mathematical Staistics Ser.). 352p. 1978. 53.50x (ISBN 0-471-02148-2, Pub. by Wiley-Interscience). Wiley.

Georgii, H. O. Canonical Gibbs Measures. (Lecture Notes in Mathematics: Vol. 760). 190p. 1979. pap. text ed. 16.00 (ISBN 0-387-09712-0). Springer-Verlag.

Gilchrist, R., ed. GLIM 82: Proceedings of the International Conference on Generalized Linear Models, 1982. (Lecture Notes in Statistics: Vol. 14). (Illus.). 188p. 1982. pap. 14.00 (ISBN 0-387-90777-7). Springer-Verlag.

Glass, Gene V. Design & Analysis of Time-Series Experiments. Willson, Victor L. & Gottman, John M., eds. LC 74-84779. (Illus.). 200p. 1975. text ed. 19.50x (ISBN 0-87081-063-4). Colo Assoc.

Golberg, Michael A. An Introduction to Probability Theory with Statistical Applications. (Mathematical Concepts in Science & Engineering Ser.: Vol. 29). 674p. 1984. 69.50x (ISBN 0-306-41645-X, Plenum Pr). Plenum Pub.

Goodman, L. A. & Kruskal, W. H. Measures of Association for Cross Classifications. (Springer Series in Statistics: Vol. 1). 1979. 18.00 (ISBN 0-387-90443-3). Springer-Verlag.

Gormulicki, B. R. & Fielding, A. Statistics, 2 Vols. 1982. 59.00x set (ISBN 0-686-44551-1, Pub. by Natl Ext England). State Mutual Bk.

Greenwood, Joseph A. & Hartley, H. O. Guide to Tables in Mathematical Statistics. LC 62-7040. pap. 160.00 (ISBN 0-317-13006-4, 2021559). Bks Demand UMI.

Grenander, Ulf. Abstract Inference. LC 80-22016. (Wiley Series in Probability & Mathematical Statistics-Probability & Mathematical Statistics Section). 526p. 1981. 44.95x (ISBN 0-471-08267-8, Pub. by Wiley Interscience). Wiley.

Gumbel, Emil J. Statistics of Extremes. LC 57-10160. 1958. 40.00x (ISBN 0-231-02190-9). Columbia U Pr.

Guttorp. Statistics Inference for Branching Processes. (Probability & Mathematical Ser.). 1986. price not set (ISBN 0-471-82291-4). Wiley.

Hacking, Ian M. Logic of Statistical Inference. 1966. 39.50 (ISBN 0-521-05165-7); pap. 14.95x (ISBN 0-521-29059-7). Cambridge U Pr.

Hajek, P. & Havranek, T. Mechanizing Hypothesis Formation: Mathematical Foundations for a General Theory. 1978. pap. 33.00 (ISBN 0-387-08738-9). Springer-Verlag.

Hald, Anders. Statistical Theory with Engineering Applications. (Wiley Series in Probability & Mathematical Statistics-Applied Probability & Statistics Section). 783p. 1952. 68.50x (ISBN 0-471-34056-1, Pub. by Wiley-Interscience). Wiley.

Harnett, D. L. Statistical Methods. 3rd ed. LC 81-3645. 736p. text ed. 36.95 (ISBN 0-201-03913-3); instr's. manual 21.00 (ISBN 0-201-03914-1). Addison-Wesley.

Harnett, Donald L. Introduction to Statistical Methods. 3rd ed. LC 81-3645. (Quantitative Methods & Statistics Ser.). (Illus.). 736p. 1982. text ed. 36.95 (ISBN 0-201-03913-3); 21.00 (ISBN 0-201-03914-1). Addison-Wesley.

Stigler, Stephen M. & Cohen, I. Bernard, eds. American Contributions to Mathematical Statistics in the Nineteenth Century: An Original Anthology, 2 vols. LC 79-8002. (Three Centuries of Science in America Ser.). (Illus.). 1980. Set. lib. bdg. 64.00x (ISBN 0-405-12590-9). Ayer Co Pubs.

Strait, Peggy T. First Course in Probability & Statistics with Applications. 581p. 1983. text ed. 29.95 (ISBN 0-15-527520-8, HC); solutions manual avail. (ISBN 0-15-527521-6). HarbraceJ.

Thompson, Colin J. Mathematical Statistical Mechanics. LC 78-70319. 1979. 29.00 (ISBN 0-691-08219-7); pap. 10.95 (ISBN 0-691-08220-0). Princeton U Pr.

Upton, Graham J. The Analysis of Cross-Tabulated Data. LC 78-4210. (Probability & Mathematical Statistics: Applied Section Ser.). 148p. 1978. 57.95x (ISBN 0-471-99659-9, Pub. by Wiley-Interscience). Wiley.

Van Der Waerden, B. L. Mathematical Statistics. LC 72-84145. (Grundlehren der Mathematischen Wissenschaften: Vol. 156). (Illus.). 1969. 41.00 (ISBN 0-387-04507-4). Springer-Verlag.

Wald, Abraham. Selected Papers in Statistics & Probability. 1955. 45.00x (ISBN 0-8047-0493-7). Stanford U Pr.

--Statistical Decision Functions. LC 77-113154. 1971. Repr. of 1950 ed. text ed. 9.95 (ISBN 0-8284-0243-4). Chelsea Pub.

Wall, F. J. Statistical Data Analysis Handbook. 576p. 1985. 49.50 (ISBN 0-07-067931-2). McGraw.

Watson, Geoffrey S. Statistics on Spheres, Vol. 6. LC 83-1328. (The University of Arkansas Lecture Notes in the Mathematical Sciences). 238p. 1983. pap. 23.50 (ISBN 0-471-88866-4, Pub. by Wiley-Interscience). Wiley.

Wolfowitz, J. Selected Papers. 642p. 1980. 45.00 (ISBN 0-387-90463-8). Springer-Verlag.

Wonnacott, Thomas H. & Wonnacott, Ronald J. Introductory Statistics. 3rd ed. (Wiley Ser. in Probability & Mathematical Statistics). 650p. 1977. 38.45 (ISBN 0-471-95982-0). Wiley.

Zacks, Shelemyahu. Theory of Statistical Inference. LC 77-132227. (Ser. in Probability & Mathematical Statistics). 609p. 1971. 71.95x (ISBN 0-471-98103-6, Pub. by Wiley-Interscience). Wiley.

MATHEMATICAL STATISTICS–BIBLIOGRAPHY

Leifman, Lev, ed. Eighteen Papers on Statistics & Probability. LC 61-9803. (Selected Translations in Mathematical Statistics & Probability: No. 15). 1981. 58.00 (ISBN 0-8218-1465-6). Am Math.

Savage, I. Richard. Bibliography of Nonparametric Statistics. LC 62-11403. 1962. pap. 7.95x (ISBN 0-674-07101-8). Harvard U Pr.

MATHEMATICAL STATISTICS–PROGRAMMED INSTRUCTION

Brown, Foster F., et al. Statistical Concepts: A Basic Program. 2nd ed. 160p. 1975. pap. text ed. 11.50 scp (ISBN 0-06-040988-6, HarpC). Har-Row.

Flast, Robert H. VisiCalc Models: Finance-Statistics-Mathematics. 240p. 1984. 15.95 (Osborne-Mcgraw). Mcgraw.

MATHEMATICAL STATISTICS–TABLES, ETC.

see also Numbers, Random

Newman, T. G. & Odell, P. L. Generation of Random Variates. Stuart, Alan, ed. (Griffin's Statistical Monographs & Courses Ser: No. 29). 1971. pap. 7.50x (ISBN 0-02-849680-9). Hafner.

MATHEMATICAL WEATHER FORECASTING

see Numerical Weather Forecasting

MATHEMATICIANS

see also Mathematics As a Profession

Albers, Donald J. & Alexanderson, G. L., eds. Mathematical People: Profiles & Interviews. 260p. 1985. 24.95 (ISBN 0-8176-3191-7). Birkhauser.

Bell, Eric T. Men of Mathematics. (Illus.). 1937. pap. 10.75 (ISBN 0-671-46401-9, Fireside). S&S.

Butzer, P. L. & Feher, F., eds. E. B. Christoffel: The Influence of His Work in Mathematics & the Physical Sciences. (Illus.). 656p. 1981. 52.95x (ISBN 0-8176-1162-2). Birkhauser.

Carlo-Rota, Gian & Moser, Jurgen, eds. Fritz John: Collected Works, 2 vols. (Contemporary Mathematicians Ser.). 1985. Set. write for info. (ISBN 0-8176-3267-0). Vol. 1 (ISBN 0-8176-3265-4). Vol. 2 (ISBN 0-8176-3266-2). Birkhauser.

Chern, S. S. Complex Manifolds Without Potential Theory. (Universitext Ser.). 1979. 18.00 (ISBN 0-387-90422-0). Springer-Verlag.

Cohen, I. Bernard, ed. Benjamin Peirce: Father of Pure Mathematics in America. An Original Anthology. LC 79-7981. (Three Centuries of Science in America Ser.). (Illus.). 1980. lib. bdg. 32.50x (ISBN 0-405-12563-1). Ayer Co Pubs.

Dedron, P. & Itard, J. Mathematics & Mathematicians, No. 1. 326p. 1978. pap. 10.00x (ISBN 0-335-00246-3, Pub. by Open Univ Pr). Taylor & Francis.

--Mathematics & Mathematicians, No. 2. 222p. 1978. pap. 10.00x (ISBN 0-335-00247-1, Pub. by Open Univ Pr). Taylor & Francis.

Dick, A. Emmy Noether: 1882-1935. (Supplement Ser.: No. 13). (Ger.). 72p. 1970. pap. 13.95x (ISBN 0-8176-0519-3). Birkhauser.

Dick, Auguste. Emmy Noether (1882-1935) 192p. 1980. pap. 14.95x (ISBN 0-8176-3019-8). Birkhauser.

Ferrante, J. & Rackoff, C. W. The Computational Complexity of Logical Theories. (Lecture Notes in Mathematics Ser.: Vol. 718). 1979. pap. 19.00 (ISBN 0-387-09501-2). Springer-Verlag.

Friedrichs. Collected Papers, 2 vols. (Contemporary Mathematicians Ser.). 1985. Set. text ed. write for info. (ISBN 0-8176-3270-0); Vol. 1. text ed. write for info. (ISBN 0-8176-3268-9); Vol. 2. text ed. write for info. (ISBN 0-8176-3269-7). Birkhauser.

H. P. Robertson - in Memoriam. iv, 63p. 1963. text ed. 7.00 (ISBN 0-89871-157-6). Soc Indus-Appl Math.

Hardy, Godfrey H. Ramanujan. 3rd ed. LC 59-10268. 1978. 12.95 (ISBN 0-8284-0136-5). Chelsea Pub.

Hofmann, Joseph E. History of Mathematics to Eighteen Hundred. (Quality Paperback Ser.: No. 144). 159p. 1967. pap. 4.95 (ISBN 0-8226-0144-3). Littlefield.

Infeld, Leopold. Whom the Gods Love: The Story of Evariste Galois, Vol. 7. LC 78-3709. (Illus.). 323p. 1978. Repr. of 1948 ed. 11.00 (ISBN 0-87353-125-6). NCTM.

Kennedy, Hubert. Peano: Life & Works of Giuseppe Peano. (Studies in the History of Modern Science: No. 4). 227p. 1980. lib. bdg. 34.00 (ISBN 90-277-1067-8, Pub. by Reidel Holland); pap. 14.95 (ISBN 90-277-1068-6, Pub. by Reidel Holland). Kluwer Academic.

Klarner, David A., ed. The Mathematical Gardiner. 382p. 1980. write for info. (ISBN 0-534-98015-5). Wadsworth Pub.

Knobloc, E., et al, eds. On the Work of Leonhard Euler: Berlin Colloquium - May 1983. (Eng. Ger. & Fr.). 252p. 1984. 37.95 (ISBN 0-317-06915-2). Birkhauser.

Lazar, A. L. & Taylor, D. C. Multipliers of Pedersen's Ideal. LC 75-44302. (Memoirs: No. 169). 111p. 1976. pap. 14.00 (ISBN 0-8218-1869-4, MEMO-169). Am Math.

Lowe, Victor. Alfred North Whitehead: The Man & His Work, Vol. 1: 1861-1910. LC 84-15467. 392p. 1985. 27.50 (ISBN 0-8018-2488-5). Johns Hopkins.

Maths & Mathematicians, 2 vols. 1984. Vol. 1. 9.00x (ISBN 0-335-00248-X, Pub. by Open Univ Pr); Vol. 2. 9.00x (ISBN 0-335-00246-3, Pub. by Open Univ Pr). Taylor & Francis.

Morgan, Bryan. Men & Discoveries in Mathematics. 1972. 12.95 (ISBN 0-7195-2587-X). Transatlantic.

Newell, Virginia K., et al, eds. Black Mathematicians & Their Works. 1980. pap. 17.95 (ISBN 0-8059-2677-1). Dorrance.

Omrcanin, Ivo. Military History of Croatia. 224p. 1983. pap. 10.95 (ISBN 0-686-46184-3). Dorrance.

Osen, Lynn M. Women in Mathematics. 224p. 1974. pap. 5.95 (ISBN 0-262-65009-6). MIT Pr.

Ostrowski, Alexander. Collected Papers, Vol. 4, X-XII. (Eng. Ger. & Fr.). 600p. 1984. 48.95 (ISBN 3-7643-1509-1); Six-vol. set. 312.95 (ISBN 3-7643-1512-1). Birkhauser.

Oxtoby, J. C., et al, eds. John von Neuman, 1903-1957. JVN. 130p. 1978. pap. 27.00 (ISBN 0-8218-0021-3). Am Math.

Professional Directory 1984. Incl. Fall Cat of Pubs, 1984-1985. 1984. 15.00 (ISBN 0-8218-0064-7). Am Math.

Reid, Constance. Jerzy Neyman-From Life. (Illus.). 320p. 1982. 22.00 (ISBN 0-387-90747-5). Springer-Verlag.

Rosen, Edward. Three Imperial Mathematicians. 120p. 1985. 20.00 (ISBN 0-89835-242-8). Abaris Bks.

Rudman, Jack. Mathematician. (Career Examination Ser.: C-479). (Cloth bdg. avail. on request). pap. 10.00 (ISBN 0-8373-0479-2). Natl Learning.

Scott, Joseph F. The Mathematical Work of John Wallis. 2nd. ed. LC 80-85524. (Illus.). xii, 240p. 1981. text ed. 16.50 (ISBN 0-8284-0314-7). Chelsea Pub.

Singh, Jagjit. Memoirs of a Mathematician Manque. 176p. 1980. text ed. 15.00x (ISBN 0-7069-1128-8, Pub. by Vikas India). Advent NY.

Tarwater, J. Dalton, et al, eds. Men & Institutions in American Mathematics. (Graduate Studies: No. 13). 136p. (Orig.). 1976. pap. 6.00 (ISBN 0-89672-023-3). Tex Tech Pr.

Turnbull, Herbert Westren. The Great Mathematicians. LC 61-16934. (Illus.). 1961. usa 12.50x (ISBN 0-8147-0419-0). NYU Pr.

Ulam, S. M. Adventures of a Mathematician. LC 75-20133. (Illus.). 320p. 1983. pap. 7.95 (ISBN 0-684-15064-6, ScribT). Scribner.

MATHEMATICS

see also Algebra; Arithmetic; Ausdehnungslehre; Axioms; Binary System (Mathematics); Biomathematics; Business Mathematics; Calculus; Combinations; Congruences (Geometry); Conic Sections; Coordinates; Curves; Decomposition (Mathematics); Determinants; Dynamics; Economics, Mathematical; Engineering Mathematics; Equations; Errors, Theory of; Forms (Mathematics); Fractions; Functions; Game Theory; Geography, Mathematical; Geometry; Graphic Methods; Groups, Theory of; Harmonic Analysis; Hyperspace; Induction (Mathematics); Kinematics; Least Squares; Logic, Symbolic and Mathematical; Maxima and Minima; Mensuration; Metric System; Numbers, Theory of; Numerals; Numeration; Permutations; Potential, Theory of; Probabilities; Projection; Quaternions; Sequences (Mathematics); Series; Set Theory; Shop Mathematics; Statics; Transformations (Mathematics); Trigonometry; Vector Analysis also headings beginning with the word Mathematical

Ablon, L. J., et al. Series in Mathematics Module, Pts. 7, 8, 9, 10, 11. Incl. Module 7. Trigonometry with Applications. LC 75-262499. 7.95 (ISBN 0-8465-0261-5); Module 8. Exponents & Logarithms. LC 75-35281 (ISBN 0-8465-0262-3); Module 9. Advanced Algebraic Techniques (ISBN 0-8465-0263-1); Module 10. Functions & Word Problems (ISBN 0-8465-0264-X); Module 11. Graphing Functions (ISBN 0-8465-0265-8). 1976. pap. 7.95 (ISBN 0-686-67410-3). Benjamin-Cummings.

Ablon, Leon, et al. Series in Mathematics Modules, 5 Modules. 1981. pap. 8.95; Module 1. pap. 8.95 (ISBN 0-8053-0131-3); Module 2. pap. 8.95 (ISBN 0-8053-0132-1); Module 3. pap. 8.95 (ISBN 0-8053-0133-X); Module 4. pap. 8.95 (ISBN 0-8053-0134-8); Rationale. pap. 4.95 (ISBN 0-8053-0136-4). Benjamin-Cummings.

--The Steps in Mathematics Modules One Thru Five. 1981. pap. 30.95 (ISBN 0-8053-0140-2). Benjamin-Cummings.

Achenbach, J. D. & Gausten, A. K. Ray Methods for Waves in Elastic Solids. (Monographs & Studies: No. 14). 300p. 1982. pap. text ed. 54.50 (ISBN 0-273-08453-4). Pitman Pub MA.

Acosta, Antonio A. & Calvo, Zoraida. Matematicas: Preparacion Para el Examen el Espanol De Equivalencia De la Escuela Superior. rev. ed. LC 80-25182. 272p. (Orig.). 1982. pap. 6.95 (ISBN 0-668-04821-2, 4821-2). Arco.

Adams, J. Frank. Lectures on Lie Groups. LC 82-51014. (Midway Reprints Ser.). 168p. 1983. pap. text ed. 11.00x (ISBN 0-226-00530-5). U of Chicago Pr.

Adams, W. Fundamentals of Mathematics for Business, Social, & Life Sciences. 1979. 31.65 (ISBN 0-13-341073-0). P-H.

Adler, Irving. The Impossible in Mathematics. LC 77-33757. (Illus.). 32p. 1957. pap. 2.50 (ISBN 0-87353-062-4). NCTM.

Adler, R. L. & Weiss, B. Similarity of Automorphisms of the Torus. LC 52-42839. (Memoirs: No. 98). 43p. 1970. pap. 9.00 (ISBN 0-8218-1298-X, MEMO-98). Am Math.

Afraimovic, V. S., et al. Transactions of the Moscow Mathematical Society, Vol. 28 (1973) LC 65-7413. 1975. 76.00 (ISBN 0-8218-1628-4, MOSCOW-28). Am Math.

Airey, Dennis D. Basic Mathematics. 1976. coil bdg. 10.95 (ISBN 0-88252-021-0). Paladin Hse.

Al-Daffa, A. A. Modern Mathematics & Intellect: Arabic Edition. 96p. 1979. pap. text ed. 6.60 (ISBN 0-471-05139-X). Wiley.

Alefeld, Gotz & Herzberger, Jurgen. Introduction to Interval Computations. Rockne, Jon, tr. from Ger. (Computer Science & Applied Mathematics Ser.). 1983. 55.00 (ISBN 0-12-049820-0). Acad Pr.

Aleksandrov, A. D., et al, eds. Mathematics: Its Content, Methods, & Meaning, 3 Vols. 2nd ed. Gould, S. H., tr. 1969. pap. 9.95 ea.; Vol. 1. pap. (ISBN 0-262-51005-7); Vol. 2. pap. (ISBN 0-262-51004-9); Vol. 3. pap. (ISBN 0-262-51003-0); pap. 27.50 set (ISBN 0-262-51014-6). MIT Pr.

Al-Hadad, Sabah. Agricultural Mathematics. 168p. 1981. pap. text ed. 10.95 (ISBN 0-8403-2450-2). Kendall-Hunt.

Ali, N., et al. Transactions of the Moscow Mathematical Society, 1975. LC 65-4713. 1977. 62.00 (ISBN 0-8218-1632-2, MOSCOW-32). Am Math.

Allard, S. Metals: Thermal & Mechanical Data. 1969. 125.00 (ISBN 0-08-006588-0). Pergamon.

Allendoerfer, Carl B. & Oakley, Cletus O. Fundamentals of Freshman Mathematics. 3rd ed. (Illus.). 1972. text ed. 32.95 (ISBN 0-07-001366-7). McGraw.

Andree, Josephine & Andree, Richard. Cryptarithms. 1978. pap. 2.95 (ISBN 0-686-23790-0); instructor's manual 2.00 (ISBN 0-686-28564-6). Mu Alpha Theta.

Andree, Josephine P., ed. Lines from the O. U. Mathematics Letter. Incl. Vol. 1, Number Extensions. 1.00; Vol. 2, Theory of GAmes. 0.75; Vol. 3, Geometric Extensions. 1.25. Mu Alpha Theta.

Andree, Josephine P, ed. More Chips from the Mathematical Log. pap. 1.25 (ISBN 0-686-00324-1). Mu Alpha Theta.

Andres, P. G., et al. Basic Mathematics for Engineers. LC 55-8369. 776p. 1944. 41.50 (ISBN 0-471-02937-8). Wiley.

Andrews, F. Emerson. Numbers, Please. 2nd enlarged ed. LC 77-20492. 1977. pap. 5.95x (ISBN 0-8077-2545-5). Tchrs Coll.

Anton, Howard & Kolman, Bernard. Applied Finite Mathematics. 3rd ed. LC 81-66947. 1982. 22.50i (ISBN 0-12-059566-4); instrs' manual 2.50i (ISBN 0-12-059571-0); study guide 6.50i (ISBN 0-12-059570-2). Acad Pr.

Anton, Howard & Kolman, B., eds. Mathematics with Applications for the Management, Life & Social Sciences. 2nd ed. LC 81-66947. 851p. 1982. text ed. 22.50i (ISBN 0-12-059561-3); instr's. manual 2.50i (ISBN 0-12-059563-X); study guide 6.50i (ISBN 0-12-059562-1). Acad Pr.

Applications in School Mathematics: 1979 Yearbook. LC 79-1137. (National Council of Teachers of Mathematics). (Illus.). 248p. 1979. 14.50 (ISBN 0-87353-139-6). NCTM.

Arnold, et al. Singularities of Differentiable Maps: Vol. 1. (Monographs in Mathematics). 1984. text ed. write for info. (ISBN 0-8176-3187-9). Birkhauser.

Arscott, et al. Remedial Mathematics for Science & Engineering. 152p. 1983. pap. text ed. 8.95 (ISBN 0-8403-3068-5). Kendall-Hunt.

Arscott-Berry. Introduction to Applied Mathematics: Summary Notes. 296p. 1983. pap. text ed. 11.95 (ISBN 0-8403-3086-3). Kendall-Hunt.

Aufmann, Richard N. & Barker, Vernon C. Basic College Mathematics: An Applied Approach. 2nd ed. LC 81-84253. 1982. pap. 25.95 (ISBN 0-395-31679-0); instr's. annotated ed. 26.95 (ISBN 0-395-32322-3); instr's. alternate Test Programm A & B 3.95 (ISBN 0-395-31680-4); solutions manual 8.50 (ISBN 0-395-32023-2); instr's. alternate test C & D 3.95 (ISBN 0-395-35435-8). HM.

Auslander, Louis, et al. Mathematics Through Statistics. LC 79-9749. 224p. 1979. pap. 13.50 (ISBN 0-88275-949-3). Krieger.

Author Index of Zentralblatt fuer Mathematik, und Ihre Grenzgebiete, 1931-1939, 2 pts. Set. pap. 146.00 (ISBN 0-685-64497-9, MREVIN 3140). Am Math.

Averbhh, V. I., et al. Transactions of the Moscow Mathematical Society, Vol. 27 (1972) LC 65-7413. 1974. 62.00 (ISBN 0-8218-1627-6, MOSCOW-27). Am Math.

Averbuh, V. I., et al. Transactions of the Moscow Mathematical Society, Vol. 24 (1971) LC 65-7413. 1974. 71.00 (ISBN 0-8218-1624-1, MOSCOW-24). Am Math.

Ayres, Frank, Jr. First-Year College Mathematics. (Schaum's Outline Ser). (Orig.). 1958. pap. 9.95 (ISBN 0-07-002650-5). McGraw.

Bailey, Frank A. Basic Mathematics. 1977. pap. 14.70x (ISBN 0-673-15064-X). Scott F.

Baker, C. C. Introduction to Mathematics. LC 66-20198. (Illus.). 1966. pap. 1.65 (ISBN 0-668-01479-2). Arco.

Ball, J. M., ed. Systems of Nonlinear Partial Differential Equations. 1983. lib. bdg. 65.00 (ISBN 90-277-1629-3, Pub. by Reidel Holland). Kluwer Academic.

Barbasin, E. A., et al. Twelve Papers on Analysis, Applied Mathematics & Algebraic Topology. LC 51-5559. (Translations Ser.: No. 2, Vol. 25). 1963. 27.00 (ISBN 0-8218-1725-6, TRANS 2-25). Am Math.

Barker, Vernon C. & Aufmann, Richard N. Essential Mathematics with Applications. LC 82-82928. 288p. 1982. pap. text ed. 12.95 (ISBN 0-395-33195-1); answer booklet 1.25 (ISBN 0-395-33196-X). HM.

Barnett, R. A. Functions & Graphs: A Precalculus Course. LC 84-12519. 800p. 1985. 31.95 (ISBN 0-07-003896-1); 12.95 (ISBN 0-07-003898-8). McGraw.

Barroso, J. A., ed. Aspects of Mathematics & Its Applications: In Honour of Professor L. Nachbin. (North-Holland Mathematical Library). 1984. write for info. (North-Holland). Elsevier.

Barrow, Isaac. Usefulness of Mathematical Learning. Kirby, J., tr. (Illus.). 458p. 1970. Repr. of 1734 ed. 32.50x (ISBN 0-7146-1591-9, F Cass Co). Biblio Dist.

Crowdis, David G. & Wheeler, Brandon W. Precalculus Mathematics. 1976. text ed. write for info. (ISBN 0-02-472030-5). Macmillan.

Crowhurst, Norman H. Taking the Mysticism from Mathematics. 2nd ed. 178p. (Orig.). 1981. pap. 7.65 (ISBN 0-89420-223-5, 297020). Natl Book.

CUPM. Recommendations for a General Mathematical Sciences Program. LC 81-83644. 1981. pap. 3.50 (ISBN 0-88385-437-6). Math Assn.

Curtiss, David R. Analytic Functions of a Complex Variable. (Carus Monograph: No. 2). 173p. 1926. 19.50 (ISBN 0-88385-002-8, CAM-02). Math Assn.

Dacorogna, B. Weak Continuity & Weak Semicontinuity of Non-Linear Functionals. (Lecture Notes in Mathematics Ser.: Vol. 922). 120p. 1982. pap. 12.00 (ISBN 0-387-11488-2). Springer-Verlag.

Dalton, Leroy C. & Snyder, Henry D., eds. Topics for Mathematics Clubs. pap. 2.80 (ISBN 0-686-05576-4). Mu Alpha Theta.

Davenport, H. The Higher Arithmetic: An Introduction to the Theory of Numbers. 172p. 1983. pap. 4.50 (ISBN 0-486-24452-0). Dover.

Davey, R. J., et al. Studies on Mesozoic & Caenozoic Dinoflagellate Cysts. (Illus.). 272p. 1983. pap. text ed. 90.00x (ISBN 0-565-00879-X, Pub. by Brit Mus Nat Hist England). Sabbot-Natural Hist Bks.

Davidson, J. New Mathematics. (Teach Yourself Ser.). 1974. pap. 4.95 (ISBN 0-679-12326-1). McKay.

Davis, Martin. Lectures on Modern Mathematics. (Notes on Mathematics & Its Applications Ser.). 196p. 1967. 57.75 (ISBN 0-677-00200-9). Gordon.

Davis, Morton. Mathematically Speaking. 484p. 1980. text ed. 20.95 (ISBN 0-15-555190-6, HC); instr's manual avail. (ISBN 0-15-555191-4). HarBraceJ.

Davis, Philip J. Schwarz Function & Its Applications. LC 74-77258. (Carus Monograph: No. 17). 241p. 1973. 16.50 (ISBN 0-88385-017-6). Math Assn.

De Boer, Paul M. Price Effects in Input-Output Relations: A Theoretical & Empirical Study for the Netherlands 1949-1967. (Lecture Notes in Economics & Mathematical Systems: Vol. 201). (Illus.). 140p. 1982. 13.00 (ISBN 0-387-11550-1). Springer-Verlag.

Dedron, P. & Itard, J. Mathematics & Mathematicians, No. 1. 326p. 1978. pap. 10.00x (ISBN 0-335-00246-3, Pub. by Open Univ Pr). Taylor & Francis.

--Mathematics & Mathematicians, No. 2. 222p. 1978. pap. 10.00x (ISBN 0-335-00247-1, Pub. by Open Univ Pr). Taylor & Francis.

DeGonzalez, Fe Acosta & DeMatos, Isabel Freire. Matematicas Modernas En el Nivel Elemental: Guia Metodologica. (Illus.). 6.25 (ISBN 0-8477-2700-9); pap. 5.00 (ISBN 0-8477-2701-7). U of PR Pr.

Demidovich, B. P. & Maron, I. A. Computational Mathematics. 668p. 1981. 10.80 (ISBN 0-8285-0704-X, Pub. by Mir Pubs USSR). Imported Pubns.

De Morgan, Augustus. On the Study & Difficulties of Mathematics. 2nd ed. 295p. 19.95 (ISBN 0-87548-187-6). Open Court.

Denholm, Richard. Basic Math with Applications. 1982. pap. text ed. 20.60x (ISBN 0-673-15233-2). Scott F.

Deutsch, R. W. & Whitney, J. W., eds. Mathematics. (Academic Program for Nuclear Power Plan Personnel Ser.: Vol. I). (Illus.). 372p. 1972. looseleaf 60.00x (ISBN 0-87683-146-3, A 326517); Lesson Plans. 500.00x (ISBN 0-87683-153-6); Practical Excercise Solutions. 25.00x (ISBN 0-87683-160-9); Quizzes & Examinations. 25.00x (ISBN 0-87683-167-6). G P Courseware.

Devi, Shakuntala. Mathematical Merry-Go-Round. 150p. 1978. 14.95x (ISBN 0-306-31031-7, Plenum Pr). Plenum Pub.

Dieudonne, J. A. Treatise on Analysis, 6 vols. Incl. Vol. 1. 1960. 33.75 (ISBN 0-12-215550-5); Vol. 2. rev. ed. 1970. 67.50 (ISBN 0-12-215502-5); Vol. 3. 1972. 68.50 (ISBN 0-12-215503-3); Vol. 4. 1974. 67.50 (ISBN 0-12-215504-1); Vol. 5. 1977. 49.50 (ISBN 0-12-215505-X); Vol. 6. 1978. 47.50 (ISBN 0-12-215506-8). (Pure & Applied Mathematics Ser.). Acad Pr.

Dieudonne, Jean. A Panorama of Pure Mathematics: As Seen by N. Bourbaki. Macdonald, I., tr. LC 80-2330. (Pure & Applied Mathematics Ser.). 1982. 37.50 (ISBN 0-12-215560-2). Acad Pr.

Dikmen, M. Theory of Thin Elastic Shells. (Surveys & Reference Works in Mathematics Ser.: No. 8). 384p. 1982. text ed. 71.95 (ISBN 0-273-08431-3). Pitman Pub MA.

Dobson, A. J. & Stokoe, J. Self-Paced Introductory Mathematics. LC 78-73315. 339p. 1983. pap. text ed. 17.95 (ISBN 0-7081-1199-8, 1616, Pub. by ANUP Australia). Australia N U P.

Dodes, Irving A. Mathematics: A Liberal Arts Approach with Basic. 2nd. ed. LC 79-131. 464p. 1980. lib. bdg. 21.50 (ISBN 0-88275-892-6). Krieger.

Dottori, D. Mathematics for Today & Tomorrow. 2nd ed. 1975. 11.32 (ISBN 0-07-082244-1). McGraw.

Dow Education Systems. Basic Industrial Mathematics: A Text Workbook. 1972. text ed. 24.10 (ISBN 0-07-017660-4). McGraw.

Dressler, Isidore. Preliminary Mathematics. 1981. text ed. 17.50 (ISBN 0-87720-243-5). AMSCO Sch.

Dressler, Isidore & Keenan, Edward P. Integrated Mathematics: Course I. (Orig.). 1980. text ed. 20.25 (ISBN 0-87720-249-4); pap. text ed. 12.92 (ISBN 0-87720-248-6). AMSCO Sch.

Dryjanski, Deborah A. Conquering Word Problems in Mathematics. 1979. incl. manual & cassettes 167.50 (ISBN 0-917792-02-5). Math Hse.

Dubbey, J. M. Development of Modern Mathematics. LC 72-88125. 153p. 1975. pap. 8.75x (ISBN 0-8448-0656-0). Crane-Russak Co.

Dubinsky, Ed & Ramanujan, M. S. On Lambda Nuclearity. LC 72-4515. (Memoirs: No. 128). 101p. 1972. pap. 10.00 (ISBN 0-8218-1828-7, MEMO-128). Am Math.

Dunmore, Charles W. & Fleisher, Rita M. Medical Terminology: Exercises in Etymology. 2nd ed. 350p. 1985. pap. text ed. 16.95 (ISBN 0-8036-2946-X, 2946-X). Davis Co.

Dyachenko, V. F. Basic Computational Math. 125p. 1979. pap. 4.95 (ISBN 0-8285-1593-X, Pub. by Mir Pubs USSR). Imported Pubns.

Dydak, J. & Segal, J. Shape Theory: An Introduction. (Lecture Notes in Mathematics: Vol. 688). 1978. pap. 15.00 (ISBN 0-387-08955-1). Springer-Verlag.

Eastham, M. S. & Kalf, H. Schrodinger Type Operators with Continuous Spectra. (Research Notes in Mathematics Ser.: No. 65). 208p. 1982. pap. text ed. 28.95 (ISBN 0-273-08526-3). Pitman Pub MA.

Eck, David J. Gauge-Natural Bundles & Generalized Gauge Theories. LC 81-12834. (Memoirs: No. 247). 50p. 1981. pap. 9.00 (ISBN 0-8218-2247-0). Am Math.

Edwards, Barry. The Readable Maths & Statistics Book. (Illus.). 336p. (Orig.). 1980. text ed. 34.95x (ISBN 0-04-310007-4). Allen Unwin.

Edwards, R. A Formal Background to Mathematics: Pt. II, A & B. (Universitext). 1170p. 1980. pap. 46.00 (ISBN 0-387-90513-8). Springer-Verlag.

Edwards, R., ed. A Formal Background to Mathematics Pt. 1, A & B Logic, Sets & Numbers, 2 pts. LC 79-15045. 1979. pap. 39.50 (ISBN 0-387-90431-X). Springer-Verlag.

Edwards, R. E. & Gaudry, G. I. Littlewood-Paley & Multiplier Theory. (Ergebnisse der Mathematik und ihrer Grenzgebiete: Vol. 90). 1977. 37.00 (ISBN 0-387-07726-X). Springer-Verlag.

Eggan, Lawrence C. & Vanden Eynden, Charles. Mathematics: Models & Applications. 1979. text ed. 22.95 (ISBN 0-669-01051-0); instr's manual 1.95 (ISBN 0-669-01052-9). Heath.

Eisen, Martin & Eisen, Carole. Finite Mathematics. 1979. text ed. write for info. (ISBN 0-02-472450-5). Macmillan.

Elliott, C. M. & Ockendon, J. R. Weak & Variational Methods for Free & Moving Boundary Problems. (Research Notes in Mathematics Ser.: No. 59). 220p. 1982. pap. text ed. 28.50 (ISBN 0-273-08503-4). Pitman Pub MA.

Elorza. Matematicas para Ciencias del Comportamiento. (Span.). 300p. 1984. pap. text ed. write for info. (ISBN 0-06-310700-7, Pub. by HarLA Mexico). Har-Row.

Emerson, Lloyd & Paquette, Laurence. Fundamental Mathematics for the Management & Social Sciences. alt. ed. 688p. 1981. text ed. 30.31 (ISBN 0-205-07166-X, 567166-3); tchrs. ed. o. p. avail. Allyn.

Erdoes, Paul, ed. Studies in Pure Mathematics: To the Memory of Paul Turan. 400p. 1983. 78.00 (ISBN 0-8176-1288-2). Birkhauser.

Erdsneker, Barbara. Mathematics Simplified & Self-Taught. 6th ed. LC 81-14912. 192p. 1982. pap. 6.95 (ISBN 0-668-05357-7, 5357). Arco.

Eremin, I. I., et al. Twelve Papers on Real & Complex Function Theory. LC 51-5559. (Translations Ser.: No. 2, Vol. 88). 1970. 37.00 (ISBN 0-8218-1788-4, TRANS 2-88). Am Math.

Eresian, W. J., et al. Mathematics & Physical Science, 2 vols. Incl. Vol. 1-Mathematics. Eresian, W. J., et al. (Illus.). 370p. 1979. text ed. 60.00x looseleaf (ISBN 0-87683-026-2); lesson plans 250.00x (ISBN 0-87683-029-7); Vol. 2-Physical Science. Eresian, W. J., et al. 318p. text ed. 60.00x looseleaf (ISBN 0-87683-027-0); lesson plan 250.00x (ISBN 0-317-11852-8). (Illus.). 688p. 1979. Set. 120.00x (ISBN 0-87683-025-4); write for info. lesson plans (ISBN 0-87683-028-9). G P Courseware.

Eves, Howard W. Mathematical Circles Adieu. 1977. write for info. (ISBN 0-87150-240-2, PWS 1941, Prindle). PWS Pubs.

--Mathematical Circles Squared. 186p. 1972. text ed. write for info. (ISBN 0-87150-154-6, PWS 1201, Prindle). PWS Pubs.

Evyatar, A. & Rosenbloom, P. Motivated Mathematics. LC 80-40491. (Illus.). 250p. 1981. 27.95 (ISBN 0-521-23308-9). Cambridge U Pr.

Ewen & Nelson. Elementary Technical Mathematics. 3rd ed. 546p. write for info. (ISBN 0-534-02861-6). Watts.

Feingold, Mordechai. The Mathematicians' Apprenticeship: Science, Universities & Society in England, 1560-1640. LC 83-1911. 256p. 1984. 39.50 (ISBN 0-521-25133-8). Cambridge U Pr.

Felker, Charles A. Shop Mathematics. 6th ed. 1984. 14.40 (ISBN 0-02-816310-9); tchrs' man 11.96 (ISBN 0-02-816320-6). Glencoe.

Fennell, Francis M. Elementary Mathematics Diagnosis & Correction Kit. 1981. pap. 24.95x comb-bound (ISBN 0-87628-295-8). Ctr Appl Res.

--Elementary Mathematics: Priorities for the 1980s. LC 81-80015. (Fastback Ser.: No. 157). 1981. pap. 0.75 (ISBN 0-87367-157-0). Phi Delta Kappa.

Fenyo, S. Modern Mathematical Methods in Technology, Vol. 2. LC 69-16400. (Applied Mathematics & Mechanics Ser.: Vol. 17). 326p. 1975. 40.50 (ISBN 0-444-10565-4, North-Holland). Elsevier.

Fenyo, S. & Frey, T. Moderne Mathematische Methoden in de Technik, Vol. III. (International Series of Numerical Mathematics: No. 18). (Ger.). 348p. 1980. pap. 64.95x (ISBN 0-8176-1097-9). Birkhauser.

Ferrara, S., et al, eds. Conformal Algebra in Space - Time & Operator Product Expansion. LC 25-9130. (Springer Tracts in Modern Physics: Vol. 67). iv, 69p. 1973. 22.50 (ISBN 0-387-06216-5). Springer-Verlag.

Findley, W., et al. Creep & Relaxation of Nonlinear Viscoelastic Materials. 368p. 1976. 81.00 (ISBN 0-444-10775-4, North-Holland). Elsevier.

Fineberg, Marjorie. Everyday Math: Tables, Graphs, & Scale. LC 79-730692. (Illus.). 1979. pap. text ed. 135.00 (ISBN 0-89290-129-2, A514-SATC). Soc for Visual.

Flicker, Y. Z. The Trace Formula & Base Change for GL(3) (Lecture Notes in Mathematics: Vol. 927). 204p. 1982. pap. 15.00 (ISBN 0-387-11500-5). Springer-Verlag.

Foley, et al. Building Math Skills. Incl. Level 1. text ed. 11.96 (ISBN 0-201-13350-4); tchr's. manual with answers 8.64 (ISBN 0-201-13359-8); avail. test & practice duplicating masters 14.44 (ISBN 0-201-13360-1); Level 2. text ed. 11.96 (ISBN 0-201-13370-9); tchr's. manual with anwers 8.64 (ISBN 0-201-13379-2); test & practice duplicating masters avail.. (Gr. 7-12 Basal, Gr. 9-12 Remedial, Gr. 7-12 Supplemental). 1981. Addison-Wesley.

Forman, William & Gavurin, Lester L. Elements of Arithmetic: Algebra & Geometry. LC 78-159159. 318p. 1972. text ed. 30.50x (ISBN 0-471-00654-8). Wiley.

Foster, et al. Mathematics for Developmental Students. 464p. 1983. pap. 19.95 (ISBN 0-8403-3016-2). Kendall-Hunt.

Francis, P. G. Mathematics for Chemists. 176p. (Orig.). 1984. text ed. 29.95 (ISBN 0-412-24980-4, 9193, Pub. by Chapman & Hall England); pap. text ed. 11.95 (ISBN 0-412-24990-1, Pub. by Chapman & Hall England). Methuen Inc.

Francis, Philip. Mathematics of the Universe: The Universe of the Mind. (Oleander Mathematics Ser.: Vol. 1). (Illus.). 1977. pap. 13.50 (ISBN 0-902675-75-3). Oleander Pr.

Francis, Philip H. Cartesian & Argand Values. (Oleander Manthematics Ser.: Vol. 3). (Illus.). 1978. pap. 13.50 (ISBN 0-900891-47-5). Oleander Pr.

Freudenthal, Hans. Weeding & Sowing: Preface to a Science of Mathematical Education. ix, 314p. 1980. lib. bdg. 47.50 (ISBN 90-277-0789-8, Pub. by Reidel Holland); pap. 15.00 (ISBN 90-277-1072-4). Kluwer Academic.

Friedrichs, K. O. From Pythagoras to Einstein. LC 65-24963. (New Mathematical Library: No. 16). 88p. 1975. pap. 8.75 (ISBN 0-88385-616-6). Math Assn.

Gabbay, S. M. Elementary Mathematics for Basic Chemistry & Physics. 128p. (Orig.). 1980. pap. 11.95 (ISBN 0-9604722-0-7). Basic Science Prep Ctr.

Gafney, Leo & Beers, John C. Essential Math Skills. Devine, Peter, ed. 224p. 1980. pap. text ed. 7.36 (ISBN 0-07-010260-0). McGraw.

Gagliardi, Richard L. & Valenza, Samuel W., Jr., eds. The Mathematics of the Energy Crisis. LC 78-53592. 96p. 1978. pap. 7.95 (ISBN 0-936918-01-2). Intergalactic NJ.

Galerstein, David H. Mastering Fundamental Mathematics. (Orig.). 1976. pap. text ed. 7.58 (ISBN 0-87720-226-5). AMSCO Sch.

Gamkrelidze, R. V., ed. Progress in Mathematics, 4 vols. Incl. Vol. 10. Mathematical Analysis. Wood, J. S., tr. pap. 29.30 (ISBN 0-317-30355-4); Vol. 11. Probability Theory, Mathematical Statistics, & Theoretical Cybernetics. Wood, J. S., tr. pap. 33.00 (ISBN 0-317-30356-2); Vol. 12. Algebra & Geometry. Choksy, Nasli H., tr. pap. 66.00 (ISBN 0-317-30357-0); Vol. 13. Probability Theory, Mathematical Statistics & Theoretical Cybernetics. Wood, J. S., tr. pap. 29.50 (ISBN 0-317-30358-9). LC 67-27902 (2024721). Bks Demand UMI.

Garcia, C. B. & Zangwill, Willard I. Pathways to Solutions, Fixed Points, & Equilibria. (Computational Math Ser.). 336p. 1981. text ed. 42.95 (ISBN 0-13-653501-1). P-H.

Garding, L. Encounter with Mathematics. LC 76-54765. 280p. 1977. 28.50 (ISBN 0-387-90229-5). Springer-Verlag.

Gardner, Martin. Martin Gardner's New Mathematical Diversions from Scientific American. LC 83-12352. (Illus.). 254p. 1984. pap. 7.95 (ISBN 0-226-28247-3). U of Chicago Pr.

--Mathematical Circus. LC 80-6135. (Illus.). 272p. 1981. pap. 4.95 (ISBN 0-394-74712-7, V-712, Vin). Random.

Garrido, L., et al, eds. Stochastic Processes in Nonequilibrium Systems: Proceedings, Sitges International School of Statistical Mechanics, June 1978, Sitges, Barcelona, Spain. (Lecture Notes in Physics: Vol. 84). 1978. pap. 25.00 (ISBN 0-387-08942-X). Springer-Verlag.

Gauss, Karl. Briefwechsel Zwischen Carl Friedrich Gauss und W. Bolyai. 1971. Repr. of 1899 ed. 26.00 (ISBN 0-384-17765-4). Johnson Repr.

--Untersuchungen ueber Hoehere Arithmetik: including Disquisitionea Arithmeticae. 2nd ed. Maser, H., tr. LC 65-17614. (Ger.). 695p. 1981. text ed. 35.00 (ISBN 0-8284-0191-8). Chelsea Pub.

Geary, A. Advanced Mathematics for Technical Students. pap. 145.50 (ISBN 0-317-08483-6, 2010171). Bks Demand UMI.

General Mathematics. (Lefax Data Bks.: No. 613). (Illus.). pap. 3.00 (ISBN 0-685-52845-6). LeFax.

Gerding, Mildred, ed. Applied Mathematics for the Petroleum Other Industries. 3rd, rev. ed. (Illus.). 274p. 1985. pap. text ed. 10.00 (ISBN 0-88698-085-2, 1.60030). PETEX.

Gewirtz, Allan & Quintas, Louis V., eds. International Conference on Combinatorial Mathematics, Second. (Annals of the New York Academy of Sciences: Vol. 319). 602p. (Orig.). 1979. pap. 112.00x (ISBN 0-89766-010-2). NY Acad Sci.

Gibson, Carol, ed. The Facts on File Dictionary of Mathematics. 224p. 1981. 14.95 (ISBN 0-87196-512-7). Facts on File.

Gill, Jack C., et al. Competency in College Mathematics. 3rd ed. LC 84-147965. (Illus.). 514p. (Orig.). 1983. pap. text ed. 19.95x (ISBN 0-943202-09-4). H & H Pub.

Gilligan, Lawrence & Nenno, Robert B. Finite Mathematics: An Elementary Approach. 2nd ed. 1979. text ed. 23.80x (ISBN 0-673-16235-4). Scott F.

Goldstein, Larry J. & Schneider, David. Finite Mathematics & Its Applications. 2nd ed. (Illus.). 528p. 1984. 31.95 (ISBN 0-13-317313-5). P-H.

Goodman, A. W. & Ratti, J. S. Finite Mathematics with Applications. 1979. text ed. 23.95x (ISBN 0-02-344760-5); write for info. Macmillan.

Goodstein, R. L. Fundamental Concepts of Mathematics. 2nd ed. 53.00 (ISBN 0-08-021665-X). Pergamon.

Goozner, Calman. Computational Skills for College Students. 1976. pap. text ed. 7.60 (ISBN 0-87720-976-6). AMSCO Sch.

Gossage, Loyce C. Basic Mathematics Review. 1985. text ed. 4.90 (ISBN 0-538-14220-0, N22). SW Pub.

Gould, S. H. & Liu, P. H. Kinship, Marriage & Mathematics. LC 80-2333. (Pure & Applied Mathematics Ser.). Date not set. write for info. (ISBN 0-12-293720-1). Acad Pr.

Gowar, Norman. An Invitation to Mathematics. (Illus.). 1979. text ed. 32.50x (ISBN 0-19-853002-1); pap. 12.95x (ISBN 0-19-853001-3). Oxford U Pr.

Grady & Wooton. Precalculus. 2nd ed. 662p. write for info. (ISBN 0-534-02841-1). Wadsworth Pub.

Graham, Lloyd A. Surprise Attack in Mathematical Problems. (Illus., Orig.). 1968. pap. 4.50 (ISBN 0-486-21846-5). Dover.

Graham, Ronald, et al. Ramsey Theory. LC 80-14110. (Wiley-Interscience Series in Discrete Mathematics). 174p. 1980. 34.50x (ISBN 0-471-05997-8, Pub. by Wiley Interscience). Wiley.

Roach, G. F. Vibration Theory. 250p. 1982. 60.00x (ISBN 0-906812-12-7, Pub. by Shiva Pub England); pap. 40.00x (ISBN 0-906812-11-9). State Mutual Bk.

Roberts, A. Wayne & Varberg, Dale E. Faces of Mathematics: An Introductory Course for College Students. 2nd ed. 492p. 1982. text ed. 25.50 scp (ISBN 0-06-045471-7, HarpC); instr's manual avail. (ISBN 0-06-365519-5). Har-Row.

Roberts, Blaine & Schulze, David L. Modern Mathematics & Economic Analysis. 1973. study guide 4.95x (ISBN 0-393-09374-3). Norton.

Robinson, R. W., et al. Combinatorial Mathematics VII: Proceedings. (Lecture Notes in Mathematics Ser.: Vol. 829). (Illus.). 256p. 1980. pap. 20.00 (ISBN 0-387-10254-X). Springer-Verlag.

Rockafellar, R. Tyrrell. Conjugate Duality & Optimization. (CBMS-NSF Regional Conference Ser.: No. 16). vi, 74p. (Orig.). 1974. pap. text ed. 10.00 (ISBN 0-89871-013-8). Soc Indus-Appl Math.

Rosenberg, R. Robert. Mathematicas Para Contabilidad y Administracion. (Span). 1972. text ed. 16.25 (ISBN 0-07-053722-4). McGraw.

Rosenblatt, Murray. Stationary Sequences & Random Fields. 396p. 1985. text ed. 30.00 (ISBN 0-8176-3264-6). Birkhauser.

Rosinger, E. E. Nonlinear Equivalence: Reduction of Pde's to Ode's & Fast Convergent Numerical Methods. (Research Notes in Mathematics: No. 77). 200p. 1983. pap. text ed. 23.95 (ISBN 0-273-08570-0). Pitman Pub MA.

Rothenberg, Ronald I. Finite Mathematics. LC 79-22637. (Self-Teaching Guide Ser.). 283p. 1980. pap. text ed. 8.95 (ISBN 0-471-04320-6, Pub. by Wiley Pr). Wiley.

Roueche, N. E. & Mink, B. Washburn. The Language of Mathematics: An Individualized Introduction. LC 78-13397. 1979. 28.95 (ISBN 0-13-522920-0). P-H.

Rubenstein, L. I. Stefan Problem. LC 75-168253. (Translations of Mathematical Monographs: Vol. 27). 1971. 56.00 (ISBN 0-8218-1577-6, MMONO-27). Am Math.

Ruberti, A., ed. Realization Theory. LC 76-21964. 1977. pap. text ed. 21.00 (ISBN 0-08-021276-X). Pergamon.

Rudman, Jack. Mathematics. (Undergraduate Program Field Test Ser.: UPFT-15). (Cloth bdg. avail. on request). pap. 9.95 (ISBN 0-8373-6015-3). Natl Learning.

--Mathematics Aide. (Career Examination Ser.: C-480). (Cloth bdg. avail. on request). pap. 8.00 (ISBN 0-8373-0480-6). Natl Learning.

Rusinoff, S. E. Mathematics for Industry. 3rd ed. (Illus.). 1968. 14.25 (ISBN 0-8269-2200-7). Am Technical.

Russell, Bertrand. Mathematics, Metaphysics & the Power of the Scientific Method, 2 vols. (Illus.). 225p. 1985. Repr. Set. 187.75 (ISBN 0-89901-215-9). Found Class Reprints.

Ryser, Herbert J. Combinatorial Mathematics. LC 65-12288. (Carus Monograph: No. 14). 154p. 1963. 19.00 (ISBN 0-88385-014-1). Math Assn.

Sachs, R. K. General Relativity for Mathematicians. LC 76-47697. (Graduate Texts in Mathematics Ser.: Vol. 48). 1977. 35.00 (ISBN 0-387-90218-X). Springer-Verlag.

Saigal, J. C. Choice of Sectors & Regions. 104p. 1969. pap. 33.75 (ISBN 0-677-61610-4). Gordon.

St. John, Michael. From Arithmetic to Algebra. 132p. (Orig.). 1980. pap. text ed. 2.95 (ISBN 0-937354-00-7, TX-334-207). Delta Systems.

Saint Paul Technical Vocational Institute Curriculum Committee. Mathematics for Careers: Consumer Applications. LC 80-67550. (Trade Mathematics Ser.). 144p. (Orig.). 1981. pap. text ed. 5.00 (ISBN 0-8273-2056-6); instr's. guide 2.85 (ISBN 0-8273-1881-2). Delmar.

--Mathematics for Careers: Fractions. LC 80-70485. (General Mathematics Ser.). 159p. (Orig.). 1981. pap. text ed. 5.00 (ISBN 0-8273-1593-7); instr's. guide 3.75 (ISBN 0-8273-1595-3). Delmar.

St. Paul Technical Vocational Institute Curriculum Committee. Mathematics for Careers: Measurement & Geometry. LC 80-67549. (General Mathematics Ser.). 161p. 1981. pap. text ed. 5.00 (ISBN 0-8273-2058-2); instr's. guide 2.85 (ISBN 0-8273-1881-2). Delmar.

Salsburg. Understanding Randomness. 104p. 1983. 25.00 (ISBN 0-8247-7057-9). Dekker.

Sanchez, David A. Ordinary & Differential Equations & Stability Theory: An Introduction. 1979. pap. text ed. 4.00 (ISBN 0-486-63828-6). Dover.

Saunders, P. T. An Introduction to Catastrophe Theory. LC 79-54172. (Illus.). 1980. 32.50 (ISBN 0-521-23042-X); pap. 11.95 (ISBN 0-521-29782-6). Cambridge U Pr.

Sawyer, W. W. Prelude to Mathematics. (Popular Science Ser.). 224p. 1983. pap. 4.50 (ISBN 0-486-24401-6). Dover.

Saxon, John. Math Seventy-Six. 300p. 1985. text ed. 18.00 (ISBN 0-939798-15-8); tchr's. ed. avail. (ISBN 0-939798-16-6). Grassdale.

Scalzo, Frank & Hughes, Rowland. A Computer Approach to Introductory College Mathematics. 1977. pap. 15.95 (ISBN 0-442-80434-2). Van Nos Reinhold.

Scandinavian Congress - 15th - Oslo - 1968. Proceedings. Aubert, K. E. & Ljunggren, W., eds. LC 70-112305. (Lecture Notes in Mathematics: Vol. 118). 1970. pap. 10.70 (ISBN 0-387-04907-X). Springer-Verlag.

Schillinger, Joseph. Mathematical Basis of the Arts. LC 76-8189. (Music Reprint Ser.). 696p. 1976. Repr. of 1948 ed. 55.00 (ISBN 0-306-70781-0). Da Capo.

Schoenstadt, A. L., et al, eds. Information Linkage Between Applied Mathematics & Industry II. LC 80-17975. 1980. 29.00 (ISBN 0-12-628750-3). Acad Pr.

Schofield, C. W. Basic Mathematics for Technicians. (Illus.). 1977. pap. text ed. 16.95x (ISBN 0-7131-3379-1). Intl Ideas.

Schofield, C. W. & Smethurst, D. Mathematics for Level-Two Technicians. (Illus.). 1979. pap. text ed. 18.95x (ISBN 0-7131-3385-6). Intl Ideas.

Schuh, J. F. Mathematical Tools for Modern Physics. 468p. 1968. 117.95x (ISBN 0-677-61090-4). Gordon.

Schwarz, Hermann A. Gesammelte Mathematische Abhandlungen, 2 vols. in 1. 2nd ed. LC 70-113147. (Ger). text ed. 39.50 (ISBN 0-8284-0260-4). Chelsea Pub.

Scott, John B. & Hutton, E. L. Mathematics for the Health Sciences. 205p. 1978. pap. text ed. 13.95x (ISBN 0-89641-009-9). American Pr.

Segel, Lee A. Mathematics Applied to Continuum Machanics. 1977. write for info. (ISBN 0-02-408700-9, 40870). Macmillan.

Seifert, Herbert & Threlfall, W. Variationsrechnung im Grossen. LC 77-160837. (Ger.). 8.95 (ISBN 0-8284-0049-0). Chelsea Pub.

Sellers, Gene. Understanding Algebra & Trigonometry. 1979. text ed. 24.95 (ISBN 0-675-08306-0). Additional supplements may be obtained from publisher. Merrill.

Setek, William. Fundamentals of Mathematics. 4th ed. 641p. Date not set. text ed. price not set (ISBN 0-02-409200-2). Macmillan.

Setek, William M., Jr. Fundamentals of Mathematics. 3rd ed. 640p. 1983. text ed. write for info. (ISBN 0-02-477960-1). Macmillan.

Shepp, Lawrence A., ed. Computed Tomography. LC 82-18508. (Proceedings of Symposia in Applied Mathematics: Vol. 27). pap. 15.00 (ISBN 0-8218-0033-7, PSAPM-27). Am Math.

Shields, Paul. Theory of Bernouilli Shifts. (Chicago Lectures in Mathematics Ser). 1973. pap. 6.00x (ISBN 0-226-75297-6). U of Chicago Pr.

Shoemaker, Terry. Performance Activities in Mathematics, 6 bks. Incl. Bk. 1 (ISBN 0-913688-10-X); Bk. 2 (ISBN 0-913688-11-8); Bk. 3 (ISBN 0-913688-12-6); Bk. 4 (ISBN 0-913688-13-4); Bk. 5 (ISBN 0-913688-14-2); Bk. 6 (ISBN 0-913688-15-0). 1974. pap. 6.64 ea. Pawnee Pub.

Signed Numbers: Level Three Texts. rev. ed. (Math Components Ser.). 48p. 1983. 2.50 (ISBN 0-88336-830-7). New Readers.

Silver, Edward S., ed. Teaching & Learning Mathematical Problem Solving: Multiple Research Perspectives. 469p. 1985. text ed. 49.95 (ISBN 0-89859-681-5); pap. 14.95 (ISBN 0-89859-759-5). L Erlbaum Assocs.

Silver, Howard A. Basic Mathematics. (Illus.). 656p. 1982. text ed. 25.95 (ISBN 0-13-062802-6). P-H.

--Mathematics: Contemporary Topics & Applications. (Illus.). 1979. text ed. 29.95 (ISBN 0-13-563304-4). P-H.

Siner, Helen B. Series in Mathematics Modules: Practical Mathematics, Module 2A. Ablon, Leon J., ed. LC 75-12083. 1975. pap. text ed. 4.95 (ISBN 0-8465-6714-8). Benjamin-Cummings.

Slade, B. A. Complete Course in Short-Cut Mathematics. 144p. 1953. 15.95 (ISBN 0-911012-11-7). Nelson-Hall.

Slisenko, A. O., ed. Studies in Constructive Mathematics & Mathematical Logic, Part 2. LC 69-12507. (Seminars in Mathematics Ser.: Vol. 8). 136p. 1970. 25.00x (ISBN 0-306-18808-2, Consultants). Plenum Pub.

Smale, S. The Mathematics of Time. (Illus.). 151p. 1980. pap. 19.50 (ISBN 0-387-90519-7). Springer-Verlag.

Smart, D. R. Fixed Point Theorems. (Cambridge Tracts in Mathematics: No. 66). (Illus.). 100p. 1980. pap. 16.95x (ISBN 0-521-29833-4). Cambridge U Pr.

Smith, D. & St. Andre, Richard. A Transition to Advanced Mathematics. LC 82-20737. 200p. 1983. text ed. 21.50 pub net (ISBN 0-534-01249-3). Brooks-Cole.

Smith, David E. A Source Book in Mathematics. 701p. 1984. pap. 12.95 (ISBN 0-486-64690-4). Dover.

Smith, Harold & Keiffer, Mildred. Pathways in Mathematics: Level II. 3rd ed. Sharpe, Glyn, ed. (Illus.). 1980. pap. text ed. 7.26x (ISBN 0-913688-37-1); tchr's. guide 6.00 (ISBN 0-686-96846-8). Pawnee Pub.

Smith, Julius & Burton, David. Basic Mathematics with Electronic Applications. (Illus.). 620p. 1972. text ed. write for info. (ISBN 0-02-412540-7). Macmillan.

Smith, Karl J. Basic Mathematics for College Students. LC 80-20492. 400p. (Orig.). 1981. pap. text ed. 19.25 pub net (ISBN 0-8185-0419-6). Brooks-Cole.

--Finite Mathematics. LC 84-21337. (Mathematics Ser.). 550p. 1984. text ed. 23.50 pub net (ISBN 0-534-03975-8). Brooks-Cole.

--Finite Mathematics: A Discrete Approach. 1975. text ed. 20.60x (ISBN 0-673-07921-X). Scott F.

--Mathematics: It's Power & Utility. LC 82-12932. (Mathematics Ser.). 500p. text ed. 21.00 pub net (ISBN 0-534-01190-X). Brooks-Cole.

--The Nature of Mathematics. 4th ed. LC 83-14455. (Mathematics Ser.). 630p. 1984. text ed. 21.00 pub net (ISBN 0-534-02806-3). Brooks-Cole.

Smith, Robert. Applied General Mathematics. LC 79-51586. (General Mathematics Ser.). (Illus.). 349p. 1982. text ed. 21.80 (ISBN 0-8273-1674-7); instr's. guide 5.25 (ISBN 0-8273-1675-5); test booklet 6.60 (ISBN 0-8273-2075-2). Delmar.

Smithsi, T. Basic Mathematical Skills. 1974. pap. 24.95 (ISBN 0-13-063420-4). P-H.

Society for Industrial & Applied Mathematics - American Mathematical Society Symposia - New York - April, 1973. Complexity of Computation: Proceedings. Karp, R. M., ed. LC 74-22062. (SIAM-AMS Proceedings: Vol 7). 1974. 34.00 (ISBN 0-8218-1327-7, SIAMS-7). Am Math.

Spargo, Edward & Harris, Raymond. Reading the Content Fields: Mathematics. (Content Skills Ser - Advanced Level). (Illus.). 96p. 1978. pap. text ed. 4.00x (ISBN 0-89061-139-4, 553A). Jamestown Pubs.

--Reading the Content Fields: Mathematics. (Content Skills Ser. - Middle Level). (Illus.). 96p. 1978. pap. text ed. 4.00x (ISBN 0-89061-129-7, 553M). Jamestown Pubs.

Sparks, Fred W. & Rees, Charles S. A Survey of Basic Mathematics. 4th ed. (Illus.). 1979. pap. text ed. 29.95 (ISBN 0-07-059902-5). McGraw.

Speiser, A. Die Geistige Arbeit. (Science & Civilization Ser.: No. 9). (Ger.). 207p. 1955. 23.95x (ISBN 0-8176-0343-3). Birkhauser.

Speiser, D., ed. Daniel Bernoulli: Werke Band 2: Mathematische Schriften. 403p. 1982. text ed. 63.95x (ISBN 0-8176-1084-7). Birkhauser.

Spence, Lawrence E. Finite Mathematics. 544p. 1981. text ed. 24.00 scp (ISBN 0-06-046369-4, HarpC); scp sol. manual 5.50 (ISBN 0-06-041842-7); instr's. manual avail. (ISBN 0-06-366385-6). Har-Row.

Sperling, Abraham & Stuart, Monroe. Mathematics Made Simple. rev. ed. LC 80-2627. (Made Simple Ser.). (Illus.). 192p. 1982. pap. 4.95 (ISBN 0-385-17481-0). Doubleday.

Spiegel, Murray R. Advanced Mathematics for Engineers & Scientists. (Schaum Outline Ser.). 1970. pap. 9.95 (ISBN 0-07-060216-6). McGraw.

Srivastava, J. N., et al. A Survey of Combinatorial Theory. LC 72-88578. 470p. 1973. 51.00 (ISBN 0-444-10425-9, North-Holland). Elsevier.

Stancl, Donald L. & Stancl, Mildred L. Applications of College Mathematics: Management, Life, & Social Sciences. 736p. 27.95 (ISBN 0-669-03860-1); instr's guide 1.95 (ISBN 0-669-03861-X); computer problem solving 8.95 (ISBN 0-669-03881-4). Heath.

Staszkow, Ronald. Developmental Mathematics: Basic Arithmetic with a Brief Introduction to Algebra. 448p. 1982. 17.50 (ISBN 0-8403-2822-2). Kendall-Hunt.

Steele, J. H., ed. Fisheries Mathematics. 1978. 39.00 (ISBN 0-12-665250-3). Acad Pr.

Steen, Lynn, ed. Undergraduate Mathematics Education in the People's Republic of China: Report of a 1983 North American Delegation. (MAA Notes Ser.: Vol. 3). 100p. 1984. pap. 5.00 (ISBN 0-88385-053-2). Math Assn.

Steen, Lynn A. Mathematics Today. LC 80-10888. (Illus.). 384p. 1980. pap. 6.95 (ISBN 0-394-74503-5, Vin). Random.

Stefani, S. & Hubbard, Lincoln B. Mathematics for Technologists in Radiology, Nuclear Medicine & Radiation Therapy. LC 78-32110. (Illus.). 240p. 1979. pap. text ed. 14.95 (ISBN 0-8016-4762-2). Mosby.

Stein, Edwin. Basic Mathematics for College Students. 7th ed. 1983. text ed. 31.36 (ISBN 0-205-07998-9, 567998); testing program performance record avail. (ISBN 0-205-08000-6). Allyn.

Stein, Edwin I. First Course in Fundamentals of Mathematics. 1978. text ed. 18.08 (ISBN 0-205-05540-0, 5655404); tchr's guide 5.12 (ISBN 0-205-05541-9, 5655412). Allyn.

--Fundamentals of Mathematics. 1980. text ed. 20.16 (ISBN 0-205-06895-2, 5668956); tchrs'. guide 6.28 (566896). Allyn.

--Fundamentals of Mathematics. 1976. text ed. 20.16 (ISBN 0-205-05003-4, 5650038); tchrs'. ed. 6.28 (ISBN 0-205-05004-2, 5650046). Allyn.

--Practical Applications in Mathematics. 1981. pap. text ed. 6.52 (ISBN 0-205-07161-9, 5671612); answer bk. 3.60 (ISBN 0-205-07178-3, 567178). Allyn.

--Refresher Mathematics. 1980. text ed. 18.32 (ISBN 0-205-06160-5, 5661609); tchrs'. guide 5.28 (ISBN 0-205-06161-3, 5661617). Allyn.

--Second Course in Fundamentals of Mathematics. 1978. text ed. 18.08 (ISBN 0-205-05538-9, 5655382); tchr's guide 5.12 (ISBN 0-205-05539-7, 5655390). Allyn.

Stein, Sherman K. Mathematics, the Man-Made Universe: An Introduction to the Spirit of Mathematics. 3rd ed. LC 75-25950. (Mathematics Ser.). (Illus.). 573p. 1976. text ed. 24.95x (ISBN 0-7167-0465-X); tchrs manual avail. W H Freeman.

Steinhoff, Richard. Basic Mathematics. LC 72-5310. 224p. 1972. 27.65 (ISBN 0-07-061123-8, G). McGraw.

Steklov Institute of Mathematics, Academy of Sciences, U S S R, No. 115. Mathematical Questions in the Theory of Wave Diffraction & Propagation: Proceedings. Babic, V. M., ed. LC 74-2363. (Proceedings of the Steklov Institute of Mathematics: No. 115). 1974. 60.00 (ISBN 0-8218-3015-5, STEKLO-115). Am Math.

Steklov Institute of Mathematics, Academy of Sciences, U.S.S.R., No. 114. Some Questions in Constructive Functional Analysis: Proceedings. LC 73-21929. (No. 114). 238p. 1974. 68.00 (ISBN 0-8218-3014-7, STEKLO-114). Am Math.

Stern, David P. Math Squared: Graph Paper Activities for Fun & Fundamentals. LC 80-15932. 115p. 1981. pap. text ed. 7.95x (ISBN 0-8077-2585-4). Tchrs Coll.

Stevens, David E. Discovering Technical Mathematics: An Introduction. LC 84-9347. 1985. text ed. 31.95 (ISBN 0-201-16365-9). Addison-Wesley.

Stewart, Ian & Tall, David. The Foundations of Mathematics. (Illus.). 1977. pap. 13.50x (ISBN 0-19-853165-6). Oxford U Pr.

Stromberg, Karl. Introduction to Classical Real Analysis. (Wadsworth International Mathematics Ser.). 576p. 1981. text ed. write for info. (ISBN 0-534-98012-0). Wadsworth Pub.

Sullivan, John. Modern College Mathematics. (Illus.). 352p. (Orig.). 1979. pap. 6.25 (ISBN 0-06-460174-9, COS 174, COS). B&N NY.

Suter, Heinrich. Die Mathematiker und Astronomen der Araber und Ihre Werke: Einschliesslich Nachtrage und Berichtungen. Repr. of 1900 ed. 30.00 (ISBN 0-384-58855-7). Johnson Repr.

Sutton, O. G. Mathematics in Action: Applications in Aerodynamics, Statistics, Weather Prediction & Other Sciences. 236p. 1984. pap. 4.95 (ISBN 0-486-24759-7). Dover.

Symposia Mathematica, Vol. 26. (Serial Publication). 243p. 1982. 37.50 (ISBN 0-12-612226-1). Acad Pr.

Symposium in Pure Mathematics - Northern Illinois Univ. May 1974. Mathematical Developments Arising from the Hilbert Problems: Proceedings, 2 pts. LC 76-20437. (Proceedings of Symposia in Pure Mathematics: Vol. 28). 1979. pap. 33.00 (ISBN 0-8218-1428-1, PSPUM-28). Am Math.

Symposium in Pure Mathematics, University of Calif. Berkeley June 1971. Tarski Symposium: Proceedings. Henkin, L., ed. LC 74-8666. (Proceedings of Symposia in Pure Mathematics: Vol. 25). 498p. 1979. pap. 45.00 with additions (ISBN 0-8218-1425-7, PSPUM-25). Am Math.

Symposium on Automatic Demonstration, Versailles, 1968. Proceedings. Laudet, M., et al, eds. LC 79-117526. (Lecture Notes in Mathematics: Vol. 125). (Illus.). 1970. pap. 18.30 (ISBN 0-387-04914-2). Springer-Verlag.

Taniuti, T. & Nishihara, K. Nonlinear Waves. Jeffrey, A., ed. (Monographs & Studies: No. 15). 320p. 1983. text ed. 65.50 (ISBN 0-273-08466-6). Pitman Pub MA.

Tarwater, J. Dalton, et al, eds. Men & Institutions in American Mathematics. (Graduate Studies: No. 13). 136p. (Orig.). 1976. pap. 6.00 (ISBN 0-89672-023-3). Tex Tech Pr.

Tate, John. Les Conjectures de Stark sur les Fonctions L d'Artin en s Equals 0, Vol. 47. (Progress in Mathematics Ser.). (Fr.). 152p. 1984. 12.95 (ISBN 0-8176-3188-7). Birkhauser.

Taub, A. H., ed. Studies in Applied Mathematics. LC 74-168565. (MAA Studies: No. 7). 217p. 1971. 16.50 (ISBN 0-88385-107-5). Math Assn.

Taylor, R. L. Stochastic Convergence of Weighted Sums of Random Elements in Linear Spaces. LC 78-13024. (Lecture Notes in Mathematics: Vol. 672). 1978. pap. 18.00 (ISBN 0-387-08929-2). Springer-Verlag.

Taylor, Ross. So You're a Mathematics Supervisor. 20p. 1981. pap. 2.50 (ISBN 0-87353-199-X). NCTM.

Taylor, S. J. Introduction to Measure & Integration. LC 73-84325. 272p. 1975. pap. text ed. 17.95x (ISBN 0-521-09804-1). Cambridge U Pr.

Three Papers on Dynamical Systems. LC 81-4981. (Translations Series Two: Vol. 116). 1981. 37.00 (ISBN 0-8218-3066-X, TRANS2-116). Am Math.

Tijonov, A. N., et al, eds. Algo Acerca de la Matematica Aplicada. 295p. 1984. 4.95 (ISBN 0-8285-2590-0, Pub. by Mir Pubns USSR). Imported Pubns.

Titchmarsh, E. C. Mathematics for the General Reader. (Illus.). 192p. 1981. pap. 3.00 (ISBN 0-486-24172-6). Dover.

Tobias, Sheila. Overcoming Math Anxiety. (Illus.). 288p. 1980. pap. 7.95 (ISBN 0-395-29088-0). HM.

Toole, Amy L. & Boehm, Ellen. Off to a Good Start: Four Hundred & Sixty-Four Readiness Activities for Reading, Math, Social Studies & Science. LC 82-13474. 230p. 1984. pap. 7.95 (ISBN 0-8027-7238-2). Walker & Co.

Towsend, Stewart. Mathematics in Sport. LC 84-6639. (Mathematics & Its Applications Ser.: 1-176). 202p. 1984. pap. text ed. 19.95x (ISBN 0-470-20082-0). Halsted Pr.

Transactions of the Moscow Mathematical Society, Vol. 23 (1970) LC 65-7413. 316p. 1972. text ed. 69.00 (ISBN 0-8218-1623-3, MOSCOW-23). Am Math.

Triola, Mario F. Mathematics & the Modern World. 2nd ed. LC 77-99264. 1978. 30.95 (ISBN 0-8053-9301-3); instr's guide 5.95 (ISBN 0-8053-9303-X). Benjamin-Cummings.

Troutman, Andria P. & Lichtenberg, Betty K. Mathematics: A Good Beginning. 2nd ed. LC 81-17997. (Mathematics Ser.). 1982. pap. text ed. 18.00 pub net (ISBN 0-8185-0492-7). Brooks-Cole.

Tuchinsky, P. M. Man in Competition with the Spruce Budworm. 60p. 1981. pap. text ed. 8.75x (ISBN 0-8176-3047-3). Birkhauser.

University of California. Publications in Mathematical & Physical Sciences, Vol. 1-3. (Partly in the original edition). pap. 55.00 (ISBN 0-384-07038-8). Johnson Repr.

Valenza, Samuel W., Jr. Conceptual Mathematics. (Illus.). 1976. pap. 9.50 (ISBN 0-936918-02-0). Intergalactic NJ.

Vanderbauwhede, A. Local Bifurcation & Symmetry. (Research Notes in Mathematics Ser.: No. 75). 320p. 1982. pap. text ed. 24.95 (ISBN 0-273-08569-7). Pitman Pub MA.

Van der Houwen, P. Construction of Integrated Formulas for Initial Value Problems. (North Holland Series in Applied Mathematics & Mechanics: Vol. 19). 1976. 68.00 (ISBN 0-444-10903-X, North-Holland). Elsevier.

Van Leuven, Edwin P. General Trade Mathematics. 2nd ed. 1952. text ed. 23.28 (ISBN 0-07-067079-X). McGraw.

Van Oystaeyen & Verschoren. Reflectors & Localization. (Lecture Notes in Pure & Applied Math.: Vol. 41). 1979. 39.75 (ISBN 0-8247-6844-2). Dekker.

Vermeersch, LaVonne F. & Southwick, Charles E. Practical Problems in Mathematics for Graphic Arts. Rev. ed. LC 82-72128. (Illus.). 184p. 1983. pap. text ed. 7.80 (ISBN 0-8273-2100-7); Instr's Guide 2.85 (ISBN 0-8273-2101-5). Delmar.

Vidal, P. Systems Echantillonnes Nonlineaires-Exercises et Problemes: Exercises et Problemes. (Theorie des Systemes Ser.). (Fr.). 124p. 1970. 40.50 (ISBN 0-677-50500-0). Gordon.

Vinik, Aggie, et al. Mathematics & Humor. LC 78-24206. (Illus.). 58p. 1978. pap. 4.00 (ISBN 0-87353-137-X). NCTM.

Vogan, D. Representation of Real Reductive Lie Groups. 1981. text ed. 38.50x (ISBN 0-8176-3037-6). Birkhauser.

Vorobyov, N. N. Criteria for Divisibility. Levine, Daniel A. & McLarnan, Timothy, trs. from Rus. LC 74-11634. (Popular Lectures in Mathematics). 1980. pap. text ed. 6.00x (ISBN 0-226-86516-9). U of Chicago Pr.

Vygodsky, M. Mathematial Handbook: Elemetary Mathematics. 422p. 1984. 7.95 (ISBN 0-8285-1701-0, Pub. by Mir Pubs USSR). Imported Pubns.

Waerden, B. L. Erwachende Wissenschaft, Vol. I: Agyptische, Babylonische und Griechische Mathematik. enl. 2nd ed. (Science & Civilization Ser.: No. 8). (Ger.). 488p. 1966. 45.95x (ISBN 0-8176-0399-9). Birkhauser.

Wain. Mathematics & Education. 1978. 24.95x (ISBN 0-442-30141-3). Van Nos Reinhold.

Washington, Allyn J. Basic Technical Mathematics. 3rd ed. LC 77-71469. 1978. pap. text ed. 31.95 (ISBN 0-8053-9520-2); instr's guide 10.95 (ISBN 0-8053-9522-9). Benjamin-Cummings.

Washington, Allyn J., et al. Essentials of Basic Mathematics. 3rd ed. 1981. 28.95 (ISBN 0-8053-9529-6). Benjamin-Cummings.

Way, Eric J. Mathematics Manual for Operators. LC 81-68898. (Illus.). 106p. 1981. pap. text ed. 19.95 (ISBN 0-250-40502-4). Butterworth.

Weber, H. R., et al. Festschrift Heinrich Weber. LC 71-125926. 1971. Repr. of 1912 ed. text ed. 25.00 (ISBN 0-8284-0246-9). Chelsea Pub.

Weil, A. Dirichlet Series & Automorphic Forms. LC 72-151320. (Lecture Notes in Mathematics: Vol. 189). 1971. pap. 15.00 (ISBN 0-387-05382-4). Springer-Verlag.

Weiss, N. A. & Yoseloff, M. L. Finite Mathematics. LC 74-20001. (Illus.). ix, 628p. 1975. text ed. 26.95x (ISBN 0-87901-039-8). Worth.

Weissglass, Julian. Exploring Elementary Mathematics: A Small-Group Approach for Teaching. LC 79-14931. (Mathematical Sciences Ser.). (Illus.). 289p. 1979. text ed. 20.00 (ISBN 0-7167-1027-7); instr's manual 3.95x (ISBN 0-7167-1223-7). W H Freeman.

Wheeler, R. E. & Wheeler, E. R. Mathematics: An Everyday Language. LC 78-13072. 483p. 1979. text ed. 33.00 (ISBN 0-471-03423-1); student supplement 12.50 (ISBN 0-471-04924-7). Wiley.

Wheeler, R. F. Rethinking Mathematical Concepts. (Mathematics & Its Applications Ser.). 314p. 1981. 61.95 (ISBN 0-470-27116-7). Halsted Pr.

Wheeler, Ruric. Modern Mathematics: An Elementary Approach. Alternative ed. LC 80-27549. 585p. 1981. text ed. 19.25 pub net (ISBN 0-8185-0413-7). Brooks-Cole.

Wheeler, Ruric E. Modern Mathematics: An Elementary Approach. 6th ed. LC 83-26163. (Mathematics Ser.). 675p. 1984. text ed. 22.75 pub net (ISBN 0-534-02843-8); pap. text ed. 7.00 student activities manual (ISBN 0-534-02844-6). Brooks-Cole.

Whipkey, Kenneth L., et al. The Power of Mathematics: Applications to the Management & the Social Sciences. 2nd ed. LC 80-19576. 622p. 1981. text ed. 34.00 (ISBN 0-471-07709-7); study guide 13.95 (ISBN 0-471-09117-0). Wiley.

White, Neil, ed. Theory of Matroids. (The Encyclopedia of Mathematics Ser.: No. 26). 448p. Date not set. price not set. (ISBN 0-521-30937-9). Cambridge U Pr.

Whitehead, Alfred N. Introduction to Mathematics. rev. ed. 1959. pap. 7.95 (ISBN 0-19-500211-3, GB). Oxford U Pr.

Whitehead, Alfred N. & Russell, Bertrand. Principia Mathematica, 3 Vols. Set. 350.00 (ISBN 0-521-06791-X). Cambridge U Pr.

--Principia Mathematica to Fifty-Six. 2nd ed. 1925-27. pap. 29.95 (ISBN 0-521-09187-X). Cambridge U Pr.

Wilder, Raymond J., ed. Evolution of Mathematical Concepts. 240p. 1978. pap. 10.00x (ISBN 0-335-00249-8, Pub. by Open Univ Pr). Taylor & Francis.

Wilder, Raymond L. Introduction to the Foundation of Mathematics. 2nd ed. LC 80-12446. 346p. 1980. Repr. of 1965 ed. 22.50 (ISBN 0-89874-170-X). Krieger.

Williamson, Richard & Trotter, Hale. Multivariable Mathematics: Linear Algebra, Calculus, Differential Equations. 2nd ed. (Illus.). 1979. ref. 38.95 (ISBN 0-13-604850-1). P-H.

Wilson, R. J., ed. Applications of Combinatorics. 140p. 1982. 60.00x (ISBN 0-906812-14-3, Pub. by Shiva Pub England); pap. 40.00x (ISBN 0-906812-14-3). State Mutual Bk.

Winograd, S. Arithmetic Complexity of Computations. LC 79-93154. (CBMS-NSF Regional Conference Ser.: No. 33). iii, 93p. 1980. pap. text ed. 13.00 (ISBN 0-89871-163-0). Soc Indus-Appl Math.

Wise, Alan. Basic Mathematics & Problem Solving. 570p. 1985. pap. text ed. 25.95 (ISBN 0-15-504979-8, HC); student guide 6.95 (ISBN 0-15-504980-1); instr's. manual avail. (ISBN 0-15-504981-X); answer key avail. (ISBN 0-15-504982-8). HarBraceJ.

Wittenberg, A. I. Vom Denken in Begriffen. (Science & Civilization Ser.: No. 12). (Ger.). 360p. 1968. 28.95x (ISBN 0-8176-0417-0). Birkhauser.

Wiznitzer, Martine R. Power Skills in Mathematics. 1979. pap. 4.95 (ISBN 0-07-055225-8). McGraw.

Wood, Martha, et al. Developmental Mathematics. 2nd ed. 1980. write for info. (ISBN 0-87150-287-9, 2272, Prindle). PWS Pubs.

Wright, Crispin. Wittgenstein on the Foundations of Mathematics. 500p. 1980. text ed. 35.00x (ISBN 0-674-95385-1). Harvard U Pr.

Yakovlev, G. N. High-School Mathematics, Pt. 1. 327p. 1985. 7.95 (ISBN 0-8285-2892-6, Pub. by Mir Pubs USSR). Imported Pubns.

--High-School Mathematics, Pt. 2. 445p. 1985. 7.95 (ISBN 0-8285-2893-4, Pub. by Mir Pubs USSR). Imported Pubns.

Yamada, T. The Schur Subgroup of the Brauer Group. (Lecture Notes in Mathematics: Vol. 397). v, 159p. 1974. pap. 13.00 (ISBN 0-387-06806-6). Springer Verlag.

Yamane, Taro. Mathematics for Economists: An Elementary Survey. 2nd ed. 1968. text ed. 33.95 (ISBN 0-13-562496-7). P-H.

Yankee, Helen M. Montessori Math: The Basics. (Basic Montessori Library Ser.). (Illus.). 22p. 1983. pap. 6.50x (ISBN 0-916011-04-6). Educ Sys Pub.

Young, Hugh D. Statistical Treatment of Experimental Data. 1962. pap. 6.95 (ISBN 0-07-072646-9). McGraw.

Yum - Ton Siu. Techniques of Extension of Analytic Objects. (Lecture Notes in Pure & Applied Mathematics Ser.: Vol. 8). Orig. Title: Techniques of Extension in Pure & Applied Mathmatics. 272p. 1974. 45.00 (ISBN 0-8247-6168-5). Dekker.

Zaitsev, V., et al. Elementary Mathematics. 590p. 1978. 10.00 (ISBN 0-8285-0719-8, Pub. by Mir Pubs USSR). Imported Pubns.

Zaslavsky, Claudia. Preparing Young Children for Math: A Book of Games. LC 79-12552. (Illus.). 1979. 10.95 (ISBN 0-8052-3723-2). Schocken.

Zawadski, Wladyslaw. Les Mathematiques Appliques a l'Economie Politique. 1965. Repr. of 1914 ed. 23.50 (ISBN 0-8337-3916-6). B Franklin.

Zippin, Leo. Uses of Infinity. LC 61-12187. (New Mathematical Library: No. 7). 151p. 1975. pap. 7.50 (ISBN 0-88385-607-7). Math Assn.

MATHEMATICS–ADDRESSES, ESSAYS, LECTURES

Abbott, James, ed. The Chauvenet Papers: A Collection of Prize-Winning Expository Papers in Mathematics. Set. 41.50 (ISBN 0-88385-439-2, CHV-012); members 31.00 (ISBN 0-317-30488-7); Vol. 1, 312p. 24.00 (ISBN 0-88385-425-2, CHV-01); members 18.50 (ISBN 0-88385-427-9); Vol. 2, 282p. 24.00 (ISBN 0-317-30489-5, CHV-02); members 18.50 (ISBN 0-317-30490-9). Math Assn.

Abhyanker, S. S. Weighted Expansions for Canonical Desingularization. (Lecture Notes in Mathematics Ser.: Vol. 910). 236p. 1982. pap. 16.00 (ISBN 0-387-11195-6). Springer-Verlag.

Abikoff, W. The Real Analytic Theory of Teichmueller Space. (Lecture Notes in Mathematics Ser.: Vol. 820). (Illus.). 144p. 1980. pap. 15.00 (ISBN 0-387-10237-X). Springer-Verlag.

Addison, J. W., et al, eds. The Theory of Models: Proceedings of the International Symposium at Berkeley, 1963. (Studies in Logic & the Foundations of Mathematics). xvi, 494p. 1965. 85.00 (ISBN 0-7204-2233-7, North-Holland). Elsevier.

Ahlfors, L. V., et al. Some Problems of Mathematics & Physics. LC 76-4884. (Translations Ser.: No. 2, Vol. 104). 1976. 55.00 (ISBN 0-8218-3054-6, TRANS 2-104). Am Math.

Aizerman, M. A., et al. Thirty-One Invited Addresses at the International Congress of Mathematicians in Moscow 1966. LC 51-5559. (Translations Ser.: No. 2, Vol. 70). 1968. 35.00 (ISBN 0-8218-1770-1, TRANS 2-70). Am Math.

Aldous, D. J., et al. Ecole d'Ete de Probabilites de Saint-Flour XIII, 1983. Hennequin, P. L., ed. (Lecture Notes in Mathematics Ser.: Vol, 1117). (Illus.). ix, 490p. 1985. pap. 25.80 (ISBN 0-387-15203-2). Springer-Verlag.

Aleksandrov, P. S., et al. Transactions of the Moscow Mathematical Society, Vol. 31 (1974) LC 65-4713. 1976. 69.00 (ISBN 0-8218-1631-4, MOSCOW-31). Am Math.

Andrunakievic, V. A., et al. Transactions of the Moscow Mathematical Society, Vol. 29 (1973) 1976. 66.00 (ISBN 0-8218-1629-2, MOSCOW-29). Am Math.

Anosov, D. V., ed. Twenty Lectures Delivered at the International Congress of Mathematicians in Vancouver, 1974. LC 77-9042. (Translation Ser. No. 2: Vol. 109). 129p. 1982. pap. 27.00 (ISBN 0-8218-3059-7, TRANS 2/109). Am Math.

Armitage, J. V., ed. Journees Arithmetiques Nineteen Eighty. LC 81-18032. (London Mathematical Society Lecture Ser.: No. 56). 350p. 1982. pap. 32.50 (ISBN 0-521-28513-5). Cambridge U Pr.

Arveson, William. Ten Lectures on Operator Algebras. LC 84-9222. (CBMS Regional Conference Series in Mathematics: Vol. 55). 104p. 1984. pap. 14.00 (ISBN 0-8218-0705-6). Am Math.

Askey, R., ed. The Collected Papers of Gabor Szego, 3 vols. 1982. text ed. 180.00x (ISBN 0-8176-3063-5). Birkhauser.

--The Collected Papers of Gabor Szego, Vol. I. 872p. 1982. text ed. 60.00x (ISBN 0-8176-3056-2). Birkhauser.

--The Collected Papers of Gabor Szego, Vol. 2. 894p. 1982. text ed. 60.00x (ISBN 0-8176-3060-0). Birkhauser.

--The Collected Papers of Gabor Szego, Vol. 3. 892p. 1982. text ed. 60.00x (ISBN 0-8176-3061-9). Birkhauser.

Aull. Rings of Continuous Function. (Lecture Notes in Pure & Applied Mathematics Ser.: Vol. 95). 336p. 1985. 65.00 (ISBN 0-8247-7144-3). Dekker.

Balslev, E., ed. Eighteenth Scandinavian Congress of Mathematicians. (Progress in Mathematics Ser.: No. 11). 528p. 1981. 35.00x (ISBN 0-8176-3040-6). Birkhauser.

Baum, Robert J., ed. Philosophy & Mathematics: From Plato to the Present. LC 73-84704. 320p. 1973. pap. 12.00x (ISBN 0-87735-514-2). Freeman Cooper.

Bratteli, O. & Jorgensen, P. E., eds. Positive Semigroups of Operators, & Applications. 1984. lib. bdg. 24.50 (ISBN 90-277-1839-3, Pub. by Reidel Holland). Kluwer Academic.

Breslow, N. E. & Whittemore, A. S., eds. Energy & Health. LC 79-63265. (SIAM-SIMS Conference Ser.: No. 6). xii, 340p. 1979. pap. text ed. 18.00 (ISBN 0-89871-000-6). Soc Indus-Appl Math.

Brjuno, A. D., et al. Transactions of the Moscow Mathematical Society, Vol. 25. LC 65-7413. 1971. text ed. 62.00 (ISBN 0-8218-1625-X, MOSCOW-25). Am Math.

Buckmaster, J. D., ed. Fluid Mechanics in Energy Conversion. LC 80-65817. (SIAM-SIMS Conference Ser.: No. 7). ix, 315p. 1980. pap. 31.00 (ISBN 0-89871-165-7). Soc Indus-Appl Math.

Ceitin, G. S., et al. Fourteen Papers on Logic, Geometry, Topology, & Algebra. LC 72-2350. (Translations Ser.: No. 2, Vol. 100). 1972. 48.00 (ISBN 0-8218-3050-3, TRANS 2-100). Am Math.

Chen, Bang-Yen. Total Mean Curvature & Submanifold of Finite Type. (Lecture Notes on Pure Mathematics: Vol. 1). 200p. 1984. 26.00x (ISBN 9971-966-02-6, Pub. by World Sci Singapore); pap. 14.00x (ISBN 9971-966-03-4, Pub. by World Sci Singapore). Taylor & Francis.

Choquet, Gustave. What Is Modern Mathematics. 46p. 1963. pap. 2.75 (ISBN 0-685-46930-1). Ed Solutions.

Ciarlet, P. G. & Roseau, M., eds. Trends & Applications of Pure Mathematics to Mechanics: Invited & Contributed Papers Presented at a Symposium at Ecole Polytechnique, Palaiseau, France, Nov. 28-Dec. 2 1983. (Lecture Notes in Physics: Vol. 195). (Fr. & Eng.). 1984. pap. 23.50 (ISBN 0-387-12916-2). Springer Verlag.

CISM (International Center for Mechanical Sciences), Dept. of Automation & Information, Univ of Geneva, 1971. Controlled & Conditioned Invariance. Basile, G., ed. (CISM Pubns. Ser.: No. 109). (Illus.). 51p. 1973. pap. 7.50 (ISBN 0-387-81132-X). Springer-Verlag.

Clifford, William K. Mathematical Papers. LC 67-28488. 1968. Repr. 35.00 (ISBN 0-8284-0210-8). Chelsea Pub.

Clunie, J. G. & Hayman, W. K., eds. Symposium on Complex Analysis. LC 73-92787. (London Mathematical Society Lecture Note Ser.: No. 12). 200p. 1974. 24.95 (ISBN 0-521-20452-6). Cambridge U Pr.

Cohen, R. S., et al, eds. Essays in Memory of Imre Lakatos. new ed. LC 76-16770. (Synthese Library Ser.: No. 99). 1976. lib. bdg. 87.00 (ISBN 90-277-0654-9, Pub. by Reidel Holland); pap. 47.50 (ISBN 90-277-0655-7, Pub. by Reidel Holland). Kluwer Academic.

--Boston Studies in the Philosophy of Science, Vol. 15: Scientific, Historical & Political Essays in Honor of Dirk J. Struik. LC 73-83556. (Synthese Library: No. 61). 652p. 1974. 76.00 (ISBN 90-277-0393-0, Pub. by Reidel Holland); pap. 47.50- (ISBN 90-277-0379-5). Kluwer Academic.

Conference, Murat-le-Quaire, March 1976. Convex Analysis & Its Applications: Proceedings. Auslender, A., ed. (Lecture Notes in Economics & Mathematical Systems: Vol. 144). 1977. soft cover 18.00 (ISBN 0-387-08149-6). Springer-Verlag.

Conference on Operator Theory, Dalhousie Univ., Halifax, 1973. Proceedings. Fillmore, P. A., ed. LC 73-14482. (Lecture Notes in Mathematics: Vol. 345). pap. 16.00 (ISBN 0-387-06496-6). Springer-Verlag.

Connor, P. E. & Perils, R. A Survey of Trace Forms of Algebraic Number Fields. (Lecture Notes on Pure Mathematics: Vol. 2). 325p. 1984. 35.00x (ISBN 9971-966-04-2, Pub. by World Sci Singapore); pap. 19.00x (ISBN 9971-966-05-0, Pub. by World Sci Singapore). Taylor & Francis.

Continuous Convergence on C (X) LC 75-16495. (Lecture Notes in Mathematics Ser.: Vol. 469). 140p. 1975. pap. 12.00 (ISBN 0-387-07179-2). Springer-Verlag.

Derrick Henry Lehmer Dedication: Dedication Issue on His 70th Birthday. (Vol. 29, No. 129). 341p. 1975. pap. 24.00 (ISBN 0-8218-0061-2, MCOM 29-129, DHL). Am Math.

Dickson, Leonard E. Collected Mathematical Papers, Vol. VI. Albert, A. Adrian, ed. LC 69-19943. 1983. lib. bdg. 55.00 (ISBN 0-8284-0306-6). Chelsea Pub.

Division of Mathematics - Committee on Support of Research in Mathematical Sciences. Mathematical Sciences: A Report. pap. 8.25 (ISBN 0-309-01681-9). Natl Acad Pr.

Dlab, V. & Gabriel, P., eds. Representation Theory I. (Lecture Notes in Mathematics Ser.: Vol. 831). 373p. 1980. pap. 26.00 (ISBN 0-387-10263-9). Springer-Verlag.

--Representation Theory II. (Lecture Notes in Mathematics: Vol. 832). 673p. 1980. pap. 43.00 (ISBN 0-387-10264-7). Springer-Verlag.

Donner, K. Extension of Positive Operators & Korovkin Theorems. (Lecture Notes in Mathematics Ser.: Vol. 904). 182p. 1982. pap. 14.00 (ISBN 0-387-11183-2). Springer-Verlag.

Dynkin, E. B., et al. Six Lectures Delivered at the International Congress of Mathematicians in Stockholm, 1962. LC 51-5559. (Translations Ser.: No. 2, Vol. 31). 1963. 15.00 (ISBN 0-8218-1731-0, TRANS 2-31). Am Math.

Education in Applied Mathematics. vii, 415p. 1967. ltd. ed. 9.00 (ISBN 0-89871-154-1). Soc Indus-Appl Math.

Egghe, L. Stopping Time Techniques for Analysts & Probabilists: London Mathematical Society Lecture. 367p. 1985. pap. 29.95 (ISBN 0-521-31715-0). Cambridge U Pr.

Eight Lectures Delivered at the International Congress of Mathematicians in Helsinki. LC 81-10769. (Translations Ser. 2: Vol. 117). 1981. 15.00 (ISBN 0-8218-3069-4). Am Math.

Equibbrium States & the Ergodic Theory of Anosov Diffeomorphisms. (Lecture Notes in Mathematics Ser.: Vol. 470). 108p. 1975. pap. 13.00 (ISBN 0-387-07187-3). Springer-Verlag.

Fadell, E. & Fournier, G., eds. Fixed Point Theory: Proceedings. (Lecture Notes in Mathematics Ser.: Vol. 886). 511p. 1981. pap. 29.00 (ISBN 0-387-11152-2). Springer-Verlag.

Fellmann, Emil, ed. Leonhard Euler, 1707-1783. (Opera Omnia, Complete Works of Leonhard Euler). (Eng. Fr. & Ger.). 500p. 1983. 29.95 (ISBN 0-8176-1343-9). Birkhauser.

Fennell, Francis, et al, eds. Selected Papers from the Sixth, Eighth & Ninth National Conference on Diagnostic & Prescriptive Mathematics. Scheer, Jan. (Illus.). 134p. 1985. pap. text ed. 8.40x (ISBN 0-940466-08-2). Research Council.

Fletcher. Quasi-Uniform Spaces. (Lecture Notes in Pure & Applied Mathematics Ser.: Vol. 77). 232p. 1982. 35.00 (ISBN 0-8247-1839-9). Dekker.

Frege, Gottlob. Collected Papers on Mathematics, Logic & Philosophy. McGuinness, Brian, ed. 416p. 1985. 39.95x (ISBN 0-631-12728-3). Basil Blackwell.

Freiman, Grigori. It Seems I Am a Jew: A Samizdat Essay. Nathanson, Melvyn B., ed. & tr. from Russian. LC 80-404. (Science & International Affairs Ser.). 114p. 1980. 9.95 (ISBN 0-8093-0962-9). S Ill U Pr.

Friedrich, Klaus. Friction & Wear of Polymer Composites. (Progress Report of the VDI-Z Series 18: No. 15). (Illus.). 102p. 1984. pap. 32.00 (ISBN 0-9907001-1-9, Pub. by VDI Verlag Gmbh Dusseldorf). Heyden.

Gamkrelidze, R. V. & Steklov, V. A., eds. L. S. Pontryagin: Selected Works, Vol. 1. 592p. 1984. text ed. 255.00 (ISBN 2-88124-105-0). Gordon.

Goldschmidt, David M. Lectures on Character Theory. LC 80-81648. (Mathematics Lecture Ser.: No. 8). 245p. 1980. text ed. 18.00 (ISBN 0-914098-17-9). Publish or Perish.

Grassl, Wolfgang, ed. Lectures in the Philosophy of Mathematics. Waismann, Friedrich. (Studien Zur Oesterreichischen Philosophie). 125p. 1981. pap. text ed. 19.00x (ISBN 90-6203-613-9, Pub. by Rodopi Holland). Humanities.

Grmela, M., ed. Global Analysis. (Lecture Notes in Mathematics: Vol. 755). 1979. pap. 25.00 (ISBN 0-387-09703-1). Springer-Verlag.

Haimes, Y. Y. & Chankong, V., eds. Decision Making with Multiple Objectives. (Lecture Notes in Economics & Mathematical Systems Ser.: Vol. 242). xi, 571p. 1985. 41.00 (ISBN 0-387-15223-7). Springer-Verlag.

Halmos, P. R. Selecta Volume One: Research Contributions. (Illus.). 458p. 1983. 38.00 (ISBN 0-387-90755-6). Springer-Verlag.

--Selecta Volume Two: Expository Writing. (Illus.). 256p. 1983. 23.00 (ISBN 0-387-90756-4). Springer-Verlag.

Hardiman, N. J. Exploring University Mathematics, 3 Vols. Vol. 1. 1967. text ed. 18.00 (ISBN 0-08-011990-5); Vol. 1. pap. 7.00 (ISBN 0-08-011991-3). Pergamon.

Hardy, Godfrey H. Ramanujan. 3rd ed. LC 59-10268. 1978. 12.95 (ISBN 0-8284-0136-5). Chelsea Pub.

Hermes, Hans. Term Logic with Choice Operator. rev. ed. LC 79-125498. (Lecture Notes in Mathematics: Vol. 6). 1970. pap. 10.70 (ISBN 0-387-04899-5). Springer-Verlag.

Hersch, Joseph & Rota, Gian-Carlo, eds. George Polya - Collected Papers: Analysis, Vol. III. (Mathematicians of Our Time Ser.: No. 22). 537p. 1984. 55.00x (ISBN 0-262-16096-X). MIT Pr.

--George Polya - Collected Papers: Probability; Combinatories; Teaching & Learning in Mathematics, Vol. IV. (Mathematicians of Our Time Ser.: No. 23). 676p. 1984. 65.00 (ISBN 0-262-16097-8). MIT Pr.

Hillman, J. A. Alexander Ideals. (Lecture Notes in Mathematics Ser.: Vol. 895). 178p. 1981. pap. 14.00 (ISBN 0-387-11168-9). Springer-Verlag.

Hirzebruch, F. & Zagier, D. The Atiyah-Singer Theorem & Elementary Number Theory. LC 74-78679. (Mathematics Lecture Ser., No. 3). 287p. 1974. pap. text ed. 18.00 (ISBN 0-914098-12-8). Publish or Perish.

Hirzebruch, F., et al, eds. Arbeitstagung Bonn, 1984. (Lecture Notes in Mathematics Ser.: Vol. 1111). v, 481p. 1985. pap. 29.20 (ISBN 0-387-15195-8). Springer-Verlag.

Hsu, P. L. Collected Papers. (Illus.). 589p. 1983. 53.00 (ISBN 0-387-90725-4). Springer-Verlag.

Hua, L. K. Selected Papers. (Illus.). 888p. 1983. 47.50 (ISBN 0-387-90744-0). Springer-Verlag.

IFAC-FIP International Conference on Digit al Computer a75211. Proceedings, 2 pts. Mansour, M. & Schaufelberger, W., eds. LC 73-21003. (Lecture Notes in Economics & Mathematical Systems, Vol. 93 & 94). 1974. Pt. 1. pap. 22.00 (ISBN 0-387-06620-9); Pt. 2. pap. 23.00 (ISBN 0-387-06621-7). Springer-Verlag.

Index of Mathematical Papers. Incl. Vol. 1. July-December, 1970. 1972. 55.00 (ISBN 0-8218-4001-0, IMP-1); Vol. 2, 2 pts. 1972. Set. 100.00 (ISBN 0-686-70178-X, IMP-2); Jan-June, 1971 (ISBN 0-8218-4002-9); July-Dec., 1971 (ISBN 0-8218-4003-7); Vol. 3, 2 pts. 1973. Set. 136.00 (ISBN 0-686-70179-8, IMP-3); Jan.-June, 1972 (ISBN 0-8218-4004-5); July-Dec., 1972 (ISBN 0-8218-4005-3); Vol. 4, 2 pts. 1973-74. Set. 136.00 (ISBN 0-686-70180-1, IMP-4); Jan.-June, 1973 (ISBN 0-8218-4006-1); July-Dec., 1973 (ISBN 0-8218-4007-X); Vol. 5. Index to Mathematical Reviews for 1973. 136.00 (ISBN 0-8218-4008-8, IMP-5); Vol. 6. Index to Mathematical Reviews for 1974. 136.00 (ISBN 0-8218-4009-6, IMP-6); Vol. 7. Index to Mathematical Reviews for 1975. 136.00 (ISBN 0-8218-4010-X, IMP-7); Vol. 8. Index to Mathematical Reviews for 1976. 205.00 (ISBN 0-8218-4011-8, IMP-8); Vol. 9. Index to Math - Reviews for 1977. 205.00 (ISBN 0-8218-4012-6, IMP-9); Cumulative Index (Author & Subject Index of Mathematics Reviews, 1973-1979. 1177.00 (ISBN 0-8218-0035-3, MREVIN-73-79). Am Math.

Jaffee & Glimm. Collected Papers, 2 vols. (Contemporary Mathematicians Ser.). Date not set. Set. text ed. price not set (ISBN 0-8176-3273-5); Vol. 1. text ed. price not set (ISBN 0-8176-3271-9); Vol. 2. text ed. price not set (ISBN 0-8176-3272-7). Birkhauser.

James, I. M., et al, eds. A Topological Tribute. (London Mathematical Society Lecture Note Ser.: No. 94). 250p. 1985. pap. 29.95 (ISBN 0-521-27815-5). Cambridge U Pr.

Jameson, G. J. Ordered Linear Spaces. LC 70-125282. (Lecture Notes in Mathematics: Vol. 141). 1970. pap. 14.70 (ISBN 0-387-04930-4). Springer-Verlag.

Jarosz, K. Perturbations of Banach Algebras. (Lecture Notes in Mathematics Ser.: Vol. 1120). v, 118p. 1985. pap. 9.80 (ISBN 0-387-15218-0). Springer-Verlag.

Jorsboe, C. G. & Mejlbro, L. The Carleson-Hunt Theorem on Fourier Series. (Lecture Notes in Mathematics Ser.: Vol. 911). 123p. 1982. pap. 12.00 (ISBN 0-387-11198-0). Springer-Verlag.

Kac, M., et al. Discrete Thoughts: Essays on Mathematics, Science, & Philosophy. 1985. write for info. (ISBN 0-8176-3285-9). Birkhauser.

Kechris, A. S., et al, eds. Cabal Seminar, 77-79: Proceedings. (Lecture Notes in Mathematics Ser.: Vol. 839). 274p. 1981. pap. 19.00 (ISBN 0-387-10288-4). Springer-Verlag.

--Cabal Seminar 79-81. (Lecture Notes in Mathematics Ser.: Vol.1019). 284p. 1983. pap. 15.00 (ISBN 0-387-12688-0). Springer-Verlag.

Kedem. Binary Time Series. (Lecture Notes in Pure & Applied Mathematics Ser.: Vol. 52). 160p. 1980. 35.00 (ISBN 0-8247-6920-1). Dekker.

Knobloch, H. W. & Schmitt, K., eds. Equadiff 82. (Lecture Notes in Mathematics Ser.: Vol. 1017). 666p. 1983. pap. 29.00 (ISBN 0-387-12686-4). Springer Verlag.

Kree, P. Ennio de Giorgi Colloquium. (Research Notes in Mathematics Ser.: No. 125). 250p. 1985. pap. text ed. 16.95 (ISBN 0-273-08680-4). Pitman Pub MA.

Lambeck, J. Torsion Theories, Additive Semantics & Rings of Quotients. LC 70-148538. (Lecture Notes in Mathematics: Vol. 177). 1971. pap. 11.00 (ISBN 0-387-05340-9). Springer-Verlag.

Lawson, H. Blaine, Jr. Lectures on Minimal Submanifolds, Vol. 1. LC 80-81649. (Mathematics Lecture Ser.: No. 9). 178p. 1980. text ed. 15.00 (ISBN 0-914098-18-7). Publish or Perish.

Levin, Simon, ed. Population Biology: Symposia in Applied Mathematics. Incl. Computer Communications. Gopinath, B., ed. 1984. write for info. Am Math.

Lighthill, J. Mathematical Biofluiddynamics. (CBMS-NSF Regional Conference Ser.: No. 17). vi, 281p. 1975. text ed. 33.00 (ISBN 0-89871-014-6). Soc Indus-Appl Math.

Littlewood, J. E. Collected Papers of J. E. Littlewood, 2 vols, Vol. 1 & Vol. 2. Cassels, J. W., ed. 1982. Vol. 1. 115.00x (ISBN 0-19-853353-5); Vol.2. 115.00x (ISBN 0-19-853355-1). Oxford U Pr.

Lokken, Roy N. The Scientific Papers of James Logan. LC 72-76613. (Transactions Ser.: Vol. 62, Pt. 6). (Illus.). 1972. pap. 2.00 (ISBN 0-87169-626-6). Am Philos.

Ludwig, D. & Cooke, K. L., eds. Epidemiology. LC 75-22944. (SIAM-SIMS Conference Ser.: No. 2). ix, 164p. 1975. pap. text ed. 20.50 (ISBN 0-89871-031-6). Soc Indus-Appl Math.

Mason, R. C. Diophantine Equations Over Function Fields. LC 84-1900. (London Mathematical Society Lecture Note Ser.: No. 96). 126p. 1984. pap. 16.95 (ISBN 0-521-26983-0). Cambridge U Pr.

Matthews, D. E., ed. Mathematics & the Life Sciences: Selected Lectures, Canadian Mathematical Congress, Aug.1975. LC 77-11151. (Lect. Notes in Biomathematics Ser.: Vol. 18). 1977. pap. text ed. 22.00 (ISBN 0-387-08351-0). Springer-Verlag.

Meyer, Paul R., ed. Papers in Mathematics. (Annals of the New York Academy of Sciences: Vol. 321). (Orig.). 1979. pap. 22.00x (ISBN 0-89766-026-9). NY Acad Sci.

Midwest Category Seminar, 4th. Reports. MacLane, S., ed. LC 78-126772. (Lecture Notes in Mathematics: Vol. 137). 1970. pap. 10.70 (ISBN 0-387-04926-6). Springer-Verlag.

Millet, Kenneth C. Piecewise Linear Concordances & Isotopies. LC 74-18328. (Memoirs Ser.: No. 153). 74p. 1974. pap. 10.00 (ISBN 0-8218-1853-8, MEMO-153). Am Math.

Mills, Stella, ed. The Collected Letters of Colin MacLaurin. 560p. 1982. text ed. 35.00x (ISBN 0-906812-08-9). Birkhauser.

Moore, Eliakim H., et al. The New Haven Mathematical Colloquium. 1910. 85.00x (ISBN 0-686-51424-6). Elliots Bks.

Nagell, Trygve, et al, eds. Selected Mathematicae Papers of Axel Thue. 1977. 40.00x (ISBN 82-00-01649-8, Dist. by Columbia U Pr). Universitet.

Neyman, J. & Pearson, E. K. Joint Statistical Papers. 299p. 1967. lib. bdg. 17.50x (ISBN 0-521-05820-1). Lubrecht & Cramer.

Nikol'sky, S M., ed. Collection of Articles, II: Dedicated to Academician I. M. Vinogradov on the Eightieth Anniversary of His Birth. LC 73-6783. (Proceedings of the Steklov Institute of Mathematics: Vol. 128). 303p. 1974. 67.00 (ISBN 0-8218-3028-7, STEKLO-128). Am Math.

Noether, Emmy. Collected Papers. 776p. 1983. 57.20 (ISBN 0-387-11504-8). Springer-Verlag.

Obata, M., ed. Selected Papers of Yano Kentaro. (North-Holland Mathematics Studies: No. 70). 366p. 1982. 53.25 (ISBN 0-444-86495-4, North Holland). Elsevier.

Oka, K. Collected Papers. 245p. 1984. 33.00 (ISBN 0-387-13240-6). Springer Verlag.

Ostrowski, Alexander. Collected Papers, Vol. 5. (Contemporary Mathematicians Ser.). 560p. 1984. text ed. 43.95x (ISBN 3-76431-510-5). Birkhauser.

Pearson, E. S. Selcted Papers. 327p. 1966. lib. bdg. 17.50x (ISBN 0-521-05926-7). Lubrecht & Cramer.

Peterson, F. P., ed. Steenrod Algebra & Its Applications: Proceedings. (Lecture Notes in Mathematics: Vol. 168). 1970. 18.00 (ISBN 0-387-05300-X). Springer-Verlag.

Pittie, H. V. Characteristic Classes of Foliations. (Research Notes in Mathematics: No. 10). 107p. (Orig.). 1976. pap. text ed. 18.95 (ISBN 0-273-00311-9). Pitman Pub MA.

Rasevskii, P. K., et al. Transactions of the Moscow Mathematical Society, Vol. 30 (1974) 1976. 50.00 (ISBN 0-8218-1630-6, MOSCOW-30). Am Math.

Roberts, F. S., ed. Energy: Mathematics & Models. LC 75-41915. (SIAM-SIMS Conference Ser.: No. 3). xxiv, 276p. 1976. pap. text ed. 24.00 (ISBN 0-89871-029-4). Soc Indus-Appl Math.

Sierpinski, Waclaw, et al. Congruence of Sets, & Other Monographs, 4 vols. in 1. Incl. On the Congruence of Sets. Sierpinski, Waclaw; Mathematical Theory of the Top. Klein, Felix; Graphical Methods. Runge, Carl; Algebraic Equations. Dickson, Leonard E. LC 67-17000. 14.95 (ISBN 0-8284-0209-4). Chelsea Pub.

Smith, J. D. Mal'cev Varieties. (Lecture Notes in Mathematics Ser.: Vol. 554). 1976. soft cover 13.00 (ISBN 0-387-07999-8). Springer-Verlag.

Smith, L. Lectures on the Eilenberg-Moore Spectral Sequence. LC 71-121060. (Lecture Notes in Mathematics: Vol. 134). 1970. pap. 10.70 (ISBN 0-387-04923-1). Springer-Verlag.

Srinivasan, B. & Sally, J. D., eds. Emmy Noether in Bryn Mawr: Proceedings of a Symposium Sponsored by the Association of Women in Mathematics in Honor of Emmy Noether's 100th Birthday. (Illus.). 182p. 1983. 30.00 (ISBN 0-387-90838-2). Springer-Verlag.

Steen, L. A., ed. Mathematics Today-Twelve Informal Essays. LC 78-7594. (Illus.). 1978. 29.50 (ISBN 0-387-90305-4). Springer-Verlag.

Steen, Lynn A., ed. Mathematics Tomorrow. (Illus.). 288p. 1981. 22.00 (ISBN 0-387-90564-2). Springer-Verlag.

Steklov Institute of Mathematics, No. 112. Collection of Articles, I: Proceedings. Petrovsky, I. G. & Nikol'sky, S. M., eds. LC 73-6783. (Proceedings of the Steklov Institute of Mathematics: No.112). 1973. 78.00 (ISBN 0-8218-3012-0, STEKLO-112). Am Math.

Streit, L. Mathematics & Physics: Lectures on Recent Results, Vol. 1. 320p. 1984. 35.00x (ISBN 9971-966-63-8, Pub. by World Sci Singapore); pap. 22.00x (ISBN 9971-966-64-6, Pub. by World Sci Singapore). Taylor & Francis.

Symposia Mathematica, Vol. 24. 1981. 47.50 (ISBN 0-12-612224-5). Acad Pr.

Symposium On Several Complex Variables, Park City, Utah, 1970. Proceedings. Brooks, R. M., ed. LC 76-153464. (Lecture Notes in Mathematics: Vol. 184). (Illus.). 1971. pap. 13.00 (ISBN 0-387-05370-0). Springer-Verlag.

Tarwater, Dalton, ed. Bicentennial Tribute to American Mathematics. LC 77-14706. 225p. 1976. 22.00 (ISBN 0-88385-424-4). Math Assn.

Thomee, V. Galerkin Finite Element Methods for Parabolic Problems. (Lecture Notes in Mathematics Ser.: Vol. 1054). vii, 237p. 1984. pap. 13.50 (ISBN 0-387-12911-1). Springer-Verlag.

Topology Symposium, Seigen, 1979. Proceedings. Neumann, W. B. & Koschorke, eds. (Lecture Notes in Mathematics: Vol. 788). 495p. 1980. pap. 34.00 (ISBN 0-387-09968-9). Springer-Verlag.

Troelstra, A. S. & Van Dalen, D., eds. The L. E. J. Brouwer Centenary Symposium: Proceedings of the Conference Held at Noordwijkerhout, June 1981. (Studies in Logic & the Foundations of Mathematics: Vol. 110). 456p. 1983. 68.00 (ISBN 0-444-86494-6, I-349-82, North Holland). Elsevier.

Weizsaecker, C. C. Barriers to Entry: A Theoretical Treatment. (Lecture Notes in Economics & Mathematical Systems Ser.: Vol. 185). (Illus.). 220p. 1980. pap. 23.00 (ISBN 0-387-10272-8). Springer-Verlag.

Yano, K. Structures on Manifolds. (Lecture Notes on Pure Mathematics: Vol. 3). 450p. 1984. 53.00 (ISBN 9971-966-15-8, Pub. by World Sci Singapore); pap. 26.00 (ISBN 9971-966-16-6, Pub. by World Sci Singapore). Taylor & Francis.

Zagier, D. B. Equivariant Pontrjagin Classes & Applications to Orbit Spaces. LC 72-90185. (Lecture Notes in Mathematics: Vol. 290). 130p. 1972. pap. 9.00 (ISBN 0-387-06013-8). Springer-Verlag.

MATHEMATICS–BIBLIOGRAPHY

American Mathematical Society. Mathematical Reviews Cumulative Author Indexes. Incl. Twenty Volume Author Index of Mathematical Reviews, 1940-59, 2 pts. 1977. 350.00 set (ISBN 0-685-22496-1, MREVIN 40-59); Author Index of Mathematical Reviews, 1960-64, 2 pts. 1966. 275.00 set (ISBN 0-8218-0026-4, MREVIN 60-64); Author Index of Mathematical Reviews, 1965-72. 1974. 550.00 (ISBN 0-8218-0027-2, MREVIN 65-72). Repr. Am Math.

Anderson, Nancy D., ed. French Mathematical Seminars. LC 78-10797. 1978. 20.00 (ISBN 0-8218-0063-9, FRENCHSEM); members 6.90. Am Math.

Askey, R., ed. The Collected Papers of Gabor Szego, 3 vols. 1982. text ed. 180.00x (ISBN 0-8176-3063-5). Birkhauser.

--The Collected Papers of Gabor Szego, Vol. I. 872p. 1982. text ed. 60.00x (ISBN 0-8176-3056-2). Birkhauser.

--The Collected Papers of Gabor Szego, Vol. 2. 894p. 1982. text ed. 60.00x (ISBN 0-8176-3060-0). Birkhauser.

--The Collected Papers of Gabor Szego, Vol. 3. 892p. 1982. text ed. 60.00x (ISBN 0-8176-3061-9). Birkhauser.

Gaffney, M. P. & Steen, L. A., eds. Annotated Bibliography of Expository Writing in the Mathematical Sciences. 282p. 1976. pap. 14.00 (ISBN 0-88385-422-8). Math Assn.

Herz, C. & Rigelhof, R., eds. P: Proceedings, 1980 Seminar on Harmonic Analysis. LC 81-19116. (Canadian Mathematical Society Conference: No. 1). 1981. pap. 16.00 (ISBN 0-8218-6000-3). Am Math.

IMPSET. Index of Mathematical Papers: MR Indexes for 1974-1977, Vols. 6-9. text ed. 418.00 (ISBN 0-317-01577-X). Am Math.

Index to Translations Selected by the American Mathematical Society, Vol. 1. 1966. 14.00 (ISBN 0-8218-0042-6, TRAN2I-1-50). Am Math.

Karpinski, Louis C. Bibliography of Mathematical Works Printed in America Through Eighteen Fifty: Reprinted with Supplement & Second Supplement to the Bibliography. Cohen, I. Bernard, ed. LC 79-7971. (Three Centuries of Science in America Ser.). (Illus.). 1980. Repr. of 1940 ed. lib. bdg. 60.00x (ISBN 0-405-12553-4). Ayer Co Pubs.

Mathematical Reviews Cumulative Index: 1973-1979, 12 Vol. 1981. pap. 1400.00 (ISBN 0-8218-0035-3). Am Math.

Mathematical Reviews Index, 1978. (IMP Ser.: No. 10). 420.00 (ISBN 0-8218-4013-4). Am Math.

Mathematical Reviews Index, 1979. (IMP Ser.: No. 11). 420.00 (ISBN 0-8218-4014-2). Am Math.

Mathematical Reviews Index, 1980. (IMP Ser.: No. 12). 420.00 (ISBN 0-8218-4016-9). Am Math.

May, K. O. Bibliography & Research Manual of the History of Mathematics. LC 71-151379. (Scholarly Reprint Ser.). 1973. 45.00x (ISBN 0-8020-7077-9). U of Toronto Pr.

Mills, Stella, ed. The Collected Letters of Colin MacLaurin. 560p. 1982. text ed. 35.00x (ISBN 0-906812-08-9). Birkhauser.

National Council of Teachers of Mathematics. Cumulative Index: The Mathematics Teacher, 1908-1965. LC 42-24844. 207p. 1967. pap. 15.00 (ISBN 0-87353-028-4). NCTM.

Schneider, David I. An Annotated Bibliography of Films & Videotapes. 282p. 1976. 10.50 (ISBN 0-88385-422-8, BFV). Math Assn.

Steen, Lynn & Seebach, J. A., eds. Fifty-Year Index of the Mathematics Magazine. 165p. 1979. pap. 11.50 (ISBN 0-88385-432-5). Math Assn.

MATHEMATICS–COLLECTED WORKS

Abbott, James, ed. The Chauvenet Papers, 2 Vols. 312p. 1979. Vol. 1, 1979, 312p. 24.00 (ISBN 0-88385-425-2); Vol. 2, 1979, 282p. 24.00 (ISBN 0-88385-427-9). Math Assn.

Abel, Niels H. Oeuvres Completes, 2 vols in 1. Sylow, L. & Lie, S., eds. Set. 65.00 (ISBN 0-384-00103-3). Johnson Repr.

Andrews, George E., ed. Percy Alexander MacMahon: Collected Papers: Combinatorics, Vol. 1. LC 77-28962. (Mathematicians of Our Time Ser.). 1978. 100.00x (ISBN 0-262-13121-8). MIT Pr.

Barrow, Isaac. Mathematical Works. Whewell, W., ed. Repr. of 1860 ed. 128.00x (ISBN 3-4870-4788-8). Adlers Foreign Bks.

Birch, B. J., et al, eds. The Collected Works of Harold Davenport, Vols. 2-4. 1978. 69.50 ea.; Vol. 2. (ISBN 0-12-099302-3); Vol. 3, 1978. (ISBN 0-12-099303-1); Vol. 4. (ISBN 0-12-099304-X); Vol. 1. 69.00 (ISBN 0-12-099301-5). Acad Pr.

Boas, R. P. Collected Works of Hidehiko Yamabe. (Notes on Mathematics & Its Applications Ser.). 154p. 1967. 38.50 (ISBN 0-677-00610-1). Gordon.

Brauer, Richard. Richard Brauer: Collected Papers, 3 vols. Wong, Warren J. & Fong, Paul, eds. 1980. Vol. 1. 75.00x (ISBN 0-262-02135-8); Vol. 2. 75.00x (ISBN 0-262-02148-X); Vol. 3. 75.00x (ISBN 0-262-02149-8). MIT Pr.

Brouwer, L. E. L. E. J. Brouwer, Collected Works: Philosophy & Foundations of Mathematics, Vol. 1. Heyting, A., ed. LC 73-75529. 628p. 1976. 127.75 (ISBN 0-444-10643-X, North-Holland). Elsevier.

Buchin, Su. Selected Mathematical Papers. 430p. 1984. text ed. 67.50 (ISBN 0-677-31300-4). Gordon.

Campbell, Douglas & Higgins, John, eds. Mathematics: People, Problems, Results. LC 83-17039. 900p. 1984. write for info. (ISBN 0-534-03199-4); pap. write for info. (ISBN 0-534-03202-8). Wadsworth Pub.

Cayley, Arthur. Collected Mathematical Papers, Vols. 1-13. 1889-1897. with index 700.00 (ISBN 0-384-07970-9); 55.00 ea.; Vol. suppl. 30.00 (ISBN 0-685-13389-3). Johnson Repr.

Chebyshev, Pafnuti L. Oeuvres: Collected Papers, 2 Vols. LC 61-17956. (Fr). 99.50 set (ISBN 0-8284-0157-8). Chelsea Pub.

Dickson, Leonard E. Collected Mathematical Papers, 5 vols. Albert, A. Adrian, ed. LC 69-19943. 3300p. 1975. Set. text ed. 195.00 set (ISBN 0-8284-0273-6). Chelsea Pub.

Hamilton, William R. Mathematical Papers of Sir William Rowan Hamilton, Vol. 3. Halberstam, H. & Ingram, R. E., eds. 1967. 140.00 (ISBN 0-521-05183-5). Cambridge U Pr.

Hardy, G. H. Collected Papers of G. H. Hardy: Including Joint Papers with J. E. Lockwood & Others, Vol. 7. 1979. 95.00x (ISBN 0-19-853347-0). Oxford U Pr.

Hermann Weyl Selecta. (Ger.). 592p. 1965. 56.95x (ISBN 0-8176-0414-6). Birkhauser.

Hilbert, David. Gesammelte Abhandlungen, 3 Vols. 3rd ed. LC 65-21834. (Ger). 1981. Set. 44.85 (ISBN 0-8284-0195-0); Vol. 1. 14.95. Chelsea Pub.

Hill, George W. The Collected Mathematical Works, 4 Vols. 1905-1907. Set. 265.00 (ISBN 0-384-23255-8). Johnson Repr.

Hurwitz Adolf: Mathematische Werke, Vol. I, Funktionentheorie. 2nd ed. (Ger.). 734p. 1962. 88.95x (ISBN 0-8176-0184-8). Birkhauser.

Hurwitz Adolf: Mathematische Werke, Vol. II, Zahlentheorie, Algebra & Geometrie. 2nd ed. (Ger.). 755p. 1963. 88.95x (ISBN 0-8176-0185-6). Birkhauser.

Jacobi, Karl G. Gesammelte Werke, 8 vols. 2nd ed. LC 68-31427. (Ger., Illus., Includes Supplementband Vorlesugen Uber Dynamik). 1969. Vols. 1-7. 170.00 (ISBN 0-8284-0226-4); Vol. 8. 15.00 (ISBN 0-8284-0227-2). Chelsea Pub.

Kodaira, Kunihiko. Collected Works, 3 vols. 540p. 1975. Set. 135.00x (ISBN 0-685-51710-1). Vol. 1. 60.00x (ISBN 0-691-08158-1); Vol. 2. 48.00x (ISBN 0-691-08163-8); Vol. 3. 48.00x (ISBN 0-691-08164-6). Princeton U Pr.

Kozesnik, Jaroslav, ed. Information Theory, Statistical Decision Functions, Random Processes, Vol. C. 1979. lib. bdg. 42.15 (ISBN 90-277-0938-6, Pub. by Reidel Holland). Kluwer Academic.

Kronecker, Leopold. Werke, 5 vols. LC 66-20394. 1969. Repr. Set. 125.00 (ISBN 0-8284-0224-8). Chelsea Pub.

Lejeune-Dirichlet, P. G. Werke, 2 Vols. in 1. Kronecker, L., ed. LC 68-54716. (Ger). 1969. Repr. 49.50 (ISBN 0-8284-0225-6). Chelsea Pub.

Lorenz, Ludwig V. Oeuvres Scientifiques De L. Lorenz, 2 Vols. 1898-1904. Set. 60.00 (ISBN 0-384-33740-6). Johnson Repr.

Minkowski, Hermann. Gesammelte Abhandlungen, 2 Vols. in 1. LC 66-28570. (Ger). 39.50 (ISBN 0-8284-0208-6). Chelsea Pub.

Plucker, Jul. Gesammelte Wissenschaftliche Abhandlungen, 2 Vols. 1971. Repr. of 1895 ed. Set. 130.00 (ISBN 0-384-46890-X). Johnson Repr.

Rademacher, Hans. Collected Papers of Hans Rademacher, 2 vols. Grosswald, Emil, ed. (Mathematicians of Our Time Ser.: Vols. 3 & 4). 1356p. 1974. 60.00x ea. Vol. 1 (ISBN 0-262-07054-5). Vol. 2 (ISBN 0-262-07055-3). Set. 115.00x. MIT Pr.

Ramanujan, S. Collected Papers. LC 62-8326. 1962. 18.95 (ISBN 0-8284-0159-4). Chelsea Pub.

Robinson. Selected Papers of Abraham Robinson, 3 vols. Korner, S., et al, eds. LC 77-92395. 1979. Vol. 1. text ed. 67.00x (ISBN 0-300-02071-6); Vol. 2. text ed. 62.00x (ISBN 0-300-02072-4); Vol. 3. text ed. 52.00x (ISBN 0-300-02073-2). Yale U Pr.

Schlaefli, Ludwig. Gesammelte Mathematische Abhandlungen, Vol. 1. (Ger.). 392p. 1953. 61.95x (ISBN 0-8176-0328-X). Birkhauser.

--Gesammelte Mathematische Abhandlungen, Vol. 2. (Ger.). 381p. 1953. 61.95x (ISBN 0-8176-0329-8). Birkhauser.

--Gesammelte Mathematische Abhandlungen, Vol. 3. (Ger.). 402p. 1956. 61.95x (ISBN 0-8176-0330-1). Birkhauser.

Smith, Henry J. Collected Mathematical Papers, 2 Vols. LC 65-11859. 65.00 (ISBN 0-8284-0187-X). Chelsea Pub.

Szego, Gabor, et al, eds. Studies in Mathematical Analysis & Related Topics: Essays in Honor of George Polya. 1962. 30.00x (ISBN 0-8047-0140-7). Stanford U Pr.

Transactions of the Moscow Mathematical Society. Incl. Vol. 12. 1963. 57.00 (ISBN 0-8218-1612-8, MOSCOW-12); Vol. 13. 1967. 47.00 (ISBN 0-8218-1613-6, MOSCOW-13); Vol. 14. 1967. 47.00 (ISBN 0-8218-1614-4, MOSCOW-14); Vol. 15. 1967. 57.00 (ISBN 0-8218-1615-2, MOSCOW-15); Vol. 16. 1968. 48.00 (ISBN 0-8218-1616-0, MOSCOW-16); Vol. 17. 1969. 50.00 (ISBN 0-8218-1617-9, MOSCOW-17); Vol. 18. 1969. 46.00 (ISBN 0-8218-1618-7, MOSCOW-18); Vol. 19. 1969. 41.00 (ISBN 0-8218-1619-5, MOSCOW-19); Vol. 20. 1971. 60.00 (ISBN 0-8218-1620-9, MOSCOW-20); Vol. 21. 1971. 54.00 (ISBN 0-8218-1621-7, MOSCOW-21); Vol. 22. 1972. 47.00 (ISBN 0-8218-1622-5). LC 65-7413. Tr. of Trudy Moskovskogo Matematiceskugo Obscestva. Am Math.

Tzafestas, S. G., ed. Selected Papers of Demetrios G. Magiros. 1985. lib. bdg. 69.00 (ISBN 90-277-2003-7, Pub. by Reidel Holland). Kluwer-Academic.

Vinogradov, I. M. Selected Works. Faddeev, L. D., et al, eds. Psv, N., tr. from Rus. (Illus.). 410p. 1985. 65.00 (ISBN 0-387-12788-7). Springer-Verlag.

Von Neumann, John. Collected Works, 6 vols. Taub, A. W., ed. Incl. Vol. 1. Logic, Theory of Sets & Quantum Mechanics. 1961. 195.00 (ISBN 0-08-009567-4); Vol. 2. Operators, Ergodic Theory & Almost Periodic Functions in a Group. 1962. 195.00 (ISBN 0-08-009568-2); Vol. 3. Rings of Operators. 1962. 195.00 (ISBN 0-08-009569-0); Vol. 4. 1963. 175.00 (ISBN 0-08-009570-4); Vol. 5. 1963. 195.00 (ISBN 0-08-009571-2); Vol. 6. Theory of Games, Astrophysics, Hydrodynamics & Meteorology. 1963. 195.00 (ISBN 0-08-009572-0). 1963. Set. 780.00 (ISBN 0-08-009566-6). Pergamon.

Weierstrass, Karl T. Mathematische Werke, 7 Vols. LC 68-7407. (Illus.). Set. 210.00 (ISBN 0-384-66490-3). Johnson Repr.

Weil, A. Oeuvres Mathematiques: Collected Papers, 1926-1978, 3 vol. set. 1980. 150.00 (ISBN 0-387-90330-5). Springer-Verlag.

Weiner, Norbert. Norbert Wiener: Collected Work: Vol. 1 Mathematical Philosophy & Foundations, Potential Theory, Brownian Movement, Wiener Integrals, Ergodic & Chaos Theories, Turbulence & Statistical Mechanics. Masani, P., ed. LC 74-17362. (Mit Mathematicians of Our Time Ser.). 1975. text ed. 70.00x (ISBN 0-262-23070-4). MIT Pr.

--Norbert Wiener: Collected Work: Vol. 2 Generalized Harmonic Analysis & Tauberian Theory, Classical Harmonic & Complex Analysis. Masani, P., ed. (Mathematicians of Our Time Ser.). 1979. 70.00x (ISBN 0-262-23092-5). MIT Pr.

Zariski, Oscar. Oscar Zariski: Collected Papers. Incl. Vol. 1. Foundations of Algebric Geometry & Resolution of Singularities. Hironaka, H. & Mumford, D., eds. 1972. 50.00x (ISBN 0-262-08049-4); Vol. 2. Holomorphic Functions & Linear Systems. Artin, M. & Mumford, D., eds. 1973. 50.00x (ISBN 0-262-01038-0); Vol. 3. Topology of Curves & Surfaces, & Special Topics in the Theory of Algebraic Varieties. Artin, M. & Mazur, B., eds. LC 73-171558. 1978. 65.00x (ISBN 0-262-24021-1); Vol. 4. Equisingularity on Algebraic Varieties. Lipman, J. & Teissier, B., eds. 1979. 75.00x (ISBN 0-262-24022-X). (Mathematicians of Our Times Ser.). MIT Pr.

MATHEMATICS–COMPETITIONS

Mathematical Buds, Vol. 3. 93p. 1984. 21.50 (ISBN 0-940790-03-3). Mu Alpha Theta.

NYSML-ARML Contests, Nineteen Seventy-Three to Nineteen Eighty-Two, Vol. 1. 127p. 1983. 5.00 (ISBN 0-940790-50-5). Mu Alpha Theta.

MATHEMATICS–CURIOSA AND MISCELLANY

Denisyuk, Yu. N. Fun with Maths & Physics. 355p. 1984. 9.95 (ISBN 0-8285-2894-2, Pub by Mir Pubs USSR). Imported Pubns.

Eves, Howard W. In Mathematical Circles, 2 Vols. 1969. Set. write for info. (ISBN 0-685-19591-0, PWS0671, Prindle); write for info. PWS Pubs.

--Mathematical Circles Revisited. (Illus.). 1971. text ed. write for info. (ISBN 0-87150-121-X, PWS0951, Prindle); text ed. write for info. (ISBN 0-685-04722-9). PWS Pubs.

Honsberger, Ross. Mathematical Gems II. LC 76-15927. (Dolciani Mathematical Expositions Ser.: No. 2). 182p. 1976. 19.00 (ISBN 0-88385-302-7). Math Assn.

Jenkins, Gerald & Wild, Anne. Mathematical Curiosities, Vol. III. 28p. 1983. pap. 3.95 (ISBN 0-13-561225-X). P-H.

Marmaduke. Marmaduke Multiply's Merry Method of Making Minor Mathematicians. facsimile ed. Bleiler, E. F., ed. viii, 170p. pap. 2.95 (ISBN 0-486-22773-1). Dover.

Vanmarcke, Erik. Random Fields: Analysis & Synthesis. (Illus.). 416p. 1983. 47.50x (ISBN 0-262-22026-1). MIT Pr.

MATHEMATICS–DATA PROCESSING

Aberth, Oliver. Computable Analysis. new ed. (Illus.). 208p. 1980. text ed. 46.50 (ISBN 0-07-000079-4). McGraw.

Abney, Darrell H., et al. Computer Mathematics for Programmers: Instructor's Manual. 1985. text ed. 5.00i (ISBN 0-12-042151-8). Acad Pr.

Ahl, David H. Computers in Mathematics: A Sourcebook of Ideas. LC 79-57487. (Illus.). 214p. 1979. pap. 15.95 (ISBN 0-916688-16-X, 12D). Creative Comp.

Automated Education Center. Hybrid Computer Application to Mathematical Models of Physical Systems. LC 70-125998. 19.00 (ISBN 0-403-04469-3). Scholarly.

Balinski, M. L. & Cottle, R. W., eds. Complementary & Fixed Point Problems. (Mathematical Programming Studies: Vol. 7). 184p. 1978. pap. 30.00 (ISBN 0-444-85123-2, North-Holland). Elsevier.

Bart, H., et al. Minimal Factorization of Matrix & Operator Functions. (Operator Theory: Advances & Applications Ser.: No. 1). 236p. 1979. pap. 20.95x (ISBN 0-8176-1139-8). Birkhauser.

Bavel, Zamir. A Math Companion for Computer Science. 1981. 23.95 (ISBN 0-8359-4300-3); pap. 18.95 (ISBN 0-8359-4299-6); solutions manual avail. (ISBN 0-8359-4301-1). Reston.

Bellman, Richard E. Introduction to the Mathematical Theory of Control Processes. LC 76-127679. (Mathematics in Science & Engineering Ser.: Vol. 40). Vol. 1 1967. 65.00 (ISBN 0-12-084801-5); Vol. 2 1971. 75.00 (ISBN 0-12-084802-3). Acad Pr.

Beltrami, E. J. Algorithmic Approach to Nonlinear Analysis & Optimization. (Mathematics in Science & Engineering Ser.: Vol. 63). 1970. 55.00 (ISBN 0-12-085560-7). Acad Pr.

Bitter, Gary. Microcomputer Applications for Calculus. 256p. 1982. pap. text ed. write for info (ISBN 0-87150-378-6, 8010, Prindle). PWS Pubs.

Bliss, Elizabeth. Data Processing Mathematics. (Illus.). 176p. 1985. text ed. 24.95 (ISBN 0-13-196155-1). P-H.

Boehm, C., ed. Calculus & Computer Science Theory: Proceedings of the Symposium Held in Rome, March 25-27, 1975. (Lecture Notes in Computer Science: Vol. 37). xiv, 370p. 1975. pap. 20.00 (ISBN 0-387-07416-3). Springer-Verlag.

Brown, Homer E. Solution of Large Networks by Matrix Methods. LC 74-34159. 256p. 1975. 40.50X (ISBN 0-471-11045-0, Pub. by Wiley-Interscience). Wiley.

Buning, Herbert & Naeve, Peter, eds. Computational Statistics. 348p. 1981. text ed. 39.20 (ISBN 3-11-008419-8). De Gruyter.

Burke, Ronald & Kramer, Arthur. Microcomputer Courseware for Technical Mathematics (Apple II & TRS-80) User's Manual. 1983. 11.70 (ISBN 0-07-009050-5). McGraw.

Burkhard, R. E. & Derigs, U. Assignment & Matching Problems: Solution Methods with FORTRAN-Programs. (Lecture Notes in Economics & Mathematical Systems Ser.: Vol. 184). 148p. 1980. pap. 18.00 (ISBN 0-387-10267-1). Springer-Verlag.

Burt, Bruce C., compiled by. Calculators: Readings from the Arithmetic Teacher & the Mathematics Teacher. LC 79-17365. (Illus.). 231p. 1979. pap. 6.25 (ISBN 0-87353-144-2). NCTM.

Calter, Paul. Problem Solving with Computers. 1972. pap. text ed. 27.65 (ISBN 0-07-009648-1). McGraw.

Chow, J. H., ed. Time-Scale Modeling of Dynamic Networks with Applications to Power Systems. (Lecture Notes in Control & Information Sciences Ser.: Vol. 46). 218p. 1982. pap. 14.00 (ISBN 0-387-12106-4). Springer-Verlag.

Claycombe, William W. & Sullivan, William G. Foundations of Mathematical Programming. (Illus.). 304p. 1975. 24.95 (ISBN 0-87909-282-3). Reston.

Clifford & Clifford. Computer Mathematics Handbook. 15.95x (ISBN 0-205-04311-9, 2043114). Allyn.

Cohon, Jared L. Multiobjective Programming & Planning. (Mathematics in Science & Engineering Ser.). 1978. 49.50 (ISBN 0-12-178350-2). Acad Pr.

Computer Math Activities, 5 Vols. Vol. 1. write for info. (ISBN 0-201-20962-4, Sch Div); Vol. 2. write for info. (ISBN 0-201-20963-2); Vol. 3. write for info. (ISBN 0-201-20964-0); Vol. 4. write for info. (ISBN 0-201-20965-9); Vol. 5. write for info. (ISBN 0-201-20966-7). Addison-Wesley.

Cook, Charles C., illus. Spatial Algorithms for Processing Land Data with a Microcomputer: Lincoln Institute Monograph. (84-2). 278p. 1984. pap. text ed. 9.00 (ISBN 0-318-03877-3). Lincoln Inst Land.

Corlett, P. N. Practical Programming. 2nd ed. LC 75-161295. (School Mathematics Project Handbooks). (Illus.). 1971. pap. 12.95x (ISBN 0-521-09740-1). Cambridge U Pr.

Cottle, R. W., et al, eds. Variational Inequalities & Complementarity Problems: Theory & Applications. LC 79-40108. 408p. 1980. 64.95 (ISBN 0-471-27610-3, Pub. by Wiley-Interscience). Wiley.

Craven, B. D. Mathematical Programming & Control Theory. (Mathematics Ser.). 1978. pap. 15.95 (ISBN 0-412-15500-1, NO. 6070, Pub. by Chapman & Hall). Methuen Inc.

Danby, J. M. Computer Applications to Differential Equations. 1985. pap. text ed. 17.95 (ISBN 0-8359-0962-X). Reston.

Daniel, Cuthbert & Wood, Fred S. Fitting Equations to Data: Computer Analysis of Multifactor Data. 2nd ed. LC 79-11110. (Probability & Mathematical Statistics Ser.: Applied Section). 1980. 38.95 (ISBN 0-471-05370-8, Pub. by Wiley-Interscience). Wiley.

Dence, Thomas P. Solving Math Problems in BASIC. (Illus.). 392p. 1983. 19.95 (ISBN 0-8306-0264-X, 1564); pap. 15.50 (ISBN 0-8306-0164-3). TAB Bks.

Dodes, Irving A. Finite Mathematics with BASIC: A Liberal Arts Approach. Rev. ed. LC 78-31505. (Illus.). 372p. 1981. Repr. of 1970 ed. lib. bdg. 21.00 (ISBN 0-88275-862-4). Krieger.

Dongarra, J. J., et al. LINPACK Users' Guide. LC 78-78206. viii, 367p. 1979. pap. text ed. 24.00 (ISBN 0-89871-172-X). Soc Indus-Appl Math.

Eckmann, J. P. & Wittwer, P. Computer Methods & Borel Summability Applied to Feigenbaum's Equation. (Lecture Notes in Physics Ser.: Vol. 227). xiv, 297p. 1985. pap. 16.60 (ISBN 0-387-15215-6). Springer-Verlag.

Elgarten, G. & Posamentier, A. S. Using Computers in Mathematics. 1983. 24.76 (ISBN 0-201-10450-4, Sch Div); 3.88 (ISBN 0-201-10449-0); solutions manual 15.40 (ISBN 0-201-10456-3). Addison-Wesley.

Elich, Carlotta J. & Elich, Joseph. Trigonometry Using Calculators. LC 79-18934. (Illus.). 1980. text ed. 23.95 (ISBN 0-201-03186-8); instr's. manual 4.00 (ISBN 0-201-03187-6). Addison-Wesley.

Fiacco. Mathematical Programming with Data Perturbations, Pt. I. (Lecture Notes in Pure & Applied Mathematics Ser.: Vol. 72). 256p. 1982. 39.75 (ISBN 0-8247-1543-8). Dekker.

Field, M. J. Several Complex Variables & Computer Manifolds Part I. LC 81-21590. (London Mathematical Society Lecture Note Ser.: No. 65). 200p. 1982. pap. 22.95 (ISBN 0-521-28301-9). Cambridge U Pr.

Flast, Robert H. VisiCalc Models: Finance-Statistics-Mathematics. 240p. 1984. 15.95 (Osborne-Mcgraw). Mcgraw.

Forsythe, George E. & Moler, C. Computer Solution of Linear Algebraic Systems. 1967. ref. ed. 30.00 (ISBN 0-13-165779-8). P-H.

Forsythe, George E., et al. Computer Methods for Mathematical Computations. (Illus.). 1977. ref. ed. 41.95 (ISBN 0-13-165332-6). P-H.

Fosdick, L., ed. Performance Evaluation of Numerical Software. 340p. 1979. 42.75 (ISBN 0-444-85330-8, North Holland). Elsevier.

Fossum, Timothy V. & Gatterdam, Ronald W. Calculus & the Computer: An Approach to Problem Solving. 1980. pap. text ed. 13.65x (ISBN 0-673-15158-1). Scott F.

Freidlin, M. I. & Wentzell, A. D. Random Perturbations of Dynamical Systems. (Grundlehren der Mathematischen Wissenschaften Ser.: Bd. 260). (Illus.). 340p. 1983. 58.00 (ISBN 0-387-90858-7). Springer-Verlag.

Gear, C. W. Numerical Initial Value Problems in Ordinary Differential Equations. (Automatic Computation Ser). (Illus.). 1971. ref. ed. 40.00 (ISBN 0-13-626606-1). P-H.

George, Alan & Liu, Joseph W. Computer Solution of Large Sparse Positive Definite. (Illus.). 256p. 1980. text ed. 41.95 (ISBN 0-13-165274-5). P-H.

Gersting, Judith L. Mathematical Structures for Computer Science. LC 82-2550. (Illus.). 432p. 1982. text ed. 28.95 (ISBN 0-7167-1305-5); solutions manual avail. W H Freeman.

Gibson, C. G. Singular Points of Smooth Mappings. (Research Notes in Mathematics Ser.: No. 25). 239p. 1979. pap. text ed. 23.95 (ISBN 0-273-08410-0). Pitman Pub MA.

Greenberg, Harvey & Maybee, John, eds. Computer-Assisted Analysis & Model Simplification. LC 80-28509. 1981. 44.50 (ISBN 0-12-299680-1). Acad Pr.

Grenander, Ulf. Mathematical Experiments on the Computer. (Pure & Applied Mathematics Ser.). 1982. 44.50 (ISBN 0-12-301750-5). Acad Pr.

Groneman, Nancy J. Business Mathematics Using Electronic Calculators. (Illus.). 240p. 1982. 21.95 (ISBN 0-13-105205-5). P-H.

Hemker, P. W. & Miller, J. J., eds. Numerical Analysis of Singular Perturbation Problems. 1979. 59.50 (ISBN 0-12-340250-6). Acad Pr.

Hermes, Hans. Term Logic with Choice Operator. rev. ed. LC 79-125498. (Lecture Notes in Mathematics: Vol. 6). 1970. pap. 10.70 (ISBN 0-387-04899-5). Springer-Verlag.

Hestenes, Marshall D. & Hill, Richard O., Jr. Trigonometry with Calculators. (Illus.). 288p. 1982. text ed. 28.95 (ISBN 0-13-930859-8). P-H.

Hoaglin, David C. & Mosteller, F., eds. Understanding Robust & Exploratory Data Analysis. LC 82-8528. (Applied Probability & Math Statistics Ser.). 447p. 1982. 39.95x (ISBN 0-471-09777-2, Pub. by Wiley-Interscience). Wiley.

Jacoby, Samuel L. & Kowalik, Janusz S. Mathematical Modeling with Computers. (Illus.). 1980. text ed. 40.00 (ISBN 0-13-561555-0). P-H.

Johnston, Robert L. Numerical Methods: A Software Approach. LC 81-12974. 276p. 1981. text ed. 32.50x (ISBN 0-471-09397-1). Wiley.

Kemeny, John G., et al. Computing for a Course in Finite Mathematics. 208p. 1985. pap. text ed. 15.95 (ISBN 0-201-13434-9). Addison-Wesley.

Kenney, Margaret. Incredible Pascal Triangle. (Motivated Math Project Activity Booklets). 91p. (Orig.). 1976. pap. text ed. 2.50 (ISBN 0-917916-16-6). Boston Coll Math.

Kennington, Jeff L. & Helgason, Richard V. Algorithms for Network Programming. LC 80-258. 291p. 1980. 40.95x (ISBN 0-471-06016-X, Pub. by Wiley Interscience). Wiley.

Klerer, Melvin & Reinfelds, Juris, eds. Interactive Systems for Experimental Applied Mathematics. 1968. 68.50 (ISBN 0-12-414650-3). Acad Pr.

Korfhage, Robert R. Discrete Computational Structures. 1974. 35.00 (ISBN 0-12-420850-9). Acad Pr.

Kosniowski, Czes. Fun Mathematics on Your Microcomputer. LC 83-1811. 1983. pap. 10.95 (ISBN 0-521-27451-6). Cambridge U Pr.

Kousourou, Gabriel, et al. An Introduction to Technical Mathematics with Computing. (Illus.). 510p. text ed. 27.00x (ISBN 0-89433-038-1). Petrocelli.

Kramer, A. D. Mathematics for Computers. 512p. 1985. price not set (ISBN 0-07-009659-7). McGraw.

Kunzi, Hans P., et al. Numerical Methods of Mathematical Optimization with ALGOL & FORTRAN Programs. LC 68-18673. (Computer Science & Applied Mathematics Ser). 1968. 45.00 (ISBN 0-12-428850-2). Acad Pr.

Lev, B. & Weiss, H. J. Introduction to Mathematical Programming: Quantitative Tools for Decision Making. 290p. 1981. 31.75 (ISBN 0-444-00591-9, North-Holland). Elsevier.

Levy, Lawrence S. Trigonometry with Calculators. 330p. 1983. text ed. write for info. (ISBN 0-02-370450-0). Macmillan.

McCready, Richard R. Office Machines: Electronic Calculators. 6th ed. LC 82-21337. 248p. 1983. pap. write for info. (ISBN 0-534-01285-X). Kent Pub Co.

Malm, Donald G. A Computer Laboratory Manual for Number Theory. 256p. 1980. pap. text ed. 9.95x (ISBN 0-933694-13-X). COMPress.

Marcus, Marvin. Discrete Mathematics: A Computational Approach Using BASIC. LC 82-14376. 329p. 1983. pap. 21.95 (ISBN 0-914894-38-2); Apple diskette 17.00 (ISBN 0-88175-001-8); IBM diskette 17.00 (ISBN 0-88175-091-3). Computer Sci.

--An Introduction to Pascal & Precalculus. 1984. 29.95 (ISBN 0-88175-009-3); tchr's diskette 17.00 (ISBN 0-88175-062-X); student's diskette 17.00 (ISBN 0-88175-061-1); solution manual 10.00 (ISBN 0-88175-063-8). Computer Sci.

--Solution Manual Discrete Mathematics: A Computational Approach Using BASIC. 92p. 1983. 15.00 (ISBN 0-88175-005-0). Computer Sci.

Merris, Russell. Introduction to Computer Mathematics. LC 85-4683. 1985. text ed. write for info. (ISBN 0-88175-083-2). Computer Sci.

Messina, P. C. & Murli, A., eds. Problems & Methodolgies in Mathematical Software Production, Sorrento, Italy 1980: Proceedings. (Lecture Notes in Computer Sciences: Vol. 142). 271p. 1982. pap. 14.50 (ISBN 0-387-11603-6). Springer-Verlag.

Molluzzo & Buckley. A First Course in Discrete Mathematics. 1985. text ed. write for info. (ISBN 0-534-05310-6). Wadsworth Pub.

Montgomery, Douglas C. & Peck, Elizabeth A. Introduction to Linear Regression Analysis. LC 81-11512. (Wiley Ser. in Probability & Mathematical Statistics - Applied Probability & Statistics Section). 504p. 1982. 38.95x (ISBN 0-471-05850-5, Pub. by Wiley-Interscience). Wiley.

Morris, Janet. How to Develop Problem Solving Using a Calculator. LC 81-9569. (Illus.). 40p. 1981. pap. 4.00 (ISBN 0-87353-175-2). NCTM.

Nahorski, Z., et al. Optimization of Discrete Time Systems: The Upper Boundary Approach. (Lecture Notes in Control & Information Sciences Ser.: Vol. 51). 137p. 1983. pap. 11.00 (ISBN 0-387-12258-3). Springer-Verlag.

Oberle, William F. Calculus and the Computer. 1986. pap. text ed. price not set (ISBN 0-201-15983-X). Addison-Wesley.

Oliver, Helen & Oliver, Bob. Trillium Basal Math-Ware: Apple Diskette. incl. tchr's manual 49.95 (ISBN 0-89824-080-8). Trillium Pr.

Pandit, S. G. & Deo, S. G. Differential Systems Involving Impulses. (Lecture Notes in Mathematics Ser.: Vol. 954). 102p. 1982. pap. 10.00 (ISBN 0-387-11606-0). Springer-Verlag.

Pavelle, Richard, ed. Applications of Computer Algebra. 1985. lib. bdg. 59.95 (ISBN 0-89838-173-8). Kluwer Academic.

Press, William, et al. Numerical Recipes: The Art of Scientific Computing. 700p. Date not set. price not set. (ISBN 0-521-30811-9). Cambridge U Pr.

Price, Wilson T. & Miller, M. Elements of Data Processing Mathematics. 2nd ed. LC 71-140239. 1971. text ed. 29.95 (ISBN 0-03-084745-1, HoltC). HR&W.

Rand, Richard H. Computer Algebra in Applied Mathematics: An Introduction to MACSYMA. (Research Notes in Mathematics: No. 94). 200p. 1983. pap. text ed. 19.95 (ISBN 0-273-08632-4). Pitman Pub MA.

Ratschek, H. H. & Rokne, J. Computer Methods for the Range of Functions. (Mathematics & Its Applications Ser.). 160p. 1984. 42.95 (ISBN 0-470-20034-0). Halsted Pr.

Rice, John R., ed. Mathematical Software. (ACM Monograph). 1971. 66.50 (ISBN 0-12-587250-X). Acad Pr.

Roberts, Peter C. Modelling Large Systems: Limits to Growth Revisited. LC 78-13339. (Orasa Text). 120p. 1978. pap. 29.95x (ISBN 0-470-26528-0); write for info. tchr's manual avail. Halsted Pr.

Rodin, E. Y. Computers & Mathematics with Applications: A Memorial Dedicated to Cornelius Lanczos. 1976. text ed. 91.00 (ISBN 0-08-020521-6). Pergamon.

Rogowski, Stephen. Problems for Computer Solution. (Illus.). 106p. 1979. pap. 4.95 student's ed. (ISBN 0-916688-13-5, 9Z); tchr's ed. 9.95 (ISBN 0-916688-14-3, 9Y). Creative Comp.

Roman, Richard A. Teaching Problem Solving & Mathematics by Computer: An Interim Report. 63p. 1974. 1.50 (ISBN 0-318-14743-2, ED 101 690). Learn Res Dev.

Rothenberg, Ronald I. Basic Computing for Calculus. 328p. 1985. 15.95 (ISBN 0-07-054011-X). McGraw.

Schittkowski, K., ed. Computational Mathematical Programming. (NATO ASI Ser.: Series F, Vol. 15). x, 451p. 1985. 48.50 (ISBN 0-387-15180-X). Springer-Verlag.

Shampine, Lawrence F. & Allen, Richard C. Numerical Computing: An Introduction. LC 72-93122. 258p. 1973. text ed. 20.95 (ISBN 0-7216-8150-6). HR&W.

Shepp, Lawrence A., ed. Computed Tomography. LC 82-18508. (Proceedings of Symposia in Applied Mathematics: Vol. 27). pap. 15.00 (ISBN 0-8218-0033-7, PSAPM-27). Am Math.

Sicks, Jon L. Investigating Secondary Mathematics with Computers. LC 85-3534. (Illus.). 278p. 1985. pap. text ed. 27.95 incl. disk (ISBN 0-317-18432-6). P-H.

Snover, Steven L. & Spikell, Mark A. Mathematical Problem-Solving with the Microcomputer: Projects to Increase Your Programming Skill. 188p. 1985. Commodore 20 & 64. pap. 19.95 incl. disk. P-H.

Society for Industrial & Applied Mathematics - American Mathematical Society Symposia - New York - March, 1971. Computers in Algebra & Number Theory: Proceedings. Birkhoff, Garrett & Hall, Marshall, Jr., eds. LC 76-167685. (SIAM-AMS Proceedings: Vol. 4). 208p. 1980. pap. 19.00 (ISBN 0-8218-1323-4, SIAMS-4). Am Math.

Stavroulakis, Peter, ed. Distributed Parameter Systems Theory, 2 pts. Incl. Pt. 1. Control. (Vol. 26) (ISBN 0-87933-071-6); Pt. 2. Estimation. (Vol. 27) (ISBN 0-87933-072-4). LC 82-21218. (Benchmark Papers in Electrical Engineering & Computer Science). 832p. 1983. 45.00 ea. (Dist. by Van Nos Reinhold); Set. 81.00 (ISBN 0-87933-103-8). Van Nos Reinhold.

Symposium in Applied Mathematics. The Influence of Computing on Mathematical Research & Education. La Salle, Joseph P., ed. LC 74-5166. (Proceedings of Symposia in Applied Mathematics: Vol. 20). 1974. 38.00 (ISBN 0-8218-1326-9, PSAPM-20). Am Math.

Tinsley, J. D. Computing in Mathematics: Some Experimental Ideas for Teachers. (School Mathematics Project Computing Ser.). (Illus.). 1971. pap. 8.95 (ISBN 0-521-09683-9). Cambridge U Pr.

Traub, J. F. & Wozniakowski, H. A General Theory of Optimal Algorithms. LC 79-8859. (ACM Monograph). 1980. 60.00 (ISBN 0-12-697650-3). Acad Pr.

Traub, J. F., ed. Algorithms & Complexity: New Directions & Recent Results. 1976. 55.00 (ISBN 0-12-697540-X). Acad Pr.

--Complexity of Sequential & Parallel Numerical Algorithms. 1973. 47.50 (ISBN 0-12-697550-7). Acad Pr.

Velleman & Hoaglin. Applications, Basics & Computing of Exploratory Data Analysis. 384p. 1981. pap. text ed. write for info. (ISBN 0-87150-409-X, Duxbury Pr). PWS Pubs.

Vemuri, V. & Karplus, Walter. Digital Computer Treatment of Partial Differential Equations. (Illus.). 480p. 1981. text ed. 39.95 (ISBN 0-13-212407-6). P-H.

Walker, Henry M. Problems for Computer Solutions Using FORTRAN. 203p. (Orig.). 1980. pap. text ed. 15.95 (ISBN 0-316-91833-4). Little.

Wand, M. Induction, Recursion & Programming. 202p. 1980. 33.50 (ISBN 0-444-00322-3, North-Holland). Elsevier.

Wang, Peter C., et al, eds. Information Linkage Between Applied Mathematics & Industry. 1979. 59.50 (ISBN 0-12-734250-8). Acad Pr.

Wardle, M. E., ed. From Problem to Program. (School Mathematics Project Computing Ser). (Illus.). 1971. 16.95 (ISBN 0-521-08301-X); pap. 6.95 (ISBN 0-521-09684-7). Cambridge U Pr.

Young, E. C. Vector & Tensor Analysis. (Pure & Applied Ser.: Vol. 48). 1978. 65.00 (ISBN 0-8247-6671-7). Dekker.

Yuen, C. K. & Fraser, D. Digital Spectral Analysis. 1979. 12.00x (ISBN 0-643-02419-0, Pub. by CSIRO). Intl Spec Bk.

--Digital Spectral Analysis. (Applicable Mathematics Ser.). 168p. 1979. pap. text ed. 24.95 (ISBN 0-273-08439-9). Pitman Pub MA.

MATHEMATICS–DICTIONARIES

Alsina, Claudi. Vocabulari Catala De Matematica Basica. (Catalan.). 48p. 1977. pap. 8.75 (ISBN 84-85008-06-5, S-50127). French & Eur.

Andrews, George E. Encyclopedia of Mathematics & Its Applications: The Theory of Partitions, Vol. 2. 1984. 34.50 (ISBN 0-521-30222-6). Cambridge U Pr.

Ballentyne, D. W. & Walker, L. E. Diccionario de Leyes y Efectos Cientificos En Quimica-Fisica Matematicas. (Span.). 216p. 14.95 (ISBN 0-686-56711-0, S-33054). French & Eur.

Bastida, Julio R. Encyclopedia of Mathematics & Its Applications: Field Extensions & Galois Theory, Vol. 22. 1984. 47.50 (ISBN 0-317-14400-6, 30242-0). Cambridge U Pr.

Biedenharn, L. C. & Louck, J. D. Encyclopedia of Mathematics & Its Applications: The Racah-Wigner Algebra in Quantum Theory, Vol. 9. 1984. 59.50 (ISBN 0-521-30229-3). Cambridge U Pr.

Biedenhern, L. C. & Louck, J. D. Encyclopedia of Mathematics & Its Applications: Angular Momentum in Quantum Physics, Vol. 8. 1984. 69.50 (ISBN 0-521-30228-5). Cambridge U Pr.

Boursin, Jean-Louis. DEMO: Dictionnaire Elementaire de Mathematiques Modernes. (Fr.). 320p. 1972. 21.95 (ISBN 0-686-56927-X, M-6045). French & Eur.

Cadillac Publishing Company & Shapiro, Max. Mathematics Encyclopedia. LC 76-23817. 1977. pap. 6.95 (ISBN 0-385-12427-9). Doubleday.

Cannon, John R. Encyclopedia of Mathematics & Its Applications: The One-Dimensional Heat Equation, Vol. 23. 1984. 59.50 (ISBN 0-317-14401-4, 30243-9). Cambridge U Pr.

Cassinelli, Gianni. Encyclopedia of Mathematics & Its Applications: The Logic of Quantum Mechanics, Vol. 15. 1984. 37.50 (ISBN 0-317-14391-3, 30235-8). Cambridge U Pr.

Chambadal, Lucien. Diccionario de las Matematicas Modernas. 2nd ed. (Span.). 264p. 1976. pap. 5.25 (ISBN 84-01-90307-6, S-12248). French & Eur.

--Dictionnaire des Mathematiques Modernes. rev. ed. (Fr.). 250p. 1972. pap. 6.95 (ISBN 0-686-56847-8, M-6625). French & Eur.

Costa, Vasco & Frances, Osvald. Diccionario de Unidadaes y Tablas de Conversion. 3rd ed. (Span.). 168p. 1977. pap. 8.75 (ISBN 84-252-0214-0, S-50579). French & Eur.

Daintith, J. & Nelson, R. D. The Penguin Dictionary of Mathematics. (Reference Ser.). 304p. 1985. pap. 5.95 (ISBN 0-14-051119-9). Penguin.

De Francis, John F. Chinese-English Glossary of the Mathematical Sciences. LC 64-16997. pap. 71.50 (ISBN 0-317-08625-1, 2004670). Bks Demand UMI.

Dictionary of Mathematics. (Eng. & Chinese.). 252p. 1974. pap. 4.95 (ISBN 0-686-92280-8, M-9575). French & Eur.

Dollard, John D. & Friedman, Charles N. Encyclopedia of Mathematics & Its Applications: Product Integration with Applications to Differential Equations, Vol. 10. 1984. 39.50 (ISBN 0-521-30230-7). Cambridge U Pr.

Downing, Douglas. Encyclopedia of Computer Terms. LC 82-11350. 160p. 1983. pap. 6.95 (ISBN 0-8120-2519-9). Barron.

Eisenreich, G. & Sube, R. Dictionary of Mathematics, 2 vols. (Eng., Fr., Ger. & Rus.). 1460p. 1982. Set. 168.00 (ISBN 0-444-99706-7). Elsevier.

Encyclopedia of Mathematics & Its Applications: Integral Geometry & Geometric Probability, Vol. 1. 1984. 42.50 (ISBN 0-317-14404-9, 30221-8). Cambridge U Pr.

English-Chinese Dictionary of Mathematical Terms. (Eng. & Chinese.). 252p. 1980. 25.00 (ISBN 0-686-92416-9, M-9293). French & Eur.

Fachlexikon ABC Mathematik. (Ger.). 624p. 1978. 30.95 (ISBN 3-87144-030-2, M-7381, Pub. by Verlag Harri Deutsch). French & Eur.

Fachlexikon ABC Mathematik. (Ger.). 1977. 30.95 (ISBN 3-87144-336-0, M-7382, Pub. by Harri Deutsch). French & Eur.

Fattorini, H. O. Encyclopedia of Mathematics & Its Applications: The Cauchy Problem, Vol. 18. 1984. 69.50 (ISBN 0-317-14396-4, 30238-2). Cambridge U Pr.

Gellert, W. Kleine Enzyklopaedie Mathematik. 2nd ed. (Ger.). 837p. 1972. 27.50 (ISBN 3-87144-104-X, M-7090). French & Eur.

Gellert, W., et al. Kleine Enzyklopaedie Mathmetik. (Ger.). 820p. 1977-78. 28.95 (ISBN 3-87144-323-9, M-7498, Pub. by Verlag Harri Deutsch). French & Eur.

Glenn, J. A. & Littler, G. H., eds. A Dictionary of Mathematics. LC 83-25739. (Illus.). 240p. 1984. 18.95x (ISBN 0-389-20451-X, 08011). B&N Imports.

Herland, Leo. Dictionary of Mathematical Sciences, 2 vols. Incl. Vol. 1. German-English. 2nd ed. xii, 320p (ISBN 0-8044-4393-9); Vol. 2. English-German. 320p (ISBN 0-8044-4394-7). LC 65-16622. (Eng. & Ger.). 22.00 ea. Ungar.

International Mathematical Union, ed. World Directory of Mathematicians 1982. 7th ed. 728p. 23.00 (ISBN 0-686-84619-2, WRLDIR/7). Am Math.

James, Glenn & James, Robert C. Mathematics Dictionary. 4th. ed. 517p. 1976. 32.50 (ISBN 0-442-24091-0). Van Nos Reinhold.

James, Gordon. Encyclopedia of Mathematics & Its Applications: The Representation Theory of the Symmetric Group, Vol. 16. 1984. 49.50 (ISBN 0-317-14393-X, 30236-6). Cambridge U Pr.

Jones, William B. & Thron, W. J. Encyclopedia of Mathematics & Its Applications: Continued Fractions, Vol. 11. 1984. 47.50 (ISBN 0-521-30231-5). Cambridge U Pr.

Jordan Ministry of Education, ed. English-Arabic Dictionary of Mathematics. 1980. 25.00x (ISBN 0-86685-330-8). Intl Bk Ctr.

Klaften, Berthold. Mathematisches Vokabular. 4th ed. (Eng. & Ger., Vocabulary of Mathematics). 1971. 13.50 (ISBN 0-686-56630-0, M-7551, Pub. by Wila). French & Eur.

Klaften, E. B. German-English, English-German Mathematical Dictionary. (Ger. & Eng.). pap. 15.00 (ISBN 0-686-77978-9). Heinman.

Lidl, Rudolf, et al. Encyclopedia of Mathematics & Its Applications: Finite Fields, Vol. 20. 1984. 69.50 (ISBN 0-317-14398-0, 30240-4). Cambridge U Pr.

Lorentz, G. G., et al. Encyclopedia of Mathematics & Its Applications: Birkhoff Interpolation, Vol. 19. 1985. 34.50 (ISBN 0-521-30239-0). Cambridge U Pr.

Lothaire, M. Encyclopedia of Mathematics & Its Applications: Combinatorics on Words, Vol. 17. 1984. 34.50 (ISBN 0-317-14395-6, 30237-4). Cambridge U Pr.

McEliece, Robert J. Encyclopedia of Mathematics & Its Applications: The Theory of Information & Coding: A Mathematical Framework for Communication, Vol. 3. (The Theory of Information & Coding Ser.). 1984. 32.50 (ISBN 0-521-30223-4). Cambridge U Pr.

Maravall Casesnoves, Dario. Diccionario de Matematica Moderna. (Span.). 332p. 1975. pap. 9.95 (ISBN 0-686-57333-1, S-50009). French & Eur.

Miller, Willard, Jr. Encyclopedia of Mathematics & Its Applications: Symmetry & Separation of Variables, Vol. 4. 1984. 34.50 (ISBN 0-521-30224-2). Cambridge U Pr.

Millington, William & Millington, T. Alaric. Dictionary of Mathematics. 1971. pap. 5.29i (ISBN 0-06-463311-X, EH 311, EH). B&N NY.

Milne-Thomson, L. M. Russian-English Mathematical Dictionary. (Mathematical Research Center Pubns., No. 7). (Rus. & Eng.). 206p. 1962. 40.00x (ISBN 0-299-02600-0). U of Wis Pr.

Milne-Thomson, Louis M. Russian-English Mathematical Dictionary: Words & Phrases in Pure & Applied Mathematics with Roots & Accents, Arranged for Easy Reference. LC 62-7217. (Mathematics Research Center, United States Army, University of Wisconsin Publication: No. 7). pap. 51.30 (ISBN 0-317-28131-3, 2055742). Bks Demand UMI.

Minc, Henryk. Encyclopedia of Mathematics & Its Applications: Permanents, Vol. 6. 1984. 32.50 (ISBN 0-521-30226-9). Cambridge U Pr.

Ministry of Education. Scientific Terms Mathematics: Japanese-English, English-Japanese. (Japanese & Eng.). 146p. 1954. Leatherette 14.95 (ISBN 0-686-92202-6, M_9346). French & Eur.

Newmark, Joseph & Lake, Frances. Mathematics As a Second Language. 2nd ed. LC 81-14935. (Mathematics Ser.). (Illus.). 600p. 1982. text ed. 29.95 (ISBN 0-201-05292-X). student supp. 6.95 (ISBN 0-201-05293-8); instr's manual 2.00 (ISBN 0-201-05294-6). Addison-Wesley.

Reck, J. Herder-Lexikon Mathematik. (Ger.). 238p. 1974. 15.95 (ISBN 3-451-16458-2, M-7445, Pub. by Herder). French & Eur.

Reck, Jurgen. Diccionario Rioduero Matematica. (Span.). 224p. 1977. leatherette 12.50 (ISBN 84-220-0832-7, S-50162). French & Eur.

Ruelle, David. Encyclopedia of Mathematics & Its Applications: Thermodynamic Formalism: The Mathematical Structures of Classical Equilibrium Statistical Mechanics, Vol. 5. 1984. 32.50 (ISBN 0-521-30225-0). Cambridge U Pr.

Silverman, Alan S. Handbook of Chinese for Mathematicians. (Current Chinese Language Project: No. 17). 1976. pap. 3.50x (ISBN 0-912966-17-3). IEAS.

Sube, Ralf. Woerterbuch der Mathematik. (Eng., Ger., Fr. & Rus.). 800p. (Dictionary of Mathematics). 1979. 80.00 (ISBN 3-87144-445-6, M-6983). French & Eur.

Tutte, W. T. Encyclopedia of Mathematics & Its Applications: Graph Theory, Vol. 21. 1984. 49.50 (ISBN 0-317-14399-9, 30241-2). Cambridge U Pr.

Vox, ed. Diccionario Monografico de Matematicas. (Span.). 287p. 1981. 20.25 (ISBN 84-7153-388-X). French & Eur.

Wagon, Stan. Encyclopedia of Mathematics & Its Applications: The Banach-Tarski Paradox, Vol. 24. (Illus.). 272p. 1985. 37.50 (ISBN 0-521-30244-7). Cambridge U Pr.

Warusfel, Andre. Dictionnaire Raisonne De Mathematiques. (Fr.). 1966. pap. 27.95 (ISBN 0-686-57257-2, M-6567). French & Eur.

MATHEMATICS–EARLY WORKS TO 1800

see also Mathematics, Greek

Abu Al-Hasan & Ahmed-Ibn Ibrahim. The Arithmetic of Al-Uqlidisi. Saidan, A. S., tr. 1978. lib. bdg. 103.00 (ISBN 90-277-0752-9, Pub. by Reidel Holland). Kluwer Academic.

De Moivre, Abraham. Doctrine of Chances, or A Method of Calculating the Probabilities of Events in Play: Including a Treatise on the Annuities of Lives. 3rd ed. LC 66-23756. 380p. 1967. 15.95 (ISBN 0-8284-0200-0). Chelsea Pub.

Descartes, Rene. Geometry. (Eng. & Fr.). 1925. pap. 4.50 (ISBN 0-486-60068-8). Dover.

Gowing, Roland. Roger Cotes: Natural Philosopher. LC 82-1154. (Illus.). 200p. 1983. 42.50 (ISBN 0-521-23741-6). Cambridge U Pr.

Hood, Thomas. A Copie of the Speeche Made by the Mathematicall Lecturer at the House of M. Thomas Smith, 4 November, 1588. LC 74-80189. (English Experience Ser.: No. 688). 16p. 1974. Repr. of 1588 ed. 3.50 (ISBN 90-221-0668-3). Walter J Johnson.

Napier, John. De Arte Logistica Joannis Naperi Merchistonii, Baronis Libri Qui Supersunt. LC 76-173010. (Maitland Club, Glasgow. Publications: No. 47). Repr. of 1839 ed. 27.50 (ISBN 0-404-52773-6). AMS Pr.

Newton, Isaac. Mathematical Papers of Isaac Newton, Vol. 3, 1670-1673. Whiteside, D. T. & Hoskin, M. A., eds. LC 65-11203. (Illus.). 155.00 (ISBN 0-521-07119-4). Cambridge U Pr.

--Mathematical Papers of Isaac Newton, Vol. 4, 1674-1684. Whiteside, D. T. & Hoskin, M. A., eds. 1971. 175.00 (ISBN 0-521-07740-0). Cambridge U Pr.

--Mathematical Papers of Isaac Newton, Vol. 5, 1683-1684. Whiteside, D. T., et al, eds. LC 65-11203. (Illus.). 600p. 1972. 175.00 (ISBN 0-521-08262-5). Cambridge U Pr.

--Mathematical Papers of Isaac Newton, Vol. 6, 1684-1691. Whiteside, D. T. & Hoskin, M. A., eds. LC 73-86046. (Illus.). 6000p. 1975. 175.00 (ISBN 0-521-08719-8). Cambridge U Pr.

--Mathematical Works, 2 Vols. Whiteside, Derek T., ed. 1964. Vol. 1. 32.00 (ISBN 0-384-41230-0); Vol. 2. 34.00 (ISBN 0-384-41232-7). Johnson Repr.

North, J. D., ed. Richard of Wallingford: An Edition of His Writings with Introduction, English Translation & Commentary, 3 vols. (Illus.). 1976. 275.00x (ISBN 0-19-858139-4). Oxford U Pr.

Oresme, Nicole, ed. De proportionibus proportionum. Grant, Edward, tr. Bd. with Ad pauca respicientes. (Medieval Science Publications Ser.). (Illus.). 488p. 1966. 50.00x (ISBN 0-299-04000-3). U of Wis Pr.

Saccheri, Girolamo. Euclides Vindicatus. 2nd ed. Halstead, George B., tr. from Lat. 1980. text ed. write for info. (ISBN 0-8284-0289-2). Chelsea Pub.

Sesiano, J. Diophantus' Arithmetica: Books IV to VI in the Arabic Translation of Qusta Ibn Luqa. (Sources in the History of Mathematics & Physical Sciences Ser.: Vol. 3). (Illus.). 502p. 1982. 79.00 (ISBN 0-387-90690-8). Springer-Verlag.

Tapp, John. The Path-Way to Knowledge: Containing the Whole Art of Arithmeticke. LC 68-54667. (English Experience Ser.: No. 66). 1968. Repr. of 1613 ed. 49.00 (ISBN 90-221-0066-9). Walter J Johnson.

MATHEMATICS–EXAMINATIONS, QUESTIONS, ETC.

Allasio, John, et al. Practice RCT Math Exam, No. 1. 1980. Set of 20. 7.50 (ISBN 0-937820-02-4). Westsea Pub.

--Practice RCT Math Exam, No. 2. 1980. Set of 20. 7.50 (ISBN 0-937820-03-2). Westsea Pub.

--Practice Rct Math Exam, No. 3. 1980. Set of 20. 7.50 (ISBN 0-937820-04-0). Westsea Pub.

--Practice RCT Math Exam, No. 5. 1980. Set of 20. 7.50 (ISBN 0-937820-06-7). Westsea Pub.

--Practice RCT Math Exam, No. 6. 1981. Set Of 20. 7.50 (ISBN 0-937820-07-5). Westsea Pub.

--Practice RCT Math Exam, No. 7. 1981. Set Of 20. 7.50 (ISBN 0-937820-08-3). Westsea Pub.

--Practice RCT Math Exam, No. 8. 1981. Set Of 20. 7.50 (ISBN 0-937820-09-1). Westsea Pub.

--Practice RCT Math Exam, No. 9. 1981. Set Of 20. 7.50 (ISBN 0-937820-21-0). Westsea Pub.

--Practice RCT Math Exams, No. 4. 1980. Set of 20. 7.50 (ISBN 0-937820-05-9). Westsea Pub.

--Practice RCT Math Exams: No. 1, Spanish Version. 1981. Set of 20. 8.50 (ISBN 0-937820-12-1); set includes 20 Westsea Original practice RCT Math exam booklets, 20 answer sheets, 1 answer key, 1 scoring conversion table. Westsea Pub.

--Practice RCT Math Exams: No. 2, Spanish Version. 1981. Set of 20. 8.50 (ISBN 0-937820-13-X); set includes 20 Westsea Original practice RCT Math exam booklets, 20 answer sheets, 1 answer key, 1 scoring conversion table. Westsea Pub.

--RCT Mathematics: A Workbook. 168p. 1980. pap. 6.95 (ISBN 0-937820-00-8); ans. key 1.95 (ISBN 0-937820-01-6). Westsea Pub.

Arco Editorial Board. College Level Examinations in Mathematics: Algebra, Algebra-Trigonometry, Trigonometry. LC 77-21106. (Illus.). 1978. pap. text ed. 5.95 (ISBN 0-668-04339-3, 4339). Arco.

Artino, Ralph A. & Gaglione, Anthony M. Contest Problem Book IV: Annual High School Examinations 1973-1982. LC 82-51076. (New Mathematical Library Ser.: No. 29). 200p. 1982. pap. 11.00 (ISBN 0-88385-629-8, 82-0151-076). Math Assn.

Bartfai, P. & Tomko, J. Point Process Queuing Problems. (Colloquia Mathematics Ser.: Vol. 24). 426p. 1981. 76.75 (ISBN 0-444-85432-0). Elsevier.

Bramson, Morris. College Board Achievement Test in Mathematics: Level I. 128p. pap. 3.95 (ISBN 0-668-05319-4). Arco.

--College Board Achievement Test in Mathematics: Level II. 128p. pap. 4.95 (ISBN 0-668-05646-0). Arco.

--Graduate Record Examination in Mathematics. 3rd ed. LC 82-16384. 144p. 1983. pap. 6.95 (ISBN 0-668-05675-4, 5675). Arco.

--Mathematics: Level II College Board Achievement Test. LC 82-8882. 128p. 1983. pap. 4.95 (ISBN 0-668-05646-0, 5646). Arco.

Braswell, James S. & Owens, Douglas T. Mathematics Tests Available in the United States & Canada. 32p. 1981. 2.50 (ISBN 0-87353-197-3). NCTM.

Brown, Walter C. Basic Mathematics Test Sheets. 1981. 0.60 (ISBN 0-87006-317-0). Goodheart.

Buros, Oscar K., ed. Mathematics Tests & Reviews. LC 75-8113. xxv, 435p. 1975. 25.00x (ISBN 0-910674-18-3). U of Nebr Pr.

Comras, Jay & Zerowin, Jeffrey. Improving College Admission Test Scores: Math Workbook. Koerner, Thomas F. & Potter, Eugenia C., eds. (Orig.). 1983. pap. text ed. write for info. (ISBN 0-88210-148-X). Natl Assn Principals.

--Improving College Admission Test Scores: Math Workbook, Teachers Manual. Koerner, Thomas F. & Potter, Eugenia C., eds. (Orig.). 1983. pap. text ed. write for info. (ISBN 0-88210-149-8). Natl Assn Principals.

Davis, Bertha. How to Take a Test. (First Bks.). (Illus.). 72p. 1984. lib. bdg. 8.90 (ISBN 0-531-04824-1). Watts.

Dodge, Howard. How to Prepare for the College Board Achievement Test - Mathematics Level II. LC 78-8655. 1979. pap. 7.95 (ISBN 0-8120-0325-X). Barron.

Erdsneker, Barbara. Mathematics Simplified & Self-Taught. 6th ed. LC 81-14912. 192p. 1982. pap. 6.95 (ISBN 0-668-05357-7, 5357). Arco.

Frieder, David. Total Math Review for the GMAT, GRE & Other Graduate School Admission Tests. LC 81-4054. 336p. 1981. pap. 10.00 (ISBN 0-668-04981-2, 4981). Arco.

Gagola, Stephen M. Notes on Primality Testing & Factoring. (MAA Notes Ser.: Vol. 4). 34p. 1984. pap. 3.50 (ISBN 0-88385-054-0). Math Assn.

Gruber, Gary R. Math Review for the GMAT. 288p. (Orig.). 1982. pap. 8.95 Softcover (ISBN 0-671-43985-5). Monarch Pr.

Guercio, E., et al. General Mathematical Ability: Preparation & Review for the Mathematics Part of the High School Equivalency Diploma Test. LC 74-19738. (GED Preparation Ser.). 160p. (Orig.). 1975. pap. 6.00 (ISBN 0-668-03689-3). Arco.

Hancock, S. F. Mathematics for Engineers: Examination Subjects for Technical Students. 2nd ed. pap. 60.00 (ISBN 0-317-30108-X, 2025277). Bks Demand UMI.

Herzog, David A. Mathematics Workbook for the GED Test. LC 82-20571. (Arco's Preparation for the GED Examination Ser.). 304p. 1983. pap. 6.95 (ISBN 0-668-05542-1). Arco.

Hockett, Shirley O. Barron's How to Prepare for the Advanced Placement Examination-Mathematics. rev. ed. 1983. pap. text ed. 9.95 (ISBN 0-8120-2071-5). Barron.

Howett, Jerry. The Mathematics Test. rev. ed. (GED Ser.). 364p. 1985. pap. 6.85 (ISBN 0-8092-5590-1). Contemp Bks.

Jenkins, Gerald & Wild, Anne. Mathematical Curiosities One: Nine Curious Models. (Illus.). 60p. 1985. pap. 4.95 (ISBN 0-906212-13-8). Parkwest Pubns.

--Mathematical Curiosities Two: Another Nine Curious Models. (Illus.). 60p. 1985. pap. 4.95 (ISBN 0-906212-14-6). Parkwest Pubns.

Johnson, David R. & Margenau, James R. Mathematics Contests: A Handbook for Mathematics Educators. LC 81-22497. (Illus.). 94p. 1982. pap. 5.00 (ISBN 0-87353-187-6). NCTM.

Kaplan, Stanley & Peters, Max, eds. Baron's Regents Exams & Answers 10th Year Mathematics. rev. ed. LC 58-18006. 300p. 1982. pap. text ed. 4.50 (ISBN 0-8120-3203-9). Barron.

Kaplan, Stanley, et al, eds. Barron's Regents Exams & Answers - 11th. Year Mathematics. rev. ed. LC 57-58722. 250p. 1983. pap. text ed. 4.50 (ISBN 0-8120-3199-7). Barron.

Koch, Harry W. Work & Compare Arithmetic. 2nd ed. 1975. 5.00 (ISBN 0-913164-58-5). Ken-Bks.

Mathematics: Subject (Advanced) Test for the GRE. pap. 6.95 (ISBN 0-668-05675-4). Arco.

Moran, Deborah, et al. GED Mathematics Test Preparation Guide: High School Equivalency Examination. (Cliffs Test Preparation Ser.). 182p. 1983. pap. 3.95 (ISBN 0-8220-2016-5). Cliffs.

National Council of Teachers of Mathematics. Evaluation in Mathematics, 26th Yearbook. Johnson, Donovan A., ed. LC 61-11906. 216p. 1961. 12.40 (ISBN 0-87353-004-7). NCTM.

Nicolescu, L. J. & Stoka, M. Mathematics for Engineers, Vol. 1. 1974. 28.00 (ISBN 0-9961001-7-2, Pub. by Abacus England). Heyden.

--Mathematics for Engineers, Vol. 2. 1974. 26.00 (ISBN 0-9961001-8-0, Pub. by Abacus England). Heyden.

Prindle, Anthony. Barron's How to Prepare for the High School Equivalency Examination (GED) General Mathematics, 4 vols. Incl. Vol. 1. Arithmetic (ISBN 0-8120-0727-1); Vol. 2. Algebra (ISBN 0-8120-0728-X); Vol. 3. Geometry, Tables & Graphics, Word Problems (ISBN 0-8120-0729-8); Vol. 4. Model Examinations (ISBN 0-8120-0730-1). LC 78-14808. 1979. pap. 2.95 ea. Barron.

Rosenberg, Richard. Lovejoy's Math Review for the SAT. (Exam Preparation Guides). (Orig.). 1983. pap. 8.95 (ISBN 0-671-47150-3). Monarch Pr.

Rudman, Jack. General Mathematical Ability (G.E.D.) (Career Examination Ser.: CS-33). (Cloth bdg. avail. on request). pap. 8.00 (ISBN 0-8373-3733-X). Natl Learning.

--Mathematics. (Teachers License Examination Ser.: G-4). (Cloth bdg. avail. on request). pap. 10.00 (ISBN 0-8373-8194-0). Natl Learning.

--Mathematics. (National Teachers Examination Ser.: NT-6). (Cloth bdg. avail. on request). pap. 11.95 (ISBN 0-8373-8416-8). Natl Learning.

--Mathematics. (Graduate Record Examination Ser.: GRE-12). (Cloth bdg. avail. on request). pap. 13.95 (ISBN 0-8373-5212-6). Natl Learning.

--Mathematics. (College-Level Examination Ser.: ATS-9C). (Cloth bdg. avail. on request). pap. 9.95 (ISBN 0-8373-5009-3). Natl Learning.

--Mathematics-Jr. H.S. (Teachers License Examination Ser.: T-40). (Cloth bdg. avail. on request). pap. 13.95 (ISBN 0-8373-8040-5). Natl Learning.

--Mathematics-Sr. H.S. (Teachers License Examination Ser.: T-41). (Cloth bdg. avail. on request). pap. 13.95 (ISBN 0-8373-8041-3). Natl Learning.

--Science & Mathematics. (National Teachers Examination Ser.: NC-5). (Cloth bdg. avail. on request). pap. 11.95 (ISBN 0-8373-8405-2). Natl Learning.

--Senior Mathematician. (Career Examination Ser.: C-2078). (Cloth. bdg. avail on request). 1977. pap. 12.00 (ISBN 0-8373-2078-X). Natl Learning.

Saunders, Brigitte. Mathematics Workbook for the SAT (College Entrance Examinations) 1980. pap. 6.95 (ISBN 0-668-04820-4). Arco.

Smith, Sanderson M. Mastering Multiple-Choice Mathematics Tests: Algebra, Geometry, Trigonometry. LC 81-20675. (Illus.). 224p. (Orig.). 1982. pap. 6.95 (ISBN 0-668-05409-3). Arco.

Wells, David. Can You Solve These? Mathematical Problems to Test Your Thinking Powers, Series One. (Illus.). 80p. 1985. pap. 4.95 (ISBN 0-906212-22-7). Parkwest Pubns.

MATHEMATICS–FORMULAE

Auth, Joanne B. Deskbook of Math Formulas & Tables. 208p. 19.95 (ISBN 0-442-20813-8); pap. 14.45 (ISBN 0-442-21106-6). Van Nos Reinhold.

Barnett, S. & Cronin, T. M. Mathematical Formulae for Engineering & Science Students. 1981. 25.00x (ISBN 0-901945-35-8, Pub. by Bradford U Pr England). State Mutual Bk.

Bartsch, Hans-Jochen. Handbook of Mathematical Formulas. 1974. 35.00 (ISBN 0-12-080050-0). Acad Pr.

Carmichael, Robert D. & Smith, Edwin R. Mathematical Tables & Formulas. 1931. pap. 3.75 (ISBN 0-486-60111-0). Dover.

Eswaran, K. S. Mathematical Formulae & Tables. 84p. 1981. 30.00x (ISBN 0-86125-149-0, Pub. by Orient Longman India). State Mutual Bk.

Fararo, Thomas J. Mathematical Ideas & Sociological Theory. 175p. 1984. text ed. 24.50 (ISBN 0-677-16635-4). Gordon.

Handbook of Mathematical Formulae for Engineers & Scientists. 1981. 29.00x (ISBN 0-686-87431-5, Pub. by Denny Pubns). State Mutual Bk.

Menzel, Donald H. Fundamental Formulas of Physics, 2 Vols. 2nd ed. (Illus.). 1960. Vol. 1. pap. text ed. 8.00 (ISBN 0-486-60595-7); Vol. 2. pap. text ed. 8.00 (ISBN 0-486-60596-5). Dover.

Mu Alpha Theta. Mathematical Buds, Vol. II. 126p. 1981. 2.50 (ISBN 0-940790-02-5). Mu Alpha Theta.

Ptak, V. & Potra, F. A. Nondiscreet Induction & Interative Processes. (Research Notes in Mathematics Ser.: No. 103). 250p. 1984. text ed. 21.95 (ISBN 0-273-08627-8). Pitman Pub MA.

Spiegel, Murray R. Mathematical Handbook of Formulas & Tables. (Schaum's Outline Ser.). 1968. pap. text ed. 9.95 (ISBN 0-07-060224-7). McGraw.

MATHEMATICS–HANDBOOKS, MANUALS, ETC.

Ashlock, Robert B. & Johnson, Martin L. Guide Each Child's Learning of Mathematics: A Diagnostic Approach to Instruction. 612p. 1983. text ed. 23.95 (ISBN 0-675-20023-7). Additional supplements may be obtained from publisher. Merrill.

Assaf, Karen & Assaf, Said. Handbook of Mathematical Calculations: For Science Students & Researchers. (Illus.). 310p. 1974. text ed. 6.50x (ISBN 0-8138-1135-X). Iowa St U Pr.

Assistantships & Fellowships in the Mathematical Sciences. 7.00 (ISBN 0-685-47853-X, ASST). Am Math.

Bronstein, I. N. & Semendyayev, K. A. Handbook of Mathematics. 20th ed. 1100p. 1985. flexible plastic cover 37.95 (ISBN 0-442-21171-6). Van Nos Reinhold.

Central State University Dept. of Mathematics. Essential Mathematics for College Freshmen. 1978. pap. text ed. 12.95 (ISBN 0-8403-2905-9, 40290501). Kendall-Hunt.

Chaundy, Theodore W., et al. The Printing of Mathematics: Aids for Authors & Editions & Rules for Compositors & Readers at the University Press, Oxford. pap. 29.80 (ISBN 0-317-10261-3, 2051896). Bks Demand UMI.

Christopher, John. Career Mathematics. (Illus.). 352p. 1986. pap. text ed. 23.95 (ISBN 0-13-114943-1). P-H.

Davidson, P. Everyday Math Made Easy. 272p. 1984. 8.95 (ISBN 0-07-049628-5). McGraw.

Gattegno, Caleb. Mathware: A Math Workshop for Home Use Kit. 1973. 38.00 (ISBN 0-87825-010-7). Ed Solutions.

Gellert, W., et al, eds. VNR Concise Encyclopedia of Mathematics. (Illus.). 816p. 1977. 22.95 (ISBN 0-442-22646-2). Van Nos Reinhold.

Grazda, Edward E., et al. Handbook of Applied Mathematics. 4th ed. LC 77-10309. 1128p. 1977. Repr. of 1966 ed. 56.50 (ISBN 0-88275-615-X). Krieger.

Konvalina, John. Basic Mathematics: Mastering Skills. 584p. 1983. pap. text ed. 21.95 (ISBN 0-15-504970-4, HC); solutions manual avail. (ISBN 0-15-504971-2). HarBraceJ.

Larkin, J. Practical Problems in Mathematics for Mechanical Drafting. LC 77-78236. 1979. pap. 7.80 (ISBN 0-8273-1670-4); instructor's guide 3.60 (ISBN 0-8273-1671-2). Delmar.

Ledermann, Walter & Vajda, Steven. Handbook of Applicable Mathematics: Analysis, Vol. 4. LC 79-42724. (Handbook of Applicable Mathematic Ser.). 865p. 1982. 85.00x (ISBN 0-471-10141-9, Pub. by Wiley-Interscience). Wiley.

Ledermann, Walter & Churchhouse, Robert F., eds. Handbook of Applicable Mathematics: Numerical Methods, Vol. 3. LC 79-42724. (Handbook of Applicable Mathematics Ser.). 592p. 1981. 85.00x (ISBN 0-471-27947-1, Pub. by Wiley-Interscience). Wiley.

Ledermann, Walter & Lloyd, Emlyn, eds. Handbook of Applicable Mathematics: Probability, Vol. 2. LC 79-42724. (Handbook of Applicable Mathematics Ser.). 450p. 1981. 85.00x (ISBN 0-471-27821-1, Pub. by Wiley-Interscience). Wiley.

Lefax Pub. Co. Editors. Manual of Mathematics. (Lefax Technical Manuals.: No. 781). (Illus.). looseleaf bdg. 9.50 (ISBN 0-685-14154-3). Lefax.

Livsic, M. S. Operators, Oscillations, Waves. LC 72-11580. (Translations of Mathematical Monographs: Vol. 34). 280p. (Orig.). 1973. 47.00 (ISBN 0-8218-1584-9, MMONO-34). Am Math.

Mardesic, S. & Segal, J. Shape Theory. (Mathematical Library Ser.: Vol. 26). 378p. 1983. 74.50 (ISBN 0-444-86286-2, North Holland). Elsevier.

Mathfile. 350p. 1983. Repr. of 1982 ed. user's guide 65.00 (ISBN 0-8218-0216-X). Am Math.

Moore & Robinson. Comprehensive Handbook for Study Skills, English, & Mathematics. 304p. 1984. pap. text ed. 28.95 (ISBN 0-8403-3325-0). Kendall-Hunt.

Olivo, C. Thomas & Olivo, Thomas P. Basic Vocational-Technical Mathematics: Fundamentals Edition. 5th ed. LC 84-23257. 240p. 1985. pap. text ed. 12.40 (ISBN 0-8273-2227-5). Delmar.

Proga, Roseanne. Basic Math. 420p. 1983. text ed. write for info. (ISBN 0-87150-452-9, 3000, Prindle). PWS Pubs.

Research & Education Association Staff. Handbook of Mathematical Scientific & Engineering Formulas, Tables, Functions, Graphs, Transforms. rev. ed. LC 80-52490. (Illus.). 1056p. (Orig.). 1984. pap. text ed. 21.85x (ISBN 0-87891-521-4). Res & Educ.

Sumner, Graham N. Mathematics for Physical Geographers. LC 78-12156. 236p. 1979. 25.95x (ISBN 0-470-26557-4). Halsted Pr.

Svenconis, Daniel J. Preparation for the S. A. T. Mathematics Examination. 2nd ed. 254p. (Orig.). 1978. pap. 9.50x (ISBN 0-930124-02-2). Transemantics.

Swartz, Clifford E. Used Math for the First Two Years of College Science. (Illus.). 320p. 1973. pap. 16.95 ref. ed. (ISBN 0-13-939736-1). P-H.

Swezey, Kenneth. Formulas, Methods, Tips & Data for Home & Workshop. rev. ed. Scharff, Robert, rev. by. LC 68-54377. (Popular Science Bk.). (Illus.). 1979. 17.26i (ISBN 0-06-014164-6, HarpT). Har-Row.

Teacher Handbook for Sequencing Math Skills: Grades K-4. (Illus.). 1979. pap. 3.95 (ISBN 0-934734-03-8). Construct Educ.

Vandegrift, John F., Sr. Basic Math Handbook for Practical Marine Engineers. Block, Richard A., ed. 168p. (Orig.). 1985. pap. 18.00 (ISBN 0-934114-64-1, BK-458). Marine Educ.

Vygodsky, M. Mathematical Handbook: Elementary Math. 422p. 1984. 7.95 (ISBN 0-8285-1701-0, Pub. by Mir Pubs USSR). Imported Pubns.

MATHEMATICS–HISTORY

see also Mathematics, Chinese; Mathematics, Greek, and similar headings

Aaboe, A. Episodes from the Early History of Mathematics. LC 63-21916. (New Mathematical Library: No. 13). 131p. 1975. pap. 8.75 (ISBN 0-88385-613-1). Math Assn.

Archibald, Raymond C. Outline of the History of Mathematics. 6th ed. pap. 7.00 (ISBN 0-384-01880-7). Johnson Repr.

--A Semicentennial History of the American Mathematical Society, 1888-1938, Vol. 1. 27.50 (ISBN 0-405-12618-2). Ayer Co Pubs.

Ball, W. Rouse, et al, eds. String Figures & Other Monographs, 4 vols. in 1. Incl. String Figures. Ball, W. R; History of the Slide Rule. Cajori, F; Non Euclidean Geometry. Carslaw, Horatio S; Methods Geometrical Construction. Petersen, Julius. LC 59-11780. 15.95 (ISBN 0-8284-0130-6). Chelsea Pub.

Ball, W. W. Short Account of the History of Mathematics. 4th ed. 1908. pap. 7.50 (ISBN 0-486-20630-0). Dover.

--A Short Account of the History of Mathematics. LC 60-3187. 1960. lib. bdg. 16.50x (ISBN 0-88307-009-X). Gannon.

Bell, Eric T. Men of Mathematics. (Illus.). 1937. pap. 10.75 (ISBN 0-671-46401-9, Fireside). S&S.

Bidwell, James K. & Clason, Robert G., eds. Readings in the History of Mathematics Education. LC 74-113172. (Illus.). 706p. 1970. 16.90 (ISBN 0-87353-087-X). NCTM.

Bledsoe, W. W. & Loveland, Donald, eds. Automated Theorem Proving: After 25 Years. LC 84-9226. (Contemporary Mathematics Ser.: Vol. 29). 366p. 1984. pap. 30.00 (ISBN 0-8218-5027-X). Am Math.

Bochner, Salomon. Role of Mathematics in the Rise of Science. 1966. 37.50x (ISBN 0-691-08028-3); pap. 10.50 (ISBN 0-691-02371-9). Princeton U Pr.

Boyer. A History of Mathematics. pap. 12.50 (ISBN 0-691-02391-3). Princeton U Pr.

Boyer, Carl B. History of Mathematics. LC 68-16506. 717p. 1968. 40.45x (ISBN 0-471-09374-2). Wiley.

--History of the Calculus & Its Conceptual Development. Orig. Title: Concepts of Calculus. 1959. pap. 5.95 (ISBN 0-486-60509-4). Dover.

Brett, William F., et al. An Introduction to the History of Mathematics, Number Theory, & Operations Research. 1974. pap. text ed. 16.50x (ISBN 0-8422-0379-6). Irvington.

Burton, David M. A History of Mathematics. 1984. text ed. 40.05 (ISBN 0-205-08095-2, 568095). Allyn.

--History of Mathematics: An Introduction. 1984. text ed. 40.05 (ISBN 0-205-08095-2, 568095). Allyn.

Cajori, Florian. A History of Mathematics. 4th ed. Nim, A. G, ed. LC 70-113120. 1979. text ed. 19.50 (ISBN 0-8284-0303-1). Chelsea Pub.

--A History of Mathematics. 4th, rev. ed. Nim, A., ed. LC 70-113120. xi, 524p. 1985. text ed. 19.50 (ISBN 0-8284-1303-7, 303). Chelsea Pub.

Cantor, Moritz B. Vorlesungen Ueber Geschichte der Mathematik, 4 Vols. 1900-08. 195.00 (ISBN 0-384-07380-8). Johnson Repr.

Clagett, Marshall. Archimedes in the Middle Ages, Vol. 1. Arabo-Latin Tradition. LC 62-7218. (Medieval Science Pubns., No. 6). (Illus.). Repr. of 1964 ed. 120.00 (ISBN 0-8357-9771-6, 2012629). Bks Demand UMI.

--Studies in Medieval Physics & Mathematics. 366p. 1980. 75.00x (ISBN 0-86078-048-1, Pub. by Variorum England). State Mutual Bk.

Cooke, R. The Mathematics of Sonya Kovalevskaya. (Illus.). 275p. 1984. 29.80 (ISBN 0-387-96030-9). Springer-Verlag.

Curtze, Maximilian. Urkunden Zur Geschichte der Mathematik Im Mittelalter & der Renaissance. (Bibliotheca Mathematica Teubneriana Ser: No. 45). (Ger). 1969. Repr. of 1902 ed. 45.00 (ISBN 0-384-10402-9). Johnson Repr.

Damon, James. The Unfolding & Determinacy Theorems for Subgroups of A & K. LC 84-9333. (Memoirs of the American Mathematical Society Ser.: Vol. 306). 90p. 1984. pap. 10.00 (ISBN 0-8218-2306-X). Am Math.

Dauben, Joseph W. The History of Mathematics from Antiquity to the Present: A Selective Bibliography. Multhauf, Robert & Wells, Ellen, eds. LC 81-43364. (Reference Library of the Humanities: Bibliographies of the History of Science & Technology Ser.). 508p. 1984. lib. bdg. 80.00 (ISBN 0-8240-9284-8). Garland Pub.

Dauben, Joseph W., ed. Mathematical Perspectives: Essays on Mathematics & Its Historical Development. LC 80-1781. 1981. 43.50 (ISBN 0-12-204050-3). Acad Pr.

Davis, Philip J. & Hersh, Reuben. The Mathematical Experience. 460p. 1981. 27.95x (ISBN 0-8176-3018-X). Birkhauser.

Davis, Phillip J. The Thread: A Mathematical Yarn. 196p. 1983. 12.95 (ISBN 0-8176-3097-X). Birkhauser.

Dickson, Leonard E. History of the Theory of Numbers, 3 Vols. LC 66-26932. 49.50 (ISBN 0-8284-0086-5). Chelsea Pub.

Dubbey, J. M. The Mathematical Work of Charles Babbage. LC 77-71409. (Illus.). 1978. 57.50 (ISBN 0-521-21649-4). Cambridge U Pr.

Dyck, Martin. Novalis & Mathematics. LC 76-164817. (North Carolina. University. Studies in the Germanic Languages & Literatures: No. 27). Repr. of 1960 ed. 27.00 (ISBN 0-404-50927-4). AMS Pr.

Engelsman, S. B., ed. Families of Curves & the Origins of Partial Differentiation. (North-Holland Mathematics Studies: No. 93). 238p. 1984. 29.00 (ISBN 0-444-86897-6, I-126-84). Elsevier.

Eves, Howard. Great Moments in Mathematics After 1650. LC 81-86186. (Dolciani Mathematical Expositions Ser.: Vol. 7). 259p. 1982. 27.00 (ISBN 0-88385-307-8). Math Assn.

--An Introduction to the History of Mathematics. 5th ed. 1983. text ed. 39.95 (ISBN 0-03-062064-3, CBS C). SCP.

Friedrichs, K. O. From Pythagoras to Einstein. LC 65-24963. (New Mathematical Library: No. 16). 88p. 1975. pap. 8.75 (ISBN 0-88385-616-6). Math Assn.

Gerhardt, Karl I. Geschichte Der Mathematik in Deutschland. Repr. of 1877 ed. 30.00 (ISBN 0-384-18150-3). Johnson Repr.

Gow, James. Short History of Greek Mathematics. LC 68-21639. 1968. 14.95 (ISBN 0-8284-0218-3). Chelsea Pub.

Heath, Thomas. Mathematics in Aristotle. LC 78-66593. (Ancient Philosophy Ser.). 305p. 1980. lib. bdg. 36.00 (ISBN 0-8240-9595-2). Garland Pub.

Heath, Thomas L. A History of Greek Mathematics, 2 vols. (Illus.). 1058p. 1981. pap. 8.50 ea. Vol. I (ISBN 0-486-24073-8). Vol. II (ISBN 0-486-24074-6). Dover.

Historia De las Ideas Modernas En la Matematica. (Serie De Matematica: No. 4). (Span.). 1974. pap. 3.50 (ISBN 0-8270-6230-3). OAS.

Hofmann, Joseph E. History of Mathematics to Eighteen Hundred. (Quality Paperback Ser.: No. 144). 159p. 1967. pap. 4.95 (ISBN 0-8226-0144-3). Littlefield.

Hogemdijk, J. P. Ibn Al-Haytham's "Composition of the Conics". (Sources in the History of Mathematics & Physical Sciences Ser.: Vol. 7). (Illus.). 400p. 1984. 98.00 (ISBN 0-387-96013-9). Springer-Verlag.

Kibre, Pearl. Studies in Medieval Science: Alchemy, Astrology, Mathematics & Medicine. 355p. 1983. 40.00 (ISBN 0-907628-21-4). Hambledon Press.

Klein, Felix. Entwicklung der Mathematik Im Neunzehnten Jahrhundert, 2 Vols. in 1. (Ger). 12.95 (ISBN 0-8284-0074-1). Chelsea Pub.

Klein, Felix, et al. Development of Mathematics in the Nineteenth Century. (LIE Groups Ser.: No. 9). 1979. 60.00 (ISBN 0-915692-28-7). Math Sci Pr.

Kline, Morris. Mathematical Thought from Ancient to Modern Times. 1972. 65.00x (ISBN 0-19-501496-0). Oxford U Pr.

--Mathematics & the Physical World. (Illus.). 496p. 1981. pap. 6.95 (ISBN 0-486-24104-1). Dover.

--Mathematics in Western Culture. (Illus.). 1964. pap. 12.95 (ISBN 0-19-500714-X, GB). Oxford U Pr.

Kreitner, John. Man's Mathematical Mind: From Thales to Weiner. 26p. 1976. pap. 1.50 (ISBN 0-913098-14-0). Myrin Institute.

Libri, Guglielmo. Histoire Des Sciences Mathematiques En Italie, 4 Vols. Repr. of 1841 ed. Set. 150.00 (ISBN 0-384-32615-3). Johnson Repr.

May, K. O. Bibliography & Research Manual of the History of Mathematics. LC 71-151379. (Scholarly Reprint Ser.). 1973. 45.00x (ISBN 0-8020-7077-9). U of Toronto Pr.

May, Kenneth O., ed. The Mathematical Association of America, Its First Fifty Years. 172p. 1972. 11.00 (ISBN 0-88385-401-5). Math Assn.

Mehrtens, H., ed. Social History of Mathematics. 320p. 1981. 29.95x (ISBN 0-8176-3033-3). Birkhauser.

Morgan, Bryan. Men & Discoveries in Mathematics. 1972. 12.95 (ISBN 0-7195-2587-X). Transatlantic.

Neugebauer, O. The Exact Sciences in Antiquity. 2nd ed. LC 57-12342. (Illus.). 256p. 1957. 22.50x (ISBN 0-87057-044-7). U Pr of New Eng.

Newton, Isaac. Mathematical Papers of Isaac Newton, Vol. 8, 1697-1722. Whiteside, D. T., ed. LC 65-11203. (Illus.). 750p. 1981. 210.00 (ISBN 0-521-20103-9). Cambridge U Pr.

Nussbaum, Roger & Peitgen, Heinz O. Special & Spurious Solutions of X(T) equals -aF(X(T-1), Vol. 51. LC 84-14568. (Memoirs of the American Mathematical Society: No. 310). 129p. 1984. pap. 13.00 (ISBN 0-8218-2311-6). Am Math.

Parkinson, Claire L. Breakthroughs: A Chronology of Great Achievements in Science & Mathematics. (Reference Books in Science). 1985. lib. bdg. 29.95 (ISBN 0-8161-8706-1). G K Hall.

Paul, Richard S. & Shaevel, M. Leonard. Essentials of Technical Mathematics. 2nd ed. (Illus.). 704p. 1982. 29.95 (ISBN 0-13-288050-4). P-H.

Popp, Walter. History of Mathematics. 160p. 1978. pap. 10.00x (ISBN 0-335-00248-X, Pub. by Open Univ Pr). Taylor & Francis.

Reid, Constance. Jerzy Neyman-From Life. (Illus.). 320p. 1982. 22.00 (ISBN 0-387-90747-5). Springer-Verlag.

Resnikoff, H. L. & Wells, R. O. Mathematics in Civilization. LC 72-83805. (Illus.). 28.50x (ISBN 0-03-085035-5); pap. text ed. 9.95x (ISBN 0-89197-843-7). Irvington.

Resnikoff, H. L. & Wells, R. O., Jr. Mathematics in Civilization. (Popular Science Ser.). 448p. 1984. pap. 9.95 (ISBN 0-486-24674-4). Dover.

Scharlau, W. & Opolka, H. From Fermat to Minkowski: Lectures on the Theory of Numbers & Its Historical Development. Buhler, W. K. & Cornell, G., trs. from German. (Undergraduate Texts in Mathematics Ser.). (Illus.). 255p. 1985. 24.00 (ISBN 0-387-90942-7). Springer-Verlag.

Scott, J. F. History of Mathematics: From Antiquity to the Beginning of the Nineteenth Century. 2nd ed. 1975. Repr. of 1960 ed. 28.50x (ISBN 0-06-496130-3, BNB-06665). B&N Imports.

Smith, David. Mathematics. LC 63-10294. (Our Debt to Greece & Rome Ser.). Repr. of 1930 ed. 17.50 (ISBN 0-8154-0207-4). Cooper Sq.

Smith, David E. History of Mathematics, 2 vols. Incl. Vol. 1. General Survey of the History of Elementary Mathematics. Repr. of 1923 ed. 10.00 (ISBN 0-486-20429-4); Vol. 2. Special Topics of Elementary Mathematics. Repr. of 1925 ed (ISBN 0-486-20430-8). pap. text ed. 10.00 ea. Dover.

--History of Mathematics, 2 vols. Set. 32.50 set (ISBN 0-8446-2955-3). Peter Smith.

Smith, David E. & Ginsberg, Jekuthiel. A History of Mathematics in America Before Nineteen Hundred. Cohen, I. Bernard, ed. LC 79-7992. (Three Centuries of Science in America Ser.). (Illus.). 1980. Repr. of 1934 ed. lib. bdg. 19.00x (ISBN 0-405-12578-X). Ayer Co Pubs.

Struik, Dirk J. A Source Book in Mathematics, 1200-1800. LC 68-21986. (Source Books in the History of the Sciences Ser.). pap. 110.80 (ISBN 0-317-09449-1, 2017753). Bks Demand UMI.

Swetz, Frank. The Treviso Arithmetic. 276p. 1984. 24.95 (ISBN 0-87548-438-7). Open Court.

Taylor, E. G. The Mathematical Practitioners. xi, 442p. Date not set. Repr. lib. bdg. 49.00 (ISBN 0-932051-39-1). Am Repr Serv.

Todhunter, Isaac. History of the Mathematical Theory of Probability. LC 51-146. 1949. 17.95 (ISBN 0-8284-0057-1). Chelsea Pub.

Turnbull, Herbert Westren. The Great Mathematicians. LC 61-16934. (Illus.). 1961. usa 12.50x (ISBN 0-8147-0419-0). NYU Pr.

Wittgenstein, Ludwig. Remarks on the Foundations of Mathematics. Von Wright, G. H. & Rhees, R., eds. Anscombe, G. E., tr. 448p. 1983. pap. text ed. 12.50x (ISBN 0-262-73067-7). MIT Pr.

Wylie, C. Ray & Barrett, Louis C. Advanced Engineering Mathematics. 5th ed. (Illus.). 1120p. 1982. 46.95x (ISBN 0-07-072188-2); solns. manual 20.00 (ISBN 0-07-072189-0). McGraw.

Zaslavsky, Claudia. Africa Counts. LC 72-91248. (Illus.). 1979. pap. 9.95 (ISBN 0-88208-104-7). Lawrence Hill.

Zeuthen, H. G. Geschichte der Mathematik Im 1600 und 1700. 32.00 (ISBN 0-384-70890-0). Johnson Repr.

--Die Mathematik Im Altertum und Im Mittelalter. 16.00 (ISBN 0-384-70892-7). Johnson Repr.

MATHEMATICS–LABORATORIES

see Computation Laboratories

MATHEMATICS–METHODOLOGY

Arnold, L. & Kotelenz, P., eds. Stochastic Space-Time Models & Limit Theories. (Mathematics & its Applications Ser.). 1985. lib. bdg. 44.00 (ISBN 90-277-2038-X, Pub. by Reidel Holland). Kluwer-Academic.

Cutler, Ann & McShane, Rudolph, trs. The Trachtenberg Speed System of Basic Mathematics. LC 81-13439. 270p. 1982. Repr. of 1960 ed. lib. bdg. 27.50x (ISBN 0-313-23200-8, CUTS). Greenwood.

Davis, Philip J. & Hersh, Reuben. The Mathematical Experience. 460p. 1981. 27.95x (ISBN 0-8176-3018-X). Birkhauser.

Ixaru, Liviu. Numerical Methods for Differential Equations & Applications. 1984. lib. bdg. 69.00 (ISBN 90-277-1597-1, Pub. by Reidel Holland). Kluwer Academic.

Jerman, Max E. & Beardslee, Edward C. Elementary Mathematics Method. (Illus.). 1978. text ed. 33.95 (ISBN 0-07-032531-6). McGraw.

LeBlanc, John F., et al. Mathematics Methods Program: Rational Numbers with Integers & Reals. (Mathematics Ser.). (Illus.). 240p. 1976. pap. text ed. 6.95 (ISBN 0-201-14612-6). Addison-Wesley.

Queen, N. Methods of Applied Mathematics. 1980. 29.95 (ISBN 0-442-30750-0). Van Nos Reinhold.

Rao, M. M. Stochastic Processes & Integration. 467p. 1981. 55.00x (ISBN 90-286-0438-3). Sijthoff & Noordhoff.

Rao, Singiresu S. Optimization Theory & Applications. 2nd ed. LC 83-12950. 747p. 1978. 26.95x (ISBN 0-470-27483-2). Halsted Pr.

Recommendations on the Mathematical Preparation of Teachers (CUPM) (MAA Notes: No. 2). 76p. 1983. pap. 5.00 (ISBN 0-88385-052-4, 83-06270). Math Assn.

Scarpellini, Bruno. Proof Theory & Intuitionistic Systems. LC 78-169705. (Lecture Notes in Mathematics: Vol. 212). 1971. pap. 14.00 (ISBN 0-387-05541-X). Springer-Verlag.

Scraton, R. E. Basic Numerical Methods: An Introduction to Numerical Mathematics on a Microcomputer. 144p. 1984. pap. text ed. 13.95 (ISBN 0-7131-3521-2). E Arnold.

Singh, Jagjit. Great Ideas on Modern Mathematics: Their Nature & Their Use. (Illus.). 14.75 (ISBN 0-8446-0911-0). Peter Smith.

Smith, C. A. Biomathematics: Principles of Mathematics for Students of Biological & General Science, Vol. 1. 4th ed. (Algebra, Geometry, Calculus). 523p. 1969. text ed. 20.75x (ISBN 0-85264-120-6). Lubrecht & Cramer.

Swetz, Frank, ed. Socialist Mathematics Education. LC 78-68025. 1979. pap. 14.00 (ISBN 0-917574-04-4). Burgundy Pr.

MATHEMATICS–OUTLINES, SYLLABI, ETC.

Bitter, et al. McGraw-Hill Mathematics, 8 levels. Incl. Level 1. text ed. 8.96 (ISBN 0-07-005761-3); Level 2. text ed. 8.96 (ISBN 0-07-005762-1); Level 3. text ed. 14.08 (ISBN 0-07-005763-X); Level 4. text ed. 14.08 (ISBN 0-07-005764-8); Level 5. text ed. 14.08 (ISBN 0-07-005765-6); Level 6. text ed. 13.28 (ISBN 0-07-005766-4); Level 7. text ed. 17.28 (ISBN 0-07-005767-2); Level 8. text ed. 17.28 (ISBN 0-07-005768-0). 1981. McGraw.

Clifford, William K. Mathematical Papers. LC 67-28488. 1968. Repr. 35.00 (ISBN 0-8284-0210-8). Chelsea Pub.

Laycock, Mary & Johnson, Connie. The Tapestry of Mathematics. new ed. (Illus.). 1978. pap. text ed. 18.95 (ISBN 0-918932-51-3). Activity Resources.

Lipschutz, Seymour. Finite Mathematics. (Schaum's Outline Ser.). 1966. pap. 8.95 (ISBN 0-07-037987-4). McGraw.

Mr. Cumulative Indices: 1959-1972 Cumulative Subject Index. Date not set. price not set. Am Math.

NCTM. How to Evaluate Your Mathematics Program. LC 81-11088. 19p. 1981. pap. 2.00 (ISBN 0-87353-183-3). NCTM.

Nielsen, Kaj L. College Mathematics. (Orig.). 1958. pap. 4.95 (ISBN 0-06-460105-6, CO 105, COS). B&N NY.

Rankin & Lightbourne. Physical Mathematics & Nonlinear Partial Differential Equations. (Lecture Notes in Pure & Applied Mathematics Ser.). 296p. 1985. 59.75 (ISBN 0-8247-7343-8). Dekker.

Schaaf, William L. Course for Teachers of Junior High School Mathematics. LC 77-177808. (Columbia University. Teachers College. Contributions to Education: No. 313). Repr. of 1928 ed. 22.50 (ISBN 0-404-55313-3). AMS Pr.

MATHEMATICS–PERIODICALS

Abbreviations of Names of Serials. 18p. 1981. 4.00 (ISBN 0-8218-0000-0, ABBR). Am Math.

Index of the American Mathematical Monthly, Vol. 1-80. LC 77-79281. 269p. 1973. 22.00 (ISBN 0-88385-426-0). Math Assn.

National Council of Teachers of Mathematics. Cumulative Index: The Mathematics Teacher, 1908-1965. LC 42-24844. 207p. 1967. pap. 15.00 (ISBN 0-87353-028-4). NCTM.

Steen, L. A. & Seebach, J. A., eds. Fifty Year Index of Mathematics Magazine. 163p. 1979. 11.50 (ISBN 0-88385-401-5, MMI). Math Assn.

MATHEMATICS–PHILOSOPHY

see also Arithmetic–Foundations; Metamathematics

Ambrose, Alice, ed. Wittgenstein's Lectures, Cambridge 1932-1935: From the Notes of Alice Ambrose & Margaret Macdonald. 225p. 1979. 25.00x (ISBN 0-8476-6151-2). Rowman.

Beller, A., et al. Coding the Universe. LC 81-2663. (London Mathematical Society Lecture Notes: No. 47). 300p. 1982. 39.50 (ISBN 0-521-28040-0). Cambridge U Pr.

Beth, E. W. Mathematical Thought. 220p. 1965. 50.95 (ISBN 0-677-00600-4). Gordon.

--Mathematical Thought: An Introduction to the Philosophy of Mathematics. (Synthese Library Ser.: No. 11). 208p. 1965. lib. bdg. 22.00 (ISBN 90-277-0070-2, Pub. by Reidel Holland). Kluwer Academic.

Beth, E. W. & Piaget, J. Mathematical Epistemology & Psychology. 348p. 1966. 73.00 (ISBN 0-677-01290-X). Gordon.

--Mathematical Epistemology & Psychology. Mays, W., tr. from Fr. (Synthese Library: No. 12). 326p. 1966. lib. bdg. 39.50 (ISBN 90-277-0071-0, Pub. by Reidel Holland). Kluwer Academic.

Black, Max. Nature of Mathematics. (Quality Paperback: No. 201). 219p. 1965. pap. 3.95 (ISBN 0-8226-0201-6). Littlefield.

Bostock, David. Logic & Arithmetic, Vol. II: Rational & Irrational Numbers. (Illus.). 1979. 49.50x (ISBN 0-19-824591-2). Oxford U Pr.

Boyer, Carl B. History of the Calculus & Its Conceptual Development. Orig. Title: Concepts of Calculus. 1959. pap. 5.95 (ISBN 0-486-60509-4). Dover.

Bulloff, J. J., et al, eds. Foundations of Mathematics: Symposium Papers Commemorating the Sixtieth Birthday of Kurt Goedel. LC 68-28757. (Illus.). 1969. 36.00 (ISBN 0-387-04490-6). Springer-Verlag.

Carnap, Rudolf. Foundations of Logic & Mathematics. (Foundations of the Unity of Science Ser: Vol. 1, No. 3). 1937. pap. 4.50x (ISBN 0-226-57578-0, P402, Phoen). U of Chicago Pr.

Carus, Paul. The Foundations of Mathematics: A Contribution to the Philosophy of Geometry. LC 75-3104. Repr. of 1908 ed. 18.00 (ISBN 0-404-59101-9). AMS Pr.

Castonguay, C. Meaning & Existence in Mathematics. LC 72-96052. (Library of Exact Philosophy: Vol. 9). 159p. 1972. 26.00 (ISBN 0-387-81110-9). Springer-Verlag.

Ceitin, G. S., et al. Five Papers on Logic & Foundations. LC 51-5559. (Translations Ser.: No. 2, Vol. 98). 292p. 1971. text ed. 35.00 (ISBN 0-8218-1798-1, TRANS 2-98). Am Math.

Cohen, R. S., et al, eds. Essays in Memory of Imre Lakatos. new ed. LC 76-16770. (Synthese Library Ser.: No. 99). 1976. lib. bdg. 87.00 (ISBN 90-277-0654-9, Pub. by Reidel Holland); pap. 47.50 (ISBN 90-277-0655-7, Pub. by Reidel Holland). Kluwer Academic.

Davis, Philip J. & Hersh, Reuben. The Mathematical Experience. 460p. 1981. 27.95x (ISBN 0-8176-3018-X). Birkhauser.

Frege, Gottlob. The Philosophical & Mathematical Correspondence. McGuinness, Brian, ed. Kaal, Hans, tr. LC 79-23199. 1980. lib. bdg. 31.00x (ISBN 0-226-26197-2). U of Chicago Pr.

--Translations from the Philosophical Writings of Gottlob Frege. 3rd ed. Geach, Peter & Black, Max, eds. 228p. 1980. 25.00x (ISBN 0-8476-6286-1); pap. 10.95x (ISBN 0-8476-6287-X). Rowman.

Fuller, R. Buckminster. Synergetics: Explorations in the Geometry of Thinking. LC 81-11798. (Illus.). 912p. 1982. pap. 13.95 (ISBN 0-02-065320-4, Collier). Macmillan.

Godel, Kurt. Consistency of the Continuum Hypothesis. (Annals of Mathematics Studies, Vol. 3). (Orig.). 1940. pap. 14.95x (ISBN 0-691-07927-7). Princeton U Pr.

Grassl, Wolfgang, ed. Lectures in the Philosophy of Mathematics. Waismann, Friedrich. (Studien Zur Oesterreichischen Philosophie). 125p. 1981. pap. text ed. 19.00x (ISBN 90-6203-613-9, Pub. by Rodopi Holland). Humanities.

Hadamard, Jacques. Psychology of Invention in the Mathematical Field. 1945. pap. text ed. 3.50 (ISBN 0-486-20107-4). Dover.

Herrmann, Robert A. The Mathematics for Mathematical Philosophy. (Monograph: No. 130). 130p. (Orig.). 1985. pap. 26.00 (ISBN 0-931441-04-8). Inst Math Philo Pr.

--Nature: The Supreme Logician. 66p. (Orig.). 1985. pap. 15.00 (ISBN 0-931441-05-6). Inst Math Philo Pr.

Howard, Homer. Mathematics Teachers' Views on Certain Issues in the Teaching of Mathematics. LC 76-176883. (Columbia University. Teachers College. Contributions to Education Ser.: No. 827). Repr. of 1941 ed. 22.50 (ISBN 0-404-55827-5). AMS Pr.

Kattsoff, Louis O. Philosophy of Mathematics. facs. ed. LC 73-84314. (Essay Index Reprint Ser). 1948. 16.50 (ISBN 0-8369-1086-9). Ayer Co Pubs.

Klenk. Wittgenstein's Philosophy of Mathematics. 1976. pap. 24.00 (ISBN 90-247-1842-2, Pub. by Martinus Nijhoff Netherlands). Kluwer Academic.

Kline, Morris. Mathematics: The Loss of Certainty. (Illus.). 1980. 25.00 (ISBN 0-19-502754-X). Oxford U Pr.

Korzybski, Alfred. Science & Sanity: An Introduction to Non-Aristotelian Systems & General Semantics. 4th ed. LC 58-6260. 806p. 1980. 23.50x (ISBN 0-937298-01-8). Inst Gen Seman.

Kuyk, Willem. Complimentarity in Mathematics. LC 77-8838. (Mathematics & Its Applications Ser.: No. 1). 1977. lib. bdg. 21.00 (ISBN 90-277-0814-2, Pub. by Reidel Holland). Kluwer Academic.

Lakatos, E. Proofs & Refutations. Worrall, J., ed. LC 75-32478. 160p. 1976. 37.50 (ISBN 0-521-21078-X); pap. 9.95 (ISBN 0-521-29038-4). Cambridge U Pr.

Lakatos, Imre. Philosophical Papers: Mathematics, Science & Epistemology, Vol. 2. Worrall, J. & Currie, G., eds. LC 77-14374. 295p. 1980. pap. 15.95 (ISBN 0-521-28030-3). Cambridge U Pr.

--Philosophical Papers: Mathematics, Science & Epistemology, Vol. 2. Worrall, J. & Currie, G., eds. LC 77-71415. 1978. 44.50 (ISBN 0-521-21769-5). Cambridge U Pr.

Lehman, Hugh. Introduction to the Philosophy of Mathematics. (American Philosophical Quarterly Library of Philosophy). 177p. 1979. 19.50x (ISBN 0-8476-6109-1). Rowman.

Lieber, Hugh G. & Lieber, Lillian R. Human Values & Science, Art & Mathematics. (Illus.). 1961. 3.95 (ISBN 0-393-06339-9). Norton.

Livingston, Eric. The Ethnomethodological Foundations of Mathematics. (Studies in Ethnomethodology). 256p. 1985. 45.00x (ISBN 0-7102-0335-7). Routledge & Kegan.

McCoy, N. H. Rings & Ideals. (Carus Monograph: No. 8). 216p. 1948. 16.50 (ISBN 0-88385-008-7). Math Assn.

Miller, J. Philip. Numbers in Presence & Absence: A Study of Husserl's Philosophy of Mathematics. 1982. lib. bdg. 29.50 (ISBN 0-686-37593-9, Pub. by Martinus Nijhoff). Kluwer Academic.

Mueller, Ian. Philosophy of Mathematics & Deductive Structure in Euclid's "Elements". (Illus.). 400p. 1981. 47.50x (ISBN 0-262-13163-3). MIT Pr.

Newton, Isaac. Mathematical Principles of Natural Philosophy & His System of the World. Cajori, Florian, rev. by. Motte, Andrew, tr. Incl. Vol. I. The Motions of Bodies. pap. 7.95x (ISBN 0-520-00928-2, CAMPUS70); Vol. II. The System of the World. pap. 7.95x (ISBN 0-520-00929-0, CAMPUS71); 50.00x (ISBN 0-520-00927-4). (Principia Ser.). 1962. pap. U of Cal Pr.

North, Gustave C. A Guidebook of Fibonacci's Inspired Mathematical Fallacies. (Illus.). 176p. 1984. 117.45x (ISBN 0-86654-123-3). Inst Econ Finan.

Odescalchi, Edmond P. Faces of Reality. LC 74-82410. (Illus.). 80p. 1975. 10.00 (ISBN 0-914226-02-9). Cyclopedia.

Polya, Gyorgy. Mathematics & Plausible Reasoning, 2 vols. Incl. Vol. 1. Induction & Analogy in Mathematics. 1954. 27.50 (ISBN 0-691-08005-4); Vol. 2. Patterns of Plausible Inference. rev. ed. 1969. 27.50 (ISBN 0-691-08006-2). Set. 45.00 (ISBN 0-685-23091-0). Princeton U Pr.

Putnam, H. Philosophical Papers: Mathematics, Matter & Methods, Vol. 1. 2nd ed. LC 75-8315. 1979. 44.50 (ISBN 0-521-22553-1); pap. 15.95 (ISBN 0-521-29550-5). Cambridge U Pr.

Russell, Bertrand. Principles of Mathematics. 2nd ed. 1964. pap. 9.95 (ISBN 0-393-00249-7, Norton Lib). Norton.

Sicha, Jeffrey. A Metaphysics of Elementary Mathematics. LC 73-79504. 456p. 1974. pap. 14.00x (ISBN 0-87023-149-9). U of Mass Pr.

Singh, Jagjit. Great Ideas of Modern Mathematics. (Illus.). 1959. pap. text ed. 5.50 (ISBN 0-486-20587-8). Dover.

Steiner, Mark. Mathematical Knowledge. LC 74-7639. (Contemporary Philosophy Ser.). 160p. 1975. 21.95x (ISBN 0-8014-0894-6). Cornell U Pr.

Swetz, Frank, ed. Socialist Mathematics Education. LC 78-68025. 1979. pap. 14.00 (ISBN 0-917574-04-4). Burgundy Pr.

Takeuti, Gaisi. Two Applications of Logic to Mathematics. (Publications of the Mathematical Society of Japan Ser.: No. 13). 1978. 23.50x (ISBN 0-691-08212-X). Princeton U Pr.

Tymoczko, Thomas. New Directions in the Philosophy of Mathematics. 1985. 15.95 (ISBN 0-8176-3163-1). Birkhauser.

Van Heijenoort, Jean, ed. From Frege to Godel: A Source Book in Mathematical Logic, 1879-1931. LC 67-10905. (Source Books in the History of the Sciences Ser). 1967. 35.00x (ISBN 0-674-32450-1); pap. 15.00x (ISBN 0-674-32449-8). Harvard U Pr.

Webb, Judson C. Mechanism, Mentalism, & Metamathematics. (Synthese Library: No. 137). xiii, 263p. 1980. lib. bdg. 29.00 (ISBN 90-277-1046-5, Pub. by Reidel Holland). Kluwer Academic.

Wedberg, Anders. Plato's Philosophy of Mathematics. LC 76-50071. 1977. Repr. of 1955 ed. lib. bdg. 18.75 (ISBN 0-8371-9405-9, WEPP). Greenwood.

Whitehead, Alfred N. & Russell, Bertrand. Principia Mathematica, 3 Vols. Set. 350.00 (ISBN 0-521-06791-X). Cambridge U Pr.

--Principia Mathematica to Fifty-Six. 2nd ed. 1925-27. pap. 29.95 (ISBN 0-521-09187-X). Cambridge U Pr.

Wilder, Raymond I. Mathematics As a Cultural System. (Foundations & Philosophy of Science & Technology Ser.). 170p. 1981. 25.00 (ISBN 0-08-025796-8). Pergamon.

Wright, C. Frege's Conception of Numbers As Objects. (Scots Philosophical Monographs: No. 2). 224p. 1983. 22.50 (ISBN 0-08-030352-8); pap. 15.50 (ISBN 0-08-025726-7). Pergamon.

MATHEMATICS–POPULAR WORKS

Adler, Irving. Readings in Mathematics. 188p. 1972. pap. 5.60 (ISBN 0-663-24123-5). NCTM.

Buxton, Laurie. Mathematics for Everyone. LC 84-22236. (Illus.). 270p. 1985. 16.95 (ISBN 0-8052-3986-3). Schocken.

Ellis, Keith. Number Power. 1980. pap. 4.95 (ISBN 0-312-57989-6). St Martin.

Hartkopf, Roy. Math Without Tears. (Nonfiction Ser.). 1985. pap. 7.95 (ISBN 0-8398-2857-8). G K Hall.

Klinger, F. Mathematics for Everyone. 1966p. 1955. 4.75 (ISBN 0-8022-0869-X). Philos Lib.

Mitchell, Charlie R. Math Anxiety: What It is & What to Do about It. (Orig.). 1984. pap. 7.95 (ISBN 0-9610794-2-8). Action Pr.

Pedoe, Dan. The Gentle Art of Mathematics. 143p. 1973. pap. 3.50 (ISBN 0-486-22949-1). Dover.

Perelman, Ya. Figures for Fun. 183p. 1979. pap. 4.95 (ISBN 0-8285-1512-3, Pub. by Mir Pubs USSR). Imported Pubns.

Peter, Rozsa. Playing with Infinity: Mathematical Explorations & Excursions. LC 75-26467. 288p. 1976. pap. text ed. 4.95 (ISBN 0-486-23265-4). Dover.

MATHEMATICS–PROBLEMS, EXERCISES, ETC.

Averbach, Bonnie & Chein, Orin. Mathematics: Problem Solving Through Recreational Mathematics. LC 80-11989. (Mathematical Sciences Ser.). (Illus.). 400p. 1980. text ed. 22.95 (ISBN 0-7167-1124-9); instrs'. guide avail.; solutions manual avail. W H Freeman.

Berman, Linda, et al. Tenth Year Mathematics. (Arco's Regents Review Ser.). 288p. (Orig.). 1982. pap. 3.95 (ISBN 0-668-05702-5, 5702). Arco.

Bezuszka, Stanley & Kenney, Margaret. Wonder-Full World of Numbers. (Contemporary Motivated Mathematics Ser.). 97p. (Orig.). 1971. pap. text ed. 1.50 (ISBN 0-917916-05-0). Boston Coll Math.

Bezuszka, Stanley, et al. Finite Differences. (Motivated Math Project Activity Booklets). 108p. (Orig.). 1976. pap. text ed. 2.50 (ISBN 0-917916-11-5). Boston Coll Math.

--Perfect Numbers. (Motivated Math Project Activity Booklets). 169p. (Orig.). 1980. pap. text ed. 3.50 (ISBN 0-917916-19-0). Boston Coll Math.

--Wonder Square. (Motivated Math Project Activity Booklets). 30p. (Orig.). 1976. pap. text ed. 1.25 (ISBN 0-917916-15-8). Boston Coll Math.

--Contemporary Motivated Mathematics, Bk. 1. (Contemporary Motivated Mathematics Ser.). 97p. (Orig.). 1972. pap. text ed. 1.50 (ISBN 0-917916-02-6). Boston Coll Math.

--Contemporary Motivated Mathematics, Bk. 2. (Comtemporary Motivated Mathematics Ser.). 97p. (Orig.). 1973. pap. text ed. 1.50 (ISBN 0-917916-03-4). Boston Coll Math.

--Contemporary Motivated Mathematics, Bk. 3. (Contemporary Motivated Mathematics Ser.). 97p. (Orig.). 1972. pap. text ed. 1.50 (ISBN 0-917916-04-2). Boston Coll Math.

Bitter, et al. McGraw-Hill Mathematics Parents Guide to Problem Solving. (McGraw-Hill Mathematics, Ser.). 16p. 1981. 1.12 (ISBN 0-07-005749-4). McGraw.

Briggaman, Joan. Practical Problems in Mathematics for Office Workers. LC 76-54051. 1977. pap. text ed. 7.40 (ISBN 0-8273-1612-7); instr.'s guide o.p. 4.25 (ISBN 0-8273-1613-5). Delmar.

Bugrov, Ya. S. & Nikolsky, S. M. Collection of Problems: Higher Mathematics. 191p. 1984. 5.95 (ISBN 0-8285-2896-9, Pub. by Mir Pubs USSR). Imported Pubns.

Bunch, Bryan. Mathematical Fallacies & Paradoxes. 1982. 18.95 (ISBN 0-442-24905-5). Van Nos Reinhold.

Chorlton, Frank. Textbook of Dynamics. 2nd ed. (Mathematics & Its Applications Ser.). 271p. 1983. 51.95x (ISBN 0-470-27407-7); pap. 32.95x (ISBN 0-470-27408-5). Halsted Pr.

Chowla, S. Riemann Hypothesis & Hilberts Tenth Problem. (Mathematics & Its Applications Ser.). 134p. 1965. 44.25 (ISBN 0-677-00140-1). Gordon.

Clifford, William K. Mathematical Papers. LC 67-28488. 1968. Repr. 35.00 (ISBN 0-8284-0210-8). Chelsea Pub.

Computer Math Activities, 5 Vols. Vol. 1. write for info. (ISBN 0-201-20962-4, Sch Div); Vol. 2. write for info. (ISBN 0-201-20963-2); Vol. 3. write for info. (ISBN 0-201-20964-0); Vol. 4. write for info. (ISBN 0-201-20965-9); Vol. 5. write for info. (ISBN 0-201-20966-7). Addison-Wesley.

Contemporary Perspectives, Inc. Problem Solving in Mathematics: Level A. (Problem Solving in Mathematics Ser.). 96p. 1982. text ed. write for info. (ISBN 0-87895-198-9); tchrs. guide avail. (ISBN 0-87895-199-7). Modern Curr.

--Problem Solving in Mathematics: Level C. (Problem Solving in Mathematics Ser.). 96p. 1982. text ed. write for info.; tchrs. guide avail. (ISBN 0-87895-349-3). Modern Curr.

--Problem Solving in Mathematics: Level D. (Problem Solving in Mathematics Ser.). 96p. 1982. text ed. write for info. (ISBN 0-87895-448-1); tchrs. guide avail. (ISBN 0-87895-449-X). Modern Curr.

--Problem Solving in Mathematics: Level E. (Problem Solving in Mathematics Ser.). 96p. 1982. text ed. write for info. (ISBN 0-87895-548-8); tchrs. guide avail. (ISBN 0-87895-549-6). Modern Curr.

--Problem Solving in Mathematics: Level F. (Problem Solving in Mathematics Ser.). 96p. 1982. text ed. write for info. (ISBN 0-87895-648-4); tchrs. guide avail. (ISBN 0-87895-649-2). Modern Curr.

Contemporary Prespectives, Inc. Problem Solving in Mathematics: Level B. (Problem Solving in Mathematics Ser.). 96p. 1982. text ed. write for info. (ISBN 0-87895-248-9); tchrs. guide avail. (ISBN 0-87895-249-7). Modern Curr.

Coscia, Donald. Computer Applications for Applied Math. 1985. pap. text ed. price not set. (ISBN 0-673-18154-5). Scott F.

DeVore, Russell B. Practical Problems in Mathematics for Heating & Cooling Technicians. LC 79-57141. (Practical Problems in Mathematics Ser.). 192p. 1981. pap. text ed. 7.80 (ISBN 0-8273-1682-8); instr's. guide 4.20 (ISBN 0-8273-1683-6). Delmar.

Dorrie, Heinrich. One Hundred Great Problems of Elementary Mathematics: Their History & Solution. Antin, David, tr. from Ger. 393p. 1965. pap. 5.95 (ISBN 0-486-61348-8). Dover.

Dressler, Isidore. Current Mathematics: A Work-Text. 1977. Bk. I. wkbk. 10.67 (ISBN 0-87720-239-7). AMSCO Sch.

Duboc, Greg. Mathematics Worksheets Generation: Apple II. 1984. 49.95. Sterling Swift.

Dynkin, E. G., et al. Mathematical Problems: An Anthology. (Pocket Mathematical Library). 76p. 1967. 24.50 (ISBN 0-677-20710-7). Gordon.

Efimov, A. V. & Demidovich, B. P. Higher Mathematics-Worked Examples & Problems with Elements of Theory Vol. 1: Linear Analysis & Fundamentals of Analysis. 511p. 1985. 9.95 (ISBN 0-8285-2890-X, Pub. by Mir Pubs USSR). Imported Pubns.

--Higher Mathematics-Worked Examples & Problems with Elements of Theory Vol. 2: Advanced Topics of Mathematical Analysis. 414p. 1985. 9.95 (ISBN 0-8285-2891-8, Pub. by Mir Pubs USSR). Imported Pubns.

Forte, Imogene & MacKenzie, Joy. Creative Math Experiences for the Young Child. rev. ed. (Illus.). 176p. 1983. pap. text ed. 8.95 (ISBN 0-86530-055-0, IP-048). Incentive Pubns.

Garrard & Boyd. Practical Problems in Mathematics for Electricians. LC 79-56247. 1981. pap. text ed. 7.40 (ISBN 0-8273-1277-6); instructor's guide 4.20 (ISBN 0-8273-1278-4). Delmar.

Gattegno, Caleb. Algebricks Exercise Workbooks 1-6. 1970. pap. 1.10 (ISBN 0-87825-001-8). Ed Solutions.

Giangrasso, et al. Basic Mathematics: A Problem Solving Approach. (Illus.). 448p. (Orig.). 1983. pap. text ed. 14.95 (ISBN 0-8403-3129-0). Kendall-Hunt.

Gleason, A. M., et al, eds. The William Lowell Putnam Mathematical Competition: Problems & Solutions - 1938-1964. LC 80-80493. 652p. 1980. 35.00 (ISBN 0-88385-428-7). Math Assn.

Gossage, Loyce C. Mathematics Skill Builder. 5th ed. 1985. pap. text ed. 5.10 (ISBN 0-538-13940-4, M95). SW Pub.

Graham, Lloyd A. Ingenious Mathematical Problems & Methods. 1959. pap. 4.95 (ISBN 0-486-20545-2). Dover.

Greitzer, Samuel L., ed. International Mathematical Olympiads 1959-1977. LC 78-54027. (New Mathematical Library: No. 27). 210p. 1979. pap. 10.00 (ISBN 0-88385-627-1). Math Assn.

Honsberger, Ross. Mathematical Morsels. LC 78-60731. (Dolciani Mathematical Exposition Ser.: No. 3). 249p. 1979. 24.00 (ISBN 0-88385-303-5). Math Assn.

Huth, Harry C. Practical Problems in Mathematics for Carpenters. 4th ed. LC 84-12174. 224p. 1985. pap. 7.80 (ISBN 0-8273-2427-8); instr's. guide 5.60 (ISBN 0-8273-2428-6). Delmar.

Kahan, Steven. Have Some Sums to Solve: The Compleat Alphametics Book. LC 77-94008. 128p. (Orig.). 1978. pap. text ed. 4.95x (ISBN 0-89503-007-1). Baywood Pub.

Kenney, Margaret. Incredible Pascal Triangle. (Motivated Math Project Activity Booklets). 91p. (Orig.). 1976. pap. text ed. 2.50 (ISBN 0-917916-16-6). Boston Coll Math.

--Mathematical Doodling. (Motivated Math Project Activity Booklets). 86p. (Orig.). 1976. pap. text ed. 2.50 (ISBN 0-917916-17-4). Boston Coll Math.

--Super Sum. (Motivated Math Project Activity Booklets). 41p. (Orig.). 1976. pap. text ed. 2.00 (ISBN 0-917916-18-2). Boston Coll Math.

Keyfitz, N. Demography Through Problems. (Problem Books in Mathematics). (Illus.). 240p. 1984. 29.50 (ISBN 0-387-90836-6). Springer-Verlag.

Larkin, J. Practical Problems in Mathematics for Mechanical Drafting. LC 77-78236. 1979. pap. 7.80 (ISBN 0-8273-1670-4); instructor's guide 3.60 (ISBN 0-8273-1671-2). Delmar.

Lebedev, N. N., et al. Worked Problems in Applied Mathematics. LC 78-67857. 1979. pap. text ed. 7.50 (ISBN 0-486-63730-1). Dover.

Lester, Frank K., Jr. & Garofalo, Joe, eds. Math Problem Solving: Issues in Research. 200p. (Orig.). 1982. pap. text ed. 14.50 (ISBN 0-89168-049-7). L Erlbaum Assocs.

Math in Action: Word Problems. (Math in Action Ser.). (Illus.). 32p. 1985. pap. text ed. 1.95 ea. (ISBN 0-317-14879-6); tchr's. ed. 14.95 (ISBN 0-88102-031-1). Math Language (ISBN 0-88102-026-5). Understanding Word Problems (ISBN 0-88102-027-3). Solving Word Problems (ISBN 0-88102-030-3). Using a Calculator (ISBN 0-88102-028-1). Estimation (ISBN 0-88102-029-X). Janus Bks.

Mauldin, D., ed. The Scottish Book. 320p. 1981. 24.95x (ISBN 0-8176-3045-7). Birkhauser.

Morris, Janet. How to Develop Problem Solving Using a Calculator. LC 81-9569. (Illus.). 40p. 1981. pap. 4.00 (ISBN 0-87353-175-2). NCTM.

National Council of Teachers of Mathematics. Problem Solving in School Mathematics, 1980 Yearbook. LC 79-27145. (Illus.). 241p. 1980. 14.50 (ISBN 0-87353-162-0). NCTM.

Newell, Alan C. Solutions in Mathematics & Physics. LC 84-71051. (CBMS-NSF Regional Conference Ser.: No. 48). xvi, 244p. (Orig.). 1985. text ed. 29.50 (ISBN 0-89871-196-7). Soc Indus Appl Math.

Newman, D. J. A Problem Seminar. (Problem Books in Mathematics). 113p. 1982. 17.00 (ISBN 0-387-90765-3). Springer-Verlag.

Polya, George. Mathematical Discovery: On Understanding, Learning, & Teaching Problem Solving. LC 81-1063. 432p. 1981. text ed. 29.50 (ISBN 0-471-08975-3). Wiley.

Polya, George, et al. The Stanford Mathematics Problem Book: With Hints & Solutions. LC 73-86270. pap. 20.00 (ISBN 0-317-09309-6, 2019663). Bks Demand UMI.

Polya, Gyorgy. How to Solve It. 1971. 25.00 (ISBN 0-691-08097-6); pap. 6.95 (ISBN 0-691-02356-5). Princeton U Pr.

--Mathematical Discovery on Understanding, Learning & Teaching Problem Solving, 2 vols. LC 62-8784. 216p. 1962. Vol. 1. 31.45x (ISBN 0-471-69333-2). Wiley.

Problems in the Constructive Trend in Mathematics. Sanin, N. A., ed. Incl. Pt. IV Proceedings. Steklov Institute of Mathematics, Academy of Sciences. (No. 93). 1970. 49.00 (ISBN 0-8218-1893-7, STEKLO-93); Part V Proceedings. Steklov Institute of Mathematics, Academy of Sciences, USSR. (No. 113). 296p. 1972. 47.00 (ISBN 0-8218-3013-9, STEKLO-113); Part VI. LC 75-11951. (No. 129). 1976. 100.00 (ISBN 0-8218-3029-5, STEKLO 129). (Proceedings of the Steklov Institute of Mathematics). Am Math.

Rappaport, E., tr. Hungarian Problem Book 2: Based on the Eotvos Competition. LC 63-16149. (New Mathematical Library: No. 12). 120p. 1975. pap. 8.75 (ISBN 0-88385-612-3). Math Assn.

Rich, Barnett. Review of Elementary Mathematics. (Schaum's Outline Ser.). (Orig.). 1977. pap. 7.95 (ISBN 0-07-052260-X). McGraw.

Ruderman, Harry, ed. Mathematical Buds, Vol. I. (Illus.). 1978. pap. text ed. 2.50 (ISBN 0-686-10172-3). Mu Alpha Theta.

Salkind, C. T., compiled by. Contest Problem Book I: Annual High School Mathematics Exams (1950-1960) LC 61-13843. (New Mathematical Library: No. 5). 154p. 1975. pap. 8.75 (ISBN 0-88385-605-0). Math Assn.

--The Contest Problem Book II: Annual High School Mathematics Exams (1961-65) LC 66-15479. (New Mathematical Library: No. 17). 112p. 1975. pap. 10.00 (ISBN 0-88385-617-4). Math Assn.

Salkind, C. T. & Earl, J. M., eds. The Contest Problem Book III: Annual High School Mathematics Exams (1966-72) LC 66-15479. (New Mathematical Library: No. 25). 186p. 1975. pap. 10.00 (ISBN 0-88385-625-5, 66-15479). Math Assn.

Schneider, Harold. Solving Math Word Problems for Students & Adults. 1965. 5.75 (ISBN 0-911642-01-3). Word-Fraction.

Schoenfeld, Alan H. Mathematical Problem Solving. Monograph ed. Date not set. 58.00 (ISBN 0-12-628870-4); pap. 29.95 (ISBN 0-12-628871-2). Acad Pr.

Schulz, Martin, ed. Elliptic Problem Solvers. 1981. 47.50 (ISBN 0-12-632620-7). Acad Pr.

Schumacher, F. Practical Problems in Mathematics for Sheet Metal Technicians. LC 71-74885. 1973. pap. text ed. 7.40 (ISBN 0-8273-0287-8); instructor's guide 3.00 (ISBN 0-8273-0288-6). Delmar.

Sinha, D. K. Catastrophe Theory & Applications. LC 81-13376. (Mathematics Ser.). 158p. 1982. 19.95x (ISBN 0-470-27303-8). Halsted Pr.

Smith, James A. Basic Mathematics, 12 bks. 3rd ed. Incl. Bk. 1. Numbers & Numerals. 1.95 (ISBN 0-916780-00-7); Bk. 2. Addition of Whole Numbers & Subtraction of Whole Numbers. 4.15 (ISBN 0-916780-01-5); Bk. 3. Multiplication of Whole Numbers. 3.25 (ISBN 0-916780-02-3); Bk. 4. Division of Whole Numbers. 3.70 (ISBN 0-916780-03-1); Bk. 5. Fractions & Fractional Numbers. 2.40 (ISBN 0-916780-04-X); Bk. 6. Addition & Subtraction of Fractional Numbers & Multiplication & Division of Fractional Numbers. 3.70 (ISBN 0-916780-05-8); Bk. 7. Decimal Numerals: Addition & Subtraction with Decimals & Multiplication & Division with Decimals. 4.15 (ISBN 0-916780-06-6); Bk. 8. Percents & Applications. 2.80 (ISBN 0-916780-07-4); Bk. 9. Formulas & Applications. 3.70 (ISBN 0-916780-08-2); Bk. 10. Measurement & Applications. 4.15 (ISBN 0-916780-09-0); Bk. 11. Measurement in Geometry. 4.15 (ISBN 0-916780-10-4); Bk. 12. Units of Measure & the Metric System. 3.25 (ISBN 0-916780-11-2). (Illus.). 1984. Bks. 1-12. pap. text ed. 35.00 (ISBN 0-916780-12-0); tchr's. manual 3.50 (ISBN 0-916780-14-7); student test booklet 4.00 (ISBN 0-916780-13-9); complete set 42.50 (ISBN 0-916780-20-1). CES.

Stark, Thomas & Pucke, Lawrence. Problems Supplement for Technical Mathematics. 1984. pap. 13.95 (ISBN 0-8053-9537-7). Benjamin-Cummings.

Steenburgen, Fran. Steenburgen Diagnostic-Prescriptive Math Program. 1978. complete program 25.00 (ISBN 0-87879-209-0). Acad Therapy.

Stokes, George G. Mathematical & Physical Papers, 5 Vols. 2nd ed. Repr. of 1905 ed. Set. 165.00 (ISBN 0-384-58370-9). Johnson Repr.

Sullivan Associates. Math Word Problems, 3 vols. 1972. pap. text ed. 2.50 each ans. (ISBN 0-686-57755-8); keys 1, 2, 3 0.50. Learning Line.

Suthney, Everette. Super Quiz II. 1983. 59.95 (ISBN 0-88408-268-7). Sterling Swift.

Tietze, Heinrich. Famous Problems of Mathematics. 2nd ed. LC 64-8910. (Illus.). 1965. 20.00x (ISBN 0-910670-11-0). Graylock.

Trigg, Charles W. Mathematical Quickies: Two Hundred & Seventy Stimulating Problems with Solutions. 224p. 1985. pap. 5.95 (ISBN 0-486-24949-2). Dover.

Wells, David. Can You Solve These? 77p. 1983. pap. 3.95 (ISBN 0-13-114074-4). P-H.

MATHEMATICS–PROGRAMMED INSTRUCTION

Aitken, Alexander C. Determinants & Matrices. LC 82-24168. (University Mathematical Texts Ser.). 144p. 1983. Repr. of 1956 ed. lib. bdg. 32.50x (ISBN 0-313-23294-6, AIDE). Greenwood.

Bajpai, A. C., et al. Mathematics for Engineers & Scientists, 2 vols. LC 72-14009. (Series of Programs on Mathematics for Scientist & Technologist). 800p. 1973. Vol. 2, 661 Pgs. 26.95 (ISBN 0-471-04374-5, Pub. by Wiley-Interscience). Wiley.

Bila, Dennis, et al. Core Mathematics. LC 74-82696. (Illus.). ix, 603p. (Prog. Bk.). 1975. text ed. 22.95x (ISBN 0-87901-035-5). Worth.

Bitter, et al. McGraw-Hill Mathematics, 8 levels. Incl. Level 1. text ed. 8.96 (ISBN 0-07-005761-3); Level 2. text ed. 8.96 (ISBN 0-07-005762-1); Level 3. text ed. 14.08 (ISBN 0-07-005763-X); Level 4. text ed. 14.08 (ISBN 0-07-005764-8); Level 5. text ed. 14.08 (ISBN 0-07-005765-6); Level 6. text ed. 13.28 (ISBN 0-07-005766-4); Level 7. text ed. 17.28 (ISBN 0-07-005767-2); Level 8. text ed. 17.28 (ISBN 0-07-005768-0). 1981. McGraw.

Burkhardt, Hugh. The Real World & Mathematics. 188p. 1981. pap. text ed. 13.95x (ISBN 0-216-91084-6). Birkhauser.

Crowhurst, Norman H. Problem Solving Arts: Part One Syllabus. 1976. pap. text ed. 9.95 (ISBN 0-89420-085-2, 256040); cassette recordings 227.10 (ISBN 0-89420-175-1, 256000). Natl Book.

Gould, Lawrence D., et al. Essentials for College Mathematics: A Programmed Text. (Illus.). 1970. pap. text ed. 7.95x (ISBN 0-89197-152-1); access pen 0.65x (ISBN 0-8290-1391-1). Irvington.

Gray, Al & Matousek, Clifford H. General Mathematics: Syllabus. 2nd ed. 1972. pap. text ed. 6.75 (ISBN 0-89420-019-4, 350899); cassette recordings 103.55 (ISBN 0-89420-148-4, 350900). Natl Book.

Howes, Vernon E. Essentials of Mathematics: Precalculus I-a Programmed Text: Algebra I. LC 75-9733. pap. 160.00 (ISBN 0-8357-9886-0, 2051295). Bks Demand UMI.

Lippa, Erik A. Mathematics for Freshman in the Life Sciences. (Illus.). 319p. (Orig.). 1977. pap. text ed. 25.00 (ISBN 0-9607980-0-5). E A Lippa.

Mathematics Research Center, Univ. of Wisconsin, Advanced Seminar. Mathematical Programming: Proceedings. Hu, T. C. & Robinson, Stephen M., eds. 1973. 19.50 (ISBN 0-12-358350-0). Acad Pr.

Roberts, Keith & Michels, Leo. Introductory Mathematics for Industry Science, & Technology. LC 85-7714. (Mathematics Ser.). 300p. 1985. pap. text ed. 25.75 (pub net) (ISBN 0-534-05148-0). Brooks-Cole.

Sackheim, George I. & Robbins, Lewis. Programmed Mathematics for Nurses. 5th ed. (Illus.). 1983. pap. text ed. write for info. (ISBN 0-02-405170-5). Macmillan.

Sullivan Associates. Programmed Mathematics Series, Bks. 9-15. 2nd ed. 1975. 5.92 ea. McGraw.

Suppes, Patrick C., et al. Computer-Assisted Instruction: Stanford's 1965-66 Arithmetic Program. (Illus.). 1968. 52.00 (ISBN 0-12-676850-1). Acad Pr.

Trafalgar House Pub. Co. Basic Mathematics & Language Skills Builder for Civil Examination Candidates. 256p. 1982. pap. 1.00 (ISBN 0-07-065110-8). McGraw.

UMAP Central Staff, compiled by. UMAP Modules, Ninteen Seventy-Seven to Seventy-Nine: Tools for Teaching. 727p. 1982. text ed. 47.95x (ISBN 0-8176-3049-X). Birkhauser.

MATHEMATICS–STATISTICAL METHODS

see Mathematical Statistics

MATHEMATICS–STUDY AND TEACHING

see also Mathematical Models

Albers, D. J. & Steen, L. A., eds. Teaching Teachers, Teaching Students. 152p. 1981. 14.95x (ISBN 0-8176-3043-0). Birkhauser.

Alberti, Del & Laycock, Mary. The Correlation of Activity-Centered Science & Mathematics. 1975. 8.50 (ISBN 0-918932-07-6). Activity Resources.

Allen, Layman E. & Ross, Joan. IMP (Instructional Math Play) Kits: Individual Solitare Kits. 15.00 (ISBN 0-911624-18-X). Wffn Proof.

American Association of School Admin. Improving Math & Science Education: Problems & Solutions. Neill, Shirley B., ed. 92p. (Orig.). 1985. pap. 13.95 (ISBN 0-87652-072-7). Am Assn Sch Admin.

Aponte, Gladys, et al. Curso Individualizado de Matematicas Basicas: Aritmetica, Algebra Elemental & Algebra Intermedia. LC 84-20838. (Span.). 356p. 1984. pap. text ed. 15.00 (ISBN 0-8477-2638-X). U of PR Pr.

Ashlock, Robert. Error Patterns in Computation. 3rd ed. 208p. 1982. pap. text ed. 10.95 (ISBN 0-675-09880-7). Merrill.

Association Of Teachers Of Mathematics. Mathematical Reflections. (Illus.). 1970. 27.50 (ISBN 0-521-07260-3); pap. 12.95 (ISBN 0-521-09582-4, 582). Cambridge U Pr.

Bauer, George. Helping Teachers Learn Mathematics: A Competency-Based Content Approach. 288p. 1984. pap. text ed. 14.95 (ISBN 0-8403-3509-1). Kendall-Hunt.

Begle, E. G. Critical Variables in Mathematics Education: Findings from a Survey of the Empirical Literature. LC 78-78131. 165p. 1979. 9.50 (ISBN 0-88385-430-9). Math Assn.

Bishop, A. J. & Nickson, Marilyn. Research on the Social Context of Mathematics Education. 84p. 1983. 10.00x (ISBN 0-7005-0613-6, Pub. by NFER Nelson UK). Taylor & Francis.

Bley, Nancy S. & Thornton, Carol A. Teaching Mathematics to the Learning Disabled. LC 81-3569. 421p. 1981. text ed. 32.00 (ISBN 0-89443-357-1). Aspen Systems.

Boeker, M. Status of the Beginning Calculus Students in Pre-Calculus College Mathematics: Study Carried Out with Students in Brooklyn College & City College of New York. LC 76-176690. (Columbia University. Teachers College. Contributions to Education: No. 922). Repr. of 1947 ed. 22.50 (ISBN 0-404-55922-0). AMS Pr.

Bond, Elias A. The Professional Treatment of the Subject Matter of Arithmetic for Teacher-Training Institutions. LC 75-176576. (Columbia University. Teachers College. Contributions to Education: No. 525). Repr. of 1934 ed. 22.50 (ISBN 0-404-55525-X). AMS Pr.

Boyd, Elizabeth N. A Diagnostic Study of Student's Difficulties in General Mathematics in First Year College Work. LC 79-176585. (Columbia University. Teachers College. Contributions to Education: No. 798). Repr. of 1940 ed. 22.50 (ISBN 0-404-55798-8). AMS Pr.

Brett, William F., et al. Contemporary College Mathematics. 320p. 1975. text ed. 22.95 (ISBN 0-8299-0038-1). West Pub.

Brissenden, T. H. F. Mathematics Teaching. 1980. text ed. 21.00 (ISBN 0-06-318159-2, IntlDept); pap. text ed. 11.90 (ISBN 0-06-318160-6). Har-Row.

Brush, Lorelei R. Encouraging Girls in Mathematics: The Problems & the Solution. LC 79-55774. (Illus.). 1980. text ed. 16.00 (ISBN 0-89011-542-7). Abt Bks.

Cawley, John F., ed. Practical Mathematics Appraisal of the Learning Disabled. LC 84-20499. 350p. 1984. 31.50 (ISBN 0-89443-559-0). Aspen Systems.

--Secondary School Mathematics for the Learning Disabled. LC 84-16946. 327p. 1984. 31.50 (ISBN 0-89443-597-3). Aspen Systems.

Challenge: A Handbook of Classroom Ideas to Motivate the Teaching of Intermediate Math. (The Spice Ser.). 1975. 6.95 (ISBN 0-89273-116-8). Educ Serv.

Chapman, L. R. The Process of Learning Mathematics. LC 71-178683. 405p. 1972. pap. text ed. 23.00 (ISBN 0-08-017357-8). Pergamon.

Cohen, Louis S. How to Teach Eureka! A Discovery Approach to the Basics in Math. new ed. 1976. manual & cassettes 179.50 (ISBN 0-917792-00-9). Math Hse.

Connolly, Austin J. KeyMath Teach & Practice Teacher's Guide. (KeyMath Teach & Practice Ser.). 1985. 7.95 (ISBN 0-88671-241-6). Am Guidance.

Corlett, P. N. Practical Programming. 2nd ed. LC 75-161295. (School Mathematics Project Handbooks). (Illus.). 1971. pap. 12.95x (ISBN 0-521-09740-1). Cambridge U Pr.

Cornelius, Michael, ed. Teaching Mathematics. 268p. 1982. pap. 15.95. Nichols Pub.

--Teaching Mathematics. LC 82-6404. (Illus.). 248p. 1982. pap. 16.50. Nichols Pub.

Davis, Philip J. & Hersh, Reuben. The Mathematical Experience. 460p. 1981. 27.95x (ISBN 0-8176-3018-X). Birkhauser.

Davis, Robert. Learning Mathematics: The Cognitive Science Approach to Mathematics Education. LC 84-2853. 300p. 1984. text ed. 34.50 (ISBN 0-89391-245-X). Ablex Pub.

Dean, Peter G. Teaching & Learning Mathematics. (The Woburn Education Ser.). 280p. 1982. 22.50x (ISBN 0-7130-0168-2, Pub by Woburn Pr England); pap. text ed. 12.50x (ISBN 0-7130-4007-6). Biblio Dist.

Demana, Franklin D., et al. Transition to College Mathematics. (Illus.). 592p. 1984. 26.95 (ISBN 0-201-11153-5); teacher's guide 3.95 (ISBN 0-201-11154-3). Addison-Wesley.

Dessart, Donald J. & Suydam, Marilyn N. Classroom Ideas from Research on Secondary School Mathematics. LC 83-8279. (Illus.). 128p. 1983. pap. 6.00 (ISBN 0-87353-207-4). NCTM.

Dienes, Z. P. Mathematics Through the Senses: Games, Dance & Art. 146p. 1973. 14.00x (ISBN 0-901225-87-8, Pub. by NFER Nelson UK). Taylor & Francis.

--The Six Stages in the Process of Learning Mathematics. Seaborne, P. L., tr. 56p. 1970. 5.00x (ISBN 0-85633-022-1, Pub. by NFER Nelson UK). Taylor & Francis.

Dubisch, Roy. Teaching of Mathematics from Intermediate Algebra Through First Year Calculus. LC 74-23520. 136p. 1975. Repr. of 1963 ed. 7.50 (ISBN 0-88275-198-0). Krieger.

Duncan, Aileen. Teaching Mathematics to Slow Learners. 160p. 1981. 35.00x (ISBN 0-7062-3666-1, Pub. by Ward Lock Ed England). State Mutual Bk.

Easterday, Kenneth E. & Henry, Loren L., eds. Activities for Junior High School & Middle School Mathematics: Readings from the Arithmetic Teacher & the Mathematics Teacher. Simpson, F. Morgan. LC 81-14024. (Illus.). 218p. 1981. pap. 8.25 (ISBN 0-87353-188-4). NCTM.

Education in Applied Mathematics. vii, 415p. 1967. ltd. ed. 9.00 (ISBN 0-89871-154-1). Soc Indus-Appl Math.

Edwards, R. E. Fourier Series: A Modern Introduction, Vol. II. rev., 2nd ed. (Graduate Texts in Mathematics Ser.: Vol. 85). 384p. 1982. 44.00 (ISBN 0-387-90651-7). Springer-Verlag.

Elsgolts, L. E. & Norkin, S. B. Introduction to the Theory & Application of Differential Equations with Deviating Arguments. 1973. 61.50 (ISBN 0-12-237750-8). Acad Pr.

El Tom, M. E., ed. Developing Mathematics in Third World Countries. (North Holland Mathematics Studies: Vol. 33). 208p. 1979. 47.00 (ISBN 0-444-85260-3, North Holland). Elsevier.

Fagerstrom, William H. Mathematical Facts & Processes Prerequisite to the Study of Calculus. LC 76-176761. (Columbia University. Teachers College. Contributions to Education Ser.: No. 572). Repr. of 1933 ed. 22.50 (ISBN 0-404-55572-1). AMS Pr.

Fang, Joong. Numbers Racket: The Aftermath of New Math. LC 68-8247. 1968. 19.50 (ISBN 0-8046-0138-0, Pub. by Kennikat). Assoc Faculty Pr.

Feldman, L. Mathematical Learning. 224p. 1969. 32.50 (ISBN 0-677-13250-6). Gordon.

Feurzeig, W., et al. The LOGO Language: Learning Mathematics Through Programming. 188p. 1977. pap. text ed. 22.95 (ISBN 0-87567-105-5). Entelek.

Fey, James T. Mathematics Teaching Today: Perspectives from Three National Surveys. 31p. 1981. pap. 3.00 (ISBN 0-87353-186-8). NCTM.

Fletcher, T. J. Some Lessons in Mathematics. pap. 12.95x (ISBN 0-521-09248-5). Cambridge U Pr.

For the Teaching of Mathematics, 3 vols. Incl. Vol. 1. Pedagogical Discussions. pap. 3.30 (ISBN 0-685-46932-8); Vol. 2. Psychological Studies, 2 pts. pap. 3.85 (ISBN 0-685-46933-6); Vol. 3. Elementary Mathematics. 133p. pap. 3.85 (ISBN 0-685-46934-4). 1963. pap. Ed Solutions.

Freudenthal, H. Mathematics As an Educational Task. LC 72-77874. (Illus.). 680p. 1973. lib. bdg. 39.50 (ISBN 90-277-0235-7, Pub. by Reidel Holland); pap. text ed. 21.00 (ISBN 90-277-0322-1). Kluwer Academic.

Freudenthal, Hans. Didactical Phenomenology of Mathematical Structures. 1983. lib. bdg. 93.50 (ISBN 90-2771-535-1, Pub. by Reidel Holland). Kluwer Academic.

Gattegno, Caleb. Arithmestics. (Illus.). 28p. 1971. pap. 2.15 (ISBN 0-87825-019-0). Ed Solutions.

--The Common Sense of Teaching Mathematics. (Common Sense of Teaching Ser.). (Illus.). 144p. 1974. pap. 6.95 (ISBN 0-87825-024-7). Ed Solutions.

--Mathematics Textbooks, 7 bks. Incl. Bk. 1. Study of Numbers up to 20. 102p. pap. text ed. 1.65 (ISBN 0-87825-011-5); Bk. 2. Study of Numbers up to 1,000. 147p. pap. text ed. 2.50 (ISBN 0-87825-012-3); Bk. 3. Applied Arithmetic. 53p. pap. text ed. 1.65 (ISBN 0-87825-013-1); Bk. 4. Fractions, Decimals, Percentages. 65p. pap. text ed. 1.65 (ISBN 0-87825-014-X); Bk. 5. Study of Numbers. 83p. pap. text ed. 1.65 (ISBN 0-87825-015-8); Bk. 6. Applied Mathematics. 104p. pap. 1.95 (ISBN 0-87825-003-4); Bk. 7. Algebra & Geometry. 92p. pap. text ed. 2.20 (ISBN 0-87825-017-4). pap. Ed Solutions.

--Notes on the Gattegno Approach to Math. 31p. 1973. 1.65 (ISBN 0-87825-043-3). Ed Solutions.

Glenn, J. A. The Third R: Towards a Numerate Society. 1978. (IntlDept); pap. text ed. 6.60 (ISBN 0-06-318076-6, IntlDept). Har-Row.

Goldstein, Amy J. & Granade, Charles, eds. Graduate Programs in the Physical Sciences & Mathematics 1986. 20th ed. (Annual Guides to Graduate Study Ser.). 650p. (Orig.). 1985. pap. 22.95 (ISBN 0-87866-345-2). Petersons Guides.

Good, Thomas, et al. Mathematics Instructions. LC 82-4646. (I. R. T. Ser.). (Illus.). 321p. 1983. 25.00 (ISBN 0-582-28342-6). Longman.

Goodson, Carcle E. & Miertschin, Susan L. Student Solutions to Accompany Technical Mathematics with Applications. 1983. pap. price not set (ISBN 0-471-89290-4). Wiley.

Hansen, Viggo P., ed. Computers in Mathematics Education: 1984 Yearbook. LC 84-2037. (Illus.). 256p. 1984. 14.50 (ISBN 0-87353-210-4). NCTM.

Heintz, Ruth. Mathematics for Elementary Teachers: A Content Approach. LC 79-18727. (Illus.). 512p. 1980. text ed. 25.95 (ISBN 0-201-03227-9); instr's. manual 3.50 (ISBN 0-201-03228-7). Addison-Wesley.

Hellmich, Eugene W. The Mathematics in Certain Elementary Social Studies in Secondary Schools & Colleges. LC 12-32085. (Columbia University. Teachers College. Contributions to Education: No. 706). Repr. of 1937 ed. 22.50 (ISBN 0-404-55706-6). AMS Pr.

Herbster, Carl p. Math Eight for Christian Schools. (Illus.). 344p. 1983. text ed. 15.95 (ISBN 0-89084-211-6); tchr's ed 29.50 (ISBN 0-89084-212-4). Bob Jones Univ Pr.

Hess, Adrien L. Mathematics Projects Handbook. 2nd ed. LC 82-2084. 47p. 1982. pap. 3.25 (ISBN 0-87353-191-4). NCTM.

Howard, Homer. Mathematics Teachers' Views on Certain Issues in the Teaching of Mathematics. LC 76-176883. (Columbia University. Teachers College. Contributions to Education Ser.: No. 827). Repr. of 1941 ed. 22.50 (ISBN 0-404-55827-5). AMS Pr.

Howell, Daisy, et al. Activities for Teaching Mathematics to Low Achievers. LC 73-93330. (Illus.). 1974. pap. 1.00 (ISBN 0-87805-052-3). U Pr of Miss.

Howett, Jerry. Building Basic Skills in Mathematics. (Orig.). 1981. pap. 5.88 (ISBN 0-8092-5877-3). Contemp Bks.

Howson, A. G., et al. Curriculum Development in Mathematics. LC 80-41205. 200p. 1981. 62.50 (ISBN 0-521-23767-X); pap. 14.95 (ISBN 0-521-27053-7). Cambridge U Pr.

Hudspeth, Kay & Hirsh, Lewis. Studying Mathematics. 64p. 1982. saddle stitch 5.95 (ISBN 0-8403-2768-4). Kendall-Hunt.

Hufendick, Lawrence H. Mathematics for the Liberal Arts Student. 163p. (Preliminary ed.). 1971. 5.00 (ISBN 0-910268-03-7); pap. 3.00 (ISBN 0-910268-04-5). Books.

Johnson, David R. & Margenau, James R. Mathematics Contests: A Handbook for Mathematics Educators. LC 81-22497. (Illus.). 94p. 1982. pap. 5.00 (ISBN 0-87353-187-6). NCTM.

Keenan, Edward P. & Gantert, Ann X. Integrated Mathematics: Course III. (Orig.). 1982. text ed. 20.25 (ISBN 0-87720-253-2); pap. text ed. 12.92 (ISBN 0-87720-252-4). AMSCO Sch.

Kolkmeyer, Alexandra. Steps for Teaching Math: An Assessment Scale for Teachers & Parents. 35p. 1985. pap. text ed. 50.00 (ISBN 0-942524-05-5). In Sight Pr NM.

Laycock, Mary & Watson, Gene. The Fabric of Mathematics: A Resource Book for Teachers. (Illus.). 18.50 (ISBN 0-918932-11-4). Activity Resources.

Lieberman, Arthur. College Mathematics for Business & the Social Sciences. LC 81-17976. (Mathematics Ser.). 618p. 1982. text ed. 23.25 pub net (ISBN 0-8185-0474-9). Brooks-Cole.

Lindquist, Mary M., ed. Selected Issues in Mathematics Education. LC 80-82903. (National Society for the Education Series on Contemporary Education Issues). 250p. 1981. 20.50x (ISBN 0-8211-1114-0); text ed. 19.50x 10 or more copies. McCutchan.

Los Angeles Unified School District, et al. FORE Mathematics. Rev. ed. Bagai, Eric & Bagai, Judith, eds. (System FORE Ser.: Vol. 4). (Illus.). 232p. 1977. 15.00x (ISBN 0-943292-04-2). Foreworks.

McCormick, Clarence. The Teaching of General Mathematics in the Secondary Schools of the United States: A Study of the Development & Present Status of General Mathematics. LC 70-178806. (Columbia University. Teachers College. Contributions to Education: No. 386). Repr. of 1929 ed. 22.50 (ISBN 0-404-55386-9). AMS Pr.

Mallett, Jerry J. & Bartch, Marian. Math Motivators, 2 vols. 1985. Vol. I, gr. 1-3. pap. 7.95 (ISBN 0-673-18264-9); Vol. II, gr. 4-6. pap. 7.95 (ISBN 0-673-18265-7). Scott F.

Marjoram, D. T. Teaching Mathematics. 1974. text ed. 14.50x (ISBN 0-435-50600-5). Heinemann Ed.

Mason, Robert D. College Mathematics: With Applications in Business & Economics. (Plaid Ser.). 1976. pap. 9.95 (ISBN 0-256-01267-9). Dow Jones-Irwin.

Math. (The Easy Way Ser.). 1982. 7.95 (ISBN 0-8120-2503-2). Barron.

Miklos, Mary O. Preparation for Criterion-Referenced Tests: A Brief Review of Mathematical Competencies for Teachers of Middle Grades. 110p. (Orig.). 1981. pap. text ed. 9.00 (ISBN 0-8191-1545-2). U Pr of Amer.

Milnor, John W. & Stasheff, James D. Characteristic Classes. LC 72-4050. (Annals of Mathematics Studies: No. 76). 250p. 1973. 32.00x (ISBN 0-691-08122-0). Princeton U Pr.

Morris, Robert. Studies in Mathematics Education, 2 Vols. Incl. Vol. 1. 129p. 1980. pap. 7.00 (ISBN 92-3-101779-9, U1013); Vol. 2. 179p. 1981. pap. 9.25 (ISBN 92-3-101905-8, U1101); Vol. 3. Mathematical Education of Primary-School Teachers. 258p. 1985. pap. 18.75 (ISBN 92-3-102141-9, U1370). (Teaching of Basic Sciences Ser.). (Illus.). 179p. Vol. 1, 1980, 129p. pap. 7.00 (ISBN 92-3-101779-9, U1013, UNESCO); Vol. 2, 1981, 179p. pap. 9.25 (ISBN 92-3-101905-8, U1101). Unipub.

Mueller, Francis J. Essential Mathematics for College Students. 3rd ed. (Illus.). 320p. 1976. pap. 25.95 (ISBN 0-13-286518-1). P-H.

National Academy Of Sciences - Division Of Mathematics Committee On Support Of Research In Mathematical Sciences. Mathematical Sciences: Undergraduate Education. 1968. pap. 6.50 (ISBN 0-309-01682-7). Natl Acad Pr.
National Convocation on Precollege Education in Math & Science, National Academy of Sciences. Science & Mathematics in the Schools: Report of a Convocation. 32p. 1982. pap. text ed. 2.00 (ISBN 0-309-03330-6). Natl Acad Pr.
National Council of Teachers of Mathematics. Cumulative Index: The Arithmetic Teacher, 1974-1983. 34p. (Orig.). 1984. pap. 10.00 (ISBN 0-87353-216-3). NCTM.
--Evaluation in Mathematics, 26th Yearbook. Johnson, Donovan A., ed. LC 61-11906. 216p. 1961. 12.40 (ISBN 0-87353-004-7). NCTM.
--Guidelines for the Preparation of Teachers of Mathematics. 32p. 1981. pap. 3.10 (ISBN 0-87353-177-9). NCTM.
--A History of Mathematics Education in the United States & Canada, 32nd Yearbk. LC 71-105864. 557p. 1970. 16.90 (ISBN 0-87353-012-8). NCTM.
--Insights into Modern Mathematics, 23rd Yearbk. Wren, F. Lynwood, ed. 440p. 1957. 14.60 (ISBN 0-87353-001-2). NCTM.
--Learning of Mathematics, Its Theory & Practice, 21st Yearbk. 355p. 1953. 14.00 (ISBN 0-87353-000-4). NCTM.
--Organizing for Mathematics Instruction: 1977 Yearbook. (Illus.). 256p. 1977. 14.50 (ISBN 0-87353-019-5). NCTM.
--Problem Solving in School Mathematics, 1980 Yearbook. LC 79-27145. (Illus.). 241p. 1980. 14.50 (ISBN 0-87353-162-0). NCTM.
NCTM. How to Evaluate Mathematics Textbooks. LC 82-2444. 1982. pap. 1.60 (ISBN 0-87353-193-0). NCTM.
--How to Evaluate Your Mathematics Program. LC 81-11088. 19p. 1981. pap. 2.00 (ISBN 0-87353-183-3). NCTM.
Noller, Ruth B., et al. Creative Problem Solving in Mathematics. (Illus.). 1978. tchr's idea bk. 2.50 (ISBN 0-914634-55-0). DOK Pubs.
Oldknow, A. J. & Smith, D. V. Learning Mathematics with Micros. LC 83-12642. (Mathematics & Its Applications Ser.). 268p. 1984. 49.95x (ISBN 0-470-27488-3, Pub. by Halsted Pr); pap. 24.95x (ISBN 0-470-27487-5). Wiley.
Olson, Alton T. Mathematics Through Paper Folding. LC 75-16115. (Illus.). 64p. 1975. pap. 3.20 (ISBN 0-87353-076-4). NCTM.
Osborne, Alan, ed. An In-Service Handbook for Mathematics Education. LC 77-7287. 260p. 1977. pap. 6.20 (ISBN 0-87353-119-1). NCTM.
Oxrieder, C. A. Your Number's Up: A Calculus Approach to Successful Math Study. 1982. text ed. 6.95 (ISBN 0-201-05526-0); instr's guide 1.50 (ISBN 0-201-05527-9). Addison-Wesley.
Page, Warren, ed. American Perspectives on the Fifth International Congress on Mathematical Education. 134p. 1984. 6.50 (ISBN 0-88385-055-9, NTE-05). Math Assn.
Pascaris, Peter A. A Guide Book for Teaching Consumer Mathematics. 322p. 1982. pap. 26.95x (ISBN 0-205-07388-3, Pub. by Longwood Div). Allyn.
Payne, Joseph N. & Goodman, F. L. Mathematics Education: Index & Bibliography, 2 vols. 1965. Set. pap. 4.50 (ISBN 0-87506-017-X). Campus.
Philadelphia Suburban School Study Council. Improving Today's Curriculum for Tomorrow's Challenges. LC 64-20044. 76p. 1964. pap. text ed. 1.50x (ISBN 0-8134-0064-3, 64). Interstate.
Polya, Gyorgy. How to Solve It. 1971. 25.00 (ISBN 0-691-08097-6); pap. 6.95 (ISBN 0-691-02356-5). Princeton U Pr.
Price, Jack, ed. Changing School Mathematics: A Responsive Process. Gawronski, J. D. LC 81-11164. (Illus.). 229p. 1981. 15.00 (ISBN 0-87353-184-1). NCTM.
Problem Solving in the Mathematics Curriculm: A Report, Recommendations & An Annotated Bibliography. 140p. 1983. 6.00 (ISBN 0-88385-051-6, NTE-01); pap. 5.00 (ISBN 0-317-30487-9). Math Assn.
Ralston, A. & Young, G. S., eds. The Future of College Mathematics: Proceedings. (Illus.). 278p. 1983. 22.00 (ISBN 0-387-90813-7). Springer-Verlag.
Reisman, Fredericka K. Teaching Mathematics: Methods & Content. 2nd ed. 1981. 25.95 (ISBN 0-395-30706-6); Instr's manual 1.25 (ISBN 0-395-30707-4). HM.
Resnick, Lauren B. & Ford, Wendy W. The Psychology of Mathematics for Instruction. LC 80-29106. 288p. 1981. text ed. 24.95x (ISBN 0-89859-029-9). L Erlbaum Assocs.
A Review of Research in Mathematics Education. Incl. Pt. A. Research on Learning & Teaching. Bell, A. W., et al. 336p. 1983. 22.00 (ISBN 0-7005-0612-8); Pt. B. Research on the Social Context of Mathematics Education. Bishop, A. J. & Nickson, Marilyn. 84p. 1983. 12.00 (ISBN 0-7005-0613-6); Pt. C. Curriculum Development & Curriculum Research - A Historical & Comparative View. Howson, A. G. 72p. 1983. 9.00 (ISBN 0-7005-0614-4). 1983. 22.00 (ISBN 0-7005-0612-8, Pub. by NFER Nelson UK). Taylor & Francis.
A Rhythmic Approach to Mathematics. LC 75-10555. (Classics in Mathematics Education Ser: Vol. 5). (Illus.). 72p. 1975. 8.40 (ISBN 0-87353-040-3). NCTM.
Robinson, Arthur E. The Professional Education of Elementary Teachers in the Field of Arithmetic. LC 78-177196. (Columbia University. Teachers College. Contributions to Education: No. 672). Repr. of 1936 ed. 22.50 (ISBN 0-404-55672-8). AMS Pr.
Rosnick, Peter. The Math Tutor. LC 82-229. 80p. 1982. pap. 4.95x (ISBN 0-582-29012-0). Longman.
Sage, Edwin R. Problem Solving with the Computer. (Illus.). 244p. (Orig.). 1969. pap. 14.95 (ISBN 0-87567-030-X). Entelek.
Schaaf, William L. Course for Teachers of Junior High School Mathematics. LC 77-177808. (Columbia University. Teachers College. Contributions to Education: No. 313). Repr. of 1928 ed. 22.50 (ISBN 0-404-55313-3). AMS Pr.
Seidlin, Joseph. Critical Study of the Teaching of Elementary College Mathematics. LC 77-177796. (Columbia University. Teachers College. Contributions to Education: No. 482). Repr. of 1931 ed. 22.50 (ISBN 0-404-55482-2). AMS Pr.
Servais, W. & Varga, T., eds. Teaching School Mathematics. (Source Books on Curricula & Methods). (Illus.). 308p. (Orig., Co-published with Penguin Books Ltd., London). 1971. pap. 7.50 (ISBN 92-3-100884-6, U661, UNESCO). Unipub.
Shuard, H. & Quadling, D. Teachers of Math. 1980. text ed. 18.35 (ISBN 0-06-318174-6, IntlDept); pap. text ed. 9.25 (ISBN 0-06-318175-4). Har-Row.
Shumway, Richard J., ed. Research in Mathematics Education. National Council of Teachers of Mathematics. LC 80-4. (Illus.). 480p. 1980. 27.00 (ISBN 0-87353-163-9). NCTM.
Sidhu, Kulbir S. The Teaching of Mathematics. 3rd. ed. xi, 382p. 1984. text ed. 35.00x (ISBN 0-86590-429-4, Pub. by Sterling Pubs India). Apt Bks.
Silbert, Jerry, et al. Direct Instruction Mathematics. (Illus., Orig.). 1981. pap. text ed. 26.95 (ISBN 0-675-08047-9). Merrill.
Skolnick, Joan, et al. How To Encourage Girls in Math & Science: Strategies for Parents & Educators. (Illus.). 192p. 1982. 15.95 (ISBN 0-13-405670-1, Spec); pap. 7.95 (ISBN 0-13-405662-0). P-H.
Sobel, Max & Maletsky, Evan. Teaching Mathematics: A Source Book for Aids, Activities, & Strategies. (Illus.). 288p. 1975. pap. text ed. 22.95 (ISBN 0-13-894121-1). P-H.
Souviney, Randall. Solving Problems Kids Care About. (Illus.). 1981. pap. 11.95 (ISBN 0-673-16534-5). Scott F.
Soviet Studies in the Psychology of Learning & Teaching Mathematics. Incl. Bk. 1. The Learning of Math Concepts. 216p (ISBN 0-87353-148-5); Bk. 2. The Structure of Mathematical Abilities. 128p (ISBN 0-87353-149-3); Bk. 3. Problem Solving in Arithmetic & Algebra. 183p (ISBN 0-87353-150-7); Bk. 4. Problem Solving in Geometry. 154p (ISBN 0-87353-151-5); Bk. 5. Development of of Spatial Abilities. 168p (ISBN 0-87353-152-3); Bk. 6. Instruction in Problem Solving. 136p (ISBN 0-87353-153-1); Bk. 7. Children's Capacity for Learning Mathematics. 261p (ISBN 0-87353-154-X); Bk. 8. Methods of Teaching Mathematics. 271p (ISBN 0-87353-155-8); Bk. 9. Problem-Solving Processes of Mentally Retarded Children. 170p (ISBN 0-87353-156-6); Bk. 10. Teaching Mathematics to Mentally Retarded Children. 224p (ISBN 0-87353-157-4); Bk. 11. Analysis & Synthesis As Problem-Solving Methods. 171p (ISBN 0-87353-158-2); Bk. 12. Problems of Instruction. 172p (ISBN 0-87353-159-0); Bk. 13. Analysis of Reasoning Processes. 231p. 1975 (ISBN 0-87353-160-4); Bk. 14. Teaching Arithmetic in the Elementary School. 202p (ISBN 0-87353-161-2). 1969. pap. 4.00 ea; pap. 22.50 set, vol. 7-14 (ISBN 0-87353-147-7). NCTM.
Stanley, Julian C., et al, eds. Mathematical Talent, Discovery, Description, & Development. LC 73-19342. (Illus.). 234p. 1974. 24.00x (ISBN 0-8018-1585-1). Johns Hopkins.
Success in Mathematics. (Success Studybooks Ser.). (Illus.). 609p. 1975. 12.00 (ISBN 0-7195-2901-8). Transatlantic.
Swabb, Barbara S. & Thomason, Mary E. Mathematics Bulletin Boards. 1971. pap. 3.95 (ISBN 0-8224-4420-8). Pitman Learning.
Swetz, Frank, ed. Socialist Mathematics Education. LC 78-68025. 1979. pap. 14.00 (ISBN 0-917574-04-4). Burgundy Pr.
Tedder, Jake D. Developing Math Skills Through Practical Application. 200p. 1985. pap. text ed. 12.95 (ISBN 0-8403-3580-6). Kendall-Hunt.
Thompson, Russell E. Precalculus Mathematics: A Short Course. LC 82-13366. 200p. (Orig.). 1982. pap. text ed. 11.25 (ISBN 0-8191-2634-9). U Pr of Amer.
Tobias, Sheila. Overcoming Math Anxiety. (Illus.). 1978. 13.95 (ISBN 0-393-06439-5). Norton.
Triola, Mario F. A Survey of Mathematics. LC 74-27627. 1973. 32.95 (ISBN 0-8465-7555-8, 57555). Benjamin-Cummings.
Underhill, Robert G. Teaching Elementary School Mathematics. 3rd ed. 1981. text ed. 23.95 (ISBN 0-675-09998-6). Additional supplements may be obtained from publisher. Merrill.
U. S. National Coordinating Center Staff & Travers, Kenneth. International Mathematics Study: Second Summary Report for the United States. 140p. 1985. pap. text ed. 7.80x (ISBN 0-87563-267-X). Stipes.
Wardle, M. E., ed. From Problem to Program. (School Mathematics Project Computing Ser). (Illus.). 1971. 16.95 (ISBN 0-521-08301-X); pap. 6.95 (ISBN 0-521-09684-7). Cambridge U Pr.
Watson, F. R. Developments in Mathematics Teaching. 156p. 1976. 25.00x (ISBN 0-7291-0085-5, Pub. by Open Bks England). State Mutual Bk.
Wenninger, Magnus J. Polyhedron Models for the Classroom. (Illus.). 80p. 1975. pap. 3.00 (ISBN 0-87353-083-7). NCTM.
Williams, David E. Mathematics Teacher's Complete Calculator Handbook. LC 83-19164. 318p. 1984. 24.95 (ISBN 0-13-563296-X, Busn). P-H.
Zill, Dennis, et al. College Mathematics for Students of Business, Life Science & Social Science. 2nd ed. 624p. 1981. text ed. write for info (ISBN 0-534-00886-0). Wadsworth Pub.

MATHEMATICS–STUDY AND TEACHING–AUDIO-VISUAL AIDS

Bestgen, Barbara J. & Reys, Robert E. Films in the Mathematics Classroom. LC 82-3442. 90p. 1982. pap. 5.80 (ISBN 0-87353-195-7). NCTM.
Blazek, Ron. Influencing Students Toward Media Center Use: An Experimental Investigation in Mathematics. LC 75-26769. (Studies in Librarianship Ser.: No. 5). 238p. 1975. pap. text ed. 9.00x (ISBN 0-8389-0201-4). ALA.

MATHEMATICS–STUDY AND TEACHING (ELEMENTARY)

Ballew, Hunter. Teaching Children Mathematics. LC 73-75000. 1973. text ed. 22.95 (ISBN 0-675-08982-4). Merrill.
Bello, Ignacio. Contemporary Basic Mathematical Skills. 2nd ed. 402p. 1983. pap. text ed. 23.95 scp (ISBN 0-06-040614-3, HarpC); answer manual avail. (ISBN 0-06-360611-9); Test Manual avail. (ISBN 0-06-360612-7). Har-Row.
Bolt, Brian. More Mathematical Activities: A Further Resource Book for Teachers. (Illus.). 160p. 1985. 10.95. Cambridge U Pr.
Bosstick, Maurice & Cable, John L. Patterns in the Sand: An Exploration in Mathematics. 2nd ed. (Illus.). 1975. text ed. write for info. (ISBN 0-02-471960-9); ans. bk free (ISBN 0-02-471970-6). Macmillan.
Bouwsma, Ward D. & Corle, Clyde G. Basic Mathematics For Elementary Teachers. LC 67-11887. pap. 88.00 (ISBN 0-317-08422-4, 2012448). BKs Demand UMI.
Caravella, Joseph R. Minicalculators in the Classroom. 64p. 1977. pap. 4.95 (ISBN 0-8106-1812-5). NEA.
Copeland, Richard W. How Children Learn Mathematics: Teaching Implications of Piaget's Research. 4th ed. 448p. 1984. text ed. write for info. (ISBN 0-02-324770-3). Macmillan.
Corle, Clyde G. Teaching Mathematics in the Elementary School. LC 64-13943. pap. 98.80 (ISBN 0-317-08697-9, 2012479). Bks Demand UMI.
D'Augustine, Charles H. Multiple Methods of Teaching Mathematics in the Elementary School. 2nd ed. (Illus.). 416p. 1984. pap. text ed. 13.50 (ISBN 0-8191-4012-0). U Pr of Amer.
Devine, Donald F. & Kaufmann, Jerome E. Elementary Mathematics. LC 76-24805. 525p. 1977. text ed. 31.95x (ISBN 0-471-20970-8); tchr's. manual 8.00 (ISBN 0-471-02394-9). Wiley.
Dubisch, Roy. Basic Concepts of Mathematics for Elementary Teachers. 2nd ed. LC 80-19446. (Mathematics Ser.). (Illus.). 483p. 1981. 26.95 (ISBN 0-201-03170-1); wkbk. 7.95 (ISBN 0-201-03156-6); instr's.manual 3.50 (ISBN 0-201-03173-6). Addison-Wesley.
Fuys, David & Tischler, Rosamond. Teaching Mathematics in the Elementary School. 1979. 23.95 (ISBN 0-316-29720-8); for info. teachers manual (ISBN 0-316-29721-6). Little.
Garner, J., et al. Research Studies in Elementary Mathematics. 1969. pap. 9.95x tchr's. ed. (ISBN 0-8290-1185-4). Irvington.
Glennon, Vincent J., ed. The Mathematical Education of Exceptional Children & Youth: An Interdisciplinary Approach. LC 80-29518. (Illus.). 408p. 1981. 19.50 (ISBN 0-87353-171-X). NCTM.
Graham, Malcolm. Modern Elementary Mathematics. 4th ed. 576p. 1984. text ed. 26.95 (ISBN 0-15-561043-0, HC); instr's manual avail. (ISBN 0-15-561044-9). HarBraceJ.
Grossnickle, Foster E. Discovering Meanings in Elementary School Mathematics. 7th ed. LC 82-21335. 401p. 1983. text ed. 30.95 (ISBN 0-03-059933-4). HR&W.
Hart, Kathleen M. Ratio: Children's Strategies & Errors. 128p. 1984. 20.00 (ISBN 0-7005-0637-3). Taylor & Francis.
Jensen, Rosalie S. & Spector, Deborach C. Teaching Mathematics to Young Children: A Basic Guide. (Illus.). 224p. 1984. 17.95 (ISBN 0-13-894212-9); pap. 8.95 (ISBN 0-13-894204-8). P-H.
Kurtz, V. Ray. Metrics for Elementary & Middle Schools. 120p. 1978. pap. 5.95 (ISBN 0-8106-1714-5). NEA.
Marks, John L. Teaching Elementary School Mathematics for Understanding. 4th ed. (Illus.). 512p. 1975. text ed. 34.95 (ISBN 0-07-040422-4). McGraw.
National Council of Teachers of Mathematics. Mathematics Learning in Early Childhood: 37th Yearbook. LC 75-6631. (Illus.). 316p. 1975. 16.90 (ISBN 0-87353-017-9). NCTM.
National Research Council. Indicators of Precollege Education in Science & Mathematics: A Preliminary Review. 212p. 1985. pap. text ed. 16.50 (ISBN 0-309-03536-8). Natl Acad Pr.
Paige, Donald D., et al. Elementary Mathematical Methods. LC 77-2683. 413p. 1982. 29.95 (ISBN 0-471-09063-8). Wiley.
Price, Shirley & Price, Merle. The Primary Math Lab. LC 78-7984. (Illus.). 1978. 14.95 (ISBN 0-673-16414-4); pap. 12.95 (ISBN 0-673-16415-2). Scott F.
Reesink, Carole J., ed. Teacher-Made Aids for Elementary School Mathematics: Readings from the Arithmetic Teacher, Vol. 2. LC 73-21581. (Illus.). 192p. 1985. pap. write for info. (ISBN 0-87353-225-2). NCTM.
Reeves, Charles A. & Clark, Thom B. Mathematics for the Elementary School Teacher. 1982. text ed. 23.80x (ISBN 0-673-16051-3). Scott F.
Reys, Robert, et al. Helping Children Learn Mathematics. (Illus.). 384p. 1984. 21.95 (ISBN 0-13-387027-8). P-H.
Richardson, Lloyd I., et al. A Mathematics Activity Curriculum for Early Childhood & Special Education. (Illus.). 1980. pap. text ed. write for info. (ISBN 0-02-399710-9). Macmillan.
Riedesel, C. Alan. Teaching Elementary School Mathematics. 4th ed. (Illus.). 416p. 1985. text ed. 27.95 (ISBN 0-13-892621-2). P-H.
Riedesel, C. Alan & Callahan, Leroy G. Elementary School Mathematics for Teachers. 1977. pap. text ed. 15.95 scp (ISBN 0-06-045412-1, HarpC). Har-Row.
Rogers, Agnes L. Experimental Tests of Mathematical Ability & Their Prognostic Value. LC 72-177201. (Columbia University. Teachers College. Contributions to Education: No. 89). Repr. of 1918 ed. 22.50 (ISBN 0-404-55089-4). AMS Pr.
Rosskopf, Myron F. Children's Mathematical Concepts: Six Piagetian Studies in Mathematics Education. LC 75-12872. (Illus.). pap. 56.00 (ISBN 0-317-09439-4, 2017767). Bks Demand UMI.
Rosskopf, Myron F., ed. Children's Mathematical Concepts: Six Piagetian Studies in Mathematical Education. LC 75-12872. 1975. text ed. 14.95x (ISBN 0-8077-2447-5). Tchrs Coll.
Schultz, James E. Mathematics for Elementary School Teachers. 2nd ed. 528p. 1982. text ed. 25.95 (ISBN 0-675-09860-2). Additional supplements may be obtained from publisher. Merrill.
Sprung, Barbara, et al. What Will Happen If... Young Children & the Scientific Method. 1985. pap. text ed. 10.95 (ISBN 0-931629-02-0). Educ Equity Con.

Suppes, Patrick C., et al. Computer-Assisted Instruction: Stanford's 1965-66 Arithmetic Program. (Illus.). 1968. 52.00 (ISBN 0-12-676850-1). Acad Pr.
Suydam, Marilyn N., ed. Alternative Courses for Secondary School Mathematics. 60p. 1985. pap. 4.50 (ISBN 0-87353-222-8). NCTM.
Thornton, et al. Teaching Mathematics to Children with Special Needs. 560p. 1983. 22.25 (ISBN 0-201-07728-0, Sch Div). Addison-Wesley.
Underhill, Richard G., et al. Diagnosing Mathematical Difficulties. (Elementary Education Ser.: No. C22). 408p. 1980. text ed. 22.95 (ISBN 0-675-08195-5). Merrill.

MATHEMATICS–STUDY AND TEACHING (SECONDARY)

Bell, Frederick H. Teaching & Learning Math in Secondary Schools. 576p. 1978. pap. text ed. write for info. (ISBN 0-697-06017-9). Wm C Brown.
Blazek, Ron. Influencing Students Toward Media Center Use: An Experimental Investigation in Mathematics. LC 75-26769. (Studies in Librarianship Ser.: No. 5). 238p. 1975. pap. text ed. 9.00x (ISBN 0-8389-0201-4). ALA.
Breslich, Ernest R. Problems in Teaching Secondary School Mathematics. 348p. 1981. Repr. of 1940 ed. lib. bdg. 40.00 (ISBN 0-89987-078-3). Darby Bks.
--The Technique of Teaching Secondary School Mathematics. 239p. 1982. Repr. of 1930 ed. lib. bdg. 45.00 (ISBN 0-89984-089-2). Century Bookbindery.
Clifton, Barbara. KET Adult Math Series Computer. Webb, Sidney, ed. (Adult Math Ser.). 40p. 1984. tchrs. guide 3.50 (ISBN 0-910475-28-8). KET.
Congdon, Allan R. Training in High-School Mathematics Essential for Success in Certain College Subjects. (Columbia University. Teachers College. Contributions to Education: No. 403). Repr. of 1930 ed. 22.50 (ISBN 0-404-55403-2). AMS Pr.
Cooney, Thomas J. & Davis, Edward J. Dynamics of Teaching Secondary School Mathematics. 448p. 1983. text ed. 24.95x (ISBN 0-88133-061-2). Waveland Pr.
Cooper, Barry. Renegotiating Secondary School Mathematics: A Study of Curriculum Change & Stability. (Studies in Curriculum History Ser.). 300p. 1985. 29.00x (ISBN 1-85000-014-X, Pub. by Falmer Pr); pap. 17.00x (ISBN 1-85000-013-1, Pub. by Falmer Pr). Taylor & Francis.
Dessart, Donald J. & Suydam, Marilyn N. Classroom Ideas from Research on Secondary School Mathematics. LC 83-8279. (Illus.). 128p. 1983. pap. 6.00 (ISBN 0-87353-207-4). NCTM.
Dressler, Isidore. Algebra I. 1966. text ed. 12.83 (ISBN 0-87720-208-7). AMSCO Sch.
--Algebra One Review Guide. (Illus., Orig.). 1966. pap. text ed. 6.83 (ISBN 0-87720-207-9). AMSCO Sch.
Erdsneker, Barbara & Saunders, Brigitte. Mathematics Workbook for the ACT. LC 82-4097. 304p. 1982. pap. 6.95 (ISBN 0-668-05443-3, 5443). Arco.
Farrell, Margaret A. & Farmer, Walter A. Systematic Instruction in Mathematics for the Middle & High School Years. LC 79-4250. (Illus.). 1980. pap. text ed. 17.30 (ISBN 0-201-02436-5, Sch Div). Addison-Wesley.
Garinger, Alan K. Adult Math. Clifton, Barbarba & Tipton, Judy, eds. 290p. 1984. wkbk. 11.00 (ISBN 0-910475-25-3). KET.
Glennon, Vincent J., ed. The Mathematical Education of Exceptional Children & Youth: An Interdisciplinary Approach. LC 80-29518. (Illus.). 408p. 1981. 19.50 (ISBN 0-87353-171-X). NCTM.
Guercio, E., et al. General Mathematical Ability: Preparation & Review for the Mathematics Part of the High School Equivalency Diploma Test. LC 74-19738. (GED Preparation Ser.). 160p. (Orig.). 1975. pap. 6.00 (ISBN 0-668-03689-3). Arco.
Johnson, D. C. & Tinsley, J. D., eds. Informatics & Mathematics in Secondary Schools: Proceedings of the IFIP TC3 Working Conference, Bulgaria. 158p. 1978. 38.50 (ISBN 0-444-85160-7, North-Holland). Elsevier.
Kastner, Bernice. Applications of Secondary School Mathematics. LC 78-8918. (Illus.). 106p. 1978. pap. 7.00 (ISBN 0-87353-127-2). NCTM.
Larcombe, Tony. Mathematical Learning Difficulties in the Secondary School: Pupil Needs & Teacher Roles. 128p. 1985. pap. 12.00 (ISBN 0-335-15020-9). Taylor & Francis.
Mallory, Virgil S. The Relative Difficulty of Certain Topics in Mathematics for Slow-Moving Ninth Grade Pupils. LC 79-177050. (Columbia University. Teachers College. Contributions to Education: No. 769). Repr. of 1939 ed. 22.50 (ISBN 0-404-55769-4). AMS Pr.
Margenau, James & Sentlowitz, Michael. How to Study Mathematics: A Handbook for Students. LC 77-5560. (Illus.). 32p. 1977. pap. 2.50 (ISBN 0-87353-115-9). NCTM.
Miklos, Mary O. Mathematical Ideas. LC 80-5871. 344p. 1980. pap. text ed. 14.00 (ISBN 0-8191-1099-X). U Pr of Amer.
Pontrjagin, L. S. Learning Higher Mathematics. (Springer Series in Soviet Mathematics). (Illus.). 320p. 1984. Vol. 1: The Method of Coordinates. pap. 29.50 (ISBN 0-387-12351-2). Vol. 2: Analysis of the Infinitely Small. Springer-Verlag.
Posamentier, Alfred. Teaching Mathematics in the Secondary School. 1981. pap. text ed. 20.95 (ISBN 0-675-08033-9). Merrill.
Prindle, Anthony. Barron's How to Prepare for the High School Equivalency Examination (GED) General Mathematics, 4 vols. Incl. Vol. 1. Arithmetic (ISBN 0-8120-0727-1); Vol. 2. Algebra (ISBN 0-8120-0728-X); Vol. 3. Geometry, Tables & Graphics, Word Problems (ISBN 0-8120-0729-8); Vol. 4. Model Examinations (ISBN 0-8120-0730-1). LC 78-14808. 1979. pap. 2.95 ea. Barron.
Rosenberger, Noah B. The Place of the Elementary Calculus in the Senior High School Mathematics. LC 71-177209. (Columbia University. Teachers College. Contributions to Education: No. 117). Repr. of 1921 ed. 22.50 (ISBN 0-404-55117-3). AMS Pr.
Schlumpf, Lester, ed. Barron's Three-Year Sequence for High School Mathematics - Course I. 250p. 1981. pap. text ed. 3.95 (ISBN 0-8120-3205-5). Barron.
Secondary School Mathematics Curriculum Improvement Study. Commentary to Booklets. (Unified Modern Mathematics Ser.: Course 6). pap. 76.30 (ISBN 0-317-29985-9, 2051822). Bks Demand UMI.
Tobin, Catherine. Math Study Skills Teacher's Guide. Marshak, David & Morimoto, Kigo, eds. 1981. pap. text ed. 3.50 (ISBN 0-88210-124-2). Natl Assn Principals.
--Math Study Skills Workshop Kit. Marshak, Daniel & Morimoto, Kigo, eds. 1981. pap. text ed. 12.50 (ISBN 0-88210-122-6). Natl Assn Principals.
Vesselo, I. R., ed. Further Training of Mathematics Teachers at Secondary Level. (International Studies in Education: No. 22). 90p. (Orig.). 1970. pap. 6.25 (ISBN 0-685-04909-4, U260, UNESCO). Unipub.
Vogeli, Bruce R. Soviet Secondary Schools for the Mathematically Talented. LC 68-30961. 100p. 1968. pap. 3.40 (ISBN 0-87353-092-6). NCTM.
Williams, Edward. Barron's Getting Ready for the High School Equivaency Examination: Beginning Preparation in Mathematics. LC 76-3662. 1976. pap. 6.95 (ISBN 0-8120-0466-3). Barron.

MATHEMATICS–TABLES, ETC.

see also Integrals; Logarithms; Ready-Reckoners; Trigonometry–Tables, etc.

Abramowitz, M. & Stegun, I. A. Pocketbook of Mathematical Functions. 468p. (Orig.). 1984. pap. 15.00 (ISBN 0-317-14892-3, Pub. by Verlagharri-Deutsch W Germany). Heyden.
Abramowitz, Milton & Stegun, Irene A., eds. Handbook of Mathematical Functions with Formulas, Graphs & Mathematical Tables. (Illus.). 1964. pap. 19.95 (ISBN 0-486-61272-4). Dover.
Auth, Joanne B. Deskbook of Math Formulas & Tables. 208p. 19.95 (ISBN 0-442-20813-8); pap. 14.45 (ISBN 0-442-21106-6). Van Nos Reinhold.
Beyer, William H. Handbook of Mathematical Sciences, 5th ed. 992p. 1978. 49.95 (ISBN 0-8493-0655-8). CRC Pr.
Beyer, William H., ed. Standard Mathematical Tables. 26th ed. 624p. 1981. 24.95 (ISBN 0-8493-0626-4). CRC Pr.
Bigsbee, Earle M. Mathematics Tables with Explanations of Tables. (Quality Paperback Ser.: No. 8). (Orig.). 1977. pap. 2.95 (ISBN 0-8226-0008-0). Littlefield.
Burington, Richard S. Handbook of Mathematical Tables & Formulas. 5th ed. LC 78-39634. (Illus.). 480p. 1973. text ed. 29.95 (ISBN 0-07-009015-7). McGraw.
Carmichael, Robert D. & Smith, Edwin R. Mathematical Tables & Formulas. 1931. pap. 3.75 (ISBN 0-486-60111-0). Dover.
Davis, Harold T. & Fisher, Vera. Tables of Mathematical Functions, Vol. 3. 1962. 8.75 (ISBN 0-911536-17-5). Trinity U Pr.
Enrick, Norbert L. Handbook of Effective Graphic & Tabular Communication. LC 79-4483. 224p. 1980. 13.75 (ISBN 0-88275-914-0). Krieger.
Eswaran, K. S. Mathematical Formulae & Tables. 84p. 1981. 30.00x (ISBN 0-86125-149-0, Pub. by Orient Longman India). State Mutual Bk.
Godfrey, Charles & Siddons, A. W. Four-Figure Tables. text ed. 3.50x (ISBN 0-521-05097-9). Cambridge U Pr.
Graham, Alexander. Kronecker Products & Matrix Calculus with Applications. LC 81-7132. (Mathematics & Its Applications Ser.). 160p. 1981. 48.95x (ISBN 0-470-27300-3). Halsted Pr.
Hackworth, Robert D. & Howland, Joseph. Introductory College Mathematics: Tables & Graphs. LC 75-23628. (Illus.). 62p. 1976. pap. text ed. 9.95 (ISBN 0-7216-4421-X). HR&W.
Halberstam, H. & Richert, H. E. Sieve Methods. 1975. 70.00 (ISBN 0-12-318250-6). Acad Pr.
Handbook of Mathematical Functions with Formulas, Graphs, & Mathematical Tables (NBS) (Selected Government Publications Ser.: 1-698). 1046p. 1964. 44.95x (ISBN 0-471-80007-4, Pub. by Wiley-Interscience). Wiley.
Jahnke, Eugene & Emde, Fritz. Tables of Functions with Formulae & Curves. 4th ed. (Ger & Eng). 1945. pap. text ed. 7.50 (ISBN 0-486-60133-1). Dover.
Johnson, William W. Addition & Subtraction Logarithms: Gaussian Tables. 1943. 3.00 (ISBN 0-685-19461-2). Powner.
Lefax Pub. Co. Editors. Mathematical Tables. (Lefax Technical Manuals.: No. 785). (Illus.). looseleaf bdg. 8.50 (ISBN 0-685-14155-1). Lefax.
--Mathematical Tables. (Lefax Data Bks.: No. 647). (Illus.). 3.00 (ISBN 0-685-52844-8). LeFax.
Shaw, A. M., ed. Handbook of Conversion Factors. 24p. 1978. 3.00x (ISBN 0-934366-01-2). Intl Research Serv.
Smoley, C. K. How to Use Smoley's Tables. Smoley, E. R. & Smoley, N. G., eds. 1976. pap. text ed. 5.00 (ISBN 0-911390-07-3). Smoley.
Spiegel, Murray R. Mathematical Handbook of Formulas & Tables. (Schaum's Outline Ser.). 1968. pap. text ed. 9.95 (ISBN 0-07-060224-7). McGraw.
Wuytack, L. Pade Approximation & Its Application. (Lecture Notes in Mathematics: Vol. 765). 392p. 1979. pap. 25.00 (ISBN 0-387-09717-1). Springer-Verlag.

MATHEMATICS–1961-

Al-Moajil, Abdullah H. & Benharbit, Abdelali. Basic Mathematics: A Pre-Calculus Course for Science & Engineering. LC 80-41685. 308p. 1981. 44.95x (ISBN 0-471-27941-2, Pub. by Wiley Interscience). Wiley.
Althoen, Steven C. & Bumcrot, Robert J. Finite Mathematics. (Illus.). 1978. text ed. 16.95x (ISBN 0-393-09046-9). Norton.
Ash, Peter F. & Robinson, Edward E. Basic College Mathematics: A Calculator Approach. LC 80-15352. (Illus.). 544p. 1981. 23.95 (ISBN 0-201-00091-1); instrs' manual 3.00 (ISBN 0-201-00092-X). Addison-Wesley.
Bajpai, A. C. & Bond, R. M. Applied Math. 349p. 1983. pap. 15.95 (ISBN 0-471-86166-9). Wiley.
Bajpai, A. C., et al. Mathematics for Engineers & Scientists, 2 vols. LC 72-14009. (Series of Programs on Mathematics for Scientist & Technologist). 800p. 1973. Vol. 2, 661 Pgs. 26.95 (ISBN 0-471-04374-5, Pub. by Wiley-Interscience). Wiley.
Baker, Jack, et al. Basic Mathematics. 2nd ed. 1985. text ed. 24.95 (ISBN 0-03-071588-1, CBS C); instr's. manual 9.95 (ISBN 0-317-30070-9). SCP.
Bakst, Aaron. Arithmetic for the Modern Age. LC 60-53374. pap. 87.30 (ISBN 0-317-08507-7, 2007243). Bks Demand UMI.
Barnett, Raymond A. & Burke, Charles J. Applied Mathematics for Business & Economics, Life Sciences & Social Sciences. (Illus.). 856p. 1983. text ed. 24.95 (ISBN 0-02-306310-6). Dellen Pub.
Bellman, R. Selective Computation. (Modern Series in Applied Mathematics: Vol. 4). 250p. 1985. 28.00x (ISBN 9971-966-86-7, Pub. by World Sci Singapore). Taylor & Francis.
Bender, Edward A. An Introduction to Mathematical Modeling. LC 77-23840. 256p. 1978. 36.50x (ISBN 0-471-02951-3, Pub. by Wiley-Interscience); solutions manual 9.00 (ISBN 0-471-03407-X). Wiley.
Bohuslov, Ronald L. Basic Mathematics for Technical Occupations. (Illus.). 480p. 1976. 26.95 (ISBN 0-13-063396-8). P-H.
Burleson, Donald R. Topics in Precalculus Mathematics. (Illus.). 544p. 1974. text ed. 27.95 (ISBN 0-13-925461-7); study guide o.p. 1.95 (ISBN 0-13-925214-2). P-H.
Campbell, Douglas & Higgins, John, eds. Mathematics: People, Problems, Results. LC 83-17039. 900p. 1984. write for info. (ISBN 0-534-03199-4); pap. write for info. (ISBN 0-534-03202-8). Wadsworth Pub.
Carman & Saunders. Modern Technical Math. 1984. write for info. (ISBN 0-534-02739-3). Wadsworth Pub.
--Modern Technical Math with Calculus. write for info. (ISBN 0-534-04305-4). Wadsworth Pub.
Childress, R. L. Fundamentals of Finite Mathematics. (Illus.). 1976. ref. ed. 27.95. P-H.
Childress, Robert L. Mathematics for Managerial Decisions. LC 73-17352. (Illus.). 656p. 1974. ref. ed. 29.95 (ISBN 0-13-562231-X). P-H.
Christy, Dennis T. Essentials of Precalculus Mathematics. 2nd ed. 598p. 1981. text ed. 25.50 scp (ISBN 0-06-041303-4, HarpC); answers to even-numbered exercises avail. (ISBN 0-06-361192-9). Har-Row.
Clar, Lawrence M. & Hart, James A. Mathematics for the Technologies. (Illus.). 1978. text ed. 27.95 (ISBN 0-13-565200-6). P-H.
Cleaves, Cheryl & Hobbs, Margie. Basic Mathematics for Trades & Technologies. (Illus.). 640p. 1983. text ed. 25.95 (ISBN 0-13-063032-2). P-H.
Cochran, James A. Applied Mathematics: Principles, Techniques, & Applications. LC 82-7055. (Mathematics Ser.). 399p. 1982. text ed. write for info (ISBN 0-534-98026-0). Wadsworth Pub.
Crown, J. Conrad & Bittinger, Marvin L. Finite Mathematics: A Modeling Approach. 2nd ed. LC 80-19472. (Mathematics Ser.). (Illus.). 480p. 1981. text ed. 29.95 (ISBN 0-201-03145-0); instrs' manual 3.50 (ISBN 0-201-03146-9). Addison-Wesley.
Devine, Donald F. & Kaufmann, Jerome E. Elementary Mathematics. LC 76-24805. 525p. 1977. text ed. 31.95x (ISBN 0-471-20970-8); tchr's. manual 8.00 (ISBN 0-471-02394-9). Wiley.
Dodge, Howard. How to Prepare for the College Board Achievement Test - Mathematics Level II. LC 78-8655. 1979. pap. 7.95 (ISBN 0-8120-0325-X). Barron.
Driver, R. D. Why Math? (Undergraduate Texts in Mathematics Ser.). (Illus.). 220p. 1984. 24.00 (ISBN 0-387-90973-7). Springer Verlag.
Ewen, Dale & Topper, Michael A. Mathematics for Technical Education. 2nd ed. (Illus.). 496p. 1983. text ed. 27.95 (ISBN 0-13-565168-9). P-H.
Freudenthal, Hans. Didactical Phenomenology of Mathematical Structures. 1983. lib. bdg. 93.50 (ISBN 90-2771-535-1, Pub. by Reidel Holland). Kluwer Academic.
Frieder, David. Total Math Review for the GMAT, GRE & Other Graduate School Admission Tests. LC 81-4054. 336p. 1981. pap. 10.00 (ISBN 0-668-04981-2, 4981). Arco.
Goodstein, R. L. Fundamental Concepts of Mathematics. 2nd ed. 1979. text ed. 53.00 (ISBN 0-08-021665-X); pap. text ed. 19.25 (ISBN 0-08-021666-8). Pergamon.
Griffiths, H. B. & Hilton, P. J. A Comprehensive Textbook of Classical Mathematics: A Contemporary Interpretation. 1978. pap. 29.50 (ISBN 0-387-90342-9). Springer-Verlag.
Groza, Vivian & Shelley, Susanne. Precalculus Mathematics. LC 76-158479. 1972. text ed. 14.95x (ISBN 0-03-077670-8). Irvington.
Gudder, Stanley. A Mathematical Journey. 1976. text ed. 28.95 (ISBN 0-07-025105-3). McGraw.
Guggenheimer, Heinrich W. Mathematics for Engineering & Science. LC 76-28336. (Applied Math Ser.). 290p. 1976. pap. 18.50 (ISBN 0-88275-462-9). Krieger.
Gulati, Bodh R. College Mathematics with Applications to the Business & Social Sciences. (Illus.). 1978. text ed. 27.50 scp (ISBN 0-06-042538-5, HarpC); ans. bklt. avail. (ISBN 0-06-362551-2). Har-Row.
Hackert. Rediscovering Mathematics. 1981. 27.95 (ISBN 0-8053-3660-5); instr's guide 4.95 (ISBN 0-8053-3661-3). Benjamin-Cummings.
Hancock. Introduction to Modern Mathematics Series 1. 1972. pap. text ed. 7.50 each incl. 5 texts (ISBN 0-8449-0210-1); tchr's manual 5.00; test 5.00. Learning Line.
--Introduction to Modern Mathematics Series 2. 1972. pap. text ed. 7.50 each incl. 4 texts (ISBN 0-8449-0220-9); tchrs' manual 5.00; test 5.00. Learning Line.
Hannon, Ralph H. Basic Technical Mathematics with Calculus. LC 76-20934. (Illus.). 1978. text ed. 24.95 (ISBN 0-7216-4497-X). SCP.
Hartnett, William E. Principles of Modern Mathematics. LC 63-7108. pap. 108.00 (ISBN 0-317-09389-4, 2051870). Bks Demand UMI.
Hashisaki, Joseph. Theory & Applications of Mathematics for Elementary School Teachers. 402p. 1983. text ed. 26.95 (ISBN 0-471-09637-7); tchr's. manual avail. (ISBN 0-471-87234-2). Wiley.
Heddens, James W., ed. Today's Mathematics. 5th ed. 688p. 1984. pap. text ed. 22.95 (ISBN 0-574-23110-2, 13-6110). SRA.
Herstein, I. N. & Kaplansky, Irving. Matters Mathematical. 2nd ed. LC 77-16091. 1978. 12.95 (ISBN 0-8284-0300-7). Chelsea Pub.
Herzog, David A. Mathematics Workbook for the GED Test. LC 82-20571. (Arco's Preparation for the GED Examination Ser.). 304p. 1983. pap. 6.95 (ISBN 0-668-05542-1). Arco.

Hofstadter, Douglas R. Goedel, Escher, Bach: An Eternal Golden Braid. LC 80-11354. (Illus.). 800p. 1980. pap. 10.95 (ISBN 0-394-74502-7, Vin). Random.

Howes, Vernon E. Essentials of Mathematics: Precalculus I-a Programmed Text: Algebra I. LC 75-9733. pap. 160.00 (ISBN 0-8357-9886-0, 2051295). Bks Demand UMI.

Hunkins, Dalton R. & Mugridge, Larry R. Applied Finite Mathematics. 2nd ed. 1985. text ed. write for info. (ISBN 0-87150-861-3, 33L2950, Prindle). PWS Pubs.

International Symposium, 3rd, December 5-9, 1977. Computing Methods in Applied Sciences & Engineering, 1977, I: Proceedings. Glowinski, R. & Lions, J. L., eds. (Lecture Notes in Mathematics: Vol. 704). 1979. pap. 22.00 (ISBN 0-387-09123-8). Springer-Verlag.

Kemeny, John G., et al. Introduction to Finite Mathematics. 3rd ed. 512p. 1974. ref. ed. 33.95 (ISBN 0-13-483834-3); answers 1.00 (ISBN 0-13-468835-X). P-H.

Kim, K. A. & Roush, F. W. Mathematics for Social Scientists. LC 79-19336. 304p. 1979. 22.50 (ISBN 0-444-99066-6, KMA/, Pub. by Elsevier). Greenwood.

Koshy, Thomas. An Elementary Approach to Mathematics. LC 75-11271. 512p. 1976. text ed. 19.90x (ISBN 0-673-16232-X). Scott F.

Kra, I. & Maskit, B., eds. Riemann Surfaces & Related Topics: Proceedings of the 1978 Stony Brook Conference. LC 79-27923. (Annals of Mathematics Studies: No.97). 400p. 1981. 35.00x (ISBN 0-691-08264-2); pap. 15.50x (ISBN 0-691-08267-7). Princeton U Pr.

Kramer, A. D. Fundamentals of Technical Mathematics with Calculus. 944p. 1984. 27.40 (ISBN 0-07-035444-8). McGraw.

Kuhfittig, Peter K. Basic Technical Mathematics with Calculus. LC 83-20978. 925p. 1984. text ed. 26.00 pub net (ISBN 0-534-03151-X); pub net solutions manual 8.00 (ISBN 0-534-03152-8). Brooks-Cole.

Lial, Margaret L. & Miller, Charles D. Finite Mathematics. 3rd ed. 1985. text ed. 26.95 (ISBN 0-673-18023-9). Scott F.

--Mathematics & Calculus with Applications. 2nd ed. 1985. text ed. 28.95x (ISBN 0-673-15896-9). Scott F.

Lynn, Rudolph E. Technical Mathematics. LC 84-7343. 712p. 1985. 31.95 (ISBN 0-471-88743-9). Wiley.

Mahler, Kurt. P-Adic Numbers & Their Functions. 2nd ed. LC 79-20103. (Cambridge Tracts in Mathematics Ser.: No. 76). 1981. 57.50 (ISBN 0-521-23102-7). Cambridge U Pr.

Malkevitch, Joseph & Meyer, Walter. Graphs, Models & Finite Mathematics. (Illus.). 480p. 1974. ref. ed. 31.95 (ISBN 0-13-363465-5). P-H.

Miller, Charles D. & Heeren, Vern E. Mathematical Ideas. 5th ed. 1985. text ed. 26.95x (ISBN 0-673-18276-2). Scott F.

Mizrahi, Abe & Sullivan, Michael. Finite Mathematics with Applications for Business & Social Sciences. 3rd ed. LC 78-12522. 1979. text ed. 25.95x (ISBN 0-471-03336-7). study guide 14.45x (ISBN 0-471-05499-2). Wiley.

Mrachek, L. & Kromschlies, C. Technical-Vocational Mathematics. LC 76-48917. 1978. pap. 25.95 (ISBN 0-13-898569-3). P-H.

Myers, Nancy. The Math Book. LC 74-14806. (Illus.). 1975. text ed. 12.00x (ISBN 0-02-849400-8). Hafner.

Pearson, John G., et al. Math Skills for the Sciences. LC 75-40065. (Wiley Self-Teaching Guides Ser). 147p. 1976. pap. 6.95 (ISBN 0-471-67541-5, Pub. by Wiley Pr). Wiley.

Peterson, John. Finite Mathematics. LC 73-10457. 1974. 12.95x (ISBN 0-89197-559-4). Irvington.

Potter, Merle C. Mathematical Methods in the Physical Sciences. (Illus.). 1978. ref. ed. 38.95 (ISBN 0-13-561134-2). P-H.

Pulsinelli, Linda. Living Mathematics: A Survey. (Illus.). 576p. 1982. 29.95 (ISBN 0-13-538819-8). P-H.

Ram, Michael. Essential Mathematics for College Physics with Calculus: A Self Study Guide. 418p. (Orig.). 1984. pap. text ed. 13.50 (ISBN 0-471-80876-8). Wiley.

Rich, Barnett. Review of Elementary Mathematics. (Schaum's Outline Ser.). (Orig.). 1977. pap. 7.95 (ISBN 0-07-052260-X). McGraw.

Riedesel, C. Alan & Callahan, Leroy G. Elementary School Mathematics for Teachers. 1977. pap. text ed. 15.95 scp (ISBN 0-06-045412-1, HarpC). Har-Row.

Smith, Douglas, et al. A Transition to Advanced Mathematics. 2nd ed. LC 85-11392. (Mathematics Ser.). 230p. 1986. text ed. 22.00 pub net. Brooks-Cole.

Smith, Karl J. Mathematics: Its Power & Utility. 2nd. ed. LC 85-9687. (Mathematics Ser.). 512p. 1985. text ed. 28.50 (pub net) (ISBN 0-534-05268-1). Brooks-Cole.

Spencer, Donald D. Computer Science Mathematics. (Mathematics Ser.). 320p. 1976. text ed. 23.95 (ISBN 0-675-08650-7). Merrill.

Sprecher, David A. Finite Mathematics. 352p. 1976. (HarpCW); 2.00 (ISBN 0-06-366389-9). Har-Row.

Stanat, Donald F. & McAllister, David F. Discrete Mathematics in Computer Science. LC 76-48915. (Illus.). 1977. 37.95 (ISBN 0-13-216150-8). P-H.

Strang, Gilbert. An Introduction to Applied Mathematics. LC 84-52450. (Illus.). 650p. 1985. 39.00scp (ISBN 0-9614088-0-4). Wellesley-Cambridge Pr.

Tremblay, J. P. & Manohar, R. Discrete Mathematical Structures with Applications to Computer Science. (Computer Science Ser.). (Illus.). 544p. 1975. text ed. 38.95 (ISBN 0-07-065142-6). McGraw.

Wade, Thomas L. & Taylor, Howard E. Fundamental Mathematics. 4th ed. (Illus.). 608p. 1974. text ed. 37.95 (ISBN 0-07-067652-6). McGraw.

Washington, Allyn J. Arithmetic & Beginning Algebra. 2nd ed. 1984. 24.95 (ISBN 0-8053-9540-7). Benjamin-Cummings.

--Basic Technical Mathematics. 4th ed. 750p. 1985. 31.95 (ISBN 0-8053-9550-4); By Zeigler & Brazen. student solutions manual 11.95 (ISBN 0-8053-9543-1). Benjamin-Cummings.

Washington, Allyn J. & Triola, Mario F. Introduction to Technical Mathematics. 3rd ed. 1984. 28.95 (ISBN 0-8053-9510-5); instr's guide 5.95 (ISBN 0-8053-9511-3). Benjamin-Cummings.

Wheeler, Ruric E. & Peeples, W. D., Jr. Finite Mathematics: With Applications to Business & the Social Sciences. LC 80-13916. 550p. 1980. text ed. 24.00 pub net (ISBN 0-8185-0418-8). Brooks-Cole.

--Modern Mathematics with Applications to Business & the Social Sciences. 3rd ed. LC 79-18636. 1980. text ed. 23.50 pub net (ISBN 0-8185-0366-1). Brooks-Cole.

Whipkey, Mary N., et al. The Power of Relevant Mathematics: The Basic Concept. (Illus.). 1977. text ed. 29.95 (ISBN 0-13-687202-6). P-H.

Willerding, Margaret. The Business of Mathematics. 1977. write for info. (ISBN 0-87150-210-0, PWS 1681, Prindle). PWS Pubs.

--First Course in College Mathematics. 4th ed. text ed. write for info. (ISBN 0-87150-285-2, Prindle); pap. text ed. write for info. PWS Pubs.

Williams, Bill R. & Crotts, Gwen. Man's Mathematical Models: Fundamental Concepts for the Nonmathematician. LC 73-93104. 384p. 1975. 22.95x (ISBN 0-88229-110-6). Nelson-Hall.

Williams, Donald R. Modern Mathematics for Business Decision-Making. 2nd ed. 1978. text ed. write for info. (ISBN 0-534-00558-6). Wadsworth Pub.

Williams, Ralph C. Mathematics for Communication: Number Relations. LC 70-123614. pap. 77.80 (ISBN 0-317-08500-X, 2007734). Bks Demand UMI.

Zill, Dennis G. & Dewar, Jacqueline M. Basic Mathematics for Calculus. 2nd ed. 448p. 1982. text ed. write for info (ISBN 0-534-01197-7). Wadsworth Pub.

MATHEMATICS, ANCIENT

Neugebauer, Otto. The Exact Sciences in Antiquity. 2nd ed. LC 69-20421. (Illus.). 1969. pap. 5.00 (ISBN 0-486-22332-9). Dover.

Sesiano, J. Diophantus' Arithmetica: Books IV to VI in the Arabic Translation of Qusta Ibn Luqa. (Sources in the History of Mathematics & Physical Sciences Ser.: Vol. 3). (Illus.). 502p. 1982. 79.00 (ISBN 0-387-90690-8). Springer-Verlag.

MATHEMATICS, ARABIC

Abu Al-Hasan & Ahmed-Ibn Ibrahim. The Arithmetic of Al-Uqlidisi. Saidan, A. S., tr. 1978. lib. bdg. 103.00 (ISBN 90-277-0752-9, Pub. by Reidel Holland). Kluwer Academic.

Al-Daffa, A. A. & Shawki, G. Mathematical Sciences in Islamic Civilization, 2 vols. (Arabic.). 400p. 1985. Vol. 1. pap. 18.00 (ISBN 0-471-87557-0); Vol. 2. pap. 18.00 (ISBN 0-471-87282-2). Wiley.

Al-Daffa, Ali A. The Muslim Contribution to Mathematics. 1977. text ed. 23.50x (ISBN 0-391-00714-9). Humanities.

Khayyam, Omar. The Algebra of Omar Khayyam. Kasir, Daoud S., ed. LC 70-177135. (Columbia University. Teachers College. Contributions to Education: No. 385). Repr. of 1931 ed. 22.50 (ISBN 0-404-55385-0). AMS Pr.

Levey, Martin & Petruck, Marvin, eds. Kushyar ibn Labban: "Principles of Hindu Reckoning". (Medieval Science Pubns., No. 8). 128p. 1965. 30.00x (ISBN 0-299-03610-3). U of Wis Pr.

Shuja Ibn Aslam, Abukamil. The Algebra of Abu Kamil, in a Commentary by Mordecai Finzi. Levey, Martin, tr. (Publications in Medieval Science No. 10). 240p. 1966. 37.50x (ISBN 0-299-03800-9). U of Wis Pr.

MATHEMATICS, BUSINESS

see Business Mathematics

MATHEMATICS, CHINESE

Current Topics in Chinese Science: Section C: Mathematics. 493p. 1984. pap. 25.00 (ISBN 0-317-11705-X). Gordon.

Current Topics in Chinese Science, Section C: Mathematics, Vol. 3. 880p. 1985. pap. text ed. 98.00 (ISBN 0-677-40405-0). Gordon.

Fitzgerald, Anne & Lane, Saunders M., eds. Pure & Applied Math in People's Republic of China. LC 77-79329. (CSCPRC Report: No. 3). 1977. pap. 9.75 (ISBN 0-309-02609-1). Natl Acad Pr.

Gould, S. H. Contemporary Chinese Research Mathematics, Vol. 2: A Report on Chinese-English Mathematical Dictionaries. 19p. 1964. 4.00 (ISBN 0-8218-0016-7, CED). Am Math.

Mikami, Y. The Development of Mathematics in China & Japan. 2nd ed. LC 74-6716. 383p. 1974. text ed. 17.95 (ISBN 0-8284-0149-7). Chelsea Pub.

Swetz, Frank. Mathematics Education in China: Its Growth & Development. 350p. 1974. 25.00x (ISBN 0-262-19121-0). MIT Pr.

Swetz, Frank & Kao, T. I. Was Pythagoras Chinese? An Examination of Right Triangle Theory in Ancient China. LC 76-41806. (Penn State Studies: No. 40). (Illus.). 1977. pap. 4.95x (ISBN 0-271-01238-2). Pa St U Pr.

MATHEMATICS, CONSTRUCTIVE

see Constructive Mathematics

MATHEMATICS, GREEK

see also Geometry–Early Works to 1800

Allman, George J. Greek Geometry from Thales to Euclid. facsimile ed. LC 75-13250. (History of Ideas in Ancient Greece Ser.). 1976. Repr. of 1889 ed. 18.00x (ISBN 0-405-07287-2). Ayer Co Pubs.

Brumbaugh, Robert S. Plato's Mathematical Imagination: The Mathematical Passages in the Dialogues & Their Interpretation. LC 55-62013. (Illus.). 1954. 20.00 (ISBN 0-527-12900-3). Kraus Repr.

Clagett, Marshall. Archimedes in the Middle Ages, Vol. 1. Arabo-Latin Tradition. LC 62-7218. (Medieval Science Pubns., No. 6). (Illus.). Repr. of 1964 ed. 120.00 (ISBN 0-8357-9771-6, 2012629). Bks Demand UMI.

Euclid. The Elements, 3 vols. Heath, Thomas L., ed. 1926. Vol. 1. pap. 7.50 (ISBN 0-486-60088-2); Vol. 2. pap. 7.50 (ISBN 0-486-60089-0); Vol. 3. pap. 7.50 (ISBN 0-486-60090-4). Dover.

Gow, James. Short History of Greek Mathematics. LC 68-21639. 1968. 14.95 (ISBN 0-8284-0218-3). Chelsea Pub.

Heath, Thomas L. A History of Greek Mathematics, 2 vols. (Illus.). 1058p. 1981. pap. 8.50 ea. Vol. I (ISBN 0-486-24073-8). Vol. II (ISBN 0-486-24074-6). Dover.

Nicomachus, Gerasenus. Introduction to Arithmetic. D'Ooge, Martin L., tr. Repr. of 1926 ed. 37.00 (ISBN 0-384-38816-7). Johnson Repr.

Sesiano, J. Diophantus' Arithmetica: Books IV to VI in the Arabic Translation of Qusta Ibn Luqa. (Sources in the History of Mathematics & Physical Sciences Ser.: Vol. 3). (Illus.). 502p. 1982. 79.00 (ISBN 0-387-90690-8). Springer-Verlag.

Szabo, Arprad. The Beginnings of Greek Mathematics. (Synthese Historical Library: No. 17). 1978. lib. bdg. 53.00 (ISBN 90-277-0819-3, Pub. by Reidel Holland). Kluwer Academic.

Tannery, Paul. La Geometrie Grecque: Comment Son Histoire Nous Est Parvenue & E Que Nous En Savons. facsimile ed. LC 75-13296. (History of Ideas in Ancient Greece Ser.). (Fr.). 1976. Repr. of 1887 ed. 13.00x (ISBN 0-405-07340-2). Ayer Co Pubs.

Taran, Leonardo. Asclepius of Tralles: Commentary to Nicomachus' Introduction to Arithmetic. LC 69-18747. (Transactions Ser.: Vol. 59, Pt. 4). 1969. pap. 2.00 (ISBN 0-87169-594-4). Am Philos.

Theon Of Smyrna. Theon of Smyrna: Mathematics Useful for Understanding Plato or, Pythagorean Arithmetic, Music, Astronomy, Spiritual Disciplines. Lawlor, Robert, tr. from Greek. LC 77-73716. (Secret Doctrine Reference Ser.). (Illus.). 200p. 1978. 12.00 (ISBN 0-913510-24-6). Wizards.

Thomas, Ivor, tr. Greek Mathematical Works, 2 Vols. (Loeb Classical Library: No. 335, 362). 12.00x. Vol. 1 (ISBN 0-674-99369-1). Vol. 2 (ISBN 0-674-99399-3). Harvard U Pr.

Tod, M. N. Ancient Greek Numerical Systems. 128p. 1979. 20.00 (ISBN 0-89005-290-5). Ares.

Toomer, G. J., tr. & commentary by. Diocles on Burning Mirrors. (Sources in the History of Mathematics & the Physical Sciences Ser.: Vol. 1). (Illus.). 240p. 1976. 42.00 (ISBN 0-387-07478-3). Springer-Verlag.

MATHEMATICS, HINDU

Levey, Martin & Petruck, Marvin, eds. Kushyar ibn Labban: "Principles of Hindu Reckoning". (Medieval Science Pubns., No. 8). 128p. 1965. 30.00x (ISBN 0-299-03610-3). U of Wis Pr.

Tirthaji, Bharati K. Vedic Mathematics. 1978. 16.50 (ISBN 0-89684-036-0, Pub. by Motilal Banarsidass India). Orient Bk Dist.

MATHEMATICS, JAPANESE

Smith, David Eugene & Mikami, Yoshio. History of Japanese Mathematics. 280p. 1914. 19.95 (ISBN 0-87548-170-1). Open Court.

MATHEMATICS, LOGIC OF

see Mathematics–Philosophy

MATHEMATICS, GERMAN

Hasse, Helmut. Mathematische Abhandlungen, 3 vols. Leopoldt, Heinrich W. & Roquette, Peter, eds. xxxvi, 1592p. 1975. 236.00x (ISBN 3-11-005931-2). De Gruyter.

Hesse, Ludwig O. Gesammelte Werke. LC 72-78370. 741p. 1972. Repr. text ed. 35.00 (ISBN 0-8284-0261-2). Chelsea Pub.

MATHEMATICS AS A PROFESSION

MAA Committee on Advisement & Personnel. Professional Opportunities in Mathematics. 11th ed. 1983. pap. 1.50 (ISBN 0-88385-440-6). Math Assn.

MATHEMATICS OF FINANCE

see Business Mathematics

MATHIEU FUNCTIONS

Meixner, J., et al. Mathieu Functions & Spheroidal Functions & Their Mathematical Foundations. (Lecture Notes in Mathematics Ser.: Vol. 837). 126p. 1980. pap. 12.00 (ISBN 0-387-10282-5). Springer-Verlag.

MATRICES

see also Eigenvalues; Games of Strategy (Mathematics); Linear Programming; Matrix Groups; Multivariate Analysis

Althoen, Steven C. & Bumcrot, Robert J. Matrix Methods in Finite Mathematics: An Introduction with Applications to Business & Industry. new ed. 350p. 1976. text ed. 26.95x (ISBN 0-393-09192-9). Norton.

Amundson, Neal R. Mathematical Methods in Chemical Engineering: Matrices & Their Application. 1966. ref. ed. 42.95 (ISBN 0-13-561084-2). P-H.

Atkinson, F. V. Multiparameter Eignevalue Problems: Matrices & Compact Operators. (Mathematics in Science & Engineering Ser.). 1972. Vol. 1. 55.00 (ISBN 0-12-065801-1); Vol. 2. write for info. (ISBN 0-12-065802-X). Acad Pr.

Ayres, Frank, Jr. Matrices. (Schaum's Outline Ser.). (Orig.). 1968. pap. 7.95 (ISBN 0-07-002656-4). McGraw.

Azar, J. J. Matrix Structural Analysis. 1972. text ed. 33.00 (ISBN 0-08-016781-0). Pergamon.

Barnett, Stephen. Matrices in Control Theory. rev. ed. LC 82-21321. 206p. 1984. lib. bdg. 14.50 (ISBN 0-89874-590-X). Krieger.

--Matrix Methods for Engineers & Scientists. 185p. 1979. pap. text ed. 23.95 (ISBN 0-07-084084-9). McGraw.

Bart, H., et al. Minimal Factorization of Matrix & Operator Functions. (Operator Theory: Advances & Applications Ser.: No. 1). 236p. 1979. pap. 20.95x (ISBN 0-8176-1139-8). Birkhauser.

Berman, Abraham & Plemmons, Robert J. Non-Negative Matrices in the Mathematical Sciences. (Computer Sciences & Applied Mathematics Ser.). 1979. 49.50 (ISBN 0-12-092250-9). Acad Pr.

Bommer, C. M. & Symonds, D. A. Skeletal Structures: Matrix. 106p. 1968. 38.50 (ISBN 0-677-61120-X). Gordon.

Boullion, Thomas L. & Odell, Patrick L. Generalized Inverse Matrices. LC 79-149768. 116p. 1971. 15.00 (ISBN 0-471-09110-3, Pub. by Wiley). Krieger.

Bronson, R. Matrix Methods: An Introduction. 1970. text ed. 21.75i (ISBN 0-12-135250-1). Acad Pr.

Brown, Homer E. Solution of Large Networks by Matrix Methods. LC 74-34159. 256p. 1975. 40.50X (ISBN 0-471-11045-0, Pub. by Wiley-Interscience). Wiley.

Campbell, Hugh G. Introduction to Matrices, Vectors & Linear Programming. 2nd ed. LC 76-22757. (Illus.). 1977. text ed. 25.95 (ISBN 0-13-487439-0). P-H.

--Matrices with Applications. (Illus.). 1968. pap. text ed. 17.95 (ISBN 0-13-565424-6). P-H.

Cline, Randall E. Elements of the Theory of Generalized Inverses of Matrices. (UMAP Modules). 94p. 1979. pap. text ed. 6.95x (ISBN 0-8176-3013-9). Birkhauser.

Cunninghame-Green, R. A. Minimax Algebra. LC 79-1314. (Lecture Notes in Economics & Mathematical Systems: Vol. 166). 1979. pap. 19.00 (ISBN 0-387-09113-0). Springer-Verlag.

Davis, Philip J. Circulant Matrices. LC 79-10551. (Pure & Applied Mathematics Ser.). 250p. 1979. 39.95 (ISBN 0-471-05771-1, Pub. by Wiley-Interscience). Wiley.

--The Mathematics of Matrices. LC 84-5647. 368p. 1984. Repr. of 1965 ed. lib. bdg. 26.50 (ISBN 0-89874-756-2). Krieger.

Davis, Stanley M., et al. Matrix. LC 77-81192. (An Organization Development Ser.). 1977. pap. text ed. 10.95 (ISBN 0-201-01115-8). Addison-Wesley.

Zichichi, A., ed. Understanding the Fundamental Constituents of Matter. LC 78-2898. (The Subnuclear Ser.). 924p. 1978. 125.00x (ISBN 0-306-38183-4, Plenum Pr). Plenum Pub.

MATTER–CONSTITUTION

see also Atoms; Chemical Structure; Dipole Moments; Electrons; Ether (Of Space); Molecular Theory; Nuclear Models; Nuclear Shell Theory; Neutrons; Protons

Amaldi, Ginestra. The Nature of Matter: Physical Theory from Thales to Fermi. Astbury, Peter, tr. LC 66-12133. 1982. pap. 11.00x (ISBN 0-226-01661-7). U of Chicago Pr.

Anderson, P. W. Basic Notions of Condensed Matter Physics: Frontiers in Physics. (No. 55). 1984. 42.95 (ISBN 0-8053-0220-4); pap. 24.95 (ISBN 0-8053-0219-0). Benjamin-Cummings.

Ballian, R. & Maynard, R., eds. Ill-Condensed Matter: Les Houches Session XXXI. xxvi, 610p. 1983. 60.00x (ISBN 9971-950-59-6, Pub. by World Sci Singapore); pap. 28.00x (ISBN 9971-950-60-X, Pub. by World Sci Singapore). Taylor & Francis.

Born, Max. Restless Universe. 2nd ed. (Illus.). viii, 315p. 1951. pap. 6.00 (ISBN 0-486-20412-X). Dover.

Burstein, Elias & De Martini, Francesco, eds. Polaritons: Proceedings, Taormina Research Conference on the Structure of Matter, 1st, Taormina, Italy, Oct, 1972. LC 73-12845. 1975. text ed. 53.00 (ISBN 0-08-017825-1). Pergamon.

Careri. Order & Disorder in Matter. 1984. 38.95 (ISBN 0-8053-1700-7); pap. 19.95 (ISBN 0-8053-1725-2). Benjamin-Cummings.

Eisberg, Robert M. Fundamentals of Modern Physics. LC 61-6770. (Illus.). 729p. 1961. 45.45x (ISBN 0-471-23463-X). Wiley.

Fano, U. & Fano, L. Physics of Atoms & Molecules: An Introduction to the Structure of Matter. LC 76-184808. 456p. 1973. text ed. 35.00x (ISBN 0-226-23782-6). U of Chicago Pr.

Gasiorowicz, Stephen. Structure of Matter: A Survey of Modern Physics. LC 78-18645. (Physics Ser.). (Illus.). 1979. text ed. 34.95 (ISBN 0-201-02511-6). Addison-Wesley.

Houwink, Roelof. Elasticity, Plasticity & Structure of Matter. 3rd ed. LC 72-154515. (Illus.). 1971. 67.50 (ISBN 0-521-07875-X). Cambridge U Pr.

Karapetyants, M. & Drakin, S. The Structure of Matter. 335p. 1974. 5.45 (ISBN 0-8285-0804-6, Pub. by Mir Pubs USSR). Imported Pubns.

Kitaigorodsky, A. I. Order & Disorder in the World of Atoms. 165p. 1980. pap. 5.95 (ISBN 0-8285-1724-X, Pub. by Mir Pubs USSR). Imported Pubns.

Matsubara, T., ed. The Structure & Properties of Matter. (Springer Series in Solid-State Sciences: Vol. 28). (Illus.). 450p. 1982. 48.00 (ISBN 0-387-11098-4). Springer-Verlag.

Polkinghorne, J. C. The Particle Play: An Account of the Ultimate Constituents of Matter. LC 79-17846. (Illus.). 138p. 1979. pap. text ed. 10.95x (ISBN 0-7167-1316-0). W H Freeman.

Samsonov, G. V., et al. A Configurational Model of Matter. LC 73-83893. (Studies in Soviet Science - Physical Sciences Ser.). (Illus.). 289p. 1973. 35.00x (ISBN 0-306-10890-9, Consultants). Plenum Pub.

Schuster, Karl. The Structure of Matter. (Siemens Programmed Instruction Ser.: No. 8). pap. 20.00 (ISBN 0-317-27769-3, 2052085). Bks Demand UMI.

Silverman, Sanford L. & Silverman, Martin G. Theory of Relationships. LC 63-13349. 1964. 6.00 (ISBN 0-8022-1571-8). Philos Lib.

Slater, John C. Quantum Theory of Molecules & Solids, Vol. 1, 3 & 4. Incl. Vol. 1. Electronic Structure of Molecules. 1963; Vol. 3. Insulators, Semiconductors & Solids. 1969; Vol. 4. The Self-Consistent Field for Molecules & Solids. 47.95 (ISBN 0-07-058038-3, C). McGraw.

Symposium of the International Astronomical Union, 53rd, Boulder, 21-26 August, 1972. Physics of Dense Matter: Proceedings. Hansen, Carl J., ed. LC 73-91431. (IAU Symposium Ser: No. 53). 1974. lib. bdg. 53.00 (ISBN 90-277-0406-6, Pub. by Reidel Holland); pap. text ed. 37.50 (ISBN 90-277-0407-4, Pub. by Reidel Holland). Kluwer Academic.

Taube, M. Evolution of Matter & Energy. (Illus.). 290p. 1985. pap. 24.00 (ISBN 0-387-13399-2). Springer-Verlag.

MATTER–PROPERTIES

see also Anisotropy; Atomic Mass; Brownian Movements; Capillarity; Chemistry, Physical and Theoretical; Colloids; Compressibility; Diffusion; Elasticity; Flocculation; Gases; Gravitation; Ions; Mass (Physics); Solution (Chemistry); Torsion; Viscosity

Cottrell, A. H. The Mechanical Properties of Matter. LC 80-12439. 340p. 1981. Repr. of 1964 ed. lib. bdg. 23.50 (ISBN 0-89874-168-8). Krieger.

Davies, P. C. W. The Forces of Nature. 2nd ed. (Illus.). 270p. Date not set. price not set (ISBN 0-521-30933-6); pap. price not set (ISBN 0-521-31392-9). Cambridge U Pr.

DeWitt, C. & DeWitt, eds. Les Houches Lectures: 1972, Black Holes. 564p. 1973. 120.75 (ISBN 0-677-15610-3). Gordon.

Eisenmenger, W., et al, eds. Phonon Scattering in Condensed Matter: Proceedings of the Fourth International Conference in Stuttgart, West Germany, August 22-26, 1983. (Springer Series in Solid-State Sciences: Vol. 51). (Illus.). 480p. 1984. 30.00 (ISBN 0-387-12954-5). Springer-Verlag.

Goodstein, David L. States of Matter. 512p. 1985. pap. 10.95 (ISBN 0-486-64927-X). Dover.

Lundqvist, Bengt & Lundqvist, Stig, eds. Collective Properties of Physical Systems: Proceedings. 1974. 68.50 (ISBN 0-12-460350-5). Acad Pr.

McMullin, Ernan. Newton on Matter & Activity. LC 77-82480. 1978. text ed. 10.95 (ISBN 0-268-01342-X). U of Notre Dame Pr.

Matsubara, T., ed. The Structure & Properties of Matter. (Springer Series in Solid-State Sciences: Vol. 28). (Illus.). 450p. 1982. 48.00 (ISBN 0-387-11098-4). Springer-Verlag.

Oparin, Alexander I. Origin of Life. 2nd ed. 1953. pap. 5.95 (ISBN 0-486-60213-3). Dover.

Pekalski, A. & Przystawa, J. A., eds. Modern Trends in the Theory of Condensed Matter: Proceedings. (Lecture Notes in Physics: Vol. 115). 587p. 1980. pap. 45.00 (ISBN 0-387-09752-X). Springer-Verlag.

Perlin Yu, E. & Wagner, M. Modern Problems in Condensed Matter Sciences: The Dynamical Jahn-Teller Effect in Localized Systems. Date not set. write for info. (ISBN 0-444-86779-1). Elsevier.

Purdue University, Thermophysical Properties Research Center. Thermophysical Properties of Matter: Specific Heat - Metallic Elements & Alloys, Vol. 4. LC 73-129616. pap. 160.00 (ISBN 0-317-26282-3, 2055697). Bks Demand UMI.

--Thermophysical Properties of Matter: Specific Heat Nonmetallic Liquids & Gases, Vol. 6. LC 73-129616. (TPRC Data Ser.). pap. 95.80 (ISBN 0-317-27798-7, 2055953). Bks Demand UMI.

--Thermophysical Properties of Matter: Thermal Conductivity - Nonmetallic Liquids & Gases. LC 73-129616. pap. 160.00 (ISBN 0-317-26375-7, 2055696). Bks Demand UMI.

Purdue University, Thermophysical Properties Reserch Center Staff & Touloukian, Y. S. Thermophysical Properties of Matter: Thermal Expansion-Nonmetallic Solids, Vol. 13. LC 73-129616. (TPRC Data Ser.). pap. 160.00 (ISBN 0-317-26280-7, 2055698). Bks Demand UMI.

Purdue University, Thermophysical Properties Research Center. Thermophysical Properties of Matter: The TPRC Data Series, Vol. 1: Thermal Conductivity; Metallic Elements & Alloys. LC 73-129616. pap. 160.00 (ISBN 0-317-28047-3, 2055777). Bks Demand UMI.

--Thermophysical Properties of Matter: The TPRC Data Series, Vol. 6 Supplement: Specific Heat: Nonmetallic Liquids & Gases. LC 73-129616. pap. 42.30 (ISBN 0-317-28042-2, 2055778). Bks Demand UMI.

Rickayzen, G. Green's Functions & Condensed Matter. 1981. 55.00 (ISBN 0-12-587950-4). Acad Pr.

Riste, T., ed. Fluctuations, Instabilities & Phase Transitions. LC 75-32413. (NATO ASI Ser. B, Physics: Vol. 11). 390p. 1975. 59.50x (ISBN 0-306-35711-9, Plenum Pr). Plenum Pub.

Ruud, Clay O. & Green, Robert E., Jr., eds. Nondestructive Methods for Material Property Determination. 420p. 1984. 65.00x (ISBN 0-306-41675-1, Plenum Pr). Plenum Pub.

Turnbull, R. M. The Structure of Matter: An Introduction to Atomic Nuclear & Particle Physics. (Illus.). 266p. 1979. pap. text ed. 22.50x (ISBN 0-216-90753-5). Intl Ideas.

Walton, Alan J. Three Phases of Matter. 2nd ed. (Illus.). 1983. 49.50x (ISBN 0-19-851957-5); pap. 24.95x (ISBN 0-19-851953-2). Oxford U Pr.

MAURY, MATTHEW FONTAINE, 1806-1873

Lewis, Charles L. Matthew Fontaine Maury. LC 79-6116. (Navies & Men Ser.). (Illus.). 1980. Repr. of 1927 ed. lib. bdg. 28.50x (ISBN 0-405-13045-7). Ayer Co Pubs.

--Matthew Fontaine Maury, the Pathfinder of the Seas. LC 72-98638. Repr. of 1927 ed. 16.00 (ISBN 0-404-03984-7). AMS Pr.

MAUSER PISTOL

Belford & Dunlap. Mauser Self Loading Pistol. 18.50 (ISBN 0-87505-108-1). Borden.

MAVAR (ELECTRONICS)

see Parametric Amplifiers

MAVERICK (AUTOMOBILE)

see Automobiles–Types–Maverick

MAXIM, HIRAM STEVENS, SIR, 1840-1916

Maxim, Hiram P. Genius in the Family. (Illus.). 1936. pap. 2.95 (ISBN 0-486-20948-2). Dover.

MAXIMA AND MINIMA

see also Calculus of Variations; Mathematical Optimization

Cunninghame-Green, R. A. Minimax Algebra. LC 79-1314. (Lecture Notes in Economics & Mathematical Systems: Vol. 166). 1979. pap. 19.00 (ISBN 0-387-09113-0). Springer-Verlag.

Danskin, J. M. Theory of Max-Min, & Its Application to Weapons Allocation Problems. (Econometrics & Operation Research: Vol. 5). (Illus.). 1967. 28.00 (ISBN 0-387-03943-0). Springer-Verlag.

Demyanov, V. & Malozemov, V. N. Introduction to Minimax. Louvish, D., tr. from Rus. LC 74-8156. 307p. 1974. 44.95x (ISBN 0-470-20850-3). Halsted Pr.

DeVore, Ronald A. & Sharpley, Robert C. Maximal Functions Measuring Smoothness. LC 83-21494. (Memoirs Ser.: No. 293). 116p. 1984. pap. 11.00 (ISBN 0-8218-2293-4). Am Math.

Elliott, Robert J. & Kalton, Nigel J. The Existence of Value in Differential Games. LC 72-4562. (Memoirs: No. 126). 67p. 1972. pap. 9.00 (ISBN 0-8218-1826-0, MEMO-126). Am Math.

Girsanov, I. V. Lectures on Mathematical Theory of Extremum Problems. Louvish, D., tr. from Rus. LC 72-80360. (Lecture Notes in Economics & Mathematical Systems: Vol. 67). (Illus.). 139p. 1972. pap. 11.00 (ISBN 0-387-05857-5). Springer-Verlag.

Gumbel, Emil J. Statistics of Extremes. LC 57-10160. 1958. 40.00x (ISBN 0-231-02190-9). Columbia U Pr.

Hight, Donald W. A Concept of Limits. 2nd ed. LC 77-80029. 1978. pap. text ed. 4.00 (ISBN 0-486-63543-0). Dover.

Kiwiel, K. C. Methods of Descent for Nondifferentiable Optimization. (Lecture Notes in Mathematics: Vol. 1133). vi, 362p. 1985. pap. 23.50 (ISBN 0-387-15642-9). Springer-Verlag.

Morse, Marston. Variational Analysis: Critical Extremals & Sturmian Extensions. LC 72-8368. (Pure & Applied Mathematics Ser.). Repr. of 1973 ed. 51.70 (ISBN 0-8357-9998-0, 2019523). Bks Demand UMI.

Niven, Ivan. Maxima & Minima Without Calculus. LC 80-81045. (Dolciani Mathematical Expositions Ser.: Vol. 6). 303p. 1982. 28.50 (ISBN 0-88385-306-X). Math Assn.

Pincus-Witten, Robert. Entries (Maximalism) (Illus.). 250p. 1983. pap. 14.95 (ISBN 0-915570-20-3). Oolp Pr.

Sperb, Rene. Maximum Principles & Their Applications. LC 81-2436. (Mathematics in Science & Engineering Ser.). 1981. 41.50 (ISBN 0-12-656880-4). Acad Pr.

MAXWELL, JAMES CLERK, 1831-1879

Buchwald, Jed Z. From Maxwell to Microphysics: Aspects of Electromagnetic Theory in the Last Quarter of the Nineteenth-Century. LC 85-1191. (Illus.). 384p. 1985. lib. bdg. 70.00x (ISBN 0-226-07882-5). U of Chicago Pr.

Campbell, Lewis & Garnett, William. Life of James Clerk Maxwell. (Sources of Science, House Ser: No. 85). 1970. Repr. of 1882 ed. 50.00 (ISBN 0-384-07295-X). Johnson Repr.

Goldman, Martin. The Demon in the Aether: The Story of James Clerk Maxwell, the Father of Modern Science. 320p. 1983. 30.00 (ISBN 0-9960042-2-X, Pub. by A Hilger England). Heyden.

Tricker, R. A. Contributions of Faraday & Maxwell to Electrical Science. 1966. pap. 11.25 (ISBN 0-08-011976-X). Pergamon.

MAXWELL EQUATIONS

Bevensee, Robert M. Handbook of Conical Antennas & Scatterers. LC 71-172793. (Illus.). 182p. 1973. 67.25 (ISBN 0-677-00480-X). Gordon.

Thomas, E. G. & Meadows, A. J. Maxwell's Equations & Their Applications. (Student Monographs in Physics). 64p. (Orig.). 1985. pap. text ed. 5.00 (ISBN 0-85274-778-0, 990300587, Pub. by Adam Hilger Techo Hse UK). Heyden.

MAY-FLIES

see also Caddis-Flies

Britt, N. Wilson. Biology of Two Species of Lake Erie Mayflies. 1962. 2.50 (ISBN 0-86727-047-0). Ohio Bio Survey.

Burks, B. D. The Mayflies, or Ephemeroptera, of Illinois. LC 75-2296. (Illus.). viii, 216p. 1975. Repr. of 1953 ed. 15.00 (ISBN 0-911836-06-3). Entomological Repr.

Leonard, Justin W. & Leonard, Fannie A. Mayflies of Michigan Trout Streams. LC 62-9726. (Bulletin Ser.: No. 43). 139p. 1962. pap. 8.00x (ISBN 0-87737-020-6). Cranbrook.

MAYA CALENDAR

see Calendar, Maya

MAYFLIES

see May-Flies

MAZDA AUTOMOBILE

see Automobiles, Foreign–Types–Mazda

MAZUT

see Petroleum As Fuel; Petroleum Products

MEALY BUGS

McKenzie, Howard L. Mealybugs of California: With Taxonomy, Biology, & Control of North American Species. (Illus.). 1968. 78.50x (ISBN 0-520-00844-8). U of Cal Pr.

Williams, D. J. Australian Mealybugs. (Illus.). 431p. 1985. 80.00x (ISBN 0-565-00953-2, Pub. by Brit Mus Nat Hist England). Sabbot-Natural Hist Bks.

MEASURABLE SETS

see Measure Theory

MEASURE, CARATHEODORY

see Caratheodory Measure

MEASURE THEORY

see also Caratheodory Measure; Ergodic Theory; Spectral Theory (Mathematics)

Abramov, L. M., et al. Ten Papers on Functional Analysis & Measure Theory. LC 51-5559. (Translations Ser.: No. 2, Vol. 49). 1966. 24.00 (ISBN 0-8218-1749-3, TRANS 2-49). Am Math.

Argabright, Loren & De Lamadrid, Jesus G. Fourier Analysis of Unbounded Measures on Locally Compact Abelian Groups. LC 74-6499. (Memoirs: No. 145). 53p. 1974. pap. 10.00 (ISBN 0-8218-1845-7, MEMO-145). Am Math.

Bahtin, I. A., et al. Eleven Papers on Differential Equations, Functional Analysis & Measure Theory. LC 51-5559. (Translations, Ser: No. 2, Vol. 51). 1966. 39.00 (ISBN 0-8218-1751-5, TRANS 2-51). Am Math.

Bauer, H. Probability Theory & Elements of Measure Theory. (Probability & Mathematical Statistics Ser.). 1981. 79.50 (ISBN 0-12-082820-0). Acad Pr.

Beckwith, T. G., et al. Mechanical Measurements. 3rd ed. 1982. 39.95 (ISBN 0-201-00036-9); solutions manual 1.50 (ISBN 0-201-00037-7). Addison-Wesley.

Bellow, A. & Kolzow, D., eds. Measure Theory: Proceedings of the Conference Held at Oberwolfach, 15-21 June, 1975. LC 76-26664. (Lecture Notes in Mathematics Ser.: Vol. 541). 1976. pap. 23.00 (ISBN 0-387-07861-4). Springer-Verlag.

Bentley, John P. Principles of Measurement Systems. LC 82-7374. 352p. (Orig.). 1984. pap. text ed. 26.00x (ISBN 0-582-30506-3). Longman.

Berberian, Sterling K. Measure & Integration. LC 74-128871. 1970. Repr. of 1965 ed. text ed. 14.95 (ISBN 0-8284-0241-8). Chelsea Pub.

Berka, Karel. Measurement: Its Concepts, Theories & Problems. 1983. 49.50 (ISBN 90-277-1416-9, Pub. by Reidel Holland). Kluwer Academic.

Billingsley, P. Convergence of Probability Measures. (Probability & Mathematical Statistics Tracts: Probability & Statistics Section). 253p. 1968. 41.95x (ISBN 0-471-07242-7, Pub. by Wiley-Interscience). Wiley.

--Weak Convergence of Measures: Applications in Probability. (CBMS-NSF Regional Conference Ser.: No. 5). v, 31p. 1971. pap. text ed. 6.50 (ISBN 0-89871-176-2). Soc Indus-Appl Math.

Bishop, Errett & Cheng, Henry. Constructive Measure Theory. LC 52-42839. (Memoirs: No. 116). 85p. 1972. pap. 9.00 (ISBN 0-8218-1816-3, MEMO-116). Am Math.

Brakke, Kenneth A. The Motion of a Surface by Its Mean Curvature. (Mathematical Notes Ser.: No. 20). 1978. 24.00 (ISBN 0-691-08204-9). Princeton U Pr.

Chae. Lebesque Integration. (Lecture Notes in Pure & Applied Mathematics Ser.: Vol. 58). 328p. 1980. 55.00 (ISBN 0-8247-6983-X). Dekker.

Cohn, Donald. Measure Theory. 276p. 1980. 24.95x (ISBN 0-8176-3003-1). Birkhauser.

Conference, 5th, Oberwolfach, Germany, Jan. 29 - Feb. 4, 1978. Probability Measures on Groups: Proceedings. Heyer, H., ed. (Lecture Notes in Mathematics: Vol. 706). 1979. pap. 22.00 (ISBN 0-387-09124-6). Springer-Verlag.

Constantinescu, C. Duality in Measure Theory. (Lecture Notes in Mathematics: Vol. 796). 197p. 1980. pap. 17.00 (ISBN 0-387-09989-1). Springer-Verlag.

Constantinescu, Corneliu. Spaces of Measures. LC 84-5815. (Studies in Mathematics: No. 4). 444p. 1984. 59.95x (ISBN 3-11-008784-7). De Gruyter.

Craven, Bruce D. Lebesgue Measure & Integral. LC 81-12151. 224p. 1982. text ed. 39.95 (ISBN 0-273-01754-3). Pitman Pub MA.

Din Standards for Technology of Length Measurement. 728.00 (ISBN 0-686-28166-7, 10051-5/11). Heyden.

Ellis, Brian D. Basic Concepts of Measurement. LC 65-19150. pap. 57.50 (ISBN 0-317-26322-6, 2024450). Bks Demand UMI.

Farrell, R. H. Techniques of Multivariate Calculation. (Lecture Notes in Mathematics: Vol. 520). 1976. pap. 20.00 (ISBN 0-387-07695-6). Springer-Verlag.

Benice, Daniel D. Precalculus Mathematics. 3rd ed. (Illus.). 544p. 1986. pap. text ed. 29.95 (ISBN 0-13-695503-7). P-H.

Bethune, J. Essentials of Drafting. 416p. 1977. text ed. 28.95 (ISBN 0-13-284430-3). P-H.

Betterley, Melvin. Sheet Metal Drafting. 2nd ed. (Illus.). 1977. pap. text ed. 26.40 (ISBN 0-07-005126-7). McGraw.

Blandford. The Complete Handbook of Drafting. (Illus.). 322p. 1982. 16.95 (ISBN 0-8306-0049-3). TAB Bks.

Boxall, V. E. Drawing & Materials. 2nd ed. (Illus.). 1975. pap. 22.50x (ISBN 0-7131-3320-1). Intl Ideas.

Brown, Walter C. Drafting for Industry. rev. ed. (Illus.). 616p. 1984. text ed. 21.00 (ISBN 0-87006-463-0); workbook 8.00 (ISBN 0-87006-464-9). Goodheart.

Colletti, Jack J. & Colletti, Paul J. A Freehand Approach to Technical Drawing. 336p. 1974. pap. 22.95 ref. ed. (ISBN 0-13-330548-1). P-H.

Cousins, M. F. Engineering Drawing form the Beginning, Vol. 2. pap. 13.25 (ISBN 0-08-006853-7). Pergamon.

D'Campo, G. Basic Technical Drawing. (Illus.). 376p. 1977. pap. 15.95x (ISBN 0-86125-432-5, Pub by Orient Longman India). Apt Bks.

Deshpande, D. L., ed. Basic Drawing. 68p. 1981. 20.00x (ISBN 0-86125-690-5, Pub. by Orient Longman India). State Mutual Bk.

Donaldson, Stanley S. Test Papers in Technical Drawing. 2nd ed. (Illus.). 104p. 1981. pap. text ed. 18.95x (ISBN 0-291-39488-4). Intl Ideas.

Duff, Jon M. Industrial Technical Illustration. 1982. 26.50 (ISBN 0-442-21957-1). Van Nos Reinhold.

Earle, James H. Basic Drafting. 1974. 3.95 (ISBN 0-932702-51-1). Creative Texas.

--Creative Drafting. 1970. 5.20 (ISBN 0-932702-52-X). Creative Texas.

--Drafting & Design. 1973. 5.20 (ISBN 0-932702-53-8). Creative Texas.

--Drafting Technology Problems. 1982. 7.15 (ISBN 0-932702-67-8). Creative Texas.

Earle, James H., et al. Drafting Fundamentals 1. 1965. 5.20 (ISBN 0-932702-54-6). Creative Texas.

--Drafting Fundamentals 2. 1969. 5.20 (ISBN 0-932702-55-4). Creative Texas.

Feirer & Lindbeck. Basic Drafting. 1978. 10.64 (ISBN 0-02-662480-X); pap. 7.32 (ISBN 0-02-662470-2); Activities for Basic Drafting 4.44 (ISBN 0-02-662550-4). Bennett IL.

Feirer, John L. & Lindbeck. Drawing & Planning for the Industrial Arts. new ed. (Illus.). 1975. text ed. 14.48 (ISBN 0-02-663480-5); tchr's guide, charts & worksheets 7.72 (ISBN 0-02-663490-2). Bennett IL.

French, T., et al. Mechanical Drawing. 10th ed. 576p. 1985. 27.44 (ISBN 0-07-022333-5). McGraw.

French, Thomas E. & Svensen, C. L. Familiar Problems in Mechanical Drawing. 1973. 9.32 (ISBN 0-07-022312-2). McGraw.

French, Thomas E. & Vierck, Charles J. Engineering Drawing & Graphic Technology. 12th ed. (Illus.). 1978. text ed. 42.95 (ISBN 0-07-022158-8). McGraw.

Fryklund, Verne C. & Kepler, Frank R. General Drafting. 4th ed. LC 78-81375. (Illus.). 1969. text ed. 14.63 (ISBN 0-87345-095-7). McKnight.

Gerevas, Lawrence E. Basic Drafting Problems. 2nd ed. 240p. 1981. pap. text ed. 13.24 scp (ISBN 0-672-97866-0); tchr's. Manual scp 7.33 (ISBN 0-672-97867-9). Bobbs.

--Drafting Technology Problems. 2nd ed. 1981. pap. write for info. (ISBN 0-02-341830-3). Macmillan.

Giachino, J. W. & Beukema, H. J. Engineering Technical Drafting. 4th ed. (Illus.). 730p. 1978. 24.00 (ISBN 0-8269-1154-4). Am Technical.

--Everyday Sketching & Drafting. 2nd ed. (Illus.). 172p. 1973. pap. 9.95 (ISBN 0-8269-1162-5). Am Technical.

Giachino, Joseph W. & Beukema, Henry J. Engineering Drafting Problems. LC 73-75065. (Illus.). pap. 26.00 (ISBN 0-317-10654-6, 2012977). Bks Demand UMI.

Giesecke, et al. Technical Drawing: With Computer Graphics. 7th ed. 872p. 1985. text ed. write for info. (ISBN 0-02-342690-X). Macmillan.

Giesecke, F. H., et al. Technical Drawing Problems. 6th ed. (Series I). 1981. pap. text ed. write for info. (ISBN 0-02-342740-X). Macmillan.

Giesecke, Frederick E., et al. Technical Drawing. 7th ed. (Illus.). 1980. text ed. write for info. (ISBN 0-02-342610-1). Macmillan.

--Technical Drawing. 8th ed. 780p. 1986. 29.00 (ISBN 0-02-342600-4). Macmillan.

Glegg, Gordon L. Making & Interpreting Mechanical Drawings. (Illus.). 1971. 8.95 (ISBN 0-521-09680-4). Cambridge U Pr.

Goetsch, David L. Structural Drafting. (Drafting Ser.). (Illus.). 355p. (Orig.). 1982. pap. text ed. 18.80 (ISBN 0-8273-1930-4); instr's. guide 4.20 (ISBN 0-8273-1931-2). Delmar.

Gorbea, J. Q. Tecnicas Mecanograficas Modernas. 3rd ed. 240p. 14.72 (ISBN 0-07-023791-3). McGraw.

Hale, E. M., et al. Introduction to Applied Drawing. rev. ed. 1962. pap. 5.28 (ISBN 0-87345-051-5). McKnight.

Hardman, William E. How To Read Shop Prints & Drawings With Blueprints. 236p. 1982. pap. text ed. 19.95 (ISBN 0-910399-01-8). Natl Tool & Mach.

Harman, Earl W. Introduction to Mechanical Drawing. new ed. 1979. pap. text ed. 10.76 (ISBN 0-205-06580-5, 3265803). Allyn.

Hoelscher, Randolph P., et al. Industrial Production on Illustration for Students, Draftsmen, & Illustrators. 2nd ed. LC 47-1150. pap. 63.00 (ISBN 0-317-10851-4, 2004414). Bks Demand UMI.

Hood, George J., et al. Geometry of Engineering Drawing. 5th ed. LC 78-12289. (Illus.). 482p. 1979. Repr. of 1969 ed. lib. bdg. 31.50 (ISBN 0-88275-756-3). Krieger.

Jensen, C. & Helsel, J. Engineering Drawing & Design. 3rd ed. 800p. 1985. 32.95 (ISBN 0-07-032533-2). McGraw.

--Fundamentals of Engineering Drawing & Design. 2nd ed. 400p. 23.95 (ISBN 0-07-032534-0). McGraw.

Jensen, C. & Mason, F. Drafting Fundamentals. 5th ed. 333p. 30.00 (ISBN 0-07-548068-9). McGraw.

Jensen, C. & Viosinet, D. Advanced Design Problems: To Accompany Engineering Drawing & Designs. 2nd ed. 1982. 10.65 (ISBN 0-07-032522-7). McGraw.

Jensen, Cecil & Helsel, Jay. Engineering Drawing & Design. 2nd ed. (Illus.). 1979. text ed. 33.25 (ISBN 0-07-032516-2). McGraw.

LeFax Pub. Co. Editors. Mechanical Drawing. (Lefax Data Bks.: No. 617). (Illus.). looseleaf bdg. 3.00 (ISBN 0-685-52841-3); pap. 3.00 (ISBN 0-685-52842-1). LeFax.

Levens, A. S. & Cooper, S. J. Problems in Mechanical Drawing. 6th ed. (Illus.). 224p. 1985. write for info. (ISBN 0-07-022334-3). McGraw.

Lexikon der Graphischen Technik. 4th ed. (Ger.). 1977. 29.95 (ISBN 3-7940-4078-3, M-7253). French & Eur.

Lieblich, Jerome H. Drawing Requirements Manual. 5th ed. 719p. 1983. perfect bdg. 32.95 (ISBN 0-912702-18-4); loose leaf 47.95 (ISBN 0-912702-17-6). Global Eng.

Lieblich, Jerome H., ed. Dimensioning & Tolerances (An Interpretation of ANSI y14.5) 96p. 1976. lib. bdg. 5.95x (ISBN 0-912702-19-2). Global Eng.

Lindbeck. Metric Practices in Drafting. 1979. pap. 7.08 (ISBN 0-02-665240-4). Bennett IL.

Lombardo, Josef V. Engineering Drawing. (College Outline Ser.). pap. 6.95 (ISBN 0-06-460086-6, CO 86, COS). B&N NY.

Lopez, Ulises M. & Warrin, George E. Mechanical Drawing. 1984. text ed. 25.95 (ISBN 0-8359-4313-5); solutions manual avail. (ISBN 0-8359-4314-3). Reston.

Los Angeles Unified School District. Drafting. LC 77-73291. 64p. 1978. pap. text ed. 4.00 (ISBN 0-02-820410-7). Glencoe.

Luzadder, Warren J. Fundamentals of Engineering Drawing: With an Intro to Interactive Computer Graphics for Design & Production. 9th ed. (Illus.). 656p. 1986. text ed. 34.95 (ISBN 0-13-338427-6). P-H.

McCabe, Francis T., et al. Mechanical Drafting Essentials. 4th ed. text ed. 23.76 (ISBN 0-13-568931-7). P-H.

Madsen, David A. Drafting: Syllabus. 1974. pap. text ed. 8.35 (ISBN 0-89420-070-4, 107015); cassette recordings 104.95 (ISBN 0-89420-140-9, 107000). Natl Book.

Madsen, David A. & Shumaker, Terence M. Civil Drafting Technology. (Illus.). 144p. 1983. 22.95 (ISBN 0-13-134890-6, 402-403). P-H.

Manual of Mechanical Drawing: How to Draw & How to Comprehend Mechanical Drawing. 27.50 (ISBN 0-87559-087-X). Shalom.

Martin, C. Leslie. Design Graphics. 2nd ed. (Illus.). 1968. text ed. write for info. (ISBN 0-02-376640-9). Macmillan.

Miller, Wilbur R. Drafting. LC 78-53388. (Basic Industrial Arts Ser.). (Illus.). 1978. 7.28 (ISBN 0-87345-793-5); softbound 5.28 (ISBN 0-87345-785-4). McKnight.

Morling, K. Geometric & Engineering Drawing. 2nd ed. (Illus.). 1974. pap. 27.50x (ISBN 0-7131-3319-8). Intl Ideas.

Nee, John G. Mechanism Drafting & Design: A Workbook. LC 80-80861. (Illus.). 1980. pap. text ed. 14.95x (ISBN 0-911168-45-1); solutions manual 3.95x (ISBN 0-911168-46-X). Prakken.

Nelson, John. Drafting for Trades & Industry - Basic Skills. LC 77-91450. (Drafting Ser.). 464p. 1979. pap. text ed. 20.80 (ISBN 0-8273-1841-3); instructor's guide 5.25 (ISBN 0-8273-1641-0). Delmar.

--Drafting for Trades & Industry - Civil. LC 77-91450. (Drafting Ser.). 942p. 1979. pap. text ed. 8.80 (ISBN 0-8273-1844-8); instructor's guide 5.25 (ISBN 0-8273-1641-0). Delmar.

--Drafting for Trades & Industry - Mechanical & Electronic. LC 77-91450. (Drafting Ser.). 328p. 1979. pap. text ed. 16.80 (ISBN 0-8273-1846-4); instructor's guide 5.25 (ISBN 0-8273-1641-0). Delmar.

Nelson, John A. & Morrison, Charles W. Proto Draft Modules. 1985. text ed. 5.50 (ISBN 0-538-33370-7, IE37). SW Pub.

Oberg, Erick V. Draftsman's Mathematical Manual. 2nd ed. LC 41-20206. pap. 67.80 (ISBN 0-317-08775-4, 2001911). Bks Demand UMI.

Omar Products, Inc. Proto Draft Modules: Simulation. 1983. 60.00 (ISBN 0-538-33360-X, IE36). SW Pub.

Ostrowsky, O. Engineering Drawing for Technicians, Vol. 1. (Illus.). 94p. 1979. pap. 18.95x (ISBN 0-7131-3408-9). Intl Ideas.

--Engineering Drawing for Technicians, Vol. 2. 96p. 1981. pap. 18.95x (ISBN 0-7131-3429-1). Intl Ideas.

Resource Systems International. Mechanical Drawing: Dimensioning. 1982. pap. text ed. 15.00 (ISBN 0-8359-4304-6). Reston.

--Mechanical Drawing: Field Sketching. 1982. pap. text ed. 15.00 (ISBN 0-8359-4305-4). Reston.

--Mechanical Drawing: Geometric Construction. 1982. pap. text ed. 15.00 (ISBN 0-8359-4306-2). Reston.

--Mechanical Drawing: Orthographic. 1982. pap. text ed. 15.00 (ISBN 0-8359-4308-9). Reston.

--Mechanical Drawing: Tools & Lettering. 1982. pap. text ed. 15.00 (ISBN 0-8359-4309-7). Reston.

Rohlmeier, Charles. Drafting: Metric. LC 79-55761. pap. 80.00 (ISBN 0-317-19778-9, 2023202). Bks Demand UMI.

Ross, Stan. World of Drafting. 1971. text ed. 18.64 (ISBN 0-87345-078-7). McKnight.

Rudman, Jack. Senior Drafting Technician. (Career Examination Ser.: C-2679). (Cloth bdg. avail. on request). pap. 10.00 (ISBN 0-8373-2679-6). Natl Learning.

--Senior Draftsman. (Career Examination Ser.: C-1575). (Cloth bdg. avail. on request). pap. 12.00 (ISBN 0-8373-1575-1). Natl Learning.

Sadamatsu, Shuzo & Sadamatsu, Junko. Design Drafting. (Illus.). 160p. 1985. pap. 25.00 (ISBN 0-442-28080-7). Van Nos Reinhold.

Schaeffer, Glen N. & Burns, W. E. Basic Mechanical Drawing. 1982. pap. 5.76 (ISBN 0-02-827940-9). Glencoe.

Segel, Yonny. Drafting Made Simple. LC 61-9550. (Made Simple Ser.). pap. 4.95 (ISBN 0-385-01348-5). Doubleday.

Spence. Basic Industrial Drafting. 1982. pap. text ed. 12.68 (ISBN 0-02-662520-2); worksheets 9.32 (ISBN 0-02-662540-7). Bennett IL.

--Drafting Technology & Practice. rev ed. 1981. text ed. 26.64 (ISBN 0-02-663440-6); worksheets 15.96 (ISBN 0-02-663460-0). Bennett IL.

Spence & Atkins. Technical Drafting. 1980. text ed. 24.72 (ISBN 0-02-665810-0); Inst. Resource Guide 80 11.20 (ISBN 0-02-665820-8). Bennett IL.

Spence, William P. Drafting: Technology & Practice. 1981. 32.50 (ISBN 0-684-16772-7). Scribner.

Spencer, Henry C., et al. Technical Drawing Problems: Series Two. 4th ed. (Illus.). 1980. pap. text ed. write for info. (ISBN 0-02-414330-8). Macmillan.

Stegman, George & Jenkins, Jerry. Technical Drawing Problems. 224p. 1987. price not set wkbk. (ISBN 0-02-416330-9). Macmillan.

Stirling, Norman. Introduction to Technical Drawing: Metric Edition. LC 79-56653. 370p. 1981. pap. text ed. 22.00 (ISBN 0-8273-1928-2). Delmar.

Syvanen, Bob. Drafting: Tips & Tricks on Drawing & Designing House Plans. LC 81-17344. (Illus.). 112p. 1982. pap. 7.95 (ISBN 0-914788-48-5). East Woods.

Thompson, Charles H. Fundamentals of Pipe Drafting. LC 58-13471. 66p. 1958. pap. 15.95x (ISBN 0-471-85998-2, Pub. by Wiley-Interscience). Wiley.

Traister, John E. Practical Drafting for the HVAC Trades. 2nd ed. (Illus.). 272p. 1984. pap. text ed. 21.95 (ISBN 0-13-689308-2). P-H.

Vezzani, A. A. & Salmonson, Donald. Reading & Detailing Assembly Drawings: Dies. LC 61-9841. 1972. 9.25x (ISBN 0-911168-10-9). Prakken.

Vogts, Raymond. Engineering Drawing & Blueprint Reading. LC 81-5047. (Illus.). 272p. 1981. pap. text ed. 8.00 (ISBN 0-668-05295-3, 5295). Arco.

Walker, John R. Exploring Metric Drafting. LC 79-24019. (Illus.). 320p. 1980. text ed. 14.64 (ISBN 0-87006-289-1). Goodheart.

Wallach, P. I. Basic Book of Drafting. (Basic Industrial Arts Ser.). (Illus.). 1979. 7.50 (ISBN 0-8269-1170-6). Am Technical.

Wallach, Paul. Metric Drafting. 1979. text ed. 22.45 (ISBN 0-02-829690-7); instrs'. manual 7.45 (ISBN 0-02-829700-8); problems book 7.95 (ISBN 0-02-829710-5). Glencoe.

Wills, Herbert, III. Leonardo's Dessert: No Pi. LC 84-27185. (Illus.). 32p. 1985. pap. 3.50 (ISBN 0-87353-221-X). NCTM.

Wirshing, J. R. & Wirshing, R. H. Civil Engineering Drafting. LC 82-17195. 352p. 1983. pap. 17.25 (ISBN 0-07-071127-5). McGraw.

Wyatt, Edwin M. Modern Drafting. (Illus., Orig.). 1962. pap. 3.00 (ISBN 0-02-829760-1). Glencoe.

Y-Fourteen Report, Digital Representation of Physical Object Shapes. 1976. pap. text ed. 4.00 (ISBN 0-685-75522-3, N00075). ASME.

Yankee, H. W. Machine Drafting & Related Technology. 2nd ed. 1981. 26.40 (ISBN 0-07-072252-8). McGraw.

Yaslow, Samuel. Elements of Mechanical Drafting. LC 78-67463. (Drafting Ser.). 375p. 1979. pap. text ed. 19.20 (ISBN 0-8273-1837-5); instructor's guide 5.25 (ISBN 0-8273-1838-3). Delmar.

Zandi, Martin. Computer-Aided Design & Drafting. LC 84-23808. 352p. 1985. text ed. 22.00 (ISBN 0-8273-2304-2); instr. guide 4.00 (ISBN 0-8273-2305-0). Delmar.

MECHANICAL DRAWING–DATA PROCESSING

Paige, Vernon. CAD Primer: Computer-Aided Design. LC 84-19548. (Illus.). 118p. (Orig.). 1985. pap. 15.00 (ISBN 0-937148-08-3). Wild Horses.

Shumaker, Terence M. & Aronson, Mike. GRID: Computer-Aided Drafting Program. 2nd ed. (Illus.). 119p. 1985. pap. text ed. 9.75x (ISBN 0-928459-00-4). Respons Logic.

--GRIDT: Digitizing Computer-Aided Drafting Program. (Illus.). 140p. 1984. pap. 9.15 (ISBN 0-928459-02-0). Respons Logic.

MECHANICAL DRAWING–EXAMINATIONS, QUESTIONS ETC.

Rudman, Jack. Chief Draftsman. (Career Examination Ser.: C-1577). (Cloth bdg. avail. on request). pap. 12.00 (ISBN 0-8373-1577-8). Natl Learning.

--Civil Engineering Draftsman. (Career Examination Ser.: C-137). (Cloth bdg. avail. on request). pap. 12.00 (ISBN 0-8373-0137-8). Natl Learning.

--Drafting Aide. (Career Examination Ser.: C-202). (Cloth bdg. avail. on request). pap. 10.00 (ISBN 0-8373-0202-1). Natl Learning.

--Drafting Technician. (Career Examination Ser.: C-2678). (Cloth bdg. avail. on request). pap. 12.00 (ISBN 0-8373-2678-8). Natl Learning.

--Draftsman. (Career Examination Ser.: C-203). (Cloth bdg. avail. on request). pap. 12.00 (ISBN 0-8373-0203-X). Natl Learning.

--Engineering Draftsman. (Career Examination Ser.: C-247). (Cloth bdg. avail. on request). pap. 12.00 (ISBN 0-8373-0247-1). Natl Learning.

--Engineering Technician (Drafting) (Career Examination Ser.: C-991). (Cloth bdg. avail. on request). pap. 12.00 (ISBN 0-8373-0991-3). Natl Learning.

--Junior Draftsman. (Career Examination Ser.: C-396). (Cloth bdg. avail. on request). pap. 12.00 (ISBN 0-8373-0396-6). Natl Learning.

--Machine Drafting. (Occupational Competency Examination Ser.: OCE-24). 14.95 (ISBN 0-8373-5774-8); pap. 13.95 (ISBN 0-8373-5724-1). Natl Learning.

--Mechanical Engineering Draftsman. (Career Examination Ser.: C-482). (Cloth bdg. avail. on request). pap. 10.00 (ISBN 0-8373-0482-2). Natl Learning.

--Senior Engineering Technician (Drafting) (Career Examination Ser.: C-1005). (Cloth bdg. avail. on request). pap. 12.00 (ISBN 0-8373-1005-9). Natl Learning.

MECHANICAL DRAWING–PROBLEMS, EXERCISES, ETC.

Bartholomew & Orr. Learning to Read & Make Mechanical Drawings. 1982. pap. text ed. 7.08 (ISBN 0-02-664820-2). Bennett IL.

Dobrovolny, J. S., et al. Problems in Engineering Drawing & Geometry, Series 12, 13, 15, 16, 21. 1964. pap. 6.80x ea. Stipes.

Hoelscher, Randolph P., et al. Problems in Engineering Drawing, Series A, B, C, D, & E. pap. 6.80x ea. Stipes.

Jensen, et al. Basic Drafting Problems. Breskin, Myrna, ed. 96p. 1981. 9.65 (ISBN 0-07-032521-9). McGraw.

Miller, William E. Basic Drafting for Interior Designers. 120p. 1982. pap. 14.95 (ISBN 0-442-26177-2). Van Nos Reinhold.

Spencer, Henry C., et al. Technical Drawing Problems: Series Three. 3rd ed. (Illus.). 1980. pap. text ed. write for info. (ISBN 0-02-414360-X). Macmillan.

MECHANICAL DRAWING–STUDY AND TEACHING

Weaver, Rip. Modern Basic Drafting. 2nd ed. LC 74-27682. (Illus.). 380p. 1979. 19.95x (ISBN 0-87201-059-7); wkbks. 9.95x ea. Wkbk. 1 (ISBN 0-87201-055-4). Wkbk. 2 (ISBN 0-87201-056-2). Gulf Pub.

MECHANICAL DRAWINGS

see Engineering Drawings

MECHANICAL ENGINEERING

Here are entered works relating to the application of the principles of mechanics to the design construction and operation of machinery.

see also Chemical Engineering; Diaphragms (Mechanical Devices); Electric Engineering; Electromechanical Devices; Heat Engineering; Horsepower (Mechanics); Machinery; Marine Engineering; Mechanical Movements; Mechanics, Applied; Power (Mechanics); Power Transmission; Production Engineering; Steam Engineering

Alexander, J. M. Strength of Materials: Fundamentals, Vol. 1. LC 80-42009. (Mechanical Engineering Ser.). 267p. 1981. 89.95x (ISBN 0-470-27119-1). Halsted Pr.

American Society of Civil Engineers, Engineering Mechanics Division. The Relation of Engineering Mechanics Research to the Practice of Civil Engineering: Engineering Mechanics Division Specialty Conference, Washington, D.C., October 12-14, 1966. LC 67-1660. (Illus.). pap. 160.00 (ISBN 0-317-11018-7, 2004904). Bks Demand UMI.

American Society of Mechanical Engineers. Cavitation State of Knowledge: Discussions Presented At the ASME Fluids Engineering & Applied Mechanics Conference, Northwestern University, Evanston, Illinois, June 16-18, 1969. Robertson, J. M. & Wislicenus, G. F., eds. LC 73-173121. pap. 20.00 (ISBN 0-317-29797-X, 2016853). Bks Demand UMI.

--The Generation of Isochronous Stress-Strain Curves: Papers Presented at the Winter Annual Meeting of ASME, New York, NY, November 26-30, 1972. LC 72-93459. (Illus.). pap. 22.80 (ISBN 0-317-08421-6, 2016821). Bks Demand UMI.

Anand, Davinder K. & Cunniff, Patrick. Engineering Mechanics: Dynamics. 450p. 1984. scp 29.10 (ISBN 0-205-07785-4, 327785). Allyn.

Arizona University, Mechanical & Energy Systems Engineering Dept. Simplified Design Guide for Estimating Photovoltaic Flat Array & System Performance. 175p. 1982. pap. 29.95x (ISBN 0-89934-168-3, P-047). Solar Energy Info.

Armen, Harry, ed. Applications of Numerical Methods to Forming Processes: AMD, Vol. 28. Jones, R. F., Jr. 208p. 1978. 30.00 (ISBN 0-685-66790-1, H00111). ASME.

Artobolevsky, I. Mechanisms in Modern Engineering Design, Vol. II. (Illus.). 1059p. 1979. 15.00 (ISBN 0-8285-0687-6, Pub. by Mir Pubs USSR). Imported Pubns.

--Mechanisms in Modern Engineering Design, Vol. III. (Illus.). 663p. 1977. 10.00 (ISBN 0-8285-0688-4, Pub. by Mir Pubs USSR). Imported Pubns.

--Mechanisms in Modern Engineering Design, Vol. IV. (Illus.). 663p. 1977. 9.45 (ISBN 0-8285-0689-2, Pub. by Mir Pubs USSR). Imported Pubns.

--Mechanisms in Modern Engineering Design, Vol. I. (Illus.). 631p. 1979. 7.45 (ISBN 0-8285-0686-8, Pub. by Mir Pubs USSR). Imported Pubns.

Atluri, Satya & Perrone, Nicholas, eds. Computer Methods for Nonlinear Solids & Structural Mechanics. 264p. 1983. pap. text ed. 50.00 (ISBN 0-317-02562-7, G00224). ASME.

Bajura, R. A. & Morrow, T. B., eds. Modeling of Environment Flow Systems. 88p. 1983. pap. text ed. 20.00 (ISBN 0-317-02634-8, H00281). ASME.

Barnet, G., et al, eds. Mechanical Fitting, Vol. 2. 2nd ed. (Engineering Craftsmen: No. H25). (Illus.). 1973. spiral bdg. 39.95x (ISBN 0-85083-186-5). Intl Ideas.

Barton, Lyndon O. Mechanism Analysis: Simplified Graphical & Analytical Techniques. (Mechanical Engineering Ser.: Vol. 32). (Illus.). 464p. 1984. 59.75 (ISBN 0-8247-7086-2). Dekker.

Basic Standards for Mechanical Engineering. (DIN Standards Ser.). (Ger.). 613.00 (ISBN 0-686-31841-2, 10041-5-1). Wiley.

Baugh, A., et al, eds. Mechanical Maintenance, Pt. I. (Engineering Craftsmen: No. J1). (Illus.). 1978. spiral bdg. 43.50x (ISBN 0-85083-016-8). Intl Ideas.

Baumeister, Theodore. Marks' Standard Handbook for Mechanical Engineers. 8th ed. (Illus.). 1978. 75.00 (ISBN 0-07-004123-7). McGraw.

Beer, F. P. & Johnston, E. R. Mechanics for Engineers, 2 vols. 3rd ed. 1976. Vol. 1: Statics. 39.00 (ISBN 0-07-004271-3); Vol. 2: Dynamics. 39.00 (ISBN 0-07-004273-X); Combined Ed. 46.00 (ISBN 0-07-004270-5). McGraw.

Beer, Ferdinand P. & Johnston, E. R., Jr. Vector Mechanics for Engineers: Dynamics. 3rd ed. 1977. text ed. 32.95 (ISBN 0-07-004281-0). McGraw.

Bennett, S. B., et al, eds. Failure Prevention & Reliability. 1977. pap. text ed. 30.00 (ISBN 0-685-86863-X, H00101). ASME.

Berger & Associates Cost Consultants, Inc. The Berger Building & Design Cost File, 1983: Mechanical, Electrical Trades, Vol. 2. LC 83-70008. 207p. 1983. pap. 26.45 (ISBN 0-942564-04-9). Building Cost File.

Bilby, B. A., et al, eds. Fundamentals of Deformation & Fracture. 630p. 1985. 79.50 (ISBN 0-521-26735-8). Cambridge U Pr.

Bogdanoff, John L. & Kozin, Frank. Probabilistic Models of Cumulative Damage. LC 84-11799. 341p. 1985. text ed. 53.50 (ISBN 0-471-88180-5, Pub. by Wiley Interscience). Wiley.

Bolotin, V. V. Random Vibrations of Elastic Systems. (Mechanics of Elastic Stability: No. 8). 480p. 1984. lib. bdg. 86.00 (ISBN 90-247-2981-5, Pub. by Martinus Nijhoff Netherlands). Kluwer Academic.

Boothroyd. Automatic Assembly. (Mechanical Engineering Ser.: Vol. 6). 352p. 1982. 45.00 (ISBN 0-8247-1531-4). Dekker.

Boresi, Arthur P., et al. Advanced Mechanics of Materials. 3rd ed. LC 77-28283. 696p. 1978. text ed. 44.50x (ISBN 0-471-08892-7). Wiley.

Branan, Carl & Mills, John. Process Evaluation & Economic Analysis. LC 76-1680. (Process Engineer's Pocket Handbook Ser.: Vol. 3). 200p. (Orig.). 1984. pap. 12.95x (ISBN 0-87201-715-X). Gulf Pub.

Braun, S., ed. MSA - Mechanical Signature Analysis. 88p. 1983. pap. text ed. 24.00 (ISBN 0-317-02630-5, G00236). ASME.

Briggs, T., et al, eds. Mechanical Fitting, Vol. 1. (Engineering Craftsmen: No. H3). 1968. spiral bdg. 37.50x (ISBN 0-85083-012-5). Intl Ideas.

British Ceramic Society, ed. The Mechanical Engineering Properties & Applications of Ceramics. 50.00x (ISBN 0-686-78852-4, Pub. by Brit Ceramic Soc England). State Mutual Bk.

British Mechanical Engineering Confederation in Association with 'Engineering' The European Economic Community & United Kingdom Engineering Companies. 57p. 1980. 78.75x (ISBN 0-89771-002-9). State Mutual Bk.

Buck, Gordon S. Machinery Alignment Tables: Face-OD & Reverse Indicator Methods. LC 83-22692. 320p. (Orig.). 1984. pap. 18.95x spiral bound (ISBN 0-87201-015-5). Gulf Pub.

Burr, A. H. Mechanical Analysis & Design. 640p. 1981. 34.00 (ISBN 0-444-00324-X); instr's. manual avail. Elsevier.

Caceres, C. A., et al, eds. Medical Devices Measurements, Quality Assurance, & Standards - STP 800. LC 82-72890. 298p. 1983. text ed. 38.00 (ISBN 0-8031-0235-6, 04-800000-54). ASTM.

CES Industries, Inc. & Nesenoff, Norman. Ed-Lab Experiment Manual: Mechanical Module. (Illus., Orig.). 1980. write for info. (ISBN 0-86711-037-6). CES Industries.

Chandra, J. & Flaherty, J. E., eds. Computational Aspects of Penetration Mechanics. (Lecture Notes in Engineering: Vol. 3). 221p. 1983. pap. 19.00 (ISBN 0-387-12634-1). Springer-Verlag.

Cheremisinoff, Nicholas P. Fluid Flow Pocket Handbook. LC 83-22619. 330p. 1984. Flexi-bound 21.95x (ISBN 0-87201-707-9). Gulf Pub.

Cheremisinoff, Nicholas P. & Cheremisinoff, Paul N. Hydrodynamics of Gas-Solids Fluidization. LC 83-18555. 1000p. 1984. 89.95x (ISBN 0-87201-352-9). Gulf Pub.

Chu, D., ed. Modal Testing & Model Refinement. 164p. 1983. pap. text ed. 34.00 (ISBN 0-317-02633-X, H00274). ASME.

Ciarlet, P. G. Topics in Mathematical Elasticity. (Studies in Mechanical Engineering). 1984. write for info. (North-Holland). Elsevier.

Combustion Dynamics & Toong, T. Y. Dynamics of Chemically Reacting Fluids. (Energy, Combustion, & Enviroment Ser.). (Illus.). 336p. 1983. text ed. 56.00 (ISBN 0-07-064976-6). McGraw.

Constance, J. D. Mechanical Engineering for Professional Engineers' Examinations. 3rd ed. 1981. 19.95 (ISBN 0-07-012457-4). McGraw.

Crouch, T. Matrix Methods Applied to Engineering Rigid Body Mechanics. LC 80-41186. 385p. 1980. 54.00 (ISBN 0-08-024245-6); pap. 19.75 (ISBN 0-08-024246-4). Pergamon.

Dean, D. L. Discrete Field Analysis of Structural Systems. (International Centre for Mechanical Sciences Ser.: No. 203). 1977. 23.00 (ISBN 0-387-81377-2). Springer-Verlag.

DED Vibrations Conference 1975, Washington, D. C. Vibration Testing--Instrumentation & Data Analysis: Presented at ASME/DED Vibrations Conference, Washington, D. C. Magrab, Edward B. & Shinaishin, Osman A., eds. LC 75-8349. (American Society of Mechanical Engineers Series - Applied Mechanics Division: Vol. 12). (Illus.). pap. 37.00 (ISBN 0-317-09976-0, 2015395). Bks Demand UMI.

Den Hamer, H. E. Interordering: A New Method of Component Orientation. (Studies in Mechanical Engineering: Vol. 2). 160p. 1981. 51.00 (ISBN 0-444-41933-0). Elsevier.

DIN Standards: Basic Standards for Mechanical Engineering. 637.00 (ISBN 0-686-28159-4, 10041-7/01). Heyden.

DIN Standards: Basic Standards for Mechanical Engineering. 1983. 581.00 (10041-5/1, Pub. by DIN Germany). Heyden.

Din Standards for Mechanical Engineering for Study & Practice. 580.00 (ISBN 0-686-28161-6, 10043-8/03). Heyden.

Doebelin, Ernest O. System Modeling & Response: Theoretical & Experimental Approaches. LC 79-27609. 587p. 1980. text ed. 52.45 (ISBN 0-471-03211-5). Wiley.

Duffy, Joseph. Power: Prime Mover of Technology. rev. ed. 1972. text ed. 21.97 (ISBN 0-87345-420-0). McKnight.

Ehringer, H. & Hoyaux, G. Energy Conservation in Transport: New Engines & Flywheels. 1983. lib. bdg. 28.00 (ISBN 90-2771-579-3, Pub. by Reidel Holland). Kluwer Academic.

Engineering Industry Training Board, ed. Training for Riggers-Erectors, 15 vols. (Illus.). 1976. Set. 67.50x (ISBN 0-89563-030-3). Intl Ideas.

Engineering Mechanics. 951p. 1979. pap. 55.00x (ISBN 0-87262-192-8). Am Soc Civil Eng.

Ewins, D. J. Modal Testing: Theory & Practice. (Mechanical Engineering Research Studies Ser.: No. 1-535). 150p. 1984. text ed. 31.95x (ISBN 0-471-90472-4, Pub. by Wiley). Wiley.

Ewins, D. J. & Srinivasan, A. V., eds. Vibrations of Bladed Disk Assemblies. 1983. pap. text ed. 34.00 (ISBN 0-317-02660-7, G00235). ASME.

An Experiment in Synopsis Publishing in the Field of Mechanical Engineering. 1981. pap. 30.00x (ISBN 0-905984-41-2, Pub. by Brit Lib England). State Mutual Bk.

Fassbender, A. G., et al. Energy Efficient Industrial Technology in Europe & Japan. LC 83-13065. (Energy Technology Review No. 85). (Illus.). 416p. 1984. 45.00 (ISBN 0-8155-0958-8). Noyes.

Fickett, Wildon & Davis, William C. Detonation. LC 77-85760. (Los Alamos Series in Basic & Applied Sciences). 1979. 42.00x (ISBN 0-520-03587-9). U of Cal Pr.

Fiftieth Anniversary Issue of the Journal of Applied Mechanics. 300p. 1983. pap. text ed. 20.00 (ISBN 0-317-02618-6, I00163). ASME.

Fletcher, L. S., ed. ASME Conference on Mechanical Engineering Education-1980: Proceedings. 181p. 1982. 15.00 (I00145). ASME.

Gamlin, A. T., et al, eds. Mechanical Maintenance & Installation: Supplementary Training Manual. (Engineering Craftsmen: No. J21S). (Illus.). 1976. 59.95x (ISBN 0-85083-332-9). Intl Ideas.

Genta, G. Kinetic Energy Storage. (Illus.). 1985. text ed. 84.95 (ISBN 0-408-01396-6). Butterworth.

Gillanders, John. Pipe & Tube Bending Manual. LC 84-631. 220p. 1984. 24.95x (ISBN 0-87201-493-2). Gulf Pub.

Glenn, Harold T. Exploring Power Mechanics. (Illus.). 1973. 15.96 (ISBN 0-02-663660-3); prog. wkbk. 5.32 (ISBN 0-02-663670-0). Bennett IL.

Gutman, I. Industrial Uses of Mechanical Vibrations. (Illus.). 332p. 1968. 20.00x (ISBN 0-8464-1110-5). Beekman Pubs.

Hamilton, Douglas M. & Robb, William. Mechanical Engineering for Public Cleansing. (Illus.). 216p. 1969. 16.75 (ISBN 0-85334-121-4, Pub. by Elsevier Applied Sci England). Elsevier.

Hartenberg, R. S., ed. National Historic Mechanical Engineering Landmarks. (Illus., Orig.). 1979. 15.00 (ISBN 0-685-96308-X, H00140). ASME.

Haviland. Handbook of Machinery Adhesives. (Mechanical Engineering Ser.). 336p. 1985. price not set (ISBN 0-8247-7467-1). Dekker.

Hench, L. L., ed. Ultrastructure Processing of Advanced Structural & Electronic Materials. LC 84-14835. (Illus.). 324p. 1985. 36.00 (ISBN 0-8155-1004-7). Noyes.

Hibbeler, R. C. Engineering Mechanics: Dynamics. 3rd ed. 512p. 1983. text ed. write for info. (ISBN 0-02-354250-0). Macmillan.

--Engineering Mechanics: Dynamics. 4th ed. 1223p. 1986. pap. price not set (ISBN 0-02-354660-3). Macmillan.

Hibbeler, Russel C. Transparency Acetates to Accompany Engineering Mechanics, Statics & Dynamics, 3rd ed. write for info.; transparency acetates avail. (ISBN 0-02-354440-6). Macmillan.

Hiscox, Gardner D. Mechanical Movements Powers & Devices. LC 78-18530. 1978. Repr. of 1907 ed. lib. bdg. 40.00 (ISBN 0-89341-512-X). Longwood Pub Group.

Horlock, J. H. Axial Flow Compressors. LC 73-75588. 222p. 1973. Repr. of 1958 ed. 14.50 (ISBN 0-88275-096-8). Krieger.

Jensen, A. & Chenoweth, H. H. Applied Engineering Mechanics. 4th ed. 464p. 30.40x (ISBN 0-07-032492-1). McGraw.

Johnson, Ray C. Optimum Design of Mechanical Elements. 2nd ed. LC 79-14363. 519p. 1980. 56.95x (ISBN 0-471-03894-6, Pub. by Wiley-Interscience). Wiley.

Joint Engineering Management Conference (23rd: 1975: Washington, D.C.) Effective Management of Engineering Resources. LC 75-329975. (Illus.). pap. 26.80 (ISBN 0-317-08475-5, 2016903). Bks Demand UMI.

Joint Engineering Management Conference (21st: 1973: St. Petersburg, Fla.) The Impact of Competitive Technology on Engineering Management: Presented at the Twenty-First Annual Joint Engineering Management Conference Held in St. Petersburg, Florida, October 25-26, 1973. LC 74-99882. (Illus.). pap. 34.80 (ISBN 0-317-08457-7, 2016896). Bks Demand UMI.

Joint Engineering Management Conference (22nd: 1974: Mexico City) International Patterns of Engineering Management: A Constructive Analysis. LC 74-99882. (Illus.). pap. 25.80 (ISBN 0-317-08464-X, 2016897). Bks Demand UMI.

Jorgensen, Eric, ed. BMW 320i: 1977-1982 Shop Manual. 1982p. (Orig.). pap. text ed. 13.95 (ISBN 0-89287-326-4, A139). Clymer Pubns.

--Chevy, Malibu, Chevelle, Monte Carlo: 1970-1984 Shop Manual. (Illus.). pap. text ed. 12.95 (ISBN 0-89287-319-1, A246). Clymer Pubns.

--Honda Twinstar 1978-1981: Service, Repair, Maintenance. (Illus.). pap. text ed. 13.95 (ISBN 0-89287-325-6, M324). Clymer Pubns.

--Kawasaki 900 & 1000cc Four, 1973-1980: Includes Shaft Drive Service Repair Performance. (Illus., Orig.). pap. text ed. 13.95 (ISBN 0-89287-321-3, M359). Clymer Pubns.

--Oldsmobile Cutlass: (Reardrive0 1970-1984 Manual. (Illus.). 342p. (Orig.). pap. text ed. 12.95 (ISBN 0-89287-324-8, A285). Clymer Pubns.

--Yamaha YZ100-490 Monoshock Singles 1975-1983: Service, Repair, Performance. (Illus.). 293p. (Orig.). pap. text ed. 13.95 (ISBN 0-89287-329-9, M413). Clymer Pubns.

Jorqgensen, Eric, ed. Datsun 210: 1979-1982 Shop Manual. (Illus.). pap. text ed. 12.95 (ISBN 0-89287-322-1, A 203). Clymer Pubns.

Karafiath, L. L. & Nowatzki, E. A. Soil Mechanics for Off-Road Vehicle Engineering. (Rock & Soil Mechanics Ser.). (Illus.). 1978. 58.00 (ISBN 0-87849-020-5). Trans Tech.

Knox, C. S. CAD-CAM Systems Implementation. (Mechanical Engineering Ser.). 352p. 1983. 39.75 (ISBN 0-8247-7041-2). Dekker.

Knox, Charles S. Engineering Documentation Flow. (Mechanical Engineering Ser.). 328p. 1984. 49.75 (ISBN 0-8247-7089-7). Dekker.

Konzo, Seichi & Bayne, James W. Opportunities in Mechanical Engineering. 2nd ed. LC 77-166404. (VGM Career Bks.). 1978. 7.95 (6552-0); pap. 5.95 (6552-8). Natl Textbk.

Kovach, Ladis D. Advanced Engineering Mathematics. LC 81-14936. (Mathematics Ser.). (Illus.). 1000p. 1982. text ed. 39.95 (ISBN 0-201-10340-0). Addison-Wesley.

Kovacik, Robert & Bono, Saverio G. Automatic Transmissions & Drive-Trains. 1984. text ed. 14.95 (ISBN 0-538-33060-0, IE06). SW Pub.

Kreith, Frank & Kreider, Jan F. Principles of Solar Engineering. LC 77-27861. (McGraw-Hill - Hemisphere Thermal & Fluids Engineering Ser.). (Illus.). 1978. 45.00 (ISBN 0-07-035476-6). McGraw.

Lee, R. R. Pocket Guide to Flanges, Fittings, & Piping Data. LC 84-669. 96p. (Orig.). 1984. pap. 9.95x (ISBN 0-87201-704-4). Gulf Pub.

Lieblich, Jerome H., ed. Dimensioning & Tolerances (An Interpretation of ANSI y14.5) 96p. 1976. lib. bdg. 5.95x (ISBN 0-912702-19-2). Global Eng.

Lindeburg, Michael R. Mechanical Engineering Review Manual. 7th ed. (Engineering Review Manual Ser.). (Illus.). 688p. 1984. pap. 36.95 (ISBN 0-932276-44-X); pap. text ed. 9.50. Prof Engine.

Mabie, Hamilton H. & Ocvirk, Fred W. Mechanisms & Dynamics of Machinery, SI Version. 3rd ed. LC 78-1382. 610p. 1978. text ed. 45.45x (ISBN 0-471-02380-9); solutions 17.50 (ISBN 0-471-04134-3). Wiley.

McKelvey, John P. & Grotch, Howard. Fisica Paraciencias E Ingenieria, Vol. I. (Span.). 1980. pap. text ed. 15.40 (ISBN 0-06-315475-7, Pub. by HarLA Mexico). Har-Row.

--Fisica Paraciencias E Ingenieria, Vol. II. (Span.). 1981. pap. text ed. 16.40 (ISBN 0-06-315476-5, Pub. by HarLA Mexico). Har-Row.

McLean, W. G. & Nelson, E. W. Schaum's Outline of Engineering Mechanics. 3rd ed. (Schaum's Outline Ser.). 1978. pap. 9.95 (ISBN 0-07-044816-7). McGraw.

Martelli, Fabrizio G. Twin Screw Extruders: A Basic Understanding. 128p. 1982. 36.50 (ISBN 0-442-26363-5). Van Nos Reinhold.

Mechanical Engineering Education in America: It's First Century. 101p. 1982. 20.00 (I00146). ASME.

Meriam, J. L. Engineering Mechanics: Statics & Dynamics Combined. LC 78-518. 540p. 1978. text ed. 50.45x (ISBN 0-471-01979-8). Wiley.

Middleton & Knowles, W. E. Mechanical Engineering at the National Research Council of Canada 1929-1951. 280p. 1984. text ed. 23.00x (ISBN 0-88920-164-1, Pub. by Laurier U Pr). Humanities.

Moss, Marvin A. Designing for Minimal Maintenance Expense: (TBC) the Practical Application of Reliability & Maintainability. (Mechanical Engineering Ser.). 288p. 1985. 39.75 (ISBN 0-8247-7314-4). Dekker.

Mueller, E. A., ed. Mechanics of Sound Generation in Flow. (IUTAM-Symposium Ser.). (Illus.). 302p. 1979. 43.70 (ISBN 0-387-09785-6). Springer-Verlag.

Mueller, J. F. Standard Application of Mechanical Details. 288p. 1985. 39.95 (ISBN 0-07-043962-1). McGraw.

Muvdi, B. B. & McNabb, J. W. Engineering Mechanics of Materials. 2nd ed. 672p. 1984. text ed. write for info. (ISBN 0-02-385770-6). Macmillan.

Nayler. Dictionary of Mechanical Engineering. 3rd ed. (Illus.). 416p. 1985. text ed. 55.95 (ISBN 0-408-01505-5). Butterworth.

Nee, John G. Mechanical Engineering Technology: Product Design & Drafting Problems. LC 83-60332. (Illus.). 163p. 1983. pap. 11.95x (ISBN 0-911168-52-4). Prakken.

--Mechanism Drafting & Design: A Workbook. LC 80-80861. (Illus.). 1980. pap. text ed. 14.95x (ISBN 0-911168-45-1); solutions manual 3.95x (ISBN 0-911168-46-X). Prakken.

Nogotov, E. F. Applications of Numerical Methods to Heat Transfer. (Illus.). 1978. pap. text ed. 48.00 (ISBN 0-07-046852-4). McGraw.

Noltingk, B. E. Jones Instrument Technology: Mechanical Measurements, Vol. I. 4th ed. (Illus.). 264p. 1985. pap. text ed. 29.95 (ISBN 0-408-01231-5). Butterworth.

Noor, A. K., ed. Impact of New Computing Systems on Computational Mechanics. 176p. 1983. pap. text ed. 34.00 (ISBN 0-317-02625-9, H00275). ASME.

Oleson, John P. Greek & Roman Mechanical Water-Lifting Devices: The History of Technology. (Phoenix Supplementary Ser.: Vol. 16). (Illus.). 624p. 1984. 95.00x (ISBN 0-8020-5597-4). U of Toronto Pr.

Osyczka, Andrzej. Multicriterion Optimization in Engineering with FORTRAN Programs. LC 83-25478. (Mechanical Engineering Series-Ellis Horwood: 1-476). 178p. 1984. 54.95x (ISBN 0-470-20019-7). Halsted Pr.

Parrish, A., ed. Mechanical Engineer's Reference Book. 11th ed. 1600p. 1973. 130.00 (ISBN 0-408-00083-X). Butterworth.

Paul, B., ed. Mechanics of Transportation Suspension Systems, AMD Vol. 15. 110p. 1975. pap. text ed. 12.00 (ISBN 0-685-62563-X, I00095). ASME.

Paul, Burton. Kinematics & Dynamics of Planar Machinery. (Illus.). 1979. text ed. 43.95 (ISBN 0-13-516062-6). P-H.

Peatfield, A. E. Teach Yourself Mechanical Engineering: Hand Tools, No. 1. (Teach Yourself Ser.). 1950. 1.00 (ISBN 0-486-21724-8). Dover.

Pefley, Richard & Newnan, Donald G. Mechanical Engineering License Review. 3rd ed. LC 79-11957. 378p. 1980. pap. 21.95 (ISBN 0-910554-28-5). Engineering.

Peterson, Rudolph E. Stress Concentration Factors. LC 53-11283. 336p. 1974. 52.95x (ISBN 0-471-68329-9, Pub. by Wiley-Interscience). Wiley.

Power Editors. Plant Energy System: Energy Systems Engineering. 1967. 69.95 (ISBN 0-07-050588-8). McGraw.

Prentis, J. M. Dynamics of Mechanical Systems. 2nd ed. LC 79-41460. 486p. 1980. 85.95x (ISBN 0-470-26938-3). Halsted Pr.

Prentis, James M. Engineering Mechanics. (Oxford Engineering Science Texts Ser.). (Illus.). 1979. text ed. 59.00x (ISBN 0-19-856205-5). Oxford U Pr.

Radiation Curing: Conference Proceedings, Vol. VI. LC 82-60954. 430p. 1982. 40.00 (ISBN 0-87263-088-9). SME.

Rao, J. S. Rotor Dynamics. 244p. 1983. 29.95x (ISBN 0-470-27448-4). Halsted Pr.

Robertson, J. M. & Wislicenus, G. F., eds. Cavitation State of Knowledge: Presented at the ASME Fluids Engineering & Applied Mechanics Conference, Northwestern University, Evanston, Ill., June 16-18, 1969. LC 73-173121. pap. 61.80 (ISBN 0-317-29952-2, 2051713). Bks Demand UMI.

Roose, Robert W., ed. Handbook of Data Sheets for Solution of Mechanical Systems Problems. (Illus.). 432p. 1984. 48.50 (ISBN 0-442-27804-7). Van Nos Reinhold.

Rothbart, H. A. Mechanical Design & Systems Handbook. 2nd ed. 1824p. 1985. 96.50 (ISBN 0-07-054020-9). McGraw.

Rudman, Jack. Assistant Mechanical Construction Engineer. (Career Examination Ser.: C-2706). (Cloth bdg. avail. on request). 1980. pap. 12.00 (ISBN 0-8373-2706-7). Natl Learning.

--Mechanical Engineer. (Career Examination Ser.: C-481). (Cloth bdg. avail. on request). pap. 10.00 (ISBN 0-8373-0481-4). Natl Learning.

Sandor, Bela I. & Richter, Karen. Engineering Mechanics: Dynamics. 2nd ed. (Illus.). 576p. 1986. text ed. 30.95 (ISBN 0-13-279050-5). P-H.

--Engineering Mechanics: Statics. 2nd ed. (Illus.). 528p. 1986. text ed. 30.95 (ISBN 0-13-279076-9). P-H.

--Engineering Mechanics: Statics & Dynamics. 2nd ed. (Illus.). 1088p. 1986. text ed. 39.95 (ISBN 0-13-279092-0). P-H.

Schlichting, Hermann. Boundary Layer Theory. 7th ed. Kestin, J., tr. from Ger. (Mechanical Engineering Ser.). (Illus.). 1979. 48.00 (ISBN 0-07-055334-3). McGraw.

Schrock, V. F., ed. Two-Phase Flow & Heat Transfer in Rod Bundles: Presented at the Winter Annual Meeting of the American Society of Mechanical Engineers, Los Angeles, November, 18, 1969. LC 73-28391. pap. 25.00 (ISBN 0-317-08165-9, 2013315). Bks Demand UMI.

Seireg, Ali A., ed. CIME (Computers in Mechanical Engineering Magazine) Research Supplement, Vol. 1. 79p. 1983. pap. text ed. 8.00 (ISBN 0-317-02556-2, G00234). ASME.

Seminar on Mechanical Engineering in a Marine Environment. 45p. 1983. pap. text ed. 12.00x (ISBN 0-85825-192-2, Pub. by Inst Engineering Australia). Brookfield Pub Co.

Sengupta, S., ed. Advances in Heat & Mass Transfer at Air Water Interfaces. 116p. 1978. 18.00 (ISBN 0-685-66789-8, H00127). ASME.

Shigley, Joseph E. & Mitchell, Larry D. Mechanical Engineering Design. 4th ed. (Mechanical Engineering Ser.). (Illus.). 778p. 1983. text ed. 45.95 (ISBN 0-07-056888-X). McGraw.

Sinclair, Bruce. A Centennial History of the American Society of Mechanical Engineers: 1880-1980. 256p. 1980. text ed. 15.00 (ISBN 0-686-69842-8, H0175H); pap. text ed. 10.00 (ISBN 0-686-69843-6, H0175P). ASME.

--A History of the American Society of Mechanical Engineers. 304p. 1980. 27.50x (ISBN 0-8020-2380-0). U of Toronto Pr.

Spiegler, K. S. Principles of Energetics. (Illus.). 175p. 1983. 27.00 (ISBN 0-387-12441-1). Springer-Verlag.

Stamper, Eugene & Droughton, John. Building Energy Systems. 1984. text ed. 35.00 (ISBN 0-8359-0587-X). Reston.

Stanley, R. C. Mechanical Properties of Solids & Fluids. (Illus.). 240p. 1972. 13.75 (ISBN 0-8088-7030-0). Davey.

Stoecker, W. F. Design of Thermal Systems. 2nd ed. (Illus.). 1980. 42.00 (ISBN 0-07-061618-3). McGraw.

Structural Optimization Symposium. AMD: Proceedings, Vol. 7. 162p. 1974. 18.00 (ISBN 0-685-48054-2, I00042). ASME.

Threlkeld, James L. Thermal Environmental Engineering. 2nd ed. 1970. ref. ed. 39.95 (ISBN 0-13-914721-7). P-H.

Trade & Technical Press Ltd, ed. Handbook of Mechanical Power Drives. 2nd ed. (Illus.). 1978. 150.00x (ISBN 0-85461-067-7). Intl Ideas.

Tucker, Allen E., ed. Communications, Vol. A. rev. ed. (Fluid Power Standards 1984 Ser.). (Illus.). 219p. 1984. 25.50 (ISBN 0-942220-71-4); Set. write for info. Natl Fluid Power.

U. S. Navy (Bureau of Naval Personnel) Basic Machines & How They Work. (Illus.). 1965. pap. 4.50 (ISBN 0-486-21709-4). Dover.

Vanmarcke, Erik. Random Fields: Analysis & Synthesis. (Illus.). 416p. 1983. 47.50x (ISBN 0-262-22026-1). MIT Pr.

Veinott, Cyril G. Computer-Aided Design of Electric Machinery. (Monographs in Modern Electrical Technology). (Illus.). 168p. 1973. 30.00x (ISBN 0-262-22016-4). MIT Pr.

Venturini, W. S. Boundary Element Method in Geomechanics. (Lecture Notes in Engineering: Vol. 4). (Illus.). 246p. 1983. pap. 21.00 (ISBN 0-387-12653-8). Springer-Verlag.

The Way Things Work: An Encyclopedia of Modern Technology, Vol. 2. 1971. 19.95 (ISBN 0-671-21086-6). S&S.

Wyskida, Richard M. & McDaniel, Don M. Modeling of Cushioning Systems. 336p. 1980. 59.25 (ISBN 0-677-05480-7). Gordon.

MECHANICAL ENGINEERING–BIBLIOGRAPHY

American Society of Mechanical Engineers. Indexes to Nineteen-Eighty Publications. (Transactions of American Society of Mechanical Engineers: Vol. 103). pap. 55.30 (ISBN 0-317-09799-7, 2016916). Bks Demand UMI.

Palyza, M. M. Useful Books of Reference for Designers (1926-1983) Held by the Science Reference Library: Pt. 3 Mechanical Engineering. 125p. (Orig.). 1984. pap. 7.50 (ISBN 0-7123-0714-1, Pub. by British Pub). Longwood Pub Group.

MECHANICAL ENGINEERING–DICTIONARIES

Bogelsack, G., et al, eds. Terminology for the Theory of Machines & Mechanisms. 30p. 1983. pap. 10.00 (ISBN 0-08-031140-7). Pergamon.

Dictionary of Mechanical Engineering. (Eng. & Chinese.). 608p. 1974. pap. text ed. 7.95 (ISBN 0-686-92389-8, M-9586). French & Eur.

European Committee of Associations of Gear & Transmission Element Manufacturers (EUROTRANS), ed. Glossary of Transmission Elements: Gears. (Illus., In 8 languages). 1976. lib. bdg. 30.00x (ISBN 3-7830-0104-8). Marlin.

Freeman, Henry G. Spezialwoerterbuch Maschinenwesen. (Ger. -Eng.). 207p. (Dictionary of Mechanical Engineering). 1971. write for info (M-7625, Pub. by Verlag W. Girardet). French & Eur.

Horner, J. G. Dictionary of Mechanical Engineering Terms. 9th rev. & enl. ed. Grahame-White, G. K., ed. 32.50 (ISBN 0-685-29250-9). Heinman.

--Dictionary of Mechanical Engineering Terms. 422p. 1967. 32.50 (ISBN 0-291-39357-8, Pub. by Technical Press UK). Heinman.

Lexikon der Graphischen Technik. 4th ed. (Ger.). 1977. 29.95 (ISBN 3-7940-4078-3, M-7253). French & Eur.

Nayler, J. L. & Nayler, G. H. Dictionary of Mechanical Engineering. 2nd ed. 1978. 39.95 (ISBN 0-408-00175-5). Butterworth.

Schulz, E. Woerterbuch der Optik und Feinmechanik: English-French-German Dictionary of Optics & Mechanical Engineering. (Eng., Fr. & Ger.). 1961. write for info. (M-90925). French & Eur.

Schulz, Ernst. Woerterbuch der Optik und Feinmechanik, Vol. 1. (Fr., Ger. & Eng., Dictionary of Optics & Mechanical Engineering). 1961. pap. 12.00 (ISBN 3-87097-036-7, M-6978). French & Eur.

--Woerterbuch der Optik und Feinmechanik, Vol. 2. (Fr., Ger. & Eng., Dictionary of Optics & Mechanical Engineering). 1961. pap. 12.00 (ISBN 3-87097-037-5, M-6977). French & Eur.

Schwartz, Vladimir V. The Illustrated Dictionary of Mechanical Engineering. (Eng. & Ger. & Fr. & Dutch & Rus.). 1984. lib. bdg. 49.50 (ISBN 90-201-1668-1, Pub. by Martinus Nijhoff Netherlands). Kluwer Academic.

Shvarts, V. V. The Concise Illustrated Russian-English Dictionary of Mechanical Engineering. (Rus. & Eng., Illus.). 224p. 1981. pap. 33.00 (ISBN 0-08-027574-5). Pergamon.

Shvarts, Vladimir. The Concise Illustrated Russian-English Dictionary of Mechanical Engineering. (Rus. & Eng.). 224p. 1980. 35.00x (ISBN 0-686-44774-3, Pub. by Collets). State Mutual Bk.

Stellhorn, Kurt. Woerterbuch Werkzeuge und Werkzeugmaschinen. (Ger. & Fr.). 1969. leatherette 56.00 (ISBN 3-7736-5260-7, M-6907). French & Eur.

Tver, David F. & Bolz, Roger W. Encyclopedic Dictionary of Industrial Technology Materials, Processes & Equipment: A New York Publication. (Illus.). 400p. 1984. 34.50 (ISBN 0-412-00501-8, 9005, Pub. by Chapman & Hall). Methuen Inc.

MECHANICAL ENGINEERING–EXAMINATIONS, QUESTIONS, ETC.

Calder, Clarence A., ed. Mechanics of Materials Exam File. LC 84-24702. (Exam File Ser.). 378p. (Orig.). 1985. pap. 9.95 (ISBN 0-910554-46-3). Engineering.

Gladstone, John. Air Conditioning & Mechanical Trades: Preparing for the Contractor's License Examination. LC 74-18258. (Illus.). 425p. 1980. pap. 19.95 (ISBN 0-930644-04-2). Engineers Pr.

Klemetson, Stanley L., ed. Fluid Mechanics Exam File. LC 84-24693. (Exam File Ser.). 218p. (Orig.). 1985. pap. 9.95 (ISBN 0-910554-48-X). Engineering.

Koch, Harry W. Mechanical Work Examinations. 1967. 7.00 (ISBN 0-913164-23-2). Ken-Bks.

Mishra, L. N., ed. Fundamentals of Mechanical Engineering: Multiple Choice Questions. 1983. text ed. 25.00x (ISBN 0-7069-2199-2, Pub. by Vikas India). Advent NY.

Rudman, Jack. Assistant Mechanical Engineer. (Career Examination Ser.: C-44). (Cloth bdg. avail. on request). pap. 12.00 (ISBN 0-8373-0044-4). Natl Learning.

--Auto Machinist. (Career Examination Ser.: C-62). (Cloth bdg. avail. on request). pap. 12.00 (ISBN 0-8373-0062-2). Natl Learning.

--Chief Supervisor of Mechanical Installations. (Career Examination Ser.: C-2482). (Cloth bdg. avail. on request). pap. 14.00 (ISBN 0-8373-2482-3). Natl Learning.

--Junior Mechanical Engineer. (Career Examination Ser.: C-402). (Cloth bdg. avail. on research). pap. 12.00 (ISBN 0-8373-0402-4). Natl Learning.

--Mechanical Engineer. (Career Examination Ser.: C-481). (Cloth bdg. avail. on request). pap. 10.00 (ISBN 0-8373-0481-4). Natl Learning.

--Mechanical Engineering Trainee. (Career Examination Ser.: C-519). (Cloth bdg. avail. on request). pap. 8.00 (ISBN 0-8373-0519-5). Natl Learning.

--Mechanical Equipment Inspector. (Career Examination Ser.: C-2045). (Cloth bdg. avail. on request). pap. 10.00 (ISBN 0-8373-2045-3). Natl Learning.

--Senior Building Mechanical Engineer. (Career Examination Ser.: C-2572). (Cloth bdg. avail. on request). pap. 14.00 (ISBN 0-8373-2572-2). Natl Learning.

--Senior Mechanical Engineer. (Career Examination Ser.: C-1648). (Cloth bdg. avail on request). 1977. pap. 12.00 (ISBN 0-8373-1648-0). Natl Learning.

Smith, Charles E., ed. Dynamics Exam File. LC 84-24699. (Exam File Ser.). 346p. (Orig.). 1985. pap. 9.95 (ISBN 0-910554-44-7). Engineering.

--Statics Exam File. LC 84-21141. (Exam File Ser.). 346p. (Orig.). 1985. pap. 9.95 (ISBN 0-910554-47-1). Engineering.

MECHANICAL ENGINEERING–HANDBOOKS, MANUALS, ETC.

American Society of Mechanical Engineers. ASME Handbook: Engineering Tables. 1956. 84.50 (ISBN 0-07-001516-3). McGraw.

--ASME Handbook: Metals Engineering-Design. 2nd ed. 1964. 72.50 (ISBN 0-07-001518-X). McGraw.

Atteberry, Pat H. Power Mechanics. LC 80-20581. (Illus.). 112p. 1980. text ed. 6.40 (ISBN 0-87006-307-3). Goodheart.

Automatic Turning Machines. 1982. 50.00x (ISBN 0-85083-217-9, Pub. by Engineering Ind). State Mutual Bk.

B-One.ThirteenM - 1979: Metric Screw Threads - M Profile. 40p. 1979. 10.00 (ISBN 0-685-25547-6, N00046). ASME.

Baumeister, E. T., ed. Standard Handbook for Mechanical Engineers. 8th ed. 1978. pap. 69.50 (ISBN 0-685-99211-X, E00028); 46.00. ASME.

Blake, Alexander. Handbook of Mechanics, Materials & Structures. (Mechanical Engineering Practice Ser.). 1000p. 1985. 71.95 (ISBN 0-471-86239-8). Wiley.

Bovay, H. E., Jr., ed. Handbook of Mechanical & Electrical Systems for Buildings. (Illus.). 864p. 1981. 62.50 (ISBN 0-07-006718-X). McGraw.

Hu, David. Cogeneration. 1984. text ed. 39.95 (ISBN 0-8359-0771-6). Reston.

Kent, R. T. Mechanical Engineers' Handbook, 2 pts. 12th ed. Carmichael, C., ed. Incl. Pt. 1. Design & Production. 1611p. 74.50x (ISBN 0-471-46959-9); Pt. 2. Mechanical Engineers' Handbook: Power. Salisbury, J. K., ed. 1409p. 77.50x (ISBN 0-471-46992-0). 1950 (Pub. by Wiley-Interscience). Wiley.

Kutz, Myer P. Mechanical Engineers' Handbook. 2256p. 1985. 72.00 (ISBN 0-471-08817-X). Wiley.

Milling One. 50.00x (ISBN 0-85083-011-7, Pub. by Engineering Ind). State Mutual Bk.

Milling Two. 1983. 50.00x (ISBN 0-85083-060-5, Pub. by Engineering Ind). State Mutual Bk.

Muller, Herbert W. Epicyclic Drive Trains: Analysis, Synthesis, & Applications. Glover, John H., ed. Mannhardt, Werner G., tr. LC 81-114220. (Illus.). 374p. 1982. 49.00 (ISBN 0-8143-1663-8). Wayne St U Pr.

Nelson, Carl A. Mechanical Trades Pocket Manual. 2nd ed. LC 83-6364. 363p. (Orig.). 1983. pap. 10.95 (ISBN 0-672-23378-9, Dist. by G K Hall). Audel.

--Millwrights & Mechanics Guide. 3rd ed. LC 82-17873. (Illus.). 1032p. 1983. 19.95 (ISBN 0-672-23373-8). Audel.

--Millwrights & Mechanics Guide. 3rd ed. LC 82-17873. (Audel Ser.). 1983. 19.95 (ISBN 0-672-23373-8). G K Hall.

Press Tool Making. 1982. 50.00x (ISBN 0-85083-168-7, Pub. by Engineering Ind). State Mutual Bk.

Vogel, Werner. The Exact Overwire Measurement of Screws, Gears, Splines & Worms. LC 72-6682. 229p. 1973. 19.95x (ISBN 0-8143-1489-9). Wayne St U Pr.

Webb, M. J. & Holtje, H. Mechanical Technician's Handbook. 1982. 42.50 (ISBN 0-07-068802-8). McGraw.

MECHANICAL ENGINEERING–PROBLEMS, EXERCISES, ETC.

Constance, J. Mechanical Engineering for Professional Engineers' Examinations. 4th ed. 624p. 1985. 34.95 (ISBN 0-07-012452-3). McGraw.

Fichera, G. Trends in Applications of Pure Mathematics to Mechanics, Vol. 1. (Monographs & Studies: No. 2). 459p. 1976. text ed. 54.50 (ISBN 0-273-00129-9). Pitman Pub MA.

Fong, J. T., et al, eds. Critical Issues in Materials & Mechanical Engineering. (PVP Ser.: Vol. 47). 276p. 1981. 40.00 (ISBN 0-686-34517-7, H00183). ASME.

Kiseliov, V. A., et al. Mecanica De Construccion En Ejemplos y Problemas. (Span., Illus.). 391p. 1973. 8.45 (ISBN 0-8285-1457-7, Pub. by Mir Pubs USSR). Imported Pubns.

Rudman, Jack. Mechanical Engineer. (Career Examination Ser.: C-481). (Cloth bdg. avail. on request). pap. 10.00 (ISBN 0-8373-0481-4). Natl Learning.

Stamper, Eugene & Dublin, Stanley W. Mechanical Engineering & Economics & Ethics for Professional Engineering Examinations. Hollander, Lawrence J., ed. (Professional Engineering Examination Ser). (Illus.). 1971. 21.55 (ISBN 0-8104-5716-4). Hayden.

Szuladzinski, Gregory. Dynamics of Structures & Machinery: Problems & Solutions. LC 80-10487. 297p. 1982. 58.95 (ISBN 0-471-09027-1, Pub. by Wiley Interscience). Wiley.

MECHANICAL ENGINEERING–TABLES, CALCULATIONS, ETC.

American Society of Mechanical Engineers. ASME Handbook: Engineering Tables. 1956. 84.50 (ISBN 0-07-001516-3). McGraw.

Anand, Davinder K. & Cunniff, Patrick. Engineering Mechanics: Statics. 450p. 1984. scp 42.11 (ISBN 0-205-07784-6, 327810). Allyn.

Anand, Davinder K. & Cunniff, Patrick F. Engineering Mechanics: Statics & Dynamics. 900p. 1984. scp 29.10 (ISBN 0-205-07810-9, 327784). Allyn.

Kamal, M. H. & Wolf, J. A., Jr. Computational Methods In Ground Transportation Systems. (AMD Ser.: Vol. 50). 1982. 40.00 (H00234). ASME.

MECHANICAL ENGINEERS

Franklin, George E. From Cotswolds to High Sierras. LC 66-20373. (Illus.). 167p. 1966. 4.00 (ISBN 0-87004-046-4). Caxton.

Mechanical Engineers in America Born Prior to 1861: A Biographical Dictionary. 330p. 1980. 20.00 (ISBN 0-686-69855-X, H00176). ASME.

Peterson, Aldor C. Applied Engineering Mechanics: Statics. 2nd ed. 260p. 1981. text ed. 38.20 (ISBN 0-205-07131-7, 327131); cancelled (ISBN 0-205-07183-X). Allyn.

MECHANICAL HANDLING

see Materials Handling

MECHANICAL MODELS

see Machinery–Models

MECHANICAL MOVEMENTS

see also Cams; Links and Link-Motion; Machinery, Kinematics Of

Bickford, John H. Mechanisms for Intermittent Motion. LC 75-184639. 272p. 1972. 28.50 (ISBN 0-8311-1091-0). Krieger.

Brown, H. T. Five Hundred Seven Mechanical Movements. 1984. pap. 7.95 (ISBN 0-917914-25-2). Lindsay Pubns.

Brown, Henry T. Five Hundred Seven Mechanical Movements. LC 81-50440. (Illus.). 102p. Repr. of 1896 ed. 12.50x (ISBN 0-935164-06-5). N T Smith.

Bucksch, H. Dictionary of Mechanisms. (Ger. & Eng.). 1976. leatherette 133.00 (ISBN 3-7625-0707-4, M-7111). French & Eur.

Chironis, Nicholas P. Mechanisms, Linkages, & Mechanical Controls. 1965. 57.75 (ISBN 0-07-010775-0). McGraw.

Dijksman, E. A. Motion Geometry of Mechanisms. LC 75-3977. (Illus.). 250p. 1976. 47.50 (ISBN 0-521-20841-6). Cambridge U Pr.

Duffy, Joseph. Analysis of Mechanisms & Robot Manipulators. 419p. 1980. 135.95x (ISBN 0-470-27002-0). Halsted Pr.

Erdman, Arthur G. & Sandor, George N. Advanced Mechanism Design: Analysis & Synthesis, Vol. 2. (Illus.). 624p. 1984. 47.95 (ISBN 0-13-011437-5). P-H.

--Mechanism Design: Analysis & Synthesis, Vol. 1. (Illus.). 544p. 1984. 41.95 (ISBN 0-13-572396-5). P-H.

Faires, Virgil M. & Keown, Robert M. Mechanism. 5th ed. LC 80-13135. 346p. 1980. Repr. of 1960 ed. lib. bdg. 21.50 (ISBN 0-89874-182-3). Krieger.

Grafstein, Paul & Schwarz, Otto M. Pictorial Handbook of Technical Devices. (Illus.). 1971. 14.00 (ISBN 0-8206-0234-5). Chem Pub.

Jones, Franklin D., et al. Ingenious Mechanisms for Designers & Inventors, 4 vols, Vols. I-IV. LC 30-14992. (Illus.). 1930-77. Set. 90.00 (ISBN 0-8311-1084-8); Vol. I, 536p. 24.95 (ISBN 0-8311-1029-5); Vol. II, 538p. 24.95 (ISBN 0-8311-1030-9); Vol. III, 536p. 24.95 (ISBN 0-8311-1031-7); Vol. IV, 493p. 24.95 (ISBN 0-8311-1032-5). Indus Pr.

Kondratiev, V. N. & Nikitin, E. E. Gas-Phase Reactions: Kinetics & Mechanisms. (Illus.). 250p. 1981. 70.00 (ISBN 0-387-09956-5). Springer-Verlag.

Lent, Deane. Analysis & Design of Mechanisms. 2nd ed. (Technology Ser.). 1970. text ed. 28.95 (ISBN 0-13-032797-2). P-H.

Mabie, Hamilton H. & Ocvirk, Fred W. Mechanisms & Dynamics of Machinery. 3rd ed. LC 74-30405. 594p. 1975. text ed. 46.00 (ISBN 0-471-55935-0); solutions 10.00 (ISBN 0-471-55938-5). Wiley.

Martin, George H. Kinematics & Dynamics of Machines. 2nd ed. (Illus.). 544p. 1982. 42.00x (ISBN 0-07-040657-X). McGraw.

Reshetov, L. Self-Aligning Mechanisms. 528p. 1982. 12.95 (ISBN 0-8285-2339-8, Pub. by Mir Pubs USSR). Imported Pubns.

Sandler, B. Z. Probabilistic Approach to Mechanisms. (Studies in Applied Mechanics: Vol. 8). 1984. 65.50 (ISBN 0-444-42306-0, I-098-84). Elsevier.

Schwamb, P. & Merrill, A. L. Elements of Mechanism. 1984. pap. 9.95 (ISBN 0-917914-15-5). Lindsay Pubns.

Shigley, Joseph E. & Uiker, John J. Theory of Machines & Mechanisms. (Mechanical Engineering Ser.). (Illus.). 576p. 1980. text ed. 44.00x (ISBN 0-07-056884-7). McGraw.

Soni, Atmaram H. Mechanism Synthesis & Analysis. LC 73-22000. pap. 126.30 (ISBN 0-317-08011-3, 2055328). Bks Demand UMI.

Suh, Chung Ha. Computer Aided Design of Mechanisms. 600p. Date not set. pap. text ed. 49.95 (ISBN 0-02-949720-5). Macmillan.

MECHANICAL PAINTING

see Painting, Industrial

MECHANICAL PRESTRESSING

see Residual Stresses

MECHANICAL QUADRATURE

see Numerical Integration

MECHANICAL SHOCK

see Shock (Mechanics)

MECHANICAL TRANSLATING

see Machine Translating

MECHANICAL WEAR

American Society for Metal. Wear & Fracture Prevention: Proceedings of a Conference Held May 21-22, 1980, Peoria, Illinois. LC 81-67226. (Materials-Metalworking Technology Ser.). pap. 79.80 (ISBN 0-317-26752-3, 2024351). Bks Demand UMI.

American Society for Metals. Source Book on Wear Control Technology: A Comprehensive Collection of Outstanding Articles from the Periodical & Reference Literature. Rigney, David A. & Glaeser, W. A., eds. LC 78-12162. (ASM Engineering Bookshelf Ser.). pap. 116.00 (ISBN 0-317-26756-6, 2024349). Bks Demand UMI.

Burwell, John T., ed. Mechanical Wear: Being the Proceedings of a Summer Conference on This Subject Held in June 1948. LC 50-1084. pap. 98.80 (ISBN 0-317-29825-9, 2051960). Bks Demand UMI.

Guttman, V. & Merz, M., eds. Corrosion & Mechanical Stress at High Temperatures. (Illus.). 477p. 1981. 52.00 (ISBN 0-85334-956-8, Pub. by Elsevier Applied Sci England). Elsevier.

Kragelsky, I. V. Friction Wear Methods. 110.00 (ISBN 0-08-025461-6). Pergamon.

Kragelsky, I. V. & Alisin, V. V., eds. Friction, Wear & Lubrication: A Complete Handbook of Tribology, 3 Vols. (Illus.). 800p. 130.00 (ISBN 0-08-027591-5, A115); firm 60.00 (ISBN 0-686-97493-X). Pergamon.

Smith, Alrick L. Reliability of Engineering Materials. (Illus.). 160p. (Orig.). 1985. pap. text ed. 35.95 (ISBN 0-408-01507-1). Butterworth.

MECHANICS

see also Acceleration (Mechanics); Animal Mechanics; Biomechanics; Deformations (Mechanics); Dynamics; Elastic Solids; Elasticity; Electromechanical Analogies; Engineering; Fluids; Force and Energy; Friction; Gases; Hydraulics; Hydrodynamics; Hydrostatics; Kinematics; Liquids; Machinery; Mass (Physics); Mathematical Physics; Matter–Properties; Mechanical Movements; Motion; Photoelasticity; Potential, Theory of; Power (Mechanics); Relativistic Mechanics; Rock Mechanics; Shock (Mechanics); Soil Mechanics; Stability; Statics; Statistical Mechanics; Steam-Engines; Strains and Stresses; Strength of Materials; Thermodynamics; Torque; Torsion; Vibration; Viscosity; Wave Mechanics; Wave-Motion, Theory of

Alonso, Marcelo & Finn, Edward J. Fundamental University Physics, 2 vols. 2nd ed. Incl. Vol. 1. Mechanics. 1979. text ed. 17.95 (ISBN 0-201-00076-8); Vol. 2. Fields & Waves. 1983. text ed. 19.95 (ISBN 0-201-00077-6). 1980. Addison-Wesley.

American Society of Mechanical Engineers. Theory of Machines & Mechanisms, 2 Vols. 1979. Set. 75.00 (ISBN 0-317-06827-X). Vol. 1, 1607p (G00148). Vol. 2, 1654p (G00149). ASME.

Andersen, Paul & Nordby, Gene M. Introduction to Structural Mechanics. LC 60-13150. pap. 88.00 (ISBN 0-317-10800-X, 2012445). Bks Demand UMI.

Andronov, A. A., et al. Seven Papers on Equations Related to Mechanics & Heat. LC 51-5559. (Translations Ser.: No. 2, Vol. 75). 1968. 34.00 (ISBN 0-8218-1775-2, TRANS 2-75). Am Math.

Arnold, V. I. Mathematical Methods in Classical Mechanics. (Graduate Texts in Mathematics Ser.: Vol. 60). (Illus.). 1978. 32.00 (ISBN 0-387-90314-3). Springer-Verlag.

Axelrad, D. R. Foundations of the Probabilistic Mechanics of Discrete Media. (Foundations & Philosophy of Science & Technology Ser.). (Illus.). 200p. 1984. 28.00 (ISBN 0-08-025234-6). Pergamon.

Barger, Vernon D. & Olsson, Martin G. Classical Mechanics: A Modern Perspective. LC 72-5697. (Illus.). 352p. 1973. text ed. 34.95 (ISBN 0-07-003723-X). McGraw.

Bartlett, James H. Classical & Modern Mechanics. LC 74-5588. 489p. 1975. 22.00 (ISBN 0-8173-3100-X); pap. 7.50 (ISBN 0-8173-3101-8). U of Ala Pr.

Bauld, Nelson. Mechanics of Materials. 2nd ed. 580p. 1985. text ed. write for info. (ISBN 0-534-05718-7, Pub. by PWS Enginering). PWS Pubs.

Beer, F. R., Jr. & Johnston, E. R. Vector Mechanics for Engineers: Combined Volume. 4th ed. 1984. 49.95 (ISBN 0-07-004438-4). McGraw.

Bell, J. F. Mechanics of Solids, Vol. 1: The Experimental Foundations of Solid Mechanics. (Illus.). 830p. 1984. pap. 36.00 (ISBN 0-387-13160-4). Springer-Verlag.

Bert, C. W., ed. Developments in Mechanics: Proceedings of the 14th Midwestern Mechanics Conference, Vol. 8. LC 61-17719. (Illus.). 626p. 39.50 (ISBN 0-8061-1291-3). U of Okla Pr.

Boresi, Arthur P. & Sidebottom, Omar. Advanced Mechanics of Materials. 4th ed. LC 84-883921. 763p. 1985. pap. text ed. 39.95x (ISBN 0-471-88392-1); write for info. (ISBN 0-471-81933-6). Halsted Pr.

Breneman, John W. Mechanics. 3rd ed. (Illus.). 1960. 28.40 (ISBN 0-07-007538-7). McGraw.

Brilla, J., ed. Trends in Applications of Pure Mathematics to Mechanics, Vol. 4. (Monographs & Studies: No. 20). 288p. 1984. text ed. 39.95 (ISBN 0-273-08606-5). Pitman Pub MA.

Brouwer, L. E. & Freudenthal, H. L. E. J. Brouwer, Collected Works, Vol. 2: Geometry, Analysis, Topology & Mechanics. 706p. 1976. 127.75 (ISBN 0-7204-2805-X, North-Holland). Elsevier.

Bullen, K. E. Introduction to the Theory of Mechanics. 8th ed. 1971. 39.50 (ISBN 0-521-08291-9). Cambridge U Pr.

Carpenter, Samuel T. Structural Mechanics. LC 75-31671. 550p. 1976. Repr. of 1966 ed. 30.50 (ISBN 0-88275-363-0). Krieger.

Chapple, M. A Level Physics: Mechanics & Heat, Vol. 1. 2nd ed. (Illus.). 336p. (Orig.). 1979. pap. text ed. 14.95x (ISBN 0-7121-0154-3, Pub. by Macdonald & Evans England). Trans-Atlantic.

Chester, W. Mechanics. (Illus.). 1980. text ed. 50.00x (ISBN 0-04-510058-6); pap. text ed. 24.95x (ISBN 0-04-510059-4). Allen Unwin.

Ciarlet, P. G. & Roseau, M., eds. Trends & Applications of Pure Mathematics to Mechanics: Invited & Contributed Papers Presented at a Symposium at Ecole Polytechnique, Palaiseau, France, Nov. 28-Dec. 2 1983. (Lecture Notes in Physics: Vol. 195). (Fr. & Eng.). 1984. pap. 23.50 (ISBN 0-387-12916-2). Springer Verlag.

CISM (International Center for Mechanical Sciences) Examples to Extremum & Variational Principles in Mechanics. Besdo, D., ed. (CISM International Centre for Mechanical Sciences Ser.: No. 65). (Illus.). 236p. 1974. pap. 23.80 (ISBN 0-387-81230-X). Springer-Verlag.

CISM (International Center for Mechanical Sciences), Dept. for General Mechanics, Technical Univ. of Brunswick, 1970. Extremum & Variational Principles in Mechanics. Lippmann, H., ed. (CISM Pubns. Ser.: No. 54). (Illus.). ii, 239p. 1972. pap. 33.10 (ISBN 0-387-81115-X). Springer-Verlag.

CISM (International Center for Mechanical Sciences) Random Processes in Mechanical Sciences. Parkus, H., ed. (CISM Pubns. Ser.: No. 9). (Illus.). vi, 169p. 1973. pap. 19.80 (ISBN 0-387-81086-2). Springer-Verlag.

Constant, F. Woodbridge. Theoretical Physics: Mechanics of Particles, Rigid & Elastic Bodies & Heat Flow. LC 78-14353. 296p. 1979. Repr. of 1954 ed. lib. bdg. 20.50 (ISBN 0-88275-738-5). Krieger.

Corben, H. C. & Stehle, Philip. Classical Mechanics. 2nd ed. LC 74-141. 402p. 1974. Repr. of 1960 ed. 25.00 (ISBN 0-88275-162-X). Krieger.

Cowan, Brian. Classical Mechanics. (Student Physics Ser.). (Illus.). 128p. (Orig.). 1984. pap. 9.95x (ISBN 0-7102-0280-6). Routledge & Kegan.

Darkov, A. & Kuznetsov, V. Structural Mechanics. Lachinov, B., tr. (Russian Monographs). 704p. 1969. 186.25 (ISBN 0-677-20830-8). Gordon.

Davis, A. Douglas. Classical Mechanics. Date not set. text ed. price not set (ISBN 0-12-206340-6). Acad Pr.

Den Hartog, Jacob P. Mechanics. 1948. pap. 7.50 (ISBN 0-486-60754-2). Dover.

Desloge, Edward A. Classical Mechanics, Vol. 1. LC 81-11407. 519p. 1982. 48.50x (ISBN 0-471-09144-8, Pub. by Wiley-Interscience). Wiley.

--Classical Mechanics, Vol. 2. LC 81-11402. 492p. 1982. 56.95x (ISBN 0-471-09145-6, Pub. by Wiley-Interscience). Wiley.

Drazin, P. G. & Reid, W. H. Hydrodynamic Stability. LC 80-40273. (Cambridge Monographs on Mechanics & Applied Mathematics). (Illus.). 539p. 1982. pap. 27.95 (ISBN 0-521-28980-7). Cambridge U Pr.

Duvant, G. & Lions, J. L. Inequalities in Mechanics & Physics. John, C., tr. from Fr. (Die Grundlehren der Mathematischen Wissenschaften: Vol. 219). (Illus.). 400p. 1976. 60.00 (ISBN 0-387-07327-2). Springer-Verlag.

Dym, C. L. Stability Theory & Its Applications to Structural Mechanics. (Mechanics of Elastic Stability Ser.: No. 3). 200p. 1974. 22.50x (ISBN 90-286-0094-9). Sijthoff & Noordhoff.

Enciclopedia de la Tecnica y de la Mecanica, 8 vols. 5th ed. (Espn.). 2920p. 1975. Set. 360.00 (ISBN 84-278-0072-X, S-14237). French & Eur.

Farmer, I. W. Strata Mechanics: Proceedings of the Symposium, Newcastle Upon Tyne, April 5-7, 1982. (Developments in Geotechnical Engineering Ser.: Vol. 32). 290p. 1982. 85.00 (ISBN 0-444-42086-X). Elsevier.

Fetter, Alexander L. & Walecka, J. Dirk. Theoretical Mechanics of Particles & Continua. (Illus.). 1980. text ed. 39.95 (ISBN 0-07-020658-9). McGraw.

Findley, W., et al. Creep & Relaxation of Nonlinear Viscoelastic Materials. 368p. 1976. 81.00 (ISBN 0-444-10775-4, North-Holland). Elsevier.

Fluegge, C. A., ed. Handbook of Physics, 54 vols, Vol. 6a, Pt. 4. (Illus.). 430p. 1974. 109.20 (ISBN 0-387-06097-9). Springer-Verlag.

Frautschi, Steven C., et al. The Mechanical Universe: Mechanics & Heat, Advanced Edition. (Illus.). 450p. Date not set. price not set (ISBN 0-521-30432-6). Cambridge U Pr.

Freeman, John & Hollis, Martin. Mechanics. LC 83-50224. (Visual Science Ser.). 48p. 1983. 13.72 (ISBN 0-382-06716-9); pap. 6.75 (ISBN 0-382-09001-2). Silver.

French, Anthony P. Newtonian Mechanics. (M.I.T. Introductory Physics Ser). (Illus.). 1971. pap. text ed. 13.95x (ISBN 0-393-09970-9). Norton.

Galilei, Galileo. Dialogues Concerning Two New Sciences. (Illus.). 1914. pap. text ed. 5.50 (ISBN 0-486-60099-8). Dover.

Gallavotti, G. The Elements of Mechanics. (Texts & Monographs in Physics). (Illus.). 528p. 1983. 48.00 (ISBN 0-387-11753-9). Springer-Verlag.

Geradin, M. B. M. Fraeijs De Veubeke Memorial Volume of Selected Papers. 791p. 1980. 57.50x (ISBN 90-286-0900-8). Sijthoff & Noordhoff.

Ghista, D. N., ed. Applied Physiological Mechanics. (Biomedical Engineering & Computation Ser.: Vol. 1). 936p. 1980. text ed. 164.25 (ISBN 3-7186-0013-7). Harwood Academic.

Granet, Irving. Technical Mechanics: Applied Statics & Dynamics. 1984p. text ed. 28.95 (ISBN 0-03-061708-1). HR&W.

Gudehus, G. Finite Elements in Geomechanics. (Wiley Series in Numerical Methods in Engineering). 573p. 1977. 105.95 (ISBN 0-471-99446-4). Wiley.

Hamel, Georg. Elementare Mechanik. 2nd ed. (Illus.). 1912. 45.00 (ISBN 0-384-21140-2). Johnson Repr.

Hamlyn, W. T. Elementary Mechanics to Structure Design in Steel. pap. 6.00x (ISBN 0-89741-003-3). Roadrunner Tech.

Hannah, John & Stephens, R. C. Mechanics of Machines: Advanced Theory & Examples. 2nd ed. (Illus.). 456p. 1972. pap. 32.50x (ISBN 0-7131-3254-X). Intl Ideas.
Harr, Milton E. Mechanics of Particulate Media: A Probabilistic Approach. (Illus.). 1977. text ed. 48.00x (ISBN 0-07-026695-6). McGraw.
Hayden, H. W. & Moffatt, W. G. The Structure & Properties of Materials: Mechanical Behavior, Vol. 3. 247p. 1965. pap. 21.95 (ISBN 0-471-36469-X). Wiley.
Heiserman, R. L. Mechanical Skills for Industrial Electricians. 1983. pap. 16.95 ea. Vol. 1, 172 pp (ISBN 0-471-86180-4). Vol. 2, 195 pp (ISBN 0-471-87579-1). Wiley.
Herman, George, ed. R. D. Mindlin & Applied Mechanics: A Collection of Studies in the Development of Applied Mechanics Dedicated to Prof. R. D. Mindlin by His Former Students. LC 73-22346. 1974. text ed. 54.00 (ISBN 0-08-017710-7). Pergamon.
Hettema, Robert M. Mechanical & Electrical Building Construction. (Illus.). 400p. 1984. 35.95 (ISBN 0-13-569608-9). P-H.
Hibbeler, R. C. Engineering Mechanics: Dynamics. 4th ed. 1223p. 1986. pap. price not set (ISBN 0-02-354660-3). Macmillan.
--Engineering Mechanics: Statics & Dynamics. 3rd ed. 960p. 1983. text ed. write for info. (ISBN 0-02-354140-7). Macmillan.
Higdon, Archie, et al. Mechanics of Materials. 3rd ed. LC 75-28453. 756p. 1976. text ed. 41.45x (ISBN 0-471-38812-2); instr's. manual avail. (ISBN 0-471-01679-9). Wiley.
--Mechanics of Materials. 4th ed. LC 84-7583. 744p. 1985. 37.95 (ISBN 0-471-89044-8). Wiley.
Hsia, Han-Min, et al, eds. Proceedings of the International Symposium on Engineering Sciences & Mechanics. LC 57-43769. (Advances in the Astronautical Sciences Ser.: Vol. 50, Pts. I & II). (Illus.). 1574p. 1983. Pt. I. lib. bdg. 120.00x (ISBN 0-87703-166-5, Pub. by Am Astronaut). Pt. II (ISBN 0-87703-167-3). fiche suppl. 6.00. Univelt Inc.
Huggins, Elisha. Graphical Mechanics: Computer & Laboratory Assisted Introduction to Mechanics. 1979. pap. text ed. 7.50x (ISBN 0-933694-02-4). COMPress.
Hunt, K. H. Kinematic Geometry of Mechanisms. (Engineering Science Ser.). (Illus.). 1978. 89.00x (ISBN 0-19-856124-5). Oxford U Pr.
Irodov, I. E. Fundamental Laws of Mechanics. 1980. pap. 6.45 (ISBN 0-8285-1803-3, Pub. by Mir Pubs USSR). Imported Pubns.
Ishlinsky, A. Advances in Theoretical & Applied Mechanics. 165p. 1981. pap. 5.95 (ISBN 0-8285-2462-9, Pub. by Mir Pubs USSR). Imported Pubns.
IUTAM International Congress, 14th. Theoretical & Applied Mechanics: Proceedings. Koiter, W. T., ed. 492p. 1977. 93.75 (ISBN 0-7204-0549-1, North-Holland). Elsevier.
Jouguet, E. Lectures De Mecanique, 2 vols. in 1. 1908-1909. 37.00 (ISBN 0-384-27940-6). Johnson Repr.
Journal of Theoretical & Applied Mechanics, ed. Two-Dimensional Turbulence. 292p. 1983. pap. 18.00 (ISBN 2-04-011785-7, Pub. by Gauthier-Villars FR). Heyden.
Kardestuncer, H. Discrete Mechanics: A Unified Approach. (International Centre for Mechanical Sciences Courses & Lectures Ser.: No. 221). (Illus.). 1976. soft cover 12.00 (ISBN 0-387-81379-9). Springer-Verlag.
Kawata, Kozo, ed. Theoretical & Applied Mechanics, Vol. 32. 537p. 1984. 89.50x (ISBN 0-86008-344-6, Pub. by U of Tokyo Japan). Columbia U Pr.
Kecs, W. & Teodorescu, P. Applications of Distribution in Mechanics. 1974. 44.00 (ISBN 0-9961000-0-8, Pub. by Abacus England). Heyden.
Kerrod, Robin. The Way It Works. (Illus.). 224p. (Orig.). 1980. 16.95 (ISBN 0-7064-1307-5, Pub. by Mayflower Bks); pap. 9.95 (ISBN 0-686-31072-1). Smith Pubs.
Khanna, K. M. Classical Mechanics. 242p. (Orig.). pap. 21.50 (ISBN 0-686-81276-X). Krieger.
Kleppner, Daniel & Kolenkow, Robert J. An Introduction to Mechanics. (Illus.). 736p. 1973. text ed. 47.95 (ISBN 0-07-035048-5). McGraw.
Knops, R. J., ed. Trends in Applications of Pure Mathematics to Mechanics, Vol. III. LC 77-351685. (Monographs & Studies: No. 11). 243p. 1981. text ed. 79.95 (ISBN 0-273-08487-9). Pitman Pub MA.
Kotkin, G. I. & Serbo, V. G. Collection of Problems in Classical Mechanics. 1971. 21.00 (ISBN 0-08-015843-9). Pergamon.
Lalanne, Michael, et al. Mechanical Vibrations for Engineers. 266p. 1983. 17.95x (ISBN 0-471-90197-0, Pub. by Wiley-Interscience). Wiley.
Levinson, L. Fundamentals of Engineering Mechanics. (Russian Monographs & Texts on the Physical Sciences). 336p. 1965. 80.95x (ISBN 0-677-20250-4). Gordon.
McCallion, H. Vibration of Linear Mechanical Systems. LC 73-181235. pap. 79.00 (ISBN 0-317-11053-5, 2006380). Bks Demand UMI.
McKenzie, Arthur E. Physics. 4th ed. 1970. 18.95x (ISBN 0-521-07698-6). Cambridge U Pr.
MacKinnon, L. Mechanics & Motion. (Oxford Physics Ser.). (Illus.). 1978. 23.50x (ISBN 0-19-851825-0); pap. 10.95x (ISBN 0-19-851843-9). Oxford U Pr.
Mason, J. Variational, Incremental & Energy Methods in Solid Mechanics & Shell Theory: IFIP World Congress. (Studies in Applied Mechanics: Vol. 4). 368p. 1980. 81.00 (ISBN 0-444-41899-7). Elsevier.
Midwestern Mechanics Conference, (7th: 1961: Michigan State University) Developments in Mechanics: Proceedings, Vol. 1. Lay, J. E. & Malvern, L. E., eds. LC 61-17719. pap. 159.00 (ISBN 0-317-09036-4, 2019387). Bks Demand UMI.
Moon, Francis C. Magneto-Solid Mechanics. LC 83-23372. 450p. 1984. 59.95x (ISBN 0-471-88536-3, Pub. by Wiley-Interscience). Wiley.
Moore, E. Neal. Theoretical Mechanics. 456p. 1983. 36.95 (ISBN 0-471-87488-4). Wiley.
Mura, T. Micromechanics of Defects in Solids. 1982. lib. bdg. 98.00 (ISBN 90-247-2560-7, Pub. by Martinus Nijhoff Netherlands). Kluwer Academic.
Nara, Harry R. Vector Mechanics for Engineers. LC 77-10175. 910p. 1977. Repr. of 1962 ed. lib. bdg. 39.50 (ISBN 0-88275-606-0). Krieger.
Nemat-Nasser, S., ed. Mechanics Today, Vols. 1-4. Incl. Vol. 1. 1973. text ed. 49.00 (ISBN 0-08-017246-6); Vol. 2. 1976. text ed. 49.00 (ISBN 0-08-018113-9); Vol. 3. 1976. text ed. 59.00 (ISBN 0-08-019882-1); Vol. 4. 1978. text ed. 88.00 (ISBN 0-08-021792-3); Vol. 5. pap. text ed. 80.00 (ISBN 0-08-024249-9); Vol. 6. pap. text ed. 55.00 (ISBN 0-08-027318-1). 1978. Set. text ed. 121.00 (ISBN 0-08-022682-5). Pergamon.
--Mechanics Today, Vol. 6. LC 80-41699. (Illus.). 225p. 1981. 55.00 (ISBN 0-08-024749-0) (ISBN 0-686-77713-1). Pergamon.
Noll, W. The Foundations of Mechanics & Thermodynamics: Selected Papers. LC 74-1651. 340p. 1974. 38.00 (ISBN 0-387-06646-2). Springer-Verlag.
Norwood, Joseph, Jr. Intermediate Classical Mechanics. (Illus.). 1979. ref. 38.95 (ISBN 0-13-469635-2). P-H.
Oden, J. T. & Becker, E. B. Computational Methods in Nonlinear Mechanics Structures. 51.00 (ISBN 0-08-026153-1). Pergamon.
Oden, J. T. & Reddy, J. N. Variational Methods in Theoretical Mechanics. 2nd, rev. ed. (Universitext Ser.). 308p. 1983. pap. 23.00 (ISBN 0-387-11917-5). Springer-Verlag.
Olenick, Richard, et al. The Mechanical Universe: Introduction to Mechanics & Heat. (Illus.). 576p. 1985. 24.95 (ISBN 0-521-30429-6). Cambridge U Pr.
Olsen, G. Elements of Mechanics of Materials. 4th ed. 1982. 31.95 (ISBN 0-13-267013-5). P-H.
Onicescu, O. Invariantive Mechanics. (International Centre for Mechanical Science Courses & Lectures Ser.: No. 218). 1976. soft cover 17.20 (ISBN 0-387-81349-7). Springer-Verlag.
Pal, J. C. A Course of Mechanics. (Illus.). xi, 399p. 1984. pap. text ed. 13.95x (ISBN 0-7069-2547-5, Pub. by Vikas India). Advent NY.
Parmley, R. O. Mechanical Components Handbook. 768p. 1984. 57.50 (ISBN 0-07-048514-3). McGraw.
Perrone, Nicholas, et al, eds. Fracture Mechanics. LC 78-16063. (Illus.). 722p. 1978. 30.00x (ISBN 0-8139-0802-7). U Pr of Va.
Phipps, LLoyd J. Mechanics in Agriculture Workbook, Pt. 1. 1983. pap. 4.95x (ISBN 0-8134-2315-5). Interstate.
--Mechanics in Agriculture Workbook, Pt. 2. 1983. pap. 4.95x (ISBN 0-8134-2316-3). Interstate.
Pindera, J. T., ed. New Physical Trends in Experimental Mechanics, Vol. 264. (International Centre for Mechanical Sciences, Courses & Lectures Ser.). (Illus.). 367p. 1981. pap. 31.70 (ISBN 0-387-81630-5). Springer-Verlag.
Plumpton, C. & Tomkys, W. H. Theoretical Mechanics in SI Units: In SI Units, Vols. 1-2. 2nd ed. 1971. Vol. 1. pap. 10.25 (ISBN 0-08-016268-1); Vol. 2. pap. 11.25 (ISBN 0-08-016591-5). Pergamon.
Powerplant Mechanics' Manual. 2nd rev. & exp. ed. LC 74-84721. (Zweng Manual Ser.). (Illus.). 1980. soft bdg. 17.95 (ISBN 0-87219-021-8). Pan Am Nav.
Proceedings: Symposium on Incremental Motion & Control Systems & Devices, 9th Annual. LC 73-647018. (Illus.). 1980. 45.00x (ISBN 0-931538-02-5). Incremental Motion.
Rabotnov, Yu. Elements of Hereditary Solid Mechanics. 387p. 1980. 9.95 (ISBN 0-8285-1537-9, Pub. by Mir Pubs USSR). Imported Pubns.
Reddy, J. N., ed. Penalty-Finite Elements Mehtods in Mechanics. (AMD Ser.: Vol. 51). 1982. 40.00 (H00235). ASME.
Research & Education Association Staff. Fluid Mechanics Dynamics Problem Solver. rev. ed. LC 83-62278. (Illus.). 960p. 1984. pap. text ed. 23.85 (ISBN 0-87891-547-8). Res & Educ.
--The Mechanics Problem Solver. rev. ed. LC 79-92403. (Illus.). 1088p. 1984. pap. text ed. 23.85x (ISBN 0-87891-519-2). Res & Educ.
Rimrott, F. P. & Tabarrok, B., eds. Theoretical & Applied Mechanics: Proceedings of the 15th International Congress, Toronto, August, 1980. 458p. 1981. 93.75 (ISBN 0-444-85411-8, North-Holland). Elsevier.
Ross, C. T. Computational Methods in Structural & Continuum Mechanics. 1982. 53.95 (ISBN 0-470-27329-1). Halsted Pr.
Rudman, Jack. Assistant Supervisor of Mechanical Installations. (Career Examination Ser.: C1117). (Cloth bdg. avail. on request). pap. 12.00 (ISBN 0-8373-1117-9). Natl Learning.
--Mechanical Maintainer - Group A. (Career Examination Ser.: C-483). (Cloth bdg. avail. on request). pap. 8.00 (ISBN 0-8373-0483-0). Natl Learning.
--Mechanical Maintainer - Group B. (Career Examination Ser.: C-484). (Cloth bdg. avail. on request). pap. 8.00 (ISBN 0-8373-0484-9). Natl Learning.
--Mechanical Maintainer - Group C. (Career Examination Ser.: C-485). (Cloth bdg. avail. on request). pap. 8.00 (ISBN 0-8373-0485-7). Natl Learning.
--Mechanical Technology. (Occupational Competency Examination Ser.: OCE-25). (Cloth bdg. avail. on request). pap. 13.95 (ISBN 0-8373-5725-X). Natl Learning.
Santilli, R. M. Foundations of Theoretical Mechanics II: Birkhoffian Generalization of Hamiltonian Mechanics. (Texts & Monographs in Physics). 370p. 1983. 69.50 (ISBN 0-387-09482-2). Springer-Verlag.
--Foundations of Theoretical Mechanics Part I: The Inverse Problem in Newtonian Mechanics. LC 78-9735. (Texts & Monographs in Physics). 1978. 45.00 (ISBN 0-387-08874-1). Springer-Verlag.
Schiehlen, W. O., ed. Dynamics of High-Speed Vehicles. (CISM International Centre for Mechanical Sciences, Courses & Lectures Ser.: Vol. 274). (Illus.). 395p. 1982. pap. 26.80 (ISBN 0-387-81719-0). Springer-Verlag.
Sears, Francis W. Mechanics, Heat, & Sound. 2nd ed. (Illus.). 1950. 23.95 (ISBN 0-201-06905-9). Addison-Wesley.
Simms, K. Introductory Mechanics for Applied Mathematics, Science & Engineering. LC 77-21857. pap. 100.25 (ISBN 0-317-08861-0, 2020975). Bks Demand UMI.
Singh, Pashupati & Prem Kumar Jha. Elementary Mechanics of Solids. LC 81-3429. 616p. 1980. 32.95x (ISBN 0-470-27149-3). Halsted Pr.
Slater, John C. & Frank, Nathaniel H. Mechanics. LC 83-6694. xiii, 297p. 1983. Repr. of 1947 ed. lib. bdg. 42.50 (ISBN 0-313-24064-7, SLME). Greenwood.
Sloane, A. Mechanics of Materials. (Illus.). 11.50 (ISBN 0-8446-2954-5). Peter Smith.
Smith, Charles E. Applied Mechanics: Statics. 2nd ed. LC 81-4232. 316p. 1982. text ed. 35.80x (ISBN 0-471-02965-3). Wiley.
Society For Experimental Stress Analysis. International Developments in Experimental Mechanics. (Illus.). 236p. 1982. 53.00 (ISBN 0-13-471680-9). P-H.
Strelkov, S. Mechanics. 560p. 1978. 12.50 (ISBN 0-8285-0791-0, Pub. by Mir Pubs USSR). Imported Pubns.
Symon, Keith R. Mechanics. 3rd ed. LC 75-128910. (Physics & Physical Science Ser). 1971. text ed. 36.95 (ISBN 0-201-07392-7). Addison-Wesley.
Symposium on Applications of Holography in Mechanics (1971: University ofSouthern California) Applications of Holography in Mechanics: Symposium. Gottenberg, W. G., ed. LC 78-172086. pap. 23.50 (ISBN 0-317-08117-9, 2016842). Bks Demand UMI.
Szabo, Istvan. Geschichte der Mechanischen Prinzipien: Und Ihre Wichtigsten Anwendungen. (Wissenschaft und Kultur: Band 32). (Ger., Illus.). 543p. 1979. 43.95x (ISBN 0-8176-1063-4). Birkhauser.
Targ, S. M. Theoretical Mechanics. (Russian Monographs). (Illus.). 424p. 1967. 74.25 (ISBN 0-677-20370-5). Gordon.
Tauchert, Theodore R. Energy Principles in Structural Mechanics. LC 80-39808. 394p. 1981. Repr. of 1974 ed. lib. bdg. 24.95 (ISBN 0-89874-309-5). Krieger.
Taylor, Thomas T. Mechanics: Classical & Quantum. 1976. pap. text ed. 26.00 (ISBN 0-08-020522-4). Pergamon.
Ter Haar, D. Elements of Hamiltonian Mechanics. 2nd ed. 1971. pap. 18.00 (ISBN 0-08-016726-8). Pergamon.
Theoretical Mechanics, 2 vols. Incl. Light, G. S. & Higham, J. B. Vol. 1. 93.00 (ISBN 0-317-27741-3); Light, G. S. & Kalsi, T. S. Vol. 2. 110.00 (ISBN 0-317-27742-1). LC 74-81553. Repr. of 1975 ed (2025227). Bks Demand UMI.
Townsend, A. A. The Structure of Turbulent Shear Flow. 2nd ed. LC 79-8526. (Cambridge Monographs on Mechanics & Applied Mathematics). (Illus.). 441p. 1980. pap. 29.95x (ISBN 0-521-29819-9). Cambridge U Pr.
Truesdale, C., ed. Mechanics of Solids, Vol. 4: Waves in Elastic & Viscoelastic Solids (Theory & Experiment) (Illus.). 350p. 1984. pap. 28.50 (ISBN 0-387-13163-9). Springer-Verlag.
Truesdell, C., ed. Mechanics of Solids, Theory of Viscoelasticity, Plasticity, Elastic Waves, & Elastic Stability, Vol. 3. (Illus.). 600p. 1984. pap. 32.00 (ISBN 0-387-13162-0). Springer-Verlag.
--Mechanics of Solids, Vol. 2: Linear Theories of Elasticity & Thermoelasticity, Linear & Nonlinear Theories of Rods, Plates, & Shells. (Illus.). 760p. 1984. pap. 34.50 (ISBN 0-387-13161-2). Springer-Verlag.
Truesdell, C. A. Six Lectures on Modern Natural Philosophy. (Illus.). 1966. 16.00 (ISBN 0-387-03684-9). Springer-Verlag.
Vaughan, J., et al, eds. Mechanical Maintenance (& Installation) II, 2 vols. (Engineering Craftsmen Ser.: No. J21). (Illus.). 342p. 1970. Set. 59.95x (ISBN 0-85083-080-X). Intl Ideas.
Wang, C. C. Mathematical Principles in Mechanics & Electromagnetism. Incl. Part A: Analytical & Continuum Mechanics. 218p (ISBN 0-306-40211-4); Part B: Electromagnetism & Gravitation. 208p (ISBN 0-306-40212-2). LC 79-11862. (Mathematical Concepts & Methods in Science & Engineering Ser.: Vols. 16 & 17). (Illus.). 208p. 1979. 35.00x ea. (Plenum Pr). Plenum Pub.
Weissler, Paul. Weekend Mechanic's Handbook: Complete Auto Repairs You Can Make. rev. ed. LC 82-3992. (Illus.). 480p. 1982. 19.95 (ISBN 0-668-05379-8); pap. 12.95 (ISBN 0-668-05384-4). Arco.
Wicks, Harry, ed. Popular Mechanics Five Hundred Home & Shop Tips. (Illus.). 160p. 1981. pap. 12.95 (ISBN 0-910990-79-4). Hearst Bks.
Wolfe, John & Phelps, E. R. Mechanics Vest Pocket Reference Book. 214p. 1983. pap. 6.95 (ISBN 0-13-571513-X). P-H.
Young, Donald F., et al. Essentials of Mechanics: A Unified First Course. (Illus.). 582p. 1974. text ed. 13.50x (ISBN 0-8138-1110-4). Iowa St U Pr.
Ziegler, H. An Introduction to Thermomechanics. 2nd rev. ed. (Series in Applied Mathematics & Mechanics: Vol. 21). 340p. 1983. 68.00 (ISBN 0-444-86503-9, I-420-82, North Holland). Elsevier.
Zita, K. Lexikon der Schulphysik: Mechanik und Akustik, Vol. 1. (Ger.). 44.00 (ISBN 3-7614-0107-8, M-7222). French & Eur.
Zorski, H., ed. Trends in Applications of Pure Mathematics to Mechanics, Vol. II. new ed. (Monographs & Studies in Mathematics: No. 5). (Illus.). 1979. 72.50 (ISBN 0-273-08421-6). Pitman Pub MA.

MECHANICS–EARLY WORKS TO 1800

Clarke, John. Demonstration of Some of the Principal Sections of Sir Isaac Newton's Principles of Natural Philosophy. 1972. Repr. of 1730 ed. 28.00 (ISBN 0-384-09226-8). Johnson Repr.
Cohen, I. Bernard. Introduction to Newton's Principia. LC 76-28770. 1971. pap. text ed. 12.00x (ISBN 0-674-46193-2). Harvard U Pr.
Drake, Stillman & Drabkin, I. E., trs. Mechanics in Sixteenth-Century Italy: Selections from Tartaglia, Benedetti, Guido Ubaldo, & Galileo. (Medieval Science Publications: No. 13). (Illus.). 442p. 1969. 30.00x (ISBN 0-299-05100-5). U of Wis Pr.
Galilei, Galileo. Dialogues Concerning Two New Sciences. Crew, Henry & De Salvio, Alfonso, trs. (University Studies Ser). Repr. of 1950 ed. 79.00 (ISBN 0-8357-9453-9, 2015284). Bks Demand UMI.
Gillispie, Charles C. Lazare Carnot Savant. LC 78-132238. 1971. 45.00 (ISBN 0-691-08082-8). Princeton U Pr.
Gowing, Roland. Roger Cotes: Natural Philosopher. LC 82-1154. (Illus.). 200p. 1983. 42.50 (ISBN 0-521-23741-6). Cambridge U Pr.
Maclaurin, Colin. Account of Sir Isaac Newton's Philosophical Discoveries. 1968. Repr. of 1748 ed. 34.00 (ISBN 0-384-34900-5). Johnson Repr.
Newton, Isaac. Sir Isaac Newton's Mathematical Principles of Natural Philosophy & His System of the World. Motte, Andrew, tr. 1962. lib. bdg. 32.50x (ISBN 0-8371-2508-1, NEMP). Greenwood.

MECHANICS–ELECTRIC ANALOGIES

see Electromechanical Analogies

BOOKS - SUBJECT INDEX

MECHANICS, APPLIED

MECHANICS–HISTORY

Drachmann, A. G. The Mechanical Technology of Greek & Roman Antiquity. (Illus.). 1963. 7.50 (ISBN 0-934454-61-2). Lubrecht & Cramer.

Drake, Stillman & Drabkin, I. E., trs. Mechanics in Sixteenth-Century Italy: Selections from Tartaglia, Benedetti, Guido Ubaldo, & Galileo. (Medieval Science Publications: No. 13). (Illus.). 442p. 1969. 30.00x (ISBN 0-299-05100-5). U of Wis Pr.

Hart, Ivor B. The Mechanical Investigations of Leonardo da Vinci. LC 82-2967. (Illus.). xiv, 240p. 1982. Repr. of 1963 ed. lib. bdg. 42.50x (ISBN 0-313-23489-2, HAMEC). Greenwood.

Hill, D. R. Al-Jazari: The Book of Knowledge of Ingenious Mechanical Devices. limited ed. LC 72-92529. 286p. 1974. 126.00 (ISBN 90-277-0329-9, Pub. by Reidel Holland). Kluwer Academic.

Mach, Ernst. The Science of Mechanics. 6th ed. McCormack, T. J., tr. from Ger. (Illus.). 634p. 1960. pap. 12.95 (ISBN 0-87548-202-3). Open Court.

Truesdell, C. A. Essays in the History of Mechanics. LC 68-17860. (Illus.). 1968. 54.00 (ISBN 0-387-04367-5). Springer-Verlag.

MECHANICS–PROBLEMS, EXERCISES, ETC.

Bloom, F. Ill-Posed Problems for Integrodifferential Equations in Mechanics & Electromagnetic Theory. LC 80-53713. (SIAM Studies in Applied Mathematics: No. 3). ix, 222p. 1981. 37.50 (ISBN 0-89871-171-1). Soc Indus-Appl Math.

Federal Aviation Administration. Aviation Mechanic Powerplant Question Book. (Aviation Maintenance Training Course Ser.). (Illus.). 79p. 1984. pap. 2.75 (ISBN 0-89100-272-3, EA-FAA-T-8080-11). Aviation Maintenance.

Habibi, Mohamad & Warisila, Robert. Mechanics: A Laboratory Manual. 2nd ed. (Illus.). 160p. 1980. pap. text ed. 9.95 (ISBN 0-89529-043-X). Avery Pub.

MECHANICS (PERSONS)

see also Automobile Mechanics; Aviation Mechanics (Persons)

Alpers, Byron J. & Afrow, Mitchell L. Metal & Machines. (Shoptalk - Vocational Reading Skills Ser.). 1978. pap. text ed. 7.88 (ISBN 0-205-05823-X, 4958233); tchr's guide 8.40 (ISBN 0-205-05824-8, 4958241). Allyn.

Bernard, John. Every Man His Own Mechanic. 14.50x (ISBN 0-392-05395-0, LTB). Sportshelf.

Rudman, Jack. Foreman of Mechanics. (Career Examination Ser.: C-1605). (Cloth bdg. avail. on request). 1977. pap. 10.00 (ISBN 0-8373-1605-7). Natl Learning.

--Maintenance Mechanic (Automated Mail Processing Equipment) (A.M.P.E) (U.S.P.S.) (Career Examination Ser.: C-1606). (Cloth bdg. avail. on request). 1984. pap. 12.00 (ISBN 0-8373-1606-5). Natl Learning.

--Toll Equipment Mechanic. (Career Examination Ser.: C-2546). (Cloth bdg. avail. on request). pap. 8.00 (ISBN 0-8373-2546-3). Natl Learning.

MECHANICS, ANALYTIC

see also Continuum Mechanics; Dynamics; Elasticity; Hydrodynamics; Hydrostatics; Kinematics; Problem of Many Bodies; Statics; Statistical Mechanics

Abraham, Ralph & Marsden, Jerrold E. Foundations of Mechanics: A Mathematical Exposition of Classical Mechanics with An Introduction to the Qualitative Theory of Dynamical Systems & Applications to the Three-Body Problem. 2nd rev. & enl. ed. 1978. 59.95 (ISBN 0-8053-0102-X). Benjamin-Cummings.

Analytical Mechanics of Gears. LC 63-21681. 546p. Date not set. pap. price not set. Buckingham Assoc.

Atteia, M., et al. Nonlinear Problems of Analysis in Geometry & Mechanics. LC 80-21647. (Research Notes in Mathematics: No. 46). 288p. (Orig.). 1981. pap. text ed. 27.00 (ISBN 0-273-08493-3). Pitman Pub MA.

Bernasconi, C. F. Relaxation Kinetics. 1976. 59.00 (ISBN 0-12-092950-3). Acad Pr.

Bleustein, Jeffrey L., ed. Mechanics & Sport AMD, Vol. 4. 318p. 1973. pap. text ed. 25.00 (ISBN 0-685-41497-3, H00007). ASME.

Cayley, Arthur. Collected Mathematical Papers, Vols. 1-13. 1889-1897. with index 700.00 (ISBN 0-384-07970-9); 55.00 ea.; Vol. suppl. 30.00 (ISBN 0-685-13389-3). Johnson Repr.

Cheng, D. G. Analysis of Linear Systems. 1959. 29.95 (ISBN 0-201-01020-8). Addison-Wesley.

Chung, T. J. & Karr, Gerald R. Development in Theoretical & Applied Mechanics, Vol. XI. 638p. 1982. 50.00 (ISBN 0-942166-00-0). U AL Dept Mech Eng.

Curry, Stephen H. & Whelpton, Robin. Manual of Laboratory Pharmacokinetics: Experiments in Biopharmaceutics, Biochemical Pharmacology, & Pharmacokinetics with a Consideration of Relevant Instrumental & Chromatographic Techniques. LC 82-2643. 189p. 1983. 24.95 (ISBN 0-471-10247-4, Pub. by Wiley-Interscience). Wiley.

Dahl, W. & Lange, K. W., eds. Kinetics of Metallurgical Processes in Steelmaking: Proceedings. (Illus.). x, 584p. 1975. 100.30 (ISBN 0-387-07366-3). Springer-Verlag.

Developments in Theoretical & Applied Mechanics, Vols. 2-4. Vol. 3. 1968. 82.00 (ISBN 0-08-012211-6); Vol. 4. 1970. 75.00 (ISBN 0-08-006513-9). Pergamon.

Developments in Theoretical & Applied Mechanics: Proceedings. 519p. 1963. 52.50x (ISBN 0-306-30162-8, Plenum Pr). Plenum Pub.

Duhamel, Jean M. Lehrbuch der Analytischen Mechanik. Schloemilch, O., ed. (Bibliotheca Mathematica Teubneriana Ser: No. 37). (Ger). 1969. Repr. of 1861 ed. 55.00 (ISBN 0-384-13230-8). Johnson Repr.

Firt, Vladimir. Statics, Formfinding & Dynamics of Air-Supported Membrane Structures. 1983. lib. bdg. 83.00 (ISBN 90-247-2672-7, Pub. by Martinus Nijhoff Netherlands). Kluwer Academic.

Fowles, Grant. Analytical Mechanics. 3rd ed. LC 76-57839. 1977. text ed. 41.95 (ISBN 0-03-089725-4, HoltC). HR&W.

--Analytical Mechanics. 4th ed. 1986. text ed. 41.95 (ISBN 0-03-004124-4, CBS C). SCP.

Fung, Y. C. Foundations of Solid Mechanics. 1965. ref. ed. 41.95 (ISBN 0-13-329912-0). P-H.

Gantmacher, F. Lectures in Analytical Mechanics. (Illus.). 286p. 1975. text ed. 15.00x (ISBN 0-8464-0551-2). Beekman Pubs.

Gantmacher, Felix R. Lectures on Analytical Mechanics. 2nd ed. write for info. (ISBN 0-8284-0311-2). Chelsea Pub.

Genta, G. Kinetic Energy Storage. (Illus.). 1985. text ed. 84.95 (ISBN 0-408-01396-6). Butterworth.

Kibble, T. W. Classical Mechanics. (Illus.). 320p. 1985. pap. text ed. 17.50 (ISBN 0-582-45023-3). Longman.

Moigno, F. Lecons De Mecanique Analytique. Repr. of 1868 ed. 50.00 (ISBN 0-384-39500-7). Johnson Repr.

Rogula, D., ed. Nonlocal Theory of Material Media. (CISM-International Centre for Mechanical Sciences, Courses & Lectures: Vol. 268). (Illus.). 278p. 1982. pap. 22.50 (ISBN 0-387-81632-1). Springer-Verlag.

Rossberg, Klaus. A First Course in Analytical Mechanics. LC 83-3602. 291p. 1983. 33.95 (ISBN 0-471-86174-X). Wiley.

Sneddon, Ian & Lowengrub, M. Crack Problems in the Classical Theory of Elasticity. LC 75-84971. (The Siam Series in Applied Mathematics). pap. 57.80 (ISBN 0-317-08602-2, 2006312). Bks Demand UMI.

Spiegel, Murray R. Theoretical Mechanics. (Schaum's Outline Ser). 1967. pap. 9.95 (ISBN 0-07-060232-8). McGraw.

MECHANICS, APPLIED

see also Engineering Models; Mechanical Engineering

Aguilar, Rodolfo J. Systems Analysis & Design in Engineering, Architecture, Construction, & Planning. (Civil Engineering & Engineering Mechanics Ser). (Illus.). 448p. 1973. ref. ed. 33.95 (ISBN 0-13-881458-9). P-H.

American Society of Mechanical Engineers. Isolation of Mechanical Vibration, Impact, & Noise: A Colloquium Presented at the ASME Design Engineering Technical Conference, Cincinnati, Ohio, Sept. 1973. Snowdon, John C. & Ungar, Eric E., eds. LC 73-84652. (ASME Applied Mechanics Division Ser.: Vol. 1). pap. 69.00 (ISBN 0-317-08486-0, 2051536). Bks Demand UMI.

Aseltine, J. A. Transform Method in Linear System Analysis. (Electrical & Electronic Eng. Ser). 1958. 48.00 (ISBN 0-07-002389-1). McGraw.

Beer, Ferdinand P. & Johnston, E. R., Jr. Vector Mechanics for Engineers Combined. 3rd ed. 1977. text ed. 39.95 (ISBN 0-07-004277-2). McGraw.

Bert, C. W., ed. Mechanics of Bimodulus Materials, Bk. No. G00150. LC 90-75422. (Applied Mechanics Division Ser.: Vol. 33). 96p. 1979. 18.00 (ISBN 0-686-62957-4). ASME.

Bradbury, Ted C. Theoretical Mechanics. LC 80-23957. 656p. 1981. Repr. of 1968 ed. text ed. 36.50 (ISBN 0-89874-235-8). Krieger.

Broersma, G. Applied Mechanics of Machine Elements in Advanced Use. 182p. 1967. 50.00x (ISBN 0-85950-040-3, Pub. by Stam Pr England). State Mutual Bk.

Brown, James. Introductory Solid Mechanics. LC 74-156805. pap. 112.00 (ISBN 0-317-07989-1, 2051225). Bks Demand UMI.

Byars, Edward F., et al. Engineering Mechanics of Deformable Bodies. 4th ed. 548p. 1983. text ed. 33.95 scp (ISBN 0-06-041109-0, HarpC); solution manual avail. (ISBN 0-06-361100-7). Har-Row.

Chia-Shun, Yih, ed. Advances in Applied Mechanics, Vol. 22. (Serial Publication Ser.). 1982. 65.00 (ISBN 0-12-002022-X). Acad Pr.

Chia-Shun Yih, ed. Advances in Applied Mechanics, Vol. 19. LC 48-8503. 1979. 65.00 (ISBN 0-12-002019-X). Acad Pr.

Chia Shun Yih, ed. Advances in Applied Mechanics, Vol. 21. (Serial Publication Ser.). 1981. 59.50 (ISBN 0-12-002021-1). Acad Pr.

Computer Conference (1969: Illinois Institute of Technology) Computational Approaches in Applied Mechanics: Presented at 1969 Computer Conference, Illinois Institute of Technology, Chicago, Ill., June 19-20, 1969. Sevin, Eugene, ed. LC 75-105936. pap. 73.30 (ISBN 0-317-08397-X, 2016812). Bks Demand UMI.

Crandall, Stephen H., et al. An Introduction to the Mechanics of Solids: SI Units. 2nd ed. (Illus.). 1978. text ed. 45.00 (ISBN 0-07-013441-3). McGraw.

Developments in Theoretical & Applied Mechanics, Vols. 2-4. Vol. 3. 1968. 82.00 (ISBN 0-08-012211-6); Vol. 4. 1970. 75.00 (ISBN 0-08-006513-9). Pergamon.

Developments in Theoretical & Applied Mechanics: Proceedings. 519p. 1963. 52.50x (ISBN 0-306-30162-8, Plenum Pr). Plenum Pub.

Dvorak, G. J. & Shield, R. T. Mechanics of Material Behavior. (Studies in Applied Mechanics: Vol. 6). 1984. 94.25 (ISBN 0-444-42169-6, I-091-84). Elsevier.

Edmunds, H. G. Mechanical Foundations of Engineering Science. LC 81-6566. 429p. 1981. 58.95x (ISBN 0-470-27253-8). Halsted Pr.

Eppler, R., ed. Laminar Turbulent Transitions. (International Union of Theoretical & Applied Mechanics). (Illus.). 432p. 1980. 43.70 (ISBN 0-387-10142-X). Springer-Verlag.

Flugge, Wilhelm, ed. Handbook of Engineering Mechanics. 1962. 89.50 (ISBN 0-07-021392-5). McGraw.

Francis, Philip H. & Lindholm, Ulric S. Advanced Experimental Techniques in the Mechanics of Materials. 462p. 1973. 101.25 (ISBN 0-677-12570-4). Gordon.

Geers, T. L. & Tong, P., eds. Survival of Mechanical Systems in Transient Environments. LC 79-954424. (Applied Mechanics Division Ser.: Vol. 36). 196p. 1979. 24.00 (ISBN 0-686-62963-9, G00153). ASME.

Hartmann, F. The Mathematical Foundation of Structural Mechanics. (Illus.). 400p. 1985. 44.00 (ISBN 0-387-15002-1). Springer-Verlag.

Hartung, R. F., ed. Computing in Applied Mechanics AMD, Vol. 18. 179p. 1976. pap. text ed. 20.00 (ISBN 0-685-75515-0, I00108). ASME.

Herman, George, ed. R. D. Mindlin & Applied Mechanics: A Collection of Studies in the Development of Applied Mechanics Dedicated to Prof. R. D. Mindlin by His Former Students. LC 73-22346. 1974. text ed. 54.00 (ISBN 0-08-017710-7). Pergamon.

Higdon, A. & Stiles. Engineering Mechanics, 2 vols. 2nd ed. Incl. Vol. I. Statics. 28.95 (ISBN 0-13-279398-9); Vol. II. Dynamics. 28.95 (ISBN 0-13-279406-3). (Civil Engineering & Engineering Mechanic Ser.). (Illus.). 928p. 1976. Set. 39.95x (ISBN 0-13-279380-6). P-H.

Higdon, A., et al. Engineering Mechanics. 3rd ed. Incl. Vol. 1. Statics. 30.95 (ISBN 0-13-279273-7); Vol. 2. Dynamics. 27.95 (ISBN 0-13-279281-8). 1968. 36.95 set (ISBN 0-13-279299-0). P-H.

Huang, T. C. Engineering Mechanics, 2 vols. Incl. Vol. 1. Statics (ISBN 0-201-03005-5); Vol. 2. Dynamics (ISBN 0-201-03006-3). 1967. 16.95 ea.; 25.95 set (ISBN 0-201-03007-1). Addison-Wesley.

Hughes, T. J., ed. Finite Element Methods for Convection Dominated Flows, Bk. No. G00151. LC 90-75379. (Applied Mechanics Division Ser.: Vol. 34). 240p. 1979. 30.00 (ISBN 0-686-62956-6). ASME.

International Congress of Applied Mechanics, 12th, Stanford University, 1968. Proceedings. Hetenyi, M. & Vincenti, W. G., eds. (Illus.). 1969. 111.00 (ISBN 0-387-04420-5). Springer-Verlag.

International Congress of Applied Mechanics, 11th, Munich, 1964. Proceedings. Goertler, H., ed. (Eng, Fr, Ger & It.). 1966. 224.20 (ISBN 0-387-03462-5). Springer-Verlag.

International Congress of Applied Mechanics, 13th, Moscow. Proceedings. Becker, E. & Mikhailov, G. K., eds. LC 58-2749. (Illus.). 370p. 1974. 70.80 (ISBN 0-387-06244-0). Springer-Verlag.

Ishihara, Tomo-o, ed. Theoretical & Applied Mechanics: Proceedings of the Japan National Congress for Applied Mechanics, Vol. 21. 550p. 1973. 50.00 (ISBN 0-86008-080-3, Pub. by U of Tokyo Japan). Columbia U Pr.

IUTAM International Congress, 14th. Theoretical & Applied Mechanics: Proceedings. Koiter, W. T., ed. 492p. 1977. 93.75 (ISBN 0-7204-0549-1, North-Holland). Elsevier.

Johnson, K. L. Contact Mechanics. 456p. 1985. 89.50 (ISBN 0-521-25576-7). Cambridge U Pr.

Juhasz, Stephen. The Applied Mechanics CumIndex, Vol. 14. 1979. 60.00 (ISBN 0-88274-013-X). R & D Pr.

Langhaar, Henry L. Energy Methods in Applied Mechanics. LC 62-10925. 350p. 1962. 43.95x (ISBN 0-471-51711-9, Pub. by Wiley-Interscience). Wiley.

Levinson, Irving J. Introduction to Mechanics. 2nd ed. 1968. text ed. 28.95 (ISBN 0-13-487660-1). P-H.

Levinson, L. Fundamentals of Engineering Mechanics. (Russian Monographs & Texts on the Physical Sciences). 336p. 1965. 80.95x (ISBN 0-677-20250-4). Gordon.

Malvern, Lawrence E. Engineering Mechanics, 2 vols. Incl. Vol. 1. Statics. ref. ed. 27.95 (ISBN 0-13-278663-X); Vol. 2. Dynamics. ref. ed. 31.95x (ISBN 0-13-278671-0). (Illus.). 352p. 1976. P-H.

Mason, J. Methods of Functional Analysis for Application in Solid Mechanics. (Studies in Applied Mechanics: Vol. 9). 392p. 1985. 87.00 (ISBN 0-444-42436-9). Elsevier.

Meriam, J. L. Engineering Mechanics, 2 vols. Incl. Vol. 1. Statics: SI Version. 397p. 1980. text ed. 36.00 (ISBN 0-471-05558-1); Arabic ed. 19.50 (ISBN 0-471-06312-6); Vol. 2. Dynamics: SI Version. 508p. text ed. 36.95 (ISBN 0-471-05559-X); Arabic ed. 19.50 (ISBN 0-471-06311-8). LC 79-11173. 1980. Wiley.

--Engineering Mechanics, 2 vols. Incl. Vol. 1. Statics. 398p. text ed. 35.45x (ISBN 0-471-59460-1); Vol. 2. Dynamics. 508p. text ed. 36.00 (ISBN 0-471-59461-X); Teacher's Manual. avail. (ISBN 0-471-02753-7). LC 77-24716. 1978. Wiley.

--Statics. 2nd ed. SI Version, ed. LC 74-11459. 381p. 1975. text ed. 35.45 (ISBN 0-471-59604-3). Wiley.

Meriman, J. L. ARA Engineering Mechanics, 2 vols. Incl. Vol. 1. SI Statics. 19.50 (ISBN 0-471-06312-6); Vol. 2. SI Dynamics. 1982. 21.50 (ISBN 0-471-06311-8). 1980. 0.00. Wiley.

Merks, J. W. Sampling & Weighing of Bulk Solids. LC 85-70381. (Illus.). 224p. 1985. 47.95x (ISBN 0-87201-860-1). Gulf Pub.

Niordson & Olhoff. Theoretical & Applied Mechanics. 1985. 83.50 (ISBN 0-317-30832-7, North-Holland). Elsevier.

Okumura, Toshie, ed. Theoretical & Applied Mechanics: Proceedings of the Japan National Congress for Applied Mechanics, Vol. 22. 528p. 1974. 50.00x (ISBN 0-86008-117-6, Pub. by U of Tokyo Japan). Columbia U Pr.

--Theoretical & Applied Mechanics: Proceedings of the Japan National Congress for Applied Mechanics, Vol. 23. 560p. 1975. 52.00x (ISBN 0-86008-138-9, Pub. by U of Tokyo Japan). Columbia U Pr.

Parker, Harry & Hauf, Harold D. Simplified Mechanics & Strength of Materials. 3rd ed. LC 76-56465. 325p. 1977. 34.95x (ISBN 0-471-66562-2, Pub. by Wiley-Interscience). Wiley.

Reddy, J. N. Energy & Variational Methods in Applied Mechanics with an Introduction to the Finite-Element Method. LC 84-3605. 545p. 1984. 52.95x (ISBN 0-471-89673-X, Pub. by Wiley-Interscience). Wiley.

Rimrott, F. P. & Tabarrok, B., eds. Theoretical & Applied Mechanics: Proceedings of the 15th International Congress, Toronto, August, 1980. 458p. 1981. 93.75 (ISBN 0-444-85411-8, North-Holland). Elsevier.

Schmitz, Norbert L. & Novotny, Donald. Introductory Electromechanics. LC 65-21815. (Illus.). pap. 82.30 (ISBN 0-317-08893-9, 2012459). Bks Demand UMI.

Selvdurai, A. P. Mechanics of Structured Media, 2 vols. (Studies in Applied Mechanics: Vol. 5). 1034p. 1981. Set. 161.75 (ISBN 0-444-41982-9); Pt. A. 79.50 (ISBN 0-444-41979-9); Pt. B. 79.50 (ISBN 0-444-41983-7). Elsevier.

Shigley, Joseph E. Applied Mechanics of Materials. (Illus.). 1975. text ed. 42.00 (ISBN 0-07-056845-6). McGraw.

Smith, C. E. Applied Mechanics: Dynamics. 2nd ed. LC 81-4732. 518p. 1982. text ed. 34.45x (ISBN 0-471-02966-1). Wiley.

Smith, Charles E. Applied Mechanics. Incl. Dynamics (ISBN 0-471-80178-X); Statics (ISBN 0-471-80460-6). 1976. text ed. 21.95x ea.; avail. tchr's manual (ISBN 0-471-01894-5); avail. tchr's manual (ISBN 0-471-01895-3). Wiley.

Smith, M. E. & Martin, J. R., eds. Recommended Guide for the Prediction of the Dispersion of Airborne Effluents, Bk. No. H00037. 3rd ed. LC 90-75471. 87p. 1979. 10.00 (ISBN 0-686-62958-2). ASME.

Takami, Hideo. Theoretical & Applied Mechanics, Vol. 28,29,30. 500p. 1981. Vol. 28. 89.50x (ISBN 0-86008-264-4, Pub. by U of Tokyo Japan); Vol. 29. 89.50x (ISBN 0-686-96691-0); Vol. 30. 89.50x (ISBN 0-86008-300-4). Columbia U Pr.

Takami, Hideo, ed. Theoretical & Applied Mechanics, Vol. 31. 500p. 1983. 89.50x (ISBN 0-86008-323-3, Pub. by U of Tokyo Japan). Columbia U Pr.

Tanaka, Hisashi, ed. Theoretical & Applied Mechanics: Proceedings of the Japan National Congress for Applied Mechanics, Vol. 24. 511p. 1976. 69.50x (ISBN 0-86008-158-3, Pub. by U of Tokyo Japan). Columbia U Pr.

Targ, S. M. Theoretical Mechanics. (Russian Monographs). (Illus.). 424p. 1967. 74.25 (ISBN 0-677-20370-5). Gordon.

Tayler, A. B. Mathematical Models in Applied Mechanics. (Applied Mathematics & Computing Science Ser.). (Illus.). 200p. 1985. 29.95 (ISBN 0-19-853533-3); pap. 14.95 (ISBN 0-19-853541-4). Oxford U Pr.

Titherington, D. & Rimmer, J. G. Applied Mechanics. 2nd ed. 192p. 1983. 9.00 (ISBN 0-07-084659-6). McGraw.

Tsuboi, Yoshikatsu, ed. Theoretical & Applied Mechanics: Proceedings of the Japan National Congress for Applied Mechanics, Vol. 25. 727p. 1977. 85.00x (ISBN 0-86008-181-8, Pub. by U of Tokyo Japan). Columbia U Pr.

U. S. National Congress of Applied Mechanics, 9th: Proceedings. 480p. 1982. 75.00 (H00228). ASME.

Von Mises, Richard & Von Karman, Theodore, eds. Advances in Applied Mechanics. Incl. Vol. 1. 1948. 80.00 (ISBN 0-12-002001-7); Vol. 2. 1951. 80.00 (ISBN 0-12-002002-5); Vol. 3. 1953. 80.00 (ISBN 0-12-002003-3); Vol. 4. Dryden, H. L., et al, eds. Tr. of Et Al. 1956. 80.00 (ISBN 0-12-002004-1); Vol. 5. 1958. 80.00 (ISBN 0-12-002005-X); Vol. 6. 1960. 80.00 (ISBN 0-12-002006-8); Vol. 7. 1962. 80.00 (ISBN 0-12-002007-6); Vol. 8. 1964. 80.00 (ISBN 0-12-002008-4); Vol. 9. Kuerti, G., ed. 1966. 80.00 (ISBN 0-12-002009-2); Vol. 10. Fascicle 1. 1967.. 11.00 (ISBN 0-12-002091-2); Vol. 11. Chia-Sun Yih, ed. 1971. 80.00 (ISBN 0-12-002011-4); Vol. 12. 1972. 80.00 (ISBN 0-12-002012-2); Vol. 13. 1973. 80.00 (ISBN 0-12-002013-0); Vol. 16. Yih, Chia-Shun, ed. 1976. 81.00 (ISBN 0-12-002016-5); lib ed 104.50 (ISBN 0-12-002043-2); microfiche 58.50 (ISBN 0-12-002044-0); Vol. 17. Yih, Chia-Shun, ed. 1977. 81.00 (ISBN 0-12-002017-3); lib. ed 104.50 (ISBN 0-12-002045-9); microfiche 48.00 (ISBN 0-12-002046-7); Vol. 18. Yih, Chia-Shun, ed. 1979. 68.50 (ISBN 0-12-002018-1); lib. ed. 89.00 (ISBN 0-12-002047-5); 50.00 (ISBN 0-12-002048-3). LC 48-8503. Acad Pr.

--Advances in Applied Mechanics, Vol. 24. (Serial Publication Ser.). 1984. 89.00 (ISBN 0-12-002024-6). Acad Pr.

--Advances in Applied Mechanics: Supplements. Incl. Suppl. 1. Rarefied Gas Dynamics: Proceedings. International Symposium on Rarefied Gas Dynamics - 2nd. Talbot, L., ed. 1961 (ISBN 0-12-002061-0); Suppl. 2. Rarefied Gas Dynamics: Proceedings. International Symposium on Rarefied Gas Dynamics - 3rd. Laurmann, John A., ed. 1963. Vol. 1-2. Vol. 1 (ISBN 0-12-002067-X). Vol. 2 (ISBN 0-12-002068-8); Suppl. 3. Rarefied Gas Dynamics: Proceedings. International Symposium on Rarefied Gas Dynamics - 4th. De Leeuw, J. H., ed. 1965-66. Vol. 1 (ISBN 0-12-002074-2). Vol. 2. 85.00 (ISBN 0-12-002075-0); Suppl. 4. Rarefied Gas Dynamics: Proceedings. International Symposium on Rarefied Gas Dynamics - 5th. Brundin, C. L., ed. 1967. Vol. 1-2. Vol. 1 (ISBN 0-12-002081-5). Vol. 2 (ISBN 0-12-002082-3); Suppl. 5. Rarefied Gas Dynamics: Proceedings. International Symposium on Rarefied Gas Dynamics - 6th. Trilling, L. & Wachman, H., eds. 1967-69. Vols. 1-2. Vol. 1 (ISBN 0-12-002085-8). Vol. 2 (ISBN 0-12-002086-6). Suppls. 1-5. 85.00 ea. Acad Pr.

Walker, Keith. Applied Mechanics for Engineering Technology. 3rd ed. 1984. text ed. 28.95 (ISBN 0-8359-0155-6). Reston.

Wan, Conrad C., ed. Applied Mechanics Aspects of Nuclear Effects in Materials: Presented at the Winter Annual Meeting of ASME, Washington, D. C., Dec. 2, 1971. LC 77-182577. pap. 52.50 (ISBN 0-317-08128-4, 2016863). Bks Demand UMI.

Wu, Theodore Y. & Hutchinson, John W., eds. Advances in Applied Mechanics, Vol. 23. (Serial Publication Ser.). 1983. 74.00 (ISBN 0-12-002023-8); lib. ed. o.p. 96.50 (ISBN 0-12-002057-2). Acad Pr.

Yamamoto, Yoshiyuki, ed. Theoretical & Applied Mechanics: Proceedings of the Japan National Congress for Applied Mechanics, Vol. 26. 579p. 1978. 79.50x (ISBN 0-86008-200-8, Pub. by U of Tokyo Japan). Columbia U Pr.

--Theoretical & Applied Mechanics: Proceedings of the Japan National Congress for Applied Mechanics, Vol. 27. 579p. 1979. 89.50x (ISBN 0-86008-245-8, Pub. by U of Tokyo Japan). Columbia U Pr.

Yih, C. S., ed. Advances in Applied Mechanics, Vol. 20. (Serial Publication Ser.). 1980. 55.00 (ISBN 0-12-002020-3); lib. ed. o.p. 60.00 (ISBN 0-12-002051-3). Acad Pr.

Yih, Chia-Shun, ed. Advances in Applied Mechanics, Vol. 14. (Serial Publication Ser.). 1974. 80.00 (ISBN 0-12-002014-9). Acad Pr.

--Advances in Applied Mechanics, Vol. 15. (Serial Publication Ser.). 1975. 80.00 (ISBN 0-12-002015-7); lib. ed. o.p. 103.00 (ISBN 0-12-002041-6). Acad Pr.

Young, Donald F. Introduction to Applied Mechanics: An Integrated Treatment for Students in Engineering, Life Science & Interdisciplinary Programs. LC 74-153162. (Illus.). 1972. 11.50x (ISBN 0-8138-1075-2). Iowa St U Pr.

MECHANICS, APPLIED–PROBLEMS, EXERCISES, ETC.

American Society of Mechanical Engineers. Computing in Applied Mechanics: Presented at the Winter Annual Meeting of the ASME, New York City, December 5-10, 1976. LC 76-28858. (American Society of Mechanical Engineers, Applied Mechanics Division: Vol. 18). pap. 46.50 (ISBN 0-317-26614-4, 2024186). Bks Demand UMI.

Beer, Ferdinand P. & Johnston, E. R., Jr. Vector Mechanics for Engineers Combined. 3rd ed. 1977. text ed. 39.95 (ISBN 0-07-004277-2). McGraw.

Hunter, Thomas A. Engineering Mechanics. (Quality Paperback Ser.: No. 46). 415p. (Orig.). 1961. pap. 4.95 (ISBN 0-8226-0046-3). Littlefield.

Nara, Harry R. Vector Mechanics for Engineers. LC 77-10175. 910p. 1977. Repr. of 1962 ed. lib. bdg. 39.50 (ISBN 0-88275-606-0). Krieger.

Stoker, J. J. Nonlinear Vibrations in Mechanical & Electrical Systems Pure & Aplied Mechanics, Vol. 2. (Pure & Applied Mathematics Ser.). 294p. 1950. 51.95 (ISBN 0-470-82830-7). Wiley.

MECHANICS, CELESTIAL

see also Astrodynamics; Moon, Theory Of; Orbits; Perturbation (Astronomy); Planets, Theory Of; Problem of Many Bodies

Abraham, Ralph & Marsden, Jerrold E. Foundations of Mechanics: A Mathematical Exposition of Classical Mechanics with An Introduction to the Qualitative Theory of Dynamical Systems & Applications to the Three-Body Problem. 2nd rev. & enl. ed. 1978. 59.95 (ISBN 0-8053-0102-X). Benjamin-Cummings.

Clagett, Marshall, tr. Nicole Oresme & the Medieval Geometry of Qualities & Motions. (Medieval Science Pubns., No. 12). (Illus.). 728p. 1968. 50.00x (ISBN 0-299-04880-2). U of Wis Pr.

Donahue, William H. & Cohen, I. Bernard, eds. The Dissolution of the Celestial Sphere. LC 80-2087. (Development of Science Ser.). (Illus.). 1981. lib. bdg. 28.00x (ISBN 0-405-13853-9). Ayer Co Pubs.

Hagihara, Yusuke. Celestial Mechanics Vol. 1: Dynamical Principles & Transformation Theory. 1970. 55.00x (ISBN 0-262-08037-0). MIT Pr.

--Celestial Mechanics, Vol. 2: Perturbation Theory, 2 pts. 1972. 60.00x ea. Pt. 1 (ISBN 0-262-08048-6). Pt. 2 (ISBN 0-262-08053-2). MIT Pr.

Kopal, Zdenek. Figures of Equilibrium of Celestial Bodies: With Emphasis on Problems of Motion of Artificial Satellites. (Mathematics Research Center Pubns., No. 3). (Illus.). 142p. 1960. 17.50x (ISBN 0-299-02010-X). U of Wis Pr.

Kovalevsky, J. Introduction to Celestial Mechanics. (Astrophysics & Space Science Library: No.7). 126p. 1967. lib. bdg. 21.00 (ISBN 90-277-0126-1, Pub. by Reidel Holland). Kluwer Academic.

Laplace, Pierre S. Celestial Mechanics, Vols. 1-4. LC 69-11316. Set. text ed. 195.00 (ISBN 0-8284-0194-2). Chelsea Pub.

--Celestial Mechanics, Vol. 5. LC 63-11316. (Mecanique Celeste, Tome V, Fr). 1969. Repr. of 1832 ed. text ed. 20.00 (ISBN 0-8284-0214-0). Chelsea Pub.

Lunar Science Symposium on Planetary Cratering Mechanics, Flagstaff, Ariz., 1976. Impact & Explosion Cratering, Planetary & Terrestrial Implications: Proceedings. Roddy, D. J., et al, eds. LC 77-24753. 900p. 1978. 165.00 (ISBN 0-08-022050-9). Pergamon.

Moser, Jurgen. Stable & Random Motions in Dynamical Systems: With Special Emphasis on Celestial Mechanics. LC 73-2481. (Annals of Mathematics Studies: No. 77). 1973. 23.50x (ISBN 0-691-08132-8). Princeton U Pr.

Moulton, Forest R. An Introduction to Celestial Mechanics. 437p. 1984. pap. 8.95 (ISBN 0-486-64687-4). Dover.

Newton, Isaac. Sir Isaac Newton's Mathematical Principles of Natural Philosophy & His System of the World. Motte, Andrew, tr. 1962. lib. bdg. 32.50x (ISBN 0-8371-2508-1, NEMP). Greenwood.

Orographic Effects in Planetary Flows. (GARP Publications Ser.: No. 23). 450p. 1980. pap. 40.00 (ISBN 0-686-71858-5, W470, WMO). Unipub.

Pollard, Harry. Celestial Mechanics. (Carus Monograph: No. 18). 134p. 1976. 19.00 (ISBN 0-88385-019-2). Math Assn.

Siegel, Carl L. & Moser, Juergen K. Lectures on Celestial Mechanics. rev. ed. Kalme, C. I., tr. from Ger. LC 71-155595. (Grundlehren der Mathematischen Wissenschaften: Vol. 187). 1971. 45.00 (ISBN 0-387-05419-7). Springer-Verlag.

Stiefel, E. L. & Scheifele, G. Linear & Regular Celestial Mechanics: Perturbed Two-Body Motion, Numerical Methods, Canonical Theory. LC 72-133369. (Die Grundlehren der Mathematischen Wissenschaften: Vol. 174). 1971. 48.00 (ISBN 0-387-05119-8). Springer-Verlag.

Szebehely, Victor G., ed. Instabilities in Dynamical Systems. (NATO Advanced Study Institutes Ser.). 1979. lib. bdg. 39.50 (ISBN 90-277-0973-4, Pub. by Reidel Holland). Kluwer Academic.

Thiry, Yves. Les Fondaments de la Mechanique Celeste. (Cours et Documents De Mathematiques et De Physique Ser.). 214p. 1970. 56.75x (ISBN 0-677-50270-2). Gordon.

MECHANICS, FRACTURE

see Fracture Mechanics

MECHANICS, NONLINEAR

see Nonlinear Mechanics

MECHANICS OF CONTINUA

see Continuum Mechanics

MECHANISMS (MACHINERY)

see Mechanical Movements

MECHANIZATION

see also Automation

Blackburn, Phil, et al. Technology, Economic Growth & the Labour Process. LC 84-22849. 272p. 1985. 29.95 (ISBN 0-312-79001-5). St Martin.

Gandhi, Mohandas K. Man vs. Machine. Hingorani, A. T., ed. 113p. (Orig.). 1980. pap. 2.50 (ISBN 0-934676-18-6). Greenlf Bks.

Giedion, Siegfried. Mechanization Takes Command. (Illus.). 1969. pap. 13.95 (ISBN 0-393-00489-9, Norton Lib). Norton.

MECHANIZATION, AGRICULTURAL

see Farm Mechanization

MECHANIZATION, MILITARY

Here are entered works on the equipping of a military force with armed and armored motor vehicles in which the force travels and engages in combat.

see also Armored Vehicles, Military; Tanks (Military Science)

Deitchman, Seymour J. Military Power & the Advance of Technology: General Purpose Military Forces in the 1980's & Beyond. Rev. ed. LC 83-50434. (Special Studies in Military Affairs). 278p. 1983. lib. bdg. 29.50x (ISBN 0-86531-573-6); pap. 13.50x (ISBN 0-86531-574-4). Westview.

English, John A. & Addicott, James, eds. The Mechanized Battlefield: A Tactical Analysis. (Illus.). 202p. 1984. pap. 30.00 (ISBN 0-08-025405-5). Pergamon.

Fuller, John F. Armored Warfare. LC 83-45766. Repr. of 1943 ed. 23.50 (ISBN 0-404-20102-4, UG446). AMS Pr.

Gordon, Don E. Electronic Warfare: Element of Strategy & Multiplier of Combat Power. (Pergamon Policy Studies on Security Affairs). (Illus.). 200p. 1982. 17.50 (ISBN 0-08-027189-8). Pergamon.

Pearton, Maurice. Diplomacy, War & Technology since Eighteen Thirty. (Studies in Government & Public Policy). 288p. 1984. pap. text ed. 9.95x (ISBN 0-7006-0254-2). U Pr of KS.

Simpkin, Brigadier R. Mechanized Infantry. (Illus.). 144p. 1980. 26.00 (ISBN 0-08-027030-1). Pergamon.

Simpkin, R. E. Human Factors in Mechanized Warfare. (Brasseys Ser.). (Illus.). 191p. 1983. 29.50 (ISBN 0-08-028340-3). Pergamon.

Travers, Timothy & Archer, Christon, eds. Men at War: Politics, Technology & Innovation in the Twentieth Century. LC 81-80545. 234p. 1982. 19.95 (ISBN 0-913750-21-2); pap. text ed. 8.95 (ISBN 0-913750-46-8). Precedent Pub.

MECHANIZATION OF LIBRARY PROCESSES

see Libraries–Automation

MECHANIZED ACCOUNTING

see Machine Accounting

MECHANIZED FARMING

see Farm Mechanization

MECHANIZED FORCES

see Mechanization, Military

MECHANIZED INFORMATION STORAGE AND RETRIEVAL SYSTEMS

see Information Storage and Retrieval Systems

MECHANIZED WARFARE

see Mechanization, Military

MEDICAL ASSISTANTS

see Medical Technologists

MEDICAL CARE–DATA PROCESSING

American Hospital Association Clearinghouse for Hospital Management Engineering, ed. Computer-Assisted Medical Record Systems: An Examination of Case Studies. 148p. 1982. pap. 18.75 (ISBN 0-87258-375-9, AHA-148200). Am Hospital.

Austin, Charles J. Information Systems for Hospital Administration. 2nd ed. LC 83-8495. (Illus.). 340p. 1983. text ed. 28.00x (ISBN 0-914904-91-4). Health Admin Pr.

Automated Hospital Information Systems: Getting the Most from the System You Select. LC 84-60126. 352p. 1984. pap. text ed. 49.00 (ISBN 0-914957-00-7). Pluribus Pr.

Brandejs, J. F., ed. Computer Assisted Physicians Offices. (Health Communications & Informatics: Vol. 5, No. 2, 1979). (Illus.). 1979. softcover 8.25 (ISBN 3-8055-3063-3). S Karger.

Brown, Montague & McCool, Barbara P. Multihospital Systems: Strategies for Organization & Management. LC 79-23439. 564p. 1980. text ed. 52.00 (ISBN 0-89443-169-2). Aspen Systems.

Cornell, Joseph A. Computers in Hospital Pharmacy Management: Fundamentals & Applications. LC 82-24381. 228p. 1983. 32.00 (ISBN 0-89443-673-2). Aspen Systems.

Cote, R. A., et al, eds. Role of Informatics in Health Data Coding & Classification Systems: Proceedings of the IFIP-IMIA International Working Conference on the Role of Informatics in Health Data Decoding & Classification Systems, Ottawa, Canada, 26-28 September, 1984. 394p. 1985. 59.25 (ISBN 0-444-87682-0, North-Holland). Elsevier.

Deconinck, F., ed. Information Processing in Medical Imaging. LC 84-1121. 1984. lib. bdg. 84.00 (ISBN 0-89838-677-2, Pub. by Martinus Nijhoff Netherlands). Kluwer Academic.

Dodson, Susan. Medical Office Applications Using Your Epson. 1985. pap. 19.95 (ISBN 0-8359-4492-1). Reston.

Drury, Barbara M., ed. Pricare's Computer Primer: For Health Professionals Managing Office Computers. LC 83-63347. 88p. (Orig.). 1984. pap. text ed. 24.95 (ISBN 0-9613095-6-3). Pricare.

Eden, Henry S. & Eden, Murray. Microcomputers in Patient Care. LC 81-1999. (Illus.). 191p. 1981. 28.00 (ISBN 0-8155-0849-2). Noyes.

Garrett, Raymond. Hospitals: A Systems Approach. 224p. 1973. 21.95 (ISBN 0-442-80238-2). Van Nos Reinhold.

Gelenbe, E., ed. Performance Eighty-Four: Models of Computer System Performance: Proceedings of the Anniversary Symposium of IFIP WG 7.3. on Computer Performance, 10th, Paris, France, 19-21 December, 1984. 560p. 1985. 68.00 (ISBN 0-444-87680-4, North-Holland). Elsevier.

Gillings & Douglass. Biostats: A Primer for Health Care Professionals. (Illus.). 275p. 1985. pap. 19.50 (ISBN 0-932137-02-4). Cavco Pubns.

Halligan, Joseph. Health Care - Softwhere. 2nd ed. Winther, Richard, ed. (Software Directories Ser.: Vol. 2). (Orig.). 1985. pap. 49.95 (ISBN 0-918451-41-8). Moore Data.

Health Care Microcomputing Sourcebook 1985: A Guide to Information for the Physician, Dentist & Health Care Professional. 500p. Date not set. pap. cancelled (ISBN 0-8352-1920-8). Bowker.

International Software Database. Software Catalog: Health Professions. 175p. 1984. 30.00 (ISBN 0-444-00952-3). Elsevier.

Lindberg, Donald A. & Collen, Morris F., eds. Computer Applications in Medical Care. (Illus.). 444p. 1982. 49.50 (ISBN 0-89352-191-4). Masson Pub.

Osswald, P. M., ed. Computers in Critical Care & Pulmonary Medicine. (Illus.). 335p. 1985. pap. 34.50 (ISBN 0-387-13840-4). Springer-Verlag.

Pearch, Nancy D. Data Systems of the National Center for Health Statistics. Olmstead, Mary, ed. (Series 1: No. 16). 50p. 1981. pap. text ed. 1.75 (ISBN 0-8406-0232-4). Natl Ctr Health Stats.

Proceedings: The Ninth Annual Symposium on Computer Applications in Medical Care. 1300p. 1985. 88.00 (ISBN 0-8186-0647-9); prepub. 79.20 (ISBN 0-317-31762-8). IEEE Comp Soc.

Readings in Microcomputers & the Mentally Handicapped. 1984. 16.00 (ISBN 0-89568-419-5). Spec Learn Corp.

Rubin, Martin, ed. Computerization & Automation in Health Facilities. 296p. 1984. 78.50 (ISBN 0-8493-5143-X). CRC Pr.

Schmitz, Homer. Hospital Information Systems. LC 79-15421. 188p. 1979. 34.00 (ISBN 0-89443-156-0). Aspen Systems.

Schofield, J. & British Computer Society (BCS) Microcomputer-Based Aids for the Disabled. 1981. pap. text ed. 34.95x (ISBN 0-471-87721-2, Pub. by Wiley Heyden). Wiley.

Sondak, Norman & Kavaler, Florence, eds. Computers in Medical Adminstration. LC 81-65100. (Artech Medical Library). (Illus.). 359p. 1981. pap. 25.00x (ISBN 0-89006-100-9). Artech Hse.

Speck, Pat K. Medical Management System Report Generator Programmer's Manual. Lozano, Alva, ed. (Illus.). 450p. 1980. text ed. 100.00 (ISBN 0-912217-08-1); pap. 90.00 (ISBN 0-317-12067-0). Afton Oaks.

--Medical Office Management Introductory Manual. Dossman, Sterly, ed. (Illus.). 110p. 1980. text ed. 75.00 (ISBN 0-912217-00-6); pap. 65.00 (ISBN 0-912217-01-4). Afton Oaks.

Standridge. Simulation in Health Care Delivery Systems Nineteen Eighty-Four. pap. 20.00 (ISBN 0-911801-02-2). Soc Computer Sim.

Weintraub, et al. Biostats: Data Analysis for Dental Health Care Profesionals. 2nd ed. (Illus.). 285p. 1985. pap. 19.50 (ISBN 0-932137-01-6). Cavco Pubns.

Worthley, John A. Managing Computers in Health Care: A Guide for Professionals. LC 82-13851. 264p. 1982. pap. text ed. 22.50x (ISBN 0-914904-80-9, 00856). Health Admin Pr.

MEDICAL CHEMISTRY

see Chemistry, Medical and Pharmaceutical

MEDICAL ELECTRONICS

see also Radiotherapy; Telemeter (Physiological Apparatus)

Bartone, John C., II. Medical Electronics & Instrumentation: Research Subject Analysis. LC 83-45291. 166p. 1983. 34.00 (ISBN 0-88164-066-2); pap. 29.95 (ISBN 0-88164-067-0). ABBE Pubs Assn.

Bergveld, P. Electromedical Instrumentation: A Guide for Medical Personnel. LC 77-85711. (Techniques of Measurement in Medicine Ser.: No. 2). (Illus.). 1980. 34.50 (ISBN 0-521-21892-6); pap. 12.95 (ISBN 0-521-29305-7). Cambridge U Pr.

Caceres, C. A., ed. Biomedical Telemetry. 1965. 76.50 (ISBN 0-12-153850-8). Acad Pr.

Consumer Medical Electronics. (Reports Ser.: No. 180). 159p. 1981. 985.00x (ISBN 0-88694-180-6). Intl Res Dev.

Cromwell, Leslie, et al. Biomedical Instrumentation & Measurements. 2nd ed. (Illus.). 1980. text ed. 31.95 (ISBN 0-13-076448-5). P-H.

Dewhurst, D. J. An Introduction to Biomedical Instrumentation. 2nd ed. 288p. 1975. text ed. 59.00 (ISBN 0-08-018755-2); pap. text ed. 31.00 (ISBN 0-08-018884-2). Pergamon.

DuBovy, Joseph L. Introduction to Biomedical Electronics. (Illus.). 1978. text ed. 25.15 (ISBN 0-07-017895-X). McGraw.

Gard, Michael F. EMI Control in Medical Electronics. White, Donald R., ed. LC 78-66192. (Illus.). 175p. 1979. text ed. 32.00 (ISBN 0-932263-19-4). White Consult.

Geddes, L. A. & Baker, L. E. Principles of Applied Biomedical Instrumentation. 2nd ed. LC 74-34390. (Biomedical Engineering & Health Systems Ser.). 616p. 1975. 46.95x (ISBN 0-471-29496-9, Pub. by Wiley-Interscience). Wiley.

Good Hospital Practice: Ethylene Oxide Gas-Ventilation Recommendations & Safe Use. 24p. 1981. pap. text ed. 35.00x (ISBN 0-910275-03-3). Assn Adv Med Instrs.

Klein, Burton R. Introduction to Medical Electronics: For Electronics & Medical Personnel. LC 83-24860. 318p. 1984. Repr. of 1976 ed. lib. bdg. 17.50 (ISBN 0-89874-729-5). Krieger.

Klemm, W. R. Applied Electronics for Veterinary Medicine & Animal Physiology. (Illus.). 484p. 1976. 41.50x (ISBN 0-398-03477-X). C C Thomas.

Market Intelligence Research Company Staff. World Medical Electronics Yearbook, 1985. 440p. Date not set. pap. text ed. 795.00 (ISBN 0-317-19557-3). Market Res Co.

Miller, H. & Harrison, D. C. Biomedical Electrode Technology. 1974. 65.00 (ISBN 0-12-496850-3). Acad Pr.

Neuman, Michael R., et al, eds. Physical Sensors for Biomedical Applications. 168p. 1980. 59.00 (ISBN 0-8493-5975-9). CRC Pr.

Roth, Herbert H., et al. Electrical Safety in Health Care Facilities. (Clinical Engineering Ser.). 1975. 55.00 (ISBN 0-12-599050-2). Acad Pr.

Stacy, Ralph W. Biological & Medical Electronics. LC 59-14465. pap. 77.00 (ISBN 0-317-28676-5, 2055293). Bks Demand UMI.

Watson, B. W., ed. IEE Medical Electronics Monographs. Incl. Vol. 1. Monographs 1-6. 255p. 1971. 22.00 (ISBN 0-901223-07-7, ME001); Vol. 2. Monographs 7-12. Hill, D. W., ed. 180p. 1974. 23.00 (ISBN 0-901223-51-4, ME002); Vol. 3. Monographs 13-17. Hill, D. W., ed. 190p. 1975. 30.00 (ISBN 0-901223-77-8, ME003); Vol. 4. Monographs 18-22. Hill, D. W., ed. 168p. 1976. 39.00 (ISBN 0-901223-84-0, ME004); Vol. 5. Monographs 23-27. Hill, D. W., ed. 1977. 39.00 (ISBN 0-901223-98-0). (Illus.). 255p (ME001, Pub. by Peregrinus England). Inst Elect Eng.

Webster, John G., et al. Electronic Devices for Rehabilitation. 446p. 1985. 45.00 (ISBN 0-471-80898-9, Pub by Wiley Med). Wiley.

Zucker, Mitchell H. Electronic Circuits for the Behavioral & Biomedical Sciences: A Reference Book of Useful Solid-State Circuits. LC 76-81921. (Illus.). 241p. 1969. text ed. 25.50x (ISBN 0-7167-0918-X). W H Freeman.

MEDICAL INSTRUMENTS AND APPARATUS

see also Lasers in Medicine

AAMI Nineteenth Annual Meeting Proceedings. annual 120p. (Orig.). 1984. pap. text ed. 25.00 (ISBN 0-910275-34-3). Assn Adv Med Instrn.

Bartone, John C., II. Medical Electronics & Instrumentation: Research Subject Analysis. LC 83-45291. 166p. 1983. 34.00 (ISBN 0-88164-066-2); pap. 29.95 (ISBN 0-88164-067-0). ABBE Pubs Assn.

Board on Toxicology & Environmental Health Hazards, National Research Council. Identifying & Estimating the Genetic Impact of Chemical Mutagens. 295p. 1983. pap. text ed. 11.50 (ISBN 0-309-03345-4). Natl Acad Pr.

Critser, James R., Jr. Medical Diagnostic Apparatus-Systems. (Ser. 10DAS-84). 1985. 100.00 (ISBN 0-88178-054-5). Lexington Data.

Donovan, Chester D. Medical Devices & Equipment: Standards, Design, Failures & Safety: Medical Subject Analysis & Research Index with Bibliography. LC 83-71665. 120p. 1984. 29.95 (ISBN 0-88164-048-4); pap. 21.95 (ISBN 0-88164-049-2). ABBE Pubs Assn.

Driscoll. Instrumental Evaluation in Biomedical Science. (Clinical & Biochemical Analysis Ser.). 312p. 1984. 59.75 (ISBN 0-8247-7184-2). Dekker.

Fratkin, Jake. WQ-Ten Electro Acupuncture Machine. Felt, Robert L., ed. 48p. (Orig.). pap. 7.95 (ISBN 0-912111-03-8). Paradigm Pubns.

Geriatric Self Health-Care Market. 1983. 1250.00 (ISBN 0-86621-040-7). Frost & Sullivan.

Good Hospital Practice: Steam Sterilization & Sterility Assurance. 28p. 1980. pap. text ed. 35.00x (ISBN 0-910275-02-5). Assn Adv Med Instrs.

Guideline for Industrial Ethylene Oxide Sterilization of Medical Devices. 20p. 1981. pap. text ed. 35.00x (ISBN 0-910275-00-9). Assn Adv Med Instrs.

Hendee, William R. The Selection & Performance of Radiologic Equipment. 400p. 1985. 48.50 (ISBN 0-683-03958-X). Williams & Wilkins.

Hoehne, K. H., ed. Digital Image Processing in Medicine: Proceedings. (Lecture Notes in Medical Informatics Ser.: Vol. 15). 197p. 1981. pap. 21.00 (ISBN 0-387-10877-7). Springer-Verlag.

Hoenig, Stuart A. & Scott, Daphne H. Medical Instrumentation & Electrical Safety: The View from the Nursing Station. LC 77-5878. 368p. 1977. pap. 26.95 (ISBN 0-471-40566-3). Krieger.

Home Health Care Products Markets. 1983. 1250.00 (ISBN 0-86621-080-6). Frost & Sullivan.

Hunt, Diana. The Doctor's Guide for Buying X-Ray Equipment & Accessories. (Illus.). 200p. 1981. text ed. write for info. Springtime.

Industrial Ethylene Oxide Sterilization of Medical Devices. (Illus.). 80p. 1981. pap. text ed. 35.00x (ISBN 0-910275-01-7). Assn Adv Med Instrs.

International Resource Development Inc. Medical Imaging Markets. 166p. 1983. 1285.00x (ISBN 0-88694-562-3). Intl Res Dev.

Ko, Wen H., ed. Bio-Medical Sensors: Implantable Indwelling Devices for Closed Loop Stimulation Systems. (Illus.). 400p. 1985. 62.00 (ISBN 0-87993-260-0). Futura Pub.

Konikiewicz, Leonard W. & Griff, Leonard C. Bioelectrography (Kirlian Photography) A New Method for Detecting Cancer & Monitoring Body Physiology. LC 80-81268. (Illus.). 210p. 1984. lib. bdg. 34.95 (ISBN 0-936692-02-2); pap. text ed. 23.95 (ISBN 0-936692-01-4). Leonard Assoc Press.

Langstrom, Carla T. Methods & Instrumentation for Medical Automation. LC 84-45004. 150p. 1984. 29.95 (ISBN 0-88164-182-0); pap. 21.95 (ISBN 0-88164-183-9). ABBE Pubs Assn.

Lung Diagnostic Function Equipment Market in EEC. 230p. 1984. 1600.00 (ISBN 0-86621-509-3). Frost & Sullivan.

Lung Function Diagnosis & Supplies Markets. 350p. 1984. 1550.00 (ISBN 0-86621-095-4). Frost & Sullivan.

Office of Technology Assessment, Congress of the United States, Washington, DC, USA. Federal Policies & the Medical Devices Industry. (Illus.). 260p. 1985. 59.95 (ISBN 0-08-032410-X). Pergamon.

Recent & Future Developments in Medical Imaging I: Proceedings of the SPIE Annual Technical Symposium, 22nd, San Diego, 1978. (SPIE Seminar Proceedings: Vol. 152). 142p. 19.00 (ISBN 0-89252-179-1); 11.00, members (ISBN 0-317-34751-9). SPIE.

Recent & Future Developments in Medical Imaging II: Proceedings of the SPIE Annual Technical Symposium, 23rd, San Diego, 1979. (SPIE Seminar Proceedings: Vol. 206). 268p. 38.00 (ISBN 0-89252-234-8); 30.00, members (ISBN 0-317-34752-7). SPIE.

Sphygmomanometers: Electronic or Automated. 35.00 (SP9). Assn Adv Med Instrn.

Tischler, Morris. Experiments in General & Biomedical Instrumentation. Haas, Mark, ed. (Illus.). 176p. 1980. pap. text ed. 18.55x (ISBN 0-07-064781-X). McGraw.

Welkowitz, Walter & Deutsch, Sid. Biomedical Instrument: Theory & Design. 1976. 36.00 (ISBN 0-12-744150-6). Acad Pr.

MEDICAL LABORATORY TECHNICIANS

see Medical Technologists

MEDICAL LABORATORY TECHNOLOGY

see Medical Technology

MEDICAL MICROBIOLOGY

see also Micro-Organisms, Pathogenic

Barnett, Margaret E. Introduction to Medical Microbiology. LC 85-4141. 210p. 1985. pap. 25.00 (ISBN 0-933195-00-1). Cal College Pr.

Bartlett, Raymond C. Medical Microbiology: Quality & Clinical Relevance. LC 73-18482. (Wiley Biomedical Health Publications Ser.). (Illus.). pap. 51.20 (ISBN 0-317-09253-7, 2055168). Bks Demand UMI.

Baum, H. & Gergely, J., eds. Molecular Aspects of Medicine, Vol. 5. (Illus.). 470p. 1983. 162.00 (ISBN 0-08-030429-X). Pergamon.

Braude, Abraham I. & McCutchan, J. Allen. Review of Medical Microbiology. (Illus.). 208p. 1983. pap. 14.50 (ISBN 0-7216-1183-4). Saunders.

Collee, J. G. Applied Medical Microbiology. (Illus.). 158p. 1981. pap. text ed. 11.95x (ISBN 0-632-00853-9). Blackwell Pubns.

Davidson, Elizabeth W., ed. Pathogenesis of Invertebrate Microbial Diseases. LC 81-65007. 576p. 1981. text ed. 42.50x (ISBN 0-86598-014-4). Allanheld.

De La Maza, M. & Patterson, E. M., eds. Medical Virology III: Proceedings of the 1983 International Symposium on Medical Virology, Oct. 19-21, 1983, Anaheim, Ca. 400p. 1984. 65.00 (ISBN 0-444-00829-2). Elsevier.

Easmon, Charles S. & Jeljaszewicz, Janusz, eds. Medical Microbiology, Vol. 4. 1984. 65.00 (ISBN 0-12-228004-0). Acad Pr.

Freeman, Bob A. Burrows Textbook of Microbiology. 22nd ed. (Illus.). 1100p. Date not set. price not set (ISBN 0-7216-3868-6). Saunders.

Gall, Lorraine S. & Curby, William A. Instrumented Systems for Microbiological Analysis of Body Fluids. 192p. 1980. 56.00 (ISBN 0-8493-5681-4). CRC Pr.

Greene, Craig E. Clinical Microbiology & Infectious Diseases of the Dog & Cat. (Illus.). 610p. 1984. 52.00 (ISBN 0-7216-4251-9). Saunders.

Jensen, Marcus M. & Wright, Donald N. Introduction to Medical Microbiology. (Illus.). 464p. 1985. text ed. 30.95 (ISBN 0-13-487380-7). P-H.

Ketchum, Paul A. Microbiology: Introduction for Health Professionals. LC 82-23709. 544p. 1984. text ed. 32.95 (ISBN 0-471-06306-1); study guide 10.95 (ISBN 0-471-88898-2). Wiley.

Linton, A. H. Microbial Interactions with Man & Animals. 270p. 1982. 53.95 (ISBN 0-471-10083-8). Wiley.

Mayo, Michael A. & Harrap, K. A., eds. Vectors in Virus Biology. (Special Publications Society General Microbiology Ser.: No. 12). 1984. 37.00 (ISBN 0-12-481480-8). Acad Pr.

Morello, Josephine A. & Mizer, Helen Eckel. Microbiology in Patient Care. 4th ed. 720p. 1984. text ed. write for info. (ISBN 0-02-383500-1). Macmillan.

Noble, W. C. Microbiology of Human Skin. 433p. 1981. 90.00x (ISBN 0-686-80441-4, Pub. by Lloyd-Luke England). State Mutual Bk.

Pelczar, Michael, Jr. & Chan, E. C. S. Elements of Microbiology. 1st ed. (Illus.). 704p. (Orig.). 1981. text ed. 33.95 (ISBN 0-07-049240-9). McGraw.

Russell, A. D. Pharmaceutical Microbiology. 3rd ed. Hugo, W. B., ed. (Illus.). 480p. 1983. pap. text ed. 29.00x (ISBN 0-632-01048-7). Blackwell Pubns.

Schlessinger, David, ed. Microbiology 1975. LC 74-33538. 1975. 28.00 (ISBN 0-914826-05-0). Am Soc Microbio.

Schrader, B. & Meier, W., eds. Raman-IR Atlas of Organic Compounds. 1974-1976. Set. 467.70x (ISBN 0-686-86853-6). Vol. 1,314p (ISBN 3-527-25539-7). Vol. 2,344p (ISBN 3-527-25541-9). Vol. 3,432p (ISBN 3-527-25542-7). VCH Pubs.

Sherris, John C., ed. Medical Microbiology: An Introduction to Infectious Diseases. 800p. 1984. 37.50 (ISBN 0-444-00854-3). Elsevier.

Smith, J. R., et al. Learning Guides for the Medical Microbiology Laboratory. 400p. 1985. pap. 19.95 (ISBN 0-471-87862-6). Wiley.

Suny Buffalo. Lab of Medical Microbiology. (Microbiology Ser.). 176p. 1983. 22.75 (ISBN 0-8247-7040-4). Dekker.

Thomas, C. G. Medical Microbiology. 5th ed. (Illus.). 416p. 1983. pap. 19.00 (ISBN 0-7216-0816-7, Pub. by Bailliere-Tindall). Saunders.

Tischer, Robert G., et al. Problem Solving in Medical Technology & Microbiology. LC 79-11337. (Illus.). 291p. 1979. pap. text ed. 12.00 (ISBN 0-89189-068-8, 45-7-010-00). Am Soc Clinical.

Treagan, Lucy & Pulliam, Lynn. Medical Microbiology Laboratory Procedures. (Illus.). 336p. 1982. spiral bdg. 19.95 (ISBN 0-7216-8901-9). Saunders.

Vieweg. European Journal of Clinical Microbiology, Vol. 1. 1983. pap. text ed. 106.500131 (ISBN 0-9904001-3-1, Pub. by Vieweg & Sohn Germany). Heyden.

Washington, J. A., II, ed. Laboratory Procedure in Clinical Microbiology. 2nd ed. (Illus.). xiv, 885p. 1985. 59.50 (ISBN 0-387-96087-2). Springer-Verlag.

MEDICAL STATISTICS

Bailey, Norman T. Mathematics, Statistics & Systems for Health. LC 77-1307. (Wiley Series Probability & Mathematical Statistics: Applied Probability & Statistics). 222p. 1977. 48.95x (ISBN 0-471-99500-2, Pub. by Wiley-Interscience). Wiley.

Brown, Byron W., Jr. & Hollander, Myles. Statistics: A Biomedical Introduction. LC 77-396. (Probability & Mathematical Statistics Ser). 456p. 1977. 34.95 (ISBN 0-471-11240-2, Pub. by Wiley-Interscience). Wiley.

Burdette, Walter J. & Gehan, Edmund A. Planning & Analysis of Clinical Studies. (Illus.). 116p. 1970. 15.25x (ISBN 0-398-00257-6). C C Thomas.

Croxton, Frederick E. Elementary Statistics: With Applications in Medicine & the Biological Sciences. (Illus.). 1953. pap. 6.95 (ISBN 0-486-60506-X). Dover.

Gore, Sheila M. & Altman, Douglas G. Statistics in Practice. 100p. 1982. 19.00x (ISBN 0-7279-0085-4, Pub. by British Med Assoc UK). Taylor & Francis.

Hospital Statistics, 1984. 262p. (Orig.). 1984. 49.50 (ISBN 0-87258-424-0, 082084). Am Hospital.

Murphy, Edmond A. Biostatistics in Medicine. LC 81-48191. (Illus.). 560p. 1982. text ed. 37.50x (ISBN 0-8018-2727-2). Johns Hopkins.

--A Companion to Medical Statistics. LC 84-21806. 288p. 1985. text ed. 27.50x (ISBN 0-8018-2612-8). Johns Hopkins.

Pearch, Nancy D. Data Systems of the National Center for Health Statistics. Olmstead, Mary, ed. (Series 1: No. 16). 50p. 1981. pap. text ed. 1.75 (ISBN 0-8406-0232-4). Natl Ctr Health Stats.

Statistical Guidelines for Contributors to Medical Journals. 1983. 5.00x (ISBN 0-8002-3869-9, Pub. by British Med Assoc UK). Taylor & Francis.

Swinscow, T. D. V. Statistics at Square One. 8th ed. 86p. 1983. 8.00x (ISBN 0-7279-0175-3, Pub. by British Med Assoc UK). Taylor & Francis.

Tanur, J. M., et al, eds. Statistics: A Guide to Biological & Health Sciences. LC 76-50856. 1977. pap. text ed. 8.95x (ISBN 0-8162-8564-0). Holden-Day.

Von Fraunhofer, J. A. & Murray, J. J. Statistics in Medical, Dental & Biological Studies. 120p. 1981. 30.00x (ISBN 0-905402-00-6, Pub. by Tri-Med England). State Mutual Bk.

MEDICAL TECHNOLOGISTS

Atkinson, Betty J. The Medical Assistant: Clinical Practice. LC 76-5301. 1976. pap. 13.80 (ISBN 0-8273-0351-3). Delmar.

Bonewit, Kathy. Clinical Competencies for the Medical Assistant. 359p. 1981. 14.95x (ISBN 0-8036-0963-9). Davis Co.

--Clinical Procedures for Medical Assistants. 1979. text ed. 19.95 (ISBN 0-7216-1846-4). Saunders.

Chernok, Norma. Your Future in Medical Assisting. LC 67-10176. (Careers in Depth Ser.). 1982. lib. bdg. 7.97 (ISBN 0-8239-0351-6). Rosen Group.

Cotton, H. & Martin, N. Aid for the Medical Assistant. 1975. 15.95 (ISBN 0-87489-003-9). Med Economics.

Doyle, Jean M. & Dennis, Robert L. The Complete Handbook for Medical Secretaries & Assistants. 2nd ed. 1978. pap. text ed. 18.95 (ISBN 0-316-18082-3, Little Med Div). Little.

Fordney, Marilyn T. & Follis, Joan J. Administrative Medical Assisting. LC 81-2141. 668p. 1982. 21.50 (ISBN 0-471-86240-1, Pub. by Wiley Med); pap. 24.50 (ISBN 0-471-06380-0); instr's. manual avail. Wiley.

Frederick, Portia M. & Kinn, Mary E. The Medical Office Assistant: Administrative & Clinical. 5th ed. (Illus.). 707p. 1981. text ed. 25.95 (ISBN 0-7216-3863-5). Saunders.

Holter, Doris J. Admission Standards & Admission Processes of Medical Technology Programs. LC 84-24627. 80p. 1985. pap. text ed. 10.00 (ISBN 0-89189-176-5, 45-9-018-00). Am Soc Clinical.

Kinn, Mary E. Student Review Manual for the Medical Office Assistant. 2nd ed. (Illus.). 298p. 1981. pap. 10.95 wkbk. (ISBN 0-7216-5439-8). Saunders.

Lawton, M. Murray, et al. Lawton & Foy's Textbook for Medical Assistants. 4th ed. LC 80-15524. (Illus.). 456p. 1980. text ed. 22.95 (ISBN 0-8016-2893-8). Mosby.

Lee, Leslie. The Lab Aide. LC 75-38567. (Illus.). 140p. 1976. pap. 9.45 (ISBN 0-8016-2912-8). Mosby.

Lindsey, Bonnie J. Clinical Medical Assistant. LC 80-11397. (Illus.). 169p. (Orig.). 1980. pap. text ed. 11.95 (ISBN 0-87619-714-4). Brady Comm.

Mummah, Hazel & Smith, Marsella. The Geriatric Assistant. (Illus.). 320p. 1980. pap. text ed. 22.50 (ISBN 0-07-044015-8). McGraw.

Perry, Henry B. & Breitner, Bina. Physician Assistants: Their Contribution to Health Care. LC 81-6260. 331p. 1982. 29.95 (ISBN 0-89885-066-5). Human Sci Pr.

Read & Burns-Cox. The Clinical Apprentice. 6th ed. 1986. price not set. PSG Pub Co.

Reedy, Barry L. The New Health Practitioners in America: A Comparative Study. 79p. 1978. 30.00x (ISBN 0-900889-68-3, Pub. by Kings Fund). State Mutual Bk.

Ring, Alvin M. Laboratory Assistants Examination Review Book. 3rd ed. 1979. 12.75 (ISBN 0-87488-455-1). Med Exam.

Rudman, Jack. Cardio-Pulmonary Technician. (Career Examination Ser.: C-1159). (Cloth bdg. avail. on request). pap. 14.00 (ISBN 0-686-66496-5). Natl Learning.

--Clinical Laboratory Investigator. (Career Examination Ser.: C-2098). (Cloth bdg. avail. on request). 1976. pap. 14.00 (ISBN 0-8373-1196-9). Natl Learning.

--Medical Equipment Technician. (Career Examination Ser.: C-2654). (Cloth bdg. avail. on request). pap. 10.00 (ISBN 0-8373-2654-0). Natl Learning.

--Medical Laboratory Technician. (Career Examination Ser.: C-2323). (Cloth bdg,. avail. on request). pap. 10.00 (ISBN 0-8373-2323-1). Natl Learning.

Schapiro, Melvin & Kuritsky, Joel. The Gastroenterology Assistant: A Laboratory Manual. (Illus.). 112p. 1972. photocopy ed. spiral bdg. 12.75x (ISBN 0-398-02618-1). C C Thomas.

Tindall, V. R. Essential Sciences for Clinicians. (Illus.). 528p. 1981. pap. text ed. 42.25 (ISBN 0-632-00733-8, B 4984-6). Mosby.

MEDICAL TECHNOLOGY

Alba. Alba's Medical Technology Board Examination Review, Vol. II. 5th ed. LC 72-172446. (Illus.). 489p. 1981. pap. text ed. 22.00 (ISBN 0-910224-06-4). Berkeley Sci.

Assembly of Engineering, Institute of Medicine, National Research Council. Medical Technology & the Health Care System: A Study of the Diffusion of Equipment-Embodied Technology. 1979. pap. text ed. 12.25 (ISBN 0-309-02865-5). Natl Acad Pr.

Baker, F. J. & Silverton, R. E. Introduction to Medical Laboratory Technology. 6th ed. 576p. 1985. pap. text ed. 25.00 (ISBN 0-407-73252-7). Butterworth.

Banta, David, et al. Toward Rational Technology in Medicine: Considerations for Health Policy. (Health Care & Society Ser.: No. 5). 1981. text ed. 28.50 (ISBN 0-8261-3200-6); pap. text ed. cancelled (ISBN 0-8261-3201-4). Springer Pub.

Banta, H. David. The Management of Health Care Technology in Nine Countries. (Springer Series on Health Care & Society: Vol. 7). 256p. 1982. 35.95 (ISBN 0-8261-3770-9). Springer Pub.

Bennington, James L. Saunders Encyclopedia & Dictionary of Laboratory Medicine & Technology. (Illus.). 1700p. 1984. 45.00 (ISBN 0-7216-1714-X). Saunders.

Bruce, A. Wayne. Basic Quality Assurance & Quality Control in the Clinical Laboratory. 179p. 1984. pap. text ed. 13.95 (ISBN 0-316-11252-6). Little.

Bryant, Neville J. Examination Review for Medical Technology. 352p. 1983. pap. 15.95 (ISBN 0-7216-2165-1). Saunders.

Business Communications Staff. Medical Diagnostic Equipment: New Developments. 1985. pap. 1500.00 (ISBN 0-89336-419-3, GB-084). BCC.

Caceres, C. A., ed. The Management of Technology in Health & Medical Care. LC 80-70587. (Artech Medical Library). (Illus.). 502p. 1981. 25.00 (ISBN 0-89006-101-7). Artech Hse.

Cooper, M. G. & Cooper, D. E. The Medical Assistant. 5th ed. 704p. 1985. price not set (ISBN 0-07-012755-7). McGraw.

Critser, James R., Jr. Cardiac Technology. (Ser. 10CT-80). 1981. 90.00 (ISBN 0-914428-81-0). Lexington Data.

--Medical Technology: Advanced Medical Apparatus-Systems. (Ser 10AMA-77). 1978. 360.00 (ISBN 0-914428-46-2). Lexington Data.

Culyer, A. J. & Horisberger, B, eds. Economic & Medical Evaluation of Health Care Technologies. (Illus.). 415p. 1983. 22.00 (ISBN 0-387-12987-1). Springer Verlag.

Daily, Elaine K. & Schroeder, John S. Hemodynamic Waveforms: Exercises in Identification & Analysis. 1st ed. LC 82-12419. (Illus.). 277p. 1983. pap. text ed. 16.95 (ISBN 0-8016-1212-8). Mosby.

Davis, Audrey B. Medicine & Its Technology: An Introduction to the History of Medical Instruments. LC 80-25202. (Contributions in Medical History Ser.: No. 7). (Illus.). 224p. 1981. lib. bdg. 45.00 (ISBN 0-313-22807-8, DMT/). Greenwood.

Donovan, Chester D. Medical Devices & Equipment: Standards, Design, Failures & Safety: Medical Subject Analysis & Research Index with Bibliography. LC 83-71665. 120p. 1984. 29.95 (ISBN 0-88164-048-4); pap. 21.95 (ISBN 0-88164-049-2). ABBE Pubs Assn.

Doucet, Lorraine. Medical Technology Review. (Illus.). 446p. 1981. pap. text ed. 15.00 (ISBN 0-397-50459-4, 65-06000, Lippincott Nursing). Lippincott.

Doucet, Lorraine D. & Packard, Albert E. Medical Technology Examination Review. 2nd ed. LC 65-8154. (Illus.). 340p. 1984. pap. text ed. 16.50 (ISBN 0-397-54486-3, Lippincott Medical). Lippincott.

Driggs, M. F. Problem-Directed & Medical Information Systems. 1979. 27.50 (ISBN 0-8151-2855-X). Year Bk Med.

Egdahl, Richard H. & Gertman, Paul M. Technology & the Quality of Health Care. LC 78-7307. 336p. 1978. text ed. 42.95 (ISBN 0-89443-025-4). Aspen Systems.

Eggert, Arthur A. Electronics & Instrumentation for the Clinical Laboratory. LC 83-10524. 432p. 1983. 26.95x (ISBN 0-471-86275-4, Pub. by Wiley Med). Wiley.

Erlich, et al. Business Administration for the Medical Assistant. 2nd ed. LC 81-67045. (Illus.). 1983. 10.95 (ISBN 0-940012-01-4). Colwell Syst.

Freeman, James A. & Beeler, Myrton F., eds. Laboratory Medicine-Urinalysis & Medical Microscopy. 2nd ed. LC 82-17254. (Illus.). 611p. 1983. text ed. 47.50 (ISBN 0-8121-0822-1). Lea & Febiger.

Gay, James & Jacobs, Barbara S., eds. The Technolgy Explosion in Medical Science: Implications for the Health Care Industry & the Public (1981-2001) (Health Care Administration Monographs: Vol. 2). 176p. 1983. text ed. 14.95 (ISBN 0-89335-181-4). SP Med & Sci Bks.

Goldman, J., ed. Health Care Technology Evaluation. (Lecture Notes in Medical Informatics: Vol. 6). 1979. pap. 17.00 (ISBN 0-387-09561-6). Springer-Verlag.

Goodman, David B., intro. by. Technology Impact: Potential Directions for Laboratory Medicine. (Annals of The New York Academy of Sciences Ser.: Vol. 428). 334p. 1984. lib. bdg. 64.00x (ISBN 0-89766-250-4); pap. 64.00x (ISBN 0-89766-251-2). NY Acad Sci.

Hahnefeld, I. W. Systematisierung von Infusionsloesungen und Grundlagen der Infusionstherapie. (Beitraege Zu Infusionstherapie und Klinische Ernaehrung: Band 5). (Illus.). 112p. 1980. pap. 9.00 (ISBN 3-8055-1395-X). S Karger.

Hamilton, Betty, ed. Medical Diagnostic Imaging Systems: Technology & Applications. (F & S Press Bk.). 232p. 1982. prof. ref. 39.50. Ballinger Pub.

Hayward, Mary & Clark, Connie. Medical Science for Medical Assistants. 1982. text ed. 19.95x (ISBN 0-02-352850-8). Macmillan.

Heusghem, Camille & Albert, Adelin, eds. Advanced Interpretation of Clinical Laboratory Data. (Clinical & Biochemical Analysis Ser.: Vol. 13). (Illus.). 448p. 1982. 65.00 (ISBN 0-8247-1744-9). Dekker.

Hinman, E. J. Advanced Medical Systems: An Assessment of the Contributions. 1979. 29.50 (ISBN 0-8151-4460-1). Year Bk Med.

Holter, Doris J. Admission Standards & Admission Processes of Medical Technology Programs. LC 84-24627. 80p. 1985. pap. text ed. 10.00 (ISBN 0-89189-176-5, 45-9-018-00). Am Soc Clinical.

Hossaini, Ali A. Medical Technology Examination Review. 2nd ed. LC 82-8758. (Illus.). 320p. 1984. 16.95 (ISBN 0-8385-6283-3, 5361). ACC.

Hossaini, Ali A., et al. Medical Technology Examination Review. LC 78-1743. (Arco Medical Review Ser.). 1978. pap. text ed. 12.00x (ISBN 0-668-04365-2). Arco.

Kirk, Clive J. Basic Medical Laboratory Technology. (Illus.). 1975. 21.00x (ISBN 0-8464-0179-7). Beekman Pubs.

Kleinfield, Sonny. A Machine Called Indomitable: The Remarkable Story of a Scientist's Inspiration, Invention, & Medical, Breakthrough. LC 85-40270. 256p. Date not set. 15.95 (ISBN 0-8129-1234-9). Times Bks.

Lieff, Jonathan D. Computers & Other Technological Aids for Psychiatric Private Practice. LC 84-6286. (Private Practice Monographs). 128p. 1984. pap. text ed. 15.00x (ISBN 0-88048-104-8). Am Psychiatric.

Lindberg, David S., et al. Williams Introduction to the Profession of Medical Technology. 4th ed. LC 84-912. (Illus.). 114p. 1984. pap. 9.50 (ISBN 0-8121-0937-6). Lea & Febiger.

McKinlay, John B., ed. Technology & the Future of Health Care. (The Milbank Readers Ser.: No. 8). 496p. 1982. text ed. 25.00x (ISBN 0-262-13183-8); pap. text ed. 12.50x (ISBN 0-262-63084-2). MIT Pr.

McNeil, Barbara J., ed. Critical Issues in Medical Technology. Cravalho, Ernest G. 448p. 1981. 28.00 (ISBN 0-86569-070-7). Auburn Hse.

Milne, Eric N. & Higgens, Charles B. Models & Techniques in Medical Imaging Research. 624p. 1983. 75.00 (ISBN 0-03-058373-X). Praeger.

Nassif, Janet Z. Health Profession Careers in Medicine's New Technology. 2nd ed. LC 78-11386. Orig. Title: Medicine's New Technology: A Career Guide. 1981. pap. 5.95 (ISBN 0-668-04436-5). Arco.

Nicholson, J. P., ed. Scientific Aids in Hospital Diagnosis. LC 76-15409. 296p. 1976. 45.00x (ISBN 0-306-30938-6, Plenum Pr). Plenum Pub.

Nukols, M. L. & Smith, K. A., eds. The Characterization of Carbon Dioxide Absorbing Agents for Life Support Equipment. (OED Ser.: Vol. 10). 1982. 40.00 (H00239). ASME.

Olanon, Katy H. Medical Technology: Subject Analysis Index with Research Bibliography. LC 85-47569. 150p. 1985. 29.95 (ISBN 0-88164-312-2); pap. 21.95 (ISBN 0-88164-313-0). ABBE Pubs Assn.

Raphael, Stanley S. Lynch's Medical Laboratory Technology. 4th ed. (Illus.). 864p. 1983. 46.95 (ISBN 0-7216-7465-8). Saunders.

Ravel. Clinical Laboratory Medicine. 4th ed. 1984. pap. 24.95 (ISBN 0-8151-7097-1). Year Bk Med.

Reiser, Stanley J. & Anbar, Michael, eds. The Machine at the Bedside: Strategies for Using Technology in Patient Care. (Illus.). 336p. 1984. 49.50 (ISBN 0-521-26718-8); pap. 14.95 (ISBN 0-521-31832-7). Cambridge U Pr.

Rossman, Sally & Reisinger, Paula. Cardiovascular Technology Exam Review. 1981. pap. text ed. 18.00 (ISBN 0-87488-180-3). Med Exam.

Russell, Louise. Technology in Hospitals: Medical Advances & Their Diffusion. (Studies in Social Economics). 1979. 26.95 (ISBN 0-8157-7630-6); pap. 9.95 (ISBN 0-8157-7629-2). Brookings.

Russell, Louise B. & Burke, Carol S. Technological Diffusion in the Hospital Sector. LC 75-37308. 240p. 1976. 8.00 (ISBN 0-89068-007-8). Natl Planning.

Scholtz. Comprehensive Review of Medical Technology. 400p. Date not set. 19.95 (ISBN 0-471-80818-0). Wiley.

Spiegel, Allen, et al, eds. Medical Technology, Health Care & the Consumer. LC 79-25559. 352p. 1981. 39.95x (ISBN 0-87705-498-3). Human Sci Pr.

Stillwell, G. Keith. Therapeutic Electricity & Ultraviolet Radiation. 3rd ed. (RML). (Illus.). 330p. 1983. lib. bdg. 39.00 (ISBN 0-683-07979-4). Williams & Wilkins.

Szolovits, Peter, ed. Artificial Intelligence in Medicine. (AAAS Selected Symposium: No. 51). 130p. 1982. softcover 26.50x (ISBN 0-89158-900-7). Westview.

Temperature Monitoring & Recording in Blood Bank: Proposed Guideline. 1984. 15.00 (ISBN 0-318-03282-1, I16-P). Natl Comm Clin Lab Stds.

Tischer, Robert G., et al. Problem Solving in Medical Technology & Microbiology. LC 79-11337. (Illus.). 291p. 1979. pap. text ed. 12.00 (ISBN 0-89189-068-8, 45-7-010-00). Am Soc Clinical.

Tresler, Kathleen M. Clinical Laboratory Tests: Significance & Nursing Implications. (Illus.). 496p. 1982. 20.95 (ISBN 0-13-137760-4). P-H.

Wagner, G., et al, eds. Technology & Health: Man & World Proceedings. (Lecture Notes in Medical Informatics Ser.: Vol. 7). 243p. 1980. pap. 24.00 (ISBN 0-387-10230-2). Springer Verlag.

Waidelich, W., ed. Optoelectronics in Medicine: Proceedings of the Fifth International Congress LASER 81. (Illus.). 239p. 1982. pap. 25.80 (ISBN 0-387-10968-4). Springer-Verlag.

Wells, P. N., ed. Scientific Basis of Medical Imaging. (Illus.). 284p. 1982. text ed. 55.00 (ISBN 0-443-01986-X). Churchill.

Wolf, Stewart & Berle, Beatrice B., eds. The Technological Imperative in Medicine. LC 81-17751. 159p. 1981. text ed. 32.50 (ISBN 0-306-40889-9, Plenum Pr). Plenum Pub.

MEDICAL ULTRASONICS

see Ultrasonics in Medicine

MEDICINE–DATA PROCESSING

Abell, Alphonse R. Recent Advances of Computers in Medicine: Guidebook for Research & Reference. LC 84-45003. 150p. 1984. 29.95 (ISBN 0-88164-166-9); pap. 21.95 (ISBN 0-88164-167-7). ABBE Pubs Assn.

Abramson, J. H. & Peritz, E. Calculator Programs for the Health Sciences. (Illus.). 1983. text ed. 42.50x (ISBN 0-19-503187-3); pap. text ed. 24.95x (ISBN 0-19-503188-1). Oxford U Pr.

Allswang, John. Physician's Guide to Computers & Computing. (Orig.). 1985. pap. write for info. (ISBN 0-8385-7851-9). ACC.

Allswang, John M., et al. Computer Power for Physicians. 225p. pap. cancelled (ISBN 0-89588-197-7). SYBEX.

Alperovitch, A., et al, eds. Evaluation of Efficacy of Medical Action. 536p. 1980. 78.75 (ISBN 0-444-85379-0). Elsevier.

Alvisi, C. Investigative Ultrasonology Two: Clinical Advances. 344p. 1981. 70.00x (ISBN 0-272-79576-3, Pub. by Pitman Bks England). State Mutual Bk.

American Hospital Association. Hospital Computer Systems Planning: Preparation of Request for Proposal. LC 84-2880. 124p. 1980. 28.00 (ISBN 0-939450-19-4, 040145). AHPI.

American Hospital Association Clearinghouse for Hospital Management Engineering, ed. Computer-Assisted Medical Record Systems: An Examination of Case Studies. 148p. 1982. pap. 18.75 (ISBN 0-87258-375-9, AHA-148200). Am Hospital.

American Medical Association, et al. Computer Assisted Medical Practice: AMA's Role. 1971. pap. 1.75 (ISBN 0-89970-028-4, OP377). AMA.

Andren, John, Jr., et al. IBM PC to Apple II BASIC Program Translation. 100p. 1984. 15.00. Med Software.

Archer, Carol R. Atlas of Computed Tomography of the Larynx. (Illus.). 200p. 1985. 27.50 (ISBN 0-87527-240-1). Green.

Asbury, A. J. ABC of Computing. 69p. 1984. 14.00 (ISBN 0-7279-0160-5, Pub. by British Med Assoc UK). Taylor & Francis.

Austin, Charles J. Information Systems for Hospital Administration. 2nd ed. LC 83-8495. (Illus.). 340p. 1983. text ed. 28.00x (ISBN 0-914904-91-4). Health Admin Pr.

Automated Education Center. An Annotated Bibliography of Biomedical Computer Applications. LC 79-120081. 19.00 (ISBN 0-403-04451-0). Scholarly.

Automated Hospital Information Systems: How to Decide What You Want. LC 84-60127. 320p. 1984. pap. text ed. 45.00 (ISBN 0-914957-01-5). Pluribus Pr.

Baert, A. L. Atlas of Computer Tomography: Volume Two, Abdominal Computer Tomography. (Illus.). 210p. 1980. 130.00 (ISBN 0-387-10093-8). Springer-Verlag.

Ball, Marion & Hannah, Kathryn. Using Computers in Nursing. 1984. text ed. 21.95 (ISBN 0-8359-8130-4); pap. text ed. 16.95 (ISBN 0-8359-8129-0). Reston.

Ball, Marion J., ed. How to Select a Computerized Hospital Information System. (Data Processing in Medicine: Vol. 2). (Illus.). 1973. 25.25 (ISBN 3-8055-1465-4). S Karger.

Bartone, J. C. Computers in Medicine: Current Medical Subject Analysis & Research Directory with Bibliography. LC 81-71809. 162p. 1983. 29.95 (ISBN 0-941864-32-4); pap. 21.95 (ISBN 0-941864-33-2). ABBE Pubs Assn.

Bartone, John C. Automatic Data Processing, Artificial Intelligence & Computers: Medical Subject Analysis with Bibliography. LC 83-71669. 144p. 1984. 29.95 (ISBN 0-88164-076-X); pap. 21.95 (ISBN 0-88164-075-1). ABBE Pubs Assn.

Bartone, John C., II. Current Status of Computers in Medicine: Medical Subject Analysis & Bibliography. LC 83-71675. 150p. 1984. 29.95 (ISBN 0-88164-093-X); pap. 21.95 (ISBN 0-88164-092-1). ABBE Pubs Assn.

Bartone, Mary R. Computer-Assisted Instruction & Education: Medical Applications & Subject Analysis with Bibliography. LC 83-71672. 146p. 1984. 29.95 (ISBN 0-88164-056-5); pap. 21.95 (ISBN 0-88164-057-3). ABBE Pubs Assn.

Bisconte, J. C. & Sklansky, J., eds. Biomedical Images & Computers: St. Pierre de Chartreuse, France 1980, Proceedings. (Lecture Notes in Medical Informatics: Vol. 17). 332p. 1982. pap. 23.00 (ISBN 0-387-11579-X). Springer-Verlag.

Blois, Marsden S. Information & Medicine: The Nature of Medical Descriptions. LC 83-24923. 300p. 1985. 27.50x (ISBN 0-520-04988-8). U of Cal Pr.

Blum, B. I., ed. Information Systems for Patient Care. (Computers & Medicine). (Illus.). 400p. 1984. 27.50 (ISBN 0-387-90912-5). Springer Verlag.

Brandejs, J. F., ed. Computer Assisted Physicians Offices. (Health Communications & Informatics: Vol. 5, No. 2, 1979). (Illus.). 1979. softcover 8.25 (ISBN 3-8055-3063-3). S Karger.

Brandejs, Jan F. & Pace, Graham. Physician's Primer on Computers: Private Practice. LC 75-39315. 208p. 1979. 23.50 (ISBN 0-669-00431-6). Lexington Bks.

Bronzino, Joseph D. Computer Applications for Patient Care. 1982. o. p. 24.95 (ISBN 0-201-10156-4, 10156, Pub. by Med-Nurse); pap. 21.95 (ISBN 0-201-10157-2, Pub. by Med-Nurse). Addison-Wesley.

Brown, Montague & McCool, Barbara P. Multihospital Systems: Strategies for Organization & Management. LC 79-23439. 564p. 1980. text ed. 52.00 (ISBN 0-89443-169-2). Aspen Systems.

Caceres, C. A., ed. Clinical Electrocardiography & Computers: A Symposium Vol. 1970. 80.50 (ISBN 0-12-153840-0). Acad Pr.

Cady. Computer Techniques in Cardiology. (Biomedical Engineering & Instrumentation Ser.: Vol. 4). 1979. 75.00 (ISBN 0-8247-6743-8). Dekker.

CAI Network Evaluation Criteria & Methodology (Seattle, Wash. Nov., 1973) 2nd. ed. 76p. 1976. 6.00 (ISBN 0-917054-10-5). Med Communications.

Caille, J. M. & Salomon, G., eds. Computerized Tomography: Proceedings. (Illus.). 310p. 1980. pap. 54.00 (ISBN 0-387-09808-9). Springer Verlag.

Cardus, D. & Vallbona, C., eds. Computers & Mathematical Models in Medicine: Proceedings. (Lecture Notes in Medical Information Ser.: Vol. 9). 315p. 1981. pap. 28.50 (ISBN 0-387-10278-7). Springer-Verlag.

Carpenter, B. Stephen, ed. Computers in Activation Analysis & Gamma-Ray Spectroscopy: Proceedings. LC 79-19600. (DOE Symposium Ser.). 904p. 1979. pap. 30.50 (ISBN 0-87079-117-6, CONF-780421); microfiche 4.50 (ISBN 0-87079-169-9, CONF-780421). DOE.

Chorafas, Dimitris N. Computer in der Medizin. (IS-Informations-Systeme). (Illus.). 127p. 1973. 20.00x (ISBN 3-11-004031-X). De Gruyter.

Chynn, K. Y. & Finby, N. Manual of Cranial Computerized Tomography. (Illus.). vi, 106p. 1982. 84.25 (ISBN 3-8055-3432-9). S Karger.

Coblentz, A. M. & Walter, J. R., eds. Systems Science in Health Care. LC 77-21046. 1978. text ed. 35.00 (ISBN 0-89433-067-5). Petrocelli.

Computer Strategies. The Medical Office Computer Handbook. 150p. 1983. looseleaf 45.00x (ISBN 0-913505-14-5). Computer Strat.

Computers in Radiotherapy: 1968 2nd International Conference. 1980. 9.00x (ISBN 0-686-69946-7, Pub. by Brit Inst Radiology England). State Mutual Bk.

Computers in the Control of Treatment Units: Applications of Modern Technology in Radiotherapy. 1980. 10.00x (ISBN 0-686-69945-9, Pub. by Brit Inst Radiology England). State Mutual Bk.

Cornell, Joseph A. Computers in Hospital Pharmacy Management: Fundamentals & Applications. LC 82-24381. 228p. 1983. 32.00 (ISBN 0-89443-673-2). Aspen Systems.

Cronenberger, J. Helen, et al. The Apple II in the Clinical Laboratory. 225p. 1984. spiral bdg. 22.50 (ISBN 0-316-15748-1). Little.

Day, Stacey B. & Brandejs, Jan F., eds. Computers for Medical Office & Patient Management. 224p. 1982. 21.95 (ISBN 0-442-21316-6). Van Nos Reinhold.

Dean, J. Michael & Booth, Frank V. Microcomputer in Critical Care: A Practical Approach. 368p. 1985. 32.50 (ISBN 0-683-02401-9). Williams & Wilkins.

Deighton, S., ed. Microprocessor Applications in Science & Medicine, 1977-1978: Bibliography. 1979. 28.00 (ISBN 0-85296-448-X). Inst Elect Eng.

DuBoulay, G. H., ed. Considerations about the Use of Computers in Radiodiagnostic Departments. 1980. 50.00x (ISBN 0-686-69947-5, Pub. by Brit Inst Radiology England). State Mutual Bk.

Eden, Henry S. & Eden, Murray. Microcomputers in Patient Care. LC 81-1999. (Illus.). 191p. 1981. 28.00 (ISBN 0-8155-0849-2). Noyes.

Ell, P. J. & Holman, B. L., eds. Computed Emission Tomography. (Illus.). 1982. 85.00x (ISBN 0-19-261347-2). Oxford U Pr.

Ell, Peter J., et al. Atlas of Computerized Emission Tomography. (Illus.). 288p. 1980. text ed. 115.00x (ISBN 0-443-02228-3). Churchill.

Enlander, Derek. Computers in Medicine: An Introduction. 120p. 1984. 15.00. Med Software.

--Microcomputer Programs in Medicine, Vol. I. (Illus.). 116p. 1983. 80.00 (ISBN 0-88672-000-1). Med Software.

--Microcomputer Programs in Medicine, Vol. II. 105p. 1984. 80.00. Med Software.

Enlander, Derek, ed. Computers in Laboratory Medicine. 1975. 39.50 (ISBN 0-12-239950-1). Acad Pr.

Enslein, K., ed. Data Acquisition & Processing in Biology & Medicine: Proceedings. Incl. Vol. 3. Rochester Conference, 1963 (ISBN 0-08-010904-7); Vol. 4. Rochester Conference, 1964; Vol. 5. Rochester Conference, 1966 (ISBN 0-08-012671-5). Vols. 3 & 5. 40.00 ea. Pergamon.

Erlich, Ann. Role of Computers in Medical Practice Management. LC 81-69069. (Illus.). 8.95 (ISBN 0-940012-18-9). Colwell Syst.

Fell, Peter J. & Skees, William D. The Doctors' Computer Handbook. (Management Ser.). (Illus.). 290p. 1984. 27.50 (ISBN 0-534-02724-5). Lifetime Learn.

Furman, William B. Continuous Flow Analysis: Theory & Practice. (Clinical & Biochemical Analysis Ser.: Vol. 3). 1976. 59.75 (ISBN 0-8247-6320-3). Dekker.

Gabrieli, Elemer R., ed. Clinically Oriented Documentation of Laboratory Data. 1972. 65.00 (ISBN 0-12-271850-X). Acad Pr.

Garrett, James F., ed. Information Systems on Technical Aids for the Disabled. (International Exchange of Experts & Information in Rehabilitation Ser.: No. 17). 34p. 1982. write for info. (ISBN 0-939986-29-9). World Rehab Fund.

Ginsberg, Stephen P. Guide to an Effective Out-Patient Ophthalmic Surgery Center. LC 84-51524. 272p. 1985. 39.50 (ISBN 0-943432-33-2). Slack Inc.

Gonzales, Laurence. Computers for Doctors. 1984. pap. 6.95 (ISBN 0-345-31478-6). Ballantine.

Gonzalez, Carlos F., et al. Computed Brain & Orbital Tomography: Technique & Interpretation. LC 76-28530. (Diagnostic & Therapeutic Radiology Ser.). 276p. 1976. 70.00x (ISBN 0-471-01692-6, Pub. by Wiley-Med). Wiley.

Good, Phillip I. A Critical Guide to Software for the IBM PC & PC Compatible Computers: Computers for Professionals in Business, Agriculture, Law & Health. LC 83-17148. (Illus.). 284p. 1983. pap. 12.95 (ISBN 0-8019-7413-5). Chilton.

GP-Info Symposium, 13-15 March, 1980, London. Computers & the General Practitioner: Proceedings. Malcolm, A. & Poyser, J., eds. (Illus.). 142p. 1981. 22.00 (ISBN 0-08-026865-X). Pergamon.

Grams, Ralph Raymond. Problem Solving, Systems Analysis, & Medicine. (Illus.). 244p. 1972. Set. 31.00x (ISBN 0-398-02298-4); companion volume - Systems Analysis wkbk. incl. (ISBN 0-398-02566-5). C C Thomas.

Griesser, G. Data Protection in Health Information Systems: Considerations & Guidelines. 218p. 1980. 42.75 (ISBN 0-444-86052-5, North Holland). Elsevier.

Griesser, G., et al. Data Protection in Health Information Systems. 2nd ed. 1983. 42.75 (ISBN 0-444-86713-9, I-410-83). Elsevier.

Guy, W & Ban, T. A., eds. The AMDP - System: Manual for the Assessment & Documentation of Psychopathology. (Illus.). 130p. 1982. pap. 12.00 (ISBN 0-387-11252-9). Springer-Verlag.

Hand, D. J. Artificial Intelligence & Psychiatry. (Scientific Basis of Psychiatry: No. 1). 266p. 1985. 39.50 (ISBN 0-521-25871-5). Cambridge U Pr.

Harris, Kenneth W. & French, Dwight K. A Methodological Study of the Quality of Mortality Medical Coding. Cox, Klaudia, ed. (Series 2: No. 81). 1979. pap. text ed. 1.75 (ISBN 0-8406-0164-6). Natl Ctr Health Stats.

Harris, Thomas R. The Use of Computers in Perinatal Medicine. LC 82-7661. 416p. 1982. 49.95 (ISBN 0-03-061513-5). Praeger.

Hefferman, Pauline Y. Diagnosis & Computers: Medical Guidebook for Reference & Research. LC 84-45001. 150p. 1984. 29.95 (ISBN 0-88164-172-3); pap. 21.95 (ISBN 0-88164-173-1). ABBE Pubs Assn.

Hendee, William R. The Physical Principles of Computed Tomography. 1983. 35.00 (ISBN 0-316-35594-1). Little.

Herman, G. T. & Natterer, F., eds. Mathematical Aspects of Computerized Tomography: Proceedings. (Lecture Notes in Medical Information Ser.: Vol. 8). 309p. 1981. pap. 28.50 (ISBN 0-387-10277-9). Springer-Verlag.

Higgins, Charles B. & Carlsson, Erik, eds. C.T. of the Heart & Great Vessels: Experimental Evaluation & Clinical Application. LC 82-71767. (Illus.). 416p. 1982. 68.00 (ISBN 0-87993-180-9). Futura Pub.

Holman, B. Leonard & Parker, J. Anthony. Computer-Assisted Cardiac Nuclear Medicine. 546p. 1981. text ed. 55.00 (ISBN 0-316-37054-1). Little.

Hunter, Tim B. The Computer in Radiology. 1985. price not set (ISBN 0-87189-235-9). Aspen Systems.

IFPtC4 Working Conference, Amsterdam, 1976. Trends in Computer-Processed Electrocardiograms: Proceedings. Van Bemmel, J. H. & Willems, J. L., eds. LC 77-1801. 438p. 1977. 61.75 (ISBN 0-7204-0723-0, North-Holland). Elsevier.

International Titisee Conference, Titisee, October 19-21, 1978. Biomedical Engineering & Data Processing in Pneumonology. Matthys, H., ed. (Progress in Respiration Research: Vol. 11). (Illus.). 1979. 49.50 (ISBN 3-8055-3012-9). S Karger.

Jacquez, John A. Computer Diagnosis & Diagnostic Methods: The Proceedings of the Second Conference on the Diagnostic Process, University of Michigan. (Illus.). 400p. 1972. 29.75x (ISBN 0-398-02521-5). C C Thomas.

Jeanmart, L., et al. Atlas of Pathological Computer Tomography: Computer Tomography of Neck, Chest, Spine, & Limbs, Vol. 3. (Illus.). 210p. 1983. 105.00 (ISBN 0-387-11439-4). Springer-Verlag.

Johannides, David F. Cost Containment Through Systems Engineering: A Guide for Hospitals. LC 79-15217. 326p. 1979. text ed. 39.75 (ISBN 0-89443-098-X). Aspen Systems.

Karanja, Linda, ed. Computers in Clinical & Biomedical Engineering. (Illus.). 120p. 1983. pap. 12.00x (ISBN 0-930844-10-6). Quest Pub.

Kazner, E., et al, eds. Computed Tomography in Intracranial Tumors: Differential Diagnosis & Clinical Aspects. Dougherty, F. C., tr. from Ger. (Illus.). 548p. 1982. 198.00 (ISBN 0-387-10815-7). Springer-Verlag.

Kember, N. F. Introduction to Computer Applications in Medicine. 176p. 1982. pap. text ed. 17.95 (ISBN 0-7131-4414-9). E Arnold.

King, Jane. Searching Internal Database: A Comparative Evaluation of their Performance in Toxicology. 1982. 70.00 (ISBN 0-905984-80-3, Brit Lib England). State Mutual Bk.

Kostrewski, B. J., ed. Current Perspectives in Health Computing. (British Computer Society Workshop Ser.). 250p. 1984. 34.50 (ISBN 0-521-26705-6). Cambridge U Pr.

Koza, Russell C., et al, eds. Health Information Systems Evaluation. LC 74-75391. (Illus.). 352p. 1974. text ed. 19.50x (ISBN 0-87081-060-X). Colo Assoc.

Kreel, L. Computer Tomography with the General Purpose Scanner. 2nd ed. 1977. incl. 240 slides 532.00 (ISBN 9-0219-3043-9, Excerpta Medica). Elsevier.

--Computerized Tomography. 2nd ed. (incl. 400 slides). 1978. pap. 532.00 (ISBN 0-444-90053-5). Elsevier.

Kronman, B. J. Analysis of a Clinical Laboratory Information System. 103p. 1975. 25.75 (LB26). Am Hospital.

Lanksch, W., et al. Computed Tomography in Head Injuries. Dougherty, F. C., tr. from Ger. (Illus.). 1979. 51.00 (ISBN 0-387-09634-5). Springer-Verlag.

Laudet, M. & Anderson, J., eds. Medical Data Processing. 776p. 1976. cancelled (ISBN 0-85066-106-4). Taylor & Francis.

Leonard, Peggy C. Building a Medical Vocabulary: A Microcomputer Course. 32p. 1984. Apple Version. 795.00 (ISBN 0-7216-1379-9); IBM-PC Version. 795.00 (ISBN 0-7216-1385-3). Saunders.

--Building a Medical Vocabulary: A Microcomputer Course & a Microcomputer Review Course. 64p. 1984. Apple Version. 995.00 (ISBN 0-7216-1383-7); IBM-PC Version. 995.00 (ISBN 0-7216-1389-6). Saunders.

--Building a Medical Vocabulary: A Microcomputer Review Course. 32p. 1984. Apple Version. 295.00 (ISBN 0-7216-1381-0); IBM-PC Version. 295.00 (ISBN 0-7216-1387-X). Saunders.

Lewis, R., ed. Computers in the Life Sciences: Applications in Research & Education. 123p. 1979. 25.00x (ISBN 0-85664-863-9, Pub. by Croom Helm Ltd). Longwood Pub Group.

Lindberg, Donald A. The Computer & Medical Care. (Illus.). 224p. 1971. 22.50x (ISBN 0-398-01131-1). C C Thomas.

Ludwig, Herbert. Computer Applications & Techniques in Clinical Medicine. LC 73-20100. (Wiley Biomedical-Health Publication Ser.). pap. 82.50 (ISBN 0-317-09245-6, 2007144). Bks Demand UMI.

McClung, Christina J. & Guerrieri, John A. Microcomputers for Medical Professionals. LC 83-5774. 157p. 1984. pap. 14.95 (ISBN 0-471-89724-8, Pub by Wiley Pr). Wiley.

Macfarlene, Peter W. Computer Techniques in Clinical Medicine. (Illus.). 272p. 1985. pap. text ed. 83.95 (ISBN 0-407-00250-2). Butterworth.

McIntosh, J. A. & McIntosh, R. P. Mathematical Modelling & Computers in Endocrinology. (Monographs on Endocrinology: Vol. 16). (Illus.). 370p. 1980. 54.00 (ISBN 0-387-09693-0). Springer-Verlag.

Mancuso, Anthony. Computed Tomography of the Head & Neck. (Illus.). 292p. 1982. lib. bdg. 60.00 (ISBN 0-683-05475-9). Williams & Wilkins.

Marg, Elwyn. Computer-Assisted Eye Examination. (Illus.). 1980. 10.00 (ISBN 0-317-17152-6). San Francisco Pr.

Marshall, Christopher. Physical Basis of Computerized Tomography. 171p. 1982. 37.50 (ISBN 0-87527-314-9). Green.

Meares, C. L. & Ingemar, C. F. Information Systems on Technical Aids for the Disabled. write for info. World Rehab.

Medical Office Software Guide. 268p. 1984. 19.95 (ISBN 0-317-04401-X). Micro Info.

Miller, Perry L. A Critiquing Approach to Expert Computer Advice. (Research Notes in Artificial Intelligence Ser.: No. 1). 128p. 1985. pap. text ed. 19.50 (ISBN 0-273-08665-0). Pitman Pub MA.

Mistretta, Charles, et al. Digital Subtraction Arteriography: An Application of Computerized Fluoroscopy. (Illus.). 164p. 1981. 43.50 (ISBN 0-8151-5915-3). Year Bk Med.

Moss, Albert & Goldberg, Henry, eds. Computed Tomography, Ultrasound & X-Ray: An Integrated Approach. LC 76-1666. 1980. 85.00 (ISBN 0-12-788525-0). Acad Pr.

Naidich, David P., et al. Computed Tomography of the Thorax. (Illus.). 336p. 1984. text ed. 79.00 (ISBN 0-89004-982-3). Raven.

Nair, Sreedhar, ed. Computers in Critical Care & Pulmonary Medicine, Vol. 1. LC 80-14503. 437p. 1980. 55.00x (ISBN 0-306-40449-4, Plenum Pr). Plenum Pub.

Neal, Patricia A. Management Information Systems for the Fee-for-Service-Prepaid Medical Group. (Going Prepaid Ser.). 143p. (Orig.). 1983. pap. 16.00 (ISBN 0-933948-76-X). Ctr Res Ambulatory.

Neiderhaus, Lee B. Computer-Assisted Diagnosis & Medical Services: Subject Analysis with Bibliography. LC 83-45292. 168p. 1984. 29.95 (ISBN 0-88164-072-7); pap. 21.95 (ISBN 0-88164-073-5). ABBE Pubs Assn.

Onoe, Morio, et al, eds. Real-Time Medical Image Processing. LC 80-23779. 257p. 1980. 45.00x (ISBN 0-306-40551-2, Plenum Pr). Plenum Pub.

Osswald, P. M., ed. Computers in Critical Care & Pulmonary Medicine. (Illus.). 335p. 1985. pap. 34.50 (ISBN 0-387-13840-4). Springer-Verlag.

Park, W. M. & Reece, B. L. Fundamental Aspects of Medical Thermography. 1980. 20.00x (ISBN 0-686-69949-1, Pub. by Brit Inst Radiology England). State Mutual Bk.

People's Computer Company. Dr. Dobb's Journal, Vol. 6. 576p. pap. 29.95. Hayden.

--Dr. Dobb's Journal of Computer Calisthenics & Orthodontia: Running Light Without Overbyte, 5 vols. Volume 1, 368 pp. pap. 25.95 each vol. (ISBN 0-8104-5475-0, 5475). Volume 2, 480 (ISBN 0-8104-5484-X, 5484). Volume 3, 480 pp (ISBN 0-8104-5490-4, 5490). Volume 4, 480 pp (5491). Volume 5, 464 pp (5492). Hayden.

Perry, Ian R. Real-Time Clinical Computing. LC 83-19267. (Medical Computing Ser.: 1-511). 131p. 1984. 39.95x (ISBN 0-471-90366-3, Res Stud Pr). Wiley.

Peyster, Robert G. & Hoover, Eric. Computerized Tomography in Orbital Disease & Neuro-Ophthalmology. (Illus.). 176p. 1984. 89.95 (ISBN 0-8151-6672-9). Year Bk Med.

Pinciroli, F. & Anderson, J., eds. Changes in Health Care Instrumentation Due to Microprocessor Technology: Proceedings. 326p. 1981. 47.00 (ISBN 0-444-86138-6, North-Holland). Elsevier.

Prakash, Omar, et al, eds. Computers in Critical Care & Pulmonary Medicine, Vol. 2. 259p. 1982. 42.50x (ISBN 0-306-40911-9, Plenum Pr). Plenum Pub.

Pressman, Robert M. Microcomputers & the Private Practitioner. LC 83-73717. (Dorsey Professional Bks.). 276p. 1984. 27.50 (ISBN 0-256-31500-0). Dorsey.

Pretschner, D. P. Personal Computing in Nuclear Medicine. (Lecture Notes in Medical Informatics: Vol. 18). 133p. 1982. pap. 13.50 (ISBN 0-387-11598-6). Springer-Verlag.

Pryor, T. Allan & Bailey, James J., eds. Computerized Interpretation of the IV. 395p. (Orig.). 1980. pap. text ed. 10.00x (ISBN 0-939204-05-3, 79-01). Eng Found.

Pryor, T. Allan, et al. Computer Systems for the Processing of Diagnostic Electrocardiograms. (Tutorial Texts Ser.). 227p. 1980. 25.00 (ISBN 0-8186-0325-9, Q325). IEEE Comp Soc.

Quetglas, G. Martin, et al. Applications of Computers in Cardiology: State of the Art & New Perspectives. 1984. 61.75 (ISBN 0-444-86824-0, I-029-84). Elsevier.

Radin, Stephen & Greenberg, Harold. Computers in the Doctor's Office. LC 84-8378. 160p. 1984. 21.95x (ISBN 0-03-069724-7). Praeger.

Randall, J. E. The Use of Microcomputers for Physiological Simulation. 1980. pap. 31.95 (ISBN 0-201-06128-7). Addison-Wesley.

Raviv, J., et al, eds. Computer Aided Tomography & Ultrasonics in Medicine. 320p. 1979. 47.00 (ISBN 0-444-85299-9, North Holland). Elsevier.

Reggia, J. A. & Tuhrim, S., eds. Computer-Assisted Medical Decision Making I. (Computers & Medicine Ser.). (Illus.). 275p. 1985. 26.50 (ISBN 0-387-96104-6). Springer-Verlag.

Reichert, Kurt L. Automation & Autoanalysis in Medicine: Research & Reference Guidebook. LC 83-45002. 150p. 1985. 29.95 (ISBN 0-88164-180-4); soft cover 21.95 (ISBN 0-88164-181-2). ABBE Pubs Assn.

Remond, A., ed. EEG Informatics: A Didactic Review of Methods & Applications of EEG Data Processing. 426p. 1977. 62.75 (ISBN 0-444-80005-0, Biomedical Pr). Elsevier.

Rienhoff, O. & Abrams, M. E., eds. Computer in the Doctor's Office. 352p. 1980. 51.00 (ISBN 0-444-86051-7, North-Holland). Elsevier.

Ripley, Kenneth L. & Murray, Alan. Introduction to Automated Arrythmia Detection. (Tutorial Texts Ser.). 335p. 1980. 25.00 (ISBN 0-8186-0338-0, Q338). IEEE Comp Soc.

Ritchie, Robert F., ed. Automated Immunoanalysis, 2 pts. (Clinical Chemistry & Biochemical Analysis Ser.: Vol. 7). (Illus.). 656p. 1978. Pt. I. 59.75 (ISBN 0-8247-6678-4); Pt. II. 59.75 (ISBN 0-8247-6679-2). Dekker.

Rodbard, David & Forti, Gianni, eds. Computers in Endocrinology. (Serono Symposia Publications: Vol. 14). 362p. 1984. text ed. 49.50 (ISBN 0-89004-368-X). Raven.

Role of Computers in Radiotherapy. (Panel Proceedings Ser.). (Illus.). 211p. 1968. pap. 13.00 (ISBN 92-0-111668-3, ISP203, IAEA). Unipub.

Rozen, P. & De Dombal, F. T., eds. Computer Aid in Gastroenterology. (Frontiers of Gastrointestinal Research: Vol. 7). (Illus.). viii, 196p. 1984. 35.00 (ISBN 3-8055-3770-0). S Karger.

Salamon, G. & Huang, Y. P. Computed Tomography of the Brain Atlas of Normal Anatomy. (Illus.). 160p. 1980. 129.00 (ISBN 0-387-08825-3). Springer-Verlag.

Sanders, Donald R. Computer Essentials for the Ophthalmologist. LC 84-51441. 160p. 1985. 29.50 (ISBN 0-943432-32-4). Slack Inc.

Schmitz, Homer. Hospital Information Systems. LC 79-15421. 188p. 1979. 34.00 (ISBN 0-89443-156-0). Aspen Systems.

Schneider, W. & Sagvall Hein, A. L., eds. Computational Linguistics in Medicine: Proceedings of the IFIP Working Conference on Computational Linguistics in Medicine. 182p. 1978. 47.00 (ISBN 0-444-85040-6, North-Holland). Elsevier.

Scholes, M., et al, eds. The Impact of Computers on Nursing: An International Review; Proceedings of the IFIP-IMIA Workshop on the Impact of Computers on Nursing, Church House, Westminster, London, 8-9 Sept., 1982, & Harrogate, England, 10-15 Sept., 1982. 590p. 1983. 60.00 (ISBN 0-444-86682-5, I-241-83, North Holland). Elsevier.

Schwartz, H. & Sondak, V. Computers & Medicine. LC 79-18948. 1979. pap. 20.00x (ISBN 0-89006-076-2). Artech Hse.

Schwartz, Marc D., ed. Using Computers in Clinical Practice: Psychotherapy & Mental Health Applications. LC 83-18648. 510p. 1984. text ed. 34.95 (ISBN 0-86656-208-7, B208). Haworth Pr.

Sellars, Dot. Computerizing Your Medical Office: A Guide for Physicians & Their Staffs. 228p. 1983. pap. 18.95 (ISBN 0-87489-305-4). Med Economics.

Shaffer, Dale E. Library Resources for Nurses: A Basic Collection for Supporting the Nursing Curriculum. 45p. 1973. pap. 3.00 (ISBN 0-915060-06-X). D E Shaffer.

Shires, David B. Computer Technology in the Health Sciences. (Illus.). 160p. 1974. 17.75x (ISBN 0-398-03005-7). C C Thomas.

Shortliffe, Edward. Computer Based Medical Consultations: Mycin. (Artificial Intelligence Ser.: Vol. 2). 264p. 1976. 33.50 (ISBN 0-444-00179-4, North-Holland). Elsevier.

Sidowski, J., et al, eds. Technology in Mental Health Care Delivery Systems. LC 79-21126. (Illus.). 1980. 35.00 (ISBN 0-89391-023-6). Ablex Pub.

Slavin, Simon, ed. Applying Computers in Social Service & Mental Health Agencies. LC 81-20102. (Administration in Social Work Ser.: Vol. 5, Nos. 3 & 4). 184p. 1982. text ed. 30.00 (ISBN 0-86656-102-1, B102). Haworth Pr.

Speck, Pat K. Medical Management System Report Generator Programmer's Manual. Lozano, Alva, ed. (Illus.). 450p. 1980. text ed. 100.00 (ISBN 0-912217-08-1); pap. 90.00 (ISBN 0-317-12067-0). Afton Oaks.

--Medical Management System's Programmer's Manual. Dossman, Sterly, ed. (Illus.). 1979. text ed. 100.00 (ISBN 0-912217-04-9); pap. 90.00 (ISBN 0-912217-05-7). Afton Oaks.

Stacy, Ralph W. & Waxman, Bruce. Computers in Biomedical Research, 4 vols. 1965-1964. Vol. 1. 80.50 (ISBN 0-12-662301-5); Vol. 2. 73.50 (ISBN 0-12-662302-3); Vol. 3. 73.50 (ISBN 0-12-662303-1); Vol. 4. 1974. 68.50 (ISBN 0-12-662304-X). Acad Pr.

Sterling, Theodor D. & Pollack, Seymour V. Computers & the Life Sciences. LC 65-27765. (Illus.). 362p. 1965. 47.50x (ISBN 0-231-02744-3). Columbia U Pr.

Stroke, George W., et al, eds. Ultrasonic Imaging & Holography: Medical, Sonar, & Optical Applications. LC 74-1371. 642p. 1974. 89.50x (ISBN 0-306-30762-6, Plenum Pr). Plenum Pub.

Tolan, Gil D. & Pryor, T. Allan, eds. Computerized Interpretation of the ECG V. 234p. (Orig.). 1980. pap. 15.00x (ISBN 0-939204-06-1, 80-13). Eng Found.

Tompkins, W. & Webster, J., eds. Design of Microcomputer-Based Medical Instrumentation. 1981. 39.95 (ISBN 0-13-201244-8). P-H.

The Use of Computers in Therapeutic Radiology: International Conference, 1966. 1980. 16.00x (ISBN 0-686-69961-0, Pub. by Brit Inst Radiology). State Mutual Bk.

Valancy, Jack. Microcomputers & Your Practice: A Guide for Physicians. LC 84-62731. (Illus.). 300p. (Orig.). 1984. pap. 17.95 (ISBN 0-931028-58-2). Pluribus Pr.

Valk, J. Computed Tomography & Cerebral Infarctions. 190p. 1980. 42.50 (ISBN 0-89004-646-8). Raven.

Wackenheim, A., et al. Atlas of Pathological Computer Tomography, Vol. 1: Cranio-Cerebral Computed Tomography. (Illus.). 150p. 1980. Set. 130.00 (ISBN 0-387-09879-8). Springer-Verlag.

Walsh, Sean. The Computer's Catalytic Role in Linking Physicians & Health Administrators in Providing Quality Assessment & Quality Assurance Programs. 49p. 1980. 2.30 (ISBN 0-318-15087-5, 147). Natl Assn Comm Health Ctrs.

Warner, Homer R. Computer-Assisted Medical Decision-Making. LC 79-52788. 1979. 33.50 (ISBN 0-12-735750-5). Acad Pr.

Waters, Kathleen & Murphy, Gretchen. Systems Analysis & Computer Applications in Health Information Management. LC 82-18468. 449p. 1982. 36.95 (ISBN 0-89443-838-7). Aspen Systems.

Wegener, O. H. Whole Body Computerized Tomography. (Illus.). 396p. 1983. 35.00 (ISBN 3-8055-2773-X). S Karger.

Werley, Harriet H. & Grier, Margaret R. Nursing Information Systems. 1981. text ed. 27.50 (ISBN 0-8261-2520-4). Springer Pub.

Wiederhold, G. Databases for Health Care. (Lecture Notes in Medical Informatics: Vol. 12). 75p. 1981. pap. 11.40 (ISBN 0-387-10709-6). Springer-Verlag.

Williams. Computer-Readable Databases, a Directory & Data Source Book: Science, Technology & Medicine. 4th ed. Date not set. write for info. (ISBN 0-444-87613-8). Elsevier.

Williams, Ben T., ed. Computer Aids to Clinical Decisions, 2 Vols. 1982. Vol. I, 168p. 63.00 (ISBN 0-8493-5575-3); Vol. II, 216p. 69.00 (ISBN 0-8493-5576-1). CRC Pr.

Wingert, F. Medical Informatics: An Introduction. (Lecture Notes in Medical Informatics Ser.: Vol. 14). 247p. 1981. text ed. 21.00 (ISBN 0-387-10870-X). Springer-Verlag.

Wolf, Paul & Enlander, Derek. Microcomputer Interpretation of Clinical Lab Results. 90p. 1984. 30.00. Med Software.

Wood, Raymond G. Computers in Radiotherapy. (Medical Computing Ser.). 171p. 1981. 64.95x (ISBN 0-471-09994-5, Pub. by Res Stud Pr). Wiley.

Worthley, John A. Managing Computers in Health Care: A Guide for Professionals. LC 82-13851. 264p. 1982. pap. text ed. 22.50x (ISBN 0-914904-80-9, 00856). Health Admin Pr.

Yamaguchi, N. & Fujisawa, K., eds. Recent Advances in EEG & EMG Data Processing. 422p. 1981. 68.00 (ISBN 0-444-80356-4, Biomedical Pr). Elsevier.

Zielstorff, Rita D., ed. Computers in Nursing. LC 80-80813. 236p. 1980. Repr. 28.50 (ISBN 0-913654-66-3). Aspen Systems.

Zimmerman, Joan & Rector, Alan. Computers for the Physician's Office, Vol. 2. LC 78-59664. (Medical Computing Ser.). 305p. 1978. 69.95 (ISBN 0-471-27888-2, Research Studies Pr). Wiley.

MEDICINE–MATHEMATICAL MODELS

Ackerman, Eugene & Gatewood, Lael C. Mathematical Models in the Health Sciences: A Computer-Aided Approach. 1979. 25.00x (ISBN 0-8166-0864-4). U of Minn Pr.

Banks, H. T. Modelling & Control in the Biomedical Sciences. LC 75-25771. (Lecture Notes in Biomathematics: Vol. 6). v, 114p. 1975. pap. 13.00 (ISBN 0-387-07395-7). Springer-Verlag.

Bellman, Richard. Mathematical Methods in Medicine. (Series in Modern Applied Mathematics: Vol. 1). xvi, 252p. 1983. 33.00x (ISBN 9971-950-20-0, Pub. by World Sci Singapore); pap. 19.00x (ISBN 9971-950-45-6, Pub. by World Sci Singapore). Taylor & Francis.

Beneken, J. E. & Lavelle, S. M., eds. Objective Medical Decision Making: Systems Approach in Acute Disease. (Lecture Notes in Medical Informatics: Vol. 22). 243p. 1983. pap. 20.00 (ISBN 0-387-12671-6). Springer-Verlag.

Berger, J., et al, eds. Mathematical Models in Medicine. (Lecture Notes in Biomathematics: Vol. 11). 1976. pap. 19.00 (ISBN 0-387-07802-9). Springer-Verlag.

Gurland, John. Stochastic Models in Medicine & Biology: Proceedings of a Symposium Conducted by the Mathematics Research Center, 1963. LC 64-14509. (U. S. Army Mathematics Research Center Ser.: No. 10). pap. 102.50 (ISBN 0-317-12991-0, 2021134). Bks Demand UMI.

Iosifescu, M. & Tautu, P. Stochastic Processes & Application in Biology & Medicine, Pt. 1: Theory. LC 73-77733. (Biomathematics, Ser.: Vol. 3). 331p. 1973. 42.00 (ISBN 0-387-06270-X). Springer-Verlag.

McIntosh, J. A. & McIntosh, R. P. Mathematical Modelling & Computers in Endocrinology. (Monographs on Endocrinology: Vol. 16). (Illus.). 370p. 1980. 54.00 (ISBN 0-387-09693-0). Springer-Verlag.

Marchuk, G. I. & Belykh, L. N., eds. Mathematical Modeling in Immunology & Medicine. 396p. 1983. 51.00 (ISBN 0-444-86588-8, I-36-83, North-Holland). Elsevier.

Shipley, Reginald A. & Clark, Richard E. Tracer Methods for in Vitro Kinetics: Theory & Applications. 1972. 45.00 (ISBN 0-12-640250-7). Acad Pr.

MEDICINE–MATHEMATICS

Bailey, Norman T. Mathematics, Statistics & Systems for Health. LC 77-1307. (Wiley Series Probability & Mathematical Statistics: Applied Probability & Statistics). 222p. 1977. 48.95x (ISBN 0-471-99500-2, Pub. by Wiley-Interscience). Wiley.

Eisenfeld, J. & Delisi, C., eds. Mathematics & Computers in Biomedical Applications. 390p. 1985. 40.00 (ISBN 0-444-87678-2). Elsevier.

Glantz, Stanton A. Mathematics for Biomedical Applications. LC 77-20320. 1979. 24.50x (ISBN 0-520-03599-2). U of Cal Pr.

Hoppensteadt, Frank C., ed. Mathematical Aspects of Physiology. LC 81-1315. (Lectures in Applied Mathematics Ser.: No. 19). 394p. 1981. 44.00 (ISBN 0-8218-1119-3, LAM-19). Am Math.

Ingram, D. & Bloch, R. F. Mathematical Methods in Medicine: Applications in Clinical Specialties, Pt. 2. 44.95 (ISBN 0-471-90046-X). Wiley.

--Mathematical Methods in Medicine: Statistical & Analytical Techniques, Part 1. LC 83-17044. (Handbook of Applicable Mathematics: 1-475). 453p. 1984. text ed. 49.95 (ISBN 0-471-90045-1, Wiley-Interscience). Wiley.

Jackson, Herbert L. Mathematics of Radiology & Nuclear Medicine. LC 70-107201. (Illus.). 180p. 1971. 12.00 (ISBN 0-87527-019-0). Green.

Ludwig, D. & Cooke, K. L., eds. Epidemiology. LC 75-22944. (SIAM-SIMS Conference Ser.: No. 2). ix, 164p. 1975. pap. text ed. 20.50 (ISBN 0-89871-031-6). Soc Indus-Appl Math.

Pretschner, D. P. Personal Computing in Nuclear Medicine. (Lecture Notes in Medical Informatics: Vol. 18). 133p. 1982. pap. 13.50 (ISBN 0-387-11598-6). Springer-Verlag.

Roach, G. F., ed. Mathematics in Medicine & Biomechanics. 236p. 1984. 29.95 (ISBN 0-906812-41-0); pap. 15.95 (ISBN 0-906812-40-2). Birkhauser.

Roberts, Keith & Michels, Leo. Mathematics for Health Sciences. LC 81-12234. (Mathematics Ser.). 442p. 1982. pap. 17.00 pub net (ISBN 0-8185-0478-1). Brooks-Cole.

Sacco, W. J. & Champion, H. R. Mathematics in Medicine. (Cyometrics Math Enrichment Ser.). 24p. (Orig.). 1981. pap. text ed. 3.00 (ISBN 0-686-36285-3). Cyometrics.

Twizell, E. H. Computational Methods for Partial Differential Equations for Biomedicine. (Mathematics & Its Applications Ser.: I-176). 180p. 1985. 57.95x (ISBN 0-470-27511-1). Halsted Pr.

MEDUSAE

Shih, C. T. A Guide to the Jellyfish of Canadian Atlantic Waters. (Illus.). 1977. pap. text ed. 5.50x (ISBN 0-660-00017-2, 56366-9, Pub. by Natl Mus Canada). U of Chicago Pr.

MEIOSIS

Anderson, Everett, et al. The Meiotic Process, I: Pairing, Recombination & Chromosome Movements. LC 72-6123. (Illus.). 189p. 1972. 29.50x (ISBN 0-8422-7019-1). Irvington.

Callebaut, M., et al. Meiosis: Current Research, 4 vols, Vol. 4. LC 72-6751. 244p. 1972. text ed. 24.50x (ISBN 0-8422-7041-8). Irvington.

John, Bernard & Lewis, Kenneth. The Meiotic Mechanism. Head, J. J., ed. LC 76-29381. (Carolina Biology Readers Ser.). (Illus.). 32p. 1984. pap. 2.00 (ISBN 0-89278-265-X, 45-9665). Carolina Biological.

Melnyk, P. L., et al. Meiosis: Current Research, 4 vols, Vol. 3. 1972. 24.50x (ISBN 0-8422-7036-1). Irvington.

Stack, Stephen M. & Lamb, B. C. The Meiotic Process, II: Pairing, Recombination, & Chromosome Movement. LC 72-6123. 208p. 1972. text ed. 29.50x (ISBN 0-8422-7031-0). Irvington.

Sybenga, J. Meiotic-Configurations. LC 75-17562. (Monographs on Theoretical & Applied Genetics: Vol. 1). (Illus.). 270p. 1975. 42.00 (ISBN 0-387-07347-7). Springer-Verlag.

MELANOPHORES

see Chromatophores

MELIOLA

Stevens, Frank L. The Genus Meliola in Porto Rico. (University of Illinois Biological Monographs: Vol. 2, No. 4). pap. 8.00 (ISBN 0-384-58110-2). Johnson Repr.

MELTING POINTS

see also Solidification

Atherton, M. P. & Gribble, C. D., eds. Migmatites, Melting & Metamorphism. 200p. 1982. 60.00x (ISBN 0-906812-26-7, Pub. by Shiva Pub England); pap. 40.00x (ISBN 0-906812-25-9). State Mutual Bk.

Pincus, Alexis G. Melting Furnace Design in the Glass Industry. LC 78-55352. (Processing in the Glass Industry Ser.). 269p. 1980. 24.95 (ISBN 0-911993-08-8). Ashlee Pub Co.

--Melting Furnace Operation in the Glass Industry. LC 77-55374. (Processing in the Glass Industry Ser.). 250p. 1980. 24.95 (ISBN 0-911993-10-X). Ashlee Pub Co.

--The Melting Process in the Glass Industry. LC 78-55368. (Processing in the Glass Industry Ser.). 257p. 1980. 24.95 (ISBN 0-911993-19-3). Ashlee Pub Co.

MEMBRANES (BIOLOGY)

see also Plasma Membranes

Abrahamsson, Sixten & Pascher, Irmin, eds. Structure of Biological Membranes. LC 76-54955. (Nobel Foundation Symposium Ser.). (Illus.). 591p. 1977. 69.50x (ISBN 0-306-33704-5, Plenum Pr). Plenum Pub.

Agin, Daniel, ed. Perspectives in Membrane Biophysics: A Tribute to Kenneth S. Cole. 324p. 1972. 69.50 (ISBN 0-677-15210-8). Gordon.

Akoyunoglou, George, ed. PhotoPhysical Process Membrane Energization, Vol. 1. 792p. 75.00 (ISBN 0-86689-006-8, 992200032). Balaban Intl Sci Serv.

--Structure & Molecular Organization of the Photosynthetic Membrane, Vol. 3. 1112p. 109.00 (ISBN 0-86689-008-4, 992200040). Balaban Intl Sci Serv.

Aloia, Roland. Membrane Fluidity in Biology, Vol. 2: General Principles. LC 82-11535. 336p. 1983. 43.00 (ISBN 0-12-053002-3). Acad Pr.

Aloia, Roland C., ed. Membrane Fluidity in Biology: Concepts of Membrane Structure, Vol. 1. 1982. 45.00 (ISBN 0-12-053001-5). Acad Pr.

Aloia, Roland C. & Boggs, Joan M., eds. Membrane Fluidity in Biology: Cellular Aspects & Disease Processes, Vol. 3. 1985. 64.50 (ISBN 0-12-053003-1). Acad Pr.

--Membrane Fluidity in Biology: Cellular Activities, Vol. 4. Date not set. price not set (ISBN 0-12-053004-X). Acad Pr.

Andreoli, Thomas E., et al, eds. Physiology of Membrane Disorders. LC 78-4071. (Illus.). 1148p. 1978. 85.00x (ISBN 0-306-31054-6, Plenum Med. Bk.). Plenum Pub.

--Membrane Physiology. 482p. 1980. pap. text ed. 19.95x (ISBN 0-306-40432-X, Plenum Pr). Plenum Pub.

Avery, J., ed. Membrane Structure & Mechanisms of Biological Energy Transduction. LC 72-95064. 608p. 1974. 57.50x (ISBN 0-306-30718-9, Plenum Pr). Plenum Pub.

Azzi, A. & Zahler, P., eds. Enzymes, Receptors & Carriers of Biological Membranes: A Laboratory Manual. (Illus.). 135p. 1984. pap. 12.00 (ISBN 0-387-13751-3). Springer-Verlag.

Martonosi, Anthony, ed. The Enzymes of Biological Membranes, Vols. 1-4. Incl. Vol. 1. Physical & Chemical Techniques. 270p. 1976. 35.00x (ISBN 0-306-35031-9); Vol. 2. Biosynthesis of Cell Components. 671p. 1976. 65.00x (ISBN 0-306-35032-7); Vol. 3. Membrane Transport. 474p. 1976. 55.00x (ISBN 0-306-35033-5); Vol. 4. Electron Transport Systems & Receptors. 446p. 1976. 55.00x (ISBN 0-306-35034-3). (Illus., Plenum Pr). Plenum Pub.

Martonosi, Anthony N., ed. The Enzymes of Biological Membranes, Vol. 1: Membrane Structure & Dynamics. 2nd, rev. ed. 439p. 1984. 59.50x (ISBN 0-306-41451-1, Plenum Pr). Plenum Pub.

--Enzymes of Biological Membranes, Vol. 2: Biosynthesis & Metabolism. 440p. 1984. 59.50x (ISBN 0-306-41452-X, Plenum Pr). Plenum Pub.

--Enzymes of Biological Membranes, Vol. 3: Membrane Transport. 2nd. ed. 665p. 1984. 89.50x (ISBN 0-306-41453-8, Plenum Pr). Plenum Pub.

--Enzymes of Biological Membranes, Vol. 4: Bioenergetics of Electron & Proton Transport. 2nd ed. 557p. 1984. 79.50x (ISBN 0-306-41454-6, Plenum Pr). Plenum Pub.

--Membranes & Transport, Vol. 1. LC 82-3690. 722p. 1982. 85.00x (ISBN 0-306-40853-8, Plenum Pr); Set price with Vol. 2. 145.00. Plenum Pub.

--Membranes & Transport, Vol. 2. LC 82-3690. 712p. 1982. Set price with Vol. 1:145.00. 85.00x (ISBN 0-306-40854-6, Plenum Pr). Plenum Pub.

Methods in Membrane Biology, Vols. 1-10. Incl. Vol. 1. 292p. 1974. 35.00x (ISBN 0-306-36801-3); Vol. 2. 376p. 1974. 35.00x (ISBN 0-306-36802-1); Vol. 3. Plasma Membranes. 262p. 1975. 35.00x (ISBN 0-306-36803-X); Vol. 4. Biophysical Approaches. 317p. 1975. 35.00x (ISBN 0-306-36804-8); Vol. 5. Transport. 213p. 1975. 35.00x (ISBN 0-306-36805-6); Vol. 6. 265p. 1976. 35.00x (ISBN 0-306-36806-4); Vol. 7. 287p. 1976. 35.00x (ISBN 0-306-36807-2); Vol. 8. 387p. 1977. 39.50x (ISBN 0-306-36808-0); Vol. 9. 410p. 1978. 39.50x (ISBN 0-306-36809-9); Vol. 10. 241p. 1979. 35.00x (ISBN 0-306-40126-6). LC 73-81094 (Plenum Pr). Plenum Pub.

Miller, M. W., et al, eds. Membrane Toxicity. LC 77-1562. (Advances in Experimental Medicine & Biology Ser: Vol. 84). 567p. 1977. 69.50x (ISBN 0-306-39084-1, Plenum Pr). Plenum Pub.

Morris, G. J. & Clarke, A., eds. Effects of Low Temperature on Biological Membranes. LC 81-67921. 1982. 55.00 (ISBN 0-12-507650-9). Acad Pr.

Mukohata, Yusuo & Packer, Lester, eds. Cation Flux Across Biomembranes. 1979. pap. text ed. 60.00 (ISBN 0-12-511050-2). Acad Pr.

Mullins, L. J., compiled by. Annual Reviews Reprints. Incl. Cell Membranes, 1975-1977. Mullins, L. J., compiled by. LC 78-55105. (Illus.). 1978. pap. text ed. 12.00 (ISBN 0-8243-2501-X); Cell Membranes, 1978-1980. Mullins, L. J., compiled by. LC 81-65983. (Illus.). pap. text ed. 28.00 (ISBN 0-8243-2503-6). (Illus.). Annual Reviews.

Nowotny, Alois, ed. Pathological Membranes. (Biomembranes Ser.: Vol. 11). 494p. 1983. 55.00x (ISBN 0-306-41065-6, Plenum Pr). Plenum Pub.

Oxender, Dale & Blume, Arthur, eds. Membrane Transport & Neuroreceptors. LC 81-8151. (Progress in Clinical & Biological Research Ser.: Vol. 63). 470p. 1981. 75.00 (ISBN 0-8451-0063-7). A R Liss.

Oxender, Dale & Fox, C. Fred, eds. Molecular Aspects of Membrane Transport: Proceedings of the ICN-UCLA Symposium Held at Keystone, Col., Mar. 1977. LC 78-541. (Progress in Clinical & Biological Research: Vol. 22). 612p. 1978. 80.00 (ISBN 0-8451-0022-X). A R Liss.

Parsons, D. S., ed. Biological Membranes. (Illus.). 1975. text ed. 24.95x (ISBN 0-19-855469-9). Oxford U Pr.

Peeters, H., ed. Protides of the Biological Fluids, Proceedings of the 29th Colliquium on Protides of the Biological Fluids, Brussels, Belgium, May 1981. (Illus.). 993p. 1982. 165.00 (ISBN 0-08-027988-0, H220). Pergamon.

Pfeffer, Wilhelm. Osmotic Investigations. (Illus.). 304p. 1985. 32.50 (ISBN 0-442-27583-8). Van Nos Reinhold.

Podesta. Membrane Physiology of Invertebrates. 624p. 1982. 99.75 (ISBN 0-8247-1503-9). Dekker.

Porcellati, Giuseppe & Di Jeso, Fernando, eds. Membrane-Bound Enzymes. LC 70-151767. (Advances in Experimental Medicine & Biology Ser.: Vol. 14). 292p. 1971. 42.50x (ISBN 0-306-39014-0, Plenum Pr). Plenum Pub.

Poste, G. & Nicolson, G. L., eds. Membrane Fusion. (Cell Surface Reviews Ser.: Vol. 5). 862p. 1978. 182.00 (ISBN 0-444-00262-6, Biomedical Pr). Elsevier.

Prince, L. M. & Sears, D. F., eds. Biological Horizons in Surface Science. 1973. 81.00 (ISBN 0-12-565850-8). Acad Pr.

Reid, Eric, et al, eds. Investigation of Membrane-Located Receptors. (Methodological Surveys in Biochemistry & Analysis Ser.: Vol. 13). 542p. 1984. 75.00x (ISBN 0-306-41499-6, Plenum Pr). Plenum Pub.

Reisfeld, Ralph A., et al. Functional & Structural Nature of Biomembranes: II. LC 73-1290. (Illus.). 214p. 1973. text ed. 19.00x (ISBN 0-8422-7045-0). Irvington.

Robinson, David G. Plant Membranes: Endo- & Plasma Membranes. LC 84-7539. (Cell Biology: A Series of Monographs: Vol. 3). 1075p. 1985. 69.50x (ISBN 0-471-86210-X). Wiley.

Rothfield, Lawrence I., ed. Structure & Function of Biological Membranes. (Molecular Biology Ser.). 1971. 77.50 (ISBN 0-12-598650-5). Acad Pr.

Saier, M. H., Jr. & Stiles, C. D. Molecular Dynamics in Biological Membranes. LC 75-12923. (Heidelberg Science Library: Vol. 22). (Illus.). 95p. (Orig.). 1975. pap. 15.00 (ISBN 0-387-90142-6). Springer-Verlag.

Salanki, J., et al, eds. Physiology of Excitable Membranes: Proceedings of the 28th International Congress of Physiological Sciences, Budapest, 1980. LC 80-41853. (Advances in Physiological Sciences: Vol. 4). (Illus.). 350p. 1981. 44.00 (ISBN 0-08-026816-1). Pergamon.

Sanadi, D. Rao, ed. Chemical Mechanisms in Bioenergetics. LC 76-26707. (ACS Monograph: 172). 1976. 33.95 (ISBN 0-8412-0274-5). Am Chemical.

Sato, Ryo & Kagawa, Yasuo, eds. Transport & Bioenergetics in Biomembranes. 262p. 1982. 45.00x (ISBN 0-306-41282-9, Plenum Pr). Plenum Pub.

Sato, Ryo & Shun-Ichi Ohnishi, eds. Structure, Dynamics, & Biogenesis of Biomembranes. 188p. 1982. 39.50x (ISBN 0-306-41283-7, Plenum Pr). Plenum Pub.

Schaefer, G. & Klingenberg, M., eds. Energy Conservation in Biological Membranes: April 6-8, 1978, Mosbach, Germany. (Colloquium Mosbach Ser.: Vol. 29). (Illus.). 1978. 48.00 (ISBN 0-387-09079-7). Springer-Verlag.

Schultz, Stanley G. Principles of Membrane Transport. LC 79-54015. (IUPAB Biophysics Ser.: No. 2). (Illus.). 1980. 34.50 (ISBN 0-521-22992-8); pap. 12.95x (ISBN 0-521-29762-1). Cambridge U Pr.

Selegny, Eric. Charged & Reactive Polymers. Incl. Vol. 3. Charged Gels & Membranes, Pt. 1. lib. bdg. 63.00 (ISBN 90-277-0665-4); Vol. 4. Charged Gels & Membranes, Pt. 2. lib. bdg. 45.00 (ISBN 90-277-0666-2). LC 76-6086. 1976 (Pub. by Reidel Holland). Kluwer Academic.

Semenza, G. & Carafoli, E., eds. Biochemistry of Membrane Transport: FEBS Symposium Number 42. (Proceedings in Life Sciences). 1977. 61.00 (ISBN 0-387-08082-1). Springer-Verlag.

Sheppard, John R. & Anderson, V. Elving, eds. Membranes & Genetic Disease. LC 82-12672. (Progress in Clinical & Biological Research Ser.: Vol. 97). 422p. 1982. 68.00 (ISBN 0-8451-0097-1). A R Liss.

Shinitzky, M. Physiology of Membrane Fluidity, 2 vols, Vols. I-II. 1984. 208 72.00, (ISBN 0-8493-6141-9); 144 55.00, (ISBN 0-8493-6142-7). CRC Pr.

Silver, Brian L. The Physical Chemistry of Membranes: An Introduction to the Structure & Dynamics of Biological Membranes. (Illus.). 432p. 1985. text ed. 50.00x (ISBN 0-04-574028-3). Allen Unwin.

Sim, Edith. Membrane Biochemistry. (Outline Studies in Biology). 80p. 1982. pap. 7.50 (ISBN 0-412-23810-1, NO. 6691, Pub. by Chapman & Hall). Methuen Inc.

Smyth, D. H., ed. Biomembranes, 2 vols. Incl. Vol. 4A. Intestinal Absorption. 580p. 59.50 (ISBN 0-306-39891-5); Vol. 4B. Intestinal Absorption. LC 72-77043. 482p. 55.00 (ISBN 0-306-39892-3). LC 72-77043. 1974. (Plenum Pr). Plenum Pub.

Snell, F., et al, eds. Physical Principles of Biological Membranes. 442p. 1970. 70.75 (ISBN 0-677-13680-3). Gordon.

Snell, F. M. & Noell, W. K., eds. Transcellular Membrane Potentials & Ionic Fluxes. (Life Sciences Ser). 140p. 1964. 41.75x (ISBN 0-677-10520-7). Gordon.

Starzak, Michael E. The Physical Chemistry of Membranes (Monograph) LC 83-4628. 1984. 47.00 (ISBN 0-12-664580-9). Acad Pr.

Streicher, E. & Seyffart, G., eds. Highly Permeable Membranes. (Contributions to Nephrology: Vol. 46). (Illus.). viii, 188p. 1985. 46.00 (ISBN 3-8055-3994-0). S Karger.

Symposium Held at the University of Nebraska Medical School, Omaha, Nebr., May, 1972. The Role of Membranes in Metabolic Regulation: Proceedings. Mehlman, Myron A. & Hanson, Richard W., eds. 1972. 65.00 (ISBN 0-12-487840-7). Acad Pr.

Thompson, Guy A. Regulation of Membrane Lipid Metabolism. 256p. 1980. 71.50 (ISBN 0-8493-5427-7). CRC Pr.

Tien, H. Ti. Bilayer Lipid Membranes (Blm) Theory & Practice. 672p. 1974. 99.75 (ISBN 0-8247-6048-4). Dekker.

Tosteson, D. C., ed. Concepts & Models. (Membrane Transport in Biology Ser.: Vol. 1). (Illus.). 1978. 99.00 (ISBN 0-387-08687-0). Springer-Verlag.

--Transport Across Single Biological Membranes. LC 78-17668. (Membrane Transport in Biology: Vol. 2). (Illus.). 1979. 99.00 (ISBN 0-387-08780-X). Springer-Verlag.

Trump, Benjamin F. & Arstila, Antti U., eds. Pathobiology of Cell Membranes, Vol. 2. LC 74-27793. 1980. 65.00 (ISBN 0-12-701502-7). Acad Pr.

Tzagoloff, Alexander, ed. Membrane Biogenesis: Mitochondria, Chloroplasts, & Bacteria. LC 75-4744. (Illus.). 476p. 1975. 55.00x (ISBN 0-306-30825-8, Plenum Pr). Plenum Pub.

Vance. Biochemistry of Lipids & Membranes. 1985. text ed. 34.95 (ISBN 0-8053-9420-6). Benjamin-Cummings.

Wade, James B. & Lewis, Simon A. Current Topics in Membranes & Transport Vol. 20: Molecular Approaches to Epethelial Transport. (Serial Publication). 1984. 65.00 (ISBN 0-12-153320-4). Acad Pr.

Weissmann, Gerald & Claiborne, Robert, eds. Cell Membranes: Biochemistry, Cell Biology & Pathology. (Illus.). 296p. 1975. text ed. 17.95 (ISBN 0-913800-06-6). HP Pub Co.

West, I. C. The Biochemistry of Membrane Transport. (Outline Studies in Biology). 96p. 1983. pap. 7.50 (ISBN 0-412-24190-0, NO. 6063). Methuen Inc.

Yagi, Kunio. Structure & Function of Biomembranes. 1979. 46.00x (ISBN 0-89955-134-3, Pub. by Japan Sci Soc Japan). Intl Spec Bk.

MEMBRANES (TECHNOLOGY)

Adelberg, Edward A. & Slayman, Carolyn, eds. Current Topics in Membranes & Transport, Vol. 23: Genes & Proteins: Transport Proteins & Receptors. 1985. 52.00 (ISBN 0-12-153323-9). Acad Pr.

Bier, Milan, ed. Membrane Processes in Industry & Biomedicine. LC 72-149647. 313p. 1971. 32.50x (ISBN 0-306-30528-3, Plenum Pr). Plenum Pub.

Bronner, Felix & Kleinzeller, Arnost, eds. Current Topics in Membranes & Transport, Vol. 18. (Serial Publication). 1983. 59.00 (ISBN 0-12-153318-2). Acad Pr.

Business Communications Staff. Membrane & Separation Technology Directory. 1985. 150.00 (ISBN 0-89336-418-5). BCC.

--Membrane & Separation Technology Patents: Patent Printouts for Membrane Market Opportunities. 1984. 150.00 (ISBN 0-89336-247-6). BCC.

Cadenhead, D. A., ed. Progress in Surface & Membrane Science, Vol. 13. (Serial Publication). 1979. 70.00 (ISBN 0-12-571813-6). Acad Pr.

Cadenhead, D. A. & Danielli, J. F., eds. Progress in Surface & Membrane Science, Vol. 14. (Serial Publication Ser.). 1981. 70.00 (ISBN 0-12-571814-4). Acad Pr.

Critser, James R., Jr. Membrane Separation Processes. (Ser. 5-80). 221p. 1981. 135.00 (ISBN 0-914428-76-4). Lexington Data.

--Membrane Separation Processes. Incl. Index & Abstracts 1967-1971. 320.00 (ISBN 0-914428-10-1). (No.5-6771). 1972. Lexington Data Inc.

--Membrane Separation Processes. (Ser. 5-78). 1979. 130.00 (ISBN 0-914428-60-8). Lexington Data.

--Membrane Separation Processes. (Ser. 5-77). 1978. 124.00 (ISBN 0-914428-54-3). Lexington Data.

--Membrane Separation Processes. (Ser. 5-72). 120p. 1973. 110.00 (ISBN 0-914428-13-6). Lexington Data.

--Membrane Separation Processes. (Ser. 5-74). 1975. 124.00 (ISBN 0-914428-25-X). Lexington Data.

--Membrane Separation Processes. (Ser. No. 5-75). 1976. 124.00 (ISBN 0-914428-33-0). Lexington Data.

--Membrane Separation Processes. (Ser. (5-76)). 1977. 124.00 (ISBN 0-914428-51-9). Lexington Data.

--Membrane Separation Processes. (Ser. 5-83). 160p. 1984. 135.00 (ISBN 0-88178-013-8). Lexington Data.

--Membrane Separation Processes. (Ser. 5-84). 197p. 1985. 140.00 (ISBN 0-88178-050-2). Lexington Data.

Dutka. Membrane Filtration. (Pollution Engineering & Technology Ser.: Vol. 17). 632p. 1981. 85.00 (ISBN 0-8247-1164-5). Dekker.

Energy Management & Membrane Technology in Food & Dairy Processing. LC 83-72936. 128p. 1983. pap. 15.50 (ISBN 0-916150-57-7). Am Soc Ag Eng.

Fendler, Janos H. Membrane Mimetic Agents: Characterizations & Applications of Micelles, Microemulsions, Monolayers, Bilayers, Vesicles, Host-Guest Systems & Polyions. LC 82-2583. 522p. 1982. 69.50 (ISBN 0-471-07918-9, Pub. by Wiley-Interscience). Wiley.

Flinn, J. E., ed. Membrane Science & Technology: Industrial, Biological, & Waste Treatment Processes. LC 77-118126. 234p. 1970. 35.00x (ISBN 0-306-30484-8, Plenum Pr). Plenum Pub.

Hatefi, D., ed. The Structural Basis of Membrane Function. 1976. 55.00 (ISBN 0-12-332450-5). Acad Pr.

Iberall, A. & Schindler, A. Physics of Membrane Transport. LC 73-87972. (Illus.). 266p. (Orig.). 1973. pap. 6.00 (ISBN 0-914780-02-6). Gen Tech Serv.

International Conference on Geomembranes: Proceedings, 2 vols. (Illus.). 1984. 49.00 (ISBN 0-318-01539-0, 22005); Vol. 1. 30.00 (ISBN 0-318-01540-4); Vol. 2. 30.00 (ISBN 0-318-01541-2). Indus Fabrics.

International Resource Development Inc. Emerging Membrane Separation Technologies. 302p. 1984. 1650.00x (ISBN 0-88694-595-X). Intl Res Dev.

Koryta, Jiri. Ions, Electrodes & Membranes. LC 81-14762. 197p. 1982. 44.95x (ISBN 0-471-10007-2, Pub. by Wiley-Interscience); pap. 22.95x (ISBN 0-471-10008-0, Pub. by Wiley-Interscience). Wiley.

Lacey, Robert & Loeb, Sidney, eds. Industrial Processing with Membranes. LC 78-21889. 360p. 1979. Repr. of 1972 ed. lib. bdg. 25.00 (ISBN 0-88275-788-1). Krieger.

Lakshminarayanaiah, N. Transport Phenomena in Membranes. 1969. 82.00 (ISBN 0-12-434250-7). Acad Pr.

London Chemical Engineering Congress, Second Session, 1977. Advance in Enzyme & Membrane Technology: Proceedings, No. 51. 100p. 1981. 70.00x (ISBN 0-85295-103-5, Pub. by Inst Chem Eng England). State Mutual Bk.

Meares, P., ed. Membrane Separation Processes. 1976. 106.50 (ISBN 0-444-41446-0). Elsevier.

Membrane Market Opportunities, P-041N. 1983. 1750.00 (ISBN 0-89336-052-X). BCC.

Membrane Processes for Industry, Symposium, May 19-20,1966. Proceedings. Feazel, Charles E. & Lacey, Robert E., eds. LC 66-30620. (Illus.). 268p. 1966. pap. 5.00 (ISBN 0-940824-00-0). S Res Inst.

Otto, Frei. Tensile Structures. 490p. 1973. pap. 19.95x (ISBN 0-262-65005-3). MIT Pr.

Selegny, Eric. Charged & Reactive Polymers. Incl. Vol. 3. Charged Gels & Membranes, Pt. 1. lib. bdg. 63.00 (ISBN 90-277-0665-4); Vol. 4. Charged Gels & Membranes, Pt. 2. lib. bdg. 45.00 (ISBN 90-277-0666-2). LC 76-6086. 1976 (Pub. by Reidel Holland). Kluwer Academic.

Torrey, S., ed. Membrane & Ultrafiltration Technology: Developments since 1981. LC 83-22009. (Chemical Technology Review Ser.: No. 226). (Illus.). 463p. 1984. 64.00 (ISBN 0-8155-0977-4). Noyes.

Tuwiner, Sidney B. Diffusion & Membrane Technology. LC 62-20783. (ACS Monograph: No. 156). 1962. 35.50 (ISBN 0-8412-0284-2). Am Chemical.

MEMORY MAPS (COMPUTER SCIENCE)

Leemon, Sheldon. Mapping the Commodore 64. 268p. (Orig.). 1984. pap. 14.95 (ISBN 0-942386-23-X). Compute Pubns.

Schank, Roger C. Dynamic Memory: A Theory of Reminding & Learning in Computers & People. LC 82-1353. 240p. 1983. 32.50 (ISBN 0-521-24858-2); pap. 11.95 (ISBN 0-521-27029-4). Cambridge U Pr.

MEMORY TUBES

see Storage Tubes

MENDEL, GREGOR JOHANN, 1822-1884

McKusick, Victor A., ed. Mendelian Inheritance in Man: Catalogs of Autosomal Dominant, Autosomal Recessive & X-linked Phenotypes. 6th ed. LC 82-47975. 1448p. 1983. lib. bdg. write for info. (ISBN 0-8018-2744-2). Johns Hopkins.

Orel, Vitezslav. Mendel. (Past Masters Ser.). (Illus.). 1984. pap. 3.95 (ISBN 0-19-287624-4). Oxford U Pr.

Stern, Curt & Sherwood, Eva R., eds. The Origin of Genetics: A Mendel Source Book. LC 66-27948. (Illus.). 179p. 1966. pap. text ed. 10.95x (ISBN 0-7167-0655-5). W H Freeman.

Skobel'tsyn, D. V., ed. Photomesic & Photonuclear Processes. LC 67-27904. (P. N. Lebedev Physics Institute Ser.: Vol. 34). 214p. 1967. 35.00 (ISBN 0-306-10791-0, Consultants). Plenum Pub.

Von Goeler, Eberhard & Weinstein, Roy, eds. Experimental Meson Spectroscopy, 1977. LC 77-94049. 456p. 1977. 22.00x (ISBN 0-930350-00-6). NE U Pr.

MESOTRONS

see Mesons

MESOZOIC PERIOD

see Geology, Stratigraphic–Mesozoic

MESSERSCHMITT AIRPLANES

Aeronautical Staff. Messerschmitt ME109. LC 65-24307. (Aero Ser.: Vol. 1). (Illus.). 1965. pap. 3.95 (ISBN 0-8168-0500-8). Aero.

Boyne, Walter J. The Messerschmitt ME 262: Arrow to the Future. LC 80-607090. (Illus.). 192p. (Orig.). 1980. 19.95 (ISBN 0-87474-276-5); pap. 10.95 (ISBN 0-87474-275-7). Smithsonian.

Feist, Uwe & Hirsch, R. S. Messerschmitt BF 110. LC 67-21486. (Aero Ser.: Vol. 16). (Illus.). 1967. pap. 3.95 (ISBN 0-8168-0560-1). Aero.

--Messerschmitt ME262. LC 67-16733. (Aero Ser.: Vol. 14). (Illus.). 1967. pap. 3.95 (ISBN 0-8168-0552-0). Aero.

Maloney, Edward T. The Messerschmitt ME-262. (Illus.). 56p. 1980. pap. 6.95 (ISBN 0-9600248-5-9, Pub. by WW Two). Aviation.

Maloney, Edward T. & Feist, Uwe. Messerschmitt ME163. LC 67-27870. (Aero Ser: Vol. 17). 1968. pap. 3.95 (ISBN 0-8168-0564-4). Aero.

Messerschmitt O-Nine Gallery. LC 73-86748. 1985. write for info. (ISBN 0-914144-00-6). Monogram Aviation.

Musciano, Walter A. Messerschmitt Aces. LC 81-20614. (Illus.). 224p. 1982. 17.95 (ISBN 0-668-04887-5). Arco.

Rice, M. S., ed. Messerschmitt ME.262: Pictorial & Design Study Including the Pilot Handbook. (Illus.). 64p. 1973. pap. 7.95 (ISBN 0-87994-020-4, Pub. by AvPubns). Aviation.

METABOLISM

see also Amino Acid Metabolism; Antimetabolites; Bioenergetics; Calcium Metabolism; Carbohydrate Metabolism; Cell Metabolism; Dormancy (Biology); Drug Metabolism; Energy Metabolism; Iron Metabolism; Lipid Metabolism; Microbial Metabolites; Mineral Metabolism; Nitrogen Metabolism; Nucleic Acid Metabolism; Nutrition; Plants–Metabolism; Protein Metabolism; Sodium Metabolism; Urea; Water Metabolism

Addink, A. D. & Spronk, N., eds. Exogenous & Endogenous Influences on Metabolic & Neural Control, Vol. 1, Invited Lectures: Proceedings of the Third Congress of the European Society for Comparative Physiology & Biochemistry, August 31-September 3, 1981, Noorwijkerhout Netherlands. (Illus.). 432p. 1982. 83.00 (ISBN 0-08-027986-4). Pergamon.

--Exogenous & Endogenous Influences on Metabolic & Neural Control, Vol. 2, Abstracts: Proceedings ot the Third Congress of the European Society for Compara07394366xxxlogy & Biochemistry, August 31-September 3, 1981, Noorwijkerhout,Netherlands. (Illus.). 260p. 1982. 55.00 (ISBN 0-08-028845-6). Pergamon.

Bakhle, Y. S. & Vane, J. R., eds. Metabolic Functions of the Lung, Vol. 4. (Lung Biology in Health & Disease Ser.). 1977. 65.00 (ISBN 0-8247-6383-1). Dekker.

Banks, P., et al. The Biochemistry of the Tissues. 2nd ed. LC 75-26739. 493p. 1976. (Pub. by Wiley-Interscience); pap. 35.95 (ISBN 0-471-01923-2, Pub. by Wiley-Interscience). Wiley.

Beets, M. G. Structure-Activity Relationships in Human Chemoreception. (Illus.). 408p. 1978. text ed. 48.25 (ISBN 0-85334-746-8, Pub. by Elsevier Applied Sci England). Elsevier.

Bergsma, D., et al, eds. Bilirubin Metabolism in the Newborn. (International Congress Ser.: No. 380). 1976. 66.00 (ISBN 0-444-15216-4, Excerpta Medica). Elsevier.

Berti, F. & Folco, G., eds. Leukotrienes & Prostacyclin. (NATO ASI Series A, Life Sciences: Vol. 154). 290p. 42.50x (ISBN 0-306-41173-3, Plenum Press). Plenum Pub.

Caldwell, J. & Paulson, G., eds. Foreign Compound Metabolism: Proceedings of the International Society for the Study of Xenobiotics Symposium, Florida, November 1983. 400p. 1984. 71.00x (ISBN 0-85066-271-0). Taylor & Francis.

Carson, E. R., et al. The Mathematical Modeling of Metabolic & Endocrine Systems: Model Formulation, Identification & Validation. (Biomedical Engineering & Health Systems Ser.). 394p. 1983. 57.50 (ISBN 0-471-08660-6). Wiley.

Cohen, Margo P. & Foa, Piero P. Special Topics in Endocrinology & Metabolism, Vol. 6. 274p. 1984. 58.00 (ISBN 0-8451-0705-4). A R Liss.

Cohen, Margo P. & Foa, Piero P., eds. Special Topics in Endocrinology & Metabolism, Vol. 1. 154p. 1979. 22.00x (ISBN 0-8451-0700-3). A R Liss.

Cohen, Margo P & Foa, Piero P., eds. Special Topics in Endocrinology & Metabolism, Vol. 3. (Special Topics in Endocrinology & Metabolism Ser.). 142p. 1982. 28.00 (ISBN 0-8451-0702-X). A R Liss.

Cohen, Margo P. & Foa, Piero P., eds. Special Topics in Endocrinology & Metabolism, Vol. 4. (Special Topics in Endocrinology & Metabolism). 270p. 1982. 38.00 (ISBN 0-8451-0703-8). A R Liss.

Cohen, Sidney. Clinical Gastroenterology: A Problem Oriented Approach. LC 82-10926. 464p. 1983. 35.00 (ISBN 0-471-08071-3, Pub. by Wiley Med). Wiley.

Cramp, D. G. Quantitative Approaches to Metabolism: The Role of Tracers & Models in Clinical Medicine. LC 81-21992. 390p. 1982. 64.95 (ISBN 0-471-10172-9, Pub. by Wiley-Interscience). Wiley.

De Bruyn, Chris, et al, eds. Purine Metabolism in Man IVA: Clinical & Therapeutic Aspects. (Advances in Experimental Medicine & Biology Ser.: Vol. 165A). 544p. 1983. 75.00x (ISBN 0-306-41363-9, Plenum Pr). Plenum Pub.

De Bruyn, Chris H., et al, eds. Purine Metabolism in Man IVB: Biochemical, Immunological, & Cancer Research. (Advances in Experimental Medicine & Biology Ser.: Vol. 165B). 509p. 1983. 69.50x (ISBN 0-306-41364-7, Plenum Pr). Plenum Pub.

Denton, R. M. & Pogson, C. I. Metabolic Regulation. 1976. pap. 7.50 (ISBN 0-412-13150-1, NO. 6085, Pub. by Chapman & Hall England). Methuen Inc.

Doelle, H. W., ed. Microbial Metabolism. LC 73-16370. (Benchmark Papers in Microbiology: Vol. 5). 424p. 1974. 59.95 (ISBN 0-87933-063-5). Van Nos Reinhold.

Dorfman, Ralph & Ungar, F., eds. Metabolism of Steroid Hormones. 1965. 95.00 (ISBN 0-12-221150-2). Acad Pr.

European Nutrition Conference, 2nd, Munich, 1976. Abstracts. Zoellner, N., et al, eds. (Nutrition & Metabolism: Vol. 20, No. 3). 1976. 15.75 (ISBN 3-8055-2441-2). S Karger.

Finkle, Bernard J. & Runeckles, Victor C., eds. Phenolic Compounds & Metabolic Regulation. LC 66-29065. 157p. 1967. 19.50x (ISBN 0-306-50023-X, Plenum Pr). Plenum Pub.

Fishman, William H., ed. Metabolic Conjugation & Metabolic Hydrolysis, 3 vols. LC 79-107556. Vol. 1, 1970. 90.00 (ISBN 0-12-257601-2); Vol. 2, 1971. 95.00 (ISBN 0-12-257602-0); Vol. 3, 1973. 90.00 (ISBN 0-12-257603-9). Acad Pr.

Freinkel, Norbert, ed. Contemporary Metabolism, Vol. 2. LC 79-643531. (Illus.). 564p. 1982. 42.50x (ISBN 0-306-40954-2, Plenum Med. Bk.). Plenum Pub.

--The Year in Metabolism, 1977. (Illus.). 468p. (Annual). 1978. 42.50x (ISBN 0-306-32002-9, Plenum Med Bk). Plenum Pub.

Gati, T., et al, eds. Nutrition-Digestion-Metabolism: Proceedings of the 28th International Congress of Physiological Sciences, Budapest, 1980. LC 80-42185. (Advances in Physiological Sciences Ser.: Vol. 12). (Illus.). 400p. 1981. 55.00 (ISBN 0-08-026825-0). Pergamon.

Gawthorne, J., et al, eds. Trace Element Metabolism in Man & Animals: Proceedings. 715p. 1982. 71.00 (ISBN 0-387-11058-5). Springer-Verlag.

Gilmour, D. Biochemistry of Insects. 1961. 56.50 (ISBN 0-12-284050-X). Acad Pr.

Greenberg, D. M., ed. Metabolic Pathways. 3rd ed. Incl. Vol. 1. 1967. 82.00 (ISBN 0-12-299251-2); Vol. 2. 1968. 71.50 (ISBN 0-12-299252-0); Vol. 3. 1969. 95.00 (ISBN 0-12-299253-9); Vol. 4. 1970. 82.00 (ISBN 0-12-299254-7); Vol. 5. Vogel, Henry J., ed. 1971. 88.00; Vol. 6. Hokin, L. E., ed. 1972. 95.00 (ISBN 0-12-299256-3). Acad Pr.

Haslam, Edwin. Metabolites & Metabolism. (International Monographs in Chemistry). (Illus.). 160p. 1985. 22.95x (ISBN 0-19-855377-3). Oxford U Pr.

Hathway, D. E., ed. Foreign Compound Metabolism in Mammals, Vols. 1-4. Incl. Vol. 1. 1960-69 Literature. 1970. 49.50 (ISBN 0-85186-008-7); Vol. 2. 1970-71 Literature. 1972. 47.00 (ISBN 0-85186-018-4); Vol. 3. 1972-73 Literature. 1975. 66.00 (ISBN 0-85186-028-1); Vol. 4. 1974-75 Literature. 1977. 68.00 (ISBN 0-85186-038-9, Royal Soc Chem London). LC 72-623875. Am Chemical.

Hayaischi, O., et al, eds. Biochemical & Medical Aspects of Tryptophan Metabolism. (Development in Biochemistry Ser.: Vol. 16). 1981. 67.25 (ISBN 0-444-80297-5). Elsevier.

Hegyeli, Ruth J., ed. Arachidonic Acid Metabolites. (Atherosclerosis Reviews Ser.: Vol. 13). 1985. text ed. price not set (ISBN 0-88167-131-2). Raven.

Herbert, R. B. Biosynthesis of Secondary Metabolites. 1981. 35.00 (ISBN 0-412-16370-5, NO.6501, Pub. by Chapman & Hall England); pap. 16.95 (ISBN 0-412-16380-2, NO.6500). Methuen Inc.

Herman, Robert H., et al, eds. Principles of Metabolic Control in Mammalian Systems. LC 79-9177. (Illus.). 690p. 1980. 45.00x (ISBN 0-306-40261-0, Plenum Pr). Plenum Pub.

Hietanen, Eino. Regulation of Serum Lipids by Physical Exercise. 192p. 1982. 64.00 (ISBN 0-8493-6330-6). CRC Pr.

Hodges, Robert E., ed. Human Nutrition-A Comprehensive Treatise, Vol. 4: Nutrition Metabolic & Clinical Applications. LC 78-27208. (Illus.). 500p. 1979. 49.50x (ISBN 0-306-40203-3, Plenum Pr). Plenum Pub.

Holick, M. F., et al, eds. Calcium, Phosphate & Vitamin D Metabolism in Pregnancy & Neonate. 554p. 1983. 111.75 (ISBN 0-444-80509-5, Biomedical Pr). Elsevier.

Hollwich, F. The Influence of Ocular Light Perception on Metabolism in Man & Animal. LC 78-17076. (Topics in Environmental Physiology & Medicine Ser.). (Illus.). 1979. 52.00 (ISBN 0-387-90315-1). Springer-Verlag.

Hutter, R., et al, eds. Antibiotics & Other Secondary Metabolites: Biosynthesis & Production. 1979. 49.00 (ISBN 0-12-363250-1). Acad Pr.

International Commission on Radiological Protection. The Metabolism of Compounds of Plutonium & Other Actinides. (ICRP Publication Ser.: No. 19). 66p. 1973. pap. 10.00 (ISBN 0-08-017119-2). Pergamon.

International Symposium Biologische Anstalt Helgoland, 3rd, 1967. Quantitative Biology of Metabolism: Models of Metabolism, Metabolic Parameters, Damage to Metabolism, Metabolic Control. Locker, A., ed. LC 68-55620. (Illus.). 1968. pap. 40.00 (ISBN 0-387-04301-2). Springer-Verlag.

Katzman, Robert & Pappius, Hanna. Brain Electrolytes & Fluid Metabolism. LC 72-77322. 419p. 1973. 36.50 (ISBN 0-683-04522-9, Pub. by W & W). Krieger.

Kervran, C. L. Biological Transmutations. (Illus.). 180p. 1980. text ed. 14.95 (ISBN 0-8464-1069-9). Beekman Pubs.

Klachko, D. M., et al, eds. Hormones & Energy Metabolism. LC 78-23943. (Advances in Experimental Medicine & Biology Ser.: Vol. 111). 212p. 1979. 35.00x (ISBN 0-306-40070-7, Plenum Pr). Plenum Pub.

Kluge, M. & Ting, I. P. Crassulacean Acid Metabolism: Analysis of an Ecological Adaptation. LC 78-12658. (Ecological Studies: Vol. 30). (Illus.). 1978. 51.00 (ISBN 0-387-08979-9). Springer-Verlag.

Lamb, Lawrence E. Metabolics: Putting Your Food Energy to Work. LC 74-1829. (Illus.). 256p. 1974. 12.95i (ISBN 0-06-012484-9, HarpT). Har-Row.

Levine, R. & Luft, R., eds. Advances in Metabolic Disorders, Vols. 1-6. Incl. Vol. 1. 1964 (ISBN 0-12-027301-2); Vol. 2. 1966 (ISBN 0-12-027302-0); Vol. 3. 1968 (ISBN 0-12-027303-9); Vol. 4. 1970 (ISBN 0-12-027304-7); Vol. 5. 1971 (ISBN 0-12-027305-5); Vol.6. 1972 (ISBN 0-12-027306-3). 75.00 ea. Acad Pr.

Levine, R. & Tuft, R., eds. Advances in Metabolic Disorders: Supplements. Incl. Suppl. 1. Early Diabetes: A Symposium. Camerini-Davalos, R. A. & Cole, H. S., eds. 1970. 75.00 (ISBN 0-12-027361-6); Suppl. 2. Vascular & Neurological Changes in Early Diabetes. Camerini-Davalos, Rafael A. & Cole, Harold S., eds. 1973. 85.00 (ISBN 0-12-027362-4). Acad Pr.

Linder, Maria C., ed. Nutritional Biochemistry & Metabolism, with Clinical Applications. 1985. 55.00 (ISBN 0-444-00910-8). Elsevier.

Lohmoeller, Lydtin H. Beta Blockers. 159p. 1980. 50.00 (ISBN 3-456-80916-6, Pub. by Holdan Bk Ltd UK). State Mutual Bk.

Luckner, M. Secondary Metabolism in Microorganisms, Plants & Animals. 2nd, rev. ed. (Illus.). 570p. 1984. 48.50 (ISBN 0-387-12771-2). Springer-Verlag.

Luckner, Martin. The Secondary Metabolism of Plants & Animals. 1972. 75.00 (ISBN 0-12-459050-0). Acad Pr.

McMurray, W. C. Essentials of Human Metabolism: The Relationship of Biochemistry to Human Physiology & Disease. 2nd ed. (Illus.). 331p. 1983. pap. text ed. 21.00 (ISBN 0-06-141643-6, 14-16437, Harper Medical). Lippincott.

Magill, Jane M. & Moore, John B., Jr. Experiments in Metabolism. (Illus.). 118p. (Orig.). 1979. pap. text ed. 5.95x plastic comb. bdg. (ISBN 0-89641-013-7). American Pr.

Mann, J. Secondary Metabolism. (Chemistry Ser.). (Illus.). 1978. text ed. 36.00x (ISBN 0-19-855506-7); pap. 17.50x (ISBN 0-19-855513-X). Oxford U Pr.

Manner, Harold. Metabolic Therapy "A". 1.00x (ISBN 0-686-29836-5). Cancer Control Soc.

Martini, Luciano & James, V. H., eds. Current Topics in Experimental Endocrinology: Vol. 5: Fetal Endocrinology & Metabolism. (Serial Publication). 1983. 55.00 (ISBN 0-12-153205-4). Acad Pr.

Massry, Shaul G., et al, eds. Phosphate & Mineral Metabolism. 500p. 1984. 69.50x (ISBN 0-306-41731-6, Plenum Pr). Plenum Pub.

Maxwell, Morton H. & Kleeman, Charles R., eds. Clinical Disorders of Fluid & Electrolyte Metabolism. 3rd ed. (Illus.). 1979. text ed. 90.00 (ISBN 0-07-040994-3). McGraw.

Mora, Jaime & Palacios, Rafael, eds. Glutamine: Metabolism, Enzymology & Regulation. 1980. 37.50 (ISBN 0-12-506040-8). Acad Pr.

Mulder, G. J. & Caldwell, J., eds. Sulfate Metabolism & Sulfate Conjugation. 312p. 1982. 42.00x (ISBN 0-85066-233-8). Taylor & Francis.

Owen, Charles A., Jr. Copper Deficiency & Toxicity: Acquired & Inherited, in Plants, Animals, & Man. LC 81-11061. (Noyes Publications-Copper in Biology & Medicine Ser.). 189p. 1982. 28.00 (ISBN 0-8155-0868-9). Noyes.

Paulson, Gaylord D., et al, eds. Xenobiotic Metabolism: In Vitro Studies. LC 79-789. (Symposium Ser.: No. 97). 1979. 33.95 (ISBN 0-8412-0486-1). Am Chemical.

Phipps, D. A. Metals & Metabolism, No. 26. (Oxford Chemistry Ser). (Illus.). 1976. pap. 12.50x (ISBN 0-19-855413-3). Oxford U Pr.

Piper, Priscilla J. Leukotrienes & Other Lipoxygenase Products: Proceedings. LC 83-175919. 368p. 1983. 69.95x (ISBN 0-471-90142-3, Res Stud Pr). Wiley.

Prasad, Ananda S. Zinc Metabolism. (Illus.). 484p. 1966. photocopy ed. 48.50x (ISBN 0-398-01518-X). C C Thomas.

Ramsden, David B. Peripheral Metabolism & Action of Thyroid Hormones, Vol. 2. (Annual Research Reviews). 1978. 28.80 (ISBN 0-88831-029-3). Eden Pr.

Reid, Eric & Leppard, J. P. Drug Metabolite Isolation & Determination. (Methodological Surveys in Biochemistry & Analysis Ser.: Vol. 12). 290p. 1983. 47.50x (ISBN 0-306-41265-9, Plenum Press). Plenum Pub.

Roe, Francis J., ed. Metabolic Aspects of Food Safety. LC 72-142181. 1971. 76.50 (ISBN 0-12-592550-6). Acad Pr.

Rohe, Fred. Metabolic Ecology. 1982. 5.95x (ISBN 0-686-37598-X). Cancer Control Soc.

Salvatore, Francesco, et al, eds. The Biochemistry of Adenosylmethionine. LC 76-25565. 1977. 75.00x (ISBN 0-231-03895-X). Columbia U Pr.

Srere, Paul A. & Estabrook, Ronald W., eds. Microenvironments & Metabolic Compartmentation. 1978. 55.00 (ISBN 0-12-660550-5). Acad Pr.

Staunton, J. Primary Metabolism: A Mechanistic Approach. (Illus.). 1978. text ed. 24.95x (ISBN 0-19-855460-5). Oxford U Pr.

Stoddart, R. W. Polysaccharide Metabolism. 224p. 1980. 35.00x (ISBN 0-85664-807-8, Pub. by Croom Helm England). State Mutual Bk.

Szymendera, Janusz. Bone Mineral Metabolism in Cancer. LC 75-104194. (Recent Results in Cancer Research: Vol. 27). (Illus.). 1970. 26.00 (ISBN 0-387-04992-4). Springer-Verlag.

Tepperman, Jay. Metabolic & Endocrine Physiology. 4th ed. (Illus.). 1980. 24.95 (ISBN 0-8151-8755-6); pap. 24.95 (ISBN 0-8151-8756-4). Year Bk Med.

Thurman, Ronald, ed. Alcohol & Aldehyde Metabolizing Systems, IV. LC 80-18745. (Advances in Experimental Medicine & Biology Ser.: Vol. 132). 850p. 1980. 95.00x (ISBN 0-306-40476-1, Plenum Pr). Plenum Pub.

Thurman, Ronald G., et al, eds. Alcohol & Aldehyde Metabolizing Systems, 3 vols. (Johnson Foundation Colloquia Ser.). 1978. Vol. 1. 70.00 (ISBN 0-12-691450-8); Vol. 2. 70.00 (ISBN 0-12-691402-8); Vol. 3, 1977. 70.00 (ISBN 0-12-691403-6); Set. 170.00 (ISBN 0-686-77325-X). Acad Pr.

Torssell, Kurt. Natural Product Chemistry: A Mechanistic & Biosynthetic Approach to Secondary Metabolism. LC 82-2045. 401p. 1983. 58.95 (ISBN 0-471-10378-0, Pub. by Wiley-Interscience). Wiley.

Weil, William B., Jr. Fluid & Electrolyte Metabolism in Infants & Children: A Unified Approach. 336p. 1978. 49.50 (ISBN 0-8089-1028-0, 794772). Grune.

White, A., et al. Hormones & Metabolic Control. 160p. 1984. pap. text ed. 11.95 (ISBN 0-7131-4437-8). E Arnold.

Whitney, Eleanor N. & Hamilton, Eva M. Understanding Nutrition. (Illus.). 1977. text ed. 18.50 (ISBN 0-8299-0052-7). West Pub.

Wilkinson, A. W. Metabolism & Response to Injury. (Illus.). 1976. 34.95 (ISBN 0-8151-9322-X). Year Bk Med.

Witzmann, Rupert F. Steroids: The Keys to Life. 288p. 1981. 31.50 (ISBN 0-442-29590-1). Van Nos Reinhold.

Wolfe, Robert R. Tracers in Metabolic Research: Radioisotope & Stable Isotope-Mass Spectrometry Methods. LC 83-19601. (Laboratory & Research Methods in Biology & Medicine Ser.: Vol. 9). 300p. 1984. 56.00 (ISBN 0-8451-1658-4). A R Liss.

Metalworking Industries as Potential Export Industries in Developing Countries. pap. 1.50 (ISBN 0-686-94685-5, UN70/2B/16, UN). Unipub.

Metalworking Industries in Developing Countries of Africa. pap. 3.00 (ISBN 0-686-94683-9, UN80 2B1, UN). Unipub.

Muhly, James D. Copper & Tin: The Distribution of Mineral Resources & the Nature of the Metals Trade in the Bronze Age, Including Supplement. new ed. (Connecticut Academy of Arts & Sciences Transaction Ser.: Vol. 43 & 46). 380p. 1976. 29.50 (ISBN 0-208-01573-6, Archon). Shoe String.

Nuclear Techniques in the Basic Metal Industries. LC 73-164980. (Proceedings Ser.). (Illus.). 634p. (Orig.). 1973. pap. 48.00 (ISBN 92-0-060073-5, ISP314, IAEA). Unipub.

Planning & Programming of the Metalworking Industries with a Special View to Exports. pap. 4.00 (ISBN 0-686-94658-8, UN72/2B/7, UN). Unipub.

Soltow, James H. Origins of Small Business: Metal Fabricators & Machinery Makers in New England, 1890-1957. LC 65-27429. (Transactions Ser.: Vol. 55, Pt. 10). 1965. pap. 1.00 (ISBN 0-87169-560-X). Am Philos.

METAL-WORK

see also Brazing; Copperwork; Electroplating; Forging; Founding; Ironwork; Metal Stamping; Metal-Working Lubricants; Metals–Cold Working; Metals–Coloring; Metals–Finishing; Pipe Bending; Plate-Metal Work; Sheet-Metal Work; Silverwork; Solder and Soldering; Steelwork; Welding

Altan, Taylan & Oh, Soo-Ik. Metal Forming: Fundamentals & Applications. 1983. 84.00 (ISBN 0-87170-167-7). ASM.

American Machinist. Metalforming: Modern Machines, Methods & Tooling for Engineers & Operating Personnel. 288p. 1982. text ed. 36.50 (ISBN 0-07-001546-5). McGraw.

American Society for Metals. Specialized Cleaning, Finishing & Coating Processes: Proceedings of a Conference Held February 5-6, 1980, Los Angeles, California. LC 81-2755. (Materials-Metalworking Technology Ser.). pap. 106.00 (ISBN 0-317-26754-X, 2024350). Bks Demand UMI.

Ammen, C. W. The Complete Handbook of Sand Casting. (Illus.). 1979. pap. 9.95 (ISBN 0-8306-1043-X, 1043). TAB Bks.

Barich, Dewey F. & Smith, Leonard C. Metal Work for Industrial Arts Shops. LC 52-8345. pap. 25.80 (ISBN 0-317-08910-2, 2004570). Bks Demand UMI.

Bedford, J. R. Metalwork Projects. pap. text ed. 6.50 (ISBN 0-686-89167-8). Transatlantic.

Bell, J., et al, eds. General Welding & Cutting. (Engineering Craftsmen: No. F10). (Illus.). 1976. spiral bdg. 49.95x (ISBN 0-85083-330-2). Trans-Atlantic.

Bellows, Guy. Chemical Machining. 2nd ed. (Machining Process Ser.MDC 82-102). (Illus.). 96p. 1982. pap. 12.50 (ISBN 0-936974-08-7). Metcut Res Assocs.

--Machining: A Process Checklist. 3rd ed. (Machining Process Ser.MDC 82-100). (Illus.). 32p. 1982. pap. 5.00 (ISBN 0-936974-07-9). Metcut Res Assocs.

Biringuccio, Vannoccio. Pirotechnia. 1966. pap. 6.95x (ISBN 0-262-52017-6). MIT Pr.

Blaser, Werner. Filigree Architecture: Metal & Glass Construction. (Eng. Fr. & Ger., Illus.). 216p. 1980. pap. 19.00 (ISBN 0-89192-298-9, Pub. by Wepf & Co). Interbk Inc.

Bragdon, Charles R. Metal Decorating from Start to Finishes. LC 61-17350. (Illus.). 1969. 5.95 (ISBN 0-87027-065-6). Cumberland Pr.

Cain, Tubal. Hardening, Tempering & Heat Treatment. (Workshop Practice Ser.: No. 1). (Illus.). 128p. 1984. pap. 13.95 (ISBN 0-85242-837-5, Pub. by Argus). Aztex.

Chapman, W. A. Workshop Technology, Pt. 1. 5th ed. (Illus.). 1976. pap. 22.95x (ISBN 0-7131-3269-8). Intl Ideas.

Cuzner, Bernard. A First Book of Metal-Work. 192p. 1980. 11.00x (ISBN 0-905418-54-9, Pub. by Gresham England). State Mutual Bk.

Daniele, Joseph W. Early American Metal Projects. LC 75-130495. 16.64 (ISBN 0-87345-142-2). McKnight.

Dieter, George. Mechanical Metallurgy. 2nd ed. (Illus.). 1976. text ed. 45.00 (ISBN 0-07-016891-1). McGraw.

Din Standards for Stamped Parts. 235.00 (ISBN 0-686-28194-2, 10924-1/67). Heyden.

Doyle, L. E., et al. Manufacturing Processes & Materials for Engineers. 2nd ed. 1969. text ed. 37.95 (ISBN 0-13-555862-X). P-H.

Doyle, Lawrence E., et al. Manufacturing Processes & Materials for Engineers. 3rd ed. (Illus.). 960p. 1985. text ed. 36.95 (ISBN 0-13-555921-9). P-H.

Dragoo, Alva W. General Shop Metalwork. rev. ed. 1964. pap. text ed. 6.64 (ISBN 0-87345-109-0). McKnight.

Feirer & Lindbeck. Basic Metalwork. 1978. 10.64 (ISBN 0-02-662610-1); pap. 7.32 (ISBN 0-02-662600-4). Bennett IL.

--Metalwork S.I. Metric Edition. 1979. text ed. 15.96 (ISBN 0-02-665150-5); student guide 6.64 (ISBN 0-02-665160-2). Bennett IL.

Feirer, J. L. & Groneman, C. H. General Metals. 6th ed. 512p. 1985. 26.96 (ISBN 0-07-020398-9); write for info. study guide (ISBN 0-07-020399-7). McGraw.

Feirer, John L. General Metals. rev., 5th ed. (Industrial Education Ser.). (Illus.). 480p. 1980. text ed. 24.60 (ISBN 0-07-020380-6). McGraw.

Feirer, John L. & Lindbeck, John R. Metalwork. rev. ed. 1970. 15.68 (ISBN 0-02-665190-4); student guide 5.12 (ISBN 0-02-665200-5). Bennett IL.

Fifer, Bill. Metal Projects, Bk. 2. 96p. 1981. 6.00 (ISBN 0-87006-172-0). Goodheart.

The Giant Book of Metalworking Projects. (Illus.). 256p. (Orig.). 1983. 19.95 (ISBN 0-8306-0357-3); pap. 12.95 (ISBN 0-8306-1357-9). TAB Bks.

Gingery, David J. The Dividing Head & Deluxe Accessories. LC 80-66142. (Build Your Own Metal Working Shop from Scrap Ser.: Bk. 6). (Illus.). 160p. (Orig.). 1982. pap. 8.95 (ISBN 0-9604330-5-8). D J Gingery.

--The Metal Lathe. LC 80-66142. (Build Your Own Metal Working Shop from Scrap Ser.: Bk. 2). (Illus.). 128p. (Orig.). 1980. pap. 7.95 (ISBN 0-9604330-1-5). D J Gingery.

--The Metal Shaper. LC 80-66142. (Build Your Own Metal Working Shop from Scrap: Bk. 3). (Illus.). 144p. (Orig.). 1980. pap. 7.95 (ISBN 0-9604330-2-3). D J Gingery.

Graham, Gregory S. Metalworking: An Introduction. 1980. text ed. write for info. (ISBN 0-534-00843-7, Breton Pubs). Wadsworth Pub.

Harris, J. N. Mechanical Working of Metals: Theory & Practice. (International Series on Materials Science & Technology: Vol. 36). (Illus.). 275p. 1983. 44.00 (ISBN 0-08-025464-0); pap. 17.50 (ISBN 0-08-025463-2). Pergamon.

Hirth, J. P. & Weertman, J., eds. Work Hardening. LC 67-29669. (Metallurgical Society Conference Ser.: No. 46). pap. 98.50 (ISBN 0-317-11258-9, 2001534). Bks Demand UMI.

Hoffmanner, A. L., ed. Metal Forming: Interrelation Between Theory & Practice. LC 70-171698. 503p. 1971. 65.00x (ISBN 0-306-30554-2, Plenum Pr). Plenum Pub.

--Metal Forming: Interrelation Between Theory & Practice: Proceedings of a Symposium, Cleveland, Ohio, 1970. LC 70-171698. pap. 129.50 (ISBN 0-317-27874-6, 2055795). Bks Demand UMI.

IBM Education Department. Precision Measurement in the Metal Working Industry. rev. ed. (Illus.). 1952. pap. 11.95x (ISBN 0-8156-2194-9). Syracuse U Pr.

International Conference on Rotary Metalworking Processes, 3rd: Proceedings. 1984. lib. bdg. 90.00x (ISBN 0-903608-55-3, Pub. by IFS Pubns UK). Air Sci Co.

Koellhoffer, Leonard. Shielded Metal Arc Welding. LC 82-8629. 271p. 1983. pap. text ed. 19.95 (ISBN 0-471-05048-2); pap. 9.95 wkbk. (ISBN 0-471-09884-1). Wiley.

Koenigsberger, T. & Tobias, S. A., eds. Proceedings of the Sixteenth Machine Tool Design & Research Conference. LC 76-5219. (International Machine Tool Design & Research Conference Ser.). 599p. 1976. text ed. 139.95x (ISBN 0-470-15100-5). Halsted Pr.

Kramer, Karl R. & Kramer, Nora. Coppercraft & Silver Made at Home. (Illus.). 14.75 (ISBN 0-8446-0170-5). Peter Smith.

Kronquist, Emil F. Metalwork for Craftsmen: A Step-by-Step Guide with 55 Projects. 13.25 (ISBN 0-8446-0171-3). Peter Smith.

Lange, K. Handbook of Metal Forming. 1985. 85.00 (ISBN 0-07-036285-8). McGraw.

Law, Ivan. Measuring & Marking Metals. (Workshop Practice Ser.: No. 6). 128p. (Orig.). 1985. pap. 9.95 (ISBN 0-85242-841-3, Pub. by Argus). Aztex.

Lindsley, E. F. Metalworking in the Home Shop. LC 83-15973. (Illus.). 309p. 1983. 29.95 (ISBN 0-442-25984-0). Van Nos Reinhold.

Little, Richard L. Metalworking Technology. (Illus.). 1976. text ed. 31.45 (ISBN 0-07-038097-X). McGraw.

Little, S. & Little, R. The Basic Book of Metalworking. (Basic Industrial Arts Ser.). (Illus.). 124p. 1984. 7.50 (ISBN 0-8269-1885-9). Am Technical.

Los Angeles Unified School District. Metalworking. LC 77-73297. 96p. 1978. pap. text ed. 4.80 (ISBN 0-02-820420-4). Glencoe.

Ludwig, Oswald A. & McCarthy, Willard J. Metalwork Technology & Practice. rev. & 7th ed. (Illus.). 1982. text ed. 20.64 (ISBN 0-87345-104-X); instr's guide 5.28; study guide 6.00. McKnight.

McCarthy, Willard J. & Repp, Victor. Machine Tool Technology. (Illus.). 1979. text ed. 21.97 (ISBN 0-87345-143-0); Study Guide 1. 4.67 (ISBN 0-87345-144-9); Study Guide 2. 4.67 (ISBN 0-87345-145-7); ans. key avail. McKnight.

McCreight, Tim. The Complete Metalsmith. LC 81-66573. (An Illustrated Handbook Ser.). (Illus.). 150p. (Orig.). 1984. pap. 9.95 spiral (ISBN 0-87192-135-9, Pub. by Davis Mass). Sterling.

--The Complete Metalsmith: An Illustrated Handbook. LC 81-66573. (Illus.). 160p. 1982. 10.95 (ISBN 0-87192-135-9). Davis Mass.

Machine Tool & Design Research International Conference, 14th & Koenigsberger, F. Proceedings. Tobias, S. A., ed. 841p. 1974. 149.95 (ISBN 0-470-49746-7). Halsted Pr.

McKnight Staff Members & Miller, Wilbur R. Metalworking. LC 78-53387. (Basic Industrial Arts Ser.). (Illus.). 1978. 7.28 (ISBN 0-87345-792-7); softbound 5.28 (ISBN 0-87345-784-6). McKnight.

Maryon, Herbert. Metalwork & Enamelling. 4th ed. (Illus.). 1971. pap. 5.95 (ISBN 0-486-22702-2). Dover.

--Metalwork & Enamelling: A Practical Treatise on Gold & Silversmiths' Work & Their Allied Crafts. 5th & rev. ed. (Illus.). 13.25 (ISBN 0-8446-0198-5). Peter Smith.

Metalworking Industries as Potential Export Industries in Developing Countries. pap. 1.50 (ISBN 0-686-94685-5, UN70/2B/16, UN). Unipub.

Metalworking Industries in Developing Countries of Africa. pap. 3.00 (ISBN 0-686-94683-9, UN80 2B1, UN). Unipub.

Metzbower, E. Source Book on Applications of the Laser in Metalworking. 1981. 54.00 (ISBN 0-87170-117-0). ASM.

Miller, Richard K. Noise Control Solutions for the Metal Products Industry. (Illus.). 120p. text ed. 45.00 (ISBN 0-89671-031-9). SEAI Tech Pubns.

--Noise Control Solutions for the Metal Products Industry, Vol. II. (Illus.). 120p. pap. text ed. 45.00 (ISBN 0-89671-021-1). SEAI Tech Pubns.

Milling: Methods & Machines. LC 82-61032. 254p. 1982. 32.00 (ISBN 0-87263-110-9). SME.

Morrisey, Thomas J. Introductory Metalworking. (South-Western Industrial Arts Ser.). (Illus.). 1984. text ed. 10.95 (ISBN 0-538-33710-9, IE71). SW Pub.

Noel Hume, Ivor. James Geddy & Sons: Colonial Craftsmen. LC 70-115038. (Archaeological Ser: No. 5). (Illus.). 45p. (Orig.). 1970. pap. 2.95 (ISBN 0-910412-10-3). Williamsburg.

Non-Ferrous Metal Works of the World. 2nd ed. 1110p. 1974. 52.50x (ISBN 0-8002-1757-8). Intl Pubns Serv.

North American Metalworking Research Conference, & Manufacturing Engineering Transactions: Proceedings, 7th, 1979. LC 79-63779. (Illus.). 1979. 65.00 (ISBN 0-87263-037-4). SME.

North American Metalworking Research Conference 5th 1977, University of Massachusetts, Amherst. North American Metalworking Research Conference Proceedings. LC 77-75743. (Manufacturing Engineering Transactions Ser.: Vol. 5). pap. 97.30 (ISBN 0-317-27743-X, 2024176). Bks Demand UMI.

North American Metalworking Research Conference 6th 1978, University of Florida. North American Metalworking Research Conference Proceedings. LC 78-51585. (Manufacturing Engineering Transaction Ser.: Vol. 6). pap. 119.50 (ISBN 0-317-27752-9, 2024177). Bks Demand UMI.

Planning & Programming of the Metalworking Industries with a Special View to Exports. pap. 4.00 (ISBN 0-686-94658-8, UN72/2B/7, UN). Unipub.

Pollack, Herman. Manufacturing & Machine Tool Operations. 2nd ed. (Illus.). 1979. ref. 29.95 (ISBN 0-13-555771-2). P-H.

Punter, Ian. Projects & Designs in Metalwork. (Illus.). 96p. 1981. 14.95 (ISBN 0-7134-3510-0, Pub. by Batsford England). David & Charles.

Robinson, B. W. Japanese Sword-Fittings & Associated Metalwork. (Baur Collection Geneva: Vol. 7). (Illus.). 448p. 1981. 265.00 (ISBN 2-88031-003-2, Pub. by Baur Foundation Switzerland). Routledge & Kegan.

Rowe, G. W. Principles of Industrial Metalworking. 430p. 1977. text ed. 65.00 (ISBN 0-7131-3381-3). E Arnold.

--Principles of Industrial Metalworking Processes. 407p. 1977. 67.50x (ISBN 0-8448-1219-6). Crane-Russak Co.

Ruley, M. J. Projects in General Metalwork. 1969. text ed. 15.28 (ISBN 0-87345-135-X). McKnight.

Rykalin, N., et al. Laser Machining & Welding. (Illus.). 1979. 57.00 (ISBN 0-08-022724-4). Pergamon.

Schey, John A. Tribology in Metalworking. 1983. 96.00 (ISBN 0-87170-155-3). ASM.

Schey, John A., ed. Metal Deformation Processes: Friction & Lubrication. LC 75-107756. (Monographs & Textbooks in Material Science: No. 1). (Illus.). pap. 160.00 (ISBN 0-317-07845-3, 2055018). Bks Demand UMI.

Schwartz, M. M. Metals Joining Manual. (Illus.). 1979. 34.50 (ISBN 0-07-055720-9). McGraw.

Shearman, William M. Metal Alloys & Patinas for Castings: For Metalsmiths, Jewelers, & Sculptors. LC 76-28729. pap. 20.00 (ISBN 0-317-27900-9, 2025450). Bks Demand UMI.

Smith, Ernest. Working in Precious Metals. 414p. 1981. 35.00x (ISBN 0-7198-0032-3, Pub. by Northwood Bks). State Mutual Bk.

Smith, R. Goodwin. English Domestic Metalwork. 64p. 1981. 30.00x (ISBN 0-85317-023-1, Pub. by Lewis Pubs). State Mutual Bk.

Society of North American Goldsmiths. Metalsmith Papers. 96p. (Orig.). 1980. pap. text ed. 12.00 (ISBN 0-9604446-0-2). SNAG.

Stewart, Richard. Modern Design in Metal. (Illus.). 1979. 18.00 (ISBN 0-7195-3537-9). Transatlantic.

Strefford, John & McMurdo, Guy. Metalwork Technology. (Illus.). 93p. 1976. 22.00x (ISBN 0-7217-4007-3, Pub. by Schofield & Sims UK). State Mutual Bk.

Tech Tran Corporation Staff. Lasers in Metalworking: A Summary & Forecast. (Illus.). 165p. 1983. spiral bdg. 50.00 (ISBN 0-918989-03-5). Tech Tran Consult.

Tubby, Pamela. Working with Metal. LC 78-65662. (Illus.). 1979. 11.95i (ISBN 0-690-01816-9); pap. 5.95i (ISBN 0-690-01826-6, TYC-T). T Y Crowell.

Utilization of Non-Ferrous Scrap Metal. pap. 2.00 (ISBN 0-686-94361-9, UN70/2B/30, UN). Unipub.

Van der Voort, G. F. Metallography: Principles & Practice. 768p. 1983. 46.00 (ISBN 0-07-066970-8). McGraw.

Vidosic, Joseph P. Metal Machining & Forming Technology. LC 64-19573. pap. 142.30 (ISBN 0-317-10972-3, 2051623). Bks Demand UMI.

Walker, John R. Exploring Metalworking. LC 75-31808. 1976. text ed. 13.20 (ISBN 0-87006-199-2); wkbk. 4.00 (ISBN 0-87006-169-0). Goodheart.

--Modern Metalworking. LC 81-6736. (Illus.). 520p. 1981. 21.00 (ISBN 0-87006-334-0); wkbk. 4.00 (ISBN 0-87006-335-9). Goodheart.

Working with Metal. (Home Repair & Improvement Ser.). (Illus.). 128p. 1981. 11.95 (ISBN 0-8094-3470-9). Time-Life.

Working with Metal. LC 82-14339. (Home Repair & Improvement Ser.). 1981. lib. bdg. 15.94 (ISBN 0-8094-3471-7, Pub. by Time-Life). Silver.

METAL-WORK–BIBLIOGRAPHY

Johnson, W., et al. Plane Strain Slip Line Fields for Metal Deformation Processes: A Source Book & Bibliography. (Illus.). 270p. 1982. 50.00 (ISBN 0-08-025452-7). Pergamon.

METAL-WORK–DICTIONARIES

Abd-El-Wahed, A. M. Metal Forming Dictionary. (Eng., Fr., Ger. & Arabic.). 386p. 1978. 45.00 (ISBN 0-686-92426-6, M-9755). French & Eur.

Clason, W. E. Elsevier's Dictionary of Metallurgy & Metal Working. (Eng., Fr., Span., Ital., Dutch & Ger.). 848p. 1978. 136.25 (ISBN 0-444-41695-1). Elsevier.

METAL-WORK–HISTORY

Waldbaum, Jane C. Metalwork from Sardis: The Finds Through 1974. (Archaeological Exploration of Sardis Monographs: No. 8). (Illus.). 280p. 1983. text ed. 40.00x (ISBN 0-674-57070-7). Harvard U Pr.

METAL-WORKING LUBRICANTS

Cox, Charles & Beck, John, eds. Management Development: Advances in Practice & Theory. 350p. 1984. 39.95x (ISBN 0-471-90388-4). Wiley.

International Conference on Jet Cutting Technology, Fourth. Proceedings, 2 vols. Stephens, H. S., ed. (Illus.). 1979. Set. pap. text ed. 60.00x (ISBN 0-900983-79-5, Dist. by Air Science Co.). BHRA Fluid.

International Symposium on Jet Cutting Technology, 3rd. Proceedings. 1977. text ed. 58.00x (ISBN 0-900983-55-8, Dist. by Air Science Co.). BHRA Fluid.

Kalpakjian, S. & Jain, S. C., eds. Metalworking Lubrication. 259p. 1980. 40.00 (ISBN 0-686-69857-6, H00159). ASME.

Nachtman. Lubricants & Lubrication in Metalworking Operations. (Manufacturing Engineering Ser.). 280p. 1985. 55.00 (ISBN 0-8247-7401-9). Dekker.

Schey, John A., ed. Metal Deformation Processes: Friction & Lubrication. LC 75-107756. (Monographs & Textbooks in Material Science: No. 1). (Illus.). pap. 160.00 (ISBN 0-317-07845-3, 2055018). Bks Demand UMI.

Society of Manufacturing Engineers. Cutting Fluids & Lubricants. (Productivity Equipment Ser.). 1985. 38.00 (ISBN 0-87263-193-1). SME.

Birau, N. & Schlott, W., eds. Melatonin - Current Status & Perspectives: Proceedings of an International Symposium on Melatonin, Held in Bremen, F. R. Germany, September 18-30, 1980. (Advances in the Biosciences Ser.: Vol. 29). (Illus.). 420p. 1981. 72.00 (ISBN 0-08-026400-X). Pergamon.

Bohner, H. O., ed. Light Metal 1985. 1525p. 1985. 80.00 (ISBN 0-89520-488-6); students 24.00 (ISBN 0-317-37220-3). Metal Soc.

--Light Metals, 1985. LC 84-29479. (Illus.). 1527p. 1985. 80.00 (ISBN 0-89520-488-6). Metal Soc.

Bourdon, J. Growth & Properties of Metal Clusters: Application to Catalysis & the Photographic Process. (Studies in Surface Science & Catalysis: Vol. 4). 550p. 1980. 95.75 (ISBN 0-444-41877-6). Elsevier.

Bramfitt, B. L. & Magonon, P. L., eds. Metallurgy of Continuous Annealed Sheet Steel. 488p. 1982. 40.00 (ISBN 0-89520-450-9); members 25.00 (ISBN 0-317-37225-4); student members 15.00 (ISBN 0-317-37226-2). Metal Soc.

Brandt. Metallurgy Fundamentals. 1985. 16.00 (ISBN 0-87006-475-4). Goodheart.

Briant, C. L. Metallurgical Aspects of Environmental Failures. (Materials Science Monographs: No. 12). 248p. 1985. 65.00 (ISBN 0-444-42491-1). Elsevier.

--Metallurgy of Environmental Fracture. (Materials Science Monographs: No. 12). 300p. 1984. write for info. Elsevier.

Brock, Geoffrey E., ed. Metallurgy of Advanced Electronic Materials: Proceedings of a Technical Conference. Philadelphia, Pennsylvania, August 27-29, 1962. LC 63-13589. (Metallurgical Society Conferences Ser.: Vol. 19). pap. 91.30 (ISBN 0-317-08053-9, 2001507). Bks Demand UMI.

Brown, Donald. Basic Metallurgy. LC 80-68584. (Mechanical Ser.). (Illus.). 323p. (Orig.). 1981. pap. text ed. 13.80 (ISBN 0-8273-1769-7); instr's. guide 3.60 (ISBN 0-8273-1770-0). Delmar.

Brown, Donald V. Metallurgy Basics. 240p. 1983. 15.95 (ISBN 0-442-21434-0). Van Nos Reinhold.

Bulk-Tonnage Metal Deposits. LC 82-62928. 1983. 97.40 (ISBN 0-942218-20-5). Minobras.

Burkin, A. R. Topics in Non-Ferrous Extractive Metallurgy. LC 80-17435. (Critical Reports on Applied Chemistry Ser.: Vol. 1). 134p. 1980. 34.95 (ISBN 0-470-27016-0). Halsted Pr.

Burkin, A. R., ed. Leaching & Reduction in Hydrometallurgy. 109p. (Orig.). 1975. pap. text ed. 40.25x (ISBN 0-900488-27-1). IMM North Am.

Business Communications Staff. New Specialty Metals & Metallurgy. 1985. pap. 1750.00 (ISBN 0-89336-454-1, GB085). BCC.

--Powder, Metallurgy: Gb-041. 1981. 725.00 (ISBN 0-89336-113-5). BCC.

Butts, Allison. Metallurgical Problems. LC 79-9867. 462p. 1981. Repr. of 1943 ed. lib. bdg. 29.50 (ISBN 0-88275-915-9). Krieger.

Caddell, Robert M. & Hosford, William F. Metal Forming: Mechanics & Metallurgy. (Illus.). 352p. 1983. text ed. 37.95 (ISBN 0-13-577700-3). P-H.

Cahalan, M. J., intro. by. Advances in Extractive Metallurgy. 1023p. 1968. text ed. 40.25x (ISBN 0-686-32508-7). IMM North Am.

Carlin, R. L., ed. Transition Metal Chemistry: A Series of Advances, Vol. 4. 1968. 75.00 (ISBN 0-8247-1079-7). Dekker.

Carlin, Richard L. Transition Metal Chemistry, Vol. 3. LC 65-27431. pap. 92.80 (ISBN 0-317-08346-5, 2017696). Bks Demand UMI.

Carter, Giles F. Principles of Physical & Chemical Metallurgy. 1979. 59.00 (ISBN 0-87170-080-8). ASM.

Centre National de la Recherche Scientifique. New Physical & Chemical Properties of Metals of Very High Purity. (Illus.). 502p. 1965. 132.95 (ISBN 0-677-10060-4). Gordon.

Chalmers, Bruce. Physical Metallurgy. LC 59-14983. (Wiley Series on the Science & Technology of Materials). pap. 117.00 (ISBN 0-317-10463-2, 2055140). Bks Demand UMI.

Chang, Y. A. & Smith, J. F. Calculation of Phase Diagrams & Thermochemistry of Alloy Phases. 286p. 30.00 (ISBN 0-89520-356-1); members 18.00 (ISBN 0-317-37185-1); student members 10.00 (ISBN 0-317-37186-X). Metal Soc.

Chaplin, Jack W. Metal Manufacturing Technology. 1976. text ed. 19.96 (ISBN 0-87345-132-5). McKnight.

Chen, E. W., ed. Magnetism & Metallurgy of Soft Magnetic Materials. 1978. 81.50 (ISBN 0-7204-0706-0, North Holland). Elsevier.

Christian, J. W. Theory of Transformations in Metals & Alloys., Part 1: Equilibrium & General Kinetic Theory. 2nd ed. LC 74-22470. 564p. 1975. text ed. 67.00 (ISBN 0-08-018031-0). Pergamon.

Committee for Fundamental Metallurgy, ed. Slag Atlas. 1981. 135.00 (ISBN 0-9960086-2-4, Pub. by Verlag Stahleisen W Germany). Heyden.

Cottrell, Alan. An Introduction to Metallurgy. LC 75-21731. 598p. 1975. pap. 29.50x (ISBN 0-8448-0767-2). Crane-Russak Co.

Cutting, G. W. Process Audits on Mineral Dressing Processes: Their Generation & Practical Use, 1978. 1981. 69.00x (ISBN 0-686-97143-4, Pub. by W Spring England). State Mutual Bk.

Dalton, Murphy L., Jr. Searching with 1 & 2 Sensor-Location Magnetometers. rev. ed. (One Hundred Forty-Eight Ser.). (Illus.). 144p. pap. text ed. 19.00 (ISBN 0-317-19114-4). M L Dalton Res.

Dancy, T. E. & Robinson, E. L., eds. Flat Rolled Products: Rolling & Treatment. LC 59-14888. (Metallurgical Society Conference Ser.: Vol. 1). pap. 37.30 (ISBN 0-317-10712-7, 2000664). Bks Demand UMI.

Delphic Forecast on "Tool Materials by Powder Metallurgy" & "Sintered Structural Components". 30p. (Orig.). 1983. pap. text ed. 9.00x (ISBN 0-904357-57-0, Metals Soc). Brookfield Pub Co.

Denyer, J. E., intro. by. International Mineral Processing Congress 1960. 5th ed. 1118p. 1960. text ed. 46.00x (ISBN 0-686-32512-5). IMM North Am.

Developments in Metallurgical Control in Basic Oxygen Steelmaking. 100p. (Orig.). 1982. pap. text ed. 15.00x (ISBN 0-904357-49-X, Metals Soc). Brookfield Pub Co.

Devereux, Owen F. Topics in Metallurgical Thermodynamics. LC 83-1115. 494p. 1983. 43.50x (ISBN 0-471-86963-5, Pub. by Wiley-Interscience). Wiley.

Douglass, D. L. & Kunz, F. W., eds. Columbium Metallurgy: Proceedings. LC 61-9442. (Metallurgy Society Conferences Ser.: Vol. 10). pap. 160.00 (ISBN 0-317-10234-6, 2000673). Bks Demand UMI.

Earhart, E. W., ed. Flat Rolled Products III: Proceedings. LC 62-18702. (Metallurgical Society Conference Ser.: Vol. 13). pap. 42.80 (ISBN 0-317-10398-9, 2000678). Bks Demand UMI.

Earhart, E. W. & Hindson, R. D., eds. Flat Rolled Products II: Semi-Finished & Finished. LC 60-10586. (Metallurgical Society Conference Ser.: Vol. 6). pap. 40.30 (ISBN 0-317-10406-3, 2000669). Bks Demand UMI.

Easterling, Ken. Introduction to the Physical Metallurgy of Welding. 208p. 1983. text ed. 59.95 (ISBN 0-408-01351-6); pap. text ed. 29.95 (ISBN 0-408-01352-4). Butterworth.

Ehrlich, Reinhart P., ed. Copper Metallurgy. LC 70-633878. pap. 94.80 (ISBN 0-317-10290-7, 2012652). Bks Demand UMI.

Emel'yanova, V. S. & Evstyukhin, A. I., eds. High Purity Metals & Alloys: Fabrication, Properties, & Testing. LC 67-19386. 175p. 1967. 35.00x (ISBN 0-306-10793-7, Consultants). Plenum Pub.

Evans, A. M., ed. Metallization Associated with Acid Magmatism. LC 76-366369. (International Geological Correlation Programme Ser.: Vol. 6). 385p. 1982. 58.95x (ISBN 0-471-09995-3, Pub. by Wiley-Interscience). Wiley.

Filippov, S. Theory of Metallurgical Processes. 296p. 1975. 10.00 (ISBN 0-8285-2231-6, Pub. by Mir Pubs USSR). Imported Pubns.

Fine, Alan H. & Geiger, H. Handbook on Material & Energy Balance Calculations in Metallurgical Processes. 45.00 (ISBN 0-89520-360-X); members 30.00 (ISBN 0-317-37227-0); student members 20.00 (ISBN 0-317-37228-9). Metal Soc.

Fine, H. A. & Gaskell, D. R., eds. Metallurgical Slags & Fluxes. LC 84-62011. (Illus.). 1116p. 1984. 72.00 (ISBN 0-89520-483-5). Metal Soc.

--Second International Symposium on Metallurgical Slags & Fluxes. 1116p. 72.00 (ISBN 0-89520-483-5, 253); members 46.00 (ISBN 0-317-37211-4); student members 23.00 (ISBN 0-317-37212-2). Metal Soc.

Fitterer, G. Applications of Fundamental Thermodynamics to Metallurgical Processes. 434p. 1967. pap. 119.25 (ISBN 0-677-10815-X). Gordon.

Foss. Basic Metallurgy. text ed. write for info. (ISBN 0-685-67274-3). Bennett IL.

Foulkes, E. C., ed. Biological Roles of Metallothionein. (Developments in Toxicology & Environmental Sciences: Vol. 9). 328p. 1981. 74.75 (ISBN 0-444-00653-2, Biomedical Pr). Elsevier.

Fox, Kenneth F., Jr. & Rinehart, C. Dean. Distribution of Copper & Other Metals in Gully Sediments of Part of Okanogan County, Washington. (Bulletin Ser.: No. 65). (Illus.). 38p. 1972. 2.00 (ISBN 0-686-34715-3). Geologic Pubns.

Friedrichs, H. Melting & Dissolution. Hinds, G. & Minuth, K. P., trs. (Illus.). 179p. 1984. pap. 25.00 (ISBN 3-514-00319-X, Pub. by Verlag Stahlusen W Germany). Heyden.

Fruehan, R. J. Ladle Metallurgy Principles & Practices. 155p. 1985. 70.00 (ISBN 0-932897-01-0). Iron & Steel.

Future Metal Strategy. 220p. (Orig.). 1980. pap. text ed. 25.00x (ISBN 0-904357-29-5, Metals Soc). Brookfield Pub Co.

Gaskell, David R. Metallurgical Thermodynamics. 2nd ed. (Materials Engineering Ser.). 560p. 1981. text ed. 48.00 (ISBN 0-07-022946-5). McGraw.

Gechneioner, K. A., Jr., et al, eds. Metallurgy at High Pressures & High Temperatures: Proceedings of a Symposium, Dallas, Texas, February 25-26, 1963. LC 64-18801. (Metallurgical Society Conferences Ser.: Vol. 22). pap. 105.80 (ISBN 0-317-10359-8, 2001510). Bks Demand UMI.

Geiger, G. H. & Poirier, D. R. Transport Phenomena in Metallurgy. LC 75-164648. 1973. text ed. 34.95 (ISBN 0-201-02352-0). Addison-Wesley.

Gilchrist, J. D. Extraction Metallurgy. 2nd ed. 1979. pap. 18.75 (ISBN 0-08-021712-5). Pergamon.

Goodenough, J. B., ed. Metal Complexes. (Structure & Bonding Ser.: Vol. 44). (Illus.). 202p. 1981. 59.00 (ISBN 0-387-10494-1). Springer-Verlag.

Gorelik, S. S. Recrystallization in Metals & Alloys. 479p. 1981. 13.00 (ISBN 0-8285-2065-8, Pub. by Mir Pubs USSR). Imported Pubns.

Gray, Phillip M., intro. by. Extraction Metallurgy '81. 441p. (Orig.). 1981. pap. text ed. 115.00x (ISBN 0-900488-59-X). IMM North Am.

Greenwood, J. D. Heavy Deposition. 216p. 1981. 60.00x (ISBN 0-85218-030-6, Pub. by Portcullio Pr). State Mutual Bk.

Grubel, Ralph O., ed. Metallurgy of Elemental & Compound Semiconductors: Proceedings. LC 61-9443. (Metallurgical Society Conference Ser.: Vol. 12). pap. 126.80 (ISBN 0-317-08023-7, 2000675). Bks Demand UMI.

Guntherodt, H. J. & Beck, H., eds. Glassy Metals II. (Topics in Applied Physics: Vol. 53). (Illus.). 410p. 1983. 44.00 (ISBN 0-387-12787-9). Springer-Verlag.

Habashi, F. Progress in Extractive Metallurgy Series, Vol. 1. 248p. 1973. 67.25 (ISBN 0-677-12220-9). Gordon.

--Progress in Extractive Metallurgy Series, Vol. 2. Date not set. price not set (ISBN 0-677-15730-4). Gordon.

Habashi, Fathi. Chalcopyrite: Its Chemistry & Metallurgy. (Illus.). 1978. text ed. 45.00x (ISBN 0-07-025383-8). McGraw.

--General Principles. (Principles of Extractive Metallurgy Ser.: Vol. 1). 424p. 1969. 75.95 (ISBN 0-677-01770-7). Gordon.

Hall, Eugene J. The Language of Mining & Metallurgy in English. (English for Careers Ser.). 1978. pap. text ed. 4.25 (ISBN 0-88345-307-X, 18521). Regents Pub.

Hanes, H. D., et al. Hot Isostatic Processing. (Metals & Ceramics Information Ctr. Ser. (McIc)). (Illus.). 93p. 1979. 31.00 (ISBN 0-935470-03-4). Battelle.

Hasson, Dennis F. & Hamilton, Howard C., eds. Advanced Processing Methods for Titanium. 320p. 1981. 36.00 (ISBN 0-317-37193-2); members 24.00 (ISBN 0-317-37194-0); student members 12.00 (ISBN 0-317-37195-9). Metal Soc.

Hatch, John E, ed. Aluminum: Properties & Physical Metallurgy. 1984. 70.00 (ISBN 0-87170-176-6). Am Soc Pub Admin.

Hausner, Henry H., et al, eds. Friction & Antifriction Materials. LC 74-127937. (Perspectives in Powder Metallurgy: Fundamentals, Methods, & Applications Ser.: Vol. 4). pap. 87.50 (ISBN 0-317-10432-2, 2019460). Bks Demand UMI.

Herbst, J. A. Control 'Eighty-Four: Mineral Metallurgical Processing. (Illus.). 441p. 1984. 45.00 (ISBN 0-89520-420-7). Soc Mining Eng.

Higgins, G. & Thomas, V. The Principles of Metallurgical Structures. write for info. Pergamon.

Higgins, Raymond A. Engineering Metallurgy, 2 Vols. Incl. Vol. 1. Applied Physical Metallurgy. 5th ed. 576p. 1983. pap. 14.50 (ISBN 0-89874-567-5); Vol. 2. Metallurgical Process Technology. 480p. pap. 14.50 (ISBN 0-89874-568-3). LC 82-19292. 1983. pap. 14.50 each (ISBN 0-89874-603-5); pap. 25.00 set. Krieger.

Hills, A. W., ed. Heat & Mass Transfer in Process Metallurgy. 252p. 1967. text ed. 26.00x (ISBN 0-686-32511-7). IMM North Am.

Hingwe, A. K., ed. Quality Control: Source Book. 1982. 54.00 (ISBN 0-87170-147-2). ASM.

Hoyle, G. Electroslag Processes: Principles & Practice. (Illus.). 215p. 1983. 50.00 (ISBN 0-85334-164-8, Pub. by Elsevier Applied Sci England). Elsevier.

Hoyt, Samuel L. Men of Metals. 1979. 7.00 (ISBN 0-87170-059-X). ASM.

Hyslop, Marjorie R. A Brief Guide to Sources of Metals Information. LC 72-87893. (Illus.). ix, 180p. 1973. text ed. 6.00 (ISBN 0-87815-008-0). Info Resources.

Institution Of Metallurgists. Progress in Metallurgical Technology. (Illus.). 1960. 15.00x (ISBN 0-677-60150-6). Gordon.

Instrumentation in the Mining & Metallurgy Industries, Vol. 10: Proceedings of the 11th Mining & Metallurgy Instrumentation Symposium. LC 73-82889. 136p. 1983. pap. text ed. 25.00x (ISBN 0-87664-771-9). Instru Soc.

Instrumentation in the Mining & Metallurgy Industries, Vol. 11: Proceedings of the 12th Mining & Metallurgy Instrumentation Symposium. 232p. 1983. pap. text ed. 35.00x (ISBN 0-87664-816-2). Instru Soc.

International Tailing Symposium, Second, Denver, Colorado, 1978. Tailing Disposal Today: Proceedings, Vol. 2. Argall, George O., Jr., ed. LC 73-78129. (A World Mining Book). (Illus.). 600p. 1979. 37.50 (ISBN 0-87930-106-6). Miller Freeman.

Ion Assisted Surface Treatment, Techniques & Processes. 140p. (Orig.). 1982. pap. text ed. 36.00x (ISBN 0-904357-48-1, Pub. by Metal Society). Brookfield Pub Co.

Javier-Son, A., ed. New Analytical Techniques for Trace Constituents of Metallic & Metal-Bearing Ores - STP 747. 135p. 1981. 15.00 (ISBN 0-8031-0743-9, 04-747000-01). ASTM.

Jeffes, J. H. & Tait, R. J., eds. Physical Chemistry of Process Metallurgy: The Richardson Conference. 266p. 1974. text ed. 72.00x (ISBN 0-900488-22-0). IMM North Am.

Johnson, C. G. & Weeks, W. R. Metallurgy. 5th ed. (Illus.). 1977. text ed. 15.95 (ISBN 0-8269-3482-X). Am Technical.

Jones, L. & Vaughan, J. Scientific & Technical Information on the Metals Industry: Report of the Metals Information Review Committee. 1982. 50.00x (ISBN 0-7123-3008-9, Pub. by Brit Lib England). State Mutual Bk.

Jones, M. J., ed. Advances in Extractive Metallurgy & Refining. 635p. 1972. text ed. 40.25x (ISBN 0-900488-06-9). IMM North Am.

--Advances in Extractive Metallurgy, 1977. 244p. 1977. text ed. 69.00x (ISBN 0-900488-37-9). IMM North Am.

--Commonwealth Mining & Metallurgical Congress, Hong Kong, 11th, 1978: Proceedings. (Commonwealth Mining & Metallurgical Congresses Ser.). 818p. 1979. text ed. 118.00x (ISBN 0-900488-45-X). IMM North Am.

--Complex Metallurgy Seventy-Eight. 143p. (Orig.). 1978. pap. text ed. 63.25x (ISBN 0-900488-42-5). IMM North Am.

--International Mineral Processing Congress 1973. 10th ed. 1209p. 1974. text ed. 72.00x (ISBN 0-900488-24-7). IMM North Am.

--Mineral Processing & Extractive Metallurgy. (Proceedings of the Ninth Commonwealth Mining & Metallurgical Congress 1969: Vol. 3). 938p. 1970. text ed. 51.75x (ISBN 0-900488-05-0). IMM North Am.

--Mining & Petroleum Geology. (Proceedings of the Ninth Commonwealth Mining & Metallurgical Congress 1969: Vol. 2). 774p. 1970. text ed. 46.00x (ISBN 0-900488-03-4). IMM North Am.

--Mining & Petroleum Technology. (Proceedings of the Ninth Commonwealth Mining & Metallurgical Congress 1969: Vol. 1). 1059p. 1970. text ed. 51.75x (ISBN 0-900488-04-2). IMM North Am.

--Physical & Fabrication Metallurgy. (Proceedings of the Ninth Commonwealth Mining & Metallurgical Congress 1969: Vol. 4). 561p. 1970. text ed. 46.00x (ISBN 0-900488-01-8). IMM North Am.

--Process Engineering of Pyrometallurgy. 105p. (Orig.). 1974. pap. text ed. 28.75x (ISBN 0-900488-23-9). IMM North Am.

Kamdar, M. H., ed. Embrittlement by Liquid & Solid Metals: Proceedings, TMS Fall Meeting, St. Louis, Missouri, 1982. LC 83-62937. (Illus.). 589p. 1984. 70.00 (ISBN 0-89520-467-3). Metal Soc.

Kaye & Street. Die Casting Metallurgy. 1982. text ed. 49.95 (ISBN 0-408-10717-0). Butterworth.

Kedves, F. J. & Beke, D. L., eds. Diffusion in Metals & Alloys: Proceedings of an International Conference Held at Tihany, Hungary. (Diffusion & Defect Monograph Ser.: Vol. 7). 685p. 1983. 84.00 (ISBN 0-87849-527-4). Trans Tech.

Klesnil, M. & Lukas, P. Fatigue of Metallic Materials. (Materials Science Monograph: Vol. 7). 240p. 1980. 61.75 (ISBN 0-444-99762-8). Elsevier.

Kovacs, T. Principles of X-Ray Metallurgy. LC 73-81852. 185p. 1969. 24.50x (ISBN 0-306-30414-7, Plenum Pr). Plenum Pub.

Kubaschewski, O. Metallurgical Thermochemistry. 5th ed. 1979. text ed. 89.00 (ISBN 0-08-020897-5); pap. text ed. 28.00 (ISBN 0-08-022107-6). Pergamon.

Kuczynski, G. C., ed. Sintering Processes. LC 79-25813. (Materials Sciences Research Ser.: Vol. 13). 585p. 1980. 85.00x (ISBN 0-306-40336-6, Plenum Pr). Plenum Pub.

Kudryk, V. & Rao, Y. K., eds. Physical Chemistry of Extractive Metallurgy. LC 84-29561. (Illus.). 497p. 1985. 70.00 (ISBN 0-89520-486-X). Metal Soc.

Kuwata. Color Atlas of Ceramo-Metal Technology, Vol. 1. 1985. write for info. (ISBN 0-912791-12-8). Ishiyaku Euro.

--Color Atlas of Ceramo-Metal Technology, Vol. 2. 1985. price not set (ISBN 0-912791-13-6). Ishiyaku Euro.

Lang, E., ed. Coatings for High Temperature Applications. (Illus.). 448p. 1984. 89.00 (ISBN 0-85334-221-0, Pub. by Elsevier Applied Sci England). Elsevier.

Leslie, William C. The Physical Metallurgy of Steels. (M-H Materials Science & Engineering Ser.). 368p. 1981. text ed. 45.00 (ISBN 0-07-037780-4). McGraw.

Lifshits, I. M., et al, eds. Electron Theory of Metals. LC 79-188919. (Illus.). 320p. 1973. 45.00x (ISBN 0-306-10873-9, Consultants). Plenum Pub.

Linchevsky, B. Methods of Metallurgical Experiment. 296p. 1982. 7.00 (ISBN 0-8285-2283-9, Pub. by Mir Pubs USSR). Imported Pubns.

Linnert, G. E. Metallurgy, Welding, Carbon & Alloy Steels- Fundamentals: WM1, Vol. 1. 3rd ed. 474p. 1965. 28.00 (ISBN 0-686-95602-8, WM1); member 21.00. Am Welding.

--Metallurgy, Welding, Carbon & Alloy Steels: Technology: WM2, Vol. 2. 3rd ed. 674p. 1967. 30.00 (ISBN 0-686-95605-2, WM2); member 22.50. Am Welding.

--Welding Metallurgy, 2 vols. Vol. 1-fundamentals, 1965. 28.00 (ISBN 0-685-65961-5); Vol. 2-technology, 1967. 20.00 (ISBN 0-685-65962-3). Am Welding.

Love, L. Carl. Principles of Metallurgy. 1985. text ed. 29.95 (ISBN 0-8359-5605-9); instrs.' manual avail. (ISBN 0-8359-5673-3). Reston.

Marder, A. R. & Goldstein, J. I., eds. Phase Transformation in Ferrous Alloys. LC 84-61582. (Illus.). 411p. 1984. 38.00 (ISBN 0-89520-481-9). Metal Soc.

Martin, J. W. & Hull, R. A. Elementary Science of Metals. LC 73-75479. (Wykeham Science Ser.: No. 1). 148p. 1974. 9.95x (ISBN 0-8448-1103-3). Crane Russak Co.

Masson, C. R. Metallurgical Slags, Pt. 2. flexi-cover 61.00 (ISBN 0-08-028684-4). Pergamon.

Materials Evaluation under Fretting Conditions-STP 780. 189p. 1982. 24.75 (ISBN 0-8031-0829-X, 04-780000-29). ASTM.

Mechanical Behaviour & Nuclear Application of Stainless Steel at Elevated Temperatures. 264p. 1982. text ed. 80.00x (ISBN 0-904357-41-4, Metals Soc). Brookfield Pub Co.

Metallurgical Society of AIME Staff. Physical Metallurgy of Metal Joining: Proceedings of a Symposium. Kossowsky, Ram & Glicksman, M. E., eds. LC 80-82303. pap. 69.50 (ISBN 0-317-26075-8, 2023772). Bks Demand UMI.

Meyers, Marc A. & Chawla, K. K. Mechanical Metallurgy: Principles & Applications. (Illus.). 752p. 1984. 40.95 (ISBN 0-13-569863-4). P-H.

Microbial Corrosion. 136p. (Orig.). 1983. pap. text ed. 36.00x (ISBN 0-904357-58-9, Metals Soc). Brookfield Pub Co.

Moffatt, H. K., et al, eds. Metallurgical Applications of Magnetohydrodynamics. 344p. 1984. pap. text ed. 70.00x (ISBN 0-904357-60-0, Metals Soc). Brookfield Pub Co.

Moffatt, William G. Handbook of Binary Phase Diagrams, 4 vols. (Illus.). 1030p. 1981. 175.00x (ISBN 0-931690-00-5). Genium Pub.

--The Index to Binary Phase Collections. LC 79-25561. 1980. 85.00x (ISBN 0-931690-12-9). Genium Pub.

Molten Salt Electrolysis in Metal Production. 73p. (Orig.). 1977. pap. text ed. 49.00x (ISBN 0-900488-39-5). IMM North Am.

Mondolf, Lucio F. & Zmeskal, Otto. Engineering Metallurgy. LC 54-12253. pap. 101.80 (ISBN 0-317-10673-2, 2003417). Bks Demand UMI.

Mueller, William M. & Shaw, Milton C., eds. Energetics in Metallurgical Phenomena, 4 vols. Vol. 1, 1965, 440p. 112.25x (ISBN 0-677-00570-9); Vol. 2, 1965, 214p. 57.75x (ISBN 0-677-01010-9); Vol. 3, 1967, 204p. 57.75x (ISBN 0-677-11120-7); Vol. 4, 1968, 392p. 106.50x (ISBN 0-677-11680-2). Gordon.

Mukherjee, K. & Majumder, J., eds. Laser Processing of Materials. 1984. avail. Metal Soc.

Mukherjee, Kali & Majumder, J., eds. Lasers in Metallurgy. 301p. 1981. 36.00 (ISBN 0-317-37206-8); 24.00 (ISBN 0-317-37207-6); students 12.00 (ISBN 0-317-37208-4). Metal Soc.

Mulholland, James A. A History of Metals in Colonial America. LC 80-15130. (Illus.). xiv, 208p. 1981. text ed. 18.75 (ISBN 0-8173-0052-X); pap. text ed. 8.95 (ISBN 0-8173-0053-8). U of Ala Pr.

Mullins, W. & Shaw, M. C. Metal Transformations. 320p. 1968. 80.95x (ISBN 0-677-10900-8). Gordon.

Multilingual Glossary of Heat Treatment Terms: Vol. 1: Theory & Processes. write for info. (Metals Soc). Brookfield Pub Co.

Murr, Lawrence E., et al, eds. Metallurgical Applications of Bacterial Leaching & Related Microbiological Phenomena. 1978. 58.00 (ISBN 0-12-511150-9). Acad Pr.

Nabarro, F. R. N., ed. Dislocations in Metallurgy. (Dislocations in Solids Ser.: Vol. 4). 464p. 1980. 102.25 (ISBN 0-444-85025-2, North Holland). Elsevier.

Neely, John E. Practical Metallurgy & Materials of Industry. 2nd ed. 406p. 1984. 29.95 (ISBN 0-471-86461-7); tchrs.' manual avail. (ISBN 0-471-80125-9). Wiley.

Nelson. Transition Metal Chemistry, Vol. 8. 496p. 75.00 (ISBN 0-8247-1656-6). Dekker.

Newton, J. Extractive Metallurgy. LC 59-14124. pap. 102.60 (ISBN 0-8357-9889-5, 2055265). Bks Demand UMI.

Ollerenshaw, R. J. Fundamental Processes Involved in the Formation of Metallurgical Fume, 1978. 1981. 80.00x (ISBN 0-686-97081-0, Pub. by W Spring England). State Mutual Bk.

Parker, R. H. An Introduction to Chemical Metallurgy: In SI-Metric Units. 2nd ed. 1978. text ed. 62.00 (ISBN 0-08-022125-4); pap. text ed. 17.50 (ISBN 0-08-022126-2). Pergamon.

Parrish, G. & Harper, G. S. Production Gas Carburizing. (Materials Engineering Practice Ser.). (Illus.). 250p. 1985. 40.00 (ISBN 0-08-027312-2); pap. 15.75 (ISBN 0-08-027319-X). Pergamon.

Pearse, M. J. An Investigation of the Oxidation & Self-Heating of Metal Sulphide Concentrates, 1979. 1982. 59.00x (ISBN 0-686-97098-5, Pub. by W Spring England). State Mutual Bk.

Pehlke, R. M. Unit Processes of Extractive Metallurgy. 400p. 1973. 34.50 (ISBN 0-444-00130-1). Elsevier.

Perspectives in Metallurgical Development. 337p. 1984. text ed. 58.00x (ISBN 0-904357-71-6, Pub. by Metals Soc). Brookfield Pub Co.

Pollack, ed. Material Science & Metallurgy. 3rd ed. 1980. text ed. 26.95 (ISBN 0-8359-4280-5); solutions manual avail. (ISBN 0-8359-4282-1). Reston.

Pryor, E. J. Mineral Processing. 3rd ed. (Illus.). 844p. 1974. Repr. of 1965 ed. 70.50 (ISBN 0-444-20010-X, Pub. by Elsevier Applied Sci England). Elsevier.

Ranwan, M. & Wezranowski, E., eds. Radiactive Tracers in Metallurgical Research. (Bibliographical Ser.: No. 42). 140p. 1974. pap. (ISBN 92-0-164074-9, ISP/21/42, IAEA). Unipub.

Rao, Y. K. Stochiometry & Thermodynamics of Metallurgical Processes. (Illus.). 800p. Date not set. price not set (ISBN 0-521-25856-1). Cambridge U Pr.

Rapidly Quenched Metals III, 2 vols. (Orig.). 1978. pap. text ed. 60.00x (ISBN 0-904357-22-8, Metals Soc). Brookfield Pub Co.

Recent Advances in Mining & Processing of Low-Grade Submarginal Mineral Deposits. LC 76-11771. 1977. text ed. 25.00 (ISBN 0-08-021051-1). Pergamon.

Residuals, Additives & Materials Properties. 341p. 1980. 85.00x (ISBN 0-85403-132-4, Metals Soc). Brookfield Pub Co.

Resource Systems International. Metallurgy: Welding. 1982. pap. text ed. 15.00 (ISBN 0-8359-4335-6). Reston.

Ritcey, G. M. & Ashbrook, A. W. Solvent Extraction: Principles & Applications to Process Metallurgy, Pt. 2. (Process Metallurgy Ser.: Vol. 1, Pt. 2). 738p. 1979. 117.00 (ISBN 0-444-41771-0). Elsevier.

Roberts, C. W. A Legacy from Victorian Enterprise (1983) The Briton Ferry Ironworks & the Daughter Companies. 277p. 1983. pap. 19.00x (ISBN 0-9509107-1-6, Metals Soc). Brookfield Pub Co.

Rod & Bar Production in the 1980's. 188p. 1982. text ed. 60.00x (ISBN 0-904357-40-6, Metals Soc). Brookfield Pub Co.

Rohde, R. W., et al, eds. Metallurgical Effects at High Strain Rates. LC 73-10497. 700p. 1973. 95.00x (ISBN 0-306-30754-5, Plenum Pr). Plenum Pub.

Rollason, E. C. Metallurgy for Engineers. 4th ed. (Illus.). 1973. pap. 28.95x (ISBN 0-7131-3282-5). Intl Ideas.

Rosenqvist, T. Principles of Extractive Metallurgy. 2nd ed. (Materials Science & Electronics Ser.). 608p. 1983. 49.95 (ISBN 0-07-053910-3). McGraw.

Rowland, T. J. & Beck, Paul A., eds. Magnetic & Inelastic Scattering of Neutrons by Metals. LC 67-29670. (Metallurgical Society Conference Ser.: Vol. 43). pap. 59.80 (ISBN 0-317-10595-7, 2001532). Bks Demand UMI.

Rudman, Jack. Metallurgist. (Career Examination Ser.: C-496). (Cloth bdg. avail. on request). pap. 12.00 (ISBN 0-8373-0496-2). Natl Learning.

Russell, K. C. Phase Stability under Irradiation. (Illus.). 206p. 1985. pap. 75.00 (ISBN 0-08-032722-2, Pub. by Aberdeen Scotland). Pergamon.

Ryan, W. Non-Ferrous Extractive Metallurgy in the United Kingdom. 234p. 1968. 34.50x (ISBN 0-686-97550-2). IMM North Am.

St. Pierre, George R., ed. Physical Chemistry of Process Metallurgy, Pt. 1. LC 60-10587. (Metallurgical Society Conferences Ser.: Vol. 7). pap. 160.00 (ISBN 0-317-10237-0, 2000670). Bks Demand UMI.

--Physical Chemistry of Process Metallurgy, Pt. 2. LC 60-10587. (Metallurgical Society Conferences Ser.: Vol. 8). pap. 160.00 (ISBN 0-317-10836-0, 2000671). Bks Demand UMI.

Samsonov, G. V. & Kislyi, P. S. High-Temperature Non-Metallic Thermocouples & Sheaths. LC 65-26628. 133p. 1967. 29.50x (ISBN 0-306-10765-1, Consultants). Plenum Pub.

Sastry, K. V., ed. Agglomeration Seventy-Seven. LC 76-58569. (Illus.). 1977. text ed. 39.00x (ISBN 0-89520-045-7). Soc Mining Eng.

Sauveur, Albert. Metallurgical Reminiscences & Dialogue. 1981. 18.00 (ISBN 0-87170-132-4). ASM.

Schuhmann, R. Metallurgical Engineering Vol. 1. Engineering Principles. (Illus.). 1952. 29.95 (ISBN 0-201-06770-6). Addison-Wesley.

Shchelov, A. Fundamentals of Metallogenic Analysis. 335p. 1979. 9.95 (ISBN 0-8285-1526-3, Pub. by Mir Pubs USSR). Imported Pubns.

Shoenberg, D. Magnetic Oscillations in Metals. LC 82-19762. (Cambridge Monographs on Physics). (Illus.). 400p. 1984. 97.50 (ISBN 0-521-22480-2). Cambridge U Pr.

Shrager, Arthur M. Elementary Metallurgy & Metallography. 2nd ed. (Illus.). 1961. pap. text ed. 5.95 (ISBN 0-486-60138-2). Dover.

Singhal, Subhash C., ed. High-Temperature Protective Coating. 390p. 1983. 50.00 (ISBN 0-89520-455-X); members 32.00 (ISBN 0-317-37209-2); student members 16.00 (ISBN 0-317-37210-6). Metal Soc.

Sohn, H. Y. & Wadsworth, M. E., eds. Rate Processes of Extractive Metallurgy. LC 78-15941. (Illus.). 484p. 1978. 65.00 (ISBN 0-306-31102-X, Plenum Pr). Plenum Pub.

Spalding, D. Brian & Afgan, Naim H., eds. Heat & Mass Transfer in Metallurgical Systems. LC 80-27193. (International Centre for Heat & Mass Transfer Ser.). (Illus.). 758p. 1981. text ed. 118.00 (ISBN 0-89116-169-4). Hemisphere Pub.

Steeb, S. & Warlimont, H., eds. Rapidly-Quenched Metals: Proceedings of the International Conference, 5th, Wurzburg, Germany, September 3-7, 1984, 2 vols. 1850p. 1985. Set. 146.25 (ISBN 0-317-19373-2, North-Holland); Vol. 1. 96.50 (ISBN 0-444-86939-5); Vol. 2. 66.75 (ISBN 0-444-86941-7). Elsevier.

Steel Castings Res. & Trade Assoc., ed. Metallurgy & Quality: Proceedings of the 25th Annual Conference 1980, Vol. 1. 1981. 80.00x (ISBN 0-686-79064-2, Pub. by Steel Castings). State Mutual Bk.

Steel Castings Res. & Trade Association, 18th Annual Conference, 1979. Modern Foundry Practice: Proceedings, 2 vols. 1973. 60.00x (ISBN 0-686-79285-8, Pub. by Steel Castings). State Mutual Bk.

Taubenblat, Pierre W. Copper Base Powder Metallurgy. LC 80-81464. (New Perspectives in Powder Metallurgy Ser.: Vol. 7). (Illus.). 232p. 1980. 42.00 (ISBN 0-918404-47-9). Metal Powder.

Tien, John K. & Elliot, John F., eds. Metallurgical Treastises. (Technology of Metallurgy Ser.). 643p. 60.00 (ISBN 0-89520-381-2); members 36.00 (ISBN 0-317-37177-0); student members 18.00 (ISBN 0-317-37178-9). Metal Soc.

Tomlenov, A. D., ed. Plastic Flow of Metals, Vol. 2. LC 75-131886. 94p. 1972. 25.00x (ISBN 0-306-17162-7, Consultants). Plenum Pub.

Tottle, C. R. An Encyclopaedia of Metallurgy & Materials. (Illus.). 448p. 1984. text ed. 97.50x (ISBN 0-7121-0571-9, Metals Soc). Brookfield Pub Co.

Umowski, Joseph S. Ferrous Metallurgy: Laboratory Manual. pap. 23.30 (ISBN 0-317-10760-7, 2004573). Bks Demand UMI.

Unterweiser, P. M., ed. Case Histories in Failure Analysis. 1979. 86.00 (ISBN 0-87170-078-6). ASM.

Upadhyaya, G. S & Dube, R. K. Problems in Metallurgical Thermodynamics & Kinetics. LC 77-7376. 1977. pap. text ed. 17.50 (ISBN 0-08-020864-9). Pergamon.

Vacuum Metallurgy Conference: Proceedings. 209p. 1985. 60.00 (ISBN 0-89520-167-4). Iron & Steel.

Van der Voort, G. F. Metallography: Principles & Practice. 768p. 1983. 46.00 (ISBN 0-07-066970-8). McGraw.

Van Vlack, Lawrence H. Elements of Material Science & Engineering. 5th ed. (Metallurgy & Materials Engineering Ser.). 550p. 1985. text ed. 38.95 (ISBN 0-201-08086-9); solution manual 2.50 (ISBN 0-201-08086-9). Addison-Wesley.

Verink, E. D., ed. Methods of Materials Selection. LC 67-29667. (Metallurgical Society Conference Ser.: Vol. 40). pap. 80.00 (ISBN 0-317-11252-X, 2001529). Bks Demand UMI.

Vogel, F. L., Jr., ed. Resonance & Relaxation in Metals. 2nd rev. ed. 423p. 1964. 42.50x (ISBN 0-306-30183-0, Plenum Pr). Plenum Pub.

Volsky, A. & Sergievskaya, E. Theory of Metallurgical Processes. 1978. 10.00 (ISBN 0-8285-1926-9, Pub. by Mir Pubs USSR). Imported Pubns.

Warner, J. C., et al, eds. Metallurgy of Uranium & Its Alloys. AEC Technical Information Center. (National Nuclear Energy Ser.: Div. IV, Vol. 12). 208p. 1953. pap. 19.00 (ISBN 0-87079-273-3, NNES-IV-12A); microfilm 10.00 (ISBN 0-87079-453-1, NNES-IV-12A). DOE.

Warren, I. H., ed. Application of Polarization Measurements in the Control of Metal Deposition. (Process Metallurgy Ser.: Vol. 3). 314p. 1984. 72.25 (ISBN 0-444-42345-1, I-229-84). Elsevier.

Waseda, Yoshio. The Structure of Non-Crystalline Materials. (Illus.). 304p. 1980. text ed. 66.95 (ISBN 0-07-068426-X). McGraw.

Webster, D., et al, eds. Beryllium Science & Technology, 2 vols. LC 78-20778. (Illus.). 1979. Vol. 1, 347p. 49.50x (ISBN 0-306-40106-1, Plenum Pr); Vol. 2, 457p. 69.50x (ISBN 0-306-40136-3). Plenum Pub.

Weiss, Alfred, ed. World Mining & Metals Technology. LC 76-19748. (Illus.). 1976. text ed. 35.00x (ISBN 0-89520-036-8). Soc Mining Eng.

Westbroek, P. & De Jong, E. W. Biomineralization & Biological Metal Accumulation. 1983. lib. bdg. 69.50 (ISBN 0-686-39596-4, Pub. by Reidel Holland). Kluwer Academic.

Westwood, A. R. & Stoloff, N. S., eds. Environment-Sensitive Mechanical Behavior. LC 66-29851. (Metallurgical Society Conferences Ser.: Vol. 35). pap. 160.00 (ISBN 0-317-11267-8, 2001524). Bks Demand UMI.

Wiffen, F. W. & Spitznagel, J. A., eds. Advanced Techniques for Characterizing Microstructures. (Technology of Metallurgy Ser.). 510p. 50.00 (ISBN 0-89520-390-1); members 32.00 (ISBN 0-317-37183-5); student members 16.00 (ISBN 0-317-37184-3). Metal Soc.

Wilkes, P. Solid State Theory in Metallurgy. LC 72-180020. (Illus.). 480p. (Orig.). 1973. pap. 24.95 (ISBN 0-521-09699-5). Cambridge U Pr.

Wilkinson, A. & Dawson, P. R. The Use of Fluxes in Reducing Metal Losses as Fume & or Dross in Secondary Brass Production, 1977. 1981. 40.00x (ISBN 0-686-97159-0, Pub. by W Spring England). State Mutual Bk.

Winkler, O., ed. Vacuum Metallurgy. Bakish, R. LC 74-118258. (Illus.). 906p. 1971. 191.50 (ISBN 0-444-40857-6). Elsevier.

World Metallurgical Congress 1957, Chicago. The Metal Plutonium. Coffinberry, A. S. & Miner, W. N., eds. LC 61-17072. pap. 114.50 (ISBN 0-317-28263-8, 2024088). Bks Demand UMI.

Yannopoulos, J. C. & Agarwal, J. C., eds. Extractive Metallurgy of Cooper: An International Symposium. LC 75-42949. Vol. 1, Pyrometallurgy & Electrolytic Refining. pap. 160.00 (ISBN 0-317-27927-0, 2025124); Vol. 2, Hydrometallurgy & Electrowinning. pap. 117.80 (ISBN 0-317-27928-9). Bks Demand UMI.

Yemel'Yanov, V. S. & Yevstyukhin, A. I., eds. Metallurgy & Metallography of Pure Metals. 348p. 1962. 94.95x (ISBN 0-677-20530-9). Gordon.

METALLURGY–AUTOMATION

see Metallurgical Plants–Automation

METALLURGY–BIBLIOGRAPHY

Palyza, M. M. Useful Books of Reference for Designers (1926-1983) Held by the Science Reference Library: Pt 1 Units in Physics, Metrication, Metallurgy, Computers in Engineering, Civil Engineering. 168p. (Orig.). 1984. pap. 7.50 (ISBN 0-7123-0712-5, Pub. by British Lib). Longwood Pub Group.

Prince, A. Multicomponent Alloy Constitution Bibliography 1955-1973. 1144p. 1978. text ed. 60.00x (ISBN 0-904357-19-8, Metals Soc). Brookfield Pub Co.

--Multicomponent Alloy Constitution Bibliography 1947-77. 544p. 1981. text ed. 50.00x (ISBN 0-904357-35-X, Metals Soc). Brookfield Pub Co.

Spande, Dennis, compiled by. A Historical Perspective on Metallurgy: A Bibliography. (Archival & Bibliographic Ser.). 1978. pap. 10.00 (ISBN 0-918456-13-4, Crossroads). African Studies Assn.

METALLURGY–DATA PROCESSING

Metallurgical Society of AIME. Computer Control in Process Metallurgy: A Short Course Sponsored by TMS-AIME Held in Las Vegas, Nevada, February 20-21, 1976. pap. 36.80 (ISBN 0-317-10708-9, 2004308). Bks Demand UMI.

O'Neil, T. J., ed. Sixteenth Application of Computers & Operations Research in the Mineral Industry. Society of Mining Engineers, Conference in Tucson, 1979. 653p. 1979. 30.00 (ISBN 0-317-35840-5, 261-1); members 22.00 (ISBN 0-317-35841-3); student members 19.00 (ISBN 0-317-35842-1). Soc Mining Eng.

Ramani, R. V., ed. Fourteenth Application of Computer Methods in the Mineral Industry. Society of Mining Engineers, Conference at the Pennsylvania State University, 1977. 1207p. 1977. 20.00 (ISBN 0-317-35828-6, 047-3); members 15.00 (ISBN 0-317-35829-4); student members 13.50 (ISBN 0-317-35830-8). Soc Mining Eng.

Use of Computers in the Fatigue Laboratory - STP 613. 172p. 1976. 20.00 (ISBN 0-8031-0593-2, 04-613000-30). ASTM.

METALLURGY–DICTIONARIES

Bader, Oliver & Theret, Michel. Diccionario Enciclopedico de Metalurgia. (Span., Fr. & Eng.). 960p. 1975. 44.95 (ISBN 84-7146-054-8, S-50132). French & Eur.

Cagnacci-Schwicker, Angelo. Dictionnaire International de Metallurgie, Mineralogie, Geologie et Industries Extractives, 2 vols. (Fr.). 1530p. 1969. Set. 95.00 (ISBN 0-686-56933-4, M-6054). French & Eur.

Clason, W. E. Elsevier's Dictionary of Metallurgy & Metal Working. (Eng., Fr., Span., Ital., Dutch & Ger.). 848p. 1978. 136.25 (ISBN 0-444-41695-1). Elsevier.

Dollinger, A., ed. Dictionary of Metallurgy. (Eng., Fr., Ger., Rus., Pol. & Slovene.). 767p. 1974. 150.00 (ISBN 0-686-92409-6, M-9893). French & Eur.

Gagnacci-Schwicker, A. & Schwicker. International Dictionary of Metallurgy, Mineralogy, Geology & the Mining & Oil Industries. (Eng., Fr., Ger. & Ital.). 1530p. 1970. 88.00 (ISBN 3-7625-0751-1, M-7482, Pub. by Bauverlag). French & Eur.

Lang, Gernot. Glossary of Technical Terms: EXtrusion of Metals German-English English-German. (Eng. & Ger.). 175p. 1982. 37.00 (ISBN 3-88355-058-2, Pub. by DGM Metallurgy Germany). IR Pubns.

Stolzel, K. Dictionary of Metallurgy & Foundry Technology: English-German. 1984. 92.75 (ISBN 0-444-99612-5, I-423-84). Elsevier.

Woerterbuch fuer Metallurgie, Mineralogie, Geologie, Bergbau und die Oelindustrie. (Eng., Fr., Ger. & Ital., Dictionary of Metallurgy, Mineralogy, Geology, Mining and Oil Industry). 1970. 88.00 (ISBN 3-7625-0751-1, M-6912). French & Eur.

METALLURGY–EARLY WORKS TO 1800

Agricola, Georgius. De Re Metallica. (Illus.). 1912. 19.95 (ISBN 0-486-60006-8). Dover.

Biringuccio, Vannoccio. Pirotechnia. 1966. pap. 6.95x (ISBN 0-262-52017-6). MIT Pr.

METALLURGY–HISTORY

Benson, Elizabeth P., ed. Pre-Columbian Metallurgy of South-America, Proceedings: A Conference at Dumbarton Oaks, October 18 & 19, 1975. LC 79-49261. (Illus.). 107p. 1979. 20.00x (ISBN 0-88402-094-0). Dumbarton Oaks.

Molloy, Peter M. The History of Metal Mining & Metallurgy: An Annotated Bibliography. LC 83-48278. (Bibliographies of the History of Science & Technology Ser.). 350p. 1985. lib. bdg. 55.00 (ISBN 0-8240-9065-9). Garland Pub.

Parr, James G. Man, Metals, & Modern Magic. LC 77-25186. 1978. Repr. of 1958 ed. lib. bdg. 24.75x (ISBN 0-313-20122-6, PAMM). Greenwood.

Smith, Cyril S., ed. The Sorby Centennial Symposium on the History of Metallurgy, Cleveland, Ohio, October 22-23, 1963. LC 65-17635. (Metallurgical Society Conference: Vol. 27). pap. 145.00 (ISBN 0-317-10418-7, 2001515). Bks Demand UMI.

Tylecote, R. F. History of Metallurgy. 192p. (Orig.). 1976. pap. text ed. 20.00x (ISBN 0-904357-06-6, Metals Soc). Brookfield Pub Co.

METALLURGY–LABORATORY MANUALS

Fine, H. Alan, ed. Extractive Metallurgy Laboratory Exercises: Instructor's Guide & Solution Manual. LC 83-81736. (Illus.). 167p. 1983. pap. 12.00 (ISBN 0-89520-462-2). Metal Soc.

Pearse, M. J. Laboratory Procedures for the Choice & Sizing of Dewatering Equipment in the Mineral Processing Industry, 1978. 1981. 75.00x (ISBN 0-686-97104-3, Pub. by W Green England). State Mutual Bk.

METALLURGY, PHYSICAL

see Physical Metallurgy

METALLURGY, POWDER

see Powder Metallurgy

METALLURGY, VACUUM

see Vacuum Metallurgy

METALORGANIC COMPOUNDS

see Organometallic Compounds

METALS

see also Alloys; Assaying; Blowpipe; Earths, Rare; Free Electron Theory of Metals; Intermetallic Compounds; Light Metals; Liquid Metals; Metallic Composites; Metallic Films; Metallic Oxides; Metallography; Mineralogy; Nonferrous Metals; Passivity (Chemistry); Precious Metals; Semimetals; Solder and Soldering; Transition Metals

also particular metals and metal groups, e.g. Iron

Abrikosov, A. A. Introduction to the Theory of Normal Metals. (Solid State Physics: Suppl. 12). 1972. 55.00 (ISBN 0-12-607772-X). Acad Pr.

Adkins, E. M., ed. Light Metals 1983: Proceedings, AIME Annual Meeting, Atlanta, 1983. LC 72-623660. (Illus.). 1254p. 1983. 55.00; members 32.00; student members 16.00. Metal Soc.

American Bureau of Metal Statistics Inc. ABMS Non-Ferrous Metal Data Publication. annual ed. 1978. 25.00 (ISBN 0-685-91837-8). Am Bur Metal.

American Bureau of Metal Statistics Editorial Staff, ed. Fifty-Second Annual Yearbook. 1973. 70.00 (ISBN 0-685-39802-1). Am Bur Metal.

American Bureau of Metal Statistics Inc. Non-Ferrous Metal Data Yearbook, 1979. (Illus.). 1980. yrbk. 70.00 (ISBN 0-686-61434-8). Am Bur Metal.

American Bureau of Metal Statistics Staff, compiled by. Year Book of the American Bureau of Metal Statistics. annual 1972. 70.00 (ISBN 0-910064-05-9). Am Bur Metal.

--Year Book of the American Bureau of Metal Statistics. LC 21-15719. 1973. 70.00 (ISBN 0-910064-06-7). Am Bur Metal.

American Society for Hospital Engineering & American Society for Hospital Purchasing & Materials Management. Silver Recovery for Hospitals. LC 80-19943. 36p. 1980. pap. 10.00 (ISBN 0-87258-331-7, 172100). AHPI.

American Society for Metals. The Inhomogeneity of Plastic Deformation: Papers Presented at a Seminar of the American Society for Metals. LC 72-95850. pap. 82.00 (ISBN 0-317-10482-9, 2019484). Bks Demand UMI.

American Society for Testing & Materials. Unified Numbering System for Metals & Alloys: Metals & Alloys Currently Covered by UNS Numbers, July, 1974. LC 75-309848. pap. 46.50 (ISBN 0-317-11264-3, 2021525). Bks Demand UMI.

American Society Of Mechanical Engineers. ASME Handbook: Metals Engineering-Design. 2nd ed. 1964. 72.50 (ISBN 0-07-001518-X). McGraw.

American Welding Society. Filler Metal Comparison Charts: A5.0. LC 78-54738. 293p. 1983. pap. 40.00; pap. 30.00 members. Am Welding.

Andersen, J. E., ed. Light Metals 1982: Proceedings, AIME Annual Meeting, Dallas, 1982. LC 72-623660. (Illus.). 1170p. 1981. 55.00. Metal Soc.

Application of Nuclear Techniques to the Study of Amorphous Metals: Supplement No. 1. (Atomic Energy Review Ser.). 294p. 1981. pap. 24.50 (ISBN 0-686-78893-1, IAERS1/81, IAEA). Unipub.

ASTM Standardization News, September, 1983. The Metal Properties Council Grows Up. write for info. Metal Prop Coun.

Avitzur. Metal Forming. (Manufacturing, Engineering, & Materials Processing Ser.: Vol. 4). 224p. 1980. 39.75 (ISBN 0-8247-6847-7). Dekker.

Basolo, Fred & Pearson, R. G. Mechanisms of Inorganic Reactions. 2nd ed. LC 66-28755. 701p. 1967. 55.00x (ISBN 0-471-05545-X, Pub. by Wiley-Interscience). Wiley.

Bass, J. & Fischer, K. H. Metals: Electronic Transport Phenomena. (Landolt Boernstein Ser.: Group III, Vol. 15, Subvol. A). (Illus.). 400p. 1982. 263.60 (ISBN 0-387-11082-8). Springer-Verlag.

Beck, H. & Gundtherodt, H. J., eds. Classy Metals, Vol. 1. (Topics in Applied Physics Ser.: Vol. 46). (Illus.). 350p. 1981. 43.00 (ISBN 0-387-10440-2). Springer-Verlag.

--Glassy Metals I. (Topics in Applied Physics: Vol. 46). (Illus.). 350p. 1981. 43.00 (ISBN 0-387-10440-2). Springer-Verlag.

Beer, S., ed. Liquid Metals: Chemistry & Physics. (Monographs & Textbks in Material Science: Vol. 4). 744p. 1972. 125.00 (ISBN 0-8247-1032-0). Dekker.

Blatt, J., et al. Thermoelectric Power of Metals. LC 76-20706. (Illus.). 264p. 1976. 55.00x (ISBN 0-306-30907-6, Plenum Pr). Plenum Pub.

Brandt, N. B. & Chudinov, S. M. Electronic Structure of Metals. 336p. 1973. 6.45 (ISBN 0-8285-0778-3, Pub. by Mir Pubs USSR). Imported Pubns.

Bruno, E. J., ed. High-Velocity Forming of Metals. LC 68-23024. (American Society of Tool & Manufacturing Engineers. Manufacturing Data Ser.). (Illus.). pap. 59.80 (ISBN 0-317-11079-9, 2016004). Bks Demand UMI.

Bunshah, R. F., ed. Techniques of Metals Research. 802p. 1968. Vol. 1, Pt. 2. 51.00 (ISBN 0-470-12197-1, Pub. by Wiley). Krieger.

--Techniques of Metals Research: Techniques Involving Extreme Environment, Nondestructive Techniques, Computer Methods in Metals Research, & Data Analysis, Vol. 7, Pt. 2. LC 69-20260. 427p. 1976. 53.50 (ISBN 0-471-12241-6). Krieger.

--Techniques of Metals Research: Techniques of Material Preparation & Handling, Vol. 1, Pt 1. LC 67-20260. 385p. 1968. 28.00 (ISBN 0-470-12195-5). Krieger.

Burke, John J. & Weiss, Volker, eds. Ultrafine-Grain Metals. (Sagamore Army Materials Research Conference Ser.: Vol. 16). 442p. 1970. 35.00x (ISBN 0-306-34516-1, Plenum Pr). Plenum Pub.

Business Communications Staff. New Specialty Metals & Metallurgy. 1985. pap. 1750.00 (ISBN 0-89336-454-1, GB085). BCC.

Caglioti, G., ed. Atomic Structure & Mechanical Properties of Metals: Proceedings. (Enrico Fermi International Summer School of Physics Ser.: Vol. 61). 664p. 1976. 159.75 (ISBN 0-7204-0490-8, North-Holland). Elsevier.

Carpovich, Eugene A. Russian-English Metals & Machines Dictionary. LC 60-12013. (Rus. & Eng.). 1960. 15.00x (ISBN 0-911484-02-7). Tech Dict.

Chalmers, Bruce. Principles of Solidification. LC 76-18772. 336p. 1977. Repr. of 1964 ed. 22.50 (ISBN 0-88275-446-7). Krieger.

Chapman, P. F. & Roberts, F. Metal Resources & Energy. (Monographs on Materials). 238p. 1983. text ed. 49.95 (ISBN 0-408-10801-0); pap. text ed. 19.95 (ISBN 0-408-10802-9). Butterworth.

Chisholm, Malcolm, ed. Reactivity of Metal-Metal Bonds. LC 81-361. (ACS Symposium Ser.: No. 155). 1981. 41.95 (ISBN 0-8412-0624-4). Am Chemical.

Clough, W. R., ed. Reactive Metals: Proceedings of the 3rd Reactive Metals Conference, Buffalo, 1958. LC 59-14889. (Metallurgical Society Conference: Vol. 2). pap. 156.30 (ISBN 0-317-10823-9, 2000665). Bks Demand UMI.

Collie, M. J., ed. Etching Compositions & Processes. LC 82-7894. (Chemical Technology Review Ser.: No. 210). (Illus.). 308p. 1983. 42.00 (ISBN 0-8155-0913-8). Noyes.

Cookson, William. Advanced Methods for Sheet Metal Work. 6th ed. (Illus.). 1975. 39.95x (ISBN 0-291-39427-2). Intl Ideas.

Coqblin, B. The Electronic Structure of Rare-Earth Metals & Alloys: The Magnetic Heavy Rare-Earths. 1978. 90.00 (ISBN 0-12-188150-4). Acad Pr.

Dickson, H., et al, eds. Thin Plate Working, Vol. 1. 2nd ed. (Illus.). 1977. 37.50x (ISBN 0-686-65561-3) (ISBN 0-85083-387-6). Intl Ideas.

Din Standards for Metallic Cast Materials: Standards for Quality Specifications, General Tolernces, Test Methods. 391.00 (ISBN 0-686-28188-8, 10708-1/53). Heyden.

Din Standards: International Comparison of Standard-Materials--Steel & Cast Iron. 2nd ed. 95.00 (ISBN 0-686-28196-9, 11131-X). Heyden.

D'Isa, Frank A. Mechanics of Metals. 1968. 21.95 (ISBN 0-201-01550-1). Addison-Wesley.

Doyle, L. E., et al. Manufacturing Processes & Materials for Engineers. 2nd ed. 1969. text ed. 37.95 (ISBN 0-13-555862-X). P-H.

Drucker, Harvey & Wildung, Raymond E., eds. Biological Implications of Metals in the Environment: Proceedings. LC 77-1039. (ERDA Symposium Ser.). 692p. 1977. pap. 25.25 (ISBN 0-87079-104-4, CONF-750929); microfiche 4.50 (ISBN 0-87079-149-4, CONF-750929). DOE.

Evans, R. W. & Wilshire, B. Creep of Metals & Alloys. 314p. 1985. text ed. 56.00x (ISBN 0-904357-59-7, Metals Soc). Brookfield Pub Co.

Fabricated Structural Metal Products. 1982. 445.00 (ISBN 0-318-00508-5). Busn Trend.

Facchetti, S., ed. Analytical Techniques for Heavy Metals in Biological Fluids: Lectures of a Course Held at the Joint Research Centre, Ispar, Italy, 22-26 June, 1981. 287p. 1983. 83.00 (ISBN 0-444-42212-9, I-183-83). Elsevier.

Farkas, J. Optimum Design of Metal Structures. 222p. 1984. 54.95x (ISBN 0-470-27482-4). Halsted Pr.

Fast, Johan D. Interaction of Metals & Gases, Vol. 1. Thermodynamics & Phase Relations. 1965. 64.00 (ISBN 0-12-249801-1). Acad Pr.

Ferreira, R., et al. Less Abundant Metals. LC 67-11280. (Structure & Bonding Ser.: Vol. 31). (Illus.). 1976. 27.00 (ISBN 0-387-07964-5). Springer-Verlag.

Filler Metal Control. (Welding Inspection Ser.: Module 28-8). (Illus.). 34p. 1979. spiral binding 6.00x (ISBN 0-87683-112-9). G P Courseware.

Formatibility Topics: Metallic Materials, STP 647. 279p. 1978. 27.75 (ISBN 0-8031-0358-1, 04-647000-23). ASTM.

Fraunhofer, J. A., et al. Protective Paint Coatings for Metals. 118p. 1981. 40.00x (ISBN 0-901994-89-8, Pub. by Portcullio Pr). State Mutual Bk.

Froment, M. Passivity of Metals & Semiconductors: Proceedings of the Fifth International Symposium on Passivity. (Thin Films Science & Technology Ser.: Vol. 4). 1984. 125.00 (ISBN 0-444-42252-8). Elsevier.

Furrer, A., ed. Crystal Field Effects in Metals & Alloys. LC 76-55802. 379p. 1977. 59.50x (ISBN 0-306-31008-2, Plenum Pr). Plenum Pub.

Grant, Nicholas J. & Giessen, Bill C., eds. Rapidly Quenched Metals. 1976. text ed. 47.50x (ISBN 0-262-07066-9). MIT Pr.

Haasen, P., et al, eds. Strength of Metals & Alloys: International Conference on the Strength of Metals & Alloys, 5th, Aachen, 1979, 3 vols. LC 79-40131. (Illus.). 1980. Set. 310.00 (ISBN 0-08-023265-5). Set. Pergamon.

Hampel, Clifford A., ed. Rare Metals Handbook. 2nd ed. LC 61-10449. 732p. 1971. Repr. of 1961 ed. 45.50 (ISBN 0-88275-024-0). Krieger.

Hartley, Frank R. & Patai, S., eds. Chemistry of the Metal Carbon Bond, Vol. 1. 1007p. 1982. 284.95 (ISBN 0-471-10058-7). Wiley.

Hatfield, William E., ed. Molecular Metals. LC 79-4284. (NATO Conference Series, Series VI: Materials Science: Vol. 1). 567p. 1979. 79.50x (ISBN 0-306-40159-2, Plenum Pr). Plenum Pub.

Hauffe, Karl. Oxidation of Metals. LC 63-17648. 452p. 1965. 45.00x (ISBN 0-306-30200-4, Plenum Pr). Plenum Pub.

Hawkins, Clifford. Absolute Configuration of Metal Complexes. LC 78-12995. 349p. 1971. 35.00 (ISBN 0-471-36280-8, Pub. by Wiley). Krieger.

Hehner, Nels E. & Ritchie, Everett J. Grid Metal Manual for Storage Batteries. (Avail. in eng. & span.). 1973. 15.00 (ISBN 0-685-56652-8). IBMA Pubns.

Hicks, G. A. & Heddle, G. M. Design & Technology Metal. 1982. 25.00x (ISBN 0-08-016897-3, Pub. by A Wheaton). State Mutual Bk.

Hoffmanner, A. L., ed. Metal Forming: Interrelation Between Theory & Practice. LC 70-171698. 503p. 1971. 65.00x (ISBN 0-306-30554-2, Plenum Pr). Plenum Pub.

Honeycombe, R. K. The Plastic Deformation of Metals. 480p. 1984. pap. text ed. 34.50 (ISBN 0-7131-3468-2). E Arnold.

Hurd, C. M. Electrons in Metals. LC 80-11429. 344p. 1981. Repr. of 1975 ed. lib. bdg. 25.50 (ISBN 0-89874-157-2). Krieger.

Johnson, Harold V. Technical Metals. 1981. text ed. 23.96 (ISBN 0-02-665850-X); student guide 5.32 (ISBN 0-02-665870-4). Bennett IL.

Kazanas, H. C. Properties & Uses of Ferrous & Nonferrous Metals. rev. ed. LC 78-70035. (Illus.). 1979. pap. 4.75x (ISBN 0-911168-39-7); instrs'. guide & answer bk. 1.95x (ISBN 0-911168-40-0). Prakken.

Keller, H. J., ed. The Chemistry & Physics of One-Dimensional Metals. LC 77-5135. (NATO ASI Series B, Physics: Vol. 25). 426p. 1977. 62.50x (ISBN 0-306-35725-9, Plenum Pr). Plenum Pub.

Khan, M. M. & Martell, Arthur E. Homogeneous Catalysis by Metal Complexes, 2 vols. Incl. Vol. 1. Activation of Small Inorganic Molecules. 86.50 (ISBN 0-12-406101-X); Vol. 2. Activation of Alkenes & Alkynes. 56.00 (ISBN 0-12-406102-8). 1974. Acad Pr.

Kimura, H. & Maddin, R. Quench Hardening in Metals. LC 74-140489. (Defects in Crystalline Solids Ser.: Vol. 3). (Illus.). 133p. 1971. 17.00 (ISBN 0-444-10114-4, North-Holland). Elsevier.

Korol'kov, Aleksei M. Casting Properties of Metals & Alloys. LC 61-18757. pap. 38.00 (ISBN 0-317-10733-X, 2003364). Bks Demand UMI.

Krenkel, P. A. Heavy Metals in the Aquatic Environment. flexi-cover 110.00x (ISBN 0-08-018068-X). Pergamon.

Lappert, M. F., et al. Metal & Metalloid Amides: Synthesis, Structure & Physical & Chemical Properties. LC 79-40253. (Chemical Science Series). 847p. 1980. 179.95x (ISBN 0-470-26573-6). Halsted Pr.

Lefax Pub. Co. Editors. Metals. (Lefax Data Bks.: No. 621). (Illus.). looseleaf bdg. 3.00 (ISBN 0-685-14158-6). Lefax.

Lifshits, I. M., et al, eds. Electron Theory of Metals. LC 79-188919. (Illus.). 320p. 1973. 45.00x (ISBN 0-306-10873-9, Consultants). Plenum Pub.

Fatigue & Fracture Toughness--Cyrogenic Behavior- STP 556. 193p. 1974. 20.25 (ISBN 0-8031-0343-3, 04-556000-30). ASTM.
Fatigue & Microstructure. 1979. 87.00 (ISBN 0-87170-075-1). ASM.
Fatigue Fractures in Welded Constructions (IIW) FF-2. 177p. 1973. 60.00 (ISBN 0-686-95614-1); 45.00. Am Welding.
Finkel'shtein, B. N. Relaxation Phenomena in Metals & Alloys. LC 62-21590. 244p. 1963. 45.00x (ISBN 0-306-10664-7, Consultants). Plenum Pub.
Frost, N. E., et al. Metal Fatigue. (Oxford Engineering Science Ser.). pap. 127.80 (ISBN 0-317-08550-6, 2051845). Bks Demand UMI.
Fuchs, H. O. & Stephens, R. I. Metal Fatigue in Engineering. LC 80-294. 1980. 45.95x (ISBN 0-471-05264-7, Pub. by Wiley-Interscience). Wiley.
Gifkins, R. C., ed. Strength of Metals & Alloys (ICSMA 6) Proceedings of the 6th International Conference, Melbourne, Australia, August 16-20, 1982, 3 Vols. LC 82-9851. (International Series on the Strength & Fracture of Materials & Structures). 1200p. 1982. 240.00 (ISBN 0-08-029325-5). Pergamon.
Handbook of Fatigue Testing, STP 566. 232p. 1974. 17.25 (ISBN 0-8031-0371-9, 04-566000-30). ASTM.
Hoo, J., ed. Rolling Contact Fatigue Testing of Bearing Steels - STP 771. 422p. 1982. 43.95 (ISBN 0-8031-0712-9, 04-771000-02). ASTM.
Hudak, Jr. & Bucci, eds. Fatigue Crack Growth Measurement & Data Analysis- STP 738. 371p. 1981. 39.00 (ISBN 0-8031-0717-X, 04-738000-30). ASTM.
The Influence of State of Stress on Low-Cycle Fatigue of Structural Materials: A Literature Survey & Interpretive Report, STP 549. 52p. 1974. pap. 5.25 (ISBN 0-8031-0375-1, 04-549000-30). ASTM.
Little, R., ed. Tables for Estimating Median Fatigue Limits - STP 731. 176p. 1981. 15.00 (ISBN 0-8031-0718-8, 04-731000-30). ASTM.
Localized Corrosion-Cause of Metal Failure, STP 516. 322p. 1972. 22.50 (ISBN 0-8031-0110-4, 04 516000 07). ASTM.
Manual on Statistical Planning & Analysis for Fatigue Experiments-STP 588. 157p. 1975. 15.00 (ISBN 0-8031-0501-0, 04-588000-30). ASTM.
Metal Fatigue Damage - Mechanism, Detection, Avoidance & Repair, STP 495. 351p. 1971. 21.00 (ISBN 0-8031-0722-6, 04 495000 30). ASTM.
Peterson, N. L. & Harkness, S. D., eds. Radiation Damage in Metals: Papers Presented at a Seminar of the American Society for Metals, Nov. 9-10, 197. LC 76-25094. (Illus.). pap. 103.80 (ISBN 0-317-08178-0, 2019485). Bks Demand UMI.
Pook, P. L. The Role of Crack Growth in Metal Fatigue. 157p. (Orig.). 1983. pap. text ed. 30.00x (ISBN 0-904357-63-5, Pub. by Metals Soc). Brookfield Pub Co.
References on Fatigue, 1965-1966. 1968. microfiche 11.00 (ISBN 0-8031-0132-5, 04-009160-30). ASTM.
Residual Stress Effects in Fatigue - STP 776. 241p. 1982. 26.50 (ISBN 0-8031-0711-0, 04-776000-30). ASTM.
Shewmon, P. G. & Zackay, V. F., eds. Response of Metals to High Velocity Deformation. LC 61-9441. (Metallurgical Society Conferences Ser.: Vol. 9). pap. 125.80 (ISBN 0-317-10938-3, 2000672). Bks Demand UMI.
Sors, L. Fatigue Design of Machine Components. 224p. 1971. text ed. 40.00 (ISBN 0-08-016138-3); write for info. xerox copyflo avail. Pergamon.
Specialty Conference on Safety & Reliability of Metal Structures. Safety & Reliability of Metal Structures: Specialty Conference, Pittsburgh, PA, Nov. 2-3, 1972. LC 78-322838. (Illus.). pap. 114.30 (ISBN 0-317-08324-4, 2019538). Bks Demand UMI.
Statistical Analysis of Fatigue Data - STP 744. 151p. 1981. 16.50 (ISBN 0-8031-0716-1, 04-744000-30). ASTM.
Stress Corrosion Cracking of Metals: A State of the Art - STP 518. 172p. 1972. 15.00 (ISBN 0-8031-0096-5, 04-518000-27). ASTM.
Thompson, Anthony W., ed. Work Hardening in Tension & Fatigue: Proceedings of a Symposium, Cincinnati, Ohio, Nov. 11, 1975. LC 77-76058. pap. 66.30 (ISBN 0-317-08184-5, 2015014). Bks Demand UMI.
Thomsen, Erich G. & Yang,. T. An Experimental Investigation of the Mechanics of Plastic Deformation of Metals. (University of California Publications in Engineering Ser.: Vol. 5, No. 4). pap. 20.00 (ISBN 0-317-10269-9, 2021186). Bks Demand UMI.
TMS-AIME Fall Meeting, Philadelphia, Oct. 3-5, 1983. Fatigue Crack Growth Threshold Concepts. Suresh, S. & Davidson, D., eds. 566p. 53.00 (ISBN 0-89520-475-4, 244); members 35.00 (ISBN 0-317-37189-4); student members 17.00 (ISBN 0-317-37190-8). Metal Soc.
Underwood, et al, eds. Chevron Notched Specimens: Testing & Stress Analysis - STP 855. 360p. 1984. 44.00 (ISBN 0-8031-0401-4, 04-855000-30). ASTM.
Use of Computers in the Fatigue Laboratory - STP 613. 172p. 1976. 20.00 (ISBN 0-8031-0593-2, 04-613000-30). ASTM.

METALS–FINISHING

see also Enamel and Enameling

Benninghoff, H. Index of Chemicals. (Eng., Ger., & Fr.). 1974. 128.00 (ISBN 0-444-41075-9). Elsevier.
Duffy, J. I., ed. Electroless & Other Nonelectrolytic Plating Techniques: Recent Developments. LC 80-19494. (Chemical Tech. Rev. 171). (Illus.). 366p. 1981. 45.00 (ISBN 0-8155-0818-2). Noyes.
Dyachenko, P. E., et al. Actual Contact Area Between Touching Surfaces. LC 64-13145. 1964. 22.50x (ISBN 0-306-10678-7, Consultants). Plenum Pub.
Lowenheim, F., ed. Guide to the Selection & Use of Electroplated & Related Finishes- STP 785. 69p. 1982. pap. 9.00 (ISBN 0-8031-0749-8, 04-785000-04). ASTM.
Mock, John A. Introduction to Prefinished Metals. LC 83-50458. 125p. 1983. 35.00 (ISBN 0-87762-329-5). Technomic.
Reid, F. H. & Goldie, W. Gold Plating Technology. 630p. 1980. 160.00x (ISBN 0-901150-02-9, Pub. by Electrochemical Scotland). State Mutual Bk.
Samuels, L. E., ed. Metallographic Polishing by Mechanical Methods. 1982. 99.00 (ISBN 0-87170-135-9). ASM.
Society Of Manufacturing Engineers & Murphy, J. A. Surface Preparation & Finishes for Metals. 1971. 49.95 (ISBN 0-07-059557-7). McGraw.
Twentieth Annual Plating & Metal Finishing Forum: Proceedings. 1984. 15.00 (ISBN 0-89883-701-4, P145). Soc Auto Engineers.
Verlag-Stahleisen, ed. The Appearance of Cracks & Fractures in Metallic Materials. 1983. 29.00 (ISBN 0-9906000-1-7, Pub. by Verlag Stahleisen W Germany). Heyden.
Wernick, S., et al. The Surface Treatment & Finishing of Aluminium & Its Alloys. 4th ed. 1274p. 1973. 175.00x (ISBN 0-85218-041-1, Pub. by Portcullio Pr). State Mutual Bk.
Yeates, R. L. Electropainting. 2nd ed. 278p. 1981. 60.00x (ISBN 0-686-87183-9, Pub. by Portcullio Pr). State Mutual Bk.

METALS–FRACTURE

see also Metals–Brittleness; Metals–Fatigue

Abelkis & Hudson, eds. Design of Fatigue & Fracture Resistant Structures - STP 761. 486p. 1982. 51.00 (ISBN 0-8031-0714-5, 04-761000-30). ASTM.
American Society for Metals Staff. Prevention of Structural Failures: The Role of NDT, Fracture Mechanics & Failure Analysis: Proceedings of Two Annual Forums, 19-22 June, 1977 & 14-16 June 1976, Tarpon Springs, Florida. LC 78-15388. (Materials-Metalworking Technology Ser.). (Illus.). pap. 90.00 (ISBN 0-317-09726-1, 2019489). Bks Demand UMI.
American Society for Testing & Materials. Flow & Fracture of Metals & Alloys in Nuclear Environments. LC 65-16810. (American Society for Testing & Materials. Special Technical Publication: No. 380). pap. 119.30 (ISBN 0-317-08035-0, 2000740). Bks Demand UMI.
--Fracture Toughness Testing & Its Applications: A Symposium Presented at the Sixty-Seventh Annual Meeting, American Society for Testing & Materials, Chicago, Ill., 1964. LC 65-16811. (American Society for Testing & Materials. Special Technical Publication: No. 381). pap. 105.80 (ISBN 0-317-08197-7, 2015506). Bks Demand UMI.
ASTM Committee G-1 on Corrosion of Metals. Environmental-Sensitive Fracture: Evaluation & Comparison of Test Methods. Dean, S. W., et al, eds. LC 83-70260. (Special Technical Publications Ser.: No. 821). 554p. 1984. text ed. 59.00 (ISBN 0-8031-0264-X, 04-821000-27). ASTM.
Chiao, T. T. & Schuster, D. M., eds. Failure Modes in Composites III. LC 76-23498. pap. 81.50 (ISBN 0-317-08667-7, 2012650). Bks Demand UMI.
Colangelo, Vito J. & Heiser, F. A. Analysis of Metallurgical Failures. LC 73-19773. (Science & Technology of Materials Ser.). 361p. 1974. 49.50x (ISBN 0-471-16450-X, Pub. by Wiley-Interscience). Wiley.
Collins, J. A. Failure of Materials in Mechanical Design: Analysis, Prediction, Prevention. LC 80-20674. 629p. 1981. 55.95x (ISBN 0-471-05024-5, Pub. by Wiley-Interscience). Wiley.
Cracks & Fracture: 9th Conference, STP 601. 1976. 51.75 (ISBN 0-8031-0318-2, 04-601000-30). ASTM.
Fast Fracture & Crack Arrest, STP 627. 429p. 1977. 42.50 (ISBN 0-8031-0341-7, 04-627000-30). ASTM.
Fatigue & Fracture Toughness--Cyrogenic Behavior- STP 556. 193p. 1974. 20.25 (ISBN 0-8031-0343-3, 04-556000-30). ASTM.
Flaw Growth & Fracture - STP 631: 10th Conference. 531p. 1977. 49.75 (ISBN 0-8031-0356-5, 04-631000-30). ASTM.
Fractography in Failure Analysis, STP 645. 395p. 1978. 36.50 (ISBN 0-8031-0359-X, 04-645000-30). ASTM.
Fractography-Microscopic Cracking Process, STP 600. 272p. 1976. 27.50 (ISBN 0-8031-0360-3, 04-600000-30). ASTM.
Fracture Toughness Evaluation by R-Curve Methods, STP 527. 118p. 1973. pap. 9.75 (ISBN 0-8031-0106-6, 04 527000 30). ASTM.
Gifkins, R. C., ed. Strength of Metals & Alloys (ICSMA 6) Proceedings of the 6th International Conference, Melbourne, Australia, August 16-20, 1982, 3 Vols. LC 82-9851. (International Series on the Strength & Fracture of Materials & Structures). 1200p. 1982. 240.00 (ISBN 0-08-029325-5). Pergamon.
Greenberg, Herman D., ed. Applications of Fracture Toughness Parameters to Structural Metals. LC 65-27851. (Metallurgical Society Conference Ser.: Vol. 31). pap. 104.50 (ISBN 0-317-11263-5, 2001519). Bks Demand UMI.
Hartley, Frank R. & Patai, Saul, eds. The Chemistry of the Metal Carbon Bond: The Nature & Cleavage of Metal-Carbon Bond, Vol. 2. (Chemistry of Functional Groups Ser.). 1000p. 1985. 280.00 (ISBN 0-471-90282-9). Wiley.
Henry, Guy & Horstmann, D. Fractography & Microfractography, Vol. 5. (De Ferri Metallographia Ser.). (Eng. Ger. & Fr., Illus.). 1979. 143.00 (ISBN 0-9960086-0-8, Pub. by Verlag Stahleisen W Germany). Heyden.
Hoeppner, David W. Fracture Prevention & Control. Proceedings of a Symposium at the 1972 Western Metal & Tool Exposition & Conference. Los Angeles, California. LC 73-86453. pap. 120.50 (ISBN 0-317-08059-8, 2050983). Bks Demand UMI.
Hutchings, F. R. & Unterweiser, P. M. Failure Analysis: The British Engine Technical Reports. 1981. 104.00 (ISBN 0-87170-116-2). ASM.
Kocanda, S. Fatigue Failure of Metals. 384p. 1978. 40.00x (ISBN 90-286-0025-6). Sijthoff & Noordhoff.
McCall, J. L. & French, P. M., eds. Metallography in Failure Analysis. LC 78-7224. 309p. 1978. 49.50x (ISBN 0-306-40012-X, Plenum Pr). Plenum Pub.
Mechanics of Crack Growth- STP 590. 502p. 1976. 45.25 (ISBN 0-8031-0509-6, 04-590000-30). ASTM.
Mecholsky, J. J. & Powell, S. R., Jr., eds. Fractography of Ceramic & Metal Failures. LC 83-71813. (Special Technical Publications Ser.: No. 827). 272p. 1984. text ed. 42.00 (ISBN 0-8031-0215-1, 04-827000-30). ASTM.
National Materials Advisory Board, National Research Council. Rapid Inexpensive Tests for Determining Fracture Toughness. LC 76-39632. 1976. pap. 9.75 (ISBN 0-309-02537-0). Natl Acad Pr.
Naumann, Friedrich K. Failure Analysis: Case Histories & Methodology. Tr. of Das Buch der Schadensfalle. 1983. 83.00 (ISBN 0-87170-171-5). ASM.
Properties Related to Fracture Toughness - STP 605. 150p. 1976. pap. 15.00 (ISBN 0-8031-0540-1, 04-605000-30). ASTM.
Resistance to Plane-Stress Fracture (R-Curve Behavior) of A572 Structural Steel, STP591. 1976. soft cover 5.25 (ISBN 0-8031-0557-6, 04-591000-30). ASTM.
Review of Developments in Plane Strain Fracture Toughness Testing, STP 463. 275p. 1970. 18.25 (ISBN 0-8031-0037-X, 04-463000-30). ASTM.
Rhodin, Thor N., ed. Physical Metallurgy of Stress Corrosion Fracture. LC 59-14890. (Metallurgical Society Conferences Ser.: Vol. 4). pap. 102.30 (ISBN 0-317-10921-9, 2000667). Bks Demand UMI.
Specialty Conference on Safety & Reliability of Metal Structures. Safety & Reliability of Metal Structures: Specialty Conference, Pittsburgh, PA, Nov. 2-3, 1972. LC 78-322838. (Illus.). pap. 114.30 (ISBN 0-317-08324-4, 2019538). Bks Demand UMI.
TMS-AIME 113th Annual Meeting, Los Angeles, Feb. 27-29, 1984. Fracture: Interactions of Microstructure, Mechanisms, & Mechanics. Landis, J. D. & Wells, J. M., eds. 512p. 58.00 (ISBN 0-89520-484-3, 255); members 39.00 (ISBN 0-317-37198-3); student members 19.00 (ISBN 0-317-37199-1). Metal Soc.
Toth, Istvan, ed. Failure Modes in Composites I. LC 73-166196. pap. 118.80 (ISBN 0-317-08674-X, 2012649). Bks Demand UMI.
Tung, P. P., et al. Fracture & Failure: Analyses, Mechanisms & Applications. 1981. 47.00 (ISBN 0-87170-113-8). ASM.
Underwood, et al, eds. Chevron Notched Specimens: Testing & Stress Analysis - STP 855. 360p. 1984. 44.00 (ISBN 0-8031-0401-4, 04-855000-30). ASTM.

METALS–HEAT TREATMENT

see also Case Hardening; Precipitation Hardening; Residual Stresses; Tempering

American Society for Metals Staff. Source Book on Heat Treating: A Discriminative Selection of Outstanding Articles from the Literature Periodicals. LC 75-25598. (ASM Engineering Bookshelf Ser.: Vol. 1: Materials & Processes). (Illus.). pap. 99.50 (ISBN 0-317-09661-3, 2051904). Bks Demand UMI.
Anderson, J. N. & Queneau, P. E., eds. Pyrometallurgical Processes in Nonferrous Metallurgy. LC 67-26570. (Metallurgical Society Conferences: Vol. 39). pap. 132.30 (ISBN 0-317-10578-7, 2001528). Bks Demand UMI.
Apblett, William R., Jr., ed. Shell & Tube Heat Exchangers. 1982. 67.00 (ISBN 0-87170-145-6). ASM.
Bell, T., ed. Heat Treatment Shanghai 83. 552p. 1984. text ed. 96.00x (ISBN 0-904357-65-1, Pub. by Metals Soc). Brookfield Pub Co.
Brooks, Charlie R. Heat Treatment of Ferrous Alloys. LC 78-16513. (Illus.). 1979. text ed. 45.00x (ISBN 0-07-008076-3). McGraw.
Brooks, Charlie R., ed. Heat Treatment, Structure, & Properties of Nonferrous Alloys. 1982. 85.00 (ISBN 0-87170-138-3). ASM.
Harris, J. N. The Shaping & Heat Treatment of Metals. write for info.; pap. write for info. (ISBN 0-685-25019-9). Pergamon.
Heat Treatment Seventy-Nine. 248p. 1980. text ed. 80.00x (ISBN 0-904357-25-2, Metals Soc). Brookfield Pub Co.
International Conference Organized by the Heat Treatment Committee of The Metals Society. Heat Treatment 84: Proceedings. 53p. 1984. text ed. 68.00x (ISBN 0-904357-70-8, Pub. by Metals Soc). Brookfield Pub Co.
Parrish, G. & Harper, G. S. Production Gas Carburizing. (Materials Engineering Practice Ser.). (Illus.). 250p. 1985. 40.00 (ISBN 0-08-027312-2); pap. 15.75 (ISBN 0-08-027319-X). Pergamon.

METALS–HIGH ENERGY FORMING

see High Energy Forming

METALS–MICROSCOPIC STRUCTURE

see Metallography

METALS–OPTICAL PROPERTIES

Jaffee, R. I., et al, eds. Refractory Metals & Alloys IV: Research & Development. LC 68-21965. (Metallurgical Society Conferences: Vol. 41). pap. 160.00 (ISBN 0-317-10586-8, 2001530). Bks Demand UMI.
Jaffee, Robert I., ed. Refractory Metals & Alloys III: Applied Aspects. LC 65-24869. (Metallurgical Society Conference Ser.: Vol. 30). pap. 160.00 (ISBN 0-317-10849-2, 2001518). Bks Demand UMI.
Semchyshen, M., ed. Refractory Metals & Alloys: Proceedings. LC 61-9444. (Metallurgical Society Conferences: Vol. 11). pap. 158.80 (ISBN 0-317-10265-6, 2000674). Bks Demand UMI.
Skobel'tsyn, D. V., ed. Optical Properties of Metals & Intermolecular Interactions. LC 72-94827. (P. N. Lebedev Physics Institute Ser.: Vol. 55). (Illus.). 228p. 1973. 55.00x (ISBN 0-306-10880-1, Consultants). Plenum Pub.

METALS–PICKLING

Mulcahy, E. W. Pickling of Steels. 95p. 1981. 50.00x (ISBN 0-901994-20-0, Pub. by Portcullio Pr). State Mutual Bk.
Straschill, M. Pickling of Metals. 196p. 1981. 35.00x (ISBN 0-85218-010-1, Pub. by Portcullio Pr). State Mutual Bk.

METALS–RADIATION EFFECTS

see Metals, Effect of Radiation On

METALS–RADIOGRAPHY

see Radiography, Industrial

METALS–RECYCLING

Data Notes Publishing Staff. Metal Recycling: Data Notes. LC 83-90729. 30p. 1983. pap. text ed. 9.95 (ISBN 0-911569-44-8, Pub. by Data Notes). Prosperity & Profits.
National Association of Recycling Industries Inc. Recycled Metals in the Nineteen Eighties. (Illus.). 188p. 1982. 40.00 (ISBN 0-686-81901-2). Natl Recycling.
Rao, S. & Dawson, P. R. Investigations on the Use of Boron-Sodium Carbonate Fluxes in Secondary Brass Melting 1979. 1981. 40.00x (ISBN 0-686-97099-3, Pub. by W Spring England). State Mutual Bk.
Sigel. Circulation of Metals in the Environment, Vol. 18. (Metal Ions in Biological Systems Ser.). 432p. 1984. 79.75 (ISBN 0-8247-7226-1). Dekker.

Turner, Francis J. Metamorphic Petrology. 2nd ed. LC 79-27496. (International Earth & Planetary Sciences Ser.). (Illus.). 512p. 1980. text ed. 54.95 (ISBN 0-07-065501-4). McGraw.

METAMORPHOSIS

see also Insects–Metamorphosis

Atherton, M. P. & Gribble, C. D., eds. Migmatites, Melting & Metamorphism. 200p. 1982. 60.00x (ISBN 0-906812-26-7, Pub. by Shiva Pub England); pap. 40.00x (ISBN 0-906812-25-9). State Mutual Bk.

Balls, Michael & Bownes, Mary, eds. Metamorphosis. (Illus.). 350p. 1985. 47.50 (ISBN 0-19-857183-6). Oxford U Pr.

Gilbert, Lawrence I. & Frieden, Earl, eds. Metamorphosis: A Problem in Developmental Biology. rev. 2nd ed. LC 81-17691. 598p. 1981. 49.50x (ISBN 0-306-40692-6, Plenum Pr). Plenum Pub.

Schachtel, Ernest G. Metamorphosis. (Psychoanalysis: Examined & Re-Examined Ser.). 344p. 1984. Repr. of 1959 ed. lib. bdg. 35.00 (ISBN 0-306-76237-4). Da Capo.

Tata, J. R. Metamorphosis. Head, J. J., ed. LC 78-52662. (Carolina Biology Readers Ser.). (Illus.). 16p. 1983. pap. 1.60 (ISBN 0-89278-246-3, 45-9646). Carolina Biological.

Zamir, Yecheskiel. Avkoan Theory & the Nature of Energy & Temperature, Vol. 3. Date not set. price not set (ISBN 0-9614730-3-7). Y Z Pubns.

METAMORPHOSIS (INSECTS)

see Insects–Development

METAPHYSICS

see also Cosmology; Knowledge, Theory Of; Space and Time

Bergson, Henri. Creative Evolution. Mitxhell, Arthur, tr. LC 83-19859. 460p. 1984. pap. text ed. 13.50 (ISBN 0-8191-3553-4). U Pr of Amer.

Burtt, E. A. The Nature & Origin of Modern Thought. (Illus.). 131p. 1984. 77.85 (ISBN 0-89901-139-X). Found Class Reprints.

Burtt, Edwin A. Metaphysical Foundations of Modern Physical Science. 2nd ed. (International Library of Psychology, Philosophy & Scientific Method). 1967. text ed. 29.00x (ISBN 0-7100-3032-0); pap. text ed. 9.45x (ISBN 0-391-01633-4). Humanities.

Collingwood, R. G. An Essay on Metaphysics. 366p. 1984. pap. 10.25 (ISBN 0-8191-3315-9). U Pr of Amer.

Comfort, Alex. Reality & Empathy: Physics, Mind & Science in the 21st Century. LC 83-9318. 1984. 39.50x (ISBN 0-87395-762-8); pap. 14.95 (ISBN 0-87395-763-6). State U NY Pr.

DeGeorge, R. T. Classical & Contemporary Metaphysics: A Source Book. 332p. 1962. 18.50 (ISBN 0-03-011310-5). Krieger.

De Guise, Giorgio. The Ignorant Man's Guide to the Mysteries of Metaphysics. (Illus.). 111p. 1984. 37.85x (ISBN 0-89266-465-7). Am Classical Coll Pr.

Faulkenstein, Dezmon A. Faulkenstein's Theories Are Loose on the Earth. 1982. 7.95 (ISBN 0-533-04690-4). Vantage.

Fisichella, Anthony J. Metaphysics: Science of Life. 2nd ed. LC 82-9726. (New Age Ser.). (Illus.). 320p. 1985. pap. 9.95 (ISBN 0-87542-229-2). Llewellyn Pubns.

Hamlyn, D. V. Metaphysics. 230p. 1984. 34.50 (ISBN 0-521-24449-8); pap. 9.95 (ISBN 0-521-28690-5). Cambridge U Pr.

Harris, Errol E. The Foundations of Metaphysics in Science. LC 83-3502. 510p. 1983. pap. text ed. 20.75 (ISBN 0-8191-3169-5). U Pr of Amer.

Hofstadter, Douglas R. Metamagical Themas. LC 83-46095. (Illus.). 852p. 1985. 24.95 (ISBN 0-465-04540-5). Basic.

Jessen, Joel. The IMPERATIVE STEP: The Step from Metaphysics to Science. 113p. 1972. pap. 7.00 (ISBN 0-942958-04-7). Kappeler Inst Pub.

Kant, Immanuel. Metaphysical Knowledge & Transcendental Problems. (Illus.). 167p. 1985. Repr. 89.55 (ISBN 0-89901-200-0). Found Class Reprints.

Kappeler, Max. Metaphysics & Science in Christian Science. (Orig.). 1985. pap. 3.50 (ISBN 0-942958-11-X). Kappeler Inst Pub.

Kogan, Barry S. Averroes & the Metaphysics of Causation. 337p. 1985. lib. bdg. 39.50x (ISBN 0-88706-063-3); pap. text ed. 14.95x (ISBN 0-88706-065-X). State U NY Pr.

Korner, Stephen. Metaphysics: Its Structure & Function. 245p. 1984. 39.50 (ISBN 0-521-26496-0). Cambridge U Pr.

Loewenberg, Jacob. Reason & the Nature of Things. LC 58-6818. (Paul Carus Lecture Ser.). xiv, 399p. 1959. 24.95 (ISBN 0-87548-105-1). Open Court.

Marcel, Gabriel. Royce's Metaphysics. LC 56-11854. pap. 45.00 (ISBN 0-317-08060-1, 2055292). Bks Demand UMI.

Norman, Ruth. Effort to Destroy: The Unarius Mission-Thwarted. 400p. (Orig.). 1984. pap. 8.95 (ISBN 0-932642-89-6). Unarius.

--Man, the Evolutionary Regenerative Spirit. 500p. 1986. text ed. 12.95 (ISBN 0-932642-95-0). Unarius.

Perrin, Stuart. The Mystical Ferryboat. (The Metaphysics Ser.). 121p. (Orig.). 1985. 16.00 (ISBN 0-943920-67-1); pap. 8.00 (ISBN 0-943920-64-7). Metamorphous Pr.

Perry, Charles M. Toward a Dimensional Reality. LC 39-11737. pap. 47.00 (ISBN 0-317-09342-8, 2016249). Bks Demand UMI.

Peters, Johannes A. Metaphysics, a Systematic Survey. LC 63-8144. (Duquesne Studies, Philosophical Ser.: No. 16). pap. 136.80 (ISBN 0-317-09337-1, 2051342). Bks Demand UMI.

Philips, Paul. Metaphysics for Daily Life. LC 80-66662. (Illus.). 98p. (Orig.). 1984. pap. 2.95 (ISBN 0-930149-01-7). Am Parapsy Res.

Plamondon, Ann L. Whitehead's Organic Philosophy of Science. LC 78-16682. 1979. 39.50x (ISBN 0-87395-387-8). State U NY Pr.

Ponce, Charles. Papers Toward Radical Metaphysics: Alchemy. 160p. (Orig.). 1984. 20.00 (ISBN 0-938190-02-4); pap. 8.95 (ISBN 0-938190-01-6). North Atlantic.

Pond, David & Pond, Lucy. The Metaphysical Handbook. LC 83-91290. (Illus.). 200p. 1984. pap. 8.95 (ISBN 0-915395-18-5). Reflecting Pond.

Prior, William J. Unity & Development in Plato's Metaphysics. 224p. 1985. cloth 24.95 (ISBN 0-8126-9000-1). Open Court.

Rescher, Nicholas. The Riddle of Existence: An Essay in Idealistic Metaphysics. (The Nicholas Rescher Ser.). 112p. (Orig.). 1985. 19.50 (ISBN 0-8191-4127-5); pap. text ed. 8.75 (ISBN 0-8191-4128-3). U Pr of Amer.

Rubinoff, Lionel. Collingwood & the Reform of Metaphysics: A Study in the Philosophy of Mind. LC 73-19150. pap. 106.80 (ISBN 0-317-08071-7, 2020519). Bks Demand UMI.

Russell, Bertrand. Mathematics, Metaphysics & the Power of the Scientific Method, 2 vols. (Illus.). 225p. 1985. Repr. Set. 187.75 (ISBN 0-89901-215-9). Found Class Reprints.

Vander-Veer, Garrett L. Bradley's Metaphysics & the Self. LC 79-99843. pap. 82.00 (ISBN 0-317-08844-0, 2013380). Bks Demand UMI.

Versfeld, Marthinus. An Essays on the Metaphysics of Descartes. LC 68-26210. 1968. Repr. of 1940 ed. 20.00 (ISBN 0-8046-0481-9, Pub. by Kennikat). Assoc Faculty Pr.

Weyl, Hermann. Open World: Three Lectures on the Metaphysical Implications of Science. 1932. 39.50x (ISBN 0-686-83658-8). Elliots Bks.

METAZOA

Clark, Robert B. Dynamics in Metazoan Evolution: The Origin of the Coelom & Segments. 1964. 45.00x (ISBN 0-19-854353-0). Oxford U Pr.

Grasse, Pierre P. & Tetry, Andree. Zoologie: Metazoaires, Vol. 2. (Methodique Ser.). 1056p. 39.95 (ISBN 0-686-56435-9). French & Eur.

Smith, D. C. & Tiffon, Y., eds. Nutrition in the Lower Metazoa: Proceedings. (Illus.). 192p. 1980. 42.00 (ISBN 0-08-025904-9). Pergamon.

Tetry, Andree. Zoologie: Metazoaires, Vol. 3. (Methodique Ser.). 1336p. 48.95 (ISBN 0-686-56436-7). French & Eur.

METEORITES

see also Meteors

Buchwald, Vagn F. Handbook of Iron Meteorites: Their History, Distribution, Composition & Structure, 3 vols. LC 74-27286. 1976. boxed set 250.00x (ISBN 0-520-02934-8). U of Cal Pr.

Dodd, Robert T. Meteorites: A Chemical-Petrologic Synthesis. LC 80-25327. (Illus.). 368p. 1981. 27.95 (ISBN 0-521-22570-1). Cambridge U Pr.

Furneaux, Rupert. The Tungus Event. 1979. pap. 1.50 (ISBN 0-8439-0619-7, Leisure Bks). Dorchester Pub Co.

Gomes, Celso P. & Keil, Klaus. Brazilian Stone Meteorites. LC 80-5333. (Illus.). 192p. 1980. 25.00x (ISBN 0-8263-0543-1). U of NM Pr.

Graham, A. L., et al. Catalogue of Meteorites. 4th ed. 400p. 1985. text ed. 84.50x (ISBN 0-565-00941-9, Pub. by Brit Mus Nat Hist England). Sabbot-Natural Hist Bks.

Heide, Fritz. Meteorites. LC 63-20906. Repr. of 1964 ed. 38.50 (ISBN 0-8357-9649-3, 2016987). Bks Demand UMI.

Huss, Glenn I. The Huss Collection of Meteorites of the American Meteorite Laboratory. (Illus.). 1976. pap. 1.00x (ISBN 0-910096-06-6). Am Meteorite.

Kuiper, Gerard P. & Middlehurst, Barbara M., eds. Moon, Meteorites & Comets. LC 62-18117. (Solar System Ser: Vol. 4). 1963. 60.00x (ISBN 0-226-45928-4). U of Chicago Pr.

LeMaire, T. R. Stones from the Stars: The Unsolved Mysteries of Meteorites. LC 79-21158. 204p. 1980. 9.95 (ISBN 0-13-846881-8). P-H.

Lunar & Planetary Institute, compiled by. Proceedings: Eleventh Lunar & Planetary Science Conference, Houston, Texas, March 17-21, 1980, 3 vols. (Geochimica & Cosmochimica Acta: Suppl. 14). 3000p. 1981. Set. 220.00 (ISBN 0-08-026314-3). Pergamon.

McCall, G. J. Meteorites & Their Origins. LC 72-7640. 352p. 1973. 26.95x (ISBN 0-470-58115-8). Halsted Pr.

McCall, G. J., ed. Meteorite Craters. (Benchmark Papers in Geology: Vol. 36). 1977. 68.00 (ISBN 0-12-787026-1). Acad Pr.

Marvin, Ursula B. Field & Laboratory Investigations of Meteorites from Victoria Land, Antarctica. Marvin, Ursula B. & Mason, Brian, eds. LC 83-20087. (Smithsonian Contributions to the Earth Sciences: No. 26). pap. 34.50 (ISBN 0-317-20102-6, 2023163). Bks Demand UMI.

Marvin, Ursula B. & Mason, Brian, eds. Catalog of Meteorites from Victoria Land, Antarctica, 1978-1980. LC 81-607125. (Smithsonian Contributions to the Earth Sciences Ser.: No. 24). pap. 25.30 (ISBN 0-317-08558-1, 2017827). Bks Demand UMI.

Mason, Brian. Handbook of Elemental Abundances in Meteorites: Reviews in Cosmochemistry & Allied Subjects. LC 71-148927. (Illus.). 566p. 1971. 149.25 (ISBN 0-677-14950-6). Gordon.

Mason, Brian H. & Taylor, S. R. Inclusions in the Allende Meteorite. LC 82-600091. (Smithsonian Contributions to the Earth Sciences Ser.: No. 25). pap. 20.00 (ISBN 0-317-08552-2, 2019305). Bks Demand UMI.

Nagy, B. Carbonaceous Meteorites. LC 73-89156. (Developments in Solar System & Space Science Ser.: Vol. 1). 747p. 1975. 128.00 (ISBN 0-444-41189-5). Elsevier.

Nininger, H. H. Arizona's Meteorite Crater. (Illus.). 1965. pap. 4.50 (ISBN 0-910096-02-3). Am Meteorite.

--Ask a Question about Meteorites. (Illus.). 1961. pap. 2.00 (ISBN 0-910096-03-1). Am Meteorite.

--A Comet Strikes the Earth. rev. ed. (Illus.). 1969. pap. 2.00 (ISBN 0-910096-04-X). Am Meteorite.

--Find a Falling Star. LC 72-83710. (Illus.). 352p. 1976. 8.95 (ISBN 0-8397-2229-X); pap. 5.95 (ISBN 0-8397-2230-3). Eriksson.

Olsen, Edward J. Meteorites: The Poor Man's Space Probe. LC 73-163905. (Augustana College Library Occasional Papers: No. 11). 18p. 1973. pap. 1.00x (ISBN 0-910182-34-5). Augustana Coll.

Pearl, Richard M. Fallen from Heaven: Meteorites & Man. 1975. pap. 2.75 (ISBN 0-940566-03-6). R M Pearl Bks.

Pejovic, Brian. Man & Meteorites. Stewart, T. H. & Stewart, S. M., eds. (Illus.). 120p. 1982. 14.95 (ISBN 0-907733-01-8). Sheridan.

Symposium on Meteorite Research, Vienna, Austria, August 7-13, 1968. Meteorite Research: Proceedings. Millman, P. N., ed. (Astrophysic & Space Science Library: No.12). 941p. 1969. lib. bdg. 89.50 (ISBN 90-277-0132-6, Pub. by Reidel Holland). Kluwer Academic.

Wasson, J. T. Meteorites: Classification & Properties. LC 74-4896. (Minerals, Rocks & Inorganic Materials Ser.: Vol. 10). (Illus.). 370p. 1974. 41.00 (ISBN 0-387-06744-2). Springer-Verlag.

Wasson, John T. Meteorites: Their Record of Early Solar-System History. LC 85-1484. (Illus.). 267p. 1985. 29.95 (ISBN 0-7167-1700-X). W H Freeman.

Wood, John A. Meteorites & the Origin of Planets. LC 68-13886. (Earth & Planetary Science Ser.). pap. 30.80 (ISBN 0-317-28252-2, 2055975). Bks Demand UMI.

METEOROLOGICAL INSTRUMENTS

see also Altimeter; Barometer; Meteorological Satellites; Thermometers and Thermometry

Commission for Instruments & Methods of Observation, 6th Session. Abridged Final Report of the Sixth Session. 98p. (Orig.). 1974. pap. 20.00 (ISBN 0-685-40958-9, W459, WMO). Unipub.

Commission for Instruments & Methods of Observations: Abridged Final Report of the Seventh Session. (Eng., Fr. & Rus.). 124p. 1977. pap. 25.00 (ISBN 92-63-10490-5, W386, WMO). Unipub.

Hawson, C. L. Performance Requirements of Aerological Instruments: An Assessment Based on Atmospheric Variability. (Technical Note Ser.: No. 112). (Illus.). 90p. 1970. pap. 15.00 (ISBN 0-686-93893-3, W87, WMO). Unipub.

Instrument Development Inquiry. 2nd ed. vi, 98p. 1976. pap. 15.00 (ISBN 0-685-77319-1, W65, WMO). Unipub.

Perry, A. E. Hot-Wire Anemometry. (Illus.). 1982. 39.00x (ISBN 0-19-856327-2). Oxford U Pr.

Sawyer, J. S. Performance Requirements of Aerological Instruments. (Technical Note Ser.: No. 45). 29p. 1962. pap. 6.50 (ISBN 0-685-57274-9, W20, WMO). Unipub.

METEOROLOGICAL LITERATURE SEARCHING

see Information Storage and Retrieval Systems–Meteorology

METEOROLOGICAL MAPS

see Meteorology–Charts, Diagrams, etc.

METEOROLOGICAL OBSERVATIONS

see Meteorology–Observations

METEOROLOGICAL OBSERVATORIES

see Meteorological Stations

METEOROLOGICAL OPTICS

see also Auroras; Rainbow; Refraction; Twilight

Corliss, William R. Rare Halos, Mirages, Anomalous Rainbows, & Related Electromagnetic Phenomena. (Catalog of Geophysical Anomalies Ser.). (Illus.). 244p. 1984. 12.95 (ISBN 0-915554-12-7). Sourcebook.

Feigelson, E. M. & Malkevich, M. S. Calculation of the Brightness of Light in the Case of Anisotropic Scattering. LC 60-8720. (Transactions (Trudy) of the Institute of Atmospheric Physics Ser.: Pt. 1). pap. 27.50 (ISBN 0-317-08290-6, 2020687). Bks Demand UMI.

Greenler, Robert. Rainbows, Halos & Glories. LC 80-143722. (Illus.). 304p. 1980. 32.50 (ISBN 0-521-23605-3). Cambridge U Pr.

McCartney, Earl J. Optics of the Atmosphere: Scattering by Molecules & Particles. LC 76-10941. (Pure & Applied Optics Ser). 408p. 1976. 60.95x (ISBN 0-471-01526-1, Pub. by Wiley-Interscience). Wiley.

Marchuk, G. I., et al. Monte Carlo Methods in Atmospheric Optics. (Springer Ser. in Optical Sciences: Vol. 12). (Illus.). 1980. 35.00 (ISBN 0-387-09402-4). Springer-Verlag.

Meinel, Aden & Meinel, Marjorie. Sunsets, Twilights, & Evening Skies. LC 83-1794. (Illus.). 200p. 1983. 32.50 (ISBN 0-521-25220-2). Cambridge U Pr.

Middleton, William E. Vision Through the Atmosphere. pap. 66.00 (ISBN 0-317-08955-2, 2014366). Bks Demand UMI.

Minnaert, M. Nature of Light & Colour in the Open Air. 1948. pap. text ed. 6.00 (ISBN 0-486-20196-1). Dover.

Report of the Second Planning Meeting for the West African Monsoon Experiment & Report of the Preparatory Meeting of the WAMEX Scientific & Management Regional Committee. (GARP Special Reports: No. 27). (Eng. & Fr.). 11p. 1978. pap. 25.00 (ISBN 0-685-60680-5, W394, WMO). Unipub.

Rozenberg, Georgii V. Twilight: A Study in Atmospheric Optics. LC 65-11345. 368p. 1966. 34.50x (ISBN 0-306-30220-9, Plenum Pr). Plenum Pub.

METEOROLOGICAL RESEARCH

American Sunbeam Staff. Weather Made to Whose Order? (Illus.). 56p. Date not set. 2.00 (ISBN 0-918700-04-3). Duverus Pub.

Bolin, Bert. The Global Atmospheric Research Programme: A Co-Operative Effort to Explore the Weather Climate of Our Planet. (Eng. & Fr.). 28p. (WMO-ICSU Publication). 1971. pap. 2.00 (W351, WMO). Unipub.

First GARP Global Experiment; Global Atmospheric Research Programme: Report. (GARP Special Reports: No. 16). 46p. (List of participants). 1975. pap. 15.00 (ISBN 0-685-62850-7, WMO). Unipub.

GARP (Global Atmospheric Research Programme), Joint Organizing Committee, 7th Session. Report. pap. 9.00 (ISBN 0-686-93930-1, W336, WMO). Unipub.

GARP (Global Atmospheric Research Programme), Joint Organizing Committee, 6th Session. Report. pap. 5.00 (ISBN 0-686-93931-X, W337, WMO). Unipub.

GARP Tropical Experiment Board, 1st Session. Report of the GARP Experiment Board 1st Session. (GARP Special Reports: No. 4). pap. 8.00 (ISBN 0-686-93934-4, W325, WMO). Unipub.

The Global Weather Experiment, 1978-79. 44p. 1981. pap. 4.00 (ISBN 0-686-73706-7, W488, WMO). Unipub.

Information on the Application of Meteorological Satellite Data in Routine Operations & Research: Abstracts, Annual Summaries & Bibliographies, Suppl. No. 3. 110p. 1980. pap. 5.00 (ISBN 0-686-62999-X, W455, WMO). Unipub.

Liljequist, Gosta H., ed. Weather & Weather Maps. (Contributions to Current Research in Geophysics: 10). 265p. 1982. text ed. 52.95x (ISBN 0-8176-1192-4). Birkhauser.

Mihara, Yoshiaki, ed. Agricultural Meteorology of Japan. LC 74-78859. 215p. 1974. text ed. 22.50x (ISBN 0-8248-0337-X, Eastwest Ctr). UH Pr.

The Monsoon Experiment. (GARP Publications Ser.: No. 18). xxvii, 214p. 1976. pap. 25.00 (ISBN 0-685-77321-3, W305, WMO). Unipub.

Pre-GATE Tests & Studies for the GARP Atlantic Tropical Experiment. (GATE Report Ser.: No. 2). (Illus.). 1974. pap. 25.00 (ISBN 0-685-50564-2, W279, WMO). Unipub.

Filippov, V. V. Quality Control Procedures for Meteorological Use. (World Weather Watch Planning Reports: No. 26). 1968. pap. 12.00 (ISBN 0-685-22334-5, W238, WMO). Unipub.

Flohn, N. Climate & Weather. (Illus., Orig.). 1968. pap. 3.95 (ISBN 0-07-021325-9). McGraw.

Forsdyke, A. G. Meteorological Factors of Air Pollution. (Technical Note Ser.: No. 114). (Illus.). 32p. 1970. pap. 10.00 (ISBN 0-685-02472-5, W86, WMO). Unipub.

From, Lester D. & Staver, Allen E. Fundamentals of Weather: A Workbook Approach. 1979. 16.50 (ISBN 0-8403-2023-X). Kendall-Hunt.

Gates, Ernest S. Meteorology & Climatology. 4th ed. (Illus.). 1972. pap. text ed. 24.95x (ISBN 0-245-52869-5). Intl Ideas.

Geiger, Rudolf. Climate Near the Ground. 4th ed. Scripta Technica Inc, tr. LC 64-23191. 1965. 35.00x (ISBN 0-674-13500-8). Harvard U Pr.

Gill, Adrian. Atmosphere-Ocean Dynamics. (International Geophysics Ser.). 1982. 60.00 (ISBN 0-12-283520-4); pap. 35.00 (ISBN 0-12-283522-0). Acad Pr.

Gille, J. C. & Kuhn, P. M. The International Radiometersonde Intercomparison Programme: 1970-71. (Technical Note Ser.: No. 128). (Illus.). xiv, 128p. 1973. pap. 20.00 (ISBN 0-685-39018-7, W135, WMO). Unipub.

Gordon, Adrian H. & Taylor, Ronald C. Computations of Surface Layer Air Trajectories, & Weather, in the Oceanic Tropics. LC 72-92065. (International Indian Ocean Expedition Meterological Monographs: No. 7). (Illus.). 112p. 1975. text ed. 20.00x (ISBN 0-8248-0253-5, Eastwest Ctr). UH Pr.

Guide to Climatatological Practices, No. 100. 125p. 1983. pap. text ed. 35.00 (ISBN 92-63-12100-1, W577, WMO). Unipub.

Guide to Hydrological Practices: Analysis, Forecasting & Other Applications, Vol. II. (WMO Ser.: No. 168). 150p. 1983. pap. text ed. 40.00 (ISBN 92-63-14168-1, W578, WMO). Unipub.

Harvey, J. G. Atmosphere & Ocean: Our Fluid Environments. LC 77-377903. 143p. 1978. pap. 16.50x (ISBN 0-8448-1293-5). Crane-Russak Co.

Hess, Seymour L. Introduction to Theoretical Meteorology. LC 78-27897. 380p. 1979. Repr. of 1959 ed. lib. bdg. 24.50 (ISBN 0-88275-857-8). Krieger.

Hetman, F. The Language of Forecasting. 556p. 1971. 74.25x (ISBN 0-677-62140-X). Gordon.

Hidore, John J. Weather & Climate: Text-Exercises-Weather Maps. LC 84-61956. 238p. 1984. pap. 15.95 (ISBN 0-941226-05-0). Park Pr Co.

Holmes, D. W. WEFAX: A Weather Data Communications Experiment. (World Weather Watch Planning Reports: No. 23). 23p. 1968. pap. 6.00 (ISBN 0-685-02476-8, W236, WMO). Unipub.

Holton, James R. Introduction to Dynamic Meteorology. 2nd ed. LC 79-6956. (International Geophysics Ser.). 1979. 24.00 (ISBN 0-12-354360-6). Acad Pr.

Hopper, A. & Vockroth, R. Upper Air Sounding Noises, 2 Pts. (Technical Note Ser.: No. 140). 1975. pap. 25.00 (ISBN 92-63-10394-1, W165, WMO). Unipub.

Houghton, David D. Handbook in Applied Meteorology. LC 84-11915. 1328p. 1985. 84.95x (ISBN 0-471-08404-2, Pub. by Wiley-Interscience). Wiley.

Houghton, Herny G. Physical Meteorology. (Illus.). 450p. 1985. text ed. 37.50x (ISBN 0-262-08146-6). MIT Pr.

Hunt, Garry E., ed. Recent Advances in Planetary Meterology. 300p. 1985. 39.50 (ISBN 0-521-25886-3). Cambridge U Pr.

International Global Data-Processing System Plan to Support the First GARP Global Experiment: Annexes. 22p. 1979. pap. 18.00 (ISBN 0-686-86845-5, W449, WMO). Unipub.

International Noctilucent Cloud Observation Manual. (Illus.). 39p. 1970. pap. 8.00 (ISBN 0-685-02467-9, W76, WMO). Unipub.

Introduction to GARP Global Atmospheric Research Programme. (GARP Publications Ser.: No. 1). x, 22p. 1969. pap. 5.00 (ISBN 0-685-22314-0, W293, WMO). Unipub.

Jehan, L. F. Dictionnaire d'Astronomie de Physique et de Meteorologie. Migne, J. P., ed. (Encyclopedie Theologique Ser.: Vol. 42). (Fr.). 780p. Repr. of 1850 ed. lib. bdg. 99.00x (ISBN 0-89241-247-X). Caratzas.

Kellogg, William W. & Schware, Robert. Climate Change & Society: Consequences of Increasing Atmospheric Carbon Dioxide. (Special Study Ser.). 170p. (Orig.). 1981. 21.50x (ISBN 0-86531-179-X); pap. 9.50x (ISBN 0-86531-180-3). Westview.

Kemp, J. F. & Young, P. Notes on Meteorology. 3rd ed. (Young & Kemp Ser.). 88p. 1971. pap. 9.95x (ISBN 0-540-00369-7). Sheridan.

Kibel, Ivan A., ed. A Collection of Articles on Dynamic Meteorology. LC 60-9255. (Soviet Research in Geophysics in English Translation Ser.: Vol. 1). pap. 46.80 (ISBN 0-317-28718-4, 2020660). Bks Demand UMI.

Kotsch, William J. & Henderson, Richard. Heavy Weather Guide. 2nd ed. (Illus.). 308p. 1984. 21.95 (ISBN 0-87021-263-X). Naval Inst Pr.

Lamb, Hubert H. Climate: Present, Past & Future, Vol. 1. (Illus.). 1972. 120.00x (ISBN 0-416-11530-6, NO.2785). Methuen Inc.

Lampton. Meterology. 1981. 9.90 (ISBN 0-531-04260-X). Watts.

Leavy, Thomas A. Basic Meteorology Lab Manual. 2nd ed. 1969. pap. text ed. 4.95 (ISBN 0-910042-06-3). Allegheny.

Leviton, R. Comparison of Sensors & Telemetry for Meteorological Rockets: Final Report. (Publications Ser.: No. 295). (Illus.). 102p. 1975. pap. 20.00 (ISBN 92-63-10395-X, W166, WMO). Unipub.

Linke, Siegfreid. Know about Weather. 28p. write for info (ISBN 0-905778-06-5). Academy Chi Pubs.

Lutgens, Frederick K. & Tarbuck, Edward J. The Atmosphere: An Introduction to Meteorology. (Illus.). 496p. 1982. text ed. 31.95 (ISBN 0-13-050120-4). P-H.

--The Atmosphere: An Introduction to Meteorology. 3rd ed. (Illus.). 576p. 1986. 30.95 (ISBN 0-13-049917-X). P H.

Lynch, David K., intro. by. Atmospheric Phenomena: Readings from Scientific American. LC 79-26987. (Illus.). 175p. 1980. text ed. 23.95x (ISBN 0-7167-1165-6); pap. 11.95 (ISBN 0-7167-1166-4). W H Freeman.

McGraw-Hill Editors. McGraw-Hill Encyclopedia of Ocean & Atmospheric Sciences. Parker, Sybil P., ed. (Illus.). 1979. 47.50 (ISBN 0-07-045267-9). McGraw.

McIntosh, D. H., et al. Essentials of Meteorology. (Wykeham Science Ser.: No. 3). 262p. 1973. pap. 11.75x (ISBN 0-8448-1354-0). Crane-Russak Co.

--Essentials of Meterology. (The Wykeham Science Ser.: No. 3). 262p. 1981. pap. cancelled (ISBN 0-85109-040-0). Taylor & Francis.

McKenzie, Alexander A. World Record Wind: Measuring Gusts of 231 Miles an Hour. (Illus.). 36p. (Orig.). 1984. pap. 2.00 (ISBN 0-9613227-0-5). A A McKenzie.

Meade, P. J. Meteorological Aspects of the Peaceful Uses of Atomic Energy: Meteorological Aspects of the Safety & Location of Reactor Plants, Pt. 1. (Technical Note Ser.: No. 33). 44p. 1960. pap. 7.00 (ISBN 0-685-22320-5, W13, WMO). Unipub.

Meeting on Education & Training in Meteorological Aspects of Atmospheric Pollution & Related Environmental Problems: Proceedings, Reseaarch Triangle Park, U.S.A., Jan.-Feb. 1977. x, 373p. 1977. pap. 40.00 (ISBN 0-685-93141-2, W379, WMO). Unipub.

Meier, Mark. Remote Sensing of Snow & Ice. (Technical Papers in Hydrology: No. 19). (Illus.). 54p. (A Contribution to the International Hydrological Programme). 1979. pap. 7.50 (ISBN 92-3-101730-6, U976, UNESCO). Unipub.

Meteorological Aspects of Air Pollution. (Technical Note Ser.: No. 106). (Illus.). 69p. (Orig.). 1970. pap. 12.00 (ISBN 0-685-04917-5, W77, WMO). Unipub.

Meteorological Services of the World. (Eng. & Fr.). 180p. 1982. pap. 24.00 loose-leaf (ISBN 0-686-83881-5, W539, WMO). Unipub.

Meteorology & the Human Environment: Lectures Presented at the 29th Session of the WMO Executive Committee. (Special Environmental Reports: No. 13). (Illus.). 49p. 1979. pap. 25.00 (ISBN 92-63-10517-0, W425, WMO). Unipub.

Meteorology & the Human Environment. pap. 2.00 (W114, WMO). Unipub.

Michigan University Greenland Expeditions 1926-1933. Reports of the Greenland Expeditions of the University of Michigan, 2 vols. LC 68-55203. (Illus.). 1968. Repr. of 1941 ed. Set. lib. bdg. 55.00x (ISBN 0-8371-3850-7, MUGE). Greenwood.

Miller, Albert & Thompson, Jack. Elements of Meteorology. 3rd ed. 1979. text ed. 23.95 (ISBN 0-675-08293-5). Merrill.

Miller, Albert & Thompson, Jack C. Elements of Meteorology. 4th ed. 448p. 1983. text ed. 26.95 (ISBN 0-675-20005-9). Additional supplements may be obtained from publisher. Merrill.

Miller, Forrest R. & Keshavamurthy, R. N. Structure of an Arabian Sea Summer Monsoon System. LC 67-29576. (International Indian Ocean Expedition Meteorological Monographs: No. 1). (Illus.). 94p. 1968. text ed. 15.00x (ISBN 0-8248-0070-2, Eastwest Ctr). UH Pr.

Moran, Joseph M. & Morgan, Micheal D. Meteorology: The Atmosphere & the Science of Weather. (Illus.). 475p. 1986. text ed. price not set (ISBN 0-8087-3241-2). Burgess.

Morel, P. Dynamic Meteorology: Lectures Delivered at the Centre Nationale D'Etudes Spatiales, Lannion, France, Aug. 7-Sept. 12, 1970. LC 72-78425. 621p. 1973. lib. bdg. 60.50 (ISBN 90-277-0344-2, Pub. by Reidel Holland). Kluwer Academic.

Moses, L. & Tomikel, John. Basic Meteorology, an Introduction to the Science. (Illus.). 130p. 1981. pap. text ed. 7.00 (ISBN 0-910042-39-X). Allegheny.

Murphy, Allan H. & Katz, Richard W., eds. Probability, Statistics, & Decision Making in Meterology. 450p. (Orig.). lib. bdg. 50.00x (ISBN 0-86531-152-8); pap. text ed. 25.00 (ISBN 0-86531-153-6). Westview.

National Research Council. Introductory Meteorology. 1918. 49.50x (ISBN 0-686-51405-X). Elliots Bks.

Nicholson, James R. Meteorological Data Catalogue. (International Indian Ocean Expedition Meteorological Monographs: No. 3). (Illus.). 59p. 1969. text ed. 20.00x (ISBN 0-8248-0082-6, Eastwest Ctr). UH Pr.

Nords, J. Collection, Storage & Retrieval of Meteorological Data. (World Weather Watch Planning Reports: No. 28). 43p. 1969. pap. 8.00 (ISBN 0-685-22296-9, W240, WMO). Unipub.

O'Neill, Gerard. High Frontier. LC 82-45263. (Illus.). 352p. 1982. pap. 8.95 (ISBN 0-385-18232-5, Anch). Doubleday.

Panchev, S. Dynamic Meteorology. 1984. lib. bdg. 74.00 (ISBN 90-277-1744-3, Pub. by Reidel Holland). Kluwer Academic.

Papers Presented at the Second WMO Scientific Conference on Weather Modification: Boulder, Colorado, 2-6 Aug. 1976. xvii, 592p. 1976. pap. 50.00 (ISBN 92-63-10443-3, W201, WMO). Unipub.

Papers Presented at the WMO Symposium on the Interpretation of Broad-Scale NWP Products for Local Forecasting Purposes: Warsaw, 11-16 Oct. 1976. xiii, 250p. 1976. pap. 30.00 (ISBN 92-63-10450-6, W206, WMO). Unipub.

Papers Presented at the WMO Technical Conference on Instruments & Methods of Observation (TECIMO) Hamburg, 27-30 July 1977. (Eng. & Fr.). vii, 264p. pap. 40.00 (ISBN 92-63-10480-8, W220, WMO). Unipub.

Parameterization of Sub-Grid Scale Processes. (GARP Publications Ser.: No. 8). (Illus.). xiii, 10p. 1972. pap. 12.00 (ISBN 0-685-34858-X, W297, WMO). Unipub.

Paul, Robert A. Meteorology Exercise Manual & Study Guide. 280p. 1986. pap. price not set lab manual (ISBN 0-8087-3371-0). Burgess.

Petterssen, Sverre. Introduction to Meteorology. 3rd ed. LC 68-15476. 1968. text ed. 51.95 (ISBN 0-07-049720-6). McGraw.

Pickett, S. T. & White, P S., eds. Natural Disturbance: The Patch Dymanics Perspective. 1985. 49.00 (ISBN 0-12-554520-7). Acad Pr.

Plate, E., ed. Engineering Meteorology. (Studies in Wind Engineering & Industrial Aerodynamics: Vol. 1). 740p. 1982. 149.00 (ISBN 0-444-41972-1, I-272-82). Elsevier.

Polar Subprogram. (GARP Publications Ser.: No. 19). 47p. 1978. pap. 15.00 (ISBN 0-685-60678-3, W392, WMO). Unipub.

Powers of Nature. LC 76-57002. (Special Publication Ser.: No. XII). (Illus.). 1978. 6.95 (ISBN 0-87044-234-1); lib. bdg. 8.50 (ISBN 0-87044-239-2). Natl Geog.

Problems in Dynamic Meteorology. 245p. 1970. pap. 10.00 (ISBN 0-685-02474-1, W83, WMO). Unipub.

Radiation Sub-Programme for the GARP Atlantic Tropical Experiment. (GATE Report Ser.: No. 4). (Illus.). 109p. (Orig.). 1974. pap. 25.00 (ISBN 0-685-40089-1, W281, WMO). Unipub.

Rainey, R. C. & Aspilden, C. Meteorology & the Migration of Desert Locusts. (Technical Note Ser.). 1963. pap. 25.00 (ISBN 0-685-22324-8, W25, WMO). Unipub.

Rasmusson, E. M. Hydrological Application of Atmospheric Vapour-Flux Analyses. (Operational Hydrology Reports: No. 11). (Illus.). x, 50p. 1977. pap. 10.00 (ISBN 92-63-10476-X, W354, WMO). Unipub.

Regional Association I, Africa: Abridged Final Report of the Sixth Session. 188p. (Orig.). 1974. pap. 25.00 (ISBN 92-63-10367-4, W141, WMO). Unipub.

Regional Association I (Africa) Abridged Final Report of the Seventh Session. (Fr.). xii, 168p. 1978. pap. 25.00 (ISBN 92-63-10503-0, W398, WMO). Unipub.

Regional Association I (Africa) Abridged Final Report of the Eighth Session. 202p. 1983. pap. text ed. 25.00 (ISBN 92-63-10607-X, W565, WMO). Unipub.

Regional Association II (Asia) Abridged Final Report of the Sixth Session (1975) (Eng., Fr. & Rus.). vi, 170p. 1975. pap. 30.00 (ISBN 92-63-10430-1, W193, WMO). Unipub.

Regional Association III (South America) Abridged Final Report of the Eighth Session, Montevideo, March 1-11, 1982. 144p. 1983. pap. 20.00 (ISBN 92-63-10594-4, W543, WMO). Unipub.

Regional Association IV, North & Central America: Abridged Final Report of the Sixth Session. 192p. (Orig.). 1974. pap. 25.00 (ISBN 0-685-50565-0, W147, WMO). Unipub.

Regional Association IV (North & Central America) Abridged Final Report of the Seventh Session, Mexico City 26 April-5 May 1977. (Illus.). 1977. pap. 25.00 (ISBN 92-63-10479-4, W366, WMO). Unipub.

Regional Association V, South-West Pacific: Abridged Final Report of the Sixth Session. 94p. (Orig.). 1974. pap. 25.00 (ISBN 92-63-10380-1, W150, WMO). Unipub.

Regional Association V (South-West Pacific) Abridged Final Report of the Seventh Session (1978) viii, 99p. 1978. pap. 25.00 (ISBN 92-63-10516-2, W418, WMO). Unipub.

Regional Association V (South-West Pacific) Abridged Final Report of the Eighth Session (1982) (Eng. & Fr.). 108p. 1983. pap. text ed. 25.00 (ISBN 92-63-10604-5, W554, WMO). Unipub.

Regional Association VI (Europe) Abridged Final Report of the Seventh Session (1978) (Illus.). xii, 125p. 1979. pap. 25.00 (ISBN 92-63-10522-7, W422, WMO). Unipub.

Regional Association VI (Europe) Abridged Final Report of the Eighth Session (1982) (Eng., Fr. & Rus.). 182p. 1983. pap. text ed. 25.00 (ISBN 92-63-10605-3, W563, WMO). Unipub.

Reifsnyder, William E. Weathering the Wilderness: The Sierra Club Guide to Practical Meteorology. LC 79-20859. (Outdoor Guides Ser.). (Illus.). 288p. 1980. pap. 8.95 (ISBN 0-87156-266-9). Sierra.

Report of the Fifteenth Session of the Joint Organizing Committee for GARP: Dubrovnik, 28 Feb.-6 Mar. 1979. 1979. pap. 25.00 (ISBN 0-686-52509-4, W432, WMO). Unipub.

Report of the Fifth Session of the Tropical Experiment Board. (GARP Special Reports: No. 11). iv, 22p. (Orig., appendices A-L). 1974. pap. 15.00 (ISBN 0-685-41137-0, W318, WMO). Unipub.

Report of the Fifth Session of WMO Executive Committee Inter-Governmental Panel on the First GARP Global Experiment. (GARP Special Reports: No. 26). (Illus.). 45p. 1978. pap. 15.00 (ISBN 0-685-27460-8, W383, WMO). Unipub.

Report of the First Session of the West African Monsoon Experiment (WAMEX) Scientific & Management Regional Committee. (GARP Special Reports: No. 31). (Eng. & Fr.). 14p. 1979. pap. 15.00 (ISBN 0-686-52645-7, W426, WMO). Unipub.

Report of the Fourteenth Session of the Joint Organizing Committee for GARP: Mexico, 13-19 April 1978. 1978. pap. 40.00 (ISBN 0-685-66642-5, W404, WMO). Unipub.

Report of the Fourth Planning Meeting for the Monsoon Experiment (MONEX) (GARP Special Reports: No. 28). (Illus.). 54p. 1978. pap. 40.00 (ISBN 0-685-65240-8, W402, WMO). Unipub.

Report of the Fourth Session of the Joint Scientific Committee. 154p. 1983. pap. text ed. 25.00 (ISBN 0-317-01270-3, W568, WMO). Unipub.

Report of the Fourth Session of the Tropical Experiment Board. (GARP Special Reports: No. 9). (Illus.). 1973. pap. 14.00 (ISBN 0-685-39013-6, W320, WMO). Unipub.

Report of the Fourth Session of WMO Executive Committee Inter-Governmental Panel on the First GARP Global Experiment. (GARP Special Reports: No. 24). v, 63p. (Appendices A-H). 1977. pap. 25.00 (ISBN 0-685-86035-3, W309, WMO). Unipub.

Report of the Ninth Session of the Joint Organizing Committee of GARP. (GATE Report Ser.). (Orig.). 1974. pap. 10.00 (ISBN 0-685-50264-3, W334, WMO). Unipub.

Report of the Second Session of the Joint Scientific Committee for GARP. 160p. 1981. pap. 25.00 (ISBN 0-686-79023-5, W507, WMO). Unipub.

Report of the Sixth Planning Meeting for the Monsoon Experiment (MONEX) (GARP Special Reports: No. 34). 104p. 1979. pap. 20.00 (W459, WMO). Unipub.

Report of the Sixth Session of WMO Executive Committee Inter-Governmental Panel on the First GARP Global Experiment. (GARP Special Reports: No. 29). 51p. 1978. pap. 25.00 (ISBN 0-685-90700-7, W411, WMO). Unipub.

Report of the Third Planning Meeting for the Monsoon Experiment (MONEX) (GARP Special Reports: No. 25). 26p. 1977. pap. 25.00 (ISBN 0-685-87432-X, W368, WMO). Unipub.

Report of the Third Session of the Inter-Governmental Panel Meeting on ALPEX. (GARP Special Reports: No. 40). 122p. 1982. pap. 15.00 (ISBN 0-686-44828-6, W548, WMO). Unipub.

METEOROLOGY-CHARTS, DIAGRAMS, ETC.

METEOROLOGY-DATA PROCESSING

METEOROLOGY-EARLY WORKS TO 1800

METEOROLOGY-HISTORY

METEOROLOGY-INDIAN OCEAN REGION

METEOROLOGY-INTERNATIONAL COOPERATION

Consolidated Report on the Voluntary Co-Operation Programme Including Projects Approved for Circulation in 1979. (Eng., Fr., Span. & Rus.). 282p. 1980. pap. 15.00 (ISBN 92-63-10545-6, W67, WMO). Unipub.

Cost & Structure of Meteorological Services with Special Reference to the Problem of Developing Countries. (Technical Note Ser.: No. 146). 52p. 1975. pap. 18.00 (ISBN 92-63-10426-3, W190, WMO). Unipub.

Eighth World Meteorological Congress: Proceedings. (Eng. & Fr.). 261p. 1980. pap. 30.00 (ISBN 92-63-10547-2, W472, WMO). Unipub.

Field Phase of the GARP Atlantic Tropical Experiment - Meteorological Atlas: Report, No. 17. (Illus.). 179p. 1975. pap. 25.00 (ISBN 0-685-62387-4, WMO). Unipub.

GARP (Global Atmospheric Research Programme), Joint Organizing Committee, 7th Session. Report. pap. 9.00 (ISBN 0-686-93930-1, W336, WMO). Unipub.

GARP (Global Atmospheric Research Programme), Joint Organizing Committee, 6th Session. Report. pap. 5.00 (ISBN 0-686-93931-X, W337, WMO). Unipub.

GARP Tropical Experiment Board, 1st Session. Report of the GARP Experiment Board 1st Session. (GARP Special Reports: No. 4). pap. 8.00 (ISBN 0-686-93934-4, W325, WMO). Unipub.

GATE. Report on the Field Phase of the Atlantic Tropical Experiment Operations. (GATE Report Ser.: No. 15). (Illus.). 148p. 1976. pap. 25.00 (ISBN 0-685-65022-7, W288, WMO). Unipub.

General Plan & Implementation Programme, 1982-1985: As Approved by the Fourteenth Session of the IOC Executive Council and the Thirty-third Session of the WMO Executive Committee. 35p. 1982. pap. 6.00 (ISBN 92-63-10582-0, W514, WMO). Unipub.

Manual on the Global Observing System. 80p. 1980. pap. 20.00 (ISBN 92-63-10544-8, W468, WMO). Unipub.

Modeling for the First GARP Global Experiment. (GARP Publications Ser.: No. 14). (Illus.). xvi, 262p. (Orig.). 1974. pap. 40.00 (ISBN 0-685-50807-2, W302, WMO). Unipub.

National Academy Of Sciences. Feasibility of a Global Observation & Analysis Experiment. 1966. pap. 5.00 (ISBN 0-309-01290-2). Natl Acad Pr.

Papers Presented at the WMO Technical Conference on Regional & Global Observation of Atmospheric Pollution Relative to Climate. (Special Environmental Reports: No. 14). 398p. 1980. pap. 31.00 (ISBN 92-63-10549-9, W466, WMO). Unipub.

Regional Association VI, Europe: Report of the 1972 Extraordinary Session. pap. 20.00 (ISBN 0-686-93896-8, W123, WMO). Unipub.

Report of a Workshop on Atmospheric Carbon Dioxide: Scientific Workshop, Washington, D.C., 1976. pap. 10.00 (ISBN 0-686-93941-7, W218, WMO). Unipub.

Report of Second Session of Tropical Experiment Council. (GARP Special Reports: No. 7). vi, 14p. 1972. pap. 5.00 (W322, WMO). Unipub.

Report of the Experts for the Development of a Data Management for the FGGE. (GARP Special Reports: No. 16). pap. 15.00 (ISBN 0-686-93939-5, W313, WMO). Unipub.

Report of the First Planning Meeting for the West African Monsoon Experiment (WAMEX) (GARP Special Reports: No. 23). 12p. 1977. pap. 25.00 (W308, WMO). Unipub.

Report of the First Session of the Intergovernmental Planning Meeting on ALPEX. (GARP Special Reports: No. 36). 35p. 1981. pap. 15.00 (ISBN 0-686-73318-5, W490, WMO). Unipub.

Report of the GARP Planning Conference. (GARP Special Reports: No. 1). pap. 5.00 (ISBN 0-686-93928-X, W328, WMO). Unipub.

Report of the Meeting on Drifting Buoys for the First GARP Global Experiment. (GARP Special Reports: No. 13). (Illus.). 80p. (Orig.). 1974. pap. 15.00 (ISBN 0-685-50808-0, W316, WMO). Unipub.

Report of the Planning Conference on the 1st GARP Global Experiment. (GARP Special Reports: No. 8). pap. 8.00 (ISBN 0-686-93938-7, W321, WMO). Unipub.

Report of the Second Session of the Inter-Governmental Planning Meeting on ALPEX. (GARP Special Reports: No. 39). 19p. 1981. pap. 15.00 (W516, WMO). Unipub.

Report of the Third Session of the Joint Scientific Committee, Dublin, March 8-15, 1982. 54p. 1982. pap. 25.00 (W542, WMO). Unipub.

Report of the 1st Session of the GARP Tropical Experiment Council. (GARP Special Reports: No. 3). pap. 3.00 (ISBN 0-686-93933-6, W326, WMO). Unipub.

Report on the GARP Tropical Experiment in the Atlantic: Interim Planning. (GARP Special Reports: No. 2). pap. 2.00 (ISBN 0-686-93929-8, W327, WMO). Unipub.

Report on the World Meteorological Congress: 7th, Geneva, April 23 - May, 1975. (Publications Ser.: No. 428). 230p. 1976. pap. 30.00 (ISBN 92-63-10428-X, WMO). Unipub.

Technical Conference on Climate: Asia & Western Pacific: Proceedings, Guangzhou, China, 5-20 Dec. 1980. 449p. 1981. pap. 28.00 (ISBN 92-63-10578-2, W518, WMO). Unipub.

Thirty-Third Session of the Executive Committee, Geneva, 1-17 June 1981: Abridged Report with Resolutions. 150p. 1981. pap. 25.00 (ISBN 92-63-10579-0, W525, WMO). Unipub.

WMO Helps the Developing Countries. 85p. 1973. pap. 2.00 (ISBN 0-685-29205-3, W110, WMO). Unipub.

World Weather Watch: Sixth Status Report on Implementation. (World Weather Watch Planning Reports). (Illus.). 225p. (Orig.). 1974. pap. 25.00 (ISBN 0-685-40087-5, W227, WMO). Unipub.

METEROLOGY–LABORATORY MANUALS

Goodman & Wang. Meteorological Instruments Laboratory Manual. 72p. 1984. pap. text ed. 9.95 (ISBN 0-8403-3313-7). Kendall-Hunt.

METEOROLOGY–OBSERVATIONS

see also Aeronautics in Meteorology; Astronautics in Meteorology; Meteorological Stations

Badgley, F. I., et al. Profiles of Wind, Temperature, & Humidity Over the Arabian Sea. LC 70-129539. (International Indian Ocean Expedition Meteorological Monographs: No. 6). (Illus.). 1972. text ed. 20.00x (ISBN 0-8248-0101-6, Eastwest Ctr). UH Pr.

Basic Synoptic Network of Observing Stations. 1978. pap. 45.00 (ISBN 0-685-42367-0, W408, WMO). Unipub.

Brooks, Charles E. & Carruthers, N. Handbook of Statistical Methods in Meteorology. LC 77-10222. Repr. of 1953 ed. 30.50 (ISBN 0-404-16202-9). AMS Pr.

Browning, K. A., ed. Nowcasting. LC 82-45030. 1982. 50.00 (ISBN 0-12-137760-1). Acad Pr.

Doviak, Richard J. & Zrnic, Dusan. Doppler Radar & Weather Observations (Monograph) LC 83-15840. 1984. 60.00 (ISBN 0-12-221420-X). Acad Pr.

Fitch, A. A., ed. Developments in Geophysical Exploration Methods, Vol. 3. (Illus.). 320p. 1982. 57.50 (ISBN 0-85334-126-5, Pub. by Elsevier Applied Sci England). Elsevier.

Forbush, Scott E & Casaverde, Mateo. Equatorial Electrojet in Peru. LC 62-51815. (Carnegie Institution of Washington Publication Ser.: No. 620). pap. 35.30 (ISBN 0-317-08543-3, 2007905). Bks Demand UMI.

Gorczynski, Wladyslaw. Comparison of Climate of the United States & Europe: Especially Poland & Her Baltic Coast. 288p. 1945. 8.00 (ISBN 0-940962-03-9). Polish Inst Art & Sci.

Guide on the Global Observing System. (Eng., Fr., Span. & Rus., Illus.). 1977. pap. 42.00 (ISBN 92-63-10488-3, W365, WMO). Unipub.

Kellogg, W. W. Meteorological Soundings in the Upper Atmosphere. (Technical Note Ser.: No. 60). 48p. 1964. pap. 8.00 (ISBN 0-685-22322-1, W28, WMO). Unipub.

Michigan University Greenland Expeditions 1926-1933. Reports of the Greenland Expeditions of the University of Michigan, 2 vols. LC 68-55203. (Illus.). 1968. Repr. of 1941 ed. Set. lib. bdg. 55.00x (ISBN 0-8371-3850-7, MUGE). Greenwood.

Potential Economic & Associated Values of the World Weather Watch. pap. 4.00 (ISBN 0-686-93902-6, W229, WMO). Unipub.

World Meteorological Organization. Meteorology in the Indian Ocean. 1965. pap. 2.00 (ISBN 0-685-22325-6, W35, WMO). Unipub.

World Weather Watch: Seventh Status Report on Implementation. (Illus.). 1975. pap. 25.00 (ISBN 92-63-10401-8, W219, WMO). Unipub.

METEOROLOGY–RESEARCH

see Meteorological Research

METEOROLOGY–STUDY AND TEACHING

Byers, Horace R. General Meteorology. 4th ed. (Illus.). 550p. 1974. text ed. 45.95 (ISBN 0-07-009500-0). McGraw.

Compendium of Meteorological Training Facilities. (Publications Ser.: No. 240). (Illus.). 1978. pap. 25.00 (ISBN 0-685-86364-6, W357, WMO). Unipub.

Compendium of Training Facilities for Meterology & Operational Hydrology. 6th ed. 590p. 1982. pap. 50.00 (ISBN 92-63-16240-9, W530, WMO). Unipub.

Conference on Meteorological Education & Training in Developing Countries in Africa: Proceedings, Algiers, 1970. (Eng. & Fr., Illus.). 362p. 1972. pap. 20.00 (ISBN 0-685-23600-5, W105, WMO). Unipub.

Education & Training in Meteorology & Meteorological Aspects of Environmental Problems: WMO-IAMAP Symposium. (Publications Ser.: No. 432). pap. 50.00 (W195, WMO). Unipub.

Guidelines for Education & Training of Meteorological Personnel. pap. 15.00 (W81, WMO). Unipub.

Guidelines for the Education & Training of Personnel in Meteorology & Operational Hydrology. 2nd ed. (Eng. & Fr., Illus.). 236p. 1977. pap. 20.00 (ISBN 92-63-12258-X, W373, WMO). Unipub.

Guidelines for the Education & Training of Personnel in Meteorology & Operational Hydrology, 3 pts. Incl. Part 1. 2nd ed. pap. 20.00 (ISBN 92-6-312258-X, W532, WMO); Education & Training of Personnel in Operating Hydrology. pap. 3.00 (ISBN 0-686-93854-2, W532); Addendum to Part 2. 35p. 1982. pap. 5.00 (W532). (Illus.). 1977 (WMO). Unipub.

Kazeck, M. & Bridwell, J. Weather Workbook. 1971. pap. 4.80x (ISBN 0-87563-045-6). Stipes.

WMO-IAMAP Symposium on Higher Education & Training: Proceedings, Rome, April 1970. (Eng & Fr.). 332p. (Orig.). 1970. pap. 20.00 (ISBN 0-685-00378-7, W91, WMO). Unipub.

World Weather Watch: Seventh Status Report on Implementation. (Illus.). 1975. pap. 25.00 (ISBN 92-63-10401-8, W219, WMO). Unipub.

METEOROLOGY–ANTARCTIC REGIONS

Kuhn, M., et al. The Radiation Budget at Plateau Station, Antarctica: Paper 5 in Meteorological Studies at Plateau Station, Antarctica. Businger, Joost A., ed. (Antarctic Research Ser.: Vol. 25). (Illus.). 1977. pap. 16.90 (ISBN 0-87590-139-5). Am Geophysical.

Lettau, H., et al. Air Temperature & Two-Dimensional Wind Profiles in the Lowest 32 Meters as a Function of Bulk Stability, Stability Related Wind Spiraling in the Lowest 32 Meters, & Variations of Temperature & Air Motion in the 0 to 32m Layer at Plateau Station, Antartica: Papers 6, 7, & 8 in Meteorological Studies at Plateau Station, Antarctica. Businger, Joost A., ed. (Antarctic Research Ser.: Vol. 25). 1977. pap. 13.50 (ISBN 0-87590-140-9). Am Geophysical.

Rubin, M. J., ed. Studies in Antarctic Meteorology. LC 66-6578. (Antarctic Research Ser.: Vol. 9). (Illus.). 231p. 1966. 18.00 (ISBN 0-87590-109-3). Am Geophysical.

METEOROLOGY, AGRICULTURAL

see also Crops and Climate

Abridged Final Report of the Seventh Session, Sofia, 17-28 Sept. 1979: Commission for Agricultural Meteorology. 1980. pap. 15.00 (ISBN 92-63-10546-4, W464, WMO). Unipub.

Agricultural Meteorology. 357p. (Orig.). 1972. pap. 35.00 (ISBN 0-685-26758-X, W112, WMO). Unipub.

Agroclimatological Data for Africa: Countries North of the Equator, Vol. 1 & Countries South of the Equator, Vol. 2, 2 vols. (Plant Production & Protection Ser.). (Illus.). 1985. Set. pap. 80.50 (F2642, FAO). Vol. 1 (ISBN 92-5-001412-0). Vol. 2 (ISBN 92-5-001413-9). Unipub.

Board on Agriculture & Renewable Resources, National Research Council. Climate & Food: Climatic Fluctuation & U. S. Agricultural Production. LC 76-46195. 1976. pap. 9.25 (ISBN 0-309-02522-2). Natl Acad Pr.

Cocheme, J. & Franqiun, P. Agroclimatology Survey of a Semi-arid Area in Africa: South of the Sahara. (Illus.). 136p. 1967. pap. 15.00 (ISBN 0-685-57271-4, W54, WMO). Unipub.

Commission for Agricultural Meteorology: Abridged Final Report of the Sixth Session. 79p. 1975. pap. 25.00 (ISBN 92-63-10402-6, W171, WMO). Unipub.

Commission for Agricultural Meteorology: Abridged Final Report of the Eighth Session. 82p. 1983. pap. text ed. 25.00 (ISBN 92-63-10612-6, W550, WMO). Unipub.

Da Mata, F. S. Soya Bean & Weather. (Technical Note Ser.: No. 160). xvi, 64p. 1978. pap. 20.00 (ISBN 92-63-10498-0, W396, WMO). Unipub.

Geiger, Rudolf. Climate Near the Ground. 4th ed. Scripta Technica Inc, tr. LC 64-23191. 1965. 35.00x (ISBN 0-674-13500-8). Harvard U Pr.

Gommes, R. A. Pocket Computers in Agrometeorology. (Plant Production & Protection Papers: No. 45). 149p. 1983. pap. 10.75 (ISBN 92-5-101336-5, F2449, FAO). Unipub.

Guide to Agricultural Meteorological Practices. 2nd ed. (Eng., Fr & Span.). 211p. 1981. pap. 25.00 (ISBN 92-63-12134-6, W520, WMO). Unipub.

Jen-Yu Wang & Barger, Gerald L., eds. Bibliography of Agricultural Meteorology. 686p. 1962. 45.00x (ISBN 0-299-02510-1). U of Wis Pr.

Omar, M. H. The Economic Value of Agrometeorological Information & Advice. (Technical Note Ser.: No. 164). 52p. 1980. pap. 10.00 (ISBN 92-63-10526-X, W478, WMO). Unipub.

Robertson, G. W. Rice & Weather. (Technical Note Ser.: No. 144). (Illus.). 40p. (CAGM Rapporteur on Meteorological Factors Affecting Rice Production). 1975. pap. 12.00 (ISBN 92-63-10423-9, W188, WMO). Unipub.

Seemann, J., et al. Agrometeorology. LC 79-9757. (Illus.). 1979. 61.00 (ISBN 0-387-09331-1). Springer-Verlag.

Smith, L. P. Methods in Agricultural Meteorology. LC 74-21868. (Developments in Atmospheric Science Ser.: Vol. 3). 210p. 1975. 59.75 (ISBN 0-444-41286-7). Elsevier.

--World Weather Watch & Meteorological Service to Agriculture. (World Weather Watch Planning Reports: No. 22). 28p. 1967. pap. 4.00 (ISBN 0-685-02477-6, W235, WMO). Unipub.

Wang, Jen Y. & Barger, Gerald L., eds. Bibliography of Agricultural Meteorology. LC 61-12212. pap. 160.00 (ISBN 0-317-27249-7, 2023710). Bks Demand UMI.

World Weather Watch Global Observing System-Satellite Sub-System: Information on Meteorological Satellite Programmes Operated by Members & Organizations. (Illus.). 50p. 1975. pap. 25.00 (ISBN 92-63-10411-5, W222, WMO). Unipub.

METEOROLOGY, MARITIME

see also Hurricanes; Typhoons

Abridged Final Report of the Seventh Session of the Regional Association II (Asia) Geneva, 2-12 June 1980. (Report Ser.). 145p. 1980. pap. 25.00 (ISBN 92-63-10567-7, W486, WMO). Unipub.

Bishop, Joseph M. A Mariner's Guide to Radiofacsimile Weather Charts. (Illus.). 128p. (Orig.). 1981. pap. 9.95 (ISBN 0-686-32920-1). Alden Electronics.

Blanchard, Duncan C. From Raindrops to Volcanoes: Adventures with Sea Surface Meteorology. LC 80-19134. (Science Study Ser.: Selected Topics in Atmospheric Sciences). (Illus.). xii, 180p. 1980. Repr. of 1967 ed. lib. bdg. 24.75x (ISBN 0-313-22638-5, BLFR). Greenwood.

Burgess, C. R. Meteorology for Seamen. metric ed. 1981. 30.00x (ISBN 0-85174-315-3, Pub. by Nautical England). State Mutual Bk.

--Meteorology for Seamen. 4th ed. 251p. 1982. text ed. 25.00x (ISBN 0-85174-315-3). Sheridan.

Commission for Marine Meteorology: Abridged Final Report of the Eighth Session, 1981. (Eng., Fr., Span. & Rus.). 113p. 1981. pap. 25.00 (ISBN 92-63-10584-7, W521, WMO). Unipub.

Commission for Marine Meteorology: Albridged Final Report of the Seventh Session (1976) 119p. 1977. pap. 25.00 (ISBN 92-63-10462-X, W212, WMO). Unipub.

Donn, William L. Meteorology. 4th ed. (Illus.). 608p. 1975. text ed. 36.55 (ISBN 0-07-017599-3). McGraw.

Fishermen & the Weather. (Fisheries Technical Papers: No. 71). 88p. 1968. pap. 7.50 (ISBN 0-686-92782-6, F1733, FAO). Unipub.

Global Data-Processing System & Meteorological Service to Shipping. (World Weather Watch Planning Reports: No. 15). 26p. 1966. pap. 12.00 (ISBN 0-685-22305-1, W231, WMO). Unipub.

Guide to Marine Meteorological Services. 1978. pap. 27.00 (ISBN 92-63-10471-9, W362, WMO). Unipub.

Handbook on Wave Analysis & Forecasting. (Eng., Fr & Span., Illus.). 1976. pap. 37.00 (ISBN 92-63-10446-8, W204, WMO). Unipub.

Hastenrath, Stefan & Lamb, Peter J. Heat Budget Atlas of the Tropical Atlantic & Eastern Pacific Oceans. LC 77-91052. (Illus.). 104p. 1978. pap. text ed. 50.00x (ISBN 0-299-07584-2). U of Wis Pr.

International List of Selected, Supplementary & Auxiliary Ships: 1976. (Publications Ser.: No. 47). 1976. pap. 21.00 (W385, WMO). Unipub.

Isemer, H. J. & Hasse, L., eds. The Bunker Climate Atlas of the North Atlantic Ocean, Vol. 1: Observations. (Illus.). 225p. 1985. 98.00 (ISBN 0-387-15568-6). Springer Verlag.

Lilly, Kenneth E., Jr. Marine Weather of Western Washington. LC 83-50478. (Illus.). 150p. (Orig.). 1983. pap. 12.95 (ISBN 0-916682-38-2). Starpath.

Manual on Marine Meteorological Services. (Eng., Fr., Span. & Rus.). 78p. 1981. pap. 20.00 (ISBN 92-63-10558-8, W503, WMO). Unipub.

Maury, Matthew F. Physical Geography of the Sea, & Its Meteorology. Leighly, John, ed. LC 63-10870. (The John Harvard Library). (Illus.). 1963. pap. 9.95x (ISBN 0-674-66652-6). Harvard U Pr.

Mertins, H. Compendium of Lecture Notes in Marine Meteorology for Class III & Class IV Personnel. (Publications Ser.: No. 434). (Eng., Fr. & Span., Illus.). 222p. 1976. pap. 25.00 (ISBN 92-63-10434-4, W187, WMO). Unipub.

Meteorological Aspects of Ice Accretion on Ships. (Reports on Marine Science Affairs: No. 10). 34p. 1975. pap. 10.00 (ISBN 0-685-55843-6, W276, WMO). Unipub.

Methods of Forecasting the State of Sea on the Basis of Meteorological Data. (Technical Note Ser.: No. 46). 35p. 1962. pap. 12.00 (ISBN 0-685-36786-X, W21, WMO). Unipub.

The Monsoon Experiment. (GARP Publications Ser.: No. 18). xxvii, 214p. 1976. pap. 25.00 (ISBN 0-685-77321-3, W305, WMO). Unipub.

Papers Presented at the WMO Technical Conference on the Applications of Marine Meteorology to the High Seas & Coastal Zone Development. (Illus.). 1977. pap. 40.00 (ISBN 92-63-10454-9, WMO). Unipub.

The Preparation & Use of Weather Maps by Mariners. (Reports on Marine Science Affairs: No. 15). 86p. 1982. pap. text ed. 11.00 (ISBN 92-63-10595-2, W555, WMO). Unipub.

Roll, Hans U. Physics of the Marine Atmosphere. (International Geophysics Ser.: Vol. 7). 1965. 57.00 (ISBN 0-12-593650-8). Acad Pr.

Sanderson, Ray. Meteorology At Sea. (Illus.). 1982. 19.95 (ISBN 0-540-07405-5). Sheridan.

--Meteorology for Yachtsmen. 1981. 40.00x (Pub. by Stanford Maritime England). State Mutual Bk.

Sea Climatology. 416p. 1981. 95.00x (ISBN 2-7108-0396-8, Pub. by Graham & Trotman England). State Mutual Bk.

Stommel, Henry & Stommel, Elizabeth. Volcano Weather: The Story of 1816, the Year Without a Summer. LC 82-19658. (Illus.). 192p. 1983. 15.95 (ISBN 0-915160-71-4). Seven Seas.

Teson, L. J. & Teson, G., Jr. Seiches et Denivellations Causees par le Vent dans Lacs, Baies, Mers, Estuaires. (Technical Note Ser.: No. 102). (Fr.). 59p. 1969. pap. 12.00 (ISBN 0-685-57270-6, W72, WMO). Unipub.

Williams, Jerome, et al. Sea & Air: The Marine Environment. 2nd ed. LC 72-93196. 338p. 1973. 15.95x (ISBN 0-87021-596-5). Naval Inst Pr.

METEOROLOGY AS A PROFESSION

Educational Research Council of America. Meteorologist. rev. ed. Kunze, Linda J. & Marchak, John P., eds. (Real People at Work Ser.: G). (Illus.). 36p. 1976. pap. text ed. 2.70 (ISBN 0-89247-054-2, 9334). Changing Times.

Harris, Miles F. & American Meteorological Society. Opportunities in Meteorology. rev. ed. LC 77-184504. (Illus.). 184p. 1972. lib. bdg. 6.60 (ISBN 0-685-27224-9); pap. 4.95 (ISBN 0-685-27225-7). Natl Textbk.

How to Become a Meteorologist. (Eng., Fr., Span. & Rus., Illus.). 16p. (Orig.). 1970. pap. 2.00 (ISBN 0-685-04913-2, W80, WMO). Unipub.

Rudman, Jack. Meteorologist. (Career Examination Ser.: C-497). (Cloth bdg. avail. on request). pap. 12.00 (ISBN 0-8373-0497-0). Natl Learning.

METEOROLOGY IN AERONAUTICS

see also Aeronautics in Meteorology

Aviation Hail Problem: Includes Other Notes on Forecasting for Jet Aircraft. (Technical Note Ser.: Nos. 37-40). pap. 17.00 (ISBN 0-685-57276-5, W25, WMO). Unipub.

Boyes, Lindy. Pilot's Weather Guide. 2nd ed. pap. text ed. 7.95 (ISBN 0-8306-2288-8, 2288). TAB Bks.

Commission for Aeronautical Meteorology, 5th Session, 1971. Report. pap. 20.00 (ISBN 0-686-93916-6, W119, WMO). Unipub.

Dabberdt, Walter F. The Whole Air Weather Guide. (Illus.). 1976. pap. 3.50 (ISBN 0-686-85668-6, Pub. by Solstice). Aviation.

Dickson, Ron R. Weather & Flight: An Introduction to Meteorology for Pilots. 186p. 1982. 16.95 (ISBN 0-13-947119-7); pap. 7.95 (ISBN 0-13-947101-4). P-H.

Federal Aviation Administration. Aviation Weather. 2nd ed. (Pilot Training Ser.). (Illus.). 219p. 1975. pap. 8.50 (ISBN 0-89100-160-3, EA-AC61-006A). Aviation Maintenance.

--Aviation Weather Services. 3rd ed. (Pilot Training Ser.). (Illus.). 123p. 1979. pap. 6.00 (ISBN 0-89100-161-1, EA-AC61-0045B). Aviation Maintenance.

Global Data-Processing System & Meteorological Service to Aviation. (World Weather Watch Planning Reports: No. 13). 40p. 1966. pap. 12.00 (ISBN 0-686-93858-5, W231, WMO). Unipub.

Global Data-Processing System & Meteorological Service to Shipping. (World Weather Watch Planning Reports: No. 15). 26p. 1966. pap. 12.00 (ISBN 0-685-22305-1, W231, WMO). Unipub.

Ground Training for the Private Pilot Licence, No. 2: Air Navigation & Aviation Meteorology. 326p. 1985. pap. 20.00x (ISBN 0-00-383111-6, Pub. by Collins England). Sheridan.

Handbook of Meteorological Forecasting for Soaring Flight. (Technical Note Ser.: No. 158). (Eng. & Fr.). x, 101p. 1978. pap. 18.00 (ISBN 92-63-10495-6, W399, WMO). Unipub.

High-Level Forecasting for Turbine-Engined Aircraft Operations over Africa & the Middle East. pap. 25.00 (ISBN 0-686-93870-4, W31, WMO). Unipub.

Jones, R. P., et al. Meteorological Problems in the Design & Operation of Supersonic Aircraft. (Technical Note Ser.: No. 89). x, 71p. 1967. pap. 9.00 (ISBN 0-685-22321-3, W55, WMO). Unipub.

Manual on Meteorological Observing in Transport Aircraft. 2nd ed. 17p. 1978. pap. 4.00 (ISBN 92-63-12197-4, W393, WMO). Unipub.

Nelson, John L. Practical Guide to Aviation Weather. 2nd ed. LC 84-16441. (Illus.). 182p. 1984. pap. 12.95 (ISBN 0-8306-2338-8, 2338). TAB Bks.

Newton, Dennis W. Severe Weather Flying. (McGraw-Hill Aviation Ser.). (Illus.). 160p. 1983. 26.50 (ISBN 0-07-046402-2). McGraw.

Simplicio, S. Utilization of Aircraft Meteorological Reports. Rev. ed. (Technical Note Ser.: No. 141). (Illus.). 34p. 1975. pap. 10.00 (ISBN 92-63-10400-X, W170, WMO). Unipub.

World Meteorological Organization. Aeronautical Meteorology. (Technical Note Ser.: No. 95). 1969. pap. 60.00 (ISBN 0-685-22293-4, W62, WMO). Unipub.

METEORS

see also Meteorites

Cristescu, Cornelia & Klepczynski, W. J., eds. Asteroids, Comets, Meteoric Matter: Proceedings. (Illus.). 333p. 1975. text ed. 60.00x (ISBN 0-87936-008-9). Scholium Intl.

Gibilisco, Stan. Comets, Meteors & Asteroids: How They Affect Earth. (Illus.). 208p. (Orig.). 1985. pap. 12.95 (ISBN 0-8306-1905-4, 1905). TAB Bks.

Hornberger, Theodore. A Goodly Gallery: William Fulke's Book of Meteors. LC 78-68390. (Memoirs Ser.: Vol. 130). 1979. pap. 6.00 (ISBN 0-87169-130-2). Am Philos.

IAU Symposium, 33rd, Tatranska Lomnica, Czechoslovakia, 1967. Physics & Dynamics of Meteors: Proceedings. Kresak, L. & Millman, P. M., eds. LC 68-26965. (IAU Symposia). 525p. 1968. lib. bdg. 53.00 (ISBN 90-277-0127-X, Pub. by Reidel Holland). Kluwer Academic.

Kronk, Gary W. Meteor Showers: A Descriptive Catalog. (Illus.). 128p. 1985. pap. text ed. 11.95x (ISBN 0-89490-072-2). Enslow Pubs.

McDonnell, J. A., ed. Cosmic Dust. LC 77-2895. 693p. 1978. text ed. 176.95x (ISBN 0-471-99512-6, Pub. by Wiley-Interscience). Wiley.

Meadows, Jack. Space Garbage: Comets, Meteors & other Solar-System Debris. (Illus.). 160p. 1985. pap. 17.95 (ISBN 0-540-01087-1, Pub. by G Philip UK). Sheridan.

Nelson, Harry E. The Resistance of the Air to Stone-Dropping Meteors. LC 53-12359. (Augustana College Library Publication Ser.: No. 24). 37p. 1953. pap. 3.00x (ISBN 0-910182-19-1). Augustana Coll.

Schiaparelli, G. V. Le Opere Publicate per Cura Della Reale Specola Di Brera, Vols. 1-11. (Sources of Science Ser.). (It). Repr. of 1930 ed. Set. 440.00 (ISBN 0-384-53780-4). Johnson Repr.

Waskin, Mel. Mrs. O'Leary's Comet. (Illus.). 175p. 1985. 13.95 (ISBN 0-89733-167-2); pap. 6.95 (ISBN 0-89733-181-8). Academy Chi Pubs.

METER (STANDARD OF LENGTH)

see Metric System

METERS, ELECTRIC

see Electric Meters

METERS, FLOW

see Flow Meters

METHANE

American Gas Association. Methane. (Special Report Ser.). 200p. 1983. 375.00 (ISBN 0-8247-7072-2). Dekker.

Clever, A. S. Methane. 100.01 (ISBN 0-08-029200-3). Pergamon.

Durbin, Enoch & McGeer, Patrick L., eds. Methane: Fuel for the Future. LC 82-13120. 350p. 1982. 47.50x (ISBN 0-306-41122-9, Plenum Pr). Plenum Pub.

Gray, Charles, Jr. & Alson, Jeff. Methanol: The Transportation Fuel of the Future (The Optimal Solution to the Acid Rain & Energy Problems) 300p. 1985. text ed. 25.00x (ISBN 0-472-10071-8); pap. text ed. 12.50x (ISBN 0-472-08063-6). U of Mich Pr.

Meynell, Peter-John. Methane: Planning a Digester. LC 77-87893. (Orig.). 1978. pap. 4.95 (ISBN 0-8052-0586-1). Schocken.

Rutan, Al. The Do's & Don't's of Methane: Gas Production for Self Sufficiency. rev. ed. (Illus.). 165p. 1979. pap. 15.00 (ISBN 0-936222-02-6). Rutan Pub.

Schumacher, M. M., ed. Landfill Methane Recovery. LC 83-3936. (Energy Tech. Rev. 84). (Illus.). 558p. (Orig.). 1983. 54.00 (ISBN 0-8155-0946-4). Noyes.

Stafford, D. A., et al. Methane Production from Waste Organic Matter. LC 78-31274. 304p. 1980. 86.50 (ISBN 0-8493-5223-1). CRC Pr.

Veal, F. J. Methane from Sorted Domestic Refuse: An Economic Assessment, 1977. 1981. 40.00x (ISBN 0-686-97114-0, Pub. by W Spring England). State Mutual Bk.

--Methane from Sorted Domestic Refuse: A Reappraisal, 1979. 1982. 40.00x (ISBN 0-686-97117-5, Pub. by W Spring England). State Mutual Bk.

Wise, Donald L., ed. Fuel Gas Production from Biomass, 2 vols. 1981. Vol. I, 280 Pgs. 83.00 (ISBN 0-8493-5990-2); Vol. II, 296 Pgs. 91.50 (ISBN 0-8493-5991-0). CRC Pr.

METHOD OF LEAST SQUARES

see Least Squares

METHOD OF WORK

see Methods Engineering

METHODS ENGINEERING

Bowditch, James & Buono, Anthony. Quality of Work Life Assessment: A Survey-Based Approach. 224p. 1982. 23.00 (ISBN 0-86569-067-7). Auburn Hse.

Butera, F. & Thurman, J. E., eds. Automation & Work Design: A Study Prepared by International Labour Office. LC 84-8169. 758p. 1984. 74.00 (ISBN 0-444-87538-7, I-318-84, Pub. by North Holland). Elsevier.

Edwards, Richard C. Contested Terrain: The Transformation of the Workplace in America. LC 78-19942. 256p. 1980. pap. 8.95x (ISBN 0-465-01413-5, TB-5051). Basic.

Glossop, R. H. Method Study & the Furniture Industry. LC 75-112711. 1970. 25.00 (ISBN 0-08-015653-3). Pergamon.

MaCoy, Ramelle & Morand, Martin J., eds. Short-Time Compensation: A Formula for Work Sharing. LC 83-13265. (Pergamon Press-Work in America Institute Ser.). 223p. 1984. 23.50 (ISBN 0-08-030148-7, 29/59/4). Pergamon.

Mumford, Enid & Weir, Mary. Computer Systems in Work Design: The Ethnics Method: Effective Technical & Human Implementation of Computer Systems. LC 78-32068. 314p. 1979. 44.95x (ISBN 0-470-26656-2). Halsted Pr.

Rosow, Jerome M. & Zager, Robert. Productivity Through Work Innovations: Complete Study. 161p. 1982. 15.00 (ISBN 0-08-029545-2). Work in Amer.

--Productivity Through Work Innovations: Executive Summary. 48p. 1982. pap. 6.50 (ISBN 0-08-029546-0). Work in Amer.

Ross, Lynne N. Work Simplification in Food Service: Individualized Instruction. LC 73-171164. (Orig., Prog. Bk.). 1972. text ed. 6.95x (ISBN 0-8138-0785-9). Iowa St U Pr.

METHYL GROUPS

see also Transmethylation

Huyduk, A. S. Propane, Butane & 2-Methylpropane. 100.01 (ISBN 0-08-029202-X). Pergamon.

Salvatore, Francesco, et al, eds. The Biochemistry of Adenosylmethionine. LC 76-25565. 1977. 75.00x (ISBN 0-231-03895-X). Columbia U Pr.

METHYLATION

see also Transmethylation

Taylor, J. H. DNA Methylation & Cellular Differentiation. (Cell Biology Monographs: Vol. 11). (Illus.). 150p. 1984. 39.50 (ISBN 0-387-81761-1). Springer Verlag.

Usdin, E. & Borchardt, R. T., eds. Transmethylation. LC 78-27647. (Developments in Neuroscience Ser.: Vol. 5). 1979. 88.50 (ISBN 0-444-00310-X, North Holland). Elsevier.

METHYLENE COMPOUNDS

Fogg, A. S. & Young. Ammonia Amines, Phosphides, Arsin. 1985. 100.00 (ISBN 0-08-026177-9). Pergamon.

METRIC RINGS

see Banach Algebras

METRIC SPACES

see also Distance Geometry

Aubin, Jean-Pierre. Applied Abstract Analysis. LC 77-2382. (Pure & Applied Mathematics Ser.). 263p. 1977. 47.50x (ISBN 0-471-02146-6, Pub. by Wiley-Interscience). Wiley.

Billingsley, P. Convergence of Probability Measures. (Probability & Mathematical Statistics Tracts: Probability & Statistics Section). 253p. 1968. 41.95x (ISBN 0-471-07242-7, Pub. by Wiley-Interscience). Wiley.

Blumenthal, Leonard M. & Menger, Karl. Studies in Geometry. LC 74-75624. (Illus.). 512p. 1970. text ed. 31.95 (ISBN 0-7167-0437-4). W H Freeman.

Borsuk, Karol. Theory of Shape. LC 76-359585. 379p. 1975. 37.50x (ISBN 0-8002-2343-8). Intl Pubns Serv.

Bryant, V. W. Metric Spaces: Interation & Application. (Illus.). 120p. 1985. 29.95 (ISBN 0-521-26857-5); pap. 9.95 (ISBN 0-521-31897-1). Cambridge U Pr.

Comfort, W. W. & Negrepontis, S. Continuous Pseudometrics. (Lecture Notes in Pure & Applied Mathematics Ser.: Vol. 14). 136p. 1975. 35.00 (ISBN 0-8247-6294-0). Dekker.

Copson, Edward T. Metric Spaces. (Cambridge Tracts in Mathematics & Mathematical Physics). 1968. 24.95 (ISBN 0-521-04722-6). Cambridge U Pr.

Kaplansky, Irving. Set Theory & Metric Spaces. 2nd ed. LC 77-7344. 1977. text ed. 9.50 (ISBN 0-8284-0298-1). Chelsea Pub.

Nadler, Sam B., Jr. & Quinn, J. Embeddability & Structure Properties of Real Curves. LC 72-4343. (Memoirs: No. 125). 74p. 1972. pap. 10.00 (ISBN 0-8218-1825-2, MEMO-125). Am Math.

Pierce, R. S. Compact Zero-Dimensional Metric Spaces of Finite Type. LC 72-11822. (Memoirs: No. 130). 64p. 1972. pap. 9.00 (ISBN 0-8218-1830-9, MEMO-130). Am Math.

Reisel, Robert R. Elementary Theory of Metric Spaces: A Course in Constructing Mathematical Proofs. (Universitext Ser.). 120p. 1982. pap. 18.00 (ISBN 0-387-90706-8). Springer-Verlag.

Rolewicz, Stefan. Metric Linear Spaces. 1985. lib. bdg. 79.00 (ISBN 90-277-1480-0, Pub. by Reidel Holland). Kluwer Academic.

Schaffer, Juan J. Geometry of Spheres in Normed Spaces. (Lecture Notes in Pure & Applied Math Ser: Vol. 20). 1976. 45.00 (ISBN 0-8247-6554-0). Dekker.

Sutherland, Wilson A. Introduction to Metric & Topological Spaces. (Illus.). 1975. 24.95x (ISBN 0-19-853155-9); pap. 16.95x (ISBN 0-19-853161-3). Oxford U Pr.

Washington, Allyn J. Basic Technical Mathematics with Calculus, Metric. 4th ed. 1985. text ed. 33.95x (ISBN 0-8053-9545-8); instr's guide 5.95 (ISBN 0-8053-9546-6). Benjamin-Cummings.

Wells, J. H. & Williams, L. R. Embeddings & Extensions in Analysis. LC 74-31234. (Ergebnisse der Mathematik und Ihrer Grenzgebiete Ser.: Vol. 84). 125p. 1975. text ed. 23.00 (ISBN 0-387-07067-2). Springer-Verlag.

METRIC SYSTEM

see also Weights and Measures

Acosta de Gonzalez, Fe. El Sistema Metrico (Modulo) (Coleccion Uprex; Serie Pedagogia: No. 57). (Span.). 1979. pap. text ed. 3.80 (ISBN 0-8477-2743-2). U of PR Pr.

Adams, Priscilla, ed. Examining the Metric Issues. 85p. 1976. pap. 4.00 (ISBN 0-916148-08-4); subscribers 3.00. Am Natl.

Albracht, James & Kurtz, Ray. Introduction to AG Metrics. text ed. 16.75x (ISBN 0-8134-1999-9). Interstate.

Alton, E. V. & Gersting, J. L. Module SI: Metric System. Ablon, L. J., et al, eds. LC 76-58669. (Ser. in Mathematical Modules). 1977. pap. text ed. 11.95 (ISBN 0-8465-0266-6). Benjamin-Cummings.

American Metric Journal Editors. Metric in a Nutshell. 2nd ed. Hopkins, Robert A., ed. LC 76-19477. 1977. 8.95 (ISBN 0-917240-06-5). Am Metric.

American Welding Society. Metric Practice Guide for the Welding Industry: A1.1. 30p. 1980. 12.00 (ISBN 0-87171-194-X); member 9.00. Am Welding.

Antoine, Valerie. Guidance for Using Metric System (SI Version) 39p. 1976. pap. 8.00 (ISBN 0-914548-23-9). Soc Tech Comm.

ASME Orientation & Guide for Use of SI (Metric) Units. 9th ed. 1982. pap. text ed. 2.00 (ISBN 0-685-41936-3, E00058). ASME.

Association for Information & Image Management. Metric Conversion Recommendations: AIIM TR1-1979. (Technical Reports Ser.). 1979. pap. text ed. 10.00 (ISBN 0-89258-063-1, T001); pap. text ed. 7.75 member. Assn Inform & Image Mgmt.

Barron's Technical Staff, compiled by. Barron's Metric Conversion Tables. LC 76-8425. (Barron's Educational Ser.). 224p. 1976. pap. text ed. 4.50 (ISBN 0-8120-0659-3). Barron.

Bartlett, David F., ed. The Metric Debate. LC 79-53270. 19.50x (ISBN 0-87081-083-9). Colo Assoc.

Batchelder, J. W. Metric Madness. (Illus.). 256p. 1981. 12.95 (ISBN 0-8159-6220-7); pap. 5.95 (ISBN 0-8159-6219-3). Devin.

Bates & Fullerton. How to Think Metric. LC 74-75325. 1974. pap. 4.95 (ISBN 0-8224-3763-5). Pitman Learning.

Benedict, John T. Metrication for the Manager. Boselovic, Len, ed. LC 77-84932. (Illus.). 1977. pap. text ed. 10.00 (ISBN 0-916148-12-2); subscribers 8.00. Am Natl.

Berggren, Don. The Magnificent Metric System: A Magical Guide to the Marvels of Metrics. LC 76-40527. (Illus., Orig.). 1976. pap. 2.95 (ISBN 0-912800-34-8). Woodbridge Pr.

Cameron, Clive A. Going Metric with the U.S. Printing Industry. 125p. 1972. pap. 11.00 (ISBN 0-317-14996-2). Tech & Ed Ctr Graph Arts RIT.

Camilli, Thomas. Make It Metric. (Illus.). 72p. (Orig.). 1982. 6.95 (ISBN 0-9607366-7-0, KP111). Kino Pubns.

Carrell, Mary J. Understanding the Metric System. 1978. pap. text ed. 3.00x (ISBN 0-88323-140-9, 229). Richards Pub.

Chisholm, L. J. Units of Weight & Measure: International (Metric) & U. S. Customary. LC 74-20726. (Illus.). 256p. 1975. Repr. of 1967 ed. 40.00x (ISBN 0-8103-4163-8). Gale.

Consumer Liaison Committee of the American National Metric Council. Metric Reference for Consumers. 1976. pap. text ed. 2.50 (ISBN 0-916148-10-6). Am Natl.

Danloux-Dumesnils, M. The Metric System: A Critical Study of Its Principles & Practice. 162p. 1969. pap. 16.95 (ISBN 0-485-12013-5, Pub. by Athlone Pr Ltd). Longwood Pub Group.

Educational Materials Sector Committee of the American National Metric Council. Metric Guide for Educational Materials: A Handbook for Teachers, Writers & Publishers. 1977. pap. text ed. 3.00 (ISBN 0-916148-09-2); subscribers 2.00. Am Natl.

Feirer. SI Metric Handbook. 1977. text ed. 25.00 (ISBN 0-02-665180-7). Bennett IL.

Follendore, Joan S. You Can Learn Metric Easily. (Illus., Orig.). 1976. pap. 1.00 (ISBN 0-916546-01-2). Racz Pub.

Friesth, E. Richard. Metrication in Manufacturing. LC 77-21838. (Illus.). 373p. 1978. 26.95 (ISBN 0-8311-1120-8). Indus Pr.

Gilbert, Thomas F. & Gilbert, Marilyn B. Thinking Metric. 2nd ed. LC 77-20190. (Self-Teaching Guide Ser.). 141p. 1978. pap. text ed. 6.95 (ISBN 0-471-03427-4, Pub. by Wiley Pr). Wiley.

Glaser, Anton. Neater by the Meter: An American Guide to the Metric System. LC 73-88193. (Illus.). 112p. (Orig.). 1974. pap. 3.50 (ISBN 0-9600324-4-4). A Glaser.

Hopkins, Robert A. The International SI System & How It Works. 3rd, rev. ed. LC 73-94128. (AMJ Publication: B.1). 300p. 1983. Repr. of 1977 ed. 16.95 (ISBN 0-686-22829-4). Am Metric.

Hunter, Helen & Wallach, Paul. Metrically Yours. LC 78-70040. pap. 20.00 (ISBN 0-317-08491-7, 2011576). Bks Demand UMI.

Jerd, Russell F. Industrial Metric Conversion. 92p. (Orig.). 1983. pap. text ed. 9.95x (ISBN 0-89917-391-8). Tichenor Pub.

Karim, G. A. & Hamilton, A. B. Metrication for the E&P Professional. LC 81-80668. (Illus.). 109p. 1981. text ed. 28.00 (ISBN 0-934634-03-3); pap. text ed. 17.00 (ISBN 0-934634-09-2). Intl Human Res.

Kempf, Albert F. & Richards, Thomas J. The Metric System Made Simple. LC 75-36631. (Made Simple Ser.). 144p. 1977. 4.95 (ISBN 0-385-11032-4). Doubleday.

Kurtz, V. Ray. Metrics for Elementary & Middle Schools. 120p. 1978. pap. 5.95 (ISBN 0-8106-1714-5). NEA.

Kverneland, Knut O. World Metric Standards for Engineering. LC 77-25875. (Illus.). 760p. 1978. 47.50 (ISBN 0-8311-1113-5). Indus Pr.

LeMaraic, A. L. & Ciaramella, J. P. Basic Guide to the Metric System. LC 75-25312. 1976. 6.95 (ISBN 0-913768-06-5, 913065). Metric Media Bk.

--The Complete Metric System with the International System of Units 51. LC 72-97799. 1974. 6.95x (ISBN 0-913768-00-6, 913006). Metric Media Bk.

LeMaraic, A. L. & Ciaramella, J. P., eds. The Metric Encyclopedia. LC 74-9235. 8.95 (ISBN 0-913768-03-0). Metric Media Bk.

Lindbeck. Metric Practices in Drafting. 1979. pap. 7.08 (ISBN 0-02-665240-4). Bennett IL.

Lowe, Kenneth E. Metrication for the Pulp & Paper Industry. LC 74-20165. (A Pulp & Paper Book). (Illus.). 192p. 1975. 35.00 (ISBN 0-87930-034-5). Miller Freeman.

Lytle, R. J. American Metric Handbook. 1981. 22.50 (ISBN 0-07-039277-3). McGraw.

Mahoney, Susan & Mills, Richard G. Metric Measurement. LC 76-731369. (Illus.). 1976. pap. text ed. 103.00 (ISBN 0-89290-128-4, 507-SAR-SATC). Soc for Visual.

Managing Metrication in Business & Industry. 203p. 1976. 37.00 (ISBN 0-8247-6469-2); subscribers 31.00. Am Natl.

Maritime Transportation Research Board, National Research Council. Maritime Metrication: A Recommended Metric Conversion Plan for the U.S. Maritime Industry. LC 76-1348. 121p. 1976. pap. 6.75 (ISBN 0-309-02447-1). Natl Acad Pr.

Marson, Ron. More Metrics Thirty-Six. LC 81-90448. (Science with Simple Things Ser.: No. 36). (Illus.). 80p. 1985. tchr. ed. 13.95 (ISBN 0-941008-36-3). Tops Learning.

Mason & Lange. Using the Metric System. (Plaid Ser.). 1976. pap. 7.95 (ISBN 0-256-01772-7). Dow Jones-Irwin.

Mechtly, E. H. The International System of Units. 1977. pap. 1.80x (ISBN 0-87563-139-8). Stipes.

Meter: A Handbook of Activities to Motivate the Teaching of the Metric System. (The Spice Ser.). 1975. 6.95 (ISBN 0-89273-118-4). Educ Serv.

Metric Conversion in the Construction Industries: Planning, Coordination & Timing. 62p. 1980. 15.00 (ISBN 0-686-70963-2); subscribers 12.00. Am Natl.

Metric Conversion Tables. pap. 2.75 (ISBN 0-06-461010-1, DI 10, BN). B&N NY.

Metric Editorial Guide. 3rd rev. ed. 1980. pap. text ed. 3.00 (ISBN 0-916148-13-0); subscribers 2.00. Am Natl.

Metric Measure. (Tops Cards Ser.: No.6). 1978. pap. 8.80 (ISBN 0-941008-06-1). Tops Learning.

Metric Planning Guide for Vocational Education. (Illus.). 72p. 1981. 12.00 (ISBN 0-89514-036-5, 10381). Am Voc Assn.

Metric Practice Guide - E 380-84. 42p. 1984. pap. 5.00 (ISBN 0-8031-0750-1, 03-503809-41). ASTM.

Metric Practice Guide - E380-84. 42p. 1984. pap. 5.00 (ISBN 0-8031-0750-1, 03-503809-41). ASTM.

Metric Series, 7 bks. Incl. Bks. 1 & 2. Measuring Metric. Cherrington, Don; Bk. 3. Metric Fundamentals. Fearon, Arthur D (ISBN 0-912450-08-8); Bk. 4. Metrics for Home Use. Massey, Opal (ISBN 0-912450-09-6); Bk. 5. Everyday Metrics. Fearon, Arthur D (ISBN 0-912450-10-X); Bk. 6. Metrics Workshop for Teachers. Cherrington, Don (ISBN 0-912450-11-8); Bk. 7. Practical Metrics. Prescott, Elizabeth (ISBN 0-912450-12-6); Bk. 8. Technical Si Metrics. Prescott, Elizabeth (ISBN 0-912450-13-4); Bk. 9. Metric Handbook. Garner, Bruce L (ISBN 0-912450-14-2). 1974. pap. 3.50 ea.; pap. 12.95 set (ISBN 0-685-42659-9). Willow Hse.

The Metric System: What It Is & How to Use It. 1975. pap. 4.00 (ISBN 0-686-10810-8). Preston.

Metrication for the Modeller. (Illus.). 40p. 1979. pap. 1.95 (ISBN 0-85344-137-5). Aztex.

Metrication: Managing the Industrial Transition - STP 574. 342p. 1975. 30.00 (ISBN 0-8031-0516-9, 04-574000-34). ASTM.

Metrication: The Australian Experience. 210p. 1975. 4.00 (ISBN 0-686-70962-4); subscribers 3.00. Am Natl.

Michaelson, M. Metric System & Metric Conversion: A Checklist of References. LC 79-83892. 1979. lib. bdg. 10.95 (ISBN 0-933474-02-4). Minn Scholarly.

Miller, David M. Understanding the Metric System: A Programed Text. new ed. 1979. pap. text ed. 8.00 (ISBN 0-205-06581-3, 566581-7); tchrs'. guide 3.20 (ISBN 0-205-06582-1, 566582-5). Allyn.

Newspaper Enterprise Association. The World Almanac Guide to Metrics. 1977. pap. 2.50 (ISBN 0-449-13828-3, GM). Fawcett.

Oppert, J. Moving to Metrics in Home Economics. LC 77-81325. 1977. 2.50 (ISBN 0-686-20043-8, 26108430). Home Econ Educ.

Ostergard, Susan, et al. The Metric World: A Survival Guide. LC 75-6919. (Illus.). 176p. 1975. pap. text ed. 13.95 (ISBN 0-8299-0059-4); instrs.' manual avail. (ISBN 0-8299-0605-3). West Pub.

Paquin, Joseph R. Fractions to Millimeters. LC 75-28052. 48p. 1975. pap. 5.95 (ISBN 0-8311-1109-7). Indus Pr.

Parker, Don H., et al. The Metric System: Syllabus. 1974. pap. text ed. 16.50 units of 10 (ISBN 0-89420-052-6, 280222); cassette recordings 18.15 (ISBN 0-89420-163-8, 280000). Natl Book.

Pedde, Lawrence D. & Foote, Warren E. Metric Manual. 278p. 1980. Repr. of 1978 ed. 46.00x (ISBN 0-8103-1020-1). Gale.

Perica, Lou & Boselovic, Len, eds. Guidelines for Writers of SI Metric Standards & Other Documents. 1975. pap. text ed. 8.00 (ISBN 0-916148-04-1); subscribers 6.00. Am Natl.

Ploutz, Paul F. The Metric System: Content & Methods. 2nd ed. (Elementary Education Ser.). 1977. pap. text ed. 12.95 (ISBN 0-675-08538-1). Merrill.

Qasim, S. H. SI Units in Engineering & Technology. 1977. pap. 7.75 (ISBN 0-08-021278-6). Pergamon.

Reid, Jane. Metrics for Everyday Use. new ed. LC 74-24660. 24p. 1975. pap. text ed. 4.16 (ISBN 0-02-665230-7). Bennett IL.

Richardson, Terry. A Guide to Metrics. LC 78-61695. (Illus.). 1978. pap. 12.00x (ISBN 0-911168-38-9). Prakken.

Schimizzi, Ned V. Mastering the Metric System. (Orig.). 1975. pap. 2.50 (ISBN 0-451-62194-8, ME2194, Ment). NAL.

Schubert, Paul & Semioli, William, trs. Conversion Tables for SI Metrication. LC 74-1104. (Illus.). 360p. 1974. 25.00 (ISBN 0-8311-1104-6). Indus Pr.

Siggson, Al, ed. The Metric System: A Review of Industrial Applications. LC 82-50572. 212p. 1982. text ed. 13.50 (ISBN 0-87263-108-7). SME.

Smoley, C. K. Smoley's Metric Four Combined Tables. Smoley, E. R. & Smoley, N. G., eds. 1400p. 1976. thumb-indexed 42.50 (ISBN 0-911390-08-1). Smoley.

Steinke, Don C. Thirty Days to Metric Mastery: For People Who Hate Math. (Illus., Orig.). 1981. pap. 6.95x (ISBN 0-9605344-0-7). Hse of Charles.

Stevens, B. Teaching the Metric System in the Foreign Language Classroom. (Language in Education Ser.: No. 32). 46p. 1980. pap. 6.95x (ISBN 0-15-599271-6). Ctr Appl Ling.

Stoecker, W. F. Using SI Units (Standard International Metric) in Heating, Air Conditioning, & Refrigeration. LC 74-26697. (Illus.). 1975. 7.50 (ISBN 0-912524-12-X). Busn News.

Teaching Classroom Metric. rev. ed. LC 76-22299. (AMJ Publication: B5.2). 145p. 1977. 9.50 (ISBN 0-917240-07-3). Am Metric.

Technical Book Division of Barron's. Metrics Made Easy. (Illus.). 1976. pap. text ed. 0.95 (ISBN 0-8120-0706-9). Barron.

Technical Division, Barron's Educational Ser., compiled by. Metric Converter. 1976. pap. text ed. 1.25 (ISBN 0-8120-0707-7). Barron.

Thornburg, Kathy R. & Thornburg, James L. Metric Magic. new ed. LC 77-93666. (Illus.). 1978. pap. text ed. 9.95 (ISBN 0-89334-014-6). Humanics Ltd.

U. S. Department of Commerce & Hopkins, R. A. NBS Metric Practice Guide & Style Manual. 5.95 (ISBN 0-917240-04-9). Am Metric.

Van Buren, Martin. Metrics for Architects, Designers & Builders. 192p. 1982. 18.95 (ISBN 0-442-28889-1). Van Nos Reinhold.

Wallach, Paul. Meet the Metric System. 1980. pap. 4.60 (ISBN 0-8224-4463-1); teacher's guide free (ISBN 0-8224-4464-X). Pitman Learning.

Wandmacher, C. Metric Units in Engineering--Going SI. LC 77-17935. (Illus.). 1978. 27.00 (ISBN 0-8311-1121-6). Indus Pr.

Whyte, W. S. & Paul, R. E. Basic Metric Surveying. 3rd ed. 336p. 1985. pap. text ed. 15.95 (ISBN 0-408-01354-0). Butterworth.

Willert, Frederic. My Metric Measurement Manual. rev. ed. (Illus.). 1975. Pgs. 120. write for info. tchrs. ed. (ISBN 0-9601144-2-4); Pgs. 88. write for info. wkbk. (ISBN 0-9601144-1-6). Pauper Pr.

Zupko, Ronald E. French Weights & Measures before the Revolution: A Dictionary of Provincial & Local Units. LC 78-3249. 256p. 1979. 25.00x (ISBN 0-253-32480-7). Ind U Pr.

METRIC TOPOLOGY

see Distance Geometry

METROLOGY

see Mensuration; Weights and Measures

METROPOLITAN TRANSPORTATION

see Urban Transportation

MHD GENERATORS

see Magnetohydrodynamic Generators

MICE

see also Jerboas

Alvarez, Ticul. Taxonomic Status of Some Mice of the Peromyscus Boylii Group in Eastern Mexico, with Description of a New Subspecies. (Museum Ser.: Vol. 14, No. 7). 10p. 1961. pap. 1.25 (ISBN 0-317-04908-9). U of KS Mus Nat Hist.

Anderson, Sydney. Subspeciation in the Meadow Mouse, Microtus Montanus, in Wyoming & Colorado. (Museum Ser.: Vol. 7, No. 7). 18p. 1954. pap. 1.25 (ISBN 0-317-04917-8). U of KS Mus Nat Hist.

--Subspeciation in the Meadow Mouse, Microtus Pennsylvanicus, in Wyoming, Colorado & Adjacent Areas. (Museum Ser.: Vol. 9, No. 4). 20p. 1956. pap. 1.25 (ISBN 0-317-04919-4). U of KS Mus Nat Hist.

Anderson, Sydney & Jones, J. Knox, Jr. Records of Harvest Mice, Reithrodontomys, from Central America, with Description of a New Subspecies from Nicaragua. (Museum Ser.: Vol. 9, No. 19). 11p. 1960. pap. 1.25 (ISBN 0-317-04926-7). U of KS Mus Nat Hist.

Baker, Rollin H. The Silky Pocket Mouse (Perognathus Flavus) of Mexico. (Museum Ser.: Vol. 7, No. 3). 9p. 1954. pap. 1.25 (ISBN 0-317-04946-1). U of KS Mus Nat Hist.

Cockrum, E. Lendell & Fitch, Kenneth L. Geographic Variation in Red-Backed Mice (Genus Clethrionomys) of the Southern Rocky Mountain Region. (Museum Ser.: Vol. 5, No. 22). 12p. 1952. pap. 1.25 (ISBN 0-317-04975-5). U of KS Mus Nat Hist.

Cockrum, Lendell E. A New Pocket Mouse (Genus Perognathus) from Kansas. (Museum Ser.: Vol. 5, Vol. 11). 4p. 1951. pap. 1.25 (ISBN 0-317-04967-4). U of KS Mus Nat Hist.

Douglas, Charles L. Comparative Ecology of Pinyon Mice & Deer Mice in Mesa Verde National Park, Colorado. (Museum Ser.: Vol. 18, No. 5). 84p. 1969. pap. 4.50 (ISBN 0-686-80275-6). U of KS Mus Nat Hist.

Elton, Charles. Voles, Mice & Lemmings. 1971. Repr. of 1942 ed. 33.10 (ISBN 3-7682-0275-5). Lubrecht & Cramer.

Finley, Robert B., Jr. A New Pinon Mouse (Peromyscus Truei) from Durango, Mexico. (Museum Ser.: Vol. 5, No. 20). 5p. 1952. pap. 1.25 (ISBN 0-317-05010-9). U of KS Mus Nat Hist.

Foster, Henry & Fox, James, eds. The Mouse in Biomedical Research: Vol. 3, Normative Biology, Immunology & Husbandry. 390p. 1983. 83.00 (ISBN 0-12-262503-X). Acad Pr.

Foster, Henry, et al, eds. The Mouse in Biomedical Research: Vol. 2, Diseases. LC 80-70669. (American College of Laboratory Animal Medicine Ser.). 1982. 80.00 (ISBN 0-12-262502-1). Acad Pr.

Foster, Henry L., et al, eds. The Mouse in Biomedical Research: Vol. 4, Experimental Biology & Oncology. 545p. 1982. 90.00 (ISBN 0-12-262504-8). Acad Pr.

--The Mouse in Biomedical Research: Vol. 1, History Genetics & Wild Mice. LC 80-70669. (ACLAM Ser.). 1981. 65.00 (ISBN 0-12-262501-3). Acad Pr.

Genoways, Hugh H. A New Species of Spiny Pocket Mouse (Genus Liomys) from Jalisco, Mexico. (Occasional Papers: No. 5). 7p. 1971. pap. 1.25 (ISBN 0-317-05016-8). U of KS Mus Nat Hist.

Gershwin, M. E. & Merchant, B., eds. Immunologic Defects in Laboratory Animals, 2 vols. (Vol. 1 380 pp.; Vol. 2 402 pp.). 1981. Vol. 1. 45.00x (ISBN 0-306-40668-3, Plenum Pr); Vol. 2. 45.00x (ISBN 0-306-40673-X); Set. 79.50x. Plenum Pub.

Gude, W. D., et al. Histological Atlas of the Laboratory Mouse. LC 81-8708. (Illus.). 164p. 1982. 29.50x (ISBN 0-306-40686-1, Plenum Pr). Plenum Pub.

Hall, E. Raymond. A New Subspecies of Pocket Mouse from Kansas. (Museum Ser.: Vol. 7, No. 11). 4p. 1954. pap. 1.25 (ISBN 0-317-04805-8). U of KS Mus Nat Hist.

--Two New Meadow Mice from Michoacan, Mexico. (Museum Ser.: Vol. 1, No. 21). 5p. 1948. pap. 1.25 (ISBN 0-317-05020-6). U of KS Mus Nat Hist.

Hall, E. Raymond & Ogilvie, Marilyn B. Conspecificity of Two Pocket Mice: Perognathus Goldmani & P. Artus. (Museum Ser.: Vol. 9, No. 18). 6p. 1960. pap. 1.25 (ISBN 0-317-04807-4). U of KS Mus Nat Hist.

Hall, E. Raymond & Villa-R, Bernardo. A New Pocket Gopher (Thomomys) & a New Spiny Pocket Mouse (Liomys) from Michoacan, Mexico. (Museum Ser.: Vol. 1, No. 14). 8p. 1948. pap. 1.25 (ISBN 0-317-05018-4). U of KS Mus Nat Hist.

Hirschhorn, Howard. All about Mice. (Illus.). 96p. (Orig.). 1974. pap. 3.95 (ISBN 0-87666-210-6, M-542). TFH Pubns.

Hogan, B., et al, eds. Manipulating the Mouse Embryo: A Laboratory Manual. (Orig.). 1985. pap. 55.00 (ISBN 0-87969-175-1). Cold Spring Harbor.

ICLAS Staff. ICLAS Manual for Genetic Monitoring of Inbred Mice. 200p. 1985. pap. 25.00x (ISBN 0-86008-366-7, Pub. by U of Tokyo Japan). Columbia U Pr.

Jones, J. Knox, Jr. Geographic Distribution of the Pocket Mouse: Perognathus Fasciatus. (Museum Ser.: Vol. 5, No. 29). 12p. 1953. pap. 1.25 (ISBN 0-317-04831-7). U of KS Mus Nat Hist.

Jones, J. Knox, Jr. & Mursaloglu, B. Geographic Variation in the Harvest Mouse, Reithrodontomys Megalotis, on the Central Great Plains & in Adjacent Regions. (Museum Ser.: Vol. 14, No. 2). 19p. 1961. pap. 1.25 (ISBN 0-317-04839-2). U of KS Mus Nat Hist.

Jones, Tony. Encyclopedia of Pet Mice. (Illus.). 224p. 1979. 12.95 (ISBN 0-87666-910-0, H-973). TFH Pubns.

Jones, William. Rats, Mice, & Cockroaches: The Dilemma & Solutions. LC 81-90323. (Illus.). 104p. (Orig.). 1982. pap. 13.95 (ISBN 0-9607272-0-5). Ramico Pubns.

Krutzsch, Philip H. North American Jumping Mice: Genus Zapus. (Museum Ser.: Vol. 7, No. 4). 124p. 1954. pap. 6.50 (ISBN 0-317-04872-4). U of KS Mus Nat Hist.

Lawyor, Timothy T. The Yucatan Deer Mouse: Peromyscus Yucatanicus. (Museum Ser.: Vol. 16, No. 4). 18p. 1965. pap. 1.25 (ISBN 0-317-04881-3). U of KS Mus Nat Hist.

Long, Charles A. Natural History of the Brush Mouse (Peromyscus Boylii) in Kansas with Description of a New Subspecies. (Museum Ser.: Vol. 14, No.6). 12p. 1961. pap. 1.25 (ISBN 0-317-04883-X). U of KS Mus Nat Hist.

Morse, Herbert C., ed. Origins of Inbred Mice. 1978. 67.00 (ISBN 0-12-507850-1). Acad Pr.

Packard, Robert L. Speciation & Evolution of the Pygmy Mice, Genus Baiomys. (Museum Ser.: Vol. 9, No. 23). 92p. 1960. pap. 4.75 (ISBN 0-686-80316-7). U of KS Mus Nat Hist.

Rafferty, Keen A., Jr. Methods in Experimental Embryology of the Mouse. LC 70-101642. (Illus.). 94p. 1970. 12.00x (ISBN 0-8018-1129-5). Johns Hopkins.

Rickart, Eric A. Reproduction Growth & Development in Two Species of Cloud Forest Peromyscus from Southern Mexico. (Occasional Papers: No. 67). 22p. 1977. pap. 1.25 (ISBN 0-317-04907-0). U of Ks Mus Nat Hist.

Willott, James F. The Auditory Psychobiology of the Mouse. (Illus.). 518p. 1983. 56.50x (ISBN 0-398-04712-X). C C Thomas.

Wirtschafter, Zoltan T. The Genesis of the Mouse Skeleton: A Laboratory Atlas. (Illus.). 192p. 1960. photocopy ed. spiral 20.50x (ISBN 0-398-02094-9). C C Thomas.

MICRO COMPUTERS

see Microcomputers

MICROANALYSIS (CHEMISTRY)

see Microchemistry

MICROBES

see Bacteria; Bacteriology; Micro-Organisms; Viruses

MICROBIAL GENETICS

see also Bacterial Genetics; Viral Genetics

Bainbridge, Brian W. The Genetics of Microbes. LC 80-15936. (Tertiary Level Biology Ser.). 193p. 1980. pap. 39.95x (ISBN 0-470-26995-2). Halsted Pr.

Fincham, J. R. Microbial & Molecular Genetics. 2nd ed. LC 75-21729. 150p. 1976. pap. 9.95x (ISBN 0-8448-0769-9). Crane-Russak Co.

Goebel, W., ed. Genetic Approaches to Microbial Pathogenicity. (Current Topics in Microbiology & Immunology Ser.: Vol. 118). (Illus.). 310p. 1985. 59.00 (ISBN 0-387-15597-X). Springer-Verlag.

Millis, N. & Pittard, A. J., eds. The Applications of Microbial Physiology & Genetics to Industrial Processes. 250p. Date not set. write for info. (ISBN 0-12-497520-8). Acad Pr.

Traul, Karl A. Microbial Tests for Mutagenicity-Carcinogenicity. (Illus.). 272p. 1985. 38.50 (ISBN 0-442-28303-2). Van Nos Reinhold.

MICROBIAL METABOLITES

see also Antibiotics; Biosynthesis

Codd, Geoffrey A., ed. Aspects of Microbial Metabolism & Ecology. (Social Publication Society General Microbiology Ser.: No. 11). 1984. 52.00 (ISBN 0-12-178050-3). Acad Pr.

Dodgeson, K. S., et al, eds. Sulfates of Microbial Origin, Vols. 1 & 2. 1982. Vol. 1, 216p. 59.00 (ISBN 0-8493-6035-8); Vol. 2, 208p. 59.00 (ISBN 0-8493-6036-6). CRC Pr.

Fiechter, A., ed. Microbial Metabolism. (Advances in Biochemical Engineering Ser.: Vol. 14). (Illus.). 1980. 46.00 (ISBN 0-387-09621-3). Springer-Verlag.

Gottschalk, G. Bacterial Metabolism. LC 78-7880. (Springer Ser. in Microbiology). (Illus.). 1979. 27.50 (ISBN 0-387-90308-9). Springer-Verlag.

Hutter, R., et al, eds. Antibiotics & Other Secondary Metabolites: Biosynthesis & Production. 1979. 49.00 (ISBN 0-12-363250-1). Acad Pr.

Kulaev, J. S., et al, eds. Environmental Regulation of Microbial Metabolism. 1985. 49.00 (ISBN 0-12-428580-5). Acad Pr.

Turner, Robert A. & Hebborn, Peter. Screening Methods in Pharmacology, Vol. 2. 1971. 68.00 (ISBN 0-12-704252-0). Acad Pr.

Turner, W. B. & Aldridge, D. C. Fungal Metabolites, Vol. II. 1983. 80.00 (ISBN 0-12-704556-2). Acad Pr.

MICROBIAL TRANSFORMATION OF CHEMICAL COMPOUNDS

see Microbiological Synthesis

MICROBIOLOGICAL SYNTHESIS

see also Fermentation

Aaronson, Sheldon, ed. Chemical Communication at the Microbial Level, Vols. I & II. 200p. 1982. Vol. I 200p. 67.00 (ISBN 0-8493-5319-X); Vol. II 200p. 67.00 (ISBN 0-8493-5320-3). CRC Pr.

Charney, William & Herzog, Hershel. Microbiological Transformation of Steroids: A Handbook. 1968. 95.00 (ISBN 0-12-169950-1). Acad Pr.

Duffy, J. I., ed. Chemicals by Enzymatic & Microbial Processes: Recent Advances. LC 80-16150. (Chemical Technology Review: No. 161). (Illus.). 386p. 1980. 48.00 (ISBN 0-8155-0805-0). Noyes.

Fonken, G. & Johnson, R. Chemical Oxidations with Microorganisms. (Oxidation in Organic Chemistry Ser.: Vol. 2). 1972. 75.00 (ISBN 0-8247-1211-0). Dekker.

Rozazza, John P., ed. Microbial Transformations of Bioactive Compounds, Vols. I & II. 1982. Vol. I, 144 pgs. 46.00 (ISBN 0-8493-6065-X); Vol. II, 200 pgs. 64.00 (ISBN 0-8493-6066-8). CRC Pr.

MICROBIOLOGY

see also Bacteriology; Biodegradation; Germfree Life; Industrial Microbiology; Marine Microbiology; Microbial Metabolites; Micro-Organisms; Microscope and Microscopy; Radioisotopes in Microbiology; Virology; Yeast

Alcamo, I. Edward. Microbiology. (Biology Ser.). (Illus.). 600p. 1983. text ed. 34.95 (ISBN 0-201-10068-1); Instrs' Manual 3.00 (ISBN 0-201-10069-X); study guide 10.95 (ISBN 0-201-11180-2); Laboratory Manual 13.95 (ISBN 0-201-11181-0) (ISBN 0-201-11182-9). Addison-Wesley.

Alexander, M., ed. Advances in Microbial Ecology, Vol. 1. (Illus.). 280p. 1977. 39.50x (ISBN 0-306-38161-3, Plenum Pr). Plenum Pub.

--Advances in Microbial Ecology, Vol. 2. (Illus.). 311p. 1978. 39.50x (ISBN 0-306-38162-1, Plenum Pr). Plenum Pub.

--Advances in Microbial Ecology, Vol. 3. (Illus.). 237p. 1979. 47.50x (ISBN 0-306-40240-8, Plenum Pr). Plenum Pub.

Ananthanarayan, R. Introduction to Medical Microbiology. 288p. 1984. pap. text ed. 15.95 (ISBN 0-86131-454-9, Pub. by Orient Longman India). Apt Bks.

Ananthanarayan, R. & Paniker, C. K. Textbook of Microbiology. 608p. 1979. 25.00x (ISBN 0-86131-032-2, Pub. by Orient Longman India). State Mutual Bk.

Ananthanarayan, R. & Paniker, Jayaram. Textbook of Microbiology. 2nd ed. (Illus.). 618p. 1982. pap. text ed. 25.00x (ISBN 0-86131-293-7, Pub. by Orient Longman Ltd India). Apt Bks.

Andersen, C. A., ed. Microprobe Analysis. LC 72-8837. 586p. 1973. 43.00 (ISBN 0-471-02835-5). Krieger.

Anderson & Sobieski. Introduction to Microbiology. 2nd ed. LC 79-20560. 1980. pap. 26.95 (ISBN 0-8016-0206-8). Mosby.

Anderson, J. M., et al, eds. Invertebrate-Microbial Interactions: Joint Symposium of the British Mycological Society & the British Ecological Society Held at the University of Exeter, September 1982. LC 83-14416. (British Mycological Society Symposium Ser.: No. 6). (Illus.). 349p. 1984. 79.50 (ISBN 0-521-25395-0). Cambridge U Pr.

Arber, W., ed. Current Topics in Microbiology & Immunology, Vol. 72. LC 15-12910. (Illus.). 200p. 1976. 50.00 (ISBN 0-387-07564-X). Springer-Verlag.

--Current Topics in Microbiology & Immunology, Vol. 78. LC 15-12910. (Illus.). 1977. 56.00 (ISBN 0-387-08499-1). Springer-Verlag.

Arber, W., et al. Current Topics in Microbiology & Immunology, Vol. 75. LC 15-12910. (Illus.). 1976. 54.00 (ISBN 3-540-08013-9). Springer-Verlag.

--Current Topics in Microbiology & Immunology, Vol. 79. LC 15-12910. 1978. 63.00 (ISBN 0-387-08587-4). Springer-Verlag.

Arber, W., et al, eds. Current Topics in Microbiology & Immunology, Vols. 40-55. Incl. Vols. 40-50 & 52-55. Chronic Infections Neuropathic Agents & Other Slow Virsus Infections. Brody, J. A., et al, eds. (Illus.). vii, 74p. 1967; Vol. 41. (Illus.). iv, 183p. 1967. 49.00 (ISBN 0-387-03755-1); Vol. 42. Insect Viruses. Maramorosch, K., ed. (Illus.). viii, 192p. 1968. 31.00 (ISBN 0-387-04071-4); Vol. 43. (Illus.). iii, 233p. (Incl. 32 pp. in German). 1968. 52.00 (ISBN 0-387-04072-2); Vol. 44. (Illus.). iii, 175p. 1968. 52.00 (ISBN 0-387-04073-0); Vol. 45. (Illus.). iii, 237p. (Incl. 61 pp. in German). 1968. 52.00 (ISBN 0-387-04074-9); Vol. 46. (Illus.). iii, 203p. (Incl. 90 pp. in German). 1968. 57.90 (ISBN 0-387-04075-7); Vol. 47. (Illus.). iii, 222p. (Incl. 29 pp. in German). 1969. 55.50 (ISBN 0-387-04445-0); Vol. 48. (Illus.). iii, 206p. 1969. 55.50 (ISBN 0-387-04446-9); Vol. 49. (Illus.). iii, 250p. 1969. 55.50 (ISBN 0-387-04447-7); Vol. 50. (Illus.). iii, 238p. 1969. 55.50 (ISBN 0-387-04448-5); Vol. 52. (Illus.). iv, 197p. 1970. 55.50 (ISBN 0-387-04787-5); Vol. 53. (Illus.). 236p. 1970. 58.50 (ISBN 0-387-05069-8); Vol. 54. (Illus.). 230p. 1971. 58.50 (ISBN 0-387-05289-5); Vol. 55. Arthropod Cell Cultures & Their Application to the Study of Viruses: Arthropod Cell Cultures & Their Application to the Study of Viruses. Weiss, E., ed. (Illus.). 340p. 1971. 58.00 (ISBN 0-387-05451-0). (Eng. & Ger., Illus.). Springer-Verlag.

--Current Topics in Microbiology & Immunology, Vol. 62. LC 73-17985. (Illus.). 170p. 1973. 43.00 (ISBN 0-387-06598-9). Springer-Verlag.

--Current Topics in Microbiology & Immunology, Vol. 63. LC 73-20915. (Illus.). 230p. 1974. 50.00 (ISBN 0-387-06599-7). Springer-Verlag.

--Current Topics in Microbiology & Immunology, Vol. 64. LC 74-3541. (Illus.). 190p. 1974. 48.00 (ISBN 0-387-06713-2). Springer-Verlag.

--Current Topics in Microbiology & Immunology, Vol. 66. LC 15-12910. (Illus.). 130p. 1974. 36.00 (ISBN 3-540-06831-7). Springer-Verlag.

--Current Topics in Microbiology & Immunology, Vol. 67. LC 15-12910. (Illus.). iv, 162p. 1974. 46.00 (ISBN 3-540-06838-4). Springer-Verlag.

--Current Topics in Microbiology & Immunology, Vol. 76. LC 15-12910. (Illus.). 1977. 54.00 (ISBN 3-540-08238-7). Springer-Verlag.

--Current Topics in Microbiology & Immunology, Vol. 77. LC 15-12910. (Illus.). 1977. 51.00 (ISBN 0-387-08401-0). Springer-Verlag.

--Current Topics in Microbiology & Immunology, Vol. 82. LC 15-12910. (Illus.). 1978. 43.00 (ISBN 0-387-08981-0). Springer-Verlag.

--Current Topics in Microbiology & Immunology, Vol. 83. LC 15-12910. (Illus.). 1978. 45.00 (ISBN 0-387-09034-7). Springer-Verlag.

--Current Topics in Microbiology & Immunology, Vol. 85. (Illus.). 1979. 57.00 (ISBN 0-387-09410-5). Springer-Verlag.

--Current Topics in Microbiology & Immunology, Vols. 86-87. (Illus.). 1980. Vol. 86. 45.00 (ISBN 0-387-09432-6); Vol. 87. 42.00 (ISBN 0-387-09433-4). Springer-Verlag.

--Current Topics in Microbiology & Immunology, Vol. 90. (Illus.). 147p. 1980. 58.00 (ISBN 0-387-10181-0). Springer-Verlag.

--Current Topics in Microbiology & Immunology, Vol. 91. (Illus.). 250p. 1981. 59.00 (ISBN 0-387-10722-3). Springer-Verlag.

Atlas, Ronald M. Basic Microbiology: Fundamentals & Applications. 1986. text ed. price not set (ISBN 0-02-304350-4). Macmillan.

--Instructor's Manual-Microbiology: Fundamentals & Applications. 144p. 1984. write for info. (instr's manual) (ISBN 0-02-304560-4). Macmillan.

Atlas, Ronald M. & Bartha, Richard. Microbial Ecology: Fundamentals & Applications. (Life Sciences Ser.). 500p. 1981. 36.95 (ISBN 0-201-00051-2). Addison-Wesley.

Bachmann, P., et al, eds. MIRDAB: Microbiological Resource Databank Catalog, 1985. 612p. 1985. 83.50 (ISBN 0-444-90387-9). Elsevier.

Balows, Albert. Essays in Microbiology. LC 68-29639. Repr. of 1968 ed. 27.40 (ISBN 0-8357-9784-8, 2013514). Bks Demand UMI.

Balows, Albert & Isenberg, Henry. Biotyping in the Clinical Microbiology Laboratory. (Illus.). 128p. 1978. photocopy ed. 18.50x (ISBN 0-398-03806-6). C C Thomas.

Baserga, Renato, et al, eds. Introduction of Macromolecules into Viable Mammalian Cells. LC 79-91743. (Wistar Symposium Ser.: Vol. 1). 354p. 1980. 35.00x (ISBN 0-8451-2000-X). A R Liss.

Bazin, M., ed. Microbial Population Dynamics, Vol. I. 216p. 1982. 69.50 (ISBN 0-8493-5951-1). CRC Pr.

Bazin, Michael. Mathematics in Microbiology. 1983. 70.00 (ISBN 0-12-083480-4). Acad Pr.

Beishir, Lois. Microbiology in Practice: Individualized Instruction for the Allied Health Sciences. 3rd ed. 320p. 1982. pap. text ed. 16.50 scp (ISBN 0-06-040587-2, HarpC); instrs'. manual avail. (ISBN 0-06-360636-4). Har-Row.

Benson, Harold J. Microbiological Applications: A Laboratory Manual in General Microbiology, Complete Version. 4th ed. 472p. 1985. write for info. wire coil (ISBN 0-697-00307-8); instr's. manual avail. (ISBN 0-697-00557-7). Wm C Brown.

--Microbiological Applications: A Laboratory Manual in General Microbiology. Short Versions. 4th ed. 368p. 1985. write for info. wire coil bdg. (ISBN 0-697-00306-X); instr's. manual avail. (ISBN 0-697-00557-7). Wm C Brown.

Berkeley, R. C. & Ellwood, D. C., eds. Microbial Polysaccharides & Polysaccharases. (Society for General Microbiology Ser.). 1979. 59.50 (ISBN 0-12-091450-6). Acad Pr.

Blakeman, J. P., ed. Microbial Ecology of the Phylloplane. LC 80-42354. 1981. 55.00 (ISBN 0-12-103750-9). Acad Pr.

Blough, H. A., et al. Current Topics in Microbiology & Immunology, Vol. 70. LC 75-12910. (Illus.). 140p. 1975. 40.00 (ISBN 0-387-07223-3). Springer-Verlag.

Board of Education & Training. Directory of Colleges & Universities Granting Degrees in Microbiology, 1980. 1980. 5.00 (ISBN 0-686-95711-3). Am Soc Microbio.

Borick, Paul M., ed. Chemical Sterilization. LC 73-4967. (Benchmark Papers in Microbiology Ser.: Vol. 1). 352p. 1973. 49.95 (ISBN 0-87933-036-8). Van Nos Reinhold.

Boyd, Robert F. General Microbiology. (Illus.). 960p. 1984. pap. text ed. 31.95 (ISBN 0-8016-0900-3). Mosby.

Branson, Dorothy. Microbiology for the Small Laboratory. (Illus.). 80p. 1972. spiral 10.50x (ISBN 0-398-02576-2). C C Thomas.

Braude, Abraham I. Microbiology: Basic Science & Medical Applications. LC 81-40588. (Illus.). 845p. 1982. pap. text ed. 24.95 (ISBN 0-7216-1920-7). Saunders.

Brenner, S., et al, eds. New Horizons in Industrial Microbiology: Philosophical Transactions of the Royal Society, 1980. rev. ed. (Ser. B: Vol. 290). (Illus.). 152p. text ed. 47.50x (ISBN 0-85403-146-4, Pub. by Dechema Germany). Scholium Intl.

Brock, Thomas D. & Brock, Katherine M. Basic Microbiology with Applications. 2nd ed. (Illus.). 1978. 33.95 (ISBN 0-13-065284-9). P-H.

Brown, M. H., ed. Meat Microbiology. (Illus.). 528p. 1982. 89.00 (ISBN 0-85334-138-9, I-305-82, Pub. by Elsevier Applied Sci England). Elsevier.

Brumfitt, W., ed. New Perspectives in Clinical Microbiology. 1978. lib. bdg. 31.50 (ISBN 90-247-2074-5, Pub. by Martinus Nijhoff Netherlands). Kluwer Academic.

Brumfitt, W., et al, eds. Combined Antimicrobial Therapy. (New Perspectives in Clinical Microbiology Ser.: No. 3). 1980. lib. bdg. 47.00 (ISBN 90-247-2280-2, Pub. by Martinus Nijhoff Netherlands). Kluwer Academic.

Buffaloe, Neal D. & Ferguson, Dale V. Microbiology. 2nd ed. LC 80-82842. (Illus.). 752p. 1981. text ed. 32.95 (ISBN 0-395-29649-8); lab manual 12.50 (ISBN 0-395-29652-8); instr's manual 1.50 (ISBN 0-395-29650-1); study guide 10.95 (ISBN 0-395-29651-X). HM.

Bull, A. T. & Slater, J. H., eds. Microbial Interactions & Communities, Vol. 1. 1982. 63.00 (ISBN 0-12-140301-7). Acad Pr.

Bull, A. T., et al. Microbial Technology: Society for General Microbiology Symposium 29. LC 78-12206. (Illus.). 1979. 75.00 (ISBN 0-521-22500-0). Cambridge U Pr.

Bu'Lock, J. D., et al. Bioactive Microbial Products: Search & Discovery. (Special Publications of the Society for General Microbiology: No. 6). 1982. 29.00 (ISBN 0-12-140750-0). Acad Pr.

Bushell, M. E. Progress in Industrial Microbiology, Vol. 18: Microbial Polysaccharides. 258p. 1983. 68.00 (ISBN 0-444-42246-3). Elsevier.

Cano, Raul J. & Colome, Jaime S. Microbiology. (Illus.). 1000p. 1985. text ed. 36.95 (ISBN 0-314-85223-9). West Pub.

Cappucino, James C. & Sherman, Natalie. Microciology Laboratory Manual. LC 82-18509. (Biology Ser.). (Illus.). 480p. 1983. pap. text ed. 19.95 (ISBN 0-201-11160-8). Addison-Wesley.

Carlile, M. J., et al. Molecular & Cellular Aspects of Microbial Evolution. LC 80-42172. (Society for General Microbiology Ser.: Symposium 32). (Illus.). 400p. 1981. 77.50 (ISBN 0-521-24108-1). Cambridge U Pr.

Carpenter, Philip L. Microbiology. 4th ed. LC 76-27056. (Illus.). 1977. text ed. 35.95 (ISBN 0-7216-2438-3); instr's manual 6.95 (ISBN 0-03-057068-9). HR&W.

Case, Christine & Johnson, Ted. Laboratory Exercises in Microbiology. 1984. 20.95 (ISBN 0-8053-5040-3); instr's guide 6.95 (ISBN 0-8053-5041-1). Benjamin-Cummings.

Christensen, Mary L. Microbiology for Nursing & Allied Health Students. (Illus.). 624p. 1982. 39.50x (ISBN 0-398-04176-8). C C Thomas.

Clifton, C. E., et al, eds. Annual Review of Microbiology, Vol. 26. LC 49-432. (Illus.). 1972. text ed. 20.00 (ISBN 0-8243-1126-4). Annual Reviews.

Cokelet, Giles R., et al, eds. Erythrocyte Mechanics & Blood Flow. LC 79-5473. (Kroc Foundation Ser.: Vol. 13). 286p. 1980. 40.00x (ISBN 0-8451-0303-2). A R Liss.

Collard, Patrick. The Development of Microbiology. LC 75-40987. pap. 52.50 (ISBN 0-317-07740-6, 2022443). Bks Demand UMI.

Cooper, M., et al, eds. Current Topics in Microbiology & Immunology, Vol. 102. (Illus.). 152p. 1983. pap. 38.00 (ISBN 0-387-12133-1). Springer-Verlag.

Crawford, Ronald L. & Hanson, R. S., eds. Microbial Growth on C. Compounds: Proceedings of the 4th International Symposium. 343p. 1984. 47.00 (ISBN 0-914826-59-X). Am Soc Microbio.

Current Topics in Microbiology & Immunology, Vol. LC 15-12910. (Illus.). 1978. 45.00 (ISBN 0-387-08781-8). Springer-Verlag.

Current Topics in Microbiology & Immunology, Vol. 114. (Illus.). 245p. 1985. 49.00 (ISBN 0-387-15103-6). Springer-Verlag.

Current Topics in Microbiology & Immunology, Vol. 71. LC 15-12910. (Illus.). 1975. 44.00 (ISBN 0-387-07369-8). Springer-Verlag.

Current Topics in Microbiology & Immunology, Vol. 88. (Illus.). 142p. 1979. 40.00 (ISBN 0-387-09415-6). Springer-Verlag.

Dalton, H. Microbial Growth on C1 Compounds. 320p. 1981. 76.95 (ISBN 0-471-26098-3, Wiley Heyden). Wiley.

Daumeister, W., ed. Electron Microscopy at Molecular Dimensions. (Proceedings in Life Sciences). (Illus.). 300p. 1980. 66.00 (ISBN 0-387-10131-4). Springer-Verlag.

Davis, Bernard D. Microbiology. 3rd ed. (Illus.). 1274p. 1980. 49.00 (ISBN 0-06-140691-0, 14-06917, Harper Medical). Lippincott.

Dawes, E. A. Microbial Energetics. (Tertiary Level Biology Ser.). (Illus.). 192p. 1985. text ed. 39.95 (ISBN 0-412-01041-0, 9432, Pub by Chapman & Hall); pap. text ed. 19.95 (ISBN 0-412-01051-8, 9433, Pub. by Chapman & Hall). Methuen Inc.

Dawson, P. S., ed. Microbial Growth. LC 74-26644. (Benchmark Papers in Microbiology Ser: Vol. 8). 400p. 1975. 68.00 (ISBN 0-12-786330-3). Acad Pr.

Dean, A. C., et al, eds. Continuous Culture: Applications & New Fields. (Continuous Culture Ser.). 364p. 1976. 62.95 (ISBN 0-470-98984-X). Halsted Pr.

DECHMA, Deutsche Gesellschaft Fuer Chemisches Apparatewesen E. V., ed. Microbiology Applied to Biotechnology: Proceedings XIIth International Congress of Microbiology. (DECHEMA Monographs: Vol. 83). 230p. (Orig.). 1979. pap. text ed. 25.80x (ISBN 3-527-10766-5). VCH Pubs.

Delaat, Adrian N. Microbiology for the Allied Health Professions. 3rd ed. LC 83-24833. (Illus.). 1984. 24.50 (ISBN 0-8121-0910-4). Lea & Febiger.

Doelle, H. W., ed. Microbial Metabolism. LC 73-16370. (Benchmark Papers in Microbiology: Vol. 5). 424p. 1974. 59.95 (ISBN 0-87933-063-5). Van Nos Reinhold.

Droop, M. R. & Jannasch, H. W., eds. Advances in Aquatic Microbiology, Vol. 1. (Serial Publication Ser.). 1977. 70.00 (ISBN 0-12-003001-2). Acad Pr.

Dubos, Rene. The Professor, the Institute, & DNA. LC 76-26812. (Illus.). 262p. 1976. 15.00x (ISBN 0-87470-022-1). Rockefeller.

Eddington, Arthur S. Science & the Unseen World. 56p. 1980. Repr. of 1929 ed. lib. bdg. 10.00 (ISBN 0-8495-1426-6). Arden Lib.

Eden, R. F. & Eden, G. Impedance Microbiology. 1984. 39.95 (ISBN 0-471-90623-9). Wiley.

Edmonds, Paul. Microbiology: An Environmental Perspective. (Illus.). 1978. text ed. write for info. (ISBN 0-02-333580-7). Macmillan.

Ellwood, D. C., et al, eds. Adhesion to Microorganisms to Surfaces. (A Volume in the Special Publications of the Society for General Microbiology Ser.). 1979. 37.00 (ISBN 0-12-236650-6). Acad Pr.

Emerson, S. U., et al. Current Topics in Microbiology & Immunology, Vol. 73. LC 15-12910. 1976. 49.00 (ISBN 0-387-07593-3). Springer-Verlag.

Erlich. Geomicrobiology. 1981. 39.75 (ISBN 0-8247-1183-1). Dekker.

Fascicle III: Microbiology. 80p. 15.00 (ISBN 0-930304-28-4). Coll Am Pathol.

Felkner. Microbial Testers: Probing Carcinogenesis. (Microbiology Ser.: Vol. 5). 1981. 45.00 (ISBN 0-8247-1244-7). Dekker.

Ferris, Elvira & Fong, Elizabeth. Microbiology for Health Careers. 2nd ed. LC 81-66764. (Allied Health Ser.). (Illus.). 192p. 1982. pap. text ed. 13.20 (ISBN 0-8273-1901-0); instr's guide 3.00 (ISBN 0-8273-1902-9). Delmar.

Fiechter, A. Microbial Reactions. (Advances in Biochemical Engineering Ser.: Vol. 23). (Illus.). 200p. 1982. 41.00 (ISBN 0-387-11698-2). Springer-Verlag.

Fiechter, A., ed. Microbial Processes. LC 72-152360. (Advances in Biochemical Engineering: Vol. 9). (Illus.). 1978. 38.00 (ISBN 0-387-08606-4). Springer-Verlag.

--New Technological Concepts. (Advances in Biochemical Engineering Ser.: Vol. 15). (Illus.). 250p. 1980. 52.00 (ISBN 0-387-09686-8). Springer-Verlag.

Fiechter, A., et al, eds. Microbiology, Theory & Application. LC 72-152360. (Advances in Biochemical Engineering Ser.: Vol. 11). 1979. 47.00 (ISBN 0-387-08990-X). Springer-Verlag.

Finegold, Sydney M. & Martin, William J. Bailey & Scott's Diagnostic Microbiology. 6th ed. LC 81-14157. (Illus.). 705p. 1982. text ed. 30.95 (ISBN 0-8016-1577-1). Mosby.

Ford, Brian J. Microbe Power. LC 76-7437. 1976. pap. 10.00 (ISBN 0-8128-1936-5). Stein & Day.

Fraenkel-Conrat, H. & Wagner, R. R., eds. Comprehensive Virology, Vol. 14: Newly Characterized Vertebrate Viruses. LC 79-810. (Illus.). 562p. 1979. 55.00x (ISBN 0-306-40231-9, Plenum Pr). Plenum Pub.

Frazer, A. C., et al. Current Topics in Microbiology & Immunology, Vol. 69. (Illus.). 200p. 1975. 46.00 (ISBN 0-387-07195-4). Springer-Verlag.

Frazier, William C. & Westhoff, Dennis. Food Microbiology. 3rd ed. (Illus.). 1978. text ed. 44.95 (ISBN 0-07-021917-6). McGraw.

Freeman, Bob A. Burrows Textbook of Microbiology. 21st ed. LC 77-16986. (Illus.). 1979. text ed. 39.50 (ISBN 0-7216-3869-4). Saunders.

Fuerst, Robert. Frobisher & Fuerst's Microbiology in Health & Disease. 15th ed. LC 82-42506. (Illus.). 669p. 1983. text ed. 28.95 (ISBN 0-7216-3944-5). Saunders.

Gall, Lorraine S. & Riely, Phyllis E., eds. Manual for the Determination of the Clinical Role of Anaerobic Microbiology. 96p. 1981. 42.00 (ISBN 0-8493-5935-X). CRC Pr.

Gaudy, Anthony & Gaudy, Elizabeth. Microbiology for Environment Science Engineers. (Water Resources & Environmental Engineering Ser.). (Illus.). 704p. 1980. 45.00 (ISBN 0-07-023035-8). McGraw.

Gauthier, Dorothy. Introductory Microbiology. 1980. spiral bdg. 11.95 (ISBN 0-88252-105-5). Paladin Hse.

Ghosh, Bijan K., ed. Organization of Prokaryotic Cell Membrane, Vols. I & II. 1981. Vol. I, 272p. 86.00 (ISBN 0-8493-5653-9); Vol. II, 224p. 86.00 (ISBN 0-8493-5654-7). CRC Pr.

Glover, S. W. & Hopwood, D. A., eds. Genetics As a Tool in Microbiology. (Society for General Microbiology Symposium: No. 31). (Illus.). 450p. 1981. text ed. 75.00 (ISBN 0-521-23748-3). Cambridge U Pr.

Gooday, G. W., et al, eds. The Eukaryotic Microbial Cell. LC 79-20741. (Society for General Microbiology Symposium: No. 30). (Illus.). 450p. 1980. 85.00 (ISBN 0-521-22974-X). Cambridge U Pr.

Gordon, John. MCQ Tutor for Students of Microbiology. 1979. pap. text ed. 19.50 (ISBN 0-8151-3805-9). Year Bk Med.

Gottfried, Sandra S. & Kelly, James L. Fundamentals in Laboratory Microbiology. (Illus.). 72p. 1984. pap. text ed. 6.95 (ISBN 0-8138-1146-5). Iowa St U Pr.

Graf, T. & Jaenisch, R., eds. Tumorviruses, Neoplastic Transformation & Differentiation. (Current Topics in Microbiology & Immunology: Vol. 101). (Illus.). 198p. 1982. 42.00 (ISBN 0-387-11665-6). Springer-Verlag.

Grainger, J. M. & Lynch, J. M., eds. Microbiological Methods for Environmental Biotechnology. (Society for Applied Bacteriology, Technical Ser.: No. 19). 1984. 65.00 (ISBN 0-12-295040-2). ACad Pr.

Grant, William D. & Long, P. E. Environmental Microbiology. LC 81-11685. (Tertiary Level Biology Ser.). 200p. 1981. pap. 29.95x (ISBN 0-470-27233-3). Halsted Pr.

Griffin, David H. Fungal Physiology. LC 81-3344. 383p. 1981. 37.50x (ISBN 0-471-05748-7). Wiley.

Habermehl, K. O., ed. Rapid Methods & Automation in Microbiology & Immunology. (Illus.). 780p. 1985. 87.00 (ISBN 0-387-13695-9). Springer-Verlag.

Harris, Kerry F., ed. Current Topics in Vector Research, Vol. II. 290p. 1984. 34.95x (ISBN 0-03-071611-X). Praeger.

Hempfing, W. P., ed. Microbial Respiration. LC 78-22097. (Benchmark Papers in Microbiology: Vol. 13). 337p. 1979. 45.95 (ISBN 0-87933-344-8). Van Nos Reinhold.

Henle, W., et al. Current Topics in Microbiology & Immunology, Vols. 94 & 95. (Illus.). 308p. 1981. 62.00 (ISBN 0-387-10803-3). Springer-Verlag.

Henle, W., et al, eds. Current Topics in Microbiology & Immunology, Vol. 97. (Illus.). 220p. 1982. 46.00 (ISBN 0-387-11118-2). Springer-Verlag.

Hepple, Peter, ed. Microbiology, Nineteen Seventy-One: Proceedings, London, 27-28 January, 1971. LC 73-168075. pap. 30.00 (ISBN 0-317-28922-5, 2023694). Bks Demand UMI.

--Microbiology: Proceedings of a Conference Held in London, 19-20 September, 1967. LC 79-353970. pap. 27.30 (ISBN 0-317-28920-9, 2023693). BKs Demand UMI.

Hewitt, W., ed. Microbiological Assay: An Introduction to Quantitative Principles & Evaluation. 1977. 45.00 (ISBN 0-12-346450-1). Acad Pr.

Higgins, I. J. & Burns, R. G. The Chemistry & Microbiology of Pollution. 1975. 46.00 (ISBN 0-12-347950-9). Acad Pr.

Hill, I. R. & Wright, S. J., eds. Pesticide Microbiology: Microbiological Aspects of Pesticide Behavior in the Environment. 1979. 98.00 (ISBN 0-12-348650-5). Acad Pr.

Hou, Ching T. Methylotrophs: Microbiology, Biochemistry & Genetics. 192p. 1984. 65.00 (ISBN 0-8493-5992-9). CRC Pr.

Hurst, A. & Nasim, A., eds. Repairable Lesions in Microorganisms. 1985. 55.00 (ISBN 0-12-362690-0). Acad Pr.

Hutzinger, O., ed. The Natural Environment & the Biogeochemical Cycles. (The Handbook of Environmental Chemistry Ser.: Vol. 1, Pt. D). (Illus.). 260p. 1985. 59.00 (ISBN 0-387-15000-5). Springer-Verlag.

International Commission on Microbiological Specifications for Foods. Microorganisms in Foods: Vol. 2, Sampling for Microbiological Analysis: Principles & Specific Applications. LC 73-2628. 1974. 30.00x (ISBN 0-8020-2143-3). U of Toronto Pr.

International Conference GIAM, 6th. Global Impacts of Applied Microbiology: Proceedings. Emejuaiwe, S. D. & Ogumbi, O., eds. 1981. 59.50 (ISBN 0-12-238280-3). Acad Pr.

International Congress of Microbiological Standardization, 12th, Annecy, 1971. Proceedings. Regamey, R. H., et al, eds. (Progress in Immunobiological Standardization: Vol. 5). 39.75 (ISBN 3-8055-1404-2). S Karger.

International Congress of Microbiological Standardization, 11th, Milan, 1968. Proceedngs. Regamey, R. H., et al, eds. (Progress in Immunobiological Standardization: Vol. 4). 1970. 46.00 (ISBN 3-8055-0400-4). S Karger.

International Symposium on Yersinia, 3rd, Montreal, September 1977. Yersinia Enterocolitica. Carter, Philip B., et al, eds. (Contributions to Microbiology & Immunology: Vol. 5). (Illus.). 1979. 66.00 (ISBN 3-8055-2927-9). S Karger.

International Symposium on Yersinia, Pasteurella & Francisella, Malmoe, April 1972. Yersinia, Pasteurella & Francisella: Proceedings. Winblad, ed. (Contributions to Microbiology & Immunology: Vol. 2). 1973. 32.00 (ISBN 3-8055-1636-3). S Karger.

Joklik, Wolfgang, ed. Zinsser Microbiology. 18th ed. (Illus.). 1328p. 1984. 59.95 (ISBN 0-8385-9978-8). ACC.

Kaminsky, Daniel, et al. Microbiology. 3rd ed. (Nursing Examination Review Book: Vol. 7). 1974. spiral bdg. 7.50 (ISBN 0-87488-507-8). Med Exam.

Kandler, O. Archaebacteria: Proceedings of the 1st International Workshop on Archebacteria, Munich 1981. (Illus.). 366p. 1982. text ed. 39.20x (ISBN 3-437-10797-6). Lubrecht & Cramer.

Kazmier, Henry E. Basic Principles of Micro-Biology. (Orig.). 1980. pap. text ed. 14.95 (ISBN 0-8403-2170-8). Kendall-Hunt.

Kelly, D. P. & Carr, N. G., eds. The Microbe Nineteen Eighty Four: Prokaryotes & Eukaryotes, Pt. II. LC 83-19004. (The Society for General Microbiology Symposium Ser.: No. 36). 300p. 1984. 59.50 (ISBN 0-521-26057-4). Cambridge U Pr.

Kerr, Thomas J. Applications in General Microbiology. 2nd ed. (Illus.). 224p. 1981. lab manual 12.95x (ISBN 0-89459-092-8). Hunter Textbks.

Ketchum. General Microbiology. 1986. price not set (ISBN 0-471-88897-4). Wiley.

Ketchum, Paul A. Microbiology: Introduction for Health Professionals. LC 82-23709. 544p. 1984. text ed. 32.95 (ISBN 0-471-06306-1); study guide 10.95 (ISBN 0-471-88898-2). Wiley.

Kim, Charles W., ed. Microbiology Review. 7th ed. LC 80-20088. 1980. pap. 12.75 (ISBN 0-87488-203-6). Med Exam.

Kingsley, V. Victor. Basic Microbiology for the Health Sciences. (Illus.). 158p. 1982. pap. 12.95 (ISBN 0-7216-5433-9). Saunders.

Klug, M. J. & Reddy, C. A., eds. Current Perspectives in Microbial Ecology. 710p. 1984. 47.00 (ISBN 0-914826-60-3). Am Soc Microbio.

Krasemann, C., ed. Infektiologisches Kolloquium I: Neues von alten Erregern und neue Erreger. (Illus.). 138p. 1983. 15.20 (ISBN 3-11-009689-7). De Gruyter.

Kurstak. Microbial Pesticides. (Microbiology Ser.: Vol. 6). 1982. 115.00 (ISBN 0-8247-1686-8). Dekker.

Lal, R., ed. Insecticide Microbiology. (Illus.). 270p. 1984. 47.00 (ISBN 0-387-13662-2). Springer-Verlag.

Larson, Elaine, ed. Clinical Microbiology & Infection Control. LC 83-15894. (Illus.). 818p. 1984. text ed. 39.95 (ISBN 0-86542-011-4). Blackwell Sci.

Lascelles, June. Microbial Photosynthesis. LC 73-12684. (Benchmark Papers in Microbioloy Ser.: Vol. 4). 401p. 1973. 51.95 (ISBN 0-87933-049-X). Van Nos Reinhold.

Laskin, Allan I. & Lechevalier, Hubert A., eds. HB Microbiology, Vol. VII. 2nd ed. 624p. 1984. 83.00 (ISBN 0-8493-7207-0). CRC Pr.

Laskin, Allen, ed. Advances in Applied Microbiology, Vol. 28. (Serial Publication Ser.). 304p. 1982. 60.00 (ISBN 0-12-002628-7). Acad Pr.

Laskin, Allen I. & Lechevalier, Hubert. CRC Handbook of Microbiology: Fungi, Algae, Protozoa & Viruses, Vol. 2. 2nd ed. 888p. 1979. 89.50 (ISBN 0-8493-7202-X). CRC Pr.

Laskin, Allen I., ed. Advances in Applied Microbiology, Vol. 29. (Serial Piblication Ser.). 1983. 55.00 (ISBN 0-12-002629-5). Acad Pr.

Laskin, Allen I. & Lechevalier, Hubert A., eds. Handbook of Microbiology, 2 vols. 2nd ed. 1984. Vol. V, 952p. 99.50 (ISBN 0-8493-7205-4); Vol. VI., 384p. 58.00 (ISBN 0-8493-7206-2). CRC Pr.

Laskin, Allen I. & Lechevalier, Hubert, eds. Handbook of Microbiology, CRC. condensed ed. LC 74-12937. 930p. 1974. pap. 19.95 (ISBN 0-87819-585-8). CRC Pr.

--Handbook of Microbiology, CRC, Vol. 1: Bacteria. 2nd ed. 770p. 1977. 69.95 (ISBN 0-8493-7201-1). CRC Pr.

--Handbook of Microbiology, CRC, Vol. 3: Microbial Composition: Amino Acids, Proteins & Nucleic Acids. 2nd ed. LC 77-12460. 1000p. 1981. 82.50 (ISBN 0-8493-7203-8). CRC Pr.

Lechene, Claude P. & Warner, Ronald, eds. Microbeam Analysis in Biology. LC 79-24948. 1980. 55.00 (ISBN 0-12-440340-9). Acad Pr.

Lee, John J. Microbiology. (Illus.). 352p. (Orig.). 1982. pap. 5.72i (ISBN 0-06-460183-8, COS CO 183). B&N NY.

Lee, Robert E. Phycology. LC 79-25402. (Illus.). 450p. 1980. 67.50 (ISBN 0-521-22530-2); pap. 21.95 (ISBN 0-521-29541-6). Cambridge U Pr.

Leive, Loretta & Schlessinger, David, eds. Microbiology - 1984. 444p. 1984. 28.00 (ISBN 0-914826-61-1). Am Soc Microbio.

Leive, Lorette, et al, eds. Microbiology, 1985. 486p. 1985. 38.00 (ISBN 0-914826-78-6). Am Soc Microbio.

Lenci, Francesco & Colombetti, Giuliano, eds. Photoreception & Sensory Transduction in Aneural Organisms. LC 80-12426. (NATO ASI Series A, Life Sciences: Vol. 33). 430p. 1980. 57.50x (ISBN 0-306-40437-0, Plenum Pr). Plenum Pub.

Lennette, Edwin H., et al, eds. Manual of Clinical Microbiology. 4th ed. (Illus.). 1149p. 1985. 61.00 (ISBN 0-914826-65-4); flexible bdg. 51.00 (ISBN 0-914826-69-7). Am Soc Microbio.

Livingston, Virginia. Microbiology of Cancer. 25.00x (ISBN 0-686-29788-1). Cancer Control Soc.

Losick, Richard & Shapiro, Lucy, eds. Microbial Development, Vol. 16. LC 84-9599. (Monogr[illegible]). 328p. 1984. 52.00 (ISBN 0-87969-17[illegible]); pap. 28.00x (ISBN 0-87969-173-5). Cold Spring Harbor.

Lynch, J. M. & Poole, N. J. Microbial Ecology: A Conceptual Approach. LC 78-13245. 266p. 1979. pap. 34.95x (ISBN 0-470-26533-7). Halsted Pr.

McKane, L. & Kandel, J. Microbiology: Essentials & Applications. 800p. 1985. 35.95 (ISBN 0-07-045125-7); study guide 13.95 (ISBN 0-07-045127-3). McGraw.

McKinney, R. E. Microbiology for Sanitary Engineers. (Sanitary & Water Resources Engineering Ser.). 1962. text ed. 42.00 (ISBN 0-07-045180-X). McGraw.

Mahy, B. W. & Pattison, J. R., eds. The Microbe Nineteen Eighty Four: Viruses, Pt. 1. LC 83-19004. (The Society for General Microbiology Symposium Ser.: No. 36). 300p. 1984. 59.50 (ISBN 0-521-26056-6). Cambridge U Pr.

Margalith, Pinhas. Flavor Microbiology. (Illus.). 328p. 1981. 31.50x (ISBN 0-398-04083-4). C C Thomas.

Margalith, Pinhas Z. Steroid Microbiology. (Illus.). 300p. 1986. price not set (ISBN 0-398-05187-9). C C Thomas.

Marshall, K. C. Interfaces in Microbial Ecology. 1976. 12.50x (ISBN 0-674-45822-2, MAIF). Harvard U Pr.

Marshall, K. C., ed. Advances in Microbial Ecology, Vol. 7. 227p. 1983. 39.50x (ISBN 0-306-41458-9, Plenum Pr). Plenum Pub.

--Microbial Adhesion & Aggregation. (Dahlem Workshop Reports, Life Sciences Research Report Ser.: Vol. 31). (Illus.). 450p. 1985. 23.50 (ISBN 0-387-13996-6). Springer-Verlag.

Martin, S. J. The Biochemistry of Viruses. LC 77-8231. (Texts in Chemistry & Biochemistry Ser.). (Illus.). 1978. 44.50 (ISBN 0-521-21678-8); pap. 15.95 (ISBN 0-521-29229-8). Cambridge U Pr.

Matthai, William C. Microbiology: A Laboratory Textbook. 360p. 1984. pap. text ed. 17.95x (ISBN 0-89787-117-0). Gorsuch Scarisbrick.

Methodology for Biomass Determinations & Microbial Activities in Sediments, STP 673. 199p. 1979. 22.50x (ISBN 0-8031-0511-8, 04-673000-16). ASTM.

Microbiology. (National Medical Ser.: Nos. 1-635). 300p. 1985. pap. text ed. 17.00 (ISBN 0-471-09625-3, Pub. by Wiley Med). Wiley.

Microbiology Reagents, Instrumentation & Supplies Market. 247p. 1985. 2000.00 (ISBN 0-86621-655-3). Frost & Sullivan.

Miller, J. Michael & Wentworth, Berttina B., eds. Methods for Quality Control in Diagnostic Microbiology. LC 85-3991. 369p. 1985. 25.00x (ISBN 0-87553-121-0). Am Pub Health.

Miller, James N. Spirochetes in Body Fluids & Tissues: Manual of Investigative Methods. (Illus.). 86p. 1971. spiral 8.75x (ISBN 0-398-01312-8). C C Thomas.

Umbreit, Wayne W., ed. Advances in Applied Microbiology. Incl. Vol. 1. 1959. 75.00 (ISBN 0-12-002601-5); Vol. 2. 1960. 75.00 (ISBN 0-12-002602-3); Vol. 3. 1961. 75.00 (ISBN 0-12-002603-1); Vol. 4. 1962. 75.00 (ISBN 0-12-002604-X); Vol. 5. 1963. 75.00 (ISBN 0-12-002605-8); Vol. 6. 1964. 75.00 (ISBN 0-12-002606-6); Vol. 7. 1965. 75.00 (ISBN 0-12-002607-4); Vol. 8. 1966. 75.00 (ISBN 0-12-002608-2); Vol. 9. 1968. 75.00 (ISBN 0-12-002609-0); Vol. 10. Perlman, D. & Umbreit, W., eds. 1968. 75.00 (ISBN 0-12-002610-4); Vol. 11. Perlman, D., ed. 1970. 75.00 (ISBN 0-12-002611-2); Vol. 12. Perlman, D. & Umbreit, W., eds. 1970. 75.00 (ISBN 0-12-002612-0); Vol. 13. Perlman, D. & Umbreit, W., eds. 1970. 75.00 (ISBN 0-12-002613-9); Vol. 14. Perlman, D. & Umbreit, W., eds. 1971. 75.00 (ISBN 0-12-002614-7); Vol. 15. Perlman, D., ed. 1972. 75.00 (ISBN 0-12-002615-5); Vol. 16. Perlman, David, ed. 1973. 75.00 (ISBN 0-12-002616-3); Vol. 21. Perlman, David, ed. 1977. 75.00 (ISBN 0-12-002621-X); Vol. 22. Perlman, David, ed. 1977. 75.00 (ISBN 0-12-002622-8); Vol. 23. Perlman, David, ed. 1978. 60.00 (ISBN 0-12-002623-6); Vol. 24. Perlman, David, ed. 1978. 60.00 (ISBN 0-12-002624-4); Vol. 25. 1979. 70.00 (ISBN 0-12-002625-2). Acad Pr.

Van der Waay, D. & Verhoef, J. New Criteria for Antimicrobial Therapy: Maintenance of Digestive Tract Colonization Resistance. (International Congress Ser.: Vol. 477). 1980. 50.25 (ISBN 0-444-90096-9). Elsevier.

Van Leeuwenhoek, Antony. The Select Works of Antony Van Leeuwenhoek: His Microscopical Discoveries in Many Works of Nature, 2 vols in 1. Egerton, Frank N., ed. Hoole, Samuel, tr. LC 77-74236. (History of Ecology Ser.). (Illus.). 1978. Repr. of 1807 ed. lib. bdg. 54.00x (ISBN 0-405-10405-7). Ayer Co Pubs.

Venkatsubramanian, K., ed. Immobilized Microbial Cells. LC 79-15794. (ACS Symposium Ser.: No. 106). 1979. 34.95 (ISBN 0-8412-0508-6); pap. 24.95 (ISBN 0-8412-0644-9). Am Chemical.

Vieweg Publishing Staff, ed. European Journal of Clinical Microbiology, 1985, Vol. 4. 1985. 106.50 (ISBN 0-9904002-3-9, Pub. by Vieweg & Sohn Germany). Heyden.

Vogt, P. K. & Koprowski, H., eds. Mouse Mammary Tumor Virus. (Current Topics in Microbiology & Immunology Ser.: Vol. 106). (Illus.). 105p. 1983. 25.00 (ISBN 0-387-12828-X). Springer-Verlag.

--Retroviruses, Vol. 2. (Current Topics in Microbiology & Immunology: Vol. 107). (Illus.). 185p. 1983. 39.50 (ISBN 0-387-12384-9). Springer-Verlag.

Volk, Wesley A. & Wheeler, Margaret. Basic Microbiology. 5th ed. 704p. 1984. text ed. 30.50 scp (ISBN 0-06-046845-9, HarpC); instr's. manual avail. (ISBN 0-06-366962-5); scp study guide 10.50 (ISBN 0-06-046846-7); transparencies avail. (ISBN 0-06-366963-3). Har-Row.

Voznaya, N. F. Chemistry of Water & Microbiology. 347p. 1981. 10.00 (ISBN 0-8285-2060-7, Pub. by Mir Pubs USSR). Imported Pubns.

Wistreich, George A. Microbiology. 4th ed. (Illus.). 704p. 1984. text ed. write for info. (ISBN 0-02-428870-5). Macmillan.

Wistreich, George A. & Lechtman, Max D. Laboratory Exercises in Microbiology. 3rd ed. 1976. lab manual 8.95x (ISBN 0-02-479210-1). Glencoe.

Wistreich, George A. & Smith, David W. Study Guide to Accompany Microbiology. 4th ed. 368p. 1984. pap. text ed. write for info. study guide (ISBN 0-02-428890-X). Macmillan.

Woolford. The Silage Fermentation. (Microbiology Ser.). 336p. 1984. 64.50 (ISBN 0-8247-7039-0). Dekker.

Yabrov, Alexander. Interferon & Nonspecific Resistance. LC 80-13677. 374p. 1980. 39.95 (ISBN 0-87705-497-5). Human Sci Pr.

Yoshii, Zensaku, et al. Atlas of Scanning Electron Microscopy in Microbiology. (Illus.). 1976. 52.00 (ISBN 0-89640-038-7). Igaku-Shoin.

Zajic, J. E. Microbial Biogeochemistry. 1969. 55.00 (ISBN 0-12-775350-8). Acad Pr.

MICROBIOLOGY–BIBLIOGRAPHY

Board of Education & Training. Bringing Life to Microbiology. 1979. 14.00 (ISBN 0-686-95719-9). Am Soc Microbio.

--Highlights in Microbiology Nineteen Seventy-Nine to Eighty, Vol. 3. (Highlights Ser.). 1981. 5.00 (ISBN 0-686-95718-0). Am Soc Microbio.

Korf, Richard P. & Gruff, Susan C. Mycotaxon Cumulative Index for Volumes I-XX (1974-1984) LC 75-640802. 232p. (Orig.). 1985. pap. text ed. 17.50 (ISBN 0-930845-00-5). Mycotaxon Ltd.

Rose, A. H., ed. Economic Microbiology, Vol. 7. 1982. 65.00 (ISBN 0-12-596557-5). Acad Pr.

Schlessinger, David, ed. Microbiology 1982. 413p. 1982. 28.00 (ISBN 0-914826-42-5). Am Soc Microbio.

MICROBIOLOGY–CLASSIFICATION

Burton, Gwendolyn. Microbiology for the Health Sciences. 2nd ed. (Illus.). 238p. 1983. text ed. 13.75 (ISBN 0-397-54397-2, 64-03380, Lippincott Nursing); wkbk. 6.50 (ISBN 0-397-54465-0, 64-04065). Lippincott.

Cowan, S. T. A Dictionary of Microbial Taxonomy. Hill, L. R., ed. LC 77-85705. (Illus.). 1978. 52.50 (ISBN 0-521-21890-X). Cambridge U Pr.

Goodfellow, M. & Board, R. G. Microbiological Classification & Identification. (Society for Applied Bacteriology Symposium Ser.: No. 8). 1980. 57.50 (ISBN 0-12-289660-2). Acad Pr.

Koneman, Elmer W. & Allen, Stephen D. Color Atlas & Textbook of Diagnostic Microbiology. 2nd ed. (Illus.). 689p. 1983. text ed. 39.50 (ISBN 0-397-50558-2, 65-07123, Lippincott Medical). Lippincott.

MICROBIOLOGY–CULTURES AND CULTURE MEDIA

Calcott, P. H. Freezing & Thawing Microbes. 74p. 1979. 40.00x (ISBN 0-904095-27-4, Pub. by Meadowfield Pr England). State Mutual Bk.

Iswaran, V. A Treatise on Media & Methods Used in Bacteriological Techniques. 2nd ed. 189p. 1980. 12.00 (ISBN 0-88065-132-6, Pub. by Messers Today & Tomorrows Printers & Publishers India). Scholarly Pubns.

Kirsop, B. E. The Stability of Industrial Organisms: UK Federation for Culture collections Symposium held at the University of Newcastle-upon-Tyne 20th July 1979. 57p. 1980. 32.00x (ISBN 0-85198-470-3, Pub. by CAB Bks England). State Mutual Bk.

Lichstein, Herman C., ed. Bacterial Nutrition. LC 82-11720. (Benchmark Papers in Microbiology: Vol. 19). 377p. 1983. 49.95 (ISBN 0-87933-439-8). Van Nos Reinhold.

MacFaddin, Jean F. Media for Isolation, Cultivation & Maintenance of Medical Bacteria, Vol. I. (Illus.). 966p. 1985. 89.95 (ISBN 0-683-05316-7). Williams & Wilkins.

Malek, Ivan & Fencl, Zdenek, eds. Continuous Cultivation of Microorganisms: Proceedings. 1970. 81.00 (ISBN 0-12-466260-9). Acad Pr.

Mather, Jennie P., ed. Mammalian Cell-Culture: The Use of Serum-Free Hormone-Supplemented Media. 302p. 1984. 39.50x (ISBN 0-306-41584-4, Plenum Pr). Plenum Pub.

Olds, R. J. Color Atlas of Microbiology. (Year Book Color Atlas Ser.). (Illus.). 288p. 1975. 39.95 (ISBN 0-8151-6542-0). Year Bk Med.

Quayle, J. R. & Bull, A. T., eds. New Dimensions in Microbiology. Mixed Substrates, Mixed Cultures, & Microbial Communities: Proceedings of a Royal Society Discussion Meeting, November 11-12, 1981. (RSL Philosophical Transactions of the Royal Society of London, Ser. B: Vol. 297, No. 1088). (Illus.). 200p. 1982. text ed. 63.00x (ISBN 0-85403-189-8, Pub. by Royal Soc London). Scholium Intl.

Strohl, William R. & Tuovinen, Olli H., eds. Microbial Chemoautotrophy. LC 83-27344. 365p. 1984. 32.50x (ISBN 0-8142-0342-6). Ohio St U Pr.

Veldkamp, H. Continous Culture in Microbial Physiology & Ecology. 74p. 1976. 39.00x (ISBN 0-904095-25-8, Pub. by Meadowfield Pr England). State Mutual Bk.

MICROBIOLOGY–DICTIONARIES

Cowan, S. T. A Dictionary of Microbial Taxonomic Usage. 1968. 7.50 (ISBN 0-934454-28-0). Lubrecht & Cramer.

English-Chinese Microbiological Dictionary. (Eng. & Chinese.). 138p. 1979. pap. 3.95 (ISBN 0-686-97368-2, M-9573). French & Eur.

Singleton, Paul & Sainsbury, Diana. Dictionary of Microbiology. LC 78-4532. 481p. 1978. 74.95x (ISBN 0-471-99658-0, Pub. by Wiley-Interscience). Wiley.

MICROBIOLOGY–HISTORY

Lechevalier, Hubert A. & Solotorovsky, Morris. Three Centuries of Microbiology. 16.25 (ISBN 0-8446-5057-9). Peter Smith.

MICROBIOLOGY–LABORATORY MANUALS

Bartholomew, James W. Laboratory Textbook & Experiments in Microbiology. rev. ed. 1977. pap. text ed. 10.95 (ISBN 0-8403-1722-0). Kendall-Hunt.

Beck, J. V., et al. Laboratory Manual for General Microbiology. 3rd ed. 1979. spiral bdg. 9.95x (ISBN 0-8087-2884-9). Burgess.

Board of Education & Training. Topic Outlines in Microbiology. 1980. 10.00 (ISBN 0-686-95715-6). Am Soc Microbio.

Bradshaw, Jack L. Laboratory Microbiology. 3rd ed. 1979. pap. text ed. 19.95 (ISBN 0-7216-1909-6, CBS C). SCP.

Brockman, Ellis. Laboratory Manual for Microbiology. new ed. LC 74-28777. 121p. 1980. pap. 15.00 (ISBN 0-87812-085-8). Pendell Pub.

Finstein, M. S. Pollution Microbiology: A Laboratory Manual. 184p. 1972. 24.75 (ISBN 0-8247-1190-4). Dekker.

Fuerst, Robert. Microbiology in Health & Disease: Laboratory Manual & Workbook. 7th ed. LC 77-16985. (Illus.). 1983. pap. text ed. 12.95 (ISBN 0-7216-3945-3). Saunders.

Kelley, Susan G. & Post, Frederick J. Basic Microbiology Techniques. 2nd ed. (Illus.). 196p. 1982. pap. 10.95x (ISBN 0-89863-053-3). Star Pub CA.

Lancaster, John H. & Clark, J. B. Microbiology: A Laboratory Science. (Illus.). 1983. lab manual 10.95x (ISBN 0-88136-007-4). Jostens.

Luginbuhl, Geraldine. General Microbiology Laboratory Manual. 2nd Ed. ed. 1981. lab manual 7.95 (ISBN 0-89459-219-X). Hunter Textbks.

Miller, Arnold I. Microbiological Laboratory Techniques. 352p. 1976. pap. text ed. 16.95 (ISBN 0-669-98384-5). Heath.

Morello, Josephine A., et al. Laboratory Manual & Workbook in Microbiology: Applications to Patient Care. 3rd ed. 280p. 1984. pap. write for info. lab manual (ISBN 0-02-383520-6). Macmillan.

Nester, Eugene & Gilstrap, Marie. Experiments in Microbiology: Accompanies Microbiology, Third Edition by Nester et al. 2nd ed. 1983. lab manual 19.95 (ISBN 0-03-062057-0, CBS C). SCP.

Otero, Raymond B. Laboratory Exercises in Microbiology. 2nd ed. 1977. pap. text ed. 8.95 (ISBN 0-8403-1743-3). Kendall-Hunt.

Seeley, Harry W., Jr. & VanDemark, Paul J. Microbes in Action: A Laboratory Manual of Microbiology. 3rd ed. (Illus.). 385p. 1981. pap. text ed. 14.95x (ISBN 0-7167-1259-8); instrs'. manual avail. W H Freeman.

Wistreich, George A. & Lechtman, Max D. Laboratory Exercises in Microbiology. 5th ed. 432p. 1984. pap. write for info. (ISBN 0-02-428900-0). Macmillan.

MICROBIOLOGY–TECHNIQUES

Aaronson, Sheldon. Experimental Microbial Ecology. 1970. 46.00 (ISBN 0-12-041050-8). Acad Pr.

Baillie, A. & Gilbert, R. J., eds. Automation, Mechanization & Data Handling in Microbiology. (Society for Applied Bacteriology Technical Ser.: No. 4). 1970. 41.50 (ISBN 0-12-073650-0). Acad Pr.

Brenner, S., et al, eds. New Horizons in Industrial Microbiology: Philosophical Transactions of the Royal Society, 1980. rev. ed. (Ser. B: Vol. 290). (Illus.). 152p. text ed. 47.50x (ISBN 0-85403-146-4, Pub. by Dechema Germany). Scholium Intl.

Chayen, Bitensky. Investigative Microtechniques in Medicine & Biology, Vol. 1. 416p. 1984. 75.00 (ISBN 0-8247-7139-7). Dekker.

Collins & Lyne. Microbiological Methods. 5th ed. 1984. text ed. 34.95 (ISBN 0-408-70957-X). Butterworth.

Mitruka, Brij M. Gas Chromatographic Applications in Microbiology & Medicine. LC 74-18002. 492p. 1975. 55.50 (ISBN 0-471-61183-2). Krieger.

Nester, Eugene & Gilstrap, Marie. Microbiology Experiments. 1982. 19.95 (ISBN 0-03-057008-5, CBS C). SCP.

Norris, J. R. & Ribbons, D. W., eds. Methods in Microbiology. Incl. Vol. 1. 1969. 90.00 (ISBN 0-12-521501-0); Vol. 2. 1970. 68.50 (ISBN 0-12-521502-9); Vol. 3A. 1970. 79.50 (ISBN 0-12-521503-7); Vol. 3B. 1970. 59.50 (ISBN 0-12-521543-6); Vol. 4. Norris, J. R., et al, eds. 1971. 95.00 (ISBN 0-12-521504-5); Vol. 5A. 1971. 69.00 (ISBN 0-12-521505-3); Vol. 5B. 1971. 62.50 (ISBN 0-12-521545-2); Vol. 6A. 1972. 93.00 (ISBN 0-12-521506-1); Vol. 6B. 1972. 60.50 (ISBN 0-12-521546-0); Vol. 7A. 1972. 77.00 (ISBN 0-12-521507-X); Vol. 7B. 1973. 66.00 (ISBN 0-12-521547-9); Vol. 8. 1973. 55.00 (ISBN 0-12-521508-8). Acad Pr.

Shapton, D. A. & Gould, G. W. Isolation Methods for Microbiologists. (Society for Applied Bacteriology Ser.: No. 3). 1969. 33.00 (ISBN 0-12-638850-4). Acad Pr.

Shapton, D. A. & Board, R. G., eds. Isolation of Anaerobes. (Society for Applied Bacteriology Technical Ser.: No. 5). 270p. 1971. 41.00 (ISBN 0-12-638840-7). Acad Pr.

Sharpe, Anthony N. & Clark, David S. Mechanizing Microbiology. (Illus.). 352p. 1978. 33.75x (ISBN 0-398-03658-6). C C Thomas.

MICROBODIES

see also Cells

Hahn, F. E., ed. Modes & Mechanisms of Microbial Growth Inhibitors. (Antibiotics Ser.: Vol. 6). (Illus.). 127p. 1983. 130.00 (ISBN 0-387-12169-2). Springer-Verlag.

Huang, Anthony H., et al. Plant Peroxisomes. LC 82-22777. (American Society of Plant Physiologists Monograph Ser.). 1983. 34.50 (ISBN 0-12-358260-1). Acad Pr.

Roberts, K. & Hyams, J. S. Microtubles. LC 79-40920. 1980. 90.00 (ISBN 0-12-590750-8). Acad Pr.

MICROCALORIMETRY

see Calorimeters and Calorimetry

MICROCHEMISTRY

see also Spot Tests (Chemistry)

Chalmers, R. A. & Masson, M. R. Microchemical Techniques, Pt. 2. pap. 31.00 (ISBN 0-08-022004-5). Pergamon.

De Bruyne, K. I., et al. Semimicro Chemistry. rev. ed. 1966. pap. text ed. 10.92 (ISBN 0-03-052860-7, Holte); tchrs' manual o.p. 1.12 (ISBN 0-03-052865-8). HR&W.

Gaetan, Jasmin & Proschek, L., eds. Microanalysis & Quantification. (Methods & Achievements in Experimental Pathology: Vol. 11). (Illus.). vi, 190p. 1984. 70.00 (ISBN 3-8055-3717-4). S Karger.

Gersh, Isidore, ed. Submicroscopic Cytochemistry, 2vols. Incl. Vol. 1. Protein & Nucleic Acids. 1974. 73.50 (ISBN 0-12-281401-0); Vol.2. Membranes,Mitochondria, & Connective Tissue. 1974. 54.00 (ISBN 0-12-281402-9). Acad Pr.

Grasserbauer, M. & Zacherl, M. K., eds. Progress in Materials Analysis, Vol. 1. (Mikrochimica Acta Ser.: Supplement 10). (Illus.). 350p. 1983. pap. 49.70 (ISBN 0-387-81759-X). Springer-Verlag.

Halpern, M. G., ed. Industrial Enzymes from Microbial Sources: Recent Advances. LC 81-1839. (Chemical Technology Review Ser.: No. 186). 1981. 45.00 (ISBN 0-8155-0843-3). Noyes.

Hutchinson, Thomas & Somlyo, Andrew. Microprobe Analysis of Biological Systems. LC 81-15015. 1981. 47.50 (ISBN 0-12-362880-6). Acad Pr.

Ikan, Rafael. Chromatography in Organic Microanalysis: A Laboratory Guide. 120p. 1983. 25.00 (ISBN 0-12-370580-0). Acad Pr.

Klimova, V. A. Basic Methods of Organic Microanalysis. 228p. 1977. 5.95 (ISBN 0-8285-0641-8, Pub. by Mir Pubs USSR). Imported Pubns.

Korenman, I. M. Introduction to Quantitative Ultramicroanalysis. 1965. 59.50 (ISBN 0-12-420550-X). Acad Pr.

Kuck, J. A., ed. Methods in Microanalysis. Incl. Vol. 5. The Determination of Oxygen, Selenium, Chromium, & Tungsten. 552p. 1977. 123.75 (ISBN 0-677-20920-7); Vol. 6. The Determination of Sulfur. 466p. 1978. 106.50 (ISBN 0-677-20770-0). Gordon.

--Methods in Microanalysis, Vols. 1-4. Incl. Vol. 1. Simultaneous Rapid Combustion. 576p. 1964. 151.50 (ISBN 0-677-10220-8); Vol. 2. Wet Combustion & Catalytic Methods in Microanalysis. 432p. 1965. 113.50 (ISBN 0-677-10230-5); Vol. 3. The Determination of Carbon & Hydrogen & the Use of New Combustion Catalysts. 602p. 1968. 159.75 (ISBN 0-677-20620-8); Vol. 4. The Determination of Carbon & Hydrogen in the Presence of Other Elements or Simultaneously with Them. 532p. 1969. 132.95 (ISBN 0-677-20630-5). LC 64-18800. Gordon.

Malissa, H., et al, eds. Nature, Aim & Methods of Microchemistry: Proceedings. (Illus.). 350p. 1981. pap. 59.50 (ISBN 0-387-81653-4). Springer-Verlag.

Ouellette, Robert J. Microchem II from Macmillan. 1984. pap. text ed. write for info. (ISBN 0-02-389600-0). Macmillan.

Schneider, Frank L. Qualitative Organic Microanalysis. 1964. 77.50 (ISBN 0-12-627750-8). Acad Pr.

Scott, V. D. & Love, G. Quantitative Electron-Probe Microanalysis. LC 83-18366. 343p. 1983. 48.95x (ISBN 0-470-27510-3). Halsted Pr.

Shinoda, Gunji K., et al, eds. X-Ray Optics & Microanalysis: Proceedings of the Sixth International Conference. 908p. 1972. 100.00x (ISBN 0-86008-077-3, Pub. by U of Tokyo Japan). Columbia U Pr.

Steyermark, Al. Quantitative Organic Microanalysis. 2nd ed. 1961. 65.00 (ISBN 0-12-670450-3). Acad Pr.

Weisz, H. Microanalysis by the Ring Oven Technique. 2nd ed. 1970. 30.00 (ISBN 0-08-015702-5). Pergamon.

MICROCINEMATOGRAPHY

Riddle, Peter. Time-Lapse Cinemicroscopy. (Biological Techniques Ser.). 1979. 29.50 (ISBN 0-12-588060-X). Acad Pr.

Rose, George G., ed. Cinemicrography in Cell Biology. 1963. 70.50 (ISBN 0-12-596850-7). Acad Pr.

MICROCIRCULATION

Conference on Microcirculation, 6th, Aalborg, 1970. Proceedings. Ditzel, J. & Lewis, D. H., eds. (Illus.). 1971. 100.00 (ISBN 3-8055-1234-1). S Karger.

Conference on Microcirculation, 6th European, Aalborg, 1970. Microcirculatory Approaches to Current Therapeutic Problems: Lung in Shock, Organ Transplantation, Diabetic Microangiopathy. Proceedings. Ditzel, J. & Lewis, D. H., eds. (Illus.). 1971. 22.25 (ISBN 3-8055-1186-8). S Karger.

Davis, E., ed. Raynaud Update: Pathophysiology & Treatment. (Advances in Microcirculation: Vol. 12). (Illus.). vi, 162p. 1985. 58.75 (ISBN 3-8055-3992-4). S Karger.

Eckart, J., ed. Kritische Bewertung aktueller Therapiemassnahmen in der Intensivmedizin. (Beitraege zur Intensiv-und Notfallmedizin: Vol. 2). (Illus.). viii, 300p. 1984. pap. 42.75 (ISBN 3-8055-3763-8). S Karger.

European Conference on Microcirculation, 8th, le Touquet 1974. Recent Advances in Critical Microcirculatory Research. Lewis, D. H., ed. (Bibliotheca Anatomica: No. 13). (Illus.). 380p. 1975. 60.00 (ISBN 3-8055-2277-0). S Karger.

Gaehtgens, P., ed. Recent Advances in Microcirculatory Research. (Bibliotheca Anatomica Series: No. 20). (Illus.). xvi, 740p. 1981. 125.75 (ISBN 3-8055-2272-X). S Karger.

Grayson, John & Zingg, Walter, eds. Microcirculation, 2 vols. Incl. Vol. 1: Blood Vessel Interactions - Systems in Special Tissues. 443p. 1976. 52.50x (ISBN 0-306-37097-2); Vol. 2: Transport Mechanisms - Disease States. 378p. 1976. 52.50x (ISBN 0-306-37098-0). LC 76-26051. (Illus., Plenum Pr). Plenum Pub.

Gross, Joseph F. & Popel, Aleksander, eds. Mathematics of Microcirculation Phenomena. 186p. 1980. text ed. 35.00 (ISBN 0-89004-449-X). Raven.

Hamer, D. W. & Biggers, J. Thick Film Hybrid Microcircuit Technology. LC 81-17178. 432p. 1983. Repr. of 1972 ed. lib. bdg. 34.95 (ISBN 0-89874-455-5). Krieger.

Hammersen, F., ed. Angiogenesis. (Mikrozirkulation in Forschung und Klinik; Progress in Applied Microcirculation: Vol. 4). (Illus.). vi, 90p. 1984. pap. 25.75 (ISBN 3-8055-3883-9). S Karger.

Hammersen, F. & Messmer, K., eds. Endothelial Cell Vesicles. (Mikrozirkulation in Forschung Und Klinik Progress in Applied Microcirculation: Vol. 9). (Illus.). xii, 120p. 1985. pap. 28.50 (ISBN 3-8055-4070-1). S Karger.

Harders, H., ed. Advances in Microcirculation, Vol. 3. 1970. 28.75 (ISBN 3-8055-0453-5). S Karger.

International Symposium, Rottach-Egern, 1971. Hemodilution: Theoretical Basis & Clinical Application; Proceedings. Messmer, K. & Schmid-Schoenbein, H., eds. (Illus.). 313p. 1972. 42.00 (ISBN 3-8055-1306-2). S Karger.

Maynaud Features, Acrocyanosis, Cryoimmunoproteins. (Advances in Microcirculation: Vol. 10). (Illus.). viii, 116p. 1982. 41.75 (ISBN 3-8055-2790-X). S Karger.

Messmer, K., ed. Structure & Function of Endothelial Cells. Hammersen, F. (Mikrozirkulation in Forschung und Klinik, Progress in Applied Microcirculation: Vol. 1). (Illus.). x, 138p. 1983. pap. 19.75 (ISBN 3-8055-3635-6). S Karger.

Messmer, K. & Fagrell, B., eds. Mikrozirkulation und arterielle Verschlusskrankheiten Muenchen, November 1980. (Illus.). vi, 222p. 1982. pap. 21.00 (ISBN 3-8055-2417-X). S Karger.

Messmer, K. & Hammersen, F., eds. Die Mikrozirkulation des Skelettmuskels. (Illus.). viii, 162p. 1985. pap. 31.50 (ISBN 3-8055-3919-3). S Karger.

--White Cell Rheology & Inflammation. (Mikrozirkulation in Forschung und Klinik; Progress in Applied Microcirculation Ser.: Vol. 7). (Illus.). x, 124p. 1985. pap. 28.75 (ISBN 3-8055-4040-X). S Karger.

Messmer, K., et al, eds. Perspectives in Methodology for Study of the Microcirculation. (Progress in Applied Microcirculation: Vol. 6). (Illus.). vi, 160p. 1984. pap. 31.50 (ISBN 3-8055-3988-6). S Karger.

Microcirculation. (Handbook of Physiology: Section 2: The Cardiovasculars System: Vol. IV). 1124p. 1984. 275.00 (ISBN 0-683-72021-X). Am Physiological.

Mortillaro, Nicholas A., ed. The Physiology & Pharmacology of the Microcirculation, Vol. 1. LC 82-20562. (Physiologic & Pharmacologic Basis of Drug Therapy Ser.). 1983. 62.00 (ISBN 0-12-508301-7). Acad Pr.

Mulvany, M. J., et al, eds. Resistance Vessels: Physiology, Pharmacology and Hypertensive Pathology. (Mikrozirkulation in Forschung & Klinik Progress in Applied Microcirculation Ser.: Vol. 8). (Illus.). x, 236p. 1985. pap. 59.75 (ISBN 3-8055-4052-3). S Karger.

Reneman, R. S. & Bollinger, A., eds. Serotonin & Microcirculation. (Mikrozirkulation in Forschung und Klinik; Progress in Applied Microcirculation Ser.: Vol. 10). (Illus.). 92p. 1985. pap. 25.75 (ISBN 3-8055-4163-5). S Karger.

Shepro, David & Fulton, George P. Microcirculation As Related to Shock. 1968. 55.00 (ISBN 0-12-639650-7). Acad Pr.

Tillmans, H., et al, eds. Microcirculation of the Heart: Theoretical & Clinical Problems. (Illus.). 360p. 1982. pap. 49.00 (ISBN 0-387-11346-0). Springer-Verlag.

Tsuchiya, M., et al. Intravital Observation of Organ Microcirculation. (International Congress Ser.: Vol. 625). 1984. 54.00 (ISBN 0-444-90374-7, I-069-84). Elsevier.

Tsuchiya, M., et al, eds. Basic Aspects of Microcirculation: Proceedings of the International Symposium, Tokyo, July 26, 1981. (International Congress Ser.: No. 578). 404p. 1982. 85.00 (ISBN 0-444-90256-2, Excerpta Medica). Elsevier.

Vaupel, P. W. & Hammersen, F., eds. Mikrozirkulation in Malignen Tumoren. (Mikrozirkulation in Forschung und Klinik. Progress in Applied Microcirculation: Vol. 2). (Illus.). vi, 126p. 1983. pap. 19.25 (ISBN 3-8055-3762-X). S Karger.

Wiedeman, Mary P., ed. Microcirculation. (Benchmark Papers in Human Physiology Ser.). 448p. 1974. 55.50 (ISBN 0-87933-066-X). Van Nos Reinhold.

Wolf-Heidegger, G., ed. Current Advances in Basic & Clinical Microcirculatory Research. (Bibliotheca Anatomica: No. 18). (Illus.). 1979. 66.50 (ISBN 3-8055-3042-0). S Karger.

MICROCLIMATOLOGY

Franklin, Thomas B. Climates in Miniature: A Study in Micro-Climate & Environment. LC 79-138234. 137p. 1972. Repr. of 1955 ed. lib. bdg. 18.75x (ISBN 0-8371-5591-6, FRCM). Greenwood.

Jones, Hamlyn G. Plants & Microclimate: A Quantitative Approach to Environmental Plant Physiology. LC 82-22043. 350p. 1983. 57.50 (ISBN 0-521-24849-3); pap. 22.95 (ISBN 0-521-27016-2). Cambridge U Pr.

Lee, Richard. Forest Microclimatology. LC 77-21961. (Illus.). 276p. 1978. 33.00x (ISBN 0-231-04156-X). Columbia U Pr.

Rosenberg, Norman J. & Blad, Blaine L. Microclimate: The Biological Environment. 2nd ed. LC 83-7031. 495p. 1983. 34.95 (ISBN 0-471-06066-6, Pub. by Wiley-Interscience). Wiley.

Unwin, D. Microclimate Measurement for Ecologists. (Biological Techniques Ser.). 1981. 33.00 (ISBN 0-12-709150-5). Acad Pr.

MICROCOMPUTERS

All about Ninety-Two Microcomputer Database Management Packages. 37p. 19.00 (ISBN 0-318-03646-0). Datapro Res.

All about Seventy Microcomputer Word Processing Packages. 51p. 25.00 (ISBN 0-318-03648-7). Datapro Res.

Allen, Belton E. Microcomputer System Software & Languages. (Tutorial Texts Ser.). 231p. 1980. 20.00 (ISBN 0-8186-0340-2, Q340). IEEE Comp Soc.

Allison, Andrew. Managing the Microminicomputer Explosion: A Guide for Manufacturers, Users & Third Party Participants. (Illus.). 250p. (Orig.). 1983. pap. 985.00 (ISBN 0-914405-00-4). Electronic Trend.

Alper, Lynne & Holmberg, Meg. Parents, Kids, & Computers. LC 84-50360. (Illus.). 145p. (Orig.). 1984. pap. 4.95 (ISBN 0-89588-151-9). SYBEX.

Alves, Jeffrey & Curtin, Dennis. Planning & Budgeting-IBM Version. (Illus.). 224p. (Orig.). 1983. pap. 15.50 (ISBN 0-930764-61-7). Curtin & London.

Anderson, Philip N. Computers & the Radio Amateur. (Illus.). 224p. 1982. 25.95 (ISBN 0-13-166306-2). P-H.

Anderson, R. G. Microcomputing. 2nd ed. (Illus.). 210p. 1984. pap. text ed. 01.95x. Trans-Atlantic.

Apple Computer Personal Guide to Personal Computers. Date not set. 2.50 (ISBN 0-317-04449-4, A2G0035). Apple Comp.

Application of Minicomputers & Microcomputers to Information Handling. 94p. 1983. pap. text ed. 13.50 (ISBN 0-317-01214-2, UPB126, UPB). Unipub.

Arca, Julie A. & Pirro, Charles F. Introduction to InfoStar. 250p. 1984. pap. cancelled (ISBN 0-89588-108-X). SYBEX.

Archer, Tod. Simplifying Microcomputer-Based Product Design With Special Development Equipment. (Illus.). 192p. 1982. lib. bdg. 26.95 (ISBN 0-13-810796-3); pap. text ed. 18.95 (ISBN 0-13-810788-2). P-H.

Artwick, Bruce. Applied Concepts in Microcomputer Graphics. (Illus.). 400p. 1984. text ed. 34.95 (ISBN 0-13-039322-3). P-H.

ASCE Technical Council on Computer Practices, New York, May, 1981. International Conference on Computing in Civil Engineering. LC 81-66346. 1222p. 1981. pap. 75.50x (ISBN 0-87262-270-3). Am Soc Civil Eng.

Asquith, George. Log Analysis by Microcomputer. 104p. 1980. 39.95x (ISBN 0-87814-118-9). Pennwell Bks.

Avison, D. E. Microcomputers & Their Commercial Applications. 112p. 1983. 9.95 (ISBN 0-632-01172-6). Computer Sci.

Ayer, Steve J. Documenting PC Systems. (Illus., Orig.). 1986. pap. text ed. 39.50 (ISBN 0-9611694-9-4). Tech Comm Assoc.

Baczynsky, Mark. Directory of Profitable Microcomputer Ventures. (Illus.). 42p. 1984. pap. 9.95 (ISBN 0-89816-011-1). Embee Pr.

Baldwin, Ed & Baldwin, Stevie. The First Family Computer Book: A Commonsense Introduction. (A Family Workshop Bk.). (Illus.). 240p. 1984. pap. 12.95 (ISBN 0-8019-7498-4). Chilton.

Balmer, James E. & Moes, Matthijs. The Portable Computer Book. 400p. 1984. 19.95 (ISBN 0-912003-36-7). Bk Co.

Barden, William, Jr. Guidebook to Small Computers. LC 80-50047. 128p. 1980. pap. 6.95 (ISBN 0-672-21698-1, 21698). Sams.

--How to Program Microcomputers. LC 77-77412. 256p. 1978. pap. 11.95 (ISBN 0-672-21459-8, 21459). Sams.

--Microcomputers for Business Applications. LC 78-64984. 256p. 1979. pap. 9.95 (ISBN 0-672-21583-7, 21583). Sams.

Bates, William. The Computer Cookbook: How to Create Small Computer Systems That Work for You. (Illus.). 380p. 1983. 24.95 (ISBN 0-13-164558-7, Spec); pap. 12.95 (ISBN 0-13-165167-6). P-H.

Bates, Williams S. The Computer Cookbook, 1984: Computers & the Computer Industry from A to Z. LC 83-40142. 416p. 1984. pap. 14.95 (ISBN 0-385-19291-6, Quantum Pr). Doubleday.

Bear, John. Computer Wimp. LC 83-40024. 296p. 1983. 14.95 (ISBN 0-89815-102-3); pap. 9.95 (ISBN 0-89815-101-5). Ten Speed Pr.

Beer, Martin D. Microcomputer Interfacing & Associated Programming Techniques. (Illus.). 300p. (Orig.). 1985. pap. text ed. 19.95x (ISBN 0-00-383034-9, Pub. by Collins England). Sheridan.

Beizer, Boris. Micro-Analysis of Computer System Performance. (Illus.). 340p. 1978. 24.50 (ISBN 0-442-20663-1). Van Nos Reinhold.

Beker, Henry & Piper, Fred. Cipher Systems: The Protection of Communications. 427p. 1984. 40.50 (ISBN 0-471-89192-4, Pub. by Wiley-Interscience). Wiley.

Bencar, Gary R. Computers for Small Business: A Step by Step Guide on How to Buy. LC 82-21710. (Illus.). 148p. 1983. pap. 9.95 (ISBN 0-935222-05-7). La Cumbre.

Bennet, William S. & Evert, Carl F., Jr. What Every Engineer Should Know about Microcomputers: Hardware-Software Design: a Step by Step Example. (What Every Engineer Should Know Ser.: Vol. 3). (Illus.). 192p. 1980. 19.75 (ISBN 0-8247-6909-0). Dekker.

Bentley, Trevor J. Making Computers Work. 158p. 1984. 19.50X (ISBN 0-8448-1485-7). Crane-Russak Co.

Berkley, Harold B., et al. Reference Card for the Dragon 32 Microcomputer. (Dragon 32 Ser.). (Illus.). 18p. (Orig.). 1983. pap. 5.95 (ISBN 0-915069-17-2). Nanos Sys.

Berner, Jeff. At Your Fingertips: Making the Most of the Micro. 202p. 1984. pap. 12.95 (ISBN 0-673-18049-2). Scott F.

Bertoni, Phil. Strangers in Computerland: Getting Comfortable with the New Magick. LC 83-18737. 224p. 1983. 16.95 (ISBN 0-86616-034-5); pap. 9.95 (ISBN 0-86616-035-3). Greene.

Bierman, Alan W. & Guiho, Gerard. Automatic Program Construction Techniques. 500p. 1984. 57.50 (ISBN 0-02-949070-7). Macmillan.

Bishop, Owen. Figuring out Facts with a Micro. (Illus.). 160p. 1985. pap. 13.95 (ISBN 0-00-383023-3, Pub. by Collins England). Sheridan.

Bittel, L. R., et al. Set for the Donut Franchise: A Microcomputer Simulation for Business in Action. 2nd ed. 48p. 1984. TRS S80 Version. 150.00 (ISBN 0-07-079357-3); Apple Version. 199.00. McGraw.

Blank, Hannah. Mastering Micros. (Illus.). 300p. 1984. 24.95. Van Nos Reinhold.

Blank, Hannah I. Mastering Micros. (Illus.). 340p. 1983. 24.95x (ISBN 0-89433-207-4). Petrocelli.

Blumenthal, Howard J. Everyone's Guide to Personal Computers. 288p. (Orig.). 1983. pap. 8.95 (ISBN 0-345-30218-4). Ballantine.

Bly, Robert W. The Personal Computer in Advertising: Using Technology to Increase Creativity. 256p. 1984. pap. 14.95 (ISBN 0-89803-003-0). Banbury Bks.

Boehmer, M. C. The Micro in Your Library. 50p. (Orig.). 1984. pap. 5.00 (ISBN 0-914677-00-4). Contemp Issues.

Bowe, Frank G. Personal Computers & Special Needs. 175p. 1984. pap. 9.95 (ISBN 0-89588-193-4). SYBEX.

Bowker's Complete Sourcebook of Personal Computing 1985. 1100p. 1984. pap. 19.95 (ISBN 0-8352-1931-3). Bowker.

Boyce, Jefferson. Understanding Microcomputer Concepts: A Guide for Beginners & Hobbyists. LC 83-62030. (Illus.). 336p. 1984. pap. text ed. 14.95 (ISBN 0-13-936956-2). P-H.

Bradbeer, Robin. Robin Bradbeer's Personal Computer Book. 3rd ed. 288p. 1984. text ed. 23.50x (ISBN 0-566-03507-3). Gower Pub Co.

Bradbeer, Robin, et al. The Beginner's Guide to Computers: Everything You Need to Know about the New Technology. (Illus.). 208p. 1982. pap. 10.95 (ISBN 0-201-11209-4). Addison-Wesley.

Brandon, Dick H. & Segelstein, Sidney. Boardroom's Complete Guide to Microcomputers. LC 83-15450. 302p. 1983. 50.00 (ISBN 0-932648-45-2). Boardroom.

Brenner, Barbara & Endreweit, Marie. Bank Street's Family Computer Book. 224p. (Orig.). 1984. pap. 6.95 (ISBN 0-345-31367-4). Ballantine.

Brobst, Harry M. Understanding Personal Computers: A Home Study Course. (Home Study Ser.). 25p. 1982. 24.00 (ISBN 0-939926-17-2); write for info. audio tape (ISBN 0-939926-16-4). Fruition Pubns.

Brown, Bruce R. Everything You Always Wanted to Know about Personal Computers but Didn't Know How to Ask. 172p. (Orig.). 1984. pap. cancelled (ISBN 0-8159-5409-3). Devin.

Brownell, Blaine A. Using Microcomputers. 1985. 16.95 (ISBN 0-8039-2291-4). Sage.

Buchsbaum, Walter. Microprocessor & Microcomputer Data Digest. 1983. text ed. 29.95 (ISBN 0-8359-4381-X). Reston.

Burke, Anna M. The Plain Brown Wrapper Book of Computers. 184p. (Orig.). 1983. pap. 9.95 (ISBN 0-936602-59-7). Kampmann.

Burton, Philip E. A Dictionary of Minicomputing & Microcomputing. 368p. 1985. pap. 20.00 (ISBN 0-8240-7286-3). Garland Pub.

Business Communications Staff. Markets for Computer Technology in the Home: G-063. 1982. 950.00 (ISBN 0-89336-300-6). BCC.

--Microcomputers: Aftermarkets, Equipment, Supplies, Services & Software. 1984. 1250.00 (ISBN 0-89336-368-5, G-081). BCC.

Bux, William & Clark, James F. Data Entry Activities for the Micro Computer. 1982. text ed. 4.40 wkbk. (ISBN 0-538-10050-8, J05). SW Pub.

Camp, et al. Microcomputer Systems Principles Featuring the 6502-KIM. (Illus.). 560p. 1979. pap. 16.95 (ISBN 0-916460-27-4). Matrix Pub.

Camuse, Ruth. Parent & Child Computer. 1986. 14.95 (ISBN 0-317-05656-5). Reston.

Cardiff, John. Farming & the Computer. Mahony, Ciaran O., ed. LC 85-9880. (Illus.). 230p. (Orig.). 1985. pap. 14.95 (ISBN 0-934125-00-7). Group Four Pubns.

Carlson, Arthur E., et al. Boyds Clothiers: Automated Accounting for the Microcomputer. 1983. 8.00 (ISBN 0-538-01150-5, A15). SW PUb.

Carr, Joseph J. Microcomputer Interfacing Handbook: A-D & D-A. (Illus.). 287p. o.p 18.95 (ISBN 0-8306-9704-7, 1271); pap. 10.95 (ISBN 0-8306-1271-8). TAB Bks.

Case, John. Digital Future: The Personal Computer Explosion-Why It's Happening & What It Means. LC 84-20775. 180p. 1985. 12.95 (ISBN 0-688-01101-2). Morrow.

Cassell, Dana K. Making Money with Your Home Computer. 128p. 1984. pap. 5.95 (ISBN 0-396-08448-6). Dodd.

Cathcart, Gloria M. & Cathcart, W. George. Learning About Computers. 192p. 1984. 10.95x (ISBN 0-7715-3681-X). Forkner.

Cayot, Billie J., et al. How to Select a Business Computer. LC 81-85927. (Successful Business Library). 150p. 1982. 29.95 (ISBN 0-916378-17-9, Oasis). PSI Res.

CES Industries, Inc. Staff. Ed-Lab Nine Hundred & Eighty Appendicies: Microcomputer Technology. (Illus.). 1981. 11.50 (ISBN 0-86711-023-6). CES Industries.

Chen, Milton & Paisley, William, eds. Children & Microcomputers. 1985. 29.00 (ISBN 0-8039-2446-1); pap. 14.95 (ISBN 0-8039-2447-X). Sage.

Ching, Chauncey. Simple Computing: What Computers Can Do for You. LC 84-33. (Orig.). 1984. pap. 9.95 (ISBN 0-915805-00-6). Total Concepts.

Chorafas, Dimitris N. Personal Computers & Data Communications. LC 84-19972. 400p. 1985. pap. text ed. 19.95 (ISBN 0-88175-052-2). Computer Sci.

Christie, Linda G. & Curry, Jesse W., Jr. The ABC's of Microcomputers: A Computer Literacy Primer. (Illus.). 218p. 1983. 15.95 (ISBN 0-13-000620-3, Spec); pap. 7.95 (ISBN 0-13-000612-2). P-H.

Church, Norm. KeepTrack File Manager for Personal Computers. 100p. 1984. pap. 9.95 (ISBN 0-88056-128-9); incl. disk 29.95 (ISBN 0-88056-185-8); incl. cassette 29.95 (ISBN 0-88056-192-0). Dilithium Pr.

Ciarcia, Steve. Ciarcia's Circuit Cellar, Vol. IV. (BYTE Bks.). (Illus.). 1984. pap. 18.95 (ISBN 0-07-010966-4). McGraw.

Clapp, Doug. Doug Clapp's Jazz Book. 1985. pap. 17.95 (ISBN 0-673-18266-5). Scott F.
Cole, Jim. Ninety-Nine Tips & Tricks for the New Pocket Computers. 128p. (Orig.). 1982. pap. 7.95 (ISBN 0-86668-019-5). ARCsoft.
Collins, Rip & Whitehead, Steve. Double Your Sales Commission Using a Personal Computer. (Micropower Ser.). 240p. 1985. pap. 14.95 (ISBN 0-697-00802-9). Wm C Brown.
Computers & Composing: How the New Technologies Are Changing Writing. 160p. 1984. 8.50x (ISBN 0-8093-1146-1). S Ill U Pr.
Computers in the City. 400p. 1983. pap. 105.00x (ISBN 0-903796-94-5, Pub. by Online). Taylor & Francis.
Cone, Paul. What You Need to Know about Computers. (Clear & Simple Ser.). (Orig.). 1984. pap. 3.95 (ISBN 0-440-59577-0, Dell Trade Pbks). Dell.
Consultant's Log. pap. 3.00 (ISBN 0-935230-09-2). Microcomputer Appns.
Consumer Guide Editors. Book of Personal Computers & Games. 54p. 1984. spiral bdg. 3.98 (ISBN 0-517-41595-X, Pub. by Beekman Hse). Outlet Bk Co.
Consumer Guide Editors & Goodman, Danny. A Parent's Guide to Personal Computers & Software. 80p. 1983. pap. 6.95 (ISBN 0-671-49173-3, 22083, Touchstone). S&S.
Cook, Rick. Using Cassette Recorders with Computers. 175p. pap. 11.95 (ISBN 0-89588-169-1). SYBEX.
Crawford, T. James, et al. Basic Keyboarding & Typewriting Applications. 1983. 7.35 (ISBN 0-538-20370-6, T37). SW Pub.
Creekmore, Wayne & Behasa, Stephanie. Through the Micromaze: A Visual Guide to Getting Organized. (Through the Micromaze Ser.: Vol. 2). 64p. 1984. pap. 9.95 (ISBN 0-912677-18-X). Ashton-Tate Bks.
Crichton, Michael. Electronic Life. 256p. 1984. pap. 3.95 (ISBN 0-345-31739-4). Ballantine.
--Electronic Life: How to Think about Computers. LC 83-48022. 1983. 12.95 (ISBN 0-394-53406-9). Knopf.
Crop, Sheldon. Office Efficiency with Personal Computers. 175p. 1984. pap. cancelled (ISBN 0-89588-165-9). SYBEX.
Curriculum Information Center, compiled by. Microcomputers in Schools, 1984-85. rev. ed. 100p. (Orig.). 1985. pap. 50.00 (ISBN 0-89770-338-3). Market Data Ret.
Curry, Jess W., Jr. & Bonner, David M., eds. Up & Running: The Small Business Computer Implementation Cookbook. (Illus.). 150p. 1984. 17.95 (ISBN 0-13-937723-9); pap. 9.95 (ISBN 0-13-937715-8). P-H.
Dagless, Erik L. & Aspinall, David. Introduction to Microcomputers. LC 81-5437. 233p. 1982. text ed. 22.95 (ISBN 0-914894-25-0). Computer Sci.
Dahmke, Mark. Microcomputer Operating Systems. 240p. 1982. pap. 18.95 (ISBN 0-07-015071-0, BYTE Bks). McGraw.
Danhof, Kenneth & Smith, Carol. Computing System Fundamentals: An Approach Based on Microcomputers. LC 79-14933. 1981. text ed. 31.95 (ISBN 0-201-01298-7); instrs' manual 2.00 (ISBN 0-201-01245-6). Addison-Wesley.
Dartnell Institute of Business Research Staff, compiled by. Dartnell's Definitive Survey of Microcomputer Practices & Usage in the United States & Canada. 325p. 1984. three-ring binder 130.50 (ISBN 0-317-04225-4). Dartnell Corp.
Datapro Reports on Microcomputers, 2 vols. Set. 625.00 (ISBN 0-318-03644-4). Datapro Res.
Davies, Owen, ed. Omni Complete Catalog of Hardware & Peripherals. 352p. 1984. 19.95 (ISBN 0-02-529830-5); pap. 12.95 (ISBN 0-02-008300-9). Macmillan.
Dennis, Terry L. & Dennis, Laurie B. Microcomputer Models for Management Science: Text & Software. (Illus.). 350p. 1985. pap. text ed. write for info. (ISBN 0-314-93171-6). West Pub.
Derfler, Frank, Jr. Microcomputer Data Communications Systems. 129p. 1982. 17.95 (ISBN 0-13-580720-4); pap. 18.95 (ISBN 0-13-580712-3). P-H.
Devon, Richard F. The First Few Bytes. 96p. 1984. pap. text ed. 5.95 (ISBN 0-8403-3250-5). Kendall-Hunt.
Dillon, T. S. & Forward, J. Microcomputer Systems: A Compendium. 400p. 1983. write for info. Elsevier.
Dirksen, A. J. Microcomputers, What They Are & How to Put Them to Productive Use. (Illus.). 392p. 1982. pap. 11.95 (ISBN 0-8306-1406-0, 1406). TAB Bks.
Ditlea, Steve, ed. Digital Deli: The Lunch Group. LC 83-40030. (Illus.). 373p. 1984. pap. 12.95 (ISBN 0-89480-591-6, 591). Workman Pub.
Dodd, Sue A. & Sandberg-Fox, Ann M. Cataloging Microcomputer Files: A Manual of Interpretation for AACR2. 228p. 1985. 40.00 (ISBN 0-8389-0401-7). ALA.
Dologite, Dorothy G. Using Small Business Computers with Lotus 1-2-3, dBASE II & Wordstar. 1985. text ed. 24.95 (ISBN 0-13-940230-6). P-H.
Douglas, I. J. Audit & Control of Mini & Microcomputers. 145p. 1982. 25.00x (ISBN 0-85012-368-2). Taylor & Francis.
Dowsing & Infotech. Microcomputer Systems, 2 vols. Set. 125.00x (ISBN 0-08-028519-8). Pergamon.
Driscoll, Frederick F. Microprocessor-Microcomputer Technology. 1983. text ed. write for info. (ISBN 0-534-01326-0, Pub. by Breton Pubs). Wadsworth Pub.
--Microprocessor-Microcomputer Technology. 520p. 1983. 29.95 (ISBN 0-442-21827-3). Van Nos Reinhold.
Dromey, R. How to Solve It by Computer. 1983. pap. 24.95 (ISBN 0-13-434001-9). P-H.
Duffett-Smith, Peter. Astronomy on Your Personal Computer. (Illus.). 240p. Date not set. price not set (ISBN 0-521-26620-3); pap. price not set (ISBN 0-521-31976-5). Cambridge U Pr.
Dwyer, Thomas A. & Critchfield, Margot. CP-M & the Personal Computer: Popular. LC 82-20703. (Microcomputer Bks.). 280p. 1983. pap. 19.95 (ISBN 0-201-10355-9). Addison-Wesley.
Edwards, C. H., Jr. Calculus & the Personal Computer. (Illus.). 192p. 1986. pap. text ed. 12.95 (ISBN 0-13-112319-X). P-H.
Edwards, Paul & Edwards, Sarah. How to Make Money with Your Personal Computer. (Handy Guide Ser.). 64p. (Orig.). 1984. pap. 3.50 (ISBN 0-88284-264-1). Alfred Pub.
Elbra, R. A. Database for the Small Computer User. 150p. 1982. pap. 20.75 (ISBN 0-471-89443-5). Wiley.
Elzey, Freeman F. Statistics: A Microcomputer Approach with Utility Supporting Software. 256p. 1984. pap. write for info. Wadsworth Pub.
Erickson, Duane E., et al. Microcomputers on the Farm: Getting Started. 56p. (Orig.). 1985. pap. 9.95 (ISBN 0-8138-1156-2). Iowa St U Pr.
Evans, Christopher. The Making of the Micro: A History of the Computer. 120p. 1981. pap. 14.95 (ISBN 0-442-22240-8). Van Nos Reinhold.
--The Micro Millennium. 1980. 10.95 (ISBN 0-670-47400-2). Viking.
Fitch, D. In Pursuit of Productivity: Making Things Happen in the Microcomputer Age. 1982. 16.95 (ISBN 0-201-04072-7). Addison-Wesley.
Fleischer, Neil T. & Gates, Calvin. The Micro Editor. 1983. text ed. 2.35 wkbk. (ISBN 0-538-23670-1, W67). SW Pub.
Flores, Ivan. The Professional Microcomputer Handbook. (Illus.). 752p. 1985. 49.95 (ISBN 0-442-22497-4). Van Nos Reinhold.
Flores, Ivan & Terry, Christopher. Microcomputer Systems. 290p. 1982. 24.50 (ISBN 0-442-26141-1). Van Nos Reinhold.
Flynn, M. J., et al, eds. Microcomputer System Design: An Advanced Course. (Lecture Notes in Computer Science Ser.: Vol. 126). 397p. 1981. pap. 22.00 (ISBN 0-387-11172-7). Springer-Verlag.
Fosegan, Joseph S. Alphabetic Indexing Rules: Application by Computer. 1984. pap. 3.70 (ISBN 0-538-11640-4, K64). SW Pub.
Fox Bourne, H. R. English Merchants. xvi, 492p. Repr. of 1886 ed. 59.00 (ISBN 0-932051-31-6). Am Repr Serv.
Freiberger, Paul & Swaine, Michael. Fire in the Valley: The Making of The Personal Computer. 300p. (Orig.). 1984. pap. 9.95 (ISBN 0-07-881121-X, 121-X). Osborne-McGraw.
Friedman, Herb. Computer Care: The Complete Guide to Microcomputer Maintenance for Home & Office. (Illus.). 224p. 14.95 (ISBN 0-13-163833-5). P-H.
Fylstra, Hilary. How to Work Smarter with Personal Computer. (VisiSeries). (Illus.). 200p. (Orig.). 1983. pap. 12.95 (ISBN 0-912213-02-7). Paladin.
--How You Can Work Smarter with Personal Computers. (The Visi Ser.). 1984. pap. 12.95 (ISBN 0-912213-02-7, VisiPress). Random.
Gadsden, S. R. & Adams, R. J. The Administration of Interlending by Microcomputer. (LIR Report 30). (Illus.). 62p. (Orig.). 1984. pap. 14.25 (ISBN 0-7123-3044-5, Pub. by British Lib). Longwood Pub Group.
Gallagher, Sharon & Van der Meer, Ron. Inside the Personal Computer: An Illustrated Introduction in 3 Dimensions. LC 84-6184. (Illus.). 1984. 19.95 (ISBN 0-89659-504-8). Abbeville Pr.
Garrison, P. Cockpit Computers & Navigation Avionics. 256p. 1982. 29.95 (ISBN 0-07-022893-0). McGraw.
Gault, J. W. & Pimmel, R. L. Introduction to Microcomputer-Based Digital Systems. (McGraw-Hill Series in Electronics). 1982. 42.00 (ISBN 0-07-023047-1). McGraw.
Gibbs, Emily A. & Perry, Jim, eds. Some of the Best from Kilobaud Microcomputing. 223p. 1980. 10.95 (BK7311). Green Pub Inc.
Gibson, Glenn A. & Liu, Yu-Cheng. Microcomputers for Engineers & Scientists. (Illus.). 1980. text ed. 38.95 (ISBN 0-13-580886-3). P-H.
Gilbert, Dennis, et al. Microcomputers: A Review of Federal Agency Experiences. (National Bureau of Standards Special Publication 500-102. Computer Science & Technology Ser.). 146p. (Orig.). 1983. pap. 5.50 (ISBN 0-318-11739-8). Gov Printing Office.
Ginter, Peter M. & Rucks, Andrew C. Basic Decision Making on the Microcomputer. 475p. 1985. pap. text ed. 23.95 (ISBN 0-394-33928-2, RanC). Random.
Givone, Donald O. & Roesser, Robert P. Microprocessors-Microcomputers: An Introduction. (Illus.). 480p. 1980. text ed. 40.00 (ISBN 0-07-023326-8). McGraw.
Gledhill, V. X. Discovering Computers. write for info. McGraw.
Glossbrenner, Alfred. The Complete Handbook of Personal Computer Communications: Everything You Need to Go Online with the World. rev., enl. ed. (Illus.). 480p. 1985. pap. 14.95 (ISBN 0-312-15760-6). St Martin.
Goldberg, Kenneth P. & Sherwood, Robert D. Microcomputers: A Parents' Guide. LC 83-1129. (Wiley Parent Education Series: No. 1-630). 196p. 1983. pap. text ed. 8.95 (ISBN 0-471-87278-4, Pub. by Wiley Pr). Wiley.
Gonzales, Laurence. Computers for Writers: User Friendly Guides. 144p. 1984. 6.95 (ISBN 0-345-31476-X). Ballantine.
Goodman, Danny. Hands-On EXCEL. 1985. pap. 19.95 (ISBN 0-673-18369-6). Scott F.
Goody, Roy W. The Intelligent Microcomputer. 354p. 1982. text ed. 28.95 (ISBN 0-574-21560-3, 13-4560); instr. guide avail. (ISBN 0-574-21561-1, 13-4561). SRA.
--Microcomputer Fundamentals. 300p. 1980. pap. text ed. 16.95 (ISBN 0-574-21540-9, 13-4540); instr's. guide avail. (ISBN 0-574-21541-7, 13-4541). SRA.
--The Versatile Microcomputer: The Motorola Family. 360p. 1984. text ed. 28.95 (ISBN 0-574-21595-6, 13-4595); free tchr's. ed (ISBN 0-574-21596-4, 13-4596). SRA.
Gorsline, George W. Sixteen-Bit Modern Microcomputers: The Intel I8086 Family. (Illus.). 496p. 1985. text ed. 32.95 (ISBN 0-13-811415-3). P-H.
Gotlieb, C. C. Computers in the Home. 65p. 1978. pap. text ed. 3.00x (ISBN 0-920380-10-7, Pub. by Inst Res Pub Canada). Brookfield Pub Co.
Graham, Ian. Computers & Video Games. write for info. EDC.
Grayson, Ashley D. & Vornholt, John. Computers to Go. Hagmann, Marnie, ed. (Illus.). 395p. 1985. pap. 12.95 (ISBN 0-671-50749-4, Pub. by Computer Bks). S&S.
Grelewicz, Richard M. Take It with You: The Complete Guide to Portable Business Computing. LC 84-5208. 246p. 1984. pap. 14.95 (ISBN 0-471-88198-8). Wiley.
Grillo, John P. & Robertson, J. D. Microcomputer Systems: An Applications Approach. 275p. 1979. pap. text ed. write for info. (ISBN 0-697-08132-X); instrs.' man. avail. (ISBN 0-697-08161-3). Wm C Brown.
Grogono, Peter. Mouse: A Language for Microcomputers. (Illus.). 200p. 1983. text ed. 17.50 (ISBN 0-89433-201-5). Petrocelli.
Gueulette, David G., ed. Microcomputers for Adult Learning: Potentials & Perils. 228p. pap. 29.27 (ISBN 0-8428-2205-4). Cambridge Bk.
Gupta, A. & Toong, Hm, eds. Insights into Personal Computers. LC 84-29707. 1985. 29.50 (ISBN 0-87942-188-6, PCO1826). Inst Electrical.
Gupton, James A., Jr. Getting Down to Business with Your Microcomputer. LC 78-68552. (Illus., Orig.). 1979. pap. 9.95 (ISBN 0-933422-00-8, A100). Sourcebooks CA.
Hallam, Stephen F., et al. Microcomputer Use: Word Processors, Spreadsheets & Databases with Accompanying Concept 3 Software. 1984. text ed. 17.50i (ISBN 0-12-319625-6). Acad Pr.
--Microcomputer Use: Word Processors, Spreadsheets, & Databases with Accompanying Concept 3 Software, IBM-MS-DOS 2.0. 1984. text ed. 21.50i (ISBN 0-12-319628-0). Acad Pr.
Hallam, Teresa A. Microcomputer Use: Word Processor, Spreadsheets, & Databases with Accompanying Concept 3 Software; Instructor's Manual. 1985. text ed. 5.00 (ISBN 0-12-319629-9). Acad Pr.
Hammond, Ray. The Musician & the Micro. (Illus.). 192p. 1983. (Pub. by Blandford Pr England); pap. 8.95x (ISBN 0-7137-1299-6). Sterling.
Harris, James R. The Aster Introduction to Microcomputers. (Monograph). (Illus.). 100p. (Orig.). 1984. pap. 20.00x (ISBN 0-943330-07-6). Aster Pub Corp.
Hartley, Michael G. & Buckley, Anne, eds. Microelectronics & Microcomputer Applications. LC 82-62245. 246p. 1983. 15.00 (ISBN 0-7190-0905-7, Pub. by Manchester Univ Pr). Longwood Pub Group.
Haven Group. The Electronic Money Machine: Profits from Your Home Computer. 240p. 1984. pap. 5.95 (ISBN 0-380-86751-6, 86751). Avon.
Head, Robert V. Information Center Resource. LC 84-61536. (Orig.). 1985. pap. write for info. (ISBN 0-89435-123-0, IC 1230). QED Info Sci.
Healey, Martin. Minicomputers & Microprocessors. LC 76-11606. 353p. 1976. pap. 19.50x (ISBN 0-8448-0970-5). Crane-Russak Co.
Heath Company Staff. Microcomputing. (Illus.). 416p. looseleaf with 2 audiocassettes 44.95 (ISBN 0-87119-082-6, EC-1000). Heathkit-Zenith Ed.
Heise, David R., ed. Microcomputers & Social Research. (Sociological Methods & Research Ser.: Vol. 9, No. 4). 6.00 (ISBN 0-686-74762-3). Sage.
Heiser, Richard S. Real Managers Use Personal Computers! 210p. (Orig.). 1984. pap. 14.95 (ISBN 0-88022-031-7, 29). Que Corp.
Heiserman, David L. Projects in Machine Intelligence for Your Home Computer. LC 81-18233. (Illus.). 103p. 1982. pap. 10.95 (ISBN 0-8306-1391-9, 1391). TAB Bks.
Heller, Rachelle & Martin, Dianne. Bits 'n Bytes about Computing for Everyone. write for info. (ISBN 0-914894-92-7). Computer Sci.
Henck, Karl N. How to Start Your Own Microcomputer Based Mail Order Business. LC 81-65513. (Illus., Orig.). 1983. pap. 9.95 (ISBN 0-939258-00-5). Bork Res.
Henderson, Richard. A Practical Guide to Performance Appraisal. 2nd ed. 1983. text ed. 25.00 (ISBN 0-8359-5576-1). Reston.
Hickel, Stephen M. The Second Ring: A Jeweler's Guide to Computers. McNamara, Sue, et al, eds. 304p. (Orig.). 1985. pap. 19.95 (ISBN 0-934253-00-5). Pimiteoui Pubns.
Highland, Harold J. Protecting Your Microcomputer System. LC 83-5858. 244p. 1984. pap. 14.95 (ISBN 0-471-89216-5, Pub by Wiley Pr). Wiley.
Hilburn, J. L. & Julich, P. Microcomputers - Microprocessors: Hardware, Software & Applications. 1976. text ed. 37.50 (ISBN 0-13-580969-X). P-H.
Hillman, H. H. Avoiding Computer Nightmares. 240p. pap. 12.95 (ISBN 0-07-028949-2). McGraw.
Hodges, William S. & Novak, Neal. Practical Programs for Home Computers. (Microcomputer Bookshelf Ser.). 200p. 1984. pap. text ed. 14.95 (ISBN 0-316-61151-4). Little.
Hodges, William S. & Novak, Neal A. Applications of Software for Homes & Businesses. (Little, Brown Microcomputer Bookshelf Ser.). 350p. (Orig.). 1984. pap. 14.95 i (ISBN 0-316-36788-5). Little.
Hoffman, Ruth. Microcomputers & Teachers. 148p. 1983. pap. text ed. 9.95 (ISBN 0-89108-119-4). Love Pub Co.
Holland, R. C. Microcomputers & Their Interfacing. (Illus.). 191p. 1984. 26.00 (ISBN 0-08-031124-5); pap. 11.00 (ISBN 0-08-031125-3). Pergamon.
--Microcomputers for Process Control. (Pergamon Materials Engineering Practice Ser.). (Illus.). 204p. 1983. 25.00 (ISBN 0-08-029957-1); pap. 12.00 (ISBN 0-08-029956-3). Pergamon.
Holt, Charles A. Microcomputer Organization. 1985. text ed. write for info. (ISBN 0-02-356350-8). Macmillan.
Holtz, Frederick. Using & Programming the AT&T 6300: Including Ready-to-Run Programs. (Illus.). 256p. 1985. 22.95 (ISBN 0-8306-0920-2, 1920); pap. 16.95 (ISBN 0-8306-1920-8). TAB Bks.
Holtz, Herman. How to Make Money with Your Micro. LC 84-3589. 324p. 1984. pap. 14.95 (ISBN 0-471-88455-3). Wiley.
Infotech. Microcomputer Software, 2 vols. Set. 145.00x (ISBN 0-08-028506-6). Pergamon.
International Resource Development Inc. Far Eastern Vendors Strategies for U. S. Microcomputer Markets. 202p. 1983. 1850.00x (ISBN 0-88694-582-8). Intl Res Dev.
--Microcomputer Operating System Strategies. 237p. 1983. 1650.00x (ISBN 0-88694-571-2). Intl Res Dev.
--PCs vs. CWPs in the Clerical Workstation of the Future. 257p. 1983. 1650.00x (ISBN 0-88694-566-6). Intl Res Dev.
--Portable Computers. 215p. 1983. 1650.00x (ISBN 0-88694-568-2). Intl Res Dev.
--Supermicros. 157p. 1984. 1650.00x (ISBN 0-88694-604-2). Intl Res Dev.
Irby, Thomas C. & Ward, D. L. Hypergraphics User's Guide: Apple II Version. 1983. 19.95 (ISBN 0-07-068143-0). McGraw.

Sagan, Hans. Beat the Odds: Microcomputer Simulations of Casino Games. 192p. 1983. pap. 9.50 (ISBN 0-8104-5181-6). Hayden.

Saiady, C. & Stokes, A. V., eds. What to Read in Microcomputing. 112p. (Orig.). 1982. pap. text ed. 23.50x (ISBN 0-566-03403-4). Gower Pub Co.

Sanders, D. H. & Fry. Computers Today: Inside Computers Today. 290p. 1985. study guide 10.95 (ISBN 0-07-054704-1). McGraw.

Schmeltz, L. R. Word Processing with Your Microcomputer. (Illus.). 256p. (Orig.). 1982. pap. 13.95 (ISBN 0-8306-1478-8, 1478). TAB Bks.

Schmidt, Allen H. & Alterman, Ira. Computing for Profits. 256p. 1984. text ed. 22.95 (ISBN 0-02-607130-4); pap. text ed. 10.95 (ISBN 0-02-008760-8). Macmillan.

Schneider, Ben Ross, Jr. My Personal Computer: And Other Family Crises. (Illus.). 245p. 1985. 15.95 (ISBN 0-02-949610-1). Macmillan.

Schroy, John O. The Fact: Fox Guide Microcomputer Information Analysis. (Illus.). 200p. 1984. pap. 19.95 (ISBN 0-914217-00-3). Dedicated Systems Corp.

Seitz, Neil. Business Forecasting: Concepts & Microcomputer Applications. 1984. 24.95 (ISBN 0-8359-0606-X); pap. text ed. 17.95 (ISBN 0-8359-0604-3); instr's. manual avail. (ISBN 0-8359-0605-1). Reston.

Shade, Gary A. Speech Systems for Your Microcomputer. (Illus.). 254p. (Orig.). 1984. 14.95 (ISBN 0-88006-073-5, BK7406). Weber Systems.

Shallis, Michael. The Silicon Idol: The Micro Revolution & Its Social Implications. LC 84-5296. 198p. 1984. 15.95 (ISBN 0-8052-3927-8). Schocken.

Shirinian, George. Microcomputer Periodicals: An Annotated Directory. 250p. 1985. pap. 24.95 (ISBN 0-8240-8717-8). Garland Pub.

Shoup, Terry E. Numerical Methods for the Personal Computer. (Illus.). 256p. 1983. pap. text ed. 19.95 (ISBN 0-13-627208-8). P-H.

Sigel, Efrem, et al. The Future of Videotext: Worldwide Prospects for Home-Office Electronic Information Services. LC 82-14836. (Communications Library). 197p. 1983. professional 34.95 (ISBN 0-86729-025-0, 409-BW). Knowledge Indus.

Simpson, Alan, ed. Planning for Office Microcomputers. (The Office of the Future Ser.: Vol. 5). 110p. (Orig.). 1982. pap. text ed. 21.00x (ISBN 0-566-03416-6). Gower Pub Co.

Simpson, Edwin L. How to Get Rich with Your Microcomputer. 109p. (Orig.). 1984. pap. 12.00 (ISBN 0-915665-03-4). Premier Publishers.

Sinclair, Ian. QL Computing. (Illus.). 182p. (Orig.). 1984. pap. 11.95 (ISBN 0-246-12595-0, Pub. by Granada England). Sheridan.

Sloan, Martha E. Introduction to Minicomputers & Microcomputers. LC 78-74693. 1980. text ed. 34.95 (ISBN 0-201-07279-3). Addison-Wesley.

The Software Catalog: Microcomputers. 1000p. 1984. 84.00 (ISBN 0-444-00745-8); incl. update 142.50 (ISBN 0-444-00776-8). Elsevier.

The Software Catalog: Microcomputers, Summer 1985, 2 pts. 2000p. 1985. 95.00 (ISBN 0-444-00959-0). Elsevier.

Soucek, Branko. Microprocessors & Microcomputers. LC 75-33123. 607p. 1976. 45.95x (ISBN 0-471-81391-5, Pub. by Wiley-Interscience). Wiley.

Souter, Gerry. The Microcomputer-Video Connection. 1985. pap. 16.95 (ISBN 0-673-18290-8). Scott F.

Spencer, Donald D. Microcomputers at a Glance. LC 77-11920. 1977. pap. 3.50x (ISBN 0-89218-021-8). Camelot Pub.

Stein, Philip G. & Shapiro, Howard M. The Joy of Minis & Micros. rev. ed. 182p. (Orig.). 1985. pap. write for info. (ISBN 0-9614514-0-8). Omnimaven Bks.

Stoller, Alan. Computer Omnibus. 150p. 1984. pap. 9.95 (ISBN 0-13-164229-4). P-H.

Sturridge, Helen, et al. The Arco Book of Electronics. LC 84-2868. (Illus.). 140p. 1984. 11.95 (ISBN 0-668-06154-5, 6154-5). Arco.

Sussman, Marvin B., ed. Personal Computers & the Family. LC 85-8459. (Marriage & Family Review Ser.: Vol. 8, Nos. 1 & 2). 216p. 1985. text ed. 24.95 (ISBN 0-86656-361-X); pap. text ed. 19.95 (ISBN 0-86656-362-8). Haworth Pr.

Svigals, Jerome. Smart Cards: The Ultimate Personal Computer. 208p. 1985. 21.95x (ISBN 0-02-948900-8). Macmillan.

Swaay, Maarten V. & Lenhert, Donald H. Fundamentals of Microcomputers. 238p. 1982. looseleaf bound 29.95 (ISBN 0-935506-04-7). Carnegie Pr.

Swanson, Paul. Microcomputer Disk Techniques. (Illus.). 224p. 1982. pap. text ed. 17.95 (ISBN 0-07-062582-4, BYTE Bks). McGraw.

Tattersfield, D. Orbits for Amateurs: With a Microcomputer. 171p. 1984. 29.95x (ISBN 0-470-27502-2). Halsted Pr.

Taylor, James B. Using Microcomputers in Social Agencies. LC 81-1759. (Human Services Guides Ser.: Vol. 19). (Illus.). 219p. 1981. pap. 7.95 (ISBN 0-8039-1617-5). Sage.

Tees, David W. & Seidel, Andrew D. Texas Cities in the Microcomputer Age. 120p. (Orig.). 1985. pap. text ed. 12.50 (ISBN 0-936440-65-1). Inst Urban Studies.

Teja, Edward R. Teaching Your Computer to Talk: A Manual of Command & Response. (Illus.). 208p. pap. 8.95 (ISBN 0-8306-1330-7, 1330). TAB Bks.

Texas Instruments Learning Center Staff. Microprocessors & Microcomputers & Switching Mode Power for Supplies. (Solid-State Electronics Technology Bks.). (Illus.). 216p. 1978. 35.00 (ISBN 0-07-063756-3). Tex Instr Inc.

--Microprocessors-Microcomputers-System Design. 534p. 1980. 32.50 (ISBN 0-07-063758-X). Tex Instr Inc.

Titus, Christopher A., et al. STD Bus Interfacing. LC 82-50652. 286p. 1982. pap. 13.95 (ISBN 0-672-21888-7, 21888). Sams.

TMS1000 Family 4-bit Microcomputers Data Manual. 2.65 (ISBN 0-317-27334-5, MP056). Tex Instr Inc.

TMS9914A GPIB Controller Data Manual. 2.00 (ISBN 0-317-27330-2, MPO33A). Tex Instr Inc.

TMS9918A-9928A-9929A Video Display Processors Data Manual. 2.00 (ISBN 0-317-27331-0, MP010A). Tex Instr Inc.

TMS99532 Single-Chip Modem Data Manual. 2.00 (ISBN 0-317-27332-9, SPPS007). Tex Instr Inc.

TMS9995 16-bit Microcomputer Data Manual. 2.00 (ISBN 0-317-27333-7, MP021A); Catalog. write for info. Tex Instr Inc.

Tocci, Ronald & Laskowski, Lester. Microprocessors & Microcomputers: Hardware & Software. 2nd ed. (Illus.). 416p. 1982. 32.95 (ISBN 0-13-581322-0); solutions manual avail. P-H.

Tomczyk, Michael. The Home Computer Wars. Mansfield, Richard, ed. (Orig.). 1984. 16.95 (ISBN 0-942386-75-2); pap. 9.95 (ISBN 0-942386-78-7). Compute Pubns.

Tompkins, W. & Webster, J., eds. Design of Microcomputer-Based Medical Instrumentation. 1981. 39.95 (ISBN 0-13-201244-8). P-H.

Toong, Hoo-min D. & Gupta, Amar. Personal Computers. LC 83-7290. (Illus.). 130p. 1983. pap. 8.95 (ISBN 0-89708-127-7). And Bks.

Tremblay, J. P. & Sorenson, P. G. The Theory & Practice of Compiler Writing. 816p. 1984. 35.95 (ISBN 0-07-065161-2). McGraw.

Tripp, Robert M., ed. The Best of Micro, Vol. 2. 224p. 1979. 8.00 (ISBN 0-938222-02-3). Computerist.

--The Best of Micro, Vol. 3. 320p. 1980. pap. 10.00 (ISBN 0-938222-04-X). Computerist.

Troutner, Joanne J. The Media Specialist, the Microcomputer, & the Curriculum. 175p. 1983. lib. bdg. 19.50 (ISBN 0-87287-367-6). Libs Unl.

TTL Data Book: Supplement, LS & S. 8.75 (ISBN 0-317-27328-0, LCC5772). Tex Instr Inc.

TTL Data Book, Vol. 3: Supplement: Additional ALS, AS. 4.95 (ISBN 0-317-27329-9, SDAD003). Tex Instr Inc.

Uhrowczik, Tedi. A Computer Summer. (Illus.). 128p. 1984. pap. 5.95 (ISBN 0-88056-318-4). Dilithium Pr.

Uston, Ken. Ken Uston Illustrated Guide to Today's Most Popular Computers. 1984. 9.95 (ISBN 0-317-13333-0). P-H.

Volunteer-The National Center & Taft Group. Basic Computer Knowledge for Nonprofits: Everything You Need to Know Made Easy. LC 85-51091. 352p. (Orig.). 1985. 3-ring binder 67.50 (ISBN 0-914756-38-9). Taft Group.

Wadsworth, Nat. Understanding Microcomputers & Small Computer Systems. (Quality Paperbacks Ser.). (Illus.). 312p. 1981. pap. 8.95 (ISBN 0-306-80143-4). Da Capo.

Waite Group Editors & Shafer, Dan. Silicon Visions: The Future of Microcomputer Technology. 320p. 1985. 18.95 (ISBN 0-89303-845-8). Brady Comm.

Waite, Mitchell & Pardee, Michael. Microcomputer Primer. 2nd ed. LC 79-67127. 384p. 1980. pap. 14.50 (ISBN 0-672-21653-1, 21653). Sams.

--Your Own Computer. 2nd ed. LC 81-51554. 224p. 1981. pap. 8.95 (ISBN 0-672-21860-7, 21860). Sams.

Wallace, W. H., ed. What's in Print: The Subject Guide to Microcomputer Magazines. 504p. 1983. pap. 14.95 vinyl (ISBN 0-8306-0611-4, 1611). TAB Bks.

Warme, Paul. BASEX. LC 79-775. 1979. pap. 9.95 (ISBN 0-07-068290-9, BYTE Bks). McGraw.

--My Micro Speaks BASEX. 164p. (Orig.). 1981. pap. 9.95 (ISBN 0-8104-5187-5). Hayden.

Warren, Jim C., Jr., ed. National Computer Conference '78 Personal Computing Digest. (Illus.). iv, 425p. 1978. pap. 14.00 (ISBN 0-88283-011-2). AFIPS Pr.

Waterford, Van. The Complete Book of Home Computers. (Illus.). 256p. (Orig.). 1982. pap. 10.95 (ISBN 0-8306-1423-0, 1423). TAB Bks.

--Microcomputer-Controlled Toys & Games & How They Work. (Illus.). 240p. (Orig.). 1983. 17.95 (ISBN 0-8306-0407-3); pap. 10.25 (ISBN 0-8306-1407-9, 1407). TAB Bks.

Waxman, Robert J. Moonlighting with Your Personal Computer. 160p. 1984. pap. 7.95 (ISBN 0-345-31652-5). Ballantine.

Weininger, Jay & Clowney, Deborah. Planning for Computer Success. 1984. 24.95 (ISBN 0-13-679440-8); pap. 17.95 (ISBN 0-13-679432-7). P-H.

Weisbecker, Joe. Home Computers Can Make You Rich. 1980. pap. 8.95 (ISBN 0-8104-5177-8). Hayden.

Werner, Michael & Warrner, Thomas. Micros, Minis & Mainframes: Computing Options for the Business Manager. LC 83-45395. 420p. 1984. pap. 19.95 (ISBN 0-8019-7303-1). Chilton.

Whitaker, D. O R on the Microcomputer. 350p. 1983. pap. 18.95 (ISBN 0-471-90084-2). Wiley.

Whitaker, David. O R on the Microcomputer. 197p. 1984. 19.95x (ISBN 0-471-90083-4). Wiley.

Whitehous, Gary, ed. Microsoftware: Statistical Analysis. 1984. 175.00 (ISBN 0-89806-084-2). Inst Indus Eng.

Whitehouse, Gary. Microsoftware: Forecasting. 1984. 175.00 (ISBN 0-89806-079-6). Inst Indus Eng.

Whitehouse, Gary, ed. Microsoftware: Operations Research. 1984. 175.00 (ISBN 0-89806-080-X). Inst Indus Eng.

Whitehouse, Gary, et al. IIE Microsoftware: Economic Analysis. 1981. 175.00 (ISBN 0-89806-013-3). Inst Indus Eng.

--IIE Microsoftware: Production Control. 1981. 175.00 (ISBN 0-89806-012-5). Inst Indus Eng.

--IIE Microsoftware: Project Management. 1981. 175.00 (ISBN 0-89806-030-3). Inst Indus Eng.

--IIE Microsoftware: Work Measurement. 1982. 175.00 (ISBN 0-89806-035-4). Inst Indus Eng.

Whitson, Dick. Your Computer Can Kill You. 1984. looseleaf 74.95 (ISBN 0-917194-15-2). Prog Studies.

Wiatrowski, Claude A. & House, Charles H. Logic Circuits & Microcomputer Systems. Cerra, Frank J., ed. (McGraw-Hill Series in Electrical Engineering: Computer Engineering & Switching Theory-Electronics & Electronic Circuits). (Illus.). 512p. 1980. text ed. 42.00 (ISBN 0-07-070090-7). McGraw.

Wilcox, Russell E. Computer & Microcomputer Systems for Small Businesses. LC 83-43246. 256p. 1984. lib. bdg. 27.50 (ISBN 0-89774-131-5). Oryx Pr.

Wild, Victor. Your Fortune in the Microcomputer Business: Getting Started, Vol. I. (Illus.). 304p. 1982. pap. 15.95 (ISBN 0-938444-04-2). Wildfire Pub.

--Your Fortune in the Microcomputer Business: Growth, Survival, Success, Vol. II. (Illus.). 256p. 1982. pap. 15.95 (ISBN 0-938444-05-0). Wildfire Pub.

Williams, Frederick & Williams, Victoria. Growing up with Computers: A Parent's Survival Guide. LC 83-62846. 288p. 1984. pap. 6.70 (ISBN 0-688-02794-6, Quill NY). Morrow.

--Microcomputers in Elementary Education: Perspectives on Implementation. LC 83-23247. 174p. 1984. text ed. write for info. (ISBN 0-534-03242-7). Wadsworth Pub.

Willis, Jerry. Peanut Butter & Jelly Guide to Computers. 2nd ed. (Illus.). 288p. 1984. pap. 14.95 (ISBN 0-88056-340-0). Dilithium Pr.

Willis, Jerry & Miller, Merl. Computers for Everybody. 3rd ed. (Illus.). 368p. 1983. pap. 9.95 (ISBN 0-88056-131-9). Dilithium Pr.

Willis, Jerry & Schrock, Jay. Exploring the Outer Limits: Telecommunications & Personal Computers. 384p. 1985. pap. 17.95 (ISBN 0-88056-349-4). Dilithium Pr.

Winger, Martin. Electronic Calculator Handbook for Pilots. (Illus.). 1978. spiral bdg. 3.95 (ISBN 0-911721-77-0, Pub. by Winger). Aviation.

Winter & Coccione. Computers Won't Byte. LC 83-51525. 128p. 1984. pap. 4.95 (ISBN 0-672-22316-3, 22316). Sams.

Witt, Howard. Navigation with a Micro-Computer. 1983. pap. text ed. 14.95 (ISBN 0-87567-082-2). Entelek.

Witten, Ian. Communicating with Microcomputers: An Introduction to the Technology of Man-Computer Communication. LC 80-40650. (Computers & People Ser.). 1980. 27.00 (ISBN 0-12-760750-1); pap. 17.00 (ISBN 0-12-760752-8). Acad Pr.

Wolff, Terris B. Microcomputer Applications: Using Small Systems Software. rev. ed. 1985. pap. text ed. 21.00 (ISBN 0-87835-813-7); instr's. manual 8.00 (ISBN 0-87835-811-0); test bank avail. (ISBN 0-87835-812-9). Boyd & Fraser.

Wollman, J. Computer Workplace. 288p. 1985. 12.95 (ISBN 0-07-071588-2, Byte Bks). McGraw.

Woodwell, Donald R. Automating Your Financial Portfolio: An Investor's Guide to Personal Computers. LC 82-73637. 220p. 1983. 19.95 (ISBN 0-87094-399-5). Dow Jones-Irwin.

--How to Get the Most Out of Your Home Computer. LC 83-9096. (Illus.). 128p. (Orig.). 1983. pap. 5.95 (ISBN 0-943392-20-9). Tribeca Comm.

Yourdon, Edward. The Perils of Personal Computing. LC 84-52806. (Illus.). 136p. (Orig.). 1985. pap. 15.00 (ISBN 0-917072-50-2). Yourdon.

Zaks, Rodnay. Protecting Your Computer: (Or How To Care For Your Computer) (Illus.). 213p. 1981. pap. 14.95 (ISBN 0-89588-239-6, C400). SYBEX.

--Your First Computer. 8.95 (ISBN 0-317-06040-6). Green Pub Inc.

--Your First Computer: A Guide to Business & Personal Computing. 3rd. updated ed. LC 83-50405. (Illus.). 257p. 1983. pap. 9.95 (ISBN 0-89588-142-X, C200A). SYBEX.

Zalewski, Donald L., ed. Microcomputers for Teachers: With Application to Mathematics & Science. (Topics for Teachers Ser.). (Illus.). 116p. (Orig.). 1982. pap. 6.00 (ISBN 0-912047-03-8). Sch Sci Math.

Zito, Tom. The Ultimate Game. Date not set. 14.95 (ISBN 0-393-01916-0). Norton.

MICROCOMPUTERS–BIBLIOGRAPHY

Nicita, Michael & Petrusna, Ronald. Reader's Guide to Microcomputer Books. 2nd, rev. ed. (Illus.). 474p. 1984. 29.95 (ISBN 0-912331-05-4); pap. 14.95 (ISBN 0-912331-04-6). Golden Lee Bk.

Nicita, Michael, et al. The Reader's Guide to Microcomputer Books. LC 84-15451. (Professional Librarian Ser.). 500p. 1984. text ed. 29.95 (ISBN 0-86729-122-2, 245-BW). Knowledge Indus.

Pratt, Allan D. A Selective Guide to the Microcomputer Literature. 64p. 1983. pap. 6.95 (ISBN 0-912087-00-5). Graham Conley.

MICROCOMPUTERS–BUSES

Bursky, Dave. The S-One Hundred Bus Handbook. 280p. 1980. pap. 17.50 (ISBN 0-8104-0897-X). Hayden.

Goodwin, James C. & Poe, Elmer C. S-100 & Other Micro Buses. 2nd ed. LC 81-50561. 208p. 1981. pap. 9.95 (ISBN 0-672-21810-0, 21810). Sams.

MICROCOMPUTERS–CONGRESSES

Butler, ed. International Conference on Computer Communication, 1974: Computer Communication Today & Up to 1985. 610p. 1974. 42.50 (ISBN 0-444-86194-7, North-Holland). Elsevier.

Buyer's Guide to Personal Computers, Peripherals & Electronic Games. 1983. pap. 5.00. Creative Comp.

Gergen, Michael & Hagen, Dolores. Computer Technology for the Handicapped. (Illus.). 253p. (Orig.). 1985. pap. text ed. 17.95 (ISBN 0-932719-00-7). Closing Gap.

Nicoud, J. D., et al, eds. Microcomputer Architectures: Proceedings of the Third EUROMICRO Symposium on Microprocessing Microprogramming, October 1977, Amsterdam. 284p. 1978. 64.00 (ISBN 0-444-85097-X, North-Holland). Elsevier.

MICROCOMPUTERS–DESIGN AND CONSTRUCTION

Blasewitz, Robert M. & Stern, Frank. Microcomputer Systems: Hardware-Software Design. 560p. 29.95 (5123). Hayden.

Bursky, Dave. Components for Microcomputer System Design. 272p. 1980. pap. 13.95 (ISBN 0-8104-0975-5). Hayden.

Cannon, Don L. Fundamentals of Microcomputer Design. LC 81-51951. (Illus.). 584p. 1982. pap. 15.00 (ISBN 0-89512-050-X, MBP30A). Tex Instr Inc.

Castellucis. Microcomputer System Analysis & Design. 1982. text ed. 19.95 (ISBN 0-8359-4368-2); solutions manual free (ISBN 0-8359-4369-0). Reston.

D'Angelo, Henry. Microcomputer Structures. 1981. 24.95 (ISBN 0-07-015294-2, BYTE Bks). McGraw.

Doty, Keith L. Fundamental Principles of Microcomputer Architecture. (Illus.). 680p. 1979. 33.95 (ISBN 0-916460-13-4). Matrix Pub.

Flynn, M. J., et al, eds. Microcomputer System Design: An Advanced Course, Dublin, 1981. 2nd ed. (Springer Study Edition). vii, 397p. 1984. pap. 19.95 (ISBN 0-387-13545-6). Springer-Verlag.

Freedman, M. David & Evans, Lansing B. Designing Systems with Microcomputers: A Systematic Approach. (Illus.). 320p. 1983. text ed. 36.95 (ISBN 0-13-201350-9). P-H.

Fudge, Don. Hi-Res Secrets Graphics Applications System. (Illus.). 240p. 1982. binder 50.00 (ISBN 0-930182-33-2). Avant Garde Pub.

Fugate, James K. Programming Tools for the IBM PC: Screen Design, Code Generator & High Memory Access. (Illus.). 272p. 1985. pap. 19.95 (ISBN 0-89303-784-2); diskette 30.00 (ISBN 0-89303-785-0). Brady Comm.

Johnson, J. & Kassel, S. The Multibus Design Guidebook. 1984. 32.50 (ISBN 0-07-032599-5). McGraw.

Kraft, George D. & Toy, Wing N. Mini-Microcomputer Hardware Design. (Illus.). 1978. ref. ed. 42.50 (ISBN 0-13-583807-X). P-H.

Nicoud, J. D., et al, eds. Microcomputer Architectures: Proceedings of the Third EUROMICRO Symposium on Microprocessing Microprogramming, October 1977, Amsterdam. 284p. 1978. 64.00 (ISBN 0-444-85097-X, North-Holland). Elsevier.

Ogdin, Carol A. Microcomputer Design. (Illus.). 1978. ref. ed. 32.95 (ISBN 0-13-580977-0); pap. 24.95 (ISBN 0-13-580985-1). P-H.

--Microcomputer System Design & Techniques. (Tutorial Texts Ser.). 374p. 1980. 24.00 (ISBN 0-8186-0259-7, Q259). IEEE Comp Soc.

Peatman, J. B. Microcomputer-Based Design. 1977. 43.95 (ISBN 0-07-049138-0). McGraw.

Pooch, U. & Chattergy, R. Designing Microcomputer Systems. (Microcomputer Ser.). 224p. 1979. pap. 12.95 (ISBN 0-8104-5679-6). Hayden.

Roberts, Steven K. Creative Design with Microcomputers. (Illus.). 400p. 1984. pap. text ed. 14.95 (ISBN 0-13-189317-3). P-H.

Texas Instruments, Inc. Microprocessors-Microcomputers-System Design. (Texas Instruments Bk. Ser.). (Illus.). 1980. 34.50 (ISBN 0-07-063758-X). McGraw.

Wehmeyer, Keith R. What Every Engineer Should Know about Micrcomputer Program Design. (What Every Engineer Should Know Ser.: Vol. 14). (Illus.). 184p. 1984. 24.75 (ISBN 0-8247-7275-X). Dekker.

Wray, Bill & Crawford, Bill. What Every Engineer Should Know about Microcomputer System Design & Debugging. (What Every Engineer Should Know Ser.: Vol. 12). (Illus.). 200p. 1984. 23.50 (ISBN 0-8247-7160-5). Dekker.

MICROCOMPUTERS–DICTIONARIES

Brown, Eugene & Tarratt, Sara L. Small Bytes: An Irreverent Computer Dictionary. 96p. 1983. pap. 4.95 (ISBN 0-02-003920-4). Macmillan.

Burton, Philip E. Dictionary of Minicomputing & Microcomputing. 1984. lib. bdg. 42.50 (ISBN 0-8240-7263-4). Garland Pub.

Chandor, Anthony. The Facts on File Dictionary of Micro Computers. 1981. 14.95 (ISBN 0-87196-597-6). Facts on File.

Christie, Linda G. & Christie, L. John. The Encyclopedia of Microcomputer Terminology: A Sourcebook for Business & Professional People. LC 84-2055. 320p. 1984. 19.95 (ISBN 0-13-276098-3); pap. 9.95 (ISBN 0-13-276080-0). P-H.

The Coleco Adam User's Encyclopedia. 1984. 14.95 (ISBN 0-317-05838-X). Bk Co.

The Computer Dictionary. 1984. pap. 5.95 (ISBN 0-671-50498-3, Wallaby). PB.

Dasenbrock, David H. User's Guide to Microcomputer Buzzwords. LC 83-60161. 110p. 1983. pap. text ed. 9.95 (ISBN 0-672-22049-0, 22049). Sams.

The DEC DICTIONARY: A Guide to Digital's Technical Terminology. LC 84-7806. (DECbooks). 376p. 1984. 21.00 (ISBN 0-932376-70-3, EY-00040-DP). Digital Pr.

Filler, Aaron. Apple Thesaurus. 896p. (Orig.). 1984. pap. 29.95 (ISBN 0-88190-346-9, BO346). Datamost.

Freiberger, Stephen & Chew, Paul. A Consumer's Guide to Personal Computing & Microcomputers. 208p. pap. 13.95 (5132). Hayden.

Godman, Arthur. Barnes & Noble Thesaurus of Computer Science: The Principles of Computer Science Explained & Illustrated. LC 83-48348. (Illus.). 256p. 1984. 13.41i (ISBN 0-06-015270-2); pap. 6.68i (ISBN 0-06-463594-5). Har-Row.

Holland, R. C. Illustrated Dictionary of Microelectronics & Microcomputers. (Illus.). 168p. 1985. 34.50 (ISBN 0-08-031634-4, Pub. by Aberdeen Scotland); pap. 13.80 (ISBN 0-08-031635-2, Pub. by Aberdeen Scotland). Pergamon.

Hordeski, Michael. Illustrated Dictionary of Microcomputer Terminology. (Illus.). 1978. pap. 10.25 (ISBN 0-8306-1088-X, 1088). TAB Bks.

Ledin, George. The Personal Computer Glossary. 1982. 3.50 (ISBN 0-88284-233-1). Alfred Pub.

McGraw-Hill Editors. Dictionary of Computers. 464p. 1985. 15.95 (ISBN 0-07-045415-9). McGraw.

Makower, Joel. Personal Computers A-Z: The Three Hundred Fifty Key Terms You Need to Understand Personal Computers. LC 83-45193. (Illus.). 224p. 1983. 15.95 (ISBN 0-385-19053-0, Quantum Pr); pap. 8.95 (ISBN 0-385-19054-9, Quantum Pr). Doubleday.

Mazloum, N. & Breskin, M. Your Personal Computer Dictionary. 160p. 1984. pap. 9.95 (ISBN 0-07-041196-4, BYTE Bks). McGraw.

Noonan, Larry. The Basic BASIC-English Dictionary: For the Apple, IBM-PC, Commodore 64, VIC-20, Atari, TRS-80, TRS-80 Color Computer, TI 99-4A, PET & Timex-Sinclair. (Illus.). 288p. 1985. pap. 19.95 (ISBN 0-88056-354-0). Dilithium Pr.

Phillips, Gary. IBM PCjr Encyclopedia. 280p. 1985. pap. 19.95 (ISBN 0-412-00671-5, NO. 9055, Pub. by Chapman & Hall). Methuen Inc.

Phillips, Gary & White, Jerry. The Atari User's Encyclopedia. Mellin, Michael F. & McCroskey, Mia, eds. 272p. (Orig.). 1983. pap. 19.95 (ISBN 0-912003-17-0). Bk Co.

Phillips, Gary, et al. The Apple User's Encyclopedia: Apple II, II Plus, IIe & III. Mellin, Michael F. & Ritz, Roberta, eds. 350p. 1983. pap. 19.95 (ISBN 0-912003-14-6). Bk Co.

Porter, Kent. The New American Computer Dictionary. rev. & expanded ed. 1985. pap. 8.95 (ISBN 0-452-25653-4, Plume). NAL.

Redlin, Paul. The Personal Computer Dictionary. 256p. 1984. pap. 10.95 (ISBN 0-471-88714-5, Pub. by Wiley Pr). Wiley.

Rosenthal, Steven. Rosenthal's Computer Glossary. 350p. 1984. 17.95 (ISBN 0-13-783192-7); pap. 10.95 cancelled (ISBN 0-13-783184-6). P-H.

Sippl, Charles. Microcomputer Dictionary. 2nd ed. LC 81-50565. 608p. 1981. pap. 16.95 (ISBN 0-672-21696-5, 21696). Sams.

Sippl, Charles J. Microcomputer Handbook. (Computer Science Ser.). 350p. 1977. 26.50 (ISBN 0-442-80324-9). Van Nos Reinhold.

Sippl, Charles J. & Carter, George. Computer Dictionary. 4th ed. LC 84-51436. 1985. 17.95 (ISBN 0-672-22205-1). Sams.

Spurlock, Loy. Applesoft Encyclopedia. (Illus.). 864p. (Orig.). Date not set. 29.95 (ISBN 0-88190-078-8, BO078). Datamost.

Steele, Guy L. The Hacker's Dictionary: A Guide to the Computer Underworld. LC 83-47573. 96p. (Orig.). 1983. pap. 5.72i (ISBN 0-06-091082-8, CN 1082, CN). Har-Row.

Sybex Staff & Zaks, Rodnay. The SYBEX Personal Computer Dictionary. LC 83-51824. (Eng., Ger., Span., Ital., Fr. & Pol.). 121p. 1984. pap. 3.95 (ISBN 0-89588-199-3). SYBEX.

MICROCOMPUTERS–DIRECTORIES

Arnold, Bob. Discount America Guide's Directory of Discount Computer Supplies. 1983. pap. text ed. 3.50 (ISBN 0-942528-05-0). Discount America.

Baczynsky, Mark. Directory of Profitable Microcomputer Ventures. (Illus.). 42p. 1984. pap. 9.95 (ISBN 0-89816-011-1). Embee Pr.

Bannister, Hank & Crane, Tim. The Guide to Computing Around Portland. rev. ed. Berard, Barbara, ed. 1984. pap. 8.95 (ISBN 0-916241-01-7). MicroConsulting NW.

Chain Store Guide Staff. Directory of Computer & Software Retailers, 1985. (Chain Store Guide Ser.). 1985. 389.00 (ISBN 0-86730-010-8, Pub. by Bus Guides Inc). Lebhar Friedman.

Datapro Research Corporation. Who's Who in Microcomputing. 1983. pap. 39.95 (ISBN 0-07-015405-8, Pub. by Datapro). McGraw.

Eighty Micro Editors. Eighty Micro's Review Guide. 480p. 1983. softcover 7.95 (ISBN 0-913531-00-6). Green Pub Inc.

Fire Service Resource Directory for Microcomputers. LC 82-62577. 92p. 1982. pap. text ed. 8.00 (ISBN 0-87765-251-1, FSP-65); pap. text ed. 7.20 members. Natl Fire Prot.

Grayson, Ashley. Simon & Schuster Guide to Briefcase Computers. 1985. pap. 12.95 (Pub. by Computer Bks). S&S.

Guide to Personal Computers in Education. Date not set. 1.95 (ISBN 0-317-04445-1, A9G0200). Apple Comp.

Hughes, Lawrence E. Data Communications for CP-M Based Micro-Computers. 1983. text ed. 21.95 (ISBN 0-8359-1229-9); pap. text ed. 15.95 (ISBN 0-8359-1228-0). Reston.

Human Connection. Using CP-M on Your Kaypro 10. (Illus.). 128p. 1984. pap. 19.50 (ISBN 0-8306-1774-4). TAB Bks.

Hunt, Alfred J. & Nielsen, Lynne C. Hunt's Directory of Microcomputer Software & Services for Civil Engineering& Construction. 384p. (Orig.). 1984. pap. text ed. 50.00 (ISBN 0-934617-00-7). Hunt Assocs Consult.

The IBM PCjr User's Encyclopedia. 1984. 14.95 (ISBN 0-912003-22-7). Bk Co.

Instructor Magazine Computer Directory for Schools. 19.95 (ISBN 0-318-01611-7). Vogeler Pub.

International Resource Development Inc. Microcomputer Publications Survey. 115p. 1983. 895.00x (ISBN 0-88694-584-4). Intl Res Dev.

International Software Database. The Software Catalog: Minicomputers, Complete 1984 Update. 1985. 15.00 (ISBN 0-444-00915-9). Elsevier.

Kelly, Brian W. & Grimes, Dennis J. Apple Computer Directory: Hardware, Software & Peripherals. (Kelly-Grimes Buyers Guide Ser.: 1-702). 469p. 1984. pap. 26.95 (ISBN 0-471-87818-9, Pub. by Wiley Pr). Wiley.

--IBM Personal Computer Directory: Hardware, Software, & Peripherals. (Kelly-Grimes Buyers Guide Ser.: No. 1-702). 581p. 1985. pap. 26.95 (ISBN 0-471-87821-9, Pub. by Wiley Pr). Wiley.

Locate: A Directory of Software Vendors Serving the Legal Profession. LC 81-67730. 118p. 1983. pap. 28.00 (ISBN 0-89707-045-3). Amer Bar Assn.

Microcomputer Aftermarkets. (Reports Ser.: No. 519). 191p. 1982. 985.00x (ISBN 0-88694-519-4). Intl Res Dev.

Microcomputer Market Place, 1986. 516p. 1986. pap. text ed. 95.00 (ISBN 0-8352-2096-6). Bowker.

Microcomputer Software Directory. 39.00 (ISBN 0-318-03640-1). Computing Pubns.

Microcomputer Vendor Directory. 9.95 (ISBN 0-317-12961-9). Auerbach.

Microcomputers Directory: Applications in Educational Settings. 1983. write for info. Harvard U Pr.

Miller, Inabeth, intro. by. Microcomputer Directory: Applications in Educational Settings. 2nd ed. 316p. 1982. 15.00 (ISBN 0-943484-00-6). Gutman Lib.

Park, Chung I. Best Microcomputer Software. LC 84-29010. 1985. pap. 3.95 (ISBN 0-939670-04-6). AD Digest.

The PC Software & Systems Directory for Computer Aided Engineering. 70p. 1985. spiral bound 79.00 (ISBN 0-932007-04-X). Mgmt Roundtable.

Petrini, Frank B., ed. Personal Computer Digest, 1985. 320p. 1985. pap. 17.95 (ISBN 0-910676-86-0). DBI.

Shirinian, George. Microcomputer Periodicals: An Annotated Directory. 250p. 1985. pap. 24.95 (ISBN 0-8240-8717-8). Garland Pub.

The Software Catalog of Microcomputers. 1983. write for info. Elsevier.

Stallings, Warren & Blissmer, Robert. Computer Annual: An Introduction to Information Systems 1984-1985. LC 83-27436. (Computers & Information Processing Systems for Business Ser.). 412p. 1984. pap. 19.45 (ISBN 0-471-88685-8). Wiley.

Van Loves Apple Software Directory, 1985. 965p. Date not set. pap. text ed. 29.95 (ISBN 0-8352-1971-2). Bowker.

Willis, Jerry. Peanut Butter & Jelly Guide to Computers. 2nd ed. (Illus.). 288p. 1984. pap. 14.95 (ISBN 0-88056-340-0). Dilithium Pr.

MICROCOMPUTERS–HANDBOOKS, MANUALS, ETC.

Ahl, David H., ed. The Best of Creative Computing, Vol. 1. LC 76-438. (Illus.). 326p. 1976. pap. 12.95 (ISBN 0-916688-01-1, 6A). Creative Comp.

Andersen, Dick & Cobb, Douglas. One-Two-Three Tips, Tricks, & Traps. 360p. 1984. pap. 16.95 (ISBN 0-88022-110-0, 127). Que Corp.

Andriole, Stephen, ed. Microcomputer Decision Support Systems: Design, Implementation & Evaluation. 1985. pap. write for info. (ISBN 0-89435-173-7). Qed Info Sci.

Apple Computer Personal Guide to Personal Computers. Date not set. 2.50 (ISBN 0-317-04449-4, A2G0035). Apple Comp.

Apple IIe Owner's Manual. Date not set. 20.00 (ISBN 0-317-04455-9, A2L2001); card supplement 15.00 (A2L2007). Apple Comp.

Apple IIe Reference Manual. Date not set. 30.00 (ISBN 0-317-04456-7, A2L2005). Apple Comp.

Apple PILOT Editor's Manual. (Apple II Plus & IIe Reference Manuals Ser.). Date not set. 15.00 (ISBN 0-317-04463-X, A2L0042). Apple Comp.

Applesoft Manual Set for IIe. (Apple II Plus & IIe Reference Manuals Ser.). Date not set. 50.00 (ISBN 0-317-04450-8, A2P2001). Apple Comp.

Applesoft Reference Manual for IIe, Vols. 1 & 2. (Apple Plus & IIe Reference Manuals). Date not set. 25.00 (ISBN 0-317-04451-6, A2L2004). Apple Comp.

Applesoft Tutorial for IIe. (Apple II Plus & IIe Reference Manuals Ser.). Date not set. 30.00 (ISBN 0-317-04452-4, A2L2003). Apple Comp.

Arneson, D. J. The Official Computer Hater's Handbook. (Orig.). 1983. pap. 3.95 (ISBN 0-440-56619-3, Dell Trade Pbks). Dell.

Arredondo, Larry. How to Choose & Successfully Use a Microcomputer: A Personal Computer, a Small Business Computer, a Professional Computer, a Desktop Computer, a Home Computer, a Portable Computer, etc. (Orig.). 1982. pap. text ed. write for info. (ISBN 0-936648-16-3, Pub. by Comp Know Ctr). Telecom Lib.

Automated Education Center. A User's Guide to the Adam System. LC 76-125997. 1969. 19.00 (ISBN 0-403-04484-7). Scholarly.

Barden, William, Jr. Guidebook to Small Computers. LC 80-50047. 128p. 1980. pap. 6.95 (ISBN 0-672-21698-1, 21698). Sams.

--What Do You Do after You Plug It In? LC 82-62199. 200p. 1983. pap. 10.95 (ISBN 0-672-22008-3, 22008). Sams.

--Z80 Microcomputer Design Projects. LC 80-50046. 208p. 1980. pap. 14.95 (ISBN 0-672-21682-5, 21682). Sams.

Barron's Computer SAT Study Program. 1983. entire pkg. 89.95 (ISBN 0-8120-7160-3). Apple IIe-48K, Apple II-48K & Apple II Plus. IBM-PC (ISBN 0-8120-7189-1). Commodore 64 (ISBN 0-8120-7192-1). mathematics wkbk., verbal wkbk., user's manual avail. Barron.

Bates, Williams S. The Computer Cookbook, 1984: Computers & the Computer Industry from A to Z. LC 83-40142. 416p. 1984. pap. 14.95 (ISBN 0-385-19291-6, Quantum Pr). Doubleday.

Beeston, Tom & Tucker, Tom. Hooking In: The Complete Underground Computer Workbook & Guide. Kadison, Ellis, ed. 176p. 1984. pap. 12.75 (ISBN 0-913425-00-1). Coltrane & Beach.

Berner, Jeff. Overcoming Computer Fear. LC 83-50714. (Illus.). 92p. 1984. pap. 3.95 (ISBN 0-89588-145-4). SYBEX.

Bertoni, Phil. Strangers in Computerland: Getting Comfortable with the New Magick. LC 83-18737. 224p. 1983. 16.95 (ISBN 0-86616-034-5); pap. 9.95 (ISBN 0-86616-035-3). Greene.

Bitter, Gary G., et al. How to Feel at Home with a Home Computer. LC 83-50901. 264p. 1983. pap. 12.95 (ISBN 0-89512-097-6). Tex Instr Inc.

Boyce, Jefferson. Microprocessor & Microcomputer Basics. (Illus.). 1979. text ed. 29.95 (ISBN 0-13-581249-6). P-H.

--Understanding Microcomputer Concepts: A Guide for Beginners & Hobbyists. LC 83-62030. (Illus.). 336p. 1984. pap. text ed. 14.95 (ISBN 0-13-936956-2). P-H.

Boyd, Alan. PC-DOS, MS-DOS: User's Guide to the Most Popular Operating System for Personal Computers. 352p. (Orig.). 1985. pap. 18.95 (ISBN 0-553-34231-2). Bantam.

Bradbeer, Robin. Learning to Use the Dragon 32 Computer: A Gower Read-out Publication. (Learning to Use Computer Ser.). (Illus.). 112p. (Orig.). 1983. pap. text ed. 12.00x (ISBN 0-566-03494-8). Gower Pub Co.

--Learning to Use the ZX Spectrum. (Learning to Use Computer Series, A Gower Read-Out Publication). 96p. (Orig.). 1982. pap. text ed. 12.00x (ISBN 0-566-03481-6). Gower Pub Co.

--Learning to Use the ZX-81 Computer. (Learning to Use Computer Series, A Gower Read-Out Publication). 86p. (Orig.). 1982. pap. text ed. 12.00x (ISBN 0-566-03451-4). Gower Pub Co.

Bradbeer, Robin, et al. The Beginner's Guide to Computers: Everything You Need to Know about the New Technology. (Illus.). 208p. 1982. pap. 10.95 (ISBN 0-201-11209-4). Addison-Wesley.

Brecher, Deborah L. The Women's Computer Literacy Handbook. (Illus.). 1985. pap. 9.95 (ISBN 0-452-25565-1, Plume). NAL.

Brickman, Bruce K. Solving the Computer Contract Dilemma: A How-To Book for Decision Makers. 176p. pap. 21.95 (6259). Hayden.

Brobst, Harry M. Understanding Personal Computers: A Home Study Course. (Home Study Ser.). 25p. 1982. 24.00 (ISBN 0-939926-17-2); write for info. audio tape (ISBN 0-939926-16-4). Fruition Pubns.

Brown, William M. Personal Computers: A Complete Handbook for Beginners. (Illus.). 250p. 1984. pap. 9.95 (ISBN 0-914091-49-2). Chicago Review.

Buchsbaum, Walter H. Personal Computers Handbook. 2nd ed. LC 83-50591. 320p. 1984. pap. 14.95 (ISBN 0-672-22094-6, 22094). Sams.

Buffington, C. Your First Personal Computer: How to Buy & Use It. 256p. 1983. pap. 8.95 (ISBN 0-07-008832-2, BYTE Bks). McGraw.

Burke, Anna M. The Plain Brown Wrapper Book of Computers. 184p. (Orig.). 1983. pap. 9.95 (ISBN 0-936602-59-7). Kampmann.

Cassel, Don. Computers Made Easy. 1984. text ed. 25.95 (ISBN 0-8359-0859-3); pap. text ed. 18.95 (ISBN 0-8359-0858-5). Reston.

Chertok, Barbara L., et al. IBM PC & XT Owner's Manual: A Practical Guide to Operations. LC 83-15576. 224p. 1983. pap. 14.95 (ISBN 0-89303-531-9). Brady Comm.

Choose Your Own Computer: A Guide to Buying the Best Personal Computer for Your Needs. (Choose Your Own Ser.). 192p. 1983. pap. 4.95 (ISBN 0-8120-2706-X). Barron.

Christensen, Conway B., ed. Programmer's Handbook to the Apple II. rev. ed. (Illus.). 108p. 1983. pap. 12.95 (ISBN 0-913249-01-7); looseleaf bdr. ed. o.p. 29.95 (ISBN 0-913249-00-9). Comp Stations.

Clarke, M. R. Advances in Computer Chess II. 142p. 1980. 16.00x (ISBN 0-85224-377-4, Pub. by Edinburgh U Pr Scotland). Columbia U Pr.

Clay, Katherine, ed. Microcomputers in Education: A Handbook of Resources. LC 82-12596. 80p. 1982. pap. 27.50 (ISBN 0-89774-064-5). Oryx Pr.

Coffron, James W. The VIC-20 Connection. LC 83-50227. (Illus.). 273p. 1983. pap. 9.95 (ISBN 0-89588-128-4). SYBEX.

Color Computer Quick Reference Guide. 4.95 (ISBN 0-317-05266-7, 26-3194). Radio Shack.

Color Computer Technical Reference Manual. 14.95 (ISBN 0-317-05265-9, 26-3193). Radio Shack.

The Computer Entrepreneur Manual. 29.95 (ISBN 0-318-02631-7). Comp Entrepreneur.

Computer Strategies. The Church Computer Handbook. 150p. 1983. looseleaf 45.00x (ISBN 0-913505-04-8). Computer Strat.

--The Dental Office Computer Handbook. 150p. 1983. looseleaf 45.00x (ISBN 0-913505-07-2). Computer Strat.

--The Grocery Store Computer Handbook. 150p. 1983. looseleaf 45.00x (ISBN 0-913505-10-2). Computer Strat.

--The Hotel Motel Computer Handbook. 180p. 1983. looseleaf 45.00x (ISBN 0-9603584-3-9). Computer Strat.

--The Investor's Computer Handbook. 150p. 1983. looseleaf 45.00x (ISBN 0-9603584-6-3). Computer Strat.

--The Motor Carrier's Computer Handbook. 150p. 1984. looseleaf 45.00x (ISBN 0-913505-15-3). Computer Strat.

--The Printer's Computer Handbook. 150p. 1984. looseleaf 45.00x (ISBN 0-913505-17-X). Computer Strat.

--The Property Management Computer Handbook. 150p. 1983. looseleaf 45.00x (ISBN 0-9603584-4-7). Computer Strat.

--The Retailer's Computer Handbook. 150p. 1983. looseleaf 45.00x (ISBN 0-9603584-8-X). Computer Strat.

The Computer User's Handbook, 1983. 1552p. 1983. 135.00 (ISBN 0-902908-17-0). Intl Pubns Serv.

Cone, Paul. What You Need to Know about Computers. (Clear & Simple Ser.). (Orig.). 1984. pap. 3.95 (ISBN 0-440-59577-0, Dell Trade Pbks). Dell.

Consumer Guide Editors. An Easy-to-Understand Guide to Home Computers. 1982. pap. 3.95 (ISBN 0-451-12031-0, Sig). NAL.

--Easy-to-Understand Guide to Home Computers. 95p. 1984. pap. 3.95 (ISBN 0-517-42584-X, Pub. by Beekman Hse). Outlet Bk Co.

Cook, Charles C., illus. Spatial Algorithms for Processing Land Data with a Microcomputer: Lincoln Institute Monograph. (84-2). 278p. 1984. pap. text ed. 9.00 (ISBN 0-318-03877-3). Lincoln Inst Land.

Cook, Rick. Using Cassette Recorders with Computers. 175p. pap. 11.95 (ISBN 0-89588-169-1). SYBEX.

Costa, Betty & Costa, Marie. A Micro Handbook for Small Libraries & Media Centers. 220p. 1983. lib. bdg. 19.50 (ISBN 0-87287-354-4). Libs Unl.

Crop, Sheldon & Mosher, Doug. Portable Computers. LC 83-50713. (Illus.). 112p. pap. cancelled (ISBN 0-89588-144-6). SYBEX.

Curnow, Ray & Curran, Susan. Learning with Your Home Computer. (Clear & Simple Home Computer Ser.: Vol. IV). (Illus.). 128p. 1984. 9.95 (ISBN 0-671-49445-7, Fireside). S&S.

Dane, P. M. Learning to Use the BBC Microcomputer: A Gower Read-Out Publication. (Learning to Use Computer Ser.). 96p. (Orig.). 1982. pap. text ed. 12.00x (ISBN 0-566-03452-2). Gower Pub Co.

Datapro Research Corp. Microcomputer Literacy Program: All about Personal Computers. 89p. 1983. write for info. manual. McGraw.

Deakin, Rose. Understanding Microcomputers: An Introduction to the New Personal Computers for Home & Office. 1983. pap. 3.50 (ISBN 0-451-12427-8, Sig). NAL.

Deken, Joseph. The Electronic Cottage: Everyday Living with Your Personal Computer in the 1980's. LC 81-14016. (Illus.). 320p. 1981. 15.95 (ISBN 0-688-00664-7). Morrow.

Dent, Arthur. The First Book of Adam the Computer. (Illus.). 208p. (Orig.). 1984. 14.95 (ISBN 0-8306-0720-X, 1720); pap. 9.95 (ISBN 0-8306-1720-5). TAB Bks.

Dickie, Margaret. Family Microcomputer-Microprocessor User's Manual: M 6805 HMOS-M 146805 CMOS. 2nd ed. (Illus.). 272p. 1983. pap. text ed. 17.95 (ISBN 0-13-541375-3). P-H.

D'Ignazio, F. How to Get Intimate with Your Computer: A Ten Step Program for Relieving Computer Anxiety. LC 83-9874. 155p. 1984. pap. 6.95 (ISBN 0-07-016901-2, BYTE Bks). McGraw.

Ditlea, Steve. The Osborne-McGraw-Hill Home Computer Guide. 1983. 11.95 (ISBN 0-07-881107-4). Mcgraw.

Dodd, Sue A. & Fox, Ann M. S. Cataloging Microcomputer Files: A Manual of Interpretation for AACR2. LC 85-1359. 228p. 1985. text ed. 40.00 (ISBN 0-8389-0401-7). ALA.

Doerr, Christine. Microcomputers & the Three R's. 2nd ed. 192p. pap. 9.95 (6300). Hayden.

Dravnieks, Dzintar E., et al, eds. IBM Personal Computer Handbook. LC 83-9953. (Illus.). 448p. (Orig.). 1983. pap. 19.95 (ISBN 0-915904-66-7). And-Or Pr.

Dromey, R. How to Solve It by Computer. 1983. pap. 24.95 (ISBN 0-13-434001-9). P-H.

Duncan, Ray. IBM PC-DOS Programmer's Reference Guide. Date not set. pap. price not set postponed (ISBN 0-89303-523-8). Brady Comm.

Dunn, Seamus & Morgan, Valerie. The Apple Personal Computer for Beginners. 1983. 17.95 (ISBN 0-13-039131-X). P-H.

Easton, Anthony T. The Under Eight Hundred Dollar Computer Buyer's Guide: Evaluating the New Generation of Small Computers. 1984. pap. 12.95 (ISBN 0-201-04191-X). Addison-Wesley.

Einhorn, Richard. Epson QX-10: Everything You Need to Know. LC 84-60790. (Illus.). 224p. 1984. pap. 12.95 (ISBN 0-688-02832-2, Quill NY). Morrow.

Erickson, Jonathan & Sayre, Robert. The Model 100 Book: A Guide to Portable Computing. 380p. (Orig.). 1984. pap. 17.95 (ISBN 0-88134-124-X, 124-X). Osborne-McGraw.

Execicom Systems Corporation. IFPS-Personal User's Manual: Release 1.0. LC 83-82445. 550p. 1984. 3 ring binder 30.00 (ISBN 0-911941-01-0). Execucom Sys Corp.

Falk, Howard. Handbook Computer Application for Small or Medium Business. LC 83-70782. 384p. 1983. 19.95 (ISBN 0-8019-7393-7). Chilton.

Flanagan, Dale. The HP Touchscreen. LC 84-60132. 280p. 1984. pap. 19.95 (ISBN 0-88022-105-4, 124). Que Corp.

Fournelle, Jerry. The User's Guide to Small Computer. 1984. pap. 9.95 (ISBN 0-671-55908-7, Pub. by Baen Bke). PB.

Fred Brown Associates Staff, ed. The Brown Book: Industry Guide for Microcomputer Pricing. (Orig.). 1985. 395.00 (ISBN 0-318-04409-9). Adventure Cap Corp.

Frederick, Franz J. Guide to Microcomputers. Assn Ed Comm Tech, ed. LC 80-68716. (Orig.). 1980. pap. 11.50 (ISBN 0-89240-038-2); pap. 9.50 members. Assn Ed Comm Tech.

Frenzel, Louis E., Jr. The Howard W. Sams Crash Course in Microcomputers. 2nd ed. LC 83-60173. 328p. 1983. pap. 21.95 (ISBN 0-672-21985-9, 21985). Sams.

Frenzel, Louis E., Jr., et al. Handbook for the IBM P C. LC 83-50939. 352p. 1984. pap. 15.95 (ISBN 0-672-22004-0, 22004). Sams.

Fry, Louis & Adams, Marsha T. The Business Microcomputer Handbook: Evaluation, Acquisition & Use. 1984. 19.45 (ISBN 0-03-071616-0). HR&W.

Garber, Brad T. Industrial Hygiene Applications of Computers. 350p. 1985. pap. text ed. 37.95 (ISBN 0-02-949340-4). Macmillan.

Genn, Robert C., Jr. & Genn, E. L. The Complete Microcomputer Handbook: With Tested BASIC Programs. LC 84-11485. (Illus.). 367p. 1984. plastic comb binding 23.95 (ISBN 0-13-162199-8). P-H.

Gledhill, V. X. Discovering Computers. write for info. McGraw.

Glossbrenner, Alfred. The Complete Handbook of Personal Computer Communications: Everything You Need to Know to Go Online with the World. 352p. 1983. pap. 14.95 (ISBN 0-312-15718-5). St Martin.

--How to Get Free Software: The Master Guide to Free Programs for Every Brand of Personal Home Computer. LC 84-31284. 432p. 1984. 14.95 (ISBN 0-312-39563-9). St Martin.

Gonzales, Laurence. User Friendly Guides: Computers for Writers. 144p. (Orig.). 1984. pap. 6.95 (ISBN 0-345-31476-X). Ballantine.

Goodman, Danny. The Simon & Schuster's Guide to Atari's "My First Computer". 128p. 1984. pap. 5.95 (ISBN 0-671-49255-1, Pub. by Computer Bks). S&S.

Goodman, Robert L. Troubleshooting Microprocessors & Digital Logic. (Illus., Orig.). 1980. 16.95 (ISBN 0-8306-9950-3); pap. 10.95 (ISBN 0-8306-1183-5, 1183). TAB Bks.

Graham, Ian & Varley, Helen. The Home Computer Handbook. 224p. 1984. 12.95 (ISBN 0-671-47221-6). S&S.

Grillo, John P. & Robertson, J. D. Data & File Management for the IBM Personal Computer. (Microcomputer Power Ser.). 191p. 1983. pap. 16.95 (ISBN 0-697-00349-3); incl. disk 32.95 (ISBN 0-697-00335-3). Wm C Brown.

Hansen, Carol. A Microcomputer User's Guide to Information Online. 192p. pap. 14.95 (6204). Hayden.

Hanson, R. N. & Rigby, S. D. Gregg Personal Keyboarding: TRS-80 Version. 96p. 1982. 36.95 (ISBN 0-07-079993-8). McGraw.

Heiserman, David L. Apple IIe Programmer's Reference Guide. LC 84-50059. 368p. 1984. pap. 19.95 (ISBN 0-672-22299-X). Sams.

Held. IBM PC User's Reference Manual. 432p. 1984. 24.95 (6262). Hayden.

Held, G. IBM PCjr User's Reference Manual. 1984. 24.95 (ISBN 0-317-05634-4, 6373). Hayden.

Held, Gil. IBM User's Manual. 384p. 1984. pap. 24.95 (6262). Hayden.

Helms, H. L. The McGraw-Hill Computer Handbook. 992p. 1983. 84.50 (ISBN 0-07-027972-1). McGraw.

Henderson, Richard. A Practical Guide to Performance Appraisal. 2nd ed. 1983. text ed. 25.00 (ISBN 0-8359-5576-1). Reston.

Herbert, Frank. Without Me You're Nothing: The Essential Guide to Home Computers. 1983. 6.95 (ISBN 0-671-49273-X). PB.

Hernandez, Ernie, Jr. Police Chief's Guide to Using Microcomputers. (Illus.). 160p. 1984. 16.95 (ISBN 0-910657-05-X). Frontline.

Hoffman, Paul & Nicoloff, Tamara. The Osborne McGraw-Hill MS-DOS User's Guide. 250p. (Orig.). 1984. 17.95 (ISBN 0-07-881131-7, 131-7). Osborne-McGraw.

Hohenstein, C. L. All about Hand-Held & Briefcase Portable Computers. 320p. 1983. pap. 9.95 (ISBN 0-07-029452-6, BYTE Bks). McGraw.

Hollerbach, Lew. A Sixty Minute Guide to Microcomputers. (Illus.). 137p. 1982. 12.95 (ISBN 0-13-811430-7); pap. 6.95 (ISBN 0-13-811422-6). P-H.

Holliday, Paul. Handbook of Software Development & Operating Procedures for Microcomputers. 250p. 1984. pap. text ed. 24.95 (ISBN 0-02-949510-5). Macmillan.

Honeysett, Martin. Microphobia: How to Survive Your Computer. (Illus.). 96p. (Orig.). 1983. pap. 3.95 (ISBN 0-943392-28-4). Tribeca Comm.

How to Use the IBM Personal Computer. 1983. pap. 3.50 (ISBN 0-88284-234-X). Alfred Pub.

Hyler, Linda, et al. A Byte of the Apple: A Beginner's Guide. (Illus.). 250p. 17.95x (ISBN 0-8359-0543-8); incl. disk 21.95 (ISBN 0-8359-0546-2). Reston.

Illowsky, Daniel & Abrash, Michael. IBM PCjr User's Guide. LC 84-50073. 19.95 (ISBN 0-672-22302-3). Sams.

InfoWorld Editors & Hogan, Thom. InfoWorld's Essential Guide to the Apple. (InfoWorld's Essential Guides Ser.). (Orig.). 1984. pap. 16.95 (ISBN 0-06-669001-3). Har Row.

Intel Staff. Components Quality Reliability Handbook. 352p. (Orig.). 1985. pap. 15.00 (ISBN 0-917017-18-8, 210997-001). Intel Corp.

--Microcontroller Handbook. 854p. 1985. pap. 18.00 (ISBN 0-917017-15-3, 210918-003). Intel Corp.

--Microsystems Components Handbook, 2 vols. rev. ed. 2700p. 1985. Set. pap. 25.00 (ISBN 0-917017-22-6, 230843-002). Intel Corp.

--OEM Systems Handbook. rev. ed. 912p. 1985. pap. 18.00 (ISBN 0-917017-17-X, 210941-003). Intel Corp.

--Reference Software Products Handbook. 352p. (Orig.). 1985. pap. 10.00 (ISBN 0-917017-24-2, 231195-001). Intel Corp.

International Resource Development Inc. Third Party Maintenance of PCs. 169p. 1984. 1650.00x (ISBN 0-88694-588-7). Intl Res Dev.

Jacques, George. Computer Fundamentals. LC 84-19815. (Computer Maintenance Ser.). (Illus.). 600p. 1984. 3 ring-binder 99.95 (ISBN 0-87119-101-6, EC-2001). HeathKit-Zenith Ed.

Johnson, Kate L. The AppleWriter IIe Handbook. (Illus.). 176p. 1984. pap. 18.95 (ISBN 0-930764-82-X). Van Nos Reinhold.

Johnston, Chris. The Microcomputer Builder's Bible. (Illus.). 320p. (Orig.). 1983. 19.95 (ISBN 0-8306-2473-2); pap. 14.50 (ISBN 0-8306-1473-7, 1473). TAB Bks.

Jones, William. The Mac Book. 1985. 17.45 (ISBN 0-03-071161-4). HR&W.

Jonovic, Donald J. The Micro-Director User Manual. 90p. 1985. looseleaf manual & diskette 125.00x (ISBN 0-915607-03-4). Jamieson Pr.

Kascmer, Joseph. The Easy Guide to Your Apple II. LC 83-60949. (Illus.). 147p. 1983. pap. 9.95 (ISBN 0-89588-122-5). SYBEX.

Kelley, James E., Jr. The IBM Personal Computer User's Guide. 352p. 1983. spiral bdg., incl. disk 29.95 (ISBN 0-440-03946-0, Banbury). Dell.

Kelley, Susan B. & Segal, Robert M. The ABZ'S of Word Processing: For Executives & Professionals. (Illus.). 64p. 1983. pap. 19.95 (ISBN 0-87396-097-1). Stravon.

King, Richard A. IBM PC-DOS Handbook. LC 83-61387. (Illus.). 296p. 1983. pap. 16.95 (ISBN 0-89588-103-9). SYBEX.

Kissell, Thomas E. Understanding & Using Programmable Controllers. (Illus.). 240p. 1986. text ed. 29.95 (ISBN 0-13-937129-X). P-H.

Kroeber, Marianne M., et al. Student Manual to Accompany Computer-Based Information Systems: A Management Approach. 160p. 1984. pap. text ed. write for info. student manual (ISBN 0-02-365390-6). Macmillan.

Kutten, L. J. Computer Buyer's Protection Guide: How to Protect Your Rights in the Microcomputer Marketplace. 96p. 1983. 19.95 (ISBN 0-13-164195-6); pap. 12.95 (ISBN 0-13-164187-5). P-H.

Lafferty, Peter. Introduction to Computing. (The Clear & Simple Home Computer Ser.: Vol. I). (Illus.). 192p. 1983. pap. 9.95 (ISBN 0-671-49442-2, Fireside). S&S.

Lancaster, Don. Cheap Video Cookbook. LC 78-51584. 256p. 1978. pap. 8.95 (ISBN 0-672-21524-1, 21524). Sams.

--Don Lancaster's Micro Cookbook, Vol. 1. LC 81-31559. 384p. 1982. pap. 15.95 (ISBN 0-672-21828-3, 21828). Sams.

Lane, J. E. Microprocessors & Information Handling. (Computing in the Eighties Ser.). 67p. 1981. pap. 15.00x (ISBN 0-85012-334-8). Intl Pubns Serv.

Lasselle, Joan & Ramsay, Carol. The ABC's of the IBM PC. LC 83-61383. (Illus.). 143p. 1983. pap. 13.95 (ISBN 0-89588-102-0). SYBEX.

Laurie, Peter. Databases: How to Manage Information on Your Micro. (Illus.). 200p. (Orig.). 1985. pap. 16.95 (ISBN 0-412-26380-7, NO. 9317, Pub. by Chapman & Hall England). Methuen Inc.

Lenk, John D. Handbook of Microcomputer Based Instrumentation & Controls. (Illus.). 384p. 1984. 27.95 (ISBN 0-13-380519-0). P-H.

--Handbook of Microprocessors, Microcomputers & Minicomputers. (Illus.). 1979. text ed. 27.95 (ISBN 0-13-380378-3). P-H.

--Handbook of Practical Microcomputer Troubleshooting. (Illus.). 1979. text ed. 25.95 (ISBN 0-8359-2757-1). Reston.

Le Noury, Daniel. Computer Crazy. LC 84-50034. (Illus.). 96p. (Orig.). 1984. pap. 5.95 (ISBN 0-89588-173-X). SYBEX.

Lewis, P. C. & Lewis, C. Student Manual for the Donut Franchise: A Microcomputer Simulation. 32p. 1984. 6.30 (ISBN 0-07-037604-2). McGraw.

Lien, David A. The IBM BASIC Handbook. LC 84-71386. (Illus.). 237p. (Orig.). 1984. pap. 14.95 (ISBN 0-932760-23-6). CompuSoft.

Linzmayer, Owen & Kennedy, Don. Insider's Guide to the Apple IIc: Tips, Shortcuts & Helpful Hints from the Professionals. (Illus.). 240p. (Orig.). pap. cancelled (ISBN 0-916688-92-5, 92-5). Creative Comp.

Lisa Online User's Manual. 1983. 40.00 (ISBN 0-317-01045-X). Learned Info.

Longley, Dennis & Shain, Michael. The Microcomputers User's Handbook, 1983-84. 324p. 1983. pap. 49.45 (ISBN 0-471-80436-3). Wiley.

Lord, Kenniston W., Jr. Learning to Use the IBM Personal Computer. LC 83-60185. 175p. 1983. pap. 14.95 (ISBN 0-89435-066-8). QED Info Sci.

Louden, Robert K. How to Use the IBM PCjr. (Handy Guide Ser.). 64p. (Orig.). 1984. pap. 3.50 (ISBN 0-88284-285-4). Alfred Pub.

Lyn, E. Ray. IBM PC & XT Handy Reference Guide. 96p. (Orig.). cancelled (ISBN 0-8306-0797-8); pap. cancelled (ISBN 0-8306-1797-3, 1797). TAB Bks.

Mace, Scott & InfoWorld Editors. InfoWorld's Essential Guide to Atari Computers. (InfoWorld's Essential Guides Ser.). 250p. (Orig.). 1984. pap. 16.95 (ISBN 0-06-669006-4). Har Row.

Margolis, Art. Troubleshooting & Repairing Personal Computers. (Illus.). 320p. 1983. pap. 14.95 (ISBN 0-8306-1539-3, 1539). TAB Bks.

Massen, Roy & Hodkinson, Dale. Does Not Compute: The Computer Users Guide. LC 84-50190. (Illus.). 96p. (Orig.). 1984. pap. 4.95 (ISBN 0-916437-00-0). Sarcastic.

Mau, Ernest E. Getting the Most from Your Micro. 288p. pap. 14.95 (6264). Hayden.

Mellin, Michael & Mikus, Michael. Connections: The Micro Communications Handbook. pap. 14.95 (ISBN 0-912003-18-9). Bk Co.

Merten, Cyndie & Meyer, Sarah. Programmer's Reference Guide for the Commodore Plus-4. 1985. pap. 19.95 (ISBN 0-673-18249-5). Scott F.

MICROCOMPUTERS–PROGRAMMING

Allen, Belton E. Microcomputer System Software & Languages. (Tutorial Texts Ser.). 231p. 1980. 20.00 (ISBN 0-8186-0340-2, Q340). IEEE Comp Soc.

Allen, Peter, ed. Microcomputer Software Distribution. 180p. 1984. pap. 985.00 (ISBN 0-931634-34-2). FIND-SVP.

Barden, William, Jr. How to Program Microcomputers. LC 77-77412. 256p. 1978. pap. 11.95 (ISBN 0-672-21459-8, 21459). Sams.

Beer, M. D. Programming Microcomputers with Pascal. 266p. 1982. pap. 13.95 (ISBN 0-442-21368-9). Van Nos Reinhold.

Benne, Bart. The Illustrated PC-FOCUS Book. LC 85-3352. (Illustrated Ser.). (Illus.). 160p. 1985. pap. 19.95 (ISBN 0-915381-73-7). Wordware Pub.

Birnes, W. J. McGraw-Hill Personal Computer Programming Encyclopedia: Languages & Operating Systems. 712p. 1985. 80.00 (ISBN 0-07-005389-8). McGraw.

Bocchino, William A. Simplified Guide to Microcomputers with Practical Programs & Applications. LC 82-3671. 256p. 1982. 19.95 (ISBN 0-13-810085-3, Busn). P-H.

Bryan, Paul. Programming Your Apple II Computer. (Illus.). 294p. 1982. 15.95o.p (ISBN 0-8306-0081-7); pap. 10.25 (ISBN 0-8306-1394-3, 1394). TAB Bks.

Burton, Kevin R. Increasing Productivity with PFS. (Illus.). 128p. (Orig.). 1984. 21.95 (ISBN 0-8306-0789-7, 1789); pap. 14.95 (ISBN 0-8306-1789-2). TAB Bks.

Campbell, Sally. Microcomputer Software Design: How to Develop Complex Application Programs. (Illus.). 232p. 1983. 21.95 (ISBN 0-13-580639-9); pap. 12.95 (ISBN 0-13-580621-6). P-H.

Chaya, Ruth K. & Miller, Joan M. More BASIC Programming for the Classroom & Home Teacher (IBM PC, IBM PCjr, Commodore, Apple, Macintosh) 262p. (Orig.). 1985. pap. text ed. 17.95X (ISBN 0-8077-2780-6). Tchrs Coll.

Chou, George. Microcomputer Programming in BASIC: With Business Applications. 2nd ed. 298p. 1984. pap. text ed. 17.50 (ISBN 0-06-041298-4, HarpC). Har Row.

Clark, Ron. Fifty-Five Color Computer Programs for the Home, School & Office. 128p. (Orig.). 1982. pap. 9.95 (ISBN 0-86668-005-5). ARCsoft.

Coburn, Edward J. Microcomputers: Hardware, Software, & Programming. 352p. 1984. pap. text ed. 15.35 scp (ISBN 0-672-98445-8); scp instr's. guide 3.67 (ISBN 0-672-98446-6); wkbk 8.75 (ISBN 0-672-98355-9). Bobbs.

Cox, Richard A. Technicians Guide To Programmable Controllers. LC 84-7715. 160p. 1984. pap. text ed. 15.00 (ISBN 0-8273-2420-0); instr's. guide 2.25 (ISBN 0-8273-2421-9). Delmar.

Crowther, Don K. Programming for Profit: How to Write & Sell Computer Programs. 272p. 1984. pap. text ed. 14.95 (ISBN 0-88190-342-6). Datamost.

Dean, Michael L. & Elmore, Paul. How to Develop & Publish Profitable Microcomputer Software. (Illus.). 150p. 1985. 33.85 (ISBN 0-87007-998-0); pap. 15.95 (ISBN 0-87007-999-9). Sourceview.

Deni, Richard L. Programming Microcomputers for Psychology Experiments. 180p. 1985. pap. text ed. write for info. (ISBN 0-534-05442-0). Wadsworth Pub.

Dewey, Patrick R. Public Access Microcomputers: A Handbook for Librarians. LC 83-26776. (Professional Librarian Ser.). 151p. 1984. professional 34.50 (ISBN 0-86729-086-2, 230-BW); pap. 27.50 professional (ISBN 0-86729-085-4). Knowledge Indus.

Elfring, Gary C. Microcomputer Assembly Language Programming. (Illus.). 224p. 1984. 29.95 (ISBN 0-442-22261-0). Van Nos Reinhold.

Ellison, D. & Tunnicliffe, W. J. How to Write Simulations Using Microcomputers. 192p. 1984. 19.95 (ISBN 0-07-084722-3). McGraw.

Engel Enterprises & Engel, C. W. Stimulating Simulations. 2nd ed. 112p. 1979. pap. 7.50 ea. (ISBN 0-8104-5170-0). Atari Version (ISBN 0-8104-5197-2, 5197). Microsoft Version (5170). VIC Version (5173). Apple Version (6317). Commodore 64 Version (5201). TI-99-4A Version (6404). Hayden.

Enlander, Derek. Microcomputer Programs in Medicine, Vol. I. (Illus.). 116p. 1983. 80.00 (ISBN 0-88672-000-1). Med Software.

Erickson, Jonathan. C-64 Telecommunications. 180p. 1984. pap. 16.95 (ISBN 0-07-881149-X, 149-X). Osborne-McGraw.

Faulk, Ed, ed. How to Write a Program II. (How to Write Ser.). (Illus.). 200p. 1983. pap. 14.95 (ISBN 0-88190-007-9, BO007). Datamost.

Field, Tim. Using MacWrite & MacPaint. (Orig.). 1984. pap. 11.95 (ISBN 0-07-881137-6, 137-6). Osborne-McGraw.

Forkner, Irvine F. BASIC Programming for Business. (Illus.). 288p. 1978. pap. text ed. 21.95x (ISBN 0-13-066423-5). P-H.

Foster, Caxton C. Programming a Microcomputer: 6502. 1978. pap. text ed. 9.95 (ISBN 0-201-01995-7). Addison-Wesley.

Foulger, R. J. Programming Embedded Microprocessors: A High-Level Language Solution. 240p. 1982. pap. 27.35 (ISBN 0-471-89421-4). Wiley.

Fox, Annie & Fox, David. Armchair BASIC: An Absolute Beginner's Guide to Programming in BASIC. 264p. (Orig.). 1982. pap. 12.95 (ISBN 0-07-047858-9, 858-9). Osborne-McGraw.

Froehlich, John P. TRS-80 More than BASIC. LC 81-52158. 224p. 1981. pap. 10.95 (ISBN 0-672-21813-5, 21813). Sams.

Gehani, Narain. C for Personal Computers: IBM PC, AT&T PC 6300 & Compatibles. LC 85-5745. 300p. 1985. pap. 19.95 (ISBN 0-88175-111-1). Computer Sci.

Godman, Arthur. The Color-Coded Guide to Microcomputers. LC 83-47884. (Illus.). 256p. 1983. 9.95i (ISBN 0-06-463590-2, EH 590). B&N NY.

--The Color-Coded Guide to Microcomputers. 1984. pap. 9.57 (ISBN 0-06-463590-2). Har-Row.

Gordon, A. M. Practical Programming for Non-Computer Professionals. 100p. 1984. pap. text ed. 18.10x (ISBN 0-471-81048-7). Wiley.

Guthery, Scott B. Learning C with Tiny C. (Illus.). 176p. (Orig.). 1985. pap. 14.95 (ISBN 0-8306-1895-3). TAB Bks.

Haas, Eileen. Getting the Most from Wordvision. 250p. (Orig.). pap. cancelled (ISBN 0-88134-148-7). Osborne-McGraw.

Hamilton, Marshall. MicroProgrammer's Market 1984. 240p. (Orig.). 1984. 18.95 (ISBN 0-8306-0200-3); pap. 13.50 (ISBN 0-8306-1700-0). TAB Bks.

Hare, Robert R. An Introduction to Personal Computing: BASIC Programming on the TRS-80. 300p. 1983. pap. write for info. Wadsworth Pub.

--Personal Computing: BASIC Programming on the TRS-80. LC 83-7502. (Computer Science Ser.). 500p. 1983. pap. text ed. 18.00 pub net (ISBN 0-534-02768-7). Brooks-Cole.

Hartnell, Tim. How to Program Your Apple IIe: If You've Never Programmed a Computer Before. 102p. 1984. 6.95 (ISBN 0-345-31662-2). Ballantine.

Hixson, Amanda C. A Buyer's Guide to Microcomputer Business Software: Accounting & Spreadsheets. 1918p. 1984. pap. 19.95 (ISBN 0-201-11065-2). Addison-Wesley.

Hodges, William S. & Novak, Neal. Practical Programs for Home Computers. (Microcomputer Bookshelf Ser.). 200p. 1984. pap. text ed. 14.95 (ISBN 0-316-61151-4). Little.

Hoornaert, Ed. A Kid's Manual for Programming the Timex-Sinclair Computers. (Illus.). 168p. 1983. 12.95 (ISBN 0-8306-0108-2); pap. 7.25 (ISBN 0-8306-0608-4, 1608). TAB Bks.

IEEE Standard 796-1983: IEEE Standard Microcomputer System Bus. 1983. 7.50 (ISBN 0-317-03956-3, SHO9001). IEEE.

Intel Staff. Introduction to the System 310 Microcomputer. rev. ed. 50p. 1984. pap. 9.00 (ISBN 0-917017-30-7, 173202-002). Intel Corp.

International Software Database. The Software Catalog: Minicomputers, Complete 1984 Update. 1985. 15.00 (ISBN 0-444-00915-9). Elsevier.

Jermann, William H. Programming Sixteen Bit Machines: The PDP-11, 8086 & M68000. (Illus.). 464p. 1986. text ed. 32.95 (ISBN 0-13-729161-2). P-H.

Joyce, Dennis & Pickering, John E. The Software Writer's Marketplace. LC 84-2063. 288p. (Orig.). 1984. lib. bdg. 19.80 (ISBN 0-89471-263-2); pap. 9.95 (ISBN 0-89471-262-4). Running Pr.

Kahn, Ed & Seiter, Charles. The Skeptical Consumer's Guide to Used Computers. 256p. (Orig.). 1985. pap. 9.95 (ISBN 0-89815-141-4). Ten Speed Pr.

Katzan, Harry, Jr. Microcomputer Graphics & Programming Techniques. 240p. 1982. 22.50 (ISBN 0-442-28419-5). Van Nos Reinhold.

Keogh, James. The Programmer's Notebook. 356p. 1984. pap. 10.95 (ISBN 0-671-47066-3, Pub. by Computer Bks). S&S.

Knight, Timothy O. Using & Programming the Adam: Including Ready-to-Run Programs. (Illus.). 128p. (Orig.). 1984. 14.95 (ISBN 0-8306-0706-4); pap. 7.95 (ISBN 0-8306-1706-X, 1706). TAB Bks.

Lancaster, Don. Micro Cookbook, Machine Language Programming, Vol. 2. 456p. 1983. pap. 15.95 (ISBN 0-672-21829-1, 21829). Sams.

Lane, John E. Choosing Programs for Microcomputers. LC 80-142911. 138p. (Orig.). 1980. pap. 22.50x (ISBN 0-85012-255-4). Intl Pubns Serv.

--Operating Systems for Microcomputers. LC 81-174400. (Computing in the Eighties: No. 1). 77p. (Orig.). 1981. pap. 12.50 (ISBN 0-85012-277-5). Intl Pubns Serv.

Langsam, Yedidyah, et al. Data Structures for Personal Computers. LC 84-3326. (Illus.). 576p. 1985. text ed. 29.95 (ISBN 0-13-196221-3). P-H.

Latham, Tony. BBC Microcomputer Disk Companion. 1984. pap. 12.95 (ISBN 0-13-069311-1). P-H.

Lee, Imsong. Microcomputer Programming & Software Support. (Tutorial Texts Ser.). 193p. 1978. 15.00 (ISBN 0-8186-0213-9, Q213). IEEE Comp Soc.

Leeson, Marjorie M. Computer Operations. 2nd ed. 512p. 1982. pap. text ed. 22.95 (ISBN 0-574-21345-7, 13-4345); instrs'. guide avail. (ISBN 0-574-21346-5, 13-4346). SRA.

Leithauser, David. Programs for Electronics, Engineers & Hobbyists. Tech Art Associates, tr. (Illus.). 100p. 1984. 14.95 (ISBN 0-88006-068-9, BK7400); Apple II, II Plus, IIe. disk 9.97 ea. (DS740011). IBM-PC (DS740012). TRS-80 Model I, III, or IV (DS740013). Weber Systems.

Leventhal, Lance. Microcomputer Experimentation with the Synertek SYM-1. (Illus.). 512p. 1983. text ed. 28.95 (ISBN 0-13-580910-X). P-H.

Leventhal, Lance A. & Walsh, Colin. Microcomputer Experimentation with Intel SDK-85. 1980. text ed. 27.95 (ISBN 0-13-580860-X). P-H.

Leventhal, Lance A. Microcomputer Experimentation with the MOS Technology KIM-1. (Illus.). 480p. 1982. 27.95 (ISBN 0-13-580779-4). P-H.

Lewis, C. & Lewis, P. Marketing Peanut Butter: A Microcomputer Simulation. 1984. Apple. 199.00 (ISBN 0-07-079587-8). IBM-PC (ISBN 0-07-079588-6). TRS-80 (ISBN 0-07-079586-X). McGraw.

Longhurst, Jean. Introduction to BASIC Programming. 129p. 1985. pap. text ed. 8.95 (ISBN 0-13-478355-7). P-H.

Lord, Kenniston W., Jr. Peachtree Software for Personal Computers: Introduction & Description. LC 83-61296. 144p. 1983. pap. 14.95 (ISBN 0-89435-069-2). QED Info Sci.

--Using the Eagle PC & 1600 Series. 304p. 1984. 23.50 (ISBN 0-442-26036-9); pap. 16.50 (ISBN 0-442-26035-0). Van Nos Reinhold.

McComic, Ira. Learning TI 99-4A Home Computer Assembly Language Programming. (Illus.). 224p. 1984. cancelled (ISBN 0-13-527870-8); pap. 16.95 (ISBN 0-13-527862-7). P-H.

McCracken, Daniel D. Guide to PL-M Programming for Microcomputer Applications. 1978. pap. text ed. 21.95 (ISBN 0-201-04575-3). Addison-Wesley.

Marshall, Garry. Programming with Graphics. (Illus.). 120p. 1983. 19.95 (ISBN 0-13-729616-9); pap. 12.95 (ISBN 0-13-729608-8). P-H.

Microcomp, Ltd. Microcomputer Software for Civil, Structural & Design Engineers: CBEAM-CM Manual & Disk. 1984. ring binder, incl. disk 495.00x (ISBN 0-87201-534-3). Gulf Pub.

Microcomputer Hardware & Software (Europe) 1985. write for info. (ISBN 0-86621-623-5, E695). Frost & Sullivan.

Microcomputer Software, 2 vols. 525.00. Datapro Res.

Microcomputer Software Training: A Directory of Diskette-Based & Video Training Packages. 89p. 1985. pap. text ed. 25.00x (ISBN 0-913203-13-0). Pacific Info.

Microcomputer Word Processing Software Market. 223p. 1985. 1575.00 (ISBN 0-86621-368-6, A1452). Frost & Sullivan.

Nash, John C. Effective Scientific Problem Solving with Small Computers. (Illus.). 272p. 1984. 19.95 (ISBN 0-8359-1594-8). Reston.

Nicks, J E. BASIC Programming Solutions for Manufacturing. (Illus.). 298p. 1982. 32.00 (ISBN 0-87263-076-5). SME.

Noggle, Joseph H. Physical Chemistry on a Microcomputer. 1985. pap. text ed. 12.95 (ISBN 0-316-61140-9). Little.

Nowak, Stephen F. & Muswick, Gary J. Getting the Most from Your Pocket Computer. (Illus.). 336p. (Orig.). 1984. 14.95 (ISBN 0-8306-0723-4, 1723); pap. 9.95 (ISBN 0-8306-1723-X). TAB Bks.

Ogdin, Carol A. Microcomputer Management & Programming. (Illus.). 1980. text ed. 31.95 (ISBN 0-13-580936-3). P-H.

--Software Design for Microcomputers. LC 78-5801. (Illus.). 1978. ref. ed. 29.95 (ISBN 0-13-821744-0); pap. 24.95 (ISBN 0-13-821801-3). P-H.

Overbeck, Wayne & Steffen, James. Computer Programs for Ham Radio. 224p. pap. 12.95 (0657). Hayden.

Page, Edward. Timex-Sinclair Computer Program Writing Workbook. 96p. 1983. 4.95 (ISBN 0-86668-810-2). ARCsoft.

Plemmons, Patrick & Myers, David. Personal Computer Buyer's Guide. (Illus.). 180p. (Orig.). 1984. pap. 12.95 (ISBN 0-912213-04-3, 900600). Paladin.

Porter, Kent. Beginning with BASIC: An Introduction to Computer Programming. (Computer Language Library). 300p. 1984. 10.95 (ISBN 0-452-25491-4, Plume). NAL.

Readings in Microcomputers & Individualized Educational Programs. 1984. 16.00 (ISBN 0-89568-418-7). Spec Learn Corp.

Regena, C. Programmer's Reference Guide to the Color Computer. 176p. (Orig.). 1984. pap. 12.95 (ISBN 0-942386-19-1). Compute Pubns.

Roberts, Don. Universal BASIC Computer Program Writing Workbook. 96p. 1983. 4.95 (ISBN 0-86668-819-6). ARCsoft.

Robillard, Mark J. Hero One: Advanced Programming & Interfacing. LC 83-50379. (Illus.). 240p. 1983. pap. 16.95 (ISBN 0-672-22165-9, 22165). Sams.

Rodwell, Peter, ed. Personal Computer Handbook: An Illustrated Guide to Choosing & Using Your Micro. LC 83-12270. (Illus.). 208p. 1983. pap. 15.95 (ISBN 0-8120-2704-3). Barron.

Roth, Pam. The First Book of Adam: Using & Programming the Coleco Adam. 227p. 1984. pap. text ed. 12.95 (ISBN 0-88022-063-5, 110). Que Corp.

Rugg, Tom & Feldman, Phil. Thirty-Two BASIC Programs for the TI 99-4A. (Illus.). 288p. 1983. pap. 19.95 (ISBN 0-88056-136-X); incl. cassette 39.95 (ISBN 0-88056-188-2); incl. disk 39.95 (ISBN 0-88056-203-X). Dilithium Pr.

Sawatzky, Jasper J. & Chen, Shu-Jen. Programming in BASIC-PLUS: VAX-11 BASIC Compatible. 2nd ed. 452p. 1985. pap. 19.95 (ISBN 0-471-88655-6). Wiley.

Scanlon, L. J. Eighty Eighty-Six, Eighty Eighty-Eight Assembly Language Programming. (Illus.). 224p. 1984. pap. 15.95 (ISBN 0-89303-424-X). Brady Comm.

Scanlon, Leo. IBM PC & XT Assembly Language: A Guide for Programmers. LC 83-3848. (Illus.). 384p. 1983. pap. 19.95 (ISBN 0-89303-241-7); bk. & diskette 54.95 (ISBN 0-89303-535-1); disk 35.00 (ISBN 0-89303-536-X). Brady Comm.

Schindler, Max, ed. Software Toolkit for Microcomputers: Improving Productivity with High-Level Languages & Operating Systems. 368p. 1983. pap. 16.95 (6256). Hayden.

Schultz, Owen C., ed. Microcomputer Programs in Print. (Illus.). 208p. (Orig.). 1983. pap. 19.95 (ISBN 0-912691-01-8). Postroad Pr Inc.

Seigel, J. B. Statistical Software for Microcomputers: A Guide to Forty Programs. 320p. 1985. pap. 99.00 (ISBN 0-444-00968-X, North-Holland). Elsevier.

Shaffer & Shaffer, Applied Research & Development, Inc. Special Effects Library: Commodore 64. 300p. 1984. incl. disk 29.95 (ISBN 0-912677-27-9). Ashton-Tate Bks.

Snover, Stephen & Spikell, Mark. How to Program Your Programmable Calculator. 1983. 8.95 (ISBN 0-13-429357-6, Spec). P-H.

Software Arts Inc. TKSolver-IBM Version PC-DOS. 300p. 1984. 399.00 (ISBN 0-07-059563-1). McGraw.

Sondak, Norman & Mallach, Efrem, eds. Advances in Microprogramming. 2nd ed. LC 75-18741. (Illus.). 470p. 1983. Repr. of 1977 ed. 30.00 (ISBN 0-89006-064-9). Artech Hse.

Staugaard, Andrew C., Jr. Microcomputer Programming & Interfacing, 6801, 68701 & 6803. LC 80-51716. 352p. 1980. pap. 14.95 (ISBN 0-672-21726-0, 21726). Sams.

--Sixty-Eight Hundred Nine Microcomputer Programming & Interfacing, with Experiments. LC 81-50567. 272p. 1981. pap. 14.95 (ISBN 0-672-21798-8, 21798). Sams.

Steiner, John P. The Standard BASIC Dictionary for Programming. LC 84-11436. 256p. 1983. 23.95 (ISBN 0-13-841560-9, Busn); pap. 19.95 (ISBN 0-13-841552-8). P-H.

Stewart, George. The C-64 Program Factory. (Illus.). 200p. 1984. pap. 12.95 (ISBN 0-07-881150-3, 150-3). Osborne-McGraw.

Sullivan, David R., et al. Computing Today: Microcomputer Concepts & Applications. LC 84-81936. 448p. 1984. pap. text ed. 23.95 (ISBN 0-395-37011-6); instr's. manual 2.00 (ISBN 0-395-37012-4). HM.

Thomas, D. A Guide to Programming the Texas Instruments 99-2 Basic Computer. (Illus.). 224p. 1983. pap. 9.95. McGraw.

--Learn BASIC: A Guide to Programming the Texas Instruments Professional Compact Computer 40. (Illus.). 256p. pap. 9.95 (ISBN 0-07-064257-5, BYTE Bks). McGraw.

Thrift, Stanley W. INSTRUCALC (TM) 1: Instrument Engineering Calculations. LC 84-12782. (Microcomputer Software for Instrument Engineers Ser.). 1984. ring binder incl. disk 595.00x (ISBN 0-87201-380-4). Gulf Pub.

Rose, A. H. & Morris, Gareth, eds. Advances in Microbial Physiology, Vol. 21. LC 67-19850. (Serial Publication Ser.). 1981. 70.00 (ISBN 0-12-027721-2). Acad Pr.

Rose, A. H., et al, eds. Advances in Microbial Physiology. Incl. Vol. 1. 1967; Vol. 2. 1968. 45.00 (ISBN 0-12-027702-6); Vol. 3. 1969. 50.00 (ISBN 0-12-027703-4); Vol. 4. 1970. 70.00 (ISBN 0-12-027704-2); Vol. 5. 1970. 60.00 (ISBN 0-12-027705-0); Vol. 6. 1971. 70.00 (ISBN 0-12-027706-9); Vol. 7. Rose, A. H. & Tempest, D. W., eds. 1972. 60.00 (ISBN 0-12-027707-7); Vol. 8. 1972. 60.00 (ISBN 0-12-027708-5); Vol. 9. 1973. 55.00 (ISBN 0-12-027709-3); Vol. 10. 1973. 60.00 (ISBN 0-12-027710-7); Vol. 14. 1977. 70.00 (ISBN 0-12-027714-X); Vol. 15. 1977. 80.00 (ISBN 0-12-027715-8); Vol. 16. 1978. 70.00 (ISBN 0-12-027716-6); Vol. 17. 1978. 70.00 (ISBN 0-12-027717-4). Acad Pr.

Rossmoore, Harold W. Microbes, Our Unseen Friends. LC 76-17795. (Illus.). 228p. 1976. o. p. 12.95 (ISBN 0-8143-1561-5); pap. 5.95 (ISBN 0-8143-1602-6). Wayne St U Pr.

Russell, A. D. & Fuller, R., eds. Cold Tolerant Microbes in Spoilage & the Environment. 1979. 33.00 (ISBN 0-12-603750-7). Acad Pr.

Shilo, Moshe, ed. Strategies of Microbial Life in Extreme Environments, LSRR 13. (Dahlem Workshop Reports Ser.: L.S.R.R. No. 13). 514p. 1979. 42.40x (ISBN 0-89573-082-0). VCH Pubs.

Skinner, F. A. & Hugo, W. B., eds. Inhibition & Inactivation of Vegetative Microbes. (Society of Applied Bacteriology Symposia Ser.: Vol. 1). 1977. 69.00 (ISBN 0-12-648065-6). Acad Pr.

Slater, J. H., et al, eds. Microbes in Their Natural Environments. LC 82-19859. (Society for General Microbiology Symposium Ser.: No. 34). 350p. 1983. 69.50 (ISBN 0-521-25063-3). Cambridge U Pr.

Stouthamer, A. H. Yield Studies in Microorganisms. 96p. 1976. 39.00x (ISBN 0-904095-20-7, Pub. by Meadowfield Pr England). State Mutual Bk.

Strange, Richard E. Microbial Response to Mild Stress. 92p. 1976. 39.00x (ISBN 0-900541-97-0, Pub. by Meadowfield Pr England). State Mutual Bk.

Waste Recovery by Micro-Organisms. 1978. pap. 13.25 (ISBN 0-685-65236-X, UM36, UNESCO). Unipub.

Weinberg, E. D. Microorganisms & Minerals. (Microbiology Ser.: Vol. 3). 1977. 85.00 (ISBN 0-8247-6581-8). Dekker.

Weiner, Jack. Microorganism Control. LC 76-57836. (Bibliographic Ser.: No. 276). 1977. pap. 23.00 (ISBN 0-87010-051-3). Inst Paper Chem.

Whitney, P. J. Microbial Plant Pathology. LC 76-20406. (Studies in the Biological Sciences Ser.). (Illus.). 1977. 12.50x (ISBN 0-87663-722-5). Universe.

Wostmann, Bernard S., et al. Germfree Research: Microflora Control & Its Application to the Biomedical Sciences. LC 84-4306. (Progress in Clinical & Biological Research Ser.: Vol. 181). 538p. 1985. 78.00 (ISBN 0-8451-5031-6). A R Liss.

MICRO-ORGANISMS, PATHOGENIC

see also Medical Microbiology

Ellner. Pathogenic Microorganisms. Date not set. write for info. (ISBN 0-444-00824-1). Elsevier.

Lucas, J. A. & Dickinson, C. H. Plant Pathology & Plant Pathogens. 2nd ed. (Illus.). 238p. 1982. pap. text ed. 19.75x (ISBN 0-632-00918-7). Blackwell Pubns.

Zadoks, Jan C. & Schein, Richard D. Epidemiology & Plant Disease Management. (Illus.). 1979. text ed. 26.95x (ISBN 0-19-502451-6); pap. text ed. 15.95x (ISBN 0-19-502452-4). Oxford U Pr.

MICROPALEONTOLOGY

Banner, F. T. & Lord, A. R., eds. Aspects of Micropalaeontology. (Illus.). 362p. 1982. text ed. 60.00x (ISBN 0-04-562003-2). Allen Unwin.

Ellison, S. P., Jr. Annotated Bibliography, & Index, of Conodonts. (Pub. Ser: 6210). (Illus.). 128p. 1962. incl. supplements 2.25 (ISBN 0-318-03316-X). Bur Econ Geology.

Funnell, B. M. & Riedel, W. R. Micropalaeontology of Oceans. 1971. 165.00 (ISBN 0-521-07642-0). Cambridge U Pr.

Haq, B. U. & Boersma, A. Introduction to Marine Micropaleontology. 376p. 1978. 32.75 (ISBN 0-444-00267-7). Elsevier.

Haq, Bilal U., ed. Nannofossil Biostratigraphy. 400p. 1984. 56.95 (ISBN 0-87933-101-1). Van Nos Reinhold.

Lord, A. R. A Stratigraphical Index of Calcareous Nannofossils. 192p. 1982. 89.95x (ISBN 0-470-27338-0). Halsted Pr.

Pierce, Richard L. Lower Upper Cretaceous Plant Microfossils from Minnesota. LC 61-64045. (Bulletin: No. 42). (Illus.). 1961. 3.75x (ISBN 0-8166-0257-3). Minn Geol Survey.

Ramsay, A. T. Oceanic Micropalaeontology, Vol. 1. 1977. 125.00 (ISBN 0-12-577301-3). Acad Pr.

Ramsay, T. S., ed. Oceanic Micropalaeontology, Vol. 2. 1978. 95.00 (ISBN 0-12-577302-1). Acad Pr.

Reiss, Z. & Hottinger, L. The Gulf of Aqaba (Elat) Ecological Micropaleontology. (Ecological Studies, Analysis & Synthesis Ser.: Vol. 50). (Illus.). 360p. 1984. 69.00 (ISBN 0-387-13486-7). Springer-Verlag.

Saito, T. & Burckle, L. H., eds. Late Neogene Epoch Boundaries. (Micropaleontology Special Publications Ser.: No. 1). 224p. 1975. 20.00 (ISBN 0-686-84248-0). Am Mus Natl Hist.

Swain, F. M., ed. Stratigraphic Micropaleontology of Atlantic Basin & Borderlands. (Developments in Paleontology & Stratigraphy Ser.: Vol. 6). 604p. 1977. 85.00 (ISBN 0-444-41554-8). Elsevier.

Tappan, Helen. The Paleobiology of Plant Protists. LC 80-14675. (Geology Ser.). (Illus.). 1028p. 1980. text ed. 95.00x (ISBN 0-7167-1109-5). W H Freeman.

MICROPHONE

Clifford. Microphones. 2nd ed. (Illus.). 264p. 1982. 14.95 (ISBN 0-8306-0097-3); pap. 10.25 (ISBN 0-8306-1475-3, 1475). TAB Bks.

Du Moncel, Theodore A. The Telephone, the Microphone, & the Phonograph. LC 74-4673. (Telecommunications Ser). (Illus.). 282p. 1974. Repr. of 1879 ed. 23.50x (ISBN 0-405-06039-4). Ayer Co Pubs.

Eargle, John. The Microphone Handbook. 1982. 31.95 (ISBN 0-914130-02-1). Elar Pub Co.

Gayford, M. L. Electroacoustics. 289p. 1971. 37.75 (ISBN 0-444-19649-8). Elsevier.

Nisbett, Alec. The Use of Microphones. (Media Manual Ser.). 168p. 1983. pap. 14.95 (ISBN 0-240-51199-9). Focal Pr.

Wile, Frederic W. Emile Berliner: Maker of the Microphone. LC 74-4699. (Telecommunications Ser). (Illus.). 380p. 1974. Repr. of 1926 ed. 29.00x (ISBN 0-405-06062-9). Ayer Co Pubs.

MICROPHOTOGRAPHY

Here are entered works on the photographing of objects of any size upon a microscopic or very small scale. To be distinguished from Photomicrography, the photographing of minute objects enlarged by means of the microscope.

see also Reader-Printers (Microphotography)

Association for Information & Image Management. All about Microfilm Cameras. (Consumer Ser.: No. C106). (Illus.). 24p. 1977. 5.00 (ISBN 0-89258-047-X, C106); member 3.75. Assn Inform & Image Mgmt.

--Document Mark (BLIP) Used in Image Mark Retrieval Systems: ANSI-AIIM MS8-1979. Rev. ed. (Standards & Recommended Practices). 1980. 6.00 (ISBN 0-89258-060-7, M008); member 5.25. Assn Inform & Image Mgmt.

--Format & Coding for Computer Output Microfilm: ANSI-AIIM MS2-1978. (Standards & Recommended Practices). 1978. 6.00 (ISBN 0-89258-054-2, M002); member 5.25. Assn Inform & Image Mgmt.

--Measuring COM Recording Speeds: AIIM MS21-1979. (Standards & Recommended Practices). 1979. 6.00 (ISBN 0-89258-058-5, M021); member 5.25. Assn Inform & Image Mgmt.

--Microfilming Newspapers: ANSI-AIIM MS111-1977. 1978. 6.00 (ISBN 0-89258-050-X); member 5.25. Assn Inform & Image Mgmt.

--Practice for Uniform Product Disclosure for Unitized Microform Readers (Microfiche, Jackets & Image Cards) ANSI/AIIM MS22-1981. (Standards & Recommended Practices). 1981. 6.00 (ISBN 0-89258-057-7, M021); member 5.25. Assn Inform & Image Mgmt.

--Specifications for Sixteen & Thirty-Five Millimeter Microfilms in Roll Form: ASNI-AIIM MS14-1978. (Standards & Recommended Practices). 1978. 6.00 (ISBN 0-89258-052-6, M014). Assn Inform Image.

Axelrod, Donald C., et al. Micrographic Film Technology: Ro11-1983. 2nd ed. Bartoli, Renator, ed. LC 83-2222. (Reference Ser.). (Illus.). 123p. 1983. 12.50 (ISBN 0-89258-059-3, R011); member 10.50. Assn Inform & Image Mgmt.

Seddon, G. Pre-Chappel Conodonts of the Llano Region, Texas. (Report of Investigations Ser.: RI 68). (Illus.). 130p. 1970. 7.50 (ISBN 0-318-03170-1). Bur Econ Geology.

Techniques of Microphotography. 1976. 3.95 (ISBN 0-87985-017-5, P52). Eastman Kodak.

MICROPROCESSORS

Adams, Charles K. Master Handbook of Microprocessor Chips. (Illus.). 378p. 1981. 18.95 (ISBN 0-8306-9633-4); pap. 11.50 (ISBN 0-8306-1299-8, 1299). TAB Bks.

Agajanian, A. H. Computer Technology: Logic, Memory, & Microprocessors; A Bibliography. 360p. 1978. 95.00x (ISBN 0-306-65174-2, IFI Plenum). Plenum Pub.

Alexandridis, Nikitas A. Microprocessor Systems Design Concepts. LC 82-18189. 623p. 1984. text ed. 32.95 (ISBN 0-914894-66-8). Computer Sci.

American Production & Inventory Control Society. Microprocessor Seminar Proceedings: January-February 1984. LC 83-73538. 287p. 1984. pap. 17.00 (ISBN 0-935406-40-9, 40640). Am Prod & Inventory.

Andrews, Michael. Programming Microprocessor Interface for Control & Instrumentation. (Illus.). 368p. 1982. 39.95 (ISBN 0-13-729996-6). P-H.

Arnold, James T. Simplified Digital Automation with Microprocessors. LC 78-51242. 1979. 44.50 (ISBN 0-12-063750-2). Acad Pr.

Aspinall, D., ed. The Microprocessor & Its Application. LC 78-54572. (Illus.). 402p. 1980. pap. 19.95 (ISBN 0-521-29798-2). Cambridge U Pr.

--The Microprocessor & Its Application. LC 78-54572. (Illus.). 1978. 52.50 (ISBN 0-521-22241-9). Cambridge U Pr.

Aspinall, David & Dagless, Erik, eds. Introduction to Microprocessors. 1977. 29.50 (ISBN 0-12-064550-5). Acad Pr.

Aumiaux, M. Microprocessor Systems. Starza, Arletta, tr. (Wiley Series in Computing). 218p. 1982. 29.95 (ISBN 0-471-10129-X). Wiley.

--The Use of Microprocessors. Hutt, Annel, tr. LC 79-42904. (Wiley Series in Computing). 198p. 1980. 34.95 (ISBN 0-471-27689-8, Pub. by Wiley Interscience). Wiley.

Auslander, David & Sagues, Paul. Microprocessors for Measurement & Control. 310p. (Orig.). 1981. pap. 15.99 (ISBN 0-07-931057-5, 57-5). Osborne-McGraw.

Baldwin, A., et al. Sixteen-Bit Microprocessors. LC 81-50564. 352p. 1981. pap. 15.95 (ISBN 0-672-21805-4, 21805). Sams.

Baldwin, J. N. Microprocessors for Industry. 144p. 1982. text ed. 19.95 (ISBN 0-408-00517-3). Butterworth.

Bansal, V. K. Design of Microprocessor Based Systems. 148p. 1985. 19.95 (ISBN 0-470-20113-4). Halsted Pr.

Barnaal, Dennis. Digital & Microprocessor Electronics for Scientific Application. 1982. pap. text ed. write for info. (ISBN 0-534-01043-1, Breton Pubs). Wadsworth Pub.

Barney, George C. Intelligent Instrumentation: Microprocessor Applications in Measurement & Control. (Illus.). 528p. 1986. text ed. 39.95 (ISBN 0-13-468943-7). P-H.

Bibbero, Robert J. Microprocessors in Industrial Control: An Independent Learning Module of the Instrument Society of America. LC 82-48556. 256p. 1983. text ed. 39.95x (ISBN 0-87664-624-0, I624-0). Instru Soc.

--Microprocessors in Instruments & Control. LC 77-9929. 301p. 1977. 32.50x (ISBN 0-471-01595-4, Pub. by Wiley-Interscience). Wiley.

Bibbero, Robert J. & Stern, David. Microprocessor Systems: Interfacing & Applications. 195p. 1982. 25.50x (ISBN 0-471-05306-6, Pub. by Wiley-Interscience). Wiley.

Bishop, Ron. Basic Microprocessors & Sixty-Eight Hundred. 1979. pap. 17.95 (ISBN 0-8104-0758-2). Hayden.

Bogart, Theodore F. Laplace Transforms & Control Systems Theory for Technology: Including Microprocessor Based Control System. LC 81-14708. (Electronic Technology Ser.). 541p. 1982. 31.95 (ISBN 0-471-09044-1); write for info solutions manual (ISBN 0-471-86325-4). Wiley.

Bowen & Behr. The Logical Design of Multiple Microprocessor Systems. (Illus.). 272p. 1980. text ed. 37.50 (ISBN 0-13-539908-4). P-H.

Boyce, Jefferson. Microprocessor & Microcomputer Basics. (Illus.). 1979. text ed. 29.95 (ISBN 0-13-581249-6). P-H.

Brey, Barry. The Microprocessor 8085A: Software, Programming & Architecture. (Illus.). 484p. 1986. text ed. 29.95 (ISBN 0-13-246711-9). P-H.

Brey, Barry B. Microprocessor-Hardware Interfacing & Applications. 448p. 1984. Additional supplements may be obtained from publisher. text ed. 29.95 (ISBN 0-675-20158-6). Merrill.

Brunner, Herb. Introduction to Microprocessors. 1982. text ed. 28.95 (ISBN 0-8359-3247-8); instr's. manual avail. (ISBN 0-8359-3248-6). Reston.

Buchsbaum, W. H. & Mauro, R. Microprocessor-Based Electronic Games. 350p. 1983. pap. 9.95 (ISBN 0-07-008722-9, BYTE Bks). McGraw.

Buchsbaum, Walter. Microprocessor & Microcomputer Data Digest. 1983. text ed. 29.95 (ISBN 0-8359-4381-X). Reston.

Burton, D. P. & Dexter, A. L. Microprocessor Systems Handbook. LC 77-88133. (Illus.). 1977. text ed. 9.50 (ISBN 0-916550-04-4). Analog Devices.

Byers, T. J. Microprocessor Support Chips: Theory, Design & Applications. 302p. (Orig.). 1982. 38.00 (ISBN 0-942412-05-2). Micro Text Pubs.

--Microprocessor Support Chips: Theory, Design, & Applications. (Illus.). 300p. 1983. 39.50 (ISBN 0-07-009518-3). McGraw.

Cahill, S. J. Designing Microprocessor: Based Digital Circuitry. (Illus.). 192p. 1985. pap. text ed. 16.95 (ISBN 0-13-200601-4). P-H.

--Digital & Microprocessor Engineering. (Electrical & Electronic Engineering Ser.). 550p. 1982. 94.95x (ISBN 0-470-27301-1); pap. 34.95 (ISBN 0-470-20093-6). Halsted Pr.

Camp & Smay. Microprocessor Systems Engineering. (Illus.). 656p. 1979. 29.95 (ISBN 0-916460-26-6). Matrix Pub.

Cannon, Don L. Sixteen-Bit Microprocessor Systems. (Solid-State Electronics Technology Bks.). 505p. 49.50 (ISBN 0-317-06598-X). Tex Instr Inc.

Cannon, Don L. & Luecke, G. Understanding Microprocessors. 2nd ed. LC 84-51247. (The Understanding Ser.). 288p. 1984. pap. text ed. 14.95 (ISBN 0-89512-160-3, LCB8451). Tex Instr Inc.

Carr, Joseph J. Eight-Bit & Sixteen-Bit Microprocessor Cookbook. (Illus.). 308p. 1983. 19.95 (ISBN 0-8306-0643-2, 1643); pap. 13.50 (ISBN 0-8306-1643-8, 1643). TAB Bks.

--Microprocessor Interfacing. (Illus.). 252p. 1982. 14.95 (ISBN 0-8306-0064-7); pap. 7.95 o.p (ISBN 0-8306-1396-X, 1396). TAB Bks.

CES Industries, Inc. Ed-Lab Experiment Manual: CES 380 Microprocessors. (Illus.). 162p. 1980. 11.50 (ISBN 0-86711-007-4). CES Industries.

CES Industries, Inc. Staff. Ed-Lab Experiment Manual: Microprocessor; Student Guide. (Illus.). 1981. write for info. (ISBN 0-86711-018-X). CES Industries.

--Ed-Lab Nine Hundred & Eighty Experiment Manual: Microcomputer Technology, Unit 2. (Unit 2). (Illus.). 11.50 (ISBN 0-86711-022-8). CES Industries.

--Ed-Lab Nine Hundred & Eighty: Microprocessor Concepts, Unit 1. (Illus.). 1981. 9.50 (ISBN 0-86711-021-X). CES Industries.

Chalmers, R. A. Microprocessors in Analytical Chemistry, Vol. 27, No. 7b. 64p. 1982. pap. 25.00 (ISBN 0-08-026284-8). Pergamon.

Chamberlin, Hal. Musical Applications of Microprocessors. 672p. 1983. pap. 21.95 (ISBN 0-317-00362-3). Hayden.

Chandor, Anthony. The Penguin Dictionary of Microprocessors. 192p. 1981. pap. 5.95 (ISBN 0-14-051100-8). Penguin.

Cherry, George. Pascal Programming Structures for Motorola Microprocessors. 1981. text ed. 24.95 (ISBN 0-8359-5465-X); pap. text ed. 16.95 (ISBN 0-8359-5471-4). Reston.

Chirlian, Paul M. Digital Circuits with Microprocessor Applications. 432p. 1981. text ed. 26.95 (ISBN 0-916460-32-0). Matrix Pub.

Cluley, J. C. Interfacing to Microprocessors. 160p. 1983. 26.50 (ISBN 0-07-011409-9). McGraw.

Coffron, J. Understanding & Troubleshooting the Microprocessors. 1980. 28.95 (ISBN 0-13-936625-3). P-H.

Coffron, James & Harmon, Bill. Microprocessor Interfacing Techniques, Vol. II. 300p. pap. cancelled (ISBN 0-89588-196-9). SYBEX.

Coffron, James W. Practical Troubleshooting for Microprocessors. (Illus.). 256p. 1981. text ed. 27.95 (ISBN 0-13-694273-3). P-H.

--Proven Techniques for Troubleshooting the Microprocessor & Home Computer Systems. (Illus.). 256p. 1984. pap. 14.95 (ISBN 0-13-731738-7). P-H.

--Your First Microprocessor: Organizing, Construction, Debugging. LC 83-62032. (Illus.). 352p. 1984. pap. 14.95 (ISBN 0-13-978446-2). P-H.

Coffron, James W. & Long, William E. Practical Interfacing Techniques for Microprocessor Systems. (Illus.). 432p. 1983. 31.95 (ISBN 0-13-691394-6). P-H.

Cooper, J. Microprocessor Background for Management Personnel. 208p. 1981. 23.95 (ISBN 0-13-580829-4). P-H.

Cornillie, O. A. Microprocessors. (EPO Applied Technology Ser.: Vol. 8). 400p. 1985. 80.00 (ISBN 0-08-030575-X). Pergamon.

Coulehan, Robert E. Introduction to Microprocessor Control in Hostile Environments. 160p. 1983. 59.95 (ISBN 0-935506-12-8). Carnegie Pr.

Crane, John. Laboratory Experiments for Microprocessor Systems. (Illus.). 192p. 1980. pap. text ed. 21.95 (ISBN 0-13-519694-9). P-H.

Daley, Henry O. Fundamentals of Microprocessors. 1983. text ed. 30.95 (ISBN 0-03-059934-2). HR&W.

Dao, Lanny V. Mastering the 8088 Microprocessor. LC 84-16419. (Illus.). 304p. (Orig.). 1984. 22.95 (ISBN 0-8306-0888-5, 1888); pap. 15.95 (ISBN 0-8306-1888-0). TAB Bks.

Davis, Thomas. Experimentation with Microprocessor Applications. (Orig.). 1980. pap. text ed. 17.95 (ISBN 0-8359-1812-2). Reston.

Parr. Beginners Guide to Microprocessors. 224p. 1982. pap. 8.95 (ISBN 0-408-00579-3). Focal Pr.

Pasahow, Edward J. Microprocessors & Microcomputers for Electronics Technicians. 1981. text ed. 19.55 (ISBN 0-07-048713-8). McGraw.

Paturzo, Bonaventura A. Making Music with Microprocessors. LC 84-8705. (Illus.). 294p. (Orig.). 1984. 16.95 (ISBN 0-8306-0729-3); pap. 11.95 (ISBN 0-8306-1729-9, 1729). TAB Bks.

Poe, Elmer. The Microprocessor Handbook. LC 83-50166. 14.95 (ISBN 0-672-22013-X). Sams.

Ramirez, E. V. & Weiss, M. Microprocessing Fundamentals: Hardware & Software. 1980. 23.50 (ISBN 0-07-051172-1). McGraw.

Rao, Guthikonda V. Microprocessors & Microcomputer Systems. rev. 2nd ed. (Illus.). 592p. 1982. 38.50 (ISBN 0-442-25626-4). Van Nos Reinhold.

Reed, Edward W. & Larman, Ian S. Fluid Power with Microprocessor Control: An Introduction. 208p. 1985. text ed. 36.95 (ISBN 0-13-322488-0). P-H.

Rich, Lloyd. Understanding Microprocessors. (Illus.). 336p. 1980. text ed. 27.95 (ISBN 0-8359-8057-X); instructor's manual avail. (ISBN 0-8359-8028-6). Reston.

Richter, L. & Le Beux, P., eds. Implementing Functions: Microprocessing & Firmware. (Proc 7th Euromicro Symp on Microproc. & Microprog. Paris '81). 500p. 1982. 74.50 (ISBN 0-444-86282-X, I-342-81, North-Holland). Elsevier.

Robillard, Mark J. Microprocessor-Based Robotics. LC 83-60160. (Intelligent Machine Ser.: Vol. I). (Illus.). 224p. 1983. pap. 16.95 (ISBN 0-672-22050-4, 22050). Sams.

Robinson, Philip R. Mastering the 68000 Microprocessor. (Illus.). 160p. 1985. 22.95 (ISBN 0-8306-0886-9, 1886); pap. 16.95 (ISBN 0-8306-1886-4). TAB Bks.

Rooney, Victor M. & Ismail, Amin R. Microprocessors & Microcomputers: A Comprehensive Study. 528p. text ed. write for info. (ISBN 0-02-402250-0). Macmillan.

Ross, P. J. A Simple Microprocessor System for Field Data Acquisition & Display. 1980. 20.00x (ISBN 0-643-02487-5, Pub. by CSJRO Australia). State Mutual Bk.

Sami, M., et al, eds. Microprocessor Systems Software: Firmware & Hardware. 372p. 1981. 64.00 (ISBN 0-444-86098-3, North-Holland). Elsevier.

Savitzky, Stephen R. Real-Time Microprocessor Systems. (Illus.). 416p. 1985. 47.50 (ISBN 0-442-28048-3). Van Nos Reinhold.

Scanlon, L. Aim Sixty-Five Laboratory Manual. (Electronic Technology Ser.). 179p. 1981. pap. text ed. 14.95 (ISBN 0-471-06488-2). Wiley.

Schindler, Max. Microprocessor Software Design. 304p. 1980. pap. 14.50 (ISBN 0-8104-5190-5). Hayden.

SEMINEX Technical Seminar & Exhibition, London, England, March 26-30, 1979. Semiconductor & Microprocessor Technology 1979: Selected Papers. Dummer, G. W. A., ed. (Illus.). 252p. 1980. pap. 55.00 (ISBN 0-08-026134-5). Pergamon.

Short, K. Microprocessors & Programmed Logic. 1980. 38.95 (ISBN 0-13-581173-2). P-H.

Simons, G. L. Introducing Microprocessors. (Illus., Orig.). 1979. pap. 24.00x (ISBN 0-85012-209-0). Intl Pubns Serv.

--Introducing Microprocessors. 177p. 1979. pap. 21.85 (ISBN 0-471-89468-0). Wiley.

Simons, L. Uses of Microprocessors. 270p. 1980. 50.00x (ISBN 0-85012-240-6, Pub. by NNC Pubns England). State Mutual Bk.

Singh, M. G., et al. Applied Industrial Control--an Introduction. (International Ser. on Systems & Control: Vol. 1). (Illus.). 450p. 1980. 62.00 (ISBN 0-08-024764-4); pap. 21.00 (ISBN 0-08-024765-2). Pergamon.

Smith, Dean L. Testing & Servicing Microprocessors. (Illus.). 325p. (Orig.). 1983. pap. text ed. 35.00x (ISBN 0-918699-04-5). D L Smith.

Smith, Noel T. An Introduction to Microprocessors: Experiments in Digital Technology. 184p. 1981. pap. 12.95 (0867). Hayden.

Soucek, Branko. Microprocessors & Microcomputers. LC 75-33123. 607p. 1976. 45.95x (ISBN 0-471-81391-5, Pub. by Wiley-Interscience). Wiley.

Staugaard, Andrew C. Microprocessor Applications. (Illus.). 838p. 1983. 99.95 (ISBN 0-87119-046-X). Heathkit-Zenith Ed.

--Microprocessor Interfacing. (Illus.). 909p. 1982. ring loose-leaf 99.95 (ISBN 0-87119-090-7, EE-3402). Heathkit-Zenith Ed.

Staugaard, Andrew C., Jr. Microprocessor Interfacing. (Illus.). 1982. pap. text ed. 24.95 (ISBN 0-87119-077-X, EB-6402); tchr's. ed. 9.95 (ISBN 0-87119-079-6); lab manual 10.95 (ISBN 0-87119-078-8). Heathkit-Zenith Ed.

Staugaard, Andrew C. Jr. & Johnson, Ron. Microprocessor Applications. (Illus.). 600p. 1984. pap. text ed. 24.95 (ISBN 0-87119-047-8, EB-6405); tchr's. ed. 9.95 (ISBN 0-87119-049-4); lab manual 10.95 (ISBN 0-87119-048-6). Heathkit-Zenith Ed.

Steckhahn, A. D. & Otter, J. Den. Industrial Applications for Microprocessors. 1982. text ed. 28.95 (ISBN 0-8359-3067-X). Reston.

Stout, David F. Microprocessor Application Handbook. (Illus.). 448p. 1982. 41.95 (ISBN 0-07-061798-8). McGraw.

Streitmatter, Gene & Fiori, Vito. Microprocessor: Theory & Application. 2nd ed. 1980. text ed. 29.95 (ISBN 0-8359-4378-X); solutions manual avail. (ISBN 0-8359-4379-8). Reston.

Subbarao, Wunnava. Microprocessors: Hardware, Software, & Design Applications. 1984. text ed. 29.95 (ISBN 0-8359-4394-1); solutions manual avail. (ISBN 0-8359-4395-X). Reston.

Swan, Tom. Programmer's Guide to the 1802: With an Assembler for Your Machine. (Illus.). 156p. (Orig.). 1981. pap. 9.50 (ISBN 0-8104-5183-2). Hayden.

Taub, Herbert. Digital Circuits & Microprocessors. (Electrical Engineering Ser.). (Illus.). 608p. 1981. text ed. 41.95 (ISBN 0-07-062945-5). McGraw.

Tedd, Mike, et al, eds. Ada for Multimicroprocessors. (Ada Companion Ser.). 250p. 1985. 29.95 (ISBN 0-521-30103-3). Cambridge U Pr.

Tedeschi, Frank P. & Kueck, Gary. One Hundred One Microprocessor Software & Hardware Projects. (Illus.). 294p. 16.95 (ISBN 0-8306-0030-2); pap. 9.95 (ISBN 0-8306-1333-1, 1333). TAB Bks.

Terrell, David. Microprocessor Technology. 1983. text ed. 27.95 (ISBN 0-8359-4392-5); solutions manual avail. (ISBN 0-8359-4393-3). Reston.

Texas Instruments Engineering Staff. Sixteen-Bit Microprocessor Systems. (Illus.). 592p. 1982. 49.50 (ISBN 0-07-063760-1). McGraw.

Texas Instruments Inc. Electronic Power Control & Digital Techniques. (Illus.). 1976. 42.50 (ISBN 0-07-063752-0). McGraw.

Texas Instruments, Inc. Microprocessors-Microcomputers-System Design. (Texas Instruments Bk. Ser.). (Illus.). 1980. 34.50 (ISBN 0-07-063758-X). McGraw.

Texas Instruments Learning Center Staff. Microprocessors & Microcomputers & Switching Mode Power for Supplies. (Solid-State Electronics Technology Bks.). (Illus.). 216p. 1978. 35.00 (ISBN 0-07-063756-3). Tex Instr Inc.

--Microprocessors-Microcomputers-System Design. 534p. 1980. 32.50 (ISBN 0-07-063758-X). Tex Instr Inc.

Tiberghien, J., et al, eds. Microprocessors & Their Applications: Proceedings of the Euromicro Symposium, 5th, Sweden, August 1979. 412p. 1980. 64.00 (ISBN 0-444-85390-1, North-Holland). Elsevier.

Titus, Jonathan & Larsen, David. Eighty-Eighty-Five-A Cookbook. LC 80-50054. 352p. 1980. pap. 15.95 (ISBN 0-672-21697-3, 21697). Sams.

Tocci, Ronald & Laskowski, Lester. Microprocessors & Microcomputers: Hardware & Software. 2nd ed. (Illus.). 416p. 1982. 32.95 (ISBN 0-13-581322-0); solutions manual avail. P-H.

--Microprocessors & Microcomputers: The 6800 Family. (Illus.). 432p. 1986. text ed. 32.95 (ISBN 0-13-581745-5). P-H.

Tokheim, Roger L. Schaum's Outline of Microprocessor Fundamentals. (Schaum's Outline Ser.). 384p. 1983. pap. text ed. 8.95 (ISBN 0-07-064958-8). Mcgraw.

Torrero, Edward A., ed. Microprocessors: New Directions for Designers. (Illus.). 144p. 1975. pap. text ed. 11.85 (ISBN 0-8104-5777-6). Hayden.

Towers, T. D. Towers' International Microprocessor Selector. (Illus.). 160p. vinyl 19.95x (ISBN 0-8306-1716-7, 1516). TAB Bks.

Triebel, Walter & Singh, Avtar. The Ninety-Nine Hundred Microprocessor: Architecture, Software, & Interface Techniques. (Illus.). 224p. 1984. text ed. 27.95 (ISBN 0-13-622853-4); pap. text ed. 14.95 (ISBN 0-13-622846-1). P-H.

Tseng, Vincent. Microprocessor Development & Development Systems. 224p. 1982. 34.95 (ISBN 0-07-065380-1). McGraw.

Turino, Jon. Microprocessors Board Testability. 100p. 175.00x (ISBN 0-686-87079-4, Pub. by Network). State Mutual Bk.

Turino, Jon & Mei, David. Microprocessor Board Testability. (Illus.). 110p. 1980. text ed. 95.00 (ISBN 0-912253-00-2). Logical Solns Tech.

Tzafestas, Spyros G., ed. Microprocessors in Signal Processing: Measurement & Control. (Microprocessor Based Systems Engineering). 1983. lib. bdg. 59.00 (ISBN 90-2771-497-5, Pub. by Reidel Holland). Kluwer Academic.

Veronis, Andrew. Advanced Microprocessor Interfacing. 1984. text ed. 22.95 (ISBN 0-8359-0056-8). Reston.

--The Complete Microprocessor Circuits Reference Manual. 1985. text ed. 39.95 (ISBN 0-8359-0806-2). Reston.

Walker, B. S. Understanding Microprocessors. LC 81-7087. 110p. 1981. pap. 14.95 (ISBN 0-470-27286-4). Halsted Pr.

Warner, Malcolm, ed. Microprocessors, Manpower & Society. LC 83-40148. 390p. 1984. 39.95 (ISBN 0-312-53187-7). St Martin.

Webster, Robin. Microprocessors Today. (Illus.). 96p. (Orig.). 1982. 12.50 (ISBN 0-7182-0463-8, Pub. by Kaye & Ward). David & Charles.

Whitbread, Martin, ed. Microprocessor Applications in Business & Industry. (Topics in Microprocessing Ser.: Book One). (Illus.). 153p. 1979. pap. text ed. 21.00 (ISBN 0-7194-0010-4, Pub. by Castle Hse England). J K Burgess.

Whitehead, Martin. Microprocessor Software. (Topics in Microprocessing Ser.: Bk. 2). 160p. 1980. 50.00x (Pub. by Castle Hse England). State Mutual Bk.

Whitworth, Ian. Sixteen-Bit Microprocessors. 300p. 1983. 21.95 (ISBN 0-13-811372-6). P-H.

William Section Symposium. Microprocessor Control Systems, the Concept - The Reality: Proceedings of the Wilmington Section Symposium. LC 82-164810. 84p. 1982. pap. text ed. 20.00x (ISBN 0-87664-688-7). Instru Soc.

Williams, G. B. Troubleshooting Microprocessor Based Systems. 1984. 28.00 (ISBN 0-08-029989-X); pap. 15.50 (ISBN 0-08-025842-5). Pergamon.

Wilmink, J. & Sami, M., eds. Microprocessing & Microprogramming: Second Symposium, Venice, 1976. 336p. 1977. 64.00 (ISBN 0-7204-0557-2, North-Holland). Elsevier.

Witting, Philip A. Fundamentals of Microprocessor Systems. 525p. 1984. pap. text ed. 24.95x (ISBN 0-86238-030-8, Pub. by Chartwell-Bratt England). Brookfield Pub Co.

Yuen, C. K. Microprocessor Systems & Their Application to Signal Processing. 1982. 49.50 (ISBN 0-12-774950-0). Acad Pr.

Zaks, Rodnay. From Chips to Systems: An Introduction to Microprocessors. LC 81-51126. (Illus.). 552p. 1981. pap. 19.95 (ISBN 0-89588-063-6, C201A). SYBEX.

--Introduction to Microprocessors. LC 78-61821. (Illus.). 104p. 1978. incl. 2 cassettes 29.95 (ISBN 0-89588-010-5). SYBEX.

Zarrella, John. Language Translators. LC 82-48049. (Microprocessor Software Engineering Concepts Ser.). 200p. (Orig.). 1982. pap. 16.95 (ISBN 0-935230-06-8). Microcomputer Appns.

Zarrella, John, ed. Microprocessor Operating Systems, Vol. 1. LC 81-80864. 166p. 1981. pap. 13.95 (ISBN 0-935230-03-3). Microcomputer Appns.

--Microprocessor Operating Systems, Vol. 2. LC 81-80864. 158p. (Orig.). 1982. pap. 13.95 (ISBN 0-935230-04-1). Microcomputer Appns.

--Microprocessor Operating Systems, Vol. 3. LC 81-80864. 152p. 1984. pap. 13.95 (ISBN 0-935230-10-6). Microcomputer Appns.

Zissos. System Design with Microprocessors. 2nd ed. 1984. 19.50; pap. write for info. (ISBN 0-12-781740-9). Acad Pr.

MICROPROCESSORS–DESIGN AND CONSTRUCTION

Camp & Smay. Microprocessor Systems Engineering. (Illus.). 656p. 1979. 29.95 (ISBN 0-916460-26-6). Matrix Pub.

Carson, John H. Design of Microprocessor Systems. (Tutorial Texts Ser.). 262p. 1979. 18.00 (ISBN 0-8186-0260-0, Q260). IEEE Comp Soc.

Coffron, James W. Your First Microprocessor: Organizing, Construction, Debugging. LC 83-62032. (Illus.). 352p. 1984. pap. 14.95 (ISBN 0-13-978446-2). P-H.

ERA. The Engineering of Microprocessor Systems: Guidelines on System Development. LC 79-40952. 1979. 25.00 (ISBN 0-08-025435-7); pap. 8.00 (ISBN 0-08-025434-9). Pergamon.

Flik, T. & Liebig, H. The Sixteen-Bit Microprocessor Systems. 300p. 1985. pap. 34.50 (ISBN 0-387-15164-8). Springer-Verlag.

Garland, Harry. Introduction to Microprocessor System Design. (Illus.). 1979. 24.95 (ISBN 0-07-022871-X); pap. 24.95 (ISBN 0-07-022870-1). McGraw.

Harmon, Thomas L. & Lawson, Barbara. Motorola MC 6800 Microprocessor Family: Assembly, Interface Design & System Design. (Illus.). 544p. 1985. text ed. 34.95 (ISBN 0-13-603960-X). P-H.

Hunter, Colin, et al. Introduction to the Intel IAPX 432 Microprocessor Architecture. 1985. pap. text ed. 22.95 (ISBN 0-8359-3222-2). Reston.

Khambata, Adi J. Microprocessors-Microcomputers: Architecture, Software & Systems. LC 81-11360. (Electronic Technology Ser.). 577p. 1982. 32.95x (ISBN 0-471-06490-4); tchr's. manual 20.00x (ISBN 0-471-86316-5). Wiley.

McGlynn, Daniel R. Microprocessors: Technology, Architecture & Applications. LC 76-137. 1976. 29.50x (ISBN 0-471-58414-2, Pub. by Wiley-Interscience). Wiley.

Mardiguian, Michel. Interference Control in Computers & Microprocessor-Based Equipment. (Illus.). 110p. 1984. text ed. 27.00 (ISBN 0-932263-23-2). White Consult.

Meade, A. H., ed. Microprocessor Systems: Design & Applications. (Infotech Computer State of the Art Reports: Vol. 11, No. 2). 248p. 1983. 445.00 (ISBN 0-08-028573-2). Pergamon.

Torrero, Edward A., ed. Microprocessors: New Directions for Designers. (Illus.). 144p. 1975. pap. text ed. 11.85 (ISBN 0-8104-5777-6). Hayden.

Travers, Donald J. Precision Signal Handling & Converter-Microprocessor Interface: A Tutorial Presentation. 90p. 1984. pap. text ed. 29.95x (ISBN 0-87664-803-0). Instru Soc.

Triebel, Walter & Singh, Avtar. The Eighty Eighty-Six Microprocessor: Architecture, Software & Interfacing Techniques. (Illus.). 352p. 1985. text ed. 31.95 (ISBN 0-13-246695-3). P-H.

--The Ninety-Nine Hundred Microprocessor: Architecture, Software, & Interface Techniques. (Illus.). 224p. 1984. text ed. 27.95 (ISBN 0-13-622853-4); pap. text ed. 14.95 (ISBN 0-13-622846-1). P-H.

--Sixteen-Bit Microprocessors: Architecture, Software, & Interface. (Illus.). 384p. 1985. text ed. 32.95 (ISBN 0-13-811407-2). P-H.

MICROPROCESSORS–PROGRAMMING

Andrews, Michael. Programming Microprocessor Interface for Control & Instrumentation. (Illus.). 368p. 1982. 39.95 (ISBN 0-13-729996-6). P-H.

Boyet, Howard. HERO 1: Advanced Programming Experiments. rev. ed. Johnson, Ron, ed. LC 84-10722. (Illus.). 305p. 1984. Repr. of 1983 ed. lab manual 24.95 (ISBN 0-87119-036-2, EB-1802). Heathkit-Zenith Ed.

Duncan, F. Microprocessor Programming & Software Development. 1980. 35.00 (ISBN 0-13-581405-7). P-H.

Eyes, David & Lichty, Ron. Programming the 65816. (Illus.). 288p. 1985. pap. 22.95 (ISBN 0-89303-789-3). Brady Comm.

Flik, T. & Liebig, H. The Sixteen-Bit Microprocessor Systems. 300p. 1985. pap. 34.50 (ISBN 0-387-15164-8). Springer-Verlag.

Foulger, R. J. Programming Embedded Microprocessors: A High-Level Language Solution. (Illus.). 240p. (Orig.). 1983. 28.00x (ISBN 0-85012-336-4). Intl Pubns Serv.

Hyde, Randy. Using 6502 Assembly Language. (Illus.). 301p. 1981. 19.95 (ISBN 0-88190-003-6, B0003). Datamost.

Krieger, Morris, et al. Structured Microprocessor Programming. LC 79-67229. (Illus.). 240p. (Orig.). 1979. pap. 25.00 (ISBN 0-917072-18-9). Yourdon.

Lane, J. E. Microprocessors & Information Handling. 60p. 1981. pap. 13.15 (ISBN 0-471-89410-9). Wiley.

Leahy, William F. Microprocessor Architecture & Programming. LC 77-1552. 252p. 1977. text ed. 29.95 (ISBN 0-471-01889-9). Krieger.

Ontario Centre for Microelectronics & Fathi. Microprocessor Software Project Management. (Electrical Engineering Ser.). 512p. 1985. 57.50 (ISBN 0-8247-7450-7). Dekker.

Short, K. Microprocessors & Programmed Logic. 1980. 38.95 (ISBN 0-13-581173-2). P-H.

Smardzewski, R. R. Microprocessor Programming & Applications for Scientists & Engineers. LC 84-13759. (Data Handling in Science & Technology Ser.: Vol. 1). 1984. 36.50 (ISBN 0-444-42407-5). Elsevier.

Triebel, Walter & Singh, Avtar. The Eighty Eighty-Six Microprocesser: Architecture, Software & Interfacing Techniques. (Illus.). 352p. 1985. text ed. 31.95 (ISBN 0-13-246695-3). P-H.

--Sixteen-Bit Microprocessors: Architecture, Software, & Interface. (Illus.). 384p. 1985. text ed. 32.95 (ISBN 0-13-811407-2). P-H.

Wester, John G. & Simpson, William D. Software Design for Microprocessors. (Solid-State Electronics Technology Bks.). (Illus.). 392p. 1976. 14.95 (ISBN 0-317-06597-1). Tex Instr Inc.

Zaks, Rodnay. Microprocessor Programming. LC 78-68645. (Illus.). 178p. 1978. incl 7 cassettes 99.95 (ISBN 0-89588-018-0). SYBEX.

--Programming Microprocessors. LC 78-61823. (Illus.). 150p. 1978. incl. 2 cassettes 29.95 (ISBN 0-89588-011-3). SYBEX.

MICROPROGRAMMING

Agrawala, Ashok K. Foundations of Microprogramming: Architecture, Software & Applications. 1976. 59.50 (ISBN 0-12-045150-6). Acad Pr.

Andrews, Michael. Principles of Firmware Engineering in Microprogram Control. LC 80-19386. (Illus.). 347p. 1980. 36.95 (ISBN 0-914894-63-3). Computer Sci.

MICROSEISMS

Hardy, H. R. Proceedings of the Third Conference on Acoustic Emission-Mircoseismic Activity in Geologic Structures & Materials. 1983. 50.00x (ISBN 0-87849-046-9). Trans Tech.

MICROSOFT (COMPUTER PROGRAM)

Aker, Sharon Z. Microsoft BASIC Programming for the Mac. 1985. pap. 17.95 (ISBN 0-673-18167-7). Scott F.

Barnard, David T., et al. Microcomputer Programming with Microsoft BASIC. (Illus.). 1983. text ed. 22.95 (ISBN 0-8359-4357-7); pap. 17.95 (ISBN 0-8359-4356-9). Reston.

Critchfield, Margot & Dwyer, Thomas. Pocket Guide to Microsoft BASIC. (Micro Computer Ser.). 1983. pap. 6.95 (ISBN 0-201-10364-8). Addison-Wesley.

Dayton, Rick. Macintosh Microsoft BASIC. price not set. P-H.

Ettlin, W. A. & Solberg, G. Microsoft BASIC Made Easy. 275p. 1983. pap. 17.95. McGraw.

Farvour, James. Microsoft BASIC Decoded & Other Mysteries. (TRS-80 Information Ser.: Vol. II). (Illus.). 312p. (Orig.). 1981. pap. 29.95 (ISBN 0-936200-01-4). Blue Cat.

Goldstein, Larry J. & Schneider, David. Microsoft BASIC for the Macintosh. (Illus.). 576p. 1984. pap. 21.95 (ISBN 0-89303-662-5). Brady Comm.

Guthrie, Anne E. The Secret Word: A Guide to the Hidden Potential of Microsoft Word. 120p. (Orig.). 1985. pap. 17.95 (ISBN 0-9614335-0-7); pap. text ed. 14.50 (ISBN 0-317-20526-9). TechnoLiteracy Assocs.

Heath Company Staff. Programming in Microsoft BASIC. (Illus.). 920p. 1981. looseleaf with 3 audiocassetes 99.95 (ISBN 0-87119-086-9, EC-1110). Heathkit-Zenith Ed.

Hoenig, Alan. Introduction to Microsoft Word for the IBM PC. (Microcomputer Power Ser.). 208p. 1984. deluxe ed. 28.95 plastic comb, incl. diskette (ISBN 0-697-00441-4); pap. 17.95 (ISBN 0-697-00437-6). Wm C Brown.

--Microsoft Word for the Macintosh: Word Processing & the Professional. (Micropower Ser.). 208p. 1985. pap. 14.95 (ISBN 0-697-00879-7). WM C Brown.

Hoffman, Paul. Microsoft Word Made Easy. 250p. (Orig.). pap. 14.95 (ISBN 0-07-881144-9, 144-9). Osborne-McGraw.

--Microsoft Word Made Easy: Macintosh Edition. LC 84-22750. 200p. 1984. pap. 15.95 (ISBN 0-07-881152-X, 152-X). Osborne-McGraw.

Kater, David A. & Kater, Richard L. The Printed Word: The Microsoft Guide to Advanced Word Processing on the Apple Macintosh. (Illus.). 336p. 1985. pap. 17.95 (ISBN 0-914845-53-5). Microsoft.

Lien, David A. Learning Microsoft BASIC for the Macintosh: New Microsoft 2.0 Version. LC 85-71339. (Illus.). 458p. (Orig.). 1985. pap. 19.95 (ISBN 0-932760-34-1). Compusoft.

Microtrend, Inc. Microsoft Windows on the IBM PC. (Microtrend Ser.). 1984. cancelled (ISBN 0-13-581661-0). P-H.

Morrill, Harriet H. Mini & Micro BASIC: Introducing Applesoft, Microsoft & BASIC Plus. (Microcomputer Bookshelf Ser.). 224p. 1983. pap. text ed. 14.50i (ISBN 0-316-58400-2); tchr's manual (ISBN 0-316-58401-0). Little.

Norton, Peter. Discovering the IBM PCjr Home Computer. (Illus.). 192p. 1984. 15.95 (ISBN 0-914845-01-2). Microsoft.

O'Malley, Timothy J. Twenty-Five Graphics Programs in Microsoft BASIC. (Illus.). 160p. 1983. 17.95 (ISBN 0-8306-0133-3, 1533); pap. 11.95 (ISBN 0-8306-0533-9). TAB Bks.

Purdum, Jack J. BASIC-80 & CP-M: Digital Research BASIC-80-Microsoft. 288p. 1983. pap. text ed. write for info. (ISBN 0-02-397020-0). Macmillan.

Rampa, Janet. Getting Started with Microsoft Word: A Step-by-Step Guide to Word Processing. (Illus.). 312p. 1984. 16.95 (ISBN 0-914845-13-6). Microsoft.

Rinearson, Peter. Word Processing Power with Microsoft Word: Professional Writing on Your IBM PC. 304p. 1985. pap. 16.95 (ISBN 0-914845-05-5). Microsoft.

--Word Processing with Style & Microsoft Word. 192p. Date not set. pap. 18.95 (ISBN 0-914845-28-4). Microsoft.

Schat, Stan. Business & Home Applications for the Macintosh Using Microsoft BASIC. 224p. 1984. pap. 14.95 (ISBN 0-89303-403-7). Brady Comm.

Seidel, Ken. Microsoft COBOL. 200p. 1983. pap. 15.95 (ISBN 0-88056-117-3). Dilithium Pr.

Weber Systems, Inc. Microsoft Windows User's Handbook. 280p. 1985. pap. 9.95 (ISBN 0-345-31999-0). Ballantine.

Williams, Robert. Microsoft Word. incl. disk 28.95 (ISBN 0-13-688037-1). P-H.

Zager, Masha & Chase, Claire. Using Microsoft Word. LC 84-60137. 300p. 1985. pap. 16.95 (ISBN 0-88022-112-7, 133); IBM PC format software 39.95 (ISBN 0-88022-151-8, 247). Que Corp.

MICROSOFT WORD (COMPUTER PROGRAM)

Scanlon, Leo J. Microsoft Word for the IBM PC. LC 84-18149. (Personal Computing Ser.). 156p. 1985. pap. write for info. (ISBN 0-13-581729-3). P-H.

MICROSOMES

Boobis, et al. Microsomes & Drug Oxidations. 420p. 1985. 80.00 (ISBN 0-85066-282-6). Taylor & Francis.

Coon, Minor J., ed. Microsomes, Drug Oxidations & Chemical Carcinogenesis, Vol. 1. LC 80-11363. 1980. 55.00 (ISBN 0-12-187701-9). Acad Pr.

--Microsomes, Drug Oxidations & Chemical Carcinogenesis, Vol. 2. LC 80-11363. 1980. 60.00 (ISBN 0-12-187702-7). Acad Pr.

Estabrook, R., et al, eds. Microsomes & Drug Oxidations. LC 73-6403. 486p. 1973. 30.00 (ISBN 0-683-02918-5, Pub. by W & W). Krieger.

Gillette, James R., et al, eds. Microsomes & Drug Oxidations: Proceedings. 1969. 65.00 (ISBN 0-12-283650-2). Acad Pr.

Harvold, Egil P. Treatement of Hemifacial Microsomia. LC 83-18758. 258p. 1983. 48.00 (ISBN 0-8451-0229-X). A R Liss.

Sato, Ryo & Kato, Ryuichi. Microsomes, Drug Oxidations & Drug Toxicology. LC 82-202706. 636p. 1982. 69.50 (ISBN 0-471-87285-7, Pub. by Wiley-Interscience). Wiley.

MICROSPORIDIA

Kudo, Roksabro. A Biologic & Taxonomic Study of the Microsporidia. (Illinois Biological Monographs: Vol. 9). Repr. of 1924 ed. 22.00 (ISBN 0-384-30600-4). Johnson Repr.

MICROSTRIP

see Microwave Wiring

MICROTECHNIQUE

see Microscope and Microscopy–Technique

MICROWAVE AMPLIFICATION BY STIMULATED EMISSION OF RADIATION

see Masers

MICROWAVE AMPLIFICATION BY VARIABLE REACTANCE

see Parametric Amplifiers

MICROWAVE CIRCUITS

Allen, J. L. & Medley, M. W., Jr. Microwave Circuit Design Using Programmable Calculators. (Illus.). 279p. 1980. 54.00 (ISBN 0-89006-089-4). Artech Hse.

Davis, A. Microwave Semiconductor Circuit Design. 1984. 47.50 (ISBN 0-442-27211-1). Van Nos Reinhold.

Edwards, T. C. Foundations for Microstrip Circuit Design. LC 80-41687. 720p. 1981. 37.95x (ISBN 0-471-27944-7, Pub. by Wiley-Interscience). Wiley.

Freeman, Ernest R. Interference Suppression Techniques for Microwave Antennas & Transmitters. (Artech Microwave Library). (Illus.). 400p. 1982. 48.00 (ISBN 0-89006-110-6). Artech Hse.

Frey, Jeffrey & Bhasin, Kul, eds. Microwave Integrated Circuits. 2nd ed. 1985. pap. text ed. 45.00 (ISBN 0-89006-160-2). Artech Hse.

Grivet, P. Physics of Transmission Lines at High & Very High Frequencies, Vol. 1. (Fr). 1970. 72.00 (ISBN 0-12-303601-1). Acad Pr.

Gupta, C., et al. Computer-Aided Design of Microwave Circuits. (Artech Microwave Library). (Illus.). 650p. 1981. 72.00x (ISBN 0-89006-106-8). Artech Hse.

Helszajn, J. Passive & Active Microwave Circuits. LC 78-5787. 274p. 1978. 49.95x (ISBN 0-471-04292-7, Pub. by Wiley-Interscience). Wiley.

Hoffman, R. K. Microwave Integrated Circuit Design Handbook. Orig. Title: Integrierte Mikrowellenshaltungen. 1985. text ed. 68.00 (ISBN 0-89006-163-7). Artech Hse.

Howes, M. J. & Morgan, D. V., eds. Microwave Devices: Device Circuit Interaction. LC 75-15887. (Solid State Devices & Circuits Ser.). 402p. 1976. 79.95 (ISBN 0-471-41729-7, Pub. by Wiley-Interscience). Wiley.

Kajfez, Darko. Notes on Microwave Circuits, Vol. 1. LC 84-223799. (Illus.). 381p. (Orig.). 1984. pap. text ed. 35.00x (ISBN 0-930071-01-8). Kajfez Con.

--Notes on Microwave Circuits, Vol. 2. (Illus.). 224p. (Orig.). 1985. pap. text ed. price not set (ISBN 0-930071-02-6). Kajfez Con.

Kurokawa, K. Introduction to the Theory of Microwave Circuits. (Electrical Science Ser.). 1969. 80.00 (ISBN 0-12-429550-9). Acad Pr.

Okoshi, T. Planar Circuits. (Springer Series in Electrophysics: Vol. 18). (Illus.). 220p. 1985. 41.50 (ISBN 0-387-13853-6). Springer-Verlag.

Pucel, R. A., ed. Monolithic Microwave Integrated Circuits. 458p. 1985. avail. (ISBN 0-87942-192-4). IEEE.

--Monolithic Microwave Integrated Circuits. (Reprint Ser.). 458p. 1985. write for info. (ISBN 0-87942-192-4). Inst Electrical.

Sazonov, D. M., et al. Microwave Circuits. 320p. 1983. 8.95 (ISBN 0-8285-2311-8, Pub. by Mir Pubs USSR). Imported Pubns.

MICROWAVE COMMUNICATION SYSTEMS

see also Closed-Circuit Television; Mobile Radio Stations; Radiotelephone

Angelakos, Diogenes J. & Everhart, Thomas E. Microwave Communications. LC 81-18556. 314p. 1983. Repr. of 1968 ed. text ed. 22.50 (ISBN 0-89874-395-8). Krieger.

Conference on Interference Problems Associated with the Operation of Microwave Communication Systems(1968: London) Conference on Interference Problems Associated with the Operation of Microwave Communication Systems, 23rd-24th April, 1968. LC 71-586382. (Institution of Electrical Engineers Conference Publications: No. 39). pap. 52.00 (ISBN 0-317-10149-8, 2007388). Bks Demand UMI.

Erst, Stephen J. Receiving Systems Design. 300p. 1984. text ed. 61.00 (ISBN 0-89006-135-1). Artech Hse.

Jakes, William C., et al, eds. Microwave Mobile Communications. LC 74-13401. 640p. 1974. 74.95x (ISBN 0-471-43720-4, Pub. by Wiley-Interscience). Wiley.

Malherbe, J. A. Microwave Transmission Line Filters. LC 78-31243. (Illus.). 1979. 43.00 (ISBN 0-89006-063-0). Artech Hse.

Van Spronsen, C. J. & Richter, L., eds. Microsystems: Architecture, Integration & Use: EUROMICRO Symposium on Microprocessing & Microprogramming, 8th, 1982. 356p. 1983. 59.75 (ISBN 0-444-86470-9, I-496-82, North Holland). Elsevier.

MICROWAVE DEVICES

see also Klystrons; Masers; Microwave Circuits; Microwave Communication Systems; Microwave Tubes; Oscillators, Microwave; Parametric Amplifiers

Allan, Thomas D. Satellite Microwave Remote Sensing. (Marine Science Ser.). 526p. 1983. 110.00x (ISBN 0-470-27397-6). Halsted Pr.

Bahr, A. J. & McGonnagle, Warren J. Microwave Nondestructive Testing Methods. (Nondestructive Monographs: Vol. 1). 102p. 1983. 24.50. Gordon.

Cogan, Adrian. Microwave Semiconductor Engineering. 1985. text ed. 50.00 (ISBN 0-89006-168-8). Artech Hse.

Coleman, James. Microwave Devices. 1982. text ed. 28.95 (ISBN 0-8359-4386-0). Reston.

Cook, Nigel P. Microwave Principles & Systems. (Illus.). 224p. 1986. text ed. 29.95 (ISBN 0-13-581596-7). P-H.

Decareau, Robert V. Microwaves in the Food Processing Industry. (Food Science & Technology Ser.). 1985. 37.50 (ISBN 0-12-208430-6). Acad Pr.

Edwards, T. C. An Introduction to Microwave Electronics. 150p. 1984. pap. text ed. 14.95 (ISBN 0-7131-3495-X). E Arnold.

Fox, J., ed. Microwave Research Institute Symposia. Incl. Vol. 1. Modern Network Synthesis. 1952; Vol. 4. Modern Advances in Microwave Techniques. LC 55-12897. 1955. o.p. (ISBN 0-470-27192-2); Vol. 5. Modern Network Synthesis. LC 56-2590. 1956; Vol. 6. Nonlinear Circuit Analysis. LC 55-3575. 1956; Vol. 9. Millimeter Waves. LC 60-10073. 1960; Vol. 11. Electromagnetics & Fluid Dynamics of Gaseaous Plasma. LC 62-13174. 1962. 38.95 (ISBN 0-470-27423-9); Vol. 13. Optical Lasers. LC 63-22084; Vol. 15. System Theory. LC 65-28522. 1965; Vol. 17. Modern Optics. LC 67-31757. 1967. o.p. (ISBN 0-470-27433-6); Vol. 19. Computer Processing in Communications. LC 77-122632. 1970; Vol. 20. Submillimeter Waves. 1971; Vol. 21. Computers & Automata. 1972; Vol. 22. Computer Communications. 1972. 46.95 (ISBN 0-471-27439-9); Vol. 24. Computer Software Engineering. 1977. Pub. by Wiley-Interscience). Wiley.

Freeman, Ernest R. Interference Suppression Techniques for Microwave Antennas & Transmitters. (Artech Microwave Library). (Illus.). 400p. 1982. 48.00 (ISBN 0-89006-110-6). Artech Hse.

Fukui, Hatsuaki, ed. Low-Noise Microwave Transistors & Amplifiers. LC 81-6994. 1981. 38.45 (ISBN 0-87942-151-7, PC01487). Inst Electrical.

Gandhi, Om P. Microwave Engineering & Applications. (Illus.). 543p. 1981. 66.00 (ISBN 0-08-025589-2); pap. 27.00 (ISBN 0-08-025588-4). Pergamon.

Garver, Robert. Microwave Diode Control Devices. LC 74-82596. 1976. 42.00 (ISBN 0-89006-022-3). Artech Hse.

Gonzalez, Guillermo. Microwave Transistor Amplifiers: Analysis & Design. (Illus.). 368p. 1984. text ed. 35.95 (ISBN 0-13-581646-7). P-H.

Graham, Edward D., Jr. & Gwyn, Charles W. Microwave Transistors. LC 74-82594. Repr. of 1975 ed. 146.50 (ISBN 0-8357-9037-1, 2015321). Bks Demand UMI.

Ha, Tri T. Solid-State Microwave Amplifier Design. LC 81-21. 326p. 1981. 47.50x (ISBN 0-471-08971-0). Wiley.

Howes, M. J. & Morgan, D. V., eds. Microwave Devices: Device Circuit Interaction. LC 75-15887. (Solid State Devices & Circuits Ser.). 402p. 1976. 79.95 (ISBN 0-471-41729-7, Pub. by Wiley-Interscience). Wiley.

--Microwave Solid State Devices & Applications. (Illus.). 256p. 1980. pap. 50.00 (ISBN 0-906048-39-7, Pub. by Peregrinus England). Inst Elect Eng.

Industrial-Commercial Microwave Equipment & Component Markets in Europe. 331p. 1983. 1600.00 (ISBN 0-86621-532-8). Frost & Sullivan.

Kudsia, Chandra M. & O'Donovan, Valentine. Microwave Filters for Communications Systems. LC 73-81239. (Modern Frontiers in Applied Science Ser.). pap. 36.00 (ISBN 0-317-08751-7, 2010076). Bks Demand UMI.

Laverghetta, Thomas S. Handbook of Microwave Testing. LC 81-67941. (Artech Microwave Library). (Illus.). 350p. 1981. 54.00x (ISBN 0-89006-070-3). Artech Hse.

--Microwave Materials & Fabrication Techniques. 450p. 1984. text ed. 55.00 (ISBN 0-89006-143-2). Artech Hse.

Liao, Samuel. Microwave Devices & Circuits. 2nd ed. LC 84-22264. (Illus.). 1985. text ed. 43.95 (ISBN 0-13-581695-5). P-H.

Matthaei, G. L., et al. Microwave Filters, Impedance-Matching Networks, & Coupling Structures. LC 80-68976. (Artech Microwave Library). (Illus.). 1098p. 1980. Repr. of 1965 ed. 79.00 (ISBN 0-89006-099-1). Artech Hse.

Microwave Test Equipment Market. 223p. 1983. 1375.00 (ISBN 0-86621-155-1, A1216). Frost & Sullivan.

Microwave Tubes in Systems - Problems & Prospects. (IEE Conference Publications Ser.: No. 241). 171p. 1984. pap. 62.00 (ISBN 0-85296-302-5). Inst Elect Eng.

Pehl, K. Microwave Technology. Orig. Title: Milkrowellenteknik. 1985. text ed. 55.00 (ISBN 0-89006-164-5). Artech Hse.

Pengelly, Raymond D. Microwave Field-Effect Transistors: Theory, Design & Applications. (Electronic Devices & Systems Research Studies). 470p. 1982. 59.95x (ISBN 0-471-10208-3, Pub. by Res Stud Pr). Wiley.

Raff, S. J. Microwave System Engineering Principles. 11.25 (ISBN 0-08-021797-4). Pergamon.

Seeger, John A. Microwave Theory, Components & Devices. (Illus.). 272p. 1986. text ed. 34.95 (ISBN 0-13-581612-2). P-H.

Soohoo, Ronald F. Microwave Magnetics. 262p. 1984. text ed. 41.25 scp (ISBN 0-06-046367-8, HarpC). Har-Row.

Steinberg, Bernard D. Microwave Imaging with Large Antenna Arrays: Radio Camera Principles & Techniques. LC 83-6705. 269p. 1983. 39.95x (ISBN 0-471-89173-8, Pub. by Wiley-Interscience). Wiley.

Torrieri, Don J. Principles of Secure Communication Systems. 1985. text ed. 61.00 (ISBN 0-89006-173-4). Artech Hse.

Tsui, James B. Microwaves Receivers & Related Components. 539p. 1985. Repr. of 1983 ed. 22.50 (ISBN 0-932146-10-4). Peninsula CA.

White, Joseph F. Microwave Semiconductor Engineering. (Electrical--Computer Science & Engineering Ser.). 558p. 1981. 32.50 (ISBN 0-442-29144-2). Van Nos Reinhold.

Young, Leo. Microwave Filters Using Parallel Coupled Lines. LC 72-168945. (Illus.). pap. 63.30 (ISBN 0-317-08872-6, 2012102). Bks Demand UMI.

MICROWAVE MEASUREMENTS

Kuzmin, A. D. & Salomonovich, A. E. Radioastronomical Methods of Antenna Measurements. (Electrical Science Monographs). 1967. 49.50 (ISBN 0-12-431150-4). Acad Pr.

Lance, Algie L. Introduction to Microwave Theory & Measurements. 1964. text ed. 29.95 (ISBN 0-07-036104-5). McGraw.

Lane, J. A. Microwave Power Measurement. (Institution of Electrical Engineers Monograph: No. 12). (Illus.). pap. 20.00 (ISBN 0-317-12994-5, 2011485). Bks Demand UMI.

MICROWAVE METEOROLOGY

see Radio Meteorology

MICROWAVE OSCILLATORS

see Oscillators, Microwave

MICROWAVE RADIO

see Radio, Short Wave

MICROWAVE RELAY SYSTEMS

see Radio Relay Systems

MICROWAVE SPECTROSCOPY

Carrington, Alan. Microwave Spectroscopy of Free Radicals. 1974. 49.50 (ISBN 0-12-160750-X). Acad Pr.

Chantry, G. W. Modern Aspects of Microwave Spectroscopy. LC 78-73876. 1980. 95.00 (ISBN 0-12-168150-5). Acad Pr.

Gordy, W. & Cook, L., eds. Technique of Organic Chemistry: Vol. 9, Pt. 2, Microwave Molecular Spectra. LC 80-16243. 747p. 1970. 67.50 (ISBN 0-471-93161-6). Krieger.

Townes, C. H. & Schawlow, A. L. Microwave Spectroscopy. LC 74-83620. (Illus.). 720p. 1975. pap. text ed. 12.95 (ISBN 0-486-61798-X). Dover.

Wilmhurst, T. H. Electron Spin Resonance Spectrometers. LC 68-8257. (Monographs on Electron Spin Resonance Ser.). 280p. 1968. 29.50x (ISBN 0-306-30372-8, Plenum Pr). Plenum Pub.

MICROWAVE TUBES

International Congress Of Microwave Tubes, 5th-Paris, 1964. Microwave Tubes: Proceedings. 1965. 132.00 (ISBN 0-12-461550-3). Acad Pr.

Kleen, Werner J. Electronics of Microwave Tubes. Lindsay, P. A., et al, trs. 1958. 63.00 (ISBN 0-12-412550-6). Acad Pr.

Okress, Ernest, ed. Microwave Power Engineering, 2 Vols. (Electrical Science Ser). 1968. Vol. 1. 80.00 (ISBN 0-12-525350-8). Acad Pr.

MICROWAVE WIRING

Bahl, I. J. & Bhartia, P. Microstrip Antennas. (Illus.). 355p. 1980. 64.00 (ISBN 0-89006-098-3). Artech Hse.

MICROWAVES

see also Microwave Devices; Microwave Measurements; Microwave Spectroscopy; Microwave Tubes; Microwave Wiring; Quantum Electronics

Adair, Eleanor R., ed. Microwaves & Thermoregulation: Symposium. 1983. 55.00 (ISBN 0-12-044020-2). Acad Pr.

Baden-Fuller, A. J. Microwaves. 2nd ed. 1979. text ed. 48.00 (ISBN 0-08-024228-6); pap. text ed. 18.00 (ISBN 0-08-024227-8). Pergamon.

Bartone, John C., II. Microwaves & Radiation: Medical Analysis Index with Research Bibliography. LC 85-47580. 150p. 1985. 29.95 (ISBN 0-88164-334-3); pap. 21.95 (ISBN 0-88164-335-1). ABBE Pubs Assn.

Business Communications Staff. The Microwave Industry: Trends, Developments. 1981. 875.00 (ISBN 0-89336-275-1, G-020R). BCC.

Collin, Robert E. Foundations for Microwave Engineering. 1966. 59.00 (ISBN 0-07-011801-9). McGraw.

Cornbleet, Sidney. Microwave Optics: The Optics of Microwave Antenna Design. (Pure & Applied Physics Ser.). 1977. 69.50 (ISBN 0-12-189650-1). Acad Pr.

Decareau, Robert V. Microwaves in the Food Processing Industry. (Food Science & Technology Ser.). 1985. 37.50 (ISBN 0-12-208430-6). Acad Pr.

Fox, J., ed. Microwave Research Institute Symposia. Incl. Vol. 1. Modern Network Synthesis. 1952; Vol. 4. Modern Advances in Microwave Techniques. LC 55-12897. 1955. o.p. (ISBN 0-470-27192-2); Vol. 5. Modern Network Synthesis. LC 56-2590. 1956; Vol. 6. Nonlinear Circuit Analysis. LC 55-3575. 1956; Vol. 9. Millimeter Waves. LC 60-10073. 1960; Vol. 11. Electromagnetics & Fluid Dynamics of Gaseous Plasma. LC 62-13174. 1962. 38.95 (ISBN 0-470-27423-9); Vol. 13. Optical Lasers. LC 63-22084; Vol. 15. System Theory. LC 65-28522. 1965; Vol. 17. Modern Optics. LC 67-31757. 1967. o.p. (ISBN 0-470-27433-6); Vol. 19. Computer Processing in Communications. LC 77-122632. 1970; Vol. 20. Submillimeter Waves. 1971; Vol. 21. Computers & Automata. 1972; Vol. 22. Computer Communications. 1972. 46.95 (ISBN 0-471-27439-9); Vol. 24. Computer Software Engineering. 1977. Pub. by Wiley-Interscience). Wiley.

Gardiol, Fred. An Introduction to Microwaves. LC 83-72774. (Illus.). 400p. 1983. 50.00 (ISBN 0-89006-134-3). Artech Hse.

Goldblith, Samuel A. & Decareau, Robert V. An Annotated Bibliography on Microwaves: Their Properties, Production, & Application to Food Processing. 1973. 32.50x (ISBN 0-262-07049-9). MIT Pr.

Grandolfo, M., et al, eds. Biological Effects & Dosimetry of Nonionizing Radiation: Radiofrequency & Microwave Energies. (NATO ASI Series A, Life Sciences: Vol. 49). 682p. 1982. 89.50x (ISBN 0-306-41017-6, Plenum Pr). Plenum Pub.

Grantham, Donald J. Antennas, Transmission Lines, & Microwaves. LC 77-25369. (The Grantham Electronics-with-Mathematics Ser.: Vol. 6). (Illus.). 1977. pap. text ed. 18.95x (ISBN 0-915668-06-8). G S E Pubns.

Gupta, K. C. Microwaves. LC 80-11904. 256p. 1980. 18.95x (ISBN 0-470-26966-9). Halsted Pr.

Heald, M. A. & Wharton, C. B. Plasma Diagnostics with Microwaves. LC 77-13781. 470p. 1978. Repr. of 1965 ed. 27.00 (ISBN 0-88275-626-5). Krieger.

Hellwege, K. H. & Hellwege, A. M., eds. Molecular Constants, Mostly from Microwaves, Molecular Beam, & Electron Resonance Spectroscopy. (Landolt-Boernstein, New Series: Group II, Vol. 14). (Illus.). 375p. (Supplement to Volumes II-4 & II-6, Subvolume b). 1983. 242.40 (ISBN 0-387-11857-8). Springer-Verlag.

Hewlitt-Packard. Microwave Theory & Applications. 1969. 29.95 (ISBN 0-13-581488-X). P-H.

Kollberg, E., ed. Microwave & Millimeter: Wave Mixers. LC 84-10887. 1984. 59.95 (ISBN 0-87942-179-7, PC01735). Inst Electrical.

Kong, Jin A., et al. Theory of Microwave Remote Sensing. LC 84-17397. 400p. 1985. text ed. 45.00x (ISBN 0-471-88860-5, Pub. by Wiley-Interscience). Wiley.

Lance, Algie L. Introduction to Microwave Theory & Measurements. 1964. text ed. 29.95 (ISBN 0-07-036104-5). McGraw.

Laverghetta, Thomas. Microwave Measurements & Techniques. LC 75-31383. 1976. 48.00 (ISBN 0-89006-053-3). Artech Hse.

Laverghetta, Thomas S. Practical Microwaves. LC 83-51119. 39.95 (ISBN 0-672-21945-X, 21945). Sams.

Lin, James C. Microwave Auditory Effects & Applications. (Illus.). 232p. 1978. 30.75x (ISBN 0-398-03704-3). C C Thomas.

Metaxas, A. C. & Meredith, R. J. Industrial Microwave Heating. (IEE Power Engineering Ser.: No. 4). 357p. 1983. pap. 80.00 (ISBN 0-906048-89-3, P0004, Pub. by Peregrinus England). Inst Elect Eng.

Okress, Ernest, ed. Microwave Power Engineering, 2 Vols. (Electrical Science Ser). 1968. Vol. 1. 80.00 (ISBN 0-12-525350-8). Acad Pr.

Peyton, Mary F., ed. Biological Effects of Microwave Radiation. LC 61-11807. 333p. 1961. 35.00x (ISBN 0-306-30113-X, Plenum Pr). Plenum Pub.

Roddy, Dennis. Microwave Technology. 1982. text ed. 21.95 (ISBN 0-8359-4390-9); instrs'. manual avail. (ISBN 0-8359-4391-7). Reston.

Saad, Theodore, ed. The Microwave Engineers' Handbook, 2 vols. LC 76-168891. 1971. 61.00 set (ISBN 0-89006-004-5); Vol. 1. 39.00 (ISBN 0-89006-002-9); Vol. 2. 39.00 (ISBN 0-89006-003-7). Artech Hse.

Skobel'tsyn, D. V., ed. Microwave-Plasma Interactions. LC 75-20239. (P. N. Lebedev Physics Institute Ser.: Vol. 73). (Illus.). 135p. 1975. 55.00 (ISBN 0-306-10915-8, Consultants). Plenum Pub.

Soares, Robert. Applications of GAAS MESFETS. LC 83-71124. (Illus.). 1983. 66.00 (ISBN 0-89006-120-3). Artech Hse.

Sodha, M. S. & Srivastava, N. C. Microwave Propagation in Ferrimagnetics. LC 81-15364. 428p. 1981. 59.50x (ISBN 0-306-40716-7, Plenum Pr). Plenum Pub.

Steneck, Nicholas H. The Microwave Debate: Technology, Science & Values in Conflict. (Illus.). 276p. 1984. 27.50x (ISBN 0-262-19230-6). MIT Pr.

Tyler, Paul E., ed. Biologic Effects of NonIonizing Radiation. (Annals of the New York Academy of Sciences: Vol. 247). 1975. 64.75x (ISBN 0-89072-761-9). NY Acad Sci.

Von Aulock, Wilhelm H., ed. Handbook of Microwave Ferrite Materials. (Illus.). 1965. 70.50 (ISBN 0-12-723350-4). Acad Pr.

Wheeler, Gershon. Introduction to Microwaves. (Illus.). 1963. ref. ed. 32.95 (ISBN 0-13-487843-4). P-H.

Williamson, CiCi & Steiner, Ann. Microwave Know-How. LC 81-90173. Orig. Title: MicroScope Savoir Faire. (Illus.). 222p. 1985. pap. 10.95 (ISBN 0-9607740-2-5). MicroScope TX.

Young, Leo, ed. Advances in Microwaves. Incl. Vol. 1. 1966. 90.00 (ISBN 0-12-027901-0); Vol. 2. 1967. 90.00 (ISBN 0-12-027902-9); Vol. 3. 1968. 90.00 (ISBN 0-12-027903-7); Vol. 4. 1969. 90.00 (ISBN 0-12-027904-5); Vol. 5. 1970. 90.00 (ISBN 0-12-027905-3); Vol. 6. 1971. 90.00 (ISBN 0-12-027906-1); Vol. 7. 1971. 90.00 (ISBN 0-12-027907-X); Suppl. 1. Theory & Design of Microwave Filters & Circuits. Matsumoto, A. 1970. 75.00 (ISBN 0-12-027961-4). Acad Pr.

MIDGET (AUTOMOBILE)

see Automobiles, Foreign–Types–Midget

MIGMATITE

Atherton, M. P. & Gribble, C. D., eds. Migmatites, Melting & Metamorphism. 200p. 1983. text ed. 39.95 (Pub. by Shiva Pub Ltd.); pap. text ed. 19.95 (Pub. by Shiva Pub Ltd.). Birkhauser.

MIGRATION OF ANIMALS

see Animal Migration

MIGRATION OF BIRDS

see Birds–Migration

MIGRATION OF FISHES

see Fishes–Migration

MIGRATION OF INSECTS

see Insects–Migration

MIGRATION OF PLANTS

see Plants–Migration

MIGRATORY BIRDS, PROTECTION OF

see Birds, Protection Of

MILITARY AERONAUTICS

see Aeronautics, Military

MILITARY AIRPLANES

see Airplanes, Military

MILITARY ARCHITECTURE

see also Fortification

Brice, Martin. Stronghold: A History of Military Architecture. (Illus.). 192p. 1984. 24.50x (ISBN 0-8052-3938-3). Schocken.

Norwood, Richard. Fortification, or Architecture Military. LC 72-6019. (English Experience Ser.: No. 545). 1973. Repr. of 1628 ed. 15.00 (ISBN 90-221-0545-8). Walter J Johnson.

Safarian, S. Design & Construction of Silos & Bunkers. 1984. 72.50 (ISBN 0-442-27801-2). Van Nos Reinhold.

Viollet-Le-Duc, Eugene. An Essay on the Military Architecture of the Middle Ages. LC 74-12651. (Illus.). 1977. Repr. of 1860 ed. lib. bdg. 22.50 (ISBN 0-8371-7747-2, VIMA). Greenwood.

MILITARY ART AND SCIENCE

see also Aeronautics, Military; Armaments; Arms and Armor; Attack and Defense (Military Science); Biological Warfare; Chemical Warfare; Classification–Books–Military Art and Science; Fortification; Mechanization, Military; Mines, Military; Naval Art and Science; Signals and Signaling; Transportation, Military also headings beginning with the word Military

Bailey, Norman & Feder, Stuart. Operational Conflict Analysis. 1973. 9.00 (ISBN 0-8183-0145-7). Pub Aff Pr.

Cushman, John H. Command & Control of Theater Forces: Adequacy. LC 85-9077. (Illus.). 250p. 1985. Repr. of 1983 ed. 25.00 (ISBN 0-916159-06-X). AFCEA Intl Pr.

Deitchman, Seymour J. Military Power & the Advance of Technology: General Purpose Military Forces in the 1980's & Beyond. Rev. ed. LC 83-50434. (Special Studies in Military Affairs). 278p. 1983. lib. bdg. 29.50x (ISBN 0-86531-573-6); pap. 13.50x (ISBN 0-86531-574-4). Westview.

Dunnigan, James F. How to Make War: A Comprehensive Guide to Modern Warfare. (Illus.). 416p. 1982. 14.50 (ISBN 0-688-00780-5). Morrow.

--How to Make War: A Comprehensive Guide to Modern Warfare. rev., upd. ed. LC 82-23065. (Illus.). 444p. 1983. pap. 8.95 (ISBN 0-688-01975-7, Quill NY). Morrow.

Eccles, Henry E. Logistics in the National Defense. LC 81-4920. (Illus.). xviii, 347p. 1981. Repr. lib. bdg. 42.50 (ISBN 0-313-22716-0, ECLO). Greenwood.

Eshel, David. Elite Fighting Units. LC 84-7419. (Illus.). 208p. 1984. 19.95 (ISBN 0-668-06206-1); pap. 14.95 (ISBN 0-668-06274-6). Arco.

Friedman, William F. Elementary Military Cryptography. rev. ed. LC 76-53119. (Cryptographic Ser.). 1976. Repr. of 1941 ed. 14.00 (ISBN 0-89412-010-7). Aegean Park Pr.

Hartmann, Gregory K. Weapons That Wait: Mine Warfare in the U. S. Navy. LC 78-71766. (Illus.). 300p. 1979. 22.95 (ISBN 0-87021-753-4). Naval Inst Pr.

Huber, R. K., ed. Systems Analysis & Modeling in Defense: Developments, Trends, & Issues. 923p. 1984. 125.00x (ISBN 0-306-41609-3, Plenum Pr). Plenum Pub.

Hughes, Wayne P., et al, eds. Military Modeling. 369p. (Orig.). 1984. pap. 17.50 (ISBN 0-930473-00-0). Military Opera Res.

International Institute for Strategic Studies. The Military Balance: Nineteen Eighty to Nineteen Eighty-One. pap. 35.80 (ISBN 0-317-26083-9, 2025154). Bks Demand UMI.

Mahan, Dennis H. Complete Treatise on Field Fortification. Repr. of 1836 ed. lib. bdg. 24.75 (ISBN 0-8371-0557-9, MAFF). Greenwood.

Preston, Anthony, ed. Warship, Vol. 1. LC 78-55455. (Illus.). 135p. 1978. 23.95 (ISBN 0-87021-975-8). Naval Inst Pr.

Slow to Take Offense: Bombers, Cruise Missles & Prudent Deterrence. 2nd ed. 136p. 1980. pap. 15.00 (ISBN 0-89206-015-8, CSIS017, CSIS). Unipub.

Willcox, A. M., et al. Command, Control & Communications (C3) (Illus.). 160p. 1983. 27.00 (ISBN 0-08-028332-2); pap. 12.50 (ISBN 0-08-028333-0). Pergamon.

Zurcher, Louis A. & Harries-Jenkins, Gwynn, eds. Supplementary Military Forces: Reserves, Militias, Auxiliaries, Vol. VIII. (War, Revolution & Peacekeeping Ser.). 278p. 1978. 28.00 (ISBN 0-8039-1109-2); pap. 14.00 (ISBN 0-8039-1110-6). Seven Locks Pr.

MILITARY ART AND SCIENCE–DATA PROCESSING

Intel Staff. Military Handbook. 480p. 1985. pap. 15.00 (ISBN 0-917017-10-2, 210461-003). Intel Corp.

Military Embedded Computer Market. 247p. 1985. 1700.00 (ISBN 0-86621-360-0, A1444). Frost & Sullivan.

Ward, J. W. & Taylor, G. N. Military Data Processing & Microcomputers: Battlefield Weapons Systems & Technology, Vol. IX. LC 82-13159. (Illus.). 225p. 1982. 26.00 (ISBN 0-08-028338-1); pap. 13.00 (ISBN 0-08-028339-X). Pergamon.

MILITARY ASTRONAUTICS

see Astronautics, Military

MILITARY AVIATION

see Aeronautics, Military

MILITARY BALLOONS

see Balloons

MILITARY ENGINEERING

see also Earthwork; Electronics in Military Engineering; Fortification; Military Architecture; Topographical Surveying

Croucher, Richard. Engineers at War Nineteen Thirty-Nine to Nineteen Forty-Five. (Illus.). 400p. 1982. pap. 13.95 (ISBN 0-85036-271-7); 30.00 (ISBN 0-85036-270-9). Dufour.

Diamant, Lincoln. Bernard Romans: Forgotten Patriot of the American Revolution, Military Engineer & Cartographer of West Point & the Hudson Valley. LC 85-5421. (Illus.). 160p. 1985. 15.95 (ISBN 0-916346-56-0). Harbor Hill Bks.

Mazmanian, Daniel A. & Nienaber, Jeanne. Can Organizations Change? Environmental Protection, Citizen Participation, & the Army Corps of Engineers. 1979. 26.95 (ISBN 0-8157-5524-4); pap. 9.95 (ISBN 0-8157-5523-6). Brookings.

Rajendran, S. Tables for Rapid Sub-Frame Analysis. 367p. 1979. pap. 20.00x (ISBN 0-8214-0517-9, 82-93508, Pub. by Singapore U Pr). Ohio U Pr.

Ruck, Hendrick W. & Ellis, John A., eds. Military Training Technology: Systematic Approaches. 192p. 1984. 24.95t (ISBN 0-03-062541-6). Praeger.

MILITARY EXPLOSIVES

see Explosives

MILITARY FIREWORKS

Macchiavelli, Niccolo. The Arte of Warre, (Certain Waies of the Orderyng of Souldiours) Whitehorne, P., tr. LC 79-26097. (English Experience Ser.: No. 135). 1969. Repr. of 1562 ed. 42.00 (ISBN 90-221-0135-5). Walter J Johnson.

MILITARY POWER

see Air Power; Military Art and Science

MILITARY SIGNALING

see Signals and Signaling

MILITARY SUPPLIES

Boyes, Jon L. & Andriole, Stephen J., eds. Issues in C3I Program Management: Requirements, Systems & Operations. (AFCEA-Signal Magazine C3I Ser.: Vol. I). (Illus.). 420p. 1984. 29.95 (ISBN 0-916159-02-7); Set. write for info. (ISBN 0-916159-01-9). AFCEA Intl Pr.

Foss, Christopher F., ed. Jane's Military Vehicle & Ground Support Equipment, 1984. 5th ed. (Jane's Yearbooks). (Illus.). 850p. 1984. 125.00x (ISBN 0-7106-0794-6). Jane's Pub Inc.

Gudgin, Peter. British Army Equipment. 80p. 1982. 8.95 (ISBN 0-85368-377-8). Stackpole.

Kemp, Anthony & Haythornthwaite, Philip. Weapons & Equipment Series, 3 vols. (Illus.). 525p. 1982. boxed set 50.00 (ISBN 0-7137-1296-1, Pub. by Blandford Pr England). Sterling.

Military Communications Market. 540p. 1983. 1425.00 (ISBN 0-86621-102-0). Frost & Sullivan.

Military C3I Market. 510p. 1984. 1750.00 (ISBN 0-86621-311-2, A1391). Frost & Sullivan.

Military Display Market. 305p. 1985. 1675.00 (ISBN 0-86621-197-7, A1261). Frost & Sullivan.

Military Embedded Computer Market. 247p. 1985. 1700.00 (ISBN 0-86621-360-0, A1444). Frost & Sullivan.

Military Fiber Optics Market (U.S.) 1985. write for info. (ISBN 0-86621-351-1, A1435). Frost & Sullivan.

Military Gallium Arsenide Semiconductor Market (U.S.) 1985. write for info. (ISBN 0-86621-423-2, A1498). Frost & Sullivan.

Military Groundbased & Shipbased Radar Market. 371p. 1984. 1475.00 (ISBN 0-86621-247-7, A1318). Frost & Sullivan.

Military Intrusion Detection Market (U.S.) 1985. write for info. (ISBN 0-86621-364-3, A1448). Frost & Sullivan.

Military Microwave Component Market. 324p. 1984. 1600.00 (ISBN 0-86621-201-9). Frost & Sullivan.

Military Power Supply Market. 297p. 1984. 1525.00 (ISBN 0-86621-268-X). Frost & Sullivan.

Military Satellite Communications Market. 305p. 1984. 1475.00 (ISBN 0-86621-219-1, A1287). Frost & Sullivan.

Military Test Equipment. 245p. 1983. 1275.00 (ISBN 0-86621-152-7, A1213). Frost & Sullivan.

Military Training Aids & Simulators (Europe) 1985. write for info. (ISBN 0-86621-745-2, E817). Frost & Sullivan.
Military Voice Digitizer Market. 216p. 1985. 1650.00 (ISBN 0-86621-390-2, A1465). Frost & Sullivan.
Monograph: External Store Environments During Flight. 100p. 1985. 25.00 (ISBN 0-915414-82-1). Inst Environ Sci.
Reilly, Robert M. United States Military Small Arms, 1816-1865. 1983. 35.00 (ISBN 0-88227-019-2). Gun Room.
The U. S. Military Trainers & Simulators Market. 1983. 1400.00 (ISBN 0-86621-092-X, A1141). Frost & Sullivan.

MILITARY VEHICLES
see Vehicles, Military

MILK
see also Butter; Cheese; Milk Plants
Burton, H., et al. Milk Sterilization. (Agricultural Planning Studies: No. 65). (Orig.). 1969. pap. 7.25 (ISBN 0-685-02454-7, F279, FAO). Unipub.
Campbell, J. R. & Marshall, R. T. The Science of Providing Milk for Man. (Agricultural Sciences Ser). 1975. 39.95 (ISBN 0-07-009690-2). McGraw.
Education & Training Comm. Oregon Association of Milk, Food & Environment Sanitarians, Inc. HTST Pasteurizer Operation Manual. (Illus.). 6.50 (ISBN 0-88246-057-9). Oreg St U Bkstrs.
FAO-WHO Joint Expert Committee on Milk Hygeine, 3rd, Geneva, 1969. Report. (Technical Report Ser: No. 453). 82p. 1970. pap. 2.00 (ISBN 92-4-120453-2, 1144). World Health.
Kon, S. K. Milk & Milk Products in Human Nutrition. 2nd, Rev. ed. (Nutritional Studies: No. 27). 80p. (Orig., 2nd Printing 1975). 1972. pap. 6.25 (ISBN 92-5-100438-2, F277, FAO). Unipub.
Lolli, Giorgio, et al. Alcohol in Italian Culture: Food & Wine in Relation to Sobriety Among Italians & Italian Americans. LC 58-9167. (Rutgers Center of Alcohol Studies: Monograph No. 3). 1958. 7.50 (ISBN 0-911290-27-3). Rutgers Ctr Alcohol.
McKenzie, Hugh A., ed. Milk Proteins, Vols. 1-2. 1971. Vol. 1. 88.00 (ISBN 0-12-485201-7); Vol. 2. 88.00 (ISBN 0-12-485202-5); Set. 143.00. Acad Pr.
Milk & Milk Products: Terminology. (Terminology Bulletins: No. 31). (Eng., Fr., Span. & Arabic.). 100p. 1979. pap. 7.50 (ISBN 92-5-000758-2, F1879, FAO). Unipub.
Mulder, H. & Walstra, P. The Milk Fat Globule: Emulsion Science as Applied to Milk Products & Comparable Foods. 296p. 1974. 59.00x (ISBN 0-85198-289-1, Pub. by CAB Bks England). State Mutual Bk.
Report of the Eighteenth Session of the Joint FAO-WHO Committee of Government Experts on the Code of Principles Concerning Milk & Milk Products. 1977. pap. 8.75 (ISBN 0-685-80150-0, F653, FAO). Unipub.
Robinson, R. K., ed. Dairy Microbiology: The Microbiology of Milk, Vol. 1. (Illus.). 258p. 1981. 42.75 (ISBN 0-85334-948-7, Pub. by Elsevier Applied Sci England). Elsevier.
--Dairy Microbiology: The Microbiology of Milk Products, Vol. 2. (Illus.). 333p. 1981. 50.00 (ISBN 0-85334-961-4, Pub. by Elsevier Applied Sci England). Elsevier.

MILK–ANALYSIS AND EXAMINATION
see also Milk–Composition
Codes of Principles Concerning Milk & Milk Products, International Standards & Standard Methods of Sampling & Analysis for Milk Products. 7th ed. (Codex Alimentarius Commission Reports). 127p. (Orig.). 1973. pap. 4.50 (ISBN 0-685-50042-X, F657, FAO). Unipub.
Westerhuis, J. H. Parturient Hypocalcaemia Prevention in Parturient Cows Prone to Milk Fever by Dietary Measures. New ed. (Agricultural Research Reports). 78p. 1974. pap. 14.00 (ISBN 90-220-0506-2, PDC63, PUDOC). Unipub.

MILK–BACTERIOLOGY
see also Dairy Bacteriology
FAO-WHO Joint Expert Committee on Milk Hygiene 1st, Geneva, 1956. Report. (Technical Report Ser: No. 124). (Eng. & Span.). 54p. 1957. pap. 1.20 (ISBN 92-4-120124-X). World Health.

MILK–COMPOSITION
see also Milk–Analysis and Examination
Galesloot, T. E. & Tinbergen, B. J., eds. Milk Proteins '84: Proceedings of the International Congress on Milk Proteins, Luxemburg, 7-11 May 1984. 325p. 1985. pap. 60.75 (ISBN 90-220-0860-6, PDC279, Pudoc). Unipub.
Milk, Our Civilization's Sham Food. 1984. pap. 4.50 (ISBN 0-916508-29-3). Happiness Pr.
Mulder, H. & Walstra, P. The Milk Fat Globule. 296p. 1974. 20.00 (ISBN 90-220-0470-8, PDC9, Pub. by PUDOC). Unipub.
WHO Food Standards Programme. Joint FAO-WHO Committee of Government Experts on the Code of Principles Concerning Milk & Milk Products: Report of the Twentieth Session, Rome, April 1982. (Joint FAO-WHO Food Standards Programme). (Eng., Fr. & Span.). 77p. 1982. pap. 7.50 (ISBN 92-5-101244-X, F2363, FAO). Unipub.

MILK–PASTEURIZATION
Education & Training Comm. Oregon Association of Milk, Food & Environment Sanitarians, Inc. HTST Pasteurizer Operation Manual. (Illus.). 6.50 (ISBN 0-88246-057-9). Oreg St U Bkstrs.

MILK–TESTING
see Milk–Analysis and Examination

MILK, DRIED
Jones, Robert E. Industry Builder: The Biography of Chester Earl Gray. (Illus.). 1948. 12.95 (ISBN 0-87015-007-3). Pacific Bks.

MILK, PASTEURIZED
see Milk–Pasteurization

MILK PLANTS
FAO-WHO Joint Expert Committee on Milk Hygiene 1st, Geneva, 1956. Report. (Technical Report Ser: No. 124). (Eng. & Span.). 54p. 1957. pap. 1.20 (ISBN 92-4-120124-X). World Health.
Hall, W. S. Standardized Pilot Milk Plants. (Animal Production & Health Papers: No. 3). (Illus.). 104p. 1976. pap. 13.25 (ISBN 92-5-100089-1, F440, FAO). Unipub.

MILK SUBSTITUTES
see Food Substitutes

MILKY WAY
Alter, G. & Ruprecht, J. The System of Open Star Clusters & the Galaxy Atlas of Open Star Clusters. 1963. 66.00 (ISBN 0-12-054250-1). Acad Pr.
Blaauw, Adriaan & Schmidt, Maarten, eds. Galactic Structure. LC 64-23428. (Stars & Stellar Systems Ser: Vol. 5). (Illus.). 1965. 50.00x (ISBN 0-226-45957-8). U of Chicago Pr.
Bok, Bart J. & Bok, Priscilla F. The Milky Way. 5th ed. LC 80-22544. (Harvard Books on Astronomy Ser.). (Illus.). 384p. 1981. text ed. 25.00 (ISBN 0-674-57503-2). Harvard U Pr.
Burton, W. B. The Large Scale Characteristics of the Galaxy. (International Astronomical Union: No. 84). 1979. lib. bdg. 73.50 (ISBN 90-277-1029-5, Pub. by Reidel Holland); pap. 37.00 (ISBN 90-277-1030-9, Pub. by Reidel Holland). Kluwer Academic.
I.A.U. Symposium, 38th, Basel, Switzerland, 1969. The Spiral Structure of Our Galaxy: Proceedings. Becker, W. & Contopoulos, G., eds. LC 75-115886. (I.A.U. Symposia). 478p. 1970. lib. bdg. 45.00 (ISBN 90-277-0109-1, Pub. by Reidel Holland). Kluwer Academic.
NATO Advanced Study Institution, Athens, Greece, September 8-19, 1969. Structure & Evolution of the Galaxy: Proceedings. Mavaridis, L. N., ed. LC 77-135107. (Astrophysics & Space Science Library: No.22). 312p. 1971. lib. bdg. 42.00 (ISBN 90-277-0177-6, Pub. by Reidel Holland). Kluwer Academic.
Shuter, W. L. Kinematics, Dynamics & Structure of the Milky Way. 1983. lib. bdg. 54.50 (ISBN 90-277-1540-8, Pub. by Reidel Holland). Kluwer Academic.
Tuve, Merle A. & Lundsager, Soren. Velocity Structures in Hydrogen Profiles: A Sky Atlas of Neutral Hydrogen Emission. (Carnegie Institution of Washington Ser.: No. 630). (Illus.). pap. 47.00 (ISBN 0-317-09033-X, 2007901). Bks Demand UMI.
Van Woerden, Hugo, et al, eds. The Milky Way Galaxy. 1985. lib. bdg. 69.00 (ISBN 90-277-1919-5, Pub. by Reidel Holland); pap. text ed. 32.50 (ISBN 90-277-1920-9). Kluwer Academic.

MILLEPEDS
Williams, Stephen R. & Hefner, Robert A. Millipedes & Centipedes of Ohio. 1928. 1.00 (ISBN 0-86727-017-9). Ohio Bio Survey.

MILLET
Chopra, Kuldip R. Technical Guideline for Sorghum & Millet: Seed Production. 110p. 1982. pap. text ed. 8.75 (ISBN 92-5-101259-8, F2377, FAO). Unipub.
Hulse, Joseph, et al. Sorghum & the Millets: Their Composition & Nutritive Value. LC 79-40871. 1980. 184.00 (ISBN 0-12-361350-7). Acad Pr.
Improvement & Production of Maize, Sorghum & Millet, 2 vols. (Plant Production & Protection Papers: Nos. 24-1 & 24-2). 703p. 1980. Set. pap. 51.75 (ISBN 0-686-74540-X, F2129, FAO). Vol. 1, General Principles, 226p (ISBN 92-5-101012-9). Vol. 2, Breeding, Agronomy & Seed Production, 500p (ISBN 92-5-101011-0). Unipub.

MILLIKAN RAYS
see Cosmic Rays

MILLING (METALLURGY)
see Ore-Dressing

MILLING (METAL-WORK)
Cain, Tubal. Milling Operations in the Lathe. (Workshop Practice Ser.: No. 5). (Illus.). 128p. (Orig.). 1984. pap. 9.95 (ISBN 0-85242-840-5, Pub. by Argus). Aztex.

MILLING MACHINERY
Here are entered works on machinery used in the process of grinding, etc.
see also Flour Mills; Mills and Mill-Work
Engineering Industry Training Board, ed. Training for Milling Machine Operators & Setters, 22 vols. (Illus.). 1977. Set. 69.95x (ISBN 0-89563-027-3). Intl Ideas.
Evans, Oliver. The Young Mill-Wright & Miller's Guide. LC 72-5047. (Technology & Society Ser.). (Illus.). 438p. 1972. Repr. of 1850 ed. 32.00 (ISBN 0-405-04699-5). Ayer Co Pubs.
Kibbe, Richard R. Milling Machine Operations. LC 84-11798. 192p. 1985. 17.95 (ISBN 0-471-89020-0). Wiley.
Lynch, A. J. Mineral Crushing & Grinding Circuits: Their Simulation, Design & Control. (Developments in Mineral Processing Ser.: Vol. 1). 342p. 1977. 72.50 (ISBN 0-444-41528-9). Elsevier.
Plaster, C., et al, eds. Milling, Vol. 1. 2nd ed. (Engineering Craftsmen: No. H4). (Illus.). 1977. spiral bdg. 38.50x (ISBN 0-85083-404-X). Intl Ideas.
Spencer, A. G., ed. Milling, Vol. 2. (Engineering Craftsmen: No. H29). (Illus.). 1969. spiral bdg. 37.50x (ISBN 0-85083-060-5). Intl Ideas.

MILLING TRADE
see Flour and Feed Trade

MILLIPEDES
see Millepeds

MILLS (BUILDINGS)
see Factories; Flour Mills

MILLS AND MILL-WORK
see also Windmills
Apps, Jerry. Mills of Wisconsin. LC 80-24684. (Illus., Orig.). 1980. pap. 12.50 (ISBN 0-915024-22-5). Tamarack Pr.
Dahl, Alf A. & Wilson, J. Douglas. Cabinetmaking & Millwork: Tools, Materials, Layout. LC 53-11586. (Books of the Building Trade). pap. 89.80 (ISBN 0-317-09679-6, 2006111). Bks Demand UMI.
Ewing, Kristine L. Mill Maintenance I: General Mill Maintenance, Fires & Explosions. LC 78-387. (Bibliographic Ser.: No. 280). 1978. pap. 30.00 (ISBN 0-87010-030-0). Inst Paper Chem.
--Mill Maintenance II: Large Machinery. LC 78-387. (Bibliographic Ser.: No. 281). 1978. pap. 13.00 (ISBN 0-87010-031-9). Inst Paper Chem.
--Mill Maintenance III: Instruments & Small Equipment. LC 78-387. (Bibliographic Ser.: No. 282). 1978. pap. 13.00 (ISBN 0-87010-032-7). Inst Paper Chem.
Miller Freeman Publications, Inc., Staff. Pulping Processes: Mill Operations, Techology, & Practices. Smith, Kenneth E., ed. LC 81-81386. (A Pulp & Paper Focus Bk). (Illus.). 216p. 1981. pap. 35.00 (ISBN 0-87930-126-0). Miller Freeman.
Uhlig, Stephen & Bhat, B. A. Choice of Technique in Maize Milling. 135p. 1980. pap. 11.50x (ISBN 0-7073-0240-4, Pub by Scottish Academic Pr Scotland). Columbia U Pr.
Williston, Ed M., ed. Small Log Sawmills: Profitable Product Selection, Process Design & Operation. LC 80-84893. (A Forest Industries Bk.). (Illus.). 368p. 1981. 52.50 (ISBN 0-87930-091-4); pap. 42.50. Miller Freeman.

MIMICRY (BIOLOGY)
see also Color of Animals
Owen, Denis. Camouflage & Mimicry. LC 82-2566. (Phoenix Ser.). (Illus.). 160p. 1982. pap. 12.50 (ISBN 0-226-64188-0). U of Chicago Pr.
Wickler, Wolfgang. Mimicry in Plants & Animals. (Illus., Orig.). 1968. pap. text ed. 3.95 (ISBN 0-07-070100-8). McGraw.

MINE DRAINAGE
International Mine Drainage Symposium, 1st, Denver, Colorado May 1979. Mine Drainage: Proceedings. Argall, George O., Jr. & Brawner, C. O., eds. LC 79-89681. (A World Mining Bk.). (Illus.). 1979. 55.00 (ISBN 0-87930-122-8). Miller Freeman.

MINE DUSTS
see also Mine Ventilation
Measurement & Control of Respirable Dust in Mining. 1980. 12.50 (ISBN 0-309-03047-1). Natl Acad Pr.
Nettleton, M. A., et al. Coal: Current Advances in Coal Chemistry & Mining Techniques, Vol. 2. 1976. text ed. 28.00x (ISBN 0-8422-7283-6). Irvington.

MINE GASES
Antsyferov, M. S., ed. Seismo-Acoustic Methods in Mining. LC 65-26634. 134p. 1966. 34.50x (ISBN 0-306-10752-X, Consultants). Plenum Pub.
Nettleton, M. A., et al. Coal: Current Advances in Coal Chemistry & Mining Techniques, Vol. 2. 1976. text ed. 28.00x (ISBN 0-8422-7283-6). Irvington.

MINE INSPECTION
Howes, M. Y. & Jones, M. J., eds. Mine Ventilation. 446p. (Orig.). 1984. pap. text ed. 104.00x (ISBN 0-900488-76-X). IMM North Am.
Rudman, Jack. Federal Mine Inspector. (Career Examination Ser.: C-1283). (Cloth bdg. avail. on request). pap. 12.00 (ISBN 0-8373-1283-3). Natl Learning.

MINE MANAGEMENT
see also Mining Engineering
Crawford, John T., III & Hustrulid, William A., eds. Open Pit Mine Planning & Design. LC 79-52269. (Illus.). 367p. 1979. text ed. 30.00x (ISBN 0-89520-253-0). Soc Mining Eng.
Howes, M. Y. & Jones, M. J., eds. Mine Ventilation. 446p. (Orig.). 1984. pap. text ed. 104.00x (ISBN 0-900488-76-X). IMM North Am.
Trotter, Donald A. The Lighting of Underground Mines. LC 83-80618. 216p. 1983. 39.95x (ISBN 0-87201-430-4). Gulf Pub.

MINE RAILROADS
California Central Coast Railways. (Illus.). 44.95 (ISBN 0-686-75183-3). Chatham Pub CA.
Curr, John. Coal Viewer & Engine Builder's Practical Companion. 2nd ed. 96p. 1970. Repr. of 1797 ed. 28.50x (ISBN 0-7146-2429-2, F Cass Co). Biblio Dist.
--Coal Viewer & Engine Builder's Practical Companion. LC 74-96376. (Illus.). Repr. of 1797 ed. lib. bdg. 22.50x (ISBN 0-678-05104-6). Kelley.
Lowenthal, Larry. Iron Mine Railroads of New Jersey. (Illus.). 145p. 1981. 17.95 (ISBN 0-686-36238-1); pap. 12.95 (ISBN 0-686-99308-X). Tri-State Rail.

MINE SURVEYING
Staley, William W. Introduction to Mine Surveying. rev. ed. (Illus.). 1964. 15.00x (ISBN 0-8047-0361-2). Stanford U Pr.
Surveying Offshore Canada Lands: For Mineral Resource Development. 1978. pap. 8.50 (ISBN 0-660-00673-1, SSC94, SSC). Unipub.

MINE SWEEPERS
Elliott, Peter. Allied Minesweeping in World War II. LC 78-61581. 132p. 1979. 12.95 (ISBN 0-87021-904-9). Naval Inst Pr.

MINE VALUATION
see also Prospecting
David, M. Geostatistical Ore Reserve Estimation. (Developments in Geomathematics: Vol. 2). 364p. 1977. 55.50 (ISBN 0-444-41532-7). Elsevier.
Henley, Stephen. Nonparametric Geostatistics. LC 81-7177. 160p. 1981. 34.95x (ISBN 0-470-27285-6). Halsted Pr.

MINE VENTILATION
Hartman, Howard L., ed. Mine Ventilation Symposium, 1st: Proceedings. LC 82-71996. (Illus.). 312p. 1982. 22.00x (ISBN 0-89520-298-0). Soc Mining Eng.

MINERAL COLLECTING
see Mineralogy–Collectors and Collecting

MINERAL INDUSTRIES
see also Ceramic Industries; Ceramics; Metallurgy; Mines and Mineral Resources; Mining Engineering
also specific types of mines and mining, e.g. Coal Mines and Mining
A. J. Wilson Mining Journal Books Ltd. The Pick & the Pen. 318p. 1980. 26.00x (ISBN 0-900117-16-8, Pub. by Mining Journal England). State Mutual Bk.
Alabama Directory of Mining & Manufacturing, 1985-86. 784p. 1985. pap. 56.00 (ISBN 0-318-02842-5). Manufacturers.
Arkansas Directory of Manufacturers, 1985. 324p. 1985. pap. 50.00 (ISBN 0-318-02844-1). Manufacturers.
Atkins, M. H. & Lowe, J. F. Economics of Pollution Control in the Non-Ferrous Metals Industry. (Illus.). 1979. 53.00 (ISBN 0-08-022458-X). Pergamon.
Banks, Ferdinand E. Resources & Energy: An Economic Analysis. LC 81-47967. 368p. 1983. 36.50x (ISBN 0-669-05203-5). Lexington Bks.
Barger, Harold & Schurr, Sam H. The Mining Industries, 1899-1939: A Study of Output, Employment, & Productivity. LC 75-19694. (National Bureau of Economic Research Ser.). (Illus.). 1975. Repr. 32.00x (ISBN 0-405-07575-8). Ayer Co Pubs.
Barnes, Marvin P. Computer-Assisted Mineral Appraisal & Feasibility. LC 79-52270. (Illus.). 167p. 1980. text ed. 33.00x (ISBN 0-89520-262-X). Soc Mining Eng.
Bernstein, Marvin. Mexican Mining Industry, 1890-1950. LC 64-18628. 1965. 39.50 (ISBN 0-87395-016-X). State U NY Pr.
Blakey, Fred. The Florida Phosphate Industry: A History of the Development & Use of a Vital Mineral. LC 73-82345. (Wertheim Publications in Industrial Relations Ser.). 1973. text ed. 15.00x (ISBN 0-674-30670-8). Harvard U Pr.
Blunden, John. Mineral Resources & Their Management. (Themes in Resource Management Ser.). 352p. 1985. pap. text ed. 17.95 (ISBN 0-582-30058-4). Longman.

Board on Mineral & Energy Resources. Redistribution of Accessory Elements in Mining & Mineral Processing: Coal & Oil Shale, Pt. I. 1979. pap. 10.75 (ISBN 0-309-02897-3). Natl Acad Pr.

--Redistribution of Accessory Elements in Mining & Mineral Processing: Uranium, Phosphate, & Alumina, Pt. II. 1979. pap. 13.75 (ISBN 0-309-02899-X). Natl Acad Pr.

--Technological Innovation & Forces for Change in the Mineral Industry. 1978. pap. 6.95 (ISBN 0-309-02768-3). Natl Acad Pr.

Burt, Roger, ed. Cornish Mining. LC 70-77258. 1969. 19.95x (ISBN 0-678-05536-X). Kelley.

Cameron, Eugene N., ed. The Mineral Position of the United States, 1975-2000. LC 72-7983. (Illus.). 182p. 1973. 15.00x (ISBN 0-299-06300-3); pap. 5.95x (ISBN 0-299-06304-6). U of Wis Pr.

Canada's Mineral Trade: The Balance of Payments & Economic Development. 113p. (Orig.). 1978. pap. text ed. 6.50 (ISBN 0-88757-011-9, Pub. by Ctr Resource Stud Canada). Brookfield Pub Co.

Canmet Minerals Research Contracts: Summaries. 49p. 1984. pap. text ed. 9.75x (ISBN 0-660-11705-3, Pub. by Canadian Govt Pub Ctr). Brookfield Pub Co.

Cook, L. H., ed. The Minerals Sector & the Australian Economy. Porter, M. G. 352p. 1984. pap. text ed. 20.00x (ISBN 0-86861-410-6). Allen Unwin.

Current Concerns in Mineral Policy. 75p. (Orig.). 1978. pap. text ed. 4.00x (ISBN 0-88757-010-0, Pub. by Ctr Resource Stud Canada). Brookfield Pub Co.

Currie, John M. & British Columbia Institute of Technology. Unit Operations in Mineral Processing. 340p. 1978. Repr. of 1973 ed. 7.20 (ISBN 0-918062-13-6). Colo Sch Mines.

Decade of Digital Computing in the Mineral Industry. LC 72-91452. 1969. 23.00x (ISBN 0-89520-010-4). Soc Mining Eng.

Employee Relations Initiatives in Canadian Mining. 85p. (Orig.). 1979. pap. text ed. 6.50x (ISBN 0-88757-014-3, Pub. by Ctr Resource Stud Canada). Brookfield Pub Co.

Employment & Training in Metallurgical Industries in the Department of Douches du Rhone, France. pap. price not set (UNESCO). Unipub.

Engineering & Mining Journal Editors, compiled by. E-MJ Operating Handbook of Mineral Processing, Vol. II. 2nd ed. 500p. 1980. 29.50 (ISBN 0-07-019527-7). McGraw.

Eucharius Roesslin. On Minerals & Mineral Products. (Ars Medica: Section 1V, Vol. 1). 1978. 112.00x (ISBN 3-11-006907-5). De Gruyter.

Goren, Simon. Mining & Drilling: Germany, Austria, Hungary. 1985. write for info. looseleaf. Oceana.

Graham, Katherine A., et al. The Administration of Mineral Exploration in the Yukon & Northwest Territories. 60p. (Orig.). 1979. pap. text ed. 4.00x (ISBN 0-686-63144-7, Pub. by Ctr Resource Stud Canada). Brookfield Pub Co.

Greaves, Thomas & Culver, William, eds. Miners & Mining in the Americas. 320p. 1985. 40.00 (ISBN 0-7190-1761-0, Pub. by Manchester Univ Pr). Longwood Pub Group.

Guidebook to Finland Tour, 1977 Prospecting Symposium. 48p. 1977. 14.50 (ISBN 0-686-38290-0). IMM North Am.

Hale, M. Cobalt: A Market Appraisal, Paper #3. (Occasional Papers of the Institution of Mining & Metallurgy Ser.). 60p. (Orig.). 1984. pap. text ed. 16.20x (ISBN 0-900488-68-9). IMM North Am.

Hodges, L. K. Mining in Central & Eastern Washington. (Shorey Prospecting Ser.). 149p. pap. 17.95 (ISBN 0-8466-1998-9, S134B). Shorey.

--Mining in Southern British Columbia. (Shorey Prospecting Ser.). (Illus.). 149p. pap. 17.95 (ISBN 0-8466-1997-0, S134C). Shorey.

--Mining in Western Washington. (Shorey Prospecting Ser.). (Illus.). 150p. pap. 17.95 (ISBN 0-8466-1999-7, S134A). Shorey.

Information Sources on the Foundry Industry. 1st Rev. ed. (Guides to Information Sources: No. 5). pap. 4.00 (UNID192, UN). Unipub.

Institution of Mining & Metallurgy & Institute of Mining Engineers, London. Rockbursts: Prediction & Control (Papers Presented at a Symposium, London, October 20, 1983) 173p. (Orig.). 1984. pap. text ed. 26.95x (ISBN 0-900488-67-0). IMM North Am.

Johnson, T. B. & Barnes, R. J., eds. Application of Computers & Operations Research in the Mineral Industry: 17th International Symposium. LC 82-70016. (Illus.). 806p. 1982. text ed. 35.00x (ISBN 0-89520-293-X). Soc Mining Eng.

Jones, M. J. & Oblatt, R., eds. Tours Guidebook, Eleventh CMMC. 76p. (Orig.). 1978. 21.75x (ISBN 0-900488-40-9). IMM North Am.

Leith, Charles K. World Minerals & World Politics. LC 74-113286. 1970. Repr. of 1931 ed. 19.50x (ISBN 0-8046-1322-2, Pub. by Kennikat). Assoc Faculty Pr.

Livermore, Robert. Bostonians & Bullion: The Journal of Robert Livermore, 1892-1915. Gressley, Gene M., ed. LC 68-12703. (Illus.). xxx, 193p. 1968. 17.95x (ISBN 0-8032-0105-2). U of Nebr Pr.

McDivitt, James & Manners, Gerald. Minerals & Men: An Exploration of the World of Minerals & Metals, Including Some of the Major Problems That Are Posed. rev. & enl. ed. LC 73-8138. (Resources for the Future Ser.). (Illus.). 192p. 1974. pap. 4.95x (ISBN 0-8018-1827-3). Johns Hopkins.

Mackenzie, Brian W. & Bolodeau, Michel L. Effects of Taxation on Base Metal Mining in Canada. 190p. (Orig.). 1979. pap. text ed. 12.50 (ISBN 0-88757-012-7, Pub. by Ctr Resource Stud Canada). Brookfield Pub Co.

Management of Uranium Mill Tailings, Low Level Waste & Hazardous Waste: Proceedings of the Seventh Symposium, 2 vols. (Orig.). 1985. pap. text ed. 38.00 (ISBN 0-910069-08-5). Geotech Engineer Prog.

Management of Uranium Mill Tailings, Low-Level Waste & Hazardous Waste: Proceedings of the Sixth Symposium, 1984. 670p. 1984. 35.00 (ISBN 0-910069-07-7). Geotech Engineer Prog.

Management of Uranium Mill Tailings, Low-Level Waste & Hazardous Waste: Proceedings of the Seventh Symposium, 1985, 2 vols. Set. write for info. (ISBN 0-910069-08-5); write for info. (ISBN 0-910069-09-3); write for info. (ISBN 0-910069-10-7). Geotech Engineer Prog.

Metallurgical Society of AIME. Water Quality Management for the Metals & Minerals Industries, a Short Course (In Conjunction with the 104th AIME Annual Meeting, New York, 1975) pap. 36.80 (ISBN 0-317-10692-9, 2004307). Bks Demand UMI.

Miller, C. George, et al. Cerre Colorade: A Case Study of the Role of Canadian Crown Corporations in Foreign Mineral Development. 60p. (Orig.). 1978. pap. text ed. 4.00x (ISBN 0-686-63142-0, Pub. by Ctr Resource Stud Canada). Brookfield Pub Co.

Miller, Richard K., et al. Noise Control Solutions for the Metal Products Industry. 1982. text ed. 45.00 (ISBN 0-89671-000-9). Fairmont Pr.

Mineral Industry Report: Northwest Territories 1976-1979. 1977. pap. 6.95 (ISBN 0-660-00490-9, SSC62, SSC). Unipub.

Mineral Industry Trends & Economic Opportunities. (Mineral Policy Ser.). 1978. pap. 2.75 (ISBN 0-685-87291-2, SSC100, SSC). Unipub.

Mineral Processing in Developing Countries. 143p. 1980. pap. 7.00 (ISBN 0-686-72714-2, UN80 2B5, UN). Unipub.

Mining & Metallurgy Instrumentation Symposium. Instrumentation in the Mining & Metallurgy Industries, Vol. 9. LC 73-83889. 212p. 1982. pap. text ed. 30.00x (ISBN 0-87664-729-8). Instru Soc.

Mining & Mineral Processing Operations in Canada, 1983. 95p. 1984. pap. text ed. 7.50x (ISBN 0-660-11581-6, Pub. by Canadian Govt Pub Ctr). Brookfield Pub Co.

Mining Journal Books Ltd., ed. World Production & Consumption of Minerals in 1978. 110p. 1982. 65.00x (ISBN 0-900117-25-7, Pub. by Mining Journal England). State Mutual Bk.

Molloy, Peter M. The History of Metal Mining & Metallurgy: An Annotated Bibliography. LC 83-48278. (Bibliographies of the History of Science & Technology Ser.). 350p. 1985. lib. bdg. 55.00 (ISBN 0-8240-9065-9). Garland Pub.

Morse, Jerome G. Nuclear Methods in Mineral Exploration & Production. (Developments in Economic Geology Ser.: Vol. 7). 280p. 1977. 68.00 (ISBN 0-444-41567-X). Elsevier.

Mular, Andrew L. & Bhappu, Roshan B., eds. Mineral Processing Plant Design. 2nd ed. LC 79-57345. (Illus.). 958p. 1980. text ed. 30.00x (ISBN 0-89520-269-7). Soc Mining Eng.

--Mineral Processing Plant Design. LC 77-26531. pap. 160.00 (ISBN 0-317-29751-1, 2017420). Bks Demand UMI.

Nelson, Don. Mines & Mining Equipment & Service Companies Worldwide, 1984-85. 500p. 1985. 79.95 (ISBN 0-419-13260-0, NO. 6900, Pub. by E & FN Spon England). Methuen Inc.

Nickel, P. E., et al. Economic Impacts & Linkages of the Canadian Mining Industry. 141p. (Orig.). 1978. pap. text ed. 8.00x (ISBN 0-88757-007-0, Pub. by Ctr Resource Stud Canada). Brookfield Pub Co.

O'Neil, Thomas J., ed. Application of Computers & Operations Research in the Mineral Industry: 16th International Symposium. LC 79-52273. (Illus.). 651p. 1979. text ed. 33.00x (ISBN 0-89520-261-1). Soc Mining Eng.

Pounds, Norman J. Ruhr: A Study in Historical & Economic Geography. LC 68-55636. (Illus.). 1968. Repr. of 1952 ed. lib. bdg. 22.50x (ISBN 0-8371-0621-4, POTR). Greenwood.

Radetzki, Marian. State Mineral Enterprises: An Investigation into Their Impact on International Mineral Markets. LC 85-2346. 184p. 1985. pap. text ed. 15.00 (ISBN 0-915707-16-0). Resources Future.

Report of IMM Mission to China. 29p. 1980. 72.00 (ISBN 0-686-38294-3). IMM North Am.

Sampling & Analysis for the Minerals Industry: Symposium held in London, November 1982. 119p. (Orig.). 1982. pap. text ed. 31.50x (ISBN 0-900488-64-6). IMM North Am.

Schofield, Charles G. Homogenization-Blending Systems Design & Control for Minerals Processing. LC 83-10784. 322p. 1983. 56.95x (ISBN 0-87201-360-X). Gulf Pub.

Shephers, R. Prehistoric Mining & Allied Industries. (Studies in Archaeology Science Ser.). 1981. 41.50 (ISBN 0-12-639480-6). Acad Pr.

Somasundaran, P., ed. Fine Particles Processing, 2 vols. LC 79-57344. (Illus.). 1865p. 1980. text ed. 50.00x (ISBN 0-89520-275-1). Soc Mining Eng.

Spisak, John F. & Jergensen, Gerald V., II, eds. Frontier Technology in Mineral Processing. LC 84-52515. (Illus.). 175p. 1985. pap. 45.00x (ISBN 0-89520-433-9, 433-9). Soc Mining Eng.

Tilton, John E. The Future of Nonfuel Minerals. 1977. 15.95 (ISBN 0-8157-8460-0). Brookings.

Tinsley, C. R., et al, eds. Finance for the Minerals Industry. LC 84-52556. (Illus.). 842p. 1985. text ed. 50.00x (ISBN 0-89520-435-5, 435-5). Soc Mining Eng.

Transnational Corporations in the Bauxite-Aluminum Industry. pap. 9.00 (UN81 2A5, UN). Unipub.

UNCTAD Secretariat. Studies in the Processing, Marketing & Distribution of Commodities: The Processing & Marketing of Manganese: Areas for International Cooperation. 57p. 1985. pap. 8.00 (UN84/2D18 5071, UN). Unipub.

Uranium Mill Tailings Management: Proceedings of the First Symposium, 1978, 2 vols. Set. 17.00 (ISBN 0-910069-11-5); Vol. 1; 172 pgs. write for info. (ISBN 0-910069-00-X); Vol. 2; 141 pgs. write for info. (ISBN 0-910069-01-8). Geotech Engineer Prog.

Uranium Mill Tailings Management: Proceedings of the Fourth Symposium, 1981. 729p. 1981. 28.00 (ISBN 0-910069-04-2). Geotech Engineer Prog.

Uranium Mill Tailings Management: Proceedings of the Fifth Symposium, 1982. 557p. 1982. 30.00 (ISBN 0-910069-06-9). Geotech Engineer Prog.

Uranium Mill Tailings Management: Proceedings of the Second Symposium, 1979. 331p. 1979. 20.00 (ISBN 0-910069-02-6). Geotech Engineer Prog.

Uranium Mill Tailings Management: Proceedings of the Third Symposium, 1980. 573p. 1980. 25.00 (ISBN 0-910069-03-4). Geotech Engineer Prog.

Voskuil, Walter H. Minerals in Modern Industry. LC 74-118424. 1970. Repr. of 1930 ed. 28.50x (ISBN 0-8046-1374-5, Pub. by Kennikat). Assoc Faculty Pr.

Warren Spring Laboratory, ed. Thesaurus of Terms for Indexing the Literature of Minerals Processing & Metals Extraction, 1974. 1981. 75.00x (ISBN 0-686-97151-5, Pub. by W Spring England). State Mutual Bk.

Westerlund, T., ed. Automation in Mining, Mineral & Metal Processing, 1983: Proceedings of the 4th IFAC Symposium, Helsinki, Finland, 22-25 August 1983. (IFAC Proceedings Ser.). 776p. 1984. 185.00 (ISBN 0-08-030569-5). Pergamon.

William Fox Mining Journal Books Ltd. Tin: The Working of a Commodity Agreement. 418p. 1980. 35.00x (ISBN 0-900117-05-2, Pub. by Mining Journal England). State Mutual Bk.

Williams, Roy E. Waste Production & Disposal in Mining, Milling & Metallurgical Industries. LC 74-20167. (A World Mining Book). (Illus.). 489p. 1975. 45.00 (ISBN 0-87930-035-3). Miller Freeman.

Wojciechowski. Mining Productivity. 1985. pap. text ed. 15.00x (ISBN 0-88757-047-X, Pub. by Ctr Resource Stud Canada). Brookfield Pub Co.

MINERAL LAND SURVEYING

see Mine Surveying

MINERAL LANDS

see Mines and Mineral Resources

MINERAL METABOLISM

Adams, Ruth & Murray, Frank. Minerals: Kill or Cure. rev. ed. 368p. (Orig.). 1974. pap. 1.95 (ISBN 0-915962-16-0). Larchmont Bks.

Alderton, Peggy. The Vitamin, Mineral Connection. 30p. 1985. pap. 2.95 (ISBN 0-317-14757-9). Books World.

Ashmead, DeWayne. Chelated Mineral Nutrition. 186p. (Orig.). 1981. pap. 5.95 (ISBN 0-86664-002-9). Intl Inst Nat Health.

--Chelated Mineral Nutrition in Plants, Animals, & Man. (Illus.). 346p. 1982. 38.75x (ISBN 0-398-04603-4). C C Thomas.

Blate, Michael. The G-Jo Institute Manual of Vitamins & Minerals. (The G-Jo Institute Self-Health Ser.). 96p. (Orig.). 1983. pap. 6.95 (ISBN 0-916878-18-X). Falkynor Bks.

Kurtzman, N. A., ed. The Donald W. Seldin Festschrift. (Journal: Mineral & Electrolyte Metabolism: Vol. 11, No. 4, 1985). (Illus.). 76p. 1985. pap. 13.75 (ISBN 3-8055-4063-9). S Karger.

Marshall, Charles W. Vitamins & Minerals: Help or Harm? (Illus.). 256p. 1983. 14.95 (ISBN 0-89313-061-3). G F Stickley.

Massry, Shaul G., et al, eds. Regulation of Phosphate & Mineral Metabolism. (Advances in Experimental Medicine & Biology Ser.: Vol. 151). 720p. 1982. 85.00x (ISBN 0-306-41020-6, Plenum Pr). Plenum Pub.

Nancollas, G. H., et al. Biological Mineralization & Demineralization: Report on the Dahlemn Workshop Berlin 1981. (Dahlem Workshop Reports: Vol. 23). (Illus.). 420p. 1982. 29.00 (ISBN 0-387-11521-8). Springer-Verlag.

Polunin, Miriam. Minerals: What They Are & Why We Need Them. (Nature's Way Ser.). 96p. 1983. pap. 1.95 (ISBN 0-7225-0524-8). Thorsons Pubs.

Solomons, Noel W. & Rosenberg, Irwin H. Absorption & Malabsorption of Mineral Nutrients. LC 84-15513. (Current Topics in Nutrition & Diseases Ser.: Vol. 12). 324p. 1984. 66.00 (ISBN 0-8451-1611-8). A R Liss.

Trace Mineral Studies with Isotopes in Domestic Animals. (Panel Proceedings Ser.). (Illus.). 151p. 1969. pap. 10.75 (ISBN 92-0-011069-X, ISP218, IAEA). Unipub.

Vaamonde, C. A., ed. Solomon Papper Festschrift, Vol. 10, No. 3. (Journal: Mineral & Electroltye Metabolism: Vol. 10, No. 3). (Illus.). vi, 76p. 1984. pap. 30.25 (ISBN 3-8055-3858-8). S Karger.

Weinberg, E. D. Microorganisms & Minerals. (Microbiology Ser.: Vol. 3). 1977. 85.00 (ISBN 0-8247-6581-8). Dekker.

MINERAL OILS

see also Petroleum

Campbell, Lindsey. Moonie & the Oil Search. (Illus.). 14.50x (ISBN 0-392-03985-0, ABC). Sportshelf.

Din Standards for Mineral Oils & Fuels: Basic Standards on Properties & Requirements, Pt. I. 179.00 (ISBN 0-686-28171-3, 10055-7/20). Heyden.

Din Standards for Mineral Oils & Fuels: Test Methods. 432.00 (ISBN 0-686-28192-6, 10792-7/57). Heyden.

MINERAL RESOURCES

see Mines and Mineral Resources

MINERAL RESOURCES IN SUBMERGED LANDS

Leipziger, Danny M. & Mudge, James L. Seabed Mineral Resources: The Economic Interests of Developing Countries. LC 76-19076. 1976. prof ref 27.50 (ISBN 0-88410-049-9). Ballinger Pub.

Surveying Offshore Canada Lands: For Mineral Resource Development. 1978. pap. 8.50 (ISBN 0-660-00673-1, SSC94, SSC). Unipub.

MINERALOGICAL CHEMISTRY

Brown, R. C., et al. The Invitro Effects of Mineral Dusts. 1980. 55.00 (ISBN 0-12-137240-5). Acad Pr.

Clark, J. R., ed. Chemistry & Physics of Minerals. (Transactions of the American Crystallographic Association Ser.: Vol. 15). 120p. 1979. pap. 15.00 (ISBN 0-686-60385-0). Polycrystal Bk Serv.

Helgeson, Harold C., et al. Handbook of Theoretical Activity Diagrams Depicting Chemical Equilibria in Geologic Systems Involving an Aqueous Phase at One ATM & Zero Degrees to 300 Degrees Centigrade. LC 73-97467. (Illus.). 253p. 1969. text ed. 7.50x (ISBN 0-87735-331-X). Freeman Cooper.

Holland, H. D. & Schidlowski, M., eds. Mineral Deposits & the Evolution of the Biosphere: Report of the Dahlem Workshop. (Dahlem Workshop Reports Ser.: Vol. 3). (Illus.). 333p. 1982. 21.00 (ISBN 0-387-11328-2). Springer-Verlag.

Laskowski, J., ed. Mineral Processing: Developments in Mineral Processing, 2 vols. (Developments in Mineral Processing Ser.). 2116p. 1981. Set. 255.50 (ISBN 0-444-99775-X). Elsevier.

Marfunin, A. S. Physics of Minerals & Inorganic Materials: An Introduction. Egorova, G. & Mishchenko, A. G., trs. from Russ. (Illus.). 1979. 58.00 (ISBN 0-387-08982-9). Springer-Verlag.

Marshall, C. Edmund. The Physical Chemistry & Mineralogy of Soils: Soils in Place, Vol. II. LC 64-20074. 313p. 1977. 45.50x (ISBN 0-471-02957-2, Pub. by Wiley-Interscience). Wiley.

Mining Chemicals. 1981. 950.00 (ISBN 0-89336-262-X, C-021). BCC.

Newton, R. C., et al, eds. Thermodynamics of Minerals & Melts, Vol. 1. (Advances in Physical Geochemistry Ser.). (Illus.). 272p. 1981. 46.00 (ISBN 0-387-90530-8). Springer-Verlag.

Rose, Arthur, et al. Geochemistry in Mineral Exploration. 2nd ed. 1980. pap. 38.00 (ISBN 0-12-596252-5). Acad Pr.

MINERALOGY

see also Crystallography; Meteorites; Mineralogical Chemistry; Petrology; Precious Stones; Rocks

also names of minerals, e.g. Feldspar, Quartz

AIME 110th Annual Meeting, Chicago, Feb. 22-26, 1981. Process Minerology: Extractive Metallurgy, Mineral Exploration, Energy Resources. Hausen, Donald M., ed. 713p. 55.00 (ISBN 0-89520-379-0, 204); members 36.00 (ISBN 0-317-37179-7); student members 18.00 (ISBN 0-317-37180-0). Metal Soc.

Anthony, John W., et al. Mineralogy of Arizona. rev. ed. LC 75-44670. 255p. 1982. 27.50x (ISBN 0-8165-0765-1); pap. 14.95 (ISBN 0-8165-0764-3). U of Ariz Pr.

Audubon Society & Chesterman, Charles W. The Audubon Society Field Guide to North American Rocks & Minerals. LC 78-54893. (Illus.). 1979. 13.50 (ISBN 0-394-50269-8). Knopf.

Bancroft, Peter. Gem & Crystal Treasures. (Illus.). 488p. 1984. 60.00 (ISBN 0-9613461-1-6). Western Enter.

Barker, Reginald W. Taxonomic Notes on the Species. LC 62-6771. (Society of Economic Paleontologists & Mineralogists, Special Publication: No. 9). pap. 65.50 (ISBN 0-317-27163-6, 2024735). Bks Demand UMI.

Bates, Robert L. Geology of the Industrial Rocks & Minerals. (Illus.). 15.25 (ISBN 0-8446-0481-X). Peter Smith.

Battey, M. H. Mineralogy for Students. 2nd ed. (Illus.). 356p. 1981. pap. text ed. 21.95x (ISBN 0-582-44005-X). Longman.

Berkheiser, Samuel W., Jr. Fetid Barite Occurrences, Western Berks County, Pennsylvania. (Mineral Resource Report: No. 84). (Illus.). 43p. 1984. pap. 5.55 (ISBN 0-8182-0053-7). Commonweal PA.

Berry, F. J. & Vaughan, D. J. Chemical Bonding: Spectroscopy in Mineral Chemistry. (Illus.). 300p. 1985. 73.00x (ISBN 0-412-25270-8, 9275, Pub. by Chapman & Hall). Methuen Inc.

Berry, L. G. & Mason, Brian. Mineralogy. 2nd ed. LC 82-16008. 561p. 1983. text ed. 38.95 (ISBN 0-7167-1424-8). W H Freeman.

Berry, Leonard G. & Mason, Brian. Mineralogy: Concepts, Descriptions, Determinations. LC 59-7841. (Geology Ser.). (Illus.). 630p. 1959. 30.95 (ISBN 0-7167-0203-7). W H Freeman.

Black, Joseph. Experiments Upon Magnesia Alba, Quicklime & Some Other Alcaline Substances. LC 79-8596. Repr. of 1898 ed. 13.50 (ISBN 0-404-18449-9). AMS Pr.

Bowen, Oliver E., Jr. Rocks & Minerals of the San Francisco Bay Region. (California Natural History Guides: No. 5). (Illus.). 1962. pap. 2.85 (ISBN 0-520-00158-3). U of Cal Pr.

Boyd, F. R., ed. The Mantle Sample: Inclusions in Kimberlites & Other Volcanics. (Illus.). 424p. 1979. 25.00 (ISBN 0-87590-213-8). Am Geophysical.

Boyd, F. R. & Meyer, H. O., eds. Kimberlites, Diatremes, & Diamonds: Their Geology, Petrology & Geochemistry. LC 78-72025. (Illus.). 408p. 1979. 25.00 (ISBN 0-87590-212-X, SP0024). Am Geophysical.

Brindley, G. W. & Brown, G., eds. Crystal Structures of Clay Minerals & Their X-Ray Identification. 495p. 1982. text ed. 70.00x (ISBN 0-903056-08-9, Mineralogical). Brookfield Pub Co.

Brown, L. P., Jr., ed. Geology of Industrial Minerals: Proceedings, 4th Forum, Austin TX, 14-15 March 1968. (Illus.). 174p. 1969. 2.00 (ISBN 0-318-03314-3). Bur Econ Geology.

Bruce, A. American Mineralogical Journal to Elucidate the Mineralogy & Geology of the U. S, Vol. 1. LC 84-62807. 1968. 24.75x (ISBN 0-02-846280-7). Hafner.

Canadian Minerals & International Economic Interdependence. (Mineral Policy Ser.). 38p. 1978. pap. 2.75 (ISBN 0-685-87290-4, SSC85, SSC). Unipub.

Catalogue of Canadian Minerals. 432p. 1983. pap. text ed. 12.50x (ISBN 0-317-28526-2, Pub. by Canadian Govt Pub Ctr). Brookfield Pub Co.

Cleaveland, Parker. An Elementary Treatise on Mineralogy & Geology. Albritton, Claude C., Jr., ed. LC 77-6513. (History of Geology Ser.). (Illus.). 1978. Repr. of 1816 ed. lib. bdg. 53.00 (ISBN 0-405-10436-7). Ayer Co Pubs.

Cox, K. G., et al. An Introduction to the Practical Study of Crystals, Minerals, & Rocks. rev. ed. LC 74-13833. 235p. 1975. pap. 21.95x (ISBN 0-470-18139-7). Halsted Pr.

Crowson, Phillip. Minerals Handbook: 1982-83. 144p. text ed. 32.95 (ISBN 0-442-21504-5). Van Nos Reinhold.

--Minerals Handbook: 1984-85. (Illus.). 304p. 1985. 49.95x (ISBN 0-87201-566-1). Gulf Pub.

Curtis, Doris M. Sedimentary Processes: Diagenesis. (Society of Economic Paleontologists & Mineralogists, Reprint Ser.: No. 1). pap. 55.50 (ISBN 0-317-27145-8, 2024747). Bks Demand UMI.

Dana, E. S. & Ford, W. E. Textbook of Mineralogy. 4th ed. 851p. 1932. 51.95x (ISBN 0-471-19305-4). Wiley.

Dana, E. S. & Hurlbut, C. S. Minerals & How to Study Them. 3rd ed. 323p. 1963. pap. 16.50 (ISBN 0-471-19195-7). Wiley.

Dana, J. D., et al. Systems of Minerology, 3 vols. 7th ed. Incl. Vol. 1. Elements, Sulfides, Sulfosalts, Oxides. 7th ed. Dana, James D., et al. 834p. 1944. 85.00 (ISBN 0-471-19239-2); Vol. 2. Halides, Nitrates, Borates, Carbonates, Sulfates, Phosphates, Arsenates, Tungstates, Molybdates. Dana, James D., et al. 1951. 94.95 (ISBN 0-471-19272-4); Vol. 3. System of Mineralogy: Silica Minerals. Dana, James D., et al. 334p. 1962. 60.00 (ISBN 0-471-19287-2). Pub. by Wiley-Interscience). Wiley.

Deer, W. A., et al. Rock Forming Minerals: Disilicates & Ring Silicates, Vol. 1B. 608p. 1985. 125.00 (ISBN 0-470-26634-1). Halsted Pr.

Deer, William A., et al. Introduction to Rock Forming Minerals. 528p. 1966. pap. 29.95x (ISBN 0-470-20516-4). Halsted Pr.

Desautels, Paul E. Rocks & Minerals. LC 73-91134. (Collector's Series: No. 1). (Illus.). 160p. 1982. 3.95 (ISBN 0-448-04088-3, G&D). Putnam Pub Group.

Dietrich, R. V. & Wicander, E. Reed. Minerals, Rock & Fossils. LC 82-20220. (Self-Teaching Guides Ser.). 212p. 1983. pap. text ed. 9.95 (ISBN 0-471-89883-X, Pub. by Wiley Pr). Wiley.

Doe, B. R. & Smith, D. K., eds. Studies in Mineralogy & Precambrian Geology: A Volume in Honor of John W. Gruner. LC 70-190173. (Geological Society of America Memoir Ser.: No. 135). pap. 93.00 (ISBN 0-317-30052-0, 2025029). Bks Demand UMI.

Ernst, W. G. Earth Materials. 1969. pap. text ed. 15.95 (ISBN 0-13-222604-9). P-H.

French, Bevan M. Progressive Contact Metamorphism of the Biwabik Iron-Formation, Mesabi Range, Minnesota. LC 68-66592. (Bulletin: No. 45). (Illus.). 1968. 4.50x (ISBN 0-8166-0478-9). Minn Geol Survey.

Fripiat, J., ed. Advanced Techniques for Clay Mineral Analysis. (Developments in Sedimentology Ser.: Vol. 34). 236p. 1982. 42.75 (ISBN 0-444-42002-9). Elsevier.

Frissel, M. J., ed. Cycling of Mineral Nutrients in Agricultural Ecosystems. (Developments in Agricultural & Managed-Forest Ecology Ser.: Vol. 3). 356p. 1978. Repr. 64.00 (ISBN 0-444-41660-9). Elsevier.

Frye, Keith. Modern Minerology. (Illus.). 336p. 1973. ref. ed. 33.95 (ISBN 0-13-595686-2). P-H.

Frye, Keith, ed. The Encyclopedia of Mineralogy. (Encylopedia of Earth Sciences Ser.: Vol. 4B). 816p. 1981. 95.00 (ISBN 0-87933-184-4). Van Nos Reinhold.

Girard, R. M. Texas Rocks & Minerals: An Amateur's Guide. (Illus.). 109p. 1964. Repr. 2.50 (ISBN 0-686-29314-2, GB 6). Bur Econ Geology.

Gupta, A. & Yagi, K. Petrology & Genesis of Leucite-Bearing Rocks. (Minerals & Rocks Ser.: Vol. 14). (Illus.). 250p. 1980. 44.00 (ISBN 0-387-09864-X). Springer-Verlag.

Hey, M. H. & Embry, P. G. An Index of Mineral Species & Varieties Arranged Chemically with an Alphabetical Index of Accepted Mineral Names & Synonyms. 2nd ed. 1975. Set. 55.00x (ISBN 0-686-37456-8). Index (ISBN 0-565-00097-7). Appendix (ISBN 0-565-00578-2). Second Appendix (ISBN 0-565-00725-4). Sabbot-Natural Hist Bks.

Holland, Heinrich D. The Chemistry of the Atmosphere & Oceans. LC 77-28176. 351p. 1978. 50.95 (ISBN 0-471-03509-2, Pub. by Wiley-Interscience). Wiley.

Hough, Jack L., ed. Turbidity Currents & the Transportation of Coarse Sediments to Deep Water: A Symposium. LC 52-2310. (Society of Economic Paleontologists & Mineralogists, Special Publication: No. 2). pap. 27.80 (ISBN 0-317-27102-4, 2024731). Bks Demand UMI.

Howell, Fred G., et al, eds. Mineral Cycling in Southeastern Ecosystems: Proceedings. LC 75-33463. (ERDA Symposium Ser.). 920p. 1975. pap. 31.00 (ISBN 0-87079-022-6, CONF-740513); microfiche 4.50 (ISBN 0-87079-276-8, CONF-740513). DOE.

Hurlbut, Cornelius S., Jr. & Klein, Cornelius. Dana's Manual of Mineralogy. 19th ed. LC 77-1131. 532p. 1977. 38.50 (ISBN 0-471-03288-3). Wiley.

International Workshop on Phosphate & Other Minerals, 5th. Phosphate & Other Minerals International Workshop: On Phosphate & Other Minerals, 5th International Workshop Abstracts. Massry, S. G., ed. (Mineral & Electrolyte Metabolism Journal: Vol. 6, No. 4-5, 1981). (Illus.). 52p. 1981. pap. 8.00 (ISBN 3-8055-3441-8). S Karger.

Jensen, M. L. & Bateman, A. M. Economic Mineral Deposits. 3rd rev. ed. LC 78-9852. 593p. 1981. text ed. 38.50 (ISBN 0-471-09043-3). Wiley.

Johnson, Wesley M. & Maxwell, John A. Rock & Mineral Analysis, Vol.27. 2nd ed. LC 81-1659. (Chemical Analysis Ser.). 489p. 1981. 80.00x (ISBN 0-471-02743-X, Pub. by Wiley-Interscience). Wiley.

Keller, W. D. Common Rocks & Minerals of Missouri. rev. ed. LC 67-66173. (Illus.). 78p. 1961. pap. 5.95x (ISBN 0-8262-0585-2). U of Mo Pr.

Kieffer, S. W. & Navrotsky, A. Microscopic to Macroscopic: Atomic Environments to Mineral Thermodynamics. Ribber, Paul H., ed. 428p. 1985. 13.00 (ISBN 0-318-17825-7). Mineralogical Soc.

Kimbler, Frank S. & Narsavage, Robert J., Jr. New Mexico Rocks & Minerals Guide. LC 81-5350. (Illus.). 76p. (Orig.). 1981. pap. 8.95 (ISBN 0-913270-97-0). Sunstone Pr.

Kirkaldy, J. F. Minerals & Rocks. (Illus.). 192p. 1982. 12.95 (ISBN 0-7137-0783-6, Pub. by Blandford Pr England). Sterling.

Klein, Cornelis & Hurlbut, Cornelius S., Jr. Manual of Mineralogy. 20th ed. 650p. 1985. 35.95x (ISBN 0-471-80580-7). Wiley.

Kobell, Franz & Ritter, V. Geschichte der Mineralogie. Repr. of 1864 ed. 50.00 (ISBN 0-384-30015-4). Johnson Repr.

Kohland, William. Mineral Identification. LC 77-73455. 1977. 9.00 (ISBN 0-910042-31-4); pap. 4.50 (ISBN 0-910042-30-6). Allegheny.

Kostov, I. & Stefanova, J. M. Sulphide Minerals. Crystal Chemistry, Parageneses and Systematics. (Illus.). 212p. 1982. text ed. 26.50x (ISBN 3-510-65110-3). Lubrecht & Cramer.

Kuzin, M. & Egorov, N. Field Manual of Minerals. 194p. 1979. 9.45 (ISBN 0-8285-1516-6, Pub. by Mir Pubs USSR). Imported Pubns.

Laporte, Leo F., ed. Reefs in Time & Space: Selected Examples from the Recent & Ancient. LC 74-165238. (Society of Economic Paleontologists & Mineralogists, Special Publication: No. 18). pap. 65.00 (ISBN 0-317-27147-4, 2024745). Bks Demand UMI.

Le Blanc, Rufus J. & Breeding, Julia G., eds. Regional Aspects of Carbonate Deposition: A Symposium. LC 57-2837. (Society of Economic Paleontologists & Mineralologists, Special Publication: No. 5). pap. 53.80 (ISBN 0-317-27104-0, 2024732). Bks Demand UMI.

Lefond, Stanley J., ed. Industrial Minerals & Rocks, 2 vols. 5th ed. LC 82-71993. (Illus.). 1508p. 1983. Set. 80.00x (ISBN 0-89520-402-9, 402-9). Soc Mining Eng.

Lisitzin, Alexander P. Sedimentation in the World Ocean with Emphasis on the Nature, Distribution & Behavior of Marine Suspensions. Rodolfo, Kelvin S., ed. LC 72-172081. (Society of Economic Paleontologists & Mineralogists, Special Publication: No. 17). pap. 58.00 (ISBN 0-317-27149-0, 2024744). Bks Demand UMI.

McConnell, D. Apatite: Its Crystal Chemistry, Mineralogy, Utilization, & Biologic Occurrences. LC 72-88060. (Applied Mineralogy Ser.: Vol. 5). (Illus.). 111p. 1973. 45.00 (ISBN 0-387-81095-1). Springer-Verlag.

MacFall, Russell P. Minerals & Gems. LC 74-28082. (Illus.). 256p. 1975. 17.50i (ISBN 0-690-00687-X). T Y Crowell.

Mackenzie, W. S. & Guilford, C. Atlas of Rock-Forming Minerals in Thin Section. 98p. 1980. pap. 28.95x (ISBN 0-470-26921-9). Halsted Pr.

McQuiston, Frank W., Jr. & Shoemaker, Robert S. Primary Crushing Plant Design. (Illus.). 1978. 33.00x (ISBN 0-89520-252-2). Soc Mining Eng.

Malaghan, Subhas G. Ultrafine Grinding & Separation of Industrial Minerals. LC 83-82078. 177p. 1983. pap. 32.00x (ISBN 0-89520-419-3, 419-3). Soc Mining Eng.

Marfunin, A. S. Spectroscopy, Luminescence & Radiation Centers in Minerals. Schiffer, W. W., tr. from Russ. (Illus.). 1979. 58.00 (ISBN 0-387-09070-3). Springer-Verlag.

Mason, Brian & Berry, L. G. Elements of Mineralogy. LC 68-13311. (Geology Ser.). (Illus.). 550p. 1968. 34.95x (ISBN 0-7167-0235-5). W H Freeman.

Middleton, Gerard V., ed. Primary Sedimentary Structures & Their Hydrodynamic Interpretation: A Symposium. LC 76-219474. (Society of Economic Paleontologists & Mineralogists, Special Publication: No. 12). pap. 68.00 (ISBN 0-317-27158-X, 2024738). Bks Demand UMI.

Milovsky, A. Mineralogy & Petrography. 437p. 1982. 10.95 (ISBN 0-8285-2310-X, Pub. by Mir Pubs USSR). Imported Pubns.

Mitchell, A. H. & Garson, M. S. Mineral Deposits & Global Tectonic Settings. (Earth Science Ser.). 1982. 50.00 (ISBN 0-12-499050-9). Acad Pr.

Mitchell, Richard S. Mineral Names: What Do They Mean? 1979. 15.95 (ISBN 0-442-24593-9). Van Nos Reinhold.

Mondadori, ed. Simon & Schuster's Guide to Rocks & Minerals. pap. 10.95 (ISBN 0-671-24417-5). S&S.

Montgomery, Arthur. The Mineralogy of Pennsylvania: 1922-1965. (Special Publication: No. 9). (Illus.). 104p. 1969. 15.00 (ISBN 0-910006-43-1). Acad Nat Sci Phila.

Moore, Nathaniel F. Ancient Mineralogy: An Inquiry Respecting Mineral Substances Mentioned by the Ancients. Albritton, Claude C., Jr., ed. LC 77-6532. (History of Geology Ser.). 1978. Repr. of 1834 ed. lib. bdg. 21.00 (ISBN 0-405-10452-9). Ayer Co Pubs.

Moscow, Vsesoiuznyi Nauchno-issledovatel'skii Institut Mineral'nogo Syr'ia. New Data on Rare Element Mineralogy (Authorized Translation from the Russian) Ginzburg, A. I., ed. LC 61-18756. pap. 36.00 (ISBN 0-317-10653-8, 2003368). Bks Demand UMI.

Nicol, A. W., ed. Physicochemical Methods of Mineral Analysis. LC 72-95070. 508p. 1975. 75.00x (ISBN 0-306-30739-1, Plenum Pr). Plenum Pub.

Niggli, Paul. Rocks & Mineral Deposits. Parker, Robert L., tr. LC 53-8082. (Geology Texts Ser.). pap. 71.50 (ISBN 0-317-29240-4, 2055547). Bks Demand UMI.

O'Donoghue. Beginners Guide to Minerals. 1983. pap. text ed. 9.95. Butterworth.

Park, W. C, et al, eds. Applied Mineralogy. LC 84-29437. (Illus.). 1194p. 1985. 90.00 (ISBN 0-89520-487-8). Metal Soc.

Pearl, Richard M. Cleaning & Preserving Minerals. 5th ed. 1980. pap. 4.00 (ISBN 0-940566-02-8). R M Pearl Bks.

Peck, W. A., ed. Bone & Mineral Research Annual 3: A Yearly Survey of Developments in the Field of Bone & Mineral Metabolism. 400p. 1985. 57.50 (ISBN 0-444-90347-X). Elsevier.

Peel, Fred W. Domestic Taxation of Hard Minerals. 2nd ed. (Resource Materials Ser.). 427p. 1983. pap. text ed. 40.00 (ISBN 0-8318-0142-5, R142). Am Law Inst.

Petruk, William, intro. by. Process Mineralogy III. LC 84-71244. (Symposia on Process Mineralogy Ser.). (Illus.). 322p. 1984. pap. 40.00 (ISBN 0-89520-426-6, 426-6). Soc Mining Eng.

Phillips, W. J. & Phillips, N. An Introduction to Mineralogy for Geologist. LC 79-42898. 344p. 1980. 69.95 (ISBN 0-471-27642-1); pap. 27.95 (ISBN 0-471-27795-9). Wiley.

Phillips, William. An Outline of Mineralogy & Geology: Intended for the Use of Those Who May Desire to Become Acquainted with the Elements of Those Sciences. Albritton, Claude C., Jr., ed. LC 77-6536. (History of Geology Ser.). (Illus.). 1978. Repr. of 1816 ed. lib. bdg. 17.00x (ISBN 0-405-10456-1). Ayer Co Pubs.

Picot, P. & Johan, Z. Atlas of Ore Minerals. (Illus.). 460p. 1983. 170.00 (ISBN 0-444-99684-2). Elsevier.

Pierrot, Roland. Chemical & Determinative Tables of Mineralogy Without the Silicates. LC 79-90000. 608p. 1980. 98.75x (ISBN 0-89352-077-2). Masson Pub.

Pough, Frederick H. A Field Guide to Rocks & Minerals. 4th ed. (Peterson Field Guide Ser.). 1976. 17.95 (ISBN 0-395-24047-6); pap. 12.95 (ISBN 0-395-24049-2). HM.

Ramdohr, Paul. The Ore Minerals & Their Intergrowths, 2 vols. 2nd ed. LC 79-40745. (International Series in Earth Sciences: Vol. 35). (Illus.). 1269p. 1981. Set. 200.00 (ISBN 0-08-023801-7). Pergamon.

Rigby, J. Keith & Hamblin, W. K., eds. Recognition of Ancient Sedimentary Environments. LC 72-194231. (Society of Economic Paleontologists & Mineralogists, Special Publication: No. 16). pap. 87.50 (ISBN 0-317-27126-1, 2024741). Bks Demand UMI.

Rittmann, A. Stable Mineral Assemblages of Igneous Rocks. LC 72-90269. (Minerals, Rocks & Inorganic Materials Ser.: Vol. 7). (Illus.). 250p. 1973. 47.00 (ISBN 0-387-06030-8). Springer-Verlag.

Rogers, Austin F. & Staples, Lloyd. Introduction to the Study of Minerals. 3rd ed. LC 75-41235. Repr. of 1937 ed. 34.50 (ISBN 0-404-14699-6). AMS Pr.

Royal Society of London Publications, et al. Mineralogy: Towards the Twenty-First Century. (Illus.). 1978. text ed. 90.00x (ISBN 0-85403-092-1). Scholium Intl.

Saggerson, E. Identification Tables for Minerals in Thin Sections. 280p. 1975. pap. text ed. 14.95x (ISBN 0-582-44343-1). Longman.

Saxena, S. K., ed. Advances in Physical Geochemistry, Vol. 2. (Illus.). 353p. 1982. 46.00 (ISBN 0-387-90644-4). Springer-Verlag.

--Kinetics & Equilibrium in Mineral Reactions. (Advances in Physical Geochemistry: Vol. 3). (Illus.). 305p. 1983. 42.00 (ISBN 0-387-90865-X). Springer-Verlag.

Perry, Milton F. Infernal Machines: The Story of Confederate Submarine & Mine Warfare. (Illus.). 231p. 1985. pap. 8.95 (ISBN 0-8071-1285-2). La State U Pr.

MINES AND MINERAL RESOURCES

see also Ceramic Materials; Mineralogy; Mining Engineering; Mining Geology; Precious Metals; Prospecting; Raw Materials

also specific types of mines and mining, e.g. Coal Mines and Mining, Gold Mines and Mining

Agterberg, F. Mineral Energy Resource Evaluation: Probabilistic Methods. Date not set. price not set. Elsevier.

Anders, Gerhard, et al, eds. The Economics of Mineral Extraction. Gramm, W. Phillip. LC 79-22949. 334p. 1980. 49.95x (ISBN 0-03-053171-3). Praeger.

The Application of Modern Transport Technology to Mineral Development in Developing Countries. pap. 12.00 (ISBN 0-686-94705-3, UN76/8/1, UN). Unipub.

Bender, F., ed. The Mineral Resources Potential of the Earth: Proceedings of the International Symposium, 2nd, Hannover, West Germany, 1979. (Illus.). 156p. 1979. pap. text ed. 21.10x (ISBN 3-510-65093-X). Lubrecht & Cramer.

Beus, A. A. & Grigorian, S. V. Geochemical Exploration Methods for Mineral Deposits. Levinson, A. A., ed. Teteruk-Schneider, Rita, tr. LC 77-75045. (Illus.). 1977. 32.00x (ISBN 0-915834-03-0). Applied Pub.

Bibliography & Index of the Geology & Mineral Resources of Washington, 1937-1956: 1937-1956. Reichert, William H. (Bulletin Ser.: No. 46). 721p. 1960. 3.00 (ISBN 0-686-34699-8). Geologic Pubns.

Biron, C. & Arioglu, E. Designs of Supports in Mines. 248p. 1983. 45.95 (ISBN 0-471-86726-8). Wiley.

Board on Mineral & Energy Resources. Redistribution of Accessory Elements in Mining & Mineral Processing: Coal & Oil Shale, Pt. I. 1979. pap. 10.75 (ISBN 0-309-02897-3). Natl Acad Pr.

--Redistribution of Accessory Elements in Mining & Mineral Processing: Uranium, Phosphate, & Alumina, Pt. II. 1979. pap. 13.75 (ISBN 0-309-02899-X). Natl Acad Pr.

Bowie, S. H., ed. Mineral Deposits of Europe: Vol. 1-Northwest Europe. 362p. 1979. 86.25x (ISBN 0-900488-44-1). IMM North Am.

British-North American Committee. Mineral Development in the Eighties: Prospects & Problems. LC 76-53628. 64p. 1977. 3.00 (ISBN 0-902594-29-X). Natl Planning.

British Sulfur Corporation. Mineral Resources of the Arab Countries. 100p. 1983. 130.00 (ISBN 0-902777-54-8, NO. 5055). Methuen Inc.

Brooks, R. R. Biological Methods of Prospecting for Minerals. LC 82-21819. 322p. 1983. 48.50 (ISBN 0-471-87400-0, Pub. by Wiley-Interscience). Wiley.

Burns, R. M. Conflict & Its Resolution in the Administration of Mineral Resources in Canada. 63p. (Orig.). 1976. pap. text ed. 5.00x (ISBN 0-88757-000-3, Pub. by Ctr Resource Stud Canada). Brookfield Pub Co.

Cargo, David N. & Mallory, Bob F. Man & His Geologic Environment. 2nd ed. LC 76-7655. 1977. text ed. 29.95 (ISBN 0-201-00894-7). Addison-Wesley.

Carlson, Ellsworth C. Kaiping Mines, Eighteen Seventy-Seven to Nineteen Twelve. rev. 2nd ed. LC 71-148943. (East Asian Monographs Ser: No. 3). 1971. pap. 11.00x (ISBN 0-674-49700-7). Harvard U Pr.

Carson, J. H. Early Recollections of the Mines. 59.95 (ISBN 0-8490-0074-2). Gordon Pr.

Collins, J. H. The Mineralogy of Cornwall & Devon. 1981. 50.00x (ISBN 0-686-97167-1, Pub. by D B Barton England). State Mutual Bk.

COMECON's Mineral Development Potential & Its Implications for Canada. (Mineral Bulletins: No. 183). 112p. 1980. pap. 5.75 (ISBN 0-660-10204-8, SSC137, SSC). Unipub.

Concise World Atlas of Geology & Mineral Deposits. 110p. 1982. 52.00x (ISBN 0-900117-28-1, Pub. by Mining Journal England). State Mutual Bk.

Cowan, Jack C. & Weintritt, Donald J. Water-Formed Scale Deposits. LC 75-5089. 606p. 1976. 79.95x (ISBN 0-87201-896-2). Gulf Pub.

David, M. Geostatistical Ore Reserve Estimation. (Developments in Geomathematics: Vol. 2). 364p. 1977. 55.50 (ISBN 0-444-41532-7). Elsevier.

Dawson, J. B. Kimberlites & Their Xenoliths. (Minerals & Rocks: Vol. 15). (Illus.). 252p. 1980. 53.00 (ISBN 0-387-10208-6). Springer-Verlag.

Deer, W. A., et al. Rock Forming Minerals: Orthosilicates, Vol. 1A. 2nd ed. 919p. 1982. 149.95x (ISBN 0-470-26633-3). Halsted Pr.

--Rock Forming Minerals, Vol. 5. 372p. 1962. 39.95x (ISBN 0-471-20524-9). Halsted Pr.

--Rock Forming Minerals, Vol. 1. 333p. 1962. 34.95x (ISBN 0-471-20518-4). Halsted Pr.

--Rock Forming Minerals, Vol. 4. 435p. 1963. 39.95x (ISBN 0-471-20523-0). Halsted Pr.

De Vore, R. William & Carpenter, Stanley B., eds. Symposium on Surface Mining Hydrology, Sedimentology, & Reclamation. LC 79-91553. (Illus.). 353p. (Orig.). 1979. pap. 33.50 (ISBN 0-89779-024-3, UKY BU119). OES Pubns.

Dictionnaire Minier Russe-Francais. (Fr. & Rus.). 1973. pap. 25.00 (ISBN 0-686-56770-6, M-6150). French & Eur.

Elsevier's Mineral & Rock Table. Lof, P., compiled by. 1982. 13.00 (ISBN 0-444-42081-9). Elsevier.

Embrey, Peter G. & Fuller, John P. A Manual of New Mineral Names, 1892-1978. 1980. 55.00x (ISBN 0-19-858501-2). Oxford U Pr.

Fischman, Leonard L. World Mineral Trends & U. S. Supply Problems. LC 80-8025. (Resources for the Future, Inc. Research Paper R-20). (Illus.). 576p. (Orig.). 1981. pap. text ed. 20.00x (ISBN 0-8018-2491-5). Johns Hopkins.

Gary, James H., ed. Proceedings of the Fourteenth Oil Shale Symposium. LC 81-10238. (Illus.). 433p. 1981. pap. text ed. 15.00 (ISBN 0-918062-46-2). Colo Sch Mines.

Gentry, Donald W. & O'Neill, Thomas J. Mine Investment Analysis. LC 84-51346. (Illus.). 502p. 1984. 50.00x (ISBN 0-89520-429-0, 429-0). Soc Mining Eng.

Govett, G. J. & Govett, M. H., eds. World Mineral Supplies. (Developments in Economic Geology: Vol. 3). 476p. 1976. 72.50 (ISBN 0-444-41366-9). Elsevier.

Gregory, C. E. Rudiments of Mining Practice. LC 83-80651. 128p. 1983. 24.00x (ISBN 0-87201-783-4). Gulf Pub.

Griffin, A. R. Mining in the East Midlands: 1550-1947. 338p. 1971. 35.00x (ISBN 0-7146-2585-X, F Cass Co). Biblio Dist.

Hartman, Howard L., et al. Mine Ventilation & Air Conditioning. 2nd ed. Mutmansky, Jan M. & Wang, Y. J., eds. LC 81-19662. 791p. 1982. 57.50x (ISBN 0-471-05690-1, Pub. by Wiley-Interscience). Wiley.

Hodges, L. K. The Reduction of Gold & Silver Ore. (Prospecting Ser.). 24p. pap. 2.95 (ISBN 0-8466-1993-8, S134D). Shorey.

Hughes, E., ed. Jobson's Mining Year Book, 1979. LC 66-2200. 305p. 1979. 50.00x (ISBN 0-8002-2224-5). Intl Pubns Serv.

IFAC Symposium, 3rd, Montreal, PQ, Canada, Aug. 1980. Automation in Mining, Mineral & Metal Processing: Proceedings. O'Shea, J. & Polis, M., eds. LC 80-40809. (Illus.). 712p. 1981. 160.00 (ISBN 0-08-026164-7). Pergamon.

The Infrared Spectra Handbook of Minerals & Clays. 1982. 265.00 (ISBN 0-8456-0080-X). Sadtler Res.

International Symposium on the Transportation & Handling of Minerals, 3rd, Vancouver, British Colmbia, Canada, Oct. 1979. Minerals Transportion: Proceedings, Vol. 3. Argall, George O., Jr., ed. LC 76-189985. (A World Mining Bk.). 1980. pap. 50.00 (ISBN 0-87930-080-9). Miller Freeman.

Interregional Seminar on the Development of Mineral Resources of the Continental Shelf: Port-of-Spain, Trinidad & Tobago. (Eng. & Fr.). pap. 5.00 (ISBN 0-686-94740-1, UN72/2A6, UN). Unipub.

Ivosevic, Stanley W. Gold & Silver Handbook: On Geology, Exploration, Production, Economics of Large Tonnage, Low Grade Deposits. (Illus.). 217p. (Orig.). 1984. pap. 29.50 (ISBN 0-9611352-3-9). S W Ivosevic.

Jaenicke, G., et al, eds. Mining Ventures in Developing Countries. (Studies of the Transnational Law of Natural Resources: No. 1). 1979. lib. bdg. 58.00 (ISBN 90-268-1037-7, Pub. by Kluwer Law Netherlands). Kluwer Academic.

Jeremic, M. L. Elements of Hydraulic Coal Mine Design. LC 83-10762. 160p. 1983. 30.95x (ISBN 0-87201-444-4). Gulf Pub.

Jobson's Mining Year Book 1981. 24th ed. LC 66-2200. (Illus.). 431p. 1981. 75.00x (ISBN 0-8002-2872-3). Intl Pubns Serv.

Jobson's Mining Year Book, 1982. 25th ed. LC 66-2200. (Illus.). 491p. 1982. 105.00x (ISBN 0-8002-3052-3). Intl Pubns Serv.

Jones, M. J., ed. Availability of Strategic Minerals. 109p. (Orig.). 1980. pap. 54.75x (ISBN 0-900488-48-4). IMM North Am.

--Commonwealth Mining & Metallurgical Congress, Hong Kong, 11th, 1978: Proceedings. (Commonwealth Mining & Metallurgical Congresses Ser.). 818p. 1979. text ed. 118.00x (ISBN 0-900488-45-X). IMM North Am.

--Geology, Mining & Extractive Processing of Uranium. 171p. (Orig.). 1977. pap. text ed. 63.25x (ISBN 0-900488-35-2). IMM North Am.

--Mineral Processing & Extractive Metallurgy. (Proceedings of the Ninth Commonwealth Mining & Metallurgical Congress 1969: Vol. 3). 938p. 1970. text ed. 51.75x (ISBN 0-900488-05-0). IMM North Am.

--Mining & Petroleum Geology. (Proceedings of the Ninth Commonwealth Mining & Metallurgical Congress 1969: Vol. 2). 774p. 1970. text ed. 46.00x (ISBN 0-900488-03-4). IMM North Am.

--Mining & Petroleum Technology. (Proceedings of the Ninth Commonwealth Mining & Metallurgical Congress 1969: Vol. 1). 1059p. 1970. text ed. 51.75x (ISBN 0-900488-04-2). IMM North Am.

--National & International Management of Mineral Resources. 350p. (Orig.). 1981. pap. text ed. 132.25x (ISBN 0-900488-58-1). IMM North Am.

--Physical & Fabrication Metallurgy. (Proceedings of the Ninth Commonwealth Mining & Metallurgical Congress 1969: Vol. 4). 561p. 1970. text ed. 46.00x (ISBN 0-900488-01-8). IMM North Am.

--Tunnelling '82. 301p. (Orig.). 1982. pap. text ed. 110.00x (ISBN 0-900488-62-X). IMM North Am.

Karelin, N. T. Mine Transport. 193p. 1981. 20.00x (ISBN 0-86125-796-0, Pub. by Orient Longman India). State Mutual Bk.

Kelly, Errol G. & Spottiswood, David J. Introduction to Mineral Processing. LC 82-2807. 491p. 1982. 74.95 (ISBN 0-471-03379-0, Pub. by Wiley-Interscience). Wiley.

Kesler, S. E. Our Finite Resources. 1975. 19.95 (ISBN 0-07-034245-8). McGraw.

Krige, D. G. Lognormal: De Wijsian Geostatistics for Ore Evaluation. 50p. 1980. 30.00x (ISBN 0-620-03006-2, Pub. by Mining Journal England). State Mutual Bk.

Kudryk, V. & Corrigan, D. A., eds. Precious Metals: Mining, Extraction, & Processing: Proceedings, AIME Annual Meeting, Los Angeles, 1984. LC 83-63270. (Illus.). 621p. 1984. 42.00 (ISBN 0-89520-469-X); members 28.00; student members 15.00. Metal Soc.

Kuhner, David & Rizzo, Tania, eds. Bibliotheca De Re Metallica: The Herbert Clark Hoover Collection of Mining & Metallurgy. LC 80-82055. (Illus.). 219p. 1980. 125.00 (ISBN 0-937368-00-8). Honnold Lib.

Kuzin, M. & Egorov, N. Field Manual of Minerals. 194p. 1979. 9.45 (ISBN 0-8285-1516-6, Pub. by Mir Pubs USSR). Imported Pubns.

Kuzvart, M. Industrial Minerals & Rocks. (Developments in Economic Geology Ser.: Vol. 18). 454p. 1984. 74.00 (ISBN 0-444-99605-2). Elsevier.

Leith, Charles K. World Minerals & World Politics. LC 74-113286. 1970. Repr. of 1931 ed. 19.50x (ISBN 0-8046-1322-2, Pub. by Kennikat). Assoc Faculty Pr.

Li, Ta M., intro. by. Mineral Resources of the Pacific Rim. LC 82-71990. (Illus.). 229p. (Orig.). 1982. pap. 30.00x (ISBN 0-89520-299-9). Soc Mining Eng.

Littlefield, Charles W. Man, Minerals, & Masters. (Illus.). 172p. 1980. pap. 7.00 (ISBN 0-89540-059-6, SB-059). Sun Pub.

Lynch, A. J., et al. Mineral & Coal Flotation Circuits: Their Simulation & Control. (Developments in Mineral Processing Ser.: Vol. 3). 292p. 1981. 61.75 (ISBN 0-444-41919-5). Elsevier.

Mackenzie, Brian W. Canada's Competitive Positon in Copper & Zinc Markets. 60p. (Orig.). 1979. pap. text ed. 5.25 (ISBN 0-686-63143-9, Pub. by Ctr Resource Stud Canada). Brookfield Pub Co.

McKercher, R. M., ed. Potash Mining Processing Transportation: Proceedings of the International Potash Technology Conference, Saskatoon, Saskatchewan, Canada, October 3-5, 1983. (Illus.). 887p. 1983. 165.00 (ISBN 0-08-025401-2). Pergamon.

McQuiston, Frank W., Jr. & Shoemaker, Robert S. Primary Crushing Plant Design. (Illus.). 1978. 33.00x (ISBN 0-89520-252-2). Soc Mining Eng.

Maull, Hanns. Energy, Minerals, & Western Security. LC 84-15410. 432p. 1985. text ed. 35.00x (ISBN 0-8018-2500-8). Johns Hopkins.

Measurement & Control of Respirable Dust in Mining. 1980. 12.50 (ISBN 0-309-03047-1). Natl Acad Pr.

Miers, John. Travels in Chili & La Plata, 2 Vols. LC 76-128416. Repr. of 1826 ed. Set. 67.50 (ISBN 0-404-04317-8). AMS Pr.

Mikesell, Raymond F. New Patterns of World Mineral Development. LC 79-90054. (British-North American Committee Ser.). 116p. 1980. 5.00 (ISBN 0-89068-049-3). Natl Planning.

Mineral Resources: Proceedings of the 3rd Session of the Committee on Natural Resources. (Mineral Resources Development Ser.: No. 43). pap. 7.00 (ISBN 0-686-92981-0, UN77/2F13, UN). Unipub.

Minerals of the World Table. 1983. 13.00 (ISBN 0-444-42135-1). Elsevier.

Mining Journal Books Ltd. Negotiation & Drafting of Mining Development Agreements. 236p. 1980. 30.00x (ISBN 0-900117-11-7, Pub. by Mining Journal England). State Mutual Bk.

Mining Journal Books Ltd., ed. Concise World Atlas of Geology & Mineral Deposits. 110p. 1981. 90.00x (ISBN 0-900117-22-2, Pub. by Mining Journal England). State Mutual Bk.

--World Production & Consumption of Minerals in 1978. 110p. 1982. 65.00x (ISBN 0-900117-25-7, Pub. by Mining Journal England). State Mutual Bk.

Mining Journal Editors. Mining Annual Review 1980. 200p. 1980. 60.00x (ISBN 0-686-69873-8, Pub. by Mining Journal England). State Mutual Bk.

Mining Journal Ltd., ed. Mining Annual Review, 1981. 600p. 1981. 95.00x (ISBN 0-686-87296-7, Pub. by Mining Journal England). State Mutual Bk.

--Mining Annual Review 1981. 100p. 1981. 100.00x (ISBN 0-686-87297-5, Pub. by Mining Journal England). State Mutual Bk.

Mousset-Jones, Pierre, ed. International Mine Ventilation Congress, 2nd: Proceedings. LC 80-52943. (Illus.). 864p. 1980. 38.00x (ISBN 0-89520-271-9). Soc Mining Eng.

Muhly, James D. Copper & Tin: The Distribution of Mineral Resources & the Nature of the Metals Trade in the Bronze Age, Including Supplement. new ed. (Connecticut Academy of Arts & Sciences Transaction Ser.: Vol. 43 & 46). 380p. 1976. 29.50 (ISBN 0-208-01573-6, Archon). Shoe String.

National & International Management of Mineral Resources. 1981. 195.00x (ISBN 0-686-97552-9, Pub. by Inst Mining England). State Mutual Bk.

National Research Council. Mineral Resources & the Environment. 1975. pap. 9.75 (ISBN 0-309-02343-2). Natl Acad Pr.

National Research Council Geophysics Research Board. Mineral Resources: Genetic Understanding for Practical Applications. 1981. pap. text ed. 12.95 (ISBN 0-309-03193-1). Natl Acad Pr.

Naylor, Peter. Discovering Lost Mines. (Discovering Ser.: No. 265). (Illus.). 64p. 1983. pap. 3.50 (ISBN 0-85263-544-3, Pub. by Shire Pubns England). Seven Hills Bks.

North, Oliver S. Mineral Exploration, Mining, & Processing Patents, 1979. LC 80-66760. (Illus.). 137p. 1980. 35.00x (ISBN 0-89520-278-6). Soc Mining Eng.

Nriagu, J. O. & Moore, P. B., eds. Phosphate Minerals. (Illus.). 470p. 1984. 57.50 (ISBN 0-387-12757-7). Springer-Verlag.

Nuclear Techniques & Mineral Resources. (Proceedings Ser.). (Illus.). 546p. 1969. pap. 39.50 (ISBN 92-0-040069-8, ISP198, IAEA). Unipub.

Nuclear Techniques & Mineral Resources: 1977. (Proceedings Ser.). (Illus.). 651p. 1977. pap. 75.25 (ISBN 92-0-060077-8, ISP464, IAEA). Unipub.

O'Neil, T. J., ed. Sixteenth Application of Computers & Operations Research in the Mineral Industry. Society of Mining Engineers, Conference in Tucson, 1979. 653p. 1979. 30.00 (ISBN 0-317-35840-5, 261-1); members 22.00 (ISBN 0-317-35841-3); student members 19.00 (ISBN 0-317-35842-1). Soc Mining Eng.

Pearson, John S. Ocean Floor Mining. LC 75-801. (Ocean Technology Review Ser: No. 2). (Illus.). 205p. 1975. 24.00 (ISBN 0-8155-0569-8). Noyes.

Persaud, Thakoor. Conflicts Between Multinational Corporations & Less Developed Countries: The Case of Bauxite Mining in the Caribbean with Special Reference to Guyana. Bruchey, Stuart, ed. LC 80-587. (Multinational Corporations Ser.). 1980. lib. bdg. 28.50x (ISBN 0-405-13378-2). Ayer Co Pubs.

Pettus, John. Fodinae Regales (The Mines Royal) 115p. 1981. Repr. of 1670 ed. text ed. 42.75x (ISBN 0-686-32510-9). IMM North Am.

Pryor, E. J. Mineral Processing. 3rd ed. (Illus.). 844p. 1974. Repr. of 1965 ed. 70.50 (ISBN 0-444-20010-X, Pub. by Elsevier Applied Sci England). Elsevier.

Radiation Protection in Mining & Milling of Uranium & Thorium. 1976. 19.95 (ISBN 92-2-101504-1). Intl Labour Office.

Ramani, R. V., ed. Fourteenth Application of Computer Methods in the Mineral Industry. Society of Mining Engineers, Conference at the Pennsylvania State University, 1977. 1207p. 1977. 20.00 (ISBN 0-317-35828-6, 047-3); members 15.00 (ISBN 0-317-35829-4); student members 13.50 (ISBN 0-317-35830-8). Soc Mining Eng.

Ramsey, Robert H. Men & Mines of Newmont: A Fifty Year History. 1973. lib. bdg. 14.00x (ISBN 0-374-96710-5). Octagon.

Rapid Excavation & Tunneling Conference, 1979. R E T C Proceedings, 2 vols. Hustrulid, William A. & Maevis, Alfred C., eds. LC 79-52280. (Illus.). 1819p. 1979. 60.00x (ISBN 0-89520-266-2). Soc Mining Eng.

Reedman, J. H. Techniques in Mineral Exploration. (Illus.). 526p. 1979. 89.00 (ISBN 0-85334-817-0, Pub. by Elsevier Applied Sci England); pap. 53.75 (ISBN 0-85334-851-0, Pub. by Elsevier Applied Sci England). Elsevier.

Reichert, William H. Bibliography & Index of the Geology & Mineral Resources of Washington, 1957-1962. (Bulletin Ser.: No. 59). 375p. 1969. 3.00 (ISBN 0-686-34714-5). Geologic Pubns.

Rendu, Jo M. Introduction to Geostatistical Methods of Mineral Evaluation. 84p. 1980. 30.00x (ISBN 0-620-03313-4, Pub. by Mining Journal England). State Mutual Bk.

Riley, Charles M. Our Mineral Resources: An Elementary Textbook in Economic Geology. 4th ed. LC 76-57669. (Illus.). 348p. 1977. Repr. of 1967 ed. lib. bdg. 19.50 (ISBN 0-88275-530-7). Krieger.

Roberts, P. & Shaw, T. Mineral Resources in Regional & Strategic Planning. 176p. 1982. text ed. 37.25x (ISBN 0-566-00395-3). Gower Pub Co.

Rucker, Edward W. The Complete Unabridged Information Manual & Reference Guide to the Oklahoma Non-Coal Mining Industry. Tommerlin, Gayle, ed. 198p. 1985. softbound 24.95 (ISBN 0-9614352-0-8). Edw Rucker Ent.

Rummery, R. A. & Howes, K. M. Management of Land Affected by Mining. 172p. 1982. 50.00x (ISBN 0-643-02275-9, Pub. by CSIRO Australia). State Mutual Bk.

Schwind-Belkin, Johanna & Caley, Earle R., eds. Eucharius Rosslin in the Younger: On Minerals & Mineral Products. (Arts Medica, Abeilung IV: Landessprachliche und Mittelalterliche Medizin I). 415p. 1978. text ed. 112.00x (ISBN 3-11006-907-5). De Gruyter.

Seminar on Petroleum Legislation. Offshore Operation: Proceedings. (Mineral Resources Development Ser.: No. 40). pap. 5.00 (ISBN 0-686-94654-5, UN73/2F/13, UN). Unipub.

Sideri, S. & Johns, S., eds. Mining for Development in the Third World: Multinationals, State Enterprises & the International Economy. LC 80-20930. (Pergamon Policy Studies on International Development). 376p. 1981. 39.00 (ISBN 0-08-026308-9). Pergamon.

Sinclair, John. Quarrying, Opencast & Alluvial Mining. (Illus.). 375p. 1969. 50.00 (ISBN 0-444-20040-1, Pub. by Elsevier Applied Sci England). Elsevier.

Skinner, Brian J. Earth Resources. 3rd ed. (Illus.). 208p. 1986. text ed. 17.95 (ISBN 0-13-223108-5); pap. text ed. 14.95 (ISBN 0-13-223090-9). P-H.

Skinner, Brian J., ed. Earth's Energy & Mineral Resources. LC 80-23495. (The Earth & Its Inhabitants: Selected Readings from American Scientist Ser.). (Illus.). 200p. 1980. pap. 9.95x (ISBN 0-913232-90-4). W Kaufmann.

Smirnov, V., ed. Studies of Mineral Deposits. 288p. 1983. 11.95 (ISBN 0-8285-2763-6, Pub. by Mir Pubs USSR). Imported Pubns.

Smith, David N. & Wells, Louis T., Jr. Negotiating Third World Mineral Agreements, Promises As Prologue. LC 75-29274. 288p. 1976. prof ref 29.95 (ISBN 0-88410-041-3). Ballinger Pub.

Somasundaran, P. & Arbiter, N., eds. Beneficiation of Mineral Fines. LC 79-91945. (Illus.). 406p. (Orig.). 1979. pap. text ed. 24.00x (ISBN 0-89520-259-X). Soc Mining Eng.

Sullivan, George. The Gold Hunter's Handbook. LC 80-5718. 208p. 1981. 15.95 (ISBN 0-8128-2788-0). Stein & Day.

Tanzer, Michael. The Race for Resources: Continuing Struggles over Minerals & Fuels. LC 80-18027. 285p. 1981. pap. 6.50 (ISBN 0-85345-541-4). Monthly Rev.

Tatsch, J. H. Mineral Deposits: Origin, Evolution, & Present Characteristics. LC 73-78206. (Illus.). 264p. 1973. 64.00 (ISBN 0-912890-01-0). Tatsch.

Van der Marel, R. & Beutelspacher, H. Atlas of Infrared Spectroscopy of Clay Minerals & Their Admixtures. 396p. 1976. 117.00 (ISBN 0-444-41187-9). Elsevier.

Vol'Pin, M. E., ed. Chemistry Reviews. (Soviet Scientific Reviews: Section B, Vol. 8). 375p. 1985. text ed. 170.00 (ISBN 3-7186-0176-1). Harwood Academic.

Weiss, Alfred, ed. World Mining & Metals Technology. LC 76-19748. (Illus.). 1976. text ed. 35.00x (ISBN 0-89520-036-8). Soc Mining Eng.

Westwood, W. & Cooper, B. S. Analytical Methods in Use in Non-Ferrous Mining & Metallurgy: A Selective Review. 54p. (Orig.). 1973. 14.50 (ISBN 0-900488-17-4). IMM North Am.

Williams, William R. Mine Mapping & Layout. (Illus.). 400p. 1983. 34.95 (ISBN 0-13-583617-4). P-H.

Woerterbuch fuer Metallurgie, Mineralogie, Geologie, Bergbau und die Oelindustrie. (Eng., Fr., Ger. & Ital., Dictionary of Metallurgy, Mineralogy, Geology, Mining and Oil Industry). 1970. 88.00 (ISBN 3-7625-0751-1, M-6912). French & Eur.

Wohlbier, H., et al, eds. Worldwide Directory of Mineral Industries Education & Research. LC 68-9304. 1968. 37.50x (ISBN 0-87201-912-8). Gulf Pub.

Wolfe, John A. Mineral Resources. (Illus.). 350p. 1984. 33.00x (ISBN 0-412-25180-9, NO. 5063, Pub. by Chapman & Hall England); pap. 18.95X (ISBN 0-412-25190-6, NO. 5064, Pub. by Chapman & Hall England). Methuen Inc.

Working Group Meeting on Environmental Managementin Mineral Resource Development: Proceedings. (Mineral Resources Development Ser.: No. 49). 141p. 1983. pap. 12.00 (ISBN 0-686-43283-5, UN82/2F9, UN). Unipub.

MINES AND MINERAL RESOURCES–DICTIONARIES

Auger, Pierre & Rousseau, Louis-Jean. Lexique Anglais-Francais De L'industrie Miniere, 1. (Eng. & Fr.). 91p. 1973. pap. 6.95 (ISBN 0-686-56905-9, M-6016). French & Eur.

Cagnacci-Schwicker, Angelo. Dictionnaire International de Metallurgie, Mineralogie, Geologie et Industries Extractives, 2 vols. (Fr.). 1530p. 1969. Set. 95.00 (ISBN 0-686-56933-4, M-6054). French & Eur.

Ersov, N. N. & Komarov, A. N., eds. Projet de Lexique Minier Russe-Francais. (Fr. & Rus.). 183p. 1972. pap. 22.50 (ISBN 0-686-56769-2, M-6468). French & Eur.

Fueyo Cuesta, Laureano. Diccionario Terminologico De Minas, Canteras y Mineralurgia. (Span.). 272p. 1973. leather 17.95 (ISBN 84-400-6971-5, S-50112). French & Eur.

Gagnacci-Schwicker, A. & Schwicker. International Dictionary of Metallurgy, Mineralogy, Geology & the Mining & Oil Industries. (Eng., Fr., Ger. & Ital.). 1530p. 1970. 88.00 (ISBN 3-7625-0751-1, M-7482, Pub. by Bauverlag). French & Eur.

Hooson, William. The Miners Dictionary. 1979. Repr. of 1747 ed. text ed. 40.25x (ISBN 0-686-32514-1). IMM North Am.

Roberts. Encyclopedia of Minerals. 2nd ed. 1984. cancelled (ISBN 0-442-26825-4). Van Nos Reinhold.

Todd, A. H. Lexicon of Terms Relating to the Assessment & Classification of Coal Resources. 140p. 1982. 99.00x (ISBN 0-86010-403-6, Pub. by Graham & Trotman England). State Mutual Bk.

Verbic, Ing S. English-Serbocroat & Serbocroat-English Geological & Mining Dictionary. (Eng. & Serbocroatian.). 528p. 1981. 90.00x (ISBN 0-686-44714-X, Pub. by Collets). State Mutual Bk.

Wyllie, R. J. & Argall, George O., Jr., eds. World Mining Glossary of Mining, Processing & Geological Terms. LC 74-20169. (A World Mining Book). 432p. 1975. 55.00 (ISBN 0-87930-031-0). Miller Freeman.

MINES AND MINERAL RESOURCES–AFRICA

Metalworking Industries in Developing Countries of Africa. pap. 3.00 (ISBN 0-686-94683-9, UN80 2B1, UN). Unipub.

Perrings, Charles. Black Mineworkers in Central Africa. LC 78-11413. 302p. 1979. text ed. 49.50x (ISBN 0-8419-0462-6, Africana). Holmes & Meier.

Postel, A. Williams. Mineral Resources of Africa. (African Handbooks Ser.: Vol. 2). (Illus.). 105p. 1943. 7.50x (ISBN 0-686-24091-X). Univ Mus of U.

South African Mining & Engineering Year Book: 1978. 27.50x (ISBN 0-8002-1994-5). Intl Pubns Serv.

Wright, J. B., et al. Geology & Mineral Resources of West Africa. (Illus.). 176p. 1985. text ed. 40.00x (ISBN 0-04-556001-3). Allen Unwin.

MINES AND MINERAL RESOURCES–ALASKA

Anderson, Eskil. Asbestos & Jade in the Kobuk River Region of Alaska. facs. ed. (Shorey Prospecting Ser.). 26p. pap. 3.95 (ISBN 0-8466-0037-4, S37). Shorey.

Knopf, Adolph. Sitka Mining District, Alaska. fasc. ed. (Geology Ser.). (Illus.). 32p. pap. 3.95 (ISBN 0-8466-8002-5, G2). Shorey.

Tussing, Arlon R. & Erickson, Gregg K. Mining & Public Policy in Alaska: Mineral Policy, the Public Lands, & Economic Development. LC 72-629327. (Joint Institute of Social & Economic Research Ser.: No. 21). 142p. 1969. pap. 5.00x (ISBN 0-295-95118-4). U of Wash Pr.

MINES AND MINERAL RESOURCES–ASIA

Braake, Alex L. Ter. Mining in the Netherlands East Indies. Wilkins, Mira, ed. LC 76-29762. (European Business Ser.). (Illus.). 1977. Repr. of 1944 ed. lib. bdg. 14.00x (ISBN 0-405-09777-8). Ayer Co Pubs.

Carlson, Ellsworth C. Kaiping Mines, Eighteen Seventy-Seven to Nineteen Twelve. rev. 2nd ed. LC 71-148943. (East Asian Monographs Ser: No. 3). 1971. pap. 11.00x (ISBN 0-674-49700-7). Harvard U Pr.

Chaston, I. R., intro. by. Asian Mining '81. 311p. (Orig.). pap. text ed. 100.00x (ISBN 0-900488-61-1). IMM North Am.

Grandy, James. Guide to Eastern Rocks & Minerals. (Illus.). 40p. pap. 3.50 (ISBN 0-88839-105-6). Hancock House.

How Japan's Metal Mining Industries Modernized. 65p. 1980. pap. 5.00 (ISBN 92-808-0083-3, TUNU089, UNU). Unipub.

Imai, Hideki, ed. Geological Studies of the Mineral Deposits in Japan & East Asia. 391p. 1978. 52.50x (ISBN 0-86008-208-3, Pub. by U of Tokyo Japan). Columbia U Pr.

Mineral Distribution Maps of Asia 1979: Reports & Studies. (Asian Economy Ser.). (Maps 1-4 with an explanatory Brochure: Mineral Resources of Asia). pap. 40.00 (UN79/2F13, UN). Unipub.

Mineral Resources of Lower Mekong Basin & Adjacent Areas of Khmer Republic, Laos, Thailand & Republic of Viet-Nam. (Mineral Resources Development Ser.: No. 39). pap. 4.00 (ISBN 0-686-94762-2, UN72/2F/12, UN). Unipub.

Report of IMM Mission to China. 29p. 1980. 72.00 (ISBN 0-686-38294-3). IMM North Am.

Scalisi, Philip & Cook, David. Classic Mineral Localities of the World: Asia & Australia, Vol. 1. 272p. 1982. 29.50 (ISBN 0-442-28685-6). Van Nos Reinhold.

Technology & Labour in Japanese Coal Mining. 65p. 1980. pap. 5.00 (ISBN 92-808-0082-5, TUNU090, UNU). Unipub.

MINES AND MINERAL RESOURCES–AUSTRALIA

Cook, L. H., ed. The Minerals Sector & the Australian Economy. Porter, M. G. 352p. 1984. pap. text ed. 20.00x (ISBN 0-86861-410-6). Allen Unwin.

Deans, Alan, ed. Australian Mining, Minerals & Oil. 610p. 1984. 110.00x (ISBN 0-317-04431-1, NO. 5060). Methuen Inc.

Harris, Stuart, ed. Social & Environmental Choice: The Impact of Uranium Mining in the Northern Territory. (Centre for Resources & Environmental Studies Mongraph: No. 3). 178p. 1981. pap. text ed. 6.95 (ISBN 0-86740-169-9, 0039, Pub. by ANUP Australia). Australia N U P.

Jones, M. J. & Oblatt, R., eds. Tours Guidebook, Eleventh CMMC. 76p. (Orig.). 1978. 21.75x (ISBN 0-900488-40-9). IMM North Am.

Morley, I. W. Black Sands: A History of the Mineral Sand Mining Industry in Eastern Australia. (Illus.). 278p. 1982. text ed. 36.50x (ISBN 0-7022-1633-X). U of Queensland Pr.

Prider, Rex T. Mining in Western Australia. 328p. 1980. 30.00x (ISBN 0-85564-153-3, Pub. by U of West Australia Pr Australia). Intl Spec Bk.

Rummery, R. A. & Howes, K. M. Management of Lands Affected by Mining. 172p. 1979. pap. 15.50 (ISBN 0-643-02275-9, C030, CSIRO). Unipub.

Scalisi, Philip & Cook, David. Classic Mineral Localities of the World: Asia & Australia, Vol. 1. 272p. 1982. 29.50 (ISBN 0-442-28685-6). Van Nos Reinhold.

MINES AND MINERAL RESOURCES–CANADA

Boadway, R. W. & Treddenick, J. M. The Impact of the Mining Industries on the Canadian Economy. 117p. (Orig.). 1977. pap. text ed. 6.00x (ISBN 0-686-63141-2, Pub. by Ctr Resource Stud Canada). Brookfield Pub Co.

Catalogue of Canadian Minerals. 432p. 1983. pap. text ed. 12.50x (ISBN 0-317-28526-2, Pub. by Canadian Govt Pub Ctr). Brookfield Pub Co.

Cousoneau, Eric & Richardson, Peter R. Gold: The World Industry & Canadian Corporate Strategy. 192p. (Orig.). 1979. pap. text ed. 13.00x (ISBN 0-88757-013-5, Pub. by Ctr Resource Stud Canada). Brookfield Pub Co.

Downing, Donald O. & Mackenzie, Brian W. Public Policy Aspects of Information Exchange in Canadian Mineral Exploration. 60p. (Orig.). 1979. pap. text ed. 4.00x (ISBN 0-686-63138-2, Pub. by Ctr Resource Stud Canada). Brookfield Pub Co.

The Future for Junior Mining in Canada. 175p. (Orig.). 1979. pap. text ed. 13.00x (ISBN 0-88757-018-6, Pub. by Ctr Resource Stud Canada). Brookfield Pub Co.

Geology & Economic Minerals of Canada, 3 pts. (Illus.). 1978. pap. 44.50 set (ISBN 0-660-00553-0, SSC96, SSC). Unipub.

Geology of Iron Deposits in Canada: Iron Ranges of the Labrador Geosyncline, Vol. 3. pap. 14.80 (SSC44, SSC). Unipub.

Gibbs, G. W. & Pintus, P. Health & Safety in the Canadian Mining Industry. 249p. (Orig.). 1978. pap. text ed. 16.00x (ISBN 0-88757-003-8, Pub. by Ctr Resource Stud Canada). Brookfield Pub Co.

Hodges, L. K. Mining in the Pacific Northwest. facs. ed. (Shorey Prospecting Ser.). 288p. pap. 39.95 (ISBN 0-8466-9134-5, SJS134). Shorey.

International Competition & the Canadian Mineral Industries. 109p. (Orig.). 1978. pap. text ed. 6.50x (ISBN 0-88757-009-7, Pub. by Ctr Resource Stud Canada). Brookfield Pub Co.

Lafkas, C. & Paterson, J. G. A Survey of Resources & a Production Cycle for the Non-Ferrous Metals. 60p. (Orig.). 1978. pap. text ed. 4.00x (ISBN 0-686-63136-6, Pub. by Ctr Resource Stud Canada). Brookfield Pub Co.

MacDonald, Wendy. Constitutional Change & the Mining Industry in Canada. 73p. 1890. write for info. (Pub. by Ctr. Resource Stud Canada). Brookfield Pub Co.

Macmillan, J. A., et al. Human Resources in Canadian Mining: A Preliminary Analysis. 176p. (Orig.). 1977. pap. 11.00 (ISBN 0-88757-004-6, Pub. by Ctr Resource Stud Canada). Brookfield Pub Co.

Mining & Mineral Processing Operations in Canada, 1983. 95p. 1984. pap. text ed. 7.50x (ISBN 0-660-11581-6, Pub. by Canadian Govt Pub Ctr). Brookfield Pub Co.

Mining to Manufacturing: Links in a Chain. (Mineral Bulletins: No. MR 175). (Illus.). 1979. pap. 9.25 (ISBN 0-660-01714-8, SSC116, SSC). Unipub.

Moore, Elwood S. American Influence in Canadian Mining. Bruchey, Stuart, ed. LC 80-561. (Multinational Corporations Ser.). (Illus.). 1980. Repr. of 1941 ed. lib. bdg. 17.00x (ISBN 0-405-13358-8). Ayer Co Pubs.

Murray, Ronald C. Provincial Mineral Policies: Saskatchewan 1944-75. 65p. (Orig.). 1978. pap. text ed. 5.00x (ISBN 0-686-63139-0, Pub. by Ctr Resource Stud Canada). Brookfield Pub Co.

Owen, Brian E. & Kops, W. J. The Impact of Policy Change on Decisions in the Mineral Industry. 116p. (Orig.). 1979. pap. text ed. 9.00x (ISBN 0-88757-015-1, Pub. by Ctr Resource Stud Canada). Brookfield Pub Co.

Prince, Michael J. Provincial Mineral Policies: Newfoundland 1945-75. 60p. (Orig.). 1977. pap. text ed. 5.00x (ISBN 0-686-63140-4, Pub. by Ctr Resource Stud Canada). Brookfield Pub Co.

Rate of Return Taxation of Minerals. 109p. (Orig.). 1977. pap. text ed. 6.50x (ISBN 0-88757-006-2, Pub. by Ctr Resource Stud Canada). Brookfield Pub Co.

Ripley, Earle A., et al. Environmental Impact of Mining in Canada. 274p. (Orig.). 1978. pap. text ed. 16.00x (ISBN 0-88757-008-9, Pub. by Ctr Resource Stud Canada). Brookfield Pub Co.

Shewchun, John S. & Curtis, David B. Solar Energy & the Canadian Mining Sector: A Demand Forecast. 60p. (Orig.). 1978. pap. text ed. 4.00x (ISBN 0-686-63137-4, Pub. by Ctr Resource Stud Canada). Brookfield Pub Co.

A Survey of Known Mineral Deposits in Canada That Are Not Being Mined. (Mineral Bulletins: No. 181). 159p. 1980. pap. 7.50 (ISBN 0-686-61081-4, SSC138, SSC). Unipub.

Thompson, G. E., ed. Canadian Minerals Yearbook, 1982. 1290p. 1984. text ed. 40.75x (ISBN 0-660-11695-2, Pub. by Energy Mines & Res Canada). Brookfield Pub Co.

Trimble, William J. The Mining Advance into the Inland Empire: A Comparative Study of the Beginnings of the Mining Industry in Idaho & Montana, Eastern Washington & Oregon & the Southern Interior of British Columbia, & of Institutions & Laws Based Upon That Industry. LC 14-31275. Repr. of 1914 ed. 27.00 (ISBN 0-384-61560-0). Johnson Repr.

Wilkinson, Bruce W. Trends in Canada's Mineral Trade. 64p. (Orig.). 1978. pap. text ed. 5.00x (ISBN 0-686-63145-5, Pub. by Ctr Resource Stud Canada). Brookfield Pub Co.

Wojciechowski, Margot J. Federal Mineral Policies, Nineteen Forty-Five to Seventy-Five: A Survey of Federal Activities That Affected the Canadian Mineral Industry. 87p. (Orig.). 1979. pap. 5.00x (ISBN 0-686-63135-8, Pub. by Ctr Resource Stud Canada). Brookfield Pub Co.

MINES AND MINERAL RESOURCES–EUROPE

Dunning, F. W. & Mykura, W., eds. Mineral Deposits of Europe: Vol. 2-Southeast Europe. 304p. 1982. text ed. 100.00x (ISBN 0-900488-63-8). IMM North Am.

Mineral Deposits of Europe: Vol. 1, Northern Europe. 362p. 1979. 90.00x (ISBN 0-686-97560-X, Pub. by Inst Mining England). State Mutual Bk.

Ridge, J. D. Annotated Bibliographies of Mineral Deposits in Europe: Northern Europe Including Examples from the U. S. S. R. in Both Europe & Asia, 2 Vols. (Illus.). 785p. 1986. Set. 215.01 (ISBN 0-08-024022-4). Pergamon.

MINES AND MINERAL RESOURCES–GREAT BRITAIN

Arnot, R. Page. The Miners: One Union, One Industry: A History of the National Union of Mineworkers 1939-46. (Illus.). 1979. text ed. 30.00x (ISBN 0-04-331074-5). Allen Unwin.

Collins, J. H. The Mineralogy of Cornwall & Devon. 1981. 50.00x (ISBN 0-686-97167-1, Pub. by D B Barton England). State Mutual Bk.

Gough, John W. Mines of Mendip. LC 67-105992. (Illus.). Repr. of 1930 ed. 27.50x (ISBN 0-678-05688-9). Kelley.

Handy, L. J. Wages Policy in the British Coalmining Industry: A Study of National Wage Bargaining. LC 80-40229. (Department of Applied Economics Monograph: No. 27). 312p. 1981. 52.50 (ISBN 0-521-23535-9). Cambridge U Pr.

Henwood, George. Cornwall's Mines & Miners. 240p. 1981. 35.00x (ISBN 0-686-97149-3, Pub. by D B Barton England). State Mutual Bk.

Leifchild, J. R. Cornwall: Its Mines & Miners. 304p. 1968. Repr. of 1857 ed. 30.00x (ISBN 0-7146-1402-5, F Cass Co). Biblio Dist.

Metcalfe, J. E. British Mining Fields. 91p. 1969. pap. text ed. 14.50x (ISBN 0-900488-00-X). IMM North Am.

Plattes, Gabriel. Discovery of Subterraneal Treasure. 60p. 1980. Repr. of 1639 ed. text ed. 34.50x (ISBN 0-686-97563-4). IMM North Am.

MINES AND MINERAL RESOURCES–MEXICO

Lyon, G. F. Journal of a Residence & Tour in the Republic of Mexico, 2 Vols. LC 72-130332. (Latin-American History & Culture Ser.). 1971. Repr. of 1828 ed. Set. 45.00x (ISBN 0-8046-1393-1, Pub. by Kennikat). Assoc Faculty Pr.

Von Humboldt, Alexander. Political Essay on the Kingdom of New Spain, 4 Vols. Black, John, tr. LC 1-20796. Repr. of 1811 ed. Set. 147.50 (ISBN 0-404-03450-0). AMS Pr.

MINES AND MINERAL RESOURCES–SOUTH AMERICA

Baird, Wellesley. Guyana Gold: The Story of Wellesley Baird Guyana's Greatest Miner. Adams, Katherine, intro. by. LC 81-51666. 210p. (Orig.). 1982. 16.00x (ISBN 0-89410-192-7); pap. 7.00x (ISBN 0-89410-193-5). Three Continents.

Gardner, George. Travels in the Interior of Brazil. LC 75-128421. Repr. of 1846 ed. 37.50 (ISBN 0-404-02678-8). AMS Pr.

Lindgren, Waldemar. Gold & Silver Deposits in North, South America. (Shorey Prospecting Ser.). 34p. pap. 4.95 (ISBN 0-8466-8006-8, G6). Shorey.

Miller, Benjamin & Singewald, Joseph T. The Deposits of South America. Wilkins, Mira, ed. LC 76-29758. (European Business Ser.). (Illus.). 1977. Repr. of 1919 ed. lib. bdg. 46.50x (ISBN 0-405-09773-5). Ayer Co Pubs.

Ribeiro Franco, Rui. Minerais do Brasil, 3 Vols. LC 73-323732. 426p. 1983. Repr. of 1972 ed. lib. bdg. 75.00x (ISBN 0-89370-754-6). Borgo Pr.

MINES AND MINERAL RESOURCES–SOVIET UNION

Alexandrov, Eugene A., compiled by. Mineral & Energy Resources of the USSR: A Selected Bibliography of Sources in English. 160p. 1980. pap. 10.00 (ISBN 0-913312-21-5). Am Geol.

MINES AND MINERAL RESOURCES–UNITED STATES

see also Mines and Mineral Resources–Alaska

Adams, Nigel. The Holden Mine. (From Discovery to Production, 1896-1938). 87p. 1981. pap. 5.00 (ISBN 0-917048-53-9). Wash St Hist Soc.

Anderson, George B. One Hundred Booming Years. Row, H. J. & Stupek, D., eds. (Illus.). 305p. 1980. 32.50 (ISBN 0-9604136-0-X). Bucyrus-Erie Co.

Arizona Industrial Minerals. 1975. 15.80 (ISBN 0-942218-00-0). Minobras.

Armes, Ethel. The Story of Coal & Iron in Alabama. LC 73-1988. (Big Business; Economic Power in a Free Society Ser.). (Illus.). Repr. of 1910 ed. 40.00 (ISBN 0-405-05072-0). Ayer Co Pubs.

Association of American Geologists & Naturalists at Philadelphia, 1840 & 1841. Proceedings. Albritton, Claude C., ed. LC 77-6507. (History of Geology Ser.). Repr. of 1843 ed. lib. bdg. 46.50x (ISBN 0-405-10430-8). Ayer Co Pubs.

Barnes, V. E. & Schofield, D. A. Potential Low-Grade Iron Ore & Hydraulic-Fracturing Sand in Cambrian Sandstones, Northwestern Llano Region, Texas. (Report of Investigations Ser.: RI 53). (Illus.). 58p. 1964. 2.00 (ISBN 0-686-29335-5). Bur Econ Geology.

Bartlett, Robert V. The Reserve Mining Controversy: Science, Technology & Environmental Quality. LC 79-48019. 312p. 1980. 17.50x (ISBN 0-253-14556-2). Ind U Pr.

Belden, L. Burr. Mines of Death Valley. (Illus.). 1985. wrappers 3.50 (ISBN 0-910856-16-8). La Siesta.

Bennett, W. A. Saline Lake Deposits in Washington. (Bulletin Ser.: No. 49). (Illus.). 129p. 1962. 1.50 (ISBN 0-686-34702-1). Geologic Pubns.

Boyum, Burton H., ed. The Mather Mine, Negaunee & Ishpeming Michigan. LC 79-89638. 87p. 1979. 18.95 (ISBN 0-938746-04-9). Marquette Cnty.

Byrd, William. Writings of Colonel William Byrd. Bassett, J. S., ed. LC 76-125631. (Research & Source Ser.: No. 518). (Illus.). 1970. Repr. of 1901 ed. lib. bdg. 32.00 (ISBN 0-8337-0442-7). B Franklin.

Colorado & Utah Industrial Minerals. 1974. 15.50 (ISBN 0-942218-01-9). Minobras.

Davies, Edward, II. Anthracite Aristocracy: Leadership & Social Change in the Hard Coal Regions of Northeastern Pennsylvania, 1800-1930. LC 85-2947. 275p. 1985. 27.00 (ISBN 0-87580-107-2). N Ill U Pr.

DeDecker, Mary. Mines of the Eastern Sierra. (Illus.). 1966. wrappers 2.95 (ISBN 0-910856-15-X). La Siesta.

Digerness, David S. Mineral Belt: Old South Park-Denver to Leadville, Vol. 1. (Illus.). 416p. 1977. 49.00 (ISBN 0-913582-20-4). Sundance.

Dornburgh, Henry. Why the Wilderness Is Called Adirondack: The Earliest Account of Founding of the MacIntyre Mine. LC 79-25055. 1980. pap. 3.95 (ISBN 0-916346-39-0). Harbor Hill Bks.

Eargle, D. H., et al. Uranium Geology & Mines, South Texas. (GB 12 Ser.). (Illus.). 59p. 1971. 1.75 (ISBN 0-686-29320-7). Bur Econ Geology.

Eckes, Alfred E., Jr. The United States & the Global Struggle for Minerals. LC 78-11082. 365p. 1979. text ed. 20.00x (ISBN 0-292-78506-2); pap. 9.95x (ISBN 0-292-78511-9). U of Tex Pr.

Galloway, W. E., et al. South Texas Uranium Province, Geologic Perspective. (Guidebook Ser.: GB 18). (Illus.). 81p. 1979. 3.00 (ISBN 0-686-29323-1, GB 18). Bur Econ Geology.

Gibson, Arrell M. Wilderness Bonanza: The Tri-State Mining District of Missouri, Kansas & Oklahoma. LC 77-177335. (Illus.). 350p. 1972. 19.95 (ISBN 0-8061-0990-4); pap. 9.95 (ISBN 0-8061-1033-3). U of Okla Pr.

Grimmett, Robert G. Cabal of Death. LC 77-15675. 292p. 1977. 7.95 (ISBN 0-89301-047-2). U Pr of Idaho.

Hibbard, W., ed. United States Minerals Issues--the Seventies, a Review; the Eighties, a Preview: 6th Annual Mineral Economics Symposium, November 12, 1980, Washington DC. 1981. pap. 30.00 (ISBN 0-08-027593-1). Pergamon.

Hodges, L. K. Mining in the Pacific Northwest. facs. ed. (Shorey Prospecting Ser.). 288p. pap. 39.95 (ISBN 0-8466-9134-5, SJS134). Shorey.

Hollister, Ovando J. The Mines of Colorado. LC 72-9452. (The Far Western Frontier Ser.). (Illus.). 454p. 1973. Repr. of 1867 ed. 26.00 (ISBN 0-405-04980-3). Ayer Co Pubs.

Holmes, Richard W. & Kennedy-Streetman, Marrianna B. Mines & Minerals of the Great American Rift. 336p. 1982. 29.50 (ISBN 0-442-28038-6). Van Nos Reinhold.

Idaho Industrial Minerals. 1975. 14.50 (ISBN 0-686-29524-2). Minobras.

Jensen, David E. Minerals of New York State. LC 78-66426. (Illus.). 1978. 12.95 (ISBN 0-932142-00-1); pap. 7.95 (ISBN 0-932142-01-X). Ward Pr.

Libecap, Gary D. The Evolution of Private Mineral Rights: Nevada's Comstock Lode. LC 77-14777. (Dissertations in American Economic History Ser.). 1978. 30.00 (ISBN 0-405-11047-2). Ayer Co Pubs.

Lincoln, Francis G. Mining Districts & Mineral Resources of Nevada. (Illus.). 1982. 14.95 (ISBN 0-913814-48-2). Nevada Pubns.

Livingston, Vaughn E., Jr. Geology & Mineral Resources of the Kelso-Cathlamet Area, Cowlitz & Wahkiakum Counties, Washington. (Bulletin Ser.: No. 54). (Illus.). 110p. 1966. 1.50 (ISBN 0-686-34707-2). Geologic Pubns.

Love, Frank. Mining Camps & Ghost Towns: Along the Lower Colorado in Arizona & California. LC 73-86960. (Great West & Indian Ser.: Vol. 42). (Illus.). 240p. 8.95 (ISBN 0-87026-031-6). Westernlore.

McGowen, J. H. & Groat, C. G. Van Horn Sandstone, West Texas: An Alluvial Fan Model for Mineral Exploration. (RI 72). (Illus.). 57p. 1982. Repr. of 1971 ed. 2.50 (ISBN 0-318-03173-6). Bur Econ Geology.

Mangone, Gerard J., ed. American Strategic Minerals. LC 84-4242. 172p. 1984. 19.50x (ISBN 0-8448-1462-8). Crane-Russak Co.

Maxwell, R. A. Mineral Resources of South Texas: Region Served Through the Port of Corpus Christi. (Report of Investigations: RI 43). (Illus.). 140p. 1962. 3.50 (ISBN 0-686-29333-9). Bur Econ Geology.

Miller, Ronald D. Mines of the High Desert. rev. ed. (Illus.). 1985. wrappers 3.50 (ISBN 0-910856-13-3). La Siesta.

Mining & Metallurgy Instrumentation Symposium. Instrumentation in the Mining & Metallurgy Industries, Vol. 7: Proceedings of the 8th Mining & Metallurgy Instrumentation Symposium. LC 73-82889. 180p. 1980. text ed. 30.00x (ISBN 0-87664-470-1). Instru Soc.

Moen, Wayne S. Geology & Mineral Deposits of the North Half of the Van Zandt Quadrangle, Whatcom County, Washington. (Bulletin Ser.: No. 50). (Illus.). 129p. 1962. 1.50 (ISBN 0-686-34703-X). Geologic Pubns.

--Mines & Mineral Deposits of Whatcom County, Washington. (Bulletin Ser.: No. 57). (Illus.). 134p. 1969. 4.50 (ISBN 0-686-34709-9). Geologic Pubns.

--Myers Creek & Wauconda Mining Districts of Northeastern Okanogan County, Washington. (Bulletin Ser.: No. 73). (Illus.). 96p. 1980. 4.00 (ISBN 0-686-34723-4). Geologic Pubns.

--St. Helens & Washougal Mining Districts of the Southern Cascades of Washington. (Information Circular Ser.: No. 60). (Illus.). 71p. 1977. 1.00 (ISBN 0-686-34732-3). Geologic Pubns.

Montana Industrial Minerals. 1975. 15.20 (ISBN 0-942218-05-1). Minobras.

Mullan, John. Miner's & Travelers' Guide to Oregon, Washington, Idaho, Montana, Wyoming, & Colorado. LC 72-9461. (The Far Western Frontier Ser.). (Illus.). 158p. 1973. Repr. of 1865 ed. 16.00 (ISBN 0-405-04989-7). Ayer Co Pubs.

Nevada Industrial Minerals. 1973. 15.00 (ISBN 0-942218-06-X). Minobras.

Pearl, Richard M. Exploring Rocks, Minerals, Fossils in Colorado. rev. ed. LC 64-25339. (Illus.). 215p. 1969. 14.95 (ISBN 0-8040-0105-7, 82-70647, Pub. by Swallow). Ohio U Pr.

Pemberton, H. Earl. Minerals of California. 672p. 1982. 29.95 (ISBN 0-442-27488-2). Van Nos Reinhold.

Poindexter, O. F., et al. Rocks & Minerals of Michigan. (Illus.). 49p. (Orig.). 1971. pap. 3.95 (ISBN 0-910726-73-6). Hillsdale Educ.

Probert, Alan. Mining in the West. (Illus.). 119p. 1981. pap. text ed. 9.95x (ISBN 0-89745-019-1). Sunflower U Pr.

Reichert, W. H. Annotated Guide to Sources of Information on the Geology, Minerals, & Ground-Water Resources of the Puget Sound Region: Washington, King County Section. (Information Circular Ser.: No. 61). (Illus.). 63p. 1978. 1.50 (ISBN 0-686-34734-X). Geologic Pubns.

Rice, Frank A. Mines of Ouray (Colorado) County. rev. ed. Benham, Jack L., ed. (Illus.). 56p. (Orig.). 1981. pap. 3.50 (ISBN 0-941026-05-1). Bear Creek Pub.

Rickard, Thomas A. A History of American Mining. (Illus.). Repr. of 1932 ed. 28.00 (ISBN 0-384-50800-6). Johnson Repr.

Rinehart, C. Dean & Fox, Kenneth F., Jr. Geology & Mineral Deposits of the Loomis Quadrangle, Okanogan County, Washington. (Bulletin Ser.: No. 64). (Illus.). 124p. 1972. 4.00 (ISBN 0-686-34713-7). Geologic Pubns.

Robinson, John W. Mines of the San Bernardinos. (California Mines Ser). (Illus., Orig.). 1985. pap. text ed. 3.50 (ISBN 0-910856-64-8). La Siesta.

Rodda, P. U., et al. Limestone & Dolomite Resources, Lower Cretaceous Rocks, Texas. (Report of Investigations: RI 56). (Illus.). 286p. 1966. Repr. 4.50 (ISBN 0-686-29338-X). Bur Econ Geology.

Shawe, Daniel R., ed. Guidebook on Fossil Fuels & Metals, Eastern Utah & Western-Southwestern Central Colorado. (Professional Contributions Ser.: No. 9). (Illus.). 150p. 1978. pap. 3.00 (ISBN 0-918062-04-7). Colo Sch Mines.

Smith, Duane A. Song of the Hammer & Drill: The Colorado San Juans, 1860-1914. Raese, Jon W. & Goldberg, J. H., eds. LC 82-4304. (Illus.). 181p. 1982. 23.16 (ISBN 0-918062-49-7). Colo Sch Mines.

Smith, Duane A. & Wieler, Hank. Secure the Shadow: Lachlan McLean, Colorado Mining Photographer. LC 80-10693. (Illus.). 82p. 1980. 13.50 (ISBN 0-918062-09-8). Colo Sch Mines.

Smith, W. Hovey. Kaolin Deposits of Central Georgia: An Introduction to Their Origin & Use. (Illus.). 92p. (Orig.). 1983. pap. 6.25 (ISBN 0-916565-01-7). Whitehall Pr.

Southern California Industrial Minerals. 1973. 14.70 (ISBN 0-942218-07-8). Minobras.

Stanton, Robert B. The Hoskaninni Papers, Mining in Glen Canyon, 1897-1902. (Glen Canyon Ser.: No. 15). Repr. of 1961 ed. 20.00 (ISBN 0-404-60654-7). AMS Pr.

Tewalt, Susan J., et al. Detailed Evaluation of Two Texas Lignite Deposits of Deltaic & Fluvial Origins. (Geological Circular Ser.: GC 82-2). (Illus.). 12p. 1982. Repr. 1.00 (ISBN 0-686-37546-7). Bur Econ Geology.

Trimble, William J. The Mining Advance into the Inland Empire: A Comparative Study of the Beginnings of the Mining Industry in Idaho & Montana, Eastern Washington & Oregon & the Southern Interior of British Columbia, & of Institutions & Laws Based Upon That Industry. LC 14-31275. Repr. of 1914 ed. 27.00 (ISBN 0-384-61560-0). Johnson Repr.

Uranium Deposits of Arizona, California & Nevada. 1978. 40.30 (ISBN 0-942218-10-8). Minobras.

Uranium Deposits of the Northern U. S. Region. 1977. 37.10 (ISBN 0-942218-11-6). Minobras.

Uranium Resources of the Central & Southern Rockies. 1979. 33.80 (ISBN 0-942218-15-9). Minobras.

Valentine, Grant M. Non-Metallic Minerals, Pt. 1. (Illus.). 258p. 1960. 3.00 (ISBN 0-686-34693-9). Geologic Pubns.

Von Mueller, Karl. Placer Miner's Manual, 3 vols. (Illus.). 1981. Vol. 1. 8.00 (ISBN 0-89316-612-X); Vol. 1. pap. 5.00 (ISBN 0-89316-611-1); Vol. 2. 8.00 (ISBN 0-89316-614-6); Vol. 2. pap. 5.00 (ISBN 0-89316-613-8); Vol. 3. 8.00 (ISBN 0-89316-616-2); Vol. 3. pap. 5.00 (ISBN 0-89316-615-4). Exanimo Pr.

Whitney, Josiah D. Metallic Wealth of the United States. LC 74-125766. (American Environmental Studies). 1970. Repr. of 1854 ed. 31.00 (ISBN 0-405-02692-7). Ayer Co Pubs.

Williams, George J., III. Calico & Other Southern California Mining Camps. (Western Americana History Ser.). (Illus., Orig.). 1985. pap. 5.95 (ISBN 0-686-79613-6). Tree by River.

Wyoming Directory of Manufacturing & Mining, 1985-86. 111p. 1985. pap. 15.00 (ISBN 0-318-02841-7). Manufacturers.

Yellig, William F., Jr. & Tek, M. Rasin. Prospects for Oil & Gas from Silurian-Niagaran Trend Areas in Michigan. (Illus.). 35p. 1976. 12.00 (ISBN 0-938654-00-4). Indus Dev Inst Sci.

Young, Otis E., Jr. Western Mining: An Informal Account of Precious-Metals Prospecting, Placering, Lode Mining, & Milling on the American Frontier from Spanish Times to 1893. LC 76-108800. (Illus.). 1970. pap. 10.95 (ISBN 0-8061-1352-9). U of Okla Pr.

Young, Otis E., Jr. & Lenon, Robert. Black Powder & Hand Steel: Miners & Machines on the Old Western Frontier. LC 75-4634. (Illus.). 200p. 1976. pap. 15.95 (ISBN 0-8061-1269-7). U of Okla Pr.

MINES AND MINING

see Mineral Industries; Mines and Mineral Resources; Mining Engineering

MINI CAR (MORRIS MINOR)

see Automobiles, Foreign–Types–Morris Mini Minor

MINI COMPUTERS

see Minicomputers

MINIATURE CAMERAS

see also individual makes of miniature cameras, e.g. Cameras–Types–Retina, etc.

Bailey, Alfred M. Nature Photography with Miniature Cameras. (Museum Pictorial Ser.: No. 1). 1951. pap. 1.10 (ISBN 0-916278-30-1). Denver Mus Natl Hist.

MINIATURE COMPUTERS

see Minicomputers

MINIATURE ELECTRONIC EQUIPMENT

see also Microelectronics; Minicomputers; Printed Circuits; Transistor Radios

Comer, David J. Electronic Design with Integrated Circuits. LC 80-23365. (Electrical Engineering Ser.). (Illus.). 416p. 1981. text ed. 27.95 (ISBN 0-201-03931-1); solutions manual 1.50 (ISBN 0-201-03932-X). Addison-Wesley.

Harrigan, Norwell, ed. Microstate Studies, Vol. 1. 1977. pap. 5.00 (ISBN 0-8130-0592-2). U Presses Fla.

Kelleher, M. D. & Yovanovich, M. M., eds. Heat Transfer in Electronic Equipment. (HTD Ser.: Vol. 20). 64p. 1981. 20.00 (ISBN 0-686-34496-0, H00206). ASME.

MINIATURE PINSCHERS

see Dogs–Breeds–Miniature Pinschers

MINIATURE TREES

see Bonsai

MINIATURIZATION (ELECTRONICS)

see Miniature Electronic Equipment

MINICOMPUTERS

see also Microcomputers; Microprocessors

All About Minicomputers. 54p. 10.00 (ISBN 0-318-17401-4); members 5.00 (ISBN 0-318-17402-2). Print Indus Am.

Application of Minicomputers & Microcomputers to Information Handling. 94p. 1983. pap. text ed. 13.50 (ISBN 0-317-01214-2, UPB126, UPB). Unipub.

Audit & Control Considerations in A Minicomputer Environment. (Computer Services Guidelines Ser.). 34p. 1981. pap. 9.00 (ISBN 0-686-84213-8). Am Inst CPA.

Bates, William. The Computer Cookbook: How to Create Small Computer Systems That Work for You. (Illus.). 380p. 1983. 24.95 (ISBN 0-13-164558-7, Spec); pap. 12.95 (ISBN 0-13-165167-6). P-H.

MINIMAX APPROXIMATION
see Chebyshev Approximation

MINING
see Mineral Industries; Mines and Mineral Resources; Mining Engineering

MINING, ELECTRIC
see Electricity in Mining

MINING ENGINEERING
see also Blasting; Boring; Electricity in Mining; Hydraulic Mining; Mine Surveying; Mine Ventilation; Petroleum Engineering; Strip Mining; Tunnels and Tunneling

Hall, Eugene J. The Language of Mining & Metallurgy in English. (English for Careers Ser.). 1978. pap. text ed. 4.25 (ISBN 0-88345-307-X, 18521). Regents Pub.

Hardy, H. Reginald & Leighton, Frederick W. Proceedings of the Second Conference on Acoustic Emission: Microseismic Activity in Geologic Structures & Materials. (Rock & Soil Mechanics Ser.). (Illus.). 500p. 1980. 45.00x (ISBN 0-87849-032-9). Trans Tech.

Hisket, J. Brent. Au & Ag Heap & Dump Leaching Practice. LC 84-71234. (Illus.). 162p. text ed. 30.00x (ISBN 0-89520-425-8, 425-8). Soc Mining Eng.

Hustrulid, William H., ed. Underground Mining Methods Handbook. LC 80-70416. (Illus.). 1754p. 1982. 120.00x (ISBN 0-89520-049-X). Soc Mining Eng.

Jones, A. H., ed. Mining Technology for Energy Resources Advances for the Eighties. 1978. 8.00 (ISBN 0-685-66805-3, G00140). ASME.

Kratzsch, H. Mining Subsidence Engineering. Fleming, R. F., tr. from Ger. (Illus.). 580p. 1983. 61.00 (ISBN 0-387-11930-2). Springer-Verlag.

Lama, R. D. & Vutukuri, V. S. Handbook on Mechanical Properties of Rocks, Vol. III. (Rock & Soil Mechanics Ser.). (Illus.). 1978. 65.00x (ISBN 0-87849-022-1). Trans Tech.

--Handbook on Mechanical Properties of Rocks, Vol. IV. (Rock & Soil Mechanics Ser.). (Illus.). 1978. 65.00x (ISBN 0-87849-023-X). Trans Tech.

Lefond, Stanley J., ed. Industrial Minerals & Rocks, 2 vols. 5th ed. LC 82-71993. (Illus.). 1508p. 1983. Set. 80.00x (ISBN 0-89520-402-9, 402-9). Soc Mining Eng.

Lewis, Robert S. Elements of Mining. 3rd ed. LC 64-14990. pap. 160.00 (ISBN 0-317-10407-1, 2016298). Bks Demand UMI.

Li Itunda Yenge. Analysis of Bulk Flow of Materials Under Gravity Caving Process, Pt. 1: Sublevel Caving in Relation to Flow in Bins & Bunkers. Raese, Jon W., ed. LC 81-129. (Colorado School of Mines Quarterly Ser.: Vol. 75, No. 4). (Illus.). 45p. 1981. pap. 8.00 (ISBN 0-686-74853-0). Colo Sch Mines.

McQuiston, Frank W., Jr. & Shoemaker, Robert S. Gold & Silver Cyanidation Plant Practice Monograph, Vol. 1. 187p. 1975. pap. text ed. 28.00x (ISBN 0-89520-027-9). Soc Mining Eng.

Mann, C. David & Kelley, Martin N., eds. RETC Proceedings, 1985. LC 85-70960. (Rapid Excavation & Tunneling Ser.). (Illus.). 1278p. 1985. 75.00x (ISBN 0-89520-441-X, 441-X). Soc Mining Eng.

Metal Structures in the Mining, Gas & Oil Industries: Metal Stuctures Conferences, 1978. 114p. (Orig.). 1978. pap. text ed. 31.50 (ISBN 0-85825-104-3, Pub. by Inst Engineering Australia). Brookfield Pub Co.

Miller Freeman Publications. Energy in Mining: Proceedings of the First International Symposium on Energy in Mining, San Francisco California, 1982. 250p. 1982. 3 ring binder 177.00 (ISBN 0-87930-145-7). Miller Freeman.

Mining & Metallurgy Instrumentation Symposium. Instrumentation in the Mining & Metallurgy Industries, Vol. 9. LC 73-83889. 212p. 1982. pap. text ed. 30.00x (ISBN 0-87664-729-8). Instru Soc.

Mining Chemicals Market. 217p. 1985. 1650.00 (ISBN 0-86621-319-8, A1402). Frost & Sullivan.

Mining Journal Books Ltd. Economics of Mineral Engineering. 223p. 1980. 25.00x (ISBN 0-900117-10-9, Pub. by Mining Journal England). State Mutual Bk.

Modes of Traditional Mining Techniques. (Project on Technology Transfer, Transformation & Development: The Japanese Experience). 21p. 1981. pap. 5.00 (ISBN 92-808-0099-X, TUNU169, UNU). Unipub.

Mular, Andrew L. & Jergensen, Gerald V., III, eds. Design & Installation of Communication Circuits. LC 82-71992. (Illus.). 1022p. 1982. 40.00x (ISBN 0-89520-401-0). Soc Mining Eng.

North, Oliver S. Mineral Exploration, Mining, & Processing Patents, 1980. (Illus.). 135p. 1982. 35.00x (ISBN 0-89520-294-8). Soc Mining Eng.

Pariseau, William G., ed. Geomechanics Applications in Underground Hardrock Mining. LC 84-72183. (Illus.). 256p. 1984. 35.00 (ISBN 0-89520-432-0, 432-0). Soc Mining Eng.

Peele, R. Mining Engineers' Handbook, 2 vols. 3rd ed. (Engineering Handbook Ser.). 2442p. 1941. Set. 112.50x (ISBN 0-471-67716-7, Pub. by Wiley-Interscience). Wiley.

Peng, Syd & Chiang, H. S. Longwall Mining. LC 83-17113. 708p. 1983. 79.95x (ISBN 0-471-86881-7, Pub. by Wiley-Interscience). Wiley.

Ramai, Raja V., ed. Longwall-Shortwall Mining: State-of-the-Art. LC 81-67436. (Illus.). 296p. 33.00x (ISBN 0-89520-288-3). Soc Mining Eng.

Ramani, R. V., ed. APCOM, Fourteenth: Proceedings. LC 76-58570. 1977. 23.00x (ISBN 0-89520-047-3). Soc Mining Eng.

Recent Advances in Mining & Processing of Low-Grade Submarginal Mineral Deposits. LC 76-11771. 1977. text ed. 25.00 (ISBN 0-08-021051-1). Pergamon.

Rickard, Thomas A. A History of American Mining. (Illus.). Repr. of 1932 ed. 28.00 (ISBN 0-384-50800-6). Johnson Repr.

--Man & Metals: A History of Mining in Relation to the Development of Civilization, 2 vols. in 1. LC 74-358. (Gold Ser.: Vol. 16). (Illus.). 1974. Repr. of 1932 ed. 74.00x (ISBN 0-405-05919-1). Ayer Co Pubs.

Robinson, D. J. & James, S. E., eds. Anodes for Electrowinning: Proceedings, AIME Annual Meeting, Los Angeles, 1984. (Illus.). 113p. 1984. pap. 17.00 (ISBN 0-89520-474-6); members 10.00; student members 10.00. Metal Soc.

Schlitt, W. J., intro. by. Interfacing Technologies in Solution Mining. LC 82-71423. (Illus.). 370p. (Orig.). 1982. pap. 30.00 (ISBN 0-89520-295-6). Soc Mining Eng.

Schlitt, W. J. & Larson, W. C., eds. Gold & Silver Leaching, Recovery & Economics. LC 81-68558. (Illus.). 148p. 1981. text ed. 20.00x (ISBN 0-89520-289-1). Soc Mining Eng.

SME Mining Engineering Handbook. LC 72-86922. 1973. 50.00x (ISBN 0-89520-021-X). Soc Mining Eng.

Society of Mining Engineers of AIME. Froth Flotation Fiftieth Anniversary Volume. Fuerstenau, D. W., ed. LC 63-46768. (Rocky Mountain Fund Ser.). pap. 160.00 (ISBN 0-317-30018-0, 2025018). Bks Demand UMI.

Southwick, Lawrence L. Ten Hints to Successful Mining. 1983. 4.95 (ISBN 0-8062-2197-6). Carlton.

Stefanko, Robert. Coal Mining Technology: Theory & Practice. Bise, Christopher J., ed. LC 82-71995. (Illus.). 410p. 1983. 45.00x (ISBN 0-89520-404-5, 404-5). Soc Mining Eng.

Stephansson, O. & Jones, M. J., eds. Application of Rock Mechanics to Cut & Fill Mining. 376p. (Orig.). 1981. pap. text ed. 132.25x (ISBN 0-900488-60-3). IMM North Am.

Stephansson, Ove, ed. Rock Bolting-Theory & Application in Mining & Underground Construction: Proceedings of the International Conference, Abisko, Sweden, 28 August 2 September 1983. 560p. 1983. lib. bdg. 45.00 (ISBN 90-6191-514-7, Pub. by Balkema RSA). IPS.

Stewart, Daniel R., ed. Design & Operation of Caving & Sublevel Stoping Mines. LC 81-68554. (Illus.). 843p. 1981. 66.00x (ISBN 0-89520-287-5). Soc Mining Eng.

Strategies for Selling Underground & Surface Mining Equipment. 320p. 1983. 1300.00 (ISBN 0-86621-082-2). Frost & Sullivan.

Sutcliffe, Harry & Wilson, John W., eds. Rapid Excavation & Tunneling Conference Proceedings, 1983, 2 vols. LC 83-70933. (Illus.). 1258p. 1983. Set. 70.00x (ISBN 0-89520-411-8, 411-8). Soc Mining Eng.

Szwilski, A. B. & Brawner, C. O., eds. Stability in Underground Mining II. LC 84-71630. (International Conferences on Stability in Underground Mining Ser.). (Illus.). 606p. 1984. 45.00x (ISBN 0-89520-430-4, 430-4). Soc Mining Eng.

Thomas, L. J. An Introduction to Mining: Exploration, Feasibility, Extraction, Rock Mechanics. LC 73-14857. 1977. pap. 24.95 (ISBN 0-470-99220-4). Halsted Pr.

Wang, Fun-Den, et al, eds. Water Jet Symposium: Proceedings. LC 81-21616. (Illus.). 248p. 1982. pap. text ed. 16.00 (ISBN 0-918062-48-9). Colo Sch Mines.

Wilson, David, ed. Design & Construction of Tailing Dams: First Seminar on Design & Construction of Tailing Dams, Nov. 6-7, 1980. LC 81-10273. (Illus.). 280p. 1981. Repr. of 1980 ed. text ed. 9.00 (ISBN 0-918062-45-4). Colo Sch Mines.

Wylie, A. W. Nuclear Assaying of Mining Boreholes: An Introduction. (Methods in Geochemistry & Geophysics Ser.: Vol. 21). 344p. 1985. 65.00 (ISBN 0-444-42357-5). Elsevier.

Yenge, Li I. Analysis of Bulk Flow of Materials Under Gravity Caving Process: Pt. 2: Theoretical and Physical Modelling of Gravity Flow of Broken Rock. Raese, Jon W., ed. LC 81-129. (Colorado School of Mines Quartering: Vol. 76, No. 3). (Illus.). 67p. 1981. pap. text ed. 8.00 (ISBN 0-686-46968-2). Colo Sch Mines.

MINING GEOLOGY

Amstutz, G. Glossary of Mining Geology. (Eng., Span., Fr. & Ger.). 196p. 1971. 36.50 (ISBN 3-432-01667-0, M-7428, Pub. by F. Enke). French & Eur.

Baumgardner, Robert W., et al. Formation of the Wink Sink, a Salt Dissolution & Collapse Feature, Winkler County, Texas. (Report of Investigations Ser.: RI 114). (Illus.). 50p. 1982. 1.50 (ISBN 0-686-37544-0). Bur Econ Geology.

Brown, Wayne S., et al, eds. Monograph on Rock Mechanics Applications in Mining. LC 76-45924. 1977. pap. text ed. 18.00x (ISBN 0-89520-046-5). Soc Mining Eng.

Erickson, A. J., Jr., ed. Applied Mining Geology. LC 84-81473. (Illus.). 222p. 1984. pap. 35.00 (ISBN 0-89520-431-2, 431-2). Soc Mining Eng.

Journel, A. G. & Huijbregts, C. J. Mining Geostatistics. 1979. 75.00 (ISBN 0-12-391050-1). Acad Pr.

Lacy, Willard C., ed. Mining Geology. LC 82-968. (Benchmark Papers in Geology: Vol. 69). 466p. 1983. 58.00 (ISBN 0-87933-426-6). Van Nos Reinhold.

Metcalfe, J. E. British Mining Fields. 91p. 1969. pap. text ed. 14.50x (ISBN 0-900488-00-X). IMM North Am.

Mining Journal Books Ltd., ed. Concise World Atlas of Geology & Mineral Deposits. 110p. 1981. 90.00x (ISBN 0-900117-22-2, Pub. by Mining Journal England). State Mutual Bk.

Riordon, P. H. & Hollister, V. F., eds. Geology of Asbestos Deposits. LC 80-52898. (Illus.). 118p. (Orig.). 1981. pap. 32.00x (ISBN 0-89520-277-8). Soc Mining Eng.

Silver, Burr A. Exploration Geology. 402p. 1982. 43.00 (ISBN 0-89419-253-1). Inst Energy.

MINING MACHINERY

see also Electricity in Mining; Hoisting Machinery

Clark, George B. Principles of Rock Drilling & Bit Wear, Pt. 2. rev. ed. Raese, Jon W., ed. LC 82-1148. (Colorado School of Mines Quarterly Ser.: Vol. 77 No. 2). (Illus.). 42p. 1982. pap. text ed. 10.00 (ISBN 0-686-79748-5). Colo Sch Mines.

Clark, J., et al. Thin Seam Coal Mining Technology. LC 82-7968. (Energy Tech. Rev. 80). (Illus.). 385p. 1983. 36.00 (ISBN 0-8155-0909-X). Noyes.

Martin, James W. & Martin, Thomas J. Surface Mining Equipment. LC 82-81951. (Illus.). 450p. 1982. 37.95 (ISBN 0-9609060-0-2). Martin Consult.

Mining Equipment Market. 274p. 1983. 1375.00 (ISBN 0-86621-557-3). Frost & Sullivan.

Mining Machinery & Equipment. 1982. 495.00 (ISBN 0-318-00500-X). Busn Trend.

Nelson, Don. Mines & Mining Equipment & Service Companies Worldwide, 1984-85. 500p. 1985. 79.95 (ISBN 0-419-13260-0, NO. 6900, Pub. by E & FN Spon England). Methuen Inc.

Stack, Barbara. Handbook of Mining & Tunnelling Machinery. LC 80-4159. 742p. 1982. 107.95x (ISBN 0-471-27937-4, Pub. by Wiley-Interscience). Wiley.

MINING RESEARCH

The Role of Innovation in the Mining & Mining Supply Industries. (Illus.). 1977. pap. 3.85 (ISBN 0-685-81707-5, SSC73, SSC). Unipub.

MINKOWSKI, HERMANN, 1864-1909

Scharlau, W. & Opolka, H. From Fermat to Minkowski: Lectures on the Theory of Numbers & Its Historical Development. Buhler, W. K. & Cornell, G., trs. from German. (Undergraduate Texts in Mathematics Ser.). (Illus.). 255p. 1985. 24.00 (ISBN 0-387-90942-7). Springer-Verlag.

MINKOWSKI SPACE

see Spaces, Generalized

MINKS

Adams, L. Mink Raising. (Illus.). 188p. 1979. pap. 3.50 (ISBN 0-936622-15-6). A R Harding Pub.

Errington, Paul L. Muskrats & Marsh Management. LC 77-14177. (Illus.). x, 183p. 1978. pap. 4.50 (ISBN 0-8032-5892-5, BB 664, Bison). U of Nebr Pr.

MINOLTA CAMERA

see Cameras–Types–Minolta

MINOR AUTOMOBILE

see Automobiles, Foreign–Types–Morris Minor

MINOR PLANETS

see Planets, Minor

MIRRORS

Heyne, Pamela. Today's Architectural Mirror: Interiors, Buildings, & Solar Designs. LC 81-10375. (Illus.). 225p. 1981. 32.50 (ISBN 0-442-23424-4). Van Nos Reinhold.

Siler, Todd. The Biomirror. (Illus.). 60p. (Orig.). 1983. pap. 6.00 (ISBN 0-914661-01-9). Feldman Fine Arts.

MISSILE GUIDANCE SYSTEMS

see Guided Missiles–Guidance Systems

MISSILES, GUIDED

see Guided Missiles

MIT

see Massachusetts Institute of Technology

MITES

see also Ticks

Balogh, J. The Oribatid Genera of the World. (Illus.). 188p. (Orig.). 1972. 21.00 (ISBN 0-685-36757-6). Entomological Repr.

Cook, David. Studies on Neotropical Water Mites. (Memoirs Ser.: No. 31). (Illus.). 644p. 1980. 50.00x (ISBN 0-686-27979-4). Am Entom Inst.

--Water Mite Genera & Subgenera. (Memoris Ser: No. 21). (Illus.). 860p. 1974. 60.00x (ISBN 0-686-08749-6). Am Entom Inst.

Cook, David R. Water Mites from India. (Memoirs Ser: No. 9). (Illus.). 411p. 1967. 30.00x (ISBN 0-686-17145-4). Am Entom Inst.

--The Water Mites of Liberia. (Memoirs Ser: No. 6). (Illus.). 418p. 1966. 30.00x (ISBN 0-686-17144-6). Am Entom Inst.

Evans, G. Owen, et al. The Terrestrial Acari of the British Isles-an Introduction to Their Morphology, Biology & Classification, Vol. 1: Introduction & Biology. (Illus.). 219p. 1961. Repr. of 1968 ed. 14.00x (ISBN 0-565-00696-7, Pub. by Brit Mus Nat Hist England). Sabbot-Natural Hist Bks.

Fransz, H. G. The Functional Response to Prey Density in an Acarine System. New ed. (Simulation Monographs). 143p. 1974. pap. 16.00 (ISBN 90-220-0509-7, PDC37, PUDOC). Unipub.

Helle, W. & Sabelis, M. Spider Mites: Their Biology & Control, Pt. A. (World Crop Pests Ser.: Vol. 1A). Date not set. write for info. (ISBN 0-444-42372-9). Elsevier.

--Spides Mites: Their Biology & Control, Pt. B. (World Crop Pests Ser.: Vol. 1B). Date not set. write for info. (ISBN 0-444-42374-5). Elsevier.

Hoy, Marjorie. Recent Advances in Knowledge of the Phytoseiidae. (Illus.). 100p. (Orig.). 1983. pap. 8.00x (ISBN 0-931876-62-1, 3284). Ag & Nat Res.

Hoy, Marjorie A. & Cunningham, Gary L. Biological Control of Pests by Mites: Proceedings of a Conference. LC 83-72136. (Illus.). 150p. (Orig.). 1983. pap. 15.00x (ISBN 0-931876-63-X, 3304). Ag & Nat Res.

Jeppson, Lee R., et al. Mites Injurious to Economic Plants. LC 72-93523. (Illus.). 1975. 70.00x (ISBN 0-520-02381-1). U of Cal Pr.

McDaniel, Burruss. How to Know the Mites & Ticks. (Pictured Key Nature Ser.). 350p. 1979. write for info. wire coil (ISBN 0-697-04757-1); pap. text ed. o.p. avail. (ISBN 0-697-04756-3). Wm C Brown.

Michael, Albert D. British Tyroglyphidae, 2 Vols. Repr. of 1903 ed. Set. 83.00 (ISBN 0-384-38875-2). Johnson Repr.

Newkirk, R. A. The Eriophyid Mites of Alfred Nalepa. (Thomas Say Foundation Ser.: Vol. 9). 138p. 1984. 20.00. Entomol Soc.

Peterson, Paul C., et al. The Feather Mite Family Eustathiidae: (Acarina: Sarcoptiformes) (Monograph: No. 21). (Illus.). 143p. 1980. pap. 15.00 (ISBN 0-910006-29-6). Acad Nat Sci Phila.

Prasad, Vikram & Cook, David. Taxonomy of Water Mite Larvae. (Memoirs Ser: No. 18). (Illus.). 326p. 1972. 30.00x (ISBN 0-686-08727-5). Am Entom Inst.

Rodriguez, J. G., ed. Recent Advances in Acarology. LC 79-17386. 1979. Vol. 1. 51.00 (ISBN 0-12-592201-9); Vol. 2. 46.50 (ISBN 0-12-592202-7). Acad Pr.

Tuttle, Donald M. & Baker, Edward W. The Spider Mites of the Southwestern United States & a Revision of the Family Tetranychidae. LC 67-30668. (Illus.). 143p. 1968. 7.50x (ISBN 0-8165-0085-1). U of Ariz Pr.

Van Der Hammen, L. A Berlese, Acari Myriopoda et Scorpiones Eighteen Eighty-Two to Nineteen Three, 12 vols. 4616p. 1980. Set. 315.00 (ISBN 90-6193-603-9, Pub. by Junk Pubs Netherlands). Kluwer Academic.

Whittington, H. B. British Trilobites of the Family Harpidae. 12.00 (ISBN 0-384-68220-0). Johnson Repr.

Zakhvatkin, A. A. Arachnoidea: Tyroglyphoidea (Acari) Ratcliffe, A. M. & Hughes, A. M., eds. Ratcliffe, A. & Hughes, A. M., trs. 1959. 10.00 (ISBN 0-934454-09-4). Lubrecht & Cramer.

MITOCHONDRIA

Bandlow, W. & Schweyen, R., eds. Mitochondria, 1977: Genetics & Biogenesis of Mitochondria. 1977. 80.00 (ISBN 3-11-007321-8). De Gruyter.

Bandlow, W., et al, eds. Genetics, Biogenetics & Bioenergetics of Mitochondria: Symposium, Sept. 1975, University of Munich, Germany. 1976. 56.00x (ISBN 3-11-006865-6). De Gruyter.

Birky, C. William, Jr., et al, eds. Genetics & Biogenesis of Mitochondria & Chloroplasts. LC 75-20271. (Ohio State University Biosciences Colloquia: No.1). (Illus.). 371p. 1976. 15.00x (ISBN 0-8142-0236-5). Ohio St U Pr.

Chappell, J. B. The Energetics of Mitochondria. rev. ed. Head, J. J., ed. LC 77-70873. (Carolina Biology Readers Ser.). (Illus.). 32p. 1979. pap. 2.00 (ISBN 0-89278-219-6, 45-9619). Carolina Biological.

Douce, R. & Day, D. A., eds. Higher Plant Cell Respiration. (New Encyclopedia of Plant Physiology Ser.: Vol. 18). (Illus.). 525p. 1985. 104.50 (ISBN 0-387-13935-4). Springer-Verlag.

Douce, Roland. Mitochondria in Higher Plants. (American Society of Plant Physiologists Monograph). 1985. 48.00 (ISBN 0-12-221280-0). Acad Pr.

Easton, A. J., et al. Analysis of Chondritic Material Using Selective Attack by Chlorine. (Illus.). 1981. spiral bdg. 21.50x (ISBN 0-565-00837-4, Pub. by Brit Mus Nat Hist England). Sabbot-Natural Hist Bks.

Erecinska, Maria & Wilson, David F., eds. Inhibitors of Mitochondrial Function. (International Encyclopedia of Pharmacology & Therapeutics Ser.: Section 107). (Illus.). 324p. 1981. 88.00 (ISBN 0-08-027380-7). Pergamon.

FEBS Meeting, Amsterdam, August, 1972, Eighth. Mitochondria & Membranes: Proceedings, Vol. 28. 1973. 30.00 (ISBN 0-444-10423-2, North-Holland). Elsevier.

Kroon, A. M. & Saccone, C., eds. The Biogenesis of Mitochondria: Transcriptional, Translational & Genetic Aspects, Proceedings. 1974. 65.00 (ISBN 0-12-426750-5). Acad Pr.

Mehlman, Myron A. & Hanson, Richard W., eds. Energy Metabolism & the Regulation of Metabolic Processes in Mitochondria. 1972. 49.50 (ISBN 0-12-487850-4). Acad Pr.

Mitochondrial Ribosomes & Mitochondrial RNA from Yeast. (Agricultural Research Reports: No. 797). 1973. pap. 4.00 (ISBN 90-220-0451-1, PDC54, PUDOC). Unipub.

Prebble, J. N. Mitochondria, Chloroplasts & Bacterial Membranes. (Illus.). 1981. text ed. 26.00x (ISBN 0-582-44133-1). Longman.

Sager, Ruth. Cytoplasmic Genes & Organelles. 1972. 37.50 (ISBN 0-12-614650-0). Acad Pr.

Schweyen, R. J., et al, eds. Mitochondria, 1983: Nucleo-Mitochondrial Interactions, Proceedings of a Conference Held in Schliersee, Germany, July 19-23, 1983. LC 83-26341. xxv, 648p. 1984. 96.00x (ISBN 3-11-009871-7). De Gruyter.

Slonimski, P., et al, eds. Mitochondrial Genes. LC 81-68894. (Monographs: Vol. 12). 520p. 1982. 82.50x (ISBN 0-87969-145-X). Cold Spring Harbor.

Symposium on Biochemistry & Biophysics of Mitochondrial Membranes. Biochemistry & Biophysics of Mitochondrial Membranes: Proceedings. Azzone, G. F., ed. 1972. 77.00 (ISBN 0-12-068950-2). Acad Pr.

Tandler, Bernard & Hoppel, Charles L. Mitochandria. (Monographs on the Ultrastructure of Cells & Organisms). 1972. 29.00 (ISBN 0-12-454143-7). Acad Pr.

Tedeschi, H. Mitochondria: Structure, Biogenesis & Transducing Functions. (Cell Biology Monographs: Vol. 4). (Illus.). 180p. 1976. 55.00 (ISBN 0-387-81317-9). Springer-Verlag.

Tzagoloff, Alexander. Mitochondria. LC 81-23373. (Cellular Organelles Ser.). 358p. 1982. 42.50 (ISBN 0-306-40799-X, Plenum Pr); pap. 19.95 (ISBN 0-306-40778-7). Plenum Pub.

Wainio, Walter W. Mammalian Mitochondrial Respiratory Chain. (Molecular Biology Ser.). 1971. 80.00 (ISBN 0-12-730650-1). Acad Pr.

MITOSIS

Little, M., et al, eds. Mitosis: Facts & Questions. LC 77-17156. (Proceedings in Life Sciences). 1977. 29.00 (ISBN 0-387-08517-3). Springer-Verlag.

Parker, Gary E., et al. Mitosis & Meiosis. 2nd ed. (EMI Programed Biology Ser.). (Illus.). 1979. pap. 6.95 (ISBN 0-88462-010-7, Ed Methods). Longman USA.

Sakai, Hikoichi & Mohri, Hideo, eds. Biological Functions of Microtubules & Related Structure: Proceedings, 13th Oji International Seminar, Tokyo, Japan, December, 1981. LC 82-11609. 1982. 39.50 (ISBN 0-12-615080-X). Acad Pr.

Zimmerman, Arthur, et al, eds. Mitosis-Cytokinesis. LC 81-14976. (Cell Biology Ser.). 1981. 65.00 (ISBN 0-12-781240-7). Acad Pr.

MIVART, ST. GEORGE JACKSON, 1827-1900

Gruber, Jacob W. A Conscience in Conflict: The Life of St. George Jackson Mivart. LC 79-17545. (Illus.). 1980. Repr. of 1960 ed. lib. bdg. 32.50x (ISBN 0-313-22041-7, GRCC). Greenwood.

MIXED CYCLOIDS (CHEMISTRY)

see Heterocyclic Compounds

MIXERS (MACHINERY)

see Mixing Machinery

MIXING

Bhatia, Mahesh V. & Cheremisinoff, Paul N. Solids Separation & Mixing. LC 79-63114. (Process Equipment Ser.: Vol. 1). 303p. 1979. 35.00 (ISBN 0-87762-272-8). Technomic.

Chance, Britton, ed. Rapid Mixing & Sampling Techniques in Biochemistry. 1964. 65.00 (ISBN 0-12-167868-7). Acad Pr.

European Conference on Mixing, 3rd. Proceedings, 2 vols. Stephens, H. S. & Stapleton, C. A., eds. (European Conferences on Mixing Ser.). 500p. 1979. Set. PLB 65.00x (ISBN 0-906085-31-4, Dist. by Air Science Co.). BHRA Fluid.

Harnby, Norman. Mixing in the Process Industries. (Monographs in Chemical Engineering). (Illus.). 256p. 1985. text ed. 87.95 (ISBN 0-408-11574-2). Butterworth.

Jimenez, J., ed. Role of Coherent Structures in Modelling Turbulence & Mixing: Proceedings. (Lecture Notes in Physics Ser.: Vol. 136). 393p. 1981. pap. 30.00 (ISBN 0-387-10289-2). Springer-Verlag.

Mixing, Second European Conference. Proceedings. Stephens, H. S. & Clarke, J. A., eds. 1978. pap. 60.00x (ISBN 0-900983-69-8, Dist. by Air Science Co.). BHRA Fluid.

Nauman, E. B. & Buffham, B. A. Mixing in Continuous Flow Systems. LC 82-24858. 304p. 1983. 45.95x (ISBN 0-471-86191-X, Pub. by Wiley-Interscience). Wiley.

Okubo, Akira. Oceanic Mixing. LC 73-133442. 151p. 1970. 19.00 (ISBN 0-403-04523-1). Scholarly.

Sweeney, Eugene T. An Introduction & Literature Guide to Mixing. (BHRA Fluid Engineering Ser., Vol. 5). 1978. 21.00x (ISBN 0-900983-77-9, Dist. by Air Science Co.). BHRA Fluid.

Symposium at Pittsburgh, Penn., June, 1974. Turbulence in Mixing Operations: Theory & Application to Mixing & Reaction. Brodkey, Robert S., ed. 1975. 57.50 (ISBN 0-12-134450-9). Acad Pr.

Uhl, Vincent & Gray, Joseph B., eds. Mixing: Theory & Practice, 2 Vols. 1966-67. Vol. 1. 71.00; Vol. 2. 71.00 (ISBN 0-12-706601-2) (ISBN 0-12-706602-0). Acad Pr.

Uram, Earl M. & Goldschmidt, Victor W., eds. Fluid Mechanics of Mixing: Presented at the Joint Meeting of the Fluids Engineering Division & the Applied Mechanics Division, Georgia Institute of Technology, Atlanta, GA, June 20-22, 1973. LC 73-81802. pap. 48.50 (ISBN 0-317-08108-X, 2016838). Bks Demand UMI.

MIXING MACHINERY

Advani, L. T. Horsepower Tables for Agitator Impellers. LC 76-2964. 175p. 1976. 29.95x (ISBN 0-87201-368-5). Gulf Pub.

MIXTURES

see also Emulsions; Solution (Chemistry)

Budnikov, P. P. & Ginstling, A. M. Principles of Solid State Chemistry. 468p. 1970. 119.50 (ISBN 0-677-61250-8). Gordon.

Cornell, John A. Experiments with Mixtures: Designs, Models & the Analysis of Mixtures Data. LC 80-22153. (Probability & Mathematical Statistics Ser.). 305p. 1981. 41.50x (ISBN 0-471-07916-2, Pub. by Wiley-Interscience). Wiley.

Everitt, B. S. & Hand, D. J. Finite Mixture Distributions. (Monographs in Applied Probability & Statistics). 143p. 1981. 22.00 (ISBN 0-412-22420-8, NO. 2234, Pub. by Chapman & Hall). Methuen Inc.

Hiza, M. J., et al. Equilibrium Properties of Fluid Mixtures: A Bibliography of Data on Fluids of Cryogenic Interest. LC 75-19000. (NSRDS Bibliographic Ser.). 165p. 1975. 85.00x (ISBN 0-306-66001-6, IFI Plenum). Plenum Pub.

Nielsen, Lawrence E. Predicting the Properties of Mixtures. 1978. 35.00 (ISBN 0-8247-6690-3). Dekker.

MO-PEDS

see Mopeds

MOBILE COMMUNICATION SYSTEMS

see also Automobiles–Radio Equipment; Mobile Radio Stations

Duff, William G. Mobile Communications. 2nd ed. (Illus.). 296p. 1980. text ed. 43.00 (ISBN 0-932263-09-7). White Consult.

Jakes, William C., et al, eds. Microwave Mobile Communications. LC 74-13401. 640p. 1974. 74.95x (ISBN 0-471-43720-4, Pub. by Wiley-Interscience). Wiley.

Lee, William C. Mobile Communications Engineering. (Illus.). 356p. 1982. 48.50 (ISBN 0-07-037039-7). McGraw.

Sams Editorial Staff. Mobile Communications Fundamentals. 1985. 34.95 (ISBN 0-317-29690-6, 22305). Sams.

MOBILE HOMES

Bernhardt, Arthur D. Building Tomorrow: The Mobile-Manufactured Housing Industry. (Illus.). 1980. text ed. 60.00 (ISBN 0-262-02134-X). MIT Pr.

Evan, John. Mobile Home Buyer's Bible. LC 79-51492. 1979. pap. 14.95 (ISBN 0-9602644-0-X). Concours Pub.

Loos, Alex & Loos, John. Chilton's Mobile Home Maintenance Guide. 1977. pap. 11.95. (ISBN 0-8019-6516-0). Chilton.

Mobile Homes. (Five Hundred Ser.). 1974. pap. 3.75 (ISBN 0-685-58221-3, 501B). Natl Fire Prot.

Raskhodoff, Nicholas M. The Complete Mobile Home Book: The Guide to Manufactured Homes. LC 80-5798. (Illus.). 240p. 1982. 21.95 (ISBN 0-8128-2781-3); pap. 14.95 (ISBN 0-8128-6137-X). Stein & Day.

Rockland, Michael A. Homes on Wheels. 192p. 1980. 15.00 (ISBN 0-8135-0892-4). Rutgers U Pr.

MOBILE RADIO STATIONS

see also Citizens Band Radio

Pannell, W. M. Frequency Engineering in Mobile Radio Bonds. 356p. 1979. cancelled. Taylor & Francis.

MODEL AIRPLANES

see Airplanes–Models

MODEL CARS

see Automobiles–Models

MODEL NETWORKS

see Electric Network Analyzers

MODEL RAILROADS

see Railroads–Models

MODEL SPACE VEHICLES

see Space Vehicles–Models

MODEL THEORY

Auerbach, Stevanne, ed. Model Programs & Their Components. LC 76-10121. (Child Care: a Comprehensive Guide Ser.: Vol. II). 297p. 1976. 24.95 (ISBN 0-87705-256-5). Human Sci Pr.

Bridge, Jane. Beginning Model Theory: The Completeness Theorem & Some Consequences. (Oxford Logic Guides Ser.). 1977. 17.95x (ISBN 0-19-853157-5). Oxford U Pr.

Cherlin, G. Model Theoretic Algebra Selected Topics. LC 76-15388. (Lecture Notes in Mathematics: Vol. 521). 1976. pap. 16.00 (ISBN 0-387-07696-4). Springer-Verlag.

Crossley, J. N. & Nerode, A. Combinatorial Factors. LC 73-10783. (Ergebnisse der Mathematik und Ihrer Grenzgebiete: Vol. 81). (Illus.). 160p. 1974. 25.00 (ISBN 0-387-06428-1). Springer-Verlag.

Farlow. Self-Organizing Methods in Modeling: GMDH Type Algorithms. (Statistics - Textbooks & Monographs). 344p. 1984. 55.00 (ISBN 0-8247-7161-3). Dekker.

Hirschfeld, J. & Wheeler, W. H. Forcing, Arithmetic, Division Rings. (Lecture Notes in Mathematics Ser.: Vol. 454). vii, 266p. 1975. pap. 17.00 (ISBN 0-387-07157-1). Springer-Verlag.

Jensen, R. R. & Prestel, A., eds. Set Theory & Model Theory: Proceedings. (Lecture Notes in Mathematics Ser.: Vol. 872). 174p. 1981. pap. 13.00 (ISBN 0-387-10849-1). Springer-Verlag.

Khalil, E. E. Modelling of Furnaces & Combustors. 1982. 41.00 (ISBN 0-9961005-3-9, Pub. by Abacus England). Heyden.

Makkai, M. & Reyes, G. First-Order Categorical Logic: Model-Theoretical Methods in the Theory of Topoi & Related Categories. LC 77-13221. (Lecture Notes in Mathematics: Vol. 611). 1977. pap. text ed. 22.00 (ISBN 0-387-08439-8). Springer-Verlag.

Mal'cev, A. I. Algebraic Systems. Seckler, B. D. & Doohovskoy, A. P., trs. from Russian. (Die Grundlehren der Mathematischen Wissenschaften: Vol. 192). 320p. 1973. 59.00 (ISBN 0-387-05792-7). Springer-Verlag.

Maurer, C. & Wraith, G. C., eds. Model Theory & Topoi. (Lecture Notes in Mathematics Ser). 354p. 1975. pap. 20.00 (ISBN 0-387-07164-4). Springer-Verlag.

Morley, Michael D., ed. Studies in Model Theory. LC 73-86564. (MAA Studies: No. 8). 197p. 1973. 16.50 (ISBN 0-88385-108-3). Math Assn.

Pillay, Anand. An Introduction to Stability Theory. (Oxford Logic Guides Ser.). 1983. 29.95x (ISBN 0-19-853186-9). Oxford U Pr.

Potier, D., ed. Modelling Techniques & Tools for Performance Analysis. 1985. 74.00 (ISBN 0-444-87696-0). Elsevier.

Prestel, A. Lectures on Formally Real Fields. (Lectures Notes in Mathematics Ser.: Vol. 1093). xi, 125p. 1984. pap. 10.00 (ISBN 0-387-13885-4). Springer-Verlag.

Reiss, David. The Family's Construction of Reality. LC 81-2703. (Illus.). 448p. 1981. text ed. 27.50x (ISBN 0-674-29415-7). Harvard U Pr.

Saracino, D. H. & Weispfenning, V. B., eds. Model Theory & Algebra: A Memorial Tribute to Abraham Robinson. LC 75-40483. (Lecture Notes in Mathematics: Vol. 498). 1975. pap. 24.00 (ISBN 0-387-07538-0). Springer-Verlag.

Shelah, S. Proper Forcing. (Lecture Notes in Mathematics: Vol. 940). 496p. 1982. pap. 27.00 (ISBN 0-387-11593-5). Springer-Verlag.

Striefel, Sebastian. How to Teach Through Modeling & Imitation. 42p. 1981. 5.00 (ISBN 0-89079-059-0). Pro Ed.

Vogt, William G. & Mickle, Marlin H., eds. Modeling & Simulation, Vol. 13: Proceedings of the Annual Pittsburgh Conference on Modeling & Simulation, 4 pts. LC 73-85004. 1744p. 1982. pap. text ed. 40.00 ea. Pt. 1; 512p (ISBN 0-87664-712-3). Pt. 2; 546p (ISBN 0-87664-713-1). Pt. 3; 408p (ISBN 0-87664-714-X). Pt. 4; 368p (ISBN 0-87664-715-8). Set. pap. text ed. 149.00 (ISBN 0-87664-716-6). Instru Soc.

MODELING, GEOLOGICAL

see Geological Modeling

MODELS, BIOLOGICAL

see Biological Models

MODELS, CHEMICAL

see Chemical Models

MODELS, MECHANICAL

see Machinery–Models

MODELS, NUCLEAR

see Nuclear Models

MODELS, ZOOLOGICAL

see Zoological Models

MODELS AND MODELMAKING

see also Architectural Models; Engineering Models; Geological Modeling; Pattern-Making; Simulation Methods; Zoological Models

also subdivision Models under names of objects, e.g. Automobiles–Models; and Machinery–Models; Surfaces, Models of

Alt, E. Winifred. Index to Handicrafts, Modelmaking & Workshop Projects, Suppl. 4. LC 36-27324. (The Useful Reference Ser. of Library Bks: Vol. 96). 1969. lib. bdg. 16.00x (ISBN 0-87305-096-7). Faxon.

Ashley, Roy. Matchstick Modelling. (Illus.). 80p. 1980. 10.95 (ISBN 0-7207-1150-9, Pub. by Michael Joseph). Merrimack Pub Cir.

Bowen, John, ed. Scale Model Warships. LC 78-25641. (Illus.). 1979. 12.95 (ISBN 0-8317-7702-8, Mayflower Bks). Smith Pubs.

Brockington, N. R. Computer Modeling in Agriculture. (Illus.). 1979. 35.00x (ISBN 0-19-854523-1). Oxford U Pr.

Bundy, Alan. The Computer Modeling of Mathematical Reasoning. 1984. 17.00 (ISBN 0-12-141252-0). Acad Pr.

Cain, Tubal. Model Engineers Handbook. rev. ed. (Illus.). 192p. 1982. pap. 9.95 (ISBN 0-85242-715-8). Aztex.

Chaney, Charles & Skee, Stanley. Plaster Mold & Model Making. LC 80-21932. 144p. 1981. Repr. of 1973 ed. text ed. 14.00 (ISBN 0-89874-282-X). Krieger.

Coleman, H. S. Teach Yourself Modelcraft. 10.00x (ISBN 0-392-08233-0, SpS). Sportshelf.

Cundell, John & King, Jim. Introducing Model Marine Steam. (Illus.). 112p. (Orig.). 1983. pap. 11.95 (ISBN 0-85242-814-6, Pub. by Argus). Aztex.

Fisher, O. Collector's Guide to Model Aero Engines. (Illus.). 132p. 1985. pap. 7.95 (ISBN 0-85242-492-2, Pub. by Argus). Aztex.

Gordon, Theron L. How to Build, Customize & Design Plastic Models. (Illus.). 192p. (Orig.). 1982. pap. 10.95 (ISBN 0-8306-1192-4, 1192). TAB Bks.

Gupta, A. K. & Lilley, D. G. Flowfield Modeling & Diagnostics. (Energy & Engineering Sciences Ser.). 400p. 1984. 49.00 (ISBN 0-9901004-5-6, Pub. by Abacus England). Heyden.

Harris, K. N. Model Boilers & Boilermaking. rev. ed. (Illus.). 185p. 1984. pap. 9.95 (ISBN 0-85242-377-2, Pub. by Argus). Aztex.

Harris, Roy D. & Maggard, Michael J. Computer Models in Operations Management: A Computer-Augmented System. 2nd ed. 1977. pap. text ed. 20.50 scp (ISBN 0-06-042664-0, HarpC); scp solutions manual 9.75 (ISBN 0-06-042666-7); source deck of all comp. progs. 30.00 (ISBN 0-06-042665-9). Har-Row.

Harrison, H. H. Model Steam Turbines. (Illus.). 62p. 1985. pap. 2.95 (ISBN 0-85242-600-3, Pub. by Argus). Aztex.

Himmelblau, David M. Process Analysis & Simulation: Deterministic Systems. (Illus.). 348p. 1968. pap. text ed. 29.95 (ISBN 0-88408-132-X). Sterling Swift.

Huckfeidt, Robert R., et al, eds. Dynamic Modeling: An Introduction. LC 82-42610. (Quantitative Applications in the Social SCiences Ser.: Vol. 27). 1982. pap. 5.00 (ISBN 0-8039-0946-2). Sage.

Jackson, Albert & Day, David. The Modelmaker's Handbook. LC 80-2702. (Illus.). 352p. 1981. 21.95 (ISBN 0-394-50788-6). Knopf.

Jensen, Phil. Building Model Trucks: An Auto World How-to-Do-It Book. (Illus.). 140p. 1978. pap. 9.95 (ISBN 0-317-16142-3). Aztex.

Laing, Gordon J. Building Scientific Models. LC 84-13616. 300p. 1985. text ed. write for info. (ISBN 0-566-00682-0). Gower Pub Co.

Lamit, Gary. Industrial Model Building. (Illus.). 528p. 1981. text ed. 35.95 (ISBN 0-13-461566-2). P-H.

Lovell, Eleanor C. & Hall, Ruth M. Index to Handicrafts, Modelmaking & Workshop Projects. (The Useful Reference Ser of Library Bks: Vol. 57). 1936. lib. bdg. 14.00x (ISBN 0-87305-057-6). Faxon.

--Index to Handicrafts, Modelmaking & Workshop Projects, Suppl. 1. (The Useful Reference Ser of Library Bks: Vol. 70). 1943. lib. bdg. 14.00x (ISBN 0-87305-070-3). Faxon.
--Index to Handicrafts, Modelmaking & Workshop Projects, Suppl. 2. (The Useful Reference Ser of Library Bks: Vol. 79). 1950. lib. bdg. 14.00x (ISBN 0-87305-079-7). Faxon.
Lykos, Peter, ed. Computer Modeling of Matter. LC 78-25828. (ACS Symposium Ser.: No. 86). 1978. 29.95 (ISBN 0-8412-0463-2). Am Chemical.
Mansir, A. Richard. A Modeller's Guide to Hull Construction. (Illus.). 64p. (Orig.). 1980. pap. 10.95 (ISBN 0-940620-01-4). Moonraker.
Marshall, Percival. Model Steamer Building. (Illus.). 52p. 1985. pap. 2.95 (ISBN 0-85242-478-7, Pub. by Argus). Aztex.
Mason, L. C. Model Four Stroke Petrol Engines. rev. ed. (Illus.). 116p. 1983. pap. 9.95 (ISBN 0-85242-431-0, Pub. by Argus). Aztex.
--Scale Model Traction Engine Building Featuring Minnie. 200p. 1985. pap. 11.95 (ISBN 0-85344-077-8, Pub. by Argus). Aztex.
Metrication for the Modeller. (Illus.). 40p. 1979. pap. 1.95 (ISBN 0-85344-137-5). Aztex.
Model & Allied Publications Plan Books (MAP) Plans Handbook 5-Scale Drawings. 80p. 1984. pap. 1.95 (ISBN 0-89404-207-6, Pub. by Argus). Aztex.
Paine, Shep & Stewart, Lane. How to Photograph Scale Models. Hayden, Bob, ed. (Illus.). 64p. (Orig.). 1984. pap. 8.95 (ISBN 0-89024-053-1). Kalmbach.
Philpott, Bryan. Making & Improving Plastic Models. LC 74-21510. (Illus.). 112p. 1975. 2.95 (ISBN 0-7153-6698-X). David & Charles.
Price, Brick. The Model-Building Handbook: Techniques Professionals Use. LC 80-70387. (Illus.). 224p. 1981. 14.95 (ISBN 0-8019-6862-3); pap. 9.95 (ISBN 0-8019-6863-1). Chilton.
Ranky, P. & Ho, C. Y. Robot Modelling: Control & Applications with Software. 380p. 1985. 45.00 (Pub. by IFS Pubns UK). Air Sci Co.
Rayman, A. A. High Speed Marine Engines. 60p. 1985. pap. 2.50 (ISBN 0-85242-540-6, Pub. by Argus). Aztex.
Rivett, Patrick. Model Building for Decision Analysis. LC 79-40739. 172p. 1980. 35.95 (ISBN 0-471-27654-5, Pub. by Wiley-Interscience). Wiley.
Santos, Saul. Scratchbuilding Model Cars. (Illus.). 224p. (Orig.). 1983. 15.95 (ISBN 0-8306-3085-6, 2085); pap. 10.95 (ISBN 0-8306-2085-0). TAB Bks.
Schleicher, Robert. The Modeler's Manual. (Illus.). 192p. 1981. 14.95 (ISBN 0-8019-6996-4); pap. 10.95 (ISBN 0-8019-6997-2). Chilton.
--Scenery & Dioramas for Modelers. LC 81-70916. 192p. 1983. 16.95 (ISBN 0-8019-7221-3); pap. 12.95 (ISBN 0-8019-7222-1). Chilton.
Shaw, Robert. The Dripping Faucet As a Model Chaotic System. (Science Frontier Express Ser.). (Illus.). 122p. 1984. pap. 15.00 (ISBN 0-942344-05-7). Aerial Pr.
Solarbo Book of Balsa Models. 100p. 1985. pap. 6.95 (ISBN 0-85242-462-0, Pub. by Argus). Aztex.
Stuart-Turner, S. M. & Greenly, Henry. The Stuart Progress. 22p. 1985. pap. 2.50 (ISBN 0-905180-08-9, Pub. by Argus). Aztex.
Takakjian, Portia & Sayles, William. Basic Handbook of Ship-Model Building. 1986. cancelled (ISBN 0-442-28403-9). Van Nos Reinhold.
Vogt, William G. & Mickle, Marlin H., eds. Modeling & Simulation, Vol. 14: Proceedings of the Annual Pittsburgh Conference on Modeling & Simulation, 4 pts. in 3 bks. LC 73-85004. 1576p. 1983. Set. pap. text ed. 149.00x (ISBN 0-87664-795-6); Pts. 1 & 2. pap. text ed. 55.00x (ISBN 0-87664-792-1); Pt. 3. pap. text ed. 55.00x (ISBN 0-87664-793-X); Pt. 4. pap. text ed. 55.00x (ISBN 0-87664-794-8). Instru Soc.
Vogy, William G. & Mickle, Marlin H., eds. Modeling & Simulation, Vol. 12: Proceedings of the Annual Pittsburgh Conference on Modeling & Simulation, 4 pts. LC 73-85004. 1776p. 1981. Set. pap. text ed. 149.00x (ISBN 0-87664-563-5); pap. text ed. 40.00x ea. Pt. 1 Energy & Environment (ISBN 0-87664-559-7). Pt. 2-Systems, Control & Computers (ISBN 0-87664-560-0). Pt. 3-Socio-economics & Biomedical (ISBN 0-87664-561-9). Pt. 4-General Modeling & Simulation (ISBN 0-87664-562-7). Instru Soc.
Ward, Roland. The Price Guide to the Models of W. H. Goss. (Price Guide Ser.). (Illus.). 182p. 1980. 29.50 (ISBN 0-902028-20-0). Antique Collect.
Wellstead, P. E. Introduction to Physical Modelling. LC 79-50528. 1980. 48.00 (ISBN 0-12-744380-0). Acad Pr.

MODELS AND MODELMAKING–RADIO CONTROL SYSTEMS

Beckman, Bob. Building & Flying Giant Scale Radio Control Aircraft. Angle, Burr, ed. (Illus.). 88p. (Orig.). 1983. pap. 9.95 (ISBN 0-89024-049-3). Kalmbach.
Boddington, David. Building & Flying Radio-Controlled Model Aircraft. (Illus.). 227p. 1985. pap. 11.95 (ISBN 0-85242-790-5, Pub. by Argus). Aztex.
--Radio Control Primer. (Illus.). 134p. 1985. pap. 9.95 (ISBN 0-85242-378-0, Pub. by Argus). Aztex.
--Scale Model Aircraft Radio Control. (Illus.). 300p. (Orig.). 1984. pap. 19.95 (ISBN 0-85242-810-3, Pub. by ARGUS). Aztex.
Burkinshaw, Bill. Introducing Radio Control Model Aircraft. (Illus.). 96p. 1983. pap. 9.95 (ISBN 0-85242-801-4). Aztex.
Drake, John. Radio Control Helicopter Models. rev. ed. (Illus.). 144p. 1983. pap. 9.95 (Pub. by Argus). Aztex.
Laidlaw-Dickson, D. J. Radio Controlled Model Racing Cars. (Illus.). 160p. 1985. pap. 11.50 (ISBN 0-85242-675-5, Pub. by Argus). Aztex.
Marks, Fred & Winter, William. Basics of Radio Control Modeling. rev. ed. Angle, Burr, ed. (Illus.). 84p. (Orig.). 1979. pap. 6.95 (ISBN 0-89024-517-7). Kalmbach.
Marks, Fred M. Getting the Most from Radio Control Systems. Angle, Burr, ed. LC 80-81430. (Illus.). 88p. (Orig.). 1980. pap. 8.95 (ISBN 0-89024-550-9). Kalmbach.
Model & Allied Publications Plan Books (MAP) Plans Handbook 3-Model Engineering. 96p. 1985. pap. 2.50 (ISBN 0-89404-205-X, Pub. by Argus). Aztex.
Model & Allied Publications Plan Books (MAP) Plans Handbook 4-Radio Control Models. 88p. 1985. pap. 2.50 (ISBN 0-89404-206-8, Pub. by Argus). Aztex.
Siposs, George G. Building & Racing Radio Control Cars & Motorcycles. Angle, Burr, ed. LC 80-84853. (Illus.). 80p. (Orig.). 1981. pap. 7.50 (ISBN 0-89024-556-8). Kalmbach.
Smeed, Vic. Introducing Radio Control Model Boats. (Illus.). 96p. 1983. pap. 9.95 (ISBN 0-85242-803-0). Aztex.
Thomas, David B. Basics of Radio Control Power Boat Modeling. Burr, Angle, ed. (Illus.). 80p. (Orig.). 1981. pap. 9.95 (ISBN 0-89024-035-3). Kalmbach.
Vale, A. M. Radio Control Model Aircraft. 192p. 1984. 27.00x (ISBN 0-905418-04-2, Pub. by Gresham England). State Mutual Bk.
Warring, R. H. Radio Controlled Model Boats. (Illus.). 112p. 1985. pap. 8.50 (ISBN 0-85242-569-4, Pub. by Argus). Aztex.
Wooley, David. Radio Controlled Fast Electric Power Boats. (Illus.). 112p. 1985. pap. 7.95 (ISBN 0-85242-753-0, Pub. by Argus). Aztex.

MODERATED REACTORS, ORGANIC
see Organic Moderated Reactors

MODERN GEOMETRY
see Geometry, Modern

MODULA-2 (COMPUTER PROGRAM LANGUAGE)

Beidler, John & Jackowitz, Paul. Modula-II. LC 85-6298. 300p. 1985. pap. write for info. (ISBN 0-87150-912-1, 37L8900). PWS Pubs.
Chirlian, Paul. Introduction to Modula 2. (Illus.). 288p. 1984. pap. 19.95. Dilithium Pr.
--Introduction to Modula 2. Morrice, Nancy, ed. 288p. 1985. pap. 19.95 (ISBN 0-916460-41-X). Matrix Pub.
Chirlian, Paul M. Introduction to Modula 2. 19.95 (ISBN 0-317-26565-2). Merl Miller Assoc.
Gleaves, R. Modula Two for Pascal Programmers. (Books on Professional Computing). (Illus.). 155p. 1984. pap. 16.95 (ISBN 0-387-96051-1). Springer-Verlag.
Greenfield, Stuart B. Invitation to Modula, No. 2. (Illus.). 280p. 1985. 29.95 (ISBN 0-317-31163-8). Van Nos Reinhold.
--Invitation to MODULA-2. (Illus.). 280p. 1985. text ed. 29.95 (ISBN 0-89433-273-2). Petrocelli.
Kaplan, Ian & Miller, Mike. Programming in Modula-2. 240p. 1984. pap. 18.95 (ISBN 0-13-729294-5). P-H.
Smedema, C. H., et al. The Programming Languages: Pascal, Modula, Chill, & Ada. 160p. 1983. 16.95. P-H.
Wiener, Richard S. & Ford, Gary A. Software Development with Modula-2. 672p. 1985. pap. 23.95 (ISBN 0-471-87834-0). Wiley.
Wiener, Richard S. & Sincovec, Richard F. Software Engineering with Modula-2 & Ada. LC 83-21827. 451p. 1984. text ed. 28.95 (ISBN 0-471-89014-6). Wiley.
Wirth, N. Programming in Modula-2. (Illus.). 176p. 1982. 13.95 (ISBN 0-387-11674-5). Springer-Verlag.
--Programming in Modula-2. 3rd corrected ed. (Texts & Monographs in Computer Science). iv, 192p. 1985. 18.95 (ISBN 0-387-15078-1). Springer-Verlag.

MODULAR ARITHMETIC

Adams, William J. Finite Mathematics: For Business & Social Science. LC 73-84448. 354p. 1974. 18.50 (ISBN 0-536-00986-4). Krieger.
Budnick, F. S. Finite Mathematics with Applications in Management & Social Sciences. 512p. 1985. 29.95 (ISBN 0-07-008861-6). McGraw.
Costello, John J., et al. Finite Mathematics with Applications. 524p. 1981. text ed. 24.95 (ISBN 0-15-527400-7, HC); solutions manual avail. (ISBN 0-15-527401-5). HarBraceJ.
Curtis, Charles W. & Reiner, Irving. Representation Theory of Finite Groups & Associative Algebras. LC 62-16994. (Pure & Applied Mathematics Ser.). 685p. 1962. 69.50 (ISBN 0-470-18975-4, Pub. by Wiley-Interscience). Wiley.
Drooyan, Irving & Wooton, William. Beginning Algebra: A Modular Approach, 8 Vols. LC 75-29776. Vol. 1. pap. 20.00 (ISBN 0-317-11109-4, 2012437); Vol. 2. pap. 26.00 (ISBN 0-317-11110-8); Vol. 3. pap. 24.30 (ISBN 0-317-11111-6); Vol. 4. pap. 20.30 (ISBN 0-317-11112-4); Vol. 5. pap. 35.80 (ISBN 0-317-11113-2); Vol. 6. pap. 35.80 (ISBN 0-317-11114-0); Vol. 7. pap. 20.50 (ISBN 0-317-11115-9); Vol. 8. pap. 26.50 (ISBN 0-317-11116-7). Bks Demand UMI.
Gallin, Daniel. Finite Mathematics. 1984. text ed. 25.80x (ISBN 0-673-16048-3). Scott F.
Gregory, Robert T. Error-Free Computation: Why It Is Needed & Methods for Doing It. LC 80-23923. 152p. (Orig.). 1980. pap. 9.50 (ISBN 0-89874-240-4). Krieger.
Gunther, F. A. & Gunther, J. Davies, eds. Residue Reviews. (Illus.). 166p. 1982. 28.50 (ISBN 0-387-90750-5). Springer-Verlag.
Harada. Factor: Categories with Applications to Direct Decomposition of Modules. (Lecture Notes in Pure & Applied Mathematics Ser.). 344p. 1983. 59.75 (ISBN 0-8247-1897-6). Dekker.
Hardy, Lane F. Finite Mathematics for the Managerial, Social, & Life Sciences. (Illus.). 450p. 1984. text ed. 28.95 (ISBN 0-314-77900-0). West Pub.
Hunkins, Dalton & Mugridge, Larry. Applied Finite Mathematics. LC 80-29563. 538p. 1981. write for info. (ISBN 0-87150-306-9, Prindle). PWS Pubs.
Katz, Nicholas & Mazur, Barry. Arithmetic Moduli of Elliptic Curves. LC 83-43079. (Annals of Mathematics Studies: No. 108). 700p. 1984. 60.00x (ISBN 0-691-08349-5); pap. 22.50x (ISBN 0-691-08352-5). Princeton U Pr.
Narkiewicz, W. Uniform Distribution of Sequences of Integers in Residue Classes. (Lecture Notes in Mathematics Ser.: Vol. 1087). vii, 125p. 1984. pap. 10.00 (ISBN 0-387-13872-2). Springer-Verlag.
Rector, Robert E. & Zwick, Earl J. Finite Mathematics & Its Applications. LC 78-69547. (Illus.). 1979. text ed. 28.50 (ISBN 0-395-27206-8); instr's. manual 1.00 (ISBN 0-395-27207-6). HM.
Residue Reviews, Vol. 78. (Illus.). 143p. 1981. 29.00 (ISBN 0-387-90566-9). Springer-Verlag.
Thomas, James W. & Thomas, Ann M. Finite Mathematics. 2nd ed. 1978. text ed. 31.83 (ISBN 0-205-05996-1, 565996); instr's man. avail. (ISBN 0-205-05997-X). Allyn.

MODULAR ARITHMETIC–PROGRAMMED INSTRUCTION

Newmark, Joseph. Using Finite Mathematics. 604p. 1981. text ed. 23.50 scp (ISBN 0-06-385752-9, HarpC); instr's. manual avail. (ISBN 0-06-375778-8). Har-Row.

MODULAR FIELDS
see also Modular Arithmetic; Quaternions

Chari, M. V. & Silvester, P., eds. Finite Elements in Electrical & Magnetic Field Problems. LC 79-1037. (Wiley Series in Numerical Methods in Engineering). 219p. 1980. 53.95 (ISBN 0-471-27578-6, Pub. by Wiley-Interscience). Wiley.
Hirschfield, J. W. Projective Geometries Over Finite Fields. (Oxford Mathematical Monographs). (Illus.). 1980. 59.00x (ISBN 0-19-853526-0). Oxford U Pr.
Lidl, Rudolf, et al. Encyclopedia of Mathematics & Its Applications: Finite Fields, Vol. 20. 1984. 69.50 (ISBN 0-317-14398-0, 30240-4). Cambridge U Pr.
Matlis, Eben. Cotorsion Modules. LC 52-42839. (Memoirs: No. 49). 66p. 1979. pap. 13.00 (ISBN 0-8218-1249-1, MEMO-49). Am Math.
Piateski-Shapiro, Iya. Complex Representations of GL (2,K) for Finite Fields K. LC 82-24484. (Contemporary Mathematics Ser.: Vol. 16). 72p. 1983. pap. 14.00 (ISBN 0-8218-5019-9). Am Math.
Schmidt, W. M. Equations Over Finite Fields: An Elementary Approach. (Lecture Notes in Mathematics: Vol. 536). 1976. soft cover 17.00 (ISBN 0-387-07855-X). Springer-Verlag.
Seligman, G. B. Modular Lie Algebras. LC 67-28452. (Ergebnisse der Mathematik & Ihrer Grenzgebiete: Vol. 40). 1967. 34.00 (ISBN 0-387-03782-9). Springer-Verlag.

MODULAR FUNCTIONS
see Functions, Modular

MODULATION (ELECTRONICS)
see also Carrier Control Systems; Radio Frequency Modulation

Cardona, M. Modulation Spectroscopy. (Solid State Physics: Suppl. 11). 1969. 76.00 (ISBN 0-12-607771-1). Acad Pr.
Connor, F. R. Modulation. (Introductory Topics in Electronics & Telecommunication Ser.). (Illus.). 1973. pap. text ed. 17.95x (ISBN 0-7131-3303-1). Intl Ideas.
--Modulation. 2nd ed. (Introductory Topics in Electronics & Telecommunication). 144p. 1982. pap. text ed. 9.95 (ISBN 0-7131-3457-7). E Arnold.
Gibson, Jerry D. & Melsa, James L. Introduction to Nonparametric Detection with Applications. (Mathematics in Science & Engineering Ser.). 1975. 70.00 (ISBN 0-12-282150-5). Acad Pr.
Nelson, Robert V. Application of Expandable Modular Control & Indicating Systems. LC 81-13401. 1981. lib. bdg. 15.95 (ISBN 0-86663-831-8). Ide Hse.
Rugh & Manning. Proposal Management Using the Modular Technique. 136p. 1982. 33.95 (ISBN 0-932146-07-4). Peninsula CA.
VanTrees, Harry L. Detection, Estimation & Modulation Theory, 2 pts. Incl. Pt. 1. Detection, Estimation & Linear Modulation Theory. 697p. 1968. 55.50x (ISBN 0-471-89955-0); Pt. 3. Radar-Sonar Signal Processing & Gaussian Signals in Noise. 626p. 1971. 75.00 (ISBN 0-471-89958-5). LC 67-23331. (Illus.). Wiley.

MODULATION THEORY
see also Modulation (Electronics); Speech Processing Systems

Cowley, J. M., et al, eds. Modulated Structures - 1979. LC 79-53846. (AIP Conference Preceedings: No. 53). (Illus.). 1979. lib. bdg. 22.00 (ISBN 0-88318-152-5). Am Inst Physics.
Norden, Hugo. Modulation Re-Defined. 6.00 (ISBN 0-8283-1406-3). Branden Pub Co.

MODULES (ALGEBRA)
see also Modular Arithmetic; Modular Fields; Finite Groups

Auslander, M. & Bridger, M. Stable Module Theory. LC 52-42839. (Memoirs: No. 94). 146p. 1969. pap. 10.00 (ISBN 0-8218-1294-7, MEMO-94). Am Math.
Baltes, H. P. & Hilf, E. R. Spectra of Finite Systems: A Review of Weyl's Problem--The Eigenvalue Distribution of the Wave Equation for Finite Domains & It Applications on the Physics of Small Systems. 116p. 1976. pap. 11.95x (ISBN 3-411-01491-1). Birkhauser.
Benice, Daniel D. Finite Mathematics with Algebra. (Illus.). 1982. Repr. of 1975 ed. text ed. 19.50x (ISBN 0-8290-0632-X). Irvington.
Bican, et al. Rings, Modules, & Preradicals. 264p. 1982. 45.00 (ISBN 0-8247-1568-3). Dekker.
Blyth, T. S. Module Theory: An Approach to Linear Algebra. (Illus.). 1977. 49.00x (ISBN 0-19-853162-1). Oxford U Pr.
Dicks, W. Groups, Trees & Projective Modules. (Lecture Notes in Mathematics: Vol. 790). 127p. 1980. pap. 13.00 (ISBN 0-387-09974-3). Springer-Verlag.
Drooyan, Irving & Wooton, William. Beginning Algebra: A Modular Approach, 8 Vols. LC 75-29776. Vol. 1. pap. 20.00 (ISBN 0-317-11109-4, 2012437); Vol. 2. pap. 26.00 (ISBN 0-317-11110-8); Vol. 3. pap. 24.30 (ISBN 0-317-11111-6); Vol. 4. pap. 20.30 (ISBN 0-317-11112-4); Vol. 5. pap. 35.80 (ISBN 0-317-11113-2); Vol. 6. pap. 35.80 (ISBN 0-317-11114-0); Vol. 7. pap. 20.50 (ISBN 0-317-11115-9); Vol. 8. pap. 26.50 (ISBN 0-317-11116-7). Bks Demand UMI.
Eichler, Martin. Projective Varieties & Modular Forms. LC 78-166998. (Lecture Notes in Mathematics: Vol. 210). 1973. pap. 11.00 (ISBN 0-387-05519-3). Springer-Verlag.
Faith, C. Algebra I: Rings, Modules, & Categories. LC 72-96724. (Die Grundlehren der Mathematischen Wissenschaften: Vol. 190). (Illus.). xxiii, 565p. 1973. 54.00 (ISBN 0-387-05551-7). Springer-Verlag.
Faith, C. & Wiegand, S., eds. Module Theory: Proceedings, Seattle, August 15-18, 1977. LC 79-4636. (Lecture Notes in Mathematics: Vol. 700). 1979. pap. 17.00 (ISBN 0-387-09107-6). Springer-Verlag.
Faith, Carl. Injective Modules & Injective Quotient Rings. (Lecture Notes in Pure & Applied Mathematics Ser.: Vol. 72). (Illus.). 120p. 1982. 25.00 (ISBN 0-8247-1632-9). Dekker.
Faith, Carl & Page, Stanley. FPF Ring Theory: Faithful Modules & Generators of Mod-R. LC 83-24067. (London Mathematical Society Lecture Note Ser.: No. 88). 176p. 1984. pap. text ed. 19.95 (ISBN 0-521-27738-8). Cambridge U Pr.
Gobel, R., et al, eds. Abelian Groups & Modules. (CISM International Centre for Mechanical Sciences Ser.: Vol. 287). (Illus.). xii, 531p. pap. 40.60 (ISBN 0-387-81847-2). Springer-Verlag.
Golan, Jonathan S. Decomposition & Dimension in Module Catagories, Vol. 33. (Lecture Notes in Pure & Applied Math Ser.). 1977. 45.00 (ISBN 0-8247-6643-1). Dekker.

Gordon, M. & Green, E. L. Modules with Cores & Amalgamations of Indecomposable Modules. LC 77-3560. (Memoirs Ser.: No. 187). 145p. 1977. pap. 14.00 (ISBN 0-8218-2187-3, MEMO-187). Am Math.

Hofmann, K. H. Lectures on Rings & Modules: Tulane University Ring & Operator Theory Year, 1970-71, Vol. 1. (Lecture Notes in Mathematics: Vol. 246). 661p. 1972. pap. 19.00 (ISBN 0-387-05760-9). Springer-Verlag.

Lucas, W. F., ed. Modules in Applied Mathematics: Differential Equation Models, Vol. 1. (Illus.). 400p. 1982. 29.50 (ISBN 0-387-90695-9). Springer-Verlag.

--Modules in Applied Mathematics, Vol. 2: Political & Related Models. (Illus.). 396p. 1983. 32.00 (ISBN 0-387-90696-7). Springer-Verlag.

--Modules in Applied Mathematics, Vol. 4: Life Science Models. (Illus.). 366p. 1983. 29.50 (ISBN 0-387-90739-4). Springer-Verlag.

Maass, H. Siegel's Modular Forms & Dirichlet Series. LC 73-171870. (Lecture Notes in Mathematics: Vol. 216). 1971. pap. 18.00 (ISBN 0-387-05563-0). Springer-Verlag.

McDonald, Bernard R. Finite Rings with Identity. (Pure & Applied Mathematics Ser.: Vol. 28). 448p. 1974. 75.00 (ISBN 0-8247-6161-8). Dekker.

Magid, Andy R. Module Categories of Analytic Groups. LC 81-10215. (Cambridge Tracts in Mathematics: No. 81). 130p. 1982. 32.50 (ISBN 0-521-24200-2). Cambridge U Pr.

Matlis, E. One-Dimensional Cohen-Macaulay Rings. (Lecture Notes in Mathematics Ser.: Vol. 327). xii, 157p. 1973. pap. 14.00 (ISBN 0-387-06327-7). Springer-Verlag.

Nastasescu, C. Graded & Filtered Rings & Modules. (Lecture Notes in Mathematics: Vol. 758). 148p. 1979. pap. 16.00 (ISBN 0-387-09708-2). Springer-Verlag.

Northcott, Douglas G. Finite Free Resolutions. LC 75-31397. (Tracts in Mathematics Ser.: No. 71). 250p. 1976. 57.50 (ISBN 0-521-21155-7). Cambridge U Pr.

Osofsky, Barbara L. Homological Dimensions of Modules. LC 72-6826. (CBMS Regional Conference Series in Mathematics: No. 12). 89p. 1979. pap. 10.00 (ISBN 0-8218-1662-4, CBMS-12). Am Math.

Reddy, J. N. The Finite Element Method: A Variational Approach. (Illus.). 480p. 1984. text ed. 39.95 (ISBN 0-07-051346-5). McGraw.

Robinson, D. J. Finiteness Conditions & Generalized Soluble Groups, Pt. 2. LC 74-189458. (Ergebnisse der Mathematik und Ihrer Grenzgebiete: Vol. 63). (Illus.). 275p. 1972. 34.00 (ISBN 0-387-05572-X). Springer-Verlag.

Spencer, E., ed. Modules for All? 47p. 1984. pap. text ed. 5.50x (ISBN 0-901116-91-2, Pub. by Scottish Coun Res UK). Humanities.

Stenstroem, B. Rings & Modules of Quotients. (Lecture Notes in Mathematics: Vol. 237). 136p. 1971. pap. 9.00 (ISBN 0-387-05690-4). Springer-Verlag.

Taylor, Martin. Classgroups of Group Rings. LC 83-26167. (London Mathematical Society Lecture Note Ser.: No. 91). 134p. 1984. pap. 17.95 (ISBN 0-521-27870-8). Cambridge U Pr.

UMAP Modules Nineteen Eighty-One: Tools for Teaching. 746p. 1982. text ed. 47.95 (ISBN 0-8176-3085-6). Birkhauser.

MOESSBAUER EFFECT

Abragam, A. L'Effet Mossbauer. (Documents on Modern Physics Ser.). 76p. 1964. pap. 30.25 (ISBN 0-677-00015-4). Gordon.

Applications of the Mossbauer Effect in Chemistry & Solid-State Physics. (Technical Reports Ser.: No. 50). (Illus.). 268p. (Orig.). 1966. pap. 18.50 (ISBN 92-0-035066-6, IDC50, IAEA). Unipub.

Cohen, Richard L. Applications of Mossbauer Spectroscopy, Vol. 2. 1980. 60.00 (ISBN 0-12-178402-9). Acad Pr.

Cohen, S. G. & Pasternak, M., eds. Perspectives in Mossbauer Spectroscopy. LC 72-97398. 254p. 1973. 35.00x (ISBN 0-306-30727-8, Plenum Pr). Plenum Pub.

Coulter, C. A. & Shatas, R. A., eds. Topics in Fields & Solids. 228p. 1968. 59.25 (ISBN 0-677-12740-5). Gordon.

Cranshaw, T. E., et al. Mossbauer Spectroscopy & Its Applications. (Illus.). 120p. Date not set. price not set (ISBN 0-521-30482-2); pap. price not set (ISBN 0-521-31521-2). Cambridge U Pr.

Dubna Conference on the Mossbauer Effect. Proceedings of the Dubna Conference on the Mossbauer Effect. 271p. 1963. 42.50x (ISBN 0-306-10662-0, Consultants). Plenum Pub.

Gol'danskii, V. I. Mossbauer Effect & Its Applications in Chemistry. LC 64-21682. 119p. 1964. 32.50x (ISBN 0-306-10677-9, Consultants). Plenum Pub.

Goldanskii, V. I. & Herber, R. H., eds. Chemical Applications of Mossbauer Spectroscopy. LC 68-18671. (Illus.). 1968. 95.00 (ISBN 0-12-287350-5). Acad Pr.

Gonser, U., ed. Moessbauer Spectroscopy II: The Exotic Side of the Methods. (Topics in Currents Physics Ser.: Vol. 25). (Illus.). 210p. 1981. 33.00 (ISBN 0-387-10519-0). Springer-Verlag.

--Mossbauer Spectroscopy. (Topics in Applied Physics Ser.: Vol. 5). (Illus.). 240p. 1975. 44.00 (ISBN 0-387-07120-2). Springer-Verlag.

Gruverman, I. J. & Seidel, C. W., eds. Mossbauer Effect Methodology, Vol. 10. LC 65-21188. 342p. 1976. 49.50x (ISBN 0-306-38810-3, Plenum Pr). Plenum Pub.

Gruverman, Irwin J., et al, eds. Mossbauer Effect Methodology, Vol. 9. 344p. 1974. 35.00x (ISBN 0-306-38809-X, Plenum Pr). Plenum Pub.

Herber, R. H., ed. Chemical Mossbauer Spectroscopy. 392p. 1984. 59.50x (ISBN 0-306-41885-1, Plenum Pr). Plenum Pub.

May, Leopold, ed. An Introduction to Mossbauer Spectroscopy. LC 76-137011. 203p. 1971. 32.50x (ISBN 0-306-30477-5, Plenum Pr). Plenum Pub.

Mossbauer Spectroscopy & Its Applications. (Panel Proceedings Ser.). (Illus.). 424p. (Orig.). 1972. pap. 32.00 (ISBN 92-0-131072-2, ISP304, IAEA). Unipub.

Perlow, Gilbert J., ed. Workshop on New Directions in Mossbauer Spectroscopy, Argonne National Lab, June 1977. LC 77-90635. (AIP Conference Proceedings: No. 38). (Illus.). 1977. lib. bdg. 15.00 (ISBN 0-88318-137-1). Am Inst Physics.

Poole, Charles P., et al. Relaxation in Magnetic Resonance: Dielectric & Mossbauer Applications. 1971. 70.50 (ISBN 0-12-561450-0). Acad Pr.

Shenoy, G. K. & Wagner, F. E., eds. Mossbauer Isomer Shifts. 956p. 1978. 146.75 (ISBN 0-7204-0314-6, North-Holland). Elsevier.

Stevens, John & Shenoy, Gopal K., eds. Mossbauer Spectroscopy & Its Chemical Applications. LC 81-17540. (Advances in Chemistry Ser.: No. 194). 1981. 69.95 (ISBN 0-8412-0593-0). Am Chemical.

Stevens, John G., ed. Cumulative Index to the Mossbauer Effect Data Indexes. Stevens, Virginia E. 365p. 1979. 125.00x (ISBN 0-306-65150-5, IFI Plenum). Plenum Pub.

Stevens, John G. & Stevens, Virginia E, eds. Mossbauer Effect Data Index, 10 vols. Incl. Vol. 1. Covering the Nineteen Sixty-Six to Nineteen Sixty-Eight Literature. 522p. 1975. 125.00x (ISBN 0-306-65162-9); Vol. 2. Covering the Nineteen Sixty-Nine Literature. 292p. 1971. 125.00x (ISBN 0-306-65140-8); Vol. 3. Covering the Nineteen Seventy Literature. 382p. 1972. 125.00x (ISBN 0-306-65141-6); Vol. 4. Covering the Nineteen Seventy-One Literature. 430p. 1972. 125.00x (ISBN 0-306-65142-4); Vol. 5. Covering the Nineteen Seventy-Two Literature. 489p. 1973. 125.00x (ISBN 0-306-65143-2); Vol. 6. Covering the Nineteen Seventy-Three Literature. 496p. 1975. 125.00x (ISBN 0-306-65144-0); Vol. 7. Covering the Nineteen Seventy-Four Literature. 408p. 1975. 125.00x (ISBN 0-306-65145-9); Vol. 8. Covering the Nineteen Seventy-Five Literature. 445p. 1976. 125.00x (ISBN 0-306-65146-7); Vol. 9. Covering the Nineteen Seventy-Six Literature. 367p. 1978. 125.00x (ISBN 0-306-65149-1); Vol. 10. Cumulative Index to the Mossbauer Effect Data Index. 365p. 1979. 125.00x (ISBN 0-306-65150-5). LC 76-146429 (IFI Plenum). Plenum Pub.

Tominaga, Takeshi & Minai, Yoshitaka. Applications of Mossbauer Spectroscopy to Environmental & Geochemical Studies. (Nuclear Science Applications: Section B, Vol. I, No. 9). 42p. 1984. 16.00 (ISBN 3-7186-0209-1). Harwood Academic.

Vertes, A., et al. Mossbauer Spectroscopy. LC 79-199. (Studies in Physical & Theoretical Chemistry: Vol. 5). 416p. 1980. 76.75 (ISBN 0-444-99782-2). Elsevier.

MOIRE METHOD

Moreland, Morey S., et al, eds. Moire Fringe Topography & Spinal Deformity: Proceedings of an International Symposium. (Illus.). 283p. 1981. 50.00 (ISBN 0-08-027518-4). Pergamon.

Theocaris, P. S. Moire Fringes in Strain Analysis. 1969. text ed. 37.00 (ISBN 0-08-012974-9); pap. text ed. 15.00 (ISBN 0-08-012973-0). Pergamon.

MOISTURE

see also Condensation (Meteorology); Evaporation; Humidity

Pande, A. Handbook of Moisture Determination & Control: Principles, Techniques, Applications, Vol. 1. 1974. 69.75 (ISBN 0-8247-6184-7). Dekker.

--Handbook of Moisture Determination & Control: Principles, Techniques, Applications, Vol. 3. 320p. 1975. 69.75 (ISBN 0-8247-6186-3). Dekker.

Wexler, Arnold, ed. Humidity & Moisture: Measurement & Control in Science & Industry, Vol. 3. 1965. (Pub. by UNR); Vol. 3, 1977 576 Pgs. 32.50 (ISBN 0-88275-080-1, Pub. by UNR). Krieger.

MOISTURE CONTROL IN BUILDINGS

see Dampness in Buildings

MOISTURE IN TEXTILES

Four Easy Steps to Mildew Control. 1982. 10.00 (ISBN 0-318-01551-X, 23020). Indus Fabrics.

MOISTURE OF SOILS

see Soil Moisture

MOLD (BOTANY)

see Molds (Botany)

MOLD, VEGETABLE

see Humus; Soils

MOLDING (FOUNDING)

see also Shell Molding (Founding)

Allsop, D. F. & Kennedy, D. Pressure Diecasting: The Technology of the Casting & the Die, Pt. 2. (Materials Engineering Practice Ser.). (Illus.). 186p. 1983. 30.00 (ISBN 0-08-027615-6); pap. 14.00 (ISBN 0-08-027614-8). Pergamon.

Calvert, E., et al, eds. Injection Moulding. (E.I.T.B. Instruction Manuals Ser.). (Illus.). 163p. 1982. pap. 39.95x spiral bdg. (ISBN 0-85083-553-4). Intl Ideas.

Coremaking, Dry-Sand & Loan Molding. 1983. pap. 6.50 (ISBN 0-917914-11-2). Lindsay Pubns.

Penn, W. S., ed. Injection Moulding of Elastomers. (Illus.). 207p. 1969. 39.00 (ISBN 0-85334-054-4, Pub. by Elsevier Applied Sci England). Elsevier.

Richardson, J. T., ed. Practical Formwork & Mould Construction. 2nd ed. (Illus.). xv, 294p. 1976. 42.75 (ISBN 0-85334-629-1, Pub. by Elsevier Applied Sci England). Elsevier.

Sarkar, A. D. Mould & Core Material for the Steel Industry. 1967. o. p. 24.00 (ISBN 0-08-012486-0). Pergamon.

Whelan, A., ed. Injection Moulding Machines. (Illus.). 486p. 1984. 81.50 (ISBN 0-85334-245-8, I-170-84, Pub. by Elsevier Applied Sci England). Elsevier.

Whelan, A. & Craft, J. L., eds. Developments in Injection Moulding, No. 2. (Illus.). 345p. 1981. 77.75 (ISBN 0-85334-741-7, Pub. by Elsevier Applied Sci England). Elsevier.

MOLDING (PLASTIC)

see Plastics–Molding

MOLDS (BOTANY)

see also Fungi; Myxomycetes

Al-Doory, Yousef & Domson, Joanne F., eds. Mould Allergy. LC 83-14951. (Illus.). 287p. 1984. text ed. 28.50 (ISBN 0-8121-0897-3). Lea & Febiger.

Christensen, Clyde M. Molds, Mushrooms, & Mycotoxins. LC 74-21808. (Illus.). 292p. 1975. 15.95x (ISBN 0-8166-0743-5). U of Minn Pr.

Malloch, David. Moulds: Their Isolation, Cultivation, & Identification. 88p. 1981. 13.95 (ISBN 0-8020-2418-1). U of Toronto Pr.

Moreau, Claude. Moulds, Toxins & Food. LC 78-8715. 477p. 1979. 103.95x (ISBN 0-471-99681-5, Pub. by Wiley-Interscience). Wiley.

Smith, E. Grant. Sampling & Identifying Allergenic Pollens & Molds: An Illustrated Manual for Physicians & Lab Technicians. (Illus.). 100p. (Orig.). 1984. pap. text ed. 41.50x (ISBN 0-930961-00-5). Blewstone Pr.

--Sampling & Identifying Allergenic Pollens & Molds: An Illustrated Manual for Physicians & Lab Technicians, Vol. 2. (Illus.). 112p. (Orig.). 1985. pap. write for info. Blewstone Pr.

Spencer, D. N., ed. The Downy Mildews. LC 81-66686. 1981. 95.00 (ISBN 0-12-656860-X). Acad Pr.

MOLECULAR ACOUSTICS

Nozdrev, V. F. Application of Ultrasonics to Molecular Physics. (Russian Monographs). (Illus.). 542p. 1963. 132.95 (ISBN 0-677-20360-8). Gordon.

Pullman, Bernard. Intermolecular Interactions: From Diatomics to Biopolymers. LC 77-24278. (Perspectives in Quantum Chemistry Ser.). 447p. 1977. 119.95 (ISBN 0-471-99507-X). Wiley.

Richards, W. G. A Bibliography of 'ab Initio' Molecular Wave Functions: Supplement for 1978-80. 1981. text ed. 69.00x (ISBN 0-19-855367-6). Oxford U Pr.

MOLECULAR ASYMMETRY

see Stereochemistry

MOLECULAR BEAMS

Eastwood, DeLyle, ed. New Directions in Molecular Luminescence - STP 822. LC 83-70423. 131p. 1983. pap. text ed. 24.00 (ISBN 0-8031-0212-7, 04-822000-39). ASTM.

Estermann, Immanuel, ed. Recent Research in Molecular Beams: A Collection of Papers Dedicated to Otto Stern on the Occasion of His 70th Birthday. 1959. 44.00 (ISBN 0-12-243250-9). Acad Pr.

Hellwege, K. H. & Hellwege, A. M., eds. Molecular Constants, Mostly from Microwaves, Molecular Beam, & Electron Resonance Spectroscopy. (Landolt-Boernstein, New Series: Group II, Vol. 14). (Illus.). 375p. (Supplement to Volumes II-4 & II-6, Subvolume b). 1983. 242.40 (ISBN 0-387-11857-8). Springer-Verlag.

Pamplin, Brian R. Molecular Beam Epitaxy. (Illus.). 178p. 1980. 44.00 (ISBN 0-08-025050-5). Pergamon.

Ploog, K. & Graf, K. Molecular Beam Epitaxy of III-V Compounds: A Comprehensive Bibliography 1958-1983. (Illus.). 235p. 1984. pap. 19.50 (ISBN 0-387-13177-9). Springer-Verlag.

Schlier, C., ed. Molecular Beams & Reaction Kinetics. (Italian Physical Society: Course No. 44). 1970. 80.00 (ISBN 0-12-368844-2). Acad Pr.

Wegener, P., ed. Molecular Beams & Low Density Gasdynamics. (Gasdynamics Ser.: Vol. 4). 1974. 62.00 (ISBN 0-8247-6199-5). Dekker.

MOLECULAR BIOLOGY

see also Genetic Code; Molecular Genetics

Agabian, Nina & Eisen, Harvey. Molecular Biology of Host-Parasite Interactions. LC 84-7874. (UCLA Symposium on Molecular & Cellular Biology, New Ser.: Vol. 13). 380p. 1984. 78.00 (ISBN 0-8451-2612-1). A R Liss.

Agranoff, B. W., et al. Progress in Molecular & Subcellular Biology, Vol. 1. Hahn, F. E., et al, eds. (Illus.). 230p. 1969. 42.00 (ISBN 0-387-04674-7). Springer-Verlag.

Agris, Paul F., ed. Biomolecular Structure & Function. 1978. 60.00 (ISBN 0-12-043950-6). Acad Pr.

Ando, T., et al. Protamines: Isolation, Characterization, Structure & Function. LC 73-77821. (Molecular Biology, Biochemistry & Biophysics Ser: Vol. 12). (Illus.). 114p. 1973. 34.00 (ISBN 0-387-06221-1). Springer-Verlag.

Balaban, M. & Eigen, M., eds. Molecular Mechanisms of Biological Recognition. 516p. 1980. 78.75 (ISBN 0-444-80130-8). Elsevier.

Baltimore, H., ed. Nobel Lectures in Molecular Biology: 1933-1975. 534p. 1977. 30.00 (ISBN 0-444-00236-7). Elsevier.

Barnes, David W., et al. Methods for Preparation of Media Supplements, & Substrata for Serum-Free Animal Cell Culture. LC 84-7203. (Cell Culture Methods for Molecular & Cell Biology Ser.: Vol. 1). 378p. 1984. 49.50 (ISBN 0-8451-3800-6). A R Liss.

--Methods for Serum-Free Culture of Cells of the Endocrine System. LC 84-7202. (Cell Culture Methods for Molecular & Cell Biology Ser.: Vol. 2). 272p. 1984. 39.00 (ISBN 0-8451-3801-4). A R Liss.

--Methods for Serum-Free Culture of Neuronal & Lymphoid Cells. LC 84-7204. (Cell Culture Methods for Molecular & Cell Biology Ser.: Vol. 4). 280p. 1984. 39.50 (ISBN 0-8451-3803-0). A R Liss.

Baum, H. & Gergely, J., eds. Molecular Aspects of Medicine, Vol. 5. (Illus.). 470p. 1983. 162.00 (ISBN 0-08-030429-X). Pergamon.

--Molecular Aspects of Medicine: Vol. 1, Complete. 600p. 1978. 77.00 (ISBN 0-08-020277-2). Pergamon.

Bayley, H. Photogenerated Reagents in Biochemistry & Molecular Biology. (Laboratory Techniques in Biochemistry & Molecular Biology Ser.: Vol. 12). 208p. 1984. pap. 22.50 (ISBN 0-444-80520-6, I-022-84). Elsevier.

Benga, G., et al, eds. Membrane Processes: Molecular Biology & Medical Applications. (Illus.). 275p. 1984. 39.50 (ISBN 0-387-90960-5). Springer Verlag.

Bentley, R. Molecular Asymmetry in Biology, Vols. 1 & 2. (Molecular Biology Ser). 1969-70. Vol. 1. 65.00 (ISBN 0-12-089201-4); Vol. 2. 82.50 (ISBN 0-12-089202-2). Acad Pr.

Berliner, L. J., ed. Spin Labeling Two: Theory & Applications. LC 75-3587. (Molecular Biology Ser.). 1979. 65.00 (ISBN 0-12-092352-1). Acad Pr.

Berliner, Lawrence J., ed. Spin Labeling: Theory & Applications. (Molecular Biology Ser.: Vol. 1). 1976. 93.00 (ISBN 0-12-092350-5). Acad Pr.

Blecher, Melvin, ed. Methods in Receptor Research, Pt. 1. (Methods in Molecular Biology Ser.: Vol. 9). 1976. 69.75 (ISBN 0-8247-6414-5). Dekker.

Borisy, Gary G., et al, eds. Molecular Biology of the Cytoskeleton. LC 84-17566. 576p. 1984. 58.00 (ISBN 0-87969-174-3). Cold Spring Harbor.

Bradshaw, L. Jack. Introduction to Molecular Biological Techniques. 1966. pap. 17.95 ref. ed. (ISBN 0-13-489187-2). P-H.

Bresler, S. E. Introduction to Molecular Biology. 1970. 74.50 (ISBN 0-12-132550-4). Acad Pr.

Bridges, J. W. & Gorrod, J. W., eds. Biological Oxidation of Nitrogen in Organic Molecules. 282p. 1972. cancelled (ISBN 0-85066-058-0). Taylor & Francis.

Bullen, G. J. & Greenslade, D. J., eds. Problems in Molecular Structure. (Illus.). 466p. 1983. 32.00 (ISBN 0-85086-083-0, NO. 8007, Pub. by Pion). Methuen Inc.

Burgess, A. W. & Nicola, N. A. Growth Factors & Stem Cells. (Molecular Biology Ser.). 1984. 31.00 (ISBN 0-12-143750-7). Acad Pr.

Butler, J. A. & Noble, D., eds. Progress in Biophysics & Molecular Biology, Vols. 5-11, & 13-30. Incl. Vol. 5. 1955. Vol. 10. 62.50 (ISBN 0-08-009293-4); Vol. 6. 1956. write for info.; Vol. 7. 1957. write for info.; Vol. 8. 1958. write for info.; Vol. 9. 1959. write for info.; Vol. 10. 1960. write for info.; Vol. 11. 1961. write for info.; Vol. 13. 1963. 60.00 (ISBN 0-08-010028-7); Vol. 14. 1964. 60.00 (ISBN 0-08-010612-9); Vol. 15. 1965; Vol. 16. 1966. 10.50 (ISBN 0-08-011581-0); Vol. 17. 1967. 60.00 (ISBN 0-08-012046-6); Vol. 18. 1968. 60.00 (ISBN 0-08-012753-3); Vol. 19, Pt. 1. 1969. 31.00 (ISBN 0-08-013034-8); Vol. 19, Pt. 2. 1969. 31.00 (ISBN 0-08-006522-8); Vol. 19, Complete. 62.50 (ISBN 0-08-006523-6); Vol. 20. 1970. 62.50 (ISBN 0-08-006627-5); Vol. 21. 1970. 60.00 (ISBN 0-08-015696-7); Vol. 22. 1971. 60.00 (ISBN 0-08-016348-3); Vol. 23. 1971. 60.00 (ISBN 0-08-016740-3); Vol. 24. 1972. 60.00 (ISBN 0-08-016868-X); Vol. 25. 1972. 60.00 (ISBN 0-08-016935-X); Vol. 26. 1973. 62.50 (ISBN 0-08-017048-X); Vol. 27. 1973. 60.00 (ISBN 0-08-017142-7); Vol. 28. 1974. 60.00 (ISBN 0-08-018005-1); Vol. 29. 1975-76. Pt. 1. 60.00 (ISBN 0-08-019719-1); Vol. 29, Pt. 2, 1975. pap. 18.50 (ISBN 0-08-019784-1); Vol. 29, Pt. 3, 1975. pap. 18.50 (ISBN 0-08-019890-2); Vol. 29, Complete, 1976. 55.00 (ISBN 0-08-020201-2); Vol. 30. 1976. Pt. 1. 60.00 (ISBN 0-08-019972-0); Pts. 2-3. 55.00 (ISBN 0-08-020207-1); Vol. 30, Complete. pap. 22.00 (ISBN 0-686-66314-4). Pergamon.

Celis, J. E. & Smith, J. D., eds. Nonsense Mutations & RNA Suppressors. 1979. 59.50 (ISBN 0-12-164550-9). Acad Pr.

Chapman, D., ed. Biomembrane Structure & Function. (Topics in Molecular & Structural Biology Ser.: Vol. 4). 414p. 1984. 71.20x (ISBN 0-89573-208-4). VCH Pubs.

Cheung, Wai Yiu, ed. Calcium & Cell Function: Vol. 1, Calmodulin. LC 80-985. (Molecular Biology Ser.). 1980. 60.00 (ISBN 0-12-171401-2). Acad Pr.

Chin, Chen-An & Song, Pill-Soon. Reactivity Indices for Biomolecules. (Graduate Studies: No. 24). (Illus.). 176p. 1981. 33.00 (ISBN 0-89672-093-4); pap. 20.00 (ISBN 0-89672-092-6). Tex Tech Pr.

Ciba Foundation. Submolecular Biology & Cancer. LC 79-10949. (Ciba Foundation Ser.: No. 67). 360p. 1979. 48.50 (ISBN 0-444-90078-0, Excerpta Medica). Elsevier.

--Submolecular Biology & Cancer. LC 79-14324. (Ciba Foundation Symposium, New Ser.: 67). pap. 90.00 (ISBN 0-317-29763-5, 2022187). Bks Demand UMI.

Cohn, Waldo E., ed. Progress in Nucleic Acid Research & Molecular Biology, Vol. 23. LC 63-15847. 1980. 49.50 (ISBN 0-12-540023-3). Acad Pr.

--Progress in Nucleic Acid Research & Molecular Biology, Vol. 24. 1980. 47.50 (ISBN 0-12-540024-1). Acad Pr.

--Progress in Nucleic Acid Research & Molecular Biology, Vol. 25. (Serial Publication). 1981. 44.00 (ISBN 0-12-540025-X). Acad Pr.

Cohn, Waldo E. & Moldave, Kivie, eds. Progress in Nucleic Acid Research & Molecular Biology, Vol. 30. (Serial Publication Ser.). 1983. 40.00 (ISBN 0-12-540030-6); lib. bdg. 47.00 o.p (ISBN 0-12-540104-3). Acad Pr.

Cold Spring Harbor Symposia on Quantitative Biology: Viral Oncogenes, Vol. 44. LC 34-8174. (Illus.). 1322p. 1980. 2 book set 164.50x (ISBN 0-87969-043-7). Cold Spring Harbor.

Crick, Francis. Of Molecules & Men. LC 66-26994. (Jesse & John Danz Lecture Ser.). 118p. 1967. pap. 5.95x (ISBN 0-295-97869-4, WP-26). U of Wash Pr.

Darnell, J. E., et al. Molecular Cell Biology. (Illus.). 1248p. 1986. text ed. write for info. (ISBN 0-7167-1448-5). W H Freeman.

Davidson, Eric H. & Firtel, Richard A. Molecular Biology of Development. (UCLA Symposium on Molecular & Cellular Biology, New Ser.: Vol. 19). 712p. 1984. 96.00 (ISBN 0-8451-2618-0). A R Liss.

Davidson, J. N., et al, eds. Progress in Nucleic Acid Research & Molecular Biology: An International Series. Incl. Vol. 3. 1964. 71.50 (ISBN 0-12-540003-9); Vol. 4. 1965. 71.50 (ISBN 0-12-540004-7); Vol. 5. 1966. 71.50 (ISBN 0-12-540005-5); Vol. 6. 1967. 71.50 (ISBN 0-12-540006-3); Vol. 7. 1967. 71.50 (ISBN 0-12-540007-1); Vol. 8. 1968. 71.50 (ISBN 0-12-540008-X); Vol. 9. 1969. 71.50 (ISBN 0-12-540009-8); Vol. 10. 1970. 71.50 (ISBN 0-12-540010-1); Vol. 11. 1971. 75.00 (ISBN 0-12-540011-X); Vol. 12. 1972. 55.00 (ISBN 0-12-540012-8); Vol. 13. 1973. 65.00 (ISBN 0-12-540013-6); Vol. 20. 1977. 59.50 (ISBN 0-12-540020-9); Vol. 21. 1978. 50.00 (ISBN 0-12-540021-7); Vol. 22. 1979. 55.00 (ISBN 0-12-540022-5). Acad Pr.

Davies, David B., et al, eds. Structural Molecular Biology Methods & Applications. LC 81-23540. (NATO Advanced Study Institutes Series A, Life Sciences: Vol. 45). 540p. 1982. 65.00x (ISBN 0-306-40982-8, Plenum Pr). Plenum Pub.

DeRobertis, E. D. & DeRobertis, E. M., Jr. Cell & Molecular Biology. 7th ed. 1980. text ed. 40.95x (ISBN 0-03-056749-1, CBS C). SCP.

--Essentials of Cell & Molecular Biology. 1981. text ed. 36.95x (ISBN 0-03-057713-6, CBS C); study guide 10.95 (ISBN 0-03-059736-6); instr's manual 9.95 (ISBN 0-03-059734-X). SCP.

Devons, Samuel, ed. Biology & the Physical Sciences. LC 78-80272. 379p. 1969. 36.50x (ISBN 0-231-03134-3). Columbia U Pr.

Dodson, Guy, et al, eds. Structural Studies on Molecules of Biological Interest: A Volume in Honour of Professor Dorothy Hodgkin. (Illus.). 1981. 42.50x (ISBN 0-19-855362-5). Oxford U Pr.

Doerfler, W., ed. The Molecular Biology of Adenoviruse 3: Thirty Years of Adenovirus Research 1953-1983. (Current Topics in Microbiology & Immunology Ser.: Vol. 111). (Illus.). 130p. 1984. 24.50 (ISBN 0-387-13138-8). Springer-Verlag.

--The Molecular Biology of Adenoviruses 2: Thirty Years of Adenovirus Research 1953-1983. (Current Topics in Microbiology & Immunology: Vol. 110). (Illus.). 290p. 1984. 49.00 (ISBN 0-387-13127-2). Springer-Verlag.

Dubnau, David A. The Molecular Biology of the Bacilli, Vol 1. LC 81-22815. (Molecular Biology Ser.). 1982. 60.00 (ISBN 0-12-222701-8). Acad Pr.

--The Molecular Biology of the Bacilli, Vol. 2. (Molecular Biology Ser.). 1985. 49.00 (ISBN 0-12-222702-6). Acad Pr.

Du Praw, Ernest J., ed. Advances in Cell & Molecular Biology. Incl. Vol. 1. 1971. 70.00 (ISBN 0-12-008001-X); Vol. 2. 1972. 80.00 (ISBN 0-12-008002-8); Vol. 3. 1975. 70.00 (ISBN 0-12-008003-6). Acad Pr.

Edelman, M., et al, eds. Methods in Chloroplast Molecular Biology. 1152p. 1983. 183.00 (ISBN 0-444-80368-8, I-518-82, Biomedical Pr). Elsevier.

Erlich, Henry, et al. Molecular Biology of Rifomycin. 182p. 1973. text ed. 28.50x (ISBN 0-8422-7089-2). Irvington.

Esposito, Michael S., ed. Yeast Molecular Biology-Recombinant DNA: Recent Advances. LC 84-4096. (Illus.). 349p. 1984. 35.00 (ISBN 0-8155-0987-1). Noyes.

Fasman, Gerald D., ed. Handbook of Biochemistry & Molecular Biology, CRC: Lipids, Carbohydrates, & Steroids Section, Vol. 1. 3rd ed. LC 75-29514. (Handbook Ser.). 570p. 1976. 76.50 (ISBN 0-87819-508-4). CRC Pr.

Feitelson, Mark. Molecular Components of Hepatitis B Virus. (Developments in Molecular Virology Ser.). 1985. lib. bdg. 33.95 (ISBN 0-89838-696-9, Pub. by Martinus Nijhoff Netherlands). Kluwer Academic.

Fermi, G. & Perutz, M. F. Haemoglobin & Myoglobin. (Atlas of Molecular Structures in Biology Ser.: No. 2). (Illus.). 1981. text ed. 49.50x (ISBN 0-19-854706-4). Oxford U Pr.

Feuer, G. & Iglesia, F. A. de la, eds. Molecular Biochemistry of Human Diseases, Vol. I. 240p. 1985. 90.00 (ISBN 0-8493-6205-9). CRC Pr.

Finean, J. B. & Engstrom, Arne. Biological Ultrastructure. 2nd ed. 1967. 69.00 (ISBN 0-12-256550-9). Acad Pr.

Florkin, Marcel & Schoffeniels, Ernest. A Molecular Approaches to Ecology. 1969. 49.00 (ISBN 0-12-261046-6). Acad Pr.

Frazier, William A. & Glaser, Luis, eds. Cellular Recognition. LC 82-6555. (UCLA Symposia on Molecular & Cellular Biology Ser.: Vol. 3). 966p. 1982. 152.00 (ISBN 0-8451-2602-4). A R Liss.

Freifelder, David. Essentials of Molecular Biology. (Illus.). 350p. 1985. write for info. (ISBN 0-86720-051-0). Jones & Bartlett.

--Molecular Biology: A Comprehensive Introduction to Prokaryotes & Eukaryotes. 979p. 1983. text ed. write for info. (ISBN 0-86720-012-X). Jones & Bartlett.

--Molecular Biology & Biochemistry: Problems & Applications. LC 78-18712. (Biology Ser.). (Illus.). 1978. pap. text ed. 14.95 (ISBN 0-7167-0068-9). W H Freeman.

--Problems for Molecular Biology: With Answers & Solutions. 299p. 1983. pap. text ed. write for info. (ISBN 0-86720-013-8). Jones & Bartlett.

Gaede, K. & Gaede, K., eds. Molecular Basis of Biological Activity, Vol. 1. 1972. 65.00 (ISBN 0-12-272850-5). Acad Pr.

Gaito, John. Molecular Psychobiology: A Chemical Approach to Learning & Other Behavior. (Illus.). 280p. 1966. 24.50x (ISBN 0-398-00635-0). C C Thomas.

Gething, Mary J., ed. Protein Transport & Secretion. (Current Communications in Molecular Biology Ser.). 220p. (Orig.). 1985. pap. 30.00 (ISBN 0-87969-183-2). Cold Spring Harbor.

Gluzman, Yakov, ed. Eukaryotic Transcription: The Role of Cis-and Trans-Acting Elements in Initiation. (Current Communications in Molecular Biology Ser.). 206p. (Orig.). 1985. pap. 30.00 (ISBN 0-87969-186-7). Cold Spring Harbor.

Goldberger, Robert F., ed. Biological Regulation & Development, Vol. 2: Molecular Organization & Cell Function. LC 78-21893. 636p. 1980. 59.50x (ISBN 0-306-40486-9, Plenum Pr). Plenum Pub.

Goldstein, Irwin J. & Etzler, Marilynn E. Chemical Taxonomy, Molecular Biology, & Function of Plant Lectins. LC 83-19937. (Progress in Clinical & Biological Research Ser.: Vol 138). 314p. 1983. 38.00 (ISBN 0-8451-0138-2). A R Liss.

Govil, G. & Hosur, R. Conformation of Biological Molecules. (NMR - Basic Principles & Progress Ser.: Vol. 20). (Illus.). 220p. 1982. 72.50 (ISBN 0-387-10769-X). Springer-Verlag.

Gratzer, W. B., ed. Readings in Molecular Biology Selected from Nature. 1971. pap. 6.95x (ISBN 0-262-57025-4). MIT Pr.

Guroff. Molecular Neurobiology. LC 79-22812. 1980. 79.50 (ISBN 0-8247-6862-0). Dekker.

Gutmann, Viktor. The Donor-Acceptor Approach to Molecular Interactions. LC 77-25012. 295p. 1978. 45.00x (ISBN 0-306-31064-3, Plenum Pr). Plenum Pub.

Hahn, F. E., ed. Progress in Molecular & Subcellular Biology, Vol. 3. LC 75-79748. (Illus.). 400p. 1973. 45.00 (ISBN 0-387-06227-0). Springer-Verlag.

--Progress in Molecular & Subcellular Biology, Vol. 8. (Illus.). 160p. 1983. 42.50 (ISBN 0-387-12590-6). Springer-Verlag.

Hahn, F. E., et al. Progress in Molecular & Subcellular Biology, Vol. 5. 1977. 45.00 (ISBN 0-387-08192-5). Springer-Verlag.

Hahn, F. E., et al, eds. Progress in Molecular & Subcellular Biology, Vol. 7. (Illus.). 260p. 1980. 56.00 (ISBN 0-387-10150-0). Springer-Verlag.

Haidemenakis, A., ed. Molecular Biology. 274p. 1970. 69.50 (ISBN 0-677-14070-3). Gordon.

Hanawalt, Philip C., illus. Molecules to Living Cells. (Scientific American Reader Ser.). (Illus.). 340p. 1985. 23.95 (ISBN 0-7167-1208-3); pap. 11.95 (ISBN 0-7167-1209-1). W H Freeman.

Handbook of Biochemistry & Molecular Biology, CRC: Cumulative Index. 295p. 1977. 56.00 (ISBN 0-8493-0511-X). CRC Pr.

Harris, J. R., ed. Electron Microscopy of Protein, Vol. 3. 1982. 51.50 (ISBN 0-12-327603-9). Acad Pr.

Hayaishi, Osamu & Ueda, Kunihiro, eds. ADP-Ribosylation Reactions: Biology & Medicine. (Molecular Biology Ser.). 674p. 1982. 75.00 (ISBN 0-12-333660-0). Acad Pr.

Heinz, Erich. Electrified Potentials in Biological Membrane Transport. (Molecular Biology, Biochemistry, & Biophysics Ser.: Vol. 33). (Illus.). 100p. 1981. 35.00 (ISBN 0-387-10928-5). Springer-Verlag.

Hindley, et al. DNA Sequencing: Laboratory Techniques in Biochemistry & Molecular Biology, Vol. 10. 384p. 1983. 83.00 (ISBN 0-444-80497-8, Biomedical Pr); pap. 27.95 (ISBN 0-444-80385-8). Elsevier.

Hoch, James A. & Setlow, Peter, eds. Molecular Biology of Microbial Differentiation: Proceedings of the Ninth International Spores Conference. 280p. 1985. 47.00 (ISBN 0-914826-75-1). Am Soc Microbio.

Hood, Leroy E., et al. Molecular Biology of Eucaryotic Cells. 1975. 26.95 (ISBN 0-8053-9851-1, 39851). Benjamin-Cummings.

Hopfinger, A. J. Intermolecular Interactions & Biomolecular Organization. LC 76-26540. 395p. 1977. 62.50 (ISBN 0-471-40910-3, Pub. by Wiley-Interscience). Wiley.

Hsieh, Kuo-Tsing. Modern Cell Biology. (Programed Biology Studies). (Illus.). 120p. (Orig., Prog. Bk.). 1975. pap. 6.95 (ISBN 0-88462-035-2, Ed Methods). Longman USA.

Huang, C. C., et al. Molecular Studies on Halogenated Deoxynucleosides. 256p. 1972. text ed. 36.50x (ISBN 0-8422-7013-2). Irvington.

Hukins, W. L., ed. Connective Tissue Matrix. (Topics in Molecular & Structural Biology Ser.: Vol. 5). 245p. 1984. 69.50x (ISBN 0-89573-209-2). VCH Pubs.

Jope, Charlene A. Cellular & Molecular Laboratory Manual. 64p. 1981. pap. text ed. 5.95 (ISBN 0-8403-2353-0). Kendall-Hunt.

Judson, Horace. The Eighth Day of Creation. 1980. 13.95 (ISBN 0-671-25410-3, Touchstone). S&S.

Kaplan, Nathan O. & Robinson, Arthur, eds. From Cyclotrons to Cytochromes: Essays in Molecular Biology & Chemistry. LC 82-1785. 1982. 70.50 (ISBN 0-12-397580-8). Acad Pr.

Key, Joe L. & Kosuge, Tsune. Cellular & Molecular Biology of Plant Stress. LC 84-28849. (UCLA Ser.: Vol. 22). 514p. 1985. 66.00 (ISBN 0-8451-2621-0). A R Liss.

Kimura, M. Molecular Evolution, Protein Polymorphism, & Neutral Theory. 363p. 1982. 48.00 (ISBN 0-387-11466-1). Springer-Verlag.

Knowles, Peter F., et al. Magnetic Resonance of Biomolecules: An Introduction to the Theory & Practice of NMR & ESR in Biological Systems. LC 75-4872. 343p. 1976. o. p. 49.95 (ISBN 0-471-49575-1, Pub. by Wiley-Interscience); pap. 29.95x (ISBN 0-471-01672-1). Wiley.

Koch, F. & Koch, G. The Molecular Biology of Poliovirus. (Illus.). 600p. 1985. 74.00 (ISBN 0-387-81763-8). Springer-Verlag.

Leshem, Y. The Molecular & Hormonal Basis of Plant Growth Regulation. LC 73-6802. 168p. 1974. 17.00 (ISBN 0-08-017649-6). Pergamon.

Likhtenshtefin, Gerktis. Spin Labeling Methods in Molecular Biology. LC 76-16500. pap. 67.80 (ISBN 0-317-28454-1, 2055151). Bks Demand UMI.

Lin, Edmund C., et al. Bacteria, Plasmids, & Phages: An Introduction to Molecular Biology. (Illus.). 352p. 1984. text ed. 35.00x (ISBN 0-674-58165-2); pap. text ed. 18.50x (ISBN 0-674-58166-0). Harvard U Pr.

Linn, Stuart M. & Roberts, Richard J., eds. Nucleases. LC 82-71651. (Monograph Ser.: Vol. 14). 378p. 1985. pap. 30.00 (ISBN 0-87969-182-4). Cold Spring Harbor.

Lwoff, Andre & Ullman, Agnes, eds. Origins of Molecular Biology: A Tribute to Jacques Monod. 1979. 33.50 (ISBN 0-12-460480-3). Acad Pr.

Mainwaring, W. P., et al. Nucleic Acid Biochemistry & Molecular Biology. (Illus.). 570p. 1982. pap. 29.60x (ISBN 0-632-00632-3, Pub. by Blackwell Sci UK). Blackwell Pubns.

Mak, Tak W. & Tannock, Ian. Cellular & Molecular Biology of Neoplasia. LC 84-14349. 228p. 1984. 58.00 (ISBN 0-8451-0236-2). A R Liss.

Malcolm, A. D., ed. Molecular Medicine, Vol. 1. (Illus.). 208p. (Orig.). 1985. pap. 24.00 (ISBN 0-904147-93-2). IRL Pr.

Malmberg, Russell, et al, eds. Molecular Biology of Plants. LC 85-11036. 150p. (Orig.). 1985. pap. 28.00 (ISBN 0-87969-184-0). Cold Spring Harbor.

Matsuno, Koichiro, et al, eds. Molecular Evolution & Protobiology. LC 83-24465. 470p. 1984. 65.00x (ISBN 0-306-41509-7, Plenum Pr). Plenum Pub.

Meister, A. Advances in Enzymology & Related Areas of Molecular Biology, Vol. 54. LC 41-9213. (Advances in Enzymology Ser.). 512p. 1983. 57.95x (ISBN 0-471-09730-6, Pub. by Wiley-Interscience). Wiley.

--Advances in Enzymology & Related Areas of Molecular Biology, Vol. 57. 464p. 1985. 55.00 (ISBN 0-471-89011-1). Wiley.

Meister, Alton. Advances in Enzymology & Related Areas of Molecular Biology, Vol. 46. LC 41-9213. 588p. 1978. 42.50 (ISBN 0-471-02993-9). Krieger.

--Advances in Enzymology & Related Areas of Molecular Biology, Vol. 52. LC 42-9213. 408p. 1981. 52.50x (ISBN 0-471-08120-5, Pub. by Wiley-Interscience). Wiley.

--Advances in Enzymology & Related Areas of Molecular Biology, Vol. 53. LC 41-9213. (Advances in Enzymology Ser.). 460p. 1982. 56.95x (ISBN 0-471-08405-0, Pub. by Wiley-Interscience). Wiley.

--Advances in Enzymology & Related Areas of Molecular Biology, Vol. 56. (AERAMB Ser.: 2-011). 520p. 1984. 50.00 (ISBN 0-471-89012-X, Pub. by Wiley-Interscience). Wiley.

Meister, Alton, ed. Advances in Enzymology & Related Areas of Molecular Biology. LC 41-9213. 317p. 1980. Vol. 48, 1979, 425p. 81.50x (ISBN 0-471-04428-8); Vol. 49, 1979, 373p. 58.50 (ISBN 0-471-04799-6); Vol. 50, 1979, 473p. 69.95 (ISBN 0-471-05309-0); Vol. 51, 1980, 317p. 54.95x (ISBN 0-471-05653-7). Wiley.

--Advances in Enzymology & Related Areas of Molecular Biology, Vol. 47. LC 41-9213. 508p. 1978. 42.50 (ISBN 0-471-04116-5). Krieger.

Meier, D. J. Molecular Basis of Transitions & Relaxations. (Midland Macromolecular Monographs). 442p. 1978. 87.95 (ISBN 0-677-11240-8). Gordon.

Murrell, J. N., et al. Molecular Potential Energy Functions. LC 84-11821. 197p. 1984. 34.95 (ISBN 0-471-90540-2, Pub. by Wiley-Interscience). Wiley.

Pies, W. & Weiss, A. Landolt-Boernstein Numerical Data & Functional Relationships in Science & Technology, New Series, Group 3: Crystal & Solid State Physics, Vol. 7g, References. 465p. 1973. 126.00 (ISBN 0-387-06541-5). Springer-Verlag.

Prausnitz, J. M. Molecular Thermodynamics of Fluid-Phase Equilibria. LC 69-16866. 1969. ref. ed. 44.95 (ISBN 0-13-599639-2). P-H.

Rostas, Francois, ed. Spectral Line Shapes: Proceedings, Seventh International Congress Aussois, France, June 11-15, 1984, Vol. 3. (Illus.). xx, 769p. 1985. 136.00x (ISBN 3-11-010119-X). De Gruyter.

Sarma, Ramaswamy H. Stereodynamics of Molecular Systems. 1979. 78.00 (ISBN 0-08-024629-X). Pergamon.

Schlier, C., ed. Molecular Beams & Reaction Kinetics. (Italian Physical Society: Course No. 44). 1970. 80.00 (ISBN 0-12-368844-2). Acad Pr.

Yardley, James T. Introduction to Molecular Energy Transfer. LC 80-10898. 1980. 36.00 (ISBN 0-12-768550-2). Acad Pr.

MOLECULAR GENETICS

Fincham, J. R. Microbial & Molecular Genetics. 2nd ed. LC 75-21729. 150p. 1976. pap. 9.95x (ISBN 0-8448-0769-9). Crane-Russak Co.

Gesellschaft Fuer Biologische Chemie, 24th, Mossbach-Baden, 1973. Regulation of Transcription & Translation in Eukaryotes: Proceedings. Bautz, E., ed. (Illus.). 300p. 1973. 52.00 (ISBN 0-387-06472-9). Springer-Verlag.

Goodman, Morris & Tashian, Richard E., eds. Molecular Anthropology: Genes & Proteins in the Evolutionary Ascent of the Primates. LC 76-45445. (Advances in Primatology Ser.). (Illus.). 479p. 1977. 49.50x (ISBN 0-306-30948-3, Plenum Pr). Plenum Pub.

Gottesman, M. Molecular Cell Genetics. 944p. 1985. 79.95 (ISBN 0-471-87925-8). Wiley.

Hamkalo, Barbara A. & Papaconstantinou, John, eds. Molecular Cytogenetics. LC 73-18008. 378p. 1973. 47.50x (ISBN 0-306-30765-0, Plenum Pr). Plenum Pub.

Hawkins, John D. Gene Structure & Expression. (Illus.). 185p. 1985. 34.50 (ISBN 0-521-25824-3); pap. 14.95 (ISBN 0-521-27726-4). Cambridge U Pr.

Lappe, Marc & Morison, Robert S., eds. Ethical & Scientific Issues Posed by Human Uses of Molecular Genetics, Vol. 265. (Annals of the New York Academy of Sciences). 208p. 1976. 26.00x (ISBN 0-89072-019-3). NY Acad Sci.

Leighton, Terrance & Loomis, William F., eds. The Molecular Genetics of Development. LC 80-532. (Molecular Biology Ser.). 1980. 60.00 (ISBN 0-12-441960-7). Acad Pr.

Lima-de-Faria, A. Molecular Evolution & Organization of the Chromosome. 1162p. 1984. 173.00 (ISBN 0-444-80407-2, I-451-83, Biomedical Pr). Elsevier.

Medvedev, Zhores A. Molecular-Genetic Mechanisms of Development. LC 71-80754. 418p. 1970. 34.50x (ISBN 0-306-30403-1, Plenum Pr). Plenum Pub.

Miller, Jeffrey H., ed. Experiments in Molecular Genetics. LC 72-78914. (Illus.). 468p. 1972. 40.00x (ISBN 0-87969-106-9). Cold Spring Harbor.

Nierlich, Donald P., et al, eds. Molecular Mechanisms in the Control of Gene Expression, Vol. 5. 1976. 65.00 (ISBN 0-12-518550-2). Acad Pr.

Puhler, A., ed. Advanced Molecular Genetics. Timmis, K. N. (Illus.). 320p. 1984. 34.50 (ISBN 0-387-12740-2). Springer-Verlag.

Rockstein, Morris & Baker, George T., eds. Molecular Genetic Mechanisms in Aging & Development. 1972. 38.50 (ISBN 0-12-591550-0). Acad Pr.

Schmitt, Francis O., et al, eds. Molecular Genetic Neuroscience. (Illus.). 512p. 1982. text ed. 90.00 (ISBN 0-89004-744-8). Raven.

Stent, Gunther S. & Calendar, Richard. Molecular Genetics: An Introductory Narrative. 2nd ed. LC 78-688. (Illus.). 773p. 1978. text ed. 35.95x (ISBN 0-7167-0048-4). W H Freeman.

Symposium On Informational Macromolecules-Rutgers University, 1962. Informational Macromolecules: Proceedings. Vogel, Henry J., et al, eds. 1963. 70.00 (ISBN 0-12-722550-1). Acad Pr.

Taylor, J. H., ed. Molecular Genetics: An Advanced Treatise, 2 pts. (Molecular Biology Ser). Pt. 1, 1962. 75.00 ea. (ISBN 0-12-684401-1). Pt. 1. Pt. 2, 1967. 75.00 (ISBN 0-12-684402-X). Acad Pr.

Taylor, J. Herbert, ed. Selected Papers on Molecular Genetics. (Perspectives in Modern Biology). (Illus., Orig.). 1965. pap. 44.00 (ISBN 0-12-684456-9). Acad Pr.

Veasey, William. Waterfowl Painting: Blue Ribbon Techniques. LC 83-61645. (Illus.). 224p. 1983. 45.00 (ISBN 0-916838-90-0). Schiffer.

Von Wettstein, D., et al, eds. Molecular Genetics in Yeast: Proceedings of the Alfred Benzon Symposium 16, Copenhagen 15-19, June 1980. 441p. 79.00x (ISBN 0-686-44536-8, Pub. by Munksgaard Denmark). State Mutual Bk.

Wassermann, G. D. Molecular Control of Cell Differentiation & Morphogenesis: A Systematic Theory. (Quantitative Approach to Life Science Ser.: Vol. 2). 1972. 99.75 (ISBN 0-8247-1766-X). Dekker.

Watson, J. D. Molecular Biology of the Gene. 3rd ed. LC 75-14791. 1976. 37.95 (ISBN 0-8053-9609-8). Benjamin-Cummings.

Winkler, U., et al. Bacterial, Phage & Molecular Genetics. 250p. 1976. pap. 18.00 (ISBN 0-387-07602-6). Springer-Verlag.

MOLECULAR ORBITALS

see also Molecular Structure

Ballard, R. E. Photoelectron Spectroscopy & Molecular Orbital Theory. LC 78-40817. 192p. 1978. 74.95x (ISBN 0-470-26542-6). Halsted Pr.

Boschke, F., ed. Molecular Orbitals. LC 51-5497. (Topics in Current Chemistry: Vol. 23). 1971. pap. 28.40 (ISBN 0-387-05504-5). Springer-Verlag.

Csizmadia, I. G., ed. Applications of MO Theory in Organic Chemistry. (Progress in Theoretical Organic Chemistry Ser.: Vol. 2). 626p. 1977. 106.50 (ISBN 0-444-41565-3). Elsevier.

Dewar, Michael J. & Dougherty, Ralph C. The PMO Theory of Organic Chemistry. LC 74-12196. (Illus.). 576p. 1975. 69.50 (ISBN 0-306-30779-0, Plenum Pr); pap. 17.50 (ISBN 0-306-20010-4). Plenum Pub.

Fleming, Ian. Frontier Orbitals & Organic Chemical Reactions. LC 76-3800. 249p. 1976. pap. 19.95x (ISBN 0-471-01819-8, Pub. by Wiley-Interscience). Wiley.

Gilchrist, T. L. & Storr, R. C. Organic Reactions & Orbital Symmetry. 2nd ed. LC 78-54578. (Cambridge Texts in Chemistry & Biochemistry Ser.). (Illus.). 1979. 75.00 (ISBN 0-521-22014-9); pap. 24.95 (ISBN 0-521-29336-7). Cambridge U Pr.

Gimarc, Benjamin M. Molecular Structure & Bonding: The Qualitative Molecular Orbital Theory. 1979. 23.00 (ISBN 0-12-284150-6). Acad Pr.

Hehre, Warren J., et al. AB Initio Molecular Orbital Theory. 848p. 1985. price not set (ISBN 0-471-81241-2). Wiley.

Heilbronner, E. & Bock, H. The HMO Model & Its Application, 3 vols. Incl. Vol. 1. Basis & Manipulation. 454p. 46.50x (ISBN 3-527-25654-7); Vol. 2. Problems with Solutions. 449p. 41.20x (ISBN 3-527-25655-5); Vol. 3. Tables of Huckel Molecular Orbitals. 190p. 25.90x (ISBN 3-527-25656-3). 1976. VCH Pubs.

Huzinaga, S., et al, eds. Gaussian Basis Sets for Molecular Calculations. (Physical Sciences Data Ser.: Vol. 16). 426p. 1984. 102.00 (ISBN 0-444-42254-4, I-398-83). Elsevier.

Jorgensen, William L. & Salem, Lionel. The Organic Chemist's Book of Orbitals. 1973. 47.50 (ISBN 0-12-390250-9); pap. 29.50 (ISBN 0-12-390256-8). Acad Pr.

Kier, Lemont B. Molecular Orbital Theory in Drug Research. LC 73-137616. (Medicinal Chemistry Ser). 1971. 60.00 (ISBN 0-12-406550-3). Acad Pr.

Orchin, Milton & Jaffe, H. H. Symmetry, Orbitals, & Spectra. LC 76-136720. 396p. 1971. 54.50 (ISBN 0-471-65550-3, Pub. by Wiley-Interscience). Wiley.

Pople, J. A. & Beveridge, D. L. Approximate Molecular Orbital Theory. 1970. text ed. 47.95 (ISBN 0-07-050512-8). McGraw.

Richards, W. Graham & Cooper, David L. Ab Initio Molecular Orbital Calculations for Chemists. 2nd ed. (Illus.). 1983. pap. 18.95x (ISBN 0-19-855369-2). Oxford U Pr.

Sackheim, George I. Atomic & Molecular Orbitals. 1965. pap. 2.80x (ISBN 0-87563-002-2). Stipes.

Simmons, Howard E. & Bunnett, Joseph F., eds. Orbital Symmetry Papers. LC 74-75425. (ACS Reprint Collection). 1974. 29.95 (ISBN 0-8412-0196-X); pap. 14.95 (ISBN 0-8412-0239-7). Am Chemical.

Sinanoglu, Oktay & Wiberg, Kenneth B. Sigma Molecular Orbital Theory. LC 77-89906. Repr. of 1970 ed. 116.30 (ISBN 0-8357-9586-1, 2016773). Bks Demand UMI.

Smith, William B. Molecular Orbital Methods in Organic Chemistry-HMO & PMO: An Introduction. (Studies in Organic Chemistry: Vol. 2). 192p. 1974. 34.50 (ISBN 0-8247-6127-8). Dekker.

Steiner, Erich. Determination & Interpretation of Molecular Wave Functions. LC 75-78120. (Monographs in Physical Chemistry: No. 3). 250p. 1976. 52.50 (ISBN 0-521-21037-2). Cambridge U Pr.

Streitweiser, Andrew & Owens, Peter H. Orbital & Electron Density Diagrams: An Application of Computer Graphics. (Illus.). 150p. 1973. pap. text ed. write for info. (ISBN 0-02-418020-3). Macmillan.

Suzuki, H. Electronic Absorption Spectra & Geometry of Organic Molecules. 1967. 98.50 (ISBN 0-12-678150-8). Acad Pr.

Van Wazer, John R. & Absar, Ilyas. Electron Densities in Molecules & Molecular Orbitals. (Physical Chemistry Ser.). 1975. 40.00 (ISBN 0-12-714550-8). Acad Pr.

Wagniere, G. H. Introduction to Elementary Molecular Orbital Theory & to Semiempirical Methods. (Lecture Notes in Chemistry: Vol. 1). 1976. pap. 11.00 (ISBN 0-387-07865-7). Springer-Verlag.

Williams, A. F. A Theoretical Approach to Inorganic Chemistry. (Illus.). 1979. 60.00 (ISBN 0-387-09073-8). Springer-Verlag.

Yates, Keith. Huckel Molecular Orbital Theory. 1978. 37.50 (ISBN 0-12-768850-1). Acad Pr.

Zahradnik, Rudolph & Pancir, Jiri. HMO Energy Characteristics. LC 75-130314. 120p. 1970. 37.50x (ISBN 0-306-65152-1, IFI Plenum). Plenum Pub.

MOLECULAR PHYSIOLOGY

see Biological Physics

MOLECULAR RAYS

see Molecular Beams

MOLECULAR REARRANGEMENTS

see Rearrangements (Chemistry)

MOLECULAR ROTATION

see also Conformational Analysis; Isomerism; Optical Rotation; Polymers and Polymerization

Lawley, K. P. Molecular Scattering: Physical & Chemical Applications. LC 74-23667. (Advances in Chemical Physics: Vol. 30). pap. 137.30 (ISBN 0-317-29408-3, 2024012). Bks Demand UMI.

Mizushima, Masataka. The Theory of Rotating Diatomic Molecules. LC 74-34080. 543p. 1975. 37.50 (ISBN 0-471-61187-5, Pub. by Wiley). Krieger.

Mizushima, San-Ichiro. Structure of Molecules & Internal Rotation. (Physical Chemistry Ser.: Vol. 2). 1954. 60.00 (ISBN 0-12-501750-2). Acad Pr.

Normand, J. M. A Lie Group: Rotation in Quantum Mechanics. 486p. 1981. 72.50 (ISBN 0-444-86125-4, North-Holland). Elsevier.

Press, W. Single-Particle Rotations in Molecular Crystals. (Springer Tracts in Modern Physics Ser.: Vol. 92). (Illus.). 140p. 1981. 29.00 (ISBN 0-387-10897-1). Springer-Verlag.

Schutte, C. J. The Theory of Molecular Spectroscopy - Vol. 1: The Quantum Mechanics & Group Theory of Vibrating & Rotating Molecules. 512p. 1976. 106.50 (ISBN 0-7204-0291-3, North-Holland). Elsevier.

Wollrab, James E. Rotational Spectra & Molecular Structure. (Physical Chemistry Ser.: Vol. 13). 1967. 74.50 (ISBN 0-12-762150-4). Acad Pr.

MOLECULAR SIEVES

see also Zeolites

Katzer, James R., ed. Molecular Sieves II. LC 77-720. (ACS Symposium Ser.: No. 40). 1977. 49.95 (ISBN 0-8412-0362-8). Am Chemical.

MOLECULAR SPECTRA

see also Vibrational Spectra

Arndt, U. W. & Wonacott, A. J. The Rotation Method in Crystallography. 276p. 1977. 70.25 (ISBN 0-7204-0594-7, Biomedical Pr). Elsevier.

ASTM Manual on Practices in Molecular Spectroscopy (E-13) 4th ed. 168p. 1980. pap. 12.50x (ISBN 0-8031-0281-X, 03-513079-39). ASTM.

Barrow, Gordon M. Structure of Molecules: An Introduction to Molecular Spectroscopy. (Orig.). 1963. pap. 18.95 (ISBN 0-8053-0521-1). Benjamin-Cummings.

Boutin, Henri & Yip, Sidney. Molecular Spectroscopy with Neutrons. LC 68-22823. 1968. 27.50x (ISBN 0-262-02042-4). MIT Pr.

Broude, V. L., et al. Spectroscopy of Molecular Excitons. (Springer Series in Chemical Physics: Vol. 16). (Illus.). 290p. 1985. 48.00 (ISBN 0-387-12409-8). Springer-Verlag.

Bunker, Philip R. The Molecular Symmetry & Spectroscopy. LC 78-51240. 1979. 55.00 (ISBN 0-12-141350-0). Acad Pr.

Coffey, William & Evans, Myron. Molecular Diffusion & Spectra. LC 83-16681. 378p. 1984. 49.95x (ISBN 0-471-87539-2, Pub. by Wiley Interscience). Wiley.

Conference on Molecular Spectroscopy. Molecular Spectroscopy: Proceedings of the 6th Conference on Molecular Spectroscopy, Organized by the Institute of Petroleum, Hydrocarbon Research Group, & Held at the University of Durham, 30 March-2 April, 1976. West, A. R., ed. LC 78-320788. pap. 149.50 (ISBN 0-317-29410-5, 2024013). Bks Demand UMI.

Downs, A. J., et al, eds. Essays in Structural Chemistry. LC 76-144136. 479p. 1971. 55.00x (ISBN 0-306-30525-9, Plenum Pr). Plenum Pub.

Gordy, W. & Cook, L., eds. Technique of Organic Chemistry: Vol. 9, Pt. 2, Microwave Molecular Spectra. LC 80-16243. 747p. 1970. 67.50 (ISBN 0-471-93161-6). Krieger.

Gorry. Basic Molecular Spectroscopy. (Illus.). 160p. 1985. pap. text ed. 15.95 (ISBN 0-408-01553-5). Butterworth.

Grosmann, M. & Ringeissen, J., eds. Molecular Spectroscopy of Dense Phases: Proceedings of the European Congress, 12th, Strasbourg, 1975. 814p. 1976. 127.75 (ISBN 0-444-41409-6). Elsevier.

Hepple, Peter, ed. Molecular Spectroscopy Nineteen Seventy-One: Proceedings, Brighton, 21-24 September, 1971. 5th ed. LC 73-152157. pap. 106.00 (ISBN 0-317-28996-9, 2023696). Bks Demand UMI.

Herzberg, Gerhard. Spectra & Structures of Simple Free Radicals: An Introduction to Molecular Spectroscopy. LC 70-124722. (Baker Non-Resident Lectureships in Chemistry Ser.). 240p. 1971. 35.00x (ISBN 0-8014-0584-X). Cornell U Pr.

Hirota, E. High-Resolution Spectroscopy in Transient Molecules. (Springer Series in Chemical Physics: Vol. 40). (Illus.). 255p. 1985. 44.00 (ISBN 0-387-15302-0). Springer-Verlag.

Lamola, Angelo, ed. Creation & Detection of the Excited State, Vol. 1, Pt. B. 1971. 85.00 (ISBN 0-8247-1403-2). Dekker.

--Creation & Detection of the Excited State, Vol. 1, Pt. A. 1971. 85.00 (ISBN 0-8247-1402-4). Dekker.

Levine, Ira N. Molecular Spectroscopy. LC 74-30477. 480p. 1975. 42.50x (ISBN 0-471-53128-6, Pub. by Wiley-Interscience). Wiley.

Long, D. A., et al. Molecular Spectroscopy, Vols. 1-6. Incl. Vol. 1. Literature up to 1972. 1973. 47.00 (ISBN 0-85186-506-2); Vol. 2. 1972-73 Literature. 1974. 56.00 (ISBN 0-85186-516-X); Vol. 3. 1973 Literature. 1975. 59.00 (ISBN 0-85186-526-7); Vol. 4. 1974-75 Literature. 1976. 47.00 (ISBN 0-85186-536-4, Pub. by Royal Soc Chem London); Vol. 5. 1975-76 Literature. 1978. 65.00 (ISBN 0-85186-546-1). LC 72-92545. Am Chemical.

Molecular Spectroscopy, Nineteen Sixty-Eight: Proceedings, Brighton, England, 17-19 April, 1968. LC 78-393156. pap. 107.80 (ISBN 0-317-28927-6, 2023695). Bks Demand UMI.

NATO Advanced Study Institute, Cambridge, England, September, 1979. Semiclassical Methods in Molecular Scattering & Spectroscopy: Proceedings. Child, M. S., ed. (NATO Advanced Study Institute Series C. Mathematical & Physical Sciences: No. 53). 344p. 1980. lib. bdg. 39.50 (ISBN 90-277-1082-1, Pub. by Reidel Holland). Kluwer Academic.

Rao, K. N. & Mathews, C. Weldon, eds. Molecular Spectroscopy: Modern Research. 1972. 75.00 (ISBN 0-12-580640-X). Acad Pr.

Rao, K. Narahari. Molecular Spectroscopy: Modern Research, Vol. 3. 1985. 85.00 (ISBN 0-12-580643-4). Acad Pr.

Richards, W. G. & Scott, P. R. Structure & Spectra of Molecules. 1985. 29.95 (ISBN 0-471-90577-1). Wiley.

Schulman, Stephen G., ed. Molecular Luminescence Spectroscopy Methods & Applications. (Chemical Analysis Ser.: No. 1-075). 1985. text ed. 85.00 (ISBN 0-471-86848-5, Pub by Wiley-Interscience). Wiley.

Schutte, C. J. The Theory of Molecular Spectroscopy - Vol. 1: The Quantum Mechanics & Group Theory of Vibrating & Rotating Molecules. 512p. 1976. 106.50 (ISBN 0-7204-0291-3, North-Holland). Elsevier.

Skobel'tsyn, D. V., ed. Electronic & Vibrational Spectra of Molecules. LC 68-26494. (P. N. Lebedev Physics Institute Ser.: Vol. 35). (Illus.). 217p. 1968. 32.50x (ISBN 0-306-10813-5, Consultants). Plenum Pub.

--Optical Properties of Metals & Intermolecular Interactions. LC 72-94827. (P. N. Lebedev Physics Institute Ser.: Vol. 55). (Illus.). 228p. 1973. 55.00x (ISBN 0-306-10880-1, Consultants). Plenum Pub.

--Research in Molecular Spectroscopy. LC 65-14628. (P. N. Lebedev Physics Institute Ser.: Vol. 27). 205p. 1965. 32.50x (ISBN 0-306-10715-5, Consultants). Plenum Pub.

Societe De Chimie Physique. Non-Radiative Transition in Molecules. 254p. 1970. 59.25x (ISBN 0-677-30610-5). Gordon.

Steinfeld, Jeffrey I. Molecules & Radiation: An Introduction to Modern Molecular Spectroscopy. 2nd ed. (Illus.). 388p. 1985. Repr. of 1974 ed. text ed. 19.95x (ISBN 0-262-19231-4). MIT Pr.

Suzuki, H. Electronic Absorption Spectra & Geometry of Organic Molecules. 1967. 98.50 (ISBN 0-12-678150-8). Acad Pr.

Truter, M. R. & Sutton, L. E. Molecular Structure by Diffraction Methods, Vols. 1-6. LC 72-95097. Vol. 1 1973. 1971-72 literature 49.00 (ISBN 0-85186-507-0, Pub. by Royal Soc Chem London); Vol. 2 1974. 1972-73 literature 52.00 (ISBN 0-85186-517-8); Vol. 3 1975. 1973-74 literature 66.00 (ISBN 0-85186-527-5); Vol. 4 1976. 1974-75 literature 73.00 (ISBN 0-85186-537-2); Vol. 5 1977. 1975-76 literature 90.00 (ISBN 0-85186-547-X); Vol. 6 1978. 1976-77 literature 84.00 (ISBN 0-85186-557-7). Am Chemical.

MOLECULAR STILLS

Gibat. The Lore of Still Building. Rev. ed. 188p. 1980. pap. 5.00 (ISBN 0-686-92658-7). Rutan Pub.

Tallgrass Research Center Editors. To Build A Still. 28p. 1980. pap. 15.00 (ISBN 0-686-92648-X). Rutan Pub.

MOLECULAR STRUCTURE

Agranovitch, V. M. & Hochstrasser, R. M., eds. Spectroscopy & Excitation Dynamics of Condensed Molecular Systems. (Modern Problems in Condensed Matter Sciences Ser.: Vol. 4). xii, 702p. 1983. 166.00 (ISBN 0-444-86313-3). Elsevier.

Balaban, M., ed. Molecular Structure & Dynamics. (Illus.). 368p. 1981. text ed. 35.00 (ISBN 0-86689-001-7, 992200148). Balaban Intl Sci Serv.

Ballhausen, C. J. & Gray, H. B. Molecular Orbital Theory. 1964. pap. text ed. 28.95 (ISBN 0-8053-0451-7, Adv Bk Prog). Benjamin-Cummings.

Bradley, W. F. & Hanson, Harold P., eds. Machine Interpretations of Patterson Functions & Alternative Direct Approaches & the Austin Symposium on Gas Phase Molecular Structure. (Transactions of the American Crystallographic Association Ser.: Vol. 2). 1966. pap. 15.00 (ISBN 0-686-60373-7). Polycrystal Bk Serv.

Breck, Donald W. Zeolite Molecular Sieves: Structure, Chemistry & Use. LC 83-26809. 784p. 1984. Repr. of 1974 ed. lib. bdg. 72.50 (ISBN 0-89874-648-5). Krieger.

Burkert, Ulrich & Allinger, Norman L., eds. Molecular Mechanics. LC 82-11442. (ACS Monographs: No. 177). 339p. 1982. lib. bdg. 64.95 (ISBN 0-8412-0584-1). Am Chemical.

Charette, Jean J. An Introduction to the Theory of Molecular Structure. LC 66-22648. pap. 50.00 (ISBN 0-317-08508-5, 2007249). Bks Demand UMI.

Daudel, D., et al, eds. Structure & Dynamics of Molecular Systems. 1985. lib. bdg. 39.50 (ISBN 90-277-1977-2, Pub. by Reidel Holland). Kluwer Academic.

Davydov, A. S. Solutions in Molecular Systems. 1985. lib. bdg. 54.00 (ISBN 90-277-1854-7, Pub. by Reidel Netherlands). Kluwer Academic.

Dunitz, Jack D. X-Ray Analysis & the Structure of Organic Molecules. LC 78-15588. (George Fisher Baker Non-Resident Lectureship Ser.). 528p. 1979. 79.50x (ISBN 0-8014-1115-7). Cornell U Pr.

Ezra, G. S. Symmetry Properties of Molecules. (Lecture Notes in Chemistry Ser.: Vol. 28). 202p. 1982. pap. 17.70 (ISBN 0-387-11184-0). Springer-Verlag.

Flygare, W. H. Molecular Structure & Dynamics. LC 77-16786. (Illus.). 1978. ref. 48.95 (ISBN 0-13-599753-4). P-H.

Griffiths, J. Color & Constitution of Organic Molecules. 1976. 55.00 (ISBN 0-12-303550-3). Acad Pr.

Gurskaya, Galina Viktorovna. The Molecular Structure of Amino Acids: Determination by X-ray Diffraction Analysis. LC 68-18821. (Illus.). pap. 32.00 (ISBN 0-317-09387-8, 2020678). Bks Demand UMI.

Hargittai, I. Sulphone Molecular Structures: Conformation & Geometry from Electron Diffraction & Microwave Spectroscopy; Structural Variations. LC 78-557. (Lecture Notes in Chemistry: Vol. 6). (Illus.). 1978. pap. 18.00 (ISBN 0-387-08654-4). Springer-Verlag.

Harris, Frank E., et al. Electronic Structure of Molecules: Algebraic & Diagrammatic Methods in Many-Fermion Theory. 400p. 1985. 49.95x (ISBN 0-471-89627-6, Pub. by Wiley-Interscience). Wiley.

Hirota, E. High-Resolution Spectroscopy in Transient Molecules. (Springer Series in Chemical Physics: Vol. 40). (Illus.). 255p. 1985. 44.00 (ISBN 0-387-15302-0). Springer-Verlag.

Hoppe, W. & Mason, R., eds. Unconventional Electron Microscopy for Molecular StructureDetermination. 1979. 48.00 (ISBN 0-9940012-3-1, Pub. by Vieweg & Sohn Germany). Heyden.

Hout, R. F., et al. A Prictorial Approach to Molecular Structure & Reactivity. LC 83-16914. 403p. 1984. 39.95x (ISBN 0-471-89703-5, Pub. by Wiley-Interscience). Wiley.

Incropera, Frank P. Introduction to Molecular Structure & Thermodynamics. LC 74-3368. (Illus.). pap. 87.80 (ISBN 0-317-09215-4, 2013059). Bks Demand UMI.

Maruani, J. & Serre, J., eds. Symmetries & Properties of Non-Rigid Molecules: A Comprehensive Survey. (Studies in Physical & Theoretical Chemisty Ser.: Vol. 23). 520p. 1983. 117.00 (ISBN 0-444-42174-2). Elsevier.

Miller, Terry A. & Bondybey, V. E., eds. Molecular Ions: Spectroscopy, Structure & Chemistry. 1984. 48.00 (ISBN 0-444-86717-1, I-438-83). Elsevier.

Pauling, Linus. The Nature of the Chemical Bond & the Structure of Molecules & Crystals: An Introduction to Modern Structural Chemistry. 3rd ed. (Baker Non-Resident Lectureship in Chemistry Ser.). (Illus.). 644p. 1960. 39.95x (ISBN 0-8014-0333-2). Cornell U Pr.

Pifat, Greta & Herak, Janok N., eds. Supramolecular Structure & Function. 374p. 1983. 49.50x (ISBN 0-306-41257-8, Plenum Pr). Plenum Pub.

Pullman, Bernard, ed. Intermolecular Forces. 576p. 1981. 76.00 (ISBN 90-277-1326-X, Pub. by Reidel Holland). Kluwer Academic.

Richards, W. G. & Scott, P. R. Structure & Spectra of Molecules. 1985. 29.95 (ISBN 0-471-90577-1). Wiley.

Starkey. Alpha Molecular Model Set for General Chemistry. 1985. 7.95 (ISBN 0-471-82511-5). Wiley.

Vilkov, L. V., et al. Determination of the Geometrical Structure of Free Molecules. 279p. 1983. 9.95 (ISBN 0-8285-2658-3, Pub. by Mir Pubs USSR). Imported Pubns.

Wheatley, P. J. Determination of Molecular Structure. 2nd, rev. ed. 264p. 1981. pap. 6.00 (ISBN 0-486-64068-X). Dover.

Wilson, E. B., Jr., et al. Molecular Vibrations: The Theory of Infrared & Raman Vibrational Spectra. (Illus.). 1980. pap. text ed. 7.00 (ISBN 0-486-63941-X). Dover.

MOLECULAR THEORY

see also Gases, Kinetic Theory Of

Albright, Lyle, et al. Pyrolysis: Theory & Industrial Practice. 446p. 1983. 65.00 (ISBN 0-12-048880-9). Acad Pr.

Bird, G. A. Molecular Gas Dynamics. (Oxford Engineering & Science Ser.). 1976. text ed. 72.00x (ISBN 0-19-856120-2). Oxford U Pr.

Cotton, F. Albert. Chemical Applications of Group Theory. 2nd ed. LC 76-129657. 386p. 1971. 38.50x (ISBN 0-471-17570-6, Pub. by Wiley-Interscience). Wiley.

Graovac, A., et al. Topological Approach to the Chemistry of Conjugated Molecules. (Lecture Notes in Chemistry: Vol. 4). 1977. pap. 14.00 (ISBN 0-387-08431-2). Springer-Verlag.

Hurley, A. C. Electron Correlation in Small Molecules. (Theoretical Chemistry Ser.). 1977. 49.50 (ISBN 0-12-362450-9). Acad Pr.

--Introduction to the Electron Theory of Small Molecules. 1977. 60.00 (ISBN 0-12-362460-6). Acad Pr.

Hush, N. S., ed. Reactions of Molecule at Electrodes. LC 70-149570. pap. 128.00 (ISBN 0-317-29338-9, 2024029). Bks Demand UMI.

Kier, L. B. & Hall, L. H. Molecular Connectivity in Chemistry & Drug Research. (Medicinal Chemistry Ser.). 1976. 58.00 (ISBN 0-12-406560-0). Acad Pr.

Kueppers, B. O. Molecular Theory of Evolution: Outline of a Physico-Chemical Theory of the Origin of Life. (Illus.). 321p. 1983. 34.00 (ISBN 0-387-12080-7). Springer-Verlag.

Mauskopf, Seymour. Crystals & Compounds: Molecular Structure & Composition in Nineteenth-Century French Science. LC 76-3197. (Transactions Ser.: Vol. 66, Pt. 3). (Illus.). 1976. pap. 7.00 (ISBN 0-87169-663-0). Am Philos.

Nash, Leonard K. The Atomic-Molecular Theory. LC 50-12355. (Harvard Case Histories in Experimental Science Ser.: Case 4). pap. 40.80 (ISBN 0-317-08941-2, 2006426). Bks Demand UMI.

Orville-Thomas, W. J., ed. Internal Rotation in Molecules. LC 73-2791. (Wiley Monographs in Chemical Physics Ser.). 606p. 1974. 144.95 (ISBN 0-471-65707-7, Pub. by Wiley-Interscience). Wiley.

Rescigno, Thomas, et al, eds. Electron-Molecule & Photon-Molecule Collisions. LC 79-15211. 365p. 1979. 55.00x (ISBN 0-306-40193-2, Plenum Pr). Plenum Pub.

Schaefer, Henry F., ed. Applications of Electronic Structure Theory. LC 77-349. (Modern Theoretical Chemistry Ser.: Vol. 4). (Illus.). 461p. 1977. 65.00x (ISBN 0-306-33504-2, Plenum Pr). Plenum Pub.

Slater, John C. Quantum Theory of Molecules & Solids, Vol. 1, 3 & 4. Incl. Vol. 1. Electronic Structure of Molecules. 1963; Vol. 3. Insulators, Semiconductors & Solids. 1969; Vol. 4. The Self-Consistent Field for Molecules & Solids. 47.95 (ISBN 0-07-058038-3, C). McGraw.

Williams, Dudley, ed. Molecular Physics, 2 pts. 2nd ed. (Methods in Experimental Physics). Pt.a, 1974. 76.50 (ISBN 0-12-476003-1); Pt.b,1974. 80.50 (ISBN 0-12-476043-0). Acad Pr.

Wilson, S. Electron Correlation in Molecules. (International Series of Monographs on Chemistry). (Illus.). 1984. 59.00x (ISBN 0-19-855617-9). Oxford U Pr.

MOLECULAR WEIGHTS

see also Atomic Weights

Billingham, N. C. Molar Mass Measurements in Polymer Science. LC 77-2823. 254p. 1977. cloth 59.95x (ISBN 0-470-99125-9). Halsted Pr.

MOLECULES

see also Dipole Moments; Energy-Band Theory of Solids; Macromolecules; Molecular Acoustics; Molecular Orbitals; Molecular Structure

Altmann, Simon L. Induced Representations in Crystals & Molecules: Point, Space & Nonrigid Molecule Groups. 1978. 59.50 (ISBN 0-12-054650-7). Acad Pr.

American Crystallographic Association. Motion in Molecules: Calculation of Crystal Packing & Non-Bonded Forces. (Program & Abstracts Ser.: Vol.12, No. 1). 58p. 1984. pap. 5.00 (ISBN 0-317-05920-3). Polycrystal Bk Serv.

Bates, D. R., et al, eds. Advances in Atomic & Molecular Physics, Vols. 1-14. Incl. Vol. 1. 1965. 85.00 (ISBN 0-12-003801-3); Vol. 2. 1966. 85.00 (ISBN 0-12-003802-1); Vol. 3. 1968. 85.00 (ISBN 0-12-003803-X); Vol. 4. 1968. 85.00 (ISBN 0-12-003804-8); Vol. 5. 1969. 85.00 (ISBN 0-12-003805-6); Vol. 6. 1970. 85.00 (ISBN 0-12-003806-4); Vol. 7. 1971. 85.00 (ISBN 0-12-003807-2); Vol. 8. 1972. 85.00 (ISBN 0-12-003808-0); Vol. 9. 1974. 78.00 (ISBN 0-12-003809-9); Vol. 10. 1974. 85.00 (ISBN 0-12-003810-2); Vol. 11. 1976. 95.00 (ISBN 0-12-003811-0); Vol. 12. 1976. 90.00 (ISBN 0-12-003812-9); Vol. 13. 1978. 90.00 (ISBN 0-12-003813-7); Vol. 14. 1979. 80.00 (ISBN 0-12-003814-5). Acad Pr.

Bates, David & Bederson, Benjamin. Advances in Atomic & Molecular Physics, Vol. 19. (Serial Publication Ser.). 1983. 65.00 (ISBN 0-12-003819-6). Acad Pr.

Bellamy, L. J. Infrared Spectra of Complex Molecules, Vol. 2. 2nd ed. 299p. 1980. 39.95 (ISBN 0-412-22350-3, NO. 6333, Pub. by Chapman & Hall England). Methuen Inc.

Berne, Bruce J. & Pecora, Robert. Dynamic Light Scattering: With Applications to Chemistry, Biology & Physics. LC 75-19140. 376p. 1976. 54.95 (ISBN 0-471-07100-5, Pub. by Wiley-Interscience). Wiley.

Birks, John B., ed. Excited States of Biological Molecules: Based on the Proceedings of the International Conference at the Calouste Gulbenkian Foundation Centre, Lisbon, Portugal, on April 18-24, 1974. LC 75-6985. (Wiley Monographs in Chemical Physics). pap. 160.00 (ISBN 0-317-29353-2, 2024005). Bks Demand UMI.

Boschke, F. L., ed. Large Amplitude Motion in Molecules One. (Topics in Current Chemistry: Vol. 81). (Illus.). 1979. 58.00 (ISBN 0-387-09310-9). Springer-Verlag.

--Large Amplitude Motion in Molecules Two. (Topics in Current Chemistry: Vol. 82). (Illus.). 1979. 53.00 (ISBN 0-387-09311-7). Springer-Verlag.

Ciba Foundation. Molecular Interactions & Activity in Proteins. LC 78-14500. (Ciba Foundation Symposium, New Ser.: 60). pap. 71.80 (ISBN 0-317-29766-X, 2022184). Bks Demand UMI.

Clementi, E. Selected Topics in Molecular Physics. (Illus.). 1972. 40.00x (ISBN 3-527-25388-2). VCH Pubs.

Coulson, C. A. The Shape & Structure of Molecules. 2nd ed. McWeeny, Roy, rev. by. 1982. 19.95x (ISBN 0-19-855517-2); pap. 10.95x (ISBN 0-19-855518-0). Oxford U Pr.

Counting Molecules-Approaching the Limit of Chemical Analysis. 1982. 5.50 (ISBN 0-910362-20-3). Chem Educ.

Davydov, A. S. Theory of Molecular Excitations. LC 72-75767. 313p. 1971. 45.00x (ISBN 0-306-30440-6, Plenum Pr). Plenum Pub.

Del Re, G., et al. Electronic States of Molecules & Atom Clusters. (Lecture Notes in Chemistry: Vol. 13). (Illus.). 180p. 1980. pap. 21.00 (ISBN 0-387-09738-4). Springer-Verlag.

Dmitriev, I. S. Molecules Without Chemical Bonds. 155p. 1981. pap. 3.50 (ISBN 0-8285-2021-6, Pub. by Mir Pubs USSR). Imported Pubns.

--Symmetry in World of Molecules. 148p. 1979. pap. 4.45 (ISBN 0-8285-1519-0, Pub. by Mir Pubs USSR). Imported Pubns.

Elias, Hans-Georg, ed. Macromolecules, Vol. 2: Synthesis, Materials, & Technology, Vol. 2. 2nd ed. 862p. 1984. 95.00x (ISBN 0-306-41085-0, Plenum Pr). Plenum Pub.

Englman, R. The Jahn-Teller Effect in Molecules & Crystals. LC 77-37113. (Wiley Monographs in Chemical Physics). (Illus.). pap. 92.50 (ISBN 0-317-09429-7, 2019668). Bks Demand UMI.

Fabian, Derek J., et al, eds. Inner-Shell & X-Ray Physics of Atoms & Solids. LC 81-11945. (Physics of Atoms & Molecules Ser.). 976p. 1981. 125.00x (ISBN 0-306-40819-8, Plenum Pr). Plenum Pub.

Fano, U. & Fano, L. Physics of Atoms & Molecules: An Introduction to the Structure of Matter. LC 76-184808. 456p. 1973. text ed. 35.00x (ISBN 0-226-23782-6). U of Chicago Pr.

Flory, P. J. Statistical Mechanics of Chain Molecules. LC 68-21490. 1969. 51.50x (ISBN 0-470-26495-0, Pub. by Wiley-Interscience). Wiley.

Fong, Francis K. Theory of Molecular Relaxation: Applications in Chemistry & Biology. LC 75-17814. (Illus.). pap. 83.00 (ISBN 0-317-09104-2, 2017400). Bks Demand UMI.

Foster, Roy, ed. Molecular Association: Including Molecular Complexes, Vol. 1. 1975. 65.00 (ISBN 0-12-262701-6). Acad Pr.

--Molecular Association: Including Molecular Complexes, Vol. 2. 1979. 95.00 (ISBN 0-12-262702-4). Acad Pr.

Fruton, Joseph S. Molecules & Life: Historical Essays on the Interplay of Chemistry & Biology. LC 72-3095. pap. 112.00 (ISBN 0-317-28456-8, 2055135). Bks Demand UMI.

Fuhrhop, J. H., et al. Large Molecules. LC 67-11280. (Structure & Bonding Ser.: Vol. 18). (Illus.). 216p. 1974. 45.00 (ISBN 0-387-06658-6). Springer-Verlag.

Gribov, Lev A. Intensity Theory for Infrared Spectra of Polyatomic Molecules. LC 64-17204. 120p. 1964. 30.00x (ISBN 0-306-10689-2, Consultants). Plenum Pub.

Hellwege, K. H., ed. Molecular Constants. (Landolt-Boerstein: Group II, Vol. 14, Subvol. A). 790p. 1983. 537.10 (ISBN 0-387-11365-7). Springer-Verlag.

Hinze, Juergen. Energy Storage & Redistribution in Molecules. 610p. 1983. 95.00x (ISBN 0-306-41272-1, Plenum Pr). Plenum Pub.

Hudson Symposium, 9th, Plattsburgh, N.Y., Apr. 1976. Homoatomic Rings, Chains & Macromolecules of Main Group Elements: Proceedings. Rheingold, A. L., ed. 616p. 1977. 106.50 (ISBN 0-444-41634-X). Elsevier.

Inoue, S. & Stephens, R. E., eds. Molecules & Cell Movement. LC 75-16666. (Society of General Physiologists Ser.: Vol. 30). 460p. 1975. 52.00 (ISBN 0-89004-041-9). Raven.

Julg, A. Crystals As Giant Molecules. (Lecture Notes in Chemistry Ser.: Vol. 9). 1978. pap. 14.00 (ISBN 0-387-08946-2). Springer-Verlag.

Kettle, S. A. Symmetry & Structure. 1985. 34.95 (ISBN 0-471-90501-1). Wiley.

Kiepenheuer, Karl O. The Sun. Pomerans, A. J., tr. LC 59-7294. (Ann Arbor Science Library). pap. 40.00 (ISBN 0-317-09534-X, 2051047). Bks Demand UMI.

Kimura, Katsumi, et al. Handbook of Hei Photoelectron Spectra of Fundamental Organic Molecules. LC 81-6449. 268p. 1981. 49.95x (ISBN 0-470-27200-7). Halsted Pr.

Kimura, Motoo, ed. The Neutral Theory of Molecular Evolution. LC 82-22225. 400p. 1984. 69.50 (ISBN 0-521-23109-4). Cambridge U Pr.

Kirkwood, John G. Dielectrics-Intermolecular Forces-Optical Rotation. Cole, Robert H., ed. (Documents on Modern Physics Ser.). (Illus.). 282p. (Orig.). 1965. 44.25 (ISBN 0-677-00405-2). Gordon.

Klinkmann, Horst, et al, eds. Middle Molecules in Uremia & Other Diseases: Analytical Techniques, Metabolic Toxicity, & Clinical Aspects. (Artificial Organs: Vol. 4). 1981. 50.00 (ISBN 0-686-73132-8); pap. 30.00 (ISBN 0-686-73133-6). Intl Soc Artifical Organs.

Landau, L. & Kitaigorodsky, A. I. Physics for Everyone: Molecules. 224p. 1980. 6.60 (ISBN 0-8285-1725-8, Pub. by Mir Pubs USSR). Imported Pubns.

Lin, S. H. & Neusser, H. J., eds. Muliphoton Spectroscopy of Molecules: Quantum Electronics: Principles & Applications. LC 83-2584. 1984. 59.00 (ISBN 0-12-450520-1). Acad Pr.

Maitland, Geoffrey C., et al. Intermolecular Forces: Their Origin & Determination. (International Series of Monographs in Chemistry). (Illus.). 1981. 79.00x (ISBN 0-19-855611-X). Oxford U Pr.

Maruzen, Benjamin. HGS Molecular Structure Models. 1969. General Chemistry Set. 16.95 (ISBN 0-8053-6971-6); Organic Chemistry Set. 16.95 (ISBN 0-8053-6970-8). Benjamin-Cummings.

Mead, C. A. Symmetry & Chirality. LC 51-5497. (Topics in Current Chemistry: Vol. 49). (Illus.). 90p. 1974. 22.00 (ISBN 0-387-06705-1). Springer-Verlag.

Molecular Structure. (Structure & Bonding Ser.: Vol. 41). (Illus.). 146p. 1980. 41.00 (ISBN 0-387-09958-1). Springer-Verlag.
Mulliken, Robert & Ermler, W. C., eds. Polyatomic Molecules. LC 80-2764. 1981. 57.50 (ISBN 0-12-509860-X). Acad Pr.
Mulliken, Robert S. & Person, Willis B. Molecular Complexes: A Lecture & Reprint Volume. LC 71-84970. pap. 129.00 (ISBN 0-317-09073-9, 2007666). Bks Demand UMI.
Mulliken, Robert S., ed. Ab Initio Calculations on Diatomic Molecules. Ermler, W. C. 1977. 33.50 (ISBN 0-12-510750-1). Acad Pr.
Neel, L., ed. Nonlinear Behaviour of Molecules, Atoms & Ions in Electric, Magnetic or Electromagnetic Fields. 516p. 1979. 100.00 (ISBN 0-444-41790-7). Elsevier.
Nye, Mary Jo. Molecular Reality: A Perspective on the Scientific Work of Jean Perrin. LC 70-171234. 1972. lib. bdg. 17.00 (ISBN 0-685-52440-X). Watson Pub Intl.
Okabe, Hideo. Photochemistry of Small Molecules. LC 78-6704. 431p. 1978. 64.50 (ISBN 0-471-65304-7, Pub. by Wiley-Interscience). Wiley.
Ratajczak, H. & Orville-Thomas, W. J. Molecular Interactions. LC 79-40825. 1980. Vol. 1, 415p. 105.95 (ISBN 0-471-27664-2, 1-500); Vol. 2, 627p. 134.95 (ISBN 0-471-27681-2). Wiley.
Rich, Alexander & Davidson, Norman, eds. Structural Chemistry & Molecular Biology: A Volume Dedicated to Linus Pauling by His Students, Colleagues, & Friends. LC 67-21127. (Illus.). 907p. 1968. 43.95x (ISBN 0-7167-0135-9). W H Freeman.
Rossman, M. G. The Molecular Replacement Method. (International Science Review). 276p. 1972. 72.75x (ISBN 0-677-13940-3). Gordon.
Ryschkewitsch, George E. Chemical Bonding & the Geometry of Molecules. LC 62-20784. (Selected Topics in Modern Chemistry Ser.). pap. 32.30 (ISBN 0-317-09188-3, 2005794). Bks Demand UMI.
Societe De Chimie Physique, 24th, Paris-Orsay, July 2-6, 1973. Molecular Motions of Liquids: Proceedings. Lascombe, J., ed. LC 73-91947. 1974. lib. bdg. 105.00 (ISBN 90-277-0431-7, Pub. by Reidel Holland). Kluwer Academic.
Symposium on Quantum, Chemistry, & Biochemistry, 8th, Jerusalem, April 1975. Environmental Effects on Molecular Structure & Properties: Proceedings. Pullman, Bernard, ed. LC 75-35543. (Jerusalem Symposium on Quantum Chemistry & Biochemistry Ser.: Vol. 8). 530p. 1976. lib. bdg. 103.00 (ISBN 90-277-0604-2, Pub. by Reidel Holland). Kluwer Academic.
Szasz. Pseudopotential Theory of Atoms & Molecules. 400p. 1985. 42.50 (ISBN 0-471-82417-8). Wiley.
Terzaghi, Eric, et al. Molecular Evolution. 450p. 1985. text ed. write for info. (ISBN 0-86720-021-9). Jones & Bartlett.
Van Lancker, J. L. Molecules, Cells & Disease. LC 77-893. (Springer Study Edition Ser.). 1977. pap. 29.00 (ISBN 0-387-90242-2). Springer-Verlag.
Van Wazer, John R. & Absar, Ilyas. Electron Densities in Molecules & Molecular Orbitals. (Physical Chemistry Ser.). 1975. 40.00 (ISBN 0-12-714550-8). Acad Pr.
Von Hippel, Arthur R., ed. Molecular Designing of Materials & Devices. 1965. 45.00x (ISBN 0-262-22006-7). MIT Pr.
Voronkov, M. G., et al. The Siloxane Bond: Physical Properties & Chemical Transformations. LC 78-16675. (Studies in Soviet Science--Physical Sciences Ser.). (Illus.). 505p. 1978. 85.00 (ISBN 0-306-10940-9, Consultants). Plenum Pub.
Weltner, W. Magnetic Atoms & Molecules. 1983. 42.50 (ISBN 0-442-29206-6). Van Nos Reinhold.
Williams, Dudley, ed. Molecular Physics, 2 pts. 2nd ed. (Methods in Experimental Physics). Pt.a, 1974. 76.50 (ISBN 0-12-476003-1); Pt.b,1974. 80.50 (ISBN 0-12-476043-0). Acad Pr.

MOLECULES–INTERNAL ROTATION
see Molecular Rotation

MOLES (ANIMALS)
Baker, Rollin H. Two New Moles (Genus Scalopus) from Mexico & Texas. (Museum Ser.: Vol. 5, No. 2). 8p. 1951. pap. 1.25 (ISBN 0-317-04938-0). U of KS Mus Nat Hist.
Smith, Guy N. Moles & Their Control. 160p. 1980. 13.50 (ISBN 0-904558-82-7). Saiga.

MOLLUSKS
see also Cephalopoda; Gasteropoda; Lamellibranchiata; Opisthobranchiata; Shells; Snails; Squids
Abbott, R. Tucker. The Best of the Nautilus: A Bicentennial Anthology of American Conchology. LC 75-41628. (Illus.). 280p. 1976. 13.95 (ISBN 0-915826-02-X). Am Malacologists.
Abbott, R. Tucker, ed. Indexes to the Nautilus: Geographical, Vols. 1-90, & Scientific Names, Vols. 61-90. 1979. Set. 24.00x (ISBN 0-915826-06-2). Am Malacologists.
Arnold, Winifred H. Glossary of a Thousand & One Terms Used in Conchology. 1965. 4.50 (ISBN 0-913792-05-5). Shell Cab.
Backhuys, W. Land & Fresh Water Molluscs of the Azores. (Illus.). 1975. pap. 60.00 (ISBN 90-04-06447-8). Heinman.
Bayer, Frederick M. & Voss, Gilbert L., eds. Studies in Tropical American Mollusks. LC 70-170142. 1971. 12.50x (ISBN 0-87024-230-X). U of Miami Pr.
Bayne, B. L., ed. Marine Mussels. LC 75-25426. (International Biological Programme Ser.: No. 10). (Illus.). 400p. 1976. 110.00 (ISBN 0-521-21058-5). Cambridge U Pr.
Blandford, W. T. & Godwin-Austen, H. N. Mollusca: Testacelldae & Zonitidae, Vol. 1. (Fauna of British India Ser.). xxxii, 332p. 1978. Repr. of 1908 ed. 30.00 (Pub. by Messers Today & Tomorrows Printers & Publishers India). Scholarly Pubns.
Blust, Robert A. The Proto-Oceanic Palatals. 193p. 1979. pap. text ed. 15.00x (ISBN 0-8248-0684-0, Pub. by Polynesian Soc). UH Pr.
Boyle, P. R. Molluscs & Man. (Studies in Biology: No. 134). 64p. 1981. pap. text ed. 8.95 (ISBN 0-7131-2824-0). E Arnold.
Caum, E. L. Check-List of Hawaiian Land & Freshwater Mollusca. (BMB Ser.: No. 56). Repr. of 1928 ed. 11.00 (ISBN 0-527-02162-8). Kraus Repr.
Clench, William J. & Turner, Ruth D. New Names Introduced by H. A. Pilsbry in the Mollusca & Crustacea. (Special Publication: No. 4). 218p. (Orig.). 1962. pap. 10.00 (ISBN 0-910006-32-6). Acad Nat Sci Phila.
Gude, G. K. Mollusca: Trochomorphidae & Janellidae, Vol. 2. xii, 522p. 1978. Repr. of 1914 ed. 30.00 (ISBN 0-88065-091-5, Pub. by Messers Today & Tomorrows Printers & Publishers India). Scholarly Pubns.
Huner, Jay V. & Brown, E. Evan. Crustacean & Mollusk Aquaculture in the United States. (Illus.). 1985. text ed. 59.00 (ISBN 0-87055-468-9). AVI.
Kolisko, E. & Kolisko, L. Zoology No. 6 Tunicatal Molluscs. 1981. 15.00x (ISBN 0-906492-42-4, Pub. by Kolisko Archive). State Mutual Bk.
Kolisko, Eugen. Zoology for Everybody: Tunicates & Molluscs, Vol. 6. (Illus.). 1983. pap. 4.50 (ISBN 0-317-07217-X, Pub. by Kolisko Archives). St George Bk Serv.
Maury, C. J. Recent Mollusks of the Gulf of Mexico: With Pleistocene & Pliocene Species from the Gulf States. 282p. 1971. Repr. 8.00 (ISBN 0-87710-361-5). Paleo Res.
Morse, D. E., et al, eds. Recent Innovations in Cultivation of Pacific Molluscs: Proceedings of an International Symposium of the California Sea Grant College Program & the Pacific Sea Grant College Programs in Alaska, Hawaii, Oregon & Washington, at La Jolla, CA, 1-3 Dec., 1982. (Developments in Aquaculture & Fisheries Science Ser.: Vol. 14). 420p. 1984. 85.25 (ISBN 0-444-42350-8). Elsevier.
Morton, J. E. Molluscs. (Hutchinson Biological Sciences Ser.). (Illus.). 244p. 1979. pap. text ed. 12.25x (ISBN 0-09-134161-2, Hutchinson U Lib). Humanities.
Preston, H. B. Mollusca: Vol. 4: Freshwater Gastropoda & Pelycypoda. (Fauna of British India Ser.). xx, 246p. 1978. Repr. of 1915 ed. 30.00 (ISBN 0-88065-177-6, Pub. by Messers Today & Tomorrows Printers & Publishers India). Scholarly Pubns.
Purchon, R. D. The Biology of the Mollusca. 2nd ed. 1977. text ed. 60.00 (ISBN 0-08-021028-7). Pergamon.
Russell-Hunter, W. D., ed. Mollusca: Ecology, Vol. 6. 1983. lib. bdg. 70.00 (ISBN 0-12-751406-6). Acad Pr.
Saleuddin, A. S. & Wilbur, Karl M., eds. The Mollusca, Vol. 5: Physiology, Pt. II. 1983. 65.00 (ISBN 0-12-751405-8). Acad Pr.
Sharabati, Doreen. Saudi Arabian Seashells. 1982. 50.00x (ISBN 0-9507641-0-8, Pub. by Cave Pubns England). State Mutual Bk.
Trueman, E. R. & Clarke, Malcolm R., eds. The Mollusca, Vol. 10: Evolution of the Mollusca. Edited Treatise ed. Date not set. price not set (ISBN 0-12-751410-4). Acad Pr.
Van Damme, Dirk. The Freshwater Mollusca of Northern Africa. (Developments in Hydrobiologia Ser.). 1985. lib. bdg. 55.00 (ISBN 90-6193-502-4, Pub. by Junk Pubs Netherlands). Kluwer Academic.
Van Der Spoel, S., et al, eds. Pathways in Malacology. 1979. lib. bdg. 53.00 (ISBN 90-313-0319-4, Pub. by Junk Pubs Netherlands). Kluwer Academic.
Verdonk, N. H., et al, eds. The Mollusca, Vol. 3: Development. 1983. 49.00 (ISBN 0-12-751403-1). Acad Pr.
Walne, Peter R. Culture of Bivalve Mollusc: Fifty Years' Experience at Conwy. 2nd ed. (Illus.). 190p. 24.50 (ISBN 0-85238-063-1, FN8, FNB). Unipub.
Wilbur, K. M. & Yonge, C. M. The Mollusca, Vol. 7: Reproduction. 1984. 70.00 (ISBN 0-12-751407-4). Acad Pr.
Wilbur, Karl M. The Mollusca: Metabolic Biochem & Molecular Biomechanics, Vol. 1. Incl. The Mollusca: Biochemistry of Mollusca Environmental Biochemissry. 49.50 (ISBN 0-12-751402-3). 1983. 62.50 (ISBN 0-12-751401-5). Acad Pr.
Wilbur, Karl M. & Yonge, C. M., eds. Physiology of Mollusca, Vol. 2. 1966. Vol. 1. 81.00 (ISBN 0-12-751302-7). Acad Pr.
Zoological Society Of London - 22nd Symposium. Studies in the Structure, Physiology & Ecology of Molluscs. Fretter, ed. 1968. 52.00 (ISBN 0-12-613322-0). Acad Pr.

MOLLUSKS–AUSTRALIA
MacPherson, J. Hope & Gabriel, C. J. Marine Molluscs of Victoria. 1962. 18.50x (ISBN 0-522-83665-8, Pub. by Melbourne U Pr). Intl Spec Bk.

MOLLUSKS–GREAT BRITAIN
Ellis, A. E. British Freshwater Bivalve Mollusca: Keys & Notes for the Identification of the Species. (A Volume in the Synopses of the British Fauna Ser.). 1978. pap. 12.00 (ISBN 0-12-236950-5). Acad Pr.
Fretter, Vera & Graham, Alastair. British Prosobranch Mollusks: Their Functional Anatomy & Ecology. (Illus.). xvi, 775p. 1962. 55.00x (ISBN 0-903874-12-1, Pub. by Brit Mus Nat Hist England). Sabbot-Natural Hist Bks.

MOLLUSKS–NEW ZEALAND
Powell, A. W. B. New Zealand Mollusca. (Illus.). 532p. 1983. 60.00 (ISBN 0-00-216906-1, Pub. by W Collins New Zealand). Intl Spec Bk.

MOLLUSKS–NORTH AMERICA
Clarke, Arthur H. The Freshwater Molluscs of Canada. (Illus.). 416p. 1982. lib. bdg. 39.95x (ISBN 0-660-00022-9, 56350-2, Pub. by Natl Mus Canada). U of Chicago Pr.
Dall, W. H. Land & Fresh Water Mollusks. Bd. with Hydroids. Nutting, C. C. (Harriman Alaska Expedition, 1899). 24.00 (ISBN 0-527-38173-X). Kraus Repr.
Keen, A. Myra & Coan, Eugene. Marine Molluscan Genera of Western North America: An Illustrated Key. 2nd ed. LC 73-80625. (Illus.). 224p. 1974. 15.00x (ISBN 0-8047-0839-8). Stanford U Pr.
Marcus, Eveline & Marcus, Ernst. American Opisthobranch Mollusks. LC 67-31694. (Studies in Tropical Oceanography Ser: No. 6). 1967. 10.00x (ISBN 0-87024-087-0). U Miami Marine.
Pilsbry, Henry A. Land Mollusca of North America: North of Mexico, Vol. I, Pts. 1 & 2. Incl. Land Mollusca of North America: North of Mexico. Pilsbry, Henry A. (Monograph: No. 3: Vol. II, Pt. 1 & 2). (Illus., Orig.). 1948. Pt. 1 - 520P., Pt. 2 - 592P. pap. 50.00 per part (ISBN 0-910006-12-1); 200.00 set, of two vols., 2 parts (ISBN 0-910006-10-5). (Monograph: No. 3). (Illus., Orig., Pt. 1, 573 pgs. - Pt. 2, 419 pgs.). 1940. pap. 50.00 per part (ISBN 0-910006-11-3); of two volumes, two parts 200.00 set (ISBN 0-910006-10-5). Acad Nat Sci Phila.

MOLLUSKS–PACIFIC OCEAN
MacFarland, Frank. Memoir IV: Studies of Opisthobranchiate Mollusks of the Pacific Coast of North America. Kessell, Howard L., ed. (Memoirs of the California Academy of Sciences Ser.). (Illus.). 546p. 1966. 40.00 (ISBN 0-940228-10-6). Calif Acad Sci.
Olsson, Axel A. Neogene Mollusks from Northwestern Ecuador. (Illus.). 258p. 1964. 12.00 (ISBN 0-87710-367-4). Paleo Res.
Tinker, Spencer W. Pacific Sea-Shells. LC 57-18069. (Illus.). 1957. bds. 7.95 (ISBN 0-8048-0464-8). C E Tuttle.

MOLLUSKS–UNITED STATES
Baker, F. C. The Fresh Water Mollusca of Wisconsin. 1973. Repr. of 1928 ed. lib. bdg. 70.00 (ISBN 3-7682-0764-1). Lubrecht & Cramer.
Baker, Frank C. The Molluscan Fauna of the Big Vermillion River, Illinois. 12.00 (ISBN 0-384-03095-5). Johnson Repr.
Bequaert, Joseph C. & Miller, Walter B. The Mollusks of the Arid Southwest. LC 72-187825. 271p. 1973. pap. 8.00x (ISBN 0-8165-0318-4). U of Ariz Pr.
Calnan, T. R. Molluscan Distribution in Copano Bay, Texas. (Report of Investigations Ser.: RI 103). (Illus.). 71p. 1980. 2.50 (ISBN 0-318-03236-8). Bur Econ Geology.
Metcalf, Artie L. Late Quaternary Mollusks of the Rio Grande Valley. LC 67-21083. 1967. pap. 3.00 (ISBN 0-87404-081-7). Tex Western.
Olsson, Axel A. & Harbison, Anne. Pliocene Mollusca of Southern Florida. LC 79-14175. (Academy of Naturl Sciences Monograph: No. 8). 602p. 1979. Repr. of 1953 ed. lib. bdg. 36.00 (ISBN 0-88275-980-9). Krieger.
Perry, Louise M. & Schwengel, Jeanne S. Marine Shells of the Western Coast of Florida. rev. ed. (Illus.). 262p. 1955. 10.00 (ISBN 0-87710-370-4); pap. 8.00 (ISBN 0-87710-369-0). Paleo Res.
Zinn, Donald J. Marine Mollusks of Cape Cod. (Natural History Ser.: No. 2). (Illus.). 80p. 1984. pap. 6.95 (ISBN 0-916275-00-0). Cape Cod Mus Nat His.

MOLLUSKS, FOSSIL
see also Ammonoidea
Agassiz, Louis. Etudes Critiques les Mollusques Fossiles: Memoire les Trigonies et Monographic Des Myes (Critical Studies on Fossil Mollusks. Gould, Stephen J., ed. LC 79-8323. (History of Paleontology Ser.). (Fr., Illus.). 1980. Repr. of 1840 ed. lib. bdg. 68.50x (ISBN 0-405-12702-2). Ayer Co Pubs.
Dall, W. H., et al. A Manual of the Recent & Fossil, Marine Pelecypod Mollusks of the Hawaiian Islands. (BMB Ser.). Repr. of 1938 ed. 34.00 (ISBN 0-527-02261-6). Kraus Repr.
Edwards, F. E. The Eocene Mollusca, 4 Vols. 1848-55. Set. 53.00 (ISBN 0-384-13860-8). Johnson Repr.
Harmer, F. W. Pliocene Mollusca, 8 Nos. 1914-24. Set. 128.00 (ISBN 0-384-21390-1). Johnson Repr.
Hoare, Richard D. Desmoinesian Brachiopoda & Mollusca from Southwest Missouri. LC 61-13508. (Illus.). 277p. 1961. 15.00x (ISBN 0-8262-0545-3). U of Mo Pr.
Maury, C. J. Recent Mollusks of the Gulf of Mexico: With Pleistocene & Pliocene Species from the Gulf States. 282p. 1971. Repr. 8.00 (ISBN 0-87710-361-5). Paleo Res.
Moore, Ellen J. Fossil Mollusks of Coastal Oregon. LC 71-634653. (Studies in Geology Ser: No. 10). (Illus.). 64p. 1971. pap. 5.95 (ISBN 0-87071-068-0). Oreg St U Pr.
Moore, Raymond C., ed. Treatise on Invertebrate Paleontology, Pt. I: Mollusca 1. LC 53-12913. (Illus.). 1960. 26.00 (ISBN 0-8137-3009-0). Geol Soc.
--Treatise on Invertebrate Paleontology, Pt. K: Mollusca 3. LC 53-12913. (Illus.). 1964. 23.75 (ISBN 0-8137-3011-2). Geol Soc.
--Treatise on Invertebrate Paleontology, Pt. N: Mollusca 6 (Bivalvia, Vols. 1-2. LC 53-12913. (Illus.). 1969. 38.25 (ISBN 0-8137-3014-7). Geol Soc.
Morris, J. & Lycett, J. Mollusca of the Great Oolite, 3 Pts. 1850-54. Set. pap. 45.00 (ISBN 0-384-40170-8). Johnson Repr.
Ostergaard, J. M. Fossil Marine Mollusks of Oahu. (BMB). pap. 8.00 (ISBN 0-527-02157-1). Kraus Repr.
--Recent & Fossil Marine Molluska of Tongatabu. (BMB). pap. 10.00 (ISBN 0-527-02237-3). Kraus Repr.
Sharpe, D. Mollusca of the Chalk, 4 Pts. Repr. of 1909 ed. Set. 23.00 (ISBN 0-384-55070-3). Johnson Repr.
Wood, S. V. Crag Mollusca, 2 Pts in 4 Nos. Repr. of 1855 ed. Set. 100.00 (ISBN 0-384-69151-X). Johnson Repr.

MOLTEN METALS
see Liquid Metals

MOLTEN SALTS
see Fused Salts

MOLYBDENUM
Boschke, F. L., ed. Aspects of Molybdenum & Related Chemistry. LC 78-13469. (Topics in Current Chemistry Ser.: Vol. 76). (Illus.). 1979. 47.00 (ISBN 0-387-08986-1). Springer-Verlag.
Chappell, Willard & Peterson, Kathy. Molybdenum in the Environment, Vol. 2: The Geochemistry, Cycling, & Industrial Uses of Molybdenum. 1977. 79.75 (ISBN 0-8247-6495-1). Dekker.
Chappell, Williard R. & Paterson, Kathy K. Molybdenum in the Environment, Vol. 1: The Biology of Molybdenum. 1976. 79.75 (ISBN 0-8247-6405-6). Dekker.
Molybdenum Resources Guidebook. 1980. 89.00 (ISBN 0-942218-04-3). Minobras.
Molybdenum Uptake by Beets in Dutch Soils. (Agricultural Research Reports: No. 775). 1972. pap. 8.25 (ISBN 90-220-0393-0, PDC189, PUDOC). Unipub.
Newton, William E. & Otsuka, Sei, eds. Molybdenum Chemistry of Biological Significance. LC 79-6374. 435p. 1980. 49.50x (ISBN 0-306-40352-8, Plenum Pr). Plenum Pub.
Parker, G. A. Analytical Chemistry of Molybdenum. (Illus.). 175p. 1983. 44.50 (ISBN 0-387-12235-4). Springer-Verlag.
Spiro, T. G. Molybdenim Enzymes. (Metal Ions in Biology Ser.). 672p. 1985. 75.00 (ISBN 0-471-88542-8). Wiley.
Sutulov, Alexander, ed. International Molybdenum Encyclopedia, 3 vols. Incl. Vol. 1. Resources & Production. 402p. 1978 (ISBN 0-87930-116-3); Vol. 2. Metallurgy & Processing. 375p. 1979 (ISBN 0-87930-117-1); Vol. 3. Products, Uses & Trade. 341p. 1980 (ISBN 0-87930-118-X). (Illus.). Set. text ed. 330.00 (ISBN 0-87930-137-6). Miller Freeman.

MOLYBDENUM ALLOYS
see also Chromium-Molybdenum Steel

--Survey of the Moon. (Illus.). 1963. 6.95 (ISBN 0-393-06330-5). Norton.
Nagel Travel Guide to the Moon. (Nagel Travel Guide Ser.). (Illus.). 176p. 1970. 23.00 (ISBN 2-8263-0059-8, Pub. by Nagel Switzerland). Hippocrene Bks.
Newton, Robert. Moon's Acceleration & Its Physical Origins, Vol. 1: As Deduced from Solar Eclipses. LC 78-2059. 1979. 37.50x (ISBN 0-8018-2216-5). Johns Hopkins.
Newton, Robert R. The Moon's Acceleration & Its Physical Origins, Vol. 2: As Deduced from General Lunar Observations. LC 78-20529. 1984. text ed. 35.00x (ISBN 0-8018-2639-X). Johns Hopkins.
Salisbury, John W. & Glaser, Peter E., eds. Lunar Surface Layer: Materials & Characteristics: Proceedings. 1964. 47.50 (ISBN 0-12-615450-3). Acad Pr.
Schultz, Peter H. Moon Morphology: Interpretations Based on Lunar Orbiter Photography. LC 74-22176. (Illus.). 644p. 1976. 60.00x (ISBN 0-292-75036-6). U of Tex Pr.
Singer, S. Fred, ed. Physics of the Moon. (Science & Technology Ser.: Vol. 13). 1967. 25.00 (ISBN 0-87703-041-3, Pub. by Am Astronaut). Univelt Inc.
Taylor, Stuart R. Lunar Science: A Post-Apollo View. LC 74-17227. 372p. 1975. text ed. 36.00 (ISBN 0-08-018274-7); pap. text ed. 17.50 (ISBN 0-08-018273-9). Pergamon.
Van Norstand, Fredric. The Moon Through the Signs. 128p. (Orig.). 1983. pap. 6.95 (ISBN 0-940058-06-5). Clancy Pubns.
Whipple, Fred L. Earth, Moon, & Planets. 3rd ed. LC 68-21987. (Books on Astronomy Series). (Illus.). 16.50x (ISBN 0-674-22400-0); pap. 5.95 (ISBN 0-674-22401-9). Harvard U Pr.

MOON–EXPLORATION

Adler, I. & Trombka, J. I. Geochemical Exploration of the Moon & the Planets. LC 78-127039. (Physics & Chemistry in Space Ser.: Vol. 3). (Illus.). 230p. 1970. 38.00 (ISBN 0-387-05228-3). Springer-Verlag.
Baldwin, Ralph B. The Measure of the Moon. LC 62-20025. pap. 136.50 (ISBN 0-317-08505-0, 2020023). Bks Demand UMI.
Cadogan, Peter. The Moon-Our Sister Planet. LC 80-41564. (Illus.). 400p. 1981. 72.50 (ISBN 0-521-23684-3); pap. 32.50 (ISBN 0-521-28152-0). Cambridge U Pr.
Hallion, Richard P. & Crouch, Tom D., eds. Apollo: Ten Years Since Tranquillity Base. LC 79-10271. (Illus.). 174p. 1979. 19.95x (ISBN 0-87474-506-3); pap. 19.95x (ISBN 0-87474-505-5). Smithsonian.
Johnson, Nicholas L. Handbook of Soviet Lunar & Planetary Exploration. (Science & Technology Ser.: Vol. 47). 276p. 1979. lib. bdg. 35.00x (ISBN 0-87703-130-4); pap. text ed. 25.00x (ISBN 0-87703-131-2). Univelt Inc.
Kopal, Z. An Introduction to the Study of the Moon. 476p. 1966. 107.75 (ISBN 0-677-01230-6). Gordon.
--The Moon: An Outline of Astronomy & Physics of Our Satellite on the Eve of the Apollo Era. (Illus.). 525p. 1969. lib. bdg. 58.00 (ISBN 9-0277-0124-5, Pub. by Reidel Holland). Kluwer Academic.
Lunar & Planetary Institute, Houston, Texas, ed. Mare Crisium: The View from Luna Twenty-Four. 733p. 1979. 54.00 (ISBN 0-08-022965-4). Pergamon.
Newton, Robert. Moon's Acceleration & Its Physical Origins, Vol. 1: As Deduced from Solar Eclipses. LC 78-2059. 1979. 37.50x (ISBN 0-8018-2216-5). Johns Hopkins.
Taylor, Stuart R. Planetary Science: A Lunar Perspective. (Illus.). 512p. 1982. 42.95X (ISBN 0-942862-00-7). Lunar & Planet Inst.

MOON–PHOTOGRAPHS, MAPS, ETC.

Baird, Michael G., ed. Moonranch. (Illus.). 1984. pap. 24.00 (ISBN 0-9608278-2-X). Winmark Pr.
Leonardi, Piero. Volcanoes & Impact Craters on the Moon & Mars. (Illus.). 446p. 1976. 102.25 (ISBN 0-444-99821-7). Elsevier.
Lowman, P. D., Jr. Lunar Panorama: A Photographic Guide to the Geology of the Moon. (Illus.). 1969. 25.00 (ISBN 0-685-00394-9). Heinman.
Whitaker, E. A., et al. The Rectified Lunar Atlas. LC 63-17721. (Photographic Lunar Atlas, Suppl: No. 2). (Illus.). 147p. 1964. 50.00x (ISBN 0-8165-0077-0). U of Ariz Pr.

MOON, FLIGHT TO THE
see Space Flight to the Moon

MOON, THEORY OF

Airy, George B. Gravitation. rev. ed. 1969. pap. 2.50 (ISBN 0-911014-02-0). Neo Pr.
Godfray, Hugh. An Elementary Treatise on the Lunar Theory. Cohen, I. Bernard, ed. LC 80-2125. (Development of Science Ser.). (Illus.). 1981. lib. bdg. 12.00x (ISBN 0-405-13847-4). Ayer Co Pubs.

MOON PROBES
see Lunar Probes

MOORS AND HEATHS
see also Fens; Marshes

Arnolds, Eef. Ecology & Coenology of Macrofungi in Grasslands & Moist Heathlands in Drenthe, the Netherlands: Pt. 1: Introduction & Synecology. (Bibliotheca Mycologica: Vol. 83). (Illus.). 410p. 1981. text ed. 48.00x (ISBN 3-7682-1314-5). Lubrecht & Cramer.
Carter Ewel, Katherine & Odum, Howard T., eds. Cypress Swamps. LC 84-5230. (Center for Wetlands Research, University of Florida). 490p. 1985. 25.00 (ISBN 0-8130-0714-3). U Presses Fla.
Dimbleby, G. W. The Development of British Heathlands & their Soils. 1962. 45.00x (ISBN 0-686-45495-2, Pub. by For Lib Comm England). State Mutual Bk.
Heal, O. W. & Perkins, D. F., eds. Production Ecology of Some British Moors & Montane Grasslands. (Ecological Studies: Vol. 27). (Illus.). 1978. 62.00 (ISBN 0-387-08457-6). Springer-Verlag.

MOOSE

Peterson, Randolph L. North American Moose. LC 56-1401. 280p. 1955. pap. 13.95 (ISBN 0-8020-6349-7). U of Toronto Pr.
Smettan, Hans. Die Moose des Kaisergebirges-Tirol. (Bryophytorum Bibliotheca Ser.: Vol. 23). 127p. 1982. pap. text ed. 18.00x (ISBN 3-7682-1331-5). Lubrecht & Cramer.

MOPEDS

Bleach, Mervyn. Moped Owners Workshop Manual: Garelli Mopeds '69 Thru '78. new ed. (Owners Workshop Manuals Ser.: No. 189). 1979. 10.50 (ISBN 0-85696-189-2, Pub. by J H Haynes England). Haynes Pubns.
Clew, Jeff & Rogers, Chris. Puch Maxi Mopeds '69 - '80. (Owners Workshop Manuals Ser.: No. 107). 1979. 10.50 (ISBN 0-85696-582-0, Pub. by J H Haynes England). Haynes Pubns.
Darlington, Mansur. Mobylette Motobecane Mopeds '66 - '76: '65 Thru '76. (Haynes Owners Workshop Manuals: No. 258). 1976. 10.50 (ISBN 0-85696-258-9, Pub by J H Haynes England). Haynes Pubns.
Fraser, Morris. Moped Maintenance & Repair. (Illus.). 256p. (Orig.). 1985. pap. 14.95 (ISBN 0-8306-1847-3, 1847). TAB Bks.

MORGAN HORSE

Mellin, Jeanne. Morgan Horse. LC 61-13021. (Illus.). 1961. pap. 9.95 (ISBN 0-8289-0153-8). Greene.
--The Morgan Horse Handbook. LC 72-91799. (Illus.). 1973. pap. 15.00 (ISBN 0-8289-0181-3). Greene.

MORPHOGENESIS
see also Botany–Morphology; Cell Differentiation; Morphology; Morphology (Animals)

Abercrombie, M. & Brachet, J., eds. Advances in Morphogenesis, 10 vols. Incl. Vol. 1. 1961 (ISBN 0-12-028601-7); Vol. 2. 1963 (ISBN 0-12-028602-5); Vol. 3. 1964. (ISBN 0-12-028603-3); Vol. 4. 1965 (ISBN 0-12-028604-1); Vol. 5. 1966 (ISBN 0-12-028605-X); Vol. 6. 1967 (ISBN 0-12-028606-8); Vol. 7. King, T. J., ed. 1968 (ISBN 0-12-028607-6); Vol. 8. King, T. J., ed. 1970 (ISBN 0-12-028608-4); Vol. 9. King, T. J., et al. 1971 (ISBN 0-12-028609-2); Vol. 10. 1973 (ISBN 0-12-028610-6). 75.00 ea. Acad Pr.
Abraham, Ralph. On Morphodynamics: Selected Papers. (Science Frontier Express Ser.). (Illus.). 255p. Date not set. pap. 25.00 (ISBN 0-942344-06-5). Aerial Pr.
Bergsma, Daniel & Lenz, Widukind, eds. Morphogenesis & Malformation of the Limb: Proceedings. LC 76-55004. (Birth Defects Original Article Ser.: Vol. 13, No. 1). 376p. 1977. 54.00x (ISBN 0-8451-1008-X). A R Liss.
Blandau, Richard J. Morphogenesis & Malformation of the Skin. LC 81-8302. (Birth Defects: Original Article Ser.: Vol. 17, No. 2). 286p. 1981. 48.00 (ISBN 0-8451-1042-X). A R Liss.
Cau, P., et al. Morphogenesis of Thyroid Follicles in Vitro. (Advances in Anatomy Embryology & Cell Biology: Vol. 52, Pt. 2). 1976. pap. 34.30 (ISBN 0-387-07654-9). Springer-Verlag.
Connelly, Thomas G., et al, eds. Morphogenesis & Pattern Formation. 312p. 1981. 50.50 (ISBN 0-89004-635-2). Raven.
Curtis, A. S. Cell Surface: Its Molecular Role in Morphogenesis. 1967. 76.50 (ISBN 0-12-199650-6). Acad Pr.
Fox, Harold. Amphibian Morphogenesis. LC 83-26526. (Bioscience Ser.). 320p. 1984. 54.50 (ISBN 0-89603-043-1). Humana.
Gribnau, A. A. & Geijsberts, L. G. Morphogenesis of the Brain in Staged Rhesus Monkey Embryos. (Advances in Anatomy, Embryology & Cell Biology Ser.: Vol. 91). (Illus.). 70p. 1985. pap. 19.50 (ISBN 0-387-13709-2). Springer-Verlag.
Henrici, Arthur T. Morphologic Variation & Rate of Growth of Bacteria. (Illus.). 194p. 1928. 18.50x (ISBN 0-398-04277-2). C C Thomas.
International Workshop on Morphogenesis & Malformation, 4th, Grand Canyon, Ariz., 1977. Morphogenesis & Malformation of the Cardiovascular System: Proceedings. Rosenquist, Glenn C. & Bergsma, Daniel, eds. LC 78-14527. (Birth Defects Original Article Ser.: Vol. 14, No. 7). 452p. 1978. 70.00x (ISBN 0-8451-1023-3). A R Liss.
Jaenicke, L., ed. Biochemistry of Differentiation & Morphogenosis. (Collequium Mosbach: Vol. 33). (Illus.). 301p. 1982. 42.00 (ISBN 0-387-12010-6). Springer-Verlag.
Jirasek, Jan E. Atlas of Human Prenatal Morphogenesis. 1983. lib. bdg. 65.00 (ISBN 0-89838-558-X, Pub. by Martinus Nijhoff Netherlands). Kluwer Academic.
Needham, Joseph. Biochemistry & Morphogenesis. 1942. 125.00 (ISBN 0-521-05797-3). Cambridge U Pr.
--Order & Life. 1968. pap. 6.95x (ISBN 0-262-64001-5). MIT Pr.
Pexieder, T. Cell Death in the Morphogenesis & Teratogenesis of the Heart. (Advances in Anatomy, Embryology & Cell Biology Ser.: Vol. 51, Pt. 3). (Illus.). 100p. (Orig.). 1975. pap. 42.50 (ISBN 0-387-07270-5). Springer-Verlag.
Sinnott, Edmund G. Problem of Organic Form. 1963. 39.50x (ISBN 0-685-69864-5). Elliots Bks.
Smith, David W. Recognizable Patterns of Human Deformation: Identification & Management of Mechanical Effects of Morphogenesis. (Major Problems in Clinical Pediatrics Ser.: Vol. 21). (Illus.). 240p. 1981. text ed. 23.95 (ISBN 0-7216-8401-7). Saunders.
Smith, Harold & Holmes, Martin G., eds. Techniques in Photomorphogenesis. (Biological Techniques Ser.). 1984. 65.00 (ISBN 0-12-652990-6). Acad Pr.
Structural Stability & Morphogenesis: An Outline of a General Theory of Models. (Illus.). 1975. 51.95 (ISBN 0-8053-9278-5); pap. 36.95 (ISBN 0-8053-9279-3). Benjamin-Cummings.
Thom, R. Structual Stability & Morphogenesis: An Outline of a General Theory of Models. Fowler, D. H., tr. from Fr. pap. 36.95 (ISBN 0-8053-9279-3). Benjamin-Cummings.
Thom, Rene F. Mathematical Models of Morphogenesis. (Mathematics & Its Applications Ser.). 305p. 1983. 59.95x (ISBN 0-470-27499-9). Halsted Pr.
Wassermann, G. D. Molecular Control of Cell Differentiation & Morphogenesis: A Systematic Theory. (Quantitative Approach to Life Science Ser.: Vol. 2). 1972. 99.75 (ISBN 0-8247-1766-X). Dekker.
Wolff, E. & Lender, T., eds. Tissue Interactions During Organogenesis. (Documents in Biology Ser.: Vol. 1). 240p. 1970. 55.75x (ISBN 0-677-13010-4). Gordon.

MORPHOLOGY
see also Morphogenesis

Abraham, Ralph. On Morphodynamics: Selected Papers. (Science Frontier Express Ser.). (Illus.). 255p. Date not set. pap. 25.00 (ISBN 0-942344-06-5). Aerial Pr.
Akhmanova, Olga. Phonology, Morphonology, Morphology. LC 72-159459. (Janua Linguarum, Ser. Minor: No. 101). 135p. 1971. pap. text ed. 16.00x (ISBN 90-2791-748-5). Mouton.
Arthur, Wallace. Mechanisms of Morphological Evolution: A Combined Genetic, Developmental & Ecological Approach. LC 83-16993. 288p. 1984. 36.00x (ISBN 0-471-90347-7, Pub. by Wiley Interscience). Wiley.
Atkinson, B. G. & Walden, S. B., eds. Changes in Gene Expression in Response to Environmental Stress. 1985. 65.00 (ISBN 0-12-066290-6). Acad Pr.
Biokinesiology Institute & Barton, John. The Atlas. (Encyclopedia of Mind & Body: Vol. 4). (Illus.). 1780p. (Orig.). 1981. pap. 125.00 (ISBN 0-937216-08-9). Biokinesiology.
Bookstein, F. L. The Measurement of Biological Shape & Shape Change. LC 78-15923. (Lecture Notes in Biomathematics Ser.: Vol. 24). 1978. pap. 14.00 (ISBN 0-387-08912-8). Springer-Verlag.
Brown, Tasman. Morphology of the Australian Skull: Studies by Multivariate Analysis. (AIAS Human Biology Ser.: No. 4). (Illus.). 1973. pap. text ed. 14.00x (ISBN 0-85575-027-8). Humanities.
Dnyansagar, V. R., et al, eds. Recent Trends & Contacts Between Cytogenetics Embryology & Morphology, 1976. (Current Trends in Life Sciences Ser.: Vol. 5). xiv, 592p. 1977. 50.00 (ISBN 0-88065-081-8, Pub. by Messers Today & Tomorrows Printers & Publishers India). Scholarly Pubns.
Dressler, Wolfgang U., et al. Leifmotifs in Natural Morphology. (Studies in Language Companion: No. 10). 400p. (Orig.). 1986. 48.00x (ISBN 90-272-3009-9). Benjamins North Am.
Dullemeijer, P., et al, eds. Morphology: Its Place & Meaning. 100p. 1983. pap. text ed. 16.00 (ISBN 90-265-0470-5, Pub. by Swets Pub Serv Holland). Swets North Am.
Evitt, William R. Sporopollenin Dinoflagellate Cysts: Their Morphology & Interpretation. LC 84-72457. (Illus.). 349p. 1985. 30.00 (ISBN 0-317-19725-8). Am Assn Strat.
Glick, David & Rosenbaum, R., eds. Techniques of Biochemical & Biophysical Morphology, Vol. 3. LC 72-153. 214p. 1977. 27.50 (ISBN 0-471-02219-5, Pub. by Wiley). Krieger.
Gosline, William A. Functional Morphology & Classification of Teleostean Fishes. LC 77-151454. (Illus.). 216p. 1971. pap. text ed. 10.00x (ISBN 0-87022-300-3). UH Pr.
Gualtierotti, T., ed. The Vestibular System: Function & Morphology. (Illus.). 560p. 1981. 99.00 (ISBN 0-387-90559-6). Springer-Verlag.
Johnson, John E, Jr., ed. Current Trends in Morphological Techniques. 272p. 1981. Vol. II. 89.50 (ISBN 0-8493-5826-4); Vol. III, 296p. 89.50 (ISBN 0-686-82889-5). CRC Pr.
Krammer, Kurt. Valve Morphology in the Genus Cymbella: C. A. Agardh. Helmcke, J. G. & Krammer, Kurt, eds. (Micromorphology of Datom Valves Ser.). (Illus.). 300p. (Orig.). 1982. lib. bdg. 59.10x (ISBN 3-7682-1333-1). Lubrecht & Cramer.
Kurten, Bjorn, ed. Teeth: Form, Function & Evolution. LC 81-10210. 456p. 1982. 57.50x (ISBN 0-231-05202-2). Columbia U Pr.
McArdle, J. Functional Morphology of the Hip & Thigh of the Lorisiformes. (Contributions to Primatology: Vol. 17). (Illus.). viii, 132p. 1981. pap. 13.75 (ISBN 3-8055-1767-X). S Karger.
McMahon, Thomas & Bonner, James. On Size & Life. (Scientific American Library). (Illus.). 255p. 1983. 27.95 (ISBN 0-7167-5000-7). W H Freeman.
Matthews, P. H. Morphology: An Introduction to the Theory of Word-Structure. LC 73-91817. (Cambridge Textbooks in Linguistics Ser.). 256p. 1974. pap. 14.95 (ISBN 0-521-09856-4). Cambridge U Pr.
Mayer, Edmund. Introduction to Dynamic Morphology. 1963. 76.50 (ISBN 0-12-480650-3). Acad Pr.
Miles, R. E. & Serra, J., eds. Geometrical Probability & Biological Structures: Buffon's 200 Anniversary. (Lecture Notes in Biomathematics: Vol. 23). 1978. pap. 19.00 (ISBN 0-387-08856-3). Springer-Verlag.
Nachtigall, W. Biological Mechanisms of Attachment: The Comparative Morphology & Bioengineering of Organs for Linkage, Suction, & Adhesion. Biederman-Thorson, M. A., tr. LC 73-17936. (Illus.). 194p. 1974. 49.50 (ISBN 0-387-06550-4). Springer-Verlag.
Noble, A. Biophysics Progression: Some Physical, Mathematical & Logical Aspects, Vol. 37, No. 1. LC 50-11295. (Illus.). 48p. 1981. pap. 25.00 (ISBN 0-08-027133-2). Pergamon.
O'Connor, Barbara H. A Color Atlas & Instruction Manual of Peripheral Blood Morphology. (Illus.). 340p. 1984. pap. text ed. 24.95 (ISBN 0-683-06624-2). Williams & Wilkins.
Oplatka, Avraham, ed. Biological Structures & Coupled Flows. (Illus.). xiv, 519p. 1982. 60.00 (ISBN 0-86689-016-5). Balaban Intl Sci Serv.
Portmann, Adolf. Animal Forms & Patterns: A Study of the Appearance of Animals. Czech, Hella, tr. from Ger. LC 67-14962. (Illus.). 1971. pap. 3.95 (ISBN 0-8052-0309-5). Schocken.
Recker, Robert R., ed. Bone Histomorphometry: Techniques & Interpretation. 312p. 1983. 89.50 (ISBN 0-8493-5373-4). CRC Pr.
Russell, Richard J. River & Delta Morphology. LC 67-29343. (Louisiana State University Studies, Coastal Studies Ser.: No. 20). pap. 20.00 (ISBN 0-317-29938-7, 2051688). Bks Demand UMI.
Sapir, E. Notes on Chasta Costa Phonology & Morphology. (Anthropological Publications Ser.: Vol. 2-2). (Illus.). 72p. 1914. 5.00x (ISBN 0-686-24092-8). Univ Mus of U.
Sarma, Ramaswamy H. Nucleic Acid Geometry & Dynamics. LC 80-10620. (Illus.). 424p. 1980. 65.00 (ISBN 0-08-024631-1); pap. 29.00 (ISBN 0-08-024630-3). Pergamon.
Serra, J. Image Analysis & Mathematical Morphology. LC 81-66397. 1982. 90.00 (ISBN 0-12-637240-3). Acad Pr.
Shipley, Kenneth G. & Banis, Carolyn S. Teaching Morphology Developmentally: Methods & Materials for Teaching Bound Morphology. 1981. 85.00 (ISBN 0-88450-728-9, 3137-B). Communication Skill.
Stevens, Peter S. Patterns in Nature. LC 73-19720. (Illus.). 256p. 1974. (Pub. by Atlantic Monthly Pr); pap. 12.45 (ISBN 0-316-81331-1). Little.
Straub, W., ed. Current Genetic, Clinical & Morphological Problems. (Developments in Ophthalmology: Vol. 3). (Illus.). vi, 218p. 1981. pap. 67.00 (ISBN 3-8055-2000-X). S Karger.

Fletcher, D. S. The Generic Names of Moths of the World, Vol. III, Geometroidea: Apoprogonidae, Axiidae, Callidulidae, Cyclidiidae, Drepanidae, Epicopeidae, Epiplemidae, Geometridae, Pterothysanidae, Sematuridae, Thyatiridae & Uranidae. Nye, I. W., ed. (Illus.). 243p. 1979. 51.00x (ISBN 0-565-00812-9, Pub. by Brit Mus Nat Hist England). Sabbot-Natural Hist Bks.
Fletcher, D. S. & Nye, I. W. The Generic Names of Moths of the World, Vol. IV: Bombycoidea, Castnioidea, Cossoidea, Mimallonoidea, Sesioidea, Sphingoidea, Zygaenoidea. (Illus.). xiv, 192p. 1982. 51.00x (ISBN 0-565-00848-X). Sabbot-Natural Hist Bks.
The Genitalia of the British Lepidoptera Geometridae. 50.00x (ISBN 0-317-07072-X, Pub. by EW Classey UK). State Mutual Bk.
Goater, B. The Butterflies & Moths of Hampshire & the Isle of Wight. 453p. 1974. 35.00x (ISBN 0-317-07037-1, Pub. by EW Classey UK). State Mutual Bk.
Hampson, G. F. Moths Lepidoptera, Vol. 1. vii, 527p. 25.00 (ISBN 0-88065-099-0, Pub. by Messers Today & Tomorrows Printers & Publishers India). Scholarly Pubns.
Hemming, F. Annotationes Leipidopterologicae. 187p. 1960-1964. 60.00x (ISBN 0-317-07026-6, Pub. by EW Classey UK). State Mutual Bk.
Heppner, John B. The Sedge Moths of North America. (Handbook Ser.: No. 1). (Illus.). 262p. (Orig.). 1985. pap. 27.95 (ISBN 0-916846-32-6). Flora & Fauna.
Hodges, Ronald W. The Moths of America North of Mexico: Fasc. 13.2a-Pyralidae; Pyraustinae; Pyraustini, Part 1. 95.00x (ISBN 0-317-07119-X, Pub. by EW Classey UK). State Mutual Bk.
--The Moths of America North of Mexico: Fasc. 13.2b-Pyralidae; Pyraustinae; Pyraustini, Part 2. 95.00x (ISBN 0-317-07121-1, Pub. by EW Classey UK). State Mutual Bk.
--The Moths of America North of Mexico: Fasc. 20.1-Bombycoidea(excluding Saturniidae) 95.00x (ISBN 0-317-07115-7, Pub. by EW Classey UK). State Mutual Bk.
--The Moths of America North of Mexico: Fasc. 22.2-Lymantriidae. 95.00x (ISBN 0-317-07118-1, Pub. by EW Classey UK). State Mutual Bk.
--The Moths of America North of Mexico: Fasc. 6.2-Gelechoidea; Oecophoridae. 95.00x (ISBN 0-317-07116-5, Pub. by EW Classey UK). State Mutual Bk.
Larsen, B. & Nakamura, I. Butterflies of East Jordan. 75p. 1983. 35.00x (ISBN 0-317-07038-X, Pub. by EW Classey UK). State Mutual Bk.
Le Moult, E. & Real, P. Les Morphos D'Amerique Du Sud Et Centrale Historique, Morphologie, Systematique, 2 vols. (Illus.). 416p. 1963. Set. 250.00x (ISBN 0-317-07113-0, Pub. by EW Classey UK). State Mutual Bk.
Lorimer, R. J. Lepidoptera of the Orkney Islands. 96p. 1983. 35.00x (ISBN 0-317-07106-8, Pub. by EW Classey UK). State Mutual Bk.
Metzler, Eric H. Annotated Checklist & Distribution Maps of the Royal Moths & Giant Silkworm Moths (Lepidoptera: Saturniidae) in Ohio. 1980. 2.50 (ISBN 0-86727-088-8). Ohio Bio Survey.
The Moths of America North of Mexico. 150.00x (ISBN 0-317-07114-9, Pub. by EW Classey UK). State Mutual Bk.
Nye, I. W. The Generic Names of Moths of the World, Vol. I: Noctuidae, Agaristidae & Nolidae. (Illus.). 568p. 1975. 76.00x (ISBN 0-565-00770-X, Pub. by Brit Mus Nat Hist England). Sabbot-Natural Hist Bks.
Nye, I. W. & Fletcher, D. S. Generic Names of Moths of the World, Vol. V: Pyraloidea. 200p. 1984. 50.00x (ISBN 0-565-00880-3, Pub. by Brit Mus Nat Hist England). Sabbot-Natural Hist Bks.
Pierce, F. N., et al. The Genitalia of the British Lepidoptera Noctuidae(Females) wrappers 40.00x (ISBN 0-317-07074-6, Pub. by EW Classey UK). State Mutual Bk.
--The Genitalia of the British Lepidoptera Noctuidae(Males) 39.00x (ISBN 0-317-07079-7, Pub. by EW Classey UK). State Mutual Bk.
Poey, P. Centurie de Leipodpteres De L'Ise de Cuda. 62p. 1971. Repr. of 1832 ed. 75.00x (ISBN 0-317-07052-5, Pub. by EW Classey UK). State Mutual Bk.
Robinson, G. S. Macrolepidoptera of Fiji & Rotuma. (A Taxonomic & Biogeographic Study). 374p. 1975. 65.00x (ISBN 0-317-07108-4, Pub. by EW Classey UK). State Mutual Bk.
Romanoff, N. M. Memoirs sur les Lepidopteres. 295.00x (ISBN 0-317-07110-6, Pub. by EW Classey UK). State Mutual Bk.
Turner, Bryan, ed. Illustrated Encyclopedia of Butterflies & Moths. (Illus.). 352p. 1979. 8.50 (ISBN 0-7064-0547-1, Mayflower Bks). Smith Pubs.
Watson, A., et al. The Generic Names of Moths of the World. Vol. II. Noctuoidea: Arctiidae, Cocytiidae, Ctenuchidae, Dilobidae, Dioptidae, Lymantriidae, Notodontidae, Strepsimanidae, Thaumatopoeidae, & Thyretidae. Nye, I. W., ed. (Illus.). xiv, 228p. 1980. 51.00x (ISBN 0-565-00811-0). Sabbot-Natural Hist Bks.
Whalley, P. E. Tropical Leaf Moths. (Illus.). 1976. text ed. 68.00x (ISBN 0-565-00782-3, Pub. by Brit Mus Nat Hist). Sabbot-Natural Hist Bks.

MOTHS–AFRICA, WEST

Carter, David. Butterflies & Moths in Britain & Europe. (Illus.). 192p. 1982. 31.50 (ISBN 0-434-10965-7, Pub. by W Heinemann Ltd). David & Charles.
Tweedie & Wilkinson. The Butterflies & Moths of Britain & Europe. pap. 8.95 (ISBN 0-00-219770-7, Collins Pub England). Greene.

MOTHS–AUSTRALIA

Abrera, Bernard. Moths of Australia. 96p. 1984. 37.00x (ISBN 0-317-07164-5, Pub. by FW Classey UK). State Mutual Bk.

MOTHS–GREAT BRITAIN

Bradley, J. D. & Fletcher, D. S. British Butterflies & Moths. 1980. 75.00x (ISBN 0-902068-08-3, Pub. by Curwen England). State Mutual Bk.
Carter, David. Butterflies & Moths in Britain & Europe. (Illus.). 192p. 1982. 31.50 (ISBN 0-434-10965-7, Pub. by W Heinemann Ltd). David & Charles.
Carter, David & Phillips, Roger, eds. Butterflies & Moths of Britain & Europe. (Illus.). 192p. (Orig.). 1982. pap. text ed. 14.95x (ISBN 0-916422-37-2, Pub. by Pan Bks England). Mad River.
Heath, John, ed. The Moths & Butterflies of Great Britain & Ireland, Vol. 1. 343p. (Orig.). 1976. text ed. 39.95x (ISBN 0-632-00331-6). Entomological Repr.
Tweedie & Wilkinson. The Butterflies & Moths of Britain & Europe. pap. 8.95 (ISBN 0-00-219770-7, Collins Pub England). Greene.

MOTHS–IRELAND

Heath, John, ed. The Moths & Butterflies of Great Britain & Ireland, Vol. 1. 343p. (Orig.). 1976. text ed. 39.95x (ISBN 0-632-00331-6). Entomological Repr.

MOTHS–NORTH AMERICA

Carter, David & Phillips, Roger, eds. Butterflies & Moths of Britain & Europe. (Illus.). 192p. (Orig.). 1982. pap. text ed. 14.95x (ISBN 0-916422-37-2, Pub. by Pan Bks England). Mad River.
Covell, Charles V., Jr. A Field Guide to the Moths of Eastern North America. LC 83-26523. (Peterson Field Guide Ser.). (Illus.). 496p. 1984. 18.95 (ISBN 0-395-26056-6); pap. 13.95 (ISBN 0-395-36100-1). HM.
Hodges, Ronald. The Moths of America North of Mexico: Pyralidae, Odontiinae & Glaphryiinae, Fasc. 13. 1b. (Illus.). 1984. 95.00x (ISBN 0-317-07159-9, Pub. by FW Classey UK). State Mutual Bk.
--The Moths of America North of Mexico: Saturniidae Pt. 1, Fasc. 20. 20a. 1984. 95.00x (ISBN 0-317-07160-2, Pub. by FW Classey UK). State Mutual Bk.
Hodges, Ronald W. The Moths of America North of Mexico: Saturniidae Pt. 2, Fasc. 20. 2b. 1984. 95.00x (ISBN 0-317-07161-0, Pub. by FW Classey UK). State Mutual Bk.
--The Moths of America North of Mexico: Sphigoidea, Fasc. 21. 1984. 95.00x (ISBN 0-317-07162-9, Pub. by FW Classey UK). State Mutual Bk.
--The Moths of America North of Mexico: Walshiidae & Cosmopterigidae, Fasc. 6. 1. 1984. 95.00x (ISBN 0-317-07163-7, Pub. by FW Classey UK). State Mutual Bk.
Holland, W. J. The Moth Book: A Guide to Moths of North America. (Illus.). 18.25 (ISBN 0-8446-0145-4). Peter Smith.
--Moth Book: A Popular Guide to a Knowledge of the Moths of North America. rev. ed. Brower, A. E., ed. LC 68-22887. (Illus.). 1968. pap. 12.50 (ISBN 0-486-21948-8). Dover.
Howard, Leland O. & Fiske, William F. The Importation into the United States of the Parasites of the Gypsy Moth & the Brown-Tail Moth: Report of Progress of Previous & Concurrent Efforts of This Kind. Egerton, Frank N., 3rd, ed. LC 77-74230. (History of Ecology Ser.). (Illus.). 1978. Repr. of 1911 ed. lib. bdg. 32.00x (ISBN 0-405-10400-6). Ayer Co Pubs.
Powell, Jerry A. Biological Interrelationship of Moths & Yucca Schottii. (Publications in Entomology Ser.: Vol. 100). 1985. 18.00x (ISBN 0-520-09681-9). U of Cal Pr.
Selman, Charles L. A Pictorial Key to the Hawkmoths (Lepidotera: Sphingidae) of Eastern United States (Except Florida) 1975. 1.50 (ISBN 0-86727-079-9). Ohio Bio Survey.

MOTHS–SOUTH AFRICA

Pinhey, Elliot C. G. Moths of Southern Africa. (Illus.). 273p. (Orig.). 1975. 41.25x (ISBN 0-624-00784-7). Entomological Repr.

MOTILITY OF CELLS

see Cells–Motility

MOTION

see also Acceleration (Mechanics); Force and Energy; Kinematics; Liapunov Functions; Mechanical Movements; Mechanics; Rotational Motion; Speed; Stability

Bickford, John H. Mechanisms for Intermittent Motion. LC 75-184639. 272p. 1972. 28.50 (ISBN 0-8311-1091-0). Krieger.
Buckley, Michael J. Motion & Motion's God: Thematic Variations in Aristotle, Cicero, Newton, & Hegel. LC 73-132234. 1971. 29.00 (ISBN 0-691-07124-1). Princeton U Pr.
Casper, Barry M. & Noer, Richard J. Revolutions in Physics. (Illus.). 1972. text ed. 20.95x (ISBN 0-393-09992-X); instructor's guide free (ISBN 0-393-09405-7). Norton.
De Groot, S. R., et al. Relativistic Kinetic Theory: Principles & Applications. 418p. 1980. 78.75 (ISBN 0-444-85453-3, North-Holland). Elsevier.
Dow, T. W. Repeal Kepler's Laws. LC 60-13372. 1960. 5.00 (ISBN 0-910340-02-1). Celestial Pr.
--Reshape Newton's Laws. LC 64-19218. 1965. 5.00 (ISBN 0-910340-03-X). Celestial Pr.
Gordon, R. J., ed. Equation of Motion, Boundry Layer Theory & Measurement. (AIChEMI Modular Instruction C-Ser.: Vol. 3). 62p. 1982. pap. 30.00 (ISBN 0-8169-0210-0). Am Inst Chem Eng.
Hackett, L. C. & Jenson, R. G. A Guide to Movement Exploration. 1973. pap. text ed. 3.95 (ISBN 0-917962-04-4). Peek Pubns.
Kuo, B. C., ed. Proceedings: Symposium on Incremental Motion Control Systems & Devices, 11th Annual. (Illus.). 332p. 1982. 45.00x (ISBN 0-931538-04-1). Incremental Motion.
--Proceedings: Symposium on Incremental Motion Control Systems & Devices, 13th Annual. (Illus.). 350p. 1984. 50.00x (ISBN 0-931538-06-8). Incremental Motion.
Landau, L. & Kitaigorodsky, A. I. Physics for Everyone: Physical Bodies. 248p. 1980. 6.60 (ISBN 0-8285-1716-9, Pub. by Mir Pubs USSR). Imported Pubns.
Morecki, A., ed. Biomechanics of Motion. (CISM-Courses & Lectures: Vol. 263). (Illus.). 217p. 1980. pap. 31.00 (ISBN 0-387-81611-9). Springer-Verlag.
Oresme, Nicole, ed. De proportionibus proportionum. Grant, Edward, tr. Bd. with Ad pauca respicientes. (Medieval Science Publications Ser.). (Illus.). 488p. 1966. 50.00x (ISBN 0-299-04000-3). U of Wis Pr.
Park, David. The Image of Eternity: Roots of Time in the Physical World. LC 79-22984. 160p. 1980. lib. bdg. 14.50x (ISBN 0-87023-286-X). U of Mass Pr.
Soldano, B. A. Mass, Measurement & Motion Sequel Two: A New Look at Maxwell's Equations & the Permittivity of Free Space. Brantley, William H., ed. (Illus.). 50p. (Orig.). 1982. pap. 7.00 (ISBN 0-943410-00-2). Grenridge Pub.
Symposium on Incremental Motion & Control Systems & Devices, 8th, Annual. Proceedings. LC 73-647018. (Illus.). 1979. 40.00x (ISBN 0-931538-01-7). Incremental Motion.
Unwin, Derick. Leyes De Movimiento De Newton. (Sp.). 1970. pap. 2.00 (ISBN 0-06-317011-6, IntlDept). Har-Row.

MOTION-PICTURE CAMERAS

see Moving-Picture Cameras

MOTION STUDY

see Time and Motion Study

MOTOR-BOATS

see also Outboard Motors

Block, Richard A. & Bramble, C. A., eds. Motorboat, Ocean & Inland Operator License Preparation Course, 2 bks. rev. ed. (Illus.). 841p. 1983. 58.00 (ISBN 0-934114-58-7). Marine Educ.
Cox, T. Motor Boat & Yachting Manual. 18th ed. (Illus.). 1973. 17.50 (ISBN 0-540-00966-0). Heinman.
Cox, Tom. Motor Boat & Yachting Manual. 18th ed. (Illus.). 356p. 1973. 17.95x (ISBN 0-8464-0644-6). Beekman Pubs.
Desmond, Kevin. Motorboating Facts & Feats. (Illus.). 256p. 1980. 19.95 (ISBN 0-900424-86-9, Pub by Guinness Superlatives England). Sterling.
Gibbs, Tony & Sports Illustrated Editors. Sports Illustrated Power Boating. LC 72-13277. 1973. pap. 2.95i (ISBN 0-397-00972-0, LP81). Har-Row.
Martenhoff, Jim. The Powerboat Handbook. (Illus.). 272p. pap. 5.95 (ISBN 0-88317-030-2). Stoeger Pub Co.
Schult, Joachim. Curious Boating Inventions. LC 74-1525. (Illus.). 150p. 1974. 14.95 (ISBN 0-8008-2103-3). Taplinger.
Warren, Nigel. Small Motor Cruises. 1979. 19.95x (ISBN 0-8464-0064-2). Beekman Pubs.
West, Jack. Modern Powerboats. 2nd ed. LC 75-662. (Illus.). pap. 60.50 (ISBN 0-317-08210-8, 2015661). Bks Demand UMI.

MOTOR BUSES

Anderson, R. C. History of Crosville Motor Services. LC 81-65955. (Illus.). 160p. 1981. 19.95 (ISBN 0-7153-8088-5). David & Charles.
Arco Editorial Board. Bus Maintainer - Bus Mechanic. 4th ed. LC 70-104878. 136p. (Orig.). 1972. pap. 8.00 (ISBN 0-668-00111-9). Arco.
Booth, Gavin. Alexander Coachbuilders. 192p. 1981. 45.00x (ISBN 0-903839-38-5, Pub. by Transport). State Mutual Bk.
From Omnibus to Motor Bus. (Illus.). 156p. 5.50 (ISBN 0-686-79879-1, 46). Shawnee County Hist.
Kaye, David. Old Buses. (Shire Album Ser.: No. 94). (Illus.). 32p. pap. 2.95 (ISBN 0-85263-613-X, Pub. by Shire Pubns England). Seven Hills Bks.
Miller, Denis. The Illustrated Encyclopedia of Trucks & Buses. (Illus.). 320p. 1982. 24.95 (ISBN 0-8317-4820-6). Smith Pubs.
Rudman, Jack. Bus Maintainer, Group A. (Career Examination Ser.: C-100). (Cloth bdg. avail. on request). pap. 10.00 (ISBN 0-8373-0100-9). Natl Learning.
--Bus Maintainer, Group B. (Career Examination Ser.: C-101). (Cloth bdg. avail. on request). pap. 10.00 (ISBN 0-8373-0101-7). Natl Learning.
--Foreman (Buses & Shops) (Career Examination Ser.: C-264). (Cloth bdg. avail. on request). pap. 10.00 (ISBN 0-8373-0264-1). Natl Learning.
Townsin, A. A. The Best of British Buses: Leyland Titans, 1927-1941, No. 1. 96p. 1981. 30.00x (ISBN 0-903839-56-3, Pub. by Transport). State Mutual Bk.
Turner, Tom. Birkenhead Buses. 48p. 1981. 10.00x (ISBN 0-903839-30-X, Pub. by Transport). State Mutual Bk.

MOTOR-CARS

see Automobiles

MOTOR CYCLES

see Motorcycles

MOTOR FLEETS

see Motor Vehicle Fleets

MOTOR FUELS

see also Airplanes–Fuel; Alcohol As Fuel; Jet Planes–Fuel; Liquid Fuels; Petroleum As Fuel; Petroleum Products

Colucci, Joseph M. & Gallopoulos, Nicholas E., eds. Future Automotive Fuels: Prospects, Performance, Perspective. LC 76-30757. (General Motors Research Symposia Ser.). 380p. 1977. 59.50x (ISBN 0-306-31017-1, Plenum Pr). Plenum Pub.
Frazier, Jack. Automobile Fuels of the 1980's: A Survey. (Illus.). 1978. pap. 4.95 (ISBN 0-685-87593-8). Solar Age Pr.
LP-Gas Engine Fuels- STP 525. 140p. 1973. 4.75 (ISBN 0-8031-0104-X, 04 525000 12). ASTM.
Paul, J. K., ed. Methanol Technology & Application in Motor Fuels. LC 78-56011. (Chemical Tech. Rev. 114, Energy Tech. Rev. 31). (Illus.). 1979. 54.00 (ISBN 0-8155-0719-4). Noyes.
Whitcomb, R. M. Non-Lead Antiknock Agents for Motor Fuels. LC 75-4474. (Chemical Technology Review Ser: No. 49). 290p. (Index of patents, inventors, companies). 1975. 36.00 (ISBN 0-8155-0573-6). Noyes.

MOTOR-TRUCKS

see also Campers and Coaches, Truck; Materials Handling; Vans

Aftermarket for Imported Cars, & Light Trucks. 232p. 1984. 1400.00 (ISBN 0-86621-174-8). Frost & Sullivan.
American Trucking Assoc. Guide to Weighing, Inspection & Accessorial Services. 1980. pap. text ed. 25.00 (ISBN 0-88711-048-7). Am Trucking Assns.
Arrow & Dodge D-Fifty Pick-Ups 1979-81. LC 80-70343. (Illus.). 192p. pap. 11.95 (ISBN 0-8019-7032-6). Chilton.
ATA Vehicle Maintenance Reporting Standards Handbook. 1983. text ed. 60.00 (ISBN 0-88711-024-X). Am Trucking Assns.
Auto-Truck Interchange Manual: Wheel Covers. 47th ed. 88p. 1982. 15.95 (ISBN 0-943032-20-2). Hollander Co.
Auto-Truck Interchange Manual: Wheel Cover Supplement. 48th ed. (Auto-Truck Interchange Ser.). (Illus.). 88p. 1982. 16.00 (ISBN 0-943032-23-7). Hollander Co.
Auto-Truck Manual: Special Wheel Supplement. 48th ed. (Auto-Truck Interchange Ser.). (Illus.). 16p. 1982. 6.00 (ISBN 0-943032-24-5). Hollander Co.
Baldwin, Nick. Trucks of the Sixties & Seventies. (Transport Library). (Illus.). 64p. 1980. 13.95 (ISBN 0-7232-2364-5, Pub. by Warne Pubs England). Motorbooks Intl.
Brady, James. On-Highway Trucks: Power Trains & Suspension Systems. 624p. 1981. text ed. 28.95 (ISBN 0-8359-5232-0). Reston.

--Motor Vehicle Program Manager. (Career Examination Ser.: C-311). (Cloth bdg. avail. on request). pap. 12.00 (ISBN 0-8373-0311-7). Natl Learning.

--Motor Vehicle Program Manager I. (Career Examination Ser.: C-312). (Cloth bdg. avail. on request). pap. 12.00 (ISBN 0-8373-0312-5). Natl Learning.

--Motor Vehicle Program Manager II. (Career Examination Ser.: C-313). (Cloth bdg. avail. on request). pap. 14.00 (ISBN 0-8373-0313-3). Natl Learning.

--Motor Vehicle Program Manager III. (Career Examination Ser.: C-314). (Cloth bdg. avail. on request). pap. 14.00 (ISBN 0-8373-0314-1). Natl Learning.

U. S. Army Standard Military Motor Vehicles, 1943. 560p. 1980. 45.00x (ISBN 0-905418-46-8, Pub. by Gresham Bks England). State Mutual Bk.

Vanderveen, Bart H. The Observer's Army Vehicles Directory to 1940. (Illus.). 378p. 1974. 15.00 (ISBN 0-7232-1540-5, Pub. by Warne Pubs England). Motorbooks Intl.

Vehicle Structural Mechanics, 3rd International Conference Proceedings. LC 79-90695. 310p. 1979. Twenty-Five papers. pap. 40.00 (ISBN 0-89883-053-2, P83). Soc Auto Engineers.

Wallace, Angelo. Automotive Literature Index: 1977-1981. 327p. 1982. pap. 29.95 (ISBN 0-9606804-4-6). Wallace Pub.

World Motor Vehicle Data Book. 1986. 35.00 (ISBN 0-317-05087-7). Motor Veh Man.

Zammit, Saviour J. Drawing Examples for Motor Vehicle Engineers. LC 78-14451. pap. 20.00 (ISBN 0-317-27768-5, 2025237). Bks Demand UMI.

MOTOR VEHICLES–EMISSION CONTROL DEVICES

see Motor Vehicles–Pollution Control Devices

MOTOR VEHICLES–EXHAUST CONTROL DEVICES

see Motor Vehicles–Pollution Control Devices

MOTOR VEHICLES–POLLUTION CONTROL DEVICES

Crouse, William H. & Anglin, Donald L. Automotive Emission Control. 3rd ed. LC 83-1015. (Automotive Technology Ser.). 288p. 1983. pap. text ed. 21.10 (ISBN 0-07-014816-3). McGraw.

Effect of Cold Weather on Motor Vehicle Emissions. pap. 2.35 (SSC30, SSC). Unipub.

Emissions: Misfueling, Catalyst Deactivation & Alternative Catalyst. 88p. 1984. 15.00 (ISBN 0-89883-809-6, SP588). Soc Auto Engineers.

Environmental Aspects of the Motor Vehicle & Its Use. (Industry Overviews: Vol. 4). 20p. 1977. pap. 6.75 (ISBN 0-686-59760-5, UNEP021, UNEP). Unipub.

Environmental Aspects of the Motor Vehicle & Its Use: A Technical Review. (Industry Technical Review Ser.: Vol. 2). 26p. 1977. pap. 6.75 (ISBN 0-686-93505-5, UNEP023, UNEP). Unipub.

Gonzales, Ron. Automotive Fuel & Emission Systems. 1985. text ed. 24.95 (ISBN 0-8359-0117-3); pap. text ed. 19.95 (ISBN 0-8359-0116-5). Reston.

Husselbee, William L. Automotive Fuel, Cooling, Lubrication & Exhaust Systems. 1984. text ed. 29.95 (ISBN 0-8359-0300-1); pap. text ed. 22.95 (ISBN 0-8359-0299-4). Reston.

Knowles, Don. Automotive Emission Controls & Computer Systems. 1984. text ed. 29.95 (ISBN 0-8359-0150-5); pap. text ed. 22.95 (ISBN 0-8359-0135-1). Reston.

Motor Vehicle Air Pollution Controls: A Global Review. 1985. 27.00 (ISBN 0-89883-835-5, SP614). Soc Auto Engineers.

National Research Council Assembly of Engineering & Motor Vehicle Nitrogen Oxides Standard Committee. NO-X Emission Controls for Heavy-Duty Vehicles: Toward Meeting a 1986 Standard. 1981. pap. text ed. 9.75 (ISBN 0-309-03226-1). Natl Acad Pr.

MOTOR VEHICLES–SMOG CONTROL DEVICES

see Motor Vehicles–Pollution Control Devices

MOTOR VEHICLES IN WAR

see Tanks (Military Science)

MOTORCYCLES

see also Mopeds

also names of motorcycles, e.g. B.S.A. motorcycle, Honda motorcycle

Arthur, Terry. The Moped Handbook. (Illus.). 1977. (Harmony); pap. 1.00 Outlet (ISBN 0-517-53107-0). Crown.

Ayton, Cyril, ed. World Motorcycles: Number One. (Illus.). 238p. 24.95 (ISBN 0-85429-360-4, F360). Haynes Pubns.

Bacon, Roy. Foreign Racing Motorcycles. 204p. 16.95 (ISBN 0-85429-295-0, F244). Haynes Pubns.

Burgess, R. W. & Clew, J. R. Always in the Picture: A History of the Velocette Motorcycle. 19.95 (ISBN 0-85429-266-7, F266). Haynes Pubns.

Caddell, Laurie & Winfield, Mike. Superbikes. LC 81-81994. (Orig.). 1981. pap. 9.95 (ISBN 0-89586-067-8). H P Bks.

Clarke, Ronald. Brough Superior: The Rolls Royce of Motorcycles. 3rd ed. (Illus.). 192p. 12.95 (ISBN 0-85429-454-6, F454). Haynes Pubns.

Clew, Jeff. British Racing Motorcycles. 183p. 16.95 (ISBN 0-85429-161-X, F161). Haynes Pubns.

--The Douglas Motorcycle: 'The Best Twin' 250p. 19.95 (ISBN 0-85429-299-3, F299). Haynes Pubns.

--The Restoration of Vintage & Thoroughbred Motorcycles. (Illus.). 200p. 15.95 (ISBN 0-85429-185-7, F185). Haynes Pubns.

--The Scott Motorcycle: The Yowling Two-Stroke. 239p. 19.95 (ISBN 0-85429-164-4, F164). Haynes Pubns.

--Suzuki. (Illus.). 235p. 17.95 (ISBN 0-317-30509-3, F243). Haynes Pubns.

Croucher, Robert M. The Observer's Book of Motorcycles. (Illus.). 192p. 1976. 4.95 (ISBN 0-7232-1572-3, Pub. by Warne Pubs England). Motorbooks Intl.

Crouse, William H. & Anglin, Donald L. Motorcycle Mechanics. LC 81-217. (Illus.). 384p. 1982. pap. text ed. 24.40 (ISBN 0-07-014781-7). McGraw.

Crowley, T. E. Discovering Old Motor Cycles. (Discovering Ser.: No. 160). (Illus.). 55p. (Orig.). 1983. pap. 3.95 (ISBN 0-85263-557-5, Pub. by Shire Pubns England). Seven Hills Bks.

Dunster, Mark. Motorcycles. LC 77-155954. (Rin: Pt. 7). 1978. pap. 4.00 (ISBN 0-89642-006-X). Linden Pubs.

Grant, Richard & Thomas, Nigel. BMX Action Bike Book. LC 84-16784. (Illus.). 48p. 1985. 5.95 (ISBN 0-668-06345-9). Arco.

Griffin, Michael M. Motorcycles: From the Inside Out (& How to Keep Them Right Side up) (Illus.). 1978. ref. ed. 18.95 (ISBN 0-13-604041-1); pap. text ed. 9.95 (ISBN 0-13-604033-0). P-H.

Kosbab, William H. Motorcycle Dictionary. Greenslade-Moore, Dianne & Lamont, Daveta, eds. LC 82-71155. 370p. 1983. pap. text ed. 14.95x (ISBN 0-89262-044-7). Career Pub.

Mosher, Lynn S. & Lear, George. Motorcycle Mechanics. (Illus.). 272p. 1977. 24.95 (ISBN 0-13-604090-X). P-H.

Page, Victor W. Early Motorcycles: Construction, Operation, Service. LC 71-158128. (Illus.). 512p. 1971. pap. 21.95 (ISBN 0-911160-62-0). Post-Era.

Renstrom, Richard. Motorcycle Milestones, Vol. 1. LC 80-66669. (Illus.). 112p. 1980. 20.00 (ISBN 0-936660-00-7); pap. 15.00 (ISBN 0-936660-01-5). Classics Unltd.

Sands, Jack. Motorcycle Marines: An Illustrated History. 32p. 1985. pap. 7.95 (ISBN 0-938242-12-1). Portrayal.

Setright, L. J. Bahnstormer: The Story of BMW Motorcycles. (Illus.). 1978. 18.95 (ISBN 0-85184-021-3, Pub. by Transport Bookman Pubns. Ltd. England). Motorbooks Intl.

--Guinness Book of Motorcycling Facts & Feats. 258p. 1980. 14.95 (ISBN 0-85112-200-0, Pub. by Guinness Superlatives England). Sterling.

Smith, Philip H. & Morrison, John C. Scientific Design of Exhaust & Intake Systems. 3rd rev. ed. LC 72-86569. (Illus.). 294p. 1972. 16.95 (ISBN 0-8376-0309-9). Bentley.

Sparks, James C. Mini & Trail Bikes: How to Build Them Yourself. (Illus.). 1976. 9.95 (ISBN 0-87690-184-4). Dutton.

Vanderveen, Bart H. Motorcycles & Scooters from Nineteen Forty-Five. (Illus.). 64p. 1972. 10.95 (ISBN 0-7232-1847-1, Pub. by Warne Pubs England). Motorbooks Intl.

Webster, Jay & Putnam, Robert. Motorcycle Operation & Service. 1985. text ed. 23.95 (ISBN 0-8359-4669-X); tchr's. manual avail. (ISBN 0-8359-4670-3). Reston.

Willoughby, Vic. Back to Basics. 120p. pap. 6.50 (ISBN 0-85429-288-8, F288). Haynes Pubns.

Woollett, Mick. Lightweight Bikes. (Illus.). 64p. 1981. pap. 5.50 (ISBN 0-7134-3913-0, Pub. by Batsford England). David & Charles.

MOTORCYCLES–MAINTENANCE AND REPAIR

Arman, Mike. Motorcycle Electrics Without Pain. (Illus.). 1980. pap. 8.00 (ISBN 0-933078-03-X). M Arman.

Arman, Mike & Heinrichs, Kurt. Harley Davidson Special Tools: Where to Get Them, How to Use Them. (Illus.). 64p. 1982. pap. text ed. 5.00 (ISBN 0-933078-07-2). M Arman.

Arthur, Terry. The Moped Handbook. (Illus.). 1977. (Harmony); pap. 1.00 Outlet (ISBN 0-517-53107-0). Crown.

Bleach, Mervyn. Honda Owner's Workshop Manual: XR75 Dirt Bikes '72-78. (Owners Workshop Manuals Ser.: No. 287). 1979. 10.50 (ISBN 0-85696-287-2, Pub. by J H Haynes England). Haynes Pubns.

Brobst, William A. Pulling Your Tail: A Primer on the Art of Motorcycle Trailering. LC 82-90072. (Illus.). 64p. 1982. pap. 5.65 (ISBN 0-9608112-0-6). Transport Env.

Brotherwood, Clive. Honda Owner's Workshop Manual: One Hundred & One Twenty-Five Singles Roads & Trails '70-75. (Owners Workshop Manuals Ser.: No. 188). 1979. 10.50 (ISBN 0-85696-188-4, Pub. by J H Haynes England). Haynes Pubns.

--Triumph 350 & 500 Unit Twins '57 - '73. new ed. (Owners Workshop Manuals Ser.: No. 137). 1979. 10.50 (ISBN 0-85696-137-X, Pub. by J H Haynes England). Haynes Pubns.

Chilton Staff. Chilton's Motorcycle & ATV Repair Manual: 1945-85. LC 85-47957. 1456p. 1986. 27.95 (ISBN 0-8019-7635-9); slipcase 28.70 (ISBN 0-8019-7636-7). Chilton.

Chilton's Automotive Editorial Staff. Chilton's Motorcycle Owner's Handbook. (Illus.). 1979. pap. 9.95 (ISBN 0-8019-6867-4, 795). Chilton.

--Chilton's Motorcycle Troubleshooting Guide. 2nd ed. LC 77-121. 1977. pap. 11.95 (ISBN 0-8019-6587-X, 6587). Chilton.

--Chilton's Repair & Tune-up Guide for Audi, 1970-1973. (Illus.). 190p. 1973. pap. 11.95 (ISBN 0-8019-5902-0). Chilton.

--Chilton's Repair & Tune-Up Guide for Honda 350-550, 1972-1977. LC 77-89115. (Chilton's Repair & Tune-Up Guides). (Illus., Orig.). 1977. pap. 10.95 (ISBN 0-8019-6603-5, 6603). Chilton.

--Yamaha 650, 1970-79. (Chilton's Repair & Tune-Up Guides). (Illus.). 1979. pap. 10.95 (ISBN 0-8019-6895-X, 6895). Chilton.

Chilton's Motorcycle Repair Manual 1981. (Illus.). 1248p. 24.95 (ISBN 0-8019-7077-6). Chilton.

Chilton's Repair & Tune-up Guide for Honda 350-360, 1968-77: Motorcycle. (Repair & Tune-up Guides Ser.). (Illus.). 1978. pap. 10.95 (ISBN 0-8019-6705-8). Chilton.

Clew, Jeff. BSA A7 & A10 Twins '47 - '54. (Owners Workshop Manuals Ser.: No. 121). 1979. 10.50 (ISBN 0-85696-121-3, Pub. by J H Haynes England). Haynes Pubns.

--Bultaco Competition Bikes '72-'75. new ed. (Owners Workshop Manuals Ser.: No. 219). 1979. 10.50 (ISBN 0-85696-219-8, Pub. by J H Haynes England). Haynes Pubns.

--Harley Davidson Owners Workshop Manual: Sportster '70 Thru '76. (Owners Workshop Manuals Ser.: No. 250). 1979. 10.50 (ISBN 0-85696-250-3, Pub. by J H Haynes England). Haynes Pubns.

--Honda Owner's Workshop Manual: Fifty Ohv & Ohc '62 Thru '71. (Owners Workshop Manuals Ser.: No. 114). 1979. 10.50 (ISBN 0-85696-114-0, Pub. by J H Haynes England). Haynes Pubns.

--Honda Owner's Workshop Manual: Sixty-Five, Seventy, Ninety & '64-72. (Owners Workshop Manuals Ser.: No. 116). 1979. 10.50 (ISBN 0-85696-116-7, Pub. by J H Haynes England). Haynes Pubns.

--Honda XL250 & 350 Trail Bikes '72 - '75. (Owners Workshop Manuals Ser.: No. 209). 1979. 10.50 (ISBN 0-85696-209-0, Pub. by J H Haynes England). Haynes Pubns.

--Honda 125, 160, 175, 200 & CD175 Twins '70 - '78: One Twenty-Five to Two Hundred Twins '64-78. (Owners Workshop Manuals Ser.: No. 067). 1979. 10.50 (ISBN 0-900550-67-8, 067, Pub. by J H Haynes England). Haynes Pubns.

--Honda 250 Elsinore '73 - '75. (Owners Workshop Manuals Ser.: No. 217). 1979. 10.50 (ISBN 0-85696-217-1, Pub. by J H Haynes England). Haynes Pubns.

--Honda 750 sohc Fours '70 - '79. (Owners Workshop Manuals Ser.: No. 131). 1979. 10.50 (ISBN 0-85696-521-9, Pub. by J H Haynes England). Haynes Pubns.

--Norton Commando '68 - '77. new ed. (Owners Workshop Manuals Ser.: No. 125). 1979. 10.50 (ISBN 0-85696-125-6, Pub. by J H Haynes England). Haynes Pubns.

--Suzuki 250 & 350 Twins '69 - '78. new ed. (Owners Workshop Manuals Ser.: No. 120). 1979. 10.50 (ISBN 0-85696-120-5, Pub. by J H Haynes England). Haynes Pubns.

--Triumph Pre-Unit Twins '47 - '60. (Owners Workshop Manuals Ser.: No. 251). 1979. 10.50 (ISBN 0-85696-251-1, Pub. by J H Haynes England). Haynes Pubns.

--Velocette Singles '53 - '70. new ed. (Owners Workshop Manuals Ser.: No. 186). 1979. 10.50 (ISBN 0-85696-186-8, Pub. by J H Haynes England). Haynes Pubns.

--Yamaha 500 Twin '73 - '79. new ed. (Owners Workshop Manuals Ser.: No. 308). 1980. 10.50 (ISBN 0-85696-308-9, Pub. by J H Haynes England). Haynes Pubns.

Clew, Jeff & Rogers, Chris. Triumph 650 & 750 4-valve Twins '63 - '83. (Owners Workshop Manuals Ser.: No. 122). 1981. 10.50 (ISBN 0-85696-579-0, Pub. by J H Haynes England). Haynes Pubns.

Clymer Publications. Bultaco Service Repair Handbook: 125-370cc, Through 1977. (Illus.). pap. 13.95 (ISBN 0-89287-174-1, M303). Clymer Pubns.

--Honda Service-Repair Handbook: CB 750SOHC Fours, 1969-1978. Jorgensen, Eric, ed. (Illus.). pap. 13.95 (ISBN 0-89287-167-9, M341). Clymer Pubns.

--Suzuki: 380-750cc Triples, 1972-1977 Service, Repair, Maintenance. (Illus.). 1977. pap. 13.95 (ISBN 0-89287-285-3, M368). Clymer Pubns.

--Yamaha Service Repair Handbook: 80-175cc Piston Port Singles, 1968-1976. (Illus.). pap. text ed. 13.95 (ISBN 0-89287-235-7, M410). Clymer Pubns.

--Yamaha: 250-400cc Piston Port Singles, 1968-76, Service, Repair, Performance. 3rd ed. Jorgensen, Eric, ed. (Illus.). pap. 13.95 (ISBN 0-89287-276-4, M415). Clymer Pubns.

Collett, George. Suzuki GT 380, 550 '72 - '77. new ed. (Owners Workshop Manuals Ser.: No. 216). 1979. 10.50 (ISBN 0-85696-216-3, Pub. by J H Haynes England). Haynes Pubns.

Collett, George & Witcomb, John. Honda 500 & 450 Twins '66 - '78. (Owners Workshop Manuals Ser.: No. 211). 1980. 10.50 (ISBN 0-85696-211-2, Pub. by J H Haynes England). Haynes Pubns.

Crouse, William H. & Anglin, Donald L. Motorcycle Mechanics. LC 81-217. (Illus.). 384p. 1982. pap. text ed. 24.40 (ISBN 0-07-014781-7). McGraw.

Daniels, Marcus. BSA Unit Singles '58 - '72. new ed. (Owners Workshop Manuals Ser.: No. 127). 1979. 10.50 (ISBN 0-85696-127-2, Pub. by J H Haynes England). Haynes Pubns.

Darlington, Mansur. BSA Pre-unit Singles '54 - '61. new ed. (Owners Workshop Manuals Ser.: No. 326). 1979. 10.50 (ISBN 0-85696-326-7, Pub. by J H Haynes England). Haynes Pubns.

--Honda CB CJ 250 & 360 Twins '74 - '78. (Owners Workshop Manuals Ser.: No. 291). 1979. 10.50 (ISBN 0-85696-291-0, Pub. by J H Haynes England). Haynes Pubns.

--Honda 125 Elsinore & MR175 '73 - '76. (Owners Workshop Manuals Ser.: No. 312). 1979. 10.50 (ISBN 0-85696-312-7, Pub. by J H Haynes England). Haynes Pubns.

--Husqvarna Competition Models '72 - '75. (Owners Workshop Manuals Ser.: No. 221). 1979. 10.50 (ISBN 0-85696-221-X, Pub. by J H Haynes England). Haynes Pubns.

--Moto-Guzzi 750, 850 & 1000 V-Twins '74 - '78. (Owners Workshop Manuals Ser.: No. 339). 1979. 10.50 (ISBN 0-85696-339-9, Pub. by J H Haynes England). Haynes Pubns.

--Suzuki GT750 (3-cyl) Models '71 - '77. new ed. (Owners Workshop Manuals Ser.: No. 302). 1979. 10.50 (ISBN 0-85696-302-X, Pub. by J H Haynes England). Haynes Pubns.

--Suzuki Trail Bikes 90 Thru 400cc's '71-'79. new ed. (Owners Workshop Manuals Ser.: No. 218). 1979. 10.50 (ISBN 0-85696-520-0, Pub. by J H Haynes England). Haynes Pubns.

--Yamaha Trail Bikes 250, 360 & 400 '68 - '79. new ed. (Owners Workshop Manuals Ser.: No. 263). 1980. 10.50 (ISBN 0-85696-519-7, Pub. by J H Haynes England). Haynes Pubns.

Darlington, Mansur & Rogers, Chris. Honda GL1000 Gold Wing '75 - '80. (Owners Workshop Manuals Ser.: No. 309). 1981. 10.50 (ISBN 0-85696-710-6, Pub. by J H Haynes England). Haynes Pubns.

Ducati Service-Repair Handbook: 160, 250,350, 450cc, Through 1974. (Illus.). 1974. pap. text ed. 13.95 (ISBN 0-89287-004-4, M306). Clymer Pubns.

Harley Davidson Owners Workshop Manual: Super & Electraglide '74 Thru '77. (Owners Workshop Manuals Ser.: No. 330). 1979. 10.50 (ISBN 0-85696-330-5, Pub. by J H Haynes England). Haynes Pubns.

Haynes, J. H. & Bange, C. D. B M W Bavaria Owners Workshop Manual: 2500, 2800, 3.0 1969 Thru 1976. (Owners Workshop Manuals Ser.: No. 348). 1979. 12.95 (ISBN 0-85696-348-8, Pub. by J H Haynes England). Haynes Pubns.

Honda CR60-500R Pro-Link: 1981-1984 Service Repair Performance. 337p. (Orig.). 1985. pap. 13.95 (ISBN 0-89287-405-8, M343). Clymer Pubns.

Honda Hawk (Motorcycle) Nineteen Seventy-Seven to Nineteen Eighty Repair Tune-up Guide. LC 79-3245. (New Automotive Bks.). 192p. 1980. 10.95 (ISBN 0-8019-6868-2). Chilton.

Jorgensen, Eric. Honda Service Repair Handbook: 350-550cc Fours, 1972-1978. Robinson, Jeff, ed. (Illus.). pap. 13.95 (ISBN 0-89287-287-X, M332). Clymer Pubns.

Jorgensen, Eric, ed. BMW 500 & 600 cc Twins, 1955-1969: Service-Repair-Performance. (Illus.). pap. 13.95 (ISBN 0-89287-224-1, M308). Clymer Pubns.

--Honda: 100-350cc 4-OHC Singles 1969-1982--Service, Repair Performance. (Illus.). pap. 13.95 (ISBN 0-89287-184-9, M315). Clymer Pubns.

--Honda 125-200 cc Twins, 1964-1977: Service, Repair, Performance. (Illus.). pap. 13.95 (ISBN 0-89287-208-X, M321). Clymer Pubns.

Fountain, Paul. The Great Mountains & Forests of South America. 1976. lib. bdg. 59.95 (ISBN 0-8490-1902-8). Gordon Pr.

Gautrat, Jacques. Dictionnaire de la Montagne. (Fr.). 256p. 1970. pap. 8.95 (ISBN 0-686-56820-6, M-6598). French & Eur.

Hsu, K. J. Mountain Building Processes. 1983. 72.50 (ISBN 0-12-357980-5). Acad Pr.

Ives, Jack D. & Barry, Roger G. Arctic & Alpine Environments. LC 74-2673. (Illus.). 980p. 1974. 134.00x (ISBN 0-416-65980-2, NO.2250). Methuen Inc.

Jerome, John. On Mountains: Thinking About Terrain. LC 78-24273. 1979. pap. 4.95 (ISBN 0-07-032535-9). McGraw.

Lyttleton, R. A. The Earth & Its Mountains. 206p. 1982. 44.95x (ISBN 0-471-10530-9, Pub. by Wiley-Interscience). Wiley.

Maeder, Herbert. Mountains of Switzerland. 1968. 15.95 (ISBN 0-04-914039-6). Allen Unwin.

Mainwaring, William L. Exploring Oregon's Central & Southern Cascades. LC 79-64841. (Illus.). 1979. pap. 7.95 (ISBN 0-918832-02-0). Westridge.

Morse, Randy. The Mountains of Canada. LC 78-71667. (Illus.). 1979. 27.50 (ISBN 0-916890-74-0). Mountaineers.

Peattie, Roderick. Mountain Geography: A Critique & Field Study. Repr. of 1936 ed. lib. bdg. 22.50x (ISBN 0-8371-2243-0, PEMG). Greenwood.

Perkis, Philip, photos by. Warwick Mountain Series. LC 78-61647. (Illus.). 1978. 24.00x (ISBN 0-932526-01-2). Nexus Pr.

Prater, Yvonne. Snoqualmie Pass: From Indian Trail to Interstate. (Illus.). 176p. (Orig.). 1981. pap. 8.95 (ISBN 0-89886-015-6). Mountaineers.

Pyatt, Edward. Guinness Book of Mountains & Mountaineering Facts & Feats. (Guinness Superlatives Ser.). (Illus.). 256p. 1980. 14.95 (ISBN 0-900424-49-4, Pub. by Guinness Superlatives England). Sterling.

Reese, Rick, ed. Montana Mountain Ranges. (Montana Geographic Series: No. 1). 100p. 1981. pap. write for info. (ISBN 0-938314-01-7). MT Mag.

Rowell, Galen. High & Wild: A Mountaineer's World. LC 79-13000. (Illus.). 160p. 1979. 29.95 (ISBN 0-87156-263-4). Sierra.

Tianshan Mountains. 1980. 20.00 (ISBN 0-8351-0738-8). China Bks.

Wheelock, Walt. Southern California Peaks. (Illus.). 1973. wrappers 1.95 (ISBN 0-910856-32-X). La Siesta.

Wheelock, Walt, ed. Desert Peaks Guide One. rev. ed. (Illus.). 1985. wrappers 2.50 (ISBN 0-910856-03-6). La Siesta.

MOUSE

see Mice

MOUTH

Bosma, James F. Oral Sensation & Perception: Second Symposium. (Illus.). 580p. 1970. photocopy ed. 54.50x (ISBN 0-398-00194-4). C C Thomas.

--Symposium on Oral Sensation & Perception. (Illus.). 376p. 1967. photocopy ed. 39.50x (ISBN 0-398-00193-6). C C Thomas.

--Third Symposium on Oral Sensation & Perception: The Mouth of the Infant. (Illus.). 484p. 1972. 58.75x (ISBN 0-398-02238-0). C C Thomas.

Cimasoni, G. Crevicular Fluid Updated. (Monographs in Oral Science: Vol. 12). (Illus.). viii, 152p. 1983. 49.50 (ISBN 3-8055-3705-0). S Karger.

Frank, R. M. & Leach, S. A., eds. Surface & Colloid Phenomena in the Oral Cavity: Methodological Aspects. Proceedings. (Illus.). 288p. 1982. pap. 34.00 (ISBN 0-904147-36-3). IRL Pr.

Gartner, Leslie P. Essentials of Oral Histology & Embryology. LC 82-90755. (Illus.). 120p. 1982. pap. text ed. 8.75 (ISBN 0-910841-00-4). Jen Hse Pub Co.

Goldberg, Hyman J. & Ripa, Louis W. Oral Hygiene in Oral Health. (Illus.). 408p. 1977. photocopy ed. 44.50x (ISBN 0-398-03590-3). C C Thomas.

Jenkins, G. Neil. The Physiology & Biochemistry of the Mouth. 4th ed. (Illus.). 608p. 1978. 42.50 (ISBN 0-632-00138-0, B 2438X, Blackwell). Mosby.

Kutscher, Austin H. & Goldberg, Ivan K. Oral Care of the Aging & Dying Patient. (Illus.). 236p. 1973. 27.50x (ISBN 0-398-02714-5). C C Thomas.

Lazzari, Eugene P., ed. CRC Handbook of Experimental Aspects of Oral Biochemistry. 384p. 1983. 98.00 (ISBN 0-8493-3162-5). CRC Pr.

Levy, B. M. Handbook of Experimental Stomatology. 224p. 1982. 59.00 (ISBN 0-8493-3161-7). CRC Pr.

Melfi, Rudy C. Permar's Oral Embryology & Microscopic Anatomy: A Textbook for Students in Dental Hygiene. 7th ed. LC 82-240. (Illus.). 206p. 1982. text ed. 15.00 (ISBN 0-8121-0835-3). Lea & Febiger.

Myers, H. M. Reprinted Selected Top Articles Published 1977, No. 1. (Karger Highlights, Oral Science One). 1979. 9.00 (ISBN 3-8055-3028-5). S Karger.

Perryman, James H., ed. Oral Physiology & Occlusion: An International Symposium. LC 78-17812. 268p. 1979. 35.00 (ISBN 0-08-023183-7). Pergamon.

Slavkin, Harold C. & Bavetta, Lucien A., eds. Developmental Aspects of Oral Biology. 1972. 82.00 (ISBN 0-12-648350-7). Acad Pr.

MOVEMENTS OF ANIMALS

see Animal Locomotion; Animal Mechanics

MOVEMENTS OF PLANTS

see Plants–Irritability and Movements

MOVIE CAMERAS

see Moving-Picture Cameras

MOVING PHOTOMICROGRAPHY

see Microcinematography

MOVING-PICTURE CAMERAS

Cermak. How to Repair Your Own 35mm Camera. 224p. 1981. o.p 14.95 (ISBN 0-8306-9637-7); pap. 10.25 (ISBN 0-8306-1270-X, 1270). TAB Bks.

Gaunt, Leonard. Focalguide to 35mm SLR. 2nd ed. (Focalguide Ser.). (Illus.). 208p. 1984. pap. cancelled (ISBN 0-240-51213-8). Focal Pr.

How to Use Your 35mm Camera. 1981. 2.50 (ISBN 0-88284-140-8). Alfred Pub.

Lipton, L. Super Eight Book. 1975. 9.95 (ISBN 0-671-22082-9, Fireside). S&S.

McGinty, Gerald P. Video Cameras: Theory & Servicing. LC 84-50791. 264p. 1984. pap. 14.95 (ISBN 0-672-22382-1, 22382). Sams.

Samuelson, David. Motion Picture Camera & Lighting Equipment. (Media Manual Ser.). (Illus.). 220p. 1977. pap. 14.95 (ISBN 0-240-50948-X). Focal Pr.

--Motion Picture Camera & Lighting Equipment. (Media Manuals Ser.). 1977. pap. 8.95 (ISBN 0-8038-4685-1). Hastings.

--Motion Picture Camera Techniques. (Media Manual Ser.). (Illus.). 1978. pap. 14.95 (ISBN 0-240-50982-X). Focal Pr.

Samuelson, David W. Motion Picture Camera Data. (Media Manual Ser.). (Illus.). 172p. 1979. pap. 14.95 (ISBN 0-240-50998-6). Focal Pr.

Souto, H. Mario. The Technique of the Motion Picture Camera. 4th., rev., enl. ed. (Library of Communication Techniques Ser.). (Illus.). 1982. 41.95 (ISBN 0-240-51123-9). Focal Pr.

MOVING-PICTURE EDITING

see Moving-Pictures–Editing

MOVING-PICTURES–EDITING

Burder, J. Technique of Editing Sixteen Millimeter Films. 4th ed. (Illus.). 152p. 1979. 25.95 (ISBN 0-240-51019-4). Focal Pr.

Burder, John. Sixteen Millimeter Film Cutting. (Media Manual Ser.). (Illus.). 160p. 1975. pap. 14.95 (ISBN 0-240-50857-2). Focal Pr.

Daley, Ken. Basic Film Technique. (Media Manual Series). (Illus.). 160p. 1980. pap. 14.95 (ISBN 0-240-51016-X). Focal Pr.

Dmytryk, Edward. On Film Editing. (Illus.). 152p. (Orig.). 1984. pap. 9.95 (ISBN 0-240-51738-5). Focal Pr.

Reisz, Karel & Millar, Gavin. Technique of Film Editing. 2nd, enl. ed. (Library of Communication Techniques Ser). (Illus.). 426p. (Orig.). 1968. pap. text ed. 16.95 (ISBN 0-240-50846-7). Focal Pr.

Walter, Ernest. Technique of the Film Cutting Room. 2nd ed. (Library of Communication Techniques Ser.). (Illus.). 320p. 1973. 35.95 (ISBN 0-240-50657-X). Focal Pr.

MOVING-PICTURES–SPECIAL EFFECTS

see Cinematography, Trick

MOWING MACHINES

see also Harvesting Machinery

Halford, David G. Old Lawnmowers. (Shire Album Ser.: No. 91). (Illus.). 32p. pap. 2.95 (ISBN 0-85263-607-5, Pub. by Shire Pubns England). Seven Hills Bks.

MS-DOS (COMPUTER OPERATING SYSTEM)

De Voney, Chris. MS-DOS User's Guide. 330p. 1984. pap. 16.95 (ISBN 0-88022-061-9, 20). Que Corp.

Hoenig, Alan. Guide to PC & MS DOS. (Microcomputer Bookshelf Ser.). 1985. pap. 15.95 (ISBN 0-316-36812-1). Little.

Hoffman, Paul & Nicoloff, Tamara. The Osborne McGraw-Hill MS-DOS User's Guide. 250p. (Orig.). 1984. 17.95 (ISBN 0-07-881131-7, 131-7). Osborne-McGraw.

Hubbard, John D. MS-DOS. (Illus.). 376p. 1984. 99.95 (ISBN 0-87119-088-5, EC-1121). Heathkit-Zenith Ed.

Human Connection. Making MS-DOS & PC-DOS Work for You. 19.95 (ISBN 0-8306-0848-6); pap. 13.95 (ISBN 0-8306-1848-1). TAB Bks.

Immers, Richard & Neufeld, Gerald. Inside Commodore DOS. (Illus., Orig.). 1984. pap. 19.95 (ISBN 0-88190-366-3, BO366). Datamost.

King, Richard A. The MS-DOS Handbook. LC 84-50354. 320p. 1984. pap. 16.95 (ISBN 0-89588-185-3). SYBEX.

Microtrend Inc. & Jackson, Charles H. MS-DOS & PC-DOS on the IBM PC. (Microtrend Ser.). 1984. 14.95 (ISBN 0-13-604281-3). P-H.

Norton, Peter. MS-DOS & PC-DOS User's Guide. LC 83-15498. (Illus.). 288p. 1983. pap. 15.95 (ISBN 0-89303-645-5). Brady Comm.

O'Day, Kate. Discovering MS-DOS. Date not set. 15.95 (ISBN 0-672-22407-0, 22407). Sams.

Shaw, Myril C. & Shaw, Susan S. Essential PC-DOS. LC 84-51218. 300p. 1985. pap. 15.95 (ISBN 0-89588-176-4). SYBEX.

Sollarzano, Henry. Quick & Easy PC-DOS & MS-DOS. 1984. pap. 3.50 (ISBN 0-88284-327-3). Alfred Pub.

Stultz, Russell. The Illustrated MS-PC-DOS Book. (Illus.). 224p. 1984. pap. 16.95 (ISBN 0-13-451063-1). P-H.

Stultz, Russell A. The Illustrated MS-PC-DOS Book. Berliner, Thomas H., ed. LC 84-22213. (Illus.). 240p. 1985. pap. 15.95 (ISBN 0-915381-53-2). WordWare Pub.

Weber Systems Inc. Staff. MS-DOS 3.0 User's Handbook. 300p. 1985. pap. 17.95 (ISBN 0-317-19097-0). Weber Systems.

Wolverton, Van. Running MS-DOS: The Microsoft Guide to Getting the Most Out of the Standard Operating System for the IBM PC & 50 Other Personal Computers. (Illus.). 384p. 1984. pap. 19.95 (ISBN 0-914845-07-1). Microsoft.

MSX (COMPUTER)

Hartnell, Tim. How to Program Your MSX Computer. (Orig.). 1985. pap. 7.95 (ISBN 0-345-32691-1). Ballantine.

Hoffman, Paul. The MSX Book. 224p. (Orig.). 1985. pap. 15.95 (ISBN 0-07-881172-4, 172-4). Osborne McGraw.

Pritchard, Joe. MSX Exposed. (Illus.). 226p. (Orig.). 1984. pap. 15.95 (ISBN 0-86161-182-9). Melbourne Hse.

Sato, Toshiyuki, et al. The Complete MSX Programmer's Guide. (Illus.). 568p. (Orig.). 1984. pap. 39.95. Melbourne Hse.

Wood, Robert C. The MSX Standard: The New Computers. (Illus.). 192p. (Orig.). 1985. 21.95 (ISBN 0-8306-0907-5, 1907); pap. 14.95 (ISBN 0-8306-1907-0). TAB Bks.

MU MESONS

see Muons

MUCK

see Humus

MUCORALES

Benjamin, Richard K. The Merosporangiferous Mucorales. (Bibl. Myco.). (Illus.). 1967. Repr. of 1965 ed. 21.00 (ISBN 3-7682-0514-2). Lubrecht & Cramer.

Zycha, H. & Siepmann, R. Mucorales. (Illus.). 35.00 (ISBN 3-7682-0145-7). Lubrecht & Cramer.

MUCOPOLYSACCHARIDES

Ragin, Douglas. Hearthrobs. 1984. 6.95 (ISBN 0-533-06052-4). Vantage.

MUCORINEAE

Blakeslee, A. F. Sexual Reproduction in the Mucorinaeae. (Biblioteca Mycologica Ser: No. 48). 1976. Repr. of 1904 ed. text ed. 14.00 (ISBN 3-7682-1064-2). Lubrecht & Cramer.

MUD-LADEN FLUIDS

see Drilling Muds

MUDS, DRILLING

see Drilling Muds

MUIR, JOHN, 1838-1914

Bade, William F. Life & Letters of John Muir, 2 Vols. LC 77-153302. (BCL Ser.: No. I). Repr. of 1924 ed. Set. 65.00 (ISBN 0-404-00444-X); cancelled. Vol. 1 (ISBN 0-404-08001-4). Vol. 2 (ISBN 0-404-08002-2). AMS Pr.

Clarke, James M. The Life & Adventures of John Muir. new ed. LC 79-64178. (Illus.). 1979. 14.95 (ISBN 0-932238-01-7, Pub. by Avant Bks). Slawson Comm.

--The Life & Adventures of John Muir. LC 79-64178. (Sierra Club Paperback Library Ser.). (Illus.). 338p. 1980. pap. 7.95 (ISBN 0-87156-241-3). Sierra.

Cohen, Michael P. The Pathless Way: John Muir & American Wilderness. LC 83-40260. 500p. 1984. 25.00 (ISBN 0-299-09720-X). U of Wis Pr.

Emanuels, George. John Muir Inventor. LC 85-60102. (Illus.). 1985. 16.50 (ISBN 0-914330-74-8); deluxe ed. 22.50. Diablo Bks.

Engberg, Robert, ed. John Muir to Yosemite & Beyond: Writings from the Years 1863-1875. Wesling, Donald. (Illus.). 194p. 1980. 21.50x (ISBN 0-299-08270-9); pap. 7.95 (ISBN 0-299-08274-1). U of Wis Pr.

Fox, Stephen R. John Muir & His Legacy: The American Conservation Movement. (Illus.). 416p. 1981. 22.00 (ISBN 0-316-29110-2). Little.

Jones, Dewitt, photos by. John Muir's America. LC 75-30536. (Illus.). 160p. (Text by T. H. Watkins). 1981. pap. 12.95 (ISBN 0-912856-64-5). Graphic Arts Ctr.

Lyon, Thomas J. John Muir. LC 72-619587. (Western Writers Ser: No. 3). (Illus.). 48p. (Orig.). 1972. pap. 2.00x (ISBN 0-88430-002-1). Boise St Univ.

Melham, Tom. John Muir's Wild America. LC 76-687. (Special Publications Ser: No. 11). (Illus.). 200p. 1976. 6.95 (ISBN 0-87044-186-8); lib. bdg. 8.50 (ISBN 0-87044-191-4). Natl Geog.

Muir, John. Letters to a Friend. LC 15-5890. 194p. 1973. 10.95 (ISBN 0-910220-48-4). Berg.

--My First Summer in the Sierra. 1979. pap. 8.95 (ISBN 0-395-28521-6). HM.

--Rambles of a Botanist among the Plants & Climates of California. Kimes, William F., intro. by. (Illus.). 43p. 1974. 10.00 (ISBN 0-87093-301-9). Dawsons.

--Travels in Alaska. LC 77-19358. 1979. pap. 7.95 (ISBN 0-395-28522-4). HM.

Smith, Herbert F. John Muir. (Twayne's United States Authors Ser). 1964. pap. 5.95x (ISBN 0-8084-0186-6, T73, Twayne). New Coll U Pr.

Wolfe, Linnie M. Son of the Wilderness: The Life of John Muir. LC 78-53294. (Illus.). 398p. 1978. 27.50x (ISBN 0-299-07730-6); pap. 10.95 (ISBN 0-299-07734-9). U of Wis Pr.

Young, S. Hall. Alaska Days with John Muir. LC 74-174351. (Illus.). Repr. of 1915 ed. 17.00 (ISBN 0-405-09110-9). Ayer Co Pubs.

MULCHING

Davies, J. W. Mulching Effects on Plant Climate & Yield. (Technical Note Ser.: No. 136). xii, 118p. 1975. pap. 20.00 (ISBN 92-63-10388-7, W159, WMO). Unipub.

Mulches. 2.25 (ISBN 0-686-21125-1). Bklyn Botanic.

Stout, Ruth. Gardening Without Work. (Illus.). 1961. Devin.

MULE DEER

Wallmo, Olof C., ed. Mule & Black-Tailed Deer of North America. LC 80-20128. (Illus.). xviii, 605p. 1981. 29.95 (ISBN 0-8032-4715-X). U of Nebr Pr.

MULES

Helmstrom, J. G. Scientific Horse, Mule & Ox Shoeing. (Shorey Lost Arts Ser.). (Illus.). 122p. pap. 8.95 (ISBN 0-8466-6029-6, U29). Shorey.

Savory, T. H. The Mule. 1979. 20.00x (ISBN 0-900541-81-4, Pub. by Meadowfield Pr England). State Mutual Bk.

Telleen, Maurice. Draft Horse Primer. LC 77-898. 400p. 1977. 14.95 (ISBN 0-87857-161-2). Rodale Pr Inc.

MULTICOMPONENT FLOW

see Multiphase Flow

MULTIMACHINE ASSIGNMENTS

see Methods Engineering

MULTIMATE (COMPUTER PROGRAM)

Barnes, Kate. Using MultiMate. LC 84-60141. 280p. 1985. 16.95 (ISBN 0-88022-114-3, 116). Que Corp.

Dreger, Carol H. The Complete Guide to MultiMate. 208p. 1984. pap. 15.95 (ISBN 0-89588-229-9). SYBEX.

Puotinen, C. J. Using the IBM Personal Computer: MultiMate. 352p. 1984. pap. 20.45 (ISBN 0-03-071411-7). HR&W.

Scanlon, Leo J. MultiMate on the IBM PC. (Illus.). 192p. 1985. pap. 16.95 (ISBN 0-89303-677-3). Brady Comm.

Stone, Paula S. & Berliner, Thomas H. The Illustrated MultiMate Book. (Illus.). 240p. 1985. pap. 16.95 (ISBN 0-915381-64-8). WordWare Pub.

Woody, Marcia K. The Software Primer MultiMate. Harper, Larry D., ed. (Software Primer Ser.). 180p. 1984. binder cancelled (ISBN 0-913871-09-5). JNZ.

MULTIPHASE FLOW

see also Two-Phase Flow

American Society of Mechanical Enginners. Measurement in Polyphase Flows: Papers Presented at the Winter Annual Meeting of the American Society of Mechanical Engineers, San Francisco, California, Dec. 10-15, 1978. Stock, David E., ed. LC 78-68328. pap. 32.80 (ISBN 0-317-08555-7, 2051712). Bks Demand UMI.

Bajura, R. A., ed. Polyphase Flow & Transport Technology. 270p. 1980. 40.00 (ISBN 0-686-69858-4, H00158). ASME.

Cooper, Paul, ed. Polyphase Flow in Turbomachinery. 1978. 40.00 (ISBN 0-685-66809-6, H00123). ASME.

Govier, George W. & Aziz, Khalid. The Flow of Complex Mixture in Pipes. LC 77-2591. 842p. 1977. Repr. of 1972 ed. 55.50 (ISBN 0-88275-547-1). Krieger.

Greenkorn. Flow Phenomena. (Energy, Power & Environment Ser.). 520p. 1983. 75.00 (ISBN 0-8247-1861-5). Dekker.

Hammitt, Frederick G. Cavitation & Multiphase Flow Phenomena. 448p. 1980. text ed. 80.00 (ISBN 0-07-025907-0). McGraw.

Heidrick, T. R., ed. Measurement in Polyphase Flows-Nineteen Eighty-Two. 129p. 30.00 (G00209). ASME.

Hetsroni, G. Handbook of Multiphase Systems. 1024p. 1981. 69.50 (ISBN 0-07-028460-1). McGraw.

Goodman, Leo A. Analyzing Qualitative Categorical Data: Log-Linear Models & Latent-Strucutre Analysis. Magidson, Jay, ed. 1978. text ed. 28.00 (ISBN 0-89011-513-3). Abt Bks.
--Analyzing Qualitative-Categorical Date: Log-Linear Models & Latent Structure Analysis. Magidson, Jay & Davis, James A., eds. 484p. 1984. Repr. of 1978 ed. lib. bdg. 32.50 (ISBN 0-8191-4105-4). U Pr of Amer.
Gordon, A. D. Classification: Methods for the Exploratory Analysis of Multivariate Data. 240p. 1981. 27.50 (ISBN 0-412-22850-5, NO.6547, Pub. by Chapman & Hall). Methuen Inc.
Green, Paul E. Analyzing Multivariate Data. 1978. text ed. 36.95 (ISBN 0-03-020786-X). Dryden Pr.
Green, Paul E. & Carroll, Douglas. Mathematical Tools for Applied Multivariate Analysis: Student Edition. 1978. 27.50 (ISBN 0-12-297552-9). Acad Pr.
Green, Paul E., ed. Mathematical Tools for Applied Multivariate Analysis. 1976. 59.50 (ISBN 0-12-297550-2). Acad Pr.
Gupta, R. P., ed. Multivariate Statistical Analysis: Proceedings of the Conference Held at Dalhousie University, Halifax, Nova Scotia, Canada, October 1979. 290p. 1980. 68.00 (ISBN 0-444-86019-3, North-Holland). Elsevier.
Hair, Joseph F., Jr., et al. Multivariate Data Analysis with Reading. 353p. 1979. text ed. write for info. (ISBN 0-02-349000-4). Macmillan.
Hamburg, Morris. Statistical Analysis for Decision Making. 3rd ed. 829p. 1983. 29.95 (ISBN 0-15-583450-9, HC); solutions manual avail. (ISBN 0-15-583451-7). HarBraceJ.
Harnett, D. L. & Murphy, J. L. Introductory Statistical Analysis. 2nd ed. 1980. 35.95 (ISBN 0-201-02758-5); student's wkbk. 9.95 (ISBN 0-201-02859-X); instructor's manual 2.95 (ISBN 0-201-02759-3). Addison-Wesley.
Harnett, Donald L. & Murphy, James L. Statistical Analysis for Business & Economics. 3rd ed. 1985. text ed. 32.95 (ISBN 0-201-10683-3). Addison Wesley.
Harris, Richard J. A Primer of Multivariate Statistics. 1975. text ed. 22.50i (ISBN 0-12-327250-5). Acad Pr.
--A Primer of Multivariate Statistics. 2nd ed. Date not set. text ed. 25.00i (ISBN 0-12-327252-1). Acad Pr.
Hartigan, John A. Clustering Algorithms. LC 74-14573. (Wiley Series in Probability & Mathematical Statistics). pap. 69.40 (ISBN 0-317-09401-7, 2019502). Bks Demand UMI.
Hawkins, D. M., ed. Topics in Applied Multivariate Analysis. LC 81-15527. (Illus.). 320p. 1981. 29.95 (ISBN 0-521-24368-8). Cambridge U Pr.
Hilton, Gordon. Intermediate Politometrics. LC 75-43733. 336p. 1976. 26.00x (ISBN 0-231-03783-X). Columbia U Pr.
Hirschberg, Nancy & Humphreys, Lloyd G. Multivariate Applications in the Social Sciences. 304p. 1982. text ed. 29.95x (ISBN 0-89859-152-X). L Erlbaum Assocs.
Hope, K. Methods of Multivariate Analysis. 288p. 1978. 56.75 (ISBN 0-677-61360-1). Gordon.
IFAC Symposium, 2nd, Indiana, USA, Sept. 1982 & Leininger, G. G. Computer Aided Design of Multivariate Technological Systems: Proceedings. (IFAC Proceedings Ser.). 632p. 1983. 150.00 (ISBN 0-08-029357-3). Pergamon.
Jacobs, F. Robert, ed. Computer Applications. (Core Business Program Ser.). (Illus.). 128p. Date not set. pap. 7.95 (ISBN 0-87196-801-0). Facts on File.
Jacobson, M. Statistical Analysis of Counting Processes. (Lecture Notes in Statistics Ser.: Vol. 12). 226p. 1982. pap. 17.00 (ISBN 0-387-90769-6). Springer-Verlag.
Jaech, J. L. Statistical Analysis of Measurement Errors. (Exxon Monographs). 1985. 29.95 (ISBN 0-471-82731-2). Wiley.
Johnson. Multivariate Statistical Simulation. (Probability & Mathematical Statistics Ser.). Date not set. price not set (ISBN 0-471-82290-6). Wiley.
Johnson, Richard A. & Wichern, Dean W. Applied Multivariate Statistical Analysis. 750p. 1982. 42.95 (ISBN 0-13-041400-X). P-H.
Johnston, R. J. Multivariate Statistical Analysis in Geography: A Primer of the General Linear Model. (Illus.). 1980. 13.95x (ISBN 0-582-30034-7). Longman.
Kachigan, Sam K. Multivariate Statistical Analysis: A Conceptual Introduction. LC 81-85445. (Illus.). 297p. 1982. text ed. 19.95x (ISBN 0-942154-00-2). Radius Pr.
Karson, Marvin J. Multivariate Statistical Methods: An Introduction. 320p. 1982. text ed. 24.95x (ISBN 0-8138-1845-1). Iowa St U Pr.
Kendall, Maurice. Multivariate Analysis. 2nd ed. (Griffin Statistical Monograph). 1980. 29.95 (ISBN 0-02-847790-1). Macmillan.
Kres, H. Statistical Tables for Multivariate Analysis: A Handbook with References to Applications. Wadsack, P., tr. (Springer Series in Statistics). (Illus.). 530p. 1983. 58.00 (ISBN 0-387-90909-5). Springer Verlag.
Krishnaiah. Multivariate Analysis: Proceedings of Third International Symposium. 1973. 86.50 (ISBN 0-12-426653-3). Acad Pr.
Krishnaiah, P. R. Analysis of Variance. (Handbook of Statistics Ser.: Vol. 1). 1002p. 1981. 115.00 (ISBN 0-444-85335-9, North-Holland). Elsevier.
--Multivariate Analysis V: Proceedings of the 5th International Symposium. 678p. 1980. 85.00 (ISBN 0-444-85321-9, North-Holland). Elsevier.
Krishnaiah, P. R., ed. Multivariate Analysis IV: Proceedings of the International Symposium, 4th, Wright State University, June, 1975. 550p. 1977. 85.00 (ISBN 0-7204-0520-3, North-Holland). Elsevier.
--Multivariate Analysis VI: Proceedings of the International Symposium, 6th, 25-29 July, 1983. 648p. 1985. 95.00 (ISBN 0-444-87602-2, North-Holland). Elsevier.
Kshirsagar, A. M. Multivariate Analysis. (Statistics Textbks & Monographs: Vol. 2). 1972. 65.00 (ISBN 0-8247-1386-9). Dekker.
Lawlis, G. Frank & Chatfield, Douglas. Multivariate Approaches for the Behavioral Sciences: A Brief Text. (Illus.). 153p. (Orig.). 1974. pap. text ed. 5.00 (ISBN 0-89672-051-9). Tex Tech Pr.
Layton, J. M. Multivariable Control Theory. (IEE Control Engineering Ser.: No. 1). (Illus.). 247p. 1976. 46.00 (ISBN 0-901223-89-1, CE001). Inst Elect Eng.
Lindeman, Richard, et al. Introduction to Bivariate & Multivariate Analysis. 1980. text ed. 26.65x (ISBN 0-673-15099-2). Scott F.
MacFarlane, A. G. Complex Variable Methods for Linear Multivariate Feedback Systems. 1981. 39.50x (ISBN 0-85066-197-8, NO.6463, Pub. by Taylor & Francis). Methuen Inc.
McKay, David, et al, eds. Data Analysis & the Social Sciences. 300p. 1983. pap. 11.95 (ISBN 0-86187-218-5). F Pinter Pubs.
Mardia, K. V., et al. Multivariate Analysis. LC 79-40922. (Probability and Mathematical Statistics Ser.). 1980. 75.00 (ISBN 0-12-471250-9); pap. 39.50 (ISBN 0-12-471252-5). Acad Pr.
Meek, Gary E. & Turner, Stephen J. Statistical Analysis for Business Decisions. 768p. 1983. text ed. 32.50 (ISBN 0-395-32274-X); instr's. manual 2.00 (ISBN 0-395-32825-X); solutions manual avail. (ISBN 0-395-34549-9). HM.
Morrison, D. F. Multivariate Statistical Methods. 2nd ed. 1976. 42.95 (ISBN 0-07-043186-8). McGraw.
Morrison, Donald F. Applied Linear Statistical Methods. 544p. 1983. 42.95 (ISBN 0-13-041020-9). P-H.
Norcliffe, G. B. Inferential Statistics for Geographers. 2nd ed. (Illus.). 272p. 1983. text ed. 15.00x (ISBN 0-09-149811-2). Sheridan.
O'Muircheartaigh, Colm A. & Payne, Clive, eds. The Analysis of Survey Data, 2 vols. LC 76-951. 1977. Vol. 1 Exploring Data Structures. 62.95x (ISBN 0-471-01706-X); Vol. 2 Model Fitting. 63.95x (ISBN 0-471-99426-X); Set. 126.00x (ISBN 0-471-99466-9, Pub. by Wiley-Interscience). Wiley.
Orloci, L., et al, eds. Multivariate Methods in Ecological Work. (Statistical Ecology Ser.: Vol. 7). 580p. 1980. 50.00 (ISBN 0-89974-004-9). Intl Co-Op.
Overall, John E. & Klett, C. James. Applied Multivariate Analysis. LC 81-20944. 522p. 1983. Repr. of 1972 ed. lib. bdg. 34.50 (ISBN 0-89874-325-7). Krieger.
Owens, D. H. Feedback & Multivariable Systems. (IEE Control Engineering Ser.: No. 7). (Illus.). 320p. 1978. 56.00 (ISBN 0-906048-03-6, CE007). Inst Elect Eng.
Parsons, Robert. Statistical Analysis: A Decision Making Approach. 2nd ed. 1978. text ed. 29.50 scp (ISBN 0-06-045016-9, HarpC); scp student solutions manual 5.95 (ISBN 0-06-045017-7). Har-Row.
Press, S. James. Applied Multivariate Analysis. 2nd ed. LC 80-26922. 624p. 1982. 31.50 (ISBN 0-88275-976-0). Krieger.
Price, G. B. Multivariable Analysis. (Illus.). 995p. 1984. 39.00 (ISBN 0-387-90934-6). Springer Verlag.
Ramsdell, Earl W. The Practical Application of Statistical Analysis in the Industrial Process. 81p. 1981. soft cover 44.95 (ISBN 0-89852-390-7, 01-01-R090). TAPPI.
Reyment, Richard, et al. Multivariate Morphometrics. 2nd ed. 1984. 33.00 (ISBN 0-12-586970-3). Acad Pr.
Rizvi, S. F. Multivariate Control System Design in the Presence of Interaction, 1978. 1981. 50.00x (ISBN 0-686-97119-1, Pub. by W Spring England). State Mutual Bk.
Roberts, Harry V. Interactive Data Analysis. Holden-Day.
Royce, Joseph R., ed. Multivariate Analysis & Psychological Theory. 1973. 84.50 (ISBN 0-12-600750-0). Acad Pr.
Schempp, W. & Zeller, K., eds. Multivariate Approximation Theory. (Internationale Schriftenreihe zur Numerischen Mathematik: No. 51). (Illus.). 455p. 1979. pap. text ed. 43.95x (ISBN 0-8176-1102-9). Birkhauser.
Schempp, Walter & Zeller, Karl, eds. Multivariate Approximation Theory Two. (International Series of Numerical Mathematics Ser.: Vol. 61). 1982. text ed. 36.95x (ISBN 0-8176-1373-0). Birkhauser.
Seber, G. F. Multivariate Observations. LC 83-21741. (Probability & Mathematical Statistics Ser.: 1-345). 686p. 1984. 49.00x (ISBN 0-471-88104-X, Pub. by Wiley-Interscience). Wiley.
Shaw, G. & Wheeler, D. Statistical Techniques in Geographical Analysis. 364p. 1985. 44.95 (ISBN 0-471-10317-9). Wiley.
Sheth, J. Multivariate Methods for Market & Survey Research. LC 76-39893. 388p. 1977. 20.00 (ISBN 0-87757-081-7). Am Mktg.
Shinskey, F. G. Controlling Multivariable Processes: An Independent Learning Module of the Instrument Society of America. LC 81-81497. 250p. 1981. text ed. 39.95x (ISBN 0-87664-529-5). Instru Soc.
Shvyrkov, V. Statistical Analysis of Data-Set Quality. LC 85-20211. (Illus.). 190p. (Orig.). 1985. pap. text ed. 33.10 (ISBN 0-942004-13-2). G Throwkoff.
Sinha. Multivariable Control: An Introduction. (Electrical Engineering Ser.). 464p. 1984. 39.75 (ISBN 0-8247-1858-5). Dekker.
Siotani, Minoru & Hayakawa, T. Modern Multivariate Statistical Analysis: A Graduate Course & Handbook. LC 82-72549. (The American Sciences Press Series in Mathematical & Management Sciences: Vol. 9). 1985. text ed. 39.50 (ISBN 0-935950-06-0). Am Sciences Pr.
SPSS Inc. Staff & Norusis, Marija J. SPSS PC: SPSS for the IBM-PC XT. LC 84-42824. 576p. (Orig.). 1984. pap. 34.95 (ISBN 0-918469-00-7). SPSS Inc.
Srivastava, M. S. & Carter, E. M. Introduction to Applied Multivariate Statistics. 394p. 1983. 36.00 (ISBN 0-444-00621-4, North-Holland). Elsevier.
Srivastava, M. S. & Khatri, C. G. An Introduction to Multivariate Statistics. LC 78-21491. 350p. 1979. 33.50 (ISBN 0-444-00302-9, North Holland). Elsevier.
Subrahmaniam, Kocherlakota & Subrahmaniam, Kathleen. Multivariate Analysis: A Selected & Abstracted Bibliography. LC 73-90690. (Statistics Textbooks & Mongraphs: Vol 4). pap. 69.00 (ISBN 0-317-08363-5, 2055052). Bks Demand UMI.
Tatsuoka, Maurice M. Multivariate Analysis: Techniques for Educational & Psychological Research. LC 78-151729. 310p. 1971. 33.95 (ISBN 0-471-84590-6). Wiley.
Tong, Y. L. Probability Inequalities in Multivariate Distribution. LC 79-27077. (Probability & Mathematical Statistics Ser.). 1980. 41.50 (ISBN 0-12-694950-6). Acad Pr.
Tzafestas, S. G., ed. Multivariable Control. 1984. lib. bdg. 49.50 (ISBN 90-277-1829-6, Pub. by Reidel Holland). Kluwer Academic.
Wang, Peter C., ed. Graphical Representation of Multivariate Data. 1978. 37.50 (ISBN 0-12-734750-X). Acad Pr.
Warwick, Kenneth M. & Morineau, Alain. Multivariate Descriptive Statistical Analysis: Correspondence Analysis & Related Techniques for Large Matrices. LC 83-21904. (Probability & Mathematical Statistical-Applied Probability & StatisticSection Ser.: 1-346). 231p. 1984. 34.95x (ISBN 0-471-86743-8, 1-346, Pub. by Wiley-Interscience). Wiley.
Whitehous, Gary, ed. Microsoftware: Statistical Analysis. 1984. 175.00 (ISBN 0-89806-084-2). Inst Indus Eng.

MUNICIPAL ENGINEERING

see also Bridges; City Planning; Drainage; Refuse and Refuse Disposal; Sanitary Engineering; Sewerage; Shore Protection; Street Cleaning; Streets; Water-Supply

Schultz, Marilyn S. & Kasen, Vivian L. Encyclopedia of Community Planning & Environmental Protection. 400p. 1983. 45.00x (ISBN 0-87196-447-3). Facts on File.

MUNICIPAL TRANSPORTATION

see Urban Transportation

MUNITIONS

see also Armaments; Firearms Industry and Trade; Weapons Systems

Cromwell, Giles. The Virginia Manufactory of Arms. LC 74-8802. 1975. 20.00 (ISBN 0-8139-0573-7). U Pr of Va.
Farley, Philip J., et al. Arms Across the Sea. LC 77-91804. 1978. 22.95 (ISBN 0-8157-2746-1); pap. 8.95 (ISBN 0-8157-2745-3). Brookings.
Gorgol, John F. The Military-Industrial Firm: A Practical Theory & Model. LC 75-170024. (Special Studies in U.S. Economic, Social, & Political Issues). 1972. 29.50x (ISBN 0-275-28229-5); pap. text ed. 12.50x (ISBN 0-89197-848-8). Irvington.
Goulden, Joseph C. & Raffio, Alexander W. The Death Merchant: The Rise & Fall of Edwin P. Wilson. LC 84-5547. 453p. 1984. 17.95 (ISBN 0-671-49341-8). S&S.
Improvised Munitions Handbook. 1982. lib. bdg. 75.00 (ISBN 0-87700-428-5). Revisionist Pr.
Kuhn, Robert L., ed. Commercializing Defense Related Technology. LC 83-21379. 270p. 1982. 29.95x (ISBN 0-03-069717-4). Praeger.
Noel-Baker, Philip. The Private Manufacture of Armaments. LC 78-145399. 1971. pap. 7.00 (ISBN 0-486-22736-7). Dover.
Swearengen, Thomas F. Tear Gas Munitions: An Analysis of Commercial Riot Gas Guns, Tear Gas Projectiles, Grenades, Small Arms Ammunition & Related Tear Gas Devices. (Illus.). 596p. 1966. photocopy ed. 60.75x (ISBN 0-398-01888-X). C C Thomas.
Tuomi & Vayrynen. Militarization & Arms Production. LC 82-16882. 320p. 1983. 32.50 (ISBN 0-312-53255-5). St Martin.

MUONS

see also Mesons

Hughes, Vernon & Wu, C. S., eds. Muon Physics. Incl. Vol. 1. 67.50 (ISBN 0-12-360601-2); Vol. 2. Weak Interactions. 111.00 (ISBN 0-12-360602-0); Vol. 3. Chemistry & Solids. 80.00 (ISBN 0-12-360603-9). 1975. Set. 220.00. Acad Pr.
Massey, Harrie, et al. Electronic & Ionic Impact Phenomena: Slow Position & Muon Collisions & Notes on Recent Advances, Vol. 5. 2nd ed. (International Series of Monographs on Physics). (Illus.). 1974. 85.00x (ISBN 0-19-851283-X). Oxford U Pr.
Walker, David C. Muon & Muonium Chemistry. LC 82-23636. (Illus.). 200p. 1984. 49.50 (ISBN 0-521-24241-X). Cambridge U Pr.

MURIATIC ACID

see Hydrochloric Acid

MUSCIDAE

Skidmore, Peter. The Biology of the Muscidae of the World. (Entomlogica Ser.). 1985. lib. bdg. 105.00 (ISBN 90-6193-139-8, Pub. by Junk Pub Netherlands). Kluwer-Academic.

MUSCLE

see also Contractility (Biology)

Bagshaw, C. R. Muscle Contraction. 80p. 1982. pap. 7.50 (ISBN 0-412-13450-0, NO. 6432, Pub. by Chapman & Hall). Methuen Inc.
Biro. Symposium on the Muscle. 1976. 11.50 (ISBN 0-9960001-9-4, Pub. by Akademiai Kaido Hungary). Heyden.
Briskey, Ernest J., et al, eds. Physiology & Biochemistry of Muscle As a Food: Proceedings, 1965, 2 vols. (Illus.). 1966. Vol. 1. 50.00x (ISBN 0-299-04110-7); Vol. 2. 50.00x (ISBN 0-299-05680-5). U of Wis Pr.
Bulbring, E. & Shuba, M. F., eds. Physiology of Smooth Muscle. LC 75-14566. 448p. 1976. 59.50 (ISBN 0-89004-051-6). Raven.
Daniel, Edwine E. & Paton, David M. Methods in Pharmacology: Smooth Muscle, Vol. 3. (Illus.). 745p. 1975. 75.00x (ISBN 0-306-35263-X, Plenum Pr). Plenum Pub.
De Villafranca, George W. Driving Force: Muscle. LC 72-189425. (Katharine Asher Engel Lecture for 1971). (Illus.). 1972. pap. 1.50 (ISBN 0-87391-010-9). Smith Coll.
Dowben, Robert M. & Shay, Jerry W., eds. Cell & Muscle Motility, Vol. 1. 414p. 1981. 45.00x (ISBN 0-306-40703-5, Plenum Pr). Plenum Pub.
--Cell & Muscle Motility, Vol. 2. 327p. 1982. text ed. 39.50 (ISBN 0-306-40798-1, Plenum Pr). Plenum Pub.
Ebashi, S., et al, eds. Muscle Contraction: Its Regulatory Mechanism. 549p. 1980. 69.50 (ISBN 0-387-10411-9). Springer-Verlag.
Forrest, John C., et al. Principles of Meat Science. LC 75-8543. (Food & Nutrition Ser.). (Illus.). 417p. 1975. text ed. 35.95 (ISBN 0-7167-0743-8). W H Freeman.
Grinnell, Alan D., et al, eds. The Regulation of Muscle Contraction: Excitation-Contraction Coupling. LC 81-4362. (UCLA Forum in Medical Sciences: Vol. 22). 1981. 35.00 (ISBN 0-12-303780-8). Acad Pr.
Gutmann, Ernest, ed. Denervated Muscle. 486p. 1962. 50.00x (ISBN 0-306-10653-1, Consultants). Plenum Pub.
Huddart, Henry. Comparative Structure & Function of Muscle. 1975. text ed. 66.00 (ISBN 0-08-017845-6). Pergamon.
Needham, Dorothy M. Machina Carnis: The Biochemistry of Muscular Contraction in Its Historical Development. (Illus.). 1972. 125.00 (ISBN 0-521-07974-8). Cambridge U Pr.
Sanadi, D. Rao, ed. Chemical Mechanisms in Bioenergetics. LC 76-26707. (ACS Monograph: 172). 1976. 33.95 (ISBN 0-8412-0274-5). Am Chemical.

Kreisel, H. Die Phytopathogehen Grosspilze Deutschlands (Basidiomycetes mit Ausschluss der Rost-und Brandpilze) (Illus.). 1979. Repr. of 1961 ed. lib. bdg. 17.50x (ISBN 3-7682-1228-9). Lubrecht & Cramer.

Krieger, L. C. Mushroom Handbook. (Illus.). 14.00 (ISBN 0-8446-2404-7). Peter Smith.

Krieger, Louis C. Mushroom Handbook. (Illus.). 1967. pap. 8.50 (ISBN 0-486-21861-9). Dover.

Lange & Hora. Collins Guide to Mushrooms & Toadstools. 29.95 (ISBN 0-00-219300-0, Collins Pub England). Greene.

Largent, David. How to Identify Mushrooms (to Genus I) Macroscopic Features. 2nd ed. (Illus.). 86p. 1977. pap. 4.95x (ISBN 0-916422-00-3). Mad River.

Largent, David, et al. How to Identify Mushrooms (to Genus III) Microscopic Features. (Illus.). 148p. 1977. pap. 8.95x (ISBN 0-916422-09-7). Mad River.

Largent, David L. & Thiers, H. How to Identify Mushrooms (to Genus II): Field Identification of Genera. (Illus.). 32p. 1977. pap. 3.95x (ISBN 0-916422-08-9). Mad River.

Lincoff, Gary. S&S Guide to Mushrooms. 1982. pap. 9.95 (ISBN 0-671-42849-7). S&S.

McIlvaine, Charles & MacAdam, Robert. One Thousand American Fungi. (Illus.). 729p. 1973. pap. 9.95 (ISBN 0-486-22782-0). Dover.

March, Andrew L. & March, Kathryn G. The Mushroom Basket: A Gourmet Introduction to the Best Common Mushrooms of the Southern Rocky Mountains, with Applications Throughout the Northern Hemisphere, & Tidbits of Mushroom Lore from Europe Russia & China. LC 82-90153. (Illus.). 162p. (Orig.). 1982. pap. 8.95 (ISBN 0-940206-02-1). Meridian Hill.

Marteka, Vincent. Mushrooms - Wild & Edible: A Seasonal Guide to the Most Easily Recognized Mushrooms. (Illus.). 1980. 19.95 (ISBN 0-393-01356-1). Norton.

Michael, E. Handbuch fuer Pilzfreunde: Vol.1: Die wichtiggsten...Pilze. Kreisel, H., ed. (German., Illus.). 392p. 1978. text ed. 26.75x (ISBN 3-437-30346-5). Lubrecht & Cramer.

--Handbuch fuer Pilzfreunde: Vol.3: Blaetterpilze, Hellblaettler & Leistlings. Kreisel, H., ed. (Illus.). 464p. 1977. text ed. 29.95 (ISBN 3-437-30348-1). Lubrecht & Cramer.

Miller, Orson K., Jr. Mushrooms of North America. rev. ed. 1979. 16.95 (ISBN 0-525-16166-X). Dutton.

Neuner, Andreas. Mushrooms & Fungi. LC 78-316610. (Nature Guides Ser.). (Illus.). 144p. 1979. pap. 5.95 (ISBN 0-7011-2328-1, Pub. by Chatto & Windus). Merrimack Pub Cir.

Orr, Robert T. & Orr, Dorothy B. Mushrooms of Western North America. LC 77-93468. (Illus.). 1980. 12.95 (ISBN 0-520-03656-5); pap. 6.95 (ISBN 0-520-03660-3). U of Cal Pr.

Rattan, S. S. & Khurana, I. P. S. The Clavaria of the Sikkim Himalayas. (Bibliotheca Mycologica Ser.: No. 66). (Illus.). 1978. pap. text ed. 8.75x (ISBN 3-7682-1212-2). Lubrecht & Cramer.

Rice, Miriam C. How to Use Mushrooms for Color. rev. ed. (Illus.). 145p. 1980. pap. 8.95x (ISBN 0-916422-19-4). Mad River.

Rinaldi, Augusto & Tyndalo, Vassili. The Complete Book of Mushrooms: Over 1,000 Species & Varieties of American, European, & Asiatic Mushrooms. (Illus.). 330p. 1974. 14.98 (ISBN 0-517-51493-1). Crown.

Singer, R. Boletinae of Florida with Notes on Extralimital Species: 4 Parts in One Vol. (Bibliotheca Mycologica Ser.: No. 58). (Illus.). 1977. lib. bdg. 21.00x (ISBN 3-7682-1145-2). Lubrecht & Cramer.

Singer, Rolf. Boletes & Related Groups in South America. (Illus.). pap. 6.40 (ISBN 3-7682-0212-7). Lubrecht & Cramer.

Sivanesan, A. Taxonomy & Pathology of Venturia Species. (Bibliotheca Mycologica Ser.: No. 59). 1977. lib. bdg. 14.00x (ISBN 3-7682-1167-3). Lubrecht & Cramer.

Smith, Alexander, et al. How to Know the Non-Gilled Mushrooms. 2nd ed. (Pictured Key Nature Ser.). 440p. 1981. write for info. wire coil (ISBN 0-697-04778-4). Wm C Brown.

Smith, Alexander H. A Field Guide to Western Mushrooms. LC 74-25949. (Illus.). 1975. 18.50 (ISBN 0-472-85599-9). U of Mich Pr.

Smith, Alexander H. & Weber, Nancy. The Mushroom Hunter's Field Guide: All Color & Enlarged. (Illus.). 336p. 1980. 14.95 (ISBN 0-472-85610-3). U of Mich Pr.

Smith, Helen V., et al. How to Know the Gilled Mushrooms. (Pictured Key Nature Ser.). 400p. 1979. avail. wire coil (ISBN 0-697-04773-3). Wm C Brown.

Snell, W. H. & Dick, E. A. The Boleti of Northeastern North America. (Illus.). 1970. 87.50 (ISBN 3-7682-0681-5). Lubrecht & Cramer.

Stamets, Paul. Psilocybe Mushrooms & Their Allies. Harris, Bob, ed. LC 77-26546. (Illus.). 1982. pap. 12.95 (ISBN 0-930180-03-8). Homestead Bk.

Stevens & Gee. How to Grow & Identify Psilocybin Mushrooms. (Illus.). 1978. perfect bdg. 5.95 (ISBN 0-686-26205-0). Pacific Pipeline.

Stuntz, Daniel. How to Identify Mushrooms (to Genus IV) Keys to Families & Genera. (Illus.). 94p. 1977. pap. 5.95x (ISBN 0-916422-10-0). Mad River.

Thiers, Harry. California Mushrooms: A Field Guide to the Boletes. LC 74-11002. (Illus.). 1974. text ed. 19.95x (ISBN 0-02-853410-7). Hafner.

Thiers, Harry D. Mushrooms of California I: The Genus Amanita. (Illus.). 60p. (Orig.). 1982. pap. 6.95x (ISBN 0-916422-24-0). Mad River.

Tylutki, Edmund E. Mushrooms of Idaho & PNW: Non-Gilled Basidiomycetes. LC 84-50764. (Northwest Naturalist Ser.). (Illus.). 264p. (Orig.). 1985. pap. 13.95 (ISBN 0-89301-097-9). U Pr of Idaho.

Watling, Roy, ed. A Literature Guide to the Identification of Mushrooms. 120p. (Orig.). 1980. pap. 9.95x (ISBN 0-916422-18-6). Mad River.

MUSHROOMS–CULTURE

see Mushroom Culture

MUSHROOMS, EDIBLE

see also Mushroom Culture

Bels-Koning, H. C. & Van Kuijk, W. M. Mushroom Terms: Polyglot on Research & Cultivation of Edible Fungi. (Eng., Fr., Ger., Ital., Span., Dutch, Danish & Lat.). 336p. 1980. pap. 83.00 (ISBN 90-220-0673-5, PDC211, Pudoc). Unipub.

Chang, S. T. & Hayes, W. A., eds. The Biology & Cultivation of Edible Mushrooms. LC 77-6591. 1978. 79.50 (ISBN 0-12-168050-9). Acad Pr.

Charles, Vera K. Introduction to Mushroom Hunting. LC 73-85355. (Illus.). 1974. Repr. of 1931 ed. 2.50 (ISBN 0-486-20667-X). Dover.

Christensen, Clyde M. Edible Mushrooms. 2nd, rev. ed. (Illus.). 136p. 1981. 12.95 (ISBN 0-8166-1049-5); pap. 6.95 (ISBN 0-8166-1050-9). U of Minn Pr.

Faubion, Nina L. Some Edible Mushrooms & How to Cook Them. 2nd ed. LC 62-15309. (Illus.). 1972. 8.95 (ISBN 0-8323-0119-1). Binford.

Gray, William D. The Use of Fungi As Food & in Food Processing, Pt. 1. (Monotopic Reprint Ser.). 1971. 11.95 (ISBN 0-87819-104-6). CRC Pr.

Kannaiyan, S., ed. A Handbook of Edible Mushrooms. 104p. 1980. 10.00 (ISBN 0-88065-141-5, Pub. by Messers Today & Tomorrows Printers & Publishers India). Scholarly Pubns.

McIlvaine, Charles & MacAdam, Robert. One Thousand American Fungi. (Illus.). 729p. 1973. pap. 9.95 (ISBN 0-486-22782-0). Dover.

McIlvaine, Charles & MacAdam, Robert K. One Thousand American Fungi. LC 72-91857. (Illus.). 1973. 30.00 (ISBN 0-87110-093-2); pap. 10.00 (ISBN 0-87110-094-0). Ultramarine Pub.

Marteka, Vincent. Mushrooms - Wild & Edible: A Seasonal Guide to the Most Easily Recognized Mushrooms. (Illus.). 1980. 19.95 (ISBN 0-393-01356-1). Norton.

Porter, Robert. The Mushroom Hunt: How to Sharpen Your Eye for the Field & Find America's Choicest Mushrooms. (Illus.). 96p. 1983. 18.95 (ISBN 0-525-24137-X, 01840-550); pap. 11.95 (ISBN 0-525-48007-2, 01160-350). Dutton.

Schmitz, Helga. Untersuchungen Zur Konservierung der Frucht Koerper des Speisepilzes Pleurotus ostreatus (Jacqu. ex Fr.) Kummer in der Partiellen Autlyse von Pilzzellwaenden. (Bibliothaca Mycologica: No. 77). (Ger., Illus.). 85p. 1980. pap. text ed. 10.50x (ISBN 3-7682-1278-5). Lubrecht & Cramer.

Stubbs, Ansel H. Wild Mushrooms Worth Knowing. LC 76-107330. Orig. Title: Wild Mushrooms of the Central Midwest. (Illus.). 160p. 1980. pap. 7.95 (ISBN 0-913504-58-0). Lowell Pr.

Survey & Cultivation of Edible Mushrooms in India, First National Symposium, Srinagar, 1976. Indian Mushroom Science I. Atal, C. K., et al, eds. (Current Trends in Life Sciences Ser.: Vol. 2). xxii, 532p. 1978. 25.00 (ISBN 0-88065-021-4, Pub. by Messers Today & Tomorrows Printers & Publishers India). Scholarly Pubns.

MUSIC–ACOUSTICS AND PHYSICS

see also Electro-Acoustics; Sound

Ando, Y. Concert Hall Acoustics. (Springer Series in Electrophysics: Vol. 17). (Illus.). 170p. 1985. 41.50 (ISBN 0-387-13505-7). Springer-Verlag.

Appelman, D. Ralph. Science of Vocal Pedagogy: Theory & Application. LC 67-10107. (Illus.). 448p. 1967. 27.50x (ISBN 0-253-35110-3); companion cassettes of 3 tapes 17.50 (ISBN 0-253-35115-4); Tape 1. 6.95 (ISBN 0-253-35112-X); Tape 2. 6.95 (ISBN 0-253-35113-8); Tape 3. 6.95 (ISBN 0-253-35114-6). Ind U Pr.

Backus, John. Acoustical Foundations of Music. 2nd ed. LC 68-54957. (Illus.). 1977. 17.95x (ISBN 0-393-09096-5, NortonC); wkbk., questions & problems avail. Norton.

Bartholomew, Wilmer T. Acoustics of Music. LC 79-17650. (Illus.). 1980. Repr. of 1942 ed. lib. bdg. 22.50x (ISBN 0-313-22087-5, BAAC). Greenwood.

Benade, A. H. Fundamentals of Musical Acoustics. (Illus.). 1976. text ed. 19.95x (ISBN 0-19-502030-8). Oxford U Pr.

Benade, Arthur H. Horns, Strings, & Harmony. LC 78-25707. (Illus.). 1979. Repr. of 1960 ed. lib. bdg. 22.50x (ISBN 0-313-20771-2, BEHO). Greenwood.

Blackwood, Easley. The Structure of Recognizable Diatonic Tunings. (Illus.). 360p. 1985. text ed. 50.00x (ISBN 0-691-09129-3). Princeton U Pr.

Broadhouse, John. Musical Acoustics: Or the Phenomena of Sound As Connected with Music. LC 72-181115. 425p. 1926. Repr. 35.00x (ISBN 0-403-01630-4). Scholarly.

Bullock, Theodore H., ed. Recognition of Complex Acoustic Signals, LSRR 5. (Dahlem Workshop Reports Ser.). 406p. 1977. 37.70x (ISBN 0-89573-089-8). VCH Pubs.

Erickson, Robert. Sound Structure in Music. LC 72-9352. (Illus.). 1975. 30.00x (ISBN 0-520-02376-5). U of Cal Pr.

Fletcher, Neville. The Physics of Music. (The Fundamentals of Senior Physics Ser.). 1976. pap. text ed. 4.95x (ISBN 0-85859-085-9, 00509); cassette 8.50x (ISBN 0-686-65412-9, 00510). Heinemann Ed.

Hall, Donald E. Musical Acoustics: An Introduction. 528p. 1979. text ed. write for info. (ISBN 0-534-00758-9). Wadsworth Pub.

Helmholtz, Hermann L. On the Sensations of Tone. 1954. pap. 9.95 (ISBN 0-486-60753-4). Dover.

Hutchins, Carleen M., ed. Musical Acoustics: Violin Family Functions, 2 pts. (Benchmark Papers in Acoustics Ser.: No. 5). 1975-76. Pt. 1. 73.00 (ISBN 0-12-786691-4); Pt. 2. 73.00 (ISBN 0-12-786692-2). Acad Pr.

Jeans, James. Science & Music. (Illus.). 1968. pap. 4.50 (ISBN 0-486-61964-8). Dover.

Levarie, Siegmund & Levy, Ernst. Tone: A Study in Musical Acoustics. 2nd ed. LC 80-29383. (Illus.). xvii, 256p. 1981. Repr. of 1980 ed. lib. bdg. 27.50x (ISBN 0-313-22499-4, LETO). Greenwood.

--Tone: A Study in Musical Acoustics. rev. ed. LC 80-16794. (Illus.). 280p. 1980. pap. 8.50x (ISBN 0-87338-250-1). Kent St U Pr.

Lloyd, Llewelyn S. Music & Sound. LC 70-107815. (Select Bibliographies Reprint Ser). 1937. 18.00 (ISBN 0-8369-5188-3). Ayer Co Pubs.

--Music & Sound. Repr. of 1937 ed. lib. bdg. 15.00x (ISBN 0-8371-4260-1, LLMS). Greenwood.

Mason, Warren P. & Thurston, R. N., eds. Physical Acoustics, Vol. 17. 1984. 89.00 (ISBN 0-12-477917-4). Acad Pr.

Mason, Warren P. & Thurston, Robert N., eds. Physical Acoustics: Principles & Methods, Vol. 15. 1981. 65.00 (ISBN 0-12-477915-8). Acad Pr.

Miller, Dayton C. The Science of Musical Sounds. 2nd ed. LC 76-181211. 286p. 1926. Repr. 39.00x (ISBN 0-403-01622-3). Scholarly.

Morgan, Joseph. The Physical Basis of Musical Sound. LC 78-5508. (Illus.). 168p. (Orig.). 1980. lib. bdg. 12.50 (ISBN 0-88275-656-7). Krieger.

Olson, Harry F. Music, Physics, & Engineering. rev. & enl. ed. (Illus.). 1966. pap. 6.95 (ISBN 0-486-21769-8). Dover.

Pierce, John R. The Science of Musical Sound. LC 82-21427. (Scientific American Library). (Illus.). 242p. 1983. 27.95 (ISBN 0-7167-1508-2). W H Freeman.

Rettinger, M. Studio Acoustics. 1981. 35.00 (ISBN 0-8206-0283-3). Chem Pub.

Rigden, John S. Physics & the Sound of Music. 2nd ed. LC 84-10401. 353p. 1985. 27.95x (ISBN 0-471-87412-4). Wiley.

Roederer, J. G. Introduction to the Physics & Psychophysics of Music. 2nd ed. (Heidelberg Science Library). (Illus.). 202p. 1975. pap. 14.95 (ISBN 3-540-90116-7). Springer-Verlag.

Rosberger, Paul. The Theory of Total Consonance. LC 71-92560. (Illus.). 108p. 1970. 16.50 (ISBN 0-8386-7570-0). Fairleigh Dickinson.

Rossing, Thomas D. Science of Sound: Musical, Electronic, Environmental. LC 80-12028. (Chemistry Ser.). (Illus.). 512p. 1981. text ed. 33.95 (ISBN 0-201-06505-3). Addison-Wesley.

Rossing, Thomas D., ed. Acoustics of Bells. 416p. 1984. 67.50 (ISBN 0-442-27817-9). Van Nos Reinhold.

Slawson, Wayne. Sound Color. LC 84-2474. 1985. 30.00x (ISBN 0-520-05185-8). U of Cal Pr.

Strong, William J. & Plitnik, George R. Music Speech High-Fidelity. 2nd ed. (Illus.). 378p. 1983. pap. 20.00x (ISBN 0-9611938-0-8). Soundprint.

Taylor, Sedley. Sound & Music: A Non-Mathematical Treatise on the Physical Constitution of Musical Sounds & Harmony. (Illus.). Repr. of 1873 ed. 24.00 (ISBN 0-384-59641-X). Johnson Repr.

Wagner, Michael. Introductory Musical Acoustics. (Illus.). 1978. pap. text ed. 13.95 (ISBN 0-89892-025-6). Contemp Pub Co of Raleigh.

White, Harvey E. & White, Donald H. Physics & Music. 422p. 1980. text ed. 37.95x (ISBN 0-03-045246-5). SCP.

Wood, Alexander. Alexander Wood's Physics of Music. 7th ed. Bowsher, J. M., ed. LC 80-20967. (Illus.). xiv, 258p. 1981. Repr. of 1975 ed. lib. bdg. 28.50x (ISBN 0-313-22644-X, WOPM). Greenwood.

Wood, Alexander, ed. The Physics of Music. 7th ed. 1975. pap. 12.95x (ISBN 0-412-21140-8, NO. 6326, Pub. by Chapman & Hall). Methuen Inc.

MUSIC–DATA PROCESSING

Hammond, Ray. The Musician & the Micro. (Illus.). 192p. 1983. (Pub. by Blandford Pr England); pap. 8.95x (ISBN 0-7137-1299-6). Sterling.

Music Made Easy: Commodore 64. 1984. incl. disk 29.95 (ISBN 0-88284-292-7). Alfred Pub.

Paturzo, Bonaventura A. Making Music with Microprocessors. LC 84-8705. (Illus.). 294p. (Orig.). 1984. 16.95 (ISBN 0-8306-0729-3); pap. 11.95 (ISBN 0-8306-1729-9, 1729). TAB Bks.

Sedelow, Walter A., Jr. & Sedelow, Sally Y., eds. Computers in Language Research. (Trends in Linguistic Ser.). 1979. pap. text ed. 27.20x (ISBN 90-279-7846-8). Mouton.

Wittlich, Gary E., et al. Microcomputers & Music. 320p. 1986. text ed. 19.95 (ISBN 0-13-580515-5). P-H.

MUSICAL INSTRUMENTS–CONSTRUCTION

Banek, Reinhold & Scoville, Jon. Sound Designs: A Handbook of Musical Instrument Building. LC 80-65364. (Illus.). 224p. (Orig.). 1980. pap. 6.95 (ISBN 0-89815-011-6). Ten Speed Pr.

Brune, John. Resonant Rubbish. 3.50 (ISBN 0-913714-66-6). Legacy Bks.

Calvert, David D. Making Your Own Stringed Instruments. (Illus.). 144p. (Orig.). 1982. pap. 8.95 (ISBN 0-8306-1379-X). TAB Bks.

Cline, Dallas. Homemade Instruments. LC 76-8073. 1976. pap. 5.95 (ISBN 0-8256-0186-X, Oak). Music Sales.

Cumpiano, W. Guitar Tradition & Technolgy. 1986. cancelled (ISBN 0-442-26845-9). Van Nos Reinhold.

Farrell, Susan C. Directory of Contemporary American Musical Instrument Makers. LC 80-24924. (Illus.). 232p. 1981. text ed. 24.00x (ISBN 0-8262-0322-1). U of Mo Pr.

Flynn, James H., Jr. Building the Balalaika, a Russian Folk Instrument. LC 84-90311. (Illus.). 55p. 1984. spiral bound 9.95 (ISBN 0-9613258-0-1). J H Flynn.

Ford, Charles, ed. Making Musical Instruments: Strings & Keyboard. LC 77-88774. (Illus.). 1979. pap. 10.95 (ISBN 0-394-73561-7). Pantheon.

Giltay, J. W. Bow Instruments: Their Form & Construction. LC 75-181164. 129p. 1923. Repr. 39.00x (ISBN 0-403-01566-9). Scholarly.

Horn, Delton T. Music Synthesizers: A Manual of Design & Construction. (Illus.). 336p. (Orig.). 1984. 16.95 (ISBN 0-8306-0565-7, 1565); pap. 12.50 (ISBN 0-8306-1565-2). TAB Bks.

Roberts, Ronald. Musical Instruments Made to be Played. (Illus.). 84p. 1976. pap. 9.95 (ISBN 0-85219-095-6, Pub. by Batsford England). David & Charles.

Siminoff, Roger H. Constructing a Five-String Banjo. (Illus.). 64p. (Orig.). 1985. pap. 14.95 (ISBN 0-88188-373-5, 00183154, Pub. by H Leonard Bks). H Leonard Pub Corp.

Sloane, Irving. Classic Guitar Construction. (Illus.). 1966. 14.00 (ISBN 0-525-08200-X, 01359-410). Dutton.

--Classic Guitar Construction. LC 84-8585. (Illus.). 96p. (Orig.). 1985. pap. 9.95 (ISBN 0-8069-7926-7). Sterling.

--Guitar Repair: A Manual of Repair for Guitars & Fretted Instruments. LC 84-8543. (Illus.). 96p. (Orig.). 1985. pap. 9.95 (ISBN 0-8069-7934-8). Sterling.

Tullberg, Helen. Lutherie, the Manufacture of Musical Instruments. 1980. 33.00x (ISBN 0-902633-41-4, Pub. by Picton England). State Mutual Bk.

Waring, Dennis. Making Folk Instruments in Wood. LC 81-50985. (Illus.). 160p. (Orig.). 1981. pap. 8.95 (ISBN 0-8069-7540-7). Sterling.

Young, Thomas C. Making of Musical Instruments. LC 79-90698. (Essay Index Reprint Ser). 1939. 20.00 (ISBN 0-8369-1317-5). Ayer Co Pubs.

MUSK OX

Reynolds, S. H. Pleistocene Ovibos. pap. 10.00 (ISBN 0-384-50430-2). Johnson Repr.

MUSKRATS

Dailey, E. J. Practical Muskrat Raising. (Illus.). 136p. pap. 3.50 (ISBN 0-936622-17-2). A R Harding Pub.

Errington, Paul L. Muskrats & Marsh Management. LC 77-14177. (Illus.). x, 183p. 1978. pap. 4.50 (ISBN 0-8032-5892-5, BB 664, Bison). U of Nebr Pr.

MUSLIM TEXTILE FABRICS

see Textile Fabrics, Islamic

MUSTANG

Amaral, Anthony. Mustang: Life & Legends of Nevada's Wild Horses. LC 76-53821. (Lancehead Ser.). (Illus.). xiv, 156p. 1977. 9.00 (ISBN 0-87417-046-X). U of Nev Pr.

Dobie, J. Frank. The Mustangs. (Illus.). 1952. pap. 8.70i (ISBN 0-316-18798-4). Little.

MUSTANG (FIGHTER PLANES)

Feist, Uwe & Maloney, Edward T. North American P-Fifty-One Mustang. LC 67-21487. (Aero Ser.: Vol. 15). 1967. pap. 3.95 (ISBN 0-8168-0556-3). Aero.

Grant, William N. The P-50 One Mustang. (Illus.). 64p. 1983. pap. 4.95 (ISBN 0-13-647875-1). P-H.

Gruenhagen, Robert W. Mustang: Story of the P-Fifty-One Fighter. LC 75-30278. (Illus.). 1980. pap. 9.95 (ISBN 0-668-04884-0). Arco.

Hess, W. N. Fighting Mustang: Chronicle of the P-51. 200p. 1985. pap. 8.95 (ISBN 0-912173-04-1). Champlin Museum.

Mikesh, Robert C. Excalibur III: Story of a P-51 Mustang. LC 78-606028. (Famous Aircraft of the National Air & Space Museum Ser.: No. 1). (Illus.). 76p. 1978. pap. 6.95 (ISBN 0-87474-635-3). Smithsonian.

Morgan, Len. The P-51 Mustang. LC 63-14945. (Famous Aircraft Ser.). (Illus.). 1979. pap. 6.95 (ISBN 0-8168-5647-8). Aero.

Rice, Michael S. Pilot's Manual for the F-82 Twin Mustang. (Illus.). 1976. pap. 7.95 (ISBN 0-87994-035-2). Aviation.

MUSTANG AUTOMOBILE

see Automobiles–Types–Mustang

MUTAGENESIS

see also Radiogenetics

Alacevic, M., ed. Progress in Environmental Mutagenesis. (Developments in Toxicology & Environmental Science Ser.: Vol. 7). 1980. 58.50 (ISBN 0-444-80241-X). Elsevier.

Berlin, A., et al. Monitoring Human Exposure to Carcinogenic & Mutagenic Agents. (International Agency for Research on Cancer Scientific Publications Ser.: No. 59). 1985. 35.00 (ISBN 0-317-17825-3). Oxford U Pr.

Bora, K. C., et al, eds. Chemical Mutagenesis: Progress in Mutation Research, Vol. 3. 360p. 1982. 87.25 (ISBN 0-444-80352-1, Biomedical Pr). Elsevier.

Butterworth, Byron E. Strategies for Short-Term Testing for Mutagens-Carcinogens. 160p. 1979. 56.00 (ISBN 0-8493-5661-X). CRC Pr.

De Serres, Frederic J., ed. Chemical Mutagens: Principles & Methods for Their Detection, Vol. 9. 320p. 1984. 42.50x (ISBN 0-306-41696-4, Plenum Pr). Plenum Pub.

De Serres, Frederick J., ed. Chemical Mutagens: Principles & Methods for their Detection, Vol. 8. 370p. 1983. 45.00x (ISBN 0-306-41336-1, Plenum Pr). Plenum Pub.

De Serres, Frederick J. & Hollaender, A., eds. Chemical Mutagens: Principles & Methods for Their Detection, Vol. 6. LC 79-640909. (Illus.). 505p. 1980. 55.00x (ISBN 0-306-40364-1, Plenum Pr). Plenum Pub.

De Serres, Frederick J. & Hollaender, Alexander, eds. Chemical Mutagens: Principles & Methods for Their Detection, Vol. 7. LC 79-640909. 523p. 1982. 55.00x (ISBN 0-306-40771-X, Plenum Pr). Plenum Pub.

De Serres, Frederick J. & Shelby, Michael D., eds. Comparative Chemical Mutagenesis. LC 81-17887. (Environmental Science Research Ser.: Vol. 24). 1125p. 1981. text ed. 115.00 (ISBN 0-306-40930-5, Plenum Pr). Plenum Pub.

Douglas, J. Fielding, ed. Carcinogenesis & Mutagenesis Testing. LC 84-12820. (Contemporary Biomedicine Ser.). 352p. 1984. 49.50 (ISBN 0-89603-042-3). Humana.

Fishbein, L. Potential Industrial Carcinogens & Mutagens. (Studies in Environmental Science: Vol. 4). 534p. 1979. 106.50 (ISBN 0-444-41777-X). Elsevier.

Frie, R W. & Brinkman, U. A., eds. Mutagenicity Testing & Related Analytical Techniques. (Current Topics in Environmental & Toxocological Chemistry Ser.). 330p. 1981. 60.25 (ISBN 0-677-16300-2). Gordon.

Generoso, W. M., et al, eds. DNA Repair & Mutagenesis in Eukaryotes. LC 80-18743. (Basic Life Sciences Ser.: Vol. 15). 470p. 1980. 55.00x (ISBN 0-306-40552-0, Plenum Pr). Plenum Pub.

Heddle, John A., ed. Mutagenicity: New Horizons in Genetic Toxicology. LC 81-22940. (Cell Biology Ser.). 1982. 65.00 (ISBN 0-12-336180-X). Acad Pr.

Hollaender, Alexander & De Serres, Frederick J., eds. Chemical Mutagens: Principles & Methods for Their Detection, 5 vols. Incl. Vol. 1. 310p. 1971. 37.50x (ISBN 0-306-37101-4); Vol. 2. 300p. 1971. 37.50x (ISBN 0-306-37102-2); Vol. 3. 304p. 1973. 37.50x (ISBN 0-306-37103-0); Vol. 4. 364p. 1976. 45.00x (ISBN 0-306-37104-9); Vol. 5. 364p. 1978. 45.00x (ISBN 0-306-37105-7). LC 73-128505. (Illus., Plenum Pr). Plenum Pub.

Hsie, Abraham W., et al, eds. Banbury Report 2: Mammalian Cell Mutagenesis: The Maturation of Test Systems. LC 79-21186. (Banbury Report Ser.). (Illus.). 504p. 1979. 52.00x (ISBN 0-87969-201-4). Cold Spring Harbor.

Kappas, A., ed. Progress in Environmental Mutagenesis & Carcinogenesis. (Progress in Mutation Research Ser.: Vol. 2). 206p. 1981. 82.75 (ISBN 0-444-80334-3, Biomedical Pr). Elsevier.

Kilbey, B. J., et al, eds. Handbook of Mutagenicity Test Procedures. 2nd, rev. ed. 860p. 1984. 150.00 (ISBN 0-444-80519-2, I-172-84). Elsevier.

Lawrence, Christopher W. Induced Mutagenesis: Molecular Mechanisms & Their Implications for Environmental Protection. (Basic Life Sciences Ser.: Vol. 23). 444p. 1983. 55.00x (ISBN 0-306-41163-6, Plenum Pr). Plenum Pub.

Lemontt, J. F. & Generoso, W. M., eds. Molecular & Cellular Mechanisms of Mutagenesis. LC 82-5300. (Basic Life Sciences Ser.: Vol. 20). 404p. 1980. 52.50x (ISBN 0-306-41006-0). Plenum Pub.

Murray, Randall, ed. Mutagens & Carcinogens. 147p. 1977. 18.50x (ISBN 0-8422-4119-1). Irvington.

Mutagens & Carcinogens. (Landmark Ser.). 1979. lib. bdg. 20.00x (ISBN 0-8422-4119-1). Ayer Co Pubs.

Prakash, Louise, et al, eds. Molecular & Environmental Aspects of Mutagenesis. (Illus.). 296p. 1975. 31.75x (ISBN 0-398-03137-1). C C Thomas.

Sorsa, Marja & Vainio, Harri, eds. Mutagens in Our Environment. LC 82-20320. (Progress in Clinical & Biological Research Ser.: Vol. 109). 514p. 1982. 50.00 (ISBN 0-8451-0109-9). A R Liss.

Stich, Hans F., ed. Carcinogens & Mutagens in the Environment: Food Products, Vol. 1. 320p. 1982. 92.50 (ISBN 0-8493-5881-7). CRC Pr.

Stitch, Hans F. Carcinogens & Mutagens: The Workplace, Vol. IV. 216p. 1985. 70.00 (ISBN 0-8493-5884-1). CRC Pr.

Sugimura, Takashi & Kondo, Sohei, eds. Environmental Mutagens & Carcinogens. LC 82-15231. 784p. 1982. 80.00 (ISBN 0-8451-3007-2). A R Liss.

Sutton, H. Eldon. Mutagenic Effects of Environmental Contaminants. (Environmental Science Ser.). 1972. 44.00 (ISBN 0-12-677950-3). Acad Pr.

Venitt, S. & Parry, J. M., eds. Mutagenicity Testing. (Practical Approach Ser.). (Illus.). 368p. (Orig.). 1984. pap. 26.00 (ISBN 0-904147-72-X). IRL Pr.

Vinyl-Chloride Mutagenesis. (Landmark Ser.). 1979. 22.50x (ISBN 0-8422-4120-5). Irvington.

Vogel, F. & Roehrborn, G., eds. Chemical Mutagenesis in Mammals & Man: Proceedings. LC 79-121062. (Illus.). 1970. 88.00 (ISBN 0-387-05063-9). Springer-Verlag.

MUTATION (BIOLOGY)

see also Chromosome Abnormalities; Evolution; Origin of Species; Variation (Biology)

Auerbach, Charlotte. Mutation Research: Problems, Results & Perspectives. 1976. 53.00 (ISBN 0-412-11280-9, NO. 6017, Pub. by Chapman & Hall). Methuen Inc.

Board on Toxicology & Environmental Health Hazards, National Research Council. Identifying & Estimating the Genetic Impact of Chemical Mutagens. 295p. 1983. pap. text ed. 11.50 (ISBN 0-309-03345-4). Natl Acad Pr.

Cold Spring Harbor Symposia on Quantitative Biology: Genes & Mutations, Vol. 16. LC 34-8174. (Illus.). 537p. 1952. 38.00x (ISBN 0-87969-015-1). Cold Spring Harbor.

Gottschalk, W. & Wolff, G. Induced Mutations in Plant Breeding. (Monographs on Theoretical & Applied Genetics Ser.: Vol. 7). (Illus.). 250p. 1983. 44.50 (ISBN 0-387-12184-6). Springer-Verlag.

Hook, Ernest & Porter, Ian, eds. Biological & Population Aspects of Human Mutation. (Birth Defects Institute Symposium Ser.: No. 11). 1981. 44.00 (ISBN 0-12-355440-3). Acad Pr.

Hsie, Abraham W., et al, eds. Banbury Report 2: Mammalian Cell Mutagenesis: The Maturation of Test Systems. LC 79-21186. (Banbury Report Ser.). (Illus.). 504p. 1979. 52.00x (ISBN 0-87969-201-4). Cold Spring Harbor.

Induced Mutations Against Plant Diseases. (Proceedings Ser.). (Illus.). 581p. 1978. pap. 68.00 (ISBN 92-0-010277-8, ISP462, IAEA). Unipub.

Induced Mutations & Plant Improvement. (Panel Proceedings Ser.). (Eng. & Span., Illus.). 554p. (Orig.). 1972. pap. 46.50 (ISBN 92-0-011072-X, ISP297, IAEA). Unipub.

Induced Mutations in Cross-Breeding. (Panel Proceedings Ser.). (Illus.). 256p. 1977. pap. 28.75 (ISBN 92-0-111676-4, ISP447, IAEA). Unipub.

Induced Mutations in Plants. (Proceedings Ser.). (Eng., Fr. & Span., Illus.). 748p. (Orig.). 1969. pap. 48.00 (ISBN 92-0-010369-3, ISP231, IAEA). Unipub.

McMahan, Forrest R. Human Mutation. LC 82-99887. (Illus.). 72p. (Orig.). 1982. pap. 3.95 (ISBN 0-910217-00-9). Synergetics WV.

Manual on Mutation Breeding. 2nd ed. (Illus.). 1977. pap. 35.25 (ISBN 92-0-115077-6, IDC119, IAEA). Unipub.

Mutations in Plant Breeding. (Panel Proceedings Ser.). (Illus.). 271p. 1966. pap. 16.00 (ISBN 92-0-011066-5, ISP129, IAEA). Unipub.

Obe, G., ed. Mutations in Man. (Illus.). 350p. 1984. 44.50 (ISBN 0-387-13113-2). Springer-Verlag.

Ohno, S. Evolution by Gene Duplication. LC 78-112882. (Illus.). 1970. 32.00 (ISBN 0-387-05225-9). Springer-Verlag.

Rice Breeding with Induced Mutations. (Technical Reports Ser.: No. 86). (Illus.). 155p. 1968. pap. 13.00 (ISBN 92-0-115068-7, IDC86, IAEA). Unipub.

Sutton, H. Eldon. Mutagenic Effects of Environmental Contaminants. (Environmental Science Ser.). 1972. 44.00 (ISBN 0-12-677950-3). Acad Pr.

Traul, Karl A. Microbial Tests for Mutagenicity-Carcinogenicity. (Illus.). 272p. 1985. 38.50 (ISBN 0-442-28303-2). Van Nos Reinhold.

Willis, John C. The Course of Evolution. LC 74-11016. 1974. 13.95x (ISBN 0-02-854860-4). Hafner.

MYCENA

Smith, A. H. North American Species of Mycena. (Bibl. Myco.: Vol. 31). 1971. Repr. of 1947 ed. 42.00 (ISBN 3-7682-0699-8). Lubrecht & Cramer.

MYCETOZOA

see Myxomycetes

MYCOBACTERIUM

Chadwick, Maureen V. Mycobacteria. (Institute of Medical Laboratory Sciences Monographs). 128p. 1983. pap. text ed. 13.00 (ISBN 0-7236-0595-5). PSG Pub Co.

Chapman, John S. The Atypical Mycobacteria & Human Mycobacteriosis. LC 77-1824. (Current Topics in Infectious Diseases Ser.). (Illus.). 216p. 1977. 32.50x (ISBN 0-306-30997-1, Plenum Pr). Plenum Pub.

Juhasz, Stephen E. & Plummer, Gordon. Host-Virus Relationships in Mycobacterium, Nocardia & Actinomyces: Proceedings. (Illus.). 248p. 1970. photocopy ed. 24.75x (ISBN 0-398-00953-8). C C Thomas.

Kubica, Wayne. The Mycobacteria: A Sourcebook. (Mycrobiology Ser.). 1984. Set. 245.00. Dekker.

Ratledge, C. & Stanford, J., eds. The Biology of the Mycobacteria, Vol. I. 1982. 76.50 (ISBN 0-12-582301-0). Acad Pr.

Ratledge, C. & Stanford, J. L., eds. Biology of the Mycobacteria, Vol. 2: Immunological & Environmental Aspects. 1983. 99.00 (ISBN 0-12-582302-9). Acad Pr.

Ratledge, Colin. The Mycobacteria. 130p. 1977. 39.00x (ISBN 0-900541-95-4, Pub. by Meadowfield Pr England). State Mutual Bk.

MYCOGENETICS

see Fungi–Genetics

MYCOLOGY

see also Fungi

Ainsworth, G. C. Introduction to the History of Mycology. LC 75-21036. (Illus.). 350p. 1976. 54.50 (ISBN 0-521-21013-5). Cambridge U Pr.

Alexopoulos, Constantine J. & Mims, Charles W. Introductory Mycology. 3rd ed. LC 79-12514. 632p. 1979. text ed. 42.50 (ISBN 0-471-02214-4). Wiley.

Anderson, J. M., et al, eds. Invertebrate-Microbial Interactions: Joint Symposium of the British Mycological Society & the British Ecological Society Held at the University of Exeter, September 1982. LC 83-14416. (British Mycological Society Symposium Ser.: No. 6). (Illus.). 349p. 1984. 79.50 (ISBN 0-521-25395-0). Cambridge U Pr.

Berger, Karl. Mycological Dictionary. 432p. 1980. 99.00x (ISBN 0-686-44735-2, Pub. by Collets). State Mutual Bk.

Beuchat, L. R. Food & Beverage Mycology. (Illus.). 1978. pap. text ed. 28.50 (ISBN 0-87055-293-7). AVI.

Bilgrami, K. S. & Misra, R. S., eds. Advancing Frontiers of Mycology & Plant Pathology: Prof. K. S. Bhargava Commemoration Volume. (Illus.). xxvi, 330p. 1982. 50.00 (ISBN 0-88065-222-5, Pub. by Messers Today & Tomorrow Printers & Publishers). Scholarly Pubns.

Carter, G. R. Diagnostic Procedures in Veterinary Bacteriology & Mycology. 4th ed. (Illus.). 526p. 1984. 39.50x (ISBN 0-398-04870-3). C C Thomas.

Couch, John N. & Bland, Charles E., eds. The Genus Coelomomyces. Date not set. 84.50 (ISBN 0-12-192650-8). Acad Pr.

Deacon, J. W. Introduction to Modern Mycology. 2nd ed. (Illus.). 272p. 1984. pap. 15.95x (ISBN 0-632-01156-4). Blackwell Pubns.

De Sole, S. Entwicklung der Drelipore von Coprinus Radiatus (Bolt.) Fr. (Bibliotheca Mycologica 88). (Illus.). 148p. 1982. pap. 17.50 (ISBN 3-7682-1343-9). Lubrecht & Cramer.

Ehrenberg, C. G. Silvae Mycologicae Berolinensis. 1972. Repr. of 1818 ed. 15.75 (ISBN 90-6123-253-8). Lubrecht & Cramer.

Ellis, M. B. Dematiaceous Hyphomycetes. 608p. 1971. 88.00x (ISBN 0-85198-027-9, Pub. by CAB Bks England). State Mutual Bk.

--More Dematiaceous Hyphomycetes. 507p. 1976. 110.00x (ISBN 0-85198-365-0, Pub. by CAB Bks England). State Mutual Bk.

Fuckel, K. Leopold. Symbolae Mycologicae. (Illus.). Repr. of 1877 ed. 90.00 (ISBN 0-384-17190-7). Johnson Repr.

Fuckel, L. Symbolae Mycologicae & Supplements. (Illus.). 1966. Repr. of 1877 ed. 70.00 (ISBN 3-7682-0358-1). Lubrecht & Cramer.

Gareth Jones, E. B. Recent Advances in Aquatic Mycology. LC 74-27179. 748p. 1976. 99.95x (ISBN 0-470-29176-1). Halsted Pr.

Gillies, R. R. Gillies & Dodds Bacteriology Illustrated. 5th ed. LC 82-23595. (Illus.). 224p. (Orig.). 1984. pap. text ed. 28.00 (ISBN 0-443-02809-5). Churchill.

Gregory, P. H. & Maddison, A. C. Epidemiology of Phytophthora on Cocoa in Nigeria. 188p. 1981. 79.00x (ISBN 0-85198-478-9, Pub. by CAB Bks England). State Mutual Bk.

Halling, Roy E. The Genus Collybia (Agaricales) in the Northeastern U. S. & Adjacent Canada. (Mycologia Memoirs: No. 8). (Illus.). 150p. 1983. 21.00 (ISBN 3-7682-1345-5). Lubrecht & Cramer.

Hanlin, Richard T. & Ulloa, Miguel. Atlas of Introductory Mycology. LC 78-65422. (Illus.). 188p. 1979. pap. text ed. 12.95 (ISBN 0-88725-003-3). Hunter Textbks.

Hawksworth, D. H. Mycologist's Handbook: An Introduction to the Principles of Taxonomy & Nomenclature in the Fungi & Lichens. 231p. 1977. cloth 50.00x (ISBN 0-85198-300-6, Pub. by CAB Bks England); pap. 39.00x (ISBN 0-85198-306-5). State Mutual Bk.

Hawksworth, D. L. Mycologist's Handbook. 231p. 1974. text ed. 21.30 (ISBN 0-85198-300-6). Lubrecht & Cramer.

Hoehnel, F. Fragmente Zur Mykologie, 2vols. 1966. 105.00 (ISBN 3-7682-0467-7). Lubrecht & Cramer.

Indian Mycologists Staff. Fungi of the Indian Subcontinent: A Collection of Papers. (Bibliotheca Mycologica Ser.: No. 91). (Illus.). 684p. 1983. text ed. 70.00x (ISBN 3-7682-1377-3). Lubrecht & Cramer.

Jackson, R. M. Mycorrhiza. (Studies in Biology: No. 159). 64p. 1984. pap. text ed. 8.95 (ISBN 0-7131-2876-3). E Arnold.

Karsten, P. A. Symbolae Ad Mycologiam Fennicam. 1966. Repr. of 1895 ed. 56.00 (ISBN 3-7682-0352-2). Lubrecht & Cramer.

Kohlmeyer, J. Index Alphabeticus Klotzschii & Rabenhorstii Herbarii Mycologici. 1962. pap. 14.00 (ISBN 3-7682-5404-6). Lubrecht & Cramer.

Kohlmeyer, Jan & Kohlmeyer, Ericka. Marine Mycology: The Higher Fungi. LC 79-14703. 1979. 76.50 (ISBN 0-12-418350-6). Acad Pr.

Koneman, Elmer W. & Roberts, Glenn. Practical Laboratory Mycology. 3rd ed. (Illus.). 224p. 1985. 22.95 (ISBN 0-683-04746-9). Williams & Wilkins.

Koske, R. E. Cookbook Statistics for Plant Pathology & Mycology. 65p. (Orig.). 1982. pap. text ed. 8.50x (ISBN 0-934454-94-9). Lubrecht & Cramer.

Laursen, Gary A. & Ammirati, Joseph F. Arctic & Alpine Mycology: The First International Symposium on Arcto-Alpine Mycology. LC 81-51281. 502p. 1981. 50.00x (ISBN 0-295-95856-1). U of Wash Pr.

Lemke, P. A. Viruses & Plasmids in Fungi. (Mycology Ser.: Vol. 1). 1979. 89.75 (ISBN 0-8247-6916-3). Dekker.

Mitchell, Thomas G., et al. Conant's Manual of Clinical Mycology. 4th ed. (Illus.). 600p. Date not set. price not set (ISBN 0-7216-6408-3). Saunders.

Moss, M. O., ed. Applied Mycology of Fusarium. Smith, J. E. LC 83-5337. (British Mycological Society Symposium: No. 7). 300p. 1984. 64.50 (ISBN 0-521-25398-5). Cambridge U Pr.

Mycology Guidebook Committee, Mycological Society of America. Mycology Guidebook. rev. ed. Stevens, Russell B., ed. LC 81-14738. (Illus.). 736p. 1981. 40.00x (ISBN 0-295-95841-3). U of Wash Pr.

New York Botanical Garden. Mycologia Index: Volumes 1-58, 1909-1966. LC 57-51730. (Mycologia Ser.). 1968. 20.00x (ISBN 0-89327-215-9). NY Botanical.

Onions, A. S., et al. Smith's Introduction to Industrial Mycology. 7th ed. 398p. 1982. 106.95x (ISBN 0-470-27294-5). Halsted Pr.

Persoon, Christiaan H. Observationes Mycologicae, Pt. 1. 1966. Repr. of 1796 ed. 15.00 (ISBN 0-384-45821-1). Johnson Repr.

Petersen, Ronald H. B & C: Mycological Association of M. J. Berkeley & M. A. Curtis. (Bibliotheca Mycologica Ser.: 72). (Illus.). 120p. 1980. pap. text ed. 10.50 (ISBN 3-7682-1258-0). Lubrecht & Cramer.

Ramsbottom, J. Fungi: An Introduction to Mycology. 1979. Repr. of 1929 ed. lib. bdg. 12.50 (ISBN 0-8495-4608-7). Arden Lib.

Razin, Shimuel, ed. Methods in Mycoplasmology: Diagnostic Mycoplasmology, Vol. 2. 1983. 55.00 (ISBN 0-12-583802-6). Acad Pr.

Robinson, Peter M. Practical Fungal Physiology. LC 78-4243. 123p. 1978. pap. 19.95 (ISBN 0-471-99656-4, Pub. by Wiley-Interscience). Wiley.

Saccardo, P. A., ed. Michelia Commentarium Mycologicum: 1879-1882, 2vols. 1969. 78.15 (ISBN 90-6123-106-X). Lubrecht & Cramer.

Sharp, Robert F. Investigative Mycology. LC 79-670321. 1978. text ed. 19.95x (ISBN 0-435-60750-2); pap. text ed. 8.95x (ISBN 0-435-60751-0). Heinemann Ed.

Singer, Martha. Mycologists & Their Taxa. (Illus.). 120p. 1984. pap. text ed. 7.00x (ISBN 3-7682-1342-0). Lubrecht & Cramer.

Snell, Walter & Dick, Esther A. Glossary of Mycology. 2nd ed. LC 77-134946. 1971. 15.00x (ISBN 0-674-35451-6). Harvard U Pr.

Stevenson, J. An Account of Fungus Exiccati Containing Material from the Americas. 1971. 70.00 (ISBN 3-7682-5436-4). Lubrecht & Cramer.

Strathern, Jeffrey N., et al, eds. The Molecular Biology of the Yeast Saccharomyces: Life Cycle & Inheritance. LC 81-68895. (Cold Spring Harbor Monograph: Vol. 11A). 751p. 1982. 94.50x (ISBN 0-87969-139-5). Cold Spring Harbor.

Trinci, A. P. & Ryley, J. F., eds. Mode of Action of Antifungal Agents. (British Mycological Society Symposium Ser.: No. 9). 390p. 1984. 79.50 (ISBN 0-521-26171-6). Cambridge U Pr.

MYCOPLASMATACEAE

Barile, M. F., et al, eds. The Mycoplasmas Vol. 1: Cell Biology. LC 78-20895. 1979. 69.00 (ISBN 0-12-078401-7). Acad Pr.

--The Mycoplasmas Vol. 2: Human & Animal Mycoplasmas. LC 78-20895. 1979. 67.00 (ISBN 0-12-078402-5). Acad Pr.

--The Mycoplasmas Vol. 3: Plant & Insect Mycoplasmas. 1979. 55.00 (ISBN 0-12-078403-3). Acad Pr.

Daniels, M. J. & Markham, P. G. Plant & Insect Mycoplasma Techniques. LC 81-13142. 369p. 1982. 54.95x (ISBN 0-470-27262-7). Halsted Pr.

Daniels, M. J. & Markham, P. J., eds. Plant & Insect Mycoplasma Techniques. 368p. 1981. 37.00 (ISBN 0-7099-0272-7, Pub. by Croom Helm Ltd). Longwood Pub Group.

Madoff, Sarabelle. Mycoplasma & the L Forms of Bacteria. (Illus.). 116p. 1971. 31.75x (ISBN 0-677-14790-2). Gordon.

Razin, Shimuel & Tully, G., eds. Methods in Mycoplasmology: Mycoplasma Characterization, Vol. 1. 1983. 62.50 (ISBN 0-12-583801-8). Acad Pr.

Sharp, John T. The Role of Mycoplasmas & Forms of Bacteria in Disease. (Illus.). 400p. 1970. photocopy ed. 39.50x (ISBN 0-398-01733-6). C C Thomas.

Smith, Paul F. Biology of Mycoplasmas. (Cell Biology Ser). 1971. 55.00 (ISBN 0-12-652050-X). Acad Pr.

MYCOSIS

see also Fungi, Pathogenic

Baker, Roger D., et al. Pathologic Anatomy of Mycoses. LC 25-11247. (Handbuch der Speziellen Pathologischen Anatomie: Vol. 3, Pt. 5). (Illus.). 1971. 318.60 (ISBN 0-387-05140-6). Springer-Verlag.

Board of Education & Training Staff. Systemic Mycoses. rev. ed. (Continuing Education Manual Ser.). 1984. 12.00 (ISBN 0-317-16825-8). Am Soc Microbio.

Palmer, Dan F., et al. Serodiagnosis of Mycotic Diseases. (Illus.). 208p. 1978. 26.25x (ISBN 0-398-03592-X). C C Thomas.

Raab, W. The Treatment of Mycosis with Imidazole Derivatives. (Illus.). 180p. 1980. pap. 16.60 (ISBN 0-387-09800-3). Springer-Verlag.

Salfelder, Karlhanns. Atlas of Deep Mycoses. LC 79-67221. (Illus.). 140p. 1980. text ed. 20.00 (ISBN 0-7216-7898-X). Saunders.

Towse, G., ed. The Role of Intravenous Miconazole in the Treatment of Systemic Mycoses. (Royal Society of Medicine International Congress & Symposium Ser.: No. 45). 64p. 1981. 16.00 (ISBN 0-8089-1399-9, 794641). Grune.

Wyllie, Thomas & Morehouse, Lawrence G., eds. Mycotoxic Fungi, Mycotoxins, Mycotoxicoses: An Encyclopedic Handbook, Vol. 1. 1977. 99.75 (ISBN 0-8247-6550-8). Dekker.

MYCOTOXINS

see also Aflatoxins

Board on Renewable Resources. Interactions of Mycotoxins in Animal Production. 197p. 1979. pap. 10.75 (ISBN 0-309-02876-0). Natl Acad Pr.

Christensen, Clyde M. Molds, Mushrooms, & Mycotoxins. LC 74-21808. (Illus.). 292p. 1975. 15.95x (ISBN 0-8166-0743-5). U of Minn Pr.

Cole, Richard J. & Cox, Richard H., eds. Handbook of Toxic Fungal Metabolites. LC 81-4082. 1981. 87.00 (ISBN 0-12-179760-0). Acad Pr.

Faulstich, H. & Kommerell, B. Amanita Toxins & Poisoning: International Amanita Symposium, Heidelberg 1978. (Illus.). 246p. 1980. pap. text ed. 32.50x. Lubrecht & Cramer.

Hayes, A. Wallace. Mycotoxin Teratogenicity & Mutagenicity. 144p. 1981. 66.00 (ISBN 0-8493-5651-2). CRC Pr.

Mycotoxin Surveillance: Prepared in Cooperation with the United Nations Environment Programme. (Food & Nutrition Papers: No. 21). 68p. 1982. pap. 7.50 (ISBN 92-5-101180-X, F2306, FAO). Unipub.

Mycotoxins: Formation, Analysis & Structure. Date not set. price not set (ISBN 0-471-90671-9). Wiley.

Perspective on Mycotoxins. (Food & Nutrition Papers: No. 13). (Eng. & Span.). 171p. 1979. pap. 11.25 (ISBN 92-5-100870-1, F1957, FAO). Unipub.

Reiss. Fungal Antigens & the Immune Response. Date not set. write for info. (ISBN 0-444-00856-X). Elsevier.

Rodricks, Joseph V., ed. Mycotoxins & Other Fungal Related Food Problems. LC 76-4547. (Advances in Chemistry Ser.: No. 149). 1976. 44.95 (ISBN 0-8412-0222-2). Am Chemical.

Shank, Ronald C. Mycotoxins & N-Nitroso Compounds: Enviornmental Risks, 2 vols. 1981. Vol. I, 296p. 81.00 (ISBN 0-8493-5307-6); Vol. II, 248 Pgs. 81.00 (ISBN 0-8493-5308-4). CRC Pr.

Steyn, P. S., ed. The Biosynthesis of Mycotoxins: A Study in Secondary Metabolism. LC 80-12013. 1980. 55.00 (ISBN 0-12-670650-6). Acad Pr.

Uraguchi, Kenji & Yamazaki, Mikio, eds. Toxicology: Biochemistry & Pathology of Mycotoxins. LC 78-8992. 288p. 1978. 54.95x (ISBN 0-470-26423-3). Halsted Pr.

MYNAHS

Bates, Henry & Busenbark, Robert. Guide to Mynahs. (Orig.). 4.95 (ISBN 0-87666-769-8, PS-633). TFH Pubns.

Low, Rosemary. Mynah Birds. (Illus.). 93p. pap. 3.95 (ISBN 0-7028-1002-9). Avian Pubns.

Weil, Martin. Mynahs. (Illus.). 96p. 1981. 4.95 (ISBN 0-87666-890-2, KW-120). TFH Pubns.

MYOLOGY

see Muscles

MYRIAPODA

see also Centipedes

Camatini, Marina, ed. Myriapod Biology. LC 79-41559. 1980. 76.50 (ISBN 0-12-155750-2). Acad Pr.

Morris, S. F. Catalogue of Type & Figured Fossil Crustacea (Exc. Ostracoda), Chelicerata & Myriapoda in the British Museum (Natural History) (Illus.). 56p. 1980. pap. 12.00x (ISBN 0-565-00828-5). Sabbot-Natural Hist Bks.

MYRIONEMA

Sauvageau, C. Sur Quelques Myrionemacees. 1897. Repr. 14.00 (ISBN 3-7682-0705-6). Lubrecht & Cramer.

MYRISTICACEAE

Landrum, Leslie R. Myrceugenia (Myrtaceae) (Flora Neotropica Monograph: No. 29). (Illus.). 1981. pap. 20.00x (ISBN 0-89327-236-1). NY Botanical.

MYSIDAE

Morgan, Mark D. Ecology of Mysidacea. 1982. text ed. 54.50 (ISBN 90-6193-761-2, Pub. by Junk Pubs Netherlands). Kluwer Academic.

MYXOMATOSIS CUNICULI

Fenner, Frank J. & Ratcliffe, F. N. Myxomatosis. LC 65-17207. pap. 103.00 (ISBN 0-317-28401-0, 2022448). Bks Demand UMI.

MYXOMYCETES

Fullmer, E. L. The Slime Molds of Ohio. 1921. 1.50 (ISBN 0-86727-010-1). Ohio Bio Survey.

Lister, Arthur L. Monograph of the Mycetozoa. 3rd ed. (Illus.). Repr. of 1925 ed. 45.00 (ISBN 0-384-32930-6). Johnson Repr.

Martin, G. W. & Alexopoulos, C. J. Myxomycetes. LC 77-88357. (Illus.). 576p. 1969. 50.00x (ISBN 0-87745-000-5). U of Iowa Pr.

Martin, G. W., et al. The Genera of the Myxomycetes. X ed. LC 83-5092. (Illus.). 198p. 1983. 35.00x (ISBN 0-87745-124-9). U of Iowa Pr.

Olive, Lindsay S. The Mycetozoans. 1975. 56.00 (ISBN 0-12-526250-7). Acad Pr.

Singer, Rolf. Mycoflora Australis. 1969. pap. 56.00 (ISBN 3-7682-5429-1). Lubrecht & Cramer.

Tilden, J. The Myxophyceae of North America & Adjacent Regions. (Bibl. Phyco.: Vol. 4). (Illus.). 1968. pap. 28.00 (ISBN 3-7682-0546-0). Lubrecht & Cramer.

N

N-WAY ALGEBRA

see Algebra, Universal

NAILS (ANATOMY)

Pierre, Maurice, ed. The Nail. (G. E. M. Ser.). (Illus.). 1981. 55.00 (ISBN 0-443-02102-3). Churchill.

NASH, JOHN HENRY, 1871-1947

Harlan, Robert D. John Henry Nash: The Biography of a Career. LC 70-628359. (U. C. Publ. in Librarianship: Vol. 7). (Illus.). Repr. of 1970 ed. 50.00 (ISBN 0-8357-9629-9, 2011834). Bks Demand UMI.

NASH-HEALEY (AUTOMOBILE)

see Automobiles, Foreign–Types–Healey

NATIONAL RESEARCH COUNCIL, CANADA

Mackenzie, Chalmers J. The Mackenzie--McNaughton Wartime Letters. Thistle, Mel, ed. LC 72-185741. pap. 48.00 (ISBN 0-317-09549-8, 2014433). Bks Demand UMI.

NATIONAL RESOURCES

see also Natural Resources;
also subdivision Economic Conditions under names of countries, regions, etc. e.g. United States–Economic Conditions

Clawson, Marion. New Deal Planning: The National Resources Planning Board. LC 80-8777. 376p. 1981. 32.50x (ISBN 0-8018-2595-4). Johns Hopkins.

NATURAL CALAMITIES

see Natural Disasters

NATURAL DISASTERS

see also Avalanches; Earth Movements; Floods; Forest Fires; Storms; Tsunamis; Volcanism

Beinin, L. Medical Consequences of Natural Disasters. (Illus.). 195p. 1985. pap. 39.00 (ISBN 0-387-15506-6). Springer-Verlag.

Bolt, B. A., et al. Geological Hazards. LC 74-32049. (Illus.). 450p. 1977. 29.50 (ISBN 0-387-90254-6). Springer-Verlag.

Bulter, J. R. & Doessel, D. P. The Economics of Natural Disaster Relief in Australia. LC 79-50570. (Centre for Research on Federal Financial Relations - Research Monograph: No. 27). 147p. (Orig.). 1980. pap. text ed. 10.00 (ISBN 0-7081-1073-8, 0565). Australia N U P.

Butler, John E. Natural Disasters. 1976. pap. text ed. 8.50x (ISBN 0-435-34068-9). Heinemann Ed.

Cohen, Stephen P. & Raghavulu, C. V. The Andhra Cyclone of Nineteen Seventy-Seven: Individual & Institutional Responses to Mass Death. 1979. 15.00x (ISBN 0-7069-0765-5, Pub. by Vikas India). Advent NY.

Engineering for Protection from Natural Disasters: Proceedings. Kanok-Nukulchai, Worsak, ed. LC 80-4169. 937p. 1980. 129.95x (ISBN 0-471-27895-5, Pub. by Wiley-Interscience). Wiley.

Griggs, Gary B. & Gilchrist, John A. Geologic Hazards, Resources, Environmental Planning. 528p. 1983. text ed. write for info. (ISBN 0-534-01226-4). Wadsworth Pub.

Natural Disasters: Selected Problems & Implications. 309p. 1980. looseleaf 15.00 (ISBN 0-88129-023-8). Wash St Bar.

Rossi, Peter, et al. Natural Hazards & Public Choice: The State & Local Politics of Hazard Mitigation. LC 82-1633. (Quantitative Studies in Social Relations Ser.). 1982. 37.50 (ISBN 0 12-598220-8). Acad Pr.

Seaman, J., et al. Epidemiology of Natural Disasters. (Contributions to Epidemiology & Biostatistics: Vol. 5). (Illus.). viii, 180p. 1984. 63.00 (ISBN 3-8055-3779-4). S Karger.

Sorkin, Alan L. Economic Aspects of Natural Hazards. LC 79-48027. (Illus.). 192p. 1981. 27.50x (ISBN 0-669-03639-0). Lexington Bks.

Terrien, Ernest J. Hazardous Materials & Natural Disaster Emergencies: Incident Action Guidebook. LC 84-51388. 64p. 1984. pap. 20.00 (ISBN 0-87762-365-1). Technomic.

Tufty, Barbara. One Thousand & One Questions Answered about Earthquakes, Avalanches, Floods & Other Natural Disasters. (The One Thousand & One Question Ser.). (Illus.). 350p. 1978. pap. 5.95 (ISBN 0-486-23646-3). Dover.

--One Thousand & One Questions Answered about Earthquakes, Avalanches, Floods & Other Natural Disasters. 14.25 (ISBN 0-8446-5826-X). Peter Smith.

Weeks, Ellen J. & Jones, Barclay G. The Social & Economic Aspects of Earthquakes & Other Natural Disasters: Risk Assessment, Hazard Mitigation, Emergency Management, Reconstruction & Recovery. (Public Administration Ser.: Bibliography P-1260). 92p. 1983. pap. 13.50 (ISBN 0-88066-630-7). Vance Biblios.

Whittow, John. Disasters: The Anatomy of Environmental Hazards. LC 79-5236. (Illus.). 406p. 1980. 22.00 (ISBN 0-8203-0499-9); pap. 9.95x (ISBN 0-8203-0542-1). U of Ga Pr.

Wright, James D. & Rossi, Peter H. After the Clean-Up: Long-Range Effects of Natural Disasters. LC 79-15768. (Contemporary Evaluation Research Ser.: Vol. 2). (Illus.). pap. 57.50 (ISBN 0-317-08995-1, 2021968). Bks Demand UMI.

NATURAL GAS

see Gas, Natural

NATURAL HISTORY

see also Aquariums; Biology; Botany; Desert Biology; Geographical Distribution of Animals and Plants; Geology; Marine Biology; Mineralogy; Paleontology; Soil Biology; Zoology

Bates, Marston. Jungle in the House: Essays in Natural & Unnatural History. LC 70-103375. 1970. 7.50 (ISBN 0-8027-0159-0). Walker & Co.

Bateson, William. Scientific Papers of William Bateson, 2 Vols. Punnett, R. C., ed. Repr. of 1928 ed. Set. 90.00 (ISBN 0-384-03533-7). Johnson Repr.

Berquam, Hazel H. Miniatures of Nature. LC 80-68645. (Illus.). 1980. pap. 4.95 (ISBN 0-8323-0383-6). Binford.

Brimley, Herbert H. North Carolina Naturalist, H. H. Brimley. facs. ed. Odum, Eugene P., ed. LC 78-134058. (Essay Index Reprint Ser). 1949. 18.00 (ISBN 0-8369-2145-3). Ayer Co Pubs.

British Museum (Natural History) Nature Stored, Nature Studied: Collections, Conservation & Allied Research at the British Museum (Natural History) (Illus.). 64p. 1981. pap. 6.50x (ISBN 0-565-00835-8, Pub. by Brit Mus Nat Hist England). Sabbot-Natural Hist Bks.

Brockie, Keith. One Man's Island: A Naturalist's View. LC 84-47708. (Illus.). 192p. 1984. 19.18i (ISBN 0-06-015360-1, HarpT). Har-Row.

Brown, Vinson. The Amateur Naturalists's Handbook. (Illus.). 448p. 1980. 15.95 (ISBN 0-13-023739-6, Spec); pap. 7.95 (ISBN 0-13-023721-3). P-H.

Buchanan, Handasyde. Nature into Art: A Treasury of Great Natural History Books. LC 79-12481. (Illus.). 1980. 25.00 (ISBN 0-8317-6337-X, Mayflower Bks). Smith Pubs.

Buckland, Francis T. Curiosities of Natural History. (Illus.). 318p. Repr. of 1858 ed. 16.95x (ISBN 0-8464-0307-2). Beekman Pubs.

Buckley, H. A., et al. Catalogue of the Ocean Deposits Collection in the British Museum (Natural History), Pt. 2: Indian & Pacific Oceans. (Illus.). 1984. 32.00x (ISBN 0-565-00863-3, Pub. by Brit Mus Nat Hist England); microfiche incl. Sabbot-Natural Hist Bks.

Buffon, Georges L. The Natural History of Oviparous Quadrupeds & Serpents: Arranged & Published from the Papers & Collections of the Count De Buffon, 4 vols. in one. Sterling, Keir B., ed. Kerr, Robert, tr. LC 77-81119. (Biologists & Their World Ser.). (Illus.). 1978. Repr. of 1802 ed. Set. lib. bdg. 132.00x (ISBN 0-405-10710-2); lib. bdg. 66.00x ea. Vol. 1 (ISBN 0-405-10711-0). Vol. 2 (ISBN 0-405-10712-9). Ayer Co Pubs.

Cecchettini, Philip A. CLEP Resourse Manual: Introduction to Natural Science. 1979. pap. text ed. 13.95 (ISBN 0-07-010309-7). McGraw.

Chalmers-Hunt, J. M., ed. Natural History Auctions, Seventeen Hundred to Nineteen Seventy-Two: A Register of Sales in the British Isles. 192p. 1976. 45.00x (ISBN 0-85667-021-9, Pub. by Sotheby Pubns England). Biblio Dist.

Copeland, Herbert F. Classification of Lower Organisms. LC 56-7944. (Illus.). 1956. 17.95x (ISBN 0-87015-059-6). Pacific Bks.

Curtis, Will, ed. The Nature of Things. LC 84-17656. 312p. 1985. 15.95 (ISBN 0-88150-028-3). Countryman.

Daehnhardt, Alfred O., ed. Natursagen, 4 vols. 1971. Repr. of 1907 ed. lib. bdg. 110.00 (ISBN 0-8337-0760-4). B Franklin.

Darwin, Charles. The Collected Papers of Charles Darwin, Vols. I & II. Barrett, Paul H., ed. LC 76-606. (Illus.). 1977. lib. bdg. 40.00x set (ISBN 0-226-13657-4); pap. 12.50 (ISBN 0-226-13658-2, P886, Phoen). U of Chicago Pr.

--Journal of Researches into the Natural History & Geology of the Countries Visited During the Voyage of H. M. S. "Beagle" Round the World, under the Command of Capt. Fitz Roy, R. A. 1977. Repr. of 1892 ed. lib. bdg. 30.00 (ISBN 0-8482-0544-8). Norwood Edns.

--Voyage of the Beagle. LC 62-2990. 1962. 6.95 (ISBN 0-385-02767-2, Anchor). Natural Hist.

Darwin, Francis. Rustic Sounds & Other Studies in Literature & Natural History. facs. ed. LC 69-17572. (Essay Index Reprint Ser). 1917. 17.00 (ISBN 0-8369-0069-3). Ayer Co Pubs.
De Grazia, Alfred. Chaos & Creation: An Introduction to Quantavolution in Human & Natural History. (Quantavolution Ser.). (Illus.). xiii, 336p. 1981. 22.00x (ISBN 0-940268-00-0). Metron Pubns.
Douglas, Charles. Natural History Notebook, No. 3. (Illus.). iv, 54p. 1980. pap. 2.50 (ISBN 0-660-10341-9, 56444-4, Pub. by Natl Mus Canada). U of Chicago Pr.
--Natural History Notebook, No. 4. (National Museum of Natural Science Ser.). (Illus.). iv, 56p. 1981. pap. 2.50 (ISBN 0-660-10321-4, 56445-2, Pub. by Natl Mus Canada). U of Chicago Pr.
Durrell, Gerald, frwd. by. The Encyclopedia of Natural History. (Octopus Book). (Illus.). 1978. 16.95 (ISBN 0-7064-0676-1, Mayflower Bks). Smith Pubs.
Dwigans, Cathy M., et al, eds. A Guide to the Museum of Natural History the University of Kansas. (Illus.). 65p. (Orig.). 1984. pap. 2.90 (ISBN 0-89338-023-7). U of KS Mus Nat Hist.
Egerton, Frank N., ed. Natural History, General & Particulor: An Original Anthology, 2 vols. LC 77-74206. (History of Ecology Ser.). (Illus.). 1978. Set. lib. bdg. 99.00x (ISBN 0-405-10376-X). Ayer Co Pubs.
Euler, Leonhard. Opera Omnia. Swiss Society of Natural Sciences Euler-Committee, ed. (Secundia Ser.: Vol. 17). 312p. 1983. text ed. 85.00 (ISBN 3-7643-1447-8). Birkhauser.
Fitch, Henry S. Spiders of the University of Kansas Natural History Reservation & Rockefeller Experimental Tract. (Miscellaneous Publications: No. 33). 202p. 1963. pap. 8.00 (ISBN 0-686-79810-4). U of KS Mus Nat Hist.
Fuentes, Carlos. Where the Air Is Clear. Hileman, Sam, tr. from Span. 376p. 1971. pap. 8.95 (ISBN 0-374-50919-0). FS&G.
Godman, John D. American Natural History: Mastogogy & Rambles of a Naturalist, Part No. 1, 3 vols. in one. LC 73-17821. (Natural Sciences in America Ser.). (Illus.). 1079p. 1974. Repr. 74.00x (ISBN 0-405-05737-7). Ayer Co Pubs.
Gould, Stephen J. Ever Since Darwin: Reflections in Natural History. (Illus.). 1979. pap. 4.95 (ISBN 0-393-00917-3). Norton.
--Hen's Teeth & Horse's Toes: Further Reflections in Natural History. (Illus.). 416p. 1984. pap. 5.95 (ISBN 0-393-30200-8). Norton.
--The Panda's Thumb: More Reflections in Natural History. (Illus.). 1980. 15.95 (ISBN 0-393-01380-4). Norton.
Grant, May B. Wildly Speaking. LC 75-122574. (Popular Ser.: No. 10). 1972. pap. 2.95 (ISBN 0-87768-005-1). Denver Mus Natl Hist.
Grinnell, Joseph. Joseph Grinnell's Philosophy of Nature: Selected Writings of a Western Naturalist. facs. ed. LC 68-20304. (Essay Index Reprint Ser). 1943. 21.50 (ISBN 0-8369-0499-0). Ayer Co Pubs.
Halbritter, Kurt. Halbritter's Plant-&-Animal World. Turnbull, Joanne & Githens, John, trs. from Ger. LC 81-2277. Orig. Title: Halbritters Tier-und Pflanzenwelt. (Illus.). 160p. 1981. 15.95 (ISBN 0-394-51805-5). Seaver Bks.
Hall, E. Raymond. In Memoriam: Charles Dean Bunker. (Miscellaneous Publications Ser.: No. 3). 11p. 1951. 1.25 (ISBN 0-317-04774-4). U of KS Mus Nat Hist.
Hay, John. The Undiscovered Country. (Illus.). 157p. 1982. 12.95 (ISBN 0-393-01571-8). Norton.
Hobson, E. W. The Domain of Natural Science. 9.25 (ISBN 0-8446-2260-5). Peter Smith.
Hobson, Ernest W. The Domain of Natural Science. LC 77-27210. (Gifford Lectures: 1921-22). Repr. of 1923 ed. 24.50 (ISBN 0-404-60467-6). AMS Pr.
Hudson, William H. The Book of a Naturalist. Repr. of 1923 ed. 35.00 (ISBN 0-404-03410-1). AMS Pr.
--A Hind in Richmond Park. Repr. of 1923 ed. 35.00 (ISBN 0-404-03413-6). AMS Pr.
--Nature in Downland. Repr. of 1923 ed. 35.00 (ISBN 0-404-03398-9). AMS Pr.
Jackson, Hartley H. Published Writings of Arthur Holmes Howell (1872-1940) (Miscellaneous Publicatoins Ser.: No. 47). 15p. 1967. 1.25 (ISBN 0-317-04776-0). U of Ks Mus Nat Hist.
Jones, William F. Nature & Natural Science: The Philosophy of Frederick Woodbridge. LC 82-48969. 197p. 1982. 20.95 (ISBN 0-87975-183-5). Prometheus Bks.
Jordan, David S. Science Sketches. new & enl. ed. (Essay Index Reprint Ser.). Repr. of 1896 ed. 18.00 (ISBN 0-518-10181-9). Ayer Co Pubs.
Kessel, Edward L., ed. A Century of Progress in the Natural Sciences, 1853-1953. LC 73-17827. (Natural Sciences in America Ser.). (Illus.). 824p. 1974. Repr. 54.00x (ISBN 0-405-05745-8). Ayer Co Pubs.
Kolisko, Eugen. Natural History. 1980. pap. 3.25 (ISBN 0-906492-21-1, Pub. by Kolisko Archives). St George Bk Serv.
Kopper, Philip. The National Museum of Natural History. 496p. 1982. 60.00 (ISBN 0-8109-1359-3). Abrams.
Lankester, Edwin R. Diversions of a Naturalist. LC 77-105024. (Essay Index Reprint Ser.). 1915. 26.50 (ISBN 0-8369-1471-6). Ayer Co Pubs.
--Science from an Easy Chair, First Series. facs. ed. LC 79-152185. (Essay Index Reprint Ser). 1910. 24.50 (ISBN 0-8369-2194-1). Ayer Co Pubs.
--Secrets of Earth & Sea. LC 76-93352. (Essay Index Reprint Ser). 1920. 19.00 (ISBN 0-8369-1301-9). Ayer Co Pubs.
Leopold, Luna B., ed. Round River: From the Journals of Aldo Leopold. (Illus.). 1972. pap. 3.95 (ISBN 0-19-501563-0, 372, GB). Oxford U Pr.
Linnaeus, Carl. Miscellaneous Tracts Relating to Natural History, Husbandry, & Physick: Calender of Flora Is Added. Egerton, Frank N., 3rd, ed. LC 77-74237. (History of Ecology Ser.). 1978. Repr. of 1762 ed. lib. bdg. 29.00x (ISBN 0-405-10406-5). Ayer Co Pubs.
Lyon, John & Sloan, Philip. From Natural History to the History of Nature: Readings from Buffon & His Critics. LC 81-1320. 432p. 1981. text ed. 19.95 (ISBN 0-268-00955-4). U of Notre Dame Pr.
Mcatee, W. L. & Harper, Francis. Published Writings of Edward Alexander Preble, 1871-1957. (Miscellaneous Publications Ser.: No. 40). 16p. 1965. 1.25 (ISBN 0-317-04779-5). U of KS Mus Nat Hist.
Magnificent Foragers: Smithsonian Explorations in the Natural Sciences. LC 78-61066. (Illus.). 223p. 1978. 16.95 (ISBN 0-89599-001-6, Dist. by Norton). Smithsonian Bks.
Le Monde de la nature. (Illus.). 1978. text ed. 26.95x (ISBN 2-03-019112-4). Larousse.
Moseley, Henry N. Notes by a Naturalist. new & rev. ed. LC 72-1710. Orig. Title: Notes by a Naturalist on the Challenger. (Illus.). Repr. of 1892 ed. 36.45 (ISBN 0-404-08159-2). AMS Pr.
Myers, George, Jr. Natural History. LC 81-80891. (Illus.). 80p. (Orig.). 1981. pap. 3.50 (ISBN 0-9602424-6-5). Paycock Pr.
Olson, Sigurd F. Listening Point. (Illus.). 1958. 13.95 (ISBN 0-394-43358-0). Knopf.
Omelyanovsky, M. E., et al. Lenin & Modern Natural Science. 422p. 1977. 6.95 (ISBN 0-8285-0198-X, Pub. by Progress Pubs USSR). Imported Pubns.
Ospovat, Dov. The Development of Darwin's Theory: Natural History, Natural Theology, & Natural Selection, 1838-1859. LC 81-4077. (Illus.). 228p. 1981. 47.50 (ISBN 0-521-23818-8). Cambridge U Pr.
Page, Jake. Pastorale: A Natural History of Sorts. LC 84-8141. (Illus.). 1985. 13.95 (ISBN 0-393-01903-9). Norton.
Pliny. Natural History. Turner, ed. Holland, tr. 1983. 70.00x (ISBN 0-900000-48-1, Pub. by Centaur Pr England). State Mutual Bk.
--Natural History, Vols. 1-5 Of 11. Warmington, E. H., ed. (Loeb Classical Library: No. 330, 352-353, 370-371). 12.50x ea. Vol. 1 (ISBN 0-674-99364-0). Vol. 2 (ISBN 0-674-99388-8). Vol. 3 (ISBN 0-674-99389-6). Vol. 4 (ISBN 0-674-99408-6). Vol. 5 (ISBN 0-674-99409-4). Harvard U Pr.
--Natural History, Vols. 6-10 Of 11. (Loeb Classical Library: No. 392-394, 418-419). 12.50x ea. Vol. 6 (ISBN 0-674-99431-0). Vol. 7 (ISBN 0-674-99432-9). Vol. 8 (ISBN 0-674-99460-4). Vol. 9 (ISBN 0-674-99433-7). Vol. 10 (ISBN 0-674-99461-2). Harvard U Pr.
Praeger, Robert L. The Way That I Went. (Illus.). 394p. (Orig.). 1980. pap. 13.50 (ISBN 0-900372-93-1, Pub. by A Figgis Ireland). Irish Bk Ctr.
Ramade, F. Ecology of Natural Resources. 231p. 1984. 54.95 (ISBN 0-471-90104-0). Wiley.
Reader's Digest Editors. Natural Wonders of the World. LC 80-50353. (Illus.). 464p. 1980. 23.95 (ISBN 0-89577-087-3, Pub. by RD Assn). Random.
Roe, Shirley A. & Cohen, I. Bernard, eds. The Natural Philosophy of Albrecht Von Haller. LC 80-2109. (Development of Science Ser.). (Illus.). 1981. lib. bdg. 40.00x (ISBN 0-405-13874-1). Ayer Co Pubs.
Russell, Dale & Harrington, Dick. Natural History Notebook, No. 5. 54p. 1982. pap. 2.50 (ISBN 0-686-97830-7, 56446-0, Pub. by Natl Mus Canada). U of Chicago Pr.
Sargent, Steven, ed. & tr. from Ger. On the Threshold of Exact Science: Selected Writings of Anneliese Maier on Late Medieval Natural Philosophy. LC 81-43524. (Middle Ages Ser.). 192p. 1982. 25.00x (ISBN 0-8122-7831-3). U of Pa Pr.
Scandone, Thomas. Emphasis: Natural History. 1979. coil binging 15.95 (ISBN 0-88252-098-9). Paladin Hse.
Schopf, J. William. Cradle of Life. Date not set. price not set (ISBN 0-87735-339-5). Freeman Cooper.
Smellie, William. The Philosophy of Natural History, 2 vols. LC 78-67541. Repr. 125.00 set (ISBN 0-404-17230-X). AMS Pr.
Steiner, Rudolf. The Boundaries of Natural Science. Amrine, Frederick, tr. from Ger. LC 83-9943. 144p. 1983. 14.95 (ISBN 0-88010-018-4). Anthroposophic.
Storer, Tracy I. & Usinger, Robert L. Sierra Nevada Natural History: An Illustrated Handbook. (Illus.). 1963. pap. 7.95 (ISBN 0-520-01227-5). U of Cal Pr.
Swain, Roger. Earthly Pleasures. (Illus.). 192p. 1981. 10.95 (ISBN 0-684-16657-7, ScribT). Scribner.
Thoreau, Henry D. The Natural History Essays. LC 80-11357. (Literature of the American Wilderness Ser.). 288p. 1980. pap. 4.95 (ISBN 0-87905-071-3, Peregrine Smith). Gibbs M Smith.
Titley, I. & Sutton, D. A. A Geographical Index to the Collections of Phaeophyta (Brown Algae) Held at the British Museum (Natural History) 1984. 15.00x (ISBN 0-565-00897-8, Pub. by Brit Mus Nat Hist England); microfiche incl. Sabbot-Natural Hist Bks.
White, Gilbert. Natural History of Selborne. 1984. 20.00x (ISBN 0-905418-22-0, Pub. by Gresham England). State Mutual Bk.
Wilkinson. Natural History. 1985. lib. bdg. 35.00 (ISBN 0-8240-9064-0). Garland Pub.
Williams. Mathematics with Applications in the Management, Natural & Social Sciences. 1985. 31.52 (ISBN 0-205-07188-0, 567188); instr. manual 7.23 (ISBN 0-205-07189-9, 567189). Allyn.
Willson, Mary F. Vertebrate Natural History. 621p. 1984. text ed. 37.95x (ISBN 0-03-061804-5). SCP.
Wilson, David S. In the Presence of Nature. LC 77-90733. (Illus.). 258p. 1978. 17.50x (ISBN 0-87023-020-4). U of Mass Pr.
Yamaguchi, K. Spectral Data of Natural Products, Vol. 2. Date not set. price not set (ISBN 0-444-40842-8). Elsevier.

NATURAL HISTORY–BIBLIOGRAPHY

Bridson, Gavin D., et al, eds. Natural History Manuscript Resources in the British Isles. LC 79-92886. 6000p. 1980. 245.00 (ISBN 0-8352-1281-5). Bowker.
Brightman, Frank, ed. Natural History Book Reviews: An International Biography. 1981. 35.00x (ISBN 0-686-72935-8, Pub by A B Academic England). State Mutual Bk.
Dryander, Jonas. Catalogus Bibliothecae Historico-Naturalis Josephi Banks, 5 vols. 1966. Set. 124.00 (ISBN 90-6123-003-9). Lubrecht & Cramer.
Freeman, R. B. The Works of Charles Darwin: An Annotated Bibliographical Handlist. rev. & 2nd ed. LC 76-30002. 235p. 1977. 24.75x (ISBN 0-208-01658-9, Pub. by St. Pauls Biblios England). U Pr of Va.
Munz, Lucile T. & Slauson, Nedra. Index to Illustrations of Living Things Outside of North America: Where to Find Pictures of Flora & Fauna. 441p. 1981. 49.50 (ISBN 0-208-01857-3, Archon). Shoe String.
Research Catalog of the Library of the American Museum of Natural History: Classed Catalog. 1978. 1050.00 (ISBN 0-8161-0238-4, Hall Library). G K Hall.

NATURAL HISTORY–DICTIONARIES

Allaby, Michael. Dictionary of the Environment. 2nd, rev. ed. (Illus.). 608p. 1984. 55.00x (ISBN 0-8147-0582-0). NYU Pr.
Brockhaus der Naturwissenschaften und der Technik. (Ger.). 832p. 35.00 (ISBN 3-7653-0019-5, M-7314, Pub. by Wiesbaden). French & Eur.
Habibi, B. Deutsch-Persisches Fachwoerterbuch Fuer Naturwissenschaft, Medezin und Landwirtschaft. (Ger. & Persian.). 240p. 1964. pap. 17.50 (ISBN 3-447-00354-5, M-7331, Pub. by Harrassowitz). French & Eur.
Historia Natural, 4 vols. 11th ed. (Espn.). 1984p. 1976. Set. leather 215.00 (ISBN 84-85009-42-8, S-50569). French & Eur.
Jehan, L. F. Dictionnaire d'Anthropologie ou Histoire Naturelle del'Homme et des Races Humaines. Migne, J. P., ed. (Nouvelle Encyclopedie Theologique Ser.: Vol. 42). (Fr.). 800p. Repr. of 1853 ed. lib. bdg. 101.50x (ISBN 0-89241-281-X). Caratzas.
--Dictionnaire Historique des Sciences Physiques et Naturelles. Migne, J. P., ed. (Troisieme et Derniere Encyclopedie Theologique Ser.: Vol. 30). (Fr.). 654p. Repr. of 1857 ed. lib. bdg. 85.00x (ISBN 0-89241-309-3). Caratzas.
Judge, Harry, et al, eds. Oxford Illustrated Encyclopedia: The Natural World, Vol. 2. (Illus.). 384p. 1985. 35.00 (ISBN 0-19-869134-3). Oxford U Pr.
Khatib, Ahmad. Dictionary of the Natural Environment: English-Arabic. 1979. pap. 7.95x (ISBN 0-86685-073-2). Intl Bk Ctr.
Lewis, Walter H. Ecology Field Glossary: A Naturalist's Vocabulary. LC 77-71856. 1977. lib. bdg. 29.95 (ISBN 0-8371-9547-0, LEF/). Greenwood.
Seager, Herbert W. Natural History in Shakespeare's Time. LC 79-160134. Repr. of 1896 ed. 24.00 (ISBN 0-404-05667-9). AMS Pr.

NATURAL HISTORY–NOMENCLATURES

see also Botany–Nomenclature

Kessel, Edward L., ed. A Century of Progress in the Natural Sciences, 1853-1953. LC 73-17827. (Natural Sciences in America Ser.). (Illus.). 824p. 1974. Repr. 54.00x (ISBN 0-405-05745-8). Ayer Co Pubs.

NATURAL HISTORY–OUTDOOR BOOKS

Barrus, Clara, ed. The Heart of Burrough's Journals. 1979. Repr. of 1928 ed. lib. bdg. 30.00 (ISBN 0-8495-0504-6). Arden Lib.
Bedichek, Roy. Adventures with a Texas Naturalist. (Illus.). 360p. 1961. pap. 8.95 (ISBN 0-292-70311-2). U of Tex Pr.
Errington, Paul L. The Red Gods Call. (Illus.). 172p. 1973. 9.50 (ISBN 0-8138-1340-9). Iowa St U Pr.
Fuller, Raymond T. Now That We Have to Walk: Exploring the Out-of-Doors. facsimile ed. LC 72-37921. (Essay Index Reprint Ser). Repr. of 1943 ed. 19.00 (ISBN 0-8369-2590-4). Ayer Co Pubs.
Godfrey, Michael A. A Sierra Club Naturalist's Guide to the Piedmont of Eastern North America. LC 79-22328. (Naturalists Guide Ser.). (Illus.). 432p. 1980. 19.95 (ISBN 0-87156-268-5); pap. 9.95 (ISBN 0-87156-269-3). Sierra.
Jefferies, Richard. Old House at Coate. LC 70-111840. (Essay Index Reprint Ser). 1948. 18.00 (ISBN 0-8369-1664-6). Ayer Co Pubs.
Kieran, John F. Nature Notes. facs. ed. LC 77-84315. (Essay Index Reprint Ser). 1941. 16.50 (ISBN 0-8369-1087-7). Ayer Co Pubs.
Leopold, Aldo. Sand County Almanac: With Other Essays on Conservation from Round River. (Illus.). 1966. 17.95 (ISBN 0-19-500619-4). Oxford U Pr.
Olson, Sigurd F. Listening Point. (Illus.). 1958. 13.95 (ISBN 0-394-43358-0). Knopf.
Pearson, Haydn S. Sea Flavor. facs. ed. LC 68-58809. (Essay Index Reprint Ser). 1948. 17.00 (ISBN 0-8369-0051-0). Ayer Co Pubs.
Sharp, Dallas L. Face of the Fields. facs. ed. LC 67-26782. (Essay Index Reprint Ser). 1911. 17.00 (ISBN 0-8369-0870-8). Ayer Co Pubs.
--Sanctuary! Sanctuary! facs. ed. LC 73-128312. (Essay Index Reprint Ser). 1926. 12.00 (ISBN 0-8369-2134-8). Ayer Co Pubs.
Sharp, William. Where the Forest Murmurs. LC 73-111865. (Essay Index Reprint Ser). 1906. 21.50 (ISBN 0-8369-1627-1). Ayer Co Pubs.
Shepard, Odell. Harvest of a Quiet Eye: A Book of Digressions. facsimile ed. LC 77-117843. (Essay Index Reprint Ser). Repr. of 1927 ed. 21.50 (ISBN 0-8369-2428-2). Ayer Co Pubs.

NATURAL HISTORY–PICTORIAL WORKS

see also Botany–Pictorial Works; Zoology–Pictorial Works

Archer, Mildred. Natural History Drawings in the India Office Library. (Illus.). 116p. 1962. 25.00x (ISBN 0-85667-082-0, Pub. by Sotheby Pubns England). Biblio Dist.
Diment, J. A., et al. Catalogue of the Natural History Drawings Commissioned by Joseph Banks on the Endeavour Voyage, Part 1: Botany - Australia. (Illus.). 183p. 1984. pap. text ed. 60.00x (ISBN 0-565-09000-3, Pub. by Brit Mus Nat Hist England). Sabbot Natural Hist Bks.
Ewan, Joseph. William Bartram: Botanical & Zoological Drawings, 1756-88. LC 68-8640. (Memoirs Ser.: Vol. 74). (Illus.). 1968. 50.00 (ISBN 0-87169-074-8). Am Philos.
Strache, Wolf. Forms & Patterns in Nature. LC 73-3468. 1973. Pantheon.
Thompson, Nedra, ed. Index to Illustrations of the Natural World: Where to Find Pictures of the Living Things of North America. LC 77-4143. (Illus.). 265p. 1983. Repr. of 1977 ed. 39.50 (ISBN 0-208-02038-1, Archon Bks). Shoe String.

NATURAL HISTORY–PRE-LINNEAN WORKS

Bacon, Francis. De Sapientia Veterum, Repr. Of 1609 Ed. Bd. with The Wisedome of the Ancients. Gorges, Arthur, tr. Repr. of 1619 ed. LC 75-27863. (Renaissance & the Gods Ser.: Vol. 20). (Illus.). 1976. lib. bdg. 88.00 (ISBN 0-8240-2068-5). Garland Pub.
Derham, William. Physico-Theology: A Demonstration of the Being & Attributes of God, from His Works of Creation. Egerton, Frank N., 3rd, ed. LC 77-74212. (History of Ecology Ser.). 1978. Repr. of 1716 ed. lib. bdg. 37.50 (ISBN 0-405-10383-2). Ayer Co Pubs.

NATURAL HISTORY–STUDY AND TEACHING

see also Nature Study

Agassiz, Louis. Methods of Study in Natural History. LC 72-125728. (American Environmental Studies). 1970. Repr. of 1863 ed. 20.00 (ISBN 0-405-02653-6). Ayer Co Pubs.

Arnspiger, Varney C. Measuring the Effectiveness of Sound Pictures As Teaching Aids. LC 71-176524. (Columbia University. Teachers College. Contributions to Education: No. 565). Repr. of 1933 ed. 22.50 (ISBN 0-404-55565-9). AMS Pr.

Brown, Robert E. & Mouser, G. W. Techniques for Teaching Conservation Education. LC 64-24115. Repr. of 1964 ed. 30.00 (ISBN 0-8357-9054-1, 2013323). Bks Demand UMI.

Goff, Paul E. Nature, Children & You. LC 81-18911. vi, 144p. 1982. 14.95 (ISBN 0-8214-0607-8, 82-83939); pap. 6.95 (ISBN 0-8214-0679-5, 82-84423). Ohio U Pr.

Gross, Phyllis P. & Railton, Esther P. Teaching Science in an Outdoor Environment: Handbook for Students, Parents, Teachers, & Camp Leaders. LC 73-173903. (California Natural History Guides: No. 30). (Illus.). 175p. 1972. 14.95x (ISBN 0-520-03092-3); pap. 5.95 (ISBN 0-520-02148-7). U of Cal Pr.

Sharpe, Grant W. Interpreting the Environment. 2nd ed. LC 81-10391. 694p. 1982. 34.00 (ISBN 0-471-09007-7). Wiley.

NATURAL HISTORY–TECHNIQUE

see also Aquariums; Insects–Collection and Preservation; Microscope and Microscopy–Technique; Plants–Collection and Preservation; Stains and Staining (Microscopy); Taxidermy; Zoological Specimens–Collection and Preservation

MacCreagh, Gordon. White Waters & Black. LC 85-8745. (Illus.). 422p. 1985. pap. 14.95 (ISBN 0-226-50016-0). U of Chicago Pr.

NATURAL HISTORY–AFRICA

Burkill, H. M. The Useful Plants of West Tropical Africa, Vol. 1. 900p. 1985. 100.00x (ISBN 0-947643-01-X, Pub. by Prospect England). U Pr of Va.

Drummond, Henry. Tropical Africa. LC 69-18651. (Illus.). Repr. of 1890 ed. 15.00x (ISBN 0-8371-2266-X, DRT&). Greenwood.

Du Chaillu, Paul B. A Journey to Ashango-Land & Further Penetration into Equatorial Africa. LC 5-9143. 1971. Repr. of 1867 ed. 23.00 (ISBN 0-384-13185-9). Johnson Repr.

Johnston, Harry H. British Central Africa. LC 78-88439. Repr. of 1897 ed. 51.00x (ISBN 0-8371-1910-3, JOB&, Pub. by Negro U Pr). Greenwood.

Kolb, Peter. The Present State of the Cape of Good-Hope: Or, a Particular Account of the Several Nations of the Hottentots, 2 vols. (Anthropology Ser.). 1969. Repr. of 1731 ed. Vol. 1. 35.00 (ISBN 0-384-30100-2); Vol. 2. 42.00 (ISBN 0-685-13553-5). Johnson Repr.

Rogers, Dilwyn J., ed. A Bibliography of African Ecology: A Geographically & Topically Classified List of Books & Articles. LC 78-19935. (Special Bibliographic Ser: No. 6). 1979. lib. bdg. 45.00x (ISBN 0-313-20552-3, RAE/). Greenwood.

Schaller, George B. Year of the Gorilla. LC 64-13946. (Illus.). 1964. pap. 5.50 (ISBN 0-226-73638-5, P209, Phoen). U of Chicago Pr.

Sweeney, Charles. Naturalist in the Sudan. LC 73-17778. (Illus.). 256p. 1974. 8.50 (ISBN 0-8008-5466-7). Taplinger.

NATURAL HISTORY–ALASKA

Bailey, Alfred M. Field Work of a Museum Naturalist: Alaska Southeast, 1919-1921; Alaska Far North, 1921-1922. (Museum Pictorial: No. 22). 1971. pap. 2.25 (ISBN 0-916278-49-2). Denver Mus Natl Hist.

Miller, Mike & Wayburn, Peggy. Alaska: The Great Land. (Illus.). 128p. 1975. pap. 7.95 (ISBN 0-684-14125-6, SL576, ScribT). Scribner.

Nelson, Richard K. Make Prayers to the Raven: A Koyukon View of the Northern Forest. LC 82-8441. 300p. 1983. 25.00x (ISBN 0-226-57162-9). U of Chicago Pr.

Staender, Vivian & Staender, Gil. Our Arctic Year. (Illus.). 1985. pap. 12.95 (ISBN 0-88240-238-2). Alaska Northwest.

NATURAL HISTORY–ALEUTIAN ISLANDS

Collins, et al. Aleutian Islands: Their People & Natural History. facsimile ed. (Illus.). 157p. Shorey.

NATURAL HISTORY–AMERICA

Chambers, Kenneth. The Country Lover's Guide to Wildlife: Mammals, Amphibians, & Reptiles of the Northeastern United States. LC 79-4338. (Illus.). 248p. 1979. 18.50 (ISBN 0-8018-2207-6). Johns Hopkins.

Fiero, G. William. Great Basin Geology. (Max C. Fleischmann Series in Great Basin Natural History). (Illus.). 200p. 1985. 22.50 (ISBN 0-87417-083-4); pap. 14.50 (ISBN 0-87417-084-2). U of Nev Pr.

Sterling, Keir B., ed. Natural Sciences in America, 58 vols. 1974. 2800.00x set (ISBN 0-405-05700-8). Ayer Co Pubs.

Tucher, Andrea. Natural History in America, 1609-1860: Printed Works in the Collections of the American Philosophical Society, the Historical Society of Pennsylvania, & the Library Company of Philadelphia. LC 83-49302. (Referance Library of Social Science-Americana to 1860). 240p. 1985. lib. bdg. 50.00 (ISBN 0-8240-8965-0). Garland Pub.

NATURAL HISTORY–ANTARCTIC REGIONS

Llano, George A., ed. Antarctic Terrestrial Biology. LC 72-92709. (Antarctic Research Ser.: Vol. 20). (Illus.). 322p. 1972. 39.00 (ISBN 0-87590-120-4). Am Geophysical.

Lowry, James K. Soft Bottom Macrobenthic Community of Arthur Harbor, Antarctica: Paper 1 in Biology of the Antarctic Seas V. Pawson, David L., ed. LC 75-22056. (Antarctic Research Ser.: Vol. 23). (Illus.). 20p. 1975. pap. 5.20 (ISBN 0-87590-123-9). Am Geophysical.

NATURAL HISTORY–ASIA

Archer, Mildred. Natural History Drawings in the India Office Library. (Illus.). 116p. 1962. 25.00x (ISBN 0-85667-082-0, Pub. by Sotheby Pubns England). Biblio Dist.

Griffith, William. Icones Plantrum Asiaticarum, 8 vols. (Illus.). 1978. Repr. of 1849 ed. Set. 800.00x (ISBN 0-89955-284-6, Pub. by Intl Bk Dist). Intl Spec Bk.

NATURAL HISTORY–AUSTRALIA

Breeden, Stanley & Breeden, Kay. Australia's North. (A Natural History of Australia Ser.: No. 3). 208p. 1980. 34.95 (ISBN 0-00-211441-0, Pub. by W Collins Australia). Intl Spec Bk.

--Wildlife of Eastern Australia. (Illus.). 260p. 1974. 12.95 (ISBN 0-8008-8332-2). Taplinger.

Evans, Howard Ensign & Evans, Mary A. Australia: A Natural History. LC 83-10471. (Illus.). 208p. 1983. 39.95 (ISBN 0-87474-418-0); pap. 19.95 (ISBN 0-87474-417-2). Smithsonian.

Gauld, I. D. An Introduction to the Ichneumonidae of Australia. (Illus.). 420p. 1984. pap. 80.00x (ISBN 0-565-00896-X, Pub. by Brit Mus Nat Hist England). Sabbot-Natural Hist Bks.

Huxley, Thomas H. & Huxley, Julian S. Diary of the Voyage of H. M. S. Rattlesnake. Repr. of 1936 ed. 22.00 (ISBN 0-527-43860-X). Kraus Repr.

Slater, Peter, et al. Field Guide to Australian Birds. LC 78-140167. (Illus.). 1971. Vol. 1, Non-Passerines. 25.00 (ISBN 0-915180-14-6); Vol. 2, Passerines. 25.00 (ISBN 0-915180-15-4). Livingston.

Spencer, Baldwin. Wanderings in Wild Australia, 2 Vols. (Illus.). Repr. of 1928 ed. Set. 110.00 (ISBN 0-384-57023-2). Johnson Repr.

Sturt, Charles. Narrative of an Expedition into Central Australia, Performed During the Years 1844-1846, 2 Vols. LC 68-55225. 1968. Repr. of 1849 ed. Set. lib. bdg. 34.00x (ISBN 0-8371-3868-X, STCA). Greenwood.

NATURAL HISTORY–BAHAMAS

Catesby, Mark. Natural History of Carolina, Florida & the Bahama Islands, Catalogue Volume. (Illus.). 50.00 (ISBN 0-384-07865-6). Johnson Repr.

Osborn, Henry F., ed. Naturalist in the Bahamas: October 12, 1861 - June 25, 1891. LC 10-13587. 1910. 10.00 (ISBN 0-404-04794-7). AMS Pr.

NATURAL HISTORY–BRAZIL

Hurt, Wesley R. The Interrelationships Between the Natural Environment & Four Sambaquis, Coast of Santa Catarina, Brazil. (Occasional Papers & Monographs: No. 1). (Illus.). 19p. 1974. 2.00. W H Mathers Mus.

NATURAL HISTORY–CANADA

Berger, Carl. Science, God, & Nature in Victorian Canada. 107p. 1983. 15.00x (ISBN 0-8020-2501-3); pap. 6.50 (ISBN 0-8020-6523-6). U of Toronto Pr.

Boily, Lise & Blanchette, Jean-Francois. The Bread Ovens of Quebec. (Illus.). 1979. pap. 8.95 (ISBN 0-660-00120-9, 56284-0, Pub. by Natl Mus Canada). U of Chicago Pr.

Denys, Nicolas. Description: Natural History of the Coasts of North America. Ganong, William F., ed. LC 68-28597. 1968. Repr. of 1908 ed. lib. bdg. 42.25x (ISBN 0-8371-3873-6, DEDH). Greenwood.

Douglas, Charles. Natural History Notebook, 2 bks. (Illus.). 1977. No. 1. pap. 2.50 (ISBN 0-660-00092-X, 56440-1, Pub. by Natl Mus Canada); No. 2. pap. 2.50 (ISBN 0-660-00094-6, 56442-8). U of Chicago Pr.

Hearne, Samuel. Journey from Prince of Wale's Fort in Hudson's Bay to the Northern Ocean. LC 78-133870. (Illus.). 1971. 19.25 (ISBN 0-8048-1007-9). C E Tuttle.

--Journey from Prince of Wales's Fort in Hudson's Bay to the Northern Ocean in the Years 1769-1772. LC 68-28601. (Illus.). 1968. Repr. of 1911 ed. lib. bdg. 32.75x (ISBN 0-8371-5045-0, HEJP). Greenwood.

Judd, W. W. & Speirs, J. Murray, eds. Naturalist's Guide to Ontario. LC 65-3239. (Illus.). 1964. pap. 8.50 (ISBN 0-8020-6039-0). U of Toronto Pr.

Laird, M. Bibliography of the Natural History of Newfoundland & Labrador. 1980. 66.50 (ISBN 0-12-434050-4). Acad Pr.

NATURAL HISTORY–CENTRAL AMERICA

Janzen, Daniel H., ed. Costa Rican Natural History. LC 82-17625. (Illus.). 832p. 1983. lib. bdg. 55.00x (ISBN 0-226-39332-1); pap. text ed. 30.00x (ISBN 0-226-39334-8). U of Chicago Pr.

NATURAL HISTORY–CHINA

Wilson, Ernest H. A Naturalist in Western China, 2 vols. LC 76-46620. 1977. Repr. of 1913 ed. write for info (ISBN 0-913728-17-9). Theophrastus.

NATURAL HISTORY–COLOMBIA

Hurt, Wesley R. & Hammen, Thomas Van D. The El Abra Rockshelter, Sabana de Bogota, Columbia, South America. (Occasional Papers & Monographs: No. 2). (Illus.). 56p. 1976. 3.00 (ISBN 0-87750-207-2). W H Mathers Mus.

NATURAL HISTORY–EUROPE

Brusewitz, Gunnar. Wings & Seasons. Wheeler, Walston, tr. from Swedish. (Illus.). 119p. 1983. 20.00 (ISBN 0-88072-029-8, Pub. by Tanager). Longwood Pub Group.

Pitard, J. & Proust, L. Les Iles Canaries, Flore de L'archipel. 1973. Repr. of 1908 ed. lib. bdg. 52.50x (ISBN 3-87429-050-6). Lubrecht & Cramer.

NATURAL HISTORY–GAMBIA

Reeve, Henry F. Gambia, Its History. LC 75-79275. (Illus.). Repr. of 1912 ed. 23.25x (ISBN 0-8371-1449-7, REG&, Pub. by Negro U Pr). Greenwood.

NATURAL HISTORY–GREAT BRITAIN

Angel, Heather, et al. The Natural History of Britain & Ireland. (Illus.). 256p. 1985. pap. 14.95 (ISBN 0-7181-2557-6, Pub. by Michael Joseph). Merrimack Pub Cir.

Bere, Rennie. The Nature of Cornwall: The County's Wildlife & Its Habitats. 196p. 1982. 39.00x (ISBN 0-86023-163-1, Pub. by Barracuda England). State Mutual Bk.

Bishop, A. C., et al. Catalogue of the Rock Collections in the British Museum (Natural History). 2nd ed. 148p. 1984. pap. text ed. 36.00x (ISBN 0-565-00875-7, Pub by Brit Mus Nat Hist England). Sabbot-Natural Hist Bks.

Bridson, Gavin D., et al, eds. Natural History Manuscript Resources in the British Isles. LC 79-92886. 6000p. 1980. 245.00 (ISBN 0-8352-1281-5). Bowker.

Dennis, Eve. Everyman's Nature Reserve: Ideas for Action. (Illus.). 256p. 1973. 7.50 (ISBN 0-7153-5918-5). David & Charles.

Freeman, R. B. British Natural History Books from the Beginning to Nineteen Hundred: A Handlist. LC 80-50228. 437p. 1980. 39.50 (ISBN 0-208-01790-9, Archon). Shoe String.

Gilpin, William. Remarks on Forest Scenery & Other Woodland Views Illustrated by the Scenes of New Forest in Hampshire. 746p. 1984. Repr. of 1791 ed. 82.00 (ISBN 0-85546-181-0, Pub. by Richmond Pub England). State Mutual Bk.

Hoeniger, F. D. & Hoeniger, J. F. Development of Natural History in Tudor England. LC 69-19336. (Folger Guides to the Age of Shakespeare Ser.). 1969. pap. 3.95 (ISBN 0-918016-29-0). Folger Bks.

--Growth of Natural History in Stuart England: From Gerard to the Royal Society. LC 69-17335. (Folger Guides to the Age of Shakespeare). 1969. pap. 3.95 (ISBN 0-918016-14-2). Folger Bks.

Hudson, William H. Land's End. Repr. of 1923 ed. 35.00 (ISBN 0-404-03404-7). AMS Pr.

Janovy, John, Jr. Keith County Journal. 1980. pap. 4.95 (ISBN 0-312-45124-5). St Martin.

Kent, Douglas H. The Historical Flora of Middlesex: An Account of the Wild Plants Found in the Watsonian Vice-County 21 from 1548 to the Present Time. (Illus.). vi, 679p. 1975. 32.50x (ISBN 0-903874-03-2, Pub by Brit Mus Nat Hist England). Sabbot-Natural Hist Bks.

Napier, P. H. Catalogue of Primates in the British Museum (Natural History) & Elsewhere in the British Isles, Part 3: Family Cercopithecidae Subfamily Colobinae. 175p. 1985. 70.00x (ISBN 0-565-00894-3, Pub. by Brit Mus Nat Hist England). Sabbot-Natural Hist Bks.

Scott, Walter S. White of Selborne. 272p. 1985. 15.75 (ISBN 0-947647-15-5, Pub. by Fanciers Supplies). Longwood Pub Group.

White, Gilbert. Natural History of Selbourne. 1974. pap. 2.95x (ISBN 0-460-01048-4, Evman). Biblio Dist.

NATURAL HISTORY–GUYANA

Beebe, William. Edge of the Jungle. 1921. 27.50 (ISBN 0-8482-7358-3). Norwood Edns.

Rodway, James. In the Guiana Forest: Studies of Nature in Relations to the Struggle for Life. LC 69-18997. (Illus.). Repr. of 1894 ed. 24.75x (ISBN 0-8371-1027-0, ROG&). Greenwood.

Waterton, Charles. Wanderings in South America, the Northwest of the United States, & the Antilles in the Years Eighteen Twelve, Eighteen Sixteen, Eighteen Twenty, & Eighteen Twenty-Four. 341p. 1968. Repr. of 1828 ed. 25.00 (ISBN 0-8398-2157-3). Parnassus Imprints.

NATURAL HISTORY–HAWAII

Kay, E. Alison, ed. Natural History of the Hawaiian Islands: Selected Readings. (Illus.). 665p. 1972. pap. 15.00x (ISBN 0-8248-0203-9). UH Pr.

Merlin, Mark D. Hawaiian Forest Plants. LC 76-36304. (Illus.). 1978. pap. 4.00 (ISBN 0-932596-00-2, Pub. by Oriental). Intl Spec Bk.

Meyen, Franz J. A Botanist's Visit to Oahu in 1831. Pultz, Mary Anne, ed. Jackson, Astrid, tr. from Ger. LC 81-7353. (Illus.). 90p. 1981. pap. 6.95 (ISBN 0-916630-23-4). Pr Pacifica.

NATURAL HISTORY–ICELAND

Oddsson, Gisli. Annalium in Islandia Farrago, & De Mirabilibus Islandiae. Hermannsson, Halldor, ed. (Islandica Ser.: Vol. 10). 1917. 12.00 (ISBN 0-527-00340-9). Kraus Repr.

NATURAL HISTORY–ISLANDS OF THE PACIFIC

Baltazar, Clare R. & Salazar, Nelia P. Philippine Insects: An Introduction. (Illus.). 1980. text ed. 17.00x (ISBN 0-8248-0675-1, Pub. by U of Philippines Pr); pap. text ed. 12.00x (ISBN 0-8248-0676-X). UH Pr.

NATURAL HISTORY–JAMAICA

Procter, G. R. Ferns of Jamaica: A Guide to The Pteridophytes. (Illus.). 610p. 1985. 82.50x (ISBN 0-565-00895-1, Pub. by Brit Mus of Nat Hist England). Sabbot Natural Hist Bks.

NATURAL HISTORY–KENYA

Coe, Malcolm. Islands in the Bush: A Natural History of the Kora National Reserve, Kenya. (Illus.). 256p. 1985. 29.95 (ISBN 0-540-01086-3, Pub. by G Philip UK). Sheridan.

NATURAL HISTORY–LATIN AMERICA

Belt, Thomas. The Naturalist in Nicaragua. (Illus.). xxxiv, 406p. 1985. lib. bdg. 30.00x (ISBN 0-226-04219-7); pap. 12.95 (ISBN 0-226-04220-0). U of Chicago Pr.

De Acosta, Joseph. The Natural & Moral History of the Indies, 2 Vols. Markham, Clements R., ed. LC 75-134715. (Hakluyt Society Ser.: No. 60-61). 1970. Set. lib. bdg. 60.50 (ISBN 0-8337-0798-1). B Franklin.

LeBoeuf, Burney & Kaza, Stephanie, eds. The Natural History of Ano Nuevo. (Illus., Orig.). 1981. pap. 9.95 (ISBN 0-910286-77-9). Boxwood.

Roosevelt, Theodore. Theodore Roosevelt's America: American Naturalists Ser. Wiley, Farida, ed. (Illus.). 1955. 14.95 (ISBN 0-8159-6714-4). Devin.

Rumphius. The Poison Tree: Selected Writings of Rumphius on the Natural History of the Indies. Beekman, E. M., tr. from Dutch & Lat. LC 81-7605. (Library of the Indies). (Illus.). 272p. 1981. lib. bdg. 20.00x (ISBN 0-87023-329-7). U of Mass Pr.

NATURAL HISTORY–LIBERIA

Johnston, Harry H. Liberia, 2 Vols. LC 71-78372. (Illus.). Repr. of 1906 ed. Set. 76.00x (ISBN 0-8371-3897-3, JOL&, Pub. by Negro U Pr). Greenwood.

NATURAL HISTORY–MADAGASCAR

Shaw, George A. Madagascar & France, with Some Account of the Island, Its People, Its Resources & Development. LC 73-82072. (Illus.). Repr. of 1885 ed. 22.50x (ISBN 0-8371-1562-0, SHM&, Pub. by Negro U Pr). Greenwood.

NATURAL HISTORY–MALAY ARCHIPELAGO

Stein, Norbert. Coniferen Im Westlichen: Malayischen Archipel. (Biogeographica Ser: No. 11). 1978. lib. bdg. 31.50 (ISBN 90-6193-212-2, Pub. by Junk Pubs Netherlands). Kluwer Academic.

NATURAL HISTORY–MELANESIA

Huxley, Thomas H. & Huxley, Julian S. Diary of the Voyage of H. M. S. Rattlesnake. Repr. of 1936 ed. 22.00 (ISBN 0-527-43860-X). Kraus Repr.

NATURAL HISTORY–MEXICO

Nelson, Edward W. Lower California & Its Natural Resources. LC 66-24189. (Illus.). 1966. 49.50x (ISBN 0-910950-00-8). Ransom Dist Co.

Rabkin, Richard & Rabkin, Jacob. Nature Guide to Florida. LC 78-23491. (Illus.). 80p. 1978. pap. 9.95 (ISBN 0-916224-44-9). Banyan Bks.
Radford, Albert E., et al. Natural Heritage: Classification, Inventory, & Information. LC 80-23087. xxi, 485p. 1981. 29.00x (ISBN 0-8078-1463-6). U of NC Pr.
Reiger, John F., ed. The Passing of the Great West: Selected Papers of George Bird Grinnell. LC 84-40696. (Illus.). 192p. (Orig.). 1985. pap. 7.95 (ISBN 0-8061-1925-X). U of Okla Pr.
Rose, Hilary & Rose, Steven. Ideology of in the Natural Sciences. 363p. 1980. pap. text ed. 11.95x (ISBN 0-87073-881-X). Schenkman Bks Inc.
Sanger, Marjory B. World of the Great White Heron. LC 67-18236. (Illus.). 1967. 14.95 (ISBN 0-8159-7214-8). Devin.
Schwartz, Susan. Nature in the Northwest: An Introduction to the Natural History & Ecology of the Northwestern United States. (Illus.). 288p. 1983. 21.95 (ISBN 0-13-610394-4); pap. 10.95 (ISBN 0-13-610386-3). P-H.
Shoman, J. Nature Realms Across America. 8.00 (ISBN 0-686-26727-3, 29). Am Forestry.
Smallwood, William M. & Smallwood, Mabel S. Natural History & the American Mind. LC 41-16864. Repr. of 1941 ed. 14.00 (ISBN 0-404-06116-8). AMS Pr.
Smith, Arthur C. Introduction to the Natural History of the San Francisco Bay Region. (California Natural History Guides: No. 1). (Illus.). 1959. 14.95x (ISBN 0-520-03099-0); pap. 3.95 (ISBN 0-520-01185-6). U of Cal Pr.
Smith, J. Lawrence. Potomac Naturalist. 1968. 8.00 (ISBN 0-87012-023-9). McClain.
Sterling, Keir B., ed. The Cabinet of Natural History & American Rural Sports, 3 vols. in one. LC 77-81115. (Biologists & Their World Ser.). (Illus.). 1978. Repr. of 1833 ed. lib. bdg. 70.50x (ISBN 0-405-10704-8). Ayer Co Pubs.
--Early Herpetological Studies & Surveys in the Eastern United States: Original Anthology. LC 77-81101. (Biologists & Their World Ser.). (Illus.). 1978. lib. bdg. 53.00x (ISBN 0-405-10685-8). Ayer Co Pubs.
Stevens, Larry. The Colorado River in Grand Canyon: A Comprehensive Guide to It's Natural & Human History. 2nd rev. ed. LC 83-61589. (Illus.). 107p. 1985. pap. 8.95 (ISBN 0-9611678-0-7); waterproof 11.25 (ISBN 0-9611678-4-X). Red Lake Bks.
Thompson, Zadock. Natural History of Vermont. LC 77-152112. (Illus.). 1971. pap. 9.25 (ISBN 0-8048-0983-6). C E Tuttle.
Trautman, Milton B. The Ohio Country from 1750-1977-A Naturalist's View. 1977. 2.50 (ISBN 0-86727-082-9). Ohio Bio Survey.
Wallace, David R. The Dark Range: A Naturalist's Night Notebook. LC 78-1452. (Illus.). 144p. 1978. 15.00 (ISBN 0-87156-212-X); pap. 8.95 (ISBN 0-87156-251-0). Sierra.
--The Dark Range: A Naturalist's Night Notebook. LC 78-1452. (Illus.). 144p. 15.00 (ISBN 0-87156-212-X); pap. 8.95 (ISBN 0-87156-251-0). Sierra.
--The Klamath Knot. LC 82-3237. (Illus.). 160p. 1983. 14.95 (ISBN 0-87156-316-9); pap. 8.95 (ISBN 0-87156-817-9). Sierra.
Wedel, Waldo R. Central Plains Prehistory: Holocene Environments & Culture Change in the Republican River Basin. LC 85-1151. (Illus.). 328p. 1985. 29.50xt (ISBN 0-8032-4729-X). U of Nebr Pr.
Zwinger, Ann. Wind in the Rock: A Naturalist Explores the Canyon Country of the Southwest. LC 78-2176. (Illus.). 1978. 16.30i (ISBN 0-06-014209-X, HarpT). Har-Row.

NATURAL HISTORY SOCIETIES

Meenan, Audrey, ed. A Directory of Natural History & Related Societies in Britain & Ireland. 407p. 1983. pap. 25.00x (ISBN 0-565-00859-5). U Pr of Va.

NATURAL RESOURCES

see also Aquatic Resources; Conservation of Natural Resources; Fisheries; Forests and Forestry; Geothermal Resources; Marine Resources; Mines and Mineral Resources; Power Resources; Reclamation of Land; Water-Power; Water Resources Development; Water-Supply; Wind Power

Abert, James G., ed. Resource Recovery Guide, Vol. 1. 608p. 1983. 44.50 (ISBN 0-442-20235-0). Van Nos Reinhold.
Alexandersson, Gunnar & Klevebring, Bjorn. World Resources: Energy Metals, Minerals. (Studies in Economic & Political Geography). 1978. 14.40x (ISBN 3-11-006577-0). De Gruyter.
Ali, S. A. Resources for Future Economic Growth. 1979. text ed. 10.50x (ISBN 0-7069-0746-9, Pub. by Vikas India). Advent NY.
Apsimon, John W., ed. The Total Synthesis of Natural Products, Vol. 4. LC 72-4075. (The Total Synthesis of Natural Products Ser.). 610p. 1981. 71.95x (ISBN 0-471-05460-7, Pub. by Wiley-Interscience). Wiley.
Aviel, Joanne F. Resource Shortages & World Politics. 162p. 1977. pap. text ed. 10.00 (ISBN 0-8191-0263-6). U Pr of Amer.
Backstrand, G. Resources, Society & Future. 1980. 47.00 (ISBN 0-08-023266-3); pap. 18.00 (ISBN 0-08-023267-1). Pergamon.
Bishop, Richard C. & Anderson, Stephen O. Natural Resource Economics: Selected Papers. 275p. 1985. 22.85x (ISBN 0-8133-0064-9). Westview.
Blinder, Alan S. & Friedman, Philip, eds. Natural Resources, Uncertainty, & General Equilibrium System Memory: Essays in Honor of Rafael Lusky. (Economic Theory & Mathematical Economics Ser.). 1977. 55.00 (ISBN 0-12-106150-7). Acad Pr.
Bliss, Christopher. Economic Growth & Resources: Natural Resources, Vol III. LC 79-4430. 1980. 40.00x (ISBN 0-312-23316-7). St Martin.
Board on Agriculture & Renewable Resources, National Research Council. Renewable Resources for Industrial Materials. LC 76-44604. 1976. pap. 9.75 (ISBN 0-309-02528-1). Natl Acad Pr.
Bohi, Douglas R. Analyzing Demand Behavior: A Study of Energy Elasticities. LC 81-47616. (Resources for the Future: Economics of Natural Resources Ser.). 192p. 1981. text ed. 19.50x (ISBN 0-8018-2705-1). Johns Hopkins.
Bohm, Peter. Deposit-Refund Systems: Theory & Applications to Environmental, Conservation, and Consumer Policy. LC 81-47617. (Resources for the Future: Economics of Natural Resources Ser.). 192p. 1981. text ed. 22.00x (ISBN 0-8018-2706-X). Johns Hopkins.
Boyd, K., ed. The Ethics of Resource Allocations. 152p. 1980. 15.00x (ISBN 0-85224-368-5, Pub. by Edinburgh U Pr Scotland). Columbia U Pr.
Brown, Lester R. Population Policies for a New Economic Era. LC 83-60702. (Worldwatch Papers). 1983. pap. text ed. 2.00 (ISBN 0-916468-52-6). Worldwatch Inst.
Brown, Lester R., et al. State of the World, 1985: A Worldwatch Institute Report on Progress Toward a Sustainable Society. (Illus.). 301p. 1985. 18.95 (ISBN 0-393-01930-6); pap. 8.95 (ISBN 0-393-30218-0). Norton.
Cambridge Information & Research Services, Ltd. World Directory of Energy Information, Vol. I: Western Europe. 336p. 1981. 85.00x (ISBN 0-87196-563-1). Facts on File.
Campos-Lopez, Enrique, ed. Renewable Resources: A Systematic Approach. 1980. 45.00 (ISBN 0-12-158350-3). Acad Pr.
Churchman, C. West & Smith, Spencer. Natural Resource Administration: Introducing a New Methodology for Management Development. (Special Study in Natural Resources & Energy Management Ser.). 180p. 1984. 20.00x (ISBN 0-86531-709-7). Westview.
Costin, A. B. & Groves, R. H. Nature Conservation in the Pacific. (Illus.). 337p. 1973. pap. 20.00 (ISBN 2-88032-051-8, IUCN37, IUCN). Unipub.
Crout, D. H. Chemistry of Natural Products. Date not set. 35.00 (ISBN 0-87735-213-5). Freeman Cooper.
Cutter, Susan L., et al. Exploitation, Conservation, Preservation: A Geographic Perspective on Natural Resource Use. LC 84-18298. (Illus.). 468p. 1985. 25.00x (ISBN 0-86598-129-9). Rowman & Allanheld.
Dahlberg, Kenneth & Bennett, John, eds. Improving Natural Resource Management: Approaches to Multidisciplinary Research. (WVST in Natural Resource & Energy Management Ser.). 360p. 1985. pap. text ed. 28.50x (ISBN 0-8133-7079-5). Westview.
Deju, Raul, et al. The Environment & Its Resources. 340p. 1972. 56.75 (ISBN 0-677-14120-3). Gordon.
Doan, Peter, et al. Local Institutional Development for Natural Resource Management. (Special Series on Local Institutional Development: No. 2). 66p. (Orig.). 1985. pap. 6.50 (ISBN 0-86731-109-6). RDC Ctr Intl Stud.
Dorner, Peter & El-Shafie, Mahmoud A., eds. Resources & Development: Natural Resource Policies & Economic Development in an Interdependent World. (Illus.). 516p. 1980. 29.50x (ISBN 0-299-08250-4). U of Wis Pr.
Dupuy, Rene-Jean. The Settlement of Disputes on the New Natural Resources: Workshop 1982. 1983. lib. bdg. 43.50 (ISBN 90-247-2901-7, Pub. by Martinus Nijhoff Netherlands). Kluwer Academic.
Energy Eighty-Three - Proceedings, Vol. II. 100p. (Orig.). 1983. pap. text ed. 15.00x (ISBN 0-85825-206-6, Pub. by Inst Engineering Australia). Brookfield Pub Co.
Energy Eighty-Three: Towards an Energy Policy for Australia - Papers, Vol. I. 329p. 1983. pap. text ed. 35.00x (ISBN 0-85825-177-9, Pub. by Inst Engineering Australia). Brookfield Pub Co.
Firey, Walter. Man, Mind, & Land: A Theory of Resource Use. LC 77-12902. 1977. Repr. of 1960 ed. lib. bdg. 21.00x (ISBN 0-8371-9834-8, FIMM). Greenwood.
Fisher, Anthony C. Resource & Environmental Economics: Natural Resources & the Environment in Economics. LC 81-9951. (Cambridge Surveys of Economic Literature Ser.). 256p. 1981. 44.50 (ISBN 0-521-24306-8); pap. 11.95 (ISBN 0-521-28594-1). Cambridge U Pr.
Friedland, Mary. Earth Resources. (Science in Action Ser.). (Illus.). 48p. 1984. pap. text ed. 2.85 (ISBN 0-88102-025-7). Janus Bks.
Higgins, G. M. & Kassam, A. H. Potential Population Supporting Capacities of Lands in the Developing World: Land Resources for Populations of the Future. Rev. ed. (Technical Report of Project: No. INT/75/P13). (Illus.). 139p. 1985. pap. 44.75 (ISBN 92-5-101411-6, F2663, FAO). Unipub.
Hinckley, A. D. Renewable Resources in Our Future. (Environmental Sciences & Applications Ser.: Vol. 8). 1980. 18.75 (ISBN 0-08-023432-1); pap. 9.25 (ISBN 0-08-023433-X). Pergamon.
Hitch, Charles J., ed. Resources for an Uncertain Future: Papers Presented at a Forum Marking the 25th Anniversary of Resources for the Future, 1977. LC 77-18378. pap. 29.30 (ISBN 0-317-26464-8, 2023800). Bks Demand UMI.
Howe, Charles W. Natural Resource Economics: Issues Analysis & Policy. LC 78-24174. 350p. 1979. 39.50 (ISBN 0-471-04527-6). Wiley.
Howe, Charles W., ed. Managing Renewable Natural Resources in Developing Countries. (Special Studies in Soc., Pol., Econ. Dev.). 212p. 1982. 24.00x (ISBN 0-86531-313-X). Westview.
Hufschmidt, Maynard M. & Hyman, Eric L., eds. Economic Approaches to Natural Resource & Environmental Quality Analysis: Proceedings & Papers of a Conference on Extended Benefit-Cost Analysis Held at the Environment & Policy Institute East-West Center, Honolulu, Hawaii, 19-26 Sept. 1979. (Natural Resources & the Environment Ser.: Vol. 5). (Illus.). 333p. 1982. pap. 18.50 (ISBN 0-907567-04-5, TYP139, TYP) (ISBN 0-907567-09-6). Unipub.
Industrial Processing of Natural Resources. pap. 5.00 (UN812B1, UN). Unipub.
Institution of Chemical Engineers. Management & Conservation of Resources: Proceedings of the Conference Organised by the Institution of Chemical Engineers at the University of Salford, UK, April 1982. (Institution of Chemical Engineers Symposium Ser.: No. 72). 206p. 1982. 45.00 (ISBN 0-08-028769-7). Pergamon.
International Conference in Bulk Materials Storage, Handling & Transportation. 396p. 1983. pap. text ed. 28.00x (ISBN 0-85825-209-0, Pub. by Inst Engineering Australia). Brookfield Pub Co.
Jarrett, Henry, et al. Science & Resources: Prospects & Implications of Technological Advance. LC 77-23132. (Resources for the Future, Inc.). (Illus.). 1977. Repr. of 1959 ed. lib. bdg. 22.50x (ISBN 0-8371-9470-9, JASR). Greenwood.
Kemp. Essays in the Economics of Exhaustible Resources. (Contributions to Economic Analysis Ser.: Vol. 150). 1984. 55.75 (ISBN 0-444-86791-0). Elsevier.
Keyes, Dale L. Land Development & the Natural Environment: Estimating Impacts. (Land Development Impact Ser.). 128p. 1976. pap. 4.95 (13500). Urban Inst.
Kneese & Sweeney. Handbook of Natural Resource & Energy Economics, 2 vols. Date not set. Set. write for info. (ISBN 0-444-87646-4). Vol. 1 (ISBN 0-444-87644-8). Vol. 2 (ISBN 0-444-87645-6). Elsevier.
Kranz, Joe & Frauen, Janice. Professional Resource Development. (Illus.). 352p. 1986. text ed. 21.95 (ISBN 0-13-725771-6). P-H.
Laboratory for Computer Graphics & Spatial Analysis, Harvard University Graduate School of Design. Computer Mapping of Natural Resources & the Environment: Plus Satellite-Derived Data Applications, Vol. 15. (The Harvard Library of Computer Graphics, Mapping Collection). (Illus.). 180p. 1981. pap. 12.50 (ISBN 0-8122-1195-2). U of Pa Pr.
Land-Water Classification. (Ecological Land Classification Ser.: No. 5). 1979. pap. 8.50 (ISBN 0-660-10039-8, SSC124, SSC). Unipub.
Macfarlane, Alan. Resources & Population. LC 75-13448. (Cambridge Studies in Social Anthropology: No. 12). (Illus.). 352p. 1976. 59.50 (ISBN 0-521-20913-7). Cambridge U Pr.
McMains, Harvey & Wilcox, Lyle, eds. Alternatives for Growth: The Engineering & Economics of Natural Resources Development. LC 77-11870. (Other Conference Ser.: No. 12). 272p. 1978. prof ref 29.95 (ISBN 0-88410-480-X). Ballinger Pub.
Maczak, Antoni & Parker, Wm. N., eds. Natural Resources in European History: A Conference Report. LC 78-24688. (Resources for the Future Ser.). 1979. pap. 8.00x (ISBN 0-8018-2237-8). Johns Hopkins.
Marks, Robert. Non-Renewable Resources & Disequilibrium Macrodynamics. LC 78-75018. 37.00 (ISBN 0-8240-4053-8). Garland Pub.
Marsh, George P. Earth As Modified by Human Action. LC 74-106906. 1970. Repr. of 1878 ed. 32.00 (ISBN 0-403-00198-6). Scholarly.
Natural Resources & the Human Environment for Food & Agriculture. (Environment Papers: No. 1). (Eng., Fr. & Span.). 70p. 1980. pap. 7.50 (ISBN 92-5-100967-8, F2132, FAO). Unipub.
The Natural Resources Programme: 1977-1981. 118p. 1982. pap. 11.75 (ISBN 92-808-0360-3, TUNU181, UNU). Unipub.
Nemetz, Peter N., ed. Resource Policy: International Perspectives. (Illus.). 371p. 1980. pap. text ed. 18.95x (ISBN 0-920380-64-6, Pub. by Inst Res Pub Canada). Brookfield Pub Co.
Novick, David. A World of Scarcities: Critical Issues in Public Policy. LC 75-42278. 194p. 1976. 45.95x (ISBN 0-470-15002-5). Halsted Pr.
O'Riordan, Timothy & Turner, R. Kerry, eds. Progress in Resource Management & Environmental Planning, Vol. 4. 304p. 1984. 64.95x (ISBN 0-471-10534-1, 1469, Pub. by Wiley-Interscience). Wiley.
Orr, David W. & Soroos, Marvin S., eds. The Global Predicament: Ecological Perspectives on World Order. LC 78-10207. xvi, 398p. 1979. 26.00x (ISBN 0-8078-1346-X); pap. 9.95x (ISBN 0-8078-1349-4). U of NC Pr.
Otter, Floyd L. & Carpenter, Edward C. Mathematics for Natural Resources Technicians. (Illus.). 92p. 1981. pap. 4.75 (ISBN 0-9614459-0-4). Otter Veterinary.
Renewable Natural Resources & the Environment: Pressing Problems in the Developing World, Vol. 2. (Natural Resources & the Environment Ser.). (Illus.). 396p. 1982. 25.00 (ISBN 0-907567-01-0, TYP102, TYP). Unipub.
Research Group on Living & Surviving. Inhabiting the Earth As a Finite World. 1979. lib. bdg. 28.00 (ISBN 0-89838-018-9, Pub. by Martinus Nijhoff Netherlands). Kluwer Academic.
Ridgeway, James. Who Owns the Earth? 1980. 15.95 (ISBN 0-02-603300-3); pap. 8.95 (ISBN 0-02-081220-5). Macmillan.
Ridker, Ronald G. & Watson, William D., Jr. To Choose a Future. LC 79-3643. (Resources for the Future Ser.). 1980. 37.00x (ISBN 0-8018-2354-4). Johns Hopkins.
Robinson, Harry. Population & Resources. 1982. 22.50x (ISBN 0-312-63120-0). St Martin.
Sasaki, A., et al. World Resources & the Development of the Earth's Surface. (Texts in Earth Sciences). 1985. 41.95 (ISBN 0-471-10536-8). Wiley.
Schachter, Oscar. Sharing the World's Resources. LC 76-28422. 1977. 19.00x (ISBN 0-231-04110-1). Columbia U Pr.
Schneider-Sawiris, Shadia. The Concept of Compensation in the Field of Trade & Environment. (Environmental Policy & Law Papers: No. 4). 37p. 1973. pap. 10.00 (ISBN 2-88032-074-7, IUCN30, IUCN). Unipub.
Seventh Session of the Committee on Natural Resources: Proceedings. (Water Resources Development Ser.: No. 54). 146p. 1981. pap. 12.00 (ISBN 0-686-82549-7, UN81/2F10, UN). Unipub.
Shaler, Nathaniel S. Man & the Earth. Repr. of 1905 ed. 20.00 (ISBN 0-384-54960-8). Johnson Repr.
Shumaker. Process Pipe Drafting. 8.00 (ISBN 0-87006-512-2). Goodheart.
Siebert, Horst. Economics of the Environment. LC 80-7442. 1981. 29.50x (ISBN 0-669-03693-5). Lexington Bks.
Simmons, I. G. Ecology of Natural Resources. 2nd ed. 432p. 1981. Vol. 2. pap. 24.95x (ISBN 0-470-27203-1). Halsted Pr.
Skinner, Brian J. Earth Resources. 2nd ed. 1976. pap. 14.95 (ISBN 0-13-223008-9). P-H.
Smith, Howard. A Naturalist's Guide to the Year. LC 84-18697. (Illus.). 256p. 1985. 18.95 (ISBN 0-525-24297-X, 01840-550). Dutton.
Stamp, Laurence D. & Wooldridge, Sidney W. London Essays in Geography. facs. ed. LC 76-80399. (Essay Index Reprint Ser). 1951. 23.75 (ISBN 0-8369-1050-8). Ayer Co Pubs.
Stoltenberg, Carl, et al. Planning Research for Resource Decisions. facsimile ed. LC 76-103839. (Illus.). 1970. pap. 10.25x (ISBN 0-8138-2260-2). Iowa St U Pr.
Storr, Eric D., ed. Bulk Transport: Solid, Liquid, Gas. 250p. 1984. pap. text ed. 30.00x (ISBN 0-85825-212-0, Pub. by Inst Engineers Australia). Brookfield Pub Co.
Tessar, Paul A., et al. Landsat: Space Technology in Natural Resource Planning. 1976. write for info. U of SD Gov Res Bur.
Tietenberg, Thomas H. Environmental Economics. 1984. text ed. 27.10x (ISBN 0-673-15558-7). Scott F.

Coan, Eugene. James Graham Cooper: Pioneer Western Naturalist. LC 80-52313. (GEM Books-Historical & Natural History Ser.). (Illus.). 210p. (Orig.). 1982. pap. 12.95 (ISBN 0-89301-071-5). U Pr of Idaho.

Cruickshank, Helen G., ed. John & William Bartram's America. (American Naturalists Ser.). (Illus.). 14.95 (ISBN 0-8159-5101-9). Devin.

Cummings, Jean. They Call Him the Buffalo Doctor. LC 73-147172. 320p. 1980. Repr. of 1971 ed. 7.00 (ISBN 0-8187-0035-1). Harlo Pr.

Cutright, Paul R. Great Naturalists Explore South America. facs. ed. LC 68-8454. (Essay Index Reprint Ser). 1940. 26.50 (ISBN 0-8369-0357-9). Ayer Co Pubs.

Cutright, Paul R. & Brodhead, Michael J. Elliott Coues: Naturalist & Frontier Historian. LC 80-12424. (Illus.). 510p. 1981. 28.50x (ISBN 0-252-00802-2). U of Ill Pr.

Darwin, Charles. The Collected Papers of Charles Darwin, Vols. I & II. Barrett, Paul H., ed. LC 76-606. (Illus.). 1977. lib. bdg. 40.00x set (ISBN 0-226-13657-4); pap. 12.50 (ISBN 0-226-13658-2, P886, Phoen). U of Chicago Pr.

--The Voyage of Charles Darwin. Ralling, Christopher, ed. LC 79-916. (Illus.). 1980. 12.50 (ISBN 0-8317-9212-4, Mayflower Bks). Smith Pubs.

Dick, John H. Other Edens: The Sketchbook of an Artist Naturalist. LC 79-67270. (Illus.). 1979. 19.95 (ISBN 0-8159-6412-9). Devin.

Durrell, Gerald & Durrell, Lee. The Amateur Naturalist. LC 83-47940. (Illus.). 192p. 1983. 22.50 (ISBN 0-394-53390-9). Knopf.

Eiseley, Loren. All the Strange Hours. 1983. 15.50 (ISBN 0-8446-5978-9). Peter Smith.

--The Night Country. LC 78-162747. (Illus.). 1971. pap. 7.95 (ISBN 0-684-13224-9, ScribT). Scribner.

Farrington, Benjamin. What Darwin Really Said. LC 82-5557. (What They Really Said Ser.). 124p. 1982. pap. 4.95 (ISBN 0-8052-0720-1). Schocken.

Geiser, Samuel W. Naturalists of the Frontier. rev. ed. LC 48-7357. (Illus.). 1948. 12.95 (ISBN 0-87074-059-8). SMU Press.

Gillham, Mary. A Naturalist in New Zealand. 16.50x (ISBN 0-392-14176-0, SpS). Sportshelf.

Haines, John. Other Days. (Illus.). 52p. 1981. 60.00x (ISBN 0-915308-29-0); pap. 5.00x (ISBN 0-915308-30-4). Graywolf.

Irvine, William. Apes, Angels & Victorians: The Story of Darwin, Huxley, & Evolution. LC 83-10344. (Illus.). 520p. 1983. pap. text ed. 18.75 (ISBN 0-8191-3282-9). U Pr of Amer.

Jenkins, Alan C. The Naturalists. (Illus.). 1978. 14.50 (ISBN 0-8317-6330-2, Mayflower Bks). Smith Pubs.

Keynes, Darwin R., ed. The Beagle Record. LC 77-82500. (Illus.). 1979. 95.00 (ISBN 0-521-21822-5). Cambridge U Pr.

LaBastille, Anne. Woodswoman. LC 75-34071. 1976. pap. 6.95 (ISBN 0-525-47504-4). Dutton.

Lawrence, Gale. The Beginning Naturalist. LC 79-89171. (Illus.). xii, 209p. (Orig.). 1979. pap. 6.95 (ISBN 0-933050-02-X). New Eng Pr VT.

Miller, Jonathan & Van Loon, Borin. Darwin for Beginners. 12.95 (ISBN 0-906495-95-4). Writers & Readers.

Mitchell, John. The Curious Naturalist. 1980. 15.95 (ISBN 0-13-195412-1, Spec); pap. 9.95 (ISBN 0-13-195404-0, Spec). P-H.

Monagan, Charles A. The Reluctant Naturalist: An Unnatural Field Guide to the Natural World. LC 83-45507. (Illus.). 224p. 1984. 10.95 (ISBN 0-689-11437-0). Atheneum.

Naturalists' Directory (International) 42nd ed. LC 5-5997. 1975. pap. 7.95 (ISBN 0-686-10195-2). World Natural Hist.

Osborn, Henry F. Cope: Master Naturalist: Life & Letters of Edward Drinker Cope, with a Bibliography of His Writings. LC 77-81135. (Biologists & Their World Ser.). (Illus.). 1978. Repr. of 1931 ed. lib. bdg. 59.50x (ISBN 0-405-10735-8). Ayer Co Pubs.

Ospovat, Dov. The Development of Darwin's Theory: Natural History, Natural Theology, & Natural Selection, 1838-1859. LC 81-4077. (Illus.). 228p. 1981. 47.50 (ISBN 0-521-23818-8). Cambridge U Pr.

Pace, Antonio, ed. Luigi Castiglioni's Viaggio: Travels in the United States of America, 1785-1787. (Illus.). 496p. 1983. text ed. 39.00x (ISBN 0-8156-2264-3). Syracuse U Pr.

Parker, Jerry. Off the Beaten Track: The Odyssey of a Naturalist. LC 85-6079. (Illus.). 1985. 17.50 (ISBN 0-916955-00-1); pap. 9.75 (ISBN 0-916955-01-X). Arcus Pub.

Pliny. The Elizabethan Zoo: A Book of Beast Both Fabulous & Authentic. Byrne, M. St. Clare, ed. Holland, Philemon & Topsell, Edward, trs. LC 79-88477. (Illus.). 192p. 1979. 17.50 (ISBN 0-87923-300-1, Nonpareil Bks.); pap. 7.95 (ISBN 0-87923-299-4). Godine.

Raven, Charles E. English Naturalists from Neckam to Ray: A Study of the Making of the Modern World. LC 47-12381. 1968. Repr. of 1947 ed. 27.00 (ISBN 0-527-74100-0). Kraus Repr.

Rehbock, Philip F. The Philosophical Naturalists: Themes in Early Nineteenth-Century British Biology. LC 83-47767. (Wisconsin Publications in the History of Science & Medicine Ser.: No. 3). (Illus.). 288p. 1983. text ed. 30.00x (ISBN 0-299-09430-8). U of Wis Pr.

Rudman, Jack. Naturalist. (Career Examination Ser.: C-1379). (Cloth bdg. avail. on request). pap. 12.00 (ISBN 0-8373-1379-1). Natl Learning.

St. John, Charles. A Scottish Naturalist: Searches & Notes of Charles St. John 1809-1856. (Illus.). 224p. 1982. 18.95 (ISBN 0-233-97390-7). Andre Deutsch.

Savage, Henry, Jr. Discovering America, Seventeen Hundred to Eighteen Seventy-Five. Morris, Richard B. & Commager, Henry S., eds. LC 78-20113. (New American Nation Ser.). (Illus.). 1979. 21.10i (ISBN 0-06-013782-7, HarpT). Har-Row.

Seward, Mark, et al, eds. A Handbook for Naturalists. 1981. 15.00x (ISBN 0-09-462390-2, Pub. by Constable Pubs England). State Mutual Bk.

Simpson, Charles T. Out of Doors in Florida: The Adventures of a Naturalist. Repr. of 1923 ed. lib. bdg. 35.00 (ISBN 0-8495-5001-7). Arden Lib.

Smith, James E. A Selection of the Correspondence of Linnaeus & Other Naturalists: From Original Manuscripts, 2 vols. Sterling, Keir B., ed. LC 77-81132. (Biologists & Their World Ser.). (Illus.). 1978. Repr. of 1821 ed. Set. lib. bdg. 99.00x (ISBN 0-405-10730-7); lib. bdg. 49.50x ea. Vol. 1 (ISBN 0-405-10731-5). Vol. 2 (ISBN 0-405-10732-3). Ayer Co Pubs.

Spoehr, Florence M. White Falcon: The House of Godeffroy & Its Commercial & Scientific Role in the Pacific. LC 63-18693. (Illus.). 1963. 8.95 (ISBN 0-87015-119-3). Pacific Bks.

Sterling, Keir B. Last of the Naturalists: The Career of C. Hart Merriam. LC 73-17847. (Natural Sciences in America Ser.). (Illus.). 500p. 1974. Repr. 28.00x (ISBN 0-405-05770-9). Ayer Co Pubs.

Swinton, A. Instructions to Young Naturalists: Fossils. 14.50x (ISBN 0-392-03503-0, SpS). Sportshelf.

Van Leeuwenhoek, Antoni. The Collected Letters of Antoni van Leeuwenhoek, 10 vols. Incl. Vol. 1. 454p. 1939; Vol. 2. 506p. 1941 (ISBN 90-265-0041-6); Vol. 3. 560p. 1948; Vol. 4. 383p. 1952 (ISBN 90-265-0043-2); Vol. 5. 457p. 1958 (ISBN 90-265-0044-0); Vol. 6. 425p. 1961 (ISBN 90-265-0045-9); Vol. 7. 427p. 1965 (ISBN 90-265-0046-7); Vol. 8. 383p. 1967 (ISBN 90-265-0047-5); Vol. 9. 482p. 1976 (ISBN 90-265-0220-6); Vol. 10. 362p. 1979 (ISBN 90-265-0285-0). (Dutch & Eng., Illus.). text ed. 105.00 ea. (Pub. by Swets Serv Holland). Swets North Am.

Weiss, Harry B. & Ziegler, Grace M. Thomas Say: Early American Naturalist. Sterling, Keir B., ed. LC 77-81137. (Biologists & Their World Ser.). (Illus.). 1978. Repr. of 1931 ed. lib. bdg. 24.50x (ISBN 0-405-10737-4). Ayer Co Pubs.

NATURALISTS–DIRECTORIES

see Scientists–Directories

NATURE

see also Man–Influence on Nature

Angier, Bradford. Wilderness Neighbors. LC 76-26303. 228p. 1982. pap. 7.95 (ISBN 0-8128-6100-0). Stein & Day.

Arguelles, Jose. Earth Ascending: An Illustrated Treatise on the Law Governing Whole Systems. LC 83-20052. (Illus.). 150p. 1984. pap. 12.95 (ISBN 0-87773-263-9, 72330-9). Shambhala Pubns.

Campbell, Joseph, ed. Spirit & Nature: Papers from the Eranos Yearbooks, Vol. 1. Manheim, Ralph & Hull, R. F., trs. from Ger. LC 54-5647. (Bollingen Ser.: No. XXX). (Illus.). 520p. (Orig.). 1982. 33.00x (ISBN 0-691-09736-4); pap. 9.95x (ISBN 0-691-01841-3). Princeton U Pr.

Cannon, Barrie R. & Cannon, George W. Coming into the Light: An Invitation. (Illus.). 1979. pap. 12.95 (ISBN 0-9603020-0-X). Voyager Pubns.

Collingwood, Robin G. Idea of Nature. 1960. pap. 7.95 (ISBN 0-19-500217-2, GB). Oxford U Pr.

Durrell, Gerald & Durrell, Lee. The Amateur Naturalist. LC 83-47940. (Illus.). 192p. 1983. 22.50 (ISBN 0-394-53390-9). Knopf.

Eckert, Allan W. Wild Season. LC 67-14449. (Illus.). 256p. 1981. 9.95 (ISBN 0-913428-32-9); pap. 4.95 (ISBN 0-913428-31-0). Landfall Pr.

Eifert, Virginia S. Essays on Nature. 274p. 1967. pap. 3.50 (ISBN 0-89792-033-3). Ill St Museum.

Einstein, Xavier. Trivia Mania: Science & Nature. 1984. pap. 2.50 (ISBN 0-317-05599-2). Zebra.

Elfner, Lynn E., et al. Guide to the Literature of Ohio's Natural Areas. 1973. 1.00 (ISBN 0-86727-067-5). Ohio Bio Survey.

Feininger, Andreas. Nature Close Up: A Fantastic Journey into Reality. (Illus.). 18.00 (ISBN 0-8446-5885-5). Peter Smith.

Fitzwarren, Albert E. The Nature of Nature from Alpha to Zeta. (Illus.). 32p. 1981. pap. 1.50 (ISBN 0-942788-07-9). Marginal Med.

Fowles, John. The Tree. (Illus.). 1980. 24.95 (ISBN 0-316-28957-4). Little.

Grant, Allen. Flashlights on Nature: A Popular Account of the Life Histories of Some Familiar Insects, Birds, Plants, Etc. 1978. Repr. of 1898 ed. lib. bdg. 25.00 (ISBN 0-8492-0088-1). R West.

Grigoryev, V. & Myakishev, G. Forces of Nature. (Illus.). 346p. 1975. 14.95x (ISBN 0-8464-1099-0). Beekman Pubs.

Haines, John. Other Days. (Illus.). 52p. 1981. 60.00x (ISBN 0-915308-29-0); pap. 5.00x (ISBN 0-915308-30-4). Graywolf.

Haken, H., ed. Chaos & Order in Nature: Proceedings of the International Symposium on Synergetics at Schloss Elmau, Bavaria, April 27-May 2, 1981. (Springer Series in Synergetics: Vol. 11). (Illus.). viii, 275p. 1981. 29.00 (ISBN 0-387-11101-8). Springer-Verlag.

Headstrom, Richard. Nature Discoveries with a Hand Lens. (Illus.). 425p. 1981. pap. 6.00 (ISBN 0-486-24077-0). Dover.

Henderson, Lawrence J. Order of Nature. facs. ed. LC 70-150186. (Select Bibliographies Reprint Ser). 1917. 18.00 (ISBN 0-8369-5699-0). Ayer Co Pubs.

Hildebrandt, Stefan & Tromba, Anthony J. Mathematics & Optimal Form. LC 84-23461. (Scientific American Library). (Illus.). 256p. 1984. text ed. 27.95 (ISBN 0-7167-5009-0). W H Freeman.

Kinkead, Eugene. A Concrete Look at Nature. (Illus.). 242p. 1974. 8.00 (ISBN 0-8129-0471-0, QH105.N7K55). E Kinkead.

--Wildness Is All Around Us. (Illus.). 178p. 1978. 10.00x (ISBN 0-87690-277-8, QH541.5.C6K56). E Kinkead.

Krook, Hans. Close to Nature: An Exploration of Nature's Microcosm. LC 84-7645. 77p. 1984. 14.45 (ISBN 0-394-54089-1). Pantheon.

Lawrence, Gale. The Beginning Naturalist. LC 79-89171. (Illus.). xii, 209p. (Orig.). 1979. pap. 6.95 (ISBN 0-933050-02-X). New Eng Pr VT.

Life Nature Library, 24 vols. Spanish Version. 12.50 ea.; French Version. 19.95 ea. French & Eur.

McKain, David W., ed. Whole Earth: Essays in Appreciation, Anger, & Hope. 384p. 1971. pap. text ed. 11.95 (ISBN 0-312-87045-0). St Martin.

Marsh, Frank L. Variation & Fixity in Nature. 150p. (Orig.). 1976. pap. 5.95 (ISBN 0-940384-02-7). Creation Res.

Massingham, H. J., ed. Essential Gilbert White of Shelborne. LC 84-48801. 384p. 1985. pap. 9.95 (ISBN 0-87923-571-3). Godine.

Moon, Jan. Living with Nature in Hawaii. rev. ed. 136p. 1979. pap. 5.95 (ISBN 0-912180-06-4). Petroglyph.

Morowitz, Harold J. Mayonnaise & the Origin of Life: Thoughts of Minds & Molecules. 256p. 1985. 15.95 (ISBN 0-684-18444-3, ScribT). Scribner.

Muir, John. Stickeen. 90p. 1981. pap. 3.95 (ISBN 0-930588-05-3). Heyday Bks.

Olwig, Kenneth R. Nature's Ideological Landscape. (London Research Series in Geography: No. 5). (Illus.). 144p. 1984. text ed. 24.95x (ISBN 0-04-710002-8). Allen Unwin.

Parsons, Christopher. True to Nature. (Illus.). 378p. 1984. 24.95 (ISBN 0-85059-530-4, Pub. by Salem Hse Ltd). Merrimack Pub Cir.

Poirot, Eugene M. Our Margin of Life. LC 78-52144. (Illus.). 139p. (Orig.). 1978. pap. 4.00 (ISBN 0-911311-06-8). Halycon Hse.

Risser, Paul G. & Cornelison, Kathy D. Man & the Biosphere. LC 79-4953. (Illus.). 109p. 1979. pap. 8.95 (ISBN 0-8061-1610-2). U of Okla Pr.

Russell, Terry & Russell, Renny. On the Loose. LC 79-15243. (Sierra Club Paperback Library). (Illus.). 128p. 1979. pap. 9.95 (ISBN 0-87156-264-2). Sierra.

Rusten, Philip. On the Growing Edge. (Illus.). 96p. 1981. 21.00 (ISBN 0-686-29722-9). Way of Seeing.

Seno, William J., ed. Up Country: Voices from the Midwestern Wilderness. LC 85-60995. (Voices from the Wilderness Ser.: No. 1). (Illus.). 256p. (Orig.). 1985. pap. 11.95 (ISBN 0-933437-00-5). Round River Pub.

Simpson, James Y. Nature: Cosmic, Human & Divine. 1929. 39.50x (ISBN 0-686-83632-4). Elliots Bks.

Smithe, Frank B. Naturalists Color Guide, Pt. III. (Illus.). 1981. 8.00 (ISBN 0-913424-05-6). Am Mus Natl Hist.

Stevens, Peter S. Patterns in Nature. LC 73-19720. (Illus.). 256p. 1974. (Pub. by Atlantic Monthly Pr); pap. 12.45 (ISBN 0-316-81331-1). Little.

Thomson, John A. The System of Animate Nature, 2 vols. LC 77-27212. (Gifford Lectures: 1915-16). Repr. of 1920 ed. Set. 49.50 (ISBN 0-404-60520-6). AMS Pr.

Trefil, James. The Unexpected Vista: A Physicist's View of Nature. Lippman, B., ed. 224p. 1985. pap. 6.95 (ISBN 0-02-096780-2, Collier). Macmillan.

Trefil, James S. The Unexpected Vista: A Physicist's View of Nature. LC 82-42654. (Illus.). 256p. 1984. 14.95 (ISBN 0-684-17869-9, ScribT). Scribner.

Verey, Rosemary. The Scented Garden. 168p. 1981. 24.95 (ISBN 0-442-28175-7). Van Nos Reinhold.

Vogl, Sonia W. & Vogl, Robert L. Teaching Nature in Cities & Towns. (Illus.). 102p. 1985. pap. text ed. 8.75x (ISBN 0-8134-2458-5, 2458). Interstate.

Whitehead, Alfred N. Concept of Nature. pap. 11.95 (ISBN 0-521-09245-0). Cambridge U Pr.

NATURE CONSERVATION

see also Wildlife Conservation

Arbib, Robert S., Jr. Lord's Woods. LC 73-139373. 1971. 6.95 (ISBN 0-393-08639-9). Norton.

Astanin, L. P. & Blagosklonov, K. N. Conservation of Nature. 149p. 1983. 5.95 (ISBN 0-8285-2602-8, Pub. by Progress Pubs USSR). Imported Pubns.

Ayensu, Edward S., et al. Our Green & Living World: The Wisdom to Save It. Goodwin, Joseph, ed. LC 84-600181. (Illus.). 256p. 1984. 25.00 (ISBN 0-89599-016-4, Dist. by Cambridge). Smithsonian Bks.

Bertram, G. L. Conservation of Sirenia: Current Status & Perspectives for Action. 1974. pap. 7.50 (ISBN 2-88032-023-2, IUCN35, IUCN). Unipub.

Brazee, Edward, ed. Index to the Sierra Club Bulletin, 1950-1976. (Bibliographic Ser.: No. 16). 60p. 1978. pap. 5.95x (ISBN 0-87071-136-9). Oreg St U Pr.

Bryant, Jeannette, ed. Conservation Directory. 27th ed. LC 70-10646. 297p. 1982. 6.00 (ISBN 0-912186-42-9). Natl Wildlife.

Cohen, Michael P. The Pathless Way: John Muir & American Wilderness. LC 83-40260. 500p. 1984. 25.00 (ISBN 0-299-09720-X). U of Wis Pr.

Cohen, Stan. The Tree Army: A Pictorial History of the Civilian Conservation Corps 1933-1943. LC 80-81071. 172p. 1980. pap. 8.95 (ISBN 0-933126-10-7). Pictorial Hist.

Conservation Foundation Staff. State of the Environment 1982. LC 82-8257. (Illus.). 439p. (Orig.). 1982. pap. 15.00 (ISBN 0-89164-070-3). Conservation Foun.

Dennis, Eve. Everyman's Nature Reserve: Ideas for Action. (Illus.). 256p. 1973. 7.50 (ISBN 0-7153-5918-5). David & Charles.

Eagles, Paul. The Planning & Management of Environmentally Sensitive Areas. pap. text ed. 13.95 (ISBN 0-582-30074-6). Longman.

Ermentrout, Robert A. Forgotten Men: The Civilian Conservation Corps. 112p. 1982. 6.50 (ISBN 0-682-49805-X). Exposition Pr FL.

Frankel, O. H. & Soule, M. E. Conservation & Evolution. LC 80-40528. (Illus.). 300p. 1981. 59.50 (ISBN 0-521-23275-9); pap. 22.95 (ISBN 0-521-29889-X). Cambridge U Pr.

Gregory, David D. & Diot, A. The Easement as a Conservation Technique. (Environmental Policy & Law Papers: No. 1). 47p. 1972. pap. 10.00 (ISBN 2-88032-071-2, IUCN18, IUCN). Unipub.

Gunter, A. Y. Big Thicket: A Challenge for Conservation. LC 73-184310. 1972. 14.95 (ISBN 0-8363-0120-X); pap. 8.50 (ISBN 0-685-02984-0). Jenkins.

Huth, Hans. Nature & the American: Three Centuries of Changing Attitudes. LC 57-12393. (Illus.). xviii, 314p. 1972. 24.50x (ISBN 0-8032-0926-6); pap. 7.50x (ISBN 0-8032-5761-9, BB 554, Bison). U of Nebr Pr.

International Convention for the Protection of New Varieties of Plants & Additional Acts. 1976. pap. 7.50 (ISBN 0-686-53008-X, WIPO20, WIPO). Unipub.

Krutilla, John V., ed. Natural Environments: Studies in Theoretical & Applied Analysis. LC 72-4441. (Resources for the Future Ser.). 360p. 1973. 27.50x (ISBN 0-8018-1446-4). Johns Hopkins.

May, Allan. A Voice in the Wilderness. LC 77-28519. (Illus.). 204p. 1978. 18.95x (ISBN 0-88229-309-5). Nelson-Hall.

Muir, John. A Rival of the Yosemite: The Canon of the South Fork of King's River, California. Jones, William R., ed. (Illus.). 24p. 1977. pap. 2.00 (ISBN 0-89646-010-X). Outbooks.

Parker, Bruce C., ed. Conservation Problems in Antarctica. LC 72-85836. (Illus.). 356p. 1972. 25.00x (ISBN 0-8139-0840-X). U Pr of Va.

Proposals for Nature Conservation in Northern Greece. (Illus.). 1971. pap. 7.50 (ISBN 2-88032-052-6, IUCN42, IUCN). Unipub.

Propositions Pour la Creation du Parc National Ivoirien De Tai. (Illus.). 1973. pap. 7.50 (ISBN 2-88032-041-0, IUCN58, IUCN). Unipub.

Stermer, Dugald. Vanishing Creatures: A Series of Portraits. (Illus.). 80p. 1980. 9.95 (ISBN 0-89581-021-2). Asian Human Pr.

NATURE STUDY

see also Animals, Habits and Behavior of; Biology; Botany; Natural History–Outdoor Books; Natural History–Study and Teaching; Zoology

Audubon Society & Pyle, Robert M. The Audubon Society Field Guide to North American Butterflies. LC 80-84240. (Illus.). 864p. 1981. 13.50 (ISBN 0-394-51914-0). Knopf.

Barrus, Clara, ed. The Heart of Burrough's Journals. 1979. Repr. of 1928 ed. lib. bdg. 30.00 (ISBN 0-8495-0504-6). Arden Lib.

Bazalgette, Leon. Henry Thoreau Bachelor of Nature. Brooks, Wyck Van, tr. LC 80-2679. (BCL Ser. I). Repr. of 1924 ed. 37.50 (ISBN 0-404-19076-6). AMS Pr.

Borland, Hal. Hal Borland's Twelve Moons of the Year. Borland, Barbara D., ed. LC 79-2164. (Illus.). 1979. 15.00 (ISBN 0-394-50496-8). Knopf.

Broome, Harvey. Faces of the Wilderness. LC 72-78038. (Illus.). 271p. 1972. 7.95 (ISBN 0-87842-027-4). Mountain Pr.

Brown, Erik. Seat in a Wild Place. LC 81-15017. (Illus.). 128p. 1983. 8.95 (ISBN 0-87233-059-1). Bauhan.

Brown, Vinson. Building Your Own Nature Museum for Study & Pleasure. (Illus.). 160p. (Orig.). 1984. lib. bdg. 12.95 (ISBN 0-668-06057-3); pap. 7.95 (ISBN 0-668-06061-1). Arco.

Burton, John. The Naturalist in London. LC 74-78247. (Regional Naturalist). (Illus.). 168p. 5.95 (ISBN 0-7153-6215-1). David & Charles.

Bystrom, Robert. Nature's Special Moments. Batts, H. Lewis, ed. & illus. (Illus.). 80p. 1975. 7.50 (ISBN 0-939294-01-X, QH-71-K3-A7). Beech Leaf.

Campbell, A. C. The Larousse Guide to the Seashore & Shallow Seas of Britain & Europe. LC 80-82755. (Larousse Nature Guides Ser.). (Illus.). 320p. (Orig.). 1981. 10.95 (ISBN 0-88332-251-X, 8068). Larousse.

Carson, Rachel. The Sense of Wonder. 1965. 12.95i (ISBN 0-06-010645-X, HarpT); PLB 10.87i (ISBN 0-06-010646-8). Har-Row.

Carter, W. Horace. Creatures & Chronicles from Cross Creek. LC 80-68460. (Illus.). 286p. (Orig.). 1981. pap. text ed. 5.95 (ISBN 0-937866-02-4). Atlantic Pub Co.

Clapper, Ronald. The Development of "Walden". A Genetic Text. LC 80-2503. 1981. 75.00 (ISBN 0-404-19051-0). AMS Pr.

Claugher, D. Scanning Nature. LC 83-5155. 116p. 1983. 24.95 (ISBN 0-521-25705-0); pap. 10.95 (ISBN 0-521-27664-0). Cambridge U Pr.

Cornell, Joseph B. Sharing Nature with Children. LC 78-74650. (Illus.). 143p. 1979. pap. 6.95 (ISBN 0-916124-14-2). Ananda.

Cornett, Jim. Wildlife of the Southwest Deserts. 2nd ed. (Illus.). 240p. 1985. pap. 5.95 (ISBN 0-937794-06-6). Nature Trails.

DeScherer, Mildred, ed. Directory of Natural Science Centers 1984. (Illus.). 1985. pap. 15.00 spiral bd. (ISBN 0-317-20046-1). Natural Sci Youth.

Feininger, Andreas. The Anatomy of Nature. 16.75 (ISBN 0-8446-5760-3). Peter Smith.

Fiedler, Judith. Field Research: A Manual for Logistics & Management of Scientific Studies in Natural Settings. LC 78-62562. (Social & Behavioral Science Ser.). (Illus.). 1978. text ed. 22.95x (ISBN 0-87589-381-3). Jossey-Bass.

Freethy, Ron. The Making of the British Countryside. LC 80-68688. (Illus.). 192p. 1981. 24.00 (ISBN 0-7153-8012-5). David & Charles.

Hamlet, John N. & Carter, W. Horace. Land That I Love. LC 79-93147. (Illus.). 295p. 1980. 10.95 (ISBN 0-937866-00-8). Atlantic Pub Co.

Harrison, James, ed. Nature's Secret World. LC 84-9169. (Illus.). 192p. 1984. 19.95 (ISBN 0-668-06213-4, 6213). Arco.

Headstrom, Richard. Adventures with a Hand Lens. 220p. 1976. pap. 3.95 (ISBN 0-486-23330-8). Dover.

Huggler, Thomas E. Westwind Woods. LC 78-106385. (Illus.). 1978. pap. 2.95 (ISBN 0-933112-00-9). Mich United Conserv.

Karlin, Sol. A. Introduction to the Living World. 1974. pap. text ed. 13.95 (ISBN 0-917962-33-8); lab manual 6.95 (ISBN 0-917962-29-X). Peek Pubns.

Keasey, Merritt S. The Saquaro Book. 72p. 1981. pap. text ed. 6.60 (ISBN 0-8403-2392-1). Kendall-Hunt.

Kidney, Dorothy B. Wilderness Journey. (Illus.). 200p. (Orig.). 1980. pap. 7.95 (ISBN 0-930096-10-X). G Gannett.

Lawrence, Gale. A Field Guide to the Familiar: Learning to Observe the Natural World. (Illus.). 336p. 1984. 19.95 (ISBN 0-13-314071-7); pap. 9.95 (ISBN 0-13-314063-6). P-H.

Lehmberg, Paul. In the Strong Woods. 160p. 1981. pap. 4.95 (ISBN 0-312-41173-1). St Martin.

Link, Michael. Outdoor Education: A Manual for Teaching in Nature's Classroom. 198p. 1981. 15.95 (ISBN 0-13-645028-8); pap. 6.95 (ISBN 0-13-645010-5). P-H.

McDonald, Ralph J. A Down-Home Gallery of American Wildlife. (Illus.). 101p. 1980. 39.95 (ISBN 0-9605428-1-7); signed numbered ed. 95.00 (ISBN 0-9605428-0-9). Countryside Studio.

Marsh, Janet. Janet Marsh's Nature Diary. (Illus.). 160p. 1984. pap. 14.95 (ISBN 0-7181-1796-4, Pub. by Michael Joseph). Merrimack Pub Cir.

Mitchell, John H. A Field Guide to Your Own Back Yard. (Illus.). 1985. 14.95 (ISBN 0-393-01923-3). Norton.

Natural Science Centers Conference 1974, Nashville, Tennessee. Proceedings. Gardner, John F., ed. (Illus., Orig.). 1975. 5.00 (ISBN 0-916544-04-4). Natural Sci Youth.

Parker, Jerry. Off the Beaten Track: The Odyssey of a Naturalist. LC 85-6079. (Illus.). 1985. 17.50 (ISBN 0-916955-00-1); pap. 9.75 (ISBN 0-916955-01-X). Arcus Pub.

Raphael, Ray. An Everyday History of Somewhere. (Illus.). 192p. 1980. pap. 8.00 (ISBN 0-933280-11-4). Island CA.

Reader's Digest Editors. Joy of Nature: How to Observe & Appreciate the Great Outdoors. LC 76-29320. (Illus.). 352p. 1977. 19.98 (ISBN 0-89577-036-9). RD Assn.

Rowlands, John J. Cache Lake Country: Life in the North Woods. (Illus.). 1978. pap. 5.95 (ISBN 0-393-00908-4). Norton.

Russell, Franklin. Watchers at the Pond. LC 80-83963. (Illus.). 272p. 1981. pap. 7.95 (ISBN 0-87923-390-7, Nonpareil Bks). Godine.

Russell, Ian. Ponds & Streams. LC 80-85505. (Wildlife Ser.). (Illus.). 52p. 1982. pap. 4.95 (ISBN 0-7153-8162-8). David & Charles.

Sharpe, Grant W. Interpreting the Environment. 2nd ed. LC 81-10391. 694p. 1982. 34.00 (ISBN 0-471-09007-7). Wiley.

Smith, V. Kerry & Krutilla, John V. Structure & Properties of a Wilderness Travel Simulator: An Application to the Spanish Peaks Area. LC 75-33766. (Resources for the Future Ser). 188p. 1976. 17.50x (ISBN 0-8018-1808-7). Johns Hopkins.

Spawls, Stephen. Sun, Sand & Snakes. LC 79-89260. (Illus.). 1980. 12.95 (ISBN 0-688-03572-8). Morrow.

The Spotter's Handbook to Wildflowers, Trees & Birds or North America. LC 79-10397. (Spotter's Guides). (Illus.). 1980. 5.95 (ISBN 0-8317-7953-5, Mayflower Bks); pap. 3.95 (ISBN 0-8317-7954-3). Smith Pubs.

Stokes, Donald W. A Guide to Nature in Winter: Northeast & North Central North America. LC 76-26861. (Illus.). 1976. 16.45 (ISBN 0-316-81720-1); pap. 8.70 (ISBN 0-316-81723-6). Little.

Van Dieren, W. & Hummelinck, M. W. Nature's Price: The Economics of Mother Earth. 224p. 1979. 15.00 (ISBN 0-7145-2696-7, Dist by Scribner); pap. 7.95 (ISBN 0-7145-2664-9). M Boyars.

Wilson, Andrew. Nature by the Month. LC 75-21181. 1976. pap. text ed. 2.95x (ISBN 0-8134-1757-0, 1757). Interstate.

Zabriskie, Jan. Plants of Deep Canyon. (Illus.). 175p. (Orig.). 1985. pap. 8.95 (ISBN 0-937794-05-8). Nature Trails.

NAUTICAL ALMANACS

see also Ephemerides

Brown, T. Nigel, ed. Brown's Nautical Almanac, 1982. 105th ed. LC 32-280. (Illus.). 967p. 1981. 37.50x (ISBN 0-8002-2868-5). Intl Pubns Serv.

Hewitt, Dick & Lees-Spalding, Tim. Macmillan & Silk Cut Nautical Almanac 1984. 800p. 1983. 80.00x (ISBN 0-333-27292-7, Pub. by Nautical England). State Mutual Bk.

NAUTICAL ASTRONOMY

see also Longitude; Navigation; Time

Birney, Arthur A. Sun Sight Navigation: Celestial for Sailors. LC 83-46034. (Illus.). 128p. 1984. pap. 12.50 (ISBN 0-87033-318-6). Cornell Maritime.

Blewitt, Mary. Celestial Navigation for Yachtsmen. LC 67-25097. 1967. 7.95 (ISBN 0-8286-0028-7). J De Graff.

Bottomley, Tom. Practical Celestial Navigation. (Illus.). 256p. (Orig.). 1983. pap. 12.95 (ISBN 0-8306-1386-2, 1386). TAB Bks.

Cotter, Charles H. The Elements of Navigation & Nautical Astronomy. 1981. 75.00x (ISBN 0-85174-270-X, Pub. by Nautical England). State Mutual Bk.

--Elements of Navigation & Nautical Astronomy. 437p. 1977. 40.00x (ISBN 0-85174-270-X). Sheridan.

Davies, Thomas D. Star Sight Reduction Tables for Forty-Two Stars: Assumed Altitude Method of Celestial Navigation. LC 79-7464. 370p. 1980. spiral 28.50x (ISBN 0-87033-250-3). Cornell Maritime.

Dunlop, G. D. Successful Celestial Navigation with H. O. 229. LC 76-8771. pap. 40.00 (ISBN 0-317-27601-8, 2025072). Bks Demand UMI.

Gray, Leonard. Celestial Navigation Planning. LC 84-45264. (Illus.). 133p. (Orig.). 1984. pap. 12.95 (ISBN 0-87033-327-5). Cornell Maritime.

Hobbs, Richard R. Marine Navigation Two: Celestial & Electronic. 2nd ed. LC 81-9538. 344p. 1981. text ed. 16.95x (ISBN 0-87021-363-6). Naval Inst Pr.

Jolly, David C. Antique Maps, Sea Charts, City Views, Celestial Charts & Battle Plans: Price Record & Handbook for 1985. (Illus.). 288p. 1985. 31.50x (ISBN 0-911775-02-1). D C Jolly.

Kittredge, Robert Y. Self-Taught Navigation. LC 73-121015. (Illus.). 1970. 9.95 (ISBN 0-87358-049-4). Northland.

Linton, Anthony. Newes of the Complement of the Art of Navigation & of the Mightie Empire of Cataia. LC 72-215. (English Experience Ser.: No. 204). 1969. Repr. of 1609 ed. 8.00 (ISBN 90-221-0204-1). Walter J Johnson.

Norville, Warren. Celestial Navigation Step by Step. 2nd ed. LC 83-47888. (Illus.). 272p. 1984. pap. 19.95 (ISBN 0-87742-177-3, C250). Intl Marine.

Pinchot, Sally, intro. by. Triton Logbook. 224p. 1984. 7.95 (ISBN 0-396-08442-7). Dodd.

Ronan, Colin, ed. The Shorter Science & Civilisation in China, Vol. 3. 280p. Date not set. price not set (ISBN 0-521-25272-5); pap. price not set (ISBN 0-521-31560-3). Cambridge U Pr.

Slocum, Jonah. Celestial Navigation. 3rd ed. 120p. 1985. softbound 16.95 (ISBN 0-317-19561-1). Basic Sci Pr.

Thompson. Celestial Navigation. 1981. 12.50 (ISBN 0-679-50965-8). McKay.

Wright, Edward. Certaine Errors in Navigation (the Voyage of George Earl of Cumberland to the Azores) LC 74-80224. (English Experience Ser.: No. 703). 1974. Repr. of 1599 ed. 29.00 (ISBN 90-221-0703-5). Walter J Johnson.

Wright, Frances W. Celestial Navigation. 2nd ed ed. LC 82-4964. (Illus.). 144p. 1982. 12.00 (ISBN 0-87033-291-0). Cornell Maritime.

NAUTICAL CHARTS

Bishop, Joseph M. A Mariner's Guide to Radiofacsimile Weather Charts. (Illus.). 128p. (Orig.). 1981. pap. 9.95 (ISBN 0-686-32920-1). Alden Electronics.

Brandon, Robin. South Biscay Pilot: The Gironde Estuary to La Coruna. (Illus.). 388p. 1977. 59.95x (ISBN 0-8464-1273-X). Beekman Pubs.

Burton, S. M. & Cunningham, G. F. Burton's Nautical Tables. 8th ed. 362p. 1974. 17.50x (ISBN 0-540-07380-6). Sheridan.

Chriss, M. & Hayes, G. R. Introduction to Charts & Their Use. 4th ed. 97p. 1977. pap. 11.00x (ISBN 0-85174-275-0). Sheridan.

Langeraar, W. Surveying & Charting of the Seas. (Elsevier Oceanography Ser.: No. 37). 612p. 1984. 54.00 (ISBN 0-444-42278-1, I-540-83). Elsevier.

Mollat, Michel & De la Ronciere, Monique. Sea Charts of the Early Explorers. LC 84-50006. (Illus.). 296p. 1985. 60.00 (ISBN 0-500-01337-3, Thames & Hudson Inc). Thames Hudson.

Moore, D. A. Marine Chartwork. 2nd ed. (Illus.). 110p. 1981. pap. 11.50 (ISBN 0-540-07269-9). Sheridan.

--Marine Chartwork & Navigation Aids. 2nd ed. 1981. 20.00x (Pub. by Stanford Maritime England). State Mutual Bk.

Motte, Geoff A. & Stout, Thomas M. Chartwork & Marine Navigation: For Fishermen & Boat Operators. 2nd ed. LC 83-46037. (Illus.). 192p. 1984. pap. 11.50 (ISBN 0-87033-314-3). Cornell Maritime.

Putman, Robert. Early Sea Charts. LC 83-8746. (Illus.). 144p. 1983. 45.00 (ISBN 0-89659-392-4). Abbeville Pr.

Squair, W. H. Modern Chartwork. rev., 5th ed. (Illus.). 368p. 1982. text ed. 35.00x (ISBN 0-85174-436-2, Pub. by Brown Son Ferguson). Sheridan.

NAUTICAL INSTRUMENTS

see also Gyroscopic Instruments; Inertial Navigation Systems

also names of nautical instruments, e.g. Compass

American Neptune Pictorial Supplements. Volume 17. Instruments of Navigation. (Illus.). 1975. pap. 3.50 (ISBN 0-87577-104-1). Peabody Mus Salem.

Barlow, William. The Navigators Supply. LC 76-38150. (English Experience Ser.: No. 430). 100p. Repr. of 1597 ed. 16.00 (ISBN 90-221-0430-3). Walter J Johnson.

Bedwell, C., ed. Developments in Electronics for Offshore Fields, Vol. 1. (Illus.). 230p. 1978. 39.00 (ISBN 0-85334-753-0, Pub. by Elsevier Applied Sci England). Elsevier.

Burch, David F. Emergency Navigation. (Illus.). 160p. 1985. 22.95 (ISBN 0-87742-204-4). Intl Marine.

Cotter, Charles H. A History of the Navigator's Sextant. (Illus.). 230p. 1983. 39.95 (ISBN 0-85174-427-3, Pub. by Brown Son & Ferguson). Sheridan.

Roy, G. J. Notes on Instrumentation & Control. Rev. ed. (Marine Engineering Ser.). 144p. 1983. pap. 9.95x (ISBN 0-540-07344-X). Sheridan.

NAUTICAL SURVEYING

see Hydrographic Surveying

NAVAL AERONAUTICS

see Aeronautics, Military

NAVAL ARCHITECTURE

see also Boat-Building; Electricity on Ships; Marine Engineering; Ship-Building; Ship Propulsion; Ships, Iron and Steel; Ships, Wooden; Stability of Ships; Trim (Of Ships); Warships; Yacht-Building;

also types of vessels, e.g. Motor-Boats

Alexsandrov, Michail. On the Dynamics of Cables with Application to Marine Use. (University of Michigan Dept. of Naval Architecture & Marine Engineering Report Ser.: No. 76). pap. 20.00 (ISBN 0-317-28262-X, 2022630). Bks Demand UMI.

Baxter, B. Naval Architecture: Examples & Theory. 240p. 1977. pap. text ed. 29.75x (ISBN 0-85264-179-6). Lubrecht & Cramer.

--Naval Architecture: Examples & Theory. 450p. 1978. 39.95x (ISBN 0-85264-179-6, Pub. by Griffin England). State Mutual Bk.

Bernitsas, Michael M. & Guha-Thakurta, S. Program HYDCYL: A Database for Calculation of Hydrodynamic Loading of Circular Cylinders. (University of Michigan, Dept. of Naval Architecture & Marine Engineering, Report: No. 267). pap. 20.00 (ISBN 0-317-27134-2, 2024682). Bks Demand UMI.

Bernitsas, Michael M. & Kekridis, Nikos S. Nonlinear Simulation of Time Dependent Towing of Ocean Vehicles. (University of Michigan Dept. of Naval Architecture & Marine Engineering Ser.: No. 283). pap. 20.00 (ISBN 0-317-30470-4, 2024824). Bks Demand UMI.

Bishop, R. E. & Price, W. G. Hydroelasticity of Ships. LC 78-67297. 1980. 105.00 (ISBN 0-521-22328-8). Cambridge U Pr.

Buxton, Ian. Big Gun Monitors: The History of the Design, Construction & Operation of the Royal Navy's Monitors. LC 80-81901. (Illus.). 215p. 1980. 21.95 (ISBN 0-87021-104-8). Naval Inst Pr.

Chapman, Frederik H. Architectura Navalis Mercatoria: Facsimile of the Classic Eighteenth Century Treatise on Shipbuilding. 152p. 75.00 (ISBN 0-229-97491-0). Sheridan.

Garden, William. Yacht Designs. LC 76-8772. (Illus.). 1977. 22.50 (ISBN 0-87742-066-1). Intl Marine.

Gillmer, Thomas C. Modern Ship Design. 2nd ed. LC 74-25031. (Illus.). 355p. 1975. text ed. 18.95x (ISBN 0-87021-388-1). Naval Inst Pr.

Hambley, Edmund C. Bridge Deck Behavior. 1976. 39.95x (ISBN 0-412-13190-0, NO.6138, Pub. by Chapman & Hall). Methuen Inc.

Hutchinson, William. A Treatise on Naval Architecture. 303p. 1980. 49.95x (ISBN 0-85177-002-9, Pub. by Conway Maritime England). State Mutual Bk.

Imron, A. & Bernitsas, M. M. Program STARI-3D: A Program for Static Risers, 3-Dimensional Analysis. (University of Michigan, Dept. of Naval Architecture & Marine Engineering, Report: No. 280). pap. 20.00 (ISBN 0-317-27124-5, 2024684). Bks Demand UMI.

Kokarakis, J. E. & Bernitsas, M. M. Static Analysis of Operating & Disconnected Risers with or Without Articulations. (University of Michigan, Dept. of Naval Architecture & Marine Engineering, University of Michigan, 1984: No. 286). pap. 29.80 (ISBN 0-317-27123-7, 2024685). Bks Demand UMI.

Kokkinis, Theodore & Bernitsas, M. M. Program FARSEP: A Program for Determination of the Far Postbuckling Section of the Secondary Equilibrium Path of Marine Risers. (University of Michigan, Dept. of Naval Architecture & Marine Engineering, Report: No. 278). pap. 20.00 (ISBN 0-317-27131-8, 2024683). Bks Demand UMI.

Landstrom, Bjorn. The Ship: An Illustrated History. LC 61-14718. (Illus.). 1983. 24.95 (ISBN 0-385-09823-5). Doubleday.

Ministry of Education. Scientific Terms Naval Architecture & Marine Engineering: Japanese-English, English-Japanese. (Japanese & Eng.). 526p. 1955. leatherette 24.95 (ISBN 0-686-92523-8, M-9337). French & Eur.

Munro-Smith, R. Elements of Ship Design. 145p. 1976. pap. 13.50x (ISBN 0-900976-39-X, Pub. by Inst Marine Eng). Intl Spec Bk.
--Ships & Naval Architecture (S. I. Units) (Illus.). 1977. pap. 22.50x (ISBN 0-900976-68-3, Pub. by Inst Marine Eng). Intl Spec Bk.
National Research Council. The Role of Design, Inspection, & Redundancy in Marine Structural Reliability. 579p. 1984. pap. text ed. 34.50 (ISBN 0-309-03488-4). Natl Acad Pr.
Petrie, George L. Simulation of the Maneuverability of Inland Waterway Tows. (University of Michigan, Dept. of Naval Architecture & Marine Engineering, Report: No. 186). pap. 23.30 (ISBN 0-317-27207-1, 2023871). Bks Demand UMI.
Rabl, S. S. Ship & Aircraft Fairing & Development: For Draftsman & Loftsmen & Sheet Metal Workers. 109p. 1941. spiral bdg. 6.00x (ISBN 0-87033-096-9). Cornell Maritime.
The Society of Naval Architects & Marine Engineers: Transactions, Vol. 87. 412p. 1980. text ed. 25.00 (ISBN 0-9603048-1-9). Soc Naval Arch.
Society of Naval Architects & Marine Engineers, Annual Meetings, 92nd, New York, Nov. 1984. Transactions, Vol. 92. (Illus.). 1985. write for info. (ISBN 0-9603048-6-X). Soc Naval Arch.
Society of Naval Architects & Marine Engineers. Transactions: Proceedings of the Society of Naval Architects & Marine Engineers Annual Meeting, 91st, New York, Nov. 1983. (Illus.). 412p. 1984. write for info. (ISBN 0-9603048-5-1). Soc Naval Arch.
Transactions: Proceedings of the Society of Naval Architects & Marine Engineers Annual Meeting, 90th, New York, Nov. 1982. (Illus.). 460p. 1983. write for info. (ISBN 0-9603048-4-3). Soc Naval Arch.

NAVAL ART AND SCIENCE
see also Marine Engineering; Military Art and Science; Navigation; Seamanship; Seamen; Ship-Building; Signals and Signaling; Warships

Brodie, Bernard. Sea Power in the Machine Age. LC 69-13840. Repr. of 1943 ed. lib. bdg. 24.75x (ISBN 0-8371-1445-4, BRSP). Greenwood.
Carlisle, Rodney P. Sovereignty for Sale. LC 81-607020. 278p. 1981. 21.95 (ISBN 0-87021-668-6). Naval Inst Pr.
Cornell, F. M. & Hoffman, A. C. American Merchant Seamans Manual. 6th ed. Hayler, William B., ed. LC 56-12402. (Illus.). 635p. 1981. 22.50x (ISBN 0-87033-267-8). Cornell Maritime.
Crenshaw, R. S., Jr. Naval Shiphandling. 4th ed. LC 74-26360. (Illus.). 496p. 1975. 19.95x (ISBN 0-87021-474-8). Naval Inst Pr.
Deutermann, P. T. OPS Officer's Manual. LC 79-89179. (Illus.). 216p. 1980. 14.95x (ISBN 0-87021-505-1). Naval Inst Pr.
Dorwart, Jeffery M. The Office of Naval Intelligence: Birth of America's First Intelligence Agency, 1865-1918. LC 79-84925. 216p. 1979. 18.95x (ISBN 0-87021-498-5). Naval Inst Pr.
Fioravanzo, Guiseppe. A History of Naval Tactical Thought. LC 78-70966. (Illus.). 312p. 1979. 16.95x (ISBN 0-87021-271-0). Naval Inst Pr.
Fire Terms: A Guide to Their Meaning & Use. (Illus.). 224p. 1980. 11.00 (ISBN 0-686-71646-9, SPP-60). Natl Fire Prot.
Griffiths, Maurice. The Hidden Menace. 160p. 1980. 35.00x (ISBN 0-85177-186-6, Pub. by Conway Maritime England). State Mutual Bk.
Jacobson, Kenneth C. The Watch Officer's Guide. 11th ed. LC 79-87470. (Illus.). 275p. 1979. 11.50x (ISBN 0-87021-749-6). Naval Inst Pr.
Koopman, Bernard O. Search & Screening: General Principles with Historical Applications. LC 79-16909. (Illus.). 400p. 1980. 59.00 (ISBN 0-08-023136-5); pap. 23.00 (ISBN 0-08-023135-7). Pergamon.
Lord, Lindsay. Nautical Etiquette & Customs. LC 76-44659. (Illus.). 63p. 1976. pap. 3.00 (ISBN 0-87033-225-2). Cornell Maritime.
Minikin, R. R. Winds, Waves, & Maritime Structures. 295p. 1963. 75.00x (ISBN 0-85264-091-9, Pub. by Griffin England). State Mutual Bk.
Naval Science Dept., U. S. Naval Academy, ed. Naval Operations Analysis. 2nd ed. LC 77-73342. 384p. 1977. 16.95x (ISBN 0-87021-440-3). Naval Inst Pr.
Navies & Men Series, 25 bks. 1980. Repr. Set. lib. bdg. 706.00x (ISBN 0-405-13030-9). Ayer Co Pubs.
Richardson, Doug. Naval Armament. (Illus.). 160p. 1982. 19.95 (ISBN 0-86720-553-9). Jane's Pub Inc.
Robison, Samuel S. A History of Naval Tactics from 1530-1930: The Evolution of Tactical Maxims. LC 75-41234. Repr. of 1942 ed. 52.50 (ISBN 0-404-14698-8). AMS Pr.
Rodgers, William L. Greek & Roman Naval Warfare. LC 79-121795. (Illus.). 555p. 1964. Repr. of 1937 ed. 14.95 (ISBN 0-87021-226-5). Naval Inst Pr.
--Naval Warfare Under Oars Fourth to Sixteenth Centuries. LC 75-121794. (Illus.). 358p. 1967. Repr. of 1940 ed. 14.95 (ISBN 0-87021-487-X). Naval Inst Pr.
Shaw, Robert L. Fighter Combat Tactics & Maneuvering. (Illus.). 432p. 1985. 28.95 (ISBN 0-87021-059-9). Naval Inst Pr.
Sundt, Wilbur. Naval Science, Vol. 4. LC 78-56425. 332p. 1979. text ed. 15.00x (ISBN 0-87021-483-7). Naval Inst Pr.
Sundt, Wilbur A. Naval Science, Vol. 1. LC 78-56425. (Illus.). 320p. 1980. 8.95x (ISBN 0-87021-456-X). Naval Inst Pr.
--Naval Science, Vol. 2. LC 78-56425. (Naval Science Ser.). (Illus.). 360p. 1981. 8.95x (ISBN 0-87021-457-8). Naval Inst Pr.
--Naval Science, Vol. 3. LC 78-56425. 305p. 1978. text ed. 12.25x (ISBN 0-87021-479-9). Naval Inst Pr.
Till, Geoffrey. Maritime Strategy & the Nuclear Age. LC 81-14559. 284p. 1982. 35.00 (ISBN 0-312-51523-5). St Martin.
Till, Geoffrey, ed. Maritime Strategy & the Nuclear Age. 2nd ed. LC 83-40344. 304p. 1984. 30.00 (ISBN 0-312-51519-7); pap. 15.95 (ISBN 0-312-51521-9). St Martin.
United States Commission to Consider the Present, Organizations of the Signal Service, Geological Survey, Coast, & Geodetic Survey, & Hydrographic Office. Testimony Before the Joint Commission to Consider the Present Organizations of the Signal Service, Geological Survey, Coast & Geodetic Survey, & the Hydrographic Office of the Navy Department: With a View to Secure Greater Efficiency, Vol. 1. 49.00 (ISBN 0-405-12518-6). Ayer Co Pubs.
Williams, Robert H. The Old Corps: A Portrait of the U. S. Marine Corps Between the Wars. LC 80-81090. (Illus.). 152p. 1982. 17.95x (ISBN 0-87021-504-3). Naval Inst Pr.
Willmott, H. P. Sea Warfare: Weapons, Tactics & Strategy. (Illus.). 165p. 1981. 22.50 (ISBN 0-917319-02-8). Sheridan.
Winters, David D. The Boat Officer's Handbook. LC 81-607042. 112p. 1981. pap. 9.95x (ISBN 0-87021-102-1). Naval Inst Pr.

NAVAL ART AND SCIENCE–DICTIONARIES

Ansted, A. A Dictionary of Sea Terms. 3rd ed. (Illus.). 360p. 1985. 24.50x (ISBN 0-85174-481-8, Pub. by Brown Son & Ferguson). Sheridan.
Cazzaroli, Gianni. Dictionnaire de la Navication. (Fr.). 392p. 1973. 23.50 (ISBN 0-686-56803-6, M-4650). French & Eur.
Falconer, William. Universal Dictionary of the Marine. LC 72-87321. (Illus.). Repr. of 1780 ed. lib. bdg. 50.00x (ISBN 0-678-05655-2). Kelley.
Gaynor, Frank, ed. New Military & Naval Dictionary. Repr. of 1951 ed. lib. bdg. 19.75x (ISBN 0-8371-2129-9, GAMN). Greenwood.
Jal, Augustin. Nouveau Glossaire Nautique, Lettre C: Revision De L'edition Publiee En 1848. (Fr.). 1978. pap. 38.40x (ISBN 90-279-7538-8). Mouton.
Kemp, P. K. The Oxford Companion to Ships & the Sea. (Illus.). 1976. 39.95 (ISBN 0-19-211553-7). Oxford U Pr.
Layton, C. W. Dictionary of Nautical Words & Terms. 2nd, rev. ed. 395p. 1982. text ed. 32.50x (ISBN 0-85174-422-2). Sheridan.
Leal Y Leal, Luis. Spanish-English, English-Spanish Naval Dictionary. 3rd, rev. & enl. ed. 232p. (Orig.). 1980. pap. 15.00 (ISBN 84-283-1089-0, Pub. by Paraninfo Spain). Heinman.
MacEwen, W. A. & Lewis, A. H. Encyclopedia of Nautical Knowledge. LC 53-9685. 626p. 1953. 20.00 (ISBN 0-87033-010-1). Cornell Maritime.
Naval Encyclopaedia. LC 73-155740. 1971. Repr. of 1884 ed. 85.00x (ISBN 0-8103-3389-9). Gale.
Nobel, John V. Naval Terms Dictionary. 1977. lib. bdg. 75.00 (ISBN 0-8490-2332-7). Gordon Pr.
Siemss, John, ed. Dictionary of Nautical Terms: Mercantile & Naval Shipping. 838p. 1984. lib. bdg. 80.00x (ISBN 0-317-13132-X). IR Pubns.
Smyth, W. H. Sailor's Word Book: An Alphabetical Digest of Nautical Terms & an Authoritative Encyclopedia of Naval Science & Nomenclature. 1977. pap. 75.00 (ISBN 0-8490-2555-9). Gordon Pr.
Tver, David F. Ocean & Marine Dictionary. LC 79-1529. 359p. 1979. 18.50 (ISBN 0-87033-246-5). Cornell Maritime.
Vandenberghe, J. P. & Chaballe, L. Y., eds. Elsevier's Nautical Dictionary. 2nd ed. 950p. 1978. 191.50 (ISBN 0-444-41694-3). Elsevier.

NAVAL ARTILLERY
see Artillery

NAVAL ASTRONAUTICS
see Astronautics, Military

NAVAL AVIATION
see Aeronautics, Military

NAVAL CONSTRUCTION
see Naval Architecture; Ship-Building

NAVAL ENGINEERING
see Marine Engineering

NAVAL SIGNALING
see Signals and Signaling

NAVIGATION
see also Astronautics in Navigation; Coastwise Navigation; Electronics in Navigation; Harbors; Hydrographic Surveying; Inland Navigation; Knots and Splices; Lighthouses; Longitude; Nautical Almanacs; Nautical Astronomy; Nautical Charts; Nautical Instruments; Naval Art and Science; Navigation (Astronautics); Ocean Currents; Pilot Guides; Pilots and Pilotage; Seamanship; Ship-Building; Signals and Signaling; Sounding and Soundings; Steam-Navigation; Stowage; Submarine Topography; Submarines; Tides; Winds; Yachts and Yachting
also names of nautical instruments, e.g. Compass, Gyroscope

Anderson, E. W. The Principles of Navigation. LC 66-70107. (Illus.). 654p. 1979. 25.00 (ISBN 0-370-00311-X, Pub. by the Bodley Head). Merrimack Pub Cir.
Appleyard, S. F. Marine Electronic Navigation. (Illus.). 256p. 1980. 34.95X (ISBN 0-7100-0533-4). Routledge & Kegan.
Bayless, Allen E. Compact Sight Reduction Tables. LC 80-15129. 32p. 1980. pap. 4.50 (ISBN 0-87033-269-4). Cornell Maritime.
Blair, Carvel H. Seamanship: A Handbook for Oceanographers. LC 76-56349. (Illus.). 238p. 1977. 9.00x (ISBN 0-87033-228-7). Cornell Maritime.
Blewitt, Mary. Celestial Navigation for Yachtsmen. LC 67-25097. 1967. 7.95 (ISBN 0-8286-0028-7). J De Graff.
Bowditch, Nathaniel. The American Practical Navigator; Being an Epitome of Navigation, 2 vols. 1977. Repr. 89.00x (ISBN 0-403-08994-8, Regency). Scholarly.
Brown, Otis S. One Day Celestial Navigation. 132p. 1984. 10.00 (ISBN 0-686-94857-2). Maryland Hist Pr.
--One Day Celestial Navigation. LC 79-67243. (Illus.). 133p. 1984. pap. 6.95 (ISBN 0-89709-132-9). Liberty Pub.
Budlong, John P. Shoreline & Sextant: Practical Coastline Navigation. 1977. 12.95 (ISBN 0-442-21928-8). Van Nos Reinhold.
Campbell, John F. History & Bibliography of the New American Practical Navigator & the American Coast Pilot. LC 64-15742. (Illus.). 1964. 25.00 (ISBN 0-87577-006-1). Peabody Mus Salem.
Cohen, Phillip M. Bathymetric Navigation & Charting. LC 79-6107. (Navies & Men Ser.). (Illus.). 1980. Repr. of 1970 ed. lib. bdg. 14.00x (ISBN 0-405-13036-8). Ayer Co Pubs.
Cotter, Charles H. The Elements of Navigation & Nautical Astronomy. 1981. 75.00x (ISBN 0-85174-270-X, Pub. by Nautical England). State Mutual Bk.
Crawford, William P. Mariner's Celestial Navigation. (Illus.). 1979. 19.95 (ISBN 0-393-60003-3). Norton.
Davies, Thomas D. Star Sight Reduction Tables for Forty-Two Stars: Assumed Altitude Method of Celestial Navigation. LC 79-7464. 370p. 1980. spiral 28.50x (ISBN 0-87033-250-3). Cornell Maritime.
Davis, John. Voyages & Works of John Davis the Navigator. Markham, Albert H., ed. & intro. by. LC 71-134714. (Hakluyt Society, First Ser.: No. 59). (Illus.). 1970. Repr. of 1880 ed. lib. bdg. 32.00 (ISBN 0-8337-2241-7). B Franklin.
Derrick, David. Navigation for Offshore & Ocean Sailors. LC 81-67008. (Illus.). 160p. 1981. 19.95 (ISBN 0-7153-8086-9). David & Charles.
Devereux, Frederick L., Jr. Practical Navigation for the Yachtsman. (Illus.). 316p. 1972. 19.95 (ISBN 0-393-03171-3). Norton.
Dixon, Conrad. Basic Coastal Navigation. (Illus.). 96p. 1973. 6.95x (ISBN 0-8464-0174-6). Beekman Pubs.
--Navigation by Pocket Calculator. (Illus.). 80p. (Orig.). 1983. pap. 4.95 (ISBN 0-229-11691-4, Pub. by Adlard Coles). Sheridan.
--Start to Navigate. (Illus.). 120p. 1977. 9.95x (ISBN 0-8464-1139-3). Beekman Pubs.
--Start to Navigate. 2nd ed. (Illus.). 128p. (Orig.). 1983. pap. 9.95 (ISBN 0-229-11706-6, Pub. by Adlard Coles). Sheridan.
Dodge, D. O. & Kyriss, S. E. Seamanship: Fundamentals for the Deck Officer. 2nd ed. LC 80-5684. (Fundamentals of Naval Science: Vol. 2). 272p. 1981. text ed. 16.95x (ISBN 0-87021-613-9). Naval Inst Pr.
Fifield, L. W. Navigation for Watchkeepers. (Illus.). 416p. 1980. text ed. 32.50x (ISBN 0-434-90564-X). Sheridan.
Frost, A. Practical Navigation for Second Mates. 5th ed. 281p. 1981. 25.00x (ISBN 0-85174-397-8). Sheridan.
--Principle & Practice of Navigation. 319p. 1978. 21.50x (ISBN 0-85174-310-2). Sheridan.
--The Principles & Practice of Navigation. 1981. 40.00x (ISBN 0-85174-310-2, Pub. by Nautical England). State Mutual Bk.
Gardner, A. C. & Creelman, W. G. Navigation for School & College. 2nd ed. 263p. 1976. 18.50x (ISBN 0-85174-236-X). Sheridan.
Graves, Frederick. Piloting. LC 80-84742. (Illus.). 288p. 1981. 8.95 (ISBN 0-87742-116-1). Intl Marine.
Gray, Leonard. Celestial Navigation Planning. LC 84-45264. (Illus.). 133p. (Orig.). 1984. pap. 12.95 (ISBN 0-87033-327-5). Cornell Maritime.
Guzzwell, John. Trekka Round the World. (Illus.). 1980. 9.95 (ISBN 0-8286-0084-8). J De Graff.
Hall, Ernie. Flotsam, Jetsam & Lagan. LC 65-20767. (Illus.). Repr. of 1965 ed. 78.90 (ISBN 0-8357-9072-X, 2015254). Bks Demand UMI.
Hart, M. R. How to Navigate Today. 5th ed. LC 68-23169. (Illus.). 121p. 1970. pap. 4.00 (ISBN 0-87033-035-7). Cornell Maritime.
Hay, David & Hay, Joan. Cruising in Strange Waters. (Illus.). 253p. 1970. 14.95x (ISBN 0-8464-0306-4). Beekman Pubs.
Hobbs, Richard R. Marine Navigation One: Piloting. 2nd ed. LC 81-9538. 320p. 1981. text ed. 16.95x (ISBN 0-87021-358-X). Naval Inst Pr.
Howard-Williams, J. Practical Pilotage. 2nd ed. 96p. 1981. 13.95 (ISBN 0-229-11657-4). Sheridan.
Howell, F. S. Navigation Primer for Fishermen. 1978. 40.00 (ISBN 0-685-63443-4). State Mutual Bk.
James, Richard & Plant, Richard M. Study Guide to the Multiple Choice Examinations for Chief Mate & Master. 2nd ed ed. LC 82-2441. 686p. 1982. 28.50x (ISBN 0-87033-288-0). Cornell Maritime.
--Study Guide to the Multiple Choice Examinations for Third & Second Mates. 4th ed ed. LC 82-2438. 1982. pap. 24.50x (ISBN 0-87033-289-9). Cornell Maritime.
Kane, G. R. Instant Navigation. 2nd ed. LC 84-70703. (Illus.). 100p. 1984. pap. text ed. 12.95 (ISBN 0-9613304-0-6). Assoc Marine.
Kemp, John F. Ocean Navigator (Reed's) 1977. 3rd ed. (Illus.). 45.00 (ISBN 0-900335-47-5). Heinman.
Lane, Carl D. & Montgomery, John. Navigation the Easy Way. (Illus.). 1949. 14.95 (ISBN 0-393-03134-9). Norton.
Layton, C. W. Harbord's Glossary of Navigation. 1981. 50.00x (ISBN 0-85174-277-7, Pub. by Nautical England). State Mutual Bk.
Levison, Henry. Astro-Navigation by Calculator. (Illus.). 112p. 1984. 16.95 (ISBN 0-7153-8553-4). David & Charles.
Maloney, Elbert S. Problems & Answers in Navigation & Piloting. 2nd ed. 96p. 1985. pap. 3.95 (ISBN 0-87021-150-1). Naval Inst Pr.
Marquez, Antonio. Tecnica de Navegacion y Pilotaje Marino. 2nd ed. USAmerica Publishing, ed. LC 84-52183. (Span., Illus.). 152p. 1985. 6.25 (ISBN 0-934763-00-3). Usamerica.
Milligan, John E. Celestial Navigation by H. O. 249. LC 74-1464. (Illus.). 111p. 1974. pap. 7.00 (ISBN 0-87033-191-4). Cornell Maritime.
Mills, H. R. Positional Astronomy & Astro-Navigation Made Easy: A New Approach Using the Pocket Calculator. LC 77-13142. 267p. 1978. 42.95x (ISBN 0-470-99324-3). Halsted Pr.
Moeller, Jan & Moeller, Bill. The Intracoastal Waterway. LC 79-66981. (Illus.). 1979. 10.00 (ISBN 0-915160-23-4). Seven Seas.
Moore, D. A. Basic Principles of Marine Navigation. (Illus.). 128p. 1979. pap. text ed. 9.50x (ISBN 0-540-00377-8). Sheridan.
--Marine Chartwork & Navigation Aids. 2nd ed. 1981. 20.00x (Pub. by Stanford Maritime England). State Mutual Bk.
Motte, Geoff A. & Stout, Thomas M. Chartwork & Marine Navigation: For Fishermen & Boat Operators. 2nd ed. LC 83-46037. (Illus.). 192p. 1984. pap. 11.50 (ISBN 0-87033-314-3). Cornell Maritime.
Motte, R. Weather Routeing of Ships. 1972. 15.00 (ISBN 0-540-00382-4). Heinman.
Noer, H. Rolf. Navigator's Pocket Calculator Handbook. LC 82-74136. (Illus.). 120p. (Orig.). 1983. pap. 16.00 spiral (ISBN 0-87033-295-3). Cornell Maritime.
Nordenskiold, Nils A. Periplus: An Essay on the Early History of Charts & Sailing Directions. Bather, Francis A., tr. from Swed. (Illus.). 1897. 189.00 (ISBN 0-8337-2572-6). B Franklin.
O'Hara, Walter J. Mariner's Gyro-Navigation Manual for Masters, Mates, Marine Engineers. LC 51-7444. (Illus.). pap. 48.00 (ISBN 0-317-08235-3, 2011305). Bks Demand UMI.
Plant, Richard M. Formulae for the Mariner. LC 78-21543. (Illus.). 79p. 1978. spiral bdg. 7.00x (ISBN 0-87033-251-1). Cornell Maritime.
Royal Yachting Association. Navigation: An RYA Manual. (Illus.). 168p. 1981. 18.95 (ISBN 0-7153-8246-2). David & Charles.

BOOKS - SUBJECT INDEX

NEMATODA

Royal Yatching Association. Navigation: An RYA Manual. (Illus.). 164p. 1984. 18.95 (ISBN 0-7153-8630-1). David & Charles.
Schlereth, Hewitt. Celestial Navigation by Star Sights. LC 83-17164. (The Cruising Navigator Ser.: Vol. 3). (Illus.). 352p. 1983. 30.00 (ISBN 0-915160-58-7). Seven Seas.
--Commonsense Coastal Navigation. (Illus.). 1982. 19.95 (ISBN 0-393-03224-8). Norton.
--Latitude & Longitude by the Noon Sight. LC 82-10632. (Cruising Navigator Ser.: Vol. 1). 320p. 1982. 30.00 (ISBN 0-915160-51-X). Seven Seas.
Schofield, Brian B. Navigation & Direction: The Story of HMS Dryad. 150p. 1982. 39.00x (ISBN 0-85937-087-9). State Mutual Bk.
Shufeldt, H. H. & Dunlap, G. D. Piloting & Dead Reckoning. 2nd ed. LC 80-606921. 164p. 1981. pap. 12.95 (ISBN 0-87021-512-4). Naval Inst Pr.
Smith, I. & Mulroney, R. A. Parallel Indexing Techniques. 1979. pap. 6.50x (ISBN 0-540-07353-9). Sheridan.
Tetley, R. M. Small Cruiser Navigation. (Illus.). 144p. 1984. 18.95 (ISBN 0-7153-8520-8). David & Charles.
Toghill, Jeff E. The Yachtsman's Navigation Manual. LC 76-24492. 1977. 12.50 (ISBN 0-8286-0077-5). J De Graff.
Townsend, Sallie & Ericson, Virginia. The Amateur Navigator's Handbook. LC 73-15985. (Illus.). 256p. 1974. 11.95i (ISBN 0-690-00192-4). T Y Crowell.
U. S. Naval Training Command. Navigation. (Nautical Ser.). (Illus.). 1977. pap. 8.95 (ISBN 0-679-50775-2). McKay.
U.S. Naval Academy. Navigation & Operations. LC 72-75502. (Fundamentals of Naval Science Ser: No. 3). 351p. 1972. 11.50x (ISBN 0-87021-491-8). Naval Inst Pr.
Van Wyck, Samuel M. & Carpenter, Max H. The Radar Book. (Illus.). x, 96p. (Orig.). 1984. pap. text ed. 17.50 (ISBN 0-87033-326-7). Cornell Maritime.
Whitaker, S. F. Night Sailing. (Illus.). 94p. 1974. 12.50x (ISBN 0-8464-1115-6). Beekman Pubs.
White, G. W. Exercises in Coastal Navigation. (Illus.). 64p. 1980. pap. text ed. 7.50x (ISBN 0-540-07265-6). Sheridan.
Wieschoff, Anne, et al, eds. The Best of Sail Navigation. (Best of Ser.). (Illus.). 288p. 1982. 15.95 (ISBN 0-914814-27-3). Sail Bks.
Wilensky, Julius M. Yachtsman's Guide to the Windward Islands. 2nd, rev. ed. Van Ost, John R., ed. LC 78-65702. (Illus.). 1978. 19.95 (ISBN 0-918752-01-9). Wescott Cove.
Wilkes, H. K. Exercises for the Ocean Yacht Navigator. 1976. 15.00 (ISBN 0-245-52871-7). Heinman.
Wilkes, Kenneth. Exercises for the Ocean Yacht Navigator. 188p. 1982. 29.00x (ISBN 0-333-32056-5, Pub. by Nautical England). State Mutual Bk.
--Ocean Yacht Navigator. 196p. 1982. 39.00x (ISBN 0-333-32077-8, Pub. by Nautical England). State Mutual Bk.
--Practical Yacht Navigator. 208p. 1982. 35.00x (ISBN 0-333-32081-6, Pub. by Nautical England). State Mutual Bk.
Willan, T. S. River Navigation in England: 1600-1750. 2nd ed. 163p. 1964. 29.50x (ISBN 0-7146-1383-5, F Cass Co). Biblio Dist.
Witt, Howard. Navigation with a Micro-Computer. 1983. pap. text ed. 14.95 (ISBN 0-87567-082-2). Entelek.
Woas, Lee. Self-Steering Without a Windvane. LC 82-10565. (Illus.). 192p. 1982. 25.00 (ISBN 0-915160-52-8). Seven Seas.
Wright, Frances W. Celestial Navigation. 2nd ed ed. LC 82-4964. (Illus.). 144p. 1982. 12.00 (ISBN 0-87033-291-0). Cornell Maritime.
--Particularized Navigation: How to Prevent Navigational Emergencies. LC 73-10239. (Illus.). 77p. 1973. pap. 5.00 (ISBN 0-87033-188-4). Cornell Maritime.
Wright, John. Dead Reckoning Navigation. (Illus.). 164p. 1973. 15.95x (ISBN 0-8464-0315-3). Beekman Pubs.

NAVIGATION–DICTIONARIES
see Naval Art and Science–Dictionaries

NAVIGATION–EARLY WORKS TO 1800
Barlow, William. The Navigators Supply. LC 76-38150. (English Experience Ser.: No. 430). 100p. Repr. of 1597 ed. 16.00 (ISBN 90-221-0430-3). Walter J Johnson.
Cuningham, William. The Cosmographical Glasse, Conteinyng the Principles of Cosmographie, Etc. LC 68-54632. (English Experience Ser.: No. 44). 1968. Repr. of 1559 ed. 49.00 (ISBN 90-221-0044-8). Walter J Johnson.
Galilei, Galileo. Galileo Galilei: Operations of the Geometric & Military Compass. Drake, Stillman, tr. from Ital. & intro. by. LC 78-606002. (Illus.). 1978. pap. text ed. 6.95x (ISBN 0-87474-383-4). Smithsonian.
Linton, Anthony. Newes of the Complement of the Art of Navigation & of the Mightie Empire of Cataia. LC 72-215. (English Experience Ser.: No. 204). 1969. Repr. of 1609 ed. 8.00 (ISBN 90-221-0204-1). Walter J Johnson.
Norwood, Richard. The Sea-Mans Practice. LC 74-28877. (English Experience Ser.: No. 755). 1975. Repr. of 1637 ed. 13.00 (ISBN 90-221-0755-8). Walter J Johnson.
--Trigonometrie, or the Doctrine of Triangles, 2 pts. LC 78-171779. (English Experience Ser.: No. 404). 362p. 1971. Repr. of 1631 ed. 53.00 (ISBN 90-221-0404-4). Walter J Johnson.
Wright, Edward. Certaine Errors in Navigation (the Voyage of George Earl of Cumberland to the Azores) LC 74-80224. (English Experience Ser.: No. 703). 1974. Repr. of 1599 ed. 29.00 (ISBN 90-221-0703-5). Walter J Johnson.

NAVIGATION–HISTORY
Finney, Ben R., compiled by. Pacific Navigation & Voyaging. (Illus.). 148p. 1976. text ed. 12.50x (ISBN 0-8248-0584-4). UH Pr.
Fire Terms: A Guide to Their Meaning & Use. (Illus.). 224p. 1980. 11.00 (ISBN 0-686-71646-9, SPP-60). Natl Fire Prot.
Nadvi, S. Arab Navigation. 15.95 (ISBN 0-686-18335-5). Kazi Pubns.
Taylor, E. G., ed. A Regiment for the Sea, & Other Writings on Navigation by William Bourne of Gravesend, a Gunner (1535-82) 464p. 1963. 20.00x (ISBN 0-686-79454-0, Pub. by Hakluyt Soc England). State Mutual Bk.
Whall, W. B. The Romance of Navigation. LC 72-83272. (Illus.). Repr. of 1930 ed. 22.00 (ISBN 0-405-09061-7). Ayer Co Pubs.

NAVIGATION–SAFETY MEASURES
see also Radio in Navigation
Burch, David F. Emergency Navigation. (Illus.). 160p. 1985. 22.95 (ISBN 0-87742-204-4). Intl Marine.
Marine Publications Intl. Ltd., ed. International Manual of Maritime Safety. 1981. 125.00x (ISBN 0-906314-00-3, Pub. by Marine Pubns Intl England). State Mutual Bk.
--Marine Personnel Safety Manual. 1981. 38.00x (ISBN 0-906314-08-9, Pub. by Marine Pubns Intl England). State Mutual Bk.
--Ships Firefighting Manual. 1981. 50.00x (ISBN 0-906314-03-8, Pub. by Marine Pubns Intl England). State Mutual Bk.
--Ships Operational Safety Manual. 1981. 195.00x (ISBN 0-906314-09-7, Pub. by Marine Pubns Intl England). State Mutual Bk.
Small Fleet Guide. 2nd ed. LC 80-85327. 96p. 1981. pap. 12.30 (ISBN 0-87912-055-X, 221.20). Natl Safety Coun.

NAVIGATION–TABLES
Caney, R. W. & Reynolds, J. E., eds. Reed's Marine Distance Tables. 4th ed. 1978. pap. 22.50 (ISBN 0-900335-51-3). Heinman.
Moeller, Jan & Moeller, Bill. The Intracoastal Waterway. LC 79-66981. (Illus.). 1979. 10.00 (ISBN 0-915160-23-4). Seven Seas.
Nichols, Daniel E. Distance Off Tables. 2nd ed. LC 43-15657. 253p. 1943. 4.00x (ISBN 0-87033-020-9). Cornell Maritime.
Norwood, Richard. Trigonometrie, or the Doctrine of Triangles, 2 pts. LC 78-171779. (English Experience Ser.: No. 404). 362p. 1971. Repr. of 1631 ed. 53.00 (ISBN 90-221-0404-4). Walter J Johnson.
Schlereth, Hewitt. Sight Reduction Tables for Small Boat Navigation. LC 82-19210. (The Cruising Navigator Ser.: Vol. 00). (Illus.). 304p. 1983. 30.00 (ISBN 0-915160-54-4). Seven Seas.

NAVIGATION, AERIAL
see Navigation (Aeronautics)

NAVIGATION (AERONAUTICS)
see also Airplanes–Piloting; Electronics in Aeronautics; Guidance Systems (Flight); Inertial Navigation (Aeronautics); Omnirange System
AGARD-NATO. Radar Techniques for Detection Tracking & Navigation. (Agardographs Ser.: No. 100). (Illus.). 616p. 1966. 164.25 (ISBN 0-677-11030-8). Gordon.
Connes, Keith. The Loran, RNAV & Nav-Comm Book. (Illus.). 1985. pap. 14.95 (ISBN 0-932579-01-9). Butterfield Pr.
Downie, Don. Cockpit Navigation Guide. 1962. 8.95 (ISBN 0-8306-9939-2); pap. 4.95 (ISBN 0-8306-2208-X, 2208). TAB Bks.
Elliot, James C. & Guerny, Gene. Pilot's Handbook of Navigation. 2nd ed. LC 76-62739. (Illus.). 384p. 1977. O. P. 16.95 (ISBN 0-8168-7326-7); pap. 14.95 (ISBN 0-8168-7330-5). Aero.
Etkin, Bernard. Dynamics of Flight Stability & Control. 2nd ed. LC 81-13058. 370p. 1982. text ed. 43.45 (ISBN 0-471-08936-2). Wiley.
Garrison, P. Cockpit Computers & Navigation Avionics. 256p. 1982. 29.95 (ISBN 0-07-022893-0). McGraw.
Ground Studies for Pilots, Vol. 3: Navigation General. 3rd ed. 240p. 1979. 22.50x (ISBN 0-246-11177-1, Pub. by Granada England). Sheridan.
Ground Training for the Private Pilot Licence, No. 2: Air Navigation & Aviation Meteorology. 326p. 1985. pap. 20.00x (ISBN 0-00-383111-6, Pub. by Collins England). Sheridan.
Harbold, Norris B. The Log of Air Navigation. 125p. 1970. pap. 8.00x (ISBN 0-89126-085-4). MA-AH Pub.
Hoyt, John R. As the Pro Flies. (Illus.). 1959. 14.95 (ISBN 0-07-030610-9). McGraw.
Practical Air Navigation. 3rd ed. 336p. 1978. pap. text ed. 10.95 (ISBN 0-88487-053-7, JS314136). Jeppesen Sanderson.
Smith, Robert. Instrument Flying Guide. 1964. pap. 5.95 (ISBN 0-8306-2217-9, 2217). TAB Bks.
Stremming, Ken & Holmes, Harold J., eds. Where Am I, VOR Course. 1976. 13.95 (ISBN 0-940766-03-5, Pub. by Haldon Bks). Aviation.
Taylor, Alan C. Aerial Banner Towing. (Illus.). 224p. 1982. pap. 7.95 (ISBN 0-8306-2303-5, 2303). TAB Bks.
Wright, Monte D. Most Probable Position: A History of Aerial Navigation to 1941. LC 72-97318. (Illus.). 300p. 1973. 29.95x (ISBN 0-7006-0092-2). U Pr of KS.

NAVIGATION (ASTRONAUTICS)
see also Space Flight; Space Vehicles
Bollinger, L. E. & Goldsmith, M., eds. Liquid Rockets & Propellants. LC 60-16913. (Illus.). 682p. 1970. 34.00 (ISBN 0-317-36836-2); members 17.50 (ISBN 0-317-36837-0). AIAA.
Dixon, Conrad. Basic Astro Navigation. (Illus.). 119p. 1973. 9.95x (ISBN 0-8464-0173-8). Beekman Pubs.
Mieville, A. D. Astronomical Navigation Without Mathematics. (Illus.). 1945. pap. text ed. 1.00 (ISBN 0-911090-17-7). Pacific Bk Supply.
Watkins, Gordon. Exercises in Astro-Navigation. (Illus.). 174p. (Orig.). 1981. pap. text ed. 11.50x (ISBN 0-540-07190-0). Sheridan.

NAVIGATION, ELECTRONICS IN
see Electronics in Navigation

NAVIGATION, INLAND
see Inland Navigation

NAVIGATION, RADAR IN
see Radar in Navigation

NAVIGATION BY BIRDS
see Bird Navigation

NAVIGATION CHARTS
see Nautical Charts

NAVIGATION LAWS
see Inland Navigation

NCR (COMPUTER)
NCR Corporation. NCR EDP Concepts Course. LC 79-63818. 512p. 1979. pap. 15.95 (ISBN 0-672-21591-8, 21591). Sams.
Sinclair, Ian. Working with MSX BASIC. (Illus.). 160p. 1984. pap. 17.95 (ISBN 0-00-383103-5, Pub. by Collins England). Sheridan.

NEBULAE
see also Galaxies; Planetary Nebulae
Aller, Lawrence H. Atoms, Stars, & Nebulae. Rev. ed. LC 76-134951. (The Harvard Books on Astronomy). (Illus.). pap. 90.80 (ISBN 0-317-09183-2, 2019508). Bks Demand UMI.
--Physics of Therman Gaseous Nebulae: Physical Processes in Gaseous Nebulae. 1984. lib. bdg. 49.50 (ISBN 90-277-1814-8, Pub. by Reidel Holland). Kluwer Academic.
Gehrels, T., ed. Planets, Stars & Nebulae Studied With Photopolarimetry. LC 73-86446. 1133p. 1974. 27.50x (ISBN 0-8165-0428-8). U of Ariz Pr.
Hubble, Edwin. The Realm of the Nebulae. LC 81-16155. (Silliman Milestones in Science Ser.). 226p. 1982. 33.00x (ISBN 0-300-02499-1); pap. 8.95x (ISBN 0-300-02500-9, Y-428). Yale U Pr.
I.A.U. Symposium, No. 46 Jodrell Bank, England, August 5-7, 1970. The Crab Nebula: Proceedings. Davies, R. D. & Smith, F. G., eds. LC 73-154735. (I.A.U. Symposia: No. 46). 470p. 1971. 50.00 (ISBN 90-277-0183-0, Pub. by Reidel Holland). Kluwer Academic.
Kaufmann, William J., III. Stars & Nebulas. LC 78-17544. (Illus.). 204p. 1978. pap. text ed. 10.95 (ISBN 0-7167-0085-9). W H Freeman.
Menzel, Donald H., ed. Selected Papers on Physical Processes in Ionized Plasmas. (Orig.). 1962. pap. text ed. 5.95 (ISBN 0-486-60060-2). Dover.
Middlehurst, Barbara M. & Aller, Lawrence H., eds. Nebulae & Interstellar Matter. LC 66-13879. (Stars & Stellar Systems Ser.: Vol. 7). (Illus.). 1968. 50.00x (ISBN 0-226-45959-4). U of Chicago Pr.
Nebula to Honor Henry Draper, Dec. 4-5, 1981. Syposium on the Orion. Glassgold, A. E. & Huggins, P. J., eds. 338p. 1982. 65.00x (ISBN 0-89766-180-X, VOL. 395C). NY Acad Sci.
Pottasch, Stuart R. Planetary Nebulae. 1984. lib. bdg. 43.00 (ISBN 90-277-1672-2, Pub. by Reidel Holland). Kluwer Academic.
Vehrenberg, Hans. Atlas of Deep Sky Splendors. 4th ed. Orig. Title: Mein Messier-Buch. Tr. of Mein Messier-Buch. (Illus.). 240p. 1983. 39.95 (ISBN 0-933346-03-4). Sky Pub.

NEC PC 8200 (COMPUTER)
Glatzer, H. & Hogan, T. On the Move with the NEC PC 8200. 256p. pap. 14.95 cancelled (ISBN 0-89303-736-2). Brady Comm.

NEC PC 8201 (COMPUTER)
GLatzer, Hal & Hogan, Thom. NEC PC 8201 User's Guide. 1984. cancelled (ISBN 0-89303-696-X). Brady Comm.

NECTURUS
Gilbert, Stephen G. Pictorial Anatomy of the Necturus. LC 78-152332. (Illus.). 54p. (Orig.). 1973. pap. text ed. 7.95x (ISBN 0-295-95149-4). U of Wash Pr.

NEGATIVE IONS
see Anions

NEGATIVES
see Photography–Negatives

NEGRO ENGINEERS
This heading discontinued January 1976. See Afro-American Engineers for later materials.
Ho, James K. K., ed. Black Engineers in the United States: A Directory. LC 73-84956. 281p. cancelled (ISBN 0-88258-136-8). Howard U Pr.

NEMATODA
Allen, M. W. & Noffsinger, Ella M. A Revision of the Marine Nematodes of the Superfamily Draconematoidea Filipjev 1918. (Publications in Zoology Ser.: Vol. 109). 1978. 16.00x (ISBN 0-520-09583-9). U of Cal Pr.
Bard, J. H. Nematicide Index. 92p. 1974. cloth 39.00x (ISBN 0-85198-309-X, Pub. by CAB Bks England). State Mutual Bk.
Barker, K. R., et al, eds. An Advanced Treatise on Meloidogyne, Vol. II: Methodology. LC 84-61978. (Illus.). 223p. 1985. text ed. 25.00 (ISBN 0-931901-02-2); text ed. 45.00 2 vol. set (ISBN 0-931901-00-6). Intl Melo Proj.
Baylis, H. A. Nematoda: Ascaroidea & Strongyloidea. (Fauna of British India Ser.). xxxvi, 416p. 1978. Repr. of 1936 ed. 30.00 (ISBN 0-88065-051-6, Pub. by Messers Today & Tomorrows Printers & PublishersIndia). Scholarly Pubns.
--Nematoda: Filaricidea, Dictophymoidea & Trichinelloidea, Vol. 2. (Fauna of British India Ser.). xxviii, 280p. 1978. Repr. of 1939 ed. 30.00 (ISBN 0-88065-052-4, Pub. by Messers Today & Tomorrows Printers & Publishers India). Scholarly Pubns.
Behme, R., et al. Biology of Nematodes: Current Studies. LC 72-8856. 219p. 1972. text ed. 24.50x (ISBN 0-8422-7043-4). Irvington.
Bird, Alan F. Structure of Nematodes. 1971. 65.00 (ISBN 0-12-099650-2). Acad Pr.
Chitwood, B. Introduction to Nematology. (Illus.). 344p. 1975. 35.00 (ISBN 0-8391-0697-1). Univ Park.
Croll, N. A., ed. The Organisation of Nematodes. 1977. 69.00 (ISBN 0-12-196850-2). Acad Pr.
Croll, Neil A. & Matthews, Bernard E. Biology of Nematodes. LC 75-555520. (Tertiary Level Biology Ser.). 201p. 1977. Repr. 26.95x (ISBN 0-470-99028-7). Halsted Pr.
Diffusion & Absorption of the Nematicide 1,3-Dichloropropene in Soil. (Agricultural Research Reports: 769). 1972. pap. 13.75 (ISBN 90-220-0378-7, PDC28, PUDOC). Unipub.
Dropkin, Victor H. Introduction to Plant Nematology. LC 80-13556. 293p. 1980. 32.50x (ISBN 0-471-05578-6, Pub. by Wiley Interscience). Wiley.
Freckman, Diana W., ed. Nematodes in Soil Ecosystems. (Illus.). 220p. 1982. text ed. 20.00x (ISBN 0-292-75526-0). U of Tex Pr.
Hetherington, Duncan C. Comparative Studies on Certain Features of Nematodes & Their Significance. (Illinois Biological Monographs: Vol. 3, No. 2). 1924. pap. 8.00 (ISBN 0-384-22760-0). Johnson Repr.
Lamberti, F. & Taylor, C. E., eds. Root-Knot Nematodes: Meloidogyne Species: Systematics, Biology & Control. 1979. 55.00 (ISBN 0-12-434850-5). Acad Pr.
Lamberti, F., et al, eds. Nematode Vectors of Plant Viruses. (NATO ASI Series A, Life Sciences: Vol. 2). 460p. 1975. 59.50x (ISBN 0-306-35602-3, Plenum Pr). Plenum Pub.
Lee, Donald Lewis & Atkinson, H. J. Physiology of Nematodes. 2d ed. LC 77-1232. (Illus.). 215p. 1977. 31.50x (ISBN 0-231-04358-9). Columbia U Pr.
Maggenti, A. R. General Nematology. (Microbiology Ser.). (Illus.). 372p. 1981. 35.00 (ISBN 0-387-90588-X). Springer-Verlag.
Mai, W. F. & Lyon, H. H. Pictorial Key to Genera of Plant-Parasitic Nematodes. 4th ed. LC 74-14082. (Illus.). 224p. 1975. 24.95x (ISBN 0-8014-0920-9). Comstock.
Nicholas, Warwick L. The Biology of Free-Living Nematodes. 2nd ed. (Illus.). 1984. 59.00x (ISBN 0-19-857587-4). Oxford U Pr.
Nickle. Plant & Insect Nematodes. 736p. 1984. 145.00 (ISBN 0-8247-7079-X). Dekker.
Norton, Don C. Ecology of Plant-Parasitic Nematodes. LC 78-1052. 268p. 1978. 48.50x (ISBN 0-471-03188-7, Pub. by Wiley-Interscience). Wiley.

Platt, Howard M. & Warwick, Richard M. Free-Living Marine Nematodes: British Enoplids, Pt. 1. LC 82-19838. (Synopses of the British Fauna Ser.: No. 28). 200p. 1983. 62.50 (ISBN 0-521-25422-1). Cambridge U Pr.

Poinar, George O. Nematodes for Biological Control of Insects. 304p. 1979. 81.50 (ISBN 0-8493-5333-5). CRC Pr.

Poinar, George O., Jr. Natural History of Nematodes. (Illus.). 320p. 1983. 40.95 (ISBN 0-13-609925-4). P-H.

Radewald, John D. Nematode Diseases of Food & Fiber Crops of the Southwestern United States. LC 77-81143. 1978. pap. 6.00 (ISBN 0-931876-16-8, 4083). Ag & Nat Res.

Rysavy, B. & Ryzhikov, K. M., eds. Helminths of Fish Eating Birds of the Palaeartic Region: Volume 1, Nematoda. (Illus.). 1978. lib. bdg. 50.00 (ISBN 90-6193-551-2, Pub. by Junk Pubs Nethherlands). Kluwer Academic.

Sasser, J. N. & Carter, C. C., eds. An Advanced Treatise on Meloidogyne: Biology & Control, Vol. I. LC 84-61978. (Illus.). 422p. 1985. Set. text ed. 65.00 (ISBN 0-931901-00-6); Vol. 1. text ed. 40.00 (ISBN 0-931901-01-4). Intl Melo Proj.

Sasser, J. N., et al. Standardization of Host Suitability Studies & Reporting of Resistance to the Root-Knot Nematodes. 1984. pap. text ed. write for info. (ISBN 0-931901-03-0). Intl Melo Proj.

Sharma, S. & Swarup, G. Cyst Forming Nematodes of India. 152p. 1984. text ed. 25.50x (ISBN 0-391-03335-2, Pub. by Cosmo India). Humanities.

Smart, Grover C., Jr. & Perry, V. G., eds. Tropical Nematology. LC 68-28872. 1968. 9.50 (ISBN 0-8130-0275-3). U Presses Fla.

Stone, A. R. & Platt, H. M., eds. Concepts in Nematode Systematics. (Systematics Symposium Special Ser.: Vol. 22). 1983. 59.50 (ISBN 0-12-672680-9). Acad Pr.

Wallace, H. R. Nematode Ecology & Plant Disease. LC 73-90720. 240p. 1973. 32.50x (ISBN 0-8448-0271-9). Crane Russak Co.

Zuckerman, B. M., et al, eds. Plant Parasitic Nematodes: Morphology, Anatomy, Taxonomy, & Ecology, Vols. 1 & 2. 1971. Vol. 1. 70.00 (ISBN 0-12-782201-1); Vol. 2. 70.00 (ISBN 0-12-782202-X). Acad Pr.

Zuckerman, Bert M. Nematodes As Biological Models: Vol. 1 Behavioral & Developmental Models. LC 79-8849. 1980. 45.00 (ISBN 0-12-782401-4). Acad Pr.

Zuckerman, Bert M., ed. Nematodes As Biological Models: Vol. 2 Aging, & Other Model Systems. LC 79-8849. 1980. 45.00 (ISBN 0-12-782402-2). Acad Pr.

NEMATOSPORA

see Yeast

NEMERTINEA

Coe, Wesley R. Biology of the Nemerteans of the Atlantic Coast of North America. 1943. pap. 49.50x (ISBN 0-686-51347-9). Elliots Bks.

Gibson, Ray. British Nemerteans. LC 81-18193. (Synopses of the British Fauna Ser.: No. 24). 200p. 1982. 37.50 (ISBN 0-521-24619-9). Cambridge U Pr.

NEON LAMPS

Miller, Samuel C. Neon Techniques & Handling: Handbook of Neon Sign & Cold Cathode Lighting. 1977. 24.00 (ISBN 0-911380-41-8). Signs of Times.

Stern, Rudi. Let There Be Neon. LC 77-25900. (Illus.). 1979. o. p. 19.95 (ISBN 0-8109-1255-4); pap. 12.50 (ISBN 0-8109-2164-2). Abrams.

NEOPRENE

see Rubber, Artificial

NEPHRITE

see Jade

NEPTUNE (PLANET)

Grosser, Morton. The Discovery of Neptune. LC 78-68017. 1979. pap. 4.50 (ISBN 0-486-23726-5). Dover.

--The Discovery of Neptune. 12.50 (ISBN 0-8446-5766-2). Peter Smith.

NERVE-CELLS

see Nerves; Neurons

NERVE TISSUE

see also Neuroglia; Neurons

Davidson, A. N., et al, eds. Functional & Structural Proteins of the Nervous System. Mandel, Paul & Morgan, Ian. LC 72-91937. (Advances in Experimental Medicine & Biology Ser.: Vol. 32). 286p. 1972. 42.50x (ISBN 0-306-39032-9, Plenum Pr). Plenum Pub.

Eichberg, Joseph. Phospholipids in Nervous Tissues. 384p. 1985. 79.50 (ISBN 0-471-86430-7). Wiley.

Popp, John A., et al, eds. Neural Trauma. LC 78-24627. (Seminars in Neurological Surgery Ser.). 408p. 1979. text ed. 53.50 (ISBN 0-89004-257-8). Raven.

Ratliff, Floyd. Mach Bands: Quantitative Studies on Neural Networks in the Retina. LC 65-10436. 1965. 35.95x (ISBN 0-8162-7045-7). Holden-Day.

Sato, Gordon, ed. Tissue Culture of the Nervous System. LC 73-79426. (Current Topics in Neurobiology Ser.: Vol. 1). (Illus.). 301p. 1973. 35.00x (ISBN 0-306-36701-7, Plenum Pr). Plenum Pub.

Tasaki, Ichiji. Physiology & Electrochemistry of Nerve Fibers. (Biophysics & Bioengineering Ser.: Vol. 3). 1982. 39.00 (ISBN 0-12-683780-5). Acad Pr.

NERVES

see also Nervous System; Neuroglia; Synapses also particular nerves, e.g. Olfactory Nerve, Optic Nerve

Burnstock, G., et al, eds. Somatic & Autonomic Nerve-Muscle Interactions: Research Monographs in Cell & Tissue Physiology, Vol. 8. 384p. 1983. 106.50 (ISBN 0-444-80458-7). Elsevier.

Conesa, Salvador H. & Argote, M. L. A Visual Aid to the Examination of Nerve Roots. (Illus.). 1976. text ed. 12.95 (ISBN 0-7216-0737-3, Pub. by Bailliere-Tindall). Saunders.

Coupland, R. E. & Forssmann, W. G., eds. Peripheral Neuroendocrine Interaction. (Illus.). 1978. pap. 51.00 (ISBN 0-387-08779-6). Springer-Verlag.

Das, G. D. & Kreutzberg, G. W. Evaluation of Interstitial Nerve Cells in the Central Nervous System: A Correlative Study Using Acetylcholinesterase & Golgi Techniques. LC 64-20582. (Advances in Anatomy, Embryology & Cell Biology: Vol. 41, Pt. 1). (Illus.). 1969. pap. 17.70 (ISBN 0-387-04091-9). Springer-Verlag.

Dorfman, Leslie J., et al, eds. Conduction Velocity Distributions: A Population Approach to Electrophysiology of Nerve; Proceedings of a Workshop, Palo Alto, California, July 1979. LC 80-29130. (Progress in Clinical & Biological Research Ser.: No. 52). 338p. 1981. 33.00x (ISBN 0-8451-0052-1). A R Liss.

Eccles, John C. The Physiology of Nerve Cells. LC 68-9181. 288p. 1957. pap. 7.95x (ISBN 0-8018-0182-6). Johns Hopkins.

Einstein, Elizabeth R. Proteins of the Brain & CSF in Health & Disease. (Illus.). 326p. 1982. 37.50x (ISBN 0-398-04657-3). C C Thomas.

Elfvin, Lars-Gosta, ed. Autonomic Ganglia. 527p. 1983. 75.00 (ISBN 0-471-10503-1, Wiley-Interscience). Wiley.

Gutmann, Ernest, ed. Denervated Muscle. 486p. 1962. 50.00x (ISBN 0-306-10653-1, Consultants). Plenum Pub.

Hammer, Kathryne. Nerve Conduction Studies. (Illus.). 166p. 1982. spiral bdg. 21.75x (ISBN 0-398-04519-4). C C Thomas.

Heistad, D. D. & Marcus, M. L. Cerebral Blood Flow: Effects of Nerves & Neurotransmitters. (Developments in Neuroscience Ser.: Vol. 14). 526p. 1982. 117.00 (ISBN 0-444-00689-3, Biomedical Pr). Elsevier.

Holbrook, Martin L. Hygiene of the Brain & Nerves & the Cure of Nervousness. LC 78-72799. Repr. of 1878 ed. 27.50 (ISBN 0-404-60862-0). AMS Pr.

Hopkins, W. G. & Brown, M. C. The Development of Nerve Cells & Their Connections. LC 83-10097. 150p. 1984. 29.95 (ISBN 0-521-25344-6); pap. 13.95 (ISBN 0-521-27325-0). Cambridge U Pr.

International Society for Cell Biology. Cellular Dynamics of the Neuron. Barondes, Samuel H., ed. (Proceedings: Vol. 8). 1970. 67.50 (ISBN 0-12-611908-2). Acad Pr.

Jenkner, F. L. Peripheral Nerve Block. LC 77-8317. (Illus.). 1977. 19.00 (ISBN 0-387-81426-4). Springer-Verlag.

Junge, Douglas. Nerve & Muscle Excitation. 2nd ed. LC 80-18158. (Illus.). 230p. 1981. pap. text ed. 17.50x (ISBN 0-87893-410-3). Sinauer Assoc.

Keynes, R. D. & Aidley, D J. Nerves & Muscle. LC 80-42150. (Cambridge Texts in the Physiological Sciences Ser.: No. 2). (Illus.). 176p. 34.50 (ISBN 0-521-23945-1); pap. 13.95 (ISBN 0-521-28362-0). Cambridge U Pr.

Landon, D. H., ed. The Peripheral Nerve. 1976. 86.00x (ISBN 0-412-11740-1, NO. 6173, Pub. by Chapman & Hall). Methuen Inc.

Levi-Montalcini, R. Nerve Cells, Transmitters & Behavior. 680p. 1980. 119.75 (ISBN 0-444-80243-6, Biomedical Pr). Elsevier.

Linden, R. J. & Kappagoda, C. T. Atrial Receptors. LC 81-10209. (Monographs of the Physiological Society: No. 39). (Illus.). 250p. 1982. 75.00 (ISBN 0-521-24188-X). Cambridge U Pr.

Mannheimer, Jeffrey S. & Lampe, Gerald N. Clinical Transcutaneous Electrical Nerve Stimulation. LC 83-21020. (Illus.). 635p. 1984. 46.00x (ISBN 0-8036-5832-X). Davis Co.

Matthews, Gary. Cellular Physiology of Nerve & Muscle. (Illus.). 225p. 1985. pap. text ed. 14.95 (ISBN 0-86542-309-1). Blackwell Pubns.

Meisami, Esmail & Brazier, Mary A. Neural Growth & Differentiation. (International Brain Research Organization Monographs: Vol. 5). 546p. 1979. text ed. 74.50 (ISBN 0-89004-378-7). Raven.

Nachmansohn, David. Chemical & Molecular Basis of Nerve Activity. 2nd & rev. ed. 1975. 50.00 (ISBN 0-12-512757-X). Acad Pr.

Ochs, Sidney. Axoplasmic Transport & Its Relation to Other Nerve Function. 462p. 1982. 56.50x (ISBN 0-471-65255-5, Pub. by Wiley-Interscience). Wiley.

Palo, Jarma, ed. Myelination & Demyelination. LC 78-4067. (Advances in Experimental Medicine & Biology Ser.: Vol. 100). 651p. 1978. 69.50x (ISBN 0-306-32700-7, Plenum Pr). Plenum Pub.

Pease, Daniel C., ed. Cellular Aspects of Neural Growth & Differentiation. LC 73-126760. (UCLA Forum in Medical Sciences: No. 14). (Illus.). 1971. 78.00x (ISBN 0-520-01793-5). U of Cal Pr.

Prasad, Keder N. Regulation of Differentiation in Mammalian Nerve Cells. (Illus.). 260p. 1980. 24.50x (ISBN 0-306-40365-X, Plenum Pr). Plenum Pub.

Shkolnik-Yarros, Ekaterina G. Neurons & Interneuronal Connections of the Central Visual System. LC 69-18115. 303p. 1971. 42.50x (ISBN 0-306-30429-5, Plenum Pr). Plenum Pub.

Wolf, Steven L., ed. Transcutaneous Electrical Nerve Stimulation. 1978. pap. 3.50 (ISBN 0-912452-21-8). Am Phys Therapy Assn.

NERVES–ANATOMY

see Neuroanatomy

NERVOUS SYSTEM

see also Biological Control Systems; Brain; Excitation (Physiology); Nerves; Neural Tube; Neuroanatomy; Neurosecretion

American Physiological Society & Kandel, Eric R. The Nervous System, Section 1: Cellular Biology of Neurona, 2 bks, Vol. 1. 1238p. 1977. Set. 135.00 (ISBN 0-683-04505-9). Williams & Wilkins.

Asanuma, Hiroshi, ed. & pref. by. Intergration in the Nervous System. LC 79-84783. (Illus.). 357p. 1979. 52.50 (ISBN 0-89640-033-6). Igaku-Shoin.

Aslin, Richard, ed. Advances in Neural & Behavioral Development. (Advances in Neural & Behav. Devel. Ser.). 296p. 1985. text ed. 34.50 (ISBN 0-89391-223-9). Ablex Pub.

Asratian, E. A. Compensatory Adaptations, Reflex Activity & the Brain. 1965. text ed. 44.00 (ISBN 0-08-010591-2). Pergamon.

Barr, Murray L. El Sistema Nervioso Humano. 2nd ed. 1975. text ed. 16.00 (ISBN 0-06-310057-6, IntlDept). Har-Row.

Barr, Murray L. & Kiernan, John A. The Human Nervous System: An Anatomical Viewpoint. 4th ed. 1983. pap. text ed. 24.75 (ISBN 0-06-140311-3, 14-03112, Harper Medical). Lippincott.

Barth, F. G., ed. Neurobiology of Arachnids. (Illus.). 400p. 1985. 69.50 (ISBN 0-387-15303-9). Springer-Verlag.

Behan, P. O., et al, eds. Immunology of Nervous System Infections: Proceedings of the Noble Bodman Symposia, London, U.K., November 12-13, 1981. (Progress in Brain Research Ser.). 59p. 1983. 104.25 (ISBN 0-444-80443-9, Biomedical Pr). Elsevier.

Boeck, P. The Paraganglia. (Handbuch der Mikroskopischen Anatomie Des Menschen: Vol. 1-8). (Illus.). 400p. 1982. 124.70 (ISBN 0-387-10978-1). Springer-Verlag.

Bolis, L., et al. Comparative Physiology of Sensory Systems. LC 83-14457. 450p. 1984. 99.50 (ISBN 0-521-25002-1). Cambridge U Pr.

Brazier, Mary A. The Electrical Activity of the Nervous System. 4th ed. 260p. 1977. 19.50 (ISBN 0-272-79403-1). Krieger.

Caputto, R. & Marsan, C. Ajmone, eds. Neural Transmission, Learning, & Memory. (International Brain Research Organization Monographs: Vol. 10). (Illus.). 286p. 1983. text ed. 76.00 (ISBN 0-89004-860-6). Raven.

Cort, Joseph. Electrolytes, Fluid Dynamics, & the Nervous System. 1966. 46.00 (ISBN 0-12-190150-5). Acad Pr.

Cotman, Carl W. & Jenson, Robert. Behavioral Neuroscience: An Introduction. 1979. instr's. manual 10.00 (ISBN 0-12-191655-3). Acad Pr.

Cotman, Carl W., ed. Neuronal Plasticity. LC 77-72807. 349p. 1978. 45.50 (ISBN 0-89004-210-1). Raven.

Cowan, W. M., et al, eds. Annual Review of Neuroscience, Vol. 4. (Illus.). 1981. text ed. 20.00 (ISBN 0-8243-2404-8). Annual Reviews.

Curtis, D. R. & McIntyre, A. K., eds. Studies in Physiology Presented to John C. Eccles. (Illus.). 1965. 25.00 (ISBN 0-387-03411-0). Springer-Verlag.

De Belleroche, J. & Dockray, G. J., eds. Cholecystokinin (CCK) in the Nervous System. 132p. 1984. text ed. 33.80x (ISBN 0-89573-369-2). VCH Pubs.

Dunkerley, Gary B. A Basic Atlas of the Human Nervous System. LC 75-14044. (Illus.). 216p. 1975. pap. text ed. 9.95x (ISBN 0-8036-2940-0). Davis Co.

Essman, Walter B., ed. Neurotransmitters, Receptors, & Drug Action. LC 79-23862. (Illus.). 220p. 1980. text ed. 35.00 (ISBN 0-89335-108-3). SP Med & Sci Bks.

Everett, N. B. Functional Neuroanatomy. 6th ed. LC 70-135680. (Illus.). 357p. 1971. text ed. 14.50 (ISBN 0-8121-0324-6). Lea & Febiger.

Eyzaguirre, Carlos & Fidone, Salvatore J. Physiology of the Nervous System. 2nd ed. (Illus.). 430p. 1975. 20.95 (ISBN 0-8151-3182-8); pap. 19.95 (ISBN 0-8151-3183-6). Year Bk Med.

Freeman, Walter J. Mass Action in the Nervous System: Examination of the Neurophysiological Basis of Adaptive Behavior Through the EEG. 1975. 78.00 (ISBN 0-12-267150-3). Acad Pr.

Gabay, Sabit, et al. Metal Ions in Neurology & Psychiatry. 384p. 1985. write for info. (ISBN 0-8451-2717-9). A R Liss.

Gabella, G. Structure of the Autonomic Nervous System. 1976. 75.00x (ISBN 0-412-13620-1, 6114, Pub. by Chapman & Hall). Methuen Inc.

Galveston Chapter, Society for Neuroscience, Galveston, TX, Feb.-March, 1981. Proteins in the Nervous System: Structure & Function: Proceedings. Haber, Bernard, et al, eds. LC 81-20903. (Progress in Clinical and Biological Research Ser.: Vol. 79). 322p. 1982. 48.00 (ISBN 0-8451-0079-3). A R Liss.

Garrod, David R. & Feldman, Joan D., eds. Development in the Nervous System. LC 80-42151. (British Society for Developmental Biology Symposium Ser.: No. 5). (Illus.). 350p. 1982. 95.00 (ISBN 0-521-23493-X). Cambridge U Pr.

Gaze, R. M. Formation of Nerve Connections. 1970. 59.50 (ISBN 0-12-278550-9). Acad Pr.

Glass, David C., ed. Neurophysiology & Emotion. LC 67-31389. (Illus.). 256p. 1967. 13.00x (ISBN 0-87470-006-X). Rockefeller.

Gottlieb, Gilbert, ed. Studies on the Development of Behavior & the Nervous System, 4 vols. Incl. Vol. 1. Behavioral Embryology. 1973. 68.00 (ISBN 0-12-609301-6); Vol. 2. Aspects of Neurogenesis. 1974. 65.00 (ISBN 0-12-609302-4); Vol. 3. Development of Neural & Behavioral Specificity. 1976. 68.00 (ISBN 0-12-609303-2); Vol. 4. Early Influences. 1978. 49.50 (ISBN 0-12-609304-0). Acad Pr.

Grenell, Robert. From Nerve to Mind. 244p. 1972. 67.25 (ISBN 0-677-12310-8). Gordon.

Guillemin, Roger, et al, eds. Neural Modulation of Immunity. 272p. 1985. text ed. 54.50 (ISBN 0-88167-049-9). Raven.

Hanin, Israel, ed. Dynamics of Neurotransmitter Function. (Illus.). 400p. 1984. text ed. 79.00 (ISBN 0-89004-832-0). Raven.

Hausman, Louis. Atlas of Consecutive Stages in the Reconstruction of the Nervous System: Atlas II. (Illus.). 100p. 1965. photocopy ed. spiral 9.50x (ISBN 0-398-00799-3). C C Thomas.

--Illustrations of the Nervous System: Atlas Three. (Illus.). 208p. 1971. 18.75x (ISBN 0-398-00800-0). C C Thomas.

Haymaker, Webb & Adams, Raymond D. Histology & Histopathology of the Nervous System, 2 vols. (Illus.). 2620p. 1982. Set. 295.00x (ISBN 0-398-03482-6). C C Thomas.

Horrocks, Lloyd A., et al, eds. Phospholipids in the Nervous System: Metabolism, Vol. 1. 400p. 1982. text ed. 58.00 (ISBN 0-89004-805-3). Raven.

Hubbard, John I., ed. The Peripheral Nervous System. LC 74-6258. (Illus.). 547p. 1974. 47.50x (ISBN 0-306-30764-2, Plenum Pr). Plenum Pub.

Hughes, Arthur F. Aspects of Neural Ontogeny. 1968. 52.50 (ISBN 0-12-360550-4). Acad Pr.

Kempf, Edward J. Autonomic Functions & the Personality. (Nervous & Mental Disease Monographs: No. 28). 1918. 19.00 (ISBN 0-384-29175-9). Johnson Repr.

Lauder, Jean & Nelson, Phillip, eds. Gene Expression & Cell-Cell Interactions in the Developing Nervous System. 274p. 1985. 42.50x (ISBN 0-306-41836-3, Plenum Pr). Plenum Pub.

Leibovic, K. N. Nervous System Theory: An Introductory Study. 1973. 52.50 (ISBN 0-12-441250-5). Acad Pr.

Levi, Giulio, et al, eds. Transport Phenomena in the Nervous System: Physiological & Pathological Aspects. LC 76-4839. (Advances in Experimental Medicine & Biology Ser.: Vol. 69). 563p. 1976. 65.00x (ISBN 0-306-39069-8, Plenum Pr). Plenum Pub.

Maletta, Gabe J. & Pirozzolo, Francis J., eds. The Aging Nervous System. LC 79-21167. (Advances in Neurogerontology Ser.: Vol. 1). 344p. 1980. 43.95x (ISBN 0-03-052136-X). Praeger.

Mann, Michael D. The Nervous System & Behavior: An Introduction. 376p. 1981. pap. text ed. 23.75x (ISBN 0-06-141576-6, 14-15769, Harper Medical). Lippincott.

Maser, Jack D., ed. Efferent Organization & the Integration of Behavior. 1973. 59.50 (ISBN 0-12-476950-0). Acad Pr.

Essman, Walter B., ed. Neurotransmitters, Receptors, & Drug Action. LC 79-23862. (Illus.). 220p. 1980. text ed. 35.00 (ISBN 0-89335-108-3). SP Med & Sci Bks.
Fariello, Ruggero G., et al, eds. Neurotransmitters, Seizures, & Epilepsy II. 392p. 1984. text ed. 63.50 (ISBN 0-88167-057-X). Raven.
Fields, L. J. Neurotransmitter Function. 1979. 38.50 (ISBN 0-8151-3220-4). Year Bk Med.
Fonnum, Frade, ed. Amino Acids As Chemical Transmitters. LC 78-2362. (NATO ASI A, Life Sciences: Vol. 16). 759p. 1978. 75.00x (ISBN 0-306-35616-3, Plenum Pr). Plenum Pub.
Granit, Ragnar. Receptors & Sensory Perception. LC 75-14597. (Mrs. Hepsa Ely Silliman Memorial Lectures). (Illus.). 369p. 1975. Repr. of 1955 ed. lib. bdg. 24.75x (ISBN 0-8371-8213-1, GRRS). Greenwood.
Heimer, L. & Roards, M. J., eds. Neuroanatomical Tract-Tracing Methods. 592p. 1981. 49.50x (ISBN 0-306-40593-8, Plenum Pr). Plenum Pub.
Hodgkin. The Conduction of the Nervous Impulse. 108p. 1982. 50.00x (ISBN 0-85323-061-7, Pub. by Liverpool Univ England). State Mutual Bk.
Hungarian Pharmacological Society, 3rd Congress, Budapest, 1979. Modulation of Neurochemical Transmission: Proceedings. Vizi, E. S., ed. LC 80-41281. (Advances in Pharmacological Research & Practice Ser.: Vol. II). (Illus.). 450p. 1981. 92.00 (ISBN 0-08-026387-9). Pergamon.
International Society for Neurovegetative Research-Tinany-1972. Neurovegetative Transmission Mechanisms: Proceedings. Csillik, B. & Kappers, J. A., eds. (Journal of Neural Transmission: Suppl. 11). (Illus.). 350p. 1974. 91.50 (ISBN 0-387-81173-7). Springer Verlag.
Iversen, L. L., et al, eds. Handbook of Psychopharmacology: Vol. 2: Principles of Receptor Research. LC 75-6851. 300p. 1975. 42.50x (ISBN 0-306-38922-3, Plenum Pr). Plenum Pub.
--Handbook of Psychopharmacology: Vol. 4: Amino Acid Neurotransmitters. LC 75-6851. 325p. 1975. 42.50x (ISBN 0-306-38924-X, Plenum Pr). Plenum Pub.
--Handbook of Psychopharmacology: Vol. 6: Biogenic Amine Receptors. LC 75-6851. 319p. 1975. 42.50x (ISBN 0-306-38926-6, Plenum Pr). Plenum Pub.
Katz. The Release of Neural Transmitter Substances. 70p. 1982. 50.00x (ISBN 0-85323-060-9, Pub. by Liverpool Univ England). State Mutual Bk.
Klein, Richard L., et al, eds. Neurotransmitter Vesicles. 1982. 61.50 (ISBN 0-12-413680-X). Acad Pr.
Kotliar, B. E. Neural Mechanism of Conditioning. (Illus.). 205p. 1984. 12.00 (ISBN 0-08-026334-8). Pergamon.
MacKenzie, E. T., et al, eds. Neurotransmitters & the Cerebral Circulation. (L. E. R. S. Monograph: Vol. 2). (Illus.). 270p. 1984. text ed. 51.00 (ISBN 0-88167-010-3). Raven.
Mardsen, C. A., ed. Measurement of Neurotransmitter Release In Vivo. (IBRO Handbook Series - Methods in the Neurosciences: Nos. 1-569). 230p. 1984. 47.00x (ISBN 0-471-90444-9, Pub. by Wiley-Interscience); pap. text ed. 21.95x (ISBN 0-471-90445-7). Wiley.
Marwaha, J. & Anderson, W. J., eds. Neuroreceptors in Health & Disease. (Monographs in Neural Sciences: Vol. 10). (Illus.). viii, 256p. 1984. 63.50 (ISBN 3-8055-3715-8). S Karger.
Moore, John W., ed. Membranes, Ions, & Impulses. LC 76-13841. 201p. 1976. 35.00x (ISBN 0-306-34505-6, Plenum Pr). Plenum Pub.
Myers, R. D. & Drucker-Colin, R. R., eds. Neurohumoral Coding of Brain Function. LC 74-7408. (Advances in Behavioral Biology Ser.: Vol. 10). 491p. 1974. 59.50x (ISBN 0-306-37910-4, Plenum Pr). Plenum Pub.
Reinoso-Suarez, Fernando & Marsan, Cosimo A., eds. Cortical Integration: Basic, Archicortical, & Cortical Association Levels of Neural Integration. (International Brain Research Organization Monograph: Vol. 11). 454p. 1984. text ed. 99.00 (ISBN 0-88167-034-0). Raven.
Stjarne, L., et al, eds. O. I. S. Seventy Five Years. 1982. 89.00 (ISBN 0-12-671480-0). Acad Pr.
Willis, W. D. The Pain System. (Pain & Headache: Vol. 8). (Illus.). x, 346p. 1985. 61.50 (ISBN 3-8055-3930-4). S Karger.
Yamamura, Henry I., et al, eds. Neurotransmitter Receptor Binding. 2nd ed. (Illus.). 256p. 1985. text ed. 54.00 (ISBN 0-88167-027-8). Raven.

NEURAL TUBE

Dobbing, John, ed. Prevention of Spina Bifida & Other Neural Tube Defects. 1983. 33.00 (ISBN 0-12-218860-8). Acad Pr.

NEUROANATOMY

Angevine, Jay B., Jr. & Cotman, Carl W. Principles of Neuroanatomy. (Illus.). 1981. 36.95x (ISBN 0-19-502885-6); pap. 18.95x (ISBN 0-19-502886-4). Oxford U Pr.
Becker, R. Frederick & Fix, James A. Outline of Functional Neuroanatomy. (Illus.). Date not set. pap. text ed. 40.00 (ISBN 0-8391-1707-8, 16896). Univ Park.
Bjorklund, A. & Hokfelt, T., eds. Methods in Chemical Neuroanatomy. (Handbook of Chemical Neuroanatomy Ser.: No. 1). xxvi, 548p. 1983. 140.50 (ISBN 0-444-90281-3, Excerpta Medica). Elsevier.
--Neuropeptides in the CNS. (Handbook of Chemical Neuroanatomy: No. 3). 550p. 1983. 123.50 (ISBN 0-444-90340-2, Biomedical Pr). Elsevier.
Bjorklund, A. & Swanson, L. W., eds. Integrated Systems of the CNS. (Handbook of Chemical Neuroanatomy: No. 4). 1984. write for info. (ISBN 0-444-90353-4, Excerpta Medica). Elsevier.
Bjorklund, A., et al. Classical Transmitters in the CNS, Pt. II. (Handbook of Chemical Neuroanatomy Ser.: Vol. 3, pt. II). 1985. 92.75 (ISBN 0-444-90352-6). Elsevier.
Bjorklund, A., et al, eds. Classical Transmitters in the CNS, Pt. I. (Handbook of Chemical Neuroanatomy Ser.: Vol. 2, pt. I). 1985. 100.00 (ISBN 0-444-90330-5, Excerpta Medica). Elsevier.
Carpenter, Malcolm. Study Guide & Self Assessment Review for the Core Text of Neuro-Anatomy. 3rd ed. 100p. 1985. pap. 15.95 (ISBN 0-683-14560-6). Williams & Wilkins.
Carpenter, Malcolm B. & Sutin, Jerome. Human Neuroanatomy. 8th ed. (Illus.). 906p. 1982. text ed. 45.50 (ISBN 0-683-01461-7). Williams & Wilkins.
Chusid, Joseph G. Correlative Neuroanatomy & Functional Neurology. 19th ed. LC 85-50602. (Illus.). 513p. 1985. lexotone cover 19.50 (ISBN 0-87041-014-8). Lange.
Conference, Bethesda, Md, June, 1981 & Chan-Palay, Victoria. Cytochemical Methods in Neuroanatomy: Proceedings. LC 82-7826. (Neurology & Neurobiology Ser.: Vol. 1). 584p. 1982. 96.00 (ISBN 0-8451-2700-4). A R Liss.
Crosby, Elizabeth C., et al, eds. Comparative Correlative Neuroanatomy of the Vertebrate Telencephalon. Carey, Joshua. (Illus.). 1982. text ed. write for info. (ISBN 0-02-325690-7). Macmillan.
DeLahunta, Alexander. Veterinary Neuroanatomy & Clinical Neurology. 2nd ed. LC 76-4246. (Illus.). 1983. text ed. 36.95 (ISBN 0-7216-3029-4). Saunders.
DeLisa, Joel A. & Mackenzie, Keith. Manual of Nerve Conduction Velocity Techniques. 158p. 1982. pap. text ed. 20.50 (ISBN 0-89004-656-5). Raven.
Dublin, William B. & Dublin, Arthur B. Atlas of Neuroanatomy for Radiologists: Surface & Sectional-with CT Scanning Correlation. LC 79-50199. (Illus.). 250p. 1982. 62.50 (ISBN 0-87527-204-5). Green.
Emson, P. C., ed. Chemical Neuroanatomy. (Illus.). 575p. 1983. text ed. 91.00 (ISBN 0-89004-608-5). Raven.
Everett, N. B. Functional Neuroanatomy. 6th ed. LC 70-135680. (Illus.). 357p. 1971. text ed. 14.50 (ISBN 0-8121-0324-6). Lea & Febiger.
Folk, Dean. External Neuroanatomy of Old World Monkeys (Cercopithecoidea) Szalay, F. S., ed. (Contributions to Primatology: Vol. 15). (Illus.). 1978. 25.25 (ISBN 3-8055-2834-5). S Karger.
Garoutte, Bill. A Survey of Functional Neuroanatomy. LC 80-84809. (Illus.). 217p. 1982. pap. text ed. 9.75x (ISBN 0-930010-04-3). Jones Med.
Gilman, Sid & Winans-Newman, Sarah. Manter & Gatz's Essentials of Clinical Neuroanatomy & Neurophysiology. 6th ed. LC 81-17437. (Essential of Medical Education Ser.). (Illus.). 218p. 1982. pap. 13.95x (ISBN 0-8036-4155-9). Davis Co.
Greengard, Paul. Cyclic Nucleotides, Phosphorylated Proteins, & Neuronal Function. LC 78-66349. (Distinguished Lecture Series of the Society of General Physiologists: Vol. 1). 134p. 1978. 22.00 (ISBN 0-89004-281-0). Raven.
Haines, Duane E. Neuroanatomy: An Atlas of Structures, Sections & Systems. (Illus.). 224p. 1983. spiral 19.50 (ISBN 0-8067-0851-4). Urban & S.
Hausman, Louis. Clinical Neuroanatomy, Neurophysiology & Neurology: With a Method of Brain Reconstruction. (Illus.). 484p. 1971. 48.50x (ISBN 0-398-00803-5). C C Thomas.
Heimer, L. The Human Brain & Spinal Cord: Functional Neuroanatomy & Dissection Guide. (Illus.). 402p. 1983. 36.95 (ISBN 0-387-90741-6); pap. 26.95 (ISBN 0-387-90740-8). Springer-Verlag.
Heimer, L. & Roards, M. J., eds. Neuroanatomical Tract-Tracing Methods. 592p. 1981. 49.50x (ISBN 0-306-40593-8, Plenum Pr). Plenum Pub.
Heym, C. & Forssmann, W. G., eds. Techniques in Neuroanatomical Research. (Illus.). 410p. 1981. 61.00 (ISBN 0-387-10686-3). Springer-Verlag.
Krieger, Dorothy T., ed. Endocrine Rhythms. LC 77-75655. (Comprehensive Endocrinology Ser.). 344p. 1979. 50.50 (ISBN 0-89004-234-9). Raven.
Lang, J. Clinical Anatomy of the Head: Neurocranium, Orbita, Craniocervical Regions. (Illus.). 489p. 1983. 490.00 (ISBN 0-387-11014-3). Springer-Verlag.
Lindsay, Robert, ed. Computer Analysis of Neuronal Structures. LC 76-50605. (Illus.). 226p. 1977. 39.50x (ISBN 0-306-30964-5, Plenum Pr). Plenum Pub.
Lissak, K., ed. Results in Neuroanatomy, Motor Organization, Cerebral Circulation & Modelling: Recent Developments in Neurobiology in Hungary, Vol. VIII. 1981. 60.00x (ISBN 0-569-08549-7, Pub. by Collet's). State Mutual Bk.
Lockard, L. Desk Reference for Neuroanatomy: A Guide to Essential Terms. LC 77-21707. 1977. 24.00 (ISBN 0-387-90278-3). Springer-Verlag.
Martinez & Martinez. Neuroanatomy: Development & Structure of the Central Nervous System. 1982. text ed. 42.00 (ISBN 0-7216-6147-5). Saunders.
Matzke, Howard A. & Foltz, Floyd M. Synopsis of Neuroanatomy. 4th ed. (Illus.). 1983. pap. 9.95x (ISBN 0-19-503244-6). Oxford U Pr.
Meisami, Esmail & Brazier, Mary A. Neural Growth & Differentiation. (International Brain Research Organization Monographs: Vol. 5). 546p. 1979. text ed. 74.50 (ISBN 0-89004-378-7). Raven.
Mitchell, George & Mayor, Donald. Essentials of Neuroanatomy. 4th ed. (Illus.). 1983. pap. text ed. 9.75 (ISBN 0-443-02450-2). Churchill.
Moyer, K. E. Neuroanatomy: Text & Illustration. 1980. pap. text ed. 24.00 scp (ISBN 0-06-044639-0, HarpC). Har-Row.
Nauta, Walle J. & Feirtag, Michael. Fundamental Neuroanatomy. LC 84-28675. (Illus.). 336p. 1985. text ed. write for info. (ISBN 0-7167-1722-0); pap. text ed. write for info. (ISBN 0-7167-1723-9). W H Freeman.
Nieuwenhuys, R., et al. The Human Central Nervous System: A Synopsis & Atlas. (Illus.). 253p. 1981. pap. 33.00 (ISBN 0-387-10316-3). Springer Verlag.
--The Human Central Nervous System: A Pictorial Survey. 2nd ed. (Illus.). 1981. pap. 33.00 (ISBN 0-387-10316-3). Springer-Verlag.
Oakley, Bruce & Schafer, Rollie. Neuroanatomy: Dissection of the Sheep Brain. (Illus.). 32p. 1980. pap. text ed. 2.98x (ISBN 0-472-08691-X). U of Mich Pr.
Pellegrino, L. J., et al. Stereotaxic Atlas of the Rat Brain. 2nd ed. LC 79-9438. 279p. 1979. 29.50x (ISBN 0-306-40269-6, Plenum Pr). Plenum Pub.
Robertson, Richard T., ed. Neuroanatomical Research Technique. (Methods in Physiological Psych. Ser.: Vol. 2). 1978. 62.50 (ISBN 0-12-590350-2). Acad Pr.
Singh, Inderbir. A Textbook of Human Neuroanatomy. 360p. 1982. 60.00x (ISBN 0-686-94065-2, Pub. by Garlandfold England); pap. 50.00x (ISBN 0-7069-1193-8). State Mutual Bk.
Snell, Richard S. Clinical Neuroanatomy for Medical Students. 1980. text ed. 31.95 (ISBN 0-316-80213-1). Little.
Strausfeld, N. J., ed. Functional Neuroanatomy. (Springer Series in Experimental Entomology). (Illus.). 440p. 1983. 79.50 (ISBN 0-387-12742-9). Springer-Verlag.
Thalamocortical Organization of the Auditory System in the Cat: Studied by Retrograde Axonal Transport of Horseradish Peroxidase. (Advances in Anatomy, Embryology, & Cell Biology Ser.: Vol. 57). (Illus.). 1979. pap. 24.00 (ISBN 0-387-09449-0). Springer-Verlag.
Verwoerd, C. D. A. & Van Oostrom, C. G. Cephalic Neural Crest & Placodes. (Advances in Anatomy, Embryology & Cell Biology: Vol. 58). (Illus.). 1979. 32.00 (ISBN 0-387-09608-6). Springer-Verlag.
Zilles, K. J. Ontogenesis of the Visual System. (Advances in Anatomy, Embryology & Cell Biology: Vol. 54, Pt. 3). (Illus.). 1978. pap. 32.00 (ISBN 0-387-08726-5). Springer-Verlag.

NEUROBIOLOGY

Altman, J. & Bayer, S. A. The Development of the Rat Spinal Chord. (Advances in Anatomy, Embryology & Cell Biology Ser.: Vol. 58). (Illus.). 160p. 1984. pap. 25.00 (ISBN 0-387-13119-1). Springer-Verlag.
Altschuler, Richard A., et al, eds. Neurobiology of Hearing: The Cochlea. 1985. text ed. price not set (ISBN 0-89004-925-4). Raven.
Aschoff, Jurgen, ed. Handbook of Behavioral Neurobiology, Vol. 4: Biological Rhythms. 582p. 1981. 55.00x (ISBN 0-306-40585-7, Plenum Pr). Plenum Pub.
Ballenger, James C. Biology of Agoraphobia. LC 84-6157. (Clinical Insights Monographs). 128p. 1984. pap. text ed. 12.00x (ISBN 0-88048-064-5). Am Psychiatric.
Barker, Jeffery L. & McKelvy, Jeffrey F. Current Methods in Cellular Neurobiology: Vol. I-Anatomical Techniques. LC 83-1282. (Neurobiology Ser.: I-662). 325p. 1983. 59.50 (ISBN 0-471-09328-9, Pub. by Wiley-Interscience). Wiley.
Barker, Jeffrey L. & McKelvy, Jeffery F. Current Methods in Cellular Neurobiology: Vol. 4 Model Systems. LC 83-1282. (Neurobiology Ser.: I-662). 192p. 1983. 49.50 (ISBN 0-471-09327-0, Pub. by Wiley-Interscience). Wiley.
Barker, Jeffrey L. & McKelvy, Jeffery F., eds. Current Methods in Cellular Neurobiology: Vol. 2: Biochemical Techniques. LC 83-1282. 319p. 1983. 59.50 (ISBN 0-471-09344-0, Pub. by Wiley-Interscience). Wiley.
--Current Methods in Cellular Neurobiology: Vol. 3: Electrophysiological & Optical Techniques. LC 83-1282. 320p. 1983. 59.50 (ISBN 0-471-09343-2, Pub. by Wiley-Interscience). Wiley.
Barth, F. G., ed. Neurobiology of Arachnids. (Illus.). 400p. 1985. 69.50 (ISBN 0-387-15303-9). Springer-Verlag.
Boulton, A. A., et al, eds. Neurobiology of the Trace Amines. LC 84-626. (Experimental & Clinical Neuroscience Ser.). (Illus.). 624p. 59.50 (ISBN 0-89603-063-6). Humana.
Bradford, H. F., ed. Neurotransmitter Interaction & Compartmentation. (NATO ASI Series A, Life Sciences: Vol. 48). 852p. 1982. 95.00x (ISBN 0-306-41015-X, Plenum Pr). Plenum Pub.
Bradford, Harry F. Chemical Neurobiology. LC 85-7037. (Illus.). 416p. 1985. text ed. write for info. (ISBN 0-7167-1694-1); study guide 8.95 (ISBN 0-7167-1641-0). W H Freeman.
Brown, Alan C. & Fyffe, E. W. Intracellular Staining of Mammalian Neurones. (Biological Techniques Ser.). 1984. for info. 23.00 (ISBN 0-12-137220-0). Acad Pr.
Brown, Ian, ed. Molecular Approaches to Neurobiology. LC 81-17593. (Cell Biology Ser.). 1982. 65.00 (ISBN 0-12-137020-8). Acad Pr.
Caplan, David, ed. Biological Studies of Mental Processes. (Illus.). 1980. 35.00x (ISBN 0-262-03061-6). MIT Pr.
Changeuz, J., et al, eds. Molecular & Cellular Interactions Underlying Higher Brain Function: Proceedings of the 9th Meeting of the International Neurobiology Society, Abbaye Royale de Fontevraud, France September 1-4, 1981. (Progress in Brain Research Ser.: No. 58). xvi, 484p. 1983. 95.75 (ISBN 0-444-80432-3, I-025-83, Biomedical Pr). Elsevier.
Chronister, R. B. & De France, J. F., eds. The Neurobiology of the Nucleus Accumbens. (Illus.). 380p. (Orig.). 1981. pap. 39.95 (ISBN 0-940090-00-7). Haer Inst.
Cold Springs Harbor Symposia on Quantitative Biology. LC 34-8174. (Molecular Neurobiology Ser.: Vol. 48). (Illus.). 920p. 1984. 137.50x (ISBN 0-87969-047-X); pap. 74.50 (ISBN 0-87969-048-8). Cold Spring Harbor.
Correia, Manning J. & Perachio, Adrian A. Contemporary Sensory Neurobiology. LC 85-142. (Progress in Clinical & Biological Research Ser.: Vol. 176). 372p. 1985. 58.00 (ISBN 0-8451-5026-X). A R Liss.
Cowan, W. Maxwell, ed. Studies in Developmental Neurobiology: Essays in Honor of Viktor Hamburger. (Illus.). 1981. text ed. 49.50x (ISBN 0-19-502927-5). Oxford U Pr.
Di Chiara, G. & Gessa, G. L., eds. Glutamate As a Neurotransmitter. (Advances in Biochemical Psychopharmacology Ser.: Vol. 27). 464p. 1981. text ed. 71.00 (ISBN 0-89004-420-1). Raven.
Dreosti, Ivor E. & Smith, Richard M., eds. Neurobiology of the Trace Elements: Vol. 1, Trace Element Neurobiology & Deficiencies. LC 83-8412. (Contemporary Neuroscience Ser.). 384p. 1983. 49.50 (ISBN 0-89603-046-6). Humana.
Eadie, M. J. & Tyrer, J. H., eds. Biochemical Neurology. LC 82-22859. 278p. 1983. 48.00 (ISBN 0-8451-3009-9). A R Liss.
Ehrenpreis, S. & Solnitsky, O., eds. Neurosciences Research. Incl. Vol. 1. 1968. 73.50 (ISBN 0-12-512501-1); Vol. 2. 1969. 73.50 (ISBN 0-12-512502-X); Vol. 3. 1970. 73.50 (ISBN 0-12-512503-8); Vol. 4. 1971. 73.50 (ISBN 0-12-512504-6); Vol. 5. 1973. 65.00 (ISBN 0-12-512505-4). Acad Pr.
Eisenstein, Edward M., ed. Aneural Organisms in Neurobiology. LC 74-28345. (Advances in Behavioral Biology Ser.: Vol. 13). 152p. 1975. 29.50x (ISBN 0-306-37913-9, Plenum Pr). Plenum Pub.

Haber, Bernard & Aprison, M. H., eds. Neuropharmacology & Behavior. LC 77-14178. (Illus.). 235p. 1978. 32.50x (ISBN 0-306-31056-2, Plenum Pr). Plenum Pub.

Haber, Bernard, et al, eds. Serotonin: Current Aspects of Neurochemistry & Function. (Advances in Experimental Medicine & Biology Ser.: Vol. 133). 840p. 1981. 89.50x (ISBN 0-306-40579-2, Plenum Pr). Plenum Pub.

Horrocks, Lloyd A., et al, eds. Phospholipids in the Nervous System: Physiological Roles, Vol. 2. 376p. 1985. text ed. 69.00 (ISBN 0-88167-068-5). Raven.

Hucho, F. Introduction to Neurochemistry. 1985. text ed. 27.50 (ISBN 0-89573-225-4). VCH Pubs.

Hucho, F. & Ovchinnikov, Y. A., eds. Toxins as Tools in Neurochemistry. xiv, 368p. 1983. 72.00x (ISBN 3-11-009593-9). De Gruyter.

Hungarian Pharmacological Society, 3rd Congress, Budapest, 1979. Modulation of Neurochemical Transmission: Proceedings. Vizi, E. S., ed. LC 80-41281. (Advances in Pharmacological Research & Practice Ser.: Vol. II). (Illus.). 450p. 1981. 92.00 (ISBN 0-08-026387-9). Pergamon.

Karczmar, A. G. & Eccles, John C., eds. Brain & Human Behavior. LC 78-160592. (Illus.). 1972. 47.00 (ISBN 0-387-05331-X). Springer-Verlag.

Kobayashi, H., et al, eds. Neurosecretion & the Biology of Neuropeptides. 580p. 1985. 64.00 (ISBN 0-387-15586-4). Springer-Verlag.

Kunos, George. Adrenoceptors & Catecholamine Action. LC 81-10431. (Neurotransmitter Receptors Ser.: Pt. B). 327p. 1983. 80.50 (ISBN 0-471-05726-6, Pub. by Wiley-Interscience). Wiley.

Lajtha, Abel, ed. Handbook of Neurochemistry, Vols. 1-7. Incl. Vol. 1. Chemical Architecture of the Nervous System. 484p. 1969. 49.50 (ISBN 0-306-37701-2); Vol. 2. Structural Neurochemistry. 562p. 1969 (ISBN 0-306-37702-0); Vol. 3. Metabolic Reactions in the Nervous System. 590p. 1970 (ISBN 0-306-37703-9); Vol. 4. Control Mechanisms in the Nervous System. 516p. 1970 (ISBN 0-306-37704-7); Vol. 5A. Metabolic Turnover in the Nervous Systems. 438p. 1971 (ISBN 0-306-37705-5); Vol. 5B. Metabolic Turnover in the Nervous System. 399p. 1971 (ISBN 0-306-37715-2); Vol. 6. Alterations of Chemical Equilibrium in the Nervous System. 584p. 1971 (ISBN 0-306-37706-3); Vol. 7. Pathological Chemistry of the Nervous System. 675p. 1972 (ISBN 0-306-37707-1). LC 68-28097. 49.50x ea. (Plenum Pr). Plenum Pub.

--Handbook of Neurochemistry, Vol. 1: Chemical Architecture of the Nervous System. LC 68-28097. pap. 127.00 (ISBN 0-317-27114-8, 2024701). Bks Demand UMI.

--Handbook of Neurochemistry, Vol. 1: Chemical & Cellular Architecture. 2nd ed. LC 82-493. 516p. 1982. 65.00x (ISBN 0-306-40861-9, Plenum Pr). Plenum Pub.

--Handbook of Neurochemistry, Vol. 10: Pathological Neurochemistry. 2nd ed. 781p. 1985. 95.00x (ISBN 0-306-41744-8, Plenum Pr). Plenum Pub.

--Handbook of Neurochemistry, Vol. 2: Experimental Neurochemistry. 2nd ed. 498p. 1982. 59.50x (ISBN 0-306-40972-0, Plenum Pr). Plenum Pub.

--Handbook of Neurochemistry, Vol. 3: Metabolism in the Nervous System. rev., 2nd ed. 724p. 89.50x (ISBN 0-306-41153-9, Plenum Pr). Plenum Pub.

--Handbook of Neurochemistry, Vol. 5: Metabolic Turnover in the Nervous System. 2nd ed. 518p. 1983. 69.50x (ISBN 0-306-41323-X, Plenum pr). Plenum Pub.

--Handbook of Neurochemistry, Vol. 6: Receptors in the Nervous System. 2nd ed. 694p. 1984. 89.50x (ISBN 0-306-41411-2, Plenum Pr). Plenum Pub.

--Handbook of Neurochemistry, Vol. 7: Structural Elements of the Nervous System. 2nd ed. 700p. 1984. 89.50x (ISBN 0-306-41440-6, Plenum Pr). Plenum Pub.

--Handbook of Neurochemistry, Vol. 8: Neurochemical Systems. 2nd. ed. 700p. 1984. 89.50x (ISBN 0-306-41579-8, Plenum Pr). Plenum Pub.

--The Handbook of Neurochemistry, Vol. 9: Alterations of Metabolites in the Nervous System. 2nd ed. 624p. 1985. 85.00x (ISBN 0-306-41743-X, Plenum Pr). Plenum Pub.

--Protein Metabolism of the Nervous System. LC 74-85373. 732p. 1970. 65.00x (ISBN 0-306-30418-X, Plenum Pr). Plenum Pub.

Lissak. Results in Neurochemistry, Neuroendocrinology, Neurophysiology & Behavior, Neuropharmacology, Neuropathology, Cybernetics, Vol. 5. 1978. 19.50 (ISBN 0-9960007-2-0, Pub. by Akademiai Kaido Hungary). Heyden.

Malick, Jeffrey B., et al, eds. Anxiolytics: Neurochemical, Behavioral, & Clinical Perspectives. (Central Nervous System Pharmacology Ser.). 232p. 1983. text ed. 51.50 (ISBN 0-89004-731-6). Raven.

Mandel, Paul & DeFeudis, F. V., eds. GABA: Biochemistry & CNS Functions. LC 79-22019. (Advances in Experimental Medicine & Biology Ser.: Vol. 123). 517p. 1979. 62.50x (ISBN 0-306-40325-0, Plenum Pr). Plenum Pub.

Margolis, R. U. & Margolis, R. K., eds. Complex Carbohydrates of Nervous Tissue. LC 78-26881. (Illus.). 419p. 1979. 49.50x (ISBN 0-306-40135-5, Plenum Pr). Plenum Pub.

Marks, Neville & Rodnight, Richard, eds. Research Methods in Neurochemistry, Vol. 1. LC 76-183563. 387p. 1972. 47.50x (ISBN 0-306-36001-2, Plenum Pr). Plenum Pub.

--Research Methods in Neurochemistry, Vol. 2. (Illus.). 432p. 1974. 42.50 (ISBN 0-306-36002-0, Plenum Pr). Plenum Pub.

--Research Methods in Neurochemistry, Vol. 3. 488p. 1975. 49.50x (ISBN 0-306-36003-9, Plenum Pr). Plenum Pub.

--Research Methods in Neurochemistry, Vol. 4. (Illus.). 461p. 1978. 45.00x (ISBN 0-306-36004-7, Plenum Pr). Plenum Pub.

--Research Methods in Neurochemistry, Vol. 5. LC 72-222263. 334p. 1981. 39.50x (ISBN 0-306-40583-0, Plenum Pr). Plenum Pub.

--Research Methods in Neurochemistry, Vol. 6. 392p. 1985. 52.50x (ISBN 0-306-41751-0, Plenum Pr). Plenum Pub.

Neuhoff, V. Proceedings of the European Society for Neurochemistry, Vol. 1. (Illus.). 280p. 1978. 51.80x (ISBN 0-89573-018-9). VCH Pubs.

Norton, William T., ed. Oligodendroglia. (Advances in Neurochemistry Ser.: Vol. 5). 338p. 1984. 49.50x (ISBN 0-306-41547-X, Plenum Pr). Plenum Pub.

Osborne, Neville N., ed. Biochemistry of Characterized Neurons. LC 76-55379. 1978. text ed. 59.00 (ISBN 0-08-021503-3). Pergamon.

Pevzner, L. V. Functional Biochemistry of the Neuroglia. LC 78-26386. (Illus.). 320p. 1979. 45.00 (ISBN 0-306-10954-9, Consultants). Plenum Pub.

Richter, D., ed. Biochemical Factors Concerned in the Functional Activity of the Nervous System. 1969. pap. 32.00 (ISBN 0-08-013311-8). Pergamon.

Siegel, George J. & Albers, R. Wayne. Basic Neurochemistry. 3rd ed. 1981. pap. text ed. 33.50 (ISBN 0-316-79002-8). Little.

Svennerholm, Lars, et al, eds. Structure & Function of the Gangliosides. LC 79-25711. (Advances in Experimental Medicine & Biology Ser.: Vol. 125). 580p. 1980. 69.50x (ISBN 0-306-40332-3, Plenum Pr). Plenum Pub.

Vizi, E. S. & Magyar, K., eds. Regulation of Transmitter Function, Basic & Clinical Aspects: Proceedings of the Meeting of the European Society for Neurochemistry, 5th, Held in Budapest, Hungary, 21-26 August 1984. (Developments in Neuroscience Ser.: Vol. 17). 572p. 1984. 122.25 (ISBN 0-444-80613-X). Elsevier.

Vizi, E. Sylvester. Non-Synaptic Interactions Between Neurons: Modulation of Neurochemical Transmission-Pharmacological & Clinical Aspects. 260p. 1984. 39.95 (ISBN 0-471-90378-7). Wiley.

Wiggins, Richard C., et al, eds. Developmental Neurochemistry. McCandless, David W. (Illus.). 272p. 1985. text ed. 35.00x (ISBN 0-292-71548-X). U of Tex Pr.

Youdim, M. B. & Lovenberg, W., eds. Essays in Neurochemistry & Neuropharmacology, Vol. 5. Sharman, D. F. & Lagnado, J. R., trs. LC 80-40964. 153p. 1981. 57.95x (ISBN 0-471-27879-3, Pub. by Wiley-Interscience). Wiley.

Zambotti, V., et al, eds. Glycolipids, Glycoproteins, & Mucopolysaccharides of the Nervous System. LC 72-78628. (Advances in Experimental Medicine & Biology Ser.: Vol. 25). 345p. 1972. 45.00 (ISBN 0-306-39025-6, Plenum Pr). Plenum Pub.

NEUROCYTE

see Neurons

NEUROGENESIS

see Developmental Neurology

NEUROGLIA

Pevzner, L. V. Functional Biochemistry of the Neuroglia. LC 78-26386. (Illus.). 320p. 1979. 45.00 (ISBN 0-306-10954-9, Consultants). Plenum Pub.

Ramon y Cajal, Santiago. The Neuron & the Glial Cell. Torre, Jack de la & Gibson, William, trs. from Span. (Illus.). 364p. 1984. 39.75x (ISBN 0-398-04908-4). C C Thomas.

NEUROKERATIN

see Keratin

NEUROLOGY

see also Developmental Neurology; Electrophysiology; Nervous System; Neurobiology; Neurochemistry; Psychology, Physiological

Abelson, Philip H., et al, eds. Neuroscience. LC 84-24524. (Illus.). 453p. 1985. text ed. 29.95 (ISBN 0-87168-309-1); pap. text ed. 14.95 (ISBN 0-87168-268-0). AAAS.

Adams, R. D. & Victor, M. Principles of Neurology. 3rd ed. 1216p. 1985. 65.00 (ISBN 0-07-000296-7). McGraw.

Addink, A. D. & Spronk, N., eds. Exogenous & Endogenous Influences on Metabolic & Neural Control, Vol. 1, Invited Lectures: Proceedings of the Third Congress of the European Society for Comparative Physiology & Biochemistry, August 31-September 3, 1981, Noorwijkerhout Netherlands. (Illus.). 432p. 1982. 83.00 (ISBN 0-08-027986-4). Pergamon.

--Exogenous & Endogenous Influences on Metabolic & Neural Control, Vol. 2, Abstracts: Proceedings ot the Third Congress of the European Society for Compara07394366xxxlogy & Biochemistry, August 31-September 3, 1981, Noorwijkerhout,Netherlands. (Illus.). 260p. 1982. 55.00 (ISBN 0-08-028845-6). Pergamon.

Aidley, D. J. The Physiology of Excitable Cells. 2nd ed. LC 77-87375. (Illus.). 1979. 79.50 (ISBN 0-521-21913-2); pap. 24.95 (ISBN 0-521-29308-1). Cambridge U Pr.

Atrens, D. M. & Curthoys, J. S., eds. Neuroscience & Behavior: An Introduction. 2nd ed. 214p. 1982. 9.00i (ISBN 0-12-066850-5). Acad Pr.

Bandler, Richard. Modulation of Sensorimotor Activity During Alterations in Behavioral States. LC 84-7952. (Neurology & Neurobiology Ser.: Vol. 12). 550p. 1984. 68.00 (ISBN 0-8451-2714-4). A R Liss.

Bannister, Roger, ed. Brain's Clinical Neurology. 6th ed. (Illus.). 1985. 35.00x (ISBN 0-19-261455-X); pap. 24.95x (ISBN 0-19-261454-1). Oxford U Pr.

Berenberg, Samuel R. Brain: Fetal & Infant. 1977. lib. bdg. 53.00 (ISBN 90-247-2022-2, Pub. by Martinus Nijhoff Netherlands). Kluwer Academic.

Bishop, Beverly & Craik, Rebecca L. Neural Plasticity. 1982. pap. 5.00 (ISBN 0-912452-38-2). Am Phys Therapy Assn.

Borsellino, A. & Cervetto, L., eds. Photoreceptors. (NATO Series A, Life Sciences: Vol. 75). 368p. 1984. 55.00x (ISBN 0-306-41629-8, Plenum Pr). Plenum Pub.

Botez, M. I. & Reynolds, E. H., eds. Folic Acid in Neurology, Psychiatry, & Internal Medicine. LC 78-57243. 550p. 1979. text ed. 71.00 (ISBN 0-89004-338-8). Raven.

Boulton, A., et al, eds. Neuromethods, Vol. 2. (Neuromethods Ser.). 500p. 1985. 59.50 (ISBN 0-89603-076-8). Humana.

Broughton, R. J., ed. Henri Gastaut & the Marseilles School's Contribution to the Neurosciences: Proceedings of the 25th & Final Colloque de Marseille. (Electroencephalography & Clinical Neurophysiology Ser.: Suppl. No. 35). 448p. 1982. 119.25 (ISBN 0-444-80363-7, Biomedical Pr). Elsevier.

Bures, Jan & Krekule, Ivan. Practical Guide to Computer Applications in Neurosciences. 398p. 1983. 54.95 (ISBN 0-471-10012-9, Pub. by Wiley-Interscience). Wiley.

Chan-Palay, Victoria & Palay, Sanford L. Coexistence of Neuroactive Substances in Neurons. LC 83-14694. (Neurosciences Ser.: I-584). 1075p. 1984. 89.95 (ISBN 0-471-89503-2, Pub. by Wiley-Interscience). Wiley.

Chaplin, James P. & Demers, Aline. Primer of Neurology & Neurophysiology. LC 78-6680. 272p. 1984. pap. 20.50 (ISBN 0-471-03027-9). Krieger.

Chusid, Joseph G. Correlative Neuroanatomy & Functional Neurology. 19th ed. LC 85-50602. (Illus.). 513p. 1985. lexotone cover 19.50 (ISBN 0-87041-014-8). Lange.

Ciba Foundation. Cerebral Vascular Smooth Muscle & Its Control. LC 77-28855. (Ciba Foundation Symposium, New Ser.: 56). pap. 102.00 (ISBN 0-317-29773-2, 2022181). Bks Demand UMI.

Conesa, Salvador H. & Argote, M. L. A Visual Aid to the Examination of Nerve Roots. (Illus.). 1976. text ed. 12.95 (ISBN 0-7216-0737-3, Pub. by Bailliere-Tindall). Saunders.

Costa, Erminio & Trabucchi, Marco, eds. Neural Peptides & Neuronal Communication. (Advances in Biochemical Psychopharmacology Ser.: Vol. 22). 670p. 1980. text ed. 88.00 (ISBN 0-89004-375-2). Raven.

Cowan, W. M., et al, eds. Annual Review of Neuroscience, Vol. 6. (Illus.). 1983. text ed. 27.00 (ISBN 0-8243-2406-4). Annual Reviews.

--Annual Review of Neuroscience, Vol. 7. (Illus.). 1984. text ed. 27.00 (ISBN 0-8243-2407-2). Annual Reviews.

Cowan, W. Maxwell, et al, eds. Annual Review of Neuroscience, Vol. 8. (Illus.). 603p. 1985. text ed. 27.00 (ISBN 0-8243-2408-0). Annual Reviews.

Delta Sleep Inducing Peptide DSIP. (Journal: European Neurology: Vol. 23, No. 5). (Illus.). 76p. 1984. pap. 15.50 (ISBN 3-8055-4011-6). S Karger.

Desmedt, John E., ed. Motor Control Mechanisms in Health & Disease: Advances in Neurology, Vol. 39. (Illus.). 1224p. 1983. 163.00 (ISBN 0-89004-723-5). Raven.

Ebbesson, Sven, ed. Comparative Neurology of the Telencephalon. LC 79-12145. (Illus.). 528p. 1980. 65.00x (ISBN 0-306-40237-8, Plenum Pr). Plenum Pub.

Edelman, Gerald M., et al, eds. Dynamic Aspects of Neocortical Function. LC 84-11825. (Neuroscience Institute Monograph). 736p. 1984. 85.00x (ISBN 0-471-80559-9, Pub. by Wiley-Interseince). Wiley.

Elam, John S. & Cancalon, Paul, eds. Axonal Transport in Neuronal Growth & Regeneration. 300p. 1984. 45.00x (ISBN 0-306-41699-9, Plenum Pr). Plenum Pub.

Endroczi, E. & De Wied, D., eds. Integrative Neurohumoral Mechanisms. (Developments in Neuroscience Ser.: Vol. 16). 560p. 1983. 40.00 (ISBN 0-444-80487-0, I-093-83, Biomedical Pr). Elsevier.

Enna, S. J. & Yamamura, H. D., eds. Neurotransmitter Receptors, 2 pts. (Receptors & Recognition Ser. B: Vols. 9 & 10). 1980. Set. 90.00x (ISBN 0-686-80428-7, NO. 2178, Pub. by Chapman & Hall); Pt. 1: Amino Acids, Peptides & Benzodiazepines. 49.95x (ISBN 0-412-16250-4, NO. 6399); Pt. 2: Biogenic Amines. 49.95x (ISBN 0-412-23130-1, 2157). Methuen Inc.

Everett, N. B. Functional Neuroanatomy. 6th ed. LC 70-135680. (Illus.). 357p. 1971. text ed. 14.50 (ISBN 0-8121-0324-6). Lea & Febiger.

Feldman, Robret G., ed. Neurology: The Physician's Guide. (Illus.). 288p. 1984. pap. text ed. 29.00 (ISBN 0-86577-111-1). Thieme-Stratton.

Fieschi, C. & Loeb, C. W., eds. Effects of Aging on Regulation of Cerebral Blood Flow & Metabolism: Abstracts. (Journal: European Neurology: Vol. 22, Suppl. 2). (Illus.). x, 64p. 1983. pap. 22.25 (ISBN 3-8055-3732-8). S Karger.

Friedlander, W., ed. Current Reviews. LC 75-14572. (Advances in Neurology Ser.: Vol. 13). 404p. 1975. 52.50 (ISBN 0-89004-000-1). Raven.

Frigyesi, T L. Subcorticual Mechanisms & Sensorimotor Activities. 293p. 1975. 110.00 (ISBN 3-456-80118-1, Pub. by Holdan Bk Ltd UK). State Mutual Bk.

Gazzaniga, Michael S., ed. Handbook of Cognitive Neuroscience. 428p. 1984. 45.00x (ISBN 0-306-41290-X, Plenum Pr). Plenum Pub.

Goetz, Christopher G. Neurotoxins in Clinical Practice. LC 85-2107. (Neurologic Illness: Diagnosis & Treatment Ser.). 400p. 1985. text ed. 55.00 (ISBN 0-89335-224-1). SP Med & Sci Bks.

Goldblatt, David. Neuroscience & Clinical Neurology Review. 224p. 1979. pap. 13.95 (ISBN 0-668-03370-3). ACC.

Grisolia, S., et al. Ramon y Cajal's Contribution to the Neurosciences. 1983. 81.00 (ISBN 0-444-80486-2). Elsevier.

Hanin, Israel & Goldberg, Alan M., eds. Progress in Cholinergic Biology: Model Cholinergic Synapses. 382p. 1982. text ed. 90.00 (ISBN 0-89004-758-8). Raven.

Hausman, Kathy A., et al. Analyzing Neurological Status. (Illus.). 125p. 1985. pap. text ed. 12.95 (ISBN 0-932491-24-3). Res Appl Inc.

Hausman, Louis. Clinical Neuroanatomy, Neurophysiology & Neurology: With a Method of Brain Reconstruction. (Illus.). 484p. 1971. 48.50x (ISBN 0-398-00803-5). C C Thomas.

Heiss, W. D. & Phelps, M. F., eds. Positron Emission Tomography of the Brain. (Illus.). 244p. 1983. 54.00 (ISBN 0-387-12130-7). Springer-Verlag.

Henry, G. & Little, N. Neurologic Emergencies: A Sympton Oriented Approach. 336p. 1985. 25.00 (ISBN 0-07-029326-0). McGraw.

Himwich, Williamina, ed. Biochemistry of the Developing Brain, Vol. 1. 408p. 1973. 79.75 (ISBN 0-8247-1316-8). Dekker.

Himwich, Williamina A., ed. Biochemistry of the Developing Brain, Vol. 2. 346p. 1974. 79.75 (ISBN 0-8247-6035-2). Dekker.

International Congress of Primatology, 3rd, Zurich, 1970. Primatology: Proceedings, 3 vols. Incl. Vol. 1. Taxonomy, Anatomy, Reproduction. Biegert, J. & Leutenegger, W., eds. (Illus.). xvi, 278p. 40.50 (ISBN 3-8055-1244-9); Vol. 2. Neurobiology, Immunology, Cytology. Biegert, J. & Leutenegger, W., eds. (Illus.). x, 245p. 38.50 (ISBN 3-8055-1245-7); Vol. 3. Behavior. Kummer, H., ed. (Illus.). x, 191p. 30.00 (ISBN 3-8055-1246-5). 1971. Set. 108.75 (ISBN 3-8055-1247-3). S Karger.

Jacobson, M., ed. Development of Sensory Systems. (Handbook of Sensory Physiology: Vol. 9). (Illus.). 1978. 135.00 (ISBN 0-387-08632-3). Springer-Verlag.

Jacoby, J. H. & Lytle, L. D., eds. Serotonin Neurotoxins. (Annals of the New York Academy of Sciences: Vol. 305). 702p. 1978. pap. 68.00x (ISBN 0-89072-061-4). NY Acad Sci.

Jewett, Don L. & Rayner, Martin D. Basic Concepts of Neuronal Function. 398p. 1984. pap. text ed. 24.95 (ISBN 0-316-46310-8). Little.

Kandel, E. R. & Schwartz, J. H., eds. Principles of Neural Science. 2nd ed. 734p. 1981. 70.00 (ISBN 0-444-00552-8, Biomedical Pr); pap. 47.50 (ISBN 0-444-00944-2, Biomedical Pr). Elsevier.

Katzman, Robert & Terry, Robert D. The Neurology of Aging. LC 82-14921. (Contemporary Neurology Ser.: No. 22). (Illus.). 249p. 1983. text ed. 41.00x (ISBN 0-8036-5231-3). Davis Co.

Kerkut, Gerald, ed. Microcomputers in the Neurosciences. (Illus.). 300p. 1985. 39.95x (ISBN 0-19-857214-X). Oxford U Pr.

Kety, Seymour S., et al, eds. Genetics of Neurological & Psychiatric Disorders. (Association for Research in Nervous & Mental Disease (ARNMD) Research Publications Ser.: Vol. 60). 312p. 1983. text ed. 52.00 (ISBN 0-89004-626-3). Raven.

Kotagal. Neurology of Childhood: Concepts & Practice. write for info. Ishiyaku Euro.

Locke, Steven E., et al, eds. Foundations of Psychoneuroimmunology. LC 84-24559. 504p. 1985. lib. bdg. 59.95x (ISBN 0-202-25138-1). Aldine Pub.

Lowenthal, A. Agar Gel Electrophoresis in Neurology. 1964. 18.00 (ISBN 0-444-40377-9). Elsevier.

Mardsen, C. A., ed. Measurement of Neurotransmitter Release In Vivo. (IBRO Handbook Series - Methods in the Neurosciences: Nos. 1-569). 230p. 1984. 47.00x (ISBN 0-471-90444-9, Pub. by Wiley-Interscience); pap. text ed. 21.95x (ISBN 0-471-90445-7). Wiley.

Marler, P. & Vandenberg, J. G., eds. Handbook of Behavioral Neurobiology, Vol. 3: Social Behavior & Communication. LC 79-308. 427p. 1979. 55.00x (ISBN 0-306-40218-1, Plenum Pr). Plenum Pub.

Massey, Janice M., ed. Basic Neurology for Electrophysiologic Monitoring. 160p. Date not set. pap. text ed. 18.00 (ISBN 0-8391-1968-2, 20672). Univ Park.

Massion, J., et al, eds. Neural Coding of Motor Performance. (Experimental Brain Research: Supplementum 2). (Illus.). 348p. 1983. 43.00 (ISBN 0-387-12140-4). Springer-Verlag.

Mayeux, Richard & Rosen, Wilma G., eds. The Dementias. (Advances in Neurology Ser.: Vol. 38). 288p. 1983. text ed. 44.00 (ISBN 0-89004-696-4). Raven.

Mesulam, Marsel. Tracing Neural Connections with Horseradish Peroxidase. LC 81-14692. (IBRO Handbook Ser.: Methods in the Neurosciences). 251p. 1982. 58.95x (ISBN 0-471-10028-5, Pub. by Wiley-Interscience); pap. 27.95x (ISBN 0-471-10029-3). Wiley.

Moskowitz, Nathan. Enzymatic Automodulation of Chemical Presynaptic Neurotrans. 238p. 1985. 33.95 (ISBN 0-03-000312-1). Praeger.

Mumenthaler, Marco. Neurologic Differential Diagnosis. Appenzeller, Otto, tr. (Ger., Illus.). 192p. 1985. pap. text ed. 27.00 (ISBN 0-86577-165-0). Thieme Stratton.

Murray, H. & Andothers, A. Thermatic Appercetion Test. 20p. 59.00 (ISBN 0-317-14306-9, Pub. by Holdan Bk Ltd UK). State Mutual Bk.

Myslobodsky, Michael, ed. Hemisyndromes: Psychobiology, Neurology, Psychiatry. LC 83-2823. 1983. 55.00 (ISBN 0-12-512460-0). Acad Pr.

Neurology. 2nd ed. (Medical Ser.). (Illus.). 64p. 1984. 12.95x (ISBN 0-935920-23-4, Pub. by Natl Medical Careers). Natl Pub Black Hills.

Oosterveld, W. J. Otoneurology. 274p. 1984. 52.00 (ISBN 0-471-90441-4, Pub. by Wiley Med). Wiley.

Oxender, Dale & Blume, Arthur, eds. Membrane Transport & Neuroreceptors. LC 81-8151. (Progress in Clinical & Biological Research Ser.: Vol. 63). 470p. 1981. 75.00 (ISBN 0-8451-0063-7). A R Liss.

Perkins, David, et al. Atlas of Clinical Neurology. (Illus.). 230p. 1985. price not set (ISBN 0-8391-2096-6, 22241). Univ Park.

Potbin, Alfred R. & Tourtellotte, Wallace W., eds. Quantitative Examination of Neurologic Functions, Vol. I. LC 84-3152. 272p. 1985. 82.00 (ISBN 0-8493-5926-0). CRC Pr.

--Quantitative Examination of Neurologic Functions, Vol. II. LC 84-3152. 208p. 1985. 67.00 (ISBN 0-8493-5927-9). CRC Pr.

Pryse-Phillips, William & Murray, T. J. Textbook of Essential Neurology. 3rd. ed. 1985. pap. price not set (ISBN 0-87488-531-0). Med Exam.

Romand, R., ed. Development of Auditory & Vestibular Systems. 1983. 59.50 (ISBN 0-12-594450-0). Acad Pr.

Rudge, Peter. Clinical Neuro-Otology. (Clinical Neurology & Neurosurgery Monographs: Vol. 4). (Illus.). 341p. 1983. text ed. 49.00 (ISBN 0-443-01918-5). Churchill.

Schlaefke, M. E., et al, eds. Central Neurone Environment & the Control Systems of Breathing & Circulation. (Proceedings in Life Sciences Ser.). 275p. 1983. 37.00 (ISBN 0-387-11671-0). Springer-Verlag.

Schoffeniels, E., et al, eds. Dynamic Properties of Glia Cells: An Interdisciplinary Approach to Their Study in the Central & Peripheral Nervous System. LC 78-40218. 1978. text ed. 81.00 (ISBN 0-08-021555-6). Pergamon.

Schulster, D. & Levitzki, A. Cellular Receptors for Hormones & Neurotransmitters. LC 79-41216. 412p. 1980. 94.95x (ISBN 0-471-27682-0, Pub. by Wiley-Interscience). Wiley.

Scott, Alwyn C. Neurophysics. LC 77-2762. Repr. of 1977 ed. 88.00 (2055136). Bks Demand UMI.

Sears, T. A., ed. Neuronal-Glial Cell Interrelationships. (Dahlem Workshop Reports Ser.: Vol. 20). (Illus.). 375p. 1982. 25.00 (ISBN 0-387-11329-0). Springer-Verlag.

Selverston, Allen I. Model Neural Networks & Behavior. 546p. 1985. 69.50x (ISBN 0-306-41949-1, Plenum Pr). Plenum Pub.

Sever, John L. & Madden, David, eds. Polyomaviruses & Human Neurological Disease. LC 82-22945. (Progress in Clinical & Biological Research Ser.: Vol. 105). 398p. 1983. 66.00 (ISBN 0-8451-0105-6). A R Liss.

Singh, Man M., et al, eds. Central Cholinergic Mechanism & Adaptive Dysfunctions. 418p. 1984. 59.50x (ISBN 0-306-41835-5, Plenum Pr). Plenum Pub.

Stone, T. Microiontophoresis & Pressure Ejection. (IBRO Handbook Ser.). 1985. 54.95 (ISBN 0-471-90607-7); pap. 27.95 (ISBN 0-471-90608-5). Wiley.

Strub, Richard L. & Black, F. William. The Mental Status Examination in Neurology. 2nd ed. LC 84-23169. (Illus.). 232p. 1985. pap. text ed. 15.95 (ISBN 0-8036-8211-5). Davis Co.

Sun, Grace Y., et al, eds. Neural Membranes. LC 83-6106. (Experimental & Clinical Neuroscience Ser.). (Illus.). 608p. 1983. 59.50 (ISBN 0-89603-052-0). Humana.

Thompson, Richard F., ed. Progress in Neuroscience. (A Scientific American Reader). (Illus.). 138p. 1985. 21.95 (ISBN 0-7167-1726-3); pap. 12.95 (ISBN 0-7167-1727-1). W H Freeman.

Tsukada, Y., ed. Perspectives on Neuroscience. (Illus.). xii, 378p. 1985. 59.50 (ISBN 0-387-15565-1). Springer-Verlag.

Usdin, E. & Hanin, I., eds. Biological Markers in Psychiatry & Neurology: Symposium on Biological Markers in Psychiatry & Neurology, Ochsner Clinic, New Orleans, U. S. A., 8-10 May 1981. 544p. 1982. 83.00 (ISBN 0-08-027987-2). Pergamon.

Vinken, P. J. & Frederiks, J. A., eds. Handbook of Clinical Neurology, 2 vols. (Revised Series I). 1985. Set. 129.75 (ISBN 0-444-90356-9). Elsevier.

Vinken, P. J., et al, eds. Handbook of Clinical Neurology: Revised Series, Vol. 45-1. 1985. write for info. (ISBN 0-444-90404-2). Elsevier.

Wallace, R. B. & Das, G. D., eds. Neural Tissue Transplantation Research: Proceedings in Life Sciences. (Illus.). 260p. 1983. 44.50 (ISBN 0-387-90833-1). Springer-Verlag.

Whitfield, I. C. Neurocommunications: An Introduction. 320p. 1984. 34.95x (ISBN 0-471-10320-9, Pub. by Wiley-Interscience). Wiley.

Wiederholt, Wigbert C., ed. Neurology for Non-Neurologists. LC 82-3995. 1982. 39.50 (ISBN 0-12-788925-6). Acad Pr.

Wigan, A. L. Duality of the Mind. Bogen, J. E., frwd. by. LC 85-50042. 368p. 1985. 30.00 (ISBN 0-934710-11-2); ltd. ed. 48.00 (ISBN 0-934710-12-0). J Simon.

Wolf, Sheldon M. Neurology Case Studies. 3rd ed. 1984. pap. text ed. 19.00 (ISBN 0-87488-006-8). Med Exam.

Yamamura, H. I. & Olsen, R. W. Psychopharmacology & Biochemistry of Neurotransmitter Receptors. (Developments in Neurology: Vol. 11). 676p. 1981. 102.00 (ISBN 0-444-00568-4, Biomedical Pr). Elsevier.

NEUROLOGY, DEVELOPMENTAL

see Developmental Neurology

NEURONS

AIP Conference Proceedings No. 89, Argonne National Laboratory, 1981. Neutron Scattering: Proceedings. Faber, John, Jr., ed. LC 82-73094. 397p. 1982. lib. bdg. 35.50 (ISBN 0-88318-188-6). Am Inst Physics.

Black, Ira B., ed. Cellular & Molecular Biology of Neuronal Development. 390p. 1984. 49.50x (ISBN 0-306-41550-X, Plenum Pr). Plenum Pub.

Brown, Alan C. & Fyffe, E. W. Intracellular Staining of Mammalian Neurones. (Biological Techniques Ser.). 1984. for info. 23.00 (ISBN 0-12-137220-0). Acad Pr.

Chalazonitis, N. & Boisson, M., eds. Abnormal Neuronal Discharges. LC 76-58750. 447p. 1978. 54.50 (ISBN 0-89004-238-1). Raven.

Chan-Palay, Victoria & Palay, Sanford L. Coexistence of Neuroactive Substances in Neurons. LC 83-14694. (Neurosciences Ser.: I-584). 1075p. 1984. 89.95 (ISBN 0-471-89503-2, Pub. by Wiley-Interscience). Wiley.

CINDA: An Index to the Literature on Microscopic Neutron Data. Incl. CINDA-A (1935-1976, 2 Vols. 1929p. 1980. Set. pap. 95.50 (ISBN 0-686-60074-6, ICIN35/76); Vol. 1 Z-50. pap. (ISBN 92-0-039079-X); Vol. 2 Z-51. pap. (ISBN 92-0-039179-6); CINDA 79 (1977-1979) 376p. 1980. pap. 33.00 (ISBN 92-0-039279-2, ICIN77/79); free supplement (ISBN 92-0-039379-9); 1977-1981. 542p. 1981. pap. 52.00 (ISBN 92-0-039081-1, ICIN81); Supplement to CINDA 81. pap. 8.25 (ISBN 92-0-039181-8, ICIN81SUPP); An Index to the Literature on Microscopic Neutron Data. IAEA). Unipub.

Cold Spring Harbor Symposia on Quantitative Biology: The Neuron, Vol. 17. LC 34-8174. (Illus.). 323p. 1953. 38.00x (ISBN 0-87969-016-X). Cold Spring Harbor.

Correia, Manning J. & Perachio, Adrian A. Contemporary Sensory Neurobiology. LC 85-142. (Progress in Clinical & Biological Research Ser.: Vol. 176). 372p. 1985. 58.00 (ISBN 0-8451-5026-X). A R Liss.

Cotman, C. W., et al, eds. Cell Surface & Neuron & Neuronal Function. Nicolson. (Cell Surface Reviews Ser.: Vol. 6). 546p. 1981. 121.75 (ISBN 0-444-80202-9, Biomedical Pr). Elsevier.

Duffy, Philip E. Astrocytes: Normal, Reactive, & Neoplastic. 236p. 1983. text ed. 45.50 (ISBN 0-89004-996-3). Raven.

Heydorn, K. Neutron Activation Analysis for Clinical Trace Element Research, Vol. I. 288p. 1984. 75.00 (ISBN 0-317-05009-5). CRC Pr.

International Symposium, Prilly-Lausanne, July 6-7, 1978. Transport Mechanisms of Tryptophan in Blood Cells, Nerve Cells, & at the Blood-Brain Barrier: Proceedings. Baumann, P., ed. (Journal of Neural Transmission: Suppl. 15). (Illus.). 1979. 64.40 (ISBN 0-387-81519-8). Springer-Verlag.

International Symposium, Switzerland, Sept. 1978. Development & Chemical Specificity Neurons: Proceedings. Cuenod, M., et al, eds. (Progress in Brain Research Ser.: Vol. 51). 1980. 111.00 (ISBN 0-444-80128-6, North Holland). Elsevier.

Kanno, T., ed. Paraneurons: Their Features & Functions. (International Congress Ser.: No. 552). 194p. 1981. 45.75 (ISBN 0-444-90194-9, Excerpta Medica). Elsevier.

Karlin, Arthur, et al, eds. Neuronal Information Transfer. (P & S Biomedical Sciences Symposia Ser.). 1978. 69.50 (ISBN 0-12-398450-5). Acad Pr.

Klopf, A. Harry. The Hedonistic Neuron: A Theory of Memory, Learning, & Intelligence. LC 80-16410. (Illus.). 140p. 1982. pap. text ed. 19.95 (ISBN 0-89116-202-X). Hemisphere Pub.

Lindsay, Robert, ed. Computer Analysis of Neuronal Structures. LC 76-50605. (Illus.). 226p. 1977. 39.50x (ISBN 0-306-30964-5, Plenum Pr). Plenum Pub.

Mintz, Stephan L. & Widmayer, Susan M., eds. Progress in the Neurosciences & Related Fields. LC 74-10822. (Studies in the Natural Sciences: Vol. 6). 92p. 1974. 25.00x (ISBN 0-306-36906-0, Plenum Pr). Plenum Pub.

Osborne, N., ed. Dale's Principle & Communication Between Neurons: Proceedings of a Colloquim of the Biochemical Society, University of Oxford, England, July 1982. 190p. 1983. 45.00 (ISBN 0-08-029789-7). Pergamon.

Osborne, Neville N., ed. Biochemistry of Characterized Neurons. LC 76-55379. 1978. text ed. 59.00 (ISBN 0-08-021503-3). Pergamon.

Pinsker, Harold & Willis, William D., Jr., eds. Information Processing in the Nervous System. 378p. 1980. text ed. 54.50 (ISBN 0-89004-422-8). Raven.

Ramon y Cajal, Santiago. The Neuron & the Glial Cell. Torre, Jack de la & Gibson, William, trs. from Span. (Illus.). 364p. 1984. 39.75x (ISBN 0-398-04908-4). C C Thomas.

Roberts, A. & Bush, B. M., eds. Neurones Without Impulses. LC 79-42572. (Society for Experimental Biology Seminar Ser.: No. 6). (Illus.). 250p. 1981. 67.00 (ISBN 0-521-23364-X); pap. 24.95 (ISBN 0-521-29935-7). Cambridge U Pr.

Rohkamm, R. Degeneration & Regeneration in Neurons of the Cerebellum. (Advances in Anatomy Embryology & Cell Biology: Vol. 53, Part 6). (Illus.). 1977. pap. 33.00 (ISBN 0-387-08519-X). Springer-Verlag.

Rowland, Lewis P., ed. Human Motor Neuron Diseases. (Advances in Neurology Ser.: Vol. 36). (Illus.). 592p. 1982. text ed. 104.50 (ISBN 0-89004-737-5). Raven.

Svendgaard, N. A., et al. Regenerative Properties of Central Monoamine Neurons: Studies in the Adult Rat Using Cerebral Iris Implants As Targets. (Advances in Anatomy, Embroyology, & Cell Biology Ser.: Vol. 51, Pt. 4). (Illus.). 70p. (Orig.). 1975. pap. 34.30 (ISBN 0-387-07299-3). Springer-Verlag.

Szentagothai, J. & Hamori, J., eds. Neuron Concept Today. 1977. 23.00 (ISBN 0-9960001-4-3, Pub. by Akademiai Kaido Hungary). Heyden.

Waxman, Stephen G., ed. Physiology & Pathobiology of Axons. LC 77-17751. 462p. 1978. 59.00 (ISBN 0-89004-215-2). Raven.

Werner, Gerhard, ed. Feature Extraction by Neurons & Behavior. 100p. 1976. pap. text ed. 8.95x (ISBN 0-262-73044-8). MIT Pr.

Wiersma, C. A., ed. Invertebrate Neurons & Behavior. 100p. 1976. pap. text ed. 8.95x (ISBN 0-262-73045-6). MIT Pr.

NEUROPHYSIOLOGY

see also Neural Transmission; Reflexes

Alexandridis, E. The Pupil. Telger, T., tr. from Ger. (Illus.). 115p. 1985. 29.90 (ISBN 0-387-96109-7). Springer-Verlag.

Barns, Marylon R., et al. Neurophysiological Basis of Patient Treatment: The Vestibular System, Vol. IV. (Illus.). 1986. pap. 12.75x (ISBN 0-936030-04-6). Stokesville Pub.

Bassler, U. Neural Basis of Elementary Behavior in Stick Insects. Strausfeld, C., tr. (Studies in Brain Function: Vol.10). (Illus.). 180p. 1983. 35.00 (ISBN 0-387-11918-3). Springer-Verlag.

Bromm, B. Pain Measurement in Man: Neurophysiological Correlates of Pain. 1984. 94.50 (ISBN 0-444-80571-0, I-389-84). Elsevier.

Buser, P. A. & Cobb, W. A., eds. Kyoto Symposia: Electroencephalography & Clinical Neurophysiology, Supp. No. 36. 770p. 1983. 204.25 (ISBN 0-444-80436-6, Biomedical Pr). Elsevier.

Chaplin, James P. & Demers, Aline. Primer of Neurology & Neurophysiology. LC 78-6680. 272p. 1984. pap. 20.50 (ISBN 0-471-03027-9). Krieger.

Cobb. Recommendations for the Practice of Clinical Neurophysiology. 1983. 9.95 (ISBN 0-444-80505-2, I-402-83). Elsevier.

Conrad & Magar, eds. Physical Principles of Neuronal & Organismic Behavior. 256p. 1973. 59.25 (ISBN 0-677-12290-X). Gordon.

Cowan, W. Maxwell, et al, eds. Annual Review of Neuroscience, Vol. 2. (Illus.). 1979. text ed. 20.00 (ISBN 0-8243-2402-1). Annual Reviews.

Creutzfeld, O., et al, eds. Sensory Motor Integration in the Nervous System. (Experimental Brain Research: Supplementum 9). (Illus.). 490p. 1984. 59.00 (ISBN 0-387-13680-0). Springer-Verlag.

Crutchfield, Carolyn A. & Barns, Marylon R. Neurophysiological Basis of Patient Treatment: Peripheral Receptors & Muscle Control, Vol. III. (Illus.). 1984. pap. 17.00x (ISBN 0-936030-03-8). Stokesville Pub.

De Jong, W., ed. Experimental & Genetic Models of Hypertension. (Handbook of Hypertension Ser.: Vol. 4). 556p. 1984. 118.75 (ISBN 0-444-90336-4, I-224-84). Elsevier.

The Dopaminergic System. (Basic & Clinical Aspects of Neuroscience Ser.). (Illus.). 50p. 1985. pap. 10.50 (ISBN 0-387-13700-9). Springer Verlag.

Evarts, Edward V., et al. Neurophysiological Approaches to Higher Brain Functions. LC 83-25922. (Neuroscience Institute Monograph Ser.: 1-693). 198p. 1984. 39.95 (ISBN 0-471-80557-2, Pub. by Wiley-Interscience). Wiley.

Freeman, Walter J. Mass Action in the Nervous System: Examination of the Neurophysiological Basis of Adaptive Behavior Through the EEG. 1975. 78.00 (ISBN 0-12-267150-3). Acad Pr.

Granit, Ragnar. The Purposive Brain. 1977. text ed. 22.50x (ISBN 0-262-07069-3); pap. 6.95x (ISBN 0-262-57054-8). MIT Pr.

Gybels, J., et al, eds. Technical Advances. (Applied Neurophysiology: Vol. 45, No. 4-5). (Illus.). iv, 208p. 1981. pap. 32.25 (ISBN 3-8055-3499-X). S Karger.
Jeannerod, Marc. The Brain Machine: The Development of Neurophysiological Thought. Urion, David, tr. from Fr. (Illus.). 192p. 1985. text ed. 16.95x (ISBN 0-674-08047-5). Harvard U Pr.
Kornblum, Sylvan & Requin, Jean, eds. Preparatory States & Processes. 400p. 1984. text ed. 39.95 (ISBN 0-89859-325-5). L Erlbaum Assocs.
Leibovic, K. N. Nervous System Theory: An Introductory Study. 1973. 52.50 (ISBN 0-12-441250-5). Acad Pr.
Lindsley & Holmes. Basic Human Neurophysiology. 1984. 32.50 (ISBN 0-444-00797-0). Elsevier.
Lissak. Results in Neurochemistry, Neuroendocrinology, Neurophysiology & Behavior, Neuropharmacology, Neuropathology, Cybernetics, Vol. 5. 1978. 19.50 (ISBN 0-9960007-2-0, Pub. by Akademiai Kaido Hungary). Heyden.
Mandel, Paul & DeFeudis, F. V., eds. GABA: Biochemistry & CNS Functions. LC 79-22019. (Advances in Experimental Medicine & Biology Ser.: Vol. 123). 517p. 1979. 62.50x (ISBN 0-306-40325-0, Plenum Pr). Plenum Pub.
Murray, R. W. Test Your Understanding of Neurophysiology. LC 83-1779. 291p. 1984. 49.50 (ISBN 0-521-24999-6); pap. 17.95 (ISBN 0-521-27127-4). Cambridge U Pr.
Nashold, B. S., et al, eds. American Society for Stereotactic & Functional Neurosurgery, Proceedings, Durham, North Carolina, April-May 1983. (Journal: Applied Neurophysiology: Vol. 46, No. 1-4). (Illus.). 244p. 1984. pap. 29.50 (ISBN 3-8055-3768-9). S Karger.
Ottoson, David. Physiology of the Nervous System. (Illus.). 528p. 1983. 45.00x (ISBN 0-19-520409-3); pap. 28.95x (ISBN 0-19-520410-7). Oxford U Pr.
Patton, Harry D., et al. Introduction to Basic Neurology. LC 75-31299. (Illus.). 1976. text ed. 24.50 (ISBN 0-7216-7113-6). Saunders.
Perris, C. & Kemali, D., eds. Neurophysiological Correlates of Normal Cognition & Psychopathology. (Advances in Biological Psychiatry: Vol. 13). (Illus.). viii, 232p. 1984. pap. 41.75 (ISBN 3-8055-3737-9). S Karger.
Pincus, Harold A. The Integration of Neuroscience & Psychiatry. LC 85-11270. (Clinical Insights Monograph). 100p. 1985. pap. text ed. 12.00X (ISBN 0-88048-073-4, 48-073-4). Am Psychiatric.
Porter, R., ed. Studies in Neurophysiology. LC 87-51674. (Illus.). 1978. 115.00 (ISBN 0-521-22019-X). Cambridge U Pr.
Remond, A., ed. EEG Informatics: A Didactic Review of Methods & Applications of EEG Data Processing. 426p. 1977. 62.75 (ISBN 0-444-80005-0, Biomedical Pr). Elsevier.
Skok, V J. Physiology of Autonomic Ganglia. 197p. 1973. 150.00 (ISBN 3-456-00360-9, Pub. by Holdan Bk Ltd UK). State Mutual Bk.
Srinivasan, S. K. & Sampath, G. Stochastic Models for Spike Trains of Single Neurons. (Lecture Notes in Biomathematics: Vol. 16). 1977. 14.00 (ISBN 0-387-08257-3). Springer-Verlag.
Stein, R. B. Nerve & Muscle: Membranes, Cells & Systems. LC 80-15028. (Illus.). 274p. 1980. 23.50x (ISBN 0-306-40512-1, Plenum Pr). Plenum Pub.
Uttal, W. R. Cellular Neurophysiology & Integration: An Interpretive Introduction. 310p. 1975. 29.95 (ISBN 0-89859-429-4). L Erlbaum Assocs.
Zrenner, E. Neurophysiological Aspects of Color Vision in Primates. (Studies of Brain Function: Vol. 9). (Illus.). 218p. 1983. 39.00 (ISBN 0-387-11653-2). Springer-Verlag.

NEUROPTERA

see also Caddis-Flies; Stone-Flies; Termites

Elliott, J. M. A Key to the Larvae & Adults of British Freshwater Megaloptera & Neuroptera. 1977. 20.00x (ISBN 0-900386-27-4, Pub. by Freshwater Bio). State Mutual Bk.
Redborg, Kurt E. & MacLeod, Ellis G. THe Developmental Ecology of Mantispa uhleri Banks: Neuroptera: Mantispidae. 1985. 15.00 (ISBN 0-317-30272-8). U of Ill Pr.

NEUROSECRETION

see also Endocrinology

Bargmann, W., et al, eds. Neurosecretion & Neuroendocrine Activity: Evolution, Structure & Function. (Illus.). 1978. 63.00 (ISBN 0-387-08637-4). Springer-Verlag.
Brooks, Chandler M., et al. Humors, Hormones, & Neurosecretions: The Origins & Development of Man's Present Knowledge of the Humoral Control of Body Functions. LC 61-14336. 1962. 39.00x (ISBN 0-87395-006-2). State U NY Pr.
Farner, Donald S. & Lederis, Karl, eds. Neurosecretion: Molecules, Cells, Systems. LC 81-21016. 558p. 1982. 69.50 (ISBN 0-306-40760-4, Plenum Pr). Plenum Pub.
International Symposium on Neurosecretion, 6th, London, 1973. Neurosecretion - the Final Neuroendocrine Pathway: Proceedings. Knowles, F. & Vollrath, L., eds. LC 74-13218. (Illus.). xii, 345p. 1974. 68.00 (ISBN 0-387-06821-X). Springer-Verlag.
Kobayashi, H., et al, eds. Neurosecretion & the Biology of Neuropeptides. 580p. 1985. 64.00 (ISBN 0-387-15586-4). Springer-Verlag.
Maddrell, Simon H. & Nordmann, Jean J. Neurosecretion. LC 79-63655. (Tertiary Level Biology Ser.). 173p. 1979. 34.95x (ISBN 0-470-26711-9). Halsted Pr.
Snaith, Philip. Clinical Neurosis. 1981. pap. text ed. 18.95x (ISBN 0-19-261251-4). Oxford U Pr.

NEUROTRANSMITTERS

see also Adrenalin; Glutamic Acid; Serotonin

Abelson, Philip H., et al, eds. Neuroscience. LC 84-24524. (Illus.). 453p. 1985. text ed. 29.95 (ISBN 0-87168-309-1); pap. text ed. 14.95 (ISBN 0-87168-268-0). AAAS.
Eichberg, Joseph. Phospholipids in Nervous Tissues. 384p. 1985. 79.50 (ISBN 0-471-86430-7). Wiley.
Fariello, Ruggero G., et al, eds. Neurotransmitters, Seizures, & Epilepsy II. 392p. 1984. text ed. 63.50 (ISBN 0-88167-057-X). Raven.
Vizi, E. Sylvester. Non-Synaptic Interactions Between Neurons: Modulation of Neurochemical Transmission-Pharmacological & Clinical Aspects. 260p. 1984. 39.95 (ISBN 0-471-90378-7). Wiley.

NEUTRINOS

Allen, J. S. Neutrino. (Investigations in Physics Ser.: No. 5). 1958. 22.50 (ISBN 0-691-08009-7). Princeton U Pr.
Faissner, Helmut, et al, eds. Proceedings of the International Neutrino Conference, Aachen 1976. 1977. 84.00 (ISBN 0-9940011-5-0, Pub. by Vieweg & Sohn Germany). Heyden.
Fiorini, Ettore, ed. Neutrino Physics & Astrophysics. LC 81-11999. (Ettore Majorana International Science Series, Physical Sciences: Vol. 12). 432p. 1982. 62.50x (ISBN 0-306-40746-9, Plenum Pr). Plenum Pub.
Jacob, M. Gauge Theories & Neutrino Physics. (Physics Reports Reprint Ser.: Vol. 2). 514p. 1979. 78.75 (ISBN 0-444-85191-7, North Holland). Elsevier.
Kuchowicz, B. Bibliography of the Neutrino. 446p. 1967. 119.25 (ISBN 0-677-11490-7). Gordon.
Lee, T. D., ed. Weak Interactions & High Energy Neutrino Physics. (Italian Physical Society Ser.: Course 32). 1966. 75.00 (ISBN 0-12-368832-9). Acad Pr.
Lewis, G. M. Neutrinos. (The Wykeham Science Ser.: No. 12). 132p. 1970. pap. cancelled (ISBN 0-85109-140-7). Taylor & Francis.
Lewis, G. M. & Wheatley, G. A. Neutrinos. LC 73-135382. (Wykeham Science Ser.: No. 12). 132p. 1970. 9.95x (ISBN 0-8448-1114-9). Crane-Russak Co.
Nieto, Michael M. & Haxton, W. C., eds. Science Underground. LC 83-70377. (AIP Conference Proceedings No. 96). 446p. 1983. lib. bdg. 38.75 (ISBN 0-88318-195-9). Am Inst Physics.
Saenz, A. W. & Uberall, H., eds. Long-Distance Neutrino Detection-Nineteen Seventy-Eight: C. L. Cowan Memorial Symposium, Catholic Univeristy. LC 79-52078. (AIP Conference Proceedings Ser.: No. 52). (Illus.). 1979. lib. bdg. 16.50 (ISBN 0-88318-151-7). Am Inst Physics.

NEUTRON ACTIVATION ANALYSIS

see Radioactivation Analysis

NEUTRON TRANSPORT THEORY

Lewis, Elmer E. & Miller, Warren F. Computational Methods of Neutron Transport. LC 84-7405. 432p. 1984. text ed. 44.95x (ISBN 0-471-09245-2, Pub. by Wiley-Interscience). Wiley.
Marchuk, G. I. & Lebedev, V. I. Numerical Methods in the Theory of Neutron Transport. 472p. 1985. text ed. 80.00 (ISBN 3-7186-0182-6); 30.00 (ISBN 3-7186-0210-5). Harwood Academic.
Osborn, Richard K. & Yip, S. Foundations of Neutron Transport Theory. (U. S. Atomic Energy Commission Monographs). 138p. 1966. 37.25 (ISBN 0-677-01170-9). Gordon.
Springer, T. Quasielastic Neutron Scattering for the Investigation of Diffusive Motions in Solids & Liquids. (Springer Tracts in Modern Physics: Vol. 64). (Illus.). 102p. 1972. 24.80 (ISBN 0-387-05808-7). Springer-Verlag.

NEUTRONS

see also Atoms; Electrons; Neutrinos; Positrons; Protons; Thermal Neutrons

Bacon, G. E. & Noakes, G. R. Neutron Physics. (Wykeham Science Ser.: No. 2). 1969. 9.95x (ISBN 0-8448-1104-1). Crane-Russak Co.
Basov, N. G., ed. Pulsed Neutron Research. LC 78-12997. (P. N. Lebedev Physics Institutes Ser.: Vol. 94). (Illus.). 112p. 1979. 49.50x (ISBN 0-306-10950-6, Consultants). Plenum Pub.
Beckurts, K. H. & Wirtz, K. Neutron Physics. rev. ed. (Illus.). 1964. 55.00 (ISBN 0-387-03096-4). Springer-Verlag.
Biological Effects of Neutron & Proton Irradiation, 2 Vols. (Illus.). 879p. (Orig., Vol. 1, 433p; Vol. 2, 446p). 1964. 24.25 ea. (IAEA). Vol. 1 (ISBN 92-0-010064-3, ISP80-1). Vol. 2 (ISBN 92-0-010164-X, ISP80-2). Unipub.
Biological Effects of Neutron Irradiation. (Proceedings Ser.). (Illus.). 484p. (Orig.). 1974. pap. 41.25 (ISBN 92-0-010474-6, ISP352, IAEA). Unipub.
Boutin, Henri & Yip, Sidney. Molecular Spectroscopy with Neutrons. LC 68-22823. 1968. 27.50x (ISBN 0-262-02042-4). MIT Pr.
British Nuclear Energy Society, ed. Radiography with Neutrons. 167p. 1975. 80.00x (ISBN 0-7277-0019-7, Pub. by Brit Nuclear England). State Mutual Bk.
Chrien, R. E., ed. Neutron Radiative Capture. (Neutron Physics & Nuclear Data in Science & Technology: Vol. 3). 200p. 1983. 65.00 (ISBN 0-08-029330-1). Pergamon.
Cierjacks, S., ed. Neutron Sources: For Applied & Pure Nuclear Research. (Neutron Physics & Nuclear Data in Science & Technology Ser.: Vol. 2). 370p. 1982. 72.00 (ISBN 0-08-029351-4). Pergamon.
Compendium of Neutron Spectra in Critically Accident Dosimetry. (Technical Reports Ser.: No. 180). (Illus.). 193p. 1978. pap. 26.25 (ISBN 92-0-125178-5, IDC180, IAEA). Unipub.
Delayed Fission Neutrons. (Illus., Orig.). 1968. pap. text ed. 16.25 (ISBN 92-0-031068-0, ISP176, IAEA). Unipub.
Doerschel, Birgit & Herforth, Lieselott. Neutronen - Personendosimetrie. (Physikalische Reihe: No. 7). (Ger., Illus.). 364p. 1980. 57.95x (ISBN 0-8176-1037-5). Birkhauser.
Egelstaff, P. A. & Poole, M. J. Experimental Neutron Thermalization. LC 79-86201. 1969. 72.00 (ISBN 0-08-006533-3). Pergamon.
Erdtmann, Gerhard. Neutron Activation Tables. (Topical Presentations in Nuclear Chemistry Ser.: Vol. 6). (Illus.). 146p. 1976. 57.50x (ISBN 3-527-25693-8). VCH Pubs.
Ero, J. & Szucs, J., eds. Nuclear Structure Study with Neutrons. LC 73-17651. 496p. 1974. 75.00x (ISBN 0-306-30770-7, Plenum Pr). Plenum Pub.
Foderaro, Anthony. Elements of Neutron Interaction Theory. LC 79-103896. 1971. text ed. 40.00x (ISBN 0-262-06033-7). MIT Pr.
Goldstein, Herbert. Fundamental Aspects of Reactor Shielding. Repr. of 1959 ed. 28.00 (ISBN 0-384-19100-2). Johnson Repr.
Guldberg, Jens, ed. Silicon. LC 81-7305. 515p. 1981. 75.00x (ISBN 0-306-40738-8, Plenum Pr). Plenum Pub.
Hetrick, David L. & Weaver, Lynn E., eds. Neutron Dynamics & Control: Proceedings. LC 66-60098. (AEC Symposium Ser.). 612p. 1966. pap. 23.50 (ISBN 0-87079-297-0, CONF-650413); microfiche 4.50 (CONF-650413). DOE.
International Conference on Fast Neutron Physics 1963: Houston, TX. Progress in Fast Neutron Physics. Phillips, G. C. & Marion, J. B., eds. LC 63-18849. (Rice University Semicentennial Publications Ser.). pap. 102.80 (ISBN 0-317-08835-1, 2020204). Bks Demand UMI.
Irvine, J. M. Heavy Nuclei, Superheavy Nuclei, & Neutron Stars. (Oxford Studies in Nuclear Physics). (Illus.). 1975. 47.00x (ISBN 0-19-851510-3). Oxford U Pr.
Lechner, R. E., et al. Neutron Scattering & Muon Spin Rotation. (Springer Tracts in Modern Physics: Vol. 101). (Illus.). 240p. 1983. 39.50 (ISBN 0-387-12458-6). Springer-Verlag.
Lovesey, Stephen W. & Scherm, Reinhard, eds. Condensed Matter Research Using Neutrons: Today & Tomorrow. (NATO ASI Series B, Physics: Vol. 112). 338p. 1985. 45.00x (ISBN 0-306-41821-5, Plenum Pr). Plenum Pub.
Mezei, F., ed. Neutron Spin Echo: Proceedings. (Lecture Notes in Physics Ser.: Vol. 128). 253p. 1980. pap. 23.00 (ISBN 0-387-10004-0). Springer-Verlag.
Mezhiborskaya, Kh. B. Photoneutron Method of Determining Beryllium. LC 61-18758. 30p. 1962. 17.50x (ISBN 0-306-10568-3, Consultants). Plenum Pub.
Mughabghsab, S. F., et al, eds. Neutron Cross Sections: Vol. I, Thermal Cross Sections & Resonance Parameters, Pt. A Z1-60. 1981. 65.00 (ISBN 0-12-509701-8). Acad Pr.
Neutron Capture Gamma-Ray Spectroscopy. (Proceedings Ser.). (Illus.). 708p. (Orig.). 1969. pap. 52.00 (ISBN 92-0-130369-6, ISP235, IAEA). Unipub.
Neutron Moisture Gauges. (Technical Reports Ser.: No. 112). (Illus., Orig.). 1970. pap. 10.50 (ISBN 92-0-165070-1, IDC112, IAEA). Unipub.
Neutron Monitoring for Radiation Protection Purposes, 2 vols. (Proceedings Ser.). (Illus., Orig.). 1974. Vol. 1. pap. 29.00 (ISBN 92-0-020173-3, ISP318-1, IAEA); Vol. 2. pap. 41.75 (ISBN 92-0-020273-X, ISP318-2). Unipub.
Neutron Nuclear Data Evaluation. (Technical Reports Ser.: No. 146). 124p. (Orig.). 1973. pap. 13.00 (ISBN 92-0-135173-9, IDC146, IAEA). Unipub.
Neutron Standard Reference Data: Proceedings. (Panel Proceedings Ser.). (Illus.). 371p. 1975. pap. 37.00 (ISBN 92-0-031074-5, ISP371, IAEA). Unipub.
Neutron Thermalization & Reactor Spectra, 2 vols. (Proceedings Ser.). (Eng., Fr. & Rus., Illus.). 1186p. (Vol. 1 - 656p., Vol. 2 - 530p.). 1968. Vol. 1. pap. 43.00 (ISBN 92-0-050068-4, ISP160-1, IAEA); Vol. 2. pap. 35.75 (ISBN 92-0-050168-0, ISP160-2). Unipub.
Nuclear Data for Reactors 1966: First Conference, 2 vols. (Proceedings Ser.). (Illus.). 1013p. 1967. Vol. 1. pap. 37.75 (ISBN 92-0-030167-3, ISP140-1, IAEA); Vol. 2. pap. 28.75 (ISBN 92-0-030267-X, ISP1402). Unipub.
Pile Neutron Research in Physics. (Proceedings Ser.). (Illus.). 656p. 1962. 30.75 (ISBN 92-0-030062-6, ISP36, IAEA). Unipub.
Pohl, H. A. Dielectrophoresis. LC 77-71421. (Cambridge Monographs on Physics). (Illus.). 1978. 125.00 (ISBN 0-521-21657-5). Cambridge U Pr.
Prompt Fission Neutron Spectra. (Panel Proceedings Ser.). (Illus.). 176p. (Orig.). 1973. pap. 14.50 (ISBN 92-0-131172-9, ISP329, IAEA). Unipub.
Protection Against Neutron Radiation. LC 73-138550. (NCRP Reports Ser.: No. 38). 1971. 9.00 (ISBN 0-913392-20-0). NCRP Pubns.
Radiation Protection & Measurements for Low-Voltage Neutron Generators. (NCRP Report Ser.: No. 72). 1984. 10.00 (ISBN 0-913392-61-8). NCRP Pubns.
Radiobiological Applications of Neutron Irradiation. (Panel Proceedings Ser.). (Illus.). 263p. (Orig.). 1972. pap. 23.50 (ISBN 92-0-011172-6, ISP325, IAEA). Unipub.
Schoenborn, Benno P., ed. Neutrons in Biology. (Basic Life Sciences Ser.: Vol. 27). 472p. 1984. 59.50x (ISBN 0-306-41508-9, Plenum Pr). Plenum Pub.
Schofield, P., ed. The Neutron & Its Applications 1982. 1983. 59.00 (ISBN 0-9960040-0-9, Pub. by A Hilger England). Heyden.
Smith, Alan B., ed. Neutron Standards & Flux Normalization: Proceedings. LC 77-611328. (AEC Symposium Ser.). 525p. 1971. pap. 21.25 (ISBN 0-87079-294-6, CONF-701022); microfiche 4.50 (ISBN 0-87079-295-4, CONF-701022). DOE.
Uhrig, Robert E., ed. Neutron Noise, Waves & Pulse Propagation: Proceedings. LC 66-60048. (AEC Symposium Ser.). 788p. 1967. pap. 27.75 (ISBN 0-87079-290-3, CONF-660206); microfiche 4.50 (ISBN 0-87079-291-1, CONF-660206). DOE.
Von, Egidy T. & Gonnewein, F., eds. Neutron-Capture Gammaray Spectroscopy 1981. 1982. 77.00 (ISBN 0-9960039-8-3, Pub. by A Hilger England). Heyden.
Von Der Hardt, Peter & Rottger, Heinz. Neutron Radiography Handbook. x, 170p. 1981. 26.00 (ISBN 90-277-1378-2, Pub. by Reidel Holland). Kluwer Academic.
Yeater, M. L., ed. Neutron Physics: Proceedings. (Nuclear Science & Technology: Vol. 2). 1962. 70.00 (ISBN 0-12-769050-6). Acad Pr.

NEUTRONS–DIFFRACTION

Arndt, Ulrich W. & Willis, B. T. Single Crystal Diffractometry. LC 66-13637. (Cambridge Monographs on Physics). pap. 88.80 (ISBN 0-317-26117-7, 2024404). Bks Demand UMI.
Bacon, G. E. Neutron Diffraction. 3rd ed. (Monographs on the Physics & Chemistry of Materials). (Illus.). 1975. 98.00x (ISBN 0-19-851353-4). Oxford U Pr.
--X-Ray & Neutron Diffraction. 1966. pap. text ed. 21.00 (ISBN 0-08-011998-0). Pergamon.
Dachs, H., ed. Neutron Diffraction. LC 78-2969. (Topics in Current Physics: Vol. 6). (Illus.). 1978. 40.00 (ISBN 0-387-08710-9). Springer-Verlag.
Izyumov, Yurii A. & Ozerov, Ruslan P. Magnetic Neutron Diffraction. LC 68-21475. 598p. 1970. 47.50x (ISBN 0-306-30371-X, Plenum Pr). Plenum Pub.

NEUTRONS–MEASUREMENT

see also Time-Of-Flight Mass Spectrometry

American Society for Testing & Materials. Symposium on Radiation Effects on Metals & Neutron Dosimetry. LC 63-12698. (American Society for Testing & Materials Ser.: Special Technical Publication, No. 341). pap. 103.80 (ISBN 0-317-10870-0, 2000139). Bks Demand UMI.

Broerse, J. J., ed. Ion Chambers for Neutron Dosimetry. (European Applied Research Reports Special Topics). 351p. 1980. 79.75 (ISBN 3-7186-0048-X). Harwood Academic.
Measurement of Absorbed Dose of Neutrons & Mixtures of Neutrons & Gamma - Rays. (NCRP Reports Ser.: No. 25). 1961. 6.00 (ISBN 0-913392-08-1). NCRP Pubns.
Measurements of Neutron Flux & Spectra for Physical & Biological Applications. (NCRP Reports Ser.: No. 23). 1960. 6.00 (ISBN 0-913392-07-3). NCRP Pubns.
Neutron Fluence Measurements. (Technical Reports Ser.: No. 107). (Illus., Orig.). 1970. pap. 14.50 (ISBN 92-0-135070-8, IDC107, IAEA). Unipub.
Neutron Monitoring. (Proceedings Ser.). (Illus.). 705p. 1967. pap. 45.00 (ISBN 92-0-020067-2, ISP136, IAEA). Unipub.

NEUTRONS–SCATTERING

Inelastic Scattering of Neutrons in Solids & Liquids: 1962, 2 Vols. (Proceedings Ser.). (Eng., Fr. & Rus., Illus.). 484p. 1963. Vol. 1. pap. 25.25 (ISBN 92-0-030363-3, ISP62-1, IAEA); Vol. 2. 26.25 (ISBN 92-0-030463-X, ISP62-2). Unipub.
Inelastic Scattering of Neutrons: 1964, 2 Vols. (Proceedings Ser.). (Eng., Fr. & Rus., Illus.). 461p. 1965. Vol. 1. 24.50 (ISBN 92-0-030365-X, ISP92/1, IAEA); Vol. 2. 32.25 (ISBN 92-0-030465-6, ISP92/2). Unipub.
Instrumentation for Neutron Inelastic Scattering Research. (Panel Proceedings Ser.). (Illus.). 290p. (Orig.). 1971. pap. 23.50 (ISBN 92-0-131070-6, ISP275, IAEA). Unipub.
Krivoglaz, M. A. Theory of X-Ray & Thermal Neutron Scattering by Real Crystals. LC 68-26771. (Illus.). 405p. 1969. 55.00x (ISBN 0-306-30347-7, Plenum Pr). Plenum Pub.
Lovesey, S. & Springer, T., eds. Dynamics of Solids & Liquids by Neutron Scattering. LC 77-4740. (Topics in Current Physics Ser: Vol. 3). 1977. 47.00 (ISBN 0-387-08156-9). Springer-Verlag.
Lovesey, Stephen W. Theory of Neutron Scattering from Condensed Matter, Vol. 1. (International Series of Monographs on Physics). (Illus.). 1984. 59.00x (ISBN 0-19-852015-8). Oxford U Pr.
Mason, Ronald & Mitchell, E. W. Neutron Scattering in Biology, Chemistry & Physics. (Phil. Trans. of the Royal Soc., Ser. B.: Vol. 290). (Illus.). 201p. 1981. Repr. text ed. 60.00x (ISBN 0-85403-151-0, Pub. by Royal Soc London). Scholium Intl.
Neutron Scattering in the Nineties: Conference Proceedings, Julich, 14-18 January 1985. (Proceedings Ser.). 621p. 1985. pap. 96.00 (ISBN 92-0-030085-5, ISP694, IAEA). Unipub.
Press, W. Single-Particle Rotations in Molecular Crystals. (Springer Tracts in Modern Physics Ser.: Vol. 92). (Illus.). 140p. 1981. 29.00 (ISBN 0-387-10897-1). Springer-Verlag.
Rowland, T. J. & Beck, Paul A., eds. Magnetic & Inelastic Scattering of Neutrons by Metals. LC 67-29670. (Metallurgical Society Conference Ser.: Vol. 43). pap. 59.80 (ISBN 0-317-10595-7, 2001532). Bks Demand UMI.
Windsor, C. G. Pulsed Neutron Scattering. 400p. 1981. 89.95x (ISBN 0-470-27131-0, PH-25 16). Halsted Pr.
--Pulsed Neutron Scattering. 432p. 1981. write for info. (ISBN 0-85066-195-1). Taylor & Francis.

NEW PRODUCTS

see also Design, Industrial

Berridge, A. E. Product Innovation & Development. 236p. 1977. text ed. 29.50x (ISBN 0-220-66325-4, Pub. by Busn Bks England). Brookfield Pub Co.
Biggadike, E. Ralph. Corporate Diversification: Entry, Strategy, & Performance. (Harvard Business School Publications, Division of Research Ser.). (Illus.). 1979. 16.00x (ISBN 0-87584-118-X). Harvard U Pr.
Buggie, Frederick D. New Product Development Strategies. 192p. 1981. 17.95 (ISBN 0-8144-5626-X). AMACOM.
Grant, Donald P. Design by Objectives: Multiple Objective Design Analysis & Evaluation in Architectural, Environmental & Product Design. LC 82-73290. 50p. (Orig.). 1982. pap. text ed. 6.00x (ISBN 0-910821-00-3). Design Meth.
Heimbold, Noreen C. & Betts, Jim. New Products: How to Create, Research, Develop & Market Them Successfully. 3rd, rev. ed. 200p. 1984. pap. 12.95 (ISBN 0-911909-00-1). New Prod Develop.
Kraushar, P. New Products & Diversifications-New Edition. 1977. 21.00x (ISBN 0-8464-0672-1). Beekman Pubs.
Leduc, Robert. How to Launch a New Product. 130p. 1966. 14.95x (ISBN 0-8464-1107-5). Beekman Pubs.
Majumdar, Badiul A. Innovations, Product Developments & Technology Transfers: An Empirical Study of Dynamic Competitive Advantage, The Case of Electronic Calculators. LC 80-1451. (Illus.). 198p. (Orig.). 1982. pap. text ed. 11.75 (ISBN 0-8191-2066-9). U Pr of Amer.
Market Intelligence Research Company Staff. Ambulatory ECG Monitoring Markets. pap. 495.00x (ISBN 0-916483-06-1). Market Res Co.
--Fiber Optic Sensor Markets. 102p. 1984. pap. text ed. 495.00x (ISBN 0-916483-03-7). Market Res Co.
--Humidity Instrumentation Markets. 114p. pap. text ed. 495.00x (ISBN 0-317-11888-9). Market Res Co.
--Nuclear Magnetic Resonance World Markets. 270p. pap. 895.00x (ISBN 0-916483-08-8). Market Res Co.
--Process Control Markets & Fiber Optics. 135p. (Orig.). 1984. pap. text ed. 495.00x (ISBN 0-916483-02-9). Market Res Co.
--Surgical Lasers: Markets in U. S., Europe, Japan. 170p. pap. 595.00 (ISBN 0-916483-07-X). Market Res Co.
--Test & Measurement Equipment World Markets. 220p. pap. text ed. 495.00x (ISBN 0-317-11889-7). Market Res Co.
--World Market Trends for Fiber Optics. 147p. pap. 125.00x (ISBN 0-916483-10-X). Market Res Co.
Morehead, John W. Finding & Licensing New Products & Technology from the U. S. A. LC 82-50568. 609p. 1982. 495.00 (ISBN 0-943420-00-8). Tech Search Intl.
Ramsey, Jackson E. Research & Development: Project Selection Criteria. LC 78-27294. (Research for Business Decisions: No. 1). 250p. 1978. 44.95 (ISBN 0-8357-0966-3). UMI Res Pr.
Sell's Directory of Products & Services, 1982. 97th ed. LC 73-640793. 938p. (Orig.). 1981. pap. 60.00x (ISBN 0-85499-509-9). Intl Pubns Serv.
Thorpe & Middendorf. Product Liability. (What Every Engineer Should Know About Ser.: Vol. 2). 1979. 24.50 (ISBN 0-8247-6876-0). Dekker.
Urban, Glen & Hauser, John R. Design & Marketing of New Products. (Illus.). 1980. 32.95 (ISBN 0-13-201269-3). P-H.
Verhage, Bronis J., et al. Strategy & Analysis in Product Development. 1981. 90.00x (ISBN 0-86176-084-0, Pub. by MCB Pubns). State Mutual Bk.

NEWFOUNDLAND DOG

see Dogs–Breeds–Newfoundland

NEWTON, ISAAC, SIR, 1642-1727

Andrade, E. N. Isaac Newton. 1979. Repr. of 1950 ed. lib. bdg. 16.00 (ISBN 0-8414-3014-4). Folcroft.
--Isaac Newton. 1950. 17.50 (ISBN 0-932062-04-0). Sharon Hill.
Ball, Rouse W. An Essay on Newton's Principia. Repr. of 1893 ed. 32.00 (ISBN 0-384-03141-2, S155). Johnson Repr.
Bechler, Z. Contemporary Newtonian Research. 1982. 39.50 (ISBN 90-277-1303-0, Pub. by Reidel Holland). Kluwer Academic.
Brewster, David. Memoirs of the Life, Writings & Discoveries of Sir Isaac Newton, 2 Vols. Repr. of 1855 ed. Set. 60.00 (ISBN 0-384-05703-9). Johnson Repr.
Brodetsky, S. Sir Isaac Newton. 1927. Repr. 20.00 (ISBN 0-8274-3425-1). R West.
Brougham, Henry & Routh, E. J. Analytical View of Sir Isaac Newton's Principia. 1972. Repr. of 1855 ed. 35.00 (ISBN 0-384-05960-0). Johnson Repr.
Burtt, Edwin A. Metaphysical Foundations of Modern Physical Science. 2nd ed. (International Library of Psychology, Philosophy & Scientific Method). 1967. text ed. 29.00x (ISBN 0-7100-3032-0); pap. text ed. 9.45x (ISBN 0-391-01633-4). Humanities.
Christianson, Gale E. In the Presence of the Creator: Issac Newton & His Times. LC 83-49211. 608p. 1984. 27.50 (ISBN 0-02-905190-8). Free Pr.
Clarke, John. Demonstration of Some of the Principal Sections of Sir Isaac Newton's Principles of Natural Philosophy. 1972. Repr. of 1730 ed. 28.00 (ISBN 0-384-09226-8). Johnson Repr.
Cohen, I. Bernard. The Newtonian Revolution. LC 79-18637. 1981. 49.50 (ISBN 0-521-22964-2). Cambridge U Pr.
--The Newtonian Revolution: With Illustrations of the Transformation of Scientific Ideas. LC 79-18637. (Illus.). 404p. 1983. pap. 17.95 (ISBN 0-521-27380-3). Cambridge U Pr.
De Villamil, Richard. Newton, the Man. 112p. 1972. Repr. of 1931 ed. 28.00 (ISBN 0-685-27503-5). Johnson Repr.
Dobbs, Betty J. The Foundation of Newton's Alchemy; or, "The Hunting of the Greene Lyon". LC 74-31795. (Illus.). 320p. 1976. 49.50 (ISBN 0-521-20786-X). Cambridge U Pr.
Dow, T. W. Repeal Kepler's Laws. LC 60-13372. 1960. 5.00 (ISBN 0-910340-02-1). Celestial Pr.
--Reshape Newton's Laws. LC 64-19218. 1965. 5.00 (ISBN 0-910340-03-X). Celestial Pr.
Edelston, J., ed. Correspondence of Sir Isaac Newton & Professor Cotes. 323p. 1969. 42.50x (ISBN 0-7146-1597-8, F Cass Co). Biblio Dist.
Hurlbutt, Robert H. Hume, Newton, & the Design Argument. LC 65-10047. pap. 58.80 (ISBN 0-317-08121-7, 2001988). Bks Demand UMI.
Koyre, Alexander. Newtonian Studies. 1965. pap. 8.50x (ISBN 0-226-45176-3). U of Chicago Pr.
Maclaurin, Colin. Account of Sir Isaac Newton's Philosophical Discoveries. 1968. Repr. of 1748 ed. 34.00 (ISBN 0-384-34900-5). Johnson Repr.
McMullin, Ernan. Newton on Matter & Activity. LC 77-82480. 1979. pap. text ed. 4.95x (ISBN 0-268-01343-8). U of Notre Dame Pr.
--Newton on Matter & Activity. LC 77-82480. 1978. text ed. 10.95 (ISBN 0-268-01342-X). U of Notre Dame Pr.
Manuel, Frank E. The Religion of Isaac Newton: The Fremantle Lectures 1973. 1974. 24.95x (ISBN 0-19-826640-5). Oxford U Pr.
Newton, Isaac. The Correspondence of Isaac Newton, Vol. 3, 1688-1694. Turnbull, H. W., ed. LC 59-65134. pap. 116.30 (ISBN 0-317-26385-4, 2024527). Bks Demand UMI.
--The Correspondence of Isaac Newton, 1718-1727, Vol. VII. Hall, A. R., et al, eds. LC 59-65134. (Illus.). 1978. 110.00 (ISBN 0-521-08723-6). Cambridge U Pr.
--The Correspondence, Seventeen Thirteen to Seventeen Eighteen, Vols. 6 & 7. Hall, A. R. & Tilling, Laura, eds. (Correspondence of Isaac Newton Ser.). (Illus.). 500p. 1976. Vol. 6. 110.00 ea. (ISBN 0-521-08722-8). Cambridge U Pr.
--Mathematical Papers of Isaac Newton, Vol. 7, 1691-1695. Whiteside, D. T. & Hoskin, M. A., eds. LC 65-11203. 1977. 200.00 (ISBN 0-521-08720-1). Cambridge U Pr.
--The Optical Papers of Isaac Newton: Vol. 1: The Optical Lectures, 1670-1672. Shapiro, Alan E., ed. LC 82-14751. (Illus.). 704p. 1984. 150.00 (ISBN 0-521-25248-2). Cambridge U Pr.
Nicholson, Marjorie H. Newton Demands the Muse: Newton's "Opticks" & the Eighteenth Century Poets. LC 78-13146. 1979. Repr. of 1966 ed. lib. bdg. 24.75x (ISBN 0-313-21044-6, NIND). Greenwood.
Pemberton, Henry. A View of Sir Isaac Newton's Philosophy. 1972. Repr. of 1728 ed. 38.00 (ISBN 0-384-45695-2). Johnson Repr.
Pullin, V. E. Sir Issac Newton: A Biographical Sketch. 1979. Repr. of 1927 ed. lib. bdg. 15.00 (ISBN 0-8495-4334-7). Arden Lib.
Rigaud, Stephen P. Historical Essay on the First Publication of Sir Isaac Newton's Principia. 1972. Repr. of 1838 ed. 24.00 (ISBN 0-384-50845-6). Johnson Repr.
Snow, A. J. Matter & Gravity in Newton's Physical Philosophy. LC 74-26293. (History, Philosophy & Sociology of Science Ser). 1975. Repr. 21.00x (ISBN 0-405-06619-8). Ayer Co Pubs.
Westfall, R. S. Never at Rest: A Biography of Isaac Newton. LC 77-84001. (Illus.). 850p. 1981. 72.50 (ISBN 0-521-23143-4). Cambridge U Pr.
Whiston, William. Sir Isaac Newton's Mathematick Philosophy More Easily Demonstrated. Repr. of 1716 ed. 38.00 (ISBN 0-384-67976-5). Johnson Repr.
Wright, J. M. A Commentary on Newton's Principia: With a Supplementary Volume, Designed for the Use of Students at the Universities, 2 Vols. 1972. Repr. of 1833 ed. Set. 75.00 (ISBN 0-384-69445-4). Johnson Repr.

NEWTON'S RINGS

see Interference (Light)

NICKEL

Betteridge, W. Nickel & Its Alloys. (Illus.). 160p. 1977. pap. 18.50x (ISBN 0-7121-0947-1, Pub. by Macdonald & Evans England). Trans-Atlantic.
--Nickel & Its Alloys. (Monographs in Toxicology). 211p. 1984. 49.95 (ISBN 0-470-20117-7). Halsted Pr.
Brown, Stanley S. & Sunderman, F. William, Jr., eds. Nickel Toxicology. 1981. 40.00 (ISBN 0-12-137680-X). Acad Pr.
Committee on Medical & Biological Effects of Environmental Pollutants. Nickel. 277p. 1975. pap. 16.50 (ISBN 0-309-02314-9). Natl Acad Pr.
Everhart, John L., ed. Engineering Properties of Nickel & Nickel Alloys. LC 74-141242. 229p. 1971. 39.50x (ISBN 0-306-30513-5, Plenum Pr). Plenum Pub.
Friend, Wayne Z. Corrosion of Nickel & Nickel-Base Alloys. LC 79-11524. (Corrosion Monographs). 459p. 1980. 72.95x (ISBN 0-471-28285-5, Pub. by Wiley-Interscience). Wiley.
Gawrilov, G. G. Chemical (Electroless) Nickel-Plating. 179p. 80.00x (ISBN 0-86108-048-3, Pub. by Portcullio Pr). State Mutual Bk.
Jacobs, J. J. & Allard, M. Nickel & Cobalt Extraction Using Organic Compounds. (European Patent Office Ser.). 500p. 1984. 100.01 (ISBN 0-08-030576-8, 16-4, 19-5). Pergamon.
Jolly, P. W. & Wilke, G. The Organic Chemistry of Nickel, 2 vols. (Organometallic Chemistry Ser.). Vol. 1, 1974. 95.00 (ISBN 0-12-388401-2); Vol. 2, 1975. 90.00 (ISBN 0-12-388402-0). Acad Pr.
Max Planck Society for the Advancement of Science, Gmelin Institute for Inorganic Chemistry. Organonickel Compounds. (Gmelin Handbuch der Anorganischen Chemie, 8th Ed., New Suppl.: Vol. 16, Pt. 1). (Illus.). 419p. 1975. 291.50 (ISBN 0-387-93294-1). Springer-Verlag.
Max Plank Society for the Advancement of Science, Gmelin Institute for Inorganic Chemistry. Nickel-Organische Verbibdunger Register-Organohickel Compounds Index for Pts. 1 & 2 of the Gmelin Handbuch. (Gmelin Handbuch der Anoranischew Chenill, 8th Ed, New Suppl.: Vol. 18). 129p. 1975. 83.20 (ISBN 0-387-93296-8). Springer-Verlag.
Milton, Charles & Milton, Daniel J. Nickel-Gold Ore of the Mackinaw Mine, Snohomish County, Washington. (Reprint Ser.: No. 4). (Illus.). 22p. 1959. 0.25 (ISBN 0-686-36913-0). Geologic Pubns.
Nriagu, Jerome O., ed. Nickel in the Environment. LC 80-16600. (Environmental Science & Technology Ser.). 833p. 1980. 140.00x (ISBN 0-471-05885-8, Pub. by Wiley Interscience). Wiley.
Specification for Nickel & Nickel-Alloy Bare Welding Rods & Electrodes: A5.14. 1983. 10.00 (ISBN 0-87171-232-6); member 7.50. Am Welding.
Specification for Nickel & Nickel-Alloy Covered Welding Electrodes: A5.11. 32p. 1983. 10.00 (ISBN 0-87171-231-8); member 7.50. Am Welding.

NICKEL-CHROMIUM ALLOYS

see also Nimonic Alloys

Friend, Wayne Z. Corrosion of Nickel & Nickel-Base Alloys. LC 79-11524. (Corrosion Monographs). 459p. 1980. 72.95x (ISBN 0-471-28285-5, Pub. by Wiley-Interscience). Wiley.

NICKEL INDUSTRY

The Nickel Industry & the Developing Countries. 100p. 1980. pap. 8.00 (ISBN 0-686-70505-X, UN80/2A2, UN). Unipub.

NICOTINE

see also Tobacco

Fazey, C. The Aetiology of Psychoactive Substance Use: A Report & Critically Annotated Bibliography on Research into the Aetiology of Alcohol, Nicotine, Opiate & Other Psychoactive Substance Use. 226p. (With the Financial Support of the United Nations Fund for Drug Abruse Control). 1977. pap. 18.00 (ISBN 92-3-101508-7, U776, UNESCO). Unipub.
Remond, A. & Izard, C. Electrophysiological Effects of Nicotine. 254p. 1980. 61.50 (ISBN 0-444-80183-9, North Holland). Elsevier.
Specifications for Plant Protection Products Nicotine Sulphate. (Specifications for Plant Protection Products). 1979. pap. 7.50 (ISBN 92-5-100552-4, F1468, FAO). Unipub.

NICOTINIC ACID

Gey, K F. & La Carlson. Metabolic Effects of Nicotinic Acid & its Derivatives. 1251p. 495.00 (ISBN 3-456-00384-6, Pub. by Holdan Bk Ltd UK). State Mutual Bk.
Weiner, Van Eys. Nicotinic Acid. (Clinical Pharmacology Ser.). 336p. 1983. 55.00 (ISBN 0-8247-7015-3). Dekker.

NIDOLOGY

see Birds–Eggs and Nests

NIGHT PHOTOGRAPHY

see Photography, Night

NIKON CAMERA

see Cameras–Types–Nikon

NILE RIVER AND VALLEY

Kassas, M. & Ghabbour, I., eds. The Nile & Its Environment. 136p. 1980. pap. 22.00 (ISBN 0-08-026081-0). Pergamon.
Said, R. The Geological Evolution of the River Nile. (Illus.). 176p. 1981. 69.00 (ISBN 0-387-90484-0). Springer-Verlag.
Shahin, M. M. Hydrology of the Nile Basin. (Developments in Water Science Ser.: Vol. 21). 575p. 1985. 92.75 (ISBN 0-444-42433-4). Elsevier.

NIMONIC ALLOYS

Betteridge, W. & Heslop, J., eds. The Nimonic Alloys. 2nd ed. LC 74-79862. (Illus.). 498p. 1974. 59.00x (ISBN 0-8448-0370-7). Crane-Russak Co.

NIOBIUM

Niobium: Physico-Chemical Properties of Its Compounds & Alloys. (Atomic Energy Review Ser.: Special Issue No. 2). 1968. pap. 14.50 (ISBN 92-0-149068-2, IAER2, IAEA). Unipub.

Stuart, Harry, ed. Niobium: Proceedings of the International Symposium: San Francisco, 1981. LC 83-63096. (Illus.). 1257p. 1984. 60.00 (ISBN 0-89520-468-1). Metal Soc.

NITRATES

Breimer, T. Environmental Factors & Cultural Measures Affecting the Nitrate of Spinach. 1982. pap. text ed. 22.00 (ISBN 90-247-3053-8, Pub. by Martinus Nijhoff Netherlands). Kluwer Academic.

Cohn, J. N. & Rittinghausen, R., eds. Mononitrates. (International Boehringer Mannheim Symposia). (Illus.). 345p. 1985. pap. 34.50 (ISBN 0-387-15107-9). Springer-Verlag.

Committee on Environmental Pollutants, National Research Council. Nitrates: An Environmental Assessment. (Scientific & Technical Assessments of Environmental Pollutants Ser.). 1978. pap. text ed. 16.75 (ISBN 0-309-02785-3). Natl Acad Pr.

Committee on Nitrate Accumulation. Accumulation of Nitrate. vii, 106p. 1972. pap. text ed. 7.50 (ISBN 0-309-02038-7). Natl Acad Pr.

Corre, W. J. & Breimer, T. Nitrate & Nitrite in Vegetables. (Literature Survey Ser.: No. 39). 91p. 1979. pap. 9.75 (ISBN 90-220-0723-5, PDC242, PUDOC). Unipub.

Effects of Agricultural Production on Nitrates in Food & Water with Particular Reference to Isotope Studies. (Panel Proceedings Ser.). (Illus.). 158p. (Orig.). 1974. pap. 13.00 (ISBN 92-0-111174-6, ISP361, IAEA). Unipub.

Engel, H. J. & Lichtlen, P., eds. Nitrates III-Cardiovascular Effects: Proceedings. (Illus.). 705p. 1981. 34.50 (ISBN 0-387-10761-4). Springer-Verlag.

National Research Council Assembly of Life Sciences. The Health Effects of Nitrates, Nitrites, & N-Nitroso Compounds. 544p. 1981. pap. text ed. 14.95 (ISBN 0-309-03230-X). Natl Acad Pr.

Needleman, P., ed. Organic Nitrates. (Handbook of Experimental Pharmacology Ser.: Vol. 40). (Illus.). xiii, 196p. 1975. 55.00 (ISBN 0-387-07048-6). Springer-Verlag.

O'Brien, Thomas F. The Nitrate Industry & Chile's Crucial Transition: 1870-1891. 232p. 1982. 30.00x (ISBN 0-8147-6159-3). NYU Pr.

Wilcox. Growth Mechanisms & Silicon Nitride. (Preparation & Properties of Solid State Materials Ser.: Vol. 7). 1982. 65.00 (ISBN 0-8247-1368-0). Dekker.

NITRATION

Albright, Lyle F. & Hanson, Carl, eds. Industrial & Laboratory Nitrations. LC 75-38712. (ACS Symposium Ser.: No. 22). 1976. 34.95 (ISBN 0-8412-0306-7). Am Chemical.

Schofield, K. Aromatic Nitration. (Illus.). 350p. 1981. 79.50 (ISBN 0-521-23362-3). Cambridge U Pr.

NITRENES

Gilchrist, T. L. & Rees, C. W. Carbenes, Nitrenes, & Arynes. 131p. 1969. pap. 12.50x (ISBN 0-306-50026-4, Plenum Pr). Plenum Pub.

Scriven. Azides & Nitrenes. 1984. 99.50 (ISBN 0-12-633480-3). Acad Pr.

NITRIC ACID

Chilton, Thomas. Strong Water: Nitric Acid, Its Sources, Methods of Manufacture, & Uses. 1968. 16.50x (ISBN 0-262-03023-3). MIT Pr.

Keleti, Cornelius. Nitric Acid & Fertilizer Nitrates. (Fertilizer Science & Technology Ser.). 424p. 1985. 95.00 (ISBN 0-8247-7332-2). Dekker.

NITRIDING

see Case Hardening

NITRO COMPOUNDS

Feuer, Henry, ed. The Chemistry of the Nitro & Nitroso Groups. LC 80-21491. 1981. Repr. of 1969 ed. Pt. 1, 780 P. text ed. (ISBN 0-89874-271-4); Pt. 2, 448 P. text ed. (ISBN 0-89874-272-2); Pts. 1 & 2. text ed. 84.50 (ISBN 0-89874-320-6). Krieger.

Rickert, Douglas E., ed. Toxicity of Nitroaromatic Compounds. LC 84-8937. (Chemical Industry Institute of Toxicology Ser.). (Illus.). 295p. 1985. 49.50 (ISBN 0-89116-304-2). Hemisphere Pub.

Schmaehl, Dietrich. Risk Assessment of N-Nitroso Compounds for Human Health. (Oncology Series: Vol. 37, No. 4). (Illus.). 120p. 1980. pap. 26.00 (ISBN 3-8055-1137-X). S Karger.

NITROGEN

see also Nitrogen Fertilizers

Alexander, Martin, ed. Biological Nitrogen Fixation: Ecology, Technology & Physiology. 248p. 1984. 42.50x (ISBN 0-306-41632-8, Plenum Pr). Plenum Pub.

Bahn, Gilbert S., ed. Reaction Rate Compilation for the H-O-N System. LC 68-20396. 254p. 1968. Repr. of 1967 ed. 74.25 (ISBN 0-677-12750-2). Gordon.

Batino. Nitrogen & Air: Gas Solubilities. LC 82-15046. (Solubility Data Ser.: Vol. 10). 1982. 100.00 (ISBN 0-08-023922-6). Pergamon.

Bothe, H. & Trebst, A., eds. Biology of Inorganic Nitrogen & Sulfur Metabolism. (Proceedings in Life Sciences Ser.). (Illus.). 370p. 1981. 52.00 (ISBN 0-387-10486-0). Springer-Verlag.

Bridges, J. W. & Gorrod, J. W., eds. Biological Oxidation of Nitrogen in Organic Molecules. 282p. 1972. cancelled (ISBN 0-85066-058-0). Taylor & Francis.

Heal, Henry. The Inorganic Heterocyclic Chemistry of Sulphur, Nitrogen & Phosphorus. 1981. 86.00 (ISBN 0-12-335680-6). Acad Pr.

Hsu, Donald K., et al. Spectral Atlas of Nitrogen Dioxide: 5530a to 6480a. 1978. 49.50 (ISBN 0-12-357950-3). Acad Pr.

Interlaboratory Cooperative Study of the Precision & Accuracy of the Measurement of Nitrogen Dioxide Content in the Atmosphere Using ASTM D 1607, DS 55. 81p. 1974. pap. 5.00 (ISBN 0-8031-0381-6, 05-055000-17). ASTM.

Jenkins, S. H. Nitrogen As a Water Pollutant. flexi-cover 99.00x (ISBN 0-08-020900-9). Pergamon.

Lee, J. A., et al, eds. Nitrogen As an Ecological Factor. (Illus.). 480p. 1983. text ed. 67.00 (ISBN 0-632-01074-6). Blackwell Pubns.

Monteith, John & Webb, Colin. Soil-Water & Nitrogen: In Mediterranean-Type Environments. 1981. 66.00 (ISBN 90-247-2406-6, Pub. by Martinus Nijhoff Netherlands). Kluwer Academic.

Nielsen, D. R. Nitrogen in the Environment, Vol. 1. 1978. 47.50 (ISBN 0-12-518401-8). Acad Pr.

Riley, F. L., ed. Progress in Nitrogen Ceramics. 1983. lib. bdg. 100.00 (ISBN 90-247-2828-2, Pub. by Martinus Nijhoff Netherlands). Kluwer Academic.

Royal Society Study Group Report Staff. The Nitrogen Cycle of the United Kingdom: A Study Group Report. (RSL Study Group Report Ser.). (Illus.). 264p. 1984. pap. text ed. 28.00 (ISBN 0-85403-227-4, Pub. by Royal Soc London). Scholium Intl.

Schofield, K. Hetero-Aromatic Nitrogen Compounds. LC 67-26477. 434p. 1968. 42.50x (ISBN 0-306-30631-X, Plenum Pr). Plenum Pub.

Stewart, W. D. & Rosswall, T., eds. The Nitrogen Cycle: Proceedings. (Royal Society of London Ser.). (Illus.). 274p. 1982. lib. bdg. 77.00x (ISBN 0-85403-183-9, Pub. by Royal Soc London). Scholium Intl.

Streuli, C. A. The Analytical Chemistry of Nitrogen & Its Compounds, 2 pts. Averell, P. R., ed. LC 68-8112. 428p. 1971. 65.00 (ISBN 0-471-83370-3). Krieger.

Takahashi, H., ed. Nitrogen Fixation & Nitrogen Cycle, Vol. 12. (Japan International Biological Program Synthesis Ser.). 161p. 1975. 20.00x (ISBN 0-86008-222-9, Pub. by U of Tokyo Japan). Columbia U Pr.

West, N. E. & Skujins, J., eds. Nitrogen in Desert Ecosystems. LC 78-17672. (US-IBP Synthesis Ser.: Vol. 9). 307p. 1978. 31.50 (ISBN 0-87933-333-2). Van Nos Reinhold.

Winneberger, John T. Nitrogen, Public Health & the Environment: Some Tools for Critical Thought. LC 81-70873. (Illus.). 77p. 1982. text ed. 19.95 (ISBN 0-250-40522-9). Butterworth.

Wright, A. Nelson & Winkler, Carl A. Active Nitrogen. (Physical Chemistry Ser.: Vol. 14). 1968. 94.00 (ISBN 0-12-765150-0). Acad Pr.

NITROGEN–ASSIMILATION AND EXCRETION

see Nitrogen Metabolism

NITROGEN–FIXATION

Ayanaba, A. & Dart, P. J., eds. Biological Nitrogen Fixation in Farming Systems of the Tropics. LC 77-1304. 377p. 1978. 86.95x (ISBN 0-471-99499-5, Pub. by Wiley-Interscience). Wiley.

Bergersen, F. J., ed. Methods for Evaluating Biological Nitrogen Fixation. LC 79-41785. 702p. 1980. cloth 139.95x (ISBN 0-471-27759-2, Pub. by Wiley-Interscience). Wiley.

Broughton, W. J. Nitrogen Fixation, Vol. 1: Ecology. (Illus.). 1981. 59.00x (ISBN 0-19-854540-1). Oxford U Pr.

Broughton, W. J., ed. Nitrogen Fixation: Rhizobium, Vols. 2 & 3. (Illus.). 1983. Vol. 2. 59.00x (ISBN 0-19-854552-5); Vol. 3, 339. 59.00x (ISBN 0-19-854555-X). Oxford U Pr.

Broughton, W. J. & Puhler, S., eds. Nitrogen Fixation: Molecular Biology, Vol. IV. (Illus.). 300p. 1985. 49.95 (ISBN 0-19-854575-4). Oxford U Pr.

Burns, R. C. & Hardy, R. W. Nitrogen Fixation in Bacteria & Higher Plants. LC 75-2164. (Molecular Biology, Biochemistry, & Biophysics Ser.: Vol. 21). (Illus.). 225p. 1975. 38.00 (ISBN 0-387-07192-X). Springer-Verlag.

Chatt, J., et al, eds. New Trends in the Chemistry of Nitrogen Fixation. 1980. 60.00 (ISBN 0-12-169450-X). Acad Pr.

Colowick, Sidney & Kaplan, Nathan, eds. Methods in Enzymology: Photosynthesis & Nitrogen Fixation, Vol. 69, Pt. C. LC 54-9110. 1980. 75.00 (ISBN 0-12-181969-8). Acad Pr.

Dobereiner, J., et al, eds. Limitations & Potentials for Biological Nitrogen Fixation in the Tropics. LC 77-28218. (Basic Life Sciences Ser.: Vol. 10). 412p. 1978. 52.50x (ISBN 0-306-36510-3, Plenum Pr). Plenum Pub.

Gibson, A. H. & Newton, W. E., eds. Current Perspective in Nitrogen Fixation. 534p. 1981. 90.00 (ISBN 0-444-80291-6, Biomedical Pr). Elsevier.

Hardy, R. W. A Treatise on Dinitrogen Fixation: Agronomy & Ecology, Sect. 4. 527p. 1977. 64.95x (ISBN 0-471-02343-4, Pub. by Wiley-Interscience). Wiley.

Isotopes in Biological Dinitrogen Fixation. (Panel Proceedings Ser.). (Illus.). 318p. 1979. pap. 35.00 (ISBN 92-0-011078-9, ISP478, IAEA). Unipub.

Ludden, P. W. & Burris, J. E., eds. Nitrogen Fixation & Carbon Dioxide Metabolism: Proceedings of the 14th Steenbock Symposium, Held 17-22 June, 1984 in Madison, Wisconsin. 448p. 1985. 72.00 (ISBN 0-444-00953-1). Elsevier.

Lyons, J. M., et al, eds. Genetic Engineering of Symbiotic Nitrogen Fixation & Conservation of Fixed Nitrogen. LC 81-4683. (Basic Life Sciences Ser.: Vol. 17). 712p. 1981. 79.50 (ISBN 0-306-40730-2, Plenum Pr). Plenum Pub.

Mishustin, E. N. & Shil'nikova, V. K. Biological Fixation of Atmospheric Nitrogen. Crozy, Alan, tr. LC 78-177914. (Illus.). 420p. 1972. 36.00x (ISBN 0-271-01110-6). Pa St U Pr.

Muller, Achim & Newton, William E., eds. Nitrogen Fixation: The Chemical-Biochemical-Genetic Interface. 380p. 1983. 55.00 (ISBN 0-306-41258-6, Plenum Press). Plenum Pub.

Newton, W. Recent Developments in Nitrogen Fixation. 1978. 74.00 (ISBN 0-12-517350-4). Acad Pr.

Orme-Johnson, William & Newton, William E., eds. Nitrogen Fixation, Vol. 2. 352p. 1980. text ed. 53.00 (ISBN 0-8391-1561-X). Univ Park.

Orme-Johnson, William H., ed. Nitrogen Fixation, Vol. 1. (Steenboek Symposia Ser.: No. 7). 414p. 1980. text ed. 53.00 (ISBN 0-8391-1560-1). Univ Park.

Postgate, J. Biological Nitrogen Fixation. 67p. 1971. 39.00x (ISBN 0-900541-64-4, Pub. by Meadowfield Pr England). State Mutual Bk.

Postgate, J. R. Fundamentals of Nitrogen Fixation. LC 82-4182. (Illus.). 200p. 1983. 39.50 (ISBN 0-521-24169-3); pap. 12.95 (ISBN 0-521-28494-5). Cambridge U Pr.

Postgate, J. R., ed. Chemistry & Biochemistry of Nitrogen Fixation. LC 70-161303. 326p. 1971. 45.00x (ISBN 0-306-30459-7, Plenum Pr). Plenum Pub.

Rao, Subba. New Developments in Biological Nitrogen Fixation. 500p. 1985. text ed. 44.50 (ISBN 0-7131-2877-1). E Arnold.

Sprent, Janet. The Biology of Nitrogen Fixing Organisms. (Illus.). 1979. text ed. 53.95 (ISBN 0-07-084087-3). McGraw.

Stewart, W. D., ed. Nitrogen Fixation by Free-Living Micro-Organisms. LC 75-2731. (International Biological Programme Ser.: Vol. 6). (Illus.). 448p. 1976. 85.00 (ISBN 0-521-20708-8). Cambridge U Pr.

Stewart, W. D. & Gallon, J. R., eds. Nitrogen Fixation. 1981. 69.50 (ISBN 0-12-669450-8). Acad Pr.

Subba Rao, N. S., ed. Recent Advances in Biological Nitrogen Fixation. 500p. 1980. text ed. 45.00x (ISBN 0-8419-5825-4). Holmes & Meier.

Vincent, J. M. Nitrogen Fixation in Legumes. 1982. 35.00 (ISBN 0-12-721980-3). Acad Pr.

NITROGEN COMPOUNDS

see also Alkaloids; Organonitrogen Compounds

Anselme, Jean-Pierre, ed. N-Nitrosamines. LC 79-12461. (ACS Symposium Ser.: No. 101). 1979. 26.95 (ISBN 0-8412-0503-5). Am Chemical.

Benson, Frederic R. High Nitrogen Compounds. LC 83-10476. 679p. 1983. 133.95 (ISBN 0-471-02652-2, Pub. by Wiley-Interscience). Wiley.

Robertson, C. P. & Herrera, R. Nitrogen Cycling in Ecosystems of Latin America & the Caribbean. 1982. 65.00 (ISBN 0-686-38400-8, Pub. by Martinus Nijhoff Netherlands). Kluwer Academic.

Royal Society Discussion Meeting. Ecological Effects of Deposited Sulphur & Nitrogen Compounds: Proceedings of a Royal Society Discussion Meeting Held on September 5-7 1983. Beament, James, et al, eds. (Philosophical Transactions of the Royal Society, Series B: Vol. 305). (Illus.). 319p. 1984. lib. bdg. 99.00x (ISBN 0-85403-229-0, Pub. by Royal Soc London). Scholium Intl.

Smith, P. A. Open-Chain Nitrogen Compounds: Chemistry of Non-Cyclic Nitrogen-Containing Organic Functional Groups. 2nd ed. 1982. text ed. 56.95 (ISBN 0-8053-8902-4). Addison-Wesley.

Streuli, C. A. The Analytical Chemistry of Nitrogen & Its Compounds, 2 pts. Averell, P. R., ed. LC 68-8112. 428p. 1971. 65.00 (ISBN 0-471-83370-3). Krieger.

Witanowski, M. & Webb, G. A., eds. Nitrogen NMR. LC 72-95065. 403p. 1973. 59.50x (ISBN 0-306-30734-0, Plenum Pr). Plenum Pub.

NITROGEN DIOXIDE

Uehara, K. & Sasada, H. High Resolution Spectral Atlas of Nitrogen Dioxide 559-597 nm. (Springer Series in Chemical Physics: Vol. 41). (Illus.). 230p. 1985. 37.00 (ISBN 0-387-15027-7). Springer-Verlag.

NITROGEN FERTILIZERS

Gasser, J. K., ed. Modelling Nitrogen from Farm Wastes. (Illus.). 195p. 1979. 26.00 (ISBN 0-85334-869-3, Pub. by Elsevier Applied Sci England). Elsevier.

Murray, T. P. & Horn, R. C. Organic Nitrogen Compounds for Use as Fertilizers. (Technical Bulletin Ser.: T-14). 64p. (Orig.). 1979. pap. 4.00 (ISBN 0-88090-013-X). Intl Fertilizer.

Nitrogen in Crop Production. 1982. write for info. Am Soc Agron.

Prins, W. H. & Arnold, G. H., eds. The Role of Nitrogen in Intensive Grassland Production: Proceedings of an International Symposium of the European Grassland Federation, Wageningen, 25-29 Aug. 1980. 171p. 1980. pap. 16.00 (ISBN 90-220-0734-0, PDC214, Pudoc). Unipub.

Simulation of Nitrogen Behaviour of Soil-Plant Systems: Papers of a Workshop: Models for the Behaviour of Nitrogen in Soil Uptake by Plant: Comparison Between Different Approaches, Wageningen, The Netherlands, 28 Jan.-1 Feb. 1980. 283p. 1981. pap. 40.00 (ISBN 90-220-0735-9, PDC223, Pudoc). Unipub.

Stevenson, F. J., ed. Nitrogen in Agricultural Soils. (ASA Monograph: No. 22). 940p. 1982. 30.00 (ISBN 0-89118-070-2). Am Soc Agron.

Whitehead, D. C. The Role of Nitrogen in Grassland Productivity: A Review of Information from Temperate Regions. 203p. 1970. 39.00x (ISBN 0-85198-015-5, Pub. by CAB Bks England). State Mutual Bk.

NITROGEN FIXATION

see Nitrogen–Fixation

NITROGEN METABOLISM

Agricultural Board. Accumulation of Nitrate. LC 72-84111. (Illus.). 144p. 1972. pap. 7.00 (ISBN 0-309-02038-7). Natl Acad Pr.

Bewley, J. D. Nitrogen & Carbon Metabolism: Symposium on the Physiology & Bio-Chemistry of Plant Productivity. (Development in Plant & Soil Sciences Ser.: No. 3). 39.50 (ISBN 90-247-2472-4, Pub. by Junk Pubs Netherlands). Kluwer Academic.

Bray, C. M. Nitrogen Metabolism in Plants. LC 82-8942. 176p. 1983. 14.95 (ISBN 0-582-44640-6). Longman.

Isotope Studies on the Nitrogen Chain. (Proceedings Ser.). (Eng., Fr. & Rus., Illus.). 343p. (Orig.). 1968. pap. 23.50 (ISBN 92-0-010068-6, ISP161, IAEA). Unipub.

Steward, F. C. & Bidwell, R. G., eds. Plant Physiology: A Treatise Vol. 8: Nitrogen Metabolism. 1983. 70.00 (ISBN 0-12-668608-4). Acad Pr.

Tracer Studies on Non-Protein Nitrogen for Ruminants, 1. (Panel Proceedings Ser.). (Illus.). 179p. 1972. pap. 16.25 (ISBN 92-0-111072-3, ISP302-1, IAEA). Unipub.

NITROGEN ORGANIC COMPOUNDS

see Organonitrogen Compounds

NITROGEN OXIDE

Klimisch, Richard L. & Larson, John G., eds. The Catalytic Chemistry of Nitrogen Oxides. LC 75-22332. (General Motors Research Symposia Ser.). 340p. 1975. 49.50x (ISBN 0-306-30875-4, Plenum Pr). Plenum Pub.

Lewis, W. H. Nitrogen Oxides Removal. LC 75-24764. (Chemical Technology Review Ser, No.55: Polution Technology Review Ser No. 25). (Illus.). 287p. 1975. 36.00 (ISBN 0-8155-0595-7). Noyes.

OECD Staff. Control Technology for Nitrogen Oxide Emissions from Stationary Sources. 167p. (Orig.). 1983. pap. 14.00x (ISBN 92-64-12485-3). OECD.

Yaverbaum, L. H. Nitrogen Oxides Control & Removal. LC 79-16141. (Pollution Technology Review Ser., No. 60: Chemical Technology Review Ser., No. 136). (Illus.). 388p. 1980. 42.00 (ISBN 0-8155-0768-2). Noyes.

NITROSO COMPOUNDS

see also Chemical Reactions

National Research Council Assembly of Life Sciences. The Health Effects of Nitrates, Nitrites, & N-Nitroso Compounds. 544p. 1981. pap. text ed. 14.95 (ISBN 0-309-03230-X). Natl Acad Pr.

NOISE POLLUTION

Barden, R. G. Sound Pollution. (Australian Environment Ser.: No.4). (Illus.). 66p. 1976. 19.75 (ISBN 0-7022-1012-9); pap. 9.95x (ISBN 0-7022-1013-7). U of Queensland Pr.

BNA"s Environmental & Safety Information Services. Noise Regulation Reporter. write for info. BNA.

Bragdon, Clifford R. Municipal Noise Legislation. text ed. 45.00 (ISBN 0-89671-018-1). SEAI Tech Pubns.

Bragdon, Clifford R., ed. Noise Pollution: A Guide to Information Sources. LC 73-17535. (Man & the Environment Information Guide Ser.: Vol. 5). 600p. 1979. 60.00x (ISBN 0-8103-1345-6). Gale.

Bugliarello, George, et al. The Impact of Noise Pollution: A Socio-Technological Introduction. 475p. 1976. 46.00 (ISBN 0-08-018166-X). Pergamon.

Floyd, Mary K. A Bibliography of Noise for 1971. LC 72-87107. 150p. 1973. 10.00x (ISBN 0-87875-031-2). Whitston Pub.

--A Bibliography of Noise, 1965-1970. LC 72-87107. xxx, 375p. 1973. 17.00x (ISBN 0-87875-029-0). Whitston Pub.

Ganguli, H. C. Human Factor Aspects of Aircraft Noise. 1972. 9.00 (ISBN 0-686-20244-9). Intl Bk Dist.

Gibbs, H. G. & Richards, T. H., eds. Stress, Vibration & Noise Analysis in Vehicles. (Illus.). 485p. 1975. 68.50 (ISBN 0-85334-642-9, Pub. by Elsevier Applied Sci England). Elsevier.

Jones, Dylan M. & Chapman, Antony J., eds. Noise & Society. LC 83-16907. 319p. 1984. 37.95x (ISBN 0-471-90357-4, Pub. by Wiley-Interscience). Wiley.

Kramer-Greene, Judith, ed. A Bibliography of Noise for 1975. LC 72-87107. 171p. 1977. 10.00x (ISBN 0-87875-099-1). Whitston Pub.

Magrab, Edward B. Environmental Noise Control. LC 75-20233. 299p. 1975. 48.50x (ISBN 0-471-56344-7, Pub. by Wiley-Interscience). Wiley.

Miller, Richard K. City Noise Index. (Illus.). 1978. pap. text ed. 35.00x (ISBN 0-89671-005-X). SEAI Tech Pubns.

--Industrial Noise Update. (Illus.). 87p. 1981. pap. text ed. 30.00 (ISBN 0-89671-025-4). SEAI Tech Pubns.

--Noise Control Solutions for the Chemical & Petroleum Industries. new ed. 1981. text ed. 45.00x (ISBN 0-89671-036-X). SEAI Tech Pubns.

--Noise Control Solutions for the Rubber & Plastics Industry. new ed. (Illus.). 1981. text ed. 45.00x (ISBN 0-89671-037-8). SEAI Tech Pubns.

--Noise Control Solutions for the Wire Industry. new ed. (Illus.). 1979. pap. text ed. 35.00x (ISBN 0-89671-006-8). SEAI Tech Pubns.

Schultz, Theodore J. Community Noise Rating. 2nd ed. (Illus.). 385p. 1982. 72.25 (ISBN 0-85334-137-0, I-303-82, Pub. by Elsevier Applied Sci England). Elsevier.

Stephens, Irving E. & Barnes, Dorothy L., eds. A Bibliography of Noise for 1976. LC 72-87107. 202p. 1978. 12.50x (ISBN 0-87875-128-9). Whitston Pub.

NOMOGRAPHY (MATHEMATICS)

Adams, Douglas P. Nomography: Theory & Application. viii, 198p. 1964. 22.50 (ISBN 0-208-00435-1, Archon). Shoe String.

Johnson, Lee H. Nomography & Empirical Equations. LC 77-16063. 160p. 1978. Repr. of 1952 ed. lib. bdg. 14.00 (ISBN 0-88275-551-X). Krieger.

Kuong, Javier F. Applied Nomography. LC 65-18920. pap. 36.00 (2024310). Bks Demand UMI.

--Applied Nomography, Vol. 2. LC 65-18920. 116p. 1968. 16.95x (ISBN 0-87201-586-6). Gulf Pub.

Palmer, E. M. Graphical Evolution. (Discrete Mathematics Ser.). 177p. 1985. 34.95 (ISBN 0-471-81577-2). Wiley.

NONAQUEOUS SOLVENTS

Janz, George J. & Tompkins, R. P. T. Non-Aqueous Electrolytes Handbook, 2 vols. Vol. 1, 1972. 130.00 (ISBN 0-12-380401-9); Vol. 2, 1974. 130.00 (ISBN 0-12-380402-7); Set. o. p. 216.00. Acad Pr.

Popovych, Orest & Tomkins, Reginald. Nonaqueous Solution Chemistry. LC 80-21693. 500p. 1981. 72.95 (ISBN 0-471-02673-5, Pub. by Wiley-Interscience). Wiley.

NONASSOCIATIVE ALGEBRAS

Beck, R. E. & Kolman, B. Computers in Nonassociative Rings & Algebras. 1977. 45.00 (ISBN 0-12-083850-8). Acad Pr.

NON-DESTRUCTIVE TESTING

see also Automatic Checkout Equipment; Ultrasonic Testing

American Society for Metals Staff. Prevention of Structural Failures: The Role of NDT, Fracture Mechanics & Failure Analysis: Proceedings of Two Annual Forums, 19-22 June, 1977 & 14-16 June 1976, Tarpon Springs, Florida. LC 78-15388. (Materials-Metalworking Technology Ser.). (Illus.). pap. 90.00 (ISBN 0-317-09726-1, 2019489). Bks Demand UMI.

Birnbaum & Free, eds. Eddy-Current Characterization of Materials & Structures - STP 722. 505p. 1981. 44.50 (ISBN 0-8031-0752-8, 04-722000-22). ASTM.

Bryant, Lawrence E. & McIntire, Paul, eds. Radiography & Radiation Testing. 2nd ed. (Nondestructive Testing Handbook). (Illus.). 925p. 1984. 99.95 (ISBN 0-931403-00-6, 128). Am Soc Nondestructive.

Erf, Robert K., ed. Holographic Nondestructive Testing. 1974. 76.00 (ISBN 0-12-241350-4). Acad Pr.

Fitting, Dale & Adler, Laszlo. Ultrasonic Spectral Analysis for Nondestructive Evaluation. LC 80-14991. 364p. 1981. 59.50x (ISBN 0-306-40484-2, Plenum Pr). Plenum Pub.

Fundamentals of Eddy Current Testing, Module 32-5. (Nondestructive Examination Techniques II Ser.). (Illus.). 46p. 1979. spiral bdg. 7.00x (ISBN 0-87683-102-1). G P Courseware.

Guidelines for the Selection & Training of Censory Panel Members - STP 758. 35p. 1981. pap. 7.25 (ISBN 0-8031-0783-8, 04-758000-36). ASTM.

Halmshaw, R. Industrial Radiology Techniques. (Wykeham Technology Ser.: No. 3). 278p. 1971. 14.00x (ISBN 0-8448-1174-2). Crane Russak Co.

Hoeller, P., ed. New Procedures in Nondestructive Testing: Proceedings, Saarbruecken, FRG, 1982. (Illus.). 604p. 1983. 51.00 (ISBN 0-387-12187-0). Springer-Verlag.

Liquid Penetrant Tests, Module 26-4. (Nondestructive Examination Techniques I Ser.). (Illus.). 62p. 1979. spiral bdg. 8.00x (ISBN 0-87683-093-9). G P Courseware.

McGonnagle, W., ed. International Advances in Nondestructive Testing, Vol. 7. 450p. 1981. 103.95 (ISBN 0-677-15700-2). Gordon.

McGonnagle, Warren J. International Advances in Nondestructive Testing, Vol. 5. 414p. 1977. 90.25 (ISBN 0-677-12000-1). Gordon.

--International Advances in Nondestructive Testing, Vol. 8. 361p. 1981. 86.75 (ISBN 0-677-16240-5). Gordon.

--Nondestructive Testing. 2nd ed. (Illus.). 468p. 1971. 58.95x (ISBN 0-677-00500-8). Gordon.

McGonnagle, Warren J., ed. International Advances in Nondestructive Testing, Vol. 6. 380p. 1979. 90.25 (ISBN 0-677-12470-8). Gordon.

--Physics & Nondestructive Testing, Vol. 1. 578p. 1967. 113.50 (ISBN 0-677-10580-0). Gordon.

--Physics & Nondestructive Testing, Vol. 2. LC 65-27852. (Illus.). 302p. 1972. 69.50x (ISBN 0-677-15250-7). Gordon.

--Physics & Nondestructive Testing, Vol. 3. LC 65-27852. (Illus.). 338p. 1972. 69.50x (ISBN 0-677-15260-4). Gordon.

Malhotra, V. M. Testing Hardened Concrete: Nondestructive Methods. (Monograph: No. 9). 1976. 29.95 (ISBN 0-685-85144-3, M-9) (ISBN 0-685-85145-1). ACI.

Monitoring Structural Integrity by Acoustic Emission, STP 571. 290p. 1975. 23.75 (ISBN 0-8031-0519-3, 04-571000-22). ASTM.

Moore, Harry D., ed. Materials & Processes for NDT Technology. (Illus.). 204p. 1984. Repr. of 1981 ed. 30.75 (ISBN 0-931403-06-5, 2250). Am Soc Nondestructive.

Nondestructive Evaluation & Flaw Criticality for Composite Materials - STP 696. 364p. 1979. 34.50x (ISBN 0-8031-0527-4, 04 696000-33). ASTM.

Nondestructive Examination Techniques II: Course 32. (Nondestructive Examination Techniques Ser.). (Illus.). 262p. pap. text ed. 44.00x looseleaf (ISBN 0-87683-097-1). G P Courseware.

Nondestructive Examination Techniques. (Illus.). 610p. 1979. pap. text ed. 95.00x looseleaf (ISBN 0-87683-088-2). G P Courseware.

Nondestructive Examination Techniques I: Course 26. (Nondestructive Examination Techniques Ser.). (Illus.). 348p. 1979. pap. text ed. 51.00x looseleaf (ISBN 0-87683-089-0). G P Courseware.

Nondestructive Rapid Identification of Metals & Alloys by Spot Tests, STP 550. 56p. 1973. pap. 4.00 (ISBN 0-8031-0528-2, 04-550000-24). ASTM.

Operation of Eddy Current Test Equipment, Module 32-6. (Nondestructive Examination Techniques II Ser.). (Illus.). 36p. 1979. spiral bdg. 7.00x (ISBN 0-87683-103-X). G P Courseware.

Operation of Magnetic Particle Test Equipment, Module 32-4. (Nondestructive Examination Techniques II Ser.). (Illus.). 44p. 1979. spiral bdg. 7.00x (ISBN 0-87683-101-3). G P Courseware.

Real-Time Radiologic Imaging - STP 716: Medical & Industrial. 352p. 1980. 36.50x (ISBN 0-8031-0546-0, 04-716000-22). ASTM.

Sharpe, R. S. Research Techniques in Non-Destructive Testing, Vol. 4. LC 79-109038. 1980. 81.00 (ISBN 0-12-639054-1). Acad Pr.

Sharpe, R. S., ed. Research Techniques in Non-Destructive Testing, Vol. 3. 1978. 79.00 (ISBN 0-12-639053-3). Acad Pr.

--Research Techniques in Non-Destructive Testing, Vol. 5. 1983. 65.00 (ISBN 0-12-639055-X). Acad Pr.

Stanford, Edwin G., et al, eds. Progress in Applied Materials Research. 1963-65. Vol. 4, 256p. 69.50x (ISBN 0-677-00920-8); Vol. 5, 248p. 69.50x (ISBN 0-677-00930-5); Vol. 6, 320p. 80.95x (ISBN 0-677-00940-2). Gordon.

Stinchcomb, W. W., et al, eds. Mechanics of Nondestructive Testing. LC 80-23808. 415p. 1980. 59.50x (ISBN 0-306-40567-9). Plenum Pub.

Tyler, et al, eds. Quality Technology Handbook. 4th ed. (Illus.). 496p. 1984. text ed. 85.00 (ISBN 0-408-01331-1). Butterworth.

NON-EUCLIDEAN GEOMETRY

see Geometry, Non-Euclidean

NONFERROUS METAL INDUSTRIES

Gill, Lafayette B. Non-Ferrous Extractive Metallurgy. LC 79-28696. 346p. 1980. 55.50x (ISBN 0-471-05980-3, Pub. by Wiley-Interscience). Wiley.

Non-Ferrous Metals Industry. (UNIDO Monographs on Industrialization of Developing Countries: Problems & Prospects: Vol. 1). pap. 4.00 (UN69/2B/39VI, UN). Unipub.

The Non-Ferrous Metals Industry, 1980. 38p. (Orig.). 1982. pap. 6.50x (ISBN 92-64-02282-1). OECD.

OECD Staff. The Non-Ferrous Metals Industry 1981. 38p. (Orig.). 1983. pap. 7.00x (ISBN 92-64-02414-X). OECD.

Preston, Lee E. Exploration for Non-Ferrous Metals: An Economic Analysis. LC 77-86409. (Resources for the Future, Inc. Publications). Repr. of 1960 ed. 19.00 (ISBN 0-404-60342-4). AMS Pr.

Robbins, Peter. Guide to Non-Ferrous Metals & Their Markets. 3rd ed. 215p. 1982. 47.50 (ISBN 0-89397-124-3). Nichols Pub.

Schmitz, Christopher J. World Non-Ferrous Metal Production & Prices, 1700-1976. 432p. 1979. 35.00x (ISBN 0-7146-3109-4, F Cass Co). Biblio Dist.

Urquhart, Elizabeth. The Canadian Nonferrous Metals Industry: An Industrial Organization Study. 159p. (Orig.). 1978. pap. text ed. 10.50 (ISBN 0-88757-005-4, Pub. by Ctr Resource Stud Canada). Brookfield Pub Co.

Worldwide Guide to Equivalent Nonferrous Metals & Alloys. 1980. 112.00 (ISBN 0-87170-101-4). ASM.

NONFERROUS METALS

see also Nonferrous Metal Industries

American Bureau of Metal Statistics Staff, compiled by. ABMS Non-Ferrous Metal Data Publication: 1974 Yearbook. rev. ed. Incl. 1974 Yearbook. American Bureau of Metal Statistics Staff, ed. 1975 (ISBN 0-910064-09-1); 1975 Yearbook. American Bureau of Metal Statistics Staff, ed. 1976 (ISBN 0-910064-09-1). LC 21-15719. 1975. 70.00 (ISBN 0-910064-08-3). Am Bur Metal.

American Bureau of Metal Statistics Staff, ed. ABMS Non-Ferrous Metal Data Publication: 1975 Yearbook. rev. ed. LC 21-15719. 1976. 70.00 (ISBN 0-910064-09-1). Am Bur Metal.

--ABMS Non-Ferrous Metal Data Publication: 1976 Year Book. rev. ed. LC 21-15719. 1977. 70.00 (ISBN 0-910064-10-5). Am Bur Metal.

American Bureau of Metal Statistics Inc. Non-Ferrous Metal Data Yearbook, 1978. (Illus.). 1979. 70.00 (ISBN 0-686-51336-3). Am Bur Metal.

Collie, M. J., ed. Extractive Metallurgy: Developments since 1980. LC 83-21996. (Chemical Technology Review Ser.: No. 227). (Illus.). 323p. 1984. 45.00 (ISBN 0-8155-0978-2). Noyes.

Deutsche Gesellschaft fur Metallkunde. Atlas of Hot Working Properties of Non-ferrous Metals: Copper & Copper Alloys, Vol. 2. 480p. text ed. 102.00 (ISBN 0-9911002-3-9, Pub. by Aluminium W Germany). Heyden.

Deutsche Gesellschoft fur Metallkunde. Atlas of Hot Working Properties of Non-ferrous Metals: Aluminium & Aluminium Alloys, Vol. 1. 245p. 1978. text ed. 87.00 (ISBN 0-9911002-2-0, Pub. by Aluminium W Germany). Heyden.

Din Standards for Non-Ferrous Metals: Aluminium, Magnesium, Titanium, & Their Wrought Alloys. 637.00 (ISBN 0-01-007042-7, 10070-7/27). Heyden.

Din Standards for Non-Ferrous Metals: Nickel, Lead, Zinc & Tin & Their Alloys. 186.00 (ISBN 0-686-28189-6, 10709-1/54). Heyden.

Din Standards: Non-Ferrous Metals: Standards for Copper & Wrought Copper Alloys. 559.00 (ISBN 0-686-28175-6, 10069-6/26). Heyden.

Engelmann, C., et al. Modern Methods for the Determination of Non-Metals in Non-Ferrous Metals: Applications to Particular Systems of Metallurgical Importance. (Illus.). xiii, 410p. 1985. 76.00x (ISBN 3-11-010342-7). De Gruyter.

Maple, M. B. & Fischer, O., eds. Superconductivity in Ternary Compounds II: Superconductivity & Magnetism. (Topics in Current Physics: Vol. 34). (Illus.). 335p. 1982. 35.00 (ISBN 0-387-11814-4). Springer-Verlag.

Material Specifications: Nonferrous Materials, 3 pts, Pt. B. (Boiler & Pressure Vessel Code Ser.: Sec. II). 1980. 110.00 (ISBN 0-686-70436-3, P0002B); loose-leaf 150.00 (ISBN 0-686-70437-1, V0002B). ASME.

Muller-Ohlsen, Lotte. Non-Ferrous Metals: Their Role in Industrial Development. 312p. 1981. 50.00x (ISBN 0-85941-190-7, Pub. by Woodhead-Faulkner England). State Mutual Bk.

Non-Ferrous Metal Data Book: 1977. LC 21-15719. 1978. write for info. (ISBN 0-685-89355-3). Am Bur Metal.

Plaksin, I. N., ed. Flotation Properties of Rare Metal Minerals. LC 67-16333. (Illus.). 91p. 1967. 8.75x (ISBN 0-911184-03-1). Primary.

Robbins, Peter. Guide to Non-Ferrous Metals & Their Markets. 3rd ed. 215p. 1982. 47.50 (ISBN 0-89397-124-3). Nichols Pub.

Ryan, W. Non-Ferrous Extractive Metallurgy in the United Kingdom. 234p. 1968. 34.50x (ISBN 0-686-97550-2). IMM North Am.

Schmitz, Christopher J. World Non-Ferrous Metal Production & Prices, 1700-1976. 432p. 1979. 35.00x (ISBN 0-7146-3109-4, F Cass Co). Biblio Dist.

Touloukian, Y. S. & Ho, C. Y. Properties of Selected Ferrous Alloying Elements, Vol. III. (M-H-CINDAS Data Series on Material Properties). 288p. 1981. text ed. 56.00 (ISBN 0-07-065034-9). McGraw.

NONFOSSIL FUELS

see Synthetic Fuels

NONLINEAR DIFFERENTIAL EQUATIONS

see Differential Equations, Nonlinear

NONLINEAR MECHANICS

Enns, Richard H., et al, eds. Nonlinear Phenomena in Physics & Biology. LC 81-15882. (NATO ASI Series B, Physics: Vol. 75). 620p. 1981. text ed. 89.50x (ISBN 0-306-40880-5, Plenum Pr). Plenum Pub.

Hagedorn, Peter. Non-Linear Oscillations. (Engineering Science Ser.). (Illus.). 1981. pap. 19.95x (ISBN 0-19-856156-3). Oxford U Pr.

Hedrick, J. K. & Paynter, H. M., eds. Nonlinear System Analysis & Synthesis, Vol. 1: Fundamental Principles, No. G00138. 146p. 1978. pap. 15.00 (ISBN 0-685-99209-8). ASME.

Hoppensteadt, F. C., ed. Nonlinear Oscillations in Biology. LC 79-26469. (Lectures in Applied Mathematics: Vol. 17). 253p. 1979. 42.00 (ISBN 0-8218-1117-7). Am Math.

Hunt, L. R. & Martin, C. F. Berkeley-Ames Workshop on Nonlinear Problems in Control & Fluid Mechanics, Pt. B. (LIE Groups Ser.: Vol. 2). 450p. 1984. 50.00 (ISBN 0-915692-37-6, 991600150). Math Sci Pr.

Jerome, Joseph. Approximation of Nonlinear Evolution Systems. (Mathematics in Science & Engineering Ser.). 244p. 1983. 47.50 (ISBN 0-12-384680-3). Acad Pr.

Jordan, H. L., et al, eds. Nonlinear Dynamics of Transcritical Flow. (Lecture Notes in Engineering: Vol. 13). vi, 203p. 1985. pap. 15.00 (ISBN 0-387-15430-2). Springer-Verlag.

Knops, R. J., ed. Nonlinear Analysis & Mechanics: Heriot-Watt Symposium, Vol. 3. (Research Notes in Mathematics Ser.: No. 30). 173p. (Orig.). 1979. pap. text ed. 22.95 (ISBN 0-273-08432-1). Pitman Pub MA.

--Nonlinear Analysis & Mechanics: Heriot-Watt Symposium, Vol. 4. LC 78-309110. (Research Notes in Mathematics Ser.: No. 39). 212p. (Orig.). 1979. pap. text ed. 23.95 (ISBN 0-273-08461-5). Pitman Pub MA.

--Nonlinear Analysis & Mechanics: Heriot-Watt Symposium, Vol. 1. (Research Notes in Mathematics Ser.: No. 17). (Orig.). 1977. pap. text ed. 23.00 (ISBN 0-273-01128-6). Pitman Pub MA.

--Nonlinear Analysis & Mechanics: Heriot-Watt Symposium, Vol. 2. (Research Notes in Mathematics Ser.: No. 27). 285p. (Orig.). 1978. pap. text ed. 27.95 (ISBN 0-273-08420-8). Pitman Pub MA.

Kouril, Frantisek & Verba, Kamil. Theory of Non-Linear & Parametric Circuits. (Mathematics & Its Applications-Ellis Horwood Ser.: 1-176). 350p. 1985. 71.95x (ISBN 0-470-20014-6). Halsted Pr.

Krylov, N. M. Introduction to Nonlinear Mechanics. (Annals of Math Studies). Repr. of 1943 ed. 11.00 (ISBN 0-527-02727-8). Kraus Repr.

Lefschetz, Solomon. Stability of Nonlinear Control Systems. (Mathematics in Science & Engineering Ser.: Vol. 13). 1965. 42.50 (ISBN 0-12-440350-6). Acad Pr.

Lyons, Richard. An Introduction to Non-Linear Devices: Passive & Active. 72p. 1983. pap. text ed. 8.95 (ISBN 0-8403-3113-4). Kendall-Hunt.

Morawetz, C. S. Lectures on Nonlinear Waves & Shocks. (Tata Institute Lectures on Mathematics Ser.). 137p. 1982. pap. 10.00 (ISBN 0-387-10830-0). Springer-Verlag.

Nasser, Nemat S. Theoretical Foundation for Large-Scale Computations for Nonlinear Material Behavior. 1984. lib. bdg. 55.50 (ISBN 90-247-3092-9, Pub. by Martinus Nijhoff Netherlands). Kluwer Academic.

Noor, A. K. & McComb, H. G., eds. Computational Methods in Nonlinear Structural & Solid Mechanics: Papers Presented at the Symposium on Computational Methods in Nonlinear Structural & Solid Mechanics, 6-8 October 1980. LC 80-41608. 1980. 185.00 (ISBN 0-08-027299-1). Pergamon.

Oden, J. T., ed. Computational Mechanics: Lectures in Computational Methods in Nonlinear Mechanics. (Lecturenotes in Mathematics Ser.: Vol. 461). vii, 328p. (Orig.). 1975. 20.00 (ISBN 0-387-07169-5). Springer-Verlag.

Riste, T., ed. Nonlinear Phenomena at Phase Transitions & Instabilities. LC 81-17780. (NATO Advanced Study Institute Series B, Physics: Vol. 77). 476p. 1982. text ed. 75.00x (ISBN 0-306-40896-1, Plenum Pr). Plenum Pub.

Sagdeev, R. Z. Nonlinear & Turbulent Processes in Physics, 3 vols. 1748p. 1984. text ed. 235.00 (ISBN 3-7186-0212-1). Harwood Academic.

--Nonlinear & Turbulent Processes in Physics, Vol. 1. 670p. 1984. text ed. 115.00 (ISBN 3-7186-0216-4). Harwood Academic.

--Nonlinear & Turbulent Processes in Physics, Vol. 2. 494p. 1984. text ed. 93.00 (ISBN 3-7186-0217-2). Harwood Academic.

--Nonlinear & Turbulent Processes in Physics, Vol. 3. 564p. 1984. text ed. 105.00 (ISBN 3-7186-0218-0). Harwood Academic.

Starzhinskii, V. M. Applied Methods in the Theory of Nonlinear Oscillations. 1980. 8.95 (ISBN 0-8285-1802-5, Pub. by Mir Pubs USSR). Imported Pubns.

Stoker, J. J. Nonlinear Elasticity. (Notes on Mathematics & Its Applications Ser.). (Illus.). 142p. (Orig.). 1968. 37.25x (ISBN 0-677-00660-8). Gordon.

--Nonlinear Vibrations in Mechanical & Electrical Systems Pure & Aplied Mechanics, Vol. 2. (Pure & Applied Mathematics Ser.). 294p. 1950. 51.95 (ISBN 0-470-82830-7). Wiley.

Walker, H. F. & Fitzgibbon, W. E., eds. Nonlinear Diffusion. LC 77-8501. (Research Notes in Mathematics Ser: No. 14). (Illus.). pap. 22.95 (ISBN 0-273-01066-2, 1066). Pitman Pub MA.

Willson, Alan N., Jr., ed. Nonlinear Networks: Theory & Analysis. LC 74-19558. 1975. 18.65 (ISBN 0-87942-046-4, PP00414). Inst Electrical.

Wunderlich, W., et al, eds. Nonlinear Finite Element Analysis in Structural Mechanics: Proceedings. (Illus.). 777p. 1981. 48.00 (ISBN 0-387-10582-4). Springer-Verlag.

NONLINEAR OPERATORS

Arnold, L. & Lefever, R., eds. Stochastic Nonlinear Systems in Physics, Chemistry, & Biology. (Springer Series in Synergetics: Vol. 8). (Illus.). viii, 237p. 1985. 33.00 (ISBN 0-387-10713-4). Springer-Verlag.

Bachar, J. M. & Hadwin, D. W., eds. Hilbert Space Operators: Proceedings, University of California Long Beach, LB CA, June 20-24, 1978. (Lecture Notes in Mathematics Ser.: Vol. 693). 1978. pap. 15.00 (ISBN 0-387-09097-5). Springer-Verlag.

Cuyt, A. Pade Approximants for Operators: Theory & Applications. (Lecture Notes in Mathematics Ser.: Vol. 1065). ix, 138p. 1984. pap. 10.50 (ISBN 0-387-13342-9). Springer-Verlag.

Gossez, J. P., et al, eds. Nonlinear Operators & the Calculus & Variations: Summer School Held in Bruxelles, 8-19 Sept. 1975. (Lecture Notes in Mathematics: Vol. 543). 1976. soft cover 17.00 (ISBN 0-387-07867-3). Springer-Verlag.

Pimbley, George H., Jr. Eigenfunction Branches of Nonlinear Operators & Their Bifurcations. LC 70-97958. (Lecture Notes in Mathematics: Vol. 104). 1969. pap. 10.70 (ISBN 0-387-04623-2). Springer-Verlag.

Rall, Louis B. Computational Solution of Nonlinear Operator Equations. LC 78-2378. 236p. (Orig.). 1979. Repr. of 1969 ed. 13.50 (ISBN 0-88275-667-2). Krieger.

Summer School, Babylon, Czechoslovakia, Sept. 1971. Theory of Nonlinear Operators. Kucera, M., ed. 1973. 50.00 (ISBN 0-12-427650-4). Acad Pr.

NONLINEAR OPTICS

see also Lasers

Akhmanov, S. A. & Khoklov, R. V. Problems of Nonlinear Optics. Sen, R., ed. Jacobi, N., tr. from Russian. LC 78-131021. 310p. 1972. 61.50 (ISBN 0-677-30400-5). Gordon.

Auston, D. H. & Eisenthal, K. B., eds. Ultrafast Phenomena IV. (Chemical Physics Ser.: Vol. 38). (Illus.). xvi, 509p. 1984. 29.00 (ISBN 0-387-13834-X). Springer-Verlag.

Baldwin, George C. An Introduction to Nonlinear Optics. LC 69-16517. 155p. 1969. 27.50x (ISBN 0-306-30388-4, Plenum Pr); pap. 8.95 (ISBN 0-306-20004-X). Plenum Pub.

Bloembergen, Nicolaas. Nonlinear Optics. (Frontiers in Physics Ser.: No. 21). 1965. 30.95 (ISBN 0-8053-0938-1). Benjamin-Cummings.

Bogoliubov, N. M. & Mitropolsky, Y. A. Asymptotic Methods in the Theory of Non-Linear Oscillations. 548p. 1961. 131.95 (ISBN 0-677-20050-1). Gordon.

Feld, M. S. & Letokhov, V. S., eds. Coherent Nonlinear Optics: Recent Advances. (Topics in Current Physics: Vol. 21). (Illus.). 377p. 1980. 51.00 (ISBN 0-387-10172-1). Springer-Verlag.

Haken, H. Light: Nonlinear Optics, Vol. 3. Date not set. write for info. (ISBN 0-444-86022-3). Elsevier.

Hanna, D. C., et al. Nonlinear Optics of Free Atoms & Molecules. MacAdam, D. L., ed. (Springer Series in Optical Sciences: Vol. 17). (Illus.). 1979. 50.00 (ISBN 0-387-09628-0). Springer-Verlag.

Harper, P. G. & Wherrett, B. S., eds. Non-Linear Optics. 1978. 69.00 (ISBN 0-12-325950-9). Acad Pr.

Levenson, Marc. Introduction to Nonlinear Laser Spectroscopy. LC 81-17608. (Quantum Electronics: Principles & Applications Ser.). 1982. 34.50 (ISBN 0-12-444720-1). Acad Pr.

Royal Society, London, England, et al. Optical Bi-Stability, Dynamical Nonlinearity & Photonic Logic: Proceedings of a Royal Society Discussion Meeting Held on 21-22, March 1984, Organized by S. D. Smith, A. Miller & B. S. Wherrett. Wherrett, B. S. & Smith, S. D., eds. (Illus.). 261p. 1985. text ed. 72.00x (ISBN 0-85403-239-8). Scholium Intl.

Shen, Y. R. Principles of Nonlinear Optics. LC 83-23259. (Pure & Applied Optics Ser.: 1-349). 563p. 1984. 49.95x (ISBN 0-471-88998-9, Pub. by Wiley-Interscience). Wiley.

Shen, Y. R., et al, eds. Nonlinear Infrared Generation. (Topics in Applied Physics Ser.: Vol. 16). 1977. 56.00 (ISBN 0-387-07945-9). Springer-Verlag.

Skobel'tsyn, D. V., ed. Investigations in Nonlinear Optics & Hyperacoustics. LC 73-79425. (P. N. Lebedev Physics Institute Ser.: Vol. 58). (Illus.). 163p. 1973. 55.00 (ISBN 0-306-10893-3, Consultants). Plenum Pub.

--Luminescence & Nonlinear Optics. LC 73-83897. (P. N. Lebedev Physics Institute Ser.: Vol. 59). (Illus.). 285p. 1973. 55.00 (ISBN 0-306-10896-8, Consultants). Plenum Pub.

--Nonlinear Optics. LC 72-107530. (P. N. Lebedev Physics Institute Ser.: Vol. 43). 203p. 1970. 29.50x (ISBN 0-306-10840-2, Consultants). Plenum Pub.

Zel'dovich, B. Y., et al. Principles of Phase Conjugation. (Springer Series in Optical Sciences: Vol. 42). (Illus.). 270p. 1985. 49.00 (ISBN 0-387-13458-1). Springer-Verlag.

Zernike, F. & Midwinter, J. E. Applied Nonlinear Optics. (Pure & Applied Optics Ser.). 199p. 1973. 41.95 (ISBN 0-317-31511-0). Wiley.

Zernike, Frits & Midwinter, John E. Applied Nonlinear Optics. LC 72-8369. (Pure & Applied Optics Ser.). 336p. 1973. 199p 38.95x (ISBN 0-471-98212-1, Pub. by Wiley-Interscience). Wiley.

NONLINEAR PROGRAMMING

Avriel, Mordecai. Nonlinear Programming: Analysis & Methods. (Illus.). 1976. 40.95 (ISBN 0-13-623603-0). P-H.

Bazaraa, M. S. & Shetty, C. M. Foundations of Optimization. (Lecture Notes in Economics & Mathematical Systems: Vol. 122). 1976. pap. 13.00 (ISBN 0-387-07680-8). Springer-Verlag.

Bazaraa, Mokhtar S. & Shetty, C. M. Nonlinear Programming: Theory & Algorithms. LC 78-986. 560p. 1979. text ed. 47.00 (ISBN 0-471-78610-1). Wiley.

Ben-Israel, Adi, et al. Optimality in Nonlinear Programming: A Feasible Directions Approach. LC 80-36746. (Pure & Applied Mathematics Ser.). 144p. 1981. cloth 37.50 (ISBN 0-471-08057-8, Pub. by Wiley-Interscience). Wiley.

Bradley, Stephen P., et al. Applied Mathematical Programming. LC 76-10426. (Illus.). 1977. text ed. 37.95 (ISBN 0-201-00464-X). Addison-Wesley.

Contribution to Theory & Practice of Nonlinear Parameter Optimization. (Agricultural Research Reports Ser.). 1975. pap. 38.00 (ISBN 90-220-0562-3, PDC22, PUDOC). Unipub.

Dan, S. Nonlinear & Dynamic Programming: An Introduction. LC 75-6503. (Illus.). vii, 164p. (Orig.). 1975. pap. text ed. 20.00 (ISBN 0-387-81289-X). Springer-Verlag.

Fiacco, Anthony V. Introduction to Sensitivity & Stability Analysis in Nonlinear Programming (Monograph) Analysis in Nonlinear Programming (Monograph) LC 82-11642. (Mathematics in Science & Engineering Ser.). 384p. 1983. 29.50 (ISBN 0-12-254450-1). Acad Pr.

Hasdorff, Lawrence. Gradient Optimization & Nonlinear Control. LC 75-40187. 280p. 1976. 29.50 (ISBN 0-471-35870-3). Krieger.

IFAC Workshop, Denver, Colorado, June 1979. Control Programs of Nonlinear Programming: Proceedings. Rauch, H. E., ed. (IFAC Proceedings). 130p. 1980. 42.00 (ISBN 0-08-024491-2). Pergamon.

IFAC Workshop, 4th, San Francisco, Calif., June 1983 & Rauch, H. E. Applications of Nonlinear Programming to Optimization & Control: Proceedings. LC 83-21936. (IFAC Proceedings). 230p. 1983. 45.00 (ISBN 0-08-030574-1). Pergamon.

International Conference on Computational Methods in Nonlinear Mechanics, 2nd, Univ. of Texas at Austin. Computational Methods in Nonlinear Mechanics: Selected Papers. Oden, J. T., ed. 160p. 1980. pap. 45.00 (ISBN 0-08-025068-8). Pergamon.

Kubicek, Milan & Hlavacek, Vladimir. Numerical Solution of Nonlinear Boundary Value Problems with Applications. (Illus.). 352p. 1983. 45.95 (ISBN 0-13-627364-5). P-H.

McCormick, Garth P. Nonlinear Programming: Theory, Algorithms & Applications. LC 82-16046. 444p. 1983. 51.95x (ISBN 0-471-09309-2, Pub. by Wiley Interscience). Wiley.

Mangasarian, O., et al, eds. Nonlinear Programming Four. LC 81-8007. 1981. 55.00 (ISBN 0-12-468662-1). Acad Pr.

Mangasarian, O. L., et al, eds. Nonlinear Programming Three. 1978. 65.00 (ISBN 0-12-468660-5). Acad Pr.

--Nonlinear Programming Two: Proceedings. 1975. 55.00 (ISBN 0-12-468650-8). Acad Pr.

Mangasarian, Olvi L. Nonlinear Programming. LC 79-4458. 236p. 1979. Repr. of 1969 ed. lib. bdg. 19.50 (ISBN 0-88275-919-1). Krieger.

Mathematics Research Center Symposium, University of Wisconsin, 1970. Nonlinear Programming. Rosen, J. B., et al, eds. 1970. 24.00 (ISBN 0-12-597050-1). Acad Pr.

Noor, A. K. & McComb, H. G., eds. Computational Methods in Nonlinear Structural & Solid Mechanics: Papers Presented at the Symposium on Computational Methods in Nonlinear Structural & Solid Mechanics, 6-8 October 1980. LC 80-41608. 1980. 185.00 (ISBN 0-08-027299-1). Pergamon.

Sposito, Vincent A. Linear & Nonlinear Programming. (Illus.). 270p. 1975. text ed. 14.95x (ISBN 0-8138-1015-9). Iowa St U Pr.

Whittle, Peter. Optimization under Constraints: Theory & Applications of Nonlinear Programming. LC 75-149574. (Wiley Series in Probability & Mathematical Statistics). pap. 62.80 (ISBN 0-317-29443-1, 2024288). Bks Demand UMI.

NONLINEAR THEORIES

see also Differential Equations, Nonlinear; System Analysis

Amann, H., et al, eds. Applications of Nonlinear Analysis in the Physical Sciences. LC 80-21067. (Surveys & References Ser.: No. 6). 352p. 1981. text ed. 81.95 (ISBN 0-273-08501-8). Pitman Pub MA.

Ansorge, R., et al, eds. Iterative Solution of Nonlinear Systems of Equations, Oberwolfach, FRG, 1982: Proceedings. (Lecture Notes in Mathematics: Vol. 953). 202p. 1982. pap. 14.00 (ISBN 0-387-11602-8). Springer-Verlag.

Atteia, M., et al. Nonlinear Problems of Analysis in Geometry & Mechanics. LC 80-21647. (Research Notes in Mathematics: No. 46). 288p. (Orig.). 1981. pap. text ed. 27.00 (ISBN 0-273-08493-3). Pitman Pub MA.

Aubin, Jean-Pierre & Ekeland, Ivar. Applied Nonlinear Analysis. (Pure & Applied Mathematics Ser.: 1237). 518p. 1984. 47.50x (ISBN 0-471-05998-6, Pub. by Wiley-Interscience). Wiley.

Aubin, T. Nonlinear Analysis on Manifolds: Monge-Ampere Equations. (Grundlehren der mathematischen Wiszenschaften: Vol. 252). 204p. 1983. 37.50 (ISBN 0-387-90704-1). Springer-Verlag.

Baker, Christopher T. & Phillips, Chris. The Numerical Solution of Nonlinear Problems. (Illus.). 1981. 42.50x (ISBN 0-19-853354-3). Oxford U Pr.

Barbu, V. Nonlinear Semigroups & Differential Equations in Banach Spaces. 252p. 1976. 32.50x (ISBN 90-286-0205-4). Sijthoff & Noordhoff.

Basov, N. G., ed. The Dissipation of Electromagnetic Waves in Plasmas. McNeill, Donald H., tr. from Russian. (Lebedev Trudy Ser.: Vol. 92). 109p. 1982. 49.50 (ISBN 0-306-10969-7, Consultants). Plenum Pub.

Bazaraa, Mokhtar S. & Shetty, C. M. Nonlinear Programming: Theory & Algorithms. LC 78-986. 560p. 1979. text ed. 47.00 (ISBN 0-471-78610-1). Wiley.

Bellman, Richard E. Methods of Nonlinear Analysis. (Mathematics in Science & Engineering Ser.: Vol. 61). Vol. 1 1970. 45.00 (ISBN 0-12-084901-1); Vol. 2. 1973. 35.00 (ISBN 0-12-084902-X). Acad Pr.

Bishop, A. R., et al. Nonlinear Problems: Present & Future. (Mathematical Studies: Vol. 61). 484p. 1982. 64.00 (ISBN 0-444-86395-8, North-Holland). Elsevier.

Blaquiere, Austin. Nonlinear System Analysis. (Electrical Science Ser.). 1966. 75.00 (ISBN 0-12-104350-9). Acad Pr.

Brackbill, Jeremiah U. & Cohen, Bruce I., eds. Multiple Time Scales. (Computational Techniques Ser.). Date not set. 75.00 (ISBN 0-12-123420-7). Acad Pr.

Byrne, George D. & Hall, Charles A., eds. Numerical Solution of Systems of Nonlinear Algebraic Equations. 1973. 60.00 (ISBN 0-12-148950-7). Acad Pr.

Casti, John L. Nonlinear System Theory. (Mathematics Science & Engineering Ser.). 1985. 45.00 (ISBN 0-12-163452-3). Acad Pr.

Chandra, Jagdish, ed. Chaos in Nonlinear Dynamical Systems. LC 84-52603. viii, 191p. 1984. text ed. 25.00 (ISBN 0-89871-052-9). Soc Indus Appl Math.

Chang, K. W. & Howes, F. A. Nonlinear Singular Perturbation Phenomena: Theory & Applications. (Applied Mathematical Sciences Ser.: Vol. 56). (Illus.). viii, 180p. 1984. pap. 18.80 (ISBN 0-387-96066-X). Springer-Verlag.

Claro, F., ed. Nonlinear Phenomena in Physics. (Springer Proceedings in Physics: Vol. 3). (Illus.). ix, 441p. 1985. 35.00 (ISBN 0-387-15273-3). Springer-Verlag.

Cronin, Jane. Fixed Points & Topological Degree in Nonlinear Analysis. LC 63-21550. (Mathematical Surveys Ser.: Vol. 11). 198p. 1982. pap. 30.00 (ISBN 0-8218-1511-3, SURV-11). Am Math.

Davidson, R. J. Methods in Nonlinear Plasma Theory. (Pure & Applied Physics Ser.). 1972. 63.00 (ISBN 0-12-205450-4). Acad Pr.

Davis, M. H. Stochastic Control & Nonlinear Filtering. (Tata Institute Lectures on Mathematics Ser.). iv, 109p. 1984. pap. 7.10 (ISBN 0-387-13343-7). Springer-Verlag.

Debnath, L. Advances in Nonlinear Waves, Vol. 2. (Research Notes in Mathematics Ser.: No. 111). 350p. 1985. pap. text ed. 25.95 (ISBN 0-273-08648-0). Pitman Pub MA.

Debnath, L., ed. Advances in Nonlinear Waves, Vol. 1. (Research Notes Ser.: No. 95). 350p. 1984. pap. text ed. 25.95 (ISBN 0-273-08609-X). Pitman Pub MA.

Deimling, K. Nonlinear Functional Analysis. (Illus.). xiv, 450p. 1985. 39.00 (ISBN 0-387-13928-1). Springer-Verlag.

Doebner, H. D. & Palev, T. D., eds. Twistor Geometry & Non-Linear Systems: Proceedings, Primorsko, Bulgaria, 1980. (Lecture Notes in Mathematics Ser.: Vol. 970). 216p. 1982. pap. 14.00 (ISBN 0-387-11972-8). Springer-Verlag.

Goessel, M. Nonlinear Time-Discrete Systems: A General Approach by Nonlinear Superposition. (Lecture Notes in Control & Information Science: Vol. 41). 112p. 1982. pap. 10.00 (ISBN 0-387-11914-0). Springer-Verlag.

Hermann, Robert, ed. Ames Research Center (NASA) Conference on Geometric Nonlinear Wave Theory, 1976. (Lie Groups; History, Frontiers & Applications Ser.: Vol. 6). 1977. pap. 17.00x (ISBN 0-915692-19-8). Math Sci Pr.

Holden, Arun V., ed. CHAOS. (Nonlinear Science: Theory & Applications Ser.). (Illus.). 304p. 1986. 42.00 (ISBN 0-7190-1811-0, Pub. by Manchester Univ Pr); pap. 17.00 (ISBN 0-317-27025-7). Longwood Pub Group.

Horsthemke, W., et al, eds. Fluctuations & Sensitivity in Nonequilibrium Systems: Proceedings of an International Conference, University of Texas, Austin, TX, March 12-16, 1984. (Proceedings in Physics Ser.: Vol. 1). (Illus.). 290p. 1984. 29.00 (ISBN 0-387-13736-X). Springer-Verlag.

Horton, C. W., Jr. & Reichl, L. E., eds. Statistical Physics & Chaos in Fusion Plasmas. LC 83-19649. (Nonequilibrium Problems in the Physical Science & Biology Ser.: 1-479). 361p. 1984. 85.00 (ISBN 0-471-88310-7, Pub. by Wiley-Interscience). Wiley.

Kalman, G. & Feix, M. R., eds. Nonlinear Effects in Plasmas. 530p. 1969. 102.95 (ISBN 0-677-12970-X). Gordon.

Karpman, V. I. Non-Linear Waves in Dispersive Media. Cap, Ferdinand, tr. 1975. text ed. 35.00 (ISBN 0-08-017720-4). Pergamon.

Knops, R. J., ed. Nonlinear Analysis & Mechanics: Heriot-Watt Symposium, Vol. 3. (Research Notes in Mathematics Ser.: No. 30). 173p. (Orig.). 1979. pap. text ed. 22.95 (ISBN 0-273-08432-1). Pitman Pub MA.

--Nonlinear Analysis & Mechanics: Heriot-Watt Symposium, Vol. 4. LC 78-309110. (Research Notes in Mathematics Ser.: No. 39). 212p. (Orig.). 1979. pap. text ed. 23.95 (ISBN 0-273-08461-5). Pitman Pub MA.

Krasnosel'skii, M. M. & Zabreiko, P. P. Geometrical Methods of Nonlinear Analysis. (Grundlehren der Mathematischen Wissenschaften: Vol. 263). xix, 409p. 1984. 48.00 (ISBN 0-387-12945-6). Springer-Verlag.

Krishnan, Venkatarama. Nonlinear Filtering & Smoothing: Introductionto Martingales, Stochastic Integrals & Estimation. LC 83-16712. 314p. 1984. 37.50x (ISBN 0-471-89840-6, Pub. by Wiley-Interscience). Wiley.

Lakshmikantham, V., ed. Nonlinear Phenomena in Mathematical Science: (Symposium) LC 82-20734. 1982. 94.50 (ISBN 0-12-434170-5). Acad Pr.

--Nonlinear Systems & Applications: An International Conference. 1977. 65.00 (ISBN 0-12-434150-0). Acad Pr.

Lakshmikanthan, V., ed. Applied Nonlinear Analysis. LC 79-10237. 1979. 65.00 (ISBN 0-12-434180-2). Acad Pr.

Leigh, J. R. Essentials of Nonlinear Control Theory. (IEE Topics in Control Ser.: No. 2). 104p. 1983. pap. 22.00 (ISBN 0-906048-96-6, TC-002). Inst Elect Eng.

Mintz, Stephan & Perlmutter, Arnold, eds. Orbis Scientiae, Nineteen Seventy-Seven: The Significance of Nonlinearity in the Natural Sciences. (Studies in the Natural Sciences Ser.: Vol. 13). 1977. 69.50x (ISBN 0-306-36913-3, Plenum Pr). Plenum Pub.

Miwa, T. & Jimbo, M., eds. Non-Linear Integrable Systems-Classical Theory & Quantum Theory: Proceedings of RIMS Symposium, Kyoto, Japan, May 13-16, 1981. vi, 290p. 1982. 29.00x (ISBN 9971-950-32-4, Pub. by World Sci Singapore). Taylor & Francis.

Olowinski, R. Numerical Methods for Non-Linear Variational Problems. (Tata Institute Lectures on Mathematics Ser.). 240p. 1980. pap. 10.00 (ISBN 0-387-08774-5). Springer-Verlag.

Pascali, D. & Sburlan, S. Nonlinear Mappings of Monotone Type. 351p. 1979. 43.00x (ISBN 90-286-0118-X). Sijthoff & Noordhoff.

Reintjes, John F. Nonlinear Optical Parametric Processes in Liquids & Gases. LC 82-11603. 1984. 67.00 (ISBN 0-12-585980-5). Acad Pr.

Rudenko, O. V. & Soluyan, S. I., eds. Theoretical Foundations of Nonlinear Acoustics. LC 77-1512. (Studies in Soviet Sciences - Physical Sciences Ser). (Illus.). 274p. 1977. 49.50x (ISBN 0-306-10933-6, Consultants). Plenum Pub.

Rugh, Wilson J. Nonlinear System Theory: The Volterra-Wiener Approach. LC 80-8874. (Johns Hopkins Series in Information Sciences & Systems). 352p. 1981. text ed. 32.50x (ISBN 0-8018-2549-0). Johns Hopkins.

Sanchez, N., ed. Nonlinear Equations in Classical & Quantum Field Theory. (Lecture Notes in Physics: Vol. 226). vii, 400p. 1985. pap. 26.80 (ISBN 0-387-15213-X). Springer-Verlag.

Schetzen, Martin. The Volterra & Weiner Theories of Nonlinear Systems. LC 79-13421. 531p. 1980. 49.95x (ISBN 0-471-04455-5, Pub. by Wiley-Interscience). Wiley.

Schmidt, Gunter & Tondl, Ales. Non-Linear Vibrations. 400p. Date not set. price not set (ISBN 0-521-26698-X). Cambridge U Pr.

Schwartz, Jacob T. Nonlinear Functional Analysis. (Notes on Mathematics & Its Applications Ser.). 244p. 1969. 44.00x (ISBN 0-677-01500-3). Gordon.

Siljak, Dragoslav D. Nonlinear Systems: The Parameter Analysis & Design. LC 68-26853. pap. 159.50 (ISBN 0-317-08564-6, 2006354). Bks Demand UMI.

Singh, S. P. & Burry, J. H., eds. Nonlinear Analysis & Applications. (Lecture Notes in Pure & Applied Mathematics Ser.: Vol. 80). (Illus.). 488p. 59.75 (ISBN 0-8247-1790-2). Dekker.

Singh, S. P., et al, eds. Topological Methods in Nonlinear Functional Analysis. LC 83-11824. (Contemporary Mathematics Ser.: Vol. 21). 218p. 1983. pap. text ed. 20.00 (ISBN 0-8218-5023-7). Am Math.

Symposium on Nonlinear Elasticity, University of Wisconsin, April, 1973. Nonlinear Elasticity: Proceedings. Dickey, R. W., ed. 1973. 24.00 (ISBN 0-12-215150-X). Acad Pr.

Takeno, S, ed. Dynamical Problems in Soliton Systems. (Springer Series in Synergetics: Vol. 30). (Illus.). 310p. 1985. 32.00 (ISBN 0-387-15372-1). Springer-Verlag.

Toda, M. Theory of Nonlinear Lattices. (Springer Series in Solid-State Sciences: Vol. 20). (Illus.). 220p. 1981. 38.00 (ISBN 0-387-10224-8). Springer-Verlag.

Tsytovich, V. N. Nonlinear Effects in Plasma. LC 69-12545. 332p. 1970. 55.00x (ISBN 0-306-30425-2, Plenum Pr). Plenum Pub.

Vinti, C., ed. Nonlinear Analysis & Optimization. (Lecture Notes in Mathematics Ser.: Vol. 1107). v, 214p. 1984. pap. 11.00 (ISBN 0-387-13903-6). Springer-Verlag.

Virdi, Kuldeep S. Non-Linear Numerical Methods in Civil Engineering. 256p. 1986. 40.00x (ISBN 0-246-11753-2, Pub. by Granada England). Sheridan.

Vojtasek, S. & Janac, K. Solution of Non-Linear Systems. Smart, G. D., ed. Dolan, Pavel, tr. from Czech. (Illus.). 1970. 14.75 (ISBN 0-8088-3929-2). Davey.

Weiland, J. C. & Wilhelmsson, H. Coherent Non-Linear Interaction of Waves in Plasmas. 1977. text ed. 54.00 (ISBN 0-08-020964-5). Pergamon.

White, R. E. An Introduction to the Finite Element Method with Applications to Nonlinear Problems. 320p. 1985. 34.95 (ISBN 0-471-80909-8). Wiley.

Woodroofe, M. Nonlinear Renewal Theory in Sequential Analysis. LC 81-84856. (CBMS-NSF Regional Conference Ser.: No. 39). v, 119p. 1982. 16.00 (ISBN 0-89871-180-0). Soc Indus Appl Math.

Yavin, Y. Numerical Studies in Nonlinear Filtering. (Lecture Notes in Control & Information Sciences Ser.: Vol. 65). vi, 273p. 1985. pap. 13.00 (ISBN 0-387-13958-3). Springer-Verlag.

Zacks, S. Parametric Statistical Inference: Basic Theory & Modern Approaches. LC 80-41715. (I.S. in Nonlinear Mathematics Series; Theory & Applications: Vol. 4). 400p. 1981. 47.00 (ISBN 0-08-026468-9). Pergamon.

NON-NEWTONIAN FLUIDS

Coleman, B. D., et al. Viscometric Flows of Non-Newtonian Fluids: Theory & Experiment. (Springer Tracts in Natural Philosophy Ser.: Vol. 5). (Illus.). 1966. 21.00 (ISBN 0-387-03672-5). Springer-Verlag.

Crochet, M. J. Numerical Simulation of Non-Newtonian Flow. (Rheology Ser.: Vol. 1). 1984. 65.50 (ISBN 0-444-42291-9). Elsevier.

Schowalter, William R. Mechanics of Non-Newtonian Fluids. LC 76-51440. 1978. text ed. 62.00 (ISBN 0-08-021778-8). Pergamon.

NONNUTRITIVE SWEETNERS

see also Sugar Substitutes

Business Communications Staff. Sugar, Sweeteners & Substitutes. 1983. 1250.00 (ISBN 0-89336-091-0, C-005R). BCC.

Grenby, T. H., et al, eds. Developments in Sweeteners, Vol. 2. (Illus.). 264p. 1983. 52.00 (ISBN 0-85334-202-4, I-206-83, Pub. by Elsevier Applied Sci England). Elsevier.

Hough, C. A., et al, eds. Developments in Sweeteners, Vol. 1. (Illus.). 192p. 1979. 42.75 (ISBN 0-85334-820-0, Pub. by Elsevier Applied Sci England). Elsevier.

NONPARAMETRIC STATISTICS

see also Order Statistics

Bueringer, Helmut & Schriever, Karl-Heinz. Nonparametric Sequential Selection Procedures. 500p. 1981. pap. 35.00x (ISBN 0-8176-3021-X). Birkhauser.

Conover, W. J. Practical Nonparametric Statistics. 2nd ed. LC 80-301. (Probability & Mathematical Statistics Ser.). 493p. 1980. 43.50 (ISBN 0-471-02867-3). Wiley.

Daniel, Wayne W. Applied Nonparametric Statistics. LC 77-74515. (Illus.). 1978. text ed. 32.50 (ISBN 0-395-25795-6); instructors manual 1.50 (ISBN 0-395-25796-4). HM.

Denker, Manfred. Theory in Nonparametric: Asymptotic Distribution. Fischer, Gerd, ed. 210p. 1985. pap. 13.00 (ISBN 3-528-08905-9, 99040031X, Pub. by Vieweg & Sohn Germany). Heyden.

Devroye, Luc & Gyorfi, Laszlo. Nonparametric Density Estimation: The L1 View. (Wiley Series in Probability & Mathematical Statistics - Probability & Mathematical Statistics Section). 368p. 1985. text ed. 37.95x (ISBN 0-471-81646-9, Pub. by Wiley-Interscience). Wiley.

Ferguson, George A. Nonparametric Trend Analysis. LC 65-13086. pap. 20.00 (ISBN 0-317-26489-3, 2023830). Bks Demand UMI.

Gnedenko, B. V. & Puri, M. L., eds. Nonparametric Statistical Inference, 2 Vols. (Colloquia Mathematica Societatis Janos Bolyai Ser.: Vol. 32). 910p. 1983. 144.75 (ISBN 0-444-86196-3, I-095-83, North Holland). Elsevier.

Henley, Stephen. Nonparametric Geostatistics. LC 81-7177. 160p. 1981. 34.95x (ISBN 0-470-27285-6). Halsted Pr.

Hollander, Myles & Wolfe, Douglas A. Nonparametric Statistical Methods. LC 72-11960. (Ser. in Probability & Mathematical Statistics). (Illus.). 503p. 1973. 38.95x (ISBN 0-471-40635-X, Pub. by Wiley-Interscience). Wiley.

Krishnaiah, P. R. & Sen, P. K., eds. Nonparametric Methods. 1985. 115.00 (ISBN 0-444-86871-2). Elsevier.

Lehmann, E. L. Nonparametrics: Statistical Methods Based on Ranks. LC 72-93538. 1975. text ed. 40.00x (ISBN 0-8162-4994-6). Holden-Day.

Puri, M. L. & Sen, P. K. Nonparametric Methods in Multivariate Analysis. LC 79-129052. (Ser. in Probability & Mathematical Statistics). 440p. 1971. 57.95x (ISBN 0-471-70240-4, Pub. by Wiley-Interscience). Wiley.

Puri, M. L., ed. Nonparametric Techniques in Statistical Inference. LC 74-116750. (Illus.). 1970. 99.50 (ISBN 0-521-07817-2). Cambridge U Pr.

Randles, Ronald H. & Wolfe, Douglas A. Introduction to the Theory of Nonparametric Statistics. LC 79-411. (Ser. in Probability & Mathematical Statistics). 450p. 1979. 48.50 (ISBN 0-471-04245-5, Pub. by Wiley-Interscience). Wiley.

Rao, Prakasa. Nonparametric Functional Estimation. 1983. 70.00 (ISBN 0-12-564020-X). Acad Pr.

Runyon, Richard P. Nonparametric Statistics: A Contemporary Approach. LC 76-55635. 1977. pap. text ed. 12.95 (ISBN 0-201-06547-9). Addison-Wesley.

Tapia, Richard A. & Thompson, James R. Nonparametric Probability Density Estimation. LC 77-17249. (Illus.). 1978. text ed. 22.00x (ISBN 0-8018-2031-6). Johns Hopkins.

Vargo, Donald L. Nonparametric Statistics: Quick & Easy on the HP-41. LC 84-81969. (Educalc Technical Ser.). 166p. 1984. pap. 16.95 (ISBN 0-936356-03-0, M-307). EduCALC Pubns.

NON-VASCULAR PLANTS

see Cryptogams

NONWOVEN FABRICS

Bhatnagar, ViJay M. Nonwovens & Disposables: New Technical-Marketing Developments. 86p. 1978. pap. 15.00 (ISBN 0-87762-256-6). Technomic.

Bhatnagar, ViJay M., ed. Nonwovens & Disposables: Proceedings of the First Canadian Symposium of Nonwovens & Disposables. LC 78-68591. (Illus.). 1978. pap. 9.95 (ISBN 0-87762-268-X). Technomic.

Dembeck, Adeline A. Guidebook to Man-Made Textile Fibers & Textured Yarns of the World: Film-To-Yarn Non-Wovens. 3rd ed. LC 68-28677. 1969. leatherette 11.00 (ISBN 0-911546-01-4). United Piece.

Weiner, Jack, et al. Nonwoven Fabrics. Incl. Vol. 1. General & Testing, Properties & Finishing, Supplement No. 2; Vol. 2. Forming Methods, Supplement No. 2; Vol. 3. Chemical & Mechanical Bonding, Supplement No. 3; Vol. 4. Uses. LC 74-100622. 1974. 15.00 ea. (ISBN 0-87010-027-0). Inst Paper Chem.

NORMAN HORSE

see Percheron Horse

NORMED LINEAR SPACES

Day, M. M. Normed Linear Spaces. 3rd ed. (Ergebnisse der Mathematik und Ihrer Grenzgebiete: Vol. 21). viii, 211p. 1973. 33.00 (ISBN 0-387-06148-7). Springer-Verlag.

The Geometry of Metric & Linear Spaces: Proceedings. Kelly, L. M., ed. (Lecture Notes in Mathematics: Vol. 490). x, 244p. 1975. pap. 17.00 (ISBN 0-387-07417-1). Springer-Verlag.

Singer, I. Best Approximation in Normed Linear Spaces by Elements of Linear Subspaces. LC 73-110407. (Grundlehren der Mathematischen Wissenschaften: Vol. 171). 1970. 46.00 (ISBN 0-387-05116-3). Springer-Verlag.

NORMED RINGS

see Banach Algebras

NORTH AMERICA–CLIMATE–MAPS

Bryson, R. A. & Hare, F., eds. Climates of North America. LC 74-477739. (World Survey of Climatology Ser.: Vol. 11). 420p. 1974. 113.00 (ISBN 0-444-41062-7). Elsevier.

NORTHERN LIGHTS

see Auroras

NORWEGIAN ELKHOUND

see Dogs–Breeds–Norwegian Elkhound

NOSTOCACEAE

Drouet, F. Revision of the Nostocaceae with Constricted Trichomes. (Beihefte zur Nova Hedwigia: No. 57). (Illus.). 1978. text ed. 35.00 (ISBN 3-7682-5457-7). Lubrecht & Cramer.

Drouet, Francis. Revision of Nostocaceae with Cylindrical Trichomes. new ed. (Illus.). 256p. 1973. 18.95x (ISBN 0-02-844060-9). Hafner.

NOTATION, MATHEMATICAL

see Mathematical Notation

NOVAE

see Stars, New

NSC-800 (MICROPROCESSOR)

Alford, Roger C. The NSC800 Microprocessor Cookbook. (Illus.). 280p. 1983. 18.95 (ISBN 0-8306-0502-9, 1502); pap. 12.95 (ISBN 0-8306-1502-4). TAB Bks.

NUCLEAR AIRCRAFT

Grey, Jerry. Aerospace Technology & Commercial Nuclear Power. 19.50 (ISBN 0-915928-69-8). AIAA.

NUCLEAR ASTROPHYSICS

Arnett, W. B., et al, eds. Nucleosynthesis. LC 67-28241. 282p. 1968. 80.95 (ISBN 0-677-11580-6). Gordon.

Audouze, Jean & Vauclair, Sylvie. An Introduction to Nuclear Astrophysics: The Formation & Evolution of Matter in the Universe. (Geophysics & Astrophysics Monographs: No. 18). 1980. lib. bdg. 39.50 (ISBN 90-277-1012-0, Pub. by Reidel Holland); pap. 21.00 (ISBN 90-277-1053-8, Pub. by Reidel Holland). Kluwer Academic.

Chretien, M. & Lipworth, E., eds. Brandeis University Summer Institute in Theoretical Physics: 1969 Lectures: Atomic Physics & Astrophysics, 2 vols. Vol. 1, 228p. 1971 ed. 66.00 (ISBN 0-677-14900-X); Vol. 2, 350p. 1973 ed. 80.00 (ISBN 0-677-14910-7). Gordon.

Greisen, Kenneth. The Physics of Cosmic X-Ray, Gamma-Ray & Particle Sources. 2nd ed. Cameron, A. G. W. & Field, G. B., eds. LC 78-135063. (Topics in Astrophysics & Space Physics Ser.). (Illus.). 124p. 1971. 28.95 (ISBN 0-677-03380-X). Gordon.

Hazard, C. & Mitton, S., eds. Active Galactic Nuclei. LC 78-67426. 1979. 49.50 (ISBN 0-521-22494-2). Cambridge U Pr.

Krueger, A. Physics of Solar Continuum Radio Bursts. 200p. 1973. 26.50x (ISBN 0-685-39164-7). Adlers Foreign Bks.

Shen, Benjamin S. & Merker, Milton, eds. Spallation Nuclear Reactions & Their Applications. new ed. (Astrophysics & Space Science Library: No. 59). 1976. lib. bdg. 39.50 (ISBN 90-277-0746-4, Pub. by Reidel Holland). Kluwer Academic.

Trefil, James S. The Moment of Creation: Big Bang Physics from Before the First Millisecond to the Present Universe. (Illus.). 240p. 1983. 15.95 (ISBN 0-684-17963-6, ScribT). Scribner.

NUCLEAR BOMB SHELTERS

Baum, G. The Earth Shelter Handbook. 15.95 (ISBN 0-937816-13-2). Tech Data.

McCarthy, Walton W. The Nuclear Shelterist. 300p. 1985. 22.50 (ISBN 0-89962-483-9). Todd & Honeywell.

Rudman, Jack. Shelter Inspector (Civil Defense) (Career Examination Ser.: C-737). (Cloth bdg. avail. on request). pap. 12.00 (ISBN 0-8373-0737-6). Natl Learning.

Teague, Edward H. Fallout Shelter Architecture: A Bibliography. (Architecture Ser.: Bibliography A 1326). 1985. pap. 2.00 (ISBN 0-89028-276-5). Vance Biblios.

NUCLEAR CHEMISTRY

Here are entered works on the application of chemical techniques to the study of the structure and properties of atomic nuclei, their transformations and reactions. Works on the chemical effects of high energy radiation on matter are entered under Radiation chemistry. Works on the chemical properties of radioactive substances and their use in chemical studies are entered under Radiochemistry.

see also Nuclear Physics; Radiation Chemistry; Radiochemistry

Arnikar, Hari J. Essentials of Nuclear Chemistry. LC 81-6818. 335p. 1982. 19.95 (ISBN 0-470-27176-0). Halsted Pr.

Benedict, Manson, et al. Nuclear Chemical Engineering. 2nd ed. (Illus.). 1008p. 1981. text ed. 49.00 (ISBN 0-07-004531-3). McGraw.

British Nuclear Energy Society, ed. Chemical Nuclear Data-Measurements & Applications. 296p. 1971. 90.00x (ISBN 0-901948-89-6, Pub. by Brit Nuclear England). State Mutual Bk.

Carnall, William T. & Choppin, Gregory R., eds. Plutonium Chemistry. LC 83-6057. (Symposium Ser.: No. 216). 484p. 1983. lib. bdg. 51.95 (ISBN 0-8412-0772-0). Am Chemical.

Cindro, N., ed. Nuclear Molecular Phenomena: Proceedings of the International Conference on Resonances in Heavy Ion Reactions, Yuogslavia-1977. 1978. 66.00 (ISBN 0-444-85116-X, North-Holland). Elsevier.

Dyer, A., ed. Gas Chemistry in Nuclear Reactors & Large Industrial Plant. 281p. 1980. 75.00x (ISBN 0-85501-449-0, Pub. by Brit Nuclear England). State Mutual Bk.

Erdtmann, Gerhard. Neutron Activation Tables. (Topical Presentations in Nuclear Chemistry Ser.: Vol. 6). (Illus.). 146p. 1976. 57.50x (ISBN 3-527-25693-8). VCH Pubs.

Friedlander, Gerhart, et al. Nuclear & Radiochemistry. 3rd ed. LC 81-1000. 684p. 1981. 54.95 (ISBN 0-471-28021-6, Pub. by Wiley-Interscience); pap. 31.95 (ISBN 0-471-86255-X, Pub. by Wiley-Interscience). Wiley.

Gamow, George & Gritchfield, C. L. Theory of Atomic Nucleus & Nuclear Energy-Sources. LC 83-45435. Repr. of 1949 ed. 49.50 (ISBN 0-404-20105-9). AMS Pr.

Hot Atom Chemistry Status Report: Proceedings, Vienna, 1974. (Panel Proceedings Ser.). (Illus.). 332p. 1976. pap. 34.25 (ISBN 92-0-141075-1, ISP393, IAEA). Unipub.

Keller, Cornelius. The Chemistry of Transuranium Elements. LC 79-173366. (Topical Presentations in Nuclear Chemistry Ser.: Vol. 3). (Illus.). 675p. 1971. 110.60x (ISBN 3-527-25389-0). VCH Pubs.

Krugers, Jan, ed. Instrumentation in Applied Nuclear Chemistry. LC 79-183561. (Illus.). 383p. 1973. 55.00x (ISBN 0-306-30562-3, Plenum Pr). Plenum Pub.

Lambrecht, Richard M. & Morcos, Nabil, eds. Nuclear & Radiochemistry Applications. LC 82-9111. (Illus.). 592p. 1982. 94.00 (ISBN 0-08-027544-3, E125); 68.00 (ISBN 0-08-029389-1). Pergamon.

Matsuura, T., ed. Hot Atom Chemistry: Recent Trends & Applications in the Physical & Life Sciences & Technology. (Studies in Physical & Theoretical Chemistry: no. 31). 532p. 1984. 111.75 (ISBN 0-444-99623-0, I-140-84). Elsevier.

Moses, A. J. Nuclear Techniques in Analytical Chemistry. LC 64-15736. (International Series on Analytical Chemistry: Vol. 20). 1965. 11.30 (ISBN 0-08-010695-1). Pergamon.

National Research Council - Committee For The Survey Of Chemistry. Nuclear Chemistry: A Current Review. 1966. pap. 4.00 (ISBN 0-309-01292-9). Natl Acad Pr.

Proceedings of the 11th Symposium on Nucleic Acids Chemistry, Japan 1983. (Nucleic Acids Symposium Ser.: No. 12). (Illus.). 224p. (Orig.). 1983. pap. 30.00 (ISBN 0-904147-53-3). IRL Pr.

Seaborg, G. T. & Loveland, W., eds. Nuclear Chemistry. LC 81-23522. (Benchmark Papers in Physical Chemistry & Chemical Physics: Vol. 5). 489p. 1982. 79.00 (ISBN 0-87933-422-3). Van Nos Reinhold.

Some Aspects of Chemical Methods in Nuclear Studies. (Atomic Energy Review Ser.: Suppl. No. 2). 274p. 1982. pap. 34.25 (ISBN 0-686-81408-8, IAER2S, IAEA). Unipub.

Tenth Symposium on Nucleic Acids Chemistry, Japan 1982: Proceedings. (Nucleic Acids Symposium Ser.: No. 11). 296p. 1982. pap. 30.00 (ISBN 0-904147-48-7). IRL Pr.

Tominaga, T. & Tachikawa, E. Modern Hot-Atom Chemistry & Its Applications. (Inorganic Chemistry Concepts Ser.). (Illus.). 160p. 1981. 52.00 (ISBN 0-387-10715-0). Springer-Verlag.

Whitson, Gary, ed. Nuclear-Cytoplasmic Interactions in the Cell Cycle. (Cell Biology Ser.). 1980. 59.50 (ISBN 0-12-747750-0). Acad Pr.

NUCLEAR COLLISIONS

Johnson, Charles W. The Cause & Effects of Nuclear Explosions. (Illus.). 310p. 1985. 8.95 (ISBN 0-932989-00-4); lib. bdg. 11.95 (ISBN 0-932989-01-2); text ed. 9.95 (ISBN 0-932989-02-0); tchr's. ed. avail. (ISBN 0-932989-03-9). Johnson Liter.

Rapaport, J., et al, eds. Neutron-Nucleus Collisions. A Probe of Nuclear Structure: Burr Oak State Park, Ohio, 1984. LC 84-73216. (AIP Conference Proceedings Ser.: No. 124). 548p. 1985. lib. bdg. 52.00 (ISBN 0-88318-323-4). Am Inst Physics.

NUCLEAR COUNTERS

see also Radiation Dosimetry; Radioactive Prospecting; Scintillation Counters; Semiconductor Nuclear Counters

Helman, Edith Z. Basic Principles of Nuclear Counting: A Programmed Text. 1975. 10.00 (ISBN 0-930914-01-5). Sci Newsletters.

Low-Background High-Efficiency Geiger-Muller Counter. (Technical Reports Ser.: No. 33). (Illus.). 32p. 1964. pap. 6.25 (ISBN 92-0-135064-3, IDC33, IAEA). Unipub.

Miller, Dudley G. Radioactivity & Radiation Detection. LC 70-146446. (Illus.). 122p. 1972. 35.75x (ISBN 0-677-01490-2). Gordon.

Neutron Monitoring. (Proceedings Ser.). (Illus.). 705p. 1967. pap. 45.00 (ISBN 92-0-020067-2, ISP136, IAEA). Unipub.

Ouseph, P. J. Introduction to Nuclear Radiation Detectors. LC 75-15744. (Illus.). 194p. 1975. 29.50x (ISBN 0-306-35302-4, Plenum Pr). Plenum Pub.

Smith, P. C., et al. The Use of Nuclear Meters in Soils Investigations. LC 67-13261. (American Society for Testing & Materials Ser.: Special Technical Publication, No. 412). pap. 35.50 (ISBN 0-317-11246-5, 2000938). Bks Demand UMI.

NUCLEAR ENERGY

see also Atomic Bomb; Masers; Nuclear Engineering; Nuclear Fission; Nuclear Industry; Nuclear Reactors

Addinall, Eric & Ellington, Henry. Nuclear Power in Perspective. 200p. 1982. 26.50 (ISBN 0-89397-110-3). Nichols Pub.

AEC Technical Information Center. Symposium on Nuclear Energy & Latin American Development: Proceedings. 166p. 1968. pap. 15.00 (ISBN 0-87079-358-6, PRNC-112). DOE.

Alexanderson, E. Pauline & Wagner, Harvey A., eds. FERMI-I: New Age for Nuclear Power. LC 78-67176. (ANS Monograph). (Illus.). 1979. 27.80 (ISBN 0-89448-017-0, 690004). Am Nuclear Soc.

Alston, Liviu L., ed. High-Voltage Technology. (United Kingdom Atomic Energy Authority, Harwell Post-Graduate Ser.). (Illus.). pap. 106.50 (ISBN 0-317-09403-3, 2051952). Bks Demand UMI.

American Assembly. The Nuclear Power Controversy. Murphy, Arthur W., ed. LC 76-40017. pap. 36.50 (ISBN 0-317-10099-8, 2015398). Bks Demand UMI.

American Society for Materials & Testing. Manual of Coating Work for Light-Water Nuclear Power Primary Containment & Other Safety-Related Facilities, 1st ed. (Illus.). 201p. 1979. 57.50x (ISBN 0-8031-0394-8, 03-401079-14). ASTM.

Argentesi, F. & Avenhaus, R., eds. Mathematical & Statistical Methods in Nuclear Safeguards. (Ispra Courses on Nuclear Engineering & Technology Ser.). 458p. 1984. 87.50 (ISBN 3-7186-0124-9). Harwood Academic.

Arnott, D. G. Our Nuclear Adventure. 1958. 6.00 (ISBN 0-8022-0040-0). Philos Lib.

Aron, Raymond. The Great Debate: Theories of Nuclear Strategy. Pawel, Ernst, tr. from Fr. LC 81-495. ix, 265p. 1981. Repr. of 1965 ed. lib. bdg. 32.50x (ISBN 0-313-22851-5, ARGR). Greenwood.

Asimov, Isaac. Worlds Within Worlds: The Story of Nuclear Energy. 1980. 10.95 (ISBN 0-89875-000-8, Pub. by U Pr Pacific); pap. 7.95 (ISBN 0-89875-001-6, Pub by U Pr Pacific). Intl Spec Bk.

Atomic Energy Review: Commemorative Issue. 102p. 1967. pap. 8.75 (ISBN 92-0-079067-4, IAER4C, IAEA). Unipub.

Atomic Energy Review Cumulative Index, Vol. 1-10, 1963-72. 70p. 1973. pap. (ISP/66, IAEA). Unipub.

Atomic Energy Review, Molybdenum: Physico-Chemical Properties of Its Compounds & Alloys. (Special Issue Ser.: No. 7). 714p. 1980. pap. 87.75 (ISBN 92-0-149080-1, IAER7S, IAEA). Unipub.

Aviel, S. David. The Politics of Nuclear Energy. LC 81-40875. (Illus.). 274p. (Orig.). 1982. lib. bdg. 26.25 (ISBN 0-8191-2201-7); pap. text ed. 13.00 (ISBN 0-8191-2202-5). U Pr of Amer.

Balchem, R. F. Guide to Nuclear Energy. 5.00 (ISBN 0-685-28365-8). Philos Lib.

Bashkin, S. & Stoner, J. O., Jr. Atomic Energy-Level & Grotrian Diagrams: Vol. 3: Vanadium I - Chromium XXIV. 550p. 1981. 115.00 (ISBN 0-444-86006-1). Elsevier.

--Atomic Energy-Level & Grotrian Diagrams, Vol. 4: Manganese I-XXV. 354p. 1983. 78.75 (ISBN 0-444-86463-6, I-517-82, North Holland). Elsevier.

--Atomic Energy Levels & Grotrian Diagrams, Vol. 1: Hydrogen 1 - Phosphorous XV. 1976. 115.00 (ISBN 0-444-10827-0, North-Holland); Addenda. 40.50 (ISBN 0-444-85236-0). Elsevier.

Bates, Abert, ed. Shut Down: Nuclear Power on Trial. (Illus.). 1979. pap. 5.00 (ISBN 0-913990-22-1). Book Pub Co.

Bates, David & Bederson, Benjamin. Advances in Atomic & Molecular Physics, Vol. 19. (Serial Publication Ser.). 1983. 65.00 (ISBN 0-12-003819-6). Acad Pr.

Bauer, G. S. & McDonald, A., eds. Nuclear Technologies in a Sustainable Energy System. (Illus.). 329p. 1983. 29.50 (ISBN 0-387-12154-4). Springer-Verlag.

Bennett, Donald J. The Elements of Nuclear Power. 2nd ed. LC 80-41121. 1981. pap. text ed. 21.95x (ISBN 0-582-30504-7). Longman.

Berger, John. Nuclear Power-the Unviable Option: A Critical Look at Our Energy Alternatives. LC 76-2181. (Illus.). 1976. pap. 4.95 (ISBN 0-87867-063-7). Ramparts.

Berger, John J. Nuclear Power: The Unviable Option. 1977. pap. 2.50 (ISBN 0-440-35994-5, LE). Dell.

Berry, W. & Roberts, J., eds. International Symposium on Materials in Nuclear Power Systems - Water Reactors: Proceedings. LC 83-63121. (Illus.). 978p. 75.00 (ISBN 0-915567-00-8); members 60.00 (ISBN 0-317-18667-1). Natl Corrosion Eng.

Billinton, R. Power System Reliability Evaluation. 310p. 1970. 52.50 (ISBN 0-677-02870-9). Gordon.

Blair, I. Taming the Atom: The Future with Nuclear Power. 1983. 27.00 (ISBN 0-9960023-8-3, Pub. by A Hilger England); pap. 11.50 (ISBN 0-9960027-2-3, Pub. by A Hilger England). Heyden.

Brandenberger, E. & Stattmann, F. Nuclear Power Dictionary, Vol. 63. (Eng. & Ger.). 456p. 1978. pap. 52.50 (ISBN 3-521-06112-4, M-7572, Verlag Karl Thiemig). French & Eur.

The Breeder Reactor & Prudent Energy Planning: A Statement by the NPA Joint Policy Committee on the Breeder Reactor & Nuclear Proliferation. 15p. (Orig.). 1980. pap. 2.00 (ISBN 0-89068-056-6). Natl Planning.

Brenner, Michael. Nuclear Power & Non-Proliferation: The Remaking of US Policy. LC 80-28561. 320p. 1981. 28.00 (ISBN 0-521-23517-0). Cambridge U Pr.

Cagnac, B. & Pebay-Peyroula, J. C. Modern Atomic Physics: Quantum Theory & Its Application, Vol. 2. LC 74-26875. 253p. 21.00 (ISBN 0-470-12921-2). Krieger.

Caldicott, Helen. Nuclear Madness. 1981. pap. 3.50 (ISBN 0-553-22774-2). Bantam.

Cameron, I. R. Nuclear Fission Reactors. LC 82-18128. 398p. 1982. 49.50x (ISBN 0-306-41073-7, Plenum Pr). PLenum Pub.

Centro Nuclear De Puerto Rico. Simposio Sobre Energia Nuclear y el Desarrollo De Latinoamerica. pap. 3.75 (ISBN 0-8477-2304-6). U of PR Pr.

Civil Engineering & Nuclear Power, 6 vols. LC 80-67611. 1974p. 1980. pap. 99.00x (ISBN 0-87262-248-7). Am Soc Civil Eng.

Clarfield, Gerard H. & Wiecek, William M. Nuclear America: Military & Civilian Nuclear Power in the United States, 1940-1980. LC 84-47565. (Illus.). 528p. 1984. 19.18 (ISBN 0-06-015336-9, HarpT). Har-Row.

Clewett, John & Critical Mass Energy Project Staff. Nuclear Power Safety Report, 1983. 1983. pap. 5.00 (ISBN 0-937188-22-0). Pub Citizen Inc.

Cohen, Bernard L. Before It's Too Late: A Scientist's Case for Nuclear Energy. 310p. 1983. (full discount avail.) 16.95 (ISBN 0-306-41425-2, Plenum Press). Plenum Pub.

Collingridge, David. Technology in the Policy Process: The Control of Nuclear Power. LC 83-9801. 200p. 1983. 22.50 (ISBN 0-312-79005-8). St Martin.

Collins, Carol C., ed. Nuclear Energy: Salvation of Suicide? 192p. 1984. 22.50 (817-7). Facts on File.

Commission on Sociotechnical Systems. N R C Trans-Bus Study. 1979. pap. 1.50 (ISBN 0-309-02929-5). Natl Acad Pr.

Conference Proceedings in the IAEA Library. 561p. (Orig.). 1972. pap. 28.75 (ISBN 92-0-179072-4, ISP326, IAEA). Unipub.

Council on Economic Priorities & Buchsbaum, Steven. Jobs & Energy: The Employment & Economic Impacts of Nuclear Power, Conservation, & Other Energy Options. Schwartz, Wendy C., ed. LC 79-91065. 1979. 35.00 (ISBN 0-87871-011-6). CEP.

Dahl, Robert A. & Brown, Ralph S., Jr. Domestic Control of Atomic Energy. LC 51-12965. 1951. pap. 2.00 (ISBN 0-527-03298-0). Kraus Repr.

Day, Langston. New Worlds Beyond the Atom. 1963. Devin.

DeLeon, Peter. Development & Diffusion of the Nuclear Power Reactor: A Comparative Analysis. LC 79-12988. 352p. 1979. prof ref 30.00 (ISBN 0-88410-682-9). Ballinger Pub.

Design Construction & Operating Experience of Demonstration LMFBRs. (Proceedings Ser.). (Illus.). 882p. 1979. pap. 96.75 (ISBN 92-0-050278-4, ISP490, IAEA). Unipub.

Deutsch, Robert W. Nuclear Power. 3rd. ed. (Illus.). 42p. 1979. pap. 3.50 (ISBN 0-87683-299-0). G P Courseware.

Doern, G. Bruce. Canadian Nuclear Policies. 1980. pap. text ed. 14.95x (ISBN 0-920380-25-5, Pub. by Inst Res Pub Canada). Brookfield Pub Co.

Duderstat. Nuclear Power. (Energy, Power, & Environment: A Ser. of Reference Bks.: Vol. 3). 1979. 34.25 (ISBN 0-8247-6829-9). Dekker.

Dunn, Lewis A. Controlling the Bomb: Nuclear Proliferation in the 1980's. LC 81-16086. (Fastsback Ser.: No. 25). 224p. 1982. 24.00x (ISBN 0-300-02820-2); pap. 7.95x (ISBN 0-300-02821-0, YF-25). Yale U Pr.

Eichner, Donald O. The Inter-American Nuclear Energy Commission: Its Goals & Achievements. Bruchey, Stuart, ed. LC 78-22676. (Energy in the American Economy Ser.). 1979. lib. bdg. 16.00x (ISBN 0-405-11979-8). Ayer Co Pubs.

El-Genk, Mohamed S. & Hoover, Mark D., eds. Space Nuclear Power Systems: The Proceedings on the First Symposium on Space Nuclear Power Systems, 2 Vols. LC 84-16634. 1985. 110.00 (ISBN 0-89464-004-6). Krieger.

El-Hinnawi, Essam E., ed. Nuclear Energy & the Environment. LC 80-40365. (Illus.). 310p. 1980. 62.00 (ISBN 0-08-024472-6). Pergamon.

Elion, H. A. & Stewart, D. C., eds. Progress in Nuclear Energy, Series 9. Incl. Vol. 4, Pt. 3; Vol. 6. 1966. 55.00 (ISBN 0-08-011583-7); Vol. 7. 1966; Vol. 9. 55.00 (ISBN 0-08-012716-9); Vol. 10. 55.00 (ISBN 0-08-013394-0); Vol. 11. 55.00 (ISBN 0-08-016920-1); Vol. 12, Pt. 1. 1975. pap. text ed. 6.50 (ISBN 0-08-018967-9). LC 59-8283. write for info. Pergamon.

La Ensenanza & La Energia Nuclear en America Latina. pap. 3.75 (ISP52, IAEA). Unipub.

Evans, N. L. & Hope, C. W. Nuclear Power: Futures, Costs & Benefits. LC 84-1806. 200p. 1984. 29.95 (ISBN 0-521-26191-0). Cambridge U Pr.

Falk, Jim. Global Fission: The Battle over Nuclear Power. (Illus.). 1982. pap. 12.95 (ISBN 0-19-554316-5). Oxford U Pr.

Fermi, Enrico. Nuclear Physics. rev. ed. LC 50-6826. (Midway Reprints Ser). 258p. 1974. pap. text ed. 15.00x (ISBN 0-226-24365-6). U of Chicago Pr.

Fermi, Laura. Atoms for the World: United States Participation in the Conference on the Peaceful Uses of Atomic Energy. LC 57-6977. (Illus.). pap. 50.00 (ISBN 0-317-08772-X, 2011227). Bks Demand UMI.

Filby, Royston H., et al, eds. Atomic & Nuclear Methods in Fossil Energy Research. LC 81-21169. 518p. 1982. 69.50x (ISBN 0-306-40899-6, Plenum Pr). Plenum Pub.

Flavin, Christopher. Nuclear Power: The Market Test. LC 83-51433. (Worldwatch Papers). 1983. pap. 2.00 (ISBN 0-916468-56-9). Worldwatch Inst.

Fraga, S., et al. Atomic Energy Levels: Data for Parametric Calculations, Vol. 4. (Physical Sciences Data Ser.). 482p. 1979. 106.50 (ISBN 0-444-41838-5). Elsevier.

Freedman, Lawrence. Britain & Nuclear Weapons. 1981. text ed. 28.00x (ISBN 0-333-30494-2). Humanities.

Freudenthal, Gideon. Atom & Individual in the Age of Newton: On the Genesis of the Mechanistic World View. 1985. lib. bdg. 49.00 (ISBN 90-277-1905-5, Reidel Holland). Kluwer Academic.

Gaines, Linda, et al. TOSCA: The Total Social Cost of Coal & Nuclear Power. LC 78-26240. 144p. 1979. prof ref 29.95 (ISBN 0-88410-086-3). Ballinger Pub.

Gamow, George & Gritchfield, C. L. Theory of Atomic Nucleus & Nuclear Energy-Sources. LC 83-45435. Repr. of 1949 ed. 49.50 (ISBN 0-404-20105-9). AMS Pr.

Garcia de La Noceda, Joaquin. Curso de Preguntas Sobre la Teoria Atomica. LC 80-26696. 500p. 1981. pap. 7.00 (ISBN 0-8477-2326-7). U of PR Pr.

Gladkov, K. The Powerhouse of the Atom. (Illus.). 303p. 1972. 14.95x (ISBN 0-8464-0741-8). Beekman Pubs.

--Powerhouse of the Atom. 1980. 15.00x (ISBN 0-89875-003-2, Pub. by U Pr Pacific). Intl Spec Bk.

Glasstone, Samuel. Sourcebook on Atomic Energy. 3rd ed. LC 79-1206. 892p. 1979. Repr. of 1967 ed. lib. bdg. 49.50 (ISBN 0-88275-898-5). Krieger.

Glasstone, Samuel & Jordan, Walter H. Nuclear Power & Its Environmental Effects. LC 80-67303. (Illus.). 400p. 1980. 25.95 (ISBN 0-89448-022-7, 690005); pap. 17.95 (ISBN 0-89448-024-3, 690006). Am Nuclear Soc.

Greenhalgh, G. The Necessity of Nuclear Power. 220p. 1980. 33.00x (ISBN 0-686-64708-4, Pub. by Graham & Trotman England). State Mutual Bk.

Grenon, M. The Nuclear Apple & the Solar Orange: Alternatives in World Energy. LC 80-40836. (Illus.). 200p. 1981. 40.00 (ISBN 0-08-026157-4); pap. 17.25 (ISBN 0-08-026156-6). Pergamon.

Grigorieff, W. W., ed. Abundant Nuclear Energy: Proceedings. LC 71-600642. (AEC Symposium Ser.). 352p. 1969. pap. 16.75 (ISBN 0-87079-130-3, CONF-680810); microfiche 4.50 (ISBN 0-87079-131-1, CONF-680810). DOE.

Grossman, Karl. Cover-Up: What You Are Not Supposed to Know About Nuclear Power. LC 80-81394. 312p. 1980. 11.95 (ISBN 0-932966-10-1). Permanent Pr.

Guhin, Michael A. Nuclear Paradox: Security Risks of the Peaceful Atom. 1976. pap. 4.25 (ISBN 0-8447-3204-4). Am Enterprise.

Gyorgy, Anna, et al. No Nukes: Everyone's Guide to Nuclear Power. LC 78-71203. (Illus.). 478p. 1979. 20.00 (ISBN 0-89608-007-2); pap. 10.00 (ISBN 0-89608-006-4). South End Pr.

Hacker, Andrew, et al. Nuclear Power in American Thought. 85p. (Orig.). 1980. pap. 2.50 (ISBN 0-931032-08-3). Edison Electric.

Hall, Eugene J. The Language of Atomic Energy in English. (English for Careers). (Illus.). 1976. pap. 4.25 (ISBN 0-88345-279-0, 18514). Regents Pub.

Hammerstrom, Gary. The Hazards of Nuclear Energy: A Policy & Planning Approach. (Learning Packages in Policy Issues Ser.: No. 3). (Illus.). 86p. (Orig.). 1977. pap. text ed. 3.00x (ISBN 0-936826-12-6). Pol Stud Assocs.
Harrigan, Gregory L. The Nuclear Quagmire. LC 84-50400. 125p. (Orig.). 1986. pap. 5.95 (ISBN 0-916403-02-5). Shanty Pr.
Hart, David. Nuclear Power in India: A Comparative Analysis. 192p. 1983. text ed. 24.00x (ISBN 0-04-338101-4). Allen Unwin.
Hawkes, Nigel. Nuclear Energy. (First Bks.). (Illus.). 40p. 1984. lib. bdg. 8.90 (ISBN 0-531-04829-2). Watts.
Hayes, Denis. Nuclear Power: The Fifth Horseman. LC 76-13243. (Worldwatch Papers). 1976. pap. 2.00 (ISBN 0-916468-05-4). Worldwatch Inst.
--Rays of Hope. 1977. pap. 4.95 (ISBN 0-393-06422-0). Norton.
Hellman, Caroline J. C. & Hellman, Richard. The Competitive Economics of Nuclear & Coal Power. LC 82-47500. 208p. 1982. 26.50x (ISBN 0-669-05533-6). Lexington Bks.
Henry, G. & Schuler, M., eds. Egypt & Nuclear Technology: "The Peace Dividend". LC 83-23243. (Significant Issues Ser.: Vol. 5, No. 9). 18p. 1983. 5.95 (ISBN 0-89206-052-2). CSI Studies.
Hogerton, John F. The Atomic Energy Deskbook. LC 63-13445. pap. 160.00 (ISBN 0-317-08578-6, 2050849). Bks Demand UMI.
Hoyle, Fred. Energy or Extinction? 2nd ed. 1980. pap. text ed. 4.50x (ISBN 0-435-54431-4). Heinemann Ed.
Hoyle, Fred & Hoyle, Geoffrey. Commonsense in Nuclear Energy. LC 80-11811. (Illus.). 88p. 1980. pap. text ed. 8.95 (ISBN 0-7167-1237-7). W H Freeman.
Hughes, Donald J. On Nuclear Energy: Its Potential for Peacetime Use. LC 57-12848. pap. 68.00 (ISBN 0-317-08411-9, 2006015). Bks Demand UMI.
Hunt, S. E. Fission, Fusion & the Energy Crisis. 2nd ed. (Illus.). 180p. 1980. 28.00 (ISBN 0-08-024734-2); pap. 11.00 (ISBN 0-08-024733-4). Pergamon.
INIS Atomindex: Five-Year Index: Report, Standard & Patent Numbers, May 1972 to June 1977. 296p. 1977. pap. 205.00 (ISBN 0-686-93138-6, IAEA). Unipub.
INIS: Character Set Representation & Coding Rules. (INIS Reference Ser.: No. 7, Rev. 2). (Illus.). 25p. 1983. pap. text ed. 5.00 (ISBN 92-0-178282-9, IN7/R2, IAEA). Unipub.
Institute for Energy Analysis. Economic & Environmental Impacts of a U. S. Nuclear Moratorium. Weinberg, Alvin M., ed. 1979. 35.00x (ISBN 0-262-23093-3). MIT Pr.
Jacobsen, Carl G. The Nuclear Era: Its History, Its Implications. LC 82-8077. 160p. 1982. 30.00 (ISBN 0-89946-158-1). Oelgeschlager.
Jessup, Philip C., ed. Atoms for Power. LC 58-6048. 1957. 3.00; pap. 1.00 (ISBN 0-936904-01-1). Am Assembly.
Kadiroglu, Osman, et al, eds. Nuclear Energy & Alternatives: Proceedings of the International Scientific Forum on an Acceptable Nuclear Energy Future of the World. LC 78-16007. 768p. 1978. prof ref 45.00x (ISBN 0-88410-081-2). Ballinger Pub.
Kaku, Michio & Trainer, Jennifer. Nuclear Power: Both Sides. (Illus.). 288p. 1983. pap. 6.95 (ISBN 0-393-30128-1). Norton.
Kaku, Michio & Trainer, Jennifer, eds. Nuclear Power, Both Sides: The Best Arguments for & Against the Most Controversial Technology. (Illus.). 384p. 1982. 16.95 (ISBN 0-393-01631-5). Norton.
Karam, R. A. & Weaver, L. E., eds. Risk-Benefit Assessments & Societal Cost of Nuclear & Other Energy Sources. 120p. 1983. pap. 44.00 (ISBN 0-08-030543-1). Pergamon.
Katz, James E. & Marwah, Onkar S. Nuclear Power in Developing Countries: An Analysis of Decision Making. LC 81-47622. 384p. 1982. 31.00x (ISBN 0-669-04700-7). Lexington Bks.
Knief, Ronald A. Nuclear Energy Technology. (Illus.). 624p. 1981. text ed. 46.00 (ISBN 0-07-035086-8). McGraw.
Kramish, Arnold. Atomic Energy in the Soviet Union. LC 59-14724. pap. 61.50 (ISBN 0-317-08466-6, 2002903). Bks Demand UMI.
Lewis, E. E. Nuclear Power Reactor Safety. LC 77-21360. 630p. 1977. 59.95x (ISBN 0-471-53335-1, Pub. by Wiley-Interscience). Wiley.
Lilienthal, David E. Atomic Energy: A New Start. LC 79-3668. 160p. 1980. 13.41i (ISBN 0-06-012617-5, HarpT). Har-Row.
--Change, Hope & the Bomb. 1963. 22.00 (ISBN 0-691-06903-4); pap. 7.95x (ISBN 0-691-01850-2). Princeton U Pr.
Lindsay, R. Bruce, ed. Energy in Atomic Physics, 1925-1960. (Benchmark Papers on Energy: Vol. 10). 400p. 1983. 45.00 (ISBN 0-87933-075-9). Van Nos Reinhold.
McCormick, Norman J. Reliability & Risk Analysis: Methods & Nuclear Power Applications. LC 81-2758. 1981. 39.50 (ISBN 0-12-482360-2). Acad Pr.
McKay, Alwyn. The Making of the Atomic Age. (Illus.). 144p. 1985. 16.95 (ISBN 0-19-219193-4); pap. 6.95 (ISBN 0-19-289174-X). Oxford U Pr.
Marshall, Walter. Nuclear Power Technology, Vol. 2: Fuel Cycle. (Illus.). 1983. 65.00x (ISBN 0-19-851958-3). Oxford U Pr.
--Nuclear Power Technology, Vol. 3: Nuclear Radiation. (Illus.). 1983. 65.00x (ISBN 0-19-851959-1). Oxford U Pr.
Martin, Daniel W. Three Mile Island: Prologue or Epilogue? 272p. 1980. prof ref 25.00 (ISBN 0-88410-629-2). Ballinger Pub.
Marx, G., ed. Nuclear Physics, Nuclear Power. 1982. 46.00 (ISBN 0-9960072-9-6, Pub. by Akademiai Kaido Hungary). Heyden.
Materials in Nuclear Energy. 1983. 56.00 (ISBN 0-87170-168-5). ASM.
Media Institute Staff. Energy Coverage-Media Panic: An International Perspective. Smith, Nelson & Theberge, Leonard, eds. LC 82-14810. (Public Communication Ser.). (Illus.). 316p. 1983. 24.95x (ISBN 0-582-29018-X). Longman.
--Television Evening News Covers Nuclear Energy: A Ten Year Perspective. (Illus.). 140p. (Orig.). 1979. pap. 35.00 (ISBN 0-937790-03-6). Media Inst.
Medvedev, Zhores A. Nuclear Disaster in the Urals. 1979. 14.95 (ISBN 0-393-01219-0). Norton.
Meehan, Richard L. The Atom & the Fault: Experts, Earthquakes, & Nuclear Power. (Illus.). 208p. 1984. 13.95 (ISBN 0-262-13199-4). MIT Pr.
Meller, Eberhard, ed. Internationalization: An Alternative to Nuclear Proliferation? LC 80-17265. (Salzburg Seminar on American Studies 1978 Ser.). 192p. 1980. text ed. 35.00 (ISBN 0-89946-049-6). Oelgeschlager.
Meyer, Leo A. Atomic Energy in Industry: A Guide for Tradesmen & Technicians. LC 62-21342. pap. 32.00 (ISBN 0-317-10136-6, 2004581). Bks Demand UMI.
--Nuclear Power in Industry. (Illus.). 1974. 9.95 (ISBN 0-8269-3402-1). Am Technical.
Miller, Jack. A Primer on Nuclear Power. 2nd ed. 1981. pap. text ed. 3.00 (ISBN 0-918552-13-3). Anvil Pr.
Moore, Harry H., ed. Survival or Suicide. facsimile ed. LC 77-134118. (Essay Index Reprint Ser). 1948. 18.00 (ISBN 0-8369-2001-5). Ayer Co Pubs.
Moore, R. V., ed. Nuclear Power. LC 77-142962. (Institution of Electrical Engineers Monograph Ser.: No. 6). (Illus.). pap. 52.00 (ISBN 0-317-12998-8, 2011486). Bks Demand UMI.
Mueller, Kimberly J. The Nuclear Power Issue: A Guide to Who's Doing What in the U. S. & Abroad. LC 79-52430. (Who's Doing What Ser.: No. 8). (Illus.). 106p. (Orig.). 1981. pap. 25.00x (ISBN 0-912102-43-8). Cal Inst Public.
Muntzing Receives ANS Nomination: Nuclear Power & Its Regulation in the United States, Vol. 7, Pt. 2. (Illus.). 125p. pap. 30.00 (ISBN 0-08-027139-1). Pergamon.
Murray, R. L. Nuclear Energy: In SI Metric Units. 2nd ed. 43.00 (ISBN 0-08-024751-2); pap. 15.00 (ISBN 0-08-024750-4). Pergamon.
Murray, Raymond L. Nuclear Energy. 2nd ed. text ed. 43.00 (ISBN 0-08-024751-2); pap. text ed. 15.00 (ISBN 0-08-024750-4). Pergamon.
Nau, Henry R. National Politics & International Technology: Nuclear Reactor Development in Western Europe. LC 73-19344. 304p. 1974. 27.50x (ISBN 0-8018-1506-1). Johns Hopkins.
Nelkin, Dorothy. Nuclear Power & Its Critics: Moral Politics at M. I. T. LC 70-147316. 6.50 (ISBN 0-8076-0722-3). Braziller.
Noakes, G. R., ed. Sources of Physics Teaching: Atomic Energy. Holography. Electrostatics, Vol. 4. 1970. pap. text ed. 18.50x (ISBN 0-85066-038-6). Intl Ideas.
Nuclear Energy & Nuclear Weapon Proliferation. 462p. 1979. 31.00x (ISBN 0-85066-184-6). Taylor & Francis.
Nuclear Power & Its Fuel Cycle. Incl. Vol. 1. Nuclear Power Prospects & Plans. pap. 79.75 (ISBN 92-0-050077-3, ISP465-1); Vol. 2, Pt. 2. The Nuclear Fuel Cycle. pap. 87.75 (ISBN 92-0-050177-X, ISP465-2); Vol. 3, Pt. 2. The Nuclear Fuel Cycle. pap. 87.75 (ISBN 92-0-050277-6, ISP465-3); Vol. 4. Radioactivity Management. pap. 87.75 (ISBN 92-0-050377-2, ISP465-4); Vol. 5. Nuclear Safety. pap. 79.75 (ISBN 92-0-050477-9, ISP465-5); Vol. 6. Nuclear Power in Developing Countries. pap. 79.75 (ISBN 92-0-050577-5, ISP465-6); Vol. 7. Nuclear Power & Public Opinion, Safeguards. pap. 79.75 (ISBN 92-0-050677-1, ISP465-7); Vol. 8. Indexes & Lists. pap. 32.25 (ISBN 92-0-050777-8, ISP465-8). Set. pap. 558.25 (ISP465SET, IAEA). Unipub.
Nuclear Power Experience: Nuclear Safety, Vols. 2-4. Incl. Vol. 2. Nuclear Power Production. 637p. 1983. pap. 99.25 (ISBN 92-0-050183-4, ISP627 2); Vol. 3. Nuclear Fuel Cycle. 893p. 1983. pap. 139.25 (ISBN 92-0-050283-0, ISP627 3); Vol. 4. Nuclear Safety. (Illus.). 873p. 1983. pap. 130.50 (ISBN 9-2005-0383-7, ISP627 4). (IAEA Proceedings Ser.). (Illus.). 1983 (IAEA). Unipub.
OAS General Secretariat Inter-American Commission of Nuclear Energy. Duodecima Reunion de la Comision Interamericana de Energia Nuclear: Informe Final del 31 de Agosto al 4 de Septiembre de 1981 La Paz, Bolivia. 50p. 1981. pap. 3.00 (ISBN 0-8270-1415-5). OAS.
OAS General Secretariat Inter-American Nuclear Energy. OAS Offical Documents Final Report: Twelfth Meeting of the Inter-American Nuclear Energy Commission, August 31 - September 4, 1981, La Paz, Bolivia. (OEA Ser. C: No. VIII.12). 52p. 1981. pap. 3.00 (ISBN 0-8270-1414-7). OAS.
Oda, N. & Takayanagi, K., eds. Electronic & Atomic Collisions: Invited Papers-11th International Conference on Physics of Electricity & Atomic Collisions, Kyoto, Japan, August 1979. 1980. 136.25 (ISBN 0-444-85434-7). Elsevier.
OECD. Nuclear Aerosols in Reactor Safety: Supplementary Report. 243p. (Orig.). 1984. pap. 40.00x (ISBN 92-64-12652-X). OECD.
OECD & NEA. Nuclear Power & Public Opinion. 118p. (Orig.). 1984. pap. 16.00x (ISBN 92-64-12608-2). OECD.
OECD Staff. Nuclear Energy & Its Fuel Cycle: Prospects to 2025. 262p. 1982. pap. 24.00 (ISBN 92-64-12306-7). OECD.
--Nuclear Energy Prospects to Two Thousand. 130p. (Orig.). 1982. pap. 14.00x (ISBN 92-64-02326-7). OECD.
OECD Staff & NEA Staff. Siting of Radioactive Waste Repositories in Geological Formations. 260p. (Orig.). 1981. pap. 15.00x (ISBN 92-6402-186-8). OECD.
Otis, Todd H. A Review of Nuclear Energy in the United States: Hidden Power. LC 81-11859. (Illus.). 192p. 1981. 29.95 (ISBN 0-03-060001-4). Praeger.
Ott, K. O. & Spnrad, Bernard I., eds. Nuclear Energy: A Sensible Alternative. 408p. 1985. 25.00x (ISBN 0-306-41441-4, Plenum Pr). Plenum Pub.
The Outlook for Nuclear Power. 1980. 3.50 (ISBN 0-309-03039-0). Natl Acad Pr.
Pacific Basin Nuclear Conference, 4th: Proceedings. 374p. 1984. 75.00 (ISBN 0-919307-30-2). Can Nuclear Assn.
Pasqualetti, Martin J. & Pijawka, K. D., eds. Nuclear Power: Assessing & Managing Hazardous Technology. 350p. 1984. 31.00x (ISBN 0-86531-811-5). Westview.
Pathak, K. K. Nuclear Policy of India. 1983. 18.50x (ISBN 0-8364-1024-6, Pub. by Gitanjali Prakashan). South Asia Bks.
Patterson, Walter C. Nuclear Power. 2nd ed. 1983. pap. 4.95 (ISBN 0-14-022499-8, Pelican). Penguin.
Peaceful Uses of Atomic Energy: Proceedings of the 4th International Conference, Geneva, 6-16 Sept. 1971, Vols. 1, 4-8, 10 & 12. Incl. Vol. 1. Opening & Closing Speeches, Special Talks, World Energy Needs & Resources & the Role of Nuclear Energy (UN72/9/1); Vol. 4. Integration of Nuclear Plants in Electrical Networks; Integrated Planning of Nuclear Industry; Fuel Materials Technology (UN72/9/4); Vol. 5. Breeder & Advanced Converter Reactors (UN72/9/5); Vol. 6. Small & Medium Power Reactors, Desalination & Agroindustrial Complexes, Role of Research & Impact of Nuclear Energy in Developing Countries (UN72/9/6); Vol. 8. Uranium & Thorium Ore Resources; Fuel Fabrication & Processing (UN72/9/8); Vol. 10. Effects of Irradiation on Fuels & Materials (UN72/9/10); Vol. 12. Nuclear Methods in Food Production, Education & Training & Public Information (UN72/9/12). (Eng., Fr., Rus. & Span., Orig.). pap. 17.00 ea. (UN). Unipub.
Peaceful Uses of Nuclear Explosions (1969-1979, Vol. 2. (Bibliographical Ser.: No. 43). 443p. 1981. pap. 62.00 (ISBN 92-0-164080-3, ISP 21 43, IAEA). Unipub.
Pentreath, R. J. Nuclear Power, Man & the Environment. (The Wykeham Science Ser.: No. 51). 268p. 1981. pap. cancelled (ISBN 0-85109-840-1). Taylor & Francis.
Performance of Nuclear Power Reactor Components. (Proceedings Ser.). (Illus.). 678p. (Orig.). 1970. pap. 52.00 (ISBN 92-0-050170-2, ISP240, IAEA). Unipub.
Perrot, M. de. Energie Nucleaire et Societe. 1982. pap. 17.50 (ISBN 0-08-027077-8). Pergamon.
Petrosyants, A. M. From Scientific Search to Atomic Industry. LC 74-24684. 374p. 1975. text ed. 17.90x (ISBN 0-8134-1661-2, 1661). Interstate.
Polanyi, Michael. Atomic Reactions. 1980. lib. bdg. 49.95 (ISBN 0-8490-3138-9). Gordon Pr.
Post, Roy G. & Seale, Robert L., eds. Water Production Using Nuclear Energy. LC 66-24303. (Illus.). pap. 98.00 (ISBN 0-317-10713-5, 2055358). Bks Demand UMI.
Pringle, Peter & Spigelman, James. The Nuclear Barons. 592p. 1983. pap. 4.95 (ISBN 0-380-62364-1, 62364-1, Discus). Avon.
Ramberg, Bennett. Global Nuclear Energy Risks: The Search for Preventive Medicine. 110p. 1985. 22.00x (ISBN 0-86531-667-8). Westview.
Resource Systems International. Nuclear Power. 1982. pap. text ed. 15.00 (ISBN 0-8359-4976-1). Reston.
Rippon, Simon. Nuclear Energy. (Illus.). 224p. 1984. 29.95 (ISBN 0-434-91731-1, Pub. by W Heinemann Ltd). David & Charles.
Risks & Benefits of Energy Systems: Proceedings of a Symposium, Julrich, 9-13 April 1983. (Proceedings Ser.). (Eng., Fr. & Rus.). 671p. 1985. pap. 104.00 (ISBN 92-0-020784-7, ISP668, IAEA). Unipub.
Risks of Nuclear Energy & Ionizing Radiation. 1981. pap. 3.00 (ISBN 0-89970-118-3). AMA.
Roberson, E. C. Atomic Energy. 13.75x (ISBN 0-392-07602-0, SpS). Sportshelf.
Roberts, L. E. Nuclear Power & Public Responsibility. LC 84-7644. 120p. 1984. 22.95 (ISBN 0-521-24718-7). Cambridge U Pr.
Rolph, Elizabeth S. Nuclear Power & the Public Safety: A Study in Regulation. LC 78-24795. (Illus.). 240p. 1979. 21.50x (ISBN 0-669-02822-3). Lexington Bks.
Rose, D. J., ed. Nuclear-Electric Power in the Asia-Pacific Region: Proceedings of the Workshop Held in Honolulu, Hawaii, 23-28 January 1983. 265p. 1985. 55.00 (ISBN 0-08-031654-9). Pergamon.
Rothmann, S. Charles, ed. Constructive Uses of Atomic Energy. facs. ed. LC 73-128304. (Essay Index Reprint Ser). 1949. 21.00 (ISBN 0-8369-2129-1). Ayer Co Pubs.
Rust, J. H. & Weaver, L. E. Nuclear Power Safety. pap. 25.00 (ISBN 0-08-021744-3). Pergamon.
Sample Analysis of a Piping System: Class One Nuclear. 1972. pap. text ed. 4.50 (ISBN 0-685-30778-6, E00063). ASME.
Schuette, D., et al, eds. The Meson Theory of Nuclear Forces & Nuclear Matter. 383p. 1980. pap. text ed. 29.95x (ISBN 3-411-01582-9). Birkhauser.
Schurr, S. H. & Marschak, J. Economic Aspects of Atomic Power. 1950. 32.00 (ISBN 0-691-04121-0). Princeton U Pr.
Secretariat for Futures Studies, Stockholm. Solar vs. Nuclear: The Solar Nuclear Alternative. 1980. 47.00 (ISBN 0-08-024758-X); pap. 18.00 (ISBN 0-08-024759-8). Pergamon.
Shaw, E. N. Europe's Nuclear Power Experiment: History of the OECD Dragon Project. (Illus.). 300p. 1982. 25.00 (ISBN 0-08-029324-7). Pergamon.
Shrader-Frechette, Kristin S. Nuclear Power & Public Policy. 2nd ed. (Orig.). 1983. pap. text ed. 10.50 (ISBN 90-277-1513-0, Pub. by Reidel Holland). Kluwer Academic.
Silber, Bettina, ed. New Directions for Nuclear Power. (Energy Policy Ser.). 60p. (Orig.). 1985. pap. 6.00 (ISBN 0-934458-08-1). Americans Energy Ind.
Snow, Donald M. Nuclear Strategy in a Dynamic World: American Policy in the Nineteen Eighties. LC 80-13634. 332p. 1981. pap. 12.95 (ISBN 0-8173-0045-7). U of Ala Pr.
Srouji, Jacque. Critical Mass: Nuclear Power, the Alternative to Energy Famine. LC 75-14532. 1977. 11.95 (ISBN 0-87695-188-4). Aurora Pubs.
Stattmann, F. Fachwoerter der Kraftwerkstechnik: Kernkraftwerke, Pt. 2. (Ger. & Eng.). 316p. 1973. pap. 13.50 (ISBN 3-521-06081-0, M-7386, Pub. by K. Thiemig). French & Eur.
--Fachwoerter der Kraftwerkstechnik: Konventionelle Dampkraftwerke, Pt. 1. (Ger.). 252p. 1971. pap. 13.50 (ISBN 3-521-06059-4, M-7385, Pub. by K. Thiemig). French & Eur.
Stewart, Hugh B. Transitional Energy Policy 1980-2030: Alternative Nuclear Technologies. (Pergamon Policy Studies on Science & Technology). 266p. 1981. 33.00 (ISBN 0-08-027183-9); pap. 13.75 (ISBN 0-08-027182-0). Pergamon.
Subrahmanyam, K., ed. Nuclear Myths & Realities: India's Dilemma. 290p. 1981. 19.95 (ISBN 0-940500-02-7, Pub. by ABC Pub Hse India). Asia Bk Corp.
The Swedish Public & Nuclear Energy: The Referendum 1980. 54p. 1981. pap. 5.00 (ISBN 92-808-0155-4, TUNU137, UNU). Unipub.
Symposium on Atomic Energy & Its Implications. facs. ed. LC 74-84341. (Essay Index Reprint Ser). 1946. 15.75 (ISBN 0-8369-1110-5). Ayer Co Pubs.
Torrens, Ian M. Interatomic Potentials. 1972. 58.50 (ISBN 0-12-695850-5). Acad Pr.
Uranium & Nuclear Issues. 156p. 1983. 25.00 (ISBN 0-919307-28-0). Can Nuclear Assn.

V. Franzen, F. Woerterbuch der Kerenergie. (Eng. & Ger., Dictionary of Nuclear Energy). 1957. 20.00 (ISBN 0-686-56618-1, M-6987). French & Eur.
Warner, Frederick, ed. The Assessment & Perception of Risk. (The Royal Society of London Ser.: Vol. 376). (Illus.). 206p. 1981. Repr. text ed. 36.00x (ISBN 0-85403-163-4, Pub. by Royal Soc London). Scholium Intl.
Weaver, Lynn E., ed. Education for Peaceful Uses of Nuclear Explosives. LC 76-101101. (Illus.). pap. 89.80 (ISBN 0-317-08638-3, 2055345). Bks Demand UMI.
Weinberg, Alvin, et al, eds. The Nuclear Connection: A Reassessment of Nuclear Power & Nuclear Proliferation. LC 84-26786. (Illus.). 304p. 1985. 27.95 (ISBN 0-317-18710-4, Pub. by Wash Inst DC); pap. 19.95 (ISBN 0-88702-205-7). Paragon Hse.
Weinberg, Alvin M., et al. The Second Nuclear Era: A New Start for Nuclear Power. LC 85-26613. 460p. 1985. 41.95 (ISBN 0-03-004144-9). Praeger.
Wilcox, Fred, ed. The Grass Roots: An Anti-Nuke Sourcebook. LC 80-11762. (Illus.). 192p. 1980. 20.95 (ISBN 0-89594-032-9); pap. 10.95 (ISBN 0-89594-031-0). Crossing Pr.
Williams, M. M. Progress in Nuclear Energy: The Role of the Boltzmann Transport Equation in Radiation Damage Calculations, Vol. 3, No. 1. LC 77-25743. (Progress in Nuclear Energy Ser.). (Illus.). 66p. 1979. pap. 43.00 (ISBN 0-08-024243-X). Pergamon.
Williams, M. M., ed. Progress in Nuclear Energy, Vol. 3, No. 2. (Illus.). 92p. 1979. pap. 43.00 (ISBN 0-08-024253-7). Pergamon.
--Progress in Nuclear Energy, Vol. 3, No. 3. 96p. 1979. pap. 43.00 (ISBN 0-08-024844-6). Pergamon.
--Progress in Nuclear Energy, Vol. 5 Complete. (Illus.). 292p. 1980. 105.00 (ISBN 0-08-027115-4). Pergamon.
Williams, M. M. & McCormick, N. J., eds. Progress in Nuclear Energy, Vol. 7. (Illus.). 228p. 1981. 115.00 (ISBN 0-08-029090-6, A999, B120). Pergamon.
--Progress in Nuclear Energy, Vol. 11. (Illus.). 310p. 1983. 120.00 (ISBN 0-08-031029-X). Pergamon.
--Progress in Nuclear Energy, Vol. 12. (Illus.). 300p. 1984. 120.00 (ISBN 0-08-031695-6). Pergamon.
--Progress in Nuclear Energy, Vol. 13. (Illus.). 300p. 1985. 138.00 (ISBN 0-08-032322-7). Pergamon.
--Progress in Nuclear Energy: Selected Staff Reports to the President's Commission on the Accident at Three Mile Island, Vol. 6. (Illus.). 436p. 1981. 105.00 (ISBN 0-08-027124-3). Pergamon.
Williams, M. M. & Sher, R., eds. Progress in Nuclear Energy: New Series. (Illus.). Vol. 1, No. 1, 1977. pap. text ed. 30.00 (ISBN 0-08-022118-1); Vol. 2, Nos. 4, 1978. pap. text ed. 21.00 (ISBN 0-08-023260-4); Vol. 2, No. 1, 1978. pap. text ed. 30.00 (ISBN 0-08-022710-4). Pergamon.
Williams, M. M. R., ed. Progress in Nuclear Energy, Vol. 3. (Illus.). 252p. 1979. 105.00 (ISBN 0-08-024875-6). Pergamon.
Williams, M. R. & McCormick, N. J., eds. Progress in Nuclear Energy, Vol. 8. 318p. 130.00 (ISBN 0-08-029684-X). Pergamon.
Williams, Roger. The Nuclear Power Decisions: British Policies, 1953-1978. 365p. 1980. 35.00 (ISBN 0-7099-0265-4, Pub. by Croom Helm Ltd). Longwood Pub Group.
Wilson, C. W. World Nuclear Directory. 7th ed. 100p. 1985. 180.00x (ISBN 0-317-31615-X, Pub. by Longman). Gale.
Winnacker & Wirtz. Nuclear Energy in Germany. LC 79-88088. 1979. 37.00 (ISBN 0-89448-018-9, 690003). Am Nuclear Soc.
Zaleski, Pierre, ed. Nuclear Energy Maturity: Proceedings of the European Nuclear Conference, 12 vols. Incl. Vol. 1. Nuclear Power Plant Design & Construction. 100.00 (ISBN 0-08-021122-4); pap. 55.00 (ISBN 0-686-67797-8); Vol. 2. Operating Experiences with Nuclear Power Plants. 100.00 (ISBN 0-08-021123-2); pap. 45.00 (ISBN 0-686-67798-6); Vol. 3. Nuclear Fuel Performance & Management Part I. 100.00 (ISBN 0-08-021124-0); pap. 45.00 (ISBN 0-686-67799-4); Vol. 4. Nuclear Fuel Performance & Management Part II. 100.00 (ISBN 0-08-021125-9); pap. 45.00 (ISBN 0-686-67800-1); Vol. 5. Nuclear Power Plant Safety & Protection. 100.00 (ISBN 0-08-021126-7); pap. 55.00 (ISBN 0-686-67801-X); Vol. 6. Nuclear Quality Assurance & Reliability. 100.00 (ISBN 0-08-021127-5); pap. 18.00 (ISBN 0-686-67802-8); Vol. 7. Nuclear Fuel Fabrication. 100.00 (ISBN 0-08-021128-3); pap. 22.00 (ISBN 0-686-67803-6); Vol. 8. Reprocessing, Transport & Waste Disposal. 100.00 (ISBN 0-08-021129-1); pap. 27.00 (ISBN 0-686-67804-4); Vol. 9. Nuclear Process Heat: Fluid Flow & Heat Transfer. 100.00 (ISBN 0-08-021130-5); pap. 36.00 (ISBN 0-686-67805-2); Vol. 10. Social Implications of Nuclear Power, Insurance & Financing; Licensing & Regulation. 100.00 (ISBN 0-08-021131-3); pap. 18.00 (ISBN 0-686-67806-0); Vol. 11. Energy Needs & Resources; Economics & Future Development of Nuclear Power Plants. 100.00 (ISBN 0-08-021132-1); pap. 18.00 (ISBN 0-686-67807-9); Vol. 12. Enrichment & Fusion. 100.00 (ISBN 0-08-021133-X); pap. 22.00 (ISBN 0-686-67808-7). 1976. Set. 825.00 (ISBN 0-08-021135-6). Set. Pergamon.
Zuckerman, Solly. Nuclear Illusion & Reality. LC 81-69996. 156p. 1982. 10.95 (ISBN 0-670-51822-0). Viking.

NUCLEAR ENERGY–DICTIONARIES

Carpovich, Eugene A. Russian-English Atomic Dictionary: Physics, Mathematics, Nucleonics. rev. ed. 2nd ed. LC 57-8256. (Rus. & Eng.). 1959. 15.00 (ISBN 0-911484-00-0). Tech Dict.
Charles, Victorin. Diccionario Atomico. (Span.). 296p. 1962. 14.95 (ISBN 0-686-56708-0, S-33057). French & Eur.
Hilgartner, Stephen, et al. Nukespeak: Nuclear Language, Visions, & Mindset. LC 82-3189. (Illus.). 320p. 1982. 14.95 (ISBN 0-87156-307-X). Sierra.
--Nukespeak: The Selling of Nuclear Technology in America. (Illus.). 296p. 1983. pap. 6.95 (ISBN 0-14-006684-5). Penguin.
Markus, John. Diccionario de Electronica y Tecnica Nuclear. (Span. & Eng.). 1052p. 75.95 (ISBN 84-267-0003-9, S-14264). French & Eur.
Mataix Lord, Mariano. Diccionario De Electronica, Informatica y Centrales Nucleares. (Fr. & Eng.). 660p. 1978. leather 59.95 (ISBN 84-267-0350-X, S-30687). French & Eur.
OECD. Glossaire de L'Energie Nucleaire. (Eng. Fr.). 446p. 1983. pap. 52.00X (ISBN 92-64-22501-3). OECD.

NUCLEAR ENERGY–ECONOMIC ASPECTS

see also Nuclear Industry

Barnett, Harold J. Atomic Energy in the United States Economy: A Consideration of Certain Industrial, Regional, & Economic Development Aspects. Bruchey, Stuart, ed. LC 78-22658. (Energy in the American Economy Ser.). (Illus.). 1979. lib. bdg. 25.50x (ISBN 0-405-11962-3). Ayer Co Pubs.
Grey, Jerry. Aerospace Technology & Commercial Nuclear Power. 19.50 (ISBN 0-915928-69-8). AIAA.
Hughes, Donald J. On Nuclear Energy: Its Potential for Peacetime Use. LC 57-12848. pap. 68.00 (ISBN 0-317-08411-9, 2006015). Bks Demand UMI.
Mullenbach, Philip. Civilian Nuclear Power: Economic Issues & Policy Formation. LC 63-10431. Repr. of 1963 ed. 10.00 (ISBN 0-527-02831-2). Kraus Repr.
Nuclear Energy Costs & Economic Development. (Proceedings Ser.: No. 239). (Illus.). 746p. (Orig.). 1970. pap. 57.25 (ISBN 92-0-050070-6, ISP239, IAEA). Unipub.
Polach, Jaroslav G. Euratom, Its Background, Issues & Economic Implications. LC 64-15292. 232p. 1964. 12.50 (ISBN 0-379-00194-2). Oceana.
Scheinman, Lawrence. Atomic Energy Policy in France Under the Fourth Republic. 1965. 32.00x (ISBN 0-691-05602-1). Princeton U Pr.

NUCLEAR ENERGY–HISTORY

Bickel, Lennard. The Deadly Element: The Story of Uranium. LC 78-66243. (Illus.). 320p. 1980. pap. 7.95 (ISBN 0-8128-6089-6). Stein & Day.
Bossong, Ken & Denman, Scott. Nuclear Power & Civil Liberties: Can We Have Both? 2nd ed. 177p. 1981. 9.50 (ISBN 0-89988-071-1). Citizens Energy.
Dale, Alfred G. Nuclear Power Development in the U. S. to Nineteen Sixty: A New Pattern in Innovation & Technologica Change. Bruchey, Stuart, ed. LC 78-22670. (Energy & the American Economy Ser.). (Illus.). 1979. lib. bdg. 16.00x (ISBN 0-405-11974-7). Ayer Co Pubs.
Del Sesto, Steven L. Science, Politics, & Controversy: Civilian Nuclear Power in the United States 1946-1974. (Special Studies in Sci., Tech., & Pub. Policy). 260p. 1981. 29.50x (ISBN 0-89158-566-4); pap. text ed. 13.50x (ISBN 0-86531-255-9). Westview.
Garrison, James. The Plutonium Culture: From Hiroshima to Harrisburg. 224p. 1981. 14.95 (ISBN 0-8264-0029-9). Continuum.
Gofman, John W. An Irreverent, Illustrated View of Nuclear Power: "Irrevy"; from Blunderland to Seabrook IV. LC 78-73212. 1979. pap. 3.95 (ISBN 0-932682-00-6). Comm Nuclear Respon.
Goldschmidt, Bertrand. The Atomic Complex: A Worldwide Political History of Nuclear Energy. LC 82-70371. Orig. Title: Le Complexe Atomique. 520p. 1982. 31.00 (ISBN 0-89448-550-4, 690007); pap. 24.00 (ISBN 0-89448-551-2, 690008). Am Nuclear Soc.
Johnson, Kenneth R. The Fulcanelli Phenomenon. 334p. 1981. 35.00x (ISBN 0-85978-051-1, Pub. by Spearman England). State Mutual Bk.
Libby, Leona M. The Uranium People. LC 79-1463. 341p. 1979. 19.95x (ISBN 0-8448-1300-1). Crane-Russak Co.
Nuclear America: A Historical Bibliography. LC 83-12227. (ABC-Clio Research Guides: No. 3). 183p. 1984. lib. bdg. 27.00 (ISBN 0-87436-360-8). ABC-Clio.
Pilat, Joseph F., et al, eds. Atoms for Peace: An Analysis after Thirty Years. (Special Studies in International Relations). 300p. 1985. softcover 26.50x (ISBN 0-8133-7051-5). Westview.
Smyth, Henry D. Atomic Energy for Military Purposes: The Official Report on the Development of the Atomic Bomb Under the Auspices of the United States Government, 1940-1945. (The Politics & Strategy of World War II Ser: No. 2). 1976. lib. bdg. 29.50 (ISBN 0-306-70767-5). Da Capo.

NUCLEAR ENERGY–INTERNATIONAL CONTROL

Atomic Safeguards: A Study in International Verification. (United Nations Studies). 12.50 (ISBN 0-686-89905-9, E.75.XV.ST/5); pap. 6.50 (ISBN 0-686-89906-7, E.75.XV.ST/5). UN.
Boardman, Robert & Keeley, James. Nuclear Exports & World Politics. LC 82-10779. 272p. 1983. 27.50 (ISBN 0-312-57976-4). St Martin.
Brodie, Bernard, ed. Absolute Weapon: Atomic Power & World Order. LC 77-167314. (Essay Index Reprint Ser.). Repr. of 1946 ed. 16.00 (ISBN 0-8369-2754-0). Ayer Co Pubs.
Howe, P. J. Transfer of Nuclear Technology. 1977. 39.00 (ISBN 0-08-022132-7). Pergamon.
Ramberg, Bennett. Destruction of Nuclear-Energy Facilities in War: The Problem & the Implications. LC 80-7691. 224p. 1980. 26.00x (ISBN 0-669-03767-2). Lexington Bks.

NUCLEAR ENERGY–LAW AND LIGISLATION

see also Radioactive Substances–Safety Regulations

Factors Relevant to the Decommissioning of Land-Based Nuclear Reactor Plants. (Safety Ser.: No. 52). 28p. 1981. pap. 7.25 (ISBN 9-2062-3080-8, ISP541, IAEA). Unipub.
Nuclear Law for a Developing World. (Legal Ser.: No. 5). 329p. 1969. pap. 25.25 (ISBN 92-0-176169-4, ISP215, IAEA). Unipub.
Qualifications & Training of Staff of the Regulatory Body for Nuclear Power Plants: A Safety Guide. (Safety Ser.: No. 50-SG-01). (Eng., Fr., Rus. & Span.). 30p. 1979. pap. 7.75 (ISBN 92-0-123179-2, ISP513, IAEA). Unipub.
Shrader-Frechette, K. S. Nuclear Power & Public Policy: The Social & Ethical Problems of Fission Technology. (Pallas Paperbacks Ser.: No. 15). 220p. 1980. lib. bdg. 20.00 (ISBN 90-277-1054-6, Pub. by Reidel Holland); pap. 10.50 (ISBN 90-277-1080-5). Kluwer Academic.
The Swedish Public & Nuclear Energy: The Referendum 1980. 54p. 1981. pap. 5.00 (ISBN 92-808-0155-4, TUNU137, UNU). Unipub.
The Use of Film Badges for Personnel Monitoring. (Safety Ser.: No. 8). pap. 7.00 (ISP43, IAEA). Unipub.

NUCLEAR ENERGY–MORAL AND RELIGIOUS ASPECTS

Aukerman, Dale. Darkening Valley. 1981. pap. 8.95 (ISBN 0-8164-2295-8, Pub. by Seabury). Winston Pr.
Cohen, Avner & Lee, Steven, eds. Nuclear Weapons & the Future of Humanity: The Fundamental Questions. LC 84-18362. (Philosophy & Society Ser.). 224p. 1985. 38.50x (ISBN 0-8476-7257-3); pap. 16.95x (ISBN 0-8476-7258-1). Rowman & Allanheld.
Dyson, Freeman, et al. Values at War: Selected Tanner Lectures on the Nuclear Crisis. 130p. (Orig.). 1983. pap. 5.95 (ISBN 0-87480-226-1). U of Utah Pr.
Hollenbach, David. Nuclear Ethics: A Christian Moral Argument. 112p. 1983. pap. 3.95 (ISBN 0-8091-2546-3). Paulist Pr.
Lackey, Douglas P. Moral Principles & Nuclear Weapons. LC 84-11540. (Philosophy & Society Ser.). (Illus.). 284p. 1984. 28.95x (ISBN 0-8476-7116-X). Rowman & Allanheld.
MacLean, Douglas, ed. The Security Gamble: Deterrence Dilemmas in the Nuclear Age. LC 84-15080. (Maryland Studies in Public Philosophy). 190p. 1984. 29.95x (ISBN 0-8476-7329-4); pap. 14.95x (ISBN 0-8476-7337-5). Rowman & Allanheld.
Nelkin, Dorothy & Pollak, Michael. The Atom Besieged: Extraparliamentary Dissent. (Illus.). 256p. 1981. 30.00x (ISBN 0-262-14034-9); pap. 7.95 (ISBN 0-262-64021-X). MIT Pr.
O'Neill, Ana M. Etica Para la Era Atomica. facsimile ed. 10.00 (ISBN 0-8477-2815-3); pap. 9.00 (ISBN 0-8477-2807-2). U of PR Pr.
Pope John Center Staff. Technological Powers & the Person: Nuclear Energy & Reproductive Technology. Lossing, Larry D. & Bayer, Edward J., eds. (Illus.). 370p. (Orig.). 1983. pap. 15.95 (ISBN 0-935372-12-1). Pope John Ctr.
Shrader-Frechette, K. S. Nuclear Power & Public Policy: The Social & Ethical Problems of Fission Technology. (Pallas Paperbacks Ser.: No. 15). 220p. 1980. lib. bdg. 20.00 (ISBN 90-277-1054-6, Pub. by Reidel Holland); pap. 10.50 (ISBN 90-277-1080-5). Kluwer Academic.
Skousen, Eric N. The War Against Nuclear Power. (Illus.). 211p. (Orig.). 1981. pap. 7.95 (ISBN 0-88080-002-X). Natl Ctr Constitutional.
Touraine, Alain, et al. Anti-Nuclear Protest: The Opposition to Nuclear Energy in France. LC 82-17666. 203p. 1983. 37.50 (ISBN 0-521-24964-3). Cambridge U Pr.
Unger, Georg. Spiritual Science & the New Nature Forces: The Nuclear Dilemma. Thomas, Nick, tr. 28p. 1981. pap. 2.95 (ISBN 0-88925-063-4, Pub. by Steiner Book Centre Canada). Anthroposophic.

NUCLEAR ENERGY–PHYSIOLOGICAL EFFECT

Clare, Frederick. They Blew Our Weather. (Illus.). 192p. 1982. 20.00 (ISBN 0-682-49824-6). Exposition Pr FL.
Eichholz, Geoffrey G. Environmental Aspects of Nuclear Power. LC 84-27759. (Illus.). 704p. 1985. 47.50 (ISBN 0-87371-017-7). Lewis Pubs Inc.
Raynaud, C., ed. Nuclear Medicine & Biology Advances: Proceedings of the Third World Congress on Nuclear Medicine & Biology, August 29 - September 2, 1982, Paris, France, 7 Vols. 3685p. 1983. Set. 500.00 (ISBN 0-08-026405-0). Pergamon.
Rosenberg, Howard L. Atomic Soldiers: American Victims of Nuclear Experiments. LC 79-3781. 192p. 1980. pap. 5.95 (ISBN 0-8070-3211-5, BP 619). Beacon Pr.

NUCLEAR ENERGY–POPULAR WORKS

Calder, Nigel. Nuclear Nightmares. 1981. pap. 4.95 (ISBN 0-14-005867-2). Penguin.
Korsunsky, M. The Atomic Nucleus. (Russian Monographs & Texts on the Physical Sciences). 456p. 1965. 80.95 (ISBN 0-677-20180-X). Gordon.
Reader, Mark, et al, eds. Atom's Eve: Ending the Nuclear Age, an Anthology. (McGraw-Hill Paperbacks Ser.). 288p. (Orig.). 1980. pap. 5.95 (ISBN 0-07-051287-6). McGraw.

NUCLEAR ENERGY–RESEARCH–LABORATORIES

Design of & Equipment for Hot Laboratories. (Proceedings Ser.). (Illus.). 550p. 1977. pap. 61.00 (ISBN 92-0-020476-7, ISP436, IAEA). Unipub.
Von der Hardt, Peter & Rottger, Heinz, eds. Handbook of Materials Testing Reactors & Associated Hot Laboratories in the European Community. 160p. 1981. 24.00 (ISBN 90-277-1347-2, Pub. by Reidel Holland). Kluwer Academic.
World Survey of Major Facilities in Controlled Fusion Research: 1976 Ed. 3rd, rev. ed. (Illus.). 868p. 1977. pap. 72.00 (ISBN 92-0-139076-9, ISP23-76, IAEA). Unipub.

NUCLEAR ENERGY AND METEOROLOGY

see also Radioactive Pollution of the Atmosphere

Application of Meteorology to Safety at Nuclear Plants. (Safety Ser.: No. 29). (Illus.). 27p. (Orig.). 1968. pap. 6.25 (ISBN 92-0-123368-X, ISP211, IAEA). Unipub.
Atmospheric Dispersion in Nuclear Power Plant Siting. (Safety Ser.: No. 50-SG-S3). (Illus.). 107p. 1981. pap. 17.75 (ISBN 92-0-623180-4, ISP549, IAEA). Unipub.
Clare, Frederick. They Blew Our Weather. (Illus.). 192p. 1982. 20.00 (ISBN 0-682-49824-6). Exposition Pr FL.

Junge, C. E. Air Chemistry & Radioactivity. (International Geophysics Ser.: Vol. 4). 1963. 65.00 (ISBN 0-12-392150-3). Acad Pr.
Meade, P. J. Meteorological Aspects of the Peaceful Uses of Atomic Energy: Meteorological Aspects of the Safety & Location of Reactor Plants, Pt. 1. (Technical Note Ser.: No. 33). 44p. 1960. pap. 7.00 (ISBN 0-685-22320-5, W13, WMO). Unipub.
Moller, F. & Rodgers, C. D. Problems of Atmospheric Radiation in GARP. (GARP Publications Ser.: No. 5). xiv, 18p. 1970. pap. 5.00 (ISBN 0-685-02468-7, W294, WMO). Unipub.
Slade, David H., ed. Meteorology & Atomic Energy: 1968. AEC Technical Information Center. LC 68-60097. 445p. 1968. pap. 19.25 (ISBN 0-87079-274-1, TID-24190); microfiche 4.50 (ISBN 0-87079-275-X, TID-24190). DOE.
Suschny, O. Measurement of Atmospheric Radioactivity. (Technical Note Ser.: No. 94). (Illus.). 109p. 1968. pap. 30.00 (ISBN 0-685-22317-5, W64, WMO). Unipub.
Symposium, Stockholm, Sweden, June 2-5, 1975. Combined Effects of Radioactive Chemical & Thermal Releases to the Environment: Proceedings. (Proceedings Ser.). (Illus.). 358p. 1976. pap. 33.00 (ISBN 92-0-020275-6, ISP404, IAEA). Unipub.

NUCLEAR ENERGY IN AGRICULTURE

see also Soils, Radioactive Substances in

Breeding for Seed Protein Improvement Using Nuclear Techniques. (Illus.). 60p. 1976. pap. 21.75 (ISBN 92-0-111475-3, ISP400, IAEA). Unipub.
Nuclear Energy Centres & Agro-Industrial Complexes. (Technical Reports Ser.: No. 140). (Illus.). 140p. (Orig.). 1973. pap. 15.00 (ISBN 92-0-145072-9, IDC140, IAEA). Unipub.
Vose, P. B. Introduction to Nuclear Techniques in Agronomy & Plant Biology. (Illus.). 1980. 63.00 (ISBN 0-08-024924-8); pap. 29.00 (ISBN 0-08-024923-X). Pergamon.
Winteringham, F. P. W. Soil & Fertilizer Nitrogen. (Technical Reports Ser.: No. 244). 107p. 1985. pap. 21.00 (ISBN 92-0-115184-5, IDC244 5071, IAEA). Unipub.

NUCLEAR ENGINEERING

see also Nuclear Fuels; Nuclear Reactors; Radioisotopes; Shielding (Radiation)

Aron, Raymond. The Great Debate: Theories of Nuclear Strategy. Pawel, Ernst, tr. from Fr. LC 81-495. ix, 265p. 1981. Repr. of 1965 ed. lib. bdg. 32.50x (ISBN 0-313-22851-5, ARGR). Greenwood.
Ash, Milton S. Nuclear Reactor Kinetics. 2nd ed. (Illus.). 1979. text ed. 75.00 (ISBN 0-07-002380-8). McGraw.
ASME-ANS International Conference on Advanced Nuclear Energy Systems, 1976. 638p. 1976. pap. 55.00 (ISBN 0-685-78340-5, H00099). ASME.
Benedict, Manson, et al. Nuclear Chemical Engineering. 2nd ed. (Illus.). 1008p. 1981. text ed. 49.00 (ISBN 0-07-004531-3). McGraw.
Benton, E. V., et al, eds. Nuclear Track Registration: Proceedings of the Fifth Pacific Northwest Conference, Hanford Engineering Development Laboratory, Westinghouse Hanford Company, Richland, Wash. USA, July 28-29 1982. 96p. pap. 55.00 (ISBN 0-08-030274-2). Pergamon.
Bracco, F. V. Stratified Charge Engines, Vol. 1. 104p. 1973. pap. 46.25 (ISBN 0-677-05165-4). Gordon.
Burton, Ralph A., ed. Bearing & Seal Design in Nuclear Power Machinery: Proceedings of the Symposium on Lubrication in Nuclear Applications, Miami Beach, Florida, June 5-7, 1967. LC 67-27785. pap. 134.80 (ISBN 0-317-10009-2, 2016809). Bks Demand UMI.
Cadwell, Jerry J. Nuclear Facility Threat Analysis & Tactical Response Procedures. (Illus.). 114p. 1983. 22.50x (ISBN 0-398-04778-2). C C Thomas.
Chiang, Hai H. Electronics for Nuclear Instrumentation, Theory & Applications. LC 82-8974. 670p. 1985. lib. bdg. 54.50 (ISBN 0-89874-483-0). Krieger.
Committee on the Safety of Nuclear Installations Specialist Meeting. Transient Two-Phase Flow: Proceedings. Plesset, Milton, et al, eds. LC 82-23422. (Illus.). 736p. 1983. text ed. 75.00 (ISBN 0-89116-258-5). Hemisphere Pub.
Companies Holding Nuclear Certificates of Authorization. (Bk. No. E00061). 55p. 1978. 65.00 (ISBN 0-685-37566-8). ASME.
Connolly, Thomas J. Foundations of Nuclear Engineering. LC 77-26916. 344p. 1978. text ed. 48.75x (ISBN 0-471-16858-0). Wiley.
Control of Semivolatile Radionuclides in Gaseous Effluents at Nuclear Facilities. (Technical Reports Ser.: No. 220). (Illus.). 56p. 1982. pap. 10.25 (ISBN 92-0-125482-2, IDC220, IAEA). Unipub.
Cornu, Aymbe & Massot, R. List of Conversion Factors for Atomic Impurities to PPM Weight. LC 68-20754. pap. 37.00 (ISBN 0-317-29352-4, 2024003). Bks Demand UMI.
Davey, W. G. & Redman, W. C. Techniques in Fast Reactor Critical Experiments. LC 79-119375. 314p. 1970. 20.40 (ISBN 0-677-02680-3, 450006). Am Nuclear Soc.
Del Bigio, G. & Gottschalk, C. M. INIS: Descriptive Cataloguing Rules. Ruckenbacker, E., ed. (INIS Reference Ser.: No. 1, Rev. 6). 90p. 1985. pap. 7.50 (ISBN 92-0-178085-0, IN1R6, IAEA). Unipub.
Deutsch, R. W. & Whitney, J. W., eds. PWR Nuclear Power Plant Technology. (Academic Program for Nuclear Power Plant Personnel Ser.: Vol. III-CPWR Version). (Illus.). 404p. 1972. looseleaf 60.00x (ISBN 0-87683-149-8, A 373977); looseleaf lesson plans 500.00x (ISBN 0-87683-156-0); looseleaf practical exercise solution 25.00x (ISBN 0-87683-163-3); looseleaf quizzes & examinations 25.00x (ISBN 0-87683-170-6). G P Courseware.
Deutsch, R. W., et al. Practical Nuclear Power Plant Technology, 2 vols. (Illus.). 1973. Set. looseleaf 120.00x (ISBN 0-87683-295-8); Vol. 1; 368p. looseleaf 60.00x (ISBN 0-87683-296-6); Vol. 2; 320pp. looseleaf 60.00x (ISBN 0-87683-297-4). G P Courseware.
Division One-Nuclear Power Plant Components: General Requirements. (Boiler & Pressure Vessel Code Ser.: Sec. 3). 1980. 55.00 (ISBN 0-686-70367-7, P0003R); pap. 80.00 loose-leaf (ISBN 0-686-70368-5, V0003R). ASME.
Duderstadt, James J. & Hamilton, Louis J. Nuclear Reactor Analysis. LC 75-20389. 650p. 1976. text ed. 54.00 (ISBN 0-471-22363-8). Wiley.
Egelstaff, P. A. & Poole, M. J. Experimental Neutron Thermalization. LC 79-86201. 1969. 72.00 (ISBN 0-08-006533-3). Pergamon.
El-Wakil, M. M. Nuclear Energy Conversion. rev. ed. LC 78-6169. 682p. 1982. 38.00 (ISBN 0-89448-015-4). Am Nuclear Soc.
--Nuclear Heat Transport. rev. ed. LC 78-61691. 514p. 1981. 32.00 (ISBN 0-317-02612-7). Am Nuclear Soc.
Foderaro, Anthony. Elements of Neutron Interaction Theory. LC 79-103896. 1971. text ed. 40.00x (ISBN 0-262-06033-7). MIT Pr.
Foster, Arthur R. & Wright, Robert L., Jr. Basic Nuclear Engineering. 4th ed. 1983. text ed. 44.26x (ISBN 0-205-07886-9, 327886) (ISBN 0-205-05698-9). Allyn.
Foust, O. J., ed. Sodium-Nak Engineering Handbook, Vol. 2. LC 70-129473. (U. S. Atomic Energy Commission Monographs). (Illus.). 402p. 1976. 103.95 (ISBN 0-677-03030-4). Gordon.
--Sodium-Nak Engineering Handbook, Vols. 3-4. (U.S. Atomic Energy Commission Monograhs). (Illus.). 1978. Vol. 3, 348p. 93.75 (ISBN 0-677-03040-1); Vol. 4, 298p. 89.25 (ISBN 0-677-03050-9). Gordon.
Fusion Reactor Design & Technology, 2 vols. 1983. pap. 46.50 (ISBN 92-0-131083-8, ISP616-1, IAEA); pap. 38.50 (ISBN 92-0-131183-4, ISP616-2). Unipub.
Garg, J. B., ed. Statistical Properties of Nuclei. LC 75-182409. 665p. 1972. 75.00x (ISBN 0-306-30576-3, Plenum Pr). Plenum Pub.
Gruen, D. M., ed. Chemistry of Fusion Technology. LC 72-89488. 394p. 1972. 55.00x (ISBN 0-306-30714-6, Plenum Pr). Plenum Pub.
Guidebook on Nuclear Techniques in Hydrology. (Technical Reports Ser.: No. 91). 439p. 1983. pap. text ed. 56.00 (ISBN 92-0-145083-4, IDC91/2, IAEA). Unipub.
Handbook on Nuclear Activation Cross-Sections. (Technical Reports: No. 156). (Illus.). 558p. 1974. pap. 43.25 (ISBN 92-0-135074-0, IDC156, IAEA). Unipub.
Harms, A. A. & Heindler, M. Nuclear Energy Synergetics: An Introduction to Conceptual Models of Integrated Nuclear Energy Systems. LC 82-16175. 252p. 1982. 37.50x (ISBN 0-306-40951-8, Plenum Pr). Plenum Pub.
Harrington, Charlene, et al. Long Term Care of the Elderly: Public Policy Issues. LC 84-17754. 280p. 1985. 29.00 (ISBN 0-8039-2214-0); pap. 14.00 (ISBN 0-8039-2215-9). Sage.
Henley, E. J., et al, eds. Advances in Nuclear Science & Technology. Incl. Vol. 1. 1962 (ISBN 0-12-029301-3); Vol. 2. 1964 (ISBN 0-12-029302-1); Vol. 4. 1968 (ISBN 0-12-029304-8); Vol. 5. Henley, E. J. & Lewins, J., eds. 1969 (ISBN 0-12-029305-6); Vol. 6. 1972 (ISBN 0-12-029306-4); Vol. 7. 1973 (ISBN 0-12-029307-2); Vol. 9. 1976 (ISBN 0-12-029309-9). 80.00 ea. Acad Pr.
--Advances in Nuclear Science & Technology, Vol. 10. LC 62-13039. 598p. 1977. 85.00x (ISBN 0-306-38230-X, Plenum Pr). Plenum Pub.
Hetrick, David L., ed. Dynamics of Nuclear Systems: Developed from the Papers Presented at the Nuclear Engineering Symposium at the University of Arizona, March 23-25, 1970. LC 73-147251. pap. 154.50 (ISBN 0-317-09044-5, 2055344). Bks Demand UMI.
INIS: Authority List for Corporate Entries & Report Prefixes. (INIS Reference Ser.: No. 6). pap. 15.50 (IN6/R10, IAEA). Unipub.
INIS: Authority List for Corporate Entries. (INIS Reference Ser.: No. 6). pap. 13.25 (IN6/R9, IAEA). Unipub.
INIS: Authority List for Journal Titles. (INIS Reference Ser.: No. 11). pap. 6.75 (IN11/R5, IAEA). Unipub.
INIS: Authority List for Journal Titles. (INIS Reference Ser.: No. 11). pap. 7.75 (IN11/R6, IAEA). Unipub.
INIS: Description of Computer Programs. (INIS Reference Ser.: No. 14). pap. 5.75 (ISBN 92-0-178675-1, IN14/R1, IAEA). Unipub.
INIS: Descriptive Cataloging Samples. (INIS Reference Ser.: No. 2). pap. 2.25 (IN2/R2, IAEA). Unipub.
INIS: Descriptive Cataloging Rules. (INIS Reference Ser.: No. 1). pap. 2.25 (IN1/R2, IAEA). Unipub.
INIS: Descriptive Cataloging Samples. (INIS Reference Ser.: No. 2). 1978. pap. 5.50 (ISBN 92-0-178278-0, IN2/R3, IAEA). Unipub.
INIS: Instructions for Submitting Abstracts. (INIS Reference Ser.: No. 4). pap. 5.50 (ISBN 92-0-178171-7, IN4/R1, IAEA). Unipub.
INIS: Manual for Index. (INIS Reference Ser.: No. 12). 108p. 1974. pap. 5.50 (ISBN 92-0-178074-5, IN12/R2, IAEA). Unipub.
INIS: Multilingual Dictionary - English-French-German-Russian, No. 1. (INIS Reference Ser.: 20). 1983. pap. 23.25 (ISBN 9-2017-8283-7, IN20/R0, IAEA). Unipub.
INIS: Self-Teaching Manual. (INIS Reference Ser.: No. 15). 1972. pap. 8.75 (ISBN 92-0-178772-3, IN15/R0, IAEA). Unipub.
INIS: Subject Categories & Scope Descriptions. (INIS Reference Ser.: No. 3). pap. 3.75 (IN3/R4, IAEA). Unipub.
INIS: Subject Indexing Samples. (INIS Reference Ser.: No. 16). pap. 7.00 (ISBN 92-0-178775-8, IN16/R0, IAEA). Unipub.
INIS: Terminology & Codes for Countries & International Organizations. (INIS Reference Ser.: 5). 14p. pap. 5.50 (ISBN 92-0-178375-2, IN5/R3, IAEA). Unipub.
Jackson, J. D., et al, eds. Annual Review of Nuclear & Particle Science, Vol. 33. LC 53-995. Orig. Title: Annual Review of Nuclear Science. (Illus.). 1983. text ed. 30.00 (ISBN 0-8243-1533-2). Annual Reviews.
Jaklovsky, Josef. Preparation of Nuclear Targets: A Comprehensive Bibliography. LC 81-12014. (IFI Data Base Library). 332p. 1981. text ed. 95.00 (ISBN 0-306-65200-5, IFI Plenum). Plenum Pub.
Jaklovsky, Josef, ed. Preparation of Nuclear Targets for Particle Accelerators. LC 81-7293. 300p. 1981. text ed. 49.50x (ISBN 0-306-40731-0, Plenum Pr). Plenum Pub.
Johnson, Noah R., intro. by. High Angular Momentum Properties of Nuclei. LC 83-8458. (Nuclear Science Research Conference Ser.). (Illus.). 520p. 1984. 74.50 (ISBN 3-7186-0169-9). Harwood Academic.
Jones, Alan V., ed. Multiphase Processes in LMFBR Safety Analysis. (Ispra Courses on Nuclear Engineering & Technology: Vol. 5). 523p. 1984. 104.00. Harwood Academic.
King, J. R., Jr., ed. Engineering & Business: Converting Engineers to Businessmen. LC 82-83563. 80p. 1982. pap. 11.00x (ISBN 0-87262-342-4). Am Soc Civil Eng.
Lacey, Robert & Loeb, Sidney, eds. Industrial Processing with Membranes. LC 78-21889. 360p. 1979. Repr. of 1972 ed. lib. bdg. 25.00 (ISBN 0-88275-788-1). Krieger.
Lakner, A. A. & Anderson, R. T. Reliability Engineering for Nuclear & Other High Technology Systems: A Practical Guide. (Illus.). 418p. 1985. 82.50 (ISBN 0-85334-286-5, Pub. by Elsevier Applied Sci England). Elsevier.
Lamarsh, John R. Introduction to Nuclear Engineering. 2nd ed. LC 82-8678. (Nuclear Science & Engineering Ser.). (Illus.). 652p. 1983. text ed. 41.95 (ISBN 0-201-14200-7). Addison-Wesley.
Lau, L. Wang. Elements of Nuclear Reactor Engineering. new ed. LC 77-156083. 256p. 1974. 69.50x (ISBN 0-677-02270-0). Gordon.
Lewins, Jeffery & Becker, Martin, eds. Advances in Nuclear Science & Technology, Vol. 14. LC 82-3654. 388p. 1982. 59.50x (ISBN 0-306-40994-1, Plenum Pr). Plenum Pub.
Lewins, Jeffery & Becker, Martin, eds. Advances in Nuclear Science & Technology, Vol. 13. LC 62-13039. 480p. 1981. 75.00x (ISBN 0-306-40637-3, Plenum Pr). Plenum Pub.
--Advances in Nuclear Science & Technology, Vol. 15. 418p. 1983. 57.50x (ISBN 0-306-41392-2, Plenum Pr). Plenum Pub.
Mader, Charles L., ed. LASL Phermex Data, Vol. 2. (The Los Alamos Scientific Series on Dynamic Material Properties). 768p. 1980. 55.00x (ISBN 0-520-04010-4). U of Cal Pr.
Mandelbaum, Michael. The Nuclear Future. LC 82-74068. 128p. 1983. 22.50x (ISBN 0-8014-1619-1); pap. 5.95x (ISBN 0-8014-9254-8). Cornell U Pr.
Ministry of Education Sciences. Scientific Terms Nuclear Engineering: Japanese-English, English-Japanese. (Japanese & Eng.). 282p. 1977. leatherette 25.00 (ISBN 0-686-92519-X, M-9336). French & Eur.
Morse, Jerome G. Nuclear Methods in Mineral Exploration & Production. (Developments in Economic Geology Ser.: Vol. 7). 280p. 1977. 68.00 (ISBN 0-444-41567-X). Elsevier.
Murphy, Glenn. Elements of Nuclear Engineering. LC 74-16147. (Illus.). 248p. 1975. Repr. of 1961 ed. 18.50 (ISBN 0-88275-155-7). Krieger.
Nea & the U. S. Dept. of Energy, Workshop, Columbus, Ohio, May 1980. Borehole & Shaft Plugging: Proceedings. OECD Staff, ed. (Illus.). 422p. (Orig.). 1980. pap. 30.00x (ISBN 92-64-02114-0). OECD.
Noggle, Joseph H. & Schirmer, Richard E. Nuclear Overhauser Effect: Chemical Applications. 1971. 61.50 (ISBN 0-12-520650-X). Acad Pr.
The Nuclear Age: Power, Proliferation, & the Arms Race. LC 84-5822. 253p. 1984. pap. 11.95 (ISBN 0-87187-311-7). Congr Quarterly.
Nuclear Data Standards for Nuclear Measurements. (Technical Reports Ser.: No. 227). (Eng.). 97p. 1984. pap. 19.25 (ISBN 92-0-135083-X, IDC227, IAEA). Unipub.
Nuclear Power Plant Steam & Mechanical Fundamentals, 12 vols. 2nd ed. (Illus.). 988p. 1981. Set. pap. text ed. 65.00x (ISBN 0-87683-300-8); lesson plans BWR set 2900.00x (ISBN 0-87683-313-X); lesson plans PWR set 2900.00x (ISBN 0-87683-314-8). G P Courseware.
Nuclear Power Plant Steam & Mechanical Fundamentals, Vol. 1. 2nd ed. (Illus.). 46p. 1981. pap. text ed. 6.00x (ISBN 0-87683-301-6). G P Courseware.
Nuclear Power Plant Steam & Mechanical Fundamentals, Vol. 2. 2nd ed. (Illus.). 100p. 1981. pap. text ed. 6.00x (ISBN 0-87683-302-4). G P Courseware.
Nuclear Power Plant Steam & Mechanical Fundamentals, Vol. 3. 2nd ed. (Illus.). 62p. 1981. pap. text ed. 6.00x (ISBN 0-87683-303-2). G P Courseware.
Nuclear Power Plant Steam & Mechanical Fundamentals, Vol. 4. 2nd ed. (Illus.). 74p. 1981. pap. text ed. 6.00x (ISBN 0-87683-304-0). G P Courseware.
Nuclear Power Plant Steam & Mechanical Fundamentals, Vol. 5. 2nd ed. (Illus.). 98p. 1981. pap. text ed. 6.00x (ISBN 0-87683-305-9). G P Courseware.
Nuclear Power Plant Steam & Mechanical Fundamentals, Vol. 6. 2nd ed. (Illus.). 86p. 1981. pap. text ed. 6.00x (ISBN 0-87683-306-7). G P Courseware.
Nuclear Power Plant Steam & Mechanical Fundamentals, Vol. 8. 2nd ed. (Illus.). 86p. 1981. pap. text ed. 6.00x (ISBN 0-87683-308-3). G P Courseware.
Nuclear Power Plant Steam & Mechanical Fundamentals, Vol. 9. 2nd ed. (Illus.). 90p. 1981. pap. text ed. 6.00x (ISBN 0-87683-309-1). G P Courseware.
Nuclear Power Plant Steam & Mechanical Fundamentals, Vol. 10. 2nd ed. (Illus.). 78p. 1981. pap. text ed. 6.00x (ISBN 0-87683-310-5). G P Courseware.
Nuclear Power Plant Steam & Mechanical Fundamentals, Vol. 11. 2nd ed. (Illus.). 66p. 1981. pap. text ed. 6.00x (ISBN 0-87683-311-3). G P Courseware.
Nuclear Power Plant Steam & Mechanical Fundamentals, Vol. 12. 2nd ed. (Illus.). 78p. 1981. pap. text ed. 6.00x (ISBN 0-87683-312-1). G P Courseware.
Nuclear Techniques & Mineral Resources: 1977. (Proceedings Ser.). (Illus.). 651p. 1977. pap. 75.25 (ISBN 92-0-060077-8, ISP464, IAEA). Unipub.
OCED Specialists Meeting, Paris, Nov. 26-8, 1979. Calculation of Three-Dimensional Rating Distributions in Operating Reactors: Proceedings. (Eng. & Fr.). 450p. (Orig.). 1980. pap. 21.50x (ISBN 92-64-02052-7, 66-80-04-3). OECD.
OECD-Nuclear Energy Agency. Regulatory & Institutional Framework for Nuclear Activities: Vol. I. (Nuclear Legislation Analytical Study). 219p. 1983. pap. 25.00 (ISBN 92-64-12534-5). OECD.
Operating Experience with Nuclear Power Stations in Member States in 1979. 392p. 1981. pap. 53.75 (ISBN 92-0-159081-4, ISP586, IAEA). Unipub.
Operating Experience with Nuclear Power Stations in Member States: Performance Analysis Report 1977. 28p. 1980. pap. 6.00 (ISBN 92-0-159179-9, ISP543, IAEA). Unipub.
Oshima, Keiichi, et al, eds. Nuclear Engineering for an Uncertain Future. LC 81-84687. 300p. 1982. text ed. 55.00x (ISBN 0-306-40953-4, Plenum Pr). Plenum Pub.

Pedersen, Knud, et al. Applied Nuclear Power for Practicing Engineers. (Professional Engineering Career Development). 1972. 15.95x (ISBN 0-8464-0143-6). Beekman Pubs.

Petrosyants, A. M. From Scientific Search to Atomic Industry. LC 74-24684. 374p. 1975. text ed. 17.90x (ISBN 0-8134-1661-2, 1661). Interstate.

Petrosy'Ants, A. M. Problems of Nuclear Science & Technology: The Soviet Union As a World Nuclear Power. 4th rev. & enl. ed. LC 80-40818. (Illus.). 400p. 1981. 62.00 (ISBN 0-08-025462-4). Pergamon.

Quality Assurance in the Procurement, Design & Manufacture of Nuclear Fuel Assemblies: A Safety Guide. (Safety Ser.: No. 50-SG-QA11). 34p. 1983. pap. text ed. 9.00 (ISBN 92-0-123283-7, ISP644, IAEA). Unipub.

Rahn, Frank, et al. A Guide to Nuclear Power Technology: A Resource for Decision-Making. LC 84-7362. 912p. 1984. 79.95x (ISBN 0-471-88914-8). Wiley.

Research Applications of Nuclear Pulsed Systems. (Panel Proceedings Ser.). (Illus.). 234p. 1967. pap. 16.25 (ISBN 92-0-151067-5, ISP144, IAEA). Unipub.

Roberts, J. T., ed. Structural Materials in Nuclear Power Systems. LC 81-1883. (Modern Perspectives in Energy Ser.). 500p. 1981. 59.50x (ISBN 0-306-40669-1, Plenum Pr). Plenum Pub.

Sample Analysis of a Piping System: Class One Nuclear. 1972. pap. text ed. 4.50 (ISBN 0-685-30778-6, E00063). ASME.

Shieh, Paulinus S. & Rahman, Inam-Ur. Introduction to Nuclear Engineering. LC 80-13160. 424p. 1981. text ed. 32.50 (ISBN 0-88275-972-8). Krieger.

Steel, L. E. Neutron Irradiation Embrittlement of Reactor Pressure Vessel Steels. (Technical Reports Ser.: No. 163). (Illus.). 235p. 1975. pap. 26.50 (ISBN 92-0-155075-8, IDC163, IAEA). Unipub.

Steps to Nuclear Power: A Guidebook. (Technical Reports Ser.: No. 164). (Illus.). 106p. 1975. pap. 14.50 (ISBN 92-0-155175-4, IDC164, IAEA). Unipub.

Stewart, Hugh B. Transitional Energy Policy 1980-2030: Alternative Nuclear Technologies. (Pergamon Policy Studies on Science & Technology). 266p. 1981. 33.00 (ISBN 0-08-027183-9); pap. 13.75 (ISBN 0-08-027182-0). Pergamon.

Thermodynamics, 2 Vols. 1966. Vol. 1. 32.25 (ISBN 92-0-040066-3, ISP109-1, IAEA); Vol. 2. 39.50 (ISBN 92-0-040166-X, ISP109-2). Unipub.

Ultimate Heat Sink & Directly Associated Heat Transport Systems for Nuclear Power Plants: A Safety Guide. (Safety Ser.: No. 50-SG-D6). (Illus.). 62p. 1981. pap. 12.25 (ISBN 92-0-123581-X, ISP581, IAEA). Unipub.

Villani, S., ed. Uranium Enrichment. (Topics in Applied Physics Ser.: Vol. 35). (Illus.). 1979. 59.00 (ISBN 0-387-09385-0). Springer-Verlag.

Wylie, A. W. Nuclear Assaying of Mining Boreholes: An Introduction. (Methods in Geochemistry & Geophysics Ser.: Vol. 21). 344p. 1985. 65.00 (ISBN 0-444-42357-5). Elsevier.

Zebroski, E. L. & Simard, R. L., eds. Information Management in the Nuclear Industry. (Illus.). 94p. 1983. pap. 40.00 (ISBN 0-08-031483-X). Pergamon.

NUCLEAR ENGINEERING–DICTIONARIES

Carpovich, Eugene A. Russian-English Atomic Dictionary: Physics, Mathematics, Nucleonics. rev. ed. 2nd ed. LC 57-8256. (Rus. & Eng.). 1959. 15.00 (ISBN 0-911484-00-0). Tech Dict.

Clason, W. E. Elsevier's Dictionary of Nuclear Science & Technology. 2nd rev. ed. (Eng., Fr., Span., Ital., Dutch & Ger.). 787p. 1970. 132.00 (ISBN 0-444-40810-X). Elsevier.

Freyberger, G. H. Abbreviations of Nuclear Power Plant Engineering. (Eng. & Ger.). 280p. 1979. 28.95 (ISBN 0-686-56591-6, M-7288, Pub. by Verlag Karl Thiemig). French & Eur.

Stattmann, F. Dictionary of Power Plant Engineering: Nuclear Power Plants, Pt. II. (Ger. & Fr.). 316p. 1973. 15.95 (ISBN 3-521-06081-0, M-7102). French & Eur.

Sube, R. Dictionary of Nuclear Engineering: English, German, French, Russian. 1985. 139.00 (ISBN 0-444-99593-5). Elsevier.

NUCLEAR ENGINEERING–INSTRUMENTS

Boland, James F. Nuclear Reactor Instrumentation (In-Core) LC 76-101310. 230p. 1970. 12.50 (ISBN 0-677-02420-7, 450015). Am Nuclear Soc.

Frederickson, F. M., ed. Snubber Design Applications & Minimization Methods. (PVP Ser.: Vol. 55). 75p. 1981. 14.00 (ISBN 0-686-34515-0, H00191). ASME.

Severud, L. K., et al, eds. Structural Considerations & Findings from Testing of Nuclear Components. (PVP Ser.: Vol. 49). 99p. 1981. 24.00 (ISBN 0-686-34519-3, H00185). ASME.

NUCLEAR ENGINEERING–SAFETY MEASURES

see also Radiation–Dosage; Radioactive Decontamination; Radioactive Waste Disposal

Atomic Industrial Forum Staff. Use of Potassium Iodide in Emergency Planning for Nuclear Power Plants: Selected Technical Papers from Radiation Issues. (Technical & Economic Reports: Radiation Protection & Environmental Considerations). 1982. 15.00 (ISBN 0-318-02243-5). Atomic Indus Forum.

The Biological Implications of Radionuclides Released from Nuclear Industries: Proceedings of Symposium Vienna 26-30 March 1979, 2 Vols. 923p. 1979. Vol. 1. pap. 67.25 (ISBN 92-0-010479-7, ISP522 1, IAEA); Vol. 2. pap. 62.00 (ISBN 92-0-010579-3, ISP522 2). Unipub.

Convention on the Physical Protection of Nuclear Material. (Legal Ser.: No. 12). 405p. 1983. pap. 52.75 (ISBN 92-0-176082-5, ISP615, IAEA). Unipub.

Criticality Control of Fissile Materials. (Illus.). 757p. (Orig.). 1966. pap. 45.00 (ISBN 92-0-020066-4, ISP114, IAEA). Unipub.

Current Nuclear Power Plant Safety Issues, 2 Vols, Vol. 1. (Proceedings Ser.). 518p. 1981. pap. 71.50 (ISBN 92-0-020181-4, ISP566/1, IAEA); pap. 93.00 (ISBN 92-0-020281-0, ISP566/2); pap. 83.50 (ISBN 92-0-020381-7, ISP566/3). Unipub.

Design, Construction, Operation, Shutdown & Surveillance of Repositories for Radioactive Wastes in Shallow Ground: Proceedures & Data. (Safety Ser.: No. 63). 62p. (Orig.). 1984. pap. 13.75 (ISBN 92-0-123384-1, ISP652, IAEA). Unipub.

Emergency Power Systems at Nuclear Power Plants: A Safety Guide. (Safety Ser.: No. 50-SG-D7). (Illus.). 50p. 1983. pap. 10.25 (ISBN 92-0-123782-0, ISP631, IAEA). Unipub.

Environmental Surveillance Around Nuclear Installations, 2 Vols. (Proceedings Ser.). (Illus.). 928p. (Vol. 1, 472p; Vol. 2, 456p). pap. 81.00 set (ISP353, IAEA); Vol. 1. pap. 40.50 (ISBN 92-0-020074-5, ISP353-1); Vol. 2. pap. 40.50 (ISBN 92-0-020174-1, ISP353-2). Unipub.

External Man-Induced Events in Relation to Nuclear Power Plant Siting: A Safety Guide. (Safety Ser.: No. 50-SG-S5). 62p. 1981. pap. 12.75 (ISBN 92-0-123081-8, ISP585, IAEA). Unipub.

Fuel Handling & Storage Systems in Nuclear Power Plants. (Safety Ser.: No. 50-SG-D10). 52p. (Orig.). 1984. pap. 12.00 (ISBN 92-0-123584-4, ISP662, IAEA). Unipub.

Guidelines for the Layout & Contents of Safety Reports for Stationary Nuclear Power Plants. (Safety Ser.: No. 34). 54p. (Orig.). 1970. pap. 7.25 (ISBN 92-0-123170-9, ISP272, IAEA). Unipub.

IAEA Safeguards - An Introduction. (Safeguards Information Ser.: Vol. 3). (Illus.). 48p. 1981. pap. 8.00 (ISBN 92-0-179081-3, ISGINF3, IAEA). Unipub.

Kottowski, H. M., ed. Safety Problems Related to Sodium Handling in Liquid Metal Fast Breeder Reactors & Large Test Facillities. (Ispra Courses on Nuclear Engineering & Technology). 258p. 1982. 38.00 (ISBN 3-7186-0087-0). Harwood Academic.

Kratzer, Myron B. Prior Consent & Nuclear Cooperation. (Technical & Economic Reports: Proliferation & Safeguards). 1983. 50.00 (ISBN 0-318-02239-7). Atomic Indus Forum.

Maintenance of Nuclear Power Plants: A Safety Guide. (Safety Ser.: No. 50-SG-07). 46p. 1983. pap. 9.75 (ISBN 92-0-123882-7, ISP604, IAEA). Unipub.

Management of Nuclear Power Plants for Safe Operation: A Safety Guide. (Safety Ser.: No. 50-SG-09). (Eng., Fr., Rus. & Span.). 56p. 1985. pap. 12.50 (ISBN 92-0-123984-X, ISP660, IAEA). Unipub.

Management of Tritium at Nuclear Facilities. (Technical Reports Ser.: No. 234). 62p. (Orig.). 1984. pap. 13.00 (ISBN 92-0-125084-3, IDC234, IAEA). Unipub.

Manual on Quality Assurance Programme Auditing. (Technical Reports Ser.: No. 237). 149p. 1985. pap. 26.50 (ISBN 92-0-155184-3, IDC237, IAEA). Unipub.

Marguglio, B. W. Quality Systems in the Nuclear Industry, STP 616. 700p. 1977. 37.75 (ISBN 0-8031-0197-X). ASTM.

Melville, Mary H. The Temporary Worker in the Nuclear Power Industry: An Equity Analysis. LC 81-65590. (CENTED Monographs: No. 1). (Illus.). 70p. 1981. pap. text ed. 5.00x (ISBN 0-939436-00-0). Ctr Tech Environ.

Nuclear Heat Application: Proceedings of a Technical Committee Meeting & Workshop, Cracow, 5-9 December 1983. (Panel Proceedings Ser.). (Eng., Fr & Rus.). 419p. 1985. pap. 65.75 (ISBN 92-0-051084-1, ISP679, IAEA). Unipub.

Nuclear Safeguards Technology 1982: Proceedings of an International Symposium on Recent Advances in Nuclear Material Safeguards Organized by the International Atomic Energy Agency & Held in Vienna, 8-12 November 1982, 2 vols. (Proceedings Ser.). 1983. Vol. 1. pap. 86.50 (ISBN 92-0-070083-7, ISP629-1, IAEA); Vol. 2. pap. 91.25 (ISBN 92-0-070183-3, ISP629-2). Unipub.

OECD Staff. Critical Flow Modeling in Nuclear Safety. 102p. 1982. pap. 13.00 (ISBN 92-64-12366-0). OECD.

Radiation Protection During Operation of Nuclear Power Plants: A Safety Guide. (Safety Ser.: No. 50-SG-05). 54p. 1983. pap. text ed. 12.00 (ISBN 92-0-123783-9, ISP654, IAEA). Unipub.

Radiation Protection Monitoring. (Proceedings Ser.). (Illus.). 556p. 1969. pap. 39.50 (ISBN 92-0-020069-9, ISP199, IAEA). Unipub.

Safeguard Techniques & Equipment: IAEA Safeguards. (Safeguards Information Ser.: No. 5). (Illus.). 35p. 1985. pap. 7.50 (ISBN 92-0-179084-8, ISGINF5, IAEA). Unipub.

Safety Analysis Methodologies for Radioactive Waste Repositories in Shallow Ground: Procedures & Data. (Safety Ser.: No. 64). 53p. (Orig.). 1984. pap. 11.75 (ISBN 92-0-123484-8, ISP656, IAEA). Unipub.

Safety Aspects of Core Management & Fuel Handling for Nuclear Power Plants: A Safety Guide. (Safety Ser.: No. 50-SG-010). 40p. 1985. pap. 10.00 (ISBN 92-0-123085-0, ISP685 5071, IAEA). Unipub.

Safety Related Instrumentation & Control Systems for Nuclear Power Plants: A Safety Guide. (Safety Ser.: No. 50-SG-D8). (Illus.). 48p. 1985. pap. 11.25 (ISBN 92-0-623184-7, ISP678, IAEA). Unipub.

Site Investigations, Design, Construction, Operation, Shutdown & Surveillance of Repositories for Low & Intermediate Level Radioactive Wastes in Rock Cavities. (Safety Ser.: No. 62). 95p. (Orig.). 1984. pap. 18.50 (ISBN 92-0-123284-5, ISP659, IAEA). Unipub.

Site Survey for Nuclear Power Plants. (Safety Ser.: No. 50-SG-S9). 48p. 1985. pap. 11.25 (ISBN 92-0-123884-3, ISP682, IAEA). Unipub.

Spinrad, Bernard I. Use of Computers in Analysis of Experimental Data & the Control of Nuclear Facilities: Proceedings. LC 67-60057. (AEC Symposium Ser.). 306p. 1967. pap. 15.75 (ISBN 0-87079-214-8, CONF-660527); microfiche 4.50 (ISBN 0-87079-215-6, CONF-660527). DOE.

Study of a Recordkeeping System for Inprocessing of Transient Workers at Nuclear Power Plants: AIF-NESP-025. (National Environmental Studies Project: NESP Reports). 1982. 50.00 (ISBN 0-318-02233-8). Atomic Indus Forum.

Surveillance of Items Important to Safety in Nuclear Power Plants: A Safety Ser. (Safety Ser.: No. 50-SG-08). 48p. 1983. pap. 9.25 (ISBN 92-0-123282-9, ISP640, IAEA). Unipub.

Thomas, A. F. & Abbey, F. Calculational Methods of Interacting Arrays of Fissile Material. LC 73-8604. 144p. 1973. text ed. 33.00 (ISBN 0-08-017660-7). Pergamon.

NUCLEAR ENGINEERING AS A PROFESSION

Manpower Development for Nuclear Power: A Guidebook. (Technical Reports Ser.: No. 200). (Illus.). 508p. 1980. pap. 72.25 (ISBN 92-0-155080-4, IDC200, IAEA). Unipub.

Working with the Atom: Careers for You. (Public Affairs & Information Program: General). 41p. 1982. pap. 1.75 (ISBN 0-318-02236-2). Atomic Indus Forum.

NUCLEAR EXCAVATION

Nuclear Techniques & Mineral Resources: 1977. (Proceedings Ser.). (Illus.). 651p. 1977. pap. 75.25 (ISBN 92-0-060077-8, ISP464, IAEA). Unipub.

Weaver, Lynn E., ed. Education for Peaceful Uses of Nuclear Explosives. LC 76-101101. (Illus.). pap. 89.80 (ISBN 0-317-08638-3, 2055345). Bks Demand UMI.

NUCLEAR EXCITATION

Belyaev, S. T. Collective Excitations in Nuclei. (Documents on Modern Physics Ser.). 84p. 1968. 38.50 (ISBN 0-677-01870-3). Gordon.

Bohr, A. Elementary Modes of Excitation in Nuclei. (Enrico Fermi Summer Institute Ser.: Vol. 69). 548p. 1978. 117.00 (ISBN 0-444-85153-4, North-Holland). Elsevier.

Demas, J. N., ed. Excited State Lifetime Measurements: Monograph. LC 82-16253. 288p. 1983. 47.50 (ISBN 0-12-208920-0). Acad Pr.

De Mayo, Paul, ed. Rearrangements in Ground & Excited States, Vol. 1. LC 79-51675. (Organic Chemistry Ser.). 1980. 84.00 (ISBN 0-12-481301-1). Acad Pr.

--Rearrangements in Ground & Excited States, Vol. 2. LC 79-51675. (Organic Chemistry Ser.). 1980. 77.00 (ISBN 0-12-481302-X). Acad Pr.

Devreese, J. T., et al, eds. Elementary Excitations in Solids, Molecules, & Atoms, 2 pts. Incl. Pt. A. 375p. 59.50x (ISBN 0-306-35791-7); Pt. B. 385p. 59.50x (ISBN 0-306-35792-5). LC 74-1247. (NATO ASI Series B, Physics: Vols. 2A & 2B). 1974 (Plenum Pr). Plenum Pub.

Lim, Edward. Excited States, Vol. 5. (Serial Publication Ser.). 220p. 1982. 55.00 (ISBN 0-12-227205-6). Acad Pr.

Lim, Edward, ed. Excited States, Vol. 6. 216p. 1982. 55.00 (ISBN 0-12-227206-4). Acad Pr.

Lim, Edward C., ed. Excited States, Vols. 1 & 2. Vol. 1, 1974. 75.00 (ISBN 0-12-227201-3); Vol. 2, 1975. 80.00 (ISBN 0-12-227202-1); Vol. 3, 1978. 70.00 (ISBN 0-12-227203-X). Acad Pr.

--Excited States, Vol. 4. (Serial Publication). 1980. 65.00 (ISBN 0-12-227204-8). Acad Pr.

Maradudin, A. A. & Nardelli, G. F. Elementary Excitations in Solids. LC 68-26772. 526p. 1969. 49.50x (ISBN 0-306-30356-6, Plenum Pr). Plenum Pub.

Sherf, Libi & Neufeld, Henry N. Pre-Excitation Syndrome: Facts & Theories. LC 78-56930. 1978. 40.00 (ISBN 0-914316-13-3). Yorke Med.

Shoppee, Charles W., ed. Excited States of Matter. (Graduate Studies: No. 2). (Illus.). 174p. (Orig.). 1973. pap. 8.00 (ISBN 0-89672-009-8). Tex Tech Pr.

Thorpe, M. F., ed. Excitations in Disordered Systems. LC 82-543. (NATO ASI Series B, Physics: Vol. 78). 718p. 1982. 105.00x (ISBN 0-306-40981-X, Plenum Pr). Plenum Pub.

Ware, William R., ed. Creation & Detection of the Excited State, Vol. 2. 240p. 1974. 85.00 (ISBN 0-8247-6113-8). Dekker.

--Creation & Detection of the Excited State, Vol. 4. 336p. 1976. 85.00 (ISBN 0-8247-6451-X). Dekker.

NUCLEAR FISSION

see also Fission Products; Neutron Transport Theory

Arnett, David W. & Truran, James W., eds. Nucleosynthesis: Challenges & New Developments. LC 85-1160. (Illus.). x, 308p. 1985. 36.00x (ISBN 0-226-02787-2); pap. 18.00 (ISBN 0-226-02788-0). U of Chicago Pr.

Duderstadt, James J. & Hamilton, Louis J. Nuclear Reactor Analysis. LC 75-20389. 650p. 1976. text ed. 54.00 (ISBN 0-471-22363-8). Wiley.

Goldschmidt, Bertrand. The Atomic Complex: A Worldwide Political History of Nuclear Energy. LC 82-70371. Orig. Title: Le Complexe Atomique. 520p. 1982. 31.00 (ISBN 0-89448-550-4, 690007); pap. 24.00 (ISBN 0-89448-551-2, 690008). Am Nuclear Soc.

Graetzerk, Hans G. & Anderson, David L. The Discovery of Nuclear Fission. Cohen, I. Bernard, ed. LC 80-2123. (Development of Science Ser.). (Illus.). 1981. lib. bdg. 12.00x (ISBN 0-405-13846-6). Ayer Co Pubs.

Natural Fission Reactors. (Panel Proceedings Ser.). (Illus.). 754p. 1979. pap. 78.75 (ISBN 92-0-051078-7, ISP475, IAEA). Unipub.

Physics & Chemistry of Fission: 1969. (Proceedings Ser.). (Illus.). 983p. (Orig.). 1969. pap. 68.00 (ISBN 92-0-030269-6, ISP234, IAEA). Unipub.

Physics & Chemistry of Fission: 1973, 2 vols. (Proceedings Ser.). (Illus.). 579p. (Orig.). 1974. Vol. 1. pap. 49.25 (ISBN 92-0-030074-X, ISP347-1, IAEA); Vol. 2. pap. 45.75 (ISBN 92-0-030174-6, ISP347-2). Unipub.

Prompt Fission Neutron Spectra. (Panel Proceedings Ser.). (Illus.). 176p. (Orig.). 1973. pap. 14.50 (ISBN 92-0-131172-9, ISP329, IAEA). Unipub.

Schmitz, F. K., et al. Fission Gas Behavior in Safety Experiments. (European Applied Research Reports, Nuclear Science & Technology Section Ser.: Vol. 5, No. 6). 204p. 1985. pap. 198.00 (ISBN 3-7186-0226-1). Harwood Academic.

Vandenbosch, Robert & Huizenga, John R. Nuclear Fission. 1973. 76.50 (ISBN 0-12-710850-5). Acad Pr.

NUCLEAR FORCES (PHYSICS)

see also Coulomb Functions

Austin, S. M., ed. The Two-Body Force in Nuclei. Crawley, G. M. LC 72-76009. 390p. 1972. 55.00x (ISBN 0-306-30598-4, Plenum Pr). Plenum Pub.

Davies, P. C. The Forces of Nature. LC 78-72084. (Illus.). 1979. 44.50 (ISBN 0-521-22523-X). Cambridge U Pr.

Zingl, H., et al, eds. Few Body Systems & Nuclear Forces: 8th International Conference Held in Graz, Austria, August 24-30, 1978. LC 78-13440. (Lecture Notes in Physics: Vol. 82). 1978. pap. 25.00 (ISBN 0-387-08917-9). Springer-Verlag.

NUCLEAR FUEL ELEMENTS

Detection & Location of Failed Fuel Elements. (Panel Proceedings Ser.). (Illus.). 241p. (Orig.). 1968. pap. 15.25 (ISBN 92-0-051168-6, ISP204, IAEA). Unipub.

Fedorov, G. B. & Smirnov, E. A. Diffusion in Reactor Materials. (Diffusion & Defect Monogr Ser.: Vol. 8). 182p. 1984. 36.00 (ISBN 0-87849-531-2). Trans Tech.

Frost, B. R. Nuclear Fuel Elements: Design-Fabrication-Performance. (International Series in Nuclear Energy). (Illus.). 244p. 1982. 39.00 (ISBN 0-08-020412-0); pap. 19.25 (ISBN 0-08-020411-2). Pergamon.

Holden, A. N. Dispersion Fuel Elements. LC 67-29666. 255p. 1967. 11.00 (ISBN 0-685-58274-4, 450017). Am Nuclear Soc.

Holden, Robert B. Ceramic Fuel Elements. LC 66-28066. 244p. 1966. 12.50 (ISBN 0-685-58271-X, 450002). Am Nuclear Soc.

Linder, P. Air Filters for Use at Nuclear Facilities. (Technical Reports Ser.: No. 122). (Illus.). 76p. (Orig.). 1970. pap. 9.75 (ISBN 92-0-125670-1, IDC122, IAEA). Unipub.

OECD Staff. Dry Storage of Spent Fuel Elements. 272p. 1982. pap. 17.00 (ISBN 92-64-02351-8). OECD.

--Safety of the Nuclear Fuel Cycle: A State-of-the-Art Report, May 1981. 162p. (Orig.). 1981. pap. text ed. 16.50x (ISBN 92-64-12213-3). OECD.

Olander, Donald R. Fundamental Aspects of Nuclear Reactor Fuel Elements, 2 vols. LC 76-6485. (ERDA Technical Information Center Ser.). 1976. Vol. 1, 624 p. pap. 23.50 (ISBN 0-87079-031-5, TID-26711-P1); Vol. 2: Solutions to Problems, 557 p, 1976. microfiche 4.50 (TID-26711-P1); pap. 22.00 (TID-26711-P2); microfiche 4.50 (ISBN 0-87079-467-1, TID-26711-P2). DOE.

Plutonium Oxygen & Uranium-Plutonium-Oxygen Systems: Thermochemical Assessment. (Technical Reports Ser.: No. 79). (Illus.). 86p. pap. 9.00 (ISBN 92-0-145167-9, IDC79, IAEA). Unipub.

Simnad, Massoud. Fuel Element Experience in Nuclear Power Reactors. LC 78-131892. 620p. 1971. 37.50 (ISBN 0-677-03260-9, 450016). Am Nuclear Soc.

Weissert & Schileo. Fabrication of Thorium Fuel Elements. LC 68-25126. 1968. 11.10 (ISBN 0-89448-007-3, 300001). Am Nuclear Soc.

NUCLEAR FUELS

see also Nuclear Fuel Elements; Reactor Fuel Reprocessing; Thorium; Uranium

Baumgaertner, F., et al, eds. Nukleare Entsorgung: Nuclear Fuel Cycle, Vol. 2. (Illus.). xiii, 352p. 1983. 65.00 (ISBN 3-527-25947-3). VCH Pubs.

Belgatom. Nuclear Fuel Supply Industry in the European Community. 141p. 85.00x (ISBN 0-686-97540-5, Pub. by Graham & Trotman England). State Mutual Bk.

Belgatom, ed. Nuclear Fuel Supply Industry in the European Community. 194p. 1983. pap. 35.00x (ISBN 0-8448-1424-5). Crane-Russak Co.

Christensen, R. Thermal Mechanical Behavior of UO2 Nuclear Fuel: Electrothermal Analysis, Vol. II. x, 122p. 1978. 19.50 (ISBN 0-938876-10-4). Entropy Ltd.

--Thermal Mechanical Behavior of UO2 Nuclear Fuel: Multi-Cycle Test Description, Vol. IV. xii, 329p. 1978. 49.50 (ISBN 0-938876-12-0). Entropy Ltd.

--Thermal Mechanical Behavior of UO2 Nuclear Fuel: Single Cycle Test Data Discriptions, Vol. III. xii, 321p. 1978. 46.50 (ISBN 0-938876-11-2). Entropy Ltd.

Christensen, R., ed. Thermal Mechanical Behavior of UO2 Nuclear Fuel, Vol. I-IV. Set. 130.00 (ISBN 0-938876-13-9). Entropy Ltd.

Corradini, M. L. & Bishop, A. A., eds. Fuel-Coolant Interactions. (HTD Ser.: Vol. 19). 113p. 1981. 24.00 (ISBN 0-686-34493-6, H00204). ASME.

Dyer, Alan, ed. Gas Chemistry in Nuclear Reactors & Large Industrial Plant: Proceedings of the Conference Held at the University of Salford, UK, 21-24 April 1980. LC 82-104413. pap. 73.80 (ISBN 0-317-30333-3, 2024810). Bks Demand UMI.

Economics of Nuclear Fuels. (Illus., Orig.). 1968. pap. 41.25 (ISBN 92-0-050668-2, ISP188, IAEA). Unipub.

European Institute for Transuranium Elements. Fission Gas Behaviour in Nuclear Fuels: Joint Research Centre Workshop, Germany, October 1978, Proceedings. Ronchi, C., et al, eds. (European Applied Research Reports Special Topics Ser.). 350p. 1979. pap. text ed. 115.50 (ISBN 3-7186-0010-2). Harwood Academic.

Experience from Operating & Fueling Nuclear Power Plants. (Proceedings Ser.). (Eng., Fr. & Span., Illus.). 721p. (Orig.). 1974. pap. 61.00 (ISBN 92-0-050274-1, ISP351, IAEA). Unipub.

Flagg, John F., ed. Chemical Processing of Reactor Fuels. (Nuclear Science and Technology Ser.: Vol. 1). 1961. 76.00 (ISBN 0-12-258250-0). Acad Pr.

Fuel & Fuel Elements for Fast Reactors, 2 vols. (Proceedings Ser.). (Eng., Fr., Rus. & Span., Illus.). 909p. (Orig.). 1974. Vol. 1. pap. 35.75 (ISBN 92-0-050074-9, ISP346/1, IAEA); Vol. 2. pap. 43.00 (ISBN 92-0-050174-5, ISP346/2). Unipub.

Fuel Handling & Storage Systems in Nuclear Power Plants. (Safety Ser.: No. 50-SG-D10). 52p. (Orig.). 1984. pap. 12.00 (ISBN 92-0-123584-4, ISP662, IAEA). Unipub.

Graves, Harvey W. Nuclear Fuel Management. LC 78-19119. 327p. 1979. text ed. 51.75x (ISBN 0-471-03136-4). Wiley.

Guidebook on Quality Control of Water Reactor Fuel. (Technical Reports Ser.: No. 221). 210p. 1983. pap. 35.50 (ISBN 92-0-155083-9, IDC221, IAEA). Unipub.

Guidebook on Spent Fuel Storage. (Technical Reports Ser.: No. 240). (Illus.). 171p. 1985. pap. 30.50 (ISBN 92-0-155384-6, IDC240, IAEA). Unipub.

Hall, E. J. & Rossi, H. H. Californium 2-52 in Teaching & Research. (Technical Reports Ser.: No. 159). (Illus.). 141p. 1974. pap. 16.00 (ISBN 92-0-115174-8, IDC159, IAEA). Unipub.

International Nuclear Fuel Cycle Evaluation, 9 vols. Incl. Vol. 1. Fuel & Heavy Water Availability: Report of INFCE Working Group 1. 314p. pap. 45.00 (ISBN 92-0-159180-2, ISP534 1); Vol. 2. Enrichment Availability: Report of INFCE Working Group 2. 157p. pap. 23.00 (ISBN 92-0-159280-9, ISP534 2); Vol.3. Assurances of Long-Term Supply of Technology, Fuel and Heavy Water and Services in the Interest of National Needs Consistent with Non-Proliferation: Report of INFCE Working Group 3. 104p. pap. 16.25 (ISBN 92-0-159380-5, ISP534 3); Vol. 4. Reprocessing, Plutonium Handling: Recycle: Report of INFCE Working Group 4. 300p. pap. 43.00 (ISBN 92-0-159480-1, ISP534 4); Vol. 5. Fast Breeders: Report of INFCE Working Group 5. 217p. pap. 32.25 (ISBN 92-0-159580-8, ISP534 5); Vol. 6. Spent Fuel Management: Report of INFCE Working Group 6. 113p. pap. 15.50 (ISBN 92-0-159680-4, ISP534 6); Vol. 7. Waste & Disposal Managements: Report of INFCE Working Group 7. (Illus.). 287p. pap. 35.50 (ISBN 92-0-159780-0, ISP534 7); Vol. 8. Advanced Fuel Cycle & Reactor Concepts: Report of INFCE Working Group 8. 181p. pap. 27.50 (ISBN 92-0-159880-7, ISP534 8); Vol. 9. INFCE Summary Volume. 285p. pap. 38.50 (ISBN 92-0-159980-3, ISP534 9). 1980. Set. pap. 278.25 (ISBN 0-686-77641-0, ISP534 1, IAEA). Unipub.

Kessler, G. Nuclear Fission Reactors: Potential Role & Risk of Converters & Breeders. (Topics in Energy Ser.). (Illus.). 257p. 1983. 41.00 (ISBN 0-387-81713-1). Springer-Verlag.

Long, Justin T. Engineering for Nuclear Fuel Reprocessing. LC 78-50886. 1023p. 1978. 68.00 (ISBN 0-89448-012-X, 300012). Am Nuclear Soc.

Meller, Eberhard, ed. Internationalization: An Alternative to Nuclear Proliferation? LC 80-17265. (Salzburg Seminar on American Studies 1978 Ser.). 192p. 1980. text ed. 35.00 (ISBN 0-89946-049-6). Oelgeschlager.

Metallurgical Society of AIME. High Temperature Nuclear Fuels. Holden, A. N., ed. LC 67-28245. (Metallurgical Society Conference Ser.: Vol. 42). pap. 131.30 (ISBN 0-317-08161-6, 2001531). Bks Demand UMI.

Mining Journal Books Ltd. Uranium & Nuclear Energy. 326p. 1980. 45.00x (ISBN 0-900117-20-6, Pub. by Mining Journal England). State Mutual Bk.

Monitoring of Airborne & Liquid Radioactive Releases from Nuclear Facilities to the Environment. (Safety Ser.: No. 46). (Illus.). 125p. 1978. pap. 15.50 (ISBN 92-0-123178-4, ISP482, IAEA). Unipub.

New Nuclear Materials Including Non-Metallic Fuels, 2 vols. (Proceedings Ser.). (Illus.). 1132p. (Vol. 1 - 564p., Vol. 2 - 568p.). Vol. 1. pap. 28.75 (ISBN 92-0-050363-2, ISP77-1, IAEA); Vol. 2. pap. 28.75 (ISBN 92-0-050463-9, ISP77-2). Unipub.

Nuclear Fuel Quality Assurance. (Proceedings Ser.). (Illus.). 488p. 1977. pap. 48.00 (ISBN 92-0-050276-8, ISP435, IAEA). Unipub.

Nuclear Materials Management. (Proceedings Ser.). (Illus.). 888p. 1966. 48.00 (ISBN 92-0-050066-8, ISP110, IAEA). Unipub.

Nuclear Power & Its Fuel Cycle. Incl. Vol. 1. Nuclear Power Prospects & Plans. pap. 79.75 (ISBN 92-0-050077-3, ISP465-1); Vol. 2, Pt. 2. The Nuclear Fuel Cycle. pap. 87.75 (ISBN 92-0-050177-X, ISP465-2); Vol. 3, Pt. 2. The Nuclear Fuel Cycle. pap. 87.75 (ISBN 92-0-050277-6, ISP465-3); Vol. 4. Radioactivity Management. pap. 87.75 (ISBN 92-0-050377-2, ISP465-4); Vol. 5. Nuclear Safety. pap. 79.75 (ISBN 92-0-050477-9, ISP465-5); Vol. 6. Nuclear Power in Developing Countries. pap. 79.75 (ISBN 92-0-050577-5, ISP465-6); Vol. 7. Nuclear Power & Public Opinion, Safeguards. pap. 79.75 (ISBN 92-0-050677-1, ISP465-7); Vol. 8. Indexes & Lists. pap. 32.25 (ISBN 92-0-050777-8, ISP465-8). Set. pap. 558.25 (ISP465SET, IAEA). Unipub.

Occupational Radiation Exposure in Nuclear Fuel Cycle Facilities. (Proceedings Ser.). (Illus.). 640p. 1980. pap. 89.50 (ISBN 92-0-020080-X, ISP527, IAEA). Unipub.

OECD Staff. Nuclear Energy & Its Fuel Cycle: Prospects to 2025. 262p. 1982. pap. 24.00 (ISBN 92-64-12306-7). OECD.

Plutonium as a Reactor Fuel. (Proceedings Ser.). (Eng., Fr & Rus., Illus.). 858p. 1967. pap. 53.75 (ISBN 92-0-050167-2, ISP153, IAEA). Unipub.

Quality Assurance & Control in the Manufacture of Metal-Clad UO2 Reactor Fuels. (Technical Reports Ser.: No. 173). (Illus.). 66p. 1976. pap. 10.50 (ISBN 92-0-155076-6, IDC173, IAEA). Unipub.

Quality Assurance in the Procurement, Design & Manufacture of Nuclear Fuel Assemblies: A Safety Guide. (Safety Ser.: No. 50-SG-QA11). 34p. 1983. pap. text ed. 9.00 (ISBN 92-0-123283-7, ISP644, IAEA). Unipub.

Reactor Burn-up Physics. (Panel Proceedings Ser.). (Illus.). 296p. (Orig.). 1973. pap. 22.50 (ISBN 92-0-051073-6, ISP336, IAEA). Unipub.

Regional Nuclear Fuel Cycle Centres, 2 vols. (Illus.). 1977. pap. 17.25 (ISBN 92-0-159177-2, ISP445-1, IAEA); pap. 36.50 (ISBN 92-0-159277-9, ISP445-2). Unipub.

Robertson, J. A. Irradiation Effects in Nuclear Fuels. LC 67-26575. 309p. 1969. 16.25 (ISBN 0-685-58270-1, 450012). Am Nuclear Soc.

Rodden, Clement J., ed. Selected Measurement Methods for Plutonium & Uranium in the Nuclear Fuel Cycle. 2nd ed. AEC Technical Information Center. LC 72-600015. 440p. 1972. pap. 19.00 (ISBN 0-87079-354-3, TID-7029); microfiche 4.50 (ISBN 0-87079-355-1, TID-7029). DOE.

Silvennoinen, P. Nuclear Fuel Cycle Optimization: Methods & Modelling Techniques. (Illus.). 138p. 1982. 28.00 (ISBN 0-08-027310-6). Pergamon.

--Reactor Core Fuel Management. 250p. 1976. text ed. 50.00 (ISBN 0-08-019853-8); pap. text ed. 21.00 (ISBN 0-08-019852-X). Pergamon.

Simnad, M. T. & Zumwalt, L. R., eds. Materials & Fuels for High-Temperature Nuclear Applications. 1964. 35.00x (ISBN 0-262-19012-5). MIT Pr.

Sol-Gel Processes for Ceramic Fuels. (Panel Procceedings Ser.). (Illus.). 179p. 1968. pap. 11.25 (ISBN 92-0-141068-9, ISP207, IAEA). Unipub.

Sorantin, H. Determination of Uranium & Plutonium in Nuclear Fuels. (Topical Presentations in Nuclear Chemistry Ser.: Vol. 5). (Illus.). 285p. 1975. 81.20x (ISBN 3-527-25475-7). VCH Pubs.

Thermal Conductivity of Uranium Dioxide. (Technical Reports Ser.: No. 59). 1966. pap. 7.50 (ISBN 92-0-145166-0, IDC59, IAEA). Unipub.

Thermodynamic & Transport Properties of Uranium Dioxide & Related Phases. (Technical Reports Ser.: No. 39). 1965. pap. 9.00 (ISBN 92-0-145065-6, IDC39, IAEA). Unipub.

Urban District Heating Using Nuclear Heat. (Panel Proceedings Ser.). (Illus.). 207p. 1977. pap. text ed. 25.25 (ISBN 92-0-051077-9, ISP461, IAEA). Unipub.

Utilization of Thorium in Power Reactors. (Technical Reports Ser.: No. 52). (Illus.). 376p. 1966. pap. 25.75 (ISBN 92-0-055066-5, IDC52, IAEA). Unipub.

Warnecke, Steven J. Uranium, Nonproliferation & Energy Security. (The Atlantic Papers: No. 37). 121p. 1980. 6.50x (ISBN 0-916672-77-8, Pub. by Atlantic Inst France). Allanheld.

World Uraniam Potential: An International Evaluation. 1979. 16.00 (ISBN 92-64-11883-7). OECD.

Wymer, Raymond G. & Vondra, Benedict L., Jr., eds. Light Water Reactor Nuclear Fuel Cycle. 272p. 1981. 77.00 (ISBN 0-8493-5687-3). CRC Pr.

Yemel'yanov, V. S. & Yevstyukin, A. I. Metallurgy of Nuclear Fuels. 1969. 110.00 (ISBN 0-08-012073-3). Pergamon.

NUCLEAR FUSION

see also Controlled Fusion; Hydrogen Bomb; Neutron Transport Theory

Committee on Nuclear & Alternative Energy Systems, National Research Council. Controlled Nuclear Fusion: Current Research & Potential Progress. 1978. pap. text ed. 5.25 (ISBN 0-309-02863-9). Natl Acad Pr.

Hulme, H. R. Nuclear Fusion. (The Wykeham Science Ser.: No. 4). 164p. 1969. pap. cancelled (ISBN 0-85109-050-8). Taylor & Francis.

Hulme, H. R. & Collieu, A. Nuclear Fusion. (Wykeham Science Ser.: No. 4). 164p. 1969. 9.95x (ISBN 0-8448-1106-8). Crane-Russak Co.

Miley, George H. Fusion Energy Conversion. LC 75-44554. (Nuclear Science Technology Ser.). (Illus.). 1976. text ed. 39.80 (ISBN 0-89448-008-1, 300009). Am Nuclear Soc.

Nuclear Fusion Special Supplement 1969: Plasma Physics & Controlled Nuclear Fusion Research. pap. 21.50 (ISBN 92-0-139069-6, ISP23-69, IAEA). Unipub.

Nuclear Fusion Supplement: 1972. pap. 30.75 (ISBN 92-0-139072-6, ISP23-72, IAEA). Unipub.

Plasma Physics & Controlled Nuclear Fusion Research: Supplement, 1972, 1971. (Illus.). 357p. (Orig.). 1973. pap. 24.25 (ISBN 92-0-139072-6, ISP 23-72, IAEA). Unipub.

Plasma Physics & Controlled Nuclear Fusion Research: 1976, 3 vols. 6th ed. (Proceedings Ser.). Vol. 1. pap. 65.00 (ISBN 92-0-130077-8, ISP439-1, IAEA); Vol. 2. pap. 66.50 (ISBN 92-0-130177-4, ISP439-2); Vol. 3. pap. 63.25 (ISBN 92-0-130277-0, ISP439-3). Unipub.

Plasma Physics & Controlled Nuclear Fusion Research: 1965. (Proceedings Ser.). (Illus.). 1778p. (Vol. 1). Vol. 1. pap. 45.00 (ISBN 92-0-030066-9, ISP111-1, IAEA); Vol. 2. pap. 57.25 (ISBN 92-0-030166-5, ISP111-2). Unipub.

Plasma Physics & Controlled Nuclear Fusion Research: 1971, 3 vols. (Illus.). Vol. 1. pap. 53.75 (ISBN 92-0-030071-5, ISP288-1, IAEA); Vol. 2. pap. 53.75 (ISBN 92-0-030171-1, ISP288-2); Vol. 3. pap. 48.00 (ISBN 92-0-030271-8, ISP288-3). Unipub.

Plasma Physics & Controlled Nuclear Fusion Research: 1982, Vol. 3. 551p. 1983. pap. text ed. 69.00 (ISBN 92-0-130283-5, ISP626/3, IAEA). Unipub.

Plasma Physics & Controlled Nuclear Fusion Research 1978: Proceedings, Seventh Conference, Innsbruck, 23-30 August 1978, 3 vols. (Proceedings Ser.). (Illus.). 1979. Vol. 1. pap. 100.00 (ISBN 92-0-130079-4, ISP495-1, IAEA); Vol. 2. pap. 84.00 (ISBN 92-0-130179-0, ISP495-2); Vol. 3. pap. 77.00 (ISBN 92-0-130279-7, ISP495-3). Unipub.

Plasma Physics & Controlled Nuclear Fusion Research, 1982: Proceedings of the Ninth International Conference on Plasma Physics & Controlled Nuclear Fusion Research Held by the International Atomic Energy Agency in Baltimore, 1-8 September 1982. (Nuclear Fusion Supplement Ser.). 1983. Vol. 1. pap. text ed. 88.25 (ISBN 92-0-130083-2, ISP626 1, IAEA); Vol. 2. pap. 97.75 (ISBN 92-0-130183-9, ISP626 2); Vol. 3. pap. text ed. 69.00 (ISBN 92-0-130283-5, ISP626 3). Unipub.

Plasma Physics & Controlled Nuclear Fusion Research 1984: Tenth Conference Proceedings, London, 12-19 September 1984, Vol. 1. (Nuclear Fusion Ser.: Suppl. 1985). 673p. 1985. pap. 105.75 (ISBN 92-0-130085-9, ISP670-1 5071, IAEA). Unipub.

Plasma Physics & Controlled Nuclear Fusion Research 1984: Tenth Conference Proceedings, London, 12-19 September 1984, Vol. 2. 667p. 1985. pap. 104.00 (ISBN 92-0-130185-5, ISP670, IAEA). Unipub.

Plasma Physics & Controlled Nuclear Fusion Research 1980, Vol. 1-2: Nuclear Fusion Supplement 1981. (Proceedings Ser.). (Illus.). 1726p. (Vol. 1). 1981. Vol. 2. pap. 101.75 (ISBN 92-0-130181-2, ISP563 2, IAEA); Vol. 1. pap. 120.00 (ISBN 92-0-130081-6, ISP563 1). Unipub.

Schramm, David N. & Arnett, W. David, eds. Explosive Nucleosynthesis: Proceedings of the Conference on Explosive Nucleosynthesis Held in Austin, Texas, on April 2-3, 1973. 313p. 1973. 17.95x (ISBN 0-292-72006-8); pap. 9.95x (ISBN 0-292-72007-6). U of Tex Pr.

Steadman, S. G., ed. Fusion Reactions Below the Coulomb Barrier. (Lecture Notes in Physics Ser.: Vol. 219). vii, 351p. 1985. pap. 23.70 (ISBN 0-387-13918-4). Springer-Verlag.

Winterberg, Friedwardt. The Physical Principles of Thermonuclear Explosive Devices. (Fusion Energy Foundation Frontiers of Science Ser.). (Illus.). xiv, 145p. 1981. softcover, xerographic reproduction 27.50. Fusion Energy Found.

NUCLEAR GEOPHYSICS

see also Radioactive Dating; Radioactive Substances

Abragam, A. & Goldman, M. Nuclear Magnetism: Order & Disorder. (International Series of Monographs in Physics). 1982. 89.00x (ISBN 0-19-851294-5). Oxford U Pr.

Fogedby, Hans C. Theoretical Aspects of Mainly Low Dimensional Magnetic Systems. (Lecture Notes in Physics Ser.: Vol. 131). 163p. 1980. pap. 15.00 (ISBN 0-387-10238-8). Springer Verlag.

Moriya, T. Spin Fluctuations in Itinerant Electron Magnetism. (Solid-State Sciences Ser.: Vol. 56). (Illus.). 260p. 1985. 35.00 (ISBN 0-387-15422-1). Springer-Verlag.

Rado, George T. & Suhl, H., eds. Magnetism: A Treatise on Modern Theory & Materials, 5 vols. 1963-1973. Vol. 1, 1963. 86.50 (ISBN 0-12-575301-2); Vol. 2A, 1965. 76.50 (ISBN 0-12-575302-0); Vol. 2B, 1967. 76.50 (ISBN 0-12-575342-X); Vol. 3, 1963. 77.00 (ISBN 0-12-575303-9); Vol. 5. o.p 78.00 (ISBN 0-12-575305-5). Acad Pr.

Steinberg, Carl P. & Cohen, Alan B. Nuclear Magnetic Resonance Imaging Technology: A Clinical, Industrial, & Policy Analysis. LC 84-601123. (Office of Technology Assessment Case Study Ser.: No. 27). 166p. (Orig.). 1984. pap. 5.50 (ISBN 0-318-11807-6). Gov Printing Office.

NUCLEAR MASSES

see Atomic Mass

NUCLEAR MEDICINE

see also Radioactivity–Physiological Effect

Alazraki, N. P. & Mishkin, F. S., eds. Fundamentals of Nuclear Medicine. 208p. 1984. 12.00 (ISBN 0-317-17711-7). Soc Nuclear Med.

Andrews, J. T., et al. Nuclear Medicine: Clinical & Technological Bases. LC 77-5040. pap. 145.00 (ISBN 0-317-07739-2, 2015188). Bks Demand UMI.

Anghileri, Leopold J., ed. General Processes of Radiotracer Localization, Vol. I. 272p. 1982. 78.00 (ISBN 0-8493-6027-7). CRC Pr.

Arcangeli, G. & Mauro, F., eds. Hyperthermia in Radiation Oncology. (Illus.). 299p. 1980. flexicover-Medical 41.50 (ISBN 0-89352-116-7, Masson Italia Editori). Masson Pub.

Atkins, Harold L. Pulmonary Nuclear Medicine. (Lung Biology in Health & Diseases Ser.). 344p. 1984. 69.75 (ISBN 0-8247-7233-4). Dekker.

Barnes, Broda O. & Barnes, Charlotte W. Heart Attack Rareness in Thyroid-Treated Patients. 104p. 1972. 12.75x (ISBN 0-398-02519-3). C C Thomas.

Biersack, H. J. & Cox, P. H., eds. Radioisotope Studies in Cardiology. (Developments in Nuclear Medicine Ser.). 1985. lib. bdg. 59.50 (ISBN 0-318-04531-1, Martinus Nijhoff Netherlands). Kluwer Academic.

Boyd, Marcia. Curriculum Guide for Nuclear Medicine Technologists. McKeown, Joan A., et al, eds. LC 82-50338. 336p. 1982. 65.00 (ISBN 0-932004-12-1). Soc Nuclear Med.

Brill, A. B., et al. Low-Level Radiation Effects: A Fact Book. 2nd ed. Bigler, Rodney E., ed. LC 82-16937. 156p. 1982. looseleaf incl. 1985 updates 32.00 (ISBN 0-932004-23-7); Updates 1985; 80p. Insert Package 10.00 (ISBN 0-317-19594-8). Soc Nuclear Med.

Brill, A. Bertrand. Low Level Radiation Fact Book. Adelstein, James, et al, eds. LC 82-16939. 156p. 1982. 27.50 (ISBN 0-932004-14-8). Soc Nuclear Med.

Bulcke, J. A. & Baert, A. L. Clinical & Radiological Aspects of Myopathies: CT Scanning-EMG-Radio-Isotopes. (Illus.). 187p. 1982. 58.00 (ISBN 0-387-11443-2). Springer-Verlag.

Carey, James E., et al, eds. CRC Manual of Nuclear Medicine Procedures. 248p. 1983. 39.50 (ISBN 0-8493-0708-2). CRC Pr.

Catsch, Alexander. Radioactive Metal Mobilization in Medicine. Kawin, Bergene, tr. (Illus.). 184p. 1964. 17.50x (ISBN 0-398-00296-7). C C Thomas.

Chandra, Ramesh. Introductory Physics of Nuclear Medicine. 2nd ed. LC 81-17149. (Illus.). 237p. 1982. text ed. 17.50 (ISBN 0-8121-0826-4). Lea & Febiger.

Choppin, G. & Ryberg, J., eds. Nuclear Chemistry: Theory & Applications. (Illus.). 1980. text ed. 105.00 (ISBN 0-08-023826-2); pap. text ed. 32.00 (ISBN 0-08-023823-8). Pergamon.

Ciba Foundation. Protein Turnover. LC 72-96519. (Ciba Foundation Symposium: New Ser.: No. 9). pap. 81.80 (ISBN 0-317-28310-3, 2022141). Bks Demand UMI.

Cohen, Jack, et al. Nuclear Magnetic Resonance in Biology & Medicine. (Life Chemistry Reports Ser.: Vol. 1, No. 4). 175p. 1983. 36.50 (ISBN 3-7186-0171-0). Harwood Academic.

Deutsch, Edward, et al, eds. Technetium in Chemistry & Nuclear Medicine. 246p. 1983. text ed. 50.50 (ISBN 8-885-03750-X). Raven.

Durakovic, Asaf. Nuclear Medicine Technologist's Handbook. 1985. 32.50 (ISBN 0-87527-311-4). Green.

Ell, P. J. & Walton, S. Radionuclide Ventricular Function Studies: Correlation with ECG, Echo & X-ray Data. 1982. text ed. 99.50 (ISBN 90-247-2639-5, Pub. by Martinus Nijhoff Netherlands). Kluwer Academic.

Enlander, Derek, ed. Computers in Laboratory Medicine. 1975. 39.50 (ISBN 0-12-239950-1). Acad Pr.

Esser, P. D. & Johnston, R. E., eds. Technology of Nuclear Magnetic Resonance. 272p. 1984. pap. 29.00 (ISBN 0-317-17712-5). Soc Nuclear Med.

Esser, Peter, et al, eds. Digital Imaging: Clinical Advances in Nuclear Medicine. LC 82-16941. (Illus.). 304p. 1983. 37.50 (ISBN 0-932004-13-X). Soc Nuclear Med.

Esser, Peter D., et al. Functional Mapping of Organ Systems & Other Computer Topics. LC 81-51827. (Illus.). 272p. 1981. 30.50 (ISBN 0-932004-09-1). Soc Nuclear Med.

Etter, Lewis E. Glossary of Words & Phrases Used in Radiology, Nuclear Medicine & Ultrasound. 2nd ed. 384p. 1970. 33.50x (ISBN 0-398-00526-5). C C Thomas.

Freeman, Leonard M. & Weissman, Heidi S., eds. Nuclear Medicine Annual, 1982. 420p. 1982. text ed. 70.50 (ISBN 0-89004-726-X). Raven.

Freeman, Leonard M. & Weissmann, Heidi S., eds. Nuclear Medicine Annual, 1984. LC 80-645231. (Illus.). 360p. 1984. text ed. 51.50 (ISBN 0-89004-453-8). Raven.

--Nuclear Medicine Annual, 1985. (Illus.). 368p. 1985. text ed. 59.50 (ISBN 0-88167-086-3). Raven.

Galle, Pierre & Masse, Roland, eds. Radionuclide Metabolism & Toxicity. (Illus.). 334p. 1982. 38.00 (ISBN 2-225-78034-X). Masson Pub.

Hardeman, M. R., et al, eds. Blood Cells in Nuclear Medicine, Pts. I & II. (Developments in Nuclear Medicine Ser.). 1984. Set. lib. bdg. 146.50 (ISBN 0-89838-660-8, Pub. by Martinus Nijhoff Netherlands); Pt. I. lib. bdg. 79.50 (ISBN 0-89838-653-5); Pt. II. lib. bdg. 79.50 (ISBN 0-89838-654-3). Kluwer Academic.

Hayes, Raymond L., et al, eds. Radioisotopes in Medicine - In Vitro Studies: Proceedings. LC 68-60071. (AEC Symposium Ser.). 753p. 1968. pap. 26.75 (ISBN 0-87079-327-6, CONF-671111); microfiche 4.50 (ISBN 0-87079-328-4, CONF-671111). DOE.

Heindel, Ned D., et al, eds. The Chemistry of Radiopharmaceuticals. LC 77-94827. (Cancer Management Ser.: Vol. 3). (Illus.). 304p. 1978. 45.50x (ISBN 0-89352-019-5). Masson Pub.

Hibbard, W. M. & Lance, S. P., eds. Laboratory Manual for Nuclear Medicine Technology. 163p. 1984. softcover 14.00 (ISBN 0-317-17713-3). Soc Nuclear Med.

Hibbard, Wanda M. A Handbook of Nuclear Pharmacy. (Illus.). 80p. 1982. spiral bdg. 18.75x (ISBN 0-398-04760-X). C C Thomas.

Hoffer, P. B. Year Book of Nuclear Medicine 1983. 1983. 44.95 (ISBN 0-8151-4527-6). Year Bk Med.

--Year Book of Nuclear Medicine, 1984. 1984. 44.95. Year Bk Med.

Hopf, M. A. & Smith, F. W. Magnetic Resonance in Medicine & Biology. (Progress in Nuclear Medicine: Vol. 8). (Illus.). viii, 180p. 1984. 70.00 (ISBN 3-8055-3868-5). S Karger.

Jasmin, G. & Simard, R. Nuclear Submicroscopy. (Methods & Achievements in Experimental Pathology: Vol. 12). (Illus.). viii, 192p. 1985. 59.75 (ISBN 3-8055-4137-6). S Karger.

Joekes, A. M., et al, eds. Radionuclides in Nephrology: Proceedings of the International Symposium, 5th, London, 1981. 384p. 1982. 46.50 (ISBN 0-8089-1521-5, 792186). Grune.

Jonckheer, M. H. & Deconinck, F., eds. X-Ray Fluorescent Scanning of the Thyroid. 1983. lib. bdg. 39.50 (ISBN 0-89838-561-X, Pub. by Martinus Nijhoff Netherlands). Kluwer Academic.

Kaufman, Leon, et al, eds. Nuclear Magnetic Resonance Imaging in Medicine. LC 81-82043. (Illus.). 240p. 1981. 34.50 (ISBN 0-89640-057-3). Igaku-Shoin.

Kim, E. E. & Haynie, T. P. Nuclear Imaging in Oncology. 256p. 1984. 52.50 (ISBN 0-8385-6973-0). ACC.

Knapp, Fern F. & Butler, Thomas A., eds. Radionuclide Generators: New Systems for Nuclear Medicine Applications. LC 83-25875. (ACS Symposium Ser.: No. 241). 236p. 1984. lib. bdg. 79.95 (ISBN 0-8412-0822-0). Am Chemical.

Kristensen, K. & Norbygaard, E., eds. Safety & Efficacy of Radiopharmaceuticals. (Developments in Nuclear Medicine Ser.). 1984. text ed. 54.00 (ISBN 0-89838-609-8, Pub. by Martinus Nijhoff Netherlands). Kluwer Academic.

Lange, Robert C. Nuclear Medicine for Technicians. LC 75-75732. pap. 45.00 (ISBN 0-317-26173-8, 2024266). Bks Demand UMI.

Leach, K. G. The Physical Aspects of Radioisotopic Organ Imaging. 1976. 25.00x (ISBN 0-686-99803-0, Pub. by Brit Inst Radiology England). State Mutual Bk.

Matin, Philip. Textbook of Clinical Nuclear Medicine. LC 85-8951. 1985. pap. text ed. 27.00 (ISBN 0-87488-419-5). Med Exam.

Medical Radioisotope Scanning: 1964, 2 vols. (Proceedings Ser.). 1964. Vol. 1. pap. 30.75 (ISBN 92-0-010264-6, ISP82-1, IAEA); Vol. 2. pap. 26.25 (ISBN 92-0-010364-2, ISP82-2). Unipub.

Medical Radioisotope Scintigraphy 1972, 2 vols. Vol. 1. pap. 66.50 (ISBN 92-0-010173-9, ISP315-1, IAEA); Vol. 2. pap. 66.50 (ISBN 92-0-010273-5, ISP315-2). Unipub.

Medical Radionuclide Imaging: Proceedings of an International Symposium on Medical Radionuclide Imaging, Organized by the International Atomic Energy Agency in Cooperation with the World Health Organization & Held in Heidelberg, September 1-5, 1980, 2 Vols. 1981. Vol. 1. pap. 79.95 (ISP564-1, IAEA); Vol. 2. pap. 87.75 (ISP564-2). Unipub.

Medical Radionuclide Imaging 1980, 2 vols. Vol. 1, 1981. pap. 87.75 (ISBN 92-0-010081-3, ISP564 1, IAEA); Vol. 2, 1982. pap. 96.75 (ISBN 92-0-010181-X, ISP564/2). Unipub.

Mettler, Fred A. & Guiberteau, Milton J. Essentials of Nuclear Medicine Imaging. 330p. 1983. 47.00 (ISBN 0-8089-1538-X, 792895). Grune.

Mettler, Fred A., Jr. & Guiberteau, Milton J. Essentials of Nuclear Medicine Imaging. LC 79-2894. 416p. 1985. 47.50 (ISBN 0-8089-1767-6). Grune.

NCRP. Protection in Nuclear Medicine & Ultrasound Diagnostic Procedures in Children. LC 83-61834. (NCRP Report Ser.: No. 73). 81p. 1983. pap. text ed. 10.00 (ISBN 0-913392-63-4). Natl Coun Radiation.

Nuclear Medicine-Factors Influencing the Choice & Use of Radionuclides in Diagnosis & Therapy: NCRP Report 70. LC 81-84121. 1982. 12.00 (ISBN 0-913392-57-X). NCRP Pubns.

Nuclear Techniques in the Study of Parasitic Infections: Proceedings of a Symposium, Vienna, 29 June-3 July 1981, Jointly Organized by IAEA, FAO, & UNEP. (Proceedings Ser.). (Illus.). 631p. 1983. pap. 81.00 (ISBN 92-0-010282-4, ISP596, IAEA). Unipub.

Nuclear Techniques in Tropical Animal Diseases & Nutritional Disorders: Proceedings of a Consultants Meeting, Vienna, 13-16 June 1983. (Panel Proceedings Ser.). 212p. 1985. pap. 33.75 (ISBN 92-0-111384-6, ISP675, IAEA). Unipub.

Nudelman, Sol & Patton, Dennis D., eds. Imaging for Medicine: Nuclear Medicine, Ultrasonics, & Thermography, Vol. 1. LC 79-25680. (Illus.). 512p. 1980. 59.50x (ISBN 0-306-40384-6, Plenum Pr). Plenum Pub.

Osbakken, Mary D., et al. Techniques, Diagnostics & Advances in Nuclear Cardiology. (Illus.). 420p. 1983. 53.50x (ISBN 0-398-04772-3). C C Thomas.

Powers, Thomas A. & James, A. Everette. Nuclear Imaging. 2nd ed. (Exercises in Diagnostic Radiology Ser.: Vol. 6). (Illus.). 250p. 1984. 18.95 (ISBN 0-7216-5109-7). Saunders.

Protection in Nuclear Medicine & Ultrasound Diagnostic Prodecures in Children. (NCRP Report Ser.: No. 73). 1984. 10.00 (ISBN 0-318-02040-8). NCRP Pubns.

Radioisotope Sample Measurement Techniques in Medicine & Biology. (Proceedings Ser.). 724p. 1965. pap. 38.50 (ISBN 92-0-010165-8, ISP106, IAEA). Unipub.

Radiopharmaceuticals from Generator-Produced Radionuclides. (Panel Proceedings Ser.). 205p. 1971. pap. 16.25 (ISBN 92-0-111471-0, ISP294, IAEA). Unipub.

Raynaud, C., ed. Nuclear Medicine & Biology Advances: Proceedings of the Third World Congress on Nuclear Medicine & Biology, August 29 - September 2, 1982, Paris, France, 7 Vols. 3685p. 1983. Set. 500.00 (ISBN 0-08-026405-0). Pergamon.

Robertson, James S., ed. Compartmental Distribution of Radiotracers. 208p. 1983. 70.00 (ISBN 0-8493-6010-2). CRC Pr.

Roth, K. NMR Tomography & Spectroscopy in Medicine: An Introduction. Telger, T. C., tr. from German. (Illus.). 130p. 1984. pap. 18.00 (ISBN 0-387-13442-5). Springer-Verlag.

Rothfeld, Benjamin, et al, eds. Nuclear Medicine in Vitro. 2nd ed. (Illus.). 420p. 1983. text ed. 57.50 (ISBN 0-397-50505-1, 65-06497, Lippincott Medical). Lippincott.

Ryo. Atlas of Nuclear Medicine Variants. 1984. 59.95 (ISBN 0-8151-7489-6). Year Bk Med.

Serafini, Aldo, ed. Nuclear Cardiology: Principles & Methods. LC 76-39783. (Topics in Cardiovascular Disease Ser.). (Illus.). 264p. 1977. 35.00x (ISBN 0-306-30952-1, Plenum Med. Bk.). Plenum Pub.

Shipley, Reginald A. & Clark, Richard E. Tracer Methods for in Vitro Kinetics: Theory & Applications. 1972. 45.00 (ISBN 0-12-640250-7). Acad Pr.

Sorenson, James A. & Phelps, Michael E. Physics in Nuclear Medicine. 404p. 1980. 43.50 (ISBN 0-8089-1238-0, 794187); slide set 310.00 (ISBN 0-8089-1530-4, 794188). Grune.

Spencer, Richard P. Interventional Nuclear Medicine. 614p. 1984. 54.50 (ISBN 0-8089-1644-0, 794234). Grune.

--Nuclear Medicine: Focus On Clinical Diagnosis. 3rd ed. LC 84-4624. 1984. text ed. write for info. (ISBN 0-87488-109-9). Med Exam.

Tauxe & Dobovsky. Nuclear Medicine in Clinical Urology & Nephrology. (Baum Ser.). 384p. 1985. 50.00 (ISBN 0-8385-6983-8). ACC.

Thrall. Diagnostic Interventions in Nuclear Medicine. 1985. 39.95 (ISBN 0-8151-8802-1). Year Bk Med.

Treves, S. T. Pediatric Nuclear Medicine. (Illus.). 360p. 1985. 74.50 (ISBN 0-387-96001-5). Springer-Verlag.

Wagner, Henry N., Jr. & Buchanan, Julia W. Nuclear Medicine Case Studies. 1985. pap. text ed. write for info. (ISBN 0-87488-196-X). Med Exam.

Young, Stuart W. Nuclear Magnetic Resonance Imaging: Basic Principles. (Illus.). 176p. 1984. text ed. 29.50 (ISBN 0-89004-998-X). Raven.

NUCLEAR MODELS

see also Nuclear Shell Theory

Bohr, A. & Mottelson, B. R. Nuclear Structure, Vol. 3: Nucleonic Correlations. Date not set. (ISBN 0-8053-1017-7, Adv Bk Prog). Benjamin-Cummings.

Davidson, John P. Collective Models of the Nucleus. LC 68-18665. 1968. 57.50 (ISBN 0-12-205250-1). Acad Pr.

Eisenberg, J. M. & Greiner, W. Nuclear Theory, Vol. 3: Microscopic Theory of the Nucleus. 2nd ed. 520p. 1976. pap. 49.00 (ISBN 0-7204-0484-3, North-Holland). Elsevier.

Green, A. E., et al. Nuclear Independent Particle Model. 1968. 77.00 (ISBN 0-12-297450-6). Acad Pr.

Kumar, Krishna. Nuclear Models & the Search for Unity in Nuclear Physics. 116p. (Orig.). 1984. pap. 16.00x (ISBN 82-00-07149-9). Universitet.

Ulehla, Ivan, et al. Optical Model of the Atomic Nucleus. Alter, G., tr. 1965. 41.00 (ISBN 0-12-707450-3). Acad Pr.

Wildermuth, K. & McClure, W. Cluster Representations of Nuclei. (Springer Tracts in Modern Physics, Vol. 41). (Illus.). 1966. 37.80 (ISBN 0-387-03670-9). Springer-Verlag.

NUCLEAR MOMENTS

see also Angular Momentum (Nuclear Physics); Nuclear Induction; Nuclear Magnetic Resonance; Nuclear Magnetism; Nuclear Spin; Paramagnetism

Eder, Gernot. Nuclear Forces: Introduction to Theoretical Nuclear Physics. 1968. pap. 12.50x (ISBN 0-262-55004-0). MIT Pr.

Lucken, E. A. Nuclear Quadrupole Coupling Constants. 1969. 57.50 (ISBN 0-12-458450-0). Acad Pr.

Rescigno, Thomas, et al, eds. Electron-Molecule & Photon-Molecule Collisions. LC 79-15211. 365p. 1979. 55.00x (ISBN 0-306-40193-2, Plenum Pr). Plenum Pub.

NUCLEAR PARTICLES

see Particles (Nuclear Physics)

NUCLEAR PHYSICS

see also Angular Correlations (Nuclear Physics); Angular Momentum (Nuclear Physics); Atomic Mass; Auger Effect; Causality (Physics); Chemistry, Physical and Theoretical; Collisions (Nuclear Physics); Cosmic Rays; Cyclotron; Electric Discharges; Isobaric Spin; Moessbauer Effect; Nuclear Astrophysics; Nuclear Chemistry; Nuclear Counters; Nuclear Engineering; Nuclear Excitation; Nuclear Fission; Nuclear Forces (Physics); Nuclear Geophysics; Nuclear Magnetism; Nuclear Models; Nuclear Moments; Nuclear Reactions; Nuclear Reactors; Nuclear Shell Theory; Nuclear Spin; Particle Accelerators; Particle Beams; Particles (Nuclear Physics); Quantum Electrodynamics; Radioactivity; Radiobiology; Scattering (Physics); Transmutation (Chemistry); Triplet State

Abrahams, K., et al, eds. Nuclear Structure. LC 81-7291. (NATO ASI Series B, Physics: Vol. 67). 442p. 1981. 69.50x (ISBN 0-306-40728-0, Plenum Pr). Plenum Pub.

Advances in Electronics & Electron Physics, Vol. 59. 306p. 1982. 60.00 (ISBN 0-12-014659-2). Acad Pr.

Ajzenberg-Selove, Fay, ed. Nuclear Spectroscopy, 2 Pts. (Pure & Applied Physics Ser.: Vol. 9). 1960. 83.00 ea. Pt. A (ISBN 0-12-046850-6). Pt. B (ISBN 0-12-046851-4). Acad Pr.

American Society for Testing & Materials. Application of Advanced & Nuclear Physics to Testing Materials. LC 65-19687. (American Society for Testing & Materials Ser.: Special Technical Publication, No. 373). pap. 35.30 (ISBN 0-317-10989-8, 2000739). Bks Demand UMI.

George F. Nuclear Theory, Nineteen Eighty-One: Proceedings of the Nuclear Theory Summer Workshop Institute of Theoretical Physics, Santa Barbara, CA, August 1981. xiii, 296p. 1982. 33.00x (ISBN 9971-950-06-5, Pub. by World Sci Singapore); pap. 19.00x (ISBN 9971-950-07-3, Pub. by World Sci Singapore). Taylor & Francis.

Goodman, Charles D., et al, eds. The PN Reaction & the Nucleon-Nucleon Force. LC 79-27785. 550p. 1980. 79.50 (ISBN 0-306-40351-X, Plenum Pr). Plenum Pub.

Grant, P. J. Nuclear Science. (Illus.). 1971. pap. text ed. 17.95x (ISBN 0-245-50419-2). Intl Ideas.

Grynberg, G. & Stora, R., eds. New Trends in Atomic Physics: Proceedings of the Les Houches Summer School, Session XXXVIII, 28 June-29 July, 1982, 2 pts. (Les Houches Summer School Proceedings Ser.: Vol. 38). 1250p. 1985. Set. 259.25 (ISBN 0-444-86823-2, North Holland); Pt. I. 138.50 (ISBN 0-444-86908-5, North Holland); Pt. II. 163.50 (ISBN 0-444-86909-3, North Holland). Elsevier.

Hamilton, H., ed. Future Directions in Studies of Nuclei Far From Stability: Proceedings of the International Symposium in Nashville, TN, Sept. 1979. 424p. 1980. 83.00 (ISBN 0-444-85448-7, North-Holland). Elsevier.

Harms, A. A. & Heindler, M. Nuclear Energy Synergetics: An Introduction to Conceptual Models of Integrated Nuclear Energy Systems. LC 82-16175. 252p. 1982. 37.50x (ISBN 0-306-40951-8, Plenum Pr). Plenum Pub.

Harnwell, G. P. & Livingood, J. J. Experimental Atomic Physics. LC 77-10147. 486p. 1979. Repr. of 1933 ed. lib. bdg. 27.50 (ISBN 0-88275-600-1). Krieger.

Heavy-Ion, High-Spin States & Nuclear Structure, 2 vols. (Illus.). 872p. 1975. Set. pap. 86.00 (ISBN 0-685-61024-1, ISP386-1&2, IAEA). Unipub.

Hellwege, K. H., ed. Molecular Constants. (Landolt-Boerstein: Group II, Vol. 14, Subvol. A). 790p. 1983. 537.10 (ISBN 0-387-11365-7). Springer-Verlag.

Henley, E. J. & Kouts, H. H., eds. Advances in Nuclear Science & Technology, Vol. 8. (Serial Publication). 1975. 80.00 (ISBN 0-12-029308-0). Acad Pr.

Henley, E. J., et al, eds. Advances in Nuclear Science & Technology. Incl. Vol. 1. 1962 (ISBN 0-12-029301-3); Vol. 2. 1964 (ISBN 0-12-029302-1); Vol. 4. 1968 (ISBN 0-12-029304-8); Vol. 5. Henley, E. J. & Lewins, J., eds. 1969 (ISBN 0-12-029305-6); Vol. 6. 1972 (ISBN 0-12-029306-4); Vol. 7. 1973 (ISBN 0-12-029307-2); Vol. 9. 1976 (ISBN 0-12-029309-9). 80.00 ea. Acad Pr.

--Advances in Nuclear Science & Technology, Vol. 10. LC 62-13039. 598p. 1977. 85.00x (ISBN 0-306-38230-X, Plenum Pr). Plenum Pub.

High-Energy Physics & Elementary Particles. (Proceedings Ser.). (Illus.). 1006p. (Orig.). 1965. pap. 39.50 (ISBN 92-0-530265-1, ISP117, IAEA). Unipub.

Hodgson, P. E. Growth Points in Nuclear Physics, Vol. 1. (Illus.). 1980. pap. 9.50 (ISBN 0-08-023079-2). Pergamon.

--Growth Points in Nuclear Physics, Vol. 2. (Illus.). 1980. pap. text ed. 10.50 (ISBN 0-08-023081-4). Pergamon.

--Nuclear Heavy-Ion Reactions. (Oxford Studies in Nuclear Physics). (Illus.). 1978. text ed. 75.00x (ISBN 0-19-851514-6). Oxford U Pr.

Hoehler, G., ed. Low Energy Hadron Interactions: Compilation of Coupling Constants & Low Energy Parameters. LC 25-9130. (Springer Tracts in Modern Physics: Vol. 55). (Illus.). 1971. 58.50 (ISBN 0-387-05250-X). Springer-Verlag.

--Nuclear Physics. LC 25-9130. (Springer Tracts in Modern Physics: Vol. 71). (Illus.). 255p. 1974. 57.90 (ISBN 0-387-06641-1). Springer-Verlag.

--Springer Tracts in Modern Physics, Vol. 53. (Illus.). 1970. 29.00 (ISBN 0-387-05016-7). Springer-Verlag.

Hoffmann, Banesh. Strange Story of the Quantum. 1959. pap. text ed. 4.95 (ISBN 0-486-20518-5). Dover.

Hornyak, William F. Nuclear Structure. 1975. 94.00 (ISBN 0-12-356050-0). Acad Pr.

Hurst, G. S. & Turner, J. E. Elementary Radiation Physics. LC 80-23962. 202p. 1981. Repr. of 1970 ed. text ed. 15.50 (ISBN 0-89874-249-8). Krieger.

Hwang, W-Y. P. & Macfarlane, M. H., eds. Hadron Substructure in Nuclear Physics: Indiana University 1983. LC 84-70165. (AIP Conference Proceedings Ser.: No. 110). 398p. 1984. lib. bdg. 43.00 (ISBN 0-88318-309-9). Am Inst Physics.

Iachello, F., ed. Interacting Bosons in Nuclear Physics. LC 79-13600. (Ettore Majorana International Science Series; Physical Sciences: Vol. 1). 201p. 1979. 42.50x (ISBN 0-306-40190-8, Plenum Pr). Plenum Pub.

IAEA Laboratory Activities: 1st Report. Incl. IAEA Laboratory Activities: 2nd Report. (Technical Reports Ser.: No. 41). (Illus.). 106p. (Orig.). 1965. pap. 6.25 (ISBN 92-0-175065-X, IDC41, IAEA); IAEA Laboratory Activities: 3rd Report. (Technical Reports Ser.: No. 55). (Illus.). 142p. (Orig.). 1966. pap. 6.25 (ISBN 92-0-175166-4, IDC55, IAEA); IAEA Laboratory Activities: 4th Report. (Technical Reports Ser.: No. 77). (Illus.). 148p. (Orig.). 1967. pap. 6.25 (ISBN 92-0-175167-2, IDC77, IAEA); IAEA Laboratory Activities: 6th Report. (Technical Reports Ser.: No. 98). (Illus.). 142p. (Orig.). 1969. pap. 13.25 (ISBN 92-0-175169-9, IDC98, IAEA); IAEA Laboratory Activities: 7th Report. (Technical Reports Ser.: No. 103). (Illus.). 101p. (Orig.). 1970. pap. 10.50 (ISBN 92-0-175070-6, IDC103, IAEA). (Technical Reports Ser.: No. 25). (Illus.). 112p. (Orig.). 1964. pap. 6.25 (ISBN 92-0-175064-1, IDC25, IAEA). Unipub.

International Atomic Energy Agency. INIS Reference Series, 16 vols. (Illus.). 1100p. (Orig.). 1969-1974. pap. 72.25 (ISBN 0-685-02939-5, IAEA). Unipub.

International Conference, Harwell, Sept. 1978. Neutron Physics & Nuclear Data: Proceedings. 1979. 55.00x (ISBN 92-64-01870-0). OECD.

International Conference on Fast Neutron Physics 1963: Houston, TX. Progress in Fast Neutron Physics. Phillips, G. C. & Marion, J. B., eds. LC 63-18849. (Rice University Semicentennial Publications Ser.). pap. 102.80 (ISBN 0-317-08835-1, 2020204). Bks Demand UMI.

International Conference on Nuclear Structure. Proceedings of the International Conference on Nuclear Structure, Kingston, Canada, August 29-September 3, 1960. Bromley, D. A. & Vogt, E. W., eds. pap. 160.00 (ISBN 0-317-08933-1, 2014144). Bks Demand UMI.

International Conference on Nuclidic Masses. Proceedings of the International Conference on Nuclidic Masses, McMaster University, Hamilton, September 12-16, 1960. Duckworth, H. E., ed. LC 61-4023. pap. 138.00 (ISBN 0-317-08945-5, 2014191). Bks Demand UMI.

International Conference on Solid State Nuclear Track Detectors, 9th, Neuherberg-Munich, 1976. Solid State Nuclear Track Detectors: Proceedings, 2 vols. Granzer, F., et al, eds. LC 77-30630. (Illus.). 1312p. 1978. Set. text ed. 285.00 (ISBN 0-08-021659-5). Pergamon.

International School of Elementary Particle Physics. Methods in Subnuclear Physics: Proceedings, 1965-1969, Vols. 1-4. Nikolic, M., ed. Incl. Vol. 1. 516p. 1968. 111.25 (ISBN 0-677-11950-X); Vol. 2. 858p. 1968. 163.25 (ISBN 0-677-11960-7); Vol. 3. 882p. 1969. 180.50 (ISBN 0-677-12790-1); Vol. 4. 1970. Part 1, 460p. 119.25 (ISBN 0-677-14340-0); Part 2, 368p. 96.25 (ISBN 0-677-14350-8); Part 3, 448p. 119.25 (ISBN 0-677-14360-5); Three Part Set. 299.25 (ISBN 0-677-13530-0); Vol. 5. 876p. 1977. Two Part Set. 119.25 (ISBN 0-677-15910-2). Gordon.

International Summer Institute in Theoretical Physics. Strong Interaction Physics. (Springer Tracts in Modern Physics: Vol. 57). 1971. 56.70 (ISBN 0-387-05252-6). Springer-Verlag.

International Summer School for Theoretical Physics-2nd - University of Karlsruhe-1969. Weak Interactions: Invited Papers. Hoehler, G., ed. (Springer Tracts in Modern Physics Ser.: Vol. 52). (Illus.). v, 214p. 1970. 44.90 (ISBN 0-387-05015-9). Springer-Verlag.

Jackson, J. D., et al, eds. Annual Review of Nuclear & Particle Science, Vol. 28. LC 53-995. (Annual Review of Nuclear Science Ser.: 1950-1977). (Illus.). 1978. text ed. 22.50 (ISBN 0-8243-1528-6). Annual Reviews.

--Annual Review of Nuclear & Particle Science, Vol. 30. LC 53-995. (Annual Review of Nuclear Science Ser.: 1950-1977). (Illus.). 1980. text ed. 22.50 (ISBN 0-8243-1530-8). Annual Reviews.

Jaech, John L. & AEC Technical Information Center. Statistical Methods in Nuclear Material Control. LC 73-600241. 409p. 1973. 18.25 (ISBN 0-87079-343-8, TID-26298); microfiche 4.50 (ISBN 0-87079-344-6, TID-26298). DOE.

Joachain, Charles J. & Post, Douglas E., eds. Atomic & Molecular Physics of Controlled Thermonuclear Fusion. (NATO ASI Series B, Physics: Vol. 101). 575p. 1983. 79.50x (ISBN 0-306-41398-1, Plenum Pr). Plenum Pub.

Jones, G. A. The Properties of Nuclei. (Oxford Physics Ser.). (Illus.). 1977. 26.50x (ISBN 0-19-851828-5). Oxford U Pr.

Jungk, Robert. Brighter Than a Thousand Suns: A Personal History of the Atomic Scientists. Cleugh, James, tr. from Ger. LC 58-8581. Orig. Title: Heller Als Tausend Sonnen. 1970. pap. 5.95 (ISBN 0-15-614150-7, Harv). HarBraceJ.

Kaplan, Irving. Nuclear Physics. 2nd ed. 1962. 34.95 (ISBN 0-201-03602-9). Addison-Wesley.

Kennedy, Hugh P. & Schrils, Rudolph, eds. Intermediate Structure in Nuclear Reactions: Lectures by Richard H. Lemmer, Leonard S. Rodberg, James E. Young, J. J. Griffin, Alexander Lande. LC 67-29341. pap. 57.80 (ISBN 0-317-26730-2, 2024360). Bks Demand UMI.

King, W. H. Isotope Shifts in Atomic Spectra. (Physics of Atoms & Molecules Ser.). 218p. 1984. 37.50x (ISBN 0-306-41562-3, Plenum Pr). Plenum Pub.

Kleppner, Daniel & Pipkin, Francis M., eds. Atomic Physics 7. LC 72-176581. 584p. 1981. 85.00 (ISBN 0-306-40650-0, Plenum Pr). Plenum Pub.

Kopferman, Hans. Nuclear Moments. (Pure & Applied Physics Ser.). 1958. microfiche 80.00 (ISBN 0-12-419951-8). Acad Pr.

Kumar, Krishna. Nuclear Models & the Search for Unity in Nuclear Physics. 116p. (Orig.). 1984. pap. 16.00x (ISBN 82-00-07149-9). Universitet.

Kutateladze, Samson S. & Borishanskii, V. M. Liquid-Metal Heat Transfer Media. 1958 ed. LC 59-4583. (Soviet Journal of Atomic Energy: No. 2). pap. 39.30 (ISBN 0-317-12995-3, 2020651). Bks Demand UMI.

Landau, L. D. & Smorodinsky, Ya. Lectures on Nuclear Theory. LC 59-8865. 108p. 1959. 15.00x (ISBN 0-306-30134-2, Plenum Pr). Plenum Pub.

Lapp, Ralph & Andrews, Howard. Nuclear Radiation Physics. 4th ed. (Illus.). 1972. 35.95 (ISBN 0-13-625988-X). P-H.

Leprince-Ringuet, Louis. Atoms & Men. Halperin, Elaine P., tr. LC 61-11292. pap. 32.00 (ISBN 0-317-08842-4, 2020200). Bks Demand UMI.

Levine, Raphael D. & Tribus, Myron, eds. The Maximum Entropy Formalism. 1979. text ed. 40.00x (ISBN 0-262-12080-1). MIT Pr.

Lewins, Jeffrey & Becker, Martin, eds. Advances in Nuclear Science & Technology, Vol. 16. 600p. 1983. 89.50x (ISBN 0-306-41486-4, Plenum Pr). Plenum Pub.

Lindgren, I., et al, eds. Atomic Physics 8. 604p. 1983. 79.50x (ISBN 0-306-41361-2, Plenum Pr). Plenum Pub.

Locher, M. P., ed. Seventh International Conference on High Energy Physics & Nuclear Structure. (Experientia Supplementa: 31). 436p. 1978. 78.95x (ISBN 0-8176-0987-3). Birkhauser.

McCarthy, I. E. Introduction to Nuclear Theory. LC 68-19781. 555p. 1968. text ed. 26.50 (ISBN 0-471-58140-2, Pub. by Wiley). Krieger.

McDowell, M. R. & Ferendeci, A. M., eds. Atomic & Molecular Processes in Controlled Thermonuclear Fusion. LC 80-238. (NATO ASI Series B, Physics: Vol. 53). 500p. 1980. 75.00x (ISBN 0-306-40424-9, Plenum Pr). Plenum Pub.

MacKinnon, Edward M. Scientific Explanation & Atomic Physics. LC 82-2702. (Illus.). 464p. 1982. lib. bdg. 31.00X (ISBN 0-226-50053-5). U of Chicago Pr.

Marmier, Pierre & Sheldon, Eric. Physics of Nuclei & Particles, Vols. 1-2. Vol. 2,1970. 41.85 (ISBN 0-12-473102-3). Acad Pr.

Marrus, Richard, et al, eds. Atomic Physics 5. LC 72-176581. 586p. 1977. 85.00x (ISBN 0-306-37195-2, Plenum Pr). Plenum Pub.

Marton, Claire, ed. Advances in Electronics & Electron Physics, Vol. 58. (Serial Publication Ser.). 1982. 75.00 (ISBN 0-12-014658-4). Acad Pr.

Marx, G., ed. Nuclear Physics, Nuclear Power. 1982. 46.00 (ISBN 0-9960072-9-6, Pub. by Akademiai Kaido Hungary). Heyden.

Massey, H. S., et al. Applied Atomic Collision Physics, Vol. 2. (Pure & Applied Physics Ser.). 1984. 80.00 (ISBN 0-12-478802-5). Acad Pr.

Massey, Harrie. New Age in Physics. 2nd ed. (Illus.). 1966. text ed. 19.50x (ISBN 0-8464-0670-5). Beekman Pubs.

Massimo, L. Physics of High Temperature Reactors. 1975. text ed. 44.00 (ISBN 0-08-019616-0). Pergamon.

Maul, Gerd G. The Nuclear Envelope & the Nuclear Matrix. LC 82-15259. (The Wistar Symposium Ser.: Vol. 2). 334p. 1982. 34.00 (ISBN 0-8451-2001-8). A R Liss.

Meeting on Polarization Nuclear Physics, Ebermannstadt, Germany, 1973. Proceedings. Fick, D., ed. (Lecture Notes in Physics Ser.: Vol. 30). (Illus.). ix, 292p. 1974. pap. 17.00 (ISBN 0-387-06978-X). Springer-Verlag.

Messel, H. & Crawford, D. F. Electron-Photon Shower Distribution Function: Tables for Lead, Copper & Air Absorbers. LC 69-16049. 1970. 255.00 (ISBN 0-08-013374-6). Pergamon.

Meyer, H. O. The Interaction Between Medium Energy Nucleons in Nuclei, Indiana University Cyclotron Facility, 1982: AIP Conference Proceedings, No. 97. LC 83-70649. (No. 97). 433p. 1983. lib. bdg. 38.50 (ISBN 0-88318-196-7). Am Inst Physics.

Minerva Symposium on Physics, Rehovot, Israel, 1973. Nuclear Structure Physics: Proceedings. Smilansky, V., et al, eds. (Lecture Notes in Physics: Vol. 23). 296p. 1973. pap. 18.30 (ISBN 0-387-06554-7). Springer-Verlag.

Mischke, Richard E. Intersections Between Particle & Nuclear Physics (Steamboat Springs, 1984: Proceedings of AIP Conference. LC 84-72790. (No. 123). 1162p. 1984. lib. bdg. 65.00 (ISBN 0-88318-322-6). Am Inst Physics.

MIT Students' System Project. Project Icarus. rev. ed. Li, Yao T. & Sandorf, Paul, eds. 1979. pap. 4.95x (ISBN 0-262-63068-0). MIT Pr.

Modern Plasma Physics Trieste Course: Basic Course Given 16 Oct. - 23 Nov. 1979 & Selected Lectures on Advanced Topics in Fusion Research Presented at the College. (Proceedings Ser.). (Illus.). 610p. 1981. pap. 83.50 (ISBN 92-0-130281-9, ISP573, IAEA). Unipub.

Morinaga, H. Developments & Borderlines of Nuclear Physics. (Italian Physical Society Course: No. 53). 1974. 60.00 (ISBN 0-12-368853-1). Acad Pr.

Munzinger, Peter B., ed. Nuclear Physics with Heavy Ions, Vol. 6. (Nuclear Science Research Conference Ser.). 492p. 1984. text ed. 108.00 (ISBN 3-7186-0196-6). Harwood Academic.

Myers, W. D. Droplet Model of Atomic Nuclei. LC 77-20790. 158p. 1977. 85.00x (ISBN 0-306-65170-X, IFI Plenum). Plenum Pub.

Nato Advanced Study Institute, C15, Ramsau, Germany, 1974. Computational Techniques in Quantum Chemistry & Molecular Physics: Proceedings. Diercksen, G. H., ed. LC 75-9913. 568p. 1975. lib. bdg. 68.50 (ISBN 90-277-0588-7, Pub. by Reidel Holland). Kluwer Academic.

NCRP. Carbon-Fourteen in the Environment. LC 84-29586. (NCRP Report Ser.: No. 81). 65p. 1985. pap. text ed. 12.00 (ISBN 0-913392-73-1). Natl Coun Radiation.

Negele & Vogt, eds. Advances in Nuclear Physics, Vol. 11. LC 67-29001. (Illus.). 434p. 1979. 59.50x (ISBN 0-306-40111-8, Plenum Pr). Plenum Pub.

Negele, J. W. & Vogt, E., eds. Advances in Nuclear Physics, Vol. 12. LC 67-29001. 272p. 1981. 49.50x (ISBN 0-306-40708-6, Plenum Pr). Plenum Pub.

Negele, J. W. & Vogt, Erich, eds. Advances in Nuclear Physics, Vol. 13. 315p. 1983. 49.50x (ISBN 0-306-41313-2, Plenum Pr). Plenum Pub.

--Advances in Nuclear Physics, Vol. 14. 282p. 1984. 49.50x (ISBN 0-306-41524-0, Plenum Pr). Plenum Pub.

Nuclear Data in Science & Technology: 1953-1975, 2 vols. (Proceedings Ser.). (Illus.). 1214p. (Orig.). 1974. pap. 53.75 (ISP343, IAEA); Vol. 1. pap. 53.75 (ISBN 92-0-030073-1, ISP 343-1); Vol. 2. pap. 53.75 (ISBN 92-0-030173-8, ISP343-2). Unipub.

Nuclear Electronics: 1961, 3 vols. (Proceedings Ser.). (Illus.). 1568p. 1962. Vol. 1. 24.00 (ISBN 92-0-030162-2, ISP42-1, IAEA); Vol. 2. 21.50 (ISBN 92-0-030262-9, ISP42-2); Vol. 3. 24.00 (ISBN 92-0-030362-5, ISP42-3). Unipub.

Nuclear Physics. (Advanced Physics Training Ser.). (Illus.). 258p. 1983. looseleaf 55.00x (ISBN 0-87683-178-1); training materials pkg. 2000.00x (ISBN 0-87683-179-X); lesson plans 1375.00x; transparencies 375.00x (ISBN 0-87683-180-3); question bank 750.00x (ISBN 0-87683-181-1). G P Courseware.

Nuclear Structure: Dubna Symposium, 1968. (Proceedings Ser.). (Illus.). 642p. 1968. pap. 39.50 (ISBN 92-0-530068-3, ISP189, IAEA). Unipub.

Nuclear Techniques & Mineral Resources. (Proceedings Ser.). (Illus.). 546p. 1969. pap. 39.50 (ISBN 92-0-040069-8, ISP198, IAEA). Unipub.

Paic, Guy & Slaus, Ivo, eds. Few Body Problems, Light Nuclei & Nuclear Interactions, 2 vols. 1969. Set. 223.25x (ISBN 0-677-13440-1); Vol. 1, 444p. 119.25x (ISBN 0-677-12760-X); Vol. 2, 482p. 132.95x (ISBN 0-677-13020-1). Gordon.

Pal, M. Theory of Nuclear Structure. 1983. 37.50 (ISBN 0-442-27524-2). Van Nos Reinhold.

Petrovich, Fred, et al, eds. Spin Excitations in Nuclei. 670p. 1984. 95.00x (ISBN 0-306-41617-4, Plenum Pr). Plenum Pub.

Physics & Material Problems of Reactor Control Rods. (Proceedings Ser.). (Illus.). 792p. 1964. 43.00 (ISBN 92-0-050364-0, ISP81, IAEA). Unipub.

Pietschmann, H. Formulae & Results in Weak Interactions. (Acta Physica Austriaca: Suppl. 12). x, 64p. 1974. pap. text ed. 26.00 (ISBN 0-387-81258-X). Springer-Verlag.

Plasma Physics & Controlled Nuclear Fusion Research 1980, Vol. 1-2: Nuclear Fusion Supplement 1981. (Proceedings Ser.). (Illus.). 1726p. (Vol. 1). 1981. Vol. 2. pap. 101.75 (ISBN 92-0-130181-2, ISP563 2, IAEA); Vol. 1. pap. 120.00 (ISBN 92-0-130081-6, ISP563 1). Unipub.

Platt, A. M., et al, eds. Nuclear Fact Book. 192p. 1985. pap. 33.00 (ISBN 3-7186-0273-3). Harwood Academic.
Racah, G., ed. Nuclear Spectroscopy. (Italian Physical Society: Course 15). 1962. 75.00 (ISBN 0-12-368815-9). Acad Pr.
Rand, Roy E. Recirculating Electron Acclerators. (Nuclear Physics Ser.: Vol. 3). 275p. 1984. 60.00 (ISBN 3-7186-0183-4). Harwood Academic.
Reid, J. M. The Atomic Nucleus. LC 84-7931. (Illus.). 280p. 1984. pap. 8.50 (ISBN 0-7190-0978-2, Pub. by Manchester Univ Pr). Longwood Pub Group.
Renner, B. Current Algebras & Their Applications. 1968. 41.00 (ISBN 0-08-012504-2). Pergamon.
Rho, Mannque & Wilkinson, Denys, eds. Mesons in Nuclei, 3 vols. 1979. Set. 261.75 (ISBN 0-444-85052-X, North Holland); Vol. 1. 102.25 (ISBN 0-444-85255-7); Vol. 2. 102.25 (ISBN 0-444-85256-5); Vol. 3. 102.25 (ISBN 0-444-85257-3). Elsevier.
Ricketts, L. W. Fundamentals of Nuclear Hardening of Electronic Equipment. 548p. 1972. 72.50 (ISBN 0-471-72100-X). Wiley.
Robson, B. A., ed. Nuclear Interactions: Conference Held in Canberra, Aug. 28-Sept. 1, 1978. (Lecture Notes in Physics: Vol. 92). 1979. pap. 28.00 (ISBN 0-387-09102-5). Springer-Verlag.
Robson, D. & Fox, J. D., eds. Nuclear Analogue States. LC 76-17849. (Benchmark Papers in Nuclear Physics Ser.: Vol. 1). 1976. 73.00 (ISBN 0-12-787356-2). Acad Pr.
Rodean, Howard C. Nuclear-Explosion Seismology. LC 73-170333. (AEC Critical Review Ser.). 164p. 1971. pap. 12.00 (ISBN 0-87079-288-1, TID-25572); microfiche 4.50 (ISBN 0-87079-289-X, TID-25572). DOE.
Rose, M. E., ed. Nuclear Orientation. (International Science Review Ser.). (Illus.). 336p. 1963. 85.75x (ISBN 0-677-00730-2). Gordon.
Ross, Graham. Grand Unified Theories. (Frontiers in Physics Ser.: No. 60). 1985. text ed. 36.95 (ISBN 0-8053-6967-8, 36937); text ed. 29.95 (ISBN 0-8053-6968-6, 36968). Benjamin-Cummings.
Rowe, D. J., ed. Dynamic Structure of Nuclear States: Proceedings of 1971 Mont Tremblant International Summer School. LC 75-186282. pap. 149.50 (ISBN 0-317-08960-9, 2014391). Bks Demand UMI.
Sandars, P. G. Atomic Physics 2. LC 69-14560. 396p. 1971. 65.00x (ISBN 0-306-37192-8, Plenum Pr). Plenum Pub.
Satchler, George R. Direct Nuclear Reactions. (International Series of Monographs on Physics). (Illus.). 1983. 89.00x (ISBN 0-19-851269-4). Oxford U Pr.
Schwandt, P. & Meyer, H. O., eds. Nuclear Physics with Stored, Cooled Beams (McCormick's Creek State Park, Indiana, 1984) LC 85-71167. (AIP Conference Proceedings Ser.: No. 128). 349p. 1985. lib. bdg. 45.60 (ISBN 0-88318-327-7). Am Inst Physics.
Segre, E., et al, eds. Annual Review of Nuclear Science, Vol. 22. LC 53-995. (Illus.). 1972. text ed. 22.50 (ISBN 0-8243-1522-7). Annual Reviews.
--Annual Review of Nuclear Science, Vol. 26. LC 53-995. (Illus.). 1976. text ed. 22.50 (ISBN 0-8243-1526-X). Annual Reviews.
--Annual Review of Nuclear Science, Vol. 27. LC 53-995. (Illus.). 1977. text ed. 22.50 (ISBN 0-8243-1527-8). Annual Reviews.
Segre, Emilio. Nuclei & Particles: An Introduction to Nuclear & Subnuclear Physics. 2nd rev. ed. 1977. 46.95 (ISBN 0-8053-8601-7). Benjamin-Cummings.
Segre, Emilio, et al, eds. Annual Review of Nuclear Science, Vol. 24. LC 53-995. (Illus.). 1974. text ed. 22.50 (ISBN 0-8243-1524-3). Annual Reviews.
--Annual Review of Nuclear Science, Vol. 25. LC 53-995. (Illus.). 1975. text ed. 22.50 (ISBN 0-8243-1525-1). Annual Reviews.
Selected Topics in Nuclear Theory. (Proceedings Ser.). (Illus.). 452p. 1963. 23.50 (ISBN 92-0-030563-6, ISP67, IAEA). Unipub.
Shen, Benjamin S. & Merker, Milton, eds. Spallation Nuclear Reactions & Their Applications. new ed. (Astrophysics & Space Science Library: No. 59). 1976. lib. bdg. 39.50 (ISBN 90-277-0746-4, Pub. by Reidel Holland). Kluwer Academic.
Shirokov, Y. M. & Yudin, N. P. Nuclear Physics, 2 vols. 749p. 1982. Set. 16.95 (ISBN 0-8285-2451-3, Pub. by Mir Pubs USSR). Imported Pubns.
Shoemaker, Christopher C. Patron-Client State Relationships: Multilateral Crises in the Nuclear Age. LC 83-17822. 220p. 1984. 29.95 (ISBN 0-03-063881-X). Praeger.
Sitenko, A. G. & Tartakovsky, V. K. Lectures on the Theory of the Nucleus. LC 74-10827. 312p. 1975. text ed. 44.00 (ISBN 0-08-017876-6). Pergamon.
Skobel'tsyn, D. V., ed. Studies in Nuclear Physics. LC 72-94830. (P. N. Lebedev Physics Institute Ser.: Vol. 53). (Illus.). 246p. 1973. 55.00 (ISBN 0-306-10882-8, Consultants). Plenum Pub.
--Studies of Nuclear Reactions. LC 66-14741. (P. N. Lebedev Physics Institute Ser.: Vol. 33). 222p. 1966. 35.00x (ISBN 0-306-10767-8, Consultants). Plenum Pub.
Smith, S. J., ed. Atomic Physics 3. LC 72-176581. 688p. 1973. 89.50x (ISBN 0-306-37193-6, Plenum Pr). Plenum Pub.
Soloviev, V. G. Theory of Complex Nuclei. 1976. text ed. 79.00 (ISBN 0-08-018053-1). Pergamon.
Stoler, P., ed. Photopion Nuclear Physics. LC 78-31569. 448p. 1979. 65.00 (ISBN 0-306-40148-7, Plenum Pr). Plenum Pub.
Sutton, Christine, ed. Building the Universe. LC 84-14454. (New Scientist Guides Ser.). (Illus.). 240p. 1985. 24.95x (ISBN 0-631-14102-2); pap. 8.95x (ISBN 0-631-14103-0). Basil Blackwell.
Theory of Nuclear Structure: Trieste Lectures, 1969. (Illus.). 961p. (Orig.). 1970. pap. 56.00 (ISBN 92-0-130070-0, ISP249, IAEA). Unipub.
Thermodynamics of Nuclear Materials: 1974, 2 Vols. (Proceedings Ser.). (Illus.). 484p. 1975. Vol. 1. pap. 46.50 (ISBN 92-0-040175-9, ISP380-1, IAEA); Vol. 2. pap. 53.75 (ISBN 0-685-54200-9, ISP380-2). Unipub.
Touschek, B., ed. Physics with Intersecting Storage Rings. (Italian Physical Society: Course 46). 1971. 92.00 (ISBN 0-12-368846-9). Acad Pr.
Tucson International Topical Conference on Nuclear Physics Held at the University of Arizona, Tucson, Jun 2-6, 1975. Effective Interactions & Operators in Nuclei: Proceedings. Barrett, B. R., ed. (Lecture Notes Physics: Vol. 40). xii, 339p. 1975. pap. 20.00 (ISBN 0-387-07400-7). Springer-Verlag.
Turnbull, R. M. The Structure of Matter: An Introduction to Atomic Nuclear & Particle Physics. (Illus.). 266p. 1979. pap. text ed. 22.50x (ISBN 0-216-90753-5). Intl Ideas.
Uhrig, Robert E., ed. Noise Analysis in Nuclear Systems: Proceedings. (AEC Symposium Ser.). 518p. 1964. pap. 21.00 (ISBN 0-87079-292-X, TID-7679); microfiche 4.50 (ISBN 0-87079-293-8, TID-7679). DOE.
VanDyke, R. S., Jr. & Fortson, E. N., eds. Atomic Physics Nine: Proceedings of the Ninth International Conference on Atomic Physics, Seattle, Washington, July 1984. 600p. 1984. 60.00x (ISBN 9971-966-80-8, 990200930, Pub. by World Sci Singapore); pap. 37.00x (ISBN 9971-966-84-0, Pub. by World Sci Singapore). Taylor & Francis.
Velo, G. & Wightman, A. S., eds. Rigorous Atomic & Molecular Physics. LC 81-12059. (NATO ASI Series B, Physics: Vol. 74). 504p. 1981. text ed. 75.00x (ISBN 0-306-40829-5, Plenum Pr). Plenum Pub.
Warren, J. B., ed. Nuclear & Particle Physics at Intermediate Energies. LC 76-8270. (NATO ASI Series B, Physics: Vol. 15). 608p. 1976. 95.00x (ISBN 0-306-35715-1, Plenum Pr). Plenum Pub.
Weise, W. Quarks & Nuclei. (International Review of Nuclear Physics Ser.: Vol. 1). 620p. 1984. 60.00x (ISBN 9971-966-61-1, Pub. by World Sci Singapore); pap. 33.00x (ISBN 9971-966-62-X, Pub. by World Sci Singapore). Taylor & Francis.
Weisskopf, Victor F., ed. Nuclear Physics. (Italian Physical Society: Course 23). 1963. 75.00 (ISBN 0-12-368823-X). Acad Pr.
Weneser, J. & Lederman, L., eds. Nuclear & Particle Physics: 1967 Annual, Vol. 1. 222p. 1969. 70.50x (ISBN 0-677-12780-4). Gordon.
--Vienna Conference Fourteen: High Energy Physics, Nineteen Sixty-Eight Supplement to Comments on Nuclear & Particle Physics. 46p. 1969. 20.95 (ISBN 0-677-13860-1). Gordon.
Wilkinson, D., ed. Proceedings of the International School of Nuclear Physics, Erice, 2-14 Sept. 1976. (Progress in Particle & Nuclear Physics Ser.: Vol. 1). 1978. 89.00 (ISBN 0-08-020327-2). Pergamon.
Wilkinson, Denys, ed. Progress in Particle & Nuclear Physics: Mesons, Isobars, Quarks & Nuclear Excitations, Vol. 11. (Illus.). 630p. 1984. 102.00 (ISBN 0-08-031489-9). Pergamon.
--Progress in Particle & Nuclear Physics, Vol. 3. 1980. 89.00 (ISBN 0-08-025020-3). Pergamon.
--Progress in Particle & Nuclear Physics, Vol. 4. (Illus.). 600p. 1980. 89.00 (ISBN 0-08-025039-4). Pergamon.
--Progress in Particle & Nuclear Physics, Vol. 5. (Illus.). 280p. 1981. 89.00 (ISBN 0-08-027109-X). Pergamon.
--Progress in Particle & Nuclear Physics, Vol. 6. 350p. 1981. 89.00 (ISBN 0-08-027117-0). Pergamon.
--Progress in Particle & Nuclear Physics, Vol. 7. (Illus.). 270p. 1981. 92.00 (ISBN 0-08-027152-9). Pergamon.
--Progress in Particle & Nuclear Physics, Vol. 12. (Illus.). 470p. 1984. 102.00 (ISBN 0-08-031500-3). Pergamon.
--Progressive in Particle & Nuclear Physics: Collective Bands in Nuclei, Vol. 9. (Illus.). 563p. 1983. 102.00 (ISBN 0-08-030036-7). Pergamon.
Yarwood, John. Atomic & Nuclear Physics. 1981. 25.00x (ISBN 0-7231-0809-9, Pub. by Univ Tutorial England). State Mutual Bk.
Yoshihara, K., et al. Periodic Table with Nuclides & Reference Data. (Illus.). 490p. 1985. pap. 69.50 (ISBN 0-387-15001-3). Springer-Verlag.
Zichichi, A., ed. The Whys of Sub-Nuclear Physics. LC 78-31740. (Subnuclear Ser.: Vol. 15). 1255p. 1979. 145.00x (ISBN 0-306-40151-7, Plenum Pr). Plenum Pub.
Zichichi, Antonio, ed. The New Aspects of Subnuclear Physics. LC 80-15088. (The Subnuclear Ser.: Vol. 16). 814p. 1981. 110.00x (ISBN 0-306-40459-1, Plenum Pr). Plenum Pub.
Zingl, H., et al, eds. Few Body Systems & Nuclear Forces 2: 8th International Conferencce Held in Graz, August 24-30, 1978. (Lecture Notes in Physics: Vol. 87). 1978. pap. 31.00 (ISBN 0-387-09099-1). Springer-Verlag.
Zu Putlitz, G., et al, eds. Atomic Physics 4. LC 72-176581. 794p. 1975. 95.00x (ISBN 0-306-37194-4, Plenum Pr). Plenum Pub.

NUCLEAR PHYSICS–ADDRESSES, ESSAYS, LECTURES

Balian, R., et al, eds. Claude Bloch Scientific Works, 2 vols. LC 74-84212. 1532p. 1975. Set. 234.00 (ISBN 0-444-10853-X, North-Holland). Elsevier.
Becker, R. L., ed. International Nuclear Physics Conference. 1967. 82.50 (ISBN 0-12-084550-4). Acad Pr.
Bederson, B., et al, eds. Atomic Physics 1. LC 69-14560. 633p. 1969. 85.00x (ISBN 0-306-30383-3, Plenum Pr). Plenum Pub.
Bohr, Niels. Niels Bohr Collected Works, Vol. 4: The System, 1920-23. Nielsen, J. Rud, ed. 766p. 1977. 149.00 (ISBN 0-7204-1804-6, North-Holland). Elsevier.
Conversi, M., et al, eds. Some Perspectives on Fundamental Nuclear & High Energy Research. 350p. 1983. pap. text ed. 50.00x (ISBN 0-911767-10-X). Hadronic Pr Inc.
Design of Radiotracer Experiments in Marine Biology Studies. (Technical Reports Ser.: No. 167). (Illus.). 292p. 1975. pap. 32.00 (ISBN 92-0-125175-0, IDC167, IAEA). Unipub.
DeWitt, C. & Gillet, V., eds. Les Houches Lectures: 1968, Nuclear Physics. 814p. 1969. 153.95 (ISBN 0-677-13380-4). Gordon.
Feng, D. H., et al, eds. Workshop on Bosons in Nuclei: Proceedings of Workshop held in Drexel, USA, Jan. 28-29, 1983. Pittel, S. 320p. 1984. 37.00x (ISBN 9971-950-18-9, Pub. by World Sci Singapore); pap. 19.00x (ISBN 9971-950-19-7, Pub. by World Sci Singapore). Taylor & Francis.
Frampton, P., et al, eds. First Workshop on Grand Unification. (LIE Groups; History, Frontiers & Applications: Vol. XI). 370p. 1980. text ed. 30.00 (ISBN 0-915692-31-7, 991600126). Math Sci Pr.
International School of Elementary Particle Physics. Methods in Subnuclear Physics: Proceedings, 1965-1969, Vols. 1-4. Nikolic, M., ed. Incl. Vol. 1. 516p. 1968. 111.25 (ISBN 0-677-11950-X); Vol. 2. 858p. 1968. 163.25 (ISBN 0-677-11960-7); Vol. 3. 882p. 1969. 180.50 (ISBN 0-677-12790-1); Vol. 4. 1970. Part 1, 460p. 119.25 (ISBN 0-677-14340-0); Part 2, 368p. 96.25 (ISBN 0-677-14350-8); Part 3, 448p. 119.25 (ISBN 0-677-14360-5); Three Part Set. 299.25 (ISBN 0-677-13530-0); Vol. 5. 876p. 1977. Two Part Set. 119.25 (ISBN 0-677-15910-2). Gordon.
Jean, M., ed. Nuclear Structure & Nuclear Reactions. (Italian Physical Society: Course 40). 1969. 90.00 (ISBN 0-12-368840-X). Acad Pr.
Klauder, John R., ed. Magic Without Magic: John Archibald Wheeler, a Collection of Essays in Honor of His 60th Birthday. LC 75-183745. (Illus.). 291p. 1972. text ed. 34.95 (ISBN 0-7167-0337-8). W H Freeman.
Kuo, T. T. & Wong, S. S., eds. Topics in Nuclear Physics - I: A Comprehensive Review of Recent Developments Lecture Notes from Peking. (Lectures Notes in Physics Ser.: Vol. 144). 567p. 1981. pap. 29.00 (ISBN 0-387-10851-3). Springer Verlag.
--Topics in Nuclear Physics - II: A Comprehensive Review of Recent Developments Lecture Notes from Peking. (Lecture Notes in Physics Ser.: Vol. 145). 511p. 1981. pap. 29.00 (ISBN 0-387-10853-X). Springer Verlag.
Maria Sklodowska-Curie: Centenary Lectures. (Proceedings Ser.). (Illus.). 198p. 1968. pap. 13.50 (ISBN 92-0-030168-1, ISP179, IAEA). Unipub.
Morse, Philip M., et al. Nuclear, Particle & Many Body Physics, 2 vols. 1972. Vol. 1. 78.00 (ISBN 0-12-508201-0); Vol. 2. 70.00 (ISBN 0-12-508202-9). Acad Pr.
Nagle, D. E., et al, eds. High Energy Physics & Nuclear Structure-1975: Conference Held at Santa Fe & Los Alamos. LC 75-26411. (AIP Conference Proceedings Ser.: No. 26). 712p. 1975. 20.50 (ISBN 0-88318-125-8). Am Inst Physics.
Porter, Charles E., ed. Statistical Theories of Spectra: Fluctuations. (Perspectives in Physics Ser.). (Illus., Orig.). 1965. pap. 46.00 (ISBN 0-12-562356-9). Acad Pr.
Reines, Frederick, ed. Cosmology, Fusion & Other Matters: A Memorial to George Gamow. LC 77-159018. (Illus.). 336p. 1972. 22.50x (ISBN 0-87081-025-1). Colo Assoc.
Schaerf, C. Intermediate Energy Nuclear Physics: Proceedings of the Intermediate School of Intermediate Energy Nuclear Physics, Florence, Italy, Aug. 19-28, 1983. 450p. 1984. 51.00x (ISBN 9971-950-22-7, Pub. by World Sci Singapore). Taylor & Francis.
Skobel'tsyn, D. V., ed. Nuclear Physics & Interaction of Particles with Matter. LC 70-120025. (P. N. Lebedev Physics Institute Ser.: Vol. 44). 269p. 1971. 37.50x (ISBN 0-306-10851-8, Consultants). Plenum Pub.
Wan, Conrad C., ed. Applied Mechanics Aspects of Nuclear Effects in Materials: Presented at the Winter Annual Meeting of ASME, Washington, D. C., Dec. 2, 1971. LC 77-182577. pap. 52.50 (ISBN 0-317-08128-4, 2016863). Bks Demand UMI.

NUCLEAR PHYSICS–DICTIONARIES

Clason, W. E. Elsevier's Dictionary of Nuclear Science & Technology. 2nd rev. ed. (Eng., Fr., Span., Ital., Dutch & Ger.). 787p. 1970. 132.00 (ISBN 0-444-40810-X). Elsevier.
Commissariat a l'Energie Atomique. Dictionnaire des Sciences et Techniques Nucleaires. 3rd ed. (Fr.). 492p. 1975. 67.50 (ISBN 0-686-56958-X, M-6081). French & Eur.
English-Russian Dictionary of Nuclear Explosions. (Eng. & Rus.). 304p. 1977. 40.00x (ISBN 0-686-44703-4, Pub. by Collets). State Mutual Bk.
Lexico De Terminos Nucleares: Diccionario Vocabulario Triligue. (Span., Eng. & Fr.). 848p. 1974. 44.95 (ISBN 84-500-6295-0, S-50124). French & Eur.
Markus, John. Vocabulario Ingles-Espanol De Electronica y Tecnica Nuclear. 2nd ed. (Span. & Eng.). 196p. pap. 16.75 (ISBN 84-267-0247-3, S-30684). French & Eur.

NUCLEAR PHYSICS–EXPERIMENTS

Exponential & Critical Experiments, 3 vols. (Proceedings Ser.). (Eng., Fr., Rus. & Span., Illus.). 1571p. (Vol. 1 480p; Vol. 2 610p; Vol. 3 481p). 1964. Vol. 1. 27.00 (ISBN 92-0-050064-1, ISP79-1, IAEA); Vol. 2. 32.25 (ISBN 92-0-050164-8, ISP79-2); Vol. 3. 27.00 (ISBN 92-0-050264-4, ISP79-3). Unipub.
Power Reactor Experiments. (Proceedings Ser.). (Illus.). 68p. (Vol. 1). Vol. 1. pap. 18.00 (ISBN 92-0-050362-4, ISP51-1, IAEA); Vol. 2. pap. 12.75 (ISBN 92-0-050462-0, ISP51-2). Unipub.

NUCLEAR PHYSICS–HISTORY

AIP & American Academy of Arts & Sciences Joint Conference, Brookline, Mass., 1967 & 1969. Exploring the History of Nuclear Physics: Proceedings, No. 7. Weiner, Charles, ed. LC 72-81883. (Illus.). 271p. 1972. 13.00 (ISBN 0-88318-106-1). Am Inst Physics.
Anderson, David L. & Cohen, I. Bernard, eds. The Discovery of the Electron. LC 80-2114. (Development of Science Ser.). (Illus.). 1981. lib. bdg. 15.00x (ISBN 0-405-13834-2). Ayer Co Pubs.
Keller, Alex. The Infancy of Atomic Physics: Hercules in His Cradle. LC 83-14233. (Illus.). 1983. 19.95x (ISBN 0-19-853904-5). Oxford U Pr.
Romer, Alfred. The Restless Atom: The Awakening of Nuclear Physics. (Illus.). 1982. pap. 3.50 (ISBN 0-486-24310-9). Dover.
Shea, William R., ed. Otto Hahn & the Rise of Nuclear Physics. 1983. lib. bdg. 49.95 (ISBN 0-686-40245-6, Pub. by Reidell Holland). Kluwer Academic.
Stuewer, Roger H., ed. Nuclear Physics in Retrospect: Proceedings of a Symposium on the 1930's. (Illus.). 1979. 27.50x (ISBN 0-8166-0869-5). U of Minn Pr.

NUCLEAR PHYSICS–INSTRUMENTS

Fenyves, E. & Haiman, O. Physical Principles of Nuclear Radiation Measurements. 1969. 86.50 (ISBN 0-12-253150-7). Acad Pr.
Nuclear Electronic Instruments in Tropical Countries. (Technical Reports Ser.: No. 13). (Illus.). 29p. 1963. pap. 6.25 (ISBN 92-0-135063-5, IDC13, IAEA). Unipub.

NUCLEAR PHYSICS–PROBLEMS, EXERCISES, ETC.

Chodos, A., et al, eds. Proceedings of the Lewes Workshop on Solutions in Nuclear & Elementary Particle Physics, Yale University, June 1984. 320p. 1985. 40.00x (ISBN 9971-966-89-1, Pub. by World Sci Singapore). Taylor & Francis.

Smith, W. Problems in Modern Physics. 190p. 1970. 40.50 (ISBN 0-677-02850-4). Gordon.

NUCLEAR PHYSICS–RESEARCH

see Nuclear Research

NUCLEAR PHYSICS–STUDY AND TEACHING

Binggeli, M. H. & Ruckenbauer, E. INIS Input Training Kit. 771p. (Orig.). 1984. pap. 67.25 (ISBN 92-0-179083-X, ISP653, IAEA). Unipub.

Tipler, Paul A. Modern Physics. 2nd ed. LC 77-58725. 1977. text ed. 33.95x (ISBN 0-87901-088-6). Worth.

NUCLEAR PHYSICS–TABLES

Cornu, Aymbe & Massot, R. List of Conversion Factors for Atomic Impurities to PPM Weight. LC 68-20754. pap. 37.00 (ISBN 0-317-29352-4, 2024003). Bks Demand UMI.

Herman, Robert C. & Hofstadter, Robert. High-Energy Electron Scattering Tables. 1960. 22.50x (ISBN 0-8047-0588-7). Stanford U Pr.

NUCLEAR POLARIZATION

see Polarization (Nuclear Physics)

NUCLEAR PLANTS

see also Boiling Water Reactors; Gas Cooled Reactors; Marine Nuclear Reactor Plants

Adamson, Greg. We All Live on Three Mile Island: The Case Against Nuclear Power. (Illus.). 160p. 1982. lib. bdg. 15.00 (ISBN 0-909196-12-5); pap. 4.95 (ISBN 0-686-79301-3). Path Pr NY.

Analyses for Soil Structure Interaction Effects for Nuclear Power Plants. 159p. 1979. pap. 13.50x (ISBN 0-87262-183-9). Am Soc Civil Eng.

Aseismic Design & Testing of Nuclear Facilities. (Technical Reports Ser.: No. 88). 49p. 1968. pap. 6.25 (ISBN 92-0-125368-0, IDC88, IAEA). Unipub.

Atomic Industrial Forum. Positive Experiences in Constructing & Operating Nuclear Power Plants Worldwide. (Technical & Economic Reports: Construction). 76p. 1984. 100.00 (ISBN 0-318-02250-8). Atomic Indus Forum.

Atomic Industrial Forum Staff. An Overview of Decommissioning Nuclear Power Plants. (Technical & Economic Reports: Decommissioning). 1983. 30.00 (ISBN 0-318-02246-X). Atomic Indus Forum.

AWS Conference, 1979. Maintenance Welding in Nuclear Power Plants: Proceedings. 176p. 1980. 25.00 (ISBN 0-87171-191-5); member 18.75. Am Welding.

Barnett, Harold J. Atomic Energy in the United States Economy: A Consideration of Certain Industrial, Regional, & Economic Development Aspects. Bruchey, Stuart, ed. LC 78-22658. (Energy in the American Economy Ser.). (Illus.). 1979. lib. bdg. 25.50x (ISBN 0-405-11962-3). Ayer Co Pubs.

Beckmann, Petr. The Health Hazards of NOT Going Nuclear. LC 76-12720. (Illus.). 188p. 1976. pap. 7.95x (ISBN 0-911762-17-5). Golem.

Behnke, W. B., Jr., et al. Clinch River: The Case for Completion. (Technical & Economic Reports). 1983. 30.00 (ISBN 0-318-02238-9). Atomic Indus Forum.

Binnie & Partners. Islands for Offshore Nuclear Power Stations. 167p. 1983. pap. 40.00x (ISBN 0-8448-1423-7). Crane-Russak Co.

Boggs, R. F. Radiological Safety Aspects of the Operation of Neutron Generators. (Safety Ser.: No. 42). (Illus.). 42p. 1976. pap. 9.25 (ISBN 92-0-123076-1, ISP427, IAEA). Unipub.

British Nuclear Energy Society, ed. Effects of Environment on Material Properties in Nuclear Energy Systems. 242p. 1971. 60.00x (ISBN 0-7277-0028-6, Pub. by Brit Nuclear England). State Mutual Bk.

Civil-Structural Inspection, Course 29. (Illus.). 260p. 1979. spiral bdg. 41.00x (ISBN 0-87683-115-3). G P Courseware.

Commission of European Communities, ed. Plutonium Recycling Scenario in Light Water Reactors: Assessment of Environmental Impact in the European Community. 240p. 1982. 29.50 (ISBN 3-7186-0118-4). Harwood Academic.

Containment & Siting of Nuclear Power Plants. (Proceedings Ser.). (Illus.). 818p. (Orig.). 1967. pap. 50.25 (ISBN 92-0-020167-9, ISP154, IAEA). Unipub.

Critical Mass Energy Project. Tube Leaks: A Consumer's & Worker's Guide to Steam Generator Problems at Nuclear Power Plants. Udell, Richard, ed. (Illus.). 64p. 1982. saddle-stitched 3.50 (ISBN 0-937188-21-2). Pub Citizen Inc.

Decommissioning of Nuclear Facilities. (Proceedings Ser.). (Illus.). 694p. 1980. pap. 95.00 (ISBN 92-0-020179-2, ISP500, IAEA). Unipub.

Design Basis Tropical Cyclone for Nuclear Power Plants: A Safety Guide. (Safety Ser.: No. 50-SG-S11B). 56p. (Orig.). 1984. pap. text ed. 12.00 (ISBN 92-0-123184-9, ISP666, IAEA). Unipub.

Design for Safety of Nuclear Power Plants: A Code of Practice. (Safety Ser.: No. 50-C-D). 44p. 1979. pap. 10.25 (ISBN 92-0-123778-2, ISP516, IAEA). Unipub.

Deutsch, R. W. & Whitney, J. W., eds. Academic Program for Nuclear Power Plant Personnel: BWR. (Illus.). 1754p. 1974. looseleaf 240.00x (ISBN 0-87683-144-7); lesson plans 2000.00x (ISBN 0-87683-151-X); practical exercise 75.00x (ISBN 0-87683-158-7); quizzes & exams 75.00x (ISBN 0-87683-165-X). G P Courseware.

--BWR Nuclear Power Plant Technology. (Academic Program for Nuclear Power Plant Personnel BWR Version Ser.: Vol. III). (Illus.). 396p. 1974. looseleaf bdg. 60.00x (ISBN 0-87683-148-X); lessons plans 500.00x (ISBN 0-87683-155-2); exercise solutions 25.00x (ISBN 0-87683-162-5); quizzes & examinations 25.00x (ISBN 0-87683-169-2). G P Courseware.

--PWR Nuclear Power Plant Technology. (Academic Program for Nuclear Power Plant Personnel Ser.: Vol. III-CPWR Version). (Illus.). 404p. 1972. looseleaf 60.00x (ISBN 0-87683-149-8, A 373977); looseleaf lesson plans 500.00x (ISBN 0-87683-156-0); looseleaf practical exercise solution 25.00x (ISBN 0-87683-163-3); looseleaf quizzes & examinations 25.00x (ISBN 0-87683-170-6). G P Courseware.

Deutsch, R. W., et al. Introduction to Boiling Water Reactor Nuclear Power Plants. (Illus.). 240p. 1976. looseleaf 60.00x (ISBN 0-87683-298-2). G P Courseware.

--Practical Nuclear Power Plant Technology, 2 vols. (Illus.). 1973. Set. looseleaf 120.00x (ISBN 0-87683-295-8); Vol. 1; 368p. looseleaf 60.00x (ISBN 0-87683-296-6); Vol. 2; 320pp. looseleaf 60.00x (ISBN 0-87683-297-4). G P Courseware.

Division One-Nuclear Power Plant Components: General Requirements. (Boiler & Pressure Vessel Code Ser.: Sec. 3). 1980. 55.00 (ISBN 0-686-70367-7, P0003R); pap. 80.00 loose-leaf (ISBN 0-686-70368-5, V0003R). ASME.

Dubrovsky, V. B. Construction of Nuclear Power Plants. 279p. 1981. 11.00 (ISBN 0-8285-2023-2, Pub. by Mir Pubs USSR). Imported Pubns.

Duderstadt, James & Kikuchi, Chihiro. Nuclear Power: Technology on Trial. 1979. 16.00 (ISBN 0-472-09311-8); pap. 9.95 (ISBN 0-472-06312-X). U of Mich Pr.

Earthquake Guidelines for Reactor Siting. (Proceedings Ser.: No. 139). (Illus.). 26p. (Orig.). 1973. pap. 6.25 (ISBN 92-0-125272-2, IDC139, IAEA). Unipub.

Earthquakes & Associated Topics in Relation to Nuclear Power Plant Siting: A Safety Guide. (Safety Ser.: No. 50-SG-S1). 69p. 1979. pap. 13.75 (ISBN 92-0-123879-7, ISP537, IAEA). Unipub.

Ebbin, Steven & Kasper, Raphael. Citizen Groups & the Nuclear Power Controversy: Uses of Scientific & Technological Information. (Environmental Studies). 318p. 1974. pap. 13.50x (ISBN 0-262-55003-2). MIT Pr.

Economic Integration of Nuclear Power Stations in Electric Power Systems. (Proceedings Ser.). (Illus.). 738p. (Orig.). 1971. pap. 59.25 (ISBN 92-0-050071-4, ISP266, IAEA). Unipub.

Emergency Power Systems at Nuclear Power Plants: A Safety Guide. (Safety Ser.: No. 50-SG-D7). (Illus.). 50p. 1983. pap. 10.25 (ISBN 92-0-123782-0, ISP631, IAEA). Unipub.

Energy, Electricity & Nuclear Power Estimates for the Period up to 2000: September, 1982. (Reference Data Ser.: No. 1). (Illus.). 57p. 1983. pap. 5.50 (ISBN 92-0-159182-9, IRDS1/2, IAEA). Unipub.

Environmental Effects of Cooling Systems at Nuclear Power Plants: Proceedings. (Proceedings Ser.). (Illus.). 832p. 1975. pap. 73.00 (ISBN 92-0-020075-3, ISP378, IAEA). Unipub.

Envirosphere Company Staff. NEPA Decision Criteria for Operating License Reviews: AIF-NESP-024. (National Environmental Studies Project: NESP Reports). 1981. 45.00 (ISBN 0-318-02232-X). Atomic Indus Forum.

Establishing the Quality Assurance Programme for a Nuclear Power Plant Project: A Safety Guide. (Safety Ser.: No.50-SG-QA1). 44p. (Orig.). 1984. pap. text ed. 10.50 (ISBN 92-0-123084-2, ISP663, IAEA). Unipub.

Experience from Operating & Fueling Nuclear Power Plants. (Proceedings Ser.). (Eng., Fr. & Span., Illus.). 721p. (Orig.). 1974. pap. 61.00 (ISBN 92-0-050274-1, ISP351, IAEA). Unipub.

External Man-Induced Events in Relation to Nuclear Power Plant Siting: A Safety Guide. (Safety Ser.: No. 50-SG-S5). 62p. 1981. pap. 12.75 (ISBN 92-0-123081-8, ISP585, IAEA). Unipub.

Faulkner, Peter T., ed. Silent Bomb: A Guide to the Nuclear Energy Controversy. (Illus.). 1977. 12.50 (ISBN 0-394-41323-7). Random.

--The Silent Bomb: A Guide to the Nuclear Energy Controversy. (Illus.). 1977. pap. 3.95 (ISBN 0-394-72270-1, Vin). Random.

Ferrara, Grace M., ed. Atomic Energy & the Safety Controversy. (Checkmark Bks). 180p. 1978. lib. bdg. 19.95 (ISBN 0-87196-297-7). Facts on File.

Fire Protection in Nuclear Power Plants: A Safety Guide. (Safety Ser.: No. 50-SG-D2). 43p. 1979. pap. 10.00 (ISBN 92-0-123779-0, ISP536, IAEA). Unipub.

Ford, Daniel, et al. Is Nuclear Power Safe? LC 75-34738. 1975. pap. 3.75 (ISBN 0-8447-2068-2). Am Enterprise.

Freeman, Leslie J. Nuclear Witnesses: Insiders Speak Out. (Illus.). 1981. 16.95 (ISBN 0-393-01456-8). Norton.

Fussell, J. B. & Burdick, G. R., eds. Nuclear Systems Reliability Engineering & Risk Assessment. LC 77-91478. xi, 849p. 1977. text ed. 48.00 (ISBN 0-89871-041-3). Soc Indus-Appl Math.

Galanin, A. D. The Theory of Thermal-Neutron Nuclear Reactors, Pt. 2. LC 58-22338. (Soviet Journal of Atomic Energy Supplement Ser.: Nos. 2-3, 1957). (Illus.). pap. 27.00 (ISBN 0-317-09426-2, 2020663). Bks Demand UMI.

Gofman, John W. & Tamplin, Arthur R. Poisoned Power: The Case Against Nuclear Power Before & After Three Mile Island. LC 79-16781. 1979. pap. 5.95 (ISBN 0-87857-288-0). Comm Nuclear Respon.

Governmental Organization for the Regulation of Nuclear Power Plants: A Code of Practice. (Safety Ser.: No. 50-C-G). 44p. 1979. pap. 10.25 (ISBN 92-0-123478-3, ISP502, IAEA). Unipub.

Green, A. E. Safety Systems Reliability. LC 82-24863. 293p. 1984. 41.95x (ISBN 0-471-90144-X, Pub. by Wiley-Interscience). Wiley.

Harrington, Charlene, et al. Long Term Care of the Elderly: Public Policy Issues. LC 84-17754. 280p. 1985. 29.00 (ISBN 0-8039-2214-0); pap. 14.00 (ISBN 0-8039-2215-9). Sage.

Hickey, Albert E., ed. Simulation & Training Technology for Nuclear Power Plant Safety. 156p. (Orig.). 1981. pap. text ed. 40.00 (ISBN 0-89785-975-8). AIR Systems.

IAEA Services & Assistance in Nuclear Power Plant Safety. 40p. 1983. pap. 7.50 (GP14, IAEA). Unipub.

In-Service Inspection for Nuclear Power Plants: A Safety Guide. (Safety Ser.: No. 50-SG-02). 47p. 1980. pap. 9.75 (ISBN 92-0-123180-6, ISP554, IAEA). Unipub.

Information to Be Submitted in Support of Licensing Applications for Nuclear Power Plants: A Safety Guide. (Safety Ser.: No. 50-Sg-G2). 44p. 1979. pap. 10.25 (ISBN 92-0-123279-9, ISP515, IAEA). Unipub.

Inglis, David R. Wind Power & Other Energy Options. LC 78-9102. (Illus.). 1978. 16.00 (ISBN 0-472-09303-7); pap. 9.95 (ISBN 0-472-06303-0). U of Mich Pr.

Inspection & Enforcement by the Regulatory Body for Nuclear Power Plants. (Safety Ser.: No. 50-SG-G4). 43p. 1980. pap. 10.25 (ISBN 9-2012-3280-2, ISP557, IAEA). Unipub.

Institute of Electrical & Electronics Engineers. IEEE Guide to the Collection & Presentation of Electrical, Electronic, Sensing, Component & Mechanical Equipment Reliability Data for Nuclear-Power Generating Stations: IEEE Standard 500 - 1984. 135.00 (ISBN 0-471-80785-0). Wiley.

Interaction of Grid Characteristics with Design & Performance of Nuclear Power Plants: A Guidebook. (Technical Reports Ser.: No. 224). (Illus.). 68p. 1983. pap. 14.50 (ISBN 92-0-155183-5, IDC224, IAEA). Unipub.

Jack Faucett Associates & S C & A Inc. Characterization of the Temporary Radiation Work Force at U. S. Nuclear Power Plants: AIF-NESP-028. (National Environmental Studies Project: NESP Reports). 1984. 50.00 (ISBN 0-318-02229-X). Atomic Indus Forum.

Karam, R. A., et al, eds. Environmental Impact of Nuclear Power Plants. LC 75-23351. 1976. text ed. 58.00 (ISBN 0-08-019956-9). Pergamon.

Keating, William T. Politics, Technology & the Environment: Technology, Assessment & Nuclear Energy. Bruchey, Stuart, ed. LC 78-22691. (Energy in the American Economy Ser.). 1979. lib. bdg. 30.00x (ISBN 0-405-11994-1). Ayer Co Pubs.

King, Lester J. & Opelka, James H., eds. Three Mile Island Clean-up: Experiences, Waste Disposal & Environmental Impact. LC 82-8817. (AIChE Symposium Series: Vol. 78). 1982. pap. 37.00 (ISBN 0-8169-0224-0, S-213); pap. 19.50 members (ISBN 0-686-47537-2). Am Inst Chem Eng.

Klema, Ernest D. & West, Robert L. Public Regulation of Site Selection for Nucler Power Plants: Present Procedures & Reform Proposals--An Annotated Bibliography. LC 77-71670. (Resources for the Future, RFF Research Paper: R-2). pap. 37.80 (ISBN 0-317-28284-0, 2019948). Bks Demand UMI.

Komanoff, Charles. Power Plant Cost Escalation: Nuclear & Coal Capital Costs, Regulation, & Economics. 336p. 1982. 28.50 (ISBN 0-442-24903-9). Van Nos Reinhold.

Maintenance of Nuclear Power Plants: A Safety Guide. (Safety Ser.: No. 50-SG-07). 46p. 1983. pap. 9.75 (ISBN 92-0-123882-7, ISP604, IAEA). Unipub.

Marchuk, Gurii I. Numerical Methods for Nuclear Reactor Calculations. LC 59-9229. (Soviet Journal of Atomic Energy. Supplement Nos. 3-4 1958 Ser.). pap. 75.00 (ISBN 0-317-08317-1, 2020653). Bks Demand UMI.

Margulova, R. Nuclear Power Stations. 432p. 1978. 10.00 (ISBN 0-8285-0691-4, Pub. by Mir Pubs USSR). Imported Pubns.

Meteorological & Hydrological Aspects of Siting & Operating of Nuclear Power Plants, 2 Vols. (Technical Note Ser.: No. 170). xiii, 125p. 1981. pap. 25.00 (ISBN 92-63-10550-2, W498, WMO); Vol. 1: Meteorological Aspects, In-Prep. Vol. 2: Hydrological Aspects. Unipub.

Milkovich, J. Consumers' Challenges to the Construction of Nuclear Power Plants--Closing the Door on Armageddon. Fogarty, John & Bennett, Blake, eds. 150p. (Orig.). 1984. pap. 17.50 (ISBN 0-9613467-0-1). J Milkovich.

Murray, Raymond L. Nuclear Energy. 2nd ed. text ed. 43.00 (ISBN 0-08-024751-2); pap. text ed. 15.00 (ISBN 0-08-024750-4). Pergamon.

National Association of Corrosion Engineers. The International Symposium on Environmental Degradation of Materials in Nuclear Power Systems-Water Reactors: Proceedings. (Illus.). 996p. 75.00 (ISBN 0-317-06633-1). Natl Corrosion Eng.

NCRP. Iodine-129: Evaluation of Releases from Nuclear Power Generation. LC 83-23145. (NCRP Report Ser.: No. 75). 74p. 1983. pap. text ed. 10.00 (ISBN 0-913392-65-0). Natl Coun Radiation.

Nuclear Energy in Latin America: The Brazilian Case. 20p. 1980. pap. 5.00 (ISBN 92-808-0183-X, TUNU077, UNU). Unipub.

Nuclear Heat Application: Proceedings of a Technical Committee Meeting & Workshop, Cracow, 5-9 December 1983. (Panel Proceedings Ser.). (Eng., Fr. & Rus.). 419p. 1985. pap. 65.75 (ISBN 92-0-051084-1, ISP679, IAEA). Unipub.

Nuclear Power Planning for Hong Kong. (Illus.). 189p. 1977. pap. 20.00 (ISBN 92-0-159077-6, ISP460, IAEA). Unipub.

Nuclear Power Plant Control & Instrumentation. (Proceedings Ser.). (Illus.). 310p. (Orig.). 1972. pap. 27.00 (ISBN 92-0-051072-8, ISP301, IAEA). Unipub.

Nuclear Power Plant Control & Instrumentation: 1978, 2 vols. (Proceedings Ser.). 1979. pap. 53.75 (ISBN 92-0-050378-0, ISP491-1, IAEA); pap. 62.75 (ISBN 92-0-050478-7, ISP491-2). Unipub.

Nuclear Power Plant Control & Instrumentation 1982. (Proceedings Ser.). 726p. 1984. pap. 113.00 (ISBN 92-0-050683-6, ISP628, IAEA). Unipub.

Nuclear Power Plant Instrumentation & Control: A Guidebook. (Technical Reports Ser.: No. 239). 386p. 1985. pap. 62.50 (ISBN 92-0-155284-X, IDC239, IAEA). Unipub.

Nuclear Power Plant Lighting. (IES Committee Reports Ser.). 1976. member 5.50 (ISBN 0-686-96218-4, CP-41); non-member 2.75 (ISBN 0-686-99736-0). Illum Eng.

Nuclear Power Plant Siting: Hydrogeologic Aspects: A Safety Guide. (Safety Ser.: No. 50SGS7). 77p. 1985. pap. 15.25 (ISBN 92-0-623284-3, ISP677 5071, IAEA). Unipub.

Nuclear Power Plant Steam & Mechanical Fundamentals, 12 vols. 2nd ed. (Illus.). 988p. 1981. Set. pap. text ed. 65.00x (ISBN 0-87683-300-8); lesson plans BWR set 2900.00x (ISBN 0-87683-313-X); lesson plans PWR set 2900.00x (ISBN 0-87683-314-8). G P Courseware.

Nuclear Power Plant Steam & Mechanical Fundamentals, Vol. 1. 2nd ed. (Illus.). 46p. 1981. pap. text ed. 6.00x (ISBN 0-87683-301-6). G P Courseware.

Nuclear Power Plant Steam & Mechanical Fundamentals, Vol. 2. 2nd ed. (Illus.). 100p. 1981. pap. text ed. 6.00x (ISBN 0-87683-302-4). G P Courseware.

Nuclear Power Plant Steam & Mechanical Fundamentals, Vol. 3. 2nd ed. (Illus.). 62p. 1981. pap. text ed. 6.00x (ISBN 0-87683-303-2). G P Courseware.

Nuclear Power Plant Steam & Mechanical Fundamentals, Vol. 4. 2nd ed. (Illus.). 74p. 1981. pap. text ed. 6.00x (ISBN 0-87683-304-0). G P Courseware.

Jean, M., ed. Nuclear Structure & Nuclear Reactions. (Italian Physical Society: Course 40). 1969. 90.00 (ISBN 0-12-368840-X). Acad Pr.

Kabir, P. K., ed. Development of Weak Interaction Theory. (International Science Review Ser.). (Illus.). 312p. 1963. 55.75 (ISBN 0-677-00320-X). Gordon.

Kennedy, Hugh P. & Schrils, Rudolph, eds. Intermediate Structure in Nuclear Reactions. LC 67-29341. (Illus.). 232p. 1968. pap. 10.00x (ISBN 0-8131-1155-2). U Pr of Ky.

Lee, T. D., ed. Weak Interactions & High Energy Neutrino Physics. (Italian Physical Society Ser.: Course 32). 1966. 75.00 (ISBN 0-12-368832-9). Acad Pr.

Mahanthappa, K. T. & Brittin, Wesley E., eds. Boulder Lecture Notes in Theoretical Physics, 1969: Vol. 12-B High Energy Collisions of Elementary Particles. 384p. 1971. 74.25x (ISBN 0-677-14560-8). Gordon.

Marshak, M. L., ed. High Energy Physics with Polarized Beams & Targets (Argonne, 1976) Proceedings. LC 76-50181. (AIP Conference Proceedings, No. 35: Subseries on Particles & Fields, No. 12). 543p. 1977. 21.50 (ISBN 0-88318-134-7). Am Inst Physics.

Nikitin, Yu P. & Rozental, I. L. High Energy Physics with Nuclei. (Studies in High Energy Physics: Vol. 5). 292p. 1984. 112.50 (ISBN 3-7186-0172-9). Harwood Academic.

Non-Destructive Testing in Nuclear Technology, 2 vols. (Proceedings Ser.). (Illus.). 839p. (Vol. 1 - 393p., Vol. 2 - 446p.). 1965. Vol. 1. 21.00 (ISBN 92-0-530065-9, ISP105-1, IAEA); Vol. 2. 24.00 (ISBN 92-0-530165-5, ISP105-2). Unipub.

Okun, L. B. Weak Interaction of Elementary Particles. 1965. pap. text ed. 21.00 (ISBN 0-08-013702-4). Pergamon.

Perl, Martin L. High Energy Hadron Physics. LC 74-6348. 584p. 1974. 52.50x (ISBN 0-471-68049-4, Pub. by Wiley-Interscience). Wiley.

Preist, T. W. & Vick, L. L., eds. Particle Interactions at High Energies. LC 67-26706. 406p. 1967. 42.50x (ISBN 0-306-30314-0, Plenum Pr). Plenum Pub.

Reeves, Hubert. Nuclear Reactions in Stellar Surfaces & Their Relations with Stellar Evolution. (Topics in Astrophysics & Space Physics Ser). (Illus.). 98p. 1971. 26.50x (ISBN 0-677-02960-8). Gordon.

Robinson, R. L., et al, eds. Reactions Between Complex Nuclei: Proceedings, 2 vols. LC 74-81324. 680p. 1975. Set. 92.75 (ISBN 0-685-57108-4); Vol. 1. 23.50 (ISBN 0-444-10664-2); Vol. 2. 78.00 (ISBN 0-444-10746-0). Elsevier.

Satchler, G. R. Introduction to Nuclear Reactions. LC 79-26275. 316p. 1980. 74.95x (ISBN 0-470-26467-5). Halsted Pr.

Schiff, Benjamin N. International Nuclear Technology Transfer: Dilemmas of Dissemination & Control. LC 83-9643. (Illus.). 226p. 1984. 35.95x (ISBN 0-86598-139-6). Rowman & Allanheld.

Skobel'tsyn, D. V., ed. Cosmic Rays & Nuclear Interactions at High Energies. LC 75-157933. (P. N. Lebedev Physics Institute Ser.: Vol. 46). 229p. 1971. 35.00x (ISBN 0-306-10862-3, Consultants). Plenum Pub.

--Nuclear Reactions & Charged-Particle Accelerators. LC 76-161. (P. N. Lebedev Physics Institute Ser.: Vol. 69). 144p. 1976. 55.50x (ISBN 0-306-10924-7, Consultants). Plenum Pub.

--Nuclear Reactions & Interaction of Neutrons & Matter. LC 74-32059. (P. N. Lebedev Physics Institute Ser.: Vol. 63). (Illus.). 161p. 1974. 55.00 (ISBN 0-306-10907-7, Consultants). Plenum Pub.

The Structure of Nuclei: Trieste Lectures 1971. (Proceedings Ser.). (Illus.). 600p. (Orig.). 1973. pap. 45.00 (ISBN 92-0-130072-7, ISP305, IAEA). Unipub.

Symposium - 3rd - Madison - 1970. Polarization Phenomena in Nuclear Reactions: Proceedings. Barschall, Henry H. & Haeberli, Willy, eds. LC 71-143762. 960p. 1971. text ed. 60.00x (ISBN 0-299-05890-5). U of Wis Pr.

Van Oers, W. T., et al, eds. Clustering Aspects of Nuclear Structure & Nuclear Reactions, Winnipeg, 1978. LC 78-64942. (AIP Conference Proceedings: No. 47). (Illus.). 1978. lib. bdg. 26.75 (ISBN 0-88318-146-0). Am Inst Physics.

Way, Katherine, ed. Atomic & Nuclear Data Reprints, 2 vols. Incl. Vol. 1. Internal Conversion Coefficients. 1973. 46.00 (ISBN 0-12-738901-6); Vol. 2. Reaction List for Charged-Particle-Induced Nuclear Reactions. McGowan, F. K. & Milner, W. T. 1973. 49.50 (ISBN 0-12-738902-4). Acad Pr.

Wildermuth, K. & McClure, W. Cluster Representations of Nuclei. (Springer Tracts in Modern Physics, Vol. 41). (Illus.). 1966. 37.80 (ISBN 0-387-03670-9). Springer-Verlag.

Yang, et al. High Energy Collisions: Third International Conference at Stony Brook, N.Y. Cole, J. A., tr. 534p. 1969. 102.95 (ISBN 0-677-13950-0). Gordon.

Zichichi, A., ed. Hadrons & Their Interactions: Current - Field Algebra, Soft Pions, Supermultiplets, & Related Topics. 1968. 97.50 (ISBN 0-12-780540-0). Acad Pr.

--Strong & Weak Interactions. 1967. 97.50 (ISBN 0-12-780545-1). Acad Pr.

NUCLEAR REACTORS

see also Boiling Water Reactors; Breeder Reactors; Gas Cooled Reactors; Heavy Water Reactors; Marine Nuclear Reactor Plants; Neutron Transport Theory; Nuclear Propulsion; Organic Cooled Reactors; Pressurized Water Reactors; Pulsed Reactors; Reactor Fuel Reprocessing; Thermal Neutrons

American Concrete Institute. Concrete for Nuclear Reactors, 3 vols. LC 72-81007. (American Concrete Institute Publication Ser.: No. SP-34). (Illus.). Vol. 1. pap. 160.00 (ISBN 0-317-10390-3, 2012301); Vol. 2. pap. 135.30 (ISBN 0-317-10391-1); Vol. 3. pap. 142.30 (ISBN 0-317-10392-X). Bks Demand UMI.

American Society of Civil Engineers, compiled by. International Seminar on Probabilistic & Extreme Load Design of Nuclear Plant Facilities. 454p. 1979. pap. 27.00x (ISBN 0-87262-146-4). Am Soc Civil Eng.

Argonne National Laboratory & AEC Technical Information Center. Reactor Physics Constants. 2nd ed. 876p. 1963. pap. 58.00 (ISBN 0-87079-337-3, ANL-5800); microfiche 4.50 (ISBN 0-87079-497-3, ANL-5800). DOE.

Ash, Milton. Optimal Shutdown Control of Nuclear Reactors. (Mathematics in Science and Engineering Ser.: Vol. 26). 1966. 49.50 (ISBN 0-12-065150-5). Acad Pr.

Ash, Milton S. Nuclear Reactor Kinetics. 2nd ed. (Illus.). 1979. text ed. 75.00 (ISBN 0-07-002380-8). McGraw.

Bankoff, S. George & Afgan, Naim H., eds. Heat Transfer in Nuclear Reactor Safety. (International Centre for Heat & Mass Transfer Ser.). (Illus.). 964p. 1982. text ed. 115.00 (ISBN 0-89116-223-2). Hemisphere Pub.

Bell, George I. & Glasstone, Samuel. Nuclear Reactor Theory. LC 78-22102. 638p. 1979. Repr. of 1970 ed. lib. bdg. 42.50 (ISBN 0-88275-790-3). Krieger.

Bender, F. Underground Siting of Nuclear Power Plants: Internationales Symposium, 1981. (Ger. & Eng., Illus.). 409p. 1982. 63.25 (ISBN 3-510-65108-1). Lubrecht & Cramer.

Blair, B., et al. Introduction to Pressurized Water Reactor Nuclear Power Plants. (Illus.). 276p. 1982. looseleaf 60.00x (ISBN 0-87683-247-8). G P Courseware.

Boland, James F. Nuclear Reactor Instrumentation (In-Core) LC 76-101310. 230p. 1970. 12.50 (ISBN 0-677-02420-7, 450015). Am Nuclear Soc.

Boyd, A. W., ed. Radiation Chemistry in Nuclear Reactor Technology. 70p. 1983. pap. 22.60 (ISBN 0-08-029156-2). Pergamon.

British Nuclear Energy Society, ed. Active Working on Reactors. 84p. 1971. 40.00x (ISBN 0-901948-86-1, Pub. by Brit Nuclear England). State Mutual Bk.

--Ferritic Steels for Fast Reactor Steam Generators, 2 vols. 510p. 1978. 150.00x (ISBN 0-686-79377-3, Pub. by Brit Nuclear England). State Mutual Bk.

--The High Temperature Reactor & Process Applications. 430p. 1975. 125.00x (ISBN 0-7277-0004-9, Pub. by Brit Nuclear England). State Mutual Bk.

--The Physics of Fast Reactor Operation & Design. 470p. 1978. 125.00x (ISBN 0-7277-0054-5, Pub. by Brit Nuclear England). State Mutual Bk.

--The Physics Problems in Thermal Reactor Design. 336p. 1967. 90.00x (ISBN 0-901948-88-8, Pub. by Brit Nuclear England). State Mutual Bk.

--Probabilistic & Extreme Load Design of Nuclear Plant Facilities. 1979. 60.00x (ISBN 0-87262-146-4, Pub. by Brit Nuclear England). State Mutual Bk.

--Structural Analysis & Design of Nuclear Plant Facilities. 553p. 1980. 45.00x (ISBN 0-87262-238-X, Pub. by Brit Nuclear England). State Mutual Bk.

--Structural Design of Nuclear Plant Facilities, 3 vols. 448p. 1973. 150.00x (ISBN 0-87262-155-3, Pub. by Brit Nuclear England). State Mutual Bk.

--Vibration in Nuclear Plant, 2 vols. 1008p. 1979. 125.00x (ISBN 0-7277-0062-6, Pub. by Brit Nuclear England). State Mutual Bk.

--Water Chemistry of Nuclear Reactor Systems. 534p. 1978. 125.00x (ISBN 0-7277-0053-7, Pub. by Brit Nuclear England). State Mutual Bk.

--Water Chemistry of Nuclear Reactor Systems, No. 2. 430p. 1981. 135.00x (ISBN 0-7277-0126-6, Pub. by Brit Nuclear England). State Mutual Bk.

--Welding & Fabrication in the Nuclear Industry. 416p. 1979. 125.00x (ISBN 0-7277-0083-9, Pub. by Brit Nuclear England). State Mutual Bk.

Burton, Ralph A., ed. Bearing & Seal Design in Nuclear Power Machinery: Proceedings of the Symposium on Lubrication in Nuclear Applications, Miami Beach, Florida, June 5-7, 1967. LC 67-27785. pap. 134.80 (ISBN 0-317-10009-2, 2016809). Bks Demand UMI.

Butt, J. Reaction Kinetic & Reactor Design. 1980. 41.95 (ISBN 0-13-753335-7). P-H.

Cameron, I. R. Nuclear Fission Reactors. LC 82-18128. 398p. 1982. 49.50x (ISBN 0-306-41073-7, Plenum Pr). PLenum Pub.

Chasan, Daniel J. The Fall of the House of WPPSS. Brewster, David, ed. 128p. (Orig.). 1985. pap. 9.95 (ISBN 0-912365-05-6). Sasquatch Pub.

Chastain, Joel W., Jr., ed. U. S. Research Reactors. AEC Technical Information Center. 78p. 1957. pap. 11.50 (ISBN 0-87079-380-2, TID-7013); microfiche 4.50 (ISBN 0-87079-483-3, TID-7013). DOE.

Clark, Melville & Hansen, K. F. Numerical Methods of Reactor Analysis. (Nuclear Science & Technology: Vol. 3). 1964. 68.50 (ISBN 0-12-175350-6). Acad Pr.

Codes for Reactor Computations. (Proceedings Ser.). (Illus., Orig.). 1961. 19.00 (ISBN 92-0-050061-7, ISP24, IAEA). Unipub.

Conduct of Regulatory Review & Assessment During the Licensing Process for Nuclear Power Plants: A Safety Guide. (Safety Ser.: No. 50-SG-G3). (Eng., Span., Rus. & Fr.). 49p. 1980. pap. 11.50 (ISBN 92-0-123480-5, ISP571, IAEA). Unipub.

Consultants Bureau. Physics & Heat Technology of Reactors. LC 59-958. (Soviet Journal of Atomic Energy. Supplement 1958: No. 1). pap. 45.00 (ISBN 0-317-08314-7, 2020654). Bks Demand UMI.

DeLeon, Peter. Development & Diffusion of the Nuclear Power Reactor: A Comparative Analysis. LC 79-12988. 352p. 1979. prof ref 30.00 (ISBN 0-88410-682-9). Ballinger Pub.

Determination of Absorbed Dose in Reactors. (Technical Reports Ser.: No. 127). (Illus.). 251p. (Orig.). 1972. pap. 22.00 (ISBN 92-0-157071-6, IDC127, IAEA). Unipub.

Developments in the Physics of Nuclear Power Reactors. (Technical Reports Ser.: No. 143). (Illus.). 291p. (Orig.). 1973. pap. 27.50 (ISBN 92-0-135073-2, IDC143, IAEA). Unipub.

Directory of Nuclear Power Reactors. Incl. Vol. 1. Power Reactors. (Superseded by Vol. 4, ISP397-1); Vol. 2. Research, Test & Experimental Reactors. pap. 11.25 (ISP397-2); Vol. 3. Research, Test & Experimental Reactors. pap. 13.00 (ISP397-3); pap. 13.75 (ISBN 92-0-152060-3, ISP379-3SUPP); Vol. 4. Power Reactors. (Replaces Vol. 1). pap. 13.75 (ISP397-4); pap. 17.50 (ISBN 92-0-152062-X, ISP397-4SUPP); Vol. 5. Research, Test & Experimental Reactors. pap. 16.00 (ISBN 92-0-152064-6, ISP397-5); Vol. 6. Research, Test & Experimental Reactors. pap. 13.50 (ISBN 92-0-152066-2, ISP397-6); Vol. 7. Power Reactors. pap. 21.00 (ISBN 92-0-152067-0, ISP397-7); Vol. 8. Research, Test & Experimental Reactors. pap. 17.75 (ISBN 92-0-152170-7, ISP397-8); Vol. 9. Power Reactors. pap. 17.75 (ISBN 92-0-152171-5, ISP397-9); Vol. 10. Power & Research Reactors. 402p. 1976. pap. 41.75 (ISBN 92-0-152076-X, ISP397-10). IAEA). Unipub.

Division Two-Code for Concrete Reactor Vessels & Containments. (Boiler & Pressure Vessel Code Ser.: Sec. 3). 1980. 90.00 (ISBN 0-686-70386-3, P00032); pap. 125.00 loose-leaf (ISBN 0-686-70387-1, V00032). ASME.

Duderstadt, James J. & Hamilton, Louis J. Nuclear Reactor Analysis. LC 75-20389. 650p. 1976. text ed. 54.00 (ISBN 0-471-22363-8). Wiley.

Dyer, A., ed. Gas Chemistry in Nuclear Reactors & Large Industrial Plant. 281p. 1980. 75.00x (ISBN 0-85501-449-0, Pub. by Brit Nuclear England). State Mutual Bk.

Dyer, Edwin A., ed. Gas Chemistry in Nuclear Reactors & Large Industrial Plants. 296p. 1980. pap. 57.95x (ISBN 0-471-25663-3, Pub. by Wiley Heyden). Wiley.

Educational Research Council of America. Nuclear Reactor Operator. Ferris, Theodore N. & Marchak, John P., eds. (Real People at Work Ser.: G). (Illus.). 36p. 1974. pap. text ed. 2.70 (ISBN 0-89247-059-3, 9339). Changing Times.

Fast Reactor Physics, 2 vols. (Proceedings Ser.). (Eng., Fr & Rus., Illus.). 1143p. (Orig., Vol. 1, 551p; Vol. 2, 592p). 1968. Vol. 1. pap. 37.00 (ISBN 0-685-12710-9, ISP165/1, IAEA); Vol. 2. pap. 41.25 (ISBN 92-0-050568-6, ISP165/2). Unipub.

Fast Reactor Physics: 1979, 2 Vols. (Proceedings Ser.). (Illus.). 512p. 1981. Vol. 1. pap. 76.00 (ISBN 92-0-050280-6, ISP529/1, IAEA). Vol. 2 (ISP529/2). Unipub.

Fast Reactors. (Bibliographical Ser.: No. 22). 561p. 1966. pap. (ISBN 92-0-054066-X, ISP/21/2, IAEA). Unipub.

The First Proceedings of Nuclear Thermal Hydraulics. 336p. 1983. 40.00 (ISBN 0-317-37149-5, 700086). Am Nuclear Soc.

Fistedis, S. H., ed. Structural Mechanics in Reactor Technology: Transactions of the 7th International Conference. (Structural Mechanics in Reactor Technology: Vol. 7). 1983. 332.00 (ISBN 0-444-86703-1). Elsevier.

Franklin, D. & Adamson, R. B. Zirconium in the Nuclear Industry - STP 824: Sixth International Symposium. LC 83-71644. 850p. 1984. text ed. 84.00 (ISBN 0-8031-0270-4). ASTM.

Fuel Burn-up Predictions in Thermal Reactors. (Panel Proceedings Ser.). (Eng. & Fr., Illus.). 243p. (Orig.). 1968. pap. 17.00 (ISBN 92-0-051068-X, ISP172, IAEA). Unipub.

Fusion Reactor Design & Technology, 2 vols. 1983. pap. 46.50 (ISBN 92-0-131083-8, ISP616-1, IAEA); pap. 38.50 (ISBN 92-0-131183-4, ISP616-2). Unipub.

Fusion Reactor Design Concepts. (Panel Proceedings Ser.). (Illus.). 784p. 1979. pap. 45.75 (ISBN 92-0-131178-8, ISP487, IAEA). Unipub.

Fusion Reactor Design Problems: Nuclear Fusion - Special Supplement 1974. (Illus.). 544p. (Orig.). 1974. pap. 45.75 (ISBN 92-0-139074-2, ISP23-74, IAEA). Unipub.

Gittus, John H., ed. Water Reactor Fuel Element Performance: Computer Modeling. (Illus.). 728p. 1983. 192.50 (ISBN 0-85334-217-2, I-171-83, Pub. by Elsevier Applied Sci England). Elsevier.

Glasstone, Samuel & Sesonske, Alexander. Nuclear Reactor Engineering. 3rd ed. 800p. 1980. 42.50 (ISBN 0-442-20057-9). Van Nos Reinhold.

Gol'denblat, I. & Nikolaenko, N. A. Calculations of Thermal Stresses in Nuclear Reactors. LC 64-13143. 78p. 1964. 25.00x (ISBN 0-306-10671-X, Consultants). Plenum Pub.

Greenspan, H., et al, eds. Computing Methods in Reactor Physics. 602p. (Orig.). 1968. 114.50 (ISBN 0-677-11890-2). Gordon.

Harrer, Joseph M. & Beckerley, James G., eds. Nuclear Power Reactor Instrumentation Systems Handbook, 2 vols. AEC Technical Information Center. LC 72-600355. Vol. 1, 313p 1973. pap. 16.00 (ISBN 0-87079-005-6, TID-25952-P1); microfiche 4.50 (ISBN 0-87079-299-7, TID-25952-P1); Vol. 2, 282p 1974. pap. 15.00 (ISBN 0-87079-144-3, TID-25952-P2); microfiche 4.50 (ISBN 0-87079-300-4, TID-25952-P2). DOE.

Henry, Allan. Nuclear Reactor Analysis. LC 74-19477. 1975. 50.00x (ISBN 0-262-08081-8). MIT Pr.

Hetrick, David L. Dynamics of Nuclear Reactors. LC 76-130109. 1971. text ed. 45.00x (ISBN 0-226-33166-0). U of Chicago Pr.

Hetsroni, G., ed. Basic Two Phase Flow Modeling in Reactor Safety & Performance: EPRI Workshop Held at Tampa, Fla. 27 Feb.--2 March 1979. 170p. 1980. pap. 50.00 (ISBN 0-08-026160-4). Pergamon.

Hickey, Albert E., ed. Simulator Training of Nuclear Reactor Operators. 151p. 1980. 15.00 (ISBN 0-89785-974-X). Am Inst Res.

Howe, J. P. & Melese-D'Hospital, G. Thorium & Gas Cooled Reactors. 1978. flexi-cover 57.00 (ISBN 0-08-024208-1). Pergamon.

International Atomic Energy Agency. Programming & Utilization of Research Reactors: Proceedings, 3 vols, Vol. 3. Eklund, Sigvard, ed. (International Atomic Energy Agency Symposia). 1962. 29.50 (ISBN 0-12-572503-5). Acad Pr.

International Tokamak Reactor: Zero Phase. (Panel Proceedings Ser.). (Illus.). 650p. 1980. pap. 82.50 (ISBN 92-0-131080-3, ISP556, IAEA). Unipub.

INTOR International Tokamak Reactor Phase 1: Report of the International Tokamak Reactor Workshop Held in Seven Sessions in Vienna during 1980 & 1981. 1982. pap. 109.50 (ISBN 92-0-131082-X, ISP619, IAEA). Unipub.

Irradiation Facilities for Research Reactors. (Proceedings Ser.). (Eng. & Fr., Illus.). 478p. (Orig.). 1973. pap. 41.25 (ISBN 92-0-050073-0, ISP316, IAEA). Unipub.

Jaeger, T. A. & Baley, B. A., eds. Structural Mechanics in Reactor Technology: Proceedings of the 5th International Conference in Berlin, Germany, August, 1979, 13 vols. 5821p. 1980. Set. pap. 276.75 (ISBN 0-444-85356-1, North Holland). Elsevier.

Jaeger, T. A. & Boley, B. A., eds. Structural Mechanics in Reactor Technology: Proceedings of the International Conference, 3rd, London, 1975, 8 pts. 3498p. 1976. Set. pap. 213.00 (ISBN 0-7204-0343-X, North-Holland). Elsevier.

--Structural Mechanics in Reactor Technology: Transactions of the 4th International Conference, San Francisco, California, August 1977, 13 vols. 6448p. 1978. pap. 298.00 (ISBN 0-444-85093-7, North-Holland). Elsevier.

Preparedness of Public Authorities for Emergencies at Nuclear Power Plants. (Safety Ser.: No. 50-SG-G6). 46p. 1982. pap. 9.50 (ISBN 92-0-123082-6, ISP601, IAEA). Unipub.

Preparedness of the Operating Organization (Licensee) for Emergencies at Nuclear Power Plants: A Safety Guide. (Safety Ser.: No. 50-SG-06). 76p. 1982. pap. 11.25 (ISBN 92-0-123182-2, ISP618, IAEA). Unipub.

NUCLEAR REACTORS–COOLING

American Society of Mechanical Engineers, Committee on Nucleonics Heat Transfer. Survey of Nucleonic Heat Transfer Research & Development. LC 72-185848. (American Society of Mechanical Engineers, Heat Transfer Division Ser.: Vol. 1). pap. 20.00 (ISBN 0-317-09936-1, 2016900). Bks Demand UMI.

AMSE. Spent Nuclear Fuel Heat Transfer; Fuel Casks & Transfer Operations: Proceedings of AMSE, Annual Winter Meeting, December 1971. Groetch, D. J. & Todreas, N., eds. LC 79-180673. (American Society of Mechanical Engineers, Heat Transfer Division Ser.: Vol. 2). pap. 20.00 (ISBN 0-317-09924-8, 2016901). Bks Demand UMI.

Cohen, Paul. Water Coolant Technology of Power Reactors. Wallin, Diane, ed. LC 79-57306. (Monograph Ser.). 250p. 1980. Repr. of 1969 ed. write for info. (ISBN 0-89448-020-0, 300016). Am Nuclear Soc.

Corradini, M. L. & Bishop, A. A., eds. Fuel-Coolant Interactions. (HTD Ser.: Vol. 19). 113p. 1981. 24.00 (ISBN 0-686-34493-6, H00204). ASME.

Foust, O. J. Sodium-Nak Engineering Handbook: Vol. 1-Sodium Chemistry & Physical Properties. LC 70-129473. (U. S. Atomic Energy Commission Monographs). 340p. 1972. 89.25 (ISBN 0-677-03020-7). Gordon.

Foust, O. J., ed. Sodium-Nak Engineering Handbook, 5 vols. 1730p. 1979. Set. 404.25 (ISBN 0-677-03070-3). Gordon.

Mueller, U. & Guenther, C., eds. Post Accident Debris Cooling: Proceedings of the Fifth Post Accident Heat Removal Information Exchange Meeting, 1982, Nuclear Research Center Karlsruhe. (Illus.). 364p. (Orig.). 1983. text ed. 30.00x (ISBN 3-7650-2034-6). Sheridan.

NUCLEAR REACTORS–FUEL

see Nuclear Fuels

NUCLEAR REACTORS–FUEL ELEMENTS

see Nuclear Fuel Elements

NUCLEAR REACTORS–MATERIALS

see also Nuclear Fuels

Analytical Chemistry of Nuclear Materials. (Technical Reports Ser.: No. 18). 88p. (Orig.). 1963. pap. 7.00 (ISBN 92-0-145163-6, IDC18, IAEA). Unipub.

Analytical Chemistry of Nuclear Materials: Second Panel Report. (Technical Reports Ser.: No. 62). (Illus.). 138p. (Orig.). 1966. pap. 11.50 (ISBN 92-0-145266-7, IDC62, IAEA). Unipub.

Foell, Wesley K. Small-Sample Reactivity Measurements in Nuclear Reactors. LC 74-144051. (ANS Monographs). 272p. 1972. 23.50 (ISBN 0-89448-003-0, 300005). Am Nuclear Soc.

Grouting Tests on Large Post-Tensioning Tendons for Secondary Nuclear Containment Structures. (PCI Journal Reprints Ser.). 16p. pap. 5.00 (ISBN 0-686-40035-6, JR103). Prestressed Concrete.

Ma, Benjamin. Nuclear Reactor Materials & Applications. 1983. 39.95 (ISBN 0-442-22559-8). Van Nos Reinhold.

New Nuclear Materials Including Non-Metallic Fuels, 2 vols. (Proceedings Ser.). (Illus.). 1132p. (Vol. 1 - 564p., Vol. 2 - 568p.). Vol. 1. pap. 28.75 (ISBN 92-0-050363-2, ISP77-1, IAEA); Vol. 2. pap. 28.75 (ISBN 92-0-050463-9, ISP77-2). Unipub.

Nuclear Data for Reactors, 2 vols. (Proceedings Ser.). (Illus.). 1702p. (Orig.). 1970. Vol. 1. pap. 57.25 (ISBN 92-0-030070-7, ISP259-1, IAEA); Vol. 2. pap. 68.00 (ISBN 92-0-030170-3, ISP259-2). Unipub.

Nuclear Materials Management. (Proceedings Ser.). (Illus.). 888p. 1966. 48.00 (ISBN 92-0-050066-8, ISP110, IAEA). Unipub.

Okrent, Hummel. Reactivity Coefficients in Large Fast Power Reactors. LC 73-119000. (ANS Monographs). 386p. 1970. 18.40 (ISBN 0-89448-006-5, 300002). Am Nuclear Soc.

Prediction of the Shift in the Brittle-Ductile Transition of Light-Water Reactor Pressure Vessel Materials. (Journal of Testing & Evaluation: Vol. 11, No. 4). 260p. 1983. write for info. Metal Prop Coun.

Reactor Plant Materials. (Illus.). 298p. 1982. looseleaf bdg. 55.00x (ISBN 0-87683-293-1); looseleaf instr's. lesson plans 1500.00x (ISBN 0-87683-294-X). G P Courseware.

Rodden, C. J., ed. Analysis of Essential Nuclear Reactor Materials. AEC Technical Information Center. LC 64-60035. 1291p. 1964. 83.50 (ISBN 0-87079-393-4, TID-21384); microfiche 4.50 (ISBN 0-87079-136-2, TID-21384). DOE.

Simnad, M. T. & Zumwalt, L. R., eds. Materials & Fuels for High-Temperature Nuclear Applications. 1964. 35.00x (ISBN 0-262-19012-5). MIT Pr.

Standard for Light Water Reactor Coolant Pressure Boundary Leak Detection: ISA Standard S67.03. 28p. 1982. pap. text ed. 16.00x (ISBN 0-87664-734-4). Instru Soc.

Steele, L. E., ed. Status of U. S. A. Nuclear Reactor Pressure Vessel Surveillance for Radiation Effects. write for info. Metal Prop Coun.

Thermodynamics of Nuclear Materials: 1967. (Eng., Fr. & Rus.). 890p. 1968. pap. 50.25 (ISBN 92-0-040068-X, ISP162, IAEA). Unipub.

Von der Hardt, Peter & Rottger, Heinz, eds. Handbook of Materials Testing Reactors & Associated Hot Laboratories in the European Community. 160p. 1981. 24.00 (ISBN 90-277-1347-2, Pub. by Reidel Holland). Kluwer Academic.

NUCLEAR REACTORS–SAFETY MEASURES

ACI Committee 349. Code Requirements for Nuclear Safety Related Concrete Structures: ACI 349-80. 1980. 59.75 (ISBN 0-685-85087-0, 349-80) (ISBN 0-685-85088-9). ACI.

Application of Meteorology to Safety at Nuclear Plants. (Safety Ser.: No. 29). (Illus.). 27p. (Orig.). 1968. pap. 6.25 (ISBN 92-0-123368-X, ISP211, IAEA). Unipub.

Bankoff, G. & Afgan, N. Heat Transfer in Nuclear Reactor. 1982. 95.00 (ISBN 0-07-003601-2). McGraw.

Bishop, A. A. & Kulacki, F. A., eds. Nuclear Reactor Safety Heat Transfer: Presented at the Winter Meeting of the ASME. LC 77-87329. pap. 20.00 (ISBN 0-317-09185-9, 2016904). Bks Demand UMI.

Bressler, M. H., et al. Criteria for Nuclear Safety Related Piping & Component Support Snubbers. (PVP: No. 45). 40p. 1980. 6.00 (ISBN 0-686-69846-0, H00172). ASME.

British Nuclear Energy Society, ed. Radiation Protection in Nuclear Power Plants & the Fuel Cycle, 2 vols. 498p. 1979. 125.00x (ISBN 0-7277-0072-3, Pub. by Brit Nuclear England). State Mutual Bk.

--Reactor Inspection Technology. 192p. 1975. 80.00x (ISBN 0-7277-0011-1, Pub. by Brit Nuclear England). State Mutual Bk.

--Safety & Siting. 136p. 1972. 59.00x (ISBN 0-901948-93-4, Pub. by Brit Nuclear England). State Mutual Bk.

Choix et Evaluation des Sites de Centrales Nucleaires du Point de Vue de la Repartition de la Population: Guide de Surete. (Safety Ser.: No. 50-SG-S4). (Fr., Eng., Rus. & Span., Illus.). 54p. 1980. pap. 11.50 (ISBN 92-0-223680-1, ISP569, IAEA). Unipub.

Containment & Siting of Nuclear Power Plants. (Proceedings Ser.). (Illus.). 818p. (Orig.). 1967. pap. 50.25 (ISBN 92-0-020167-9, ISP154, IAEA). Unipub.

Detection & Location of Failed Fuel Elements. (Panel Proceedings Ser.). (Illus.). 241p. (Orig.). 1968. pap. 15.25 (ISBN 92-0-051168-6, ISP204, IAEA). Unipub.

Dhillon, Balbir S. Power System Reliability, Safety & Management. LC 82-72852. (Illus.). 350p. 1983. 45.00 (ISBN 0-250-40548-2). Butterworth.

Earthquake Guidelines for Reactor Siting. (Proceedings Ser.: No. 139). (Illus.). 26p. (Orig.). 1973. pap. 6.25 (ISBN 92-0-125272-2, IDC139, IAEA). Unipub.

Fire Protection Practice for Nuclear Reactor. (Eight Hundred & Nine Hundred Ser.). 1974. pap. 3.50 (ISBN 0-685-58215-9, 802). Natl Fire Prot.

Freeman, Leslie J. Nuclear Witnesses: Insiders Speak Out. (Illus.). 1981. 16.95 (ISBN 0-393-01456-8). Norton.

Fussell, J. B. & Burdick, G. R., eds. Nuclear Systems Reliability Engineering & Risk Assessment. LC 77-91478. xi, 849p. 1977. text ed. 48.00 (ISBN 0-89871-041-3). Soc Indus-Appl Math.

Graham, John. Fast Reactor Safety. (Nuclear Science & Technology Ser.: Vol. 8). 1971. 76.00 (ISBN 0-12-294950-1). Acad Pr.

Guideline for Design & Analysis of Nuclear Safety Related Earth Structures, N-725. Standard. 35p. 1983. pap. 16.00x (ISBN 0-87262-375-0). Am Soc Civil Eng.

IAEA Safeguards for State's Systems of Accounting & Control of Nuclear Materials. 1980 ed. 28p. pap. 7.00 (ISBN 0-686-81862-8, ISGINF2, IAEA). Unipub.

Jones, O. C., Jr. & Bankoff, S. G., eds. Symposium on the Thermal & Hydraulic Aspects of Nuclear Reactor Safety - Light Water Reactors, Vol. 1. 1977. pap. text ed. 25.00 (ISBN 0-685-86878-8, G00127). ASME.

Nuclear Aerosols in Reactor Safety: June, 1979. (Document Ser.). 266p. 1979. 18.75x (ISBN 92-64-11977-9). OECD.

Nuclear Energy Agency & Organization for Economic Cooperation & Development. Plate Inspection Programme, PISC: November, 1979. (Illus.). 78p. (Orig.). 1980. pap. text ed. 7.50x (ISBN 92-64-12028-9, 66 80 02 1). OECD.

Nuclear Power Experience: Nuclear Safety, Vols. 2-4. Incl. Vol. 2. Nuclear Power Production. 637p. 1983. pap. 99.25 (ISBN 92-0-050183-4, ISP627 2); Vol. 3. Nuclear Fuel Cycle. 893p. 1983. pap. 139.25 (ISBN 92-0-050283-0, ISP627 3); Vol. 4. Nuclear Safety. (Illus.). 873p. 1983. pap. 130.50 (ISBN 9-2005-0383-7, ISP627 4). (IAEA Proceedings Ser.). (Illus.). 1983 (IAEA). Unipub.

Nuclear Safeguards Technology: 1978, 2 vols. (Proceedings Ser.). (Illus.). 1590p. 1978. Set. pap. 105.00 (ISBN 92-0-070079-9, ISP497 1, IAEA); pap. 116.50 (ISP497 2, IAEA). Unipub.

Nuclear Safeguards Technology 1982: Proceedings of an International Symposium on Recent Advances in Nuclear Material Safeguards Organized by the International Atomic Energy Agency & Held in Vienna, 8-12 November 1982, 2 vols. (Proceedings Ser.). 1983. Vol. 1. pap. 86.50 (ISBN 92-0-070083-7, ISP629-1, IAEA); Vol. 2. pap. 91.25 (ISBN 92-0-070183-3, ISP629-2). Unipub.

OECD-NEA. Reference Seismic Ground Motions in Nuclear Safety Assessments. (Illus.). 171p. (Orig.). 1980. pap. text ed. 16.00x (ISBN 92-64-12100-5). OECD.

Okrent, David. Nuclear Reactor Safety: On the History of the Regulatory Process. LC 80-53958. 392p. 1981. 39.50x (ISBN 0-299-08350-0). U of Wis Pr.

Osterhout, Marilyn M., ed. Decontamination & Decommissioning of Nuclear Facilities. LC 80-10223. 820p. 1980. 115.00x (ISBN 0-306-40429-X, Plenum Pr). Plenum Pub.

Principles & Standards of Reactor Safety. (Proceedings Ser.). (Illus.). 650p. (Orig.). 1974. pap. 57.25 (ISBN 92-0-020373-6, ISP342, IAEA). Unipub.

Quality Assurance in the Manufacture of Items for Nuclear Power Plants: A Safety Guide. (Safety Ser.: No. 50-SG-QA8). 40p. 1981. pap. 8.50 (ISBN 92-0-123181-4, ISP577, IAEA). Unipub.

Quality Assurance Organization for Nuclear Power Plants: A Safety Guide. (Safety Ser.: No. 50-SG-QA7). (Illus.). 52p. 1983. pap. text ed. 12.00 (ISBN 92-0-123183-0, ISP606, IAEA). Unipub.

Recurring Inspection of Nuclear Reactor Steel Pressure Vessels. (Bibliographical Ser.: No. 34). 214p. 1968. pap. (STI/PUB/21/34, IAEA). Unipub.

Recurring Inspection of Nuclear Reactor Steel Pressure Vessels. (Technical Reports Ser.: No. 81). (Illus.). 239p. 1981. pap. 18.50 (ISBN 0-686-93880-1, IDC81, IAEA). Unipub.

Rolph, Elizabeth S. Nuclear Power & the Public Safety: A Study in Regulation. LC 78-24795. (Illus.). 240p. 1979. 21.50x (ISBN 0-669-02822-3). Lexington Bks.

Rust, J. H. & Weaver, L. E. Nuclear Power Safety. pap. 25.00 (ISBN 0-08-021744-3). Pergamon.

Safe Operation of Critical Assemblies & Research Reactors. (Safety Ser.: No. 4). (Eng., Fr., Rus. & Span.). 104p. 1961. pap. (ISBN 92-0-123061-3, ISP29, IAEA). Unipub.

Safe Operation of Nuclear Power Plants. (Safety Ser.: No. 31). (Illus.). 125p. (Orig.). 1969. pap. 12.50 (ISBN 92-0-123169-5, ISP222, IAEA). Unipub.

Safe Operation of Research Reactors & Critical Assemblies 1984: Code of Practice & Annexes. (Safety Ser.: No. 35). 216p. 1985. pap. 36.00 (ISBN 92-0-123784-7, ISP667, IAEA). Unipub.

Safety Functions & Component Classification from BWR, PWR & PTR: A Safety Guide. (Safety Ser.: No. 50-SG-D1). 68p. 1980. pap. 11.75 (ISBN 92-0-123979-3, ISP542, IAEA). Unipub.

Safety Related Instrumentation & Control Systems for Nuclear Power Plants: A Safety Guide. (Safety Ser.: No. 50-SG-D8). (Illus.). 48p. 1985. pap. 11.25 (ISBN 92-0-623184-7, ISP678, IAEA). Unipub.

Science Applications, Inc. Evaluation of an Environs Exposure Rate Monitoring System for Post-Accident Assessment: AIF-NESP 023. (National Environmental Studies Project: NESP Reports). 1981. 50.00 (ISBN 0-318-02231-1). Atomic Indus Forum.

Shimizu, Akinao & Aoki, Katsutada. Application of Invariant Imbedding to Reactor Physics. (Nuclear Science & Technology Ser). 1972. 55.00 (ISBN 0-12-640150-0). Acad Pr.

Site Survey for Nuclear Power Plants: A Safety Guide. (Safety Ser.: No. 50-SG-S9). (Eng., Fr., Rus. & Span.). 48p. 1985. pap. 11.25 (ISBN 92-0-123884-3, ISP678, IAEA). Unipub.

Specification for the Design, Fabrication & Erection of Steel Safety-Related Structures for Nuclear Facilities: AISC-ANSI N690. 288p. 1984. 10.00 (ISBN 0-318-17777-3, S327). Am Inst Steel Construct.

Steele, L. E., ed. Status of U. S. A. Nuclear Reactor Pressure Vessel Surveillance for Radiation Effects- STP 784. LC 82-71751. 277p. 1983. text ed. 29.50 (ISBN 0-8031-0229-1, 04-784000-35). ASTM.

Von der Hardt, P. & Rottger, H. Aspects of Nuclear Reactor Safety: Proceedings. (European Applied Research Reports Special Topics Ser.). 646p. 1980. lib. bdg. 61.50 (ISBN 3-7186-0016-1). Harwood Academic.

Webb, Richard E. The Accident Hazards of Nuclear Power Plants. LC 75-37173. (Illus.). 240p. 1976. pap. 8.95 (ISBN 0-87023-210-X). U of Mass Pr.

Williams, M. M. Nuclear Safety. (Illus.). 1979. pap. 20.00 (ISBN 0-08-024752-0). Pergamon.

Wood, J. Computational Methods in Reactor Shielding. (Illus.). 450p. 1981. 61.00 (ISBN 0-08-028685-2); pap. 21.00 (ISBN 0-08-028686-0). Pergamon.

Wood, William C. Nuclear Safety: Risks & Regulation. 1983. pap. 4.95 (ISBN 0-8447-3508-6). Am Enterprise.

NUCLEAR REACTOR FUEL REPROCESSING

see Reactor Fuel Reprocessing

NUCLEAR RESEARCH

Bethge, K., et al, eds. Nuclear Physics Methods in Materials Research: Proceedings of the 7th Divisional Conference. 1980. 46.00 (ISBN 0-9940013-9-8, Pub. by Vieweg & Sohn Germany). Heyden.

Braunbek, Werner. Pursuit of the Atom. 1959. 9.95 (ISBN 0-87523-115-2). Emerson.

Brookhaven National Laboratory. Brookhaven Lectures: Vistas in Research. Incl. Vol. 1. 220p. 1967 (ISBN 0-677-11550-4); Vol. 2. 208p. 1968 (ISBN 0-677-12950-5); Vol. 3. 198p. 1968 (ISBN 0-677-12990-4); Vol. 4. 188p. 1969 (ISBN 0-677-13500-9). 57.75 ea. Gordon.

Chemistry Research & Chemical Techniques Based on Research Reactors. (Technical Reports Ser.: No. 17). (Illus.). 264p. (Orig.). 1963. pap. 17.00 (ISBN 92-0-045063-6, IDC17, IAEA). Unipub.

Crewe, Albert V. & Katz, Joseph J. Nuclear Research U. S. A. Knowledge for the Future. (Illus.). 10.00 (ISBN 0-8446-0564-6). Peter Smith.

Dellums, Ronald V., et al. Nuclear California: An Investigative Report. Kaplan, David E., ed. LC 82-1213. (Illus.). 144p. (Orig.). 1982. pap. 5.95 (ISBN 0-9607166-0-2). Greenpeace-Ctr Invest Re.

Heilbron, J. L., et al. Lawrence & His Laboratory: Nuclear Science at Berkeley, 1931-1961. LC 81-83681. (Illus.). 106p. (Orig.). 1981. pap. 3.00x (ISBN 0-918102-09-X). U Cal Hist Sci Tech.

Henley, E. J., et al, eds. Advances in Nuclear Science & Technology, Vol. 11. LC 62-13039. 576p. 1978. 85.00x (ISBN 0-306-40030-8, Plenum Pr). Plenum Pub.

Hodgson, P. E. Growth Points in Nuclear Physics, Vol. 3. (Illus.). 200p. 1981. pap. 10.30 (ISBN 0-08-026484-0). Pergamon.

IAEA Research Contracts: 10th Annual Report. Incl. IAEA Research Contracts: 11th Annual Report. (Technical Reports Ser.: No. 125). (Illus.). 285p. (Orig.). 1971. pap. 23.75 (ISBN 92-0-175071-4, IDC125, IAEA); IAEA Research contracts: 12th Annual Report. (Technical Reports Ser.: No. 134). 192p. (Orig.). 1972. pap. 18.50 (ISBN 92-0-175072-2, IDC134, IAEA); IAEA Research Contracts: 13th Annual Report. (Technical Reports Ser.: No. 144). 238p. (Orig.). pap. 23.75 (ISBN 92-0-175073-0, IDC144, IAEA); IAEA Research Contracts: 14th Annual Report. (Technical Reports Ser.: No. 154). 184p. (Orig.). 1974. pap. 19.00 (ISBN 92-0-175074-9, IDC154, IAEA); IAEA Research Contracts: 3rd Annual Report. (Technical Reports Ser.: No. 16). (Illus.). 82p. 1963. pap. 6.25 (ISBN 92-0-175063-3, IDC16, IAEA); IAEA Research Contracts: 4th Annual Report. (Technical Reports Ser.: No. 28). (Illus.). 134p. 1964. pap. 6.25 (ISBN 92-0-175164-8, IDC28, IAEA); IAEA Research Contracts: 5th Annual Report. (Technical Reports Ser.: No. 42). (Illus.). 127p. 1965. pap. 6.25 (ISBN 92-0-175165-6, IDC42, IAEA); IAEA Research Contracts: 6th Annual Report. (Technical Reports Ser.: No. 53). (Illus.). 131p. 1966. pap. 6.25 (ISBN 92-0-175066-8, IDC53, IAEA); IAEA Research Contracts: 7th Annual Report. (Technical Reports Ser.: No. 74). (Illus.). 223p. 1967. pap. 6.25 (ISBN 92-0-175067-6, IDC74, IAEA); IAEA Research Contracts: 9th Annual Report. (Technical Reports Ser.: No. 97). (Illus.). 474p. 1969. pap. 17.00 (ISBN 92-0-175069-2, IDC97, IAEA). (Technical Reports Ser.: No. 105). 214p. (Orig.). 1970. pap. 18.50 (ISBN 92-0-175170-2, IDC105, IAEA). Unipub.

International School on Electro & Photonuclear Reactions, First Course, Erice, June 2-17, 1976. International School on Electro & Photonuclear Reactions I: Proceedings. Schaerf, C., ed. (Lecture Notes in Physics: Vol. 61). 1977. soft cover 32.00 (ISBN 3-540-08139-9). Springer-Verlag.

--International School on Electro & Photonuclear Reactions II: Proceedings. Schaerf, C., ed. (Lecture Notes in Physics: Vol. 62). 1977. 19.00 (ISBN 0-387-08140-2). Springer-Verlag.

International University Courses on Nuclear Physics, 10th, Schladming, Austria, 1971. Concepts in Hadron Physics: Proceedings. (Acta Physica Austriaca: Suppl. 8). (Illus.). xvi, 424p. 1971. 63.80 (ISBN 0-387-81032-3). Springer-Verlag.

Jackson, J. D., et al, eds. Annual Review of Nuclear & Particle Science, Vol. 31. LC 53-995. (Annual Review of Nuclear Science Ser.: 1950-1977). (Illus.). 1981. text ed. 22.50 (ISBN 0-8243-1531-6). Annual Reviews.

MacAvoy, Paul W. Economic Strategy for Developing Nuclear Breeder Reactors. 1969. 32.50x (ISBN 0-262-13054-8). MIT Pr.

Manual for the Operation of Research Reactors. (Technical Reports Ser.: No. 37). 194p. 1964. pap. 13.00 (ISBN 92-0-155364-1, IDC37, IAEA). Unipub.

Plasma Physics & Controlled Nuclear Fusion Research 1984: Tenth Conference Proceedings, London, 12-19 September 1984, Vol. 2. 667p. 1985. pap. 104.00 (ISBN 92-0-130185-5, ISP670, IAEA). Unipub.

Pollard, Ernest C. Radiation: One Story of the M. I. T. Radiation Lab. 1940-1945. (Illus.). 197p. 1982. pap. 8.00 (ISBN 0-9612798-1-8). Woodburn Pr.

Safe Operation of Research Reactors & Critical Assemblies 1984: Code of Practice & Annexes. (Safety Ser.: No. 35). 216p. 1985. pap. 36.00 (ISBN 92-0-123784-7, ISP667, IAEA). Unipub.

Segre, E., et al, eds. Annual Review of Nuclear Science, Vol. 23. LC 53-995. (Illus.). 1973. text ed. 22.50 (ISBN 0-8243-1523-5). Annual Reviews.

Siting of Reactors & Nuclear Research Centres. (Proceedings Ser.). (Illus.). 511p. 1963. 25.25 (ISBN 92-0-020263-2, ISP72, IAEA). Unipub.

Structure of Medium-Heavy Nuclei 1979. (Reports on Progress in Physics: No. 49). 1981. 80.00 (ISBN 0-9960032-9-0, Pub. by Inst Physics England). Heyden.

Wilhelmi, Z. & Sikora, B. Heavy Ions & Nuclear Structure. (Nuclear Science Research Conference Ser.: Vol. 5). 483p. 1983. 98.50 (ISBN 3-7186-0164-8). Harwood Academic.

NUCLEAR ROCKETS

AGARD-NATO. Nuclear Thermal & Electric Rocket Propulsion. (Agardographs Ser.: No. 101). 650p. 1967. 172.25 (ISBN 0-677-11040-5). Gordon.

Committee on Advanced Nuclear Systems National Research Council. Advanced Nuclear Systems for Portable Power in Space. 60p. 1983. pap. 13.50 (ISBN 0-309-03427-2). Natl Acad Pr.

NUCLEAR SALINE WATER CONVERSION PLANTS

British Nuclear Energy Society, ed. Nuclear Desalination. 64p. 1968. 60.00x (ISBN 0-901948-94-2, Pub. by Brit Nuclear England). State Mutual Bk.

Guide to the Costing of Water from Nuclear Desalination Plants. (Technical Reports Ser.: No. 80). (Illus.). 83p. (Orig.). 1967. pap. 7.75 (ISBN 92-0-145267-5, IDC80, IAEA). Unipub.

Guide to the Costing of Water from Nuclear Desalination Plants. (Technical Reports Ser.: No. 151). (Illus.). 79p. (Orig.). 1974. pap. 10.00 (ISBN 92-0-145273-X, IDC151, IAEA). Unipub.

Nuclear Energy for Water Desalination. (Illus.). 133p. 1966. pap. 11.50 (ISBN 92-0-145066-4, IDC51, IAEA). Unipub.

NUCLEAR SCATTERING

see Scattering (Physics)

NUCLEAR SHELL THEORY

Brody, T. A. & Moshinsky, M. Tables of Transformation Brackets for Nuclear Shell-Model Calculations. 2nd ed. 250p. 1967. 69.50 (ISBN 0-677-01320-5). Gordon.

Craseman, Bernard, ed. Atomic Inner-Shell Processes, 2 vols. Incl. Vol. 1. Production & Decay of Inner-Shell Vacancies. 1975. 80.00 (ISBN 0-12-196901-0); Vol. 2. Experimental Approaches & Applications. 1975. 66.00 (ISBN 0-12-196902-9). Acad Pr.

Crasemann, Bernd, ed. Atomic Inner-Shell Physics. (Physics of Atoms & Molecules Ser.). 733p. 1985. 97.50x (ISBN 0-306-41847-9, Plenum Pr). Plenum Pub.

Irvine, J. M. Heavy Nuclei, Superheavy Nuclei, & Neutron Stars. (Oxford Studies in Nuclear Physics). (Illus.). 1975. 47.00x (ISBN 0-19-851510-3). Oxford U Pr.

Koiter, W. T. & Mikhailov, G. K., eds. Theory of Shells: Proceedings of the IUTAM Symposium on Shell Theory, 3rd Symposium, Russia, August 1978. 704p. 1980. 110.75 (ISBN 0-444-85338-3, North-Holland). Elsevier.

Lawson, R. D. Theory of the Nuclear Shell Model. (OSNP). (Illus.). 1980. text ed. 89.00x (ISBN 0-19-851516-2). Oxford U Pr.

Olszak, W., ed. Thin Shell Theory: New Trends & Applications. (CISM Courses & Lectures Ser.: Vol. 240). (Illus.). 301p. 1980. pap. 28.00 (ISBN 0-387-81602-X). Springer-Verlag.

The Structure of Nuclei: Trieste Lectures 1971. (Proceedings Ser.). (Illus.). 600p. (Orig.). 1973. pap. 45.00 (ISBN 92-0-130072-7, ISP305, IAEA). Unipub.

NUCLEAR SHIELDING

see Shielding (Radiation)

NUCLEAR SHIPS

see also Marine Nuclear Reactor Plants

Latham, Robert F. Introduction to Marine Engineering. LC 58-1831. (Illus.). 208p. 1958. 11.95x (ISBN 0-87021-317-2). Naval Inst Pr.

National Research Council, Maritime Transportation Research Board. Nuclear Merchant Ships. (Illus.). xi, 125p. 1974. pap. 10.75 (ISBN 0-309-02318-1). Natl Acad Pr.

Safety Considerations in the Use of Ports & Approaches by Nuclear Merchant Ships. (Safety Ser.: No. 27). 20p. 1968. pap. 6.25 (ISBN 92-0-123168-7, ISP206, IAEA). Unipub.

NUCLEAR SPECTROSCOPY

see also Hyperfine Interactions

Ajzenberg-Selove, Fay, ed. Nuclear Spectroscopy, 2 Pts. (Pure & Applied Physics Ser.: Vol. 9). 1960. 83.00 ea. Pt. A (ISBN 0-12-046850-6). Pt. B (ISBN 0-12-046851-4). Acad Pr.

Anthony, Evans E. Handbook of Tritium NMR Spectroscopy & Applications. LC 84-15273. 1985. 39.95 (ISBN 0-471-90583-6). Wiley.

Axenrod, Theodore & Webb, Graham. Nuclear Magnetic Resonance Spectroscopy of Nuclei Other Than Protons. LC 80-27361. 424p. 1981. Repr. of 1974 ed. lib. bdg. 32.50 (ISBN 0-89874-290-0). Krieger.

Bertsch, G. F., ed. Nuclear Spectroscopy: Proceedings. (Lecture Notes in Physics: Vol. 119). 250p. 1980. pap. 23.00 (ISBN 0-387-09970-0). Springer-Verlag.

Boumans, P. W., ed. Atomic Absorption Spectroscopy: Past, Present & Future, Pt. 2: To Commemorate the 25th Anniversary of Alan Walsh's Landmark Paper in Spectrochimica Acta. (Spectrochimica Acta B: Vol. 36, No. 5). iv, 92p. 1981. pap. 17.50 (ISBN 0-08-026287-2). Pergamon.

--Line Coincidence Tables for Inductively Coupled Plasma Atomic Emission Spectrometry, 2 vols. (Fr., Illus.). 941p. 1981. 250.00 (ISBN 0-08-026269-4). Pergamon.

--Line Coincidence Tables for Inductively Coupled Plasma Atomic Emission Spectrometry, 2 vols. (Span., Illus.). 941p. 1981. 250.00 (ISBN 0-08-026270-8). Pergamon.

Brugel, W., ed. Handbook of NMR Spectral Parameters, 3 vols. 990p. casebound set 625.00 (ISBN 0-471-25617-X, Pub. by Wiley Heyden). Wiley.

Brugel, Werner. Nuclear Magnetic Resonance Spectra & Chemical Structure. 1968. 58.50 (ISBN 0-12-137450-5). Acad Pr.

Caudano, R. & Verbist, J., eds. Electron Spectroscopy. 1136p. 1975. 149.00 (ISBN 0-444-41291-3). Elsevier.

Cerney, Joseph, ed. Nuclear Spectroscopy & Reactions, 4 pts. Set. 274.50; Pt. A 1974. 92.00 (ISBN 0-12-165201-7); Pt. B 1974. 94.00 (ISBN 0-12-165202-5); Pt. C 1974. 94.00 (ISBN 0-12-165203-3); Pt. D 1975. 65.00 (ISBN 0-12-165204-1). Acad Pr.

Chakrabarti, C. L., ed. Progress in Analytical Atomic Spectroscopy, Vol. 5. (Illus.). 470p. 1983. 114.00 (ISBN 0-08-030418-4). Pergamon.

Chakrabarti, C. L. & Sturgeon, R. E., eds. Progress in Analytical Atomic Spectroscopy, Vol. 6. (Illus.). 444p. 1985. 132.00 (ISBN 0-08-032307-3). Pergamon.

Christian, Gary D. & Feldman, Fredric J. Atomic Absorption Spectroscopy: Applications in Agriculture, Biology & Medicine. LC 78-23204. 512p. 1979. Repr. of 1970 ed. lib. bdg. 30.50 (ISBN 0-88275-797-0). Krieger.

Colloquium Spectroscopicum Internationale. Atomic Spectroscopy: XXI Colloquium Spectroscopicum Internationale, 8th International Conferenceon Atomic Spectroscopy, Cambridge, July 1-6, 1979: Keynote Lectures. LC 81-197242. pap. 71.30 (ISBN 0-317-29347-8, 2024000). Bks Demand UMI.

Crasemann, Bernd, ed. Atomic Inner-Shell Physics. (Physics of Atoms & Molecules Ser.). 733p. 1985. 97.50x (ISBN 0-306-41847-9, Plenum Pr). Plenum Pub.

Ejiri, H. & Fukuda, T. Nuclear Spectroscopy & Nuclear Interactions: New Development of Inbeam Spectroscopy & Exotic Nuclear Spectroscopy-Proceedings of the Symposium Held at Osaka, Japan, March 1984. 550p. 1984. 56.00x (ISBN 9971-966-54-9, Pub. by World Sci Singapore). Taylor & Francis.

Emsley, J. W. & Sutcliffe, L. H., eds. Progress in NMR Spectroscopy: Vol. 11 Complete. LC 66-17931. 282p. 1978. 96.00 (ISBN 0-08-020325-6). Pergamon.

--Progress in Nuclear Magnetic Resonance Spectroscopy, Vols. 1-10. Incl. Vol. 1. 1962. 76.00 (ISBN 0-08-011322-2); Vol. 2. 1963; Vol. 3. 1965; Vol. 4. 1966. 76.00 (ISBN 0-08-012717-7); Vol. 5. 1970. 76.00 (ISBN 0-08-012834-3); Vol. 6. 1971; Vol. 7. 1971; Vol. 8, 3 pts. 1972. Vol. 8, Complete. 76.00 (ISBN 0-08-017018-8); Pts. 1-3. pap. 15.50 ea.; Pt. 1. pap. -1971 (ISBN 0-08-016662-8); Pt. 2. pap. -1971 (ISBN 0-08-016757-8); Pt. 3. pap. -1972 (ISBN 0-08-016857-4); Vol. 9, 3 pts. Vol. 9, Complete. 76.00 (ISBN 0-08-017704-2); Pts. 1-3. pap. 13.75 ea.; Vol. 10. Pt. 1, 1975. pap. 8.00 (ISBN 0-08-017703-4); Pt. 2, 1976. pap. 14.00 (ISBN 0-08-019463-X); Pts. 3 & 4, 1977. 75.00 (ISBN 0-08-019464-8); One Vol. Ed. 76.00 (ISBN 0-08-019466-4). write for info. Pergamon.

Emsley, J. W., et al. High Resolution Nuclear Magnetic Resonance Spectroscopy. 1966. 54.00 (ISBN 0-08-011824-0). Pergamon.

Faraggi, H. & Ricci, R. A. Nuclear Spectroscopy & Nuclear Reactions with Heavy Ions. (Enrico Fermi Summer School of Physics: No. 62). 596p. 1976. 123.50 (ISBN 0-7204-0450-9, North-Holland). Elsevier.

Hamilton, Joseph H. & Manthuruthil, Jose, eds. Radioactivity in Nuclear Spectroscopy, 2 vols. 1524p. 1972. Set. 272.75 (ISBN 0-677-14220-X); Vol. 1, 592p. 135.25 (ISBN 0-677-12410-4); Vol. 2, 932p. 175.75 (ISBN 0-677-12420-1). Gordon.

Hanle, W. & Kleinpoppen, H., eds. Progress in Atomic Spectroscopy: Pts. A & B, 2 vols. LC 78-18230. (Physics of Atoms & Molecules Ser.). 1978. 140.00x set (ISBN 0-685-92702-4, Plenum Pr); Pt. A, 755p. 85.00x (ISBN 0-306-31115-1); Pt. B, 820p. 89.50x (ISBN 0-306-31116-X). Plenum Pub.

Harris, Robin K. Nuclear Magnetic Resonance Spectroscopy. 250p. 1983. text ed. 34.95 (ISBN 0-273-01684-9). Pitman Pub MA.

International Conference on Solid State Nuclear Track Detectors, 10th, Lyon, France, July 1979. Solid State Nuclear Track Detectors: Proceedings. Francois, H., et al, eds. LC 79-41577. (Illus.). 1082p. 1980. 145.00 (ISBN 0-08-025029-7). Pergamon.

Jackman, L. M. & Sternhell, S. Applications of Nuclear Magnetic Resonance Spectroscopy in Organic Chemistry. 2nd ed. 1969. pap. 19.50 (ISBN 0-08-022953-0). Pergamon.

Kaufmann, E. N. & Shenoy, G. K., eds. Nuclear & Electron Resonance Spectroscopies Applied to Materials Science. (Materials Research Society Proceedings Ser.: Vol. 3). 558p. 1981. 77.75 (ISBN 0-444-00597-8, North-Holland). Elsevier.

Levy, George C. & Lichter, Robert L. Nitrogen-Fifteen Nuclear Magnetic Resonance Spectroscopy. LC 78-4016. 221p. 1979. 34.50 (ISBN 0-471-02954-8, Pub by Wiley-Interscience). Wiley.

Maeir, Clifford L. The Role of Spectroscopy in the Acceptance of the Internally Structured Atom. Cohen, I. Bernard, ed. LC 80-2093. (Development of Science Ser.). (Illus.). 1981. lib. bdg. 50.00x (ISBN 0-405-13858-X). Ayer Co Pubs.

Mooney, E. F., ed. Annual Reports on NMR Spectroscopy. Incl. Vol. 1. 1968. 69.00 (ISBN 0-12-505350-9); Vol. 5B. 1974. 80.00 (ISBN 0-12-505345-2); Vol. 6, 2 pts. 1976-78. Pt. B. 49.50 (ISBN 0-12-505346-0); Pt. C. 95.00 (ISBN 0-12-505347-9); Vol. 7. 1978. 60.00 (ISBN 0-12-505307-X); Vol. 8. 1978. 85.00 (ISBN 0-12-505308-8); Vol. 9. 1979. 75.00 (ISBN 0-12-505309-6). Acad Pr.

Mooney, E. F. & Webb, G. A., eds. Annual Reports on NMR Spectroscopy, Vol. IIA. 1981. 84.00 (ISBN 0-12-505311-8). Acad Pr.

--Annual Reports on NMR Spectroscopy, Vol. 12. 1982. 70.00 (ISBN 0-12-505312-6). Acad Pr.

Moretto, L. G. & Ricci, R. A., eds. Nuclear Structure & Heavy Ion Dynamics: Proceedings of the International School of Physics "Enrico Fermi" Course LXXXVII, Varenna, Italy, 27 July-6 Aug, 1982. (Enrico Fermi International Summer School of Physics Ser.: Vol. 87). 492p. 1984. 102.00 (ISBN 0-444-86826-7, North Holland). Elsevier.

Nuclear Spectroscopy of Fission Products 1979: Grenoble. (Institute of Physics Conference Ser.: No. 51). 1980. 80.00 (ISBN 0-9960033-1-2, Pub. by Inst Physics England). Heyden.

Pecker-Wimel, C. Introduction a la Spectroscopie Des Plamas. (Cours & Documents de Mathematiques & de Physique Ser.). 168p. (Orig.). 1967. 44.25x (ISBN 0-677-50130-7). Gordon.

Progress in Nuclear Magnetic Resonance Spectroscopy, Vol. 13. Complete. 87.50x (ISBN 0-08-026027-6). Pergamon.

Racah, G., ed. Nuclear Spectroscopy. (Italian Physical Society: Course 15). 1962. 75.00 (ISBN 0-12-368815-9). Acad Pr.

Roth, K. NMR Tomography & Spectroscopy in Medicine: An Introduction. Telger, T. C., tr. from German. (Illus.). 130p. 1984. pap. 18.00 (ISBN 0-387-13442-5). Springer-Verlag.

Rybakov, Boris V. & Sidorov, V. A. Fast Neutron Spectroscopy. 1958 ed. Vlasov, N. A., ed. LC 60-8723. (Soviet Journal of Atomic Energy: Supplement: No. 6). pap. 32.80 suppl. (ISBN 0-317-08815-7, 2020649). Bks Demand UMI.

Schrenk, William G. Analytical Atomic Spectroscopy. LC 75-22102. (Modern Analytical Chemistry Ser.). (Illus.). 380p. 1975. 55.00x (ISBN 0-306-33902-1, Plenum Pr). Plenum Pub.

Shaw, Derek. Fourier Transform N.M.R. Spectroscopy. 2nd, rev. ed. (Studies in Physical & Theoretical Chemistry: Vol. 30). 304p. 1984. 72.25 (ISBN 0-444-42285-4, I-248-84). Elsevier.

Simons, W. W. & Zanger, M. Sadtler Guide to the NMR Spectra of Polymers. 1973. 125.00 (ISBN 0-85501-098-3). Sadtler Res.

Sukhodrev, N. K. Research on Spectroscopy & Luminescence, Part 3: On Excitation Spectra in Spark Discharges. LC 62-12860. (P. N. Lebedev Physics Institute Ser.: Vol. 15). 53p. 1962. 22.50x (ISBN 0-306-17043-4, Consultants). Plenum Pub.

Von Goeler, Eberhard & Weinstein, Roy, eds. Experimental Meson Spectroscopy, 1977. LC 77-94049. 456p. 1977. 22.00x (ISBN 0-930350-00-6). NE U Pr.

Wang, C. H. Spectroscopy of Condensed Media: Dynamics of Molecular Interactions. 1985. 74.00 (ISBN 0-12-734780-1). Acad Pr.

Welz, Bernhard. Atomic Absorption Spectroscopy. (Illus.). 267p. 1976. 40.00x (ISBN 3-527-25680-6). VCH Pubs.

NUCLEAR SPIN

see also Magnetic Resonance; Polarization (Nuclear Physics); Spin-Lattice Relaxation

Carruthers, Peter A. Spin & Isospin in Particle Physics. LC 72-160021. (Illus.). 268p. 1971. 69.50 (ISBN 0-677-02580-7). Gordon.

Daniels, James M. Oriented Nuclei: Polarized Targets & Beams. (Pure & Applied Physics Ser.: Vol. 20). 1965. 59.50 (ISBN 0-12-202950-X). Acad Pr.

Fox, John D. & Robson, D., eds. Isobaric Spin in Nuclear Physics: Proceedings. 1966. 76.00 (ISBN 0-12-263850-6). Acad Pr.

McWeeny, R. Spins in Chemistry. (Current Chemical Concepts Ser). 1970. 39.50 (ISBN 0-12-486750-2). Acad Pr.

Wolf, Dieter. Spin Temperature & Nuclear Spin Relaxation in Matter: Basic Principles & Applications. (International Series of Monographs on Physics). (Illus.). 1979. text ed. 49.95x (ISBN 0-19-851295-3). Oxford U Pr.

NUCLEAR SUBMARINES

Dalgleish, D. Douglas & Schweikart, Larry. Trident. LC 83-16777. (Science & International Affairs Ser.). (Illus.). 384p. 1984. 32.50 (ISBN 0-8093-1126-7). S Ill U Pr.

Preston, Anthony. Dreadnought to Nuclear Submarine. (The Ship Series, National Maritime Museum). (Illus.). 1980. 10.95 (ISBN 0-11-290319-3). Sheridan.

NUCLEAR TRANSFORMATIONS

see Nuclear Reactions

NUCLEAR UNDERGROUND EXPLOSIONS

see Underground Nuclear Explosions

NUCLEAR WARFARE

see also Atomic Bomb; Hydrogen Bomb; Nuclear Warfare

Abt, Clark C. A Strategy for Terminating Nuclear War. (Special Study Ser.). 200p. 1985. pap. 19.85x (ISBN 0-8133-7050-7). Westview.

Adams, Ruth & Cullen, Sue, eds. The Final Epidemic: Physicians & Scientists on Nuclear War. 266p. (Orig.). 1982. pap. 4.95 (ISBN 0-941682-00-5). Educ Found for Nucl Sci.

Aizenstat, A. J. Survival for All: The Alternative to Nuclear War with a Practical Plan for Total Denuclearization. LC 84-28231. 224p. 1985. 14.95 (ISBN 0-932755-14-3). Billner & Rouse.

Asher, Marty. Fifty-Seven Reasons Not to Have a Nuclear War. (Illus.). 120p. (Orig.). 1984. pap. 4.95 (ISBN 0-446-38167-5). Warner Bks.

Barash, David P. & Lipton, Judith E. Stop Nuclear War! A Handbook. LC 82-48162. 396p. 1982. (GP); pap. 7.95 (ISBN 0-394-62433-5, E835, Ever). Grove.

Barnaby, Frank. Prospects for Peace. (Illus.). 105p. 1980. 24.00 (ISBN 0-08-027399-8); pap. 12.75 (ISBN 0-08-027398-X). Pergamon.

Barstow, David O., ed. The Threat of Nuclear Annihilation: A Psychotherapeutic View-A Special Issue of Pilgrimage. 72p. 1984. pap. 9.95 (ISBN 0-89885-213-7). Human Sci Pr.

Beckman, Petr. The Health Hazards of Not Going Nuclear. 1980. pap. 2.50 (ISBN 0-686-97299-6). Ace Bks.

Bensen, David W. & Sparrow, Arnold H., eds. Survival of Food Crops & Livestock in the Event of Nuclear War: Proceedings. LC 77-170334. (AEC Symposium Ser.). 745p. 1971. 26.75 (ISBN 0-87079-219-9, CONF-700909); microfiche 4.50 (ISBN 0-87079-220-2, CONF-700909). DOE.

Blackett, Patrick M. Studies of War: Nuclear & Conventional. LC 78-16364. (Illus.). 1978. Repr. of 1962 ed. lib. bdg. 27.50x (ISBN 0-313-20575-2, BLSW). Greenwood.

Bracken, Paul. The Command & Control of Nuclear Forces. LC 83-42874. 288p. 1983. 25.00x (ISBN 0-300-02946-2). Yale U Pr.

Briggs, Raymond. When the Wind Blows. LC 82-5780. (Illus.). 40p. 1982. 10.95 (ISBN 0-8052-3829-8). Schocken.

Brodie, Bernard. Strategy in the Missile Age. (Rand Corporation Research Studies). 1959. pap. 12.95 (ISBN 0-691-01852-9). Princeton U Pr.

Bulletin of the Atomic Scientists, ed. The Final Epidemic: Physicians & Scientists on Nuclear War. 252p. 1982. pap. 4.95 (ISBN 0-941682-00-5, 03874-2). U of Chicago Pr.

Campbell, Christopher. Nuclear Weapons Fact Book. LC 84-1977. (Illus.). 192p. 1984. 18.95 (ISBN 0-89141-208-5). Presidio Pr.

Cassel, Christine, et al, eds. Nuclear Weapons & Nuclear War: A Source Book for Health Professionals. Abraham, Henry. LC 83-24511. 564p. 1984. 29.95 (ISBN 0-03-063872-0); pap. 12.95 (ISBN 0-03-063873-9). Praeger.

Chazov, Y., et al. Nuclear War: The Medical & Biological Consequences. 239p. 1984. pap. 3.95 (ISBN 0-8285-2834-9, Pub. by Novosti Pr USSR). Imported Pubns.

Clark, I. C. Limited Nuclear War. 1982. 25.00 (ISBN 0-691-07644-8). Princeton U Pr.

Cohen, S. T. The Neutron Bomb: Political, Technological & Military Issues. LC 78-63388. (Special Reports Ser.). 95p. 1978. 6.50 (ISBN 0-89549-009-9). Inst Foreign Policy Anal.

Cruit, Ronald L. & Cruit, Robert L. Survive the Coming Nuclear War: How to Do It. LC 81-48445. (Illus.). 208p. 1984. pap. 8.95 (ISBN 0-8128-6222-8). Stein & Day.

The Day after Midnight: The Effects of Nuclear War. Riordan, Michael, ed. (Illus.). 143p. (Orig.). 1982. pap. 7.95 (ISBN 0-917352-11-4). Cheshire.

The Effects of Nuclear War. 1980. 10.95 (ISBN 0-916672-36-0). Allanheld.

Effects of Nuclear War. LC 79-600080. (Office of Technology Assessment NS 89 Ser.). 151p. (Orig.). 1979. pap. 6.50 (ISBN 0-318-11780-0). Gov Printing Office.

Ehrlich, Robert. Waging Nuclear Peace: The Technology & Politics of Nuclear Weapons. 1984. lib. bdg. 39.50 (ISBN 0-87395-919-1); pap. 12.95 (ISBN 0-87395-920-5). State U NY Pr.

Feldman, Shai. Israeli Nuclear Deterrence: A Strategy for the 1980's. LC 82-9679. 314p. 1983. 27.50x (ISBN 0-231-05546-3); pap. 12.00x (ISBN 0-231-05547-1). Columbia U Pr.

Ford, Daniel, et al. Beyond the Freeze: The Road to Nuclear Sanity. LC 82-72504. (Orig.). 1982. pap. 6.95 (ISBN 0-8070-0484-7, BP646). Beacon Pr.

Frank, Lewis A. Soviet Nuclear Planning. LC 76-57804. (Orig.). 1976. pap. 4.25 (ISBN 0-8447-3237-0). Am Enterprise.

Freedman, Lawrence. The Evolution of Nuclear Strategy. 1981. 35.00x (ISBN 0-312-27269-3). St Martin.

Frei, Daniel. Risks of Unintentional Nuclear War. 255p. 1982. 19.00x (ISBN 0-8002-3317-4). Intl Pubns Serv.

Frei, Daniel & Catrina, Christian. Risks of Unintentional Nuclear War. 255p. 1983. pap. 19.00 (ISBN 0-86598-106-X, UN82/0/1, UN). Unipub.

--Risks of Unintentional Nuclear War. LC 82-16333. 288p. 1983. pap. text ed. 12.50 (ISBN 0-86598-106-X). Allanheld.

--Risks of Unintentional Nuclear War. 19.00 (ISBN 0-686-84919-1, E.82.O.1). UN.

Goodwin, Peter. Nuclear War: The Facts on Your Survival. (Illus.). 128p. 1981. (Rutledge Pr); pap. 5.95 (ISBN 0-8317-6458-9). Smith Pubs.

Greene, Owen, et al. Nuclear Winter: The Evidence & the Risks. 252p. 1985. pap. 9.95 (ISBN 0-7456-0177-4); 34.95 (ISBN 0-7456-0176-6). Basil Blackwell.

Greene, Owne & Rubin, Barry. London after the Bomb: What a Nuclear Attack Really Means. (Illus.). 1982. pap. 4.95 (ISBN 0-19-285123-3). Oxford U Pr.

Griffiths, Franklyn & Polanyi, John C., eds. The Dangers of Nuclear War. LC 79-18825. 1979. 25.00 (ISBN 0-8020-2356-8); pap. 10.00 (ISBN 0-8020-6389-6). U of Toronto Pr.

Ground Zero. Hope: Nuclear War & the 1984 Elections. 96p. (Orig.). 1983. pap. 3.95 (ISBN 0-671-50226-3, Long Shadow). PB.

Harwell, M. A. Nuclear Winter. (Illus.). xxi, 179p. 1984. 16.95 (ISBN 0-387-96093-7). Springer-Verlag.

International Physicians for the Prevention of Nuclear War, et al. Last Aid: The Medical Dimensions of Nuclear War. Chivian, Eric & Chivian, Suzanna, eds. LC 82-13472. (Illus.). 338p. 1982. pap. 11.95 (ISBN 0-7167-1435-3). W H Freeman.

Kahan, Jerome H. Security in the Nuclear Age: Developing U.S. Strategic Arms Policy. 351p. 1975. 26.95 (ISBN 0-8157-4818-3); pap. 9.95 (ISBN 0-8157-4817-5). Brookings.

Katz, Arthur M. Life after Nuclear War: The Economic & Social Impacts of Nuclear Attacks on the United States. LC 81-1300. 464p. 1981. pap. 15.95 (ISBN 0-88410-907-0). Ballinger Pub.

Kearney, Cresson. Nuclear War Survival Skills. 1981. pap. 9.95 (ISBN 0-939002-02-7). Caroline Hse.

Kegley, Charles W., Jr. & Wittkopf, Eugene R., eds. The Nuclear Reader: Strategy, Weapons, War. LC 84-51846. 352p. 1985. pap. text ed. 10.95 (ISBN 0-312-57979-9); 27.50 (ISBN 0-312-57982-9). St Martin.

Kissinger, Henry A. Nuclear Weapons & Foreign Policy. abr. ed. Quigg, Philip, ed. 1969. pap. 6.95 (ISBN 0-393-00494-5, Norton Lib). Norton.

Kraybill, Donald B. Facing Nuclear War. LC 82-11765. 320p. (Orig.). 1982. pap. 8.95 (ISBN 0-8361-3312-9). Herald Pr.

--Facing Nuclear War. LC 82-11765. 320p. 1982. pap. 8.95 (ISBN 0-8361-3308-0). Herald Hse.

Leaning, Jennifer & Keyes, Langley, eds. The Counterfeit Ark: Crisis Relocation for Nuclear War. LC 83-15519. 368p. 1983. 29.95x (ISBN 0-88410-940-2); pap. 14.95 (ISBN 0-88410-941-0). Ballinger Pub.

Lens, Sidney. The Day Before Doomsday: An Anatomy of the Nuclear Arms Race. LC 78-53086. 1978. pap. 8.50x (ISBN 0-8070-0491-X, BP584). Beacon Pr.

McCracken, Samuel. The War Against the Atom. LC 81-66105. 1982. 18.50 (ISBN 0-465-09062-1). Basic.

McNaught, L. W. Nuclear, Biological & Chemical Warfare. (Brassey's Battlefield Weapons Systems & Technology Ser.: Vol. 4). 60p. 1984. 27.00 (ISBN 0-08-028328-4); pap. 12.50 (ISBN 0-08-028329-2). Pergamon.

Martin, Thomas L., Jr. & Latham, Donald C. Strategy for Survival. LC 63-17720. (Illus.). Repr. of 1963 ed. 99.80 (ISBN 0-8357-9624-8, 2011564). Bks Demand UMI.

Meyer, Stephen M. The Dynamics of Nuclear Proliferation. (Illus.). 225p. 1984. lib. bdg. 20.00x (ISBN 0-226-52148-6). U of Chicago Pr.

Mooney, Tom. Black Tuesday: A Story of Nuclear War. pap. 3.00 (ISBN 0-317-28511-4). Mooney.

National Research Council. The Effects on the Atmosphere of a Major Nuclear Exchange. 208p. 1985. pap. text ed. 14.50 (ISBN 0-309-03528-7). Natl Acad Pr.

Nuclear Radiation in Warfare. 150p. 1981. 21.00 (ISBN 0-85066-217-6). Taylor & Francis.

Peterson, Jeannie & Hinrichsen, Don, eds. Nuclear War: The Aftermath. LC 82-18517. (Illus.). 196p. 1982. 15.00 (ISBN 0-08-028175-3). Pergamon.

Pringle, Laurence. Nuclear War: From Hiroshima to Nuclear Winter. LC 85-10195. (Illus.). 128p. 1985. PLB 11.95 (ISBN 0-89490-106-0). Enslow Pubs.

Radiological Factors Affecting Decision-Making in a Nuclear Attack. LC 74-20064. (NCRP Reports Ser.: No. 42). 1974. 8.00 (ISBN 0-913392-24-3). NCRP Pubns.

Richards, Jerrold. Nuclear War & You: Before, During, After. LC 84-70562. 272p. (Orig.). 1984. pap. 6.95 (ISBN 0-9613278-0-4). CFPR Pubns.

Schell, Jonathan. The Fate of the Earth. 1982. 11.95 (ISBN 0-394-52559-0). Knopf.

Secacca, Sandra. Up in Arms: A Common Cause Guide to Understanding Nuclear Arms Policy. (Illus.). 130p. 1984. pap. text ed. 3.50 (ISBN 0-914389-01-7). Common Cause.

Sharfman, Peter. Effects of Nuclear War. LC 79-600080. 283p. 1984. 55.00x (ISBN 0-8103-0999-8). Gale.

Sibley, C. Bruce. Surviving Doomsday. 1977. 10.00x (ISBN 0-686-87233-9, Pub. by Shaw & Sons). State Mutual Bkq.

Somerville, John, ed. Soviet Marxism & Nuclear War: An International Debate. LC 80-25820. (Contributions in Philosophy: No. 18). 176p. 1981. lib. bdg. 29.95 (ISBN 0-313-22531-1, SSM/). Greenwood.

Suddaby, Adam. The Nuclear War Game: Facts & Information Everyone Should Know. 1984. pap. 9.95 (ISBN 0-582-38483-4). Caroline Hse.

Thompson, E. P. & Smith, Dan, eds. Protest & Survive. LC 81-81692. 288p. 1981. pap. 4.95 (ISBN 0-85345-582-1). Monthly Rev.

Van Gogh, Anna. Promise Me War: A Preview of a Brighter Tomorrow. Anderson, Jack, ed. 424p. 1984. 29.95 (ISBN 0-913829-03-X); pap. 14.95 (ISBN 0-913829-00-5). Lucy Mary Bks.

Van Ornum, William & Van Ornum, Mary W. Talking to Children about Nuclear War. 160p. 1984. 12.95 (ISBN 0-8264-0248-8); pap. 7.95 (ISBN 0-8264-0247-X). Crossroad NY.

Windass, S., ed. Avoiding Nuclear War: Common Security As a Strategy for the Defence of the West. 275p. 1985. 22.70 (ISBN 0-08-031175-X, Pub. by Aberdeen Scotland); pap. 12.90 (ISBN 0-08-031184-9, Pub. by Aberdeen Scotland). Pergamon.

Woolsey, R. James, ed. Nuclear Arms: Ethics, Strategy, Politics. LC 83-26580. 289p. 1984. 22.95 (ISBN 0-917616-56-1); pap. 8.95 (ISBN 0-917616-55-3). ICS Pr.

NUCLEAR WASTES

see Radioactive Wastes

NUCLEAR WEAPONS

see also Atomic Bomb; Ballistic Missiles; Hydrogen Bomb

Aldridge, Robert C. Counterforce Syndrome: A Guide to U. S. Nuclear Weapons & Strategic Doctrine. rev. ed. (Illus.). 86p. 1979. pap. 4.95 (ISBN 0-89758-008-7). Inst Policy Stud.

Arnott, D. G. Our Nuclear Adventure. 1958. 6.00 (ISBN 0-8022-0040-0). Philos Lib.

Assembly of Mathematical & Physical Sciences, National Research Council. Long-Term Worldwide Effects of Multiple Nuclear-Weapons Detonations. LC 75-29733. xvi, 213p. 1975. pap. 14.95 (ISBN 0-309-02418-8). Natl Acad Pr.

Beaton, Leonard & Maddox, John. The Spread of Nuclear Weapons. LC 76-16061. (Studies in International Security: No. 5). 1976. Repr. of 1962 ed. lib. bdg. 24.75x (ISBN 0-8371-8949-7, BENW). Greenwood.

Beres, Louis R., ed. Security or Armageddon: Israel's Nuclear Strategy. LC 84-48505. 1985. pap. 12.95x (ISBN 0-669-11131-7). Lexington Bks.

Bertsch, Kenneth A. & Shaw, Linda S. The Nuclear Weapons Industry. 405p. 1984. pap. text ed. 45.00. Investor Ctr.

Blate, Michael. Help Defuse the Bomb...Now! Easy Effective Ways You Can Help Prevent Nuclear Holocaust. (G-Jo Institute Life Enhancement Ser.). (Illus.). 60p. 1984. pap. 3.95 (ISBN 0-916878-29-5). Falkynor Bks.

Bracken, Paul. The Command & Control of Nuclear Forces. LC 83-42874. 264p. 1985. pap. 7.95 (ISBN 0-300-03398-2, Y-522). Yale U Pr.

Campbell, Christopher. Nuclear Weapons Fact Book. LC 84-1977. (Illus.). 192p. 1984. 18.95 (ISBN 0-89141-208-5). Presidio Pr.

Cartwright, J. & Critchley, J. Cruise, Pershing & SS-20: The Search for Consensus: Nuclear Weapons in Europe. 188p. 1985. 22.75 (ISBN 0-08-031201-2, Pub by BDP); pap. 12.50 (ISBN 0-08-031202-0). Pergamon.

Cassel, Christine, et al, eds. Nuclear Weapons & Nuclear War: A Source Book for Health Professionals. Abraham, Henry. LC 83-24511. 564p. 1984. 29.95 (ISBN 0-03-063872-0); pap. 12.95 (ISBN 0-03-063873-9). Praeger.

Clarfield, Gerard H. & Wiecek, William M. Nuclear America: Military & Civilian Nuclear Power in the United States, 1940-1980. LC 84-47565. (Illus.). 528p. 1984. 19.18 (ISBN 0-06-015336-9, HarpT). Har-Row.

Cochran, Thomas B., et al. Nuclear Weapons Databook, Vol. I: U. S. Nuclear Forces & Capabilities. LC 82-24376. 360p. 1983. prof. ref. 38.00x (ISBN 0-88410-172-X); pap. 19.95 (ISBN 0-88410-173-8). Ballinger Pub.

--Nuclear Weapons Databook, Vol. II: U. S. Nuclear Weapons Production Complex. 400p. 1986. 39.95x (ISBN 0-88410-932-1); pap. 19.95 (ISBN 0-88410-933-X). Ballinger Pub.

Comprehensive Study on Nuclear Weapons. (Disarmament Study Ser.: No. 1). 172p. 1981. pap. 13.00 (ISBN 0-686-78450-2, UN81111, UN). Unipub.

Craig, P. P. & Jungerman, J. A. The Nuclear Arms Race: Technology & Society. 464p. 1985. 23.95 (ISBN 0-07-013345-X). McGraw.

Cunningham, Ann Marie & Fitzpatrick, Mariana, eds. Future Fire: Weapons for the Apocalypse. LC 82-17381. 274p. 1983. pap. 8.95 (ISBN 0-446-37031-2). Warner Bks.

Dahl, Robert A. Controlling Nuclear Weapons: Democracy Versus Guardianship. (Frank W. Abrams Lectures Ser.). 128p. 1985. text ed. 14.95 (ISBN 0-317-18287-0); pap. 8.95 (ISBN 0-317-18288-9). Syracuse U Pr.

Durie, Sheila & Edwards, Rob. Fueling the Nuclear Arms Race: The Links between Nuclear Power & Nuclear Weapons. 129p. (Orig.). 1982. pap. 5.95 (ISBN 0-86104-372-3, Pub by Pluto Pr). Longwood Pub Group.

Ehrlich, Robert. Waging Nuclear Peace: The Technology & Politics of Nuclear Weapons. 1984. lib. bdg. 39.50 (ISBN 0-87395-919-1); pap. 12.95 (ISBN 0-87395-920-5). State U NY Pr.

Freedman, Lawrence. The Evolution of Nuclear Strategy. 473p. 1983. pap. 10.95 (ISBN 0-312-27270-7). St Martin.

Galtung, Johan. Environment, Development, & Military Activity Towards Alternative Security Doctrines. 128p. (Orig.). 1983. 15.00x (ISBN 82-00-06360-7). Universitet.

Green, William C. Soviet Nuclear Weapons Policy: A Research Guide. 250p. 22.50x (ISBN 0-86531-817-4). Westview.

Greene, Owen, et al. Nuclear Winter: The Evidence & the Risks. 252p. 1985. pap. 9.95 (ISBN 0-7456-0177-4); 34.95 (ISBN 0-7456-0176-6). Basil Blackwell.

Hogg, Ian & Chant, Christopher. Nuclear War in the Eighties. LC 83-47534. (Illus.). 224p. 1983. 19.18i (ISBN 0-06-015196-X, HarpT); pap. 9.57i (CN1079, HarpT). Har-Row.

Jones, Rodney W., ed. Small Nuclear Forces & U. S. Security Policy: Threats & Potential Conflicts in the Middle East & South Asia. LC 83-47790. 304p. 1984. 25.50x (ISBN 0-669-06736-9). Lexington Bks.

Kaplan, Fred. The Wizards of Armageddon: Strategists of the Nuclear Age. 1983. 18.95 (ISBN 0-671-42444-0). S&S.

Kapur, Ashok. International Nuclear Proliferation: Multilateral Diplomacy & Regional Aspects. LC 78-19744. (Praeger Special Studies). 400p. 1979. 43.95 (ISBN 0-03-046316-5). Praeger.

Kegley, Charles W., Jr. & Wittkopf, Eugene R., eds. The Nuclear Reader: Strategy, Weapons, War. LC 84-51846. 352p. 1985. pap. text ed. 10.95 (ISBN 0-312-57979-9); 27.50 (ISBN 0-312-57982-9). St Martin.

Kelleher, Catherine M. Germany & the Politics of Nuclear Weapons. LC 75-16168. (Institute of War & Peace Studies). (Illus.). 372p. 1975. 32.00x (ISBN 0-231-03960-3). Columbia U Pr.

Knorr, Klaus. On the Uses of Military Power in the Nuclear Age. (Center of International Studies Ser.). 1966. 22.50x (ISBN 0-691-05626-9). Princeton U Pr.

Krass, A. S., et al. Uranium Enrichment & Nuclear Weapon Proliferation. LC 83-8486. 270p. 1983. 33.00x (ISBN 0-8002-3079-5). Taylor & Francis.

Laird, Robbin. France, the Soviet Union, & the Nuclear Weapons Issue. (Special Studies in International Relations). 150p. 1985. pap. 15.95x (ISBN 0-8133-7018-3). Westview.

Leone, Bruno, ed. Nuclear Arms: Nineteen Eighty-Four Supplement. (Opposing Viewpoints SOURCES Ser.). 120p. pap. text ed. 7.95 (ISBN 0-89908-518-0). Greenhaven.

Leone, Bruno, et al, eds. Nuclear Arms: Nineteen Eighty-Five Supplement. (Opposing Viewpoints Sources Ser.). 100p. 1985. pap. text ed. 9.95 (ISBN 0-89908-509-1). Greenhaven.

Liddell Hart, Basil H. The Revolution in Warfare. LC 79-22632. 1980. Repr. of 1947 ed. lib. bdg. 24.75x (ISBN 0-313-22173-1, LHRW). Greenwood.

Malone, Peter. The British Nuclear Deterrent: A History. LC 84-40046. 224p. 1984. 27.50 (ISBN 0-312-10410-3). St Martin.

Neidle, Stephen. Topics in Nucleic Acid Structure. LC 81-1316. 221p. 1981. 64.95x (ISBN 0-470-27161-2). Halsted Pr.
Ninth Symposium on Nucleic Acids Chemistry, Tokyo. Proceedings. (Nucleic Acids Symposium Series: No. 10). 256p. 1981. 25.00 (ISBN 0-904147-32-0). IRL Pr.
Nucleic Acids Chemistry Eighth Symposium, Japan 1980: Proceedings. (Nucleic Acids Symposium Ser.: No. 8). 208p. 1980. 20.00 (ISBN 0-904147-28-2). IRL Pr.
Nucleic Acids Chemistry: Proceedings of the Symposium, 12th, Japan, 1984. (Nucleic Acids Symposium Ser.: No. 15). (Illus.). 210p. (Orig.). 1984. 40.00 (ISBN 0-904147-94-0). IRL Pr.
Osterman, L. A. Methods of Protein & Nucleic Acid Research: Electrophoresis, Isoelectric Focusing, Ultracentrifugation, Vol. 1. (Illus.). 370p. 1984. 59.00 (ISBN 0-387-12735-6). Springer-Verlag.
--Methods of Protein & Nucleic Acid Research: Immunoelectrophoresis - Application of Radioisotopes. (Illus.). 220p. 1984. 38.00 (ISBN 0-387-13094-2). Springer-Verlag.
Parthier, B. & Boulter, D., eds. Nucleic Acids & Proteins in Plants II: Structure, Biochemistry, & Physiology of Nucleic Acids. (Encyclopedia of Plant Physiology: Vol. 14 B). (Illus.). 774p. 1982. 130.00 (ISBN 0-387-11140-9). Springer-Verlag.
Progress in Nucleic Acid Research, Vol. 28. (Serial Publication). 1983. 39.50 (ISBN 0-12-540028-4). Acad Pr.
Research Symposium on Complexes of Biologically Active Substances with Nucleic Acids & Their Modes of Action. Proceedings. Hahn, F. E., et al, eds. (Progress in Molecular & Subcellular Biology: Vol. 2). (Illus.). 1971. 45.00 (ISBN 0-387-05321-2). Springer-Verlag.
Rickwood, D. & Hames, B. D., eds. Gel Electrophoresis of Nucleic Acids: A Practical Approach. (Practical Approach Ser.). 260p. 1982. 20.00 (ISBN 0-904147-24-X). IRL Pr.
Saenger, W. Principles of Nucleic Acid Structure. (Springer Advanced Texts in Chemistry). (Illus.). xx, 556p. 1983. 44.00 (ISBN 0-387-90762-9); pap. 24.95 (ISBN 0-387-90761-0). Springer-Verlag.
Sarma, Ramaswamy H. Nucleic Acid Geometry & Dynamics. LC 80-10620. (Illus.). 424p. 1980. 65.00 (ISBN 0-08-024631-1); pap. 29.00 (ISBN 0-08-024630-3). Pergamon.
Science Press Staff, ed. Nucleic Acids & Proteins: The Proceedings of China-West Germany Symposium on Nucleic Acids & Proteins. 662p. 1981. 47.50 (ISBN 0-442-20072-2). Van Nos Reinhold.
Spiro, Thomas G., ed. Nucleic Acid-Metal Ion Interactions, Vol. 1. LC 79-13808. (Metals Ions in Biology Ser.). 256p. 1980. 55.95 (ISBN 0-471-04399-0, Pub. by Wiley-Interscience). Wiley.
Steiner, Robert F. & Weinryb, Ira, eds. Excited States of Proteins & Nucleic Acids. LC 75-138521. 478p. 1971. 55.00x (ISBN 0-306-30509-7, Plenum Pr). Plenum Pub.
Sundaralingham, M. & Rao, S. R., eds. Structure & Conformation of Nucleic Acids & Protein-Nuclein Acid Interactions. (Illus.). 1975. text ed. 53.00 (ISBN 0-8391-0764-1). Univ Park.
Symposium on Nucleic Acids Chemistry, 4th, Kyoto, 1976. Proceedings. (Nucleic Acids Symposium Ser.: No. 2). 162p. 20.00 (ISBN 0-904147-41-X). IRL Pr.
Symposium on Nucleic Acids Chemistry, 5th, Mishima, Japan, 1977. Proceedings. (Nucleic Acids Symposium Ser.: No. 3). 196p. 20.00 (ISBN 0-904147-46-0). IRL Pr.
Symposium on Nucleic Acids Chemistry, 6th, Nagoya, Japan, 1978. Proceedings. (Nucleic Acids Symposium Ser.: No. 5). 233p. 20.00 (ISBN 0-904147-43-6). IRL Pr.
Symposium on Nucleic Acids Chemistry, 7th, Okayama, Japan, 1979. Proceedings. (Nucleic Acids Symposium Ser.: No. 6). 206p. 20.00 (ISBN 0-904147-44-4). IRL Pr.
Symposium on the Chemistry of Nucleic Acid Components, 3rd, Czechoslovakia, 1975. Proceedings. (Nucleic Acids Symposium Ser.: No. 1). 198p. 20.00 (ISBN 0-904147-40-1). IRL Pr.
Ts'o. Basic Principles of Nucleic Chemistry. 1974. Vol. 1. 82.00 (ISBN 0-12-701901-4); Vol. 2, 1974. 77.00 (ISBN 0-12-701902-2). Acad Pr.
Ursprung, H., ed. Nucleic Acid Hybridization in the Study of Cell Differentiation. LC 70-188705. (Results & Problems in Cell Differentiation: Vol. 3). (Illus.). 120p. 1972. 24.00 (ISBN 0-387-05742-0). Springer-Verlag.
Vogel, H. J., ed. Nucleic Acid-Protein Recognition. 1977. 75.00 (ISBN 0-12-722560-9). Acad Pr.
Wang, Shih Y., ed. Photochemistry & Photobiology of Nucleic Acids, 2 vols. 1976. Vol. 1. 95.00 (ISBN 0-12-734601-5); Vol. 2. 85.00 (ISBN 0-12-734602-3). Acad Pr.
Weissbluth, Mitchel, ed. Quantum Aspects of Polypeptides & Polynucleotides: A Symposium Held at Stanford University, California, March 25-29, 1963. LC 64-9806. (Biopolymers Symposia: No.1). pap. 143.30 (ISBN 0-317-08769-X, 2007395). Bks Demand UMI.
Zorback, W. Werner & Tipson, R. Stuart, eds. Synthetic Procedures in Nucleic Acid Chemistry: Vol. 1. 570p. (Orig.). 1968. 31.00 (ISBN 0-470-98415-5). Krieger.
--Synthetic Procedures in Nucleic Acid Chemistry: Vol. 2. 686p. (Orig.). 1973. 54.25 (ISBN 0-471-98418-3). Krieger.

NUCLEONS
see Particles (Nuclear Physics)

NUCLEOPROTEINS

Busch, Harris. Histones & Other Nuclear Proteins. 1965. 49.00 (ISBN 0-12-147656-1). Acad Pr.
King, Jonathan, ed. Protein & Nucleic Acids Structure. 1984. text ed. 29.95 (ISBN 0-8053-5403-4). Benjamin-Cummings.

NUCLEOSIDES

Agris, Paul F. The Modified Nucleosides of Transfer RNA: A Bibliography of Biochemical & Biophysical Studies From 1970-1979. LC 80-81197. 220p. 1980. 32.00 (ISBN 0-8451-0207-9). A R Liss.
Bloch, Alexander, ed. Chemistry, Biology, & Clinical Uses of Nucleoside Analogs, Vol. 255. (Annals of the New York Academy of Sciences). 610p. 1975. 71.00x (ISBN 0-89072-009-6). NY Acad Sci.
Hall, Ross H. Modified Nucleosides in Nucleic Acids. LC 73-122745. (Molecular Biology Ser). 1971. 55.00x (ISBN 0-231-03018-5). Columbia U Pr.
Harmon, Robert E., ed. Chemistry & Biology of Nucleosides & Nucleotides. 1978. 55.00 (ISBN 0-12-326140-6). Acad Pr.
Huang, C. C., et al. Molecular Studies on Halogenated Deoxynucleosides. 256p. 1972. text ed. 36.50x (ISBN 0-8422-7013-2). Irvington.
Nass, G., ed. Modified Nucleosides & Cancer: Workshop, Freiburg, FRG, 1981. (Recent Results in Cancer Research: Vol. 84). (Illus.). 440p. 1983. 52.00 (ISBN 0-387-12024-6). Springer-Verlag.
Rideout, Janet L., et al. Nucleosides, Nucleotides & Their Biological Applications. LC 83-15745. 1983. 33.50 (ISBN 0-12-587980-6). Acad Pr.
Suhadolnik, Robert J. Nucleosides As Biological Probes. LC 79-10719. 346p. 1979. 96.50 (ISBN 0-471-05317-1, Pub. by Wiley-Interscience). Wiley.
Tattersall, M. H. & Fox, R. M., eds. Nucleosides in Cancer Treatment: Rational Approaches to Antimetabolite Selectivity & Modulation. LC 80-70775. (Ludwig Symposia Ser.: Vol. 1). 1981. 49.50 (ISBN 0-12-683820-8). Acad Pr.
Walker, R. T., et al, eds. Nucleoside Analogues: Chemistry, Biology, & Medical Applications. LC 79-19432. (NATO ASI Series A, Life Sciences: Vol. 26). 468p. 1979. 59.50 (ISBN 0-306-40302-1, Plenum Pr). Plenum Pub.

NUCLEOTIDES
see also Nucleosides

Alfred Benzon Symposium - 1st. Role of Nucleotides for the Function & Conformation of Enzymes. Kalckar, H. M., et al, eds. 1970. 70.00 (ISBN 0-12-394550-X). Acad Pr.
Brooker, Gary, et al, eds. Current Methodology. LC 78-55806. (Advances in Cyclic Nucleotide Research Ser.: Vol. 10). 271p. 1979. 41.00 (ISBN 0-89004-265-9). Raven.
Cramer, Hinrich & Schultz, Joachim. Cyclic Three Prime, Five Prime -Nucleotides: Mechanisms of Action. LC 76-45361. 554p. 1977. 91.95 (ISBN 0-471-99456-1, Pub. by Wiley-Interscience). Wiley.
Daly, John. Cyclic Nucleotides in the Nervous System. LC 76-62999. (Illus.). 415p. 1977. 45.00x (ISBN 0-306-30971-8, Plenum Pr). Plenum Pub.
De Serres, Frederick J., ed. Genetic Consequences of Nucleotide Pool Imbalance. (Basic Life Sciences Ser.: Vol. 31). 504p. 1985. 69.50x (ISBN 0-306-41902-5, Plenum Pr). Plenum Pub.
Dumont, Jacques E., et al, eds. Cyclic Nucleotides: Proceedings of the Fourth International Conference, Brussels, Belgium. (Advances in Cyclic Nucleotide Research: Vol. 14). 756p. 1981. text ed. 113.50 (ISBN 0-89004-546-1). Raven.
Everse, Johannes, et al, eds. The Pyridine Nucleotide Coenzymes. 416p. 1982. 60.00 (ISBN 0-12-244750-6). Acad Pr.
Frunder, H., ed. Effects & Metabolism of Insulin & Cyclic Nucleotides. (Illus.). 1978. stitched 22.00x (ISBN 0-685-87201-7). Adlers Foreign Bks.
Gen Bank-Embl. Nucleotide Sequences Nineteen Eighty-Five, Parts 1-4. (Special Supplement to Nucleic Acids Research). 2000p. (Orig.). 1985. pap. 120.00 set (ISBN 0-947946-25-X); Pt. 1. pap. 40.00 part (ISBN 0-947946-26-8). Pt. 2 (ISBN 0-947946-27-6). Pt. 3 (ISBN 0-947946-28-4). Pt. 4 (ISBN 0-947946-29-2). IRL Pr.
Greengard, P. & Robison, G. A., eds. Advances in Cyclic Nucleotide Research, Vol. 6. LC 71-181305. 368p. 1975. 50.50 (ISBN 0-89004-042-7). Raven.
Greengard, Paul. Cyclic Nucleotides, Phosphorylated Proteins, & Neuronal Function. LC 78-66349. (Distinguished Lecture Series of the Society of General Physiologists: Vol. 1). 134p. 1978. 22.00 (ISBN 0-89004-281-0). Raven.
Greengard, Paul & Robison, Alan, eds. Advances in Cyclic Nucleotide Research, Vol 13. 352p. 1980. text ed. 54.50 (ISBN 0-89004-471-6). Raven.
Greengard, Paul & Robison, G. Alan, eds. Advances in Cyclic Nucleotide Research, Vol. 3. 416p. 1973. text ed. 50.50 (ISBN 0-911216-38-3). Raven.
--Advances in Cyclic Nucleotide Research, Vol. 4. LC 71-181305. 498p. 1974. 57.00 (ISBN 0-911216-76-6). Raven.
--Advances in Cyclic Nucleotide Research, Vol. 11. LC 71-181305. 397p. 1979. text ed. 57.00 (ISBN 0-89004-363-9). Raven.
Greengard, Paul, et al, eds. Cyclic Nucleotides & Protein Phosphorylation: Fifth International Conference, Milan, Italy. (Advances in Cyclic Nucleotide & Protein Phosphorylation Research). (Illus.). 722p. 1984. Vol. 17. text ed. 104.50 (ISBN 0-89004-349-3); Vol. 17A-Abstracts, 192. pap. 21.50 (ISBN 0-89004-409-0). Raven.
--New Assay Methods for Cyclic Nucleotides. (Advances in Cyclic Nucleotide Research Ser.: Vol. 2). 145p. 1972. text ed. 27.50 (ISBN 0-911216-21-9). Raven.
Greengard, Paul G. & Robison, Alan, eds. Advances in Cyclic Nucleotide Research, Vol. 15. 532p. 1983. text ed. 78.00 (ISBN 0-89004-881-9). Raven.
Hamet, Pavel & Sands, Howard, eds. Pathophysiological Aspects of Cyclic Nucleotides. (Advances in Cyclic Nucleotide Research: Vol. 12). 470p. 1980. text ed. 70.00 (ISBN 0-89004-454-6). Raven.
Harmon, Robert E., ed. Chemistry & Biology of Nucleosides & Nucleotides. 1978. 55.00 (ISBN 0-12-326140-6). Acad Pr.
Henderson, J. Frank & Paterson, A. R. Nucleotide Metabolism. 1973. 55.00 (ISBN 0-12-340550-5). Acad Pr.
International Conference on Cyclic Amp, 2nd, July, 1974. Advances in Cyclic Nucleotide Research: Proceedings. Drummond, G. I., et al, eds. LC 74-24679. (Advances in Cyclic Nucleotide Research Ser.: Vol. 5). 886p. 1975. 96.50 (ISBN 0-89004-021-4). Raven.
International Conference on Cyclic Nucleotide, 3rd, New Orleans, la., July 1977. Advances in Cyclic Nucleotide Research: Proceedings, Vol. 9. George, William J. & Ignarro, Louis, eds. LC 77-84555. 831p. 1978. 95.00 (ISBN 0-89004-240-3). Raven.
Janik, Borek. Physicochemical Characteristics of Oligonucleotides & Polynucleotides. LC 70-165692. 213p. 1971. 24.50x (ISBN 0-306-65155-6, IFI Plenum). Plenum Pub.
Kebabian, J. W., ed. Cyclic Nucleotides Part II: Physiology & Pharmacology. (Handbook of Experimental Pharmacology Ser.: Vol. 58). 1000p. 1982. 227.00 (ISBN 0-387-11239-1). Springer-Verlag.
Metrology of Radionuclides. (Proceedings Ser.). (Illus.). 480p. 1960. 15.75 (ISBN 92-0-030060-X, ISP6, IAEA). Unipub.
Nathanson, J. A. & Kobabian, J. W., eds. Cyclic Nucleotides, Part I: Biochemistry. (Handbook of Experimental Pharmacology Ser.: Vol. 58, Pt. I). (Illus.). 736p. 1982. 187.00 (ISBN 0-387-10786-X). Springer-Verlag.
Palmer, Gene C., ed. Neuropharmacology of Cyclic Nucleotides: Role of CAMP in Affective Disorders, Epilepsy & Modified Behavioral States. LC 78-23490. (Illus.). 316p. 1979. text ed. 22.50 (ISBN 0-8067-1521-9). Urban & S.
Scheit, Karl H. Nucleotide Analogs: Synthesis & Biological Function. LC 79-25445. 288p. 1980. 64.50 (ISBN 0-471-04854-2, Pub. by Wiley-Interscience). Wiley.
Strada, Samuel J. & Thompson, W. Joseph, eds. Cyclic Nucleotide Phosphodiesterases. (Advances in Cyclic Nucleotide & Protein Phosphorylation Research Ser.: Vol.16). (Illus.). 460p. 1984. 59.50 (ISBN 0-89004-779-0). Raven.
Sund, Horst, ed. Pyridine Nucleotide: Dependent Dehydrogenases. 513p. 1977. text ed. 66.00x (ISBN 3-11007-091-X). De Gruyter.

NUCLEUS (CELLS)
see Cell Nuclei; Cells

NUCLEUS OF THE ATOM
see Nuclear Physics

NUMBER CONCEPT
see also Numeration

Bottoni, Lois & Reynolds, Patti, eds. Numbers One-Ten. (Golden Step Ahead Workbks.). (Illus.). 36p. 1984. wkbk. 1.95 (ISBN 0-307-23537-8, 3537, Golden Bks). Western Pub.
Concepto De Numero. (Serie De Matematica: No. 7). (Span.). 1968. pap. 3.50 (ISBN 0-8270-6250-8). OAS.
Coutourat, Louis. De l'Infini Mathematique. LC 68-56776. (Research & Source Works Ser.: No. 262). (Fr). 1969. Repr. of 1896 ed. 35.50 (ISBN 0-8337-0706-X). B Franklin.
Daniel, Wanda R. & Dunlap, Howard G. Help with Capitalization, Abbreviations, & Numbers. 1984. pap. text ed. 3.32 (ISBN 0-395-34821-8); tchr's manual 1.00 (ISBN 0-395-34822-6). HM.
Dantzig, Tobias. Number: The Language of Science. 4th rev. ed. (Illus.). 340p. 1967. pap. text ed. 10.95x (ISBN 0-02-906990-4). Free Pr.
Drob, Ralph E. Number Mastery. Smith, Donald E., ed. (Michigan Tracking Ser.). 1974. pap. text ed. 2.45x (ISBN 0-914004-46-8). Ulrich.
Frege, Gottlob. Foundations of Arithmetic: A Logico-Mathematical Enquiry into the Concept of Numbers. Austin, J. L., tr. LC 68-8996. (Eng. & Ger.). 1968. 17.95 (ISBN 0-8101-0023-1); pap. 9.95 (ISBN 0-8101-0605-1). Northwestern U Pr.
Grossmann, Reinhart. Ontological Reduction. LC 72-85604. (Indiana University Humanities Ser.: No. 72). pap. 42.00 (ISBN 0-317-09304-5, 2055221). Bks Demand UMI.
Mendelson, Elliott. Number Systems & the Foundations of Analysis. LC 84-21839. 370p. 1985. Repr. of 1973 ed. lib. bdg. 24.95 (ISBN 0-89874-818-6). Krieger.
Piaget, Jean. Child's Conception of Number. 1965. pap. 5.95 (ISBN 0-393-00324-8, Norton Lib). Norton.
Schwaller de Lubicz, R. A. The Study of Numbers. 96p. 1985. pap. 5.95 (ISBN 0-89281-073-4). Inner Tradit.
Sondheimer, Ernst & Rogerson, Alan. Numbers & Infinity: An Historical Account of Mathematical Concepts. LC 81-7660. 150p. 1981. 22.95 (ISBN 0-521-24091-3); pap. 9.95 (ISBN 0-521-28433-3). Cambridge U Pr.

NUMBER STUDY
see Arithmetic–Study and Teaching

NUMBER THEORY
see Numbers, Theory of

NUMBERS, COMPLEX
see also Algebra, Universal; Ausdehnungslehre; Functions; Numbers, Real; Quaternions; Vector Analysis

Beardon, A. F. Complex Analysis: The Argument Principle in Analysis & Topology. LC 78-8540. 239p. 1979. 69.95x (ISBN 0-471-99671-8, Pub. by Wiley-Interscience). Wiley.
Chillingworth, H. R. Complex Variables. LC 72-86178. 280p. 1973. pap. text ed. 21.00 (ISBN 0-08-016939-2). Pergamon.
Conway, J. B. Functions of One Complex Variable. 2nd ed. (Graduate Texts in Mathematics Ser.: Vol. 11). (Illus.). 1978. 29.80 (ISBN 0-387-90328-3). Springer-Verlag.
Hawkins, F. M. & Hawkins, J. Q. Complex Numbers & Elementary Complex Functions. 154p. 1970. 41.75 (ISBN 0-677-61110-2). Gordon.
Kogbetliantz, E. G. Handbook of First Complex Prime Numbers, 2 vol. set. LC 78-142082. 1014p. 1971. 186.25 (ISBN 0-677-02920-9). Gordon.
Kohn, J. J., et al, eds. Several Complex Variables. 280p. 1984. 24.95 (ISBN 0-8176-3189-5). Birkhauser.
Lang, S. Complex Analysis. (Graduate Texts in Mathematics Ser.: Vol. 103). (Illus.). 385p. 1985. 39.00 (ISBN 0-387-96085-6). Springer-Verlag.
Levi, Judith N. The Syntax & Semantics of Complex Nominals. 1978. 29.50 (ISBN 0-12-445150-0). Acad Pr.
Maass, H. Modular Functions of One Complex Variables. (Tata Institute Lectures on Mathematics Ser.). vii, 266p. 1983. pap. 7.10 (ISBN 0-387-12874-3). Springer-Verlag.
Markushevich, A. I. Complex Numbers & Conformal Mapping. (Russian Tracts on the Physical Sciences Ser.). 70p. 1962. 19.75x (ISBN 0-677-20280-6). Gordon.
Nevanlinna, Rolf & Paatero, Viekko. Introduction to Complex Analysis. 2nd ed. 360p. 1982. text ed. 15.95 (ISBN 0-8284-0310-4). Chelsea Pub.
Schwerdtfeger, Hans. Geometry of Complex Numbers. LC 62-53580. (Mathematical Expositions Ser.: No. 13). pap. 50.00 (ISBN 0-317-09112-3, 2014404). Bks Demand UMI.
Seminar on Complex Multiplication, Institute for Advanced Study, Princeton & Borel, A. Proceedings. (Lecture Notes in Mathematics: Vol. 21). 1966. pap. 10.70 (ISBN 0-387-03604-0). Springer-Verlag.
Silverman, Richard A. Introductory Complex Analysis. 372p. 1984. pap. 8.00 (ISBN 0-486-64686-6). Dover.
Sveshnikov, A. & Tikhonov, A. Theory of Functions of a Complex Variable. 311p. 1978. 5.95 (ISBN 0-8285-0747-3, Pub. by Mir Pubs USSR). Imported Pubns.

Hecke, Erich. Algebraische Zahlen. 2nd ed. LC 50-3732. (Ger). 1970. 12.95 (ISBN 0-8284-0046-6). Chelsea Pub.

Hejhal, D. A. The Selberg Trace Formula for PSL; 2, IR, Vol. 2. (Lecture Notes in Mathematics: Vol. 1001). 806p. 1983. pap. 38.00 (ISBN 0-387-12323-7). Springer-Verlag.

Henrici, Peter. Computational Analysis with the HP-25 Pocket Calculator. LC 77-1182. 280p. 1977. pap. 26.50 (ISBN 0-471-02938-6, Pub. by Wiley-Interscience). Wiley.

Hua, L. K. Introduction to Number Theory. Shiu, Peter, tr. from Chinese. (Illus.). 572p. 1982. 49.00 (ISBN 0-387-10818-1). Springer-Verlag.

Hua, L. K. & Wang, Y. Applications of Number Theory to Numerical Analysis. 241p. 1981. 42.00 (ISBN 0-387-10382-1). Springer-Verlag.

Husserl. Philosophie der Arithmetik. (Husserliana Ser: No. 12). 1970. lib. bdg. 50.00 (ISBN 90-247-0230-5, Pub. by Martinus Nijhoff Netherlands). Kluwer Academic.

Igusa, J. I. Lectures on Forms of Higher Degree. (Tata Institute Lecture Notes). 1979. pap. 15.00 (ISBN 0-387-08944-6). Springer-Verlag.

International Conference, Sonderforschungsbereich Theoretische Mathematik,University of Bonn, July 1976. Modular Functions of One Variable: Proceedings, No. 6. Serre, J. P. & Zagier, D. B., eds. (Lecture Note in Mathematics: Vol. 627). 1977. pap. 22.00 (ISBN 0-387-08530-0). Springer-Verlag.

Ireland, K. & Rosen, Michael. A Classical Introduction to Modern Number Theory. (Graduate Texts in Mathematics Ser.: Vol. 84). (Illus.). 341p. 1982. 33.00 (ISBN 0-387-90625-8). Springer-Verlag.

Iyanaga, S. The Theory of Numbers. (Mathematical Library: Vol. 8). 542p. 1976. 106.50 (ISBN 0-444-10678-2, North-Holland). Elsevier.

Jager, H. Number Theory Noordwijkerhout Nineteen Eighty-Three: Proceedings of the Journees Arithmetiques Held at Noordwijkerhout, The Netherlands July 11-15, 1983. (Lecture Notes in Mathematics Ser.: Vol. 1068). v, 296p. 1984. pap. 18.50 (ISBN 0-387-13356-9). Springer-Verlag.

Kac, Mark. Statistical Independence in Probability Analysis & Number Theory. (Carus Monograph: No. 12). 93p. 1959. 16.50 (ISBN 0-88385-012-5). Math Assn.

Khinchin, Aleksander Y. Three Pearls of Number Theory. LC 52-2385. 1952. 9.00x (ISBN 0-910670-04-8). Graylock.

Knopp, M. I., ed. Analytic Number Theory: Proceedings. (Lecture Notes in Mathematics Ser.: Vol. 899). 478p. 1982. pap. 27.00 (ISBN 0-387-11173-5). Springer-Verlag.

Koblitz, N. P-Adic Analysis. (London Mathematical Society Lecture Note Ser.: No. 46). 150p. 1980. pap. 17.95 (ISBN 0-521-28060-5). Cambridge U Pr.

--P-Adic Numbers, P-Adic Analysis & Zeta Functions. 2nd ed. (Graduate Tests in Mathematics Ser.: Vol. 58). (Illus.). 288p. 1984. 28.00 (ISBN 0-387-96017-1). Springer-Verlag.

Koblitz, Neal, ed. Modern Trends in Number Theory Related to Fermat's Last Theorem. (Progress in Mathematics Ser.: Vol. 26). 470p. 1982. text ed. 30.00 (ISBN 0-8176-3104-6). Birkhauser.

Korobov, N. M., et al. Eight Papers on Algebra & Number Theory. LC 51-5559. (Translations, Ser.: No. 2, Vol. 4). 1956. 23.00 (ISBN 0-8128-1704-4, TRANS 2-4). Am Math.

Landau, Edmund. Elementare Zahlentheorie. LC 49-235. (Ger). 12.00 (ISBN 0-8284-0026-1). Chelsea Pub.

--Elementary Number Theory. 2nd ed. LC 57-8494. 13.95 (ISBN 0-8284-0125-X). Chelsea Pub.

--Foundations of Analysis. 2nd ed. LC 60-15580. 1960. text ed. 10.95 (ISBN 0-8284-0079-2). Chelsea Pub.

--Grundlagen der Analysis: With Complete German-English Vocabulary. 4th ed. LC 60-7485. (Ger). o. p. 6.95; pap. 4.95 (ISBN 0-8284-0141-1). Chelsea Pub.

--Vorlesungen Ueber Zahlentheorie, 3 Vols. in One. LC 49-235. (Ger). 35.00 (ISBN 0-8284-0032-6). Chelsea Pub.

Lang, S. Introduction to Modular Forms. (No. 222). (Illus.). 1976. 34.00 (ISBN 0-387-07833-9). Springer-Verlag.

Langlands, Robert P. Euler Products. LC 72-151580. (Yale Mathematical Monographs: Vol. 1). pap. 20.00 (ISBN 0-317-09487-4, 2016790). Bks Demand UMI.

Leblanc, John F., et al. Mathematics-Methods Program: Number Theory. (Mathematics Ser.). (Illus.). 128p. 1976. pap. text ed. 3.95 (ISBN 0-201-14624-X); instr's. manual 2.00 (ISBN 0-201-14625-8). Addison-Wesley.

Lejeune-Dirichlet, P. G. & Dedekind, R. Zahlentheorie. 4th ed. LC 68-54716. (Ger). 1969. text ed. 39.50 (ISBN 0-8284-0213-2). Chelsea Pub.

LeVeque, William J., ed. Reviews in Number Theory. LC 74-11335. 1974. Set. paper 400.00 (ISBN 0-685-26205-7, REVNUM); Vol. 1. 90.00 (ISBN 0-8218-0203-8, REVNUM-1); Vol. 2. 90.00 (ISBN 0-8218-0204-6, REVNUM-2); Vol. 3. 90.00 (ISBN 0-8218-0205-4, REVNUM-3); Vol. 4. 90.00 (ISBN 0-8218-0206-2, REVNUM-4); Vol. 5. 90.00 (ISBN 0-8218-0207-0, REVNUM-5); Vol. 6. 90.00 (ISBN 0-8218-0208-9, REVNUM-6). Am Math.

Lion, Gerard & Vergne, Michele, eds. The Weil Representation, Maslov Index & Theta Series. (Progress in Mathematics Ser.: No. 6). 346p. 1980. pap. text ed. 24.00x (ISBN 0-8176-3007-4). Birkhauser.

Local Analysis of Selberg's Trace Formula. (Lecture Notes in Mathematics: Vol. 1040). iii, 128p. 1983. pap. 10.00 (ISBN 0-387-12713-5). Springer-Verlag.

Luneburg, H. Vorlesungen uber Zalentheorie. (Elemente der Mathematik Von Hoeheren Standpunkt Aus: Vol. 8). (Ger.). 108p. 1978. pap. 21.95x (ISBN 0-8176-0932-6). Birkhauser.

MacMahon, Percy A. Combinatory Analysis, 2 Vols. in 1. LC 59-10267. 29.50 (ISBN 0-8284-1137-9). Chelsea Pub.

Malm, Donald G. A Computer Laboratory Manual for Number Theory. 256p. 1980. pap. text ed. 9.95x (ISBN 0-933694-13-X). COMPress.

Malyshev, A. V., ed. Studies in Number Theory. LC 68-31238. (Seminars in Mathematics Ser.: Vol. 1). 66p. 1968. 18.50x (ISBN 0-306-18801-5, Consultants). Plenum Pub.

Mann, Henry B. Addition Theorems: The Addition Theorems of Group Theory & Number Theory. LC 76-16766. 124p. 1976. Repr. of 1965 ed. text ed. 12.50 (ISBN 0-88275-418-1). Krieger.

Masi, Michael. Boethian Number Theory: A Translation of the De Institutione Arithmetica. (Studies in Classical Antiquity: No. 6). 197p. 1983. pap. text ed. 27.75x (ISBN 90-6203-785-2). Humanities.

Mathews, George B. Theory of Numbers. 2nd ed. LC 61-17958. 13.95 (ISBN 0-8284-0156-X). Chelsea Pub.

Minkowski, Hermann. Diophantische Approximationen. LC 56-13056. (Ger). 11.95 (ISBN 0-8284-0118-7). Chelsea Pub.

--Geometrie der Zahlen. (Bibliotheca Mathematica Teubneriana: No. 40). (Ger). 1969. Repr. of 1910 ed. 30.00 (ISBN 0-384-39040-4). Johnson Repr.

Mordell, L. J. Two Papers on Number Theory. 80p. 1972. 4.50x (ISBN 0-685-27556-6). Adlers Foreign Bks.

Moreno, Carlos J. Advanced Analytic Number Theory, Pt.1. LC 82-22620. (Contemporary Mathematical Ser.). 192p. 1983. Vol. 15. pap. 18.00 (ISBN 0-8218-5015-6). Am Math.

Motohashi, Y. Sieve Methods & Prime Numbers Theory. (Tata Institute Lectures on Mathematics Ser.). xi, 205p. 1983. pap. 9.00 (ISBN 0-387-12281-8). Springer-Verlag.

Nagell, Trygve. Introduction to Number Theory. 309p. 1981. 15.95 (ISBN 0-8284-0163-2). Chelsea Pub.

Narkiewicz, W. Number Theory. Kanemitsu, S., tr. 360p. 1984. 37.00x (ISBN 9971-950-13-8, Pub. by World Sci Singapore); pap. 21.00x (ISBN 9971-950-26-X, Pub. by World Sci Singapore). Taylor & Francis.

Nathanson, M. B., ed. Number Theory: Carbondale Nineteen Seventy-Nine. (Lecture Notes in Mathematics: Vol. 751). 342p. 1979. pap. 20.00 (ISBN 0-387-09559-4). Springer-Verlag.

--Number Theory Day: Proceedings of the Conference Held at Rockefeller University, New York, 1976. LC 77-26055. (Lecture Notes in Mathematics Ser: Vol. 626). 1977. pap. 18.00 (ISBN 0-387-08529-7). Springer-Verlag.

Niven, Ivan & Zuckerman, Herbert S. An Introduction to the Theory of Numbers. 4th ed. LC 79-24869. 355p. 1980. text ed. 38.50x (ISBN 0-471-02851-7); solutions manual avail. (ISBN 0-471-06394-0). Wiley.

Number Systems. (Computer Literacy Ser.). pap. 4.95 (ISBN 0-318-04025-5). Sperry Comp Syst.

Ore, Oystein. Invitation to Number Theory. LC 67-20607. (New Mathematical Library: No. 20). 129p. 1975. pap. 8.75 (ISBN 0-88385-620-4). Math Assn.

Parent, D. P. Exercises in Number Theory. Cole, M., tr. from Fr. (Problem Books in Mathematics). x, 542p. 1984. 38.00 (ISBN 0-387-96063-5). Springer-Verlag.

Pieper, H. Variationen uber ein Zahlenthroretisches Them von Carl Friedrich Gauss. (Science & Civilization Ser.: No. 33). (Ger.). 160p. 1978. 16.95x (ISBN 0-8176-0959-8). Birkhauser.

Pogorzelski, Henry A. & Ryan, William J. Foundations of Semiological Theory of Numbers. 590p. (Orig.). 1982. pap. text ed. 29.95 (ISBN 0-89101-053-X). U Maine Orono.

Polya, G. & Szego, G. Problems & Theorems in Analysis II: Theory of Functions, Zeros, Polynomials, Determinants, Number Theory, Geometry. Billigheimer, C. E., tr. (Illus.). 1977. pap. text ed. 24.00 (ISBN 0-387-90291-0). Springer-Verlag.

Pringsheim, Alfred. Vorlesungen Uber Zahlen & Funktionenlehre, 2 Vols. (Bibliotheca Mathematica Teubneriana Ser: Nos. 28-29). (Ger). 1969. Repr. of 1916 ed. Set. 145.00 (ISBN 0-384-47885-9). Johnson Repr.

Rademacher, Hans. Lectures on Elementary Number Theory. LC 76-30495. 156p. 1977. Repr. of 1964 ed. lib. bdg. 11.50 (ISBN 0-88275-499-8). Krieger.

Resource Systems International. Applied Math: I. 1982. pap. text ed. 15.00 (ISBN 0-8359-0140-8). Reston.

Robinson, Abraham. Numbers & Ideals. LC 65-16747. (Illus.). 1965. 14.95x (ISBN 0-8162-7234-4). Holden-Day.

Rosen, Kennith H. Elementary Number Theory & Its Applications. 1984. 29.95 (ISBN 0-201-06561-4). Addison-Wesley.

Rota, Gian-Carlo, ed. Studies in Algebra & Number Theory. LC 79-4638. (Advances in Mathematics Supplementary Studies: Vol. 6). 1979. 70.00 (ISBN 0-12-599153-3). Acad Pr.

Scharlau, W. & Opolka, H. From Fermat to Minkowski: Lectures on the Theory of Numbers & Its Historical Development. Buhler, W. K. & Cornell, G., trs. from German. (Undergraduate Texts in Mathematics Ser.). (Illus.). 255p. 1985. 24.00 (ISBN 0-387-90942-7). Springer-Verlag.

Schroeder, M. R. Number Theory in Science & Communication. (Springer Series in Information Sciences: Vol. 7). (Illus.). 350p. 1984. 28.00 (ISBN 0-387-12164-1). Springer-Verlag.

Schweiger, F. Metrical Theory of Jacobi-Perron Algorithm. LC 73-9201. (Lecture Notes in Mathematics: Vol. 334). v, 111p. 1973. pap. 13.00 (ISBN 0-387-06388-9). Springer-Verlag.

Scott, Norman R. Computer Number Systems & Arithmetic. LC 84-9964. (Illus.). 240p. 1985. text ed. 39.95 (ISBN 0-13-164211-1). P-H.

Seminar on Complex Multiplication, Institute for Advanced Study, Princeton & Borel, A. Proceedings. (Lecture Notes in Mathematics: Vol. 21). 1966. pap. 10.70 (ISBN 0-387-03604-0). Springer-Verlag.

Serre, J. P. Local Fields. Greenberg, M. J., tr. from Fr. LC 79-12643. (Graduate Texts in Mathematics: Vol. 67). (Illus.). 1979. 33.00 (ISBN 0-387-90424-7). Springer-Verlag.

Serre, Jean-Pierre & Shimura, Goro, eds. Geometry & Number Theory: A Volume in Honor of Andre Weil. LC 83-48062. 608p. 1983. text ed. 48.00x (ISBN 0-8018-3091-5). Johns Hopkins.

Shanks, Daniel. Solved & Unsolved Problems in Number Theory. 2nd ed. LC 77-13019. 1978. text ed. 12.95 (ISBN 0-8284-0297-3). Chelsea Pub.

--Solved & Unsolved Problems in Number Theory. 3rd, rev. ed. LC 77-13010. vii, 304p. 1985. text ed. 18.95 (ISBN 0-317-30640-5, 297). Chelsea Pub.

Shapiro, Harold N. Introduction to the Theory of Numbers. LC 82-10929. (Pure & Applied Mathematics Ser.). 459p. 1983. 45.95x (ISBN 0-471-86737-3, Pub. by Wiley-Interscience). Wiley.

Shimura, G. Automorphic Functions & Number Theory. LC 68-25132. (Lecture Notes in Mathematics Ser.: Vol. 54). (Orig.). 1968. pap. 10.70 (ISBN 0-387-04224-5). Springer-Verlag.

Siegel, C. L. Topics in Complex Function Theory, 3 vols. Incl. Vol. 1. Elliptical Functions & Uniformization Theory. 186p. 1969. 40.50x (ISBN 0-471-79070-2); Vol. 2. Automorphic Functions & Abelian Integrals. 193p. 1972. 48.50x (ISBN 0-471-79080-X); Vol. 3. Abelian Functions & Modular Functions of Several Variables. Tretkoff, M. & Gottschling, E., trs. 244p. 1973. 48.50x (ISBN 0-471-79090-7). LC 69-19931. (Pure & Applied Mathematics Ser., Pub. by Wiley-Interscience). Wiley.

Sierpinski, W. & Schinzel, A. Elementary Theory of Numbers. Date not set. price not set (ISBN 0-444-86662-0, North-Holland). Elsevier.

Smith, Henry J. Report on the Theory of Numbers. LC 64-8080. 1966. 15.95 (ISBN 0-8284-0186-1). Chelsea Pub.

Sneath, Peter H. & Sokal, Robert R. Numerical Taxonomy: The Principles & Practice of Numerical Classification. LC 72-1552. (Biology Ser.). (Illus.). 573p. 1973. 43.95x (ISBN 0-7167-0697-0). W H Freeman.

Spencer, Donald D. Computers in Number Theory. LC 81-17452. (Illus.). 250p. 1982. pap. 16.95 (ISBN 0-914894-27-7). Computer Sci.

Stark, Harold M. An Introduction to Number Theory. 1978. pap. text ed. 13.95x (ISBN 0-262-69060-8). MIT Pr.

Steklov Institute of Mathematics, Academy of Sciences, U.S.S.R., No. 82 & Postinikov, A. G. Ergodic Problems in the Theory of Congruences & of Diophantine Approximations: Proceedings. (Proceedings of the Steklov Institute of Mathematics: No. 82). 1967. 33.00 (ISBN 0-8218-1882-1, STEKLO-82). Am Math.

Symposium at the Centre for Research in Mathematics, University of Montreal, Sept., 1971. Applications of Number Theory to Numerical Analysis: Proceedings. Zaremba, S. K., ed. 1972. 64.50 (ISBN 0-12-775950-6). Acad Pr.

Symposium in Pure Mathematics, Houston, January 1967. Number Theory, Vol. 12. LeVeque, W. J. & Straus, E. G., eds. LC 70-78057. (Proceedings of Symposia in Pure Mathematics). 1969. 23.00 (ISBN 0-8218-1412-5, PSPUM-12). Am Math.

Symposium in Pure Mathematics - Pasadena - 1963. Theory of Numbers: Proceedings. Whiteman, A. L., ed. LC 65-17382. (Proceedings of Symposia in Pure Mathematics: Vol. 8). 216p. 1979. pap. 27.00 with additions (ISBN 0-8218-1408-7, PSPUM-8). Am Math.

Symposium in Pure Mathematics, St. Louis, 1972. Analytic Number Theory: Proceedings. Diamond, H. G., ed. LC 72-10198. (Proceedings of Symposia in Pure Mathematics: Vol. 24). 1973. 48.00 (ISBN 0-8218-1424-9, PSPUM-24). Am Math.

Symposium in Pure Mathematics, Stony Brook, N.Y. 1969. Number Theory Institute, Nineteen Sixty-Nine: Proceedings. Lewis, Donald J., ed. LC 76-125938. (Proceeding of Symposia in Pure Mathematics: Vol. 20). 1971. 44.00 (ISBN 0-8218-1420-6, PSPUM-20). Am Math.

Toledo, S. A. Tableau Systems for First Order Number Theory & Certain Higher Order Theories. LC 75-6738. (Lecture Notes in Mathematics Ser.: Vol. 447). iii, 339p. 1975. pap. 20.00 (ISBN 0-387-07149-0). Springer-Verlag.

Trost, E. Primzahlen. 2nd rev. ed. (Elemente der Mathematik Von Hoeheren Standpunkt Aus: Vol. 2). (Ger.). 100p. 1968. pap. 16.95 (ISBN 0-8176-0387-5). Birkhauser.

Turan, P. Topics in Number Theory. (Colloquia Mathematica Societatis Janos Bolyai: Vol. 13). 456p. 1976. 74.50 (ISBN 0-7204-0454-1, North-Holland). Elsevier.

Turan, Paul, et al, eds. Number Theory & Analysis: A Collection of Papers in Honor of Edmund Landau (1877-1938) LC 68-8991. pap. 88.80 (ISBN 0-317-09421-1, 2019393). Bks Demand UMI.

Valenza, Samuel W., Jr. The Professor Googol Flying Time Machine & Atomic Space Capsule Math Primer. 3rd ed. (Illus.). 196p. 1974. 10.95 (ISBN 0-936918-00-4). Intergalactic NJ.

Vaughan, R. C. The Hardy-Littlewood Method. (Cambridge Tracts in Mathematics: No. 80). 160p. 1981. 39.50 (ISBN 0-521-23439-5). Cambridge U Pr.

Vinogradov, I. Fundamentos de la Teoria De los Numeros. (Span.). 107p. 1977. 6.45 (ISBN 0-8285-1686-3, Pub. by Mir Pubs USSR). Imported Pubns.

Vinogradov, I. M., ed. Number Theory: Proceedings, International Conference, Moscow, 1971. LC 75-14189. (Proceedings of the Steklov Institute of Mathematics: Vol. 132). 1975. 62.00 (ISBN 0-8218-3032-5, STEKLO-132). Am Math.

Weil, A. Basic Number Theory. 3rd ed. LC 74-13963. (Die Grundlehren der Mathematischen Wissenschaften Ser.: Vol. 144). xviii, 325p. 1974. 33.00 (ISBN 0-387-06935-6). Springer-Verlag.

Weil, Andre. Number Theory. 384p. 1984. text ed. 24.95 (ISBN 0-8176-3141-0). Birkhauser.

Weyl, Hermann. Algebraic Theory of Numbers. rev. ed. (Annals of Mathematics Studies: No. 1). (Orig.). 1954. pap. 26.50x (ISBN 0-691-07908-0). Princeton U Pr.

Yates, Samuel. Repunits & Repetends. LC 82-50241. 215p. 1982. pap. 13.00 (ISBN 0-9608652-0-9). S Yates.

Zassenhaus, Hans. Number Theory & Algebra: Collected Papers Dedicated to Henry B. Mann, Arnold E. Ross & Olga Taussky-Todd. 1977. 77.00 (ISBN 0-12-776350-3). Acad Pr.

NUMBERS, TRANSCENDENTAL

Baker, Alan R. Transcendental Number Theory. LC 74-82591. 148p. 1975. 34.50 (ISBN 0-521-20461-5). Cambridge U Pr.

Chudnovsky, G. V. Contributions to the Theory of Transcendental Numbers. LC 83-15728. (Mathematical Surveys Monographs Ser.: No. 19). 450p. 1984. 80.00 (ISBN 0-8218-1500-8). Am Math.

Mahler, K. Lectures on Transcendental Numbers. Divis, B. & Le Veque, W. J., eds. 1976. 17.00 (ISBN 0-387-07986-6). Springer-Verlag.

Remson, Irwin, et al. Numerical Methods in Subsurface Hydrology. LC 75-142139. 389p. 1971. 64.50 (ISBN 0-471-71650-2, Pub. by Wiley-Interscience). Wiley.

Samoilenko, A. M. & Ronto, N. I. Numerical-Analytic Methods of Investigating Periodic Solutions. 183p. 1979. pap. 4.95 (ISBN 0-8285-1514-X, Pub. by Mir Pubs USSR). Imported Pubns.

Sartaj Sahni. Concepts in Discrete Mathematics. 436p. 1981. text ed. 32.00 (ISBN 0-942450-00-0). Camelot Pub MN.

Sawyer, W. W. A First Look at Numerical Functional Analysis. (Oxford Applied Mathematics & Computing Science Ser.). (Illus.). 1978. pap. 15.95x (ISBN 0-19-859629-4). Oxford U Pr.

Scaife, B. K. Studies in Numerical Analysis. 1974. 55.00 (ISBN 0-12-621150-7). Acad Pr.

Scarborough, James B. Numerical Mathematical Analysis. 6th ed. 608p. 1966. 32.50x (ISBN 0-8018-0575-9). Johns Hopkins.

Scheid, Francis. Numerical Analysis. (Schaum's Outline Ser). (Orig.). 1968. pap. 9.95 (ISBN 0-07-055197-9). McGraw.

Schwartz, J. T., ed. Mathematical Aspects of Computer Science: Proceedings of a Symposium, New York City, Apr. 1966. LC 67-16554. (Proceedings of Symposia in Applied Mathematics: Vol. 19). 1978. pap. 20.00 (ISBN 0-8218-1319-6, PSAPM-19). Am Math.

Shaeffer, Ralph E. Calculator Layout: The Numerical Concept, 2 vols. Dale, Jean, ed. LC 83-90855. (Illus.). 135p. (Orig.). 1983. Vol. 1. pap. text ed. 28.00x (ISBN 0-9611418-0-8). R Shaeffer.

Shaw, R., et al, eds. Innovative Numerical Analysis for the Engineering Sciences. LC 80-14005. 811p. 1980. 40.00x (ISBN 0-8139-0867-1). U Pr of Va.

Smith, H. V. Tables for Numerical Integration. 32p. 1982. 30.00x (ISBN 0-85264-272-5, Pub. by Griffin England). State Mutual Bk.

Southworth, R. & De Leeuw, S. Digital Computation & Numerical Methods. 1965. text ed. 45.00 (ISBN 0-07-059799-5). McGraw.

Stark, Peter A. Introduction to Numerical Methods. (Illus.). 1970. text ed. write for info. (ISBN 0-02-416110-1). Macmillan.

Stoer, J. & Bulirsch, R. Introduction to Numerical Analysis. Bartels, R., et al, trs. from Ger. (Illus.). 1980. pap. 28.00 (ISBN 0-387-90420-4). Springer-Verlag.

Streeter, Donald N. The Scientific Process & the Computer. LC 73-21744. pap. 120.00 (ISBN 0-317-08515-8, 2007078). Bks Demand UMI.

Stummel, F. & Hainer, K. Introduction to Numerical Analysis. 276p. 1980. pap. 22.00x (ISBN 0-7073-0130-0, Pub. by Scottish Academic Pr). Columbia U Pr.

Swaszek, Peter F. Quantization. 352p. 1985. 49.95 (ISBN 0-442-28124-2). Van Nos Reinhold.

Symposium in Applied Mathematics, Santa Monica Calif, 1953. Numerical Analysis: Proceedings, Vol. 6. Curtiss, J. H., ed. LC 50-1183. (Proceedings of Symposia in Applied Mathematics). 303p. 1956. 35.00 (ISBN 0-8218-1306-4, PSAPM-6). Am Math.

Symposium on the Theory of Numerical Analysis. Proceedings. Morris, J. L., ed. LC 70-155916. (Lecture Notes in Mathematics: Vol. 193). 1971. pap. 11.00 (ISBN 0-387-05422-7). Springer-Verlag.

Szidarovszky, F. & Yakowitz, S., eds. Principles & Procedures of Numerical Analysis. LC 78-12070. (Mathematical Concepts & Methods in Science & Engineering Ser.: Vol. 14). 343p. 1978. 35.00x (ISBN 0-306-40087-1, Plenum Pr). Plenum Pub.

Talbot, Sandra, et al. Elements of Computer Mathematics. LC 84-21388. (Mathematics Ser.). 425p. 1985. text ed. 23.50 pub. net (ISBN 0-534-04392-5). Brooks-Cole.

Temam, R. Navier-Stokes Equations: Theory & Numerical Analysis. 3rd, rev. ed. (Studies in Mathematics & Its Applications: Vol. 2). 526p. 1985. 81.50 (ISBN 0-444-87558-1); pap. 35.00 (ISBN 0-444-87559-X, North-Holland). Elsevier.

Thompson, Thomas M. From Error-Correcting Codes Through Spere Packing to Simple Groups. (Carus Monograph: No. 21). 242p. 1984. 24.00 (ISBN 0-88385-023-0, 82062784). Math Assn.

Todd, John. Basic Numerical Mathematics, Vol. 1: Numerical Analysis. (International Series of Numerical Mathematics: No. 14). 1981. 29.50 (ISBN 0-12-692401-5). Acad Pr.

Turan, Paul, et al, eds. Number Theory & Analysis: A Collection of Papers in Honor of Edmund Landau (1877-1938) LC 68-8991. pap. 88.80 (ISBN 0-317-09421-1, 2019393). Bks Demand UMI.

Turner, P. R., ed. Numerical Analysis, Lancaster 1984. (Lecture Notes in Mathematics: Vol. 1129). xiv, 179p. 1985. pap. 12.00 (ISBN 0-387-15234-2). Springer-Verlag.

Van Bokhoven, W. M. & Jess, J. Numerical Methods. Date not set. price not set. Elsevier.

Vandergraft, James S. Introduction to Numerical Computations. (Computer Science & Applied Mathematics Ser.). 1978. 35.00 (ISBN 0-12-711350-9). Acad Pr.

Vandergraft, James S., ed. Introduction to Numerical Computations. LC 82-16252. (Computer Science & Applied Mathematics Ser.). 369p. 1983. 32.00 (ISBN 0-12-711356-8). Acad Pr.

Watson, G. A., ed. Numerical Analysis. LC 75-45241. (Lecture Notes in Mathematics: Vol. 506). 1976. pap. 16.00 (ISBN 0-387-07610-7). Springer-Verlag.

--Numerical Analysis Dundee 1981: Proceedings. (Lecture Notes in Mathematics: Vol. 912). 245p. 1982. pap. 19.00 (ISBN 0-387-11199-9). Springer-Verlag.

--Numerical Analysis: Proceedings. (Lecture Notes in Mathematics Ser.: Vol. 773). 184p. 1980. pap. 15.00 (ISBN 0-387-09740-6). Springer-Verlag.

Watson, W. A., et al. Numerical Analysis. 224p. 1981. 30.00x (ISBN 0-7131-2817-8, Pub. by E Arnold England). State Mutual Bk.

Werner, H. & Wuytack, L., eds. Computational Aspects of Complex Analysis. Bunger, H. J. 1983. PLB 54.00 (ISBN 90-2771-571-8, Pub. by Reidel Holland). Kluwer Academic.

Wilkes, M. V. Short Introduction to Numerical Analysis. (Illus., Orig.). pap. 8.95 (ISBN 0-521-09412-7, 412). Cambridge U Pr.

Woolf, E., et al, eds. Numerical Analysis & Data Processing. 400p. (Orig.). 1985. pap. text ed. 32.50x (ISBN 0-7121-0495-X). Trans-Atlantic.

Yakowitz & Sziderovszky. An Introduction to Numerical Computations. 600p. 1986. text ed. price not set write for info. (ISBN 0-02-430810-2). Macmillan.

Zadeh, L. A., et al, eds. Computing Methods in Optimization Problems Two. 1969. 65.00 (ISBN 0-12-775250-1). Acad Pr.

NUMERICAL ANALYSIS–DATA PROCESSING

Abney, Darrell H., et al. Computer Mathematics for Programmers. 1984. text ed. 18.00i (ISBN 0-12-042150-X). Acad Pr.

Ascher & Russell, eds. Numerical Boundary Value ODE's. (Progress in Scientific Computing: No. 6). 1985. text ed. write for info. (ISBN 0-8176-3302-2). Birkhauser.

Atkinson, L. V. & Harley, P. J. An Introduction to Numerical Methods with Pascal. 1982. pap. text ed. 17.95 (ISBN 0-201-13788-7). Addison-Wesley.

Beck, R. E. & Kolman, B. Computers in Nonassociative Rings & Algebras. 1977. 45.00 (ISBN 0-12-083850-8). Acad Pr.

Beckett, Royce & Hurt, James. Numerical Calculations & Algorithms. LC 81-20894. 1983. 19.50 (ISBN 0-89874-415-6). Krieger.

Berztiss, A. T. Data Structures: Theory & Practice. 2nd ed. (Computer Science & Applied Mathematics Ser.). 586p. 1975. 24.00i (ISBN 0-12-093552-X). Acad Pr.

Bjorck, Ake & Dahlquist, Germund. Numerical Methods. Anderson, N., tr. (Illus.). 576p. 1974. ref. ed. 42.95 (ISBN 0-13-627315-7). P-H.

Calter, Paul. Mathematics for Computer Technology. (Illus.). 608p. 1986. text ed. 29.95 (ISBN 0-13-562190-9). P-H.

Cheney, Ward & Kincaid, David. Numerical Mathematics & Computing. 2nd ed. LC 84-27420. (Mathematics Ser.). 512p. 1985. text ed. 25.25 pub net (ISBN 0-534-04356-9). Brooks-Cole.

Cheney, Ward E. & Kincaid, David. Numerical Mathematics & Computing. 2nd ed. 400p. 1984. write for info. solutions manual. Wadsworth Pub.

Chytil, M. P., et al. Mathematical Foundations of Computer Science 1984: Praha, Czechoslovakia, September 3-8, 1984. (Lecture Notes in Computer Science Ser.: Vol. 176). xi, 581p. pap. 28.00 (ISBN 0-387-13372-0). Springer-Verlag.

Clifford & Clifford. Computer Mathematics Handbook. 15.95x (ISBN 0-205-04311-9, 2043114). Allyn.

Conley, William C. Computer Optimization Techniques. rev. ed. (Illus.). 350p. 1984. text ed. 29.95 (ISBN 0-89433-213-9). Petrocelli.

Cooke, D. J. & Bez, H. E. Computer Mathematics. LC 83-7588. (Cambridge Computer Science Texts Ser.: No. 18). (Illus.). 425p. 1984. 49.50 (ISBN 0-521-25341-1); pap. 19.95 (ISBN 0-521-27324-2). Cambridge U Pr.

Dew, P. M. & James, K. R. Introduction to Numerical Computation in Pascal. 304p. 1983. pap. 19.00 (ISBN 0-387-91216-9). Springer-Verlag.

Dodes, I. Numerical Analysis for Computer Science. 618p. 1978. text ed. 30.00 (ISBN 0-444-00238-3, North-Holland). Elsevier.

--Numerical Analysis for Computer Science. 618p. 1980. 32.00 (ISBN 0-317-30899-8, North-Holland). Elsevier.

Dorn, William S. & McCracken, Daniel D., eds. Numerical Methods with FORTRAN IV Case Studies. LC 77-37365. 477p. 1972. 44.50 (ISBN 0-471-21918-5). Wiley.

Evans, D. J., ed. Software for Numerical Mathematics. 1974. 73.00 (ISBN 0-12-243750-0). Acad Pr.

Forsythe, George E., et al. Computer Methods for Mathematical Computations. (Illus.). 1977. ref. ed. 41.95 (ISBN 0-13-165332-6). P-H.

Gastinel, Noel. Linear Numerical Analysis. LC 70-108619. 1971. 68.00 (ISBN 0-12-277150-8). Acad Pr.

Gear, C. W. Numerical Initial Value Problems in Ordinary Differential Equations. (Automatic Computation Ser). (Illus.). 1971. ref. ed. 40.00 (ISBN 0-13-626606-1). P-H.

Green, William R. Computer-Aided Data Analysis: A Practical Guide. 256p. 1985. 29.95x (ISBN 0-471-80928-4). Wiley.

Grenander, Ulf. Mathematical Experiments on the Computer. (Pure & Applied Mathematics Ser.). 1982. 44.50 (ISBN 0-12-301750-5). Acad Pr.

Hart, John F., et al. Computer Approximations. LC 77-16187. 352p. 1978. Repr. of 1968 ed. lib. bdg. 22.50 (ISBN 0-88275-642-7). Krieger.

Henrici, P. & Henrici, M. L. Numerical Analysis Demonstrations on the HP-33E. 234p. 1982. pap. 15.00 (ISBN 0-471-05943-9). Wiley.

Henrici, Peter. Computational Analysis with the HP-25 Pocket Calculator. LC 77-1182. 280p. 1977. pap. 26.50 (ISBN 0-471-02938-6, Pub. by Wiley-Interscience). Wiley.

--The Essentials of Numerical Analysis with Pocket Calculator Demonstrations. LC 81-10468. 409p. 1982. text ed. 38.50 (ISBN 0-471-05904-8); avail. solns. manual (ISBN 0-471-09704-7). Wiley.

Iazeolla, G., et al, eds. Mathematical Computer Performance & Reliability: Proceedings of the International Workshop held in Pisa, Italy, 26-30, 1983. 430p. 1984. 50.00 (ISBN 0-444-86892-5). Elsevier.

Jacobs, D., ed. Numerical Software: Needs & Availability. (Institute of Mathematics & Its Applications Conference Ser.). 1978. 45.00 (ISBN 0-12-378660-6). Acad Pr.

James, M. L., et al. Applied Numerical Methods for Digital Computation with FORTRAN & CSMP. 2nd ed. 1977. text ed. 32.50 scp (ISBN 0-7002-2499-8, HarpC); solution manual avail. (ISBN 0-06-363255-1). Har-Row.

Johnston, Robert L. Numerical Methods: A Software Approach. LC 81-12974. 276p. 1981. text ed. 32.50x (ISBN 0-471-09397-1). Wiley.

Kuo, Shan S. Computer Applications of Numerical Methods. LC 78-164654. 1972. text ed. 31.95 (ISBN 0-201-03956-7). Addison-Wesley.

LaFara, Robert L. Computer Methods for Science & Engineering. (Illus.). 1973. 16.10 (ISBN 0-8104-5766-0). Hayden.

Liffick, Blaise W., ed. Numbers in Theory & Practice. (Orig.). 1979. pap. 13.95 (ISBN 0-07-037827-4, BYTE Bks). McGraw.

Linz, Peter. Theoretical Numerical Analysis: An Introduction to Advanced Techniques. LC 78-15178. (Pure & Applied Mathematics: Texts, Monographs & Tracts). 1979. 34.95x (ISBN 0-471-04561-6, Pub. by Wiley-Interscience). Wiley.

Lipschutz, Seymour. Schaum's Outline of Essential Computer Mathematics. 256p. 1982. pap. 9.95 (ISBN 0-07-037990-4). McGraw.

Miller, R. E. & Thatcher, J. W., eds. Complexity of Computer Computations. LC 72-85736. (IBM Research Symposia Ser.). 225p. 1972. 39.50x (ISBN 0-306-30707-3, Plenum Pr). Plenum Pub.

Miller, Webb. The Engineering of Numerical Software. LC 84-9830. (Computational Mathematics Ser.). (Illus.). 192p. 1985. text ed. 33.95 (ISBN 0-13-279043-2). P-H.

Piessens, R., et al. Quadpack: A Subroutine Package for Automatic Integration. (Springer Series in Computational Mathematics: Vol. 1). (Illus.). 301p. 1983. pap. 24.00 (ISBN 0-387-12553-1). Springer-Verlag.

Pizer, Stephen M. Numerical Computing & Mathematical Analysis. (Computer Science Ser). (Illus.). 544p. 1975. text ed. 30.95 (ISBN 0-574-19155-0, 13-4025). SRA.

Pizer, Stephen M. & Wallace, Victor L. To Compute Numerically: Concepts & Strategies. 1982. text ed. 29.95 (ISBN 0-316-70940-9); tchr's manual avail. (ISBN 0-316-70941-7). Little.

Prather, Ronald E. Discrete Mathematical Structures for Computer Science. LC 75-25014. (Illus.). 680p. 1976. text ed. 34.50 (ISBN 0-395-20622-7); solutions manual 3.50 (ISBN 0-395-20623-5). HM.

Rice, John R. Numerical Methods, Software & Analysis. LC 82-24927. 800p. 1983. IMSL Reference Ed. 41.95 (ISBN 0-07-052209-X); IMSL Reference Ed. 20.95 (ISBN 0-07-052208-1). McGraw.

Scalzo, Frank & Hughes, Rowland. A Computer Approach to Introductory College Mathematics. 1977. pap. 15.95 (ISBN 0-442-80434-2). Van Nos Reinhold.

Schendel, U. Introduction to Numerical Methods for Parallel Computers. (Mathematics & Its Applications Ser.). 151p. 1984. 21.95x (ISBN 0-470-20091-X). Halsted Pr.

Schwartz, J. T., ed. Mathematical Aspects of Computer Science: Proceedings of a Symposium, New York City, Apr. 1966. LC 67-16554. (Proceedings of Symposia in Applied Mathematics: Vol. 19). 1978. pap. 20.00 (ISBN 0-8218-1319-6, PSAPM-19). Am Math.

Schwefel, Hans-Paul. Numerical Optimization of Computer Models. LC 81-173223. 389p. 1981. 42.95 (ISBN 0-471-09988-0, Pub. by Wiley-Interscience). Wiley.

Shampine, Lawrence F. & Allen, Richard C. Numerical Computing: An Introduction. LC 72-93122. 258p. 1973. text ed. 20.95 (ISBN 0-7216-8150-6). HR&W.

Shoup, Terry E. Applied Numerical Methods for the Microcomputer. (Illus.). 272p. 1984. text ed. 29.50 (ISBN 0-13-041418-2). P-H.

--Numerical Methods for the Personal Computer. (Illus.). 256p. 1983. pap. text ed. 19.95 (ISBN 0-13-627208-8). P-H.

Smith, J. M. Mathematical Modeling & Digital Simulation for Engineers & Scientists. LC 76-52419. 332p. 1977. 40.50x (ISBN 0-471-80344-8, Pub. by Wiley-Interscience). Wiley.

Society for Industrial & Applied Mathematics - American Mathematical Society Symposia - New York - March, 1971. Computers in Algebra & Number Theory: Proceedings. Birkhoff, Garrett & Hall, Marshall, Jr., eds. LC 76-167685. (SIAM-AMS Proceedings: Vol. 4). 208p. 1980. pap. 19.00 (ISBN 0-8218-1323-4, SIAMS-4). Am Math.

Steklov Institute of Mathematics, Academy of Sciences, U S S R, No. 96. Automatic Programming, Numerical Methods & Functional Analysis: Proceedings. Faddeeva, V. N., ed. (Proceedings of the Steklov Institute of Mathematics: No. 96). 1970. 47.00 (ISBN 0-8218-1896-1, STEKLO-96). Am Math.

Texas Instruments Learning Center Staff. Calculator Analysis for Business & Finance. 288p. 1977. 29.95 (ISBN 0-317-06592-0). Tex Instr Inc.

Thompson, William J. Computing in Applied Science. LC 83-21625. 325p. 1984. text ed. 28.50 (ISBN 0-471-09355-6). Wiley.

Turner, P. R., ed. Topics in Numerical Analysis: Proceedings, S.E.R.C. Summer School, Lancaster, 1981. (Lecture Notes in Mathematics Ser.: Vol. 965). 202p. 1982. pap. 13.00 (ISBN 0-387-11967-1). Springer-Verlag.

Vemuri, V. & Karplus, Walter. Digital Computer Treatment of Partial Differential Equations. (Illus.). 480p. 1981. text ed. 39.95 (ISBN 0-13-212407-6). P-H.

NUMERICAL ANALYSIS LABORATORIES

see Computation Laboratories

NUMERICAL CALCULATIONS

see also Computation Laboratories; Differential Equations–Numerical Solutions; Differential Equations, Linear–Numerical Solutions; Differential Equations, Partial–Numerical Solutions; Digital Filters (Mathematics); Monte Carlo Method

Alefeld, G. & Crigorieff, R. D., eds. Fundamentals of Numerical Computation: International Conference. (Computing Supplementum: No. 2). (Illus.). 250p. 1980. pap. 57.90 (ISBN 0-387-81566-X). Springer-Verlag.

Balakrishna, A. V. & Neustadt, Lucien W., eds. Computing Methods in Optimization Problems: Proceedings. 1964. 55.00 (ISBN 0-12-076950-6). Acad Pr.

Bartholomew-Biggs, Michael. The Essentials of Numerical Computation. (The Hatfield Poytechnic Computer Science Ser.). 241p. (Orig.). 1982. pap. text ed. 19.50x (ISBN 0-86238-029-4, Pub. by Chartwell-Bratt England). Brookfield Pub Co.

Chen, Ching-Chih & Hernon, Peter. Numeric Databases. LC 83-25761. 320p. 1984. pap. 35.00 (ISBN 0-89391-247-6). Ablex Pub.

Faddeeva, V. N. Computational Methods of Linear Algebra. 1959. pap. 7.50 (ISBN 0-486-60424-1). Dover.

Fosdick, L., ed. Performance Evaluation of Numerical Software. 340p. 1979. 42.75 (ISBN 0-444-85330-8, North Holland). Elsevier.

Fox, Leslie. Introduction to Numerical Linear Algebra. (Monographs on Numerical Analysis Ser.). 1965. 19.95x (ISBN 0-19-500325-X). Oxford U Pr.

Furman, T. T. Approximate Methods in Engineering Design. LC 80-40891. (Mathematics in Science & Engineering Ser.). 408p. 1981. 65.00 (ISBN 0-12-269960-2). Acad Pr.

Glowinski, R., et al, eds. Computing Methods in Applied Sciences & Engineering. (Lecture Notes in Economics & Mathematical Systems Ser.: Vol. 134). 1976. soft cover 23.00 (ISBN 0-387-07990-4). Springer-Verlag.

--Computing Methods in Applied Sciences. (Lecture Notes in Physics Ser.: Vol. 58). (Eng. & Fr.). 1976. soft cover 23.00 (ISBN 0-387-08003-1). Springer-Verlag.

Hammerlin, G. & Hoffmann, K. H., eds. Improperly Posed Problems & Their Numerical Treatment. (International Series of Numerical Mathematics: Vol. 63). 264p. 1983. text ed. 24.95 (ISBN 3-7643-1538-5). Birkhauser.

Henrici, Peter. Error Propagation for Difference Methods. LC 76-18838. 82p. 1977. Repr. of 1963 ed. 8.50 (ISBN 0-88275-448-3). Krieger.

Langer, Rudolph Ernest, ed. Frontiers of Numerical Mathematics: A Symposium Conducted by the Mathematics Research Center, United States Army & the National Bureau of Standards at the University of Wisconsin, Madison, Wisconsin, October 30 & 31, 1959. LC 60-60026. (U.S. Army Mathematical Research Center Publication Ser.: No. 4). pap. 36.00 (ISBN 0-317-08424-0, 2004656). Bks Demand UMI.

Marchuk, G. I. Differential Equations & Numerical Mathematics: Proceedings of a U. S. S. R. Council of Ministers for Science & Technology, Moscow. LC 81-81912. (Illus.). 176p. 1982. 55.00 (ISBN 0-08-026491-3, D120). Pergamon.

Milne, W. E. Numerical Calculus. 1949. 40.00x (ISBN 0-691-08011-9). Princeton U Pr.

Reid, K. Relationship Between Numerical Computation & Programming Language. 378p. 1982. 32.00 (ISBN 0-444-86377-X, North-Holland). Elsevier.

Richtmyer, Robert D. & Morton, K. W. Difference Methods for Initial-Value Problems. 2nd ed. LC 67-13959. (Pure & Applied Mathematics Ser.). (Illus.). 405p. 1967. 53.50 (ISBN 0-470-72040-9, Pub. by Wiley-Interscience). Wiley.

Rozsa, P., ed. Numerical Methods. (Colloquia Mathematica Ser.: Vol. 22). 632p. 1980. 93.75 (ISBN 0-444-85407-X, North-Holland). Elsevier.

Society for Industrial & Applied Mathematics-American Mathematical Society Symposia-N.C.-April, 1968. Numerical Solution of Field Problems in Continuum Physics: Proceedings. Birkhoff, G. & Varga, R. S., eds. LC 75-92659. (SIAM-AMS Proceedings: Vol. 2). 1970. 27.00 (ISBN 0-8218-1321-8, SIAMS-2). Am Math.

Stiefel, E. L. Introduction to Numerical Mathematics. Rheinboldt, W. C., tr. 1963. 29.50 (ISBN 0-12-671150-X); problem bklt. o.p. free (ISBN 0-685-05133-1). Acad Pr.

Symposium at the Centre for Research in Mathematics, University of Montreal, Sept., 1971. Applications of Number Theory to Numerical Analysis: Proceedings. Zaremba, S. K., ed. 1972. 64.50 (ISBN 0-12-775950-6). Acad Pr.

Symposium in Applied Mathematics-Atlantic City & Chicago-1962. Experimental Arithmetic, High Speed Computing & Mathematics: Proceedings. Metropolis, N. C., et al, eds. LC 63-17582. (Proceedings of Symposia in Applied Mathematics: Vol. 15). 1963. 27.00 (ISBN 0-8218-1315-3, PSAPM-15). Am Math.

Thompson, J. F., ed. Numerical Grid Generation: Proceedings of the Symposium on the Numerical Generation of Curvilenear Coordinate Systems & Use in the Numerical Solution of Partial Differential Equations, Nashville, Tennessee, April 13-16, 1982. 944p. 1982. 95.00 (ISBN 0-444-00757-1, North Holland). Elsevier.

Todd, John. Basic Numerical Mathematics, Vol. 2: Numerical Algebra. 1978. 32.50 (ISBN 0-12-692402-3). Acad Pr.

Watson, G. A. Approximation Theory & Numerical Methods. LC 79-42725. 229p. 1980. 34.95 (ISBN 0-471-27706-1, Pub. by Wiley-Interscience). Wiley.

Zienkiewicz, O. C., et al, eds. Numerical Methods in Offshore Engineering. LC 77-12565. (Numerical Methods in Engineering Ser.). 582p. 1978. 115.95x (ISBN 0-471-99591-6, Pub. by Wiley-Interscience). Wiley.

NUMERICAL FILTERS

see Digital Filters (Mathematics)

NUMERICAL INTEGRATION

Anderson, Norman H. Foundations of Information Integration Theory: Foundations, Vol. 1. LC 80-1769. (Information Integration Ser.). 1981. 44.00 (ISBN 0-12-058101-9). Acad Pr.

Antoine, Jean-Pierre & Tirapegui, Enrique, eds. Functional Integration: Theory & Application. LC 80-21935. 365p. 1980. 55.00x (ISBN 0-306-40573-3, Plenum Pr). Plenum Pub.

Arthurs, A. M. & Bhagavan, M. R., eds. Functional Integration & Its Applications. 1975. 68.00x (ISBN 0-19-853346-2). Oxford U Pr.

Constantinescu, Corneliu, et al. Integration Theory: Measure & Integral, Vol. I. (Pure & Applied Mathematics Ser.). 576p. 1985. text ed. 48.50x (ISBN 0-471-04479-2, Pub. by Wiley-Interscience). Wiley.

Davis, Philip J. & Rabinowitz, Philip. Methods of Numerical Integration. 2nd ed. LC 83-13522. (Computer Science & Mathematics Monograph). 1984. 52.00 (ISBN 0-12-206360-0). Acad Pr.

Dollard, John D. & Friedman, Charles N. Encyclopedia of Mathematics & Its Applications: Product Integration with Applications to Differential Equations, Vol. 10. 1984. 39.50 (ISBN 0-521-30230-7). Cambridge U Pr.

Engels, H. Numerical Quadrature & Cubature. LC 79-41235. (Computational Mathematics and Application Ser.). 1980. 74.00 (ISBN 0-12-238850-X). Acad Pr.

Fichtenholz, G. M. The Definite Integral. Silverman, R. A., tr. from Rus. LC 78-149513. (Pocket Mathematical Library Ser.). (Illus.). 98p. 1973. 30.25 (ISBN 0-677-21090-6). Gordon.

Ghizzetti, A. & Ossicini, A. Quadrature Formulae. 1970. 43.50 (ISBN 0-12-281750-8). Acad Pr.

Hammerlin, G., ed. Numerical Integration. (International Series of Numerical Mathematics: Vol. 57). 275p. text ed. 31.95x (ISBN 0-8176-1254-8). Birkhauser.

Hammerlin, Gunther. Numerische Integration. (Internationale Schriftenreihe zur Numerischen Mathematik: No. 45). (Ger. & Eng.). 320p. 1979. pap. 34.95 (ISBN 0-8176-1014-6). Birkhauser.

Hinze, J., ed. Numerical Integration of Differential Equations & Large Linear Systems: Proceedings, Bielefeld, FRG, 1980. (Lecture Notes in Mathematics: Vol. 968). 412p. 1982. pap. 22.00 (ISBN 0-387-11970-1). Springer-Verlag.

Janssen, A. J. & Van der Steen, P. Integration Theory. (Lecture Notes in Mathematics Ser.: Vol. 1078). v, 224p. 1984. pap. 13.50 (ISBN 0-387-13386-0). Springer-Verlag.

McShane, E. J. Order-Preserving Maps & Integration Processes. (Annals of Mathematics Studies). Repr. of 1953 ed. 11.00 (ISBN 0-527-02747-2). Kraus Repr.

Pitt, H. R. Measure & Integration for Use. (Institute of Mathematics & Its Applications Monograph). 156p. 1985. 17.95 (ISBN 0-19-853608-9). Oxford U Pr.

Rao, M. M. Stochastic Processes & Integration. 467p. 1981. 55.00x (ISBN 90-286-0438-3). Sijthoff & Noordhoff.

Smith, H. V. Tables for Numerical Integration. 1982. pap. text ed. 5.95x (ISBN 0-02-852670-8). Macmillan.

NUMERICAL SEQUENCES

see Sequences (Mathematics)

NUMERICAL WEATHER FORECASTING

Haltiner, G. J. & Williams, R. T. Numerical Prediction & Dynamic Meteorology. 2nd ed. 477p. 1980. 44.00x (ISBN 0-471-05971-4). Wiley.

NURSERIES (HORTICULTURE)

see also Plant Propagation

Berninger, Louis M. Profitable Garden Center Management. 2nd ed. (Illus.). 1981. 20.95 (ISBN 0-8359-5633-4); instrs's manual avail. (ISBN 0-8359-5634-2). Reston.

Davidson, Harold & Mechlenburg, Roy. Nursery Management: Administration & Culture. (Illus.). 464p. 1981. text ed. 29.95 (ISBN 0-13-627455-2). P-H.

Selected Papers in Greenhouse & Nursery Engineering. 117p. 1984. 30.00 (ISBN 0-317-06801-6). Am Soc Ag Eng.

Selected Papers in Greenhouse & Nursery Mechanization Concepts. 112p. 1984. 27.00 (ISBN 0-317-06802-4). Am Soc Ag Eng.

Toogood, Alan & Stanley, John. The Modern Nurseryman. (Illus.). 432p. 1981. 32.95 (ISBN 0-571-11544-6); pap. 16.95 (ISBN 0-571-11547-0). Faber & Faber.

Williams, George S. Nursery Crops & Landscape Designs for Agribusiness Studies. 2nd ed. 1984. text ed. 9.75x; pap. 13.00 (ISBN 0-8134-2310-4). Interstate.

NURSERY STOCK

see also Nurseries (Horticulture); Shrubs; Trees

Lamb, Kelly & Lamb, Bowbrick. Nursery Stock Manual. 300p. 1981. 30.00x (ISBN 0-686-75420-4, Pub. by Grower Bks). State Mutual Bk.

NURSES AND NURSING–DATA PROCESSING

Corbett, Nancy A. & Beveridge, Phyllis. Computer Simulations for Clinical Nursing, Vol. 2. 1984. Apple II version. 495.00 (ISBN 0-7216-1343-8); IBM-PC version. 495.00 (ISBN 0-7216-1368-3). Saunders.

--Computer Simulations in Clinical Nursing, Vol. 1. 1984. Apple II Complete Package. 495.00 (ISBN 0-7216-1023-4); Apple II. additional wkbk. 9.95 (ISBN 0-7216-1154-0); IBM-PC Version. 495.00 (ISBN 0-7216-1365-9). Saunders.

Grobe, Susan J. Computer Primer & Resource for Nurses. (Illus.). 180p. 1984. pap. text ed. 9.75 (ISBN 0-397-54485-5, Lippincott Nursing). Lippincott.

Pocklington, Dorothy B. & Guttman, Linda. Nursing Reference for Computer Literature. LC 64-4271. 1984. pap. text ed. 12.95 (ISBN 0-397-54487-1, Lippincott Nursing). Lippincott.

Saba, Virginia K. & McCormick, Kathleen. Essentials of Computers for Nurses. (Illus.). 548p. 1985. pap. text ed. price not set (ISBN 0-397-54457-X, Lippincott Nursing). Lippincott.

St. Lawrence, Kathleen. Computerized Clinical Nursing Reference Information System. (Illus., Orig.). 1985. pap. text ed. 24.95 (ISBN 0-916207-10-2). Oryn Pubns Inc.

Walker. What Every Nurse Should Know about Computers. LC 64-4420. 1984. 9.75 (ISBN 0-397-54502-9, Lippincott Nursing). Lippincott.

NUTATION

I.A.U. Symposium No. 78, Kiev, USSR, May 23-28, 1977, et al. Nutation & the Earth's Rotation: Proceedings. Smith, M. L. & Bender, P. L., eds. 284p. 1980. lib. bdg. 34.00 (ISBN 90-277-1113-5, Pub. by Reidel Holland); pap. 21.00 (ISBN 90-277-1114-3). Kluwer Academic.

Klein, Felix. Ueber Die Theorie Des Kreisels. 1965. 60.00 (ISBN 0-384-29720-X). Johnson Repr.

NUTHATCHES

Bent, Arthur C. Life Histories of North American Nuthatches, Wrens, Thrashers & Their Allies. (Illus.). 1948. pap. 9.95 (ISBN 0-486-21088-X). Dover.

--Life Histories of North American Nuthatches, Wrens, Thrashers & Their Allies. (Illus.). 14.75 (ISBN 0-8446-1640-0). Peter Smith.

NUTRITION

see also Absorption (Physiology); Animal Nutrition; Diet; Feeds; Food; Metabolism; Minerals in the Body; Vitamins

also subdivision Nutrition under subjects, e.g. Children–Nutrition

Abelson, Philip H., ed. Food: Politics, Economics, Nutrition & Research. LC 75-18785. (Science Compendium Ser.: Vol. 2). (Illus.). 1975. casebound 10.00 (ISBN 0-87168-215-X). AAAS.

Abraham, Sidney, et al. Caloria & Selected Nutrient Values of Persons Age 1-74 Years, U. S., 1971-74. Stevenson, Taloria, ed. (Ser. 11: No. 209). 1978. pap. 1.50 (ISBN 0-8406-0147-6). Natl Ctr Health Stats.

Abravnel, Elliot D. & King, Elizabeth A. Dr. Abravnel's Body Type Diet & Lifetime Nutrition Plan. 256p. 1984. pap. 3.95 (ISBN 0-553-23973-2). Bantam.

Acciardo, Marcia. Light Eating for Survival. (Illus.). 106p. (Orig.). 1978. pap. text ed. 5.95 (ISBN 0-933278-05-5). Twen Fir Cent.

Adams, Ruth & Murray, Frank. Megavitamin Therapy. 286p. (Orig.). 1973. pap. 3.95 (ISBN 0-915962-03-9). Larchmont Bks.

--Minerals: Kill or Cure. rev. ed. 368p. (Orig.). 1974. pap. 1.95 (ISBN 0-915962-16-0). Larchmont Bks.

--Seeds, Grains, Nuts. 1.75x (ISBN 0-915962-07-1). Cancer Control Soc.

Addleman, Frank G. The Winning Edge: Nutrition for Athletic Fitness & Performances. 228p. 1984. 16.95 (ISBN 0-13-961145-2); pap. 7.95 (ISBN 0-13-961137-1). P-H.

Adrian, J., ed. Dictionary of Food, Nutrition & Biochemsitry. (Illus.). 240p. 1985. 29.00 (ISBN 0-89573-404-4, Pub. by Ellis Horwood Ltd UK). VCH Pubs.

Aebi, H., et al. Problems in Nutrition Research Today. LC 81-66375. 1981. 33.00 (ISBN 0-12-044420-8). Acad Pr.

Ahnefeld, F. W., et al, eds. Parenteral Nutrition. Babad, A., tr. from Ger. LC 75-34213. (Illus.). 200p. 1975. pap. 21.00 (ISBN 0-387-07518-6). Springer-Verlag.

Aihara, Herman. Acid & Alkaline. 2nd ed. (Orig.). 1980. pap. 2.50 (ISBN 0-918860-35-0). G Ohsawa.

Alfin-Slater, Roslyn & Kritchevsky, David, eds. Human Nutrition-A Comprehensive Treatise, Vol. 3A: Nutrition & the Adult-Macronutrients. LC 79-25119. (Illus.). 308p. 1980. 35.00x (ISBN 0-306-40287-4, Plenum Pr). Plenum Pub.

--Human Nutrition-A Comprehensive Treatise, Vol. 3B: Nutrition & the Adult-Micronutrients. LC 79-3888. (Illus.). 450p. 1980. 49.50x (ISBN 0-306-40288-2, Plenum Pr). Plenum Pub.

Alfin-Slater, Roslyn B. & Aftergood, Lilla. Nutrition for Today. (Contemporary Topics in Health Science Ser). 64p. 1973. pap. text ed. write for info. (ISBN 0-697-07340-8). Wm C Brown.

Alford, Betty B. & Bogle, Margaret L. Nutrition During the Life Cycle. 384p. 1982. 29.95 (ISBN 0-13-627810-8). P-H.

Ali, Shahrazad. How Not to Eat Pork: Or Life Without the Pig. LC 85-70171. (Illus.). 120p. (Orig.). 1985. pap. 5.95 (ISBN 0-933405-00-6). Civilized Pubns.

Anderson, Linnea, et al. Nutrition in Health & Disease. 17th ed. (Illus.). 794p. 1982. text ed. 26.50 (ISBN 0-397-54282-8, 64-02085, Lippincott Nursing). Lippincott.

Arab, L., et al. Nutrition & Health. (Illus.). xviii, 244p. 1982. pap. 20.50 (ISBN 3-8055-3465-5). S Karger.

Arlin, Marian T. The Science of Nutrition. 2nd ed. (Illus.). 352p. 1977. text ed. write for info. (ISBN 0-02-303840-3, 30384). Macmillan.

Arnold O. Beckman Conference in Clinical Chemical. Human Nutrition: Clinical & Biochemical Aspects: Proceedings. Garry, Philip J., ed. LC 81-65736. 405p. 1981. 35.00 (ISBN 0-915274-15-9); members 25.00. Am Assn Clinical Chem.

Arnott, Marilyn S., et al, eds. Molecular Interrelations of Nutrition & Cancer. (M. D. Anderson Symposium on Fundamental Cancer Research Ser.: 34th Annual). 490p. 1982. text ed. 83.50 (ISBN 0-89004-701-4). Raven.

Arnow, E. Earle. Food Power: A Doctor's Guide to Common Sense Nutrition. LC 75-185419. (Illus.). 305p. 1972. 19.95x (ISBN 0-911012-37-0). Nelson-Hall.

Aronson, Virginia & Fitzgerald, Barbara. Guidebook for Nutrition Counselors. 484p. 1980. 19.50 (ISBN 0-8158-0387-7). Chris Mass.

Asahina, K. & Shigiya, R., eds. Physiological Adaptability & Nutritional Status of the Japanese (B, Vol. 4. (Japan International Biological Program Synthesis Ser.). 250p. 1975. 32.50x (ISBN 0-86008-214-8, Pub. by U of Tokyo Japan). Columbia U Pr.

Ashley, Richard & Duggal, Heidi. Dictionary of Nutrition. 1983. pap. 3.50 (ISBN 0-671-49407-4). PB.

Ashmead, Dewayne. Chelated Mineral Nutrition in Plants, Animals, & Man. (Illus.). 346p. 1982. 38.75x (ISBN 0-398-04603-4). C C Thomas.

Atkins, Robert. Nutrition Breakthrough. 1979. 12.95x (ISBN 0-688-03644-9); pap. 3.50x (ISBN 0-553-20279-0). Cancer Control Soc.

Atkins, Robert C. Dr. Atkins Nutrition Breakthrough: How to Treat Your Medical Condition Without Drugs. 1982. pap. 3.50 (ISBN 0-553-20279-0). Bantam.

Austin, James E., ed. Nutrition Programs in the Third World: Cases & Readings. LC 80-21083. 480p. 1981. text ed. 35.00 (ISBN 0-89946-024-0). Oelgeschlager.

Austin, James E. & Zeitlin, Marian F., eds. Nutrition Intervention in Developing Countries: An Overview. LC 80-29223. (Nutrition Intervention in Developing Countries Ser.). 256p. 1981. text ed. 35.00 (ISBN 0-89946-077-1). Oelgeschlager.

Aykroyd, W. R. & Doughty, Joyce. Legumes in Human Nutrition. 2nd ed. (Food & Nutrition Papers: No. 20). (Eng., Fr. & Span.). 160p. 1982. pap. 11.75 (ISBN 92-5-101181-8, F2329, FAO). Unipub.

Aykroyo, W. R. & Doughty, J. Legumes in Human Nutrition. (Nutritional Studies: No. 19). 138p. (5th Printing 1977). 1964. pap. 7.25 (ISBN 92-5-100440-4, F257, FAO). Unipub.

Bauer, Cathy & Andersen, Juel. The Tofu Cookbook. 1979. 9.95 (ISBN 0-87857-246-5). Rodale Pr Inc.

Beaton, G. H. & McHenry, E. W., eds. Nutrition: A Comprehensive Treatise, 3 vols. Incl. Vol. 1. Macronutrients & Nutrient Elements. 1964. 85.50 (ISBN 0-12-084101-0); Vol. 2. Vitamins, Nutrient Requirements & Food Selections. 1964. 85.50 (ISBN 0-12-084102-9); Vol. 3. Nutritional Status: Assessment & Application. 1966. 73.00 (ISBN 0-12-084103-7). Acad Pr.

Beeson, Kenneth & Matrone, Gennard. The Soil Factor in Nutrition: Animal & Human. (Nutrition & Clinical Nutrition Ser.: Vol. 2). 1976. 39.75 (ISBN 0-8247-6484-6). Dekker.

Beiler, Henry. Food Is Your Best Medicine. pap. 2.95x (ISBN 0-394-71837-2). Cancer Control Soc.

Bender. Dictionary of Nutrition & Food Techonology. 5th ed. 1983. text ed. 34.95. Butterworth.

Bender, Arnold. Food Processing & Nutrition. (Food Science & Technology Ser.). 1978. 41.50 (ISBN 0-12-086450-9). Acad Pr.

Berg, Alan. The Nutrition Factor: Its Role in National Development. 1973. 22.95 (ISBN 0-8157-0914-5); pap. 8.95 (ISBN 0-8157-0913-7). Brookings.

Bernard, Raymond. Nutritional Methods of Blood Regeneration, Pt. 1. 53p. 1960. pap. 8.95 (ISBN 0-88697-037-7). Life Science.

Bickel, H. & Schutz, Y., eds. Digestion & Absorption of Nutrients. (International Journal for Vitamin & Nutrition Research, Supplement: No. 25). (Illus.). 94p. (Orig.). 1983. pap. 15.00 (ISBN 3-456-81335-X, Pub. by Hans Huber). J K Burgess.

Bieler, H. G. Food Is Your Best Medicine. 256p. 1982. pap. 2.95 (ISBN 0-345-30190-0). Ballantine.
Bijlani, L. Eating Scientifically. 188p. 1979. 30.00x (ISBN 0-86125-049-4, Pub. by Orient Longman India). State Mutual Bk.
Birch, G. G. & Parker, K. J., eds. Food & Health: Science & Technology. (Illus.). xii, 532p. 1976. 76.00 (ISBN 0-85334-875-8, Pub. by Elsevier Applied Sci England). Elsevier.
Birch, G. G., et al, eds. Health & Food. 224p. 1972. 24.00 (ISBN 0-85334-558-9, Pub. by Elsevier Applied Sci England). Elsevier.
Bland, Jeffery. Nutraerobics: The Complete Individualized Nutrition & Fitness Program for Life after 30. LC 83-47716. 320p. 1983. 16.30 (ISBN 0-06-250053-8, HarpR). Har-Row.
Bland, Jeffrey. Bioflavonoids. Mindell, Earl & Passwater, Richard, eds. (Good Health Guides Ser.). 26p. 1984. pap. 1.45 (ISBN 0-87983-330-0). Keats.
--Octacosanol, Carnitine, & Other "Accessory" Nutrients. Passwater, Richard A. & Mindell, Earl, eds. (Good Health Guide Ser.). 36p. 1982. pap. text ed. 1.45 (ISBN 0-87983-316-5). Keats.
Blaxter, K., ed. Food, Nutrition & Climate. Fowden, L. (Illus.). 422p. 1982. 72.25 (ISBN 0-85334-107-9, Pub. by Elsevier Applied Sci England). Elsevier.
Bloch, Abby & Margie, Joyce D. Nutrition & the Cancer Patient. LC 81-70351. 269p. 1983. pap. 11.95 (ISBN 0-8019-7120-9). Chilton.
Board on Agriculture & Renewable Resources. Nutrient Requirements of Non-Human Primates. 83p. 1978. pap. 6.50 (ISBN 0-309-02786-1). Natl Acad Pr.
Bodwell, C. E. Evaluation of Proteins for Humans. (Illus.). 1977. lib. bdg. 56.50 (ISBN 0-87055-215-5). AVI.
Bolton, Edward R. Oils, Fats & Fatty Foods: Their Practical Examination. 4th ed. Williams, K. A., ed. LC 67-73132. pap. 124.00 (ISBN 0-317-09891-8, 2004594). Bks Demand UMI.
Borsook, Henry. Vitamins: What They Are. (Orig.). pap. 2.50 (ISBN 0-515-05834-3). Jove Pubns.
Bourne, G. H., ed. Human & Animal Nutrition. (World Review of Nutrition & Dietetics: Vol. 32). (Illus.). 1978. 63.00 (ISBN 3-8055-2855-8). S Karger.
--Human & Veterinary Nutrition. (World Review of Nutrition & Dietetics: Vol. 26). (Illus.). 1977. 70.75 (ISBN 3-8055-2392-0). S Karger.
--Human & Veterinary Nutrition, Biochemical Aspects of Nutrients. (World Review of Nutrition & Dietetics: Vol. 30). (Illus.). 1978. 63.00 (ISBN 3-8055-2789-6). S Karger.
--Human Nutrition & Animal Feeding. (World Review of Nutrition & Dietetics: Vol. 37). (Illus.). xii, 292p. 1981. 105.25 (ISBN 3-8055-2143-X). S Karger.
--Human Nutrition & Nutrition & Pesticides in Cattle. (World Review of Nutrition & Dietetics: Vol. 35). (Illus.). 238p. 1980. 81.75 (ISBN 3-8055-0442-X). S Karger.
--Nutrients & Energy. (World Review of Nutrition & Dietetics: Vol. 42). (Illus.). xii, 228p. 1983. 84.25 (ISBN 3-8055-3710-7). S Karger.
--Nutrition Education & Modern Concepts of Food Assimilation. (World Review of Nutrition & Dietetics: Vol. 40). (Illus.). xii, 192p. 1982. 69.50 (ISBN 3-8055-3519-8). S Karger.
--Nutrition in Disease & Development. (World Review of Nutrition & Dietetics: Vol. 39). (Illus.). x, 194p. 1982. 68.25 (ISBN 3-8055-3459-0). S Karger.
--Nutritional Considerations in a Changing World. (World Review of Nutrition & Dietetics: Vol. 44). (Illus.). x, 218p. 1984. 70.25 (ISBN 3-8055-3837-5). S Karger.
--World Review of Nutrition & Dietetics, Vol. 12. 1970. 81.75 (ISBN 3-8055-0663-5). S Karger.
--World Review of Nutrition & Dietetics, Vol. 13. 1971. 41.75 (ISBN 3-8055-1180-9). S Karger.
--World Review of Nutrition & Dietetics, Vol. 14. 1972. 57.25 (ISBN 3-8055-1282-1). S Karger.
--World Review of Nutrition & Dietetics, Vol. 15. (Illus.). 300p. 1972. 48.75 (ISBN 3-8055-1397-6). S Karger.
--World Review of Nutrition & Dietetics, Vol. 17. (Illus.). 300p. 1973. 61.50 (ISBN 3-8055-1336-4). S Karger.
--World Review of Nutrition & Dietetics, Vol. 18. 1973. 99.00 (ISBN 3-8055-1458-1). S Karger.
--World Review of Nutrition & Dietetics, Vol. 19. (Illus.). 319p. 1974. 70.25 (ISBN 3-8055-1589-8). S Karger.
--World Review of Nutrition & Dietetics, Vol. 21. (Illus.). x, 327p. 1975. 81.00 (ISBN 3-8055-2133-2). S Karger.
--World Review of Nutrition & Dietetics, Vol. 22. (Illus.). 1975. 84.25 (ISBN 3-8055-2135-9). S Karger.
--World Review of Nutrition & Dietetics, Vol. 23. (Illus.). xii, 315p. 1975. 75.75 (ISBN 3-8055-2243-6). S Karger.
--World Review of Nutrition & Dietetics, Vol. 24. (Illus.). 250p. 1976. 64.75 (ISBN 3-8055-2344-0). S Karger.
--World Review of Nutrition & Dietetics, Vol. 25. (Illus.). 300p. 1976. 73.25 (ISBN 3-8055-2363-7). S Karger.
--World Review of Nutrition & Dietetics, Vol. 37: Human Nutrition & Animal Feeding. (Illus.). xii, 292p. 1981. 105.25 (ISBN 3-8055-2143-X). S Karger.
--World Review of Nutrition & Dietetics, Vol. 38: Physiology & Social Nutrition & Nutritional Education. (Illus.). x, 230p. 1981. 69.50 (ISBN 3-8055-3048-X). S Karger.
Bourne, G. H. & Cama, H. R., eds. Vitamin & Carrier Functions of Polyprenoids. (World Review of Nutrition & Dietetrics: Vol. 31). (Illus.). 1978. 58.75 (ISBN 3-8055-2801-9). S Karger.
Bourne, Geoffrey H., ed. Some Aspects of Human & Veterinary Nutrition. (World Review of Nutrition & Dietetics: Vol. 28). 1978. 68.75 (ISBN 3-8055-2672-5). S Karger.
--Some Special Aspects of Nutrition. (World Review of Nutrition & Dietetics: Vol. 33). (Illus.). 1979. 67.25 (ISBN 3-8055-2942-2). S Karger.
Bourne, H. C., ed. Some Aspects of Human Nutrition. (World Review of Nutrition & Dietetics: Vol. 27). 1977. 48.75 (ISBN 3-8055-2393-9). S Karger.
Boykin-Stith, Lorraine & D'Angelo, Rosemary. A Comprehensive Review of Clinical Nutrition. LC 81-50667. 121p. 1981. pap. 14.95x (ISBN 0-938860-02-X). Westville Pub Co.
Boykin-Stith, Lorraine & Williams, Barbara K. A Comprehensive Review of Nutrition. LC 80-54647. 155p. (Orig.). 1980. pap. 14.95x (ISBN 0-938860-00-3). Westville Pub Co.
Bradshaw, Lois E. & Mazlen, Roger G. Nutrition in Health Care. LC 79-89882. 1979. pap. 6.95 (ISBN 0-917634-06-3). Creative Infomatics.
Bragg, Paul. Toxicless Diet - Purification. 1.75x (ISBN 0-686-29873-X). Cancer Control Soc.
Bragg, Paul C. & Bragg, Patricia. Healthful Eating Without Confusion. 11th ed. LC 71-152392. pap. 4.95 (ISBN 0-87790-024-8). Health Sci.
--Shocking Truth About Water. 24th ed. LC 77-101348. pap. 4.95 (ISBN 0-87790-000-0). Health Sci.
Brandt, Johanna. The Grape Cure. 2.00x (ISBN 0-686-29874-8). Cancer Control Soc.
Brennen, R. O. Nutrigenetics: Relieving Hypoglycemia. 8.95x (ISBN 0-87131-187-9). Cancer Control Soc.
Brisson, Germain J. Lipids in Human Nutrition. LC 81-17013. (Illus.). 200p. 1981. text ed. 22.50 (ISBN 0-937218-12-X). J K Burgess.
Brody, Jane. Jane Brody's Nutrition Book: A Lifetime Guide to Good Eating for Better Health & Weight Control by the Personal Health Columnist for the New York Times. LC 80-25117. (Illus.). 576p. 1981. 12.98 (ISBN 0-393-01429-0). Norton.
Bronfen, Nan. Nutrition for a Better Life: A Sourcebook for the 80's. LC 80-17326. (Illus.). 240p. (Orig.). 1980. pap. 8.95 (ISBN 0-88496-152-4). Capra Pr.
Bunnelle, Hasse. Food for Knapsackers & Other Trail Travellers. LC 74-162395. (Totebooks Ser.). 144p. 1971. pap. 4.95 (ISBN 0-87156-049-6). Sierra.
Burk, Dean. Vitamin B17, B15, Brief Foods-Vitamins. 1.50 (ISBN 0-686-29881-0). Cancer Control Soc.
Burkitt, Dennis. Eat Right to Stay Healthy. 1979. 5.95x (ISBN 0-668-04682-1). Cancer Control Soc.
Calabrese, Edward J. Nutrition & Environmental Health: The Influence of Nutritional Status on Pollutant Toxicity & Carcinogenicity, 2 vols. Incl. Vol. 1. The Vitamins. 91.95 (ISBN 0-471-04833-X); Vol. 2. Minerals & Macronutrients. 544p. 74.95 (ISBN 0-471-08207-4). LC 9-21089. (Environmental Science & Technology Ser.). 1980 (Pub. by Wiley-Interscience). Wiley.
Calcium Requirements: Report of a WHO Expert Group, Rome, 1961. (Nutrition Meetings Reports: No. 30). 54p. 1962. pap. 4.75 (ISBN 0-686-93129-7, F86, FAO). Unipub.
Caliendo, Mary A. The Nutrition Crisis: Alternatives for Change. (Illus.). 1979. pap. text ed. write for info. (ISBN 0-02-318340-3). Macmillan.
Carbohydrates in Human Nutrition: A Joint WHO Report. (Food & Nutrition Papers: No. 15). (Eng., Fr. & Span.). 89p. (2nd Printing 1983). 1980. pap. 7.50 (ISBN 92-5-100903-1, F2040, FAO). Unipub.
Carlin, Joseph M. A Food Service Guide to the Nutrition Program for the Elderly. rev. ed. 1975. pap. text ed. 6.50 (ISBN 0-89634-013-9, 023). Systems Planning.
Chandra, R. K. & Newberne, P. M. Nutrition, Immunity & Infection: Mechanisms of Interaction. LC 77-21209. (Illus.). 262p. 1977. 29.50x (ISBN 0-306-31058-9, Plenum Pr). Plenum Pub.
Chandra, R. K., ed. Progress in Food & Nutrition Science. (Illus.). 198p. 1984. pap. 84.00 (ISBN 0-08-030928-3). Pergamon.
Chaney, Margaret S., et al. Nutrition. 9th ed. LC 78-69546. (Illus.). 1979. text ed. 31.95 (ISBN 0-395-25448-5). HM.
Charley, Helen. Food Science. 2nd ed. LC 81-11366. 564p. 1982. 29.00 (ISBN 0-471-06206-5); text ed. 26.95 (ISBN 0-471-06160-3). Wiley.
Cheraskin, E. & Ringsdorf, W. Diet & Disease. 7.95x (ISBN 0-87983-143-X). Cancer Control Soc.
Chicago Dietetic Association & South Suburban Dietetic Association. Manual of Clinical Dietetics. LC 80-53899. 1981. text ed. 25.00 (ISBN 0-7216-2537-1); physician's guide 29.95 (ISBN 0-7216-2539-8). Saunders.
Chomicki, William P. Your Secret to Vibrant Good Health. 1984. 4.95 (ISBN 0-8062-1802-9). Carlton.
Chrispeels, Maarten J. & Sadava, David. Plants, Food, & People. LC 76-46498. (Illus.). 278p. 1977. text ed. 25.95 (ISBN 0-7167-0378-5); pap. text ed. 13.95 (ISBN 0-7167-0377-7). W H Freeman.
Christakis, George, ed. Nutritional Assessment in Health Programs. LC 74-120960. 90p. 1973. 6.00x (ISBN 0-87553-116-4, 070). Am Pub Health.
Church, D. C., ed. Digestive Physiology & Nutrition of Ruminants: Nutrition, Vol. 2. 2nd ed. 1979. text ed. 27.50x (ISBN 0-9601586-5-0). O & B Bks.
Clark, Linda. Light on Your Health Problems. LC 72-83522. (Pivot Original Health Book). 240p. 1972. pap. 1.50 (ISBN 0-87983-026-3). Keats.
Clydesdale, Fergus. Food Science & Nutrition: Current Issues & Answers. (Illus.). 1979. ref. 22.95. P-H.
Clydesdale, Fergus S. & Francis, F. J. Food, Nutrition & You. (Illus.). 1977. lib. bdg. 17.95 (ISBN 0-13-323048-1); pap. text ed. 16.95 (ISBN 0-13-323030-9). P-H.
Commission on International Relations. World Food & Nutrition Study: Supporting Papers, 5 vols. 1977. Vol. I. pap. 8.25 (ISBN 0-309-02647-4); Vol. II. pap. 8.25 (ISBN 0-309-02726-8); Vol. III. pap. 8.50 (ISBN 0-309-02730-6); Vol. IV. pap. 7.50 (ISBN 0-309-02727-6); Vol. V. pap. 7.50 (ISBN 0-309-02646-6). Natl Acad Pr.
Corbin, Cheryl. Nutrition. LC 80-11138. (Illus.). 208p. 1981. pap. 8.95 (ISBN 0-03-048276-3, Owl Bks.). HR&W.
Cordingley, E. W. Principles & Practice of Naturopathy. 25p. 1971. pap. 2.95 (ISBN 0-88697-034-2). Life Science.
Correa, Hector & El Torky, Mohamed A. The Biological & Social Determinants of the Demographic Transition. LC 82-16042. (Illus.). 298p. (Orig.). 1983. lib. bdg. 27.50 (ISBN 0-8191-2754-X); pap. text ed. 13.50 (ISBN 0-8191-2755-8). U Pr of Amer.
Crisp, Arthur H. & Stonehill, Edward. Sleep, Nutrition & Mood. LC 75-16121. 173p. 1976. 48.95 (ISBN 0-471-18688-0, Pub. by Wiley-Interscience). Wiley.
Cunningham, John J. Contemporary Clinical Nutrition: A Conspectus. 288p. 1985. pap. text ed. 19.95 (ISBN 0-89313-068-0). G F Stickley Co.
--Introduction to Nutritional Physiology. (Illus.). 400p. 1983. 22.95x (ISBN 0-89313-031-1); text ed. 22.95x (ISBN 0-686-38084-3). G F Stickley.
Cureton, Thomas K. The Physiological Effects of Wheat Germ Oil on Humans in Exercise: Forty-Two Physical Training Programs Utilizing 894 Humans. (Illus.). 552p. 1972. 47.50x (ISBN 0-398-02270-4). C C Thomas.
Dadd, Debra L., et al. Nutritional Analysis System: A Physician's Manual for Evaluation of Therapeutic Diets. 154p. 1982. pap. 19.50x spiral (ISBN 0-398-04681-6). C C Thomas.
Daly, Katherine M., et al. Nutrition & Eating Problems of Oral & Head-Neck Surgeries: A Guide to Soft & Liquid Meals. (Illus.). 414p. 1985. 38.50x (ISBN 0-398-04914-9). C C Thomas.
Darby, W. J., et al, eds. Annual Review of Nutrition, Vol. 1. (Illus.). 1981. text ed. 20.00 (ISBN 0-8243-2801-9). Annual Reviews.
--Annual Review of Nutrition, Vol. 2. (Illus.). 1982. text ed. 22.00 (ISBN 0-8243-2802-7). Annual Reviews.
D'Asaro, Barbara. Be Young & Vital: The Nutrition-Exercise Plan. LC 78-24260. (Illus.). 191p. 1979. pap. 7.95 (ISBN 0-89490-022-6). Enslow Pubs.
Davidson, Stanley, et al. Human Nutrition & Dietetics. 7th ed. (Illus.). 1979. text ed. 37.00 (ISBN 0-443-01765-4); pap. text ed. 49.50 (ISBN 0-443-01764-6). Churchill.
Davis, Adelle. Eat Right to Keep Fit. 3.95x. Cancer Control Soc.
--Let's Eat Right to Keep Fit. 1970. pap. 3.95x (ISBN 0-451-07951-5). Cancer Control Soc.
--Let's Eat Right to Keep Fit. rev. ed. LC 75-134581. 1970. 8.95 (ISBN 0-15-150304-4). HarBraceJ.
Debry, G., ed. Nutrition, Food & Drug Interactions in Man. (World Review of Nutrition & Dietetics: Vol. 43). (Illus.). x, 210p. 1984. 70.75 (ISBN 3-8055-3800-6). S Karger.
De Spain, June. Little Cyanide Cookbook: B-17 Recipes. 5.95 (ISBN 0-912986-00-X). Cancer Control Soc.
Detoxification Diet. 0.50 (ISBN 0-686-29908-6). Cancer Control Soc.
Deutsch, Ronald. Realities of Nutrition. LC 76-23508. (Berkeley Series in Nutrition). (Illus.). 1976. pap. 12.95 (ISBN 0-915950-19-7). Bull Pub.
Deutsch-Skandinavisches Symposium, Kopenhagen, 1978. Parenterale Ernaehrung (Forschung und Praxis) Zoellner, N., ed. (Beitraege zu Infusionstherapie und Klinische Ernaehrung: Band 1). (Illus.). 1978. pap. 7.25 (ISBN 3-8055-2963-5). S Karger.
Dietary Fats & Oils in Human Nutrition. (Food & Nutrition Papers: No. 26). 102p. 1980. pap. 23.50 (ISBN 92-5-100802-7, F2094, FAO). Unipub.
Dunn, Martha D. Fundamentals of Nutrition. (Illus.). 580p. 1983. text ed. 19.95 (ISBN 0-8436-2284-9). Van Nos Reinhold.
Dusek, Dorothy E. Thin & Fit: Your Personal Lifestyle. 288p. 1982. pap. text ed. write for info. (ISBN 0-534-01077-6). Wadsworth Pub.
Eisenman, Patricia & Johnson, Dennis. Coaches' Guide to Nutrition & Weight Control. LC 81-82452. (Illus.). 255p. 1982. pap. text ed. 10.95 (ISBN 0-931250-25-0, BE150025). Human Kinetics.
Energy & Protein Requirements: Report of a Joint FAO-WHO Ad Hoc Expert Committee. (Food & Nutrition Papers: No. 7). (Illus.). 118p. (3rd Printing 1977). 1973. pap. 4.25 (ISBN 92-5-100303-3, F124, FAO). Unipub.
Ensminger, A. H. & Ensminger, M. E. Foods & Nutrition Encyclopedia, 2 vols. (Illus.). 2432p. 1983. Set. 99.00x (ISBN 0-941218-05-8). Pegus Pr.
Ensminger, M. E. & Olentine, C. G., Jr. Feeds & Nutrition. (Illus.). 1978. Complete, 1417 Pgs. 49.50 (ISBN 0-941218-01-5); Abridged, 824 Pgs. 35.50 (ISBN 0-941218-02-3). Ensminger.
Escott-Stump, Sylvia. Nutrition & Diagnosis-Related Care. LC 84-17145. (Illus.). 344p. 1985. pap. 23.50 (ISBN 0-8121-0950-3). Lea & Febiger.
European Nutrition Conference, 2nd, Munich, 1976. Abstracts. Zoellner, N., et al, eds. (Nutrition & Metabolism: Vol. 20, No. 3). 1976. 15.75 (ISBN 3-8055-2441-2). S Karger.
Evaluation of the Toxicity of a Number of Antimicrobials & Antioxidants. (Nutrition Meetings Reports: No. 31). 104p. (2nd Printing 1974). 1962. pap. 4.75 (ISBN 92-5-101812-X, F133, FAO). Unipub.
Eversaul, George A. Clinical Nutrition. Date not set. 85.00 (ISBN 0-9601978-2-6, 0-9601-7826). G A Eversaul.
Exton-Smith & Caird. Metabolic & Nutritional Disorders in the Elderly. 238p. 1980. 26.00 (ISBN 0-7236-0537-8). PSG Pub Co.
Falkner, F. & Tanner, J. M., eds. Human Growth, Vol. 3: Neurobiology & Nutrition. 624p. 1979. 45.00x (ISBN 0-306-34463-7, Plenum Pr). Plenum Pub.
FAO-WHO Joint Committee Expert Committee on Nutrition, 8th. Proceedings. (Technical Report Ser: No. 477). 80p. 1971. pap. 2.00 (ISBN 92-4-120477-X, 413). World Health.
FAO-WHO Joint Expert Committee on Food Additives, Geneva, 1975. Evaluation of Certain Food Additives: 19th Report of the Joint FAO-WHO Expert Committee on Food Additives, Geneva, 1975. (Nutrition Meetings Reports: No. 55). 23p. 1975. pap. 4.75 (ISBN 92-5-101811-1, F129, FAO). Unipub.
Ferguson, James M. & Taylor, C. Barr. A Change for Heart: Your Family & the Food You Eat. 1978. pap. 5.95 (ISBN 0-915950-22-7). Bull Pub.
Fiennes, R. N., ed. Biology of Nutrition, Pts. 1-2. Incl. Pt. 1. The Evolution & Nature of Living Systems; Pt. 2. The Organizations & Nutritional Methods of Life Forms. 688p. 1972. Set. text ed. 150.00 (ISBN 0-08-016470-6). Pergamon.
Fitness & Nutrition. (Nutrition Education Source Ser.). (Orig.). 1981. pap. 4.00 (ISBN 0-910869-11-1). Soc Nutrition Ed.
Fitzgerald, Thomas K., ed. Nutrition & Anthropology in Action. (Studies of Developing Countries: No. 21). (Orig.). 1976. pap. text ed. 16.50x (ISBN 90-232-1447-1). Humanities.
Food & Nutrition Board. Recommended Dietary Allowances: Ninth Edition. (Illus.). 1980. pap. 8.50 (ISBN 0-309-02941-4). Natl Acad Pr.

Food & Nutrition Board - Division of Biology & Agriculture. Maternal Nutrition & the Course of Pregnancy. LC 72-605179. (Illus., Orig.). 1970. pap. text ed. 9.95 (ISBN 0-309-01761-0). Natl Acad Pr.

Food & Nutrition Terminology: Definitions of Selected Terms & Expressions in Current Use. (Terminology Bulletins: No. 28). (Eng., Fr. & Span.). 55p. (2nd Printing 1976). 1974. pap. 7.50 (ISBN 92-5-000061-8, F1194, FAO). Unipub.

Food Deprivation. (Landmark Ser.). 1979. 29.00x (ISBN 0-8422-4127-2). Irvington.

Food, Nutrition & Agriculture Guidelines for Agriculture Training Curricula in Africa. (Food & Nutrition Papers: No. 22). (Eng. & Fr.). 205p. 1982. pap. 15.50 (ISBN 92-5-101176-1, F2293, FAO). Unipub.

Foods & Nutrition Encyclopedia, 2 vols. 79.95. Ency Brit Inc.

Fredericks, Carlton. Calorie & Carbohydrate Guide. 1982. pap. 2.95 (ISBN 0-671-46941-X, 43059). PB.

Freedland, R. A. & Briggs, S. A Biochemical Approach to Nutrition. 1977. pap. 7.50 (ISBN 0-412-13040-8, NO.6113, Pub. by Chapman & Hall). Methuen Inc.

Freidman, Mendel, ed. Nutritional Improvement of Food & Feed Proteins. LC 78-17278. (Advances in Experimental Medicine & Biology Ser.: Vol. 105). 894p. 1978. 95.00x (ISBN 0-306-40026-X, Plenum Pr). Plenum Pub.

Friedman, Mendel, ed. Protein Nutritional Quality of Foods & Feeds, Pt. 2: Quality Factors-Plant Breeding, Composition, Processing & Antinutrients. (Nutrition & Clinical Nutrition Ser.: Vol. 1). 1975. 95.00 (ISBN 0-8247-6282-7). Dekker.

Frigerio, A. & Milon, H., eds. Chromatography & Mass Spectrometry in Nutrition Science & Food Safety: Proceedings of the International Symposium in Chromatography & Mass Spectrometry in Nutrition Science & Food Safety, Montreux, June 19-22, 1983. (Analytical Chemistry Symposium Ser.: No. 21). 306p. 1985. 109.25 (ISBN 0-444-42339-7, I-315-84). Elsevier.

Frompovich, Catherine J. Understanding Body Chemistry & Hair Mineral Analysis. Koppenhaver, April M., ed. 128p. 1982. pap. text ed. 4.95 (ISBN 0-935322-18-3). C J Frompovich.

Fulwood, Robinson & Johnson, Clifford L. Hematological & Nutritional Biochemistries References Data of Persons 6 Months-74 Years of Age: United States, 1976-1980. Cox, Klaudia, tr. (Ser. 11: No. 232). 60p. 1982. pap. 1.95 (ISBN 0-8406-0267-7). Natl Ctr Health Stats.

Gallender, Carolyn N. & Gallender, Demos. Dietary Problems & Diets for the Handicapped. 224p. 1979. 16.25x (ISBN 0-398-03838-4). C C Thomas.

Gastineau, Clifford F., et al, eds. Fermented Food Beverages in Nutrition. (Nutrition Foundation Ser.). 1979. 70.00 (ISBN 0-12-277050-1). Acad Pr.

Gates, June. Basic Foods. 2nd ed. LC 80-26409. 636p. 1981. text ed. 28.95 (ISBN 0-03-049846-5, HoltC). HR&W.

Gati, T., et al, eds. Nutrition-Digestion-Metabolism: Proceedings of the 28th International Congress of Physiological Sciences, Budapest, 1980. LC 80-42185. (Advances in Physiological Sciences Ser.: Vol. 12). (Illus.). 400p. 1981. 55.00 (ISBN 0-08-026825-0). Pergamon.

Gerard, Ralph W., ed. Food for Life. LC 52-14880. 1965. pap. 3.25x (ISBN 0-226-28790-4, P527, Phoen). U of Chicago Pr.

Gifft, Helen, et al. Nutrition, Behavior & Change. LC 79-170033. 1972. ref. ed. 25.95 (ISBN 0-13-627836-1). P-H.

Goforth, Allene, ed. Food & Nutrition: A Bibliographic Guide to the Microform Collection. 96p. 1981. pap. text ed. 50.00 (ISBN 0-667-00591-9). Microfilming Corp.

Goodhart, Robert S. & Shils, Maurice E., eds. Modern Nutrition in Health & Disease. 6th ed. LC 79-16842. (Illus.). 1370p. 1980. text ed. 47.50 (ISBN 0-8121-0645-8). Lea & Febiger.

Goodstein, Richard L., ed. Eating & Weight Disorders: Advances in Treatment & Research. (Springer Series on Behavior Therapy & Behavioral Medicine: Vol. 8). 192p. 1983. 23.95x (ISBN 0-8261-3830-6). Springer Pub.

Goulart, Frances S. The Official Eating to Win Cookbook: Super Foods for Super Athletic Performance. LC 81-40806. 224p. 1983. 16.95 (ISBN 0-8128-2832-1). Stein & Day.

Gussow, Joan. The Feeding Web: Issues in Nutritional Ecology. LC 78-8579. 1978. pap. 13.95 (ISBN 0-915950-15-4). Bull Pub.

Guthrie, Helen A. & Braddock, Karen S. Programmed Nutrition. 2nd ed. LC 77-15942. (Illus.). 332p. 1978. pap. text ed. 15.95 (ISBN 0-8016-2003-1). Mosby.

Haas, Robert. Nutritional Guide to Fast Food. (Illus.). 160p. 1982. pap. 6.95 (ISBN 0-682-49909-9, Banner). Exposition Pr FL.

Hafen, Brent Q. Nutrition, Food & Weight Control: A Practical Guide. 320p. 1980. pap. text ed. 19.07 (ISBN 0-205-06826-X, 6268269); tchr's ed. free (ISBN 0-205-06828-6, 6268285). Allyn.

--Nutrition, Food & Weight Control: Expanded Edition. 361p. 1980. 28.95x (ISBN 0-205-06825-1, 6268250, Pub. by Longwood Div). Allyn.

Hambraeus, Leif, ed. Nutrition in Europe. 150p. 1981. text ed. 35.00x (ISBN 0-86598-059-4, Pub. by Almquist & Wiksell Sweden). Allanheld.

Hamilton, Eva M. & Whitney, Eleanor N. Nutrition. 2nd ed. (Illus.). 650p. 1982. 26.95 (ISBN 0-314-66862-4). West Pub.

--Nutrition: Concepts & Controversies. 2nd ed. (Illus.). 732p. 1982. pap. text ed. 24.95 (ISBN 0-314-63249-2); 9.95 (ISBN 0-314-63251-4). West Pub.

Hansen, R. Gaurth & Wyse, Bonita W. Nutritional Quality Index of Foods. (Illus.). 1979. text ed. 39.50 (ISBN 0-87055-320-8). AVI.

Haresign, Lewis. Recent Advances in Animal Nutrition, 1981 (SAFS) 1982. text ed. 59.95 (ISBN 0-408-71014-4). Butterworth.

--Recent Development in Ruminant Nutrition. 1982. 19.95 (ISBN 0-408-10804-5). Butterworth.

Haskell, William, et al, eds. Nutrition & Athletic Performance. 284p. (Orig.). 1982. pap. 19.95 (ISBN 0-915950-56-1). Bull Pub.

Hathcock, John, ed. Nutritional Toxicology, Vol. 1. LC 82-4036. (Nutrition: Basic & Applied Science Ser.). 1982. 65.00 (ISBN 0-12-332601-X). Acad Pr.

Hathcock, John N. & Coon, Julius, eds. Nutrition & Drug Interrelations. 1978. 65.00 (ISBN 0-12-332550-1). Acad Pr.

Hawkins, Harold F. Applied Nutrition. 224p. 1977. Repr. of 1947 ed. lexatone 9.95 (ISBN 0-87881-069-2). Mojave Bks.

Hegsted, D. M., et al, eds. Nutrition Reviews' Present Knowledge in Nutrition. 4th ed. LC 76-44616. 605p. (Orig.). 1976. pap. 8.50 (ISBN 0-935368-15-9). Nutrition Found.

Hegyeli, Ruth J., ed. Nutrition & Cardiovascular Disease. (Progress in Biochemical Pharmacology: Vol. 19). (Illus.). x, 316p. 1982. 98.50 (ISBN 3-8055-3571-6). S Karger.

Heinerman, John. Complete Book of Spices: Their Medical, Nutritional & Cooking Uses. LC 82-80700. 1983. 15.95 (ISBN 0-87983-347-5); pap. 12.95 (ISBN 0-87983-281-9). Keats.

Hensley, E. S. Basic Concepts of World Nutrition. 302p. 1981. pap. 21.75x (ISBN 0-398-04544-5). C C Thomas.

Hetzel, B. S. & Frith, H. J. The Nutrition of Aborigines in Relation to the Ecosystems of Central Australia. 150p. 1978. pap. 7.25 (ISBN 0-643-00306-1, C031, CSIRO). Unipub.

Hetzel, B. S. & Frith, H. J., eds. The Nutrition of Aborigines in Relation to the Ecosystem of Central Australia. 1979. 8.00x (ISBN 0-643-00306-1, Pub. by CSIRO). Intl Spec Bk.

Hill, Graham L. Nutrition & the Surgical Patient. (Clinical Surgery International Ser.: Vol. 2). (Illus.). 323p. 1981. 34.00 (ISBN 0-443-02249-6). Churchill.

Hodges, Robert E. Nutrition in Medical Practice. LC 77-11337. (Illus.). 363p. 1980. text ed. 24.50 (ISBN 0-7216-4706-5). Saunders.

Hoffer, Abram & Walker, Morton. Nutrients to Age Without Senility. 1980. pap. 2.95x (ISBN 0-87983-218-5); 10.95x (ISBN 0-87983-217-7). Cancer Control Soc.

Hofmann, Lieselotte, ed. The Great American Nutrition Hassle. LC 78-51947. 422p. 1978. pap. 13.95 (ISBN 0-87484-446-0). Mayfield Pub.

Holmes, Marjorie. God & Vitamins. 368p. 1982. pap. 3.50 (ISBN 0-380-56994-9, 68536-1). Avon.

Homola, Samuel. Doctor Homola's Macro-Nutrient Diet for Quick, Permanent Weight Loss. LC 81-38340. 240p. 1981. 14.95 (ISBN 0-13-216952-5, Parker). P-H.

Hood, Lamartine F. & Wardrip, E. K. Carbohydrates & Health. (Illus.). 1977. text ed. 30.00 (ISBN 0-87055-223-6). AVI.

Howard, Rosanne B. Nutrition in Clinical Care. 2nd ed. Herbold, Nancy H., ed. (Illus.). 800p. 1982. 36.00x (ISBN 0-07-030514-5). McGraw.

Howe, Phyllis. Basic Nutrition in Health & Disease: Including Selection & Care of Food. 7th ed. 450p. 1981. pap. text ed. 16.50 (ISBN 0-7216-4796-0). Saunders.

Howell, Edward. Food Enzymes for Health & Longevity. (Illus.). 154p. 1981. pap. text ed. 5.95 (ISBN 0-933278-06-3). Twen Fir Cent.

Hulse, Joseph, et al. Sorghum & the Millets: Their Composition & Nutritive Value. LC 79-40871. 1980. 184.00 (ISBN 0-12-361350-7). Acad Pr.

Hunter, Beatrice. The Natural Foods Cookbook. 2.95x. Cancer Control Soc.

Hunter, Beatrice T. Brewer's Yeast, Wheat Germ, Lecithin & Other High Power Foods. (Good Health Guide Ser.). 1982. pap. 1.45 (ISBN 0-87983-278-9). Keats.

--Wheat, Millet & Other Grains. (Good Health Guide Ser.). 1982. pap. 1.45 (ISBN 0-87983-289-4). Keats.

Hurley, Lucille. Developmental Nutrition. (Illus.). 1979. text ed. 25.95 (ISBN 0-13-207639-X). P-H.

IDRC, Ottawa. Agriculture, Food & Nutrition Sciences Division: The First Five Years. 49p. 1977. pap. 5.00 (ISBN 0-88936-130-4, IDRC89, IDRC). Unipub.

Inglett, G. E. & Charalambous, George, eds. Tropical Foods: Chemistry & Nutrition, Vol. 1. 1979. 39.50 (ISBN 0-12-370901-6). Acad Pr.

Integrating Nutrition into Agricultural & Rural Development Projects: Six Case Studies. (Nutrition in Agriculture Ser.: No. 2). 132p. 1985. pap. 10.00 (ISBN 92-5-102150-3, F2693 5071, FAO). Unipub.

International College of Applied Nutrition. Nutrition-Applied Personally. 3.00x (ISBN 0-686-29754-7). Cancer Control Soc.

International Congress of Nutrition, Mexico, Sept. 1972. Proceedings, 4 vols. 1975. Set. 178.75 (ISBN 3-8055-1394-1). S Karger.

International Planned Parenthood Federation, ed. Health, Nutrition & Population in Human Settlements. (Occasional Essay Ser.: No. 5). 1977. 10.00x (ISBN 0-686-87106-5, Pub. by Intl Planned Parent). State Mutual Bk.

Irwin, M. Isabel, et al. Nutritional Requirements of Man: A Conspectus of Human Research. LC 80-50451. 592p. 1980. pap. 12.50 (ISBN 0-935368-23-X). Nutrition Found.

Jaqua, Ida & McClenahan, Pat. Nutrition for the Whole Family: A Guide to Better Health for Parents, Teachers, & Children. (Illus.). 156p. 1982. 11.95 (ISBN 0-13-627547-8); pap. 5.95 (ISBN 0-13-627539-7). P-H.

Jelliffe, Derrick B., ed. Human Nutrition-A Comprehensive Treatise, Vol. 2: Nutrition & Growth. (Illus.). 472p. 1979. 49.50x (ISBN 0-306-40128-2, Plenum Pr). Plenum Pub.

Jenks, Jorian. The Stuff We're Made of: The Positive Approach to Health through Nutrition. 1959. 5.00 (ISBN 0-8159-6829-9). Devin.

Jensen, Bernard D. Vital Foods-Total Health. 5.95x (ISBN 0-686-29759-8). Cancer Control Soc.

Jerome, Norge W., et al, eds. Nutritional Anthropology: Contemporary Approaches to Diet & Culture. (Illus.). ix, 433p. (Orig.). 1980. pap. 12.80 (ISBN 0-913178-55-1). Redgrave Pub Co.

Johnson, Roberta, ed. Whole Foods for the Whole Family. LC 81-81988. (Illus.). 352p. 1981. pap. 10.95 (ISBN 0-912500-09-3). La Leche.

Johnston, B. F. & Greaver, J. P. Manual on Food & Nutrition Policy. (Food & Nutrition Papers: No. 15). 95p. 1969. pap. 5.50 (ISBN 92-5-100436-6, F265, FAO). Unipub.

Jones, Susan S. Nutrition & Exercise for the over Fifty's. Passwater, Richard A. & Mindell, Earl R., eds. (Good Health Guide Ser.). 32p. 1983. pap. 1.45 (ISBN 0-87983-305-X). Keats.

Jordan, Henry, et al. Eating Is Okay: A Radical Approach to Weight Loss. Gelman, Steve, ed. 1978. pap. 2.50 (ISBN 0-451-12731-5, DE2731, Sig). NAL.

Junkin, Brock & Junkin, Elizabeth. Eat Cheaper. 80p. 1982. 5.50 (ISBN 0-682-49787-8). Exposition Pr FL.

Jurgens, Marshall H. Animal Feeding & Nutrition. 4th ed. 1978. wire coil bdg. 22.95 (ISBN 0-8403-2669-6, 40266902). Kendall Hunt.

Kadans, Joseph N. Encyclopedia of Fruits, Vegetables, Nuts & Seeds for Healthful Living. 1973. 12.95 (ISBN 0-13-275412-6, Reward); pap. 4.95 (ISBN 0-13-275420-7). P-H.

Kaibara, Ekiken. Yojokun: Japanese Secret of Good Health. 1974. 9.95 (ISBN 0-89346-101-6, Pub. by Tokuma Shoten); pap. 2.95 (ISBN 0-89346-047-8). Heian Intl.

King, Maurice H., et al. Nutrition for Developing Countries: With Special Reference to the Maize, Cassava & Millet Areas of Africa. (Illus.). 1973. pap. text ed. 19.95 (ISBN 0-19-572244-2). Oxford U Pr.

Kirkpatrick, Jean. Nutrition & the Woman Alcoholic. 2.75 (ISBN 0-686-35776-0). WFS.

Kirschner, H. E. Live Food Juices. 4.95x (ISBN 0-686-29769-5). Cancer Control Soc.

Knudsen, Odin K. & Scandizzo, Pasquale L. Nutrition & Food Needs in Developing Countries. (Working Paper: No. 328). 73p. 1979. 3.00 (ISBN 0-686-36199-7, WP-0328). World Bank.

Kolisko, Eugen. Nutrition II. 2nd ed. 1979. pap. 4.25 (ISBN 0-906492-12-2, Pub. by Kolisko Archives). St George Bk Serv.

Kowtaluk, Helen. Discovering Nutrition. 1980. text ed. 12.80 (ISBN 0-02-663380-9); tchr's guide 9.32 (ISBN 0-02-663390-6); student guide 5.32 (ISBN 0-02-663400-7). Bennett IL.

Kraus, Barbara. Calories & Carbohydrates. 6th, rev. ed. 1985. pap. 6.95 (ISBN 0-452-25663-1, Plume). NAL.

Krehl, Willard & Moss, N. Henry, eds. Clinical Nutrition in Health Care Facilities. LC 79-66103. (Orig.). 1979. pap. text ed. 4.95x (ISBN 0-89313-019-2). G F Stickley Co.

Krehl, Willard A. The Role of Citrus in Health & Disease. LC 76-4502. 1976. 6.50 (ISBN 0-8130-0532-9). U Presses Fla.

Kretchmer, Norman, intro. by. Human Nutrition: Readings from Scientific American. LC 78-17367. (Illus.). 275p. 1978. pap. text ed. 13.95x (ISBN 0-7167-0182-0). W H Freeman.

Kreutler, Patricia. Nutrition in Perspective. (Illus.). 1980. text ed. 26.95 (ISBN 0-13-627752-7); wkbk. 13.95 (ISBN 0-13-627778-0). P-H.

Kunin, Richard. Mega-Nutrition. 1980. 6.95x (ISBN 0-452-25344-6). Cancer Control Soc.

Kuo, Peter T., et al, eds. Health & Obesity. 200p. 1983. text ed. 39.50 (ISBN 0-89004-809-6). Raven.

Kupsinel, Penelope E. & Harker, Charlotte S. Questions & Problems on Nutrition. LC 74-81202. 1974. pap. text ed. 4.95x (ISBN 0-8134-1663-9, 1663). Interstate.

Kurtz, Robert C., ed. Nutrition In Gastrointestinal Disease. (Contemporary Issues in Clinical Nutrition: Vol. 1). (Illus.). 1981. text ed. 20.00 (ISBN 0-443-08128-X). Churchill.

Labuza, Theodore P. Food & Your Well-Being. (Illus.). 1977. pap. text ed. 17.95 (ISBN 0-8299-0129-9); instrs.' manual & study guide 7.50 (ISBN 0-8299-0162-0). West Pub.

Labuza, Theodore P. & Sloan, A. Elizabeth. Contemporary Nutrition Controversies. (Illus.). 1979. pap. text ed. 16.95 (ISBN 0-8299-0258-9). West Pub.

--Food for Thought. 2nd ed. (Illus.). 1977. pap. text ed. 9.50 (ISBN 0-87055-244-9). AVI.

Lag, Jul, ed. Survey of Geomedical Problems. 272p. 1980. 24.00x (ISBN 82-00-12654-4). Universitet.

Lamb, Lawrence E. Metabolics: Putting Your Food Energy to Work. LC 74-1829. (Illus.). 256p. 1974. 12.95i (ISBN 0-06-012484-9, HarpT). Har-Row.

Lamb, M. W. & Harden, M. L. Meaning of Human Nutrition. 1975. pap. text ed. 11.25 (ISBN 0-08-017079-X). Pergamon.

Lappe, Frances M. Diet for a Small Planet. rev ed. 432p. 1975. spiral bdg. 7.95 (ISBN 0-345-28919-6); pap. 2.75 (ISBN 0-345-29515-3). Ballantine.

Larsen, Carl. Even the Dog Won't Eat My Meat Loaf. LC 79-19887. 1980. pap. 5.95 (ISBN 0-89645-011-2). Media Ventures.

Larson, Gena. Fact-Book on Better Food for Better Babies & Their Families. LC 72-83519. (Pivot Original Health Book). 128p. 1972. pap. 2.25 (ISBN 0-87983-023-9). Keats.

--Fundamentals in Foods. 1.75x (ISBN 0-686-29781-4). Cancer Control Soc.

Lasota, Marcia. The New Fast Food Calorie Guide. (Illus., Orig.). Date not set. pap. 3.95 (ISBN 0-933474-09-1, Gabriel Bks). Minn Scholarly.

Latham, M. C. Planning & Evaluation of Applied Nutrition Programmes. (Food & Nutrition Papers: No. 16). 125p. (Orig., 3rd Printing 1977). 1972. pap. 11.00 (ISBN 92-5-100439-0, F319, FAO). Unipub.

Lehman, S. C. Nutrition & Food Preparation & Preventive Care & Maintenance. (Lifeworks Ser.). 1981. 7.96 (ISBN 0-07-037094-X). McGraw.

Lesser, Michael. Nutrition & Vitamin Therapy. 7.95x (ISBN 0-394-17600-6); pap. 2.50 (ISBN 0-553-14437-5). Cancer Control Soc.

--Nutrition & Vitamin Therapy. LC 79-52100. 1980. pap. 7.95 (ISBN 0-394-17600-6, E748, Ever). Grove.

Leverton, Ruth M. Food Becomes You. facsimile ed. (Illus.). 1965. 10.45x (ISBN 0-8138-2405-2). Iowa St U Pr.

Leviton, Richard. Tofu, Tempeh, Miso & Other Soyfoods. Passwater, Richard A. & Mindell, Earl R., eds. (Good Health Guide Ser.). 36p. 1982. pap. 0.95 (ISBN 0-87983-284-3). Keats.

Li, A. K., et al. Fluid Electroytes, Acid Base & Nutrition. 1980. 12.00 (ISBN 0-12-448150-7). Acad Pr.

Linder, Maria C., ed. Nutritional Biochemistry & Metabolism, with Clinical Applications. 1985. 55.00 (ISBN 0-444-00910-8). Elsevier.

Lindlahr, Victor H. You Are What You Eat. LC 80-19722. 128p. 1980. Repr. of 1971 ed. lib. bdg. 13.95x (ISBN 0-89370-604-3). Borgo Pr.

--You Are What You Eat. LC 80-19722. 1971. pap. 3.95 (ISBN 0-87877-004-6, H-4). Newcastle Pub.

Lloyd, L. E., et al. Fundamentals of Animal Nutrition. 2nd ed. LC 77-16029. (Animal Science Ser.). (Illus.). 466p. 1978. text ed. 31.95 (ISBN 0-7167-0566-4). W H Freeman.

Lowenberg, Miriam E., et al. Food & People. 3rd ed. LC 78-19172. 382p. 1979. 33.95 (ISBN 0-471-02690-5). Wiley.

Lusk, Graham. The Elements of the Science of Nutrition. 4th ed. (Nutrition Foundations Reprint Ser.). (Illus.). Repr. 46.00 (ISBN 0-384-34203-5). Acad Pr.
--The Fundamental Basis of Nutrition. 1923. 24.50x (ISBN 0-686-51390-8). Elliots Bks.
--Nutrition. LC 75-23660. (Clio Medica: No. 10). (Illus.). Repr. of 1933 ed. 13.00 (ISBN 0-404-58910-3). AMS Pr.
McEntire, Patricia. Mommy I'm Hungry: How to Feed Your Child Nutritiously. LC 81-68292. 168p. 1982. pap. 5.95 (ISBN 0-917982-11-8). Cougar Bks.
McLaren, Donald S. Nutrition in the Community: A Critical Look at Nutrition Policy Planning & Programs. 2nd ed. LC 82-6992. 472p. 1983. 58.95 (ISBN 0-471-10294-6, Pub. by Wiley-Interscience). Wiley.
MacNeil, Karen. The Book of Whole Foods: Nutrition & Cuisine. LC 80-5490. (Illus.). 356p. (Orig.). 1981. pap. 8.95 (ISBN 0-394-74012-2, V-012, Vin). Random.
Manocha, S. L. Nutrition & Our Overpopulated Planet. (Illus.). 488p. 1975. spiral 49.50x (ISBN 0-398-03180-0). C C Thomas.
Martin, W. Coda. A Matter of Life. 1965. 6.95 (ISBN 0-8159-6202-9). Devin.
Mason, Marion, et al. Nutrition & the Cell: The Inside Story. LC 72-95734. (Illus.). Repr. of 1973 ed. 17.50 (ISBN 0-8357-9636-1, 2013104). Bks Demand UMI.
Mauron, Jean, ed. Nutrition Adequacy: Nutrients Available & Needs. (Experimentia Supplementum Ser.: Vol. 44). 384p. 1983. text ed. 39.95 (ISBN 3-7643-1479-6). Birkhauser.
Mayer, Jean. Human Nutrition: Its Physiological, Medical & Social Aspects, A Series of 82 Essays. (Illus.). 740p. 1979. 23.75x (ISBN 0-398-02359-X). C C Thomas.
Mayer, Jean & Dwyer, Johanna, eds. Food & Nutrition Policy in a Changing World. (Illus.). 1979. pap. text ed. 13.95 (ISBN 0-19-502364-1). Oxford U Pr.
Miller, C. D. Food Values of Poi, Taro, & Limu. pap. 8.00 (ISBN 0-527-02140-7). Kraus Repr.
Minnich, Jerry. Gardening for Maximum Nutrition. (Illus.). 244p. 1983. 15.95 (ISBN 0-87857-475-1). Rodale Pr Inc.
Minor, Lewis J. L. J. Minor Foodservice Standards Series: Vol. 1-Nutritional Standards. (Illus.). 1983. text ed. 19.50 (ISBN 0-87055-425-5). AVI.
--L. J. Minor Foodservice Standards Series: Vol. 2-Sanitation, Safety, Environmental Standards. (Illus.). 1983. text ed. 19.50 (ISBN 0-87055-428-X). AVI.
Mitchell, H. H. & Edman, Marjorie. Nutrition & Climatic Stress: With Particular Reference to Man. (Illus.). 256p. 1951. 24.75x (ISBN 0-398-04365-5). C C Thomas.
Mitchell, Harold H. Comparative Nutrition of Man & Domestic Animals, Vol. 2. 1964. 63.50 (ISBN 0-12-499602-7). Acad Pr.
Mosley, W. H., ed. Nutrition & Human Reproduction. LC 77-28738. 526p. 1978. 65.00x (ISBN 0-306-31122-4, Plenum Pr). Plenum Pub.
Moss, N. Henry & Mayer, Jean, eds. Food & Nutrition in Health & Disease. (Annals of the New York Academy of Sciences: Vol. 300). 474p. 1977. 42.00x (ISBN 0-89072-046-0). NY Acad Sci.
Muller, H. G. & Tobin, G. Nutrition & Food Processing. 1980. pap. 30.00 (ISBN 0-87055-363-1). AVI.
Nagy, Steven & Attaway, John, eds. Citrus Nutrition & Quality. LC 80-22562. (ACS Symposium Ser.: No. 143). 1980. 38.95 (ISBN 0-8412-0595-7). Am Chemical.
Naito, H., ed. Nutrition & Heart Disease. (Monographs of the American College of Nutrition: Vol. 5). 365p. 1982. text ed. 35.00 (ISBN 0-89335-119-9). SP Med & Sci Bks.
Nasset, Edmund S. Nutrition Handbook. 3rd ed. (Illus.). 176p. (Orig.). pap. 6.01i (ISBN 0-06-463513-9, EH 513). B&N NY.
National Research Council. World Food & Nutrition Study: Potential Contributions of Research, Commission on International Relations. 1977. pap. 11.50 (ISBN 0-309-02628-8). Natl Acad Pr.
National Research Council Assembly of Life Sciences-Food & Nutrition Board. Assessing Changing Food Consumption Patterns. 296p. 1981. pap. text ed. 16.00 (ISBN 0-309-03135-4). Natl Acad Pr.
Neilson, Bruce J. & Cronin, L. Eugene, eds. Estuaries & Nutrients. LC 81-83901. (Contemporary Issues in Science & Society Ser.). (Illus.). 656p. 1981. 69.50 (ISBN 0-89603-035-0). Humana.
Neuberger, A. & Jukes, T. Human Nutrition: Current Issues & Controversies. 250p. 1982. text ed. 35.00 (ISBN 0-937218-37-5). J K Burgess.
New York Academy of Sciences, Feb 20-22, 1980. Micronutrient Interactions: Vitamins, Minerals, & Hazardous Elements, Vol. 355. Levander, O. A. & Cheng, Lorraine, eds. LC 80-25622. 372p. 1980. 74.00x (ISBN 0-89766-099-4); pap. 74.00x (ISBN 0-89766-100-1). NY Acad Sci.
Newbold, H. L. Mega-Nutrients for Your Nerves. 1983. pap. 3.95 (ISBN 0-425-06571-5). Berkley Pub.
Norris, P. About Honey: Nature's Elixir for Health. 1982. pap. 2.95 (ISBN 0-87904-043-2). Lust.
Null, Gary. Gary Null's Nutrition Sourcebook for the Eighties. 320p. 1983. 15.95 (ISBN 0-02-590900-2); pap. 7.95 (ISBN 0-02-059500-X). Macmillan.
Null, Gary & Null, Steve. The Complete Handbook of Nutrition. 1973. pap. 3.95 (ISBN 0-440-11613-9). Dell.
--The Complete Handbook of Nutrition. LC 78-187994. (The Health Library: Vol. 1). 340p. 1972. 7.95 (ISBN 0-8315-0124-3). Speller.
Null, Gary, et al. The Complete Question & Answer Book of General Nutrition. LC 79-187997. (The Health Library: Vol. 5). 184p. 1972. 9.95 (ISBN 0-8315-0128-6). Speller.
Nutrition: A Review of the WHO Programme 1965-1971. (WHO Chronicle Reprint: Vol. 26, No. 4-5). (Also avail. in French & Spanish). 1972. pap. 0.80 (ISBN 92-4-156020-7). World Health.
Nutrition & Working Efficiency. (Freedom from Hunger Campaign Basic Studies: No. 5). 47p. (3rd Printing 1966). 1966. pap. 4.50 (ISBN 92-5-101820-0, F302, FAO). Unipub.
Nutrition for Athletes: A Handbook for Coaches. 64p. 1980. 6.25 (ISBN 0-88314-136-1, 241-25140). AAHPERD.
O'Banion, Dan R. The Ecological & Nutritional Treatment of Health Disorders. (Illus.). 228p. 1981. 25.75x (ISBN 0-398-04455-4). C C Thomas.
Obert, Jessie C. Community Nutrition. LC 77-13992. 452p. 1978. text ed. 35.00 (ISBN 0-471-65236-9). Wiley.
Osborne, D. R. & Voogt, P. The Analysis of Nutrients in Foods. (Food Science & Technology Ser.). 1978. 44.00 (ISBN 0-12-529150-7). Acad Pr.
Pacey, Arnold, compiled by. Gardening for Better Nutrition. (Illus.). 64p. (Orig.). 1978. pap. 7.75x (ISBN 0-903031-50-7, Pub. by Intermediate Tech England). Intermediate Tech.
Passmore, R., et al. Handbook on Human Nutritional Requirements. (Also avail. in french, & spanish). 1974. pap. 4.80 (ISBN 92-4-140061-7). World Health.
Passwater, Richard. Super-Nutrition-Healthy Hearts. 3.50x (ISBN 0-686-29823-3). Cancer Control Soc.
--Supernutrition. 3.50x (ISBN 0-671-42172-7). Cancer Control Soc.
Pearson, Paul B. & Greenwell, J. Richard, eds. Nutrition, Food & Man: An Interdisciplinary Perspective. LC 80-10297. 159p. 1980. pap. 5.95 (ISBN 0-8165-0706-6). U of Ariz Pr.
Pennington, Jean A. Dietary Nutrient Guide. (Illus.). 1976. pap. text ed. 24.50 (ISBN 0-87055-196-5). AVI.
Pennsylvania State University Nutrition Education Curriculum Study. Nutrition in a Changing World: Grade Four. LC 80-20736. (Illus.). 152p. (Orig.). 1981. pap. text ed. 11.95x (ISBN 0-8425-1864-9). Brigham.
Perez-Polo, J. Regino & De Vellis, Jean, eds. Growth & Trophic Factors. LC 83-954. (Progress in Clinical & Biological Research Ser.: Vol. 118). 592p. 1983. 45.00 (ISBN 0-8451-0118-8). A R Liss.
Peshek, Robert J. Balancing Body Chemistry with Nutrition. 1977. 20.00 (ISBN 0-9605902-0-X). Color Coded Charting.
--Nutrition for a Healthy Heart. (Illus.). 1979. 20.00 (ISBN 0-9605902-2-6). Color Coded Charting.
--Student's Manual for Balancing Body Chemistry with Nutrition. 1977. 20.00 (ISBN 0-9605902-1-8). Color Coded Charting.
Phillips, David A. Guidebook to Nutritional Factors in Foods. LC 79-10010. 1979. pap. 5.95 (ISBN 0-912800-71-2). Woodbridge Pr.
Pigden, W. J. & Balch, C. C., eds. Standardization of Analytical Methodology for Feeds: Proceedings of a Workshop Held in Ottawa, Canada, 4-12 Mar. 1979. 128p. 1980. pap. 13.00 (ISBN 0-88936-217-3, IDRC134, IDRC). Unipub.
Pike, Arnold. Viewpoint on Nutrition. LC 80-24024. 221p. 1980. Repr. of 1973 ed. lib. bdg. 15.95x (ISBN 0-89370-621-3). Borgo Pr.
Plummer, Mary A. Foods & Nutrition: Syllabus. 1976. pap. text ed. 5.25 (ISBN 0-89420-001-1, 167070); cassette recordings 58.10 (ISBN 0-89420-147-6, 167040). Natl Book.
Posner, Barbara M. Nutrition & the Elderly: Policy Development, Program Planning, & Evaluation. LC 77-17683. 208p. 1979. 24.50x (ISBN 0-669-02085-0). Lexington Bks.
Powell, Eric F. A Home Course in Nutrition. 104p. 1978. pap. 8.95x (ISBN 0-8464-1019-2). Beekman Pubs.
Price, Weston. Nutrition & Physical Degeneration. 27.50x (ISBN 0-916764-00-1). Cancer Control Soc.
Price, Weston A. Nutrition & Physical Degeneration. 9th ed. (Illus.). 560p. 1977. 23.00 (ISBN 0-916764-00-1). Price-Pottenger.
Procedures for the Testing of International Food Additives to Establish Their Safety for Use. (Nutrition Meetings Reports: No. 17). 19p. (2nd Printing 1974). 1958. pap. 4.50 (ISBN 92-5-101822-7, F336, FAO). Unipub.
Protein Supply-Demands: Changing Styles. 1982. 1250.00 (ISBN 0-89336-287-5, GA-049). BCC.
Pyke, Magnus. Man & Food. 1970. pap. 3.95 (ISBN 0-07-050990-5). McGraw.
Rand, W. M. & Uauy, R. Protein-Energy Requirement Studies in Developing Countries: Results of International Research. (Food & Nutrition Bulletins: Suppl. 10). 369p. 1984. pap. 31.25 (ISBN 92-808-0481-2, TUNU224, UNU). Unipub.
Rao, V. K. Food, Nutrition & Poverty. x, 154p. 1982. text ed. 25.00x (ISBN 0-7069-1886-X, Pub. by Vikas India). Advent NY.
Rasper, Vladimir F., ed. Cereal Polysaccharides in Technology & Nutrition. 184p. 1984. pap. 23.00 (ISBN 0-913250-36-8). Am Assn Cereal Chem.
Rechcigi, M. Nutrient Elements & Toxicants. (Comparative Animal Nutrition: Vol. 2). (Illus.). 1977. 41.75 (ISBN 3-8055-2351-3). S Karger.
Rechcigl, M., ed. Food, Nutrition & Health. (World Review of Nutrition & Dietetics: Vol. 16). (Illus.). 350p. 1973. 76.75 (ISBN 3-8055-1398-4). S Karger.
--Handbook of Nutritive Value of Processed Food: Food for Human Use, Vol. I. 696p. 1982. 84.50 (ISBN 0-8493-3951-0). CRC Pr.
Rechcigl, M., Jr., ed. Nitrogen, Electrolytes Water & Metabolism. (Comparative Animal Nutrition: Vol. 3). (Illus.). 1979. 55.50 (ISBN 3-8055-2829-9). S Karger.
--Physiology of Growth & Nutrition. (Comparative Animal Nutrition: Vol. 4). (Illus.). xii, 344p. 1981. pap. 106.00 (ISBN 3-8055-1199-X). S Karger.
Rechcigl, Miloslav, Jr., ed. Culture Media for Micro-Organisms & Plants, Vol. 3. 644p. 1977. 19.95 (ISBN 0-8493-2738-5). CRC Pr.
--Man, Food & Nutrition. LC 73-81478. (Uniscience Ser). 344p. 1973. 49.00 (ISBN 0-87819-040-6). CRC Pr.
Rechigl, M., Jr., ed. Nutrition & the World Food Problem. (Illus.). 1978. 5.50 (ISBN 3-8055-2779-9). S Karger.
Reed, Pat B. Nutrition: An Applied Science. (Illus.). 650p. 1980. text ed. 30.95 (ISBN 0-8299-0311-9); instrs.' manual avail. (ISBN 0-8299-0570-7). West Pub.
Report of the Nutrition Problems in Latin America: 4th Conference, Guatemala City, 1957. 1959. pap. 4.75 (ISBN 0-685-36327-9, F370, FAO). Unipub.
Report of the Second Joint FAO-WHO Conference on Food Additives: Rome, June, 1963. (Nutrition Meetings Reports: No. 34). 13p. 1974. pap. 5.00 (ISBN 92-5-101825-1, F381, FAO). Unipub.
Requirements of Vitamin A, Thiamine, Riboflavin & Niacin: Report of a Joint FAO-WHO Expert Group. (Nutrition Meetings Reports: No. 41). 86p. (3rd Printing 1978). 1967. pap. 5.25 (ISBN 92-5-100453-6, F1467, FAO). Unipub.
Reuben, David. Everything You Always Wanted to Know about Nutrition. 1979. pap. 3.95 (ISBN 0-380-44370-8, 69385). Avon.
Roberts, Lydia J. Nutricion. Torres, Rosa M., tr. LC 77-23108. 1978. pap. 12.00 (ISBN 0-8477-2777-7). U of PR Pr.
Robinson, Corinee H. & Lawler, Marilyn R. Normal & Therapeutic Nutrition. 16th ed. 1982. text ed. write for info. (ISBN 0-02-402370-1). Macmillan.
Robson, John R., et al. Malnutrition, Its Causation & Control. 632p. 1972. Set. 80.95 (ISBN 0-677-03140-8). Gordon.
Roche, Alex F. & Falkner, Frank, eds. Nutrition & Malnutrition: Identification & Measurement. LC 74-13950. (Advances in Experimental Medicine & Biology Ser.: Vol. 49). 375p. 1974. 49.50x (ISBN 0-306-39049-3, Plenum Pr). Plenum Pub.
Roe, Campbell. Drugs & Nutrients. (Drugs & the Pharmaceutical Science Ser.). 568p. 1984. 99.75 (ISBN 0-8247-7054-4). Dekker.
Roe, Daphne A. Clinical Nutrition for the Health Scientist. 144p. 1980. 52.00 (ISBN 0-8493-5417-X). CRC Pr.
Rolander-Chilo, Brita, ed. Nutritional Research: An International Approach. (Illus.). 1979. text ed. 33.00 (ISBN 0-08-024399-1). Pergamon.
Rosenbaum, Ernest, et al. Nutrition for the Cancer Patient. (Orig.). 1980. pap. 7.95 (ISBN 0-915950-38-3). Bull Pub.
Rynders, Barbara B. Eat It, Its Good for You! 1978. pap. 2.98 (ISBN 0-9601872-0-0). B Rynders Pubns.
Sahn, David E. & Lockwood, Richard, eds. Methods for the Evaluation of the Impact of Food & Nutrition Programmes. (Food & Nutrition Bulletins: Suppl. 8). 291p. 1984. pap. 31.25 (ISBN 92-808-0473-1, TUNU225, UNU). Unipub.
Salter, Charles A. & De Lerma, Carlotta S. Knee-High Nutrition. Darst, Sheila S., ed. 1984. 12.95 (ISBN 0-89896-094-0); pap. 7.95 (ISBN 0-317-11663-0). Larksdale.
Santos, W. J., et al, eds. Nutrition & Food Science: Present Knowledge & Utilization, 3 vols. LC 79-27952. 1980. Vol. 1, 822p. 89.50x (ISBN 0-306-40342-0, Plenum Pr); Vol. 2, 968p. 95.00x (ISBN 0-306-40343-9); Vol. 3, 832p. 89.50x (ISBN 0-306-40344-7). Plenum Pub.
Sauberlich, Howerde E., et al. Laboratory Tests for the Assessment of Nutritional Status. LC 74-77908. (Monotopic Reprint Ser.). 136p. 1974. Repr. 19.95 (ISBN 0-8493-0121-1). CRC Pr.
Scheider, William L. Nutrition: Basic Concepts & Applications. (Illus.). 560p. 1983. pap. 27.95 (ISBN 0-07-055230-4). McGraw.
Schmandt, Jurgen, et al, eds. Nutrition Policy in Transition. LC 79-9628. (Illus.). 320p. 1980. 27.50x (ISBN 0-669-03596-3). Lexington Bks.
Schofield, Sue. Development & the Problems of Village Nutrition. LC 78-73290. 174p. 1979. Repr. of 1978 ed. text ed. 22.95x (ISBN 0-916672-21-2). Allanheld.
--Development & the Problems of Village Nutrition. 174p. 1979. 25.00x (ISBN 0-85664-836-1). Rowman.
Schreiber, William M. Fast Food Nutritional Guide: How to Survive a Big Mac Attack! 48p. 1982. pap. 2.50 (ISBN 0-914091-15-8). Chicago Review.
Schrimshaw, Nevin S. & Wallerstein, Mitchel B., eds. Nutrition Policy Implementation: Issues & Experience. (Illus.). 572p. 1982. 65.00x (ISBN 0-306-40858-9, Plenum Pr). Plenum Pub.
Scientific American Editors. Food & Agriculture: A Scientific American Book. (Illus.). 154p. 1976. text ed. 20.95x (ISBN 0-7167-0382-3); pap. 10.95x (ISBN 0-7167-0381-5). W H Freeman.
Scott, Cyril. Crude Black Molasses. 1980. pap. 2.95 (ISBN 0-87904-010-6). Lust.
Scrimshaw, Nevin S. & Altschul, Aaron M., eds. Amino Acid Fortification of Protein Foods. 1971. 45.00x (ISBN 0-262-19091-5). MIT Pr.
Scrimshaw, Nevin S. & Behar, Moises, eds. Nutrition & Agricultural Development. LC 76-2043. (Basic Life Sciences Ser.: Vol. 7). (Illus.). 524p. 1976. 65.00x (ISBN 0-306-36507-3, Plenum Pr). Plenum Pub.
Sheinken, David, et al. The Food Connection: How the Things You Eat Affect the Way You Feel. LC 78-11208. 1979. 10.00 (ISBN 0-672-52518-6). Bobbs.
Silano, V., et al, eds. Improvement of Nutritional Quality of Food Crops: A State of the Art Report. Bansul, H. C. & Bozzini, A. (Plant Production & Protection Papers: No. 34). 96p. 1981. pap. 7.50 (ISBN 92-5-101166-4, F2298, FAO). Unipub.
Silberman, Howard & Eisenberg, Daniel. Parenteral & Enteral Nutrition for the Hospitalized Patient. (Illus.). 320p. 1982. pap. 33.95. ACC.
Soffer, Alfred. Potassium Therapy: A Seminar. (Illus.). 124p. 1968. photocopy ed. 12.75x (ISBN 0-398-01807-3). C C Thomas.
Somogyi, J. C., ed. Foreign Substances & Nutrition. Tarjan, R. (Bibliotheca Nutritio et Dieta: No. 29). (Illus.). viii, 132p. 1980. pap. 35.50 (ISBN 3-8055-0621-X). S Karger.
Somogyi, J. C. & Varela, G., eds. Nutritional Deficiencies in Industrialized Countries. (Bibliotheca Nutritioc et Dieta: Vol. 30). (Illus.). viii, 172p. 1981. 54.50 (ISBN 3-8055-1994-X). S Karger.
Sorenson, Joyce & Murray, Nancy. General Nutrition. (Menus for Better Health Ser.). 36p. (Orig.). 1983. pap. 1.95 (ISBN 0-911638-07-5). Witkower.
Souci, S. W. & Fachmann, W. Food Composition & Nutrition Tables. 1982. 75.00 (ISBN 0-9960099-8-1, Pub. by Wissenschaftliche W Germany). Heyden.
Sperber. Sociology of Nutrition & Public Health. (Traditional Healing Ser.: No. 9). Date not set. cancelled (ISBN 0-932426-15-8, Trado-Medic Bks). Conch Mag.
Springer, Ninfa S. Nutrition Casebook on Developmental Disabilities. LC 81-21383. 1982. 20.00x (ISBN 0-8156-2266-X); pap. 12.95x (ISBN 0-8156-2259-7). Syracuse U Pr.
Stare, Fredrick J. & McWilliams, Margaret. Nutrition for Good Health. LC 74-81644. 1974. 8.95x (ISBN 0-916434-11-7). Plycon Pr.
--Nutrition for Good Health. 224p. 1982. 13.95 (ISBN 0-89313-064-8). G F Stickley.

Mrak, E. M., et al, eds. Advances in Food Research, Vols. 1-24. Incl. Vol. 1. 1948. 70.00 (ISBN 0-12-016401-9); Vol. 2. 1949. 70.00 (ISBN 0-12-016402-7); Vols. 3-5. Vol. 3, 1951. 70.00 (ISBN 0-12-016403-5); Vol. 4, 1953. 70.00 (ISBN 0-12-016404-3); Vol. 5, 1954. 70.00 (ISBN 0-12-016405-1); Vol. 6. 1955. 70.00 (ISBN 0-12-016406-X); Vols. 7-8. 1957-58. Vol. 7. 70.00 (ISBN 0-12-016407-8); Vol. 8. 70.00 (ISBN 0-12-016408-6); Vol. 9. Chichester, C. O., et al, eds. 1960. 70.00 (ISBN 0-12-016409-4); Vols. 11-13. 1963-64. Vol. 10, 1963. 70.00 (ISBN 0-12-016410-8); Vol. 11, 1963. 70.00 (ISBN 0-12-016411-6); Vol. 12, 1964. 70.00 (ISBN 0-12-016412-4); Vol. 13, 1964. 70.00 (ISBN 0-12-016413-2); Vol. 14. 1965. 70.00 (ISBN 0-12-016414-0); Vol. 15. 1967. 70.00 (ISBN 0-12-016415-9); Vol. 16. 1968. 70.00 (ISBN 0-12-016416-7); Vol. 17. 1969. 70.00 (ISBN 0-12-016417-5); Vol. 18. 1970. 70.00 (ISBN 0-12-016418-3); Vol. 19. 1971. 70.00 (ISBN 0-12-016419-1); Vol. 20. 1973. 70.00 (ISBN 0-12-016420-5); Vol. 21. 1975. 70.00 (ISBN 0-12-016421-3); Vol. 22. 1976. 70.00 (ISBN 0-12-016422-1) (ISBN 0-12-016487-6); Vol. 23. 1977. 70.00 (ISBN 0-12-016423-X); Vol. 24. 1978. 70.00 (ISBN 0-12-016424-8). Vols. 1-22. 70.00 ea. Acad Pr.

Nutrition Action. 20.00 (ISBN 0-686-95914-0). Ctr Sci Public.

Nutrition in Industry, Nineteen Forty-Six. Bd. with Chilean Development Corporation - A Study in National Planning to Raise Living. Finer, Herman. (I.L.O. Studies & Reports: Nos. 4 & 5). Repr. 41.00 (ISBN 0-317-16638-7). Kraus Repr.

Oddy, Derek T. & Miller, Derek S., eds. The Making of the Modern British Diet. 235p. 1976. 17.50x (ISBN 0-87471-803-1). Rowman.

Pearson, Paul B. & Greenwell, J. Richard, eds. Nutrition, Food & Man: An Interdisciplinary Perspective. LC 80-10297. 159p. 1980. pap. 5.95 (ISBN 0-8165-0706-6). U of Ariz Pr.

Peshek, Robert J. Clinical Nutrition Using the Seven Lines of Defense Against Disease. 1980. 10.00 (ISBN 0-9605902-3-4). Color Coded Charting.

Pinstrup-Andersen, Per. Nutritional Consequences of Agricultural Projects: Conceptual Relationships & Assessment Approaches. (Working Paper: No. 456). 93p. 1981. 5.00 (ISBN 0-686-36057-5, WP-0456). World Bank.

Report of the Nutrition Committee for South & East Asia: 4th Session, Tokyo, 1956. (Nutrition Meetings Reports: No. 14). 50p. 1957. pap. 4.50 (ISBN 92-5-101828-6, F361, FAO). Unipub.

Selvey, Nancy & White, Philip L. Nutrition in the Nineteen Eighties: Constraints on Our Knowledge. LC 81-8454. (Progress in Clinical & Biological Research Ser.: Vol. 67). 620p. 1981. 80.00 (ISBN 0-8451-0067-X). A R Liss.

Somogyi, J. C. World-Wide Problems of Nutrition Research & Nutrition Education. (Bibliotheca Nutritio et Dieta: No. 32). (Illus.). xvi, 76p. 1982. pap. 32.00 (ISBN 3-8055-3586-4). S Karger.

Wolf, Wayne R. Biological Reference Materials: Availability, Uses & Need for Validation of Nutrient Measurement. LC 84-7568. 272p. 1984. text ed. 60.00X (ISBN 0-471-80636-6, Pub. by Wiley-Interscience). Wiley.

Wurtman, Judith J. Eating Your Way Through Life. LC 77-84121. 231p. 1979. pap. text ed. 14.50 (ISBN 0-685-99040-0). Raven.

Wurtman, R. J. & Lieberman, H., eds. Research Strategies for Assessing the Behavioural Effects of Foods & Nutrients: Proceedings of Conference of the Center for Brain Sciences & Metabolism Charitable Trust, Massachusetts Institute of Technology, Cambridge, USA. (Illus.). 136p. 1984. 32.00 (ISBN 0-08-030862-7). Pergamon.

NUTRITION–STUDY AND TEACHING

Audiovisual Resources in Food & Nutrition: 1970-1978. 232p. 1979. 42.50 (ISBN 0-912700-50-5). Oryx Pr.

Bavly, Sarah. Family Food Consumption in Palestine. LC 76-176544. (Columbia University. Teachers College. Contributions to Education: No. 946). Repr. of 1949 ed. 22.50 (ISBN 0-404-55946-8). AMS Pr.

Bender, A. E. & Bender, D. A. Nutrition for Medical Students. LC 82-133881. 380p. 1982. 48.95x (ISBN 0-471-28041-0, Pub. by Wiley-Interscience). Wiley.

Bingham, Nelson E. Teaching Nutrition in Biology Classes: An Experimental Investigation of High School Biology Pupils in Their Study of the Relation of Food to Physical Well-Being. LC 74-176565. (Columbia University. Teachers College. Contributions to Education: No. 772). Repr. of 1939 ed. 22.50 (ISBN 0-404-55772-4). AMS Pr.

Bourne, G. H., ed. Physiology & Social Nutrition & Nutritional Education. (World Review of Nutrition & Dietetics: Vol. 38). (Illus.). x, 230p. 1982. 69.50 (ISBN 3-8055-3048-X). S Karger.

Clarke, Helen. The Professional Training of the Hospital Dietician. LC 70-176651. (Columbia University. Teachers College. Contributions to Education: No. 602). Repr. of 1934 ed. 22.50 (ISBN 0-404-55602-7). AMS Pr.

Holmes, A. C. Visual Aids in Nutrition Education: A Guide to Their Preparation & Use. 154p. (Orig.). 1968. pap. 11.00 (ISBN 92-5-100502-8, F463, FAO). Unipub.

Knight, Margaret. Teaching Nutrition & Food Science. 1976. pap. 12.95 (ISBN 0-7134-3099-0, Pub. by Batsford England). David & Charles.

LaBuza, Theodore P. The Nutrition Crisis: A Reader. LC 75-20459. (Illus.). 512p. 1975. pap. text ed. 16.95 (ISBN 0-8299-0063-2). West Pub.

Nutrition Education Curricula: Relevance Design & the Problem of Change. (Educational Studies & Documents: No. 18). 56p. 1975. pap. 5.00 (ISBN 92-3-101287-8, U433, UNESCO). Unipub.

Report of the Symposium on Education & Training in Nutrition in Europe: Bad Homburg, 1959. (Nutrition Meetings Reports: No. 26). 56p. 1960. pap. 4.50 (ISBN 0-686-92825-3, F387, FAO). Unipub.

Rudman, Jack. Public Health Nutritionist. (Career Examination Ser.: C-632). (Cloth bdg. avail. on request). pap. 10.00 (ISBN 0-8373-0632-9). Natl Learning.

Way, Wendy L. & Nitzke, Susan A. Techniques for Meeting Nutrition Education Needs. 1981. 4.00 (ISBN 0-686-34525-8). Home Econ Educ.

NUTRITION OF PLANTS

see Plants–Nutrition

NUTRITION RESEARCH

see Nutrition–Research

NUTS

Adams, Ruth & Murray, Frank. Seeds, Grains, Nuts. 1.75x (ISBN 0-915962-07-1). Cancer Control Soc.

Boethal, D. J. & Eikenbary, R. D., eds. Pest Management Programs for Deciduous Tree Fruits & Nuts. LC 79-12616. 267p. 1979. 39.50x (ISBN 0-306-40178-9, Plenum Pr). Plenum Pub.

Brooks, Reid M. & Olmo, Harold P. Register of New Fruit & Nut Varieties. 2nd rev. & enl. ed. LC 76-100017. 512p. 1972. 37.50x (ISBN 0-520-01638-6). U of Cal Pr.

Cashew Nut Processing. (Agricultural Services Bulletins: No. 6). (Eng., Fr. & Span., Illus.). 86p. 1969. pap. 7.50 (ISBN 92-5-100740-3, F702, FAO). Unipub.

Kadans, Joseph N. Encyclopedia of Fruits, Vegetables, Nuts & Seeds for Healthful Living. 1973. 12.95 (ISBN 0-13-275412-6, Reward); pap. 4.95 (ISBN 0-13-275420-7). P-H.

Micke, Warren, et al. Almond Orchard Management. LC 78-66204. 1978. pap. 6.00x (ISBN 0-931876-27-3, 4092). Ag & Nat Res.

O'Brien, Michael & Cargill, Burton F. Principles & Practices of Harvesting & Handling for Fruits & Nuts. (Illus.). 1983. lib. bdg. 62.50 (ISBN 0-87055-413-1). AVI.

Recommended International Code of Hygienic Practice for Tree Nuts. (CAC-RCP Ser.: No. 136). 12p. (Orig.). 1974. pap. 4.50 (ISBN 0-685-41472-8, F668, FAO). Unipub.

Stebbins, Robert L. & Walheim, Lance. Western Fruit, Berries & Nuts: How to Select, Grow & Enjoy. (Illus.). 192p. (Orig.). pap. 9.95 (ISBN 0-89586-078-3). H P Bks.

Sunset Editors. Fruits, Nuts & Berries: How To Grow. LC 84-80621. (Illus.). 112p. (Orig.). 1984. pap. 5.95 (ISBN 0-376-03092-5). Sunset Lane.

Walters, S. M., et al, eds. The European Garden Flora: Mononcotyledons, Pt. 2-Juncaceae to Orchidaceae, Vol. 2. (Illus.). 318p. 1984. 59.50 (ISBN 0-521-25864-2). Cambridge U Pr.

Weschcke, Carl. Growing Nuts in the North. (Illus.). 124p. 1954. 5.00 (ISBN 0-87542-881-9). Llewellyn Pubns.

Woodroof, J. G. Tree Nuts Production, Processing Products. 2nd ed. (Illus.). 1979. lib. bdg. 65.00 (ISBN 0-87055-254-6). AVI.

O

OAK

Cottam, Walter P., et al. Oak Hybridization at the University of Utah. (State Arboretum of Utah Ser.: Publication No. 1, 1982). (Illus.). 96p. 1982. 15.00 (ISBN 0-942830-00-8); pap. 10.00x (ISBN 0-942830-01-6). State Arbor.

Miller, Howard & Lamb, Samuel. Oaks of North America. (Illus.). 336p. 1984. 15.95 (ISBN 0-87961-136-7); pap. 9.95 (ISBN 0-87961-137-5). Naturegraph.

Trelease, W. The American Oaks. (Plant Monograph Ser.). (Illus.). 1969. 52.50 (ISBN 3-7682-0600-9). Lubrecht & Cramer.

OATS

Baum, B. R. Oats - Wild & Cultivated: A Monograph of the Genus Avena L. (Poaceae) 480p. 1977. 85.00x (ISBN 0-660-00513-1, Pub. by CAB Bks England). State Mutual Bk.

Coffman, F. A., ed. Oats & Oat Improvement. (Illus.). 1961. 4.50 (ISBN 0-89118-009-5). Am Soc Agron.

Interrelationships Between Potassium & Magnesium Absorption by Oats. (Agricultural Reseach Reports: No. 642). 1964. pap. 7.25 (ISBN 90-220-0103-2, PDC163, PUDOC). Unipub.

OBSERVATIONS, METEOROLOGICAL

see Meteorology–Observations

OBSERVATORIES, ASTRONOMICAL

see Astronomical Observatories

OBSERVATORIES, METEOROLOGICAL

see Meteorological Stations; Meteorology–Observations

OCEAN

see also Diving, Submarine; Underwater Exploration; Oceanography;
also names of oceans, e.g. Pacific Ocean

Barton, Robert. The Oceans. 336p. 1980. 24.95x (ISBN 0-87196-414-7). Facts on File.

Bolin, Bert, ed. The Atmosphere & the Sea in Motion. LC 59-14858. (Illus.). 512p. 1960. 10.00x (ISBN 0-87470-000-0). Rockefeller.

Borgese, Elisabeth M. & Ginsburg, Norton, eds. Ocean Yearbook, No. 5. LC 79-642855. 600p. 1985. lib. bdg. 49.00x est. (ISBN 0-226-06606-1). U of Chicago Pr.

--Ocean Yearbook: 2. LC 79-642855. 1981. 40.00x (ISBN 0-226-06603-7). U of Chicago Pr.

Borgese, Elizabeth M. & Ginsburg, Norton. Ocean Yearbook: 3. LC 79-642855. 672p. 1982. lib. bdg. 49.00x (ISBN 0-226-06604-5). U of Chicago Pr.

Borgese, Elizabeth M. & Ginsburg, Norton, eds. Ocean Yearbook: 1. 1979. 30.00x (ISBN 0-226-06602-9). U of Chicago Pr.

Bowen, F. The Sea: Its History & Romance, 4 vols. 1977. lib. bdg. 400.00 (ISBN 0-8490-2581-8). Gordon Pr.

Boyles, Allan. Acoustic Waveguides: Applications to Oceanic Science. LC 83-17000. 321p. 1984. 46.95x (ISBN 0-471-88771-4, Pub. by Wiley Interscience). Wiley.

Carson, Rachel L. Sea Around Us. 1954. pap. 3.95 (ISBN 0-451-62164-6, ME2164, Ment). NAL.

Chia, L. S. & MacAndrews, C. Southeast Asian Seas: Frontiers for Development. 1982. 36.50 (ISBN 0-07-099247-9). McGraw.

Coker, Robert E. This Great & Wide Sea: An Introduction to Oceanography & Marine Biology. (Illus.). pap. 4.95xi (ISBN 0-06-130551-0, TB551, Torch). Har-Row.

Couper, Alastair, ed. The Times Atlas of the Oceans. (Illus.). 256p. 1983. 79.95 (ISBN 0-442-21661-0). Van Nos Reinhold.

Cousteau, Jacques. Jacques Cousteau: The Ocean World. (Illus.). 1979. 60.00 (ISBN 0-8109-0777-1). Abrams.

Douglas, John S. Story of the Oceans. LC 78-106686. Repr. of 1952 ed. lib. bdg. 26.00x (ISBN 0-8371-3357-2, DOSO). Greenwood.

Fine, John C. Exploring the Sea. (Illus.). 160p. 1982. 14.95 (ISBN 0-937548-03-0). Plexus Pub.

Finn, Daniel P. Managing the Ocean Resources of the United States: The Role of the Federal Marine Sanctuary Program. (Lecture Notes in Coastal & Estuarine Studies: Vol. 2). (Illus.). 193p. 1982. pap. 18.00 (ISBN 0-387-11583-8). Springer-Verlag.

Garrett, William & Smagin, V. M. Determination of the Atmospheric Contribution of Petroleum Hydrocarbons to the Oceans. (Special Environmental Reports: No. 6). (Illus.). 27p. 1976. pap. 16.00 (ISBN 92-63-10440-9, W252, WMO). Unipub.

Gibbs, R. J. & Shaw, R. P., eds. Transport Processes in Lakes & Oceans. LC 77-11099. (Marine Science Ser.: Vol. 7). 296p. 1977. 49.50x (ISBN 0-306-35507-8, Plenum Pr). Plenum Pub.

Goldberg, Edward D., ed. The Sea: Marine Chemistry. LC 62-18366. (Ideas & Observations on Progress in the Study of the Seas Ser.: Vol. 5). 895p. 1974. 94.95x (ISBN 0-471-31090-5, Pub. by Wiley-Interscience). Wiley.

Gran Diccionario Infantil Marin, 4 vols. (Espn.). 840p. 1979. Set. 128.00 (ISBN 84-7102-150-1, S-50032). French & Eur.

Great Britain Challenger Office. Report on the Scientific Results of the Voyage of H. M. S. Challenger During the Years 1873-1876, 50 Vols. (Illus.). 1880-1895. Set. 5000.00 (ISBN 0-384-19750-7). Johnson Repr.

Groves, Donald G. & Hunt, Lee M. The Ocean World Encyclopedia. LC 79-21093. (Illus.). 1980. 49.95 (ISBN 0-07-025010-3). McGraw.

Haine, Edgar A. Disaster at Sea. LC 81-66272. (Illus.). 388p. 1982. 30.00 (ISBN 0-8453-4719-5). Cornwall Bks.

Harvey, John G. Atmosphere & Ocean: Our Fluid Environments. 144p. 1981. 30.00x (ISBN 0-686-78984-9, Pub. by Artemis England). State Mutual Bk.

Heezen, B. C. Influence of Abyssal Circulation on Sedimentary Accumulations in Space & Time. (Developments in Sedimentology Ser.: Vol. 23). 216p. 1977. 53.25 (ISBN 0-444-41569-6). Elsevier.

Kester, Dana R., et al. Wastes in the Ocean: Dredged Material Disposal in the Ocean, Vol. 2. (Environmental Science & Technology Ser.). 299p. 1983. 49.95x (ISBN 0-471-09771-3, Pub. by Wiley-Interscience). Wiley.

Lane, Ferdinand. Mysterious Sea. LC 73-128268. (Essay Index Reprint Ser). 1947. 22.00 (ISBN 0-8369-1971-8). Ayer Co Pubs.

LeTan, Pierre. Visit with a Mermaid. LC 82-15149. (Illus.). 32p. 1983. 7.95 (ISBN 0-517-54894-1, C N Potter). Crown.

El Mar, Gran Enciclopedia Salvat, 10 vols. (Espn.). 3000p. 1975. Set. 320.00 (ISBN 84-7137-428-5, S-50560). French & Eur.

Navarro Dagnino, Juan. Vocabulario Maritimo Ingles-Espanol y Espanol-Ingles. 5th ed. (Span. & Eng.). 151p. 1976. pap. 8.50 (ISBN 84-252-0225-6, S-12239). French & Eur.

The Ocean Realm. LC 77-93399. (Special Publication Ser.: 13). (Illus.). 1978. 6.95 (ISBN 0-87044-251-1); lib. bdg. 8.50 (ISBN 0-87044-256-2). Natl Geog.

Rowe, Beverly. Sea Gems. (Illus.). 64p. 1982. 22.00 (ISBN 0-88014-046-1). Mosaic Pr OH.

Rutland, Jonathan. The Sea. LC 83-50392. (Silver Burdett Color Library). 48p. 1983. 14.00 (ISBN 0-382-06729-0). Silver.

Sackett, Russell. The Edge of the Sea. (Planet Earth Ser.). (Illus.). 176p. 1983. 14.95 (ISBN 0-8094-4332-5). Time Life.

Saturday Evening Post Editors. The Saturday Evening Post Book of the Sea & Ships. LC 78-61519. (Illus.). 160p. 1978. 18.95 (ISBN 0-89387-023-4, Co-Pub by Sat Eve Post). Curtis Pub Co.

The Sea: A Select Bibliography on the Legal, Political, Economic & Technological Aspects, 1975-1978. (Eng. & Fr.). pap. 5.00 (ISBN 0-686-94863-7, UN78/1/3, UN). Unipub.

The Sea: A Select Bibliography on the Legal, Political, Economic & Technological Aspects, 1975-1976. (Eng. & Fr.). pap. 3.00 (ISBN 0-686-94864-5, UN76/1/6, UN). Unipub.

Shepherd, Stella. Like a Mantle, the Sea. LC 73-85450. (Illus.). 184p. 1971. 9.50x (ISBN 0-8214-0133-5, 82-81362). Ohio U Pr.

Sluyter, E. H. & Raddon, Ethel. Ocean Waves & Progressive Oscillatory Waves: Syllabus. 1977. pap. text ed. 4.35 (ISBN 0-89420-015-1, 234011); cassette recordings 39.30 (ISBN 0-89420-165-4, 234000). Natl Book.

Third United Nations Conference on the Law of the Sea: Official Records, Vol. IX. 191p. 1979. pap. 14.00 (ISBN 0-686-68976-3, UN79 5 3, UN). Unipub.

Trefil, James. A Scientist at the Seashore. LC 84-14112. (Illus.). 208p. 1985. 16.95 (ISBN 0-684-18235-1, ScribT). Scribner.

Vinogradov, A. P. & Udintsev, G. B., eds. The Rift Zones of the World Ocean. Kaner, N., tr. LC 75-16178. 503p. 1975. 96.95x (ISBN 0-470-90838-6). Halsted Pr.

Wegener, A. The Origins of Continents & Oceans. (Illus.). 14.75 (ISBN 0-8446-3143-4). Peter Smith.

Wegener, Alfred. Origin of Continents & Oceans. Biram, John, tr. (Illus.). 1966. pap. 5.95 (ISBN 0-486-61708-4). Dover.

Wilson, David A. Song of the Sea. 40p. (Orig.). 1970. pap. 1.50 (ISBN 0-934852-04-9). Lorien Hse.

OCEAN–RESEARCH

see Oceanographic Research

OCEAN-ATMOSPHERE INTERACTION

see also Ocean Waves

Barth, Michael C. & Titus, James G. Greenhouse Effect & Sea Level Rise. 384p. 1984. 24.50 (ISBN 0-442-20991-6). Van Nos Reinhold.

Dobson, F., et al, eds. Air-Sea Interaction: Instruments & Methods. LC 80-17895. 815p. 1980. 59.50x (ISBN 0-306-40543-1, Plenum Pr). Plenum Pub.

Hastenrath, Stefan & Lamb, Peter J. Heat Budget Atlas of the Tropical Atlantic & Eastern Pacific Oceans. LC 77-91052. (Illus.). 104p. 1978. pap. text ed. 50.00x (ISBN 0-299-07584-2). U of Wis Pr.

Houghton, John T., ed. The Global Climate. LC 83-7602. (Illus.). 350p. 1984. 52.50 (ISBN 0-521-25138-9). Cambridge U Pr.

The Influence of the Ocean on Climate: Lectures Presented at the 28th Session of the WMO Executive Committee. (No. 11). 44p. 1977. pap. 10.00 (ISBN 92-63-10472-7, W277, WMO). Unipub.

Komar, Paul D. Beach Processes & Sedimentation. (Illus.). 464p. 1976. 43.95 (ISBN 0-13-072595-1). P-H.
LeBond, P. H. & Mysak, L. A. Waves in the Ocean. (Oceanography Ser.: Vol. 20). 602p. 1981. 49.00 (ISBN 0-444-41926-8). Elsevier.
McCormick, Michael E. Ocean Wave Energy Conversion. LC 81-494. (Alternate Energy Ser.). 233p. 1981. 47.50x (ISBN 0-471-08543-X, Pub. by Wiley-Interscience). Wiley.
Mei, Chiang C. The Applied Dynamics of Ocean Surface Waves. LC 82-8639. 740p. 1982. 80.50x (ISBN 0-471-06407-6, Pub. by Wiley-Interscience). Wiley.
Meyer, R. E. & Meyer, R. E., eds. Waves on Beaches & Resulting Sediment Transport. 1972. 26.50 (ISBN 0-12-493250-9). Acad Pr.
Ocean Wave Measurement & Analysis, 2 vols. 935p. 1974. pap. 62.00x (ISBN 0-87262-116-2). Am Soc Civil Eng.
Phillips, O. M. The Dynamics of the Upper Ocean. 2nd ed. LC 76-26371. (Cambridge Monographs on Mechanics & Applied Mathematics Ser.). (Illus.). 1977. 69.50 (ISBN 0-521-21421-1). Cambridge U Pr.
Provis, D. G., ed. Waves on Water of Variable Depth. (Lecture Notes in Physics: Vol. 64). 1977. 18.00 (ISBN 0-387-08253-0). Springer-Verlag.
Russell, Robert C. Waves & Tides. LC 73-135252. (Illus.). 348p. Repr. of 1953 ed. lib. bdg. 22.50x (ISBN 0-8371-5171-6, RUWT). Greenwood.
Swamp Group, ed. Ocean Wave Modeling. 262p. 1985. 49.50x (ISBN 0-306-41685-9, Plenum Pr). Plenum Pub.
Trefil, James. A Scientist at the Seashore. LC 84-14112. (Illus.). 208p. 1985. 16.95 (ISBN 0-684-18235-1, ScribT). Scribner.

OCEANARIUMS
see Marine Aquariums

OCEANEERING
see Ocean Engineering

OCEANOGRAPHERS
see also Oceanography As a Profession

Craig, Robert D. & Clement, Russell T., eds. Who's Who In Oceania: 1980-1981. 1981. 12.95 (ISBN 0-939154-13-7); pap. 7.95 (ISBN 0-939154-14-5). Inst Polynesian.
Lewis, Charles L. Matthew Fontaine Maury. LC 79-6116. (Navies & Men Ser.). (Illus.). 1980. Repr. of 1927 ed. lib. bdg. 28.50x (ISBN 0-405-13045-7). Ayer Co Pubs.
Rudman, Jack. Oceanographer. (Career Examination Ser.: C-550). (Cloth bdg. avail. on request). pap. 12.00 (ISBN 0-8373-0550-0). Natl Learning.
U. S. Directory of Marine Scientists, 1982. 1982. 12.25 (ISBN 0-309-03281-4). Natl Acad Pr.
Varley, Allen, ed. Who's Who in Ocean Freshwater Science. 336p. 165.00x (ISBN 0-582-90050-6, Pub. by Longman). Gale.

OCEANOGRAPHIC INSTRUMENTS

McConnell, A. No Sea too Deep: History of Oceanographic Instruments. 188p. 1982. 43.00 (ISBN 0-9960020-9-X). Heyden.

OCEANOGRAPHIC RESEARCH
see also Underwater Exploration

Beebe, William. The Arcturus Adventure: An Account of the New York Zoological Society's First Oceanographic Expedition. 1926. 27.50 (ISBN 0-8482-0138-8). Norwood Edns.
Drew, E. A., et al, eds. Underwater Research. 1976. 68.00 (ISBN 0-12-221950-3). Acad Pr.
Gautier, Catherine & Fieux, Michele, eds. Large-Scale Oceanographic Experiments & Satellites. 1984. lib. bdg. 48.00 (ISBN 90-277-1786-9, Pub. by Reidel Holland). Kluwer Academic.
Global Ocean Research. (Reports on Marine Science Affairs: No. 1). 47p. (Orig.). 1970. pap. 5.00 (ISBN 0-685-04911-6, W267, WMO). Unipub.
Guide to the Measurement of Marine Primary Production Under Some Special Conditions. (Monographs on Oceanographic Methodology: No. 3). (Illus.). 73p. (Orig.). 1973. pap. 5.00 (ISBN 92-3-101099-9, U278, UNESCO). Unipub.
Hulm, Peter. A Strategy for the Seas: The Regional Seas Programme Past & Future. 28p. 1984. 5.00 (UNEP090, UNEP). Unipub.
Jane's Ocean Technology, 1974-1975. 79.50 (ISBN 0-531-02744-9). Key Bk Serv.
Jane's Ocean Technology 1978. 79.50x (ISBN 0-686-73472-6). Key Bk Serv.
Kuperman, William A. & Jensen, Finn B., eds. Bottom-Interacting Ocean Acoustics. LC 80-24616. (NATO Conference Series IV-Marine Sciences: Vol. 5). 730p. 1981. 95.00x (ISBN 0-306-40624-1, Plenum Pr). Plenum Pub.
Marchuk, G. I. & Kagan, B. A. Ocean Tides: Mathematical Models & Numerical Experiments. Cartwright, D. E., tr. LC 82-18898. (Illus.). 240p. 1984. 72.00 (ISBN 0-08-026236-8). Pergamon.
Means of Acquisition & Communication of Ocean Data, 2 vols. (Report on Marine Science Affairs: Nos. 6&7). (Illus., Orig.). 1973. Vol. 1 Ocean Data Requirements & Communication Facilities. pap. 40.00 (ISBN 0-685-34558-0, W272, WMO); Vol. 2 Surface, Sub-surface & Upper-Air Observations. pap. 80.00 (ISBN 0-685-34559-9, W271). Unipub.
Muratov, M. Origin of Continents & Ocean Basins. 191p. 1977. 6.45 (ISBN 0-8285-0797-X, Pub. by Mir Pubs USSR). Imported Pubns.
Ocean Observing System Development Programme. (Intergovernmental Oceanographic Commission Technical Ser.: No. 27). 31p. 1985. pap. 7.50 (ISBN 92-3-102289-X, U1440, UNESCO). Unipub.
The R-V Pillsbury Deep-Sea Biological Expedition to the Gulf of Guinea, 1964-1965. Incl. Part 1. 1966. 5.50x (ISBN 0-87024-085-4); Part 2. 1970. 7.95x (ISBN 0-87024-190-7). (Studies in Tropical Oceanography Ser: No. 4). U Miami Marine.
Rodenhuis, David R., ed. The Final Plan for the GATE Sub-Programme Data Centres. 1976. pap. 25.00 (ISBN 0-685-74526-0, W275, WMO). Unipub.
Schlee, Susan. On Almost Any Wind: The Saga of the Oceanographic Research Vessel "Atlantis". LC 78-58038. (Illus.). 336p. 1978. 24.95x (ISBN 0-8014-1160-2). Cornell U Pr.
Steward, Robard H. Methods of Satellite Oceanography. LC 83-18017. 1985. 32.50x (ISBN 0-520-04226-3). U of Cal Pr.
Tsuchiya, Mizuki. Upper Waters of the Intertropical Pacific Ocean. LC 68-9513. (Oceanographic Studies: No. 4). 50p. 1968. text ed. 8.50x (ISBN 0-8018-0636-4). Johns Hopkins.
Van Andel, Tjeerd. Tales of An Old Ocean. (Illus.). 1978. pap. 8.95 (ISBN 0-393-03213-2, Norton Lib); pap. 3.95 (ISBN 0-393-00883-5). Norton.
Wooster, Warren S. Freedom of Oceanic Research. LC 73-81050. 256p. 1973. 18.00x (ISBN 0-8448-0214-X). Crane-Russak Co.
Zooplankton Sampling. (Monographs on Oceanographic Methodology: No. 2). 174p. (3rd Printing 1979). 1968. pap. 13.75 (ISBN 92-3-101194-4, U737, UNESCO). Unipub.

OCEANOGRAPHY
see also Abyssal Zone; Astronautics in Oceanography; Chemical Oceanography; Coasts; Hydrography; Diving, Submarine; Marine Biology; Meteorology, Maritime; Navigation; Ocean; Ocean-Atmosphere Interaction; Ocean Bottom; Ocean Currents; Ocean Engineering; Ocean Temperature; Ocean Waves; Oceanographers; Oceanographic Instruments; Oceanographic Research; Sea-Water; Sounding and Soundings; Submarine Geology; Tides; Underwater Exploration

Adam, Robert E. Oceans of the World: Syllabus. 1978. pap. text ed. 5.35 (ISBN 0-89420-041-0, 233021); cassette recordings 70.85 (ISBN 0-89420-166-2, 233000). Natl Book.
Agence de Cooperation Culturelle et Technique, ed. Vocabulaire De L'oceanologie. (Fr.). 431p. 1976. pap. 49.95 (ISBN 0-686-57252-1, M-6560). French & Eur.
Angel, M. V. Progress in Oceanography, Vol. 8. (Illus.). 296p. 1980. 115.00 (ISBN 0-08-022963-8). Pergamon.
Angel, M. V. & O'Brien, J. Progress in Oceanography, Vol. 9, Nos. 1-4. (Illus.). 246p. 1982. 115.00 (ISBN 0-08-027116-2). Pergamon.
Angel, M. V. & O'Brien, J., eds. Progress in Oceanography, Vol. 10. (Illus.). 226p. 1982. 106.00 (ISBN 0-08-029121-X). Pergamon.
Angel, M. V. & O'Brien, J. J., eds. Progress in Oceanography, Vol. 12. (Illus.). 470p. 1984. 150.00 (ISBN 0-08-031504-6). Pergamon.
--Progress in Oceanography, Vol. 13. (Illus.). 520p. 1985. 160.00 (ISBN 0-08-032724-9, Pub. by Aberdeen Scotland). Pergamon.
Angel, Martin V., ed. A Voyage of Discovery: George Deacon 70th Anniversary Volume. new ed. LC 76-57958. 1977. 145.00 (ISBN 0-08-021380-4). Pergamon.
Anikouchine, William & Sternberg, Richard. The World Ocean. 2nd ed. (Illus.). 512p. 1981. 31.95 (ISBN 0-13-967778-X). P-H.
Baker, Joseph T. & Murphy, Vreni, eds. Handbook of Marine Science: Section B, Compounds from Marine Organisms, Vol. 1. 216p. 1976. 54.00 (ISBN 0-87819-391-X). CRC Pr.
Banner, F. T. & Collins, M. B. Northwest European Shelf Seas: The Sea-Bed & the Sea in Motion, Vol. 2, Physical & Chemical Oceanography & Physical Resources. (Oceanography Ser.: Vol. 24B). 338p. 1980. 95.75 (ISBN 0-444-41739-7). Elsevier.
Barkley, Richard A. Oceanographic Atlas of the Pacific Ocean. (Illus.). 1969. text ed. 50.00x (ISBN 0-87022-050-0). UH Pr.
Barnes, H. Oceanography & Marine Biology. 1959. 10.75 (ISBN 0-08-026258-9). Pergamon.
Barnes, Harold, ed. Oceanography & Marine Biology: An Annual Review, Vol. 15. 1977. 75.00 (ISBN 0-900015-39-X). Taylor-Carlisle.
--Oceanography & Marine Biology: An Annual Review, Vol. 16. 1978. 80.00 (ISBN 0-900015-44-6). Taylor-Carlisle.
--Oceanography & Marine Biology: Annual Review, Vol. 14. 1976. 75.00 (ISBN 0-900015-37-3). Taylor-Carlisle.
Barnes, M. Oceanography & Marine Biology: An Annual Review, Vol. 20. (Illus.). 778p. 1983. 82.80 (ISBN 0-08-028460-4). Pergamon.
Barnes, M., ed. Oceanography & Marine Biology: An Annual Review, Vol. 21. (Oceanography & Marine Biology Ser.). (Illus.). 590p. 1983. 82.80 (ISBN 0-08-030360-9). Pergamon.
Barnes, Margaret, ed. Oceanography & Marine Biology: An Annual Review. LC 64-1930. (Oceanography & Marine Biology Ser.: Vol. 22). (Illus.). 590p. 1984. 76.80 (ISBN 0-08-030392-7). Pergamon.
Barnes, Margaret & Barnes, Harold, eds. Oceanography & Marine Biology: An Annual Review, Vol. 18. (Illus.). 528p. 1980. 63.00 (ISBN 0-08-025732-1). Pergamon.
Barton, Robert. Atlas of the Sea. LC 73-18541. (John Day Bk.). (Illus.). 128p. 1974. 10.95i (ISBN 0-381-98267-X). T Y Crowell.
Bascom, Willard. Waves & Beaches: The Dynamics of the Ocean Surface. rev. updated ed. LC 79-7038. (Illus.). 1980. pap. 8.95 (ISBN 0-385-14844-5, Anchor Pr). Doubleday.
Beebe, William. The Arcturus Adventure: An Account of the New York Zoological Society's First Oceanographic Expedition. 1926. 27.50 (ISBN 0-8482-0138-8). Norwood Edns.
Beer, T. Environmental Oceanography: An Introduction to the Behaviour of Coastal Waters. LC 82-18099. (PIL Ser.). (Illus.). 109p. 1983. 30.00 (ISBN 0-08-026291-0); pap. 13.00 (ISBN 0-08-026290-2). Pergamon.
Belderson, R. H., et al. Sonographs of the Sea Floor: A Picture Atlas. 185p. 1972. 87.25 (ISBN 0-444-40984-X). Elsevier.
Bernabo, M. & Picchi, F. Grande Dizionario di Marina: Inglese-Italiano, Italiano-Inglese. (Eng. & Ital.). 963p. 1970. 95.00 (ISBN 0-686-92551-3, M-9298). French & Eur.
Bischoff, J. L. & Piper, D. Z., eds. Marine Geology & Oceanography of the Pacific Manganese Nodule Province. LC 79-12475. (Marine Science Ser.: Vol. 9). 855p. 1979. 89.50x (ISBN 0-306-40187-8, Plenum Pr). Plenum Pub.
Bishop, Joseph M. Applied Oceanography. LC 83-26091. (Ocean Engineering Ser.: 1-194). 300p. 1984. text ed. 32.95x (ISBN 0-471-87445-0, Pub. by Wiley-Interscience). Wiley.
Boje, R. & Tomczak, M., eds. Upwelling Ecosystems. (Illus.). 1978. pap. 34.00 (ISBN 0-387-08822-9). Springer-Verlag.
Borgese, Elisabeth M. & Ginsburg, Norton, eds. Ocean Yearbook, No. 5. LC 79-642855. 600p. 1985. lib. bdg. 49.00x est. (ISBN 0-226-06606-1). U of Chicago Pr.
--Ocean Yearbook: 4. LC 79-642855. 620p. 1984. text ed. 49.00x (ISBN 0-226-06605-3). U of Chicago Pr.
Bowden, K. F. The Physical Oceanography of Coastal Waters. 302p. 1983. 71.95x (ISBN 0-470-27505-7). Halsted Pr.
Boyer, Robert E. Oceanography Fact Book. LC 74-1649. (Fact Bks.). (Illus.). 48p. 1974. pap. text ed. 5.95 (ISBN 0-8331-1707-6). Hubbard Sci.
Braynard, Frank O., frwd. by. A Descriptive Catalogue of the Marine Collection to Be Found at India House. 2nd ed. LC 73-7088. (Illus.). 280p. 1973. 100.00x (ISBN 0-8195-4065-X). Wesleyan U Pr.
Bretschneider, Charles L. Topics in Ocean Engineering, 3 vols. Incl. Vol. 1. 428p. 1969 (ISBN 0-87201-598-X); Vol. 2. (Illus.). 229p. 1970 (ISBN 0-87201-599-8); Vol. 3. 328p. 1976 (ISBN 0-87201-600-5). LC 78-87230. 29.50x ea. Gulf Pub.
Brewer, P. G. Oceanography: The Present & the Future. (Illus.). 392p. 1983. 42.00 (ISBN 0-387-90720-3). Springer-Verlag.
Broecker, W. S. & Peng, T. H. Tracers in the Sea. (Illus.). 690p. 1982. text ed. 40.00 (ISBN 0-86542-310-5). Blackwell Sci.
Brown, Seyom, et al. Regimes for the Ocean, Outer Space, & Weather. 1977. 22.95 (ISBN 0-8157-1156-5); pap. 8.95 (ISBN 0-8157-1155-7). Brookings.
Brunn Memorial Lectures. Incl. 1971: Presented at the 7th Session of the IOC Assembly, UNESCO, Paris, Oct. 26-Nov. 6, 1961. (No. 10). 43p. 1972. pap. 5.00 (ISBN 92-3-101014-X, U61); 1973: Presented at the 8th Session of the IOC Assembly, UNESCO, Paris Nov. 5-17, 1973. (No. 11). 63p. 1975. pap. 5.00 (ISBN 92-3-101274-6, U62); 1975. (No. 15). 1978 (ISBN 92-3-101526-5, U794); 1977, 10th Session, Paris, 1977. Intergovernmental Oceanographic Commission Assembly. (No. 19). 64p. 1979 (ISBN 92-3-101746-2, U794); 1979: Presented at the 11th Session of the IOC Assembly, UNESCO, Paris, Nov. 1, 1979. (No. 21). 40p. 1981. pap. 5.00 (ISBN 92-3-101947-3, U1129). (Intergovernmental Oceanographic Commission Technical Ser.). (Orig.). pap. 5.00 (UNESCO). Unipub.
Bryan, George M. & Heirtzler, James R. Ocean Margin Drilling Program Atlases, Vol. 5. (Regional Atlas Ser.). 1984. write for info. spiral bdg (ISBN 0-86720-255-6, Marine Sci Intl). Jones & Bartlett.
Burke, William T. Ocean Sciences, Technology, & the Future International Law of the Sea. LC 66-63004. 91p. (Orig.). 1966. pap. 1.50 (ISBN 0-8142-0031-1). Ohio St U Pr.
Capurro, L. R. & Reid, Joseph L., eds. Contributions on the Physical Oceanography of the Gulf of Mexico. LC 71-135998. (Texas A&M University Oceanographic Studies on the Gulf of Mexico: Vol. 2). 288p. 1972. 29.95x (ISBN 0-87201-347-2). Gulf Pub.
Center for Ocean Management Studies. Comparative Marine Policy. 272p. 1981. 29.95x (ISBN 0-686-77546-5). Bergin & Garvey.
Charlier, Roger H. & Gordon, Bernard L. Ocean Resources: An Introduction to Economic Oceanography. LC 78-61393. (Illus.). 1978. pap. text ed. 11.00 (ISBN 0-8191-0599-6). U Pr of Amer.
Charnock, H. & Deacon, G., eds. Advances in Oceanography. LC 78-17970. 364p. 1978. 59.50x (ISBN 0-306-40019-7, Plenum Pr). Plenum Pub.
CICAR II: Symposium on Progress in Marine Research in the Caribbean & Adjacent Regions: Papers on Oceanography, Meteorology & Geophysics, Caracas, 12-16 July 1976. (Fisheries Reports: No. 200, Suppl. 25X). (Eng. & Span.). 647p. 1979. pap. 30.25 (ISBN 92-5-000707-8, F1598, FAO). Unipub.
Clay, Clarence S. & Medwin, Herman. Acoustical Oceanography: Principles & Applications. LC 77-1133. (Ocean Engineering Ser.). 544p. 1977. text ed. 59.95x (ISBN 0-471-16041-5, Pub. by Wiley-Interscience). Wiley.
Collias, Eugene E. & Andreeva, Svetlana I. Puget Sound Marine Environment: An Annotated Bibliography. LC 77-24231. 402p. 1978. pap. 13.50x (ISBN 0-295-95570-8, Pub. by Washington Sea Grant). U of Wash Pr.
Committee On Oceanography & Committee On Ocean Engineering. Oceanic Quest: The International Decade of Ocean Exploration. (Orig.). 1969. pap. 6.00 (ISBN 0-309-01709-2). Natl Acad Pr.
Costlow, John D., ed. Fertility of the Sea, 2 vols. LC 74-132383. (Illus.). 646p. 1971. Set. 121.50 (ISBN 0-677-14730-9). Gordon.
Cracknell, Arthur P., ed. Remote Sensing Applications in Marine Science & Technology. 1983. lib. bdg. 78.00 (ISBN 90-2771-608-0, Pub. by Reidel Holland). Kluwer Academic.
Crease, J., et al, eds. Essays on Oceanography: A Tribute to John Swallow. (Illus.). 578p. 1984. 162.00 (ISBN 0-08-032339-1). Pergamon.
Csanady, G. T. Circulation in the Coastal Ocean. 1982. 52.50 (ISBN 90-277-1400-2, Pub. by Reidel Holland). Kluwer Academic.
Davis, Richard A. Principles of Oceanography. 2nd ed. LC 76-10436. (Illus.). 1977. text ed. 27.95 (ISBN 0-201-01464-5). Addison-Wesley.
Deacon, G. E. R. & Deacon, Margaret B., eds. Modern Concepts of Oceanography. LC 81-6239. (Benchmark Papers in Geology Ser.: Vol. 61). 386p. 1982. 48.95 (ISBN 0-87933-390-1). Van Nos Reinhold.
Deacon, Margaret B. Oceanography: Concepts & History. LC 76-27682. (Benchmark Papers in Geology Ser.: Vol. 35). 1978. 44.50 (ISBN 0-87933-202-6). Van Nos Reinhold.
De Sylva, Donald P. The Alfred C. Glassell, Jr. - University of Miami Argosy Expedition to Ecuador: Part 1: Introduction & Narrative. LC 72-125657. (Studies in Tropical Oceanography Ser: No. 11). 1972. 6.95x (ISBN 0-87024-171-0). U Miami Marine.
Diemer, Ferdinand, et al, eds. Advanced Concepts in Ocean Measurements for Marine Biology. LC 79-24802. (Belle Baruch Library Ser.: Vol. 10). (Illus.). xvi, 572p. 1980. text ed. 39.95x (ISBN 0-87249-388-1). U of SC Pr.
Dietrich, Gunther, et al. General Oceanography: An Introduction. 2nd ed. LC 80-12919. 626p. 1980. 74.95x (ISBN 0-471-02102-4, Pub. by Wiley-Interscience). Wiley.

Pickard, G. L. Descriptive Physical Oceanography. 4th ed. (International Series in Geophysics). (Illus.). 1982. text ed. 39.00 (ISBN 0-08-026280-5); pap. text ed. 11.95 (ISBN 0-08-026279-1). Pergamon.

Pickard, G. L. & Pond, S. Introductory Dynamic Oceanography. 2nd ed. LC 77-4427. (Illus.). 368p. 1978. text ed. 45.00 (ISBN 0-08-028729-8); pap. text ed. 12.50 (ISBN 0-08-028728-X). Pergamon.

Pipkin, Bernard W., et al. Laboratory Exercises in Oceanography. (Illus.). 255p. 1977. lab. manual 12.95 (ISBN 0-7167-0181-2); tchrs. manual avail. W H Freeman.

Pirie, R. Gordon, ed. Oceanography: Contemporary Readings in Ocean Sciences. 2nd ed. (Illus.). 1977. pap. text ed. 13.95x (ISBN 0-19-502119-3). Oxford U Pr.

Platt, T., et al. Mathematical Models in Biological Oceanography. (Monographs on Oceanographic Methodology: No. 7). (Illus.). 157p. 1982. pap. 18.75 (ISBN 92-3-101922-8, U1200, UNESCO). Unipub.

PROBES: A Prospectus on Processes & Resources of the Bering Sea Shelf Nineteen Seventy-Five to Nineteen Eighty-Five. write for info. (ISBN 0-914500-05-8). U of AK Inst Marine.

Rasmusson, E. M. Hydrological Application of Atmospheric Vapour-Flux Analyses. (Operational Hydrology Reports: No. 11). (Illus.). x, 50p. 1977. pap. 10.00 (ISBN 92-63-10476-X, W354, WMO). Unipub.

Regional Association IV (North & Central America) Abridged Final Report of the Seventh Session, Mexico City 26 April-5 May 1977. (Illus.). 1977. pap. 25.00 (ISBN 92-63-10479-4, W366, WMO). Unipub.

Reid, Joseph L., ed. Antarctic Oceanology One. LC 78-151300. (Antarctic Research Ser.: Vol. 15). (Illus.). 343p. 1971. 28.50 (ISBN 0-87590-115-8). Am Geophysical.

Reid, Joseph L., Jr. Northwest Pacific Ocean Waters in Winter. LC 72-12351. (Oceanographic Studies: No. 5). (Illus.). 96p. 1973. 12.00x (ISBN 0-8018-1466-9). Johns Hopkins.

Report of the Decade: The International Decade of Ocean Exploration. 4.75 (ISBN 0-318-18094-4, NSF -82-16). NSF.

Report of the Fifth Session of WMO Executive Committee Inter-Governmental Panel on the First GARP Global Experiment. (GARP Special Reports: No. 26). (Illus.). 45p. 1978. pap. 15.00 (ISBN 0-685-27460-8, W383, WMO). Unipub.

Report of the First Session of the West African Monsoon Experiment (WAMEX) Scientific & Management Regional Committee. (GARP Special Reports: No. 31). (Eng. & Fr.). 14p. 1979. pap. 15.00 (ISBN 0-686-52645-7, W426, WMO). Unipub.

Report of the Fourth Planning Meeting for the Monsoon Experiment (MONEX) (GARP Special Reports: No. 28). (Illus.). 54p. 1978. pap. 40.00 (ISBN 0-685-65240-8, W402, WMO). Unipub.

Report of the Fourth Session of WMO Executive Committee Inter-Governmental Panel on the First GARP Global Experiment. (GARP Special Reports: No. 24). v, 63p. (Appendices A-H). 1977. pap. 25.00 (ISBN 0-685-86035-3, W309, WMO). Unipub.

Report on the Agro-Ecological Zones Project: Methodology & Results for South & Central America, Vol. 3. (World Soil Resources Reports: No. 48-3). (Eng. & Span.). 251p. 1982. pap. 19.75 (ISBN 92-5-101081-1, F2225, FAO). Unipub.

Rezak, Richard & Henry, Vernon J., eds. Contributions on the Geological & Geophysical Oceanography of the Gulf of Mexico. LC 73-149761. (Texas A&M University Oceanographic Studies on the Gulf of Mexico: Vol. 3). 303p. 1972. 29.95x (ISBN 0-87201-348-0). Gulf Pub.

Riley, S. P. & Skirrow, G., eds. Chemical Oceanography, 6 vols. 2nd ed. Vol. 1. 1975. 95.00 (ISBN 0-12-588601-2); Vol. 2. 1975. 95.00 (ISBN 0-12-588602-0); Vol. 3. 1975. 95.00 (ISBN 0-12-588603-9); Vol. 4. 1975. 60.00 (ISBN 0-12-588604-7); Vol. 5. 1976. 70.00 (ISBN 0-12-588605-5); Vol. 6. 1976. 70.00 (ISBN 0-12-588606-3). Acad Pr.

Robinson. Satellite Oceanography: An Introduction for Oceanographers & Remote-Sensing Scientist. (Marine Science Ser.). 1985. 59.95 (ISBN 0-470-20148-7). Wiley.

Robinson, A. R. Eddies in Marine Science. (Topics in Atmospheric & Oceanographic Sciences Ser.). (Illus.). 625p. 1983. 47.00 (ISBN 0-387-12253-2). Springer-Verlag.

Rona, Peter A., ed. Mid-Atlantic Ridge, Part 1 & 2. LC 76-47736. (Microform Publication: No. 5). (Illus.). 1976. 9.00 (ISBN 0-8137-6005-4). Geol Soc.

Ross, D. A. Opportunities & Uses of the Ocean. LC 79-12694. (Illus.). 1979. 26.50 (ISBN 0-387-90448-4). Springer-Verlag.

Ross, David A. Introduction to Oceanography. 3rd ed. (Illus.). 528p. 1982. 31.95 (ISBN 0-13-491357-4). P-H.

Royal Society Discussion Meeting, June 2-3, 1982. Results of the Royal Society Joint-Air-Sea Interaction Project (JASIN) Proceedings. Charnock, H. & Pollard, R. T., eds. (Phil. Trans Royal Society, Series A: Vol. 308). (Illus.). 229p. 1983. Repr. text ed. 70.00x (ISBN 0-85403-206-1, Pub. by Royal Soc London). Scholium Intl.

Royce, William F. Introduction to the Practice of Fishery Science. 1984. 35.00 (ISBN 0-12-600960-0). Acad Pr.

Sachs, Moshe Y., ed. Sea-Bed Nineteen Sixty-Nine, 7 vols. LC 73-171925. 1971. Set. 590.00 (ISBN 0-405-02587-4); 71.50; Index. 88.00 (ISBN 0-405-02595-5). Ayer Co Pubs.

Schopf, Thomas J. Paleoceanography. LC 79-12546. (Illus.). 1980. 25.00x (ISBN 0-674-65215-0). Harvard U Pr.

Scientific American Editors. The Ocean: A Scientific American Book. LC 71-102897. (Illus.). 140p. 1969. pap. text ed. 10.95x (ISBN 0-7167-0997-X). W H Freeman.

Scientific Report of the Intercalibration Exercise: The IOC-WMO-UNEP, Pilot Project on Monitoring Background Levels of Selected Pollutants in Open Ocean Waters. (Intergovernmental Oceanographic Commission Technical Ser.: No. 22). 91p. 1983. pap. 5.25 (ISBN 92-3-102077-3, U1260, UNESCO). Unipub.

Sears, M. & Merriman, D., eds. Oceanography: The Past. (Illus.). 812p. 1980. 44.00 (ISBN 0-387-90497-2). Springer-Verlag.

Sears, M. & Warren, Bruce, eds. Progress in Oceanography, Vols. 1 & 4-6. LC 63-15353. text ed. write for info. Vol. 1 1964 (ISBN 0-08-010199-2). Vol. 4 1967 (ISBN 0-08-012124-1). Vol. 5 1969. (ISBN 0-08-012631-6). Vol. 6, 1974 (ISBN 0-08-017707-7). Pergamon.

Seeber, G. & Apel, J. R., eds. Geodetic Features of the Ocean Surface & Their Implications. 1984. Repr. lib. bdg. 42.00 (ISBN 90-277-1840-7, Pub. by Reidel Holland). Kluwer Academic.

Shepard, Francis & Dill, Robert. Submarine Canyons & Other Sea Valleys. LC 66-13451. 381p. 1966. 24.00 (ISBN 0-471-78315-3, Pub. by Wiley). Krieger.

Shor, Alexander & Uchipi, Elazar. Ocean Margin Drilling Program Atlases, Vol. 2. (Regional Atlas Ser.). 1984. write for info. spiral bdg (ISBN 0-86720-252-1, Marine Sci Intl). Jones & Bartlett.

Shor, Alexander N. & Uchipi, Elazar. Ocean Margin Drilling Program Atlases, Vol. 3. (Regional Atlas Ser.). 1984. write for info. spiral bdg (ISBN 0-86720-253-X, Marine Sci Intl). Jones & Bartlett.

Siedler, G., et al. GATE: Containing Results from the GARP Atlantic Tropical Experiment (GATE) Including the Proceedings of the GATE Symposium on Oceanography & Surface Layer Meteorology, Kiel May 1978. 140.00 (ISBN 0-08-023983-8). Pergamon.

Sluyter, E. H. & Raddon, Ethel. Ocean Waves & Progressive Oscillatory Waves: Syllabus. 1977. pap. text ed. 4.35 (ISBN 0-89420-015-1, 234011); cassette recordings 39.30 (ISBN 0-89420-165-4, 234000). Natl Book.

Smith, F. Walton & Kalber, F. A., eds. Handbook in Marine Science, CRC: Section A, Oceanography. LC 73-88624. 640p. 1974. Vol. 1. 59.95 (ISBN 0-87819-389-8); Vol. 2, 390p. 56.00 (ISBN 0-87819-390-1). CRC Pr.

Sorensen, Robert M. Basic Coastal Engineering. LC 77-29256. (Ocean Engineering Ser.). 227p. 1978. 39.95 (ISBN 0-471-81370-2, Pub. by Wiley-Interscience). Wiley.

Steinbeck, John & Ricketts, Edward F. Sea of Cortez: A Leisurely Journal of Travel & Research. (Illus.). 640p. Repr. of 1941 ed. 30.00 (ISBN 0-911858-08-3). Appel.

Stern, Melvin E. Ocean Circulation Physics. (International Geophysics Ser.). 1975. 57.50 (ISBN 0-12-666750-0). Acad Pr.

Stevenson, Merritt R., et al. A Marine Atlas of the Pacific Coastal Waters of South America. LC 79-85448. (Illus.). 1970. 110.00x (ISBN 0-520-01616-5). U of Cal Pr.

Stockman, Robert H. The Intergovernmental Oceanographic Commission: An Uncertain Future. (Washington Sea Grant Ser.). 150p. 1974. pap. 5.50x (ISBN 0-295-95371-3). U of Wash Pr.

Stommel, Henry & Fieux, Michele. Oceanographic Atlases: A Guide to Their Geographic Coverage & Contents. LC 78-70786. 1978. 15.00 (ISBN 0-915176-22-X); pap. 7.50x (ISBN 0-915176-21-1). Job Shop.

Stommel, Henry & Yoshida, Kozo, eds. Kuroshio: Physical Aspects of the Japan Current. LC 72-378. (Illus.). 527p. 1972. 42.50x (ISBN 0-295-95225-3). U of Wash Pr.

Stowe, Keith S. Ocean Science. 2nd ed. LC 82-16120. 673p. 1983. pap. text ed. 35.50 (ISBN 0-471-86719-5); tchrs' manual avail. (ISBN 0-471-87151-6). Wiley.

Swallow, Mary, ed. Progress in Oceanography, Vol. 7. Incl. Pt. 1. Midwater Fishes in the Eastern North Atlantic. 1976. pap. 8.50 (ISBN 0-08-020877-0); Pt. 2. The Mixing & Spreading of Medoc. 1976. pap. 7.50 (ISBN 0-08-020888-6); Pt. 3. 1977. pap. 6.50 (ISBN 0-08-020890-8); Pt. 4. Observations of Rossby Waves Near Site D. 1977. pap. 6.00 (ISBN 0-08-020892-4); Pts. 5 & 6. Date not set. 17.50 (ISBN 0-08-022069-X); Vol. 7 Complete. Date not set. 76.00 (ISBN 0-08-020329-9). LC 63-15353. pap. write for info. Pergamon.

Takenouti, Y. & Hood, D. W., eds. Bering Sea Oceanography: An Update Nineteen Seventy-Two to Nineteen Seventy-Four. 7.00 (ISBN 0-914500-06-6). U of AK Inst Marine.

Taylor, Geoffrey I. Scientific Papers, 4 vols. Batchelor, G. K., ed. Incl. Vol. 1. Mechanics of Solids. 95.00 (ISBN 0-521-06608-5); Vol. 2. Meteorology, Oceanography & Turbulent Flow. 1960. 95.00 (ISBN 0-521-06609-3); Vol. 3. Aerodynamics & the Mechanics of Projectiles & Explosions. 1963. 95.00 (ISBN 0-521-06610-7); Vol. 4. Mechanics of Fluids: Miscellaneous Topics. (Illus.). 1971. 95.00 (ISBN 0-521-07995-0). Cambridge U Pr.

Tchernia, P. Descriptive Regional Oceanography. Densmore, D., tr. (Pergamon Marine Ser.: Vol. 3). (Illus.). 256p. 1980. 62.00 (ISBN 0-08-020925-4); pap. 21.00 (ISBN 0-08-020919-X). Pergamon.

Thomasson, E. M., compiled by. Study of the Sea: The Development of Marine Research Under the Auspices of the International Council for the Exploration of the Sea. (Illus.). 272p. 1981. 78.75 (ISBN 0-85238-112-3, FN92, FNB). Unipub.

Thurman, Harold V. Essentials of Oceanography. 512p. 1983. text ed. 20.95 (ISBN 0-675-20031-8). Additional supplements may be obtained from the publisher. Merrill.

--Introductory Oceanography. 4th ed. 544p. 1985. text ed. 28.95 (ISBN 0-675-20375-9). Additional supplements may be obtained from publisher. Merrill.

Timchenko, I. E. Stochastic Modeling of Ocean Dynamics. 320p. 1984. text ed. 135.00 (ISBN 3-7186-0231-8). Harwood Academic.

Time Series of Ocean Measurements, Vol. 1. (Intergovernmental Oceanographic Commission Technical Ser.: No. 24). 46p. 1983. pap. text ed. 5.00 (ISBN 92-3-102171-0, U1324, UNESCO). Unipub.

Toba, Y. & Mitsuyasu, H., eds. The Ocean Surface. 1985. lib. bdg. 69.00 (ISBN 90-277-2021-5, Pub. by Reidel Holland). Kluwer-Academic.

Toksoz, M. N., et al. Oceanic Ridges & Arcs: Geodynamic Processes. (Developments in Geotectonics Ser.: Vol. 14). 538p. 1980. 34.00 (ISBN 0-444-41839-3). Elsevier.

Tolmazin, David. Elements of Dynamic Oceanography. 192p. 1985. text ed. 35.00x (ISBN 0-04-551070-9); pap. text ed. 19.95x (ISBN 0-04-551071-7). Allen Unwin.

Tooley, M. J. Sea-Level Changes: North-West England During the Flandrian Stage. (Research Studies in Geography Ser.). (Illus.). 1979. 39.00x (ISBN 0-19-823228-4). Oxford U Pr.

Turekian, Karl K. Oceans. 2nd ed. (Illus.). 160p. 1976. 15.95 (ISBN 0-13-630426-5). P-H.

Tyler, John E., ed. Light in the Sea. (Benchmark Paper in Optics Ser.: Vol. 3). 1977. 61.50 (ISBN 0-12-787595-6). Acad Pr.

Van Andel, Tjeerd. Science at Sea: Tales of an Old Ocean. LC 81-9867. (Illus.). 186p. 1981. 19.95x (ISBN 0-7167-1363-2); pap. 10.95 (ISBN 0-7167-1364-0). W H Freeman.

Van Dorn, William G. Oceanography & Seamanship: A Guide for Ocean Cruising. LC 73-15377. (Illus.). 550p. 1974. 22.50 (ISBN 0-396-06888-X). Dodd.

Van Loon, H. Climates of the Ocean. (World Survey of Climatology Ser.: Vol. 15). 300p. 1984. 173.00 (ISBN 0-444-41337-5, I-090-84). Elsevier.

Van Micghan, J. Meteorological Aspects of the Contributions Presented at the Joint Oceanographic Assembly: Edinburgh, 13-24 Sept. 1976. (Reports on Marine Science Affairs: No. 12). (Eng. & Fr.). v, 17p. 1978. pap. 10.00 (ISBN 92-63-10499-9, W420, WMO). Unipub.

Vilhjalmsson, Thor. The Deep Blue Sea: Pardon the Ocean. 57p. 1981. pap. 6.00 (ISBN 0-910477-01-9). LoonBooks.

Voipio, A., ed. The Baltic Sea. (Oceanography Ser.: Vol. 30). 418p. 1981. 119.25 (ISBN 0-444-41884-9). Elsevier.

Wallace, W. Development of the Chlorinity-Salinity Concept in Oceanography. LC 72-97440. (Elsevier Oceanography Ser.: Vol. 7). 240p. 1974. 70.25 (ISBN 0-444-41118-6). Elsevier.

Warren, Bruce A. & Wunsch, Carl, eds. Evolution of Physical Oceanography: Scientific Surveys in Honor of Henry Stommel. 664p. 1981. 50.00x (ISBN 0-262-23104-2). MIT Pr.

Wefer, Gerold, et al, eds. The Harrington Sound Project, Kiel University Bermuda Biological Station Special Publication, No. 19. (Illus.). 94p. (Orig.). 1981. pap. 6.00 (ISBN 0-917642-19-8). Bermuda Bio.

Wenk, Edward, Jr. The Politics of the Ocean. LC 72-5814. (Illus.). 608p. 1972. 22.50x (ISBN 0-295-95240-7). U of Wash Pr.

Williams, Jerome, et al. Sea & Air: The Marine Environment. 2nd ed. LC 72-93196. 338p. 1973. 15.95x (ISBN 0-87021-596-5). Naval Inst Pr.

Withner, Carl L., ed. The Orchids: Scientific Studies. LC 84-19435. 618p. 1985. Repr. of 1974 ed. lib. bdg. 52.50 (ISBN 0-89874-809-7). Krieger.

Wolff, W. J., ed. Ecology of the Wadden Sea: Basic Data for the Management of Europe's Largest Marine Wetland. 2094p. 1983. lib. bdg. 85.00 (ISBN 90-6191-062-5, Pub. by Balkema RSA). IPS.

Wooster, Warren S. Freedom of Oceanic Research. LC 73-81050. 256p. 1973. 18.00x (ISBN 0-8448-0214-X). Crane-Russak Co.

OCEANOGRAPHY–BIBLIOGRAPHY

Gordon, Robert & Spaulding, Malcolm. A Bibliography of Numerical Models for Tidal Rivers, Estuaries & Coastal Waters. (Marine Technical Report Ser.: No. 32). 1974. pap. 2.00 (ISBN 0-938412-03-5). URI MAS.

Sears, Mary, compiled by. Oceanographic Index, Woods Hole Oceanographic Institution Author Cumulation, 1971-1974: Woods Hole Oceanpgraphic Institution Author Cumulation, 1971-1974. 1976. lib. bdg. 120.00 (ISBN 0-8161-0029-2, Hall Library). G K Hall.

--Oceanographic Index, Woods Hole Oceanographic Institution, Regional Cumulation, 1971-1974: Woods Hole Oceanographic Institution, Regional Cumulation, 1971-1974. 1976. lib. bdg. 110.00 (ISBN 0-8161-0943-5, Hall Library). G K Hall.

--Oceanographic Index, Woods Hole Oceanographic Institution, Subject Cumulation 1971-1974, 2 vols. 1976. Set. lib. bdg. 240.00 (ISBN 0-8161-0030-6, Hall Library). G K Hall.

--Oceanographic Index: Author Cumulation, 1946-1970: Woods Hole Oceanographic Institution, Mass, 3 vols. 1972. Set. 298.00 (ISBN 0-8161-0931-1, Hall Library). G K Hall.

--Oceanographic Index: Regional Cumulation, 1946-1970: Woods Hole Oceanographic Institution, Mass. 1972. 100.00 (ISBN 0-8161-0117-5, Hall Library). G K Hall.

--Oceanographic Index: Subject Cumulation, 1946-1971: Woods Hole Oceanographic Institution, Mass, 4 vols. 1972. Set. 395.00 (ISBN 0-8161-0932-X, Hall Library). G K Hall.

--Oceanographic Index: Organismal Cumulation, 1946-1973, Marine Organisms, Chiefly Planktonic: Woods Hole Oceanographic Institution, Mass, 3 vols. 1454p. 1974. Set. lib. bdg. 270.00 (ISBN 0-8161-0933-8, Hall Library). G K Hall.

University of California - San Diego. Catalogs of the Scripps Institution of Oceanography Library, 4 pts. Incl. Pt. 1. Author-Title Catalog, 7 vols. 1970. Set. 665.00 (ISBN 0-8161-0860-9); Pt. 2. Subject Catalog, 2 vols. 1970. Set. 200.00 (ISBN 0-8161-0112-4); Pt. 3. Shelf List, 2 vols. 1970. Set. 185.00 (ISBN 0-8161-0113-2); Pt. 4. Shelf List of Documents, Reports & Translations Collection. 1970. 95.00 (ISBN 0-8161-0114-0). Hall Library). G K Hall.

--Catalogs of the Scripps Institution of Oceanography Library, First Supplement to Pt. 1, Author-Title Catalog, 3 vols. 1973. 330.00 (ISBN 0-8161-0897-8, Hall Library). G K Hall.

--Catalogs of the Scripps Institution of Oceanography Library, First Supplement to Pts. 2-4, Subject Catalog, Shelf List, Shelf List of Documents & Reports. 1974. 110.00 (ISBN 0-8161-1144-8, Hall Library). G K Hall.

OCEANOGRAPHY–RESEARCH

see Oceanographic Research

OCEANOGRAPHY, PHYSICAL

see Oceanography

OCEANOGRAPHY AS A PROFESSION

Gordon, Bernard L., ed. Marine Careers: Selected Papers. 42p. 1974. 2.00 (ISBN 0-910258-02-3). Book & Tackle.

Ocean Sciences Board, National Research Council. Doctoral Scientists in Oceanography. 1981. pap. text ed. 9.25 (ISBN 0-309-03133-8). Natl Acad Pr.

Wood, Jonathan S. Your Future in the Science of Oceanography. (Careers in Depth Ser.). (Illus.). 1982. lib. bdg. 8.97 (ISBN 0-8239-0438-5). Rosen Group.

OCEANOLOGY
see Oceanography

OCHROLECHIA

Verseghy, K. Gattung Ochrolechia. 1962. pap. 14.00 (ISBN 3-7682-5401-1). Lubrecht & Cramer.

OCTOPUS
see also Cephalopoda

Cousteau, Jacques-Yves & Diole, Philippe. Octopus & Squid: The Soft Intelligence. LC 72-76141. 304p. 1973. 12.95 (ISBN 0-385-06896-4). Doubleday.

Young, John Z. Anatomy of the Nervous System of Octopus Vulgaris. (Illus.). 1971. 75.00x (ISBN 0-19-857340-5). Oxford U Pr.

--Model of the Brain. 1964. 35.00x (ISBN 0-19-857333-2). Oxford U Pr.

ODONTOGLOSSAE
see Flamingos

ODORS
see also Deodorization; Perfumes

Amoore, John E. Molecular Basis of Odor. (Illus.). 216p. 1970. 21.00x (ISBN 0-398-00039-5). C C Thomas.

Bailey, J. C. & Viney, N. J. Analysis of Odours by Gas Chromatography & Allied Techniques, 1979. 1981. 75.00x (ISBN 0-686-97023-3, Pub. by W Spring England). State Mutual Bk.

Bedborough, D. R. & Trott, P. E. The Sensory Measurement of Odours by Dynamic Dilution, 1979. 1981. 69.00x (ISBN 0-686-97168-X, Pub. by W Spring England). State Mutual Bk.

Board on Toxicology & Environmental Health Hazards. Odors from Stationary & Mobile Sources. 1979. pap. 21.95 (ISBN 0-309-02877-9). Natl Acad Pr.

Brown, Richard E. & MacDonald, David W., eds. Social Odours in Mammals, 2 vols. (Illus.). 1985. Vol. 1. 60.00x (ISBN 0-19-857546-7); Vol. 2. 45.00x (ISBN 0-19-857617-X). Oxford U Pr.

Carleton, A. J. Absorption of Odours: Summary Report, 1979. 1981. 65.00x (ISBN 0-686-97007-1, Pub. by W Spring England). State Mutual Bk.

Compilation of Odor & Taste Threshold Values Data-DS 48A. 508p. 1978. 27.50 (ISBN 0-8031-0306-9, 05-048010-36). ASTM.

Dorling, T. A. Activated Carbon Adsorption in Odour Control: The Adsorption of Styrene Vapour, 1979. 1981. 65.00x (ISBN 0-686-97008-X, Pub. by W Spring England). State Mutual Bk.

Engen, Trygg. The Perception of Odors. (Series in Cognition & Perception). 1982. 30.00 (ISBN 0-12-239350-3). Acad Pr.

Jellinek, J. Stephan. The Use of Fragrance in Consumer Products. Incl. LC 75-2106. 219p. 1975. 47.00 (ISBN 0-471-44151-1, Pub. by Wiley-Interscience). Wiley.

Jennings, Walter & Shibamoto, Takayuki. Qualitative Analysis of Flavor & Fragrance Volatiles by Glass Capillary Gas Chromtography. LC 79-26034. 1980. 53.00 (ISBN 0-12-384250-6). Acad Pr.

Louden, Louise & Weiner, Jack. Odors & Odor Control. (Bibliographic Ser.: No. 267). 1976. pap. 25.00 (ISBN 0-87010-040-8). Inst Paper Chem.

Odor Control for Wastewater Facilities ('79) (Manual of Practice Ser.: No. 22). (Illus.). 70p. Date not set. pap. 8.00 (ISBN 0-943244-17-X). Water Pollution.

Pope, D. & Moss, R. L. Current Odour Problems & Control Techniques in the UK, 1980. 1981. 35.00x (ISBN 0-686-97053-5, Pub. by W Spring England). State Mutual Bk.

Summer, W. Odour Pollution of Air: Causes & Control. 1972. 45.00x (ISBN 0-249-44022-9). Intl Ideas.

OECANTHINAE
see Crickets

OEDOGONIACEAE

Gauthier-Lievre, L. Oedogoniacees Africaines. (Illus.). 1964. 28.00 (ISBN 3-7682-0216-X). Lubrecht & Cramer.

Hirn, K. E. Monographie & Iconographie der Oedogoniaceen. (Illus.). 1960. pap. 70.00 (ISBN 3-7682-7056-4). Lubrecht & Cramer.

OFFICE EQUIPMENT AND SUPPLIES
see also Accounting Machines; Calculating-Machines; Electronic Office Machines; Typewriters

Barcomb, David. Office Automation: A Survey of Tools & Technology. 241p. 1981. pap. 21.00 (ISBN 0-932376-15-0, EY-00004-DP). Digital Pr.

The Business & Technology Videolog. LC 78-74186. 1981. pap. 39.50 (ISBN 0-88432-070-7). Video-Forum.

Computer & Business Equipment Manufacturers Association. The Computer & Business Equipment Industry Marketing Data Book. 177p. (Orig.). 1983. pap. 55.50 (ISBN 0-912797-02-9). CBEMA.

Condon, M. A. Office System Printer: A Practical Evaluation Guide. 100p. 1982. pap. 14.20 (ISBN 0-471-89413-3). Wiley.

--Office Workstations. (Office Technology in the 80's Ser.: Vol. 6). 197p. (Orig.). 1982. pap. 15.00x (ISBN 0-85012-387-9). Taylor & Francis.

Edwards, Nancy M., ed. Office Automation. 1983. 34.95 (ISBN 0-442-22202-5). Van Nos Reinhold.

International Labour Office, Geneva. Audiovisual, Draughting, Office, Reproduction & Other Ancillary Equipment & Supplies: Equipment Planning Guide for Vocational & Technical Training & Education Programmes. (No. 15). (Illus.). 279p. (Orig.). 1982. pap. 22.80 (ISBN 92-2-102112-2). Intl Labour Office.

Katzan, Harry, Jr. Office Automation: A Manager's Guide. 224p. 1982. 32.50 (ISBN 0-8144-5752-5). AMACOM.

Lieberman, Mark A., et al. Office Automation: A Manager's Guide for Improved Productivity. LC 81-23114. 331p. 1982. 34.95x (ISBN 0-471-07983-9, Pub. by Wiley-Interscience). Wiley.

McKenzie, Jimmy C. & Hughes, Robert J. Office Machines: A Practical Approach. 2nd ed. 352p. 1983. write for info. wire coil (ISBN 0-697-08088-9); instr's solutions manual avail. (ISBN 0-697-08194-X); practice set avail. (ISBN 0-697-08096-X). Wm C Brown.

Naffah, N. Office Information Systems. 656p. 1982. 76.75 (ISBN 0-444-86398-2, North-Holland). Elsevier.

Office Automation: Current Perspectives. (Special Interest Packages Ser.). pap. 23.00 (PO20); pap. 18.00 member. Assn Inform & Image Mgmt.

Office Automation Markets. (Reports Ser.: No. 182). 170p. 1981. 985.00x (ISBN 0-88694-182-2). Intl Res Dev.

Office Automation Software Market. 336p. 1985. 1750.00 (ISBN 0-86621-291-4, A1368). Frost & Sullivan.

Office Consumables & the Automated Office. (Reports Ser.: No. 199). 168p. 1982. 1285.00x (ISBN 0-88694-199-7). Intl Res Dev.

Office Lighting. 1982. 13.50 (ISBN 0-686-47863-0, RP-1). Illum Eng.

Peck, Phyllis J. & Konkel, Gilbert J. Office Technology for the Nontechnical Manager. LC 84-81648. 224p. 1982. pap. 13.95x (ISBN 0-911054-07-3). Office Pubns.

Simons. Automating Your Office. 1984. 24.00x (ISBN 0-85012-402-6). Intl Pubns Serv.

Simpson, Alan, ed. Planning for Office Microcomputers. (The Office of the Future Ser.: Vol. 5). 110p. (Orig.). 1982. pap. text ed. 21.00x (ISBN 0-566-03416-6). Gower Pub Co.

Snodgrass, Tod J. Office Purchasing Guide: How to Save up to Fifty Percent on Office Supplies & Furniture, Business Forms & Printing, Office Machines & Equipment. LC 85-5156. (Illus.). 256p. (Orig.). 1985. 29.95 (ISBN 0-933051-02-6); pap. 17.95 (ISBN 0-933051-01-8). Lowen Pub.

Thurber, Kenneth A. Office Automation Systems. (Tutorial Texts Ser.). 201p. 1980. 20.00 (ISBN 0-8186-0339-9, Q339). IEEE Comp Soc.

Wainwright, Judith & Francis, Arthur. Office Automation, Organisation & the Nature of Work. LC 84-18717. 240p. 1984. text ed. 34.50x (ISBN 0-566-00729-0). Gower Pub Co.

Wilson, P. A. & Pritchard, J. A. Office Technology Benefits. 180p. 1983. pap. 27.35 (ISBN 0-471-89414-1). Wiley.

OFFICE PRACTICE–AUTOMATION

American Law Institute-American Bar Association Joint Committee. Law & Computers in the Mid-Sixties: Course of Study Transcript. 399p. 1966. pap. 2.18 (ISBN 0-317-32232-X, B239). Am Law Inst.

Barcomb, David. Office Automation: A Survey of Tools & Technology. 241p. 1981. pap. 21.00 (ISBN 0-932376-15-0, EY-00004-DP). Digital Pr.

--Office Automation: A Survey of Tools & Technology. 256p. 1981. 15.00 (ISBN 0-686-98086-7). Telecom Lib.

Bergerud, Marly & Gonzalez, Jean. Word Information Processing: Concepts of Office Automation. 2nd ed. LC 83-19815. (Word Processing Ser.: 1-388). 528p. 1984. text ed. 26.95. Wiley.

Bikson, Tora K. New Technology in the Office: Planning for People. (Studies in Productivity: Highlights of the Literature Ser.: Vol. 40). 1985. 35.00 (ISBN 0-08-029514-2). Work in Amer.

Blaazer, Caroline & Molyneux, Eric. Supervising the Electronic Office. 202p. 1984. text ed. 29.50x (ISBN 0-566-02448-9). Gower Pub Co.

Cecil, Paula B. Office Automation: Concepts & Application. 3rd ed. 1984. 23.95 (ISBN 0-8053-1763-5); instr's guide 7.95 (ISBN 0-8053-1764-3); study guide 6.95 (ISBN 0-8053-1765-1). Benjamin-Cummings.

Chorafas, Dimitris N. Office Automation: The Productivity Challenge. (Illus.). 304p. 1982. text ed. 36.95 (ISBN 0-13-631028-1). P-H.

Christie, Bruce. Human Factors of Information Technology in the Office. LC 84-20903. (Information Processing Ser.). 1985. 26.95 (ISBN 0-471-90631-X). Wiley.

Cohen, Aaron & Cohen, Elaine. Planning the Electronic Office. (Illus.). 256p. 1983. 37.50 (ISBN 0-07-011583-4). McGraw.

Cohen, B. G. F., ed. Human Aspects in Office Automation. (Elsevier Series in Office Automation: no. 1). 340p. 1984. 50.00 (ISBN 0-444-42327-3, I-133-84). Elsevier.

Compute Editors. MacOffice: Using the Macintosh for Everything. (Orig.). 1985. pap. 18.95 (ISBN 0-87455-006-8). Compute Pubns.

Dang-Tan, Chau & Dang-Tan, Hau. How to Automate Your Office. LC 84-45793. 250p. 1985. 85.00 (ISBN 0-8144-5803-3). Amacom.

Derfler, Frank, Jr. & Stallings, Frank. A Manager's Guide to Local Networks. (Illus.). 154p. 1983. 21.95 (ISBN 0-13-549766-3); pap. 14.95 (ISBN 0-13-549758-2). P-H.

Derrick, John & Oppenheim, Phillip. A Handbook of New Office Technology. 320p. 1982. 110.00x (ISBN 0-7126-0020-5, Pub. by Century Pub Co). State Mutual Bk.

Doswell, Andrew. Office Automation. LC 82-6988. (Wiley Series Information Processing). 283p. 1983. 29.95 (ISBN 0-471-10457-4, Pub. by Wiley-Interscience). Wiley.

Edwards, Nancy M. Office Automation: A Glossary & Guide. 275p. 1984. text ed. 59.50 (ISBN 0-471-81859-3). Wiley.

Edwards, Nancy M. & Shaw, Carmine, eds. Office Automation: A Glossary & Guide. LC 82-4714. (Information & Communications Management Guides Ser.). 275p. 1982. 59.50 (ISBN 0-86729-012-9, 703-BW). Knowledge Indus.

Field, R. M. A Glossary of Office Automation Terms. 32p. 1982. pap. text ed. 15.00x (ISBN 0-914548-42-5). Univelt Inc.

--A Glossary of Office Automation Terms. Society for Technical Communications, ed. 32p. (Orig.). 1982. pap. text ed. 15.00x (ISBN 0-914548-42-5). Soc Tech Comm.

Finn, Nancy B. The Electronic Office. (Illus.). 160p. 1983. pap. 15.95 (ISBN 0-13-251819-8). P-H.

First Local Area Networks Exposition, 1982. Date not set. 125.00. Info Gatekeepers.

Firth, R. J. Viewdata Systems: A Practical Evaluation Guide. (Office Technology in the Eighties Ser.). (Illus.). 114p. (Orig.). 1982. pap. 15.00x (ISBN 0-85012-370-4). Taylor & Francis.

Galitz, Wilbert O. The Office Environment: Automations Impact on Tomorrow's Workplace. 1984. pap. 14.95 (ISBN 0-916875-00-8). Admin Mgmt Soc.

Gant, Wanda & Casale, James F., eds. Making Business Systems Effective: The Papers & Proceedings of Syntopican XIII. 500p. (Orig.). 1985. pap. text ed. 30.00 (ISBN 0-935220-13-5). Assn Info Sys.

Goldthwaite, John. Office Automation Conference Digest. 373p. 1985. 28.00 (ISBN 0-88283-045-7). AFIPS Pr.

Gower Publishing Co., Ltd. Staff, ed. A Planning Guide to Office Automation. 123p. 1984. text ed. 41.95x (ISBN 0-566-02503-5). Gower Pub Co.

Greenwood, Frank & Greenwood, Mary. Office Automation: The Challenge of Technology. 1984. text ed. 22.50 (ISBN 0-8359-5165-0). Reston.

Gregory, Judith & Marshall, Daniel, eds. Office Automation: Jekyll or Hyde. LC 83-60764. 240p. (Orig.). 1983. pap. 12.95 (ISBN 0-912663-00-6). Work Women Educ.

Hines, V. Douglas. Office Automation: Tools & Methods for System Building. 501p. 1985. 29.95 (ISBN 0-471-80562-9). Wiley.

Kalow, Samuel J. & Ross, Ercole. Office Systems: A Manager's Guide to Integrating Word Processing, Data Processing & Telecommunications for the Automated Office. 224p. 1984. 18.95 (ISBN 0-13-633156-4, Spec); pap. 10.95 (ISBN 0-13-633149-1, Spec). P-H.

Katzan, Harry, Jr. Office Automation: A Manager's Guide. 224p. 1982. 32.50 (ISBN 0-8144-5752-5). AMACOM.

Konkel, Gilbert J. & Peck, Phyllis J. Word Processing & Office Automation: A Supervisory Perspective. LC 82-80637. (Illus.). 168p. 1982. pap. 12.95x (ISBN 0-911054-05-7). Office Pubns.

Lieberman, Mark A., et al. Office Automation: A Manager's Guide for Improved Productivity. LC 81-23114. 331p. 1982. 34.95x (ISBN 0-471-07983-9, Pub. by Wiley-Interscience). Wiley.

McCandless, Cathie. Computer Shorthand: Medical Dictation & Transcription. (Computer Shorthand Ser.). 385p. 1984. pap. text ed. 24.95x (ISBN 0-471-89695-0); practice dictation 295.00 (ISBN 0-471-80659-5). Wiley.

McFarland & Kitterman. Secretarial Procedures for the Automated Office. 1984. text ed. 24.95 (ISBN 0-8359-6957-6); instr's manual avail. (ISBN 0-8359-6598-8). Reston.

Matthews, et al. Palmetto Insurance Company: A Computerized Office Simulation. 1984. 6.20 (ISBN 0-538-26700-3, Z70). SW Pub.

Medley, Don B., et al. The Automated Office. 1985. 19.95 (ISBN 0-538-10890-8, J89). SW Pub.

Mullins, Carolyn & West, Thomas. The Office Automation Primer: Harnessing Information Technologies for Greater Productivity. 158p. 1982. 18.95 (ISBN 0-13-631085-0); pap. 9.95 (ISBN 0-13-631077-X). P-H.

Oberst, B. B. & Reid, R. A., eds. Computer Application to Private Office Practices. (Illus.). 145p. 1984. 29.50 (ISBN 0-387-90933-8). Springer Verlag.

Office Automation Markets. (Reports Ser.: No. 182). 170p. 1981. 985.00x (ISBN 0-88694-182-2). Intl Res Dev.

Office Machines Course. 1979. text ed. 5.75 wkbk. (ISBN 0-538-13800-9, M80). SW Pub.

Office Procedures & Technology. 1984p. 15.64 (ISBN 0-87350-334-1); wkbk 7.07 (ISBN 0-87350-340-6); tchr's. manual 4.95 (ISBN 0-87350-338-4); tchr's. key to wkbk. 7.50 (ISBN 0-87350-337-6); test booklet 1.78 (ISBN 0-87350-339-2). Milady.

Otway, Harry J. & Peltu, Malcolm. New Office Technology: Human & Organizational Aspects. LC 82-24473. 244p. 1983. text ed. 29.50 (ISBN 0-89391-198-4). Ablex Pub.

Paterson. Word Processing & the Automated Office. (Wiley Series in Engineering Management). 150p. 1985. 24.95 (ISBN 0-470-20147-9). Wiley.

Peltu, Malcolm. A Guide to the Electronic Office. 196p. 1982. 40.00x (ISBN 0-85227-267-7, Pub. by Assoc Bus Pr England). State Mutual Bk.

Piovia, Sara. A Commonsense Guide to Law Office Automation. 240p. 1984. 19.95 (ISBN 0-13-152836-X); pap. 12.95 (ISBN 0-13-152802-5). P-H.

The Practical Lawyer's Manual for Automatic Law Office Typing & Word Processing. 116p. 1979. pap. 7.50 (ISBN 0-317-30702-9, F113). Am Law Inst.

Price, S. G. Introducing the Electronic Office. 161p. 1979. pap. 25.15 (ISBN 0-471-89467-2). Wiley.

Quinn, Karen T., ed. Advances in Office Automation. 350p. 1984. 34.95 (ISBN 0-471-90398-1). Wiley.

Remer, Daniel. Computer Power for Your Law Office. LC 83-61382. (Illus.). 142p. 1983. pap. 19.95 (ISBN 0-89588-109-8). SYBEX.

Roberts, Alan & Freer, Carolee. Computer Shorthand: Skill Building & Transcription. 376p. (Orig.). 1984. pap. text ed. 24.95 (ISBN 0-471-89665-9). Wiley.

Roberts, J. H. Implementing a Pilot Plan for Office Automation. 100p. 1984. pap. text ed. 11.20 (ISBN 0-471-81050-9). Wiley.

Rosen, Arnold & Bahniuk, Margaret H. Administrative Procedures for the Electronic Office. 2nd ed. LC 84-13141. 519p. 1985. 26.95 (ISBN 0-471-80854-7); study guide 9.95 (ISBN 0-471-81879-8). Wiley.

Rosenthal, Steven. Rosenthal's Dictionary of the Automated Office. 350p. 1984. 19.95 (ISBN 0-13-783218-4); pap. 12.95 cancelled (ISBN 0-13-783200-1). P-H.

Rullo. Advances in Office Automation Management, Vol. 1. 1981. write for info. Wiley.

Ruprecht, Mary M. & Wagoner, Kathleen P. Managing Office Automation. LC 83-17046. 680p. 1984. 29.95 (ISBN 0-471-88731-5). Wiley.

Saffady, William. The Automated Office: An Introduction to the Technology. Plunka, Gene A., ed. (Reference Ser.). 241p. 1981. 17.75 (ISBN 0-89258-072-0, R017); member 13.25. Assn Inform & Image Mgmt.

St. John Bate, Joseph & Burgess, Ross. The Automated Office. (Illus.). 180p. 1985. pap. 15.95 (ISBN 0-00-383008-X, Pub. by Collins England). Sheridan.

Schroeder, Betty L. CPS Review for Office Technology, Module 6. 130p. 1984. pap. text ed. 18.95x (ISBN 0-471-86155-3); pap. text ed. 89.95x set of six (ISBN 0-471-86149-9). Wiley.

Smith, H. T., et al. Automated Office Systems Management. 604p. 1985. 29.95 (ISBN 0-471-86148-0). Wiley.

Smith, Harold T. The Office Revolution: Strategies for Managing Tomorrow's Workforce. (Illus.). 132p. (Orig.). 1983. 21.95 (ISBN 0-318-04032-8); pap. 14.95 members (ISBN 0-318-04033-6). Admin Mgmt.

Stokes. Integrated Office Systems. (Illus.). 363p. 1982. 445.00s (ISBN 0-08-028568-6). Pergamon.

Stone, R. The Push-Button Manager: A Guide to Office Automation. 224p. 1985. 7.50 (ISBN 0-07-084782-7). McGraw.

Tapscott, Don. Office Automation: A User-Driven Method. LC 82-15133. 264p. 1982. 29.50x (ISBN 0-306-41071-0, Plenum Pr). Plenum Pub.
--Office Automation: A User-Driven Method. (Applications of Modern Technology in Business Ser.). 264p. 1985. pap. 14.95x (ISBN 0-306-41973-4, Plenum Pr). Plenum Pub.
Thurber, Kenneth A. Office Automation Systems. (Tutorial Texts Ser.). 201p. 1980. 20.00 (ISBN 0-8186-0339-9, Q339). IEEE Comp Soc.
Uhlig, Ronald P. & Farber, David J. The Office of the Future. 378p. 1979. 35.00 (ISBN 0-686-98082-4). Telecom Lib.
Wagenvoord, James. Computerspace: Home Office Strategies That Work for Computers. LC 83-22111. (Illus.). 128p. 1984. pap. 9.95 (ISBN 0-399-51020-6, Perigee). Putnam Pub Group.
Westin, Alan F. The Office Automation Controversy: Technology, People & Social Policy. 200p. 1985. 29.95 (ISBN 0-86729-103-6, 713-BW). Knowledge Indus.
Westley. Office Automation, 2 vols. (Infotech Computer State of the Art Reports). 600p. 1980. Set. 310.00 (ISBN 0-08-028513-9). Pergamon.
Whitehead, John. Planning the Electronic Office. LC 85-21275. (Information Technology Ser.). 192p. 1985. 29.00 (ISBN 0-7099-3621-4, Pub. by Croom Helm Ltd). Longwood Pub Group.
Williamson & York, Inc. The Professional Workstation: Requirements & Marketing Opportunities in the Engineering Environment. 250p. 1983. write for info. C I M Systems.

OFFSET PRINTING

Chambers, Harry T. The Management of Small Offset Print Departments. 2nd ed. 217p. 1979. text ed. 31.50x (ISBN 0-220-67007-2, Pub. by Busn Bks England). Brookfield Pub Co.
Clifton, Merritt. The Samisdat Method: A Guide to Do-It-Yourself Offset Printing. 1978. pap. 2.00 (ISBN 0-686-12106-6). Samisdat.
Eastman Kodak Company, ed. Lithographic Offset Presses: An Illustrated Guide. LC 78-58634. (Illus.). 1978. pap. 5.25 (ISBN 0-87985-219-4, Q-215). Eastman Kodak.
Latimer, Henry. Production Planning & Repro Mechanicals for Offset Printing. (Illus.). 1980. 37.50 (ISBN 0-07-036621-7). McGraw.
Makarius, Theodore F. Operation of the Offset Press. 255p. 20.00 (ISBN 0-317-14453-7). Perfect Graphic.
Red Sun Collective. What Is Offset Printing? A Red Sun Press Guide to the Preparation of Materials for Printing. Red Sun Press, ed. (Illus.). 100p. (Orig.). 1984. pap. text ed. 3.00 (ISBN 0-932728-04-9). Red Sun Pr.
Robinson, Paul. Instant Print Estimator: Offset Prices That Reflect Your Costs. rev. ed. (Illus.). 550p. 1981. loose-leaf 69.95x (ISBN 0-9607084-0-5). Cushman Pubs.
Rudman, Jack. Offset Photographer. (Career Examination Ser.: C-560). (Cloth bdg. avail. on request). pap. 12.00 (ISBN 0-8373-0560-8). Natl Learning.
--Offset Pressman. (Career Examination Ser.: C-561). (Cloth bdg. avail. on request). pap. 12.00 (ISBN 0-8373-0561-6). Natl Learning.
--Offset Printing Machine Operator. (Career Examination Ser.: C-562). (Cloth bdg. avail. on request). pap. 12.00 (ISBN 0-8373-0562-4). Natl Learning.

OFFSHORE INSTALLATIONS

see Offshore Structures

OFFSHORE STRUCTURES

Behavior of Offshore Structures, 2nd International Conference. Boss Seventy-Nine: Proceedings, 3 vols. 1500p. Set. pap. 146.00x (ISBN 0-906085-34-9, Dist. by Air Science Co). BHRA Fluid.
Binnie & Parners & EEC Commission. Islands for Offshore Nuclear Power Stations. 160p. 1981. 85.00x (ISBN 0-686-80926-2, Pub. by Graham & Trotman England). State Mutual Bk.
Block, Richard A. & Collins, Charles B., eds. Standard Operations Manual for the Marine Transportation Sector of the Offshore Mineral & Oil Industry. 61p. (Orig.). 1979. pap. text ed. 5.00 (ISBN 0-934114-09-9, BK-116). Marine Educ.
Brebbia, C. A. Dynamic Analysis of Offshore Structures. (Illus.). 1979. 69.95 (ISBN 0-408-00393-6). Butterworth.
Carneiro, F. L., et al. Offshore Structures Engineering, Vol. 5. LC 84-80880. (Offshore Structures Engineering Ser.). 832p. 1984. 49.95x (ISBN 0-87201-607-2). Gulf Pub.
Carneiro, F. L., et al, eds. Offshore Structures Engineering, Vol. 4. LC 82-81336. (Offshore Structures Engineering Ser.). 584p. 1982. 49.95x (ISBN 0-87201-612-9). Gulf Pub.
Chandler, K. A. Marine & Offshore Corrosion. 2nd ed. 432p. 1985. text ed. 79.95 (ISBN 0-408-01175-0). Butterworth.
Chen, W. F. & Han, D. J. Tubular Members in Offshore Structures. (Surveys in Structural Engineering & Structural Mechanics Ser.). 1985. text ed. 34.95 (ISBN 0-273-08581-6). Pitman Pub MA.
Chryssostomidis, Chryssostomos & Connor, Jerome J., eds. Behaviour of Off-Shore Structures: Proceedings of the Third International Conference, 2 Vols. LC 82-11749. (Illus.). 1622p. 1982. Set. text ed. 179.00 (ISBN 0-89116-343-3). Hemisphere Pub.
Chung, J. S., ed. Offshore Mechanics-Artic Engineering-Deepsea Systems Symposium, First: Proceedings, 2 Vols, Vol. 2. 289p. 1982. 45.00 (I00148). ASME.
Chung, J. S. & Lunardini, V. J., eds. Offshore Mechanics & Arctic Engineering Symposium, 2nd International: Proceedings. 812p. 1983. pap. text ed. 100.00 (ISBN 0-317-02642-9, I00156). ASME.
Cox, R. A., ed. Offshore Medicine: Medical Care of Employees in the Offshore Oil Industry. (Illus.). 208p. 1982. 35.60 (ISBN 0-387-11111-5). Springer-Verlag.
Crawford. Marine & Offshore Pumping & Piping Systems. 1981. text ed. 54.95 (ISBN 0-408-00548-3). Butterworth.
Dawson, Thomas H. Offshore Structural Engineering. (Illus.). 352p. 1983. text ed. 41.95 (ISBN 0-13-633206-4). P-H.
Dowling, P. J., et al, eds. Offshore Structures Engineering, Vol. 3: Buckling of Shells in Offshore Structures. LC 81-83737. (Offshore Structures Engineering Ser.). 582p. 1982. 49.95x (ISBN 0-87201-611-0). Gulf Pub.
Frieze, P. A., et al, eds. Marine & Offshore Safety: Proceedings of an International Conference Held at Glasgow, U. K., Sept. 7-9, 1983. (Developments in Marine Technology Ser.: Vol. 1). 612p. 1984. 129.75 (ISBN 0-444-42383-4). Elsevier.
Gilbert, John T. E., ed. Environmental Planning Guidelines for Offshore Oil & Gas Development. (Illus.). 64p. 1982. pap. text ed. 6.00x (ISBN 0-8248-0792-8, Eastwest Ctr). UH Pr.
Goda, Toshimi. Random Seas & Design of Maritime Structures. 320p. 1985. 37.50x (ISBN 0-86008-369-1, Pub. by U of Tokyo Japan). Columbia U Pr.
Gowar, R. G., ed. Developments in Fire Protection of Offshore Platforms, Vol. 1. (Illus.). 232p. 1978. text ed. 46.25 (ISBN 0-85334-792-1, Pub. by Elsevier Applied Sci England). Elsevier.
Graff, William J. Introduction to Offshore Structures: Design, Fabrication, Installation. LC 81-6259. 372p. 1981. 29.95x (ISBN 0-87201-694-3). Gulf Pub.
Haggard, Russell, ed. Orientation for Offshore Crane Operations. Rev. ed. (Rotary Drilling Ser.: Unit V: Offshore Technology Lesson 8). (Illus.). 35p. (Orig.). 1983. pap. text ed. 4.50 (ISBN 0-88698-042-9, 2.50810). Petex.
Herbich. Offshore Pipeline Design Elements. (Ocean Engineering Ser.: Vol. 3). 240p. 1981. 49.75 (ISBN 0-8247-1388-5). Dekker.
--Seafloor Scour: Design Guidelines for Ocean Founded Structures. (Ocean Engineering Ser.). 288p. 1984. 59.75 (ISBN 0-8247-7095-1). Dekker.
Hsu, Teng H. Applied Offshore Structural Engineering. LC 84-628. 200p. 1984. 29.95x (ISBN 0-87201-750-8). Gulf Pub.
Institution of Civil Engineers Staff, ed. Design & Construction of Offshore Structures. 183p. 1977. 55.50x (ISBN 0-7277-0041-3). Am Soc Civil Eng.
--Fatigue in Offshore Structural Steels. 136p. 1981. 33.50x (ISBN 0-7277-0108-8). Am Soc Civil Eng.
International Labour Office. Safety & Health in the Construction of Fixed Offshore Installations in the Petroleum Industry. (International Labour Office Code of Pracice Ser.). xi, 135p. (Orig.). 1982. pap. 11.40 (ISBN 92-2-102900-X). Intl Labour Office.
International Offshore Mechanics & Arctic Engineering Symposium, 3rd: Proceedings. 1983. pap. text ed. write for info (IX0161). ASME.
Johnson, Peter, et al, eds. Offshore Manual International. 172p. 1981. 30.00x (ISBN 0-333-32078-6, Pub. by Nautical England). State Mutual Bk.
Jones, Michael E. Deepwater Oil Production & Manned Underwater Structures. 265p. 1981. 100.00x (ISBN 0-86010-339-0, Pub. by Graham & Trotman England). State Mutual Bk.
Karlsen, Jan E. & Qvale, Thoralf U. Safety & Offshore Working Conditions. 110p. (Orig.). 1984. pap. 18.00x (ISBN 82-00-06371-2). Universitet.
Kirk, Colin L., ed. Dynamic Analysis of Offshore Structures. LC 81-85403. 128p. 1982. 29.95x (ISBN 0-87201-026-0). Gulf Pub.
Le Tirant, P. Seabed Reconnaissance & Offshore Soil Mechanics for the Installation of Petroleum Structures. 512p. 1980. 87.00x (ISBN 0-86010-196-7, Pub. by Graham & Trotman England). State Mutual Bk.
Lobo, F. L., et al. Offshore Structures Engineering, Vol. 1. LC 78-74102. (Offshore Structures Engineering Ser.). 424p. 1979. 43.50x (ISBN 0-87201-608-0). Gulf Pub.
Long Service from Offshore Structure. 1981. 100.00x (ISBN 0-686-97085-3, Pub. by Marine Mgmt England). State Mutual Bk.
McClelland, Bromlette & Reifel, Michael, eds. Planning & Design of Fixed Offshore Platforms. LC 84-27078. (Illus.). 1056p. 1985. 89.50 (ISBN 0-442-25223-4). Van Nos Reinhold.
Maier, G., ed. Case Histories in Offshore Engineering. (CISM International Centre for Mechanical Sciences Ser.: Vol. 283). (Illus.). ix, 365p. 1985. pap. 29.00 (ISBN 0-387-81817-0). Springer Verlag.
Middleditch, Brian S., ed. Environmental Effects of Offshore Oil Production: The Buccaneer Gas & Oil Field Study. LC 81-11934. (Marine Science Ser.: Vol. 14). 464p. 1981. 69.50x (ISBN 0-306-40826-0, Plenum Pr). Plenum Pub.
Mitchell, Edward J., ed. Question of Offshore Oil. LC 76-16665. pap. 42.80 (ISBN 0-317-29838-0, 2017492). Bks Demand UMI.
Morgan, Max J. Dynamic Positioning of Offshore Vessels. 513p. 1978. 51.95x (ISBN 0-87814-044-1). Pennwell Bks.
Mousseli, A. H. Offshore Pipeline Design, Analysis & Methods. 193p. 1981. 49.95x (ISBN 0-87814-156-1). Pennwell Bks.
North Sea Corrosion - What Have We Learnt? 1981. 110.00x (ISBN 0-686-97105-1, Pub. by Marine Mgmt England). State Mutual Bk.
Offshore Oil & Gas Yearbook Nineteen Eighty One-Nineteen Eighty Two: UK & Continental Europe. 4th ed. (Illus.). 329p. 1982. 120.00x (ISBN 0-85038-498-2). Intl Pubns Serv.
Offshore Welded Structures: Guide for the Conception & Design of Tubular Welded Joints. LC 84-73153. (Illus.). 400p. (Orig.). 1985. pap. 59.95x (ISBN 0-87201-601-3). Gulf Pub.
Peters, A. F., ed. Impact of Offshore Oil Operations. (Illus.). 205p. 1974. 35.25 (ISBN 0-85334-453-1, Pub. by Elsevier Applied Sci England). Elsevier.
Puech, Alain. The Use of Anchors in Offshore Petroleum Operations. LC 84-71684. (Illus.). 112p. 1984. 39.95x (ISBN 0-87201-042-2). Gulf Pub.
Ranney, M. W. Offshore Oil Technology: Recent Developments. LC 79-83771. (Energy Technology Review Ser. 38, Ocean Technology Review Ser. 8). (Illus.). 339p. 1979. 42.00 (ISBN 0-8155-0741-0). Noyes.
Rushbrook, F. Fire Aboard: The Problems of Prevention & Control in Ships, Port Installations & Offshore Structures. 2nd ed. (Illus.). 1979. 75.00 (ISBN 0-686-77984-3). Heinman.
Safety & Health in the Construction of Fixed Offshore Installations in the Petroleum Industry. (Codes of Practice Ser.). vi, 132p. 1981. pap. 11.40 (ISBN 92-2-102900-X, ILO200, ILO). Unipub.
Sarpkaya, Turgut & Isaacson, Michael. Mechanics of Wave Forces on Offshore Structures. 624p. 1981. 39.50 (ISBN 0-442-25402-4). Van Nos Reinhold.
Seminar on Petroleum Legislation. Offshore Operation: Proceedings. (Mineral Resources Development Ser.: No. 40). pap. 5.00 (ISBN 0-686-94654-5, UN73/2F/13, UN). Unipub.
Vendrell, J. Oil Rig Moorings Handbook. 38p. 1977. pap. 10.50x (ISBN 0-85174-293-9). Sheridan.
Walker, A. C., et al. Buckling of Offshore Structures. LC 83-83188. 460p. 1984. 64.95x (ISBN 0-87201-067-8). Gulf Pub.
Wave & Wind Directionality: Applications to the Design of Offshore Structures. 574p. (Orig.). 1983. 89.95 (ISBN 0-87201-906-3). Gulf Pub.
Whitehead, Harry. An A-Z of Offshore Oil & Gas. 2nd ed. LC 82-84656. 438p. 1983. 44.50x (ISBN 0-87201-052-X). Gulf Pub.
Wilson, James F. Dynamics of Offshore Structures. LC 83-19862. (Ocean Engineering: A Wiley Ser.: 1-194). 546p. 1984. 59.95x (ISBN 0-471-87568-6, Pub. by Wiley-Interscience). Wiley.
Wright, Stephen G., ed. Geotechnical Practice in Offshore Engineering. LC 83-70397. 637p. 1983. pap. 47.50x (ISBN 0-87262-360-2). Am Soc Civil Eng.
Yudhibir & Balasubramaniam, A. S., eds. Geotechnical Aspects of Coastal & Offshore Structures: Proceedings of the Symposium on Geotechnical Aspects of Coastal & Offshore Structure, Bangkok, 14-18 December 1981. 288p. 1983. lib. bdg. 40.00 (ISBN 90-6191-515-5, Pub. by Balkema RSA). IPS.
Zinkowski, Nicholas B. Commercial Oilfield Diving. 2nd ed. LC 78-7214. (Illus.). 328p. 1978. 19.00x (ISBN 0-87033-235-X). Cornell Maritime.

OFT (FLIGHT SIMULATOR)

see Flight Simulators

OHM'S LAW

see also Electric Measurements

CES Industries, Inc. Staff. Ed-Lab Eighty Exercise Manual: Programming for Ohm's Law. (Illus.). 1982. write for info. (ISBN 0-86711-058-9). CES Industries.

OIL

see Mineral Oils; Oils and Fats; Petroleum

OIL BURNERS

Burkhardt, Charles H. Domestic & Commercial Oil Burners. 3rd ed. LC 68-31659. (Illus.). 1969. text ed. 30.40 (ISBN 0-07-009039-4). McGraw.
Field, Edwin M. Oil Burners. 4th ed. LC 83-22308. (Illus.). 1984. 12.95 (ISBN 0-672-23394-0). Audel.
--Oil Burners. 3rd ed. 320p. 1977. 9.95 (ISBN 0-672-23277-4). Audel.
Green, A. E., ed. An Alternative to Oil: Burning Coal with Gas; the Benefits of Burning Coal & Natural Gas Mixtures in Boilers Originally Designed for Oil. LC 82-1894. (Illus.). xi, 140p. (Orig.). 1982. pap. 8.95 (ISBN 0-8130-0724-0). U Presses Fla.
Installation of Oil Burning Equipment. (Thirty Ser). 88p. 1973. pap. 3.50 (ISBN 0-685-44166-0, 31). Natl Fire Prot.
Prevention of Furnace Explosions in Fuel Oil-Fired Multiple Burner Boiler-Furnaces. (Eighty-Ninety Ser.). 84p. 1974. pap. 3.50 (ISBN 0-685-44131-8, 85D). Natl Fire Prot.
Rudman, Jack. Install Oil Burner Equipment (License) (Career Examination Ser.: C-1317). (Cloth bdg. avail. on request). pap. 10.00 (ISBN 0-8373-1317-1). Natl Learning.

OIL CONSERVATION

see Petroleum Conservation

OIL ENGINES

see Gas and Oil Engines

OIL FIELDS

see also Oil Well Drilling; Petroleum; Petroleum–Pipe Lines

Allain, Louis J. Capital Investment Models of the Oil & Gas Industry: A Systems Approach. Bruchey, Stuart, ed. LC 78-22654. (Energy in the American Economy Ser.). (Illus.). 1979. lib. bdg. 42.00x (ISBN 0-405-11959-3). Ayer Co Pubs.
Amyx, James W., et al. Petroleum Reservoir Engineering Physical Properties. 1960. 52.95 (ISBN 0-07-001600-3). McGraw.
Baker, Ron. Treating Oil Field Emissions. 2nd ed. Taylor, Lydia, ed. (Illus.). 112p. (Orig.). 1974. pap. text ed. 6.00 (ISBN 0-88698-121-2, 3.50030). Petex.
Buck, Joan. Petroleum Lands & Leasing. 184p. 1983. 39.95 (ISBN 0-87814-239-8). PennWell Bks.
Chaballe, L. Y. & Masuy, L. Elsevier's Oil & Gas Field Dictionary. 672p. (in 6 languages plus Arabic suppl.). 1980. 138.50 (ISBN 0-444-41833-4). Elsevier.
Craig, Bruce. Practical Oil-Field Metallurgy. LC 83-4060. 200p. 1983. 49.95x (ISBN 0-87814-232-0, P-4328). Pennwell Bks.
Dickey, Parke A., et al. Oil & Gas Geology of the Oil City Quadrangle, Pennsylvania. (Mineral Resource Report: No. 25). (Illus.). 201p. pap. 9.95 (ISBN 0-8182-0032-4). Commonweal PA.
DiStasio, J. I., ed. Chemicals for Oil Field Operations: Recent Developments. LC 81-11052. (Chem. Tech. Rev. 195: Energy Tech. Rev. 69). (Illus.). 307p. 1982. 48.00 (ISBN 0-8155-0861-1). Noyes.
Galloway, W. E., et al. Atlas of Major Texas Oil Reservoirs. 139p. 1983. 40.00 (ISBN 0-318-03333-X). Bur Econ Geology.
Hoskins, James C., II. The Petroleum Landman: Basic Practices & Procedures. 26.00 (ISBN 0-318-02009-2). IED Pub Hse.
Hughes, Richard V. Oil Property Valuation. x ed. LC 77-2945. (Illus.). 324p. 1978. lib. bdg. 24.00 (ISBN 0-88275-402-5). Krieger.
Hunt, A. Lee. Pocket Guide to Supervising in the Oilfield. 36p. (Orig.). 1983. pap. 4.95x (ISBN 0-87201-714-1). Gulf Pub.
Jacobsen, Norman H. Oil Field Diving: The Diver's Story. LC 84-90315. (Illus.). 150p. (Orig.). 1984. pap. 9.95x (ISBN 0-9613260-0-X). Jacobsen Prop.
Levorsen, Arville I. Stratigraphic Type Oil Fields, 2 vols. 1976. lib. bdg. 250.00 (ISBN 0-8490-2694-6). Gordon Pr.
Liddle, R. A. The Van Oil Field, Van Zandt County, Texas. (Bull 3601 Ser.). 79p. 1936. 1.50 (ISBN 0-318-03307-0). Bur Econ Geology.
Lowe, et al, eds. New Mexico Petroleum Land Practices. (IED Book Ser.). 42.00 (ISBN 0-318-02003-3). IED Pub Hse.
Lytle, William S., et al. A Summary of Oil & Gas Developments in Pennsylvania: 1955 t0 1959. (Mineral Resource Report: No. 45). (Illus.). 133p. pap. 14.40 (ISBN 0-8182-0036-7). Commonweal PA.
McGlade, William G. Oil & Gas Geology of the Amity & Claysville Quadrangles, Pennsylvania. (Mineral Resource Report: No. 54). (Illus.). 131p. 1984. pap. 29.30 (ISBN 0-8182-0022-7). Commonweal PA.

Sinha, Mihir K. & Padgett, Larry. Reservoir Engineering Techniques Using FORTRAN. (Illus.). 225p. 1984. text ed. 45.00 (ISBN 0-934634-50-5). Intl Human Res.

Smith, Charles R. Mechanics of Secondary Oil Recovery. LC 74-32220. 512p. 1975. Repr. of 1966 ed. 35.50 (ISBN 0-88275-270-7). Krieger.

Timmerman, E. H. Practical Reservoir Engineering, Vol. 1. 365p. 1981. 71.95x (ISBN 0-87814-168-5). Pennwell Bks.

OIL SEEDS

see Oilseeds

OIL-SHALES

see also Petroleum

American Chemical Society, Division of Fuel Chemistry. Chemistry & Geochemistry of Oil Shales: Preprints of Papers Presented at Seattle, Washington, March 20-25, 1983. (American Chemical Society, Division of Fuel Chemistry, Preprints of Papers Ser.: Vol. 28, No. 3). pap. 62.80 (ISBN 0-317-28800-8, 2020320). Bks Demand UMI.

--Oil Shale, Tar Sands, & Related Materials: General Papers: Storch Award Symposium: Preprints of Papers Presented at San Francisco, California, August 24-29, 1980. (Preprints of Papers: Vol. 25, No. 3). pap. 74.50 (ISBN 0-317-28241-7, 2013279). Bks Demand UMI.

Byers, Charles W. Shales: Depositional Processes & Environments. (Illus.). 225p. 1986. text ed. write for info. (ISBN 0-934634-67-X). Intl Human Res.

Chong, K. P. & Ward-Smith, J., eds. Mechanics of Oil Shale. 603p. 1984. 112.50 (ISBN 0-85334-273-3, Pub. by Elsevier Applied Sci England). Elsevier.

Ellis, Theodore J. The Potential Role of Oil Shale in the U. S. Energy Mix: Questions of Development & Policy Formulation in an Environment Age. Bruchey, Stuart, ed. LC 78-22677. (Energy in the American Economy Ser.). (Illus.). 1979. lib. bdg. 23.00x (ISBN 0-405-11980-1). Ayer Co Pubs.

Gary, J. H., ed. Proceedings of the Twelfth Oil Shale Symposium. 395p. 1979. 11.00 (ISBN 0-918062-08-X). Colo Sch Mines.

Gary, James H., ed. Oil Shale Symposium Proceedings: 18th. (Illus.). 360p. 1985. pap. text ed. 25.00x (ISBN 0-918062-62-4). Colo Sch Mines.

--Proceedings of the Eleventh Oil Shale Symposium. (Illus.). 389p. 1978. pap. 5.00 (ISBN 0-918062-03-9). Colo Sch Mines.

--Proceedings of the Fifteenth Oil Shale Symposium. LC 82-4294. (Illus.). 597p. 1982. pap. 20.00 (ISBN 0-918062-50-0). Colo Sch Mines.

--Proceedings of the Thirteenth Oil Shale Symposium. LC 80-18711. (Oil Shale Ser.). (Illus.). 391p. (Orig.). 1980. pap. 12.00 (ISBN 0-918062-39-X). Colo Sch Mines.

--Sixteenth Oil Shale Symposium Proceedings. (Illus.). 600p. 1983. pap. text ed. 25.00 (ISBN 0-918062-56-X). Colo Sch Mines.

Grissom, M. Catherine, ed. Oil Shales & Tar Sands: A Bibliography, Supplement 2. 588p. 1984. pap. 38.25 (ISBN 0-87079-526-0, DOE/TIC-3367); microfiche 4.50 (ISBN 0-87079-527-9, DOE/TIC-3367). DOE.

Jensen, Howard, et al, eds. Analytical Chemistry of Liquid Fuel Sources: Tar Sands, Oil Shale, Coal, & Petroleum. LC 78-10399. (Advances in Chemistry Ser.: No. 170). 1978. 34.95 (ISBN 0-8412-0395-4). Am Chemical.

Miknis, Francis P. & McKay, John F., eds. Geochemistry & Chemistry of Oil Shales. LC 83-11801. (ACS Symposium Ser.: No. 230). 565p. 1983. lib. bdg. 59.95x (ISBN 0-8412-0799-2). Am Chemical.

Nowacki, Perry, ed. Oil Shale Technical Data Handbook. LC 80-27547. (Energy Tech. Rev. 63: Chemical Tech. Rev. 182). (Illus.). 309p. 1981. 48.00 (ISBN 0-8155-0835-2). Noyes.

Penner, S. S. & Iceman, L. Energy II-Non-Nuclear Energy Technologies, Vol. II. (Illus.). 888p. 1984. 77.00 (ISBN 0-08-031943-2); pap. 29.95 (ISBN 0-08-031942-4). Pergamon.

Petersen, Kathy, ed. Oil Shale: The Environmental Challenges III. (Proceedings of an International Symposium Ser.: No III). (Illus.). 261p. 1983. text ed. 11.00 (ISBN 0-918062-54-3). Colo Sch Mines.

Peterson, Kathy, ed. Oil Shale: The Environmental Challenges. LC 81-10118. (Proceedings of International Symposium Aug. 11-14, 1980, Vail, Colorado). (Illus.). 380p. 1981. text ed. 10.00 (ISBN 0-918062-43-8). Colo Sch Mines.

Peterson, Kathy K., ed. Oil Shale: The Environmental Challenges II. LC 82-14759. (Illus.). 392p. 1982. 11.00 (ISBN 0-918062-51-9). Colo Sch Mines.

Pettit, Rhonda, ed. Eastern Oil Shale Symposium Proceedings, 1983. (Illus.). 300p. 1983. pap. text ed. 25.00 (ISBN 0-86607-022-2, IMMR83/089). KY Ctr Energy Res.

Raese, Jon W. & Baughman, Gary L., eds. Oil Shale Symposium Proceedings Index 1964-82. LC 82-19839. 110p. 1982. pap. text ed. 30.00 (ISBN 0-918062-52-7). Colo Sch Mines.

Robl, Tom & Koppenaal, Dave. The Chemical & Engineering Properties of Eastern Oil Shale. Pettit, Rhonda, ed. 303p. (Orig.). 1982. pap. text ed. 10.00 (ISBN 0-86607-014-1). KY Ctr Energy Res.

Ruebens, John & Gary, J. H., eds. Proceedings of the Tenth Oil Shale Symposium. LC 75-17946. (Illus.). 256p. 1977. pap. 3.50 (ISBN 0-918062-01-2). Colo Sch Mines.

Russell, Paul L. History of Western Oil Shale. LC 80-66410. (Illus.). 176p. 1980. 49.50 (ISBN 0-86563-000-3). Ctr Prof Adv.

Stauffer, H. C., ed. Oil Shale, Tar Sands, & Related Materials. LC 81-10948. (ACS Symposium Ser.: No. 163). 1981. 39.95 (ISBN 0-8412-0640-6). Am Chemical.

Steele, Henry B. Economic Potentialities of Synthetic Liquid Fuels from Oil Shale. Bruchey, Stuart, ed. LC 78-22751. (Energy in the American Economy Ser.). (Illus.). 1979. lib. bdg. 40.00x (ISBN 0-405-12015-X). Ayer Co Pubs.

Strausz, Otto P. & Lown, Elizabeth M., eds. Oil Sand & Oil Shale Chemistry. LC 78-19168. (Illus.). 384p. 1978. pap. 37.80x (ISBN 0-89573-102-9). VCH Pubs.

Synthetic Fuels from Oil Shale & Tar Sands (Symposium III) 707p. 1983. 75.00 (ISBN 0-910091-48-X). Inst Gas Tech.

Tissot, B., pref. by. Kerogen-Insoluble Organic Matter from Sedimentary Rocks. 560p. 1980. 175.00x (ISBN 0-86010-220-3, Pub. by Graham & Trotman England). State Mutual Bk.

Yen, T. F. & Chilingarian, G. V. Oil Shale. (Developments in Petroleum Science Ser.: Vol. 5). 292p. 1976. 68.00 (ISBN 0-444-41408-8). Elsevier.

OIL TANKERS

see Tankers

OIL WELL BLOWOUTS

Adams, Neal. Workover Well Control. 308p. 1981. 53.95x (ISBN 0-87814-142-1). Pennwell Bks.

Blowout Prevention. 3rd, rev. ed. (Rotary Drilling Ser.: Unit III, Lesson 3). (Illus.). 97p. (Orig.). 1980. pap. text ed. 5.00 (ISBN 0-88698-051-8, 2.30330). PETEX.

Fischer, D. W., ed. Managing Technological Accidents: Two Blowouts in the North Sea: Proceedings of an IIASA Workshop on Blowout Management. (IIASA Proceedings Ser.: Vol. 16). (Illus.). 242p. 1982. 55.00 (ISBN 0-08-029346-8). Pergamon.

Mills, Peter G. Blowout Prevention: Theory & Applications. LC 84-4507. (Illus.). 224p. 1984. 56.00 (ISBN 0-934634-78-5). Intl Human Res.

Subsea Blowout Preventers & Marine Riser Systems. (Rotary Drilling Ser.: Unit III, Lesson 4). (Illus.). 58p. (Orig.). 1976. pap. text ed. 5.00 (ISBN 0-88698-052-6, 2.30410). PETEX.

OIL WELL DRILLING

see also Drilling Muds; Oil Well Blowouts

Albornoz, Fernando, ed. The Auxiliaries. Quiroga, Roberto, tr. (Rotary Drilling Ser.: Unit I, Lesson 9). (Span., Illus.). 60p. (Orig.). 1983. pap. text ed. 5.00 (ISBN 0-88698-037-2, 2.10922). PETEX.

--The Drill Stem. 2nd ed. Quiroga, Roberto, tr. (Rotary Drilling Ser.: Unit I, Lesson 3). (Span., Illus.). 51p. (Orig.). 1983. pap. text ed. 5.00 (ISBN 0-88698-031-3, 2.10322). PETEX.

--The Rotary, Kelly, & Swivel. Quiroga, Roberto, tr. (Rotary Drilling Ser.: Unit I, Lesson 4). (Span., Illus.). 69p. (Orig.). 1982. pap. text ed. 5.00 (ISBN 0-88698-032-1, 2.10422). PETEX.

--The Rotary Rig & its Components. Carmona-Agosto, Vivian, tr. (Rotary Drilling Ser.: Unit I, Lesson 1). (Span., Illus.). 47p. (Orig.). 1980. pap. text ed. 5.00 (ISBN 0-88698-029-1, 2.10132). PETEX.

Alperovitch, I. M., et al. Magnetotellurics in Oil Exploration in the U.S.S.R. Keller, G. V., tr. Vozoff, K. & Asten, M., eds. 65p. 1982. pap. 12.00 (ISBN 0-931830-19-2). Soc Exploration.

Angel, R. R. Volume Requirements for Air & Gas Drilling. (Air & Gas Drilling Technology Ser.: Vol. 2). 94p. (Orig.). 1958. 12.95x (ISBN 0-87201-890-3). Gulf Pub.

Baker, Ron. A Primer of Oilwell Drilling. 4th ed. Gerding, Mildred, ed. (Illus.). 94p. (Orig.). 1982. pap. text ed. 8.50 (ISBN 0-88698-116-6, 2.00040). Petex.

Baldwin, Pamela L. & Baldwin, Malcolm F. Onshore Planning for Offshore Oil: Lessons from Scotland. LC 75-606. (Illus.). 1975. pap. 5.00 (ISBN 0-89164-001-0). Conservation Foun.

Blowout Prevention. 3rd, rev. ed. (Rotary Drilling Ser.: Unit III, Lesson 3). (Illus.). 97p. (Orig.). 1980. pap. text ed. 5.00 (ISBN 0-88698-051-8, 2.30330). PETEX.

Boyd, W. E. Control of Formation Pressure. (Well Servicing & Workover: Lesson 9). (Illus.). 44p. (Orig.). 1971. pap. text ed. 4.50 (ISBN 0-88698-065-8, 3.70910). PETEX.

--Fishing Tools & Techniques. (Well Servicing & Workover Ser.: Lesson 10). (Illus.). 48p. (Orig.). 1971. pap. text ed. 4.50 (ISBN 0-88698-066-6, 3.71010). PETEX.

Brantly, J. E. History of Oil Well Drilling. LC 78-149757. (Illus.). 1548p. 1971. 59.95x (ISBN 0-87201-634-X). Gulf Pub.

Brock, Jim. Analyzing Your Logs Vol. II: Advanced Open Hole Interpretation. Brock, Jannye, ed. (Illus.). 160p. (Orig.). 1984. pap. 30.00 (ISBN 0-916647-02-1). Petro-Media.

Buialov, N. I., et al. Quantitative Evaluation of Predicted Reserves of Oil & Gas (Authorized Translation from the Russian) LC 64-7759. pap. 20.00 (ISBN 0-317-10640-6, 2003359). Bks Demand UMI.

Canadian Association of Oilwell Drilling Contractors. Drilling Rig Task Details & Performance Standards, 5 vols. (Orig.). 1982. Set. 42.25x (ISBN 0-87201-927-6). Rig Manager (ISBN 0-87201-929-2). Driller (ISBN 0-87201-930-6). Derrickhand (ISBN 0-87201-931-4). Motorhand (ISBN 0-87201-932-2). Floorhand (ISBN 0-87201-933-0). Gulf Pub.

--An Introduction to Oilwell Drilling & Servicing. LC 82-12027. 98p. (Orig.). 1982. pap. 6.95x (ISBN 0-87201-202-6). Gulf Pub.

--Servicing Rig Task Details & Performance Standards, 4 vols. (Orig.). 1982. Set. pap. 33.80x (ISBN 0-87201-928-4). Rig Manager (ISBN 0-87201-934-9). Rig Operator (ISBN 0-87201-935-7). Derrickhand (ISBN 0-87201-936-5). Floorhand (ISBN 0-87201-937-3). Gulf Pub.

Carmona-Agosto, Vivian, ed. The Bit. Albornoz, Fernando, tr. (Rotary Drilling Ser.: Unit I, Lesson 2). (Span., Illus.). 59p. (Orig.). 1981. pap. text ed. 5.00 (ISBN 0-88698-030-5, 2.10232). PETEX.

--Safety on the Rig. rev. ed. Albornoz, Fernando, tr. from Eng. (Rotary Drilling Ser.: Unit I, Lesson6). (Span., Illus.). 77p. 1981. pap. text ed. 5.00 (ISBN 0-88698-038-0, 2.11032). PETEX.

Carmona-Agosto, Vivian, et al, eds. Wind, Waves, & Weather. Rossman, Marcela, tr. from Eng. (Rotary Drilling Series, Unit V: Lesson 1). (Span., Illus.). 44p. 1982. pap. text ed. 4.50 (ISBN 0-88698-046-1, 2.50112). PETEX.

Carneiro, F. L., et al, eds. Offshore Structures Engineering, Vol. 2. LC 78-74102. (Offshore Structures Engineering Ser.). 600p. 1980. 49.95x (ISBN 0-87201-609-9). Gulf Pub.

Chemicals for Enhanced Oil Recovery: C-014R. 1983. 1500.00 (ISBN 0-89336-210-7). BCC.

Chenevert, M., et al. HP-41CV Applied Drilling Engineering Manual. LC 82-20983. 152p. (Orig.). 1983. 29.95x (ISBN 0-87201-355-3); Bar Code Supplement pap. 48p. 49.95x (ISBN 0-87201-356-1). Gulf Pub.

Chillingarian, G. V. Drilling & Drilling Fluids. (Development in Petroleum Science Ser.: Vol. 11). 1981. 119.25 (ISBN 0-444-41867-9). Elsevier.

Collip, Bruce G. Buoyancy, Stability & Trim. (Rotary Drilling Ser.: Unit V, Lesson 3). (Illus.). 30p. (Orig.). 1976. pap. text ed. 4.50 (ISBN 0-88698-071-2, 2.50310). PETEX.

Commission of the European Communities. New Technologies for Exploration & Exploitation of Oil & Gas Resources, Vol. 11. 600p. 1979. 75.00x (ISBN 0-86010-159-2, Pub. by Graham & Trotman England). State Mutual Bk.

Control of Drilling. 100p. 1982. 90.00x (ISBN 0-686-92040-6, Pub. by Graham & Trotman England). State Mutual Bk.

Controlled Directional Drilling. 2nd, rev. ed. (Rotary Drilling Ser.: Unit III, Lesson 1). (Illus.). 41p. (Orig.). 1974. pap. text ed. 5.00 (ISBN 0-88698-049-6, 2.30120). PETEX.

Craft, Benjamin C., et al. Well Design: Drilling & Production. 1962. ref. ed. 44.95x (ISBN 0-13-950022-7). P-H.

Cranmer, John L. Basic Drilling Engineering Manual. LC 82-12322. 160p. 1982. 64.95x (ISBN 0-87814-199-5, P-4312). Pennwell Bks.

Cyrus, Cinda. Well Cementing. Paxson, Jeanette R., ed. (Oil & Gas Production Ser.). (Illus.). 82p. (Orig.). 1983. pap. text ed. 5.00 (ISBN 0-88698-112-3, 3.30610). Petex.

Drilling Mud. rev. ed. (Rotary Drilling Ser.: Unit II, Lesson 2). (Illus., Orig.). 1975. pap. text ed. 5.00 (ISBN 0-88698-054-2, 2.20220). PETEX.

French Petroleum Institute Staff. Drilling Mud & Cement Slurry Rheology Manual. LC 81-85417. 108p. 1982. 29.95x (ISBN 0-87201-780-X). Gulf Pub.

Geological & Mud Logging in Drilling Control. LC 80-82500. 81p. 1982. 23.50x (ISBN 0-87201-433-9). Gulf Pub.

Geophysics Research Board. Continental Scientific Drilling. 1979. pap. 5.95 (ISBN 0-309-02872-8). Natl Acad Pr.

Gerding, Mildred. The Rotary Rig & Its Components: Canadian Metric Edition. 3rd ed. (Rotary Drilling Ser.: Unit I, Lesson 1). (Illus.). 1979. pap. text ed. 5.00 (ISBN 0-88698-017-8). PETEX.

Gerding, Mildred, ed. Helicopter Safety. rev. ed. (Rotary Drilling Ser.: Unit 5, Lesson 7). (Illus.). 37p. (Orig.). 1980. pap. text ed. 4.50 (ISBN 0-88698-075-5, 2.50710). PETEX.

--The Rotary Rig & Its Components. 3rd ed. (Rotary Drilling Ser.: Unit I, Lesson 1). (Illus.). Date not set. pap. text ed. 5.00 (ISBN 0-88698-005-4, 2.10130). PETEX.

--Well Service & Workover Profitability. (Well Servicing & Workover Ser.: Lesson 12). (Illus.). 32p. 1980. pap. text ed. 4.50 (ISBN 0-88698-068-2, 3.71220). PETEX.

Gowar, R. G., ed. Developments in Fire Protection of Offshore Platforms, Vol. 1. (Illus.). 232p. 1978. text ed. 46.25 (ISBN 0-85334-792-1, Pub. by Elsevier Applied Sci England). Elsevier.

Gray, George & Darley, H. C. Composition & Properties of Oil Well Drilling Fluids. 4th ed. LC 79-28157. 630p. 1980. 59.95x (ISBN 0-87201-129-1). Gulf Pub.

Grayson, C. Jackson, Jr. Decisions Under Uncertainty: Drilling Decisions by Oil & Gas Operators. Bruchey, Stuart, ed. LC 78-22686. (Energy in the American Economy Ser.). (Illus.). 1979. Repr. of 1960 ed. lib. bdg. 32.50x (ISBN 0-405-11989-5). Ayer Co Pubs.

Haggard, Russell, ed. Orientation for Offshore Crane Operations. Rev. ed. (Rotary Drilling Ser.: Unit V: Offshore Technology Lesson 8). (Illus.). 35p. (Orig.). 1983. pap. text ed. 4.50 (ISBN 0-88698-042-9, 2.50810). Petex.

Haggard, Rusty. Diving & Equipment. 2nd, rev. ed. Janicek, Nancy, ed. (Rotary Drilling Ser.: Unit V, Lesson 5). (Illus.). 45p. (Orig.). 1982. pap. text ed. 4.50 (ISBN 0-88698-073-9, 2.50520). PETEX.

Hall, R. Stewart. Drilling & Producing Offshore. LC 82-18956. 267p. 1983. 49.95x (ISBN 0-87814-213-4, P-4249). Pennwell Bks.

Handbook of Rheology for Drilling Fluids & Cement Slurries. 152p. 1982. 90.00x (ISBN 2-7108-0373-9, Pub. by Graham & Trotman England). State Mutual Bk.

Hardy, George. Pooling & Unitization: Rocky Mountains. 620p. 1984. 39.00 (ISBN 0-89419-339-2). Inst Energy.

Harris, L. M. Design for Reliability in Deepwater Floating Drilling Operations. 266p. 1980. 49.95 (ISBN 0-87814-082-4). Pennwell Bks.

Henderson, Celina, ed. Spread Mooring Systems. Rossman, Marcela, tr. from Eng. (Rotary Drilling Ser.: Unit V, Lesson 2). (Span., Illus.). 53p. (Orig.). 1982. pap. text ed. 4.50 (ISBN 0-88698-045-3, 2.50212). PETEX.

Institut du Petrole Francaise, ed. Drilling Data Handbook. LC 79-56343. 412p. 1980. 49.95x (ISBN 0-87201-204-2). Gulf Pub.

Introduction to Oilwell Service & Workover. (Well Servicing & Workover Ser.: Lesson I). (Illus.). 73p. (Orig.). 1971. pap. text ed. 5.00 (ISBN 0-88698-057-7, 3.70110). PETEX.

Janicek, Nancy, ed. Drilling a Straight Hole. 3rd, rev. ed. (Rotary Drilling Ser.: Unit II, Lesson 3). (Illus.). 37p. (Orig.). 1982. pap. text ed. 5.00 (ISBN 0-88698-055-0, 2.20320). PETEX.

Janicek, Nancy J., ed. Controlled Directional Drilling. Rev. ed. (Rotary Drilling Ser.). (Illus.). 50p. (Orig.). 1974. pap. text ed. 5.00 (ISBN 0-88698-099-2). Petex.

Kirkley, Charles, ed. Making Hole. 2nd, rev. ed. (Rotary Drilling Ser.: Unit II, Lesson 1). (Illus.). 38p. (Orig.). 1983. pap. text ed. 5.00 (ISBN 0-88698-053-4, 2.20120). PETEX.

Kruse, Curtis. Jacking Systems & Rig Moving Procedures. (Rotary Drilling Ser.: Unit V, Lesson 4). (Illus.). 52p. (Orig.). 1976. pap. text ed. 4.50 (ISBN 0-88698-072-0, 2.50410). PETEX.

Leecraft, Jodie. Diesel Engines & Electric Power. (Rotary Drilling Ser.: Unit I, Lesson 11). (Illus.). 90p. (Orig.). 1982. pap. text ed. 5.00 (ISBN 0-88698-027-5, 2.11121). PETEX.

Leecraft, Jodie, ed. The Auxiliaries. 2nd ed. (Rotary Drilling Ser.: Unit I, Lesson 9). (Illus.). 48p. 1981. pap. text ed. 5.00 (ISBN 0-88698-013-5, 2.10920). PETEX.

--The Auxiliaries: Canadian Metric Edition. rev. ed. (Rotary Drilling Ser.: Unit I, Lesson 9). (Illus.). Date not set. pap. text ed. 5.00 (ISBN 0-88698-025-9, 2.10921). PETEX.

--The Bit. 3rd ed. (Rotary Drilling Ser.: Unit I, Lesson 2). (Illus.). 60p. Date not set. pap. text ed. 5.00 (ISBN 0-88698-006-2, 2.10230). PETEX.

--The Bit: Canadian Metric Edition. (Rotary Drilling Ser.: Unit I, Lesson 2). (Illus.). 60p. (Orig.). 1980. pap. text ed. 5.00 (ISBN 0-88698-018-6, 2.10231). PETEX.

--The Blocks & Drilling Line. rev. ed. Albornoz, Fernando, tr. (Rotary Drilling Ser.: Unit I, Lesson 5). (Span., Illus.). 51p. (Orig.). 1981. pap. text ed. 5.00 (ISBN 0-88698-033-X, 2.10520). PETEX.

--Diseases of Annual Edible Oilseed Crops, Vol. II. 176p. 1985. 58.00 (ISBN 0-8493-5381-5). CRC Pr.

--Diseases of Annual Edible Oilseed Crops, Vol. III. 168p. 1985. 57.00 (ISBN 0-8493-5382-3). CRC Pr.

Pesce, Celestino. Oil Palms & Other Oilseeds of the Amazon. Johnson, Dennis V., ed. Schultes, Richard E. & Borges, Ricardo, trs. from Portuguese. LC 85-11958. (Studies in Economic Botony). Tr. of Oleaginosas da Amazonia. (Illus.). 1985. 24.95x (ISBN 0-917256-28-X). Ref Pubns.

Report of the Fifteenth Session of the Intergovernmental Group on Oilseeds, Oils & Fats to the Committee on Commodity Problems: Rome, March 1981. (Eng., Fr. & Span.). 12p. 1981. pap. 7.50 (ISBN 92-5-101065-X, F2128, FAO). Unipub.

OILSEEDS

see also Oils and Fats; Seeds

Induced Mutations - A Tool in Plant Research: Proceedings of a Symposium, Vienna, 9-13 March 1981, Jointly Organized by IAEA and FAO. (Proceedings Ser.). (Illus.). 538p. 1981. pap. 16.50 (ISBN 0-686-82544-6, ISP591, IAEA); pap. 18.00 (ISP 591-2). Unipub.

Kramer, J. K. & Saver, F. D., eds. High & Low Erucic Acid Rapeseed Oils: Production, Usage, Chemistry & Toxilogical Evaluation. LC 82-13805. 1983. 79.50 (ISBN 0-12-425080-7). Acad Pr.

Oilseeds. (Commodity Projections). 1979. pap. 6.00 (ISBN 0-686-59429-0, F1606, FAO). Unipub.

Report of the Intergovernmental Group on Oilseeds, Oils, & Fats to the Committee on Commodity Problems. Incl. Tenth Session. 19p. 1976. pap. 7.50 (ISBN 0-685-68966-2, F1117); Eleventh Session. (Illus.). 29p. 1978. pap. 7.50 (ISBN 0-685-20384-0, F1143); Thirteenth Session. 34p. 1979. pap. 7.00 (ISBN 0-686-93098-3, F1639); Fourteenth Session, Rome, April 1980. 38p. 1981. pap. 7.50 (ISBN 92-5-100937-6, F2044). FAO). Unipub.

OLD ENGLISH SHEEPDOGS

see Dogs–Breeds–Old English Sheepdog

OLD MILLS

see Flour Mills; Mills and Mill-Work

OLD RED SANDSTONE (GEOLOGY)

see Geology, Stratigraphic–Devonian

OLEFINS

Cook, J. Gordon. Handbook of Polyolefin Fibers. 608p. 1967. 90.00x (ISBN 0-900541-50-4, Pub. by Meadowfield Pr England). State Mutual Bk.

Dragutan, A. T., et al. Olefin Metathesis & Ring-Opening Polymerization of Cyclo-Olefins. 400p. 1985. text ed. 64.95 (ISBN 0-471-90267-5, Pub. by Wiley-Interscience). Wiley.

Fray, G. I. & Saxton, R. G. The Chemistry of Cyclo-Octatetraene & Its Derivatives. LC 76-57096. 1978. Cambridge U Pr.

Henman, T. J., ed. World Index of Polyolefin Stabilizers. 348p. 1983. 185.00x (ISBN 0-87201-920-9). Gulf Pub.

Ivin, K. J. Olefin Metathesis. 1983. 70.00 (ISBN 0-12-377050-5). Acad Pr.

Sittig, Marshall. Polyolefin Production Processes-Latest Developments. LC 76-9491. (Chemical Technology Review: No. 70). (Illus.). 385p. 1976. 39.00 (ISBN 0-8155-0622-8). Noyes.

OLEOMARGARINE

Committee on Agriculture, U.S. House of Representatives. Oleomargarine. LC 75-26318. (World Food Supply Ser). (Illus.). 1976. Repr. of 1949 ed. 31.00x (ISBN 0-405-07794-7). Ayer Co Pubs.

Pabst, W. R., Jr. Butter & Oleomargarine. LC 70-76644. (Columbia University. Studies in the Social Sciences: No. 427). Repr. of 1937 ed. 15.00 (ISBN 0-404-51427-8). AMS Pr.

OLEUM

see Sulphuric Acid

OLFACTORY BRAIN

see Rhinencephalon

OLFACTORY NERVE

see also Septum (Brain)

Cagan, Robert H. & Kare, Morley R., eds. Biochemistry of Taste & Olfaction. (Nutrition Foundation Ser.). 1981. 55.00 (ISBN 0-12-154450-8). Acad Pr.

Pfaff, Donald, ed. Taste, Olfaction & the Central Nervous System: A Festschrift in Honor of Carl Pfaffmann. LC 84-43054. 346p. 1985. cloth 29.95 (ISBN 0-87470-039-6). Rockefeller.

Valnet, Jean. The Practice of Aromatherapy: Holistic Health & the Essential Oils of Flowers & Herbs. LC 82-4968. (Illus.). 279p. 1982. pap. 8.95 (ISBN 0-89281-026-2). Destiny Bks.

OLIGOCENE PERIOD

see Geology, Stratigraphic–Oligocene

OLIGOCHAETA

Brinkhurst, Ralph O. & Cook, David G., eds. Aquatic Oligochaete Biology. LC 79-28164. 538p. 1980. 69.50x (ISBN 0-306-40338-2, Plenum Pr). Plenum Pub.

Gates, G. E. Burmese Earthworms: An Introduction to the Systematics & Biology of Megadrile Oligochaetes with Special Reference to Southeast Asia. LC 72-83461. (Transactions Ser.: Vol. 62, Pt. 7). (Illus.). 1972. pap. 5.00 (ISBN 0-87169-627-4). Am Philos.

Jamieson, B. G. Ultrastructure of the Oligochaeta. LC 81-66699. 1982. 146.50 (ISBN 0-12-380180-X). Acad Pr.

Kuhne, Walter G. The Liassic Therapsid Oligokyphus. (Illus.). iii, 150p. 1956. 21.50x (ISBN 0-565-00115-9, Pub. by British Mus Nat Hist England). Sabbot-Natural Hist Bks.

Stephenson, J. The Oligochaeta. (Illus.). 1930. 70.00 (ISBN 3-7682-0750-1). Lubrecht & Cramer.

OLIGOSACCHARIDES

Stanek, Jaroslav, et al. Oligosaccharides. Mayer, Karel, tr. 1965. 80.00 (ISBN 0-12-663756-3). Acad Pr.

OLIVE

Establishment of Olive Research Networks: Report of a Meeting Held at Cordoba, Spain, September 19-20, 1974. (Illus.). 1975. pap. 7.50 (ISBN 0-685-62393-9, F1093, FAO). Unipub.

Report of the Third Session of the FAO Olive Production Committee. (Illus.). 1977. pap. 15.50 (ISBN 92-5-100223-1, F1098, FAO). Unipub.

OLIVE INDUSTRY AND TRADE

China: Development of Olive Production: Report of a Study Tour to the People's Republic of China, Sept. 25 - Oct, 19, 1979. (Plant Production & Protection Papers: No. 23). 163p. 1980. pap. 11.75 (ISBN 92-5-100995-3, F2097, FAO). Unipub.

The Stabilization of the Olive Oil Market. (Commodity Policy Studies: No. 9). 55p. 1955. pap. 4.75 (ISBN 0-686-92739-7, F437, FAO). Unipub.

Suarez, Martinez & Herrera, Gomez. Manual of Olive Oil Technology. 2nd ed. Moreno, Martinez, ed. 164p. 1984. pap. 12.50 (F2558, FAO). Unipub.

OLYMPUS CAMERA

see Cameras–Types–Olympus

OMNIRANGE SYSTEM

Lonergan, T. & Frederick, C. The VOR. 1983. pap. 8.95 (ISBN 0-8104-5186-7). Hayden.

OMR

see Organic Moderated Reactors

ONIONS

OECD Staff. International Standardisation of Fruit & Vegetables: Onions. rev. ed. 50p. 1984. pap. 14.00 (ISBN 92-64-02495-6). OECD.

Voss, Ronald E. Onion Production in California. LC 79-55403. (Illus.). 1979. pap. 5.00 (ISBN 0-931876-35-4, 4097). Ag & Nat Res.

ON-LINE BIBLIOGRAPHIC SEARCHING

Armstrong, C. J. & Large, J. A. A Microcomputer Teaching Package for On-Line Bibliographic Searching: Complete Package. (R&D Report: No. 5741). (Illus., Orig.). 1984. manual, wkbk, floppy discs 90.00 (ISBN 0-7123-3023-2, Pub. by Croom Helm Ltd); pap. text ed. 10.50 wkbk. only (ISBN 0-7123-3024-0). Longwood Pub Group.

Association of Research Libraries, Systems & Procedures Exchange Center. Online Catalogs. (SPEC Kit & Flyer Ser.: No. 96). 97p. 1983. 20.00 (ISBN 0-318-03460-3); members 10.00. Assn Res Lib.

Byerly, Greg. Online Searching: A Dictionary & Bibliographic Guide. 288p. 1983. lib. bdg. 27.50 (ISBN 0-87287-381-1). Libs Unl.

Cochrane, Pauline A. Redesign of Catalogs & Indexes for Improved Online Subject Access: Selected Papers of Pauline A. Cochrane. LC 85-42722. 384p. 1985. lib. bdg. 45.00 (ISBN 0-89774-158-7). Oryx Pr.

Fayen, Emily G. The Online Catalog: Improving Public Access to Library Materials. LC 83-12009. (Professional Librarian Ser.). 148p. 1983. professional o.s.i. 34.50 (ISBN 0-86729-054-4); pap. 27.50 professional (ISBN 0-86729-053-6, 235-BW). Knowledge Indus.

Feinberg, Hilda, ed. Indexing Specialized Formats & Subjects. LC 82-23155. 300p. 1983. 37.50 (ISBN 0-8108-1608-3). Scarecrow.

Gilreath, Charles L. Computer Literature Searching: Research Strategies & Databases. 180p. 1984. softcover 22.00x (ISBN 0-86531-526-4). Westview.

Hall, James L. & Brown, Marjorie J., eds. Online Bibliographic Databases: An International Directory. 3rd ed. 250p. 1983. 95.00x (ISBN 0-8103-0530-5, Pub. by Aslib England). Gale.

Harvard Business Review: HBR ONLINE. (HBR Ser.). Online database. write for info. (ISBN 0-471-87063-3); User's guide. 50.00 (ISBN 0-471-89144-4). Wiley.

Hawkins, Donald. Online Information Retrieval Bibliography 1964-1979. 175p. 1980. 25.00x (ISBN 0-938734-00-8). Learned Info.

HBR. Harvard Business Review: HBR ONLINE Thesaurus. (HBR Ser.). 1982. 50.00 (ISBN 0-317-31839-X). Wiley.

Henry, Malcolm, et al. Online Searching: An Introduction. LC 80-40242. (Illus.). 220p. 1980. 39.95 (ISBN 0-408-10696-4). Butterworth.

Holmes, P. L. On-line Information Retrieval: An Introduction & Guide to the British Library's Short Term Experimental Information Network Project. Experimental Use of Non-Medical Information Services, 2 Vols. 1978. Vol. 1. 40.00x ea. (ISBN 0-905984-11-0, Pub. by Brit Lib England). Vol. 2 (ISBN 0-905984-02-1). State Mutual Bk.

Hoover, Ryan E., ed. Online Search Strategies. LC 82-17179. (Professional Librarian Ser.). 345p. 1982. professional 37.50 (ISBN 0-86729-005-6, 225-BW); pap. 29.50 professional (ISBN 0-86729-004-8). Knowledge Indus.

Houghton, Bernard & Convey, John. On Line Information Retrieval Systems: An Introductory Manual to Principles & Practice. 2nd ed. 224p. 1984. 21.50 (Pub. by Bingley England). Shoe String.

Hyman, M. & Wallis, E. Mini-Computers & Bibliographic Information Retrieval. 1980. 40.00x (ISBN 0-85350-144-0, Pub. by Brit Lib England). State Mutual Bk.

Katz, Bill, ed. Reference & Online Services Handbook: Guidelines, Policies & Procedures, Vol. II. 596p. 1985. lib. bdg. 37.50 (ISBN 0-918212-74-X). Neal-Schuman.

Keenan, Stella. How to go On-Line: Guidelines for the Establishment of On-Line Services in Public Libraries. 1980. 30.00x (ISBN 0-905984-57-9, Pub. by Brit Lib England). State Mutual Bk.

Key Papers on the Use of Computer-Based Bibliographic Services, 1973. 1973. 10.00 (ISBN 0-317-13885-5, 342-BW). Knowledge Indus.

Lee, Joann. Online Searching: The Basics, Settings, & Management. 240p. 1984. lib. bdg. 23.50 (ISBN 0-87287-380-3). Libs Unl.

Maloney, James J., ed. Online Searching Technique & Management. LC 83-11954. vii, 195p. 1983. pap. text ed. 25.00x (ISBN 0-8389-3285-1). ALA.

Matthews, Joseph R. Public Access to Online Catalogs. 2nd ed. (Library Automation Planning Guides Ser.). 497p. 1985. pap. text ed. 35.00 (ISBN 0-918212-89-8). Neal Schuman.

--Public Access to Online Catalogs: A Planning Guide for Managers. 345p. 1982. pap. text ed. 28.50 (ISBN 0-910965-00-5). Online.

Matthews, Joseph R. & Lawrence, Gary S. Using Online Catalogs: A Nationwide Survey. (Illus.). 255p. 1983. pap. 27.95 (ISBN 0-918212-76-6). Neal-Schuman.

Meadow, Charles T. & Cochrane, Pauline. Basics of Online Searching. LC 80-23050. (Information Science Ser.). 245p. 1981. 25.50x (ISBN 0-471-05283-3, Pub. by Wiley-Interscience). Wiley.

Moore, Nick, ed. On-Line Information in Public Libraries: A Review of Recent British Research. 69p. 1981. 35.00x (ISBN 0-905984-76-5, Pub. by Brit Lib England). State Mutual Bk.

Oulton, A. J. The On-Line Public Library. 1982. pap. 55.00x (ISBN 0-905984-78-1, Brit Lib England). State Mutual Bk.

Palmer, Roger C. Online Reference & Information Retrieval. (Library Science Text). 140p. (Orig.). 1982. pap. text ed. 18.50 (ISBN 0-87287-347-1). Libs Unl.

Schmittroth, John, Jr., ed. Online Database Search Services Directory, 2 pts. 1983. Set. pap. 120.00x (ISBN 0-8103-1698-6). Gale.

Sears, Jean L. & Moody, Marilyn K. Using Government Publications: Searching by Subjects & Agencies, Vol. 1. LC 83-43249. 256p. 1985. lib. bdg. 67.50 (ISBN 0-89774-094-7). Oryx Pr.

Subject Thesaurus for Bowker Online Databases. 571p. 1984. 25.00 (ISBN 0-8352-1889-9). Bowker.

Tedd, Lucy A. The Teaching of On-Line Cataloguing & Searching & the Use of New Technology in UK Schools of Librarianship & Information Science. 126p. 1981. pap. 40.00x (ISBN 0-905984-67-6, Pub. by Brit Lib England). State Mutual Bk.

Tolle, John E. Public Access Terminals: Determining Quantity Requirements. LC 84-164540. (OCLC Library Information & Computer Science Ser.). (Illus.). 161p. (Orig.). 1983. pap. 14.50 (ISBN 0-933418-51-5). OCLC Online Comp.

Tze-Chung Li. An Introduction to Online Searching. LC 84-6686. (Contributions in Librarianship & Information Science: No. 50). (Illus.). xvi, 289p. 1985. lib. bdg. 27.95 (ISBN 0-313-24274-7, LIO/). Greenwood.

Vickery, B. C. The Use of On-line Search in Teaching: An Assessment of Projects Carried Out by U.K. Schools of Library & Information Studies. 1977. 30.00x (ISBN 0-905984-05-6, Pub. by Brit Lib England). State Mutual Bk.

Vulton, A. J. & Pearce, A. On-Line Experiments in Public Libraries. 1980. 30.00x (ISBN 0-905984-56-0, Pub. by Brit Lib England). State Mutual Bk.

Yeates, R. Prestel in the Public Library: Reactions to the General Public to Prestel & its Potential for Conveying Local Information. 1982. 55.00x (ISBN 0-905984-79-X, Pub. by Brit Lib England). State Mutual Bk.

Zorena, P. Basic User's Guide to Full-Text Chemical Databases: How to Search ACS Journals & the Kirk-Othmer Encyclopedia Online. (On Line Chemical Information Ser.). 1985. pap. 20.00 (ISBN 0-471-82806-8). Wiley.

ON-LINE DATA PROCESSING

see also On-Line Bibliographic Searching; Real-Time Data Processing; Time-Sharing Computer Systems

Abbott, Joe. On-Line Programming: A Management Guide. 110p. (Orig.). 1981. pap. 20.00x (ISBN 0-85012-295-3). Intl Pubns Serv.

Academic Microfile. 1983. 720.00. Learned Info.

Adler, Mortimer J. Paideia Problems & Possibilities. 96p. 1983. 7.95 (ISBN 0-02-500220-1); pap. 3.95 (ISBN 0-02-013050-3). Macmillan.

Arthur. Application of On-Line Analytical Instrumentation to Process Control. LC 82-70694. (Activated Sludge Process Control Ser.). 222p. 1982. 39.95 (ISBN 0-250-40539-3). Butterworth.

Audit & Control Considerations in an On-Line Environment. (Computer Services Guidelines Ser.). 32p. 1983. pap. 8.50 (ISBN 0-317-02602-X). Am Inst CPA.

Auster, Ethel, ed. Managing Online Reference Services. 300p. 1986. pap. text ed. 35.00 (ISBN 0-918212-93-6). Neal-Schuman.

Automated Education Center. Management of On Line Systems. 1969. 19.00 (ISBN 0-403-04473-1). Scholarly.

--On Line Computing Systems. LC 65-21221. 19.00 (ISBN 0-403-04475-8). Scholarly.

Binder, M. B. Vidotex & Teletext: New Online Resources for Libraries. (Foundations of Library & Information Science Ser.: Vol. 21). 1985. 47.50 (ISBN 0-89232-612-3). Jai Pr.

Black, W. Wayne. An Introduction to On-Line Computers. LC 70-141580. (Illus.). 462p. 1971. 85.75 (ISBN 0-677-02930-6). Gordon.

Butcher, D. W. On-Line Monitoring of Continuous Process Plant. 326p. 1984. 83.95x (ISBN 0-470-27504-9). Halsted Pr.

Cane, Mike. The Computer Phone Book. 1983. pap. 14.95 (ISBN 0-452-25446-9, Plume). NAL.

--Computer Phone Book Online Guide for the Commodore Computers. 496p. 1984. pap. 9.95 (ISBN 0-451-82084-3, Sig). NAL.

Ching-hih Chen & Schweizer, Susanna. Online Bibliographic Searching: Learning Manual. 244p. 1981. 24.95 (ISBN 0-918212-59-6). Neal-Schuman.

Cluley, John C. Computer Interfacing & On-Line Operation. LC 74-16952. (Computer Systems Engineering Ser.). (Illus.). 181p. 1975. 19.50x (ISBN 0-8448-0567-X). Crane-Russak Co.

Collier, Harry, et al, eds. Electronic Publishing Review: The International Journal of the Transfer of Published Information via Videotex & Online Media. 1984. per year 66.00 (ISBN 0-317-00229-5). Learned Info.

Condon, M. A. Office Workstations. (Office Technology in the 80's Ser.: Vol. 6). 197p. (Orig.). 1982. pap. 15.00x (ISBN 0-85012-387-9). Taylor & Francis.

Conference on Trend in On-Line Computer Control Systems, 2nd., University of Sheffield, 1975. Trend in On-Line Computer Control Systems: 21-24 April, 1975. LC 76-355944. (Institution of Electrical Engineers Conference Publication Ser.: 127). (Illus.). pap. 72.50 (ISBN 0-317-10838-7, 2012129). Bks Demand UMI.

The Data Comms Market in Western Europe 1981-87. (Online Seminar 1981). 179p. (Orig.). 1981. pap. text ed. 75.95 (ISBN 0-903796-72-4, Pub. by Online Conferences England). Brookfield Pub Co.

Data Processing in Physical Distribution Management. (Online Conference). 176p. (Orig.). 1978. pap. text ed. 54.00 (ISBN 0-903796-24-4, Pub. by Online Conferences England). Online.

Davies, Owens & Edelhart, Mike. Omni Online Database Directory 1985. rev. ed. 384p. 1985. pap. 14.95 (ISBN 0-02-079920-9, Collier). Macmillan.

Down, P. J. Fault Diagnosis in Data Communications Systems. LC 78-30112. (Illus.). 1982. pap. 35.00 (ISBN 0-85012-186-8). Intl Pubns Serv.

Economics Abstracts International Online User Manual. 1983. 30.00 (ISBN 0-317-01044-1). Learned Info.

Edelhart, Mike & Davies, Owen. Omni: Online Database Directory. 384p. 1983. 19.95 (ISBN 0-02-535000-5); pap. 10.95 (ISBN 0-02-079910-1). Macmillan.

Birnes, W. J. McGraw-Hill Personal Computer Programming Encyclopedia: Languages & Operating Systems. 712p. 1985. 80.00 (ISBN 0-07-005389-8). McGraw.

Calingaert, Peter. Operating System Elements: A User Perspective. (Illus.). 304p. 1982. 26.95 (ISBN 0-13-637421-2). P-H.

Carr, Joseph J. CMOS-TTL-A: User's Guide with Projects. (Illus.). 336p. 1984. 19.95 (ISBN 0-8306-0650-5); pap. 13.50 (ISBN 0-8306-1650-0, 1650). TAB Bks.

Chandler, Lana J. Invitation to DOS-JCL for Application Programmers. (Illus.). 120p. 1985. pap. text ed. 12.00 (ISBN 0-89433-271-6). Petrocelli.

--Invitation to DOS JCL for Application Programmers. (Illus.). 120p. 1985. pap. 12.00 (ISBN 0-89433-271-6). Van Nos Reinhold.

Coffman, Edward G., Jr. & Denning, Peter J. Operating Systems Theory. LC 73-491. 400p. 1973. ref. ed. 34.95 (ISBN 0-13-637868-4). P-H.

Cohen, Leo J. Operating System Analysis & Design. LC 79-118984. 1971. text ed. 13.25 (ISBN 0-8104-5643-5). Hayden.

Conn, Richard. ZCPR3: The Manual. LC 84-61790. 352p. (Orig.). 1985. pap. 19.95 (ISBN 0-918432-59-6). NY Zoetrope.

DOS User's Manual for IIe. Date not set. 20.00 (ISBN 0-317-04457-5, A2L2002). Apple Comp.

Finkel, Raphael A. An Operating Systems Vade Mecum. 320p. 1986. text ed. 32.95 (ISBN 0-13-637455-7). P-H.

Flynn, M. J., et al. Operating Systems: An Advanced Course. (Springer Study Editions). 593p. 1979. pap. 23.00 (ISBN 0-387-09812-7). Springer-Verlag.

Freeman, Donald E. & Perry, Olney R. I-O Design: Data Management in Operating Systems. (Illus.). 1977. text ed. 25.95x (ISBN 0-8104-5789-X). Hayden.

Holt, Richard C., et al. Structured Concurrent Programming with Operating Systems Applications. 1978. pap. text ed. 21.95 (ISBN 0-201-02937-5). Addison-Wesley.

Intel Staff. Development Systems Handbook. rev. ed. 560p. 1985. pap. 15.00 (ISBN 0-917017-16-1, 210940-003). Intel Corp.

--Introduction to the IRMX 86 Operating System. rev. ed. 182p. 1981. pap. 10.00 (ISBN 0-917017-34-X, 983124-004). Intel Corp.

Janson, Philippe A. Operating Systems: Structures & Mechanisms. LC 84-20391. 260p. 1985. 29.50 (ISBN 0-12-380230-X). Acad Pr.

Johannesson, Goran. Programmable Control Systems. 136p. 1985. pap. text ed. 22.50x (ISBN 0-86238-046-4, Pub. by Chartwell-Bratt England). Brookfield Pub Co.

Kaisler, Stephen H. The Design of Operating Systems for Small Computer Systems. LC 82-6912. 667p. 1982. 37.50x (ISBN 0-471-07774-7, Pub. by Wiley-Interscience). Wiley.

Kane, Gerry. Guide to Popular Operating Systems. 1984. pap. 18.95 (ISBN 0-673-18048-4). Scott F.

Katzan, Harry, Jr. & Tharayil, Davis. Invitation to MVS: Logic & Debugging. (Illus.). 300p. 1984. text ed. 29.95 (ISBN 0-89433-081-0). Petrocelli.

Kurzban, Stanley A., et al. Operating Systems Principles. 2nd ed. (Illus.). 432p. 1984. 34.50 (ISBN 0-442-25734-1). Van Nos Reinhold.

Lanciaux, D. Operating Systems: Theory & Practice. 398p. 1979. 64.00 (ISBN 0-444-85300-6, North Holland). Elsevier.

Lane, J. E. Operating Systems for Microcomputers. 77p. 1981. pap. 10.95 (ISBN 0-471-89416-8). Wiley.

Lane, John E. Operating Systems for Microcomputers. LC 81-174400. (Computing in the Eighties: No. 1). 77p. (Orig.). 1981. pap. 12.50 (ISBN 0-85012-277-5). Intl Pubns Serv.

Levy, Henry M. Capability-Based Computer Systems. 250p. 1983. 28.00 (ISBN 0-932376-22-3, EY-00011-DP). Digital Pr.

Lister, A. M. Fundamentals of Operating Systems. 2nd ed. 161p. 1980. pap. 13.95 (ISBN 0-387-91170-7). Springer-Verlag.

Lowe, Doug. OS Utilities. LC 80-84103. (Illus.). 185p. (Orig.). 1981. pap. 15.00 (ISBN 0-911625-11-9). M Murach & Assoc.

Madnick, Stuart & Donovan, John. Operating Systems. (Illus.). 640p. 1974. text ed. 44.95 (ISBN 0-07-039455-5). McGraw.

Ousterhout, John K. Medusa: A Distributed Operating System. LC 81-7509. (Distributed Database Systems Ser.: No. 1). 152p. 1981. 34.95 (ISBN 0-8357-1201-X). UMI Res Pr.

Pascal Operating System Manual. (Apple II Plus & IIe Reference Manuals). Date not set. 25.00 (ISBN 0-317-04469-9, A2L0028). Apple Comp.

Peterson, James L. Operating System Concepts. 1985. text ed. 35.95 (ISBN 0-201-06089-2). Addison Wesley.

Peterson, James L. & Silberschatz, Abraham. Operating System Concepts. LC 82-22766. (Computer Science Ser.). (Illus.). 576p. 1983. 34.95 (ISBN 0-201-06097-3). Addison-Wesley.

Rus, Teodor. Data Structures & Operating Systems. LC 77-3262. (Wiley Series in Computing). pap. 94.00 (ISBN 0-317-26154-1, 2024377). Bks Demand UMI.

Sanden, Bo. Systems Programming with JSP. 188p. 1985. pap. text ed. 19.95x (ISBN 0-86238-054-5, Pub. by Chartwell-Bratt England). Brookfield Pub Co.

Seiden, Eric A. LYTTLE Operating System Manual. Dar Systems International Staff, ed. 400p. (Orig.). Date not set. pap. cancelled 3-ring binder (ISBN 0-916163-32-6); manual on disk for word processors 45.00 (ISBN 0-916163-33-4). Dar Syst.

Shaw, Alan C. Logical Design of Operating Systems. (Illus.). 304p. 1974. 34.95 (ISBN 0-13-540112-7). P-H.

Stagner, Walter. OASIS User's Handbook. 300p. (Orig.). 1985. pap. 17.95 (ISBN 0-317-19098-9). Weber Systems.

Tsichritzis, Dionysios C. & Bernstein, Philip. Operating Systems. (Computer Science & Applied Mathematics Ser.). 298p. 1974. 24.00i (ISBN 0-12-701750-X). Acad Pr.

Turner, Raymond W. Operating Systems: Design & Implementation. 296p. 1986. text ed. price not set (ISBN 0-02-421820-0). Macmillan.

Worth, Don & Lechner, Pieter. Beneath Apple DOS. 1981. 19.95 (ISBN 0-912985-00-3, 6493). Quality Soft.

Worth, Don D. & Lechner, Pieter M. Beneath Apple ProDos. LC 84-61383. (Illus.). 288p. 1984. pap. 19.95 (ISBN 0-912985-05-4, 5054). Quality Soft.

Zarrella, John. Operating Systems: Concepts & Principles. LC 79-122639. (Microprocessor Software Engineering Concepts Ser.). (Illus.). 156p. (Orig.). 1979. pap. 13.95 (ISBN 0-935230-00-9). Microcomputer Appns.

Zarrella, John, ed. Microprocessor Operating Systems, Vol. 1. LC 81-80864. 166p. 1981. pap. 13.95 (ISBN 0-935230-03-3). Microcomputer Appns.

--Microprocessor Operating Systems, Vol. 2. LC 81-80864. 158p. (Orig.). 1982. pap. 13.95 (ISBN 0-935230-04-1). Microcomputer Appns.

--Microprocessor Operating Systems, Vol. 3. LC 81-80864. 152p. 1984. pap. 13.95 (ISBN 0-935230-10-6). Microcomputer Appns.

Zolotow, Nina & Goldman, Joshua. System 1032 User's Guide. rev. ed. (Illus.). 702p. 1985. looseleaf 32.50x (ISBN 0-912055-10-3). Software Hse.

OPERATIONAL AMPLIFIERS

Boyce, Jefferson C. Operational Amplifiers for Technicians. 1983. text ed. write for info. (ISBN 0-534-01243-4, Pub. by Breton Pubs). Wadsworth Pub.

Clayton, G. Operational Amplifiers. 2nd ed. 1979. text ed. 39.95 (ISBN 0-408-00370-7). Butterworth.

Coughlin, Robert F. & Driscoll, Frederick F., Jr. Operational Amplifiers & Linear Integrated Circuits. 2nd ed. (Illus.). 400p. 1982. 34.95 (ISBN 0-13-637785-8). P-H.

Faulkenberry, Luces M. An Introduction to Operational Amplifiers: With Linera IC Applications. 2nd ed. LC 81-13043. (Electronic Technology Ser.). 560p. 1982. text ed. 31.95x (ISBN 0-471-05790-8); solutions manual 5.00 (ISBN 0-471-86319-X). Wiley.

Graeme, Jerald G. Designing with Operational Amplifiers: Applications, Alternatives. (Illus.). 1977. 44.50 (ISBN 0-07-023891-X). McGraw.

Jung, Walter G. IC Op-Amp Cookbook. 2nd ed. LC 80-50052. (Illus.). 1980. pap. 15.95 (ISBN 0-672-21695-7). Sams.

Marston, R. M. One Hundred & Ten OP-AMP Projects. (Illus.). 128p. 1975. pap. 7.95 (ISBN 0-8104-0701-9). Hayden.

Melen, Roger & Garland, Harry. Understanding IC Operational Amplifiers. 2nd ed. LC 77-99109. 160p. 1978. pap. 8.95 (ISBN 0-672-21511-X). Sams.

Rutkowski, George B. Handbook of Integrated-Circuit Operational Amplifiers. (Illus.). 304p. 1975. ref. ed. 24.95 (ISBN 0-13-378703-6). P-H.

Shepherd, I. E. Operational Amplifiers. LC 80-40770. (Illus.). 256p. 1981. text ed. 55.00x (ISBN 0-582-46089-1). Longman.

Wait, John V., et al. Introduction to Operational & Amplifier Theory Applications. (Illus.). 480p. 1975. text ed. 48.00 (ISBN 0-07-067765-4). McGraw.

OPERATIONAL ANALYSIS
see Operations Research

OPERATIONAL CALCULUS
see Calculus, Operational

OPERATIONAL RESEARCH
see Operations Research

OPERATIONS, CALCULUS OF
see Calculus of Operations

OPERATIONS RESEARCH
see also Maintainability (Engineering); Mathematical Optimization; Network Analysis (Planning); Queuing Theory; Research, Industrial; Simulation Methods; Statistical Decision; Systems Engineering

Ackoff, R. L. Progress in Operations Research, Vol. 1. LC 61-10415. (Operations Research Ser.: No. 5). Repr. of 1961 ed. 98.30 (ISBN 0-8357-9966-2, 2051575). Bks Demand UMI.

Albach, H. & Bergendahl, G., eds. Production Theory & Its Applications: Proceedings of a Workshop. (Lecture Notes in Economics & Mathematical Systems Ser.: Vol. 139). 1977. pap. 13.00 (ISBN 0-387-08062-7). Springer-Verlag.

Anderson, David R., et al. An Introduction to Management Science: Quantitative Approaches to Decision Making. 4th ed. (Illus.). 752p. 1985. text ed. 30.95 (ISBN 0-314-85214-X). West Pub.

Andrew. Computational Methods in Operations Research. (Cybernetics & Systems Ser.). 1984. 25.00 (ISBN 0-9901002-9-4, Pub. by Abacus England). Heyden.

Arsene, Grigore, ed. Dilation Theory, Toeplitz Operators, & Other Topics. (Operators Theory: Vol. II). 400p. 1983. text ed. 39.95 (ISBN 3-7643-1516-4). Birkhauser.

Avi-Itzhak, Benjamin. Developments in Operations Research, 2 vols. LC 78-141897. (Illus.). 652p. 1971. Set. 157.25 (ISBN 0-677-30510-9); Vol. 1,308p. 80.95 (ISBN 0-677-30830-2); Vol 2.,344p. 93.75 (ISBN 0-677-30840-X). Gordon.

Bailey, Norman T. Mathematics, Statistics & Systems for Health. LC 77-1307. (Wiley Series Probability & Mathematical Statistics: Applied Probability & Statistics). 222p. 1977. 48.95x (ISBN 0-471-99500-2, Pub. by Wiley-Interscience). Wiley.

Bandyopadhyay, R. & Padwal, S. M. Introduction to Operational Research & Data Management. 400p. Date not set. text ed. price not set (ISBN 0-7069-1234-9, Pub. by Vikas India). Advent NY.

Baumgartel, Hellmut & Wollenberg, Manfred. Mathematical Scattering Theory. (Operator Theory: Advances & Applications, Vol. 9). 1983. text ed. 44.95 (ISBN 3-7643-1519-9). Birkhauser.

Baumol, W. Economic Theory & Operations Analysis. 4th ed. 1977. 32.95 (ISBN 0-13-227132-X). P-H.

Beer, Stafford. Decision & Control: The Meaning of Operational Research & Management Cybernetics. LC 66-25668. 556p. 1966. 52.95x (ISBN 0-471-06210-3, Pub. by Wiley-Interscience). Wiley.

--Platform for Change. LC 73-10741. 457p. 1975. 48.95x (ISBN 0-471-06189-1, Pub. by Wiley-Interscience). Wiley.

Beilby, M. H. Economics & Operational Research. 1976. 37.50 (ISBN 0-12-085750-2). Acad Pr.

Bohigian, Haig E. The Foundations & Mathematical Models of Operations Research with Extensions to the Criminal Justice System. LC 75-186274. (Illus.). xxiii, 282p. (Orig.). 1972. pap. 12.95 (ISBN 0-933390-01-7). Gazette Pr.

Box, George E. & Draper, Norman R. Evolutionary Operation: A Statistical Method for Process Improvement. LC 68-56159. (Applied Probability & Mathematical Statistics Ser). 237p. 1969. 42.50x (ISBN 0-471-09305-X, Pub. by Wiley-Interscience). Wiley.

Bradley, Hugh E. The Operations Research & Management Science CumIndex, Vol. 10. 1979. 60.00 (ISBN 0-88274-009-1). R & D Pr.

Brans, J. P., ed. Operational Research, 1981. 984p. 1982. 127.75 (ISBN 0-444-86223-4, North-Holland). Elsevier.

Bronson, R. Schaum's Outline of Operations Research. (Schaum Paperback Ser.). 1982. pap. 9.95 (ISBN 0-07-007977-3). McGraw.

Budnick, Frank S., et al. Principles of Operations Research for Management. 1977. 33.50x (ISBN 0-256-01796-4). Irwin.

Burkard, R. E., et al. Algebraic & Combinatorial Methods in Operations Research: Proceedings of the Workshop on Algebraic Structures in Operations Research. (Mathematics Studies, Vol. 95; Annals of Discrete Mathematics: No. 19). 382p. 1984. 55.75 (ISBN 0-444-87571-9, North-Holland). Elsevier.

Byrd, J. & Moore, L. T. Decision Models for Management. 1982. 34.95x (ISBN 0-07-009511-6). McGraw.

Cabot, A. Victor & Hartnett, Donald L. Introduction to Management Science. LC 76-20024. (Illus.). 1977. text ed. 38.95 (ISBN 0-201-02746-1). Addison-Wesley.

Conolly, B. Techniques in Operational Research: Models, Search & Randomization, Vol. 2. LC 80-41741. (Mathematics & Its Applications Ser.). 340p. 1981. 89.95x (ISBN 0-470-27130-2). Halsted Pr.

Cook, Thomas M. & Russell, Robert A. Contemporary Operations Management: Text & Cases. 2nd ed. (Illus.). 528p. 1984. 30.95 (ISBN 0-13-170449-4). P-H.

Croucher, John S. Operations Research: A First Course. (Illus.). 320p. 1980. 32.00 (ISBN 0-08-024798-9); pap. 14.85 (ISBN 0-08-024797-0). Pergamon.

Daellenbach, Hans G. & George, John A. Introduction to Operations Research Techniques. 2nd ed. 1983. text ed. 41.43 (ISBN 0-205-07718-8, EDP 107718); answer book (ISBN 0-205-05756-X). Allyn.

Dean, Burton V., ed. Operations Research in Research & Development. LC 77-18041. 302p. 1978. Repr. of 1963 ed. lib. bdg. 18.50 (ISBN 0-88275-647-8). Krieger.

Domschke, W. & Drexl, A. Location & Layout Planning. (Lecture Notes in Economics & Mathematical Systems Ser.: Vol. 238). iv, 134p. 1985. pap. 12.30 (ISBN 0-387-13908-7). Springer-Verlag.

Doty, James. Journal of Operations. 12.00 (ISBN 0-87770-204-7). Ye Galleon.

Duckworth, Walter E., et al. A Guide to Operational Research. 3rd ed. 1977. 9.95 (ISBN 0-412-13500-0, NO. 6092, Pub. by Chapman & Hall). Methuen Inc.

Eiselt, Horst A. & Von Frajer, Helmut. Operations Research Handbook: Standard Algorithms & Methods with Examples. 1977. 29.60x (ISBN 3-11-007055-3). De Gruyter.

Emshoff, James R. & Sisson, Roger L. Design & Use of Computer Simulation Models. (Illus.). 1970. write for info. (ISBN 0-02-333720-6, 33372). Macmillan.

Fabrycky, Walter J. & Torgerson, Paul. Applied Operations Research & Management Science. (Illus.). 576p. 1984. 34.95 (ISBN 0-13-041459-X). P-H.

Fitzsimmons, J. A. & Sullivan, R. S. Service Operations Management. 464p. 1982. 34.95x (ISBN 0-07-021215-5). McGraw.

Gass, Saul I., ed. Operations Research: Mathematics & Models. LC 81-10849. (Proceedings of Symposia in Applied Mathematics: Vol. 25). 198p. pap. 12.00 (ISBN 0-8218-0029-9, PSAPM-25). Am Math.

Ghosal, Amitava. Applied Cybernetics: Its Relevance to Operations Research. (Studies in Operations Research Ser.). 176p. 1978. 38.50 (ISBN 0-677-05410-6). Gordon.

Greene, James H. Operations Management: Productivity & Profit. 1984. text ed. 39.95 (ISBN 0-8359-5250-9); instrs' manual avail. (ISBN 0-8359-5251-7). Reston.

Gribik & Kortanek. Extremal Methods of Operations Research. (Pure & Applied Mathematics Ser.). 456p. 1986. price not set (ISBN 0-8247-7474-4). Dekker.

Grouchko, Daniel, ed. Operations Research & Reliability. LC 72-172824. (Illus.). 642p. 1971. 132.95 (ISBN 0-677-14610-8). Gordon.

Gupta, Shiv K. & Cozzolino, John M. Fundamentals of Operations Research for Management. LC 73-94384. (Illus.). 1975. text ed. 32.00x (ISBN 0-8162-3476-0); solutions manual 6.50x (ISBN 0-8162-3486-8). Holden-Day.

Haley, K., ed. Operational Research Nineteen Seventy-Eight. 1114p. (Proceedings). 1979. 127.75 (ISBN 0-444-85230-1, North-Holland). Elsevier.

Hammer, G. & Pallaschke, D., eds. Selected Topics in Operations Research & Mathematical Economics: Proceedings of the Eighth Symposium on Operations Research Held at the University of Karlsruhe, West Germany, August 22-25, 1984. (Lecture Notes in Economics & Mathematical Systems). ix, 478p. 1984. pap. 30.00 (ISBN 0-387-12918-9). Springer-Verlag.

Hammer, L. Ivanescu & Rudeanu, S. Boolean Methods in Operations Research & Related Areas. LC 67-21932. (Econometrics & Operations Research Ser.: Vol. 7). (Illus.). 1968. 38.00 (ISBN 0-387-04291-1). Springer-Verlag.

Harvey, C. M. Operations Research: An Introduction to Linear Optimization & Decision Analysis. 454p. 1979. 33.00 (ISBN 0-444-00300-2). Elsevier.

Hauptmann, H., et al, eds. Operations Research & Economic Theory: Essays in Honor of Martin J. Beckmann. (Illus.). xi, 378p. 1984. 28.50 (ISBN 0-387-13652-5). Springer-Verlag.

Henn, R., et al, eds. Optimization & Operations Research: Proceedings of a Workshop Held at the University of Bonn, October 2-8, 1977. (Lecture Notes in Econometrics & Operations Research Ser.: Vol. 157). 1978. pap. 17.00 (ISBN 0-387-08842-3). Springer-Verlag.

Hesse, Rick & Woolsey, Gene. Applied Management Science. 384p. 1980. pap. text ed. 19.95 (ISBN 0-574-19345-6, 13-2345); instr's. guide avail. (ISBN 0-574-19346-4, 13-2346). SRA.

Hettich, R., ed. Semi-Infinite Programming: Proceedings. (Lecture Notes in Control & Information Science: Vol. 15). (Illus.). 1979. pap. 14.00 (ISBN 0-387-09479-2). Springer-Verlag.

Heyman, D. P. & Sobel, M. J. Stochastic Models in Operations Research, Vol. 1: Stochastic Processes & Operating Characteristics. 1982. 41.95x (ISBN 0-07-028631-0). McGraw.

Hillier, Frederick S. & Lieberman, Gerald J. Operations Research. 2nd ed. LC 73-94383. 816p. 1974. text ed. 32.95x (ISBN 0-8162-3856-1). Holden-Day.

Holzman. Mathematical Programming for Operations Researchers. (Industrial Engineering Ser.: Vol. 6). 392p. 1981. 55.00 (ISBN 0-8247-1499-7). Dekker.

--Operations Research Support Methodology. (Industrial Engineering--a Ser. of Reference Books & Textbooks: Vol. 2). 1979. 75.00 (ISBN 0-8247-6771-3). Dekker.

Hu, T. C., et al. Combinatorial Algorithms. LC 81-15024. (Computer Science Ser.). 500p. 1981. text ed. 28.95 (ISBN 0-201-03859-5); program manual 15.00 (ISBN 0-201-11469-0). Addison-Wesley.

Jaiswal, N. K. Priority Queues. (Mathematics in Science & Engineering Ser.: Vol. 50). 1968. 65.00 (ISBN 0-12-380050-1). Acad Pr.

Jaiswal, N. K., ed. Scientific Management of Transport Systems: Proceedings International Conference, New Delhi, Nov. 26-28, 1980. 378p. 1981. 55.50 (ISBN 0-444-86205-6, North-Holland). Elsevier.

Johnson, Rodney D. & Siskin, Bernard R. Quantitative Techniques for Business Decisions. (Illus.). 544p. 1976. 30.95 (ISBN 0-13-746990-X). P-H.

Kaufmann, Arnold & Faure, R. Introduction to Operations Research. Sneyd, Henry C., tr. LC 67-23162. (Mathematics in Science & Engineering Ser.: Vol. 47). (Illus.). 1968. 60.00 (ISBN 0-12-402360-6). Acad Pr.

Kidd, John, ed. Managing with Operational Research. LC 85-40079. 256p. 1985. 29.95x (ISBN 0-312-51227-9). St Martin.

Kingsman, B. G. Raw Materials Purchasing: An Operational Research Approach. (Frontiers of Operational Research & Applied Systems Analysis Ser.: Vol. 4). (Illus.). 376p. 1985. 45.00 (ISBN 0-08-029976-8); pap. 32.00 (ISBN 0-08-029975-X). Pergamon.

Kohlas, Jurg. Stochastic Methods of Operations Research. LC 81-21574. 160p. 1982. 39.50 (ISBN 0-521-23899-4); pap. 14.95 (ISBN 0-521-28292-6). Cambridge U Pr.

Kothari, C. R. An Introduction to Operational Research. 383p. 1982. text ed. 30.00x (ISBN 0-7069-1749-9, Pub by Vikas India); pap. 10.95 (ISBN 0-7069-1750-2). Advent NY.

Lange, Oskar. Optimal Decisions. 304p. 1972. text ed. 37.00 (ISBN 0-08-016053-0). Pergamon.

McCloskey, Joseph F., et al, eds. Operations Research for Management, Vol. 1. (Operations Research Ser). 410p. 1954. Vol. 1. 37.50x (ISBN 0-8018-0404-3). Johns Hopkins.

Marlow, W. H. Mathematics for Operations Research. LC 78-534. 483p. 1978. 58.95x (ISBN 0-471-57233-0, Pub. by Wiley-Interscience). Wiley.

Morse, Philip M. & Bacon, L. W. Operations Research for Public Systems. LC 67-27347. 1967. pap. text ed. 10.95x (ISBN 0-262-13010-6). MIT Pr.

Morse, Philip M. & Kimball, George E. Methods of Operations Research. (Illus.). 179p. 1980. Repr. of 1946 ed. 21.95 (ISBN 0-932146-03-1). Peninsula CA.

Muth, Eginhard J. Transform Methods with Applications to Engineering & Operations Research. (Illus.). 1977. ref. ed. O.P. 29.95 (ISBN 0-13-928861-9). P-H.

Nagel, Stuart S. & Neef, Marian. Operations Research Methods. LC 76-25693. (Sage University Papers Ser.: Quantitative Applications in the Social Sciences, No. 2). 76p. 1976. pap. 5.00 (ISBN 0-8039-0651-X). Sage.

Neumann, K. & Pallaschke, D., eds. Contributions to Operations Research. (Lectures Notes in Economics & Mathematical Systems: Vol. 240). v, 190p. 1985. pap. 17.30 (ISBN 0-387-15205-9). Springer-Verlag.

Nijkamp, Peter & Spronk, Jaap, eds. Multiple Criteria Analysis: Operational Methods. 288p. 1981. 21.00x (ISBN 0-566-00412-7, 04707-4, Pub. by Gower Pub Co England). Lexington Bks.

Palmer, Colin. Quantitative Aids for Management Decision Making. 212p. 1979. text ed. 30.50x (ISBN 0-566-00284-1). Gower Pub Co.

Pearcy, Carl M. Some Recent Developments in Operator Theory. LC 78-8754. (Conference Board of the Mathematical Sciences Ser.: No. 36). 73p. 1980. pap. 11.00 (ISBN 0-8218-1686-1, CBMS 36). Am Math.

Prekopa, A., ed. Progress in Operations Research, 2 Vols. (Colloquia Mathematica Societatis Janos Bolyai: No. 12). 968p. 1976. Set. 95.75 (ISBN 0-7204-2836-X, North-Holland). Elsevier.

Raff, Ellison S., ed. Computers & Operations Research: Environmental Applications. 1977. pap. text ed. 38.00 (ISBN 0-08-021348-0). Pergamon.

Reed, John H. The Application of Operations Research to Court Delay. LC 72-89647. (Special Studies in U.S. Economic, Social & Political Issues). 1973. 39.50x (ISBN 0-275-06690-8). Irvington.

Richmond, Samuel B. Operations Research for Management Decisions. LC 68-20552. (Illus.). 615p. 1968. 42.50 (ISBN 0-471-06620-6). Wiley.

Rochat, Jean-Claude. Mathematiques pour la Question de l'Environment. (Interdisciplinary Systems Research Ser.: No. 74). (Fr., Illus.). 413p. 1980. pap. 45.95x (ISBN 0-8176-1126-6). Birkhauser.

Roubens, M., ed. Advances in Operations Research: Proceedings of the European Congress on Operation Research, 2nd, Stockholm, Sweden, November 29, 1977. 1977. 81.00 (ISBN 0-7204-0718-4, North-Holland). Elsevier.

Schmidt, J. William & Davis, Robert P. Foundation of Analysis in Operations Research. LC 80-987. (Operations Research & Industrial Engineering Ser.). 1981. 32.00 (ISBN 0-12-626850-9). Acad Pr.

Sengupta, S. Sankar. Operations Research in Sellers' Competition: A Stochastic Microtheory. LC 67-13528. 228p. 1967. 13.50 (ISBN 0-471-77625-4, Pub. by Wiley). Krieger.

Sezepesi, G & Szekely, B. Systems Analysis & Operations Research Dictionary. (Hungarian, Eng., Fr., Ger., & Rus.). 154p. 1980. 30.00x (ISBN 0-569-08617-5, Pub. by Collets). State Mutual Bk.

Siemens, Nicolai, et al. Operations Research: Planning, Operating & Information Systems. LC 70-184529. 1973. text ed. 19.95 (ISBN 0-02-928740-5). Free Pr.

Singh, Jagjit. Great Ideas of Operations Research. 14.75 (ISBN 0-8446-2947-2). Peter Smith.

Stahl, I., ed. Operational Gaming: An International Approach. LC 83-17399. (Frontiers of Operational Research & Applied Systems Analysis: Vol. 3). 340p. 1983. 32.50 (ISBN 0-08-030836-8); pap. 17.50 (ISBN 0-08-030870-8). Pergamon.

Stainton, R. S. Operational Research & Its Management Implications. 128p. (Orig.). 1977. pap. text ed. 14.95x (ISBN 0-7121-1522-6). Trans-Atlantic.

Stevens, Roger T. Operational Test & Evaluation: A Systems Engineering Process. LC 85-5193. 298p. 1985. Repr. of 1979 ed. lib. bdg. write for info. (ISBN 0-89874-845-3). Krieger.

Taha, Hamdy A. Operations Research. 3rd ed. 1982. text ed. write for info. (ISBN 0-02-418860-3). Macmillan.

Thesen, Arne, ed. Computer Methods in Operations Research. (Operations Research & Industrial Engineering Ser). 1978. 27.50 (ISBN 0-12-686150-1). Acad Pr.

Thierauf, Robert J. An Introductory Approach to Operations Research. LC 82-7835. 428p. 1982. Repr. of 1978 ed. lib. bdg. 31.50 (ISBN 0-89874-503-9). Krieger.

Thierauf, Robert J. & Klekamp, Robert C. Decision Making Through Operations Research. 2nd ed. LC 74-19473. (Management & Administration Ser.). 650p. 1975. 44.50x (ISBN 0-471-85861-7); instructors manual o.p. 8.50x (ISBN 0-471-85856-0); pap. write for info. (ISBN 0-471-85857-9). Wiley.

Turban & Meredith. Fundamentals of Management Science. 3rd ed. 1985. 30.95x (ISBN 0-256-03078-2); study guide 9.95x (ISBN 0-256-03079-0). Business Pubns.

Tzafestas, S. G. Optimization & Control of Dynamic Operational Research Models. (Systems & Control Ser.: Vol. 4). 438p. 1982. 63.75 (ISBN 0-444-86380-X, North-Holland). Elsevier.

Vajda, S. Planning by Mathematics. LC 73-330815. (Topics in Operational Research Ser.). (Illus.). pap. 37.50 (ISBN 0-317-10739-9, 2051913). Bks Demand UMI.

Wagner, Harvey M. Principles of Operations Research with Applications to Managerial Decisions. 2nd ed. (Illus.). 1088p. 1975. 39.95 (ISBN 0-13-709592-9). P-H.

Wentzel, E. Operations Research: A Methodological Approach. 256p. 1983. 5.95 (ISBN 0-8285-2569-2, Pub. by Mir Pubs USSR). Imported Pubns.

Whisler, William D., ed. Applications on Management Science & Operations Research Methods. 249p. 1974. pap. text ed. 14.95x (ISBN 0-8422-0376-1). Irvington.

White, Douglas, et al. Operational Research Techniques, Vol. 2. 328p. 1974. 31.00x (ISBN 0-8464-0687-X). Beekman Pubs.

Whitehouse, Gary E. & Wechsler, Ben L. Applied Operations Research: A Survey. LC 76-16545. 434p. 1976. 46.00x (ISBN 0-471-94077-1); solutions manual 5.00x (ISBN 0-471-02552-6). Wiley.

Woolsey, Robert E. & Swanson, Huntington S. Operations Research for Immediate Application: A Quick and Dirty Manual. Orig. Title: Quick & Dirty Manual: Operations Research for Immediate Application. 1975. pap. text ed. 16.50 scp (ISBN 0-06-047233-2, HarpC). Har-Row.

Worms, G. Modern Methods of Applied Economics. 242p. 1970. 55.75x (ISBN 0-677-01990-4). Gordon.

OPERATOR ALGEBRAS

Araki, H. & Effros, E. G., eds. Geometric Methods in Operator Algebras. (Research Notes in Mathematics Ser.: No. 123). 400p. 1985. pap. text ed. write for info. (ISBN 0-273-08683-9). Pitman Pub MA.

Araki, H., et al, eds. Operator Algebras & Their Connections with Topology & Ergodic Theory. (Lecture Notes in Mathematics: Vol. 1132). vi, 594p. 1985. pap. 35.50 (ISBN 0-387-15643-7). Springer-Verlag.

Kakosyan, A. V., et al. Characterization of Distributions by the Method of Intensively Monotone Operators. (Lecture Notes in Mathematics Ser.: Vol. 1088). x, 175p. 1984. pap. 12.00 (ISBN 0-387-13857-9). Springer-Verlag.

OPERATOR THEORY

see also Differential Operators; Linear Operators; Nonlinear Operators; Operator Algebras

Dym, Harry, et al, eds. Topics in Operator Theory Systems & Networks, Vol. 12. (Operator Theory Ser.). 300p. 1984. write for info. (ISBN 3-7643-1550-4). Birkhauser.

Rosenblum, Marvin & Rovnyak, James. Hardy Classes & Operator Theory. (OXMM Ser.). 192p. 1985. 39.95x (ISBN 0-19-503591-7). Oxford U Pr.

OPERATORS, DIFFERENTIAL

see Differential Operators

OPERATORS, LINEAR

see Linear Operators

OPERATORS, NONLINEAR

see Nonlinear Operators

OPERCULATES

see Discomycetes

OPHIDIA

see Snakes

OPHIOLOGY

see Snakes

OPHTHALMOLOGY

see also Eye

Chignell, A. H. Retinal Detachment Surgery. (Illus.). 1980. 40.00 (ISBN 0-387-09475-X). Springer-Verlag.

Corboy, J. M. The Retinoscopy Book: A Manual for Beginners. rev. ed. LC 79-65451. 143p. 1979. text ed. 19.50 (ISBN 0-913590-67-3). Slack Inc.

Duke-Elder, Stewart, ed. System of Ophthalmology Series. Incl. Vol. 1. The Eye in Evolution. (Illus.). 843p. 1958. 65.00 (ISBN 0-8016-8282-7); Vol. 2. The Anatomy of the Visual System. (Illus.). 901p. 1961. 67.50 (ISBN 0-8016-8283-5); Vol. 3, Pt. 1. Normal & Abnormal Development: Embryology. (Illus.). 330p. 1963. 51.50 (ISBN 0-8016-8285-1); Vol. 3, Pt. 2. Normal & Abnormal Development: Congenital Deformities. (Illus.). 1190p. 1964. 72.50 (ISBN 0-8016-8286-X); Vol. 4. The Physiology of the Eye & of Vision. (Illus.). xx, 734p. 1968. 79.50 (ISBN 0-8016-8296-7); Vol. 5. Ophthalmic Optics & Refraction. (Illus.). xix, 879p. 1970; Vol. 7. The Foundations of Ophthalmology: Heredity, Pathology, Diagnosis & Therapeutics. (Illus.). 829p. 1962. 69.50 (ISBN 0-8016-8284-3); Vol. 8. Diseases of the Outer Eye: Conjunctiva, Cornea & Sclera, 2 vols. (Illus.). 1242p. 1965. 100.00 (ISBN 0-8016-8287-8); Vol. 9. Diseases of Uveal Tract. (Illus.). xvi, 978p. 1966. 85.00 (ISBN 0-8016-8290-8); Vol. 10. Diseases of the Retina. (Illus.). xv, 878p. 1967. 85.00 (ISBN 0-8016-8295-9); Vol. 11. Diseases of the Lens & Vitreous: Glaucoma & Hypotony. (Illus.). xx, 779p. 1969. 85.00 (ISBN 0-8016-8297-5); Vol. 12. Neuro-Ophthalmology. (Illus.). xxi, 994p. 1971. 89.50 (ISBN 0-8016-8299-1); Vol. 14. Injuries, 2 vols. 1357p. 1972. Set. 125.00 (ISBN 0-8016-8300-9). Mosby.

Enoch, Jay M., et al. Quantitative Layer-by-Layer Perimetry: An Extented Analysis. (Current Ophthalmology Monographs). (Illus.). 256p. 1980. 39.00 (ISBN 0-8089-1282-8, 791165). Grune.

Huber, A. & Klein, D., eds. Neurogenetics & Neuro-Opthalmology. (Developments in Neurology Ser.: Vol. 5). 432p. 1982. 78.75 (ISBN 0-444-80378-5, I-499-82, Biomedical Pr). Elsevier.

International Council of Opthalmology, ed. Perimetric Standards & Perimetric Glossary. 1979. lib. bdg. 29.00 (ISBN 90-6193-600-4, Pub. by Junk Pubs Netherlands). Kluwer Academic.

Jalie, M. The Principles of Ophthalmic Lenses. 1981. 79.00x (ISBN 0-686-45410-3, Pub. by Assn Disp Opt England). State Mutual Bk.

Janney, G. D. & Tunnacliffe, A. H. Worked Problems in Ophthalmic Lenses. 1981. 40.00x (ISBN 0-686-45414-6, Pub. by Assn Disp Opt England). State Mutual Bk.

Keates, Richard & Fry, S. M. Ophthalmic Neodymuim: Yag Lasers. LC 83-60644. 96p. 1983. 19.50 (ISBN 0-943432-04-9). Slack Inc.

Kwitko, Marvin L. & Weinstock, Frank J., eds. Geriatric Ophthalmology. 480p. 1985. 59.50 (ISBN 0-8089-1687-4, 792412). Grune.

Lawwill, T. ERG, VER & Psychophysics. (Documenta Ophthalmologica Proceedings: Vol. 13). 1976. lib. bdg. 63.00 (ISBN 90-6193-153-3, Pub. by Junk Pubs. Netherlands). Kluwer Academic.

Lerman, Sidney, ed. Radiant Energy & the Eye. (Illus.). 1980. text ed. write for info. (ISBN 0-02-369970-1). Macmillan.

L'Esperance. Ophthalmic Lasers: Photocoagulation, Photoradiation & Surgery. 2nd ed. 1983. 81.50 (ISBN 0-8016-2823-7). Mosby.

Roy, F. Hampton. Ocular Syndromes & Systemic Diseases. 400p. 1985. 44.50 (ISBN 0-8089-1686-6, 793670). Grune.

Society of Photo-Optical Instrumentation Engineers, Seminar. Photo-Optical Data Reduction: Proceedings, Vol. 2. 1964. 29.00 (ISBN 0-89252-003-5). Photo-Optical.

Spaeth, George L. & Schwartz, Louis. Laser Therapy of the Anterior Segment: A Practical Approach. LC 83-50367. 176p. 1984. 49.50 (ISBN 0-943432-14-6). Slack Inc.

Straub, W., ed. Current Genetic, Clinical & Morphological Problems. (Developments in Ophthalmology: Vol. 3). (Illus.). vi, 218p. 1981. pap. 67.00 (ISBN 3-8055-2000-X). S Karger.

Tolentino, Felipe L., et al. Vitreoretinal Disorders: Diagnosis & Management. LC 73-81838. (Illus.). Repr. of 1976 ed. 120.00 (ISBN 0-8357-9562-4, 2012283). Bks Demand UMI.

Van Buren, J. M. The Retinal Ganglion Cell Layer: A Physiological Anatomical Correlation in Man & Primates of the Normal Topographical Anatomy of the Retinal Ganglion Cell Layer & Its Alterations with Lesions of the Visual Pathways. (Illus.). 160p. 1963. photocopy ed. 16.00x (ISBN 0-398-04422-8). C C Thomas.

Volker-Dieben, H. J. The Effect of Immunological & Non-Immunological Factors on Corneal Graft Survival. (Monographs in Opthalmology). 1984. lib. bdg. 45.50 (ISBN 90-6193-808-2, Pub. by Junk Pubs Netherlands). Kluwer Academic.

OPISTHOBRANCHIATA

MacFarland, Frank. Memoir IV: Studies of Opisthobranchiate Mollusks of the Pacific Coast of North America. Kessell, Howard L., ed. (Memoirs of the California Academy of Sciences Ser.). (Illus.). 546p. 1966. 40.00 (ISBN 0-940228-10-6). Calif Acad Sci.

Marcus, Eveline & Marcus, Ernst. American Opisthobranch Mollusks. LC 67-31694. (Studies in Tropical Oceanography Ser: No. 6). 1967. 10.00x (ISBN 0-87024-087-0). U Miami Marine.

Thompson, T. E. Biology of Ophisthobranch Molluscs, Vol. 1. (Illus.). 1976. 45.00x (ISBN 0-903874-04-0, Pub. by Brit Mus Nat Hist). Sabbot-Natural Hist Bks.

Thompson, T. E. & Brown, G. H. Biology of Opisthobranch Molluscs, Vol. 2. (Illus.). 280p. 1984. 78.00x (ISBN 0-903874-18-0, Pub. by Brit Mus Nat Hist England). Sabbot-Natural Hist Bks.

OPOSSUMS

Russell, Rupert. Spotlight on Possums. (Illus.). 91p. 1980. 18.00x (ISBN 0-7022-1478-7). U of Queensland Pr.

OPPANOL

see Rubber, Artificial

OPPENHEIMER, J. ROBERT, 1904-1967

Goodchild, Peter. J. Robert Oppenheimer: Shatterer of Worlds. LC 85-13194. (Illus.). 304p. 1985. pap. 10.95 (ISBN 0-88064-021-9). Fromm Intl Pub.

Kunetka, James W. Oppenheimer: The Years of Risk. 336p. 1982. 15.95 (ISBN 0-13-638007-7). P-H.

Newman, Steven L. & Christopher, Mark S. Get Oppenheimer! 288p. cancelled (ISBN 0-8129-0927-5). Times Bks.

Oppenheimer, Robert. Robert Oppenheimer: Letters & Recollections. Smith, Alice K. & Weiner, Charles, eds. LC 80-10106. (Harvard Paperbacks Ser.). 408p. 1981. pap. 8.95 (ISBN 0-674-77606-2). Harvard U Pr.

Smith, Alice K. & Weiner, Charles, eds. Robert Oppenheimer: Letters & Recollections. LC 80-10106. 1980. 20.00x (ISBN 0-674-52833-6). Harvard U Pr.

United States Atomic Energy Commission & Oppenheimer, J. Robert, eds. In the Matter of J. Robert Oppenheimer. 1971. pap. 12.50x (ISBN 0-262-71002-1). MIT Pr.

OPTICAL CHARACTER RECOGNITION DEVICES

Smith, John W. & Merali, Zinat. Optical Character Recognition: The Technology & It's Applications. (LIR Report 33). (Orig.). 1985. pap. 19.50 (ISBN 0-7123-3047-X, Pub. by British Lib). Longwood Pub Group.

OPTICAL CRYSTALLOGRAPHY
see Crystal Optics

OPTICAL DATA PROCESSING
see also Computers–Optical Equipment; Information Display Systems; Optical Pattern Recognition

Barrekette, E. S., et al, eds. Optical Information Processing, Vol. 2. LC 77-17579. 463p. 1978. 69.50x (ISBN 0-306-34472-6, Plenum Pr). Plenum Pub.

Barrett, R. Developments in Optical Disc Technology & the Implications for Information Storage & Retrieval. (R&D Report: No. 5623). (Illus.). 80p. (Orig.). 1981. pap. 71.25 (ISBN 0-905984-71-4, Pub. by British Lib). Longwood Pub Group.

Biotechnology Equipment & Supplies. (Reports Ser.: No. 513). 179p. 1982. 985.00x (ISBN 0-88694-513-5). Intl Res Dev.

Brock, ed. Robot Vision & Sensory Control: Proceedings of the Second International Conference, Stuttgart, BRD, Nov. 1982. iv, 388p. 1983. 85.00 (ISBN 0-444-86548-9, North-Holland). Elsevier.

Carnegie Symposium on Cognition, Eighth Annual. Visual Information Processing: Proceedings. Chase, William G., ed. 1973. 49.50 (ISBN 0-12-170150-6). Acad Pr.

Casasent, D., ed. Optical Data Processing: Applications. (Topics in Applied Physics: Vol. 23). (Illus.). 1978. 57.00 (ISBN 0-387-08453-3). Springer-Verlag.

Cathey, W. Thomas. Optical Information Processing & Holography. LC 73-14604. (Pure & Applied Optics Ser.). 398p. 1974. 40.95 (ISBN 0-471-14078-3, Pub. by Wiley-Interscience). Wiley.

Chien, Y. T. Interactive Pattern Recognition. (Electrical Engineering & Electronics Ser.: Vol. 3). 1978. 55.00 (ISBN 0-8247-6631-8). Dekker.

Data Extraction & Classification from Film: Proceedings of the SPIE, Annual Technical Symposium, 21st, San Diego, 1977. (SPIE Seminar Proceedings: Vol. 117). 152p. 9.00 (ISBN 0-89252-144-9); members 4.00 (ISBN 0-317-34616-4). SPIE.

Digest of Papers from the SPIE International Optical Computing Conference, Italy, 1976. 158p. 16.00 (ISBN 0-317-34624-5); members 12.00 (ISBN 0-317-34625-3). SPIE.

Digest of Papers from the SPIE International Optical Computing Conference, Washington, D.C., 1975. 180p. 16.00 (ISBN 0-317-34626-1); members 12.00 (ISBN 0-317-34627-X). SPIE.

Effects Technology, Inc. Design Manual for Fiber Optic CODEC Link, Vol. V. (User Manual & Handbook Ser.). 150p. 1981. pap. 50.00 (ISBN 0-686-39228-0). Info Gatekeepers.

Frieden, B. R., ed. The Computer in Optical Research: Methods & Applications. (Topics in Applied Physics: Vol. 41). (Illus.). 400p. 1980. 66.00 (ISBN 0-387-10119-5). Springer-Verlag.

Grimson, Eric L. From Images to Surfaces: A Computational Study of the Human Early Visual System. (Artificial Intelligence Ser.). (Illus.). 274p. 1981. 35.00x (ISBN 0-262-07083-9). MIT Pr.

Hall, Ernest L. Computer Image Processing & Recognition. (Computer Science & Applied Mathematics Ser.). 1979. 36.50 (ISBN 0-12-318850-4). Acad Pr.

Harger, Robert O. Optical Communication Theory. (Benchmark Papers in Electrical Engineering & Computer Science: Vol. 18). 1977. 55.00 (ISBN 0-12-786630-2). Acad Pr.

Huang, T. S. & Tretiak, O. J. Picture Bandwidth Compression. LC 74-135062. 746p. 1972. 188.50x (ISBN 0-677-14680-9, 1468). Gordon.

Institute for Telecommunication Sciences. A User's Manual for Optical Waveguide Communications. (User Manual & Handbook Ser.: Vol. I). 287p. 1978. 95.00. Info Gatekeepers.

International Optical Computing Conference I, 1980: Proceedings of the SPIE Technical Symposium East, Washington, D.C., 1980. (SPIE Seminar Proceedings: Vol. 231). 326p. 30.00 (ISBN 0-89252-260-7); members 23.00 (ISBN 0-317-34699-7). SPIE.

International Optical Computing Conference II, 1980: Proceedings of the SPIE Technical Symposium East, Washington, D.C., 1980. (SPIE Seminar Proceedings: Vol. 232). 240p. 30.00 (ISBN 0-89252-261-5); members 23.00 (ISBN 0-317-34700-4). SPIE.

Kingslake, Rudolf. Optical System Design. 1983. 32.00 (ISBN 0-12-408660-8). Acad Pr.

Lee, S. H., ed. Optical Information Processing: Fundamentals. (Topics in Applied Physics Ser.: Vol. 48). (Illus.). 330p. 1981. 53.00 (ISBN 0-387-10522-0). Springer-Verlag.

Lipkin, Bernice S. & Rosenfeld, Azriel, eds. Picture Processing & Psychopictorics. 1970. 70.00 (ISBN 0-12-451550-9). Acad Pr.

Menczel, J., et al, eds. Osteoporosis: Proceedings of an International Symposium Held at the Jerusalem Osteoporosis Center in June, 1981. 440p. 1983. 58.00x (ISBN 0-471-10156-7). Wiley.

Nesterikhin, Yu E., et al, eds. Optical Information Processing, Vol. 1. LC 75-42415. 401p. 1976. 65.00x (ISBN 0-306-30899-1, Plenum Pr). Plenum Pub.

Optical Computing: Critical Review of Technology, Vol. 456. 1984. 43.00 (ISBN 0-89252-491-X). Photo-Optical.

Optical Information Storage: Proceedings of the SPIE Technical Symposium East, Washington, D.C., 1979. (SPIE Seminar Proceedings: Vol. 177). 156p. 37.00 (ISBN 0-89252-205-4); 29.00, members (ISBN 0-317-34709-8). SPIE.

Reichardt, W., ed. Processing of Optical Data by Organisms & by Machines. (Italian Physical Society: Course No. 43). 1970. 95.00 (ISBN 0-12-368843-4). Acad Pr.

Rogers, G. L. Noncoherent Optical Processing. LC 77-5453. 192p. 1977. text ed. 33.95 (ISBN 0-471-73055-6). Krieger.

Rosenfeld, Azriel & Kak, Avinash C. Digital Picture Processing. 2nd ed. LC 81-17611. (Computer Science & Applied Mathematics Ser.). 1982. Vol. 1. 40.00 (ISBN 0-12-597301-2); Vol. 2. 35.00 (ISBN 0-12-597302-0). Acad Pr.

Schumaker, Robert A., et al. Study for Applying Computer-Generated Images to Visual Stimulation. LC 74-131394. 142p. 1969. 19.00 (ISBN 0-403-04536-3). Scholarly.

Selected Papers in Optical Computing: Supplement to Proceedings of the SPIE International Optical Computing Conference, Italy, 1976. 84p. 8.00 (ISBN 0-317-34755-1); members 6.00 (ISBN 0-317-34756-X). SPIE.

Siemens. Optical Communications: A Telecommunications Review. 220p. 1984. 39.95x (ISBN 0-471-90368-X, Pub. by Wiley-Interscience). Wiley.

Society of Photo-Optical Instrumentation Engineers, Seminar. Acquisition & Analysis of Pictorial Data: Proceedings, Vol. 48. 1975. 28.00 (ISBN 0-89252-060-4). Photo-Optical.

--Image Information Recovery: Proceedings, Vol. 16. 1968. 29.00 (ISBN 0-89252-019-1). Photo-Optical.

Society of Photographic Scientists & Engineers. Optical Data Display, Processing & Storage: 2nd SPSE Symposium, Advance Printing of Paper Summaries Presented March 15-19, 1981, the Aladdin Hotel, Las Vegas, Nevada. pap. 33.30 (ISBN 0-317-08015-6, 2015861). Bks Demand UMI.

Ullman, Shimon. The Interpretation of Visual Motion. (Artificial Intelligence Ser.). (Illus.). 229p. 1979. text ed. 30.00x (ISBN 0-262-21007-X). MIT Pr.

U. S. Department of Commerce. Technical Digest-Symposium on Optical Fiber Measurements. 1980. pap. 50.00. Info Gatekeepers.

Yu, Francis T. S. Optical Information Processing. LC 82-11057. 562p. 1982. 62.50x (ISBN 0-471-09780-2, Pub. by Wiley-Interscience). Wiley.

OPTICAL INSTRUMENTS
see also Astronomical Instruments; Computers–Optical Equipment; Glass; Lenses; Microscope and Microscopy; Mirrors; Petrographic Microscope; Telescope
also names of specific instruments, e.g. Spectroscope

Barrett, R. Further Developments in Optical Disc Technology & Applications. (LIR Report 27). (Illus.). 43p. (Orig.). 1984. pap. 14.25 (ISBN 0-7123-3038-0, Pub. by British Lib). Longwood Pub Group.

Beaven, G. L., et al. Optical Fibres. (Illus.). 400p. 1986. 100.00 (ISBN 0-08-030577-6). Pergamon.

Bindmann, W. Fachwoerterbuch Optik und Optischer Geraetebau. (Eng. & Ger.). 408p. (Dictionary of Optics and Optical Devices). 1974. 75.00 (ISBN 3-7684-6411-3, M-7402, Pub. by Dausien). French & Eur.

Cherin, Allen H. An Introduction to Optical Fibers. (McGraw-Hill Series in Electrical Engineering). (Illus.). 336p. 1982. text ed. 44.00 (ISBN 0-07-010703-3). McGraw.

CISM (International Center for Mechanical Sciences), Dept. for General Mechanics, 1971. Optical Filtering. Parkus, H., ed. (CISM Pubns. Ser.: No. 94). (Illus.). 59p. 1973. pap. 10.70 (ISBN 0-387-81130-3). Springer-Verlag.

Eccles, M. J., et al. Low Light Level Detectors in Astronomy. LC 82-12881. (Cambridge Astrophysics Ser.). (Illus.). 200p. 1983. 42.50 (ISBN 0-521-24088-3). Cambridge U Pr.

Horne, D. F. Optical Production Technology. 2nd ed. 1983. 90.00 (ISBN 0-9960025-8-8, Pub. by A Hilger England). Heyden.

Horne, Douglas F. Optical Instruments & Their Applications. (Illus.). xiv, 270p. 1980. 90.00 (ISBN 0-9960019-6-4, Pub. by A Hilger England). Heyden.

Information Gatekeepers Inc. Fiber Optics & Market Trends in Japan. 1982. 200.00 (ISBN 0-686-39229-9). Info Gatekeepers.

Johnson, B. K. Optics & Optical Instruments: An Introduction with Special Reference to Practical Applications. 14.50 (ISBN 0-8446-5921-5). Peter Smith.

Jurek, B. Optical Surfaces. 218p. 1977. 57.50 (ISBN 0-444-99868-3). Elsevier.

Kingslake, R., ed. Applied Optics & Optical Engineering: A Comprehensive Treatise, 5 vols. Incl. Vol. 1. Light: Its Generation & Modification. 1965 (ISBN 0-12-408601-2); Vol. 2. The Detection of Light & Infrared Radiation. 1965 (ISBN 0-12-408602-0); Vol. 3. Optical Components. 1966 (ISBN 0-12-408603-9); Vol. 4. Optical Instruments, Part I. 1967 (ISBN 0-12-408604-7); Vol. 5. Optical Instruments, Part 2. 1969 (ISBN 0-12-408605-5). 72.00 ea. Set. Acad Pr.

Kingston, R. H. Detection of Optical & Infrared Radiation. (Springer Series in Optical Sciences: Vol. 10). (Illus.). 1978. 29.00 (ISBN 0-387-08617-X). Springer-Verlag.

Kressel, H., ed. Semiconductor Devices for Optical Communication. 2nd, updated ed. (Topics in Applied Physics Ser.: Vol. 39). (Illus.). 325p. 1982. pap. 27.00 (ISBN 0-387-11348-7). Springer-Verlag.

Levenson, Jordan. How to Buy & Understand Refracting Telescopes. LC 81-81885. (Illus., Orig.). 1981. pap. 18.95x (ISBN 0-914442-09-0). Levenson Pr.

Luxmoore, A. R., ed. Optical Transducers & Techniques in Engineering Measurement. (Illus.). 1983. 64.75 (ISBN 0-85334-203-2, Pub. by Elsevier Applied Sci England). Elsevier.

O'Shea, D. C. Elements of Modern Optical Design. 1985 ed. (Pure & Applied Optics Ser.). 42.95 (ISBN 0-471-07796-8). Wiley.

Ross, Douglas A. Optoelectronic Devices & Optical Imaging Techniques. (Electrical & Electronic Engineering Ser.). (Illus.). 137p. 1979. text ed. 27.50x (ISBN 0-333-24292-0); pap. text ed. 18.50x (ISBN 0-333-25335-3). Scholium Intl.

Smith, W. J. Modern Optical Engineering. 1966. 58.75 (ISBN 0-07-058690-X). McGraw.

Society of Photo-Optical Instrumentation Engineers, Seminar. Application of Optical Instrumentation: Proceedings, Vol. 47. 1975. 15.00 (ISBN 0-89252-059-0). Photo-Optical.

--Effective Systems Integration & Optical Design I: Proceedings. 176p. 1975. 11.00 (ISBN 0-89252-066-3). Photo-Optical.

--Optical Instrumentation: A Problem-Solving Tool in Automotive Safety Engineering & Bio-Mechanics, Proceedings, Vol. 34. 28.00 (ISBN 0-89252-045-0). Photo Optical.

--Optical Instrumentation: A Tool for Solving Problems in Security, Surveillance & Law Enforcement, Proceedings, Vol. 33. 28.00 (ISBN 0-89252-044-2). Photo Optical.

Society of Photo-Optical Instrumentation Engineers, Annual Technical Symposium, 13th, Wash. D. C. Proceedings. 1968. 8.00 (ISBN 0-89252-086-8). Photo-Optical.

Society of Photo-Optical Instrumentation Engineers, Annual Technical Symposium, 14th San Francisco. Proceedings. 1969. 8.00 (ISBN 0-89252-087-6). Photo-Optical.

Society of Photo-Optical Instrumentation Engineers, Seminar. Remote Sensing of Earth Resources & the Environment: Proceedings, Vol. 27. 168p. 1971. 29.00 (ISBN 0-89252-037-X). Photo-Optical.

U. S. Navy (Bureau of Naval Personnel) Basic Optics & Optical Instruments. (Illus.). 1969. pap. 7.95 (ISBN 0-486-22291-8). Dover.

Zimmer, H. G. Geometrical Optics. Wilson, R. N., tr. LC 72-94095. (Applied Physics & Engineering Ser.: Vol. 9). (Illus.). 1970. 27.50 (ISBN 0-387-04771-9). Springer-Verlag.

OPTICAL MASERS
see Lasers

OPTICAL MEASUREMENTS

Dahneke, Barton E. Measurement of Suspended Particles by Quasi-Elastic Light Scattering. 570p. 1983. 48.50 (ISBN 0-471-87289-X, Pub. by Wiley-Interscience). Wiley.

Levi, Leo, ed. Handbook of Tables of Functions for Applied Optics, CRC. LC 73-88627. (Handbook Ser.). 640p. 1974. 76.50 (ISBN 0-87819-371-5). CRC Pr.

Marcuse, D. Principles of Optical Fiber Measurements. LC 80-2339. 1981. 49.50 (ISBN 0-12-470980-X). Acad Pr.

Weissberger, Arnold, et al, eds. Techniques of Chemistry: Vol. I, Pt. 3C, Physical Methods of Chemistry: Polarimetry. LC 49-48584. 528p. 1972. 47.95 (ISBN 0-471-92732-5). Krieger.

OPTICAL MINERALOGY

Gribble, C. D. & Hall, A. J. A Practical Introduction to Optical Mineralogy. (Illus.). 200p. 1985. text ed. 30.00x (ISBN 0-04-549007-4); pap. text ed. 14.95x (ISBN 0-04-549008-2). Allen Unwin.

Jones, Norris W. & Bloss, Donald F. Laboratory Manual for Optical Mineralogy. (Orig.). 1979. pap. text ed. 13.95x (ISBN 0-8087-1058-3). Burgess.

Kerr, Paul E. Optical Mineralogy. 4th ed. (Illus.). 1977. text ed. 47.95 (ISBN 0-07-034218-0). McGraw.

Marfunin, A. S. Spectroscopy, Luminescence & Radiation Centers in Minerals. Schiffer, W. W., tr. from Russ. (Illus.). 1979. 58.00 (ISBN 0-387-09070-3). Springer-Verlag.

Phillips, W. Revell & Griffen, Dana T. Optical Mineralogy: The Nonopaque Minerals. LC 80-12435. (Illus.). 677p. 1981. text ed. 47.95x (ISBN 0-7167-1129-X). W H Freeman.

Phillips, William R. Mineral Optics: Principles & Techniques. LC 78-134208. (Geology Ser.). (Illus.). 249p. 1971. text ed. 37.95x (ISBN 0-7167-0251-7). W H Freeman.

OPTICAL PATTERN RECOGNITION
see also Optical Character Recognition Devices

Biberman, L. M., ed. Perception of Displayed Information. LC 72-97695. (Optical Physics & Engineering Ser.). (Illus.). 345p. 1973. 55.00 (ISBN 0-306-30724-3, Plenum Pr). Plenum Pub.

Cathey, W. Thomas. Optical Information Processing & Holography. LC 73-14604. (Pure & Applied Optics Ser.). 398p. 1974. 40.95 (ISBN 0-471-14078-3, Pub. by Wiley-Interscience). Wiley.

DiBartolo, Baldassare. Optical Interactions in Solids. LC 67-31206. 260p. 1968. 32.50 (ISBN 0-471-21276-8). Krieger.

Kaufmann, A. Introduction to the Theory of Fuzzy Subsets, Vol. 1: Fundamental Theoretical Elements. 1975. 67.50 (ISBN 0-12-402301-0). Acad Pr.

Zadeh & Fu, King-Sun, eds. Fuzzy Sets & Their Applications to Cognitive & Decision Processes. 1975. 60.00 (ISBN 0-12-775260-9). Acad Pr.

OPTICAL ROTATION
see also Polarization (Light)

Barron, Lawrence D. Molecular Light Scattering & Optical Activity. 425p. 1983. 72.50 (ISBN 0-521-24602-4). Cambridge U Pr.

Crabbe, Pierre. ORD & CD in Chemistry & Biochemistry: An Introduction. 1972. 41.50 (ISBN 0-12-194650-9). Acad Pr.

Kirkwood, John G. Dielectrics-Intermolecular Forces-Optical Rotation. Cole, Robert H., ed. (Documents on Modern Physics Ser.). (Illus.). 282p. (Orig.). 1965. 44.25 (ISBN 0-677-00405-2). Gordon.

Mason, S. F. Molecular Optical Activity & the Chiral Discriminations. LC 82-1125. (Illus.). 250p. 1982. 44.50 (ISBN 0-521-24702-0). Cambridge U Pr.

Mason, Stephen F., ed. Optical Activity & Chiral Discrimination. (NATO Advanced Study Institutes Ser., Math & Physical Sciences: No. 48). 1979. lib. bdg. 45.00 (ISBN 90-277-0982-3). Kluwer Academic.

Mizushima, San-Ichiro. Structure of Molecules & Internal Rotation. (Physical Chemistry Ser.: Vol. 2). 1954. 60.00 (ISBN 0-12-501750-2). Acad Pr.

OAS General Secretariat Dept. of Scientific & Technological Affairs. Actividad Optica, Dispersion Rotatoria Optica y Dicroismo Circular En Quimica Organica. 2nd ed. (Quimica Ser.: Monografia No. 11). (Span.). 70p. 1981. pap. 3.50 (ISBN 0-8270-1418-X). OAS.

OPTICAL SCANNERS
see also Optical Character Recognition Devices; Perceptrons

Gottlieb, Milton, et al. Electro-Optical & Acoustic-Optical Scanning & Deflection. (Optical Engineering Ser.: Vol. 3). (Illus.). 208p. 1983. 35.00 (ISBN 0-8247-1811-9). Dekker.

Society of Photo-Optical Instrumentation Engineers, Seminar. Scanners & Imagery Systems for Earth Observation: Proceedings, Vol. 51. 1975. 28.00 (ISBN 0-89252-063-9). Photo-Optical.

OPTICAL WAVE GUIDES

Adams, M. J. An Introduction to Optical Waveguides. LC 80-42059. 401p. 1981. cloth 63.95x (ISBN 0-471-27969-2, Pub. by Wiley Interscience). Wiley.

Barnoski, Michael K., ed. An Introduction to Integrated Optics. LC 74-5444. 515p. 1974. 59.50x (ISBN 0-306-30784-7, Plenum Pr). Plenum Pub.

Clarricoats, P. J., ed. Optical-Fibre Waveguides. (IEE Reprint Ser.: No. 1). 335p. 1975. pap. 32.00 (ISBN 0-901223-76-X, RE001, Pub. by Peregrinus England). Inst Elect Eng.

Newman, Paul. Optical Resolution Procedures for Chemical Compounds, Vol. 1: Amines & Related Compounds. 1981. 52.50 (ISBN 0-9601918-0-1). Optical Resolution.
--Optical Resolution Procedures for Chemical Compounds, Vol. 2: Acids, 2 pts. LC 78-61452. 1981. Set. 79.00 (ISBN 0-9601918-3-6). Pt. I, 566p (ISBN 0-9601918-1-X). Pt. II, 580p (ISBN 0-9601918-2-8). Optical Resolution.
Newton, Isaac. Opticks. 1952. pap. text ed. 6.50 (ISBN 0-486-60205-2). Dover.
--Opticks, or a Treatise of the Reflections, Refractions, Inflections & Colours of Light. 16.00 (ISBN 0-8446-5799-9). Peter Smith.
Nicholson, Marjorie H. Newton Demands the Muse: Newton's "Opticks" & the Eighteenth Century Poets. LC 78-13146. 1979. Repr. of 1966 ed. lib. bdg. 24.75x (ISBN 0-313-21044-6, NIND). Greenwood.
Nussbaum, A. & Phillips, R. Contemporary Optics for Scientists & Engineers. 1976. 41.95 (ISBN 0-13-170183-5). P-H.
Omar, Saleh Beshara. Ibn Al-Haytham's Optics: A Study of the Origins of Experimental Science. LC 76-42611. (Studies in Islamic Philosophy & Science). (Illus.). 1977. 20.00x (ISBN 0-88297-015-1). Bibliotheca.
Optical Society of America. Optics Index. 20.00 (ISBN 0-9600380-2-7). Optical Soc.
Ostrowsky, D. B. Fiber & Integrated Optics. (NATO ASI Ser. B, Physics: Vol. 41). 430p. 1979. 65.00x (ISBN 0-306-40162-2, Plenum Pr). Plenum Pub.
Ostrowsky, D. B. & Spitz, E., eds. New Directions in Guided Wave & Coherent Optics, 2 Vols. 1984. lib. bdg. 95.00 set (ISBN 90-247-2938-6, Pub. by Martinus Nijhoff Netherlands). Kluwer Academic.
Palmer, C. Harvey. Optics: Experiments & Demonstrations. 340p. 1962. 25.00x (ISBN 0-8018-0518-X). Johns Hopkins.
Papoulis, Athanasios. Systems & Transforms with Applications in Optics. LC 81-5995. 484p. 1981. Repr. of 1968 ed. lib. bdg. 29.50 (ISBN 0-89874-358-3). Krieger.
Pecham, John. John Pecham & the Science of Optics: Perspectiva Communis. Lindberg, David C., ed. LC 72-98122. (Publication in Medieval Science No. 14). 1970. 40.00x (ISBN 0-299-05730-5). U of Wis Pr.
Pressley, Robert J. Handbook of Lasers, CRC: With Selected Data on Optical Technology. LC 72-163066. (Handbook Ser.). (Illus.). 631p. 1971. 49.95 (ISBN 0-87819-381-2). CRC Pr.
REA Staff. Optics Problem Solver. rev. ed. LC 81-50899. 832p. 1984. 23.85 (ISBN 0-87891-526-5). Res & Educ.
Robertson, E. R., ed. The Engineering Uses of Coherent Optics. LC 75-22978. 560p. 1976. 150.00 (ISBN 0-521-20879-3). Cambridge U Pr.
Robson, B. A. The Theory of Polarization Phenomena. (Oxford Studies in Physics). (Illus.). 1974. 35.00x (ISBN 0-19-851453-0). Oxford U Pr.
Rousseau, Denis L., ed. Optical Techniques. (Physical Techniques in Biological Ser.: Vol. 1B). 1984. 65.00 (ISBN 0-12-599322-6). Acad Pr.
Rozenberg, Georgii V. Twilight: A Study in Atmospheric Optics. LC 65-11345. pap. 92.00 (ISBN 0-317-27113-X, 2024702). Bks Demand UMI.
Rubin, Melvin L. Optics for Clinicians. 2nd ed. LC 72-97862. (Illus.). 1974. 30.00x (ISBN 0-937404-01-2). Triad Pub FL.
Ruda, M. C., ed. International Conference on Nonimagiging Concentrators, Vol. 441. 116p. 42.00 (ISBN 0-89252-476-6). Photo-Optical.
Ruth, W. Lexikon der Schulphysik: Optik und Relativitaet, Vol. 4. (Ger.). 42.00 (ISBN 3-7614-0109-4, M-7226). French & Eur.
Saleh, B. Photoelectronic Statistics: With Applications to Spectroscopy & Optical Communication. LC 77-9936. (Springer Ser. in Optical Sciences: Vol. 6). (Illus.). 1977. 46.00 (ISBN 0-387-08295-6). Springer-Verlag.
Schulz, E. Woerterbuch der Optik und Feinmechanik: English-French-German Dictionary of Optics & Mechanical Engineering. (Eng., Fr. & Ger.). 1961. write for info. (M-90925). French & Eur.
Schulz, Ernst. Woerterbuch der Optik und Feinmechanik, Vol. 1. (Fr., Ger. & Eng., Dictionary of Optics & Mechanical Engineering). 1961. pap. 12.00 (ISBN 3-87097-036-7, M-6978). French & Eur.
--Woerterbuch der Optik und Feinmechanik, Vol. 2. (Fr., Ger. & Eng., Dictionary of Optics & Mechanical Engineering). 1961. pap. 12.00 (ISBN 3-87097-037-5, M-6977). French & Eur.
Sears, Francis W. Optics. 3rd ed. 1949. 24.95 (ISBN 0-201-06915-6). Addison-Wesley.
Skobel'tsyn, D. V., ed. Optical Studies in Liquids & Solids. LC 69-12523. (P. N. Lebedev Physics Institute Ser.: Vol. 39). 266p. 1969. 35.00x (ISBN 0-306-10821-6, Consultants). Plenum Pub.
Smith, F. Graham & Thomson, J. H. Optics. LC 71-146547. (Manchester Physics Ser). 350p. 1971. 26.95x (ISBN 0-471-80360-X, Pub. by Wiley-Interscience). Wiley.
Smith, W. J., et al, eds. Optical Specifications: Components & Systems, Vol. 406. 139p. 46.00 (ISBN 0-89252-441-3). Photo-Optical.
Snyder, A. W. & Menzel, R., eds. Photoreceptor Optics. LC 75-6700. (Illus.). 550p. 1975. 59.00 (ISBN 0-387-07216-0). Springer-Verlag.
Solid State Optical Control Devices, Vol. 464. 1984. 43.00 (ISBN 0-89252-499-5). Photo-Optical.
Soroko, L. M. Holography & Coherent Optics. LC 78-4479. (Illus.). 834p. 1978. 99.50x (ISBN 0-306-40101-0, Plenum Pr). Plenum Pub.
Spatial Light Modulators & Applications, Vol. 465. 1984. 43.00 (ISBN 0-89252-500-2). Photo-Optical.
Stavroudis, O. N. Modular Optical Design. (Springer Series in Optical Sciences: Vol. 28). (Illus.). 199p. 1982. 43.00 (ISBN 0-387-10912-9). Springer-Verlag.
Steffens, Henry J. The Development of Newtonian Optics in England. (Illus.). 1977. 20.00 (ISBN 0-88202-048-X, Sci Hist). Watson Pub Intl.
Stroke, George W. Introduction to Coherent Optics & Halography. 2nd ed. (Illus.). 1969. 47.50 (ISBN 0-12-673956-0). Acad Pr.
Swenson, Loyd S., Jr. The Ethereal Aether: A History of the Michelson-Morley-Miller Aether-Drift Experiments, 1880-1930. (Illus.). 382p. 1972. 22.50x (ISBN 0-292-72000-9). U of Tex Pr.
Systems Integrated & Optical Design II - Another Look: Proceedings of the SPIE-SPSE Technical Symposium East, Reston, Va, 1977. (SPIE Seminar Proceedings: Vol. 103). 136p. 10.00 (ISBN 0-89252-130-9); members 10.00 (ISBN 0-317-34766-7). SPIE.
Tamir, T., ed. Integrated Optics. (Topics in Applied Physics Ser.: Vol. 7). (Illus.). 1979. pap. 27.50 (ISBN 0-387-09673-6). Springer-Verlag.
Tarasov, L. V. Laser Age in Optics. 206p. 1985. 6.95 (ISBN 0-8285-2075-5, Pub. by Mir Pubs USSR). Imported Pubns.
Tenquist, D. W., et al. University Optics, 2 vols. 1970. Set. 131.95x (ISBN 0-677-62090-X); Vol. 1, 350p. 75.25x (ISBN 0-677-62070-5); Vol. 2, 390p. 75.25x (ISBN 0-677-62080-2). Gordon.
Tunnacliffe, A. H. Introduction to Visual Optics. 1981. 79.00x (ISBN 0-686-45407-3, Pub. by Assn Disp Opt England). State Mutual Bk.
Tunnacliffe, A. H. & Hirst, J. S. Optics. 1981. 90.00x (ISBN 0-686-45408-1, Pub. by Assn Disp Opt England). State Mutual Bk.
Ward, Gray, ed. Integrated Optics & Optical Communications. 1974. pap. 12.95x (ISBN 0-8422-0402-4). Irvington.
Weik, Martin H. Fiber Optics & Lightwave Communications Standard Dictionary. 320p. 1980. 23.95 (ISBN 0-442-25658-2). Van Nos Reinhold.
Weissberger, A. & Rossiter, B. W., eds. Techniques of Chemistry: Optical, Spectroscopic & Radioactivity Methods: Iternferometry, Light Scattering, Microscopy, Microwave & Magnetic Resonance Spectroscopy, Vol. 1, Pt. 3A. 732p. 1972. 60.00 (ISBN 0-471-92729-5). Krieger.
Welford, W. T. Optics. 2nd ed. (Oxford Physics Ser.). 1981. pap. text ed. 17.95x (ISBN 0-19-851847-1); cloth 37.50x (ISBN 0-19-851846-3). Oxford U Pr.
Welford, W. T. & Winston, Roland. The Optics of Nonimaging Concentrators: Light & Solar Energy. 1978. 46.50 (ISBN 0-12-745350-4). Acad Pr.
Williams, Charles S. & Becklund, Orville A. Optics: A Short Course for Engineers & Scientists. LC 83-164. 414p. 1984. Repr. of 1972 ed. text ed. 39.50 (ISBN 0-89874-617-5). Krieger.
Wiltse, J. C., ed. Millimeter Wave Technology, Vol. 423. 177p. 42.00 (ISBN 0-89252-458-8). Photo-Optical.
Wolf, E. Progress in Optics, Vol. 21. 1984. 65.00 (ISBN 0-444-86761-9). Elsevier.
Wolf, E., ed. Progress in Optics, Vols. 9-17. (North-Holland); Vol. 11, 1973. 64.00 (ISBN 0-444-10497-6); Vol. 12, 1975. 64.00 (ISBN 0-7204-1512-8); Vol. 13, 1976. 55.50 (ISBN 0-444-10806-8); Vol. 14, 1977. 74.50 (ISBN 0-444-10914-5); Vol. 15, 1978. 68.00 (ISBN 0-7204-1515-2); Vol. 16, 1979. 81.00 (ISBN 0-444-85087-2); Vol. 17, 1980. 68.00 (ISBN 0-444-85309-X). Elsevier.
--Progress in Optics, Vol. 18. 364p. 1980. 68.00 (ISBN 0-444-85445-2, North-Holland). Elsevier.
--Progress in Optics, Vol. 19. 394p. 1981. 57.50 (ISBN 0-444-85444-4, North Holland). Elsevier.
--Progress in Optics, Vol. 20. 400p. 1984. 61.75 (ISBN 0-444-86736-8). Elsevier.
--Progress in Optics, Vol. 22. 424p. 1985. 65.00 (ISBN 0-444-86923-9, North-Holland). Elsevier.
Young, Hugh D. Fundamentals of Waves, Optics & Modern Physics. 2nd ed. 1975. 42.95 (ISBN 0-07-072521-7). McGraw.
Young, M. Applied Optics. (Series in Optical Sciences: Vol. 5). 1977. 33.00 (ISBN 0-387-08126-7). Springer-Verlag.
Yu, F. T. White-Light Optical Signal Processing. (Pure & Applied Optics Ser.). 320p. 1985. write for info. (ISBN 0-471-80954-3). Wiley.
Yu, Francis T. Optics & Information Theory. LC 83-16273. 240p. 1984. Repr. of 1976 ed. lib. bdg. 29.95 (ISBN 0-89874-678-7). Krieger.
Zahradnik, Milos. The Production & Application of Fluorescent Brightening Agents. LC 81-16355. 147p. 1982. 34.95 (ISBN 0-471-10125-7, Pub. by Wiley-Interscience). Wiley.
Zebrowski, Ernest, Jr. Practical Optics. (Illus.). 30p. (Orig.). 1982. pap. text ed. 2.95 (ISBN 0-943908-00-0). ITEC.

OPTICS–ATLASES

Harburn, G., et al. Atlas of Optical Transforms. LC 75-14718. 104p. 1975. 34.50x (ISBN 0-8014-0986-1). Cornell U Pr.

OPTICS–TABLES, ETC.

Boll, Richard Henry. Tables of Light-Scattering Functions: Relative Indices of Less Than Unity & Infinity. LC 57-7175. pap. 93.00 (ISBN 0-317-08493-3, 2011234). Bks Demand UMI.
Rousseau, M. & Mathieu, Jean P. Problems in Optics. 376p. 1973. text ed. 37.00 (ISBN 0-08-016980-5). Pergamon.

OPTICS, ELECTRONIC

see Electron Optics

OPTICS, FIBER

see Fiber Optics

OPTICS, GEOMETRICAL

ASTM Standards on Color & Appearance Measurement. 265p. 1983. 39.00 (ISBN 0-8031-0822-2, 03-512083-14). ASTM.
Buchdahl, H. A. Optical Aberration Coefficients. 2nd ed. LC 68-19165. 1969. pap. 6.95 (ISBN 0-486-62010-7). Dover.
--Optical Aberration Coefficients. 11.25 (ISBN 0-8446-1760-1). Peter Smith.
Cornbleet, S. Microwave & Optical Ray Geometry. LC 83-16737. 152p. 1984. cloth 36.95x (ISBN 0-471-90315-9, Pub. by Wiley-Interscience). Wiley.
Herzberger, Max. Modern Geometrical Optics. LC 77-9030. 516p. 1978. Repr. of 1958 ed. 29.50 (ISBN 0-88275-585-4). Krieger.
Horemis, Spyros. Optical & Geometric Patterns & Designs. 1970. pap. 5.50 (ISBN 0-486-22214-4). Dover.
Kline, Morris & Kay, Irvin W. Electromagnetic Theory & Geometrical Optics. LC 78-14351. (Pure & Applied Mathemetics Ser.: Vol. 12). 540p. 1979. Repr. of 1965 ed. lib. bdg. 30.50 (ISBN 0-88275-739-3). Krieger.
Machado, M. A. & Narducci, L. M., eds. Optics in Four Dimensions-1980: ICO Ensenada. LC 80-70771. (AIP Conference Proceedings: No. 65). 745p. 1981. lib. bdg. 40.75 (ISBN 0-88318-164-9). Am Inst Physics.
Ogle, Kenneth N. Optics: An Introduction for Ophthalmologists. 2nd ed. (Illus.). 288p. 1979. photocopy 30.50 (ISBN 0-398-01417-5). C C Thomas.
Zimmer, H. G. Geometrical Optics. Wilson, R. N., tr. LC 72-94095. (Applied Physics & Engineering Ser.: Vol. 9). (Illus.). 1970. 27.50 (ISBN 0-387-04771-9). Springer-Verlag.

OPTICS, LINEAR

see Nonlinear Optics

OPTICS, METEOROLOGICAL

see Meteorological Optics

OPTICS, NONLINEAR

see Nonlinear Optics

OPTICS, PHOTOGRAPHIC

see Photographic Optics

OPTICS, PHYSICAL

see also Crystal Optics; Electromagnetic Theory; Photoelasticity

Egan, Walter G. & Hilgeman, Theodore W. Optical Properties of Inhomogeneous Materials: Applications to Geology, Astronomy, Chemistry & Engineering. LC 78-20043. 1979. 45.00 (ISBN 0-12-232650-4). Acad Pr.
Garbuny, Max. Optical Physics. 1965. 33.00 (ISBN 0-12-275350-X). Acad Pr.
Green, George. Mathematical Papers. LC 70-92316. 19.95 (ISBN 0-8284-0229-9). Chelsea Pub.
Lorenz, Ludwig V. Oeuvres Scientifiques De L. Lorenz, 2 Vols. 1898-1904. Set. 60.00 (ISBN 0-384-33740-6). Johnson Repr.
Mark, Harry H. Optokinetics: A Treatise on the Motions of Lights. LC 81-71626. (Illus.). 150p. 1982. 9.95 (ISBN 0-9608152-0-1). H Mark-Corbett.
Pockels, Friedrich C. Lehrbuch der Kristalloptik. (Bibliotheca Mathematica Teubneriana Ser: No. 39). (Ger). 1969. Repr. of 1906 ed. 53.00 (ISBN 0-384-47000-9). Johnson Repr.
Skobel'tsyn, D. V., ed. Optical Methods of Investigating Solid Bodies. LC 65-10524. (P. N. Lebedev Physics Institute Ser.: Vol. 25). 188p. 1965. 35.00x (ISBN 0-306-10713-9, Consultants). Plenum Pub.
Stokes, George G. Mathematical & Physical Papers, 5 Vols. 2nd ed. Repr. of 1905 ed. Set. 165.00 (ISBN 0-384-58370-9). Johnson Repr.
Strong, John. Concepts of Classical Optics. LC 57-6918. (Physics Ser.). (Illus.). 692p. 1958. 34.95x (ISBN 0-7167-0301-7). W H Freeman.

OPTICS, PHYSIOLOGICAL

see also Color Vision; Eye; Vision

Acers, Thomas E. Congenital Abnormalities of the Optic Nerve & Related Forebrain. LC 82-24962. (Illus.). 75p. 1983. 14.50. (ISBN 0-8121-0889-2). Lea & Febiger.
Arden, G. B., ed. The Visual System: Neurophysiology, Biophysics, & Their Clinical Applications. LC 72-77461. (Advances in Experimental Medicine & Biology Ser.: Vol. 24). 347p. 1972. 49.50x (ISBN 0-306-39024-8, Plenum Pr). Plenum Pub.
Hering, Ewald. Outlines of a Theory of the Light Sense. LC 64-11130. (Illus.). 1964. 22.50x (ISBN 0-674-64900-1). Harvard U Pr.
LeGrand, Y. & El Hage, S. G. Physiological Optics. (Springer Ser. in Optical Sciences: Vol. 13). (Illus.). 350p. 1980. pap. 52.00 (ISBN 0-387-09919-0). Springer-Verlag.
Linksz, Arthur. Physiology of the Eye: Vol. I Optics. LC 50-5797. (Illus.). 366p. 1953. 71.50 (ISBN 0-8089-0267-9, 792561). Grune.
Reichardt, W., ed. Processing of Optical Data by Organisms & by Machines. (Italian Physical Society: Course No. 43). 1970. 95.00 (ISBN 0-12-368843-4). Acad Pr.
Tunnacliffe, A. H. Introduction to Visual Optics. 1981. 79.00x (ISBN 0-686-45407-3, Pub. by Assn Disp Opt England). State Mutual Bk.
Wehner, R., ed. Information Processing in the Visual Systems of Arthropods. LC 72-91887. 340p. 1972. pap. 32.00 (ISBN 0-387-06020-0). Springer-Verlag.
Zinchenko, V. P. & Vergiles, N. Yu. Formation of Visual Images: Studies of Stabilized Retinal Images. LC 70-185458. 68p. 1972. 25.00x (ISBN 0-306-10871-2, Consultants). Plenum Pub.

OPTICS, QUANTUM

see Quantum Optics

OPTIMIZATION (MATHEMATICS)

see Mathematical Optimization

OPTIMIZATION THEORY

see Mathematical Optimization

ORANGE

McPhee, John. Oranges. LC 66-20125. 149p. 1967. 7.50 (ISBN 0-374-22688-1); pap. 5.25 (ISBN 0-374-51297-3). FS&G.
Pectinesterases from the Orange Fruit: Their Purification, General Characteristics & Juice Cloud Destablizing Properties. 1979. pap. 16.00 (ISBN 90-220-0709-X, PDC147, Pudoc). Unipub.

ORANGUTANS

Maple, Terry L. Orang-Utan Behavior. (Van Nostrand Reinhold Primate Behavior & Development Ser.). 272p. 1980. text ed. 34.50 (ISBN 0-442-25154-8). Van Nos Reinhold.

ORBIT (INFORMATION RETRIEVAL SYSTEM)

Palmer, Roger C. Online Reference & Information Retrieval. (Library Science Text). 140p. (Orig.). 1982. pap. text ed. 18.50 (ISBN 0-87287-347-1). Libs Unl.

ORBITALS, ATOMIC

see Atomic Orbitals

ORBITALS, MOLECULAR

see Molecular Orbitals

ORBITING VEHICLES

see Artificial Satellites; Space Stations

ORBITS

see also Artificial Satellites–Orbits; Mechanics, Celestial

Dow, T. W. Repeal Kepler's Laws. LC 60-13372. 1960. 5.00 (ISBN 0-910340-02-1). Celestial Pr.
Escobal, Pedro R. Methods of Orbit Determination. LC 75-11889. 500p. 1976. Repr. of 1965 ed. 35.00 (ISBN 0-88275-319-3). Krieger.
Kepler, Johann. Somnium: The Dream, or Posthumous Work on Lunar Astronomy. Rosen, Edward, tr. LC 65-20639. pap. 72.30 (ISBN 0-317-07803-8, 2004977). Bks Demand UMI.
Moser, Jurgen & Kyner, Walter T. Lectures on Hamiltonian Systems, & Rigorous & Formal Stability of Orbits about an Oblate Planet. LC 52-42839. (Memoirs: No. 81). 87p. 1979. pap. 12.00 (ISBN 0-8218-1281-5, MEMO-81). Am Math.
Moulton, Forest R. Periodic Orbits. 1920. 39.00 (ISBN 0-384-40235-6). Johnson Repr.
Symposium in Applied Mathematics, New York, 1957. Orbit Theory: Proceedings, Vol. 9. Birkhoff, G. & Langer, R. E., eds. LC 50-1183. (Proceedings of Symposia in Applied Mathematics). 195p. 1959. 24.00 (ISBN 0-8218-1309-9, PSAPM-9). Am Math.

Symposium, University of Sao Paulo, 1969. Periodic Orbits, Stability & Resonances: Proceedings. Giacaglia, G. E., ed. LC 74-124848. 530p. 1970. lib. bdg. 50.00 (ISBN 90-277-0170-9, Pub. by Reidel Holland). Kluwer Academic.

Szebehely, Victor G. Theory of Orbits in the Restricted Problem of Three Bodies. 1967. 51.50 (ISBN 0-12-680650-0). Acad Pr.

ORCHARDS

see Fruit-Culture

ORCHID CULTURE

Arditti, Joseph, ed. Orchid Biology: Reviews & Perspectives, I. LC 76-25648. (Illus.). 328p. 1977. 45.00x (ISBN 0-8014-1040-1). Cornell U Pr.

Birk, Lance A. The Paphiopedilum Grower's Manual. (Illus.). 208p. 1984. 75.00x (ISBN 0-9612826-0-6). Pisang Pr.

Black, Peter M. The Complete Book of Orchid Growing. 160p. 1981. 40.00x (ISBN 0-7063-5512-1, Pub. by Ward Lock Ed England). State Mutual Bk.

Correll, Donovan S. Native Orchids of North America North of Mexico. LC 78-62270. (Illus.). 1950. 35.00x (ISBN 0-8047-0999-8). Stanford U Pr.

Darwin, Charles R. The Various Contrivances by Which Orchids are Fertilised by Insects. 2nd ed. LC 72-3892. (Illus.). xvi, 300p. 1972. write for info. (ISBN 0-404-08406-0). AMS Pr.

Dressler, Robert L. The Orchids: Natural History & Classification. LC 80-24561. (Illus.). 352p. 1981. text ed. 30.00x (ISBN 0-674-87525-7). Harvard U Pr.

Fast, Gertrud. Orchideenkultur: Botanische Grundlagen Pflanzenbeschreibungen. 2ND ed. (Illus.). 1981. 38.95 (ISBN 3-8001-6133-8). Lubrecht & Cramer.

Kramer, Jack. Orchids for Your Home. 144p. 1974. pap. 1.95 (ISBN 0-346-12143-4). Cornerstone.

Kramer, Jack & Crafton, Roy L. Miniature Orchids to Grow & Show. (Illus.). 1982. 15.95 (ISBN 0-393-01632-3). Norton.

Moir, W. W. & Moir, May A. Creating Oncidinae Intergenerics. LC 81-16182. (Illus.). 111p. 1982. pap. text ed. 12.00x (ISBN 0-8248-0784-7). UH Pr.

Noble, Mary. You Can Grow Orchids. 4th, rev. ed. (Illus.). 136p. 1980. pap. 7.95 (ISBN 0-913928-04-6). McQuerry-Orchid.

Northen, Rebecca T. Orchids as House Plants. rev. ed. (Illus.). 160p. 1976. pap. 2.95 (ISBN 0-486-23261-1). Dover.

Rentoul, J. N. Growing Orchids, Bk. 4: The Australasian Families. (Growing Orchids Ser.). (Illus.). 224p. 1985. 26.95 (ISBN 0-88192-020-7, Dist. by Intl Spec Bk); pap. 19.95 (ISBN 0-88192-021-5). Timber.

--Growing Orchids Book Three: Vandas, Dendrobiums & Others. (Illus.). 241p. 1983. 26.95 (ISBN 0-917304-22-5); pap. 19.95 (ISBN 0-917304-32-2). Timber.

--Growing Orchids Book Two: The Cattleyas & other Epiphytes. (Illus.). 218p. 1982. 26.95 (ISBN 0-917304-20-9); pap. 19.95 (ISBN 0-917304-28-4). Timber.

--Growing Orchids, Vol. 1: Cymbidiums & Slippers. LC 81-3023. (Illus.). 170p. 1980. 29.95 (ISBN 0-295-95839-1). U of Wash Pr.

Rittershausen, Brian & Rittershausen, Wilma. Orchids As Indoor Plants. (Illus.). 90p. 1983. pap. 7.95 (ISBN 0-7137-1303-8, Pub. by Blandford Pr England). Sterling.

Rittershausen, Wilma, ed. An Illustrated Guide to Growing Your Own Orchids. LC 83-83424. (Illustrated Gardening Guides Ser.). (Illus.). 160p. 1984. 9.95 (ISBN 0-668-06197-9, 6179-9). Arco.

Sheviak, Charles J. An Introduction to the Ecology of the Illinois Orchidaceae. (Scientific Papers: Vol. XIV). (Illus.). 89p. 1974. pap. 3.75 (ISBN 0-89792-055-4). Ill St Museum.

Van Royen, P. The Genus Corybas (Orchidaceae) in its Eastern Areas. (Phanerogamarum Monographiae: No. 16). (Illus.). 176p. 1983. lib. bdg. 35.00x (ISBN 3-7682-1367-6). Lubrecht & Cramer.

Williams, B. S. & Williams, H. Orchid Growers Manual. 7th ed. 1973. Repr. of 1894 ed. 52.50 (ISBN 3-7682-0043-4). Lubrecht & Cramer.

Winterringer, Glen S. Wild Orchids of Illinois. (Popular Science Ser.: Vol. VII). (Illus.). 130p. 1967. pap. 3.00 (ISBN 0-89792-028-7). Ill St Museum.

Withner, Carl L., ed. The Orchids: Scientific Studies. LC 73-20496. (Illus.). 604p. 1974. 52.50x (ISBN 0-471-95715-1, Pub. by Wiley-Interscience). Wiley.

ORCHIDS

see also Orchid Culture

Ames, Blanche. Drawings of Florida Orchids. (Orchid Ser.). (Illus.). 1980. Repr. of 1959 ed. text ed. 15.00 (ISBN 0-930576-22-5). E M Coleman Ent.

Ames, Oakes. Orchidaceae: Illustrations & Studies of the Family Orchidaceae Volume IV: the Genus Habenaria in North America. (Orchid Ser.). (Illus.). 1980. Repr. of 1910 ed. text ed. 25.00 (ISBN 0-930576-23-3). E M Coleman Ent.

Ames, Oaks. Studies In the Family Corchidaceae, 7 Vols. (Illus.). 1610p. 1982. Repr. Set. 145.00 (ISBN 0-9608918-0-3); 27.00 ea. Vol. I (ISBN 0-9608918-1-1). Vol. II (ISBN 0-9608918-2-X). Vol. III (ISBN 0-9608918-3-8). Vol. IV. (ISBN 0-9608918-4-6); Vol. V. (ISBN 0-9608918-5-4); Vol. VI. (ISBN 0-9608918-6-2). Vol. VII (ISBN 0-9608918-7-0). Twin Oaks Bks.

Arditti, Joseph. Orchid Biology: Reviews & Perspectives, Vol I. (Illus.). 1977. 45.00x (ISBN 0-8014-1040-1). Comstock.

Arditti, Joseph, ed. Orchid Biology, No. III. LC 76-25648. (A Comstock Bk.). (Illus.). 416p. 1983. 49.50x (ISBN 0-8014-1512-8). Cornell U Pr.

--Orchid Biology: Reviews & Perspectives, II. LC 76-25648. (Illus.). 400p. 1982. 45.00x (ISBN 0-8014-1276-5). Cornell U Pr.

--Orchid Biology: Reviews & Perspectives, Vol. III. (Illus.). 416p. 1983. 49.50x (ISBN 0-8014-1512-8). Comstock.

Ball, John S. Southern African Epiphytic Orchids. 1978. 200.00x (ISBN 0-86036-119-5, Pub. by Collins England). State Mutual Bk.

Banerjee, M. L. & Thapa, B. B. Orchids of Nepal. (International Bioscience Ser.: No. 4). (Illus.). 150p. 1978. 9.00 (ISBN 0-88065-023-0, Pub. by Messers Today & Tomorrows Printers & Publishers India). Scholarly Pubns.

Banerji, M. L. Orchids of Nepal. (Illus.). 135p. (Orig.). 1982. text ed. 12.50 (ISBN 0-934454-95-7). Lubrecht & Cramer.

Banerji, M. L. & Pradhan, Prabha. The Orchids of Nepal Himalaya. (Illus.). 640p. 1983. lib. bdg. 189.00 (ISBN 3-7682-1366-8). Lubrecht & Cramer.

Bateman, James. The Orchidaceae of Mexico & Guatemala. 250.00 (ISBN 0-384-03530-2). Johnson Repr.

Bennett, Keith S. The Tropical Asiatic Slipper Orchids: Genus Paphiopedilum. (Illus.). 91p. 1985. 15.95 (ISBN 0-207-14887-2, Pub. by Salem Hse Ltd). Merrimack Pub Cir.

Black, Peter M. The Complete Handbook of Orchid Growing. 160p. 1980. 17.65 (ISBN 0-8129-0951-8). Times Bks.

Blackmore, Stephen. Bee Orchids. (Shire Natural History Ser.: No. 3). (Orig.). 1985. pap. 3.95 (ISBN 0-85263-745-4, Pub. by Shire Pubns England). Seven Hills Bks.

Cameron, Jean W. The Orchids of Maine. 1976. pap. 3.50 (ISBN 0-89101-001-7). U Maine Orono.

Casper, S. J. & Krausch, H. D. Suesswasserflora von Mitteleuropa: Pteridophyta und Antophyta, Part 1 - Lycopodiaceae bis Orchidaceae, Vol. 23. Pascher, A., et al, eds. (Ger., Illus.). 403p. 1980. lib. bdg. 37.00 (ISBN 0-318-00460-7). Lubrecht & Cramer.

Chew Kang, Lee. Orchids. (Illus.). 1979. 15.00 (ISBN 0-89860-032-4). Eastview.

Cogniaux, Alfredus. Orchidaceae, 4 vols. (Flora Brasiliensis Ser.: Vol. 3, Pts. 4-6). (Lat., Illus.). 970p. 1975. Repr. Set. lib. bdg. 157.50x (ISBN 3-87429-080-8). Lubrecht & Cramer.

Darnell, A. W. Orchids for the Outdoor Garden: A Descriptive List of the World's Orchids for the Use of Amateur Gardeners. LC 76-23979. (Illus.). 512p. 1976. pap. 7.50 (ISBN 0-486-23406-1). Dover.

Darwin, Charles. Fertilization of Orchids by Insects. (Orchid Ser.). 1980. Repr. of 1862 ed. text ed. 27.50 (ISBN 0-930576-20-9). E M Coleman Ent.

De La Bathie, H. Perrier. Flora of Madagascar: Orchids. Humbert, H., ed. Beckman, Steven D., tr. from French. LC 82-90881. (Illus.). 542p. 1982. 65.00x (ISBN 0-9609434-0-4). S D Beckman.

Dunsterville, G. C. & Garay, L. A. Orchids of Venezuela, 3 vols. 1980. pap. 40.00 (ISBN 0-87544-000-2). Museum Bks.

--Venezuelan Orchids Illustrated, Vol. 6. 1975. 30.00 (ISBN 0-87544-001-0). Museum Bks.

Du Petit-Thouars, Aubert-Aubert. Histoire Particuliere Des Plantes Orchidees Recueillies sur les Trois Iles Australes d'Afrique. (Orchid Ser.). (Illus.). 1980. Repr. of 1822 ed. text ed. 15.00 (ISBN 0-930576-24-1). E M Coleman Ent.

Duthie, J. F. The Orchids of the Western Himalaya. (Illus.). 1967. Repr. of 1906 ed. 105.00 (ISBN 3-7682-0465-0). Lubrecht & Cramer.

Fitch, Charles M. All about Orchids. LC 80-1806. (Illus.). 288p. 1981. 15.95 (ISBN 0-385-15848-3). Doubleday.

Fitch, W. H., illus. Refugium Botanicum or Figurs & Descriptions from Living Specimens of Little Known or New Plants of Botanical Interest, Vol. II. (Orchid Ser.). (Illus.). 1980. Repr. text ed. 27.50 (ISBN 0-930576-19-5). E M Coleman Ent.

Hooker, J. D. A Century of Indian Orchids. (Calutta Royal Bot. Gard. Ser.). (Illus.). 1967. 70.00 (ISBN 3-7682-0464-2). Lubrecht & Cramer.

Hooker, W. J. Icones Plantarum: On Orchids, Vols. 21 & 22. (Ser. 4). 1967. Vol. 21. 21.00 ea. Vol. 22 (ISBN 3-7682-0853-2) (ISBN 3-7682-0854-0). Lubrecht & Cramer.

Hunt, P. Francis. The Orchid. (Octopus Bk.). (Illus.). 1979. 40.00 (ISBN 0-7064-0808-X, Mayflower Bks). Smith Pubs.

Hunt, P. Francis & Grierson, Mary. The Country Life Book of Orchids. 1981. 100.00x (ISBN 0-686-78784-6, Pub. by RHS Ent England). State Mutual Bk.

Keenan, P. E. Orchids: A Guide to All Species Found in Maine. (Maine Geographic Ser.). (Illus.). 48p. 1983. pap. 2.95 (ISBN 0-89933-068-1). Delorme Pub.

Kraenzlin, F. W. Orchidacearum Genera et Species. (Plant Monograph Reprint Ser.: No. 6). (Illus.). 1969. Repr. of 1904 ed. 70.00 (ISBN 3-7682-0649-1). Lubrecht & Cramer.

Kraenzlin, R. Monographie von Masdevallia Ruiz et Pavon Lothiana Kraenz: Scaphosepalum Pfitzer, Cryptophoranthus Bearb, Rodr., Pseudostomeria Kraenzl. (Feddes Repertorium: Beiheft 34). (Ger.). 240p. 1980. Repr. of 1925 ed. lib. bdg. 32.20x (ISBN 3-87429-184-7). Lubrecht & Cramer.

Lindley, John. Folia Orchidacea: A Enumeratiion of the Known Species of Orchids, 2 vols. in 1. 1983. Repr. of 1964 ed. 50.00 (ISBN 90-6123-088-8). Lubrecht & Cramer.

--The Genera & Species of Orchidaceous Plants, 7 vols. in 1. 1984. Repr. of 1964 ed. 50.00 (ISBN 90-6123-091-8). Lubrecht & Cramer.

Luer, Carlyle A. Native Orchids of Florida. (Illus.). 1972. 28.00x (ISBN 0-89327-014-8). NY Botanical.

--Native Orchids of the United States & Canada. (Illus.). 1975. 33.00x (ISBN 0-89327-015-6). NY Botanical.

Millar, Andree. Orchids of Papua New Guinea: An Introduction. LC 78-54152. (Illus.). 112p. 1978. 25.00x (ISBN 0-295-95605-4). U of Wash Pr.

Moir, W. W. & Moir, May A. Creating Oncidinae Intergenerics. LC 81-16182. (Illus.). 111p. 1982. pap. text ed. 12.00x (ISBN 0-8248-0784-7). UH Pr.

--Laeliinae Intergenerics. LC 82-4887. (Illus.). 61p. 1982. pap. text ed. 12.00x (ISBN 0-8248-0814-2). UH Pr.

Orchids. 2.25 (ISBN 0-686-21148-0). Bklyn Botanic.

Orchids Nineteen Seventy-One to Seventy-Five. 1982. 55.00x (ISBN 0-900629-85-1, Pub. by RHS Ent England). State Mutual Bk.

Orchids Nineteen Seventy-Six to Eighty. 1982. 65.00x (ISBN 0-906603-20-X, Pub. by RHS Ent England). State Mutual Bk.

Orchids Nineteen Sixty-One to Seventy. 1982. 60.00x (ISBN 0-900629-38-X, Pub. by RHS Ent England). State Mutual Bk.

The Orchids of South Central Africa. 192p. 1981. 49.00x (ISBN 0-460-04295-5, Pub. by J M Dent England). State Mutual Bk.

Piers, Frank. Orchids of East Africa. 2nd rev. ed. (Illus.). 1984. pap. 29.95 (ISBN 3-7682-0569-X). Lubrecht & Cramer.

Plaxton, Elmer H., ed. North American Terrestrial Orchids: Symposium II - Proceedings & Lectures. LC 82-62805. (Illus.). 144p. 1983. pap. 17.95 (ISBN 0-9610332-0-7). Mich Orchid Soc.

Ritterhausen, Brian & Ritterhausen, Wilma. Orchids in Color. (Illus.). 1979. 12.50 (ISBN 0-7137-0859-X, Pub. by Blandford Pr England). Sterling.

Schlechter, R. Beitraege zur Orchideenkunde von Colombia. (Feddes Repertorium Ser.: Beiheft 27). (Ger.). 183p. 1980. Repr. of 1924 ed. lib. bdg. 27.30x (ISBN 3-87429-182-0). Lubrecht & Cramer.

--Beitraege zur Orchideenkunde von Zentralamerika, 2 vols. in 1. (Feddes Repertorium: Beiheft 17 & 18). (Ger.). 402p. 1980. Repr. of 1922 ed. lib. bdg. 47.25x (ISBN 3-87429-181-2). Lubrecht & Cramer.

--Orchidaceae Perrieriannae: Zur Orchideenkunde der Insel Madagascar. (Feddes Repertorium: Beiheft 33). (Ger.). 391p. 1980. Repr. of 1925 ed. lib. bdg. 40.25x (ISBN 3-87429-183-9). Lubrecht & Cramer.

--Orchideenflora von Rio Grande do Sul. (Feddes Repertorium: Beiheft 35). (Ger.). 108p. 1980. Repr. of 1925 ed. lib. bdg. 20.65x (ISBN 3-87429-185-5). Lubrecht & Cramer.

Segerback, L. B., ed. Orchids of Nigeria. (Illus.). 122p. 1983. lib. bdg. 37.50 (ISBN 90-6191-217-2, Pub. by Balkema RSA). IPS.

Stewart, J. & Hennessey, E. F. Orchids of America. LC 81-6589. 159p. 50.00 (ISBN 0-395-31771-1). HM.

Van Der Pijl, L. & Dodson, Calaway H. Orchid Flowers: Their Pollination & Evolution. LC 66-28521. (Illus.). 1966. 14.95 (ISBN 0-87024-069-2). U of Miami Pr.

Van Royen, P. The Orchids of the High Mountains of New Guinea. (Illus.). 784p. 1980. 70.00 (ISBN 3-7682-1261-0). Lubrecht & Cramer.

Veitch, James. Manual of Orchidaceous Plants: 1887-1894, 2 vols. (Illus.). 1981. Set. 100.00 (ISBN 90-6123-180-9). Lubrecht & Cramer.

Williams & Arlott. A Field Guide to the Orchids of Britain & Europe. 29.95 (ISBN 0-00-219314-0, Collins Pub England). Greene.

Williams, John G. & Williams, Andrew E. Field Guide to Orchids of North America. LC 82-23677. (Illus.). 144p. 1983. flexi-cover 10.95 (ISBN 0-87663-415-3). Universe.

Williamson, Graham. Orchids of South Central Africa. 1981. 60.00x (ISBN 0-686-78777-3, Pub. by RHS Ent England). State Mutual Bk.

Withner, C. L. The Orchids: Scientific Survey. (Illus.). 648p. 1959. 39.95x (ISBN 0-471-06827-6, Pub. by Wiley-Interscience). Wiley.

ORDER STATISTICS

see also Nonparametric Statistics

Barlow, R. E., et al. Statistical Inference Under Order Restrictions: The Theory & Application of Isotonic Regression. LC 74-39231. (Probability & Statistics Ser.). (Illus.). 388p. 1972. 74.95x (ISBN 0-471-04970-0, Pub. by Wiley-Interscience). Wiley.

Gibbons, Jean D., et al. Selecting & Ordering Populations: A New Statistical Methodology. LC 77-3700. (Probability & Mathematical Statistics). 569p. 1977. 55.50x (ISBN 0-471-02670-0, Pub. by Wiley-Interscience). Wiley.

Harter, H. Leon. The Chronological Annotated Bibliography of Order Statistics: Vol. II, 1950-1959. LC 81-66077. (The American Sciences Press Series in Mathematical & Management Sciences: Vol. 8). 1983. 149.50 (ISBN 0-935950-05-2). Am Sciences Pr.

ORDNANCE RESEARCH

William Roy, Seventeen Twenty-Six to Seventeen Ninety: Pioneer of the Ordnance Survey. 1981. pap. 10.00x (ISBN 0-7141-0387-X, Pub. by Brit Lib England). State Mutual Bk.

ORDOVICIAN PERIOD

see Geology, Stratigraphic–Ordovician

ORE-DEPOSITS

see also Ores

Barnes, H. L., ed. Geochemistry of Hydrothermal Ore Deposits. 2nd ed. LC 79-354. 798p. 1979. 42.50x (ISBN 0-471-05056-3, Pub. by Wiley-Interscience). Wiley.

Bastin, Edson S. Interpretation of Ore Textures. LC 51-3907. (Geological Society of America, Memoir Ser.: No. 45). pap. 32.30 (ISBN 0-317-10251-6, 2007947). Bks Demand UMI.

Baumann, Ludwig. Introduction to Ore Deposits. 1976. 12.50x (ISBN 0-7073-0207-2, Pub. by Scottish Academic Pr Scotland). Columbia U Pr.

Klemm, D. D. & Schneider, H. J., eds. Time- & Strata- Bound Ore Deposits. (Illus.). 1979. 59.00 (ISBN 0-387-08502-5). Springer-Verlag.

Lebedev, L. M. Metacolloids in Endogenic Deposits. LC 65-25241. (Monographs in Geoscience Ser.). 1967. 42.50x (ISBN 0-306-30295-0, Plenum Pr). Plenum Pub.

Netschert, Bruce C. & Landsberg, Hans H. The Future Supply of the Major Metals: A Reconnaissance Survey. LC 76-58923. (Resources for the Future Ser.). (Illus.). 1978. Repr. of 1961 ed. lib. bdg. 24.75 (ISBN 0-8371-9472-5, NEMM). Greenwood.

Ore Deposits of the United States. LC 68-24170. 1968. 35.00x (ISBN 0-89520-008-2). Soc Mining Eng.

Park, Charles F. & Guilbert, John M. The Geology of Ore Deposits. 4th ed. LC 85-10099. (Illus.). 768p. 1985. text ed. write for info. (ISBN 0-7167-1456-6). W H Freeman.

Park, Charles F., Jr. & MacDiarmid, Roy A. Ore Deposits. 3rd ed. LC 75-14157. (Geology Ser.). (Illus.). 529p. 1975. text ed. 32.95x (ISBN 0-7167-0272-X). W H Freeman.

Recent Advances in Mining & Processing of Low-Grade Submarginal Mineral Deposits. LC 76-11771. 1977. text ed. 25.00 (ISBN 0-08-021051-1). Pergamon.

Relation of Ore Deposition to Doming in the North American Cordillera. LC 60-2730. (Geological Society of America, Memoir Ser.: No. 77). pap. 32.80 (ISBN 0-317-10779-8, 2007960). Bks Demand UMI.

Wolf, K. H. Handbook of Strata-Bound & Stratiform Ore Deposits, Pt. 4. Date not set. write for info. (ISBN 0-444-42248-X). Elsevier.

ORE-DRESSING

see also Flotation

Arbiter, N. Nathaniel, ed. Milling Methods in the Americas. 625p. 1965. 125.00x (ISBN 0-677-10690-4). Gordon.

Arbiter, Nathaniel, ed. Seventh International Mineral Processing Congress: Proceedings, 1965. 625p. 1965. 144.50x (ISBN 0-677-10690-4). Gordon.

Inculet, Ion I. Electrostatic Mineral Separation. (Electrostatics & Electrostatic Applications Ser.). 1984. 29.95 (ISBN 0-471-90576-3). Wiley.

Lynch, A. J. Mineral Crushing & Grinding Circuits: Their Simulation, Design & Control. (Developments in Mineral Processing Ser.: Vol. 1). 342p. 1977. 72.50 (ISBN 0-444-41528-9). Elsevier.

Milling Machine Work. 1953. pap. text ed. 14.00 (ISBN 0-8273-0185-5). Delmar.

Processing of Low-Grade Uranium Ores. (Panel Proceedings Ser.). (Illus.). 247p. 1967. pap. 16.25 (ISBN 92-0-041067-7, ISP146, IAEA). Unipub.

Richards, Robert H., et al. Textbook of Ore Dressing. 3rd, rev. ed. LC 40-10540. pap. 156.00 (ISBN 0-317-29998-0, 2051848). Bks Demand UMI.

Taggart, Arthur F. Handbook of Mineral Dressing. (Engineering Handbook Ser.-). 1905p. 1945. 89.95 (ISBN 0-471-84348-2, Pub. by Wiley-Interscience). Wiley.

OREGON PINE

see Douglas Fir

ORES

see also Metallurgy; Metals; Mineralogy; Mines and Mineral Resources; Ore-Deposits; also names of specific ores, e.g. Iron Ores

Amstutz, G. C., ed. Ore Genesis: The State of the Art. (Illus.). 780p. 1982. 69.00 (ISBN 0-387-11139-5). Springer-Verlag.

Amstutz, G. C. & Bernard, A. J., eds. Ores in Sediments. (International Union of Geological Sciences: Ser. a, No. 3). (Illus.). 1973. pap. 36.00 (ISBN 0-387-05712-9). Springer-Verlag.

Craig, James R. & Vaughan, David J. Ore Microscopy. LC 80-39786. 406p. 1981. 37.50 (ISBN 0-471-08596-0, Pub. by Wiley-Interscience). Wiley.

Evans, A. Introduction to Ore Geology. (Geoscience Texts Ser.: Vol. 2). 1980. 54.00 (ISBN 0-444-19473-8); pap. 24.50 (ISBN 0-444-19472-X). Elsevier.

Gass, I. G., ed. Volcanic Processes in Ore Genesis. 188p. (Orig.). 1980. pap. text ed. 46.00x (ISBN 0-900488-33-6). IMM North Am.

Iron & Steel Society of AIME. Iron & Steel Society of AIME: 2nd Proceedings, Chicago Meeting, February 23-25, 1981, Sponsered by the Process Technology Division, Iron & Steel Society of AIMMPE, Vol. 2. pap. 80.80 (ISBN 0-317-26610-1, 2024187). Bks Demand UMI.

Jones, M. J., ed. Complex Sulphide Ores. 278p. (Orig.). 1980. pap. text ed. 161.00x (ISBN 0-900488-51-4). IMM North Am.

Ramdohr, Paul. The Ore Minerals & Their Intergrowths, 2 vols. 2nd ed. LC 79-40745. (International Series in Earth Sciences: Vol. 35). (Illus.). 1269p. 1981. Set. 200.00 (ISBN 0-08-023801-7). Pergamon.

Schumann, Walter. Stones & Minerals: Minerals, Precious Stones, Rocks, Ores. (Illus.). 226p. 1985. 6.98 (ISBN 0-8069-5526-0). Sterling.

Uytenbogaardt, E. W. & Burke, E. A. Tables for Microscopic Identification of Ore Minerals. (Earth Science Ser.). 430p. 1985. pap. 10.95 (ISBN 0-486-64839-7). Dover.

Wills, B. A. Mineral Processing Technology: An Introduction to the Practical Aspects of Ore Treatment & Mineral Recovery. 2nd ed. LC 80-41698. (International Series on Materials Science & Technology: Vol. 29). (Illus.). 450p. 1981. 60.00 (ISBN 0-08-031160-1); pap. 20.00 (ISBN 0-08-027323-8). Pergamon.

ORES–ANALYSIS

see Assaying

ORESME, NICOLE, 1323-1382

Grant, Edward, ed. Nicole Oresme & the Kinematics of Circular Motion: Tractatus De Commensurabilitate Vel Incommensurabilitate Motuum Celi. Grant, Edward, tr. LC 79-133238. (Medieval Science Ser). (Illus.). 438p. 1971. 50.00x (ISBN 0-299-05830-1). U of Wis Pr.

ORGAN–CONSTRUCTION

Audsley, George A. The Art of Organ Building, 2 vols. Incl. Vol. 1. Proem. (Illus.). x, 600p. 19.95 (ISBN 0-486-21314-5); Vol. 2. Specifications of Organs. (Illus.). iv, 750p. 19.95 (ISBN 0-486-21315-3). Dover.

Blanchard, Homer D., ed. Organs of Our Time. Rev. ed. LC 82-90079. (Illus.). 231p. 1982. 24.00 (ISBN 0-930112-06-7). Praestant.

Klais, Hans G. & Steinhaus, Hans. The Bamboo Organ in the Catholic Parish Church of St. Joseph at las Pinas, Province of Rizal, on the Island of Luzon, Philippines. Blanchard, Homer, tr. from Ger. LC 77-9579. (Illus.). 1977. 20.00x (ISBN 0-930112-02-4). Praestant.

Klotz, Hans. Organ Handbook. LC 69-11068. 1969. 8.75 (ISBN 0-570-01306-2, 99-1187). Concordia.

Lewis, Walter & Lewis, Thomas. Modern Organ Building. LC 77-8738. 1977. Repr. of 1911 ed. lib. bdg. 30.00 (ISBN 0-89341-074-8). Longwood Pub Group.

Matthews, John. The Restoration of Organs. (Music Ser.). (Illus.). 170p. 1981. Repr. of 1920 ed. lib. bdg. 22.50 (ISBN 0-306-76098-3). Da Capo.

Ogasapian, John. Organ Building in New York City, 1700 to 1900. LC 78-300889. (Illus.). 1977. pap. text ed. 26.00x (ISBN 0-913746-10-X). Organ Lit.

Reinburg, Peggy K. Arp Schnitger, Organ Builder: Catalyst for the Centuries. LC 81-47829. (Illus.). 192p. 1982. 18.50x (ISBN 0-253-30927-1). Ind U Pr.

Rimbault, Edward F. The Early English Organ Builders & Their Works. LC 77-75182. 1977. Repr. of 1864 ed. lib. bdg. 15.00 (ISBN 0-89341-062-4). Longwood Pub Group.

Sayer, Michael. Samuel Renn: English Organ Builder. 1974. 40.00x (ISBN 0-85033-078-5, Pub. by Phillimore England). State Mutual Bk.

Seidel, J. J. The Organ & Its Construction. (Music Reprint Ser.). 218p. 1981. Repr. of 1855 ed. 25.00 (ISBN 0-306-76106-8). Da Capo.

Sumner, William. The Organ: Its Evolution, Principles of Construction & Use. 3rd ed. LC 73-181272. 544p. 1962. Repr. 59.00x (ISBN 0-403-01695-9). Scholarly.

ORGANIC CHEMISTRY

see Chemistry, Organic

ORGANIC COOLED REACTORS

Bojtech, O. T., compiled by. Organic Coolants & Moderators. (Bibliographical Ser.: No. 17). 173p. 1975. pap. 11.25 (ISBN 92-0-054065-1, IDC70, IAEA). Unipub.

Organic Liquids as Reactor Coolants & Moderators. (Technical Reports Ser.: No. 70). (Illus.). 148p. 1967. pap. 12.50 (ISBN 92-0-055067-3, IDC70, IAEA). Unipub.

ORGANIC FARMING

see also Organic Gardening

Bezdicek, D. F., et al, eds. Organic Farming: Current Technology & Its Role in a Sustainable Agriculture. (Casa Special Publication Ser.). 192p. 1984. 12.00 (ISBN 0-89118-076-1). Am Soc Agron.

Corley, Hugh. Organic Small Farming. Bargyla & Rateaver, Gylver, eds. LC 74-33122. (Conservation Gardening & Farming Ser: Ser. C). 1975. pap. 10.00 (ISBN 0-9600698-4-4). Rateavers.

Engelken, Ralph & Engelken, Rita. The Art of Natural Farming & Gardening. 1981. 9.95 (ISBN 0-942066-00-6). Barrington IA.

Howard, Sir Albert. The Soil & Health: A Study of Organic Agriculture. LC 70-179077. (Illus.). 335p. 1972. pap. 5.95 (ISBN 0-8052-0334-6). Schocken.

Jenks, Jorian. The Stuff We're Made of: The Positive Approach to Health through Nutrition. 1959. 5.00 (ISBN 0-8159-6829-9). Devin.

Leatherbarrow, Margaret. Gold in the Grass. Bargyla & Rateaver, Gylver, eds. LC 75-23179. (Conservation Gardening & Farming Ser: Ser. C). 1975. pap. 10.00 (ISBN 0-9600698-8-7). Rateavers.

Oelhaf, Robert C. Organic Agriculture: Economic & Ecological Comparisons with Conventional Methods. 271p. 1978. 32.95x (ISBN 0-470-26427-6). Halsted Pr.

Philbrick, John & Philbrick, Helen. Gardening for Health & Nutrition: The Bio-Dynamic Way. LC 79-150428. (Illus.). 96p. 1973. pap. 4.00 (ISBN 0-89345-223-8, Steinerbks). Garber Comm.

Shacklady, Cyril A., ed. The Use of Organic Residues in Rural Communities. 177p. 1983. pap. text ed. 15.00 (ISBN 92-808-0362-X, TUNU212, UNU). Unipub.

Stephenson, W. A. Seaweed in Agriculture & Horticulture. 3rd ed. Bargyla & Rateaver, Gylver, eds. LC 74-12812. (Conservation Gardening & Farming Ser: Ser. C). 1974. pap. 7.00 (ISBN 0-9600698-3-6). Rateavers.

Stevens, Richard L. Organic Gardening in Hawaii. (Illus.). 72p. 1981. pap. 4.95 (ISBN 0-912180-40-4). Petroglyph.

Sykes, Friend. Humus Farming. Bargyla & Rateaver, Gylver, eds. (Conservation Gardening & Farming Ser.). pap. write for info. (ISBN 0-9600698-7-9). Rateavers.

Todd, Nancy J. & Todd, John. Bioshelters, Ocean Arks, City Farming: Ecology as the Basis of Design. LC 83-51436. (Illus.). 256p. 1984. 25.00 (ISBN 0-87156-348-7); pap. 10.95 (ISBN 0-87156-814-4). Sierra.

Turner, F. Newman. Fertility Farming. Rateaver, Bargyla & Rateaver, Gylver, eds. (Conservation Gardening & Farming Ser). pap. write for info (ISBN 0-685-61014-4). Rateavers.

--Fertility Pastures & Cover Crops. Bargyla & Rateaver, Gylver, eds. LC 74-33123. (Conservation Gardening & Farming Ser: Ser. C). pap. 10.00 (ISBN 0-9600698-6-0). Rateavers.

ORGANIC GARDENING

see also Organic Farming

Engelken, Ralph & Engelken, Rita. The Art of Natural Farming & Gardening. 1981. 9.95 (ISBN 0-942066-00-6). Barrington IA.

Foster, Catherine O. The Organic Gardener. pap. 8.95 (ISBN 0-394-71785-6, V-785, Vin). Random.

Kolisko, E. & Kolisko, L. Agriculture of Tomorrow. 2nd ed. (Illus.). 1978. (Pub. by Kolisko Archive Publications); pap. 15.95 (ISBN 0-906492-44-0). St George Bk Serv.

Kreuter, Marie-Luise. The MacMillan Book of Organic Gardening. (Illus.). 128p. 1985. pap. 5.95 (ISBN 0-02-063150-2). MacMillan.

Organic Gardening & Minnich, Jerry. The Rodale Guide to Composting. (Illus.). 1979. 14.95 (ISBN 0-87857-212-0). Rodale Pr Inc.

Organic Gardening & Farming Magazine, ed. Encyclopedia of Organic Gardening. LC 77-25915. 1978. 24.95 (ISBN 0-87857-225-2); deluxe 27.95 (ISBN 0-87857-351-8). Rodale Pr Inc.

Shewell-Cooper, W. E. Compost Gardening. LC 74-18416. (Illus.). 1975. 12.95x (ISBN 0-02-852110-2). Hafner.

Smith, Marny. Gardening with Conscience: The Organic-Intensive Method. 96p. (Orig.). 1981. pap. 3.95 (ISBN 0-8164-2325-3, Pub. by Seabury). Winston Pr.

Smith, Robert F., Jr. Organic Gardening in the West: Raising Vegetables in a Short, Dry Growing Season. (Illus.). 1976. pap. 4.95 (ISBN 0-913270-60-1). Sunstone Pr.

Stevens, Richard L. Organic Gardening in Hawaii. (Illus.). 72p. 1981. pap. 4.95 (ISBN 0-912180-40-4). Petroglyph.

Yepsen, Roger B., Jr. The Encyclopedia of Natural Insect & Disease Control. (Illus.). 496p. 1984. 24.95 (ISBN 0-87857-488-3, 01-051-0). Rodale Pr Inc.

ORGANIC MATTER IN SOIL

see Humus

ORGANIC MODERATED REACTORS

Bojtech, O. T., compiled by. Organic Coolants & Moderators. (Bibliographical Ser.: No. 17). 173p. 1975. pap. 11.25 (ISBN 92-0-054065-1, IDC70, IAEA). Unipub.

ORGANICULTURE

see Organic Farming; Organic Gardening

ORGANOBORON COMPOUNDS

Brown, Herbert C., et al. Organic Syntheses Via Boranes. LC 74-20520. 283p. 1975. 45.50 (ISBN 0-471-11280-1, Pub. by Wiley-Interscience). Wiley.

Cragg, Gordon. Organoboranes in Organic Synthesis. (Studies in Organic Chemistry: Vol. 1). 440p. 1973. 75.00 (ISBN 0-8247-6018-2). Dekker.

Grimes, Russell N., ed. Metal Interactions with Boron Clusters. LC 82-9068. (Modern Inorganic Chemistry Ser.). (Illus.). 342p. 1982. 49.50x (ISBN 0-306-40933-X, Plenum Pr). Plenum Pub.

Mikhailov, B. M. & Bubnov, Yu N. Organoboron Compounds in Organic Synthesis. 560p. 1984. 224.00 (ISBN 3-7186-0113-3). Harwood Academic.

Noeth, H. & Wrackmeyer, H. Nuclear Magnetic Resonance Spectroscopy of Boron Compounds. LC 77-14148. (NMR: Vol 14). 1978. 100.00 (ISBN 0-387-08456-8). Springer-Verlag.

Onak, Thomas. Organoborane Chemistry. (Organoborane Chemistry Ser.). 1975. 85.00 (ISBN 0-12-526550-6). Acad Pr.

Smith, K. Organometallic Compounds of Boron. (Chapman & Hall Chemistry Sourcebooks Ser.). 316p. 1985. lib. bdg. 49.95 (ISBN 0-412-26790-X, Pub by Chapman & Hall). Methuen Inc.

ORGANOCHLORINE COMPOUNDS

Blair, Ectyl H., ed. Chlorodioxins: Origin & Fate. LC 73-84139. (Advances in Chemistry Ser: No. 120). 1973. 24.95 (ISBN 0-8412-0181-1). Am Chemical.

Committee on Impacts of Stratospheric Change, National Research Council. Halocarbons: Environmental Effects of Chlorofluoromethane Release. 125p. 1976. pap. 7.75 (ISBN 0-309-02529-X). Natl Acad Pr.

Moriarty, F., ed. Organochlorine Insecticides: Persistent Organic Pollutants. 1975. 58.50 (ISBN 0-12-506750-X). Acad Pr.

ORGANOFLUORINE COMPOUNDS

see also Fluorocarbons

Banks, R. E. Preparation Properties & Industrial Applications of Organofluorine Compounds. (Ellis Horwood Series in Chemical Science). 352p. 1982. 89.95 (ISBN 0-470-27526-X). Halsted Pr.

Filler, R. & Kobayashi, Y., eds. Biomedical Aspects of Fluorine Chemistry. 256p. 1983. 74.50 (ISBN 0-444-80466-8, I-133-83, Biomedical Pr). Elsevier.

Hudlicky, M. Chemistry of Organic Fluorine Compounds. 1962. write for info. (ISBN 0-02-357750-9). Macmillan.

Hudlicky, Milos. Chemistry of Organic Fluorine Compounds. LC 73-14377. 903p. 1976. text ed. 172.95x (ISBN 0-470-41835-4). Halsted Pr.

ORGANOGRAPHY

see Botany–Organography

ORGANOIRON COMPOUNDS

Knox, G. R. Organometallic Compounds of Iron. (Chapman & Hall Chemistry Sourcebook Ser.). 488p. 1985. lib. bdg. 49.95x (ISBN 0-412-26850-7, 9547, Pub. by Chapman & Hall). Methuen Inc.

Lovenberg, Walter, ed. Iron-Sulfur Proteins, 3 vols. Incl. Biological Properties. Vol. 1, 1973. 78.00 (ISBN 0-12-456001-6); Molecular Properties. Vol. 2, 1974. 72.00 (ISBN 0-12-456002-4); Vol. 3. 1977. 81.00 (ISBN 0-12-456003-2). 1973. Acad Pr.

Reutov, O. A. Advances in Organometallic Chemistry. 261p. 1985. pap. 9.95 (ISBN 0-8285-2884-5, Pub. by Mir Pubs USSR). Imported Pubns.

Rosenblum, Myron. Chemistry of the Iron Group Metallocenes: Ferrocene, Ruthenocene, Osmocene, Pt. 1. 241p. 1965. text ed. 15.00 (ISBN 0-470-73671-2, Pub. by Wiley). Krieger.

Siderophores from Microorganisms & Plants. (Structure & Bonding Ser.: Vol. 58). (Illus.). 160p. 1984. 30.00 (ISBN 0-387-13649-5). Springer-Verlag.

ORGANOLEAD COMPOUNDS

Grandjean, Philippe, ed. Biological Effects of Organolead Compounds. 288p. 1984. 84.00 (ISBN 0-8493-5309-2). CRC PR.

Harrison, P. G. Organometallic Compounds of Germanium, Tin, & Lead. (Chapman & Hall Chemistry Sourcebook Ser.). 192p. 1985. lib. bdg. 33.00x (ISBN 0-412-26810-8, 9542, Pub. by Chapman & Hall). Methuen Inc.

Ratcliffe, Jennifer M. Lead in Man & the Environment. LC 81-2905. (Ellis Horwood Series in Environmental Sciences). 240p. 1981. 81.95 (ISBN 0-470-27184-1). Halsted Pr.

Reutov, O. A. Advances in Organometallic Chemistry. 261p. 1985. pap. 9.95 (ISBN 0-8285-2884-5, Pub. by Mir Pubs USSR). Imported Pubns.

Seyferth, D. & King, R., eds. Organometallic Chemistry Reviews: Annual Surveys 1975 - Silicon-Tin-Lead. (Journal of Organometallic Chemistry Library: Vol. 4). 548p. 1977. 106.50 (ISBN 0-444-41591-2). Elsevier.

ORGANOMERCURY COMPOUNDS

Larock, R. C. Organomercury Compounds in Organic Synthesis. (Reactivity & Structure Ser.: Vol. 22). 420p. 1985. 94.00 (ISBN 0-387-13749-1). Springer-Verlag.

ORGANOMETALLIC COMPOUNDS

see also particular organometallic compounds, e.g. Organomagnesium Compounds

Abel, E. W. & Stone, F. G. Organometallic Chemistry, Vols. 1-7. Incl. Vol. 1. 1971 Literature. 1972. 41.00 (ISBN 0-85186-501-1); Vol. 2. 1972 Literature. 1973. 49.00 (ISBN 0-85186-511-9); Vol. 3. 1973 Literature. 1974. 54.00 (ISBN 0-85186-521-6); Vol. 4. 1974 Literature. 1975. 68.00 (ISBN 0-85186-531-3); Vol. 5. 1975 Literature. 1976. 73.00 (ISBN 0-85186-541-0); Vol. 6. 1976 Literature. 1977. 86.00 (ISBN 0-85186-551-8); Vol. 7. 1978. 93.00 (ISBN 0-85186-561-5, Pub. by Royal Soc Chem London). LC 72-83459. Am Chemical.

Alper, Howard. Transition Metal Organometallics in Organic Synthesis, 2 vols. (Organic Chemistry Ser.). Vol. 1, 1976. 66.00 (ISBN 0-12-053101-1); Vol. 2, 1978. 43.50 (ISBN 0-12-053102-X). Acad Pr.

Aylett, B. J. Organometallic Compounds, Vol. 1, Pt. 2: Groups IV & V. 4th ed. 1979. 85.00 (ISBN 0-412-13020-3, NO. 6018, Pub. by Chapman & Hall). Methuen Inc.

Bauer, K. & Haller, G. Organometallic Compounds - Models of Synthesis, Physical Constants & Chemical Reactions, Vol. 1: Compounds of Transition Metals. 2nd ed. Dub, M., ed. LC 66-28249. xxvi, 1171p. 1975. 83.00 (ISBN 0-387-07196-2). Springer-Verlag.

Becker, E. I. & Tsutsui, M., eds. Organometallic Reactions & Syntheses, Vol. 6. LC 74-92108. (Illus.). 314p. 1977. 55.00 (ISBN 0-306-39906-7, Plenum Pr). Plenum Pub.

Becker, Ernest I. & Tsutsui, Minoru, eds. Organometallic Reactions, 2 vols. LC 74-92108. 1971. Vol. 1, 400pp. 29.50 (ISBN 0-471-06135-2); Vol. 2, 462pp. 32.50 (ISBN 0-471-06130-1). Krieger.

Bird, C. W. Transition Metal Intermediates in Organic Synthesis. 1967. 62.50 (ISBN 0-12-099750-9). Acad Pr.

Blackborow, J. R. & Young, D. Metal Vapour Synthesis in Organometallic Chemistry. LC 79-9844. (Reactivity & Structure Ser.: Vol. 9). (Illus.). 1979. 63.00 (ISBN 0-387-09330-3). Springer-Verlag.

Brewster, J. H., ed. Aspects of Mechanism & Organometallic Chemistry. LC 78-21684. 361p. 1979. 59.50x (ISBN 0-306-40071-5, Plenum Pr). Plenum Pub.

Brinckman, F. E. & Bellama, J. M., eds. Organometals & Organometalloids: Occurrence & Fate in the Environment. LC 78-24316. (ACS Symposium Ser.: No. 82). 1978. 44.95 (ISBN 0-8412-0461-6). Am Chemical.

--Handbook of Organosilicon Compounds: Advances Since 1961, Vol. 4. 1008p. 1975. 125.00 (ISBN 0-8247-6269-X). Dekker.
--Handbook of Organosilicon Compounds: Advances Since 1961, Vol.1. 768p. 1975. 125.00 (ISBN 0-8247-6259-2). Dekker.
Borisov, S. N., et al. Organosilicon Derivatives of Phosporus & Sulphur. LC 74-159028. 338p. 1971. 45.00x (ISBN 0-306-30511-9, Plenum Pr). Plenum Pub.
--Organosilicon Heteropolymers & Heterocompounds. LC 69-13393. (Monographs in Inorganic Chemistry Ser.). 633p. 1970. 55.00x (ISBN 0-306-30379-5, Plenum Pr). Plenum Pub.
Boschke, F. L., ed. Bioactive Organo-Silicon Compounds. LC 79-12799. (Topics in Current Chemistry Ser.: Vol. 84). (Illus.). 1979. 57.00 (ISBN 0-387-09347-8). Springer-Verlag.
Kwart, H. & King, K. Delta-Orbital Involvement in the Organo-Chemistry of Silicon, Phosphorus & Sulfur. LC 77-1555. (Reactivity & Structure: Vol. 3). 1977. 56.00 (ISBN 0-387-07953-X). Springer-Verlag.
Seyferth, D. & King, R., eds. Organometallic Chemistry Reviews: Annual Surveys 1975 - Silicon-Tin-Lead. (Journal of Organometallic Chemistry Library: Vol. 4). 548p. 1977. 106.50 (ISBN 0-444-41591-2). Elsevier.
Seyferth, D., et al, eds. Organometallic Chemistry Reviews: Organosilicon Reviews. (Journal of Organometallic Chemistry Library: Vol. 2). 404p. 1976. 106.50 (ISBN 0-444-41488-6). Elsevier.
Weber, William P. Silicon Reagents for Organic Synthesis. (Reactivity & Structure: Vol. 14). 450p. 1983. 110.00 (ISBN 0-387-11675-3). Springer-Verlag.

ORGANOSULPHUR COMPOUNDS

Ando, W. Photo Oxidation of Organo-Sulfur Compounds. (Sulfur Reports Ser.). 80p. 1981. flexicover 22.00 (ISBN 3-7186-0073-0). Harwood Academic.
Ashworth, M. R. The Determination of Sulphur-Containing Groups. (The Analysis of Organic Materials & International Series of Monographs, No. 2). Vol. 1 1973. 45.00 (ISBN 0-12-065001-0); Vol. 2 1976. 55.00 (ISBN 0-12-065002-9); Vol. 3 1977. 55.00 (ISBN 0-12-065003-7). Acad Pr.
Block, Eric, ed. Reactions of Organosulfur Compounds. 1978. 38.50 (ISBN 0-12-107050-6). Acad Pr.
Board on Toxicology & Environmental Health, National Research Council. Sulfur Oxides. 1979. pap. text ed. 10.50 (ISBN 0-309-02862-0). Natl Acad Pr.
Borisov, S. N., et al. Organosilicon Derivatives of Phosporus & Sulphur. LC 74-159028. 338p. 1971. 45.00x (ISBN 0-306-30511-9, Plenum Pr). Plenum Pub.
Cavallini, D., et al, eds. Natural Sulfur Compounds: Novel Biochemical & Structural Aspects. 565p. 1980. 69.50x (ISBN 0-306-40335-8, Plenum Pr). Plenum Pub.
Drozd, V. N. & Zefirov, N. S. Sigmatropic Additions & Cyclosubstitutions in Five-Membered Heterocyclic Compounds Containing Exocyclic Double Bonds. (Sulfur Reports Ser.). 45p. 1981. flexicover 16.50 (ISBN 3-7186-0081-1). Harwood Academic.
Freidlina, R. Kh., ed. Organic Sulfur Chemistry: Ninth International Symposium on Organic Sulfur Chemistry, Riga, USSR, 9-14 June 1980. (IUPAC Symposium Ser.). (Illus.). 270p. 1981. 72.00 (ISBN 0-08-026180-9). Pergamon.
Kwart, H. & King, K. Delta-Orbital Involvement in the Organo-Chemistry of Silicon, Phosphorus & Sulfur. LC 77-1555. (Reactivity & Structure: Vol. 3). 1977. 56.00 (ISBN 0-387-07953-X). Springer-Verlag.
Lovenberg, W., ed. Iron-Sulfur Proteins, 3 vols. Incl. Biological Properties. Vol. 1, 1973. 78.00 (ISBN 0-12-456001-6); Molecular Properties. Vol. 2, 1974. 72.00 (ISBN 0-12-456002-4); Vol. 3. 1977. 81.00 (ISBN 0-12-456003-2). 1973. Acad Pr.
McFarland, J. W. Sulfonyl Isocyanates & Sulfonyl Isothiocyanates. (Sulfur Reports Ser.). 54p. 1981. flexicover 16.50 (ISBN 3-7186-0082-X). Harwood Academic.
Mason, D. McA. & Hakewill, H., Jr. Identification & Determination of Organic Sulfur in Utility Gases. (Research Bulletin Ser.: 5). iv, 51p. 1959. 5.00 (ISBN 0-317-34308-4). Inst Gas Tech.
Maw, G. A. Biochemistry of S-Methyl-L-Cysteine & Its Principal Derivatives. (Sulfur Reports Ser.). 31p. (Orig.). 1982. pap. text ed. 23.00 (ISBN 3-7186-0112-5). Harwood Academic.
Nudelman, Abraham. The Chemistry of Optically Active Sulphur Compounds. 262p. 1984. 60.95 (ISBN 0-677-16390-8). Gordon.
Preston, Seaton T. & Pankratz, Ronald. A Guide to the Analysis of Thioalcohols & Thioethers: (Mercaptans & Alkyl Sulfides) by Gas Chromatography. rev. ed. 1981. spiral plastic bdg. 25.00 (ISBN 0-913106-16-X). PolyScience.
Sudworth, J. L. & Tilley, A. R. The Sodium-Sulfur Battery. 400p. 1985. 60.00 (ISBN 0-412-16490-6). Methuen Inc.
Suter, C. M. Organic Chemistry of Sulfur. 864p. 1971. 132.95x (ISBN 0-677-65130-9). Gordon.
Torchinskii, Yu M. Sulfhydyl & Disulfide Groups of Proteins. LC 73-83903. (Studies in Soviet Sciences - Life Sciences). (Illus.). 285p. 1974. 45.00x (ISBN 0-306-10888-7, Consultants). Plenum Pub.
Trost, Barry M. & Melvin, Lawrence S., Jr. Sulfer Ylides: Emerging Synthetic Intermediates. (Organic Chemistry Ser.). 1975. 75.00 (ISBN 0-12-701060-2). Acad Pr.

ORGANOTIN COMPOUNDS

Boschke, F. L., ed. Organotin Compounds. (Topics in Current Chemistry Ser.: Vol. 104). (Illus.). 150p. 1982. 36.00 (ISBN 0-387-11542-0). Springer-Verlag.
Max Planck Society for the Advancement of Science, Gmelin Institute for Inorganic Chemistry. Organotin Compounds. (Gmelin Handbuch der Anorganischen Chemie, 8th Ed., New Suppl.: Vol. 26, Pt. 1). 182p. 1975. 126.50 (ISBN 0-387-93291-7). Springer-Verlag.
Poller, R. C. Chemistry of Organotin Compounds. (Organometallic Chemistry Ser). 1970. 75.00 (ISBN 0-12-560750-4). Acad Pr.
Seyferth, D. & King, R., eds. Organometallic Chemistry Reviews: Annual Surveys 1975 - Silicon-Tin-Lead. (Journal of Organometallic Chemistry Library: Vol. 4). 548p. 1977. 106.50 (ISBN 0-444-41591-2). Elsevier.

ORGANOTITANIUM COMPOUNDS

Feld, Raoul & Cowe, Peter L. Organic Chemistry of Titanium. 213p. 1965. 29.50x (ISBN 0-306-30629-8, Plenum Pr). Plenum Pub.

ORGANS (ANATOMY)

Banks, William J. Histology & Comparative Organology: A Text-Atlas. LC 79-24569. 296p. 1980. Repr. of 1974 ed. lib. bdg. 25.50 (ISBN 0-89874-084-3). Krieger.
Kessel, Richard G. & Kardon, Randy H. Tissues & Organs: A Text-Atlas of Scanning Electron Microscopy. LC 78-23886. (Illus.). 317p. 1979. text ed. 46.95 (ISBN 0-7167-0091-3); pap. text ed. 23.95 (ISBN 0-7167-0090-5); slides avail. (ISBN 0-7167-1231-8). W H Freeman.
Tyson, Charles A., ed. Organ Function Tests in Toxicity Evaluation. Sawhney, Daljit S. LC 85-4947. (Illus.). 237p. 1985. 42.00 (ISBN 0-8155-1036-5). Noyes.

ORGANS, CULTURE OF

Cau, P., et al. Morphogenesis of Thyroid Follicles in Vitro. (Advances in Anatomy Embryology & Cell Biology: Vol. 52, Pt. 2). 1976. pap. 34.30 (ISBN 0-387-07654-9). Springer-Verlag.
Lutz, H., ed. Invertebrate Organ Cultures. (Documents in Biology Ser.: Vol. 2). 264p. 1970. 69.50x (ISBN 0-677-30100-6). Gordon.
Thomas, J. Andre, ed. Organ Culture. (Fr). 1970. 86.00 (ISBN 0-12-688150-2). Acad Pr.

ORIENTATION

Brown, Terry & Hunter, Rob. The Concise Book of Orienteering. 1979. pap. 2.95 (ISBN 0-686-70999-3). Vanguard.
Burton, Maurice. The Sixth Sense of Animals. LC 72-6622. (Illus.). 192p. 1973. 7.95 (ISBN 0-8008-7232-0). Taplinger.
Lynn, R. Attention, Arousal & the Orientation Reaction. 1966. text ed. 23.00 (ISBN 0-08-011524-1); pap. text ed. 11.25 (ISBN 0-08-013840-3). Pergamon.
Ratliff, Donald E. Map, Compass, & Campfire. LC 64-8453. (Illus.). 1970. pap. 3.50 (ISBN 0-8323-0129-9). Binford.
Rock, Irvin. Orientation & Form. 1974. 33.00 (ISBN 0-12-591250-1). Acad Pr.
Symposium On Animal Orientation - Garmisch-Partenkirchen - 1962. Proceedings. Autrum, H., et al, eds. (Advances in Biology: Vol. 26). (Illus.). 1963. 34.30 (ISBN 0-387-02963-X). Springer-Verlag.
Von Frisch, Karl. Dance Language & Orientation of Bees. Chadwick, Leigh E., tr. LC 67-17321. (Illus., Ger). 1967. 30.00x (ISBN 0-674-19050-5, Belknap Pr). Harvard U Pr.
Williams, Charles W. Direction: The Essential Dimension. 1960. 8.95 (ISBN 0-8315-0003-4). Speller.

ORIGIN OF LIFE
see Life–Origin

ORIGIN OF MAN
see Man–Origin

ORIGIN OF SPECIES
see also Hybridization; Natural Selection; Phylogeny; Variation (Biology)

Barrett, Paul, et al, eds. Concordance to Darwin's "Origin of Species". 864p. 1981. 49.50x (ISBN 0-8014-1319-2). Cornell U Pr.
Darwin, Charles. Origin of Species. 1962. pap. 4.95 (ISBN 0-02-092120-9, Collier). Macmillan.
--Origin of Species. pap. 3.50 (ISBN 0-451-62102-6, ME2102, Ment). NAL.
--The Origin of Species. abr. ed. Appleman, Philip, ed. 1975. pap. text ed. 3.95x (ISBN 0-393-09219-4). Norton.
--The Origin of Species. Irvine, Charlotte & Irvine, William, eds. LC 56-7502. pap. 3.95 (ISBN 0-8044-6105-8). Ungar.
--The Origin of the Species. (Rowman & Littlefield University Library). 488p. 1972. 15.00x (ISBN 0-87471-662-4); pap. 8.00x (ISBN 0-87471-663-2). Rowman.
Darwin, Charles R. Foundations of the Origin of Species. Darwin, Francis, ed. LC 10-1422. 1909. 16.00 (ISBN 0-527-21610-0). Kraus Repr.
De Vries, H. Mutation Theory, 2 Vols. in 1. Farmer, J. B. & Darbishire, trs. 1909-1910. 58.00 (ISBN 0-527-93470-4). Kraus Repr.
Dobzhansky, Theodosius. Genetics & the Origin of Species. Eldredge, Niles & Gould, Stephen Jay, eds. (Classics of Modern Evolution Ser.). 416p. 1982. pap. 18.00x (ISBN 0-231-05475-0). Columbia U Pr.
--Genetics of the Evolutionary Process. LC 72-127363. 505p. 1971. 40.00x (ISBN 0-231-02837-7); pap. 17.00x (ISBN 0-231-08306-8). Columbia U Pr.
Ehrlich, Paul R. & Ehrlich, Anne H. Extinction: The Causes & Consequences of the Disappearance of Species. 400p. 1983. pap. 4.50 (ISBN 0-345-28895-5). Ballantine.
Endler, John A. Geographic Variation, Speciation, & Clines. LC 76-45896. (Monographs in Population Biology: No. 10). (Illus.). 1977. 28.50 (ISBN 0-691-08187-5); pap. 12.50 (ISBN 0-691-08192-1). Princeton U Pr.
Himmelfarb, Gertrude. Darwin & the Darwinian Revolution. 1968. pap. 9.95 (ISBN 0-393-00455-4, Norton Lib.). Norton.
--Darwin & the Darwinian Revolution. 16.25 (ISBN 0-8446-1240-5). Peter Smith.
Jameson, D. L. Genetics of Speciation. (Benchmark Papers in Genetics: Vol. 9). 1977. 56.00 (ISBN 0-12-786756-2). Acad Pr.
Mayr, Ernst. Systematics & the Origin of Species. Eldrige, Niles & Gould, Stephen J., eds. (Classics in Evolution Ser.). 384p. 1982. pap. 16.00x (ISBN 0-231-05499-8). Columbia U Pr.
Morse, Ph. A., ed. The Perception of Species-Specific Vocalizations. (Brain, Behavior & Evolution Journal: Vol. 16, No. 5-6). (Illus.). iv, 144p. 1980. pap. 13.25 (ISBN 3-8055-0733-X). S Karger.

ORISKANY FORMATION
see Geology, Stratigraphic–Devonian

ORNAMENTAL SHRUBS

Flint, Harrison. The Country Journal Book of Hardy Trees & Shrubs. (Illus.). 176p. (Orig.). 1983. pap. 10.00 (ISBN 0-918678-02-1). Historical Times.

ORNAMENTAL TREES

Adams, Bill. Trees for Southern Landscapes. LC 76-15457. (Illus.). 96p. (Orig.). 1976. pap. 6.95x (ISBN 0-88415-881-0, Pub. by Pacesetter Pr). Gulf Pub.
Flint, Harrison. The Country Journal Book of Hardy Trees & Shrubs. (Illus.). 176p. (Orig.). 1983. pap. 10.00 (ISBN 0-918678-02-1). Historical Times.
Grace, Julie, ed. Ornamental Conifers. (Illus.). 224p. 1983. 34.95 (ISBN 0-917304-83-7). Timber.
Herda, D. J. Growing Trees Indoors. LC 78-31764. 256p. 1979. 22.95x (ISBN 0-88229-346-X). Nelson-Hall.
Pirone, P. P. Tree Maintenance. 5th ed. (Illus.). 1978. 49.95 (ISBN 0-19-502321-8). Oxford U Pr.

ORNITHOLOGISTS

Cutright, Paul R. & Brodhead, Michael J. Elliott Coues: Naturalist & Frontier Historian. LC 80-12424. (Illus.). 510p. 1981. 28.50x (ISBN 0-252-00802-2). U of Ill Pr.
Hume, Edgar E. Ornithologists of the United States Army Medical Corps: Thirty-Six Biographies. Sterling, Keir B., ed. LC 77-81131. (Biologists & Their World Ser.). (Illus.). 1978. Repr. of 1942 ed. lib. bdg. 49.50x (ISBN 0-405-10729-3). Ayer Co Pubs.
Stephens, Lorain & Traylor, Melvin A., Jr. Ornithological Gazetteer of Peru. vi, 273p. 1983. 16.00 (ISBN 0-317-03914-8). Mus Comp Zoo.
Sutton, George M. Bird Student: An Autobiography. (Corrie Herring Hooks Ser.: No. 4). (Illus.). 232p. 1980. 15.95 (ISBN 0-292-70727-4). U of Tex Pr.
Wallace, George J. My World of Birds: Memoirs of an Ornithologist. 345p. 1979. 12.50 (ISBN 0-8059-2586-4). Dorrance.
Zusi, Richard. Roger Tory Peterson at the Smithsonian: On the 15th Anniversary of a Field Guide to the Birds. (Illus.). 72p. pap. 9.95x (ISBN 0-87474-997-2). Smithsonian.

ORNITHOLOGY

Ali, Salim. Fieldguide to the Birds of the Eastern Himalayas. (Illus.). 1978. 24.00x (ISBN 0-19-560595-0). Oxford U Pr.
Allen, Elsa G. The History of American Ornithology Before Audubon. (Illus.). 1979. Repr. of 1951 ed. 45.00 (ISBN 0-934626-00-6). W G Arader.
Belding, Lyman. Land Birds of the Pacific District. Repr. of 1890 ed. 37.00 (ISBN 0-384-03792-5). Johnson Repr.
Brusewitz, Gunnar. Wings & Seasons. Wheeler, Walston, tr. from Swedish. (Illus.). 119p. 1983. 20.00 (ISBN 0-88072-029-8, Pub. by Tanager). Longwood Pub Group.
Burger, Joanna. Pattern, Mechanism, & Adaptive Significance of Territoriality in Herring Gulls (Larus argentatus) 92p. 1984. 9.00 (ISBN 0-943610-41-9). Am Ornithologists.
Chapman, Frank M. Essays in South American Ornithogeography: Original Anthology. Sterling, Keir B., ed. LC 77-81087. (Biologists & Their World Ser.). (Illus.). 1978. lib. bdg. 59.50x (ISBN 0-405-10663-7). Ayer Co Pubs.
Check-list if Birds of the World, Vol. 2: Galliformes, Gruiformes, Charadriiformes. x, 401p. 1934. 15.00 (ISBN 0-686-35812-0). Mus Comp Zoo.
Check-list of Birds of the World, Vol 6: Piciformes. xiii, 259p. 1948. 15.00 (ISBN 0-686-35817-1). Mus Comp Zoo.
Check-list of Birds of the World, Vol. 13: Emberizinae, Catamblyrhynchinae, Cardinalinae, Thraupinae, Tersininae. xvi, 443p. 1970. 20.00 (ISBN 0-686-35824-4). Mus Comp Zoo.
Check-list of Birds of the World, Vol. 12: Pachycephalinae, Aegithalidae, Remizidae, Paridae, Sittidae, Certhiidae, Rhabdornithidae, Climacteridae, Dicaeidae, Nectariniidae, Zosteropidae, Meliphagidae. xii, 495p. 1967. 20.00 (ISBN 0-686-35823-6). Mus Comp Zoo.
Check-list of Birds of the World, Vol. 14: Parulidae, Drepanididae, Vireonidae, Icteridae, Fringillinae, Carduelinae, Estrildidae, Viduinae. xii, 443p. 1968. 20.00 (ISBN 0-686-35825-2). Mus Comp Zoo.
Check-list of Birds of the World, Vol. 1: Struthioniformes, Tinamiformes, Procellariiformes, Sphenisciformes, Gaviiformes, Podicipediformes, Pelecaniformes, Ciconiiformes, Phoenicopteriformes, Falconiformes, Anseriformes. xviii, 547p. 1979. 30.00 (ISBN 0-686-35810-4). Mus Comp Zoo.
Check-list of Birds of the World, Vol. 4: Cuculiformes, Strigiformes, Caprimulgiformes, Apodes. xiv, 291p. 1940. 15.00 (ISBN 0-686-35815-5). Mus Comp Zoo.
Check-list of Birds of the World, Vol. 5: Trochili, Coliiformes, Trogoniformes, Coraciiformes. xiv, 306p. 1945. 15.00 (ISBN 0-686-35816-3). Mus Comp Zoo.
Check-list of Birds of the World, Vol. 8: Tyrannidae, Pipridae, Cotingidae, Oxyruncidae, Phytotomidae, Pittidae, Philepittidae, Acanthisittidae, Menuridae, & Atrichornithidae. xv, 365p. 1979. 25.00 (ISBN 0-686-35819-8). Mus Comp Zoo.
Check-list of Birds of the World, Vol. 9: Alaudidae, Hirundinidae, Motacillidae, Campephagidae, Pycnonotidae, Irenidae, Laniidae, Vangidae, Bombycillidae, Dulidae, Cinclidae, Troglodytidae, Mimidae. xii, 506p. 1960. 15.00 (ISBN 0-686-35820-1). Mus Comp Zoo.
Checklist of Birds of the World, Vol. 15 Bubalornithinae, Passerinae, Ploceinae, Sturnidae, Oriolidae, Dicruridae, Callaeidae, Grallinidae, Artamidae, Cracticidae, Ptilonorhynchidae, Paradisaeidae, Corvidae. xii, 315p. 1962. 15.00 (ISBN 0-686-35826-0). Mus Comp Zoo.
Checklist of Birds of the World, Vol. 7: Eurylaimidae, Dendrocolaptidae, Furnariidae, Formicariidae, Conopophagidae, Rhinocryptidae. xii, 318p. 1951. 15.00 (ISBN 0-686-35818-X). Mus Comp Zoo.
Chestlist of Birds of the World, Vol. 3 Columbiformes, Psittaciformes. xi, 311p. 1937. 15.00 (ISBN 0-686-35814-7). Mus Comp Zoo.
Contributions to the History of American Ornithology. LC 73-17810. (Natural Sciences in America Ser.). 382p. 1974. Repr. 19.00x (ISBN 0-405-05727-X). Ayer Co Pubs.
Cramp, Stanley, ed. Handbook of the Birds of Europe, the Middle East, & North Africa: The Birds of the Western Palearctic, Vol. 3: Waders to Gulls. (Illus.). 1983. 98.00x (ISBN 0-19-857506-8). Oxford U Pr.
Cruickshank, Allan D. & Cruickshank, Helen. One Thousand & One Questions Answered About Birds. LC 75-41881. (The One Thousand & One Questions Ser.). (Illus.). 320p. 1976. pap. 4.95 (ISBN 0-486-23315-4). Dover.
Farner, Donald S. & King, James R. Avian Biology, 5 vols. Vol. 1, 1971. 89.50 (ISBN 0-12-249401-6); Vol. 2, 1972. 89.50 (ISBN 0-12-249402-4); Vol. 3, 1973. 79.50 (ISBN 0-12-249403-2); Vol. 4, 1974. 69.50 (ISBN 0-12-249404-0); Vol. 5, 1975. 94.50. Acad Pr.
Grzybowski, Joseph A. & Schnell, Gary D. Oklahoma Orinthology: An Annotated Bibliography. 192p. 19.95 (ISBN 0-317-12257-6). U of Okla Pr.

Hamerstrom, Frances. Birding with a Purpose: Of Raptors, Gaboons, & Other Creatures. (Illus.). 130p. 1984. 13.95 (ISBN 0-8138-0228-8). Iowa St U Pr.

Hickling, R. D., ed. Enjoying Ornithology. (Illus.). 300p. 1984. 30.00 (ISBN 0-85661-036-4). Buteo.

Johnston, Richard F., ed. Current Ornithology, Vol. 1. 405p. 1983. 39.50x (ISBN 0-306-41339-6, Plenum Pr). Plenum Pub.

--Current Ornithology, Vol. 2. 343p. 1984. 39.50x (ISBN 0-306-41780-4, Plenum Pr). Plenum Pub.

Kepler, Angela K. Comparative Study of Todies (Todidae), with Emphasis on the Puerto Rican Tody, Todus Mexicanus. (Illus.). 206p. 1977. 11.75 (ISBN 0-686-35805-8, 16). Nuttall Ornith.

King, A. S. & McLelland, J., eds. Form & Function in Birds, Vol. 1. LC 79-50523. 1980. 74.00 (ISBN 0-12-407501-0). Acad Pr.

--Forms & Function in Birds, Vol. 2. 1981. 80.00 (ISBN 0-12-407502-9). Acad Pr.

Lanyon, Wesley E. The Comparative Biology of the Meadowlarks (Sturnella) in Wisconsin. (Illus.). 66p. 1957. cloth bdg. 6.00 (ISBN 0-686-35784-1, 1); pap. 4.00 (ISBN 0-686-37167-4). Nuttall Ornith.

Mayr, Ernst & Short, Lester L. Species Taxa of North American Birds: A Contribution to Comparative Systematics. (Illus.). 127p. 1970. 7.00 (ISBN 0-686-35797-3, 9). Nuttall Ornith.

Nicholson, E. M. The Study of Birds: An Introduction to Ornithology. 1979. Repr. of 1929 ed. lib. bdg. 15.00 (ISBN 0-8492-1969-8). R West.

Nuttall Ornithological Club. Bulletin of the Nuttall Ornithological Club: A Quarterly Journal of Ornithology, 8 vols. in 3. LC 73-17834. (Natural Sciences in America Ser.). (Illus.). 1826p. 1974. Repr. Set. 122.00x (ISBN 0-405-05754-7); Vol. 1. 41.00x (ISBN 0-405-05755-5); Vol. 2. 41.00x (ISBN 0-405-05756-3); Vol. 3. 40.00x (ISBN 0-405-05757-1). Ayer Co Pubs.

Pasquier, Roger F. Watching Birds: An Introduction to Ornithology. 1980. pap. 9.95 (ISBN 0-395-29068-6). HM.

Paynter, Raymond A. Ornithological Gazetteer of Argentina. (Illus.). vi, 509p. 1985. 24.50 (ISBN 0-317-20167-0). Mus Comp Zoo.

Paynter, Raymond A., Jr. Avian Energetics. (Illus.). 334p. 1974. 17.00 (ISBN 0-686-35804-X). Nuttall Ornith.

--Ornithological Gazetteer of Venezuela. (Illus.). iii, 245p. 1982. 13.75 (ISBN 0-686-38914-X). Mus Comp Zoo.

Paynter, Raymond A., Jr. & Traylor, Melvin A., Jr. Ornithological Gazetteer of Colombia. (Illus.). v, 311p. 1981. 13.75 (ISBN 0-686-35831-7). Mus Comp Zoo.

Paynter, Raymond A., Jr., et al. Ornithological Gazetteer of Paraguay. (Illus.). iv, 43p. 1977. 2.25 (ISBN 0-686-35829-5). Mus Comp Zoo.

--Ornithological Gazetteer of Bolivia. (Illus.). vi, 80p. 1975. 2.50 (ISBN 0-686-35827-9). Mus Comp Zoo.

--Ornithological Gazetteer of Ecuador. viii, 152p. 1977. 5.75 (ISBN 0-686-35828-7). Mus Comp Zoo.

Petrak, Margaret L., ed. Diseases of Cage & Aviary Birds. 2nd ed. LC 81-3792. (Illus.). 680p. 1982. text ed. 89.50 (ISBN 0-8121-0692-X). Lea & Febiger.

Pettingill, Olin S., Jr. Ornithology at the University of Michigan Biological Station & the Birds of the Region. (Illus.). viii, 118p. 1974. pap. text ed. 5.00 (ISBN 0-939294-00-1, QL-684-M5-P4). Beech Leaf.

--Ornithology in Laboratory & Field. 5th ed. 1985. text ed. 24.00i (ISBN 0-12-552455-2). Acad Pr.

Rand, David M. & Paynter, Raymond A., Jr. Ornithological Gazetteer of Uruguay. iv, 75p. 1981. 5.00 (ISBN 0-686-35832-5). Mus Comp Zoo.

Richards, Lawrence P. & Bock, Walter J. Functional Anatomy & Adaptive Evolution of the Feeding Apparatus in the Hawaiian Honeycreeper Genus Loxops (Drepanididae. 173p. 1973. 9.00. Am Ornithologists.

Richmond, Chandler S. Beyond the Spring: Cordelia Stanwood of Birdsacre. (Illus.). xvi, 156p. (Orig.). 1978. 14.95 (ISBN 0-932448-00-3); pap. 7.95 (ISBN 0-932448-01-1). Latona Pr.

Ricklefs, Robert E., ed. Audubon Conservation Report No. 6: Report of the Advisory Panel on the California Condor. (Audubon Conservation Report Ser.). 1978. pap. 1.50 (ISBN 0-930698-04-5). Natl Audubon.

Sibley, Charles G. & American Ornithologists' Union, eds. Proceedings: International Ornithological Congress, 13th, 2 vols. 1250p. 1963. 10.00 (ISBN 0-943610-00-1). Am Ornithologists.

Skutch, Alexander F. Life Histories of Central American Highland Birds. (Publications: No.7). (Illus.). 213p. 1967. 8.00 (ISBN 0-686-35794-9). Nuttall Ornith.

--New Studies of Tropical American Birds. (Publications: No.19). (Illus.). 281p. 1981. 29.50 (ISBN 0-686-35809-0). Nuttall Ornith.

--Studies of Tropical American Birds. (Publications: No.10). (Illus.). 228p. 1972. 12.00 (ISBN 0-686-35798-1). Nuttall Ornith.

Stegmann, Boris C. Relationships of the Superorders Alectoromorphae & Charadriomorphae (Aves) A Comparative Study of the Avian Hand. (Publications: No.17). (Illus.). 119p. 1978. 10.00 (ISBN 0-686-35806-6). Nuttall Ornith.

Van Tyne, Josselyn & Berger, Andrew J. Fundamentals of Ornithology. 2nd. ed. LC 75-20430. 808p. 1976. 53.50x (ISBN 0-471-89965-8, Pub. by Wiley-Interscience). Wiley.

Wallace, George J. & Mahan, Harold D. An Introduction to Ornithology. 3rd ed. LC 74-480. (Illus.). 1975. text ed. write for info. (ISBN 0-02-423980-1). Macmillan.

Wood, D. Scott, et al. World Inventory Of Avian Skeletal Specimens, 1982. 224p. 1982. bound 25.00 (ISBN 0-943610-36-2). AM Ornithologists.

--World Inventory of Avian Spirit Specimens, 1982. 181p. 1982. bound 25.00 (ISBN 0-943610-37-0). AM Ornithologists.

Wood, Scott & Jenkinson, Marion A. World Inventory of Avian Anatomical Specimens, 1982: Geographic Analysis. 290p. 1984. bound 25.00 (ISBN 0-943610-42-7). Am Ornithologists.

ORNITHOLOGY, ECONOMIC

see Birds, Injurious and Beneficial

OROGRAPHY

see Mountains

ORRERIES

see Planetaria

ORTEGA Y GASSET, JOSE, 1883-1955

McClintock, Robert. Man & His Circumstances: Ortega As Educator. LC 76-149404. 1971. text ed. 22.95x (ISBN 0-8077-1726-6). Tchrs Coll.

Marias, Julian. Jose Ortega y Gasset: Circumstances & Vocation. Lopez-Morillas, Frances M., tr. LC 71-88141. pap. 122.50 (ISBN 0-8357-9729-5, 2016239). Bks Demand UMI.

Ouimette, Victor. Jose Ortega y Gasset. (World Authors Ser.). 1982. lib. bdg. 16.95 (ISBN 0-8057-6466-6, Twayne). G K Hall.

Raley, Harold. Jose Ortega Y Gasset: Philosopher of European Unity. LC 78-148689. 272p. 1971. 17.50 (ISBN 0-8173-6612-1). U of Ala Pr.

Silver, Philip. Ortega As Phenomenologist. LC 78-667. 1978. 24.00x (ISBN 0-231-04544-1). Columbia U Pr.

Weigert, Andrew J. Life & Society: A Meditation on the Social Thought of Jose Ortega y Gassett. 250p. 1983. text ed. 19.95x (ISBN 0-8290-1278-8). Irvington.

ORTHOGONAL FUNCTIONS

see Functions, Orthogonal

ORTHOGONAL POLYNOMIALS

see also Chebyshev Polynomials

Askey, Richard. Orthogonal Polynomials & Special Functions. (CBMS-NSF Regional Conference Ser.: No. 21). vii, 110p. (Orig.). 1975. pap. text ed. 16.00 (ISBN 0-89871-018-9). Soc Indus-Appl Math.

Beckmann, Petr. Orthogonal Polynomials for Engineers & Physicists. LC 72-87318. 1973. 25.00x (ISBN 0-911762-14-0). Golem.

Boas, R. P., Jr. & Buck, R. C. Polynomial Expansions of Analytic Functions. 2nd ed. (Ergebnisse der Mathematik und Ihrer Grenzgebiete: Vol. 19). (Illus.). 1964. 23.10 (ISBN 0-387-03123-5). Springer-Verlag.

Chihara, T. S. An Introduction to Orthogonal Polynomials. (Mathematics & Its Applications Ser.). 262p. 1978. 65.95 (ISBN 0-677-04150-0). Gordon.

Freud, Geza. Orthogonal Polynomials. LC 76-134028. 1971. 50.00 (ISBN 0-08-016047-6). Pergamon.

Geronimus, L. Ya. Orthogonal Polynomials: Estimates, Asymptotic Formulas, & Series of Polynomials Orthogonal on the Unit Circle & on an Interval. LC 60-53450. 242p. 1961. 32.50x (ISBN 0-306-10565-9, Consultants). Plenum Pub.

ORTHOGONAL SERIES

see Series, Orthogonal

ORTHOGRAPHIC PROJECTION

Quinlan, Charles, Jr. Orthographic Projection Simplified. rev. ed. 1982. pap. text ed. 6.36 (ISBN 0-87345-057-4). McKnight.

ORTHOPTERA

see also Cockroaches; Crickets; Locusts

Cipriano, Joseph. Photographic Manual of Regional Orthopaedic Tests. 200p. 1985. lib. bdg. 24.95 (ISBN 0-683-01700-4). Williams & Wilkins.

Harz, H. & Kaltenbach, A. The Orthopters of Europe, Vol. 3. (Entomologica Ser: Vol. 12). 1976. lib. bdg. 84.00 (ISBN 90-6193-122-3, Pub. by Junk Pubs Netherlands). Kluwer Academic.

Herrera, L. Catalogue of the Orthoptera of Spain. 1982. 37.00 (ISBN 90-6193-131-2, Pub. by Junk Pubs Netherlands). Kluwer Academic.

Kirby, W. F. Orthoptera - Acriidae. (Fauna of British India Ser.). x, 278p. 1973. Repr. of 1914 ed. 12.00 (ISBN 0-88065-147-4, Pub. by Messers Today & Tomorrows Printers & Publishers India). Scholarly Pubns.

Rehn, James A. & Grant, Harold J., Jr. A Monograph of the Orthoptera of North America (North of Mexico, Vol. 1. (Monograph: No. 12). (Illus.). 257p. (Orig.). 1961. pap. 18.00 (ISBN 0-910006-18-0). Acad Nat Sci Phila.

OSBORNE (COMPUTER)

Anbarlian, H. An Introduction to SuperCalc Spreadsheeting on the Osborne. incl. diskette 49.95 (ISBN 0-07-001701-8, BYTE Bks). McGraw.

How to Use SuperCalc: For the Osborne. 1983. 34.95 (ISBN 0-88056-179-3). Dilithium Pr.

Lord, Kenniston W., Jr. Using the Osborne Personal Computer. (Illus.). 336p. 1983. 19.95 (ISBN 0-442-26010-5); pap. 12.95 (ISBN 0-442-26054-7). Van Nos Reinhold.

Osborne, Adam & Dvorak, John. Hypergrowth: the Rise & Fall of Osborne Computer Corporation. Business Management Research, ed. (Illus.). 1984. 19.95 (ISBN 0-918347-00-9). Idthekkethan.

Philips, Sheldon W. & King, Brian L. OSGLAS: General Ledger Accounting System for Osborne Computers. (Key-By-Key Ser.). (Illus.). 240p. (Orig.). 1983. pap. write for info. (ISBN 0-534-02872-1); write for info. templates on disk. Wadsworth Pub.

--OSGLAS: Payroll for Osborne Computers. (Key-By-Key Ser.). (Illus.). 150p. 1983. pap. write for info. (ISBN 0-534-02874-8); write for info. Wadsworth Pub.

Realval: Osborne Version. 80p. 250.00 (ISBN 0-07-021123-X). McGraw.

Regis, Margaret. OSDEX: A Comprehensive Index to the Osborne 1 User's Manual. 64p. (Orig.). 1983. pap. 5.95 (ISBN 0-914083-00-7). Periscope Pr.

Understanding the Osborne I. (Calabrese Understanding Ser.: Vol. 3). (Illus.). 298p. 1984. pap. 14.95 (ISBN 0-911699-21-X). Calabrese Pubns.

Willis, Jerry, et al. Things to Do with Your Osborne Computers. 1983. pap. 3.95 (ISBN 0-451-12852-4, Sig). NAL.

Zimmerman, Steven & Conrad, Leo. Osborne Business Applications. cancelled 17.95 (ISBN 0-89303-746-X). Brady Comm.

OSCILLATIONS

see also Damping (Mechanics); Electric Noise; Frequencies of Oscillating Systems; Transients (Dynamics)

Basov, N. G., ed. The Kinetics of Simple Models in the Theory of Oscillations. LC 78-5936. (P.N. Lebedev Physics Institute Ser.: Vol. 90). (Illus.). 216p. 1978. 59.50 (ISBN 0-306-10948-4, Consultants). Plenum Pub.

Braginsky, V. B., et al. Systems with Small Dissipation. Gliner, Erast, tr. (Illus.). 152p. 1985. lib. bdg. 28.00x (ISBN 0-226-07072-7); pap. 12.00x (ISBN 0-226-07073-5). U of Chicago Pr.

Buckley, R. Oscillations & Waves. (Student Monographs in Physics). 64p. 1985. pap. write for info. (Pub. by Adam Hilger Techo Hse UK). Heyden.

Chandra, J. & Scott, A. C., eds. Coupled Nonlinear Oscillators: Proceedings of the Joint U. S. Army-Center for Nonlinear Studies Workshop, Los Alamos, New Mexico, 21-23 July, 1981. (North-Holland Mathematics Studies: No. 80). 124p. 1983. 36.25 (ISBN 0-444-86677-9, North Holland). Elsevier.

Cox, J. P. Theory of Stellar Pulsation. LC 79-3198. (Ser. in Astrophysics: No. 2). (Illus.). 1980. 57.50x (ISBN 0-691-08252-9); pap. 16.50x (ISBN 0-691-08253-7). Princeton U Pr.

Donocik, Rudolf. Theory of Phase-Controlled Oscillations. (Illus.). 296p. 1971. 40.00x (ISBN 0-7165-1314-5, Pub. by Irish Academic Pr Ireland). Biblio Dist.

Gardner, Floyd M. Phaselock Techniques. 2nd ed. LC 78-20777. 285p. 1979. 32.50x (ISBN 0-471-04294-3, Pub by Wiley-Interscience). Wiley.

Gulshaw, B., et al. Avalanche Diode Oscillators. LC 79-308906. 160p. 1978. pap. text ed. 27.00x (ISBN 0-85066-102-1). Taylor & Francis.

Halanay, A. Differential Equations: Stability, Oscillations, Time Lags. (Mathematics in Science & Engineering Ser.: Vol. 23). 1966. 83.00 (ISBN 0-12-317950-5). Acad Pr.

Krasnoselsky, Mark A. Operator of Translation Along the Trajectories of Differential Equations. LC 67-22349. (Translations of Mathematical Monographs: Vol. 19). 1968. Repr. of 1950 ed. 37.00 (ISBN 0-8218-1569-5, MMONO-19). Am Math.

Kreith, K. Oscillation Theory. LC 73-79366. (Lecture Notes in Mathematics: Vol. 324). 109p. 1973. pap. 12.00 (ISBN 0-387-06258-0). Springer-Verlag.

Kuramoto, Y. Chemical Oscillations, Waves, & Turbulence. (Springer Series in Synergetics: Vol. 19). (Illus.). 170p. 1984. 32.00 (ISBN 0-387-13322-4). Springer-Verlag.

Lefschetz, S. Contributions to the Theory of Nonlinear Oscillations, Vols. 1-3 & 5, 1950-1960. (Annals of Mathematics Studies). Vol. 1. 24.00 (ISBN 0-527-02736-7); Vol. 2. 11.00 (ISBN 0-527-02745-6); Vol. 3. 23.00 (ISBN 0-527-02753-7); Vol. 5. 21.00 (ISBN 0-527-02761-8). Kraus Repr.

Lefschetz, Solomon, ed. Contributions to the Theory of Nonlinear Oscillations, Vol. 4. (Annals of Mathematics Studies: No. 41). (Orig.). 1958. pap. 22.00 (ISBN 0-691-07932-3). Princeton U Pr.

Livsic, M. S. Operators, Oscillations, Waves. LC 72-11580. (Translations of Mathematical Monographs: Vol. 34). 280p. (Orig.). 1973. 47.00 (ISBN 0-8218-1584-9, MMONO-34). Am Math.

Mickens, Ronald E. An Introduction to Nonlinear Oscillations. LC 80-13169. (Illus.). 320p. 1981. text ed. 84.50 (ISBN 0-521-22208-7). Cambridge U Pr.

Migulin, V., ed. Basic Theory of Oscillations. Yankovsky, George, tr. 400p. 1983. 11.95 (ISBN 0-8285-2743-1, Pub. by Mir Pubs USSR). Imported Pubns.

Minorsky, Nicholas N. Non Linear Oscillation. LC 74-8918. 734p. 1974. Repr. of 1962 ed. 42.50 (ISBN 0-88275-186-7). Krieger.

Nayfeh, Ali H. & Mook, Dean T. Nonlinear Oscillations. LC 78-27102. (Pure & Applied Mathematics Ser.). 704p. 1979. 64.50x (ISBN 0-471-03555-6, Pub. by Wiley-Interscience). Wiley.

Panovko, Ya. G. & Gubanova, I. I. Stability & Oscillations of Elastic Systems: Paradoxes, Fallacies, & New Concepts. LC 65-11341. 291p. 1965. 40.00x (ISBN 0-306-10735-X, Consultants). Plenum Pub.

Paquet, J. C. & Le Maitre, J. F. Methodes Pratiques d'Etude des Oscillations Non Lineaires: Theorie Des Systemes. 172p. 1970. 56.75x (ISBN 0-677-50200-1). Gordon.

Rocard, Yves. Dynamic Instability: Automobiles, Aircraft, Suspension Bridges. Meyer, M. L., tr. (Illus.). 1958. 12.00 (ISBN 0-8044-4833-7). Ungar.

Starzhinskii, V. M. Applied Methods in the Theory of Nonlinear Oscillations. 1980. 8.95 (ISBN 0-8285-1802-5, Pub. by Mir Pubs USSR). Imported Pubns.

OSCILLATORICEAE

Drouet, Francis. Revision of the Classification of the Oscillatoriaceae. (Monograph: No. 15). (Illus.). 370p. 1968. lib. bdg. 18.00 (ISBN 0-910006-23-7). Acad Nat Sci Phila.

Gomont, M. Monographie Des Oscillariees: 1892-93, 2 parts in 1 vol. (Illus.). 1962. 28.00 (ISBN 3-7682-0038-8). Lubrecht & Cramer.

OSCILLATORS, CRYSTAL

Bottom, Virgil E. Introduction to Quartz Crystal Unit Design. (VNR Electrical Computer Serverice & Engineering Ser.). 272p. 1982. 28.50 (ISBN 0-442-26201-9). Van Nos Reinhold.

Frerking, Marvin E. Crystal Oscillator Design & Temperature Compensation. 1978. 24.95 (ISBN 0-442-22459-1). Van Nos Reinhold.

Matthys, Robert J. Crystal Oscillator Circuits. LC 82-17564. 233p. 1983. 35.95x (ISBN 0-471-87401-9, Pub. by Wiley-Interscience). Wiley.

Parzen, Benjamin. Design of Crystal & Other Harmonic Oscillators. LC 82-13620. 454p. 1983. 53.50x (ISBN 0-471-08819-6, Pub. by Wiley-Interscience). Wiley.

OSCILLATORS, ELECTRIC

see also Oscillators, Crystal; Oscillators, Microwave; Phase-Locked Loops; Pulse Generators; Transients (Electricity)

Blanchard, Alain A. Phase-Locked Loops: Application to Coherent Receiver Design. LC 75-30941. 1976. 49.95x (ISBN 0-471-07941-3, Pub. by Wiley-Interscience). Wiley.

Vendelin, George D. Design of Amplifiers & Oscillators by the S-Parameter Method. LC 81-13005. 190p. 1982. 31.95x (ISBN 0-471-09226-6, Pub. by Wiley-Interscience). Wiley.

OSCILLATORS, MICROWAVE

Howes, M. J. & Morgan, D. V., eds. Variable Impedance Devices. LC 78-4122. (Solid State Devices & Circuits Ser.). 291p. 1978. 69.95 (ISBN 0-471-99651-3, Pub. by Wiley-Interscience). Wiley.

OSCILLOGRAPH

Basic Oscillography. 1976. pap. 2.50 (ISBN 0-87985-123-6, P130). Eastman Kodak.

OSCILLOSCOPE

see Cathode Ray Oscilloscope

OSMOREGULATION

Fitzsimons, J. T. The Physiology of Thirst & Sodium Appetite. LC 78-16212. (Physiological Society Monographs: No. 35). 1979. 95.00 (ISBN 0-521-22292-3). Cambridge U Pr.

Gerick, David J. Water, Water Everywhere. (Illus.). 1978. 20.00 (ISBN 0-916750-75-2). Dayton Labs.
Gilles, R. Mechanisms of Osmoregulation in Animals: Maintenance of Cell Volume. LC 78-4608. 667p. 1979. 144.95x (ISBN 0-471-99648-3, Pub. by Wiley-Interscience). Wiley.
Maloiy, G. W., ed. Comparative Physiology of Osmoregulation in Animals, Vol. 2. LC 77-93492. 1980. 49.50 (ISBN 0-12-467002-4). Acad Pr.
Pequeux, A., et al, eds. Osmoregulation in Estuarine & Marine Animals: Proceedings of the Invited Lectures to a Symposium Organized Within the 5th Conference of the European Society for Comparative Physiology & Biochemistry - Taormina, Sicily, Italy, Sept 5-8, 1983. (Lecture Notes on Coastal & Estuarine Studies: Vol. 9). x, 221p. 1984. pap. 17.00 (ISBN 0-387-13353-4). Springer-Verlag.
Pickford, Grace E., et al. Studies on the Blood Serum of the Euryhaline Cyprinodont Fish, Fundulus Heteroclitus, Adapted to Fresh or to Salt Water. (Transactions of the Connecticut Academy of Arts & Sciences Ser.: Vol. 43). 1969. pap. 10.50 (ISBN 0-208-00907-8). Shoe String.
Rains, Donald W., et al, eds. Genetic Engineering of Osmoregulation: Impact of Plant Productivity for Food, Chemicals, & Energy. LC 80-14972. (Basic Life Sciences Ser.: Vol. 14). 395p. 1980. 49.50x (ISBN 0-306-40454-0, Plenum Pr). Plenum Pub.
Rankin, J. C. & Danenport, J. Animal Osmoregulation: Testing of Polymers. LC 81-17491. (Tertiary Level Biology Ser.). 202p. 1981. 42.95x (ISBN 0-470-27207-4). Halsted Pr.
Skadauge, E. Osmoregulation in Birds. (Zoophysiology Ser.: Vol. 12). (Illus.). 250p. 1981. 56.00 (ISBN 0-387-10546-8). Springer-Verlag.

OSMOSIS
see also Absorption (Physiology); Biological Transport; Electro-Osmosis; Permeability; Porosity; Solution (Chemistry)
Hoornaert, P. Reverse Osmosis. (EPO Applied Technology Ser.: Vol. 4). 220p. 1984. 55.00 (ISBN 0-08-031144-X). Pergamon.
Lonsdale, H. K. & Podall, H. E., eds. Reverse Osmosis Membrane Research. LC 72-87518. 503p. 1972. 75.00x (ISBN 0-306-30710-3, Plenum Pr). Plenum Pub.
Pfeffer, Wilhelm. Osmotic Investigations. (Illus.). 304p. 1985. 32.50 (ISBN 0-442-27583-8). Van Nos Reinhold.
Sourirajan, S. Reverse Osmosis. 1970. 81.00 (ISBN 0-12-655650-4). Acad Pr.

OSTEOLOGY
see Bones; Skeleton

OSTRACODA
Bate, R. H., et al. Fossil & Recent Ostracods. (British Micropalaeontological Society Ser.). 350p. 1982. 112.95x (ISBN 0-470-27314-3). Halsted Pr.
Biology & Paleobiology of Ostracoda: Symposium, 1972, No. 282. (Bulletin of American Paleontology). (Illus.). 1975. pap. 25.00 (ISBN 0-87710-294-5). Paleo Res.
Furtos, Norma C. The Ostracoda of Ohio. 1933. 2.00 (ISBN 0-86727-028-4). Ohio Bio Survey.
Hanai, Tetsuro, et al, eds. Checklist of Ostracoda from Japan & Its Adjacent Seas. 119p. 1977. 22.50x (ISBN 0-86008-180-X, Pub. by U of Tokyo Japan). Columbia U Pr.
--Checklist of Ostracoda from Southeast Asia. 236p. 1981. 32.50 (ISBN 0-86008-267-9, Pub. by U of Tokyo Japan). Columbia U Pr.
Howe, Henry V. & Laurencich, Laura. Introduction to the Study of Cretaceous Ostracoda. LC 58-9761. pap. 135.00 (ISBN 0-317-29862-3, 2019564). Bks Demand UMI.
Loffler, H. & Danielopol, D., eds. Ecology & Zoogeography of Ostracoda. (Illus.). 1977. lib. bdg. 79.00 (ISBN 90-6193-581-4, Pub. by Junk Pubs. Netherlands). Kluwer Academic.
Neale, J. W. The Taxonomy, Morphology & Ecology of Recent Ostracoda. 1969. 30.80 (ISBN 0-934454-77-9). Lubrecht & Cramer.
Stout, Larry N. Review & Index Through 1975 of Genus Candona (Ostracoda) in North America (Exclusive of Pre-Quaternary Species) LC 76-47833. (Microform Publication: No. 6). (Illus.). 1976. 3.00 (ISBN 0-8137-6006-2). Geol Soc.

OSTREA
see Oysters

OSTWALD, WILHELM, 1853-1932
Slosson, Edwin E. Major Prophets of To-Day. facs. ed. LC 68-8493. (Essay Index Reprint Ser.). 1914. 20.00 (ISBN 0-8369-0882-1). Ayer Co Pubs.

OTARIA
see Seals (Animals)

OTTERS
Laidler, Liz. Otters in Britain. (Illus.). 192p. 1982. 19.95 (ISBN 0-7153-8069-9). David & Charles.
Wayre, Philip. The River People: Adventuring with Otters. LC 75-33551. (Illus.). 215p. 1976. 9.95 (ISBN 0-8008-6797-1). Taplinger.

OTTERS, SEA
see Sea-Otters

OUGHTRED, WILLIAM, 1575-1660
Cajori, Florian. William Oughtred: A Great Seventeenth-Century Teacher of Mathematics. vi, 106p. 1916. 12.00x (ISBN 0-87548-174-4). Open Court.

OUTBOARD MOTORS
Chilton Staff. Chilton's Repair & Tune-up Guide: Outboard Motors 0-65 HP 1975-85. LC 85-47974. 512p. (Orig.). 1986. pap. 16.95 (ISBN 0-8019-7630-8). Chilton.
--Chilton's Repair & Tune-up Guide: Outboard Motors 70 HP & Above 1975-1985. LC 85-47975. 512p. (Orig.). 1986. pap. 16.95 (ISBN 0-8019-7631-6). Chilton.
Chrysler-Force: 3.5-140 HP Outboards, 1966-1984. (Illus.). 300p. 1985. pap. 22.95 (ISBN 0-317-17451-7). Western Marine Ent.
Corcoran, Lawrence. Outboard Service Guide. Corcoran, Lynn, ed. 1977. pap. text ed. 3.25 (ISBN 0-686-24789-2). L Corcoran.
Stagner, Eugene W. Understanding the Outboard Motor. 1984. text ed. 34.95 (ISBN 0-8359-8059-6). Reston.
Suzuki: 2-140 Hp Outboards, 1977-1984. (Illus.). 300p. 1985. pap. 22.95 (ISBN 0-89287-406-6). Western Marine Ent.

OUTER SPACE
see also Space Environment
Bhatt, S. Legal Controls of Outer Space. 372p. 45.00x (ISBN 0-686-78834-6, Pub. by Bks India England). State Mutual Bk.
Brown, Seyom, et al. Regimes for the Ocean, Outer Space, & Weather. 1977. 22.95 (ISBN 0-8157-1156-5); pap. 8.95 (ISBN 0-8157-1155-7). Brookings.
Calder, Nigel. Spaceships of the Mind. (Illus.). 1978. 14.95 (ISBN 0-670-66021-3). Viking.
Clarke, Arthur C. Challenge of the Spaceship. 1980. pap. 2.50 (ISBN 0-671-82139-3). PB.
--The Promise of Space. 336p. 1985. pap. 3.50 (ISBN 0-425-07565-6) (ISBN 0-317-13693-3). Berkley Pub.
Collins, M. Fred. Space Shots. LC 78-68713. (Illus.). 1979. pap. 7.95 (ISBN 0-8129-0823-6). Times Bks.
Colloquium on the Law of Outer Space - International Institute of Space Law of the International Astronautical Federation, 12th, 1969. Proceedings. Schwartz, Mortimer D., ed. iii, 336p. (Orig.). 1970. pap. text ed. 27.50x (ISBN 0-8377-0407-3). Rothman.
Colloquium on the Law of Outer Space-International Institute of Space Law of the International Astronautical Federation, 13th, 1970. Proceedings. Schwartz, Mortimer D., ed. iii, 381p. 1971. pap. text ed. 27.50x (ISBN 0-8377-0408-1). Rothman.
Colloquium on the Law of Outer Space - International Institute of Space Law of the International Astronautical Federation, 19th, 1976. Proceedings. Schwartz, Mortimer D., ed. 419p. 1977. pap. text ed. 27.50x (ISBN 0-8377-0414-6). Rothman.
Davies, Owen, ed. The Omni Book of Space. 1983. pap. 3.95 (ISBN 0-8217-1275-6). Zebra.
Duedney, Daniel. Space: The High Frontier in Perspective. LC 82-50920. (Worldwatch Papers). 1982. pap. 2.00 (ISBN 0-916468-49-6). Worldwatch Inst.
ESLAB Symposium, 6th, Noordwijk, the Netherlands, Sept. 1972. Photon & Particle Interactions with Surfaces in Space: Proceedings. Grard, R. J., ed. LC 73-83561. (Astrophysics & Space Science Library: No. 37). 600p. 1973. lib. bdg. 84.00 (ISBN 90-277-0381-7, Pub. by Reidel Holland). Kluwer Academic.
Feldman, Anthony. Space. 336p. 1980. 24.95 (ISBN 0-87196-416-3). Facts on File.
Katz, James E., ed. People in Space: Policy Perspectives for a "Star Wars" Century. (Illus.). 1985. 29.95 (ISBN 0-88738-052-2); pap. 14.95 (ISBN 0-88738-609-1). Transaction Bks.
Mirabito, Michael M. The Exploration of Outer Space with Cameras: A History of the NASA Unmanned Spacecraft Missions. LC 83-776. (Illus.). 208p. 1983. lib. bdg. 19.95x (ISBN 0-89950-061-7). McFarland & Co.
Morfill, G. E., ed. Dust in Space & Comets: Proceedings of the Topical Meeting of the COSPAR Interdisciplinary Scientific Commission B (Meetings B1 & B2) of the COSPAR 25th Plenary Meeting, Graz, Austria, 25 June-7 July 1984. (Illus.). 324p. 1985. pap. 49.50 (ISBN 0-08-032745-1, Pub by PPL). Pergamon.
Oser, H., et al, eds. Life Sciences & Space Research XXI (2) Proceedings of Workshops VII & XI & of the COSPAR Interdisciplinary Scientific Commission F (Meetings F1, F3, F5, F6, F7, & F9) of the COSPAR 25th Plenary Meeting Held in Graz, Austria, 25 June - 7 July 1984. (Illus.). 334p. 1985. pap. 49.50 (ISBN 0-08-032752-4, Pub by PPL). Pergamon.
Osman, Tony. Space History. (Illus.). 235p. 1983. 16.95 (ISBN 0-312-74945-7). St Martin.
Outer Space: A Selective Bibliography. pap. 11.00 (UN82/1/12, UN). Unipub.
Outer Space: Battlefield of the Future? 180p. 1978. 18.00x (ISBN 0-85066-130-7). Taylor & Francis.
Ridpath, Ian. Space. LC 83-50389. (Silver Burdett Color Library). 48p. 1983. 14.00 (ISBN 0-382-06726-6). Silver.
Robinson, George S. Living in Outer Space: Biological Foundations of Space Law. 1976. pap. 9.00 (ISBN 0-8183-0243-7). Pub Aff Pr.
Taubenfeld, Howard J., ed. Space & Society. LC 64-21185. 196p. 1964. 12.50 (ISBN 0-379-00210-8). Oceana.
United Nations. The World in Space: A Survey of Space Activities & Issues. Prepared for Unispace. (Illus.). 704p. 1982. text ed. 54.95 (ISBN 0-13-967745-3). P-H.
The United Nations & Outer Space. pap. 3.00 (ISBN 0-686-94844-0, UN77/1/9, UN). Unipub.

OUTER SPACE–EXPLORATION
see also Astronautics–International Cooperation; Lunar Probes
AAS - AAAS Symposium - Montreal - 1964. Towards Deeper Space Penetration. Van Driest, Edard R., ed. (Science & Technology Ser.: Vol. 2). 1964. 20.00x (ISBN 0-87703-030-8, Pub. by Am Astronaut). Univelt Inc.
Adelman, Benjamin & Adelman, Saul J. Bound for the Stars: An Enthusiastic Look at the Opportunities & Challenges Space Exploration Offers. (Illus.). 368p. 1981. text ed. 17.95 (ISBN 0-13-080390-1, Spec); pap. text ed. 8.95 (ISBN 0-13-080382-0). P-H.
Allan, Joseph P. & Martin, Russell. Entering Space: An Astronaut's Odyssey. rev., enl. ed. (Illus.). 240p. (Orig.). 1985. 24.95 (ISBN 0-941434-76-1); pap. 16.95 (ISBN 0-941434-74-5). Stewart Tabori & Chang.
American Astronautical Society. Advances in the Astronautical Sciences. Incl. Vol. 6. Sixth Annual Meeting, New York, 1960. Jacobs, H. & Burgess, E., eds. 45.00x (ISBN 0-87703-007-3); Vol. 9. Fourth Western Regional Meeting, San Francisco, 1961. Jacobs, H. & Burgess, E., eds. 45.00x (ISBN 0-87703-010-3); Vol. 11. Eighth Annual Meeting, Washington, 1962. 45.00x (ISBN 0-87703-012-X); Vol. 13. Ninth Annual Meeting, Interplanetary Missions, Los Angeles, 1963. Burgess, E., ed. 45.00x (ISBN 0-87703-014-6). Am Astronaut). Univelt Inc.
Blaine, J. C. End of an Era in Space Exploration. Jacobs, H., ed. (Science & Technology: Vol. 42). (Illus.). 1976. 25.00x (ISBN 0-87703-080-4, Pub. by Am Astronaut). Univelt Inc.
Calder, Nigel. Spaceships of the Mind. 1979. pap. 6.95 (ISBN 0-14-005231-3). Penguin.
Charbonneau, Gary. Index to Aerospace Historian: Cumulative Index by Author, Title, & Subject 1954-1973. 106p. 1974. pap. text ed. 12.00x (ISBN 0-89126-011-0). MA-AH Pub.
Clarke, Arthur C. Report on Planet Three & Other Speculations. LC 74-156515. 1972. 9.95i (ISBN 0-06-010793-6, HarpT). Har-Row.
Deutsch, Armin J. & Klemperer, Wolfgang B., eds. Space Age Astronomy: An International Symposium. 1962. 92.50 (ISBN 0-12-213550-4). Acad Pr.
Elliot, Jeffrey M. The Future of the Space Program - Large Corporations & Society: Discussions with 22 Science-Fiction Writers. LC 80-19754. (Great Issues of the Day Ser.: Vol. 1). 64p. (Orig.). 1981. lib. bdg. 12.95x (ISBN 0-89370-140-8); pap. text ed. 4.95x (ISBN 0-89370-240-4). Borgo Pr.
Flinn, E., ed. Scientific Results of Viking Project. (Illus.). 725p. 1977. 15.00 (ISBN 0-87590-207-3). Am Geophysical.
Gatland, Kenneth. The Illustrated Encyclopedia of Space Technology: A Comprehensive History of Space Exploration. 288p. 1981. 24.95 (ISBN 0-517-54258-7, Harmony). Crown.
Goodman, John C., ed. Space, Our Next Frontier. 1985. spiral bd. 6.95 (ISBN 0-943802-14-8). Natl Ctr Pol.
Handbook of Soviet Lunar & Planetary Exploration, Vol. 47. (Science & Technology Ser.). 1979. lib. bdg. 35.00x (ISBN 0-87703-105-3, Pub. by Am Astronaut); pap. 25.00x (ISBN 0-87703-106-1). Univelt Inc.
Handbook of Soviet Manned Space Flight, Vol 48. (Science & Technology Ser.). 1980. lib. bdg. 45.00x (ISBN 0-87703-115-0, Pub. by Am Astronaut); pap. 35.00x (ISBN 0-87703-116-9). Univelt Inc.
Hartmann, William K. & Miller, Ron. Out of the Cradle: Exploring the Frontiers Beyond Earth. (Illus.). 192p. (Orig.). 1984. (ISBN 0-89480-813-3, 813); pap. 11.95 (ISBN 0-89480-770-6, 770). Workman Pub.
Harvey, J. W., et al, eds. Solar-Space Observations & Stellar Prospects: Proceedings of the Topical Meeting of the COSPAR Interdisciplinary Scientific Commission E (Meetings E1, E2 & E6) of the COSPAR 25th Plenary Meeting, Graz, Austria, 25 June-7 July 1984. (Illus.). 184p. 1985. pap. 49.50 (ISBN 0-08-032743-5, Pub. by PPL). Pergamon.
Heath, Gloria W., ed. Space Safety & Rescue Nineteen Eighty-Two to Nineteen Eighty-Three. (Science & Technology Ser.: Vol. 58). (Illus.). 378p. (Orig.). 1984. lib. bdg. 50.00x (ISBN 0-87703-202-5, Pub. by Am Astro Soc); pap. text ed. 40.00x (ISBN 0-87703-203-3). Univelt Inc.
Ingram, C. D. Time Warp & a Time to Speak. 1985. 7.95 (ISBN 0-533-06503-8). Vantage.
Jasani, B., ed. Outer Space: A New Dimension of the Arms Race. 424p. 1982. 41.00x (ISBN 0-85066-231-1). Taylor & Francis.
Jasentuliyana, N. & Chipman, R., eds. International Space Programmes & Policies: Proceedings of the 2nd United Nations Conference on the Exploration & Peaceful Uses of Outer Space (UNISPACE), Vienna, Austria, August 1982. 1984. 65.00 (ISBN 0-444-87572-7, North-Holland). Elsevier.
Johnston, Richard S., et al, eds. Future U. S. Space Programs, 2 pts. (Advances in the Astronautical Sciences: Vol. 38). (Illus.). 1979. lib. bdg. 85.00x (ISBN 0-87703-119-3, Pub. by Am Astronaut); Pt. I. 45.00x (ISBN 0-87703-098-7); Pt. II. 40.00x (ISBN 0-87703-099-5); microfiche suppl. 10.00x (ISBN 0-87703-129-0). Univelt Inc.
Ling, Edwin R., Sr. The National Space Technology Laboratories. 32p. 1984. 2.95 (ISBN 0-87397-265-1). Strode.
--Space Crescent. 1984. 24.95 (ISBN 0-87397-264-3). Strode.
Lowman, P. D., Jr. Space Panorama. (Illus.). 1968. 35.00 (ISBN 0-685-12042-2). Heinman.
Macvey, John W. Colonizing Other Worlds: A Field Manual. LC 83-40006. (Illus.). 256p. 1984. 17.95 (ISBN 0-8128-2943-3). Stein & Day.
--Where Will We Go When the Sun Dies? LC 80-5386. (Illus.). 264p. 1983. 16.95 (ISBN 0-8128-2698-1). Stein & Day.
Massey, Harrie & Pardoe, G. K., eds. Industrialization of Space in the 1990's. (Illus.). 140p. 1984. lib. bdg. 46.00 (ISBN 0-85403-233-9, Pub. by Royal Soc London). Scholium Intl.
Massey, Harry & Runcorn, S. K., eds. Planetary Exploration: Proceedings. (Royal Society of London Ser.). (Illus.). 167p. 1982. text ed. 55.00x (ISBN 0-85403-185-5, Pub. by Royal Soc London). Scholium Intl.
Morgenthaler, G. W. & Morra, R. G., eds. Unmanned Exploration of the Solar System. (Advances in the Astronautical Sciences Ser.: Vol. 19). 1965. 45.00x (ISBN 0-87703-021-9, Pub. by Am Astronaut). Univelt Inc.
Morrison, David & Samz, Jane. Voyage to Jupiter. (NASA SP 439 Ser.). 211p. 1980. pap. 9.00 (ISBN 0-318-11840-8). Gov Printing Office.
Napolitano, L. G. Space Activity: Impact on Science & Technology. 110.00 (ISBN 0-08-020365-5). Pergamon.
--Space & Energy. 90.00 (ISBN 0-08-021053-8). Pergamon.
--Space Developments for the Future of Mankind. 140.00 (ISBN 0-08-025454-3). Pergamon.
Napolitano, Luigi G. Space Two Thousand. LC 83-8795. 709p. 65.00 (ISBN 0-915928-73-6). AIAA.
Needell, Allan, ed. The First Twenty-Five Years in Space: A Symposium. LC 83-600210. 165p. 1983. 12.50 (ISBN 0-87474-668-X). Smithsonian.
New Dimensions Foundation, ed. Worlds Beyond: The Everlasting Frontier. LC 78-54345. 320p. 1978. pap. 6.95 (ISBN 0-915904-36-5). And-Or Pr.
Oberg, James E. Red Star in Orbit. (Illus.). 1981. 16.95 (ISBN 0-394-51429-7). Random.
Out of This World: An Illustrated Guide to Space Technology & Exploration. 128p. 1985. 14.95 (ISBN 0-668-06335-1). Arco.
Powers, Robert M. Planetary Encounters. LC 78-16516. (Illus.). 288p. 1978. 19.95 (ISBN 0-8117-1270-2). Stackpole.
Ramo, Simon, et al, eds. Peacetime Uses of Outer Space. LC 76-52430. (Illus.). 1977. Repr. of 1961 ed. lib. bdg. 24.75x (ISBN 0-8371-9368-0, RAPU). Greenwood.
Schneider, W. C. & Hanes, T. E., eds. Skylab Results, 2 pts, Pt. 1 & 2. (Advances in the Astronautical Sciences Ser.: Vol. 31). 1975. write for info. (Pub. by Am Astronaut); microfiche 55.00x (ISBN 0-87703-072-3). Univelt Inc.

Bannister, J. V. & Bannister, W. H., eds. Biological & Clinical Aspects of Superoxide & Superoxide Dismutase. (Developments in Biochemistry Ser.: Vol. 11B). 1980. 68.25 (ISBN 0-444-00443-2). Elsevier.

Bannister, J. V. & Hill, H. A., eds. Chemical & Biochemical Aspects of Superoxide & Superoxide Dismutase. (Developments in Biochemistry Ser.: Vol. 11A). 414p. 1980. 68.25 (ISBN 0-444-00442-4). Elsevier.

Ciba Foundation. Monoamine Oxidase & Its Inhibition. LC 76-10396. (Ciba Foundation Symposium, New Ser.: 39). pap. 106.80 (2022167). Bks Demand UMI.

Cockayne, B. & Jones, D. W., eds. Modern Oxide Materials: Preparation, Properties & Device Applications. 1972. 59.50 (ISBN 0-12-177750-2). Acad Pr.

Diggle, John & Vijh, Ashok K., eds. Oxides & Oxide Films, Vol. 3. (The Anodic Behavior of Metals & Semiconductors Ser.). 352p. 1976. 75.00 (ISBN 0-8247-6314-9). Dekker.

--Oxides & Oxide Films, Vol. 4. (The Anodic Behavior of Metals & Semiconductors Ser.). 1976. 75.00 (ISBN 0-8247-6315-7). Dekker.

Hehner, Nels E. & Ritchie, Everett J. Lead Oxides: Chemistry, Technology, Battery Manufacturing Uses, History. 1974. 15.00 (ISBN 0-685-56653-6). IBMA Pubns.

Hellwege, K. H., ed. Landolt-Boernstein Numerical Data & Functional Relationships in Science & Technology, New Series, Group 3: Crystal & Solid State Physics, Vols. 1-6. Incl. Vol. 1. Elastic, Piezoelectric, Piezooptic & Electrooptic Constants of Crystals. Bechman, R. & Hearmon, R. F. x, 160p. 1966; Vol. 2. Elastic, Piezoelectric, Piezooptic, Electrooptic Constants, & Non-Linear Dielectric Susceptibilities of Crystals. Bechman, R., et al. (Illus.). ix, 232p. 1969; Vol. 3. Ferro- & Antiferroelectric Substances. Mitsui, T., et al. (Illus.). viii, 584p. 1969; Vol. 4, Pt. A. Magnetic & Other Properties of Oxides & Related Compounds. Goodenough, J. B., et al. (Illus.). xv, 367p. 1970. 130.20 (ISBN 0-387-04898-7); Vol. 4, Pt. B: Magnetic & Other Properties of Oxides & Related Compounds. Bonnenberg, F., et al. (Illus.). xvi, 666p. 1970. 235.20 (ISBN 0-387-05176-7); Vol. 5. Structure Data of Organic Crystals, 2 vols. Schudt, E. & Weitz, G. (Illus.). 1971. Set. 428.40 (ISBN 0-387-05177-5); Vol. 6. Structure Data of Elements & Intermetallic Phases. Eckerlin, P. & Kandler, H. 1971. 346.50 (ISBN 0-387-05500-2). LC 62-53136. Springer-Verlag.

Katritzky, A. R. & Lagowski, J. J. Chemistry of Heterocyclic Oxides. 1971. 95.00 (ISBN 0-12-401250-7). Acad Pr.

Magnetic & Other Properties of Oxides & Related Compounds: Part B: Spinels, Fe Oxides & Fe-Me- O-Compounds. (Landolt-Boernstein Ser. Group III: Vol. 12). (Illus.). 770p. (Suppl & extension to vol. 4). 1980. 331.80 (ISBN 0-387-09421-0). Springer-Verlag.

Samsonov, G. V. The Oxide Handbook. 2nd rev. ed. Johnston, Robert K., tr. from Russian. LC 80-23223. (IFI Data Base Library). 480p. 1982. 95.00 (ISBN 0-306-65177-7, IFI Plenum). Plenum Pub.

Seltzer, M. S., ed. Defects & Transport in Oxides. Jaffee, R. I. LC 74-19162. 611p. 1974. 89.50x (ISBN 0-306-30824-X, Plenum Pr). Plenum Pub.

Smith, R. & Howe, J., eds. Beryllium Oxide. 1964. 72.00 (ISBN 0-317-17784-2). Elsevier.

Sorensen, O. Toft, ed. Non-Stoichiometric Oxides. LC 80-2342. (Materials Science Ser.). 1981. 70.00 (ISBN 0-12-655280-0). Acad Pr.

Toropov, N. A. & Barzakovskii, V. P. High-Temperature Chemistry of Silicates & Other Oxide Systems. LC 65-25264. 216p. 1966. 34.50x (ISBN 0-306-10749-X, Consultants). Plenum Pub.

Toropov, N. A., ed. Chemistry of High Temperature Materials. LC 74-79891. (Illus.). 237p. 1969. 35.00x (ISBN 0-306-10820-8, Consultants). Plenum Pub.

Vijh, Ashok K., ed. Oxides & Oxide Films, Vol. 5. (The Anodic Behavior of Metals & Semiconductor Ser.). 1977. 65.00 (ISBN 0-8247-6580-X). Dekker.

Young. Oxides of Nitrogen, Sulfur & Chlorine: Gas Solubilities. (IUPAC Solubility Data Ser.: Vol. 8). 1981. 100.00 (ISBN 0-08-023924-2). Pergamon.

OXO-COMPOUNDS

see also Aldehydes; Carbonyl Compounds; Ketones

Pies, W. & Weiss, A. Schluesselelemente. (Landolt-Boernstein New Ser, Crystal Structure Data of Inorganic Compounds, Group 3: Vol. 7e). (Illus.). 780p. 1975. 340.20 (ISBN 0-387-07334-5). Springer-Verlag.

West, Robert. The Oxocarbons. LC 80-515. (Organic Chemistry Ser.). 1980. 43.00 (ISBN 0-12-744580-3). Acad Pr.

OXYACETYLENE WELDING AND CUTTING

American Welding Society. Committee on Filler Metal. Specification for Carbon, Steel Filler Metals for Gang Shielded Arc Welding: AWS A5.18. LC 79-50636. 21p. 1979. pap. 10.00 (ISBN 0-87171-173-7). Am Welding.

Balchin, N. C., et al, eds. Oxy-Acetylene Welding. (Engineering Craftsmen: No. F25). (Illus.). 1977. spiral bdg. 39.95x (ISBN 0-85083-396-5). Intl Ideas.

Greenly, H. & Evans, Martin. Walschaerts' Valve Gear. (Illus.). 64p. 1985. pap. 3.95 (ISBN 0-317-14791-9, Pub. by Argus). Aztex.

Jefferson, T. B. Jefferson's Gas Welding Manual. 4th ed. (Monticello Bks). 136p. 1982. pap. 5.00 (ISBN 0-686-12006-X). Jefferson Pubns.

--The Oxyacetylene Weldor's Handbook. 7th ed. (Monticello Bks). 320p. 1972. 7.50 (ISBN 0-686-12005-1). Jefferson Pubns.

Jefferson, Ted B. & Jefferson, D. T. Jefferson's Gas Welding Manual. 4th ed. (Monticello Bks). 140p. 1982. pap. 6.50 (ISBN 0-686-29440-8). Jefferson Pubns.

Jennings, Royalston F. Gas & A.C. Arc Welding & Cutting. 3rd ed. 1956. pap. text ed. 6.64 (ISBN 0-87345-119-8). McKnight.

Minnick. GTAW Handbook. 14.00 (ISBN 0-87006-514-9). Goodheart.

Recommended Practices for Gas Metal Arc Welding: AWS C5.6. LC 78-73281. (Illus.). 58p. 1979. pap. text ed. 20.00 (ISBN 0-87171-166-4); member 15.00. Am Welding.

Schell, Frank R. Welding Procedures: Electric Arc. LC 76-14084. 1977. pap. text ed. 8.00 (ISBN 0-8273-1603-8); instr's manual 5.25 (ISBN 0-8273-1697-6). Delmar.

--Welding Procedures: Oxyacetylene. LC 76-4306. 1977. pap. text ed. 8.00 (ISBN 0-8273-1600-3); instr's. guide 5.25 (ISBN 0-8273-1697-6). Delmar.

Shielded Metal Arc & Oxyacetylene Welding. (Welding Inspection Ser.: Module 28-2). (Illus.). 46p. 1979. spiral bdg. 7.00x (ISBN 0-87683-106-4). G P Courseware.

Specification for Iron, Steel, & Oxyfuel Gas Welding Rods: A5.2. 8p. 1980. 10.00 (ISBN 0-87171-200-8); member 7.50. Am Welding.

OXYGEN

see also Oxo-Compounds; Ozone

Bahn, Gilbert S., ed. Reaction Rate Compilation for the H-O-N System. LC 68-20396. 254p. 1968. Repr. of 1967 ed. 74.25 (ISBN 0-677-12750-2). Gordon.

Bulk Oxygen Systems at Consumer Sites. (Fifty Ser). 1974. pap. 2.00 (ISBN 0-685-58094-6, 50). Natl Fire Prot.

Caughey, Winslow S., ed. Biochemical & Clinical Aspects of Oxygen. LC 79-23522. 1979. 67.50 (ISBN 0-12-164380-8). Acad Pr.

Cohen, G. & Greenwald, M. D., eds. Oxy Radicals & Their Scavenger Systems, Vol. 1. 339p. 1983. 80.00 (ISBN 0-444-00746-6, Biomedical Pr). Elsevier.

Fatt, Irving. Polarographic Oxygen Sensor: Its Theory of Operation & Its Application in Biology, Medicine & Technology. LC 82-6581. 290p. (Orig.). 1982. Repr. of 1976 ed. 59.95 (ISBN 0-89874-511-X). Krieger.

Hayaishi, Osamu, ed. Molecular Mechanisms of Oxygen Activation. (Molecular Biology Ser.). 1974. 83.00 (ISBN 0-12-333640-6). Acad Pr.

Hilado, Carlos J., ed. Flammability Handbook for Plastics. 2nd, rev. ed. LC 72-82519. 201p. 1974. pap. 35.00 (ISBN 0-87762-139-X). Technomic.

Kintzinger, J. P. & Marsmann, H. Oxygen-Seventeen & Silicon-Twenty-Nine. (NMR-Basic Principles & Progress Ser.: Vol. 17). (Illus.). 235p. 1981. 50.00 (ISBN 0-387-10414-3). Springer-Verlag.

Kirby, A. J. The Anomeric Effect & Related Stereoelectronic Effects at Oxygen. (Reactivity & Structure: Vol. 15). (Illus.). 200p. 1983. 53.00 (ISBN 0-387-11684-2). Springer-Verlag.

Lubbers, D. W., et al, eds. Oxygen Transport to Tissue V. (Advances in Experimental Medicine & Biology Ser.: Vol. 169). 938p. 1984. 125.00x (ISBN 0-306-41610-7, Plenum Pr). Plenum Pub.

Max Planck Society for the Advancement of Science, Gemelin Institute for Inorganic Chemistry & Delyannis, A. A. Oxygen: Walter Desalting. (Gmelin Handbuch der Anorganischen Chemie, 8th Ed). (Illus.). 339p. 1974. 218.40 (ISBN 0-387-93280-1). Springer-Verlag.

Meijne, N. G. Hyperbaric Oxygen & Its Clinical Value: With Special Emphasis on Biochemical & Cardiovascular Aspects. (Illus.). 288p. 1970. 30.75x (ISBN 0-398-01280-6). C C Thomas.

Nozaki, Mitsuhiro & Yamamoto, Shozo, eds. Oxygenases & Oxygen Metabolism Symposium. 654p. 1982. 55.00 (ISBN 0-12-522780-9). Acad Pr.

Rodgers, M. A. & Powers, E. L., eds. Oxygen & Oxy-Radicals in Chemistry & Biology. LC 81-19096. 1981. 70.00 (ISBN 0-12-592050-4). Acad Pr.

Schaap, A. P., ed. Singlet Molecular Oxygen. LC 76-3496. (Benchmark Papers in Organic Chemistry Ser.: Vol. 5). 400p. 1976. 75.00 (ISBN 0-12-787415-1). Acad Pr.

Semenza, G. Of Oxygen, Fuels & Living Matter, Vol. 2, Pt. 2. (Evolving Life Sciences: Recollections on Scientific Ideas & Events Ser.). 508p. 1982. text ed. 74.95x (ISBN 0-471-27924-2, Pub. by Wiley-Interscience). Wiley.

Spiro, Thomas G., ed. Metal Ion Activation of Dioxygen, Vol. 2. LC 79-13808. (Metal Ions in Biology Ser.). 247p. 1980. 64.50 (ISBN 0-471-04398-2, Pub. by Wiley-Interscience). Wiley.

Wasserman, Harry H. & Murray, Robert W., eds. Singlet Oxygen. LC 77-25737. (Organic Chemistry Ser.). 1979. 82.00 (ISBN 0-12-736650-4). Acad Pr.

OXYGEN–INDUSTRIAL APPLICATIONS

see also Metallurgy; Oxyacetylene Welding and Cutting; Steel–Metallurgy

Battino. Oxygen & Ozone: Gas Solubilities. (Solubility Data Ser.). 1981. 100.00 (ISBN 0-08-023915-3). Pergamon.

OXYGEN IN THE BODY

see also Anoxemia

Autor, Anne, ed. Pathology of Oxygen. 360p. 1982. 70.00 (ISBN 0-12-068620-1). Acad Pr.

Balentine, J. Douglas. Pathology of Oxygen Toxicity. 346p. 1982. 55.00 (ISBN 0-12-077080-6). Acad Pr.

Bannister, J. V., ed. The Biology & Chemistry of Active Oxygen. (Developments in Biochemistry Ser.: Vol. 26). 280p. 1984. 55.00 (ISBN 0-444-00924-8). Elsevier.

Bicher, Haim I. & Bruley, Duane F., eds. Oxygen Transport to Tissue IV. (Advances in Experimental Medicine & Biology: Vol. 159). 650p. 1983. 85.00x (ISBN 0-306-41192-X, Plenum Pr). Plenum Pub.

--Oxygen Transport to Tissue, Vol. 1, 2 pts, Vol. I. Incl. Pt. A, Instrumentation, Methods, & Physiology. 702p. 1973. 75.00x (ISBN 0-306-39093-0); Pt. B: Pharmacology, Mathematical Studies & Neonatology. 552p. 1973. 69.50x (ISBN 0-306-39094-9). LC 73-13821. (Advances in Experimental Medicine & Biology Ser.: Vols. 37A & 37B, Plenum Pr). Plenum Pub.

Bruley, Duane, et al, eds. Oxygen Transport to Tissue VI. (Advances in Experimental Medicine & Biology Ser.: Vol. 180). 924p. 1985. 125.00x (ISBN 0-306-41887-8, Plenum Pr). Plenum Pub.

Ehrly, A. M., ed. Determination of Tissue Oxygen Pressure in Patients. (Illus.). 112p. 1983. 20.00 (ISBN 0-08-029785-4). Pergamon.

Gilbert, Daniel L., ed. Oxygen & Living Processes: An Interdisciplinary Approach. (Topics in Environmental Physiology & Medicine Ser.). (Illus.). 401p. 1981. 69.00 (ISBN 0-387-90554-5). Springer Verlag.

Grote, Jurgon, et al, eds. Oxygen Transport to Tissue II. LC 75-25951. (Advances in Experimental Medicine & Biology Ser.: Vol. 75). 804p. 1976. 85.00x (ISBN 0-306-39075-2, Plenum Pr). Plenum Pub.

Hershey, Daniel, ed. Blood Oxygenation. LC 74-122626. 374p. 1970. 37.50x (ISBN 0-306-30486-4, Plenum Pr). Plenum Pub.

Ho, C. & Eaton, W. A., eds. Hemoglobin & Oxygen Binding. 486p. 1982. 95.00 (ISBN 0-444-00571-4, Biomedical Pr). Elsevier.

Kovach, A. G., et al. Oxygen Transport to Tissue: Proceedings of a Satellite Symposium of the 28th International Congress of Physiological Sciences, Budapest, Hungary, 1980. Dora, E., ed. LC 80-42249. (Advances in Physiological Sciences Ser.: Vol. 25). (Illus.). 500p. 1981. 66.00 (ISBN 0-08-027346-7). Pergamon.

Loeppky, J. A. & Riedesel, M. L., eds. Oxygen Transport to Human Tissues: A Symposium in Honor of Ulrich C. Luft, VA Medical Center, Albuquerque, N.M., June 1981. 378p. 1982. 81.50 (ISBN 0-444-00677-X, Biomedical Pr). Elsevier.

Lubbers, D. W., et al, eds. Oxygen Transport to Tissue V. (Advances in Experimental Medicine & Biology Ser.: Vol. 169). 938p. 1984. 125.00x (ISBN 0-306-41610-7, Plenum Pr). Plenum Pub.

Meijne, N. G. Hyperbaric Oxygen & Its Clinical Value: With Special Emphasis on Biochemical & Cardiovascular Aspects. (Illus.). 288p. 1970. 30.75x (ISBN 0-398-01280-6). C C Thomas.

Silver, I. A., et al, eds. Oxygen Transport to Tissue III. LC 77-17140. (Advances in Experimental Medicine & Biology Ser.: Vol. 94). 815p. 1978. 85.00 (ISBN 0-306-32694-9, Plenum Pr). Plenum Pub.

OXYGEN STEELMAKING

see Steel–Metallurgy

OXYMURIATIC ACID

see Chlorine

OYSTERS

Galtsoff, Paul S., compiled by. Bibliography of Oysters & Other Marine Organisms Associated with Oyster Bottoms & Estuarine Ecology. 1972. lib. bdg. 88.50 (ISBN 0-8161-0945-1, Hall Reference). G K Hall.

Kennedy, Victor S. & Breisch, Linda L. Maryland's Oyster: Research & Management. pap. 8.00 (ISBN 0-317-17753-2). MD Sea Grant Col.

--Maryland's Oysters: An Annotated Bibliography. pap. 8.00 (ISBN 0-943676-01-0). MD Sea Grant Col.

Kochiss, John M. Oystering from New York to Boston. LC 74-5965. (The American Maritime Library: Vol. 7). (Illus.). 251p. 1974. 10.00 (ISBN 0-8195-4074-9); ltd. ed. 30.00 (ISBN 0-8195-4075-7). Mystic Seaport.

Korringa, P. Farming Cupped Oysters of the Genus Crassostrea. (Developments in Aquaculture & Fisheries Science Ser.: Vol. 2). 224p. 1976. 55.50 (ISBN 0-444-41333-2). Elsevier.

--Farming the Flat Oyster of the Genus Ostrea. (Developments in Aquaculture & Fisheries Science Ser.: Vol. 3). 238p. 1976. 55.50 (ISBN 0-444-41334-0). Elsevier.

Peffer, Randall S. The Watermen. LC 79-9896. 1979. 15.95 (ISBN 0-8018-2177-0). Johns Hopkins.

Quayle, D. B. Ostras Tropicales: Cultivo y Metodos. 84p. 1981. pap. 6.00 (ISBN 0-88936-266-1, IDRC-TS17S, IDRC). Unipub.

--Tropical Oyster Culture: A Selected Bibliography. 40p. 1975. pap. 5.00 (ISBN 0-88936-066-9, IDRC52, IDRC). Unipub.

Wennersten, John R. The Oyster Wars of Chesapeake Bay. LC 81-5810. (Illus.). 159p. 1981. 12.95 (ISBN 0-87033-263-5). Tidewater.

OZONE

Air Quality Meteorology & Atmospheric Ozone - STP 653. 639p. 1978. 55.00 (ISBN 0-8031-0275-5, 04-653000-17). ASTM.

Aquatic Applications of Ozone. 28.00 (ISBN 0-317-07460-1). Intl Ozone.

Bailey, Philip S. Ozone Reactions with Organic Compounds: A Symposium Sponsored by the Division of Petroleum Chemistry at the 161st Meeting of the American Chemical Society, Los Angeles, California, March 29-30, 1971. LC 75-88560. (American Chemical Society Advances in Chemistry Ser.: Vol. 112). pap. 35.30 (ISBN 0-317-26313-7, 20204237). Bks Demand UMI.

Battino. Oxygen & Ozone: Gas Solubilities. (Solubility Data Ser.). 1981. 100.00 (ISBN 0-08-023915-3). Pergamon.

Biswas, Asit K., ed. The Ozone Layer: Synthesis of Papers Based on the UNEP Meeting on the Ozone Layer, Washington DC, March 1977. LC 79-42879. (Environmental Sciences & Applications Ser.: Vol. 4). 1980. 68.00 (ISBN 0-08-022429-6). Pergamon.

Bower, Frank A. & Ward, Richard B., eds. Stratospheric Ozone & Man, Vol. I: Stratospheric Ozone. 232p. 1981. 74.50 (ISBN 0-8493-5753-5). CRC Pr.

--Stratospheric Ozone & Man, Vol. II: Man's Interactions & Concerns. 280p. 1981. 79.50 (ISBN 0-8493-5755-1). CRC Pr.

Committee on Impacts of Stratospheric Change, et al. Protection Against Depletion of Stratospheric Ozone by Chlorofluorocarbons. LC 79-57247. xvii, 392p. (Orig.). 1979. pap. text ed. 10.25 (ISBN 0-309-02947-3). Natl Acad Pr.

Conkin, Barbara M. & Conkin, James E. Stratigraphy: Foundation & Concepts. 1984. 45.00 (ISBN 0-442-21747-1). Van Nos Reinhold.

Cumberland, John H., et al, eds. Economics of Managing Chlorofluorocarbons: Stratospheric Ozone & Climate Issues. LC 82-11279. (Resources for the Future Ser.). 536p. 1982. text ed. 28.00x (ISBN 0-8018-2963-1). Johns Hopkins.

Environmental Studies Board, National Research Council. Causes & Effects of Stratospheric Ozone Reduction: An Update. 339p. 1982. pap. text ed. 13.95 (ISBN 0-309-03248-2). Natl Acad Pr.

Fochtman, Edward G., et al, eds. Forum on Ozone Disinfection. LC 76-51563. 1977. text ed. 18.00 (ISBN 0-918650-01-1); text ed. 25.00 non-members (ISBN 0-918650-00-3). Intl Ozone.

Horvath, M., et al. Ozone. (Topics in Inorganic & General Chemistry Ser.: No. 20). 1985. 72.25 (ISBN 0-444-99625-7). Elsevier.

International Symposium on Ozone Technology, 5th. 30.00 (ISBN 0-317-07464-4). Intl Ozone.

McCormick, M. P. & Lovill, J. E., eds. Space Observations of Aerosols & Ozone: Proceedings of the Topical Meeting of the COSPAR Interdisciplinary Scientific Commission A (Meetings A1 & A2) of the COSPAR 24th Plenary Meeting held in Ottawa, Canada, 16 May-2 June, 1982, Vol. 2/5. (Illus.). 120p. 1983. pap. 45.00 (ISBN 0-08-030427-3). Pergamon.

Advances in Electrophoretic Painting: 1978-80. (Bibliographies in Paint Technology Ser.: No. 36). 85p. 1982. 45.00x (ISBN 0-686-44657-7, Pub. by Chandler England). State Mutual Bk.

Catalog of Existing Small Tools for Surface Preparation & Support Equipment for Blasters & Painters. 1984. 25.00 (ISBN 0-318-03373-9). SSPC.

Electrophoretic Paint Deposition. 2nd ed. 62p. 1970. 40.00x (ISBN 0-686-44665-8, Pub. by Chandler England). State Mutual Bk.

Guidlines for Centrifugal Blast Cleaning. 1984. 15.00 (ISBN 0-318-03372-0). SSPC.

Internal Can Linings. 54p. 1978. 40.00x (ISBN 0-686-44669-0, Pub. by Chandler England). State Mutual Bk.

O'Neil, Isabel. Art of the Painted Finish for Furniture & Decoration. (Illus.). 1971. 19.95 (ISBN 0-688-01070-9). Morrow.

Procedure Handbook: Surface Preparation & Painting of Tanks & Closed Areas. 1984. 25.00 (ISBN 0-318-03379-8). SSPC.

Remedial Painting of Weathering Steel: State of the Art Survey. 1984. 30.00 (ISBN 0-318-03369-0). SSPC.

Reynolds, Hezekiah. Directions for House & Ship Painting. (AAS Facsimiles: No. 1). (Illus., Orig.). 1978. pap. 2.95 (ISBN 0-912296-16-X, Dist. by U Pr of Va). Am Antiquarian.

Rudman, Jack. Bridge Painter. (Career Examination Ser.: C-93). (Cloth bdg. avail. on request). pap. 10.00 (ISBN 0-8373-0093-2). Natl Learning.

--Foreman Bridge Painter. (Career Examination Ser.: C-1412). (Cloth bdg. avail. on request). pap. 10.00 (ISBN 0-8373-1412-7). Natl Learning.

--Maintenance Painter. (Career Examination Ser.: C-1358). (Cloth bdg. avail. on request). pap. 10.00 (ISBN 0-8373-1358-9). Natl Learning.

--Maintenance Painter Foreman. (Career Examination Ser.: C-1359). (Cloth bdg. avail. on request). pap. 12.00 (ISBN 0-8373-1359-7). Natl Learning.

--Painter. (Career Examination Ser.: C-570). (Cloth bdg. avail. on request). pap. 12.00 (ISBN 0-8373-0570-5). Natl Learning.

Surface Texture: Profile Measurement. 1984. 25.00 (ISBN 0-318-03377-1). SSPC.

Thirty-Three Year Report on Water Tank Painting. 1984. 30.00 (ISBN 0-318-03365-8). SSPC.

PAINTS
see Paint

PAIR SYSTEM
see Binary System (Mathematics)

PALEOBIOLOGY
see Paleobotany; Paleoecology; Paleontology

PALEOBOTANY
see also Plankton, Fossil;
also names of individual genera and species of fossil plants

Andrews, Henry N. The Fossil Hunters: In Search of Ancient Plants. LC 79-24101. (Illus.). 420p. 1980. 37.50x (ISBN 0-8014-1248-X). Cornell U Pr.

Axelrod, Daniel I. Contributions to the Neogene Paleobotany of Central California. (U. C. Publications in Geological Sciences Ser.: Vol. 121). 222p. 1981. pap. 24.50x (ISBN 0-520-09621-5). U of Cal Pr.

Barefoot, A. C. & Hankins, Frank W. Identification of Modern Tertiary Woods. (Illus.). 1982. 98.00x (ISBN 0-19-854378-6). Oxford U Pr.

Basson, Philip W. Fossil Flora of the Drywood Formation of Southwestern Missouri. LC 67-63045. (Illus.). 184p. 1968. 18.00x (ISBN 0-8262-7516-8). U of Mo Pr.

Carnegie Institution Of Washington. Eocene Flora of Western America. Repr. of 1937 ed. 28.00 (ISBN 0-685-02242-0). Johnson Repr.

--Miocene & Pliocene Floras of Western North America. Repr. of 1938 ed. 23.00 (ISBN 0-685-02185-8). Johnson Repr.

--Studies of the Pleistocene Palaeobotany of California. Repr. of 1934 ed. 19.00 (ISBN 0-685-02051-7). Johnson Repr.

--Studies of the Pliocene Palaeobotany of California. Repr. of 1933 ed. 19.00 (ISBN 0-685-02164-5). Johnson Repr.

Chandler, M. E. Upper Eocene Flora of Hordle, Pts. 1-2. 1925-26. Set. 20.00 (ISBN 0-384-08455-9). Johnson Repr.

Chaney, Ralph W. & Sanborn, Ethel I. Goshen Flora of West Central Oregon. Repr. 19.00 (ISBN 0-384-08461-3). Johnson Repr.

Crawford, Gary W. Paleoethnobotany of the Kameda Peninsula Jomon. (Anthropological Papers: No. 73). (Illus.). 200p. 1983. pap. 8.00x (ISBN 0-932206-95-6). U Mich Mus Anthro.

Dilcher, D. L. & Taylor, T. N., eds. Biostratigraphy of Fossil Plants: Sucessional & Paleoecological Analyses. LC 79-27418. 259p. 1980. 34.50 (ISBN 0-87933-373-1). Van Nos Reinhold.

Engler, A. Versuch einer Entwicklungsgeschichte der Pflanzenwelt Insbesondere der Florengebiete Seit der Tertiaerperiode. 1971. 63.00 (ISBN 3-7682-0749-8). Lubrecht & Cramer.

Foord, H. The Carboniferous Cephalopoda of Ireland, Vols. 55, 57, Nos. 259, 269. Repr. of 1901 ed. 25.00 ea. Johnson Repr.

Gensel, Patricia G. & Andrews, Henry N. Plant Life in the Devonian. (Illus.). 396p. 1984. 29.95 (ISBN 0-03-062002-3). Praeger.

Harris, Thomas M. Yorkshire Jurassic Flora: Vol. II, Caytoniales, Cycadales, & Pteridisperms. (Illus.). 1964. 34.00x (ISBN 0-565-00622-3, Pub. by Brit Mus Nat Hist). Sabbot-Natural Hist Bks.

--Yorkshire Jurassic Flora: Vol. III, Bennettitales. (Illus.). 1969. 34.00x (ISBN 0-565-00675-4, Pub. by Brit Mus Nat Hist). Sabbot-Natural Hist Bks.

--Yorkshire Jurassic Flora: Vol. IV, Ginkgoales & Czekanowskiales. (Illus.). 1974. 52.00x (ISBN 0-565-00724-6, Pub. by Brit Mus Nat Hist). Sabbot-Natural Hist Bks.

--Yorkshire Jurassic Flora: Vol. V, Coniferales. (Illus.). 1979. 52.00x (ISBN 0-565-00803-X, Pub. by Brit Mus Nat Hist). Sabbot-Natural Hist Bks.

Harris, Thomas Maxwell. Yorkshire Jurassic Flora: Vol. I, Thallophyta-Pteridophyta. (Illus.). 1961. 31.00x (ISBN 0-565-00148-5, Pub. by Brit Mus Nat Hist). Sabbot-Natural Hist Bks.

Hickey, Leo J. Stratigraphy & Paleobotany of the Golden Valley Formation (Early Tertiary) of Western North Dakota. LC 76-50970. (Memoir: No. 150). (Illus.). 1977. 34.00 (ISBN 0-8137-1150-9). Geol Soc.

Hsen Hsu Hu. Miocene Flora from Shantung Province, China. Repr. of 1940 ed. 28.00 (ISBN 0-384-24720-2). Johnson Repr.

Hughes, Norman F. Paleobiology of Angiosperm Origins: Problems of Mesozoic Seed-Plant Evolution. LC 75-3855. (Illus.). 216p. 1976. 57.50 (ISBN 0-521-20809-2). Cambridge U Pr.

Janssen, Raymond E. Leaves & Stems from Fossil Forests. rev. ed. (Popular Science Ser.: Vol. I). (Illus.). 190p. 1979. pap. 4.00 (ISBN 0-89792-077-5). Ill St Museum.

--Some Fossil Plant Types of Illinois. (Scientific Papers Ser.: Vol. I). (Illus.). 124p. 1940. 3.00x (ISBN 0-89792-094-5); pap. 2.00x (ISBN 0-89792-000-7). Ill St Museum.

Knowlton, Frank H. Plants of the Past, a Popular Account of Fossil Plants. LC 76-94246. (Illus.). Repr. of 1927 ed. 19.50 (ISBN 0-404-03735-6). AMS Pr.

Leakey, Meave G. & Leakey, Richard E., eds. Koobi Fora: Research Projects, Vol. 1. (Illus.). 1978. text ed. 65.00x (ISBN 0-19-857392-8). Oxford U Pr.

Lowenstam, Heinz A. Biostratigraphic Studies of the Niagaran Inter-Reef Formations of Northeastern Illinois. (Scientific Papers Ser.: Vol. IV). (Illus.). 146p. 1948. 3.00 (ISBN 0-89792-093-7); pap. 2.00 (ISBN 0-89792-005-8). Ill St Museum.

Martin, Paul S. The Last Ten Thousand Years: A Fossil Pollen Record of the American Southwest. LC 63-11984. (Illus.). 87p. 1963. 14.95x (ISBN 0-8165-0050-9). U of Ariz Pr.

Napier, P. H. Catalogue of Primates in the British Museum (Natural History) Part 1: Families Callitrichidae & Cebidae. 1976. pap. 22.50x (ISBN 0-565-00744-0, Pub. by Brit Mus Nat Hist). Sabbot-Natural Hist Bks.

Niklas, Karl J., ed. Paleobotany, Paleoecology, & Evolution, 2 vols. LC 81-1838. 1981. Vol. 1. 50.00 (ISBN 0-03-059136-8); Vol. 2. 50.00 (ISBN 0-03-056656-8); Set. 90.00 (ISBN 0-03-060038-3). Praeger.

Pandey, S. N., et al. Textbook of Botany: Vol. II. 9th ed. viii, 531p. 1981. text ed. 40.00x (ISBN 0-7069-2397-9, Pub. by Vikas India). Advent NY.

Pierce, Richard L. Lower Upper Cretaceous Plant Microfossils from Minnesota. LC 61-64045. (Bulletin: No. 42). (Illus.). 1961. 3.75x (ISBN 0-8166-0257-3). Minn Geol Survey.

Romans, Robert C. & McCann, Patricia S. Bibliography of Ohio Paleobotany. 1974. 1.00 (ISBN 0-86727-073-X). Ohio Bio Survey.

Shukla, A. C. Essentials of Paleobotany. Misra, S. P., ed. (Illus.). 1975. 13.50 (ISBN 0-7069-0381-1). Intl Bk Dist.

Shukla, A. C. & Misra, S. P. Essentials of Paleobotany. 2nd ed. (Illus.). 1982. text ed. 22.50x (ISBN 0-7069-1450-3, Pub. by Vikas India). Advent NY.

Stewart, Wilson N. Paleobotany & the Evolution of Plants. LC 82-21986. 1983. 32.50 (ISBN 0-521-23315-1). Cambridge U Pr.

Streel, M., et al, eds. Advances in Paleozoic Botany. 1972. Repr. 27.75 (ISBN 0-444-41080-5). Elsevier.

Tappan, Helen. The Paleobiology of Plant Protists. LC 80-14675. (Geology Ser.). (Illus.). 1028p. 1980. text ed. 95.00x (ISBN 0-7167-1109-5). W H Freeman.

Taylor, Thomas N. Paleobotany: An Introduction to Fossil Plant Biology. (Illus.). 576p. 1981. 46.95x (ISBN 0-07-062954-4). McGraw.

Tidwell, William D. Common Fossil Plants of Western North America. LC 75-4640. (Illus.). 1975. pap. 7.95 (ISBN 0-8425-1301-9). Brigham.

Tiffney, Bruce, ed. Geological Factors & the Evolution of Plants. LC 84-27053. 304p. 1985. text ed. 25.00x (ISBN 0-300-03304-4). Yale U Pr.

Van Landingham, S. L. Miocene Non-Marine Diatoms from the Yakima Region in South Central Washington. (Illus.). 1965. pap. 16.00 (ISBN 3-7682-5414-3). Lubrecht & Cramer.

Walker, D. & West, R. G., eds. Studies in the Vegetation History of the British Isles. 89.50 (ISBN 0-521-07565-3). Cambridge U Pr.

PALEOCENE PERIOD
see Geology, Stratigraphic–Paleocene

PALEOCLIMATOLOGY
see also Dendrochronology

Berger, A. L., et al, eds. Milankovitch & Climate: Understanding the Response to Astronomical Forcing. 1984. lib. bdg. 64.00 (ISBN 90-277-1791-5, Pub. by Reidel Holland). Kluwer Academic.

Bowen, Robert. Paleotemperature Analysis. (Methods in Geochemistry & Geophysics Ser.: Vol. 2). 265p. 1966. 74.50 (ISBN 0-444-40074-5). Elsevier.

Bradley, Raymond S. Quaternary Paleoclimatology: Methods of Paleoclimatic Reconstruction. (Illus.). 1985. text ed. 50.00x (ISBN 0-04-551067-9); pap. text ed. 24.95x (ISBN 0-04-551068-7). Allen Unwin.

Brooks, C. E. Climate Through the Ages. 1970. pap. 6.95 (ISBN 0-486-22245-4). Dover.

Butzer, Karl W. Environment & Archeology: An Ecological Approach to Prehistory. 2nd ed. LC 74-115938. (Illus.). 703p. 1971. text ed. 39.95x (ISBN 0-202-33023-0). Aldine Pub.

--Quarternary Stratigraphy & Climate in the Near East. 1958. pap. 20.00 (ISBN 0-384-06790-5). Johnson Repr.

Cline, R. M. & Hays, J. D., eds. Investigation of Late Quaternary Paleoceanography & Paleoclimatology. LC 75-40889. (Memoir: No. 145). (Illus.). 1976. 30.00 (ISBN 0-8137-1145-2). Geol Soc.

Frenzel, Burkhard. Climatic Fluctuations of the Ice Age. Nairn, A. E., tr. from Ger. LC 70-170788. (Illus.). 252p. 1973. text ed. 22.50 (ISBN 0-8295-0226-2). UPB.

Grayson, Donald K. A Bibliography of the Literature on North American Climates of the Past Thirteen Thousand Years. LC 75-5131. (Reference Library of Natural Science: No. 2). 160p. 1975. lib. bdg. 22.00 (ISBN 0-8240-9992-3). Garland Pub.

Hecht, A. D. Paleoclimate Analysis & Modeling. (Environmental Science & Technology Ser.). 456p. 1985. 49.95 (ISBN 0-471-86527-3). Wiley.

Lamb, Hubert H. Climate: Present, Past & Future, Vol. 1. (Illus.). 1972. 120.00x (ISBN 0-416-11530-6, NO.2785). Methuen Inc.

Libby, Leona M. Past Climates: Tree Thermometers, Commodities, & People. (Illus.). 157p. 1983. text ed. 25.00x (ISBN 0-292-73019-5). U of Tex Pr.

Mahaney, W. C., ed. Quaternary Paleoclimate. 480p. 1981. 50.00x (ISBN 0-86094-076-4, Pub. by GEO Abstracts England). State Mutual Bk.

Pearson, Ronald. Climate & Evolution. 1979. 49.00 (ISBN 0-12-548250-7). Acad Pr.

Velichko, A. A., et al, eds. Late Quaternary Environments of the Soviet Union. LC 83-25892. (Illus.). 320p. 1984. 45.00x (ISBN 0-8166-1250-1). U of Minn Pr.

PALEOECOLOGY

Aigner, T. Storm Depositional Systems. (Lecture Notes in Earth Sciences: Vol. 3). vii, 174p. 1985. pap. 14.50 (ISBN 0-387-15231-8). Springer-Verlag.

Bakels, C. C. Analecta Praehistorica Leidensia: XI. 1978. pap. 42.00 (ISBN 90-6021-427-7, Pub. by Leiden Univ Holland). Kluwer Academic.

Behrensmeyer, Anna K. & Hill, Andrew P., eds. Fossils in the Making: Vertebrate Taphonomy & Paleoecology. LC 79-19879. (Prehistoric Archaeology & Ecology Ser.). (Illus.). 1980. lib. bdg. 20.00x (ISBN 0-226-04169-7); pap. text ed. 8.00x (ISBN 0-226-04168-9). U of Chicago Pr.

Berglund, B. Handbook of Holocene Palaeoecology & Palaeohydrology. 1985. 90.00 (ISBN 0-471-90691-3). Wiley.

Birks, H. J. Quaternary Paleoecology. (Illus.). 300p. 1980. text ed. 89.50 (ISBN 0-8391-4127-0). Univ Park.

Boucot, Arthur. Principles of Benthic Marine Paleo-Ecology. LC 79-8535. 1981. 66.50 (ISBN 0-12-118980-5). Acad Pr.

Dodd, Robert J. & Stanton, Robert J., Jr. Paleoecology, Concepts & Applications. LC 80-19623. 559p. 1981. 49.95x (ISBN 0-471-04171-8, Pub. by Wiley-Interscience). Wiley.

Gall, J. C. Ancient Sedimentary Environments & the Habitats of Living Organisms: Introduction to Palaeoecology. Wallace, P., tr. from Fr. (Illus.). 230p. 1983. 26.00 (ISBN 0-387-12137-4). Springer-Verlag.

Hansen, Henry P. Paleoecology of Two Peat Deposits on the Oregon Coast. (Studies in Botany Ser: No. 3). 32p. 1941. pap. 3.95x (ISBN 0-87071-013-3). Oreg St U Pr.

Harris, Arthur H. Late Pleistocene Vertebrate Paleoecology of the West. (Illus.). 303p. 1985. text ed. 25.00x (ISBN 0-292-74645-8). U of Tex Pr.

King, Frances B. Plants, People & Paleoecology. (Scientific Papers Ser.: Vol. XX). (Illus., Orig.). 1985. pap. text ed. write for info. (ISBN 0-89792-100-3). Ill St Museum.

Modderman, P. J. Analecta Praehistorica Leidensia: X. (Illus.). 1978. pap. 31.50 (ISBN 90-6021-432-3, Pub. by Leiden Univ Holland). Kluwer Academic.

Niklas, Karl J., ed. Paleobotany, Paleoecology, & Evolution, 2 vols. LC 81-1838. 1981. Vol. 1. 50.00 (ISBN 0-03-059136-8); Vol. 2. 50.00 (ISBN 0-03-056656-8); Set. 90.00 (ISBN 0-03-060038-3). Praeger.

Rau, Weldon W. Foraminifera, Stratigraphy & Paleoecology of the Quinault Formation, Point Grenville-Raft River Coastal Area, Washington. (Bulletin Ser.: No. 62). (Illus.). 41p. 1970. 3.00 (ISBN 0-686-34711-0). Geologic Pubns.

Rhodes, R. Sanders, II. Paleoecology & Regional Paleoclimatic Implications of the Farmdalian Craigmile & Woodfordian Waubonsie Mammalian Local Faunas, Southwestern Iowa. (Reports of Investigations Ser.: No. 40). (Illus.). viii, 51p. (Orig.). 1984. pap. text ed. 5.00 (ISBN 0-89792-103-8). Ill St Museum.

Schafer, Wilhelm. Ecology & Palaeoecology of Marine Environments. Craig, G. Y., ed. Oertel, Irmgard, tr. from Ger. LC 72-81105. 624p. 1972. 30.00x (ISBN 0-226-73581-8). U of Chicago Pr.

Shipman, Pat. Life History of a Fossil: Introduction to Taphonomy & Paleoecology. (Illus.). 1981. text ed. 19.95x (ISBN 0-674-53085-3). Harvard U Pr.

--Taphonomy of Rampithecus Wickeri at Fort Ternan Kenya. (Museum Briefs Ser.: No. 26). (Illus.). v, 37p. 1982. pap. 2.00 (ISBN 0-913134-26-0). Mus Anthro MO.

PALEOETHNOGRAPHY
see Archaeology

PALEOGEOGRAPHY

Allchin, Bridget, et al, eds. The Prehistory & Palaeogeography of the Great Indian Desert. 1978. 73.00 (ISBN 0-12-050450-2). Acad Pr.

Hallam, A. Atlas of Palaeobiogeography, 1972. 531p. 1973. 106.50 (ISBN 0-444-40975-0). Elsevier.

Khudoley, K. M. & Meyerhoff, A. A. Paleogeography & Geological History of Greater Antilles. LC 77-129999. (Geological Society of America Memoir Ser.: No. 129). pap. 53.80 (ISBN 0-317-29130-0, 2025024). Bks Demand UMI.

Markovskii, N. I. Paleogeographic Principles of Oil & Gas Prospecting. LC 75-12798. 256p. 1979. 74.95x (ISBN 0-470-57215-9). Halsted Pr.

Miall, A. D. Principles of Sedimentary Basin Analysis. (Illus.). 550p. 1984. 39.00 (ISBN 0-387-90941-9). Springer-Verlag.

Ross, Charles A., ed. Paleogeographic Provinces & Provinciality. LC 74-193154. (Society of Economic Paleontologists & Mineralogists, Special Publication: No. 21). pap. 60.80 (ISBN 0-317-27151-2, 2024743). Bks Demand UMI.

Zambrano, E. & Vasquez, E. Paleogeographic & Petroleum Synthesis of Western Venezuela. 70p. 1972. 60.00x (ISBN 2-7108-0194-9, Pub. by Graham & Trotman England). State Mutual Bk.

PALEOLIMNOLOGY

Horie, S. Lake Biwa. (Monographiae Biologicae). 1985. lib. bdg. 145.00 (ISBN 90-6193-095-2, Pub. by Junk Pubs Netherland). Kluwer Academic.

PALEOMAGNETISM
see also Continental Drift

Cox, Allan, ed. Plate Tectonics & Geomagnetic Reversals. LC 73-4323. (Geology Ser.). (Illus.). 702p. 1973. text ed. 44.95 (ISBN 0-7167-0259-2); pap. text ed. 30.95 (ISBN 0-7167-0258-4). W H Freeman.

McElhinney, M. W. Palaeomagnetism & Plate Tectonics. LC 72-80590. (Earth Science Ser). (Illus.). 368p. 1973. 74.50 (ISBN 0-521-08707-4). Cambridge U Pr.

McElhinny, M. W., et al. Global Reconstruction & the Geomagnetic Field During the Palaeozoic. 1981. 29.50 (ISBN 90-277-1231-X, Pub. by Reidel Holland). Kluwer Academic.

Tarling, D. H. Palaeomagnetism: Principles & Applications in Geology, Geophysics & Archaeology. (Illus.). 1983. 55.00 (ISBN 0-412-23920-5, NO. 6758, Pub. by Chapman & Hall); pap. 29.95 (ISBN 0-412-25100-0, NO. 6759). Methuen Inc.

Van der Voo, R., et al, eds. Plate Reconstruction from Paleozoic Paleomagnetism. (Geodynamics Ser.: Vol. 12). 136p. 1984. 20.00 (ISBN 0-87590-512-9). Am Geophysical.

PALEONTOLOGISTS

Bird, Roland T. Bones for Barnum Brown: Adventures of a Dinosaur Hunter. Schreiber, V. Theodore, ed. LC 84-24047. (Illus.). 192p. 1985. 29.95 (ISBN 0-87565-007-4); pap. 12.95 (ISBN 0-87565-011-2). Tex Christian.

Lambrecht, K. & Quenstedt, W. A. Paleontologi: A Biographical & Bibliographical Register of Paleontologists, Pt. 72. Albritton, Claude C., Jr., ed. LC 77-6526. (History of Geology Ser.). 1978. Repr. of 1938 ed. lib. bdg. 40.00x (ISBN 0-405-10445-6). Ayer Co Pubs.

Scott, William B. Some Memories of a Paleontologist. Cohen, I. Bernard, ed. LC 79-7988. (Three Centuries of Science in America Ser.). 1980. Repr. of 1939 ed. lib. bdg. 28.50x (ISBN 0-405-12570-4). Ayer Co Pubs.

Simpson, George G. Discoverers of the Lost World: An Account of Some of Those Who Brought Back to Life South American Mammals Long Buried in the Abyss of Time. LC 84-2243. (Illus.). 240p. 1984. 25.00x (ISBN 0-300-03188-2). Yale U Pr.

Teilhard De Chardin, Pierre. Lettres De Voyage (1923-1955) 1961. pap. 12.95 (ISBN 0-685-11292-6). French & Eur.

PALEONTOLOGY

see also Extinct Animals; Living Fossils; Micropaleontology; Paleobotany; Sedimentary Structures

also mollusks, Fossil; Vertebrates, Fossil, and similar headings

Abel, Othenio. Palaobiologie und Stammeschichte: Paleobiology & Phylogeny. Gould, Stephen J., ed. LC 79-8320. (The History of Paleontology Ser.). (Ger., Illus.). 1980. Repr. of 1929 ed. lib. bdg. 40.00x (ISBN 0-405-12701-4). Ayer Co Pubs.

Afshar, Freydoun. Taxonomic Revision of the Superspecific Groups of the Cretaceous & Cenozoic Tellinidae. LC 72-98019. (Geological Society of America Ser.: No. 119). pap. 57.80 (ISBN 0-317-28386-3, 2025467). Bks Demand UMI.

Andel, Tjeerd H., et al. Cenozoic History & Paleoceanography of the Central Equatorial Pacific Ocean: A Regional Synthesis Deep Sea Drilling Project Data. LC 75-20815. (Geological Society of America Memoir Ser.: No. 143). pap. 57.80 (ISBN 0-317-29104-1, 2023732). Bks Demand UMI.

Babin, Claude. Elements of Palaeontology. LC 79-1323. 446p. 1980. 72.95 (ISBN 0-471-27577-8, Pub. by Wiley-Interscience); pap. 31.95x (ISBN 0-471-27576-X). Wiley.

Ball, H. W., pref. By. British Palaeozoic Fossils. 4th ed. (Illus.). vi, 203p. 1975. pap. 10.50x (ISBN 0-686-27503-9, Pub. by Brit Mus Nat Hist). Sabbot-Natural Hist Bks.

Barker, Reginald W. Taxonomic Notes on the Species. LC 62-6771. (Society of Economic Paleontologists & Mineralogists, Special Publication: No. 9). pap. 65.50 (ISBN 0-317-27163-6, 2024735). Bks Demand UMI.

Basic Academics, 10 Modules. (Illus.). 940p. 1982. Set. spiral bdg. 100.00x (ISBN 0-87683-224-9); instr's. manual 150.00x (ISBN 0-87683-235-4); lesson plans 35.00x (ISBN 0-87683-246-X). G P Courseware.

Bayer, U. Pattern Recognition Problems in Geology & Paleontology. (Lecture Notes in Earth Sciences: Vol. 2). vii, 229p. 1985. pap. 19.50 (ISBN 0-387-13983-4). Springer-Verlag.

Beede, J. W. & Kniker, H. T. Species of the Genus Schwagerina & Their Stratigraphic Significance. (Bull Ser.: 2433). (Illus.). 96p. 1924. 1.00 (ISBN 0-686-29344-4, BULL 2433). Bur Econ Geology.

Beerbower, James R. Search for the Past: An Introduction to Paleontology. 2nd ed. LC 68-18060. (Illus.). 1968. ref. ed. 34.95 (ISBN 0-13-797316-0). P-H.

Benchley, P. J. Fossils & Climate. 352p. 1984. text ed. 49.95 (ISBN 0-471-90418-X, Pub. by Wiley-Interscience). Wiley.

Bernard, Felix. Elements de Paleontologie. Gould, Stephen J., ed. LC 79-8325. (The History of Paleontology Ser.). (Fr., Illus.). 1980. Repr. of 1895 ed. lib. bdg. 97.50x (ISBN 0-405-12705-7). Ayer Co Pubs.

Binford, Lewis R. Faunal Remains from Klasies River Mouth: Monograph. LC 83-15909. 1984. 39.50 (ISBN 0-12-100070-2). Acad Pr.

Black, Rhona M. Elements of Palaeontology. (Illus.). 1970. 67.50 (ISBN 0-521-07445-2); pap. 21.95 (ISBN 0-521-09615-4). Cambridge U Pr.

Blake, J. F. Cornbrash Fauna, Pts. 1 & 2. Repr. of 1905 ed. Set. 18.00 (ISBN 0-384-04669-X). Johnson Repr.

Bliss, Richard, et al. Fossils: Key to the Present. 1980. pap. 4.95 (ISBN 0-89051-058-X). Master Bks.

Bolliger, Markus. Die Gattung Pulmonaria in Westeuropa. (Phanerogamarum Monographiae VIII). (Ger.). 250p. (Orig.). 1982. text ed. 47.25x (ISBN 3-7682-1338-2). Lubrecht & Cramer.

Boucot, A. J. Evolution & Extinction Rate Controls. (Developments in Palaeontology & Stratigraphy Ser.: Vol. 1). 428p. 1975. 98.00 (ISBN 0-444-41182-8). Elsevier.

Boule, Marcellin. Fossil Men: Elements of Human Paleontology. LC 78-72691. Repr. of 1923 ed. 69.50 (ISBN 0-404-18262-3). AMS Pr.

--L' Homme Fossile de la Chapelle aux Saints. LC 78-72692. Repr. of 1913 ed. 46.50 (ISBN 0-404-18263-1). AMS Pr.

Bowen, Robert. Paleotemperature Analysis. (Methods in Geochemistry & Geophysics Ser.: Vol. 2). 265p. 1966. 74.50 (ISBN 0-444-40074-5). Elsevier.

Brasier, M. D. Microfossils. (Illus., Orig.). 1980. text ed. 30.00x (ISBN 0-04-562001-6); pap. text ed. 15.95x (ISBN 0-04-562002-4). Allen Unwin.

Broadhead, T. W., ed. Lophophorates: Notes for A Short Course Organized by J. T. Dutro. Jr. & R. S. Boardman. (University of Tennessee Studies in Geology). (Illus.). iv, 251p. 1981. pap. 6.00 (ISBN 0-910249-03-2). U of Tenn Geo.

Broadhead, T. W. & Waters, J. A., eds. Echinoderms: Notes for a Short Course. (University of Tennessee Studies in Geology). (Illus.). iv, 235p. 1980. pap. 6.00 (ISBN 0-910249-01-6). U of Tenn Geo.

Brouwer, A. General Palaeontology. Kaye, R. H., tr. LC 67-18435. (Illus.). 1968. pap. 2.45x (ISBN 0-226-07602-4). U of Chicago Pr.

Buckland, William. Geology & Mineralogy Considered with Reference to Natural Theology, 2 vols. Gould, Stephen J., ed. LC 79-8326. (The History of Paleontology Ser.). (Illus.). 1980. Repr. of 1836 ed. Set. lib. bdg. 69.00x (ISBN 0-405-12706-5); lib. bdg. 34.50x ea. Vol. 1 (ISBN 0-405-12707-3). Vol. 2 (ISBN 0-405-12708-1). Ayer Co Pubs.

Butzer, Karl W. Environment & Archeology: An Ecological Approach to Prehistory. 2nd ed. LC 74-115938. (Illus.). 703p. 1971. text ed. 39.95x (ISBN 0-202-33023-0). Aldine Pub.

Carnegie Institution Of Washington. Contributions to Paleontology. Repr. of 1930 ed. 19.00 (ISBN 0-685-02235-8). Johnson Repr.

Casanova, Richard L. & Ratkevich, Ronald P. Illustrated Guide to Fossil Collecting. rev., 3rd ed. LC 81-18788. (Illus.). 240p. 1981. lib. bdg. 12.95 (ISBN 0-87961-112-X); pap. 6.95 (ISBN 0-87961-113-8). Naturegraph.

Castell, C. P., et al. British Caenozoic Fossils: Tertiary & Quaternary. 5th ed. (Illus.). vi, 132p. 1975. pap. 8.50x (ISBN 0-686-27501-2, Pub. by Brit Mus Nat Hist). Sabbot-Natural Hist Bks.

Cleevely, R. J. World Palaeontological Collections. 450p. 1982. 100.00x (ISBN 0-7201-1655-4). Mansell.

Cline, R. M. & Hays, J. D., eds. Investigation of Late Quaternary Paleoceanography & Paleoclimatology. LC 75-40899. (Memoir: No. 145). (Illus.). 1976. 30.00 (ISBN 0-8137-1145-2). Geol Soc.

Colbert, Edwin H. The Great Dinosaur Hunters & Their Discoveries. LC 84-4204. 384p. 1984. pap. 6.95 (ISBN 0-486-24701-5). Dover.

Cope, Edward D. The Origin of the Fittest: Essays on Evolution & the Primary Factors of Organic Evolution, 2 vols. in one. LC 73-17813. (Natural Sciencesin America Ser.). 1066p. 1974. Repr. 69.50x (ISBN 0-405-05729-6). Ayer Co Pubs.

Cowgill, et al. History of Laguna De Petenixil: A Small Lake in Northern Guatemala. (Connecticut Academy of Arts Sciences Memoirs Ser.: Vol. 17). (Illus.). 126p. 1966. pap. 15.00 (ISBN 0-208-00784-9). Shoe String.

Cracraft, Joel & Eldredge, Niles, eds. Phylogenetic Analysis & Paleonology. LC 78-31404. (Illus.). 256p. 1979. 39.00x (ISBN 0-231-04692-8); pap. 14.00x (ISBN 0-231-04693-6). Columbia U Pr.

Crimes, T. P. & Harper, J. C. Trace Fossils Two: Geological Journal Special Issue, Vol. 9. (Liverpool Geological Society & the Manchester Geological Association Ser.). 360p. 1977. 94.95 (ISBN 0-471-27756-8, Pub. by Wiley-Interscience). Wiley.

Croucher, Ronald & Woolley, Alan R. Fossils, Minerals & Rocks: Collection & Preservation. LC 82-1282. (Illus.). 64p. 1982. 7.95 (ISBN 0-521-24736-5, Copublished with the British Museum). Cambridge U Pr.

Curtis, Doris M. Sedimentary Processes: Diagenesis. (Society of Economic Paleontologists & Mineralogists, Reprint Ser.: No. 1). pap. 55.50 (ISBN 0-317-27145-8, 2024747). Bks Demand UMI.

Cuvier, Georges. Essay on the Theory of the Earth: Mineralogical Notes, & an Account of Cuvier's Geological Discoveries. Albritton, Claude C., Jr., ed. Kerr, Robert, tr. LC 77-6517. (History of Geology Ser.). (Illus.). 1978. Repr. of 1817 ed. lib. bdg. 32.00 (ISBN 0-405-10439-1). Ayer Co Pubs.

--Memoirs on Fossil Elephants & on Reconstruction of the Genera Palaeotherium & Anoplotherium. Gould, Stephen J., ed. LC 79-8327. (Fr., Illus.). 1980. Repr. of 1812 ed. lib. bdg. 80.00x (ISBN 0-405-12709-X). Ayer Co Pubs.

Danielli, H. C. The Fossil Alga Girvanella Nicholson & Etheridge. 20.00x (ISBN 0-686-78656-4, Pub. by Brit Mus Pubns England). State Mutual Bk.

De Beer, Gavin. Archaeopteryx Lithographica: A Study Based on the British Museum Specimen. (Illus.). 68p. 1966. Repr. of 1954 ed. 22.50x (ISBN 0-565-00224-4, Pub. by Brit Mus Nat Hist England). Sabbot-Natural Hist Bks.

Denison, Robert. Acanthodii. Kuhn, O. & Schultze, H. P., eds. (Handbook of Paleoichthyology: Vol. 5). (Illus.). 62p. 1979. text ed. 41.30x (ISBN 3-437-30291-4). Lubrecht & Cramer.

--Placodermi. Kuhn, O. & Schultz, H. P., eds. (Handbook of Paleoichthyology: Vol. 2). (Illus.). 128p. 1978. text ed. 55.05x (ISBN 3-437-30265-5). Lubrecht & Cramer.

Dietrich, R. V. & Wicander, E. Reed. Minerals, Rock & Fossils. LC 82-20220. (Self-Teaching Guides Ser.). 212p. 1983. pap. text ed. 9.95 (ISBN 0-471-89883-X, Pub. by Wiley Pr). Wiley.

D'Orbigny, Alcide. Cours Elementaire de Paleontologie et de Geologie Stratgraphiques, Vol. 2, Pt. 2. (Fr.). 33.00 (ISBN 0-405-12744-8). Ayer Co Pubs.

D'Orbigny, Alcide D. Cours Elementaire de Paleontologie et de Geologie Stratigraphiques: Beginning Course in Paleontology & Stratigraphic Geology, 2 vols. in 3. Gould, Stephen J., ed. LC 79-8339. (The History of Paleontology Ser.). (Fr., Illus.). 1980. Repr. of 1849 ed. Set. lib. bdg. 98.00x (ISBN 0-405-12725-1); Vol. 1. 33.00 (ISBN 0-405-12726-X); Vol. 2. 33.00 (ISBN 0-405-12727-8). Ayer Co Pubs.

Driesch, Angela von den. A Guide to the Measurement of Animal Bones from Archaeological Sites. LC 76-49773. (Peabody Museum Bulletins: No. 1). (Illus.). 1976. pap. text ed. 10.00x (ISBN 0-87365-950-3). Peabody Harvard.

Dunbar, Carl O. & Waage, Karl M. Historical Geology. 3rd ed. LC 72-89681. (Illus.). 556p. 1969. text ed. 39.95x (ISBN 0-471-22507-X). Wiley.

Dyer, Judith & Schram, Frederick. A Manual of Invertebrate Paleontology. (Illus.). 165p. (Orig.). 1983. pap. text ed. 6.80 (ISBN 0-87563-237-8). Stipes.

Edwards, W. N. The Early History of Palaeontology. (Illus.). 1976. pap. 2.75x (ISBN 0-565-00658-4, Pub. by Brit Mus Nat Hist). Sabbot-Natural Hist Bks.

Emerson, B. K., et al. Geology & Paleontology. (Harriman Alaska Expedition, 1899 Ser.). Repr. of 1904 ed. 41.00 (ISBN 0-527-38164-0). Kraus Repr.

Flint, Richard F. Earth & Its History. (Illus.). 500p. 1973. text ed. 13.95x (ISBN 0-393-09377-8). Norton.

Fox, Norman. Fossils: Hard Facts from the Earth. LC 81-68315. 1981. pap. 3.95 (ISBN 0-89051-077-6); tchr's guide 2.95x (ISBN 0-686-33037-4). Master Bks.

Frailey, David. An Early Miocene (Arikareean) Fauna from North-Central Florida (the Sb-1a Local Fauna) (Occasional Papers: No. 75). 20p. 1978. pap. 1.25 (ISBN 0-686-79817-1). U of KS Mus Nat Hist.

Fundamentals of Fossil Simulator Instructor Training. 270p. 1984. looseleaf 50.00x (ISBN 0-87683-370-9). G P Courseware.

Gaudry, Albert. Essai Paleontologie Philosophique: Ouvage Faisant Echainementd Monde Animal les Temps Geologiques: Essay in Philosophical Paleontology: a Sequel to the Interconnections of the Animal World in Geologic Time. Gould, Stephen J., ed. LC 79-8331. (History of Paleontology Ser.). (Fr., Illus.). 1980. Repr. of 1896 ed. lib. bdg. 21.00x (ISBN 0-405-12712-X). Ayer Co Pubs.

Goldring, Winifred. Handbook of Paleontology for Beginners & Amateurs: The Fossils, Pt. 1. (Illus.). 394p. 1960. Repr. 6.75 (ISBN 0-87710-363-1). Paleo Res.

Gould, Stephen J., ed. The Complete Works of Vladimir Kovalevsky: Original Anthology. LC 79-8354. (The History of Paleontology Ser.). (Fr., Ger., Eng., Illus.). 1980. lib. bdg. 68.50x (ISBN 0-405-12750-2). Ayer Co Pubs.

--The Evolution of Gryphaea: Original Anthology. LC 79-8357. (The History of Paleontology Ser.). (Illus.). 1980. lib. bdg. 37.00x (ISBN 0-405-12751-0). Ayer Co Pubs.

--The History of Paleontology, 34 bks, Vols. 1-20. (Illus.). 1980. Repr. Set. lib. bdg. 2077.00x (ISBN 0-405-12700-6). Ayer Co Pubs.

--Louis Dollo's Papers on Paleontology & Evolution: Original Anthology. LC 79-8355. (The History of Paleontology Ser.). (Fr. & Eng., Illus.). 1980. lib. bdg. 63.00x (ISBN 0-405-12752-9). Ayer Co Pubs.

Gregory, K. J., ed. Background to Palaeohydrology: A Perspective. 408p. 1983. 59.95x (ISBN 0-471-90179-2, Pub. by Wiley-Interscience). Wiley.

Hakansson, H. & Gerloff, J., eds. Diatomaceae III: Festschrift Niels Foged on the Occassion of his 75th Birthday. (Nova Hedwigia Beiheft: 73.). (Eng. & Ger., Illus.). 386p. (Orig.). 1982. lib. bdg. 59.10x (ISBN 3-7682-5473-9). Lubrecht & Cramer.

Hallam, A. Atlas of Palaeobiogeography, 1972. 531p. 1973. 106.50 (ISBN 0-444-40975-0). Elsevier.

Hallam, A., ed. Patterns of Evolution: As Illustrated by the Fossil Record. (Developments in Paleontology & Stratigraphy Ser.: Vol. 5). 592p. 1977. 93.75 (ISBN 0-444-41495-9). Elsevier.

Hamilton, et al. Larousse Guide to Minerals, Rocks & Fossils. LC 77-71167. 1977. 15.95 (ISBN 0-88332-079-7, 8095); pap. 9.95 (ISBN 0-88332-078-9, 8094). Larousse.

Hansan, Hans J. & Lykke-Anderson, Anna-Lisa. Wall Structure & Classification of Fossil & Recent Elphidiid & Nonionid Foraminifera. 1976. 19.00x (ISBN 0-686-75227-9). Universitet.

Harrison, Jessica A. The Carnivora of the Edson Local Fauna (Late Hemphillian) Kansas. LC 83-600029. (Smithsonian Contributions to Paleobiology: No. 54). pap. 20.00 (ISBN 0-317-29737-6, 2022200). Bks Demand UMI.

Heilprin, Angelo. The Geographical & Geological Distribution of Animals: The International Science Series Vol. 57. LC 73-17824. (Natural Sciences in America Ser.). (Illus.). 458p. 1974. Repr. 31.00x (ISBN 0-405-05742-3). Ayer Co Pubs.

Heirtzler, J. R., et al, eds. Indian Ocean Geology & Biostratigraphy. LC 77-88320. (Special Publication Ser.). (Illus.). 616p. 1978. 25.00 (ISBN 0-87590-208-1). Am Geophysical.

Hilber, Oswald. Die Gattung Pleurotus Kummer Unter Besonderer Beruecksichtigung des Pleurotus-Eryngii-Komplexes. (Bibliotheca Mycologica Ser.: Vol. 87). (Ger., Illus.). 447p. (Orig.). 1982. text ed. 70.00x (ISBN 3-7682-1335-8). Lubrecht & Cramer.

Hill, Dorothy. Treatise on Invertebrate Paleontology, Part E, Vol. 1: Archaeocyatha. rev. & enl. ed. Teichert, Curt, ed. LC 53-12913. Tr. of Treatise on Invertebrate Paleontology, Part E - Archaeocyatha & Porifera by Vladimir J. Okulitch. (Illus.). xxx, 158p. 1972. 16.00 (ISBN 0-8137-3105-4). Geol Soc.

Hill, Dorothy, ed. Treatise on Invertebrate Paleontology, Pt. F, Suppl. 1: Coelenterata (Anthozoa: Rugosa & Tabulata) LC 53-12913. (Illus.). 1981. 38.00 (ISBN 0-8137-3029-5). Geol Soc.

Hind, W. Carboniferous Lamellibranchiata, Vol. 2. Repr. of 1905 ed. 40.00 (ISBN 0-384-23280-9). Johnson Repr.

Hitchcock, Edward. A Report on the Sandstone of the Connecticut Valley, Especially Its Fossil Footmarks. LC 73-17825. (Natural Sciences in America Ser.). (Illus.). 256p. 1974. Repr. 29.00x (ISBN 0-405-05743-1). Ayer Co Pubs.

Hoare, Richard. Journal of Paleontology, Vols. 26-50, 1952-1976. 1980. 21.95 (ISBN 0-87972-145-6); pap. 10.95 (ISBN 0-87972-146-4). Bowling Green Univ.

Honjo, S., ed. Ocean Biocoenosis: Microfossil Counterparts in Sediment Traps. (Micropaleontology Special Publications Ser.: No. 5). 1982. 50.00 (ISBN 0-686-84259-6). Am Mus Natl Hist.

Horowitz, A. S. & Potter, P. E. Introductory Petrography of Fossils. LC 73-142385. (Illus.). 1971. 56.00 (ISBN 0-387-05275-5). Springer-Verlag.

Hoskins, Donald M., et al. Fossil Collecting in Pennsylvania. 3rd, Rev. ed. (General Geology Report Ser.: No. 40). (Illus.). 215p. (Orig.). 1983. pap. 3.25 (ISBN 0-8182-0019-7). Commonweal PA.

Hough, Jack L., ed. Turbidity Currents & the Transportation of Coarse Sediments to Deep Water: A Symposium. LC 52-2310. (Society of Economic Paleontologists & Mineralogists, Special Publication: No. 2). pap. 27.80 (ISBN 0-317-27102-4, 2024731). Bks Demand UMI.

Hurzeler, Johannes. Contribution a L'odontologie et a la Phylogenese du Genre Pliopithecus Gervais. Bd. with Die Primatenfunde aus der miozanen Spaltenfullung von Neudorf an der March, Devin ska Nova Ves, Tschechoslowakei. Zapfe, Helmuth. 1961. LC 78-72721. 1954. 79.50 (ISBN 0-404-18296-8). AMS Pr.

Jehan, L. F. Dictionnaire de Cosmogonie et de Paleontologie. Migne, J. P., ed. (Nouvelle Encyclopedie Theologique Ser.: Vol. 48). (Fr.). 732p. Repr. of 1854 ed. lib. bdg. 93.00x (ISBN 0-89241-286-0). Caratzas.

Jessen, Hans L. Schultergurtel & Pectoralflosse Bei Actinopterygiern. (Fossils & Strata Ser: No. 1). 101p. 1973. 25.00x (ISBN 8-200-09288-7, Dist. by Columbia U Pr). Universitet.

Keller, Fred, et al. Introduction to Historical Geology. (Illus.). 1979. lab manual 8.95x (ISBN 0-89459-194-0). Hunter Textbks.

Kier, Porter M. Fossil Spatangoid Echinoids of Cuba. LC 83-600065. (Smithsonian Contributions to Paleobiology: No. 55). pap. 85.50 (ISBN 0-317-28248-4, 2022657). Bks Demand UMI.

King, James E. Fossils. (Story of Illinois Ser.: No. 14). (Illus.). 68p. 1982. pap. 1.00 (ISBN 0-89792-092-9). Ill St Museum.

Kloidt, M. & Lysek, G. Die Epiphylle Pilzfora von Acer Platanoides L. (Bibliotheca Mycologica 86 Ser.). 144p. (Orig.). 1982. 19.70 (ISBN 3-7682-1332-3). Lubrecht & Cramer.

Kurten, Bjorn. The Age of Mammals. LC 79-177479. (Illus.). 250p. 1972. 30.00x (ISBN 0-231-03624-8); pap. 13.00x (ISBN 0-231-03647-7). Columbia U Pr.

--The Cave Bear Story. Life & Death of a Vanished Animal. LC 76-3723. (Illus.). 163p. 1976. 21.50x (ISBN 0-231-04017-2). Columbia U Pr.

Lambert, Mark. Fossils. Lye, Keith, ed. LC 79-12921. (Arco Fact Guides in Color). (Illus.). 1979. 6.95 (ISBN 0-668-04805-0). Arco.

Lane, N. Gary. Life of the Past. 1978. pap. text ed. 18.95 (ISBN 0-675-08411-3). Merrill.

Laporte, Leo F., intro. by. The Fossil Record & Evolution. LC 81-17401. (Readings from Scientific American Ser.). (Illus.). 225p. 1982. text ed. 28.95 (ISBN 0-7167-1402-7); pap. text ed. 14.95 (ISBN 0-7167-1403-5). W H Freeman.

Laporte, Leo F., ed. Reefs in Time & Space: Selected Examples from the Recent & Ancient. LC 74-165238. (Society of Economic Paleontologists & Mineralogists, Special Publication: No. 18). pap. 65.00 (ISBN 0-317-27147-4, 2024745). Bks Demand UMI.

Leary, Richard L. Paleozoic Paleozoological Type & Figured Specimens. (Inventory of the Collections Ser.). 259p. Ill St Museum.

Le Blanc, Rufus J. & Breeding, Julia G., eds. Regional Aspects of Carbonate Deposition: A Symposium. LC 57-2837. (Society of Economic Paleontologists & Mineralogists, Special Publication: No. 5). pap. 53.80 (ISBN 0-317-27104-0, 2024732). Bks Demand UMI.

Lehmann, Ulrich. Palaeontologisches Woerterbuch. (Ger.). 1977. pap. 15.95 (ISBN 3-423-03039-9, M-7577, Pub. by Dtv). French & Eur.

Leidy, Joseph. The Extinct Mammalian Fauna of Dakota & Nebraska, & a Account of Some Allied Forms from Other Localities: Synopsis of the Mammalian Remains of North America. 2nd ed. LC 73-17828. (Natural Sciences in America Ser.: Vol. 3). (Illus.). 536p. 1974. Repr. 37.50x (ISBN 0-405-05746-6). Ayer Co Pubs.

Lisitzin, Alexander P. Sedimentation in the World Ocean with Emphasis on the Nature, Distribution & Behavior of Marine Suspensions. Rodolfo, Kelvin S., ed. LC 72-172081. (Society of Economic Paleontologists & Mineralogists, Special Publication: No. 17). pap. 58.00 (ISBN 0-317-27149-0, 2024744). Bks Demand UMI.

Luff, Rosemary-Margaret. Animal Remains in Archaeology. (Shire Archaeology Ser.: No. 33). (Illus.). 64p. 1983. pap. 5.95 (ISBN 0-85263-633-4, Pub. by Shire Pubns England). Seven Hills Bks.

MacDonald, James. A Fossil Collector's Handbook: A Paleontology Field Guide. (Illus.). 240p. 1983. 16.95 (ISBN 0-13-329235-5); pap. 8.95 (ISBN 0-13-329227-4). P-H.

MacFall, Russell & Wollin, Jay C. Fossils for Amateurs: A Guide to Collecting & Preparing Invertebrate Fossils. 2nd ed. 384p. 1983. 17.95 (ISBN 0-442-26348-1); pap. 11.95 (ISBN 0-442-26350-3). Van Nos Reinhold.

McKerrow, W. Stuart, ed. The Ecology of Fossils: An Illustrated Guide. (Illus.). 1978. text ed. 37.50x (ISBN 0-262-13144-7); pap. 12.50 (ISBN 0-262-63086-9). MIT Pr.

Mantell, Gideon A. The Medals of Creation: Or, First Lessons in Geology & the Study of Organic Remains, 2 vols. 2nd rev. ed. Gould, Stephen J., ed. LC 79-8334. (The History of Paleontology Ser.). (Illus.). 1980. Repr. of 1854 ed. Set. lib. bdg. 80.00x (ISBN 0-405-12716-2); lib. bdg. 40.00x ea. Vol. 1 (ISBN 0-405-12717-0). Vol. 2 (ISBN 0-405-12718-9). Ayer Co Pubs.

Martinsson, Anders, ed. Taxonomy, Ecology & Identity of Conodonts: Fossils & Strata No. 15. 192p. (Orig.). 1984. pap. 35.00x (ISBN 82-00-06737-8). Universitet.

Matthew, William D. Climate & Evolution. LC 73-17830. (Natural Sciences in America Ser.). (Illus.). 150p. 1974. Repr. 12.00x (ISBN 0-405-05748-2). Ayer Co Pubs.

Meggers, Betty J. Amazonia: Man & Culture in a Counterfeit Paradise. LC 74-141427. (Worlds of Man Ser.). 1971. 17.95x (ISBN 0-88295-608-6); pap. 8.95x (ISBN 0-88295-609-4). Harlan Davidson.

Mellett, J. S. Paleobiology of North American Hyaenodon (Mammalia Creodonta) Szalay, F. S., ed. (Contributions to Vertebrate Evolution: Vol. 1). 1977. 32.00 (ISBN 3-8055-2379-3). S Karger.

Mial, L. C. Sirenoid Ganoids, Vol. 2. Repr. of 1907 ed. 70.00 (ISBN 0-384-38760-8). Johnson Repr.

Middlemiss, F. A. Fossils. 2nd ed. (Introducing Geology Ser.). 1976. pap. text ed. 5.95x (ISBN 0-04-560005-8). Allen Unwin.

Middleton, Gerard V., ed. Primary Sedimentary Structures & Their Hydrodynamic Interpretation: A Symposium. LC 76-219474. (Society of Economic Paleontologists & Mineralogists, Special Publication: No. 12). pap. 68.00 (ISBN 0-317-27158-X, 2024738). Bks Demand UMI.

Miller, Hugh. The Testimony of the Rocks: Or, Geology in Its Bearings on Two Theologies, Natural & Revealed. Gould, Stephen J., ed. LC 79-8336. (The History of Paleontology Ser.). (Illus.). 1980. Repr. of 1857 ed. lib. bdg. 42.00x (ISBN 0-405-12720-0). Ayer Co Pubs.

Moody, Richard. Fossils. (Illus.). 128p. 1979. 8.95 (ISBN 0-600-36313-9). Transatlantic.

Moore, Ellen J. Fossil Mollusks of Coastal Oregon. LC 71-634653. (Studies in Geology Ser: No. 10). (Illus.). 64p. 1971. pap. 5.95 (ISBN 0-87071-068-0). Oreg St U Pr.

Moore, Raymond C., ed. Treatise on Invertebrate Paleontology, Pt. N: Mollusca 6 (Bivalvia, Vol. 3 (Oysters) LC 53-12913. (Illus.). 1971. 19.50 (ISBN 0-8137-3026-0). Geol Soc.

Munthe, Jens. Catalog of Fossil Type & Figured Specimens in the Milwaukee Public Museum. 27p. 1980. 2.75 (ISBN 0-89326-065-7). Milwaukee Pub Mus.

Neale, J. M. & Brasier, M. D. Microfossils From Recent & Fossil Shelfseas. (British Micropalaeontological Society Ser.). 355p. 1981. 96.95x (ISBN 0-470-27220-1). Halsted Pr.

Nicholson, Henry A. The Ancient Life-History of the Earth: A Comprehensive Outline of the Principles & Leading Facts of Paleontological Science. Gould, Stephen J., ed. LC 79-83338. (The History of Paleontology Ser.). (Illus.). 1980. Repr. of 1877 ed. lib. bdg. 30.00x (ISBN 0-405-12724-3). Ayer Co Pubs.

Nield, E. W. & Tucker, V. C. Palaeontology: An Introduction. (Illus.). 250p. 1985. 25.00 (ISBN 0-08-023854-8); pap. 12.50 (ISBN 0-08-023853-X). Pergamon.

Oakley, Kenneth P., et al, eds. Catalogue of Fossil Hominids. Incl. Pt. 1. Africa. 223p. pap. text ed. 35.00x; Pt. 2. Europe. pap. text ed. 56.00x (ISBN 0-565-00711-4); Pt. 3. Americas, Asia Australasia. pap. text ed. 38.50x (ISBN 0-565-00767-X). (Illus.). 1980. pap. (Pub. by Brit Mus Nat Hist). Sabbot-Natural Hist Bks.

Owen, Richard. Paleontology: Or, a Systematic Summary of Extinct Animals & Their Geological Relations. Gould, Stephen J., ed. LC 79-8342. (The History of Paleontology Ser.). (Illus.). 1980. Repr. of 1860 ed. lib. bdg. 37.00x (ISBN 0-405-12732-4). Ayer Co Pubs.

Packard, Earl L. New Turtle from the Marine Miocene of Oregon. (Studies in Geology Ser: No. 2). 32p. 1940. pap. 3.95x (ISBN 0-87071-062-1). Oreg St U Pr.

Parkinson, James. Organic Remains of a Former World, 3 vols. Albritton, Claude C., Jr., ed. LC 77-6534. (History of Geology Ser.). (Illus.). 1978. lib. bdg. 99.00 (ISBN 0-405-10454-5). Ayer Co Pubs.

Parmalee, Paul W., et al. Pleistocene & Recent Vertebrate Faunas from Crankshaft Cave, Missouri. (Reports of Investigations Ser.: No.14). (Illus.). 37p. 1969. pap. 1.00 (ISBN 0-89792-036-8). Ill St Museum.

Phillips, D. Catalogue of the Type & Figured Specimens of Mesozoic Ammonoidea in the British Museum (Natural History) 1977. pap. 28.00x (ISBN 0-565-00790-4, Pub. by Brit Mus Nat Hist). Sabbot-Natural Hist Bks.

Pictet, Francois J. Traite Elementaire De Paleontologie Histoire Naturelle Des Animaux Fossiles Consideres Ans Leur S Rapports Zoologiques et Geologiques, 4 vols. Gould, Stephen J., ed. LC 79-8344. (History of Paleontology Ser.). (Fr., Illus.). 1980. Repr. of 1844 ed. Set. lib. bdg. 174.00x (ISBN 0-405-12734-0); lib. bdg. 43.50x ea. Vol. 1 (ISBN 0-405-12735-9). Vol. 2 (ISBN 0-405-12736-7). Vol. 3 (ISBN 0-405-12737-5). Vol. 4 (ISBN 0-405-12738-3). Ayer Co Pubs.

Pojeta, J., Jr. & Pope, J. K., eds. Studies in Paleontology & Stratigraphy. (Illus.). 456p. 1975. 25.00 (ISBN 0-87710-296-1). Paleo Res.

Potter, P. E. & Pettijohn, F. J. Paleocurrents & Basin Analysis. 2nd ed. LC 76-30293. (Illus.). 1977. 39.00 (ISBN 0-387-07952-1). Springer-Verlag.

Pregill, Gregory. Late Pleistocene Herpetofaunas from Puerto Rico. (Miscellaneous Papers: No. 71). 72p. 1981. 4.25 (ISBN 0-317-04884-8). U of KS Mus Nat Hist.

Quenstedt, Friedrich A. Handbuch der Petrefaktenkunde: Handbook for the Study of Fossile. Gould, Stephen J., ed. LC 79-8345. (The History of Paleontology Ser.). (Ger., Illus.). 1980. Repr. of 1852 ed. Set. lib. bdg. 124.00x (ISBN 0-405-12739-1); lib. bdg. 62.00x ea. Vol. 1 (ISBN 0-405-12745-6). Vol. 2 (ISBN 0-405-12749-9). Ayer Co Pubs.

Raup, David M. & Stanley, Steven M. Principles of Paleontology. 2nd ed. LC 77-17443. (Illus.). 481p. 1978. text ed. 31.95x (ISBN 0-7167-0022-0). W H Freeman.

Renzglia, Karen S. Comparative Developmental Investigation of the Gametophyte Generation in the Metzgeriales (Hepatophyta) (Bryophytorum Bibliotheca Ser.: 24). (Illus.). 253p. (Orig.). 1982. text ed. 47.25x (ISBN 3-7682-1336-6). Lubrecht & Cramer.

Rigby, J. Keith & Hamblin, W. K., eds. Recognition of Ancient Sedimentary Environments. LC 72-194231. (Society of Economic Paleontologists & Mineralogists, Special Publication: No. 16). pap. 87.50 (ISBN 0-317-27126-1, 2024741). Bks Demand UMI.

Rixon, A. E. Fossil Animal Remains: Their Preparation & Conservation. (Illus.). 304p. 1976. pap. 39.50 (ISBN 0-485-12028-3, Pub. by Athlone Pr Ltd). Longwood Pub Group.

Robison, R. A., ed. Treatise on Invertebrate Paleontology, Part G: Bryoza, Vol. 1. rev. ed. 1983. 48.00 (ISBN 0-8137-3107-0). Geol Soc.

--Treatise on Invertebrate Paleontology, Pt. W, Suppl. 2: Conodonta. LC 53-12913. (Illus.). 1981. 18.00 (ISBN 0-8137-3028-7). Geol Soc.

Rudwick, Martin J. The Meaning of Fossils: Episodes in the History of Palaeontology. 2nd ed. LC 84-28080. (Illus.). 288p. 1985. pap. 11.95 (ISBN 0-226-73103-0). U of Chicago Pr.

Sarjeant, W. A. S., ed. Terrestrial Trace Fossils. LC 82-21393. (Benchmark Papers in Geology: Vol. 76). 432p. 1983. 46.50 (ISBN 0-87933-079-1). Van Nos Reinhold.

Schindewolf, Otto H. Grundfragen der Palontologie: Geologische Zeitmessung, Organische Stammesentwicklung, Biologische Systematick (Basic Question of Paleontology: Geologic Chronology, Organic Phylogeny, Biologic Systematics. Gould, Stephen J., ed. LC 79-8347. (Ger., Illus.). 1980. Repr. of 1950 ed. lib. bdg. 46.00x (ISBN 0-405-12741-3). Ayer Co Pubs.

Schmalhausen, Ivan I. Origin of Terrestrial Vertebrates. Kelso, Leon, tr. 1968. 66.00 (ISBN 0-12-625750-7). Acad Pr.

Schopf, Thomas J., ed. Models in Paleobiology. LC 72-78387. (Illus.). 250p. 1972. 12.95x (ISBN 0-87735-325-5). Freeman Cooper.

Schopf, Thomas J. & Gould, Stephen J., eds. Presidential Addresses of the Paleontological Society: Original Anthology. LC 79-8358. (The History of Paleontology Ser.). (Illus.). 1980. lib. bdg. 60.00x (ISBN 0-405-12753-7). Ayer Co Pubs.

Schultze, Hans-Peter, et al. Type & Figured Specimens of Fossil Vertebrates in the Collection of the University of Kansas Museum of Natural History: Part I. Fossil Fishes. (Miscellaneous Papers: No. 73). 53p. 1982. 8.25 (ISBN 0-317-04815-5). U of KS Mus Nat Hist.

Scott, J. Palaeontology: An Introduction. (Illus.). 1973. 12.50 (ISBN 0-900707-22-4). Heinman.

Scott, James. Palaentology. 160p. 49.00x (ISBN 0-89771-000-2). State Mutual Bk.

--Palaeontology: An Introduction. 1978. 9.95 (ISBN 0-8008-6213-9). Taplinger.

Seposki, J. John, Jr. A Compendium of Fossil Marine Families. 125p. 1982. 18.50 (ISBN 0-89326-081-9). Milwaukee Pub Mus.

Shipman, Pat. Life History of a Fossil: Introduction to Taphonomy & Paleoecology. (Illus.). 1981. text ed. 19.95x (ISBN 0-674-53085-3). Harvard U Pr.

Simpson, George G. Attending Marvels: A Patagonian Journal. LC 82-13438. (Phoenix Ser.). 296p. 1982. pap. 9.50 (ISBN 0-226-75935-0). U of Chicago Pr.

--Fossils & the History of Life. LC 83-4423. (Scientific American Library). (Illus.). 239p. 1983. 27.95 (ISBN 0-7167-1564-3). W H Freeman.

--Fossils & the Theory of Life. (Illus.). 1984. 27.95 (ISBN 0-317-13779-4). W H Freeman.

Skinner, Brian J., ed. Paleontology & Paleoenvironments. (The Earth & Its Inhabitants: Selected Readings from American Scientist Ser.). (Illus.). 210p. (Orig.). 1981. pap. 10.95x (ISBN 0-913232-93-9). W Kaufmann.

Smith, Andrew. Echinoid Palaeobiology. (Special Topics in Palaeontology Ser.). (Illus.). 224p. 1984. text ed. 35.00x (ISBN 0-04-563001-1); pap. text ed. 19.95x (ISBN 0-04-563002-X). Allen Unwin.

Smith, Fred H. & Spencer, Frank. The Origins of Modern Humans: A World Survey of Fossil Evidence. LC 84-859. 612p. 1984. 70.00 (ISBN 0-8451-0233-8). A R Liss.

Spoczynska, Joy O. Fossils: A Study in Evolution. (Illus.). 208p. 1971. 12.50x (ISBN 0-87471-061-8). Rowman.

Sutherland, Patrick K. & Manger, Walter L., eds. Biostratigraphy, Vol. 2. 640p. 75.00 (ISBN 0-8093-1169-0). S Ill U Pr.

Swinton, W. E. Fossil Birds. 3rd ed. (Illus.). 1975. pap. text ed. 3.25x (ISBN 0-565-05397-3, Pub. by Brit Mus Nat Hist). Sabbot-Natural Hist Bks.

Symposium on Silica in Sediments, 1958. Silica in Sediments: A Symposium. Ireland, H. Andrew, ed. LC 60-50. (Society of Economic Paleontologists & Mineralogists, Special Publication: No. 7). pap. 49.30 (ISBN 0-317-27166-0, 2024734). Bks Demand UMI.

Takayanagi, T. & Saito, T., eds. Progress in Micropaleontology: Papers in Honor of Professor Kiyoshi Asano. (Micropaleontology Special Publications Ser.). 422p. 1976. 35.00 (ISBN 0-686-84247-2). Am Mus Natl Hist.

Tasch, Paul. Paleobiology of the Invertebrates: Data Retrieval from the Fossil Record. 2nd ed. LC 79-14929. 975p. 1980. text ed. 52.95 (ISBN 0-471-05272-8). Wiley.

Traverse, A. Paleopalynology. 500p. 1985. text ed. 75.00x (ISBN 0-04-561001-0); pap. text ed. 34.95x (ISBN 0-04-561002-9). Allen Unwin.

Valentine, James W., ed. Phanerozoic Diversity Patterns: Profiles in Microevolution. LC 84-42904. (Series in Geology & Paleontology). (Illus.). 430p. 1985. text ed. 50.00x (ISBN 0-691-08374-6); pap. text ed. 15.00x (ISBN 0-691-08375-4). Princeton U Pr.

Van Landingham, S. L. Catalogue of the Fossil & Recent Genera & Species of Diatoms & Their Syhonyms: Navicula, Pt. 5. 2963p. 1975. text ed. 35.00x (ISBN 3-7682-0475-8). Lubrecht & Cramer.

--Catalogue of the Fossil & Recent Genera & Species of Diatoms & Their Synonyms: Neidium-Rhocicosigma, Pt. 6. 3605p. 1978. text ed. 35.00x (ISBN 3-7682-0476-6). Lubrecht & Cramer.

Velikovsky, Immanuel. Earth in Upheaval. 1980. pap. 3.95 (ISBN 0-671-52465-8). PB.

Von Zittel, K. A. Geschichte der Geologie und Paleontologie. 1889. 50.00 (ISBN 0-384-71020-4). Johnson Repr.

--Text-Book of Palaeontology, 3 vols. Eastmann, C. R. & Woodward, A. Smith, eds. Incl. Vol. 2. Vertebrates I: Pisces, Amphibia, Reptile, Aves. 17.50 (ISBN 3-7682-7100-5); Vol. 3. Mammalia. 16.00 (ISBN 3-7682-7103-X). 1964. Set. 85.00 (ISBN 3-7682-7100-5). Lubrecht & Cramer.

Watson, D. M. Paleontology & Modern Biology. 1951. 49.50x (ISBN 0-686-83673-1). Elliots Bks.

Weishampel, D. B. Evolution of Jaw Mechanisms in Ornithopod Dinosaurs. (Advances in Anatomy, Embryology, & Cell Biology Ser.: Vol. 87). (Illus.). 110p. 1984. pap. 24.00 (ISBN 0-387-13114-0). Springer-Verlag.

Whittington, H. B. The Burgess Shale. LC 85-2297. 160p. 1985. 25.00x (ISBN 0-300-03348-6). Yale U Pr.

Wiley, E. O. The Phylogeny & Biogeography of Fossil Recent Gars (Actincopterygii: Lepisosteidae) (Miscellaneous Publications: No. 64). 111p. 1976. pap. 5.75 (ISBN 0-686-79832-5). U of KS Mus Nat Hist.

Wilson, Robert W. The Condylarth Genus Ellipsodon. (Museum Ser.: Vol. 9, No. 5). 12p. 1956. 1.25 (ISBN 0-317-04818-X). U of KS Mus Nat Hist.

Yatkola, Daniel & Tanner, Lloyd G. Brachypothermian: From the Tertiary North America. (Occasional Papers: No. 77). 11p. 1979. 1.25 (ISBN 0-317-04821-X). U of KS Mus Nat Hist.

Yen, T. F. & Kawahara, F. K., eds. Chemical & Geochemical Aspects of Fossil Energy Extraction. LC 82-72858. (Illus.). 266p. 1983. 45.00 (ISBN 0-250-40462-1). Butterworth.

Zangerl, R. Chondrichthyes I: Paleozoic Elasmobranchii. Kuhn, O. & Schultz, H. P., eds. (Handbook of Paleoichthyology: Vol. 3A). (Illus.). 115p. 1981. text ed. 72.25X (ISBN 3-437-30337-6). Lubrecht & Cramer.

Ziegler, B. Introduction to Palaeobiology: General Paleontology. Muir, R., tr. LC 82-15843. (Geology Ser.). 225p. 1983. 74.95X (ISBN 0-470-27552-9); pap. 29.95 (ISBN 0-470-20067-7). Halsted Pr.

PALEONTOLOGY–BIBLIOGRAPHY

Bibliography of Fossil Vertebrates, 1969-1972. (Geological Society of America Memoir Ser.: No. 141). pap. 160.00 (ISBN 0-317-10855-7, 2007185). Bks Demand UMI.

Selected Works in Nineteenth Century North American Paleontology. LC 73-17841. (Natural Sciences in America Ser.). 482p. 1974. Repr. 25.00x (ISBN 0-405-05763-6). Ayer Co Pubs.

Shimer, Harvey W. & Shrock, Robert R. Index Fossils of North America. (Illus.). 1944. 75.00x (ISBN 0-262-19001-X). MIT Pr.

Simpson, George G. American Mesozoic Mammalia. (Illus.). 1929. 150.00x (ISBN 0-685-89733-8). Elliots Bks.

PALEONTOLOGY–SCANDINAVIA

Bassett, Michael G. & Cocks, Leonard R. A Review of Silvrian Brachiopods from Gotland. (Fossils & Strata Ser: No. 3). 1974. 10.50x (ISBN 8-200-09349-2, Dist. by Columbia U Pr). Universitet.

Vidal, Gonzalo. Late Precambrian Microfossils from the Visingso Beds in Southern Sweden. (Fossils & Strata: No.9). 1976. pap. text ed. 18.00x (ISBN 8-200-09418-9, Dist. by Columbia U Pr). Universitet.

PALEONTOLOGY–SOUTH AMERICA

Kier, Porter M. Fossil Spatangoid Echinoids of Cuba. LC 83-600065. (Smithsonian Contributions to Paleobiology: No. 55). pap. 85.50 (ISBN 0-317-28248-4, 2022657). Bks Demand UMI.

Stirton, R. A., et al. Descriptive & Interpretive Studies of South American Platyrrhine Fossils: 1891-1952. LC 78-72716. 41.50 (ISBN 0-404-18291-7). AMS Pr.

PALEONTOLOGY–UNITED STATES

Baker, Frank C. Life of the Pleistocene or Glacial Period. LC 74-80996. (BCL Ser. I). 1969. Repr. of 1920 ed. 37.50 (ISBN 0-404-00449-0). AMS Pr.

Bardack, David. Localities of Fossil Vertebrates Obtained from the Niobrara Formation (Cretaceous) of Kansas. (Museum Ser.: Vol. 17,No. 1). 14p. 1965. 1.25 (ISBN 0-317-04783-3). U of KS Mus Nat Hist.

Bennett, Debra K. The Fossil Fauna from Lost & Found Quarries (Hemphillian: Latest Miocene), Wallace County, Kansas. (Occasional Papers: No. 79). 24p. 1979. pap. 1.50 (ISBN 0-686-79812-0). U of KS Mus Nat Hist.

Bird, Roland T. Bones for Barnum Brown: Adventures of a Dinosaur Hunter. Schreiber, V. Theodore, ed. LC 84-24047. (Illus.). 192p. 1985. 29.95 (ISBN 0-87565-007-4); pap. 12.95 (ISBN 0-87565-011-2). Tex Christian.

Bulletins of American Paleontology, Vol. 27. 25.00 set (ISBN 0-87710-256-2). Paleo Res.

Bulletins of American Paleontology, Vol. 28. 25.00 set (ISBN 0-87710-257-0). Paleo Res.

Bulletins of American Paleontology, Vol. 29. 25.00 set (ISBN 0-87710-258-9). Paleo Res.

Bulletins of American Paleontology, Vol. 30. 25.00 set (ISBN 0-87710-259-7). Paleo Res.

Bulletins of American Paleontology, Vol. 31. 25.00 set (ISBN 0-87710-260-0). Paleo Res.

Bulletins of American Paleontology, Vol. 32. 25.00 set (ISBN 0-87710-261-9). Paleo Res.

Bulletins of American Paleontology, Vol. 33. 25.00 set (ISBN 0-87710-262-7). Paleo Res.

Bulletins of American Paleontology, Vol. 34. 25.00 set (ISBN 0-87710-263-5). Paleo Res.

Bulletins of American Paleontology, Vol. 35. 25.00 set (ISBN 0-87710-264-3). Paleo Res.

Bulletins of American Paleontology, Vol. 36. 25.00 set (ISBN 0-87710-265-1). Paleo Res.

Bulletins of American Paleontology, Vol. 37. 25.00 set (ISBN 0-87710-266-X). Paleo Res.

Bulletins of American Paleontology, Vol. 38. 25.00 set (ISBN 0-87710-267-8). Paleo Res.

Bulletins of American Paleontology, Vol. 39. 25.00 set (ISBN 0-87710-268-6). Paleo Res.

Bulletins of American Paleontology, Vol. 40. 25.00 set (ISBN 0-87710-269-4). Paleo Res.

Bulletins of American Paleontology, Vol. 41. 25.00 set (ISBN 0-87710-270-8). Paleo Res.

Bulletins of American Paleontology, Vol. 42. 25.00 set (ISBN 0-87710-271-6). Paleo Res.

Bulletins of American Paleontology, Vol. 43. 25.00 set (ISBN 0-87710-272-4). Paleo Res.

Bulletins of American Paleontology, Vol. 44. 25.00 set (ISBN 0-87710-273-2). Paleo Res.

Bulletins of American Paleontology, Vol. 45. 25.00 set (ISBN 0-87710-274-0). Paleo Res.

Bulletins of American Paleontology, Vol. 46. 25.00 set (ISBN 0-87710-275-9). Paleo Res.

Bulletins of American Paleontology, Vol. 47. 25.00 set (ISBN 0-87710-276-7). Paleo Res.

Bulletins of American Paleontology, Vol. 48. 25.00 set (ISBN 0-87710-277-5). Paleo Res.

Bulletins of American Paleontology, Vol. 49. 25.00 set (ISBN 0-87710-278-3). Paleo Res.

Bulletins of American Paleontology, Vol. 50. 25.00 set (ISBN 0-87710-279-1). Paleo Res.

Bulletins of American Paleontology, Vol. 52. 25.00 set (ISBN 0-87710-281-3). Paleo Res.

Bulletins of American Paleontology, Vol. 53. 25.00 set (ISBN 0-87710-282-1). Paleo Res.

Bulletins of American Paleontology, Vol. 54. 25.00 set (ISBN 0-87710-283-X). Paleo Res.

Bulletins of American Paleontology, Vol. 64. Incl. No. 278. Palynology of the Almond Formation (Upper Cretaceous). Rock Springs Uplift, Wyoming. Stone, J. F. 1973. pap. 10.00 (ISBN 0-87710-216-3); No. 279. Tabulate Corals & Echinoderms from the Pennsylvanian Winterset Limestone, Hogshooter Formation, Northeastern Oklahoma. Strimple, H. L. & Cocke, J. M. 1973. pap. write for info.; No. 280. Stratigraphy & Genera of Calcareous Foraminifera of the Fraileys Facies (Mississippian) of Central Kentucky. Browne, R. G. & Pohl, E. R. 1973. pap. 3.50 (ISBN 0-87710-218-X); No. 281. Crinoid Studies, 2 pts. Pabian, R. K. & Strimple, H. L. 1974. Set. pap. 4.00 (ISBN 0-87710-219-8). Some Pennsylvanian Crinoids From Nebraska. Pt. II. Some Permian Crinoids From Nebraska, Kansas & Oklahoma. pap. 25.00 set (ISBN 0-87710-293-7). Paleo Res.

Bulletins of American Paleontology, Vol. 66. Incl. No. 283. Middle-Ordovician Crinoids from Southwestern Virginia & Eastern Tennessee. Brower, J. C. & Veinus, Julia. (Illus.). 1974. pap. 5.00 (ISBN 0-87710-221-X); No. 284. Gastropoda of the Fox Hill Formation (Maestrichtian) of North Dakota. Erickson, J. M. (Illus.). 1977. pap. 4.25 (ISBN 0-87710-222-8); No. 285. Late Cenozoic Corals of South Florida. Weisbord, N. E. (Illus.). 1974. pap. 10.50 (ISBN 0-87710-223-6); No. 286. Neogene Biostratisgraphy (Ostracoda) of Southern Hispaniola. Bold, W. A. van den. (Illus.). 1974. pap. 4.25 (ISBN 0-87710-224-4). pap. 25.00 set (ISBN 0-87710-295-3). Paleo Res.

Bulletins of American Paleontology, Vol. 68. Incl. No. 288. North American Paracrinoidea: Ordovician Echinodermata. Parsley, R. L. & Mintz, L. W. (Illus.). 1975. pap. 4.75 (ISBN 0-87710-226-0); No. 289. Ostracodes from the Late Neogene of Cuba. Bold, W. A. van den. 1975. pap. 2.50 (ISBN 0-87710-227-9); No. 290. Cirripedia of Florida & Surrounding Waters (Acrothracica & Rhizocephala) (Illus.). pap. 2.90 (ISBN 0-87710-228-7). pap. 25.00 set (ISBN 0-87710-297-X). Paleo Res.

Bulletins of American Paleontology, Vol. 69. 25.00 set (ISBN 0-87710-298-8). Paleo Res.

Bulletins of American Paleontology, Vol. 70. Incl. No. 292. Bathyal Gastropods of the Family Turridae in the Early Oligocene Keasey Formation in Oregon. Hickman, C. S. (Illus.). 1976. pap. 12.50 (ISBN 0-685-85223-7); No. 293. Two Foraminiferal Assemblages from the Duplin Marl in Georgia & South Carolina. Herrick, S. M. (Illus.). 1976. pap. 3.50 (ISBN 0-87710-231-7); No. 294. Cenozoic Naticidae (Mollusca: Gastropoda) of the Northeastern Pacific. Marincovich, L. (Illus.). pap. 17.50 (ISBN 0-87710-232-5). pap. 25.00 set (ISBN 0-87710-299-6). Paleo Res.

Bulletins of American Paleontology, Vol. 72. 25.00 set (ISBN 0-87710-301-1). Paleo Res.

Bulletins of American Paleontology, Vol. 73. 25.00 set (ISBN 0-87710-302-X). Paleo Res.

Bulletins of American Paleontology, Vol. 75. 25.00 set (ISBN 0-87710-304-6). Paleo Res.

Bulletins of American Paleontology, Vol. 76. 25.00 set (ISBN 0-87710-305-4). Paleo Res.

Bulletins of American Paleontology, Vol. 77. 25.00 set (ISBN 0-87710-306-2). Paleo Res.

Bulletins of American Paleontology, Vol. 78. 25.00 set (ISBN 0-87710-381-X). Paleo Res.

Bulletins of American Paleontology, Vol. 79. 25.00 set (ISBN 0-87710-382-8). Paleo Res.

Bulletins of American Paleontology, Vol. 80. 25.00 set (ISBN 0-87710-385-2). Paleo Res.

Bulletins of American Paleontology, Vol. 81. 25.00 set (ISBN 0-87710-388-7). Paleo Res.

Carnegie Institution Of Washington. Papers Concerning the Palaeontology of California, Arizona & Idaho. Repr. of 1934 ed. 19.00 (ISBN 0-685-02119-X). Johnson Repr.

--Papers Concerning the Palaeontology of California, Nevada & Oregon. Repr. of 1935 ed. 19.00 (ISBN 0-685-02120-3). Johnson Repr.

--Papers Concerning the Palaeontology of California, Oregon & the Northern Great Basin Province. Repr. of 1932 ed. 19.00 (ISBN 0-685-02121-1). Johnson Repr.

--Papers Concerning the Palaeontology of the Cretaceous & Later Tertiary of Oregon, of the Pliocene of North-Western Nevada, & of the Late Miocene & Pleistocene of California. Repr. of 1928 ed. 19.00 (ISBN 0-685-02122-X). Johnson Repr.

--Studies on the Fossil Flora & Fauna of the Western United States. Repr. of 1925 ed. 19.00 (ISBN 0-685-02175-0). Johnson Repr.

Carpenter, F. M., et al. Coal Age Fossils from Mazon Creek. (Scientific Papers Ser.: Vol. III, Nos. 1-4). (Illus.). 147p. 1979. pap. 4.00 (ISBN 0-89792-082-1). Ill St Museum.

Chaney, Ralph W. & Sanborn, Ethel I. Goshen Flora of West Central Oregon. Repr. 19.00 (ISBN 0-384-08461-3). Johnson Repr.

Downs, Theodore. Fossil Vertebrates of Southern California. LC 68-26065. (California Natural History Guides: No. 23). (Illus., Orig.). 1968. pap. 1.75 (ISBN 0-520-00352-7). U of Cal Pr.

Foley, Robert L. Late Pleistocene (Woodfordian) Vertebrates from the Driftless Area of Southwestern Wisconsin, the Moscow Fissure Local Fauna. (Reports of Investigations Ser.: No. 39). (Illus.). x, 50p. (Orig.). 1984. pap. text ed. 5.00 (ISBN 0-89792-102-X). Ill St Museum.

Foreman, Brian & Schultze, Peter. A New Gymnarthrid Microsaur from the Lower Permian of Kansas with a Review of the Tuditanomorph Microsaurs (Amphibia) (Occasional Papers: No. 91). 25p. 1981. 1.50 (ISBN 0-317-04814-7). U of KS Mus Nat Hist.

Fox, Richard C. Two New Pelycosaurs from the Lower Permian of Oklahoma. (Museum Ser.: Vol. 12, No. 6). 11p. 1962. 1.25 (ISBN 0-317-04792-2). U of KS Mus Nat Hist.

Galbreath, Edwin C. A New Extinct Emydid Turtle from the Lower Pliocene of Oklahoma. (Museum Ser.: Vol. 1, No. 16). 16p. 1948. 1.25 (ISBN 0-317-04796-5). U of Ks Mus Nat Hist.

--Pliocene & Pleistocene Records of Fossil from Western Kansas & Oklahoma. (Museum Ser.: Vol. 1, no. 17). 4p. 1948. 1.25 (ISBN 0-317-04798-1). U of KS Mus Nat Hist.

Hall, E. Raymond & Dalquest, Walter W. A New Doglike Carnivore, Genus Cynarctus, from the Clarendonian, Pliocene, of Texas. (Museum Ser.: Vol. 14, No. 10). 4p. 1962. 1.25 (ISBN 0-317-04806-6). U of KS Mus Nat Hist.

Hanna, G. Dallas & Hanna, Marcus A. Foraminifera from the Eocene of Cowlitz River, Lewis County, Washington. (Publications in Geology Ser.: I-4). (Illus.). 7p. 1924. pap. 10.00x (ISBN 0-295-73789-1, UWPG 1-4). U of Wash Pr.

Harris, John M. & Jefferson, George, eds. Rancho La Brea: Treasures of the Tar Pits. (Illus.). 96p. 1985. pap. 9.95 (ISBN 0-317-31585-4). U of Wash Pr.

Hitchcock, Edward. A Report on the Sandstone of the Connecticut Valley, Especially Its Fossil Footmarks. LC 73-17825. (Natural Sciences in America Ser.). (Illus.). 256p. 1974. Repr. 29.00x (ISBN 0-405-05743-1). Ayer Co Pubs.

Hoare, Richard D. Desmoinesian Brachiopoda & Mollusca from Southwest Missouri. LC 61-13508. (Illus.). 277p. 1961. 15.00x (ISBN 0-8262-0545-3). U of Mo Pr.

Howard, Hildegarde. Eagles & Eagle-Like Vultures of the Pleistocene of Rancho La Brea. Repr. of 1932 ed. 19.00 (ISBN 0-384-24430-0). Johnson Repr.

Krishtalka, L. & West, Robert M. Paleontology & Geology of the Bridger Formation, Southern Green River Basin, Southwestern Wyoming: Part Two - The Bridgerian Insectivore Entomolestes Granseri. 1977. 0.75 (ISBN 0-89326-027-4). Milwaukee Pub Mus.

Krishtalka, Leonard & West, R. M. Paleonology & Geology of the Bridger Formation, Southern Green River Basin, Southwestern Wyoming: Part Four - The Geolabididae (Mammalia, Insectivora) 1979. 0.75 (ISBN 0-89326-050-9). Milwaukee Pub Mus.

Lawrence, Barbara. Mammals Found at the Awatovi Site. (HU PMP Ser.). (Illus.). 1951. pap. 15.00 (ISBN 0-527-01290-4). Kraus Repr.

Leary, Richard L. Early Pennsylvanian Geology & Paleobotany of the Rock Island County, Illinois Area. (Reports of Investigations: No. 37). (Illus.). 100p. 1981. pap. 3.50 (ISBN 0-89792-089-9). Ill St Museum.

Levenson, James B. The Southern-Mesic Forest of Southeastern Wisconsin: Species, Composition & Community Structure. (Illus.). 246p. 1981. 12.50 (ISBN 0-89326-068-1). Milwaukee Pub Mus.

Major, Alan. Collecting Fossils. LC 74-33907. (Illus.). 202p. 1975. 8.95 (ISBN 0-312-14945-X). St Martin.

Martin, Larry C. New Rodents from the Lower Miocene Gering Formation of Western Nebraska. (Occasional Papers: No. 32). 12p. 1974. 1.25 (ISBN 0-317-04809-0). U of KS Mus Nat Hist.

Nitecki, Matthew H., ed. Mazon Creek Fossils. LC 79-10104. 1979. 41.00 (ISBN 0-12-519650-4). Acad Pr.

Orr, William & Orr, Elizabeth. Handbook of Oregon Plant & Animal Fossils. LC 81-90259. (Illus.). 285p. (Orig.). 1981. 10.95 (ISBN 0-9606502-0-2). W&E Orr.

Packard, Earl L. Fossil Baleen from the Pliocene of Cape Blanco, Oregon, Fossil Sea Lion from Cape Blanco, Oregon, & A Pinniped Humerus from the Astoria Miocene of Oregon. (Studies in Geology Ser: Nos. 5, 6, & 7). (Illus.). 32p. 1947. pap. 3.95x (ISBN 0-87071-065-6). Oreg St U Pr.

Palaeontographia Americana, Vol. 9. 32.50 (ISBN 0-87710-386-0). Paleo Res.

Palaeontographica Americana. Incl. No. 47. A Revision of the Family Seraphsidae (Gastropoda: Strombacea) Jung, Peter. 1974. 6.00 (ISBN 0-87710-348-8); No. 49. Comparative Morphology & Shell History of the Ordovician Strophomenacea (Brachiopoda) Pope, J. K. 1976. 6.50 (ISBN 0-87710-350-X); No. 50. Evolution & Classification of Cenozoic North American & European Lucinidae (Mollusca, Bivalvia) Bretsky, Sara. 12.50 (ISBN 0-87710-351-8); No. 51. Morphology & Anatomy of Aneurophyton: A Progymnosperm from the Late Devonian of New York. Serlin, B. S. & Banks, H. P. 3.75 (ISBN 0-87710-352-6). (Illus.). Set. 40.00 (ISBN 0-87710-360-7). Paleo Res.

Palaeontographica Americana, Vol. 2. Incl. No. 9. Devonian Brevicones of New York & Adjacent Areas. Flower, Rousseau H. 1938. o. p. 4.00 (ISBN 0-87710-310-0); No. 11. Notes on Giant Fasciolarias. Smith, Burnett. 1940. 0.50 (ISBN 0-87710-312-7); No. 12. The Titusvillidae, Paleozoic & Recent Branching Hexactinellida. Caster, Kenneth E. 1941. 2.00 (ISBN 0-87710-313-5). (Illus.). 30.00 set (ISBN 0-87710-354-2). Paleo Res.

Palaeontographica Americana, Vol. 3. Incl. No. 13. Notes on Structure & Phylogeny of Eurysiphonate Cephalopods. Flower, Rousseau H. 1941. 2.60 (ISBN 0-87710-314-3); No. 15. Two Abnormal Busycon Shells. Smith, Burnett. 1943. 0.40 (ISBN 0-87710-316-X); No. 16. Fish Remains from the Middle Devonian Bone Beds of the Cincinnati Arch Region. Wells, John W. 1944. 2.25 (ISBN 0-87710-317-8); No. 17. Two Spine Rows in a Florida Busycon Contrarium. Smith, Burnett. 1944. 0.40 (ISBN 0-87710-318-6); No. 18. A New Jellyfish (Kirklandia Texana Caster) from the Lower Cretaceous of Texas. Caster, Kenneth E. 1945. 2.50 (ISBN 0-87710-319-4); No. 20. Some Species of Platystrophia from the Trenton of Ontario & Quebec. Sinclair, G. Winston. 1946. 0.75 (ISBN 0-87710-321-6); No. 21. Observations on Gastropod Protoconchs. Smith, Burnett. 1946. Pt. III. Some Protoconchs In Busycon, Fusinus, Heilprinia, Hesperisterna & Urosalpinx. o. p. 0.75 (ISBN 0-685-85237-7); No. 22. Two Marine Quaternary Localities. Smith, Burnett. 1948. 1.00 (ISBN 0-87710-323-2); No. 23. Studies of Carboniferous Crinoids: Oklahoma & Nebraska, 4 pts. 2.00 (ISBN 0-87710-324-0); No. 24. Stereotoceras & Brevicoceratidae. Flower, R. H. 1950. 2.00 (ISBN 0-87710-325-9); No. 25. The Pelecypod Genus Venericardia in the Paleocene & Eocene of Western North America. Verastegui, P. 1953. 8.00 (ISBN 0-87710-326-7). (Illus.). 35.00 set (ISBN 0-87710-355-0). Paleo Res.

Palaeontographica Americana, Vol. 4. Incl. No. 29. Dalmanellidae of the Cincinnatian. Hall, Donald D. 1962. 2.25 (ISBN 0-87710-330-5); No. 30. The Pelecypod Genus Byssonchia in the Cincinnatian at Cincinnati, Ohio. Pojeta, John, Jr. 1962. 5.00 (ISBN 0-87710-331-3); No. 32. Upper Ordovician Eurypterids of Ohio. Caster, K. E. & Kjellesvig-Waering, E. N. 1964. o. p. 4.00 (ISBN 0-87710-333-X). (Illus.). 35.00 set (ISBN 0-87710-356-9). Paleo Res.

Palaeontographica Americana, Vol. 5. Incl. No. 34. Upper Tertiary Arcacea of the Mid-Atlantic Coastal Plain. Bird, S. O. 1965. 4.00 (ISBN 0-87710-335-6); No. 35. Dimyarian Pelecypods of the Mississippi Marshall Sandstone of Michigan. Driscoll, Egbert G. 1965. 4.60 (ISBN 0-87710-336-4); No. 36. North American Ambonychiidae (Pelecypoda) Pojeta, John, Jr. 1977. 7.00 (ISBN 0-87710-337-2). (Illus.). 50.00 set (ISBN 0-87710-357-7). Paleo Res.

Palaeontographica Americana, Vol. 6. Incl. No. 38. Lycopsid Stems & Roots & Sphenopsid Fructifications & Stems from the Upper Freeport Coal of Southeastern Ohio. Abbott, Maxine L. 1968. 5.00 (ISBN 0-87710-339-9); No. 39. Cenozoic Evolution of the Alticostate Venericards in Gulf & East Coastal North America. Heaslip, William G. 1968. 6.50 (ISBN 0-87710-340-2); No. 40. Carboniferous Crinoids of Texas with Stratigraphic Implications. Strimple, H. L. & Watkins, W. T. 1969.. (Illus.). 40.00 (ISBN 0-87710-358-5). Paleo Res.

Palaeontographica Americana, Vol. 7. Incl. No. 42. Torreites Sanchezi (Douville) from Jamaica. Jung, Peter. 1970. 1.25 (ISBN 0-87710-343-7); No. 43. The Cancellariid Radula & Its Interpretation. Olsson, A. A. 1970. 1.25 (ISBN 0-87710-344-5); No. 44. Ontogeny & Sexual Dimorphism of Lower Paleozoic Trilobita. Chung-Hung Hu. 1971. 12.50 (ISBN 0-87710-345-3); No. 45. Rudists of Jamaica. Chubb, L. J. 1971. 8.50 (ISBN 0-87710-346-1); No. 46. Crinoids Rom the Girardeau Limestone. Brower, J. C. 1973. 20.00 (ISBN 0-87710-347-X). (Illus.). Set. 45.00 (ISBN 0-87710-359-3). Paleo Res.

Technical Association of the Pulp & Paper Industry. Protein Binders in Paper & Paperboard Coating: A Project of the Coating Committee. Strauss, R., ed. LC 75-929. (TAPPI Monograph Ser.: No. 36). pap. 37.00 (ISBN 0-317-28874-1, 2020304). Bks Demand UMI.

--Synthetic Binders in Paper Coatings: A Project of the Coating Binders Committee. Sinclair, Alvin R., ed. LC 75-7557. (TAPPI Monograph Ser.: No. 37). pap. 37.80 (ISBN 0-317-28872-5, 2020305). Bks Demand UMI.

--Thermal Spray Coatings. Meringolo, Vince, ed. pap. 20.00 (ISBN 0-317-20542-0, 2022827). Bks Demand UMI.

Technical Association the Pulp & Paper Industry. Paper Coating Additives Test Procedures by Functional Profile: A Project of the Coating Binders Committee of Coating & Graphic Arts Division. Lewis, R. W., ed. pap. 28.00 (ISBN 0-317-29319-2, 2022346). Bks Demand UMI.

Yin, Robert I., ed. Paper Coating Additives: Description of Functional Properties & List of Available Products. 4th ed. 72p. 1982. pap. 34.95 (ISBN 0-89852-401-6, 01 01 R101). TAPPI.

PAPER MAKING AND TRADE

see also Wood Pulp Industry

Allan, David R., ed. Uncoated Groundwood Papers: Proceedings of the First Uncoated Groundwood Papers Conference, New York, New York, November 1983. LC 84-60473. (Illus.). 112p. (Orig.). pap. 97.00 (ISBN 0-87930-155-4). Miller Freeman.

Amigo, Eleanor & Neuffer, Mark. Beyond the Adirondacks: The Story of St. Regis Paper Company. LC 80-1798. (Contributions in Economics & Economic History Ser.: No. 35). (Illus.). xi, 219p. 1980. lib. bdg. 27.50x (ISBN 0-313-22735-7, AFN/). Greenwood.

Amsalem, Michel A. Technology Choice in Developing Countries: The Textile & Pulp & Paper Industries. (Illus.). 224p. 1983. 30.00x (ISBN 0-262-01072-0). MIT Pr.

Annual Meeting Preprints. Incl. Annual Meeting Preprints. 346p. 1976. 4.95 (01-05-0176). 286p. 1975. soft cover 4.95 (ISBN 0-686-98472-2, 01-05-0175). TAPPI.

Annual Meeting Proceedings. 309p. 1979. 4.95 (ISBN 0-686-98469-2, 01-05-0179). TAPPI.

Annual Meeting Proceedings. Incl. Annual Meeting Proceedings. 309p. 1979. 4.95 (01-05-0179); Annual Meeting Proceedings. 416p. 1980. pap. 19.95 (01-05-0180); Annual Meeting Proceedings. 449p. 1982. pap. 44.95 (01050182). 239p. 1978. soft cover 4.95 (ISBN 0-686-98470-6, 01-05-0178). TAPPI.

Annual Meeting: Proceedings. 449p. 1982. pap. 44.95 (ISBN 0-686-43236-3, 01050182). TAPPI.

Annual Meeting: Proceedings. 416p. 1980. pap. 19.95 (ISBN 0-686-43237-1, 01 05 0180). TAPPI.

Arthur, Jett C, Jr., ed. Textile & Paper Chemistry & Technology. LC 77-7938. (ACS Symposium Ser.: No. 49). 1977. 27.95 (ISBN 0-8412-0377-6). Am Chemical.

Aspects Ecologiques de L'Industrie des Pates Et Papiers Etude Technique. 1983. pap. 5.50 (UNEP087, UNEP). Unipub.

Atchinson, Joseph E. Nonwood Plant Fiber Pulping Progress Report. LC 82-80290. (No. 13). 148p. 1983. pap. 48.95 (ISBN 0-89852-404-0, 01 01 R104). TAPPI.

Atchison, Joseph, ed. Nonwood Plant Fiber Pulping, No. 14. (Illus.). 1985. pap. 49.95 (ISBN 0-89852-416-4). TAPPI.

Atchison, Joseph E., et al, eds. Nonwood Plant Fiber Pulping, 13 Vols. 1835p. 1983. soft cover 297.95 (ISBN 0-686-98535-4, 01-01-NPFS). TAPPI.

Atkins, John F. The Paper Machine Wet Press Manual. LC 79-6366. (TAPPI PRESS Books). (Illus.). 120p. 1979. 14.95 (ISBN 0-89852-042-8, 01-02 B042). TAPPI.

Balston, Thomas. James Whatman, Father & Son. Bidwell, John, ed. LC 78-74386. (Nineteenth-Century Book Arts & Printing History Ser.: Vol. 1). (Illus.). 1979. lib. bdg. 26.00 (ISBN 0-8240-3875-4). Garland Pub.

--William Balston, Paper Maker, 1759-1849. Bidwell, John, ed. LC 78-74387. (Nineteenth-Century Book Arts & Printing History Ser.: Vol. 2). (Illus.). 1979. lib. bdg. 26.00 (ISBN 0-8240-3876-2). Garland Pub.

Barrett, Timothy. Japanese Papermaking: Traditions, Tools & Techniques. LC 83-5790. (Illus.). 320p. 1984. 32.50 (ISBN 0-8348-0185-X). Weatherhill.

Barton, Jack S., et al. Future Technical Needs & Trends in the Paper Industry II. (TAPPI PRESS Reports). (Illus.). 82p. 1976. pap. 19.95 (ISBN 0-89852-364-8, 01-01-R064). TAPPI.

Battista, Orlando A., ed. Synthetic Fibers in Papermaking. LC 64-13211. 340p. 1964. text ed. 21.00 (ISBN 0-470-05894-3, Pub. by Wiley). Krieger.

Bidwell, John. The Size of the Sheet in America: Paper-Moulds Manufactured by N & D Sellers of Philadelphia. (Illus.). 1978. pap. 4.00x (ISBN 0-912296-31-3, Dist. by U Pr of Va). Am Antiquarian.

Bigl, Joseph H., et al. Blade Coating Technology. Clark, C. Wells, ed. (TAPPI PRESS Reports). (Illus.). 84p. (Orig.). 1978. pap. 24.95 (ISBN 0-89852-373-7, 01-01-R073). TAPPI.

Casey, James P. Pulp & Paper: Chemistry & Technology, Vol. 4. 3rd ed. LC 79-13435. 2609p. 1983. 81.00 (ISBN 0-471-03178-X, Pub. by Wiley-Interscience). Wiley.

Clark, James D. Pulp Technology & Treatment for Paper. rev. ed. (Illus.). 880p. 1985. price not set (ISBN 0-87930-164-3). Miller Freeman.

Clark, James d'A. Pulp Technology & Treatment for Paper. LC 78-59149. (A Pulp & Paper Book). (Illus.). 752p. 1978. 75.00 (ISBN 0-87930-066-3). Miller Freeman.

Cote, Wilfred A., ed. Papermaking Fibers: A Photomicrographic Atlas. (Renewable Materials Institute Ser.). (Illus.). 200p. 1980. pap. text ed. 12.00x (ISBN 0-8156-2228-7). Syracuse U Pr.

Davis, Charles T. The Manufacture of Paper. LC 72-5042. (Technology & Society Ser.). (Illus.). 625p. 1972. Repr. of 1886 ed. 34.00 (ISBN 0-405-04694-4). Ayer Co Pubs.

Dickson, Ted & Harben, Peter, eds. Raw Materials for the Pulp & Paper Industry. 100p. (Orig.). 1984. pap. text ed. 38.50 (ISBN 0-913333-01-8). Metal Bulletin.

Edde, Howard. Environmental Control for Pulp & Paper Mills. LC 83-22011. (Pollution Technology Review Ser.: No. 108). (Illus.). 179p. 1984. 32.00 (ISBN 0-8155-0979-0). Noyes.

Environmental Aspects of the Pulp & Paper Industry. (Industry Overviews: Vol. 1). 27p. 1977. pap. 6.75 (ISBN 0-686-93516-0, UNEP017, UNEP). Unipub.

Environmental Conference: Proceedings. 298p. 1982. pap. 44.95 (ISBN 0-686-43240-1, 01 05 0382). TAPPI.

Estimated Production of Pulp, Paper, & Paperboard in Certain Countries in 1974. (Forestry Papers: No. 11). 49p. 1975. pap. 11.50 (ISBN 0-686-92796-6, F773, FAO). Unipub.

Estimated Production of Pulp, Paper, & Paperboard in Certain Countries in 1976. (Forestry Papers: No. 28). 48p. 1977. pap. 7.50 (ISBN 0-686-92798-2, F1269, FAO). Unipub.

Estimated Production of Pulp, Paper & Paperboard in Certain Countries in 1981: FAO Advisory Committee on Pulp and Paper, 23rd Session, Rome, 9-12 June 1982. 30p. 1982. pap. 7.50 (ISBN 0-686-84613-3, F2327, FAO). Unipub.

Euro-Data Analysts. Profits & Markets in the Global Paper, Paperboard, & Packaging Industries. (Illus.). 180p. 1983. pap. 595.00 (ISBN 0-87930-152-X, 541). Miller Freeman.

Evanoff, Philip C. & Gerlach, Werner, eds. Surface Strength Terminology. (Illus.). 65p. 1983. pap. 39.95 non-members (ISBN 0-89852-411-3); pap. 26.77 members. TAPPI.

Ewing, Kristine L. Care & Maintenance of Paper Machine Clothing. LC 76-53915. (Bibliographic Ser.: No. 274). 1977. pap. 12.00 (ISBN 0-87010-048-3). Inst Paper Chem.

Finney, Frederick M. Dictionary of Syngraphics & Associated Terms. 96p. 1983. 8.95 (ISBN 0-89421-031-9). Challenge Pr.

Fuentes, Ernesto F., et al. Nonwood Plant Fiber Pulping: Progress Report, No. 11. (TAPPI PRESS Reports). (Illus.). 99p. 1981. pap. 38.95 (ISBN 0-89852-391-5, 01 01 R091). TAPPI.

Glaister, Geoffrey. Glaister's Glossary of the Book: Terms Used in Paper-Making, Printing, Bookbinding, & Publishing. LC 76-47975. 1979. 75.00 (ISBN 0-520-03364-7). U of Cal Pr.

Gose, Charles J., Jr., ed. Corrugator Roll Wear Measurement. 1983. TAPPI members 20.07 (ISBN 0-89852-415-6); nonmembers 29.95. TAPPI.

Guide for Planning Pulp & Paper Enterprises. (Forestry Ser.: No. 1). (Illus.). 379p. (Orig., 2nd Printing 1977). 1973. 30.50 (ISBN 92-5-100058-1, F217, FAO). Unipub.

Hagemeyer, Robert W., et al. Future Technical Needs & Trends in the Paper Industry III. (TAPPI PRESS Reports). (Illus.). 102p. 1979. pap. 29.95 (ISBN 0-89852-378-8, 01-01-R078). TAPPI.

Halpern, M. G. Paper Manufacture. LC 75-2944. (Chemical Technology Review Ser: No. 47). (Illus.). 379p. 1975. 36.00 (ISBN 0-8155-0576-0). Noyes.

--Synthetic Paper from Fibers & Films. LC 75-14913. (Chemical Technology Review: No. 52). (Illus.). 265p. 1976. 36.00 (ISBN 0-8155-0587-6). Noyes.

Halpern, M. G., ed. Pulp Mill Processes: Developments since 1977. LC 81-16782. (Pollution Technology Review 85; Chemical Technology Review: No. 198). (Illus.). 371p. 1982. 48.00 (ISBN 0-8155-0871-9). Noyes.

Heiser, Edward J. & Allswede, Jerry L., eds. Blade Coating Defect Terminology. (Illus.). 53p. 1982. pap. 24.95 (ISBN 0-686-43234-7, 01 01 R094). TAPPI.

Heller, Jules. Papermaking. (Illus.). 1978. 22.50 (ISBN 0-8230-3895-5). Watson-Guptill.

Henderson, J. S., ed. The NCE Recovery Boiler Precipitator: Mill Experience & Design Implications. LC 83-70306. (Illus.). 72p. 1983. pap. 64.95 (ISBN 0-89852-406-7). TAPPI.

Horacek, Robert G. Deinking by Washing. Corwin, Harold E., ed. (Recycling of Papermaking Fibers Ser.). (Illus.). 33p. 1983. pap. 19.95 (ISBN 0-89852-409-1). TAPPI.

Hot Melt Adhesives & Coatings: Course Notes. 100p. 1981. soft cover 39.95 (ISBN 0-686-98539-7, 01-06-1681). TAPPI.

Huber, Joan E., ed. Kline Guide to the Paper Industry. 4th ed. (Illus.). 343p. 1979. pap. 70.00 (ISBN 0-917148-10-X). Kline.

Hunter, Dard. Papermaking. (Illus.). 1978. pap. 8.95 (ISBN 0-486-23619-6). Dover.

Hyzer, Donald V., ed. Project Implementation: Project Case Histories, Vol. 2. (Illus.). 242p. 1982. pap. 44.95 (ISBN 0-89852-402-4, 01 01 R102). TAPPI.

IFAC Conference, 4th, Ghent, Belgium, June 1980. Instrumentation & Automation in the Paper, Rubber, Plastics & Polymerisation Industries: Proceedings. Van Cauwenberghe, A., ed. LC 80-41889. (IFAC Proceedings Ser.). (Illus.). 550p. 1981. 130.00 (ISBN 0-08-024487-4). Pergamon.

Information Sources on the Utilization of Agricultural Residues for the Production of Panels, Pulp, & Paper. (UNIDO Guides to Information Sources: No. 35). 99p. 1980. pap. 4.00 (ISBN 0-686-70504-1, UNID234, UN). Unipub.

Instrumentation in the Pulp & Paper Industry, Vol. 20: Proceedings of the Pulp & Paper Instrumentation Symposium, 22th. LC 73-82889. 72p. 1984. pap. text ed. 30.00x (ISBN 0-87664-838-3). Instru Soc.

International Pulp Bleaching Conference: Proceedings. 223p. 1982. pap. 44.95 (ISBN 0-686-43244-4, 01 05 1282). TAPPI.

International Sulfite Pulping Conference: Proceedings. 223p. 1982. pap. 44.95 (ISBN 0-686-43245-2, 01 05 1782). TAPPI.

International Symposium on Transport & Handling in the Pulp & Paper Industry, Third, Vancouver, B. C. Sept. 1978. Transport & Handling in the Pulp & Paper Industry, Vol. 3: Proceedings. Kalish, John, ed. LC 74-20162. (A Pulp & Paper Book). (Illus.). 240p. 1979. 37.50 (ISBN 0-87930-109-0). Miller Freeman.

International Symposium on Transport & Handling in the Pulp & Paper Industry, 4th, London, England, Nov. 1980. Transport & Handling in the Pulp & Paper Industry, Vol. 4: Proceedings. Kalish, John E., ed. LC 74-20162. (A Pulp & Paper Bk). (Illus.). 208p. 1981. 59.50 (ISBN 0-87930-127-9). Miller Freeman.

Kline, James E. Paper & Paperboard Manufacturing & Converting Fundamentals. LC 81-85073. (A Pulp & Paper Bk.). (Illus.). 232p. 1982. pap. 39.50 (ISBN 0-87930-134-1). Miller Freeman.

Koretsky, Elaine. Color for the Hand Papermaker. LC 83-62415. (Illus.). 180p. 1983. special ed. 200.00x (ISBN 0-9612216-3-1); pap. text ed. 35.00x (ISBN 0-9612216-0-7). Carriage Hse Pr.

Lavigne, John R. Instrumentation Applications for the Pulp & Paper Industry. LC 77-93837. (A Pulp & Paper Book). (Illus.). 1979. 35.00 (ISBN 0-87930-074-4). Miller Freeman.

--An Introduction to Paper Industry Instrumentation. rev. ed. LC 77-89603. (A Pulp & Paper Book). (Illus.). 1977. 39.50 (ISBN 0-87930-069-8). Miller Freeman.

Lewtya, John, ed. Paper Machine Energy Factors. 24p. 1983. 11.95 (ISBN 0-89852-413-X); TAPPI members 8.00. TAPPI.

Loeber, E. G., ed. Supplement to E. J. Labarre's Dictionary & Encyclopaedia of Paper & Paper-Making. 114p. text ed. 23.75 (ISBN 90-265-0038-6, Pub. by Swets Pub Serv). Swets North Am.

Louden, Louise. Foam & Foam Control. LC 77-73609. (Bibliographic Ser.: No. 277). 1977. pap. 28.00 (ISBN 0-87010-049-1). Inst Paper Chem.

--Noise Control in the Pulp & Paper Industry. (Bibliographic Ser.: No. 264, Suppl. 1). 1981. pap. 10.00 (ISBN 0-87010-063-7). Inst Paper Chem.

--Pulping of Bagasse & Other Papermaking Fibers. LC 76-29080. (Bibliographic Ser.: No. 270). 1976. pap. 20.00 (ISBN 0-87010-045-9). Inst Paper Chem.

Lowe, Kenneth E. Metrication for the Pulp & Paper Industry. LC 74-20165. (A Pulp & Paper Book). (Illus.). 192p. 1975. 35.00 (ISBN 0-87930-034-5). Miller Freeman.

McCloskey, John T., et al. Nonwood Plant Fiber Pulping: Progress Report, No. 9. (TAPPI PRESS Reports). (Illus.). 112p. 1978. pap. 38.95 (ISBN 0-89852-375-3, 01 01 R075). TAPPI.

McGill, R. J. Measurement & Control in Papermaking. 420p. 1980. 97.50 (ISBN 0-9960019-7-2, Pub. by A Hilger England). Heyden.

Making Paper. (Illus.). 64p. 1982. 10.00 (ISBN 0-686-47653-0); members 8.00. Am Craft.

Miller Freeman Publications, Inc., Staff. Energy Management & Conservation in Pulp & Paper Mills. Coleman, Matthew, ed. LC 81-81000. (A Pulp & Paper Focus Bk.). (Illus.). 206p. 1981. pap. 32.50 (ISBN 0-87930-099-X). Miller Freeman.

--Maintenance Methods for the Pulp & Paper Industry. Coleman, Matthew, ed. LC 80-82934. (A Pulp & Paper Focus Bk.). (Illus.). 192p. 1980. pap. 29.50 (ISBN 0-87930-088-4). Miller Freeman.

Miller Freeman Publications Inc., Staff. Publication Papers: An Appraisal of the Future of Paper Printing & Publishing at the Start of the Electronic Era, Proceedings of the PPI Publications Papers Conference, Amsterdam, September, 1982. Kalish, John, ed. LC 83-61154. (Illus.). 79p. 1983. pap. 65.00 (ISBN 0-87930-150-3). Miller Freeman.

Miller, Richard K. Noise Control Solutions for the Paper Industry. (Illus.). 80p. text ed. 45.00 (ISBN 0-89671-033-5). SEAI Tech Pubns.

Miller, Richard K., et al. Noise Control Solutions for the Paper Products Industry. 45.00 (ISBN 0-89671-001-7). Fairmont Pr.

Munsell, Joel. Chronology of the Origin & Progress of Paper & Paper-Making. Bidwell, John, ed. LC 78-74389. (Nineteenth-Century Book Arts & Printing History Ser.: Vol. 4). 1980. lib. bdg. 33.00 (ISBN 0-8240-3878-9). Garland Pub.

Nader, Ralph. The Paper Plantation. LC 73-1907. (Ralph Nader Study Group Reports). 288p. 1974. 11.95 (ISBN 0-670-53807-8, Grossman). Viking.

Navarro, Jaime. Evaluation of Mixed Tropical Hardwoods for Pulp & Paper Manufacture. (Illus.). 160p. 1976. pap. 11.00 (ISBN 92-5-100041-7, F776, FAO). Unipub.

Needham, Joseph & Tsuen-Hsuin, Tsien. Science & Civilization in China: Chemistry & Chemical Technology Part 1: Paper & Printing, Vol. 5. (Illus.). 485p. 1985. 89.50 (ISBN 0-521-08690-6). Cambridge U Pr.

Nonwoven Fibers & Binders: Seminar Notes. 70p. 1981. soft cover 34.95 (ISBN 0-686-98538-9, 01-06-1381). TAPPI.

Ortner, Herbert E. Recycling of Papermaking Fibers: Flotation Deinking. Corwin, Harold E., ed. pap. 20.00 (ISBN 0-317-20560-9, 2022814). Bks Demand UMI.

Paper Synthetic Conference: Proceedings. 364p. 1982. pap. 44.95 (ISBN 0-686-43243-6, 01 05 0782). TAPPI.

Parham, Russell A. & Gray, Richard L. The Practical Identification of Wood Pulp Fibers. 212p. 1982. 34.95 (ISBN 0-89852-400-8, 01 01R0100). TAPPI.

Perkins, Joseph K., ed. Brown Stock Washing Using Rotary Filters. (Illus.). 1983. TAPPI members 30.12 (ISBN 0-89852-414-8); nonmembers 44.95. TAPPI.

Phillips, F. H. The Pulping & Papermaking Potential of Tropical Hardwoods, Vol. 1. 1980. 20.00x (ISBN 0-643-00339-8, Pub. by CSJRO). State Mutual Bk.

Phillips, F. H. & Logan, A. F. The Pulping & Paper Making Potential of Tropical Hardwoods VI: Mixed Species from the Gogol Timber Area, Papua New Guinea. (Division of Chemical Technology Technical Papers: No. 10). 32p. 1979. 6.00 (ISBN 0-643-00339-8, C064, CSIRO). Unipub.

Pulp & Paper Chemical Market. 336p. 1985. 1800.00 (ISBN 0-86621-686-3, E758). Frost & Sullivan.

Pulp & Paper industry. (UNIDO Guides to Information Sources: No. 11). pap. 4.00 (ISBN 0-686-93281-1, UNID121, UN). Unipub.

Pulp & Paper Instrumentation Symposium. Instrumentation in the Pulp & Paper Industry, Vol. 19: Proceedings of the Pulp & Paper Instrumentation Symposium. LC 73-82889. 52p. 1981. pap. text ed. 15.00x (ISBN 0-87664-517-1). Instru Soc.

--Instrumentation in the Pulp & Paper Industry, Vol. 18: Proceedings of the Pulp & Paper Instrumentation Symposium. LC 73-82889. 71p. 1980. pap. text ed. 15.00x (ISBN 0-87664-475-2). Instru Soc.

Wyatt, M. Colby, ed. The Performance of Paper Made with Thermomechanical Pulp: A Workshop on Thermomechanical Pulp. (TAPPI PRESS Reports). 11p. 1978. pap. 4.95 (ISBN 0-89852-374-5, 01-01-R074). TAPPI.

Yin, Robert I., ed. Paper Coating Additives: Description of Functional Properties & List of Available Products. 4th ed. 72p. 1982. pap. 34.95 (ISBN 0-89852-401-6, 01 01 R101). TAPPI.

PAPER MAKING AND TRADE–BIBLIOGRAPHY

Hunter, Dard. Literature of Papermaking, 1390-1800. LC 68-56797. (Bibliography & Reference Ser.: No. 411). (Illus.). 1971. Repr. of 1925 ed. lib. bdg. 35.50 (ISBN 0-8337-1769-3). B Franklin.

Labarre, E. J. Dictionary & Encyclopaedia of Paper & Paper-Making. 2nd, rev. ed. 500p. 1952. text ed. 71.50 (ISBN 90-265-0037-8, Pub. by Swets Pub Serv Holland). Swets North Am.

Louden, Louise. Pulping of Bagasse & Other Papermaking Fibers. LC 76-29080. (Bibliographic Ser.: No. 270). 1976. pap. 20.00 (ISBN 0-87010-045-9). Inst Paper Chem.

Pollock, Vera & Weiner, Jack. Corrosion of Pulp & Paper Mill Equipment. LC 76-21187. (Bibliographic Ser.: No. 269). 1976. pap. 40.00 (ISBN 0-87010-054-8). Inst Paper Chem.

Pulp & Paper Industry Division Index to Technical Papers, 1960-1983. 80p. 1984. pap. text ed. 12.00x (ISBN 0-87664-804-9). Instru Soc.

Roth, Lillian, et al. Corrosion of Pulp & Paper Mill Equipment, Suppl. 1. LC 76-21187. (Bibliographic Ser.: No. 269, Suppl. 1). 1979. pap. 45.00 (ISBN 0-87010-056-4). Inst Paper Chem.

Technical Association of the Pulp & Paper Industry. Engineering Drying Bibliography. Hansen, Alan J., ed. (Technical Association of the Pulp & Paper Industry, CA Report: No. 46). pap. 23.00 (ISBN 0-317-28938-1, 2020295). Bks Demand UMI.

Weiner, Jack. Microorganism Control. LC 76-57836. (Bibliographic Ser.: No. 276). 1977. pap. 23.00 (ISBN 0-87010-051-3). Inst Paper Chem.

Weiner, Jack, et al. Paper & Its Relation to Printing. 2nd ed, suppl. 1 ed. LC 62-51039. (Bibliographic Ser.: No. 164, Supplement 2). 1973. pap. 24.00 (ISBN 0-87010-005-X). Inst Paper Chem.

PAPERBOARD

Kline, James E. Paper & Paperboard Manufacturing & Converting Fundamentals. LC 81-85073. (A Pulp & Paper Bk.). (Illus.). 232p. 1982. pap. 39.50 (ISBN 0-87930-134-1). Miller Freeman.

Mark. Handbook of Physical & Mechanical Testing of Paper & Paperboard, Vol. 1. 821p. 1983. 95.00 (ISBN 0-8247-1871-2). Dekker.

PARABOLA

see also Conic Sections

Dawes, William M. The Hyperbola & the Parabola. LC 72-86314. 75p. 1973. text ed. 9.75 (ISBN 0-8283-1485-3). Branden Pub Co.

Wolf, Joseph. Classification & Fourier Inversion for Parabolic Subgroups with Square Integrable Nilradical. LC 79-21155. (Memoirs: No. 225). 166p. 1979. pap. 12.00 (ISBN 0-8218-2225-X). Am Math.

PARABOLIC CYLINDER FUNCTIONS

see Weber Functions

PARACELSUS, 1493-1541

Jung, C. G. Alchemical Studies. Adler, Gerhard, et al, eds. Hull, R. F., tr. (The Collected Works of C. G. Jung: No. 13). 1968. 35.00 (ISBN 0-691-09760-7); pap. 13.50x (ISBN 0-691-01849-9). Princeton U Pr.

Pachter, Henry M. Magic into Science: The Story of Paracelsus. 360p. 1982. Repr. of 1951 ed. lib. bdg. 35.00 (ISBN 0-8495-4408-4). Arden Lib.

Pagel, W. Paracelsus. 2nd ed. (Illus.). xii, 400p. 1982. 59.25 (ISBN 3-8055-3518-X). S Karger.

Stillman, John M. Theophrastus Bombastus von Hohenheim Called Paracelsus. LC 79-8625. (Illus.). viii, 184p. Repr. of 1920 ed. 34.50 (ISBN 0-404-18491-X). AMS Pr.

Webster, Charles. From Paracelsus to Newton: Magic & the Making of Modern Science. LC 82-4586. (Illus.). 120p. 1983. 22.95 (ISBN 0-521-24919-8). Cambridge U Pr.

PARACHUTES

Butler, Manley C., Jr. How to Get an FAA TSO for Parachutes. 112p. 1984. pap. text ed. 34.95x (ISBN 0-930747-00-3). Tech Info Pubn.

Poynter, Dan. The Parachute Manual: A Technical Treatise on Aerodynamic Decelerators. 3rd, rev. ed. LC 83-13350. (Illus.). 592p. 1984. lab manual 44.95 (ISBN 0-915516-35-7). Para Pub.

PARAFFINS

Mozes, G. Parafin Products: Properties, Technologies, Applications. (Developments in Petroleum Products Ser.: Vol. 14). 336p. 1983. 83.00 (ISBN 0-444-99712-1). Elsevier.

PARAGORDIUS

May, Henry G. Contributions to the Life Histories of Gordius Robustus Leidy & Paragordius Varius: Leidy. (Illus.). Repr. of 1920 ed. 12.00 (ISBN 0-384-36060-2). Johnson Repr.

PARAKEET

see Budgerigars; Parrots

PARALLEL PROCESSING (ELECTRONIC COMPUTERS)

Akl, Selim G. Parallel Sorting Algorithms. Date not set. pap. 24.95 (ISBN 0-12-047681-9). Acad Pr.

--Parallel Sorting Alogorithms. Date not set. 49.00 (ISBN 0-12-047680-0). Acad Pr.

Barringer, H. A Survey of Verification Techniques for Parallel Programs. (Lecture Notes in Computer Science: Vol. 191). vi, 115p. 1985. pap. 11.20 (ISBN 0-387-15239-3). Springer-Verlag.

Becker, J. D. & Eisele, I., eds. WOPPLOT 83 Parallel Processing-Logic, Organization, & Technology: Proceeding of a Workshop Held at the Federal Armed Forces Unversity Munich (HSBwM) Neububerg, Bavaria, Germany, June 27-29, 1983. (Lecture Notes in Physics: Vol. 196). v, 189p. 1984. pap. 13.00 (ISBN 0-387-12917-0). Springer Verlag.

Evans, D. J., ed. Parallel Processing Systems: An Advanced Course. LC 81-38445. (Illus.). 350p. 1982. 44.50 (ISBN 0-521-24366-1). Cambridge U Pr.

Feilmeier, M., et al, eds. Parallel Computing: Proceedings of the International Conference, Freie Universitat, Berlin, 26-28, Sept., 1983. 566p. 1984. 74.00 (ISBN 0-444-87528-X, North Holland). Elsevier.

Hoare, C. A. Communicating Sequential Processes. (International Book Ser.). (Illus.). 224p. 1985. text ed. 35.00 (ISBN 0-13-153271-5). P-H.

Hwang, Kai & Briggs, Faye A. Computer Architecture & Parallel Processing. 848p. 1984. 45.95 (ISBN 0-07-031556-6). McGraw.

Knoedel, W. & Schneider, H. J., eds. Parallel Processes & Related Automata. (Computing Supplementum Ser.: No. 3). 203p. 1981. pap. 52.00 (ISBN 0-387-81606-2). Springer-Verlag.

Kowalik, J. S., ed. High-Speed Computation. (NATO ASI Series, Series F: Computer & Systems Sciences: No. 7). 455p. 1984. 46.60 (ISBN 0-387-12885-9). Springer-Verlag.

Kuhn, Robert H. & Padua, David A. Parallel Processing. (Tutorial Texts Ser.). 498p. 1981. 36.00 (ISBN 0-8186-0367-4, Q367). IEEE Comp Soc.

Matney, Roy M., 2nd & Roth, C. H., Jr. Parallel Computing Structures & Algorithms for Logic Design Problems. LC 72-133318. 124p. 1969. 19.00 (ISBN 0-403-04518-5). Scholarly.

Oleinick, Peter N. Parallel Algorithms on a Multiprocessor. Stone, Harold S., ed. LC 82-4954. (Computer Science Ser.: Systems Programming: No. 4). 126p. 1982. 34.95 (ISBN 0-8357-1327-X). UMI Res Pr.

Paddon, D. J., ed. Supercomputers & Parallel Computations. (The Institute of Mathematics & Its Applications Conference Ser.). (Illus.). 1984. 39.00x (ISBN 0-19-853601-1). Oxford U Pr.

Schendel, U. Introduction to Numerical Methods for Parallel Computers. (Mathematics & Its Applications Ser.). 151p. 1984. 21.95x (ISBN 0-470-20091-X). Halsted Pr.

Stone, Jonathan. Parallel Processing in the Visual Systems: The Classification of Retinal Ganglion Cells & Its Impact on the Neurobiology of Vision. (Perspectives in Vision Research Ser.). 430p. 1983. 55.00x (ISBN 0-306-41220-9, Plenum Pr). Plenum Pub.

PARALLELS (GEOMETRY)

see also Axioms; Geometry–Foundations; Geometry, Non-Euclidean

Cameron, P. J. Parallelisms of Complete Designs. LC 75-32912. (London Mathematical Society Lecture Note Ser.: No. 23). (Illus.). 1976. 22.95 (ISBN 0-521-21160-3). Cambridge U Pr.

Stackel, Paul. Die Theorie der Parallellinien Von Euklid Bis Auf Gauss. (Bibliotheca Mathematica Teubneriana Ser.: No. 41). (Ger.). Repr. of 1895 ed. 39.00 (ISBN 0-384-57410-6). Johnson Repr.

PARAMAGNETIC RESONANCE, ELECTRONIC

see Electron Paramagnetic Resonance

PARAMAGNETISM

see also Electron Paramagnetic Resonance

LaMar, G. N., et al, eds. NMR of Paramagnetic Molecules: Principles & Applications. 1973. 91.50 (ISBN 0-12-434550-6). Acad Pr.

Low, William, ed. Paramagnetic Resonance, 2 Vols. 1963. Set. 130.50 (ISBN 0-12-456266-3); Vol. 1. 88.00 (ISBN 0-12-456201-9); Vol. 2. 88.00 (ISBN 0-12-456202-7). Acad Pr.

Parsonage, P. Design & Testing of Paramagnetic Liquid Separation Systems, 1978. 1981. 69.00x (ISBN 0-686-97054-3, Pub. by W Spring England). State Mutual Bk.

Segal, E. Mathematical Cosmology & Extragalactic Astronomy. (Pure & Applied Mathematics Ser.: Vol. 68). 1976. 29.50 (ISBN 0-12-635250-X). Acad Pr.

Selwood, Pierce W. Adsorption & Collective Paramagnetism. 1962. 49.00 (ISBN 0-12-636550-4). Acad Pr.

PARAMETRIC AMPLIFIERS

Brosowski, Bruno. Parametric Semi-Infinite Optimization, Vol. 22. (Methoden und Verfaliren der Mathematischen Physik). 260p. 1981. pap. 32.95. P Lang Pubs.

Control of Distributed Parameter Systems: Joint Automatic Control Conference, 1969, University of Colorado. LC 75-94121. pap. 27.00 (ISBN 0-317-11045-4, 2016912). Bks Demand UMI.

Huseyin, K. Vibrations & Stability of Multiple Parameter System. (Mechanics of Elastic Stability: No. 3). 228p. 1978. 37.50x (ISBN 90-286-0136-8). Sijthoff & Noordhoff.

Kimmich, H. P. Monitoring of Vital Parameters During Extracorporal Circulation. (Illus.). x, 334p. 1981. soft cover 80.50 (ISBN 3-8055-2059-X). S Karger.

Vincent, Thomas L. & Grantham, Walter J. Optimality in Parametric Systems. LC 81-1870. 243p. 1981. 42.95x (ISBN 0-471-08307-0, Pub. by Wiley-Interscience). Wiley.

Zacks, S. Parametric Statistical Inference: Basic Theory & Modern Approaches. LC 80-41715. (I.S. in Nonlinear Mathematics Series; Theory & Applications: Vol. 4). 400p. 1981. 47.00 (ISBN 0-08-026468-9). Pergamon.

PARAMPHISTOMIDAE

Stunkard, Horace W. Studies on North American Polystomidae Aspidogastridae & Paramphistomidae. (Illus.). Repr. of 1917 ed. 12.00 (ISBN 0-384-58730-5). Johnson Repr.

PARASITE-HOST RELATIONSHIPS

see Host-Parasite Relationships

PARASITES

see also Agricultural Pests; Fungi, Pathogenic; Insects, Injurious and Beneficial; Parasitism also names of parasitic orders, classes, etc., e.g. Cestoda, Nemathelminthes, Ticks

Baker, A. S. Bibliography of the Helminth Parasites of New Zealand (1879-1971) 79p. 1973. 30.00x (ISBN 0-85198-265-4, Pub. by CAB Bks England). State Mutual Bk.

Barnard, C. J., ed. Producers & Scroungers Strategics of Exploitation & Parasitism. 267p. 1984. 39.95 (ISBN 0-412-00541-7, NO. 9017, Pub. by Chapman & Hall England). Methuen Inc.

Bilharziasis & Malaria. (Bulletin of WHO: Vol. 35, No. 3). 178p. 1966. pap. 3.60 (ISBN 0-686-09213-9). World Health.

Canning, E. V. & Wright, C. A., eds. Behavioural Aspects of Parasite Transmission. (Zoological Journal of the Linean Society Ser.: Vol. 5). 1973. 47.50 (ISBN 0-12-158650-2). Acad Pr.

Cheng, Thomas C. General Parasitology. 1973. text ed. 32.00i (ISBN 0-12-170750-4). Acad Pr.

Donaldson, R. J. Parasites & Western Man. (Illus.). 232p. 1979. text ed. 32.00 (ISBN 0-8391-1432-X). Univ Park.

Esch, Gerald W. & Nikol, Brent B., eds. Regulation of Parasite Populations. 1977. 39.50 (ISBN 0-12-241750-X). Acad Pr.

Ewing, Henry E. Manual of External Parasites. (Illus.). 226p. 1929. photocopy ed. 22.50x (ISBN 0-398-04253-5). C C Thomas.

Fallis, A. M., ed. Ecology & Physiology of Parasites: A Symposium Held at University of Toronto, 1970. LC 70-151365. pap. 67.00 (ISBN 0-317-26914-3, 2023613). Bks Demand UMI.

Flynn, Robert J. Parasites of Laboratory Animals. LC 77-171165. (Illus.). 884p. 1973. 37.00x (ISBN 0-8138-0470-1). Iowa St U Pr.

Gaafar, S. M., et al. Parasites, Pests & Predators. (World Animal Science Ser.: Vol. B2). Date not set. write for info. (ISBN 0-444-42175-0). Elsevier.

Hassell, Michael P. The Dynamics of Arthropod Predator-Prey Systems. LC 78-51169. (Monographs in Population Biology: No. 13). 1978. 27.50 (ISBN 0-691-08208-1); pap. 10.95 (ISBN 0-691-08215-4). Princeton U Pr.

Howard, Leland O. & Fiske, William F. The Importation into the United States of the Parasites of the Gypsy Moth & the Brown-Tail Moth: Report of Progress of Previous & Concurrent Efforts of This Kind. Egerton, Frank N., 3rd, ed. LC 77-74230. (History of Ecology Ser.). (Illus.). 1978. Repr. of 1911 ed. lib. bdg. 32.00x (ISBN 0-405-10400-6). Ayer Co Pubs.

Human Antiparasitic Drugs: Pharmacology & Usage. LC 84-13110. 1985. 23.25 (ISBN 0-471-90253-5). Wiley.

Jacobs, Leon, ed. Parasitic Zoonoses: Section C, 3 vols. (CRC Handbook Series in Zoonoses). 1982. Volume I, 400 pp. 86.00 (ISBN 0-8493-2916-7); Volume II, 360 pp. 79.50 (ISBN 0-8493-2917-5); Volume III, 384. 86.00 (ISBN 0-8493-2918-3). CRC Pr.

Klein, Aaron E. The Parasites We Humans Harbor. (Illus.). 1981. 12.95 (ISBN 0-525-66693-1). Lodestar Bks.

Levine, Norman D., ed. Natural Nidality of Diseases & Questions of Parasitology. Plous, Frederick K., Jr., tr. LC 68-11027. (Illus.). Repr. of 1968 ed. 94.10 (ISBN 0-8357-9691-4, 2019031). Bks Demand UMI.

Lombardero, Oscar J. Los Nombres Cientificos de los Parasitos y Su Significado. 2nd ed. (Span.). 90p. 1978. 12.50 (ISBN 0-686-56662-9, S-33068). French & Eur.

McKelvey, John J., Jr., et al, eds. Vectors of Disease Agents: Interactions with Plants, Animals, & Men. LC 80-18676. 256p. 1981. 49.95 (ISBN 0-03-056887-0). Praeger.

Marchalonis, John J., ed. Contemporary Topics in Immunobiology, Vol. 12: Immunobiology of Parasites & Parasitic Infections. 490p. 1984. 59.50x (ISBN 0-306-41418-X, Plenum Pr). Plenum Pub.

Ogbourne, C. P. & Duncan, J. L. Strongylus Vulgaris in the Horse: Its Biology & Veterinary Importance. 40p. 1977. 40.00x (ISBN 0-85198-393-6, Pub. by CAB Bks England). State Mutual Bk.

Price, Peter W. Evolutionary Biology of Parasites. LC 79-3227. (Monographs in Population Biology: No. 15). 1980. 25.00 (ISBN 0-691-08256-1); pap. 10.95 (ISBN 0-691-08257-X). Princeton U Pr.

Pritchard, Mary H. & Kruse, Gunther O., eds. The Collection & Preservation of Animal Parasites. LC 81-19869. iv, 141p. (Orig.). 1982. pap. 10.95x (ISBN 0-8032-8704-6). U of Nebr Pr.

Rohde, Klaus. Ecology of Marine Parasites. LC 81-12934. (Australian Ecology Ser.). (Illus.). 245p. 1982. text ed. 25.00 (ISBN 0-7022-1660-7); pap. text ed. 12.95 (ISBN 0-7022-1670-4). U of Queensland Pr.

Scott, Donald R. & O'Keeffe, Larry E., eds. Lygus Bug: Host Plant Interactions. 39p. (Collection of papers). 1977. 1.95 (ISBN 0-89301-037-5). U Pr of Idaho.

Slutzky, Gerald M., ed. Biochemistry of Parasites: Proceedings of Satellite Conference of the 13th Annual Meeting of the Federation of European Biochemical Societies (FEBS), Jerusalem, August 1980. (Illus.). 236p. 1981. 44.00 (ISBN 0-08-026381-X). Pergamon.

Van Den Bossche, ed. Comparative Biochemistry of Parasites. 1972. 67.50 (ISBN 0-12-711050-X). Acad Pr.

Wakelin, Derek. Immunity to Parasites: How Animals Control Parasite Infection. 192p. 1984. pap. text ed. 16.95 (ISBN 0-7131-2889-5). E Arnold.

Yuncker, Truman G. Revision of the North American & West Indian Species of Cuscuta. (Illinois Biological Monographs: Vol. 6, Nos. 2 & 3). 12.00 (ISBN 0-384-70540-5). Johnson Repr.

PARASITES–ARTHROPODA

Shephard, M. R. Arthropods as Final Hosts of Nematodes & Nematomorphs. 248p. 1974. 49.00x (ISBN 0-85198-310-3, Pub. by CAB Bks England). State Mutual Bk.

PARASITES–BIBLIOGRAPHY

Jenkins, D. W. Pathogens, Parasites & Predators of Medically Important Arthropods. (WHO Bulletin Supplement: Vol. 30). 1964. pap. 3.60 (ISBN 92-4-168301-5). World Health.

PARASITES–BIRDS

Stroud, Robert. Bird Disease by Stroud. 14.95 (ISBN 0-87666-435-4, AP-926). TFH Pubns.

PARASITES–DOMESTIC ANIMALS

Gaafar, S. M., et al, eds. Pathology of Parasitic Diseases. LC 72-108014. (Illus.). 408p. 1971. 15.00 (ISBN 0-911198-28-8). Purdue U Pr.

Gibson, T. E., ed. Weather & Parasitic Animal Disease. (Technical Note Ser.: No. 159). 174p. 1978. pap. 30.00 (ISBN 92-63-10497-2, W410, WMO). Unipub.

Henson, J. B. & Campbell, M., eds. Theileriosis: Report of a Workshop Held in Nairobi, Kenya, 7-9 Dec. 1976. (Illus.). 112p. 1977. pap. 10.00 (ISBN 0-88936-124-X, IDRC86, IDRC). Unipub.

Molyneux, D. H., et al. The Biology of Trypansoma & Leishmania: Parasites of Man & Domestic Animals. 274p. 1983. 36.00x (ISBN 0-8002-3078-7). Taylor & Francis.

Soulsby, E. J. Helminths, Arthropods & Protozoa of Domesticated Animals. 7th ed. (Illus.). 809p. 1982. text ed. 57.50 (ISBN 0-8121-0780-2). Lea & Febiger.

Trypanotolerant Livestock in West & Central Africa. (Animal Production & Health Papers: No. 20-1 & 20-2). (Eng. & Fr.). 1980. Set. pap. 33.00 (ISBN 92-5-100978-3, F2152, FAO). Vol. 1, General Study, 155p. Vol. 2, Country Studies, 308p. Unipub.

PARASITES–FISHES

Bangham, Ralph V. A Resurvey of the Fish Parasites of Western Lake Erie. 1972. 1.00 (ISBN 0-86727-061-6). Ohio Bio Survey.

Bowman, Thomas E. & Tareen, Inam U. Cymothoidae from Fishes of Kuwait (Arabian Gulf)(Crustacea: Isopoda) LC 83-600096. (Smithsonian Contributions to Zoology Ser.: No. 382). pap. 20.00 (ISBN 0-317-29613-2, 2021865). Bks Demand UMI.

Hoffman, Glen L. & Meyer, Fred P. Parasites of Freshwater Fishes. (Illus.). 224p. 1974. pap. 19.95 (ISBN 0-87666-130-4, PS-208). TFH Pubns.

Hoffman, Glenn L. Parasites of North American Freshwater Fishes. LC 67-14063. 1967. 42.50x (ISBN 0-520-00565-1). U of Cal Pr.

Kabats. Parasites & Diseases & Fish Cultures. 1985. 54.00 (ISBN 0-85066-285-0, Pub. by Falmer Pr). Taylor & Francis.

Paperna, Ilan. Parasites, Infections & Diseases of Fish in Africa. (Commission for Inland Fisheries of Africa (CIFA): Technical Papers: No. 7). (Eng. & Fr.). 224p. 1980. pap. 16.00 (ISBN 92-5-100982-1, F2032, FAO). Unipub.

Scott, T. & Scott, A. British Parasitic Copepoda, 2 Vols in 1. Repr. of 1913 ed. 28.00 (ISBN 0-384-54470-3). Johnson Repr.

Yamaguti, Satyu. Monogenetic Trematodes of Hawaiian Fishes. (Illus.). 287p. 1968. text ed. 20.00x (ISBN 0-87022-891-9). UH Pr.

PARASITES–INSECTS

Carter, Walter. Insects in Relation to Plant Disease. 2nd ed. LC 73-4362. pap. 160.00 (ISBN 0-317-28102-X, 2055731). Bks Demand UMI.

Egerton, Frank N., ed. Ecological Studies on Insect Parasitism: An Original Anthology. LC 77-73820. (History of Ecology Ser.). 1978. lib. bdg. 24.50x (ISBN 0-405-10389-1). Ayer Co Pubs.

Poinar, George O. Nematodes for Biological Control of Insects. 304p. 1979. 81.50 (ISBN 0-8493-5333-5). CRC Pr.

Poinar, George O., Jr. & Thomas, Gerald M. Insect Pathogens & Parasites: Laboratory Guide. 408p. 1984. 49.50x (ISBN 0-306-41680-8, Plenum Pr). Plenum Pub.

Price, Peter W., ed. Evolutionary Strategies of Parasitic Insects & Mites. LC 75-11524. 235p. 1975. 39.50x (ISBN 0-306-30851-7, Plenum Pr). Plenum Pub.

Steinhaus, Edward A. Insect Microbiology: An Account of the Microbes Associated with Insects & Ticks. (Illus.). 1967. Repr. of 1946 ed. 26.95x (ISBN 0-02-852920-0). Hafner.

Wilcox, John A. Host Plants of Chrysomelidae, Leaf Beetles, of Northeastern United States & Eastern Canada. 1978. pap. text ed. 4.95 (ISBN 0-916846-09-1). World Natural Hist.

PARASITES–VERTEBRATES

Davis, John W. & Anderson, Roy C., eds. Parasitic Diseases of Wild Mammals. facsimile ed. LC 72-103854. (Illus.). 1971. pap. 25.65x (ISBN 0-8138-2455-9). Iowa St U Pr.

PARASITIC PLANTS

see also Fungi; Symbiosis

also names of parasitic plants

Cheeke, Peter R. & Shull, L. R. Natural Toxicants in Feeds & Poisonous Plants. (Illus., Orig.). 1985. deluxe ed. 69.50 (ISBN 0-87055-482-4). AVI.

Kuijt, Job. The Biology of Parasitic Flowering Plants. LC 68-9722. (Illus.). 1969. 55.00x (ISBN 0-520-01490-1). U of Cal Pr.

PARASITISM

see also Host-Parasite Relationships; Predation (Biology)

All India Symposium, Jabalpur, Feb. 24-27, 1978. Physiology of Parasitism: Proceedings. Agarwal, G. P. & Bilgrami, K. S., eds. (Current Trends in Life Sciences: Vol. 7). vi, 478p. 1979. 50.00 (ISBN 0-88065-004-4, Pub. by Messers Today & Tomorrows Printers & Publishers India). Scholarly Pubns.

Cook, Clayton B., et al, eds. Cellular Interactions in Symbiosis & Parasitism. LC 79-23304. (Ohio State University Biosciences Colloquia: No. 5). (Illus.). 321p. 1980. 25.00x (ISBN 0-8142-0315-9). Ohio St U Pr.

Koch, William. Neoplastic & Viral Parasitism. 1961. pap. 4.00x (ISBN 0-318-00143-8). Cancer Control Soc.

Mahadevan, A., ed. Physiology of Host Pathogen Interaction, 1977. (Current Trends in Life Sciences Ser.: Vol. 6). viii, 496p. 1979. 40.00 (ISBN 0-88065-152-0, Pub. by Messers Today & Tomorrows Printers & Publishers India). Scholarly Pubns.

Moulder, James W. Biochemistry of Intracellular Parasitism. LC 62-12636. (Illus.). 1962. 12.50x (ISBN 0-226-54248-3). U of Chicago Pr.

Read, Clark P. Parasitism & Symbiology: An Introductory Text. LC 75-110390. Repr. of 1970 ed. 81.50 (ISBN 0-8357-9947-6, 2055139). Bks Demand UMI.

Rosen, David. The Role of Hyperparasitism in Biological Control: A Symposium. LC 81-65779. (Illus.). 55p. 1981. pap. 3.00 (ISBN 0-931876-47-8, 4103). Ag & Nat Res.

PARASITOLOGY

see also Parasites; Parasitism

Advances in Parasitology, Vol. 21. (Serial Publication). 336p. 1982. 56.00 (ISBN 0-12-031721-4). Acad Pr.

Advances in Parasitology, Vol. 22. (Serial Publication). 416p. 1983. 60.00 (ISBN 0-12-031722-2). Acad Pr.

Arme, C., et al. Studies in Parasitology in Memory of Clark P. Read. Byram, J. E. & Stewart, George, eds. (Rice University Studies: Vol. 62, No. 4). 236p. 1977. pap. 10.00x (ISBN 0-89263-230-5). Rice Univ.

August, J. Thomas. Molecular Parasitology. (John Jacob Abel Symposia on Drug Development Ser.). 1984. 37.00 (ISBN 0-12-068060-2). Acad Pr.

Baker, J. R., ed. Advances in Parasitology, Vol. 24. 1985. 60.00 (ISBN 0-12-031724-9). Acad Pr.

Baker, John R. & Muller, Ralph. Advances in Parasitology, Vol. 23. LC 62-22124. (Serial Publication). 1985. 40.00 (ISBN 0-12-031723-0). Acad Pr.

Barriga, Omar O. Immunology of Parasitic Infections. (Illus.). 368p. (Orig.). 1981. pap. text ed. 31.50 (ISBN 0-8391-1621-7). Univ Park.

Beaver, Paul C. & Jung, Rodney C. Clinical Parasitology. 9th ed. LC 83-11338. (Illus.). 825p. 1984. text ed. 51.50 (ISBN 0-8121-0876-0). Lea & Febiger.

Cheng, Thomas C. General Parasitology. 1973. text ed. 32.00i (ISBN 0-12-170750-4). Acad Pr.

Cox, F. E., ed. Modern Parasitology: A Textbook of Parasitology. (Illus.). 358p. 1982. pap. text ed. 25.00x (ISBN 0-632-00612-9). Blackwell Pubns.

Crompton, D. W. & Newton, B. A., eds. Trends & Perspectives in Parasitology, No. 1. LC 80-42159. (Illus.). 150p. 1981. 29.95 (ISBN 0-521-23821-8); pap. 11.95 (ISBN 0-521-28242-X). Cambridge U Pr.

--Trends & Perspectives in Parasitology, No. 2. LC 80-42159. (Illus.). 91p. 1982. 21.95 (ISBN 0-521-24830-2); pap. 8.95 (ISBN 0-521-28989-0). Cambridge U Pr.

Dawes, B. & Lumsden, W. H., eds. Advances in Parasitology, Vol. 16. (Serial Publication Ser.). 1978. 70.00 (ISBN 0-12-031716-8). Acad Pr.

Esch, Gerald W. & Nikol, Brent B., eds. Regulation of Parasite Populations. 1977. 39.50 (ISBN 0-12-241750-X). Acad Pr.

Food & Nutrition Board, National Research Council. Prevention of Microbial & Parasitic Hazard Associated with Processed Foods: A Guide for the Food Processor. 164p. 1975. pap. 7.25 (ISBN 0-309-02345-9). Natl Acad Pr.

Garnham, P. C. Progress in Parasitology. (Heath Clark Lectures, 1968). (Illus.). 224p. 1971. 45.00 (ISBN 0-485-26321-1, Pub. by Athlone Pr Ltd). Longwood Pub Group.

Gauld, I. D. & Mitchell, P. A. The Taxonomy, Distribution & Host Preferences of African Parasitic Wasps of the Subfamily Ophioninae (Hymenoptera; Inchenumonidae) 1978. 90.00x (ISBN 0-85198-409-6, Pub. by CAb Bks England). State Mutual Bk.

--The Taxonomy, Distribution & Host Preferences of Indo-Papuan Paraditic Wasps of the Subfamily Ophioninae (Hymenoptera; Ichneumonidae) 611p. 1981. 89.00 (ISBN 0-85198-482-7, Pub. by CAB Bks England). State Mutual Bk.

Griffiths, Henry J. A Handbook of Veterinary Parasitology: Domestic Animals of North America. LC 78-50021. 1978. 20.00x (ISBN 0-8166-0834-2); pap. 12.95x (ISBN 0-8166-0828-8). U of Minn Pr.

Hudson, L., ed. The Biology of Trypanosomes: Current Topics in Microbiology & Immunology Ser, Vol. 117. (Current Topics in Microbiology & Immunology: Vol. 117). (Illus.). 195p. 1985. 44.00 (ISBN 0-387-15512-0). Springer-Verlag.

Kennedy, C. R., ed. Ecological Aspects of Parasitology. 1976. 123.00 (ISBN 0-7204-0602-1, North-Holland). Elsevier.

Leiva, Manuel R. Relacion Hospedante-Parasito Mecanismo De Patogenicidad De los Microorganismos. (Serie Biologia: No. 14). 91p. 1981. pap. 3.50 (ISBN 0-8270-1322-1). OAS.

Levine, Norman D., ed. Natural Nidality of Diseases & Questions of Parasitology. Plous, Frederick K., Jr., tr. LC 68-11027. (Illus.). Repr. of 1968 ed. 94.10 (ISBN 0-8357-9691-4, 2019031). Bks Demand UMI.

Lumsden, W. H., et al, eds. Advances in Parasitology, Vol. 18. (Serial Publication Ser.). 1980. 59.50 (ISBN 0-12-031718-4). Acad Pr.

--Advances in Parasitology, Vol. 19. (Serial Publication Ser.). 224p. 1982. 47.00 (ISBN 0-12-031719-2). Acad Pr.

--Advances in Parasitology, Vol. 20. (Serial Publication Ser.). 1982. 70.00 (ISBN 0-12-031720-6). Acad Pr.

Marquardt, William C. & Demaree, Richard S. Principles of Parasitology. 592p. 1985. text ed. write for info. (ISBN 0-02-376250-0). Macmillan.

Mettrick, D. F. & Desser, S. S., eds. Parasites-Their World & Ours: Proceedings of the Fifth International Congress of Parasitology, Toronto, Canada, August 7-14, 1982. 465p. 1982. 64.00 (ISBN 0-444-80433-1, Biomedical Pr). Elsevier.

Meyer, Marvin C. & Olsen, O. Wilford. Essentials of Parasitology. 3rd ed. 288p. 1980. write for info. wire coil (ISBN 0-697-04684-2). Wm C Brown.

The Microsporidian Paradites of Platyleminthes: EU Canning. 32p. 1975. 49.00x (ISBN 0-85198-380-4, Pub. by CAB Bks England). State Mutual Bk.

Noble, Elmer R. & Noble, Glenn A. Parasitology: The Biology of Animal Parasites. 5th ed. LC 81-20686. (Illus.). 522p. 1982. text ed. 34.50 (ISBN 0-8121-0819-1). Lea & Febiger.

Oberhofer, Thomas R. Manual of Practical Medical Microbiology & Parasitology. 499p. 1985. pap. text ed. 29.95 (ISBN 0-471-80543-2, Pub. by Wiley Med). Wiley.

Ogbourne, C. P. & Duncan, J. L. Strongylus Vulgaris in the Horse: Its Biology & Veterinary Importance. 40p. 1977. 40.00x (ISBN 0-85198-393-6, Pub. by CAB Bks England). State Mutual Bk.

Practical Parasitology - General Laboratory Techniques & Parasitic Protozoa: Animal Husbandry - Notes for Students. pap. 4.50 (F329, FAO). Unipub.

Price, C. J. & Reed, C. J. Practical Parasitology: General Laboratory Techniques & Parasitic Protozoa Notes for Students of Animal Husbandry. 112p. 1970. pap. 3.00 (ISBN 92-5-101581-3, F330, FAO). Unipub.

Schmidt, Gerald D. & Roberts, Larry S. Foundations of Parasitology. 2nd ed. LC 81-1342. (Illus.). 795p. 1981. pap. text ed. 28.95 (ISBN 0-8016-4344-9). Mosby.

Shephard, M. R. Arthropods as Final Hosts of Nematodes & Nematomorphs. 248p. 1974. 49.00x (ISBN 0-85198-310-3, Pub. by CAB Bks England). State Mutual Bk.

Snail Control in the Prevention of Bilharziasis. (Monograph Ser: No. 50). (Eng, Fr, & Rus., Illus.). 247p. 1966. 8.00 (ISBN 92-4-140050-1). World Health.

Spencer, H., et al. Tropical Pathology. (Spezielle Pathologische Anatomie Ser. Special Ed.: Vol. 8). (Illus.). 765p. 1973. 139.00 (ISBN 0-387-06208-4). Springer Verlag.

Stary, P., ed. Aphid Parasites of the Central Asian Area. (Illus.). 1979. pap. 26.00 (ISBN 90-6193-599-7, Pub. by Junk Pubs Netherlands). Kluwer Academic.

Strickland, Thomas G. Immunoparasitology: Principles & Methods in Malaria & Schistosomiasis Research. Hunter, Kenneth W., ed. LC 82-626. 304p. 1982. 45.95 (ISBN 0-03-061499-6). Praeger.

Taylor, Angela & Baker, John, eds. Methods of Cultivating Parasites in Vitro. 1978. 59.00 (ISBN 0-12-685550-1). Acad Pr.

Taylor, Angela E. & Muller, Ralph, eds. The Relevance of Parasitology to Human Welfare Today. (Symposia of the British Society for Parasitology Ser.: Vol. 16). (Illus.). 1978. pap. 19.75 (ISBN 0-632-00422-3, B 4884-X, Blackwell). Mosby.

Ukoli, F. M. Introduction to Parasitology in Tropical Africa. LC 82-6910. 400p. 1984. 36.00x (ISBN 0-471-10371-3, Pub. by Wiley-Interscience); pap. 14.95x (ISBN 0-471-10465-5). Wiley.

Van Der Hammen, L., ed. A. Berlese: Complete Acarological Works, 5 vols. (Illus.). 1977. lib. bdg. 263.00 set (ISBN 90-6193-582-2, Pub. by Junk Pub Netherlands). Kluwer Academic.

Vogtle, F., et al, eds. Host Guest Complex Chemistry III. (Topics in Current Chemistry Ser.: Vol. 121). (Illus.). 250p. 1984. 40.00 (ISBN 0-387-12821-2). Springer-Verlag.

Warren, K. S. & Bowers, J. Z., eds. Parasitology: A Global Perspective. (Illus.). 270p. 1983. 43.00 (ISBN 0-387-90840-4). Springer-Verlag.

Warren, Kenneth S. & Purcell, Elizabeth F., eds. The Current Status & Future of Parasitology. LC 81-84673. (Illus.). 296p. 1982. pap. 10.00 (ISBN 0-914362-37-2). J Macy Foun.

PARASITOLOGY–CULTURES AND CULTURE MEDIA

German Science Foundation Staff, ed. Recent German Research on Problems of Parasitology, Animal Health & Animal Breeding in the Tropics & Subtropics. 135p. 1984. pap. 17.50 (ISBN 0-317-27026-5). VCH Pubs.

PARASITOLOGY–LABORATORY MANUALS

Cable, Raymond M. An Illustrated Laboratory Manual of Parasitology. 5th ed. 1977. spiral bdg. 13.95x (ISBN 0-8087-0373-0). Burgess.

Laboratory Training Manual on the Use of Nuclear Techniques in Animal Parasitology: Immunology & Pathophysiology. (Technical Reports Ser.: No. 160). (Illus.). 164p. (Orig.). 1981. pap. 17.00 (ISBN 92-0-115274-4, IDC160, IAEA). Unipub.

Laboratory Training Manual on the Use of Nuclear Techniques in Animal Parasitology: A Joint Undertaking by the Food & Agriculture Organization of the United Nations & the International Atomic Energy Agency. (Technical Reports Ser.: No. 219). (Illus.). 335p. 1983. pap. text ed. 40.75 (ISBN 92-0-115182-9, IDC219, IAEA). Unipub.

Macy, Ralph W. & Berntzen, Allen K. Laboratory Guide to Parasitology: With Introduction to Experimental Methods. (Illus.). 316p. 1971. spiral 17.75x (ISBN 0-398-02154-6). C C Thomas.

PARATHYROID GLANDS

Draper, M. W. & Nissenson, R. A., eds. Parathyroid Hormone. (Journal: Mineral & Electrolyte Metabolism: Vol. 8, No. 3-4). (Illus.). vi, 124p. 1982. pap. 33.25 (ISBN 3-8055-3550-3). S Karger.

PARENTAL BEHAVIOR IN ANIMALS

see also Animals, Infancy of

Bell, Robert W. & Smotherman, William F., eds. Maternal Influences & Early Behavior. LC 78-17074. (Illus.). 465p. 1980. text ed. 60.00 (ISBN 0-89335-059-1). SP Med & Sci Bks.

Gubernick, David J. & Klopfer, Peter H., eds. Parental Care in Mammals. LC 80-36692. 478p. 1981. 39.50x (ISBN 0-306-40533-4, Plenum Pr). Plenum Pub.

Skutch, Alexander F. Parent Birds & Their Young. LC 75-2195. (Corrie Herring Hooks Ser.: No. 2). (Illus.). 521p. 1976. 45.00 (ISBN 0-292-76424-3). U of Tex Pr.

PAREXIC ANALYSIS

see Numerical Analysis

PARGETTING

see Plastering

PARKWAYS

see Express Highways

PARROTS

see also Budgerigars; Cockateels

Alderton, David. Parrots, Lories & Cockatoos. 200p. 1982. 21.95 (ISBN 0-86230-041-X). Triplegate.

Bates, Henry & Busenbark, Robert. Parrots. (Orig.). pap. 2.95 (ISBN 0-87666-427-3, M-506). TFH Pubns.

Bates, Henry J. & Busenbark, Robert I. Parrots & Related Birds. (Illus.). 543p. 19.95 (ISBN 0-87666-967-4, TFH H-912). TFH Pubns.

Bosch, Klaus & Weede, Ursula. Encyclopedia of Amazon Parrots. Lambrich, Annemarie, tr. (Illus.). 208p. 1984. 24.95 (ISBN 0-87666-871-6, H-1055). TFH Pubns.

Burr, Elisha W. Diseases of Parrots. (Illus.). 318p. 1982. 24.95 (ISBN 0-87666-843-0, H-1037). TFH Pubns.

Decoteau, A. E. The Handbook of Amazon Parrots. (Illus.). 221p. 1980. 14.95 (ISBN 0-87666-892-9, H-1025). TFH Pubns.

--The Handbook of Macaws. (Illus.). 128p. 1982. 19.95 (ISBN 0-87666-844-9, H-1044). TFH Pubns.

De Grahl, Wolfgang. The Parrot Family: Parakeets-Budgerigars-Cockatiels-Lovebirds-Lories-Macaws. LC 83-17940. (Illus.). 176p. 1985. 12.95 (ISBN 0-668-06039-5); pap. 7.95 (ISBN 0-668-06043-3). Arco.

Duke Of Bedford. Parrots & Parrot-Like Birds. 14.95 (ISBN 0-87666-428-1, H-931). TFH Pubns.

Forshaw, Joseph M. Australian Parrots. 2nd ed. (Illus.). 224p. 1980. 75.00 (ISBN 0-686-62188-3); write for ltd. ed. Eastview.

--Parrots of the World. (Illus.). 1977. Repr. of 1973 ed. 34.95 (ISBN 0-87666-959-3, PS-753). TFH Pubns.

Freud, Arthur. All about the Parrots. LC 79-25568. (Illus.). 304p. 1984. 17.95 (ISBN 0-87605-815-2). Howell Bk.

Grahl, Wolfgang de. The Parrot Family. LC 83-17940. (Illus.). 176p. 1984. 12.95 (ISBN 0-668-06039-5). Arco.

Greene, W. T. Parrots in Captivity. (Illus.). 1979. 29.95 (ISBN 0-87666-979-8, H-1018). TFH Pubns.

Hargrave, Lyndon L. Mexican Macaws: Comparative Osteology. LC 72-125168. (Anthropological Papers: No. 20). 67p. 1970. pap. 4.95x (ISBN 0-8165-0212-9). U of Ariz Pr.

Harmon, Ian. Australian Parrots in Bush & Aviary. LC 81-68497. (Illus.). 240p. 1982. 29.00 (ISBN 0-7153-8259-4). David & Charles.

Harris, Robbie. Grey-Cheeked Parakeets & Other Brotogeris. (Illus.). 160p. 1985. text ed. 9.95 (ISBN 0-86622-049-6, PS-830). TFH Pubns.

Hayward, Jim. Lovebirds & Their Color Mutations. (Illus.). 112p. 1980. 14.95 (ISBN 0-7137-0949-9, Pub. by Blandford Pr England). Sterling.

Lear, Edward. Illustrations of the Family of Psittacidae, or Parrots. (Illus.). 1978. Repr. 1300.00. Johnson Repr.

Lendon, Alan. Australian Parrots in Field & Aviary. (Illus.). 344p. 1979. 32.95 (ISBN 0-207-12424-8). Avian Pubns.

Low, Rosemary. Lories & Lorikeets. (Illus.). 1979. pap. 14.95 (ISBN 0-87666-980-1, PS-773). TFH Pubns.

--Parrots: Their Care & Breeding. (Illus.). 670p. 1980. 55.00 (ISBN 0-7137-0876-X, Pub. by Blandford Pr England). Sterling.

Mulawka, Edward J. Taming & Training Parrots. (Illus.). 1981. 19.95 (ISBN 0-87666-989-5, H-1019). TFH Pubns.

--Yellow-Fronted Amazon Parrots. (Illus.). 160p. 12.95 (ISBN 0-87666-835-X, PS-781). TFH Pubns.

Paradise, Paul R. African Grey Parrots. (Illus.). 1979. 4.95 (ISBN 0-87666-977-1, KW-018). TFH Pubns.

--Amazon Parrots. (Illus.). 1979. 4.95 (ISBN 0-87666-985-2, KW-012). TFH Pubns.

Plath, Carl & Davis, Malcolm. This Is the Parrot. 9.95 (ISBN 0-87666-431-1, PS-653). TFH Pubns.

Rogers, Cyril H. Parrot Guide. 2nd ed. (Illus.). 256p. 14.95 (ISBN 0-87666-546-6, PL-2984). TFH Pubns.

Spiotta, Loren. Macaws. (Illus.). 1979. 4.95 (ISBN 0-87666-975-5, KW-003). TFH Pubns.

Starika, W. A. & Richardson, E. L., eds. The T.F.H. Book of Parrots: With a Special Illustrated Section on Surgical Sexing William C. Satterfield. (Illus.). 80p. 1982. 6.95 (ISBN 0-87666-806-6, HP-015). TFH Pubns.

Teitler, Risa. Amazon Parrots, Taming. (Illus.). 1979. 4.95 (ISBN 0-87666-881-3, KW-039). TFH Pubns.

Vriends, Matthew M. & Axelrod, Herbert R. Parrots. (Illus.). 1979. 4.95 (ISBN 0-87666-995-X, KW-032). TFH Pubns.

PARTICLE, DYNAMICS OF A

see Dynamics of a Particle

PARTICLE ACCELERATORS

see also Cyclotron; Linear Accelerators; Particle Beams

Arrons, J., et al, eds. Particle Acceleration Mechanics in Astrophysics. LC 79-55844. (AIP Conference Proceedings: No. 56). (Illus.). 425p. lib. bdg. 22.00 (ISBN 0-88318-155-X). Am Inst Physics.

Artin, Emil & Tate, J. Class Field Theory. (Math Lecture Notes Ser.: No. 6). 259p. 1967. pap. text ed. 30.95 (ISBN 0-8053-0291-3). Benjamin-Cummings.

Carrigan, R. A., Jr. & Huson, F. R., eds. The State of Particle Accelerators & High Energy Physics (Fermilab Summer School, 1981) LC 82-73861. (AIP Conference Proceedings Ser.: No. 92). 337p. 1982. lib. bdg. 33.75 (ISBN 0-88318-191-6). Am Inst Physics.

Goldsmith, Maurice & Shaw, Edwin. Europe's Giant Accelerator. 288p. 1977. 33.00x (ISBN 0-85066-121-8). Taylor & Francis.

Institute of Physics. Charged Particle Tracks in Solid & Liquids. (Institute of Physics Conference Ser.: No. 8). 1969. 49.00 (ISBN 0-9960028-7-1, Pub. by Inst Physics England). Heyden.

Kapitza, S. P. & Melekhin, V. N. The Microtron. Rowe, Ednor, ed. Sviatoslavsky, I. N., tr. (Accelerators & Storage Rings: Vol. 1). 222p. 1978. lib. bdg. 34.75 (ISBN 0-906346-01-0). Harwood Academic.

Livingston, M. Stanley. Particle Accelerators: A Brief History. LC 69-18038. (Illus.). 1969. 8.95x (ISBN 0-674-65470-6). Harvard U Pr.

Marion, Jerry B. & Van Patter, Douglas M., eds. Nuclear Research with Low Energy Nuclear Accelerators. 1967. 77.00 (ISBN 0-12-472259-8). Acad Pr.

Month, Melvin. Physics of High Energy Particle Accelerators: SLAC Summer School, 1982, No. 105. LC 83-72986. (AIP Conference Proceedings: No. 105). 1102p. 1983. lib. bdg. 55.50 (ISBN 0-88318-304-8). Am Inst Physics.

Month, Melvin, et al, eds. Physics of High Energy Particle Accelerators: BNL-SUNY Summer School. LC 85-70057. (AIP Conference Proceedings: No. 127). 970p. 1985. lib. bdg. 65.00 (ISBN 0-88318-326-9). Am Inst Physics.

Olson, C. L. & Schumacher, U. Collective Ion Acceleration. (Springer Tracts in Modern Physics: Vol. 84). (Illus.). 1979. 39.00 (ISBN 0-387-09066-5). Springer-Verlag.

Radiation Protection Design Guidelines for Zero Point One to One Hundred MeV Particle Accelerator Facilities. LC 76-52067. (NCRP Reports Ser.: No. 51). 1977. 9.00 (ISBN 0-913392-33-2). NCRP Pubns.

Scharf, Waldemar. Particle Accelerators & Their Uses, Vol. 4. (Accelerators & Storage Rings Ser.). 1000p. 1985. text ed. 159.00 (ISBN 3-7186-0034-X) (ISBN 0-317-20114-X). Harwood Academic.

Touschek, B., ed. Physics with Intersecting Storage Rings. (Italian Physical Society: Course 46). 1971. 92.00 (ISBN 0-12-368846-9). Acad Pr.

PARTICLE BEAMS

see also Particles (Nuclear Physics)

Prelec, Krsto, ed. Production & Neutralization of Negative Ions & Beams: International Symposium, Brookhaven, 1983. 3rd ed. LC 84-70379. (AIP Conference Proceedings Ser.: No. 111). 778p. 1984. lib. bdg. 53.75 (ISBN 0-88318-310-2). Am Inst Physics.

Schwandt, P. & Meyer, H. O., eds. Nuclear Physics with Stored, Cooled Beams (McCormick's Creek State Park, Indiana, 1984) LC 85-71167. (AIP Conference Proceedings Ser.: No. 128). 349p. 1985. lib. bdg. 45.60 (ISBN 0-88318-327-7). Am Inst Physics.

PARTICLE BOARD

Maloney, Thomas M. Modern Particleboard & Dry-Process Fiberboard Manufacturing. LC 76-47094. (A Forest Industries Book). (Illus.). 1977. 50.00 (ISBN 0-87930-063-9). Miller Freeman.

Plywood, Fibreboard & Particle Board. (Terminology Bulletins: No. 30). (Eng., Fr., Ital., Ger. & Span.). 162p. 1976. pap. 11.75 (F1218, FAO). Unipub.

PARTICLES

see also Colloids; Dust; Fluidization; Light–Scattering

AIP Conference, Boston 1974. Experimental Meson Spectroscopy 1974: Proceedings, No. 21. Garelick, David A., ed. LC 74-82628. 452p. 1974. 19.00 (ISBN 0-88318-120-7). Am Inst Physics.

AIP Conference, Philadelphia 1974. Neutrinos-1974: Proceedings, No. 22. Baltay, Charles, ed. LC 74-82413. 1974. 16.00 (ISBN 0-88318-121-5). Am Inst Physics.

AIP Conference Proceedings No. 87, Fermilab School, Physics of High Energy Particle Accelerators: Proceedings. Carrigan, R. A., et al, eds. LC 82-72421. 960p. 1982. lib. bdg. 48.00 (ISBN 0-88318-186-X). Am Inst Physics.

AIP Conference Proceedings No. 90. Los Alamos, 1982. Laser Acceleration of Particles. Channell, Paul J., ed. LC 82-73361. 276p. 1982. lib. bdg. 32.00 (ISBN 0-88318-190-8). Am Inst Physics.

Allen, T. Particle Size Measurement. 3rd ed. (Powder Technology Ser.). 1981. 64.00x (ISBN 0-412-15410-2, NO. 6386, Pub. by Chapman & Hall). Methuen Inc.

Alpha: Emitting Particles in Lungs. LC 75-17147. (NCRP Reports Ser.: No. 46). 1975. 7.00 (ISBN 0-913392-28-6). NCRP Pubns.

Andric, I., et al, eds. Particle Physics 1980. 1981. 91.50 (ISBN 0-444-86174-2). Elsevier.

Artsimovich, L. A. & Lukyanov, S. Y. Motion of Charged Particles in Electric & Magnetic Fields. 1980. 8.95 (ISBN 0-8285-1871-8, Pub. by Mir Pubs USSR). Imported Pubns.

ASTM Committee E-29 on Particle Size. Liquid Particle Size Measurement Techniques. Tichkoff, J. M., et al, eds. LC 83-73515. (Special Technical Publication Ser.: No. 848). 200p. 1984. text ed. 37.00 (ISBN 0-8031-0227-5, 04-848000-41). ASTM.

Barth, Howard G., et al, eds. Modern Methods of Particle Size Analysis. Elving, P. J. & Winefordner, J. D. LC 84-3630. (Chemical Analysis: A Series of Monographs on Analytical Chemistry & its Applications: 1-075). 309p. 1984. text ed. 55.00x (ISBN 0-471-87571-6, Pub. by Wiley Interscience). Wiley.

Beddow, J. K. Particulate Science & Technology. (Illus.). 1980. 57.50 (ISBN 0-8206-0254-X). Chem Pub.

Beddow, J. K. & Meloy, T. P., eds. Testing & Characterization of Powders & Fire Particles. (Powder Advisory Centre Publication Ser. (POWTECH)). 176p. 1979. 57.95 (ISBN 0-471-25602-1, Wiley Heyden). Wiley.

Beddow, John K., ed. Particulate Systems: Technology & Fundamentals. LC 82-1099. (Illus.). 362p. 1983. 69.95 (ISBN 0-89116-241-0). Hemisphere Pub.

Boal, D. H. & Kamal, A. N., eds. Particles & Fields 1. LC 78-2509. 470p. 1978. 55.00 (ISBN 0-306-31147-X, Plenum Pr). Plenum Pub.

Clift, Roland, et al. Bubbles, Drops & Particles. LC 77-6592. 1978. 58.50 (ISBN 0-12-176950-X). Acad Pr.

Committee on Particulate Control Technology, National Research Council. Controlling Airborne Particles. xi, 114p. (Orig.). 1980. pap. text ed. 9.50 (ISBN 0-309-03035-8). Natl Acad Pr.

Dahneke, Barton E. Measurement of Suspended Particles by Quasi-Elastic Light Scattering. 570p. 1983. 48.50 (ISBN 0-471-87289-X, Pub. by Wiley-Interscience). Wiley.

Domokos, G. & Kovesi-Domokos, S., eds. Particles & Gravity: Proceedings of the Johns Hopkins Workshop on Current Problems in Particle Theory, June 8, 1984. 400p. 1984. 44.00x (ISBN 9971-966-78-6, Pub. by World Sci Singapore). Taylor & Francis.

European Federation of Chemical Engineering. Particle Technology: Proceedings of the European Federation of Chemical Engineering, European Symposium, Amsterdam, Holland, June 3-5, 1980, Vols. A & B. Schonert, K., et al, eds. (E FCE Publication Ser.: No. 7). 1232p. 1980. text ed. 85.00x (ISBN 3-921567-27-0, Pub. by Dechema Germany). Scholium Intl.

Fayed, M. E. & Otten, Lambert, eds. Handbook of Powder Science & Technology. (Illus.). 656p. 1984. 79.50 (ISBN 0-442-22610-1). Van Nos Reinhold.

Flamm, D. & Schoberl, F. Quantum Numbers, Gauge Theories & Hadron Spectroscopy. (Quark Models in Elementary Particles Ser.). 384p. 1982. 77.25 (ISBN 0-677-16270-7). Gordon.

Fundamentals of Magnetic Particle Testing, Module 32-3. (Nondestructive Examination Techniques II Ser.). (Illus.). 46p. 1979. spiral bdg. 7.00x (ISBN 0-87683-100-5). G P Courseware.

Gaisser, T. K., ed. Cosmic Rays & Particle Physics - Nineteen Seventy-Eight: Bartol Conference. LC 79-50489. (AIP Conference Proceedings Ser.: No. 49). (Illus.). 1979. lib. bdg. 23.50 (ISBN 0-88318-148-7). Am Inst Physics.

Griffeath, D. Additive & Cancellative Interacting Particle Systems. (Lecture Notes in Mathematics: Vol. 724). 1979. pap. 13.00 (ISBN 3-540-09508-X). Springer-Verlag.

Halliday, Ian & McIntosh, Bruce A., eds. Solid Particles in the Solar System. (International Astronomical Union Symposium: No. 90). 432p. 1980. PLB 50.00 (ISBN 90-277-1164-X, Pub. by Reidel Holland); pap. 26.50 (ISBN 90-277-1165-8). Kluwer Academic.

Honerkamp, J. & Pohlmeyer, J., eds. Structural Elements in Particle Physics & Statistical Mechanics. (NATO ASI Series B, Physics: Vol. 82). 470p. 1983. 69.50x (ISBN 0-306-41038-9, Plenum Pr). Plenum Pub.

Institution of Chemical Engineers, ed. POWTECH Eighty-Five: Proceedings of the International Symposium on Particle Technology Held in Birmingham, UK, 5-7 March 1985. (Institution of Chemical Engineers Symposium Ser.: Vol. 91). 270p. 1985. 24.00 (ISBN 0-08-031443-0). Pergamon.

Jancewicz, Bernard & Lukierski, Jerzy, eds. Quantum Theory of Particles & Fields: Birthday Volume Dedicated to Jan Lopuszanski. 292p. 32.00x (ISBN 9971-950-77-4, Pub. by World Sci Singapore). Taylor & Francis.

Jelinek, Z. K. Particle Size Analysis. Bryce, W. A., tr. LC 73-14415. (Elles Horwood Series in Analytical Chemistry). (Illus.). 178p. 1974. 58.95 (ISBN 0-470-44148-8). Halsted Pr.

Kaufmann, William J., III, intro. by. Particles & Fields: Readings from Scientific American. LC 80-10669. (Illus.). 139p. 1980. text ed. 20.95 (ISBN 0-7167-1233-4); pap. text ed. 10.95 (ISBN 0-7167-1234-2). W H Freeman.

Kaye, Brian H. Direct Characterization of Fineparticles. LC 81-1734. (Chemical Analysis: A Series of Monographs on Analytic Chemistry & Its Applications). 398p. 1981. 85.00x (ISBN 0-471-46150-4, Pub. by Wiley-Interscience). Wiley.

Klabunde, Kenneth J. Chemistry of Free Atoms & Particles. 1980. 35.00 (ISBN 0-12-410750-8). Acad Pr.

Klabunde, Kenneth J., ed. Thin Films from Free Atoms & Particles. Date not set. price not set (ISBN 0-12-410755-9). Acad Pr.

Konopinski, Emil J. Classical Descriptions of Motion: The Dynamics of Particle Trajectories, Rigid Rotations, & Elastic Waves. LC 71-75626. (A Series of Books in Physics). pap. 129.30 (ISBN 0-317-12988-0, 2055550). Bks Demand UMI.

Kopilov, G. Elementary Kinematics of Elementary Particles. 270p. 1983. pap. 4.95 (ISBN 0-8285-2712-1, Pub. by Mir Pubs USSR). Imported Pubns.

Murphy, Charles H. Handbook of Particle Sampling & Analysis Methods. 354p. 1984. text ed. 49.50x (ISBN 0-89573-116-9). VCH Pubs.

Ogawa, Akira. Seperation of Particles from Air & Gases. 1984. Vol. I, 176p. 63.00 (ISBN 0-317-05129-6); Vol. II, 208p. 63.00 (ISBN 0-317-05130-X). CRC Pr.

Particle Size Analysis, Loughborough University of Technology, 4th, 1981. Particle Size Analysis: Proceedings. Stanley-Wood, N. & Allen, T., eds. 461p. 1982. text ed. 74.95x (ISBN 0-471-26221-8, Pub. by Wiley-Interscience). Wiley.

Perera, Frederica P. & Ahmed, A. Karim. Respirable Particles: Impact of Airborne Fine Particulates on Health & Environment. LC 79-13163. 208p. 1979. prof. ref. 29.95 (ISBN 0-88410-090-1). Ballinger Pub.

Prosser, Reese T. New Formulation of Particle Mechanics. LC 52-42839. (Memoirs Ser.: No. 61). 57p. 1980. pap. 10.00 (ISBN 0-8218-1261-0, MEMO-61). Am Math.

Ryder. Elementary Particles & Symmetries. (Documents on Modern Physics Ser.). 278p. 1975. 49.95 (ISBN 0-677-05130-1). Gordon.

Somasundaran, P., ed. Fine Particles Processing, 2 vols. LC 79-57344. (Illus.). 1865p. 1980. text ed. 50.00x (ISBN 0-89520-275-1). Soc Mining Eng.

Symposium on Inhaled Particles & Vapours. Inhaled Particles: Proceedings, Vol. V. Walton, W. H., ed. (Illus.). 900p. 1982. 165.00 (ISBN 0-08-026838-2). Pergamon.

Symposium on Ultrafine Particles Indianapolis, 1961. Ultrafine Particles. Kuhn, W. E., ed. LC 63-20239. (Electrochemical Society Ser.). pap. 143.50 (ISBN 0-317-11065-9, 2007076). Bks Demand UMI.

Taglauer, E. & Heiland, W., eds. Inelastic Particle-Surface Collisions: Proceedings. (Springer Series in Chemical Physics: Vol. 17). (Illus.). 329p. 1981. pap. 33.00 (ISBN 0-387-10898-X). Springer-Verlag.

Taylor, J. C. Gauge Theories of Weak Interactions. LC 75-9092. (Cambridge Monographs on Mathematical Physics: No. 3). (Illus.). 200p. 1976. 54.50 (ISBN 0-521-20896-3); pap. 15.95x (ISBN 0-521-29518-1). Cambridge U Pr.

Vonsovsky, S. V. Magnetism of Elementary Particles. 295p. 1975. 6.45 (ISBN 0-8285-0792-9, Pub. by Mir Pubs USSR). Imported Pubns.

Wesson, Paul, ed. Gravity, Particles, & Astrophysics. (Astrophysics & Space Science Library Ser.: No. 79). 276p. 1980. lib. bdg. 34.00 (ISBN 90-277-1083-X, Pub. by Reidel). Kluwer Academic.

PARTICLES (NUCLEAR PHYSICS)

see also Angular Momentum (Nuclear Physics); Collisions (Nuclear Physics); Coupling Constants; Nuclear Forces (Physics); Particle Accelerators; Particle Beams; Polarization (Nuclear Physics); Regge Trajectories; Transport Theory; Tunneling (Physics); Van Allen Radiation Belts;

also names of particles–e.g. Electrons, Neutrons, Protons

Aceleradores De Particulas. (Serie De Fisica: No. 7). (Span.). 1982. pap. 3.50 (ISBN 0-8270-1539-9). OAS.

AIP Conference, Univ. of California at Irvine, Dec., 1971. Particle Physics 1971: Proceedings, No. 6. Bander, M., et al, eds. LC 72-81239. 185p. 1972. 11.00 (ISBN 0-88318-105-3). Am Inst Physics.

Aitchison. Gauge Theories in Particle Physics. 1981. pap. 36.00 (ISBN 0-9960022-2-7, Pub. by Inst Physics England). Heyden.

Aly, H. H. Lectures on Particles & Fields. 385p. 1970. 85.75 (ISBN 0-677-13740-0). Gordon.

Bacry, Henri. Lectures on Group Theory & Particle Theory. LC 72-78879. (Documents on Modern Physics Ser.). (Illus.). 598p. 1977. 132.95 (ISBN 0-677-30190-1). Gordon.

Bars, Itzhak, et al, eds. Symmetries in Particle Physics. 320p. 1984. 47.50x (ISBN 0-306-41801-0, Plenum Pr). Plenum Pub.

Basov, N. G., ed. Strong & Electromagnetic Interactions of Elementary Particles & Nuclei. LC 80-21933. (The Lebedev Physics Institute Ser.: Vol. 95). (Illus.). 214p. 1980. 65.00 (ISBN 0-306-10965-4, Consultants). Plenum Pub.

Bates, David R. & Bederson, Benjamin, eds. Advances in Atomic & Molecular Physics, Vol. 15. LC 65-18423. (Serial Publication Ser.). 1979. 70.00 (ISBN 0-12-003815-3). Acad Pr.

Beddow, John K. & Meloy, Thomas P. Advanced Particulate Morphology: Theory & Practice. 208p. 1980. 69.00 (ISBN 0-8493-5781-0). CRC Pr.

Bernstein, Jeremy. Elementary Particles & Their Currents. LC 68-21404. (Physics Ser.). (Illus.). 322p. 1968. text ed. 32.95 (ISBN 0-7167-0324-6). W H Freeman.

Bilic, N., et al, eds. Frontiers in Particle Physics 1983: Adriatic Meeting on Particle Physics, IV, Dubrovnik, Yugoslavia, June 6-15, 1983. 550p. 1984. 60.00x (ISBN 9971-950-57-X, Pub. by World Sci Singapore). Taylor & Francis.

Blecher, M. & Gotow, K., eds. Low Energy Tests of Conservation Laws in Particle Physics: Conference Proceedings, Blacksburg, Virginia, 1983. LC 84-71157. (AIP Conference Proceedings: No. 114, Subseries on Particles & Fields No. 33). 322p. 1984. lib. bdg. 40.50 (ISBN 0-88318-313-7). Am Inst Physics.

Blokhintsev, D. I. Space & Time in the Microworld. Smith, Z., tr. from Rus. LC 72-77871. Orig. Title: Prostranstuo I Uremja V Micromire. 330p. 1973. lib. bdg. 60.50 (ISBN 90-277-0240-3, Pub. by Reidel Holland). Kluwer Academic.

Massey, Harrie, et al. Electronic & Ionic Impact Phenomena, Vol. 4: Recombination & Fast Collisions of Heavy Particles. 2nd ed. (International Series of Monographs on Physics). (Illus.). 1974. 105.00x (ISBN 0-19-851253-8). Oxford U Pr.

Meschan, Isadore. Roentgen Signs in Clinical Diagnosis. LC 56-8031. (Illus.). pap. 160.00 (ISBN 0-317-07868-2, 2013532). Bks Demand UMI.

Meyer, H. O. The Interaction Between Medium Energy Nucleons in Nuclei, Indiana University Cyclotron Facility, 1982: AIP Conference Proceedings, No. 97. LC 83-70649. (No. 97). 433p. 1983. lib. bdg. 38.50 (ISBN 0-88318-196-7). Am Inst Physics.

Michaudon, A., et al, eds. Nuclear Fission & Neutron-Induced Fission Cross-Sections. LC 80-41822. (Neutron Physics & Nuclear Data in Science & Technology Ser.: Vol. 1). (Illus.). 270p. 1981. 66.00 (ISBN 0-08-026125-6). Pergamon.

Miller, R. B. An Introduction to the Physics of Intense Charged Particle Beams. LC 82-557. 362p. 1982. 45.00x (ISBN 0-306-40931-3, Plenum Pr). Plenum Pub.

Mischke, Richard E. Intersections Between Particle & Nuclear Physics (Steamboat Springs, 1984: Proceedings of AIP Conference. LC 84-72790. (No. 123). 1162p. 1984. lib. bdg. 65.00 (ISBN 0-88318-322-6). Am Inst Physics.

Mitter, H., ed. Electroweak Interactions, Schladming (Graz), Austria 1982: Proceedings. (Acta Physia Austriaca Supplementum: Vol. 24). (Illus.). 474p. 1982. 39.20 (ISBN 0-387-81729-8). Springer-Verlag.

Molinari, A. From Nuclei to Particles. 536p. 1982. 115.00 (ISBN 0-444-86158-0, North-Holland). Elsevier.

Morse, Philip M., et al. Nuclear, Particle & Many Body Physics, 2 vols. 1972. Vol. 1. 78.00 (ISBN 0-12-508201-0); Vol. 2. 70.00 (ISBN 0-12-508202-9). Acad Pr.

Muirhead, H. Notes on Elementary Particle Physics. 264p. 1972. text ed. 34.00 (ISBN 0-08-016550-8). Pergamon.

Muller, B. The Physics of the Quark-Gluon Plasma. (Lecture Notes in Physics Ser.: Vol. 225). vii, 142p. 1985. pap. 8.70 (ISBN 0-387-15211-3). Springer-Verlag.

Mutter, K. H. & Schilling, K., eds. Current Topics in Elementary Particle Physics. LC 81-10652. (NATO ASI Series B, Physics: Vol. 70). 352p. 1981. text ed. 52.50x (ISBN 0-306-40801-5, Plenum Pr). Plenum Pub.

Nambu, Y. Quarks: Frontiers in Elementary Particle Physics. 250p. 1985. 33.00x (ISBN 9971-966-65-4, Pub. by World Sci Singapore); pap. 19.00x (ISBN 9971-966-66-2, Pub. by World Sci Singapore). Taylor & Francis.

Niekisch, E. A. Springer Tracts in Modern Physics, Vol. 61. Hoehler, G., ed. LC 25-9130. (Illus.). 200p. 1972. 44.30 (ISBN 0-387-05739-0). Springer-Verlag.

Nieuwenhuizen, P. V., et al, eds. Supergravity, Supersymmetry: Proceedings of Trieste Spring School, Italy 1984. 500p. 1984. 60.00x (ISBN 9971-966-75-1, Pub. by World Sci Singapore); pap. 28.00x (ISBN 9971-966-76-X, Pub. by World Sci Singapore). Taylor & Francis.

Nikolic, M., ed. Analysis of Scattering & Decay. (Documents on Modern Physics Ser.). 344p. (Orig.). 1968. 66.00x (ISBN 0-677-12810-X). Gordon.

--Kinematics & Multi-Particle Systems. (Documents on Modern Physics Ser.). 324p. (Orig.). 1968. 69.50x (ISBN 0-677-01800-2). Gordon.

Novozhilov, Y. V. Elementary Particles. 208p. 1961. 59.25x (ISBN 0-677-20470-1). Gordon.

Novozhilov, Yuri V. Introduction to Elementary Particle Theory. Rosner, Jonathon L., tr. 1974. text ed. 76.00 (ISBN 0-08-017954-1). Pergamon.

Okun, L. B. Particle Physics, Vol. 2. (Contemporary Concept in Physics Ser.). 223p. 1985. text ed. 44.00 (ISBN 3-7186-0228-8); pap. 12.00 (ISBN 3-7186-0229-6). Harwood Academic.

Omnes, Roland. Introduction to Particle Physics. LC 75-172471. 414p. 1972. 71.95x (ISBN 0-471-65372-1, Pub. by Wiley-Interscience). Wiley.

O'Neill, Gerald K. & Cheng, David. Elementary Particle Physics: An Introduction. LC 79-17878. (Illus.). 1979. text ed. 44.95 (ISBN 0-201-05463-9). Addison-Wesley.

Panvini, R. S., ed. Particle Searches & Discoveries: Proceedings, International Conference, Vanderbilt University, 1-3 March 1976. LC 76-19949. (AIP Conference Proceedings Ser.: No. 30). 1976. 18.50 (ISBN 0-88318-129-0). Am Inst Physics.

Panvini, R. S. & Alam, M. S., eds. Novel Results in Particle Physics. LC 82-73954. (AIP Conf. Proc.: No. 93). 384p. 1982. lib. bdg. 35.00 (ISBN 0-88318-192-4). Am Inst Physics.

Panvini, R. S. & Csorna, S. E., eds. High Energy E Plus E Minus Interactions Vanderbilt 1980. LC 80-53377. (AIP Conference Proceedings Ser.: No. 62). 405p. 1980. lib. bdg. 23.00 (ISBN 0-88318-161-4). Am Inst Physics.

Papadopoulou, T. First Hellenic School on Elmentary Particle Physics: Proceedings held in Corfu, Greece, Sept. 12-30, 1982. 650p. 1984. 67.00x (ISBN 9971-950-99-5, Pub. by World Sci Singapore). Taylor & Francis.

Parikh, J. C. Group Symmetries in Nuclear Structure. LC 77-17451. (Nuclear Physics Monographs Ser.). (Illus.). 287p. 1978. 39.50x (ISBN 0-306-31043-0, Plenum Pr). Plenum Pub.

Perlmutter, A. & Scott, L. F., eds. New Frontiers in High-Energy Physics. LC 78-15767. (Studies in the Natural Sciences Ser.: Vol. 14). 680p. 1978. 95.00x (ISBN 0-306-40037-5, Plenum Pr). Plenum Pub.

Peterson, V. S. & Pakvasa, S., eds. Proceedings of the Eighth Hawaii Topical Conference in Particle Physics, 1979. (Particle Physics Conference Proceedings). 644p. 1980. pap. text ed. 20.00x (ISBN 0-8248-0716-2). UH Pr.

Pickering, Andrew. Construction Quarks: A Sociological History of Particle Physics. LC 84-235. (Illus.). 488p. 1984. lib. bdg. 30.00x (ISBN 0-226-66798-7). U of Chicago Pr.

Pilkuhn, H. Relativistic Particle Physics. LC 79-10666. (Texts & Monographs in Physics). (Illus.). 1979. 55.00 (ISBN 0-387-09348-6). Springer-Verlag.

Powtech Conference Staff. Particle Technology: Proceedings of the Powtech Conference, 1981, No. 63. 500p. 1981. 150.00x (ISBN 0-85295-133-7, Pub. by Inst Chem Eng England). State Mutual Bk.

Puppi, G., ed. Old & New Problems in Elementary Particles. 1968. 72.00 (ISBN 0-12-567250-0). Acad Pr.

Quill, Lawrence L., ed. The Chemistry & Metallurgy of Miscellaneous Materials. AEC Technical Information Center. (National Nuclear Energy Ser.: Division IV, Vol. 19c). 172p. 1955. pap. 16.00 (ISBN 0-87079-161-3, TID-5212); microfilm 10.00 (ISBN 0-87079-162-1, TID-5212). DOE.

Recami, E., ed. Tachyons, Monopoles & Related Topics: Proceedings of the First Session of the Interdisciplinary Seminars on "Tachyons & Related Topics," Erice, September 1976. 1978. 41.50 (ISBN 0-444-85165-8, North-Holland). Elsevier.

Renner, B. Current Algebras & Their Applications. 1968. 41.00 (ISBN 0-08-012504-2). Pergamon.

Roberto, J. B., et al, eds. Advanced Photon & Particle Techniques for the Characterization of Defects in Solids, Vol. 41. LC 85-5061. 1985. text ed. 43.00 (ISBN 0-931837-06-5). Materials Res.

Roy, R. R. & Reed, R. D. Interactions of Photons & Leptons with Matter. LC 68-23487. 1969. 61.00 (ISBN 0-12-601350-0). Acad Pr.

Ruhl, Werner, ed. Field Theoretical Methods in Particle Physics. LC 80-11773. (NATO ASI Series B, Physics: Vol. 55). 608p. 1980. 89.50x (ISBN 0-306-40444-3, Plenum Pr). Plenum Pub.

Ryder, Lewis H. Quantum Field Theory. (Illus.). 350p. 1985. pap. 74.50 (ISBN 0-521-23764-5). Cambridge U Pr.

Satz, H., ed. Many Degrees of Freedom in Particle Theory. LC 78-27. (NATO ASI Series B, Physics: Vol. 31). 574p. 1978. 85.00x (ISBN 0-306-35731-3, Plenum Pr). Plenum Pub.

Schaaf, M. Reduction of the Product of Two Irreducible Unitary Representations of the Proper Orthochronous Quantummechanical Poincare Group. LC 72-139677. (Lecture Notes in Physics: Vol. 5). 1970. pap. 10.70 (ISBN 0-387-05194-5). Springer-Verlag.

Scholten, Olaf, ed. Proceedings of the Workshop on Interacting Boson-Boson & Boson-Fermion Systems, Michigan, May 1984. 400p. 1985. 51.00x (ISBN 9971-966-82-4, Pub. by World Sci Singapore). Taylor & Francis.

Schwartz, Laurent. Application des Distributions a l'Etude des Particles Elementaires en Mecanique Quantique. (Cours & Documents de Mathematiques & de Physique Ser.). (Fr.). 148p. 1969. 40.50 (ISBN 0-677-50090-4). Gordon.

--Application of Distributions to the Theory of Elementary Particles in Quantum Mechanics. LC 68-17535. (Documents on Modern Physics Ser.). (Illus.). 144p. 1969. 46.25x (ISBN 0-677-30090-5). Gordon.

Schwinger, Julian. Particles & Sources. (Documents on Modern Physics Ser.). 100p. 1969. 32.50x (ISBN 0-677-02060-0). Gordon.

Skobel'tsyn, D. V., ed. Nucleon Compton Effect at Low & Medium Energies. LC 69-12521. (P. N. Lebedev Physics Institute Ser.: Vol. 41). (Illus.). 217p. 1969. 27.50x (ISBN 0-306-10828-3, Consultants). Plenum Pub.

--Theory of Collective Particle Acceleration & Relativistic Electron Beam Emission. (P. N. Lebedev Physics Institute Ser.: Vol. 66). (Illus.). 213p. 1975. 55.00 (ISBN 0-306-10917-4, Consultants). Plenum Pub.

--Theory of Interaction of Elementary Particles at High Energies. LC 73-83900. (P. N. Lebedev Physics Institute Ser.: Vol. 57). (Illus.). 258p. 1974. 55.00 (ISBN 0-306-10899-2, Consultants). Plenum Pub.

Stefanini, A., ed. Miniaturization of High-Energy Physics Detectors. LC 82-16495. (Ettore Majorana International Science Series: Physical Sciences: Vol. 14). 260p. 1983. 45.00x (ISBN 0-306-41133-4, Plenum Pr). Plenum Pub.

Steinberger, J., ed. Selected Topics in Particle Physics. (Italian Physical Society: Course 41). 1968. 65.00 (ISBN 0-12-368841-8). Acad Pr.

Sudarshan, E. C. & Ne'Eman, Y., eds. The Past Decade in Particle Theory. LC 71-181810. 832p. 1973. 149.25 (ISBN 0-677-12010-9). Gordon.

Sutton, Christine. The Particle Connection: The Most Exciting Scientific Chase Since DNA & the Double Helix. LC 84-10595. 352p. 1984. 16.95 (ISBN 0-671-49659-X). S&S.

Symposium on Meson-, Photo-, & Electroproduction at Low & Intermediate Energies, Bonn, 1970. Proceedings. LC 25-9130. (Springer Tracts in Modern Physics: Vol. 59). 1971. 56.70 (ISBN 0-387-05494-4). Springer-Verlag.

Tassie, L. J. The Physics of Elementary Particles. LC 73-175761. (A Longman Text Ser.). pap. 66.80 (ISBN 0-317-09207-3, 2013566). Bks Demand UMI.

Trefil, James S. From Atoms to Quarks: The Strange World of Particle Physics. (Illus.). 240p. 1982. pap. 7.95 (ISBN 0-684-17460-X, ScribT). Scribner.

Turnbull, R. M. The Structure of Matter: An Introduction to Atomic Nuclear & Particle Physics. (Illus.). 266p. 1979. pap. text ed. 22.50x (ISBN 0-216-90753-5). Intl Ideas.

Urban, P., ed. Contacts Between High Energy Physics & Other Fields of Physics: Proceedings. (Acta Physica Austriaca: Suppl. 18). (Illus.). 1977. 122.80 (ISBN 0-387-81454-X). Springer-Verlag.

--Current Problems in Elementary Particle & Mathematical Physics. (Acta Physica Austriaca: Supplementum 15). (Illus.). 1976. 87.40 (ISBN 0-387-81401-9). Springer-Verlag.

Vlasov, A. A. Many-Particle Theory & Its Application to Plasma. (Russian Monographs). (Illus.). 418p. 1961. 78.75x (ISBN 0-677-20330-6). Gordon.

Warren, J. B., ed. Nuclear & Particle Physics at Intermediate Energies. LC 76-8270. (NATO ASI Series B, Physics: Vol. 15). 608p. 1976. 95.00x (ISBN 0-306-35715-1, Plenum Pr). Plenum Pub.

Weinberg, Steven. The Discovery of Subatomic Particles. LC 82-23157. (Scientific American Library). (Illus.). 206p. 1983. smyth casebound 27.95 (ISBN 0-7167-1488-4). W H Freeman.

Wiik, B. H. & Wolf, G. Electron Position Interactions. Hohler, G., ed. (Springer Tracts in Modern Physics: Vol. 86). (Illus.). 1979. 43.00 (ISBN 0-387-09604-3). Springer-Verlag.

Wilkinson, Denys, ed. Progress in Particle & Nuclear Physics, Vol. 3. 1980. 89.00 (ISBN 0-08-025020-3). Pergamon.

--Progress in Particle & Nuclear Physics, Vol. 5. (Illus.). 280p. 1981. 89.00 (ISBN 0-08-027109-X). Pergamon.

--Progress in Particle & Nuclear Physics, Vol. 6. 350p. 1981. 89.00 (ISBN 0-08-027117-0). Pergamon.

--Progress in Particle & Nuclear Physics, Vol. 7. (Illus.). 270p. 1981. 92.00 (ISBN 0-08-027152-9). Pergamon.

Williams, W. S. Introduction to Elementary Particles. 2nd ed. LC 73-84251. (Pure & Applied Physics Ser.: Vol. 12). 1971. 69.00 (ISBN 0-12-756756-9). Acad Pr.

Yount, David & Dobson, Peter N., eds. Proceedings of the Fourth Topical Conference in Particle Physics (1971) 550p. 1972. pap. text ed. 25.00x (ISBN 0-8248-0210-1). UH Pr.

Zamir, Yecheskiel. Avkoan Theory: Avkoan Principle-A Principle of the Tiniest Particle, Vol. 1. 2nd ed. (Illus.). 51p. (Orig.). 1985. 7.95 (ISBN 0-9614730-1-0); pap. 4.95 (ISBN 0-9614730-0-2). Y Z Pubns.

Zichichi, A., ed. Elementary Processes at High Energy, Pts. A-B, Pts. A-b. 1972. 80.50 ea. (ISBN 0-12-780586-9) (ISBN 0-12-780587-7). Acad Pr.

--Hadrons & Their Interactions: Current - Field Algebra, Soft Pions, Supermultiplets, & Related Topics. 1968. 97.50 (ISBN 0-12-780540-0). Acad Pr.

--Subnuclear Phenomena, Pts. A-B. 1971. 80.00 ea. Pt. A (ISBN 0-12-780580-X). Pt. B (ISBN 0-12-780582-6). Acad Pr.

--Symmetries in Elementary Particle Physics. 1965. pap. 39.00 (ISBN 0-12-780556-7). Acad Pr.

--Theory & Phenomenology in Particle Physics, 2 pts. 1969. Pt. A. 77.00 (ISBN 0-12-780571-0); Pt. B. 88.00 (ISBN 0-12-780572-9); Set. 126.00. Acad Pr.

Zichlichi, A., ed. Recent Developments in Particle Symmetries. 1966. 64.50 (ISBN 0-12-780562-1). Acad Pr.

PARTICLES, RADIATION

see also Scattering (Physics)

Hills, Christopher. Supersensonics: The Science of Radiational Paraphysics. LC 75-46093. (Illus.). 609p. (Orig.). 1978. pap. 24.95 (ISBN 0-916438-18-X, Dist. by New Era Pr). Univ of Trees.

Schulz, M. & Lanzerotti, L. J. Particle Diffusion in the Radiation Belts. LC 73-11949. (Physics & Chemistry in Space: Vol. 7). (Illus.). ix, 250p. 1974. 55.00 (ISBN 0-387-06398-6). Springer-Verlag.

PARTITIONS (MATHEMATICS)

Andrews, George E. Encyclopedia of Mathematics & Its Applications: The Theory of Partitions, Vol. 2. 1984. 34.50 (ISBN 0-521-30222-6). Cambridge U Pr.

--Number Theory: The Theory of Partitions. LC 76-41770. (Encyclopedia of Mathematics & Its Applications: Vol. 2). (Illus.). 1976. text ed. 32.00 (ISBN 0-201-13501-9). Addison-Wesley.

--On the General Rogers-Ramanujan Theorem. LC 74-18067. (Memoirs: No. 152). 86p. 1974. pap. 10.00 (ISBN 0-8218-1852-X, MEMO-152). Am Math.

--Partitions: Yesterday & Today. 56p. (Orig.). 1980. pap. text ed. 5.00 (ISBN 0-9597579-0-2). Australia N U P.

--Stet. LC 84-3059. (Memoirs: No. 301). 48p. 1984. pap. 8.00 (ISBN 0-8218-2302-7). Am Math.

Dickson, Leonard E. Researches on Waring's Problem. LC 35-19856. (Carnegie Institution of Washington Publication Ser.: No. 464). pap. 66.30 (ISBN 0-317-09159-X, 2015710). Bks Demand UMI.

Erdos, P., et al, eds. Combinational Set Theory: Partition Relations for Cardinals. (Studies in Logic & the Foundations of Mathematics: Vol. 106). 348p. 1984. 52.00 (ISBN 0-444-86157-2, North Holland). Elsevier.

MacMahon, Percy A. Combinatory Analysis, 2 Vols. in 1. LC 59-10267. 29.50 (ISBN 0-8284-1137-9). Chelsea Pub.

Stanley, Richard. Ordered Structures & Partitions. LC 52-42839. (Memoirs: No. 119). 104p. 1972. pap. 9.00 (ISBN 0-8218-1819-8, MEMO-119). Am Math.

Steklov Institute of Mathematics, Academy of Sciences, USSR & Stogrin, M. I. Regular Dirichlet-Voronoi Partitions for the Second Triclinic Group: Proceedings. LC 75-23284. (Proceedings of the Steklov Institute of Mathematics: No.123). 116p. 1975. 39.00 (ISBN 0-8218-3023-6, STEKLO-123). Am Math.

Whitworth, William A. Choice & Chance with One Thousand Exercises. 5th ed. 1965. Repr. of 1901 ed. 8.95x (ISBN 0-02-854750-0). Hafner.

PASCAL, BLAISE, 1623-1662

Adamson, Donald. Pascal: A Critical Biography. LC 81-8033. 200p. 1985. 28.50x (ISBN 0-389-20098-0, 06871). B&N Imports.

Bishop, Morris. Pascal, the Life of Genius. LC 68-9538. (Illus.). 1968. Repr. of 1936 ed. lib. bdg. 27.75x (ISBN 0-8371-0021-6, BILG). Greenwood.

Cailliet, Emile. Clue to Pascal. LC 74-113306. 1970. Repr. of 1944 ed. 14.50x (ISBN 0-8046-1008-8, Pub. by Kennikat). Assoc Faculty Pr.

--Pascal: The Emergence of Genius. 2nd ed. LC 75-94602. 383p. Repr. of 1961 ed. lib. bdg. 22.50x (ISBN 0-8371-2537-5, CAP). Greenwood.

Davidson, Hugh M. The Origins of Certainty: Means & Meanings in Pascal's "Pensees". LC 78-12768. 1979. lib. bdg. 16.00x (ISBN 0-226-13716-3). U of Chicago Pr.

De Sainte-Beuve, Charles-Augustin. Port-Royal, 3 tomes. 1953-1955. Set. 79.95 (ISBN 0-685-11502-X). French & Eur.

Dube, Pierre H. & Davidson, Hugh M. A Concordance to Pascal's "Les Provinciales". LC 79-54323. (Garland Reference Library of the Humanities). 1000p. 1980. lib. bdg. 121.00 (ISBN 0-8240-9536-7). Garland Pub.

Duclaux, Mary. Portrait of Pascal. 1927. Repr. 25.00 (ISBN 0-8274-3188-0). R West.

Goldmann, Lucien. Hidden God. Thody, Philip, tr. (International Library of Philosophy & Scientific Method Ser.). 1976. text ed. 24.00x (ISBN 0-7100-3621-3). Humanities.

Kummer, Irene. Blaise Pascal: Das Heil Im Widerspruch. 1978. 56.80x (ISBN 3-11-007253-X). De Gruyter.

Mortimer, Ernest. Blaise Pascal: The Life & Work of a Realist. 1979. Repr. of 1959 ed. lib. bdg. 25.00 (ISBN 0-8414-6341-7). Folcroft.

--Blaise Pascal: The Life & Work of a Realist. LC 76-847. (Illus.). 240p. 1976. Repr. of 1959 ed. lib. bdg. 17.75x (ISBN 0-8371-8747-8, MOBP). Greenwood.

--Blaise Pascal: The Life & Work of a Realist. 240p. 1982. Repr. of 1959 ed. lib. bdg. 40.00 (ISBN 0-89760-563-2). Telegraph Bks.

Pascal, Blaise. The Thoughts, Letters, & Opuscules of Blaise Pascal. 1978. Repr. of 1864 ed. lib. bdg. 35.00 (ISBN 0-8492-2094-7). R West.

Paul, C. Kegan. The Thoughts of Blaise Pascal: Translated from the Text of M. Auguste Molinier. 1978. Repr. of 1888 ed. 30.00 (ISBN 0-8492-2095-5). R West.

Renyi, Alfred. Letters on Probability. Vekerdi, Laslo, tr. from Hung. LC 74-179559. (Waynebooks Ser: No. 33). (Eng.). 86p. 1973. pap. 3.95x (ISBN 0-8143-1465-1). Wayne St U Pr.

St. Cyres, Viscount. Pascal. 1909. Repr. 25.00 (ISBN 0-8274-3103-1). R West.

Saint-Beuve. Port Royal, 3 vols. Vol. 1. 37.50 (ISBN 0-686-56564-9); Vol. 2. 37.50 (ISBN 0-686-56565-7); Vol. 3. 35.95 (ISBN 0-686-56566-5). French & Eur.

Soltau, Roger H. Pascal: The Man & the Message. Repr. of 1927 ed. lib. bdg. 15.00 (ISBN 0-8371-4341-1, SOPS). Greenwood.

Stewart, H. F. Blaise Pascal. 1973. Repr. of 1942 ed. 6.00 (ISBN 0-8274-1623-7). R West.

Stewart, Hugh F. Blaise Pascal. LC 77-16601. 1977. Repr. of 1942 ed. lib. bdg. 8.50 (ISBN 0-8414-7801-5). Folcroft.

Tullock. Pascal. 1898. Repr. 20.00 (ISBN 0-8274-3104-X). R West.

Wetsel, David. L' Ecriture et le Reste: The "Pensees" of Pascal in the Exegetical Tradition of Port-Royal. LC 81-9610. (Illus.). 256p. 1981. 22.50x (ISBN 0-8142-0324-8). Ohio St U Pr.

PASCAL (COMPUTER PROGRAM LANGUAGE)

Alagic, S. & Arbib, M. A. The Design of Well-Structured & Correct Programs. LC 77-27087. (Texts & Monographs in Computer Science). 1978. 23.00 (ISBN 0-387-90299-6). Springer-Verlag.

Allan, Boris. Introducing Pascal. (Illus.). 170p. 1984. pap. 13.95 (ISBN 0-246-12322-2, Pub. by Granada England). Sheridan.

Anderson, Ronald W. From BASIC to Pascal. (Illus.). 324p. 18.95 (ISBN 0-8306-2466-X, 1466); pap. 11.50 (ISBN 0-8306-1466-4, 1466). TAB Bks.

ANSI-IEEE 770X3.97-1983: IEEE Standard Pascal Computer Programming Language. 1983. 17.95 (ISBN 0-471-88944-X, SHO8912). IEEE.

Apple Computer Pascal Manual Set. (Lisa Reference Manuals). Date not set. 95.00 set (ISBN 0-317-04436-2, A6L0111). Apple Comp.

Atkinson, L. V. & Harley, P. J. An Introduction to Numerical Methods with Pascal. 1982. pap. text ed. 17.95 (ISBN 0-201-13788-7). Addison-Wesley.

Atkinson, Laurence. Pascal Programming. LC 80-40126. (Computing Ser.). 428p. 1980. 58.95x (ISBN 0-471-27773-8); pap. 19.95 (ISBN 0-471-27774-6). Wiley.

Attikiouzel. Pascal for Electronic Engineers. 1984. 22.50 (ISBN 0-442-30596-6). Van Nos Reinhold.

Augenstein, Moshe & Tenenbaum, Aaron M. Data Structures Using Pascal. (Illus.). 528p. 1981. text ed. 34.95 (ISBN 0-13-196501-8). P-H.

Austing, Richard H., et al. Advanced Placement Test in Computer Science (Pascal) 160p. 1985. pap. 8.95 (ISBN 0-668-06095-6). Arco.

Ball, William E. & Pollack, Seymour V. Guide to Structured Programming & Pascal. 450p. Date not set. text ed. price not set info. (ISBN 0-03-056844-7, HoltC). HR&W.

Barron, D. W. Pascal: The Language & Its Implementation. (Computing Ser.). 301p. 1981. 44.95x (ISBN 0-471-27835-1, Pub. by Wiley-Interscience). Wiley.

Beer, M. D. Programming Microcomputers with Pascal. 266p. 1982. pap. 13.95 (ISBN 0-442-21368-9). Van Nos Reinhold.

Beer, Martin. Programming with Pascal. 256p. 1982. 17.95 (ISBN 0-442-21368-9). Van Nos Reinhold.

Behforooz, Ali & Holoien, Martin O. Problem Solving & Structured Programming with Pascal. 350p. 1984. pap. write for info. Wadsworth Pub.

Behforooz, Ali & Shurma, Onka P. Pascal Syntax. 1985. pap. text ed. 8.95 (ISBN 0-8359-5453-6). Reston.

Belford, G. & Liu, C. L. Pascal. (Illus.). 384p. 1984. pap. 23.95 (ISBN 0-07-038138-0). McGraw.

Berentes, Drew. MacPascal Programming. 1985. 22.95 (ISBN 0-8306-0891-5, 1891); pap. 16.95 (ISBN 0-8306-1891-0). TAB Bks.

Blume, C. & Jakob, W. PASRO Pascal for Robots. (Illus.). 145p. 1985. 22.00 (ISBN 0-387-15120-6). Springer-Verlag.

Bohl, Marilyn. Information Processing: With PASCAL. 3rd ed. 1982. text ed. 21.95 (ISBN 0-574-21390-2, 13-4390). instr. guide avail. (ISBN 0-574-21391-0, 13-4391). SRA.

Borgerson, Mark J. A BASIC Programmer's Guide to Pascal. LC 81-16281. 118p. 1982. pap. text ed. 11.95 (ISBN 0-471-09293-2, Pub. by Wiley Pr). Wiley.

Bowen, Kenneth A. Speaking Pascal: A Computer Language Primer. 236p. (Orig.). 1981. pap. 14.50 (ISBN 0-8104-5164-6). Hayden.

Bowles. Microcomputer Problem Solving Using Pascal. 2nd ed. 500p. 1984. 17.95 (ISBN 0-387-90822-6). Springer-Verlag.

Bowles, K. L., et al. Problem Solving Using UCSD Pascal. 2nd ed. (Illus.). 350p. 1984. pap. 17.95 (ISBN 0-387-90822-6). Springer Verlag.

Bowles, Ken. Beginner's Manual for the UCSD Pascal System. (Orig.). 1980. pap. 14.95 (ISBN 0-07-006745-7, BYTE Bks). McGraw.

Bowyer, Kevin & Tomboulian, Sherryl. Pascal Programming for the IBM PC: IBM DOS, Pascal & UCSD P-System Pascal. LC 83-3921. (Illus.). 352p. 1983. pap. 19.95 (ISBN 0-89303-280-8); bk. & diskette 49.95 (ISBN 0-89303-761-3); disk 30.00 (ISBN 0-89303-762-1). Brady Comm.

Bowyer, Kevin W. & Tomboulian, Sherryl J. Pascal for the IBM-PC: Turbo Pascal, PC-DOS Pascal, & UCSD p-System Pascal. rev. & expanded ed. (Illus.). 438p. 1984. pap. 19.95 (ISBN 0-89303-766-4). Brady Comm.

Brainerd, Walter S., et al. Pascal Programming: A Spiral Approach. LC 82-70213. 597p. (Orig.). 1982. pap. text ed. 25.00x (ISBN 0-87835-122-1); solutions manual avail. Boyd & Fraser.

Brecher, J. & Cherry, G. Macintosh Pascal. 1985. 17.95 (ISBN 0-8359-4174-4). Reston.

Brecher, Jerry & Cherry, George. Macintosh Pascal. (Illus.). 360p. 17.95 (ISBN 0-317-13084-6). P-H.

Brown, Douglas. From Pascal to C: An Introduction to the C Programming Language. 176p. 1985. write for info. (ISBN 0-534-04602-9). Wadsworth Pub.

Brown, Peter. Pascal from BASIC. 1982. pap. 12.95 (ISBN 0-201-10158-0). Addison-Wesley.

Bryant, Ry & Vaget, Brian W., eds. Simulation in Strongly Typed Languages: Ada, Pascal, Simula... (SCS Simulation Ser.: Vol. 13, No. 2). 1984. 30.00 (ISBN 0-317-05019-2). Soc Computer Sim.

Camara, Jose & Puccetti, Frederick. Getting Started in Pascal Programming. (Illus.). 208p. (Orig.). 1984. 19.95 (ISBN 0-8306-0188-0, 1588); pap. 12.95 (ISBN 0-8306-0588-6). TAB Bks.

Carmony, Lowell A. & Holliday, Robert. Pascal on the Macintosh. LC 84-19895. 370p. text ed. cancelled (ISBN 0-88175-032-8, Dist. by Har-Row). Computer Sci.

Carmony, Lowell A. & Holliday, Robert L. Macintosh Pascal. LC 84-19901. (Illus.). 315p. 1985. pap. 19.95 (ISBN 0-88175-081-6); student's diskette 20.00 (ISBN 0-88175-088-3); solutions diskette 15.00 (ISBN 0-88175-089-1). Computer Sci.

Carmony, Lowell A., et al. Apple Pascal: A Self-Study Guide for the Apple II Plus, IIe, & IIc. LC 84-19950. (Illus.). 233p. 1985. pap. text ed. 18.95 (ISBN 0-88175-076-X); diskette 15.00 (ISBN 0-88175-095-6). Computer Sci.

--Problem Solving in Apple Pascal: Teacher's Guide & Solution Manual. 1984. 15.00 (ISBN 0-88175-021-2). Computer Sci.

Carter, Lynn R. An Analysis of Pascal Programs. Stone, Harold, ed. LC 82-4925. (Computer Science: Systems Programming: No. 6). 202p. 1982. 44.95 (ISBN 0-8357-1331-8). UMI Res Pr.

Chernicoff. Macintosh Pascal. Date not set. price not set. Hayden.

Cherry, George. Pascal Programming Structures for Motorola Microprocessors. 1981. text ed. 24.95 (ISBN 0-8359-5465-X); pap. text ed. 16.95 (ISBN 0-8359-5471-4). Reston.

Cherry, George W. Pascal Programming Structures: An Introduction to Systematic Programming. (Illus.). 336p. 1980. text ed. 20.95 O.P. (ISBN 0-8359-5463-3); pap. text ed. 18.95 (ISBN 0-8359-5462-5). Reston.

Chirlian, Paul M. Pascal. 224p. 1980. pap. 12.95 (ISBN 0-916460-28-2). Matrix Pub.

Clark, Randy & Koehler, Stephen. The UCSD Pascal Handbook. (Software Ser.). (Illus.). 384p. 1982. text ed. 24.95 (ISBN 0-13-935544-8); pap. text ed. 18.95 (ISBN 0-13-935536-7). P-H.

Collins, W. J. Intermediate Pascal Programming: A Case Study Approach. (Computer Science Ser.). 416p. 1985. price not set (ISBN 0-07-044652-0). McGraw.

Collins, William. Introduction to Computer Programming with Pascal. 350p. Date not set. pap. text ed. price not set (ISBN 0-02-323780-5). Macmillan.

Conlan, Jim. IBM PC Pascal. (IBM Personal Computer Ser.). 318p. 1984. pap. 17.95 (ISBN 0-471-87936-3). Wiley.

Conway, Richard, et al. Programming for Poets: A Gentle Introduction Using Pascal. (Orig.). 1979. pap. text ed. 16.95 (ISBN 0-316-15411-3). Little.

--A Primer on Pascal. 2nd ed. 430p. 1981. pap. text ed. 16.95 (ISBN 0-316-15416-4). Little.

Cooper, Doug. Standard Pascal User Reference Manual. 1983. pap. 12.95 (ISBN 0-393-30121-4). Norton.

Cooper, Doug & Clancy, Michael. Oh! Pascal! 1982. pap. 20.95x (ISBN 0-393-95205-3). Norton.

--Oh! Pascal! 2nd ed. 1985. pap. text ed. 23.95x (ISBN 0-393-95445-5); instructor's manual avail. (ISBN 0-393-95447-1). Norton.

Cooper, J. W. Introduction to Pascal for Scientists. LC 80-28452. 260p. 1981. 28.95x (ISBN 0-471-07885-8, Pub. by Wiley-Interscience). Wiley.

Cooper, James W. The Laboratory Microcomputer: Programming in Pascal & MC68000 Assembly Language on the IBM System 9000. LC 84-10437. 328p. 1984. text ed. 29.00 (ISBN 0-471-81036-3, Pub. by Wiley-Interscience). Wiley.

Cortesi, David & Cherry, George. Personal Pascal: Compiled Pascal for the IBM Personal Computer. (Illus.). 1983. text ed. 24.95 (ISBN 0-8359-5523-0); pap. text ed. 17.95 (ISBN 0-8359-5522-2). Reston.

Crandall, Richard E. Pascal Applications for the Sciences. LC 82-24832. (Self-Teaching Guides). 224p. 1983. pap. text ed. 16.95 (ISBN 0-471-87242-3, 1-581). Wiley.

Dale, Nell & Orshalick, David. Pascal for Programmers. LC 82-48796. 1983. 19.84 (ISBN 0-669-06373-8). Heath.

Dale, Nell B. & Orshalick, David W. Introduction to Pascal & Structured Design. 448p. 1983. pap. 20.95 (ISBN 0-669-06962-0); instr's. manual 1.95 (ISBN 0-669-05888-2). Heath.

Davidson, Gregory. Practical Pascal Programs. (Illus.). 205p. pap. 15.99 (ISBN 0-07-582633-X, BYTE Bks). McGraw.

Dennis, Terry L. Apple Pascal: A Problem-Solving Approach. (Illus.). 400p. 1985. pap. text ed. 16.95 (ISBN 0-314-85228-X). West Pub.

DesChamps, D. J. Why Pascal? 125p. 1984. pap. cancelled (ISBN 0-88056-302-8). Dilithium Pr.

Downing, Douglas. Computer Programming in Pascal the Easy Way. (Easy Way Ser.). 256p. 1984. pap. 8.95 (ISBN 0-8120-2799-X). Barron.

Drummond. Pascal Supplement. 2nd ed. 1985. write for info. (ISBN 0-07-054716-5). McGraw.

Duntemann, Jeff. Complete Turbo Pascal. 1985. pap. 19.95 (ISBN 0-673-18111-1). Scott F.

Dyck, et al. Computing: An Introduction to Structured Problem Solving Using Pascal. 1981. text ed. 26.95 (ISBN 0-8359-0902-6); instr's. manual free (ISBN 0-8359-0903-4). Reston.

Eisenbach, Susan & Sadler, Christopher. Pascal for Programmers. (Illus.). 201p. 1981. pap. 16.00 (ISBN 0-387-10473-9). Springer-Verlag.

Findlay, William & Watt, David. Pascal: An Introduction to Methodical Programming. 2nd ed. LC 78-11540. 404p. 1981. pap. 19.95 (ISBN 0-914894-73-0). Computer Sci.

Findlay, William & Watt, David A., eds. Pascal: An Introduction to Methodical Programming. 3rd ed. text ed. 16.95 (ISBN 0-273-02188-5). Pitman Pub MA.

Finger, Susan. Pascal Programming for Engineers Using VPS. 368p. 1983. pap. 12.95 (ISBN 0-8403-3026-X). Kendall-Hunt.

Forkner, Irvine H. Pascal Programming. LC 84-17467. (Computer Science Ser.). 300p. 1985. pap. text ed. 14.50 pub net (ISBN 0-534-04215-5). Brooks-Cole.

--Pascal Programming Business, Management Science, & Social Science Applications. 250p. 1984. pap. write for info. Wadsworth Pub.

Forsyth, Richard S. Pascal at Work & Play. 250p. 1982. 35.00 (ISBN 0-412-23370-3, NO. 6638, Pub. by Chapman & Hall); pap. 12.95 (ISBN 0-412-23380-0, NO. 6639). Methuen Inc.

Fox, David & Waite, Mitchell. Pascal Primer. LC 80-53275. 208p. 1981. pap. 17.95 (ISBN 0-672-21793-7, 21793). Sams.

Fuori, William. Pascal Programming for the IBM PC & PC XT. 1984. cancelled (ISBN 0-317-06174-7). Reston.

Gallo, Michael A. & Nenno, Robert B. Computers in Society with BASIC & Pascal. 1985. pap. text ed. write for info. (ISBN 0-87150-852-4, 37L8700). PWS Pubs.

Garrison, Paul. Turbo Pascal for BASIC Programmers. 250p. 1985. pap. 14.95 (ISBN 0-88022-167-4, 184). Que Corp.

Gear, C. William. Programming in Pascal. 224p. 1983. text ed. 14.95 (ISBN 0-574-21360-0, 13-4360). SRA.

Gilbert, Harry M. & Larky, Arthur I. Practical Pascal. 1984. 14.95 (ISBN 0-538-10400-7, J40). SW Pub.

Gilder, Jules H. & Barrus, J. Scott. Pascal Programs in Science & Engineering. 2nd ed. 384p. pap. 18.95 (6265). Hayden.

Goldberg, Charles H., et al. Pascal. (Programming Language Ser.). (Illus.). 1984. pap. text ed. 23.75 (ISBN 0-87835-139-6); instr's. manual 8.00 (ISBN 0-87835-142-6). Boyd & Fraser.

Goodman, Paul & Zeldin, Alan. The MacPascal Book. (Illus.). 320p. 1985. pap. 19.95 (ISBN 0-89303-644-7). Brady Comm.

Gottfried, B. S. Programming with Pascal. (Schaum's Outline Ser.). 320p. 1983. 8.95 (ISBN 0-07-023849-9). McGraw.

Graham, Neill. Programming the IBM Personal Computer: Pascal. 1984. 19.45 (ISBN 0-03-061982-3). HR&W.

Graham, Roger. Practical Pascal for Microcomputers. LC 83-10213. 230p. 1984. pap. 14.95 (ISBN 0-471-88234-8, Pub. by Wiley Pr). Wiley.

Gray, Susan H. Pascal Simplified: A Guide for the First-Time User. LC 85-14197. 150p. 1985. text ed. 21.50x (ISBN 0-8476-7428-2, Helix Bks.); pap. 9.95 (ISBN 0-8226-0394-2). Rowman & Allanheld.

Grier, Sam. Pascal for the Eighties. LC 84-28518. (Computer Science Ser.). 448p. 1985. pap. text ed. 18.50 pub net (ISBN 0-534-04674-6). Brooks-Cole.

Grogono, P. & Nelson, S. H. Problem Solving & Computer Programming in. 1982. pap. text ed. 17.95 (ISBN 0-201-02460-8). Addison-Wesley.

Grogono, Peter. Problem Solving Techniques Pascal. (Business & Computer Science Ser.). 320p. 1982. pap. text ed. 17.95 (ISBN 0-201-02460-8). Addison-Wesley.

--Programming in Pascal. rev. ed. LC 79-24640. 384p. 1980. pap. text ed. 19.95 (ISBN 0-201-02775-5). Addison-Wesley.

--Programming in Pascal: Computer Science. (Illus.). 512p. 1984. 23.95 (ISBN 0-201-12070-4). Addison-Wesley.

Haigh, Roger & Radford, Loren. UCSD Pascal: Featuring the Apple IIe & II Plus. 461p. 1983. text ed. write for info (ISBN 0-87150-457-X, 8090). PWS Pubs.

Halpern, Richard. Microcomputer Graphics Using Pascal: Apple Version. 250p. 1985. pap. text ed. 22.50 scp (ISBN 0-06-042583-0, HarpC). Har-Row.

--Microcomputer Graphics Using Pascal: IBM Version. 238p. 1985. pap. text ed. 24.95 scp (ISBN 0-06-042584-9, HarpC). Har-Row.

Hansen, B. Brinch Hansen on Pascal Compilers. (Illus.). 256p. Date not set. text ed. 27.95 (ISBN 0-13-083098-4). P-H.

Harrow, Keith & Jones, Jacqueline. Problem Solving Using IBM PC Pascal. (Illus.). 592p. 1986. pap. text ed. 21.95 (ISBN 0-13-721358-1). P-H.

Hartmann, A. C. A Concurrent Pascal Compiler for Minicomputers. Goos, G. & Hartmanis, J., eds. (Lecture Notes in Computer Science Ser.: Vol. 50). 1977. pap. 11.95 (ISBN 0-387-08240-9). Springer-Verlag.

Hassell, Johnette & Law, Victor J. Standard Pascal: An Introduction to Structured Software Design: Workbook. (Illus.). 288p. 1985. pap. write for info. (ISBN 0-697-00274-8). Wm C Brown.

Hawksley, Chris. Pascal Programming: A Beginner's Guide to Computers & Programming. LC 82-19760. 200p. 1983. 27.95 (ISBN 0-521-25302-0); pap. 10.95 (ISBN 0-521-27292-0). Cambridge U Pr.

Heath Company Staff. Programming in Pascal. (Illus.). 513p. 1981. 99.95 (ISBN 0-87119-093-1, EC-1111). Heathkit-Zenith Ed.

Heiserman, David L. Pascal. (Illus.). 350p. (Orig.). 1980. 16.95 (ISBN 0-8306-9934-1); pap. 11.50 (ISBN 0-8306-1205-X, 1205). TAB Bks.

Hergert, Douglas & Kalash, Joseph T. Apple Pascal Games. LC 81-16577. (Illus.). 371p. 1981. pap. 15.95 (ISBN 0-89588-074-1, P360). SYBEX.

Hergert, Richard & Hergert, Douglas. Doing Business with Pascal. LC 82-62361. (Illus.). 371p. 1983. pap. text ed. 17.95 (ISBN 0-89588-091-1). SYBEX.

--Doing Business with Pascal. 371p. 17.95 (ISBN 0-317-00353-4). SYBEX.

Holt, Charles A. Microcomputer Systems: Hardware, Assembly Langauge, & Pascal. 547p. 1986. text ed. price not set write for info. (ISBN 0-02-356370-2). Macmillan.

Holt, R. C. & Hume, J. N. Programming Standard Pascal. (Illus.). 400p. 1980. pap. text ed. 18.95 (ISBN 0-8359-5690-3). Reston.

--UCSD Pascal: A Beginner's Guide to Programming Microcomputers. 368p. 1982. 24.95 (ISBN 0-8359-7915-6); pap. 19.95 (ISBN 0-8359-7913-X). Reston.

Horowitz, Ellis & Sahni, Sartaj. Fundamentals of Data Structures in Pascal. rev. ed. LC 83-10136. 542p. 1984. 31.95 (ISBN 0-914894-94-3). Computer Sci.

Hume, J. N. & Holt, R. C. Pascal under UNIX. 1983. text ed. 22.95 (ISBN 0-8359-5446-3); pap. text ed. 16.95 (ISBN 0-8359-5445-5). Reston.

Hunter, Bruce H. Fifty Pascal Programs. LC 84-50351. 338p. 1984. pap. 19.95 (ISBN 0-89588-110-1). SYBEX.
Hunter, R. Compilers: Their Design & Construction Using Pascal. (Computing Ser.). 1985. write for info. (ISBN 0-471-90720-0). Wiley.
Hyde, Randy. P-Source. 464p. (Orig.). 1983. pap. text ed. 24.95 (ISBN 0-88190-004-4, BO342). Datamost.
Institute of Electrical & Electronics Engineers, Inc. American National Standard Institute: Standard Pascal Computer Language. 128p. 1983. 17.95 (ISBN 0-471-88944-X). Wiley.
Intel Staff. Pascal-86 User's Guide. rev. ed. 396p. (Orig.). 1983. pap. 35.00 (ISBN 0-917017-27-7, 121539-004). Intel Corp.
Introduction to Pascal. (Computer Literacy Ser.). pap. 16.95 (ISBN 0-318-04029-8). Sperry Comp Syst.
Jensen, K. & Wirth, N. Pascal User Manual & Report. 3rd. ed. (Springer Study Edition). (Illus.). xvi, 266p. 1985. pap. 14.00 (ISBN 0-387-96048-1). Springer-Verlag.
Jensen, K. & Wirth, N. E. Pascal: User's Manual & Report. viii, 167p. 1978. 8.60 (ISBN 3-540-90144-2, DM 19,80). Springer-Verlag.
Jensen, Kathleen & Wirth, Niklaus. Pascal-User Manual & Report. 2nd ed. LC 75-16462. (Springer Study Edition Ser.). 180p. 1978. pap. 11.95 (ISBN 0-387-90144-2). Springer-Verlag.
Jones, Richard M. Introduction to Pascal & Computer Applications. 460p. 1983. scp 26.76 (ISBN 0-205-07937-7, 207937). Allyn.
Jume, J. N. & Holt, R. C. Vax Pascal. text ed. 24.95 (ISBN 0-8359-8247-5); pap. text ed. 19.95 (ISBN 0-8359-8246-7). Reston.
Katzan, Harry, Jr. Invitation to Pascal. (Illus.). 242p. 1981. text ed. 17.50 (ISBN 0-89433-103-5). Petrocelli.
Keller, A. First Course in Computer Programming with Pascal. 256p. 1982. 23.95 (ISBN 0-07-033508-7). McGraw.
Kemp, R. Pascal for Students. 256p. 1982. pap. text ed. 14.95 (ISBN 0-7131-3447-X). E Arnold.
Kennedy, Michael & Soloman, Martin B. Pascal: Program Development with Ten Instruction Pascal Subset (Tips) & Standard Pascal. (Illus.). 512p. 1982. text ed. 21.95 (ISBN 0-13-652735-3). P-H.
Kernighan, Brian W. & Plauger, P. J. Software Tools in Pascal. LC 81-3629. 1981. pap. 21.95 (ISBN 0-201-10342-7); tape 75.00 (ISBN 0-201-10343-5). Addison-Wesley.
Kieburtz, Richard B. Structured Programming & Problem Solving with Pascal. (Illus.). 1978. pap. 21.95 (ISBN 0-13-854869-2). P-H.
Klotz, Jerome H. & Meyer, R. Daniel. Biostatistical Microcomputing in Pascal. LC 84-27546. (Probability & Statistics). 150p. 1985. 19.95x (ISBN 0-8476-7357-X). Rowman & Allanheld.
Koffman, E. B. Pascal: A Problem Solving Approach. 1982. pap. text ed. 16.95 (ISBN 0-201-10341-9). Addison-Wesley.
Koffman, Elliot B. Problem Solving & Structured Programming in Pascal. 2nd ed. LC 84-16811. 1985. text ed. 23.95 (ISBN 0-201-11736-3). Addison-Wesley.
Kronick, Scott. Macintosh Pascal Illustrated. LC 85-3907. 1985. 16.95 (ISBN 0-201-11675-8). Addison-Wesley.
Lamie. Pascal Programming. 1986. pap. price not set (ISBN 0-471-82308-2). Wiley.
Lamprey, Roger H., et al. Programming Principles Using Pascal. 650p. 1985. text ed. 22.50 scp (ISBN 0-06-043842-8, HarpC); instr's. manual, trans. masters, solutions manual avail. (ISBN 0-06-363830-4). Har-Row.
Lecarme, Olivier & Nebut, Jean-Louis. Pascal for Programmers. LC 83-16205. (Illus.). 272p. 1984. 22.95 (ISBN 0-07-036958-5). McGraw.
Ledgard, Henry. ANSI-IEEE Pascal Standard: The American Pascal Standard. 1984. write for info. Springer-Verlag.
Ledgard, Henry & Singer, Andrew. Elementary Pascal. 384p. 1982. pap. text ed. 17.95 (ISBN 0-574-21380-5, 13-4380). SRA.
--Elementary Pascal. 1982. 20.00 (ISBN 0-394-52424-1). Random.
--Elementary Pascal: Learning to Program Your Computer in Pascal with Sherlock Holmes. LC 81-69671. 324p. (Orig.). 1982. pap. 12.95 (ISBN 0-394-70800-8, Vin). Random.
--Pascal for the Macintosh. LC 84-24503. 456p. 1985. pap. text ed. 18.95 (ISBN 0-201-11772-X). Addison-Wesley.
Ledgard, Henry F., et al. Pascal with Style: Programming Proverbs. 1979. pap. text ed. 10.50 (ISBN 0-8104-5124-7). Hayden.
Ledin, George. Understanding Pascal. (An Alfred Handy Guide Ser.). 63p. 1981. 3.50 (ISBN 0-88284-149-1). Alfred Pub.
Leestma, Sanford & Nyhoff, Larry. Pascal: Programming & Problem Solving. 320p. 1985. 17.95 (ISBN 0-02-369540-4). Macmillan.
--Programming with Pascal. 384p. 1984. pap. text ed. write for info. (ISBN 0-02-369460-2). Macmillan.
Lewis, Gerard. Macintosh Pascal: Learning to Program Right the First Time. 312p. 1984. pap. cancelled (ISBN 0-88693-165-7). Banbury Bks.
--Macintosh: The Appliance of the Future. 288p. 1984. pap. 14.95 (ISBN 0-88693-031-6). Banbury Bks.
Lewis, Ted G. Pascal for the IBM Personal Computer. LC 82-22750. 288p. 1983. pap. 15.95 (ISBN 0-201-05464-7). Addison-Wesley.
Lewis, Theodore G. Pascal Programming for the Apple. 224p. 1981. O.P. 20.95 (ISBN 0-8359-5455-2); pap. 14.95 (ISBN 0-8359-5454-4). Reston.
Lewis, William E. Problem-Solving Principles for Pascal Programmers: Applied Logic, Psychology & Grit. 179p. pap. 10.95 (ISBN 0-8104-5767-9). Hayden.
Lightfood, D. Teach Yourself Computer Programming in Pascal. 1984. pap. 6.95 (ISBN 0-679-10539-5). McKay.
Lines, Martin V. Pascal As a Second Language. (Illus.). 224p. 1984. pap. text ed. 21.95 (ISBN 0-13-652925-9). P-H.
Lings, Brian. Information Structures: A Uniform Approach Using Pascal. 250p. 1985. 45.00 (ISBN 0-412-26490-0, Pub. by Chapman & Hall England); pap. 19.95 (ISBN 0-412-26500-1). Methuen Inc.
--Information Structures: A Uniform Approach Using Pascal. 250p. 1985. 45.00 (ISBN 0-412-26490-0, 9565); pap. 19.95 (ISBN 0-412-26500-1, 9566). Methuen Inc.
Luehrmann, Arthur & Peckham, Herbert. Apple Pascal: A Hands-on Approach. (Programming Language Ser.). (Illus.). 384p. 1982. pap. 23.95 spiral bdg. (ISBN 0-07-049171-2). McGraw.
--Hands-on Pascal: For the IBM Personal Computer. (Personal Programmimg Ser.). 448p. 1984. pap. text ed. write for info. (ISBN 0-07-049176-3). McGraw.
MacCallum, Iain. Pascal for the Apple. 1983. incl. disk 35.00 (ISBN 0-13-652909-7). P-H.
--UCSD Pascal for the IBM PC. (Illus.). 500p. 1985. 33.90 (ISBN 0-13-936063-8). P-H.
McDermott, Vern, et al. Learning Pascal Step by Step. LC 84-19869. 236p. 1985. text ed. 19.95 (ISBN 0-88175-045-X); tchr's ed. 23.95 (ISBN 0-88175-046-8). Computer Sci.
McGlynn, Daniel R. Fundamentals of Microcomputer Programming: Including Pascal. LC 82-8645. 332p. 1982. pap. 18.95 (ISBN 0-471-08769-6, Pub. by Wiley-Interscience). Wiley.
McNitt, Lawrence. Invitation to Pascal for the TRS-80. 1985. 16.95 (ISBN 0-89433-253-8). Petrocelli.
Mallozzi, John S. & DeLillo, Nicholas J. Computability with Pascal. LC 83-24450. (Illus.). 193p. 1984. text ed. 26.95 (ISBN 0-13-164443-2). P-H.
Mandell, Steven L. Computers & Data Processing Today with Pascal. (Illus.). 450p. 1983. pap. text ed. 24.95 (ISBN 0-314-70647-X). West Pub.
--Computers & Data Processing Today with Pascal. 2nd ed. (Illus.). 550p. 1985. pap. text ed. 27.95 (ISBN 0-314-96080-5). West Pub.
--A Pascal Supplement for Computers & Data Processing Today. 150p. 1983. write for info (ISBN 0-314-77494-7). West Pub.
Marcus, Jeffrey & Marcus, Marvin. Computing Without Mathematics: BASIC & Pascal Applications (School Edition) LC 85-4144. 300p. (Orig.). 1985. pap. 32.95 (ISBN 0-88175-110-3); pap. text ed. 21.95 (ISBN 0-88175-105-7); wkbk. 10.00 (ISBN 0-88175-115-4); diskette 15.00 (ISBN 0-88175-106-5). Computer Sci.
Marcus, Marvin. An Introduction to Pascal & Precalculus. 1984. 29.95 (ISBN 0-88175-009-3); tchr's diskette 17.00 (ISBN 0-88175-062-X); student's diskette 17.00 (ISBN 0-88175-061-1); solution manual 10.00 (ISBN 0-88175-063-8). Computer Sci.
Matuszek, David L. Quick Pascal. LC 82-8354. 179p. 1982. pap. text ed. 14.95x (ISBN 0-471-86644-X). Wiley.
Mazlack, Lawrence J. Structured Problem Solving with Pascal. 1983. pap. text ed. 22.95 (ISBN 0-03-060153-3). HR&W.
Mendelson, Bert. A First Course in Programming with Pascal. 385p. 1982. scp 28.15 (ISBN 0-205-07823-0, 207823). Allyn.
Miller, Alan R. Pascal Programs for Scientists & Engineers. LC 81-51128. (Scientists & Engineers Ser.: No. 1). (Illus.). 374p. 1981. pap. 17.95 (ISBN 0-89588-058-X, P340). SYBEX.
Miller, Lawrence H. Programming & Problem Solving: A Second Course with Pascal. 624p. 1986. text ed. write for info. (ISBN 0-201-05531-7). Addison-Wesley.
Moffat, David V. Common Algorithms in Pascal with Programs for Reading. (Software Ser.). 192p. 1983. pap. 12.95 (ISBN 0-13-152637-5). P-H.
--UCSD Pascal Examples & Exercises. (Illus.). 224p. 1986. pap. text ed. 14.95 (ISBN 0-13-935396-8). P H.
Moll, Robert & Folsom, Rachel. Macintosh Pascal. LC 84-81937. 494p. pap. 23.95 (ISBN 0-395-37574-6); solutions manual 2.00 (ISBN 0-395-37575-4). HM.
Moore, John B. Pascal: Text & Reference. 2nd ed. 1989. pap. text ed. 22.95 (ISBN 0-8359-5440-4). Reston.
Moore, Lawrie. Foundations of Programming with Pascal. LC 80-40146. (Computers & Their Applications Ser.). 238p. 1981. pap. 19.95x (ISBN 0-470-27281-3). Halsted Pr.
Moser. Programming Proverbs for Pascal Students. 1985. pap. price not set (ISBN 0-471-82309-0). Wiley.
Nanney, T. Ray. Computing & Problem Solving with Pascal. LC 84-2071. (P-H Software Ser.). (Illus.). 592p. 1985. pap. text ed. 23.95 (ISBN 0-13-164799-7). P-H.
Page, E. S. & Wilson, L. B. Information Representation & Manipulation Using Pascal. LC 82-4505. (Cambridge Computer Science Texts: No. 15). (Illus.). 275p. 1983. 32.50 (ISBN 0-521-24954-6); pap. 13.95 (ISBN 0-521-27096-0). Cambridge U Pr.
Pardee, Michael. Pascal Primer for the IBM PC. (Plume-Waite Computer Ser.). (Illus.). 1984. pap. 17.95 (ISBN 0-452-25496-5, Plume). NAL.
Pasahow, E. Pascal for Electronics. 208p. 1985. 11.95 (ISBN 0-07-048724-3). McGraw.
Pascal Language Reference Manual. (Apple II Plus & IIe Reference Manuals Ser.). Date not set. 20.00 (ISBN 0-317-04468-0, A2L0027). Apple Comp.
Pascal Operating System Manual. (Apple II Plus & IIe Reference Manuals). Date not set. 25.00 (ISBN 0-317-04469-9, A2L0028). Apple Comp.
Pascal Program Preparation Tools Manual. (Apple III Reference Manuals). Date not set. 20.00 (ISBN 0-317-04437-0, A3L0005). Apple Comp.
Pascal Programmer's Manual, 2 vols. (Apple III Reference Manuals). Date not set. 30.00 (ISBN 0-317-04438-9, A3L0003). Apple Comp.
Pascal Technical Reference Manual. (Apple III Reference Manuals). Date not set. 50.00 (ISBN 0-317-04439-7, A3L0006). Apple Comp.
Pemberton, Steven & Daniels, Martin. Pascal Implementation: The P4 Compiler, 2 Vols. LC 81-20184. 172p. 1982. pap. 37.95x (ISBN 0-470-27386-0). Halsted Pr.
Perrott, Ronald M. & Allison, Donald H. Pascal for FORTRAN Programmers. LC 82-7253. 347p. 1984. 19.95 (ISBN 0-914894-09-9). Computer Sci.
Pollack, Seymour V. Introducing Pascal. LC 83-10756. 371p. 1984. pap. text ed. 19.95 (ISBN 0-03-060563-6). HR&W.
--Programming the IBM Personal Computer: UCSD Pascal. LC 82-21249. 400p. 1983. pap. 40.45 with diskette (ISBN 0-03-063669-8); pap. 20.95 (ISBN 0-03-062637-4). HR&W.
--UCSD Pascal Programming. 1985. pap. text ed. 21.95x (ISBN 0-03-069393-4). HR&W.
Poole, Lon & Davidson, Gregory. Practical Pascal Programs. 206p. (Orig.). 1982. pap. 16.95 (ISBN 0-931988-74-8, 74-8). Osborne-McGraw.
Porter, Kent. Practical Programming in Pascal: An Introduction to Computer Programming. 1985. 14.95 (ISBN 0-452-25568-6, Plume). NAL.
Prather, Ronald E. Problem-Solving Principles: Programming with Pascal. (Illus.). 352p. 1982. text ed. 22.95 (ISBN 0-13-721316-6); pap. text ed. 20.95 (ISBN 0-13-721308-5). P-H.
Presley & Corica. Guide to Programming in Apple Pascal. 1986. 19.95 (ISBN 0-931717-21-3); 19.95 (ISBN 0-931717-27-2). Lawrenceville Pr.
Press, William, et al. Numerical Recipes: The Art of Scientific Computing. 700p. Date not set. price not set. (ISBN 0-521-30811-9). Cambridge U Pr.
Price, David. Pascal: A Considerate Approach. 198p. 1982. 17.95 (ISBN 0-13-652818-X). P-H.
--Pascal: A Considerate Approach. 2nd ed. 1984. pap. 12.95 (ISBN 0-13-652884-8). P-H.
--UCSD Pascal: A Considerate Approach. (Illus.). 193p. 1983. 19.95 (ISBN 0-13-935478-6); pap. 12.95 (ISBN 0-13-935460-3). P-H.
Reynolds. Program Design & Data Structures in PASCAL. 1986. text ed. write for info. Wadsworth Pub.
Richards, James. Pascal. 1982. 17.00i (ISBN 0-12-587520-7); instr's. manual 10.00i (ISBN 0-12-587521-5). Acad Pr.
Rohl, J. S. Recursion Via Pascal. (Computer Science Texts Ser.: No. 19). (Illus.). 200p. 1984. 34.50 (ISBN 0-521-26329-8); pap. 14.95 (ISBN 0-521-26934-2). Cambridge U Pr.
--Writing Pascal Programs. LC 82-14591. (Cambridge Computer Science Texts Ser.: No. 16). (Illus.). 250p. 1983. 27.95 (ISBN 0-521-25077-3); pap. 12.95 (ISBN 0-521-27196-7). Cambridge U Pr.
Rohl, J. S. & Barrett, H. J. Programming Via Pascal. LC 79-17433. (Cambridge Computer Science Texts Ser.: No. 12). 300p. 1980. 42.50 (ISBN 0-521-22628-7); pap. 18.95 (ISBN 0-521-29583-1). Cambridge U Pr.
Rushton, Jeremy. Pascal with Your BASIC Micro. 136p. 1983. pap. 9.95 (ISBN 0-672-22036-9, 22036). Sams.
Sahni, Sartaj. Software Development in Pascal. 1985. text ed. 32.00 (ISBN 0-942450-01-9). Camelot Pub MN.
Sand, Paul. The First Book of Macintosh Pascal. 272p. (Orig.). 1985. pap. 17.95 (ISBN 0-07-881165-1, 165-1). Osborne McGraw.
Sand, Paul A. Advanced Pascal Programming Techniques. (Illus.). 350p. (Orig.). 1983. pap. 19.95 (ISBN 0-88134-105-3, 105-8). Osborne-McGraw.
Savitch, Walter J. Pascal: An Introduction to the Art & Science of Programming. 1984. pap. 24.95x (ISBN 0-8053-8370-0); instr's. guide 15.95 (ISBN 0-8053-8371-9). Benjamin-Cummings.
Schneider, G. Michael & Bruell, Steven C. Advanced Programming & Problem Solving with Pascal. LC 81-1344. 506p. 1981. text ed. 34.50 (ISBN 0-471-07876-X). Wiley.
Schneider, G. Michael & Weingart, Steven W. An Introduction to Programming & Problem Solving with Pascal. 2nd ed. LC 82-2809. 480p. 1982. 27.45 (ISBN 0-471-08216-3); pap. 23.00 (ISBN 0-471-80447-9). Wiley.
Schneider, M. G., et al. Study Guide to Accompany an Introduction to Programming & Problem Solving with Pascal. 2nd ed. 189p. pap. 7.95 (ISBN 0-471-88347-6). Wiley.
Seiter, Charles & Weiss, Robert. Pascal for BASIC Programmers. (Microbooks Popular Ser.). 224p. 1982. pap. 10.95 (ISBN 0-201-06577-0). Addison-Wesley.
Sherman, C. & Holder, S. Elements of Pascal: A Problem Solving Approach for Business. 198p. 1984. pap. 10.45 (ISBN 0-471-80651-X). Wiley.
Skilton, F. R. Understanding Pascal. 400p. 1984. write for info. (ISBN 0-697-08256-3); instr's. manual avail. (ISBN 0-697-08279-2). Wm C Brown.
Skvarcius, R. Problem Solving Using Pascal: Algorithm Developmental & Programming Concepts. 640p. 1983. pap. text ed. write for info (ISBN 0-87150-440-5, 8080). PWS Pubs.
Smedema, C. H., et al. The Programming Languages: Pascal, Modula, Chill, & Ada. 160p. 1983. 16.95. P-H.
SofDesign Inc. Exploring Pascal: A Compiler for Beginners. Presser, Rich & Leddy, John, eds. 320p. 1985. incl. disk 39.95 (ISBN 0-912677-25-2). Ashton-Tate Bks.
Starkey, J. Denbigh & Ross, Rockford. Fundamental Programming & Problem Solving in Pascal. International ed. 625p. 1984. 17.00 (ISBN 0-314-77810-1). West Pub.
--Fundamental Programming: Pascal. 352p. 1982. pap. text ed. write for info. (ISBN 0-314-71811-7). West Pub.
--Fundamental Programming with Pascal. (Illus.). 625p. 1984. pap. text ed. 24.95 (ISBN 0-314-77806-3). West Pub.
Swan. Pascal Programs for Business. 1983. 18.95 (ISBN 0-317-02343-8, 6270); disks & documentation 59.95 (7270). Hayden.
--Pascal Programs for Games & Graphics. 224p. 1983. 15.95 (ISBN 0-317-02344-6, 6271); disks & documentation 49.94 (7271). Hayden.
Swan, Tom. Pascal Programs for Data Base Management. 256p. 18.95 (6272); pap. 49.95 disks & documentation (7272). Hayden.
Syslo, Maciej, et al. Discrete Optimization Algorithms with Pascal Programs. (Illus.). 544p. 1983. text ed. 45.00 (ISBN 0-13-215509-5). P-H.
Taylor, R. P. Programming Primer: A Graphic Introduction to Computer Programming with BASIC & Pascal. LC 81-2209. 1982. 21.95 (ISBN 0-201-07400-1). Addison-Wesley.
Tiberghien, Jacques. The Pascal Handbook. LC 80-53283. (Illus.). 485p. 1981. pap. 19.95 (ISBN 0-89588-053-9, P320). SYBEX.
Tiny Pascal Fig-FORTH. 10.00 (ISBN 0-318-01357-6). Mountain View Pr.
Tomek, I. & Muldner, T. Guide to PMS: A Pascal Primer. 304p. 1985. 16.95 (ISBN 0-07-064959-6). McGraw.
Tomek, Ivan. The First Book of Josef: An Introduction to Computer Programming. (Illus.). 320p. 1983. pap. text ed. 14.95 (ISBN 0-13-318287-8). P-H.
Tremblay, Jean P. & Bunt, Richard B. Structured Pascal. 448p. 1980. pap. text ed. 24.95 (ISBN 0-07-065159-0). McGraw.
Tucker, Allen B., Jr. Apple Pascal: A Programming Guide. LC 82-912. 247p. 1982. pap. text ed. 19.95 (ISBN 0-03-059547-9). HR&W.
--Introduction to Programming with ESP & Pascal. LC 82-21240. 362p. 1983. pap. text ed. 20.95 (ISBN 0-03-059148-1). HR&W.

Underkoffler, Milton. Introduction to Structured Programming with Pascal. 376p. 1983. pap. text ed. write for info. (ISBN 0-87150-394-8, 8040). PWS Pubs.

Vile, Richard. Programming Your Own Adventure Games in Pascal. (Illus.). 320p. (Orig.). 1984. 19.95 (ISBN 0-8306-0768-4); pap. 13.95 (ISBN 0-8306-1768-X, 1768). TAB Bks.

Walker, Billy K. A Structured Approach to Pascal. 1983. pap. 12.95x (ISBN 0-256-02827-3). Irwin.

Washington Apple Pi, Ltd. Staff. Perfect Pascal Programs. Platt, Robert, ed. LC 84-24017. (Illus.). 288p. (Orig.). 1985. 22.95 (ISBN 0-8306-0894-X, 1894); pap. 16.95 (ISBN 0-8306-1894-5). TAB Bks.

Wells, Timothy. A Structured Approach to Building Programs: Pascal, Vol. 3. (Orig.). 1985. pap. text ed. write for info. (ISBN 0-917072-46-4). Yourdon.

Wichmann, Brian A. & Ciechanowicz, Z. J., eds. Pascal Compiler Validation. LC 82-23882. 176p. 1983. 26.95 (ISBN 0-471-90133-4, Pub. by Wiley-Interscience). Wiley.

Willner, Eliakim & Demchak, Barry. Advanced Programming in UCSD Pascal. 336p. 1985. text ed. 22.95 (ISBN 0-13-011628-9); pap. 17.95 (ISBN 0-13-011610-6). P-H.

Wilson, I. R. & Addyman, A. M. A Practical Introduction to Pascal. 2nd ed. 236p. 1982. pap. 14.95 (ISBN 0-387-91210-X, BSI 6192). Springer-Verlag.

Wood, Derick. Paradigms & Programming with Pascal. LC 82-19714. 425p. 1984. text ed. 27.95 (ISBN 0-914894-45-5). Computer Sci.

Wood, Steve. Using Turbo Pascal. 350p. (Orig.). 1985. pap. 19.95 (ISBN 0-07-881148-1). Osborne-McGraw.

Zwass, Vladimir. Programming in Pascal. 320p. (Orig.). 1985. pap. 8.61i (ISBN 0-06-460201-X, CO 201). B&N NY.

PASSENGER PIGEONS

Eckert, Allan W. The Silent Sky: The Incredible Extinction of the Passenger Pigeon. LC 65-20745. 244p. 1973. pap. 4.95 (ISBN 0-913428-15-9). Landfall Pr.

Schorger, Arlie W. The Passenger Pigeon: Its Natural History & Extinction. (Illus.). 424p. 1973. 23.95 (ISBN 0-8061-1035-X); pap. 11.95 (ISBN 0-8061-1384-7). U of Okla Pr.

PASSERIFORMES

see also Finches; Sparrows; Thrashers; Wood Warblers

Bent, Arthur C. Life Histories of North American Blackbirds, Orioles, Tanagers & Allies. (Illus.). 1958. 16.75 (ISBN 0-8446-1631-1). Peter Smith.

--Life Histories of North American Blackbirds, Orioles, Tanagers & Their Allies. (Illus.). 1958. pap. 7.95 (ISBN 0-486-21093-6). Dover.

--Life Histories of North American Thrushes, Kinglets & Their Allies. (Illus.). 1949. pap. 7.95 (ISBN 0-486-21086-3). Dover.

--Life Histories of North American Thrushes, Kinglets & Their Allies. (Illus.). 14.50 (ISBN 0-8446-1643-5). Peter Smith.

Dwight, Jonathan, Jr. The Sequence of Plumages & Moults of the Passerine Birds of New York, Vol. 13. (Annals of the New York Academy of Sciences). Repr. of 1900 ed. 10.00x (ISBN 0-89072-004-5). NY Acad Sci.

PASSIVITY (CHEMISTRY)

Tomashov, N. D. & Chernova, G. P. Passivity & Protection of Metals Against Corrosion. LC 66-19933. 208p. 1967. 45.00 (ISBN 0-306-30276-4, Plenum Pr). Plenum Pub.

PASTEUR, LOUIS, 1822-1895

Hume, D. Bechamp vs. Pasteur? 1981. 15.95x (ISBN 0-686-76726-8). B Of A.

Mechnikov, et al. Founders of Modern Medicine. facs. ed. Berger, D., tr. LC 78-142669. (Essay Index Reprint Ser). 1939. 21.00 (ISBN 0-8369-2111-9). Ayer Co Pubs.

Radot, Rene V. The Life of Pasteur. 1923. 35.00 (ISBN 0-8274-4255-6). R West.

PASTEURIZATION OF MILK

see Milk–Pasteurization

PASTRY

see also Cake

Healy, Bruce & Bugat, Paul. Mastering the Art of French Pastry. 284p. 1984. 23.95 (ISBN 0-8120-5456-3). Barron.

PASTURES

see also Forage Plants; Grasses; Grazing

Chessmore, Roy A. Profitable Pasture Management. LC 78-70056. 1979. 14.50 (ISBN 0-8134-2056-3, 2056). Interstate.

Glossary of Terms Used in Pasture & Range Survey Research, Ecology, Management. 153p. 1976. pap. 14.00 (ISBN 0-685-68955-7, F925, FAO). Unipub.

Humphreys, Ross. Tropical Pastures & Fodder Crops. (Intermediate Tropical Agriculture Ser.). (Illus.). 1978. pap. text ed. 6.50x (ISBN 0-582-60303-X). Longman.

Penning de Vries, F. W. & Djiteye, M. A., eds. La Productivite des Paturages Saheliens: Une Etude des Sols, des Vegetations et de l'Exploitation de Cette Resource Naturelle. (Agricultural Research Reports: No. 918). 548p. (English summary). 1982. 41.50 (ISBN 90-220-0806-1, PDC246, PUDOC). Unipub.

Rensburg, H. V. van. Management & Utilization of Pastures: East Africa: Pt. 1, Kenya; Pt. 2 Tanzania; Pt. 3 Uganda, 3 Pts. (Pasture & Fodder Crop Studies: No. 3). (Eng. & Fr.). 124p. (2nd Printing 1978). 1969. pap. 10.50 (ISBN 92-5-100420-X, F1970, FAO). Unipub.

Shaw, N. H. & Bryan, W. W. Tropical Pasture Research: Principles & Methods. 454p. 1976. 90.00x (ISBN 0-85198-358-8, Pub. by CAB Bks England). State Mutual Bk.

Strange, L. R. Human Influences in African Pastureland Environments: With Special Reference to the Arid & Semiarid Pastoral Regions of Eastern Africa. (Pasture & Fodder Crop Studies: No. 8). 102p. 1980. pap. 7.50 (ISBN 92-5-100874-4, F2076, FAO). Unipub.

--An Introduction to African Pastureland Production with Special Reference to Farm & Rangeland Environments of Eastern Africa. (Pasture & Fodder Crop Studies: No. 6). 204p. 1980. pap. 14.75 (ISBN 92-5-100872-8, F2075, FAO). Unipub.

Turner, F. Newman. Fertility Pastures & Cover Crops. Bargyla & Rateaver, Gylver, eds. LC 74-33123. (Conservation Gardening & Farming Ser: Ser. C). pap. 10.00 (ISBN 0-9600698-6-0). Rateavers.

Whiteman, Peter C. Tropical Pasture Science. (Illus.). 1980. 58.00x (ISBN 0-19-859471-2); pap. 24.50x (ISBN 0-686-96830-1). Oxford U Pr.

Wilson, John R. Plant Relations in Pastures. 425p. 1978. pap. 45.00 (ISBN 0-643-00264-2, C005, CSIRO). Unipub.

Wilson, John R., ed. Plant Relations in Pastures. 1978. 35.00x (ISBN 0-643-00264-2, Pub. by CSIRO). Intl Spec Bk.

PATENT LAWS AND LEGISLATION

see also Patent Practice

Blaustein, Paul H. Learned Hand on Patent Law. LC 82-63003. 350p. 1983. lib. bdg. 50.00 (ISBN 0-9610490-0-6); text ed. 50.00 (ISBN 0-686-88645-3). Pineridge Pub.

Bowman, Ward S., Jr. Patent & Antitrust Law: A Legal & Economic Appraisal. 1973. 25.00x (ISBN 0-226-06925-7). U of Chicago Pr.

Chisum. Patents, 6 vols. 1983. Updates avail. loose-leaf 400.00 (#525); looseleaf 1983 208.50; looseleaf 1984 291.00. Bender.

Choate, Robert A. & Francis, William H. Patent Law, Cases & Materials Also Including Trade Secrets - Copyrights - Trademaks. 2nd ed. LC 80-27863. (American Casebook Ser.). 1110p. 1981. text ed. 28.95 (ISBN 0-8299-2124-9). West Pub.

Communications Law 1984, 2 vols. (Patents, Copyrights, Trademarks, & Literary Property Ser.). 1871p. 1984. Set. 35.00 (ISBN 0-686-80167-9, G4-3754). PLI.

Conlin, David, et al. Intellectual Property Rights in Biotechnology Worldwide. 320p. 1986. pap. 80.00x (ISBN 0-943818-15-X). Stockton Pr.

Crespi, R. S. Patenting in the Biological Sciences: A Practical Guide for Research Scientists in Biotechnology & the Pharmaceutical & Agrochemical Industries. LC 81-19771. 211p. 1982. 39.95 (ISBN 0-471-10151-6, Pub. by Wiley-Interscience). Wiley.

Current Developments in Patent Law, 1984. (Patents, Copyrights, Trademarks, & Literary Property Course Handbook Ser.). 452p. 1984. 35.00 (ISBN 0-686-79964-X, G4-3742). PLI.

Demaret, Paul. Patents, Territorial Restrictions, & EEC Law: A Legal & Economic Analysis. (IIC Studies: Vol. 2). 147p. 1978. pap. 26.50x (ISBN 0-89573-016-2). VCH Pubs.

Directory of Patent Attorneys & Agents. LC 80-23400. 328p. 1980. pap. 11.00 (ISBN 0-08-026343-7). Pergamon.

Dunner, Donald R. Patent Law Perspectives, 6 vols. 2nd ed. LC 82-61193. 1970. A Year's Service. 560.00; Annual Renewal. 460.00; looseleaf 1983 375.00; looseleaf 1984 425.00. Bender.

Flanagan, John R. How to Prosecute Patent Applications: A Self-Study Course Using Actual Inventions. LC 84-60154. 250p. 1985. pap. 29.95 (ISBN 0-913995-01-0). Patent Ed.

Foreign Patent Litigation. (Patents, Copyrights, Trademarks & Literary Property Course Handbook Ser.: Vol. 171). 327p. 1983. 35.00 (ISBN 0-317-11430-1, G4-3734). PLI.

Greene, Orville & Durr, Frank. The Practical Inventor's Handbook. LC 78-26666. (Illus.). 1979. 39.95 (ISBN 0-07-024320-4). McGraw.

Hall, Thos. B. The Infringement of Patents for Inventions, Not Designs - with Sole Reference to the Opinions of the Supreme Court of the United States. 275p. 1983. Repr. of 1893 ed. lib. bdg. 27.50x (ISBN 0-8377-0707-2). Rothman.

Hamburg, C. Bruce. Patent Law Handbook, 1984-85. (Intellectual Property Library). 1984. 42.50 (ISBN 0-87632-254-2). Boardman.

Holmes, William C. Antitrust & Intellectual Property Law. LC 83-2600. 1983. 85.00 (ISBN 0-87632-324-7). Boardman.

Horwitz. Patent Office Rules & Practice: Release 21, 8 vols. 1983. Updates avail. 480.00 (605); looseleaf 1983 392.00; looseleaf 1984 397.50. Bender.

--Patent Office Rules & Practice: Release 38. 1983. write for info. (605). Bender.

Infringement of Copyrights. (Nineteen Eighty to Eighty-One Patents, Copyrights, Trademarks & Literary Property Course Handbook Ser.). 275p. (Orig.). 1981. pap. text ed. 35.00 (ISBN 0-686-78752-8, G4-3691). PLI.

Infringement of Patents. (Infringement of Patents, Copyrights, & Trademarks Library). 333p. 1981. 35.00 (ISBN 0-686-80216-0, G4-3689). PLI.

Inventive Activity in the Asian & the Pacific Region. 152p. 1981. pap. 8.25 (ISBN 92-805-0028-7, WIPO66, WIPO). Unipub.

Jehoran, H. Cohen, ed. Protection of Geographic Denominations of Goods & Services. (Monographs in Industrial Property & Copyright Law: Vol. III). 216p. 1980. 37.50 (ISBN 90-286-0090-6). Sijthoff & Noordhoff.

Johnston, Dan. Design Protection. 128p. 1978. 16.95x (ISBN 0-85072-088-5, Pub. by Design Council England). Intl Spec Bk.

Klitzman, Maurice H. Patent Interference: Law & Practice. 300p. 1984. 45.00 (ISBN 0-317-04076-6). PLI.

Ladas, Stephen. Patents, Trademarks, & Related Rights: National & International Protection, 3 vols. LC 73-89709. 1888p. 1974. text ed. 125.00x (ISBN 0-674-65775-6). Harvard U Pr.

Law & Business Inc. & Legal Times Seminars, eds. Patent Re-Examination. (Seminar Course Handbooks). 1983. pap. 30.00 (C0085X, Law & Business). HarBraceJ.

Marcy, William, ed. Patent Policy: Government, Academic, & Industry Concepts. LC 78-9955. (ACS Symposium Ser.: No. 81). 1978. 24.95 (ISBN 0-8412-0454-3). Am Chemical.

Matthew Bender Publishers. Patent Law Perspectives. 1983. write for info. (532). Bender.

Miller, Arthur R. & Davis, Michael. Intellectual Property: Patents, Trademarks & Copyright in a Nutshell. LC 83-12454. (Nutshell Ser.). 428p. 1983. pap. text ed. 8.95 (ISBN 0-314-74524-6). West Pub.

Model Law for Developing Countries on Inventions. 1965. pap. 7.50 (ISBN 0-686-53017-9, WIPO46, WIPO). Unipub.

Nash & Rawicz. Patents & Technical Data. 654p. 1983. 35.00x (ISBN 0-318-03085-3). GWU Natl Law.

National Association of Credit Management. Patent-Trademark Law & Practice: Digest of Commercial Laws of the World, 3 Bdrs. LC 65-22163. 1975. bds. 225.00x Looseleaf (ISBN 0-379-01025-9, 83-1). Oceana.

Nelson, Lester, ed. Digest of Patent & Trademark Laws of the World, 3 vols. (Digest of Commercial Laws of the World Ser.). 1975. Set. 225.00 (ISBN 0-379-01025-9). Oceana.

Patent Antitrust 1982. (Patents, Copyrights, Trademarks, & Literary Property Course Handbook Ser.). 349p. 1982. 35.00 (ISBN 0-686-79969-0, G4-3707). PLI.

Patent Antitrust, 1984. (Patents, Copyrights, Trademarks & Literary Property Course Handbook Ser.: Vol. 177). 340p. 1984. 35.00 (ISBN 0-317-11432-8, G4-3743). PLI.

Patent Law Annual, Southwestern Legal Foundation: Proceedings, 1st-21st, 1963-1983. bound set 840.00x (ISBN 0-317-02327-6); per vol. bd. 42.50; microfilm avail. Rothman.

Patent Litigation. (Patents, Copyrights, Trademarks, & Literary Property Course Handbook Ser.: Vol. 170). 434p. 1983. 35.00 (ISBN 0-317-11428-X, G4-3733). PLI.

Patlaw: USPQ. write for info. BNA.

Pennsylvania Bar Institute. Patents, Trademarks, Copyrights & Trade Secrets: Pennsylvania Legal Practice Course Materials. 60p. 1984. 15.00 (ISBN 0-318-02157-9, PLP-84(10)). PA Bar Inst.

Penrose, Edith T. The Economics of the International Patent System. LC 78-64301. (Johns Hopkins University. Studies in the Social Sciences. Extra Volumes.: 30). Repr. of 1951 ed. 12.50 (ISBN 0-404-61399-3). AMS Pr.

--The Economics of the International Patent System. 247p. 1973. Repr. of 1951 ed. lib. bdg. 18.75x (ISBN 0-8371-6653-5, PEEI). Greenwood.

Product Counterfeiting: Remedies. (Patents, Copyrights, Trademarks & Literary Property Course Handbook: Vol. 180). 332p. 1984. 35.00 (ISBN 0-317-11486-7, G4-3744). PLI.

Richardson, Robert O. How to Get Your Own Patent. LC 80-54340. (Illus.). 128p. 1981. O.P. 16.95 (ISBN 0-8069-5564-3); pap. 8.95 (ISBN 0-8069-8990-4). Sterling.

Robbins, Frank E. Defense of Prior Invention Patent Infringement Litigation. LC 77-84298. 1977. 20.00 (ISBN 0-685-86093-0, G1-0645). PLI.

Rosenberg, Peter D. Patent Law Fundamentals, 2 vols. 2nd ed. LC 80-10710. 1980. 135.00 (ISBN 0-87632-098-1). Boardman.

Rotondi, Mario. Draft of a Model Law on Trademarks, Patents, & Models. LC 72-181274. 362p. 1971. 17.50 (ISBN 0-379-20090-2). Oceana.

Section of Patent, Trademark & Copyright Law: Committee Reports, 1930-1984. Bound Set. 535.00x (ISBN 0-686-89507-X, Pub.by ABA); Per Vol. Bdg., 1930-1960. 9.50; Per Vol. Bdg., 1961-1984. 15.00. Rothman.

Section of Patent, Trademark & Copyright Law: Proceedings, 1935-1984, 48 vols. Bound Set. 505.00x (ISBN 0-686-89510-X, Pub. by ABA); Per Vol. Bdg., 1935-1945, 1947-1959. 9.50; Per Vol. Bdg., 1960-1984. 15.00. Rothman.

Shepard's Citations, Inc. Shepard's United States Patents & Trademark Citations: A Compilation of Citations to United States Patents, Trademarks & Copyrights, & to Related Decisions by the Courts & Commissioner of Patents, 2 vols. LC 68-6238. 1968. 55.00 ea. (Shepards-McGraw). McGraw.

--Shepard's United States Patents & Trademarks Citations: A Compilation of Citations to United States Patents, Trademarks, & Copyrights, & to Related Decisions by the Courts & Commissioner of Patents, 2 vols. LC 68-6238. 1968. Supplement 1968-80 173.00 (ISBN 0-686-90290-4, Shepards-McGraw). McGraw.

Taxation Committee of the Patent Law Association of Chicago, ed. Tax Guide for Patents, Trademarks & Copyrights. 5th ed. 1984. 37.50 (ISBN 0-87632-318-2). Boardman.

Technology Licensing. (Patents, Copyrights, Trademarks, & Literary Property Ser.: 2 Vols.). 1113p. 1982. 35.00 (ISBN 0-686-80168-7, G4-3681). PLI.

Two Hundred Years of English & American Patent, Trademark & Copyright Law. 136p. 1977. pap. 5.00 (ISBN 0-686-47990-4). Amer Bar Assn.

Ullrich, Hanns. Standards of Patentability for European Inventions. (IIC Studies: Vol. 1). 137p. 1977. pap. 34.20x (ISBN 3-527-25695-4). VCH Pubs.

U. S. Trademark Association. Notes from the Patent Office, 2 vols. LC 65-23627. (Incl. periodic suppls). 1974. looseleaf 97.00 (ISBN 0-88238-027-3); 1980 supplement 22.00 (ISBN 0-685-25467-4). Law-Arts.

Vaughan, Floyd L. The United States Patent System. LC 72-6846. 355p. 1972. Repr. of 1956 ed. lib. bdg. 22.50x (ISBN 0-8371-6499-0, VAPS). Greenwood.

PATENT PRACTICE

Calvert, Robert, ed. The Encyclopedia of Patent Practice & Invention Management. LC 74-1028. 880p. 1974. Repr. of 1964 ed. 49.50 (ISBN 0-88275-181-6). Krieger.

Directory of Patent Attorneys & Agents. LC 80-23400. 328p. 1980. pap. 11.00 (ISBN 0-08-026343-7). Pergamon.

Flanagan, John R. How to Prepare Patent Applications: A Self-Study Course Book Using Actual Inventions. LC 83-61896. 260p. 1983. pap. 29.95 (ISBN 0-913995-00-2). Patent Ed.

--How to Prosecute Patent Applications: A Self-Study Course Using Actual Inventions. LC 84-60154. 250p. 1985. pap. 29.95 (ISBN 0-913995-01-0). Patent Ed.

Muncheryan, Hrand M. Patent It Yourself. (Illus.). 180p. (Orig.). 1982. 14.95 (ISBN 0-8306-2429-5, 1429); pap. 8.95 (ISBN 0-8306-1429-X). TAB Bks.

Patent Law Annual, Southwestern Legal Foundation: Proceedings, 1st-21st, 1963-1983. bound set 840.00x (ISBN 0-317-02327-6); per vol. bd. 42.50; microfilm avail. Rothman.

Sviridov, Wipo. International Symposium on the Role of Patent Information on Transfer to Technology: Varna, Bulgaria May 27th to 30th, 1980, Vol. 3. (Illus.). 200p. 1981. pap. 13.25 (ISBN 0-08-027555-9). Pergamon.

PATENTS

see also Inventions; Patent Laws and Legislation

Calvert, Robert, ed. The Encyclopedia of Patent Practice & Invention Management. LC 74-1028. 880p. 1974. Repr. of 1964 ed. 49.50 (ISBN 0-88275-181-6). Krieger.

Dible, Donald. What Everyone Should Know about Patents, Trademarks, & Copyright. LC 78-6780. 1981. text ed. 14.95 (ISBN 0-8359-8641-1); pap. 12.95 (ISBN 0-8359-8640-3). Reston.

Dicaro, Deborah. Patents. Spigai, Frances, ed. LC 82-72565. (Database Search Aids Ser.: Vol. 6). 174p. (Orig.). 1983. pap. 25.00 (ISBN 0-939920-08-5). Database Serv.

DOE Technical Information Center. Patents (DOE) Available for Licensing: A Bibliography Covering January 1974 Through December 1980. 284p. 1982. pap. 17.00 (ISBN 0-87079-445-0, DOE/TIC-3398); microfiche 4.50 (ISBN 0-87079-456-6, DOE/TIC-3398). DOE.

--Patents (DOE) Available for Licensing: A Bibliography for the Period 1966-1974. 60p. 1983. pap. 9.25 (ISBN 0-87079-512-0, DOE/TIC-3398 SUPPL. 1); microfiche 4.50 (ISBN 0-87079-513-9, DOE/TIC-3398 SUPPL. 1). DOE.

Fenner, T. W. & Everett, J. L. Inventor's Handbook. 1968. 17.00 (ISBN 0-8206-0070-9). Chem Pub.

Fiber Optics Patent Directory, 1881-1979. LC 79-93150. 161p. 1980. 74.00x (ISBN 0-935714-01-4). Patent Data.

Gausewitz, Richard. Patent Pending: Today's Inventors & Their Inventions. (Illus.). 240p. 1984. Repr. of 1983 ed. 14.95 (ISBN 0-916943-00-3). Alson Pub.

Gausewitz, Richard L. Patent Pending: Today's Inventors & Their Inventions. LC 82-9341. (Illus.). 240p. 1983. 14.95 (ISBN 0-8159-6522-2). Devin.

Goldstein, Paul. Copyright, Patent, Trademark & Related State Doctrines: Cases & Materials on the Law of Intellectual Property. 2nd ed. LC 81-3201. (University Casebook Ser.). 955p. 1981. text ed. 25.00 (ISBN 0-88277-029-2). Foundation Pr.

--Copyright, Patent, Trademark & Related State Doctrines: Cases & Materials on the Law of Intellectual Property. 2nd ed. (University Casebook Ser.). 183p. 1982. pap. text ed. write for info. tchrs. manual (ISBN 0-88277-105-1). Foundation Pr.

Great Britain, Patent Office. Patents for Inventions, 2 vols. Bunnell, Peter C. & Sobieszek, Robert A., eds. LC 76-23063. (Sources of Modern Photography Ser.). (Illus.). 1979. Repr. of 1903 ed. Set. lib. bdg. 103.00x (ISBN 0-405-09626-7); lib. bdg. 45.00x ea. Vol. 1 (ISBN 0-405-09627-5). Vol. 2 (ISBN 0-405-09628-3). Ayer Co Pubs.

Greer, Thomas J., Jr. Writing & Understanding U. S. Patent Claims. 125p. 1979. pap. 17.50 (ISBN 0-87215-238-3). Michie Co.

Griliches, Zvi. R & D, Patents, & Productivity. LC 83-18121. (National Bureau of Economic Research Conference Ser.). 528p. 1984. lib. bdg. 50.00x (ISBN 0-226-30883-9). U of Chicago Pr.

Grubb, Philip W. Patents for Chemists. (Illus.). 1982. 45.00x (ISBN 0-19-855153-3). Oxford U Pr.

Information for Industry (IFI) Staff, compiled by. Patent Intelligence & Technology Report: 1977. 1978. 295.00 (ISBN 0-306-68407-1, IFI Plenum). Plenum Pub.

Inlow, Edgar B. The Patent Grant. LC 78-64209. (Johns Hopkins University. Studies in the Social Sciences. Sixty-Seventh Ser. 1949: 2). Repr. of 1950 ed. 18.00 (ISBN 0-404-61314-4). AMS Pr.

The International Index of Patents: Chemical U. S.: 1790-1960, 6 vols. 1964. Set. 500.00x (ISBN 0-87471-015-4). Rowman.

The International Index of Patents: Electrical: U. S. 1790-1960, 5 vols. 1964. Set. 450.00x (ISBN 0-87471-058-8). Rowman.

Klaften, B. & Allison, F. C. Woerterbuch der Patentfachsprache. 4th ed. (Eng. & Ger., Dictionary of Technical Terms of Patents). 1971. 54.00 (ISBN 3-87910-105-1, M-6974). French & Eur.

Konold, et al. What Every Engineer Should Know about Patents. (What Every Engineer Should Know Ser.: Vol. 1). 1979. 24.30 (ISBN 0-8247-6805-1). Dekker.

Maynard, John T. Understanding Chemical Patents: A Guide for the Inventor. LC 77-28097. 1978. 19.95 (ISBN 0-8412-0347-4). Am Chemical.

Meinhardt, Peter. Inventions, Patents & Trade Marks in Great Britain. 1971 ed. 397p. 25.00 (ISBN 0-686-37380-4). Beekman Pubs.

Mount, Ellis, ed. Role of Patents in Sci-Tech Libraries. LC 82-2885. (Science & Technology Libraries Ser.: Vol. 2, No. 2). 97p. 1982. 25.00 (ISBN 0-86656-114-5, B114). Haworth Pr.

Muncheryan, Hrand M. Patent It Yourself. (Illus.). 180p. (Orig.). 1982. 14.95 (ISBN 0-8306-2429-5, 1429); pap. 8.95 (ISBN 0-8306-1429-X). TAB Bks.

Newby, F. How to Find Out About Patents. 1967. pap. 11.75 (ISBN 0-08-012332-5). Pergamon.

Ratzlaff, John T. Dr. Nikola Tesla--Complete Patents. 2nd ed. LC 79-67722. (Illus.). 500p. lib. bdg. 32.00 (ISBN 0-9603536-8-2). Tesla Bk Co.

Schwenck, James E. & McNair, Eric P. How to Become a Successful Inventor: Design a Gadget in Your Spare Time & Strike It Rich! 1974. 7.95 (ISBN 0-8038-3031-9). Hastings.

Sittig, Marshall. Metal & Inorganic Waste Reclaiming Encyclopedia. LC 80-21669. (Pollution Tech. Rev. 70; Chem. Tech. Rev. 175). (Illus.). 591p. (Orig.). 1981. 54.00 (ISBN 0-8155-0823-9). Noyes.

Stockbridge, V. D. Digest of U. S. Patents Relating to Breech-Loading & Magazine Small Arms, 1836-1873. (Illus.). 1963. 12.50 (ISBN 0-910598-02-9). Flayderman.

Szendy, Gyorgy L. Woerterbuch des Pantentwesens in 5 Sprachen. (Ger., Eng., Fr., Span. & Rus., Dictionary of Patents in Five Languages). 1974. 76.00 (ISBN 3-18-400269-1, M-6935). French & Eur.

V. Hoffmeister, Johannes. Woerterbuch der Philosophischen Begriffe. 2nd ed. (Ger.). 38.00 (ISBN 3-7873-0164-X, M-6975). French & Eur.

V. Uexkuell, Detlev. Woerterbuch der Patentpraxis. (Ger. & Eng., Dictionary of Patent Practice). 1976. 57.00 (ISBN 3-452-18239-8, M-6973). French & Eur.

Whitehurst, Bert W. Franchise Your Inventions. (Illus.). 70p. 1982. lib. bdg. 15.00x (ISBN 0-686-78701-3); pap. text ed. 10.00x (ISBN 0-686-78702-1). Galleon-Whitehurst.

World Symposium on the Importance of the Patent System to Developing Countries. 1978. pap. 13.75 (ISBN 0-685-65239-4, WIPO52, WIPO). Unipub.

PATENTS–UNITED STATES

Critser, James R., Jr. Membrane Separation Processes. (Ser. 5-78). 1979. 130.00 (ISBN 0-914428-60-8). Lexington Data.

Dick, Trevor J. An Economic Theory of Technological Change: The Case of Patents & United States Railroads, 1871-1950. LC 77-14769. (Dissertations in American History Ser.). 1978. 17.00 (ISBN 0-405-11031-6). Ayer Co Pubs.

Duffy, J. I., ed. Snack Food Technology: Recent Developments. LC 81-16757. (Food Technical Review: No. 55). (Illus.). 255p. 1982. 36.00 (ISBN 0-8155-0873-5). Noyes.

Leggett, M. D., ed. Subject-Matter Index of Patents for Inventions Issued by the United States Patent Office from 1790 to 1873, Inclusive, 3 vols. LC 75-24110. (America in Two Centuries Ser). 1976. Repr. of 1874 ed. Set. 158.00x (ISBN 0-405-07737-8); Vol. 1. 53.00x (ISBN 0-405-07738-6); Vol. 2. 53.00x (ISBN 0-405-07739-4); Vol. 3. 53.00x (ISBN 0-405-07740-8). Ayer Co Pubs.

Two Thousand Five Hundred Fiber Optics Patent Abstracts: 1881-1979. LC 79-93149. (Illus.). 382p. 1980. 167.50x (ISBN 0-935714-00-6). Patent Data.

Vaughan, Floyd L. The United States Patent System. LC 72-6846. 355p. 1972. Repr. of 1956 ed. lib. bdg. 22.50x (ISBN 0-8371-6499-0, VAPS). Greenwood.

PATHOGENIC BACTERIA

see Bacteria, Pathogenic

PATHOGENIC FUNGI

see Fungi, Pathogenic

PATHOGENIC MICRO-ORGANISMS

see Micro-Organisms, Pathogenic

PATHOGENIC PROTOZOA

see Protozoa, Pathogenic

PATHOLOGICAL BOTANY

see Plant Diseases

PATHOLOGICAL CHEMISTRY

see Chemistry, Medical and Pharmaceutical; Physiological Chemistry

PATHOLOGY, VEGETABLE

see Plant Diseases

PATTERN-MAKING

see also Founding; Mechanical Drawing; Molding (Founding); Sheet-Metal Work–Pattern-Making

Acebedo, Medara. How to Make Your Own Basic Patterns. (Illus.). 64p. 1982. 8.95 (ISBN 0-89962-245-3). Todd & Honeywell.

Ammen, C. W. Constructing & Using Wood Patterns. (Illus.). 266p. 1983. 17.95 (ISBN 0-8306-0110-4, 1510); pap. 12.50 (ISBN 0-8306-1510-5). TAB Bks.

Chinoy, N. J., ed. The Role of Ascorbic Acid in Growth, Differentiation & Metabolism of Plants. (Advances in Agricultural Biotechnology Ser.). 1984. lib. bdg. 46.50 (ISBN 90-247-2908-4, Pub. by Martinus Nijhoff Netherlands). Kluwer-Academic.

Davison, Marguerite P. A Handweavers Pattern Book. rev ed. (Illus.). 1951. 18.00 (ISBN 0-9603172-0-1). M P Davison.

Day, Lewis F. Pattern Design. LC 78-21373. (Illus.). 1979. 14.95 (ISBN 0-8008-6268-6, Pentalic); pap. 9.95 (ISBN 0-8008-6270-8, Pentalic). Taplinger.

Frankland, Thomas W. Pipe Template Layout. (Illus., Orig.). 1967. pap. 6.95 (ISBN 0-02-802400-1). Glencoe.

Handford, Jack. Professional Pattern Grading. LC 79-91230. (Illus.). 1980. 16.95 (ISBN 0-916434-34-6). Plycon Pr.

--Professional Pattern Making for Designer's of Women's Wear & Men's Casual Wear. LC 74-78635. (Illus.). 1984. spiral bdg. 18.95x (ISBN 0-916434-20-6). Plycon Pr.

Hollen, Norma R. Pattern Making by the Flat Pattern Method. 5th ed. LC 80-70048. 1981. spiral bdg. 15.95x (ISBN 0-8087-3173-4). Burgess.

Hornung, Clarence P. Allover Patterns for Designers & Craftsmen. 13.25 (ISBN 0-8446-5493-0). Peter Smith.

Jones, Walter B. Job Analysis & Curriculum Construction in the Metal Trades Industry: A Contribution to the Study of Curriculum Construction in Vocational Education Based on Job Analysis of Pattern Makers Trade. LC 70-176920. (Columbia University. Teachers College. Contributions to Education: No. 227). Repr. of 1926 ed. 22.50 (ISBN 0-404-55227-7). AMS Pr.

Melliar, Margaret. Pattern Cutting. 1977. 14.95 (ISBN 0-7134-2897-X, Pub. by Batsford England). David & Charles.

Olson, Nancy. Patterngrams: How to Copy Designs at Home. 2nd ed. LC 72-78471. (Illus.). 1979. pap. 10.00 (ISBN 0-87005-312-4). Fairchild.

Schlotzhauer, Joyce M. Curves Unlimited: Expanding the Curved Two-Patch System to Soften Shapes & Create New Pattern. (Orig.). 1984. pap. 24.95 (ISBN 0-914440-78-0). EPM Pubns.

Shoben, Martin & Ward, Janet. Pattern Cutting & Making Up: Vol. 3, The Professional Approach. (Illus.). 192p. 1981. 32.00 (ISBN 0-7134-3561-5, Pub. by Batsford England); pap. 17.95 (ISBN 0-7134-3562-3). David & Charles.

Ward, Shoben & Ward, Janet. Pattern Cutting & Making Up: Vol. 1, Basic Techniques & Sample Development. 1980. 32.00 (ISBN 0-7134-3338-8, Pub. by Batsford England); pap. 17.95 (ISBN 0-7134-3339-6). David & Charles.

Wolfe, Mary Gorgen. Clear-Cut Pattern Making (by the Flat Pattern Method) LC 81-16511. 221p. 1982. 25.95x (ISBN 0-471-09937-6); avail. tapes (ISBN 0-471-08655-X). Wiley.

PATTERN PERCEPTION

Ahuja, Narendra & Schachter, Bruce J. Pattern Models. LC 82-11070. 309p. 1983. 45.95 (ISBN 0-471-86194-4, Pub. by Wiley-Interscience). Wiley.

Albrecht, D. G., ed. Recognition of Pattern & Form, Austin, Texas 1979: Proceedings. (Lecture Notes in Biomathematics: Vol. 44). 225p. 1982. pap. 17.00 (ISBN 0-387-11206-5). Springer-Verlag.

Andrews, Harry C. Introduction to Mathematical Techniques in Pattern Recognition. LC 82-6543. 262p. 1983. Repr. of 1972 ed. 27.50 (ISBN 0-89874-506-3). Krieger.

Baird, Henry S. Model-Based Image Matching Using Location. (Association for Computing Machinery Distinguished Dissertation Award Ser.: 1984). (Illus.). 115p. 1985. text ed. 25.00 (ISBN 0-262-02220-6). MIT Pr.

Batchelor, Bruce G., ed. Pattern Recognition. LC 77-12488. (Illus.). 501p. 1977. 55.00 (ISBN 0-306-31020-1, Plenum Pr). Plenum Pub.

Chen, C. H., ed. Pattern Recognition & Signal Processing, No. 29. (NATO Advanced Study Institute Ser.). 666p. 1978. 46.00x (ISBN 90-286-0978-4). Sijthoff & Noordhoff.

Chien, Y. T. Interactive Pattern Recognition. (Electrical Engineering & Electronics Ser.: Vol. 3). 1978. 55.00 (ISBN 0-8247-6631-8). Dekker.

Dacey, Michael F. Status of Pattern Analysis: Identification of Problems in the Statistical Analysis of Spatial Arrangement. (Discussion Paper Ser.: No. 3.). 1963. pap. 5.75 (ISBN 0-686-32171-5). Regional Sci Res Inst.

Duda, Richard O. & Hart, Peter E. Pattern Classification & Scene Analysis. LC 72-7008. 482p. 1973. 58.95x (ISBN 0-471-22361-1, Pub. by Wiley-Interscience). Wiley.

Fu, K. S. Applications of Pattern Recognition. 288p. 1982. 96.50 (ISBN 0-8493-5729-2). CRC Pr.

Fu, K. S., ed. Digital Pattern Recognition. 2nd ed. (Communication & Cybernetics: Vol. 10). (Illus.). 234p. 1980. pap. 36.00 (ISBN 0-387-10207-8). Springer-Verlag.

Fu, King Sun. Syntactic Pattern Recognition & Applications. (Advances in Computing Science & Technology Ser.). (Illus.). 640p. 1982. text ed. 52.00 (ISBN 0-13-880120-7). P-H.

Fu, King Sun, ed. Synactic Pattern Recognition, Applications. (Communication & Cybernetics: Vol. 14). (Illus.). 1977. 56.00 (ISBN 0-387-07841-X). Springer-Verlag.

Grenander, U. Pattern Synthesis: Lectures in Pattern Recognition, Vol. 1. LC 76-209. (Applied Mathematical Sciences: Vol. 18). 1976. pap. 24.00 (ISBN 0-387-90174-4). Springer-Verlag.

Gronander, U. Regular Structures: Lectures in Pattern Theory III. (Applied Mathematical Sciences Ser: Vol. 33). 569p. 1981. pap. 28.50 (ISBN 0-387-90560-X). Springer-Verlag.

Haken, H., ed. Pattern Formation by Dynamic Systems & Pattern Recognition. (Springer Series in Synergetics). (Illus.). 305p. 1979. 42.00 (ISBN 0-387-09770-8). Springer-Verlag.

Hand, D. J. Kernel Discriminant Analysis. (Pattern Recognition & Image Processing Research Studies). 250p. 1982. 42.95 (ISBN 0-471-10211-3, Pub. by Res Stud Pr). Wiley.

Kanal, L. N. & Rosenfeld, A., eds. Progress in Pattern Recognition, Vol. 1. 392p. 1982. 53.25 (ISBN 0-444-86325-7, North-Holland). Elsevier.

Kandel, A. Fuzzy Techniques in Pattern Recognition. 356p. 1982. 40.50 (ISBN 0-471-09136-7). Wiley.

Kolers, P. A., et al, eds. Processing of Visible Language, Vol. 1. LC 79-13530. 553p. 1979. 59.50 (ISBN 0-306-40186-X, Plenum Pr). Plenum Pub.

Kovalevsky, V. A. Image Pattern Recognition. (Illus.). 241p. 1980. 39.00 (ISBN 0-387-90440-9). Springer-Verlag.

Krishnaiah, P. R. & Kanal, L. Classification, Pattern Recognition & Reduction of Dimension. (Handbook of Statistics: Vol. 2). 904p. 1983. 115.00 (ISBN 0-444-86217-X, North-Holland). Elsevier.

Latombe, Jean-Claude, ed. Artificial Intelligence & Pattern Recognition in Computer-Aided Design: Proceedings of the IFIP Working Conference, Grenoble, France, March 17-19, 1978. 510p. 1979. 76.75 (ISBN 0-444-85229-8, North Holland). Elsevier.

Nieman, H. Pattern Analysis. (Springer Series in Information Sciences: Vol. 4). (Illus.). 305p. 1981. 42.00 (ISBN 0-387-10792-4). Springer-Verlag.

Oja, E. Subspace Methods of Pattern Recognition. 186p. 1983. 49.95x (ISBN 0-471-90311-6, 1-516, Pub. by Wiley-Interscience). Wiley.

Pal, S. K. & Dutta-Majumder, D. Fuzzy Mathematical Approach in Pattern Recognition Problems. 350p. 1985. 29.95x (ISBN 0-470-27463-8). Halsted Pr.

Pavlidis, T. Structural Pattern Recognition. LC 77-21105. (Springer Ser. in Electrophysics: Vol. 1). (Illus.). 1977. 30.00 (ISBN 0-387-08463-0). Springer-Verlag.

Sayre, Kenneth M. Recognition: Study in the Philosophy of Artificial Intelligence. 1965. 16.95 (ISBN 0-268-00228-2). U of Notre Dame Pr.

Suen, Ching Y. & DeMori, Renato, eds. Computer Analysis & Perception: Auditory Signals, Vol. II. 176p. 1982. 66.00 (ISBN 0-8493-6306-3). CRC Pr.

--Computer Analysis & Perception: Visual Signals, Vol. I. 176p. 1982. 60.00 (ISBN 0-8493-6305-5). CRC Pr.

Varmuza, K. Pattern Recognition in Chemistry. (Lecture Notes in Chemistry Ser.: Vol. 21). (Illus.). 217p. 1980. pap. 25.00 (ISBN 0-387-10273-6). Springer-Verlag.

Watanabe, Satosi. Pattern Recognition: Human & Mechanical. LC 84-7354. 352p. 1985. text ed. 30.00x (ISBN 0-471-80815-6, Pub by Wiley-Interscience). Wiley.

PAVEMENTS

see also Roads; Streets

AASHTO Interim Guide for Design of Pavement Structures, Chap. III. rev. ed. 128p. 1972. pap. 5.00 (ISBN 0-686-32351-3, GDPS-2). AASHTO.

Design of Concrete Airport Pavement. 61p. 1973. pap. 4.00 (ISBN 0-89312-056-1, EB050P). Portland Cement.

Finney, Edwin A. Better Concrete Pavement Serviceability. (Monograph). 1973. 23.85 (ISBN 0-685-85140-0, M-7). ACI.

Gilson, George. Concrete Flatwork Manual. 160p. (Orig.). 1982. pap. 7.75 (ISBN 0-910460-93-0). Craftsman.

Guide to Successful Street Paving. 12p. 1976. pap. 1.40 (ISBN 0-89312-159-2, PA048P). Portland Cement.

Guidelines for Skid Resistant Pavement Design. 1976. 2.00 (ISBN 0-686-29463-7). AASHTO.

Haas, Ralph & Hudson, W. Ronald. Pavement Management Systems. LC 81-17229. 478p. 1982. Repr. of 1978 ed. text ed. 31.50 (ISBN 0-89874-407-5). Krieger.

Maintenance of Joints & Cracks in Concrete Pavement. 1976. pap. 1.15 (ISBN 0-89312-156-8, IS188P). Portland Cement.

Recycling of Biruminous Pavements, STP 662. 153p. 1978. pap. 16.00x (ISBN 0-8031-0776-5, 04-662000-08). ASTM.

Surface Texture Versus Skidding - STP 583. 154p. 1975. 12.00 (ISBN 0-8031-0786-2, 04-583000-37). ASTM.

Thelen, Edmund & Howe, L. Fielding, Jr. Porous Pavement. LC 78-4314. (Illus., Orig.). 1977. pap. 8.95 (ISBN 0-89168-010-1). L Erlbaum Assocs.

Walkway Surfaces, STP 649: Measurement of Slip Resistance. 117p. 1978. pap. 8.00 (ISBN 0-8031-0596-7, 04-649000-47). ASTM.

Yoder, E. J. & Witczak, M. W. Principles of Pavement Design. 2nd ed. LC 75-12555. 711p. 1975. 54.95x (ISBN 0-471-97780-2, Pub. by Wiley-Interscience). Wiley.

PAVEMENTS, ASPHALT

Wallace, Hugh A. & Martin, J. R. Asphalt Pavement Engineering. 1967. 46.50 (ISBN 0-07-067923-1). McGraw.

PAVING

see Pavements

PC-1211 (COMPUTER)

Librach, Hank. Pocket Computer Primer. LC 82-80270. 96p. (Orig.). 1982. pap. 9.95 (ISBN 0-942412-00-1); pre-recorded cassette 8.95 (ISBN 0-686-87024-7). Micro Text Pubns.

PC-DOS (COMPUTER OPERATING SYSTEM)

Ashley, Ruth & Fernandez, Judi N. PC-DOS: A Self-Teaching Guide. 2nd ed. 1985. pap. 16.95 (ISBN 0-471-82471-2). Wiley.

Busch, David D. PC-DOS Customized: Create Your Own DOS Commands for the IBM-PC, XT & AT. 176p. 1985. pap. 14.95 (ISBN 0-89303-753-2). Brady Comm.

De Voney, Chris. PC-DOS User's Guide. 354p. 1984. pap. 16.95 (ISBN 0-88022-040-6, 30). Que Corp.

Duncan, Ray. IBM PC-DOS Programmer's Reference Guide. Date not set. pap. price not set postponed (ISBN 0-89303-523-8). Brady Comm.

Farvour, James L. TRS-DOS 2.3 Decoded & Other Mysteries. (TRS-80 Information Ser.: Vol. 6). (Illus.). 298p. (Orig.). 1982. pap. 29.95 (ISBN 0-936200-07-3). Blue Cat.

Human Connection. Making MS-DOS & PC-DOS Work for You. 19.95 (ISBN 0-8306-0848-6); pap. 13.95 (ISBN 0-8306-1848-1). TAB Bks.

Mackie, Peter. The World of PC-DOS. 125p. 1984. pap. 9.95 (ISBN 0-88056-145-9); IBM-PC, IBM-PC XT, Compaq. incl. disk 29.95. Dilithium Pr.

Microtrend Inc. & Jackson, Charles H. MS-DOS & PC-DOS on the IBM PC. (Microtrend Ser.). 1984. 14.95 (ISBN 0-13-604281-3). P-H.

Murtha & Petrie. PC-DOS Companion. LC 83-50996. 168p. 1983. pap. 15.95 (ISBN 0-672-22039-3, 22039). Sams.

Norton, Peter. MS-DOS & PC-DOS User's Guide. LC 83-15498. (Illus.). 288p. 1983. pap. 15.95 (ISBN 0-89303-645-5). Brady Comm.

--PC-DOS: Introduction High-Performance Computing. (Illus.). 336p. 1985. pap. 17.95 (ISBN 0-89303-752-4). Brady Comm.

Sollarzano, Henry. Quick & Easy PC-DOS & MS-DOS. 1984. pap. 3.50 (ISBN 0-88284-327-3). Alfred Pub.

Stultz, Russell. The Illustrated MS-PC-DOS Book. (Illus.). 224p. 1984. pap. 16.95 (ISBN 0-13-451063-1). P-H.

Understanding PC-DOS. 1984. pap. 14.95 (ISBN 0-911699-25-2). Calabrese Pubns.

PCJR (COMPUTER)

see Ibm Pcjr (Computer)

PC XT (COMPUTER)

see Ibm Personal Computer Xt

PDP-11 (COMPUTER)

Cichanowski, Gerald W. Macro Eleven Programming & PDP Eleven Organization. LC 82-11498. 248p. 1982. pap. text ed. 12.95x (ISBN 0-910554-38-2). Engineering.

Desautels, Edouard J. Assembly Language Programming for PDP-11 & LSI-11 Computers: An Introduction to Computer Organization. 574p. 1982. pap. 23.95 (ISBN 0-697-08164-8); solutions manual avail. (ISBN 0-697-08165-6). Wm C Brown.

Diehr, George, et al. BASIC Programming for the VAX & PDP-11. LC 83-21689. 473p. 1984. pap. text ed. 23.50 (ISBN 0-471-86817-5); write for info. tchr's. ed. (ISBN 0-471-80224-7). Wiley.

Early, G. Assembly Language: Macro II & PDP II. (Computer Science Ser.). 560p. 1983. 27.95 (ISBN 0-07-018782-7). McGraw.

Eckhouse, Richard H., Jr. & Morrison, L. Robert. Minicomputer Systems: Organization, Programming & Applications (PDP-11) 2nd ed. (Illus.). 1979. text ed. 37.50 (ISBN 0-13-583914-9). P-H.

Gill, Arthur. Machine & Assembly Language Programming of the PDP-11. 2nd ed. (Illus.). 224p. 1983. text ed. 28.95 (ISBN 0-13-541888-7). P-H.

Kapps, Charles S. & Stafford, Robert L. Assembly Language for the PDP-11. LC 80-39985. 353p. 1981. text ed. write for info. (ISBN 0-87150-304-2, 37L 8000, Prindle). PWS Pubs.

MacEwen, Glenn H. Introduction to Computer Systems: Using the PDP-Eleven & Pascal. (Computer Science Ser.). (Illus.). 400p. 1980. text ed. 40.95 (ISBN 0-07-044350-5). McGraw.

Micro-PDP-11 Handbook. 401p. 1983. pap. 10.00 (ISBN 0-932376-38-X, EB-24944-DP). Digital Pr.

Nie, N. H. & Hull, C. H. SPSS-Eleven: The SPSS Batch System for the DEC PDP-11. 2nd rev. ed. 1982. 16.95x (ISBN 0-07-046546-0). McGraw.

Parker, Alan J. BASIC for Business for the VAX & PDP-11. 2nd ed. 1983. text ed. 22.95 (ISBN 0-8359-0358-3); pap. text ed. 18.95 (ISBN 0-8359-0357-5); instr's Manual avail. (ISBN 0-8359-0360-5). Reston.

PDP-11 Architecture Handbook. 272p. 1983. pap. 15.00 (ISBN 0-932376-37-1, EB-23657-DP). Digital Pr.

PDP-11 Microcomputer Interfaces Handbook. 627p. 1983. 17.00 (ISBN 0-932376-59-2, EB-23144-DP). Digital Pr.

PDP-11 Software Handbook. rev. ed. 405p. 1984. pap. 15.00 (ISBN 0-932376-64-9, EB-25398-DP). Digital Pr.

PDP 11-04-24-34A-44-70 Processor Handbook. 483p. 1981. pap. 15.00 (ISBN 0-932376-55-X, EB-19402-DP). Digital Pr.

Sebesta, Robert W. PDP-11 Structured Assembly Language Programming. 352p. 1985. text ed. 29.95 (ISBN 0-8053-7005-6); instr's. guide 5.95 (ISBN 0-8053-7006-4). Benjamin Cummings.

Shapiro, Harvey. Assembly Language Programming for the PDP-11. 349p. 1984. text ed. 27.95 (ISBN 0-87484-704-4). Mayfield Pub.

Singer, Michael. PDP-11 Assembler Language Programming & Machine Organization. 178p. 1980. 22.95 (ISBN 0-471-04905-0). Wiley.

Stone, Harold & Siewiorek, Daniel. Introduction to Computer Organization & Data Structures: PDP-11 Edition. 11th ed. (Illus.). 352p. 1975. text ed. 39.95 (ISBN 0-07-061720-1). McGraw.

PEAFOWL

Bergmann, Josef. The Peafowl of the World. (Illus.). 192p. 1980. 21.75 (ISBN 0-904558-51-7). Saiga.

PEANUT BUTTER

The Peanut Butter Market. (Food & Beverage Studies). 1980. 295.00 (ISBN 0-686-31519-7). Busn Trend.

PEANUTS

Groundnuts. Rev. ed. (Better Farming Ser.: No. 17). 40p. 1977. pap. 7.50 (ISBN 92-5-100619-9, F75, FAO). Unipub.

Hogendorn, J. S. Nigerian Groundnut Exports: Origins & Early Developments. (Illus.). 1978. 34.95x (ISBN 0-19-575443-3). Oxford U Pr.

Johnson, F. Roy. The Peanut Story. rev ed. (Illus.). 1977. Repr. of 1964 ed. 10.00 (ISBN 0-930230-33-7). Johnson NC.

Porter, D. M., et al, eds. Compendium of Peanut Diseases. LC 84-70853. (Illus.). 73p. 1984. pap. text ed. 17.00 (ISBN 0-89054-055-1). Am Phytopathol Soc.

Umen, D. P. Biology of Peanut Flowering. 1981. 30.00x (ISBN 0-686-76625-3, Pub. by Oxford & IBH India). State Mutual Bk.

Woodroof, J. G. Peanuts: Production, Processing, Products. 3rd ed. (Illus.). 1983. lib. bdg. 62.50 (ISBN 0-87055-417-4). AVI.

PEAT

Development of Pure Peat Mixture for Raising Plants with Blocks. (Agricultural Research Reports: No. 668). 1965. pap. 5.50 (ISBN 90-220-0128-8, PDC164, PUDOC). Unipub.

Fuchsman, Charles H. Peat: Industrial Chemistry & Technology. LC 79-52791. 1980. 39.50 (ISBN 0-12-264650-9). Acad Pr.

Hansen, Henry P. Paleoecology of Two Peat Deposits on the Oregon Coast. (Studies in Botany Ser: No. 3). 32p. 1941. pap. 3.95x (ISBN 0-87071-013-3). Oreg St U Pr.

Luettig, G. W., ed. Recent Technologies of the Uses of Peat: Reports of the International Symposium. (Illus.). 223p. 1983. pap. text ed. 35.20x (ISBN 3-510-65115-4). Lubrecht & Cramer.

Robinson, D. W. & Lamb, J. G., eds. Peat in Horticulture. 1976. 41.00 (ISBN 0-12-590160-7). Acad Pr.

PEBBLES

see Rocks

PECTIN

Characterization of Pectin Lyases on Pectins & Methyl Oligogalacturonates. (Agricultural Research Reports: 780). 1972. pap. 14.00 (ISBN 90-220-0408-2, PDC20, PUDOC). Unipub.

Pectinesterases from the Orange Fruit: Their Purification, General Characteristics & Juice Cloud Destablizing Properties. 1979. pap. 16.00 (ISBN 90-220-0709-X, PDC147, Pudoc). Unipub.

PEDIATRICS

Barness, Lewis. Advances in Pediatrics, Vol. 30. 1984. 55.95 (ISBN 0-8151-0503-7). Year Bk Med.

Campion, Margaret R. Hydrotheraphy in Paediatrics. 256p. 1985. 31.00 (ISBN 0-87189-106-9, Pub by W. Heinemann). Aspen Systems.

--Hydrotherapy in Paediatrics. 256p. 1985. 31.00 (ISBN 0-87189-106-9, Pub. by W. Heinemann). Aspen Systems.

DeLuca, H. F. & Anast, C. S., eds. Pediatric Diseases Related to Calcium. 450p. 1980. 56.00 (ISBN 0-444-00361-4, Biomedical Pr). Elsevier.

Finberg, Laurence, et al. Water & Electrolytes in Pediatrics: Physiology, Pathophysiology & Treatment. (Illus.). 272p. 1982. 39.00 (ISBN 0-7216-3625-X). Saunders.

Gans, Stephen L. Pediatric Endoscopy. 202p. 1983. 41.50 (ISBN 0-8089-1547-9, 791514). Grune.

Haller, Jack O. & Shkolnik, Arnold. Ultrasound in Pediatrics. (Clinics in Diagnostic Ultrasoun Ser.: Vol. 8). (Illus.). 306p. 1981. text ed. 26.00 (ISBN 0-443-08155-7). Churchill.

Hicks, Jocelyn M. & Boeckx, Roger L. Pediatric Clinical Chemistry. (Illus.). 752p. 1984. 80.00 (ISBN 0-7216-4661-1). Saunders.

Levine, Melvin D., et al. Developmental-Behavioral Pediatrics. (Illus.). 1296p. 1983. 79.00 (ISBN 0-7216-5744-3). Saunders.

Meites, Samuel, ed. Pediatric Clinical Chemistry. rev. ed. LC 80-66259. 513p. 1981. 35.00 (ISBN 0-915274-12-4); members 30.00. Am Assn Clinical Chem.

Rossi, E. & Oetliker, O., eds. Nephrologie im Kindesalter III. (Paediatrische Fortbildungskurse fuer die Praxis: Bd. 45). (Ger., Illus.). 1978. 22.75 (ISBN 3-8055-2825-6). S Karger.

Russo, Raymond M., et al. Advanced Textbook of Sexual Development & Disorders in Childhood & Adolescence. (Advanced Textbook Ser.). 1983. pap. text ed. 25.00 (ISBN 0-87488-485-3). Med Exam.

Smith, David W. Growth & Its Disorders: Basics & Standards, Approach & Classifications, Growth Deficiency Disorders, Growth Excess Disorders, Obesity. LC 76-20114. (Major Problem in Clinical Pediatrics: Vol. 15). pap. 42.30 (ISBN 0-317-26141-X, 2025005). Bks Demand UMI.

Strauss, Jose, ed. Neonatal Kidney & Fluid-Electrolytes. 1983. lib. bdg. 46.00 (ISBN 0-89838-575-X, Pub. by Martinus Nijhoff Netherlands). Kluwer Academic.

Sty, John R. Pediatric Nuclear Medicine. 224p. 1981. 49.95 (ISBN 0-8385-7801-2). ACC.

Treves, S. T. Pediatric Nuclear Medicine. (Illus.). 360p. 1985. 74.50 (ISBN 0-387-96001-5). Springer-Verlag.

PEDOLOGY (SOIL SCIENCE)

see Soil Science

PEIRCE, CHARLES SANTIAGO SANDERS, 1839-1914

Apel, Karl-Otto. Charles Sanders Peirce: From Pragmatism to Pragmaticism. Krois, John M., tr. from Ger. LC 81-3337. Orig. Title: Der Denkweg Von Charles Sanders Peirce. 288p. 1981. lib. bdg. 22.50x (ISBN 0-87023-177-4). U of Mass Pr.

Buchler, Justus. Charles Peirce's Empiricism. 1966. lib. bdg. 24.00x (ISBN 0-374-91064-2). Octagon.

Freeman, Eugene, ed. The Relevance of Charles Peirce. (Monist Library of Philosophy). 412p. 1983. cloth 29.95 (ISBN 0-914417-00-2). Hegeler Inst.

Ketner, Kenneth L. & Cook, James E., eds. Charles Sanders Peirce: Contributions to The Nation, Pt. 3: 1901-1908. (Graduate Studies: No. 19). 208p. 1979. 22.00 (ISBN 0-89672-070-5); pap. 16.00 (ISBN 0-89672-069-1). Tex Tech Pr.

Ketner, Kenneth L. & Cook, James E.compiled by. Charles Sanders Peirce: Contributions to the Nation Pt. 1: 1869-1893. (Graduate Studies: No. 10). 306p. 1975. 15.00 (ISBN 0-89672-020-9); pap. 10.00 (ISBN 0-89672-019-5). Tex Tech Pr.

Reilly, Francis E. Charles Peirce's Theory of Scientific Method. LC 79-105527. (Orestes Brownson Ser: No. 7). 1970. 25.00 (ISBN 0-8232-0880-X). Fordham.

PEIRCE, CHARLES SANTIAGO SANDERS, 1839-1914–BIBLIOGRAPHY

Robin, Richard S., ed. Annotated Catalogue of the Papers of Charles S. Peirce. LC 67-28217. 296p. 1968. 17.50x (ISBN 0-87023-029-8). U of Mass Pr.

PEKINGESE SPANIELS

see Dogs–Breeds–Pekingese Spaniels

PELECYPODA

see Lamellibranchiata

PELTIER COOLING

see Thermoelectric Cooling

PELTIER HEAT

see Thermoelectric Apparatus and Appliances

PENGUINS

Ainley, David G. & LeResche, Robert E. Breeding Biology of the Adelie Penguin. LC 82-17573. (Illus.). 198p. 1983. text ed. 29.50x (ISBN 0-520-04838-5). U of Cal Pr.

Jouventin, Pierre. Visual & Vocal Signals in Penguins, Their Evolution & Adaptive Characters. (Advances in Ethology: Vol. 24). (Illus.). 152p. (Orig.). 1981. pap. text ed. 24.00 (ISBN 3-489-61436-4). Parey Sci Pubs.

Muller-Schwarze, Dietland. The Behavior of Penguins: Adapted to Ice & Tropics. (Animal Behavior Ser.). (Illus.). 160p. 1984. 29.50x (ISBN 0-87395-866-7); pap. 10.95x (ISBN 0-87395-867-5). State U NY Pr.

Peterson, Roger T. Penguins. LC 79-10101. 1979. 25.00 (ISBN 0-395-27092-8). HM.

Simpson, George G. Pengins: Past & Present, Here & There. LC 75-27211. (Illus.). pap. 6.95 08/1982 162pp (ISBN 0-300-03095-9, Y-473). Yale U Pr.

Soper, Tony & Sparks, John. Penguins. LC 67-25577. 1967. 12.50 (ISBN 0-8008-6275-9). Taplinger.

Traut, Dennis. Penguin's Penguins. (Illus.). 48p. 1982. pap. 2.95 (ISBN 0-14-005987-3). Penguin.

PENTAX CAMERA

see Cameras–Types–Pentax

PENTOSES

Wood, Terry & Landau, Bernard R. The Pentose Phosphate Pathway. Date not set. price not set (ISBN 0-12-762860-6). Acad Pr.

PEONIES

Nehrling, Arno & Nehrling, Irene. Peonies Outdoors & In. LC 75-17125. (Illus.). 320p. 1975. pap. 5.95 (ISBN 0-486-23229-8). Dover.

Stearn, W. T. & Davis, P. H. Peonies of Greece: A Taxonomic Historical Survey of the Genus Paeonia in Greece. (Illus.). 136p. 1984. 56.00x (ISBN 0-565-00975-3, Pub by Brit Mus Nat Hist England). Sabbot-Natural Hist Bks.

PEPPER (SPICE)

Bailey, Walter. A Short Discourse of the Three Kindes of Peppers in Common Use. LC 77-38145. (English Experience Ser.: No. 425). 48p. Repr. of 1588 ed. 7.00 (ISBN 90-221-0425-7). Walter J Johnson.

PEPSIN

Elodi, P., ed. Proteinase Action. (Symposia Biologica Hungary Ser.: Vol. 25). 500p. 1984. 55.00 (ISBN 0-9910002-7-7, Pub. by Akademiai Kaido Hungary). Heyden.

PEPTIDE HORMONES

ACTH & Related Peptides: Structure, Regulation, & Action, Vol. 297. (Annals of the New York Academy of Sciences). 664p. 1977. 60.00x (ISBN 0-89072-043-6). NY Acad Sci.

Back, Nathan, et al, eds. Pharmacology of Hormonal Polypeptides & Proteins. LC 68-19184. (Advances in Experimental Medicine & Biology Ser.: Vol. 2). 671p. 1968. 55.00x (ISBN 0-306-39002-7, Plenum Pr). Plenum Pub.

Bolis, Liana, et al, eds. Peptide Hormones, Biomembranes & Cell Growth. 304p. 1985. 49.50x (ISBN 0-306-41816-9, Plenum Pr). Plenum Pub.

Bryant-Greenwood, G. D., et al, eds. Relaxin. 402p. 1982. 81.00 (ISBN 0-444-00643-5, Biomedical Pr). Elsevier.

Chayen, J. The Cytochemical Bioassay of Polypeptide Hormones. (Monographs on Endocrinology: Vol. 17). (Illus.). 230p. 1980. 51.00 (ISBN 0-387-10040-7). Springer-Verlag.

Choh Hao Li, ed. Hormonal Proteins & Peptides: Prolactin, Vol. 8. LC 80-11061. 1980. 44.00 (ISBN 0-12-447208-7). Acad Pr.

Hakanson, Rolf & Thorell, Jan, eds. Biogenetics of Neurohormonal Peptides. 1985. 42.00 (ISBN 0-12-317450-3). Acad Pr.

Hesch, R. D., ed. Peptide Hormones As Mediators in Immunology & Oncology. (Serono Symposia Publications Ser.). Date not set. text ed. write for info. (ISBN 0-89004-609-3). Raven.

Li, Choh H., ed. Hormonal Proteins & Peptides, 7 vols. Incl. Vol. 1. 1973. 49.50 (ISBN 0-12-447201-X); Vol. 2. 1973. 59.50 (ISBN 0-12-447202-8); Vol. 3. 1975. 67.50 (ISBN 0-12-447203-6); Vol. 4. 1977. 49.50 (ISBN 0-12-447204-4); Vol. 5. Lipotropin & Related Peptides. 1978. 47.50 (ISBN 0-12-447205-2); Vol. 6. Thyroid Hormones. 1978. 71.50 (ISBN 0-12-447206-0); Vol. 7. Hypothalmic Hormones. 1979. 49.50 (ISBN 0-12-447207-9). LC 78-5444. Acad Pr.

Li, Choh Hao, ed. Hormonal Proteins & Peptides, Vol. 10: B-Endorphin. LC 81-10994. 1981. 55.00 (ISBN 0-12-447210-9). Acad Pr.

McKerns, Kenneth W. & Pantic, Vladmir, eds. Hormonally Active Brain Peptides: Stucture & Function. LC 82-9147. (Biochemical Endocrinology Ser.). 652p. 1982. 75.00x (ISBN 0-306-40865-1, Plenum Pr). Plenum Pub.

Miles International Symposium, 12th. Polypeptide Hormones: Proceedings. Beers, Roland F. & Bassett, Edward, eds. 544p. 1980. text ed. 86.50 (ISBN 0-89004-462-7). Raven.

Pierce, John G., ed. Proteins & Peptides Hormones. LC 82-6159. (Benchmark Papers in Biochemistry: Vol. 4). 459p. 1982. 62.00 (ISBN 0-87933-417-7). Van Nos Reinhold.

Porter, John C., ed. Hypothalamic Peptide Hormones & Pituitary Regulation. LC 77-22461. (Advances in Experimental Medicine & Biology Ser.: Vol. 87). 374p. 1977. 49.50x (ISBN 0-306-32687-6, Plenum Pr). Plenum Pub.

Rodriguez, E. M. & Van Wimersma Greidanus, T. B., eds. The Cerebrospinal Fluid (CSF) & Peptide Hormones. (Frontiers of Hormone Research: Vol. 9). (Illus.). viii, 220p. 1982. 56.25 (ISBN 3-8055-2823-X). S Karger.

PEPTIDES

Albertini, A. & Rigosa, C., eds. International Symposium on C-Peptide. (Illus.). 180p. 1979. text ed. 37.50x (ISBN 0-686-29670-2, Pub. by Piccin Italy). J K Burgess.

Analysis, Networks, Peptides. (Advances in Polymer Science Ser.: Vol. 65). (Illus.). 230p. 1984. 44.00 (ISBN 0-387-13656-8). Springer-Verlag.

Atassi, M. Z. & Benjamini, E., eds. Immunobiology of Proteins & Peptides II. (Advances in Experimental Medicine & Biology: Vol. 150). 238p. 1982. 35.00x (ISBN 0-306-41110-5, Plenum Pr). Plenum Pub.

Atassi, M. Z. & Stavitsky, A. B., eds. Immunobiology of Proteins & Peptides I. LC 78-5083. (Advances in Experimental Medicine & Biology Ser.: Vol. 98). 523p. 1978. 59.50x (ISBN 0-306-32698-1, Plenum Pr). Plenum Pub.

Bergmeyer, H. U., ed. Methods of Enzymatic Analysis: Enzymes 3-Peptides, Protinases & Their Inhibitors, Vol. 5. 3rd ed. 558p. 1984. 120.00x (ISBN 0-89573-235-1). VCH Pubs.

Birr, C. Aspects of the Merrifield Peptide Synthesis. (Reactivity & Structure Ser.: Vol. 8). (Illus.). 1978. 28.00 (ISBN 0-387-08872-5). Springer-Verlag.

Birr, C., ed. Methods of Peptide & Protein Sequence Analysis: Proceedings of the International Conference on Solid Phase, 3rd, Heidelberg, October 1-4, 1979. 532p. 1980. 92.00 (ISBN 0-444-80218-5, Biomedical Pr). Elsevier.

Bizollon, C. A., ed. Physiological Peptides & New Trends in Radioimmunology. 370p. 1981. 59.25 (ISBN 0-444-80358-0, Biomedical Pr). Elsevier.

Blaha, K & Malon, P., eds. Peptides, 1982: Proceedings of the 17th European Peptide Symposium, Prague, Czechoslovakia, August 29-September 3, 1982. (Illus.). 846p. 1982. 112.00 (ISBN 3-11-009574-2). De Gruyter.

Blout, E. R., et al. Peptides, Polypeptides & Proteins. LC 74-22202. 656p. 1974. 38.00 (ISBN 0-471-08387-9). Krieger.

Bodansky, Miklos. Peptide Synthesis. 2nd ed. LC 83-22190. 224p. 1985. Repr. of 1976 ed. lib. bdg. write for info. (ISBN 0-89874-709-0). Krieger.

Bodanszky, M. Principles of Peptide Synthesis. (Reactivity & Structure Ser.: Vol. 16). (Illus.). 240p. 1984. 49.00 (ISBN 0-387-12395-4). Springer-Verlag.

Bodanszky, M., et al. The Practice of Peptide Synthesis. (Reactivity & Structure, Concepts in Organic Chemistry Ser.: Vol. 21). 240p. 1984. 49.50 (ISBN 0-387-13471-9). Springer-Verlag.

Bodanszky, Miklos O., et al. Peptide Synthesis. 2nd ed. LC 76-16099. (Interscience Monographs on Organic Chemistry). 208p. 1976. 43.50x (ISBN 0-471-08451-4, Pub. by Wiley-Interscience). Wiley.

Burgen, Sir Arnold, et al. Neuroactive Peptides. (Proceedings of the Royal & Society, Series B.: Vol. 210). (Illus.). 192p. 1980. text ed. 35.00x (ISBN 0-85403-149-9, Pub. by Royal Soc London). Scholium Intl.

Choh Hao Li, ed. Hormonal Proteins & Peptides: Gonadotropic Hormones, Vol. XI. LC 82-22770. 1983. 47.50 (ISBN 0-12-447211-7). Acad Pr.

--Hormonal Proteins & Peptides: Techniques in Protein Chemistry, Vol. 9. LC 80-11061. (Hormonal Proteins & Peptides Ser.). 1980. 49.50 (ISBN 0-12-447209-5). Acad Pr.

Ciba Foundation. Peptide Transport in Bacteria & Mammalian Cut. LC 72-76006. (Ciba Foundation Symposium Ser.: No. 4). pap. 42.50 (ISBN 0-317-28325-1, 2022136). Bks Demand UMI.

Costa, E. & Trabucci, M., eds. Regulatory Peptides: From Molecular Biology to Function. (Advances in Biochemical Psychopharmacology Ser.: Vol. 33). 588p. 1982. text ed. 85.00 (ISBN 0-89004-797-9). Raven.

Costa, Erminio & Trabucchi, Marco, eds. Neural Peptides & Neuronal Communication. (Advances in Biochemical Psychopharmacology Ser.: Vol. 22). 670p. 1980. text ed. 88.00 (ISBN 0-89004-375-2). Raven.

Critser, James R., Jr. Proteins-Peptides: Preparations & Applications. (Ser. 15-84). 182p. 1985. 125.00 (ISBN 0-88178-024-3). Lexington Data.

Davies, J. S., ed. Amino Acids & Peptides. (Chemistry Sourcebooks Ser.). 800p. 69.95 (ISBN 0-412-26950-3, Pub. by Chapman & Hall). Methuen Inc.

Dence, Joseph B. Steroids & Peptides: Selected Chemical Aspects for Biology, Biochemistry & Medicine. LC 79-21236. 418p. 1980. 74.95 (ISBN 0-471-04700-7, Pub. by Wiley-Interscience). Wiley.

Desiderio, D. M. Analysis of Neuropeptides by Liquid Chromatography & Mass Spectrometry. (Techniques & Instrumentation in Analytical Chemistry Ser.: No. 6). 236p. 1984. 61.00 (ISBN 0-444-42418-0). Elsevier.

Devenyi, T. & Gergely, J. Amino Acid Peptides & Proteins. 1974. 56.00 (ISBN 0-444-41127-5). Elsevier.

Eberle, A. N., et al, eds. Perspectives in Peptide Chemistry. (Illus.). xii, 444p. 1980. 61.75 (ISBN 3-8055-1297-X). S Karger.

Elmore, D. T. Peptides & Proteins. LC 68-21392. (Cambridge Chemistry Texts Ser). (Illus.). 1968. 32.50 (ISBN 0-521-07107-0); pap. 9.95x (ISBN 0-521-09535-2). Cambridge U Pr.

Endroczi, E., et al, eds. Neuropeptides & Psychosomatic Processes. 1984. 79.00 (ISBN 0-9910000-6-4, Pub. by Akademiai Kaido Hungary). Heyden.

--Neuropeptides, Neurotransmitters & Regulation of Endocrine Processes: Proceedings of the International Conference on Intergrative Neurohumoral Mechanisms. 1984. 56.00 (ISBN 0-9910000-5-6, Pub. by Akademiai Kaido Hungary). Heyden.

--Neuropeptides, Neurotransmitters, & Regulation of Endocrine: Processes-Neuropeptides & Psychosomatic, 2 Vols. 1984. 113.00 (ISBN 0-9910000-7-2, Pub. by Akademiai Kaido Hungary). Heyden.

Erdoes, E. G., ed. Bradykinin, Kallidin, & Kallikrein-Supplement. (Handbook of Experimental Pharmacology: Vol. 25, Suppl.). (Illus.). 1979. 212.40 (ISBN 0-387-09356-7). Springer-Verlag.

European Peptide Symposium, 9th, France, 1968. Peptides: Proceedings. Bricas, E., ed. 1968. 24.50 (ISBN 0-444-10156-X, North-Holland). Elsevier.

Fraioli, F., et al, eds. Opioid Peptides in the Periphery: Proceedings of the International Symposium on Opioid Peptides in Periphery under the Patronage of the Italian National Council of Research Held in Rome, Italy, 23-25 May, 1984. (Developments in Neuroscience Ser.: Vol. 18). 298p. 1985. 58.00 (ISBN 0-444-80624-5). Elsevier.

Gainer, Harold, ed. Peptides in Neurobiology. LC 76-54766. (Current Topics in Neurobiology Ser.). (Illus.). 484p. 1977. 49.50x (ISBN 0-306-30978-5, Plenum Pr). Plenum Pub.

Goodman, Murray, ed. Peptides, Polypeptides, & Proteins: Interactions & Their Biological Implications, Vol. 22. 588p. 1983. text ed. 47.50x (ISBN 0-471-88679-3, Pub. by Wiley-Interscience). Wiley.

Gregory, R. A., ed. Regulatory Peptides of Gut & Brain. (British Medical Bulletin Ser.: Vol. 38, No. 3). 99p. 1983. pap. text ed. 19.50 (ISBN 0-443-02660-2). Churchill.

Gross, Erhard, ed. The Peptides: Analysis, Synthesis, Biology: Vol. 3 Protection of Functional Groups in Peptides Synthesis. 1981. 55.00 (ISBN 0-12-304203-8). Acad Pr.

Gross, Erhard & Meiehnhofer, Hohannes, eds. The Peptides: Analysis, Synthesis, Biology, Vol. 5. (Special Methods in Peptide Synthesis Ser.: Part B). 1983. 79.50 (ISBN 0-12-304205-4). Acad Pr.

Gross, Erhard & Meienhofer, Johannes, eds. The Peptides: Analysis, Synthesis, Biology: Vol. I, Pt. a, Major Methods of Peptide Bond Formation. LC 78-31958. 1979. 65.00 (ISBN 0-12-304201-1). Acad Pr.

--The Peptides: Analysis, Synthesis, Biology: Vol. 4, Modern Techniques of Peptide & Amino Acid Anaysis. 1981. 59.50 (ISBN 0-12-304204-6). Acad Pr.

Gross, Erhard & Meinhoper, Johannes, eds. The Peptides: Analysis, Synthesis, Biology, Vol. 2: Special Methods in Peptide Synthesis, Pt. A. LC 78-31958. 1980. 65.50 (ISBN 0-12-304202-X). Acad Pr.

Gross, Franz, et al, eds. Enzymatic Release of Vasoactive Peptides: Eighth Workshop Conference HOECHST. (Illus.). 432p. 1980. text ed. 59.00 (ISBN 0-89004-458-9). Raven.

Hearn. Peptide & Protein Reviews, Vol. 2. 336p. 1983. 52.50 (ISBN 0-8247-7135-4). Dekker.

Hearn, Milton W. & T. W. Hearn, Etal, eds. High Performance Liquid Chromatography of Proteins & Peptides: Proceedings of First International Symposium. 1983. 35.00 (ISBN 0-12-335780-2). Acad Pr.

Hearn, Milton W., ed. Peptide & Protein Reviews, Vol. 4. (Illus.). 256p. 1984. 52.50 (ISBN 0-8247-7292-X). Dekker.

Jakubke, Hans-Dieter & Jeschkeit, Hans. Aminoacids, Peptides & Proteins: An Introduction. 1st English ed. Cotterrell, G. P. & Jones, J. H., trs. LC 77-23945. 336p. 1978. 49.95x (ISBN 0-470-99279-4). Halsted Pr.

Kleinkauf, Horst & Van Dohren, Hans, eds. Peptide Antibiotics. (Illus.). 479p. 1982. 76.00x (ISBN 3-11-008484-8). De Gruyter.

Krieger, Dorothy T., et al. Brain Peptides. 1030p. 1983. 97.50 (ISBN 0-471-09433-1, Pub. by Wiley-Interscience). Wiley.

Lande, Saul, ed. Progress in Peptide Research, Vol. 2. LC 76-153298. 404p. 1972. 106.50x (ISBN 0-677-13610-2). Gordon.

Law, Harry D. The Organic Chemistry of Peptides. LC 75-126888. pap. 60.80 (ISBN 0-317-29324-9, 2024015). Bks Demand UMI.

Levy, A., et al, eds. Endogenous Peptides & Centrally Acting Drugs. (Progress in Biochemical Pharmacology: Vol. 16). (Illus.). xvi, 160p. 1980. 35.00 (ISBN 3-8055-0831-X). S Karger.

Li, Choh H., ed. Hormonal Proteins & Peptides, 7 vols. Incl. Vol. 1. 1973. 49.50 (ISBN 0-12-447201-X); Vol. 2. 1973. 59.50 (ISBN 0-12-447202-8); Vol. 3. 1975. 67.50 (ISBN 0-12-447203-6); Vol. 4. 1977. 49.50 (ISBN 0-12-447204-4); Vol. 5. Lipotropin & Related Peptides. 1978. 47.50 (ISBN 0-12-447205-2); Vol. 6. Thyroid Hormones. 1978. 71.50 (ISBN 0-12-447206-0); Vol. 7. Hypothalmic Hormones. 1979. 49.50 (ISBN 0-12-447207-9). LC 78-5444. Acad Pr.

Liu, T. Y., et al, eds. Chemical Synthesis & Sequencing of Peptides & Proteins. (Developments in Biochemistry Ser.: Vol. 17). 1981. 68.50 (ISBN 0-444-00623-0, Biomedical Pr). Elsevier.

Lombardini, Barry J. & Kenny, Alexander D. The Role of Peptides & Amino Acids As Neurotransmitters. LC 81-8335. (Progress in Clinical & Biological Research Ser.: Vol. 68). 248p. 1981. 40.00 (ISBN 0-8451-0068-8). A R Liss.

Lottspeich, F. & Henschen, A., eds. High Performance Liquid Chromatography in Protein & Peptide Chemistry. (Illus.). 1982. 58.00x (ISBN 3-11-008542-9). De Gruyter.

McCann & Dhindsa. Role of Peptides & Proteins in the Control of Reproduction. 370p. 1983. 75.00 (ISBN 0-444-00737-7, Biomedical Pr). Elsevier.

McKerns, Kenneth W. & Pantic, Vladmir, eds. Hormonally Active Brain Peptides: Stucture & Function. LC 82-9147. (Biochemical Endocrinology Ser.). 652p. 1982. 75.00x (ISBN 0-306-40865-1, Plenum Pr). Plenum Pub.

Martin, Joseph B., ed. Neuropeptides in Neurologic & Psychiatric Disease. (Association for Research in Nervous & Mental Disease, (ARNMD), Research Publications Ser.: Vol. 64). 1985. text ed. price not set (ISBN 0-88167-147-9). Raven.

Martinez, J. L., et al, eds. Endogenous Peptides & Learning & Memory Processes. LC 81-12691. (Behavioral Biology Ser.). 1981. 65.00 (ISBN 0-12-474980-1). Acad Pr.

Millar, R. P., ed. Neuropeptides: Biochemical & Physiological Studies. (Illus.). 368p. 1981. text ed. 50.00 (ISBN 0-443-02265-8). Churchill.

Motta, M. & Zanishi, M., eds. Pititary Hormones & Related Peptides. (Serono Symposium: No. 49). 1982. 59.50 (ISBN 0-12-509160-5). Acad Pr.

Najjar, V. A. Immunologically Active Peptides. 1982. lib. bdg. 55.00 (ISBN 90-6193-842-2, Pub by Junk Pubs Netherlands). Kluwer Academic.

Neurotensin: A Brain & Gastrointestinal Peptide, Vol. 400. 80.00x (ISBN 0-89766-190-7); pap. 80.00x (ISBN 0-89766-191-5). NY Acad Sci.

Offord, R. E. & Dibello, C., eds. Semisynthetic Peptides & Proteins. 1978. 49.50 (ISBN 0-12-524350-2). Acad Pr.

Peptide & Protein Reviews, Vol. 1. (Illus.). 256p. 1983. 35.00 (ISBN 0-8247-7053-6). Dekker.

Peptide & Protein Reviews, Vol. 3. (Illus.). 240p. 1984. 52.50 (ISBN 0-8247-7241-5). Dekker.

Pettit, G. R. Synthetic Peptides, Vol. 4. 478p. 1977. 110.75 (ISBN 0-444-41521-1). Elsevier.

--Synthetic Peptides, Vol. 5. 404p. 1980. 110.75 (ISBN 0-444-41895-4). Elsevier.

--Synthetic Peptides, Vol. 6. 512p. 1982. 153.25 (ISBN 0-444-42080-0). Elsevier.

Pettit, George R. Synthetic Peptides, Vol. 3. 1975. 81.00 (ISBN 0-12-552403-X). Acad Pr.

Said, Sami I., ed. Vasoactive Intestinal Peptide. (Advances in Peptide Hormone Research Ser.). 528p. 1982. text ed. 74.50 (ISBN 0-89004-443-0). Raven.

Sairam, M. R. & Atkinson, L. E., eds. Gonadal Proteins & Peptides & Their Biological Significance: Proceedings of the International Symposium Held at Le Chateau, Montebello, Quebec, June 1984. 450p. 1984. 60.00x (ISBN 9971-966-85-9, Pub. by World Sci Singapore). Taylor & Francis.

Satellite Symposium International Congress of Pharmacology, Lucknow, India 8th, July 1981. Current Status of Centrally Acting Peptides: Proceedings, Vol. 38. Dhawan, B. N., ed. LC 82-3825. (Illus.). 288p. 1982. 72.00 (ISBN 0-08-028008-0). Pergamon.

Schlesinger. Neurophypophyseal Peptide Hormones & Other Biologically Active Peptides. (Developments in Endocrinology Ser.: Vol. 13). 294p. 1981. 75.25 (ISBN 0-444-00605-2, Biomedical Pr). Elsevier.

Schroder, Eberhard & Lubke, Kraus, eds. The Peptides, 2 vols. Incl. Vol. 1. Methods of Peptide Synthesis. 1965. 92.00 (ISBN 0-12-629801-7); Vol. 2. Synthesis, Occurrence & Action of Biologically Active Polypeptides. 1966. Acad Pr.

Scully, Michael F. & Kakkar, Vijay V., eds. Chromogenic Peptide Substrates. (Illus.). 304p. 1979. text ed. 37.50 (ISBN 0-443-01840-5). Churchill.

Sheppard, R. C., ed. Amino-acids, Peptides, & Proteins, Vols. 1-9. Incl. Vol. 1. 1968 Literature. 1970. 32.00 (ISBN 0-85186-004-4, Royal Soc Chem London); Vol. 2. 1969 Literature. 1971. 32.00 (ISBN 0-85186-014-1); Vol. 3. 1970 Literature. 1972. 32.00 (ISBN 0-85186-024-9); Vol. 4. 1971 Literature. 1973. 38.00 (ISBN 0-85186-034-6); Vol. 5. 1972 Literature. 1974. 41.00 (ISBN 0-85186-044-3); Vol. 6. 1973 Literature. 1975. 49.00 (ISBN 0-85186-054-0); Vol. 7. 1974 Literature. 1976. 54.00 (ISBN 0-85186-064-8); Vol. 8. 1975 Literature. 1977. 70.00 (ISBN 0-85186-074-5); Vol. 9. 1976 Literature. 1978. 80.00 (ISBN 0-85186-084-2). LC 72-92548. Am Chemical.

Skrabanek, Petr & Powell, David. Substance P, Vol. 2. Horrobin, D. F., ed. LC 80-646426. (Annual Research Reviews Ser.). 175p. 1980. 26.00 (ISBN 0-88831-073-0). Eden Pr.

Thody, A. J., ed. The MSH Peptides. 1981. 42.50 (ISBN 0-12-687850-1). Acad Pr.

Udenfriend, Sidney, ed. The Peptides: Analysis, Synthesis, Biology, Vol. 7. Open-ended Treatise ed. Date not set. price not set (ISBN 0-12-304207-0). Acad Pr.

Voelter, W. & Wuensch, E., eds. Chemistry of Peptides & Proteins, Vol. 1. xv, 533p. 1982. 78.40x (ISBN 3-11-008604-2). De Gruyter.

Wehr. HPLC of Peptides & Proteins. 1985. write for info. (ISBN 0-471-26107-6). Wiley.

Weinstein. Chemistry & Biochemistry of Amino Acids, Peptides, & Proteins, Vol. 7. 472p. 1983. 75.00 (ISBN 0-8247-7027-7). Dekker.

Weinstein, B. Chemistry & Biochemistry of Amino Acids, Peptides, & Proteins, Vol. 1. LC 75-142896. pap. 47.50 (ISBN 0-317-08528-X, 2055061). Bks Demand UMI.

Weinstein, Boris, ed. Chemistry & Biochemistry of Amino Acids, Peptides & Proteins, Vol. 3. 336p. 1974. 75.00 (ISBN 0-8247-6204-5). Dekker.

--Chemistry & Biochemistry of Amino Acids, Peptides, & Proteins: A Survey of Recent Developments, Vol. 4. LC 75-142896. pap. 88.00 (ISBN 0-317-29935-2, 2021511). Bks Demand UMI.

--Chemistry & Biochemistry of Amino Acids, Peptides & Proteins, Vol. 6. 336p. 1982. 75.00 (ISBN 0-8247-1363-X). Dekker.

--Peptides: Chemistry & Biochemistry; Proceedings of the 1st American Peptide Symposium, Yale University, Aug. 1968. LC 70-107760. pap. 139.00 (ISBN 0-317-29565-9, 2021510). Bks Demand UMI.

Wrinch, Dorothy M. Chemical Aspects of the Structure of Small Peptides: An Introduction. LC 62-160. pap. 50.30 (ISBN 0-317-09409-2, 2020699). Bks Demand UMI.

PERCENTAGE

Howett, J. Basic Skills with Decimals & Percents. 128p. 1980. pap. text ed. 3.67 (ISBN 0-8428-2118-X). Cambridge Bk.

Saint Paul Technical Vocational Institute Curriculum Committee. Mathematics for Careers: Percents. LC 79-51557. (General Mathematics Ser.). 165p. 1981. pap. text ed. 5.00 (ISBN 0-8273-1880-4); instructor's guide 2.85 (ISBN 0-8273-1881-2). Delmar.

PERCENTAGE–PROGRAMMED INSTRUCTION

Loose, Frances F. Decimals & Percentages. reusable ed. (Illus.). 96p. 1977. 7.50 (ISBN 0-89039-200-5); answer key incl. Ann Arbor FL.

PERCEPTION

see also Perceptrons; Space Perception

Adam, G. Perception, Consciousness, Memory: Reflections of a Biologist. LC 73-20153. 229p. 1980. 29.50x (ISBN 0-306-30776-6, Plenum Pr). Plenum Pub.

Adolfson, John A. & Berghage, Thomas E. Perception & Performance Underwater. LC 73-23009. 380p. 1974. 24.50 (ISBN 0-471-00900-8, Pub. by Wiley). Krieger.

Albrecht, D. G., ed. Recognition of Pattern & Form, Austin, Texas 1979: Proceedings. (Lecture Notes in Biomathematics: Vol. 44). 225p. 1982. pap. 17.00 (ISBN 0-387-11206-5). Springer-Verlag.

Dodwell, Peter C. & Caelli, Terrence M., eds. Figural Synthesis. 320p. 1984. 34.95 (ISBN 0-89859-382-4). L Erlbaum Assocs.

Egan, James P. Signal Detection & ROC-Analysis. (Academic Press Ser. in Cognition & Perception). 1975. 49.00 (ISBN 0-12-232850-7). Acad Pr.

Engen, Trygg. The Perception of Odors. (Series in Cognition & Perception). 1982. 30.00 (ISBN 0-12-239350-3). Acad Pr.

Simmonds, James G. & Mann, James E., Jr. A First Look at Perturbation Theory. LC 84-20181. 1985. lib. bdg. write for info. (ISBN 0-89874-816-X). Krieger.

PERTURBATION (ASTRONOMY)

see also Problem of Many Bodies

Airy, George B. Gravitation. rev. ed. 1969. pap. 2.50 (ISBN 0-911014-02-0). Neo Pr.

PERTURBATION (MATHEMATICS)

see also Differential Equations–Numerical Solutions; Perturbation (Astronomy); Perturbation (Quantum Dynamics)

Chang, K. W. & Howes, F. A. Nonlinear Singular Perturbation Phenomena: Theory & Applications. (Applied Mathematical Sciences Ser.: Vol. 56). (Illus.). viii, 180p. 1984. pap. 18.80 (ISBN 0-387-96066-X). Springer-Verlag.

Dewar, Michael J. & Dougherty, Ralph C. The PMO Theory of Organic Chemistry. LC 74-12196. (Illus.). 576p. 1975. 69.50 (ISBN 0-306-30779-0, Plenum Pr); pap. 17.50 (ISBN 0-306-20010-4). Plenum Pub.

Eckhaus, W. Asymptotic Analysis of Singular Perturbations. (Studies in Mathematics & Its Applications: Vol. 9). 286p. 1979. 59.75 (ISBN 0-444-85306-5, North Holland). Elsevier.

Eckhaus, W. & De Jager, E. M., eds. Theory & Applications of Singular Perturbations, Oberwolfach, Germany 1981: Proceedings. (Lecture Note in Mathematics: Vol. 942). 372p. 1982. pap. 21.00 (ISBN 0-387-11584-6). Springer-Verlag.

Faris, W. G. Self-Adjoint Operators. (Lecture Notes in Mathematics Ser.: Vol. 433). vii, 115p. 1975. pap. 13.00 (ISBN 0-387-07030-3). Springer-Verlag.

Grabmuller, H. Singular Perturbation Techniques Applied to Integro-Differential Equations. (Research Notes in Mathematics: No. 20). 148p. (Orig.). 1978. pap. text ed. 22.95 (ISBN 0-273-08409-7). Pitman Pub MA.

Howes, F. A. Boundary-Interior Layer Interactions in Nonlinear Singular Perturbation Theory. LC 78-8693. 108p. pap. 13.00 (ISBN 0-8218-2203-9, MEMO-203). Am Math.

Kato, T. Perturbation Theory for Linear Operators. 2nd ed. (Grundlehren der Mathematischen Wissenschaften, A Series of Comprehensive Studies in Mathematics: Vol. 132). (Illus.). xxi, 619p. 1976. 50.00 (ISBN 0-387-07558-5). Springer-Verlag.

--A Short Introduction to Perturbation Theory for Linear Operators. (Illus.). 176p. 1982. 24.00 (ISBN 0-387-90666-5). Springer-Verlag.

Kevorkian, J. & Cole, J. D. Perturbation Methods in Applied Mathematics. (Applied Mathematical Sciences Ser.: Vol. 34). (Illus.). 558p. 1985. Repr. of 1981 ed. 48.50 (ISBN 0-387-90507-3). Springer-Verlag.

Meyer, Richard & Parter, Seymour, eds. Singular Pertubations & Symptotics. LC 80-24946. 1980. 36.50 (ISBN 0-12-493260-6). Acad Pr.

Miranker, Willard L. Numerical Methods for Stiff Equations & Singular Perturbation Problems. (Mathematics & Its Applications Ser.: No. 5). 216p. 1980. lib. bdg. 30.00 (ISBN 90-277-1107-0, Pub. by Reidel Holland). Kluwer Academic.

Nayfeh. Problems in Perturbation. 1985. 36.95 (ISBN 0-471-82292-2). Wiley.

Nayfeh, Ali H. Introduction to Perturbation Techniques. LC 80-15233. 519p. 1981. 47.95x (ISBN 0-471-08033-0, Pub. by Wiley-Interscience). Wiley.

Nayfeh, Ali-Hasan. Perturbation Methods. LC 72-8068. (Pure & Applied Mathematics Ser.). 425p. 1973. 42.95x (ISBN 0-471-63059-4, Pub. by Wiley-Interscience). Wiley.

O'Malley, Robert E., ed. Asymptotic Methods & Singular Perturbations: Proceedings of a Symposium, New York, April 1976. LC 76-27872. (SIAM-AMS Proceedings: Vol. 10). 1976. 30.00 (ISBN 0-8218-1330-7, SIAMS10). Am Math.

O'Malley, Robert E., Jr. Introduction to Singular Perturbations. (Applied Mathematics & Mechanics: An International Series of Monographs, Vol. 14). 1974. 55.00 (ISBN 0-12-525950-6). Acad Pr.

Polkinghorne, J. C. Models of High Energy Processes. LC 79-296. (Monographs on Mathematical Physics). (Illus.). 1980. 34.50 (ISBN 0-521-22369-5). Cambridge U Pr.

Rellich, Franz. Perturbation Theory of Eigenvalue Problems. (Notes on Mathematics & Its Applications Ser). 138p. (Orig.). 1969. 37.25 (ISBN 0-677-00680-2). Gordon.

Smith, Donald R. Singular Perturbation Theory: An Introduction with Applications. 576p. 1985. 42.50 (ISBN 0-521-30042-8). Cambridge U Pr.

PERTURBATION (QUANTUM DYNAMICS)

Arrighini, G. P. Intermolecular Forces & Their Evaluation by Perturbation Theory. (Lecture Notes in Chemistry Ser.: Vol. 25). 243p. 1981. pap. 18.60 (ISBN 0-387-10866-1). Springer-Verlag.

Breuer, R. A. Gravitational Perturbation Theory & Synchrotron Radiation. (Lecture Notes in Physics: Vol. 44). 210p. 1975. pap. 14.00 (ISBN 0-387-07530-5). Springer-Verlag.

PERTURBATION THEORY

see Perturbation (Mathematics)

PEST CONTROL

see also Insect Control; Weed Control; and similar headings; also subdivision Control under names of pests

Agricultural Board. Principles of Plant & Animal Pest Control, Vol. 1, Plant-Disease Development & Control. 1968. pap. 7.00 (ISBN 0-309-01596-0). Natl Acad Pr.

--Principles of Plant & Animal Pest Control, Vol. 2, Weed Control. 1968. pap. 11.50 (ISBN 0-309-01597-9). Natl Acad Pr.

Agricultural Board Division of Biology & Agriculture. Principles of Plant & Animal Pest Control, Vol. 3, Insect-Pest Management & Control. 1969. pap. 12.75 (ISBN 0-309-01695-9). Natl Acad Pr.

Agriculture Board. Principles of Plant & Animal Pest Control, Vol. 6, Effects Of Pesticides On Fruit & Vegetable Physiology. 1968. pap. 5.95 (ISBN 0-309-01698-3). Natl Acad Pr.

Akesson, N. B. & Yates, W. E. The Use of Aircraft for Mosquito Control, Oct. 1982. 96p. 10.00 (ISBN 0-686-84357-6). Am Mosquito.

Alford, D. V. & Upstone, M. E. Pests & Disease Control in Fruit & Hops. 105p. 1980. 30.00x (ISBN 0-901436-60-7, Pub. by CAB Bks England). State Mutual Bk.

Alford, David V. A Colour Atlas of Fruit Pests: Their Recognition, Biology & Control. (Illus.). 310p. 1984. text ed. 58.00x (ISBN 0-7234-0816-5, Pub. by Wolfe Medical England). Sheridan.

Apple, J. Lawrence & Smith, Ray F., eds. Integrated Pest Management. LC 76-17549. (Illus.). 213p. 1976. 32.50x (ISBN 0-306-30929-7, Plenum Pr). Plenum Pub.

Application of Remote Sensing Techniques for Improving Desert Locust Survey & Control. (Illus.). 92p. 1977. pap. 10.50 (ISBN 92-5-100112-X, F721, FAO). Unipub.

Beroza, Morton, ed. Pest Management with Insect Sex Attractants. LC 76-1873. (ACS Symposium Ser: No. 23). 1976. 24.95 (ISBN 0-8412-0308-3). Am Chemical.

Bibliography on Rodent Pest Biology & Control: 1960-1969, 4 Vols, Pts. 1-4. 947p. 1971. pap. 64.75 set (ISBN 0-686-79527-X, F2201, FAO). Unipub.

Bohlen, E. Crop Pests in Tanzania & Their Control. 2nd rev. ed. (Illus.). 142p. 1978. lib. bdg. 34.00 (ISBN 3-489-65126-X). Parey Sci Pubs.

Bos, J. The Isolating Effect of Greenhouses on Anthropod Pests & Its Significance for Integrated Pest Management. 92p. 1984. pap. text ed. 12.25 (ISBN 90-220-0839-8, PDC266, Pudoc). Unipub.

Bottrell, Dale G. Guidelines for Integrated Control of Maize Pests. (Plant Production & Protection Papers: No. 18). (Eng. & Fr., Illus.). 98p. 1978. pap. 14.50 (ISBN 92-5-100875-2, F1942, FAO). Unipub.

Bowen, W. R., compiled by. Turfgrass Pests. 60p. 1980. pap. 6.00 (ISBN 0-931876-39-7, 4053). Ag & Nat Res.

British Crop Protection Conference-Pests & Diseases: Vol. 1, 2, & 3. 1977. Set. 100.00x (ISBN 0-901436-11-9, Pub. by BCPC Pubns England). State Mutual Bk.

Burton, Vernon, et al. Study Guide for Agricultural Pest Control Advisers: Insects, Mites & Other Invertebrates & Their Control in California. rev. ed. LC 81-68756. 128p. 1981. pap. 4.00x (ISBN 0-931876-49-4, 4044). Ag & Nat Res.

Conway, Gordon R. Pest & Pathogen Control: Strategy, Tactics & Policy Models. (ILASA International Series on Applied Systems Analysis). 508p. 1984. 60.00x (ISBN 0-471-90349-3, 1-696, Pub. by Wiley-Interscience). Wiley.

Crop Loss Assessment Methods: FAO Manual on the Evaluation & Prevention of Losses by Pests, Diseases, & Weeds. (Illus.). 1976. looseleaf bdg. 16.80 (ISBN 0-685-67374-X, FAO); suppl. 1 4.80 (ISBN 0-685-67375-8). Unipub.

Curran, David F. The Ginseng Disease & Pest Reference Guide. Curran, Patricia A., ed. (Illus.). 152p. (Orig.). 1985. spiral 60.00 (ISBN 0-318-04401-3). D F Curran Prods.

Davidson, Ralph H. & Lyon, William F. Insect Pests of Farm, Garden & Orchard. 7th ed. LC 78-31366. 596p. 1981. pap. text ed. 24.00 (ISBN 0-471-86314-9). Wiley.

Division of Biology and Agriculture - Agricultural Board. Principles of Plant & Animal Pest Control, Vol. 4, Control Of Plant Parasitic Nematodes. 1968. pap. 11.50 (ISBN 0-309-01696-7). Natl Acad Pr.

Dover, Michael J. A Better Mousetrap: Innovative Technologies for Agricultural Pest Management, No. 4. Courrier, Kathleen, ed. (Illus., Orig.). Date not set. pap. text ed. 3.50 (ISBN 0-915825-09-0). World Resources Inst.

Dunning, R. A. Pest & Disease Control in Vegetables, Potatoes & Sugar Beet. 97p. 1980. 35.00x (Pub. by CAB Bks England). State Mutual Bk.

Edwards, Stephen R. & Bell, Bruce M., eds. Pest Control in Museums: A Status Report. (Orig.). 1981. pap. 15.00 (ISBN 0-942924-01-0). Assn Syst Coll.

Elements of Integrated Control of Sorghum Pests. (Plant Production & Protection Papers: No. 19). (Eng., Fr. & Span., Illus.). 167p. 1979. pap. 12.00 (ISBN 92-5-100884-1, F1943, FAO). Unipub.

Environmental Studies Board, National Research Council. Contemporary Pest Control Practices & Prospects: Report of the Executive Committee. LC 75-43468. (Pest Control Ser.: An Assessment of Present & Alternative Technologies, Vol. 1). 506p. 1976. pap. 13.25 (ISBN 0-309-02410-2). Natl Acad Pr.

Environmental Studies Board, Natl Research Council. Pest Control: An Assesssment of Present & Alternative Technologies, Vols. 1-3 &5. 1976. pap. 27.00 set (ISBN 0-309-02409-9). Natl Acad Pr.

--Pest Control & Public Health. LC 75-45777. (Pest Control Ser.: Vol.5). 282p. 1976. pap. 9.50 (ISBN 0-309-02414-5). Natl Acad Pr.

Flaherty, Donald L., et al, eds. Grape Pest Management. LC 80-70846. (Illus.). 312p. (Orig.). 1981. pap. 25.00x (ISBN 0-931876-44-3, 4105). Ag & Nat Res.

Flint, Mary L. & Kobbe, Brunhilde. Integrated Pest Management for Citrus. LC 83-82076. (Illus.). 100p. (Orig.). 1983. pap. 15.00x (ISBN 0-931876-65-6, 3303). Ag & Nat Res.

Flint, Mary L. & Van Den Bosch, Robert. Introduction to Integrated Pest Management. LC 80-28479. 255p. 1981. 19.95x (ISBN 0-306-40682-9, Plenum Pr). Plenum Pub.

Flint, Mary L., ed. Integrated Pest Management for Alfalfa Hay. LC 81-65780. (Illus.). 96p. (Orig.). 1981. pap. 15.00x (ISBN 0-931876-46-X, 4104). Ag & Nat Res.

Frishman, Austin M. Preparation for Pesticide Certification Examinations: Questions & Answers for Commercial Pesticide Applicators. LC 79-18406. 176p. (Orig.). 1980. pap. 10.00 (ISBN 0-668-04761-5). Arco.

Gibson, Miles E. Agricultural Aviation. 100p. (Orig.). 1974. pap. 9.95 (ISBN 0-942306-02-3). Diversified Pub Co.

--Agricultural Pilot & Chemicals. (Illus.). 75p. (Orig.). 1974. pap. 9.95 (ISBN 0-942306-05-8). Diversified Pub Co.

--All about Crop Dusting. 95p. (Orig.). 1968. pap. 9.95 (ISBN 0-942306-01-5). Diversified Pub Co.

--A Million Dollar Aviator. 109p. (Orig.). 1976. pap. text ed. 9.95 (ISBN 0-942306-04-X). Diversified Pub Co.

--So You Think You Want to Be a Crop-Duster. rev. ed. (Illus.). 140p. 1978. pap. 9.95 (ISBN 0-942306-00-7). Diversified Pub Co.

Grainge, Michael, et al. Plant Species Reportedly Possessing Pest-Control Properties: A Database. (East-West Resource Systems Institute RM Ser.: NO. 84-1). vi, 240p. 1984. velobound 20.00 (ISBN 0-86638-057-4). E W Center HI.

Gunn, D. L. & Rainey, R. C. Strategy & Tactics of Control of Migrant Pests. (Royal Society Discussion Ser.). (Illus.). 240p. 1980. text ed. 66.50x (ISBN 0-85403-117-0, Pub. by Royal Soc England). Scholium Intl.

Gunther, F. A. & Gunther, J. Davies, eds. Residue Reviews, Vol. 69. LC 62-18595. 1978. 27.50 (ISBN 0-387-90306-2). Springer-Verlag.

Hatfield, Jerry L. & Thomason, Ivan J., eds. Biometerology in Integrated Pest Management. LC 81-22780. 1982. 49.50 (ISBN 0-12-332850-0). Acad Pr.

Hill, D. S. Agricultural Insect Pests of the Tropics & Their Control. 2nd ed. LC 81-24216. (Illus.). 500p. 1983. 75.00 (ISBN 0-521-24638-5). Cambridge U Pr.

Hills, F. J., et al. Sugarbeet Pest Management: Aphid-Borne Viruses. (Illus.). 12p. (Orig.). 1982. pap. 2.00 (ISBN 0-931876-60-5, 3277). Ag & Nat Res.

--Sugarbeet Pest Management: Leaf Diseases. (Illus.). 12p. (Orig.). 1982. pap. 2.00 (ISBN 0-931876-59-1, 3278). Ag & Nat Res.

Hoy, Marjorie A. & Cunningham, Gary L. Biological Control of Pests by Mites: Proceedings of a Conference. LC 83-72136. (Illus.). 150p. (Orig.). 1983. pap. 15.00x (ISBN 0-931876-63-X, 3304). Ag & Nat Res.

Huffaker, C. B., ed. Biological Control. LC 74-619. 530p. 1974. pap. 12.95x (ISBN 0-306-20008-2, Rosetta). Plenum Pub.

Huffaker, Carl B., ed. New Technology of Pest Control. LC 79-4369. (Environmental Science & Technology Ser.). 500p. 1980. 45.50x (ISBN 0-471-05336-8, Pub. by Wiley-Interscience); pap. 45.50 (ISBN 0-471-05327-9). Wiley.

IPM Manual Group Staff & Flint, Mary L. Integrated Pest Management for Almonds. LC 85-70728. (Illus.). 144p. (Orig.). Date not set. pap. 15.00 (ISBN 0-931876-73-7, 3308). Ag & Nat Res.

Jotwani, M. G. & Young, W. R. Control of Sorghum Shoot Fly. 330p. 1981. 35.00x (ISBN 0-686-76630-X, Pub. by Oxford & IBH India). State Mutual Bk.

Kaukeinen, D. E. Vertebrate Pest Control & Management Materials, 4th Symposium - STP 817. LC 83-70429. 305p. 1984. text ed. 44.00 (ISBN 0-8031-0213-5, 04-817000-48). ASTM.

Kilgore, Wendell W. & Doutt, Richard L. Pest Control: Biological, Physical & Selected Chemical Methods. 1967. 76.50 (ISBN 0-12-406650-X). Acad Pr.

Mallis, Arnold, et al. Handbook of Pest Control. New 6th ed. Story, Keith & Moreland, Dan, eds. (Illus.). 1115p. 1982. text ed. 65.00 (ISBN 0-942588-00-2). Franzak & Foster.

Matthews, G. A. Pest Management. (Illus.). 288p. 1985. text ed. 35.00 (ISBN 0-582-47011-0). Longman.

Metcalf, Robert L. & Luckmann, William H. Introduction to Insect Pest Management. 2nd ed. LC 82-4794. (Environmental Science & Technology: A Wiley-Interscience Series of Texts & Monographs). 577p. 1982. 34.95x (ISBN 0-471-08547-2, Pub. by Wiley-Interscience). Wiley.

Morgan, W. M. & Ledieu, M. S. Pest & Disease Control in Glasshouse Crops. 106p. 1979. 30.00x (Pub. by BCPC Pubns England). State Mutual Bk.

Morse, Roger A., ed. Honey Bee Pests, Predators & Diseases. LC 78-58027. (Illus.). 400p. 1978. 42.50x (ISBN 0-8014-0975-6). Comstock.

National Research Council, Environmental Studies Board. Urban Pest Management. 1980. pap. text ed. 11.95 (ISBN 0-309-03125-7). Natl Acad Pr.

Nordlund, Donald A., et al, eds. Semiochemicals: Their Role in Pest Control. 306p. 1981. 48.50x (ISBN 0-471-05803-3, Pub. by Wiley-Interscience). Wiley.

Norton, G. A. & Hollings, C. S., eds. Pest Management: Proceedings of an International Conference, 25-29 October 1976, Laxenburg, Austria. LC 78-40825. 1979. text ed. 72.00 (ISBN 0-08-023427-5). Pergamon.

Pests & Disease Control in Glasshouse Crops. 106p. 1979. 42.00x (ISBN 0-901436-52-6, Pub. by CAB Bks England). State Mutual Bk.

Pimentel, David, ed. Handbook of Pest Management in Agriculture. 1981. vol. 1, 296 pgs., July 1981 76.00 (ISBN 0-8493-5855-8); vol. 2, 336 pgs., Aug. 1981 89.50 (ISBN 0-8493-3842-5); vol. 3, 672 pgs., Sept. 1981 89.50 (ISBN 0-8493-3843-3). CRC Pr.

Report of the Seventh Session of the FAO Panel of Experts on Integrated Pest Control. (Illus.). 1978. pap. 7.50 (ISBN 92-5-100433-1, F1348, FAO). Unipub.

Report of the Sixth Session of the FAO Panel of Experts on Integrated Pest Control. 1976. pap. 7.50 (ISBN 92-5-100012-3, F1107, FAO). Unipub.

Roberts, Daniel A. Fundamentals of Plant-Pest Control. LC 77-16135. (Illus.). 242p. 1978. text ed. 27.95x (ISBN 0-7167-0041-7). W H Freeman.

Roberts, Philip S. & Thomason, Ivan J. Sugarbeet Pest Management: Nematodes. (Illus.). 36p. 1981. pap. text ed. 3.00 (ISBN 0-931876-52-4, 3272). Ag & Nat Res.

Rudman, Jack. Exterminator. (Career Examination Ser.: C-236). (Cloth bdg. avail. on request). pap. 12.00 (ISBN 0-8373-0236-6). Natl Learning.

--Housing Exterminator. (Career Examination Ser.: C-2283). (Cloth bdg. avail. on request). 1977. 10.00 (ISBN 0-8373-2283-9). Natl Learning.

--Pest Control Aide. (Career Examination Ser.: C-2030). (Cloth bdg. avail. on request). pap. 10.00 (ISBN 0-8373-2030-5). Natl Learning.

Schafer, Jr. & Walker, eds. Vertebrate Pest Control & Management Materials: Third Conference - STP 752. 206p. 1981. 23.00 (ISBN 0-8031-0760-9, 04-752000-48). ASTM.

Scopes, N., ed. Pest & Disease Control Handbook. 450p. 1979. 99.00x (ISBN 0-901436-42-9, Pub. by CAB Bks England). State Mutual Bk.

Simulation of Lime Aphid Population Dynamics. 165p. 1980. pap. 28.00 (ISBN 90-220-0706-5, PDC186, PUDOC). Unipub.

Smith, Edward H. & Pimentel, David, eds. Pest Control Strategies. 1978. 39.00 (ISBN 0-12-650450-4). Acad Pr.

Stark, R. W. & Gittins, A. R., eds. Pest Management for the Twenty-First Century. 1973. 1.75 (ISBN 0-89301-009-X). U Pr of Idaho.

Study Guide for Agricultural Pest Control Advisers on Nematodes & Nematicides. rev. ed. (Illus.). 40p. 1981. pap. text ed. 2.00 (ISBN 0-931876-51-6, 4045). Ag & Nat Res.

Test Methods for Vertebrate Pest Control & Management Materials - STP 625. 256p. 1977. 26.00 (ISBN 0-8031-0199-6, 04-625000-48). ASTM.

Vertebrate Pest Control & Management Materials - STP 680: Second Conference. 330p. 1979. 31.50x (ISBN 0-8031-0761-7, 04-680000-48). ASTM.

Ware, George W. Complete Guide to Pest Control: With & Without Chemicals. LC 80-52306. 1980. 18.50 (ISBN 0-913702-09-9). Thomson Pub CA.

Waters, William E., et al. Integrated Pest Management in Pine-Bark Beetle Ecosystems. LC 85-15160. (Environmental Science & Technology Ser.). 1985. 44.95 (ISBN 0-471-05328-7, Pub. by Wiley-Interscience). Wiley.

Westwood, Melvin N. Temperate-Zone Pomology. LC 77-26330. (Illus.). 428p. 1978. text ed. 38.95x (ISBN 0-7167-0196-0). W H Freeman.

Whitehead, D. L. & Bowers, W. S., eds. Natural Products for Innovative Pest Management. (Current Themes in Tropical Science Ser.: Vol. 2). (Illus.). 550p. 1983. 99.50 (ISBN 0-08-028893-6). Pergamon.

Wilson, M. Curtis, et al. Practical Insect Pest Management: Fundamentals of Applied Entomology, No. 1. 2nd ed. LC 76-46901. (Illus.). 1977. 9.95x (ISBN 0-88133-031-0). Waveland Pr.

--Practical Insect Pest Management: Insects of Vegetables & Fruit, Vol. 3. 2nd ed. LC 81-70506. (Illus.). 144p. 1982. pap. text ed. 7.95x (ISBN 0-917974-65-4). Waveland Pr.

Youdeowei, Anthony & Service, Mike. Pest & Vector Management in the Tropics. LC 81-20845. (Illus.). 320p. 1983. text ed. 45.00x (ISBN 0-582-46348-3). Longman.

PEST CONTROL–BIOLOGICAL CONTROL

Burges, H. D., ed. Microbial Control of Pests & Plant Diseases, 1970 to 1980. LC 80-41480. 960p. 1981. 90.00 (ISBN 0-12-143360-9). Acad Pr.

Del Fosse, E. S. Proceedings of the Fifth International Symposium on Biological Control of Weeds. 647p. 1981. pap. 90.00x (ISBN 0-643-02837-4, Pub. by CAB Bks England). State Mutual Bk.

Dunn, P. H. Proceedings of the Second International Symposium on Biological Control of Weeds. 220p. 1973. 40.00x (ISBN 0-85198-299-9, Pub. by CAB Bks England). State Mutual Bk.

Goden, D. Pest Slugs & Snails: Biology & Control. Gruber, S., tr. from Ger. (Illus.). 470p. 1983. 75.00 (ISBN 0-387-11894-2). Springer-Verlag.

Greathead, D. J. A Review of Biological Control in the Ethiopian Region. 162p. 1971. cloth 42.00x (ISBN 0-85198-022-8, Pub. by CAB Bks England). State Mutual Bk.

Huffaker, C. B., ed. Biological Control. LC 79-157149. (Illus.). 530p. 1971. 55.00x (ISBN 0-306-30532-1, Plenum Pr). Plenum Pub.

Huffaker, C. B. & Messenger, P. S., eds. Theory & Practice of Biological Control. 1977. 83.00 (ISBN 0-12-360350-1). Acad Pr.

Rao, V. P. Biological Control of Pests in Fiji. 38p. 1971. 30.00x (ISBN 0-85198-115-1, Pub. by CAB Bks England). State Mutual Bk.

--A Review of the Biological Control of Insects & other Pests in Southeast Asia & the Pacific Regions. 149p. 1971. 42.00x (ISBN 0-85198-114-3, Pub. by CAB Bks England). State Mutual Bk.

Rao, V. P. & Ghani, M. A., eds. Studies on Predators of Adelges spp. in the Himalayas. 116p. 1972. 39.00x (ISBN 0-85198-186-0, Pub. by CAB Bks England). State Mutual Bk.

Samways, Michael J. Biological Control of Pests & Weeds. (Studies in Biology: No. 132). 64p. 1981. pap. text ed. 8.95 (ISBN 0-7131-2822-4). E Arnold.

Simmonds, F. T., ed. Proceedings of the First International Symposium on Biological Control of Weeds, 1969. 110p. 1970. 40.00x (ISBN 0-85198-134-8, Pub. by CAB Bks England). State Mutual Bk.

Swan, D. J. A Review of the Work on Predators, Parasites & Pathogens for the Control of Oryctes Rhinoceros (L) in Pacific Area. 64p. 1974. 39.00x (ISBN 0-85198-332-4, Pub. by CAB Bks England). State Mutual Bk.

Wapshere, A. J. Proceedings of the Third International Symposium on Biological Control of Weeds. 140p. 1974. 45.00x (ISBN 0-85198-307-3, Pub. by CAB Bks England). State Mutual Bk.

Welch, S. M. & Croft, B. A. The Design of Biological Monitoring Systems for Pest Management. 77p. 1980. pap. 16.00 (PDC150, PUDOC). Unipub.

Wilson, F. A Review of the Biological Control of Insects & Weeds in Australia & Australian New Guinea. 104p. 1960. cloth 30.00x (ISBN 0-85198-065-1, Pub. by CAB Bks England). State Mutual Bk.

PEST RESISTANCE OF PLANTS

see Plants–Disease and Pest Resistance

PESTICIDES

see also Fungicides; Herbicides; Insecticides; Spraying and Dusting Residues in Agriculture

Agro-Pesticide Distribution & Use in Asian Countries: Report of a Multi-Country Study Mission. 219p. 1983. pap. text ed. 14.75 (ISBN 92-833-2006-9, APO135, APO). Unipub.

Aizawa, Hirayasu. Metabolic Maps of Pesticides. (Ecotoxicology & Environmental Quality Ser.). 1982. 45.00 (ISBN 0-12-046480-2). Acad Pr.

Akesson, Norman B. & Yates, Wesley E. Pesticide Application Equipment & Techniques. (Agricultural Services Bulletins: No. 38). 261p. 1979. pap. 18.75 (ISBN 92-5-100835-3, F1894, FAO). Unipub.

Bandal, S. Kris, et al, eds. The Pesticide Chemist & Modern Toxicology. LC 81-10790. (ACS Symposium Ser.: No. 160). 1981. 49.95 (ISBN 0-8412-0636-8). Am Chemical.

Banki, L. Bioassay of Pesticides in the Laboratory. 1978. casebound 34.50 (ISBN 0-9960000-2-X, Pub. by Akademiai Kaido Hungary). Heyden.

Bard, J. H. Nematicide Index. 92p. 1974. cloth 39.00x (ISBN 0-85198-309-X, Pub. by CAB Bks England). State Mutual Bk.

Barrons, Keith C. Are Pesticides Really Necessary? LC 80-54684. 245p. 1981. pap. 6.95 (ISBN 0-89526-888-4). Regnery-Gateway.

Bohmont, Bert L. The New Pesticide User's Guide. 1983. text ed. 23.95 (ISBN 0-8359-4890-0); instr's. manual free (ISBN 0-8359-4891-9). Reston.

Bourne, G. H., ed. Human Nutrition & Nutrition & Pesticides in Cattle. (World Review of Nutrition & Dietetics: Vol. 35). (Illus.). 238p. 1980. 81.75 (ISBN 3-8055-0442-X). S Karger.

Bowman, M. C., ed. Analysis of Pesticides by Chromatographic Methods. new ed. 1976. 25.00 (ISBN 0-912474-08-4). Preston Pubns.

Buchel, K. H. Chemistry of Pesticides. LC 82-17327. (Environmental Science & Technology Ser.). 618p. 1983. 110.00 (ISBN 0-471-05682-0, Pub. by Wiley-Interscience). Wiley.

Bull, David. A Growing Problem: Pesticides & the Third World Poor. pap. 9.95 (ISBN 0-85598-064-8). Inst Food & Develop.

Busvine, J. R. Recommended Methods for Meausurment of Pest Resistance to Pesticides. (Plant Production & Protection Papers: No. 21). (Eng. & Fr.). 136p. 1980. pap. 9.75 (ISBN 92-5-100883-3, F2079, FAO). Unipub.

Cardarelli, Nate F. Controlled Release Pesticides Formulations. LC 75-46632. (Uniscience Ser.). 224p. 1976. 66.00 (ISBN 0-8493-5114-6). CRC Pr.

Champ, B. R. & Dyte, C. E. Report of the FAO Global Survey of Pesticide Susceptibility of Stored Grain Pests. (Plant Production & Protection Papers: No. 5). 297p. 1976. pap. 10.00 (ISBN 92-5-100022-0, F1394, FAO). Unipub.

Chau, A. S. & Afghan, B. K. Analysis of Pesticides in Water, Vol. 3. 264p. 1982. 76.50 (ISBN 0-8493-5212-6). CRC Pr.

Chau, S. Y., ed. Analysis of Pesticides in Water, Significance, Principles, Techniques, & Chemistry: Significance, Principles, Techniques, & Chemistry, Vol. I. Afghan, B. K. 216p. 1982. 71.50 (ISBN 0-8493-5210-X). CRC Pr.

Code of Practice for Safe Use of Pesticides. 28p. 1976. pap. 6.00 (ISBN 0-643-00171-9, C011, CSIRO). Unipub.

Commission of the European Communities. Organophosphorus Pesticides Criteria (Dose-Effect Relationships) for Organophosphorus Compounds. Derache, R., ed. 1977. pap. text ed. 44.00 (ISBN 0-08-021993-4). Pergamon.

Committee on Prototype Explicit Analysis for Pesticides. Regulating Pesticides. xiii, 288p. 1980. pap. text ed. 12.50 (ISBN 0-309-02946-5). Natl Acad Pr.

Corbett, J. R., et al, eds. The Biochemical Mode of Action of Pesticides. 2nd ed. 1984. 65.00 (ISBN 0-12-187860-0). Acad Pr.

Cremlyn, R. Pesticides: Preparation & Mode of Action. LC 77-28590. 1978. 57.95 (ISBN 0-471-99631-9, Pub. by Wiley-Interscience); pap. 28.95 (ISBN 0-471-27669-3). Wiley.

Critser, James R., Jr. Pesticides. (Ser. 13-78). 1979. 195.00 (ISBN 0-914428-63-2). Lexington Data.

Crosby, Donald G., ed. Natural Pest Control Agents. LC 66-22355. (Advances in Chemistry Ser.: No. 53). 1966. 15.95 (ISBN 0-8412-0054-8). Am Chemical.

Das. Pesticide Analysis. 1981. 55.25 (ISBN 0-8247-1087-8). Dekker.

Division of Biology & Agriculture. Degradation of Synthetic Organic Molecules in the Biosphere. (Illus.). 352p. 1972. pap. 20.95 (ISBN 0-309-02046-8). Natl Acad Pr.

Elliot, J. G. & Wilson, B. J., eds. The Influence of the Weather on the Efficiency & Safety of Pesticide Application: The Drift of Herbicides. (Occasional Pub. Ser.: No. 3). 130p. (Orig.). 1983. pap. 18.00x (ISBN 0-89955-416-4, Pub. by BCPC England). Intl Spec Bk.

Eto, Morifusa. Organophosphorus Pesticides: Organic & Biological Chemistry. LC 73-90239. (Uniscience Ser.). 375p. 1974. 74.00 (ISBN 0-8493-5021-2). CRC Pr.

FAO Panel of Experts on Pesticide Specifications, Registration Requirements & Application Standards: Report of the First Session of a Group on Pesticide Registration Requirements, Rome, June 28-July 4, 1977. pap. 7.50 (ISBN 92-5-100371-8, F1253, FAO). Unipub.

FAO-WHO Experts on Pesticide Residues. Evaluation of Some Pesticide Residues in Food: Monographs. Incl. 1971. (No. 1). 1972. pap. 6.00 (ISBN 92-4-166501-7, 688); 1972. (No. 2). 1973. pap. 10.00 (ISBN 92-4-166502-5); 1973. (No. 3). 1974. pap. 8.40 (ISBN 92-4-166503-3); 1974. (No. 4). 1975. pap. 19.20 (ISBN 92-4-166504-1). (Pesticide Residues Ser.). (Also avail. in French). pap. World Health.

FAO-WHO Experts on Pesticide Residues. Geneva, 1968. Pesticide Residues in Food: Report. (Technical Report Ser.: No. 417). (Also avail. in French & Spanish). 1969. pap. 2.00 (ISBN 92-4-120417-6). World Health.

FAO-WHO Experts on Pesticide Residues. Rome, 1970. Pesticide Residues in Food: Report. (Technical Report Ser.: No. 474). (Also avail. in French & Spanish). 1971. pap. 2.00 (ISBN 92-4-120474-5). World Health.

FAO-WHO Experts on Pesticide Residues. Geneva, 1971. Pesticide Residues in Food: Report. (Technical Report Ser.: No. 502). (Also avail. in French, Russian & Spanish). 1972. pap. 1.60 (ISBN 92-4-120502-4). World Health.

FAO-WHO Experts on Pesticide Residues. Rome, 1972. Pesticide Residues in Food: Report. (Technical Report Ser.: No. 525). (Also avail. in french & spanish). 1973. pap. 1.60 (ISBN 92-4-120525-3). World Health.

FAO-WHO Experts on Pesticide Residues. Geneva, 1973. Pesticide Residues in Food: Report. (Technical Report Ser.: No. 545). (Also avail. in French, Russian & Spanish). 1974. pap. 2.40 (ISBN 92-4-120545-8). World Health.

FAO-WHO Experts on Pesticide Residues. Rome, 1975. Pesticide Residues in Food: Report. (Technical Report Ser.: No. 574). (Also avail. in French & Spanish). 1975. pap. 2.40 (ISBN 92-4-120574-1). World Health.

Federal Institute for Biology in Agriculture & Forestry, Institute for Plant Protection Agent Research, Berlin-Dahlem & Ebing, Winifried. Gaschromatographie der Pflanzenschutzmittel: Tabellarische Literaturreferate, 5 vols. new ed. (Ger.). Vol. I, 1970. 20.00 (ISBN 0-913106-09-7); Vol. II, 1972. 15.00 (ISBN 0-913106-10-0); Vol. III. 15.00 (ISBN 0-913106-11-9); Vol. IV. 15.00 (ISBN 0-913106-12-7); Vol. V, 1975. 15.00 (ISBN 0-913106-13-5). PolyScience.

Fest, C. & Schmidt, K. J. The Chemistry of Organphosphorous Pesticides. (Illus.). 380p. 1982. 80.00 (ISBN 0-387-11303-7). Springer-Verlag.

Follweiler, Joanne M. & Sherma, Joseph, eds. Handbook of Chromatography, Pesticides & Related Organic Chemicals. 368p. 1984. 67.00 (ISBN 0-8493-4010-1). CRC Pr.

Frehse, H. & Geissbuhler, H., eds. Pesticide Residues: A Contribution to Their Interpretation, Relevance & Legislation. (International Union of Pure & Applied Chemistry). 1979. text ed. 44.00 (ISBN 0-08-023931-5). Pergamon.

Georghiou, G. P. & Saito, Tetsuo, eds. Pest Resistance to Pesticides. 822p. 1983. 89.50x (ISBN 0-306-41246-2, Plenum Pr). Plenum Pub.

Green, Maurice B. & West, T. F. Chemicals for Crop Protection & Pest Control. 2nd ed. LC 77-4881. 1977. pap. text ed. 16.25 (ISBN 0-08-019013-8). Pergamon.

Guide to Codex Maximum Limits for Pesticide Residues: Prepared in Collaboration with UNEP. (CAC-PR Ser.: No. 1 - 1978 First Issue). 209p. 1978. pap. 15.50 (ISBN 92-5-100683-0, F1581, FAO). Unipub.

Gunther, Francis A., ed. Residues of Pesticides & Other Contaminants in the Total Environment. (Residue Reviews: Vol. 91). (Illus.). 160p. 1984. 24.00 (ISBN 0-387-90998-2). Springer-Verlag.

--Residues of Pesticides & Other Contaminants in the Total Environment. (Residue Reviews Ser.: Vol. 92). (Illus.). 210p. 1984. 29.50 (ISBN 0-387-96018-X). Springer-Verlag.

--Residues of Pesticides & Other Contaminants in the Total Environment. (Residue Reviews Ser.: Vol. 93). (Illus.). 255p. 1984. 29.50 (ISBN 0-387-96019-8). Springer-Verlag.

Haque, Rizwanel & Biros, Francis J., eds. Mass Spectrometry & NMR Spectroscopy in Pesticide Chemistry. LC 73-20005. (Environmental Science Research Ser.: Vol. 4). 348p. 1974. 49.50x (ISBN 0-306-36304-6, Plenum Pr). Plenum Pub.

Hartley, G. S. Physical Principles of Pesticide Behaviour: The Dynamics of Applied Pesticide in the Local Environment in Relation to Biological Responses. Graham-Bryce, I. J., ed. (Vol. 1). 1980. 90.00 (ISBN 0-12-328401-5). Acad Pr.

Harvey, John, Jr. & Zweig, Gunter, eds. Pesticide Analytical Methodology. LC 80-19470. (ACS Symposium Ser.: No. 136). 1989. 44.95 (ISBN 0-8412-0581-7). Am Chemical.

Haskell, P. T., ed. Pesticide Application: Principles & Practice. (Illus.). 450p. 1985. 49.00 (ISBN 0-19-854542-8). Oxford U Pr.

Hassall, Kenneth A. The Chemistry of Pesticides: Their Metabolism, Mode of Action & Uses in Crop Protection. (Illus.). 372p. (Orig.). 1982. 79.50x (ISBN 0-89573-054-5). VCH Pubs.

Hemming, C. F. & Taylor, T. H., eds. International Study Conference on the Current & Future Problems of Acridology: Proceedings. 524p. 1972. 55.00x (ISBN 0-85135-073-9, Pub. by Centre Overseas Research). State Mutual Bk.

Hutson, D. H. & Roberts, T. R. Progress in Pesticide Biochemistry, Vol. 1. LC 80-41419. 346p. 1981. 79.95 (ISBN 0-471-27920-X, Pub. by Wiley-Interscience). Wiley.

--Progress in Pesticide Biochemistry, Vol. 2. 226p. 1982. text ed. 58.95 (ISBN 0-471-10118-4, Pub. by Wiley-Interscience). Wiley.

--Progress in Pesticide Biochemistry, Vol. 3. 449p. 1983. 199.95 (ISBN 0-471-90053-2, Pub. by Wiley Interscience). Wiley.

Impact Monitoring of Agricultural Pesticides. (Illus.). 1976. pap. 12.00 (ISBN 92-5-100052-2, F935, FAO). Unipub.

Industrial Production & Formulation of Pesticides in Developing Countries: Chemistry & Production of Pesticides, Vol. 2. pap. 5.00 (ISBN 0-686-94476-3, UN73/2B/10, UN). Unipub.

International Congress of Pesticide Chemistry, 4th, Zurich, 1978. Advances in Pesticide Science: Proceedings, 3 vols. Geissbuehler, H., et al, eds. 1979. Set. text ed. 265.00 (ISBN 0-08-022349-4). Pergamon.

International Congress of Pesticides Chemistry, 4th, Zurich, July 1978. World Food Production--Environment--Pesticides: Plenary Lectures. Geissbuehler, H., et al, eds. (IUPAC Symposia). 1979. text ed. 35.00 (ISBN 0-08-022374-5). Pergamon.

International IUPAC Congress-2nd. Pesticide Chemistry: Proceedings of the International IUPAC Congress, 2nd Congress, 6 vols. Tahori, A. S., ed. Set. 443.75x (ISBN 0-677-12120-2); Vol. 1, 506p., 1972. 101.25x (ISBN 0-677-12130-X); Vol. 2, 310p., 1971. 69.50x (ISBN 0-677-12140-7); Vol. 3, 236p., 1971. 62.50x (ISBN 0-677-12150-4); Vol. 4, 618p., 1971. 129.50x (ISBN 0-677-12160-1); Vol. 5, 578p., 1972. 123.75x (ISBN 0-677-12170-9); Vol. 6, 584p., 1972. 121.50x (ISBN 0-677-12180-6). Gordon.

Jensen, A. A. Residues of Pesticides & Other Contaminants in the Total Environment. (Residue Reviews: Vol. 89). 155p. 1983. 31.00 (ISBN 0-387-90884-6). Springer-Verlag.

Kalshoven, L. G. Pests of Crops of Indonesia. 702p. 1982. 125.00 (ISBN 0-444-00686-9). Elsevier.

Kaneko, T. M. & Akesson, N. B., eds. Pesticide Formulations & Application Systems: Third Symposium - STP 828. LC 83-71898. 152p. 1984. text ed. 19.00 (ISBN 0-8031-0221-6, 04-828000-48). ASTM.

Khan, S. U. Pesticides in the Soil Environment. (Fundamental Aspects of Pollution Control & Environmental Science Ser.: Vol. 5). 240p. 1980. 53.25 (ISBN 0-444-41873-3). Elsevier.

Kurstak. Microbial Pesticides. (Microbiology Ser.: Vol. 6). 1982. 115.00 (ISBN 0-8247-1686-8). Dekker.

Laboratory Traning Manual on the Use of Nuclear Techniques in Pesticide Research. (Technical Reports Ser.: No. 225). 291p. 1983. pap. text ed. 44.00 (ISBN 92-0-115083-0, IDC225, IAEA). Unipub.

Lee, Robert E., Jr. Air Pollution from Pesticides & Agricultural Processes. (Uniscience Ser.). 280p. 1976. 69.00 (ISBN 0-8493-5157-X). CRC Pr.

Mandava, H. Bhushan, ed. CRC Handbook of Natural Pesticides, Vol. I. 595p. 1985. 108.00 (ISBN 0-8493-3651-1). CRC Pr.

Manual on the Use of FAO Specifications for Plant Protection Products. 51p. (Orig.). 1972. pap. 4.50 (ISBN 0-685-23607-2, F267, FAO). Unipub.

Marini-Bettolo, G. B., ed. Natural Products & the Protection of Plants: Proceedings of a Study Week of the Pontifical Academy of Sciences, October 18-23, 1976. 846p. 1978. 191.50 (ISBN 0-444-41620-X). Elsevier.

Matthews, G. A. Pesticide Application Methods. LC 77-26033. (Illus.). 1979. 17.95x (ISBN 0-582-46351-3). Longman.

Model Extension Leaflet of Pest Resistance to Pesticides. (Specifications for Plant Protection Products: No. 10). 1971. pap. 7.50 (F1995, FAO). Unipub.

Narahashi, Toshio, ed. Neurotoxicology of Insecticides & Pheromones. LC 78-10913. 316p. 1979. 42.50x (ISBN 0-306-40067-7, Plenum Pr). Plenum Pub.

Newton, Michael. Handbook of Weed & Insect Control Chemicals for Forest Resource Managers. 160p. 1981. 24.95x (ISBN 0-917304-25-X); pap. 17.95x (ISBN 0-917304-63-2). Timber.

Perring, F. H. & Mellanby, K. Ecological Effects of Pesticide. (A Linnean Society Symposium Ser.). 1978. 39.50 (ISBN 0-12-551350-X). Acad Pr.

Pest Resistance to Pesticides & Crop Loss Assessment: Report of the Third Session of the FAO Panel of Experts, Held in Kyoto, Japan, 6 August 1980. (Plant Production & Protection Papers: No. 6). (Eng., Fr. & Span.). 42p. 1981. pap. 7.50 (ISBN 92-5-101104-4, F2231, FAO). Unipub.

Pest Resistance to Pesticides & Crop Loss Assessment: Report of the 2nd Session of the FAO Panel of Experts Held in Rome, Aug.-Sept. 1978, Vol. 2. (Plant Production & Protection Papers: No. 6). (Eng., Fr. & Span.). 47p. 1979. pap. 7.50 (ISBN 92-5-100762-4, F1838, FAO). Unipub.

Pesticide Industry. (Guides to Information Sources: No. 10). pap. 4.00 (ISBN 0-686-93219-6, UNID280, UN). Unipub.

Pesticide Residues in Food. Incl. Report of the 1975 Joint FAO-WHO Meeting, Geneva, Nov.-Dec. 1975. 45p. 1976. pap. 6.25 (ISBN 92-5-100040-9, F315); Report of the Joint FAO-WHO Meeting, 1976. (No. 8). 35p. 1978. pap. 6.75 (ISBN 92-5-100317-3, F1393, FAO); Report of the Joint Meeting of the FAO Panel of Experts on Pesticide Residues & the WHO Expert Committee on Pesticide Residues, Geneva, December 1977. 1978. pap. 7.50 (ISBN 92-5-100578-8, F1510); Report of the Joint Meeting of the FAO Panel of Experts on Pesticide Residues in Food & the WHO Expert Group on Pesticides Residues, Geneva, December 1979. (No. 20). 97p. 1980. pap. 8.00 (ISBN 92-5-100922-8, F1936); Report, 1980. (No. 26). (Eng., Fr. & Span.). 88p. 1981. pap. 7.50 (ISBN 92-5-101058-7, F2180); Monographs 1980: Data & Recommendations of the Joint Meeting of the FAO Panel of Experts on Pesticide Residues in Food & the Environment & the WHO Expert Group on Pesticide Residues, Rome, October 6-15, 1980. (No. 26). 460p. 1981. pap. 33.75 (ISBN 92-5-101148-6, F2282); Report of the Joint Committee of FAO-WHO Panel of Experts on Pesticide Residue in Food & the Environment & the WHO Expert Group on Pesticides, Geneva, Nov. 23-Dec. 12, 1981. (No. 37). 69p. 1982. pap. 7.50 (ISBN 92-5-101202-4, F2307); Index & Summary, 1965-1978. (No. 11). 41p. 1979. pap. 7.50 (ISBN 92-5-100652-0, F1551); Report of the Joint FAO-WHO Meeting, Rome, November-December 1982, 2 vols. (Nos. 46 & 49). (Eng., Fr. & Span.). 79p. 1983. Report. pap. 7.50 (ISBN 92-5-101360-8, F2501); Evaluations. pap. 31.00 (ISBN 92-5-101432-9, F2542); 1983. (No. 56). 68p. 1984. pap. 7.50 (ISBN 92-5-102094-9, F2593). (Plant Production & Protection Papers). (Eng., Fr. & Span., Orig., FAO). Unipub.

Pesticide Residues in Food Evaluations 1981: The Monographs. (Plant Production & Protection Papers: No. 42). 576p. 1982. pap. 41.00 (ISBN 92-5-101306-3, F2399, FAO). Unipub.

Pesticide Residues in Food: Report of the Joint Meeting, Rome, November 1970. (Agricultural Planning Studies: No. 87). 44p. 1971. pap. 4.50 (ISBN 92-5-101534-1, F310, FAO). Unipub.

Pesticide Residues in Food: Report of the 1974 Joint FAO-WHO Expert Meeting. (Agricultural Planning Studies: No. 97). pap. 6.25 (F314, FAO). Unipub.

Pesticides in the Modern World: A Symposium Prepared by Members of the Cooperative Programme of Agro-Allied Industries with FAO & Other United Nations Organizations. pap. 8.25 (F1084, FAO). Unipub.

Plimmer, Jack R., ed. Pesticide Chemistry in the Twentieth Century. LC 76-51748. (ACS Symposium Ser: No. 37). 1977. 19.95 (ISBN 0-8412-0532-9). Am Chemical.

--Pesticide Residues & Exposure. LC 81-20568. (ACS Symposium Ser.: No. 182). 1982. 27.95 (ISBN 0-8412-0701-1). Am Chemical.

Preston, Seaton T. & Pankratz, Ronald. A Guide to the Analysis of Pesticides by Gas Chromatography. 1981. spiral plastic bdg. 35.00 (ISBN 0-913106-15-1). PolyScience.

Radioisotopes in the Detection of Pesticide Residues. (Panel Proceedings Ser.). (Illus.). 116p. 1966. pap. 7.25 (ISBN 92-0-111166-5, ISP123, IAEA). Unipub.

Recommended International Maximum Limits for Pesticide Residues. 2nd ed. 20p. 1978. pap. 4.50 (ISBN 92-5-100719-5, F611, FAO). Unipub.

Report of the Ad Hoc Government Consultation on International Standardization of Pesticide Registration Requirements. 1978. pap. 7.50 (ISBN 92-5-100562-1, F1415, FAO). Unipub.

Report of the Ad Hoc Government Consultation on Pesticides in Agriculture & Public Health. 42p. 1975. pap. 7.50 (ISBN 0-685-59221-9, F1087, FAO). Unipub.

Rice, Elroy L. Pest Control with Nature's Chemicals: Allelochemics & Pheromones in Gardening & Agriculture. LC 83-47838. (Illus.). 240p. 1983. 28.50x (ISBN 0-8061-1853-9). U of Okla Pr.

Rodenticides: Analyses, Specifications, Formulations. (Plant Production & Protection Papers: No. 16). 81p. 1979. pap. 7.50 (ISBN 92-5-100798-5, F1867, FAO). Unipub.

Rosen, Joseph D., et al, eds. Sulfur in Pesticide Action & Metabolism. LC 81-7916. (ACS Symposium Ser.: No. 158). 1981. 34.95 (ISBN 0-8412-0635-X). Am Chemical.

Rudd, Robert L. Pesticides & the Living Landscape. LC 64-14506. pap. 84.00 (ISBN 0-317-29744-9, 2015653). Bks Demand UMI.

Rudman, Jack. Pesticide Control Inspector. (Career Examination Ser.: C-2561). (Cloth bdg. avail. on request). pap. 10.00 (ISBN 0-8373-2561-7). Natl Learning.

--Senior Pesticide Control Inspector. (Career Examination Ser.: C-2562). (Cloth bdg. avail. on request). pap. 12.00 (ISBN 0-8373-2562-5). Natl Learning.

Safe, S. & Hutzinger, O. Mass Spectrometry of Pesticides & Pollutants. LC 73-83415. (Uniscience Ser). 220p. 1973. 59.50 (ISBN 0-8493-5033-6). CRC Pr.

Scher, Herbert B. Advances in Pesticide Formulation Technology. LC 84-6394. (ACS Symposium Ser.: No. 254). 250p. 1984. lib. bdg. 44.95 (ISBN 0-8412-0840-9). Am Chemical.

Scher, Herbert B., ed. Controlled Release Pesticides. LC 77-22339. (ACS Symposium Ser.: No. 53). 1977. 29.95 (ISBN 0-8412-0382-2). Am Chemical.

Seymour, K. G., ed. Pesticide Formulations & Application Systems: Second Conference - STP 795. LC 82-72891. 111p. 1983. pap. text ed. 14.00 (ISBN 0-8031-0233-X, 04-795000-48). ASTM.

Sheets, T. J. & Pimentel, David, eds. Pesticides: Contemporary Roles in Agriculture, Energy, & the Environment. LC 78-71497. (Contemporary Issues in Science & Society Ser.). 186p. 1979. 39.50 (ISBN 0-89603-005-9). Humana.

Siewierski, M., ed. Determination & Assessment of Pesticide Exposure: Proceedings of a Working Conference Held in Hershey, Pennsylvania, October 29-31, 1980. (Studies in Environmental Science: No. 24). 222p. 1984. 72.25 (ISBN 0-444-42416-4). Elsevier.

Simms, R. C., et al. Residue of Pesticides & other Contaminants in the Total Environment. (Residue Reviews: Vol. 88). (Illus.). 164p. 1983. 25.00 (ISBN 0-387-90851-X). Springer-Verlag.

Sittig, Marshall, ed. Pesticide Manufacturing & Toxic Materials Control Encyclopedia. LC 80-19373. (Chemical Tech. Rev. 168; Env. Health Rev. 3; Pollution Tech. Rev. 69). (Illus.). 810p. 1981. 96.00 (ISBN 0-8155-0814-X). Noyes.

Specifications for Pesticides Used in Public Health: Insecticides, Rodenticides, Molluscicides, Repellents, Methods. 4th ed. (Also avail. in French & Spanish). 1973. 16.00 (ISBN 92-4-154022-2). World Health.

Spindler, M., et al. Residues of Pesticides & Other Contaminants in the Total Environment. (Residue Reviews Ser.: Vol. 90). 145p. 1983. 24.00 (ISBN 0-387-90905-2). Springer-Verlag.

Stimmann, M. W. Pesticide Application & Safety Training. LC 80-52766. 1977. pap. text ed. 8.00x (ISBN 0-931876-17-6, 4070). Ag & Nat Res.

Storage of Pesticides in Portable Containers. 1974. pap. 2.00 (ISBN 0-685-58203-5, 43D-T). Natl Fire Prot.

Street, J. Pesticide Selectivity. 1975. 55.00 (ISBN 0-8247-6335-1). Dekker.

Thomson, W. T. Tree, Turf & Ornamental Pesticide Guide. rev. ed. 150p. 1983. pap. text ed. 12.00 (ISBN 0-913702-22-6). Thomson Pub CA.

Tordoir, W. F. & Van Hemstra-Lequin, E. A., eds. Field Worker Exposure During Pesticide Application. (Studies in Environmental Science: Vol. 7). 208p. 1980. 51.00 (ISBN 0-444-41879-2). Elsevier.

The Use of FAO Specifications for Plant Protection Products. 2nd, Rev. ed. (Plant Production & Protection Papers: No. 13). (Eng., Fr. & Span.). 92p. 1979. pap. 7.50 (ISBN 92-5-100704-7, F1597, FAO). Unipub.

Van Heemstra-Lequin, A. H. & Tordoir. Education & Safe Handling in Pesticide Application. (Studies in Environmental Science: Vol. 18). 302p. 1982. 68.00 (ISBN 0-444-42041-X). Elsevier.

Van Valkenburg, J. W., ed. Pesticidal Formulations Research: Physical & Colloidal Chemical Aspects. LC 74-81252. (Advances in Chemistry Ser: No. 86). 1969. 21.95 (ISBN 0-8412-0087-4). Am Chemical.

Van Valkenburg, W., ed. Pesticide Formulations. LC 72-86610. pap. 93.30 (ISBN 0-8357-9091-6, 2055053). Bks Demand UMI.

Ware, George W. Pesticides: Theory & Applications. LC 82-7412. (Illus.). 291p. 1982. pap. text ed. 23.95 (ISBN 0-7167-1416-7). W H Freeman.

Watson, David L. & Brown, A. W., eds. Pesticide Management & Insecticide Resistance. 1977. 55.50 (ISBN 0-12-738650-5). Acad Pr.

WHO Expert Committee. Geneva, 1971, 19th. WHO Expert Committee on Insecticides: Report. (Technical Report Ser.: No. 475). (Also avail. in French & Spanish). 1971. pap. 1.20 (ISBN 92-4-120475-3). World Health.

WHO Expert Committee on Insecticides. Geneva, 1972, 20th. Safe Use of Pesticides: Report. (Technical Report Ser.: No. 513). (Also avail. in French & Spanish). 1973. pap. 2.40 (ISBN 92-4-120513-X). World Health.

Whorton, James, et al. Before Silent Spring: Pesticides in Pre-DDT America. LC 74-2984. 316p. 1975. 29.00x (ISBN 0-691-08139-5). Princeton U Pr.

Worthing, Charles R., ed. The Pesticide Manual: A World Compendium. 825p. 1984. 150.50 (ISBN 0-901436-44-5, Pub. by BCPC Pubns England). State Mutual Bk.

Worthing, Charles R. & Walker, S. Barrie, eds. The Pesticide Manual. 7th ed. 700p. 1983. 65.00x (ISBN 0-901436-77-1, Pub. by B C P C England). Intl Spec Bk.

Wright, et al, eds. Pesticide Tank Mix Applications: First Conference - STP 764. 100p. 1982. pap. 13.95 (ISBN 0-8031-0828-1, 04-764000-48). ASTM.

Zehr, Eldon I., ed. Methods for Evaluating Plant Fungicides, Nematicides, & Bactericides. LC 78-63414. 141p. 1978. lib. bdg. 18.00 (ISBN 0-89054-025-X). Am Phytopathol Soc.

Zweig, Gunter & Lawrence, James, eds. Analytical Methods for Pesticides & Plant Growth Regulators, Vol. 12: High Performance Liquid Chromatography (HPLC) of Pesticides. LC 63-16560. 1982. 45.00 (ISBN 0-12-784312-4). Acad Pr.

PESTICIDES–ENVIRONMENTAL ASPECTS

Barrons, Keith C. Are Pesticides Really Necessary? LC 80-54684. 245p. 1981. pap. 6.95 (ISBN 0-89526-888-4). Regnery-Gateway.

Carson, Rachel. Silent Spring. (Illus.). 1962. 16.95 (ISBN 0-395-07506-8). HM.

Chau, S. Y., ed. Analysis of Pesticides in Water, Significance, Principles, Techniques, & Chemistry: Significance, Principles, Techniques, & Chemistry, Vol. I. Afghan, B. K. 216p. 1982. 71.50 (ISBN 0-8493-5210-X). CRC Pr.

Committee on Pesticide Decision Making, National Research Council. Pesticide Decision Making. LC 77-94524. (Analytical Studies for the U. S. Environmental Protection Agency Ser.). (Illus.). 1978. pap. text ed. 7.50 (ISBN 0-309-02734-9). Natl Acad Pr.

Dover, Michael & Croft, Brian. Getting Tough: Public Policy & the Management of Pesticide Resistance. (Illus.). 77p. 1984. pap. text ed. 3.50 (ISBN 0-915825-03-1). World Resources Inst.

Edwards, C. A., ed. Environmental Pollution by Pesticides. LC 72-95067. (Environmental Science Research Ser.: Vol. 3). 552p. 1973. 65.00x (ISBN 0-306-36303-8, Plenum Pr). Plenum Pub.

Edwards, Clive E. Persistent Pesticides in the Environment. LC 79-141881. (Uniscience Ser). 170p. 1974. 46.00 (ISBN 0-685-38667-8). CRC Pr.

FAO-WHO Esperts on Pesticide Residues. Geneva, 1975. Pesticide Residues in Food: Report. (Technical Report Ser.: No. 592). (Also avail. in French & Spanish). 1976. pap. 2.40 (ISBN 92-4-120592-X). World Health.

FAO-WHO Experts on Pesticide Residues. Rome, 1969. Pesticide Residues in Food: Report. (Technical Report Ser.: No. 458). (Also avail. in French, Russian & Spanish). 1970. pap. 2.00 (ISBN 92-4-120458-3). World Health.

Fowden, L. & Graham-Bryce, I. J., eds. Crop Protection Chemicals: Directions of Future Development. (Illus.). 212p. 1981. lib. bdg. 63.00x (ISBN 0-85403-175-8, Pub. by Royal Soc London). Scholium Intl.

Guenzi, W. D., ed. Pesticides in Soil & Water. (Illus.). 1974. 14.00 (ISBN 0-89118-756-1). Soil Sci Soc Am.

Gunther, F. A., ed. Residue Reviews: Residues of Pesticides & Other Contaminants in the Total Environment, 2 vols. LC 62-18595. (Residue Reviews Ser.). (Illus.). viii, 168p. 1973. Vol. 48. 29.00 (ISBN 0-387-90064-0); Vol. 49. 29.00 (ISBN 0-387-90068-3). Springer-Verlag.

Gunther, F. A. & Gunther, J. Davies, eds. Residue Reviews, Vol. 55. (Residues of Pesticides & Other Contaminants in the Total Environment Ser.). (Illus.). 180p. 1975. text ed. 25.00 (ISBN 0-387-90102-7). Springer-Verlag.

Gunther, Francis A., ed. Residues of Pesticides & Other Contaminants in the Total Environment. (Residue Reviews: Vol. 91). (Illus.). 160p. 1984. 24.00 (ISBN 0-387-90998-2). Springer-Verlag.

--Residues of Pesticides & Other Contaminants in the Total Environment. (Residue Reviews Ser.: Vol. 92). (Illus.). 210p. 1984. 29.50 (ISBN 0-387-96018-X). Springer-Verlag.

--Residues of Pesticides & Other Contaminants in the Total Environment. (Residue Reviews Ser.: Vol. 93). (Illus.). 255p. 1984. 29.50 (ISBN 0-387-96019-8). Springer-Verlag.

Hallenbeck, W. H. & Burns, K. M. Pesticides & Human Health. vii, 176p. 1985. 24.80 (ISBN 0-387-96050-3). Springer-Verlag.

Haque, Rizwanel, ed. Environmental Dynamics of Pesticides. Freed, V. H. LC 74-28273. (Environmental Science Research Ser.: Vol. 6). 395p. 1975. 52.50x (ISBN 0-306-36306-2, Plenum Pr). Plenum Pub.

Hartley, G. S. Physical Principles of Pesticide Behaviour: The Dynamics of Applied Pesticide in the Local Environment in Relation to Biological Responses. Graham-Bryce, I. J., ed. (Vol. 1). 1980. 90.00 (ISBN 0-12-328401-5). Acad Pr.

Hartley, G. S. & Graham-Bryce, I. Physical Principles of Pesticide Behavior: The Dynamics of Applied Pesticide in the Local Environment in Relation to Biological Responses, Vol. 2. 1981. 74.50 (ISBN 0-12-328402-3). Acad Pr.

Headley, Joseph C. & Lewis, J. N. The Pesticide Problem: An Economic Approach to Public Policy. LC 66-28503. pap. 39.80 (ISBN 0-317-28861-X, 2020964). Bks Demand UMI.

Hill, I. R. & Wright, S. J., eds. Pesticide Microbiology: Microbiological Aspects of Pesticide Behavior in the Environment. 1979. 98.00 (ISBN 0-12-348650-5). Acad Pr.

J. J. Keller & Associates, Inc., ed. Pesticides Guide. LC 79-54216. (22G). 600p. 1985. 90.00 (ISBN 0-934674-12-4). J J Keller.

Kaufman, Donald D., et al, eds. Bound & Conjugated Pesticide Residues. LC 76-13011. (ACS Symposium Ser.: No. 29). 1976. 34.95 (ISBN 0-8412-0334-2). Am Chemical.

Kennedy, Maurice V., ed. Disposal & Decontamination of Pesticides. LC 78-8645. (ACS Symposium Ser.: No. 73). 1978. 29.95 (ISBN 0-8412-0433-0). Am Chemical.

Khan, Mohammad A., ed. Pesticides in Aquatic Environments. LC 77-5380. (Environmental Science Research Ser.: Vol. 10). 271p. 1977. 37.50x (ISBN 0-306-36310-0, Plenum Pr). Plenum Pub.

McEwen, F. L. & Stephenson, G. R. The Use & Significance of Pesticides in the Environment. LC 78-23368. 538p. 1979. 43.95x (ISBN 0-471-03903-9, Pub. by Wiley-Interscience). Wiley.

McKenna, et al. Pesticide Regulation Handbook. 1983. pap. 125.00 (ISBN 0-88057-059-8). Exec Ent Inc.

Magee, Philip S., et al, eds. Pesticide Synthesis Through Rational Approaches. LC 84-11062. (ACS Symposium Ser.: No. 255). 352p. 1984. lib. bdg. 54.95x (ISBN 0-8412-0852-2). Am Chemical.

Matsumara, Fumio & Boush, G. Mallory, eds. Environmental Toxicology of Pesticides. 1972. 72.00 (ISBN 0-12-480450-0). Acad Pr.

Miller, Morton W. & Berg, George G. Chemical Fallout: Current Research on Persistent Pesticides. (Illus.). 560p. 1972. 49.75x (ISBN 0-398-01313-6). C C Thomas.

Miyamoto, J. & Kearney, P. C., eds. Pesticide Chemistry: Human Welfare & the Environment: Proceedings of the 5th International Congress of Pesticide Chemistry, Kyoto, Japan, 29 August - 4 September 1982, 4 Vols. (IUPAC Symposium Ser.). 1750p. 1983. Set. 390.00 (ISBN 0-08-029219-4). Pergamon.

Norris, Ruth & Ahmed, A. Karim, eds. Pills, Pesticides & Profits: The International Trade in Toxic Substances. LC 81-11001. 182p. 1982. pap. 12.95 (ISBN 0-88427-050-5). North River.

Nuclear Techniques for Studying Pesticide Residue Problems. (Panel Proceedings Ser.). (Illus.). 88p. (Orig.). 1970. pap. 9.25 (ISBN 92-0-111470-2, ISP252, IAEA). Unipub.

Recommended International Maximum Limits for Pesticide Residues. (CAC-RS 1978). 31p. 1979. pap. 5.50 (ISBN 92-5-100658-X, F1571, FAO). Unipub.

Recommended International Maximum Limits for Pesticide Residues. 2nd ed. 20p. 1978. pap. 4.50 (ISBN 92-5-100719-5, F611, FAO). Unipub.

Recommended International Maximum Limits for Pesticide Residues: Fourth Series. 1974. pap. 4.50 (ISBN 92-5-100230-4, F605, FAO). Unipub.

Recommended International Standard for Pesticide Residues: Second Series. 1970. pap. 4.50 (F639, FAO). Unipub.

Recommended International Tolerances for Pesticide Residues. 1972. pap. 0.00 write for info. (F585, FAO). Unipub.

Report on the FAO Expert Consultation on Pesticide & the Environment. 1978. pap. 7.50 (ISBN 92-5-100422-6, F1317, FAO). Unipub.

Residue Reviews, Vol. 70. (Illus.). 1979. 27.50 (ISBN 0-387-90398-4). Springer-Verlag.

Residue Reviews, Vol. 71. (Illus.). 1979. 30.50 (ISBN 0-387-90389-5). Springer-Verlag.

Rudd, Robert L. Environmental Toxicology: A Guide to Information Sources. LC 73-17540. (Man & the Environmrnt Information Guide Ser.: Vol. 7). 1977. 60.00x (ISBN 0-8103-1342-1). Gale.

Second Expert Consultation on Environmental Criteria for Registration of Pesticides: Rome, May 1981. (Plant Production & Protection Papers: No. 28). (Eng., Fr. & Span.). 64p. 1981. pap. 7.50 (ISBN 92-5-101131-1, F2258, FAO). Unipub.

Sheail, John. Pesticides & Nature Conservation: The British Experience, 1950-1975. (Illus.). 300p. 1985. 27.95 (ISBN 0-19-854150-3). Oxford U Pr.

Sheets, T. J. & Pimentel, David, eds. Pesticides: Contemporary Roles in Agriculture, Energy, & the Environment. LC 78-71497. (Contemporary Issues in Science & Society Ser.). 186p. 1979. 39.50 (ISBN 0-89603-005-9). Humana.

Swenzey, Sean & Daxl, Rainer. Breaking the Circle of Poison: The IPM Revolution in Nicaragua. pap. 4.00 (ISBN 0-317-02669-0). Inst Food & Develop.

The Trouble with Temik: An Historical-Environmental Look at Long Island Agriculture & Pesticide Usage. 12.95 (ISBN 0-317-03376-X); pap. 7.95 (ISBN 0-317-03377-8). De Young Pr.

Vance, Mary. Pesticides & the Environment: Monographs. (Public Administration Ser.: Bibliography P 1638). 1985. pap. 6.75 (ISBN 0-89028-328-1). Vance Biblios.

Vettorazzi, G., ed. International Regulatory Aspects for Pesticide Chemicals, Vol. II. 256p. 1982. 77.00 (ISBN 0-8493-5608-3). CRC Pr.

Wasserstrom, Robert F. & Wiles, Richard. Field Duty: U. S. Farmworkers & Pesticide Safety, No. 3. Courrier, Kathleen, ed. (Illus.). 78p. (Orig.). 1985. pap. text ed. 3.50 (ISBN 0-915825-08-2). World Resources Inst.

White-Stevens, Robert, ed. Pesticides in the Environment, Vol. 2. 1976. 85.00 (ISBN 0-8247-1783-X). Dekker.

Woolson, E. A., ed. Arsenical Pesticides. LC 74-31378. (ACS Symposium Ser.: No. 7). 1975. 18.95 (ISBN 0-8412-0243-5). Am Chemical.

PESTICIDES–TOXICOLOGY

Brown, V. K. Acute Toxicity in Theory & Practice: With Special Reference to the Toxicoloty of Pesticides. LC 79-42905. (Monographs in Toxicology; Environmental & Safety Aspects). 159p. 1980. 41.95 (ISBN 0-471-27690-1, Pub. by Wiley-Interscience). Wiley.

Chambers, Janice E. & Yarbrough, James D., eds. Effects of Chronic Exposures to Pesticides on Animal Systems. 262p. 1982. text ed. 71.50 (ISBN 0-89004-756-1). Raven.

Chapman, Frank M. The Handbook of Birds, 2 vols. (Illus.). 367p. 1985. Repr. of 1898 ed. Set. 177.45 (ISBN 0-89901-211-6). Found Class Reprints.

Ecobichon, D. J. & Joy, R. M., eds. Pesticides & Neurological Diseases. 296p. 1982. 76.00 (ISBN 0-8493-5571-0). CRC Pr.

Eesa, Naeem M. & Cutkomp, Laurence K. Glossary of Pesticide Toxicology & Related Terms. 80p. (Orig.). 1984. pap. 10.00 (ISBN 0-913702-28-5). Thomson Pub CA.

Fairchild, Edwardj. Agricultural Chemical & Pesticides: Handbook of the Toxic Effects. (Illus.). 230p. 1978. text ed. 60.00 (ISBN 0-7194-0002-3, Pub. by Castle Hse England). J K Burgess.

FAO-WHO Experts on Pesticide Residues. Rome, 1969. Pesticide Residues in Food: Report. (Technical Report Ser.: No. 458). (Also avail. in French, Russian & Spanish). 1970. pap. 2.00 (ISBN 92-4-120458-3). World Health.

Fleck, Raymond F. & Hollaender, Alexander, eds. Genetic Toxicology: An Agricultural Perspective. (Basic Life Sciences: Vol. 21). 560p. 1982. 65.00x (ISBN 0-306-41135-0, Plenum Pr.). Plenum Pub.

Hallenbeck, W. H. & Burns, K. M. Pesticides & Human Health. vii, 176p. 1985. 24.80 (ISBN 0-387-96050-3). Springer-Verlag.

Kohn, G. K., ed. Mechanism of Pesticide Action. LC 74-22484. (ACS Symposium Ser.: No. 2). 1974. 14.95 (ISBN 0-8412-0551-5). Am Chemical.

Marquis, Judith K., ed. Contemporary Issues in Pesticide Toxicology & Pharmacology. (Concepts in Toxicology: Vol. 2). (Illus.). x, 120p. 1986. 38.00 (ISBN 3-8055-4215-1). S Karger.

Shankland, D. L., et al, eds. Pesticide & Venom Neurotoxicity. LC 77-25006. 293p. 1978. 45.00 (ISBN 0-306-31123-2, Plenum Pr). Plenum Pub.

Vettorazzi, G. International Regulatory Aspects for Pesticide Chemicals. 232p. 1979. 71.50 (ISBN 0-8493-5607-5). CRC Pr.

Wasserstrom, Robert F. & Wiles, Richard. Field Duty: U. S. Farmworkers & Pesticide Safety, No. 3. Courrier, Kathleen, ed. (Illus.). 78p. (Orig.). 1985. pap. text ed. 3.50 (ISBN 0-915825-08-2). World Resources Inst.

Weir, David & Schapiro, Mark. Circle of Poison: Pesticides & People in a Hungry World. LC 81-13384. 101p. 1981. pap. 3.95 (ISBN 0-935028-09-9). Inst Food & Develop.

WHO Scientific Group. Geneva, 1974. Chemical & Biochemical Methodology for the Assessment of Hazards of Pesticides for Man: Report. (Technical Report Ser.: No. 560). (Also avail. in French & Spanish). 1975. pap. 2.40 (ISBN 92-4-120560-1). World Health.

Whorton, James, et al. Before Silent Spring: Pesticides in Pre-DDT America. LC 74-2984. 316p. 1975. 29.00x (ISBN 0-691-08139-5). Princeton U Pr.

PESTICIDES AND THE ENVIRONMENT

see Pesticides–Environmental Aspects

PESTS

see also Agricultural Pests; Household Pests; Insects, Injurious and Beneficial; Parasites; Zoology, Economic;
also names of Pests, e.g. Boll-Weevil

Cauquil, J. Cotton Boll Rot. 1981. 45.00x (ISBN 0-686-76631-8, Pub. by Oxford & IBH India). State Mutual Bk.

Gaafar, S. M., et al. Parasites, Pests & Predators. (World Animal Science Ser.: Vol. B2). Date not set. write for info. (ISBN 0-444-42175-0). Elsevier.

Kitching, R. L. & Jones, R. E., eds. The Ecology of Pests. 254p. 1982. 30.00x (ISBN 0-643-00408-4, Pub. by CSIRO Australia). State Mutual Bk.

--The Ecology of Pests: Some Australian Case Histories. 254p. 1981. pap. 15.50 (ISBN 0-643-00408-4, CO65, CSIRO). Unipub.

Laird, Marshall, ed. Commerce & the Spread of Pests & Disease Vectors. LC 83-16627. (Illus.). 368p. 1984. text ed. 34.95x (ISBN 0-03-062137-2). Praeger.

Pirone, Pascal P. Diseases & Pests of Ornamental Plants. 5th ed. LC 77-26893. 566p. 1978. 32.50x (ISBN 0-471-07249-4, Pub. by Wiley-Interscience). Wiley.

Welch, S. M. & Croft, B. A. The Design of Biological Monitoring Systems for Pest Management. 77p. 1980. pap. 16.00 (PDC150, PUDOC). Unipub.

--The Design of Biological Monitoring Systems for Pest Management. LC 79-10960. (Simulation Monographs). 76p. 1979. pap. 23.95x (ISBN 0-470-26632-5). Halsted Pr.

PET (COMPUTER)

Adamis, Eddie. BASIC Subroutines for Commodore Computers. LC 82-21874. 312p. 1983. pap. text ed. 12.95 (ISBN 0-471-86541-9, Pub. by Wiley Pr). Wiley.

Arotsky, J. & Glassbrook, D. W. An Introduction to Microcomputing with the PET. 288p. 1983. pap. text ed. 16.95 (ISBN 0-7131-3475-5). E Arnold.

Berenbon, Howard. Mostly BASIC: Applications for Your PET. LC 80-53274. 160p. 1980. Book 1. pap. 13.95 (ISBN 0-672-21790-2, 21790). Sams.

--Mostly BASIC: Applications for Your PET, Bk. 2. LC 80-53274. 224p. 1983. pap. 13.95 (ISBN 0-672-22001-6, 22001). Sams.

Brain, David, et al. The BASIC Conversions Handbook for Apple, TRS-80 & PET Users. 80p. (Orig.). 1982. pap. 9.95 (ISBN 0-8104-5534-X). Hayden.

Business Communications Staff. Pet Industry Outlook. 1985. pap. 1500.00 (ISBN 0-89336-439-8, GA-034N). BCC.

Cassel, Don. BASIC 4.0 Programming for the Commodore PET-CBM. (Micropower Ser.). 224p. 1983. plastic comb 16.95 (ISBN 0-697-08265-2); incl. disk o.p. 29.95 (ISBN 0-697-09908-3). Wm C Brown.

Chance, David. Thirty-Three Challenging Computer Games for the TRS-80, Apple & PET. (Illus.). 252p. 15.95 (ISBN 0-8306-9703-9, 1275); pap. 9.25 (ISBN 0-8306-1275-0). TAB Bks.

Compute Magazine, ed. Compute's First Book of PET-CBM. (Illus.). 244p. (Orig.). 1981. pap. 12.95 (ISBN 0-942386-01-9). Compute Pubns.

Downey, James M. & Rogers, Steven M. PET Interfacing. LC 81-50568. 264p. 1981. pap. 16.95 (ISBN 0-672-21795-3). Sams.

Dunn, Seamus & Morgan, Valerie. The PET Personal Computer for Beginners. 1983. pap. 19.95 (ISBN 0-13-661827-8). P-H.

--The PET Personal Computer for Beginners. 1982. 25.99 (ISBN 0-13-661835-9). P-H.

Greenberg, Gary. C-BIMS: Cassette-Based Information Management System for the PET. (Illus.). 224p. (Orig.). 1983. 16.95 (ISBN 0-8306-0489-8); pap. 10.95 (ISBN 0-8306-1489-3, 1489). TAB Bks.

Haigh, Roger W. & Radford, Loren E. BASIC for Microcomputers: Apple, TRS-80, PET. 337p. 1983. 21.95 (ISBN 0-442-27843-8). Van Nos Reinhold.

Hallgren, Richard. Interface Projects for the PET-CBM. (Illus.). 200p. Date not set. cancelled (ISBN 0-13-469494-5); pap. cancelled (ISBN 0-13-469486-4). P-H.

Hampshire, Nick. Library of PET Subroutines. 140p. (Orig.). 1982. pap. 17.95 (ISBN 0-8104-1050-8); 1 PET disk & documentation 25.00. Hayden.

--PET Graphics. 224p. 1983. pap. 19.75 (ISBN 0-317-00355-0); 1 PET disk & documentation 25.00. Hayden.

Haskell, Richard. PET-CBM BASIC. (Illus.). 154p. 1982. 18.95 (ISBN 0-13-661769-7); pap. 12.95 (ISBN 0-13-661751-4). P-H.

Haugo, J. E. Introduction to Microcrocomputers: PET Set. 1982. 73.28 (ISBN 0-07-079225-9). McGraw.

Marshall, Garry. Learning to Use the PET Computer. (Learning to Use Computer Series, A Gower Read-Out Publication). 98p. (Orig.). 1982. pap. text ed. 12.00x (ISBN 0-566-03427-1). Gower Pub Co.

Noonan, Larry. Basic BASIC-English Dictionary for the Apple, PET & TRS-80. (Illus.). 154p. 1983. 17.95 (ISBN 0-8306-1521-0, 1521). TAB Bks.

Peckham, Herbert D. Hands-on BASIC with a PET. (Illus.). 1982. pap. 23.95 (ISBN 0-07-049157-7, BYTE Bks). McGraw.

A PET in the Classroom. 1983. tchr's manual 14.95 (ISBN 0-88056-121-1); activity wkbk. 5.95 (ISBN 0-88056-122-X). Dilithium Pr.

Poirot, James & Retzlaff, Don. Microcomputer Workbook: PET Commodore Edition. 110p. (Orig.). 1981. pap. text ed. 6.95 (ISBN 0-88408-147-8). Sterling Swift.

Poirot, James L. & Retzlaff, Don. How to Program in BASIC: PET Commodore Edition. 1979. pap. 69.00 disks (ISBN 0-317-05323-X). Sterling Swift.

Ryan, Michael A. The PET Index. 216p. 1982. pap. text ed. 17.95 (ISBN 0-566-03426-3). Gower Pub Co.

Smith, Alan M., ed. PCDex: Magazine Resource Guide for Commodore 64, VIC-20 & PET-CBM Personal Computers. 216p. (Orig.). 1984. pap. 14.95 (ISBN 0-918391-00-8). Altacom.

Weber, Jeffrey R. User's Guide to PET-CBM Computers. LC 80-70466. (How to Use Your Personal Computer Ser.). 330p. 1983. pap. 13.95 (ISBN 0-9604892-8-2). Weber Systems.

PETROGRAPHIC MICROSCOPE

McSween, H. Y., Jr. & Broadhead, T. W. An Introduction to the Petrographic Microscope: A Programmed Text. (Illus.). iii, 53p. 1982. lab manual 5.00 (ISBN 0-910249-04-0). U of Tenn Geo.

Wright, Frederic E. The Methods of Petrographic-Microscopic Research. 1977. lib. bdg. 75.00 (ISBN 0-8490-2229-0). Gordon Pr.

PETROGRAPHY

see Petrology

PETROLATUM

Curtis, Doris M., et al. How to (Try to) Find on Oil Field. 94p. 1981. 23.95x (ISBN 0-87814-166-9). Pennwell Bks.

PETROLEUM

see also Boring; Oil Fields; Petroleum Products

Alternative Arrangements for Petroleum Development: A Guide for Government Policy-Makers & Negotiators. 70p. 1983. pap. text ed. 10.00 (ISBN 0-686-46312-9, UN82/2A22, UN). Unipub.

Altgelt & Gouw. Chromatography in Petroleum Analysis. (Chromatographic Science Ser.: Vol. 11). 1979. 85.00 (ISBN 0-8247-6790-X). Dekker.

American Society for Testing & Institute of Petroleum. Petroleum Measurement Tables. 1973. (Pub. by Elsevier Applied Sci England); British Ed. 39.00 (ISBN 0-444-39994-1); Metric Ed. 48.00 (ISBN 0-444-39993-3). Elsevier.

Arrow, Kenneth J. & Kalt, Joseph P. Petroleum Price Regulation: Should We Decontrol? 1979. pap. 4.25 (ISBN 0-8447-3359-8). Am Enterprise.

Association of Desk & Derrick Clubs of America. D & D Standard Oil Abbreviator. 2nd ed. LC 72-96172. 230p. 14.95 (ISBN 0-87814-017-4). Pennwell Bks.

Atkinson, G. Origin & Chemistry of Petroleum: Proceedings of the Third Annual Karcher Symposium, Oklahoma, 1979. Zuckerman, J. J., ed. (Illus.). 120p. 1981. 33.00 (ISBN 0-08-026179-5). Pergamon.

Berger, Bill & Anderson, Ken. Petroleo Moderno. Pena, Gus, tr. from Eng. (Span.). 284p. 1980. 15.95 (ISBN 0-87814-136-7). Pennwell Bks.

Brooks, J., ed. Organic Maturation Studies & Fossil Fuel Exploration. LC 80-41958. 1981. 60.00 (ISBN 0-12-135760-0). Acad Pr.

Burcik, Emil J. Properties of Petroleum Reservoir Fluids. LC 57-5906. (Illus.). 190p. 1979. Repr. of 1957 ed. text ed. 29.00 (ISBN 0-934634-00-9). Intl Human Res.

Coleman, Hywel. Petroleum: Upstream. (Science & Technical Readers Ser.). (Orig.). 1980. pap. text ed. 2.95x (ISBN 0-435-29001-0). Heinemann Ed.

Colombia Ministerio De Obras Publicas Y Transporte & Inter-American Development Bank. The Impact of Energy Costs on the Transport Sector in Latin America: Proceedings of a Seminar Held in Bogota, Colombia Between December 1-3, 1983. LC 83-189959. (Illus.). v, 405p. Date not set. price not set. IADB.

Cram, Ire H., ed. Future Petroleum Provinces of the United States: Their Geology & Potential, 2 vols. LC 73-165867. (American Association of Petroleum Geologists Memoirs: No. 15). Vol. 1. pap. 160.00 (ISBN 0-317-10271-0, 2050024); Vol. 2. pap. 160.00 (ISBN 0-317-10272-9). Bks Demand UMI.

Crump, G. B., ed. Petroanalysis 81: Advances in Analytical Chemistry in the Petroleum Industry. Proceedings of the Institute of Petroleum (IP) 456p. 1983. 89.95 (ISBN 0-471-26217-X, Pub. by Wiley Interscience). Wiley.

Dahlberg, E. C. Applied Hydrodynamics in Petroleum Exploration. (Illus.). 161p. 1982. pap. 24.00 (ISBN 0-387-90677-0). Springer-Verlag.

Davidson, Martin J. & Gottlieb, Benjamin M., eds. Unconventional Methods in Exploration for Petroleum & Natural Gas, No. III. LC 83-8653. (Illus.). 282p. 1984. 50.00 (ISBN 0-87074-188-8). SMU Press.

Davis, Jerome D. High-Cost Oil & Gas Resources. (Illus.). 266p. 1981. 40.00 (ISBN 0-85664-588-5, Pub. by Croom Held Ltd). Longwood Pub Group.

Decroocq, Daniel. Catalytic Cracking of Heavy Petroleum Fractions. LC 84-71685. (Illus.). 136p. 1984. 42.95x (ISBN 0-87201-143-7). Gulf Pub.

Development of Petroleum & Natural Gas Resources in Asia & the Far East: Proceedings, Vols. 1 & 3. (Mineral Resources Development Ser.: No. 41). Vol. 1. pap. 19.00 (ISBN 0-686-93048-7, UN73/2F/14V2, UN); Vol. 3. pap. 8.50 (ISBN 0-686-98882-5). Unipub.

Engel, Bernard. Alaskan Crude. 1981. pap. 2.25 (ISBN 0-8439-0827-0). Dorchester Pub Co.

Fox, A. F. World of Oil. 1964. pap. 7.75 (ISBN 0-08-010686-2). Pergamon.

Frankel, Paul H. Essentials of Petroleum: A Key to Oil Economics. 2nd, rev. ed. 188p. 1969. 28.50x (ISBN 0-7146-1220-0, F Cass Co). Biblio Dist.

Gesner, Abraham. Practical Treatise on Coal, Petroleum & Other Distilled Oils. 2nd ed. Gesner, George W., ed. LC 67-29511. Repr. of 1865 ed. 25.00x (ISBN 0-678-00440-4). Kelley.

Gilbert, Chester G. & Pogue, Joseph E. Petroleum: A Resource Interpretation. 1980. lib. bdg. 49.95 (ISBN 0-8490-3109-5). Gordon Pr.

Glover, Sheldon L. Preliminary Report on Petroleum & Natural Gas in Washington. (Report of Investigations Ser.: No. 4). (Illus.). 24p. 1936. 0.25 (ISBN 0-686-34727-7). Geologic Pubns.

Goodier, J. L., et al. Spill Prevention & Fail-Safe Engineering for Petroleum & Related Products. LC 83-2204. (Pollution Tech. Rev. 100). (Illus.). 329p. (Orig.). 1983. 36.00 (ISBN 0-8155-0944-8). Noyes.

Hallwood, C. Paul & Sinclair, Stuart W. Oil Debt & Development: OPEC in the Third World. 208p. 1981. pap. text ed. 10.95x (ISBN 0-04-382027-1). Allen Unwin.

Harbaugh, John W., et al. Probability Methods in Oil Exploration. LC 76-50631. 269p. 1977. 42.95 (ISBN 0-471-35129-6, Pub. by Wiley-Interscience). Wiley.

Henry, J. T. Early & Later History of Petroleum. LC 76-107917. Repr. of 1873 ed. 45.00x (ISBN 0-678-00622-9). Kelley.

--Early & Later History of Petroleum with Authentic Facts in Regard to Its Development in Western Pennsylvania, 2 vols in 1. (Illus.). 1965. 21.00 (ISBN 0-8337-1658-1). B Franklin.

Herald, F. A., ed. Occurrence of Oil & Gas in West Texas. (Publication Ser.: 5716). (Illus.). 442p. 1957. 9.00 (ISBN 0-686-29362-2). Bur Econ Geology.

Hofstader, Robert A., et al, eds. Analysis of Petroleum for Trace Metals. LC 76-46297. (Advances in Chemistry Ser.: No. 156). 1976. 34.95 (ISBN 0-8412-0349-0). Am Chemical.
Hunt, John M. Petroleum Geochemistry & Geology. LC 79-1281. (Illus.). 617p. 1979. text ed. 46.95 (ISBN 0-7167-1005-6). W H Freeman.
Institute of Petroleum, ed. Continuous Density Measurement. 1979. 35.00x (ISBN 0-686-87265-7, Pub. by Inst Petroleum). State Mutual Bk.
Institute of Petroleum (IP) Expanding Uses of Petroleum. 1982. 35.95 (ISBN 0-471-26176-9). Wiley.
Kaylin, Arleen & Bowen, Douglas, eds. Update 1980. LC 79-27511. (The Great Contemporary Issues Ser.). (Illus.). 1980. write for info. (ISBN 0-405-13086-4). Ayer Co Pubs.
Kinghorn, Robert R. An Introduction to the Physics & Chemistry of Petroleum. 420p. 1983. 42.95x (ISBN 0-471-90054-0, Pub. by Wiley-Interscience). Wiley.
Kramer, Karlheinz. Erdoel Lexicon. 5th ed. (Eng. & Ger., Lexicon of Petroleum). 1972. 48.00 (ISBN 3-7785-0233-6, M-7366, Pub. by Heuthig). French & Eur.
Leipnitz, E. Dictionary of Petroleum-Industry & Petroleum Chemistry. (Polyglot.). 1979. 40.75x (ISBN 3-87097-073-1). Adlers Foreign Bks.
Linderman, Charles W., ed. International Technical Conference on Slurry Tranportation, 2nd: Proceedings. LC 77-81416. (Illus.). 152p. 1977. pap. 40.00 (ISBN 0-932066-02-X). Slurry Tech.
Lovejoy, Wallace F. Methods of Estimating Reserves of Crude Oil, Natural Gas, & Natural Gas Liquids. LC 65-24790. pap. 45.50 (ISBN 0-317-26470-2, 2023805). Bks Demand UMI.
McCain, William D., Jr. Properties of Petroleum Fluids. LC 73-78008. 325p. 1974. 49.95x (ISBN 0-87814-021-2). Pennwell Bks.
Malins, Donald C., ed. Effects of Petroleum on Arctic & Subarctic Marine Environments & Organisms: Biological Effects, Vols. 1 &2. 1977. Vol. 1. 39.00 (ISBN 0-12-466901-8); Vol. 2. 37.50 (ISBN 0-12-466902-6). Acad Pr.
Muskat, Morris. Physical Principles of Oil Production. LC 81-80667. (Illus.). 922p. 1981. Repr. of 1949 ed. text ed. 48.00 (ISBN 0-934634-07-6). Intl Human Res.
Netschert, Bruce C. The Future Supply of Oil & Gas: A Study of the Availability of Crude Oil, Natural Gas, & Natural Gas Liquids in the United States in the Period Through 1975. LC 77-23269. (Resources for the Future Ser.). 1977. Repr. of 1958 ed. lib. bdg. 18.75 (ISBN 0-8371-9473-3, NEOG). Greenwood.
Neumann, H. J., et al. Composition & Properties of Petroleum. 137p. 1981. pap. 18.95x (ISBN 0-470-27139-6). Halsted Pr.
Northern Development & Technology Assessment Systems: A Study of Petroleum Development Programs. (Science Council of Canada Background Studies: No. 34). 1977. pap. 6.95 (ISBN 0-685-77313-2, SSC65, SSC). Unipub.
Odell, Peter R. & Vallenilla, Luis. Pressures of Oil. 215p. 1978. text ed. 14.50 (ISBN 0-06-318086-3, Pub. by Har-Row Ltd England). Har-Row.
Oil & Natural Gas Resources of Canada 1976: Oil Sands & Heavy Oils - the Prospects, 2 pts. 1978. pap. 5.50 set (ISBN 0-685-89403-7, SSC97, SSC); Vol. 1. pap. (ISBN 0-660-00859-9); Vol. 2. pap. (ISBN 0-685-89404-5). Unipub.
Okandan, Ender, ed. Heavy Crude Oil Recovery. 1984. lib. bdg. 54.50 (ISBN 90-247-2951-3, Pub. by Martinus Nijhoff Netherlands). Kluwer Academic.
Pelofsky, Arnold H., ed. Heavy Oil Gasification. (Energy, Power & Environment Ser.: Vol. 1). 1977. 39.75 (ISBN 0-8247-6638-5). Dekker.
Robinson, Colin & Morgan, Jon. North Sea Oil in the Future. 1978. text ed. 26.00x (ISBN 0-8419-5043-1). Holmes & Meier.
Royal Dutch-Shell Group of Companies. The Petroleum Handbook. 6th, rev. ed. 710p. 1983. 127.50 (ISBN 0-444-42118-1). Elsevier.
Shear Stability of Multigrade Oils - IP Fleet Test, DS49-S1. (Data Ser.). 36p. 1974. pap. 4.00x (ISBN 0-8031-0566-5, 05-049001-12). ASTM.
Stocking, George W. The Mexican Oil Problem. 1976. lib. bdg. 59.95 (ISBN 0-8490-0618-X). Gordon Pr.
Tatsch, J. H. Petroleum Deposits: Origin, Evolution, & Present Characteristics. LC 73-93625. (Illus.). 378p. 1974. 50.00 (ISBN 0-912890-06-1). Tatsch.
Teh Fu Yen, ed. Shale Oil, Tar Sands, & Related Fuel Sources: A Symposium Co-Sponsored by the Division of Fuel Chemistry & the Division of Petroleum Chemistry of the American Chemical Society. LC 76-16510. (Advances in Chemistry Ser.: No. 151). (Illus.). pap. 47.80 (ISBN 0-317-10922-7, 2051257). Bks Demand UMI.
United Nations Institute for Training & Research. International Conference on the Future Supply of Nature-Made Petroleum & Gas: Proceedings. 1977. pap. text ed. 61.00 (ISBN 0-08-021735-4). Pergamon.
Valkovic, Vlado. Trace Elements in Petroleum. 269p. 1978. 41.95x (ISBN 0-87814-084-0). Pennwell Bks.
VDI. Synthetic Crude from Oil Sands. (Progress Report of the VDI-Z, Series 3: No. 80). 108p. (Orig.). 1983. pap. 34.00 (ISBN 0-9907000-1-1, Pub. by VDI W Germany). Heyden.
Wheeler, Robert R. & Whited, Maurine. Oil from Prospect to Pipeline. 5th ed. LC 84-15755. (Illus.). 160p. (Orig.). 1985. pap. 8.95x (ISBN 0-87201-636-6). Gulf Pub.
Woodland, A. W., ed. Petroleum & the Continental Shelf of Northwest Europe: Geology, Vol. 1. (Illus.). 501p. 1975. 92.50 (ISBN 0-85334-648-8, Pub. by Elsevier Applied Sci England). Elsevier.

PETROLEUM–BIBLIOGRAPHY

Aziz, K. & Settari, A. Petroleum Reservoir Simulation. (Illus.). 475p. 1979. 89.00 (ISBN 0-85334-787-5, Pub. by Elsevier Applied Sci England). Elsevier.
Stacy, Charles M. Bibliography of Petroleum Dictionaries. 35p. (Orig.). 1984. 9.75 (ISBN 0-916409-00-7). Specialized Intl Biblio.

PETROLEUM–DRILLING FLUIDS

see Drilling Muds

PETROLEUM–GEOLOGY

see also Oil Well Logging; Oil Well Logging, Electric; Oil Well Logging, Radiation

Al'tovskii, M. E., et al. Origin of Oil & Oil Deposits. LC 60-13948. 107p. 1961. 30.00x (ISBN 0-306-10564-0, Consultants). Plenum Pub.
American Association of Petroleum Geologists (26th: 1941: Houston) Staff. Possible Future Oil Provinces of the United States & Canada. Levorsen, A. I., ed. LC 41-23448. pap. 40.00 (ISBN 0-317-29056-8, 2023744). Bks Demand UMI.
American Petroleum Instiitute. Manual of Petroleum Measurement Standards. LC 80-67080. (Chapter 11.1 -- Volume Correction Factors: Vol. VI). (Illus.). 563p. 1980. write for info. (ISBN 0-89364-027-1). Am Petroleum.
Brooks, Jim & Welte, Dietrich H. Advances in Petroleum Geochemistry, Vol. 1. (Serial Publication Ser.). 1984. 49.50 (ISBN 0-12-032001-0). Acad Pr.
Chapman, R. E. Petroleum Geology. (Developments in Petroleum Science Ser.: Vol. 16). 416p. 1983. 44.25 (ISBN 0-444-42165-3, I-424-83). Elsevier.
--Petroleum Geology: A Concise Study. LC 72-97426. 310p. 1976. pap. 30.00 (ISBN 0-444-41432-0). Elsevier.
Dickey, Parke A. Petroleum Development Geology. 2nd ed. 428p. 1981. 49.95x (ISBN 0-87814-174-X). Pennwell Bks.
Dutton, S. P. Petroleum Source Rock Potential & Thermal Maturity, Palo Duro Basin, Texas. (Geological Circular Ser.: GC 80-10). (Illus.). 48p. 1980. 1.50 (ISBN 0-318-03137-X). Bur Econ Geology.
Dutton, S. P., et al. Petroleum Potential of the Palo Duro Basin, Texas Panhandle. (Report of Investigations: RI 123). (Illus.). 87p. 1982. 5.00 (ISBN 0-318-03264-3). Bur Econ Geology.
Earney, Fillmore C. Petroleum & Hard Minerals from the Sea. LC 80-17653. (Scripta Series in Geography). 291p. 1980. 53.95x (ISBN 0-470-27009-8, Pub. by Halsted Pr). Wiley.
Evaporite Deposits: Illustration & Interpretation of Some Environmental Sequences. 282p. 1980. 129.00x (ISBN 2-7108-0385-2, Pub. by Graham & Trotman England). State Mutual Bk.
Exlog. Field Geologist's Training Guide. (The Exlog Series of Petroleum Geology & Engineering Handbooks). (Illus.). 298p. 1985. text ed. 34.00 (ISBN 0-317-14155-4). Intl Human Res.
--Theory & Applications of Drilling Fluid Hydraulics. (The Exlog Series of Petroleum Geology & Engineering Handbooks). (Illus.). 208p. 1985. text ed. 27.00 (ISBN 0-88746-045-3). Intl Human Res.
EXLOG Staff. Formation Evaluation: Geological Procedures. Whittaker, Alun, ed. (The EXLOG Series of Petroleum Geology & Engineering Handbooks). (Illus.). 175p. 1985. text ed. 29.00 (ISBN 0-88746-054-2). Intl Human Res.
Fisher, W. L., et al. Delta Systems in the Exploration for Oil & Gas: Syllabus for Research Colloquium Held in Austin, August 1969. (Illus.). 212p. 1982. Repr. of 1969 ed. 6.00 (ISBN 0-318-03366-6). Bur Econ Geology.
Gary, James H., ed. Oil Shale: Proceedings of the Seventeenth Symposium. (Illus.). 440p. 1984. pap. text ed. 25.00 (ISBN 0-918062-58-6). Colo Sch Mines.
Giles, A. B. & Wood, D. H. Oakwood Salt Dome, East Texas: Geologic Framework, Growth History, & Hydrocarbon Production. (Geological Circular Ser.: GC 83-1). (Illus.). 55p. 1983. 2.50 (ISBN 0-318-03156-6). Bur Econ Geology.
Glennie, K. W., ed. Introduction to the Petroleum Geology of the North Sea. 236p. 1984. pap. text ed. 31.00x (ISBN 0-632-01268-4, Pub. by Blackwell Sci UK). Blackwell Pubns.
Graham & Trotman Ltd., ed. Nigeria: Its Petroleum Geology, Resources & Potential, Vol. 1. 176p. 1982. 110.00x (ISBN 0-86010-264-5, Pub. by Graham & Trotman England). State Mutual Bk.
Hedberg, Hollis D., et al, eds. Petroleum Geochemistry, Genesis & Migration. (AGI Reprint Ser.). (Illus.). 296p. 1983. pap. write for info (ISBN 0-913312-77-0). Am Geol.
Hobson, G. D. & Tiratsoo, E. N. Introduction to Petroleum Geology. rev., 2nd ed. LC 80-85239. 382p. 1985. 49.95x (ISBN 0-87201-401-0). Gulf Pub.
Hooks, McCloskey & Assoc., ed. Federal & State Regulation of Oil & Gas Exploration & Development on the Outer Continental Shelf. 369p. 1983. 65.00 (ISBN 0-89419-278-7). Inst Energy.
Institute of Petroleum. Recommended Practice for Radio Silence When Conducting Wireline Services Involving the Use of Explosives. 37p. 1984. pap. 24.95 (ISBN 0-471-90653-0). Wiley.
Jain, K. C. & DeFigueiredo, R. J., eds. Concepts & Techniques in Oil & Gas Exploration. 289p. 1982. 37.00 (ISBN 0-931830-22-2); members 30.00. Soc Exploration.
Jones, M. J., ed. Mining & Petroleum Geology. (Proceedings of the Ninth Commonwealth Mining & Metallurgical Congress 1969: Vol. 2). 774p. 1970. text ed. 46.00x (ISBN 0-900488-03-4). IMM North Am.
Landes, Kenneth K. Petroleum Geology. 2nd ed. LC 74-26700. 458p. 1975. Repr. of 1959 ed. 28.50 (ISBN 0-88275-226-X). Krieger.
--Petroleum Geology of the United States. LC 77-101975. 571p. 1970. 87.95x (ISBN 0-471-51335-0, Pub. by Wiley-Interscience). Wiley.
Levorsen, A. I. Geology of Petroleum. 2nd ed. LC 65-25242. (Geology Ser.). (Illus.). 724p. 1967. 37.95 (ISBN 0-7167-0230-4). W H Freeman.
Liddle, R. A. The Van Oil Field, Van Zandt County, Texas. (Bull 3601 Ser.). 79p. 1936. 1.50 (ISBN 0-318-03307-0). Bur Econ Geology.
Link, Dr. Peter K. Basic Petroleum Geology. 235p. 1982. 40.00 (ISBN 0-930972-01-5). Oil & Gas.
Link, Peter K. Basic Petroleum Geology. (Illus.). 235p. 1982. 43.00 (ISBN 0-930972-01-5, P-7039). Pennwell Bks.
Mason, John F., ed. Petroleum Geology in China. 263p. 1981. 39.95x (ISBN 0-87814-163-4). Pennwell Bks.
Megill, R. E. An Introduction to Exploration Economics. 2nd ed. LC 75-153985. 180p. 1979. 44.95x (ISBN 0-87814-115-4). Pennwell Bks.
--Long Range Exploration Planning. 96p. 1985. 33.95 (ISBN 0-87814-286-X). PennWell Bks.
Moody, Graham B. Petroleum Exploration Handbook: A Practical Manual Summarizing the Application of Earth Sciences to Petroleum Exploration. (Illus.). 1961. 75.00 (ISBN 0-07-042867-0). McGraw.
Morton, R. A., et al. Continuity & Internal Properties of Gulf Coast Sandstones & Their Implications for Geopressured Fluid Production. (Report of Investigations Ser.: RI 132). (Illus.). 70p. 1983. 3.00 (ISBN 0-318-03287-2). Bur Econ Geology.
Newendorp, Paul D. Decision Analysis for Petroleum Exploration. LC 75-10936. 668p. 1976. 69.95 (ISBN 0-87814-064-6). Pennwell Bks.
North, F. K. Petroleum Geology. (Illus.). 750p. 1985. text ed. 60.00x (ISBN 0-04-553003-3); pap. text ed. 34.95x (ISBN 0-04-553004-1). Allen Unwin.
Okandan, Ender, ed. Heavy Crude Oil Recovery. 1984. lib. bdg. 54.50 (ISBN 90-247-2951-3, Pub. by Martinus Nijhoff Netherlands). Kluwer Academic.
Petrakis, Leon & Weiss, F. T., eds. Petroleum in the Marine Environment. LC 79-25524. (ACS Advances in Chemistry Ser.: No. 185). 1980. 54.95 (ISBN 0-8412-0475-6). Am Chemical.
Petroleum Exploration Strategies in Developing Countries. 272p. 1981. 75.00x (ISBN 0-86010-346-3, Pub. by Graham & Trotman England). State Mutual Bk.
Petroleum Geology & Reservoirs. (Well Servicing & Workover Ser.: Lesson 2). (Illus.). 65p. (Orig.). pap. text ed. 5.00 (ISBN 0-88698-058-5, 3.70210). PETEX.
Pirson, Sylvain J. Geologic Well Log Analysis. 3rd ed. LC 82-24218. 476p. 1983. 29.95x (ISBN 0-87201-902-0); 32 p Bar Code Supplement 49.95x (ISBN 0-87201-903-9). Gulf Pub.
Plummer, H. J., et al. Calcareous Foraminifera in the Brownwood Shale Near Bridgeport, Texas & Foraminifera of the Cisco Group in Texas. (Bull Ser.: 3019). (Illus.). 90p. 1930. 1.00 (ISBN 0-318-03305-4). Bur Econ Geology.
Porstendorfer, G. Principles of Magneto-Telluric Prospecting. (Geoexploration Monographs: Ser. 1, No. 5). (Illus.). 118p. 1975. lib. bdg. 31.20x (ISBN 3-4431-3007-0). Lubrecht & Cramer.
Robinson, Joseph E., ed. Computer Applications in Petroleum Geology. LC 82-3113. (Computer Methods in the Geosciences Ser.). 164p. 1982. 26.95 (ISBN 0-87933-444-4); pap. 16.95 (ISBN 0-87933-432-0). Van Nos Reinhold.
Roehl, P. O. & Choquette, P. W. Carbonate Petroleum Reservoir. (Casebooks in Earth Sciences Ser.). (Illus.). 480p. 1985. 59.00 (ISBN 0-387-96012-0). Springer-Verlag.
Selley, Richard C. Elements of Petroleum Geology. LC 84-24718. (Illus.). 449p. 1985. text ed. 44.95 (ISBN 0-7167-1630-5). W H Freeman.
--Petroleum Geology for Geophysicists & Engineers. LC 82-81124. (Short Course Handbooks). (Illus.). 88p. 1983. text ed. 23.00 (ISBN 0-934634-49-1); pap. 15.00 (ISBN 0-934634-42-4). Intl Human Res.
Sengbush, Ray L. Introduction to Petroleum Exploration. 191p. 1985. text ed. price not set (ISBN 0-88746-047-X). Intl Human Res.
Silver, Burr A. Subsurface Exploration Stratigraphy. 45.00 (ISBN 0-318-02024-6). IED Pub Hse.
--Techniques of Using Geologic Data. 32.00 (ISBN 0-318-02025-4). IED Pub Hse.
Silvia, M. T. & Robinson, E. A. Deconvolution of Geophysical Time Series in the Exploration of Oil & Natural Gas. (Developments in Petroleum Science Ser.: Vol. 10). 252p. 1979. 61.75 (ISBN 0-444-41679-X). Elsevier.
Takken, Suzanne, ed. Handbook on Petroleum Exploration. 172p. 1978. 24.00 (ISBN 0-89419-021-0); pap. 14.00 (ISBN 0-685-41833-2). Inst Energy.
Tissot, B. P. & Welte, D. H. Petroleum Formation & Occurence. rev. & enl. ed. (Illus.). 610p. 1984. 44.50 (ISBN 0-387-13281-3). Springer-Verlag.
Valencia, M., ed. Hydrocarbon Potential of the South China Sea: Possibilities of Joint Development: Proceedings of the EAPI-CCOP Workshop, East-West Center, Honolulu, Hawaii, USA. 260p. 1982. 26.00 (ISBN 0-08-028692-5). Pergamon.
Whiteman, Arthur. Nigeria: Its Petroleum Geology, Resources & Potential, Vol. 2. 238p. 1982. 110.00x (ISBN 0-86010-265-3, Pub. by Graham & Trotman England). State Mutual Bk.
World Petroleum Congress. Proceedings of the Ninth World Petroleum Congress: Exploration & Transportation, Vol. 3. 390p. 1975. 111.00 (ISBN 0-85334-665-8, Pub. by Elsevier Applied Sci England). Elsevier.
Wrather, W. E. & Lahee, F. H., eds. Problems of Petroleum Geology, 2 vols. 1976. lib. bdg. 250.00 (ISBN 0-8490-2485-4). Gordon Pr.
Zambrano, E. & Vasquez, E. Paleogeographic & Petroleum Synthesis of Western Venezuela. 70p. 1972. 60.00x (ISBN 2-7108-0194-9, Pub. by Graham & Trotman England). State Mutual Bk.

PETROLEUM–MICROBIOLOGY

Atlas, Ronald M., ed. Petroleum Microbiology. 500p. 1984. text ed. 55.00 (ISBN 0-02-949000-6). Macmillan.

PETROLEUM–PIPE LINES

Contingency Planning Considerations: Northern Oil & Gas Pipelines. 1979. pap. 9.00 (ISBN 0-685-96906-1, SSC125, SSC). Unipub.
Cookenboo, Leslie, Jr. Crude Oil Pipe Lines & Competition in the Oil Industry & Costs of Operating Crude Oil Pipe Lines. Bruchey, Stuart, ed. LC 78-22669. (Rice Institute Pamphlet: Energy in the American Economy Ser.: Vol. 41, No. 1). (Illus.). 1979. Repr. of 1955 ed. lib. bdg. 25.50x (ISBN 0-405-11973-9). Ayer Co Pubs.
Cranmer, John L. Basic Pipeline Engineering Manual. 240p. 1983. 64.95 (ISBN 0-87814-244-4). Pennwell Bks.
Hansen, John A. U. S. Oil Pipeline Markets: Structure, Pricing, & Public Policy. Schmalensee, R., ed. (Regulation of Economic Activity Ser.). 176p. 1983. 27.50x (ISBN 0-262-08128-8). MIT Pr.
Hosmanek, Max. Pipeline Construction. Cyrus, Cinda, ed. (Illus.). 122p. (Orig.). 1984. pap. text ed. 8.50 (ISBN 0-88698-096-8, 4.00030). Petex.
Hydrogeological Considerations in Northern Pipeline Development. pap. 5.00 (SSC50, SSC). Unipub.

--Manual of Petroleum Measurement Standards. LC 80-67080. (Chapter 11.1 -- Volume Correction Factors). 1980. write for info. (ISBN 0-89364-035-2). Am Petroleum.

--Manual of Petroleum Measurements Standards. LC 80-67080. (Chapter 11.1 -- Volume Correction Factors: Vol. VII). (Illus.). 958p. 1980. write for info. (ISBN 0-89364-029-8). Am Petroleum.

Ariman, T., ed. Earthquake Behavior & Safety of Oil & Gas Storage Facilities, Buried Pipelines & Equipment, Vol. 77. 478p. 1983. pap. text ed. 70.00 (ISBN 0-317-02615-1, H00263). ASME.

Artificial Lift Methods. (Well Servicing & Workover Ser.: Lesson 5). (Illus.). 45p. (Orig.). 1971. pap. text ed. 4.50 (ISBN 0-88698-061-5, 3.70510). PETEX.

Atteraas, L., et al, eds. Underwater Technology-Offshore Petroleum: Proceedings of the International Conference, Bergen, Norway, April 14-16 1980. LC 80-40414. 450p. 1980. 78.00 (ISBN 0-08-026141-8). Pergamon.

Baker, Ron. Treating Oil Field Emissions. 2nd ed. Taylor, Lydia, ed. (Illus.). 112p. (Orig.). 1974. pap. text ed. 6.00 (ISBN 0-88698-121-2, 3.50030). Petex.

Baldwin, Pamela L. & Baldwin, Malcolm F. Onshore Planning for Offshore Oil: Lessons from Scotland. LC 75-606. (Illus.). 1975. pap. 5.00 (ISBN 0-89164-001-0). Conservation Foun.

Belov, P. Fundamentals of Petroleum Chemicals Technology. Sobolev, David, tr. from Russian. (Illus.). 430p. 1970. 16.00x (ISBN 0-8464-0438-9). Beekman Pubs.

Block, Richard A. & Collins, Charles B., eds. The M&O Master's Handbook. (Illus.). 271p. (Orig.). 1979. pap. text ed. 15.00 (ISBN 0-934114-16-1, BK-117). Marine Educ.

Blowout Prevention. 3rd, rev. ed. (Rotary Drilling Ser.: Unit III, Lesson 3). (Illus.). 97p. (Orig.). 1980. pap. text ed. 5.00 (ISBN 0-88698-051-8, 2.30330). PETEX.

Boyd, W. E. Control of Formation Pressure. (Well Servicing & Workover: Lesson 9). (Illus.). 44p. (Orig.). 1971. pap. text ed. 4.50 (ISBN 0-88698-065-8, 3.70910). PETEX.

--Fishing Tools & Techniques. (Well Servicing & Workover Ser.: Lesson 10). (Illus.). 48p. (Orig.). 1971. pap. text ed. 4.50 (ISBN 0-88698-066-6, 3.71010). PETEX.

Boyd, William. Principles of Drilling Fluid Control. (Illus.). 215p. 1978. pap. text ed. 8.00 (ISBN 0-88698-096-8). Petex.

Brenner, Robert L. Petroleum Stratigraphy: A Guide for Nongeologists. 193p. 1984. 27.00 (ISBN 0-934634-38-6). Intl Human Res.

Bustin, W. & Dukek, W. Electrostatic Hazards in the Petroleum Industry. (Electrostatics & Electrostatic Application Ser.). 100p. 1983. 26.95 (ISBN 0-471-90163-6, Pub. by Res Stud Pr). Wiley.

Carmona-Agosto, Vivian, ed. The Bit. Albornoz, Fernando, tr. (Rotary Drilling Ser.: Unit I, Lesson 2). (Span., Illus.). 59p. (Orig.). 1981. pap. text ed. 5.00 (ISBN 0-88698-030-5, 2.10232). PETEX.

--Safety on the Rig. rev. ed. Albornoz, Fernando, tr. from Eng. (Rotary Drilling Ser.: Unit I, Lesson6). (Span., Illus.). 77p. 1981. pap. text ed. 5.00 (ISBN 0-88698-038-0, 2.11032). PETEX.

Carneiro, F. L., et al. Offshore Structures Engineering, Vol. 5. LC 84-80880. (Offshore Structures Engineering Ser.). 832p. 1984. 49.95x (ISBN 0-87201-607-2). Gulf Pub.

Chenevert, Martin & Roye, J. PIPECALC (TM) 1: Practical Pipeline Hydraulics. LC 84-9007. (Microcomputer Software for Pipeline Engineers Ser.). 1984. incl. disk 295.00x (ISBN 0-87201-741-9). Gulf Pub.

Chenevert, Martin E. & Hollo, Reuven. TI-Fifty-Nine Drilling Engineering Manual. LC 81-1110. 249p. 1981. 65.95 (ISBN 0-87814-161-8). Pennwell Bks.

Clearance of Oil from Water Surfaces: The Oil Mop Recovery Device, 1978. 1981. 40.00x (ISBN 0-686-97043-8, Pub. by W Spring England). State Mutual Bk.

Coenen, George L. Basic Electronics for the Petroleum Industry: Unit I. Greenlaw, Martha, ed. (Illus.). 33p. (Orig.). 1980. pap. text ed. 4.50 (ISBN 0-88698-100-X, 1.41130). Petex.

--Basic Electronics for the Petroleum Industry: Unit II. 3rd ed. Greenlaw, Martha, ed. (Illus.). 51p. (Orig.). 1980. pap. text ed. 4.50 (ISBN 0-88698-102-6, 1.41230). Petex.

--Basic Electronics for the Petroleum Industry: Unit III. Greenlaw, Martha, ed. (Illus.). 55p. (Orig.). 1980. pap. text ed. 4.50 (ISBN 0-88698-103-4, 1.41330). Petex.

--Basic Electronics for the Petroleum Industry: Unit IV. 3rd ed. Greenlaw, Martha, ed. (Illus.). 54p. (Orig.). 1980. pap. text ed. 4.50 (ISBN 0-88698-104-2, 1.41430). Petex.

--Basic Electronics for the Petroleum Industry: Unit V. Greenlaw, Martha, ed. (Illus.). 35p. (Orig.). 1980. pap. text ed. 4.50 (ISBN 0-88698-105-0, 1.41530). Petex.

Collip, Bruce G. Buoyancy, Stability & Trim. (Rotary Drilling Ser.: Unit V, Lesson 3). (Illus.). 30p. (Orig.). 1976. pap. text ed. 4.50 (ISBN 0-88698-071-2, 2.50310). PETEX.

Constant, Nicholas J. Improved Recovery. LC 83-62119. (Oil & Gas Production Ser.: Lesson 8). (Illus., Orig.). 1983. pap. text ed. 7.50 (ISBN 0-88698-044-5, 3.30810). PETEX.

Controlled Directional Drilling. 2nd, rev. ed. (Rotary Drilling Ser.: Unit III, Lesson 1). (Illus.). 41p. (Orig.). 1974. pap. text ed. 5.00 (ISBN 0-88698-049-6, 2.30120). PETEX.

Cranmer, John L. Basic Pipeline Engineering Manual. 240p. 1983. 64.95 (ISBN 0-87814-244-4). Pennwell Bks.

Cyrus, Cinda. A Primer of Oilwell Service & Workover. 3rd ed. Gerding, Mildred, ed. (Illus.). 106p. (Orig.). 1979. pap. text ed. 6.50 (ISBN 0-88698-117-4, 3.60030). Petex.

--Well Cementing. Paxson, Jeanette R., ed. (Oil & Gas Production Ser.). (Illus.). 82p. (Orig.). 1983. pap. text ed. 5.00 (ISBN 0-88698-112-3, 3.30610). Petex.

Davia, N. C. & Thomas, D. An Assessment of the Model Six-V Oil Skimm ER Supplied by Engineering & General Equipment Ltd., 1980. 1981. 30.00x (ISBN 0-686-97036-5, Pub. by W Spring England). State Mutual Bk.

Dawe, R. A. & Wilson, D. C., eds. Developments in Petroleum Engineering, No. 1. 288p. 1985. 54.00 (ISBN 0-85334-358-6, Pub. by Elsevier Applied Sci England). Elsevier.

De Malherbe, R. & De Malherbe, M. C. Risk Analysis in Some Production & Refining Systems in the Petroleum Industry. 1981. 41.00 (ISBN 0-9961073-3-9, Pub. by VDI W Germany). Heyden.

Donaldson, E. C. Enhanced Oil Recovery, 1: Fundamentals & Analyses. (Developments in Petroleum Science Ser.: Vol. 17A). 1985. 65.00 (ISBN 0-444-42206-4, I-456-84). Elsevier.

Drilling Mud. rev. ed. (Rotary Drilling Ser.: Unit II, Lesson 2). (Illus., Orig.). 1975. pap. text ed. 5.00 (ISBN 0-88698-054-2, 2.20220). PETEX.

Duchscherer, W., Jr. Geochemical Hydrocarbon Prospecting with Case Histories. 208p. 1984. write for info. (ISBN 0-87814-261-4). PennWell Bks.

Eaton, David. Shale Oil Technology: Status of the Industry. (Working Papers Ser.: No. 7). 39p. 1977. pap. 2.50 (ISBN 0-318-00185-3). LBJ Sch Pub Aff.

Ely, John. Stimulation Treatment Handbook. 272p. 1985. 39.95 (ISBN 0-87814-284-3). PennWell Bks.

Enhanced Oil Recovery by Displacement with Saline Solutions. LC 79-84033. 148p. 1979. 21.95x (ISBN 0-87201-263-8). Gulf Pub.

Evans, Frank L., Jr. Equipment Design Handbook for Refineries & Chemical Plants, 2 Vols. 2nd ed. LC 79-50245. Vol. 1, 196p. 1979 37.95x (ISBN 0-87201-254-9); Vol. 2, 370p. 1980 41.95x (ISBN 0-87201-255-7). Gulf Pub.

EXLOG. Mud Logging: Principles & Interpretations. (The Exlog Series of Petroleum Geology & Engineering Handbooks). (Illus.). 98p. 1985. text ed. 26.00 (ISBN 0-88746-044-5). Intl Human Res.

EXLOG Staff. Formation Evaluation: Geological Procedures. Whittaker, Alun, ed. (The EXLOG Series of Petroleum Geology & Engineering Handbooks). (Illus.). 175p. 1985. text ed. 29.00 (ISBN 0-88746-054-2). Intl Human Res.

--Theory & Evaluation of Formation Pressures: A Pressure Detection Reference Handbook. Whittaker, Alun, ed. (EXLOG Series of Petroleum Geology & Engineering Handbooks). (Illus.). 225p. 1985. text ed. 32.00 (ISBN 0-88746-052-6). Intl Human Res.

Fayers, F. J. Enhanced Oil Recovery. (Developments in Petroleum Science Ser.: Vol. 13). 596p. 1981. 78.75 (ISBN 0-444-42033-9). Elsevier.

Fertl, W. H. Abnormal Formation Pressures. (Developments in Petroleum Science: Vol. 2). 382p. 1976. 47.00 (ISBN 0-444-41328-6). Elsevier.

Gas Processors Suppliers Assn. Engineering Data Book: English Units 9th ed, SI Units 1st ed. 1981. 41.95 (ISBN 0-686-45985-7, P-7020). Pennwell Bks.

Gatlin, Carl. Petroleum Engineering: Drilling & Well Completion. 1960. ref. ed. 42.95 (ISBN 0-13-662155-4). P-H.

Gerding, Mildred. The Rotary Rig & Its Components: Canadian Metric Edition. 3rd ed. (Rotary Drilling Ser.: Unit I, Lesson 1). (Illus.). 1979. pap. text ed. 5.00 (ISBN 0-88698-017-8). PETEX.

Gerding, Mildred, ed. Applied Mathematics for the Petroleum Other Industries. 3rd, rev. ed. (Illus.). 274p. 1985. pap. text ed. 10.00 (ISBN 0-88698-085-2, 1.60030). PETEX.

--The Rotary Rig & Its Components. 3rd ed. (Rotary Drilling Ser.: Unit I, Lesson 1). (Illus.). Date not set. pap. text ed. 5.00 (ISBN 0-88698-005-4, 2.10130). PETEX.

--Well Service & Workover Profitability. (Well Servicing & Workover Ser.: Lesson 12). (Illus.). 32p. 1980. pap. text ed. 4.50 (ISBN 0-88698-068-2, 3.71220). PETEX.

Giuliano, Francis A., ed. Introduction to Oil & Gas Technology. 2nd ed. (Short Course Handbooks). (Illus.). 194p. 1981. text ed. 32.00 (ISBN 0-934634-48-3); pap. text ed. 24.00. Intl Human Res.

Goins, W. C. & Sheffield, Riley. Blowout Prevention. 2nd ed. LC 70-101145. (Practical Drilling Technology Ser.: Vol. 1). 336p. 1983. 39.95x (ISBN 0-87201-073-2). Gulf Pub.

Gore, Nancy. Wireline Operations. LC 83-62077. (Oil & Gas Production Ser.: Lesson 10). (Illus.). 80p. (Orig.). 1983. pap. text ed. 5.00 (ISBN 0-88698-043-7, 3.31010). PETEX.

Gottleib, Benjamin M., ed. Unconventional Methods in Exploration for Petroleum & Natural Gas II. (Illus.). 280p. 1981. 50.00 (ISBN 0-87074-179-9). SMU Press.

Goudy, Linda M., ed. Hart's Petroleum Professionals, 1985. 2nd ed. 568p. 1985. pap. text ed. 40.00 (ISBN 0-912553-06-5). Hart Pubns.

Grona, Nancy. Basic Electricity for the Petroleum Industry. 2nd ed. (Illus.). 146p. (Orig.). 1978. pap. text ed. 5.50 (ISBN 0-88698-079-8, 1.40020). PETEX.

Grona, Nancy & Skinner, Mary L. Operation of Electrified & Automatic Leases. 2nd ed. Gerding, Mildred, ed. (Illus.). 114p. (Orig.). 1978. pap. text ed. 5.50 (ISBN 0-88698-113-1, 3.20020). Petex.

Haggard, Russell, ed. Orientation for Offshore Crane Operations. Rev. ed. (Rotary Drilling Ser.: Unit V: Offshore Technology Lesson 8). (Illus.). 35p. (Orig.). 1983. pap. text ed. 4.50 (ISBN 0-88698-042-9, 2.50810). Petex.

Haggard, Rusty. Diving & Equipment. 2nd, rev. ed. Janicek, Nancy, ed. (Rotary Drilling Ser.: Unit V, Lesson 5). (Illus.). 45p. (Orig.). 1982. pap. text ed. 4.50 (ISBN 0-88698-073-9, 2.50520). PETEX.

Hallenburg, James K. Geophysical Logging for Mineral & Engineering Applications. 264p. 1983. 69.95 (ISBN 0-87814-235-5). Pennwell Bks.

Hankinson, R. L. & Hankinson, R. L., Jr. LANDSTAR TM: The Landman's Encyclopedia Database. 1985. incl. floppy disk 995.00x (ISBN 0-87201-422-3). Gulf Pub.

Henderson, Celina, ed. Spread Mooring Systems. Rossman, Marcela, tr. from Eng. (Rotary Drilling Ser.: Unit V, Lesson 2). (Span., Illus.). 53p. (Orig.). 1982. pap. text ed. 4.50 (ISBN 0-88698-045-3, 2.50212). PETEX.

Hepple, P. & Institute of Petroleum. Expanding Uses of Petroleum. (Illus.). 105p. 1966. 13.00 (ISBN 0-444-39958-5, Pub. by Elsevier Applied Sci England). Elsevier.

Heroy, W. B., ed. Unconventional Methods in Exploring Petroleum & Natural Gas. (Illus.). 256p. 1969. 50.00 (ISBN 0-87074-184-5). SMU Press.

Hobson, G. D., ed. Modern Petroleum Technology: Pts. 1 & 2. 5th ed. 1000p. 1984. Set. 225.00 (ISBN 0-471-26249-8, Pub. by Wiley Interscience). Wiley.

Holcomb, Eldon. Arithmetic for Rig Personnel. 59p. (Orig.). 1982. pap. text ed. 2.00 (ISBN 0-88698-106-9, 1.61010). Petex.

Hoskins, James C., II. The Petroleum Landman: Basic Practices & Procedures. 26.00 (ISBN 0-318-02009-2). IED Pub Hse.

Hosmanek, Max. Pipeline Construction. Cyrus, Cinda, ed. (Illus.). 122p. (Orig.). 1984. pap. text ed. 8.50 (ISBN 0-88698-096-8, 4.00030). Petex.

Howell, J. K. & Hogwood, E. E. Electrified Oil Production. 344p. 1981. 47.95 (ISBN 0-87814-167-7, P-4275). Pennwell Bks.

Hsu, Teng H. Applied Offshore Structural Engineering. LC 84-628. 200p. 1984. 29.95x (ISBN 0-87201-750-8). Gulf Pub.

Ikoku, Chi U. Natural Gas Production Engineering. LC 83-21617. 517p. 1984. 39.50 (ISBN 0-471-89483-4). Wiley.

Institute of Petroleum. Institute of Petroleum: Petroleum Measurement, Instrumentation for Primary Measurement, Pt. XII, Sect. 3. 40p. 1983. 22.95 (ISBN 0-471-26282-X). Wiley.

--Recommended Practice for Radio Silence When Conducting Wireline Services Involving the Use of Explosives. 37p. 1984. pap. 24.95 (ISBN 0-471-90653-0). Wiley.

Institute of Petroleum (Great Britain) Staff. Metrication-UK: Units for the Measurement of Crude Oil & Petroleum Products. LC 74-183161. pap. 20.00 (2023700). Bks Demand UMI.

International Labour Office Staff. Small-Scale Oil Extraction from Groundnuts & Copra: Technical Memorandum, No. 5. (Technology Ser.). xi, 111p. (Orig.). 1983. pap. 8.55 (ISBN 92-2-103503-4). Intl Labour Office.

The International Transfer of Technology in Establishment of the Petrochemical Industry in Developing Countries. pap. 3.00 (UN75/15/RR12, UN). Unipub.

Introduction to Oilwell Service & Workover. (Well Servicing & Workover Ser.: Lesson I). (Illus.). 73p. (Orig.). 1971. pap. text ed. 5.00 (ISBN 0-88698-057-7, 3.70110). PETEX.

Janicek, Nancy, ed. Drilling a Straight Hole. 3rd, rev. ed. (Rotary Drilling Ser.: Unit II, Lesson 3). (Illus.). 37p. (Orig.). 1982. pap. text ed. 5.00 (ISBN 0-88698-055-0, 2.20320). PETEX.

Jenkins, G. Oil Economists' Handbook: 1984. 292p. 1983. 77.75 (ISBN 0-85334-207-5, I-264-83, Pub. by Elsevier Applied Sci England). Elsevier.

Jensen, Johannes & Sorensen, Bent. Fundamentals of Energy Storage. LC 83-10348. (Alternate Energy Ser.: 1-326). 345p. 1983. 45.95x (ISBN 0-471-08604-5, 1-326, Pub. by Wiley-Interscience). Wiley.

Johansen, Robert T. & Berg, Robert L., eds. Chemistry of Oil Recovery. LC 78-27298. (ACS Symposium Ser.: No. 91). 1979. 34.95 (ISBN 0-8412-0477-2). Am Chemical.

Kay, Deven L., ed. Western Oil Reporter: Rocky Mountain Petroleum Directory, 1985. 31st. ed. 1056p. 1985. pap. text ed. 32.00 (ISBN 0-912553-03-0). Hart Pubns.

Kirkley, Charles, ed. Corrosion Control. (Oil & Gas Production Ser.). (Illus.). 76p. (Orig.). 1982. pap. text ed. 5.00 (ISBN 0-88698-110-7, 3.30110). Petex.

--Making Hole. 2nd, rev. ed. (Rotary Drilling Ser.: Unit II, Lesson 1). (Illus.). 38p. (Orig.). 1983. pap. text ed. 5.00 (ISBN 0-88698-053-4, 2.20120). PETEX.

Kruse, Curtis. Jacking Systems & Rig Moving Procedures. (Rotary Drilling Ser.: Unit V, Lesson 4). (Illus.). 52p. (Orig.). 1976. pap. text ed. 4.50 (ISBN 0-88698-072-0, 2.50410). PETEX.

Latil, M. Enhanced Oil Recovery. LC 79-56344. 236p. (Orig.). 1980. pap. 29.95x (ISBN 0-87201-775-3). Gulf Pub.

Lee, M. A. The Droplet Size Distribution of Oils Emulsified in Sea Water by Concentrate Dispersants, 1980. 1981. 30.00x (ISBN 0-686-97064-0, Pub. by W Spring England). State Mutual Bk.

Leecraft, Jodie. Diesel Engines & Electric Power. (Rotary Drilling Ser.: Unit I, Lesson 11). (Illus.). 90p. (Orig.). 1982. pap. text ed. 5.00 (ISBN 0-88698-027-5, 2.11121). PETEX.

Leecraft, Jodie, ed. The Auxiliaries. 2nd ed. (Rotary Drilling Ser.: Unit I, Lesson 9). (Illus.). 48p. 1981. pap. text ed. 5.00 (ISBN 0-88698-013-5, 2.10920). PETEX.

--The Auxiliaries: Canadian Metric Edition. rev. ed. (Rotary Drilling Ser.: Unit I, Lesson 9). (Illus.). Date not set. pap. text ed. 5.00 (ISBN 0-88698-025-9, 2.10921). PETEX.

--The Bit. 3rd ed. (Rotary Drilling Ser.: Unit I, Lesson 2). (Illus.). 60p. Date not set. pap. text ed. 5.00 (ISBN 0-88698-006-2, 2.10230). PETEX.

--The Bit: Canadian Metric Edition. (Rotary Drilling Ser.: Unit I, Lesson 2). (Illus.). 60p. (Orig.). 1980. pap. text ed. 5.00 (ISBN 0-88698-018-6, 2.10231). PETEX.

--The Blocks & Drilling Line. rev. ed. Albornoz, Fernando, tr. (Rotary Drilling Ser.: Unit I, Lesson 5). (Span., Illus.). 51p. (Orig.). 1981. pap. text ed. 5.00 (ISBN 0-88698-033-X, 2.10520). PETEX.

--The Blocks & Drilling Line: Canadian Metric Edition. (Rotary Drilling Ser.: Unit I, Lesson 5). (Illus.). 51p. (Orig.). pap. text ed. 5.00 (ISBN 0-88698-021-6, 2.10510). PETEX.

--Circulating Systems. 3rd, rev. ed. (Rotary Drilling Ser.: Unit I, Lesson 8). (Illus.). 47p. (Orig.). 1981. pap. text ed. 5.00 (ISBN 0-88698-024-0, 2.10831). PETEX.

--Circulating Systems. 3rd ed. (Rotary Drilling Ser.: Unit I, Lesson 8). (Illus.). 52p. (Orig.). 1981. pap. text ed. 5.00 (ISBN 0-88698-012-7, 2.10830). PETEX.

--Diesel Engines & Electric Power. 2nd ed. (Rotary Drilling Ser.: Unit I, Lesson 11). (Illus.). 99p. (Orig.). 1981. pap. text ed. 5.00 (ISBN 0-88698-015-1, 2.11120). PETEX.

--The Drill Stem. 2nd ed. (Rotary Drilling Ser.: Unit I, Lesson 3). (Illus.). 52p. (Orig.). 1981. pap. text ed. 5.00 (ISBN 0-88698-007-0, 2.10320). PETEX.

--The Drill Stem: Metric Version. 2nd, rev. ed. (Rotary Drilling Ser.: Unit I, Lesson 3). (Illus.). 40p. (Orig.). 1981. pap. text ed. 5.00 (ISBN 0-88698-019-4, 2.10321). PETEX.

--The Hoist. 2nd ed. (Rotary Drilling Ser.: Unit I, Lesson 6). (Illus.). 40p. (Orig.). 1982. pap. text ed. 5.00 (ISBN 0-88698-010-0, 2.10620). PETEX.

--The Hoist: Metric Edition. 3rd, rev. ed. (Rotary Drilling Ser.: Unit I, Lesson 6). (Illus.). 32p. (Orig.). 1982. pap. text ed. 5.00 (ISBN 0-88698-022-4, 2.10621). PETEX.

--Mud Pumps & Conditioning Equipment. 2nd, rev. ed. (Rotary Drilling Ser.: Unit I, Lesson 12). (Illus.). 67p. (Orig.). 1982. pap. text ed. 5.00 (ISBN 0-88698-016-X, 2.11220). PETEX.

--Mud Pumps & Conditioning Equipment: Metric Version. 2nd, rev. ed. (Rotary Drilling Ser.: Unit I, Lesson 12). (Illus.). 63p. (Orig.). 1982. pap. text ed. 5.00 (ISBN 0-88698-028-3, 2.11221). PETEX.

--Rotary, Kelly, & Swivel. 2nd ed. (Rotary Drilling Ser.: Unit I, Lesson 4). (Illus.). 57p. (Orig.). pap. text ed. 5.00 (ISBN 0-88698-008-9, 2.10420). PETEX.

--Rotary, Kelly & Swivel: Canadian Metric Edition. 2nd ed. (Rotary Drilling Ser.: Unit I, Lesson 4). (Illus.). 1981. pap. text ed. 5.00 (ISBN 0-88698-020-8, 2.10421). PETEX.

--Safety on the Rig. (Rotary Drilling Ser.: Unit I, Lesson 10). (Illus.). 72p. 1981. pap. text ed. 5.00 (ISBN 0-88698-014-3, 2.11030). PETEX.

Leecraft, Jodie & Greenlaw, Martha, eds. Safety on the Rig: Canadian Metric Version. 3rd, rev. ed. (Rotary Drilling Ser.: Unit I, Lesson 10). (Illus.). 63p. 1981. pap. text ed. 5.00 (ISBN 0-88698-026-7, 2.11031). PETEX.

Life Offshore. (Rotary Drilling Ser.: Unit V, Lesson 9). (Illus.). 28p. (Orig.). 1978. pap. text ed. 4.50 (ISBN 0-88698-076-3, 2.50910). PETEX.

Liljestrand, Walter & Lawson, Gordon. Handbook 5: Degassers. LC 83-161604. (Mud Equipment Manual Ser.). (Illus.). 120p. (Orig.). 1985. pap. 21.95x (ISBN 0-87201-617-X). Gulf Pub.

Longley, Mark, ed. Testing & Completing. 2nd ed. (Rotary Drilling Ser.: Unit II: Normal Drilling Operations, Lesson 5). (Illus.). 56p. (Orig.). 1983. pap. text ed. 5.00 (ISBN 0-88698-121-2, 2.20520). Petex.

Ludwigson, John, ed. Nineteen Eighty-Four Hazardous Material Spills Conference: Prevention, Behavior, Control & Cleanup of Spills & Water Sites. LC 84-80663. (Illus.). 458p. 1984. pap. 56.00 (ISBN 0-86587-064-0). Gov Insts.

McCoy, R. L. PETROCALC (TM) 7: Applied Well Log Analysis. LC 85-12564. (PETROCALC (TM) Software for Petroleum Engineers Ser.). 80p. 1985. incl. floppy disk 495.00x (ISBN 0-87201-734-6). Gulf Pub.

McCray, Arthur W. & Cole, Frank W. Oil Well Drilling Technology. (Illus.). 1979. Repr. of 1959 ed. 24.95x (ISBN 0-8061-0423-6). U of Okla Pr.

Mayer-Gurr, Alfred. Petroleum Engineering. LC 76-6449. (Geology of Petroleum Ser: Vol. 3). 208p. 1976. pap. text ed. 19.95x (ISBN 0-470-15082-3). Halsted Pr.

Meehan, Nathan D. & Vogel, Eric L. HP-Forty-One Reservior Engineering Manual. LC 82-22704. 364p. 1982. 59.95x (ISBN 0-87814-186-3). Pennwell Bks.

Mesko, A. Fundamentals of Digital Filtering with Applications in Geophysical Prospecting for Oil. LC 83-5835. 512p. 1984. 69.95x (ISBN 0-470-27444-1). Halsted Pr.

Moore, Preston. Drilling Practices Manual. 2nd ed. 480p. 1985. 64.95t (ISBN 0-87814-292-4). PennWell Bks.

Mosburg, Lewis G., Jr., ed. Basic Land Management Handbook. 36.00 (ISBN 0-318-01991-4). IED Pub Hse.

Musser, E. G. Designing Offsite Facilities by Use of Routing Diagrams. LC 83-5608. 62p. (Orig.). 1983. pap. 34.95x comb bound (ISBN 0-87201-628-5). Gulf Pub.

Nelson, W. L. Petroleum Refinery Engineering. 4th ed. 960p. 1958. 79.95 (ISBN 0-686-45981-4, P-7013). Pennwell Bks.

Nichols, J. A. Dispersant Gels for Treating Surfaces Contaminated with Residual Oils, 1975. 1981. 30.00x (ISBN 0-686-97059-4, Pub. by W Spring England). State Mutual Bk.

--Dispersant Gels for Treating Surfaces Contaminated with Residual Oils, 1979. Lynch, B., rev. by. 1981. 39.00x (ISBN 0-686-97061-6, Pub. by W Spring England). State Mutual Bk.

Oil Companies Materials Association (OCMA) DFCP-5 Drilling Fluid Materials Starch. 1980. pap. 21.95 (ISBN 0-471-25920-9). Wiley.

Open-Hole Fishing. 2nd, rev. ed. (Rotary Drilling Ser.: Unit III, Lesson 2). (Illus.). 40p. (Orig.). 1975. pap. text ed. 5.00 (ISBN 0-88698-050-X, 2.30220). PETEX.

Owen, D. B., ed. The Search for Oil: Some Statistical Methods and Techniques. (Statistics: Textbooks & Monographs Ser.: Vol.13). 208p. 1975. 49.75 (ISBN 0-8247-6342-4). Dekker.

Paxson, Jeanette. Basic Tools & Equipment for the Oil Field. (Illus.). 109p. (Orig.). 1982. pap. 5.50 (ISBN 0-88698-100-X, 1.80010). Petex.

Paxson, Jeanette, ed. Casing & Cementing. (Rotary Drilling Ser.: Lesson 4, Unit 2). (Illus.). 53p. (Orig.). Date not set. pap. text ed. 5.00 (ISBN 0-88698-056-9, 2.20420). PETEX.

PC-Technology, Inc. Pumper II. 72p. 1985. loose leaf binder 695.00 (ISBN 0-87814-291-6). PennWell Bks.

PETEX. Well Cleanout & Repair Methods. (Well Servicing & Workover Ser.: Lesson 8). (Illus.). 32p. 1971. pap. text ed. 4.50 (ISBN 0-88698-064-X, 3.70810). PETEX.

--Well Stimulation Treatments. (Well Servicing & Workover Ser.: Lesson 11). (Illus.). 44p. 1971. pap. text ed. 4.50 (ISBN 0-88698-067-4, 3.71110). PETEX.

Petroleum Geology & Reservoirs. (Well Servicing & Workover Ser.: Lesson 2). (Illus.). 65p. (Orig.). pap. text ed. 5.00 (ISBN 0-88698-058-5, 3.70210). PETEX.

Pettit, Rhonda, ed. Eastern Oil Shale Symposium Proceedings, 1983. (Illus.). 300p. 1983. pap. text ed. 25.00 (ISBN 0-86607-022-2, IMMR83/089). KY Ctr Energy Res.

Production Rig Equipment. (Well Servicing & Workover Ser.: Lesson 6). (Illus.). 39p. (Orig.). 1971. pap. text ed. 4.50 (ISBN 0-88698-062-3, 3.70610). PETEX.

Ranney, M. W. Offshore Oil Technology: Recent Developments. LC 79-83771. (Energy Technology Review Ser. 38, Ocean Technology Review Ser. 8). (Illus.). 339p. 1979. 42.00 (ISBN 0-8155-0741-0). Noyes.

Roebuck, Field, Jr. Applied Petroleum Reservoir Technology. 38.00 (ISBN 0-318-02016-5). IED Pub Hse.

Sandrea, Rafael & Nielsen, Ralph. Dynamics of Petroleum Reservoirs Under Gas Injection. LC 74-4829. 180p. 1974. 18.95x (ISBN 0-87201-219-0). Gulf Pub.

Schultz, W. P., et al, eds. Enhanced Oil Recovery for the Independent Producer. (Illus.). 340p. 1985. pap. 40.00 (ISBN 0-87074-203-5). SMU Press.

Serra, O. Fundamentals of Well-Log Interpretation: The Acquisition of Logging Data, Vol. 1. (Developments in Petroleum Science Ser.: Vol. 15A). 440p. 1984. 100.00 (ISBN 0-444-42132-7). Elsevier.

Shah, D. O., ed. Surface Phenomena in Enhanced Oil Recovery. LC 81-8704. 886p. 1981. 125.00x (ISBN 0-306-40757-4, Plenum Pr). Plenum Pub.

Silver, Burr A. Subsurface Exploration Stratigraphy. 342p. 1983. 45.00 (ISBN 0-89419-254-X). Inst Energy.

--Techniques of Using Geologic Data. 154p. 1983. 32.00 (ISBN 0-89419-260-4). Inst Energy.

Skinner, David. Hydrogen Sulfide in Production Operations. Longley, Mark, ed. (Oil & Gas Production Ser.). (Illus.). 47p. (Orig.). 1982. pap. text ed. 5.00 (ISBN 0-88698-111-5, 3.30310). Petex.

Skinner, David R. Fluid Flow, Artificial Lift, Gathering, & Processing. LC 81-6264. (Introduction to Petroleum Production Ser.: Vol. 2). 234p. 1982. 24.95x (ISBN 0-87201-768-0). Gulf Pub.

--Reservoir Engineering, Drilling, Well Completions. LC 81-6264. (Introduction to Petroleum Productions Ser.: Vol. 1). 190p. 1981. 22.95x (ISBN 0-87201-767-2). Gulf Pub.

--Well Site Facilities: Water Handling, Storage, Control Systems. LC 81-6264. (Introduction to Petroleum Production Ser.: Vol. 3). 176p. 1982. 22.95x (ISBN 0-87201-769-9). Gulf Pub.

Slider, H. C. Worldwide Practical Petroleum Reservoir Engineering Methods. LC 83-4067. 825p. 1983. 79.95 (ISBN 0-87814-234-7, P-4334). Pennwell Bks.

Spread Mooring Systems. (Rotary Drilling Ser.: Unit V, Lesson 2). (Illus.). 1976. pap. text ed. 4.50 (ISBN 0-88698-070-4, 2.50210). PETEX.

Subsea Blowout Preventers & Marine Riser Systems. (Rotary Drilling Ser.: Unit III, Lesson 4). (Illus.). 58p. (Orig.). 1976. pap. text ed. 5.00 (ISBN 0-88698-052-6, 2.30410). PETEX.

Sukhanov, V. Petroleum Processing. 408p. 1982. 8.95 (ISBN 0-8285-2438-6, Pub. by Mir Pubs USSR). Imported Pubns.

Susman, George O. World Oil's Cementing Oil & Gas Wells: Including Casing Handling Procedures. (World Oil Handbook Ser.: Vol. 3). pap. 20.00 (ISBN 0-317-26814-7, 2024313). Bks Demand UMI.

Symposium on Heat Treated Steels for Elevated Temperature Service (1966: New Orleans) Heat-Treated Steels for Elevated Temperature Service: Symposium Held as Part of the 21st Annual Petroleum-Mechanical Engineering Conference. Semchyshen, M., ed. LC 66-28396. (Illus.). pap. 45.80 (ISBN 0-317-08414-3, 2016819). Bks Demand UMI.

Symposium on Twenty-five Years of Progress in Petroleum Technology, New York, 1951. Progress in Petroleum Technology: A Collection of the Papers. LC 51-6844. (Advances in Chemistry Ser.: No. 5). (Illus.). pap. 98.00 (ISBN 0-317-10874-3, 2050182). Bks Demand UMI.

Takken, Suzanne. Petroleum Exploration Handbook. 24.00 (ISBN 0-318-01993-0). IED Pub Hse.

Thumann, Albert. Fundamentals of Energy Engineering. 1983. 29.95 (ISBN 0-13-338327-X). Fairmont Pr.

University Course in Digital Seismic Methods Used in Petroleum Exploration. 294p. 1980. 25.00 (ISBN 0-910835-04-7). Goose Pond Pr.

University Microfilms International. Society of Petroleum Engineers Technical Papers, 2 vols. LC 80-28727. 1981. Set. 275.00 (ISBN 0-8357-0217-0, Pub. by Collections & Curr). Univ Microfilms.

Van Golf-Racht, T. Fundamentals of Fractures Reservoir Engineering. (Developments in Petroleum Science Ser.: Vol. 12). 710p. 1982. 85.00 (ISBN 0-444-42046-0). Elsevier.

Vessel Inspection & Maintenance. (Rotary Drilling Ser., Unit V,: Lesson 6). (Illus.). 37p. 1977. pap. text ed. 4.50 (ISBN 0-88698-074-7). PETEX.

Wasan, Darsh & Payatakes, Alkis, eds. Interfacial Phenomena in Enhanced Oil Recovery. LC 82-3941. (AICHE Symposium Ser.: Vol. 78). 126p. 1982. pap. 32.00 (ISBN 0-8169-0220-8, S-212); pap. 17.00 members. Am Inst Chem Eng.

Well Completion Methods. (Well Servicing & Workover: Lesson 4). (Illus.). 49p. 1971. pap. text ed. 4.50 (ISBN 0-88698-060-7, 3.70410). PETEX.

Well Logging Methods. (Well Servicing & Workover: Lesson 3). (Illus.). 46p. 1971. pap. text ed. 4.50 (ISBN 0-88698-059-3, 3.70310). PETEX.

Whalen, Bruce R. Basic Instrumentation. 3rd ed. (Illus.). 289p. 1983. pap. text ed. 12.00 (ISBN 0-88698-003-8, 1.20030). Petex.

White, Irvin L., et al. North Sea Oil & Gas: Implications for Future United States Development. LC 73-21222. (Illus.). 176p. (Orig.). 1973. pap. 7.95x (ISBN 0-8061-1182-8). U of Okla Pr.

White, Philip D. & Moss, Jon T. Thermal Recovery Methods. 384p. 1983. 55.95 (ISBN 0-87814-214-2, P-4292). Pennwell Bks.

Whyte, Thaddeus E., Jr. & Yon, Carmen M., eds. Industrial Gas Separations. LC 83-6440. (ACS Symposium Ser.: No. 223). 292p. 1983. lib. bdg. 34.95x (ISBN 0-8412-0780-1). Am Chemical.

Winston, W. P. Petroleum Law Guide 1984. 136p. 1983. 29.75 (ISBN 0-85334-231-8, Pub. by Elsevier Applied Sci England). Elsevier.

Young, William J. Organization of Instrumentation Guidelines. 114p. 1982. 37.95x (ISBN 0-87814-187-1). Pennwell Bks.

Zaba, Joseph & Doherty, W. T. Practical Petroleum Engineers' Handbook. 5th ed. LC 58-12306. 948p. 1970. 49.95x (ISBN 0-87201-744-3). Gulf Pub.

Zaijic, J. E., et al, eds. Microbial Enhanced Oil Recovery. 174p. 1983. 49.95x (ISBN 0-87814-212-6, P-4321). Pennwell Bks.

PETROLEUM ENGINEERING–DATA PROCESSING

Sigma Energy Consultants. PETROCALC (TM) 4: Well History Record Keeping System. LC 85-937. (PETROCALC (TM) Software for Petroleum Engineers Ser.). 1985. 3-ring binder incl. disk 495.00x (ISBN 0-87201-730-3). Gulf Pub.

--PETROCALC (TM) 5: Production History & Future Projection. LC 85-938. (PETROCALC (TM) Software for Petroleum Engineers Ser.). 1985. 3-ring binder incl. disk 495.00x (ISBN 0-87201-731-1). Gulf Pub.

Sinclair, Richard & Chenevert, Martin. PETROCALC (TM) 6: Wellbore Stimulation. LC 85-9806. (PETROCALC (TM) Software for Petroleum Engineers Ser.). (Illus.). 64p. 1985. incl. floppy disk 395.00x (ISBN 0-87201-732-X). Gulf Pub.

Sinha, Mihir K. & Padgett, Larry. Reservoir Engineering Techniques Using FORTRAN. (Illus.). 225p. 1984. text ed. 45.00 (ISBN 0-934634-50-5). Intl Human Res.

Talwar, Mahesh. CHEMCALC (TM) 4: Multiphase Flow, Compressible Flow, & Incompressible Flow. LC 85-843. (CHEMCALC (TM) Software for Chemical Engineers Ser.). 1985. 395.00 (ISBN 0-87201-088-0). Gulf Pub.

PETROLEUM ENGINES

see Gas and Oil Engines

PETROLEUM GAS, LIQUEFIED

see Liquefied Petroleum Gas

PETROLEUM GEOLOGY

see Petroleum–Geology

PETROLEUM INDUSTRY AND TRADE

see also Automobiles–Service Stations; Oil Industries; Petroleum–Refining; Petroleum Chemicals Industry; Petroleum Products

Abdel-Barr, Hussein A. The Market Structure of International Oil with Special Reference to the Organization of Petroleum Exporting Countries. Bruchey, Stuart, ed. LC 78-22653. (Energy in the American Economy Ser.). (Illus.). 1979. lib. bdg. 30.50x (ISBN 0-405-11958-5). Ayer Co Pubs.

Adelman, M. A. The World Petroleum Market. LC 72-4029. (Resources for the Future Ser.). (Illus.). 456p. 1973. 37.00x (ISBN 0-8018-1422-7). Johns Hopkins.

Ahrari, Mohammed E. The Dynamics of Oil Diplomacy: Conflict & Concensus. Bruchey, Stuart, ed. LC 80-608. (Multinational Corporations Ser.). 1980. lib. bdg. 45.00x (ISBN 0-405-13360-X). Ayer Co Pubs.

Alaska Geographic Staff, ed. Alaska's Oil-Gas & Minerals Industry. (Alaska Geographic Ser.: Vol. 9, No. 4). pap. 12.95 Album Style (ISBN 0-88240-170-X). Alaska Northwest.

Al-Chalabi, Fadhil J. OPEC & the International Oil Industry: A Changing Structure. (Illus.). 1980. pap. 9.95 (ISBN 0-19-877155-X). Oxford U Pr.

Allain, Louis J. Capital Investment Models of the Oil & Gas Industry: A Systems Approach. Bruchey, Stuart, ed. LC 78-22654. (Energy in the American Economy Ser.). (Illus.). 1979. lib. bdg. 42.00x (ISBN 0-405-11959-3). Ayer Co Pubs.

Allen, Loring. OPEC Oil. LC 79-19284. 288p. 1979. text ed. 35.00 (ISBN 0-89946-002-X). Oelgeschlager.

Allvine, Fred C. & Patterson, James M. Competition Ltd, the Marketing of Gasoline. LC 70-180491. pap. 65.40 (ISBN 0-317-28578-5, 2055197). Bks Demand UMI.

Al-Otaiba, M. S. OPEC & the Petroleum Industry. 208p. 1976. 25.00 (ISBN 0-85664-262-2, Pub. by Croom helm Ltd). Longwood Pub Group.

Al-Otaiba, Mana S. Essays on Petroleum. 176p. 1982. 21.50 (ISBN 0-7099-1921-2, Pub. by Croom Helm Ltd). Longwood Pub Group.

Amuzegar, Jahngir. Oil Exporters' Economic Development in an Interdependent World. (Occasional Papers: No. 18). 99p. 1983. pap. 5.00 (ISBN 0-317-04016-2). Intl Monetary.

Anderson, Jack & Boyd, James. Fiasco. LC 80-45037. 386p. 1983. 17.50 (ISBN 0-8129-0943-7). Times Bks.

Annual Report, 1952. 1952. pap. 40.00 (ISBN 0-686-30730-5). Munger Oil.

Annual Report, 1953. 1953. pap. 40.00 (ISBN 0-686-30731-3). Munger Oil.

Annual Report, 1954. 1954. pap. 40.00 (ISBN 0-686-30732-1). Munger Oil.

Annual Report, 1955. 1955. pap. 40.00 (ISBN 0-686-30733-X). Munger Oil.

Aperjis, Dimitri. The Oil Market in the Nineteen Eighties: OPEC Oil Policy & Economic Development. LC 81-15050. 240p. 1982. Prof. Ref. 35.00x (ISBN 0-88410-903-8). Ballinger Pub.

Baker, George. Mexico's Petroleum Sector. LC 83-4178. 312p. 1983. 49.95x (ISBN 0-87814-237-1, P-4332). Pennwell Bks.

Balassa, Bela. The Policy Experience of Twelve Less Developed Countries, 1973-1978. (Working Paper: No. 449). 36p. 1981. pap. 3.00 (ISBN 0-686-39745-2, WP-0449). World Bank.

Ball, Max W., et al. This Fascinating Oil Business. LC 64-15660. (Illus.). 1979. pap. 11.95 (ISBN 0-672-52584-4). Bobbs.

Banks, Ferdinand E. Resources & Energy: An Economic Analysis. LC 81-47967. 368p. 1983. 36.50x (ISBN 0-669-05203-5). Lexington Bks.

Barker, T. S. & Brailovsky, Vladimiro, eds. Oil or Industry: Energy, Industrialization & Economic Policy in Canada, Mexico, Norway, the Netherlands & the United Kingdom. LC 81-67884. 1981. 55.00 (ISBN 0-12-078620-6). Acad Pr.

Beckenstein, Alan, et al. Performance Measurement of the Petroleum Industry: Functional Profitability & Alternatives. LC 79-1951. (Illus.). 1979. 26.50x (ISBN 0-669-03017-1). Lexington Bks.

Berger, Bill & Anderson, Ken. Modern Petroleum. 2nd ed. 255p. 1981. 39.95x (ISBN 0-87814-172-3). Pennwell Bks.

Boyle, William C. Designing Production Safety Systems. 264p. 1979. 39.95 (ISBN 0-87814-096-4). Pennwell Bks.

British-North American Committee. Higher Oil Prices: Worldwide Financial Implications. LC 75-29675. 64p. 1975. 3.00 (ISBN 0-902594-27-3). Natl Planning.

Brooks, Benjamin T. Peace, Plenty, & Petroleum. LC 75-6463. (The History & Politics of Oil Ser). 197p. 1976. Repr. of 1944 ed. 17.50 (ISBN 0-88355-283-3). Hyperion Conn.

Buck, Joan. Petroleum Lands & Leasing. 184p. 1983. 39.95 (ISBN 0-87814-239-8). PennWell Bks.

Bustin, W. & Dukek, W. Electrostatic Hazards in the Petroleum Industry. (Electrostatics & Electrostatic Application Ser.). 100p. 1983. 26.95 (ISBN 0-471-90163-6, Pub. by Res Stud Pr). Wiley.

California-Alaska Oil & Gas Review of 1976. 1977. 40.00 (ISBN 0-686-28274-4). Munger Oil.

Challa, Krishna. Investment & Returns in Exploration & the Impact on the Supply of Oil & Natural Gas Reserves. Bruchey, Stuart, ed. LC 78-22667. (Energy in the American Economy Ser.). (Illus.). 1979. lib. bdg. 16.00x (ISBN 0-405-11971-2). Ayer Co Pubs.

Chevalier, Jean-Marie. The New Oil Stakes. Rock, Ian, tr. from Fr. 187p. 1973. text ed. 14.75x (ISBN 0-8464-1182-2). Beekman Pubs.

Commission of the European Communities. New Technologies for Exploration & Exploitation of Oil & Gas Resources, Vol. 11. 600p. 1979. 75.00x (ISBN 0-86010-159-2, Pub. by Graham & Trotman England). State Mutual Bk.

Cortese, Charles F., ed. The Social Impact of Energy Development in the West. 1985. pap. text ed. 12.95x (ISBN 0-8290-1083-1). Irvington.

Deegan, James F. An Econometric Model of the Gulf Coast Oil & Gas Exploration Industry. Bruchey, Stuart, ed. LC 78-22672. (Energy in the American Economy Ser.). (Illus.). 1979. lib. bdg. 16.00x (ISBN 0-405-11975-5). Ayer Co Pubs.

Denny, Ludwell. We Fight for Oil. 1979. lib. bdg. 59.95 (ISBN 0-8490-3014-5). Gordon Pr.

Dewan, John. Modern Open-Hole Log-Interpretation. LC 83-4228. 360p. 1983. 54.95 (ISBN 0-87814-233-9, P-4302). Pennwell Bks.

Doran, Charles F. Myth, Oil & Politics: Introduction to the Political Economy of Petroleum. LC 77-4571. (Illus.). 1977. 14.95 (ISBN 0-02-907580-7). Free Pr.

Eckbo, Paul L. The Future of World Oil. LC 76-16809. 160p. 1976. prof ref 29.95x (ISBN 0-88410-455-9). Ballinger Pub.

Elf-Aquitaine, et al. Exploration for Carbonate Petroleum Reservoirs. LC 81-13144. 213p. 1982. 45.95x (ISBN 0-471-08603-7, Pub. by Wiley-Interscience). Wiley.

Emerging Energy & Chemical Applications of Methanol: Opportunities for Developing Countries. viii, 73p. 1982. pap. 5.00 (ISBN 0-8213-0018-0). World Bank.

Emerson, Steven. The American House of Saud: The Secret Petrodollar Connection. 1985. 18.95 (ISBN 0-531-09778-1). Watts.

Evans, Douglas. Western Energy Policy. LC 78-23315. 1979. 25.00x (ISBN 0-312-86392-6). St Martin.

Feinberg, William J., ed. The Whole World Oil Directory, 1985. 1985. Set. pap. 103.00 (ISBN 0-938184-13-X). Whole World.

Financial Solidarity for Development, 2 vols. pap. 15.00 (ISBN 0-686-68958-5, UN792D92V, UN); pap. 15.00 (ISBN 0-686-68957-7, UN792D9V2). Unipub.

Fitzgerald, Joseph. Black Gold with Grit. 240p. 1978. 16.95 (ISBN 0-686-74129-3). Superior Pub.

Fulda, Michael. Oil & International Relations: Energy, Trade, Technology & Politics. Bruchey, Stuart, ed. LC 78-22681. (Energy in the American Economy Ser.). (Illus.). 1979. lib. bdg. 23.00x (ISBN 0-405-11984-4). Ayer Co Pubs.

Garrison, Paul. Investing in Oil in the Eighties. 130p. 1981. 39.95x (ISBN 0-87814-151-0). Pennwell Bks.

Gerding, Mildred, ed. Applied Mathematics for the Petroleum Other Industries. 3rd, rev. ed. (Illus.). 274p. 1985. pap. text ed. 10.00 (ISBN 0-88698-085-2, 1.60030). PETEX.

--Fundamentals of Petroleum. 2nd ed. (Illus.). 292p. (Orig.). 1981. pap. text ed. 10.00 (ISBN 0-88698-048-8, 1.00020). PETEX.

--Well Service & Workover Profitability. (Well Servicing & Workover Ser.: Lesson 12). (Illus.). 32p. 1980. pap. text ed. 4.50 (ISBN 0-88698-068-2, 3.71220). PETEX.

Ghadar, Fariborz & Stobaugh, Robert. The Petroleum Industry in Oil-Importing Developing Countries. LC 81-48556. 240p. 1983. 28.00x (ISBN 0-669-05419-4). Lexington Bks.

Ghosh, Arabinda. Competition & Diversification in the United States Petroleum Industry. LC 84-24932. (Illus.). 176p. 1985. lib. bdg. 35.00 (ISBN 0-89930-064-2, GHC/, Quorum). Greenwood.

--OPEC, the Petroleum Industry, & United States Energy Policy. LC 82-13245. (Illus.). 206p. 1983. lib. bdg. 35.00 (ISBN 0-89930-010-3, GOU/, Quorum). Greenwood.

Gisselquist, David. Oil Prices & Trade Deficits: U. S. Conflicts with Japan & West Germany. LC 79-20632. (Praeger Special Studies). 158p. 1980. 37.95 (ISBN 0-03-052381-8). Praeger.

Goins, W. C. & Sheffield, Riley. Blowout Prevention. 2nd ed. LC 70-101145. (Practical Drilling Technology Ser.: Vol. 1). 336p. 1983. 39.95x (ISBN 0-87201-073-2). Gulf Pub.

Grayson, C. Jackson, Jr. Decisions Under Uncertainty: Drilling Decisions by Oil & Gas Operators. Bruchey, Stuart, ed. LC 78-22686. (Energy in the American Economy Ser.). (Illus.). 1979. Repr. of 1960 ed. lib. bdg. 32.50x (ISBN 0-405-11989-5). Ayer Co Pubs.

Hanighen, Frank C. The Secret War. LC 75-6476. (History & Politics of Oil Ser.). 316p. 1976. Repr. of 1934 ed. 21.65 (ISBN 0-88355-294-9). Hyperion Conn.

Harney. Oil from Shale. (Special Report Ser.). 289p. 1983. 375.00 (ISBN 0-8247-1777-5). Dekker.

Harris, L. M. Design for Reliability in Deepwater Floating Drilling Operations. 266p. 1980. 49.95 (ISBN 0-87814-082-4). Pennwell Bks.

Hawdon, David, ed. The Energy Crisis Ten Years After. LC 83-40189. 224p. 1984. 21.95 (ISBN 0-312-25123-8). St Martin.

Hepple, P., ed. Joint Problems of the Oil & Water Industries. (Illus.). 195p. 1967. 29.75 (ISBN 0-444-39953-4, Pub. by Elsevier Applied Sci England). Elsevier.

Hepple, Peter, ed. The Expanding Uses of Petroleum: Report of the Summer Meeting of the Institute of Petroleum, held at Torquay, 1966. LC 67-77992. pap. 27.80 (ISBN 0-317-29031-2, 2023690). Bks Demand UMI.

--Petroleum Supply & Demand: Report of the Summer Meeting of the Institute of Petroleum held at Brighton, 1965. LC 66-5547. pap. 38.00 (ISBN 0-317-29000-2, 2023698). Bks Demand UMI.

Institute of Petroleum. The Effective Use of Petroleum. 265p. 1979. 49.95x (ISBN 0-471-25792-3, Pub. by Wiley Heyden). Wiley.

--Health & Hazards in a Changing Oil Scene: Procedings of the Institute of Petroleum 1982 Annual Conference, London, UK. 201p. 1983. 37.95 (ISBN 0-471-26270-6). Wiley.

--Model Code of Safe Practice: Drilling, Production & Pipeline Operations in Marine Areas, Pt. 8. 2nd ed. 72p. 1980. 35.95x (ISBN 0-471-25809-1). Wiley.

--Petroleum Measurement Manual - Automatic Tank Gauging: Proceedings, Pt. V. 42p. 1982. 48.95x (ISBN 0-471-26147-5, Pub. by Wiley Heyden). Wiley.

--Petroleum Measurement Manual: Fidelity & Security of Measurement - Data Transmission Systems Section 1, Pt. XIII. 32p. 1977. 35.95x (ISBN 0-471-25782-6). Wiley.

--Petroleum Measurement Manual: Tank Calibration Section I- Liquid Calibration Methods, Pt. II. 120p. 1981. 38.95x (ISBN 0-471-25802-4). Wiley.

--Petroleum Measurement Manual: Tank Calibration Section II: Horizontal & Inclined Cylindrical Tanks Measuring Methods, Pt. II. 128p. 1972. 34.95 (ISBN 0-471-25803-2). Wiley.

--Standards for Petroleum & Its Products: Part 1: Methods for Analysis & Testing. 41st ed. 359p. 1982. 154.95 (ISBN 0-471-26146-7). Wiley.

--Standards for Petroleum & Its Products, Vols. 1 & 2. 43rd ed. 1800p. 1984. Pt. 1, Methods of Analysis & Testing. 154.95 (ISBN 0-471-90455-4). Wiley.

--Storage & Piped Distribution of Heating Oil Safety Code, Vol. 10. 1971. 16.75 (ISBN 0-444-39962-3). Elsevier.

Institute of Petroleum (Great Britain) Staff. Recommended SI & Other Metric Units for the Petroleum & Petrochemical Industries, Including Basic Rules of the Oil Companies Materials Association. rev. ed. LC 72-10438. pap. 20.00 (ISBN 0-317-26012-X, 2023699). Bks Demand UMI.

Institute of Petroleum Standards for Petroleum & Its Products, Part 1: Methods for Analysis & Testing, 2 vols. 1981. Set. 145.00x (ISBN 0-471-26146-7). Wiley.

Institution of Civil Engineers Staff, ed. The Marine Environment & Oil Facilities. 168p. 1979. 27.75x (ISBN 0-7277-0075-8). Am Soc Civil Eng.

International Labour Office Staff. Small-Scale Oil Extraction from Groundnuts & Copra: Technical Memorandum, No. 5. (Technology Ser.). xi, 111p. (Orig.). 1983. pap. 8.55 (ISBN 92-2-103503-4). Intl Labour Office.

Jenkins, G. Oil Economists' Handbook: 1985. 378p. 1985. 90.00 (ISBN 0-85334-325-X, Pub. by Elsevier Applied Sci England). Elsevier.

Johnson, Arthur M. The Challenge of Change: The Sun Oil Company, 1945-1977. LC 82-14395. (Illus.). 500p. 1983. 30.00x (ISBN 0-8142-0340-X). Ohio St U Pr.

Kalt, Joseph P. The Economics & Politics of Oil Price Regulation: Federal Policy in the Post-Embargo Era. (Regulation of Economic Activity Ser.: No. 4). 336p. 1981. 47.50x (ISBN 0-262-11079-2). MIT Pr.

Kemeziz, Paul, III & Wilson, Ernest J. The Decade of Energy Policy: Policy Analysis in Oil Importing Countries. LC 84-15936. 288p. 1984. 27.95x (ISBN 0-03-062783-4). Praeger.

Kim, Y. Y. & Thompson, R. G. Oil & Gas Supplies in the Lower Forty-Eight States. LC 78-53816. 110p. 1978. 20.95x (ISBN 0-87201-816-4). Gulf Pub.

Klitz, J. Kenneth. North Sea Oil: Resource Requirements for UK Development. (Illus.). 1981. 40.00 (ISBN 0-08-024442-4). Pergamon.

Koopman, George, et al. Oil & the International Economy: Lessons from the Two Price Shocks. 431p. 1985. pap. 16.95 (ISBN 0-88738-616-4). Transaction Bks.

Krapels, Edward N., ed. Pricing Petroleum Products: Strategies of Eleven Industrial Nations, Vol. 1. (Illus.). 272p. 1983. 85.00 (ISBN 0-07-035374-3). McGraw.

Langenkamp, R. D. Handbook of Oil Industry Terms & Phrases. 4th ed. 360p. 1984. 29.95x (ISBN 0-87814-258-4). Pennwell Bks.

Langenkamp, Robert D. Oil Business Fundamentals. 146p. 1982. 21.95x (ISBN 0-87814-198-7, P-4288). Pennwell Bks.

Lehman, Edward R. Profits, Profitability, & the Oil Industry. Bruchey, Stuart, ed. LC 78-22694. (Energy in the American Economy Ser.). (Illus.). 1979. lib. bdg. 23.00x (ISBN 0-405-11997-6). Ayer Co Pubs.

Le Tirant, P. Seabed Reconnaissance & Offshore Soil Mechanics for the Installation of Petroleum Structures. 512p. 1980. 87.00x (ISBN 0-86010-196-7, Pub. by Graham & Trotman England). State Mutual Bk.

Leyland, Eric. Oil Man. (Illus.). 9.50x (ISBN 0-392-04084-0, SpS). Sportshelf.

Lieberman, Norman P. Troubleshooting Refinery Processes. 2nd ed. 440p. 1984. 65.95 (ISBN 0-87814-263-0). PennWell Bks.

Lilly, Willene J. The Petroleum Secretary's Handbook. 2nd ed. LC 84-27384. 336p. 1985. 35.95 (ISBN 0-87814-278-9). Pennwell Bks.

Lovejoy, Wallace F. & Homan, Paul T. Economic Aspects of Oil Conservation Regulation. (Resources for the Future Ser). 310p. 1967. 22.50x (ISBN 0-8018-0397-7). Johns Hopkins.

Lowe, John S. Oil & Gas in a Nutshell. LC 83-6811. (Nutshell Ser.). 443p. 1983. pap. text ed. 8.95 (ISBN 0-314-73469-4). West Pub.

Lyon, Jim. Dome Petroleum: The Inside Story of Its Rise & Fall. (Illus.). 1983. 16.95 (ISBN 0-8253-0183-1). Beaufort Bks NY.

MacAvoy, Paul W., ed. Federal Energy Administration Regulation: Ford Administration Papers. 1977. pap. 6.25 (ISBN 0-8447-3248-6). Am Enterprise.

McCaslin, John C. Petroleum Exploration Worldwide. LC 82-22499. 192p. 1983. 59.95x (ISBN 0-87814-220-7, P-4307). Pennwell Bks.

McCoy, R. D., et al. Current Research in Petroleum Fuels, I. (Energy & Environmental Studies: Petroleum Research). 1976. text ed. 30.00x (ISBN 0-8422-7293-3). Irvington.

McCray, A. W. Petroleum Evaluations & Economic Decision. (Illus.). 544p. 1975. 44.95 (ISBN 0-13-662213-5). P-H.

McDonald, Philip R. Factors Influencing Fuel Oil Growth. Bruchey, Stuart, ed. LC 78-22700. (Energy in the American Economy Ser.). (Illus.). 1979. lib. bdg. 32.50x (ISBN 0-405-12002-8). Ayer Co Pubs.

McNair, Will. Electric Drilling Rig Handbook. 222p. 1980. 45.95x (ISBN 0-87814-120-0). Pennwell Bks.

Manes, Rene P. The Effects of United States Oil Import Policy on the Petroleum Industry. Bruchey, Stuart, ed. LC 78-22696. (Energy in the American Economy Ser.). (Illus.). 1979. lib. bdg. 32.50x (ISBN 0-405-11999-2). Ayer Co Pubs.

Mangone, Gerard J. The Future of Gas & Oil from the Sea. 240p. 1983. 35.00 (ISBN 0-442-26164-0). Van Nos Reinhold.

Manne, Alan S. Scheduling of Petroleum Refinery Operations. LC 56-6518. (Economic Studies: No. 98). (Illus.). 1956. 12.50x (ISBN 0-674-79080-4). Harvard U Pr.

Marks, Alex. Petroleum Storage Principles. LC 83-6309. 432p. 1983. 83.95x (ISBN 0-87814-238-X, P-4289). Pennwell Bks.

Mathews, J. J. Life & Death of an Oilman: The Career of E. W. Marland. 1974. pap. 7.95 (ISBN 0-8061-1238-7). U of Okla Pr.

Mattione, Richard P. OPEC's Investments & the International Financial System. LC 84-23242. 210p. 1985. 26.95 (ISBN 0-8157-5510-4); pap. 9.95 (ISBN 0-8157-5509-0). Brookings.

Maurer, William. Advanced Drilling Techniques. 698p. 1980. 69.95x (ISBN 0-87814-117-0). Pennwell Bks.

Megill, R. E. Long Range Exploration Planning. 96p. 1985. 33.95 (ISBN 0-87814-286-X). PennWell Bks.

Meloe, Torleif. United States Control of Petroleum Imports: A Study of the Federal Government's Role in the Management of Domestic Oil Supplies. Bruchey, Stuart, ed. LC 78-22701. (Energy in the American Economy Ser.). (Illus.). 1979. lib. bdg. 25.50x (ISBN 0-405-12003-6). Ayer Co Pubs.

Mercier, C. Petrochemical Industry & Possibilities of Its Establishment in Developing Countries. 202p. 1971. 80.95x (ISBN 0-677-61370-9). Gordon.

Mezerik, A. G., ed. Handbook of State Owned Oil Enterprises, Nineteen Seventy-Eight to Nineteen Seventy-Nine. 1979. pap. 100.00x (ISBN 0-685-99740-5). Intl Review.

Mezerik, Avrahm G., ed. Directory of State & Cooperative Oil Enterprises. 1963. pap. 15.00x (ISBN 0-685-13193-9, 78). Intl Review.

Mikesell, Raymond F. Petroleum Company Operations & Agreements in the Developing Countries. LC 83-43265. 160p. 1984. pap. text ed. 20.00 (ISBN 0-915707-07-1). Resources Future.

Miller, Richard K., et al. Noise Control Solutions for the Chemical & Petroleum Industries. 45.00 (ISBN 0-89671-010-6). Fairmont Pr.

Miller's Oil & Gas Federal Income Taxation: 1983. 21st ed. 744p. pap. 27.50 (ISBN 0-317-04213-0). Commerce.

Mosburg, Lewis G., ed. Problems & Pitfalls in Exploration Agreements. 764p. 50.00 (ISBN 0-89419-277-9). Inst Energy.

Mosburg, Lewis G., Jr., ed. Petroleum Land Practices, 2 vols. 1264p. 1981. Set. 60.00 (ISBN 0-89419-270-1). Vol. I (ISBN 0-89419-268-X). Vol. II (ISBN 0-89419-269-8). Inst Energy.

Niblock, Tim & Lawless, Richard, eds. Prospects for the World Oil Industry. LC 85-4186. 160p. 1985. 29.00 (ISBN 0-7099-4104-8, Pub. by Croom Helm Ltd). Longwood Pub Group.

Nordhauser, Norman. The Quest for Stability: Domestic Oil Policy, 1919-1935. Freidel, Frank, ed. LC 78-62510. (Modern American History Ser.: Vol. 15). 190p. 1979. lib. bdg. 29.00 (ISBN 0-8240-3638-7). Garland Pub.

Nore, Peter & Turner, Terisa, eds. Oil & Class Struggle. 324p. (Orig.). 1980. 35.00x (ISBN 0-905762-38-X, Pub. by Zed Pr England); pap. 8.95x (ISBN 0-905762-27-4, Pub. by Zed Pr England). Biblio Dist.

Oil Field Subsurface Injection of Water - STP Six Hundred Forty-One. 122p. 1977. pap. 10.75 (ISBN 0-8031-0530-4, 04-641000-16). ASTM.

Organization of Petroleum Exporting Countries. Annual Statistical Bulletin 1979. LC 74-640556. (Illus.). 185p. (Orig.). 1980. pap. 30.00x (ISBN 0-8002-2788-3). Intl Pubns Serv.

Payne, F. William. Energy Management & Control Systems Handbook. LC 83-48149. 350p. 1984. text ed. 39.00 (ISBN 0-915586-89-4). Fairmont Pr.

Perry, Charles. The West, Japan, & Cape Route Imports: The Oil & Non-Fuel Mineral Trades. LC 82-80947. (Special Report Ser.). 88p. 1982. 7.50 (ISBN 0-89549-042-0). Inst Foreign Policy Anal.

Peters, A. F., ed. Impact of Offshore Oil Operations. (Illus.). 205p. 1974. 35.25 (ISBN 0-85334-453-1, Pub. by Elsevier Applied Sci England). Elsevier.

The Petrochemical Industry: Trends in Production & Investment to 1985. 1979. 8.00 (ISBN 92-64-11890-X). OECD.

Petroleum Cooperation Among Developing Countries. pap. 11.00 (ISBN 0-686-94663-4, UN77/2A3, UN). Unipub.

Pettengill, Samuel B. Hot Oil: The Problem of Petroleum. LC 75-6483. (The History & Politics of Oil Ser.). xviii, 308p. 1976. Repr. of 1936 ed. 24.75 (ISBN 0-88355-300-7). Hyperion Conn.

Prast, William G. & Lax, Howard L. Oil-Futures Markets: An Introduction. LC 82-48622. 208p. 1983. 25.50x (ISBN 0-669-06354-1). Lexington Bks.

Puech, Alain. The Use of Anchors in Offshore Petroleum Operations. LC 84-71684. (Illus.). 112p. 1984. 39.95x (ISBN 0-87201-042-2). Gulf Pub.

Quick, Allen N. & Buck, Neal A. Strategic Planning for Exploration Management. (Illus.). 161p. 1984. 32.00 (ISBN 0-934634-66-1). Intl Human Res.

Ramsey, James B., ed. Bidding & Oil Leases, Vol. 25. Walter, Ingo I. LC 79-3169. (Contemporary Studies in Economic & Financial Analysis Monographs). 320p. (Orig.). 1980. lib. bdg. 36.00 (ISBN 0-89232-148-2). Jai Pr.

Rintoul, William. Drilling Ahead. LC 81-50167. (Illus.). 300p. 1981. 19.95 (ISBN 0-934136-09-2, Valley Pub). Western Tanager.

Riva, Joseph P., Jr. World Petroleum Resources & Reserves. (Special Study). (Illus.). 250p. 1983. lib. bdg. 48.00x (ISBN 0-86531-446-2). Westview.

Roebuck, Field, Jr. Applied Petroleum Reservoir Technology. 469p. 1983. 38.00 (ISBN 0-89419-263-9). Inst Energy.

Roncaglia, Alessandro. International Oil Market. Kregel, J. A., ed. LC 84-5555. Tr. of L'Economi del Petrolio. 1985. 30.00 (ISBN 0-87332-282-7); pap. 14.95 (ISBN 0-87332-290-8). M E Sharpe.

Rondot, Jean. La Compagnie Francaise Des Petroles: Du Franc-or Au Petrole-Franc. Wilkins, Mira, ed. LC 76-29773. (European Business Ser.). Tr. of The French Petroleum Company: from the Gold Franc to the Petroleum Franc. (Fr.). 1977. Repr. of 1962 ed. lib. bdg. 17.00x (ISBN 0-405-09785-9). Ayer Co Pubs.

Sanpersen, Harold W. The Inevitable Revolution in the World Oil Markets. (The Most Meaningful Contemporary Historical Trends Library). (Illus.). 131p. 1981. 67.75x (ISBN 0-930008-86-3). Inst Econ Pol.

Schumacher, M. M., ed. Heavy Oil & Tar Sands Recovery & Upgrading: International Technology. LC 82-2229. (Energy Tech Rev.: No. 78). (Illus.). 552p. 1982. 48.00 (ISBN 0-8155-0893-X). Noyes.

Carson, W. G. The Other Price of Britain's Oil: Safety & Control in the North Sea. 220p. 1981. 40.00x (ISBN 0-85520-392-7, Pub. by Robertson & Co England). State Mutual Bk.

Ferrier, Ronald W. The History of the British Petroleum Company: The Developing Years 1901-1932, Vol. 1. LC 81-18019. 696p. 1982. 74.50 (ISBN 0-521-24647-4). Cambridge U Pr.

Griffiths, Trevor. Oi for England. 48p. 1982. pap. 4.95 (ISBN 0-571-11977-8). Faber & Faber.

Kuczynski, Irving. British Offshore Oil & Gas Policy. LC 79-53210. (Outstanding Dissertations in Economics Ser.). 280p. 1984. lib. bdg. 36.00 (ISBN 0-8240-4059-7). Garland Pub.

Mannners, Ian R. North Sea Oil & Environmental Planning: The United Kingdom Experience. 344p. 1982. text ed. 37.50x (ISBN 0-292-76475-8). U of Tex Pr.

Parsler, Ron & Shapiro, Dan. The Social Impact of Oil in Scotland. 192p. 1980. text ed. 36.50x (ISBN 0-566-00375-9). Gower Pub Co.

Rosie, George. The Ludwig Initiative: A Cautionary Tale of North Sea Oil. 152p. 1981. 39.00x (ISBN 0-906391-00-8, Pub. by Mainstream). State Mutual Bk.

PETROLEUM INDUSTRY AND TRADE–NORTH SEA REGION

Jones, David K., ed. The Impact of North Sea Hydrocarbons. (Illus.). 1978. pap. text ed. 29.00 (ISBN 0-08-022263-3). Pergamon.

PETROLEUM INDUSTRY AND TRADE–NORWAY

Hansen, Thorvald B. Offshore Adventure: A Pictorial History of the Norwegian Petroleum Industry. (Illus.). 64p. 1984. 44.00x (ISBN 82-00-06406-9). Universitet.

Lind, T. & Mackay, G. A. Norwegian Oil Policies. 1980. Repr. 21.50x (ISBN 0-7735-0510-5). McGill-Queens U Pr.

PETROLEUM INDUSTRY AND TRADE–UNITED STATES

Alnasrawi, Abbas. Arab Oil & United States Energy Requirements. (Monograph No. 16). 42p. (Orig.). 1982. pap. 5.95 (ISBN 0-937694-52-5). Assn Arab-Amer U Grads.

Anderson, Irvine H. Aramco, the United States, & Saudi Arabia: A Study of the Dynamics of Foreign Oil Policy, 1933-1950. LC 80-8535. 288p. 1981. 23.50x (ISBN 0-691-04679-4). Princeton U Pr.

Boatright, Mody C. & Owens, William A. Tales from the Derrick Floor: A People's History of the Oil Industry. LC 81-19725. (Illus.). xx, 284p. 1982. 22.50x (ISBN 0-8032-1177-5); pap. 6.50 (ISBN 0-8032-6067-9, BB 804, Bison). U of Nebr Pr.

Bouhabib, Abdallah R. The Long-Run of New Reserves of Crude Oil in the U. S., 1966-1973. Bruchey, Stuart, ed. LC 78-22665. (Energy in the American Economy Ser.). (Illus.). 1979. lib. bdg. 17.00x (ISBN 0-405-11968-2). Ayer Co Pubs.

California-Alaska Oil & Gas Review for 1969. 1970. 40.00 (ISBN 0-686-28269-8). Munger Oil.

California-Alaska Oil & Gas Review for 1971. 40.00 (ISBN 0-686-28270-1). Munger Oil.

California-Alaska Oil & Gas Review for 1972. 40.00 (ISBN 0-686-28271-X). Munger Oil.

California-Alaska Oil & Gas Review for 1973. 1974. 40.00 (ISBN 0-686-28272-8). Munger Oil.

California-Alaska Oil & Gas Review of 1975. 1976. 40.00 (ISBN 0-686-28273-6). Munger Oil.

California Gas & Oil Exploration: 1963 Annual. 1964. 40.00 (ISBN 0-686-28263-9). Munger Oil.

California Oil & Gas Exploration 1956. 1956. pap. 40.00 (ISBN 0-686-30734-8). Munger Oil.

California Oil & Gas Exploration 1957. 1957. pap. 40.00 (ISBN 0-686-30735-6). Munger Oil.

California Oil & Gas Exploration 1959. 1959. pap. 40.00 (ISBN 0-686-30736-4). Munger Oil.

California Oil & Gas Exploration: 1960 Annual. 1961. 40.00 (ISBN 0-686-28261-2). Munger Oil.

California Oil & Gas Exploration: 1962 Annual. 1963. 40.00 (ISBN 0-686-28262-0). Munger Oil.

California Oil & Gas Exploration: 1964 Annual. 1965. 40.00 (ISBN 0-686-28264-7). Munger Oil.

California Oil & Gas Exploration: 1965 Annual. 1966. 40.00 (ISBN 0-686-28265-5). Munger Oil.

California Oil & Gas Exploration: 1966 Annual. 1967. 40.00 (ISBN 0-686-28266-3). Munger Oil.

California Oil & Gas Exploration: 1967 Annual. 1968. 40.00 (ISBN 0-686-28267-1). Munger Oil.

California Oil & Gas Exploration: 1968 Annual. 1969. 40.00 (ISBN 0-686-28268-X). Munger Oil.

California Oil & Gas Review, 1977. 1978. 40.00 (ISBN 0-686-16192-0). Munger Oil.

Erickson, Edward W. Economic Incentives, Industrial Structure & the Supply of Crude Oil Discoveries in the U. S., 1946-58-59. Bruchey, Stuart, ed. LC 78-22678. (Energy in the American Economy Ser.). (Illus.). 1979. lib. bdg. 14.00x (ISBN 0-405-11981-X). Ayer Co Pubs.

Franks, Kenny A. & Lambert, Paul F. Early California Oil: A Photographic History, 1865-1940. LC 84-40134. (The Montague History of Oil Ser.: No. 4). (Illus.). 260p. 1985. 34.50 (ISBN 0-89096-206-5). Tex A&M Univ Pr.

Froh, Riley. Wildcatter Extraordinary. 208p. 1984. 11.95 (ISBN 0-911225-03-X). Clearstream Pr.

Giddens, Paul H. The Birth of the Oil Industry. LC 72-2839. (Use & Abuse of America's Natural Resources Ser.). (Illus.). 292p. 1972. Repr. of 1938 ed. 23.50 (ISBN 0-405-04507-7). Ayer Co Pubs.

Halbouty, Michel & Clark, James. Spindletop. LC 52-7149. 306p. 1980. Repr. of 1952 ed. 18.95x (ISBN 0-87201-791-5). Gulf Pub.

Halevi, Marcus & Andrasko, Kenneth. Alaska Crude: Visions of the Last Frontier. (Illus.). 1977. pap. 7.95 (ISBN 0-316-33879-6). Little.

Hardy, George, ed. Pooling & Unitization in Louisiana. 465p. 1983. 39.00 (ISBN 0-89419-315-5). Inst Energy.

--Pooling & Unitization in Texas. 336p. 1984. 39.00 (ISBN 0-89419-336-8). Inst Energy.

Horwich, George & Mitchell, Edward J., eds. Policies for Coping with Oil Supply Disruptions. 1982. 15.95 (ISBN 0-8447-2232-4); pap. 7.95 (ISBN 0-8447-2233-2). Am Enterprise.

Ise, John. The United States Oil Policy. LC 72-2846. (Use & Abuse of America's Natural Resources Ser). (Illus.). 584p. 1972. Repr. of 1928 ed. 34.00 (ISBN 0-405-04512-3). Ayer Co Pubs.

Johnson, Arthur M. Pipelines: A Study in Private Enterprise & Public Policy, 1862-1906. LC 81-23728. (Illus.). xiii, 307p. 1982. Repr. of 1956 ed. lib. bdg. 37.50x (ISBN 0-313-23409-4, JODEV). Greenwood.

Kelley, Dana R., et al. The Petroleum Industry & the Future Petroleum Province in Pennsylvania. 2nd ed. (Mineral Resource Report Ser.: 65). (Illus.). 39p. pap. 2.00. Commonweal Env.

Kuntz, Eugene, ed. Pooling & Unitization in Oklahoma. 411p. 1983. 39.00 (ISBN 0-89419-310-4). Inst Energy.

Litchfield, Carter, et al. The Bethlehem Oil Mill Seventeen Forty-Five to Nineteen Thirty-Four: German Technology in Early Pennsylvania. LC 82-61069. (Illus.). 128p. 1984. 22.50 (ISBN 0-917526-02-3). Olearius Edns.

Lowe, et al, eds. New Mexico Petroleum Land Practices. (IED Book Ser.). 42.00 (ISBN 0-318-02003-3). IED Pub Hse.

Lowe, John S., ed. New Mexico Petroleum Land Practice. 672p. 1982. 42.00 (ISBN 0-89419-248-5). Inst Energy.

McDonald, Stephen L. Petroleum Conservation in the United States: An Economic Analysis. LC 71-149242. (Resources for the Future Ser.). (Illus.). 288p. 1971. 22.50x (ISBN 0-8018-1261-5). Johns Hopkins.

Merklein, Helmut & Murchison, William. Those Gasoline Lines & How They Got There. LC 79-55245. 150p. 1980. lib. bdg. 10.95 (ISBN 0-933028-10-5); pap. 5.95 (ISBN 0-933028-09-1). Fisher Inst.

Olien, Roger M. & Olien, Diana D. Wildcatters: Texas Independent Oilmen. Lubeck, Scott, ed. (Illus.). 256p. 1984. 16.95 (ISBN 0-932012-85-X). Texas Month Pr.

Pratt, Joseph. The Growth of a Refining Region, Vol. 4. Porter, Glenn, ed. LC 77-7797. (Industrial Development & the Social Fabric Ser.). 313p. (Orig.). 1980. lib. bdg. 29.50 (ISBN 0-89232-090-7). Jai Pr.

Ramsey, James B. The Oil Muddle: Control vs. Competition. 144p. 1985. pap. text ed. 7.25 (ISBN 0-8191-4483-5). U Pr of Amer.

Ridgeway, James & Conner, Bettina. New Energy: Understanding the Crisis & a Guide to An Alternative Energy System. LC 74-16669. (Institute for Policy Studies Ser.). 228p. 1975. 9.95x (ISBN 0-8070-0504-5). Beacon Pr.

Rintoul, William. Oildorado: Boom Times on the West Side. LC 78-50141. (Illus.). 240p. 1980. pap. 7.95 (ISBN 0-934136-07-6, Valley Calif). Western Tanager.

Riva, Joseph P., Jr., et al. Prospects for U. S. Conventional Oil & Gas Production to the Year 2000. (WVSS in Natural Resources & Energy Management Ser.). 150p. 1985. pap. text ed. 22.50x (ISBN 0-8133-7067-1). Westview.

Rundell, Walter, Jr. Oil in West Texas & New Mexico: A Pictorial History of the Permian Basin. LC 81-48376. (Illus.). 200p. 1982. 24.50 (ISBN 0-89096-125-5). Tex A&M Univ Pr.

Sobel, Lester A., ed. Energy Crisis, Vol. 3: 1975-77. LC 74-75154. 1977. lib. bdg. 19.95 (ISBN 0-87196-280-2); 59.95 set (ISBN 0-686-85940-5). Facts on File.

State & Federal Exploratory Wells & Core Holes Drilled off the West Coast of Continental U.S.A. Prior to 1974. 1975. 40.00 (ISBN 0-686-28277-9). Munger Oil.

U. S. Dept. of the Interior. Hearings Before the Secretary of the Interior on Leasing of Oil Lands & Natural-Gas Wells in Indian Territory & Territory of Oklahoma: May 8, 24, 25 & 29, & June 7, & 19, 1906. LC 72-2841. (Use & Abuse of America's Natural Resources Ser.). 92p. 1972. Repr. of 1906 ed. 14.00 (ISBN 0-405-04509-3). Ayer Co Pubs.

Wagner, Walter R. & Lytle, William S. Greater Pittsburgh Region Revised Surface Structure & Its Relation to Oil & Gas Fields. (Information Circular Ser.: No. 80). (Illus.). 20p. 1984. pap. 1.85 (ISBN 0-8182-0030-8). Commonweal PA.

Wampler, Ralph L. Forced Pooling! A Guide for Oklahoma Mineral Owners. 1982. pap. 14.95 (ISBN 0-943264-01-4). San Anselmo Pub.

White, Gerald T. Scientists in Conflict: The Beginnings of the Oil Industry in California. LC 68-31651. (Illus.). 272p. 1968. 10.00 (ISBN 0-87328-032-6). Huntington Lib.

Wildavsky, Aaron & Tenenbaum, Ellen. The Politics of Mistrust: Estimating American Oil & Gas Resources. LC 80-29049. (Managing Information Ser.: Vol. 1). (Illus.). 364p. 1981. 29.95 (ISBN 0-8039-1582-9). Sage.

--The Politics of Mistrust: Estimating American Oil & Gas Resources. LC 80-29049. (Managing Information Ser.: Vol. 1). (Illus.). 364p. 1981. pap. 14.95 (ISBN 0-8039-1583-7). Sage.

PETROLEUM PIPE LINES

see Petroleum–Pipe Lines

PETROLEUM POLLUTION OF WATER

see Oil Pollution of Water

PETROLEUM PRODUCTS

see also Coal-Tar Products; Lubrication and Lubricants; Petroleum–Refining; Petroleum As Fuel; Petroleum;

also names of specific products, e.g. Gasoline

American Society for Materials & Testing. Low-Temperature Pumpability Characteristics of Engine Oils in Full-Scale Engines, DS 57. 104p. 1975. pap. 16.00 (ISBN 0-8031-0392-1, 05-057000-12). ASTM.

ASTM & Other Specifications for Petroleum Products & Lubricants, 1984. 4th ed. 350p. 1984. 40.00 (ISBN 0-8031-0835-4, 03-402384-12). ASTM.

Eckbo, Paul L. The Future of World Oil. LC 76-16809. 160p. 1976. prof ref 29.95x (ISBN 0-88410-455-9). Ballinger Pub.

Falbe, Jurgen, ed. Chemical Feedstocks from Coal. LC 81-3022. 647p. 1982. 115.95 (ISBN 0-471-05291-4, Pub. by Wiley-Interscience). Wiley.

Institute of Petroleum. Guidelines on User Precautionary Labelling for Suppliers of Packaged Petroleum Products. (Institute of Petroleum Ser.). 34p. 1983. pap. 19.95x (ISBN 0-471-26257-9, Pub. by Wiley-Interscience). Wiley.

--Standards for Petroleum & Its Products: Part 1: Methods for Analysis & Testing. 41st ed. 359p. 1982. 154.95 (ISBN 0-471-26146-7). Wiley.

--Standards for Petroleum & Its Products, Vols. 1 & 2. 43rd ed. 1800p. 1984. Pt. 1, Methods of Analysis & Testing. 154.95 (ISBN 0-471-90455-4). Wiley.

Miscellaneous ASTM Standards for Petroleum Products. 15th ed. 1300p. 1981. 54.00 (ISBN 0-8031-0518-5, 03-402081-12). ASTM.

Schelling, Thomas C. Thinking Through the Energy Problem. LC 79-4583. (CED Supplementary Paper). 1979. pap. 5.00 (ISBN 0-87186-242-5). Comm Econ Dev.

Significance of ASTM Tests for Petroleum Products, STP-7C. 216p. 1977. pap. 11.75 (ISBN 0-8031-0567-3, 04-007030-12). ASTM.

Waddams, A. L. Chemicals from Petroleum. 4th ed. LC 79-56811. 375p. 1980. 16.50x (ISBN 0-87201-104-6). Gulf Pub.

--Chemicals from Petroleum. 1962. 12.95x (ISBN 0-685-21897-X). Wehman.

PETROLEUM REFINING

see Petroleum–Refining

PETROLEUM WASTE

see also Oil Pollution of Water

Beychok, Milton R. Aqueous Wastes: From Petroleum & Petrochemical Plants. LC 67-19834. Repr. of 1967 ed. 95.00 (ISBN 0-8357-9839-9, 2051229). Bks Demand UMI.

PETROLOGY

see also Crystallography; Geochemistry; Geology; Mineralogy; Paleomagnetism; Rocks

also varieties of rock, e.g. Quartz

Allegre, C. J. & Hart, S. R., eds. Trace Elements in Igneous Petrology. (Developments in Petrology: Vol. 5). 1978. Repr. 72.50 (ISBN 0-444-41658-7). Elsevier.

Amstutz, G. C., ed. Spilites & Spilitic Rocks. (International Union of Geological Sciences: Ser. A, No. 4). (Illus.). 450p. 1974. 46.00 (ISBN 0-387-06448-6). Springer-Verlag.

Bayly, Brian. Introduction to Petrology. 1968. text ed. 34.95 (ISBN 0-13-491621-2). P-H.

Best, Myron G. Igneous & Metamorphic Petrology. LC 81-17530. (Illus.). 630p. 1982. text ed. 37.95 (ISBN 0-7167-1335-7). W H Freeman.

Binns, R. A. & McBryde, I. A Petrological Analysis of Ground-Edge Artifacts from Northern New South Wales. (AIAS Prehistory & Material Culture Ser.: No. 10). (Illus., Orig.). 1972. pap. text ed. 11.50x (ISBN 0-85575-025-1). Humanities.

Borradaile, G. J., et al, eds. Atlas of Deformational & Metamorphic Rock Fabrics. (Illus.). 530p. 1982. 64.00 (ISBN 0-387-11278-2). Springer-Verlag.

Bowen, Oliver E., Jr. Rocks & Minerals of the San Francisco Bay Region. (California Natural History Guides: No. 5). (Illus.). 1962. pap. 2.85 (ISBN 0-520-00158-3). U of Cal Pr.

Caribbean Geological Conference (5th: 1968: St. Thomas, Virgin Islands) Staff. Caribbean Geophysical, Tectonic & Petrological Studies. Donnelly, Thomas D., ed. LC 74-165441. (Geological Society of America Memoir Ser.: No. 130). pap. 68.50 (ISBN 0-317-29126-2, 2025025). Bks Demand UMI.

Chayes, Felix. Ratio Correlation: A Manual for Students of Petrology & Geochemistry. LC 71-146110. 1971. text ed. 7.00x (ISBN 0-226-10218-1); pap. text ed. 3.00x (ISBN 0-226-10220-3). U of Chicago Pr.

Cook, Earl F., ed. Tufflavas & Ignimbrites. 1966. 23.95 (ISBN 0-444-00008-9, North Holland). Elsevier.

Ehlers, Ernest G. & Blatt, Harvey. Petrology: Igneous, Sedimentary, & Metamorphic. LC 81-12517. (Illus.). 732p. 1982. text ed. 37.95 (ISBN 0-7167-1279-2). W H Freeman.

Ernst, W. G. Earth Materials. 1969. pap. text ed. 15.95 (ISBN 0-13-222604-9). P-H.

--Petrologic Phase Equilibria. LC 76-3699. (Illus.). 333p. 1976. 41.95 (ISBN 0-7167-0279-7). W H Freeman.

Filby, Royston H., et al, eds. Atomic & Nuclear Methods in Fossil Energy Research. LC 81-21169. 518p. 1982. 69.50x (ISBN 0-306-40899-6, Plenum Pr). Plenum Pub.

Folk, Robert L. Petrology of Sedimentary Rocks. 4th ed. LC 80-83557. (Illus.). 1980. 15.95x (ISBN 0-914696-14-9). Hemphill.

Gupta, A. & Yagi, K. Petrology & Genesis of Leucite-Bearing Rocks. (Minerals & Rocks Ser.: Vol. 14). (Illus.). 250p. 1980. 44.00 (ISBN 0-387-09864-X). Springer-Verlag.

Haldorsen, Sylvi. The Petrography of Tills: A Study from Ringsaker, Southeastern Norway. (Geological Survey of Norway Ser: No. 336, Bulletin 44). 32p. 1978. pap. 12.00x (ISBN 82-00-31370-0, Dist. by Columbia U Pr). Universitet.

Hatch, F. H., et al. Petrology of the Igneous Rocks. 13th ed. (Textbook of Petrology Ser.). (Illus.). 1972. pap. text ed. 15.95x (ISBN 0-04-552009-7). Allen Unwin.

Hekinian, R. Petrology of the Ocean Floor. (Oceanography Ser.: Vol. 33). 394p. 1983. 85.00 (ISBN 0-444-41967-5). Elsevier.

Huang, Walter T. Petrology. 1962. text ed. 55.00 (ISBN 0-07-030750-4). McGraw.

Hughes, C. J. Igneous Petrology. (Developments in Petrology Ser.: Vol. 7). 552p. 1982. 30.00 (ISBN 0-444-42011-8). Elsevier.

Hyndman, D. W. Petrology of Igneous & Metamorphic Rocks. 2nd ed. 720p. 1985. 38.95 (ISBN 0-07-031658-9). McGraw.

Irvine, T. N. Petrology of the Duke Island Ultramafic Complex, Southeastern Alaska. LC 73-87233. (Geological Society of America Memoir Ser.: NO. 138). pap. 77.50 (ISBN 0-317-28981-0, 2023736). Bks Demand UMI.

Jackson, K. C. Textbook of Lithology. 1970. text ed. 48.95 (ISBN 0-07-032143-4). McGraw.

Keller, W. D. Common Rocks & Minerals of Missouri. rev. ed. LC 67-66173. (Illus.). 78p. 1961. pap. 5.95x (ISBN 0-8262-0585-2). U of Mo Pr.

Kempe, D. R. & Harvey, Anthony P., eds. The Petrology of Archaeological Artifacts. (Illus.). 1983. 69.00x (ISBN 0-19-854418-9). Oxford U Pr.

Kornprobst, J., ed. Kimberlites: I. Kimberlites & Related Rocks; Kimberlites: The Mantle & Crust-Mantle Relationships: Developments in Petrology, 2 Vols. 860p. 1984. Vol. 1-11A. 54.00 (ISBN 0-444-42273-0, I-538-83); Vol. 2-11b. 50.00 (ISBN 0-444-42274-9). Elsevier.

Krumbein, William & Pettijohn, F. J. Manual of Sedimentary Petrography. LC 39-3391. (The Century Earth Science Ser.). pap. 140.80 (ISBN 0-317-26297-1, 2055690). Bks Demand UMI.

Le Maitre, R. W. Numerical Petrology. (Developments in Petrology Ser.: No. 8). 282p. 1982. 57.50 (ISBN 0-444-42098-3, I-038-84). Elsevier.

Maaloe, S. Principles of Igneous Petrology. (Illus.). 415p. 1985. 49.50 (ISBN 0-387-13520-0). Springer-Verlag.

McBirney, A. R. Igneous Petrology. 1985. 38.75 (ISBN 0-87735-323-9). Freeman Cooper.

McBride, E. F. Sedimentary Petrology & History of the Haymond Formation (Pennsylvanian), Marathon Basin, Texas. (Report of Investigations Ser.: RI 57). 101p. 1966. 2.50 (ISBN 0-686-29339-8). Bur Econ Geology.

McCall, G. J. H., ed. Ophiolitic & Related Melanges. LC 81-13490. (Benchmark Papers in Geology: Vol. 66). 464p. 1983. 56.00 (ISBN 0-87933-421-5). Van Nos Reinhold.

Mason, R. Petrology of the Metamorphic Rocks. (Textbook of Petrology Ser.). (Illus.). 1978. pap. text ed. 14.95x (ISBN 0-04-552014-3). Allen Unwin.

Milovsky, A. Mineralogy & Petrography. 437p. 1982. 10.95 (ISBN 0-8285-2310-X, Pub. by Mir Pubs USSR). Imported Pubns.

Moorhouse, Walter W. Study of Rocks in Thin Section. 1959. text ed. 36.95 scp (ISBN 0-06-044610-2, HarpC). Har-Row.

Nockolds, S. T., et al. Petrology for Students. 8th ed. LC 76-52186. (Illus.). 1978. 77.50 (ISBN 0-521-21553-6); pap. 24.95x (ISBN 0-521-29184-4). Cambridge U Pr.

Pearl, Richard M. Exploring Rocks, Minerals, Fossils in Colorado. rev. ed. LC 64-25339. (Illus.). 215p. 1969. 14.95 (ISBN 0-8040-0105-7, 82-70647, Pub. by Swallow). Ohio U Pr.

Powell, Roger. Equilibrium Thermodynamics in Petrology: An Introduction. 1978. text ed. 21.60 (ISBN 0-06-318061-8, IntlDept); pap. text ed. 15.70 (ISBN 0-06-318073-1, IntlDept). Har-Row.

Sander, B. An Introduction to the Study of Fabrics of Geological Bodies. 1970. 110.00 (ISBN 0-08-006660-7). Pergamon.

Sood, Mohan K. Modern Igneous Petrology. LC 81-820. 244p. 1981. 39.95x (ISBN 0-471-08915-X, Pub. by Wiley-Interscience). Wiley.

Stach, E., et al. Textbook of Coal Petrology. 3rd, rev. & enl. ed. Murchison, D. G., et al, eds. Murchison, D. G., tr. (Illus.). 536p. 1982. lib. bdg. 48.00x (ISBN 3-443-01018-0). Lubrecht & Cramer.

Stanton, R. L. Ore Petrology. (International Series in the Earth & Planetary Sciences). (Illus.). 736p. 1971. text ed. 55.95 (ISBN 0-07-060843-1). McGraw.

Strakhov, N. M. Principles of Lithogenesis, 3 Vols. LC 62-15800. Vol. 1, 245p, 1967. 45.00x (ISBN 0-306-17051-5, Consultants); Vol. 2, 609p, 1969. 55.00 (ISBN 0-306-17052-3); Vol. 3, 500p, 1969. 49.50 (ISBN 0-306-17053-1). Plenum Pub.

Tomkeieff, S. I. Dictionary of Petrology. 680p. 1983. 107.95 (ISBN 0-471-10159-1). Wiley.

Tucker, M. E. Sedimentary Petrology: An Introduction, Vol.3. (Geoscience Texts Ser.). 252p. 1981. pap. 24.95x (ISBN 0-470-27160-4). Halsted Pr.

Turner, Francis J. Metamorphic Petrology. 2nd ed. LC 79-27496. (International Earth & Planetary Sciences Ser.). (Illus.). 512p. 1980. text ed. 54.95 (ISBN 0-07-065501-4). McGraw.

Way, Douglas S. Terrain Analysis: A Guide to Site Selection Using Aerial Photographic Interpretation. 2nd ed. (Community Development Ser.: Vol. 1). (Illus.). 1978. 48.95 (ISBN 0-87933-318-9). Van Nos Reinhold.

Williams, Howel, et al. Petrography: An Introduction to the Study of Rocks in Thin Sections. LC 54-5872. (Geology Ser.). (Illus.). 406p. 1954. 27.95x (ISBN 0-7167-0206-1). W H Freeman.

--Petrography: An Introduction to the Study of Rocks in Thin Sections. 2nd ed. LC 82-5072. (Illus.). 626p. 1983. text ed. 38.95 (ISBN 0-7167-1376-4). W H Freeman.

Winkler, H. G. Petrogenesis of Metamorphic Rocks: Springer Study Edition. 5th ed. LC 79-14704. (Illus.). 1979. pap. 19.50 (ISBN 0-387-90413-1). Springer-Verlag.

Wright, Frederic E. The Methods of Petrographic-Microscopic Research. 1977. lib. bdg. 75.00 (ISBN 0-8490-2229-0). Gordon Pr.

Zubkov, V. General Petrography. (Illus.). 228p. 1967. 14.95x (ISBN 0-8464-0447-8). Beekman Pubs.

PETROLOGY–LABORATORY MANUALS

Hutchison, Charles S. Laboratory Handbook of Petrographic Techniques. LC 73-17336. 527p. 1974. 58.95 (ISBN 0-471-42550-8, Pub. by Wiley-Interscience). Wiley.

PETROLOGY–NOMENCLATURE

see Rocks–Classification and Nomenclature

PETRUNKEVITCH, ALEXANDER IVANOVITCH, 1875-

Colebrook, C. Spider, Egg, & Microcosm: Three Men & Three Worlds of Science. LC 55-9287. 1955. 8.00 (ISBN 0-9600476-1-1). E Kinkead.

Woodruff, Lorande R., et al. In Honor of Alexander Petrunkevitch. (Connecticut Academy of Arts & Sciences Transaction: Vol. 36). 1945. 29.50 (ISBN 0-208-00946-9). Shoe String.

PETS

see also Cage-Birds; Domestic Animals also particular species of animals, e.g. Cats, Dogs, etc.

Brandt, Leonore. Raccoon Family Pets. pap. 2.95 (ISBN 0-87666-216-5, AP-7500). TFH Pubns.

Brann, Donald R. How to Build Pet Housing, Bk. 751. LC 75-269. 1978. pap. 6.95 (ISBN 0-87733-751-9). Easi-Bild.

Business Communications Staff. The Pet Industry: Outlook. 1985. cancelled (ISBN 0-89336-164-X, GA-034N). BCC.

Fogle, Bruce. Interrelations Between People & Pets. (Illus.). 370p. 1981. 32.75x (ISBN 0-398-04169-5). C C Thomas.

Henley, Diana, et al. ASPCA Guide to Pet Care. LC 74-114389. (Illus.). 1970. pap. 1.25 (ISBN 0-8008-0453-8). Taplinger.

Herriot, James, et al. Animal Stories: Tame & Wild. LC 85-12575. (Illus.). 224p. 1985. 9.98 (ISBN 0-8069-4722-5). Sterling.

Levinson, Boris M. Pet-Oriented Child Psychotherapy. 228p. 1969. 13.75x (ISBN 0-398-01118-4). C C Thomas.

Manolson, Frank, ed. The Pet Encyclopedia. LC 81-1851. 368p. 1981. 24.95 (ISBN 0-8407-4079-4). Nelson.

Miller, Evelyn. How to Raise & Train an Airedale. (Illus.). pap. 2.95 (ISBN 0-87666-233-5, DS-1002). TFH Pubns.

O'Connor, Richard F. Ident-A-Dog: A Complete Identification Record of Your Dog. (Ident-A Ser.). (Illus.). 32p. (Orig.). 1985. pap. 2.95 (ISBN 0-913243-98-1). O'Connor Hse-Pubs.

Piper, Blanche. Four Footed Members of the Family. LC 84-209401. (Illus.). 1980. 4.95 (ISBN 0-89962-002-7). Todd & Honeywell.

Pronek, Neal. Oscars. 1972. 5.95 (ISBN 0-87666-765-5, PS-687). TFH Pubns.

Schwartz, Charlotte. Friend to Friend: Dogs That Help Mankind. 192p. 1984. pap. 12.95 (ISBN 0-87605-545-5). Howell Bk.

Snedigar, Robert. Our Small Native Animals: Their Habits & Care. (Illus.). 1963. pap. 5.95 (ISBN 0-486-21022-7). Dover.

--Our Small Native Animals: Their Habits & Care. rev. ed. (Illus.). 14.75 (ISBN 0-8446-2961-8). Peter Smith.

Stamm, G. W. Popular Mechanics Veterinary Guide for Farmers. new ed. LC 75-18653. (Illus.). 304p. 1975. 14.95 (ISBN 0-910990-61-1). Hearst Bks.

PEUGEOT (AUTOMOBILE)

see Automobiles, Foreign–Types–Peugeot

PFAFF'S PROBLEM

Schouten, Jan A. & Van Der Kulk, W. Pfaff's Problem & Its Generalizations. LC 75-77140. 1969. Repr. of 1949 ed. 19.50 (ISBN 0-8284-0221-3). Chelsea Pub.

PFEIL (FIGHTER PLANES)

Nowarra, Heinz J. & Maloney, Edward T. Dornier D-335. LC 66-22652. (Aero Ser: Vol. 9). (Illus.). 1966. pap. 3.95 (ISBN 0-8168-0532-6). Aero.

PH

see Hydrogen-Ion Concentration

PHAGOCYTOSIS

see also Reticulo-Endothelial System

Rossi, F. & Patriarca, P., eds. Biochemistry & Function of Phagocytes. LC 81-19251. (Advances in Experimental Medicine & Biology, Ser.: Vol. 141). 716p. 1982. 85.00 (ISBN 0-306-40887-2, Plenum Pr). Plenum Pub.

PHANEROGAMS

see also Angiosperms; Gymnosperms

Cronquist, Arthur. How to Know the Seed Plants. (Pictured Key Nature Ser.). 250p. 1979. wire coil (ISBN 0-697-04761-X). Wm C Brown.

Esau, Katherine. Anatomy of Seed Plants. 2nd ed. LC 76-41191. 550p. 1977. text ed. 39.45 (ISBN 0-471-24520-8). Wiley.

Guedes, M. Morphology of Seed Plants. (Plant Science Ser.: No. 2). (Illus.). 1979. lib. bdg. 16.80x (ISBN 3-7682-1195-9). Lubrecht & Cramer.

Jackson, B. D., et al, eds. Index Kewensis Supplements. Incl. Vol. 1. 1866-1895. Durand, T. & Jackson, B. D., eds. 1901-06; Vol. 4. 1906-1910. Prain, D., ed. 1913; Vol. 6. 1916-1920. Hill, A. W., ed. 1926. 68.00x (ISBN 0-19-854315-8); Vol. 7. 1921-1925. Hill, A. W., ed. 1929. 63.00x (ISBN 0-19-854316-6); Vol. 8. 1926-1930. Hill, A. W., ed. 1933. 68.00x (ISBN 0-19-854317-4); Vol. 10. 1936-1940. Hill, A. W. & Salisbury, E. J., eds. 1947; Vol. 12. 1951-1955. Taylor, George, ed. 1959; Vol. 13. 1956-1960. Taylor, George, ed. 1966. 68.00x (ISBN 0-19-854354-9); Vol. 14. 1961-1965. Taylor, George, ed. 1970. 68.00x (ISBN 0-19-854370-0); Vol. 15. 1966-1970. Heslop-Harrison, J., compiled by. 1973; Vol. 16. 1971-1976. Brenan, J. P., ed. 1980. 140.00x (ISBN 0-19-854531-2). Oxford U Pr.

Rydberg, Per A. Flora of the Prairies & Plains of Central North America. (Illus.). 1965. Repr. of 1932 ed. 23.95x (ISBN 0-02-851240-5). Hafner.

PHARMACEUTICAL ARITHMETIC–PROGRAMMED INSTRUCTION

Sackheim, George I. & Robbins, Lewis. Programmed Mathematics for Nurses. 5th ed. (Illus.). 1983. pap. text ed. write for info. (ISBN 0-02-405170-5). Macmillan.

Weaver, Mabel E., et al. Programmed Mathematics of Drugs & Solutions. rev. ed. 128p. 1984. pap. text ed. 7.50 (ISBN 0-397-54475-8, 64-04164, Lippincott Nursing). Lippincott.

PHARMACEUTICAL CHEMISTRY

see Chemistry, Medical and Pharmaceutical

PHARMACEUTICAL RESEARCH

Adrian, R. H., et al, eds. Reviews of Physiology, Biochemistry & Pharmacology, Vol. 83. LC 74-3674. (Illus.). 1978. 51.00 (ISBN 0-387-08907-1). Springer-Verlag.

August, J. T., ed. Monoclonal Antibodies in Drug Development. (Illus.). 237p. (Orig.). 1982. lexitone 24.00 (ISBN 0-9609094-0-0). Am Phar & Ex.

Bartosek, Ivan, et al, eds. Animals in Toxicological Research. (Monographs of the Mario Negri Institute for Pharmacological Research). 224p. 1982. text ed. 38.50 (ISBN 0-89004-811-8). Raven.

Bergman & Gittins. Statistical Methods for Planning Pharmaceutical Research. (Statistics-Textbook & Monographs Ser.). 280p. 1985. write for info. (ISBN 0-8247-7146-X). Dekker.

Bindra, Jasjit S. & Lednicer, Daniel. Chronicles of Drug Discovery, Vol. 2. LC 81-11471. 272p. 1983. cloth 48.50 (ISBN 0-471-89135-5, Pub. by Wiley-Interscience). Wiley.

Breimer, D. D. & Speiser, P., eds. Topics in Pharmaceutical Sciences II: Proceedings of the 43rd International Congress of the F.I.P., Montreux, Switzerland September 5-9,1983. 1984. 69.25 (ISBN 0-444-80549-4, I-009-84, Biomedical Pr). Elsevier.

Christoffersen, Ralph E. & Olson, Edward C., eds. Computer-Assisted Drug Design. LC 79-21038. (ACS Symposium Ser.: No. 112). 1979. 59.95 (ISBN 0-8412-0521-3). Am Chemical.

Chu, E. & Generoso, W., eds. Mutation, Cancer, & Malformation. (Environmental Science Research Ser.: Vol. 31). 855p. 1984. 97.50x (ISBN 0-306-41820-7, Plenum Press). Plenum Pub.

Edelmann, A., et al, ed. Radioactivity for Pharmaceutical & Allied Research Laboratories. 1960. 52.50 (ISBN 0-12-230850-6). Acad Pr.

Endo, H., et al, eds. Chemistry & Biological Actions of 4-Nitroquinoline 1-Oxide. LC 6-129622. (Recent Results in Cancer Research: Vol. 34). (Illus.). 1971. 26.00 (ISBN 0-387-05230-5). Springer-Verlag.

Endrenyi, Laszlo, ed. Kinetic Data Analysis: Design & Analysis of Enzyme & Pharmacokinetic Experiments. LC 81-120. 438p. 1981. 69.50x (ISBN 0-306-40724-8, Plenum Pr). Plenum Pub.

Florey, Klaus, ed. Analytical Profiles of Drug Substances, Vol. 10. 1981. 60.00 (ISBN 0-12-260810-0). Acad Pr.

Galli, Claudio, et al, eds. Phospholipases & Prostaglandins. LC 77-87457. (Advances in Prostaglandin & Thromboxane Research Ser.: Vol. 3). 218p. 1978. 40.00 (ISBN 0-89004-201-2). Raven.

Goldberg, Morton E., ed. Pharmacological & Biochemical Properties of Drug Substances, Vol. 2. 257p. 1977. 36.00 (ISBN 0-917330-25-0). Am Pharm Assn.

Harper, N. J. & Simmonds, A. B., eds. Advances in Drug Research, Vol. 13. (Serial PUblication). 1984. 59.00 (ISBN 0-12-013313-X). Acad Pr.

Harper, N. J. & Simmons, A. B., eds. Advances in Drug Research, 6 vols, Vols. 8-14. (Serial Publication). 1984. Vol. 8, 1975. 60.00 (ISBN 0-12-013308-3); Vol. 9, 1975. 40.00 (ISBN 0-12-013309-1); Vol. 10, 1975. 40.00 (ISBN 0-12-013310-5); Vol. 11, 1978. 50.00 (ISBN 0-12-013311-3); Vol. 12, 1978. 60.00 (ISBN 0-12-013312-1); Vol. 14. 69.50 (ISBN 0-12-013314-8). Acad Pr.

Johnson, E. M. & Kochhar, D. M., eds. Teratogenesis & Reproductive Toxicology. (Handbook of Experimental Pharmacology Ser.: Vol. 65). (Illus.). 400p. 1983. 118.00 (ISBN 0-387-11906-X). Springer-Verlag.

Jucker, E., ed. Progress in Drug Research, Vol. 25. 500p. 1981. text ed. 126.95x (ISBN 0-8176-1179-7). Birkhauser.

Jucker, Ernst. Progress in Drug Research, Vol. 28. 1984. text ed. 88.95x (ISBN 3-76431-556-3). Birkhauser.

Jucker, Ernst, ed. Progress in Drug Research, Vol. 26. 412p. 1982. text ed. 103.95 (ISBN 0-8176-1261-0). Birkhauser.

Kier, Lemont B. Molecular Orbital Theory in Drug Research. LC 73-137616. (Medicinal Chemistry Ser). 1971. 60.00 (ISBN 0-12-406550-3). Acad Pr.

Munson. Pharmaceutical Analysis: Modern Methods, Pt. B. (Drugs & Pharmaceutical Science Ser.). 512p. 1984. 79.75 (ISBN 0-8247-7251-2); text ed. 39.75. Dekker.

Nodine, John H. & Siegler, Peter E., eds. Animal & Clinical Pharmacologic Techniques in Drug Evaluation. LC 64-19787. pap. 160.00 (ISBN 0-317-29951-4, 2051708). Bks Demand UMI.

Sears, M. L., ed. Pharmacology of the Eye. (Handbook of Experimental Pharmacology Ser.: Vol. 69). 784p. 1984. 189.00 (ISBN 0-387-12578-7). Springer-Verlag.

Usdin, Earl, et al, eds. Frontiers in Biochemical & Pharmacological Research in Depression. (Advances in Biochemical Psychopharmacology Ser.: Vol. 39). (Illus.). 482p. 1984. text ed. 87.00 (ISBN 0-89004-243-8). Raven.

Vukovich, Matoren N. The Clinical Research Process in the Pharmaceutical Sciences. (Drugs & the Pharmaceutical Science Ser.). 608p. 1983. 59.75 (ISBN 0-8247-1914-X). Dekker.

Wardell, William M. & Lasagna, Louis. Regulation & Drug Development. 1975. pap. 3.50 (ISBN 0-8447-3167-6). Am Enterprise.

PHARMACY

see also Botany, Medical; Chemistry, Medical and Pharmaceutical; Drugs

Bonal, Joaquin & Poston, J. W., eds. Clinical Pharmacy Education & Patient Education: Proceedings of the European Symposium on Clinical Pharmacy, 12th, Barcelona, 1983. (Progress in Clinical Pharmacy Ser.: No. 6). 322p. 1984. 49.50 (ISBN 0-521-26610-6). Cambridge U Pr.

Brandon, Milan L. Corticosteroids in Medical Practice. (Illus.). 608p. 1962. 48.50x (ISBN 0-398-00215-0). C C Thomas.

Computer Strategies. The Pharmacy Computer Handbook. rev ed. 140p. 1983. looseleaf 45.00x (ISBN 0-9603584-2-0). Computer Strat.

Eckelman, W. C., ed. Technetium Ninety-Nine-M: Generators, Chemistry, & Preparation of Radiopharmaceuticals. (Illus.). 168p. 1983. 25.00 (ISBN 0-08-029144-9). Pergamon.

Florey, Klaus, ed. Analytical Profiles of Drug Substances, Vol. 11. LC 70-187259. 1982. 55.00 (ISBN 0-12-260811-9). Acad Pr.

Fukushima, H., et al. Index Guide to Drug Information Retrieval. 280p. 1979. 63.50 (ISBN 0-444-80139-1, Biomedical Pr). Elsevier.

Graedon, Joe. The New People's Pharmacy: Drug Breakthroughs of the '80s. 19.95 (ISBN 0-553-05072-9); pap. 8.95 (ISBN 0-553-34134-0). Bantam.

Hibbard, Wanda M. A Handbook of Nuclear Pharmacy. (Illus.). 80p. 1982. spiral bdg. 18.75x (ISBN 0-398-04760-X). C C Thomas.

Hoppe, Heinz A. & Levring, Tore, eds. Marine Algae in Pharmaceutical Science, Vol. 2. (Illus.). 309p. 1982. 56.00 (ISBN 3-11-008626-3). De Gruyter.

International Congress on Pharmacy: Proceedings, 2nd, Boston, 17-20 July 1980. LC 80-70866. 1980. 6.00 (ISBN 0-686-73989-2). Am Assn Coll Pharm.

Pharmaceutical Society of Great Britain, ed. Pharmaceutical Handbook. 19th ed. 800p. 1980. 35.00 (ISBN 0-85369-130-4, Pub. by Pharmaceutical). Rittenhouse.

Roda, E., ed. Bile Acids in Gastroenterology. 250p. 1983. text ed. 45.00 (ISBN 0-85200-488-5, Pub. by MTP Pr England). Kluwer Academic.

Russell, Charles, et al. Interpersonal Communication in Pharmacy: An Interactionist Approach. (Illus.). 176p. 1981. pap. 16.95 (ISBN 0-8385-4306-5). ACC.

Singer, Walter. Pharmacy Review. 3rd. ed. 188p. (Orig.). 1984. pap. 15.95 (ISBN 0-8385-7840-3). ACC.

Smith, Harry A. Principles & Methods of Pharmacy Management. 2nd ed. LC 80-17560. (Illus.). 413p. 1980. text ed. 19.50 (ISBN 0-8121-0765-9). Lea & Febiger.

PHARMACY–DATA PROCESSING

Bobon, D. & Baumahn, U., eds. AMDP System in Pharmacopsychiatry. (Modern Problems of Pharmacopsychiatry: Vol. 20). (Illus.). vi, 234p. 1983. 56.25 (ISBN 3-8055-3637-2). S Karger.

Computer Strategies. The Pharmacy Computer Handbook. rev ed. 140p. 1983. looseleaf 45.00x (ISBN 0-9603584-2-0). Computer Strat.

Cornell, Joseph A. Computers in Hospital Pharmacy Management: Fundamentals & Applications. LC 82-24381. 228p. 1983. 32.00 (ISBN 0-89443-673-2). Aspen Systems.

Ducrot, H., et al, eds. Computer Aid to Drug Therapy & to Drug Monitoring. 444p. 1978. 61.75 (ISBN 0-444-85188-7, North-Holland). Elsevier.

Fraade, David J., ed. The Aster Guide to Computer Applications in the Pharmaceutical Industry: An Overview of System Manufacturers' Hardware & Software. (Illus.). 250p. (Orig.). 1984. pap. 45.00x (ISBN 0-943330-05-X). Aster Pub Corp.
--Automation of Pharmaceutical Operations. 360p. 1983. 57.50 (ISBN 0-943330-02-5). Aster Pub Corp.
Manell, P. & Johansson, S. G., eds. The Impact of Computer Technology on Drug Information: Proceedings of the IFIP-IMIA Working Conference, Uppsala, Sweden, October 26-28, 1981. 262p. 1982. 34.00 (ISBN 0-444-86451-2, North Holland). Elsevier.
Stuper, Andrew J., et al. Computer Assisted Studies of Chemical Structure & Biological Function. LC 78-12337. 220p. 1979. 56.95 (ISBN 0-471-03896-2, Pub. by Wiley-Interscience). Wiley.

PHASE CHANGES (STATISTICAL PHYSICS)
see Phase Transformations (Statistical Physics)
Walas, Stanley M. Phase Equilibria in Chemical Engineering. (Illus.). 736p. 1984. text ed. 49.95 (ISBN 0-409-95162-5). Butterworth.

PHASE CONTRAST MICROSCOPE
see Phase Microscope

PHASE DIAGRAMS
Alper, Allan M., ed. Phase Diagrams: Materials Science & Technology Vol. 5: Crystal Chemistry, Stoichiometry, Spinodal Decomposition, Properties of Inorganic Phases. (Refractory Materials Ser.: Vol. 6-V). 1978. 70.00 (ISBN 0-12-053205-0). Acad Pr.
Alper, Allen, ed. Phase Diagrams: Materials Science & Technology. Incl. Part 1. Theory, Principles & Techniques of Phase Diagrams. 1970. 77.00 (ISBN 0-12-053201-8); Part 2. The Use of Phase Diagrams in Metals, Refractories, Ceramics, Glass & Electronic Materials. 1970. 77.00 (ISBN 0-12-053202-6); Part 3. The Use of Phase Diagrams in Electronic Materials & Glass Technology. 1970. 77.00 (ISBN 0-12-053203-4); Pt. 4. The Use of Phase Diagrams in Technical Materials. 1976. 72.00 (ISBN 0-12-053204-2). (Refractory Materials Ser: Vol. 6). Acad Pr.
Gordon, Paul. Principles of Phase Diagrams in Materials Systems. LC 82-14073. 248p. 1983. Repr. of 1968 ed. 19.50 (ISBN 0-89874-408-3). Krieger.
Helgeson, Harold C., et al. Handbook of Theoretical Activity Diagrams Depicting Chemical Equilibria in Geologic Systems Involving an Aqueous Phase at One ATM & Zero Degrees to 300 Degrees Centigrade. LC 73-97467. (Illus.). 253p. 1969. text ed. 7.50x (ISBN 0-87735-331-X). Freeman Cooper.
Hoffman, E. J. Phase & Flow Behavior in Petroleum Production. LC 81-68122. (Illus.). 915p. 1981. 225.00x (ISBN 0-9601552-3-6). Energon Co.
Kaufman, L. & Bernstein, H. Computer Calculation of Phase Diagrams: With Special Reference to Refractory Metals. (Refractory Materials Ser: Vol. 4). 1970. 81.00 (ISBN 0-12-402050-X). Acad Pr.
Levin, Ernest M. & McMurdie, Howard F., eds. Phase Diagram for Ceramists, Vol. II. 625p. 1969. 40.00 (ISBN 0-916094-05-7). Am Ceramic.
--Phase Diagrams for Ceramists: With Commentaries, Vol. III. 513p. 1975. 40.00 (ISBN 0-916094-06-5). Am Ceramic.
Levin, Ernest M., et al. Phase Diagram for Ceramist's 1964 Basic Volume, Vol. 1. (Illus.). 40.00 (ISBN 0-916094-04-9). Am Ceramic.
Morse, S. A. Basalts & Phase Diagrams: An Introduction to the Quantitative Use of Phase Diagrams in Igneous Petrology. (Illus.). 400p. 1980. 33.00 (ISBN 0-387-90477-8). Springer-Verlag.
Perel'man, Fanya M. Phase Diagrams of Multicomponent Systems: Geometric Methods. LC 66-12705. 82p. 1966. 24.50x (ISBN 0-306-10746-5, Consultants). Plenum Pub.
Smith, Geraldine, ed. Phase Diagrams for Ceramist, Vol. V. 1983. 80.00 (ISBN 0-916094-47-2). Am Ceramic.
--Phase Diagrams for Ceramists: Cumulative Index. 1984. 15.00 (ISBN 0-916094-60-X). Am Ceramic.
Wisniak, J. Phase Diagrams: A Literature Source Book, 2 vols. (Physical Sciences Data Ser.: Vol. 10). 2102p. 1981. Set. 298.00 (ISBN 0-444-41981-0). Elsevier.

PHASE DIFFERENCE MICROSCOPE
see Phase Microscope

PHASE-LOCKED LOOPS
Geiger, Dana F. Phaselock Loops for DC Motor Speed Control. LC 80-29578. 206p. 1981. 32.50 (ISBN 0-471-08548-0, Pub. by Wiley-Interscience). Wiley.
Heath Company Staff. Phase-Locked Loops. rev. ed. (Electronic Technology Ser.). (Illus.). 268p. 1979. looseleaf with experimental pts. 49.95 (ISBN 0-87119-025-7); pap. text ed. 18.95 (ISBN 0-87119-023-0); tchr's. ed 9.95 (ISBN 0-87119-024-9). Heathkit-Zenith Ed.
Lindsey, W. C. & Simon, M. K. Phase Locked Loops & Their Applications. (IEEE Press Reprint Ser.). 1977. 40.95 (ISBN 0-471-04175-0); (Pub. by Wiley-Interscience). Wiley.

PHASE MICROSCOPE
Ross, K. F. Phase Contrast & Interference Microscopy. 1967. 26.00 (ISBN 0-312-60410-6). St Martin.
Wade, Glen, ed. Acoustic Imaging: Cameras, Microscopes, Phased Arrays & Holographic Systems. LC 76-21. 325p. 1976. 52.50x (ISBN 0-306-30914-9, Plenum Pr). Plenum Pub.

PHASE RULE AND EQUILIBRIUM
see also Alloys; Chemical Equilibrium; Phase Diagrams; Vapor-Liquid Equilibrium
Bereron, Clifton G. & Risbud, Subhas H., eds. Introduction to Phase Equilibria in Ceramic Systems. 1984. 30.00 (ISBN 0-916094-58-8). Am Ceramic.
Giessen, B. C., ed. Developments in the Structural Chemistry of Alloy Phases. LC 77-94080. 288p. 1969. 32.50x (ISBN 0-306-30428-7, Plenum Pr). Plenum Pub.
Ginell, R. Association Theory: The Phases of Matter & Their Transformations. (Studies in Physical & Theoretical Chemistry: Vol. 1). 224p. 1979. 47.00 (ISBN 0-444-41753-2). Elsevier.
Hiza, M. J., et al. Equilibrium Properties of Fluid Mixtures: A Bibliography of Data on Fluids of Cryogenic Interest. LC 75-19000. (NSRDS Bibliographic Ser.). 165p. 1975. 85.00x (ISBN 0-306-66001-6, IFI Plenum). Plenum Pub.
Newton, R. C., et al, eds. Thermodynamics of Minerals & Melts, Vol. 1. (Advances in Physical Geochemistry Ser.). (Illus.). 272p. 1981. 46.00 (ISBN 0-387-90530-8). Springer-Verlag.
Null, Harold R. Phase Equilibrium in Process Design. LC 78-23527. 288p. 1980. Repr. of 1970 ed. lib. bdg. 19.50 (ISBN 0-88275-808-X). Krieger.
Prausnitz, J. M. Molecular Thermodynamics of Fluid-Phase Equilibria. LC 69-16866. 1969. ref. ed. 44.95 (ISBN 0-13-599639-2). P-H.
Reisman, Arnold. Phase Equilibria. (Physical Chemistry Ser: Vol. 19). 1970. 83.00 (ISBN 0-12-586350-0). Acad Pr.
Stanley, H. Eugene. Introduction to Phase Transitions & Critical Phenomena. (International Series of Monographs on Physics). (Illus.). 1971. text ed. 24.95x (ISBN 0-19-501458-8). Oxford U Pr.
Storvick, Truman S. & Sandler, Stanley I., eds. Phase Equilibria & Fluid Properties in the Chemical Industry: Estimation & Correlation. LC 77-13804. (ACS Symposium Ser.: No. 60). 1977. 49.95 (ISBN 0-8412-0393-8). Am Chemical.
Wetmore, F. E. & Leroy, D. J. Principles of Phase Equilibria. 11.50 (ISBN 0-8446-0961-7). Peter Smith.

PHASE TRANSFORMATIONS (STATISTICAL PHYSICS)
Biggs, N. L. Interaction Models. LC 77-80827. (London Mathematical Society Lecture Ser.: No. 30). (Illus.). 1977. 19.95x (ISBN 0-521-21770-9). Cambridge U Pr.
Block, Stanley, ed. Mechanisms of Phase Transitions. (Transactions of the American Crystallographic Association Ser.: Vol. 7). 154p. 1971. pap. 15.00 (ISBN 0-686-60378-8). Polycrystal Bk Serv.
Bruce, A. D., et al. Structural Phase Transitions. 326p. 1981. 33.00x (ISBN 0-85066-206-0). Taylor & Francis.
Domb, C. & Green, M., eds. Phase Transitions & Critical Phenomena. Vol. 1. 1973. 83.00 (ISBN 0-12-220301-1); Vol. 2. 1972. 84.50 (ISBN 0-12-220302-X); Vol. 5a. 1976. 69.50 (ISBN 0-12-220305-4); Vol. 5B. 1976. 69.50 (ISBN 0-12-220351-8); Vol. 6. 1977. 99.50 (ISBN 0-12-220306-2). Acad Pr.
--Phase Transitions & Critical Phenomena: Series Expansion for Lattice Models, Vol. 3. 1974. 99.00 (ISBN 0-12-220303-8). Acad Pr.
Domb, C. M. & Lebowitz, Joel L., eds. Phase Transitions & Critical Phenomena, Vol. 7. 1983. 60.00 (ISBN 0-12-220307-0). Acad Pr.
Doremus, R. H. Rates of Phase Transformations. Date not set. 29.00 (ISBN 0-12-220530-8). Acad Pr.
Fisher, Robert A. Optical Phase Conjugation. (Quantum Electronics Princples & Applications Ser.). 612p. 1983. 59.50 (ISBN 0-12-257740-X). Acad Pr.
Hauptman, Herbert & Karle, Jerome. Solution of the Phase Problem, Pt. 1: The Centrosymmetric Crystal. (American Crystallographic Association Monograph: Vol. 3). 87p. 1953. pap. 3.00 (ISBN 0-686-60369-9). Polycrystal Bk Serv.
Henisch, H. K., et al, eds. Phase Transitions & Their Applications in Materials Science. LC 73-14411. 300p. 1974. text ed. 45.00 (ISBN 0-08-017955-X). Pergamon.
Koch, S. W. Dynamics of First-Order Phase Transitions in Equilibrium & Nonequilibrium Systems. (Lecture Notes in Physics Ser.: Vol. 207). iii, 148p. 1984. pap. 9.50 (ISBN 0-387-13379-8). Springer-Verlag.
Mouritsen, O. G. Computer Studies of Phase Transitions & Critical Phenomena. (Series in Computational Physics). (Illus.). 210p. 1984. 24.50 (ISBN 0-387-13397-6). Springer-Verlag.
Mueller, K. A. & Rigamonti, A., eds. Local Properties at Phase Transitions: Proceedings. (Enrico Fermi International Summer School of Physics: 59). 884p. 1976. 172.50 (ISBN 0-7204-0448-7, North-Holland). Elsevier.
Mueller, K. A. & Thomas, H., eds. Structural Phase Transitions, Vol. I. (Topics in Current Physics Ser.: Vol. 23). (Illus.). 190p. 1981. 33.00 (ISBN 0-387-10329-5). Springer-Verlag.
Mutaftschiev, B. Interfacial Aspects of Phase Transformation. 1982. 79.00 (ISBN 90-277-1440-1, Pub. by Reidel Holland). Kluwer Academic.
Nolfi, Frank V., Jr., ed. Phase Transformations During Irradiation. (Illus.). 363p. 1983. 70.50 (ISBN 0-85334-179-6, Pub. by Elsevier Applied Sci England). Elsevier.
Owens, Frank J., et al, eds. Magnetic Resonance of Phase Transitions. LC 78-67881. 1979. 65.00 (ISBN 0-12-531450-7). Acad Pr.
Patashinskii, A. Z., et al. Fluctuation Theory of Phase Transitions. Shepherd, P. J., ed. (International Series in Natural Philosophy: Vol. 98). (Illus.). 1979. text ed. 72.00 (ISBN 0-08-021664-1). Pergamon.
Rao, C. N. & Rao, K. J. Phase Transition in Solids: An Approach to the Study of Chemistry & Physics of Solids. (Illus.). 1978. text ed. 61.95x (ISBN 0-07-051185-3). McGraw.
Riste, T., ed. Electron-Phonon Interactions & Phase Transitions. LC 77-14590. (NATO ASI Series B, Physics: Vol. 29). 432p. 1977. 62.50x (ISBN 0-306-35729-1, Plenum Pr). Plenum Pub.
Sinai, Ya G. Theory of Phase Transition. 164p. 1983. 30.00 (ISBN 0-08-026469-7, C111, D125). Pergamon.
Tsakalakos, T. Phase Transformations in Solids. (Materials Research Society Ser.: Vol. 21). 1984. 105.00 (ISBN 0-444-00901-9). Elsevier.

PHASE TRANSITIONS (STATISTICAL PHYSICS)
see Phase Transformations (Statistical Physics)

PHEASANTS
Delacour, Jean. Pheasant Breeding & Care. (Illus.). 1978. 14.95 (ISBN 0-87666-434-6, AP-6450). TFH Pubns.
--The Pheasants of the World. 2nd ed. 432p. 1983. 55.00 (ISBN 0-904558-37-1). Triplegate.
Fitzsimons, J. O'C. Pheasants & Their Enemies. (Illus.). 112p. 1979. 13.50 (ISBN 0-904558-56-8). Saiga.
Gerrits, H. A. Pheasants: Including Their Care in the Aviary. rev. ed. (Illus.). 144p. 1974. 14.95 (ISBN 0-7137-0683-X, Pub by Blandford Pr England). Sterling.

PHENOLOGY
see also Birds–Migration; Crops and Climate; Plants, Flowering Of
Lieth, H., ed. Phenology & Seasonality Modeling. LC 73-23022. (Ecological Studies - Analysis & Synthesis Ser.: Analysis & Synthesis, Vol. 8). (Illus.). 480p. 1974. 75.00 (ISBN 0-387-06524-5). Springer-Verlag.
Miller, P. J., ed. Fish Phenology: Anabolic Adaptiveness in Teleosts, No. 44. LC 79-40966. (Symposia of the Zoological Society of London). 1980. 60.00 (ISBN 0-12-613344-1). Acad Pr.
Podolsky, Alexander S. New Phenology: Elements of Mathematical Forecasting in Ecology. LC 83-16723. 480p. 1984. 64.95 (ISBN 0-471-86451-X, Pub. by Wiley-Interscience). Wiley.
Smith, N. V. The Acquisition of Phonology. LC 72-95409. 228p. 1973. 39.50 (ISBN 0-521-20154-3). Cambridge U Pr.

PHENOLS
Preston, Seaton T., Jr. & Pankratz, Ronald. A Guide to the Analysis of Phenols by Gas Chromatography. 1978. spiral bdg 25.00 (ISBN 0-913106-04-6). PolyScience.
Taylor, William I. & Battersby, Alan R., eds. Oxidative Coupling of Phenols. LC 67-21702. (Organic Substances of Natural Origin Ser.: Vol. 1). (Illus.). pap. 100.30 (ISBN 0-317-07827-5, 2017690). Bks Demand UMI.

PHENOMENA, CRITICAL (PHYSICS)
see Critical Phenomena (Physics)

PHEROMONES
Beroza, Morton, ed. Pest Management with Insect Sex Attractants. LC 76-1873. (ACS Symposium Ser: No. 23). 1976. 24.95 (ISBN 0-8412-0308-3). Am Chemical.
Blum, Murray S. & Blum, Nancy A. Insect Pheromones. LC 82-25974. 200p. 1984. 19.95t (ISBN 0-03-056962-1). Praeger.
Brady, U. Eugene, et al. Pheromones: Current Research, 2 vols, Vol. 2. 157p. 1974. text ed. 28.50x (ISBN 0-8422-7212-7). Irvington.
Hummel, H. E. & Miller, T. A., eds. Techniques in Pheremone Research. (Springer Series in Expereimental Entomology). (Illus.). 450p. 1984. 62.00 (ISBN 0-387-90919-2). Springer-Verlag.
Jacobson, Martin. Insect Sex Pheromones. 1972. 71.50 (ISBN 0-12-379350-5). Acad Pr.
Narahashi, Toshio, ed. Neurotoxicology of Insecticides & Pheromones. LC 78-10913. 316p. 1979. 42.50x (ISBN 0-306-40067-7, Plenum Pr). Plenum Pub.
Shorey, H. H. Animal Communication by Pheromones. 1976. 39.00 (ISBN 0-12-640450-X). Acad Pr.
Shorey, H. H. & McKelvey, John J., Jr. Chemical Control of Insect Behavior: Theory & Application. LC 76-46573. (Environmental Science & Technology Ser.). 414p. 1977. 48.50x (ISBN 0-471-78840-6, Pub. by Wiley-Interscience). Wiley.
Struble, D. L., et al. Pheromones: Current Research, 2 vols, Vol. 1. 176p. 1974. text ed. 28.50x (ISBN 0-8422-7211-9). Irvington.
Vandenbergh, John G., ed. Pheromones & Reproduction in Mammals. LC 82-22776. 1983. 41.50 (ISBN 0-12-710780-0). Acad Pr.

PHILOSOPHY–DATA PROCESSING
Sloman, Aaron. The Computer Revolution in Philosophy: Philosophy, Science & Models of Mind. (Harvester Studies in Cognitive Science). 1978. text ed. 27.75x (ISBN 0-391-00830-7); pap. text ed. 16.00x (ISBN 0-391-00831-5). Humanities.

PHILOSOPHY AND SCIENCE
see Science–Philosophy

PHILOSOPHY OF NATURE
see also Cosmology; Uniformity of Nature
Armstrong, D. M. What Is a Law of Nature? (Cambridge Studies in Philosophy). 190p. 1985. pap. 9.95 (ISBN 0-521-31481-X). Cambridge U Pr.
Beckett, L. C. Movement & Emptiness. 1969. pap. 1.45 (ISBN 0-8356-0414-4, Quest). Theos Pub Hse.
Ekirch, Arthur A., Jr. Man & Nature in America. LC 63-14925. xvi, 231p. 1973. pap. 4.75 (ISBN 0-8032-5785-6, BB 574, Bison). U of Nebr Pr.
Fisk, Milton. Nature & Necessity: An Essay in Physical Ontology. LC 72-85605. (Indiana University Humanities Ser.: No. 73). pap. 79.00 (ISBN 0-317-09316-9, 2055220). Bks Demand UMI.
Jones, William F. Nature & Natural Science: The Philosophy of Frederick Woodbridge. LC 82-48969. 197p. 1982. 20.95 (ISBN 0-87975-183-5). Prometheus Bks.
Kant, Immanuel. The Philosophy of Nature & the Destinies of Mankind. (Illus.). 178p. 1985. 87.75 (ISBN 0-89266-501-7). Am Classical Coll Pr.
Leiss, William. The Domination of Nature. LC 74-6090. 252p. 1974. pap. 6.95x (ISBN 0-8070-4161-0, BP492). Beacon Pr.
--The Domination of Nature. LC 75-188358. 1972. 6.95 (ISBN 0-8076-0646-4). Braziller.
Lindberg, David C. Roger Bacon's Philosophy of Nature: A Critical Edition. (Illus.). 1983. 84.00x (ISBN 0-19-858164-5). Oxford U Pr.
Lucas, John R. Space, Time & Causality: An Essay in Natural Philosophy. 180p. 1985. 28.00x (ISBN 0-19-875057-9); pap. 10.95x (ISBN 0-19-875058-7). Oxford U Pr.
Ruse, Michael. Nature Animated. 1983. 49.50 (ISBN 90-277-1403-7, Pub. by Reidel Holland). Kluwer Academic.
Shea, William R. Nature Mathematized. 1983. 56.50 (ISBN 90-277-1402-9, Pub. by Reidel Holland). Kluwer Academic.
Whitehead, Alfred N. Nature & Life. LC 34-9604. (Illus.). 1969. Repr. of 1934 ed. lib. bdg. 18.75 (ISBN 0-8371-0751-2, WHNL). Greenwood.

PHLEBOGRAPHY
see Veins–Radiography

PHLOEM
Aronoff, S., ed. Phloem Transport. LC 75-15501. (NATO ASI Series A: Life Sciences: Vol. 4). 646p. 1975. 79.50x (ISBN 0-306-35604-X, Plenum Pr). Plenum Pub.
Crafts, Alden S. & Crisp, Carl E. Phloem Transport in Plants. LC 71-125130. (Biology Ser.). (Illus.). 481p. 1971. text ed. 39.95 (ISBN 0-7167-0683-0). W H Freeman.
Esau, K. The Phloem. (Encyclopedia of Plant Anatomy: Vol. 2). (Illus.). 505p. 1969. lib. bdg. 75.20X (ISBN 3-443-14002-5). Lubrecht & Cramer.
Wooding, F. B. P. Phloem. rev. ed. Head, J. J., ed. LC 77-70872. (Carolina Biology Readers Ser.). (Illus.). 16p. 1978. pap. 1.60 (ISBN 0-89278-215-3, 45-9615). Carolina Biological.

PHLOGISTON
see Chemistry–Phlogiston

PHOCAENA
see Porpoises

PHONOGRAPH
see also Electro-Acoustics; Sound–Recording and Reproducing

Senger, H., ed. Blue Light Effects in Biological Systems. (Proceedings in Life Sciences). (Illus.). 550p. 1984. 55.50 (ISBN 0-387-13462-X). Springer Verlag.
Shlyapintokh, V. Photochemical Conversion & Stabilization of Polymers. LC 83-62287. 320p. 1984. text ed. write for info. (ISBN 0-02-949690-X, Pub. by Hanser International). Macmillan.
Smith, K. C., ed. The Science of Photobiology. 442p. 1977. 39.50x (ISBN 0-306-31051-1, Rosetta); pap. 18.95x (ISBN 0-306-20029-5). Plenum Pub.
Smith, Kendric C. & Hanawalt, Philip C. Molecular Photobiology: Inactivation & Recovery. (Molecular Biology Ser, Vol. 6). 1969. 49.00 (ISBN 0-12-651450-X). Acad Pr.
Smith, Kendric C., ed. Photochemical & Photobiological Reviews, Vol. 4. LC 75-43689. 343p. 1979. 59.50x (ISBN 0-306-40225-4, Plenum Pr). Plenum Pub.
--Photochemical & Photobiological Reviews, Vol. 6. LC 75-43689. 214p. 1981. 39.50x (ISBN 0-306-40662-4, Plenum Pr). Plenum Pub.
Tometsko, Andrew M. & Richard, Frederic M., eds. Applications of Photochemistry in Probing Biological Targets. LC 80-15368. (Annals of the New York Academy of Sciences: Vol. 346). 502p. 1980. 100.00x (ISBN 0-89766-080-3); pap. 100.00x (ISBN 0-89766-081-1). NY Acad Sci.
Williams, Theodore P. & Baker, B. N., eds. The Effect of Constant Light on Visual Processes. LC 79-26293. 465p. 1980. 59.50 (ISBN 0-306-40328-5, Plenum Pr). Plenum Pub.
Wolken, Jerome J. Photoprocesses, Photoreceptors, & Evolution. 1975. 48.00 (ISBN 0-12-762050-8). Acad Pr.
Zewail, Ahmed, ed. Photochemistry & Photobiology, Vol. 1. 784p. 1984. text ed. 95.00 (ISBN 3-7186-0173-7). Harwood Academic.
--Photochemistry & Photobiology, Vol. 2. 720p. 1984. text ed. 95.00x (ISBN 3-7186-0179-6). Harwood Academic.

PHOTOCELLS

see Photoelectric Cells

PHOTOCHEMISTRY

see also Photobiology

Adamson, Arthur W. & Fleischauer, Paul D., eds. Concepts of Inorganic Photochemistry. LC 84-5776. 456p. 1984. Repr. of 1975 ed. lib. bdg. 34.50 (ISBN 0-89874-762-7). Krieger.
Advances in Photochemistry. Advances in Photochemistry, Vol. 7. LC 63-13592. pap. 106.00 (ISBN 0-317-09792-X, 2006493). Bks Demand UMI.
Allen, N. S. & Schnabel, W., eds. Photochemistry & Photophysics of Polymers. 440p. 1984. 126.00 (ISBN 0-85334-269-5, I-256-84, Pub. by Elsevier Applied Sci England). Elsevier.
Arnold, D. R., et al. Photochemistry: An Introduction. 1974. 45.00 (ISBN 0-12-063350-7). Acad Pr.
Ashmore, Philip G., et al, eds. Photochemistry & Reaction Kinetics. LC 67-105417. pap. 98.50 (ISBN 0-317-26113-4, 2024403). Bks Demand UMI.
Auston, D. H. & Eisenthal, K. B., eds. Ultrafast Phenomena IV. (Chemical Physics Ser.: Vol. 38). (Illus.). xvi, 509p. 1984. 29.00 (ISBN 0-387-13834-X). Springer-Verlag.
Barltrop, J. A. & Coyle, J. D. Principles of Photochemistry. LC 78-16622. pap. 55.80 (ISBN 0-317-20842-X, 2024796). Bks Demand UMI.
Bayley, H. Photogenerated Reagents in Biochemistry & Molecular Biology. (Laboratory Techniques in Biochemistry & Molecular Biology Ser.: Vol. 12). 208p. 1984. pap. 22.50 (ISBN 0-444-80520-6, I-022-84). Elsevier.
Bensasson, R. V. & Truscott, T. G. Flash Photolysis & Pulse Radiolysis: Contributions to the Chemistry of Biology & Medicine. (Illus.). 272p. 1983. 50.00 (ISBN 0-08-024949-3). Pergamon.
Boschke, F., ed. Photochemistry. (Topics in Current Chemistry Ser.: Vol. 46). (Illus.). iv, 236p. 1974. 45.00 (ISBN 0-387-06592-X). Springer-Verlag.
Bryce, Smith, ed. Photo Chemistry, Vol. 15. 576p. 1985. 197.00 (ISBN 0-85186-135-0, Pub. by Royal Soc Chem UK). Heyden.
Bryce-Smith, D. Photochemistry, Vols. 1-10. Incl. Vol. 1. 1968-69 Literature. 1970. 30.00 (ISBN 0-85186-005-2); Vol. 2. 1969-70 Literature. 1971. 47.00 (ISBN 0-85186-015-X); Vol. 3. 1970-71 Literature. 1972. 47.00 (ISBN 0-85186-025-7); Vol. 4. 1971-72 Literature. 1973. 50.00 (ISBN 0-85186-035-4); Vol. 5. 1972-73 Literature. 1974. 56.00 (ISBN 0-85186-045-1); Vol. 6. 1973-74 Literature. 1975. 70.00 (ISBN 0-85186-055-9); Vol. 7. 1974-75 Literature. 1976. 82.00 (ISBN 0-85186-065-6); Vol. 8. 1975-76 Literature. 1977. 95.00 (ISBN 0-85186-075-3); Vol. 9. 1976-77 Literature. 1978. 97.00 (ISBN 0-85186-085-0); Vol. 10. 1979. 102.00 (ISBN 0-85186-590-9). LC 73-17909. Am Chemical.
Bryce-Smith, D. & Gilbert, A. The Organic Photochemistry of Benzene-I. 18p. 1976. pap. text ed. 14.00 (ISBN 0-08-020464-3). Pergamon.
Chapman, O. L., ed. Organic Photochemistry, Vol. 1. 1967. 69.75 (ISBN 0-8247-1095-9). Dekker.
--Organic Photochemistry, Vol. 3. 320p. 1973. 69.75 (ISBN 0-8247-1096-7). Dekker.
Connolly, John S. Photochemical Conversion & Storage of Solar Energy. LC 81-12853. 1981. 55.00 (ISBN 0-12-185880-4). Acad Pr.
Cowan, D. O. & Drisko, R. L., eds. Elements of Organic Photochemistry. LC 75-28173. (Illus.). 586p. 1976. 35.00x (ISBN 0-306-30821-5, Plenum Pr). Plenum Pub.
Coxon, J. M. & Halton, B. Organic Photochemistry. LC 73-82447. (Chemistry Texts Ser). (Illus.). 270p. 1974. pap. 18.95 (ISBN 0-521-09824-6). Cambridge U Pr.
Cundall, R. B. & Gilbert, A. Photochemistry. (Studies in Modern Chemistry Ser.). 220p. 1970. 19.50x (ISBN 0-306-50009-4, Plenum Pr). Plenum Pub.
Eisenthal, K. B., et al, eds. Picosecond Phenomena III, Garmisch Partenkirchen, FRG, 1982: Proceedings. (Springer Series in Chemical Physics: Vol. 23). (Illus.). 401p. 1982. 33.00 (ISBN 0-387-11912-4). Springer-Verlag.
Gratzel, M., ed. Energy Resources Through Photochemistry & Catalysis. LC 83-9938. 573p. 1983. 65.00 (ISBN 0-12-295720-2). Acad Pr.
Guderian, R., ed. Air Pollution by Photochemical Oxidants. (Ecological Studies, Analysis & Synthesis: Vol. 52). (Illus.). 380p. 1985. 55.50 (ISBN 0-387-13966-4). Springer-Verlag.
Guillet, James. Polymer Photophysics & Photochemistry: An Introduction to the Study of Photoprocesses in Macromolecules. 391p. 1985. 79.50 (ISBN 0-521-23506-5). Cambridge U Pr.
Gurevich, Yu. Y., ed. Photoelectrochemistry. LC 78-21541. (Illus.). 255p. 1979. 49.50x (ISBN 0-306-10953-0, Consultants). Plenum Pub.
Hall, D. O. & Palz, W., eds. Photochemical, Photoelectrochemical & Photobiological Processes. 1982. 32.50 (ISBN 90-277-1371-5, Pub. by Reidell Holland). Kluwer Academic.
Hall, D. O., et al, eds. Photochemical, Photoelectrochemical & Photobiological Processes. 1983. lib. bdg. 46.00 (ISBN 90-277-1614-5, Pub. by Reidel Holland). Kluwer Academic.
Hayata, Yoshihiro & Dougherty, Thomas J., eds. Lasers & Hematoporphyrin Derivative in Cancer. LC 83-22554. (Illus.). 128p. 1983. text ed. 59.00 (ISBN 0-89640-095-6). Igaku-Shoin.
Horspool, W. M. Aspects of Organic Photochemistry. 1976. 55.00 (ISBN 0-12-356650-9). Acad Pr.
Inorganic Photochemistry: State of the Art. 1983. 7.50 (ISBN 0-910362-23-8). Chem Educ.
Lahmani, F., ed. Photophysics & Photochemistry above 6 EV: Proceedings of the International Meeting of the Societe de Chimie Physique, 38th, Bombannes, 21-27 September, 1984. (Studies in Physical & Theoretical Chemistry: Vol. 35). 672p. 1985. 139.00 (ISBN 0-444-42463-6). Elsevier.
Lehn, J. M. Preparative Organic Photochemistry. (Topics in Current Chemistry Ser.: Vol. 103). (Illus.). 94p. 1982. 23.00 (ISBN 0-387-11388-6). Springer-Verlag.
Levine, Joel S., ed. The Photochemistry of Atmospheres: Earth, the Other Planets, & Comets. 1985. 79.50 (ISBN 0-12-444920-4). Acad Pr.
McKellar, J. F. & Allen, N. S. Photochemistry of Man Made Polymers. (Illus.). 306p. 1975. 55.50 (ISBN 0-85334-799-9, Pub. by Elsevier Applied Sci England). Elsevier.
Murov, Steven L. Handbook of Photochemistry. 1973. 69.75 (ISBN 0-8247-6164-2). Dekker.
Nagel, M. R., et al. Illumination, Color, A Contrast Tables: Naturally Illuminated Objects. 1978. 63.00 (ISBN 0-12-513750-8). Acad Pr.
NATO Advanced Study Institute, 1973. Chemical Spectroscopy & Photochemistry in the Vacuum: Proceedings. Sandorfy, C., et al, eds. LC 73-91209. (NATO Advanced Studies Institute Ser: No. C-8). 1974. lib. bdg. 74.00 (ISBN 90-277-0418-X, Pub. by Reidel Holland). Kluwer Academic.
Neporent, B. S., ed. Elementary Photoprocesses in Molecules. LC 68-28094. (Illus.). 339p. 1968. 49.50x (ISBN 0-306-10810-0, Consultants). Plenum Pub.
Noyes, William A., Jr. & Leighton, Philip A. The Photochemistry of Gases. 10.00 (ISBN 0-8446-2670-8). Peter Smith.
Okabe, Hideo. Photochemistry of Small Molecules. LC 78-6704. 431p. 1978. 64.50 (ISBN 0-471-65304-7, Pub. by Wiley-Interscience). Wiley.
Padwa, A. Organic Photochemistry, Vol. 4. 1979. 69.75 (ISBN 0-8247-6908-2). Dekker.
Padwa, Albert. Organic Photochemistry, Vol. 5. 512p. 1981. 79.75 (ISBN 0-8247-1343-5). Dekker.
--Organic Photochemistry, Vol. 6. 1983. 79.75 (ISBN 0-8247-7003-X). Dekker.
Photochemical Oxydants & Their Presursors in the Atmosphere: Effects, Formation, Transport & Abatement. (Document Ser.). 120p. 1979. 7.50x (ISBN 92-64-11838-1). OECD.
Photochemical Smog: Contribution of Volatile Organic Compounds. 98p. 1982. pap. 9.50 (ISBN 92-64-12297-4). OECD.
Photochemistry & Organic Synthesis. (Topics in Current Chemistry Ser.: Vol. 129). (Illus.). 280p. 1985. 49.50 (ISBN 0-387-15141-9). Springer-Verlag.
Pitts, J. N., et al, eds. Advances in Photochemistry, Vol. II. 538p. 1979. text ed. 35.95 (ISBN 0-471-04797-X, 2-020, Pub. by Wiley-Interscience). Wiley.
Pitts, James N., et al, eds. Advances in Photochemistry. LC 63-13592. 1980. Vol. 11, 1979, 538p. 87.00 (ISBN 0-471-04797-X); Vol. 12, 1980, 459p. 81.00 (ISBN 0-471-06286-3). Wiley.
Pitts, James N., Jr., et al, eds. Advance in Photochemistry, Vol. 10. LC 63-13592. 488p. 1977. 49.50 (ISBN 0-471-02145-8). Krieger.
--Advances in Photochemistry, Vol. 9. 566p. 1974. 39.50 (ISBN 0-471-69092-9). Krieger.
Rabek, J. F. Experimental Methods in Photochemistry & Photophysics. 1098p. 1982. 260.00 (ISBN 0-471-10090-0). Wiley.
Reck, Ruth A. & Hummel, John R., eds. Interpretation of Climate & Photochemical Models, Ozone & Temperature Measurements: AIP Conference Proceedings, No. 82, La Jolla Institute, March 9-11, 1981. LC 82-71345. 320p. 1982. 33.00 (ISBN 0-88318-181-9). Am Inst Physics.
Reinhold, L., et al, eds. Progress in Phytochemistry, Vol. 6. LC 68-24347. (Illus.). 1980. 96.00 (ISBN 0-08-024946-9). Pergamon.
Reinisch, R. F., ed. Photochemistry of Macromolecules. LC 70-127936. 229p. 1970. 39.50x (ISBN 0-306-30499-6, Plenum Pr). Plenum Pub.
Reiser, A., ed. Photochemistry Seven: IUPAC Symposium on Photochemistry, Leuven, Belgium, 24-28 July, 1978, Seventh IUPAC Symposium. (IUPAC Symposia Ser.). 1979. 44.00 (ISBN 0-08-022358-3). Pergamon.
Roberts, Ralph. Applications of Photochemistry. LC 83-51826. 101p. 1984. pap. 25.00 (ISBN 0-87762-340-6). Technomic.
Roffey, C. G. Photopolymerization of Surface Coatings. LC 81-12916. 353p. 1982. 54.95 (ISBN 0-471-10063-3, Pub. by Wiley-Interscience). Wiley.
Rohatgi-Mukherjee, K. K. Fundamentals of Photochemistry. LC 78-12088. 347p. 1979. 18.95 (ISBN 0-470-26547-7). Halsted Pr.
Schiavello, Mario. Photoelectrochemistry, Photocatalysis & Photoreactors Fundamentals & Developments. 1985. lib. bdg. 84.00 (ISBN 90-277-1946-2, Pub. by Reidel Holland). Kluwer Academic.
Schmidt, Gerhard M. Solid State Photochemistry. (Monographs in Modern Chemistry: Vol. 8). (Illus.). 280p. 1976. 50.60x (ISBN 3-527-25671-7). VCH Pubs.
Schoenberg, A. Preparative Organic Photochemistry. 2nd ed. LC 67-16134. (Illus.). 1968. 98.00 (ISBN 0-387-04325-X). Springer-Verlag.
Smith, Kendric C., ed. Photochemical & Photobiological Reviews, Vol. 4. LC 75-43689. 343p. 1979. 59.50x (ISBN 0-306-40225-4, Plenum Pr). Plenum Pub.
--Photochemical & Photobiological Reviews, Vol. 6. LC 75-43689. 214p. 1981. 39.50x (ISBN 0-306-40662-4, Plenum Pr). Plenum Pub.
Thomas, L. & Rishbeth, H., eds. Photochemical & Transport Processes in the Upper Atmosphere. LC 76-26741. 1977. pap. text ed. 30.00 (ISBN 0-08-021312-X). Pergamon.
Tometsko, Andrew M. & Richard, Frederic M., eds. Applications of Photochemistry in Probing Biological Targets. LC 80-15368. (Annals of the New York Academy of Sciences: Vol. 346). 502p. 1980. 100.00x (ISBN 0-89766-080-3); pap. 100.00x (ISBN 0-89766-081-1). NY Acad Sci.
Turro, N. J. Modern Molecular Photochemistry. 1981. pap. 27.95x (ISBN 0-8053-9354-4). Benjamin-Cummings.
Vogel, Hermann. The Chemistry of Light & Photography. LC 72-9242. (The Literature of Photography Ser.). Repr. of 1875 ed. 23.50 (ISBN 0-405-04946-3). Ayer Co Pubs.
Volman, David, et al, eds. Advances in Photochemistry, Vol 13. 1985. 80.00 (ISBN 0-471-81523-3). Wiley.
Wrighton, Mark, ed. Inorganic & Organometallic Photochemistry. LC 78-17616. (Advances in Chemistry Ser.: No. 168). 1978. 39.95 (ISBN 0-8412-0398-9). Am Chemical.
Wrighton, Mark S., ed. Interfacial Photoprocesses: Energy Conversion & Synthesis. LC 79-26245. (ACS Advances in Chemistry Ser.: No. 184). 1980. 54.95 (ISBN 0-8412-0474-8). Am Chemical.
Zewail, Ahmed, ed. Photochemistry & Photobiology, Vol. 1. 784p. 1984. text ed. 95.00 (ISBN 3-7186-0173-7). Harwood Academic.
--Photochemistry & Photobiology, Vol. 2. 720p. 1984. text ed. 95.00x (ISBN 3-7186-0179-6). Harwood Academic.

PHOTOCONDUCTIVITY

Bube, Richard H. Photoconductivity of Solids. LC 78-1084. 484p. 1978. Repr. of 1960 ed. 28.50 (ISBN 0-88275-660-5). Krieger.
Mort, J. & Pai, C. M., eds. Photoconductivity & Related Phenomena. LC 76-16160. 502p. 1976. 81.00 (ISBN 0-444-41463-0). Elsevier.
Patsis, A. V. & Seanor, D. A. Photoconductivity in Polymers. LC 74-80461. (Illus.). 349p. (Orig.). 1976. 19.95 (ISBN 0-87762-129-2). Technomic.

PHOTOCOPYING PROCESSES

see also Blue-Prints; Electrophotography; Reader-Printers (Microphotography); Thermography (Copying Process)

Baumgarten, Jon A. & Latman, Alan. Corporate Copyright & Information Practices. LC 83-234204. (Illus.). iv, 200p. Date not set. price not set (Law & Business). HarBraceJ.
Eastman Kodak Company. Phototypesetting with Kodak Products, 1980. LC 75-36853. (Illus.). 48p. 1982. 8.00 (ISBN 0-87985-168-6, Q-5). Eastman Kodak.
Special Librarians Association. Library Photocopying & the U. S. Copyright Law of 1976: An Overview for Librarians & Their Counsel. pap. 22.00 (ISBN 0-317-10264-8, 2016136). Bks Demand UMI.

PHOTOELASTICITY

Aben, Hillar. Integrated Photoelasticity. (Illus.). 1979. 48.00x (ISBN 0-07-000043-3). McGraw.
CISM (International Center for Mechanical Sciences), Dept. for Mechanics of Deformable Bodies, 1970. Photoelasticity in Theory & Practice. Brcic, V., ed. (CISM International Center for Mechanical Sciences Ser.: No. 59). (Illus.). 242p. 1975. pap. 23.30 (ISBN 0-387-81081-1). Springer-Verlag.
Dally, James W. & Riley, William F. Experimental Stress Analysis. 2d ed. LC 77-393. (Illus.). 1977. text ed. 43.00x (ISBN 0-07-015204-7). McGraw.
Frocht, Max M. Photoelasticity, Vol. 2. LC 41-15564. (Illus.). pap. 130.80 (ISBN 0-317-08372-4, 2017833). Bks Demand UMI.
Hearn, E. J. & Mech, M. I. Photoelasticity. 78p. 1971. 39.00x (ISBN 0-900541-14-8, Pub. by Meadowfield Pr England). State Mutual Bk.
Symposium of International Union of Theoretical & Applied Mechanics, Brussels, Belgium, 1973. Photoelastic Effect & Its Applications: Proceedings. Kestens, J., ed. (Illus.). 650p. 1975. 66.10 (ISBN 0-387-07278-0). Springer-Verlag.
Theocaris, P. S. & Gdoutos, E. E. Matrix Theory of Photoelasticity. (Springer Series in Optical Sciences: Vol. 11). (Illus.). 1979. 49.00 (ISBN 0-387-08899-7). Springer-Verlag.
Zandman, Felix, et al. Photoelastic Coatings. (Society for Experimental Stress Analysis Monograph: No. 3). (Illus.). 174p. 1977. text ed. 9.95x (ISBN 0-8138-0035-8). Iowa St U Pr.

PHOTOELECTRIC CELLS

see also Remote Control

Aatec Publications, ed. Solar Census: Photovoltaics Edition. LC 84-71602. 200p. 1984. pap. 14.95 (ISBN 0-937948-05-5). Aatec Pubns.
American Institute of Architects. Architect's Handbook of Energy Practice: Photovoltaics. (Illus.). 56p. 1982. pap. 18.00x (ISBN 0-913962-56-2). Am Inst Arch.
Beghi, Giogio. Performance of Solar Energy Converters: Thermal Collectors & Photovoltaic Cells. 1983. lib. bdg. 69.50 (ISBN 90-277-1545-9, Pub. by Reidel Holland). Kluwer Academic.
Buresch, M. Photovoltaic Energy Systems: Design & Installation. 352p. 1983. 27.50 (ISBN 0-07-008952-3). McGraw.
Byers, T. J. Twenty Selected Solar Projects: Making Photovoltaics Work for You. 1984. 19.95 (ISBN 0-13-934779-8); pap. 11.95 (ISBN 0-13-934761-5). P-H.
CES Industries, Inc. Ed-Lab Eight Hundred Experiment Manual: Photocell Sensor. (Illus., Orig.). 1983. write for info. (ISBN 0-86711-049-X). CES Industries.
--Ed-Lab Eighty Experiment Manual: Photocell Sensor. (Illus., Orig.). 1983. write for info. (ISBN 0-86711-036-8). CES Industries.
Davidson, Homer L. Thirty Three Photovoltaic Projects. (Illus.). 272p. (Orig.). 1982. 16.95 (ISBN 0-8306-2467-8, 1467); pap. 10.95 (ISBN 0-8306-1467-2). TAB Bks.

Todd, Hollis N. & Zakia, Richard D. Photographic Sensitometry. LC 75-82445. 312p. 1981. pap. 14.95 (ISBN 0-87100-000-8, 2000). Morgan.

PHOTOGRAPHIC SLIDES

see Slides (Photography)

PHOTOGRAPHIC SUPPLIES

see Photography–Apparatus and Supplies

PHOTOGRAPHIC SURVEYING

see also Photographic Interpretation; Photography, Aerial

The Rephotographic Survey Project Staff. Second View: The Rephotographic Survey Project. LC 84-3600. (Illus.). 224p. 1985. 65.00 (ISBN 0-8263-0751-5). U of NM Pr.

PHOTOGRAPHS–CONSERVATION AND RESTORATION

Caring for Photographs. Rev. ed. (Life Library of Photography). 1983. 15.95 (ISBN 0-8094-4420-8). Time Life.

Eastman Kodak Company. Conservation of Photographs (F-40) 156p. (Orig.). 1985. pap. 29.95 (ISBN 0-87985-352-2). Eastman Kodak.

Keefe, Laurence E., Jr. & Inch, Dennis. The Life of a Photograph: Archival Processing, Matting, Framing & Storage. (Illus.). 1983. 24.95 (ISBN 0-240-51701-6). Focal Pr.

Orth, Thomas W., ed. Selected Bibliography: Photographic Conservation. 8p. 1979. pap. 10.00 (ISBN 0-317-14995-4). Tech & Ed Ctr Graph Arts RIT.

Preservation of Photographs. LC 79-54197. (Illus.). 60p. 1979. pap. 5.50 (ISBN 0-87985-212-7, F-30). Eastman Kodak.

Society of Photographic Scientists & Engineers. International Symposium: the Stability & Preservation of Photographic Images: Advanced Printing of Paper Summaries, August 29-September 1, 1982, th Public Archives of Canada, Ottawa, Ontario. pap. 20.00 (ISBN 0-317-28842-3, 2017861). Bks Demand UMI.

Wilhelm, Henry & Brower, Carol. The Stability & Preservation of Color & B&W Photographic Materials. LC 84-6921. (Illus.). 400p. 1985. 49.95 (ISBN 0-911515-00-3). Preserv Pub Co.

Winger, Howard & Smith, Richard. Deterioration & Preservation of Library Materials. LC 78-115971. (Studies in Library Science). 1970. 14.00x (ISBN 0-226-90201-3). U of Chicago Pr.

PHOTOGRAPHY

see also Astronomical Photography; Calotype; Cameras; Cinematography; Color Photography; Electrophotography; Kirlian Photography; Lenses, Photographic; Macrophotography; Microphotography; Photomechanical Processes; Photomicrography; Slides (Photography); Stereoscope

also headings beginning with the word Photographic

Abramson, Sue. Extended Frames. 32p. 1981. spiral bdg. 10.00 (ISBN 0-930794-21-4). Station Hill Pr.

Adams, Ansel. The Camera. (The Ansel Adams Photography Ser.: Bk. 1). (Illus.). 1980. 16.50 (ISBN 0-8212-1092-0, 125121, Pub. by Museum Mod Art). NYGS.

Adams, George. How to Photograph a Woman. 1979. pap. 5.95 (ISBN 0-380-43117-3, 43117-3). Avon.

Amphoto Corporation. Thirty-Five Millimeter Photography Simplified. rev. ed. (Modern Photo Guides Ser). (Illus.). 96p. 1974. Repr. 7.95t (ISBN 0-13-918888-6, Spec). P-H.

Anthony And Company. Illustrated Catalogue of Photographic Equipment & Material for Amateurs. Orig. Title: Illustrated Photographic Catalogue. 1970. pap. 7.95 (ISBN 0-87100-016-4). Morgan.

Avon, Dennis & Hawkins, Andrew. Photography: A Complete Guide to Technique. (Illus., Orig.). 1979. (Amphoto); pap. 16.95 (ISBN 0-8174-2191-2). Watson-Guptill.

Baines, Harry. Science of Photography. 3rd ed. LC 73-19208. 318p. 1969. 26.95x (ISBN 0-471-04340-0). Halsted Pr.

Barthes, Roland. Camera Lucida: Reflections on Photography. Howard, Richard, tr. (Illus.). 119p. 1981. 10.95 (ISBN 0-8090-3340-2); pap. 6.95 (ISBN 0-8090-1398-3). Hill & Wang.

Berrin, Elliott R. Investigative Photography. 1983. 4.65 (ISBN 0-686-40876-4, TR-83-1). Society Fire Protect.

Blaker, Alfred A. Photography: Art & Technique. LC 79-23536. (Illus.). 460p. 1980. text ed. 34.95 (ISBN 0-7167-1115-X); pap. text ed. 19.95 (ISBN 0-7167-1116-8); reference manual incl. W H Freeman.

Buchloh, Benjamin H., ed. Carl Andre-Hollis Frampton, Twelve Dialogues 1962-1963. (The Nova Scotia Ser.). (Illus.). 134p. 1981. 22.50x (ISBN 0-8147-0579-0). NYU Pr.

Bunnell, Peter C. & Sobieszek, Robert A., eds. The Literature of Photography, 62 bks. 1973. Set. 1301.50 (ISBN 0-405-04889-0). Ayer Co Pubs.

--The Sources of Modern Photography Series, 51 bks. (Illus.). 1979. Vols. 1-25. lib. bdg. 559.00x (ISBN 0-405-09597-X); Vols. 26-51. lib. bdg. 1393.00x (ISBN 0-405-18980-X). Ayer Co Pubs.

Burchfield, Jerry. Darkroom Art. (Illus.). 168p. 1981. (Amphoto); pap. 14.95 (ISBN 0-8174-3708-8). Watson-Guptill.

Cavallo, Robert & Kahan, Stuart. The Business of Photography. 1981. Outlet 3.98 (ISBN 0-517-53945-4, Michelman Books). Crown.

Cole, Stanely. Amphoto Guide to Basic Photography. (Illus.). 1978. (Amphoto); pap. 7.95 (ISBN 0-8174-2115-7). Watson-Guptill.

Coleman, A. D., et al. Photography A-V Program Directory. LC 80-83469. (Illus.). 224p. 1980. 28.00x (ISBN 0-936524-00-6). PMI Inc.

Craven, George M. How Photography Works. (Illus.). 150p. 1986. pap. text ed. 12.95 (ISBN 0-13-400789-1). P-H.

--Object & Image. 2nd ed. 400p. 1982. 29.95 (ISBN 0-13-628966-5). P-H.

Curl, David H. Photocommunication: A Guide to Creative Photography. (Illus.). 1979. pap. text ed. write for info. (ISBN 0-02-326350-4). Macmillan.

Davanne, A. La Photographie, 2 vols. in 1. Bunnell, Peter C. & Sobieszek, Robert A., eds. LC 76-23052. (Sources of Modern Photography Ser.). (Fr., Illus.). 1979. lib. bdg. 37.00x (ISBN 0-405-09615-1). Ayer Co Pubs.

Davis, Phil. Photography. 4th ed. 462p. 1982. pap. text ed. write for info. (ISBN 0-697-03219-1); instructor's manual avail. (ISBN 0-697-03220-5). Wm C Brown.

Delamotte, Philip H. The Practice of Photography. 2nd ed. LC 72-9193. (The Literature of Photography Ser.). Repr. of 1855 ed. 15.00 (ISBN 0-405-04903-X). Ayer Co Pubs.

Dibert, Ken. Photography: Three Generations. LC 76-15520. 9.95 (ISBN 0-912216-11-5). Angel Pr.

Dixon, Dwight R. & Dixon, Paul B. Photography: Experiments & Projects. (Illus.). 1976. pap. text ed. write for info. (ISBN 0-02-329840-5). Macmillan.

Dugan, Tom. Photography Between Covers: Interviews with Photo Book Makers. LC 79-9260. (Illus.). 1979. 15.00 (ISBN 0-87992-012-2). Light Impressions.

Eastman Kodak Company. Analysis, Treatment & Disposal of Ferricyanide in Photographic Effluents. LC 79-57024. 72p. 1980. pap. 5.75 (ISBN 0-87985-245-3, J-54). Eastman Kodak.

--Kodak Guide to 35 MM Photography. LC 79-54310. (Illus.). 286p. (Orig.). 1981. text ed. 19.95 (ISBN 0-87985-242-9, AC-95H); pap. 9.95 (ISBN 0-87985-236-4, AC-95S). Eastman Kodak.

Eastman Kodak Company, ed. Basic Photography for the Graphic Arts. 4th ed. LC 72-88626. (Illus.). 57p. (Orig., Major revision). 1982. pap. 8.50 (ISBN 0-87985-033-7, Q1). Eastman Kodak.

--Camera-Back Silver Masking with Three-Aim Point Control. (Illus.). 1976. pap. 3.50 (ISBN 0-87985-185-6, Q-7B). Eastman Kodak.

--KW-Nineteen, Advanced B-W Photography. (Kodak Workshop Ser.). (Illus.). 96p. (Orig.). Date not set. pap. 8.95 (ISBN 0-87985-304-2). Eastman Kodak.

--KW-Twenty, the Art of Seeing. (Kodak Workshop Ser.). (Illus.). 96p. (Orig.). Date not set. pap. 8.95 (ISBN 0-87985-305-0). Eastman Kodak.

Eastman Kodak Company Staff, ed. Images, Images, Images: The Book of Programmed Multi-Image Production (S-12) 3rd ed. (Illus.). 264p. 1983. pap. 24.95 (ISBN 0-87985-327-1). Eastman Kodak.

Eisenstaedt, Alfred. Eisenstaedt's Guide to Photography. (Handbook Ser.). (Illus.). 176p. 1981. pap. 12.95 (ISBN 0-14-046483-2). Penguin.

Elliston, P., ed. Photography. (Fundamentals of Senior Physics Ser.). 1979. pap. text ed. 7.95x (ISBN 0-85859-187-1, 00500). Heinemann Ed.

Engrand, Bernard. L' Industrie Photographique en France. Bunnell, Peter C. & Sobieszek, Robert A., eds. LC 78-67656. (Sources of Modern Photography Ser.). (Fr.). 1979. Repr. of 1934 ed. lib. bdg. 17.00x (ISBN 0-405-09897-9). Ayer Co Pubs.

Evrard-Blanquart, L. D. La Photographie. Bunnell, Peter C. & Sobieszk, Robert A., eds. LC 76-23042. (Sources of Modern Photography Ser.). 1979. Repr. of 1870 ed. lib. bdg. 14.00x (ISBN 0-405-09604-6). Ayer Co Pubs.

Frair, John & Ardoin, Birthney. Effective Photography. (Illus.). 496p. 1982. 26.95 (ISBN 0-13-244459-3); pap. 23.95 (ISBN 0-13-244442-9). P-H.

Freeman, Michael. Instant Film Photography. (Illus.). 224p. 1985. 17.95 (ISBN 0-88162-117-X, Pub. by Salem Hse Ltd). Merrimack Pub Cir.

--The Thirty-Five Millimeter Handbook. (Illus.). 320p. 1980. 25.00 (ISBN 0-87165-093-2, Amphoto). Watson-Guptill.

Freund, Gisele. Photography & Society. 256p. 1981. 35.00x (ISBN 0-86092-049-6, Pub. by Fraser Bks). State Mutual Bk.

Gaunt, Leonard & Petzold, Paul. The Focal Encyclopedia of Photography. Rev., enlarged ed. 1700p. 1969. desk ed. 30.95 (ISBN 0-240-50680-4). Focal Pr.

Gerace, P. & Mangione, S. Communication: Photography. 1976. pap. 8.84 (ISBN 0-13-153239-1). P-H.

Gernsheim, Helmut. The Origins of Photography. 3rd, rev. ed. LC 82-80979. (Illus.). 1983. slipcased 50.00 (ISBN 0-500-54080-2). Thames Hudson.

Graves, Carson. The Zone System for 35mm Photographers: A Basic Guide to Exposure Control. (Illus.). 112p. 1982. pap. 13.95 (ISBN 0-930764-39-0). Curtin & London.

Great Britain, Patent Office. Patents for Inventions, 2 vols. Bunnell, Peter C. & Sobieszek, Robert A., eds. LC 76-23063. (Sources of Modern Photography Ser.). (Illus.). 1979. Repr. of 1903 ed. Set. lib. bdg. 103.00x (ISBN 0-405-09626-7); lib. bdg. 45.00x ea. Vol. 1 (ISBN 0-405-09627-5). Vol. 2 (ISBN 0-405-09628-3). Ayer Co Pubs.

Haberstich, D. Modern Photographers on Photography. 1978. 10.95 (ISBN 0-13-596510-1, Spec); pap. 6.95 (ISBN 0-13-596502-0, Spec). P-H.

Hattersley, Ralph. Beginner's Guide to Photography. rev. ed. LC 81-43043. 160p. 1982. pap. 7.95 (ISBN 0-385-17705-4, Dolp). Doubleday.

Hawken, William R. You & Your Camera. (Illus.). 160p. 1977. pap. 6.95 (ISBN 0-8174-0560-7, Amphoto). Watson-Guptill.

Hedgecoe, John. The Book of Photography. (Illus.). 1976. 19.95 (ISBN 0-394-49818-6); pap. text ed. 19.00 (ISBN 0-394-32047-6). Knopf.

--The Book of Photography. LC 83-49189. (Illus.). 256p. 1984. pap. 12.95 (ISBN 0-394-72466-6). Knopf.

--John Hedgecoe's Complete Photography Course. 1979. 17.95 (ISBN 0-671-25000-0). S&S.

--John Hedgecoe's Complete Photography Course. 1983. pap. 10.95 (ISBN 0-671-47501-0). S&S.

Hedgecoe, John & Langford, Michael. Photography: Materials & Methods. (Oxford Paperbacks Handbooks for Artists). (Illus.). 1971. pap. 9.95x (ISBN 0-19-289909-0). Oxford U Pr.

Helprin, Ben. Photographic Self-Assignments. LC 79-51528. (Photography How-to Ser.). (Illus.). 1979. pap. 4.50 (ISBN 0-8227-4015-X). Petersen Pub.

Holmes, Edward. An Age of Cameras. rev. ed. (Illus.). 160p. 1978. text ed. 14.95 (ISBN 0-85242-346-2, 3346). Morgan.

Horenstein, Henry. Beyond Basic Photography: A Technical Manual. 1977. pap. 9.70i (ISBN 0-316-37312-5). Little.

How to Improve Your Photography. (Illus.). pap. 14.95 (ISBN 0-89586-121-6). H P Bks.

Jacobs, Lou. How to Take Great Pictures with Your SLR. LC 74-82515. (Illus.). 200p. 1974. pap. 7.95 (ISBN 0-912656-26-3). H P Bks.

James, T. H., ed. Theory of the Photographic Process. 4th ed. 1977. 68.95 (ISBN 0-02-360190-6, 36019). Macmillan.

Janus, ed. Man Ray: The Photographic Image. (Illus.). 232p. 1981. pap. 39.00x (ISBN 0-86092-045-3, Pub. by Fraser Bks). State Mutual Bk.

Jenkins, Reese V. Images & Enterprise: Technology & the American Photographic Industry, 1839-1925. LC 75-11348. (Studies in the History of Technology). (Illus.). 374p. 1976. 32.50x (ISBN 0-8018-1588-6). Johns Hopkins.

Kardon, Janet. Photography: A Sense of Order. (Illus.). 60p. 1981. pap. 12.00 (ISBN 0-88454-027-8). U of Pa Contemp Art.

Klindt, Steven, ed. New American Photography. (Illus.). 48p. 1981. pap. 10.00 (ISBN 0-932026-06-0). Columbia College Chi.

Knight, Arthur. The Liveliest Art. rev ed. 1979. pap. 3.95 (ISBN 0-451-62285-5, ME2285, Ment). NAL.

Kowaliski, Paul. Applied Photographic Theory. LC 72-613. (Wiley Ser. on Photographic Sciences & Technology & Graphic Arts). pap. 135.80 (ISBN 0-8357-9838-0, 2016154). Bks Demand UMI.

Krejcarek, Philip. Photography: Simple Truths. 1978. pap. 6.00 (ISBN 0-686-15968-3). P Krejcarek.

Kuhn, Willy. Die Photographische Industrie Deutschland. Bunnell, Peter C. & Sobieszek, Robert A., eds. LC 78-67657. (Sources of Modern Photography Ser.). (Ger.). 1979. Repr. of 1929 ed. lib. bdg. 17.00x (ISBN 0-405-09899-5). Ayer Co Pubs.

LaCour & Lathrop. Photo Technology. 3rd ed. (Illus.). 432p. 1977. 14.95 (ISBN 0-8269-2629-0). Am Technical.

Lahue, Kalton C. Wide Angle Photography. LC 77-74100. (Photography How-to Ser.). (Illus.). 1977. pap. 3.95 (ISBN 0-8227-4014-1). Petersen Pub.

Langford, Michael. Better Photography. (Illus.). 1978. pap. 9.95 (ISBN 0-240-50983-8). Focal Pr.

--The Master Guide to Photography. LC 82-80133. 1982. 35.00 (ISBN 0-394-50873-4). Knopf.

--The Step-by-Step Guide to Photography. LC 78-54894. (Illus.). 1978. 19.95 (ISBN 0-394-41604-X). Knopf.

--Story of Photography. (Illus.). 1980. pap. 13.95 (ISBN 0-240-51044-5). Focal Pr.

Langford, Michael J. Advanced Photography. rev., 4th ed. (Illus.). 335p. 1980. pap. text ed. 20.95 (ISBN 0-240-51028-3). Focal Pr.

LaPlante, Jerry C. Photographers on Photography. LC 78-7063. (Illus.). 1979. pap. 5.95 (ISBN 0-8069-8560-7). Sterling.

Larmore, Lewis. Introduction to Photographic Principles. (Illus.). pap. 3.75 (ISBN 0-486-21385-4). Dover.

Lathrop, I. T. & LaCour, M. The Basic Book of Photography. (Basic Industrial Arts Ser.). (Illus.). 122p. 1984. 7.50 (ISBN 0-8269-2610-X). Am Technical.

Leary, Michael E. Photography: From Theory to Practice. (Illus.). 168p. 1984. 24.95x (ISBN 0-89863-078-9); pap. text ed. 15.95 (ISBN 0-89863-073-8). Star Pub CA.

Lerebours, N. P. A Treatise on Photography. LC 72-9215. (The Literature of Photography Ser.). Repr. of 1843 ed. 17.00 (ISBN 0-405-04923-4). Ayer Co Pubs.

London, Barbara. A Short Course in Pentax Photography. (Illus., Orig.). 1979. 14.95 (ISBN 0-930764-14-5); pap. 9.95 (ISBN 0-930764-05-6). Curtin & London.

London, Barbara & Boyer, Richard. Photographing Outdoors with Your Automatic Camera. (Your Automatic Camera Ser.). (Illus.). 144p. (Orig.). 1981. pap. 6.95 (ISBN 0-930764-19-6). Curtin & London.

McKnight Staff Members & Miller, Wilbur R. Photography. LC 78-53393. (Basic Industrial Arts Ser.). (Illus.). 1978. 7.28 (ISBN 0-87345-797-8); softbound 5.28 (ISBN 0-87345-789-7). McKnight.

Malcolm, Janet. Diana & Nikon: Essays on the Aesthetic of Photography. LC 78-74547. (Illus.). 176p. 1981. 17.95 (ISBN 0-87923-273-0); pap. 8.95 (ISBN 0-87923-387-7). Godine.

Marvullo, Joe. Improving Your Color Photography. (Illus.). 175p. 1982. 14.95 (ISBN 0-13-453522-7). P-H.

Marzio, Peter C. Democratic Art: An Exhibition on the History of Chromolithography in America, 1840-1900. LC 79-90049. (Illus.). 112p. 1979. pap. 12.50 (ISBN 0-88360-034-X). Amon Carter.

Mitchell, Bob. Amphoto Guide to Travel Photography. (Illus.). 1979. (Amphoto); pap. 7.95 (ISBN 0-8174-2144-0). Watson-Guptill.

Mitchell, Earl N. Photographic Science. LC 83-19808. 404p. 1984. text ed. 33.50x (ISBN 0-471-09046-8); write for info. tchr.'s manual (ISBN 0-471-89580-6); lab manual 11.95 (ISBN 0-471-86501-X). Wiley.

Morgan, Barbara, ed. Photomontage: Barbara Morgan. LC 80-81142. 64p. (Orig.). pap. 9.95 (ISBN 0-87100-171-3). Morgan.

Newhall, Beaumont, ed. Photography: Essays & Images; Illustrated Readings in the History of Photography. (Illus.). 328p. 1981. 32.50 (ISBN 0-87070-387-0, 706949, Pub. by Museum Mod Art); pap. 16.95 (ISBN 0-87070-385-4, 706957, Pub. by Museum Mod Art). NYGS.

Page, Andre. Photographic Interpretation. (Illus.). 128p. 1973. 7.50 (ISBN 0-7207-0633-5). Transatlantic.

Perisic, Zoran. Special Optical Effects. LC 80-41005. (Illus.). 1980. 33.95 (ISBN 0-240-51007-0). Focal Pr.

Photographic Principles: Developing & Printing. (Illus.). 1981. 4.38 (ISBN 0-9601006-5-2). G T Yeamans.

Photography: The U. K. Photographic Market. 65p. 1985. 150.00x (ISBN 0-686-71955-7, Pub. by Euromonitor). State Mutual Bk.

Picker, Fred. The Zone VI Workshop. (Illus.). 128p. 1978. 9.95 (ISBN 0-8174-0574-7, Amphoto). Watson-Guptill.

Pierson & Mayer. La Photographie Consideree Comme Art et Comme Industrie. Bunnell, Peter C. & Sobieszk, Robert A., eds. LC 76-24666. (Sources of Modern Photography Ser.). (Fr.). 1979. Repr. of 1862 ed. lib. bdg. 21.00x (ISBN 0-405-09643-7). Ayer Co Pubs.

Polaroid Corporation Staff. Photomicrography with Polaroid Land Films. (Illus.). 54p. (Orig.). 1985. pap. 6.95 (ISBN 0-240-51703-2). Focal Pr.

--Polaroid Black & White Land Films. (Illus.). 72p. (Orig.). 1983. pap. 6.95 (ISBN 0-240-51705-9). Focal Pr.

--Kodak Professional Photoguide. (No. R-28). (Illus.). 40p. 1977. 11.50 (ISBN 0-87985-100-7). Eastman Kodak.

Eastman Kodak Company, ed. The Joy of Photography. Bd. with More Joy of Photography. 288p. (Illus.). 312p. 1982. Set. pap. 27.90 (ISBN 0-201-99239-6). Addison-Wesley.

Eastman Kodak Company Staff. Kodak Guide to 35mm Photography (AC-95S) LC 83-83259. (Illus.). 286p. 1984. pap. 9.95 (ISBN 0-87985-347-6). Eastman Kodak.

Eder, Joseph M. Ausfuhrliches Handbuch der Photographie: 1891-93, 4 Vols. (Illus.). 476p. Set. pap. 300.00 (ISBN 0-686-82589-6). Saifer.

Family Workshop Inc. Focus on Photography. LC 83-45387. 160p. (Orig.). 1984. pap. 12.95 (ISBN 0-8019-7499-2). Chilton.

Feininger, Andreas. Total Photography. (Illus.). 252p. 1982. 14.95 (ISBN 0-8174-3531-X, Amphoto). Watson-Guptill.

Fondiller, Harvey V., ed. Popular Photography Answer Book. 256p. 1980. 14.95 (ISBN 0-87165-039-8, Amphoto). Watson-Guptill.

Freeman, Michael. Photo School: A Step by Step Course in Photography. (Illus.). 224p. 1982. 24.95 (ISBN 0-8174-5402-0, Amphoto). Watson-Guptill.

--Salem House Concise Guide to Photography: The Professional Manual for the Amateur Photographer. (Illus.). 176p. 1985. pap. 11.95 (ISBN 0-88162-096-3, Pub. by Salem Hse Ltd). Merrimack Pub Cir.

--The Thirty-Five Millimeter Handbook: A Complete Course from Basic Techniques to Professional Applications. 1985. 14.98 (ISBN 0-89471-339-6). Running Pr.

Gassan, Arnold H. Handbook for Contemporary Photography. 4th ed. LC 77-14576. (Illus.). 1977. 14.95 (ISBN 0-87992-009-2); pap. 8.95x (ISBN 0-87992-008-4). Light Impressions.

Gaunt, Leonard. Canon Reflex Way. 4th ed. (Camera Way Ser.). (Illus.). 500p. 1986. 29.95 (ISBN 0-240-51220-0). Focal Pr.

Graduating Photography. (Illus.). 116p. Date not set. cancelled (ISBN 0-686-89251-8, Peregrine Smith). Gibbs M Smith.

Grimm, Tom & Grimm, Michele. The Good Guide for Bad Photographers: How to Avoid Mistakes & Take Better Pictures. LC 82-2139. (Illus.). 256p. 1982. pap. 7.95 (ISBN 0-452-25474-4, Z5474, Plume). NAL.

H P Books, ed. How to Select & Use Your SLR System. LC 81-82138. 1981. 7.95 (ISBN 0-89586-112-7). H P Bks.

Hattersley, Ralph. Beginning Photography: Beginner's Guide to Photography, Beginner's Guide to Darkroom Techniques, Beginner's Guide to Photographing People. rev. ed. LC 80-2741. (Illus.). 544p. 1981. 15.95 (ISBN 0-385-17318-0). Doubleday.

Haveman, Josepha. Workbook in Creative Photography. 1976. 5.95 (ISBN 0-87100-048-2). Morgan.

Hawken, William. Zoom Lens Photography. (Illus., Orig.). 1981. pap. 10.95 (ISBN 0-930764-29-3). Curtin & London.

Hawkins, Andrew & Avon, Dennis. Photography: The Guide to Technique. (Illus.). 272p. 1984. 19.95 (ISBN 0-7137-1456-5, Pub. by Blandford Pr England); pap. 12.95 (ISBN 0-7137-1411-5, Pub. by Blandford Pr England). Sterling.

The Here's How Book of Photography, Vol. 2. LC 73-184546. 414p. 1977. 12.95 (ISBN 0-87985-200-3, AE-101). Eastman Kodak.

How to Catch the Action. LC 82-62978. (Kodak Library of Creative Photography). 1984. lib. bdg. 15.94 (ISBN 0-86706-216-9, Pub. by Time-Life). Silver.

Hunt, Robert. A Manual of Photography. 3rd ed. LC 72-9212. (The Literature of Photography Ser.). Repr. of 1853 ed. 25.50 (ISBN 0-405-04920-X). Ayer Co Pubs.

Hurter, Bill. Techniques in Portrait Photography. (Masterclass Photography Ser.). (Illus.). 176p. 1983. 12.95 (ISBN 0-13-900621-4). P-H.

Jacobson, R. E., et al, eds. The Manual of Photography. 7th ed. (Illus.). 682p. 1978. pap. 23.95 (ISBN 0-240-51239-1). Focal Pr.

Keppler, Herbert. The Nikon-Nikkormat Way. 3rd ed. (Camera Way Bks.). (Illus.). 512p. 1983. 32.95 (ISBN 0-240-51185-9). Focal Pr.

Kodak. How to Take Good Pictures. 192p. 1981. pap. 5.95 (ISBN 0-345-29745-8). Ballantine.

Kodak Pocket Guide to Great Picture Taking. 112p. 1984. pap. 5.95 (ISBN 0-671-54137-4). S&S.

Langford, Michael. Basic Photography. new, rev., 4th ed. (Illus.). 397p. 1977. pap. text ed. 18.95 (ISBN 0-240-50955-2). Focal Pr.

--Better Photography. (Illus.). 1978. pap. 9.95 (ISBN 0-240-50983-8). Focal Pr.

--Michael Langford's 35 MM Handbook. LC 82-48555. 1983. 16.95 (ISBN 0-394-53129-9); pap. 9.95 (ISBN 0-394-71369-9). Knopf.

--Step by Step Guide to Photography. LC 78-54894. 1979. pap. text ed. 16.00 (ISBN 0-394-32373-4, KnopfC). Knopf.

Lathrop, Irvin I. & LeCour, Marshall. Photo Technology Laboratory Manual. pap. 28.00 (ISBN 0-317-10693-7, 2011577). Bks Demand UMI.

Logan, Larry L. Professional Photographer's Handbook-Nikon School Edition. LC 81-90008. (Illus.). 116p. (Orig.). 1981. pap. 11.95 (ISBN 0-9603856-1-4). Logan Design.

London, Barbara. A Short Course in Canon Photography. (Illus.). 144p. 1983. pap. 11.95 (ISBN 0-930764-52-8, Co.-Pub. by Van Nos Reinhold). Curtin & London.

--A Short Course in Canon Photography. rev. ed. 1983. pap. 11.95 (ISBN 0-930764-52-8). Van Nos Reinhold.

--A Short Course in Minolta Photography. (Illus.). 144p. 1983. pap. 11.95 (ISBN 0-930764-53-6, Co.-Pub. by Van Nos Reinhold). Curtin & London.

--A Short Course in Nikon Photography. (Illus.). 144p. 1983. pap. 11.95 (ISBN 0-930764-54-4, Co.-Pub. by Van Nos Reinhold). Curtin & London.

--A Short Course in Olympus Photography. (Illus.). 144p. 1983. pap. 11.95 (ISBN 0-930764-55-2, Co.-Pub. by Van Nos Reinhold). Curtin & London.

--A Short Course in Pentax Photography. (Illus.). 144p. 1983. pap. text ed. 11.95 (ISBN 0-930764-56-0, Co.-Pub. by Van Nos Reinhold). Curtin & London.

--A Short Course in Photography. (Illus.). 144p. 1983. pap. 11.95 (ISBN 0-930764-51-X). Curtin & London.

Lovell, R. P., et al. Handbook of Photography. 1984. pap. text ed. write for info. (ISBN 0-534-03177-3). Wadsworth Pub.

Noemer, Fred E. The Handbook of Modern Halftone Photography: With Complete Concepts & Practices. 8th ed. (Illus.). 200p. 19.90 (ISBN 0-911126-05-8). Perfect Graphic.

Paine, Shep & Stewart, Lane. How to Photograph Scale Models. Hayden, Bob, ed. (Illus.). 64p. (Orig.). 1984. pap. 8.95 (ISBN 0-89024-053-1). Kalmbach.

Photo-Lab-Index. 38th ed. LC 40-847. 1400p. 1981. looseleaf 54.95 (ISBN 0-87100-051-2, 2051). Morgan.

Polaroid Corporation Staff. Polaroid 35mm Slide System. (Illus., Orig.). 1984. pap. 13.95 (ISBN 0-240-51707-5). Focal Pr.

Rehm, Karl M. Basic Black & White Photography. LC 75-42568. (Illus.). 192p. 1977. pap. 9.95 (ISBN 0-8174-2403-2, Amphoto). Watson-Guptill.

Reynolds, Clyde, ed. Camera Techniques. (Illus.). 336p. 1983. 29.95 (ISBN 0-240-51245-6). Focal Pr.

Society of Photographic Scientists & Engineers. SPSE Handbook of Photographic Science & Engineering. LC 72-10168. (Wiley Ser. on Photographic Science & Technology & the Graphic Arts). 1416p. 1973. 96.50x (ISBN 0-471-81880-1, Pub. by Wiley-Interscience). Wiley.

Special Problems. Rev. ed. (Life Library of Photography). 1982. 15.95 (ISBN 0-8094-4400-3). Time-Life.

Spitzing, G. Two Hundred Photo Tips. (Photo Tips Ser.). (Illus.). 80p. 1980. pap. 4.95 (ISBN 0-85242-502-3, 3469). Morgan.

Stensvold, Mike, ed. Blueprint Series, Vol. 2. LC 73-82543. (Photography How-to Ser.). (Illus.). 1978. pap. 3.95 (ISBN 0-8227-4017-6). Petersen Pub.

Stroebel, Leslie. Photographic Filters. LC 72-83109. 144p. 1974. pap. 8.95 (ISBN 0-87100-028-8, 2028). Morgan.

--View Camera Technique. 5th ed. (Illus.). 312p. 1986. 25.95 (ISBN 0-240-51711-3). Focal Pr.

Taylor, Herb, et al. How to Use Your 35mm Camera. LC 81-71227. (Modern Photo Guides). (Illus.). 120p. (Orig.). 1982. pap. 7.95 (ISBN 0-385-18144-2). Avalon Comm.

--Natural Light & Night Photography. LC 81-71223. (Modern Photo Guides). (Illus.). 120p. (Orig.). 1982. pap. 7.95 (ISBN 0-385-18156-6). Avalon Comm.

Voogel, E. & Keyzer, P. Two Hundred Slide Tips. (Photo Tips Ser.). (Illus.). 102p. (Orig.). 1980. pap. 4.95 (ISBN 0-85242-502-3, 3471). Morgan.

Werge, John. The Evolution of Photography. LC 72-9245. (The Literature of Photography Ser.). Repr. of 1890 ed. 23.50 (ISBN 0-405-04949-8). Ayer Co Pubs.

White, Minor & Zakia, Richard D. The New Zone System Manual. rev. ed. (Illus., Orig.). 1984. pap. 12.95 (ISBN 0-87100-195-0, 2195). Morgan.

Wildi, Ernst. Hasselblad Manual. 2nd ed. (Camera Ways Bks.). (Illus.). 302p. 1982. 34.95 (ISBN 0-240-51186-7). Focal Pr.

PHOTOGRAPHY–HIGH-SPEED

see Photography, High-Speed

PHOTOGRAPHY–HISTORY

Aperture History of Photography Series Giftpak, Set 1. Incl. Henri Cartier Bresson. LC 76-21993 (ISBN 0-89381-000-2); Jacques Lartique. LC 76-22000 (ISBN 0-89381-001-0); Dorothea Lange. LC 76-22001 (ISBN 0-89381-078-9); Alfred Stieglitz. LC 76-25728 (ISBN 0-89381-004-5); Wynn Bullock. LC 76-25727 (ISBN 0-89381-003-7). (Illus.). 90p. 1976. Set. pap. 39.95 over boards (ISBN 0-685-63920-7); set avail. (ISBN 0-89381-038-X). Aperture.

Buckland, Gail. Fox Talbot & the Invention of Photography. 216p. 1981. 60.00x (ISBN 0-85967-599-8, Pub. by Scolar England). State Mutual Bk.

Camera Notes: The Official Organ of the Camera Club of New York, 6 vols. in 3. (Photography Ser.). (Repr. of 1897-1903 eds.). 1978. Set. 350.00 (ISBN 0-306-77553-0); 150.00 ea. Vol. 1, 1897-1899 (ISBN 0-306-77554-9). Vol. 2, 1899-1901 (ISBN 0-306-77555-7). Vol. 3, 1901-1903 (ISBN 0-306-77556-5). Da Capo.

Darrah, William C. Cartes De Visite in Nineteenth Century Photography. (Illus.). 222p. 1981. 27.00 (ISBN 0-913116-05-X). W. C. Darrah.

Eder, Josef M. History of Photography. 19.00 (ISBN 0-8446-5687-9). Peter Smith.

Feldvebel, Thomas P. The Ambrotype: Old & New. LC 80-65216. (Illus.). 51p. 1980. pap. 9.95 (ISBN 0-89938-001-8). Tech & Ed Ctr Graph Arts RIT.

Fouque, Victor. The Truth Concerning the Invention of Photography: Nicephore Niepce-His Life, Letters, & Works (1867) LC 72-9198. (The Literature of Photography Ser.). Repr. of 1935 ed. 17.00 (ISBN 0-405-04907-2). Ayer Co Pubs.

Gilbert, George. Photography: The Early Years, a Historical Guide for Collectors. LC 78-20163. (Illus.). 181p. 1980. 21.10i (ISBN 0-06-011497-5, HarpT). Har-Row.

Harrison, W. Jerome. A History of Photography Written As a Practical Guide & an Introduction to Its Latest Developments. LC 72-9204. (The Literature of Photography Ser.). Repr. of 1887 ed. 18.00 (ISBN 0-405-04913-7). Ayer Co Pubs.

Japan Photographers Association. A Century of Japanese Photography. (Illus.). 1981. 47.50 (ISBN 0-394-51232-4). Pantheon.

Kravtes, T. P., et al, eds. Documents on the History of the Invention of Photography. LC 76-24664. (Sources of Modern Photography Ser.). (Rus. & Fr., Illus.). 1979. Repr. of 1949 ed. lib. bdg. 40.00x (ISBN 0-405-09641-0). Ayer Co Pubs.

McCausland, Elizabeth. Eyewitness: The Growth of Photography. Peters, Susan D., ed. (Illus.). 250p. Date not set. 22.50 (ISBN 0-8180-1421-0). Horizon.

Mentienne, A. La Decouverte de la Photographie en 1839. Bunnell, Peter C. & Sobieszek, Robert A., eds. LC 76-23037. (Sources in Modern Phtography Ser.). (Fr.). 1979. Repr. of 1892 ed. lib. bdg. 17.00x (ISBN 0-405-09600-3). Ayer Co Pubs.

Newhall, Beaumont. The Daguerreotype in America. (Illus.). 176p. 1976. pap. 7.95 (ISBN 0-486-23322-7). Dover.

--The History of Photography: From 1839 to the Present Day. 5th rev. ed. 1982. 40.00 (ISBN 0-87070-380-3, 365211); pap. 18.95 (ISBN 0-87070-381-1, 365238). NYGS.

--The Latent Image: The Discovery of Photography. 160p. 1983. pap. 8.95x (ISBN 0-8263-0673-X). U Of NM Pr.

Olshaker, Mark. The Polaroid Story: Edwin Land & the Polaroid Experience. LC 77-15965. (Illus.). 292p. 1983. pap. 9.95 (ISBN 0-8128-6093-4). Stein & Day.

Potonniee, Georges. The History of the Discovery of Photography. LC 72-9222. (The Literature of Photography Ser.). Repr. of 1936 ed. 22.00 (ISBN 0-405-04929-3). Ayer Co Pubs.

Rance, Adrian B. A Victorian Photographer in Southampton. 1982. 40.00x (ISBN 0-686-75448-4, Pub. by Cave Pubns England). State Mutual Bk.

Reilly, James. The Albumen & Salted Paper Book. LC 80-14340. (Extended Photo Media Ser.: No. 2). (Illus.). 1980. clothbound o.p. 15.00 (ISBN 0-87992-020-3); pap. text ed. 8.95x (ISBN 0-87992-014-9). Light Impressions.

Rinhart, Floyd & Rinhart, Marion. The American Daguerreotype. LC 80-24743. (Illus.). 448p. 1981. 65.00 (ISBN 0-8203-0549-9). U of Ga Pr.

Snelling. History & Practice of the Art of Photography: The 1849 First Edition. 228p. 1970. 8.95 (ISBN 0-87100-014-8, 2014). Morgan.

Sobieszek, Robert A., ed. Early Experiments with Direct Color Photography, 3 bks. LC 76-34668. (Sources of Modern Photography Ser.). (Fr. & Eng.). 1979. Set. lib. bdg. 34.50x (ISBN 0-405-09645-3). Ayer Co Pubs.

--Two Pioneers of Color Photography: Cros & Du Hauron. LC 76-24667. (Sources of Modern Photography Ser.). (Fr.). 1979. lib. bdg. 37.00x (ISBN 0-405-09644-5). Ayer Co Pubs.

Stenger, Erich. The History of Photography. Bunnell, Peter C. & Sobieszek, Robert A., eds. LC 76-23050. (Sources of Modern Photography Ser.). (Illus.). 1979. Repr. of 1939 ed. lib. bdg. 21.00x (ISBN 0-405-09611-9). Ayer Co Pubs.

Story, Alfred T. The Story of Photography. 1979. Repr. of 1904 ed. lib. bdg. 25.00 (ISBN 0-8495-4947-7). Arden Lib.

Tausk, Peter. Photography in the Twentieth Century. (Illus.). 344p. 1980. 26.50 (ISBN 0-240-51031-3). Focal Pr.

Wade, John. A Short History of the Camera. (Illus.). 144p. (Orig.). 1979. pap. 8.95 (ISBN 0-85242-640-2, 3640). Morgan.

PHOTOGRAPHY–INDUSTRIAL APPLICATIONS

see Photography, Industrial

PHOTOGRAPHY–LENSES

see Lenses, Photographic

PHOTOGRAPHY–LIGHTING

see also Photography–Exposure

Boord, W. Arthur, ed. Sun Artists (Original Series, Nos. 1-8. LC 72-9184. (The Literature of Photography Ser.). Repr. of 1891 ed. 44.00 (ISBN 0-405-04895-5). Ayer Co Pubs.

Brooks, David. How to Control & Use Photographic Lighting. LC 80-82382. (Orig.). 1980. pap. 10.95 (ISBN 0-89586-059-7). H P Bks.

Carlson, Verne & Carlson, Sylvia. Professional Lighting Handbook. (Illus.). 224p. 1985. 22.95 (ISBN 0-240-51721-0). Focal Pr.

Eastman Kodak Company, ed. KW-Seventeen, Existing-Light Photography. (Kodak Workshop Ser.). 96p. (Orig.). Date not set. pap. 8.95 (ISBN 0-87985-302-6). Eastman Kodak.

H P Books, ed. How to Use Light Creatively. LC 18-8237. 1981. 7.95 (ISBN 0-89586-113-5). H P Bks.

Hattersley, R. Photographic Lighting. 1978. 15.95 (ISBN 0-13-665323-5, Spec); pap. 6.95 (ISBN 0-13-665315-4). P-H.

Hunt, Robert. Researches on Light. LC 72-9213. (The Literature of Photography Ser.). Repr. of 1844 ed. 24.50 (ISBN 0-405-04921-8). Ayer Co Pubs.

Jacobs, Lou, Jr. Amphoto Guide to Lighting. (Illus.). 1979. (Amphoto); pap. 7.95 (ISBN 0-8174-2140-8). Watson-Guptill.

Kerr, Norm. Technique of Photographic Lighting. (Illus.). 1979. 9.95 (ISBN 0-8174-6024-1, Amphoto). Watson-Guptill.

--Techniques of Photographic Lighting. (Illus.). 208p. 1982. pap. 9.95 (ISBN 0-8174-6024-1, Amphoto). Watson-Guptill.

Light & Film. 1982. write for info. (ISBN 0-8094-4166-7). Time-Life.

Lincoln, Adams W., ed. Sunlight & Shadow. LC 76-24669. (Sources of Modern Photography Ser.). (Illus.). 1979. Repr. of 1897 ed. lib. bdg. 17.00x (ISBN 0-405-09646-1). Ayer Co Pubs.

Mastering Composition & Light. LC 82-62976. (Kodak Library of Creative Photography). 1984. lib. bdg. 15.94 (ISBN 0-86706-210-X, Pub. by Time-Life). Silver.

Smith, D. Studio Lighting Handbook. 1986. pap. cancelled (ISBN 0-930764-67-6). Van Nos Reinhold.

Thorpe, Don. Amphoto Guide to Available Light Photography. (Amphoto Guide Ser.). (Illus.). 1980. (Amphoto); pap. 7.95 (ISBN 0-8174-2149-1). Watson-Guptill.

PHOTOGRAPHY–LIGHT FILTERS

Eastman Kodak Company. Using Filters. LC 81-67034. (The Kodak Workshop Ser.). (Illus.). 96p. (Orig.). 1981. pap. 8.95 (ISBN 0-87985-277-1, KW-13). Eastman Kodak.

Hypia, Jorma. The Complete Tiffen Filter Manual. (Illus.). 136p. 1981. pap. 9.95 (ISBN 0-8174-3700-2, Amphoto). Watson-Guptill.

Taylor, Herb, ed. How to Use Filters. LC 81-71221. (Modern Photo Guide Ser.). (Illus.). 120p. 1982. pap. 7.95 (ISBN 0-385-18148-5). Doubleday.

Taylor, Herb, et al. How to Use Filters. LC 81-71221. (Modern Photo Guides). (Illus.). 120p. (Orig.). 1982. pap. 7.95 (ISBN 0-385-18148-5). Avalon Comm.

PHOTOGRAPHY–NEGATIVES

see also Photography–Developing and Developers

Adams, Ansel. The Negative. (The New Ansel Adams Photography Ser.: Bk. 2). (Illus.). 288p. 1981. 18.95 (ISBN 0-8212-1131-5). NYGS.

Gotze, H. Black & White Negatives: Exposure & Development. (Photo Tips Ser.). (Illus.). 96p. (Orig.). 1980. pap. 4.95 (ISBN 0-85242-709-3, Fountain Press). Morgan.

PHOTOGRAPHY–PRINTING PROCESSES

see also Color Photography–Printing Processes

Bunnell, Peter C., ed. Nonsilver Printing Processes: Four Selections, 1886-1927. LC 72-9221. (The Literature of Photography Ser.). 22.00 (ISBN 0-405-04928-5); pap. 4.50 (ISBN 0-685-32643-8). Ayer Co Pubs.

Burbank, W. H. Photographic Printing Methods: A Practical Guide to the Professional & Amateur Worker. 3rd ed. LC 72-9185. (The Literature of Photography Ser.). Repr. of 1891 ed. 20.00 (ISBN 0-405-04896-3). Ayer Co Pubs.

Carter, Kenneth. Photography Simplified for Archivists. Gill, Rowland P., ed. (A Collegiate Guide to Archival Science Ser.: No. 5). 16p. (Orig.). 1948. pap. text ed. 3.75 (ISBN 0-910653-10-0, 8101-K). Archival Servs.

Eastman Kodak Co., ed. Practical Steps to Quality Printing. 24p. 1977. pap. 5.00 (ISBN 0-87985-209-7, Q-72). Eastman Kodak.

Eastman Kodak Company. Basic Developing, Printing, Enlarging in Black-&-White. 4th ed. LC 82-82731. (Illus.). 72p. 1977. pap. 3.95 (ISBN 0-87985-182-1, AJ-2). Eastman Kodak.

Eastman Kodak Company, ed. Using Kodak Ektachrome R-3 & R-3000 Chemicals. (Illus.). 118p. 1985. wkbk. 60.00 (ISBN 0-87985-361-1). Eastman-Kodak.

Hafey, John & Shillea, Tom. The Platinum Print. LC 79-55710. (Illus.). 119p. (Orig.). 1979. pap. 14.95 (ISBN 0-89938-000-X). Tech & Ed Ctr Graph Arts RIT.

Hattersley, Ralph. Photographic Printing. (Illus.). 1977. 15.95 (ISBN 0-13-665299-9, Spec); pap. 6.95 (ISBN 0-13-665281-6, Spec). P-H.

Hawken, William R. You & Your Prints. (Illus.). 1978. (Amphoto); pap. 6.95 (ISBN 0-8174-2114-9). Watson-Guptill.

Manella, Douglas. Amphoto Guide to Black-&-White Processing & Printing. (Illus.). 1979. (Amphoto); pap. 7.95 (ISBN 0-8174-2135-1). Watson-Guptill.

Parry, Pamela J., compiled by. Photography Index: A Guide to Reproductions. LC 78-20013. 1979. lib. bdg. 35.00 (ISBN 0-313-20700-3, PPI/). Greenwood.

The Print. Rev. ed. (Life Library of Photography). 1982. 15.95 (ISBN 0-8094-4162-4). Time-Life.

Reilly, James. The Albumen & Salted Paper Book. LC 80-14340. (Extended Photo Media Ser.: No. 2). (Illus.). 1980. clothbound o.p. 15.00 (ISBN 0-87992-020-3); pap. text ed. 8.95x (ISBN 0-87992-014-9). Light Impressions.

Robinson, Henry P. & Abney, W. D. The Art & Practice of Silver Printing. LC 72-9227. (The Literature of Photography Ser.). Repr. of 1881 ed. 15.00 (ISBN 0-405-04933-1). Ayer Co Pubs.

Trapmore, Alison. Color Printing. (Photographer's Library Ser.). (Illus.). 168p. pap. cancelled (ISBN 0-240-51113-1). Focal Pr.

PHOTOGRAPHY–PROCESSING

Barger, Susan M., ed. Selected Bibliography: Photographic Processes in Use Before 1880. LC 84-84390. 149p. 1980. pap. 37.50 (ISBN 0-89938-003-4). Tech & Ed Ctr Graph Arts RIT.

Bingham, Robert J. Photogenic Manipulation. LC 72-9182. (The Literature of Photography Ser.). (Illus.). Repr. of 1852 ed. 12.00 (ISBN 0-405-04893-9). Ayer Co Pubs.

Birnbaum, Hubert C. Black & White Darkroom Techniques. LC 81-67033. (Kodak Workshop Ser.). (Illus.). 96p. (Orig.). 1981. pap. 8.95 (ISBN 0-87985-274-7, KW-15). Eastman Kodak.

Brodatz, Phil. Photographics: A Workshop in High-Contrast Techniques. (Illus.). 96p. 1981. 10.95 (ISBN 0-8174-5417-9, Amphoto). Watson-Guptill.

Carroll, B. H., et al. Introduction to Photographic Theory: The Silver Halide Process. LC 79-26802. 355p. 1980. 45.95X (ISBN 0-471-02562-3, Pub. by Wiley Interscience). Wiley.

Casagrande, Bob. Better Black & White Darkroom Techniques. (Master Class Photography Ser.). (Illus.). 176p. 1984. pap. 8.95 (ISBN 0-13-071324-4). P-H.

Coe, Brian. Guide to Early Photographic Processes. (Illus.). 112p. (Orig.). 1984. pap. 18.95 (ISBN 0-905209-40-0, Pub. by Victoria & Albert Mus UK). Faber & Faber.

Construction Materials for Photographic Processing Equipment: Eastman Kodak Company K-12. (Illus.). 1980. pap. 5.95 (ISBN 0-87985-250-X). Eastman Kodak.

Crawford, William. The Keepers of Light: A History & Working Guide to Early Photographic Processes. LC 79-88815. 324p. 1979. pap. 24.95 (ISBN 0-87100-158-6, 2158). Morgan.

Croucher, J. H. & Le Gray, Gustave. Plain Directions for Obtaining Photographic Pictures by the Calotype & Energiatype, Also Upon Albumenized Paper & Glass, by Collodion & Albumen, Etc., Etc, Pts. 1-3. LC 72-9191. (The Literature of Photography Ser.). Repr. of 1853 ed. 23.50 (ISBN 0-405-04901-3). Ayer Co Pubs.

Dillaye, Frederic. La Theorie, la Pratique et L'art En Photographie Avec le Procede Au Gelatino Bromure D'argent. Bunnell, Peter C. & Sobieszek, Robert A., eds. LC 76-23053. (Sources of Modern Photography Ser.). (Fr., Illus.). 1979. Repr. of 1891 ed. lib. bdg. 44.00x (ISBN 0-405-09618-6). Ayer Co Pubs.

Duren, Lista & McDonald, Billy. Building Your Own Home Darkroom Step-by-Step. 1982. pap. 14.95 (ISBN 0-442-22089-8). Van Nos Reinhold.

Eastman Kodak Company. Kodak Color Darkroom Dataguide. 7th ed. (Illus.). 34p. 1982. pap. 20.00 spiral bound (ISBN 0-87985-086-8, R-19). Eastman Kodak.

--KODAK Complete Darkroom DATAGUIDE. 5th ed. Orig. Title: QSL Adress Book. 58p. (Orig.). 1984. pap. 19.95 (ISBN 0-87985-355-7). Eastman Kodak.

--Processing Chemicals & Formulas. LC 73-82620. (Illus.). 52p. 1977. pap. 1.95 (ISBN 0-87985-069-8, J-1). Eastman Kodak.

Eastman Kodak Company, ed. Black & White Film & Paper Processing & Process Monitoring. (Illus.). 1984. pap. 6.00 (ISBN 0-318-11894-7, Z-128). Eastman-Kodak.

--Copy Preparation & Platemaking Using KODAK PMT Materials. (Illus.). 1980. pap. 4.50 (ISBN 0-87985-261-5, Q-71). Eastman Kodak.

--KW Twenty-One, Darkroom Expression. (Kodak Workshop Ser.). (Illus.). 96p. Date not set. pap. 8.95 (ISBN 0-87985-300-X). Eastman Kodak.

--Photofabrication Methods with Kodak Photo Resists. 1983. pap. 3.75 (ISBN 0-87985-013-2, P246). Eastman Kodak.

Eastman Kodak Company Staff. Creative Darkroom Techniques (AG-18) 3rd & rev. ed. LC 73-87110. (Illus.). 292p. 1983. pap. 15.95 (ISBN 0-87985-309-3). Eastman Kodak.

--Printing Color Negatives (E-66) rev. ed. (Illus.). 72p. 1982. pap. 8.95 (ISBN 0-87985-322-0). Eastman Kodak.

Fineman, Mark. The Home Darkroom. 2nd ed. LC 72-79608. (Illus.). 96p. 1976. pap. 5.95 (ISBN 0-8174-0555-0, Amphoto). Watson-Guptill.

Floyd, Wayne. The Double Exposure Book. (Illus.). 88p. (Orig.). 1985. pap. text ed. 9.95 (ISBN 0-9613160-0-4). W Floyd.

Gaunt, Leonard. Film & Paper Processing. (Photographer's Library). (Illus.). 168p. 1982. pap. 15.95 (ISBN 0-240-51110-7). Focal Pr.

Gotze, H. Prints: Processing & Enlarging in Black & White. (Photo Tips Ser.). (Illus.). 1980. pap. 4.95 (ISBN 0-85242-632-1). Morgan.

Grill, Tom & Scanlon, Mark. The Essential Darkroom Book: A Complete Guide to Black & White Processing. (Illus.). 176p. 1983. pap. 14.95 (ISBN 0-8174-3838-6, Amphoto). Watson-Guptill.

Grimm, Tom & Grimm, Michele. The Basic Darkroom Book: A Complete Guide to Processing & Printing Color & Black-&-White Photographs. (Orig.). 1978. pap. 8.95 (ISBN 0-452-25544-9, Z5544, Plume). NAL.

H P Books, ed. Basic Guide to Black & White Darkroom Techniques. 96p. 1982. pap. 7.95 (ISBN 0-89586-196-8). H P Bks.

--Basic Guide to Color Darkroom Techniques. (Illus.). 96p. (Orig.). 1983. pap. 7.95 (ISBN 0-89586-260-3). H P Bks.

--Basic Guide to Creative Darkroom Techniques. 96p. 1982. pap. 7.95 (ISBN 0-89586-197-6). H P Bks.

Haist, Grant. Modern Photographic Processing, 2 vols. LC 78-17559. (Photographic Science & Technology & Graphic Arts Ser.). 781p. 1979. Set. 134.95 (ISBN 0-471-04286-2); Vol. 1. 74.95 (ISBN 0-471-02228-4); Vol. 2. 77.95 (ISBN 0-471-04285-4, Pub. by Wiley-Interscience). Wiley.

Hattersley, Ralph. Beginner's Guide to Darkroom Techniques. LC 76-1063. (Illus.). 1976. pap. 7.95 (ISBN 0-385-11073-1, Dolp). Doubleday.

--Beginning Photography: Beginner's Guide to Photography, Beginner's Guide to Darkroom Techniques, Beginner's Guide to Photographing People. rev. ed. LC 80-2741. (Illus.). 544p. 1981. 15.95 (ISBN 0-385-17318-0). Doubleday.

Hawken, William R. You & Your Prints. (Illus.). 1978. (Amphoto); pap. 6.95 (ISBN 0-8174-2114-9). Watson-Guptill.

Kelley, Jain. Darkroom Two. LC 78-69948. (Illus.). 160p. (Orig.). 1979. pap. 17.95 (ISBN 0-912810-21-1). Lustrum Pr.

Kodak Black & White Darkroom Dataguide. 7th ed. (Illus.). 36p. 1980. spiral bound 12.95 (ISBN 0-87985-269-0, R-20). Eastman Kodak.

Lahue, Kalton C. The Darkroom Guide. (Petersen's Photographic Library: Vol. 1). (Illus.). 160p. 1980. pap. 8.95 (ISBN 0-8227-4039-7). Petersen Pub.

--Photo Retouching & Restoration. LC 78-78395. (Photography How-to Ser.). (Illus.). 1979. pap. 4.50 (ISBN 0-8227-4034-6). Petersen Pub.

Lahue, Kalton C. & PhotoGraphic Magazine Editors. Creative Darkroom Techniques. LC 73-82536. (Photography How-to Ser.). (Illus.). 80p. 1973. pap. 4.95 (ISBN 0-8227-0018-2). Petersen Pub.

Langford, Michael. The Darkroom Handbook. 128p. 1982. 65.00x (ISBN 0-85223-188-1, Pub. by Ebury Pr England). State Mutual Bk.

Lewis, Eleanor, ed. Darkroom. LC 76-57201. (Illus.). 184p. (Orig.). 1979. pap. 17.50 (ISBN 0-912810-19-X). Lustrum Pr.

Manella, Douglas. Amphoto Guide to Black-&-White Processing & Printing. (Illus.). 1979. (Amphoto); pap. 7.95 (ISBN 0-8174-2135-1). Watson-Guptill.

Miller, Ray. Building a Home Darkroom, KW-14. LC 81-66622. (The Kodak Workshop Ser.). (Illus.). 96p. 1981. pap. 8.95 (ISBN 0-87985-273-9). Eastman Kodak.

Nadler, Bob. Advanced B & W Darkroom Book. (Illus.). 1979. pap. 6.95 (ISBN 0-8174-2947-6, Amphoto). Watson-Guptill.

--Basic Black & White Darkroom Book. (Illus.). 96p. 1978. pap. 6.95 (ISBN 0-8174-2938-7, Amphoto). Watson-Guptill.

--The Illustrated B&W Darkroom Book. LC 79-9933. (Illus.). 1979. 21.95 (ISBN 0-933596-01-4). F-Twenty-Two Pr.

Roberts, Fred M. Darkroom Logbook for Photographers. 94p. 1973. pap. 9.50 (ISBN 0-912746-04-1). F M Roberts.

Saltzer, Joseph. Zone System Calibration Manual. 64p. 1979. mechanical binding 14.95 (ISBN 0-8174-2421-0, Amphoto). Watson-Guptill.

--A Zone System for All Formats. (Illus.). 1979. 25.00 (ISBN 0-8174-2419-9, Amphoto). Watson-Guptill.

Schofield, Jack, ed. Darkroom Book. (Illus.). 256p. 1981. 25.00 (ISBN 0-87165-106-8, Amphoto). Watson-Guptill.

--The Darkroom Book. (Illus.). 256p. 1985. pap. 16.95 (ISBN 0-8174-3757-6, Amphoto). Watson-Guptill.

Scopick, David. The Gum Bichromate Book: Contemporary Methods for Photographic Printmaking. LC 78-8122. (Extended Photo Media Ser.: No. 1). (Illus., Orig.). 1978. pap. 7.95 (ISBN 0-87992-010-6). Light Impressions.

Silver Masking of Transparencies with Three-Aim-Point Control. 1980. pap. 4.00 (ISBN 0-87985-259-3, Q-7A). Eastman Kodak.

Sobieszek, Robert A., ed. The Collodion Process & the Ferrotype: Three Accounts, 1854-1872. LC 72-9190. (The Literature of Photography Ser.). 20.00 (ISBN 0-405-04900-5). Ayer Co Pubs.

Stroebel, Leslie, et al. Photographic Materials & Processes. 512p. 1985. pap. 34.95 (ISBN 0-240-51752-0). Butterworth.

Voogel, E. & Keyser, P. Two Hundred Darkroom Tips - Black & White. (Photo Tips Ser.). (Illus.). 102p. (Orig.). 1980. pap. 4.95 (ISBN 0-85242-573-2, 3573). Morgan.

Welzen, J. V. Two Hundred Darkroom Tips - Colour. (Photo Tips Ser.). (Illus.). 96p. 1980. pap. 4.95 (ISBN 0-85242-574-0, 3575). Morgan.

Wilson, Edward L. The American Carbon Manual; Or, the Production of Photographic Prints in Permanent Pigments. LC 72-9246. (The Literature of Photography Ser.). Repr. of 1868 ed. 18.00 (ISBN 0-405-04950-1). Ayer Co Pubs.

PHOTOGRAPHY–RESEARCH

De Saint-Victor, Niepce. Recherches Photographiques. Bunnell, Peter C. & Sobieszek, Robert A., eds. LC 76-23058. (Sources of Modern Photography Ser.). (Fr.). 1979. Repr. of 1855 ed. lib. bdg. 17.00x (ISBN 0-405-09622-4). Ayer Co Pubs.

PHOTOGRAPHY–RETOUCHING

Lahue, Kalton C. Photo Retouching & Restoration. LC 78-78395. (Photography How-to Ser.). (Illus.). 1979. pap. 4.50 (ISBN 0-8227-4034-6). Petersen Pub.

Ourdan, J. P. The Art of Retouching by Burrows & Colton. LC 72-9187. (The Literature of Photography Ser.). Repr. of 1880 ed. 14.00 (ISBN 0-405-04898-X). Ayer Co Pubs.

Podracky, John. Photographic Retouching & Airbrush Techniques. (Illus.). 1980. text ed. 19.95 (ISBN 0-13-665257-3). P-H.

PHOTOGRAPHY–SCIENTIFIC APPLICATIONS

see also Astronomical Photography; Optics–Atlases; Photographic Interpretation; Photography, High-Speed; Photography, Submarine; Photomicrography; Radiography; Technical Illustration

Blaker, Alfred A. Handbook for Scientific Photography. LC 77-24661. (Illus.). 319p. 1977. text ed. 35.95 (ISBN 0-7167-0285-1). W H Freeman.

Darius, Jon. Beyond Vision: One Hundred Historic Scientific Photographs. LC 84-4405. (Illus.). 1984. 29.95 (ISBN 0-19-853245-8). Oxford U Pr.

Dowdell, John & Zakia, Richard. Zone Systemizer. LC 73-87272. 63p. 1973. 14.95 (ISBN 0-87100-040-7). Morgan.

Draper, John W. Scientific Memoirs. LC 72-9194. (The Literature of Photography Ser.). Repr. of 1878 ed. 32.00 (ISBN 0-405-04904-8). Ayer Co Pubs.

George, J. D., et al, eds. Underwater Photography & Television for Scientists. (Illus.). 250p. 1985. 26.95 (ISBN 0-19-854141-4). Oxford U Pr.

Michaelis, Anthony R. Research Films in Biology, Anthropology, Psychology & Medicine. 1955. 76.50 (ISBN 0-12-493350-5). Acad Pr.

Morton, Richard A., ed. Photography for the Scientist. 2nd ed. 1985. 98.00 (ISBN 0-12-508370-X). Acad Pr.

Newman, A. A., ed. Photographic Techniques in Scientific Research, Vol. 2. 1976. 77.50 (ISBN 0-12-517960-X). Acad Pr.

--Photographic Techniques in Scientific Research, Vol. 3. 1979. 90.00 (ISBN 0-12-517963-4). Acad Pr.

Ninth Biennial Workshop on Color Aerial Photography in the Plant Sciences & Related Fields. 204p. 1984. pap. 28.00 (ISBN 0-937294-56-X); pap. 21.00 members' price. ASP & RS.

Rogers, Garry F., et al, eds. Bibliography of Repeat Photography for Evaluating Landscape Change. (Illus.). 176p. 1984. 12.50x (ISBN 0-87480-239-3). U of Utah Pr.

Society of Photographic Scientists & Engineers. International Symposium on Still Camera Technology: Advanced Printing of Paper Summaries, March 21-23,1983, the Dunes Hotel & Country Club, Las Vegas, Nevada. pap. 20.00 (ISBN 0-317-28846-6, 2020629). Bks Demand UMI.

Zweifel, Frances W. Handbook of Biological Illustration. LC 61-19734. (Orig.). 1961. pap. 6.00x (ISBN 0-226-99699-9, P510, Phoen). U of Chicago Pr.

PHOTOGRAPHY–SENSITOMETRY

see Photographic Sensitometry

PHOTOGRAPHY–SPECIAL EFFECTS

see also Photography, Trick

Carroll, Don & Carroll, Marie. Focus on Special Effects: Locating Pictures That Exist Only in Your Mind. (Illus.). 184p. 1982. 24.95 (ISBN 0-8174-3885-8, Amphoto). Watson-Guptill.

Langford, Michael. The Book of Special Effects Photography. LC 81-82591. (Illus.). 168p. 1982. 16.50 (ISBN 0-394-52107-2). Knopf.

--The Book of Special Effects Photography. 168p. 1982. 39.00x (ISBN 0-85223-209-8, Pub. by Ebury Pr England). State Mutual Bk.

Moser, Lida. Amphoto Guide to Special Effects. (Illus.). 168p. 1980. (Amphoto); pap. 7.95 (ISBN 0-8174-3524-7). Watson-Guptill.

Stensvold, Mike. In Camera Special Effects. (Masterclass Photography Ser.). (Illus.). 176p. 1983. 12.95 (ISBN 0-13-453803-X). P-H.

--In-Camera Special Effects. 176p. 1985. 9.95 (ISBN 0-13-453795-5). P-H.

PHOTOGRAPHY–STUDIOS AND DARK ROOMS

Here are entered works on the construction and physical layout of studios and dark rooms.

Bluffield, Robert. Making & Managing a Photographic Studio in Britain. (Illus.). 144p. 1982. 17.95 (ISBN 0-7153-8245-4). David & Charles.

Coote, Jack H. Monochrome Darkroom Practice. (Illus.). 320p. 1982. 31.50 (ISBN 0-240-51061-5); pap. 13.95 (ISBN 0-240-51700-8). Focal Pr.

Curtin, Dennis. Into Your Darkroom: Step-by-Step. (Illus.). 96p. (Orig.). 1981. pap. 12.95 (ISBN 0-930764-24-2). Curtin & London.

Curtin, Dennis & DeMaio, Joe. The Darkroom Handbook: A Complete Guide to the Best Design, Construction & Equipment. (Illus.). 1979. 17.95 (ISBN 0-930764-08-0); pap. 12.95 (ISBN 0-930764-06-4). Curtin & London.

Duren, Lista & McDonald, Billy. Build Your Own Home Darkroom. (Illus.). 160p. 1982. pap. 14.95 (ISBN 0-930764-26-9). Curtin & London.

--Building Your Own Home Darkroom Step-by-Step. 1982. pap. 14.95 (ISBN 0-442-22089-8). Van Nos Reinhold.

Eastman Kodak Company. Photolab Design. 52p. 1977. pap. 2.00 (ISBN 0-87985-098-1, K-13). Eastman Kodak.

How to Use Your Darkroom. 1981. 2.50 (ISBN 0-88284-145-9). Alfred Pub.

Robinson, Henry P. The Studio: And What to Do in It. LC 72-9231. (The Literature of Photography Ser.). Repr. of 1891 ed. 15.00 (ISBN 0-405-04937-4). Ayer Co Pubs.

Spitzing, Gunter. The Darkroom. (Illus.). 396p. 1984. cancelled (ISBN 0-240-51219-7). Focal Pr.

Studio. rev. ed. (Life Library of Photography). (Illus.). 1982. 15.95 (ISBN 0-8094-4416-X). Time-Life.

Taylor, Herb, et al. Black & White Home Developing & Printing. LC 81-71226. (Modern Photo Guides). (Illus.). 120p. (Orig.). 1982. pap. 7.95 (ISBN 0-385-18164-7). Avalon Comm.

PHOTOGRAPHY–SUPPLIES

see Photography–Apparatus and Supplies

PHOTOGRAPHY, AERIAL

see also Aerial Photography in Anthropology; Aerial Photography in Archaeology; Aerial Photography in Geography; Aerial Photography in Geology; Photographic Interpretation; Photographic Reconnaissance Systems; Remote Sensing

American Society of Photogrammetry, ed. Eighth Biennial Workshop on Color Aerial Photography in the Plant Sciences & Related Fields. 167p. pap. 16.00 (17.00 member) (ISBN 0-937294-34-9). ASP & RS.

Brock, G. C. Physical Aspects of Aerial Photography. (Illus.). 11.25 (ISBN 0-8446-1743-1). Peter Smith.

Church, Earl & Quinn, Alfred O. Elements of Photogrammetry. rev. ed. (Illus.). 1948. 8.95x (ISBN 0-8156-2002-0). Syracuse U Pr.

Eastman Kodak Company Editors. Kodak Data for Aerial Photography (M-29) 5th ed. LC 75-44815. (Illus.). 136p. 1982. pap. 15.00 (ISBN 0-87985-298-4). Eastman Kodak.

Gousen, Doeko. Aerial Photo Interpretation in Soil Survey. (Soils Bulletins: No. 6). (Eng., Fr. & Span.). 116p. (3rd. Printing 1976). 1967. pap. 8.50 (ISBN 92-5-100105-7, F1151, FAO). Unipub.

Little, Robert T. Astrophotography: A Step-by-Step Approach. (Illus.). 128p. 1985. 19.95x (ISBN 0-02-948980-6). Macmillan.

Paine, David P. Aerial Photography & Image Interpretation for Resource Management. LC 81-4287. 571p. 1981. 40.50 (ISBN 0-471-01857-0). Wiley.

Schneider, Sigfried. Luftbild und Luftbildinterpretation. (Lehrbuch der Allgemeinen Geographie Ser.: Vol. 11). (Illus.). xvi, 532p. 1974. 78.00x (ISBN 3-11-002123-4). De Gruyter.

Smith, Frank K. How to Take Great Photos from Airplanes. (Modern Aircraft Ser). (Illus.). 1978. pap. 8.95 (ISBN 0-8306-2251-9, 2251). TAB Bks.

Steward, Robard H. Methods of Satellite Oceanography. LC 83-18017. 1985. 32.50x (ISBN 0-520-04226-3). U of Cal Pr.

Strandberg, Carl H. Aerial Discovery Manual. LC 67-19945. (Photographic Science & Technology & the Graphic Arts Ser.). 249p. 1967. pap. 42.95x (ISBN 0-471-83170-0, Pub. by Wiley-Interscience). Wiley.

PHOTOGRAPHY, APPLIED

see also Photocopying Processes

Dennis, Ervin A. Applied Photography. LC 84-23047. 512p. 1985. text ed. 18.60 (ISBN 0-8273-2292-5); instr's. guide 4.80 (ISBN 0-8273-2294-1); student manual 6.80 (ISBN 0-8273-2293-3). Delmar.

PHOTOGRAPHY, ASTRONOMICAL

see Astronomical Photography

PHOTOGRAPHY, BIOLOGICAL

see Photography, Submarine; Photography of Animals; Photography of Birds; Photography of Insects; Photography of Plants; Photomicrography

PHOTOGRAPHY, CLOSE-UP

see also Macrophotography

Eastman Kodak Company, ed. KW Twenty-Two, Close-Up Photography. (Kodak Workshop Ser.). (Illus.). 96p. Date not set. pap. 8.95 (ISBN 0-87985-301-8). Eastman Kodak.

Hawken, William R. Close-up Photography. (Illus.). 132p. (Orig.). 1982. pap. 10.95 (ISBN 0-930764-33-1). Curtin & London.

PHOTOGRAPHY, FLASH-LIGHT

see also Photography, High-Speed

Bailey, James. How to Select & Use an Electronic Flash. (Illus.). 1983. pap. 11.95 (ISBN 0-89586-144-5). H P Bks.

Lefkowitz, Lester. Electronic Flash (KW-12) LC 81-66623. (Kodak Workshop Ser.). (Illus.). 96p. 1981. pap. 8.95 (ISBN 0-87985-271-2). Eastman Kodak.

Taylor, Herb, ed. Flash Photography. LC 82-70158. (Modern Photo Guide Ser.). (Illus.). 120p. 1982. pap. 7.95 (ISBN 0-385-18150-7). Doubleday.

Taylor, Herb, et al. Flash Photography. LC 82-70158. (Modern Photo Guides). (Illus.). 120p. (Orig.). 1982. pap. 7.95 (ISBN 0-385-18150-7). Avalon Comm.

PHOTOGRAPHY, HIGH-SPEED

Dalton, Stephen. Split Second: The World of High-Speed Photography. (Illus.). 144p. 1985. 17.95 (ISBN 0-88162-063-7, Pub. by Salem Hse Ltd). Merrimack Pub Cir.

Dubovik, A. S. Photographic Recording of High-Speed Processes. 1968. 72.00 (ISBN 0-08-012017-2). Pergamon.

High-Speed Photography. 60p. 1981. pap. 6.75 (ISBN 0-87985-165-1, G44). Eastman Kodak.

Riper, Walker V., et al. Nature Photography with High Speed Flash. (Museum Pictorial Ser.: No. 5). 1952. pap. 1.10 (ISBN 0-916278-34-4). Denver Mus Natl Hist.

PHOTOGRAPHY, INDUSTRIAL

Martin, Derald. Professional Industrial Photography. (Illus.). 176p. 1980. 19.95 (ISBN 0-8174-4008-9, Amphoto). Watson-Guptill.

Super-Eight Photographic Surveillance. 1972. pap. 1.00 (ISBN 0-87985-134-1, P233). Eastman Kodak.

PHOTOGRAPHY, INFRA-RED

Ciesla, William M., intro. by. Color Aerial Photography in the Pl Sc & Related Fields: Seventh Biennial Workshop. 255p. 1979. pap. 12.00 (7.00 member) (ISBN 0-937294-11-X). ASP & RS.

Eastman Kodak Company. Applied Infrared Photography. LC 81-65754. 84p. 1981. pap. text ed. 6.00 (ISBN 0-87985-288-7, M-28). Eastman Kodak.

Kodak Infrared Films. (Illus.). 1981. pap. text ed. 3.25 (ISBN 0-87985-293-3, N-17). Eastman Kodak.

Lillesand, Thomas M., intro. by. Thermosense I: Proceedings. 244p. 1978. pap. 10.00 (ISBN 0-937294-13-6); pap. 6.00 members. ASP & RS.

Paduano, Joseph. The Art of Infrared Photography: A Comprehensive Guide to the Use of Black & White Infrared Film. LC 84-61014. (Illus.). 80p. 1984. pap. 12.95 (ISBN 0-87100-238-8, 2238). Morgan.

PHOTOGRAPHY, KIRLIAN

see Kirlian Photography

PHOTOGRAPHY, LENSLESS

see Holography

PHOTOGRAPHY, NIGHT

Here are entered Outdoor views taken at night. Not to be confused with Photography–Artifical Light.

Hepworth, T. C. Evening Work for Amateur Photographers. LC 72-9207. (The Literature of Photography Ser.). Repr. of 1890 ed. 18.00 (ISBN 0-405-04916-1). Ayer Co Pubs.

Taylor, Herb, ed. Natural Light & Night Photography. LC 81-71223. (Modern Photo Guide Ser.). (Illus.). 120p. 1982. pap. 7.95 (ISBN 0-385-18156-6). Doubleday.

Taylor, Herb, et al. Natural Light & Night Photography. LC 81-71223. (Modern Photo Guides). (Illus.). 120p. (Orig.). 1982. pap. 7.95 (ISBN 0-385-18156-6). Avalon Comm.

PHOTOGRAPHY, SUBMARINE

Cousteau, Jacques-Yves & Dumas, Frederic. The Silent World. LC 52-5431. 1953. 15.00i (ISBN 0-06-010890-8, HarpT). Har-Row.

Diamondis, Peter J. Underwater Photography Now. LC 83-136151. (Illus.). 154p. 1983. 14.95 (ISBN 0-9612110-0-8). P J Diamondis.

George, J. D., et al, eds. Underwater Photography & Television for Scientists. (Illus.). 250p. 1985. 26.95 (ISBN 0-19-854141-4). Oxford U Pr.

Greenberg, Jerry. Manfish with a Camera. (Illus.). 48p. pap. 2.50 (ISBN 0-686-75253-8). Banyan Bks.

Hall, Howard. Howard Hall's Guide to Successful Underwater Photography. (Illus.). 192p. (Orig.). 1982. pap. text ed. 14.95 (ISBN 0-932248-03-9). Marcor Pub.

Hersey, John B., ed. Deep-Sea Photography. LC 66-16038. (Oceanographic Studies: No. 3). (Illus.). 368p. 1968. 35.00x (ISBN 0-8018-0270-9). Johns Hopkins.

Riefenstahl, Leni. Coral Gardens. LC 78-2163. (Illus.). 1978. 29.95i (ISBN 0-06-013591-3, HarpT). Har-Row.

Rosenthal, Beverly. The Amazing World of Underwater Photography. LC 83-60110. (Strange but True Ser.). 1983. 10.00 (ISBN 0-382-06689-8). Silver.

Schulke, Flip. Underwater Photography for Everyone. 1978. 17.95 (ISBN 0-13-936450-1). P-H.

Smith, Paul F., ed. Underwater Photography: Scientific & Engineering Applications. LC 84-2279. 1984. 44.50 (ISBN 0-442-27962-0). Van Nos Reinhold.

Society of Photo-Optical Instrumentation Engineers, Seminar. Underwater Photo-Optical Instrumentation Applications, 1968: Proceedings, Vol. 12. 28.00 (ISBN 0-89252-015-9). Photo-Optical.

Turner, John. Underwater Photography. (Illus.). 136p. 1982. pap. 30.50 (ISBN 0-240-51122-0). Focal Pr.

Wallin, Douglas. Basics of Underwater Photography. (Illus.). 128p. 1975. 7.95 (ISBN 0-8174-0578-X, Amphoto). Watson-Guptill.

PHOTOGRAPHY, TRICK

see also Cinematography, Trick; Photography–Special Effects

Taylor, Herb, ed. Trick Photography. LC 81-71309. (Modern Photo Guide Ser.). (Illus.). 120p. 1982. pap. 7.95 (ISBN 0-385-18154-X). Doubleday.

Taylor, Herb, et al. Trick Photography. LC 81-71309. (Modern Photo Guides). (Illus.). 120p. (Orig.). 1982. pap. 7.95 (ISBN 0-385-18154-X). Avalon Comm.

PHOTOGRAPHY IN INDUSTRY

see Photography, Industrial

PHOTOGRAPHY OF ANIMALS

Cloudsley-Thompson, John, et al. Nightwatch: The Natural World from Dusk to Dawn. (Illus.). 1983. 24.95 (ISBN 0-87196-271-3). Facts on File.

Dickinson, Darol. Photographing Livestock: The Complete Guide. LC 79-88468. (Illus.). pap. 7.95 (ISBN 0-87358-200-4). Northland.

Ghorpade, M. Y. Sunlight & Shadows. (Illus.). 128p. 1983. 24.00 (ISBN 0-575-03283-9, Gollancz England). David & Charles.

Guilfoyle, Ann & Rayfield, Susan. Wildlife Photography. (Illus.). 176p. 1982. 24.95 (ISBN 0-8174-6417-4, Amphoto). Watson-Guptill.

Marchington, John & Clay, Anthony. An Introduction to Bird & Wildlife Photography in Still & in Movie. (Illus.). 1974. 14.00 (ISBN 0-571-10171-2). Transatlantic.

Preston-Mafham, Ken. Practical Wildlife Photography. LC 80-40792. (Practical Photography Ser.). (Illus.). 168p. 1982. 24.95 (ISBN 0-240-51081-X). Focal Pr.

Spero, James. North American Mammmals: A Photographic Album for Artists & Designers. 1980. 11.75 (ISBN 0-8446-5667-4). Peter Smith.

Warner, L. J. Mammal Photography & Observation: A Practical Guide. 1979. 24.00 (ISBN 0-12-735650-9). Acad Pr.

PHOTOGRAPHY OF ART

Shulman, Julius. The Photography of Architecture & Design: The Photography Buildings, Interiors, & the Visual Arts. (Illus.). 1977. 27.50 (ISBN 0-8230-7429-3, Whitney Lib). Watson-Guptill.

PHOTOGRAPHY OF BIRDS

Cruickshank, Allan D. Cruickshank's Photographs of Birds of America. LC 77-70078. (Illus.). 1977. pap. 7.95 (ISBN 0-486-23497-5). Dover.

Line, Les & Russell, Franklin. The Audubon Society Book of Wild Birds. LC 76-17306. (Audubon Society Ser.). (Illus.). 1976. 50.00 (ISBN 0-8109-0661-9). Abrams.

Marchington, John & Clay, Anthony. An Introduction to Bird & Wildlife Photography in Still & in Movie. (Illus.). 1974. 14.00 (ISBN 0-571-10171-2). Transatlantic.

Morris, Frank T. Finches of Australia: A Folio. (Illus.). 124p. 65.00 (ISBN 0-7018-1000-9). Eastview.

Warham, John. Technique of Bird Photography. 4th ed. (Illus.). 304p. 1983. 39.95 (ISBN 0-240-51084-4). Focal Pr.

PHOTOGRAPHY OF INSECTS

Lindsley, P. E. Insect Photography for the Amateur. 52p. 1977. 21.00x (ISBN 0-686-75580-4, Pub. by Amateur Entomol Soc). State Mutual Bk.

PHOTOGRAPHY OF PLANTS

American Society of Photogrammetry, ed. Eighth Biennial Workshop on Color Aerial Photography in the Plant Sciences & Related Fields. 167p. pap. 16.00 (17.00 member) (ISBN 0-937294-34-9). ASP & RS.

Fell, Derek. How to Photograph Flowers, Plants & Landscapes. LC 80-82571. (Photography Ser.). (Orig.). 1980. pap. 7.95 (ISBN 0-89586-068-6). H P Bks.

Fitch, Charles M. Rodale Book of Garden Photography. (Illus.). 176p. 1981. pap. 12.95 (ISBN 0-8174-5781-X, Amphoto). Watson-Guptill.

PHOTOGRAVURE

see also Photomechanical Processes

Bunnell, Peter C., ed. Nonsilver Printing Processes: Four Selections, 1886-1927. LC 72-9221. (The Literature of Photography Ser.). 22.00 (ISBN 0-405-04928-5); pap. 4.50 (ISBN 0-685-32643-8). Ayer Co Pubs.

Denison, Herbert. A Treatise on Photogravure. Lyons, Nathan, ed. LC 73-22263. (Visual Studies Reprint Ser.). 1974. pap. 6.50 (ISBN 0-87992-004-1). Light Impressions.

--A Treatise on Photogravure. Lyons, Nathan, ed. (Reprint & Research Ser.). (Illus.). 142p. 1974. 11.95 (ISBN 0-87992-005-X); pap. 6.50 (ISBN 0-87992-004-1). Visual Studies.

PHOTOIONIZATION OF GASES

Lawley, K. P., ed. Lawley: Photodissociation & Photoionisation. (Advances in Chemical Physics Ser.). 1985. 64.95 (ISBN 0-471-90211-X). Wiley.

Wuilleumier, F. J., ed. Photoionization & Other Probes of Many Electron Interactions. LC 76-16512. (NATO ASI Series B, Physics: Vol. 18). 472p. 1976. 75.00 (ISBN 0-306-35718-6, Plenum Pr). Plenum Pub.

PHOTOLITHOGRAPHY

see also Photomechanical Processes

Swerdlow, Robert M. The Step-By-Step Guide to Photo-Offset Lithography. (Illus.). 400p. 1982. 27.95 (ISBN 0-13-846584-3). P-H.

PHOTOLYSIS (CHEMISTRY)

see Photochemistry

PHOTOMACROGRAPHY

see Macrophotography

PHOTOMECHANICAL PROCESSES

see also Electrophotography; Photocopying Processes; Photoengraving; Photolithography; Phototypesetting

Bruyninckx, Jozef. Phototypography & Graphic Arts Dimension Control Photography. LC 74-115394. (Illus.). 150p. 1976. 18.25 (ISBN 0-911126-03-1). Perfect Graphic.

Eastman Kodak Company, ed. More Special Effects for Reproduction. LC 76-52137. (Illus.). 1977. pap. 12.00 (ISBN 0-87985-188-0, Q-171). Eastman Kodak.

Frieser, Hellmut. Photographic Information Recording. LC 75-20097. Tr. of Photographische Informationsaufzeichnung. 592p. 1975. 106.95 (ISBN 0-470-28117-0). Halsted Pr.

Yule, John A. Principles of Color Reproduction. LC 66-26764. 411p. 1967. 59.95x (ISBN 0-471-98030-7, Pub. by Wiley-Interscience). Wiley.

PHOTOMETRY

see also Color; Flame; Photometry; Light; Optics; Spectrophotometry

American Association for the Advancement of Science Staff. Astronomical Photoelectric Photometry. Wood, Frank B., ed. LC 53-12745. pap. 37.30 (ISBN 0-317-07843-7, 2000204). Bks Demand UMI.

Calder, A. B. Photometric Methods of Analysis. (Illus.). 1969. 43.50 (ISBN 0-9960017-0-0, Pub. by A Hilger England). Heyden.

Egan. Photometry & Polarization in Remote Sensing. 480p. 1985. 68.00 (ISBN 0-444-00892-6). Elsevier.

Hall, Douglas S. & Genet, Russell M. Photoelectric Photometry of Variable Stars. 2nd ed. 300p. 1984. pap. 23.95 (ISBN 0-911351-04-3). Fairborn Observ.

IES Guide for the Selection, Care & Use of Electrical Instruments in the Photometric Laboratory. 12p. 5.50 (ISBN 0-686-47885-1, LM-28); member 3.25. Illum Eng.

IES Practical Guide to Photometry. 8.00 (ISBN 0-686-47888-6, LM-36). Illum Eng.

Photometric Measurements of HID Lamps. (Measurement & Testing Guides Ser.). 1975. 4.50 (ISBN 0-686-96322-9, LM-51); members 2.00 (ISBN 0-686-99765-4). Illum Eng.

Photometric Measurements of Roadway Sign Installations. (Measurement & Testing Guides Ser.). 1976. member 2.00 (ISBN 0-686-96326-1, LM-52); non-member 4.00 (ISBN 0-686-99766-2). Illum Eng.

Photometric Testing of Indoor Fluorescent Luminaires. (Measurement & Testing Guides Ser.). 1972. 4.00 (ISBN 0-686-96289-3, LM-41); members 2.00 (ISBN 0-686-99755-7). Illum Eng.

Photometric Testing: Outdoor Fluorescent Luminares. (Measurement & Testing Guides Ser.). 1975. member 2.75 (ISBN 0-686-96231-1, LM-10); non-member 5.50 (ISBN 0-686-99740-9). Illum Eng.

Piller, H. Microscope Photometry. LC 76-58893. 1977. 41.00 (ISBN 0-387-08094-5). Springer-Verlag.

Practical Guide to Photometry. (Measurement & Testing Guides Ser.). 1971. 8.00 (ISBN 0-686-96270-2, LM-36); members 4.00 (ISBN 0-686-99751-4). Illum Eng.

Predetermination of Contrast Rendition Factors for the Calculations of ESI. (Measurement & Testing Guides Ser.). 1973. 9.00 (ISBN 0-686-96280-X, LM-39); member 4.50 (ISBN 0-686-99753-0). Illum Eng.

Sawicki, Eugene. Photometric Organic Analysis: Basic Principles with Applications. LC 70-116768. (Chemical Analysis Ser.: Vol. 31). pap. 160.00 (ISBN 0-317-08871-8, 2006491). Bks Demand UMI.

Sawicki, Eugene & Sawicki, Carole R. Aldehydes-Photometric Analysis, 5 vols. (Analysis of Organic Materials Ser.). 1975. Vol. 1. 55.00 (ISBN 0-12-620501-9); Vol. 2. 59.00 (ISBN 0-12-620502-7); Vol. 3, 1976. 58.00 (ISBN 0-12-620503-5); Vol. 4. 1977. 55.00 (ISBN 0-12-620504-3); Vol. 5. 85.00 (ISBN 0-12-620505-1). Acad Pr.

Snell, Forster D. Photometric & Fluorometric Methods of Analysis: Metals, 2 pts. LC 77-25039. 2192p. 1978. Set. 395.95 (ISBN 0-471-81014-2, Pub. by Wiley-Interscience). Wiley.

Svehla & Wilson. Photometric Methods in Inorganic Trace Analysis. (Wilson & Wilson's Comprehensive Analytical Chemistry Ser.: Vol. 20). 1985. 100.00 (ISBN 0-444-99588-9). Elsevier.

Wolpert, Robert C. & Genet, Russell M. Advances in Photoelectric Photometry, Vol. 1. LC 82-84767. 240p. (Orig.). 1983. pap. 23.95 (ISBN 0-911351-01-9). Fairborn Observ.

Wolpert, Robert C. & Genet, Russell M., eds. Advances in Photoelectric Photometry, Vol. 2. 200p. (Orig.). 1984. pap. 23.95 (ISBN 0-911351-05-1). Fairborn Observ.

PHOTOMETRY, ASTRONOMICAL

Genet, Russell M., ed. Solar System Photometry Handbook. LC 83-21382. (Illus.). 224p. 1983. pap. text ed. 17.95 (ISBN 0-943396-03-4). Willmann-Bell.

Ghedini, Silvano. Software for Photometric Astronomy. LC 82-8574. (Illus.). 224p. 1982. pap. text ed. 26.95 (ISBN 0-943396-00-X). Willmann-Bell.

Golay, M. Introduction to Astronomical Photometry. Thornley, G. J., tr. from Fr. LC 73-91430. (Astrophysics & Space Science Library: No. 41). 1974. lib. bdg. 63.00 (ISBN 90-277-0428-7, Pub. by Reidel Holland). Kluwer Academic.

PHOTOMICROGRAPHY

see also Microcinematography; Microradiography; Microscope and Microscopy; Optics–Atlases; Photography–Scientific Applications; Stereology

PHYLLOSCOPUS

Ticehurst, Claud. Systematic Review of the Genus Phylloscopus, Willow Warblers or Leaf-Warblers. (Illus.). Repr. of 1938 ed. 30.00 (ISBN 0-384-60540-0). Johnson Repr.

PHYLLOTAXIS

Williams, R. F. The Shoot Apex & Leaf Growth. (Illus.). 280p. 1975. 44.50 (ISBN 0-521-20453-4). Cambridge U Pr.

PHYLOGENY

see also Evolution; Origin of Species; Paleontology

Arvey, M. Dale. Phylogeny of the Waxwings & Allied Birds. (Museum Ser.: Vol. 3, No. 3). 58p. 1951. pap. 3.00 (ISBN 0-317-04583-0). U of KS Mus Nat Hist.

Brooks, Daniel R., et al. Principles & Methods of Phylogenetic Systematics: A Cladistics Workbook. (Special Publication Ser.: No. 12). (Illus.). v, 92p. (Orig.). 1984. pap. 6.50 (ISBN 0-89338-022-9). U of KS Mus Nat Hist.

Cracraft, Joel & Eldredge, Niles, eds. Phylogenetic Analysis & Paleonology. LC 78-31404. (Illus.). 256p. 1979. 39.00x (ISBN 0-231-04692-8); pap. 14.00x (ISBN 0-231-04693-6). Columbia U Pr.

Eldredge, Niles & Cracraft, Joel. Phylogenetic Patterns & the Evolutionary Process: Method & Theory in Comparative Biology. LC 80-375. 349p. 1984. pap. 15.00x (ISBN 0-317-13103-6). Columbia U Pr.

Gould, Stephen J. Ontogeny & Phylogeny. 1977. 25.00x (ISBN 0-674-63940-5, Belknap Pr). Harvard U Pr.

--Ontogeny & Phylogeny. 520p. 1985. pap. 8.95 (ISBN 0-674-63941-3, Belknap Pr). Harvard U Pr.

Gregory, William K. Evolution Emerging: A Survey of Changing Patterns from Primeval Life to Man, 2 vols. LC 73-17822. (Natural Sciences in America Ser.). (Illus.). 1808p. 1974. Repr. Set. 122.00x (ISBN 0-405-05738-5); 61.00 ea. Vol.1 (ISBN 0-405-05739-3). Vol.2 (ISBN 0-405-05740-7). Ayer Co Pubs.

Jean Piaget Foundation Archives, Geneva. Phylogeny & Ontogeny. (Human Development Journal: Vol. 27, no. 5-6). (Illus.). vi, 134p. 1984. pap. 16.75 (ISBN 3-8055-3904-5). S Karger.

Jope, Charlene A. Organismic & Environmental Laboratory Manual. 144p. 1981. pap. text ed. 9.95 (ISBN 0-8403-2322-0). Kendall-Hunt.

Margulis, Lynn & Schwartz, Karlene V. Five Kingdoms: An Illustrated Guide to the Phyla of Life on Earth. LC 81-7845. (Illus.). 338p. 1982. text ed. 28.95x (ISBN 0-7167-1212-1). W H Freeman.

Wiley, Edward O. Phylogenetics: Theory & Practice of Phylogenetic Systematics. LC 81-5080. 439p. 1981. 45.50x (ISBN 0-471-05975-7, Pub. by Wiley-Interscience). Wiley.

PHYLOGENY (BOTANY)

Eldredge, Niles & Cracraft, Joel. Phylogenetic Patterns & the Evolutionary Process. LC 80-375. (Illus.). 1980. 42.00x (ISBN 0-231-03802-X); pap. 15.00. Columbia U Pr.

Hennig, Willi. Insect Phylogeny. LC 80-40853. 514p. 1981. 89.95 (ISBN 0-471-27848-3, Pub. by Wiley-Interscience). Wiley.

--Phylogenetic Systematics. Davis & Zangerl, trs. LC 78-31969. 280p. 1979. Repr. of 1966 ed. 22.50x (ISBN 0-252-00745-X). U of Ill Pr.

Joysey, K. A. & Friday, A. E., eds. Problems of Phylogenetic Reconstruction. (Systematics Assoc. Special Volume: No. 21). 1982. 66.00 (ISBN 0-12-391250-4). Acad Pr.

Phytochemical Society. Phytochemical Phylogeny: Proceedings. Harborne, J. B., ed. 1970. 61.50 (ISBN 0-12-324666-0). Acad Pr.

PHYLOGEOGRAPHY–MAPS

see also Vegetation Mapping

Moore, D. M., ed. Green Planet: The Story of Plant Life on Earth. LC 82-4287. (Illus.). 288p. 1982. 29.95 (ISBN 0-521-24610-5). Cambridge U Pr.

PHYSICAL ANTHROPOLOGY

see also Anthropometry; Craniology; Fossil Man; Human Biology; Human Evolution; Human Genetics; Man–Influence of Environment; Primates; Race

Abdushelishvili, M. G., et al. Contributions to the Physical Anthropology of Central Asia & the Caucasus. Field, Henry, ed. Heath, Barbara, tr. LC 79-158217. (Harvard University, Peabody Museum of Archaeology & Ethnology. Russian Translation Ser.: Vol. 3, No. 2). 1968. lib. bdg. 67.50 (ISBN 0-404-52645-4). AMS Pr.

Ankel-Simons, Friderun. A Survey of Living Primates & Their Anatomy. 288p. 1983. pap. text ed. write for info. (ISBN 0-02-303500-5). Macmillan.

Baker, P. T., ed. The Biology of High-Altitude Peoples. LC 76-50311. (International Biological Programme Ser.: No. 14). (Illus.). 1978. 79.50 (ISBN 0-521-21523-4). Cambridge U Pr.

Barrett, M., et al. Occasional Papers in Human Biology, Vol. I. 1979. pap. text ed. 11.50x (ISBN 0-391-00999-0). Humanities.

Bennett, Kenneth A. Fundamentals of Biological Anthropology. 550p. 1979. text ed. write for info. (ISBN 0-697-07553-2). Wm C Brown.

Birdsell, J. B., et al, eds. Occasional Papers in Human Biology, Vol. 2. (Illus.). 1979. pap. text ed. 13.00x (ISBN 0-391-00998-2). Humanities.

Brace, C. Loring & Metress, James F., eds. Man in Evolutionary Perspective. LC 72-14184. Repr. of 1973 ed. 121.50 (ISBN 0-8357-9926-3, 2012618). Bks Demand UMI.

Bunak, Viktor V., et al. Contributions to the Physical Anthropology of the Soviet Union. Howells, William W., tr. LC 60-1045. (Harvard University. Peabody Museum of Archaeology & Ethnology. Russian Translation Ser.: Vol. 1, Pt. 2). Repr. of 1960 ed. lib. bdg. 32.50 (ISBN 0-404-52642-X). AMS Pr.

Campbell, Bernard G. Humankind Emerging. 4th ed. 1985. pap. text ed. 23.95 (ISBN 0-316-12553-9); tchr's. ed. avail. (ISBN 0-316-12554-7). Little.

Chapple, Eliot D. The Biological Foundations of Individuality & Culture. LC 79-23284. 388p. (Orig.). 1980. lib. bdg. 19.50 (ISBN 0-89874-041-X). Krieger.

Delson, Eric. Ancestors: The Hard Evidence. 378p. 1985. 49.50 (ISBN 0-8451-0249-4). A R Liss.

Duverus, Delamer. Somatic Reasoning: Teleological Entelechies Patterns in Time. 2nd ed. 36p. (Orig.). 1981. pap. 3.50 (ISBN 0-918700-11-6). Duverus Pub.

Fishberg, Maurice. Materials for the Physical Anthropology of the Eastern European Jews. LC 6-2111. (American Anthro. Association Memoirs). 1905. 14.00 (ISBN 0-527-00500-2). Kraus Repr.

Gjessing, Lieve. Contribution to the Somatology of Periodic Catatonia. Marshall, H., tr. 1976. text ed. 89.00 (ISBN 0-08-015650-9). Pergamon.

Greulich, William W. Somatic & Endocrine Studies of Puberal & Adolescent Boys. (SRCD: Vol. 7, No. 3). 1942. pap. 16.00 (ISBN 0-527-01524-5). Kraus Repr.

Harrison, G. A., et al. Human Biology: An Introduction to Human Evolution, Variation, Growth, & Ecology. 2nd ed. (Illus.). 1977. pap. text ed. 18.95x (ISBN 0-19-857165-8). Oxford U Pr.

Hiorns, R. W., ed. Demographic Patterns in Developed Societies. (Symposia of the Society for the Study of Human Biology Ser.: Vol. 19). 240p. 1980. cancelled (ISBN 0-85066-185-4). Taylor & Francis.

Hooton, Ernest A. Indians of Pecos Pueblo. 1930. 200.00x (ISBN 0-686-83582-4). Elliots Bks.

Hunter, David E. & Whitten, Phillip, eds. Readings in Physical Anthropology & Archaeology. 1978. pap. text ed. 12.95 scp (ISBN 0-06-043023-0, HarpC); instr's manual avail. (ISBN 0-06-363027-3). Har-Row.

Iscan, M. Yasar, ed. A Topical Guide to the American Journal of Physical Anthropology 1964-1980, Vol. 22-53. LC 82-21696. 234p. 1983. 24.00 (ISBN 0-8451-0224-9). A R Liss.

Johnston, Francis E. Physical Anthropology. 496p. 1982. pap. text ed. write for info. (ISBN 0-697-07564-8); instrs.' manual avail. (ISBN 0-697-07566-4). Wm C Brown.

Jolly, Clifford & Plog, Fred. Physical Anthropology. 4th ed. 496p. 1986. pap. text ed. 18.95 (ISBN 0-394-35428-1, KnopfC). Knopf.

--Physical Anthropology & Archeology. 3rd ed. 1982. pap. text ed. 20.00 (ISBN 0-394-32672-5, KnopfC). Knopf.

Jones, F. W. Measurements & Landmarks in Physical Anthropology. (American Anthro. Association Memoirs). Repr. of 1929 ed. 11.00 (ISBN 0-527-02169-5). Kraus Repr.

Jordan, Paul. Face of the Past. LC 84-40355. (Illus.). 152p. 1985. 25.00x (ISBN 0-87663-453-6). Universe.

Joseph, N. R. Physicochemical Anthropology, Part I: Human Behavioral Structure. (Illus.). 1978. 33.25 (ISBN 3-8055-2793-4). S Karger.

Jurmain, et al. Understanding Physical Anthropology & Archaeology. (Illus.). 1981. pap. text ed. 21.95 (ISBN 0-8299-0388-7). West Pub.

Keleman, Stanley. Somatic Reality. 128p. 1979. 12.95 (ISBN 0-934320-00-4). Center Pr.

Kelemon, Stanley. Somatic Reality. LC 79-88485. 1979. 7.95 (ISBN 0-686-82345-1). Sci & Behavior.

Kelso, A. J. & Trevathan, Wenda. Physical Anthropology. 3rd ed. (Illus.). 352p. 1984. pap. text ed. 24.95 (ISBN 0-13-666298-6). P-H.

Kennedy, G. E. Paleoanthropology. 1980. 36.95 (ISBN 0-07-034046-3). McGraw.

Kennedy, William J. Adventures in Anthropology: A Reader in Physical Anthropology. (Illus.). 1977. pap. text ed. 15.95 (ISBN 0-8299-0094-2). West Pub.

Lasker, Gabriel W. & Tyzzer, Robert N. Physical Anthropology. 3rd ed. 1982. pap. text ed. 27.95 (ISBN 0-03-047551-1). HR&W.

Leakey, L. S. & Bestor, William S., eds. Adam or Ape: A Sourcebook of Discoveries about Early Man. 540p. cancelled (ISBN 0-87073-700-7); pap. text ed. cancelled (ISBN 0-87073-701-5). Schenkman Bks Inc.

Leigh, R. W. Dental Morphology & Pathology of Prehistoric Guam. (BMM Ser.). (Orig.). 1929. pap. 10.00 (ISBN 0-527-01668-3). Kraus Repr.

Lessa, W. A. Appraisal of Constitutional Typologies. LC 44-4905. (Amer Anthro Assn Memoirs). 1943. pap. 16.00 (ISBN 0-527-00561-4). Kraus Repr.

Livingstone, Frank B. Data on the Abnormal Hemoglobins & Glucose-Six-Phosphate Dehydrogenase Deficiency in Human Populations. (Technical Reports: No. 3). (Contribution 1 in Contributions in Human Biology). 1973. pap. 2.50x (ISBN 0-932206-12-3). U Mich Mus Anthro.

MacCurdy, G. G. Human Skulls from Gazelle Peninsula. (Anthropological Publications Ser.: Vol. 6 no.1). (Illus.). 21p. 1914. 5.00x (ISBN 0-686-24089-8). Univ Mus of U.

Montagu, M. F. An Introduction to Physical Anthropology. 3rd ed. (Illus.). 788p. 1960. photocopy ed. 69.50x (ISBN 0-398-04367-1). C C Thomas.

Nelson, Harry & Jurmain, Robert. Introduction to Physical Anthropology. (Illus.). 1979. pap. text ed. 18.50 (ISBN 0-8299-0240-6). West Pub.

--Introduction to Physical Anthropology. 3rd ed. (Illus.). 600p. 1985. pap. text ed. 22.95 (ISBN 0-314-85282-4). West Pub.

Osborne, Richard H. & Bennett, Kenneth A. Centers for Training in Physical Anthropology. 1979. pap. 3.00 (ISBN 0-686-36571-2). Am Anthro Assn.

Rock, J. F. A Monographic Study of the Hawaiian Species of the Tribe Lobelioideae, Family Campanulaceae. (BMB). (Orig.). 1919. 116.00 (ISBN 0-527-01651-9). Kraus Repr.

Sheldon, William. Atlas of Men: A Guide for Somatotyping the Adult Male of All Ages. 1970. Repr. of 1954 ed. 27.95x (ISBN 0-02-852160-9). Hafner.

Skinner, Mark F. & Sperber, Geoffrey H., eds. Atlas of Radiographs of Early Man. LC 82-13989. 360p. 1982. 70.00 (ISBN 0-8451-0218-4). A R Liss.

Spencer, Frank, ed. A History of American Physical Anthropology: 1930-1980. 1982. 44.50 (ISBN 0-12-656660-7). Acad Pr.

Steele, E. J. Somatic Selection & Adaptive Evolution. 100p. 1980. 30.00x (ISBN 0-686-69937-8, Pub. by Croom Helm England). State Mutual Bk.

Stein, Philip L. & Rowe, Bruce M. Physical Anthropology. 3rd ed. 512p. 1982. 27.95x (ISBN 0-07-061151-3). McGraw.

Trinkaus, Erick. The Slanidar Neandertals. LC 83-2488. (Monograph). 1983. 47.50 (ISBN 0-12-700550-1). Acad Pr.

Van Vark, G. & Howells, W. W., eds. Multivariate Statistical Methods in Physical Anthropology. 1984. lib. bdg. 61.00 (ISBN 90-2771-734-6, Pub. by Reidel Holland). Kluwer Academic.

Weiss, Mark L. & Mann, Alan E. Human Biology & Behavior: An Anthropological Perspective. 4th ed. 1985. text ed. 22.95 (ISBN 0-316-92894-1); tchr's. ed. avail. (ISBN 0-316-92896-8). Little.

Wetherington, Ronald K. Laboratory Exercises in Physical Anthropology. (Illus.). 108p. 1970. spiral 9.75x (ISBN 0-398-02051-5). C C Thomas.

Williams, George D. Maya-Spanish Crosses in Yucatan. (HU PMP). 1931. 18.00 (ISBN 0-527-01228-9). Kraus Repr.

Wolfe, Linda D. & Leiberman, Leslie S. Physical Anthropology: A Laboratory Text. (Illus.). 180p. 1985. pap. text ed. 13.95 (ISBN 0-89892-049-3). Contemp Pub Co of Raleigh.

Yearbook of Physical Anthropology Ser. Incl. Vol. 9. 1953-1961. Lasker, Gabriel, ed. pap. 5.00 (ISBN 0-686-36572-0); Vol. 16. 1972. Buettner-Janusch, John, ed. pap. 5.00 (ISBN 0-686-36573-9); Vol. 18. 1974. Buettner-Janusch, John, ed. pap. 6.00 (ISBN 0-686-36574-7); Vol. 19. 1975. Buetter-Janusch, John, ed. pap. 6.00 (ISBN 0-686-36575-5); Vol. 21. 1978. Bennett, Kenneth A., ed. pap. 6.00 (ISBN 0-686-36576-3); Vol. 22. 1979. Bennett, Kenneth A., ed. pap. 6.00 (ISBN 0-686-36577-1). Am Anthro Assn.

PHYSICAL CHEMISTRY

see Chemistry, Physical and Theoretical

PHYSICAL DISTRIBUTION OF GOODS

see also Packaging; Warehouses

Christopher, Martin & Gattorna, John. Controlling the Distribution Function. 1977. 90.00x (ISBN 0-903763-77-X, Pub. by MCB Pubns). State Mutual Bk.

Christopher, Martin, et al. Effective Distribution Management. 1978. 90.00x (ISBN 0-903763-78-8, Pub. by MCB Pubns). State Mutual Bk.

Computer Strategies. The Distributor's Computer Handbook. 150p. 1983. looseleaf 45.00x (ISBN 0-913505-08-0). Computer Strat.

Cooke, Peter N. Energy Saving in Distribution. 288p. 1981. text ed. 54.00x (ISBN 0-566-02155-2). Gower Pub Co.

Dannenberg, William P., et al. Introduction to Wholesale Distribution. (Illus.). 1978. 25.95 (ISBN 0-13-500777-1); stud. ed. o.p. 16.95 (ISBN 0-685-85447-7). P-H.

Davis, Grant M. & Dillard, John E., Jr. Physical Logistics Management. LC 83-10300. (Illus.). 566p. 1983. lib. bdg. 35.75 (ISBN 0-8191-3342-6); pap. text ed. 22.00 (ISBN 0-8191-3343-4). U Pr of Amer.

Dawson, John A. Commercial Distribution in Europe. LC 81-2123. 1982. 27.50 (ISBN 0-312-15264-7). St Martin.

Gilmour, Peter. Physical Distribution Management in Australia. 1974. 95.00x (ISBN 0-7015-1793-X, Pub. by MCB Pubns). State Mutual Bk.

Herron, David P. The Use of Computers in Physical Distribution Management. 1980. 90.00x (ISBN 0-86176-058-1, Pub. by MCB Pubns). State Mutual Bk.

Heskett, J. L., et al. Case Problems in Business Logistics. 360p. 1973. pap. 25.95 (ISBN 0-471-06599-4). Wiley.

J. J. Keller & Associates. Transportation & Distribution Dictionary. Laux, Patricia, ed. 350p. (Orig.). 1985. pap. write for info. (ISBN 0-934674-53-1, 23-H). J J Keller.

Johnson, James C. Readings in Contemporary Physical Dist. & Logistics. 4th ed. 352p. 1981. pap. text ed. write for info. (ISBN 0-02-360960-5). Macmillan.

Lancioni, Richard. Distribution Challenges for the 1980s. 1981. 90.00x (ISBN 0-86176-074-3, Pub. by MCB Pubns). State Mutual Bk.

Maister, David. Organising for Physical Distribution. 1977. 90.00x (ISBN 0-905440-51-X, Pub. by MCB Pubns). State Mutual Bk.

Rakowski, James P., ed. Transportation Economics: A Guide to Information Sources. LC 73-17584. (Economics Information Guide Series: Vol. 5). 200p. 1976. 60.00x (ISBN 0-8103-1307-3). Gale.

Ray, David, et al. Handbook of Distribution Costing & Control. 1980. 150.00x (ISBN 0-86176-063-8, Pub. by MCB Pubns). State Mutual Bk.

Rudman, Jack. Distribution Clerk - Machine (U.S.P.S.) (Career Examination Ser.: C-2255). (Cloth bdg. avail. on request). 1977. pap. 10.00 (ISBN 0-8373-2255-3). Natl Learning.

Stock, James R. Energy-Ecology Impacts on Distribution. 1978. 80.00x (ISBN 0-905440-53-6, Pub. by MCB Pubns). State Mutual Bk.

Studies in the Processing, Marketing & Distribution of Commodities: The Processing & Marketing of Coffee - Areas for International Cooperation. (Illus.). 51p. 1985. pap. 7.00 (UN84/2D11, UN). Unipub.

Taff, Charles A. Management of Physical Distribution & Transportation. 7th ed. 1984. 28.95x (ISBN 0-256-03022-7). Irwin.

PHYSICAL GEOGRAPHY

see also Agricultural Geography; Caves; Climatology; Coast Changes; Continents; Earth; Earth Movements; Earthquakes; Erosion; Geochemistry; Geophysics; Glaciers; Hydrography; Ice; Lakes; Landforms; Landslides; Man–Influence on Nature; Meteorology; Mountains; Ocean; Ocean Currents; Oceanography; Paleogeography; Rivers; Sedimentation and Deposition; Shore Lines; Speleology; Tides; Volcanoes; Water, Underground; Watersheds; Winds

also Lakes, Mountains, Ocean, Plains, Rivers, Valleys, and other geographical terms

Biogeographical Processes. (Processes in Physical Geography: No. 5). 136p. 1982. pap. text ed. 8.95x (ISBN 0-04-574016-X). Allen Unwin.

Bradshaw, Michael J. Earth: The Living Planet. LC 77-946. 302p. 1977. text ed. 32.95x (ISBN 0-470-99107-0). Halsted Pr.

Briggs, David & Smithson, Peter. Fundamentals of Physical Geography. LC 85-2495. (Illus.). 576p. 1985. pap. 15.95 (ISBN 0-09-160951-8, Pub. by Hutchinson Educ). Longwood Pub Group.

Brook, George, et al. Exercises in Physical Geography. (Illus.). 350p. 1984. 14.95 (ISBN 0-89892-054-X). Contemp Pub Co of Raleigh.

Burchfiel, B. Clark, et al. Physical Geology: The Structure & Processes of the Earth. 496p. 1982. text ed. 27.95 (ISBN 0-675-09913-7). Additional Supplement May Be Obtained From Publisher. Merrill.

Butzer, Karl W. Recent History of an Ethiopian Delta: The Omo River & the Level of Lake Rudolf. LC 70-184080. (Research Papers Ser.: No. 136). 184p. 1971. pap. 10.00 (ISBN 0-89065-043-8). U Chicago Dept Geog.

Chappe, D'Auteroche. Journey into Siberia, Made by Order of the King of France. LC 77-115518. (Russia Observed Ser). Repr. of 1770 ed. 24.50 (ISBN 0-405-03074-6). Ayer Co Pubs.

Chhibber, Harbans L. The Physiography of Burma. LC 72-179178. (Illus.). Repr. of 1933 ed. 17.50 (ISBN 0-404-54808-3). AMS Pr.

Porter, D. & Easterling, K. Phase Transformations in Metals & Alloys. 1981. pap. 23.95 (ISBN 0-442-30440-4). Van Nos Reinhold.

Smallman, R. E. Modern Physical Metallurgy. 4th ed. 1985. text ed. 59.95 (ISBN 0-408-71050-0); pap. text ed. 35.95 (ISBN 0-408-71051-9). Butterworth.

Tien, John K., et al, eds. Alloy & Microstructural Design. 1976. 77.00 (ISBN 0-12-690850-8). Acad Pr.

Tyrkiel, E. F. Dictionary of Physical Metallurgy. (Eng., Ger., Fr., Pol. & Rus.). 402p. 1978. 91.50 (ISBN 0-444-99810-1). Elsevier.

Verhoeven, John D. Fundamentals of Physical Metallurgy. LC 75-4600. 567p. 1975. text ed. 50.75x (ISBN 0-471-90616-6). Wiley.

PHYSICAL OCEANOGRAPHY

see Oceanography

PHYSICAL OPTICS

see Optics, Physical

PHYSICAL ORGANIC CHEMISTRY

see Chemistry, Physical Organic

PHYSICAL RESEARCH

see Physics–Research

PHYSICAL WEATHER FORECASTING

see Numerical Weather Forecasting

PHYSICISTS

see also Physics As a Profession

Abbott, David, ed. The Biographical Dictionary of Scientists: Physicists. LC 84-9211. (The Biographical Dictionary of Scientists Ser.). 220p. 1984. 18.95x (ISBN 0-911745-79-3). P Bedrick Bks.

Aris, Rutherford & Davis, H. Ted, eds. Springs of Scientific Creativity: Essays on Founders of Modern Science. LC 82-23715. (Illus.). 352p. 1983. 32.50x (ISBN 0-8166-1087-8). U of Minn Pr.

Bernstein, Jeremy. Hans Bethe: Prophet of Energy. 224p. 1985. pap. 7.95 (ISBN 0-87548-313-5). Open Court.

Braunbek, Werner. Pursuit of the Atom. 1959. 9.95 (ISBN 0-87523-115-2). Emerson.

Broda, Engelbert. Ludwig Boltzmann: Man, Physicist, Philosopher. LC 82-80707. (Illus.). 179p. 1983. 22.50 (ISBN 0-918024-24-2). Ox Bow.

Brown, Sanborn C. Count Rumford, Physicist Extraordinary. LC 78-25712. (Illus.). 1979. Repr. of 1962 ed. lib. bdg. 27.50x (ISBN 0-313-20772-0, BRCR). Greenwood.

Buckley, Paul & Peat, F. David. A Question of Physics: Conversations in Physics & Bio. LC 78-8096. 1978. 20.00x (ISBN 0-8020-2295-2). U of Toronto Pr.

Caroe, Gwendolen M. William Henry Bragg, Eighteen Sixty-Two to Nineteen Forty-Two. LC 77-84799. (Illus.). 1978. 34.50 (ISBN 0-521-21839-X). Cambridge U Pr.

Cole, K. C. Sympathetic Vibrations: Reflections on Physics As a Way of Life. LC 85-7555. (Illus.). 352p. 1985. pap. 7.95 (ISBN 0-553-34234-7). Bantam.

Davy, Humphry B. The Collected Works of Sir Humphry Davy, 9 Vols. Davy, John, ed. 1972. Repr. Set. 260.00 (ISBN 0-384-11010-X). Johnson Repr.

Elsasser, Walter M. Memoirs of a Physicist in the Atomic Age. (Illus.). 1978. 20.00 (ISBN 0-88202-178-8). Watson Pub Intl.

Fessenden, Helen M. Fessenden: Builder of Tomorrows. LC 74-4681. (Telecommunications Ser.). (Illus.). 376p. 1974. Repr. of 1940 ed. 20.00x (ISBN 0-405-06047-5). Ayer Co Pubs.

Feynman, Richard P. Surely You're Joking, Mr. Feynman! Adventures of a Curious Character. Hutchings, Edward, ed. 1985. 16.95 (ISBN 0-393-01921-7). Norton.

French, A. P., ed. Einstein: A Centenary Volume. LC 78-25968. (Illus.). 1979. text ed. 25.00x (ISBN 0-674-24230-0); pap. 9.95 (ISBN 0-674-24231-9). Harvard U Pr.

Frisch, Otto R. What Little I Remember. LC 78-18096. (Illus.). 227p. 1980. pap. 13.95 (ISBN 0-521-28010-9). Cambridge U Pr.

Goldsmith, Maurice. Frederic Joliot-Curie. 1976. text ed. 16.25x (ISBN 0-85315-342-6). Humanities.

Guettinger, W. & Eikemeier, H., eds. Structural Stability in Physics: Proceedings of Two International Symposia. (Springer Ser. in Synergetics). (Illus.). 1979. 43.00 (ISBN 0-387-09463-6). Springer-Verlag.

Hart, Ivor B. Great Physicists. LC 71-117804. (Essay Index Reprint Ser). 1927. 14.00 (ISBN 0-8369-1656-5). Ayer Co Pubs.

Heathcote, Niels H. Nobel Prize Winners in Physics, 1901-1950. facsimile ed. LC 76-167354. (Essay Index Reprint Ser: Life of Science Library). Repr. of 1953 ed. 36.00 (ISBN 0-8369-2455-X). Ayer Co Pubs.

Jaffe, Bernard. Michelson & the Speed of Light. LC 78-25969. (Illus.). 1979. Repr. of 1960 ed. lib. bdg. 24.75x (ISBN 0-313-20777-1, JAMI). Greenwood.

Jungk, Robert. Brighter Than a Thousand Suns: A Personal History of the Atomic Scientists. Cleugh, James, tr. from Ger. LC 58-8581. Orig. Title: Heller Als Tausend Sonnen. 1970. pap. 5.95 (ISBN 0-15-614150-7, Harv). HarBraceJ.

Kargon, Robert H. The Rise of Robert Millikan: Portrait of a Life in American Science. (Illus.). 206p. 1982. 27.50 (ISBN 0-8014-1459-8). Cornell U Pr.

Kevles, Daniel J. The Physicists. 1978. 15.95 (ISBN 0-394-46631-4). Knopf.

--The Physicists: The History of a Scientific Community in Modern America. LC 78-23592. 1979. pap. 10.95 (ISBN 0-394-72669-3, Vin). Random.

Kuhn, Thomas S., et al. Sources for History of Quantum Physics. LC 66-26634. (Memoirs Ser.: Vol. 68). 1967. 7.50 (ISBN 0-87169-068-3). Am Philos.

Kurylo, Friedrich & Susskind, Charles. Ferdinand Braun: A Life of the Nobel Prize Winner & Inventor of the Cathode-Ray Oscilloscope. (Illus.). 304p. 1981. 42.50x (ISBN 0-262-11077-6). MIT Pr.

Mann, Wilfrid B. Was There a Fifth Man? Quintessential Recollections. (Illus.). 128p. 1981. 19.50 (ISBN 0-08-027445-5). Pergamon.

Moray, John E. The Sea of Energy. 5th ed. (Illus.). 275p. 1978. 22.50 (ISBN 0-9606374-0-0, 264-334); pap. 9.35 (ISBN 0-9606374-1-9). Cosray Res.

Morse, Philip M. In at the Beginnings: A Physicist's Life. LC 76-40010. 1977. text ed. 30.00x (ISBN 0-262-13124-2). MIT Pr.

Newton, Isaac. The Correspondence of Isaac Newton, 1718-1727, Vol. VII. Hall, A. R., et al, eds. LC 59-65134. (Illus.). 1978. 110.00 (ISBN 0-521-08723-6). Cambridge U Pr.

Peierls, Rudolf. Bird of Passage: Recollections of a Physicist. (Illus.). 472p. 1985. 29.50x (ISBN 0-691-08390-8). Princeton U Pr.

Post, Robert C. Physics, Patents & Politics: A Biography of Charles Grafton Page. (Illus.). 1977. 20.00 (ISBN 0-88202-046-3, Sci Hist). Watson Pub Intl.

Ridley, B. K. Time, Space & Things. 2nd ed. LC 83-20979. 224p. 1984. 29.95 (ISBN 0-521-26293-3); pap. 9.95 (ISBN 0-521-26920-2). Cambridge U Pr.

Rutherford, Ernest & Boltwood, Bertram B. Rutherford & Boltwood: Letters on Radioactivity. Badash, Lawrence, ed. LC 78-81411. (Yale Studies in the History of Science & Medicine Ser.: No. 4). (Illus.). pap. 100.50 (ISBN 0-8357-9490-3, 2016787). Bks Demand UMI.

Segre, Emilio. From X-Rays to Quarks: Modern Physicists & Their Discoveries. (Illus.). 337p. 1985. pap. 12.95 (ISBN 0-7167-1147-8). W H Freeman.

Shea, William R. & Bunge, M. A., eds. Rutherford & Physics at the Turn of the Century. 1979. 20.00x (ISBN 0-88202-184-2). Watson Pub Intl.

Snow, C. P. The Physicists. LC 81-80861. (Illus.). 103p. 1981. 15.95 (ISBN 0-316-80221-2). Little.

Stokes, George G. Memoir & Scientific Correspondence of the Late Sir George Gabriel Stokes, 2 Vols. LC 7-29029. Repr. of 1907 ed. Set. 95.00 (ISBN 0-384-58383-0). Johnson Repr.

Thompson, Silvanus P. Philipp Reis: Inventor of the Telephone. LC 74-4696. (Telecommunications Ser). (Illus.). 200p. 1974. Repr. of 1883 ed. 16.00x (ISBN 0-405-06060-2). Ayer Co Pubs.

Volkenstein, M. V. Physics & Biology. 1982. 27.50 (ISBN 0-12-723140-4). Acad Pr.

Wheaton, Bruce R. & Heilbron, J. L., eds. An Inventory of Published Letters to & from Physicists 1900-1950. LC 80-51581. (Berkeley Papers in History of Science: No. 6). 1983. pap. 20.00x (ISBN 0-918102-06-5). U Cal Hist Sci Tech.

Who's Who in Atoms. 6th ed. 1977. 250.00x (ISBN 0-85280-201-3). Intl Pubns Serv.

Wybourne, Brian G. Classical Groups for Physicists. LC 73-17363. 415p. 1974. 51.95 (ISBN 0-471-96505-7, Pub. by Wiley-Interscience). Wiley.

PHYSICS

see also Agricultural Physics; Astrophysics; Biological Physics; Capillarity; Chemistry, Physical and Theoretical; Compressibility; Cosmic Physics; Critical Phenomena (Physics); Diffusion; Dynamics; Elasticity; Electricity; Electrons; Ether (Of Space); Evaporation; Field Theory (Physics); Friction; Gases; Geophysics; Gravitation; Heat; Hydraulics; Hydrostatics; Ions; Kinematics; Light; Liquids; Magnetism; Magnetohydrodynamics; Mathematical Physics; Matter; Mechanics; Meteorology; Molecular Dynamics; Motion; Music–Acoustics and Physics; Optics; Permeability; Physical Metallurgy; Pneumatics; Quantum Theory; Radiation; Radioactivity; Solid State Physics; Sound; Statics; Thermodynamics; Viscosity; Weights and Measures

Abbott, A. F. Ordinary Level Physics. 3rd ed. 1977. pap. text ed. 16.00x (ISBN 0-435-67005-0). Heinemann Ed.

Aberg, T., et al. Corpuscles & Radiation in Matter I. (Encyclopedia of Physics: Vol. 31). (Illus.). 670p. 1982. 131.20 (ISBN 0-387-11313-4). Springer-Verlag.

Abro, A. The Rise of the New Physics. 2nd ed. (Illus.). 994p. 1951. pap. 6.95 ea.; Vol. 1. pap. (ISBN 0-486-20003-5); Vol. 2. pap. (ISBN 0-486-20004-3). Dover.

Acosta, Virgilio, et al. Fisica Moderna. (Span.). 1975. pap. text ed. 15.00 (ISBN 0-06-310010-X, IntlDept). Har-Row.

Ahner, Walter L. & Kastan, Harold G. Review Text in Physics. (Illus., Orig.). 1966. pap. text ed. 7.42 (ISBN 0-87720-171-4). AMSCO Sch.

Ahrens, L. H. Physics & Chemistry of the Earth, Vol. 10. (Illus.). 270p. 1980. 105.00 (ISBN 0-08-020287-X). Pergamon.

AIP Conference Proceedings No. 84, APS-AISI, Leigh University, 1981. Physics in the Steel Industry: Proceedings. Schwerer, Fred C., ed. LC 82-72033. 409p. 1982. lib. bdg. 36.00 (ISBN 0-88318-183-5). Am Inst Physics.

AIP Conference Proceedings No. 85 Madsion, Wisconsin, 1982. Proton-Antiproton Collider Physics: Proceedings. Barger, V., et al, eds. LC 82-72141. 676p. 1982. lib. bdg. 42.00 (ISBN 0-88318-184-3). Am Inst Physics.

AIP Conference, Univ. of British Columbia, Vancouver, 1972. Cyclotrons 1972: Proceedings, No. 9. Burgerson, J. J. & Strathdee, A., eds. LC 72-92798. 836p. 1972. 19.00 (ISBN 0-88318-108-8). Am Inst Physics.

Aitchison, Ian J. & Paton, J. E., eds. Progress in Nuclear Physics, Vol. 13: Rudolf Peierls & Theoretical Physics - Proceedings of the Peierls Symposium. 1977. 16.50 (ISBN 0-08-021621-8). Pergamon.

Alberi, G. & Bajzer, Z., eds. Applications of Physics to Medicine & Biology: Proceedings of the International Conference, Trieste, Italy, March 30-April 3, 1982. 688p. 1983. 67.00x (ISBN 9971-950-42-1, Pub. by World Sci Singapore). Taylor & Francis.

Alder, A. B. Methods in Computational Physics: Advances in Research & Applications, Vol. 18. Date not set. price not set (ISBN 0-12-460818-3). Acad Pr.

Alder, B., et al, eds. Methods in Computational Physics: Advances in Research & Applications. Incl. Vol. 1. Statistical Physics. 1963. 68.00 (ISBN 0-12-460801-9); Vol. 2. Quantum Mechanics. 1963. 68.00 (ISBN 0-12-460802-7); Vol. 3. Fundamental Methods in Hydrodynamics. 1964. 68.00 (ISBN 0-12-460803-5); Vol. 4. Applications in Hydrodynamics. 1965. 68.00 (ISBN 0-12-460804-3); Vol. 5. Nuclear Particle Kinematics. 1966. 68.00 (ISBN 0-12-460805-1); Vol. 6. Nuclear Physics. 1967. 68.00 (ISBN 0-12-460806-X); Vol. 7. Astrophysics. 1967. 68.00 (ISBN 0-12-460807-8); Vol. 8. Energy Bands of Solids. 1968. 68.00 (ISBN 0-12-460808-6); Vol. 9. Plasma Physics. 1970. 71.50 (ISBN 0-12-460809-4); Vol. 10. Atomic & Molecular Scattering. 1971. 71.50 (ISBN 0-12-460810-8); Vol. 11. Seismology, Surface Waves & Earth Oscillations. Bolt, Bruce A., et al, eds. 1972. 63.50 (ISBN 0-12-460811-6); Vol. 12. Seismology, Body Waves & Sources. Bolt, Bruce A., ed. 1972. 63.50 (ISBN 0-12-460812-4); Vol. 13. Geophysics. Bolt, Bruce A., et al, eds. 1973. 90.00 (ISBN 0-12-460813-2); Vol. 14. Radio Astronomy. 1975. 68.50 (ISBN 0-12-460814-0); Vol. 15. Vibration Properties of Solids. Gilat, Gideon, et al, eds. 1976. 83.00 (ISBN 0-12-460815-9); Vol. 16. Computer Applications to Controlled Fusion Research. Killeen, John, ed. 1976. 89.50 (ISBN 0-12-460816-7); Vol. 17. General Circulation Models of the Atmosphere. Chang, Julius, ed. 1977. 71.50 (ISBN 0-12-460817-5); lib ed. 91.50 (ISBN 0-12-460878-7); microfiche 52.00 (ISBN 0-12-460879-5). Acad Pr.

Alonso, Marcelo & Finn, Edward J. Fundamental University Physics, 2 vols. 2nd ed. Incl. Vol. 1. Mechanics. 1979. text ed. 17.95 (ISBN 0-201-00076-8); Vol. 2. Fields & Waves. 1983. text ed. 19.95 (ISBN 0-201-00077-6). 1980. Addison-Wesley.

Alvarenga, Beatriz. Fisica General, Vol. I. (Span.). 1980. pap. text ed. 8.60 (ISBN 0-06-310011-8, Pub. by HarLA Mexico). Har-Row.

--Fisica General, Vol. II. (Span.). 1980. pap. text ed. 9.30 (ISBN 0-06-310014-2, Pub. by HarLA Mexico). Har-Row.

--Fisica General. 2nd ed. (Span.). 1024p. 1983. pap. text ed. write for info (ISBN 0-06-310016-9, Pub. by HarLA Mexico). Har-Row.

Alvarenga, Beatriz & Alvarenga, Maximo. Fisica General. 1976. text ed. 12.40 (ISBN 0-06-310012-6, IntlDept). Har-Row.

Amaldi, E., et al. Electroproduction at Low Energy & Hadron Form Factors. (Springer Tracts in Modern Physics: Vol. 83). (Illus.). 1979. 37.00 (ISBN 0-387-08998-5). Springer-Verlag.

American Association For The Advancement Of Science - New York - 1949. Present State of Physics. facsimile ed. Brackett, Frederick S., ed. LC 75-99617. (Essay Index Reprint Ser.). 1954. 27.50 (ISBN 0-8369-1542-9). Ayer Co Pubs.

American Society for Testing & Materials. Application of Advanced & Nuclear Physics to Testing Materials. LC 65-19687. (American Society for Testing & Materials Ser.: Special Technical Publication, No. 373). pap. 35.30 (ISBN 0-317-10989-8, 2000739). Bks Demand UMI.

Anderson, Elmer. Introduction to Modern Physics. 1982. text ed. 35.95 (ISBN 0-03-058512-0, CBS C); Instr's manual 20.00 (ISBN 0-03-058513-9). SCP.

--Modern Physics & Quantum Mechanics. 1971. text ed. 35.95 (ISBN 0-7216-1220-2, CBS C). SCP.

Anderson, Herbert L., ed. Physics Vade Mecum. LC 81-69849. 340p. 1981. 25.00 (ISBN 0-88318-289-0). Am Inst Physics.

Andrade, E. N. An Approach to Modern Physics. 11.25 (ISBN 0-8446-0456-9). Peter Smith.

Arecchi, F. T., et al, eds. Coherence in Spectroscopy & Modern Physics. LC 78-14474. (NATO ASI Series B, Physics: Vol. 37). 410p. 1978. 62.50x (ISBN 0-306-40050-2, Plenum Pr). Plenum Pub.

Arfken, George. Answers to Miscellaneous Problems: Mathematical Methods for Physicists. 1985. text ed. 2.00i (ISBN 0-12-059822-1). Acad Pr.

--University Physics. 1984. text ed. 31.00i (ISBN 0-12-059860-4); student's solution manual 6.50i (ISBN 0-12-059867-1); study guide 9.75i (ISBN 0-12-059868-X); instrs. manual 1.50i (ISBN 0-12-059865-5); transparency masters 50.00i (ISBN 0-12-059870-1). Acad Pr.

--University Physics: International Edition. 1984. 20.00 (ISBN 0-12-059858-2). Acad Pr.

Aristotle. Physics, 2 vols, Vols. I & II. Charlton, ed. 1983. Set. 12.95x (ISBN 0-317-06326-X). Oxford U Pr.

Arya, Atam P. Elementary Modern Physics. new ed. LC 73-1466. 1974. text ed. 24.95 (ISBN 0-201-00304-X). Addison-Wesley.

--Introductory College Physics. (Illus.). 1979. text ed. 31.95 (ISBN 0-02-304000-9); instrs'. manual avail.; student study guide avail. Macmillan.

Asimov, Isaac. Asimov on Physics. 1978. pap. 3.95 (ISBN 0-380-41848-7, 63602-6, Discus). Avon.

--Understanding Physics: Light, Magnetism & Electricity. (Signet Science Ser). 1969. pap. 3.95 (ISBN 0-451-62304-5, ME2304, Ment). NAL.

--Understanding Physics: Motion, Sound & Heat. (Signet Science Ser.). 1969. pap. 4.50 (ISBN 0-451-62365-7, ME2202, Ment). NAL.

--Understanding Physics: The Electron, Proton & Neutron. (Signet Science Ser). 1969. pap. 4.50 (ISBN 0-451-62402-5, ME2190, Ment). NAL.

Ausloos, P., ed. Kinetics of Ion-Molecule Reactions. LC 79-367. (NATO ASI Ser. B, Physics: Vol. 40). 516p. 1979. 75.00x (ISBN 0-306-40153-3, Plenum Pr). Plenum Pub.

Bagehot, Walter. Physics & Politics. 1881. 30.00 (ISBN 0-932062-08-3). Sharon Hill.

Baierlein, Ralph. Newtonian Dynamics. (Illus.). 336p. 1983. text ed. 37.95 (ISBN 0-07-003016-2). McGraw.

Baker, Adolph. Modern Physics & Anti-Physics. LC 74-109506. 1970. pap. 12.95 (ISBN 0-201-00485-2). Addison-Wesley.

Baltes, H. P., ed. Inverse Source Problems in Optics. LC 78-12076. (Topics in Current Physics: Vol. 9). (Illus.). 1978. 28.00 (ISBN 0-387-09021-5). Springer-Verlag.

Barbe, D. F., ed. Charge-Coupled Devices. (Topics in Applied Physics Ser.: Vol. 38). (Illus.). 1980. 45.00 (ISBN 0-387-09832-1). Springer-Verlag.

Basdevant, J. L. & Gastmans, R., eds. Fundamental Interactions: Cargese 1981. LC 82-10164. (NATO Advanced Study Institutes Series B, Physics: Vol. 85). 714p. 1982. 95.00x (ISBN 0-306-41116-4, Plenum Pr). Plenum Pub.

Basic Physics. (Basic Academics Ser.: Module 7). (Illus.). 105p. 1982. spiral bdg. 10.00x (ISBN 0-87683-231-1); instr's manual 15.00x (ISBN 0-87683-242-7). G P Courseware.

Bassani, F., et al, eds. Highlights of Condensed Matter Theory: Proceedings of the International School of Physics, Enrico Fermi, Course LXXXIX Varenna, Italy, June 28 - July 16, 1983. (Enrico Fermi International Summer School of Physics Ser.). 89p. 1984. write for info. (North-Holland). Elsevier.

Bauer, R. S., ed. Surfaces & Interfaces: Physics & Electronics. 650p. 1984. 77.00 (ISBN 0-444-86784-8, I-200-84, North Holland). Elsevier.

Beauchamp, K. G. Walsh Functions & Their Applications. (Techniques of Physics Ser.). 1976. 39.50 (ISBN 0-12-084050-2). Acad Pr.

Dita, P. & Georgescu, V., eds. Gauge Theories: Fundamentals Interactions & Rigorous Results. (Progress in Physics Ser.: Vol. 5). 389p. 1982. 22.50x (ISBN 0-8176-3095-3). Birkhauser.

Dittman, Richard & Schmeig, Glenn. Physics in Everyday Life. Rogers, Janice L. & Zappa, C. R., eds. LC 78-13381. (Schaum's Outline Seri). (Illus.). 1979. text ed. 28.95 (ISBN 0-07-017056-8). McGraw.

Dixon, Robert T. The Dynamic World of Physics. 512p. 1984. text ed. 24.95 (ISBN 0-675-20093-8). Additional supplements may be obtained from publisher. Merrill.

Douglas, Shawhan. Physics with the Computer. (Orig.). 1981. tchr's ed. 24.95 (ISBN 0-87567-037-7); student's ed. 14.95; incl. diskettes 150.00. Entelek.

Drake, Stillman, tr. from Lat. Galileo Galilei: "Two New Sciences". 366p. 1974. 27.50x (ISBN 0-299-06400-X). U of Wis Pr.

Duffey, George H. Theoretical Physics: Classical & Modern Views. LC 79-23794. 704p. 1980. Repr. of 1973 ed. lib. bdg. 34.50 (ISBN 0-89874-062-2). Krieger.

Durand, Loyal & Pondrom, Lee G., eds. High Energy Physics, 1980: International Conference, Madison Wisconsin, 2 pts. (AIP Conference Proceedings Ser.: No. 68). 1622p. 1981. lib. bdg. 85.00 (ISBN 0-88318-167-3). Am Inst Physics.

Duvant, G. & Lions, J. L. Inequalities in Mechanics & Physics. John, C., tr. from Fr. (Die Grundlehren der Mathematischen Wissenschaften: Vol. 219). (Illus.). 400p. 1976. 60.00 (ISBN 0-387-07327-2). Springer-Verlag.

Ebe, John A. Point: Instant of Time. (Fundamentals of Mechanics Ser.: Vol. 1). 60p. lib. bdg. write for info. Ebe.

Edmonds, Dean S., Jr. Cioffari's Experiments in College Physics, 7th ed. 456p. pap. 16.95 (ISBN 0-669-04492-X). Heath.

Edwards, C., ed. Gravitational Radiation, Collapsed Objects & Exact Solution: Proceedings. (Lecture Notes in Physics: Vol. 124). (Illus.). 487p. 1980. 35.00 (ISBN 0-387-09992-1). Springer-Verlag.

Ehlers, J., et al. Lectures in Statistical Physics. (Lecture Notes in Physics: Vol. 28). (Illus.). vi, 342p. 1974. pap. 17.00 (ISBN 0-387-06711-6). Springer-Verlag.

Ehlers, J., et al, eds. Imaging Processes & Coherence in Physics. (Lecture Notes in Physics Ser.: Vol. 112). 573p. 1980. pap. 39.00 (ISBN 3-540-09727-9). Springer-Verlag.

Eisberg, Robert M. & Lerner, Lawrence S. Physics, Foundations & Applications, 2 Vols. 720p. 1981. Vol. 1. text ed. 34.95x (ISBN 0-07-019091-7); Vol. 2. text ed. 34.95x (ISBN 0-07-019092-5). McGraw.

--Physics: Foundations & Applications, Combined Vol. (Illus.). 1552p. 1981. 47.95x (ISBN 0-07-019110-7). McGraw.

Elliot, J. P. & Dawber, P. G. Symmetry in Physics, Vols. 1 & 2. 1985. Vol. 1. pap. 15.95 ea. (ISBN 0-19-520455-7). Vol. 2 (ISBN 0-19-520456-5). Oxford U Pr.

Elwell, D. & Pointon, A. J. Physics for Engineers & Scientists. 2nd ed. LC 77-16193. 356p. 1979. pap. 28.95x (ISBN 0-470-26872-7). Halsted Pr.

Epstein, Lewis C. Thinking Physics. (Illus.). 562p. 1985. pap. 14.95 (ISBN 0-935218-06-8). Insight Pr Ca.

--Thinking Physics Is Gedanken Physics. 2nd, enl. ed. (Illus.). 600p. 1983. 14.95x (ISBN 0-935218-04-1). Insight Pr CA.

Epstein, Lewis C. & Hewitt, P. Thinking Physics, Pt. II. (Illus.). 253p. 1981. pap. 6.95x (ISBN 0-935218-01-7). Insight Pr CA.

Eresian, W. J., et al. Mathematics & Physical Science, 2 vols. Incl. Vol. 1-Mathematics. Eresian, W. J., et al. (Illus.). 370p. 1979. text ed. 60.00x looseleaf (ISBN 0-87683-026-2); lesson plans 250.00x (ISBN 0-87683-029-7); Vol. 2-Physical Science. Eresian, W. J., et al. 318p. text ed. 60.00x looseleaf (ISBN 0-87683-027-0); lesson plan 250.00x (ISBN 0-317-11852-8). (Illus.). 688p. 1979. Set. 120.00x (ISBN 0-87683-025-4); write for info. lesson plans (ISBN 0-87683-028-9). G P Courseware.

Euler, Manfred. Physikunterricht: Anspruch und Realitaet, Vol. 5. (Didaktik und Naturewissenshaft). (Ger.). 254p. 1982. 30.55 (ISBN 3-8204-7103-0). P Lang Pubs.

Ewan, Dale & Heaton, Leroy. Physics for Technical Education. (Illus.). 720p. 1981. text ed. 29.95 (ISBN 0-13-674127-4). P-H.

Ewen, Dale & Schurter, Neil. Physics for Career Education. 2nd ed. (Illus.). 448p. 1982. 27.95 (ISBN 0-13-672329-2). P-H.

Experimento, Razonamiento y Creacion En Fisica. rev. ed. (Serie De Fisica: No. 5). (Span.). 1977. pap. 3.50 (ISBN 0-8270-6165-X). OAS.

Fabian, Derek J., et al, eds. Inner-Shell & X-Ray Physics of Atoms & Solids. LC 81-11945. (Physics of Atoms & Molecules Ser.). 976p. 1981. 125.00x (ISBN 0-306-40819-8, Plenum Pr). Plenum Pub.

Feinberg, Gerald. What Is the World Made of: The Achievements of Twentieth-Century Physics. LC 76-18342. (Illus.). 1978. (Anch); pap. 6.95 (ISBN 0-385-07694-0). Doubleday.

Ferbel, Thomas, ed. Techniques & Concepts of High-Energy Physics II. (NATO ASI Series B, Physics: Vol. 99). 350p. 1983. 49.50x (ISBN 0-306-41385-X, Plenum Pr). Plenum Pub.

Ference, Michael, Jr., et al. Analytical Experimental Physics. 3rd ed. LC 55-5124. (Illus.). 1956. 17.50x (ISBN 0-226-24299-4). U of Chicago Pr.

Feynman, R. P., et al. Feynman Lectures on Physics, 3 Vols. Vol. 1. text ed. 19.95 (ISBN 0-201-02116-1); Vol. 2. text ed. 19.95 (ISBN 0-201-02117-X); Vol. 3. text ed. 19.95 (ISBN 0-201-02118-8); Set. text ed. 52.95 (ISBN 0-201-02115-3); exercises for vols 2 & 3 o. p. 3.25. Vol. 2 Excercises o. p. Vol. 3 (ISBN 0-201-02019-X). Addison-Wesley.

Feynman, Richard P. Character of Physical Law. (Illus.). 1967. pap. 5.95 (ISBN 0-262-56003-8). MIT Pr.

Fleming, Phyllis J. Language of Physics. LC 77-76110. (Physics Ser.). 1978. text ed. 23.95 (ISBN 0-201-02472-1); 5.95 (ISBN 0-201-02474-8). Addison-Wesley.

Fluegge, E., ed. Encyclopedia of Physics, 54 vols, Vols. 11-12, 14-19. Incl. Vol. 11, Pt. 1. Acoustics One. Tr. of Akustik One. (Illus.). 1961. 123.90 (ISBN 0-387-02686-X); Vol. 11, Pt. 2. Acoustics Two. Tr. of Akustik Two. (Illus.). 1962. 97.40 (ISBN 0-387-02841-2); Vol. 12. Thermodynamics of Gases. Tr. of Thermodynamik der Gase. (Illus.). 1958. 147.50 (ISBN 0-387-02292-9); Vol. 14. Low Temperature Physics One. Tr. of Kaeltephysik One. (Illus.). 1956. 70.80 (ISBN 0-387-02037-3); Vol. 15. Low Temperature Physics Two. Tr. of Kaeltephysik Two. (Illus.). 1956. 109.20 (ISBN 0-387-02038-1); Vol. 16. Electric Fields & Waves. Tr. of Elekrische Felder und Wellen. (Illus.). 1958. 153.40 (ISBN 0-387-02293-7); Vol. 17. Dielectrics. Tr. of Dielektrika. (Illus.). 1956. 94.40 (ISBN 0-387-02039-X); Vol. 18, Pt. 1. Magnetism. Wijn, H. P., ed. Tr. of Magnetismus. (Illus.). 1969. 153.40 (ISBN 0-387-04164-8); Vol. 18, Pt. 2. Ferromagnetism. Wijn, H. P., ed. Tr. of Ferromagnetismus. (Illus.). 1966. 153.40 (ISBN 0-387-03548-6); Vol. 19. Electrical Conductivity One. Tr. of Elektrische Leitungsphaenomene 1. (Illus.). 1956. 82.60 (ISBN 0-387-02040-3). Springer-Verlag.

--Encyclopedia of Physics, 54 vols, Vols. 21-23, 25, 27, 28, 30, 32, 34-35. Incl. Vol. 21. Electron Emission. Gas Discharges One. Tr. of Elektronen-Emission Gas-Entladungen 1. (Illus.). 1956. 129.80 (ISBN 0-387-02041-1); Vol. 22. Gas Discharges Two. Tr. of Gasentladungen Two. (Illus.). 1956. 126.90 (ISBN 0-387-02042-X); Vol. 23. Electrical Instruments. Pannenborg, A. E., ed. Tr. of Elektrische Instrumente. (Illus.). 1967. 153.40 (ISBN 0-387-03852-3); Vol. 25, Pt. 1. Crystal Optics, Diffraction. Tr. of Kristalloptik, Beugung. (Illus.). 1961; Vol. 25, Pts. 2a-2c. Light & Matter. Genzel, L., ed. Tr. of Licht und Materie. (Illus.). Pt. 2a, 1967. 88.50 (ISBN 0-387-03853-1); Pt. 2b, 1974. 116.90 (ISBN 0-387-06638-1); Pt. 2c, 1970. 94.40 (ISBN 0-387-04856-1); Vol. 27. Spectroscopy One. Tr. of Spektroskopie One. (Illus.). 1964. 115.10 (ISBN 0-387-03153-7); Vol. 28. Spectroscopy Two. Tr. of Spektroskopie Two. 1957. 97.40 (ISBN 0-387-02167-1); Vol. 30. X-Rays. Tr. of Roentgenstrahlen. (Illus.). 1957. 88.50 (ISBN 0-387-02168-X); Vol. 32. Structural Research. Tr. of Strukturforsc2'hung. (Illus.). 1957. 141.60 (ISBN 0-387-02169-8); Vol. 34. Corpuscles & Radiation in Matter Two. Tr. of Korpuskeln und Strahlung in Materie 2. (Illus.). 1958. 76.70 (ISBN 0-387-02295-3); Vol. 35. Atoms One. Tr. of Atome One. (Illus.). 1957. 97.40 (ISBN 0-387-02170-1). Springer-Verlag.

--Encyclopedia of Physics, 54 vols, Vols. 46-49, 51-54. Incl. Vol. 46, Pt. 1. Cosmic Rays One. 1961. 97.40 (ISBN 0-387-02689-4); Vol. 46, Pt. 2. Cosmic Rays Two. Sitte, K., ed. 1967. 159.30 (ISBN 0-387-03855-8); Vol. 47. Geophysics One. 1956. 116.90 (ISBN 0-387-02046-2); Vol. 48. Geophysics Two. 1957. 194.70 (ISBN 0-387-02174-4); Vol. 49. Geophysics Three, 4 pts. Bartels, J. & Rower, K., eds. (Illus.). Pt. 1, 1966. 112.10 (ISBN 0-387-03549-4); Pt. 2, 1967. 112.10 (ISBN 0-686-96891-3); Pt. 3, 537p, 1971. 159.30 (ISBN 0-387-05570-3); Pt. 4, 592p, 1972. 140.50 (ISBN 0-387-05583-5); Vol. 51. Astrophysics Two: Stellar Structure. Tr. of Astrophysik Two - Sternaufbau. (Illus.). 1958. 171.10 (ISBN 0-387-02299-6); Vol. 52. Astrophysics Three: The Solar System. Tr. of Astrophysik Three - das Sonnensystem. (Illus.). 1959. 141.60 (ISBN 0-387-02416-6); Vol. 53. Astrophysics Four: Stellar Systems. Tr. of Astrophysik Four - Sternsysteme. (Illus.). 1959. 141.60 (ISBN 0-387-02417-4); Vol. 54. Astrophysics Five: Miscellaneous. Tr. of Astrophysik Five - Verschiedenes. (Illus.). 1962. 97.40 (ISBN 0-387-02844-7). Springer-Verlag.

Fluegge, S., ed. Encyclopedia of Physics, 54 vols, Vols. 3-4, 6, 8-10. Incl. Vol. 3, Pt. 1. Principles of Classical Mechanics & Field Theory. Tr. of Prinzipien der Klassischen Mechanik und Feldtheorie. (Illus.). viii, 902p. 1960; Vol. 3, Pt. 3. The Non-Linear Field Theories of Mechanics. Truesdell, C. & Noll, W. Tr. of Die Nicht-Linearen Feldtheorien der Mechanik. (Illus.). viii, 602p. 1965. 174.10 (ISBN 0-387-03313-0); Vol. 4. Principles of Electrodynamics & Relativity. Tr. of Prinzipien der Elektrodynamik und Relativitatstheorie. (Illus.). vi, 290p. 1962. 97.40 (ISBN 0-387-02840-4); Vol. 6. Elasticity & Plasticity. Tr. of Elastizitaet und Plastizitaet. (Illus.). viii, 642p. 1958. 141.60 (ISBN 0-387-02290-2); Vol. 6a, Pt. 1. Mechanics of Solids One. Truesdell, C., ed. (Illus.). 1973. 175.90 (ISBN 0-387-05873-7); Vol. 6a, Pt. 2. Mechanics of Solids Two. Truesdell, C., ed. (Illus.). 1972. 205.40 (ISBN 0-387-05535-5); Vol. 6a, Pt. 3. Mechanics of Solids Three. Truesdell, C., ed. (Illus.). 1973. 164.10 (ISBN 0-387-05536-3); Vol. 8, Pt. 1. Fluid Dynamics One. Tr. of Stroemungsmechanik One. (Illus.). 1959. 129.80 (ISBN 0-387-02411-5); Vol. 8, Pt. 2. Fluid Dynamics Two. Tr. of Stroemungsmechanik Two. (Illus.). 1963. 182.90 (ISBN 0-387-02997-4); Vol. 9. Fluid Dynamics Three. Tr. of Stroemungsmechanik Three. (Illus.). 1960. 194.70 (ISBN 0-387-02548-0); Vol. 10. Structure of Liquids. Tr. of Struktur der Fluessigkeiten. (Illus.). vi, 686p. 1960. 94.40 (ISBN 0-387-02549-9). Tr. of Handbuch der Physik. (Eng., Fr. & Ger.). Springer-Verlag.

--Encyclopedia of Physics, 54 vols, Vols. 37-42, 44-45. Incl. Vol. 37, Pt. 1. Atoms Three - Molecules One. Tr. of Atome 3 - Molekuele 1. (Illus.). vi, 439p. 1959. 118.00 (ISBN 0-387-02412-3); Vol. 37, Pt. 2. Molecules Two. Tr. of Molekule 2. (Illus.). vi, 303p. 1961. 97.40 (ISBN 0-387-02688-6); Vol. 38, Pt. 2. Neutrons & Related Gamma Ray Problems. Tr. of Neutronen und Verwandte Gammastrahlewprobleme. (Illus.). vi, 868p. 1959. 171.10 (ISBN 0-387-02413-1); Vol. 39. Structure of Atomic Nuclei. Tr. of Bauder Atomkerne. (Illus.). vi, 566p. 1971. 123.90 (ISBN 0-387-02171-X); Vol. 40. Nuclear Reactions One. Tr. of Kernreaktionen One. (Illus.). vi, 553p. 1957. 123.90 (ISBN 0-387-02172-8); Vol. 41, Pt. 1. Nuclear Reactions Two: Theory. Tr. of Kernreaktionen 2: Theorie. (Illus.). viii, 580p. 1959. 141.60 (ISBN 0-387-02414-X); Vol. 41, Pt. 2. Beta Decay. Tr. of Betazerfall. (Illus.). vi, 117p. 1962. 47.20 (ISBN 0-387-02843-9); Vol. 42. Nuclear Reactions Three. Tr. of Kernreaktionen 3. (Illus.). viii, 626p. 1957. 129.80 (ISBN 0-387-02173-6); Vol. 44. Nuclear Instrumentation One. Creutz, E., ed. Tr. of Instrumentelle Hilfsmittel der Kernphysik 1. (Illus.). viii, 473p. 1959. 123.90 (ISBN 0-387-02415-8); Vol. 45. Nuclear Instrumentation Two. Creutz, E., ed. Tr. of Instrumentelle Hilfsmittel der Kernphysik 2. (Illus.). viii, 544p. 1958. 129.80 (ISBN 0-387-02297-X). Springer-Verlag.

Fong, Peter. Physical Science, Energy & Our Environment. (Illus.). text ed. write for info. (ISBN 0-02-338660-6). Macmillan.

Ford, Kenneth. Classical & Modern Physics, 3 vols. Incl. Vol. 1. 1972; Vol. 2. Ford, Kenneth W. 1972. text ed. 33.50x (ISBN 0-471-00724-2); answer manual o.p. 7.50 (ISBN 0-471-00945-8); Vol. 3. 1974. text ed. 35.50x (ISBN 0-471-00878-8); answer manual o.p. 6.95 (ISBN 0-471-00946-6). LC 76-161385. 1973. combined ed. for vols. 1 & 2 o.p. 35.95 (ISBN 0-471-00666-1). Wiley.

Frampton, P. H. & Van Dam, H., eds. Third Workshop on Grand Unification. (Progress in Physics Ser.: Vol. 6). 384p. 1982. text ed. 27.50 (ISBN 0-8176-3105-4). Birkhauser.

Freeman, Ira M. Physics Made Simple. rev. ed. LC 65-13090. (Made Simple Ser.). pap. 4.95 (ISBN 0-385-08727-6). Doubleday.

Fujita, Shugeji. Statistical & Thermal Physics, Pt. 1. LC 83-22250. 1985. write for info. (ISBN 0-89874-689-2). Krieger.

--Statistical & Thermal Physics, Pt. 2. 1986. write for info. (ISBN 0-89874-866-6). Krieger.

Fuller, Harold Q., et al. Physics: Including Human Application. 1978. text ed. 25.75 scp (ISBN 0-06-042214-9, HarpC); scp lab manual 11.50 (ISBN 0-06-042212-2); scp study guide 9.50 (ISBN 0-06-042213-0). Har-Row.

Fundamental Physics with Reactor Neutrons & Neutrinos: 1977. (Institute of Physics Conference Ser.: No. 42). 1978. 55.00 (ISBN 0-9960032-2-3, Pub. by Inst Physics England). Heyden.

Fundamentals of Physical Science. rev. ed. (Illus.). 240p. 1982. Set. training materials 4900.00x (ISBN 0-87683-055-6); pap. text ed. 60.00x (ISBN 0-87683-056-4); looseleaf lesson plans 3375.00x (ISBN 0-87683-057-2); transparencies 1125.00x (ISBN 0-87683-058-0); question bank 1550.00x (ISBN 0-87683-059-9). G P Courseware.

Gabbay, S. M. Elementary Mathematics for Basic Chemistry & Physics. 128p. (Orig.). 1980. pap. 11.95 (ISBN 0-9604722-0-7). Basic Science Prep Ctr.

Gaillard, M. K. & Stora, R. Gauge Theories in High Energy Physics, 2 Vols. (Les Houches Summer School Proceedings Ser.: Vol. 37). 1984. Set. 231.00 (ISBN 0-444-86543-8, I-080-84, North-Holland); Vol. 1. 146.25 (ISBN 0-444-86722-8); Vol. 2. 109.75 (ISBN 0-444-86723-6). Elsevier.

Galeev, A. A. & Sudan, R. N., eds. Basic Plasma Physics II. (Handbook of Plasma Physics Ser.: Vol. 2). 850p. 1985. 183.50 (ISBN 0-444-86645-0, North-Holland). Elsevier.

Gallimore, J. G. Transverse Paraphysics: The New Science of Space, Time & Gravity Control. LC 82-50823. (Illus.). 359p. (Orig.). 1982. pap. text ed. 35.00 (ISBN 0-9603536-4-X). Tesla Bk Co.

Garrido, L. A., et al, eds. The Many-Body Problem. LC 77-94344. 333p. 1969. 34.50x (ISBN 0-306-30444-9, Plenum Pr). Plenum Pub.

Gas-Filled Detectors. (Advanced Health Physics Training Ser.). (Illus.). 115p. 1983. Set. training materials package 1700.00x (ISBN 0-87683-187-0); looseleaf 45.00x (ISBN 0-87683-188-9); lesson plans 1250.00x (ISBN 0-87683-189-7); transparencies 250.00x (ISBN 0-87683-190-0); question bank 625.00x (ISBN 0-87683-191-9). G P Courseware.

Gastaldi, Ugo & Klapisch, Robert, eds. Physics at LEAR with Low-Energy Cooled Antiprotons. (Ettore Majorana International Science Series, Physical Sciences: Vol. 17). 902p. 1984. 125.00x (ISBN 0-306-41384-1, Plenum Pr). Plenum Pub.

Gautreau, Ronald & Savin, William. Schaum's Outline of Modern Physics. (Schaum's Outline Ser.). (Illus.). 1978. pap. 9.95 (ISBN 0-07-023062-5). McGraw.

Giancoli, Douglas C. General Physics. (Illus.). 976p. 1984. text ed. 42.95 (ISBN 0-13-350884-6). P-H.

--General Physics, Vol. II. LC 84-8432. (Illus.). 480p. 1984. text ed. 25.95 (ISBN 0-13-350992-3). P-H.

--General Physics, Vol. I. (Illus.). 480p. 1984. text ed. 25.95 (ISBN 0-13-350984-2). P-H.

--The Ideas of Physics. 2nd ed. (Illus.). 528p. 1978. text ed. 23.95 (ISBN 0-15-540559-4, HC); instructor's manual avail. (ISBN 0-15-540560-8). HarBraceJ.

--Physics: Principles with Applications. 2nd ed. (Illus.). 864p. 1985. text ed. 35.95 (ISBN 0-13-672627-5); study guide by Joseph Boyle 12.95 (ISBN 0-13-672635-6). P-H.

Gimblett, F. & Hood, K. Chemistry, Physics & Technology of Macromolecular Inorganic Compounds & Materials, Pt. 1. 1969. 27.00 (ISBN 0-686-92699-4). Elsevier.

--Chemistry, Physics & Technology of Macromolecular Inorganic Compounds & Materials, Pt. 2. 1970. 27.00 (ISBN 0-686-92697-8). Elsevier.

Ginzberg, V. L. Theoretical Physics & Astrophysics. Haar, D. Ter, tr. (International Series in Natural Philosophy: Vol. 99). (Illus.). 1979. pap. 37.00 (ISBN 0-08-023066-0). Pergamon.

Ginzburg, V. L. & Lebedev, P. N. Waynflete Lectures on Physics: Selected Topics in Contemporary Physics & Astrophysics. Haar, D. ter, tr. LC 82-24619. (International Series in Natural Philosophy: Vol. 106). (Illus.). 133p. 1983. 25.00 (ISBN 0-08-029147-3). Pergamon.

Kursunoglu, Behram, ed. Fundamental Interactions in Physics. LC 73-84002. (Studies in the Natural Sciences: Vol. 2). 408p. 1973. 65.00x (ISBN 0-306-36902-8, Plenum Pr). Plenum Pub.

Kursunoglu, Behram & Perlmutter, Arnold, eds. Gauge Theories, Massive Neutrinos & Proton Decay. LC 81-11923. (Studies in the Natural Sciences: Vol. 18). 402p. 1981. text ed. 62.50x (ISBN 0-306-40821-X, Plenum Pr). Plenum Pub.

Kursunoglu, Behram, et al, eds. Fundamental Interactions in Physics & Astrophysics. LC 73-18315. (Studies in the Natural Sciences: Vol. 3). 470p. 1973. 69.50x (ISBN 0-306-36903-6, Plenum Pr). Plenum Pub.

--Recent Developments in High-Energy Physics. LC 80-19774. (Studies in the Natural Sciences Ser.: Vol. 17). 320p. 1980. 52.50x (ISBN 0-306-40565-2, Plenum Pr). Plenum Pub.

--Theories & Experiments in High-Energy Physics. LC 75-16281. (Studies in the Natural Sciences: Vol. 9). 494p. 1975. 75.00x (ISBN 0-306-36909-5, Plenum Pr). Plenum Pub.

Kyame, Joseph J. Mathematical Methods of Physics. (Illus.). 460p. 1979. pap. 15.95x (ISBN 0-89641-017-X). American Pr.

Landau, L. & Kitaigorodsky, A. I. Physics for Everyone: Molecules. 224p. 1980. 6.60 (ISBN 0-8285-1725-8, Pub. by Mir Pubs USSR). Imported Pubns.

Landau, L. D. & Lifshitz, E. M. Course on Theoretical Physics: Statistical Physics, Vol. 5, Pt. 1. 3rd ed. (Illus.). 1980. text ed. 81.00 (ISBN 0-08-023039-3); pap. text ed. 22.50 (ISBN 0-08-023038-5). Pergamon.

--A Shorter Course of Theoretical Physics. Incl. Vol. 1. Mechanics & Electrodynamics. 1972. 19.00 (ISBN 0-08-016739-X); Vol. 2. Quantum Mechanics. 1974. 25.00 (ISBN 0-08-032616-1). LC 74-167927. 1986. price not set (ISBN 0-08-025049-1). Pergamon.

Landau, L. D., et al. Course of Theoretical Physics, 10 vols. Incl. Vol. 1. Mechanics. 3rd ed. 1976. text ed. 15.50 (ISBN 0-08-021022-8); Vol. 2. The Classical Theory of Fields. 4th ed. 1976. text ed. 15.00 (ISBN 0-08-016019-0); Vol. 3. Quantum Mechanics - Non-Relativistic Theory. 3rd ed. 1977. text ed. 25.00 (ISBN 0-08-020940-8); Vol. 4, Pts. 1-2. Relativistic Quantum Theory. Pt. 1. text ed. 20.00 (ISBN 0-08-016025-5); Pt. 2. text ed. 15.50 (ISBN 0-08-017175-3); Vol. 5. Statistical Physics. 2nd ed. 1969. text ed. 50.00 (ISBN 0-08-023039-3); pap. text ed. 20.00 (ISBN 0-08-023038-5); Vol. 6. Fluid Mechanics. 1959; Vol. 7. Elasticity Theory. 2nd ed. 1970; Vol. 8. Electrodynamics of Continuous Media. 1960; Vol. 9. 3rd ed. 1978. text ed. 35.00 (ISBN 0-08-023073-3); pap. text ed. 15.00 (ISBN 0-08-023072-5). write for info. Pergamon.

Landsberg, G. S., ed. Textbook of Elementary Physics, 3 vols. MIR Publishers, tr. from Rus. Incl. Vol. 1. Mechanics, Heat & Molecular Physics; Vol. 2. Electricity & Magnetism; Vol. 3. Oscillations, Waves, Optics & Structure of the Atom. (Illus.). 1485p. 1975. text ed. 48.00x set (ISBN 0-8464-0913-5). Beekman Pubs.

Langbein, D. Theory of Van der Waals Attraction. LC 25-9130. (Springer Tracts in Modern Physics: Vol. 72). (Illus.). 150p. 1974. 46.10 (ISBN 0-387-06742-6). Springer-Verlag.

Larson, Dewey B. New Light on Space & Time. LC 65-24256. (Illus.). 1977. pap. 6.00 (ISBN 0-913138-08-8). North Pacific.

--Nothing but Motion. LC 79-88078. (Illus.). 1979. 9.50 (ISBN 0-913138-07-X). North Pacific.

Latin American School Of Physics-University of Mexico, 1965. Many-Body Problems & Other Selected Topics in Theoretical Physics, Vol. 1. Moshinsky, M., et al, eds. LC 67-31518. (Illus.). 968p. 1967. Set. 231.00 (ISBN 0-677-11500-8); pap. 54.00x (ISBN 0-677-12935-1). Gordon.

Lavender. New Land for Old. 1981. cased 25.50 (ISBN 0-9960021-0-3, Pub. by Inst Physics England); pap. 15.50 (ISBN 0-9960021-1-1, Pub. by Inst Physics England). Heyden.

Lazarus, David & Raether, Manfred. Practical Physics: How Things Work. (Illus.). 1984. pap. text ed. 11.20x (ISBN 0-87563-167-3). Stipes.

Lee, H. C. An Introduction to Kaluza-Klein Theories: Proceedings of the Workshop on Kaluza-Klein Theories, Chalk River, Canada, Aug. 11-16, 1983. 380p. 1984. 42.00x (ISBN 9971-966-19-0, Pub. by World Sci Singapore); pap. 21.00x (ISBN 9971-966-20-4, Pub. by World Sci Singapore). Taylor & Francis.

Lefax Pub. Co. Editors. Physical & Thermodynamic Data. (Lefax Data Bks.: No. 646). (Illus.). looseleaf bdg. 3.00 (ISBN 0-685-14162-4). Lefax.

--Physics. (Lefax Data Bks.: No. 632). (Illus.). pap. 3.00 (ISBN 0-685-14164-0). LeFax.

Lehrman. Physics the Easy Way. (The Easy Way Ser.). 1984. pap. 7.95 (ISBN 0-8120-2658-6). Barron.

Lemon, Harvey B. From Galileo to the Nuclear Age: An Introduction to Physics. (Phoenix Science Ser.). pap. 120.00 (ISBN 0-317-08845-9, 2020104). Bks Demand UMI.

Levine, Celotta & Levine, Judah. Methods of Experimental Physics, Vol. 22. 1985. 80.00 (ISBN 0-12-475964-5). Acad Pr.

Levy, M. & Lurcat, F., eds. Cargese Lecture Notes, 1965: Application of Mathematics to Problems in Theoretical Physics. 516p. 1967. 132.95x (ISBN 0-677-11660-8). Gordon.

Lindner, C. C. & Rosa, A. Topics on Steiner Systems. (Annals of Discrete Mathematics Ser.: Vol. 7). 350p. 1980. 74.50 (ISBN 0-444-85484-3, North-Holland). Elsevier.

Lindsay, Robert B. & Margenau, Henry. Foundations of Physics. LC 80-84973. 560p. 1981. 29.00 (ISBN 0-918024-18-8); pap. text ed. 15.00 (ISBN 0-918024-17-X). Ox Bow.

Long, Dale D. Physics Around You. 608p. 1980. text ed. write for info. (ISBN 0-534-00770-8). Wadsworth Pub.

Lorenz, Hans. Lehrbuch der Technischen Physik, 4 Vols. (Classics in the History of Engineering Science Ser). (Ger). 1968. Repr. of 1902 ed. Set. 145.00 (ISBN 0-384-33720-1). Johnson Repr.

Luhr, Overton. Physics Tells Why: An Explanation of Some Common Physical Phenomena. 2nd ed. LC 51-30387. (Illus.). pap. 99.30 (ISBN 0-317-09229-4, 2012363). Bks Demand UMI.

Lutz, H. O., et al, eds. Fundamental Processes in Energetic Atomic Collisions. (NATO ASI Series B, Physics: Vol. 103). 678p. 1983. 95.00x (ISBN 0-306-41465-1, Plenum Pr). Plenum Pub.

Ma, Shang-Keng. Modern Theory of Critical Phenomena. LC 76-8386. (Frontiers in Physics: Vol. 46). (Illus.). 1976. pap. 31.95 (ISBN 0-8053-6671-7). Benjamin-Cummings.

McAlexander, Aaron. Hands-On Applied Physics. LC 79-356. 1979. text ed. 26.95 (ISBN 0-8053-7030-7). Benjamin-Cummings.

McCliment, Edward R. Physics. 913p. 1984. text ed. 30.95 (ISBN 0-15-570585-7, HC); solutions manual avail. (ISBN 0-15-570586-5); study guide avail. (ISBN 0-15-570587-3). HarBraceJ.

McCrea, W. H., et al, eds. The Constants of Physics. (Philosophical Transactions of the Royal Society: Ser. A, Vol. 310). (Illus.). 153p. 1984. Repr. lib. bdg. 50.00 (ISBN 0-85403-224-X, Pub. by Royal Soc London). Scholium Intl.

McDiarmid, D. R. & Gattinger, R., eds. Instruments & Analysis Techniques for Space Physics: Proceedings of Workshop VI of the COSPAR 24th plenary meeting held in Ottawa, Canada, 16 May-2 June, 1982, Vol. 2/7. (Illus.). 200p. 1983. pap. 45.00 (ISBN 0-08-030431-1). Pergamon.

McGervey, John D. Introduction to Modern Physics. 2nd ed. 756p. 1983. text ed. 28.00i (ISBN 0-12-483560-0). Acad Pr.

--Introduction to Modern Physics. 2nd ed. 1984. pap. text ed. 20.00 (ISBN 0-12-483562-7). Acad Pr.

McGonnagle, Warren J., ed. Physics & Nondestructive Testing, Vol. 2. LC 65-27852. (Illus.). 302p. 1972. 69.50x (ISBN 0-677-15250-7). Gordon.

--Physics & Nondestructive Testing, Vol. 3. LC 65-27852. (Illus.). 338p. 1972. 69.50x (ISBN 0-677-15260-4). Gordon.

McGregor, Donald R. The Inertia of the Vacuum: A New Foundation for Theoretical Physics. (Illus.). 96p. 1981. 6.00 (ISBN 0-682-49722-3, University). Exposition Pr FL.

McGuinness, Brian, ed. Ludwig Boltzmann: Theoretical Physics & Philosophical Problems, Selected Writings. Foulkes, Paul, tr. LC 74-79571. (Vienna Circle Collection Ser: No. 5). Orig. Title: Populare Schriften. 270p. 1974. lib. bdg. 33.50 (ISBN 90-277-0249-7, Pub. by Reidel Holland); pap. 17.00 (ISBN 90-277-0250-0). Kluwer Academic.

Machlup. Physics. Date not set. price not set (ISBN 0-471-82426-7). Wiley.

McKelvey, John P. & Grotch, Howard. Fisica Paraciencias E Ingenieria, Vol. I. (Span.). 1980. pap. text ed. 15.40 (ISBN 0-06-315475-7, Pub. by HarLA Mexico). Har-Row.

--Fisica Paraciencias E Ingenieria, Vol. II. (Span.). 1981. pap. text ed. 16.40 (ISBN 0-06-315476-5, Pub. by HarLA Mexico). Har-Row.

McKenzie, Arthur E. Physics. 4th ed. 1970. 18.95x (ISBN 0-521-07698-6). Cambridge U Pr.

Magnetic Properties of Coordination & Organometallic Transition Metal Compounds: Supplement 2. LC 62-53136. (Landolt-Boernstein Ser. Group II: Vol. 10). (Illus.). 1979. 386.40 (ISBN 0-387-08722-2). Springer-Verlag.

Mahanthappa, K. T. & Brittin, Wesley E., eds. Boulder Lecture Notes in Theoretical Physics, 1969: Vol. 12-A, Ferromagnetism & Quantum Optics. 220p. 1971. 47.25x (ISBN 0-677-14550-0). Gordon.

--Boulder Lecture Notes in Theoretical Physics, 1969: Vol. 12-C, Mathematical Methods in Field Theory & Complex Analytic Varieties. 296p. 1971. 67.25x (ISBN 0-677-14570-5). Gordon.

Manheimer, Wallace M. An Introduction to Trapped-Particle Instability in Tokamaks. LC 77-8530. (ERDA Critical Review Ser.: Advances in Fusion Science & Engineering). 104p. 1977. pap. 10.50 (ISBN 0-87079-105-2, TID-27157); microfiche 4.50 (ISBN 0-87079-251-2, TID-27157). DOE.

Manin, Y. I. Mathematics & Physics. (Progress in Physics Ser.: No. 3). 112p. 1981. 12.50x (ISBN 0-8176-3027-9). Birkhauser.

March, Robert H. Physics for Poets. 2nd ed. (Illus.). 1977. text ed. 33.95 (ISBN 0-07-040243-4). McGraw.

Marcus, Abraham & Thrower, J. Robert. Introduction to Applied Physics. LC 77-6082. 1985. text ed. 24.00 (ISBN 0-534-04746-7). Breton Pubs.

Marcus, Abraham & Thrower, James R. Introduction to Applied Physics. 450p. 1980. text ed. write for info. (ISBN 0-534-00825-9, Breton Pubs). Wadsworth Pub.

Marion, Jerry. Physics in the Modern World: Study Guide. 2nd ed. 1980. 23.25i (ISBN 0-12-472280-6); 5.00i (ISBN 0-12-472284-9). Acad Pr.

Marion, Jerry B. Physics & the Physical Universe. 3rd ed. LC 79-9387. 190p. 1980. text ed. 36.50 (ISBN 0-471-03430-4); pap. 12.95 study guide (ISBN 0-471-05815-7); answers avail. (ISBN 0-471-05818-1). Wiley.

Marion, Jerry B. & Hornyak, William F. Physics for Scientists & Engineers, Vol. 1. 1982. text ed. 35.95 (ISBN 0-03-049486-9, CBS C); instr's manual 20.00 (ISBN 0-03-058282-2); Vols. 1 & 2. study guide 18.95. SCP.

--Physics for Scientists & Engineers, Vol. 2. 1982. text ed. 34.95 (ISBN 0-03-049491-5, CBS C); instr's manual 18.95 (ISBN 0-03-058282-2); Vols. 1 & 2. study guide 16.95. SCP.

--Physics for Scientists & Engineers: Combined Volume. 1982. text ed. 51.00 (ISBN 0-03-062831-8, CBS C). SCP.

--Principles of Physics. LC 83-7709. 772p. 1984. text ed. 39.95x (ISBN 0-03-049481-8). SCP.

Martin, B. R. Statistics for Physicists. 1971. 39.00 (ISBN 0-12-474750-7). Acad Pr.

Martin, M. C. & Hewett, C. A. Elements of Classical Physics. LC 73-3450. 1975. text ed. 31.00 (ISBN 0-08-017098-6). Pergamon.

Marton, C. & Edmonds, Peter, eds. Methods of Experimental Physics: Ultrasonic, Vol. 19. LC 79-26343. 1981. 80.00 (ISBN 0-12-475961-0). Acad Pr.

Marton, C. & Septier, A., eds. Advances in Electronics & Electron Physics Supplement, No. 13C. (Serial Publication). 544p. 1983. 74.50 (ISBN 0-12-014576-6). Acad Pr.

Marton, Claire, ed. Advances in Electronics & Electron Physics, Vol. 56. (Serial Publication Ser.). 1981. 75.00 (ISBN 0-12-014656-8). Acad Pr.

--Advances in Electronics & Electron Physics, Vol. 57. (Serial Publication Ser.). 1981. 85.00 (ISBN 0-12-014657-6). Acad Pr.

Marton, L., ed. Advances in Electrotronics & Electron Physics, Vol. 63. 1985. 75.00 (ISBN 0-12-014663-0). Acad Pr.

Marton, L. & Marton, C., eds. Advances in Electronics and Electron Physics, Vol. 52. 1980. 94.50 (ISBN 0-12-014652-5). Acad Pr.

Marton, L. & Richard, Patrick, eds. Methods of Experimental Physics: Atomic Physics Accelerators, Vol. 17. (Serial Pub.). 1980. 80.00 (ISBN 0-12-475959-9). Acad Pr.

Mathematics I. (Basic Mathematics Ser.: Module 3). (Illus.). 100p. 1982. spiral bdg. 10.00x (ISBN 0-87683-227-3); instr's manual 15.00x (ISBN 0-87683-238-9). G P Courseware.

Mayants, Lazar. The Enigma of Probability & Physics. 392p. 1984. 69.00 (ISBN 90-277-1674-9, Pub. by Reidel Holland). Kluwer Academic.

Melton, L. R. An Introductory Guide to Information Sources in Physics. 1978. pap. 4.50 (ISBN 0-9960017-9-4, Pub. by A Hilger England). Heyden.

Merken, Mel. Physical Science, with Modern Applications. 3rd ed. 1985. text ed. 35.95 (ISBN 0-03-070448-0, CBS C). SCP.

Merrill, John J. & Hamblin, W. Kenneth. Physical Science Fundamentals. LC 81-70312. 336p. (Orig.). 1982. text ed. 24.95x (ISBN 0-8087-3996-4). Burgess.

Messiah, Albert. Quantenmechanik, Band Two: Zwei Auflage Ubersetzt aus dem Franzosischen von Joachim Streubel. (Ger., Illus.). 585p. 1985. 27.60x (ISBN 3-11-010265-X). De Gruyter.

Methods & Techniques of Mathematical Physics: Proceedings of Conferences held in Oberwolfach, Sept. 16-22, 1979: Mathematical Methods of Plasmaphysics, Vol. 20. 297p. 1980. pap. 27.35. P Lang Pubs.

Milani, Myrna M. & Smith, Brian R. A Primer of Rotational Physics. LC 84-13518. 1985. 15.00 (ISBN 0-943290-02-3); pap. 10.00 (ISBN 0-943290-01-5). Fainshaw Pr.

Milewski, B. Supersymmetry & Supergravity, 1983: Proceedings of the XIX Winter School & Workshop Theoretical Physics, Karpacz, Poland, February 14-26, 1983. 588p. 1983. 60.00x (ISBN 9971-950-23-5, Pub. by World Sci Singapore); pap. 33.00x (ISBN 9971-950-97-9, Pub. by World Sci Singapore). Taylor & Francis.

Miller, Arthur I. Imagery in Scientific Thought: Creating 20th-Century Physics. 320p. 1984. 24.95 (ISBN 0-8176-3196-8). Birkhauser.

Miller, Franklin, Jr. College Physics. 5th ed. 876p. 1982. text ed. 28.95 (ISBN 0-15-511737-8, HC); solution manual avail. (ISBN 0-15-511738-6); study guide by Robert Stanley 9.95 (ISBN 0-15-511739-4). HarBraceJ.

Mintz, Stephan & Perlmutter, Arnold, eds. New Pathways in High Energy Physics, Pt. 1: Magnetic Charge & Other Fundamental Approaches. LC 76-20476. (Studies in the Natural Sciences Ser.: Vol. 10). 415p. 1976. 65.00x (ISBN 0-306-36910-9, Plenum Pr). Plenum Pub.

--New Pathways in High Energy Physics, Pt. 2: New Particles - Theories & Experiments. LC 76-20476. (Studies in the Natural Sciences Ser.: Vol. 11). 421p. 1976. 65.00x (ISBN 0-306-36911-7, Plenum Pr). Plenum Pub.

--Orbis Scientiae, Nineteen Seventy-Seven: The Significance of Nonlinearity in the Natural Sciences. (Studies in the Natural Sciences Ser.: Vol. 13). 1977. 69.50x (ISBN 0-306-36913-3, Plenum Pr). Plenum Pub.

Mintz, Stephan L., et al, eds. Fundamental Theories in Physics. LC 74-9659. (Studies in the Natural Sciences: Vol. 5). 255p. 1974. 45.00x (ISBN 0-306-36905-2, Plenum Pr). Plenum Pub.

Month, M. & Herrera, J. C., eds. Nonlinear Dynamics & the Beam-Beam Interaction. LC 79-57341. (AIP Conference Proceedings: No. 57). (Illus.). 340p. lib. bdg. 20.50 (ISBN 0-88318-156-8). Am Inst Physics.

Moreau, Nancy. A General Physics Review. (Illus.). 160p. (Orig.). 1981. pap. text ed. 3.00 (ISBN 0-9606036-2-X). N & N Pub.

--General Physics Review. 2nd ed. (Illus.). 189p. 1985. pap. text ed. 4.00 (ISBN 0-9606036-5-4). N & N Pub.

Morrison & Eames. Powers of Ten. LC 82-5504. (Scientific American Library). (Illus.). 164p. 1985. pap. 19.95 (ISBN 0-7167-6003-7). W H Freeman.

Morton, Charles. Charles Morton's Compendium Physicae. Hornberger, Theodore, ed. 237p. 1940. 30.00x (ISBN 0-8139-0943-0, Colonial Society of Massachusetts). U Pr of Va.

Mulligan, J. Introductory College Physics. 768p. 1985. 33.95 (ISBN 0-07-044036-0); study guide 10.95 (ISBN 0-07-044040-9). McGraw.

Mulligan, Joseph F. Practical Physics: The Production & Conservation of Energy. (Illus.). 1980. text ed. 28.95 (ISBN 0-07-044032-8). McGraw.

Nabarro, F. R. Moving Dislocations. (Dislocations in Solids Ser.: Vol. 3). 354p. 1980. 68.00 (ISBN 0-444-85015-5, North-Holland). Elsevier.

Nakajima, S. The Physics of Elementary Excitations. (Springer Ser. in Solid-State Sciences: Vol. 12). (Illus.). 340p. 1980. 53.80 (ISBN 0-387-09921-2). Springer-Verlag.

NATO Advanced Study Institute, Denver, Colorado, June, 1973. Scattering Theory in Mathematical Physics: Proceedings. LaVita, J. A. & Marchand, J. P., eds. LC 73-91205. 1974. lib. bdg. 47.50 (ISBN 90-277-0414-7, Pub. by Reidel Holland). Kluwer Academic.

Nelson, Edward. Quantum Fluctuations. LC 84-26449. (Princeton Series in Physics). 155p. 1985. 32.00 (ISBN 0-691-08378-9); pap. 12.95 (ISBN 0-691-08379-7). Princeton U Pr.

Newton College of the Sacred Heart. Physical Science Two. 1972. text ed. 15.40 (ISBN 0-13-671354-8); pap. text ed. 9.56 (ISBN 0-13-671339-4); testing manual & achiev. tests 39.60 (ISBN 0-13-671156-1). P-H.

O'Dwyer, John. College Physics. 2nd ed. 808p. write for info. (ISBN 0-534-02950-7). Wadsworth Pub.

Ohanian, Hans. Physics, Vols. I & II. 1985. Combined ed. text ed. 36.95x (ISBN 0-393-95401-3); Vol. I. text ed. 22.95x (ISBN 0-393-95404-8); Vol. II. text ed. 22.95x (ISBN 0-393-95407-2); study guide 12.95x (ISBN 0-393-95413-7); solutions manual avail. (ISBN 0-393-95410-2). Norton.

Oldenberg, Otto & Rasmussen, N. Modern Physics for Engineers. 1966. text ed. 47.95 (ISBN 0-07-047653-5). McGraw.

Olivo, T. & Olivo, C. T. Fundamentals of Applied Physics. 3rd ed. LC 83-71503. 440p. 1984. text ed. 23.80 (ISBN 0-8273-2159-7); wkbk. 7.80 (ISBN 0-8273-2161-9); instr's guide 5.25 (ISBN 0-8273-2160-0). Delmar.

Solid State Physics: Advances in Research & Applications. Incl. Vol. 1. 1955 (ISBN 0-12-607701-0); Vol. 2. 1956 (ISBN 0-12-607702-9); Vol. 3. 1956 (ISBN 0-12-607703-7); Vol. 4. 1957 (ISBN 0-12-607704-5); Vol. 5. 1957 (ISBN 0-12-607705-3); Vol. 6. 1958 (ISBN 0-12-607706-1); Vol. 7. 1958 (ISBN 0-12-607707-X); Vol. 8. 1959 (ISBN 0-12-607708-8); Vol. 9. 1959 (ISBN 0-12-607709-6); Vol. 10. 1960 (ISBN 0-12-607710-X); Vol. 11. 1960 (ISBN 0-12-607711-8); Vol. 12. 1961 (ISBN 0-12-607712-6); Vol. 13. 1962 (ISBN 0-12-607713-4); Vol. 14. 1963 (ISBN 0-12-607714-2); Vol. 15. 1963 (ISBN 0-12-607715-0); Vol. 16. 1964 (ISBN 0-12-607716-9); Vol. 17. 1965 (ISBN 0-12-607717-7); Vol 18. 1966 (ISBN 0-12-607718-5); Vol. 19. 1967 (ISBN 0-12-607719-3); Vol. 20. 1968 (ISBN 0-12-607720-7); Vol. 21. 1968 (ISBN 0-12-607721-5); Vol. 22. 1969 (ISBN 0-12-607722-3); Vol. 23. 1970 (ISBN 0-12-607723-1); Vol. 24. 1970 (ISBN 0-12-607724-X); Vol. 25. 1970 (ISBN 0-12-607725-8); Vol. 26. 1971 (ISBN 0-12-607726-6); Vol. 27. 1972 (ISBN 0-12-607727-4); Vol. 28. 1973 (ISBN 0-12-607728-2); Vol. 29. 1974 (ISBN 0-12-607729-0). 74.50 ea. Acad Pr.

Sommer, A. H. Photoemissive Materials. LC 79-9461. 268p. 1980. Repr. of 1968 ed. lib. bdg. 19.50 (ISBN 0-89874-009-6). Krieger.

Sorenson, James A. & Phelps, Michael E. Physics in Nuclear Medicine. 404p. 1980. 43.50 (ISBN 0-8089-1238-0, 794187); slide set 310.00 (ISBN 0-8089-1530-4, 794188). Grune.

Spears, Jacqueline & Zollman, Dean. Fascination of Physics. (Illus.). 544p. 1985. text ed. 26.95x (ISBN 0-8053-6974-0); instr's guide 5.95 (ISBN 0-8053-6975-9, 36975). Benjamin-Cummings.

Sproull, Robert L. & Phillips, W. Andrew. Modern Physics: The Quantum Physics of Atoms, Solids, & Nuclei. 3rd ed. LC 79-26680. 682p. 1980. 42.95 (ISBN 0-471-81840-2). Wiley.

Stafleu. Time & Again: A Systematic Analysis of the Foundations of Physics. 1981. 19.95x (ISBN 0-88906-108-4). Radix Bks.

Standford & Tanner. Physics for Students of Science & Engineering. 1985. pap. text ed. 20.00i (ISBN 0-12-663375-4). Acad Pr.

Stanford, A. L. & Tanner, J. M. Physics for Students of Science & Engineering: Workbook. 1985. text ed. 9.00i (ISBN 0-12-663382-7). Acad Pr.

Stanford, A. L. & Tanner, James L. Physics for Students of Science & Engineering. 1984. text ed. 31.00i (ISBN 0-12-663380-0). Acad Pr.

Stephenson, Reginald J. Exploring in Physics: A New Outlook on Problems in Physics. (Midway Reprint Ser). 1974. pap. 4.25x (ISBN 0-226-77276-4). U of Chicago Pr.

Stipe, Gordon J. The Development of Physical Theories. LC 77-13632. 494p. (Orig.). 1979. Repr. of 1967 ed. lib. bdg. 29.50 (ISBN 0-88275-623-0). Krieger.

Stollberg, Robert & Hill, Faith F. Physics: Fundamental & Frontiers. rev. ed. 1980. text ed. 24.24 (ISBN 0-395-26649-1); laboratory suppl. 3.52 (ISBN 0-395-18242-5); progress tests 63.88 (ISBN 0-395-18240-9); 12.44 (ISBN 0-395-26650-5). HM.

Strother, G. K. & Weber, Robert L. Physics with Applications in Life Sciences. (Illus.). 1977. text ed. 34.95 (ISBN 0-395-21718-0); instr's. manual 1.00 (ISBN 0-395-21719-9). HM.

Suckley, Michael H. Analyzing the Physical Universe. 1979. coil bdg. 18.95 (ISBN 0-88252-063-6). Paladin Hse.

Suh, Nam P. Tribophysics. 528p. 1986. text ed. 75.00 (ISBN 0-13-930983-7). P-H.

Swartz, C. Prelude to Physics. 202p. 1983. pap. 18.95 (ISBN 0-471-06028-3). Wiley.

Swartz, C. E. Phenomenal Physics. LC 80-16690. 741p. 1980. 38.50 (ISBN 0-471-83880-2); avail. tchr's manual (ISBN 0-471-07914-6). Wiley.

Swimme, Brian. The Universe Is a Green Dragon: A Cosmic Creation Story. (Illus.). 173p. (Orig.). 1984. pap. 8.95 (ISBN 0-939680-14-9). Bear & Co.

Taffel, Alexander. Physics: Its Methods & Meanings. 1981. text ed. 23.80 (ISBN 0-205-07074-4, 7370741); tchr'sguide 11.96 (ISBN 0-205-07075-2, 737075); lab manual 9.32 (ISBN 0-205-07076-0, 737076); tests 43.20 (ISBN 0-205-07078-7, 737078). Allyn.

Theoretical Physics. (Proceedings Ser.). (Illus.). 638p. 1963. 32.25 (ISBN 92-0-030263-7, ISP61, IAEA). Unipub.

Thomas, Edward. From Quarks to Quasars: An Outline of Modern Physics. (Illus.). 294p. 1977. 19.50 (ISBN 0-485-12024-0, Pub. by Athlone Pr Ltd). Longwood Pub Group.

Thomas, Ursula & Twaddell, Freeman. Lesestoff. Incl. Physik & Chemie. LC 76-11313 (ISBN 0-299-07194-4); Mensch & Gesellschaft. LC 46-1323 (ISBN 0-299-07184-7); Literatur. LC 76-11317 (ISBN 0-299-07174-X); Biologie. LC 76-11322 (ISBN 0-299-07164-2). 1977. pap. text ed. 6.00x ea. U of Wis Pr.

Thompson, D. O. & Chimenti, Dale E., eds. Review of Progress in Quantitative Nondestructive Evaluation, Vol. 2. 1840p. 1983. 225.00x (ISBN 0-306-41350-7, Plenum Pr). Plenum Pub.

Thompson, G. H. B. Physics of Semiconductor Laser Devices. 549p. 1980. 84.95 (ISBN 0-471-27685-5). Wiley.

Thomson, Joseph J. Electricity & Matter. 1911. 42.50x (ISBN 0-686-83533-6). Elliots Bks.

Tilley, Donald E. Contemporary College Physics. LC 78-57146. 1979. pap. text ed. 37.95 (ISBN 0-8053-9290-4); instr's guide 9.95 (ISBN 0-8053-9291-2). Benjamin-Cummings.

--University Physics for Science & Engineering. LC 75-14974. 1976. 38.95 (ISBN 0-8465-7536-1); instr's guide 6.95 (ISBN 0-8465-7537-X). Benjamin-Cummings.

Tilley, Donald E. & Thumm, Walter. Physics for College Students. LC 72-89140. 800p. 1974. 37.95 (ISBN 0-8465-7538-8). Benjamin-Cummings.

Tipler, Paul A. Modern Physics. 2nd ed. LC 77-58725. 1977. text ed. 33.95x (ISBN 0-87901-088-6). Worth.

--Physics. 2nd ed. LC 81-70205. (Illus.). xxiv, 1078p. 1982. text ed. 38.95 (ISBN 0-87901-135-1); Vol. 1 Chpts. 1-19. 24.95 (ISBN 0-87901-182-3); Vol. 2 Chpts. 20-37. 24.95 (ISBN 0-87901-183-1); study guide 11.95 (ISBN 0-87901-180-7). Worth.

Tippens, P. E. Applied Physics. 3rd ed. 880p. 1984. 31.00 (ISBN 0-07-064977-4); study guide 14.15 (ISBN 0-07-064978-2). McGraw.

Tippens, Paul E. Basic Technical Physics. LC 82-7182. 512p. 1983. text ed. 19.55 (ISBN 0-07-064971-5). Mcgraw.

Toraldo Di Francia, G. Investigation of the Physical World. LC 80-12791. (Illus.). 480p. 1981. 70.00 (ISBN 0-521-23338-0); pap. 22.95 (ISBN 0-521-29925-X). Cambridge U Pr.

Trefil, James S. Physics As a Liberal Art. LC 77-6729. 1978. text ed. 20.00 (ISBN 0-08-019863-5). Pergamon.

Trigg, George L., ed. Crucial Experiments in Modern Physics. LC 75-21567. 141p. 1975. pap. 7.95x (ISBN 0-8448-0765-6). Crane-Russak Co.

Trower, W. Peter & Bellini, Gianpaolo, eds. Physics in Collision: High-Energy ee-ep-pp Interactions, Vol. 1. LC 82-620. 525p. 1982. 75.00 (ISBN 0-306-40996-8, Plenum Pr). Plenum Pub.

Tuck, T. & Makram-Ebeid, S. Semi-Insulating 111-V Materials: Evian 1982. 400p. 1982. 165.00x (ISBN 0-906812-22-4, Pub. by Shiva Pub England). State Mutual Bk.

Turi, Edith A., ed. Thermal Characterization of Polymeric Materials. LC 81-17578. 1981. 98.00 (ISBN 0-12-703780-2). Acad Pr.

Turko, L. & Pekalski, A., eds. Developments in the Theory of Fundamental Interactions. (Studies in High Energy Physics: Vol. 3). 598p. 1981. 57.25 (ISBN 3-7186-0104-4). Harwood Academic.

Valentin, L. Subatomic Physics: Nuclei & Particles, 2 vols. 600p. 1981. Set. 106.50 (ISBN 0-444-86117-3, North-Holland). Elsevier.

Van Der Merwe, Alwyn, ed. Old & New Questions in Physics, Cosmology, Philosophy, & Theoretical Biology: Essays in Honor of Wolfgang Yourgrau. 936p. 1983. 95.00x (ISBN 0-306-40962-3, Plenum Pr). Plenum Pub.

Van Heuvelen, Allan. Physics: A General Introduction. 1982. text ed. 31.95 (ISBN 0-316-89710-8); tchrs' manual avail. (ISBN 0-316-89711-6); students' guide 10.95 (ISBN 0-316-89712-4); TB avail. (ISBN 0-316-89713-2). Little.

Van Kampen, N. G. Stochastic Processes in Physics & Chemistry. 420p. 1982. 76.75 (ISBN 0-444-86200-5, North-Holland); pap. 28.00 (ISBN 0-444-86650-7). Elsevier.

Velarde, Manuel G., ed. Nonequilibrium Cooperative Phenomena in Physics & Related Fields. (NATO ASI Series B, Physics: Vol. 116). 546p. 1985. 85.00x (ISBN 0-306-41833-9, Plenum Pr). Plenum Pub.

Vladimirov, V. S. Equations of Mathematical Physics. Yankovsky, Eugene, tr. 464p. 1984. 10.95 (ISBN 0-8285-2877-2, Pub. by Mir Pubs Ussr). Imported Pubns.

Von Baeyer, Hans C. Rainbows, Snowflakes & Quarks: Physics & the World Around Us. (Illus.). 192p. 1984. 16.95 (ISBN 0-07-067545-7). McGraw.

Von Franz, Marie-Louise. Alchemical Active Imagination. (Seminar Ser.: No. 14). 116p. (Orig.). 1979. pap. 9.50 (ISBN 0-88214-114-7). Spring Pubns.

Walker, Jearl. The Flying Circus of Physics. LC 75-5670. 224p. 1975. text ed. 18.45x (ISBN 0-471-91808-3). Wiley.

Wall, Jesse D. Introductory Physics: A Problem-Solving Approach. 1977. text ed. 24.95 (ISBN 0-669-00188-0). Heath.

Ward, Charlotte R. This Blue Planet: Introduction to Physical Science. 417p. 1972. text ed. 24.95 (ISBN 0-316-92230-7); instuctor's Manual avail. (ISBN 0-316-92222-6). Little.

Warren, Mashuri L. Introductory Physics. LC 78-22089. (Illus.). 683p. 1979. text ed. 27.95x (ISBN 0-7167-1008-0); tchr's manual avail. W H Freeman.

Weast, Robert C. Handbook of Chemistry & Physics. 63rd ed. 2432p. 1982. 59.95 (ISBN 0-8493-0463-6). CRC Pr.

Weidner. Physics. 1985. write for info. (ISBN 0-205-08078-2, 738078). Allyn.

Weidner & Sells. Elementary Classical Physics, Vol. 1. 2nd ed. 1985. 35.64 (ISBN 0-205-03597-3, 733597). Allyn.

--Elementary Modern Physics. 3rd ed. 1985. 38.57 (ISBN 0-205-06559-7, 736559). Allyn.

Weidner, Richard T. & Sells, Robert L. Elementary Physics: Classical & Modern. 1975. text ed. 43.67 (ISBN 0-205-04647-9, 7346476); instr's. manual o. p. free (ISBN 0-205-04648-7). Allyn.

Weinreich, Gabriel. Notes for General Physics. (Illus.). 250p. 1972. 6.00 (ISBN 0-911014-16-0); pap. 2.95 (ISBN 0-911014-17-9). Neo Pr.

Wells, D. A. & Slusher, H. S. Schaum's Outline of Physics for Engineering & Science. (Schaum's Outline Ser.). 336p. 1983. pap. 8.95 (ISBN 0-07-069254-8). McGraw.

Wess, Julius & Bagger, Jonathan. Supersummetry & Supergravity. (Princeton Series in Physics). 192p. 1983. 42.50 (ISBN 0-691-08327-4); pap. 12.50 (ISBN 0-691-08326-6). Princeton U Pr.

Will, Clifford M. Theory & Experiment in Gravitational Physics. (Illus.). 384p. 1985. pap. 24.95 (ISBN 0-521-31710-X). Cambridge U Pr.

Williams, J. E., et al. Modern Physics. 1976. text ed. 25.92 (ISBN 0-03-089763-7, HoltE); tchr's guide 14.96 (ISBN 0-03-089795-5). HR&W.

Wilson, Jerry. Technical College Physics. 1982. text ed. 33.95 (ISBN 0-03-057912-0, CBS C); instr's. manual 20.00 (ISBN 0-03-058491-4); study guide 12.95 (ISBN 0-03-058492-2). SCP.

Wilson, Jerry D. Physics: Concepts & Aplications. 2nd ed. (Illus.). 848p. 1981. text ed. 27.95 (ISBN 0-669-03373-1); instr's guide 1.95 (ISBN 0-669-01948-8); student guide 16.95 (ISBN 0-669-03362-6); lab guide 16.95 (ISBN 0-669-01947-X). Heath.

--Physics: Concepts & Applications. 1977. text ed. 20.95x (ISBN 0-669-96180-9); instructor's manual free (ISBN 0-669-00243-7). Heath.

Wolf, K. B., ed. Group Theoretical Methods in Physics: Proceedings. (Lecture Notes in Physics: Vol. 135). 629p. 1980. 48.00 (ISBN 0-387-10271-X). Springer-Verlag.

Wolkenstein, V. S. Problems in General Physics. 349p. 1975. 9.45 (ISBN 0-8285-1957-9, Pub. by Mir Pubs USSR). Imported Pubns.

Woolfson, M. M. Trends in Physics 1978. (Illus.). 1979. 87.50 (ISBN 0-9960017-8-6, Pub. by A Hilger England). Heyden.

Yavorsky, B. Modern Handbook of Physics. 712p. 1982. 13.95 (ISBN 0-8285-2372-X, Pub. by Mir Pubs USSR). Imported Pubns.

Yavorsky, B. & Detlaf, A. Handbook of Physics. 965p. 1975. 15.00 (ISBN 0-8285-0786-4, Pub. by Mir Pubs USSR). Imported Pubns.

Yavorsky, B. M. & Pinsky, A. A. Fundamentals of Physics, 2 vols. 1030p. 1974. Set. 11.50 (ISBN 0-8285-0781-3, Pub. by Mir Pubs USSR). Imported Pubns.

Yavorsky, B. M. & Seleznov, Y. A. Physics: A Refresher Course. 654p. 1979. 12.00 (ISBN 0-8285-1539-5, Pub. by Mir Pubs USSR). Imported Pubns.

Young, Hugh D. Fundamentals of Waves, Optics & Modern Physics. 2nd ed. 1975. 42.95 (ISBN 0-07-072521-7). McGraw.

Zafiratos, C. Physics. LC 75-14034. 911p. 1976. 41.00 (ISBN 0-471-98104-4). Wiley.

Zafiratos, C. D. Physics. 2nd ed. 797p. 1985. 38.95 (ISBN 0-471-06309-6); solutions manual 9.95 (ISBN 0-471-81185-8). Wiley.

Zebrowski, Ernest, Jr. Physics for the Technician. 1974. text ed. 27.40 (ISBN 0-07-072780-5). McGraw.

--Practical Physics. (Illus.). 1980. 22.85 (ISBN 0-07-072788-0). McGraw.

Zichichi, Antonino, ed. The Unity of the Fundamental Interactions. (The Subnuclear Ser.: Vol. 19). 760p. 1983. 110.00x (ISBN 0-306-41242-X, Plenum Press). Plenum Pub.

Ziman, John M. Models of Disorder. LC 77-82527. (Illus.). 1979. 87.50 (ISBN 0-521-21784-9); pap. 29.95 (ISBN 0-521-29280-8). Cambridge U Pr.

Zinoviev, A. A. Logical Physics. 1983. lib. bdg. 59.00 (ISBN 90-277-0734-0, Pub. by Reidel Holland). Kluwer Academic.

Zukav, Gary. The Dancing Wu Li Masters: An Overview of the New Physics. (A Bantam New Age Bk.). 384p. 1980. pap. 4.50 (ISBN 0-553-24914-2). Bantam.

--The Dancing Wu Li Masters: An Overview of the New Physics. LC 78-25827. (Illus.). 1979. 14.95 (ISBN 0-688-03402-0); pap. 8.95 (ISBN 0-688-08402-8). Morrow.

PHYSICS–ADDRESSES, ESSAYS, LECTURES

Ahlfors, L. V., et al. Some Problems of Mathematics & Physics. LC 76-4884. (Translations Ser.: No. 2, Vol. 104). 1976. 55.00 (ISBN 0-8218-3054-6, TRANS 2-104). Am Math.

Bai-Lin, Hao. Chaos. 586p. 1984. 56.00 (ISBN 9971-966-50-6, Pub. by World Sci Singapore); pap. 26.00x (ISBN 9971-966-51-4, Pub. by World Sci Singapore). Taylor & Francis.

Balachandran, A. P. & Trahern, G. C. Lectures on Group Theory for Physicists. (Monographs & Textbooks on Physical Sciences). 110p. 1984. pap. text ed. 20.00x (ISBN 88-7088-088-5, Pub. by Bibliopolis, Italy). Humanities.

Barut, A. O. & Brittin, Wesley E., eds. Lectures in Theoretical Physics, Vol. 14A: Topics in Strong Interactions. (Illus.). 455p. 1972. text ed. 22.50x (ISBN 0-87081-043-X). Colo Assoc.

Barut, Asim O. & Brittin, Wesley E., eds. Lectures in Theoretical Physics Vol. 13: Desitter & Conformal Groups & Their Applications. 1971. 22.50x (ISBN 0-87081-014-6); pap. text ed. 10.00x (ISBN 0-87081-039-1). Colo Assoc.

Barut, Asim O., et al, eds. Quantum Space & Time-the Quest Continues: Studies & Essays in Honour of Louis de Broglie, Paul Dirac & Eugene Wigner. (Monographs in Physics). (Illus.). 680p. 1984. pap. 49.50 (ISBN 0-521-31911-0). Cambridge U Pr.

Berger, C., ed. Photon-Photon Collisions. (Lecture Notes in Physics Ser.: Vol. 191). 417p. 1983. pap. 22.00 (ISBN 0-387-12691-0). Springer-Verlag.

Bernasconi, J. & Schneider, Toni, eds. Physics in One Dimension: Proceedings. (Springer Ser. in Solid-State Sciences: Vol. 23). (Illus.). 368p. 1981. 37.00 (ISBN 0-387-10586-7). Springer-Verlag.

Blum, W., et al, eds. W. Heisenberg: Gesammelte Werke - Collected Works. 509p. 1984. 39.50 (ISBN 0-387-13020-9). Springer-Verlag.

Born, M. Physics in My Generation. 2nd rev. ed. LC 68-59281. (Heidelberg Science Lib: Vol. 7). (Illus.). 1969. pap. 12.95 (ISBN 0-387-90008-X). Springer-Verlag.

Brittin, W., ed. Lectures in Theoretical Physics, Vol. 14 B: Mathematical Methods in Theoretical Physics. LC 59-13034. (Illus.). 520p. 1973. 22.50x (ISBN 0-87081-047-2). Colo Assoc.

Brittin, Wesley E. & Odabasi, Halis, eds. Topics in Modern Physics: Tribute to E. U. Condon. LC 70-135286. 1971. 19.50x (ISBN 0-87081-010-3). Colo Assoc.

Bunge, M., ed. Studies in the Foundations, Methodology & Philosophy of Science, 4 vols. Incl. Vol. 1. Delaware Seminar in the Foundations of Physics. (Illus.); Vol. 2. Quantum Theory & Reality. 1967. 28.00 (ISBN 0-387-03993-7); Vol. 3, Pt. 1. The Search for System. (Illus.). xii, 536p. 1967. 54.50 (ISBN 0-387-03994-5); Vol. 3, Pt. 2. The Search for Truth. (Illus.). viii, 374p. 1967. 47.00 (ISBN 0-387-03995-3); Vol. 4. Problems in the Foundations of Physics. (Illus.). 1971. 28.00 (ISBN 0-387-05490-1). LC 71-163433. Springer-Verlag.

Castellani, C., et al, eds. Disordered Systems & Localization: Proceedings. (Lecture Notes in Physics Ser.: Vol. 149). 308p. 1981. pap. 22.00 (ISBN 0-387-11163-8). Springer-Verlag.

Cernuschi, Felix. Experimento, Razonamiento y Creacion en Fisica. 3rd ed. (Serie de Fisica Monografia: No. 5). 151p. 1981. pap. text ed. 3.50 (ISBN 0-8270-1417-1). OAS.

Conn, G. K. & Fowler, G. N., eds. Essays in Physics. Vol. 4. 1972. pap. 24.00 (ISBN 0-12-184804-3); Vol. 5, 1974. pap. 25.00 (ISBN 0-12-184805-1); Vol. 6, 1976. pap. 24.00 (ISBN 0-12-184806-X). Acad Pr.

Cowley, J. M. Diffraction Physics. 2nd, rev. ed. 1981. 68.00 (ISBN 0-444-86121-1). Elsevier.

Dirac, Pam, et al. Directions in Physics: Lectures Delivered During a Visit to Australia & New Zealand, August & September, 1975. LC 77-24892. 95p. 1978. 24.50x (ISBN 0-471-02997-1, Pub. by Wiley-Interscience). Wiley.

Eguch, T. & Yamaguchi, Y., eds. Tokyo Topical Symposium on High Energy Physics, 1982: Proceedings of the Symposium Tokyo, Japan, Sept. 7-11, 1982. vi, 392p. 1983. 46.00x (ISBN 9971-950-74-X, Pub. by World Sci Singapore). Taylor & Francis.

Einstein, Albert. Essays in Physics. (Philosphical Paperback Ser.). 75p. 1985. pap. 3.95 (ISBN 0-8022-2482-2). Philos Lib.

Enz, C. P. & Mehra, J., eds. Physical Reality & Mathematical Description: Dedicated to Josef Maria Jauch on the Occasion of His Sixtieth Birthday. LC 74-81937. xxiii, 552p. 1974. lib. bdg. 66.00 (ISBN 90-277-0513-5, Pub. by Reidel Holland). Kluwer Academic.

Falk, H., ed. CCNY Physics Symposium: In Celebration of Melvin Lax's Sixtieth Birthday. 364p. (Orig.). 1983. pap. text ed. write for info. (ISBN 0-9611452-0-X). City Coll Physics.

Ferrando, A., et al, eds. SU3 X SU2 X U1 & Beyond: Proceedings of the XIIIth GIFT International Seminar on Theoretical Physics & Xth Winter Meeting on Fundamentals Physics Masella, Girona, Spain, Jan. 28-Feb. 6, 1982. 516p. 1983. 60.00x (ISBN 9971-950-79-0, Pub. by World Sci Singapore). Taylor & Francis.

Feynman, R. P., et al. Feynman Lectures on Physics, 3 Vols. Vol. 1. text ed. 19.95 (ISBN 0-201-02116-1); Vol. 2. text ed. 19.95 (ISBN 0-201-02117-X); Vol. 3. text ed. 19.95 (ISBN 0-201-02118-8); Set. text ed. 52.95 (ISBN 0-201-02115-3); exercises for vols 2 & 3 o. p. 3.25. Vol. 2 Excercises o. p. Vol. 3 (ISBN 0-201-02019-X). Addison-Wesley.

Freund, Peter G. & Goebel, C. J., eds. Quanta: Essays in Theorectical Physics Dedicated to Gregory Wentzel. LC 70-108268. pap. 107.50 (ISBN 0-317-08085-7, 2019966). Bks Demand UMI.

Fronsdal, C., et al. Selected Papers of Julian Schwinger. (Mathematical Physics & Applied Mathematics Ser.: No. 4). 1979. lib. bdg. 29.50 (ISBN 90-277-0974-2, Pub. by Reidel Holland); pap. 11.95 (ISBN 90-277-0975-0, Pub. by Reidel Holland). Kluwer Academic.

Gamow, George. Mister Tompkins in Paperback. (Illus., Orig.). 1967. bds. 29.95 (ISBN 0-521-06905-X); pap. 7.95 (ISBN 0-521-09355-4). Cambridge U Pr.

Goeke, K. & Reinhard, P. G. Time Dependent Hartree-Fock & Beyond, Bad Honnef, FRG, 1982 Proceedings. (Lecture Notes in Physics: Vol. 171). 426p. 1982. pap. 23.00 (ISBN 0-387-11950-7). Springer-Verlag.

Guth, Alan H., et al, eds. Asymptotic Realms of Physics: Essays in Honor of Francis E. Low. (Illus.). 336p. 1983. 40.00x (ISBN 0-262-07089-8). MIT Pr.

Haken, H. Evolution of Order & Chaos in Physics, Chemistry, & Biology: Schloss Elmau, FRG, 1982 Proceedings. (Springer Series in Synergetics: Vol. 17). (Illus.). 287p. 1982. 35.00 (ISBN 0-387-11904-3). Springer-Verlag.

Harnad, J. P. & Shnider, S., eds. Geometrical & Topological Methods in Gauge Theories: Proceedings. (Lecture Notes in Physics: Vol. 129). 155p. 1980. pap. 17.00 (ISBN 0-387-10010-5). Springer-Verlag.

Hietarinta, J. & Montonen, C., eds. Integrable Quantum Field Theories: Proceedings. (Lecture Notes in Physics Ser.: Vol. 151). 251p. 1982. pap. 20.00 (ISBN 0-387-11190-5). Springer-Verlag.

Les Houches Lectures. Incl. 1961, Low Temperature Physics. DeWitt, C., et al, eds. 654p. 1962. 161.95x (ISBN 0-677-10090-6); 1962, Geophysics: the Earth's Environment. DeWitt, C., et al, eds. 638p. 1963. 132.95x (ISBN 0-677-10100-7); 1963, Relativity, Groups & Topology. DeWitt, C. & DeWitt, B. S., eds. 956p. 1964. 246.25x (ISBN 0-677-10080-9); 1964, Quantum Optics & Electronics. DeWitt, C., et al, eds. 633p. 1965. 166.50 (ISBN 0-677-10530-4); 1965, High Energy Physics. DeWitt, C. & Jacob, M., eds. 522p. 1965. 98.25x (ISBN 0-677-10760-9); 1967, Many-Body Physics. DeWitt, C. & Balian, R., eds. 444p. 1968. 119.25x (ISBN 0-677-12700-6). Gordon.

Huang, Kerson, ed. Physics & Our World: A Symposium in Honor of Victor F. Weisskopf MIT 1974. LC 76-7207. (AIP Conference Proceeding: No. 28). 164p. 1976. 15.00 (ISBN 0-88318-127-4). Am Inst Physics.

Jacob, M., ed. CERN: 25 Years of Physics. (Physics Reports Reprint Bk.: Vol. 4). 560p. 1981. 74.50 (ISBN 0-444-86146-7, North-Holland). Elsevier.

Kang, K., et al. Grand Unification, Fifth Workshop: Held at Brown University, Providence, RI, April 12-14, 1984. 480p. 1984. 52.00x (ISBN 9971-966-58-1, Pub. by World Sci Singapore); pap. 26.00x (ISBN 9971-966-59-X, Pub. by World Sci Singapore). Taylor & Francis.

Kathren, Ronald L., et al, eds. Computer Applications in Health Physics. (Illus.). 822p. 1984. 35.00 (ISBN 0-9613108-0-4). Health Phys Soc.

Khalatnikov, I. M., ed. Physics Reviews, Vol. 4. (Soviet Scientific Reviews Ser.: Section A). 296p. 1982. 170.00 (ISBN 3-7186-0106-0). Harwood Academic.

Khalatnikov, I. M. & Landau, L. D., eds. Physics Reviews, Vol. 5. (Soviet Scientific Reviews Ser.: Section A). LC 725-128292. 1984. 170.00 (ISBN 3-7186-0138-9). Harwood Academic.

Kneubuhl, F. K. & Moss, T. S., eds. Infrared Physics Three: Papers from the Third International Conference (CIRP 3) Held in Zurich, Switzerland, 23-27 July 1984. 550p. 1985. pap. 80.00 (ISBN 0-08-031442-2, Pub. by Aberdeen Scotland). Pergamon.

Korner, J. G., et al, eds. Current Induced Reactions. (Lecture Notes in Physics: Vol. 56). 1976. soft cover 27.00 (ISBN 3-540-07866-5). Springer-Verlag.

Koslow, Arnold. The Changeless Order. LC 67-24207. (Science Ser). 1967. 7.50 (ISBN 0-8076-0429-1). Braziller.

Laszlo, Ervin & Sellon, Emily B., eds. Vistas in Physical Reality. LC 75-34356. (Illus.). 228p. 1976. 39.50x (ISBN 0-306-30884-3, Plenum Pr). Plenum Pub.

Lavoisier, Antoine. Essays, Physical & Chemical. Thomas, H., tr. 511p. 1970. Repr. of 1776 ed. 45.00x (ISBN 0-7146-1604-4, F Cass Co). Biblio Dist.

Levy, M., ed. Cargese Lectures in Physics, 1972, Vol. 7. 418p. 1977. 91.50x (ISBN 0-677-15750-9). Gordon.

Levy, M. & Bessis, D., eds. Cargese Lectures in Physics, Vol. 5. 556p. 1972. 132.95x (ISBN 0-677-15180-2). Gordon.

Levy, Maurice, ed. Cargese Lectures in Physics, 1966-1968, Vols. 1-3. (Orig.). 1967-69. Vol. 1, 1967, 438p. 113.50x (ISBN 0-677-11650-0); Vol. 2, 1968, 432p. 80.95x (ISBN 0-677-12720-0); Vol. 3, 1969, 686p. 124.50x (ISBN 0-677-13580-7). Gordon.

Levy, Maurice & Kastler, D., eds. Cargese Lectures in Physics, 1969, Vol. 4. 398p. 1970. 106.50 (ISBN 0-677-13910-1). Gordon.

Marion, J. B. General Physics with Bioscience Essays. 2nd ed. 592p. 1985. 36.45 (ISBN 0-471-89878-3); study guide 9.95 (ISBN 0-471-81340-0). Wiley.

Massey, H. A Perspective of Physics: Volume 4, Selections from Nineteen Seventy-Nine Comments on Modern Physics. 384p. 1981. 57.75 (ISBN 0-677-16190-5). Gordon.

Nath, P., et al. Applied N-1 Supergravity, Vol. 1. (ICIP Lecture Series in Theoretical Physics Lectures). 1984. 22.00x (ISBN 9971-966-48-4, Pub. by World Sci Singapore); pap. 10.00x (ISBN 9971-966-49-2). Taylor & Francis.

Ne'Emann, Yuval, ed. Jerusalem Einstein Centennial Symposium. (Illus.). 528p. 1980. text ed. 54.95 (ISBN 0-201-05289-X). Addison-Wesley.

Newman, H. D., ed. Electroweak Effects at High Energies. (Ettore Majorana, International Science Ser.: Physical Sciences-Vol. 21). 848p. 1985. 129.50x (ISBN 0-306-41904-1, Plenum Pr). Plenum Pub.

Nobel Foundation. Nobel Lectures in Physics, 1901-1970, 4 vols. Incl. Vol. 1. 1901-1921. 1967. 76.75 (ISBN 0-444-40416-3); Vol. 2. 1922-1941. 1965 (ISBN 0-444-40417-1); Vol. 3. 1942-1962. 1964 (ISBN 0-444-40418-X); Vol. 4. 1963-1970. 1973 (ISBN 0-444-40993-9). 76.75 ea. Elsevier.

Pakvas, S. & Tuan, S. F., eds. Selected Lectures from the Hawaii Topical Conferences in Particle Physics, 2 vols. 1006p. 1982. Set. 88.00x (ISBN 9971-950-36-7, Pub. by World Sci Singapore); Set. pap. 42.00x (ISBN 9971-950-16-2, Pub. by World Sci Singapore). Taylor & Francis.

Parry, W. E., ed. Essays in Theoretical Physics: In Honor of Dirk ter Haar. (Illus.). 352p. 1984. 50.00 (ISBN 0-08-026523-5). Pergamon.

Pauli, Wolfgang. Pauli Lectures on Physics. Enz, C. P., ed. Marguilies, S. & Lewis, H. R., trs. Incl. Vol. 1. Electrodynamics. LC 76-155320 (ISBN 0-262-66033-4); Vol. 2. Optics & the Theory of Electrons. LC 72-7802 (ISBN 0-262-66034-2); Vol. 3. Thermodynamics & the Kinetic Theory of Gases. LC 72-7803 (ISBN 0-262-66035-0); Vol. 4. Statistical Mechanics. LC 72-7804 (ISBN 0-262-66036-9); Vol. 5. Wave Mechanics. LC 72-7805 (ISBN 0-262-66037-7); Vol. 6. Selected Topics in Field Quantization. LC 72-7807 (ISBN 0-262-66038-5). 1973. pap. text ed. 30.00x set (ISBN 0-262-66032-6); pap. text ed. 6.95x ea. MIT Pr.

Pictronero, L. & Tosatti, E., eds. Physics of Intercalation Compounds: Proceedings. (Springer Series in Solid-State Sciences: Vol. 38). (Illus.). 323p. 1981. 31.00 (ISBN 0-387-11283-9). Springer-Verlag.

Pippard, A. B. Reconciling Physics With Reality: An Inagural Lecture. LC 70-187082. pap. 20.00 (ISBN 0-317-08599-9, 2051384). Bks Demand UMI.

Prasanna, A. R., et al, eds. Gravitation, Quanta & the Universe: Proceedings of the Einstein Centenary Symposium Held at Ahmedabad, India 29 January to 3 February, 1979. LC 80-17051. 326p. 1980. 58.95x (ISBN 0-470-27007-1). Halsted Pr.

Raman, Chandrasekhara V. New Physics. facs. ed. LC 72-128292. (Essay Index Reprint Ser). 1951. 17.00 (ISBN 0-8369-2020-1). Ayer Co Pubs.

Rudaz, S. & Walsh, T., eds. Sixth Workshop on Grand Unification: Proceedings of the Sixth Workshop on Grand Unification. 500p. 1985. 60.00x (ISBN 0-317-27184-9, Pub. by World Sci Singapore). Taylor & Francis.

Schwartz, John H. Superstrings, 2 Vols. 950p. 1985. 90.00x (ISBN 0-317-27175-X, Pub by World Sci Singapore); pap. 42.00x (ISBN 0-317-27176-8). Taylor & Francis.

Seiler, Hansjakob, ed. Apprehension: Das Sprachliche Erfassen von Gegenstaenden. Incl. Pt. I. Bereich & Ordnung der Phaenomene. 300p. 1982. 44.00x (ISBN 3-87808-985-6); Pt. II. Die Techniken & Ihr Zuzammenhang in Einzelsprachen. 1983. 44.00x (ISBN 3-87808-984-8); Pt. III. 1982. price not set (ISBN 3-87808-983-X). Benjamins North Am.

Seligman, Thomas H., ed. Group Theory & Its Applications in Physics, 1980: Latin American School of Physics, Mexico City. (AIP Conference Proceedings: No. 71). 349p. 1981. lib. bdg. 32.00 (ISBN 0-88318-170-3). Am Inst Physics.

Streit, L. Mathematics & Physics: Lectures on Recent Results, Vol. 1. 320p. 1984. 35.00x (ISBN 9971-966-63-8, Pub. by World Sci Singapore); pap. 22.00x (ISBN 9971-966-64-6, Pub. by World Sci Singapore). Taylor & Francis.

Surface Physics. (Tracts in Modern Physics: Vol. 77). (Illus.). 130p. 1975. 35.00 (ISBN 0-387-07501-1). Springer-Verlag.

Symposium, Nice, 1973. Hyperfunctions & Theoretical Physics: Proceedings. Pham, F. L., ed. (Lecture Notes in Mathematics Ser.: Vol. 449). iv, 218p. 1975. pap. 16.00 (ISBN 0-387-07151-2). Springer-Verlag.

Symposium on Classical & Quantum Mechanical Aspects of Heavy Ion Collisions, Max-Planck-Institut Fuer. Kernphysik, Heidelberg, Oct 2-5, 1974. Proceedings. Harney, H. L., et al, eds. LC 74-32179. (Lecture Notes in Physics Ser: Vol. 33). viii, 312p. 1975. pap. 19.00 (ISBN 0-387-07025-7). Springer-Verlag.

Ter Haar, D., ed. Collected Papers of P. L. Kapitza, Vol. 4. (Illus.). 384p. 1984. 100.00 (ISBN 0-08-026505-7). Pergamon.

Ter Haar, D. & Scully, M. O., eds. Willis E. Lamb, Jr. A Festschrift on the Occasion of His 65th Birthday. (Physics Reports Reprint Book: Vol. 3). 518p. 1979. 76.75 (ISBN 0-444-85253-0, North Holland). Elsevier.

Thooft, G., et al, eds. Recent Developments in Gauge Theories. LC 80-18528. (NATO ASI Series B, Physics: Vol. 59). 446p. 1980. 69.50x (ISBN 0-306-40479-6, Plenum Pr). Plenum Pub.

Urban, P., ed. Contacts Between High Energy Physics & Other Fields of Physics: Proceedings. (Acta Physica Austriaca: Suppl. 18). (Illus.). 1977. 122.80 (ISBN 0-387-81454-X). Springer-Verlag.

Wigner, Eugene P. Symmetries & Reflections. LC 79-89843. 1979. pap. text ed. 10.00 (ISBN 0-918024-16-1). Ox Bow.

Wilber, Ken, ed. Quantum Questions: Mystical Writings of the Great Physicists. LC 83-20332. (New Science Library). 200p. 1984. pap. 8.95 (ISBN 0-87773-266-3). Shambhala Pubns.

Wolf, K. B., ed. Nonlinear Phenomena. (Lecture Notes in Physics Ser.: Vol. 189). 453p. 1983. pap. 25.00 (ISBN 0-387-12730-5). Springer-Verlag.

PHYSICS–APPARATUS AND INSTRUMENTS

see Physical Instruments

PHYSICS–BIBLIOGRAPHY

Brush, Stephen G. & Belloni, Lanfranoo. The History of Modern Physics: An International Bibliography. LC 82-49291. (The History of Science & Technology Ser.: Vol. 4). 400p. 1983. lib. bdg. 42.00 (ISBN 0-8240-9117-5). Garland Pub.

Home, R. W. & Gittins, Mark J. The History of Classical Physics: A Selected, Annotated Bibliography. Multhauf, Robert & Wells, Ellen, eds. LC 83-48276. (Bibliographies of the History of Science & Technology Ser.). 300p. 1984. lib. bdg. 53.00 (ISBN 0-8240-9067-5). Garland Pub.

Kuhn, Thomas S., et al. Sources for History of Quantum Physics. LC 66-26634. (Memoirs Ser.: Vol. 68). 1967. 7.50 (ISBN 0-87169-068-3). Am Philos.

Marton, Claire, ed. Advances in Electronics & Electron Physics, Vol. 58. (Serial Publication Ser.). 1982. 75.00 (ISBN 0-12-014658-4). Acad Pr.

Palyza, M. M. Useful Books of Reference for Designers (1926-1983) Held by the Science Reference Library: Pt 1 Units in Physics, Metrication, Mettallurgy, Computers in Engineering, Civil Engineering. 168p. (Orig.). 1984. pap. 7.50 (ISBN 0-7123-0712-5, Pub. by British Lib). Longwood Pub Group.

Princeton University. Dictionary Catalog of the Princeton University Plasma Physics Laboratory Library, First Supplement. 1973. lib. bdg. 160.00 (ISBN 0-8161-1032-8, Hall Library). G K Hall.

Yates, B. How to Find Out About Physics. 1965. pap. 7.75 (ISBN 0-08-011288-9). Pergamon.

PHYSICS–COLLECTED WORKS

Benedek, G. B. & Villars, F. M. Physics with Illustrative Examples from Medicine & Biology, 2 vols. 1974. 25.95 ea.; Vol. 1. 23.95 (ISBN 0-201-00551-4). Vol. 2 (ISBN 0-201-00558-1). Addison-Wesley.

Bohr, Niels. Niels Bohr Collected Works, Vol. 1: Early Work, 1905-1911. Nielsen, J. R., ed. 608p. 1973. 125.75 (ISBN 0-444-10003-2, North-Holland). Elsevier.

Brueckner, Keith A., ed. Advances in Theoretical Physics, 2 Vols. Vol. 1 1965. 68.50 (ISBN 0-12-038501-5); Vol. 2 1968. 60.00 (ISBN 0-12-038502-3). Acad Pr.

Fermi, Enrico. Collected Papers of Enrico Fermi, 2 vols. Segre, Emilio, ed. Incl. Vol. 1. Italy, 1921-38. 60.00x (ISBN 0-226-24359-1); Vol. 2. United States, 1939-54. 60.00x (ISBN 0-226-24360-5). LC 60-12465. 1965. U of Chicago Pr.

Fresnel, Augustin J. Oeuvres Completes, 3 vols. (Lat.). Repr. of 1866 ed. 160.00 (ISBN 0-384-16770-5). Johnson Repr.

Green, George. Mathematical Papers. LC 70-92316. 19.95 (ISBN 0-8284-0229-9). Chelsea Pub.

Hoehler, G., ed. Springer Tracts in Modern Physics, Vol. 40. (Eng. & Ger., Illus.). 1966. 34.30 (ISBN 0-387-03669-5). Springer-Verlag.

Kirkwood, John G. Collected Papers, 8 vol. set. 1951p. 1968. 374.50 (ISBN 0-677-01720-0). Gordon.

Lagemann, Robert T. The Garland Collection of Classical Physics Apparatus at Vanderbilt University. LC 84-81830. (Illus.). 317p. (Orig.). 1984. pap. 12.95 (ISBN 0-9613702-0-3). Folio Pubs.

Lavoisier, Antoine-L. Oeuvres de Lavoisier, 6 Vols. (Illus.). Repr. of 1893 ed. Set. 210.00 (ISBN 0-384-31677-8). Johnson Repr.

Lorenz, Ludwig V. Oeuvres Scientifiques De L. Lorenz, 2 Vols. 1898-1904. Set. 60.00 (ISBN 0-384-33740-6). Johnson Repr.

Minkowski, Hermann. Gesammelte Abhandlungen, 2 Vols. in 1. LC 66-28570. (Ger). 39.50 (ISBN 0-8284-0208-6). Chelsea Pub.

Stokes, George G. Mathematical & Physical Papers, 5 Vols. 2nd ed. Repr. of 1905 ed. Set. 165.00 (ISBN 0-384-58370-9). Johnson Repr.

Szilard, Leo. Collected Works of Leo Szilard: Scientific Papers. Feld, Bernard T. & Szilard, Gertrud W., eds. 1972. 47.50x (ISBN 0-262-06039-6). MIT Pr.

Ter Haar, D. Collected Papers of L. C. Landau. 856p. 1965. 139.95 (ISBN 0-677-20550-3). Gordon.

--L. D. Landau, Vol. 2. 1969. pap. 8.50 (ISBN 0-08-006450-7). Pergamon.

Thomson, James. Collected Papers in Physics & Engineering. LC 70-137300. Repr. of 1912 ed. 35.00 (ISBN 0-404-06422-1). AMS Pr.

Walker, Jearl, intro. by. The Physics of Everyday Phenomena: Readings from Scientific American. LC 79-9287. (Illus.). 86p. 1979. pap. text ed. 8.95x (ISBN 0-7167-1126-5). W H Freeman.

PHYSICS–DATA PROCESSING

Agrawala, A. K. & Tripathi, S. K., eds. Performance Eighty-Three: Proceedings of the International Symposium on Computer Performance Modelling, Measurement & Evaluation, 9th, College Park, Maryland, May 25-27, 1983. 488p. 1984. 49.00 (ISBN 0-444-86673-6, I-467-83, North Holland). Elsevier.

Ames, W. F., et al, eds. Scientific Computing: Proceedings of the IMACS World Congress on Systems, Simulation, & Scientific Computation, Tenth, Montreal, Canada, 8-13 Aug., 1982. (IMACS Transactions on Scientific Computation Ser.: Vol. 1). 364p. 1983. 51.00 (ISBN 0-444-86607-8, North Holland). Elsevier.

Arfken, George. Computer Software: For University Physics. 1984. text ed. write for info. (ISBN 0-12-059869-8). Acad Pr.

Bork, A., ed. Computer Assisted Learning in Physics Education. LC 80-41129. (Illus.). 80p. 1980. 36.00 (ISBN 0-08-025812-3). Pergamon.

Brody, T. A. Symbol Manipulation Techniques for Physics. (Documents on Modern Physics Ser.). 104p. 1968. 44.25 (ISBN 0-677-01820-7). Gordon.

Computing as a Language of Physics. (Illus.). 616p. (Orig.). 1973. pap. 44.50 (ISBN 92-0-130172-3, ISP306, IAEA). Unipub.

Gottlieb, Herbert H. Physics: Lab Experiments & Correlated Computer Aids. 1981. 10.50 (ISBN 0-318-01172-7). Microphys Prog.

Greenspan, H., et al, eds. Computing Methods in Reactor Physics. 602p. (Orig.). 1968. 114.50 (ISBN 0-677-11890-2). Gordon.

Holland, C. D. & Liapis, A. I. Computer Methods for Solving Dynamic Separation Problems. (Illus.). 512p. 1983. text ed. 48.00 (ISBN 0-07-029573-5). McGraw.

International Conference on Solid State Nuclear Track Detectors, 11th, Bristol, UK, Sept. 1981. Solid State Nuclear Track Detectors: Proceedings. Fowler, P. H. & Clapham, V. M., eds. (Illus.). 958p. 1982. 195.00 (ISBN 0-08-026509-X, C120, C140). Pergamon.

International Conference on Solid State Nuclear Track Detectors, 10th, Lyon, France, July 1979. Solid State Nuclear Track Detectors: Proceedings. Francois, H., et al, eds. LC 79-41577. (Illus.). 1082p. 1980. 145.00 (ISBN 0-08-025029-7). Pergamon.

International Conference on Solid State Nuclear Track Detectors, 9th, Neuherberg-Munich, 1976. Solid State Nuclear Track Detectors: Proceedings, 2 vols. Granzer, F., et al, eds. LC 77-30630. (Illus.). 1312p. 1978. Set. text ed. 285.00 (ISBN 0-08-021659-5). Pergamon.

Kathren, Ronald L., et al, eds. Computer Applications in Health Physics. (Illus.). 822p. 1984. 35.00 (ISBN 0-9613108-0-4). Health Phys Soc.

Mattson, J., et al, eds. Spectroscopy & Kinetics. (Computers in Chemistry & Instrumentation Ser: Vol. 3). 352p. 1973. 69.75 (ISBN 0-8247-6058-1). Dekker.

Merrill, John R. Using Computers in Physics. LC 80-5681. 271p. 1980. pap. text ed. 13.25 (ISBN 0-8191-1134-1). U Pr of Amer.

Miwa, T. & Jimbo, M., eds. Non-Linear Integrable Systems-Classical Theory & Quantum Theory: Proceedings of RIMS Symposium, Kyoto, Japan, May 13-16, 1981. vi, 290p. 1982. 29.00x (ISBN 9971-950-32-4, Pub. by World Sci Singapore). Taylor & Francis.

Nelson, Walter R. & Jenkins, T. M., eds. Computer Techniques in Shielding & Dosimetry. LC 79-20872. (Ettore Majorana International Science Ser., Physical Sciences: Vol. 3). 530p. 1980. 79.50x (ISBN 0-306-40307-2, Plenum Pr). Plenum Pub.

Numerical Reactor Calculations. (Proceedings Ser.). (Illus.). 836p. (Orig.). 1972. pap. 59.50 (ISBN 92-0-030072-3, ISP307, IAEA). Unipub.

Patterson, G. A. Engine Thermodynamics with a Pocket Calculator. 2nd ed. 149p. 1983. 14.95 (ISBN 0-917410-07-6). Basic Sci Pr.

Rader, Richard. Entelek Computer-Based Physics Lab. 133p. 1976. pap. text ed. 14.95 (ISBN 0-87567-035-0); incl. diskette 80.00. Entelek.

Rosenfeld, A., ed. Digital Picture Analysis. (Topics in Applied Physics Ser: Vol. 11). 1976. 44.00 (ISBN 0-387-07579-8). Springer-Verlag.

Simon, Sheridan. The Physics Disk. 80p. 1985. pap. text ed. 29.95 incl. disk (ISBN 0-13-672387-X). P-H.

Skobel'tsyn, D. V., ed. Programming & Computer Techniques in Experimental Physics. LC 71-118860. (P. N. Lebedev Physics Institute Ser.: Vol. 45). 126p. 1970. 25.00x (ISBN 0-306-10843-7, Consultants). Plenum Pub.

Spinrad, Bernard I. Use of Computers in Analysis of Experimental Data & the Control of Nuclear Facilities: Proceedings. LC 67-60057. (AEC Symposium Ser.). 306p. 1967. pap. 15.75 (ISBN 0-87079-214-8, CONF-660527); microfiche 4.50 (ISBN 0-87079-215-6, CONF-660527). DOE.

Volta Memorial Conference, Como, Italy, 1977. Stochastic Behavior in Classical & Quantum Hamiltonian Systems: Proceedings. Casati, G. & Ford, J., eds. (Lecture Notes in Physics: Vol. 93). 1979. pap. 22.00 (ISBN 0-387-09120-3). Springer-Verlag.

Wood, J. Computational Methods in Reactor Shielding. (Illus.). 450p. 1981. 61.00 (ISBN 0-08-028685-2); pap. 21.00 (ISBN 0-08-028686-0). Pergamon.

PHYSICS–DICTIONARIES

Alekseev, P. M. English-Russian Glossary of Physics Terms. (Eng. & Rus.). 288p. 1980. 35.00x (ISBN 0-686-44696-8, Pub. by Collets). State Mutual Bk.

Ballentyne, D. W. & Walker, L. E. Diccionario de Leyes y Efectos Cientificos En Quimica-Fisica Matematicas. (Span.). 216p. 14.95 (ISBN 0-686-56711-0, S-33054). French & Eur.

Becker, U. Herder-Lexikon Weltaumphysik. (Ger.). 240p. 1975. pap. 17.95 (ISBN 3-451-16463-9, M-7461, Pub. by Herder). French & Eur.

Becker, Udo. Diccionario Rioduero: Fisica Del Espacio. (Span.). 264p. 1978. leatherette 13.25 (ISBN 84-220-0846-7, S-50163). French & Eur.

Besancon, Robert M., ed. The Encyclopedia of Physics. 3rd ed. 1985. 149.50 (ISBN 0-442-25778-3). Van Nos Reinhold.

Bindmann. Festkoerperphysik und Elektronische Technik. (Eng. & Ger.). 1104p. (Dictionary of Solid State Physics and Electrical Engineering). 1972. 83.95 (ISBN 3-87097-055-3, M-7410, Pub. by Brandstetter). French & Eur.

Bindmann, W. Dictionary of Solid State Physics & Electronics Technology: English-German, German-English. (Technical Dictionary). 1973. 31.50x (ISBN 0-685-27547-7). Adlers Foreign Bks.

Birdmann, G. English-German, German, English Solid State Physics & Electronics Dictionary. (Eng. & Ger.). 1103p. 1980. 100.00x (ISBN 0-569-07204-2, Pub. by Collet's). State Mutual Bk.

Chang, S. Chinese-English Dictionary of Physical Terms. (Eng. & Ger.). 405p. 1969. pap. 75.00 (ISBN 0-686-56601-7, M-7322, Pub. by Harrassowitz). French & Eur.

Clason, W. E. Elsevier's Dictionary of General Physics. (Eng., Fr., Span., Ital., Dutch & Ger.). 859p. (Polyglot). 1962. 123.50 (ISBN 0-444-40122-9). Elsevier.

Daintith, John, ed. Dictionary of Physics. 216p. 1982. pap. 6.25i (ISBN 0-06-463560-0, EH-560). Har-Row.

--The Facts on File Dictionary of Physics. 248p. 1981. 14.95 (ISBN 0-87196-511-9). Facts on File.

De Vries, L. Woerterbuch der Reinen und Angewandten Physik, Vol. 1. (Ger. & Eng., Dictionary of Physics & Applied Physics). 1964. 38.00 (ISBN 3-486-30942-0, M-6954). French & Eur.

--Woerterbuch der Reinen und Angewandten Physik, Vol. 2. (Eng. & Ger., Dictionary of Physics & Applied Physics). 1964. 38.00 (ISBN 0-686-56615-7, M-6962). French & Eur.

De Vries, L. & Clason, W. E. Dictionary of Pure & Applied Physics: German-English. 367p. 46.75 (ISBN 0-444-40168-7). Elsevier.

Dictionary of Physics. (Eng. & Chinese.). 1689p. 1978. 19.95 (ISBN 0-686-92341-3, M-9287). French & Eur.

English-Russian Dictionary of Minimum Physics. (Eng. & Rus.). 287p. 1980. leatherette 7.95 (ISBN 0-686-97372-0, M-9123). French & Eur.

Fluegge, E., ed. Encyclopedia of Physics, 54 vols, Vols. 11-12, 14-19. Incl. Vol. 11, Pt. 1. Acoustics One. Tr. of Akustik One. (Illus.). 1961. 123.90 (ISBN 0-387-02686-X); Vol. 11, Pt. 2. Acoustics Two. Tr. of Akustik Two. (Illus.). 1962. 97.40 (ISBN 0-387-02841-2); Vol. 12. Thermodynamics of Gases. Tr. of Thermodynamik der Gase. (Illus.). 1958. 147.50 (ISBN 0-387-02292-9); Vol. 14. Low Temperature Physics One. Tr. of Kaeltephysik One. (Illus.). 1956. 70.80 (ISBN 0-387-02037-3); Vol. 15. Low Temperature Physics Two. Tr. of Kaeltephysik Two. (Illus.). 1956. 109.20 (ISBN 0-387-02038-1); Vol. 16. Electric Fields & Waves. Tr. of Elekrische Felder und Wellen. (Illus.). 1958. 153.40 (ISBN 0-387-02293-7); Vol. 17. Dielectrics. Tr. of Dielektrika. (Illus.). 1956. 94.40 (ISBN 0-387-02039-X); Vol. 18, Pt. 1. Magnetism. Wijn, H. P., ed. Tr. of Magnetismus. (Illus.). 1969. 153.40 (ISBN 0-387-04164-8); Vol. 18, Pt. 2. Ferromagnetism. Wijn, H. P., ed. Tr. of Ferromagnetismus. (Illus.). 1966. 153.40 (ISBN 0-387-03548-6); Vol. 19. Electrical Conductivity One. Tr. of Elektrische Leitungsphaenomene 1. (Illus.). 1956. 82.60 (ISBN 0-387-02040-3). Springer-Verlag.

--Encyclopedia of Physics, 54 vols, Vols. 21-23, 25, 27, 28, 30, 32, 34-35. Incl. Vol. 21. Electron Emission. Gas Discharges One. Tr. of Elektronen-Emission Gas-Entladungen 1. (Illus.). 1956. 129.80 (ISBN 0-387-02041-1); Vol. 22. Gas Discharges Two. Tr. of Gasentladungen Two. (Illus.). 1956. 126.90 (ISBN 0-387-02042-X); Vol. 23. Electrical Instruments. Pannenborg, A. E., ed. Tr. of Elektrische Instrumente. (Illus.). 1967. 153.40 (ISBN 0-387-03852-3); Vol. 25, Pt. 1. Crystal Optics, Diffraction. Tr. of Kristalloptik, Beugung. (Illus.). 1961; Vol. 25, Pts. 2a-2c. Light & Matter. Genzel, L., ed. Tr. of Licht und Materie. (Illus.). Pt. 2a, 1967. 88.50 (ISBN 0-387-03853-1); Pt. 2b, 1974. 116.90 (ISBN 0-387-06638-1); Pt. 2c, 1970. 94.40 (ISBN 0-387-04856-1); Vol. 27. Spectroscopy One. Tr. of Spektroskopie One. (Illus.). 1964. 115.10 (ISBN 0-387-03153-7); Vol. 28. Spectroscopy Two. Tr. of Spektroskopie Two. 1957. 97.40 (ISBN 0-387-02167-1); Vol. 30. X-Rays. Tr. of Roentgenstrahlen. (Illus.). 1957. 88.50 (ISBN 0-387-02168-X); Vol. 32. Structural Research. Tr. of Strukturforsc2'hung. (Illus.). 1957. 141.60 (ISBN 0-387-02169-8); Vol. 34. Corpuscles & Radiation in Matter Two. Tr. of Korpuskeln und Strahlung in Materie 2. (Illus.). 1958. 76.70 (ISBN 0-387-02295-3); Vol. 35. Atoms One. Tr. of Atome One. (Illus.). 1957. 97.40 (ISBN 0-387-02170-1). Springer-Verlag.

--Encyclopedia of Physics, 54 vols, Vols. 46-49, 51-54. Incl. Vol. 46, Pt. 1. Cosmic Rays One. 1961. 97.40 (ISBN 0-387-02689-4); Vol. 46, Pt. 2. Cosmic Rays Two. Sitte, K., ed. 1967. 159.30 (ISBN 0-387-03855-8); Vol. 47. Geophysics One. 1956. 116.90 (ISBN 0-387-02046-2); Vol. 48. Geophysics Two. 1957. 194.70 (ISBN 0-387-02174-4); Vol. 49. Geophysics Three, 4 pts. Bartels, J. & Rower, K., eds. (Illus.). Pt. 1, 1966. 112.10 (ISBN 0-387-03549-4); Pt. 2, 1967. 112.10 (ISBN 0-686-96891-3); Pt. 3, 537p, 1971. 159.30 (ISBN 0-387-05570-3); Pt. 4, 592p, 1972. 140.50 (ISBN 0-387-05583-5); Vol. 51. Astrophysics Two: Stellar Structure. Tr. of Astrophysik Two - Sternaufbau. (Illus.). 1958. 171.10 (ISBN 0-387-02299-6); Vol. 52. Astrophysics Three: The Solar System. Tr. of Astrophysik Three - das Sonnensystem. (Illus.). 1959. 141.60 (ISBN 0-387-02416-6); Vol. 53. Astrophysics Four: Stellar Systems. Tr. of Astrophysik Four - Sternsysteme. (Illus.). 1959. 141.60 (ISBN 0-387-02417-4); Vol. 54. Astrophysics Five: Miscellaneous. Tr. of Astrophysik Five - Verschiedenes. (Illus.). 1962. 97.40 (ISBN 0-387-02844-7). Springer-Verlag.

Fluegge, S., ed. Encyclopedia of Physics, 54 vols, Vols. 3-4, 6, 8-10. Incl. Vol. 3, Pt. 1. Principles of Classical Mechanics & Field Theory. Tr. of Prinzipien der Klassischen Mechanik und Feldtheorie. (Illus.). viii, 902p. 1960; Vol. 3, Pt. 3. The Non-Linear Field Theories of Mechanics. Truesdell, C. & Noll, W. Tr. of Die Nicht-Linearen Feldtheorien der Mechanik. (Illus.). viii, 602p. 1965. 174.10 (ISBN 0-387-03313-0); Vol. 4. Principles of Electrodynamics & Relativity. Tr. of Prinzipien der Elektrodynamik und Relativitatstheorie. (Illus.). vi, 290p. 1962. 97.40 (ISBN 0-387-02840-4); Vol. 6. Elasticity & Plasticity. Tr. of Elastizitaet und Plastizitaet. (Illus.). viii, 642p. 1958. 141.60 (ISBN 0-387-02290-2); Vol. 6a, Pt. 1. Mechanics of Solids One. Truesdell, C., ed. (Illus.). 1973. 175.90 (ISBN 0-387-05873-7); Vol. 6a, Pt. 2. Mechanics of Solids Two. Truesdell, C., ed. (Illus.). 1972. 205.40 (ISBN 0-387-05535-5); Vol. 6a, Pt. 3. Mechanics of Solids Three. Truesdell, C., ed. (Illus.). 1973. 164.10 (ISBN 0-387-05536-3); Vol. 8, Pt. 1. Fluid Dynamics One. Tr. of Stroemungsmechanik One. (Illus.). 1959. 129.80 (ISBN 0-387-02411-5); Vol. 8, Pt. 2. Fluid Dynamics Two. Tr. of Stroemungsmechanik Two. (Illus.). 1963. 182.90 (ISBN 0-387-02997-4); Vol. 9. Fluid Dynamics Three. Tr. of Stroemungsmechanik Three. (Illus.). 1960. 194.70 (ISBN 0-387-02548-0); Vol. 10. Structure of Liquids. Tr. of Struktur der Fluessigkeiten. (Illus.). vi, 686p. 1960. 94.40 (ISBN 0-387-02549-9). Tr. of Handbuch der Physik. (Eng., Fr & Ger.). Springer-Verlag.

--Encyclopedia of Physics, 54 vols, Vols. 37-42, 44-45. Incl. Vol. 37, Pt. 1. Atoms Three - Molecules One. Tr. of Atome 3 - Molekuele 1. (Illus.). vi, 439p. 1959. 118.00 (ISBN 0-387-02412-3); Vol. 37, Pt. 2. Molecules Two. Tr. of Molekule 2. (Illus.). vi, 303p. 1961. 97.40 (ISBN 0-387-02688-6); Vol. 38, Pt. 2. Neutrons & Related Gamma Ray Problems. Tr. of Neutronen und Verwandte Gammastrahlewprobleme. (Illus.). vi, 868p. 1959. 171.10 (ISBN 0-387-02413-1); Vol. 39. Structure of Atomic Nuclei. Tr. of Bauder Atomkerne. (Illus.). vi, 566p. 1971. 123.90 (ISBN 0-387-02171-X); Vol. 40. Nuclear Reactions One. Tr. of Kernreaktionen One. (Illus.). vi, 553p. 1957. 123.90 (ISBN 0-387-02172-8); Vol. 41, Pt. 1. Nuclear Reactions Two: Theory. Tr. of Kernreaktionen 2: Theorie. (Illus.). viii, 580p. 1959. 141.60 (ISBN 0-387-02414-X); Vol. 41, Pt. 2. Beta Decay. Tr. of Betazerfall. (Illus.). vi, 117p. 1962. 47.20 (ISBN 0-387-02843-9); Vol. 42. Nuclear Reactions Three. Tr. of Kernreaktionen 3. (Illus.). viii, 626p. 1957. 129.80 (ISBN 0-387-02173-6); Vol. 44. Nuclear Instrumentation One. Creutz, E., ed. Tr. of Instrumentelle Hilfsmittel der Kernphysik 1. (Illus.). viii, 473p. 1959. 123.90 (ISBN 0-387-02415-8); Vol. 45. Nuclear Instrumentation Two. Creutz, E., ed. Tr. of Instrumentelle Hilfsmittel der Kernphysik 2. (Illus.). viii, 544p. 1958. 129.80 (ISBN 0-387-02297-X). Springer-Verlag.

Glazebrook, Richard, ed. A Dictionary of Applied Physics, 5 vols. Set. 120.00 (ISBN 0-8446-1199-9); 24.00 ea. Peter Smith.

Gray, H. J. & Isaacs, A., eds. A New Dictionary of Physics. rev. ed. LC 75-307635. Orig. Title: Dictionary of Physics. (Illus.). 640p. 1975. 40.00x (ISBN 0-582-32242-1). Longman.

Hoefling, O. Lexikon der Schulphysik: Atomphysik, Vol. 5. (Ger.). 47.00 (ISBN 3-7614-0110-8, M-7227). French & Eur.

Hyman, Charles J., ed. Dictionary of Physics & Allied Sciences: German-English. LC 77-6949. (Ger. & Eng.). 1978. 30.00 (ISBN 0-8044-4433-1). Ungar.

Idlin, Ralph, ed. Dictionary of Physics & Allied Sciences: English-German. LC 77-6950. (Eng. & Ger.). 1978. 30.00 (ISBN 0-8044-4435-8). Ungar.

Isaacs, Alan, ed. The Multilingual Energy Dictionary. LC 80-26793. pap. 72.00 (ISBN 0-317-26081-2, 2025155). Bks Demand UMI.

Jehan, L. F. Dictionnaire d'Astronomie de Physique et de Meteorologie. Migne, J. P., ed. (Encyclopedie Theologique Ser.: Vol. 42). (Fr.). 780p. Repr. of 1850 ed. lib. bdg. 99.00x (ISBN 0-89241-247-X). Caratzas.

--Dictionnaire Historique des Sciences Physiques et Naturelles. Migne, J. P., ed. (Troisieme et Derniere Encyclopedie Theologique Ser.: Vol. 30). (Fr.). 654p. Repr. of 1857 ed. lib. bdg. 85.00x (ISBN 0-89241-309-3). Caratzas.

Jesse, A. Physics Terminology. (Fr. Ger. & Eng.). 129p. 1980. pap. 24.95 (ISBN 3-7625-0963-8, M-9310). French & Eur.

Laitier, Gabriel. Dictionnaire de Physique. (Fr.). 276p. 1968. pap. 35.00 (ISBN 0-686-56988-1, M-6328). French & Eur.

Lerner, Rita G. & Trigg, George L., eds. Encyclopedia of Physics. 1980. text ed. 139.95 (ISBN 0-201-04313-0). Addison-Wesley.

McAinsh, T. F., ed. Encyclopedia of Physics in Medicine & Biology. (Illus.). 650p. 1985. 135.00 (ISBN 0-08-029154-6). Pergamon.

McGraw Hill, ed. Encyclopedia of Physics. 1352p. 1983. 63.50 (ISBN 0-07-045253-9). McGraw.

McGraw-Hill Editors. Dictionary of Physics. 656p. 1985. write for info. (ISBN 0-07-045418-3). McGraw.

Meyers Physik-Lexikon. (Ger.). 1973. 46.00 (ISBN 3-411-00921-7, M-7561, Pub. by Bibliographisches Institut). French & Eur.

Ministry of Education. Scientific Terms Physics: Japanese-English, English-Japanese. (Japanese & Eng.). 221p. 1954. 14.95 (ISBN 0-686-92514-9, M-9343). French & Eur.

Parker, Sybil P. McGraw-Hill Dictionary of Physics. 1985. pap. 15.95. McGraw.

Pitt, Valerie H., ed. The Penguin Dictionary of Physics. (Reference Ser.). 1977. pap. 5.95 (ISBN 0-14-051071-0). Penguin.

Precis Thesaurus: Physics. 1981. 55.00x (ISBN 0-686-99804-9, Pub. by Brit Lib England). State Mutual Bk.

Rickard, Teresa. The Barnes & Noble Thesaurus of Physics: Fundamentals of Physics Explained & Illustrated. LC 83-47598. (Science Fundamentals Ser.). (Illus.). 256p. 1984. 13.95i (ISBN 0-06-015214-1, HarpT). Har-Row.

Rickard, Terry. Barnes & Noble Thesaurus of Physics. (Illus.). 256p. 1984. pap. 6.68i (ISBN 0-06-463582-1, EH 582). B&N NY.

Sauermost, R. Herder-Lexikon Physik. (Ger.). 1975. 15.95 (ISBN 0-686-56480-4, M-7449, Pub. by Herder). French & Eur.

Sauermost, Rolf. Diccionario Rioduero: Fisica. (Span.). 256p. 1976. leatherette 9.95 (ISBN 84-220-0763-0, S-50167). French & Eur.

Smirnova, L. A. Russian-English Phrase-Book for Physicists. 336p. 1968. leatherette 4.95 (ISBN 0-686-92126-7, M-9109). French & Eur.

Sube, R. & Eisenreich, G. Physics Dictionary, 3 vols. 2895p. 1980. 185.00x (ISBN 0-569-07879-2, Pub. by Collet's). State Mutual Bk.

Sube, R. & Eisenreich, G., eds. Physics Dictionary, 3 vols. (Eng., Ger., Fr & Rus.). 1974. 260.00x (ISBN 3-87144-143-0). Adlers Foreign Bks.

Sube, Ralf & Eisenreich, Gunther. Woerterbuch Physik, 3 vols. (Eng., Ger., Fr & Rus., Dictionary of Physics). 1970. Set. 312.00 (ISBN 3-87144-143-0, M-6909). French & Eur.

Thewlis, J. Concise Dictionary of Physics: And Related Subjects. 2nd ed. LC 79-40209. 1979. 72.00 (ISBN 0-08-023048-2). Pergamon.

Thewlis, J., ed. Encyclopaedic Dictionary of Physics, 9 vols., 5 suppls. Incl. Vol. 1. Abbe Refractometer to Compensated Bars. 1961. 37.00 (ISBN 0-08-006540-6); Vol. 2. Compensator to Epecadmium Neutrons. 1961. 37.00 (ISBN 0-08-006541-4); Vol. 3. Epitaxy to Intermediate Image. 1961. 37.00 (ISBN 0-08-006542-2); Vol. 4. Intermediate Stage to Neutron Resonance Level. 1962. 37.00 (ISBN 0-08-006543-0); Vol. 5. Neutron Scattering to Radiation Constants. 1962. 37.00 (ISBN 0-08-006544-9); Vol. 6. Radiation, Continuous, to Stellar Luminosity. 1962. 37.00 (ISBN 0-08-006545-7); Vol. 7. Stellar Magnitude to Zwitter Ion. 1963. 37.00 (ISBN 0-08-006546-5); Vol. 8. Subject & Author Indexes. 1963. 37.00 (ISBN 0-08-006749-2); Vol. 9. Multilingual Glossary. 1964. 77.50 (ISBN 0-08-009928-9); Supplementary Volumes, 5 vols. 1966. Vol 1, 1966. 25.00 (ISBN 0-08-011835-6); Vol 2, 1967. 31.00 (ISBN 0-08-011889-5); Vol. 3, 1969. 31.00 (ISBN 0-08-012447-X); Vol. 4, 1971. 42.50 (ISBN 0-08-006359-4); Vol. 5, 1975. 50.00 (ISBN 0-08-017056-0); Vol. 6, Date Not Set. price not set (ISBN 0-08-020642-5). 755.00 set (ISBN 0-08-018296-8). Pergamon.

Tolstoi, D. M. English-Russian Physics Dictionary. (Eng. & Rus.). 848p. 1978. 75.00x (ISBN 0-686-44700-X, Pub. by Collets). State Mutual Bk.

Tolstoi, D. M., ed. English-Russian Physics Dictionary. LC 78-40718. (Eng. & Rus.). 1979. 89.00 (ISBN 0-08-023057-1). Pergamon.

PHYSICS–DIRECTORIES

Fachlexikon ABC Physik, 2 vols. (Ger.). 1784p. 1974. Set. 95.00 (ISBN 3-87144-003-5, M-7383, Pub. by Verlag Harri Deutsch). French & Eur.

Shea, Dion, ed. Directory of Physics & Astronomy Staff Members, 1984-85. 412p. 1984. pap. 30.00 (ISBN 0-88318-458-3). Am Inst Physics.

--Graduate Programs in Physics, Astronomy & Related Fields, 1984-85. 912p. 1984. pap. 17.50 (ISBN 0-88318-459-1). Am Inst Physics.

--Speakers, Tours & Films, 1984-85. 176p. (Orig.). 1984. pap. 10.00 (ISBN 0-88318-269-6). Am Inst Physics.

PHYSICS–EARLY WORKS TO 1800

Accademia Del Cimento. Essays of Natural Experiments Made in the Academie Del Cimento. Waller, R., tr. (Illus.). Repr. of 1684 ed. 18.00 (ISBN 0-384-00260-9). Johnson Repr.

Aristotle. Aristotle's Physics. Apostle, H. G., tr. from Gr. LC 80-80037. (Apostle Translations of Aristotle's Works Ser.: Vol. 2). 386p. 1980. text ed. 21.60x (ISBN 0-9602870-2-7); pap. text ed. 10.80x (ISBN 0-9602870-3-5). Peripatetic.

--Aristotle's Physics. Hope, Richard, tr. LC 61-5498. xiv, 242p. 1961. pap. 6.25x (ISBN 0-8032-5093-2, BB 122, Bison). U of Nebr Pr.

--Aristotles's Physics, Bks. 1 & 2. Charlton, W., ed. (Clarendon Aristotle Ser.). 1970. 12.95x (ISBN 0-19-872026-2). Oxford U Pr.

--Physica. Ross, W. David, ed. (Oxford Classical Texts Ser). 1950. 17.50x (ISBN 0-19-814514-4). Oxford U Pr.

--Physics, 2 Vols. (Loeb Classical Library: No. 228, 255). 12.50x ea. Bks. 1-4 (ISBN 0-674-99251-2). Bks. 5-8 (ISBN 0-674-99281-4). Harvard U Pr.

--Physics. rev. ed. Ross, W. David, ed. 1936. 67.50x (ISBN 0-19-814109-2). Oxford U Pr.

Boscovich, Roger J. Theory of Natural Philosophy. (Illus.). 1966. pap. 7.95x (ISBN 0-262-52003-6). MIT Pr.

Eckermann, Willigis. Der Physikkommentar Hugolins von Orvieto Oesa: Ein Beitrag zur Erkenntnislehre des spaetmittelalterlichen Augustinismus. (Spaetmittelalter und Reformation, Vol. 5). 160p. 1972. 23.60x (ISBN 3-11-003714-9). De Gruyter.

Galilei, Galileo. Dialogues Concerning Two New Sciences. (Illus.). 1914. pap. text ed. 5.50 (ISBN 0-486-60099-8). Dover.

--Dialogues Concerning Two New Sciences. Crew, Henry & De Salvio, Alfonso, trs. (University Studies Ser). Repr. of 1950 ed. 79.00 (ISBN 0-8357-9453-9, 2015284). Bks Demand UMI.

Hauksbee, Francis. Physico-Mechanical Experiments on Various Subjects. 2nd ed. (Sources of Science Ser: No. 90). 1970. Repr. of 1719 ed. 28.00 (ISBN 0-384-21785-0). Johnson Repr.

Langton, Christopher. An Introduction into Physicke. LC 75-25797. (English Experience Ser.: No. 281). 1970. Repr. of 1550 ed. 16.00 (ISBN 90-221-0281-5). Walter J Johnson.

Newton, Isaac. Newton's Philosophy of Nature. Thayer, H. Standish, tr. (Library of Classics Ser: No. 16). 1953. pap. text ed. 7.95x (ISBN 0-02-849700-7). Hafner.

Power, Henry & Hall, M. B. Experimental Philosophy, 3 Bks. 1966. Repr. of 1664 ed. 22.00 (ISBN 0-384-47480-2). Johnson Repr.

Rohault, Jacques. A System of Natural Philosophy, 2 Vols. (Sources of Science, House Ser.: No. 50). Repr. of 1723 ed. Set. 65.00 (ISBN 0-384-51760-9). Johnson Repr.

PHYSICS–EXAMINATIONS, QUESTION, ETC.

Cronin, Jeremiah A., et al. University of Chicago Graduate Problems in Physics with Solutions. 1979. pap. 9.00x (ISBN 0-226-12109-7, P809, Phoen). U of Chicago Pr.

Gewirtz, Herman. How to Prepare for the College Board Achievement Test - Physics. 3rd ed. LC 79-9283. 1980. Barron.

Gewirtz, Herman, ed. Barron's Regents Exams & Answers Physics. rev. ed. LC 56-39359. 250p. 1982. pap. text ed. 4.50 (ISBN 0-8120-3167-9). Barron.

Moreau, Nancy. A Regents Physics Review. Garnsey, Wayne, ed. (Illus.). 225p. 1985. pap. text ed. 2.50 (ISBN 0-9606036-8-9). N & N Pub.

Rudman, Jack. Assistant Physicist. (Career Examination Ser.: C-2087). (Cloth bdg. avail. on request). 1977. pap. 12.00 (ISBN 0-8373-2087-9). Natl Learning.

--Chemistry, Physics & General Science. (National Teachers Examination Ser.: NT-7). (Cloth bdg. avail. on request). pap. 11.95 (ISBN 0-8373-8417-6). Natl Learning.

--Junior Physicist. (Career Examination Ser.: C-405). (Cloth bdg. avail. on request). pap. 12.00 (ISBN 0-8373-0405-9). Natl Learning.

--Physical Sciences. (Graduate Record Area Examination Ser.: GRE-43). 21.95 (ISBN 0-8373-5293-2); pap. 13.95 (ISBN 0-8373-5243-6). Natl Learning.

--Physicist. (Career Examination Ser.: C-586). (Cloth bdg. avail. on request). pap. 12.00 (ISBN 0-8373-0586-1). Natl Learning.

--Physics. (Graduate Record Examination Ser.: GRE-15). (Cloth bdg. avail. on request). pap. 13.95 (ISBN 0-8373-5215-0). Natl Learning.

--Physics & General Science - Sr. H.S. (Teachers License Examination Ser.: T-46). (Cloth bdg. avail. on request). pap. 13.95 (ISBN 0-8373-8046-4). Natl Learning.

PHYSICS–EXPERIMENTS

see also Electricity–Experiments

Achinstein, Peter & Hannaway, Owen, eds. Observation, Experiment, & Hypothesis in Modern Physical Science. 1985. 37.50 (ISBN 0-262-01083-6). MIT Pr.

Cioffari, Bernard & Edmonds, Dean. Experiments in College Physics. 7th ed. 1983. pap. text ed. 17.95x (ISBN 0-669-04492-X). Heath.

Eadie, W. T., et al. Statistical Methods in Experimental Physics. LC 75-157034. 296p. 1972. 42.50 (ISBN 0-444-10117-9, North-Holland). Elsevier.

France, P. W. Experiments in Elementary Physics. 2nd ed. 1981. pap. text ed. 12.95x (ISBN 0-89917-311-X). TIS Inc.

Greenberg, Leonard H. Discovery in Physics for Scientists & Engineers. 2nd ed. LC 74-4565. (Illus.). 316p. 1975. pap. text ed. 20.95 (ISBN 0-7216-4246-2). HR&W.

Harris, N. & Hemmerling, E. M. Experiments in Applied Physics. 3rd ed. 1980. text ed. 16.95 (ISBN 0-07-026818-5). McGraw.

Hoehler, G., ed. Springer Tracts in Modern Physics, Vol. 65. LC 25-9130. (Illus.). 148p. 1972. 37.80 (ISBN 0-387-05876-1). Springer-Verlag.

Kruse, Olan E. General Physics Demonstration Manual. 1973. pap. 9.00x wkbk. (ISBN 0-934786-06-2). G Davis.

Marton, Claire, ed. Methods of Experimental Physics: Fluid Dynamics, Vol. 18A. LC 79-26343. 1981. 65.00 (ISBN 0-12-475960-2). Acad Pr.

--Methods of Experimental Physics: Fluid Dynamics, Vol. 18B. 1981. 57.50 (ISBN 0-12-475956-4). Acad Pr.

Marton, L. & Marton, C. Methods of Experimental Physics: Nuclear Methods in Soli State Physics, Vol. 21. 1983. 69.00 (ISBN 0-12-475963-7). Acad Pr.

Marton, L., ed. Methods of Experimental Physics. Incl. Vol. 1. Classical Methods. Estermann, Immanuel, ed. 1959. 75.00 (ISBN 0-12-475901-7); Vol. 4. Atomic & Electron Physics, Pts. A-B. Hughes, Vernon W. & Schultz, Howard L., eds. 1967. Pt. A. 92.00 (ISBN 0-12-475904-1); Pt. B. 76.50 (ISBN 0-12-475944-0); Vol. 6. Solid State Physics. Lark-Horovitz, K. & Johnson, Vivian A., eds. 1959. Pt. A. 74.00 (ISBN 0-12-475906-8); Pt. B. 74.00 (ISBN 0-12-475946-7); Vol. 7. Atomic & Electron Physics: Atomic Interactions. Bederson, B. & Fite, W., eds. 1968. Pt. A. 85.00 (ISBN 0-12-475907-6); Pt. B. 83.00 (ISBN 0-12-475947-5); Vol. 8. Problems & Solutions for Students. Marton, L. & Hornyak, W. F., eds. 1969. 60.00 (ISBN 0-12-475908-4); Vol. 9. Plasma Physics. Griem, Hans R. & Lovberg, Ralph H., eds. 1970-71. Pt. A. 79.50 (ISBN 0-12-475909-2); Pt. B. 71.00 (ISBN 0-12-475949-1); Vol. 10. Physical Principles of Far-Infrared Radiation. Robinson, L. C. 1973. 82.50 (ISBN 0-12-475910-6). Acad Pr.

--Methods of Experimental Physics: Quantum Electronics, Vol. 15A. (Methods of Experimental Physics Ser.). 1979. 70.00 (ISBN 0-12-475915-7). Acad Pr.

--Methods of Experimental Physics: Vacuum Physics & Technology, Vol. 14. (Methods of Experimental Physics Ser.). 1979. 76.00 (ISBN 0-12-475914-9). Acad Pr.

Meiners, Harry F., ed. Physics: Demonstration Experiments, 2 vols. LC 84-23409. 1518p. 1985. Repr. of 1970 ed. lib. bdg. 96.50 (ISBN 0-89874-821-6). Krieger.

Melissinos, Adrian. Experiments in Modern Physics. 1966. text ed. 27.25i (ISBN 0-12-489850-5). Acad Pr.

Mintz, Stephan & Perlmutter, Arnold, eds. New Pathways in High Energy Physics, Pt. 2: New Particles - Theories & Experiments. LC 76-20476. (Studies in the Natural Sciences Ser.: Vol. 11). 421p. 1976. 65.00x (ISBN 0-306-36911-7, Plenum Pr). Plenum Pub.

Nelkon, M. & Ogborn, J. M. Advanced Level Practical Physics. 4th ed. 1970. text ed. 14.50x (ISBN 0-435-68655-0). Heinemann Ed.

Preston, D. W., et al. Experiments in Physics: A Laboratory Manual. 161p. 1983. pap. 13.95 (ISBN 0-471-88548-7). Wiley.

Preston, Daryl W. Experiments in Physics, Calculus Version. 1985. pap. text ed. 16.50 (ISBN 0-471-80571-8). Wiley.

Rothman, Milton A. Discovering the Natural Laws: The Experimental Basis of Physics. LC 78-171318. (Illus.). 1972. 5.95 (ISBN 0-385-05211-1). Doubleday.

Smith, Brian J. Practical Construction Science. LC 79-40562. (Longman Technician Ser.: Construction & Civil Engineering). pap. 87.00 (ISBN 0-317-27785-5, 2025235). Bks Demand UMI.

Squires, G. L. Practical Physics. 3rd ed. 200p. Date not set. price not set (ISBN 0-521-24952-X); pap. price not set (ISBN 0-521-27095-2). Cambridge U Pr.

Taylor, G. R. Introductory Physics Experiments. 176p. 1977. text ed. 9.95 (ISBN 0-89459-009-X). Hunter Textbks.

Trigg, George L. Landmark Experiments in 20th Century Physics. LC 74-21664. 309p. 1975. 24.50x (ISBN 0-8448-0602-1); pap. 14.50x (ISBN 0-8448-0603-X). Crane-Russak Co.

PHYSICS–FORMULAE

Fischbeck, H. J. & Fishbeck, K. H. Formulas, Facts, & Constants for Students & Professionals in Engineering, Chemistry, & Physics. 270p. 1982. pap. 16.00 (ISBN 0-387-11315-0). Springer-Verlag.

Lynn, B. W. & Wheater, J. F., eds. Radiative Corrections in SU (2) L X U (1) Proceedings of the Workshop on Radiative Corrections in SU (2) L X U (1), Miramore, Trieste, Italy, June 6-8. 340p. 1984. 35.00x (ISBN 9971-966-26-3, Pub. by World Sci Singapore); pap. 21.00X (ISBN 9971-966-28-X, Pub. by World Sci Singapore). Taylor & Francis.

Myung, H. C., et al, eds. Applications of Lie-Admissable Algebras in Physics, Vol. 2. 595p. 1978. pap. text ed. 55.00x (ISBN 0-911767-04-5). Hadronic Pr Inc.

Nording, Carl & Osterman, Jonny. Physics Handbook: Elementary Constants & Units, Tables, Formulae & Diagrams & Mathematical Formulae. 431p. 1982. text ed. 23.95x (ISBN 0-86238-000-6, Pub. by Chartwell-Bratt England). Brookfield Pub Co.

PHYSICS–HISTORY

see also Physics–Early Works to 1800

Achinstein, Peter & Hannaway, Owen, eds. Observation, Experiment, & Hypothesis in Modern Physical Science. 1985. 37.50 (ISBN 0-262-01083-6). MIT Pr.

Aris, Rutherford & Davis, H. Ted, eds. Springs of Scientific Creativity: Essays on Founders of Modern Science. LC 82-23715. (Illus.). 352p. 1983. 32.50x (ISBN 0-8166-1087-8). U of Minn Pr.

Asimov, Isaac. The History of Physics. LC 83-6478. (Illus.). 720p. 1984. 29.95 (ISBN 0-8027-0751-3). Walker & Co.

Bauer, Henry H. Beyond Velikovsky: The History of a Public Controversy. LC 83-17935. (Illus.). 368p. 1984. 21.95 (ISBN 0-252-01104-X). U of Ill Pr.

Bechler, Z. Contemporary Newtonian Research. 1982. 39.50 (ISBN 90-277-1303-0, Pub. by Reidel Holland). Kluwer Academic.

Bellone, Enrico. The World on Paper: Studies on the Second Scientific Revolution. Giaconni, Mirella & Giaconni, Ricardo, trs. from Italian. Orig. Title: Il Mondo di Carta. 1980. text ed. 27.50x (ISBN 0-262-02147-1). MIT Pr.

Brush, S. G. The Kind of Motion We Call Heat: A History of the Kinetic Theory of Gases in the Nineteenth Century, 2 bks. (Studies in Statistical Mechanics: Vol. 6). 1976. Bk. 1. 53.25 (ISBN 0-7204-0370-7, North-Holland); Bk. 2. 93.75 (ISBN 0-7204-0482-7); Set. 121.25 (ISBN 0-686-67836-2). Elsevier.

Brush, Stephen G. The Temperature of History, Phases of Science & Culture in the Nineteeth Century. LC 77-11999. (Studies in the History of Science). (Illus.). 1978. lib. bdg. 18.95 (ISBN 0-89102-073-X). B Franklin.

Brush, Stephen G. & Belloni, Lanfranoo. The History of Modern Physics: An International Bibliography. LC 82-49291. (The History of Science & Technology Ser.: Vol. 4). 400p. 1983. lib. bdg. 42.00 (ISBN 0-8240-9117-5). Garland Pub.

Brush, Stephen G., ed. Resources for the History of Physics: Guide to Books & Audiovisual Materials, Guide to Original Works of Historical Importance & Their Translations into Other Languages. LC 70-186306. pap. 48.00 (ISBN 0-317-10599-X, 2022324). Bks Demand UMI.

Burtt, Edwin A. Metaphysical Foundations of Modern Physical Science. 2nd ed. (International Library of Psychology, Philosophy & Scientific Method). 1967. text ed. 29.00x (ISBN 0-7100-3032-0); pap. text ed. 9.45x (ISBN 0-391-01633-4). Humanities.

Casimir, Hendrik B. Haphazard Reality: Half a Century of Science. LC 82-48112. (Sloan Foundation Books). 356p. 1983. 19.23i (ISBN 0-06-015028-9, HarpT). Har-Row.

Clagett, Marshall. Giovanni Marliani & Late Medieval Physics. LC 70-181929. (Columbia University Studies in the Social Sciences: No. 483). Repr. of 1941 ed. 12.50 (ISBN 0-404-51483-9). AMS Pr.

--Studies in Medieval Physics & Mathematics. 366p. 1980. 75.00x (ISBN 0-86078-048-1, Pub. by Variorum England). State Mutual Bk.

Cohen, Robert S. Physical Sciences & the History of Physics. 1984. lib. bdg. 39.50 (ISBN 90-277-1615-3, Pub by Reidel Holland). Kluwer Academic.

De Broglie, Louis. Revolution in Physics: A Non-Mathematical Survey of Quanta. Niemeyer, Ralph W., tr. LC 76-95113. Repr. of 1953 ed. lib. bdg. 18.75x (ISBN 0-8371-2582-0, BRRP). Greenwood.

Duhem, Pierre. To Save the Phenomena: An Essay on the Idea of Physical Theory from Plato to Galileo. Doland, Edmund & Maschler, Chaninah, trs. LC 71-77978. xxvi, 120p. 1985. pap. text ed. 9.00x. U of Chicago Pr.

Duhem, Pierre M. The Evolution of Mechanics. Oravas, G. A., ed. (Genesis & Method Ser.: No. 1). Orig. Title: L' Evolution de la Mecanique. 234p. 1980. Repr. 47.50x (ISBN 90-286-0688-2). Sijthoff & Noordhoff.

Einstein, Albert & Infeld, Leopold. Evolution of Physics. 1967. pap. 9.95 (ISBN 0-671-20156-5, Touchstone Bks). S&S.

Fierz, Markus & Weisskopf, V. F., eds. Theoretical Physics in the Twentieth-Century: A Memorial Volume to Wolfgang Pauli. LC 60-15886. pap. 85.00 (ISBN 0-317-08596-4, 2007408). Bks Demand UMI.

Gamow, George. Thirty Years that Shook Physics: The Story of Quantum Theory. 240p. 1985. pap. 4.95 (ISBN 0-486-24895-X). Dover.

Gerland, Ernst. Geschichte der Physik Von Den Altesten Zeitem Bis Zum Ausgange Des Achtzehnten Jahrhunderts. Repr. of 1913 ed. 50.00 (ISBN 0-384-18180-5). Johnson Repr.

Gillmor, C. Stewart. Coulomb & the Evolution of Physics & Engineering in Eighteenth Century France. LC 79-155006. (Illus.). 1971. 34.50x (ISBN 0-691-08095-X). Princeton U Pr.

Goudsmit, Samuel A. Alsos. (History of Modern Physics 1800-1950 Ser.: Vol. 1). (Illus.). 1983. Repr. of 1947 ed. 28.00x (ISBN 0-938228-09-9). Tomash Pubs.

Grant, E. Physical Science in the Middle Ages. LC 77-8393. (History of Science Ser.). (Illus.). 1978. pap. 10.95 (ISBN 0-521-29294-8). Cambridge U Pr.

Gunter, Pete A. Bergson & the Evolution of Physics. LC 77-77844. pap. 90.00 (ISBN 0-317-08063-6, 2019683). Bks Demand UMI.

Harman, P. M., ed. Wranglers & Physicists: Studies on Cambridge Mathematical Physics in the Nineteenth Century. LC 85-1485. 320p. 1985. 27.00 (ISBN 0-7190-1756-4, Pub. by Manchester Univ Pr). Longwood Pub Group.

Hart, Ivor B. Great Physicists. LC 71-117804. (Essay Index Reprint Ser). 1927. 14.00 (ISBN 0-8369-1656-5). Ayer Co Pubs.

Heilbron, J. L. Elements of Early Modern Physics. LC 81-40327. 300p. 1981. 36.00x (ISBN 0-520-04554-8); pap. 10.95 (ISBN 0-520-04555-6). U of Cal Pr.

Heilbron, J. L. & Wheaton, Bruce R., eds. Literature on the History of Physics in the 20th Century. LC 80-51580. (Berkeley Papers in the History of Science: No. 5). (Orig.). 1981. pap. 20.00x (ISBN 0-918102-05-7). U Cal Hist Sci Tech.

Hermann, A. Lexikon der Schulphysik: Geschichte der Physik, Vol. 6. (Ger.). 35.00 (ISBN 3-7614-0131-0, M-7228). French & Eur.

--Lexikon der Schulphysik: Geschichte der Physik, Vol. 7. (Ger.). 45.00 (ISBN 3-7614-0153-1, M-7229). French & Eur.

Hermann, A. & Meyenn, K. V., eds. Wolfgang Pauli: Scientific Correspondence with Bohr, Einstein, Heisenberg, Vol. I: 1919-1929. (Sources in the History of Mathematics & Physical Sciences Ser.: Vol. 2). (Illus.). 1979. 110.00 (ISBN 0-387-08962-4). Springer-Verlag.

Hesse, Mary B. Forces & Fields. LC 74-106693. (Illus.). 318p. Repr. of 1962 ed. lib. bdg. 24.75x (ISBN 0-8371-3366-1, HEFF). Greenwood.

Hoppe, Edmund. Geschichte Der Physik. 1926. 18.00 (ISBN 0-384-24310-X). Johnson Repr.

International Working Seminar on the Role of the History of Physics in Physics Education. History in the Teaching of Physics: Proceedings. Brush, Stephen G. & King, Allen L., eds. LC 71-188602. 128p. 1972. 10.00x (ISBN 0-87451-065-1). U Pr of New Eng.

Jaki, Stanley L. Relevance of Physics. LC 66-20583. 1967. 25.00x (ISBN 0-226-39143-4). U of Chicago Pr.

Kapitza, Petr L. Experiment, Theory, Practice. (Boston Studies in the Philosophy of Science: No. 46). 1980. lib. bdg. 47.00 (ISBN 90-277-1061-9, Pub. by Reidel Holland); pap. 14.75 (ISBN 90-277-1062-7). Kluwer Academic.

Kevles, Daniel J. The Physicists. 1978. 15.95 (ISBN 0-394-46631-4). Knopf.

--The Physicists: The History of a Scientific Community in Modern America. LC 78-23592. 1979. pap. 10.95 (ISBN 0-394-72669-3, Vin). Random.

Kuhn, S. Thomas & Heilbron, John L. Sources for History of Quantum Physics: An Inventory & Report. LC 66-26634. (American Philosophical Society, Memoirs Ser.: Vol. 68). pap. 47.50 (ISBN 0-317-08066-0, 2019709). Bks Demand UMI.

Kuhn, Thomas S., et al. Sources for History of Quantum Physics. LC 66-26634. (Memoirs Ser.: Vol. 68). 1967. 7.50 (ISBN 0-87169-068-3). Am Philos.

Lemon, Harvey B. From Galileo to the Nuclear Age: An Introduction to Physics. (Phoenix Science Ser.). pap. 120.00 (ISBN 0-317-08845-9, 2020104). Bks Demand UMI.

Lindsay, Robert B. The Nature of Physics: A Physicist's Views on the History & Philosophy of His Science. LC 68-10642. 220p. 1968. 20.00x (ISBN 0-87057-107-9). U Pr of New Eng.

McCormmach, Russell K., et al, eds. Historical Studies in the Physical Sciences. LC 77-75220. (Illus.). 1978. Vol. 8 1977. text ed. 27.50x (ISBN 0-8018-1907-5); Vol. 9 1978. text ed. 27.50x (ISBN 0-8018-2045-6). Johns Hopkins.

McGucken, William. Nineteenth-Century Spectroscopy: Development of the Understanding of Spectra, 1802-1897. LC 74-94886. pap. 62.30 (ISBN 0-317-08471-2, 2011868). Bks Demand UMI.

Massey, Harrie. New Age in Physics. 2nd ed. (Illus.). 1966. text ed. 19.50x (ISBN 0-8464-0670-5). Beekman Pubs.

Mehra, J. The Solvay Conferences on Physics: Aspects of the Development of Physics Since 1911. LC 75-28332. 424p. 1976. lib. bdg. 79.00 (ISBN 90-277-0635-2, Pub. by Reidel Holland). Kluwer Academic.

Mehra, Jagdish, ed. The Physicist's Conception of Nature. LC 73-75765. 1973. lib. bdg. 118.50 (ISBN 90-277-0345-0, Pub. by Reidel Holland). Kluwer Academic.

Miller. Frontiers in Physics: Nineteen Hundred to Nineteen Eleven. 1985. price not set (ISBN 0-8176-3203-4). Birkhauser.

Millikan, Robert A. Evolution in Science & Religion. LC 72-85283. 104p. 1973. Repr. of 1927 ed. 19.50x (ISBN 0-8046-1702-3, Pub. by Kennikat). Assoc Faculty Pr.

Monson, Milton W., Sr. Physics Is Constipated. 1983. 19.95 (ISBN 0-533-05190-8). Vantage.

Moyer, Albert E. American Physics in Transition: Conceptual Shifts in the Late Nineteenth Century. (History of Modern Physics 1800-1950 Ser.: Vol. 3). (Illus.). 1983. 30.00x (ISBN 0-938228-06-4). Tomash Pubs.

Rusk, Rogers D. Atoms, Men & Stars: A Survey of the Latest Developments of Physical Science & Their Relation to Life. facsimile ed. LC 70-156712. (Essay Index Reprint Ser.). Repr. of 1937 ed. 24.50 (ISBN 0-8369-2332-4). Ayer Co Pubs.

Sambursky, Samuel. Physics of the Stoics. LC 72-6045. 153p. 1973. Repr. of 1959 ed. lib. bdg. 15.00x (ISBN 0-8371-6489-3, SAPS). Greenwood.

Schneer, Cecil J. The Evolution of Physical Science: Major Ideas from Earliest Times to the Present. 416p. 1984. pap. text ed. 13.50 (ISBN 0-8191-3790-1). U Pr of Amer.

Schuster, Arthur. The Progress of Physics During 33 Years, 1875-1908. LC 74-26289. (History, Philosophy & Sociology of Science Ser.). 1975. Repr. 14.00x (ISBN 0-405-06615-5). Ayer Co Pubs.

Thomson, J. J. Recollections & Reflections. LC 74-26297. (History, Philosophy & Sociology of Science Ser). (Illus.). 1975. Repr. 36.50x (ISBN 0-405-06622-8). Ayer Co Pubs.

U. S. National Committee for the International Union of Pure & Applied Physics. Physics Fifty Years Later. (Illus.). 416p. 1973. 16.75 (ISBN 0-309-02138-3). Natl Acad Pr.

Weart, Spencer. Scientists in Power. LC 78-21670. (Illus.). 1979. text ed. 22.50x (ISBN 0-674-79515-6). Harvard U Pr.

Willson. A European Experiment: The Launching of the Jet Project. 1981. 23.00 (ISBN 0-9960021-8-9, Pub. by Inst Physics England). Heyden.

PHYSICS–LABORATORY MANUALS

Ahner, Walter L. & Diamond, Sheldon R. Laboratory Manual in Physics. 2nd ed. (Orig.). 1967. 7.33 (ISBN 0-87720-174-9); tchrs' ed. 4.55 (ISBN 0-87720-175-7). AMSCO Sch.

--Workbook & Laboratory Manual in Physics. 2nd ed. (Illus., Orig.). 1967. wkbk. 9.25 (ISBN 0-87720-176-5). AMSCO Sch.

Alexander, Ralph W. & Sparlin, Don M. Physics Laboratory Manual. 176p. 1981. 12.95 (ISBN 0-8403-2289-5). Kendall-Hunt.

American Institute of Physics. American Institute of Physics Handbook. 3rd ed. LC 71-109244. (Illus.). 2368p. 1972. 99.50 (ISBN 0-07-001485-X). McGraw.

Baird, et al. Physics Laboratory Manual. 2nd ed. 144p. 1984. pap. text ed. 13.95 (ISBN 0-8403-3209-2). Kendall Hunt.

Bernard, C. H. & Epp, C. D. Laboratory Experiments in College Physics. 5th ed. 437p. 1980. 19.45 (ISBN 0-471-05441-0). Wiley.

Brosowski, Bruno & Martensen, Erich, eds. Approximation & Optimization in Mathematical Physics. 205p. 1983. pap. 25.80 (ISBN 3-8204-7631-8). P Lang Pubs.

Carr, Howard & Simon, Marllin. Physics: A Laboratory Textbook. 2nd ed. (Illus.). 1981. pap. text ed. 15.95x lab manual (ISBN 0-89892-039-6). Contemp Pub Co of Raleigh.

Case, Lloyd A. Laboratory Physics. LC 76-7374. (Illus.). 144p. 1976. pap. text ed. 6.00x (ISBN 0-8422-0535-7). Irvington.

CES Industries, Inc. Ed-Lab Experiment Manual: CES 308 Resolvers. (Illus.). 1981. write for info. (ISBN 0-86711-013-9). CES Industries.

Cromer, Alan. Experiments in Physics. 192p. 1981. pap. text ed. 10.95 (ISBN 0-8403-2804-4, 40280401). Kendall-Hunt.

Goodrich, Roy G. Physics Laboratory Textbook. (Illus.). 442p. 1985. pap. text ed. 17.95 (ISBN 0-89892-031-0). Contemp Pub Co of Raleigh.

Henry, Dennis C., et al. Experiments in Light, Electricity, & Modern Physics, Laboratory Manual. 1978. pap. text ed. 7.95 (ISBN 0-8403-1889-8). Kendall-Hunt.

Hetland, Philip R. Physics Experiments for Laboratory & Life. 1978. pap. text ed. 10.95 (ISBN 0-8403-1907-X). Kendall-Hunt.

Kruse, Olan E., et al. Technical Physics Laboratory Manual. 1971. pap. 9.00x wkbk. (ISBN 0-934786-07-0). G Davis.

Leighton, Robert B. & Vogt, Rochus E. Exercises in Introductory Physics. (Physics Ser). (Orig.). 1969. pap. text ed. 5.95 (ISBN 0-201-04215-0). Addison-Wesley.

Marchini, Robert. Laboratory Manual for Physics 2111 & 2511. 96p. 1981. pap. text ed. 8.95 (ISBN 0-8403-2469-3). Kendall-Hunt.

Meiners, H., et al. Laboratory Physics. 2nd ed. 1985. pap. 20.95 (ISBN 0-471-03675-7). Wiley.

Meiners, H. F., et al. Laboratory Physics. 436p. 1972. 24.95 (ISBN 0-471-59159-9). Wiley.

Moriber, George & Hudes, Isidore. Laboratory Studies in the Physical Sciences. rev ed. 1979. 10.95 (ISBN 0-8403-2032-9). Kendall-Hunt.

O'Kelly, Lewis. Laboratory Manual for Physics 2112 & 2512. 96p. 1982. pap. 7.95 (ISBN 0-8403-2635-1). Kendall-Hunt.

Skolil, Lester L. & Smith, Louis E. Modern College Physics: A Laboratory Manual. Pt. 1, 3rd Ed. 1973, 368 p. write for info. wire coil (ISBN 0-697-05807-7); Pt. 2, 2nd Ed. 1974, 352 p. write for info. wire coil (ISBN 0-697-05808-5). Wm C Brown.

Stanford, A. L., Jr. Laboratory Textbook for College Physics. 2nd ed. (Illus.). 200p. 1984. pap. text ed. 11.95 (ISBN 0-89892-057-4). Contemp Pub Co of Raleigh.

Tortorici, Marianne R. & Hunt, Hiram M. Radiation Physics Laboratory Manual. (Illus.). 194p. (Orig.). 1984. 10.95x (ISBN 0-940122-14-6); instr's. manual 15.95x (ISBN 0-940122-15-4). Multi Media Co.

Wall, Clifford N., et al. Physics Laboratory Manual. 3rd ed. 1972. pap. text ed. 18.95 (ISBN 0-13-674101-0). P-H.

White, Marsh W. & Manning, Kenneth V. Experimental College Physics. 3rd ed. (Illus.). 1954. text ed. 30.95 (ISBN 0-07-069749-3). McGraw.

Wood, Lowell T. General Physics Lab Manual, Vol. 2. 3rd ed. (Illus.). 70p. 1982. pap. text ed. 4.95x (ISBN 0-89641-113-3). American Pr.

--General Physics Laboratory Manual, Vol. 1. 3rd ed. (Illus.). 80p. 1982. pap. text ed. 4.95x (ISBN 0-89641-076-5). American Pr.

Wood, Robert M. Experiments for an Introductory Physics Course. 1978. pap. text ed. 7.95 (ISBN 0-8403-1940-1). Kendall-Hunt.

PHYSICS–MATHEMATICAL MODELS

Bishop, A. R., et al, eds. Fronts, Interfaces & Patterns: Proceedings of the 3rd International Conference, Held at the Centre for Non-linear Studies, Los Alamos, NM, 2-6 May, 1983. 436p. 1984. 63.00 (ISBN 0-444-86906-9, North Holland). Elsevier.

Davidson, Ronald C. & Marion, Jerry B. Mathematical Methods for Introductory Physics with Calculus. 2nd ed. LC 79-19656. 232p. 1980. pap. text ed. 18.95x (ISBN 0-7216-2919-9). SCP.

Emch, G. G. Mathematical & Conceptual Foundations of Twentieth Century Physics. (Mathematical Studies: Vol. 100). 1985. 55.00 (ISBN 0-444-87585-9, North-Holland). Elsevier.

Flato, Moshe, et al, eds. Applications of Group Theory in Physics & Math. Incl. Large-Scale Computations in Fluid Mechanics. Osher, Stanley, ed. (Lectures in Applied Mathematics: Vol. 21). 1984. write for info. Am Math.

Jernigan, R., et al, eds. The Role of Language in Problem Solving One: Proceedings of the Symposium, the Johns Hopkins University Applied Physics Laboratory, Laurel, MD, 29-31 Oct., 1984. 406p. 1985. 55.75 (ISBN 0-444-87764-9, North Holland). Elsevier.

Lieb, Elliott H. & Mattis, Daniel C., eds. Mathematical Physics in One Dimension: Exactly Soluble Models of Interacting Particles. (Perspectives in Physics: A Series of Reprint Collections). 565p. 1966. 65.00 (ISBN 0-12-448750-5). Acad Pr.

Nording, Carl & Osterman, Jonny. Physics Handbook: Elementary Constants & Units, Tables, Formulae & Diagrams & Mathematical Formulae. 431p. 1982. text ed. 23.95x (ISBN 0-86238-000-6, Pub. by Chartwell-Bratt England). Brookfield Pub Co.

Pointon, Anthony J. An Introduction to Statistical Physics for Students. (A Longman Text Ser.). (Illus.). pap. 53.50 (ISBN 0-317-09211-1, 2013565). Bks Demand UMI.

Rushton, Albert, ed. Mathematical Models & Design Methods in Solid-Liquid Seperation. 1985. lib. bdg. 49.50 (ISBN 90-247-3140-2, Pub. by Martinus Nijhoff Netherlands). Kluwer Academic.

Trautman, A. Differential Geometry for Physicists. (Monographs & Textbooks in Physical Sciences). 100p. 1984. pap. text ed. 20.00x (ISBN 88-7088-087-7, Pub. by Bibliopolis, Italy). Humanities.

Wallace, Philip R. Mathematical Analysis of Physical Problems. (Physics Ser.). 616p. 1984. pap. 11.95 (ISBN 0-486-64676-9). Dover.

Williams. Mathematics with Applications in the Management, Natural & Social Sciences. 1985. 31.52 (ISBN 0-205-07188-0, 567188); instr. manual 7.23 (ISBN 0-205-07189-9, 567189). Allyn.

PHYSICS–METHODOLOGY

Busse, W. & Zelazny, R., eds. Computing in Accelerator Design & Operation. (Lecture Notes in Physics Ser.: Vol. 215). xii, 574p. 1984. pap. 28.00 (ISBN 0-387-13909-5). Springer-Verlag.

Chisholm, J. S. & Morris, R. M. Mathematical Methods in Physics. 2nd, rev. ed. 720p. 1983. 51.00 (ISBN 0-444-86621-3, North Holland). Elsevier.

De Greaf, Donald E. Microphysics. (Illus.). 640p. 1985. pap. text ed. 17.50x (ISBN 0-930402-13-8). Crystal MI.

Denardo, G., et al, eds. Group Theoretical Methods in Physics: Proceedings of the XIIth International Colloquium, Held at the International Centre for Theoretical Physics, Trieste, Italy, Sept. 5-11, 1983. (Lecture Notes in Physics Ser.: Vol. 201). xxvii, 518p. 1984. pap. 23.00 (ISBN 0-387-13335-6). Springer-Verlag.

Eadie. Statistical Methods in Experimental Physics. 1984. Repr. 42.50 (ISBN 0-317-11385-2). Elsevier.

Johnson, David E. & Johnson, Johnny R. Mathematical Methods in Engineering & Physics. 208p. 1982. 38.95 (ISBN 0-13-561126-1). P-H.

Squires, G. L. Practical Physics. 3rd ed. 200p. Date not set. price not set (ISBN 0-521-24952-X); pap. price not set (ISBN 0-521-27095-2). Cambridge U Pr.

Zachary, W. W., ed. International Colloquium on Group Theoretical Methods in Physics: Proceedings of the XIII Colloquium Held at College Park, Maryland, USA, May 1984. 650p. 1985. 74.00x (ISBN 9971-966-87-5, 0990200884, Pub. by World Sci Singapore); pap. 37.00x (ISBN 9971-966-88-3, Pub. by World Sci Singapore). Taylor & Francis.

PHYSICS–OUTLINES, SYLLABI, ETC.

Beiser, Arthur. Physical Science. (Schaum's Outline Ser.). 320p. 1974. pap. text ed. 6.95 (ISBN 0-07-004376-0). McGraw.

Bennett, Clarence E. College Physics. 6th ed. LC 67-16622. (Illus.). 1967. pap. 5.95 (ISBN 0-06-460021-1, CO 21, COS). B&N NY.

Clemensen, Jessie. Study Outlines in Physics; Construction & Experimental Evaluation. LC 71-176654. (Columbia University. Teachers College. Contributions to Education: No. 553). Repr. of 1933 ed. 22.50 (ISBN 0-404-55553-5). AMS Pr.

PHYSICS–PHILOSOPHY

see also Causality (Physics)

Achinstein, Peter & Hannaway, Owen, eds. Observation, Experiment, & Hypothesis in Modern Physical Science. 1985. 37.50 (ISBN 0-262-01083-6). MIT Pr.

Bobrow, Daniel G., ed. Qualitative Reasoning about Physical Sciences. 504p. 1985. text ed. 22.50x (ISBN 0-262-02218-4, Pub. by Bradford). MIT Pr.

Boltzmann, Ludwig. Theoretical Physics & Philosophical Problems: Selected Writings. McGuinness, Brian, ed. Foulke, Paul, tr. from Ger. LC 74-79571. (Vienna Circle Collection: No. 5). 270p. 1974. lib. bdg. 46.00 (ISBN 90-277-0249-7, Pub. by Reidel Holland); pap. 24.00 (ISBN 90-277-0250-0). Kluwer Academic.

Bunge, M. Philosophy of Physics. LC 72-86103. (Synthese Library: No. 45). 248p. 1973. lib. bdg. 34.00 (ISBN 90-277-0253-5, Pub. by Reidel Holland). Kluwer Academic.

Capek, M. Bergson & Modern Physics: A Re-Interpretation & Re-Evaluation. LC 79-146967. (Synthese Library: No. 37). 414p. 1971. 42.00 (ISBN 90-277-0186-5, Pub. by Reidel Holland). Kluwer Academic.

Cohen, R. S. & Seeger, R. J., eds. Boston Studies in the Philosophy of Science: Ernst Mach, Physicist & Philosopher, Vol. 6. (Synthese Library: No. 27). 295p. 1970. 29.00 (ISBN 90-277-0016-8, Pub. by Reidel Holland). Kluwer Academic.

Cohen, R. S. & Stachel, J., eds. Leon Rosenfeld: Selected Papers. (Synthese Library Ser.: No. 100). 1976. lib. bdg. 97.50 (ISBN 90-277-0651-4, Pub. by Reidel Holland); pap. 37.00 (ISBN 90-277-0652-2). Kluwer Academic.

Colloquium for the Philosophy of Science, Boston, 1969-1972. Boston Studies in the Philosophy of Science, Vol 13: Logical & Epistemological Studies in Contemporary Physics, Proceedings. Cohen, R. S. & Wartofsky, M. W., eds. LC 73-83557. (Synthese Library: No.59). 462p. 1974. 53.00 (ISBN 90-277-0391-4); pap. 28.95 (ISBN 90-277-0377-9). Kluwer Academic.

Colloquium for the Philosophy of Science, Boston, 1964-1966. Boston Studies in the Philosophy of Science, Vol 3: In Memory of Norwood Russell Hanson. Cohen, R. S. & Wartofsky, M. W., eds. (Synthese Library: No. 14). 489p. 1967. 45.00 (ISBN 90-277-0013-3, Pub. by Reidel Holland). Kluwer Academic.

Colodny, Robert G., ed. From Quarks to Quasars: Philosophical Problems of Modern Physics. LC 84-29456. (Pittsburgh Series in Philosophy of Science). (Illus.). 496p. 1986. 50.00x (ISBN 0-8229-3515-5). U of Pittsburgh Pr.

--Paradigms & Paradoxes: The Philosophical Challenge of the Quantum Domain. LC 79-158189. (Philosophy of Science Ser). 1972. 39.95x (ISBN 0-8229-3235-0). U of Pittsburgh Pr.

Davies, P. C. The Accidental Universe. LC 81-21592. (Illus.). 160p. 1982. 22.95 (ISBN 0-521-24212-6); pap. 10.95 (ISBN 0-521-28692-1). Cambridge U Pr.

Davies, Paul. Superforce: The Search for a Grand Unified Theory of Nature. LC 84-5473. 288p. 1984. 16.95 (ISBN 0-671-47685-8). S&S.

Duhem, Pierre. Aim & Structure of Physical Theory. LC 53-6383. 1962. pap. text ed. 5.95x (ISBN 0-689-70064-4, 13). Atheneum.

Eddington, Arthur S. The Nature of the Physical World. LC 77-27200. (Gifford Lectures: 1927). Repr. of 1928 ed. 27.50 (ISBN 0-404-60478-1). AMS Pr.

Feyerabend, Paul & Maxwell, Grover, eds. Mind, Matter & Method: Essays in Philosophy & Science in Honor of Herbert Feigl. LC 66-13467. 1966. 17.50x (ISBN 0-8166-0379-0). U of Minn Pr.

Frank, Philipp. Foundations of Physics. LC 46-4908. (Foundations of the Unity of Science Ser: Vol. 1, No. 7). 1946. pap. 1.95x (ISBN 0-226-57582-9, P406, Phoen). U of Chicago Pr.

Frey, Gerhard, ed. Bela Juhos: Selected Papers. Foulkes, Paul, tr. LC 76-17019. (Vienna Circle Collection Ser: No. 7). 1976. lib. bdg. 55.00 (ISBN 90-277-0686-7, Pub. by Reidel Holland); pap. 28.95 (ISBN 90-277-0687-5). Kluwer Academic.

Friedrich, Lawrence W., ed. Nature of Physical Knowledge. 1960. 9.95 (ISBN 0-87462-420-7). Marquette.

Gal-Or, B. Cosmology, Physics & Philosophy. (Illus.). 522p. 1981. 34.00 (ISBN 0-387-90581-2). Springer-Verlag.

Gaukroger, Stephen. Explanatory Structures-Concepts of Explanation in Early Physics & Philosophy. (Harvester Studies in Philosophy Ser.: No. 6). 1978. text ed. 29.00x (ISBN 0-391-00899-4). Humanities.

Gregory, Richard L. Mind in Science: A History of Explanations in Psychology & Physics. LC 81-7732. (Illus.). 648p. 1981. 34.50 (ISBN 0-521-24307-6). Cambridge U Pr.

Heisenberg, Werner. Physics & Philosophy: The Revolution in Modern Science. (World Perspectives Ser.). pap. 5.95xi (ISBN 0-06-130549-9, TB549, Torch). Har-Row.

Hesse, Mary B. Forces & Fields. LC 74-106693. (Illus.). 318p. Repr. of 1962 ed. lib. bdg. 24.75x (ISBN 0-8371-3366-1, HEFF). Greenwood.

Reno, Robert C. A Physics Review for the MCAT. (Illus.). 82p. (Orig.). 1984. pap. 6.95 (ISBN 0-916615-00-6). Bks of Sci.

Rogers, E. M. Teaching Physics for the Inquiring Mind. 1962. pap. 8.95x (ISBN 0-691-08002-X). Princeton U Pr.

Swift, Digby G. Physics for Rural Development: A Sourcebook for Teachers & Extension Workers in Developing Countries. LC 82-2748. 257p. 1983. 37.95x (ISBN 0-471-10364-0, Pub. by Wiley-Interscience). Wiley.

Van Cleave, Janice P. Teaching the Fun of Physics. (Illus.). 224p. 1985. 16.95 (ISBN 0-13-892423-6); pap. 9.95 (ISBN 0-13-892415-5). P-H.

Von Baravalle, Hermann. Introduction to Physics in the Waldorf Schools: The Balance Between Art & Science. 2nd ed. 1967. pap. 2.95 (ISBN 0-916786-10-2, Pub by Waldorf School Monographs). St George Bk Serv.

Yurkewicz, William, Jr. A Guidebook for Teaching Physics. (Guidebook for Teaching Ser.). 375p. 1985. pap. 28.95x (ISBN 0-205-08355-2, 238355, Pub. by Longwood Div). Allyn.

PHYSICS–TABLES, ETC.

Angus, S., ed. International Thermodynamic Tables of the Fluid State-5. 1978. text ed. 72.00 (ISBN 0-08-021981-0). Pergamon.

--International Thermodynamic Tables of the Fluid State-6. 1979. text ed. 97.00 (ISBN 0-08-022372-9). Pergamon.

--International Thermodynamic Tables of the Fluid State-7. 1980. text ed. 110.00 (ISBN 0-08-022373-7). Pergamon.

Bernard, Gary D. & Ishimaru, Akira. Tables of the Anger & Lommel-Weber Functions. LC 62-17144. (Illus.). 74p. 1962. pap. 15.00x (ISBN 0-295-73956-8). U of Wash Pr.

Fischbeck, H. J. & Fishbeck, K. H. Formulas, Facts, & Constants for Students & Professionals in Engineering, Chemistry, & Physics. 270p. 1982. pap. 16.00 (ISBN 0-387-11315-0). Springer-Verlag.

Hellwege, K. H., ed. Landolt-Boernstein Numerical Data & Functional Relationships in Science & Technology, New Series, Group 4: Macroscopic & Technical Properties of Matter, Vol. 1, Densities Of Nonaquesous Solutions: Phosphorescence Of Inorganic Substances. 1974. 249.90 (ISBN 0-387-06269-6). Springer-Verlag.

--Landolt-Boernstein Numerical Data & Functional Relationships in Science & Technology, New Series, Group 1: Nuclear Particle & Physics, Vols. 1-8. Incl. Vol. 1. Energy Levels of Nuclei. (Illus.). 814p. 1961. 149.10 (ISBN 0-387-02715-7); Vol. 2. Nuclear Radii. Collard, H. R., et al. Schopper, H., ed. (Illus.). viii, 54p. 1967. 25.20 (ISBN 0-387-03894-9); Vol. 3. Numerical Tables for Angular Correlation Computations in Alpha, Beta & Gamma Spectroscopy. Appel, H. Schopper, H., ed. vi, 1202p. 1968. 226.80 (ISBN 0-387-04218-0); Vol. 4. Numerical Tables for Beta-Decay & Electron Capture. Behrens, H. & Jaenecke, J. Schopper, H., ed. (Illus.). viii, 316p. 1968. 75.60 (ISBN 0-387-04593-7); Vol. 5, Pt. A. Q-Values & Excitation Functions of Nuclear Reactions, Pt.A: Q-Values. Keller, K. A., et al. 1972. 247.80 (ISBN 0-387-06031-6); Vol. 5, Pt. B. Q-Values & Excitation Functions of Nuclear Reactions, Pt. B: Excitation Functions for Charged-Particle Induced Nuclear Reactions. Keller, K. A., et al. 1973. 153.30 (ISBN 0-387-06167-3); Vol. 5, Pt. C. Estimation of Unknown Excitation Functions & Thick-Target Yields for p, d, He & Reactions. Diddens, A. N., et al. 1974. 79.80 (ISBN 0-387-06723-X); Vol. 6. Properties & Production Spectra of Elementary Particles. Diddens, A. N., et al. Schopper, H., ed. 1972. 75.60 (ISBN 0-387-06047-2); Vol. 7. Elastic & Charge Exchange Scattering of Elementary Particles. Schopper, H., ed. 210.00 (ISBN 0-387-06248-3); Vol. 8. Photoproduction of Elementary Particles. Genzel, H. & Joos, P. J. 142.80 (ISBN 0-387-06249-1). Springer-Verlag.

--Landolt-Boernstein Numerical Data & Functional Relationships in Science & Technology, New Series, Group 3: Crystal & Solid State Physics, Vols. 1-6. Incl. Vol. 1. Elastic, Piezoelectric, Piezooptic & Electrooptic Constants of Crystals. Bechman, R. & Hearmon, R. F. x, 160p. 1966; Vol. 2. Elastic, Piezoelectric, Piezooptic, Electrooptic Constants, & Non-Linear Dielectric Susceptibilities of Crystals. Bechman, R., et al. (Illus.). ix, 232p. 1969; Vol. 3. Ferro- & Antiferroelectric Substances. Mitsui, T., et al. (Illus.). viii, 584p. 1969; Vol. 4, Pt. A. Magnetic & Other Properties of Oxides & Related Compounds. Goodenough, J. B., et al. (Illus.). xv, 367p. 1970. 130.20 (ISBN 0-387-04898-7); Vol. 4, Pt. B: Magnetic & Other Properties of Oxides & Related Compounds. Bonnenberg, F., et al. (Illus.). xvi, 666p. 1970. 235.20 (ISBN 0-387-05176-7); Vol. 5. Structure Data of Organic Crystals, 2 vols. Schudt, E. & Weitz, G. (Illus.). 1971. Set. 428.40 (ISBN 0-387-05177-5); Vol. 6. Structure Data of Elements & Intermetallic Phases. Eckerlin, P. & Kandler, H. 1971. 346.50 (ISBN 0-387-05500-2). LC 62-53136. Springer-Verlag.

Kaye, G. W. & Laby, T. H. Tables of Physical & Chemical Constants. 14th rev. ed. Bailey, A. E., et al, eds. LC 73-85205. (Illus.). 320p. 1973. text ed. 25.00x (ISBN 0-582-46326-2). Longman.

Tuma, Jan J. Handbook of Physical Calculations. 2nd ed. (Illus.). 512p. 1982. 41.95 (ISBN 0-07-065439-5). McGraw.

PHYSICS, ASTRONOMICAL

see Astrophysics

PHYSICS, BIOLOGICAL

see Biological Physics

PHYSICS, NUCLEAR

see Nuclear Physics

PHYSICS, TERRESTRIAL

see Geophysics

PHYSICS AS A PROFESSION

Cole, K. C. Sympathetic Vibrations: Reflections on Physics As a Way of Life. LC 85-7555. (Illus.). 352p. 1985. pap. 7.95 (ISBN 0-553-34234-7). Bantam.

Conference on Changing Career Opportunities, Pennsylvania State Univ., Aug. 1977. Physics Careers, Employment & Education. Perl, Martin L., ed. LC 77-9403. (AIP Conference Proceedings: No. 39). (Illus.). 1978. lib. bdg. 18.50 (ISBN 0-88318-138-X). Am Inst Physics.

Rudman, Jack. Physical Science Aide. (Career Examination Ser.: C-583). (Cloth bdg. avail. on request). pap. 10.00 (ISBN 0-8373-0583-7). Natl Learning.

--Physical Science Technician. (Career Examination Ser.: C-584). (Cloth bdg. avail. on request). pap. 10.00 (ISBN 0-8373-0584-5). Natl Learning.

PHYSICS RESEARCH

see Physics–Research

PHYSIOGRAPHY

see Geology; Geomorphology; Physical Geography

PHYSIOLOGICAL ACOUSTICS

see Hearing; Music–Acoustics and Physics

PHYSIOLOGICAL CHEMISTRY

see also Absorption (Physiology); Animal Heat; Bioenergetics; Biological Chemistry; Biosynthesis; Blood–Analysis and Chemistry; Carbohydrates; Cells; Chemistry, Medical and Pharmaceutical; Chemistry, Organic; Enzymes; Fat; Histochemistry; Homeostasis; Metabolism; Osmosis; Oxidation, Physiological; Poisons; Proteins; Toxins and Antitoxins; Vitamins also Minerals in the Body; Sugar in the Body; and similar headings

Adrian, R. H., et al, eds. Reviews of Physiology, Biochemistry & Pharmacology, Vol. 82. (Illus.). 1978. 52.00 (ISBN 0-387-08748-6). Springer-Verlag.

Berndt, A., et al. Organic C-Centered Radicals. LC 62-53136. (Landolt-Boernstein,Group II: Vol. 9, Pt. 8). (Illus.). 1977. 327.60 (ISBN 0-387-08152-6). Springer-Verlag.

Conder, John R. & Young, Colin L. Physiochemical Measurements by Gas Chromatography. LC 78-9899. 1979. 139.95 (ISBN 0-471-99674-2, Pub. by Wiley-Interscience). Wiley.

Davis, Albert R. The Anatomy of Biomagnetism. 1982. 7.95 (ISBN 0-533-05046-4). Vantage.

Greenberg, D. M., ed. Metabolic Pathways. 3rd ed. Incl. Vol. 1. 1967. 82.00 (ISBN 0-12-299251-2); Vol. 2. 1968. 71.50 (ISBN 0-12-299252-0); Vol. 3. 1969. 95.00 (ISBN 0-12-299253-9); Vol. 4. 1970. 82.00 (ISBN 0-12-299254-7); Vol. 5. Vogel, Henry J., ed. 1971. 88.00; Vol. 6. Hokin, L. E., ed. 1972. 95.00 (ISBN 0-12-299256-3). Acad Pr.

Havemann, K. & Janoff, A., eds. Neutral Proteases of Human Polymorphonuclear Leukocytes: Biochemistry, Physiology & Clinical Significance. LC 78-7037. (Illus.). 480p. 1978. text ed. 44.50 (ISBN 0-8067-0801-8). Urban & S.

International Symposium on Renal Handling of Sodium, Brestenberg, 1971. Recent Advances in Renal Physiology. Wirz, H. & Spinelli, F., eds. 300p. 1972. 41.75 (ISBN 3-8055-1405-0). S Karger.

Jones, Norman L. Blood Bases & Acid-Base Physiology. LC 81-6372. (Illus.). 1980. text ed. 10.95 (ISBN 0-913258-65-2). Thieme-Stratton.

Keller, H. U. & Till, G. O. Leucocyte Locomotion & Chemotaxis. (Agents & Actions Supplements Ser.: Vol. 12). 425p. 1983. text ed. 49.95 (ISBN 0-8176-1489-3). Birkhauser.

Levandowsky, M. & Hunter, S. H., eds. Biochemistry & Physiology of Protozoa, Vol. 4. 2nd ed. 1983. 69.50 (ISBN 0-12-444604-3). Acad Pr.

Liebowitz, Michael R. The Chemistry of Love. 224p. 1984. pap. 2.95 (ISBN 0-425-06989-3). Berkley Pub.

Lyalikov, L. Problems in Physiochemical Analysis. MIR Publishers, tr. 268p. 1975. 15.00x (ISBN 0-8464-0762-0). Beekman Pubs.

Nachmansohn, David. Chemical & Molecular Basis of Nerve Activity. 2nd & rev. ed. 1975. 50.00 (ISBN 0-12-512757-X). Acad Pr.

Peeters, H., ed. Phosphatidylcholine. (Illus.). 1976. 22.50 (ISBN 0-387-07828-2). Springer-Verlag.

Pullman, Bernard, ed. Frontiers in Physicochemical Biology. 1979. 66.00 (ISBN 0-12-566960-7). Acad Pr.

Quay, W. B. Pineal Chemistry: In Cellular & Physiological Mechanisms. (Illus.). 448p. 1974. 44.75x (ISBN 0-398-02802-8). C C Thomas.

Sankar, D. Siva. Quantitative Problems in Physical & Chemical Biology. Date not set. price not set (ISBN 0-685-77285-3). PJD Pubns.

Silverstein, Robert M. & Muller-Schwarze, Dietland, eds. Chemical Signals in Vertebrates 3. 378p. 1983. 52.50x (ISBN 0-306-41254-3, Plenum Pr). Plenum Pub.

Szent-Gyorgyi, Albert. Bioelectronics. 1968. 24.50 (ISBN 0-12-680945-3). Acad Pr.

Weiner, J. S., ed. Physiological Variation & Its Genetic Basis. (Symposia of the Society for the Study of Human Biology Ser.: Vol. 17). 180p. 1977. cancelled (ISBN 0-85066-108-0). Taylor & Francis.

PHYSIOLOGICAL CHEMISTRY–LABORATORY MANUALS

Janik, Borek. Physicochemical Characteristics of Oligonucleotides & Polynucleotides. LC 70-165692. 213p. 1971. 24.50x (ISBN 0-306-65155-6, IFI Plenum). Plenum Pub.

PHYSIOLOGICAL DATA TRANSMISSION

see Telemeter (Physiological Apparatus)

PHYSIOLOGICAL EFFECT OF LIGHT ON PLANTS

see Plants, Effect of Light On

PHYSIOLOGICAL OPTICS

see Optics, Physiological

PHYSIOLOGICAL OXIDATION

see Oxidation, Physiological

PHYSIOLOGICAL PSYCHOLOGY

see Psychology, Physiological

PHYSIOLOGISTS

Bowditch, Henry P. The Life & Writings of Henry Pickering Bowditch: An Original Anthology, 2 vols. Cohen, I. Bernard, ed. LC 79-7950. (Three Centuries of Science in America Ser.). (Illus.). 1980. Set. lib. bdg. 80.00x (ISBN 0-405-12531-3). Ayer Co Pubs.

Brooks, Chandler McC., et al, eds. The Life & Contributions of Walter Bradford Cannon, 1871-1945. LC 74-20825. 1975. 39.50x (ISBN 0-87395-261-8). State U NY Pr.

Engelmann, Th. W. Th. W. Engelmamn: Some Papers & His Bibliography. 264p. 1984. pap. text ed. 32.75x (ISBN 90-6203-656-2, Pub. by Radopi Holland). Humanities.

Hawker, Margot, et al. The Older Patient & the Role of the Physiologist. 2nd ed. Dick, Donald, intro. by. (Illus.). 160p. 1985. pap. 8.95 (ISBN 0-571-13427-0). Faber & Faber.

PHYSIOLOGY

see also Absorption (Physiology); Adaptation (Physiology); Anatomy; Animal Heat; Animal Mechanics; Blood–Circulation; Body Temperature; Bones; Cells; Electrophysiology; Excitation (Physiology); Fertilization (Biology); Growth; Homeostasis; Metabolism; Muscles; Nervous System; Neurophysiology; Nutrition; Perspiration; Physiological Chemistry; Pregnancy; Psychology, Physiological; Reproduction; Respiration; Rheology; Secretion; Senses and Sensation; Vibration–Physiological Effect also names of organs and secretions, e.g. Heart, Kidneys, Bile, Gastric Juice

Adolph, E. F. Origins of Physiological Regulations. 1968. 38.00 (ISBN 0-12-044360-0). Acad Pr.

Adrain, R. H., et al, eds. Reviews of Physiology, Biochemistry & Pharmacology, Vol. 90. (Illus.). 300p. 1981. 52.00 (ISBN 0-387-10657-X). Springer-Verlag.

Adrian, R. H. Reviews of Physiology, Biochemistry, & Pharmacology, Vol. 88. (Illus.). 264p. 1981. 54.00 (ISBN 0-387-10408-9). Springer-Verlag.

Adrian, R. H., ed. Reviews of Physiology, Biochemistry & Pharmacology, Vol. 73. LC 74-3674. (Illus.). 190p. 1975. 57.00 (ISBN 0-387-07357-4). Springer-Verlag.

--Reviews of Physiology, Biochemistry & Pharmacology, Vol. 89. (Illus.). 260p. 1981. 56.00 (ISBN 0-387-10495-X). Springer-Verlag.

--Reviews of Physiology, Biochemistry, & Pharmacology, Vol. 95. (Illus.). 235p. 1983. 45.50 (ISBN 0-387-11736-9). Springer-Verlag.

Adrian, R. H., et al, eds. Reviews of Physiology, Biochemistry & Pharmacology, Vol. 70. (Illus.). 260p. 1974. 52.00 (ISBN 0-387-06716-7). Springer-Verlag.

--Reviews of Physiology, Biochemistry & Pharmacology, Vol. 71. (Illus.). vi, 175p. 1974. 57.00 (ISBN 0-387-06939-9). Springer-Verlag.

--Reviews of Physiology, Biochemistry & Pharmacology, Vol. 76. LC 74-3674. (Illus.). 1976. 71.00 (ISBN 0-387-07757-X). Springer-Verlag.

--Reviews of Physiology, Biochemistry & Pharmacology, Vol. 78. LC 74-3674. 1977. 61.00 (ISBN 0-387-07975-0). Springer-Verlag.

--Reviews of Physiology, Biochemistry & Pharmacology, Vol. 80. LC 74-3674. (Illus.). 1977. 56.00 (ISBN 0-387-08466-5). Springer-Verlag.

--Reviews of Physiology, Biochemistry & Pharmacology, Vol. 81. LC 74-3674. (Illus.). 1978. 56.00 (ISBN 0-387-08554-8). Springer-Verlag.

--Reviews of Physiology, Biochemistry & Pharmacology, Vol. 82. (Illus.). 1978. 52.00 (ISBN 0-387-08748-6). Springer-Verlag.

--Reviews of Physiology, Biochemistry & Pharmacology, Vol. 83. LC 74-3674. (Illus.). 1978. 51.00 (ISBN 0-387-08907-1). Springer-Verlag.

--Reviews of Physiology, Biochemistry & Pharmacology, Vol. 85. (Illus.). 1979. 51.00 (ISBN 0-387-09225-0). Springer-Verlag.

--Reviews of Physiology, Biochemistry & Pharmacology, Vol. 91. (Illus.). 240p. 1981. 42.00 (ISBN 0-387-10961-7). Springer-Verlag.

--Reviews of Physiology, Biochemistry, & Pharmacology, Vol. 92. (Illus.). 220p. 1982. 42.50 (ISBN 0-387-11105-0). Springer-Verlag.

--Reviews of Physiology, Biochemistry & Pharmacology, Vol. 94. (Illus.). 225p. 1982. 46.00 (ISBN 0-387-11701-6). Springer-Verlag.

--Reviews of Physiology, Biochemistry & Pharmacology, Vol. 96. (Illus.). 194p. 1983. 41.00 (ISBN 0-387-11849-7). Springer-Verlag.

--Reviews of Physiology, Biochemistry, & Pharmacology, Vol. 97. (Illus.). 176p. 1983. 37.50 (ISBN 0-387-12135-8). Springer-Verlag.

American Physiologial Society. Handbook of Physiology: Circulation, Section 2, the Cardiovascular System, 3 vols. Berne, Robert & Sperelakis, Nick, eds. Incl. Vol. 1. Heart; Vol. 2. Vascular Smooth Muscle; Vol. 3. Microcirculation. 1979. 130.00 (ISBN 0-683-00605-3). Williams & Wilkins.

American Physiological Society. Incl. The Nervous System: Section 1, Volume 1: Cellular Biology of Neurons. Kandel, Eric R. 1238p. 1977. 135.00 (ISBN 0-683-04505-9); The Nervous System: Section 1, Volume II: Motor Control. Brooks, Vernon B. 1548p. 1981. 245.00 (ISBN 0-683-01105-7); The Cardiovascular System: Section 2, Volume I: The Heart. Berne, Robert M. & Sperelakis, N. 978p. 1979. 130.00 (ISBN 0-683-00605-3); The Cardiovascular System: Section 2, Volume II: Vascular Smooth Muscle. Bohr, David F., et al. 694p. 1980. 95.00 (ISBN 0-683-00606-1); The Respiratory System: Section 3, Volume I. Fenn, Wallace O. & Rahn, Hermann. 934p. 1964. 32.00 (ISBN 0-683-03148-1); Adaptation to the Environment: Section 4. Dill, D. B., et al. 1068p. 1964. 32.00 (ISBN 0-683-02570-8); Adipose Tissue: Section 5. Renold, Albert E. & Cahill, George F., Jr. 832p. 1965. 28.00 (ISBN 0-683-07232-3); Alimentary Canal: Section 6, Volume I: Control of Food & Water Intake. Code, Charles F. 486p. 1967. 22.00 (ISBN 0-683-01951-1); Alimentary Canal: Section 6, Volume II: Secretion, Code, Charles F. 662p. 1968. 32.00 (ISBN 0-683-01952-X); Alimentary Canal: Section 6, Volume III: Intestinal Absorption. Code, Charles F. 490p. 1968. 22.00 (ISBN 0-683-01953-8); Alimentary Canal: Section 6, Volume IV: Motility. Code, Charles F. 804p. 1968. 38.50 (ISBN 0-683-01954-6); Alimentary Canal: Section 6, Volume V: Bile, Digestion, Ruminal Physiology. Code, Charles F. 582p. 1968. 30.00 (ISBN 0-683-01955-4); Endocrinology: Section 7, Volume I: Endocrine Pancreas. Steiner, Donald F. & Freinkel, Norbert. 731p. 1972. 45.00 (ISBN 0-683-03588-6); Endocrinology: Section 7, Volume II: Female Reproductive System. Greep, Roy O. 1973. Pt. 1, 666 p. 44.50 (ISBN 0-683-03564-9); Pt. 2, 381pp. 25.00 (ISBN 0-683-03565-7); Endocrinology: Section 7, Volume III: Thyroid. Greer, Monte A. & Solomon, David H. 500p. 1974. 38.00 (ISBN 0-683-03566-5); Endocrinology: Section 7, Volume IV: The Pituitary Gland & Its Neuroendocrine Control, 2 Pts. Knobil, Ernst & Sawyer, Wilbur H. 1974. Pt. 1, 584 pp. 49.50 (ISBN 0-683-03568-1); Pt. 2, 607 pp. 49.50 (ISBN 0-683-03569-X); Endocrinology: Section 7, Volume V: Male Reproductive System. Hamilton, David W. & Greep, Roy O. 527p. 1975. 47.50 (ISBN 0-683-03567-3); Endocrinology: Section 7, Volume VI: Adrenal Gland. Blaschko, Hermann, et al. 754p. 1975. 75.00 (ISBN 0-683-03570-3); Endocrinology: Section 7, Volume VII: Parathyroid Gland. Aurbach, Gerald D. 488p. 1976. 55.00; Renal Physiology: Section 8. Orloff, Jack & Berliner, Robert W. 1090p. 1973. 72.50 (ISBN 0-683-06652-8); Reactions to Environmental Agents: Section 9. Lee, Douglas H. 667p. 1977. 80.00 (ISBN 0-683-03000-0). (Handbook of Physiology Ser.). Waverly Pr.

Anderson, D. J., ed. Physiology: Past, Present, & Future: A Symposium in Honour of Yngve Zotterman, University of Bristol, July 11 & 12, 1979. LC 80-40957. (Illus.). 168p. 1980. 32.00 (ISBN 0-08-025480-2). Pergamon.

Anderson, Paul D. Basic Human Anatomy & Physiology: Clinical Implications for the Health Professionals. LC 83-23511. 450p. 1984. pap. text ed. 16.00x pub net (ISBN 0-534-03089-0). Wadsworth Health.

Anthony, Catherine P. & Thibodeau, Gary A. Structure & Function of the Body. 7th ed. (Illus.). 374p. 1984. pap. text ed. 14.95 (ISBN 0-8016-0296-3). Mosby.

--Textbook of Anatomy & Physiology. 11th ed. LC 82-12555. (Illus.). 887p. 1983. text ed. 28.95 (ISBN 0-8016-0289-0). Mosby.

Autrum, H., et al, eds. Handbook of Sensory Physiology, 8 vols. Incl. Vol. 1. Principles of Receptor Physiology. Loewenstein, W. R., ed. 1971. 76.00 (ISBN 0-387-05144-9); Vol. 2. Somatosensory System. Iggo, A., ed. 1973. 158.00 (ISBN 0-387-05941-5); Vol. 3, Pt. 1. Enteroceptors. Neil, E., ed. 1972. 39.50 (ISBN 0-387-05523-1); Vol. 3, Pt. 2. Muscle Receptors. Hunt, C. C., et al. 1974. 78.00 (ISBN 0-387-06891-0); Vol. 4. Chemical Sense. Beidler, L. M., ed. 1971. Pt. 1 Olfaction. 63.00 (ISBN 0-387-05291-7); Pt. 2. Taste. 58.00 (ISBN 0-387-05501-0); Vol. 5, Pt. 1. Auditory System. 152.00 (ISBN 0-387-06676-4); Vol. 6, Pt. 1. Vestibular System. Kornhuber, H. H., ed. 148.00 (ISBN 0-387-06889-9); Vol. 7, Pt. 1. Photochemistry of Vision. Dartnall, H. J., ed. 1972. 93.00 (ISBN 0-387-05145-7); Vol. 7, Pt. 2. Physiology of Photoreceptor Organs. Fuortes, M. G., ed. 1972. 115.00 (ISBN 0-387-05743-9); Vol. 7, Pts. 3A & 3B. Central Processing of Vision Information. Jung, R., ed. LC 70-190496. 1973. Pt. A. 149.00 (ISBN 0-387-05769-2); Pt. B. 137.00 (ISBN 0-387-06056-1). Pt. B; Vol. 7, Pt. 4. Visual Psychophysics. Jameson, D. & Hurvich, L. M., eds. 1972. 125.00 (ISBN 0-387-05146-5); Vol. 8. Perception. Teuber, H. L., ed. 155.00 (ISBN 0-387-08300-6). Springer-Verlag.

Badeer, H. S. Cardiovascular Physiology. (Karger Continuing Education Series: Vol. 6). (Illus.). xvi, 276p. 1984. 24.75 (ISBN 3-8055-3796-4). S Karger.

Baeyens, Dennis A. Experimental Physiology. 96p. (Orig.). 1981. lab manual 8.95x (ISBN 0-89459-131-2). Hunter Textbks.

Banks, P., et al. The Biochemistry of the Tissues. 2nd ed. LC 75-26739. 493p. 1976. (Pub. by Wiley-Interscience); pap. 35.95 (ISBN 0-471-01923-2, Pub. by Wiley-Interscience). Wiley.

Barber, C., et al. Dictionary of Physiological Measurement. 1984. pap. text ed. 11.00 (ISBN 0-85200-737-X, Pub. by MTP Pr England). Kluwer Academic.

Barcroft, J. Features in the Architecture of Physiological Functions. 1972. Repr. of 1938 ed. 21.50x (ISBN 0-02-840820-9). Hafner.

Bell, George H., et al, eds. Textbook of Physiology. 10th ed. (Illus.). 600p. 1980. pap. 35.00 (ISBN 0-443-02152-X). Churchill.

Benson, Harold J. & Talaro, Arthur. Physiological Applications. 318p. 1982. write for info. wire coil (ISBN 0-697-04717-2); instr's. handbook avail. (ISBN 0-697-04723-7). Wm C Brown.

Bergner, Erik E., et al, eds. Compartments, Pools & Spaces in Medical Physiology: Proceedings. LC 67-61865. (AEC Symposium Ser.). 521p. 1967. pap. 21.00 (ISBN 0-87079-167-2, CONF-661010); microfiche 4.50 (ISBN 0-87079-168-0, CONF-661010). DOE.

Berne, R. M., et al, eds. Annual Review of Physiology, Vol. 45. LC 39-15404. (Illus.). 1983. text ed. 27.00 (ISBN 0-8243-0345-8). Annual Reviews.

--Annual Review of Physiology, Vol. 46. LC 39-15404. (Illus.). 1984. text ed. 27.00 (ISBN 0-8243-0346-6). Annual Reviews.

Bevan, James. The Simon & Schuster Handbook of Anatomy & Physiology. 8.50 (ISBN 0-671-24998-3); 8.95 (ISBN 0-317-00952-4). S&S.

Blashko, H., et al. Reviews of Physiology, Biochemistry & Pharmacology, Vol. 98. (Illus.). 260p. 1983. 48.50 (ISBN 0-387-12817-4). Springer-Verlag.

Bolis, L., et al, eds. Comparative Physiology: Locomotion, Respiration, Transport & Blood: Proceedings of the International Congress Held in Acquasparta, 1972. 1973. 42.75 (ISBN 0-444-10556-5); pap. 25.75 (ISBN 0-686-44058-7). Elsevier.

Boolootian, Richard A. Elements of Human Anatomy & Physiology. LC 76-3681. 550p. 1976. text ed. 22.95 (ISBN 0-8299-0086-1); instrs.' manual avail. (ISBN 0-8299-0460-3). West Pub.

Boyer, A. L. Dictionnaire de Physiologie. Migne, J. P., ed. (Troisieme et Derniere Encyclopedie Theologique Ser.: Vol. 58). (Fr.). 776p. Repr. of 1861 ed. lib. bdg. 98.50x (ISBN 0-89241-324-7). Caratzas.

Brooks, Paynton & Brooks. The Human Body: Structure & Function in Health & Disease. 2nd ed. LC 79-24085. (Illus.). 1980. pap. text ed. 25.95 (ISBN 0-8016-0808-2). Mosby.

Brown, Arthur M. & Stubbs, Donald W., eds. Medical Physiology. LC 82-8585. (Illus.). 904p. 1983. 35.95 (ISBN 0-471-05207-8). Wiley.

Brown, B. H. & Smallwood, R. H. Medical Physics & Physiological Measurement. (Illus.). 544p. 1982. text ed. 31.95 (ISBN 0-632-00704-4, B 0893-7). Mosby.

Brown, J. H. U. & Gann, Donald, eds. Engineering Principles in Physiology, 2 vols. Vol. 1, 1973. 65.00 (ISBN 0-12-136201-9); Vol. 2, 1973. 76.50 (ISBN 0-12-136202-7). Acad Pr.

Brown, L., et al, eds. Reviews of Physiology & Biochemistry. Incl. Vol. 57. 1966. 64.90 (ISBN 0-387-03499-4); Vol. 59. 1967. 73.80 (ISBN 0-387-03783-7); Vol. 60. 1968. 79.70 (ISBN 0-387-04103-6); Vol. 61. 1969; Vol. 62. 1970. o.p. (ISBN 0-387-04811-1); Vol. 63. 1971; Vol. 64. 1972. o.p.; Vol. 65. 1972; Vol. 66. 1972; Vol. 67. 1972; Vol. 68. 1973. Springer-Verlag.

Bullock, Barbara, et al, eds. Pathophysiology: Adaptations & Alterations in Function. 1984. 35.95 (ISBN 0-316-11479-0) (ISBN 0-316-11481-2). Little.

Burke, S. R. Human Anatomy & Physiology for the Health Sciences. 465p. 1980. 19.95 (ISBN 0-471-05598-0). Wiley.

Byrd, Ronald James & Browning, Freddie Melton. A Laboratory Manual for Exercise Physiology. (Illus.). 168p. 1972. spiral bdg. 17.50x (ISBN 0-398-02459-6). C C Thomas.

Cahe, L A., et al, eds. Antidromic Vasodilatation & Neurogenic Inflammation: Satellite Symposium of the 29th International Congress of Physiological Sciences Newcastle Australia 1983. 353p. 1984. 46.00 (Pub. by Akademiai Kiado Hungary). Heyden.

Calder, William A., III. Size, Function, & Life History. (Illus.). 448p. 1984. text ed. 32.50x (ISBN 0-674-81070-8). Harvard U Pr.

Cambridge Communication Ltd. Anatomy & Physiology: A Self Instructional Course, 5 vols. (Illus.). 1985. Set. pap. text ed. 24.75 (ISBN 0-443-03395-1); Bk. 1. The Human Body & the Reproductive System. pap. text ed. 4.95 (ISBN 0-443-03170-3); Bk. 2. The Endocrine Glands & the Nervous System. pap. text ed. 4.95 (ISBN 0-443-03206-8); Bk. 3. The Locomotor System & the Special Senses. pap. text ed. 4.95 (ISBN 0-443-03207-6); BK. 5. The Urinary System & the Digestive System. pap. text ed. 4.95 (ISBN 0-443-03209-2). Churchill.

Carlson, Anton J., et al. The Machinery of the Body. rev. & enl. ed. LC 61-14536. 1961. 30.00x (ISBN 0-226-09279-8). U of Chicago Pr.

Carlson, Neil R. Physiology of Behavior. 2nd ed. 704p. 1981. text ed. 32.84 (ISBN 0-205-07262-3, 797262-8); tchr's. ed. avail. (ISBN 0-205-07263-1); wkbk. 15.24 (ISBN 0-205-07264-X, 797264). Allyn.

Case, R. M., ed. Variations in Human Physiology. LC 84-11301. (Integrative Studies in Human Physiology). 241p. 1985. text ed. 21.00 (ISBN 0-7190-1086-1, Pub. by Manchester Univ Pr); pap. text ed. 9.00 (ISBN 0-7190-1732-7). Longwood Pub Group.

Cena, K. & Clark, J. A., eds. Bioengineering, Thermal Physiology & Comfort. (Studies in Environmental Science: Vol. 10). 290p. 1981. 64.00 (ISBN 0-444-99761-X). Elsevier.

Chaffee, Ellen E., et al. Basic Physiology & Anatomy. 4th ed. LC 79-15976. 628p. 1980. text ed. 27.50x (ISBN 0-397-54227-5, Lippincott Nursing). Lippincott.

Cluff, Leila L. Anatomy & Physiology Clarified for Effective Learning. 2nd ed. Printing Inc. Art Staff, tr. LC 82-81215. (Illus.). 300p. (Orig.). 1982. pap. 8.95 (ISBN 0-89829-114-3). Health Ed Aids.

Cohen, Bernard, ed. Vestibular & Oculomotor Physiology: International Meeting of the Barany Society, Vol. 374. LC 81-14230. 892p. 1981. 177.00x (ISBN 0-89766-137-0); pap. 177.00x (ISBN 0-89766-138-9). NY Acad Sci.

Coleman, Thomas G., ed. Computer Simulation of Physiological Systems. 40p. pap. 10.00 (ISBN 0-686-36684-0). Soc Computer Sim.

Comroe, J. H., Jr., et al, eds. Annual Review of Physiology, Vol. 36. LC 39-15404. (Illus.). 1974. text ed. 20.00 (ISBN 0-8243-0336-9). Annual Reviews.

Corradino, R. A., ed. Functional Regulation at the Cellular & Molecular Levels: Proceedings of Conference, Ithaca, N. Y., July 21-24, 1981. 1982. 80.00 (ISBN 0-444-00676-1, Biomedical Pr). Elsevier.

Crowe, John H. & Clegg, James S., eds. Anhydrobiosis. LC 73-12354. (Benchmark Papers in Biological Concepts Ser.: Vol. 2). 477p. 1973. 55.00 (ISBN 0-87933-039-2). Van Nos Reinhold.

Crowley, Leonard V. Introductory Concepts in Anatomy & Physiology. LC 76-2249. (Illus.). Repr. of 1976 ed. 115.50 (ISBN 0-8357-9612-4, 2015077). Bks Demand UMI.

Crozier, Alan. Biochemistry & Physiology of Gibberellins, 2 vols. LC 83-13862. 576p. 1983. Vol. 1. 62.50 (ISBN 0-03-059054-X); Vol. 2. 59.50x (ISBN 0-03-059056-6). Praeger.

Cunningham, John J. Introduction to Nutritional Physiology. (Illus.). 400p. 1983. 22.95x (ISBN 0-89313-031-1); text ed. 22.95x (ISBN 0-686-38084-3). G F Stickley.

Davis, Bowman O., et al. Conceptual Human Physiology. 640p. 1985. text ed. 34.95 (ISBN 0-675-20252-3); study guide 11.50 (ISBN 0-675-20420-8); additional supplements avail. Merrill.

Davson, Hugh & Segal, M. B. Introduction to Physiology, Vols. 1-3. Incl. Vol. I. Basic Mechanisms. 576p. 1975. 29.50 (ISBN 0-8089-0896-0, 791001); Vol. II. Basic Mechanisms. 494p. 1975; Vol. III. Control Mechanisms. 656p. 1976. 29.50 (ISBN 0-686-57753-1, 791003). Grune.

--Introduction to Physiology: Vol. IV, Mechanisms of Motor Control. 620p. 1978. 29.50 (ISBN 0-8089-0899-5, 791004). Grune.

--Introduction to Physiology, Vol. V: Control of Reproduction. 610p. 1980. 54.50 (ISBN 0-8089-0900-2, 791005). Grune.

Day, James A. Perspectives in Kinanthropometry. 1985. text ed. write for info. (ISBN 0-87322-008-0, BDAY0008). Human Kinetics.

Dean, W. B. & Farrar, G. E., Jr. Basic Concepts of Anatomy & Physiology. 2nd ed. (Illus.). 400p. 1982. pap. text ed. 15.50 (ISBN 0-397-54378-6, 64-03208, Lippincott Medical). Lippincott.

DeCoursey, Russell M. Laboratory Manual of Human Anatomy & Physiology. 2nd ed. (Illus.). 256p. 1974. pap. text ed. 18.95 (ISBN 0-07-016239-5). McGraw.

DeVries, Herbert A. Physiology of Exercise for Physical Education & Athletics. 3rd ed. 592p. 1980. text ed. write for info. (ISBN 0-697-07169-3). Wm C Brown.

Dienhart, Charlotte M. Basic Human Anatomy & Physiology. 3rd ed. LC 78-64706. (Illus.). 1979. pap. text ed. 13.50 (ISBN 0-7216-3082-0). Saunders.

Donnelly, Patricia J. & Wistreich, George A. Laboratory Manual for Anatomy & Physiology: With Cat Dissection. 636p. 1982. pap. text ed. 20.50 scp (ISBN 0-06-046644-8, HarpC); instr's manual avail. (ISBN 0-06-361701-3). Har-Row.

Donnersberger, Anne B., et al. A Manual of Anatomy & Physiology. fetal pig ed. 1978. pap. text ed. 17.95 (ISBN 0-669-01490-7); answer key 1.95 (ISBN 0-669-01632-2). Heath.

Eckert, Roger. Animal Physiology. LC 77-6648. (Biology Ser.). (Illus.). 558p. 1978. text ed. 30.95 (ISBN 0-7167-0570-2). W H Freeman.

Edelman, I. S., et al, eds. Annual Review of Physiology, Vol. 41. LC 39-15404. (Illus.). 1979. text ed. 20.00 (ISBN 0-8243-0341-5). Annual Reviews.

--Annual Review of Physiology, Vol. 42. LC 39-15404. (Illus.). 1980. text ed. 20.00 (ISBN 0-8243-0342-3). Annual Reviews.

--Annual Review of Physiology, Vol. 44. LC 39-15404. (Illus.). 1982. text ed. 22.00 (ISBN 0-8243-0344-X). Annual Reviews.

--Annual Review of Physiology, Vol. 43. LC 39-15404. (Illus.). 1981. text ed. 20.00 (ISBN 0-8243-0343-1). Annual Reviews.

Ellory, J. C. & Young, T. Red Cell Membranes: A Methodological Approach. (Biological Techniques Ser.). 1982. 55.00 (ISBN 0-12-237140-2). Acad Pr.

Feher, O. & Joo, F., eds. Cellular Analogues of Conditioning & Neural Plasticity: Proceedings of a Satellite Symposium of the 28th International Congress of Physiological Sciences, Szeged, Hungary, 1980. LC 80-41992. (Advances in Physiological Sciences: Vol. 36). (Illus.). 300p. 1981. 44.00 (ISBN 0-08-027372-6). Pergamon.

Ferruzzi, Donald R. Human Anatomy & Physiology: A Laboratory Manual, Vol. 1. 4th ed. (Illus.). 222p. 1985. 17.95 (ISBN 0-9609098-1-8). Biomat Pub Co.

Fontaine, Maurice. Physiologie. (Methodique Ser.). 1956p. 52.50 (ISBN 0-686-56432-4). French & Eur.

Fox, Stuart I. Human Physiology. 736p. 1984. text ed. write for info. (ISBN 0-697-08232-6); lab manual avail. (ISBN 0-697-04724-5); instr's manual avail. (ISBN 0-697-00254-3); transparencies avail. (ISBN 0-697-04942-6). Wm C Brown.

--Laboratory Guide to Human Physiology: Concepts & Clinical Applications. 3rd ed. 336p. 1984. write for info wire coil (ISBN 0-697-04724-5); write for info. Wm C Brown.

Frohlich, Edward D. Pathophysiology: Altered Regulatory Mechanisms in Disease. 3rd ed. 992p. 1983. text ed. 37.50 (ISBN 0-397-52103-0, 65-07040, Lippincott Medical). Lippincott.

Ganong, William F. Review of Medical Physiology. 12th ed. LC 85-50920. (Illus.). 583p. 1985. lexotone cover 22.50 (ISBN 0-87041-138-1). Lange.

Gelfand, I. M., et al, eds. Structural-Functional Organization of Biological Systems. 448p. 1971. 27.50x (ISBN 0-262-07042-1). MIT Pr.

Ghai, C. L. A Textbook of Practical Physiology. xiii, 239p. 1984. pap. text ed. 15.95x (ISBN 0-7069-2592-0, Pub. by Vikas India). Advent NY.

Gilula, Norton B., ed. Membrane-Membrane Interactions. (Society of General Physiologists Ser.: Vol. 34). 230p. 1980. text ed. 42.00 (ISBN 0-89004-377-9). Raven.

Glossary of Physiological Terms. (Rus., Eng., Fr. & Ger.). 116p. 1980. 30.00x (ISBN 0-686-44718-2, Pub. by Collets). State Mutual Bk.

Gravitational Physiology: Proceedings of the 28th International Congress of Physiological Sciences, Budapest, 1980. LC 80-42103. (Advances in Physiological Sciences: Vol. 19). (Illus.). 350p. 1981. 40.00 (ISBN 0-08-027340-8). Pergamon.

Green, John H. Basic Clinical Physiology. 3rd ed. (Illus.). 1978. pap. text ed. 16.95x (ISBN 0-19-263331-7). Oxford U Pr.

--An Introduction to Human Physiology. 4th ed. (Illus.). 1976. pap. text ed. 25.00x (ISBN 0-19-263328-7). Oxford U Pr.

Greep, Roy O., ed. Reproductive Physiology IV. (International Review of Physiology Ser.: Vol. 27). (Illus.). 352p. 1983. text ed. 49.50 (ISBN 0-8391-1555-5, 14206). Univ Park.

Griffiths, Mary. Introduction to Human Physiology. 2nd ed. 1981. text ed. write for info. (ISBN 0-02-347230-8). Macmillan.

Grinnell, Alan D. & Moody, William J., Jr. The Physiology of Excitable Cells. LC 83-12063. (Neurology & Neurobiology Ser.: Vol. 5). 620p. 1983. 72.00 (ISBN 0-8451-2704-7). A R Liss.

Gross, J. F., et al, eds. Modern Techniques in Physiological Sciences. 1974. 79.50 (ISBN 0-12-304450-2). Acad Pr.

Guild, Warren R., et al. Physiology for Nurses: A Guide for Nurses, Allied Health Professionals & Physician Assistants. LC 73-5321. (Trainex Manual Ser.). (Illus.). 289p. 1973. 9.95 (ISBN 0-685-41086-2). Trainex Pr.

Guyton, Arthur C. Physiology of the Human Body. 6th ed. 1984. text ed. 37.95 (ISBN 0-03-058339-X, CBS C). SCP.

Hainsworth, F. Reed. Animal Physiology: Adaptations in Function. (Life Sciences Ser.). (Illus.). 600p. 1981. text ed. 36.95 (ISBN 0-201-03401-8). Addison-Wesley.

Hall, Thomas S. History of General Physiology. Incl. Vol. I (ISBN 0-226-31353-0, P656); Vol. II (ISBN 0-226-31354-9, P657). 1969. pap. 6.50x ea. (Phoen). U of Chicago Pr.

Harley, John P. Human Physiology Lecture Notes. 1984. pap. text ed. 13.25 (ISBN 0-89917-440-X). Tichenor Pub.

Haupt, R., et al. Introductory Physiology & Anatomy: A Laboratory Guide. 4th ed. 1977. pap. text ed. write for info. (ISBN 0-02-351710-7). Macmillan.

Henfrey, Arthur, ed. Botanical & Physiological Memoirs. Repr. of 1853 ed. 55.00 (ISBN 0-384-22310-9). Johnson Repr.

Ho, Betty Y. Living Function of Sleep, Life & Aging. LC 79-13810. (Illus., Orig.). 1967. pap. 3.50 (ISBN 0-9600148-0-2). Juvenescent.

Hoar, William S. General & Comparative Physiology. 3rd ed. (Illus.). 928p. 1983. 38.95 (ISBN 0-13-349308-3). P-H.

Hoar, William S. & Hickman, Cleveland P. General & Comparative Physiology: A Laboratory Companion. 3rd ed. 1983. pap. 16.95 (ISBN 0-13-349316-4). P-H.

Hofmann, E. Reviews of Physiology, Biochemistry & Pharmacology, Vol. 75. LC 74-3674. 1976. 71.00 (ISBN 0-387-07639-5). Springer-Verlag.

Hole, John W., Jr. Essentials of Human Anatomy & Physiology. 600p. 1982. text ed. write for info. (ISBN 0-697-04730-X); info. instr's. manual avail. (ISBN 0-697-04741-5); study guide avail. (ISBN 0-697-04742-3); transparencies avail. (ISBN 0-697-04941-8). Wm C Brown.

--Essentials of Human Anatomy & Physiology. 2nd ed. 608p. 1986. text ed. price not set (ISBN 0-697-00778-2); instr's. manual avail.; price not set student study guide (ISBN 0-697-00997-1); price not set lab manual (ISBN 0-697-00615-8); instr's. manual for lab manual avail. (ISBN 0-697-04959-0). Wm C Brown.

--Human Anatomy & Physiology. 3rd ed. (Illus.). 896p. 45.00 (ISBN 0-684-18184-3, ScribT). Scribner.

Holtzmeier, Dawn K. Applied Anatomy & Physiology: A Laboratory Manual & Workbook for Health Careers. 304p. 1983. pap. text ed. 21.95 (ISBN 0-8403-2915-6). Kendall-Hunt.

Hoppensteadt, Frank C., ed. Mathematical Aspects of Physiology. LC 81-1315. (Lectures in Applied Mathematics Ser.: No. 19). 394p. 1981. 44.00 (ISBN 0-8218-1119-3, LAM-19). Am Math.

Horvath, S. M. & Yousef, M., eds. Environmental Physiology: Aging, Heat & Altitude. 468p. 1981. 96.00 (ISBN 0-444-00583-8, Biomedical Pr). Elsevier.

Hulliger, M., et al. Reviews of Physiology, Biochemistry & Pharmacology, Vol. 101. (Illus.). 255p. 1984. 35.50 (ISBN 0-387-13679-7). Springer-Verlag.

Hurvich, Leo M. Color Vision. LC 80-19077. (Illus.). 280p. 1981. pap. text ed. 35.00x (ISBN 0-87893-337-9). Sinauer Assoc.

International Congress of Physiological Sciences, Munich, 1971. Proceedings, 2 vols. 1971. Set. pap. 57.90 (ISBN 0-387-05618-1). Springer-Verlag.

International Primatological Society, 7th Congress, Bangalore, January 1979. Non-Human Primates As Models for Study of Human Reproduction. Anand Kumar, T. C., ed. (Illus.). 252p. 1980. pap. 38.00 (ISBN 3-8055-0540-X). S Karger.

Iyengar, G. V., et al. The Elemental Composition of Human Tissues & Body Fluids. 151p. 1978. 34.20x (ISBN 0-89573-003-0). VCH Pubs.

Jacob, Stanley W. & Francone, Clarice A. Elements of Anatomy & Physiology. LC 75-28795. (Illus.). 251p. 1976. text ed. 12.95 (ISBN 0-7216-5088-0). Saunders.

Jensen, David. Principles of Physiology. 2nd ed. (Illus.). 1085p. 1980. 42.50 (ISBN 0-8385-7931-0). ACC.

Kehoe, et al. Workbook for Introductory Human Anatomy & Physiology. 144p. 1983. wkbk. 8.50 (ISBN 0-8403-3091-X). Kendall-Hunt.

Kleitman, Nathaniel. Sleep & Wakefulness. rev. ed. LC 63-17854. 1963. 40.00x (ISBN 0-226-44071-0). U of Chicago Pr.

Knobil, Ernst, et al, eds. Annual Review of Physiology, Vol. 40. LC 39-15404. (Illus.). 1978. text ed. 20.00 (ISBN 0-8243-0340-7). Annual Reviews.

Koshland, Daniel E., Jr. Bacterial Chemotaxis As a Model Behavioral System. (Distinguished Lecture Series of the Society of General Physiologists: Vol. 2). 210p. 1980. text ed. 28.50 (ISBN 0-89004-468-6). Raven.

Landau, Barbara R. Essential Human Anatomy & Physiology. 2nd ed. 1980. text ed. 30.40x (ISBN 0-673-15249-9). Scott F.

Langley, L. L., et al. Dynamic Anatomy & Physiology. 5th ed. (Illus.). 1980. text ed. 38.00 (ISBN 0-07-036275-0). McGraw.

Larsen, James B. & Billings, Jeffrey D. Laboratory Manual for Human Physiology. 128p. 1982. pap. text ed. 8.95 (ISBN 0-8403-2782-X). Kendall-Hunt.

Lash, James & Burger, Max M., eds. Cell & Tissue Interactions. LC 77-83689. (Society of General Physiologists Ser: Vol. 32). 331p. 1977. 42.50 (ISBN 0-89004-180-6). Raven.

Lawrence, Jean M. Human Physiology. 1983. 7.95 (ISBN 0-88252-019-9). Paladin Hse.

Layman, Dale P. The Terminology of Anatomy & Physiology: A Programmed Approach. LC 82-13448. 293p. 1983. pap. 11.95 (ISBN 0-471-86262-2, Pub. by Wiley Med). Wiley.

Lerner, Richard M. On the Nature of Human Plasticity. 208p. 1984. 29.95 (ISBN 0-521-25651-8). Cambridge U Pr.

Lote, Christopher J. Principles of Renal Physiology. (Illus.). 179p. 1982. pap. text ed. 15.50x (ISBN 0-7099-0079-1, Pub. by Croom Helm England). Sheridan.

Luciano, Dorothy S., et al. Human Function & Structure. (Illus.). 1978. text ed. 35.95 (ISBN 0-07-038942-X). McGraw.

Lyons, Richard T. & Reed, Ray. An Instructional Manual for Anatomy & Physiology. 1984. pap. text ed. 19.95 (ISBN 0-89917-434-5). Tichenor Pub.

Mcclintic, J. R. Physiology of the Human Body. 3rd ed. 615p. 1985. 33.95 (ISBN 0-471-87483-3); pap. price not set (ISBN 0-471-83099-2). Wiley.

McClintic, J. Robert. Basic Anatomy & Physiology of the Human Body. 2nd ed. LC 79-14295. 762p. 1980. text ed. 37.95x (ISBN 0-471-03876-8); pap. 16.45x experiments (ISBN 0-471-05118-7). Wiley.

--Physiology of the Human Body. 2nd ed. LC 77-27066. 647p. 1978. text ed. 38.45x (ISBN 0-471-02664-6). Wiley.

Macey, Robert I. Human Physiology. 2nd ed. (Illus.). 224p. 1975. pap. 18.95 ref. ed. (ISBN 0-13-445288-7). P-H.

McKendrick, John G. The Principles of Physiology. 15.00 (ISBN 0-8274-4238-6). R West.

McMurray, W. C. Essentials of Human Metabolism: The Relationship of Biochemistry to Human Physiology & Disease. 2nd ed. (Illus.). 331p. 1983. pap. text ed. 21.00 (ISBN 0-06-141643-6, 14-16437, Harper Medical). Lippincott.

McNaught, Ann B. & Callander, Robin. Illustrated Physiology. 4th ed. (Illus.). 291p. 1983. pap. text ed. 16.00 (ISBN 0-443-02713-7). Churchill.

Malone, K. & Schneider, J. M. Workbook for Basic Human Anatomy & Physiology: Traditional & Innovative Exercises. 363p. 1983. pap. text ed. 14.50 (ISBN 0-471-09244-4). Wiley.

Mantegazza, Paola. Physiology & Expression. 327p. 1981. Repr. lib. bdg. 45.00 (ISBN 0-89987-567-X). Darby Bks.

Marieb, Elaine. Essentials of Human Anatomy & Physiology. 1984. 18.95 (ISBN 0-201-15882-5, Med-Nurse). Addison-Wesley.

Marks, G. C. & Kozlowski, T. T., eds. Ectomycorrhizae: Their Ecology & Physiology. (Physiological Ecology Ser.). 1973. 77.00 (ISBN 0-12-472850-2). Acad Pr.

Marmarelis, P. Z. & Marmarelis, V. Z. Analysis of Physiological Systems: The White-Noise Approach. LC 78-497. (Illus.). 503p. 1978. 69.50x (ISBN 0-306-31066-X, Plenum Pr). Plenum Pub.

Martin, Constance R. Endocrine Physiology. (Illus.). 1984. 47.50x (ISBN 0-19-503359-0). Oxford U Pr.

Mason, E. B. Physiology. 1983. 34.95 (ISBN 0-8053-6885-X); instr's. guide 6.95 (ISBN 0-8053-6886-8). Benjamin-Cummings.

Mehner, A. & Hartfiel, W., eds. Handbuch der Gefluegelphysiologie, 2 Pts. (Illus.). 1156p. 1984. Set. 170.25 (ISBN 3-8055-3738-7). S Karger.

Mei, N., et al. Progress in Sensory Physiology, Vol. 4. (Illus.). 136p. 1983. 32.00 (ISBN 0-387-12498-5). Springer-Verlag.

Miller, Marjorie A., et al. Kimber-Gray-Stackpole's Anatomy & Physiology. 17th ed. (Illus.). 640p. 1977. text ed. write for info. (ISBN 0-02-381220-6). Macmillan.

Millis, N. & Pittard, A. J., eds. The Applications of Microbial Physiology & Genetics to Industrial Processes. 250p. Date not set. write for info. (ISBN 0-12-497520-8). Acad Pr.

Moat, Albert G. Microbial Physiology. LC 79-11323. 600p. 1979. 41.50x (ISBN 0-471-07258-3, Pub. by Wiley-Interscience). Wiley.

Moscovitz, Toni. Physiology of Diving. (Illus.). 1978. 20.00 (ISBN 0-916750-44-2). Dayton Labs.

Mueller, Johannes. Elements of Physiology. Baly, William, tr. from Ger. LC 78-72814. (Brainedness, Handedness, & Mental Abilities Ser.). Repr. of 1843 ed. 60.00 (ISBN 0-404-60884-1). AMS Pr.

Nalbandov, A. V. Reproductive Physiology of Mammals & Birds: The Comparative Physiology of Domestic & Laboratory Animals & Man. 3rd ed. LC 75-25890. (Animal Science Ser.). (Illus.). 334p. 1976. 29.95x (ISBN 0-7167-0843-4). W H Freeman.

National Medical Series. Physiology. 350p. 1984. pap. text ed. 17.00 (ISBN 0-471-09627-X, 1-635, Pub. by Wiley Med). Wiley.

Neal, Kenneth G. & Kalbus, Barbara H. Anatomy & Physiology: A Laboratory Manual & Study Guide. 4th ed. 424p. 1983. pap. text ed. 18.95x (ISBN 0-8087-1449-X). Burgess.

Nicpon-Marieb, Elaine. Human Anatomy & Physiology. 2nd ed. 1985. Cat Edition. spiral bdg. 21.95x (ISBN 0-8053-6726-8); Fetal Pig Edition. spiral bdg. 21.95x (ISBN 0-8053-6727-6); solutions manual 5.59 (ISBN 0-8053-6728-4). Benjamin-Cummings.

Obal, F. & Benedek, G., eds. Environmental Physiology: Proceedings of the 28th International Congress of Physiological Sciences, Budapest, 1980 (Including the Satellite Symposium on Sports Physiology) LC 80-42102. (Advances in Physiological Sciences: Vol. 18). (Illus.). 375p. 1981. 44.00 (ISBN 0-08-027339-4). Pergamon.

Panke, Thomas W. & Mcleod, Charles. Pathophysiology of Thermal Injury: A Practical Approach. LC 79-3237. 384p. 1985. 53.00 (ISBN 0-8089-1754-4). Grune.

Physiology Workbook. 1984. text ed. 14.95 (ISBN 0-409-08631-2). Butterworth.

PreTest Services, Inc. Physiology: PreTest Self-Assessment & Review. 3rd ed. Dise, Craig A., ed. (Basic Science Ser.). 196p. 1982. review book 12.95 (ISBN 0-07-051936-6). McGraw.

Prezbindowski, Kathleen. Guide to Learning Anatomy & Physiology. (Illus.). 362p. 1980. pap. text ed. 12.95 (ISBN 0-8016-4040-7). Mosby.

Reed, Gretchen M. & Sheppard, Vincent F. Regulation of Fluid & Electrolyte Balance: A Programmed Instruction in Clinical Physiology. 2nd ed. LC 76-20109. (Illus.). 1977. pap. text ed. 12.95 (ISBN 0-7216-7513-1). Saunders.

Reith, Edward J., et al. Textbook of Anatomy & Physiology. 2nd ed. (Illus.). 1978. pap. text ed. 34.00 (ISBN 0-07-051873-4). McGraw.

Reviews of Physiology, Biochemistry & Pharmacology, Vol. 100. (Illus.). 250p. 1984. 36.50 (ISBN 0-387-13327-5). Springer-Verlag.

Reviews of Physiology, Biochemistry & Pharmacology, Vol. 102. (Illus.). 265p. 1985. 47.00 (ISBN 0-387-15300-4). Springer-Verlag.

Reviews of Physiology, Biochemistry & Pharmacology, Vol. 84. (Illus.). 1978. 51.00 (ISBN 0-387-08984-5). Springer-Verlag.

Reviews of Physiology, Biochemistry & Pharmacology, Vol. 86. (Illus.). 1979. 57.00 (ISBN 0-387-09488-1). Springer-Verlag.

Reviews of Physiology, Biochemistry & Pharmacology, Vol. 99. (Illus.). 240p. 1984. 40.00 (ISBN 0-387-12989-8). Springer-Verlag.

Rogers, Terence A. Elementary Human Physiology. LC 61-11245. (Illus.). Repr. of 1961 ed. 107.30 (ISBN 0-8357-9880-1, 2016101). Bks Demand UMI.

Rose, A. H. & Morris, G., eds. Advances in Microbial Physiology, Vol. 20. LC 67-19850. 1980. 65.00 (ISBN 0-12-027720-4). Acad Pr.

Rose, A. H., et al, eds. Advances in Microbial Physiology, Vol. 24. (Serial Publication Ser.). 1983. 65.00 (ISBN 0-12-027724-7). Acad Pr.

Rowett, H. G. Basic Anatomy & Physiology. (Illus.). 1973. text ed. 13.25 (ISBN 0-7195-2872-0). Transatlantic.

Ruch, Theodore C. & Patton, Harry D., eds. Physiology & Biophysics. 2nd ed. Incl. Vol. 1. The Brain & Neural Function. text ed. 38.00 (ISBN 0-7216-7821-1); Vol. 2. Circulation, Respiration & Fluid Balance. 495p. text ed. 30.00 (ISBN 0-7216-7818-1); Vol. 3. Digestion, Metabolism, Endocrine Function & Reproduction. text ed. 30.00 (ISBN 0-7216-7819-X); Vol. 4. Excitable Tissues & Reflex Control of Muscle. 39.50 (ISBN 0-7216-7817-3). LC 73-180188. (Illus.). 1973-82. Saunders.

Rudman, Jack. Anatomy & Physiology. (College Proficiency Examination Ser.: CLEP-37). (Cloth bdg. avail. on request). pap. 9.95 (ISBN 0-8373-5437-4). Natl Learning.

Russell, George K. Laboratory Investigations in Human Physiology. (Illus.). 1978. pap. text ed. write for info. (ISBN 0-02-404680-9). Macmillan.

Salanki, J., et al, eds. Physiology of Non-Excitable Cells: Proceedings of the 28th International Congress of Physiological Sciences, Budapest, 1980. LC 80-41874. (Advances in Physiological Sciences: Vol. 3). (Illus.). 350p. 1981. 44.00 (ISBN 0-08-026815-3). Pergamon.

--Physiology of Excitable Membranes: Proceedings of the 28th International Congress of Physiological Sciences, Budapest, 1980. LC 80-41853. (Advances in Physiological Sciences: Vol. 4). (Illus.). 350p. 1981. 44.00 (ISBN 0-08-026816-1). Pergamon.

Sanford, Paul A. Digestive System Physiology. (Physiological Principles in Medicine Ser.: No. 2). 180p. 1982. 30.00x (ISBN 0-7131-4380-0, Pub. by E Arnold). State Mutual Bk.

Schmidt, Robert F., ed. Fundamentals of Sensory Physiology. 2nd, rev. ed. Biederman-Thorson, M. A., tr. (Springer Study Edition Ser.). (Illus.). 286p. 1981. pap. 22.00 (ISBN 0-387-10349-X). Springer-Verlag.

Schmidt-Nielsen, Knut. Animal Physiology. 3rd ed. (Biological Science & Foundations of Modern Biology Ser). 1970. ref. ed. o.p. 16.95x (ISBN 0-13-037390-7); pap. 13.95x ref. ed. (ISBN 0-13-037382-6). P-H.

--Animal Physiology: Adaptation & Environment. 3rd ed. LC 83-7766. (Illus.). 600p. 1983. 29.95 (ISBN 0-521-25973-8). Cambridge U Pr.

Schneiderman, Carl R. Basic Anatomy & Physiology In Speech & Hearing. LC 83-26290. (Illus.). 228p. 1984. pap. text ed. 17.50 (ISBN 0-933014-05-8). College Hill.

Schottelius, Byron A. & Schottelius, Dorothy D. Textbook of Physiology. 18th ed. LC 77-17844. (Illus.). 624p. 1978. text ed. 25.95 (ISBN 0-8016-4356-2). Mosby.

Selkurt, Ewald E. Physiology. 5th ed. 691p. 1984. text ed. 31.95 (ISBN 0-316-78038-3). Little.

Sergeev, B. F. Physiology for Everyone. 343p. 1978. pap. 4.95 (ISBN 0-8285-0829-1, Pub. by Mir Pubs USSR). Imported Pubns.

Shapovalou, I. A., et al. Reviews of Physiology, Biochemistry & Pharmacology, Vol. 72. LC 74-3674. (Illus.). 200p. 1975. 68.00 (ISBN 0-387-07077-X). Springer-Verlag.

Silverstein, Alvin. Human Anatomy & Physiology. 2nd ed. LC 79-13053. 767p. 1983. text ed. 38.50x (ISBN 0-471-79165-2). transp. avail. (ISBN 0-471-09892-2); tests avail. (ISBN 0-471-07781-X); tchrs.' manual avail. (ISBN 0-471-03121-6). Wiley.

Sinclair, Walton B. The Biochemistry & Physiology of the Lemon & Other Citrus Fruits. LC 83-72137. (Illus.). 1000p. (Orig.). 1983. 55.00x (ISBN 0-931876-64-8, 3306). Ag & Nat Res.

Sinning, Wayne E. Experiments & Demonstrations in Exercise Physiology. LC 74-4591. (Illus.). 162p. 1975. pap. text ed. 16.95 (ISBN 0-7216-8313-4); instr's manual 3.95 (ISBN 0-03-057268-1). HR&W.

Solomon, Eldra P. & Davis, P. William. Human Anatomy & Physiology. 1983. text ed. 39.95 (ISBN 0-03-059992-X, CBS C); instr's manual 20.00 (ISBN 0-03-059993-8); study guide 13.95 (ISBN 0-03-059994-6). SCP.

Squires, Bruce. Basic Terms in Anatomy & Physiology. (Illus.). 165p. 1981. pap. 10.95 (ISBN 0-7216-8537-4). Saunders.

Steen, Edwin B. & Ashley Montagu. Anatomy & Physiology, 2 vols. Incl. Cells, Tissues, Integument, Skeletal, Muscular & Digestive Systems, Blood, Lymph, Circulatory System. rev. ed. 1984. Vol. I. 6.68 (ISBN 0-06-460190-0, 98); Urinary, Respiratory & Nervous Systems, Sensations & Sense Organs, Endocrine & Reproductive Systems. 1971. Vol. II. 5.95 (ISBN 0-06-460099-8, CO 99). COS). Har-Row.

--Advances in Comparative Physiology & Biochemistry, Vol. 7. 1978. 80.00 (ISBN 0-12-011506-9). Acad Pr.

Lowenstein, O. E., ed. Advances in Comparative Physiology & Biochemistry, Vols. 1-4. 80.00 ea. Vol. 1, 1962 (ISBN 0-12-011501-8). Vol. 2 (ISBN 0-12-011502-6). Vol. 3 (ISBN 0-12-011503-4). Vol. 4, 1971 (ISBN 0-12-011504-2). Vols. 5-7. Vol. 7 (ISBN 0-12-011507-7). Acad Pr.

Pequeux, A., et al, eds. Osmoregulation in Estuarine & Marine Animals: Proceedings of the Invited Lectures to a Symposium Organized Within the 5th Conference of the European Society for Comparative Physiology & Biochemistry - Taormina, Sicily, Italy, Sept 5-8, 1983. (Lecture Notes on Coastal & Estuarine Studies: Vol. 9). x, 221p. 1984. pap. 17.00 (ISBN 0-387-13353-4). Springer-Verlag.

Pethes, G. & Frenyo, V. L. Advances in Animal & Comparative Physiology: Proceedings of the 28th International Congress of Physiological Sciences, Budapest, 1980. LC 80-41894. (Advances in Physiological Sciences: Vol. 20). (Illus.). 400p. 1981. 55.00 (ISBN 0-08-027341-6). Pergamon.

Ramsay, James A. Physiological Approach to the Lower Animals. 2nd ed. LC 68-21398. (Illus.). 1968. pap. 12.95x (ISBN 0-521-09537-9). Cambridge U Pr.

Schmidt-Nielsen, Knut. How Animals Work. LC 77-174262. (Illus.). 100p. 1972. 22.95 (ISBN 0-521-08417-2); pap. 8.95x (ISBN 0-521-09692-8). Cambridge U Pr.

Schmidt-Nielsen, Knut, et al, eds. Comparative Physiology: Water, Ions & Fluid Mechanics. LC 77-7320. (Illus.). 1978. 64.50 (ISBN 0-521-21696-6). Cambridge U Pr.

--Comparative Physiology: Primitive Mammals. LC 77-7320. (Illus.). 1980. 54.50 (ISBN 0-521-22847-6). Cambridge U Pr.

Swenson, Melvin J., ed. Dukes' Physiology of Domestic Animals. 9th rev. ed. (Illus.). 928p. 1977. text ed. 39.50x (ISBN 0-8014-1076-2). Comstock.

Vanegas, Horacio, ed. Comparative Neurology of the Optic Tectum. 841p. 1984. 125.00x (ISBN 0-306-41236-5, Plenum Pr). Plenum Pub.

Wood & Lenfant. Evolution of Respiratory Processes. LC 79-4051. (Lung Biology in Health & Disease Ser.: Vol. 13). 1979. 69.75 (ISBN 0-8247-6793-4). Dekker.

PHYSIOLOGY, EXPERIMENTAL

Holmes, Frederick L. Claude Bernard & Animal Chemistry. LC 73-88497. (Commonwealth Fund Publications Ser). 640p. 1974. text ed. 37.50x (ISBN 0-674-13485-0). Harvard U Pr.

Lesch, John E. Science & Medicine in France: The Emergence of Experimental Physiology, 1790-1855. LC 83-12749. (Illus.). 276p. 1984. text ed. 25.00x (ISBN 0-674-79400-1). Harvard U Pr.

PHYSIOLOGY, MOLECULAR

see Biological Physics

PHYSIOLOGY OF PLANTS

see Plant Physiology

PHYSOPODA

see Thrips

PHYTOCHEMISTRY

see Botanical Chemistry

PHYTOGEOGRAPHY

see also Island Flora and Fauna; Plants–Migration

Affolter, James M. A Monograph of the Genus Lilaeopsis (Umbelliferae) Anderson, Christiane, ed. LC 85-1291. (Systematic Botany Monographs: Vol. 6). (Illus.). 140p. (Orig.). 1985. pap. 18.00 (ISBN 0-912861-06-1). Am Soc Plant.

Beatley, Janice C. & ERDA Technical Information Center. Vascular Plants of the Nevada Test Site & Central Southern Nevada: Ecologic & Geographic Distributions. LC 76-21839. 316p. 1976. pap. 16.00 (ISBN 0-87079-033-1, TID-26881); microfiche 4.50 (ISBN 0-87079-216-4, TID-26881). DOE.

Box, E. O. Macroclimate & Plant Forms: An Introduction to Predictive Modeling in Phytogeography. (Tasks for Vegetation Science Ser.: No. 1). 272p. 1981. 69.50 (ISBN 90-6193-941-0, Pub. by Junk Pubs Netherlands). Kluwer Academic.

Collinson, A. S. Introduction to World Vegetation. 1977. pap. text ed. 10.95 (ISBN 0-04-581013-3). Allen Unwin.

Daubenmire, Rexford. Plant Geography: With Special Reference to North America. (Physiological Cology Ser.). 1978. 47.00 (ISBN 0-12-204150-X). Acad Pr.

De Laubenfels, David J. Mapping the World's Vegetation: Regionalization of Formations & Flora. (Geographical Ser.: No. 4). (Illus.). 304p. 1975. text ed. 27.95x (ISBN 0-8156-2172-8). Syracuse U Pr.

Denny, Patrick, ed. The Ecology & Management of African Wetland Vegetation. (Geobotany Ser.). 1985. lib. bdg. 78.50 (ISBN 90-6193-509-1, Pub. by Junk Pubs Netherlands). Kluwer-Academic.

Drude, Oscar. Handbuch der Pflanzengeographie: Handbook of Phytogeography. Egerton, Frank N., 3rd, ed. LC 77-74213. (History of Ecology Ser.). (Illus.). 1978. Repr. of 1890 ed. lib. bdg. 46.50x (ISBN 0-405-10384-0). Ayer Co Pubs.

Egerton, Frank N., ed. Ecological Phytogeography in the Nineteenth Century: An Original Anthology. LC 77-74218. (History of Ecology Ser.). 1978. lib. bdg. 51.00x (ISBN 0-405-10388-3). Ayer Co Pubs.

Eyre, S. R., ed. World Vegetation Types. LC 78-147779. 264p. 1971. 39.00x (ISBN 0-231-03503-9). Columbia U Pr.

Flint, Harrison L. Landscape Plants for Eastern North America: Exclusive of Florida & the Immediate Gulf Coast. LC 82-16068. 677p. 1983. 59.95x (ISBN 0-471-86905-8, Pub. by Wiley-Interscience). Wiley.

Gleason, Henry A. & Cronquist, Arthur. Natural Geography of Plants. LC 64-15448. (Illus.). 420p. 1964. 55.00x (ISBN 0-231-02668-4). Columbia U Pr.

Good, Ronald. The Geography of Flowering Plants. 4th ed. LC 73-85684. (Illus.). 584p. 1974. text ed. 33.00x (ISBN 0-582-46611-3). Longman.

Hulten, E. The Amphi-Atlantic Plants & Their Phytogeographic Connections. (Illus.). 1973. 84.00 (ISBN 3-87429-041-7). Lubrecht & Cramer.

Jones, Gareth E. Vegetation Productivity. LC 78-40985. (Topics in Applied Geography Ser.). pap. 28.00 (ISBN 0-317-20789-X, 2025270). Bks Demand UMI.

Kellman, Martin C. Plant Geography. 2nd ed. LC 80-5079. 1980. 26.00 (ISBN 0-312-61461-6). St Martin.

Laufer, Berthold. The American Plant Migration, Vol.1: The Potato. (Field Museum of Natural History). (Illus.). 1938. 11.00 (ISBN 0-527-01888-0). Kraus Repr.

Marshall, Alan G., ed. Fourier, Hadamand, & Hilbert Transforms in Chemistry. LC 81-20984. 550p. 1982. text ed. 75.00x (ISBN 0-306-40904-6, Plenum Pr). Plenum Pub.

Meyen, Franz J. Outlines of the Geography of Plants: Native Country, the Culture, & the Uses of the Principal Cultivated Plants on Which the Prosperity of Nations Is Based. Egerton, Frank N., ed. LC 77-74239. (History of Ecology Ser.). 1978. Repr. of 1846 ed. lib. bdg. 35.50x (ISBN 0-405-10408-1). Ayer Co Pubs.

Phillips, W. Louis, compiled by. Index to Plant Distribution Maps in North American Periodicals Through 1972. 1976. lib. bdg. 115.00 (ISBN 0-8161-0009-8, Hall Library). G K Hall.

Plants of Yellowstone & Grand Teton National Parks. (Nature & Scenic Bks.). pap. 5.95 (ISBN 0-937512-02-8). Wheelwright UT.

Raunkiaer, Christen. The Life Forms of Plants & Statistical Plants Geography. Egerton, Frank N., 3rd, ed. Gilbert-Carter, H. & Fausboll, A., trs. LC 77-74249. (History of Ecology Ser.). (Illus.). 1978. Repr. of 1934 ed. lib. bdg. 51.00x (ISBN 0-405-10418-9). Ayer Co Pubs.

Riley, Denis R. & Young, Anthony. World Vegetation. 1967. 9.95x (ISBN 0-521-06083-4). Cambridge U Pr.

Romans, Robert C., ed. Geobotany I. LC 76-51249. 308p. 1977. 49.50x (ISBN 0-306-31007-4, Plenum Pr). Plenum Pub.

--Geobotany II. LC 81-13992. 271p. 1981. text ed. 45.00x (ISBN 0-306-40832-5, Plenum Pr). Plenum Pub.

Schimper, A. F. Plant Geography Upon a Physiological Basis. Fisher, W. R., tr. (Illus.). 1960. Repr. of 1903 ed. 70.00 (ISBN 3-7682-0901-6). Lubrecht & Cramer.

Skottsberg, C. Juan Fernandez & Hawaii: A Phytogeographical Discussion. (BMB Ser.: BMB 16). pap. 8.00 (ISBN 0-527-02119-9). Kraus Repr.

Sterling, Keir B., ed. Essays on North American Plant Geography from the Nineteenth Century: Original Anthology. LC 77-81124. (Biologists & Their World Ser.). (Illus.). 1978. lib. bdg. 38.50x (ISBN 0-405-10720-X). Ayer Co Pubs.

Stott, Philip. Historical Plant Geography. (Illus.). 192p. 1981. text ed. 30.00x (ISBN 0-04-580010-3); pap. text ed. 14.95x (ISBN 0-04-580011-1). Allen Unwin.

Strachey & Winterbottom. Catalogue of the Plants of Kumaon: And of the Adjacent Portions of Garhwal & Tibet. 1978. Repr. of 1918 ed. 25.00x (ISBN 0-89955-256-0, Pub. by Intl Bk Dist). Intl Spec Bk.

Transeau, E. N. & Williams, P. E. Distribution Maps of Certain Plants in Ohio. 1929. 1.00 (ISBN 0-86727-019-5). Ohio Bio Survey.

Vale, Thomas R. Plants & People: Vegetation Change in North America. Knight, C. Gregory, ed. LC 82-8865. (Resource Publications in Geography Ser.). (Illus., Orig.). 1982. pap. 5.00 (ISBN 0-89291-151-4). Assn Am Geographers.

Von Humboldt, Alexander. Essai sur la Geographie Des Plantes: Essays on the Geography of Plants. Egerton, Frank N., 3rd, ed. LC 77-74253. (History of Ecology Ser.). 1978. Repr. of 1807 ed. lib. bdg. 14.00x (ISBN 0-405-10422-7). Ayer Co Pubs.

White, James, ed. Studies on Plant Demography: A Festschrift for John L. Harper. Date not set. price not set (ISBN 0-12-746630-4). Acad Pr.

Zohary, M. Geobotanical Foundations of the Middle East. 762p. 1973. text ed. 255.00 (ISBN 90-265-0157-9, Pub. by Swets Pub Serv Holland). Swets North Am.

PHYTOGRAPHY

see Botany

PHYTOHORMONES

see Plant Hormones

PHYTOLOGY

see Botany

PHYTOPATHOGENIC BACTERIA

see Bacteria, Phytopathogenic

PHYTOPATHOGENIC FUNGI

see Fungi, Phytopathogenic

PHYTOPATHOLOGY

see Plant Diseases

PHYTOPHTORA

Erwin, D. C., et al, eds. Phytophthora: It's Biology, Taxonomy, Ecology & Pathology. 392p. 1983. text ed. 76.00 (ISBN 0-89054-050-0). Am Phytopathol Soc.

Old, K. M. Phytophthora & Forest Management in Australia. 118p. 1979. pap. 7.25 (ISBN 0-643-02523-5, C055, CSIRO). Unipub.

Ribeiro, O. K. A Source Book of the Genus Phytophtora. (Illus.). 1978. lib. bdg. 28.00 (ISBN 3-7682-1200-9). Lubrecht & Cramer.

Tucker, C. M. The Taxonomy of the Genus Phytophtora. (Illus.). 21.00 (ISBN 3-7682-0515-0). Lubrecht & Cramer.

Zentmyer, George A., ed. Phytophthora Cinnamoni & the Diseases It Causes. LC 80-67516. (Monograph Ser.: No. 10). 96p. 1980. 9.50 (ISBN 0-89054-030-6). Am Phytopathol Soc.

PHYTOPLANKTON

see also Algae; Primary Productivity (Biology)

Contant, H. & Duthie, H. C. The Phytoplankton of Lac St-Jean, Quebec. (Bibliotheca Phycologica Ser.: No. 40). (Illus.). 1978. pap. text ed. 14.00x (ISBN 3-7682-1198-3). Lubrecht & Cramer.

Fogg, G. E. Algal Cultures & Phytoplankton Ecology. 2nd ed. LC 74-27308. (Illus.). 192p. 1975. 22.50x (ISBN 0-299-06760-2). U of Wis Pr.

Goldman, Charles R., ed. Primary Productivity in Aquatic Environments. 1966. 33.50x (ISBN 0-520-01425-1). U of Cal Pr.

Holm-Hansen, O., et al, eds. Marine Phytoplankton & Productivity: Proceedings of the Invited Lectures to a Symposium Organized within the 5th Conference of the European Society for Cooperative Physiology & Biochemistry, Taurmina, Sicily, Sept. 5-8, 1983. (Lecture Notes on Coastal & Estaurine Studies: Vol. 8). vii, 175p. 1984. pap. 15.00 (ISBN 0-387-13333-X). Springer-Verlag.

Morris, I., ed. The Physiological Ecology of Phytoplankton. (Studies in Ecology: Vol. 7). 1981. 78.50x (ISBN 0-520-04308-1). U of Cal Pr.

Reynolds, C. S. The Ecology of Freshwater Photoplankton. LC 83-7211. (Cambridge Studies in Ecology). (Illus.). 300p. 1984. 57.50 (ISBN 0-521-23782-3); pap. 24.95 (ISBN 0-521-28222-5). Cambridge U Pr.

Smith, DeBoyd L. A Guide to Marine Coastal Plankton & Marine Invertebrate Larvae. LC 76-62564. (Illus.). 1978. pap. text ed. 9.95 (ISBN 0-8403-1672-0). Kendall-Hunt.

Smith, G. M. Phytoplankton of the Inland Lakes of Wisconsin, 2 vols. in one. 1977. Repr. of 1924 ed. 42.00 (ISBN 3-7682-1134-7). Lubrecht & Cramer.

Sournia, A. Phytoplankton Manual. (Monographs on Oceanographic Methodology: No. 6). 337p. 1978. 28.25 (ISBN 92-3-101572-9, U900, UNESCO). Unipub.

Taylor, F. J. Phytoplankton of the South Western Indian Ocean. (Illus.). 1966. pap. 4.80 (ISBN 3-7682-0462-6). Lubrecht & Cramer.

Wood, R. D. Guide to the Phytoplankton of Narragansett Bay, Rhode Island. 1967. 3.75 (ISBN 0-9603898-1-4). R D Wood.

PHYTOSOCIOLOGY

see Plant Communities

PI

Beckmann, Petr. History of Pi. 4th ed. LC 77-24777. (Illus.). 1977. 12.95x (ISBN 0-911762-18-3). Golem.

Black, Thomas F. Why Is PI. 6.95x (ISBN 0-89741-012-2). Roadrunner Tech.

PIAGET, JEAN, 1896-

Copeland, Richard W. How Children Learn Mathematics: Teaching Implications of Piaget's Research. 4th ed. 448p. 1984. text ed. write for info. (ISBN 0-02-324770-3). Macmillan.

Dasen, Pierre. Piagetian Psychology. 1977. 33.95 (ISBN 0-89876-080-1). Gardner Pr.

Jacob, S. H. Foundations for Piagetian Education. 96p. 1985. lib. bdg. 18.25 (ISBN 0-8191-4327-8). U Pr of Amer.

Modgil, Sohan. Piagetian Research: A Handbook of Recent Studies. 492p. 1974. 100.00x (ISBN 0-85633-030-2, Pub. by NFER Nelson UK). Taylor & Francis.

Modgil, Sohan & Modgil, Celia. Piagetian Research: Compilation & Commentary, 8 vols. 172p. 1976. Vol. 1, pts. I, II, & III. 14.00x (ISBN 0-85633-089-2, Pub. by NFER Nelson UK); Vol. 2, pts. I & II, 280p. 18.00x (ISBN 0-85633-097-3); Vol. 3, pts. I & II, 318p. 20.00x (ISBN 0-85633-098-1); Vol. 4, pts. I & II, 332. 20.00x (ISBN 0-85633-103-1); Vol. 5, pts. I & II, 384p. 23.00x (ISBN 0-85633-105-8); Vol. 6, pt 1, 224p. 18.00x (ISBN 0-85633-106-6); Vol. 7, pt. 1, 192p. 18.00x (ISBN 0-85633-107-4); Vol. 8, pt. I, 240p. 18.00x (ISBN 0-85633-108-2); Set. 124.00. Taylor & Francis.

Neimark, Edith D., et al, eds. Moderators of Competence: Challenges to the Universality of Piagetian Theory. 240p. 1985. text ed. 29.95 (ISBN 0-89859-531-2). L Erlbaum Assocs.

Rosskopf, Myron F. Children's Mathematical Concepts: Six Piagetian Studies in Mathematics Education. LC 75-12872. (Illus.). pap. 56.00 (ISBN 0-317-09439-4, 2017767). Bks Demand UMI.

Seltman, Muriel & Seltman, Peter. Piaget's Logic: A Critique of Genetic Epistemology. 420p. 1985. text ed. 40.00x (ISBN 0-04-370154-X). Allen Unwin.

Wadsworth, Barry J. Piaget's Theory of Cognitive & Affective Development. 3rd ed. LC 83-13637. 190p. 1984. pap. text ed. 12.95 (ISBN 0-582-28425-2). Longman.

PIANO–CONSTRUCTION

Jackson, Jim. Tuning & Repairing Your Own Piano. (Illus.). 192p. (Orig.). 1984. pap. 12.50 (ISBN 0-8306-1678-0, 1678). TAB Bks.

PIANO–TUNING

Bradley, Jack. How to Tune, Repair & Regulate Pianos: A Practical Guide. LC 85-60253. (Illus.). 158p. (Orig.). 1985. pap. 19.95 (ISBN 0-931856-03-5). Hill Springs Pubns.

Gurlik, Philip, Jr. The Piano: A Piano Technicians Guide for the Piano Owner. 40p. (Orig.). 1985. pap. 2.95 (ISBN 0-918464-66-8). Bookman Hse.

Jackson, Jim. Tuning & Repairing Your Own Piano. (Illus.). 192p. (Orig.). 1984. pap. 12.50 (ISBN 0-8306-1678-0, 1678). TAB Bks.

Sullivan, Anita T. The Seventh Dragon: The Riddle of Equal Temperment. new ed. LC 84-22627. (Illus.). 100p. (Orig.). 1985. 18.00 (ISBN 0-943920-22-1); pap. 10.00 (ISBN 0-943920-21-3). Metamorphous Pr.

PICKLING

see Canning and Preserving

PICKLING (METALS)

see Metals–Pickling

PICTURE TUBES

see Television Picture Tubes

PIERS

see also Wharves

Construction & Protection, Piers & Wharves. (Eighty-Ninety Ser). 1971. pap. 2.00 (ISBN 0-685-58143-8, 87). Natl Fire Prot.

Derucher & Heins. Bridges & Pier Protective Systems & Devices. (Civil Engineering Ser.: Vol. 1). 1979. 49.75 (ISBN 0-8247-6895-7). Dekker.

PIES

see Pastry

PIEZO-ELECTRIC OSCILLATORS

see Oscillators, Crystal

PIEZO-ELECTRICITY

see Pyro- and Piezo-Electricity

PIG

see Swine

PIG IRON

see Cast Iron

PIGEONS

see also Passenger Pigeons; White-Winged Dove

Abs, Michael. Physiology & Behaviour of the Pigeon. 1983. 63.00 (ISBN 0-12-042950-0). Acad Pr.

Aerts, Jan. Pigeon Racing: Advanced Techniques. (Illus.). 192p. 1981. pap. 7.95 (ISBN 0-571-11572-1). Faber & Faber.

Allen, William H., Jr. How to Raise & Train Pigeons. LC 58-7602. (Illus.). 160p. 1982. 13.95 (ISBN 0-8069-3706-8); lib. bdg. 16.79 (ISBN 0-8069-3707-6). Sterling.

--Pigeons: How to Raise & Train Them. pap. 2.00 (ISBN 0-87980-118-2). Wilshire.

Belding, D. V. Racing Pigeons. 1982. 14.95 (ISBN 0-86230-014-2). Triplegate.

Bent, Arthur C. Life Histories of North American Gallinaceous Birds. (Illus.). 1932. pap. 8.00 (ISBN 0-486-21028-6). Dover.

--Life Histories of North American Gallinaceous Birds. (Illus.). 15.25 (ISBN 0-8446-1635-4). Peter Smith.

Chiasson, Robert B. Laboratory Anatomy of the Pigeon. 3rd ed. (Laboratory Anatomy Ser.). 96p. 1984. write for info. wire coil (ISBN 0-697-04927-2). Wm C Brown.

Delacour, Jean. Wild Pigeons & Doves. rev. ed. (Illus.). 189p. 1980. 14.95 (ISBN 0-87666-968-2, AP-6810). TFH Pubns.

Foy, Charles. Pigeons for Pleasure & Profit. (Illus.). 1972. pap. 4.00 (ISBN 0-911466-19-3). Swanson.

Goodwin, Derek. Pigeons & Doves of the World. 3rd ed. LC 76-55484. (Illus.). 496p. 1983. 48.50x (ISBN 0-8014-1434-2). Comstock.

--Pigeons & Doves of the World. 3rd. ed. LC 81-70700. (Illus.). 466p. 1983. 48.50x (ISBN 0-8014-1434-2). Cornell U Pr.

Gos, Michael W. Doves. (Illus.). 96p. 1981. 4.95 (ISBN 0-87666-828-7, KW-123). TFH Pubns.

Granda, A. M. & Maxwell, J. H., eds. Neural Mechanisms of Behavior in the Pigeon. LC 78-24064. (Illus.). 452p. 1979. 59.50x (ISBN 0-306-40096-0, Plenum Pr). Plenum Pub.

Hayes, Gordon. The Pigeons That Went to War. LC 81-90046. (Illus.). 160p. 1981. 9.95 (ISBN 0-9605880-1-9). G H Hayes.

Levi, Wendell M. Encyclopedia of Pigeon Breeds. 1965. 50.00 (ISBN 0-910876-02-9). Levi Pub.

--The Pigeon. 1981. Repr. 42.50 (ISBN 0-910876-01-0). Levi Pub.

McClary, Douglas. The Show Racer. (Illus.). 146p. 1976. 11.95 (ISBN 0-571-10761-3). Faber & Faber.

Naether, Carl. Pigeons. (Illus.). 96p. Date not set. 4.95 (ISBN 0-87666-837-6, KW-148). TFH Pubns.

Rotondo, Joe, ed. Rotondo on Racing Pigeons. (Illus.). 330p. 1981. 35.00 (ISBN 0-686-69815-0). North Am Fal Hunt.

Rowan, M. K. The Doves, Parrots, Louries & Cuckoos of Southern Africa. (Illus.). 429p. 1984. 38.00 (ISBN 0-88072-093-X, Pub. by Tanager). Longwood Pub Group.

Swanson, Leslie C. Pigeons, Racing Homer Facts & Secrets. 1958. pap. 2.50 (ISBN 0-911466-17-7). Swanson.

--Pigeons, Racing Homer Topics. 1955. pap. 2.50 (ISBN 0-911466-18-5). Swanson.

Wheeler, Harry G. Exhibition & Flying Pigeons. 350p. 1978. 16.50 (ISBN 0-904558-27-4). Saiga.

Whitney, Leon F. Keep Your Pigeons Flying. 2nd ed. Osman, Colin, ed. LC 61-11434. (Illus.). 256p. 1983. pap. 9.95 (ISBN 0-8397-4402-1). Eriksson.

Zweers, G. A. The Feeding System of the Pigeon (Columba Livia L) (Advances in Anatomy, Embryology, & Cell Biology Ser.: Vol. 73). (Illus.). 120p. 1982. pap. 28.00 (ISBN 0-387-11332-0). Springer-Verlag.

PIGMENTATION

see Color of Animals

PIGMENTS

see also Coloring Matter; Dyes and Dyeing; Paint;
also names of pigments

Britton, G. The Biochemistry of Natural Pigments. LC 82-9512. (Cambridge Texts in Chemistry & Biochemistry). (Illus.). 275p. 1983. 62.50 (ISBN 0-521-24892-2). Cambridge U Pr.

Crown, David A. Forensic Examination of Paints & Pigments. 276p. 1968. 24.75x (ISBN 0-398-00372-6). C C Thomas.

Fox, Denis. Animal Biochromes & Structural Colours. LC 72-89801. 1976. 46.00x (ISBN 0-520-02347-1). U of Cal Pr.

Gettens, Rutherford J. & Stout, George L. Painting Materials: A Short Encyclopedia. (Illus.). 1965. pap. 5.00 (ISBN 0-486-21597-0). Dover.

Gutcho, M. H., ed. Inorganic Pigments: Manufacturing Processes. LC 80-16319. (Chemical Technology Review No. 166). 488p. 1980. 54.00 (ISBN 0-8155-0811-5). Noyes.

Hill, H. Earl & Prane, Joseph W., eds. Applied Techniques in Statistics for Selected Industries: Coatings, Paints & Pigments. LC 83-21750. 671p. 1984. 85.00 (ISBN 0-471-03791-5, Pub. by Wiley-Interscience). Wiley.

Lubs, H. A., ed. Chemistry of Synthetic Dyes & Pigments. LC 64-7905. (A C S Ser: No. 127). 750p. 1971. Repr. of 1955 ed. 47.50 (ISBN 0-88275-039-9). Krieger.

Myers, R. & Long, J. S. Pigments, Pt.1. (Treatise on Coatings Ser.: Vol. 3). (Illus.). 592p. 1975. 175.00 (ISBN 0-8247-1475-X). Dekker.

Parfitt, G. D., ed. Dispersion of Powders in Liquids: With Special Reference to Pigments. 3rd ed. (Illus.). 533p. 1981. 81.50 (ISBN 0-85334-990-8, Pub. by Elsevier Applied Sci England). Elsevier.

Patterson, David, ed. Pigments: An Introduction to Their Physical Chemistry. (Illus.). 210p. 1967. 27.75 (ISBN 0-444-20009-6, Pub. by Elsevier Applied Sci England). Elsevier.

Patton, Temple C., ed. Pigment Handbook, 3 vols. LC 73-529. 1978p. 1973. Set. 412.00 (ISBN 0-471-67127-4, Pub. by Wiley-Interscience). Wiley.

Symposium on Biochemistry & Physiology of Visual Pigments, Bochum Univ., Germany, 1972. Proceedings. Langer, H., ed. (Illus.). xiv, 366p. 1973. 38.00 (ISBN 0-387-06204-1). Springer-Verlag.

Technical Association of the Pulp & Paper Industry Staff. Paper Coating Pigments: A Project of the Coating Pigments Committee. Hagemeyer, Robert W., ed. LC 76-13421. (TAPPI Monograph Ser.: no. 38). pap. 59.00 (ISBN 0-317-28426-6, 2020306). Bks Demand UMI.

Thompson, Daniel V. Materials & Techniques of Medieval Painting. Orig. Title: Materials of Medieval Painting. 1957. pap. 4.50 (ISBN 0-486-20327-1). Dover.

Wolman, Moshe, ed. Pigments in Pathology. 1969. 89.50 (ISBN 0-12-762450-3). Acad Pr.

PIGS

see Swine

PILES (CIVIL ENGINEERING)

see Piling (Civil Engineering)

PILING (CIVIL ENGINEERING)

Fleming, et al. Piling Engineering. 1985. 69.95 (ISBN 0-470-20144-4). Wiley.

Fleming, W. G. & Sliwinski, Z. J. The Use & Influence of Bentonite in Bored Pile Construction. 93p. 1977. 35.00x (ISBN 0-86017-031-4, Pub. by Ciria Pubns Dept). State Mutual Bk.

Healy, P. R. & Weltman, A. J. Survey of Problems Associated with the Installation of Displacement Piles. 54p. 1980. 60.00 (ISBN 0-86017-145-0, Pub. by Ciria Pubns Dept). State Mutual Bk.

Hobbs, N. B. & Healy, P. R. Piling in Chalk. 126p. 1979. 70.00x (ISBN 0-86017-119-1, Pub. by Ciria Pubns Dept). State Mutual Bk.

Nikolaev, B. A. Pile Driving by Electroosmosis. LC 61-18759. 62p. 1962. 25.00x (ISBN 0-306-10578-0, Consultants). Plenum Pub.

Poulos, H. G. & Davis, E. H. Pile Foundation Analysis & Design. LC 80-14658. (Geotechnical Engineering Ser.). 397p. 1980. text ed. 52.75x (ISBN 0-471-02084-2). Wiley.

Reimbert, M. & Reimbert, A. Retaining Walls, Anchorages & Sheet Piling: Part1. LC 74-77789. (Series on Rock & Soil Mechanics). Orig. Title: Murs De Soutenements. (Illus.). 284p. 1974. 40.00x (ISBN 0-87849-009-4). Trans Tech.

Thorburn, S. & Thorburn, J. Q. Review of the Problems Associated with the Construction of Cost-in-Place Concrete Piles. 42p. 1977. 40.00x (ISBN 0-86017-020-9, Pub. by Ciria Pubns Dept). State Mutual Bk.

Tomlinson, M. J. Pile Design & Construction Practice. (Viewpoint Ser.). (Illus.). 1981. 59.00x (ISBN 0-7210-1013-X). Scholium Intl.

Weltman, A. J. Integrity Testing of Piles: A Review. 36p. 1977. 30.00x (ISBN 0-86017-035-7, Pub. by Ciria Pubns Dept). State Mutual Bk.

--Pile Load Testing Procedures. 52p. 1980. 40.00x (ISBN 0-86017-136-1, Pub. by Ciria Pubns Dept). State Mutual Bk.

Weltman, A. J. & Healy, P. R. Piling in "Boulder Clay" & Other Glacial Tills. 78p. 1978. 60.00x (ISBN 0-86017-103-5, Pub. by Ciria Pubns Dept). State Mutual Bk.

Weltman, A. J. & Little, J. A. A Review of Bearing Pile Types. 82p. 1979. 35.00x (ISBN 0-86017-018-7, Pub. by Ciria Pubns Dept). State Mutual Bk.

Weltman, A. J., ed. Noise & Vibration from Piling Operations. 68p. 1980. 60.00x (ISBN 0-86017-137-X, Pub. by Ciria Pubns Dept). State Mutual Bk.

West, A. S. Piling Practice. (Illus.). 122p. 1975. 17.50 (ISBN 0-408-70288-5). Transatlantic.

PILLARS

see Columns

PILOT (COMPUTER PROGRAM LANGUAGE)

Apple PILOT Editor's Manual. (Apple II Plus & IIe Reference Manuals Ser.). Date not set. 15.00 (ISBN 0-317-04463-X, A2L0042). Apple Comp.

Apple PILOT Language Manual. (Apple II Plus & IIe Reference Manuals Ser.). Date not set. 20.00 (ISBN 0-317-04464-8, A2L0041). Apple Comp.

Conlon, Tom. PILOT: The Language & How to Use It. (Illus.). 1984. pap. 17.95 (ISBN 0-13-676247-6). P-H.

Ledin, Victor. Understanding PILOT. (Handy Guide Ser.). 64p. (Orig.). 1983. pap. 3.50 (ISBN 0-88284-251-X). Alfred Pub.

PILOT. (Alfred's Language Bks.). 1981. pap. 3.50 (ISBN 0-317-04682-9). Alfred Pub.

Starkweather, John A. User's Guide to PILOT. 240p. 1984. 19.95 (ISBN 0-13-937755-7); pap. 12.95 (ISBN 0-13-937748-4). P-H.

PILOT CHARTS

see Nautical Charts

PILOT GUIDES

Coles, Adland & Bradley, David. Creeks & Harbours of the Solent. 144p. 1982. 60.00x (ISBN 0-333-31808-0, Pub. by Nautical England). State Mutual Bk.

Department of Transportation. Private Pilot Practical Test Standards: S. E. Land. 114p. (Orig.). pap. text ed. 4.95 (ISBN 0-941272-25-7). Astro Pubs.

F.A.A. How to Become a Pilot: The Step by Step Guide to Flying. LC 74-8723. (Illus.). pap. 8.95 (ISBN 0-8069-8386-8). Sterling.

Fillingham, Paul. Pilot's Guide to the Lesser Antilles. LC 78-27491. (Illus.). 1979. 15.95 (ISBN 0-07-020815-8). McGraw.

Forman, Peter N. Flying Hawaii: A Pilot's Guide to the Islands. (Illus.). 160p. (Orig.). 1983. pap. 10.25 (ISBN 0-8306-2361-2, 2361). TAB Bks.

French Pilot, Vol.1. 224p. 1980. 30.00x (ISBN 0-686-69883-5, Pub. by Nautical England). State Mutual Bk.

Kellogg, Orson. Every Pilot's Guide to Fuel Economy. 1980. pap. 4.95 (ISBN 0-935802-00-2, Pub. by Taxlogs Unltd). Aviation.

Kurt, T. Pilot Fitness. 1986. cancelled (ISBN 0-442-23150-4). Van Nos Reinhold.

Rice, Michael S., ed. Pilots Manual for Curtiss P-40 Warhawk. (Illus.). 24p. 1972. pap. 6.95 (ISBN 0-87994-018-2, Pub. by AvPubns). Aviation.

--Pilot's Manual for Lockheed P-38 Lightning. (Illus.). 68p. 1972. pap. 6.95 (ISBN 0-87994-019-0, Pub. by AvPubns). Aviation.

--Pilots Manual for Republic P-47 Thunderbolt. (Illus.). 62p. 1973. pap. 6.95 (ISBN 0-87994-022-0, Pub. by AvPubns). Aviation.

Robson, Malcolm. Channel Islands Pilot. 176p. 1980. 27.00 (ISBN 0-245-53413-X, Pub. by Nautical England). State Mutual Bk.

--Channel Islands Pilot. 176p. 1982. 40.00x (ISBN 0-333-32051-4, Pub. by Nautical England). State Mutual Bk.

--French Pilot: Omonville to Reguier (The East, Vol. 1. 224p. 1982. 45.00x (ISBN 0-333-32063-8, Pub. by Nautical England). State Mutual Bk.

Robson, Malcom. French Pilot, Vol. 2. 256p. 1980. 33.00x (ISBN 0-245-53382-6, Pub. by Nautical England). State Mutual Bk.

Smith, Frank K. Flying the Bahamas: The Weekend Pilot's Guide. (Illus.). 240p. (Orig.). 1983. pap. 11.50 (ISBN 0-8306-2351-5, 2351). TAB Bks.

Taylor, Richard L. IFR for VFR Pilots. 1983. 13.95 (ISBN 0-02-616630-5). Macmillan.

Wright, Edward. Certaine Errors in Navigation (the Voyage of George Earl of Cumberland to the Azores) LC 74-80224. (English Experience Ser.: No. 703). 1974. Repr. of 1599 ed. 29.00 (ISBN 90-221-0703-5). Walter J Johnson.

PILOTLESS AIRCRAFT

see Guided Missiles

PILOTS AND PILOTAGE

see also Navigation; Pilot Guides

Aviation Maintenance Publishers. Pilot Logbook. 70p. 1979. text ed. 2.50 (ISBN 0-89100-112-3, EA-PLO-2). Aviation Maintenance.

Bottomley, Tom. Practical Piloting. (Illus.). 182p. (Orig.). 1983. pap. 10.25 (ISBN 0-8306-0619-X, 1619). TAB Bks.

Boyd, K. T. ATP-FAR 135: Airline Transport Pilot. (Illus.). 168p. 1983. pap. 17.50 (ISBN 0-8138-0510-4). Iowa St U Pr.

Christy, Joe. The Private Pilot's Handy Reference Guide. (Illus.). 224p. 1980. 14.95 (ISBN 0-8306-9663-6, 2325); pap. 11.95 (ISBN 0-8306-2325-6, 2325). TAB Bks.

Curry, Jane. The River's in My Blood: Riverboat Pilots Tell Their Stories. LC 82-11068. (Illus.). xx, 298p. 1985. pap. 7.95 (ISBN 0-8032-6316-3, BB-916, Bison). U of Nebr Pr.

Federal Aviation Administration. Aviation Instructor's Handbook. (Pilot Training Ser.). 120p. 1977. pap. 6.00 (ISBN 0-89100-170-0, EA-AC60-14). Aviation Maintenance.

--Commercial Pilot Flight Test Guide. 2nd ed. (Pilot Training Ser.: Pilot Training Ser.). 29p. 1975. pap. 4.75 (ISBN 0-89100-172-7, EA-AC61-55A). Aviation Maintenance.

--Instrument Flying Handbook. 3rd ed. (Pilot Training Ser.). (Illus.). 271p. 1980. pap. 8.50 (ISBN 0-89100-257-X, EA-AC61-27C). Aviation Maintenance.

--Pilot's Handbook of Aeronautical Knowledge. 2nd ed. (Pilot Training Ser.). (Illus.). 257p. 1971. pap. 11.00 (ISBN 0-89100-223-5, EA-AC61-23B). Aviation Maintenance.

Griffin, Jeff W. Cold Weather Flying. (Modern Aviation Ser.). 1980. 9.95 (ISBN 0-8306-9711-X). TAB Bks.

Maloney, Elbert S. Problems & Answers in Navigation & Piloting. 2nd ed. 96p. 1985. pap. 3.95 (ISBN 0-87021-150-1). Naval Inst Pr.

Marquez, Antonio. Tecnica de Navegacion y Pilotaje Marino. 2nd ed. USAmerica Publishing, ed. LC 84-52183. (Span., Illus.). 152p. 1985. 6.25 (ISBN 0-934763-00-3). Usamerica.

Martin, Nancy. Sea & River Pilots. (Illus.). 1979. 20.00x (ISBN 0-900963-72-7, Pub. by Terence Dalton England). State Mutual Bk.

Musciano, Walter A. Messerschmitt Aces. LC 81-20614. (Illus.). 224p. 1982. 17.95 (ISBN 0-668-04887-5). Arco.

Robson, Malcolm. Channel Islands Pilot. 176p. 1980. 27.00 (ISBN 0-245-53413-X, Pub. by Nautical England). State Mutual Bk.

Verne, Jules. The Danube Pilot. 3.95 (ISBN 0-685-27948-0). Assoc Bk.

PINE

see also individual species, e.g. Yellow Pine

Adlard, P. G. & Richardson, K. F. Stand Density & Stem Taper in Pinus Patula: Schiede & Deppe. 1978. 30.00x (ISBN 0-85074-047-9, Pub. by For Lib Comm England). State Mutual Bk.

Adlard, P. G., et al. Wood Density Variation in Plantation-Grown Pinus Patula from the Viphya Plateau, Malawi. 1978. 40.00x (ISBN 0-85074-045-2, Pub. by For Lib Comm England). State Mutual Bk.

Armitage, F. B. & Burley, J. Pinus Kesiya. 1980. 39.00x (ISBN 0-85074-030-4, Pub. by For Lib Comm England). State Mutual Bk.

Axelrod, Daniel I. History of the Maritime Closed-Cone Pines, Alta & Baja California. (U. C. Publications in Geological Sciences Ser.: Vol. 120). 1980. pap. 15.50x (ISBN 0-520-09620-7). U of Cal Pr.

Bowmen, M. R. & Whitmore, T. C. A Second Look at Agathis. 1980. 30.00x (ISBN 0-85074-053-3, Pub. by For Lib Comm England). State Mutual Bk.

Burley, J. & Palmer, E. R. Pulp & Wood Densitometric Properties of Pinus Caribaea from Fiji. 1979. 30.00x (ISBN 0-85074-046-0, Pub. by For Lib Comm England). State Mutual Bk.

Cronartium Ribicola: Its Growth & Reproduction in the Tissues of the Eastern White Pine, No. 86. 1964. 1.50 (ISBN 0-686-20698-3). SUNY Environ.

Greaves, A. Review of Pinus Caribaea. 1980. 30.00x (ISBN 0-85074-052-5, Pub. by For Lib Comm England). State Mutual Bk.

Identification of Pines of the United States, Native & Introduced, by Needle Structure, No. 32. 1942. 0.25 (ISBN 0-686-20691-6). SUNY Environ.

Johnson, Anne & Johnson, Russ. Ancient Bristlecone Pine Forest. LC 70-126317. pap. 2.95 (ISBN 0-912494-03-4). Chalfant Pr.

Ladell, J. L. Needle Density, Pith Size & Tracheid Length in Pine. 1963. 30.00x (ISBN 0-686-45538-X, Pub. by For Lib Comm England). State Mutual Bk.

Lamb, A. F. Pinus Caribaea, Vol. 1. 1978. 50.00x (ISBN 0-85074-015-0, Pub. by For Lib Comm England). State Mutual Bk.

Lanner, Ronald M. The Pinon Pine: A Natural & Cultural History. LC 81-119. (Illus.). 208p. 1981. 13.50 (ISBN 0-87417-065-6); pap. 8.50 (ISBN 0-87417-066-4). U of Nev Pr.

Mirov, Nicholas T. The Genus Pinus. (Illus.). 602p. 1967. 34.50 (ISBN 0-471-06838-1, Pub. by Wiley-Interscience). Wiley.

Mirov, Nicholas T. & Hasbrouck, Jean. The Story of Pines. LC 74-30899. (Illus.). 160p. 1976. 12.95 (ISBN 0-253-35462-5). Ind U Pr.

Peterson, Russell. The Pine Tree Book. (Illus.). 1980. 14.95 (ISBN 0-89616-005-X); pap. 7.95 (ISBN 0-89616-006-8). Brandywine.

Plumptre, R. A. Some Wood Properties of Pinus Patula from Uganda & Techniques Developed. 1978. 30.00x (ISBN 0-85074-032-0, Pub. by For Lib Comm England). State Mutual Bk.

Ross, Opal. Fields & Pine Trees. 1977. 8.00 (ISBN 0-87770-184-9); pap. 5.95 (ISBN 0-87770-177-6). Ye Galleon.

Whitmore, T. C. A First Look at Agathis. 1977. 30.00x (ISBN 0-85074-018-5, Pub. by For Lib Comm England). State Mutual Bk.

Wolffsohn, A. Fire Control in Tropical Pine Forests. 1981. 30.00x (ISBN 0-85074-056-8, Pub. by For Lib Comm England). State Mutual Bk.

Wormald, T. J. Pinus Patula. 1975. 50.00x (ISBN 0-85074-025-8, Pub. by For Lib Comm England). State Mutual Bk.

PINE BARRENS

Forman, Richard R., ed. Pine Barrens: Ecosystem & Landscape. LC 79-9849. (Natural Resource Management Ser.). 1979. 55.00 (ISBN 0-12-263450-0). Acad Pr.

Goldstein, Joan. Environmental Decision Making in Rural Locales: The Pine Barrens. LC 81-5208. 186p. 1981. 29.95 (ISBN 0-03-059604-1). Praeger.

McPhee, John. The Pine Barrens. LC 67-22439. (Illus.). 157p. 1968. 11.95 (ISBN 0-374-23360-8); pap. 5.25 (ISBN 0-374-51442-9). FS&G.

Parnes, Robert. Canoeing the Jersey Pine Barrens. Rev. ed. LC 81-9681. (Illus.). 286p. (Orig.). 1981. pap. 8.95 (ISBN 0-914788-44-2). East Woods.

PINEAL BODY

Oksche & Pevet. Pineal Organ: Photobiology, Biochronometry & Endocrinology. (Developments in Endocrinology Ser.: Vol. 14). 366p. 1982. 64.25 (ISBN 0-444-80387-4, Biomedical Pr). Elsevier.

Quay, W. B. Pineal Chemistry: In Cellular & Physiological Mechanisms. (Illus.). 448p. 1974. 44.75x (ISBN 0-398-02802-8). C C Thomas.

Pritsker, Alan B. & Young, Robert E. Simulation with GASP-PL-I: A PL-I Based Continuous-Discrete Simulation Language. LC 75-23182. pap. 87.80 (ISBN 0-317-11035-7, 2022490). Bks Demand UMI.

Rockey, C. J. Structured PL-1 Programming with Business Applications. 544p. 1981. pap. 8.95 (ISBN 0-697-08141-9); solutions manual avail. (ISBN 0-697-08145-1). Wm C Brown.

Rockey, Clarence J. Structured PL-1 Programming. 2nd ed. LC 84-72271. 576p. 1985. pap. text ed. write for info. (ISBN 0-697-08180-X); write for info. (ISBN 0-697-00305-1). Wm C Brown.

Ruston, Henry. Programming with PL-1. (Illus.). 1978. text ed. 30.95 (ISBN 0-07-054350-X). McGraw.

SAS Institute Inc., ed. SAS Programmer's Guide, 1981 Edition. (SAS Programmer's Guide). 208p. (Orig.). 1980. pap. 9.95 (ISBN 0-917382-17-X). SAS Inst.

Shortt, Joseph & Wilson, Thomas C. Problem Solving & the Computer: A Structured Concept with PL 1 (PLC) 2nd ed. 1979. pap. text ed. 22.95 (ISBN 0-201-06916-4). Addison-Wesley.

Smedley, Dan. Programming the PL-1 Way. (Illus.). 300p. 1982. 15.95 (ISBN 0-8306-0092-2); pap. 9.95 (ISBN 0-8306-1414-1, 1414). TAB Bks.

Tremblay, Jean P. & Bunt, Richard B. Structured PL-1 (PL-C) Programming. 1979. pap. text ed. 24.95x (ISBN 0-07-065173-6). McGraw.

Underkoffler, Milton. Introduction to Structured Programming with PL-1 & PL-C. 1980. write for info. (ISBN 0-87150-292-5, 2302, Prindle). PWS Pubs.

Xenakis, John. Structured PL-1 Programming: An Introduction. 1979. pap. text ed. write for info. (ISBN 0-87872-190-8, Duxbury Pr). PWS Pubs.

PLACENTA

Baur, R. Morphometry of the Placental Exchange Area. LC 77-3148. (Advances in Anatomy, Embryology & Cell Biology: Vol. 53, No. 1). 1977. pap. 22.00 (ISBN 0-387-08159-3). Springer-Verlag.

Beaconsfield, P. Placenta-a Neglected Experimental Animal. 1979. 80.00 (ISBN 0-08-024430-0); pap. 30.00 (ISBN 0-08-024435-1). Pergamon.

Beaconsfield, R. & Birdwood, G., eds. Placenta: The Largest Human Biopsy. (Illus.). 174p. 1982. 44.00 (ISBN 0-08-028028-5). Pergamon.

Bischof, P. Placental Proteins. (Contributions to Gynecology & Obstetrics: Vol. 12). (Illus.). viii, 96p. 1984. 28.25 (ISBN 3-8055-3853-7). S Karger.

Chard, T. & Klopper, A. I. Placental Function Tests. (Illus.). 96p. 1982. pap. 25.90 (ISBN 0-387-11529-3). Springer-Verlag.

Faber, J. Job & Thornburg, Kent L. Placental Physiology: Structure & Function of Fetomaternal Exchange. (Illus.). 208p. 1983. text ed. 40.50 (ISBN 0-89004-978-5). Raven.

Heap, R. B., et al. Placenta: Structure & Function. 208p. 1982. 80.00x (ISBN 0-906545-07-2, Pub. by Journals Repro England). State Mutual Bk.

Kaufmann, P. & Davidoff, M. The Guinea-Pig Placenta. (Advances in Anatomy, Embryology & Cell Biology: Vol 53 Pt. 2). 1977. soft cover 26.00 (ISBN 0-387-08179-8). Springer-Verlag.

Kaufmann, P. & King, B. F., eds. Structural & Functional Organization of the Placenta. (Bibliotheca Anatomica: No. 22). (Illus.). viii, 164p. 1982. 65.25 (ISBN 3-8055-3520-1). S Karger.

Klopper, A., ed. Immunology of the Human Placenta & Proteins: Supplement to the Quarterly Journal "Placenta", Vol. 4. 136p. 1982. 42.95 (ISBN 0-03-062117-8). Praeger.

Klopper, A. I. & Chard, T., eds. Placental Proteins. (Illus.). 1979. pap. 41.00 (ISBN 0-387-09406-7). Springer-Verlag.

Miller, R. K. The Placenta: Receptors, Pathology & Toxicology. Thiede, H., ed. 390p. 1982. 69.50 (ISBN 0-03-063037-1). Praeger.

Moghissi, Kamran S. & Hafez, E. S., eds. The Placenta: Biological & Clinical Aspects. (Illus.). 412p. 1974. photocopy ed. 44.50x (ISBN 0-398-02999-7). C C Thomas.

Soma, H., ed. Morphological & Functional Aspects of Placental Dysfunction. (Contributions to Gynecology & Obstetrics: Vol. 9). (Illus.). viii, 180p. 1982. pap. 54.50 (ISBN 3-8055-3510-4). S Karger.

Steven, D., ed. Comparative Placentation: Essays in Structure & Function. (Monographs for Students of Medicine). 1976. 29.50 (ISBN 0-12-668050-7). Acad Pr.

Strong, S. J. & Corney, G. The Placenta in Twin Pregnancy. 1967. 59.00 (ISBN 0-08-012223-X). Pergamon.

Wallenburg, H. C. S. Transfer Across the Primate & Non-Primate Placenta. Van Kreel, B. K. & Van Dijk, J. P., eds. LC 80-41905. 300p. 1982. 59.95 (ISBN 0-03-063036-3). Praeger.

Yao, Alice C. & Lind, John. Placental Transfusion: A Clinical & Physiological Study. 188p. 1982. 19.75x (ISBN 0-398-04437-6). C C Thomas.

PLACER MINING

see Hydraulic Mining

PLAINS

see also Deserts; Pampas; Prairies; Steppes; Tundras

Perry, Richard. Life in Desert & Plain. LC 75-34733. (The Many Worlds of Wildlife Ser.). (Illus.). 256p. 1976. 10.95 (ISBN 0-8008-4798-9). Taplinger.

PLANARIA

Chandebois, R. Histogenesis & Morphogenesis in Planarian Regeneration. Wolsky, A., ed. (Monographs in Developmental Biology: Vol. 11). (Illus.). 200p. 1976. 38.50 (ISBN 3-8055-2285-1). S Karger.

Reynoldson, T. B. A Key to the British Species of Freshwater Triclads. 2nd ed. 1978. 20.00x (ISBN 0-900386-34-7, Pub. by Freshwater Bio). State Mutual Bk.

PLANE CURVES

see Curves, Plane

PLANE GEOMETRY

see Geometry, Plane

PLANE TRIGONOMETRY

see Trigonometry, Plane

PLANES (HAND TOOLS)

Greenfield Tool Company. Eighteen Fifty-Four Price List of Joiners' Bench Planes & Moulding Tools. Roberts, Kenneth D., ed. 32p. 1981. pap. 2.50 (ISBN 0-913602-43-4). K Roberts.

Roberts, Jook. Leonard Bailey & Co.'s Illustrated Catalogue & Price List of Patent Adjustable Bench Planes, Etc. 1876. (Illus.). 48p. 1981. pap. text ed. 5.00 (ISBN 0-913602-42-6). K Roberts.

Roberts, Kenneth D., ed. Chapin-Stephens Catalog No. 114. 1975. Repr. 5.00 (ISBN 0-913602-10-8). K Roberts.

--Ohio Tool Companies Adjustable Planes Nineteen Hundred Fifteen. (Illus.). 32p. 1981. pap. 3.00 (ISBN 0-913602-47-7). K Roberts.

--Price List of Joiners' Bench Planes & Moulding Tools, Greenfield Tool Co., 1854. 30p. 1981. pap. 2.00 (ISBN 0-913602-43-4). K Roberts.

Roberts, Kenneth D., intro. by. Stanley Rule & Level Co. 1872 Price List of Boxwood & Ivory Rules, Levles, Iron & Wood Bench Planes, Etc. (Illus.). 48p. 1981. pap. 5.00 (ISBN 0-913602-44-2). K Roberts.

Roberts, Kenneth D., ed. Stanley Rule & Level Co.'s Combination Planes. 1975. 5.0001054698x (ISBN 0-913602-09-4). K Roberts.

Sandusky Tool Co. Illustrated List of Planes, Etc. 1978. Repr. of 1877 ed. 4.50 (ISBN 0-913602-24-8). K Roberts.

Sellens, Alvin. The Stanley Plane: A History & Descriptive Inventory. LC 75-9509. (Illus.). 1975. 13.50 (ISBN 0-9612068-0-2). Sellens.

--Woodworking Planes: A Descriptive Register of Wooden Planes. LC 78-52687. (Illus.). 1978. 13.50 (ISBN 0-9612068-1-0). Sellens.

PLANETARIA

The Elementary & Classmate Planetariums. rev. ed. 32p. (Orig.). 1980. pap. text ed. 4.15 (ISBN 0-943956-01-3). Trippensee Pub.

PLANETARY NEBULAE

Gurzadyan, G. A. Planetary Nebulae. 328p. 1969. 80.95 (ISBN 0-677-20220-2). Gordon.

--Planetary Nebulae. Hummer, D. G., ed. & tr. LC 69-11664. 314p. 1971. lib. bdg. 45.00 (ISBN 90-277-0117-2, Pub. by Reidel Holland). Kluwer Academic.

I.A.U Symposium, 34th, Tatranska Lomnica, Czechoslovakia, 1967. Planetary Nebulae: Proceedings. Osterbrock, D. E. & O'Dell, C. R., eds. (IAU Symposia: No. 34). 469p. 1968. lib. bdg. 45.00 (ISBN 90-277-0134-2, Pub. by Reidel Holland). Kluwer Academic.

I.A.U. Symposium, 76th. Planetary Nebulae: Proceedings. Terzian, Yervant, ed. 1978. lib. bdg. 47.50 (ISBN 90-277-0872-X, Pub. by Reidel Holland); pap. 31.50 (ISBN 90-277-0873-8, Pub. by Reidel Holland). Kluwer Academic.

Kafatos, M. & Henry, R. B., eds. The Crab Nebula & Related Supernova Remnants. (Illus.). 320p. Date not set. price not set (ISBN 0-521-30530-6). Cambridge U Pr.

PLANETOIDS

see Planets, Minor

PLANETS

see also Life on Other Planets; Mechanics, Celestial; Satellites; Solar System; Stars; Transits also individual planets, e.g. Mars (Planet)

Ackerman, Diane. The Planets: A Cosmic Pastoral. LC 76-14840. (Illus.). 1976. 6.95 (ISBN 0-688-03088-2). Morrow.

Adler, I. & Trombka, J. I. Geochemical Exploration of the Moon & the Planets. LC 78-127039. (Physics & Chemistry in Space Ser.: Vol. 3). (Illus.). 230p. 1970. 38.00 (ISBN 0-387-05228-3). Springer-Verlag.

Airy, George B. Gravitation. rev. ed. 1969. pap. 2.50 (ISBN 0-911014-02-0). Neo Pr.

Bauer, S. J. Physics of Planetary Ionospheres. LC 72-15455. (Physics & Chemistry in Space Ser.: Vol. 6). (Illus.). 230p. 1973. 55.00 (ISBN 0-387-06173-8). Springer-Verlag.

Black, D. C. & Matthews, Mildred S., eds. Protostars & Planets II. LC 85-11223. 1985. 45.00 (ISBN 0-8165-0950-6). U of Ariz Pr.

Briggs, Geoffrey A. & Taylor, Frederick W. The Cambridge Photographic Atlas of the Planets. LC 81-38529. (Illus.). 224p. 1982. 27.95 (ISBN 0-521-23976-1). Cambridge U Pr.

Chamberlain, Joseph W. Theory of Planetary Atmospheres: An Introduction to Their Physics & Chemistry. (International Geophysics Ser.). 1978. 35.00 (ISBN 0-12-167250-6). Acad Pr.

Chapman, Clark R. Planets of Rock & Ice: From Mercury to the Moons of Saturn. (Illus.). 256p. 1982. 13.95 (ISBN 0-684-17484-7, ScribT). Scribner.

Cheyne, Charles H. An Elementary Treatise in the Planetary Theory. Cohen, I. Bernard, ed. LC 80-2117. (Development of Science Ser.). (Illus.). 1981. lib. bdg. 15.00x (ISBN 0-686-73597-8). Ayer Co Pubs.

--An Elementary Treatise on the Planetary Theory. 15.00 (ISBN 0-405-13837-7). Ayer Co Pubs.

Cole, G. H. & Watton, W. G. The Structure of Planets. LC 77-18646. (Wykeham Science Ser.: No. 45). 232p. 1977. 19.50x (ISBN 0-8448-1309-5). Crane-Russak Co.

Cook, A. H. Interiors of the Planets. (Cambridge Planetary Science Ser.: No. 1). (Illus.). 360p. 1981. 72.50 (ISBN 0-521-23214-7). Cambridge U Pr.

Coradini, A. & Fulchignoni, M., eds. The Comparative Study of the Planets. 1982. 59.50 (ISBN 90-277-1406-1, Pub. by Reidel Holland). Kluwer Academic.

Davies, Merton & Murray, Bruce C. The View from Space: Photographic Exploration of the Planets. LC 75-16887. 1971. pap. 11.00x (ISBN 0-231-08330-0). Columbia U Pr.

Gehrels, T., ed. Planets, Stars & Nebulae Studied With Photopolarimetry. LC 73-86446. 1133p. 1974. 27.50x (ISBN 0-8165-0428-8). U of Ariz Pr.

Glass, Billy P. Introduction to Planetary Geology. LC 81-17057. (Planetary Science Ser.: No. 2). (Illus.). 1982. 32.50 (ISBN 0-521-23579-0); pap. cancelled (ISBN 0-521-28052-4). Cambridge U Pr.

Goody, Richard & Walker, James C. Atmospheres. (Foundations of Earth Science Ser). (Illus.). 160p. 1972. ref. ed. o.p. 8.95 (ISBN 0-13-050096-8); pap. 15.95 ref. ed. (ISBN 0-13-050088-7). P-H.

Greeley, Ronald. Planetary Landscapes. (Illus.). 256p. 1985. 39.95x (ISBN 0-04-551080-6). Allen Unwin.

Greenberg, Richard & Brahic, Andre, eds. Planetary Rings. LC 84-125. 785p. 1983. 35.00x (ISBN 0-8165-0828-3). U of Ariz Pr.

Grossinger, Richard. The Night Sky: The Science & Anthropology of the Stars & Planets. LC 81-5293. 544p. 1981. 16.95 (ISBN 0-87156-288-X). Sierra.

Guerin, P., ed. Planetes et satellites: Mondes de l'espace. rev. ed. (Fr., Illus.). 1970. 40.50x (ISBN 0-685-14042-3). Larousse.

Hartmann, William K. Moons & Planets. 2nd ed. 528p. 1983. text ed. write for info. (ISBN 0-534-00719-8). Wadsworth Pub.

Hubbard, William B. Planetary Interiors. 1984. 42.50 (ISBN 0-442-23704-9). Van Nos Reinhold.

Hunt, Garry, ed. Uranus & the Outer Planets: Proceedings of the IAU-RAS Colloquium, No. 60. LC 81-17047. (Illus.). 350p. 1982. 39.50 (ISBN 0-521-24573-7). Cambridge U Pr.

I.A.U. Symposium, 40th, Marfa, Texas, 1969. Planetary Atmospheres: Proceedings. Sagan, C., et al, eds. LC 77-140566. (I.A.U. Symposia: No. 40). 408p. 1971. lib. bdg. 42.00 (ISBN 90-277-0165-2, Pub. by Reidel Holland). Kluwer Academic.

Inglis, Stuart J. Planets, Stars, & Galaxies. 4th ed. LC 75-31542. 336p. 1976. pap. text ed. 33.50x (ISBN 0-471-42738-1). Wiley.

International Symposium on Solar Terrestrial Physics. Physics of Solar Planetary Environments: Proceedings, 2 vols. Williams, Donald J., ed. LC 76-29443. (Illus.). 1038p. 1976. pap. 10.00 (ISBN 0-87590-204-9). Am Geophysical.

King, Henry C. & Millburn, John R. Geared to the Stars: The Evolution of Planetariums, Orreries & Astronomical Clocks. LC 78-18262. 1978. 80.00 (ISBN 0-8020-2312-6). U of Toronto Pr.

Kondratyev, K. Y. & Hunt, G. E. Weather & Climate on Planets. (Illus.). 750p. 1981. 105.00 (ISBN 0-08-026493-X). Pergamon.

Kuiper, Gerard P. & Middlehurst, Barbara M., eds. Planets & Satellites. LC 54-7183. (Solar System Ser.: Vol. 3). 1961. 50.00x (ISBN 0-226-45927-6). U of Chicago Pr.

Lewis, John S. & Primm, Ronald G. Planets & Their Atmospheres: Origin & Evolution (Monograph) LC 83-10001. (International Geophysics Ser.). 1983. 59.00 (ISBN 0-12-446580-3); pap. 29.50 (ISBN 0-12-446582-X). Acad Pr.

Libin, Arthur D., ed. ASI Tables of Diurnal Planetary Motion. LC 75-22432. 190p. 1975. pap. 4.25 (ISBN 0-88231-025-9). ASI Pubs Inc.

Lunar & Planetary Institute, Houston, Texas, U. S. A., ed. Proceedings of the Conference on Multi-Ring Basins. 300p. 1981. 39.00 (ISBN 0-08-028045-5). Pergamon.

Lunar & Planetary Science Conference, 12th, Houston, Mar. 16-20, 1981. Proceedings. Lunar & Planetary Institute, ed. (Geochimica et Cosmochimica Acta Ser.: No. 16). (Illus.). 2000p. 1982. 195.00 (ISBN 0-08-028074-9). Pergamon.

Lunar & Planetary Science Conference, 10th, Houston, Texas, March 19-23, 1979. Proceedings, 3 vols. LC 79-22554. (Illus.). 3200p. 1980. 240.00 (ISBN 0-08-025128-5). Pergamon.

Masterson, Amanda R., ed. Index to the Proceedings of the Lunar & Planetary Science Conferences, Houston, Texas, 1970-1978. LC 79-20109. (Illus.). 325p. 1979. 39.00 (ISBN 0-08-024620-6). Pergamon.

Miller, Pat B. Pluto. LC 78-60924. (Illus.). 1978. pap. 3.50 (ISBN 0-9601846-1-9). PM Ent.

Moore, Thomas. The Planets Within. LC 81-65457. (Illus.). 224p. 1982. 26.50 (ISBN 0-8387-5022-2). Bucknell U Pr.

Murray, Bruce. The Planets. LC 82-21067. (Scientific American Reader Ser.). (Illus.). 120p. 1983. pap. text ed. 10.95 (ISBN 0-7167-1468-X). W H Freeman.

Murray, Bruce, et al. Earthlike Planets: Surfaces of Mercury, Venus, Earth, Moon, Mars. LC 80-19608. (Illus.). 387p. 1981. text ed. 33.95x (ISBN 0-7167-1148-6); pap. text ed. 17.95x (ISBN 0-7167-1149-4). W H Freeman.

Newton, Robert R. Ancient Planetary Observations & the Validity of Ephemeris Time. LC 75-44392. 768p. 1976. 37.50x (ISBN 0-8018-1842-7). Johns Hopkins.

Oberg, James E. New Earths: Restructuring Earth & Other Planets. 1983. pap. 8.95 (ISBN 0-452-00623-6, [illegible], Mer). NAL.

O'Reilly, W., ed. Magnetism, Planetary Rotation, & Convention in the Solar System: Retrospect & Prospect, Vol. 7. (Geophysical Surveys Ser.: Nos. 1, 2 & 3). 1985. lib. bdg. 49.00 (ISBN 90-277-2050-9, Pub. by Reidel Holland). Kluwer Academic.

Ponnamperuma, Cyril, ed. Chemical Evolution of the Giant Planets. 1976. 32.00 (ISBN 0-12-561350-4). Acad Pr.

--Comparative Planetology. 1978. 37.50 (ISBN 0-12-561340-7). Acad Pr.

Preiss, Byron, ed. The Planets. LC 85-47649. (Illus.). 304p. 1985. pap. 24.95 (ISBN 0-553-05109-1). Bantam.

Ridpath, Ian & Tirion, Wil. Universe Guide to Stars & Planets. LC 84-24133. (Illus.). 384p. 1985. 19.95 (ISBN 0-87663-366-1); pap. 10.95 (ISBN 0-87663-859-0). Universe.

Shorthill, R. W., ed. Progress in Planetary Exploration. (Advances in Space Research: Vol. 1, No. 8). (Illus.). 224p. 1981. pap. 32.00 (ISBN 0-08-028384-5). Pergamon.

Stiller, H. & Sagdeev, R. Z., eds. Planetary Interiors. (Advances in Space Research Ser.: Vol. 1, No. 7). (Illus.). 265p. 1981. pap. 37.00 (ISBN 0-08-028382-9). Pergamon.

Strong, James. Search for the Solar System: The Role of Unmanned Interplanetary Probes. (Illus.). 1973. 12.95x (ISBN 0-8464-0827-9). Beekman Pubs.

Summer Advanced Study Institute Symposium, University of Orleans, France, July 31-Aug. 11, 1972. Physics & Chemistry at Upper Atmospheres: Proceedings. McCormac, B. M., ed. LC 72-92533. (Astrophysics & Space Science Library: No. 35). 385p. 1973. lib. bdg. 60.50 (ISBN 90-277-0283-7, Pub. by Reidel Holland). Kluwer Academic.

Szebehely, Victor, ed. Dynamics of Planets & Satellites & Theories of Their Motion. (Astrophysics & Space Science Library: No. 72). 1978. lib. bdg. 47.50 (ISBN 90-277-0869-X, Pub. by Martinus Nijhoff Netherlands). Kluwer Academic.

Taylor, Stuart R. Planetary Science: A Lunar Perspective. (Illus.). 512p. 1982. 42.95X (ISBN 0-942862-00-7). Lunar & Planet Inst.

Velikovsky, Immanuel. Worlds in Collision. 1950. 12.95 (ISBN 0-385-04541-7). Doubleday.

Whipple, Fred L. Earth, Moon, & Planets. 3rd ed. LC 68-21987. (Books on Astronomy Series). (Illus.). 16.50x (ISBN 0-674-22400-0); pap. 5.95 (ISBN 0-674-22401-9). Harvard U Pr.

Williams, G. E., ed. Megacycles: Long-Term Episodity in Earth & Planetary History. LC 79-19908. (Benchmark Papers in Geology: Vol. 57). 448p. 1981. 57.50 (ISBN 0-87933-366-9). Van Nos Reinhold.

Wood, John A. Meteorites & the Origin of Planets. LC 68-13886. (Earth & Planetary Science Ser.). pap. 30.80 (ISBN 0-317-28252-2, 2055975). Bks Demand UMI.

Zharkov, V. N. The Interior Structure of the Earth & Planets. Hubbard, C. W., tr. from Rus. (Soviet Scientific Reviews, Astrophysics & Space Physics Reviews Supplement Ser.). Date not set. price not set (ISBN 3-7186-0067-6). Harwood Academic.

Zharkov, V. N. & Trubitsyn, V. P. Planetary Interiors. Hubbard, W. B., ed. (Astronomy & Astrophysics Ser.: Vol. 6). 399p. 1978. pap. text ed. 24.00 (ISBN 0-912918-15-2, 0015). Pachart Pub Hse.

PLANETS, MINOR

Cristescu, Cornelia & Klepczynski, W. J., eds. Asteroids, Comets, Meteoric Matter: Proceedings. (Illus.). 333p. 1975. text ed. 60.00x (ISBN 0-87936-008-9). Scholium Intl.

Gehrels, T., ed. Asteroids. LC 79-19686. 1181p. 1979. 35.00x (ISBN 0-8165-0695-7). U of Ariz Pr.

Gibilisco, Stan. Comets, Meteors & Asteroids: How They Affect Earth. (Illus.). 208p. (Orig.). 1985. pap. 12.95 (ISBN 0-8306-1905-4, 1905). TAB Bks.

PLANETS, THEORY OF

see also Mechanics, Celestial

Benjamin, Francis S., Jr. & Toomer, G. J., eds. Campanus of Novara & Medieval Planetary Theory: "Theorica planetarum". (Medieval Science Ser: No. 16). (Illus.). 508p. 1971. 40.00 (ISBN 0-299-05960-X). U of Wis Pr.

Hanson, N. R. & Humphreys, W. C., Jr. Constellations & Conjectures. LC 70-159654. (Synthese Library: No. 48). (Illus.). 282p. 1973. lib. bdg. 39.50 (ISBN 90-277-0192-X, Pub. by Reidel Holland). Kluwer Academic.

Kopal, Zdenek. Figures of Equilibrium of Celestial Bodies: With Emphasis on Problems of Motion of Artificial Satellites. (Mathematics Research Center Pubns., No. 3). (Illus.). 142p. 1960. 17.50x (ISBN 0-299-02010-X). U of Wis Pr.

Lunar & Planetary Institute, Houston, Texas. Basaltic Volcanism on Terrestrial Planets. (Illus.). 1200p. 1982. 66.00 (ISBN 0-08-028086-2); student ed. 45.00 (ISBN 0-08-028807-3). Pergamon.

Orographic Effects in Planetary Flows. (GARP Publications Ser.: No. 23). 450p. 1980. pap. 40.00 (ISBN 0-686-71858-5, W470, WMO). Unipub.

PLANIMETER

Larsgaard, Mary L. Topographic Mapping of the Americas, Australia, & New Zealand. LC 84-3874. 230p. 1984. text ed. 45.00 (ISBN 0-87287-276-9). Libs Unl.

PLANKTON

see also Fresh-Water Biology; Phytoplankton

Apstein, C. Die Pyrocysteen der Plankton-Expedition der Humboldt-Stiftung. 1971. Repr. of 1909 ed. 7.00 (ISBN 3-7682-0807-9). Lubrecht & Cramer.

Bougis, P., ed. Marine Plankton Ecology. 1976. 106.50 (ISBN 0-444-11033-X, North-Holland). Elsevier.

Brandt, K. & Apstein, C., eds. Nordisches Plankton: 1911-42, 7 vols. 1964. 372.00 (ISBN 90-6123-110-8). Lubrecht & Cramer.

Buttner-Kolisko, Agnes. Plankton Rotifers: Biology & Taxonomy. Kolisko, G., tr. from German. (Die Binnengewaesser). (Illus.). 146p. 1974. pap. text ed. 19.25x (ISBN 0-318-00462-3). Lubrecht & Cramer.

Clarke, Thomas A., et al. Biology of Plankton. 206p. 1972. text ed. 29.00x (ISBN 0-8422-7016-7). Irvington.

Davis, Charles C. Marine & Fresh Water Plankton. (Illus.). 562p. 1955. 18.50x (ISBN 0-87013-016-1). Mich St U Pr.

Dumont, H. J. & Tundisi, J. G. Tropical Zooplankton. (Developments in Hydrobiology Ser.: No. 23). 344p. 1984. 84.00 (ISBN 90-6193-774-4, Pub. by Junk Pubs Netherlands). Kluwer Academic.

Hohn, Matthew H. Qualitative & Quantitative Analyses of Plankton Diatoms. 1969. 6.00 (ISBN 0-86727-057-8). Ohio Bio Survey.

Kennett, James P. & Srinivasan, M. S. Neogene Planktonic Foraminifera: A Phylogenetic Atlas. LC 82-23401. 288p. 1983. 38.95 (ISBN 0-87933-070-8). Van Nos Reinhold.

Kerfoot, W. Charles, ed. Evolution & Ecology of Zooplankton Communities. LC 80-50491. (Illus.). 817p. 1980. 70.00x (ISBN 0-87451-180-1). U Pr of New Eng.

Kofoid, C. A. The Plankton of the Illinois River, 1894-99. (Bibliotheca Phycologica Ser.: No. 29). 1977. Repr. of 1903 ed. lib. bdg. 52.50x (ISBN 3-7682-1104-5). Lubrecht & Cramer.

Kofoid, Charles A. The Plankton of the Illinois River, 1894-1899: Quantitative Investigations & General Results, Pt.1. Egerton, Frank N., 3rd, ed. LC 77-74235. (History of Ecology Ser.). (Illus.). 1978. Repr. of 1903 ed. lib. bdg. 46.50x (ISBN 0-405-10404-9). Ayer Co Pubs.

Lebour, M. V. The Planktonic Diatoms of Northern Seas. (Ray Society Publication Ser.: No. 116). (Illus.). 244p. 1978. Repr. of 1930 ed. lib. bdg. 21.00x (ISBN 3-87429-147-2). Lubrecht & Cramer.

Long Term Observation of Plankton Fluctuation in the Central Adriatic. (General Fisheries Council of the Mediterranean (GFCM): Studies & Reviews: No. 41). (Eng. & Fr.). 39p. 1969. pap. 7.50 (ISBN 92-5-001960-2, F1801, FAO). Unipub.

Ludwig, William B. & Roach, Lee S. Studies on the Animal Ecology of the Hocking River Basin: The Bottom Invertebrates of the Hocking River & The Plankton of the Hocking River. 1932. 2.00 (ISBN 0-86727-025-X). Ohio Bio Survey.

Marr, John, ed. Kuroshio: A Symposium on the Japan Current. 624p. 1970. 30.00x (ISBN 0-8248-0090-7, Eastwest Ctr). UH Pr.

Newell, G. E. & Newell, R. C. Marine Plankton: Practical Guide. 1966. pap. text ed. 12.25x (ISBN 0-09-110541-2, Hutchinson U Lib). Humanities.

Omori, M. & Ikeda, T. Methods in Zooplankton Ecology. 322p. 1984. 44.95 (ISBN 0-471-80107-0, Pub. by Wiley Interscience). Wiley.

Pontin, Rosalind M. A Key to the Freshwater Planktonic & Semi-Planktonic Rotifera of the British Isles. 1978. 25.00x (ISBN 0-900386-33-9, Pub. by Freshwater Bio). State Mutual Bk.

Raymont, J. E. Plankton & Productivity in the Oceans: Zooplankton, Vol. 2. 2nd ed. (Illus.). 700p. 1983. 90.00 (ISBN 0-08-024404-1); pap. 45.00 (ISBN 0-08-024403-3). Pergamon.

Raymont, John E., et al. Plankton & Productivity in the Oceans: Vol. 1, Phytoplankton. 2nd ed. (Illus.). 1980. text ed. 89.00 (ISBN 0-08-021552-1); pap. text ed. 19.95 (ISBN 0-08-021551-3). Pergamon.

Saito, Tsunemasa, et al. Systematic Index of Recent & Pleistocene Planktonic Foraminifera. (Illus.). 190p. 1981. 29.50x (ISBN 0-86008-280-6, Pub. by U of Tokyo Japan). Columbia U Pr.

Schuett, F. Die Peridineen der Plankton-Expedition der Humboldt-Stiftung I: Allgemeiner Teil. (Illus.). 1978. Repr. of 1895 ed. 35.00 (ISBN 3-7682-0806-0). Lubrecht & Cramer.

Steele, John H., ed. Spatial Pattern in Plankton Communities. LC 78-12017. (NATO Conference Series IV, Marine Science: Vol. 3). 480p. 1978. 69.50x (ISBN 0-306-40057-X, Plenum Pr). Plenum Pub.

Steidinger, K. A. & Walker, L. M. Marine Plankton Life Cycle Strategies. 168p. 1984. 58.00 (ISBN 0-8493-5222-3). CRC Pr.

Strickland, Richard M. The Fertile Fjord: Plankton in Puget Sound. (A Puget Sound Bk.). (Illus.). 160p. (Orig.). 1983. pap. 8.95 (ISBN 0-295-95979-7, Pub. by Wash Sea Grant). U of Wash Pr.

Van der Spoel, S. & Heyman, R. P. A Comparative Atlas of Zooplankton: Biological Patterns in the Oceans. 200p. 1983. pap. 51.50 (ISBN 0-387-12573-6). Springer-Verlag.

Van der Spoel, S. & Pierrot-Bults, A. C., eds. Zoogeography & Diversity in Plankton. LC 79-9494. 410p. 1979. 96.00x (ISBN 0-470-26798-4). Halsted Pr.

Wille, N. Die Schizophyceen der Plankton-Expedition der Hunboldt-Stiftung. (Illus.). 1968. Repr. of 1904 ed. 14.70 (ISBN 3-7682-0808-7). Lubrecht & Cramer.

Zooplankton Fixation & Preservation. (Monographs on Oceanographic Methodology: No. 4). (Illus.). 350p. 1976. pap. 18.75 (ISBN 92-3-101272-X, U736, UNESCO). Unipub.

Zooplankton Sampling. (Monographs on Oceanographic Methodology: No. 2). 174p. (3rd Printing 1979). 1968. pap. 13.75 (ISBN 92-3-101194-4, U737, UNESCO). Unipub.

PLANKTON, FOSSIL

Bolli, Hans & Saunders, John B., eds. Plankton Stratigraphy. (Earth Science Ser.). (Illus.). 800p. 1984. 125.00 (ISBN 0-521-23576-6). Cambridge U Pr.

PLANNING, CITY

see City Planning

PLANS

see Architectural Drawing; Geometrical Drawing; Maps; Mechanical Drawing

PLANT ANATOMY

see Botany–Anatomy

PLANT ASSIMILATION

see Plants–Assimilation

PLANT ASSOCIATIONS

see Plant Communities

PLANT-BREEDING

see also Grafting; Grain–Breeding; Hybridization, Vegetable; Plant Genetics; Plant Propagation; Plants–Disease and Pest Resistance; Tree Breeding

Agriculture Board, National Research Council. Genetic Engineering of Plants: Agricultural Research Opportunities & Policy Concerns. 1984. pap. text ed. 9.50 (ISBN 0-309-03434-5). Natl Acad Pr.

Allard, Robert W. Principles of Plant Breeding. LC 60-14240. 485p. 1960. 37.50 (ISBN 0-471-02310-8). Wiley.

Broertjes, C. Induced Variability in Plant Breeding: Proceedings of the International Symposium of the Section Mutation & Polyploidy of the European Association for Research on Plant Breeding EUCARPIA, Wageningen, The Netherlands, Aug. 31-Sept. 4, 1981. 149p. (25 papers, 12 posters). 1982. pap. 22.25 (ISBN 90-220-0796-0, PDC236, Pudoc). Unipub.

Chaudhary, H. K. Elementary Principles of Plant Breeding. 1981. 35.00x (ISBN 0-686-76634-2, Pub. by Oxford & IBH India). State Mutual Bk.

Christiansen, M. N. & Lewis, Charles F., eds. Breeding Plants for Less Favorable Environments. LC 81-10346. 459p. 1982. 57.50 (ISBN 0-471-04483-0, Pub. by Wiley-Interscience). Wiley.

Frankel, R. & Galun, E. Pollination Mechanisms, Reproduction & Plant Breeding. (Monographs on Theoretical & Applied Genetics: Vol. 2). 1977. 39.00 (ISBN 0-387-07934-3). Springer-Verlag.

Frey, Kenneth J., ed. Plant Breeding II. 498p. 1981. 22.95x (ISBN 0-8138-1550-9). Iowa St U Pr.

Gleba, Y. Y. & Sytnik, K. M. Protoplast Fusion: Genetic Engineering in Higher Plants. (Monographs on Theoretical & Applied Genetics: Vol. 8). (Illus.). 245p. 1984. 55.00 (ISBN 0-387-13284-8). Springer-Verlag.

Gottschalk, W. & Wolff, G. Induced Mutations in Plant Breeding. (Monographs on Theoretical & Applied Genetics Ser.: Vol. 7). (Illus.). 250p. 1983. 44.50 (ISBN 0-387-12184-6). Springer-Verlag.

Hanson, C. H., ed. The Effect of FDA Regulations (GRAS) on Plant Breeding & Processing. (Illus.). 1974. pap. 3.25 (ISBN 0-89118-507-0). Crop Sci Soc Am.

Hardarson, G. & Lie, T. A., eds. Breeding Legumes for Enhanced Symbiotic Nitrogen Fixation. (Advances in Agricultural Biotechnology Ser.). 1985. lib. bdg. 36.00 (ISBN 90-247-3123-2, Pub. by Martinus Nijhoff Netherlands). Kluwer-Academic.

Hendriksen, A. J. T. & Sneep, J., eds. Plant Breeding Perspectives. 460p. (13 colour plates, over 700 refs.). 1979. 63.50 (ISBN 90-220-0697-2, PDC122, PUDOC). Unipub.

Induced Mutations in Cross-Breeding. (Panel Proceedings Ser.). (Illus.). 256p. 1977. pap. 28.75 (ISBN 92-0-111676-4, ISP447, IAEA). Unipub.

Janick, Jules, ed. Plant Breeding Reviews, Vol. 1. (Plant Breeding Reviews Ser.). (Illus.). 1983. PLB 45.00 (ISBN 0-87055-397-6). AVI.

--Plant Breeding Reviews, Vol. 2. (Plant Breeding Reviews Ser.). (Illus.). 1984. lib. bdg. 45.00 (ISBN 0-87055-454-9). AVI.

Janick, Jules, et al, eds. Plant Breeding Reviews, Vol. 3. (Plant Breeding Reviews Ser.). 1985. 45.00 (ISBN 0-87055-487-5). AVI.

Lange, W. & Zeven, A. C., eds. Efficiency in Plant Breeding: Proceedings, Congress of the European Association for Research on Plant Breeding, Wageningen, the Netherlands, 19-24 June, 1983. (Illus.). 383p. 1985. 47.75 (ISBN 90-220-0856-8, PDC272, Pudoc). Unipub.

Manual on Mutation Breeding. 2nd ed. (Illus.). 1977. pap. 35.25 (ISBN 92-0-115077-6, IDC119, IAEA). Unipub.

Mayo, Oliver. The Theory of Plant Breeding. (Illus.). 1980. text ed. 76.00x (ISBN 0-19-854536-3). Oxford U Pr.

Muhammed, Amir, et al, eds. Genetic Diversity in Plants. LC 77-9475. (Basic Life Sciences Ser.: Vol. 8). (Illus.). 518p. 1977. 57.50x (ISBN 0-306-36508-1, Plenum Pr). Plenum Pub.

Mutations in Plant Breeding. (Panel Proceedings Ser.). (Illus.). 271p. 1966. pap. 16.00 (ISBN 92-0-011066-5, ISP129, IAEA). Unipub.

Mutations in Plant Breeding - 2. (Panel Proceedings Ser.). (Illus.). 315p. 1968. pap. 21.50 (ISBN 92-0-111368-4, ISP182, IAEA). Unipub.

Nelson, R. R., ed. Breeding Plants for Disease Resistance: Concepts & Applications. LC 71-128175. (Illus.). 412p. 1973. 28.75x (ISBN 0-271-01141-6). Pa St U Pr.

New Approaches to Breeding for Improved Plant Protein. (Panel Proceedings Ser.). (Illus.). 193p. 1969. pap. 14.50 (ISBN 92-0-111069-3, ISP212, IAEA). Unipub.

Neyra, Carlos A. Biochemical Basis Plant Breeding: Carbon Metabolism, Vol. 1. 192p. 1985. 60.00 (ISBN 0-8493-5741-1). CRC Pr.

North, C. Plant Breeding & Genetics in Horticulture. LC 79-10436. 150p. 1979. pap. 24.95x (ISBN 0-470-26661-9). Halsted Pr.

Nuclear Techniques for Seed Protein Improvement. (Panel Proceedings Ser.). (Illus.). 442p. (Orig.). 1973. pap. 33.75 (ISBN 92-0-111073-1, ISP320, IAEA). Unipub.

Plant Breeding Symposium. Plant Breeding: A Symposium. Frey, Kenneth J., ed. LC 66-21642. pap. 109.50 (ISBN 0-317-30428-3, 2024932). Bks Demand UMI.

Polyploidy & Induced Mutations in Plant Breeding. (Panel Proceedings Ser.). (Illus.). 414p. (Orig.). 1974. pap. 32.00 (ISBN 92-0-011074-6, ISP359, IAEA). Unipub.

Practicals in Plant Breeding: A Manual Cum Practical Record. 1981. 35.00x (ISBN 0-686-76660-1, Pub. by Oxford & IBH India). State Mutual Bk.

Rees, H., et al, eds. The Manipulation of Genetic Systems in Plant Breeding. (Royal Society of London Ser.). (Illus.). 209p. 1981. lib. bdg. 55.00x (ISBN 0-85403-165-0, Pub. by Royal Soc London). Scholium Intl.

Reinert, J. & Bajaj, Y. P., eds. Applied & Fundamental Aspects of Plant Cell, Tissue & Organ Culture. (Illus.). 1976. 120.00 (ISBN 0-387-07677-8). Springer-Verlag.

Rubenstein, Irwin, et al, eds. Genetic Improvement of Crops: Emergent Techniques. 232p. 1980. 22.50x (ISBN 0-8166-0966-7). U of Minn Pr.

Russell, G. E., ed. Progress in Plant Breeding, Vol. 1. (Illus.). 288p. 1985. text ed. 79.95 (ISBN 0-407-00780-6). Butterworth.

Russell, Gordon E. Plant Breeding for Pest & Disease Resistance. 1978. 79.95 (ISBN 0-408-10613-1). Butterworth.

Selection in Mutation Breeding. (Panel Proceedings Ser.). (Illus.). 180p. 1985. pap. 29.00 (ISBN 92-0-111284-X, ISP665, IAEA). Unipub.

Sharp, W. R., et al, eds. Plant Cell & Tissue Culture: Principles & Applications. LC 78-13080. (Ohio State University Biosciences Colloquia: No. 4). (Illus.). 908p. 1979. 37.50x (ISBN 0-8142-0287-X). Ohio St U Pr.

Sinha, U. & Sinha, Sunita. Cytogenetics: Plant Breeding & Evolution. 1980. text ed. 30.00x (ISBN 0-7069-0469-9, Pub. by Vikas Indig). Advent NY.

Smith, H. C. & Wratt, G. S., eds. Plant Breeding in New Zealand. (Illus.). 300p. (Orig.). 1983. pap. 34.95 (ISBN 0-409-70137-8). Butterworth.

Srb, Adrian M., ed. Genes, Enzymes, & Populations. LC 73-15867. (Basic Life Sciences Ser.: Vol. 2). (Illus.). 374p. 1973. 45.00x (ISBN 0-306-36502-2, Plenum Pr). Plenum Pub.

Tomes, Dwight & Christie, Bert. Plant Breeding. 1982. text ed. 19.95 (ISBN 0-8359-5550-8); instrs'. manual avail. (ISBN 0-8359-5551-6). Reston.

Verghese, T. M., ed. Vistas in Plant Sciences: Special Volume in Genetics & Plant Breeding, Vol. III. 166p. 1978. 14.00 (ISBN 0-88065-203-9, Pub. by Messers Today & Tomorrow Printers & Publishers India). Scholarly Pubns.

Verma, D. P. & Hohn, T., eds. Genes Involved in Microbe-Plant Interactions. (Plant Gene Research). (Illus.). 420p. 1984. 55.00 (ISBN 0-387-81789-1). Springer-Verlag.

Vose, P. B. & Blixt, S. G., eds. Crop Breeding: A Contemporary Basis. (Illus.). 450p. 1983. 99.00 (ISBN 0-08-025505-1). Pergamon.

Welsh, James R. Fundamentals of Plant Genetics & Breeding. LC 80-14638. 304p. 1981. text ed. 34.95 (ISBN 0-471-02862-2). Wiley.

Wood, D. R., ed. Crop Breeding. (Foundation for Modern Crop Science Ser.: Vol. 4). (Illus.). 1983. 18.00 (ISBN 0-89118-036-2). Am Soc Agron.

PLANT CELLS AND TISSUES

see also Cell Differentiation; Chromatophores; Phloem; Plastids

Ammirato, Philip, et al, eds. Handbook of Plant Cell Culture: Crop Species, Vol. 3. (Handbook of Plant Cell Culture Ser.). 650p. 1984. 53.00 (ISBN 0-02-949010-3). Macmillan.

Bell, L. N. Energetics of the Photosynthezing Plant Cell. (Soviet Scientific Reviews Supplement Series Physicochemical Biology: Vol. 5). 420p. 1985. text ed. 175.00 (ISBN 3-7186-0195-8). Harwood Academic.

Bhojwani, S. S. & Razdan, M. N. Plant Tissue Culture: Theory & Practice. (Developments in Crop Science Ser.: Vol. 5). 1984. 113.50 (ISBN 0-444-42164-5, I-075-84). Elsevier.

Brett, C. T. & Hillman, J. R., eds. Biochemistry of Plant Cell Walls. (Society for Experimental Biology Seminar Ser.: Vol. 28). 250p. 1985. 34.50 (ISBN 0-521-30487-3). Cambridge U Pr.

Bryant, J. A. & Francis, D., eds. The Cell Division Cycle in Plants. (Illus.). 240p. 1985. 34.50 (ISBN 0-521-30046-0). Cambridge U Pr.

Burgess, J. An Introducton to Plant Cell Development. (Illus.). 246p. 1985. 54.50 (ISBN 0-521-30273-0); pap. 19.95 (ISBN 0-521-31611-1). Cambridge U Pr.

Burnett, J. H. & Trinci, A. P., eds. Fungal Walls & Hyphal Growth. LC 78-72082. (Illus.). 1980. 82.50 (ISBN 0-521-22499-3). Cambridge U Pr.

Calder, Malcolm D. & Bernhardt, Peter. The Biology of Mistletoes. LC 83-71158. 1984. 55.00 (ISBN 0-12-155055-9). Acad Pr.

Conger, B. V., ed. Cloning Agricultural Plants via In Vitro Techniques. LC 80-23852. 280p. 1981. 85.00 (ISBN 0-8493-5797-7). CRC Pr.
Cutler, E. F. & Alvin, K. L. The Plant Cuticle. (Linn Soc Symposium Ser.: No. 10). 1982. 90.00 (ISBN 0-12-199920-3). Acad Pr.
Cutter, Elizabeth G. Plant Anatomy, Pt. I: Cells & Tissues. 2nd ed. (Illus.). 1978. text ed. 18.95 (ISBN 0-201-01236-7). Addison-Wesley.
Dixon, R. A., ed. Plant Cell Culture: A Practical Approach. (A Practical Approach Ser.). (Illus.). 250p. (Orig.). 1985. pap. 25.00 (ISBN 0-947946-22-5). IRL Pr.
Dodds, John H. & Roberts, Lorin W. Experiments in Plant Tissue Culture. LC 81-6106. (Illus.). 192p. 1982. 34.50 (ISBN 0-521-23477-8); pap. 12.95 (ISBN 0-521-29965-9). Cambridge U Pr.
Dodds, John H., ed. Plant Genetic Engineering. 208p. Date not set. price not set. (ISBN 0-521-25966-5). Cambridge U Pr.
Frey-Wyssling, A. The Plant Cell Wall. 3rd rev. ed. 1976. 107.30 (ISBN 3-443-14009-2). Lubrecht & Cramer.
Garcia, ed. Structure, Function & Biosynthesis of Plant Cell Walls. 524p. 1984. pap. 19.00 (ISBN 0-317-12494-3). Am Soc of Plan.
Giles, Kenneth L. & Sen, S. K., eds. Plant Cell Culture in Crop Improvement. (Basic Life Sciences Ser.: Vol. 22). 514p. 1982. 65.00x (ISBN 0-306-41160-1, Plenum Pr). Plenum Pub.
Gornik, E., et al, eds. Physics of Narrow Gap Semiconductors: Proceedings. (Lecture Notes in Physics Ser.: Vol. 152). 485p. 1982. 30.00 (ISBN 0-387-11191-3). Springer-Verlag.
Gunning, B. E. & Robards, A. W., eds. Intercellular Communication in Plants: Studies on Plasmodesmata. (Illus.). 300p. 1976. 46.00 (ISBN 0-387-07570-4). Springer-Verlag.
Hall, J. L. Electron Microscopy & Cytochemistry of Plant Cells. 1979. (Biomedical Pr); pap. 59.75 (ISBN 0-444-80135-9). Elsevier.
Hall, J. L. & Flowers, T. J. Plant Cell Structure & Metabolism. 2nd ed. (Illus.). 480p. (Orig.). 1982. pap. 22.00x (ISBN 0-582-44408-X). Longman.
Hall, John I. Isolation of Membranes & Organelles from Plants Cells. Moore, Anthony L., ed. (Biological Techniques Ser.). 1983. 49.50 (ISBN 0-12-318820-2). Acad Pr.
Halliwell, Barry. Chloroplast Metabolism: The Structure & Function of Chloroplasts in Green Leaf Cells. (Illus.). 1981. 50.00x (ISBN 0-19-854549-5); pap. 15.95 (ISBN 0-19-854585-1). Oxford U Pr.
Hu Han, ed. Plant Tissue Culture: Proceedings of the Bejiny (Peking) Symposium. LC 80-12359. (Pitman International Ser. in Bioscience). 538p. 1980. text ed. 87.95 (ISBN 0-273-08488-7). Pitman Pub MA.
Johri, B. M., ed. Experimental Embryology of Vascular Plants. (Illus.). 265p. 1982. 49.50 (ISBN 0-387-10334-1). Springer-Verlag.
Ledbetter, M. C. & Porter, K. Introduction to the Fine Structure of Plant Cells. LC 70-134021. (Illus.). 1970. 36.00 (ISBN 0-387-05195-3). Springer-Verlag.
Linskens, H. F. & Heslop-Harrison, J., eds. Cellular Interactions. (Encyclopedia of Plant Physiology Ser.). (Illus.). 850p. 1984. 140.00 (ISBN 0-387-12738-0). Springer-Verlag.
Luettge, U. & Pitman, M. G., eds. Transport in Plants Two, Pts. A & B. Incl. Pt. A. Cells. Robertson, R. A., frwd. by. (Illus.). 440p. 80.00 (ISBN 0-387-07452-X); Pt. B. Tissues & Plants. (Illus.). 480p. 85.00 (ISBN 0-387-07453-8). (Encyclopedia in Plant Physiology Ser.: Vol. 2). 1976. Springer-Verlag.
Maksymowych, R. Analysis of Leaf Development. LC 72-83585. (Developmental & Cell Biology Monographs: No. 1). (Illus.). 112p. 1973. 37.50 (ISBN 0-521-20017-2). Cambridge U Pr.
Markham, R., et al, eds. Modification of Cells. LC 74-81326. 350p. 72.50 (ISBN 0-444-10699-5, North-Holland). Elsevier.
Marme & Marre. Plasmalemma & Tonoplast: Their Functions in the Plant Cell. (Developments in Plant Biology: Vol. 7). 446p. 1982. 76.75 (ISBN 0-444-80409-9, Biomedical Pr). Elsevier.
Matile, P. The Lytic Compartment of Plant Cells. LC 75-5931. (Cell Biology Monographs: Vol. 1). (Illus.). xiii, 183p. 1975. 55.00 (ISBN 0-387-81296-2). Springer-Verlag.
Miller, M. W. & Kuehnert, C. C., eds. The Dynamics of Meristem Cell Populations. LC 70-185045. (Advances in Experimental Medicine & Biology Ser.: Vol. 18). 324p. 1972. 42.50x (ISBN 0-306-39018-3, Plenum Pr). Plenum Pub.
Plant Cell Culture. (Advances in Biochemical Engineering - Biotechnology Ser.: Vol. 31). (Illus.). 140p. 1985. 29.50 (ISBN 0-387-15489-2). Springer-Verlag.
Reinert, J. & Bajaj, Y. P., eds. Applied & Fundamental Aspects of Plant Cell, Tissue & Organ Culture. (Illus.). 1976. 120.00 (ISBN 0-387-07677-8). Springer-Verlag.
Roberts, Lorin W. Cytodifferentiation in Plants: Xylogenesis as a Model System. LC 75-10041. (Developmental & Cell Biology Ser.). pap. 43.50 (ISBN 0-317-26380-3, 2024522). Bks Demand UMI.
Sharp, W. R., et al, eds. Plant Cell & Tissue Culture: Principles & Applications. LC 78-13080. (Ohio State University Biosciences Colloquia: No. 4). (Illus.). 908p. 1979. 37.50x (ISBN 0-8142-0287-X). Ohio St U Pr.
Smith, H., ed. The Molecular Biology of Plant Cells. (Botanical Monographs: Vol. 14). 1978. 52.50x (ISBN 0-520-03465-1). U of Cal Pr.
Staba, E. John. Plant Tissue Culture As a Source of Biochemicals. 304p. 1980. 82.00 (ISBN 0-8493-5557-5). CRC Pr.
Stern, Kingsley R. Introductory Plant Biology. 2nd ed. 640p. 1982. instrs.' manual o.p. avail. (ISBN 0-697-04716-4); lab manual o.p. avail. (ISBN 0-697-04572-2); transparencies avail. (ISBN 0-697-04784-9). Wm C Brown.
Strogonov, B. P., et al. Structure & Function of Plant Cells in Saline Habitats. Gollak, B., ed. Mercado, A., tr. from Rus. LC 73-13609. (Illus.). 284p. 1973. 55.95x (ISBN 0-470-83406-4). Halsted Pr.
Thorpe, Trevor A., ed. Plant Tissue Culture: Methods & Application in Agriculture. 1981. 25.00 (ISBN 0-12-690680-7). Acad Pr.
Van Vloten-Doting, Lous, et al, eds. Molecular form & Function of the Plant Genome. (NATO ASI Series A, Life Sciences: Vol. 83). 706p. 1985. 82.50x (ISBN 0-306-41913-0, Plenum Pr). Plenum Pub.
Vasil, Indra K. Plant Improvement & Somatic Cell Genetics - Symposium. 1982. 23.50 (ISBN 0-12-714980-5). Acad Pr.
Vasil, Indra K., ed. Cell Culture & Somatic Cell Genetics of Plants: Cell Growth, Cytodifferentiation, Cryopreservation, Vol. 2. Date not set. price not set (ISBN 0-12-715002-1). Acad Pr.

PLANT CHEMISTRY
see Botanical Chemistry; Plants–Chemical Analysis

PLANT CLASSIFICATION
see Botany–Classification

PLANT COMMUNITIES
see also Botany–Ecology; Halophytes; Plant Indicators

Beadle, N. C. The Vegetation of Australia. LC 81-2662. (Illus.). 656p. 1981. 125.00 (ISBN 0-521-24195-2). Cambridge U Pr.
Costin, Alec B., et al. Kosciusko Alpine Flora. (Illus.). 408p. 1979. 35.00x (ISBN 0-643-02473-5, Pub. by Brit Mus Nat Hist England). Sabbot-Natural Hist Bks.
Curtis, John T. Vegetation of Wisconsin: An Ordination of Plant Communities. (Illus.). 672p. 1959. 27.50 (ISBN 0-299-01940-3). U of Wis Pr.
Gehu, J. M., ed. Colloques Phytosociologiques VII: Lille 1978, le Vegetation des Sols Tourbeux. (Fr.). 556p. 1981. lib. bdg. 52.50x (ISBN 3-7682-1260-2). Lubrecht & Cramer.
--Documents Phytosociologiques. (Fr., Illus.). 521p. 1981. lib. bdg. 52.50x (ISBN 3-7682-1298-X). Lubrecht & Cramer.
--Documents Phytosociologiques, IV: Festschrift R. Tuexen", 2 vols. (Illus.). 1979. Set. lib. bdg. 70.00x (ISBN 3-7682-1233-5). Lubrecht & Cramer.
McIntosh, R. P., ed. Phytosociology. LC 77-20258. (Benchmark Papers in Ecology: Vol. 6). 388p. 1978. 43.95 (ISBN 0-87933-312-X). Van Nos Reinhold.
Moore, Randy, ed. Vegetative Compatibility Responses in Plants. LC 83-72004. (Illus.). 163p. 1983. pap. 19.50 (ISBN 0-918954-40-1). Baylor Univ Pr.
Oosting, Henry J. The Study of Plant Communities: An Introduction to Plant Ecology. 2nd ed. LC 56-11029. (Illus.). 440p. 1956. 29.95x (ISBN 0-7167-0703-9). W H Freeman.
Poissonet, P., ed. Vegetation Dynamics in Grasslands, Heathlands & Mediterranean Ligneous Formations. 1982. lib. bdg. 85.00 (ISBN 0-686-36955-6, Pub. by Junk Pubs Netherlands). Kluwer Academic.
Scott, Jane. Botany in the Field: An Introduction to Plant Communities for the Amateur Naturalist. LC 83-19180. (Illus.). 176p. 1984. 16.95 (ISBN 0-13-080300-6); pap. 8.95 (ISBN 0-13-080292-1). P-H.
Specht, R. J. & Roe, Ethel M. Conservation of Major Plant Communities in Australia & Papua New Guinea. (2 microfiches). 1974. 6.00 (ISBN 0-643-00094-1, C051, CSIRO). Unipub.
Warming, Eugenius & Vahl, Martin. Oecology of Plants: An Introduction to the Study of Plant-Communities. Egerton, Frank N., 3rd, ed. LC 77-74254. (History of Ecology Ser.). 1978. Repr. of 1909 ed. lib. bdg. 34.50x (ISBN 0-405-10423-5). Ayer Co Pubs.

PLANT DESIGN
see Factories–Design and Construction

PLANT DISEASES
see also Deficiency Diseases in Plants; Fungi, Pathogenic; Fungi, Phytopathogenic; Fungi in Agriculture; Insects As Carriers of Disease; Parasitic Plants; Plant Quarantine; Plants–Disease and Pest Resistance; Rusts (Fungi); Virus Diseases of Plants
also subdivision Disease and Pests under particular subjects, e.g. Trees–Diseases and Pests

Agricultural Board. Principles of Plant & Animal Pest Control, Vol. 1, Plant-Disease Development & Control. 1968. pap. 7.00 (ISBN 0-309-01596-0). Natl Acad Pr.
--Principles of Plant & Animal Pest Control, Vol. 2, Weed Control. 1968. pap. 11.50 (ISBN 0-309-01597-9). Natl Acad Pr.
Agricultural Board Division of Biology & Agriculture. Principles of Plant & Animal Pest Control, Vol. 3, Insect-Pest Management & Control. 1969. pap. 12.75 (ISBN 0-309-01695-9). Natl Acad Pr.
Agriculture Board. Principles of Plant & Animal Pest Control, Vol. 6, Effects Of Pesticides On Fruit & Vegetable Physiology. 1968. pap. 5.95 (ISBN 0-309-01698-3). Natl Acad Pr.
Agrios, George N. Plant Pathology. 2nd ed. 1978. 25.00i (ISBN 0-12-044560-3). Acad Pr.
Ainsworth, G. C. Introduction to the History of Plant Pathology. LC 80-40476. 220p. 1981. 75.00 (ISBN 0-521-23032-2). Cambridge U Pr.
American Phytopathological Society - Sourcebook Committee. Sourcebook of Laboratory Exercises in Plant Pathology. Kelman, Arthur, ed. (Illus.). 388p. 1967. 19.95 (ISBN 0-7167-0813-2). W H Freeman.
Asada, Y., et al, eds. Plant Infection: The Physiological & Biochemical Basis. 362p. 1982. 58.00 (ISBN 0-387-11873-X). Springer-Verlag.
Ayres, P. G. Effects of Disease on the Physiology of the Growing Plant. LC 80-42175. (Society for Experimental Biology Symposium Ser.: No. 11). (Illus.). 200p. 1982. 54.50 (ISBN 0-521-23306-2); pap. 22.95 (ISBN 0-521-29898-9). Cambridge U Pr.
Baker, K. F. & Cook, R. J. Biological Control of Plant Pathogens. LC 82-70786. 433p. 1982. Repr. of 1974 ed. text ed. 32.50 (ISBN 0-89054-045-4); text ed. 27.50 members. Am Phytopathol Soc.
Baker, Kenneth F., et al, eds. Annual Review of Phytopathology, Vol. 11. LC 63-8847. (Illus.). 1973. text ed. 20.00 (ISBN 0-8243-1311-9). Annual Reviews.
--Annual Review of Phytopathology, Vol. 12. LC 63-8847. (Illus.). 1974. text ed. 20.00 (ISBN 0-8243-1312-7). Annual Reviews.
Baker, Kenneth P., et al, eds. Annual Review of Phytopathology, Vol. 10. LC 63-8847. (Illus.). 1972. text ed. 20.00 (ISBN 0-8243-1310-0). Annual Reviews.
--Annual Review of Phytopathology, Vol. 13. LC 63-8847. (Illus.). 1975. text ed. 20.00 (ISBN 0-8243-1313-5). Annual Reviews.
--Annual Review of Phytopathology, Vol. 14. LC 63-8847. (Illus.). 1976. text ed. 20.00 (ISBN 0-8243-1314-3). Annual Reviews.
--Annual Review of Phytopathology, Vol. 15. LC 63-8847. (Illus.). 1977. text ed. 20.00 (ISBN 0-8243-1315-1). Annual Reviews.
Barnes, Ervin H. Atlas & Manual of Plant Pathology. 2nd ed. LC 79-10575. 343p. 1979. 24.50x (ISBN 0-306-40168-1, Plenum Pr). Plenum Pub.
Baruah, H. K. Textbook of Plant Pathology. 486p. 1979. 50.00 (ISBN 0-686-84470-X, Pub. by Oxford & I B H India). State Mutual Bk.
BCPC Pests & Diseases, 1981, 3 vols. 930p. 1982. Vol. 1. pap. 90.00x set (ISBN 0-901436-66-6, Pub. by B C P C England). Vol. 2 (ISBN 0-901436-67-4). Vol. 3 (ISBN 0-901436-68-2). Intl Spec Bk.
Bilgrami, K. S. & Dube, H. C. Textbook of Modern Plant Pathology. 1976. 13.50 (ISBN 0-7069-0421-4). Intl Bk Dist.
Bilgrami, K. S. & Dube, R. C. Textbook of Modern Plant Pathology. 6th ed. 1984. pap. text ed. 15.95x (ISBN 0-7069-2630-7, Pub. by Vikas India). Advent NY.
Bilgrami, K. S. & Misra, R. S., eds. Advancing Frontiers of Mycology & Plant Pathology: Prof. K. S. Bhargava Commemoration Volume. (Illus.). xxvi, 330p. 1982. 50.00 (ISBN 0-88065-222-5, Pub. by Messers Today & Tomorrow Printers & Publishers). Scholarly Pubns.
Bos, L. Introduction to Plant Virology. LC 82-12679. 158p. 1983. 14.95x (ISBN 0-582-44680-5). Longman.
--Symptoms of Virus Diseases in Plants: With Index of Names & Symptoms. 3rd ed. (Eng., Ital., Span. & Dutch., Illus.). 225p. 1978. 21.00 (ISBN 90-220-0658-1, PDC6, Pudoc). Unipub.
Bourke, P. Austin. Forecasting from Weather Data of Potato Blight & Other Plant Diseases & Pests. (Technical Note Ser.). 1955. pap. 4.00 (ISBN 0-685-22304-3, W4, WMO). Unipub.
Box, L. Symptoms of Virus Diseases in Plants. 1981. 165.00x (ISBN 0-686-76669-5, Pub. by Oxford & IBH India). State Mutual Bk.
British Crop Protection Council Conference: Pests & Diseases, 1979, 3 vols. 890p. 1982. Set. pap. text ed. 55.00x (ISBN 0-901436-55-0, Pub. by B C P C England). Intl Spec Bk.
Buczacki, S. T. Zoosporic Plant Pathogens: A Modern Perspective. 1983. 60.00 (ISBN 0-12-139180-9). Acad Pr.
Burchill, R. T. Methods in Plant Pathology. 43p. 1981. 30.00x (ISBN 0-85198-491-6, Pub. by CAB Bks England). State Mutual Bk.
Butler, E. J. Fungi & Disease in Plants. 1978. Repr. of 1918 ed. 37.50x (ISBN 0-89955-282-X, Pub. by Intl Bk Dist). Intl Spec Bk.
Callow, J. A. Biochemical Plant Pathology. 484p. 1983. 69.95x (ISBN 0-471-90092-3, Pub. by Wiley-Interscience). Wiley.
Campbell, C. Lee. The Fischer-Smith Controversy: Are There Bacterial Diseases of Plants. LC 80-85458. (Phytopathology Classic Ser.: No. 13). (Illus.). 65p. 1981. 8.50 (ISBN 0-89054-014-4). Am Phytopathol Soc.
Cook, Allyn A. Diseases of Tropical & Subtropical Field, Fiber & Oil Plants. (Illus.). 545p. 1981. text ed. 45.00x (ISBN 0-02-949300-5). Macmillan.
--Diseases of Tropical & Subtropical Vegetables & Other Food Plants. LC 78-57055. 1978. 35.00x (ISBN 0-02-843080-8). Hafner.
Cook, James R. & Baker, Kenneth F. Nature & Practice of Biological Control of Plant Pathogens. LC 83-71224. (Illus.). 539p. 1983. text ed. 43.00 (ISBN 0-89054-053-5). Am Phytopathol Soc.
Cook, R. James, et al, eds. Annual Review of Phytopathology, Vol. 23. LC 63-8847. (Illus.). 535p. 1985. text ed. 27.00 (ISBN 0-8243-1323-2). Annual Reviews.
Crop Loss Assessment Methods: FAO Manual on the Evaluation & Prevention of Losses by Pests, Diseases, & Weeds. (Illus.). 1976. looseleaf bdg. 16.80 (ISBN 0-685-67374-X, FAO); suppl. 1 4.80 (ISBN 0-685-67375-8). Unipub.
Daly, Joseph M. & Deverall, Joseph M., eds. Toxins in Plant Pathogenesis. 1983. 25.00 (ISBN 0-12-200780-8). Acad Pr.
Dean, C. G. Red Ring Disease of Coconut. 70p. 1979. 49.00x (ISBN 0-85198-455-X, Pub. by CAB Bks England). State Mutual Bk.
Diagnosis of Sharka (Plum Pox) & Host Range of Its Inciting Virus. (Agricultural Research Reports: 796). 1973. pap. 4.00 (ISBN 90-220-0453-8, PDC26, PUDOC). Unipub.
Dickinson, C., ed. Microbiology of Aerial Plant Surfaces. 1976. 99.50 (ISBN 0-12-215050-3). Acad Pr.
Division of Biology and Agriculture - Agricultural Board. Principles of Plant & Animal Pest Control, Vol. 4, Control Of Plant Parasitic Nematodes. 1968. pap. 11.50 (ISBN 0-309-01696-7). Natl Acad Pr.
Durbin, R. D., ed. Toxins in Plant Disease. LC 80-70601. (Physiology Ecology Ser.). 1981. 65.00 (ISBN 0-12-225050-8). Acad Pr.
Ebbels, D. L. & King, J. E., eds. Plant Health: The Scientific Basis for Administrative Control of Plant Diseases & Pests, Vol. 2. (Organized by the Federation of British Plant Pathologists). 322p. 1979. 69.95x (ISBN 0-470-26954-5). Halsted Pr.
Egerton, Frank N., 3rd, ed. Phytopathological Classics of the Eighteenth Century: An Originial Anthology. LC 77-74247. (History of Ecology Ser.). (Illus.). 1978. lib. bdg. 47.50x (ISBN 0-405-10416-2). Ayer Co Pubs.
--Phytopathologlical Classics of the Nineteenth Century: An Original Anthology. LC 77-74246. (History of Ecology Ser.). (Illus.). 1978. lib. bdg. 34.50x (ISBN 0-405-10415-4). Ayer Co Pubs.
Evans, H. C. Pod Rot of Cacao Caused by Moniliophthora (Monilia) Roreri. 44p. 1981. 39.00x (ISBN 0-85198-484-3, Pub. by CAB Bks England). State Mutual Bk.
Firman, I. D. & Waller, J. M. Coffee Berry Diseases & Other Colletotrichum Diseases of Coffee. 53p. 1977. 40.00x (ISBN 0-85198-367-7, Pub. by CAB Bks England). State Mutual Bk.
Francki, R. I., ed. The Plant Viruses: Polyhedral Virions with Tripartite Genomes, Vol. 1. (The Viruses Ser.). 297p. 1985. 49.50x (ISBN 0-306-41958-0, Plenum Pr). Plenum Pub.
Francki, R. I., et al, eds. Atlas of Plant Viruses, Vol. II. 304p. 1985. 87.00 (ISBN 0-8493-6502-3). CRC Pr.
Fry, William E. Principles of Plant Disease Management. 366p. 1982. 25.50 (ISBN 0-12-269180-6). Acad Pr.
Gregory, P. H. & Maddison, A. C. Epidemiology of Phytophthora on Cocoa in Nigeria. 188p. 1981. 79.00x (ISBN 0-85198-478-9, Pub. by CAB Bks England). State Mutual Bk.
Grogan, Raymond G., et al, eds. Annual Review of Phytopathology, Vol. 16. LC 63-8847. (Illus.). 1978. text ed. 20.00 (ISBN 0-8243-1316-X). Annual Reviews.
--Annual Review of Phytopathology, Vol. 17. LC 63-8847. (Illus.). 1979. text ed. 20.00 (ISBN 0-8243-1317-8). Annual Reviews.

Davidson Pratt, J. & West, T. F. Services for the Chemical Industry. 1968. pap. 11.50 (ISBN 0-08-012664-2). Pergamon.
Elonka, S. M. Standard Basic Math & Applied Plant Calculations. 1977. text ed. 28.50 (ISBN 0-07-019297-9). McGraw.
Lewis, B. T. & Marron, J. P. Facilities & Plant Engineering Handbook. 1974. 69.50 (ISBN 0-07-037560-7). McGraw.
Moffat, Donald W. Manual de Formulas, Graficos y Tablas del Ingeniero de Plantas. Loinaz, Jorge, tr. LC 85-80464. Tr. of Plant Engineer's Manual of Fomulas, Charts & Tables. (Span., Illus.). 328p. 1985. 65.00 (ISBN 0-9612412-1-7). Lineal Cleworth.
Murphy, James A., ed. Plant Engineering Management, Vol. 5. LC 74-144106. (Manufacturing Management Ser.). (Illus.). 1971. text ed. 12.50 (ISBN 0-87263-027-7). SME.
Nailen, Richard L. The Plant Engineer's Guide to Industrial Electric Motors. (Illus.). 498p. 1985. text ed. 54.95 (ISBN 0-943876-01-X). Baldner J V.
Nutt, Merle C. Functional Plant Planning, Layout & Materials Handling. LC 70-114266. 1970. text ed. 18.95 (ISBN 0-682-47092-9, University). Exposition Pr FL.
Polimeros, George. Energy Cogeneration Handbook: Criteria for Central Plant Design. LC 80-27186. (Illus.). 264p. 1981. 45.00 (ISBN 0-8311-1130-5). Indus Pr.
Weisman, Joel & Eckart, L. E. Modern Power Plant Engineering. (Illus.). 528p. 1984. text ed. 41.95 (ISBN 0-13-597252-3). P-H.

PLANT EVOLUTION
see Plants–Evolution

PLANT FUNGI
see Fungi, Pathogenic

PLANT GENETICS

Bogart, Ralph, ed. Genetics Lectures, Vol. 3. LC 73-87943. 192p. 1974. pap. 9.00x (ISBN 0-87071-433-3). Oreg St U Pr.
Broertjes, C. & Van Harten, A. M. The Application of Mutation Breeding Methods in the Improvement of Vegetatively Propagated Crops. (Developments in Crop Science Ser.: Vol. 2). 316p. 1978. 76.75 (ISBN 0-444-41618-8). Elsevier.
Burley, Gibson J. & Speight, M. R. The Adoption of Agricultural Practices for the Development of Heritable Resistance to Pests & Pathogens in Forest Crops. 1980. 30.00x (ISBN 0-85074-057-6, Pub. by For Lib Comm England). STate Mutual Bk.
Cereal Grain Protein Improvement: Proceedings of the Final Research Co-ordination Meeting of the FAO-IAEA-GSF-SIDA Co-ordinated Research Programme, Vienna, 6-10 December 1982. (Panel Proceedings Ser.). (Illus.). 388p. 1984. pap. 61.00 (ISBN 92-0-111184-3, ISP664, IAEA). Unipub.
Dudits, D. & Farkas, G. L., eds. Cell Genetics in Higher Plants. 1976. 17.00 (ISBN 0-9960002-2-4, Pub. by Akademiai Kaido Hungary). Heyden.
Eldridge, K. G. An Annotated Bibliography of Genetic Variation in Eucalyptus Camaldulensis. 1975. 30.00x (ISBN 0-85074-023-1, Pub. by For Lib Comm England). State Mutual Bk.
Frankel, O. H. & Hawkes, J. G., eds. Crop Genetic Resources for Today & Tomorrow. LC 74-82586. (International Biological Programme Ser.: Vol. 2). (Illus.). 544p. 1975. 95.00 (ISBN 0-521-20575-1). Cambridge U Pr.
Genetic Interaction Between Phaseolus Vulgaris & Bean Common Mosaic Virus with Implications for Strain Identification & Breeding for Resistance. (Agricultural Research Reports: No. 872). 1978. pap. 20.00 (ISBN 90-220-0671-9, PDC123, PUDOC). Unipub.
Gleba, Y. Y. & Sytnik, K. M. Protoplast Fusion: Genetic Engineering in Higher Plants. (Monographs on Theoretical & Applied Genetics: Vol. 8). (Illus.). 245p. 1984. 55.00 (ISBN 0-387-13284-8). Springer-Verlag.
Grant, Verne. Genetics of Flowering Plants. LC 74-13555. (Illus.). 1975. 52.50x (ISBN 0-231-03694-9); pap. 22.00x (ISBN 0-231-08363-7). Columbia U Pr.
Hardarson, G. & Lie, T. A., eds. Breeding Legumes for Enhanced Symbiotic Nitrogen Fixation. (Advances in Agricultural Biotechnology Ser.). 1985. lib. bdg. 36.00 (ISBN 90-247-3123-2, Pub. by Martinus Nijhoff Netherlands). Kluwer-Academic.
Hohn, B. & Dennis, E. S., eds. Genetic Flux in Plants. (Plant Gene Research Ser.). (Illus.). 240p. 1985. 39.00 (ISBN 0-387-81809-X). Springer-Verlag.
Improvement of Oil-Seed & Industrial Crops by Induced Mutations: Group Meetings on the Use of Induced Mutations for the Improvement of Oil-Seed & Other Industrial Crops Organized by the Joint FAO/IAEA Division of Isotope Radiation & Applications of Atomic Energy for Food & Agriculture Development & Held in Vienna From November 17-21, 1980. (Illus.). 353p. 1982. pap. 46.25 (ISBN 92-0-011082-7, ISP608, IAEA). Unipub.
Induced Mutations - A Tool in Plant Research: Proceedings of a Symposium, Vienna, 9-13 March 1981, Jointly Organized by IAEA and FAO. (Proceedings Ser.). (Illus.). 538p. 1981. pap. 16.50 (ISBN 0-686-82544-6, ISP591, IAEA); pap. 18.00 (ISP 591-2). Unipub.
Induced Mutations in Vegetatively Propagated Plants. (Panel Proceedings Ser.). (Illus.). 222p. (Orig.). 1974. pap. 17.75 (ISBN 92-0-111473-7, ISP339, IAEA). Unipub.
Induced Mutations in Vegetatively Propogated Plants, 2: Proceedings of the Final Research Coordination Meeting on the Improvement of Vegetatively Propagated Crops & Tree Crops Through Induced Mutations Organized by the Joint FAO/IAEA Division of Isotope & Radiation Applications of Atomic Energy for Food & Agricultural Development & Held in Coimbatore, India, from 11-15 February 1980. (Panel Proceedings Ser.). (Illus.). 310p. 1982. pap. 40.25 (ISBN 92-0-111182-7, ISP519, IAEA). Unipub.
Ledoux, Lucien, ed. Genetic Manipulations with Plant Material. LC 75-12547. (NATO ASI Series A, Life Sciences: Vol. 3). 614p. 1975. 62.50x (ISBN 0-306-35603-1, Plenum Pr). Plenum Pub.
Love, A. & Love, D. Plant Chromosomes. 1975. 12.60 (ISBN 3-7682-0966-0). Lubrecht & Cramer.
McIvor, J. G., ed. Genetic Resources of Forage Plants. Bray, R. A. (Illus.). 337p. 1983. text ed. 30.00x (ISBN 0-643-03462-5, Pub. by CSIRO Australia). Intl Spec Bk.
McIvor, J. G. & Bray, R. A., eds. Genetic Resources of Forage Plants. 337p. 1983. text ed. 54.00 (ISBN 0-643-03462-5, CO70, CSIRO). Unipub.
Magnien, E. & De Nettancourt, D., eds. Genetic Engineering of Plants & Micro-Organisms Important for Agriculture. (Advances in Argicultural Biotechnology Ser.). 1985. lib. bdg. 36.00 (ISBN 90-247-3131-3, Pub. by Martinus Nijhoff Netherlands). Kluwer Academic.
Moore, D. M. Plant Cytogenetics. 1976. pap. 6.95 (ISBN 0-412-13440-3, NO. 6202, Pub. by Chapman & Hall England). Methuen Inc.
Muhammed, Amir, et al, eds. Genetic Diversity in Plants. LC 77-9475. (Basic Life Sciences Ser.: Vol. 8). (Illus.). 518p. 1977. 57.50x (ISBN 0-306-36508-1, Plenum Pr). Plenum Pub.
Nester, Eugene & Kosuge, Tsau ne, eds. Plant - Microbe Interactions: Molecular & Genetic Perspectives, Vol. 1. 400p. 1984. text ed. 38.00 (ISBN 0-02-949470-2). Macmillan.
Nitzsche, Werner & Wenzel, Gerhard. Haploids in Plant Breeding. (Advances in Plant Breeding Ser.: Vol. 8). (Illus.). 101p. 1977. pap. text ed. 28.00 (ISBN 3-489-75010-1). Parey Sci Pubs.
Owens, Lowell D. Genetic Engineering: Applications to Agriculture. LC 83-3252. (Beltsville Symposia in Agricultural Research: No. 7). (Illus.). 352p. 1983. text ed. 42.50x (ISBN 0-86598-112-4). Rowman & Allanheld.
Rees, H., et al, eds. The Manipulation of Genetic Systems in Plant Breeding. (Royal Society of London Ser.). (Illus.). 209p. 1981. lib. bdg. 55.00x (ISBN 0-85403-165-0, Pub. by Royal Soc London). Scholium Intl.
Riley, Ralph & Lewis, K. R., eds. Chromosome Manipulation & Plant Genetics: The Contributions to a Symposium Held During the Tenth International Botanical Congress, Edinburgh, 1964. LC 66-71193. pap. 33.50 (ISBN 0-317-28828-8, 2020701). Bks Demand UMI.
Roebbelen, Gerhard & Sharp, Eugene L. Mode of Inheritance, Interaction & Application of Genes Conditioning Resistance to Yellow Rust. (Advances in Plant Breeding Ser.: Vol. 9). (Illus.). 88p. (Orig.). 1978. pap. text ed. 25.00 (ISBN 3-489-71110-6). Parey Sci Pubs.
Tanksley, S. D. & Orton, T. J., eds. Isozymes in Plant Genetics & Breeding: Parts A & B, 2 pts. (Developments in Plant Genetics & Breeding Ser.: Pts. 1A & B). 1983. Pt. A. 106.50 (ISBN 0-444-42226-9); Pt. B. 106.50 (ISBN 0-444-42227-7). Set (ISBN 0-444-42228-5). Elsevier.
Verghese, T. M., ed. Vistas in Plant Sciences: Special Volume in Genetics & Plant Breeding, Vol. III. 166p. 1978. 14.00 (ISBN 0-88065-203-9, Pub. by Messers Today & Tomorrow Printers & Publishers India). Scholarly Pubns.
Verma, D. P. & Hohn, T., eds. Genes Involved in Microbe-Plant Interactions. (Plant Gene Research). (Illus.). 420p. 1984. 55.00 (ISBN 0-387-81789-1). Springer-Verlag.
Walden, David B., ed. Maize Breeding & Genetics. LC 78-6779. 794p. 1978. 82.95x (ISBN 0-471-91805-9, Pub. by Wiley-Interscience). Wiley.
Welsh, James R. Fundamentals of Plant Genetics & Breeding. LC 80-14638. 304p. 1981. text ed. 34.95 (ISBN 0-471-02862-2). Wiley.
Witcombe, John R. & Erskine, William, eds. Genetic Resources & Their Exploitation - Chickpeas, Faba Beans, & Lentils. (Advances Agricultural Biotechnology Ser.). 1984. lib. bdg. 36.50 (ISBN 90-247-2939-4, Pub. by Martinus Nijhoff Netherlands). Kluwer-Academic.
Witt, Steven C. QuickBook: Genetic Engineering of Plants. (Illus.). 53p. (Orig.). 1983. pap. 7.95 (ISBN 0-912005-02-5). CA Agri Lnd Pr.
Yeatman, Christopher W., et al, eds. Plant Genetic Resources: A Conservation Imperative. (AAAS Ser.). 1985. 24.50x (ISBN 0-8133-0129-7). Westview.

PLANT GEOGRAPHY
see Phytogeography

PLANT GROWTH
see Growth (Plants)

PLANT HORMONES

Addicott, Fredrick T., ed. Abscisic Acid. LC 81-23406. 624p. 1983. 75.00 (ISBN 0-03-055831-X). Praeger.
Crozier, Alan & Hillman, John R., eds. The Biosynthesis & Metabolism of Plant Hormones. (Society for Experimental Biology Seminar Ser.: No. 23). 300p. 1985. 29.95 (ISBN 0-521-26424-3). Cambridge U Pr.
Jacobs, William P. Plant Hormones & Plant Development. LC 78-54580. (Illus.). 1979. 22.95 (ISBN 0-521-22062-9). Cambridge U Pr.
Kaldewey, Harald & Vardar, Yusuf. Hormonal Regulation in Plant Growth & Development. LC 72-86049. (Illus.). 535p. 1972. 55.90x (ISBN 3-527-25436-6). VCH Pubs.
Kirby, Celia. Hormone Weedkillers. 60p. (Orig.). 1981. pap. 10.00x (ISBN 0-901436-62-3, Pub. by B C P C England). Intl Spec Bk.
Leshem, Y. The Molecular & Hormonal Basis of Plant Growth Regulation. LC 73-6802. 168p. 1974. 17.00 (ISBN 0-08-017649-6). Pergamon.
Macmillan, J., ed. Hormonal Regulation of Development I: Molcular Aspects of Plant Hormones. (Encyclopedia of Plant Physiology Ser.: Vol. 9). (Illus.). 681p. 1980. 148.00 (ISBN 0-387-10161-6). Springer-Verlag.
Moore, T. C. Biochemistry & Physiology of Plant Hormones. LC 79-11492. (Illus.). 1979. 29.50 (ISBN 0-387-90401-8). Springer-Verlag.
Pharis, R. P. & Reid, D. M., eds. Hormonal Regulation of Development III. (Encyclopedia of Plant Physiology Ser.: Vol. 11). (Illus.). 870p. 1985. 139.50 (ISBN 0-387-10197-7). Springer-Verlag.
Scott, T. K., ed. Hormonal Regulation of Development II: The Functions of Hormones from the Level of the Cell to the Whole Plant. (Encyclopedia of Plant Physiology Ser.: Vol. 10). (Illus.). 320p. 1984. 76.00 (ISBN 0-387-10196-9). Springer Verlag.
Thimann, Kenneth V. Hormone Action in the Whole Life of Plants. LC 76-26641. (Illus.). 464p. 1977. 40.00x (ISBN 0-87023-224-X). U of Mass Pr.
Weaver, Robert J. Plant Growth Substances in Agriculture. LC 71-166964. (Plant Science Ser.). (Illus.). 594p. 1972. text ed. 45.95x (ISBN 0-7167-0824-8). W H Freeman.
Went, R. W., et al. Phytohormones. (Landmark Reprint in Plant Science Ser.). 1978. Repr. of 1937 ed. text ed. 22.50x (ISBN 0-86598-004-7). Allanheld.

PLANT INDICATORS

Chikishev, A. G. Plant Indicators of Soil, Rocks & Subsurface Waters. LC 65-15596. 210p. 1965. 37.50x (ISBN 0-306-10730-9, Consultants). Plenum Pub.
Guderian, R. Air Pollution: Phytotoxicity of Acidic Gases & Its Significance in Air Pollution Control. LC 76-50626. (Ecological Studies: Vol. 22). 1977. 36.00 (ISBN 0-387-08030-9). Springer-Verlag.

PLANT INTRODUCTION
see also Plants, Cultivated

Anderson, Alexander W. How We Got Our Flowers. (Illus.). 10.75 (ISBN 0-8446-1533-1). Peter Smith.
Baker, H. G. & Stebbins, G. L., eds. The Genetics of Colonizing Species. 1965. 74.50 (ISBN 0-12-075150-X). Acad Pr.
Milne, Lorus J. & Milne, Margery. Ecology Out of Joint: New Environments & Why They Happen. LC 76-48933. (Illus.). 1977. 8.95 (ISBN 0-684-14846-3, ScribT). Scribner.
Russell, Norman. Introduction to Plant Science: A Humanistic & Ecological Approach. LC 75-1445. (Illus.). 302p. 1975. pap. text ed. 18.50 (ISBN 0-8299-0043-8); instrs.' manual avail. (ISBN 0-8299-0603-7). West Pub.

PLANT LAYOUT
see also Assembly-Line Methods; Machinery in Industry; Materials Handling

Domschke, W. & Drexl, A. Location & Layout Planning. (Lecture Notes in Economics & Mathematical Systems Ser.: Vol. 238). iv, 134p. 1985. pap. 12.30 (ISBN 0-387-13908-7). Springer-Verlag.
Economic Development Foundation. Manual on Plant Layout & Materials Handling. LC 72-186284. 80p. 1971. 7.25 (ISBN 92-833-1011-X, APO45, APO). Unipub.
Tompkins, James A. & White, John A. Facilities Planning. LC 83-21715. 675p. 1984. text ed. 37.50 (ISBN 0-471-03299-9). Wiley.
White, John A. & Francis, Richard L. Facility Layout & Location: An Analytical Approach. LC 73-18455. (Int'l. Series in Industrial & Systems Engineering). (Illus.). 448p. 1974. ref. ed. 33.95x (ISBN 0-13-299149-7). P-H.
Wireman, Terry. Plant Layout & Material Handling. 1984. text ed. 27.95 (ISBN 0-8359-5577-X). Reston.

PLANT MAINTENANCE
see also Industrial Housekeeping; Machinery

Bloch, Heinz P. & Geitner, Fred K. Machinery Component Maintenance & Repair. LC 84-15738. (Practical Machinery Management for Process Plants Ser.: Vol. 3). (Illus.). 576p. 1985. 59.95x (ISBN 0-87201-453-3). Gulf Pub.
Cooling, W. Colebrook. Simplified Low-Cost Maintenance Control. rev. ed. 128p. 1983. 24.95 (ISBN 0-8144-5657-X). Am Mgmt Assns.
Cooling, Wilmer. Simplified Low-cost Maintenance Control. LC 82-18380. pap. 30.50 (ISBN 0-317-20412-2, 2023501). Bks Demand UMI.
Energy Task Force. Controlling Energy Through Microprocessor Utilization. 77p. 21.00 (ISBN 0-913359-13-0). Assn Phys Plant Admin.
Information Sources on Industrial Maintenance & Repair. (UNIDO Guides to Information Sources: No.36). 86p. 1980. pap. 4.00 (ISBN 0-686-70501-7, UNID236, UN). Unipub.
Introduction to Maintenance Planning in Manufacturing Establishments. pap. 5.00 (ISBN 0-686-94671-5, UN75/2B/6, UN). Unipub.
Kelly, A. Maintenance Planning & Control. (Illus.). 264p. 1983. text ed. 39.95 (ISBN 0-408-01375-3). Butterworth.
Kletz, Trevor A. What Went Wrong? Case Histories of Process Plant Disasters. LC 84-23483. (Illus.). 224p. 1985. 39.95x (ISBN 0-87201-339-1). Gulf Pub.
Langley, Billy C. Plant Maintenance. 1985. text ed. 29.95 (ISBN 0-8359-5578-8). Reston.
Lyons. Handbook of Industrial Lighting. 1981. text ed. 49.95 (ISBN 0-408-00525-4). Butterworth.
Maintenance of Factory Service Two, 2 vols. 1982. 52.00x (ISBN 0-85083-077-X, Pub. by Engineering Ind). State Mutual Bk.
Maintenance of Factory Services One. 1982. 52.00x (ISBN 0-85083-028-1, Pub. by Engineering Ind). State Mutual Bk.
Mann, Lawrence, Jr. Maintenance Management. Rev. ed. LC 81-47628. 512p. 1983. 33.00x (ISBN 0-669-04715-5). Lexington Bks.
Marks, Nolan. On the Spot Repair Manual for Commercial Food Equipment. LC 82-81598. (Illus.). 132p. 1982. pap. 19.95 (ISBN 0-941712-01-X). INtl Pub Corp OH.
Nichols, Herbert L., Jr. Heavy Equipment Repair. 2nd ed. LC 80-80644. (Illus.). 1980. 20.00 (ISBN 0-911040-14-5). North Castle.
O'Keefe, William & Elliott, Thomas C., eds. Solving Plant Problems: Design, Operation, Maintenance. LC 84-12605. (Illus.). 272p. 1984. 29.95 (ISBN 0-07-050585-3). McGraw.
Plant Maintenance Program. (Manual of Practice, Operations & Maintenance: No. 3). 112p. (Orig.). 1982. pap. text ed. 10.00 (ISBN 0-943244-38-2). Water Pollution.
Rudman, Jack. Heavy Equipment Repair Supervisor. (Career Examination Ser.: C-2614). (Cloth bdg. avail. on request). pap. 12.00 (ISBN 0-8373-2614-1). Natl Learning.
--Maintenance Man. (Career Examination Ser.: C-463). (Cloth bdg. avail. on request). pap. 10.00 (ISBN 0-8373-0463-6). Natl Learning.
--Maintenance Man Trainee. (Career Examination Ser.: C-464). (Cloth bdg. avail. on request). pap. 10.00 (ISBN 0-8373-0464-4). Natl Learning.
--Operations & Maintenance Trainee. (Career Examination Ser.: C-554). (Cloth bdg. avail. on request). pap. 10.00 (ISBN 0-8373-0554-3). Natl Learning.
--Plant Maintenance Engineer. (Career Examination Ser.: C-2480). (Cloth bdg. avail. on request). pap. 10.00 (ISBN 0-8373-2480-7). Natl Learning.
--Plant Maintenance Mechanic. (Career Examination Ser.: C-1393). (Cloth bdg. avail. on request). pap. 8.00 (ISBN 0-8373-1393-7). Natl Learning.
--Plant Maintenance Supervisor. (Career Examination Ser.: C-1559). (Cloth bdg. avail. on request). pap. 10.00 (ISBN 0-8373-1559-X). Natl Learning.

Sutcliffe, J. F. & Pate, J. S., eds. The Physiology of the Garden Pea. 1978. 78.50 (ISBN 0-12-677550-8). Acad Pr.

Sweeney, B. M. Rhythmic Phenomena in Plants. (Experimental Botany Monographs, Vol. 3). 1969. 33.50 (ISBN 0-12-679050-7). Acad Pr.

Tanner, W. & Loewus, F. A., eds. Plant Carbohydrates II: Extracellular Carbohydrates. (Encyclopedia of Plant Physiology: Vol. 13 B). (Illus.). 800p. 1981. 127.00 (ISBN 0-387-11007-0). Springer-Verlag.

Tesar, M. B. etal, ed. Physiological Basis for Crop Growth & Develpment. 341p. 1984. 20.00 (ISBN 0-89118-037-0). Am Soc Agron.

Thornley, J. H. Mathematical Models in Plant Physiology: Quantitative Approach to Problems in Plant & Crop Physiology. 1976. 62.00 (ISBN 0-12-690550-9). Acad Pr.

Ting, Irwin P. & Gibbs, Martin, eds. Crassulacean Acid Metabolism. 316p. 1982. pap. 15.00 (ISBN 0-943088-00-3). Am Soc of Plant.

Vaughan, D. & Malcolm, R. E., eds. Soil Organic Matter & Biological Activity. (Developments in Plant & Soil Sciences). 1985. lib. bdg. 59.50 (ISBN 90-247-3154-2, Pub. by Martinus Nijhoff Netherlands). Kluwer Academic.

Walter, H. Vegetation of the Earth: In Relation to Climate & the Eco-Physiological Conditions. 2nd ed. Wieser, J., tr. LC 72-85947. (Heidelberg Science Library: Vol. 15). (Illus.). xvi, 240p. 1979. pap. 19.00 (ISBN 0-387-90404-2). Springer-Verlag.

Wareing, P. F. & Smith, H., eds. Photoperception by Plants. (Philosphical Transactions of the Royal Society: Series B, Vol. 303). (Illus.). 190p. 1984. text ed. 63.00x (ISBN 0-85403-220-7, Pub. by Royal Soc London). Scholium Intl.

Wilkins, Malcolm B., ed. Advanced Plant Physiology. 528p. 1984. text ed. 35.95 (ISBN 0-273-01853-1). Pitman Pub MA.

Wilson, John R., ed. Plant Relations in Pastures. 1978. 35.00x (ISBN 0-643-00264-2, Pub. by CSIRO). Intl Spec Bk.

Wintermans, J. F. & Kuiper, P. J., eds. Biochemistry & Metabolism of Plant Lipids: Proceedings of the International Symposium on the Biochemistry & Metabolism of Plant Lipids, Fifth, Groningen, the Netherlands, June 7-10, 1982. (Developments in Plant Biology Ser.: Vol. 8). 600p. 1982. 85.00 (ISBN 0-444-80457-9, Biomedical Pr). Elsevier.

Witham, et al. Exercises in Plant Physiology. 1985. pap. write for info. (ISBN 0-87150-944-X, Prindle). PWS Pubs.

Wood, R. K., ed. Active Defense Mechanisms in Plants. LC 81-15706. (NATO ASI Series A, Life Sciences: Vol. 37). 391p. 1981. 55.00 (ISBN 0-306-40814-7, Plenum Pr). Plenum Pub.

Woodbury, William. Plant Physiology. 1984. text ed. 22.95 (ISBN 0-8359-5556-7). Reston.

Zimmermann, M. H. & Milburn, J. A., eds. Transport in Plants One Pholoem Transport. LC 75-20178. (Encyclopedia of Plant Physiology New Ser.: Vol. 1). (Illus.). 550p. 1975. 95.00 (ISBN 0-387-07314-0). Springer-Verlag.

PLANT PHYSIOLOGY–LABORATORY MANUALS

Cherry, Joe H. Molecular Biology of Plants: A Text Manual. (A Molecular Biology Ser.). 204p. 1973. 29.50x (ISBN 0-231-03642-6). Columbia U Pr.

Machlis, Leonard & Torrey, John G. Plants in Action: A Laboratory Manual of Plant Physiology. (Illus.). 282p. 1956. pap. text ed. 12.95x (ISBN 0-7167-0702-0). W H Freeman.

McInnis, Thomas, Jr. Plant Biology Laboratory. 1975. wire coil bdg. 6.95 (ISBN 0-88252-024-5). Paladin Hse.

PLANT PIGMENTS

see also Carotinoids; Plastids; Quinone

Eskin, N. Michael. Plant Pigments, Flavors & Textures: The Chemistry & Biochemistry of Selected Compounds. LC 78-22523. (Food Science & Technology Ser.). 1979. 35.00 (ISBN 0-12-242250-3). Acad Pr.

Goodwin, T. W., ed. Chemistry & Biochemistry of Plant Pigments, Vol. 1. 2nd ed. 1976. 90.00 (ISBN 0-12-289901-6). Acad Pr.

--Chemistry & Biochemistry of Plant Pigments, Vol. 2. 2nd ed. 1976. 70.00 (ISBN 0-12-289902-4). Acad Pr.

PLANT REGULATORS

Nickell, Louis G. Plant Growth Regulators: Agricultural Uses. (Illus.). 173p. 1982. 26.00 (ISBN 0-387-10973-0). Springer Verlag.

Nickell, Louis G., ed. Plant Growth Regulating Chemicals, 2 Vols. 1983. Vol. I, 288p. 89.00 (ISBN 0-8493-5002-6); Vol. II, 264p. 83.00 (ISBN 0-8493-5003-4). CRC Pr.

Plimmer, Jack R., ed. Pesticide Chemistry in the Twentieth Century. LC 76-51748. (ACS Symposium Ser: No. 37). 1977. 19.95 (ISBN 0-8412-0532-9). Am Chemical.

Scott, Tom, ed. Plant Regulation & World Agriculture. LC 79-14597. (NATO ASI Series A, Life Sciences: Vol. 22). 575p. 1979. 69.50x (ISBN 0-306-40180-0, Plenum Pr). Plenum Pub.

Weaver, Robert J. Plant Growth Substances in Agriculture. LC 71-166964. (Plant Science Ser.). (Illus.). 594p. 1972. text ed. 45.95x (ISBN 0-7167-0824-8). W H Freeman.

PLANT POPULATIONS

Dirzo, Rodolfo & Sarukhan, Jose, eds. Perspectives on Plant Population Ecology. LC 83-20182. (Illus.). 450p. 1984. text ed. 47.50x (ISBN 0-87893-142-2); pap. text ed. 28.75x (ISBN 0-87893-143-0). Sinauer Assoc.

Harper, J. L. Population Biology of Plants. 1977. 75.00 (ISBN 0-12-325850-2). Acad Pr.

--Population Biology of Plants. LC 76-16973. 1981. pap. 36.00 (ISBN 0-12-325852-9). Acad Pr.

Scott, Tom, ed. Plant Regulation & World Agriculture. LC 79-14597. (NATO ASI Series A, Life Sciences: Vol. 22). 575p. 1979. 69.50x (ISBN 0-306-40180-0, Plenum Pr). Plenum Pub.

Solbrig, Otto T., ed. Demography & Evolution in Plant Populations. (Botanical Monographs Ser.: Vol. 15). 1980. monograph 44.00x (ISBN 0-520-03931-9). U of Cal Pr.

Solbrig, Otto T., et al, eds. Topics in Plant Population Biology. LC 78-27630. (Illus.). 1979. 55.00x (ISBN 0-231-04336-8). Columbia U Pr.

White, J., ed. The Population Structure of Vegetation. (Handbook of Vegetation Science). 1985. lib. bdg. 97.50 (ISBN 90-6193-184-3, Pub. by Junk Pubs Netherlands). Kluwer-Academic.

PLANT PROPAGATION

see also Grafting; Plant-Breeding; Seeds

Adriance, Guy W. & Brison, Fred R. Propagation of Horticultural Plants. 2nd ed. LC 79-9753. 308p. 1979. Repr. of 1955 ed. lib. bdg. 19.50 (ISBN 0-88275-965-5). Krieger.

Ashri, A., et al. Sesame - Status & Improvement: Proceedings of Expert Consultation, Rome, Italy, Dec. 1980. (Plant Production & Protection Papers: No. 29). 203p. 1981. pap. 14.75 (ISBN 92-5-101122-2, F2259, FAO). Unipub.

Browse, Phillip M. Step-by-Step Guide to Plant Propagation. 1979. pap. 9.95 (ISBN 0-671-24832-4, Fireside). S&S.

Conger, B. V., ed. Cloning Agricultural Plants via In Vitro Techniques. LC 80-23852. 280p. 1981. 85.00 (ISBN 0-8493-5797-7). CRC Pr.

The Effect of Cutting Treatments on Dry Matter Production of Lolium Perenne & Dactylis. 1963. pap. 5.00 (ISBN 90-220-0099-0, PDC162, PUDOC). Unipub.

Fitz, Franklin H. A Gardener's Guide to Propagating Food Plants. (Illus.). 160p. 1983. 11.95 (ISBN 0-684-17655-6, ScribT). Scribner.

Fretz, Thomas A., et al. Plant Propagation Laboratory Manual. 3rd rev. ed. 1979. text ed. 13.95x (ISBN 0-8087-0668-3). Burgess.

Hartmann, Hudson T. & Kester, Dale E. Plant Propagation: Principles & Practices. 4th ed. (Illus.). 704p. 1983. text ed. 31.95 (ISBN 0-13-681007-1). P-H.

Henke, Randolph, et al. Tissue Culture in Forestry & Agriculture. (Basic Life Sciences Ser.: Vol. 32). 390p. 1985. 55.00x (ISBN 0-306-41919-X, Plenum Pr). Plenum Pub.

Hills, Lawrence D. The Propagation of Alpines. (Illus.). 1976. Repr. of 1959 ed. write for info (ISBN 0-913728-11-X). Theophrastus.

Hutchinson, William A. Plant Propagation & Cultivation. (Illus.). 1980. pap. text ed. 19.50 (ISBN 0-87055-340-2). AVI.

Improvement of Oil-Seed & Industrial Crops by Induced Mutations: Group Meetings on the Use of Induced Mutations for the Improvement of Oil-Seed & Other Industrial Crops Organized by the Joint FAO/IAEA Division of Isotope Radiation & Applications of Atomic Energy for Food & Agriculture Development & Held in Vienna From November 17-21, 1980. (Illus.). 353p. 1982. pap. 46.25 (ISBN 92-0-011082-7, ISP608, IAEA). Unipub.

Induced Mutations in Vegetatively Propogated Plants, 2: Proceedings of the Final Research Coordination Meeting on the Improvement of Vegetatively Propagated Crops & Tree Crops Through Induced Mutations Organized by the Joint FAO/IAEA Division of Isotope & Radiation Applications of Atomic Energy for Food & Agricultural Development & Held in Coimbatore, India, from 11-15 February 1980. (Panel Proceedings Ser.). (Illus.). 310p. 1982. pap. 40.25 (ISBN 92-0-111182-7, ISP519, IAEA). Unipub.

James, Wilma R. Propagate Your Own Plants. LC 78-18248. (Illus.). 149p. 1978. 11.95 (ISBN 0-87961-073-5); pap. 5.95 (ISBN 0-87961-072-7). Naturegraph.

Jinkin's Grape & Seedling Nursery. Art of Propagation. facs. ed. (Shorey Lost Arts Ser.). 34p. pap. 2.95 (ISBN 0-8466-6045-8, U45). Shorey.

Nelson, J. H. The Propagation Wizard's Handbook. 136p. 1978. pap. 6.95 (ISBN 0-88006-000-X, BK7302). Green Pub Inc.

Plumridge, Jack. How to Propagate Plants. (Illus.). 1979. 12.95x (ISBN 0-85091-043-9, Pub. by Lothian). Intl Spec Bk.

Propagation. 2.25 (ISBN 0-686-21126-X). Bklyn Botanic.

Reinert, J. & Bajaj, Y. P., eds. Applied & Fundamental Aspects of Plant Cell, Tissue & Organ Culture. (Illus.). 1976. 120.00 (ISBN 0-387-07677-8). Springer-Verlag.

Rodent Pests - Biology & Control: Bibliography. (Plant Production & Protection Papers: No. 7). 836p. 1977. pap. 29.50 (ISBN 92-5-100435-8, F1334, FAO). Unipub.

Toogood, Alan. Propagation. LC 80-6164. (Illus.). 336p. 1981. 13.95 (ISBN 0-8128-2772-4). Stein & Day.

--Propagation. 256p. 1980. 39.00x (ISBN 0-460-04377-3, Pub. by J M Dent England). State Mutual Bk.

Wright, John. Propagation: How to Grow Plants Using Seeds, Cutting & Other Methods. (Illus.). 96p. (Orig.). 1985. pap. 3.95 (ISBN 0-7137-1611-8, Pub. by Blandford Pr England). Sterling.

Wright, R. C. Simple Plant Propagation. LC 77-70396. (Illus.). 1978. pap. 3.95 (ISBN 0-8120-0795-6). Barron.

PLANT QUARANTINE

Hewitt, William B. & Chiarappa, L. Plant Health & Quarantine in International Transfer of Genetic Resources. 360p. 1977. 69.95 (ISBN 0-8493-5413-7). CRC Pr.

Weber, Gustavus A. The Plant Quarantine & Control Administration: Its History, Activities & Organization. LC 72-3076. (Brookings Institution. Institute for Government Research. Service Monographs of the U.S. Government: No. 59). Repr. of 1930 ed. 29.00 (ISBN 0-404-57159-X). AMS Pr.

PLANT REPRODUCTION

see Plants–Reproduction

PLANT RESPIRATION

see Plants–Respiration

PLANT SOCIETIES

see Plant Communities

PLANT TAXONOMY

see Botany–Classification

PLANT TRANSLOCATION

Baker, D. A. Transport Phenomena in Plants. (Outline Studies in Biology Ser.). 1978. pap. 7.50 (ISBN 0-412-15360-2, NO. 6022, Pub. by Chapman & Hall). Methuen Inc.

Crafts, Alden S. & Crisp, Carl E. Phloem Transport in Plants. LC 71-125130. (Biology Ser.). (Illus.). 481p. 1971. text ed. 39.95 (ISBN 0-7167-0683-0). W H Freeman.

Kursanov, A. L. Assimilate Transport in Plants. 1984. 181.00 (ISBN 0-444-80508-7, I-195-84). Elsevier.

Luettge, U., ed. Microautoradiography & Electron Probe Analysis: Their Application to Plant Physiology. LC 72-97599. (Illus.). 280p. 1972. pap. 29.00 (ISBN 0-387-05950-4). Springer-Verlag.

Luettge, U. & Pitman, M. G., eds. Transport in Plants Two, Pts. A & B. Incl. Pt. A. Cells. Robertson, R. A., frwd. by. (Illus.). 440p. 80.00 (ISBN 0-387-07452-X); Pt. B. Tissues & Plants. (Illus.). 480p. 85.00 (ISBN 0-387-07453-8). (Encyclopedia in Plant Physiology Ser.: Vol. 2). 1976. Springer-Verlag.

Moorby, J. Transport Systems in Plants. (Integrated Themes in Biology Ser.). (Illus.). 176p. (Orig.). 1981. pap. text ed. 14.95x (ISBN 0-582-44379-2). Longman.

Raven, John A. Energetics & Transport in Aquatic Plants. LC 84-12525. (MBL Lectures in Biology Ser.: Vol. 4). 576p. 1984. 83.00 (ISBN 0-8451-2203-7). A R Liss.

PLANT-WATER RELATIONSHIPS

Chapman, Homer D. & Pratt, Parker F. Methods of Analysis for Soils, Plants, & Waters. 2nd ed. 310p. 1982. pap. text ed. 8.00x (ISBN 0-931876-55-9, 4034). Ag & Nat Res.

Kozlowski, T. T. Water Deficits & Plant Growth: Additional Woody Crop Plants. Riker, A. J., ed. (Vol. 7). 1983. 37.00 (ISBN 0-12-424157-3). Acad Pr.

Kozlowski, Theodore T., ed. Water Deficits & Plant Growth, 5 vols. LC 68-14658. Tr. of Et Al. Vol. 1 1968. 66.00 (ISBN 0-12-424150-6); Vol. 2 1968. 56.00 (ISBN 0-12-424152-2); Vol. 3 1972. 56.00 (ISBN 0-12-424153-0); Vol. 4 1976. 61.50 (ISBN 0-12-424154-9); Vol. 5, 1978. 50.00 (ISBN 0-12-424155-7). Acad Pr.

Kramer, Paul J., ed. Water Relations of Plants. 428p. 1983. 35.00 (ISBN 0-12-425040-8). Acad Pr.

Lassahn, Pamela, et al, eds. Anticipated & Abnormal Plant Transients in Light Water Reactors. 1470p. 1984. 225.00x (ISBN 0-306-41718-9, Plenum Pr). Plenum Pub.

Milburn, J. A. Water Flow in Plants. LC 77-30743. (Integrated Themes in Biology Ser.). (Illus.). 1979. pap. text ed. 18.50x (ISBN 0-582-44387-3). Longman.

Pospisilova, J. & Solarova, J., eds. Water in Plants Bibliography: 1979, Vol. 5. 39.50 (ISBN 90-619-3905-4, Pub. by Junk Pubs Netherlands). Kluwer Academic.

Pospisilova, Jana, ed. Water in Plants Bibliography. 1978. pap. 25.00 (ISBN 90-6193-902-X, Dr. W. Junk Pub). Kluwer Academic.

Pospisilova, Jana & Solarova, J., eds. Water in Plants Bibliography, Vol. 3. 1979. pap. 29.00 (ISBN 9-0619-3903-8, Pub. by Junk Pubs Holland). Kluwer Academic.

--Water in Plants Bibliography, Vol. 4. vi, 156p. 1980. pap. 42.15 (ISBN 90-6193-904-6, Dr W Junk Pub). Kluwer Academic.

Simpson, G. M. Water Stress on Plants. LC 81-7376. (Illus.). 336p. 1981. 48.95 (ISBN 0-03-056698-3). Praeger.

Slavic, B. Methods of Studying Plant-Water Relations. (Aecological Studies: Vol. 9). (Illus.). 480p. 1974. 55.00 (ISBN 0-387-06686-1). Springer Verlag.

Troller, John A. & Christian, J. H. Water Activity & Food. (Food Science & Technology Ser.). 1978. 39.50 (ISBN 0-12-700650-8). Acad Pr.

Turner, N. C. & Kramer, P. J. Adaptation of Plants to Water & High Temperature Stress. LC 79-24428. 482p. 1980. text ed. 56.50x (ISBN 0-471-05372-4, Pub. by Wiley-Interscience). Wiley.

Value to Agriculture of High-Quality Water from Nuclear Desalination. 1969. pap. 12.00 (ISBN 92-0-041069-3, IAEA). Unipub.

Weinberg, Michael, ed. Atmospheric Water Vapor Resources for Rainfall As They Are Related to Water-Synthesis in Plant-Life, Annotated Bibliography. 45p. 1978. 3.00 (ISBN 0-9601014-5-4); facsimile ed. avail. Weinberg.

Weinberg, Michael A. Plants Are Waters' Factories: A Book About Drouth. LC 75-4850. 110p. 1976. pap. 1.95 (ISBN 0-9601014-1-1). Weinberg.

Wiebe, H. H., et al. Measurement of Plant & Soil Water Status. 71p. (Orig.). 1971. pap. 0.50 (ISBN 0-87421-003-8). Utah St U Pr.

PLANTATION CROPS

see Tropical Crops

PLANTING

see Agriculture; Trees

PLANTS

see also Alpine Flora; Aquatic Plants; Botany; Climbing Plants; Cryptogams; Dye Plants; Fertilization of Plants; Floriculture; Flowers; Forage Plants; Forcing (Plants); Growth (Plants); Insectivorous Plants; Paleobotany; Parasitic Plants; Phanerogams; Plants, Useful; Poisonous Plants; Pollen; Rare Plants; Succulent Plants; Tropical Plants; Weeds

also names of individual plants, and headings beginning with the word Plant

Adams, George & Whicher, Olive. The Plant Between Sun & Earth. LC 82-50276. (Illus.). 224p. (Orig.). 1982. pap. 12.95 (ISBN 0-87773-232-9, 71231-5). Shambhala Pubns.

Adriance, Guy W. & Brison, Fred R. Propagation of Horticultural Plants. 2nd ed. LC 79-9753. 308p. 1979. Repr. of 1955 ed. lib. bdg. 19.50 (ISBN 0-88275-965-5). Krieger.

Arber, Agnes. National Philosophy of Plant Form. LC 84-3606. 1970. Repr. of 1950 ed. 15.95x (ISBN 0-02-840360-6). Hafner.

Arnett, Ross H., Jr. & Arnett, Mary E., eds. The Naturalists' Directory of Plant Collectors & Identifiers, International, Pt. II, No. 4. 4th ed. (Naturalists' Directory (International) Ser.). 96p. (Orig.). 1985. pap. cancelled (ISBN 0-916846-16-4). Flora & Fauna.

Ayensu, Edward S. & DeFilipps, Robert A. Endangered & Threatened Plants of the United States. LC 77-25138. (Illus.). 403p. 1978. 35.00x (ISBN 0-87474-222-6). Smithsonian.

Bailey, Liberty H. Hortus Third: A Concise Dictionary of Plants Cultivated in the United States & Canada. (Illus.). 1976. 125.00 (ISBN 0-02-505470-8). Macmillan.

Baumeister, W. Pflanzenlexikon. (Ger.). 1280p. 1969. pap. 49.95 (ISBN 3-499-16100-1, M-7580). French & Eur.

Beckett, Kenneth A. The Concise Encyclopedia of Garden Plants. (Illus.). 440p. 1984. 19.95 (ISBN 0-85613-534-8, Pub. by Salem Hse Ltd). Merrimack Pub Cir.

Begon, Michael & Mortimer, Martin. Population Ecology: A Unified Study of Animal & Plants. LC 81-5641. (Illus.). 256p. 1981. pap. text ed. 18.95x (ISBN 0-87893-067-1). Sinauer Assoc.

Bir, S. S. Aspects of Plant Sciences, Vol. III. 170p. 1980. 15.00 (ISBN 0-88065-172-5, Pub. by Messers Today & Tomorrows Printers & Publishers India). Scholarly Pubns.

Bir, S. S., ed. Aspects of Plant Sciences, Vol. VI. (Illus.). 261p. 1983. 19.00x (ISBN 0-88065-235-7, Pub. by Messers Today & Tomorrow Printers & Publishers). Scholarly Pubns.

Bruggen, Theodore Van. The Vascular Plants of South Dakota. 2nd ed. 476p. 1985. pap. text ed. 24.95x (ISBN 0-8138-0650-X). Iowa St U Pr.

California Academy of Sciences Vascular Plant Type Collection Index. 200.00 (ISBN 0-930466-90-X). Meckler Pub.

Capon, Brian. Investigations into the Biology of Plants. 1981. coil bdg. 8.95 (ISBN 0-88252-041-5). Paladin Hse.

Carr, D. J. & Carr, S. G., eds. People & Plants in Australia. 450p. 1981. 50.00 (ISBN 0-12-160720-8); pap. 40.00 (ISBN 0-12-160722-4). Acad Pr.

--Plants & Man in Australia. 350p. 1981. 40.00 (ISBN 0-12-160723-2); pap. 35.00 (ISBN 0-12-160724-0). Acad Pr.

Chinoy, N. J., ed. The Role of Ascorbic Acid in Growth, Differentiation & Metabolism of Plants. (Advances in Agricultural Biotechnology Ser.). 1984. lib. bdg. 46.50 (ISBN 90-247-2908-4, Pub. by Martinus Nijhoff Netherlands). Kluwer-Academic.

Clausen, Jens, et al. Effect of Varied Environments on Western North American Plants. (Experimental Studies on the Nature of Species, Vol. 1). (Illus.). 459p. 1940. pap. 16.50 (ISBN 0-87279-530-6, 520). Carnegie Inst.

Commonwealth Scientific & Industrial Research Institute. A Curious & Diverse Flora. Commonwealth Scientific & Industrial Research Institute & Australian Academy of Science, eds. 1982. slides 35.00x (ISBN 0-89955-361-3, Pub. by CSIRO). Intl Spec Bk.

Cook, J. Gordon. ABC of Plant Terms. 293p. 1968. 39.00x (ISBN 0-900541-56-3, Pub. by Meadowfield Pr England). State Mutual Bk.

--Your Guide to the Plant Kingdom. 304p. 40.00x (ISBN 0-900541-55-5, Pub. by Meadowfield Pr England). State Mutual Bk.

Cooperrider, Tom S., ed. Endangered & Threatened Plants of Ohio. LC 81-82268. 1982. 10.00 (ISBN 0-86727-091-8). Ohio Bio Survey.

Coutinho, A. Pereira. Flora de Portugal. 2A ed. dirigido pel Ruy Telles Plahinha. (Historia Naturalis Classica 98). 1973. Repr. lib. bdg. 70.00x (ISBN 3-7682-0931-8). Lubrecht & Cramer.

Creso, Irene, ed. Vascular Plants of Western Washington. LC 84-72043. (Illus.). 520p. (Orig.). 1984. pap. 14.95 (ISBN 0-9613916-0-X). Creso.

Cronquist, Arthur. Vascular Flora of the Southeastern United States: Vol. 1-Asteraceae. Radford, Albert E., ed. LC 79-769. xv, 261p. 1980. 25.00x (ISBN 0-8078-1362-1). U of NC Pr.

DeRoo, Sally. Exploring Our Environment: A Resource Guide-Manual-Plants. (Illus.). 168p. 1977. instr.'s manual 6.00 (ISBN 0-89039-208-0). Ann Arbor Fl.

Dirr, Michael. Manual of Woody Landscape Plants. 3rd ed. (Illus.). 1983. 29.80x (ISBN 0-87563-231-9); pap. text ed. 22.80x (ISBN 0-87563-226-2). Stipes.

Dommerques, Y. & Krupa, S. V. Interactions Between Non-Pathogenic Soil Microorganisms & Plants. (Developments in Agricultural & Managed-Forest Ecology: Vol. 4). 476p. 1978. 117.00 (ISBN 0-444-41638-2). Elsevier.

Dormer, Kenneth J. Shoot Organization in Vascular Plants. LC 70-39412. (Illus.). 256p. 1972. text ed. 22.95x (ISBN 0-8156-5032-9). Syracuse U Pr.

Duncan, U. K. Flora of East Ross-Shire. 272p. 1980. 37.00x (ISBN 0-317-07066-5, Pub. by EW Classey UK). State Mutual Bk.

Edmonds, John. Container Plant Manual. 172p. 1981. 40.00x (ISBN 0-686-75410-7, Pub. by Grower Bks). State Mutual Bk.

Encylopedie Illustree Du Monde Vegetal. (Fr.). 600p. 14.95 (ISBN 0-686-57160-6, M-6219). French & Eur.

Faber, Phyllis M. Common Wetland Plants of Coastal California. (Illus.). 120p. 1982. 12.00 (ISBN 0-9607890-0-6). Pickleweed.

Fahn, A. Secretory Tissues in Plants. 1979. 53.00 (ISBN 0-12-247650-6). Acad Pr.

Fitter, A. H. & Hay, R. K. Environmental Physiology of Plants. (Experimental Botany Ser.). 1981. 55.00 (ISBN 0-12-257760-4); pap. 27.00 (ISBN 0-12-257762-0). Acad Pr.

Forbes, J. C. & Watson, R. D. Agricultural Botany. 250p. 1986. pap. text ed. write for info. (ISBN 0-7131-2891-7). E Arnold.

Frenkel, Robert E. Ruderal Vegetation along Some California Roadsides. (California Library Reprint Ser.: No. 92). 1978. Repr. of 1970 ed. 21.00x (ISBN 0-520-03589-5). U of Cal Pr.

Friedland, Mary K. Green Plants. (Science in Action Ser.). (Illus.). 48p. 1982. pap. text ed. 2.85 (ISBN 0-915510-76-6). Janus Bks.

Galston, A., et al. Life of the Green Plant. 3rd ed. 1980. 23.95 (ISBN 0-13-536326-8); pap. 20.95 (ISBN 0-13-536318-7). P-H.

Gerard, John. The Herbal or General History of Plants. (Illus.). xiv, 1678p. 1975. Repr. of 1633 ed. 75.00 (ISBN 0-486-23147-X). Dover.

Gerarde, John. The Herball or Generall Historie of Plantes. 303p. 1984. Repr. of 1597 ed. text ed. 85.00x (ISBN 0-86590-238-0). Apt Bks.

Gleason, Henry A. & Cronquist, Arthur. Manual of Vascular Plants. 810p. 1963. text ed. write for info. (ISBN 0-87150-760-9, Pub. by Willard Grant Pr). PWS Pubs.

Grace, J. Plant-Atmosphere Relationships. LC 82-19177. (Outline Studies in Ecology). 80p. 1983. pap. 7.50 (ISBN 0-412-23180-8, NO. 6783, Pub. by Chapman & Hall). Methuen Inc.

--Plant Response to Wind. (Experimental Botany Ser.). 1978. 47.50 (ISBN 0-12-294450-X). Acad Pr.

Graham, C. F. & Wareing, P. F. Developmental Control in Animals & Plants. 2nd ed. (Illus.). 424p. 1984. pap. text ed. 32.50x (ISBN 0-632-00758-3, Pub. by Blackwell Sci UK). Blackwell Pubns.

Guia de Peces y Plantas de Acuario. (Span.). Date not set. Leatherette 44.95 (ISBN 0-686-97406-9, S-36344). French & Eur.

Hansen, Bertel. Balanophoraceae. LC 79-28385. (Flora Neotropica Monograph: No. 23). 1980. 10.50x (ISBN 0-89327-195-0). NY Botanical.

Harlow, William M. Art Forms from Plant Life. LC 75-25002. Orig. Title: Patterns of Life: The Unseen World of Plants. (Illus.). 1974. pap. 6.50 (ISBN 0-486-23262-X). Dover.

Hay, Roy & Synge, Patrick M. The Color Dictionary of Flowers & Plants for Home & Garden. (Illus.). 584p. 1982. pap. 12.95 (ISBN 0-517-52456-2). Crown.

Hebrew University Conference, Rehovot, Israel. Optimizing the Soil Physical Environment Toward Greater Crop Yields: Proceedings. Hillel, D., ed. 1972. 37.50 (ISBN 0-12-348540-1). Acad Pr.

Heiser, Charles B., Jr. Of Plants & People. LC 84-40688. (Illus.). 272p. 1985. 24.95 (ISBN 0-8061-1931-4). U of Okla Pr.

Hewitt, E. J., ed. Nitrogen Assimilation of Plants. 1979. 98.00 (ISBN 0-12-346360-2). Acad Pr.

Hicks, Ray R., Jr. & Stephenson, George K. Woody Plants of the Western Gulf Region. (Illus.). 1978. pap. text ed. 13.95 (ISBN 0-8403-1880-4). Kendall-Hunt.

Hooker, J. D. & Jackson, B. D., eds. Index Kewensis Plantarum Phanerogamarum (Linnaeus to the Year 1885, 2 vols. 1977. Repr. text ed. 456.00x set (ISBN 3-87429-117-0). Lubrecht & Cramer.

Hornabrook, R. W. Essays on Kuru. 150p. 1975. 49.00x (ISBN 0-317-07064-9, Pub. by EW Classey UK). State Mutual Bk.

Hotchkiss, Neil. Common Marsh Underwater & Floating-Leaved Plants of the United States & Canada. LC 74-187019. (Illus.). 250p. 1972. pap. 6.00 (ISBN 0-486-22810-X). Dover.

Huang, Anthony H., et al. Plant Peroxisomes. LC 82-22777. (American Society of Plant Physiologists Monograph Ser.). 1983. 34.50 (ISBN 0-12-358260-1). Acad Pr.

Janick, Jules, et al. Plant Science: An Introduction to World Crops. 3rd ed. LC 81-4897. (Illus.). 868p. 1981. text ed. 30.95 (ISBN 0-7167-1261-X). W H Freeman.

Jolivet, Pierre. Insects & Plants. (Handbook Ser.: No. 2). (Illus.). 208p. (Orig.). 1985. pap. 19.95 (ISBN 0-916846-25-3). Flora & Fauna.

Jones, G. Neville & Fuller, George D. Vascular Plants of Illinois. (Scientific Papers Ser.: Vol. VI). (Illus.). 593p. 1955. 10.00 (ISBN 0-89792-012-0). Ill St Museum.

Juscafresa Serrat, Baudillo. Enciclopedia Ilustrada De la Flora: Medicinal, Toxica, Aromatica y Condimenticia. (Espn.). 528p. 1975. 25.50 (ISBN 84-7003-208-9, S-50505). French & Eur.

Kent, Douglas H. The Historical Flora of Middlesex: An Account of the Wild Plants Found in the Watsonian Vice-County 21 from 1548 to the Present Time. (Illus.). vi, 679p. 1975. 32.50x (ISBN 0-903874-03-2, Pub by Brit Mus Nat Hist England). Sabbot-Natural Hist Bks.

Kerrich, G. J., et al, eds. Key Words to the Fauna & Flora of the British Isles & Northwestern Europe. (Systematic Association Special Ser.). 1978. 40.00 (ISBN 0-12-405550-8). Acad Pr.

Khoshoo, T. N. & Nair, P. K. Progress in Plant Research, 2 vols, Vols. 1 & 2. (Orig.). 1979. Set. 82.50 (ISBN 0-686-75230-9). Vol. 1 - Applied Morphology & Allied Subjects. Vol. 2 - Plant Improvement & Horticulture. Krieger.

Kirkbride, Joseph H., Jr. A Revision of the Genus Declieuxia (Rubiaceae) LC 66-6394. (Memoirs of the New York Botanical Garden Ser.: Vol. 28, No. 4). 1976. pap. 10.95x (ISBN 0-89327-010-5). NY Botanical.

Kloppenburg-Versteegh, J. The Traditional Use of Malay Plants & Herbs. Kaufman, Aileen, tr. from Dutch. LC 79-89939. Orig. Title: Het Gebruik Van Indische Planten. (Illus.). 1985. cancelled (ISBN 0-86164-152-3, Pub by Momenta Publishing Ltd U. K.). Hunter Hse.

Koedam, A. & Margaris, N. Aromatic Plants. 1982. text ed. 41.50 (ISBN 90-247-2720-0, Pub. by Martinus Nijhoff Netherlands). Kluwer Academic.

Koopowitz, Harold & Kaye, Hilary. Plant Extinction: A Global Crisis. LC 82-62894. (Illus.). 256p. 1983. 16.95 (ISBN 0-913276-44-8). Stone Wall Pr.

Kozlowski, T. T. & Riker, A. J., eds. Flooding & Plant Growth. LC 83-15811. (Physiological Ecology Ser.). 1984. 60.00 (ISBN 0-12-424120-4). Acad Pr.

Kuehn, H. H. Identification of Woody Plants: Summer & Winter Characteristics. 1978. pap. text ed. 10.50 (ISBN 0-89669-007-5). Collegium Bk Pubs.

L. H. An Atlas of the Biologic Resources of the Hudson Estuary. (Illus.). 104p. (Orig.). 1977. pap. 5.50 (ISBN 0-89062-096-2, Pub. by Boyce Thompson Inst Plant Res). Pub Ctr Cult Res.

Laetsch, Watson M. Plants: Basic Concepts in Botany. 1979. text ed. 25.95 (ISBN 0-316-51186-2); tchrs' manual avail. (ISBN 0-316-51185-4). Little.

Lange, Herbert. Vox--Enciclopedia Cultural, Tomo 8: Plantas. (Espn.). 210p. 1977. leatherette 29.95 (ISBN 84-7153-495-9, S-50501). French & Eur.

Levitt, Dulcie. Plants & People: Aboriginal Uses of Plants on Groote Eylandt. (AIAS New Ser.: No. 22). (Illus.). 166p. 1981. (Pub. by Australian Inst Australia); pap. text ed. 22.50x (ISBN 0-391-02205-9, Pub. by Australian Inst Australia). Humanities.

Lleras, Eduardo. Trigoniaceae. LC 77-91706. (Flora Neotropica Monograph: No. 19). 1978. pap. 7.25x (ISBN 0-89327-198-5). NY Botanical.

Lloyd, Francis E. Guayule (Parthenium Argentatum Gray): A Rubber-Plant of the Chihuahuan Desert. (Illus.). 213p. 1911. pap. 8.00 (ISBN 0-87279-140-8, 139). Carnegie Inst.

Mabey, Richard. Plantcraft: A Guide to the Everyday Use of Wild Plants. LC 77-82824. (Illus.). 1979. pap. 5.95 (ISBN 0-87663-937-6). Universe.

Malmberg, Russell, et al, eds. Molecular Biology of Plants. LC 85-11036. 150p. (Orig.). 1985. pap. 28.00 (ISBN 0-87969-184-0). Cold Spring Harbor.

Martin, W. C. & Hutchins, R. Flora of New Mexico, 2 vols. (Illus.). 3000p. 1980. Set. lib. bdg. 140.00 (ISBN 3-7682-1263-7). Lubrecht & Cramer.

Mass, P. J. M. Renealmia (Zingiberaceae-Zingiberoideae) Costoideae (Additions) (Zingiberaceae) LC 77-72241. (Flora Neotropica Monograph: No. 18). 1977. pap. 21.00x (ISBN 0-89327-192-6). NY Botanical.

Matsuo, T., ed. Adaptability in Plants, Vol. 6. (Japan International Biological Program Synthesis Ser.). 1975. 26.00 (ISBN 0-86008-216-4, Pub. by U of Tokyo Japan). Columbia U Pr.

Meikle, R. D. Flora of Cyprus, Vol. 1. (Illus.). xii, 832p. 1977. 46.00x (ISBN 0-9504876-3-5, Pub. by Brit Mus Nat Hist England). Sabbot-Natural Hist Bks.

Merrill, Elmer D. Plant Life of the Pacific World. LC 80-51195. (Illus.). 312p. 1982. Repr. of 1945 ed. 13.50 (ISBN 0-8048-1370-1). C E Tuttle.

--Plant Life of the Pacific World. (Illus.). 1945. 11.50x (ISBN 0-686-51288-X). Elliots Bks.

Moir, May A. The Garden Watcher. LC 82-24728. (Illus.). 117p. 1983. pap. text ed. 12.00x (ISBN 0-8248-0789-8). UH Pr.

Moss, E. H. Flora of Alberta. 2nd ed. Packer, John G., rev. by. (Illus.). 704p. 1983. text ed. 45.00x (ISBN 0-8020-2508-0). U of Toronto Pr.

Nadakavukaren, Mathew J. & McCracken, Derek. Botany: An Introduction to Plant Biology. (Illus.). 520p. (Orig.). 1985. pap. text ed. 24.95 (ISBN 0-314-85279-4). West Pub.

Nair, P. K., ed. Aspects of Plant Sciences, Vol. I. 210p. 1976. 12.00 (ISBN 0-88065-170-9, Pub. by Messers Today & Tomorrows Printers & Publishers India). Scholarly Pubns.

--Aspects of Plant Sciences, Vol. II. 164p. 1979. 12.00 (ISBN 0-88065-171-7, Pub. by Messers Today & Tomorrows Printers & Publishers India). Scholarly Pubns.

--Glimpses in Plant Research: Vol. 6, Botanical Monographs & Reviews. 393p. 1984. text ed. 60.00x (ISBN 0-7069-2132-1, Pub. by Vikas India). Advent NY.

Nelson, Ruth A. Plants of Zion National Park: Wildflowers, Trees, Shrubs & Ferns. LC 74-28958. (Illus.). 344p. 1976. 10.00x (ISBN 0-915630-00-1); pap. text ed. 6.95x (ISBN 0-915630-01-X). Zion.

New Mexico Native Plant Protection Advisory Committee. A Handbook of Rare & Endemic Plants of New Mexico. LC 82-16865. (New Mexico Natural History Ser.). (Illus.). 291p. 1984. 24.95x (ISBN 0-8263-0722-1); pap. 12.95 (ISBN 0-8263-0723-X). U of NM Pr.

Nicholls, Richard. The Plant Doctor: Growing & Healing Indoor Plants. LC 74-31542. (Illus.). 128p. (Orig.). 1975. lib. bdg. 12.90 (ISBN 0-914294-13-X); pap. 4.95 (ISBN 0-914294-14-8). Running Pr.

Ninth Biennial Workshop on Color Aerial Photography in the Plant Sciences & Related Fields. 204p. 1984. pap. 28.00 (ISBN 0-937294-56-X); pap. 21.00 members' price. ASP & RS.

Perry, Frances, ed. Simon & Schuster's Complete Guide to Plants & Flowers. (Illus.). 1976. pap. 10.95 (ISBN 0-671-22247-3). S&S.

The Plant - the Living Plant - the Root. (Economic & Social Development Papers: No. 1). (Illus.). 1977. pap. 7.50 (ISBN 92-5-100140-5, F59, FAO). Unipub.

The Plant: The Stem, the Buds, & the Leaves. Rev. ed. (Better Farming Ser.: No. 2). (Illus.). 30p. 1977. pap. 7.50 (ISBN 92-5-100141-3, F60, FAO). Unipub.

Plants 1945-1966. pap. 13.00 (F938, FAO). Unipub.

Raven, Peter H., et al. Biology of Plants. 3rd ed. 1981. text ed. 36.95 (ISBN 0-87901-132-7); lab manual 13.95x; prep guide avail. (ISBN 0-87901-143-2). Worth.

Reeves, Robert G. Flora of South Central Texas. Orig. Title: Flora of South Central Texas. 1977. pap. text ed. 11.50x (ISBN 0-934786-00-3). G Davis.

Ritchie, J. C. Past & Present Vegetation of the Far Northwest Canada. 272p. 1984. 35.00x (ISBN 0-8020-2523-4). U of Toronto Pr.

Rodriguez, Eloy, et al, eds. Biology & Chemistry of Plant Trichomes. 244p. 1983. 39.50x (ISBN 0-306-41393-0, Plenum Pr). Plenum Pub.

Rose, Peter Q. Ivies. (Illus.). 180p. 1980. 17.50 (ISBN 0-7137-0969-3, Pub. by Blandford Pr England). Sterling.

Ross-Craig, Stella. Drawings of British Plants, 8 vols. Incl. Vol. 1 (ISBN 0-7135-1137-0); Vol. 2 (ISBN 0-7135-1138-9); Vol. 3 (ISBN 0-7135-1139-7); Vol. 4; Vol. 5 (ISBN 0-7135-1141-9); Vol. 6 (ISBN 0-7135-1142-7); Vol. 7 (ISBN 0-7135-1143-5); Vol. 8. (Illus.). 1980. 256.25 set (ISBN 0-7135-1110-9); 32.50 ea. Lubrecht & Cramer.

Roth, Charles E. The Plant Observer's Guidebook: A Field Botany Manual for the Amateur Naturalist. (Illus.). 240p. 1984. 17.95 (ISBN 0-13-680752-6); pap. 9.95 (ISBN 0-13-680745-3). P-H.

Russell, E. W. Soil Conditions & Plant Growth. 10th ed. LC 74-168964. (Illus.). 867p. 1974. text ed. 35.00x (ISBN 0-582-44048-3). Longman.

Sampson, Arthur W. & Jespersen, Beryle S. California Range Brushlands & Browse Plants. (Illus.). 162p. 1981. pap. text ed. 6.00x (ISBN 0-931876-54-0, 4010). Ag & Nat Res.

Sill, Webster H., Jr. Plant Protection: An Integrated Interdisciplinary Approach. (Illus.). 298p. 1982. 23.95x (ISBN 0-8138-1665-3). Iowa St U Pr.

Singer, Rolf. Marasmieae (Basidiomycetes-Tricholomataceae) LC 76-21378. (Flora Neotropica Monograph: No. 17). 1976. pap. 25.00x (ISBN 0-89327-009-1). NY Botanical.

Sleumer, H. O. Flacourtiaceae. LC 79-22365. (Flora Neotropica Monograph: No. 22). 1980. 47.50x (ISBN 0-89327-194-2). NY Botanical.

Smith, Alexander H. & Singer, Rolf. Monograph on the Genus Galerina Earle. (Illus.). 1964. 21.95x (ISBN 0-02-852460-8). Hafner.

Smith, H. & Grierson, D., eds. Molecular Biology of Plant Development. LC 81-43687. (Botanical Monographs: Vol. 18). (Illus.). 500p. 1982. 68.50x (ISBN 0-520-04675-7). U of Cal Pr.

Smith, James P. & York, Richard, eds. Inventory of Rare & Endangered Vascular Plants of California. (Special Publication Ser.: No. 1). 192p. (Orig.). 1984. pap. 10.95x (ISBN 0-943460-10-7). Calif Native.

Stephens, Homer A. Trees, Shrubs, & Woody Vines in Kansas. LC 69-10357. (Illus.). 1969. pap. 9.95 (ISBN 0-7006-0057-4). U Pr of KS.

Steward, F. C. & Bidwell, R. G., eds. Plant Physiology: A Treatise Vol. 8: Nitrogen Metabolism. 1983. 70.00 (ISBN 0-12-668608-4). Acad Pr.

Still, Steven. Herbaceous Plants. (Illus.). 203p. 1982. text ed. 21.80x (ISBN 0-87563-212-2); pap. text ed. 16.80x (ISBN 0-87563-211-4). Stipes.

Stone, Doris M. The Lives of Plants: Exploring the Wonders of Botany. (Illus.). 256p. 1983. 15.95 (ISBN 0-684-17907-5, ScribT). Scribner.

Swartley, John C. Eastern Hemlock & Its Variations. LC 79-18983. 272p. 1980. 25.00 (ISBN 0-8240-7407-6). Garland Pub.

Synge, P. & Hay, R. Dictionary of Garden Plants & Flowers in Colour: May 1981. 1981. 60.00x (ISBN 0-686-78769-2, Pub. by RHS Ent England). State Mutual Bk.

Tanner, Heather & Tanner, Robin. Woodland Plants. LC 82-5558. (Illus.). 216p. 1982. with slipcover 60.00 (ISBN 0-8052-3821-2). Schocken.

Teho, Fortunato. Plants of Hawaii. (Illus.). pap. 3.95 (ISBN 0-912180-13-7). Petroglyph.
Thimann, Kenneth V. Senescence in Plants. 288p. 1980. 82.00 (ISBN 0-8493-5803-5). CRC Pr.
Thomas, Graham S. Perennial Garden Plants. rev ed. (Illus.). 404p. 1982. 29.95x (ISBN 0-460-04575-X, Pub. by J M Dent England). Biblio Dist.
--Plants for Ground-Cover. (Illus.). 308p. 1977. 22.50x (ISBN 0-460-03994-6, Pub. by J M Dent England). Biblio Dist.
Titchmarsh, Alan. The Larousse Guide to House Plants. LC 82-81524. (Nature Guides Ser.). (Illus.). 272p. (Orig.). 1982. pap. 9.95 (ISBN 0-88332-281-1, 8217). Larousse.
Tivy, Joy. Biogeography: A Study of Plants in the Ecosystem. 2nd ed. LC 80-41366. (Illus.). 459p. 1982. pap. text ed. 14.95x (ISBN 0-582-30009-6). Longman.
Tompkins, Peter & Bird, Christopher. The Secret Life of Plants: A Fascinating Account of the Physical, Emotional, & Spiritual Relations Between Plants & Man. LC 72-9160. 402p. 1984. pap. 7.64i (ISBN 0-06-091112-3, CN 1112, CN). Har-Row.
Trakimas, Winifred, et al. Blueprint of the Plant: A Laboratory Manual of Botany. 2nd ed. 178p. pap. text ed. 10.95x (ISBN 0-8087-3614-0). Burgess.
Van Der Maarel, Eddy & Werger, Marinus J., eds. Plant Species & Plant Communities. 1978. lib. bdg. 37.00 (ISBN 90-6193-591-1, Pub. by Junk Pubs Netherlands). Kluwer Academic.
Van Der Pijl, L. Principles of Dispersal in Higher Plants. (Illus.). 250p. 1982. 29.50 (ISBN 0-387-11280-4). Springer-Verlag.
Vascular Plant Types & Early Authentic Specimens of the Academy of Natural Sciences of Philadelphia Index. 350.00 (ISBN 0-930466-87-X). Meckler Pub.
Verey, Rosemary. The Scented Garden. 168p. 1981. 24.95 (ISBN 0-442-28175-7). Van Nos Reinhold.
Walsh, L. M. & Beaton, J. D., eds. Soil Testing & Plant Analysis. (Illus.). 471p. 1973. 10.00 (ISBN 0-89118-755-3). Soil Sci Soc Am.
Walther, Eric. Echeveria. (Illus.). 426p. 1972. 25.00 (ISBN 0-940228-05-X). Calif Acad Sci.
Webb, Ralph C. A Guide to the Plants of Pinnacles. Jackson, Earl, ed. LC 72-172690. (Illus.). 78p. 1971. pap. 1.00 (ISBN 0-911408-25-8). SW Pks Mnmts.
Wetherell, D. F. Plant Tissue Culture. Head, John J., ed. LC 83-70600. (Carolina Biology Readers Ser.). (Illus.). 16p. 1984. pap. 1.60 (ISBN 0-89278-342-7, 45-9742). Carolina Biological.
Whittaker, Robert H. Ordination of Plant Communities. 1982. 29.50 (ISBN 90-6193-565-2, Pub. by Junk Pubs Netherlands). Kluwer Academic.
Wickens, G. E., et al. Plants For Arid Lands. (Illus.). 500p. 1985. text ed. 50.00x (ISBN 0-04-581019-2). Allen Unwin.
Winterringer, Glen S. & Evers, Robert A. New Records for Illinois Vascular Plants. (Scientific Papers Ser.: Vol. XI). 135p. 1960. pap. 3.25 (ISBN 0-89792-020-1). Ill St Museum.
Wodehouse, Roger P. Hayfever Plants: Their Appearance, Distribution, Time of Flowering, & Their Role in Hayfever. 2nd, rev. ed. LC 70-130511. pap. 72.00 (ISBN 0-317-29158-0, 2055597). Bks Demand UMI.
Wunderlin, Richard. Guide to the Vascular Plants of Central Florida. LC 82-11117. 1983. 25.00 (ISBN 0-8130-0748-8). U Presses Fla.

PLANTS–ABSORPTION OF WATER
see also Plants–Water Requirements

Pierre, W. H., et al, eds. Plant Environment & Efficient Water Use. (Illus.). 1966. 6.00 (ISBN 0-89118-001-X). Am Soc Agron.

PLANTS–ANATOMY
see Botany–Anatomy

PLANTS–ASSIMILATION
see also Plant Translocation

Ashmead, Dewayne. Chelated Mineral Nutrition in Plants, Animals, & Man. (Illus.). 346p. 1982. 38.75x (ISBN 0-398-04603-4). C C Thomas.
Darwin, Charles R. Insectivorous Plants. 2nd rev. ed. LC 70-151602. Repr. of 1893 ed. 27.50 (ISBN 0-404-01928-5). AMS Pr.
DeWit, C. T., et al. Simulation of Assimilation, Respiration & Transpiration of Crops. LC 78-11384. 140p. 1978. pap. 26.95x (ISBN 0-470-26494-2). Halsted Pr.
Harborne, J. B. Phytochemical Methods: A Guide to Modern Techniques of Plant Analysis. 300p. 1984. text ed. 33.00 (ISBN 0-412-25550-2, 9124, Pub. by Chapman & Hall England). Methuen Inc.
Robinson, J. B. Annotated Bibliography of Colour Illustrated Mineral Deficiency Symptoms in Tropical Crops. 84p. 1974. 49.00x (ISBN 0-85198-304-9, Pub. by CAB Bks England). State Mutual Bk.
Robinson, J. B., ed. Diagnosis of Mineral Disorders in Plants, 5 vols. 1984. Vol. 1, Principles. 50.00 (ISBN 0-8206-0311-2); Vol. 2, Vegetables. 62.50 (ISBN 0-8206-0312-0). Chem Pub.
--Diagnosis of Mineral Disorders in Plants: Vegetables, Vol. II. 100p. 1982. 75.00x (ISBN 0-11-240804-4, Pub. by HMSO). State Mutual Bk.
Sutcliffe, J. F. & Baker, D. A. Plants & Mineral Salts. 1975. 54.00x (ISBN 0-686-84465-3, Pub. by Oxford & I B H India). State Mutual Bk.
Van Steenis, C. Rheophytes of the World: An Account of Flood - Resistant Flowering Plants & Ferns & the Theory of Autonomous Evolution. 424p. 1981. 75.00 (ISBN 90-286-0840-0). Sijthoff & Noordhoff.

PLANTS–CHEMICAL ANALYSIS
see also Botanical Chemistry; Chlorophyll; Plants–Assimilation

Dey, P. M. & Dixon, R. A. Biochemistry of Storage Carbohydrates in Green Plants. 1985. 79.00 (ISBN 0-12-214680-8). Acad Pr.
Evans, David P., et al, eds. Handbook of Plant Cell Culture, Vol. 1: Techniques for Propagation & Breeding. LC 82-73774. 1983. 53.00 (ISBN 0-02-949230-0). Macmillan.
Gardner, Franklin P., et al. Physiology of Crop Plants. (Illus.). 328p. 1985. 21.95x (ISBN 0-8138-1376-X). Iowa St U Pr.
Goodwin, T. W. & Mercer, E. I. Introduction to Plant Biochemistry. 2nd ed. (Illus.). 400p. 1982. pap. 33.00 (ISBN 0-08-024921-3). Pergamon.
Jensen, U. & Fairbrothers, D. E., eds. Protein & Nucleic Acids in Plant Systematics. LC 83-14689. (Proceedings in Life Sciences Ser.). (Illus.). 408p. 1983. 47.00 (ISBN 0-387-12667-8). Springer-Verlag.
Nes. Biochemistry of Function of Isopentenods in Plants. 550p. 1984. 99.75 (ISBN 0-8247-1909-3). Dekker.
Robinson, J. B. Flourine-Its Occurrence, Analysis, Effects on Plants: Diagnosis & Control. 36p. 1978. 30.00x (ISBN 0-85198-431-2, Pub. by CAB Bks England). State Mutual Bk.
Smith, P. The Chemotaxonomy of Plants. (Contemporary Biology Ser). 324p. 1978. pap. 18.00 (ISBN 0-444-19455-X). Univ Park.
Stumpf, P. K. & Conn, E. E., eds. The Biochemistry of Plants: A Comprehensive Treatise, Secondary Plant Products, Vol. 7. LC 80-13168. 1981. 85.00 (ISBN 0-12-675407-1). Acad Pr.

PLANTS–CLASSIFICATION
see Botany–Classification

PLANTS–COLLECTION AND PRESERVATION
see also Herbaria

Holmgren, Patricia, ed. New York Botanical Garden Vascular Plant Type Collection Index. 600p. 1985. lib. bdg. 350.00 (ISBN 0-930466-86-1). Meckler Pub.
Plant Collecting. 1970. 0.35 (ISBN 0-686-20732-7). SUNY Environ.
Womersley, J. S. Plant Collecting & Herbarium Development: A Manual. (Plant Production & Protection Papers: No. 33). 148p. 1981. pap. 10.75 (ISBN 92-5-101144-3, F2283, FAO). Unipub.

PLANTS–COLOR
see Color of Plants

PLANTS–DISEASE AND PEST RESISTANCE

Alford, D. V. & Upstone, M. E. Pest & Disease Control in Fruit & Hops. 97p. (Orig.). 1981. pap. 9.95x (ISBN 0-901436-60-7, Pub. by B C P C England). Intl Spec Bk.
--Pests & Disease Control in Fruit & Hops. 105p. 1980. 30.00x (ISBN 0-901436-60-7, Pub. by CAB Bks England). State Mutual Bk.
Attwood, P., ed. Crop Protection Handbook: Cereals. 85.00x (ISBN 0-901436-72-0, Pub. by CAB Bks England). State Mutual Bk.
Austin, R. B. Decision Making in the Practice of Crop Protection. 250p. 1982. 70.00x (ISBN 0-901436-71-2, Pub. by CAB Bks England). State Mutual Bk.
British Crop Protection Conference-Pests & Diseases: Vol. 1, 2, & 3. 1977. Set. 100.00x (ISBN 0-901436-11-9, Pub. by BCPC Pubns England). State Mutual Bk.
Burley, Gibson J. & Speight, M. R. The Adoption of Agricultural Practices for the Development of Heritable Resistance to Pests & Pathogens in Forest Crops. 1980. 30.00x (ISBN 0-85074-057-6, Pub. by For Lib Comm England). STate Mutual Bk.
Busvine, J. R. Recommended Methods for Meausurment of Pest Resistance to Pesticides. (Plant Production & Protection Papers: No. 21). (Eng. & Fr.). 136p. 1980. pap. 9.75 (ISBN 92-5-100883-3, F2079, FAO). Unipub.
CAB Books, ed. British Crop Protection Conference: Weeds, 3 vols. 1976. Set. 125.00x (ISBN 0-901436-40-2, Pub. by CAB Bks England). State Mutual Bk.
--Crop Loss Assessment Methods: FAO Manual on the Evaluation & Prevention of Losses by Pests, Disease & Weeds. 276p. 1971. 59.00x (ISBN 0-85198-185-2, Pub. by CAB Bks England). State Mutual Bk.
Deverall, B. J. Defence Mechanisms of Plants. LC 76-12917. (Monographs in Experimental Biology Ser.: No. 19). (Illus.). 1977. 27.95 (ISBN 0-521-21335-5). Cambridge U Pr.
Dixon, G. R. Plant Pathogens & Their Control in Horticulture. (Sciences in Horticulture Ser.). (Illus.). 265p. (Orig.). 1984. pap. text ed. 16.50x (ISBN 0-333-35912-7). Scholium Intl.
Dunning, R. A. Pest & Disease Control in Vegetables, Potatoes & Sugar Beet. 97p. 1980. 35.00x (Pub. by CAB Bks England). State Mutual Bk.
Dunning, R. A., et al. Pest & Disease Control in Vegetables, Potatoes & Sugar Beet. 97p. (Orig.). 1981. pap. 9.95x (ISBN 0-901436-59-3, Pub. by B C P C England). Intl Spec Bk.
Flint, Mary L., ed. Integrated Pest Management for Tomatoes. LC 82-70536. 112p. 1982. pap. text ed. 15.00x (ISBN 0-931876-56-7, 3274). Ag & Nat Res.
Guide to Pollution Control in Fertilizer Plants. (Fertilizer Industry Ser.: No. 9). pap. 2.50 (ISBN 0-686-93250-1, UN77/2B2, UN). Unipub.
Hedin, Paul A., ed. Host Plant Resistance to Pests. LC 77-13823. (ACS Symposium Ser.: No. 62). 1977. 28.95 (ISBN 0-8412-0389-X). Am Chemical.
--Plant Resistance to Insects. LC 82-22622. (ACS Symposium Ser.: No. 208). 375p. 1983. lib. bdg. 49.95 (ISBN 0-8412-0756-9). Am Chemical.
Iswaran, V. A Manual for the Proper Use of Inoculants & Pelleting for Legumes. (Illus.). 195p. 1983. 15.00 (ISBN 0-88065-239-X, Pub. by Messers Today & Tomorrow Printers & Publishers India). Scholarly Pubns.
Lamberti, F. & Waller, J. M., eds. Durable Resistance in Crops. (NATO ASI Series A, Life Sciences: Vol. 55). 450p. 1983. 62.50x (ISBN 0-306-41183-0, Plenum Press). Plenum Pub.
Lebaron, Homer M. & Gressel, Jonathan, eds. Herbicide Resistance in Plants. LC 81-16381. 401p. 1982. 53.50x (ISBN 0-471-08701-7, Pub. by Wiley-Interscience). Wiley.
Lucas, G. B. & Campbell, C. L. Introduction to Plant Diseases: Identification & Management. Lucas, L. T., ed. (Illus.). 1985. text ed. 29.50 (ISBN 0-87055-473-5). AVI.
Mahadevan. Biochemical Aspects of Plant Disease Resistance: Post-Infectional Defense Mechanisms, Pt. II. (International Bio Science Monograph: No. 13). 1982. write for info. (ISBN 0-88065-244-6, Pub. by Messers Today & Tomorrow Printers & Publishers). Scholarly Pubns.
Mahadevan, A. Biochemical Aspects of Plant Disease Resistance: Performed Inhibitory Substance 'Prohibitions, Pt. 1. (International Bio Science Monograph: No. 11). (Illus.). xiv, 400p. 1982. 59.00 (ISBN 0-88065-225-X, Pub. by Messers Today & Tomorrow Printers & Publishers). Scholarly Pubns.
Marini-Bettolo, G. B., ed. Natural Products & the Protection of Plants: Proceedings of a Study Week of the Pontifical Academy of Sciences, October 18-23, 1976. 846p. 1978. 191.50 (ISBN 0-444-41620-X). Elsevier.
Maxwell, Fowder G. & Jennings, Peter R. Breeding Plants Resistant to Insects. LC 79-13462. (Environmental Science & Technology: Texts & Monographs). 683p. 1980. 40.50x (ISBN 0-471-03268-9, Pub. by Wiley-Interscience). Wiley.
Metlitsky, L. V. & Ozeretskovskaya, O. L. Plant Immunity. LC 68-25383. 114p. 1968. 29.50x (ISBN 0-306-30344-2, Plenum Pr). Plenum Pub.
Morgan, W. M. & Ledieu, M. S. Pest & Disease Control in Glasshouse Crops. 106p. (Orig.). 1981. pap. 9.95x (ISBN 0-901436-52-6, Pub. by B C P C England). Intl Spec Bk.
Morgan, W. M., et al. Pest & Disease Control of Protected Crops, Outdoor Bulbs & Corms. 115p. 1983. pap. 9.00x (ISBN 0-901436-82-8, Pub. by B C P C England). Intl Spec Bk.
Nelson, R. R., ed. Breeding Plants for Disease Resistance: Concepts & Applications. LC 71-128175. (Illus.). 412p. 1973. 28.75x (ISBN 0-271-01141-6). Pa St U Pr.
Noordam, D. Identification of Plant Viruses: Methods & Experiments. (Illus.). 205p. 1974. pap. 16.00 (ISBN 90-220-0464-3, PDC43, PUDOC). Unipub.
Pathank, P. K. & Heinrichs, E. A. A Bibliography of Varietal Resistance to the Rice Gall Midge, Orseolia Oryzael (Wood-Mason) 45p. 1982. 30.00x (ISBN 0-85198-493-2, Pub. by CAB Bks England). State Mutual Bk.
Pest Resistance to Pesticides & Crop Loss Assessment: Report of the Third Session of the FAO Panel of Experts, Held in Kyoto, Japan, 6 August 1980. (Plant Production & Protection Papers: No. 6). (Eng., Fr. & Span.). 42p. 1981. pap. 7.50 (ISBN 92-5-101104-4, F2231, FAO). Unipub.
Pest Resistance to Pesticides & Crop Loss Assessment: Report of the 2nd Session of the FAO Panel of Experts Held in Rome, Aug.-Sept. 1978, Vol. 2. (Plant Production & Protection Papers: No. 6). (Eng., Fr. & Span.). 47p. 1979. pap. 7.50 (ISBN 92-5-100762-4, F1838, FAO). Unipub.
Pest Resistance to Pesticides in Agriculture. 38p. 1970. pap. 7.50 (ISBN 0-686-70624-2, F1984, FAO). Unipub.
Pests & Disease Control in Glasshouse Crops. 106p. 1979. 42.00x (ISBN 0-901436-52-6, Pub. by CAB Bks England). State Mutual Bk.
Plumb, R. T. & Thresh, J. M. Plant Virus Epidemiology. (Illus.). 388p. 1983. 48.00x (ISBN 0-632-01028-2, Pub. by Blackwell UK). Blackwell Pubns.
Riker, Tom. The Healthy, Garden Book. 1978. pap. 7.95 (ISBN 0-8128-6009-8). Stein & Day.
Scopes, N., ed. Pest & Disease Control Handbook. 450p. 1979. 99.00x (ISBN 0-901436-42-9, Pub. by CAB Bks England). State Mutual Bk.
Scopes, Nigel. Pest & Disease Control Handbook. 2nd ed. 672p. 1983. 57.00x (ISBN 0-901436-78-X, Pub. by B C P C England). Intl Spec Bk.
Smith, P. M., et al. Pest & Disease Control of Hardy Nursery Stock, Bedding Plants & Turf. 195p. 1983. pap. 13.00x (ISBN 0-901436-83-6, Pub. by B C P C England). Intl Spec Bk.
Soils & Crop Protection Chemicals. (Monograph Ser.: No. 27). 200p. (Orig.). 1984. pap. 32.00x (ISBN 0-901436-80-1, Pub. by B C P C England). Intl Spec Bk.
Vanderplank, J. E. Disease Resistance in Plants. 2nd ed. LC 83-21328. 1984. text ed. 34.50 reference (ISBN 0-12-711442-4). Acad Pr.
Williams, R. D. Crop Protection Handbook: Grassland & Forage Legumes. 1983. 95.00x (ISBN 0-901436-70-4, Pub. by BCPC Pubns England). State Mutual Bk.
Wilson, Charles L. & Graham, Charles L., eds. Exotic Plant Pests & North American Agriculture. 1983. 65.00 (ISBN 0-12-757880-3). Acad Pr.

PLANTS–DISEASES
see Plant Diseases

PLANTS–DROUGHT RESISTANCE
see also Plants, Effect of Drought on

Van-Ollenbach, Aubrey. Planting Guide to the Middle East. 1979. 49.50 (ISBN 0-85139-513-9, Pub. by Architectural Pr). Nichols Pub.

PLANTS–ECOLOGY
see Botany–Ecology

PLANTS–EMBRYOLOGY
see Botany–Embryology

PLANTS–EVOLUTION

Briggs, David & Walters, S. M. Plant Variation & Evolution. 2nd ed. LC 83-14310. (Illus.). 350p. 1984. 59.50 (ISBN 0-521-25706-9); pap. 17.95 (ISBN 0-521-27665-9). Cambridge U Pr.
Carlquist, Sherwin. Ecological Strategies of Xylem Evolution. LC 74-76382. (Illus.). 1975. 36.50x (ISBN 0-520-02730-2). U of Cal Pr.
Coulter, John M. Evolution of Sex in Plants. (Illus.). 1973. Repr. of 1914 ed. lib. bdg. 10.75x (ISBN 0-02-843230-4). Hafner.
Darlington, C. D. Chromosome Botany & the Origins of Cultivated Plants. rev. ed. 1973. 18.95x (ISBN 0-02-843670-9). Hafner.
Delevoryas, Theodore. Plant Diversification. 2nd ed. LC 76-30858. 144p. 1977. pap. text ed. 17.95x (ISBN 0-03-080133-8, HoltC). HR&W.
De Vries, H. Mutation Theory, 2 Vols. in 1. Farmer, J. B. & Darbishire, trs. 1909-1910. 58.00 (ISBN 0-527-93470-4). Kraus Repr.
Gerarde, John. The Herball or Generall Historie of Plantes. 303p. 1984. Repr. of 1597 ed. text ed. 85.00x (ISBN 0-86590-238-0, Pub. by Neeraj Pub Hse New Delhi). Apt Bks.
Godwin, Harry. History of the British Flora: A Factual Basis for Phytogeography. 2nd ed. (Cambridge Science Classics Ser.). 551p. 1984. pap. 34.50 (ISBN 0-521-26941-5). Cambridge U Pr.
Good, Ronald. Features of Evolution in the Flowering Plants. LC 74-82210. (Illus.). 416p. 1974. pap. text ed. 6.95 (ISBN 0-486-61591-X). Dover.
--Features of Evolution in the Flowering Plants. (Illus.) 11.50 (ISBN 0-8446-5194-X). Peter Smith.
Grant, Verne. Plant Speciation. 2nd ed. LC 81-6159. (Illus.). 544p. 1981. 52.50x (ISBN 0-231-05112-3); pap. 18.50x (ISBN 0-231-04460-7). Columbia U Pr.
Hughes, Norman F. Paleobiology of Angiosperm Origins: Problems of Mesozoic Seed-Plant Evolution. LC 75-3855. (Illus.). 216p. 1976. 57.50 (ISBN 0-521-20809-2). Cambridge U Pr.

Scagel, Robert F., et al. Plants: An Evolutionary Survey. 757p. 1984. write for info. (ISBN 0-534-00677-9); pap. write for info. (ISBN 0-534-02802-0). Wadsworth Pub.

Stebbins, George L. Variations & Evolution in Plants. LC 50-9426. (Columbia Biological Ser.: No. 16). (Illus.). 643p. 1950. 75.00x (ISBN 0-231-01733-2). Columbia U Pr.

Van Steenis, C. Rheophytes of the World: An Account of Flood - Resistant Flowering Plants & Ferns & the Theory of Autonomous Evolution. 424p. 1981. 75.00 (ISBN 90-286-0840-0). Sijthoff & Noordhoff.

PLANTS–FLOWERING

see Plants, Flowering Of

PLANTS–GENETICS

see Plant Genetics

PLANTS–GEOGRAPHICAL DISTRIBUTION

see Phytogeography

PLANTS–GROWTH

see Growth (Plants)

PLANTS–HYBRIDIZATION

see Hybridization, Vegetable

PLANTS–IDENTIFICATION

Affolter, James M. A Monograph of the Genus Lilaeopsis (Umbelliferae) Anderson, Christiane, ed. LC 85-1291. (Systematic Botany Monographs: Vol. 6). (Illus.). 140p. (Orig.). 1985. pap. 18.00 (ISBN 0-912861-06-1). Am Soc Plant.

Baumgardt, John P. How to Identify Flowering Plant Families. (Illus.). 269p. 1982. pap. 22.95 (ISBN 0-917304-21-7). Timber.

Britten, James, et al, eds. William Turner, Libellus de re Herbaria 1538, the Names of Herbes 1548. ix, 275p. 1965. Repr. of 1548 ed. 22.50x (ISBN 0-318-02524-8, Pub by Brit Mus Nat Hist England). Sabbot-Natural Hist Bks.

Britton, Nathaniel L. & Brown, Addison. Illustrated Flora of the Northern United States & Canada, 3 Vols. (Illus.). 1970. pap. 12.95 ea.; Vol. 1. pap. (ISBN 0-486-22642-5); Vol. 2. pap. (ISBN 0-486-22643-3); Vol. 3. pap. (ISBN 0-486-22644-1). Dover.

Clifford, H. T. & Ludlow, Gwen. Keys to the Families & Genera of Queensland. 2nd ed. (Flowering Plants (Magnoliophyta)). (Illus.). 1979. pap. 19.95x (ISBN 0-7022-1225-3). U of Queensland Pr.

Dirr, Michael. Photographic Manual for Woody Landscape Plants. (Illus.). 1978. text ed. 24.00x (ISBN 0-87563-156-8); pap. text ed. 16.40 (ISBN 0-87563-153-3). Stipes.

Dwelley, Marilyn J. Trees & Shrubs of New England. LC 79-52448. (Illus., Orig.). 1980. pap. 12.95 (ISBN 0-89272-064-6). Down East.

Elisens, Wayne J. Monograph of the Maurandyinae (Scrophulariaceae-Antirrhineae) Anderson, Christiane, ed. LC 85-1266. (Systematic Botany Monographs: Vol. 5). (Illus.). 97p. (Orig.). 1985. pap. 12.00 (ISBN 0-912861-05-3). Am Soc Plant.

Hicks, Ray R., Jr. & Stephenson, George K. Woody Plants of the Western Gulf Region. (Illus.). 1978. pap. text ed. 13.95 (ISBN 0-8403-1880-4). Kendall-Hunt.

Kartesz, John T. & Kartesz, Rosemarie. Synonymized Checklist of the Vascular Flora of the United States, Canada, & Greenland. xlviii, 494p. 1980. 35.00x (ISBN 0-8078-1422-9). U of NC Pr.

Kresanek, Jaroslav. Healing Plants. (Illus.). 224p. 1985. 8.95 (ISBN 0-668-06306-8). Arco.

McGuire, Diane K., ed. Beatrix Farrand's Plant Book for Dumbarton Oaks. LC 80-12169. (Illus.). 1980. 20.00x (ISBN 0-88402-095-9); pap. 10.00x (ISBN 0-88402-102-5). Dumbarton Oaks.

Mohlenbrock, Robert H. Flowering Plants: Lilies to Orchids. LC 69-16118. (Illustrated Flora of Illinois Ser.). (Illus.). 304p. 1970. 22.95x (ISBN 0-8093-0408-2). S Ill U Pr.

Plants of Deep Canyon: The Central Coachella Valley of California. LC 79-63644. 1979. 14.95 (ISBN 0-942290-03-8). Boyd Deep Canyon.

Roxburgh, William. Flora Indica: Descriptions of Indian Plants. 842p. 1971. Repr. of 1832 ed. 52.50 (ISBN 0-686-81241-7). Krieger.

Shaw, Richard J. & On, Danny. Plants of Waterton-Glacier National Parks & the Northern Rockies. Orig. Title: Plants of Waterton-Glacier National Parks. 160p. 1981. pap. 6.95 (ISBN 0-87842-137-8). Mountain Pr.

Smith, James P. & York, Richard, eds. Inventory of Rare & Endangered Vascular Plants of California. 3rd ed. (Special Publication Ser.: No. 1). 192p. (Orig.). 1985. pap. 10.95x (ISBN 0-943460-10-7). Calif Native.

Stevens, John E. Discovering Wild Plant Names. 1985. (ISBN 0-913714-59-3). Legacy Bks.

Stubbendieck, J. & Hatch, Stephan L. North American Range Plants. 2nd ed. LC 82-8560. xii, 464p. 1982. p. 26.95xo. (ISBN 0-8032-4140-2); pap. 13.95x (ISBN 0-8032-9132-9). U of Nebr Pr.

Tykac, J. & Vanek, V. A Field Guide in Color to Plants. LC 79-13564. (Field Guide in Color Ser.). (Illus.). 1979. 6.95 (ISBN 0-7064-1056-4, Mayflower Bks). Smith Pubs.

Walters, S. M., et al, eds. The European Garden Flora: Mononcotyledons, Pt. 2-Juncaceae to Orchidaceae, Vol. 2. (Illus.). 318p. 1984. 59.50 (ISBN 0-521-25864-2). Cambridge U Pr.

Wiggins, Ira L. Flora of Baja California. LC 77-92948. (Illus.). 1054p. 1980. 75.00x (ISBN 0-8047-1016-3). Stanford U Pr.

PLANTS–IMMUNITY

see Plants–Disease and Pest Resistance

PLANTS–IRRITABILITY AND MOVEMENTS

see also Insectivorous Plants

Darwin, Charles R. The Power of Movement in Plants. 2nd ed. LC 65-23402. 1966. Repr. of 1881 ed. lib. bdg. 55.00 (ISBN 0-306-70921-X). Da Capo.

--The Power of Movement in Plants. 3rd ed. LC 72-3901. (Illus.). x, 592p. 1972. 42.50 (ISBN 0-404-08415-X). AMS Pr.

Fallah, Skaidrite M. Evoked Biological Responses of Plants - Annotated Bibliography. 60p. 1974. pap. 3.95 (ISBN 0-917200-03-9). ESPress.

Haupt, W. & Feinleib, M. E., eds. Physiology of Movements. (Encyclopedia of Plant Physiology: Vol. 7). (Illus.). 1979. 118.00 (ISBN 0-387-08776-1). Springer-Verlag.

Plant Nutrient Supply & Movement. (Technical Reports Ser.: No. 48). 160p. 1965. pap. 12.50 (ISBN 92-0-115265-5, IDC48, IAEA). Unipub.

Retallack, Dorothy. The Sound of Music & Plants. (Illus.). 96p. 1973. pap. 3.00 (ISBN 0-87516-170-7). De Vorss.

PLANTS–METABOLISM

see also Plant Translocation

Chibnall, Albert C. Protein Metabolism in the Plant. 1939. 39.50x (ISBN 0-685-69795-9); pap. 19.50x (ISBN 0-685-69796-7). Elliots Bks.

Creasy, Leroy L. & Hrazdina, Geza, eds. Cellular & Subcellular Localization in Plant Metabolism. LC 82-7560. (Recent Advances in Phytochemistry Ser.: Vol. 16). 288p. 1982. 39.50x (ISBN 0-306-41023-0, Plenum Pr). Plenum Pub.

Duffus, C. M. & Duffus, J. H. Carbohydrate Metabolism in Plants. LC 82-22855. (Illus.). 192p. (Orig.). 1984. 13.95 (ISBN 0-582-44642-2). Longman.

Geissman, T. A. & Crout, D. H. Organic Chemistry of Secondary Plant Metabolism. LC 71-81384. 1969. pap. 20.00 (ISBN 0-87735-201-1). Freeman Cooper.

Hall, J. L. & Flowers, T. J. Plant Cell Structure & Metabolism. 2nd ed. (Illus.). 480p. (Orig.). 1982. pap. 22.00x (ISBN 0-582-44408-X). Longman.

Lewis, D. H., ed. Storage Carbohydrates in Vascular Plants. (Society for Experimental Biology Seminar Ser.: No. 19). (Illus.). 256p. 1985. 69.50 (ISBN 0-521-23698-3). Cambridge U Pr.

Owen, Charles A., Jr. Copper Deficiency & Toxicity: Acquired & Inherited, in Plants, Animals, & Man. LC 81-11061. (Noyes Publications-Copper in Biology & Medicine Ser.). 189p. 1982. 28.00 (ISBN 0-8155-0868-9). Noyes.

Richter, Gerhard. Plant Metabolism. 450p. 1980. 60.95x (ISBN 0-85664-955-4, Pub. by Croom Helm England). State Mutual Bk.

--Plant Metabolism. 475p. text ed. 29.50 (ISBN 0-85664-955-4). Univ Park.

Smith, H., ed. Plants & the Daylight Spectrum. LC 81-66697. 1982. 59.00 (ISBN 0-12-650980-8). Acad Pr.

Vickery, Brian & Vickery, Margaret. Secondary Plant Metabolism. 350p. 1981. text ed. 53.00 (ISBN 0-8391-1676-4). Univ Park.

PLANTS–MIGRATION

Laufer, Berthold. The American Plant Migration, Vol.1: The Potato. (Field Museum of Natural History). (Illus.). 1938. 11.00 (ISBN 0-527-01888-0). Kraus Repr.

Vale, Thomas R. Plants & People: Vegetation Change in North America. Knight, C. Gregory, ed. LC 82-8865. (Resource Publications in Geography Ser.). (Illus., Orig.). 1982. pap. 5.00 (ISBN 0-89291-151-4). Assn Am Geographers.

PLANTS–MORPHOLOGY

see Botany–Morphology

PLANTS–MOVEMENTS

see Plants–Irritability and Movements

PLANTS–NOMENCLATURE

see Botany–Nomenclature

PLANTS–NOMENCLATURE (POPULAR)

see Plant Names, Popular

PLANTS–NUTRITION

see also Deficiency Diseases in Plants; Hydroponics; Photosynthesis

Ashmead, Dewayne. Chelated Mineral Nutrition in Plants, Animals, & Man. (Illus.). 346p. 1982. 38.75x (ISBN 0-398-04603-4). C C Thomas.

Blaser, R. E. Agronomy & Health. 1970. pap. free (ISBN 0-89118-026-5). Am Soc Agron.

Development of Pure Peat Mixture for Raising Plants with Blocks. (Agricultural Research Reports: No. 668). 1965. pap. 5.50 (ISBN 90-220-0128-8, PDC164, PUDOC). Unipub.

An Experimental Study of Influence of Micro-Elements on Uptake of Macroelements by Plants. 1961. pap. 4.00 (ISBN 90-220-0202-0, PDC159, PUDOC). Unipub.

Food for Plants. (Discovering Soils Ser.: No. 6). 33p. 1978. pap. 6.00 (ISBN 0-643-02170-1, C013, CSIRO). Unipub.

Fried, Maurice & Broeshart, Hans. Soil-Plant System in Relation to Inorganic Nutrition. (Atomic Energy Commission Monographs). 1967. 23.50 (ISBN 0-12-268050-2). Acad Pr.

Fussell, G. E. Crop Nutrition: Science & Practice Before Liebig. 236p. 1971. 8.50x (ISBN 0-87291-026-1). Coronado Pr.

Gauch, Hugh G. Inorganic Plant Nutrition. LC 72-76542. 488p. 1972. 49.50 (ISBN 0-87933-003-1). Van Nos Reinhold.

Improved Use of Plant Nutrients: Report of an Expert Consultation on Better Exploitation of Plant Nutrients, Rome, 18-22 April 1977. (Soils Bulletins: No. 37). 159p. (2nd Printing 1981). 1978. pap. 11.75 (ISBN 92-5-100583-4, F1455, FAO). Unipub.

Isotopes in Plant Nutrition & Physiology. (Proceedings Ser.). (Eng., Fr., Rus. & Span., Illus.). 594p. (Orig.). 1967. pap. 41.75 (ISBN 92-0-010067-8, ISP137, IAEA). Unipub.

Lauchli, A. & Bieleski, R. L., eds. Inorganic Plant Nutrition. (Encyclopedia of Plant Physiology: Vol. 15, Part A & B). (Illus.). 900p. 1983. 150.00 (ISBN 0-387-12103-X). Springer-Verlag.

Mortvedt, J. J., ed. Micronutrients in Agriculture. (Illus.). 1972. 12.50 (ISBN 0-89118-754-5). Soil Sci Soc Am.

Plant Nutrient Supply & Movement. (Technical Reports Ser.: No. 48). 160p. 1965. pap. 12.50 (ISBN 92-0-115265-5, IDC48, IAEA). Unipub.

Riker, Tom. The Healthy, Garden Book. 1978. pap. 7.95 (ISBN 0-8128-6009-8). Stein & Day.

Robinson, J. B. Annotated Bibliography of Colour Illustrated Mineral Deficiency Symptoms in Tropical Crops. 84p. 1974. 49.00x (ISBN 0-85198-304-9, Pub. by CAB Bks England). State Mutual Bk.

Samish, R. M. Recent Advances in Plant Nutrition, 2 vols. LC 78-179403. (Illus.). 1972. Set. 144.50 (ISBN 0-677-14390-7); Vol. 1, 368p. 77.50 (ISBN 0-677-12360-4); Vol. 2, 410p. 85.75 (ISBN 0-677-12370-1). Gordon.

Sutcliffe, J. F. & Baker, D. A. Plantis & Mineral Sales. 1981. 32.00x (ISBN 0-686-76657-1, Pub. by Oxford & IBH India). State Mutual Bk.

Tinker, P. B. & Lauchli, Andre, eds. Advances in Plant Nutrition. (Advances in Plant Nutrition Ser.: Vol. 1). 320p. 1984. 32.95x (ISBN 0-03-070087-6). Praeger.

Traynor, Joe. Ideas in Soil & Plant Nutrition. (Orig.). 1980. pap. 5.00 (ISBN 0-9604704-0-9); pap. text ed. 5.00 (ISBN 0-9604704-0-9). Kovak Bks.

Van Eysings, Roorda & Smilde, K. W. Nutritional Disorders in Tomatoes, Cucumbers & Lettuce Underglass. 130p. 1981. 63.00x (ISBN 90-220-0737-5, Pub. by CAB Bks England). State Mutual Bk.

PLANTS–PATHOLOGY

see Plant Diseases

PLANTS–PEST RESISTANCE

see Plants–Disease and Pest Resistance

PLANTS–RADIATION EFFECTS

see Plants, Effect of Radiation On

PLANTS–REPRODUCTION

see also Fertilization of Plants; Spores (Botany)

Blakeslee, A. F. Sexual Reproduction in the Mucorinaeae. (Biblioteca Mycologica Ser: No. 48). 1976. Repr. of 1904 ed. text ed. 14.00 (ISBN 3-7682-1064-2). Lubrecht & Cramer.

Buckles, Mary P. The Flowers Around Us: A Photographic Essay on Their Reproductive Structures. LC 82-24815. 128p. 1985. 29.95 (ISBN 0-8262-0402-3). U of Mo Pr.

Coulter, John M. Evolution of Sex in Plants. (Illus.). 1973. Repr. of 1914 ed. lib. bdg. 10.75x (ISBN 0-02-843230-4). Hafner.

Johnson, Christopher B. Physiological Processes of Limiting Plant Productivity. 1981. text ed. 99.95 (ISBN 0-408-10649-2). Butterworth.

Meudt, Werner J., ed. Strategies of Plant Reproduction. LC 82-11594. (Beltsville Symposia in Agricultural Research Ser.: Vol. 6). (Illus.). 400p. 1983. text ed. 39.50x (ISBN 0-86598-054-3). Allanheld.

Nitzsche, Werner & Wenzel, Gerhard. Haploids in Plant Breeding. (Advances in Plant Breeding Ser.: Vol. 8). (Illus.). 101p. 1977. pap. text ed. 28.00 (ISBN 3-489-75010-1). Parey Sci Pubs.

Thomas, E., et al. From Single Cells to Plants. (The Wykeham Science Ser.: No. 38). 188p. 1975. pap. cancelled (ISBN 0-85109-520-8). Taylor & Francis.

Toogood, Alan. Propagation. LC 80-6164. (Illus.). 336p. 1982. pap. 12.95 (ISBN 0-8128-6149-3). Stein & Day.

Trichlorofon. (Specifications for Plant Protection Products: No. 7.50). pap. 7.50 (F2004, FAO). Unipub.

Trifluralin. (Specifications for Plant Protection Products: No. 30). 1977. pap. 7.50 (F2013, FAO). Unipub.

Triometon. (Specifications for Plant Protection Products: No. 44). 1977. pap. 7.50 (ISBN 92-5-100553-2, F2021, FAO). Unipub.

Van Den Ende, Herman. Sexual Interactions in Plants. 1976. 39.00 (ISBN 0-12-711250-2). Acad Pr.

Willson, Mary F. Plant Reproductive Ecology. LC 82-24826. 282p. 1983. 39.95 (ISBN 0-471-08362-3, Pub. by Wiley-Interscience). Wiley.

Willson, Mary F. & Burley, Nancy. Mate Choice in Plants. LC 83-42590. (Monographs in Population Biology: No. 19). (Illus.). 244p. 1983. 35.00x (ISBN 0-691-08333-9); pap. 12.50x (ISBN 0-691-08334-7). Princeton U Pr.

PLANTS–RESPIRATION

DeWit, C. T., et al. Simulation of Assimilation, Respiration & Transpiration of Crops. LC 78-11384. 140p. 1978. pap. 26.95x (ISBN 0-470-26494-2). Halsted Pr.

Douce, R. & Day, D. A., eds. Higher Plant Cell Respiration. (New Encyclopedia of Plant Physiology Ser.: Vol. 18). (Illus.). 525p. 1985. 104.50 (ISBN 0-387-13935-4). Springer-Verlag.

Lemon, Edgar R. CO-Two & Plants: The Reponse of Plants to Rising Levels of Atmospheric Carbon Dioxide. 350p. 1983. softcover 26.50x (ISBN 0-86531-597-3). Westview.

Opik, Helgi. Respiration of Higher Plants. (Studies in Biology: No. 120). 64p. 1980. pap. text ed. 8.95 (ISBN 0-7131-2801-1). E Arnold.

Palmer, John M., ed. The Physiology & Biochemistry of Plant Respiration. (Society for Experimental Biology Seminar Ser.: No. 20). 250p. 1984. 59.50 (ISBN 0-521-23697-5). Cambridge U Pr.

Zelitch, Israel. Photosynthesis, Photorespiration & Plant Productivity. 1971. 56.00 (ISBN 0-12-779250-3). Acad Pr.

PLANTS–SOILLESS CULTURE

see Hydroponics

PLANTS–TRANSLOCATION

see Plant Translocation

PLANTS–TRANSPIRATION

see also Plants–Water Requirements

DeWit, C. T., et al. Simulation of Assimilation, Respiration & Transpiration of Crops. LC 78-11384. 140p. 1978. pap. 26.95x (ISBN 0-470-26494-2). Halsted Pr.

Planting & Transplanting. 1982. 2.25. Bklyn Botanic.

PLANTS–WATER REQUIREMENTS

see also Plant-Water Relationships

CAB Books, ed. Lentils: International Center for Agricultural Research in Dry Areas. 216p. 1981. 99.00x (ISBN 0-85198-475-4, Pub. by CAB Bks England). State Mutual Bk.

Stone, John F. Plant Modification for More Efficient Water Use, Vol. 14. (Developments in Agricultural & Managed Forest Ecology Ser.: Vol. 1). 330p. 1975. Repr. 53.25 (ISBN 0-444-41273-5). Elsevier.

Van-Ollenbach, Aubrey. Planting Guide to the Middle East. 1979. 49.50 (ISBN 0-85139-513-9, Pub. by Architectural Pr). Nichols Pub.

PLANTS, CULTIVATED

see also Annuals (Plants); Floriculture; Flowers; Perennials; Plants, Edible; Tropical Plants

Alefeld, F. Landwirtschaftliche Flora. 1966. Repr. of 1866 ed. lib. bdg. 42.70x (ISBN 3-87429-001-8). Lubrecht & Cramer.

Allen, H. Direct Drilling & Reduced Cultivations. (Illus.). 219p. 22.95 (ISBN 0-85236-113-0, Pub. by Farming Pr Uk). Diamond Farm Bk.

Bailey, Liberty H. Manual of Cultivated Plants. rev. ed. 1949. 37.95 (ISBN 0-02-505520-8). Macmillan.

Benzing, David H. Biology of the Bromeliads. 305p. (Orig.). 1980. pap. 14.95x (ISBN 0-916422-21-6). Mad River.

Bosel, T. K. & Bhattacharjee, S. K. Garden Plants. 282p. 1980. 50.00x (ISBN 0-686-84453-X, Pub. by Oxford & I B H India). State Mutual Bk.

Broertjes, C. & Van Harten, A. M. The Application of Mutation Breeding Methods in the Improvement of Vegetatively Propagated Crops. (Developments in Crop Science Ser.: Vol. 2). 316p. 1978. 76.75 (ISBN 0-444-41618-8). Elsevier.

Burton, W. G. Post-Harvest Physiology of Food Crops. (Illus.). 320p. 1982. 35.00x (ISBN 0-582-46038-7). Longman.

CAB Books, ed. Lentils: International Center for Agricultural Research in Dry Areas. 216p. 1981. 99.00x (ISBN 0-85198-475-4, Pub. by CAB Bks England). State Mutual Bk.

El Cultivo y la Utilizacion del Tarwi: Lupinus Mutabilis Sweet. (Plant Production & Protection Papers: No. 36). (Span.). 248p. 1982. pap. 17.75 (ISBN 92-5-301197-1, F2479, FAO). Unipub.

Darlington, C. D. Chromosome Botany & the Origins of Cultivated Plants. rev. ed. 1973. 18.95x (ISBN 0-02-843670-9). Hafner.
Denno, Robert F. & McClure, Mark S. Variable Plants & Herbivores in Natural & Managed Systems. 1983. 64.00 (ISBN 0-12-209160-4). Acad Pr.
Flocker, William J. & Hartmann, Hudson T. Plant Science: Growth, Development & Utilization of Cultivated Plants. (Illus.). 688p. 1981. text ed. 32.95 (ISBN 0-13-681056-X). P-H.
Galston, Arthur W. Green Wisdom. (Illus.). 240p. 1983. pap. 6.95 (ISBN 0-399-50713-2, Wideview). Putnam Pub Group.
Gerard, John. Catalogus Arborum, Fructicum Ac Plantarum Tam Indigenarum Quam Exoticarum in Horto Johannis Gerardi. LC 73-6132. (English Experience Ser.: No. 598). 22p. 1973. Repr. of 1599 ed. 6.00 (ISBN 0-685-72641-X). Walter J Johnson.
Greene, Wilhelmina F. & Blomquist, Hugo L. Flowers of the South: Native & Exotic. xiv, 208p. 1953. 9.95 (ISBN 0-8078-0635-8). U of NC Pr.
Handelsman, Judith & Baerwald, Sara. Greenworks: Tender Loving Care for Plants. LC 73-1854. 1974. pap. 1.95 (ISBN 0-02-062890-0). Macmillan.
Hawkes, J. G. The Diversity of Crop Plants. (Illus.). 208p. 1983. text ed. 20.00x (ISBN 0-674-21286-X). Harvard U Pr.
Joiner, Jasper N. Foliage Plant Production. (Illus.). 608p. 1981. text ed. 32.95 (ISBN 0-13-322867-3). P-H.
King, Eleanor A. Bible Plants for American Gardens. LC 75-3646. (Illus.). 224p. 1975. pap. 4.50 (ISBN 0-486-23188-7). Dover.
Kyte, Ann. Plants from Test Tubes. (Illus.). 196p. 1983. pap. 22.95x (ISBN 0-917304-50-0). Timber.
Langer, R. H. & Hill, G. D. Agricultural Plants. LC 80-41536. (Illus.). 300p. 1982. 44.50 (ISBN 0-521-22450-0); pap. 17.95 (ISBN 0-521-29506-8). Cambridge U Pr.
Li Hui-Lin. The Origin & Cultivation of Shade & Ornamental Trees. LC 62-11271. (Illus.). 288p. 1974. pap. 9.95 (ISBN 0-8122-1070-0, Pa Paperbks). U of Pa Pr.
Meyen, Franz J. Outlines of the Geography of Plants: Native Country, the Culture, & the Uses of the Principal Cultivated Plants on Which the Prosperity of Nations Is Based. Egerton, Frank N., ed. LC 77-74239. (History of Ecology Ser.). 1978. Repr. of 1846 ed. lib. bdg. 35.50x (ISBN 0-405-10408-1). Ayer Co Pubs.
Milthorpe, F. L. & Moorby, J. Introduction to Crop Physiology. 2nd ed. LC 78-26380. (Illus.). 1980. o.p 49.50 (ISBN 0-521-22624-4); pap. 18.95 (ISBN 0-521-29581-5). Cambridge U Pr.
Thompson, R. & Casey, R. Perspectives for Peas & Lupins As Protein Crops. 1983. 54.50 (ISBN 90-247-2792-8, Pub. by Martinus Nijhoff Netherlands). Kluwer Academic.
Zeven, A. C. & De Wet, J. M. J. Dictionary of Cultivated Plants & Their Regions of Diversity: Excluding Most Ornamentals, Forest Trees & Lower Plants. 2nd ed. 263p. 1983. 38.75 (ISBN 90-220-0785-5, PDC241, Pudoc). Unipub.
Zhukovsky, P. M. & Zeven, A. C. Dictionary of Cultivated Plants & Centres of Diversity: Excluding Ornamentals, Forest Trees & Lower Plants. (Illus.). 200p. 1975. 36.00 (ISBN 90-220-0549-6, PDC27, Pudoc). Unipub.

PLANTS, CULTIVATED–BIBLIOGRAPHY

Elliot, W. Roger & Jones, David L. Encyclopedia of Australian Plants Suitable for Cultivation, Vol. 2. (Illus.). 517p. 59.95 (ISBN 0-85091-143-5). Intl Spec Bk.

PLANTS, EDIBLE

see also Mushrooms, Edible

Angier, Bradford. Field Guide to Edible Wild Plants. LC 73-23042. (Illus.). 256p. 1974. pap. 9.95 (ISBN 0-8117-2018-7). Stackpole.
Atta, Marian Van. Wild Edibles, Identification for Living off the Land. rev. ed. LC 84-62805. (Living off the Land Ser.). (Illus.). 64p. 1985. pap. text ed. 4.95 (ISBN 0-938524-01-1). Geraventure.
Berglund, Berndt & Bolsby, Clare E. The Complete Outdoorsman's Guide to Edible Wild Plants. LC 77-82243. (Illus.). 1978. pap. 4.95 (ISBN 0-684-15481-1). Scribner.
Beshoar, Daniel. Violet Soup: Common Edible Plants of the Rockies. (Illus.). 70p. 1982. 8.00 (ISBN 0-86541-009-7); pap. 4.00 (ISBN 0-86541-010-0). Filter.
Brouk, B. Plants Consumed by Man. 1975. 73.50 (ISBN 0-12-136450-X). Acad Pr.
Clifton, Claire. Edible Flowers. (Illus.). 96p. 1984. 10.95 (ISBN 0-07-011382-3). McGraw.
Cribb, A. B. & Cribb, J. W. Wild Food in Australia. 1980. pap. 6.50x (ISBN 0-00-634436-4, Pub. by W Collins Australia). Intl Spec Bk.
Elias, Thomas & Dykeman. Field Guide to North American Edible Wild Plants. LC 82-18785. 286p. 1983. 19.95 (ISBN 0-442-22200-9). Van Nos Reinhold.
Elliott, Douglas. Roots: An Underground Botany. LC 75-46234. (Illus.). 160p. 1976. pap. 7.95 (ISBN 0-85699-132-5). Chatham Pr.
Furlong, Marjorie & Pill, Virginia. Wild Edible Fruits & Berries. LC 74-32015. (Illus.). 64p. 1974. 11.95 (ISBN 0-87961-033-6); pap. 5.95 (ISBN 0-87961-032-8). Naturegraph.
Gibbons, Euell. Stalking the Wild Asparagus. 1970. pap. 6.95 field guide ed. (ISBN 0-679-50223-8). McKay.
Harrington, H. D. Edible Native Plants of the Rocky Mountains. LC 67-29685. (Illus.). 292p. 1974. pap. 9.95 (ISBN 0-8263-0343-9). U of NM Pr.
--Western Edible Wild Plants. LC 77-190061. (Illus.). 1972. pap. 6.95 (ISBN 0-8263-0218-1). U of NM Pr.
Harris, Ben C. Eat the Weeds. LC 69-12302. 1969. pap. 3.95 (ISBN 0-517-51730-2). Barre.
--Eat the Weeds. LC 73-83951. 176p. 1973. pap. 1.50 (ISBN 0-87983-066-2). Keats.
Hedrick. Sturtevant's Edible Plants of the World. 686p. 1972. pap. 10.95 (ISBN 0-486-20459-6). Dover.
--Sturtevant's Edible Plants of the World. 18.50 (ISBN 0-8446-4552-4). Peter Smith.
Heiser, Charles B., Jr. Of Plants & People. LC 84-40688. (Illus.). 272p. 1985. 24.95 (ISBN 0-8061-1931-4). U of Okla Pr.
--The Sunflower. LC 74-15906. (Illus.). 198p. 1981. pap. 6.95 (ISBN 0-8061-1743-5). U of Okla Pr.
Howorth, Peter. Foraging along the Pacific Coast: From Mexico to Puget Sound. LC 84-21450. (Illus.). 250p. (Orig.). 1985. pap. 9.95 (ISBN 0-88496-228-8). Capra Pr.
Kirk, Donald R. Wild Edible Plants of Western North America. color ed. LC 75-5998. (Illus.). 343p. 1975. 11.95 (ISBN 0-87961-037-9); pap. 5.95 (ISBN 0-87961-036-0). Naturegraph.
Kunkel, G. Plants for Human Consumption: Annotated Checklist of Edible Phanerogams & Ferns. 393p. 1984. lib. bdg. 36.75X (ISBN 3-87429-216-9). Lubrecht & Cramer.
MacPherson, Alan & MacPherson, Sue. Edible & Useful Wildplants of the Urban West. LC 79-20899. (Illus.). 1979. pap. 9.95 (ISBN 0-87108-533-X). Pruett.
Main, Jody S. & Jamello, Nancy. Sprout Booklet & Stainless Screen Steel. (Living on This Planet Ser.). (Illus.). 14p. 1982. pap. 1.50 (ISBN 0-937148-01-6). Wild Horses.
Main, Jody S. & Jamello, Nancy P. Sprouts Are Good: Sprout Booklet. (Living On This Planet Ser.). (Illus.). 14p. 1982. pap. 0.83 (ISBN 0-937148-00-8). Wild Horses.
March, Kathryn G. & March, Andrew L. Common Edible & Medicinal Plants of Colorado, with Recipes & Prescriptions. LC 79-91117. (Illus.). 89p. (Orig.). 1979. pap. 5.95 (ISBN 0-940206-01-3). Meridian Hill.
Medsger, Oliver P. Edible Wild Plants. (Illus.). 359p. 1972. pap. 6.95 (ISBN 0-02-080910-7, Collier). Macmillan.
Peterson, Lee. A Field Guide to Eastern Edible Wild Plants. (Peterson Field Guide Ser.). 1984. 16.95 (ISBN 0-395-20445-3); pap. 10.95 (ISBN 0-395-31870-X). HM.
Richardson, Joan. Wild Edible Plants of New England: A Field Guide. (Illus.). 250p. 1985. pap. 9.95 (ISBN 0-89933-009-6). Globe Pequot.
Robinson, Peggy. Profiles of Northwest Plants: Food Uses, Medicinal Uses, & Legends. 2nd ed. (Illus.). 168p. 1979. pap. 5.95 (ISBN 0-686-27923-9). P Robinson.
Saunders, Charles F. Edible & Useful Wild Plants of the United States & Canada. 12.50 (ISBN 0-8446-5451-5). Peter Smith.
Sweet, Muriel. Common Edible & Useful Plants of the East & Midwest. LC 75-8914. (Illus.). 79p. 1975. 9.95 (ISBN 0-87961-035-2); pap. 3.95 (ISBN 0-87961-034-4). Naturegraph.
Tomikel, John. Edible Wild Plants of Eastern United States & Canada. LC 75-25198. (Illus.). 100p. 1976. 8.00x (ISBN 0-910042-22-5); pap. 3.95 (ISBN 0-910042-21-7). Allegheny.
--Edible Wild Plants of Pennsylvania & New York. LC 72-89403. 1973. 5.00 (ISBN 0-910042-14-4); pap. 2.50 (ISBN 0-910042-13-6). Allegheny.
Turner, Nancy J. & Szczawinski, Adam F. Edible Wild Fruits & Nuts of Canada. (Illus.). 1979. pap. 9.95 spiral bdg. (ISBN 0-660-00128-4, 56328-6, Pub. by Natl Mus Canada). U of Chicago Pr.
Yanovsky, Elias. Food Plants of the North American Indians. 1980. lib. bdg. 49.95 (ISBN 0-8490-3108-7). Gordon Pr.

PLANTS, EFFECT OF AIR POLLUTION ON

Dugger, Mack, ed. Air Pollution Effects on Plant Growth. LC 74-26543. (ACS Symposium Ser.: No. 3). 1974. 19.95 (ISBN 0-8412-0223-0). Am Chemical.
Grace, J., et al. Plants & Their Atmospheric Environment. (British Ecological Society Symposia Ser.). 419p. 1981. 89.95x (ISBN 0-470-27125-6). Halsted Pr.
Guderian, R. Air Pollution: Phytotoxicity of Acidic Gases & Its Significance in Air Pollution Control. LC 76-50626. (Ecological Studies: Vol. 22). 1977. 36.00 (ISBN 0-387-08030-9). Springer-Verlag.
Koziol, Michael J. & Whatley, F. R., eds. Gaseous Air Pollutants & Plant Metabolism. 1984. text ed. 99.95 (ISBN 0-408-11152-6). Butterworth.
Lauenroth, W. K. & Preston, E. M., eds. The Effects of SO2 on a Grassland: A Case Study in the Northern Great Plains of the United States. (Ecological Studies, Analysis & Synthesis: Vol. 45). (Illus.). 270p. 1984. 32.00 (ISBN 0-387-90943-5). Springer-Verlag.
Mansfield, T. A., ed. Effects of Air Pollutants on Plants. LC 75-32449. (Society for Experimental Biology Seminar Ser.: No. 1). (Illus.). 180p. 1976. 44.50 (ISBN 0-521-21087-9); pap. 17.95x (ISBN 0-521-29039-2). Cambridge U Pr.
Mukammal, E. D. Review of Present Knowledge of Plant Injury by Air Pollution: Report of the CAGM Rapporteur on Non-Radioactive Pollutants of the Biosphere & Their Injurious Effects on Plants, Animals & Yields. (Technical Note Ser.: No. 147). 27p. 1976. pap. 12.00 (ISBN 92-63-10431-X, W194, WMO). Unipub.
Treshow, Michael, ed. Air Pollution & Plant Life. LC 83-5905. (Environmental Monographs & Symposia: 1-505). 400p. 1984. 75.00x (ISBN 0-471-90103-2, Pub. by Wiley-Interscience). Wiley.

PLANTS, EFFECT OF COLD ON

see also Frost Protection

Influences of Temperature on Apachis Hypogaea: With Special Reference to Its Pollen Viability. 1963. pap. 6.75 (ISBN 90-220-0086-9, PDC160, PUDOC). Unipub.
Levitt, J. Responses of Plants to Environmental Stresses: Vol. I: Chilling, Freezing, & High Temperature Stresses. 2nd ed. (Physiological Ecology Ser.). 1980. 35.00 (ISBN 0-12-445501-8). Acad Pr.
Li, Paul H. & Sakai, A., eds. Plant Cold Hardiness & Freezing Stress. 1978. 47.50 (ISBN 0-12-447650-3). Acad Pr.
Roberts, D. W. & Miska, J. P. Cold Hardiness & Winter Survival of Plants 1965-1975. 470p. 1980. pap. 125.00x (ISBN 0-85198-477-0, Pub. by CAB Bks England). State Mutual Bk.
Stamp, Peter. Chilling Tolerance of Young Plants Demonstrated on the Example of Maize. (Advances in Agronomy & Crop Science Ser.: Vol. 7). (Illus.). 83p. (Orig.). 1984. pap. 21.00 (ISBN 3-489-71310-9). Parey Sci Pubs.

PLANTS, EFFECT OF DROUGHT ON

see also Plants–Drought Resistance

Stone, J. F. & Willis, W. O., eds. Plant Production & Management under Drought Conditions: Papers Presented at the Symposium, 4-6 Oct., 1982, Held at Tulsa, OK. (Developments in Agricultural & Managed-Forest Ecology Ser.: Vol. 12). 398p. 1983. Repr. 74.50 (ISBN 0-444-42214-5). Elsevier.

PLANTS, EFFECT OF LIGHT ON

see also Artificial Light Gardening

Mohr, H. Lecture on Photomorphogenesis. LC 72-83443. (Illus.). 300p. 1972. pap. 26.00 (ISBN 0-387-05879-6). Springer-Verlag.
Ott, John N. My Ivory Cellar. (Illus.). 8.50 (ISBN 0-8159-6217-7). Devin.
Smith, Harold & Holmes, Martin G., eds. Techniques in Photomorphogenesis. (Biological Techniques Ser.). 1984. 65.00 (ISBN 0-12-652990-6). Acad Pr.
Wareing, P. F. & Smith, H., eds. Photoperception by Plants. (Philosophical Transactions of the Royal Society: Series B, Vol. 303). (Illus.). 190p. 1984. text ed. 63.00x (ISBN 0-85403-220-7, Pub. by Royal Soc London). Scholium Intl.
Whatley, F. R. & Whatley, J. M. Light & Plant Life. (Studies in Biology: No. 124). 96p. 1980. pap. text ed. 8.95 (ISBN 0-7131-2785-6). E Arnold.

PLANTS, EFFECT OF MINERALS ON

see also Deficiency Diseases in Plants

Lepp, N. W., ed. Effect of Heavy Metal Pollution on Plants: Vol. 1, Effects of Trace Metals on Plant Function. (Pollution Monitoring Ser.). (Illus.). 352p. 1981. 55.50 (ISBN 0-85334-959-2, Pub. by Elsevier Applied Sci England). Elsevier.
--Effect of Heavy Metal Pollution on Plants: Vol. 2, Metals in the Environment. (Pollution Monitoring Ser.). (Illus.). 257p. 1981. 46.25 (ISBN 0-85334-923-1, Pub. by Elsevier Applied Sci England). Elsevier.
Loneragan, J. F. Copper in Soils & Plants. 1981. 47.50 (ISBN 0-12-455520-9). Acad Pr.

PLANTS, EFFECT OF POLLUTION ON

see also Plants, Effect of Air Pollution on

Murray, Frank, ed. Fluoride Emissions: Their Monitoring & Effects on Vegetation & Ecosystems. 234p. 1982. 36.00 (ISBN 0-12-511980-1). Acad Pr.
Ormrod, D. P. Pollution & Horticulture. (Fundamental Aspects of Pollution Control & Environmental Science Ser.: Vol. 4). 260p. 1978. 53.75 (ISBN 0-444-41726-5). Elsevier.

PLANTS, EFFECT OF RADIATION ON

Effects of Low Doses of Radiation on Crop Plants. (Technical Reports Ser.: No. 64). (Illus.). 58p. (Orig.). 1966. pap. 7.00 (ISBN 92-0-115466-6, IDC64, IAEA). Unipub.
Gausman, Harold W. Plant Leaf Optical Properties in Visible & Near-Infrared Light. (Graduate Studies: No. 29). (Illus.). 78p. 1985. 25.00 (ISBN 0-89672-132-9); pap. 10.00 (ISBN 0-89672-131-0). Tex Tech Pr.
Improving Plant Protein by Nuclear Techniques. (Proceedings Ser.). (Eng., Fr., Rus. & Span., Illus.). 460p. (Orig.). 1970. pap. 35.75 (ISBN 92-0-010170-4, ISP258, IAEA). Unipub.
Induced Mutations in Cross-Breeding. (Panel Proceedings Ser.). (Illus.). 256p. 1977. pap. 28.75 (ISBN 92-0-111676-4, ISP447, IAEA). Unipub.
Induced Mutations in Plants. (Proceedings Ser.). (Eng., Fr. & Span., Illus.). 748p. (Orig.). 1969. pap. 48.00 (ISBN 92-0-010369-3, ISP231, IAEA). Unipub.
Isotopes & Radiation in Plant Pathology. (Technical Reports Ser.: No. 66). pap. 9.00 (ISBN 92-0-015166-3, IDC66, IAEA). Unipub.
Isotopes & Radiation in Soil-Plant Nutrition Studies. (Proceedings Ser.). (Eng., Fr., Rus. & Span., Illus.). 624p. (Orig.). 1965. pap. 32.00 (ISBN 92-0-010265-4, ISP108, IAEA). Unipub.
Laboratory Training Manual on the Use of Isotopes & Radiation in Soil-Plant Relations Research. (Technical Reports Ser.: No. 29). (Illus.). 166p. 1964. pap. 10.00 (ISBN 92-0-115064-4, IDC29, IAEA). Unipub.
Limiting Steps in Ion Uptake by Plants from Soil. (Technical Reports Ser.: No. 65). (Illus.). 154p. 1966. pap. 12.50 (ISBN 92-0-115566-2, IDC65, IAEA). Unipub.
Radiation Effects & After-Effects in the Clear Polymethyl Methacrylate Dosimeter. (Agricultural Research Reports: 763). Date not set. pap. 12.00 (ISBN 90-220-0361-2, PDC78, PUDOC). Unipub.

PLANTS, EFFECT OF SALINITY ON

see Plants, Effect of Salts on

PLANTS, EFFECT OF SALTS ON

Staples, Richard C. & Toenniessen, Gary H. Salinity Tolerance in Plants: Strategies for Crop Improvement. LC 83-14759. (Environmental Science & Technology: Texts & Monographs: 1-121). 443p. 1984. 49.95 (ISBN 0-471-89674-8, Pub. by Wiley-Interscience). Wiley.
Value to Agriculture of High-Quality Water from Nuclear Desalination. 1969. pap. 12.00 (ISBN 92-0-041069-3, IAEA). Unipub.

PLANTS, EFFECT OF TEMPERATURE ON

see also Frost Protection

Levitt, J. Responses of Plants to Environmental Stresses: Vol. I: Chilling, Freezing, & High Temperature Stresses. 2nd ed. (Physiological Ecology Ser.). 1980. 35.00 (ISBN 0-12-445501-8). Acad Pr.
Money, D. C. Climate, Soils & Vegatation. 1981. 25.00x (ISBN 0-7231-0769-6, Pub. by Univ Tutorial England). State Mutual Bk.
Olien, Charles R. & Smith, Myrtle N. Analysis & Improvement of Plant Cold Hardiness. 224p. 1980. 69.00 (ISBN 0-8493-5397-1). CRC Pr.
School of Rural Economics & Related Studies, ed. Climate Advantage in Horticultural Production. 1981. 15.00x (ISBN 0-686-78798-6, Pub. by Sch Rural Econ England). State Mutual Bk.

PLANTS, FLOWERING OF

Baumgardt, John P. How to Identify Flowering Plant Families. (Illus.). 269p. 1982. pap. 22.95 (ISBN 0-917304-21-7). Timber.
Bernier, Georges, ed. The Physiology of Flowers, 2 vols. 1981. Vol. I, 168p. 56.00 (ISBN 0-8493-5709-8); Vol. II 248p. 81.50 (ISBN 0-8493-5710-1). CRC Pr.
Dyer, R. A. The Genera of South African Flowering Plants, 2 Vols. Incl. Vol. 1. Dicotyledons. 756p. text ed. 12.50 (ISBN 0-621-02854-1); Vol. 2. Monocotyledons. 284p. text ed. 12.50 (ISBN 0-621-02863-0). 1983 (Pub. by Dept Agriculture & Fish S Africa). Intl Spec Bk.
Geesink, R., et al, eds. Thonner's Analytical Key to the Families of Flowering Plants. (Leiden Botanical Ser.: Vol. 5). 200p. 37.00 (ISBN 90-6021-461-7, Pub. by Junk Pubs Netherlands). Kluwer Academic.
Gibbs, R. Darnley. Chemotaxonomy of Flowering Plants, 4 vols. (Illus.). 2500p. 1974. 150.00x set (ISBN 0-7735-0098-7). McGill-Queens U Pr.

Melrose, D. B. Plasma Astrophysics: Nonthermal Processes in Diffuse Magnetized Plasmas, Vol.1: The Emission,Absorption & Transfer of Waves in Plasmas. 280p. 1979. 61.50 (ISBN 0-677-02340-5). Gordon.
--Plasma Astrophysics: Nonthermal Processes in Diffuse Magnetized Plasmas, Vol. 2: Astrophysical Applications, 2 Vols. 1979. price, 714p 138.75 set (ISBN 0-677-03490-3); each 90.25 (ISBN 0-677-02130-5). Gordon.
Menzel, Donald H., ed. Selected Papers on Physical Processes in Ionized Plasmas. (Orig.). 1962. pap. text ed. 5.95 (ISBN 0-486-60060-2). Dover.
Miyamoto, Kenro. Plasma Physics for Nuclear Fusion. (Illus.). 623p. 1980. text ed. 60.00x (ISBN 0-262-13145-5). MIT Pr.
Montgomery, David C. Theory of the Unmagnetized Plasma. (Illus.). 412p. 1971. 75.25x (ISBN 0-677-03350-8). Gordon.
Moravcsik, M. J., ed. Recent Developments in Particle Physics. (Nuclear Physics Ser.). 272p. (Orig.). 1966. 74.25x (ISBN 0-677-11010-3). Gordon.
Nasser, Essam. Fundamentals of Gaseous Ionization & Plasma Electronics. LC 77-125275. (Wiley Series in Plasma Physics). pap. 89.30 (ISBN 0-317-08904-8, 2055184). Bks Demand UMI.
Nicholson, Dwight R. Introduction to Plasma Theory. LC 82-13658. (Plasma Physics Ser.). 292p. 1983. text ed. 38.50x (ISBN 0-471-09045-X). Wiley.
Nishida, A., ed. Magnetospheric Plasma Physics. 364p. 1982. 49.50 (ISBN 90-277-1345-6, Pub. by Reidel Holland). Kluwer Academic.
Oskam, H. J., ed. Plasma Processing of Materials. LC 84-14806. (Illus.). 268p. 1985. 36.00 (ISBN 0-8155-1003-9). Noyes.
Pai Shih-I. Magnetogasdynamics & Plasma Dynamics. (Illus.). 1962. 29.00 (ISBN 0-387-80608-3). Springer-Verlag.
Pecker-Wimel, C. Introduction a la Spectroscopie Des Plamas. (Cours & Documents de Mathematiques & de Physique Ser.). 168p. (Orig.). 1967. 44.25x (ISBN 0-677-50130-7). Gordon.
Plasma Chemistry, Vol. 1. LC 79-25770. (Topics in Current Chemistry: Vol. 89). (Illus.). 150p. 1980. 52.00 (ISBN 3-540-09825-9). Springer-Verlag.
Plasma Chemistry, Vol. 2. LC 79-25770. (Topics in Current Chemistry: Vol. 90). (Illus.). 140p. 1980. 52.00 (ISBN 3-540-09826-7). Springer-Verlag.
Plasma Physics & Controlled Nuclear Fusion Research: 1968, 2 vols. (Proceedings Ser.). (Illus.). 1834p. (Vol. 1). 1968. Vol. 1. pap. 68.00 (ISBN 92-0-530168-X, ISP192-1, IAEA); Vol. 2. pap. 57.25 (ISBN 92-0-530268-6, ISP 192-2). Unipub.
Plasma Physics & Controlled Nuclear Fusion Research: 1982, Vol. 3. 551p. 1983. pap. text ed. 69.00 (ISBN 92-0-130283-5, ISP626/3, IAEA). Unipub.
Plasma Physics & Controlled Nuclear Fusion Research 1978: Proceedings, Seventh Conference, Innsbruck, 23-30 August 1978, 3 vols. (Proceedings Ser.). (Illus.). 1979. Vol. 1. pap. 100.00 (ISBN 92-0-130079-4, ISP495-1, IAEA); Vol. 2. pap. 84.00 (ISBN 92-0-130179-0, ISP495-2); Vol. 3. pap. 77.00 (ISBN 92-0-130279-7, ISP495-3). Unipub.
Plasma Physics & Controlled Nuclear Fusion Research 1984: Tenth Conference Proceedings, London, 12-19 September 1984, Vol. 1. (Nuclear Fusion Ser.: Suppl. 1985). 673p. 1985. pap. 105.75 (ISBN 92-0-130085-9, ISP670-1 5071, IAEA). Unipub.
Plasma Physics: Culham Summer School. (Institute of Physics Conference Ser.: No. 20). 1974. 55.00 (ISBN 0-9960029-9-5, Pub. by Inst Physics England). Heyden.
Plasma Physics: Proceedings Ser. 649p. 1965. 35.50 (ISBN 92-0-030265-3, ISP89, IAEA). Unipub.
Plasma Space Sciences Symposium: Proceedings. 386p. 1965. 106.50 (ISBN 0-677-00640-3). Gordon.
Pozhela, J. Plasma & Current Instabilities in Semiconductors. Germogenova, O. A., tr. (International Series in the Science of the Solid State: Vol. 18). (Illus.). 314p. 1981. 72.00 (ISBN 0-08-025048-3). Pergamon.
Princeton University. Dictionary Catalog of the Princeton University Plasma Physics Laboratory Library, 4 vols. 1970. Set. lib. bdg. 395.00 (ISBN 0-8161-0881-1, Hall Library). G K Hall.
Rosenbluth, M. N., ed. Advanced Plasma Theory. (Italian Physical Society Ser.: Course 25). 1964. 75.00 (ISBN 0-12-368825-6). Acad Pr.
Rostas, Francois, ed. Spectral Line Shapes: Proceedings, Seventh International Congress Aussois, France, June 11-15, 1984, Vol. 3. (Illus.). xx, 769p. 1985. 136.00x (ISBN 3-11-010119-X). De Gruyter.
Russell, C. T., ed. Active Experiments in Space Plasmas. (Advances in Space Research: Vol. 1, No. 2). (Illus.). 468p. 1981. pap. 65.00 (ISBN 0-08-027158-8). Pergamon.
Rye, B. J. & Taylor, J. C. Physics of Hot Plasmas. 455p. 1970. 47.50x (ISBN 0-306-30479-1, Plenum Pr). Plenum Pub.
Schindler, Karl, ed. Cosmic Plasma Physics. LC 78-188924. 369p. 1972. 49.50x (ISBN 0-306-30582-8, Plenum Pr). Plenum Pub.
Schmidt, George. Physics of High Temperature Plasmas. 2nd ed. 1979. 39.50 (ISBN 0-12-626660-3). Acad Pr.
Schwarz, H. J., et al, eds. Laser Interaction & Related Plasma Phenomena, Vol. 5. LC 79-135851. 863p. 1981. 95.00x (ISBN 0-306-40545-8, Plenum Pr). Plenum Pub.
Skobel'tsyn, D. V., ed. Plasma Physics. LC 68-26495. (P. N. Lebedev Physics Institute Ser.: Vol. 32). (Illus.). 202p. 1968. 35.00x (ISBN 0-306-10790-2, Consultants). Plenum Pub.
--Theory of Plasmas. LC 74-34269. (P. N. Lebedev Physics Institute Ser.: Vol. 61). (Illus.). 255p. 1975. 55.00x (ISBN 0-306-10904-2, Consultants). Plenum Pub.
Stacey, Weston M. Fusion Plasma Analysis. LC 80-19955. 376p. 1981. 44.95 (ISBN 0-471-08095-0, Pub. by Wiley-Interscience). Wiley.
Sturrock, P. A., ed. Plasma Astrophysics. (Italian Physical Society: Course 39). 1967. 70.00 (ISBN 0-12-368839-6). Acad Pr.
Symposia in Applied Mathematics - New York - 1965. Magneto-Fluid & Plasma Dynamics: Proceedings. Grad, H., ed. LC 66-20436. (Proceedings of Symposia in Applied Mathematics: Vol. 18). 1967. 23.00 (ISBN 0-8218-1318-8, PSAPM-18). Am Math.
Symposium On The Dynamics Of Fluids And Plasmas. Dynamics of Fluids & Plasmas: Proceedings. Pai, S. I., ed. 1967. 84.00 (ISBN 0-12-544250-5). Acad Pr.
Theoretical & Computational Plasma Physics. (Proceedings Ser.). (Illus.). 516p. 1978. pap. 58.50 (ISBN 92-0-130078-6, ISP474, IAEA). Unipub.
Tidman, D. A. Shock Waves in Collisionless Plasmas. Krali, N. A., ed. LC 74-13711. 187p. (Orig.). 1971. 16.25 (ISBN 0-471-86785-3). Krieger.
Tsytovich, V. N. Nonlinear Effects in Plasma. LC 69-12545. 332p. 1970. 55.00x (ISBN 0-306-30425-2, Plenum Pr). Plenum Pub.
Veprek, S. & Venugopalan, M., eds. Plasma Chemistry, Vol. IV. (Topics in Current Chemistry Ser.: Vol. 107). (Illus.). 186p. 1983. 36.00 (ISBN 0-387-11828-4). Springer-Verlag.
--Plasma Chemistry: Volume III. (Topics in Current Chemistry: Vol. 94). (Illus.). 160p. 1980. 44.50 (ISBN 0-387-10166-7). Springer-Verlag.
Volkov, et al. Collective Phenomena in Current Carrying Plasma. 264p. 1984. text ed. 90.00 (ISBN 2-88124-016-X). Gordon.
Weiland, J. C. & Wilhelmsson, H. Coherent Non-Linear Interaction of Waves in Plasmas. 1977. text ed. 54.00 (ISBN 0-08-020964-5). Pergamon.
Wentzel, Donat A. & Tidman, Derek A., eds. Plasma Instabilities in Astrophysics. (Illus.). 430p. 1969. 106.50x (ISBN 0-677-13520-3). Gordon.
Wilhelmsson, Hans, ed. Plasma Physics: Nonlinear Theory & Experiments. LC 76-46955. (Nobel Foundation Symposium Ser.). (Illus.). 513p. 1977. 79.50 (ISBN 0-306-33706-1, Plenum Pr). Plenum Pub.
Williams, B., ed. Film Preparation & Etching Using Vacuum or Plasma Technology: Proceedings of the SIRA International Seminar, Brighton, U. K., 22-24 March 1983. 100p. 1984. 27.50 (ISBN 0-08-031150-4). Pergamon.
Yasuda, H. Plasma Polymerization: A Monograph. Date not set. 62.00 (ISBN 0-12-768760-2). Acad Pr.
Yeh, K. C. & Liv, C. H. Theory of Ionospheric Waves. (International Geophysics Ser., Vol. 17). 1972. 70.00 (ISBN 0-12-770450-7). Acad Pr.

PLASMA ACCELERATORS

see also Plasma Jets; Plasma Rockets

Kash, Sidney W., ed. Plasma Acceleration. LC 60-13869. pap. 31.30 (ISBN 0-317-09232-4, 2000312). Bks Demand UMI.

PLASMA DIAGNOSTICS

see also Physical Measurements; Plasma (Ionized Gases)

Georges, George C. Lagrangian & Hamiltonian Formulation of Plasma Problems. LC 70-141694. 74p. 1969. 17.50 (ISBN 0-403-04503-7). Scholarly.
Podgornyi, I. M. Topics in Plasma Diagnostics. LC 72-137010. 214p. 1971. 35.00x (ISBN 0-306-30489-9, Plenum Pr). Plenum Pub.
Sheffield, John. Plasma Scattering of Electromagnetic Radiation. 1975. 76.00 (ISBN 0-12-638750-8). Acad Pr.
Tolok, V. T. Recent Advances in Plasma Diagnostics, Vol. 1, Optical Techniques. LC 70-140828. 130p. 1971. 27.50x (ISBN 0-306-19101-6, Consultants). Plenum Pub.
Tolok, V. T., ed. Recent Advances in Plasma Diagnostics, Vol. 3, Corpuscular, Correlation, Bolometric, and Other Techniques. LC 70-140828. 73p. 1971. 20.00x (ISBN 0-306-19103-2, Consultants). Plenum Pub.

PLASMA DYNAMICS

see also Magnetohydrodynamics

Alexandrov, A. F., et al. Principles of Plasma Electrodynamics. (Springer Series in Electrophysics: Vol. 9). (Illus.). 510p. 1984. 49.50 (ISBN 0-387-12613-9). Springer-Verlag.
Babuel-Peyrissac, Jean-Paul. Equations Cinetiques des Fluides & des Plasmas. (Cours & Documents de Mathematiques & de Physique Ser.). 306p. 1975. 129.50 (ISBN 0-677-50630-9). Gordon.
Birdsall. Plasma Physics via Computer. 512p. 1983. text ed. 45.00 (ISBN 0-07-005371-5). McGraw.
Cairns, R A. Plasma Physics. 224p. 1985. 34.00 (ISBN 0-317-14039-6, Pub. by Blackie & Son UK); pap. 17.00 (ISBN 0-317-14040-X). Heyden.
Chen, Francis F. Introduction to Plasma Physics & Controlled Fusion: Vol. 1: Plasma Physics. 2nd ed. 400p. 1984. 24.50x (ISBN 0-306-41332-9, Plenum Pr). Plenum Pub.
Dembovsky, V. Plasma Metallurgy: The Principles. (Materials Science Monographs: No. 23). 280p. 1985. 109.25 (ISBN 0-444-99603-6). Elsevier.
Frieser, R. G. & Mogab, C. J., eds. Plasma Processing: Symposium on Plasma Etchins & Deposition, Proceedings. LC 81-65237. (Electrochemical Society Proceedings Ser.: Vol. 81-1). (Illus.). pap. 87.00 (ISBN 0-317-09584-6, 2051749). Bks Demand UMI.
Gekker, I. R. Interaction of Strong Electromagnetic Fields with Plasmas. Sykes, J. B. & Franklin, R. N., trs. (Oxford Studies in Physics). (Illus.). 1982. 69.00x (ISBN 0-19-851467-0). Oxford U Pr.
Gormezano, C. & Leotta, G. G., eds. Heating in Toroidal Plasmas III: Proceedings of the 3rd Joint Varenna-Grenoble International Symposium, Grenoble, France, 22-26 March 1982, 3 vols. 1224p. 1982. pap. 165.00 set (ISBN 0-08-029984-9). Pergamon.
Gunther, K. & Radtka, R. Electrical Properties & Weekly Nonideal Plasmas. (Experientia Supplementum Ser.: Vol. 49). 1984. text ed. 19.95x (ISBN 3-764316-35-7). Birkhauser.
Heald, M. A. & Wharton, C. B. Plasma Diagnostics with Microwaves. LC 77-13781. 470p. 1978. Repr. of 1965 ed. 27.00 (ISBN 0-88275-626-5). Krieger.
Hora, H. Nonlinear Plasma Dynamics at Laser Irradiation. (Lecture Notes in Physics Ser.: Vol. 102). 1979. pap. 17.00 (ISBN 0-387-09502-0). Springer-Verlag.
Hora, Heinrich & Miley, George H., eds. Laser Interaction & Related Plasma Phenomena, Vol. 6. 1180p. 1984. 135.00x (ISBN 0-306-41395-7, Plenum Pr). Plenum Pub.
International Conference on the Microwave Behavior of Ferrimagnetics & Plasmas, London, 1965. The Microwave Behaviour of Ferrimagnetics & Plasmas. LC 66-36909. (Institution of Electrical Engineers Conference Publications: No. 13). pap. 109.30 (ISBN 0-317-10123-4, 2007385). Bks Demand UMI.
Laing, E. W. Plasma Physics. 30.00x (ISBN 0-686-97016-0, Pub. by Scottish Academic Pr Scotland). State Mutual Bk.
Lasers in Fluid Mechanics & Plasmdynamics. 26.50 (ISBN 0-317-06660-9). AIAA.
Leontovich, M. A., ed. Reviews of Plasma Physics, Vol. 8. LC 64-23244. 472p. 1980. 65.00x (ISBN 0-306-17068-X, Consultants Bureau). Plenum Pub.
Lockheed Symposium on Magnetohydrodynamics, Palo Alto, 1962. Propagation & Instabilities in Plasmas. 7th ed. LC 63-19236. pap. 38.80 (ISBN 0-317-12970-8, 2000318). Bks Demand UMI.
Lockheed Symposium on Magnetohydrodynamics, (5th: 1960: Palo Alto) Radiation & Waves in Plasmas. Mitchner, Morton, ed. LC 61-14651. pap. 41.80 (ISBN 0-317-07864-X, 2000319). Bks Demand UMI.
Plasma Physics & Controlled Nuclear Fusion Research 1984: Tenth Conference Proceedings, London, 12-19 September 1984, Vol. 2. 667p. 1985. pap. 104.00 (ISBN 92-0-130185-5, ISP670, IAEA). Unipub.
Raether, H. Excitation of Plasmas & Interband Transitions by Electrons. (Springer Tracts in Modern Physics: Vol. 88). (Illus.). 190p. 1980. 38.00 (ISBN 0-387-09677-9). Springer-Verlag.
Sitenko, A. G. Fluctuations & Non-Linear Wave Interactions in Plasmas. Kocherga, O. D., tr. LC 80-41990. (International Series in Natural Philosophy: Vol. 107). (Illus.). 290p. 1982. 66.00 (ISBN 0-08-025051-3, C135). Pergamon.
Szekely, J. & Apelian, D., eds. Plasma Processing & Synthesis of Materials: Proceedings of Symposium, 1983, Boston, MA, Materials Research Society. (Materials Research Society Symposia Ser.: Vol. 30). 306p. 1984. 64.00 (ISBN 0-444-00895-0, North Holland). Elsevier.
Venugopalan, M., ed. Reactions under Plasma Conditions. LC 78-132857. Vol. 1. pap. 153.30 (ISBN 0-317-10852-2, 22006313); Vol. 2. pap. 155.50 (ISBN 0-317-10853-0). Bks Demand UMI.

PLASMA INSTABILITIES

see also Electromagnetic Fields; Magnetohydrodynamics; Plasma (Ionized Gases)

AIP Conference, Princeton, 1970. Feedback & Dynamic Control of Plasmas: Proceedings, No. 1. Chu, T. K. & Hendel, H. W., eds. LC 70-141596. 364p. 1970. 14.00 (ISBN 0-88318-100-2). Am Inst Physics.
Cap, Ferdinand. Handbook of Plasma Instabilities, Vol. I. 1976. 55.00 (ISBN 0-12-159101-8). Acad Pr.
Hasegawa, A. Plasma Instabilities & Nonlinear Effects. LC 74-18072. (Physics & Chemistry in Space Ser.: Vol. 8). (Illus.). xi, 217p. 1975. 49.00 (ISBN 0-387-06947-X). Springer-Verlag.
Mikhailovskii, A. B. Theory of Plasma Instabilities, 2 vols. Incl. Vol. 1. Instabilities of a Homogeneous Plasma. 307p. 1974 (ISBN 0-306-17181-3); Vol. 2. Instabilities of an Inhomogeneous Plasma. 332p. 1974 (ISBN 0-306-17182-1). LC 73-83899. (Studies in Soviet Science - Physical Sciences Ser.). 1974. 49.50x ea. (Consultants). Plenum Pub.
Pardo, William B. & Robertson, Harry S., eds. Plasma Instabilities & Anomalous Transport. LC 66-25666. (Illus.). 1966. pap. 9.95x (ISBN 0-87024-064-1). U of Miami Pr.
Pineda, Alvaro A., ed. Selective Plasma Component Removal. LC 84-80840. (Illus.). 232p. 1984. 35.00 (ISBN 0-87993-228-7). Futura Pub.
Potemra, Thomas A., ed. Magnetospheric Currents. (Geophysical Monograph: No. 28). (Illus.). 357p. 1984. 33.00 (ISBN 0-87590-055-0). Am Geophysical.
Tsytovich, V. N. Theory of Turbulent Plasma. LC 75-31720. (Studies in Soviet Science - Physical Sciences Ser.). (Illus.). 535p. 1977. 85.00x (ISBN 0-306-10894-1, Consultants). Plenum Pub.
Von Engel, A. Electric Plasmas: Their Nature & Uses. LC 83-6166. 250p. 1983. 36.00x (ISBN 0-8002-3076-0). Taylor & Francis.

PLASMA JET (ROCKETS)

see Plasma Rockets

PLASMA JETS

Gerdeman, D. A. & Hecht, N. L. Arc Plasma Technology in Materials Science. (Applied Mineralogy: Vol. 3). (Illus.). 1972. 45.00 (ISBN 0-387-81041-2). Springer-Verlag.
O'Brien, R. L. Plasma Arc Metalworking Processes, PMP. 160p. 1967. 10.00 (ISBN 0-685-65957-7); member 7.50. Am Welding.
Rosciszewski, Jan. Ionizing Fronts in Plasma Propulsion & Power Generation Systems. LC 70-131402. 191p. 1969. 19.00 (ISBN 0-403-04532-0). Scholarly.

PLASMA MEMBRANES

see also Cells–Permeability

American Chemical Society,164th National Meeting. Biogenesis of Plant Cell Wall Polysaccharides: Proceedings. Loewus, Frank, ed. 1973. 94.00 (ISBN 0-12-455350-8). Acad Pr.
Benga, Gheorghe, ed. Structure & Properties of Cell Membranes, 3 vols. 1985. Vol. I, 288 pgs. price not set (ISBN 0-8493-5764-0); Vol. II, 304 pgs. price not set (ISBN 0-8493-5765-9); Vol. III, 336 pgs. price not set (ISBN 0-8493-5766-7). CRC Pr.
Chapman, D. Biological Membranes, 3 vols. Vol. 1 1968. o.s.i 70.00 (ISBN 0-12-168540-3); Vol. 2 1973. 60.00 (ISBN 0-12-168542-X); Vol. 3 1976. 60.00 (ISBN 0-12-168544-6). Acad Pr.
Cole, Kenneth S. Membranes, Ions & Impulses: A Chapter of Classical Biophysics. LC 67-24121. (Biophysics Ser.: No. 1). (Illus.). 1971. 53.00x (ISBN 0-520-00251-2). U of Cal Pr.
Curtis, A. S. Cell Surface: Its Molecular Role in Morphogenesis. 1967. 76.50 (ISBN 0-12-199650-6). Acad Pr.
Daems, W. T., et al, eds. Cell Biological Aspects of Disease: The Plasma Membrane & Lysosomes. (Boerhaave Series for Postgraduate Medical Education: No. 19). 330p. 1981. PLB 68.50 (ISBN 90-6021-466-8, Pub. by Leiden Univ Netherlands). Kluwer Academic.
Dalton, Albert J. & Haguenau, Francoise, eds. Membranes. (Ultrastructure in Biological Systems Ser.). 1968. 47.50 (ISBN 0-12-200940-1). Acad Pr.
Duncan, C. J. & Hopkins, C. R., eds. Secretory Mechanisms. LC 79-10003. (Society for Experimental Biology Symposium: No. 33). (Illus.). 1980. 82.50 (ISBN 0-521-22684-8). Cambridge U Pr.

Elson, Elliot, et al, eds. Cell Membranes: Methods & Review, Vol. 1. 211p. 1983. 29.50x (ISBN 0-306-41298-5, Plenum Pr). Plenum Pub.

Evans, W. H. Preparation & Characterisation of Mammalian Plasma Membranes. (Techniques in Biochemistry & Molecular Biology Ser.: Vol. 7, Pt. 1). 1978. pap. 28.00 (ISBN 0-7204-4222-2, 7:1). Elsevier.

Garcia, ed. Structure, Function & Biosynthesis of Plant Cell Walls. 524p. 1984. pap. 19.00 (ISBN 0-317-12494-3). Am Soc of Plan.

George, James N., et al, eds. Platelet Membrane Glycoproteins. 412p. 1985. 59.50x (ISBN 0-306-41857-6, Plenum Pr). Plenum Pub.

Godfraind, K. & Meyer, P., eds. Cell Membrane in Function & Dysfunction of Vascular Tissue, 1981. (Argenteuil Symposia Ser.: Vol. 5). 278p. 1981. 80.50 (ISBN 0-444-80316-5, Biomedical Pr). Elsevier.

Gomperts, B. D. The Plasma Membrane: Models for Its Structure & Function. 1977. 39.50 (ISBN 0-12-289450-2). Acad Pr.

Hagiwara, Susumu. Membrane Potential-Dependent Ion Channels in Cell Membrane: Phylogenetic & Developmental Approaches. (Distinguished Lecture Series of the Society of General Physiologists: Vol. 3). (Illus.). 128p. 1983. text ed. 36.00 (ISBN 0-89004-717-0). Raven.

Hennessen, W., ed. Standardization of Albumin, Plasa Substitutes & Plasmapheresis. (Developments in Biological Standardization: Vol. 48). (Illus.). viii, 326p. 1981. pap. 32.00 (ISBN 3-8055-2496-X). S Karger.

Kepner, G. R., ed. Cell Membrane Permeability & Transport. LC 79-11930. (Benchmark Papers in Human Physiology: Vol. 12). 410p. 1979. 50.00 (ISBN 0-87933-352-9). Van Nos Reinhold.

Kreuzer, F. & Slegers, J. F., eds. Biomembranes, Vol. 3: Passive Permeability of Cell Membranes. LC 78-140830. 536p. 1972. 55.00x (ISBN 0-306-39803-6, Plenum Pr). Plenum Pub.

Kuo, Hyh-Fa, ed. Phospholipids & Cellular Regulation, Vols. I & II. 1985. Vol. I. price not set, 288p. (ISBN 0-8493-5537-0); Vol. II. price not set, 304p. (ISBN 0-8493-5538-9). CRC Pr.

Lucy, J. A. The Plasma Membrane. rev. ed. Head, J. J., ed. LC 77-75589. (Carolina Biology Readers Ser.). (Illus.). 16p. 1979. pap. 1.60 (ISBN 0-89278-281-1, 45-9681). Carolina Biological.

Malhotra, S. K. The Plasma Membrane. (Membrane Transport in Life Science Ser.). 209p. 1983. 69.95 (ISBN 0-471-09325-4, 1-429, Pub. by Wiley-Interscience). Wiley.

Moore, John W., ed. Membranes, Ions, & Impulses. LC 76-13841. 201p. 1976. 35.00x (ISBN 0-306-34505-6, Plenum Pr). Plenum Pub.

Mullins, L. J., compiled by. Annual Reviews Reprints. Incl. Cell Membranes, 1975-1977. Mullins, L. J., compiled by. LC 78-55105. (Illus.). 1978. pap. text ed. 12.00 (ISBN 0-8243-2501-X); Cell Membranes, 1978-1980. Mullins, L. J., compiled by. LC 81-65983. (Illus.). pap. text ed. 28.00 (ISBN 0-8243-2503-6). (Illus.). Annual Reviews.

Nicolau, Claude, ed. Virus Transformed Cell Membranes. 1979. 66.00 (ISBN 0-12-518650-9). Acad Pr.

Nombela, C., ed. Microbial Cell Wall Synthesis & Autolysis: Proceedings of a Symposium Sponsored by the Federation of European Microbiological Societies, Madrid, July 3-6, 1984. 328p. 1985. 70.50 (ISBN 0-444-80636-9). Elsevier.

Passow, H. & Staempfli, R., eds. Laboratory Techniques in Membrane Biophysics: An Introductory Course. LC 69-19291. (Illus.). 1969. pap. 29.00 (ISBN 0-387-04592-9). Springer-Verlag.

Pfeffer, Wilhelm. Osmotic Investigations. (Illus.). 304p. 1985. 32.50 (ISBN 0-442-27583-8). Van Nos Reinhold.

Poste & Nicholson. The Synthesis, Assembly & Turnover of Cell Surface Components. (Cell Surface Reviews: Vol. 4). 884p. 1978. 79.95 (ISBN 0-444-00232-4, Biomedical Pr). Elsevier.

Poste, G. & Nicholson, G., eds. The Cell Surface in Animal Embryogenesis & Development. (Cell Surface Reviews: Vol. 1). 766p. 1977. 142.75 (ISBN 0-7204-0597-1, Biomedical Pr). Elsevier.

--Virus Infection & the Cell Surface. (Cell Surface Reviews: Vol. 2). 342p. 1977. 92.00 (ISBN 0-7204-0598-X, Biomedical Pr). Elsevier.

Poste, G. & Nicolson, G., eds. Dynamic Aspects of Cell Surface Organization. (Cell Surface Reviews Ser.: Vol. 3). 1977. 142.75 (ISBN 0-7204-0623-4, Biomedical Pr). Elsevier.

Robinson, David G. Plant Membranes: Endo- & Plasma Membranes. LC 84-7539. (Cell Biology: A Series of Monographs: Vol. 3). 1075p. 1985. 69.50x (ISBN 0-471-86210-X). Wiley.

Solheim, B. Cell Wall Biochemistry Related to Specificity in Host-Plant Pathogen Interactions. 1977. pap. 43.00x (ISBN 82-00-05141-2, Dist. by Columbia U Pr). Universitet.

Stein, W. D., ed. Movement of Molecules Across Cell Membranes. (Theoretical & Experimental Biology: Vol. 6). 1967. 65.00 (ISBN 0-12-664650-3). Acad Pr.

Tao, Mariano, ed. Membrane Abnormalities & Disease, 2 vols. 1982. Vol. 1, 160 Pgs. 48.00 (ISBN 0-8493-6160-5); Vol. 2, 192 Pgs. 48.00 (ISBN 0-8493-6161-3). CRC Pr.

Tindall, Richard S. A., ed. Therapeutic Apheresis & Plasma Perfusion. LC 82-17236. (Progress in Clinical & Biological Research Ser.: Vol. 106). 492p. 1982. 48.00 (ISBN 0-8451-0106-4). A R Liss.

Trump, Benjamin F. & Arstila, A. U., eds. Pathobiology of Cell Membranes, 2 vols, Vol. 1. 1975. 75.00 (ISBN 0-12-701501-9). Acad Pr.

Wallach, D. F. The Plasma Membrane: Dynamic Perspectives, Genetics & Pathology. LC 72-85948. (Heidelberg Science Library: Vol. 18). (Illus.). 179p. 1972. pap. 15.00 (ISBN 0-387-90047-0). Springer-Verlag.

Wallach, Donald. Plasma Membranes & Diseases. LC 79-50529. 1980. 49.50 (ISBN 0-12-733150-6). Acad Pr.

Wallach, Donald F. Proteins of Animal Cell Plasma Membranes, Vol. 2. Horrobin, D. F., ed. (Annual Research Reviews). 1979. 28.00 (ISBN 0-88831-048-X). Eden Pr.

Weed, Robert I., et al. The Red Cell Membrane. LC 70-170193. (Illus.). 192p. 1971. 58.00 (ISBN 0-8089-0736-0, 794770). Grune.

Wellach, Donald F. Proteins of Animal Cell Plasma Membranes, Vol. 1. 1978. 19.20 (ISBN 0-88831-011-0). Eden Pr.

Wolf, Stewart & Murray, Allen K., eds. Composition & Function of Cell Membranes: Application to the Pathophysiology of Muscle Diseases. LC 81-17892. (Advances in Experimental Medicine & Biology Ser.: Vol. 140). 300p. 1981. text ed. 42.50 (ISBN 0-306-40883-X, Plenum Pr). Plenum Pub.

PLASMA PROPULSION

see Plasma Rockets

PLASMA PROTEINS

see also Immunoglobulins

Koblet, H., et al. Physiology & Pathophysiology of Plasma Protein Metabolism. 240p. 1965. 50.00 (ISBN 3-456-00107-X, Pub. by Holdan Bk Ltd UK). State Mutual Bk.

Kushner, Irving, et al, eds. C-Relative Protein & the Plasma Protein Response to Tissue Injury. (Annals of The New York Academy of Sciences Ser.: Vol. 389). 482p. 1982. lib. bdg. 100.00 (ISBN 0-89766-193-1); pap. 100.00 (ISBN 0-89766-194-X). NY Acad Sci.

Nose, Yukihiko, et al, eds. Plasmapheresis: Therapeutic Applications & New Techniques. (Illus.). 462p. 1983. text ed. 70.50 (ISBN 0-89004-980-7). Raven.

Putnam, Frank W., ed. The Plasma Proteins: Structure, Function & Genetic Control, Vol. 4. 2nd ed. 1984. 65.00 (ISBN 0-12-568404-5). Acad Pr.

Rothschild, Marcus A. & Waldmann, Thomas, eds. Plasma Protein Metabolism: Regulation of Synthesis, Distribution & Degradation. 1970. 72.00 (ISBN 0-12-598750-1). Acad Pr.

Wallach, Donald F. Proteins of Animal Cell Plasma Membranes, Vol. 2. Horrobin, D. F., ed. (Annual Research Reviews). 1979. 28.00 (ISBN 0-88831-048-X). Eden Pr.

PLASMA ROCKETS

Chapman, Brian. Glow Discharge Processes: Sputtering & Plasma Etching. LC 80-17047. 406p. 1980. 48.95x (ISBN 0-471-07828-X, Pub. by Wiley-Interscience). Wiley.

PLASMA SPECTROSCOPY

Alfven, H. Cosmic Plasma. 1981. 39.50 (ISBN 90-277-1151-8, Pub. by Reidel Holland). Kluwer Academic.

Barnes. Applications of Plasma Emission Spectrochemistry. 160p. 1979. 45.95 (ISBN 0-471-25595-5, Pub. by Wiley Heyden). Wiley.

--Developments in Plasma Emission Spectrochemistry. write for info. (ISBN 0-85501-621-3). Wiley.

Barnes, R. M., ed. Plasma Spectrochemistry: Proceedings of the Winter Conference, Orlando, Florida, January 4-9, 1982. 436p. 1983. 50.00 (ISBN 0-08-028745-X). Pergamon.

Boumans, P. W. Line Coincidence Tables for Inductively Coupled Plasma Atomic Emission Spectrometry, 2 vols. 2nd ed. LC 84-6402. (Illus.). 944p. 1984. Set. 235.00 (ISBN 0-08-031404-X). Pergamon.

Carr, Timothy W., ed. Plasma Chromatography. 274p. 1984. 37.50x (ISBN 0-306-41432-5, Plenum Pr). Plenum Pub.

Szekely, J. & Apelian, D., eds. Plasma Processing & Synthesis of Materials: Proceedings of Symposium, 1983, Boston, MA, Materials Research Society. (Materials Research Society Symposia Ser.: Vol. 30). 306p. 1984. 64.00 (ISBN 0-444-00895-0, North Holland). Elsevier.

Thompson, Michael & Walsh, J. N. Handbook of Inductively-Coupled Plasma Spectrometry. LC 83-7212. 230p. 1983. 79.95 (ISBN 0-412-00371-6, NO. 5039, Pub. by Chapman & Hall). Methuen Inc.

PLASMA TORCH

see Plasma Jets

PLASMODIOPHORALES

Karling, John S. Plasmodiophorales. 2nd rev. ed. 1968. 24.95x (ISBN 0-02-847510-0). Hafner.

PLASMOGENY

see Life–Origin

PLASTER

see also Cement; Concrete

Allen, Dorothy S. Plaster & Bisque Art: Gold Leafing, Hummel, Lacquer, Marble & Woodtone Finishes. Cole, Tom, ed. LC 80-70317. (Plaster Art, Step by Step Ser.). (Illus.). 56p. 1981. pap. 1.95 (ISBN 0-9605204-2-2). Dots Pubns.

--Plaster & Bisque Art with Acrylics. Cole, Tom, ed. LC 80-70317. (Plaster Art, Step by Step Ser.). (Illus.). 75p. 1981. pap. 1.95 (ISBN 0-9605204-1-4). Dots Pubns.

Durran, C. P. Dublin Decorative Plasterwork. 1967. 25.00 (ISBN 0-693-01112-2). Transatlantic.

Volkart, K. Gips - Woerterbuch. (Ger.). 176p. 1971. 68.00 (ISBN 3-7625-0460-1, M-7426, Pub. by Bauverlag). French & Eur.

Volkart, K. H. Gypsum & Plaster Dictionary. (Ger., Eng. & Fr.). 176p. 1971. 68.00 (ISBN 3-7625-0460-1, M-7437, Pub. by Bauverlag). French & Eur.

PLASTER CASTS

Chaney, Charles & Skee, Stanley. Plaster Mold & Model Making. LC 80-21932. 144p. 1981. Repr. of 1973 ed. text ed. 14.00 (ISBN 0-89874-282-X). Krieger.

PLASTERING

Beard, Geoffrey. Stucco & Decorative Plasterwork in Europe. LC 82-49006. (Icon Editions). (Illus.). 165p. 1983. 48.08i (ISBN 0-06-430383-7, HarpT). Har-Row.

Pegg, Brian F. & Stagg, William D. Plastering: A Craftsman's Encyclopedia. 276p. 1976. text ed. 14.75 (ISBN 0-258-97007-3, Pub. by Granada England). Brookfield Pub Co.

Rudman, Jack. Foreman Plasterer. (Career Examination Ser.: C-2270). (Cloth bdg. avail. on request). 1977. pap. 10.00 (ISBN 0-8373-2270-7). Natl Learning.

--Plasterer. (Career Examination Ser.: C-589). (Cloth bdg. avail. on request). pap. 8.00 (ISBN 0-8373-0589-6). Natl Learning.

Stagg, W. D. & Pegg, B. Plastering: A Craftsman's Encyclopedia. (Illus.). 1976. 21.00x (ISBN 0-8464-0726-4). Beekman Pubs.

--Plastering: A Craftsman's Encyclopedia. 276p. 1976. pap. 16.00x (ISBN 0-246-11387-1, Pub. by Granada England). Sheridan.

Van Den Branden, F. & Hartsell, Thomas L. Plastering Skills. (Illus.). 544p. (Orig.). 1985. pap. 21.95 (ISBN 0-8269-0657-5, Pub. by Am Technical). Sterling.

Van Den Branden, Felicien & Hartsell, Thomas L. Plastering Skill & Practice. LC 72-165182. (Illus.). pap. 137.50 (ISBN 0-317-10858-1, 2010124). Bks Demand UMI.

PLASTIC ANALYSIS (THEORY OF STRUCTURES)

ACI Committee 340. Design Handbook in Accordance with the Strength Design Method of ACI 318-77: Columns, Vol. 2. 1978. binder 55.50 (ISBN 0-685-85093-5, SP-17A78). ACI.

Bares, R. A., ed. Plastics in Material & Structural Engineering: Proceedings ICP-RILEM-IBK International Symposium, Prague, June 23-25, 1981. (Developments in Civil Engineering Ser.: Vol. 5). 962p. 1982. 164.00 (ISBN 0-444-99710-5). Elsevier.

Beedle, Lynn S. Plastic Design of Steel Frames. LC 58-13454. 406p. 1974. 56.95x (ISBN 0-471-06171-9, Pub. by Wiley-Interscience). Wiley.

Disque, Robert O. Applied Plastic Design in Steel. LC 77-10512. 256p. 1978. Repr. of 1971 ed. lib. bdg. 16.50 (ISBN 0-88275-312-6). Krieger.

Hodge, Philip G. Plastic Analysis of Structures. rev. ed. LC 80-26340. 444p. 1981. 32.50 (ISBN 0-89874-161-0). Krieger.

Nielsen, M. P. Limit Analysis & Concrete Plasticity. (Illus.). 1984. 42.95 (ISBN 0-13-536623-2). P-H.

Save, M. A. & Massonnet, C. C. Plastic Analysis & Design of Plates, Shells & Disks, Vol. 15. 478p. 1972. 93.75 (ISBN 0-444-10113-6, North-Holland). Elsevier.

Sherwood, John N. The Plastically Crystalline State: Orientationally-Disordered Crystals. LC 78-16086. 383p. 1979. 94.95 (ISBN 0-471-99715-3, Pub. by Wiley-Interscience). Wiley.

PLASTIC BUILDING MATERIALS

see Plastics in Building

PLASTIC COATING

see also Electronic Apparatus and Appliances–Plastic Embedment

Acrylic Powder Coatings. 59p. 1977. 40.00x (ISBN 0-686-44642-9, Pub. by Chandler England). State Mutual Bk.

Coatings: Plastics & Elastomers as Protective Coatings. 155p. 1984. 78.00 (ISBN 0-317-12670-9). T-C Pubns CA.

Gillies, M. T., ed. Solventless & High Solids Industrial Finishes: Recent Developments. LC 80-21553. (Chemical Technology Review: No. 179). (Illus.). 342p. 1981. 48.00 (ISBN 0-8155-0828-X). Noyes.

Roffey, C. G. Photopolymerization of Surface Coatings. LC 81-12916. 353p. 1982. 54.95 (ISBN 0-471-10063-3, Pub. by Wiley-Interscience). Wiley.

Seymour, R. B. Plastics vs. Corrosives. LC 81-21996. (Society of Plastics Engineers Monographs). 285p. 1982. text ed. 54.95x (ISBN 0-471-08182-5, Pub. by Wiley-Interscience). Wiley.

Urethanes in Elastomers & Coating, Vol. 2. LC 73-90089. (Major Papers from the Journal of Elastomers & Plastics). 205p. pap. 9.95 (ISBN 0-87762-234-5). Technomic.

PLASTIC CRAFT

see Plastics Craft

PLASTIC EMBEDMENT (ELECTRONICS)

see Electronic Apparatus and Appliances–Plastic Embedment

PLASTIC FILMS

Benning, Calvin J. Plastic Films for Packaging: Technology Applications & Process Economics. 192p. 1983. 35.00 (ISBN 0-87762-320-1). Technomic.

Handbook of Films, Sheets & Laminates. 85.00 (ISBN 0-686-48144-5, 0305). T-C Pubns CA.

Oswin, C. R. Plastic Films & Packaging. (Illus.). xi, 214p. 1975. 27.75 (ISBN 0-85334-641-0, Pub. by Elsevier Applied Sci England). Elsevier.

Pinner, S. H., ed. Modern Packaging Films. LC 67-26705. 249p. 1967. 32.50x (ISBN 0-306-30632-8, Plenum Pr). Plenum Pub.

PLASTIC FOAMS

Berlin, A. A., et al. Foam Based on Reactive Oligomers. 301p. 1982. 49.00 (ISBN 0-87762-307-4). Technomic.

Flammability of Cellular Plastics, Part 2. (Fire & Flammability Ser.: Vol. 19). 154p. 1981. pap. 25.00 (ISBN 0-87762-298-1). Technomic.

Foamed Plastics: Polyurethane Foams. 80p. 1982. 78.00 (ISBN 0-317-12676-8, LS20). T-C Pubns CA.

Foamed Plastics: Styrene, Epoxy & Other Polymeric Foams. 100p. 1984. 78.00 (ISBN 0-317-12677-6, LS114). T-C Pubns CA.

Foams Desk-Top Data Bank. 85.00 (ISBN 0-686-48141-0, 0304). T-C Pubns CA.

Foams: Molding Thermosetting & Thermoplastic Structural Foam. 137p. 1983. 78.00 (ISBN 0-317-12678-4, LS115). T-C Pubns CA.

Frisch, K. C. & Saunders, J. H., eds. Plastic Foams, Pt.2. (Monographs on Plastics: Vol. 1). 592p. 1973. 115.00 (ISBN 0-8247-1219-6). Dekker.

Frisch, Kurt C. & Saunders, J. H., eds. Plastic Foams, Pt.1. LC 71-157837. (Monographs on Plastics). Repr. of 1972 ed. 116.00 (ISBN 0-8357-9092-4, 2055059). Bks Demand UMI.

Hilyard, N. C. Mechanics of Cellular Plastics. 1981. text ed. 58.00x (ISBN 0-02-949390-0). Macmillan.

Hilyard, N. C., ed. Mechanics of Cellular Plastics. (Illus.). 401p. 1982. 64.00 (ISBN 0-686-48139-9, 1906). T-C Pubns CA.

Moody & Thomas. Chromatographic Separation with Foamed Plastics & Rubbers. (Chromatographic Science Ser.). 176p. 1982. 35.00 (ISBN 0-8247-1549-7). Dekker.

Nadeau, Herbert G., ed. Fire Property Data-Cellular Plastics. 167p. 1981. pap. 25.00 (ISBN 0-87762-293-0). Technomic.

Plastic Foams: Proceedings of a Special Conference, Los Angeles. (Illus.). 188p. 1980. 32.00 (ISBN 0-938648-03-9). T-C Pubns CA.

Semerdjiev, S. Introduction to Structural Foam. (SPE Processing Ser.). (Illus.). 133p. 1982. 18.00 (ISBN 0-686-48142-9, 1603). T-C Pubns CA.

Storage of Cellular Rubber & Plastics. (Two Hundred Ser). 1974. pap. 2.00 (ISBN 0-685-58171-3, 231B). Natl Fire Prot.

Structural Foam Applications, 1973-March 1983. 127p. 1983. 78.00 (ISBN 0-686-48314-6, LS116). T-C Pubns CA.

Structural Foam: Finishing & Decorating, 1977-Sept. 1983. 55p. 1983. 78.00 (ISBN 0-686-48315-4, LS117). T-C Pubns CA.

Structural Foam Plastics Directory & Marketing Guide. LC 83-50698. 70p. 1983. pap. 45.00 (ISBN 0-87762-333-3). Technomic.

Technomic's Staff, ed. Cellular Plastics in Transportation. LC 75-32680. 1975. pap. 9.95x (ISBN 0-685-63886-3). Technomic.

U. S. Foamed Plastics Markets & Directory 1984. LC 63-59134. 68p. pap. 40.00 (ISBN 0-87762-374-0). Technomic.
Wendle, Bruce C., et al, eds. Engineering Guide to Structural Foams. LC 76-16932. (Illus.). 1976. pap. 25.00x (ISBN 0-87762-218-3). Technomic.

PLASTIC INDUSTRIES
see Plastics Industry and Trade

PLASTIC LAMINATES
see Laminated Plastics

PLASTIC MATERIALS
see Plastics

PLASTIC MOLDING
see Plastics–Molding

PLASTIC PACKAGING
see Plastics in Packaging

PLASTIC PACKAGING (ELECTRONICS)
see Electronic Apparatus and Appliances–Plastic Embedment

PLASTIC TOOLS
Benjamin, William P. Plastic Tooling: Techniques & Applications. LC 75-39845. (Illus.). 256p. 1972. 57.00 (ISBN 0-07-004554-2). McGraw.

PLASTICITY
see also Buckling (Mechanics); Dislocations in Crystals; Dislocations in Metals; Elastic Plates and Shells; Materials–Creep; Plasticizers; Plastics; Plates (Engineering); Rheology
Argon, Ali, ed. Constitutive Equations in Plasticity. 1975. text ed. 35.00x (ISBN 0-262-01042-9). MIT Pr.
Bishop, Beverly & Craik, Rebecca L. Neural Plasticity. 1982. pap. 5.00 (ISBN 0-912452-38-2). Am Phys Therapy Assn.
Brownw, Dik. Hagar the Horrible, No. 2. 128p. 1985. pap. 1.95 (ISBN 0-441-31460-0). Ace Bks.
Cotman, Carl W., ed. Synaptic Plasticity. 460p. text ed. write for info (ISBN 0-89862-654-4). Guilford Pr.
Gollin, Eugene S., ed. Developmental Plasticity: Behavioral & Biological Aspects of Variations in Development. LC 80-2331. (Developmental Psychology Ser.). 1981. 37.50 (ISBN 0-12-289620-3). Acad Pr.
Harper, Charles A. Handbook of Plastics & Elastomers. 950p. 1975. 74.50 (ISBN 0-07-026681-6). McGraw.
Houwink, Roelof. Elasticity, Plasticity & Structure of Matter. 3rd ed. LC 72-154515. (Illus.). 1971. 67.50 (ISBN 0-521-07875-X). Cambridge U Pr.
Johnson, W. & Mellor, P. B. Engineering Plasticity. LC 83-18446. (Engineering Science Ser.: 1-467). 646p. 1983. pap. text ed. 34.95x (ISBN 0-470-20012-X). Halsted Pr.
Kovacs, T. & Zsoldos, L. Dislocations & Plastic Deformations. LC 73-6995. 364p. 1974. 28.00 (ISBN 0-08-017062-5). Pergamon.
Malhotra, V. M., ed. Developments in the Use of Superplasticizers. LC 81-65667. (SP-68). 572p. (Orig.). 1981. pap. 51.75 (ISBN 0-686-95243-X). ACI.
Massonnet, C., et al. Plasticity in Structural Engineering, Fundamentals & Applications. (CISM,, International Center for Mechanical Sciences: Vol. 241). (Illus.). 302p. 1979. pap. 35.00 (ISBN 0-387-81350-0). Springer-Verlag.
Mendelson, Alexander. Plasticity: Theory & Application. LC 82-21231. 368p. 1983. Repr. of 1968 ed. lib. bdg. 24.50 (ISBN 0-89874-582-9). Krieger.
--Plasticity: Theory & Application. LC 68-12718. (Macmillan Series in Applied Mechanics). pap. 91.80 (ISBN 0-317-10993-6, 2003540). Bks Demand UMI.
Padmanabham, K. A. & Davies, G. J. Superplasticity. (Materials Research & Engineering: Vol. 2). (Illus.). 292p. 1980. pap. 39.00 (ISBN 0-387-10038-5). Springer-Verlag.
Sawczuk, A. & Bianchi, G., eds. Plasticity Today-Modelling, Methods & Applications: Proceedings of an International Symposium on Current Trends & Results in Plasticity, Held at the International Centre for Mechanical Sciences, Udine, Italy, 27-30 June 1983. (Illus.). 864p. 1985. 142.50 (ISBN 0-85334-302-0, Pub. by Elsevier Applied Sci England). Elsevier.
Stricklin, J. A. & Saczalski, K. J., eds. Constitutive Equations in Viscoplasticity: Computational & Engineering Aspects AMD, Vol. 20. 214p. 1976. pap. text ed. 20.00 (ISBN 0-685-75516-9, I00106). ASME.
Thomas, Tracy Y. Plastic Flow & Fracture in Solids. (Mathematics in Science & Engineering Ser: Vol. 2). 1961. 60.00 (ISBN 0-12-688450-1). Acad Pr.
Tomlenov, A. D., ed. Plastic Flow of Metals, Vol. 1. LC 75-131886. 114p. 1971. 25.00x (ISBN 0-306-10850-X, Consultants). Plenum Pub.
Valanis, K. C., ed. Constitutive Equations in Viscoplasticity: Phenomenological & Physical Aspects AMD, Vol. 21. 80p. 1976. pap. text ed. 14.00 (ISBN 0-685-75517-7, I00107). ASME.
Washizu, K. Variational Methods in Elasticity & Plasticity. 3rd ed. (Illus.). 540p. 1982. 110.00 (ISBN 0-08-026723-8). Pergamon.
Wessel, E. T. & Loss, F. J., eds. Elastic-Plastic Fracture Test Methods - STP 856: The User's Experience. LC 84-70607. (Illus.). 430p. 1985. text ed. 49.00 (ISBN 0-8031-0419-7, 04-856000-30). ASTM.
Yong, R. N. & Selig, E. T., eds. Application of Plasticity & Generalized Stress-Strain in Geotechnical Engineering. LC 81-71796. 359p. 1982. pap. 27.25x (ISBN 0-87262-294-0). Am Soc Civil Eng.

PLASTICIZERS
see also Solvents
Sears, J. Kern & Darby, Joseph R. The Technology of Plasticizers. LC 80-10225. (SPE Monographs). 1166p. 1982. 148.50x (ISBN 0-471-05583-2, Pub. by Wiley-Interscience). Wiley.
--The Technology of Plasticizers. (SPE Monograph). (Illus.). 1166p. 1981. 148.50 (ISBN 0-686-48137-2, 0813). T-C Pubns CA.

PLASTICS
see also Acetal Resins; Aminoplastics; Brittleness; Chemistry, Organic–Synthesis; Condensation Products (Chemistry); Elastomers; Electronic Apparatus and Appliances–Plastic Embedment; Epoxy Resins; Extrusion (Plastics); Glass Reinforced Plastics; Gums and Resins; Heat Resistant Materials; Laminated Plastics; Pipe, Plastic; Plastic Analysis (Theory of Structures); Plastic Films; Plastic Foams; Plastic Tools; Plasticity; Plastics in Building; Polyesters; Reinforced Plastics; Rubber, Artificial; Thermoplastics; Vinyl Polymers
also names of plastics, e.g. Nylon
Ahmed, Mukhtar. Coloring of Plastics. LC 78-26186. 240p. 1979. 22.50 (ISBN 0-442-20267-9). Krieger.
--Coloring of Plastics: Theory & Practice. 1979. 24.50 (ISBN 0-442-20267-9). Van Nos Reinhold.
Albright, Lyle F. Processes for Major Addition-Type Plastics & Their Monomers. rev. ed. LC 80-12568. 300p. 1985. lib. bdg. 32.50 (ISBN 0-89874-074-6). Krieger.
American Society for Electroplated Plastics Staff. Standards & Guidelines for Electroplated Plastics. 3rd ed. (Illus.). 160p. 1984. 36.00 (ISBN 0-13-842310-5). P-H.
Arnold, Lionel K. Introduction to Plastics. (Illus.). 1968. pap. 8.95x (ISBN 0-8138-1272-0). Iowa St U Pr.
Ash, M. & Ash, I. Encyclopedia of Plastics, Polymers & Resins Vol. 1, A-G. 1981. 75.00 (ISBN 0-8206-0290-6). Chem Pub.
--Encyclopedia of Plastics, Polymers & Resins Vol. 2, H-O. 1982. 75.00 (ISBN 0-8206-0296-5). Chem Pub.
--Encyclopedia of Plastics, Polymers & Resins Vol. 3, P-Z. 1983. 75.00 (ISBN 0-8206-0303-1). Chem Pub.
Baer, Eric, ed. Engineering Design for Plastics. LC 75-1222. 1216p. 1975. Repr. of 1964 ed. 68.50 (ISBN 0-88275-281-2). Krieger.
Baijal, M. D., ed. Plastics Polymer Science & Technology. (SPE Monograph). (Illus.). 945p. 1982. 172.50 (ISBN 0-686-48131-3, 0815). T-C Pubns CA.
Baijal, Mahendra D., ed. Plastic Polymers Science & Technology. LC 31-13066. (Society of Plastic Engineers Monographs). 945p. 1982. 172.50x (ISBN 0-471-04044-4, Pub. by Wiley-Interscience). Wiley.
Baird, Ronald J. & Baird, David. Industrial Plastics. LC 81-13514. (Illus.). 320p. 1982. 16.80 (ISBN 0-87006-402-9). Goodheart.
Baker, John & Heyman, J. Plastic Design of Frames, 2 vols. Incl. Vol. 1. Fundamentals; Vol. 2. Applications. 47.50 (ISBN 0-521-07984-5). LC 69-19370. (Illus.). 1969-1971. Cambridge U Pr.
Bares, R. A., ed. Plastics in Material & Structural Engineering. (Illus.). 962p. 1982. 164.00 (ISBN 0-686-48179-8, 0706). T-C Pubns CA.
Beck, Ronald D. Plastic Product Design. 2nd ed. 424p. 1980. 32.95 (ISBN 0-442-20632-1). Van Nos Reinhold.
--Plastic Product Design. 2nd ed. (Illus.). 424p. 1980. 33.00 (ISBN 0-686-48180-1, 0206). T-C Pubns CA.
Bikales, Norbert M., ed. Molding of Plastics. LC 78-172950. 230p. pap. text ed. 16.00 (ISBN 0-471-07233-8). Krieger.
Birley, Arthur W. & Scott, Martyn J. Plastics Materials. 1982. (Pub. by Chapman & Hall); pap. 23.00x (ISBN 0-412-00221-3, NO. 5022). Methuen Inc.
Boyer, Raymond F., ed. Technological Aspects of the Mechanical Behavior of Polymers. LC 74-181576. (Applied Polymer Symposia: No. 24). Repr. of 1974 ed. 23.00 (ISBN 0-8357-9378-8, 2007371). Bks Demand UMI.
Braun, Dietrich. Identification of Plastics. 1982. pap. text ed. 14.50 (ISBN 0-02-949260-2). Macmillan.
--Identification of Plastics: Qualitative Analysis of Plastics Using Simple Methods. (Illus.). 100p. 1982. 21.00 (ISBN 0-686-48113-5, 1901). T-C Pubns CA.
Briston, J. H. & Gosselin, C. C. Introduction to Plastics. 7.50 (ISBN 0-685-28367-4). Philos Lib.
Brown, R. L. E. Design & Manufacture of Plastic Parts. 204p. 1980. 57.95 (ISBN 0-471-05324-4). Wiley.
Brydson, J. & Peacock, D. G., eds. Principles of Plastics Extrusion: A Teaching Programmer. (Illus.). 108p. 1973. 9.25 (ISBN 0-85334-563-5, Pub. by Elsevier Applied Sci England). Elsevier.
Burlace, C. J. & Whalley, L. Waste Plastics & Their Potential for Recycle, 1977. 1981. 40.00x (ISBN 0-686-97166-3, Pub. by W Spring England). State Mutual Bk.
Business Communications Staff. Interpenetrating Networks. 1984. 1500.00 (ISBN 0-89336-375-8, P-075). BCC.
--Membrane & Separation Technology Patents: Patent Printouts for Membrane Market Opportunities. 1984. 150.00 (ISBN 0-89336-247-6). BCC.
--Multi-Layer Films: Markets, Technology: P-063. 1982. 1500.00 (ISBN 0-89336-292-1). BCC.
--Opportunities in Specialty Plastics. 1983. 1950.00 (ISBN 0-89336-365-0, P-073). BCC.
--Plastics Compounding. 1985. 1950.00 (ISBN 0-89336-345-6, P-070). BCC.
--Plastics Conference Proceedings, 1982. 1983. 125.00 (ISBN 0-686-84693-1). BCC.
--Plastics Conference Proceedings, 1983. 1984. 125.00 (ISBN 0-89336-376-6). BCC.
--Plastics Conference Proceedings: 7th Annual. 1981. 105.00 (ISBN 0-89336-311-1). BCC.
--Plastics Forming. 1984. 1500.00 (ISBN 0-89336-401-0, P-079). BCC.
--Plastics UV Stability. 1984. 1750.00 (ISBN 0-89336-402-9, P-080). BCC.
--Plastics vs. Other Pipes, P-043R. 1984. 1500.00 (ISBN 0-89336-270-0). BCC.
--Transparent Plastics: Developments Trends, P-053. 1982. 1500.00 (ISBN 0-89336-201-8). BCC.
Butters, Gordon, ed. Plastics Pneumatic Conveying & Bulk Storage. (Illus.). 296p. 1981. 57.50 (ISBN 0-85334-983-5, Pub. by Elsevier Applied Sci England). Elsevier.
Buttrey, D. N., ed. Plastics in Furniture. (Illus.). 183p. 1976. 24.00 (ISBN 0-85334-647-X, Pub. by Elsevier Applied Sci England). Elsevier.
Cherry, Raymond. General Plastics: Projects & Procedures. rev. ed. (Illus.). 1967. text ed. 16.64 (ISBN 0-87345-162-7). McKnight.
Cook, J. Gordon. Your Guide to Plastics. 320p. 1968. 40.00x (ISBN 0-900541-52-0, Pub. by Meadowfield Pr England). State Mutual Bk.
Crawford, R. J. Plastics Engineering. (Illus.). 360p. 1981. pap. 28.00 (ISBN 0-08-026263-5). Pergamon.
Crompton, T. R. The Analysis of Plastics. (Series in Analytical Chemistry: Vol. 8). (Illus.). 452p. 1984. 54.00 (ISBN 0-08-026251-1). Pergamon.
D'Alelio, Gaetano F. & Parker, John A., eds. Ablative Plastics: Papers. LC 76-143687. (Illus.). pap. 124.80 (ISBN 0-317-07830-5, 2055032). Bks Demand UMI.
Davis, A. & Sims, D. Weathering of Polymers. (Illus.). 300p. 1983. 64.75 (ISBN 0-85334-226-1, I-266-83, Pub. by Elsevier Applied Sci England). Elsevier.
Dealy, John M. Rheometers for Molten Plastics: A Practical Guide to Testing & Property Measurement. 300p. 1981. 39.50 (ISBN 0-442-21874-5). Van Nos Reinhold.
Deanin, Rudolph D. & Crugnola, Aldo M., eds. Toughness & Brittleness of Plastics. LC 76-41267. (Advances in Chemistry Ser.: No. 154). 1976. 49.95 (ISBN 0-8412-0221-4). Am Chemical.
Degradable Plastics. 43p. 1982. 37.00x (ISBN 0-686-44663-1, Pub. by Chandler England). State Mutual Bk.
Din Standards for Plastics: Duroplast-resins & Duroplast-molding Materials. 431.00 (ISBN 0-01-005652-1, 10056-7/21). Heyden.
Din Standards for Plastics: Half-Finished Products & Finished Products. 355.00 (ISBN 0-01-078925-1, 10789-5/51). Heyden.
Din Standards Natural Rubber & Elastomers. 322.00 (ISBN 0-686-28185-3, 10704-1/47). Heyden.
Din Standards: Plastic Pipes, Pipeline Components & Pipe Joints. 239.00 (ISBN 0-686-28187-X, 10790-1/52). Heyden.
Din Standards: Plastics: Testing Standards for Mechanical, Thermal & Electrical Properties, Pt. I. 384.00 (ISBN 0-686-28169-1, 10053-5/18). Heyden.
Din Standards: Plastics Two: Test Standards for Chemical, Optical - Usability & Processing Properties. 601.00 (ISBN 0-686-28186-1, 10705-6/48). Heyden.
Disposal of Plastics with Minimum Environmental Impact, STP 533. 68p. 1973. 4.25 (ISBN 0-8031-0083-3, 04 533000 19). ASTM.
Disque, Robert O. Applied Plastic Design in Steel. LC 79-153190. pap. 63.80 (ISBN 0-317-11073-X, 2007244). Bks Demand UMI.
Driver, Walter E. Plastics Chemistry & Technology. LC 78-24011. 1979. 26.50 (ISBN 0-442-22156-8). Van Nos Reinhold.
Duck, E. W. Plastics & Rubbers. 1972. 10.00 (ISBN 0-8022-2076-2). Philos Lib.
Dym, Joseph B. Product Design with Plastics: A Practical Manual. (Illus.). 288p. 1983. 28.95 (ISBN 0-8311-1141-0). Indus Pr.
Edwards, Lauton. Industrial Arts Plastics. rev. ed. 1974. 17.92 (ISBN 0-02-664630-7). Bennett IL.
Ehrenstein, G. W. & Erhard, G. Designing with Plastics. 200p. 1984. 35.00 (ISBN 0-02-948770-6). Macmillan.
El-Desouti, H. Y. Plastic Technology Dictionary. (Eng., Fr., Ger. & Arabic.). 331p. 1980. 45.00 (ISBN 0-686-92400-2, M-9754). French & Eur.
Ethylene Copolymers: P-061. 1984. 1250.00 (ISBN 0-89336-290-5). BCC.
Evans, R., ed. Physical Testing of Plastics - STP 736. 125p. 1981. 15.00 (ISBN 0-8031-0768-4, 04-736000-19). ASTM.
Flammability of Solid Plastics, Part 2. (Family & Flammability Ser.: Vol. 17). 208p. 1981. 25.00 (ISBN 0-87762-296-5). Technomic.
Frados, Joel. Plastics Engineering Handbook of the SPI. 4th ed. 1976. 49.50 (ISBN 0-442-22469-9). Van Nos Reinhold.
Frados, Joel, ed. Plastics Engineering Handbook of the SPI. 4th ed. 909p. 1976. 49.50 (ISBN 0-686-48143-7, 0208). T-C Pubns CA.
Gaechter, R. & Mueller, H. Plastics Additives Handbook. LC 83-62289. 320p. 1984. text ed. 59.00 (ISBN 0-02-949430-3, Pub. by Hanser International). Macmillan.
Garner, David P. & Stahl, G. Allan, eds. The Effects of Hostile Environments on Coatings & Plastics. LC 83-9230. (ACS Symposium Ser.: No. 229). 339p. 1983. lib. bdg. 47.95x (ISBN 0-8412-0798-4). Am Chemical.
Grandilli, Peter A. Technician's Handbook of Plastics. 272p. 1981. 22.95 (ISBN 0-442-23870-3). Van Nos Reinhold.
--Technician's Handbook of Plastics. 246p. 1981. 23.00 (ISBN 0-686-48117-8, B327). T-C Pubns CA.
Gray, G. W. & Winsor, P. A., eds. Liquid Crystals & Plastic Crystals: Preparation, Constitution & Applications, Vol. 1. LC 73-11504. (Illus.). 383p. 1974. 74.95 (ISBN 0-470-32339-6). Halsted Pr.
--Liquid Crystals & Plastic Crystals: Physico-Chemical Properties & Methods of Investigation, Vol. 2. LC 73-11505. (Illus.). 314p. 1974. 79.95 (ISBN 0-470-32340-X). Halsted Pr.
Green, Andrew, ed. Emerging High Performance Structural Plastic Technology. LC 82-70767. 85p. 1982. pap. 16.00x (ISBN 0-87262-305-X). Am Soc Civil Eng.
Greene, Francis T., et al, eds. Quality Assurance of Polymeric Materials & Products: STP 846. LC 83-73514. (Illus.). 145p. 1985. pap. text ed. 24.00 (ISBN 0-8031-0408-1, 04-846000-19). ASTM.
Guillet, J., ed. Polymers & Ecological Problems. LC 73-81406. (Polymer Science & Technology Ser.: Vol. 3). 230p. 1973. 42.50x (ISBN 0-306-36403-4, Plenum Pr). Plenum Pub.
Handbook of Films, Sheets & Laminates. 85.00 (ISBN 0-686-48144-5, 0305). T-C Pubns CA.
Hertzberg, Richard W. & Manson, John A. Fatigue of Engineering Plastics. LC 79-6786. 1980. 42.00 (ISBN 0-12-343550-1). Acad Pr.
Hess, Harry L. Plastics Laboratory Procedures. LC 78-26948. 1980. pap. 18.76 scp (ISBN 0-672-97138-0); pap. 3.67 scp answer key (ISBN 0-672-97268-9). Bobbs.
Hilado, Carlos J., ed. Flammability Handbook for Plastics. 2nd, rev. ed. LC 72-82519. 201p. 1974. pap. 35.00 (ISBN 0-87762-139-X). Technomic.
Hill, R. The Mathematical Theory of Plasticity. (Engineering Science Ser.). 1983. pap. 26.95x (ISBN 0-19-856162-8). Oxford U Pr.
Holmes, M. & Just, D. J. GRP in Structural Engineering. 298p. 1984. 51.00 (ISBN 0-85334-232-6, Pub. by Elsevier Applied Sci England). Elsevier.
International Plastics Selector, Inc. The Adhesives Desk-Top Data Bank. 95.00 (ISBN 0-686-48215-8, 0301). T-C Pubns CA.
--Specifications for Adhesives. 55.00 (ISBN 0-686-48216-6, 0308). T-C Pubns CA.
International Symposium on Rate Processes in Plastic Deformation, Cleveland, 1972, Staff. Rate Processes in Plastic Deformation of Materials: The John E. Dorn Symposium, Proceedings. Li, J. C. & Mukherjee, A. K., eds. LC 73-86454. (Materials-Metalworking Technology Ser.: No. 4). pap. 160.00 (ISBN 0-317-09740-7, 2050984). Bks Demand UMI.
IPC Business Press Staff, ed. European Plastics Buyers' Guide. 110.00x (ISBN 0-617-00304-1, Pub. by IPC England). State Mutual Bk.
Jones, Roger F., ed. Handbook of Short Fiber Reinforced Plastics. 1985. text ed. 34.50 (ISBN 0-412-00791-6, 9226, Pub. by Chapman & Hall England). Methuen Inc.

Brown, R. L. E. Design & Manufacture of Plastic Parts. 204p. 1980. 57.95 (ISBN 0-471-05324-4). Wiley.
Bruins, Paul. Basic Principles of Rotational Molding. 294p. 1971. 55.75 (ISBN 0-677-14980-8). Gordon.
Business Communications Staff. Large Molded Parts. 1984. 1750.00 (ISBN 0-89336-400-2, P-078). BCC.
Calvert, E., et al, eds. Injection Moulding. (E.I.T.B. Instruction Manuals Ser.). (Illus.). 163p. 1982. pap. 39.95x spiral bdg. (ISBN 0-85083-553-4). Intl Ideas.
De Cleir, Piaras V. Polymers in Injection Molding. LC 85-51316. 170p. 1985. 44.00 (ISBN 0-938648-25-X). T-C Pubns CA.
Design & Manufacture of Plastic Injection Moulds. (Productivity Ser.: No. 13). 70p. 1979. pap. 8.25 (ISBN 92-833-1703-3, APO93, APO). Unipub.
Foams: Molding Thermosetting & Thermoplastic Structural Foam. 137p. 1983. 78.00 (ISBN 0-317-12678-4, LS115). T-C Pubns CA.
Gastrow, Hans & Stoeckhert, Klaus. Injection Molds: Examples for Design & Construction. LC 83-62286. 280p. 1983. text ed. 49.50 (ISBN 0-02-949440-0, Pub. by Hanser International). Macmillan.
Glanvill, A. B. & Denton, E. N. Injection-Mould Design Fundamentals. (Illus.). 1965. 27.95 (ISBN 0-8311-1033-3). Indus Pr.
Honeycombe, R. K. The Plastic Deformation of Metals. 480p. 1984. pap. text ed. 34.50 (ISBN 0-7131-3468-2). E Arnold.
Injection Molding Extrusion & Moldmaking: Proceedings of SPE Pactec '80. 365p. 28.00 (ISBN 0-686-48233-6, 1503). T-C Pubns CA.
Injection Molding, Extrusion, Mold Making & Design, Machinery & Equiptment, Color & Decorating, & Management: Proceedings of SPE Pactec '81, August 25-27, 1981, Los Angeles, California. 388p. 25.00 (ISBN 0-686-48161-5, 1506). T-C Pubns CA.
Injection Molding Machinery & Accessories. 300p. 1983. 78.00 (ISBN 0-317-12681-4, LS118). T-C Pubns CA.
Injection Molding of Plastics. 2nd ed. (Illus.). 198p. 1984. 30.00 (ISBN 0-317-20185-9). T-C Pubns CA.
Injection Molding of Plastics, 1979. LC 80-53542. (Illus.). 1983. 78.00 (ISBN 0-938648-00-4, LS119). T-C Pubns CA.
Injection Molding-Plastics. 300p. 1983. 78.00 (ISBN 0-317-12682-2, LS119). T-C Pubns CA.
Johannaber, Friedrich. Injection Molding Machines. LC 81-85871. 312p. 1983. text ed. 40.00 (ISBN 0-02-949420-6, Pub. by Hanser International). Macmillan.
Kresta, Jiri E., ed. Reaction Injection Molding: Polymer Chemistry & Engineering. LC 84-24560. (ACS Symposium Ser.: No. 270). 302p. 1985. lib. bdg. 59.95x (ISBN 0-8412-0888-3). Am Chemical.
Learning Systems Ltd, ed. Elements of Injection Moulding of Thermoplastics. (Illus., Orig.). 1969. pap. text ed. 5.95 (ISBN 0-85334-043-9). Transatlantic.
Mold Release Agents for Rubbers & Plastics, 1973-Jan. 1983. 162p. 1983. 78.00 (ISBN 0-686-48316-2, LS130). T-C Pubns CA.
Reaction Injection Molding of Polymers. 126p. 1984. 78.00 (ISBN 0-686-48332-4, LS43). T-C Pubns CA.
Robinson, J. S., ed. Plastics Molding: Equipment, Processes, & Materials. LC 81-90745. x, 299p. 1981. pap. 42.00 (ISBN 0-942378-00-8). Polymers & Plastics Tech Pub Hse.
Rosato, Dominick V. & Rosato, Donald V. Injection Molding Handbook. (Illus.). 960p. 1985. 86.50 (ISBN 0-442-27815-2). Van Nos Reinhold.
Rubin, Irvin I. Injection Molding: Theory & Practice. LC 73-5. (S P E Monographs: Vol. 1). 657p. 1973. 64.50x (ISBN 0-471-74445-X, Pub. by Wiley-Interscience). Wiley.
--Injection Molding: Theory & Practice. (SPE Monograph). 657p. 1972. 64.50 (ISBN 0-686-48157-7, 0804). T-C Pubns CA.
Schwartz, Seymour & Goodman, Sidney. Plastics Materials & Processes. 832p. 1982. 94.50 (ISBN 0-442-22777-9). Van Nos Reinhold.
Stoeckhert, Klaus. Mold-Making Handbook. LC 83-62285. 484p. 1983. text ed. 68.00 (ISBN 0-02-949670-5, Pub. by Hanser International). Macmillan.
Tobin, William J. Quality Control Manual for Injection Molding. 85p. 1978. 34.50 (ISBN 0-938648-13-6, 0909). T-C Pubns CA.
Weir, C. I. Introduction to Injection Molding. Mendoza, Luis E., tr. (SPE Processing Ser.). (Span., Illus.). 92p. 26.50 (ISBN 0-686-48174-7, 1102). T-C Pubns CA.
Weir, Clifford I. Introduction to Injection Molding. (SPE Processing Ser.). (Illus.). 83p. 1975. 9.50 (ISBN 0-686-48158-5, 1602). T-C Pubns CA.

PLASTICS, CELLULAR
see Plastic Foams

PLASTICS ADDITIVES
see Plastics–Additives

PLASTICS CRAFT

Angle, Burr, ed. Hints & Tips for Plastic Modeling. (Illus.). 1980. pap. 4.75 (ISBN 0-89024-546-0). Kalmbach.
Cherry, Raymond. General Plastics: Projects & Procedures. rev. ed. (Illus.). 1967. text ed. 16.64 (ISBN 0-87345-162-7). McKnight.
DiNoto, Andrea. Art Plastic: Designed for Living. LC 83-73418. (Illus.). 228p. 1984. 45.00 (ISBN 0-89659-437-8). Abbeville Pr.
Edwards, Lauton. Industrial Arts Plastics. rev. ed. 1974. 17.92 (ISBN 0-02-664630-7). Bennett IL.

PLASTICS IN BUILDING

Benjamin, B. S. Structural Design with Plastics. 2nd ed. 416p. 1981. 34.50 (ISBN 0-442-20167-2). Van Nos Reinhold.
Buildings, Fire Safety Aspects of Polymeric Materials: National Academy of Sciences, Vol. 7. LC 77-79218. 210p. 1979. 19.00 (ISBN 0-87762-228-0). Technomic.
Hollaway, L. Glass Reinforced Plastics in Construction: Engineering Aspects. LC 77-13952. 228p. 1978. 52.95x (ISBN 0-470-99338-3). Halsted Pr.
Horne, M. R. & Morris, L. J. Plastic Design of Low-Rise Frames. (Structural Mechanics Ser.). (Illus.). 256p. 1982. 50.00x (ISBN 0-262-08123-7). MIT Pr.
Montella. Plastics in Architecture. (Plastics Engineering Ser.). 280p. 1985. 49.75 (ISBN 0-8247-7396-9). Dekker.
Plastics Used as Building or Construction Materials, 1975-May 1983. 201p. 1983. 78.00 (ISBN 0-686-48319-7, LS136). T-C Pubns CA.
Selected Abstracts on Structural Applications of Plastics. (Manual & Report on Engineering Practices Ser.: No. 47). 80p. 1967. pap. 4.00x (ISBN 0-87262-221-5). Am Soc Civil Eng.
Tentative Guide for Plastics in Building Construction. 52p. 1973. pap. 2.00 (ISBN 0-685-44143-1, 205M-T). Natl Fire Prot.

PLASTICS IN PACKAGING
see also Plastic Foams

Bruins, Paul F., ed. Packaging with Plastics. LC 72-78922. 220p. 1974. 48.75 (ISBN 0-677-12200-4). Gordon.
Business Communications Staff. Plastic Alternatives to the Metal Can. 1984. 1950.00 (ISBN 0-89336-386-3, P-077). BCC.
--Plastics vs. the Metal Can. 1984. 1950.00 (ISBN 0-89336-386-3, P-077). BCC.
Deitsch, Marian, ed. Kline Guide to Packaging. Rich, Susan. (Illus.). 324p. 1980. pap. 70.00. Kline.
Farnham, Stanley E. Guide to Thermoformed Plastic Packaging: Sales Builder-Cost Cutter. LC 72-156481. 472p. 1972. 21.95 (ISBN 0-8436-1206-1). Van Nos Reinhold.
Oswin, C. R. Plastic Films & Packaging. (Illus.). xi, 214p. 1975. 27.75 (ISBN 0-85334-641-0, Pub. by Elsevier Applied Sci England). Elsevier.
Pinner, S. H., ed. Modern Packaging Films. LC 67-26705. 249p. 1967. 32.50x (ISBN 0-306-30632-8, Plenum Pr). Plenum Pub.
Sacharow, Stanley & Griffin, Roger C., Jr. Basic Guide to Plastics in Packaging. LC 72-91986. 224p. 1973. 22.95 (ISBN 0-8436-1208-8). Van Nos Reinhold.
Technomic's Staff, ed. Cellular Plastics in Transportation. LC 75-32680. 1975. pap. 9.95x (ISBN 0-685-63886-3). Technomic.

PLASTICS INDUSTRY AND TRADE

Baker, John F., et al. The Steel Skeleton, Vol. 2: Plastic Behaviour & Design. LC 54-3769. pap. 111.80 (ISBN 0-317-26067-7, 2024427). Bks Demand UMI.
Berry, Richard M. Plastics Additives Marketing Guide & Company Directory. LC 77-150351. 125p. 1972. pap. 7.95 (ISBN 0-87762-058-X). Technomic.
Brown, R. L. Design & Manufacture of Plastic Parts. (Illus.). 204p. 1980. 58.00 (ISBN 0-686-48177-1, 0802). T-C Pubns CA.
Business Communications Staff. Plastics in Business Machines. 1985. pap. 1950.00 (ISBN 0-89336-443-6, P-064R). BCC.
--Plastics International Trade: P-058. 1981. 800.00 (ISBN 0-89336-259-X). BCC.
--Plastics Planning Guide: 1980-1981. 6th ed. 1981. 85.00 (ISBN 0-89336-288-3). BCC.
--Polyester Growth Markets. (Illus.). 1983. 1250.00 (ISBN 0-89336-100-3, P-047R). BCC.
Developing of Plastics Industries in Developing Countries. pap. 3.00 (ISBN 0-686-94788-6, UN70/2B/27, UN). Unipub.
DuBois, J. Harry. Plastics History, U. S. A. LC 79-156480. (Illus.). 464p. 1972. 24.95 (ISBN 0-8436-1203-7). Van Nos Reinhold.
Friedel, Robert. Pioneer Plastic: The Making & Selling of Celluloid. LC 81-69818. (Illus.). 192p. 1983. 21.50x (ISBN 0-299-09170-8). U of Wis Pr.
Glenz, Wolfgang W., ed. The Plastics Industry in Western Europe. 158p. 1984. 19.95. Macmillan.
IFAC Conference, 4th, Ghent, Belgium, June 1980. Instrumentation & Automation in the Paper, Rubber, Plastics & Polymerisation Industries: Proceedings. Van Cauwenberghe, A., ed. LC 80-41889. (IFAC Proceedings Ser.). (Illus.). 550p. 1981. 130.00 (ISBN 0-08-024487-4). Pergamon.
Jambro, D. Manufacturing Processes: Plastics. 1976. pap. text ed. 8.84 (ISBN 0-13-555623-6). P-H.
Kollonitsch, Valerie & Deitsch, Marian, eds. Kline Guide to the Plastics Industry. 2nd ed. LC 82-83394. (Illus.). 340p. 1982. pap. 155.00 (ISBN 0-917148-16-9). Kline.
Levy, Sidney. Plastics Extrusion Technology Handbook. LC 81-6587. (Illus.). 300p. 1981. 33.95 (ISBN 0-8311-1095-3). Indus Pr.
Machining Processes & Properties of Plastics & Elastomers, 1973-June 1982. 125p. 1982. 78.00 (ISBN 0-686-48307-3, LS125). T-C Pubns CA.
Meeting of the Minds: Marketing Polyurethane Technology. (SPI Conference Ser.). 354p. 1982. pap. 55.00 (ISBN 0-87762-317-1). Technomic.
Miller, Richard K. Robots in Industry: Applications for the Plastics Industry. 2nd ed. 180p. 1984. pap. text ed. 125.00 (ISBN 0-89671-053-X). SEAI Tech Pubns.
Miller, Richard K., et al. Noise Control Solutions for the Rubber & Plastics Industry. 45.00 (ISBN 0-686-74624-4). Fairmont Pr.
Nondestructive Test Methods in the Rubber & Plastics Industries, 1983-1984. 50p. 1984. 78.00 (ISBN 0-686-48317-0, LS128). T-C Pubns CA.
Plastic & Rubber Working Machinery. (Machinery Studies). 1980. 350.00 (ISBN 0-686-31531-6). Busn Trend.
Plastics Planning Conference: Proceedings 1984. 1985. pap. 125.00 (ISBN 0-89336-427-4). BCC.
Prevention of Dust Explosions in the Plastic Industry. (Sixty Ser.). 51p. 1970. pap. 2.00 (ISBN 0-685-46073-8, 654). Natl Fire Prot.
Reinforced Plastics Industry. 1982. 950.00 (ISBN 0-89336-267-0, P 055). BCC.
Sittig, M. Pollution Control in the Plastics & Rubber Industry. LC 75-2940. (Pollution Technology Review Ser: No. 18). (Illus.). 306p. 1975. 36.00 (ISBN 0-8155-0572-8). Noyes.
Society of Plastics Engineers. Advances in Technology Yield Profitability: 7th Annual Pacific Technical Conference, Feb. 22-24, 1983. pap. 111.00 (ISBN 0-317-29605-1, 2021699). Bks Demand UMI.
--Automation, Tooling & Thermosets: Regional Technical Conference, Mar. 3 & 4, 1983, Ramada Inn, Airport West, Mississauga, Ontario, Canada - Ontario Section & Thermoset Division, Society of Plastics Engineers. pap. 52.30 (ISBN 0-317-29608-6, 2021698). Bks Demand UMI.
--Decorating Plastics RETEC: Technical Papers, Society of Plastics Engineers, Decorating Division, Dec. 2 & 3, 1982, Hyatt Regency Dearborn, Dearborn, Michigan. pap. 34.80 (ISBN 0-317-29610-8, 2021696). Bks Demand UMI.
--Plastics-Engineering Today for Tomorrow's World: ANTEC 83, 41st Annual Technical Conference Proceedings, May 2-5, 1983, Hyatt Regency in Chicago. pap. 160.00 (ISBN 0-317-28683-8, 2020447). Bks Demand UMI.
--Plastics in a World Economy: ANTEC '84, 42nd Technical Conference & Exhibition. pap. 160.00 (ISBN 0-317-19848-3, 2023008). Bks Demand UMI.
--Plastics in the Electrical Industry: Technical Papers, Regional Technical Conference, March 3-4, 1980, Milwaukee, Wisconsin. (Illus.). pap. 57.30 (ISBN 0-317-08863-7, 2012018). Bks Demand UMI.
Society of the Plastics Industry. Plastics Industry Safety Handbook. 328p. 1973. 18.95 (ISBN 0-8436-1207-X). Van Nos Reinhold.
Structural Foam Plastics Directory & Marketing Guide. LC 83-50698. 70p. 1983. pap. 45.00 (ISBN 0-87762-333-3). Technomic.
Technical Insights Inc. Robots in Industry: Applications for the Plastics Industry. LC 82-99928. 163p. 1984. 125.00 (ISBN 0-89671-041-6). Tech Insights.
Throne. Plastics Processing Engineering. 1979. 115.00 (ISBN 0-8247-6700-4). Dekker.
U. S. Foamed Plastics Markets & Directory 1984. LC 63-59134. 68p. pap. 40.00 (ISBN 0-87762-374-0). Technomic.
Van Cauwenbergue, A. R., ed. Instrumentation & Automation in the Paper, Rubber, Plastics & Polymerization Industries: Proceedings of the Fifth International IFAC-IMEKO Symposium, Antwerp, Belgium, 11-13 October 1983. (IFAC Proceedings Ser.). 528p. 1984. 120.00 (ISBN 0-08-031112-1). Pergamon.
Welling, Manfred S. German-English Glossary of Plastics Machinery Terms. (Ger. & Eng.). 280p. 1981. text ed. 14.00x (ISBN 0-02-949800-7, Pub. by Hanser International). Macmillan.
Yescombe, E. R. Plastics & Rubbers: World Sources of Information. 512p. 1976. 55.50 (ISBN 0-85334-675-5, Pub. by Elsevier Applied Sci England). Elsevier.

PLASTIDS
see also Chloroplasts; Chromatophores

Kirk, J. T. & Tilney-Basset, R. A. The Plastids: Their Chemistry, Structure, Growth & Inheritance. 960p. 1979. 178.75 (ISBN 0-444-80022-0, Biomedical Pr). Elsevier.

PLATE-METAL WORK
see also Metal Stamping

Dickson, H., et al, eds. Thin Plate Working, Vol. 2. (Engineering Craftsmen: No. D22). (Illus.). 1969. spiral bdg. 37.50x (ISBN 0-85083-033-8). Intl Ideas.
Reid, F. H. & Goldie, W., eds. Gold Plating Technology. (Illus.). 1974. 125.00 (ISBN 0-685-58546-8). Heinman.
Rowney, J. M., et al, eds. Thick Plate Working, Vol. 2. (Engineering Craftsmen: No. D21). (Illus.). 1969. spiral bdg. 37.50x (ISBN 0-85083-047-8). Intl Ideas.
Thick Plate Working, Vol. 1. (Engineering Craftsmen: No. D1). (Illus.). 1969. spiral bdg. 37.50x (ISBN 0-85083-025-7). Intl Ideas.

PLATE TECTONICS
see also Continental Drift

Bird, John, ed. Plate Tectonics. rev. ed. (Illus.). 986p. 1980. pap. 25.00 (ISBN 0-87590-223-5). Am Geophysical.
Bonini, William E., et al, eds. The Caribbean-South American Plate Boundary & Regional Tectonics. (Memoir Ser.: No. 162). (Illus.). 1984. 47.50. Geol Soc.
Bowin, Carl. Caribbean Gravity Field & Plate Tectonics. LC 76-16261. (Geological Society of America Special Papers: No. 169). pap. 33.80 (ISBN 0-317-29080-0, 2023738). Bks Demand UMI.
Caribbean Geological Conference (5th: 1968: St. Thomas, Virgin Islands) Staff. Caribbean Geophysical, Tectonic & Petrological Studies. Donnelly, Thomas D., ed. LC 74-165441. (Geological Society of America Memoir Ser.: No. 130). pap. 68.50 (ISBN 0-317-29126-2, 2025025). Bks Demand UMI.
Condie, Kent C., ed. Plate Tectonics & Crustal Evolution. 2nd ed. (Illus.). 350p. 1982. 72.00 (ISBN 0-08-028076-5); pap. 32.00 (ISBN 0-08-028075-7). Pergamon.
Cox, Allan & Hart, Robert B. Plate Tectonics: The Plate Tectonics Game. (Illus.). 350p. 1985. pap. text ed. 14.95 (ISBN 0-86542-313-X). Blackwell Pubns.
Cox, Allan, ed. Plate Tectonics & Geomagnetic Reversals. LC 73-4323. (Geology Ser.). (Illus.). 702p. 1973. text ed. 44.95 (ISBN 0-7167-0259-2); pap. text ed. 30.95 (ISBN 0-7167-0258-4). W H Freeman.
Davies, P. A. & Runcorn, S. K., eds. Mechanisms of Continental Drift & Plate Tectonics. 1981. 72.00 (ISBN 0-12-206160-8). Acad Pr.
Dewey, J. F., et al, eds. Tectonics: A Selection of Papers. 150p. 23.00 (ISBN 0-08-028742-5). Pergamon.
Ernst, W. G., ed. Metamorphism & Plate Tectonic Regimes. LC 74-23374. (Benchmark Papers in Geology Ser: No. 17). 448p. 1975. 76.00 (ISBN 0-12-786447-4). Acad Pr.
Garfunkel, Zvi, ed. Mantle Flow & Plate Theory. (Benchmark Papers in Geology: No. 84). (Illus.). 416p. 1984. 59.50 (ISBN 0-442-22734-5). Van Nos Reinhold.
Gayer, R., ed. The Tectonic Evolution of the Caledonide-Appalachian Origin. (Monograph on Intedisciplinary Earth Science Research & Applications). (Orig.). 1985. pap. write for info. (ISBN 0-9904001-9-0, Pub. by Sohn Germany). Heyden.
Geophysics Research Board. Continental Tectonics. (Studies in Geophysics). xii, 197p. 1980. pap. text ed. 14.95 (ISBN 0-309-02928-7). Natl Acad Pr.
Gill, J. Orogenic Andesites & Plate Tectonics. (Minerals & Rocks Ser.: Vol. 16). (Illus.). 300p. 1981. 38.50 (ISBN 0-387-10666-9). Springer-Verlag.
Glen, William. Continental Drift & Plate Tectonics. (Physics & Physical Science Ser.). 192p. 1975. pap. text ed. 12.95 (ISBN 0-675-08799-6). Merrill.
Hashimoto, M. & Uyeda, S., eds. Accretion Tectonics in the Circum-Pacific Regions. 1983. lib. bdg. 85.00 (ISBN 90-2771-561-0, Pub. by Reidel Holland). Kluwer Academic.
Hutton, D. W. & Sanderson, D. J., eds. Variscan Tectonics of the North Atlantic Region. (Illus.). 260p. 1984. text ed. 60.00x (ISBN 0-632-01203-X). Blackwell Pubns.
Jaroszewski, W. Fault & Fold Tectonics. (Geology Ser.: I-528). 550p. 1984. 97.00x (ISBN 0-470-27478-6). Halsted Pr.

Smith, Arthur J. Professional Plumbing Techniques: Illustrated & Simplified. LC 84-8883. (Illus.). 266p. 1984. 16.95 (ISBN 0-8306-0763-3, 1763). TAB Bks.

Step-by-Step Basic Plumbing. (Step by Step Home Repair Ser.). (Illus.). 96p. 1981. pap. 6.95 (ISBN --696-01405-X). BH&G.

Sullivan, James A. Plumbing: Installation & Design. (Illus.). 480p. 1980. text ed. 24.95 (ISBN 0-8359-5552-4); instr's manual avail. (ISBN 0-8359-5553-2). Reston.

Sunset Editors. Basic Plumbing Illustrated. LC 82-83221. (Illus.). 96p. 1983. pap. 5.95 (ISBN 0-376-01466-0, Sunset Bks). Sunset-Lane.

Thiesse, James L. Plumbing Fundamentals. (Contemporary Construction Ser.). (Illus.). 192p. 1981. 21.56 (ISBN 0-07-064191-9). McGraw.

Traister, John E. Planning & Designing Plumbing Systems. (Illus.). 224p. 1983. pap. 13.00 (ISBN 0-910460-39-6). Craftsman.

PLUMBING–ESTIMATES

Galeno, Joseph J. Plumbing Estimating Handbook. LC 76-57182. (Plumbing Ser.). 256p. 1976. pap. text ed. 15.00 (ISBN 0-8273-1764-6). Delmar.

Herkimer, Herbert. Cost Manual for Piping & Mechanical Construction. 1958. 18.50 (ISBN 0-8206-0029-6). Chem Pub.

Massey, Howard C. Estimating Plumbing Costs. 224p. (Orig.). 1982. pap. 17.25 (ISBN 0-910460-82-5). Craftsman.

Miller, William C. & Gallina, Leonard. Estimating & Cost Control in Plumbing Design. 176p. 1980. 22.50 (ISBN 0-442-23347-7). Van Nos Reinhold.

Page, John S. & Nation, Jim G. Estimator's Piping Man-Hour Manual. 3rd ed. LC 75-28602. (Estimator's Man-Hour Library). 220p. 1976. 39.95x (ISBN 0-87201-700-1). Gulf Pub.

PLUMBING–EXAMINATIONS, QUESTIONS, ETC.

Oravetz, Jules. Questions & Answers for Plumbers Examinations. 2nd ed. LC 73-85726. (Illus.). 1985. pap. 9.95 (ISBN 0-8161-1703-9). Audel.

Rudman, Jack. Assistant Plumbing Engineer. (Career Examination Ser.: C-2705). (Cloth bdg. avail. on request). 1980. pap. 12.00 (ISBN 0-8373-2705-9). Natl Learning.

--Master Plumber. (Career Examination Ser.: C-476). (Cloth bdg. avail. on request). pap. 12.00 (ISBN 0-8373-0476-8). Natl Learning.

--Plumber. (Career Examination Ser.: C-591). (Cloth bdg. avail. on request). pap. 10.00 (ISBN 0-8373-0591-8). Natl Learning.

--Plumber's Helper. (Career Examination Ser.: C-592). (Cloth bdg. avail. on request). pap. 8.00 (ISBN 0-8373-0592-6). Natl Learning.

--Plumbing. (Occupational Competency Examination Ser.: OCE-29). (Cloth bdg. avail. on request). pap. 13.95 (ISBN 0-8373-5729-2). Natl Learning.

--Plumbing Engineer. (Career Examination Ser.: C-2713). (Cloth bdg. avail. on request). 1980. pap. 12.00 (ISBN 0-8373-2713-X). Natl Learning.

--Plumbing Inspector. (Career Examination Ser.: C-593). (Cloth bdg. avail. on request). pap. 10.00 (ISBN 0-8373-0593-4). Natl Learning.

--Plumbing Supervisor. (Career Examination Ser.: C-2583). (Cloth bdg. avail. on request). pap. 10.00 (ISBN 0-8373-2583-8). Natl Learning.

--Senior Plumbing Inspector. (Career Examination Ser.: C-1740). (Cloth bdg. avail. on request). 12.00 (ISBN 0-8373-1740-1). Natl Learning.

--Supervising Plumbing Inspector. (Career Examination Ser.: C-1049). (Cloth bdg. avail. on request). pap. 10.00 (ISBN 0-8373-1049-0). Natl Learning.

PLUMBING FOR MICROWAVES

see Microwave Wiring

PLUTO

Green, Jeff. Pluto: The Evolutionary Cause of Incarnation, Vol. I. Buske, Terry, ed. (Modern Astrology Ser.). 360p. (Orig.). 1985. pap. 12.95 (ISBN 0-87542-296-9, L-296). Llewellyn Pubns.

Moore, Patrick & Tombaugh, Clyde. Out of the Darkness: The Planet Pluto. LC 80-36881. (Illus.). 224p. 1980. 14.95 (ISBN 0-8117-1163-3). Stackpole.

Whyte, Anthony J. & Wise, Herbert A. The Planet Pluto. LC 79-23998. 1980. 23.00 (ISBN 0-08-024648-6). Pergamon.

PLUTONIUM

see also Nuclear Fuels; Transplutonium Elements

Carnall, William T. & Choppin, Gregory R., eds. Plutonium Chemistry. LC 83-6057. (Symposium Ser.: No. 216). 484p. 1983. lib. bdg. 51.95 (ISBN 0-8412-0772-0). Am Chemical.

Cleveland, Jess M. The Chemistry of Plutonium. LC 78-60617. (ANS Monograph). (Illus.). 1979. Repr. of 1970 ed. 49.00x (ISBN 0-89448-013-8, 300014). Am Nuclear Soc.

Hodge, H. C., et al, eds. Uranium, Plutonium & the Transplutonic Elements. (Handbook of Experimental Pharmacology: Vol. 36). (Illus.). xxiii, 995p. 1973. 220.00 (ISBN 0-387-06168-1). Springer-Verlag.

Makarov, Evgeniis S. Crystal Chemistry of Simple Compounds of Uranium, Thorium, Plutonium, Neptunium. Uvarov, E. B., tr. from Rus. LC 59-14486. pap. 38.30 (ISBN 0-317-08925-0, 2003366). Bks Demand UMI.

Milyukova, M. S. Analytical Chemistry of Plutonium. (Analytical Chemistry of the Elements). 440p. 1971. 37.95x (ISBN 0-470-60415-8). Halsted Pr.

Miner, William N., ed. Plutonium Nineteen-Seventy & Other Actinides: Proceedings of the 4th International Conference on Plutonium & Other Actinides, Santa Fe, New Mexico, October 5-9, 1970. (Nuclear Metallurgy Ser.: Vol. 17). Part I. pap. 133.00 (ISBN 0-317-10226-5); Part II. pap. 137.50 (ISBN 0-317-13005-6). Bks Demand UMI.

Patterson, Walter C. The Plutonium Business & the Spread of the Bomb. LC 84-22181. 288p. 1985. Repr. of 1984 ed. 16.95 (ISBN 0-87156-837-3, Dist. by Random). Sierra.

Pitcher, W. S. & Aguirre, L., eds. Bibliography of Circum-Pacific Plutonism. (Mircoform Publication Ser.: No. 12). 1982. 6.00 (ISBN 0-8137-6012-7). Geol Soc.

Plutonium as a Reactor Fuel. (Proceedings Ser.). (Eng., Fr. & Rus., Illus.). 858p. 1967. pap. 53.75 (ISBN 92-0-050167-2, ISP153, IAEA). Unipub.

Plutonium: Physico-Chemical Properties of Its Compounds & Alloys. (Atomic Energy Review Ser.: No. 1, Special Issue). 1966. pap. 7.25 (ISBN 92-0-149066-6, IAER1, IAEA). Unipub.

Sachs, Robert G., ed. National Energy Issues: How Do We Decide? Plutonium As a Test Case. LC 79-18341. (American Academy of Arts & Sciences Ser.). 360p. 1980. prof ref 30.00 (ISBN 0-88410-620-9). Ballinger Pub.

Safe Handling of Plutonium. (Safety Ser.: No. 39). (Illus.). 135p. (Orig.). 1974. pap. 15.00 (ISBN 92-0-123473-2, ISP358, IAEA). Unipub.

Sorantin, H. Determination of Uranium & Plutonium in Nuclear Fuels. (Topical Presentations in Nuclear Chemistry Ser.: Vol. 5). (Illus.). 285p. 1975. 81.20x (ISBN 3-527-25475-7). VCH Pubs.

Taube, M. Plutonium: A General Survey. LC 79-89985. (Topical Presentations in Nuclear Chemistry Ser.: Vol. 4). (Illus.). 242p. 1974. 51.80x (ISBN 3-527-25455-2). VCH Pubs.

The Uranium-Carbon & Plutonium-Carbon Systems: A Thermochemical Assessment. (Technical Reports Ser.: No. 14). (Illus.). 44p. 1963. pap. 6.25 (ISBN 92-0-145063-X, IDC14, IAEA). Unipub.

Use of Plutonium for Power Production. (Technical Reports Ser.: No. 49). (Illus.). 162p. 1965. pap. 12.50 (ISBN 92-0-055165-3, IDC49, IAEA). Unipub.

Wilkinson, W. D., ed. Extractive & Physical Metallurgy of Plutonium & Its Alloys: Based on a Symposium Held in San Francisco, California, February 16-17, 1959. LC 60-10588. pap. 81.00 (ISBN 0-317-10454-3, 2051948). Bks Demand UMI.

Yemel'yanov, V. S. & Yevstyukin, A. I. Metallurgy of Nuclear Fuels. 1969. 110.00 (ISBN 0-08-012073-3). Pergamon.

PLYMOUTH AUTOMOBILE

see Automobiles–Types–Plymouth

PLYWOOD

see also Veneers and Veneering

Baldwin, Richard F. Plywood Manufacturing Practices. 2nd rev. ed. LC 80-84894. (A Forest Industries Bk.). (Illus.). 344p. 1981. 42.50 (ISBN 0-87930-092-2). Miller Freeman.

Capron, J. Hugh. Wood Laminating. rev. ed. 1972. 16.64 (ISBN 0-87345-046-9). McKnight.

Lees, Alfred W. Sixty-Seven Prizewinning Plywood Projects. (Illus.). 384p. 1985. 27.95 (ISBN 0-943822-40-8). Rodale Pr Inc.

Plywood & Other Wood-Based Panels. (Orig.). 1966. pap. 20.00 (ISBN 0-685-09398-0, F323, FAO). Unipub.

Plywood Clinic, 6th, Portland, Oregon, March 1978. Modern Plywood Techniques, Vol. 6: Proceedings. LC 74-20159. (Plywood Clinic Library: A Forest Industries Bk.). (Illus.). 80p. 1978. pap. 27.50 (ISBN 0-87930-104-X). Miller Freeman.

Plywood, Fibreboard & Particle Board. (Terminology Bulletins: No. 30). (Eng., Fr., Ital., Ger. & Span.). 162p. 1976. pap. 11.75 (F1218, FAO). Unipub.

Sellers. Plywood & Adhesive Technology. 840p. 1985. write for info. (ISBN 0-8247-7407-8). Dekker.

Seventh Plywood Clinic, Portland, Oregon, March, 1979. Modern Plywood Techniques: Proceedings, Vol. 7. LC 74-20159. (Plywood Clinic Library (A Forest Industries Bk)). (Illus.). 1979. pap. 27.50 (ISBN 0-87930-115-5). Miller Freeman.

PNEUMATIC BUILDINGS

see Air-Supported Structures

PNEUMATIC CONTROL

Eacho, E. M., et al. Pneumatic Measurement & Control Applications, 3 vol. set. (Illus.). 1981. Set. lib. bdg. 154.00x (ISBN 0-87683-010-6); Vol. 1, 400 p. text ed. 60.00x looseleaf (ISBN 0-87683-011-4); Vol. 2, 160p. looseleaf 47.00x (ISBN 0-87683-013-0); Vol. 3, 160p. lab manual solutions looseleaf 47.00x (ISBN 0-317-12060-3); lesson plans, looseleaf 1250.00x (ISBN 0-87683-014-9). G P Courseware.

McCord. Designing Pneumatic Control Circuits, Vol. 2. (Mechanical Engineering Ser.). 160p. 1983. 26.75 (ISBN 0-8247-1910-7). Dekker.

Wray, Lynn & Meyer, Leo. National Standards for Total System Balance: Air Distribution-Hydronic Systems-Sound. 1982. 45.00 (ISBN 0-910289-00-X). Assoc Air Balance.

PNEUMATIC MACHINERY

see also Air-Turbines; Pneumatic Control; Pneumatic-Tube Transportation

Andersen, Blaine W. The Analysis & Design of Pneumatic Systems. LC 76-16767. 314p. 1976. Repr. of 1967 ed. text ed. 21.50 (ISBN 0-88275-435-1). Krieger.

Clark, S. K. & Dodge, R. N. A Handbook for the Rolling Resistance of Pneumatic Tires. (Illus.). 78p. 1979. 12.00 (ISBN 0-938654-26-8, TIRES). Indus Dev Inst Sci.

Fawcett, J. R. Pneumatic Circuits & Low Cost Automation. 150p. 1982. 70.00x (Trade & Tech). State Mutual Bk.

Hydraulic & Pneumatic Cylinders. 200p. 1982. 75.00x (ISBN 0-85461-049-9, Pub. by Trade & Tech). State Mutual Bk.

Lyons, William C. Air & Gas Drilling Manual. LC 83-12944. (Air & Gas Drilling Technology Ser.: Vol. 1). 194p. 1984. comb bound 32.50x (ISBN 0-87201-014-7). Gulf Pub.

Patrick, Dale R. & Patrick, Stephen. Instrumentation Training Course, 2 vols. 2nd ed. Incl. Vol. 1, Pneumatic Instruments. pap. 16.95 (ISBN 0-672-21579-9, 21579); Vol. 2, Electronic Instruments. pap. 15.95 (ISBN 0-672-21580-2, 21580). LC 79-63866. 1979. Set. pap. 27.95 (ISBN 0-672-21581-0). Sams.

PNEUMATIC TRANSMISSION

see Pneumatic-Tube Transportation

PNEUMATIC-TUBE TRANSPORTATION

see also Fans (Machinery)

Kraus, Milton N. & Chemical Engineering Magazine. Pneumatic Conveying of Bulk Materials. (Chemical Engineering Bks.). 352p. 1980. 39.95 (ISBN 0-07-010724-6). McGraw.

Marchello, J. M. & Gomezplata, A., eds. Gas-Solids Handling in the Process Industry. (Chemical Processing & Engineering: an International Ser.: Vol. 8). 336p. 1976. 65.00 (ISBN 0-8247-6302-5). Dekker.

Pneumatic Transport of Solids in Pipes, 4th International Conference. Proceedings. Stephens, H. S. & Stapleton, C. A., eds. (Illus.). 1979. pap. text ed. 62.00x (ISBN 0-900983-86-8, Dist by Air Science Co.). BHRA Fluid.

Pneumotransport Five: Proceedings. (International Conference on Pneumatic Transport of Solids in Pipes Ser.). (Illus.). 467p. 1980. pap. 87.00x (ISBN 0-686-77573-2, Dist. by Air Science Co.). BHRA Fluid.

Stoess, H. A., Jr. Pneumatic Conveying. 2nd ed. LC 83-6915. 277p. 1983. 41.95x (ISBN 0-471-86935-X, Pub. by Wiley-Interscience). Wiley.

Thorton, Wendy A., ed. The Pneumotransport Bibliography. 1972. text ed. 26.00x (ISBN 0-900983-17-5, Dist. by Air Science Co.). BHRA Fluid.

PNEUMATICS

see also Aerodynamics; Gases; Pneumatic Machinery; Sound

Applied Hydraulics & Pneumatics in Industry. 260p. 1982. 75.00x (ISBN 0-686-92052-X, Trade & Tech). State Mutual Bk.

Conant, James B., ed. Robert Boyle's Experiments in Pneumatics. (Havard Case Histories in Experimental Science: Case 1). (Illus.). pap. 20.00 (ISBN 0-317-08773-8, 2022240). Bks Demand UMI.

Eacho, E. M., et al. Pneumatic Measurement & Control Applications, 3 vol. set. (Illus.). 1981. Set. lib. bdg. 154.00x (ISBN 0-87683-010-6); Vol. 1, 400 p. text ed. 60.00x looseleaf (ISBN 0-87683-011-4); Vol. 2, 160p. looseleaf 47.00x (ISBN 0-87683-013-0); Vol. 3, 160p. lab manual solutions looseleaf 47.00x (ISBN 0-317-12060-3); lesson plans, looseleaf 1250.00x (ISBN 0-87683-014-9). G P Courseware.

Fawcett, J. R. Pneumatic Circuits & Low Cost Automation. 150p. 1969. 25.00x (ISBN 0-85461-029-4, Pub. by Trade & Tech England). Brookfield Pub Co.

Hay, E., ed. Slurry Transportation & Pneumatic Handling. 104p. 1983. pap. text ed. 24.00 (ISBN 0-317-03527-4, H00256). ASME.

Holbrook, Edward L. & Chen, Pah I. Design of Pneumatic & Fluidic Control Systems. LC 84-61668. (Illus.). 431p. 1984. 28.95 (ISBN 0-9613851-0-3). Pech Pub.

Institute for Power System. Pneumatic Data, Vol. 2. 130p. 1979. 50.00x (ISBN 0-686-65623-7). State Mutual Bk.

--Pneumatic Data, Vol. 3. 100p. 1979. 50.00x (ISBN 0-686-65624-5). State Mutual Bk.

--Pneumatic Engineering Calculations. 120p. 1979. 50.00x (ISBN 0-686-65625-3). State Mutual Bk.

--Pneumatic Handbook. 5th ed. 700p. 1979. 150.00x (ISBN 0-85461-068-5). State Mutual Bk.

--Pneumatic Power Glossary. 80p. 1979. 30.00x (ISBN 0-686-65626-1). State Mutual Bk.

International Conference on Hydraulics, Pneumatics & Fluidics in Control & Automation. Proceedings. 1977. text ed. 58.00x (ISBN 0-900983-53-1, Dist. by Air Science Co.). BHRA Fluid.

Irvine, Thomas F. & Hartnett, James P. Steam & Air Tables in SI Units. 1975. 9.50 (ISBN 0-07-032054-3). McGraw.

Johnson, Olaf A. Fluid Power: Pneumatics. LC 74-12996. 256p. 1975. pap. 9.50 (ISBN 0-8269-3675-X). Krieger.

Kraus, Milton N. & Chemical Engineering Magazine. Pneumatic Conveying of Bulk Materials. (Chemical Engineering Bks.). 352p. 1980. 39.95 (ISBN 0-07-010724-6). McGraw.

Moore, D. F. The Friction of Pneumatic Tyres. 220p. 1975. 59.75 (ISBN 0-444-41323-5). Elsevier.

Neubert, G. Dictionary of Hydraulics & Pneumatics: English-German-Russian-Slovene. (Eng., Ger., Rus. & Slovene.). 226p. 1973. 75.00 (ISBN 0-686-92602-1, M-9896). French & Eur.

Neubert, Gunter. Dictionary of Hydraulics & Pneumatics. 226p. 1980. 40.00x (ISBN 0-569-08523-3, Pub. by Collet's). State Mutual Bk.

Pneumatic Data. 1982. 65.00x (ISBN 0-686-92046-5, Trade & Tech). State Mutual Bk.

Pneumatic Engineering Calculations. 1982. 45.00x (ISBN 0-686-92047-3, Trade & Tech). State Mutual Bk.

Pneumatic Handbook. 6th ed. (Illus.). 600p. 1982. text ed. 122.50x (ISBN 0-85461-090-1). Brookfield Pub Co.

Principles of Pneumatics. 100p. 1982. 59.00x (ISBN 0-85461-010-3, Pub. by Trade & Tech). State Mutual Bk.

Stewart, Harry L. Pneumatics & Hydraulics. 3rd ed. LC 75-36658. (Illus.). 1976. 10.95 (ISBN 0-672-23237-5, 23237). Audel.

Stoess, H. A., Jr. Pneumatic Conveying. 2nd ed. LC 83-6915. 277p. 1983. 41.95x (ISBN 0-471-86935-X, Pub. by Wiley-Interscience). Wiley.

Trade & Techinical Press Editors. Applied Hydraulics & Pneumatics in Industry. 260p. 1968. 32.50x (ISBN 0-85461-077-4, Pub by Trade & Tech England). Brookfield Pub Co.

Trade & Technical Press Editors. Pneumatic Data, Vol. 3. 100p. 1978. 21.00x (ISBN 0-85461-069-3, Pub by Trade & Tech England). Brookfield Pub Co.

--Pneumatic Engineering Calculations. 120p. 1969. 21.00x (ISBN 0-85461-038-3, Pub by Trade & Tech England). Brookfield Pub Co.

--Pneumatic Handbook. 5th ed. 700p. 1978. 105.00 (ISBN 0-85461-068-5, Pub by Trade & Tech England). Brookfield Pub Co.

--Principles of Pneumatics. 100p. 1967. 25.00x (ISBN 0-85461-010-3, Pub by Trade & Tech England). Brookfield Pub Co.

Warring, R. H. Pneumatic Handbook. 6th ed. LC 82-82850. 448p. 1982. 66.00x (ISBN 0-87201-726-5). Gulf Pub.

Wilson, Frank W., ed. Pneumatic Controls for Industrial Application. LC 65-13379. (Manufacturing Data Ser.). (Illus.). 1965. pap. 9.00 (ISBN 0-87263-007-2). SME.

POCKET BATTLESHIPS

see Warships

POCKET GOPHERS

Baker, Rollin H. The Pocket Gophers (Genus Thomomys) of Coahuila, Mexico. (Museum Ser.: Vol. 5, No. 28). 16p. 1953. pap. 1.25 (ISBN 0-317-04945-3). U of KS Mus Nat Hist.

Downhower, Jerry F. & Hall, E. Raymond. The Pocket Gopher in Kansas. (Miscellaneous Ser.: No. 44). 32p. 1966. pap. 1.75 (ISBN 0-686-80276-4). U of KS Mus Nat Hist.

Durrant, Stephen D. The Pocket Gophers (Genus Thomomys) of Utah. (Museum Ser.: Vol. 1, No. 1). 82p. 1946. pap. 4.25 (ISBN 0-686-80277-2). U of KS Mus Nat Hist.

Hall & Raymond, E. A New Pocket Gopher (Genus Thomomys) from Eastern Colorado. (Museum Ser.: Vol. 5, No. 8). 5p. 1951. pap. 1.25 (ISBN 0-317-05066-4). U of KS Mus Nat Hist.

Hall, E. Raymond. A New Pocket Gopher (Genus Thomomys) from Wyoming & Colorado. (Museum Ser.: Vol. 5, No.13). 4p. 1951. pap. 1.25 (ISBN 0-317-04791-4). U of KS Mus Nat Hist.

Azzam, R. M. & Bashara, N. M. Ellipsometry & Polarized Light. 530p. 1977. 113.00 (ISBN 0-444-10826-2, North-Holland). Elsevier.
Bertin, J. & Loeb, J. Experimental & Theoretical Aspects of Induced Polarization. Incl. Vol. 1. Presentation & Application of the IP Method. 43.30 (ISBN 3-443-13009-7); Vol. 2. Macroscopic & Microscopic Theories. 22.40 (ISBN 3-443-13010-0). 1976. 76.30 set. Lubrecht & Cramer.
Francon, Maurice & Mallick, S. Polarization Interferometers: Applications in Microscopy & Macroscopy. LC 75-147194. (Wiley Ser. in Pure & Appied Optics). pap. 43.00 (ISBN 0-317-29330-3, 2024021). Bks Demand UMI.
Heller, Wilfried, et al. Depolarization & Related Ratios of Light Scattering by Spheroids. LC 74-13816. 105p. 1974. 12.00 (ISBN 0-8143-1527-5). Wayne St U Pr.
Marshak, M. L., ed. High Energy Physics with Polarized Beams & Targets (Argonne, 1976) Proceedings. LC 76-50181. (AIP Conference Proceedings, No. 35: Subseries on Particles & Fields, No. 12). 543p. 1977. 21.50 (ISBN 0-88318-134-7). Am Inst Physics.
Pockels, Friedrich C. Lehrbuch der Kristalloptik. (Bibliotheca Mathematica Teubneriana Ser: No. 39). (Ger). 1969. Repr. of 1906 ed. 53.00 (ISBN 0-384-47000-9). Johnson Repr.
Shurcliff, William A. Polarized Light: Production & Use. LC 62-11405. pap. 54.50 (ISBN 0-317-08051-2, 2051980). Bks Demand UMI.
Swindell, William, ed. Polarized Light. LC 74-26881. (Benchmark Papers in Optics Ser: No. 1). 418p. 1975. 66.00 (ISBN 0-12-787498-4). Acad Pr.
Thomas, G. H., ed. High Energy Physics with Polarized Beams & Polarized Target (Argonne, 1978) LC 79-64565. (AIP Conference Proceedings: No. 51). (Illus.). 1979. lib. bdg. 24.00 (ISBN 0-88318-150-9). Am Inst Physics.
Velluz, L., et al. Optical Circular Dichroism: Principles Measurements, & Applications. (Illus.). 1969. 34.20x (ISBN 3-527-25289-4). VCH Pubs.
Weissberger, Arnold, et al, eds. Techniques of Chemistry: Vol. I, Pt. 3C, Physical Methods of Chemistry: Polarimetry. LC 49-48584. 528p. 1972. 47.95 (ISBN 0-471-92732-5). Krieger.

POLARIZATION (NUCLEAR PHYSICS)

International Summer Institute in Theoretical Physics. Strong Interaction Physics. (Springer Tracts in Modern Physics: Vol. 57). 1971. 56.70 (ISBN 0-387-05252-6). Springer-Verlag.
Joseph, C. & Soffer, J., eds. International Symposium of High-Energy Physics with Polarized Beams & Polarized Targets. (Experientia Supplementa Ser.: No. 38). 800p. 1981. pap. text ed. 78.95x (ISBN 0-8176-1189-4). Birkhauser.
Ohlsen, G. G., et al, eds. Polarization Phenomena in Nuclear Physics, 1980: Fifth International Symposium, Santa Fe. (AIP Conference Proceedings: No. 69). 1536p. 1981. lib. bdg. 84.00 (ISBN 0-88318-168-1). Am Inst Physics.
Sanderson, R. T., ed. Polar Convalense. 1983. 21.50 (ISBN 0-12-618080-6). Acad Pr.

POLAROGRAPH AND POLAROGRAPHY

Gnaiger, E. & Forstner, H., eds. Polarographic Oxygen Sensors: Aquatic & Physiological Applications. (Illus.). 370p. 1983. 52.00 (ISBN 0-387-11654-0). Springer-Verlag.
Kambara, Tomihito. Modern Aspects of Polarography. LC 66-28449. 245p. 1966. 35.00x (ISBN 0-306-30278-0, Plenum Pr). Plenum Pub.
Mairanovskii, Stal' G. Catalytic & Kinetic Waves in Polarography. LC 68-10535. (Illus.). 352p. 1968. 39.50x (ISBN 0-306-30339-6, Plenum Pr). Plenum Pub.
Milner, George W. The Principles & Applications of Polarography & Other Electroanalytical Processes. LC 57-3248. pap. 160.00 (ISBN 0-317-09850-0, 2004947). Bks Demand UMI.
Polarografia. (Serie De Quimica: No. 13). (Span.). 1974. pap. 3.50 (ISBN 0-8270-6385-7). OAS.
Schmidt, Helmut & Von Stackelberg, Mark. Modern Polarographic Methods. Maddison, R. E., tr. 1963. 33.00 (ISBN 0-12-626950-5). Acad Pr.
Smyth, W. Franklin, ed. Polarography of Molecules of Biological Significance. 1979. 62.50 (ISBN 0-12-653050-5). Acad Pr.
Zuman, P. Elucidation of Organic Electrode Processes. (Current Chemical Concepts Ser.). 1969. 49.50 (ISBN 0-12-782750-1). Acad Pr.
--Topics in Organic Polarography. LC 77-104331. 540p. 1970. 62.50x (ISBN 0-306-30454-6, Plenum Pr). Plenum Pub.
Zuman, Petr. Substituent Effects in Organic Polarography. LC 63-17643. 384p. 1967. 37.50x (ISBN 0-306-30238-1, Plenum Pr). Plenum Pub.

POLAROID LAND (CAMERA)

see Cameras–Types–Polaroid Land

POLARONS

Devreese, J. T., ed. Polarons in Ionic Crystals & Polar Semiconductors: Proceedings of the 1971 Antwerp Advanced Study Institute. 1976. 76.75 (ISBN 0-444-10409-7, North-Holland). Elsevier.

POLDERS

Early Senescence of Rice & Drechslera Oryzae in the Wagenigen Polder. (Agricultural Research Reports). 1977. pap. 14.00 (ISBN 90-220-0621-2, PDC108, PUDOC). Unipub.
Introduction of Ophiobolus Graminis Into New Polders & Its Decline. (Agricultural Research Reports: No. 713). 1968. pap. 8.25 (ISBN 90-220-0177-6, XPUDOC, PUDOC). Unipub.

POLEMONIACEAE

Grant, Karen A. & Grant, Verne. Flower Pollination in the Phlox Family. LC 65-19809. 180p. 1965. 26.00x (ISBN 0-231-02843-1). Columbia U Pr.

POLICE–DATA PROCESSING

Hernandez, Ernie, Jr. Police Chief's Guide to Using Microcomputers. (Illus.). 160p. 1984. 16.95 (ISBN 0-910657-05-X). Frontline.
--Police Handbook for Applying the Systems Approach & Computer Technology. LC 82-17662. (Illus.). 231p. 1982. 26.95 (ISBN 0-910657-00-9); pap. 19.95 (ISBN 0-910657-01-7). Frontline.
Huls, Mary E. Computers in Police Work: A Selective Bibliography. (Public Administration Ser.: Bibliography P 1628). 1985. pap. 2.00 (ISBN 0-89028-298-6). Vance Biblios.

POLICE–EQUIPMENT AND SUPPLIES

Beall, James R. & Downing, Robert E. Helicopter Utilization in Municipal Law Enforcement: Administrative Considerations. (Illus.). 96p. 1973. 14.75x (ISBN 0-398-02780-3). C C Thomas.
Bristow, Allen P. The Search for an Effective Police Handgun. (Illus.). 256p. 1973. 26.75x (ISBN 0-398-02554-1). C C Thomas.
Leonard, V. A. The New Police Technology. (Illus.). 360p. 1980. photocopy ed. 40.50x (ISBN 0-398-03967-4). C C Thomas.
Robinson, Roger H. The Police Shotgun Manual. (Illus.). 168p. 1973. 14.75x (ISBN 0-398-02630-0). C C Thomas.
Williams, Mason. The Law Enforcement Book of Weapons, Ammunition & Training Procedures: Handguns, Rifles & Shotguns. (Illus.). 544p. 1977. photocopy 55.50x (ISBN 0-398-03576-8). C C Thomas.

POLISHES

see also Waxes

Cleaning, Polishing & Sanitation Products. 260p. 1984. 550.00 (ISBN 0-686-32750-0). Busn Trend.

POLISHING

see Grinding and Polishing

POLITICAL SCIENCE–DATA PROCESSING

Janda, Kenneth. Data Processing: Applications to Political Research. 2nd ed. LC 65-15476. (Handbooks for Research in Political Behavior Ser). 1969. text ed. 16.95 (ISBN 0-8101-0260-9); pap. text ed. 6.95x (ISBN 0-8101-0259-5). Northwestern U Pr.

POLLED ABERDEEN CATTLE

see Aberdeen-Angus Cattle

POLLEN

Binding, G. J. About Pollen. 1982. pap. 4.95x (ISBN 0-317-07289-7, Regent House). B of A.
Birks, H. J. & Gordon, A. D. Numerical Methods in Quarternary Pollen Analysis. Date not set. price not set (ISBN 0-12-101250-6). Acad Pr.
Brown, Grafton T. Pollen-Slide Studies. (Illus.). 142p. 1949. photocopy ed. 19.50x (ISBN 0-398-00235-5). C C Thomas.
Hansen, Henry P. Paleoecology of Two Peat Deposits on the Oregon Coast. (Studies in Botany Ser: No. 3). 32p. 1941. pap. 3.95x (ISBN 0-87071-013-3). Oreg St U Pr.
Heslop-Harrison, J. Aspects of the Structure, Cytochemistry & Germination of the Pollen of Rye. LC 79-41655. 1980. 26.50 (ISBN 0-12-344950-2). Acad Pr.
Heusser, Calvin J. Pollen & Spores of Chile: Modern Types of Pteridophyta, Gymnospermae, & Angiospermae. LC 75-114322. 167p. 1971. 19.95x (ISBN 0-8165-0213-7). U of Ariz Pr.
Huntley, Brian & Birks, H. J. An Atlas of Past & Present Pollen Maps for Europe: 0-13,000 Years Ago. LC 82-21613. 650p. 1983. 185.00 (ISBN 0-521-23735-1). Cambridge U Pr.
Katiyar, Kamlesh. Studies in the Pollen Morphology of Rosales. Nair, P. K., ed. (Advances in Pollen Spore Research Ser.: Vol. 8). (Illus.). 150p. 1982. 15.00 (ISBN 0-88065-226-8, Pub. by Messers Today & Tomorrow Printers & Publishers). Scholarly Pubns.
Knox. Pollen Allergy. (Studies in Biology: No. 107). 1979. 5.95 (ISBN 0-8391-0257-7). Univ Park.
Lewis, Walter H., et al. Airborne & Allergenic Pollen of North America. LC 82-21183. (Illus.). 288p. 1984. text ed. 60.00x (ISBN 0-8018-2940-2). Johns Hopkins.
Markgraf, Vera & D'Antoni, Hector L. Pollen Flora of Argentina: Modern Pollen & Spore Types of Pteridophyta, Gymnospermae, & Angiospermae. LC 78-3770. 208p. 1978. pap. 19.95x (ISBN 0-8165-0649-3). U of Ariz Pr.
Martin, Paul S. The Last Ten Thousand Years: A Fossil Pollen Record of the American Southwest. LC 63-11984. (Illus.). 87p. 1963. 14.95x (ISBN 0-8165-0050-9). U of Ariz Pr.
Nair, P. K., ed. Advances in Pollen Spore Research, Vol. IV. 160p. 1979. 12.00 (ISBN 0-88065-168-7, Pub. by Messers Today & Tomorrows Printers & Publishers India). Scholarly Pubns.
--Advances in Pollen Spore Research, Vols. V - VII. 285p. 1980. 30.00 (ISBN 0-88065-169-5, Pub. by Messers Today & Tomorrows Printers & Publishers India). Scholarly Pubns.
--Advances in Pollen Spore Research, Vol. 1. 167p. 1975. 12.00 (ISBN 0-88065-165-2, Pub. by Messers Today & Tomorrows Printers & Publishers India). Scholarly Pubns.
Ogden, Eugene C., et al. Manual for Sampling Airborne Pollen. (Illus.). 1974. pap. 16.95x (ISBN 0-02-849820-8). Hafner.
Parkhill, Joe M. The Wonderful World of Pollen. 160p. (Orig.). 1982. pap. text ed. 6.95 (ISBN 0-936744-06-5). Country Bazaar.
Punt, W., ed. The Northwest European Pollen Flora, Vol. 1. 416p. 1976. 51.00 (ISBN 0-444-41421-5). Elsevier.
Smith, E. Grant. Sampling & Identifying Allergenic Pollens & Molds: An Illustrated Manual for Physicians & Lab Technicians. (Illus.). 100p. (Orig.). 1984. pap. text ed. 41.50x (ISBN 0-930961-00-5). Blewstone Pr.
--Sampling & Identifying Allergenic Pollens & Molds: An Illustrated Manual for Physicians & Lab Technicians, Vol. 2. (Illus.). 112p. (Orig.). 1985. pap. write for info. Blewstone Pr.
Srivastava, D. Studies on the Pollen Biology of Certain Cultivated Malvaceae. Nair, P. K., ed. (Advances in Pollen Spore Research Ser.: Vol. 9). (Illus.). 175p. 1982. 15.00x (ISBN 0-88065-227-6, Pub. by Messers Today & Tomorrow Printers & Publishers). Scholarly Pubns.
Stanley, R. G. & Linskens, H. F. Pollen: Biology, Biochemistry, & Management. (Illus.). x, 307p. 1974. 36.00 (ISBN 0-387-06827-9). Springer-Verlag.
Wodehouse, Roger P. Pollen Grains: Their Structure, Identification, & Significance in Science & Medicine. LC 59-15783. pap. 143.50 (ISBN 0-317-29159-9, 2055596). Bks Demand UMI.

POLLINATION

see Fertilization of Plants

POLLUTION

see also Air–Pollution; Environmental Engineering; Factory and Trade Waste; Radioactive Fallout; Refuse and Refuse Disposal; Spraying and Dusting Residues in Agriculture; Water–Pollution;

also subdivision Pollution under subjects, e.g. Air–Pollution; Water–Pollution

Abbott, R. Tucker, ed. Indexes to the Nautilus: Geographical, Vols. 1-90, & Scientific Names, Vols. 61-90. 1979. Set. 24.00x (ISBN 0-915826-06-2). Am Malacologists.
American Association for the Advancement of Science, Dallas, December, 1968. Global Effects of Environmental Pollution: A Symposium. Singer, S. F., ed. LC 78-118129. 218p. 1970. lib. bdg. 26.00 (ISBN 90-277-0151-2, Pub. by Reidel Holland). Kluwer Academic.
Anderson, Frederick R., et al. Environmental Improvement Through Economic Incentives. LC 76-47400. (Resources for the Future Ser.). 208p. 1978. text ed. 18.50x (ISBN 0-8018-2000-6); pap. text ed. 6.00x (ISBN 0-8018-2100-2). Johns Hopkins.
Andrews, W. Guide to the Study of Environmental Pollution. 1972. text ed. 12.40 (ISBN 0-13-370858-6); pap. text ed. 9.84 (ISBN 0-13-370833-0). P-H.
Atkins, M. H. & Lowe, J. F. Case Studies in Pollution Control in the Textile Dyeing & Finishing Industries: A Study in Non-Technical Language of Essential Information on the Economics of Control, the Problems & Their Solutions. 1979. 53.00 (ISBN 0-08-022457-1). Pergamon.
Attenborough, Keith & Pollitt, C., eds. Pollution: The Professionals & the Public. 216p. 1977. pap. 11.00x (ISBN 0-335-00037-1, Pub. by Open Univ Pr). Taylor & Francis.
Barrekette, E. S., ed. Pollution: Engineering & Scientific Solutions. LC 72-91328. (Environmental Science Research Ser.: Vol. 2). 799p. 1973. 79.50 (ISBN 0-306-36302-X, Plenum Pr). Plenum Pub.
Bayne, Brian L., ed. The Effects of Stress & Pollution on Marine Animals. LC 84-18145. 400p. 1984. 45.95x (ISBN 0-03-057019-0). Praeger.
Benarde, Melvin. Our Precarious Habitat. rev. ed. (Illus.). 384p. 1973. 8.25 (ISBN 0-393-06360-7); pap. 6.95x (ISBN 0-393-09372-7). Norton.
Berry, Brian J. & Horton, Frank E. Urban Environmental Management: Planning for Pollution Control. (Illus.). 448p. 1974. 34.95 (ISBN 0-13-939611-X). P-H.
Berthouex, P. Mac & Rudd, Dale F. Strategy of Pollution Control. LC 76-29008. 579p. 1977. text ed. 48.45 (ISBN 0-471-74449-2). Wiley.
Bigart, Robert, ed. Environmental Pollution in Montana. LC 71-169032. 261p. 1972. O.P. 8.50 (ISBN 0-87842-037-1); pap. 4.95 (ISBN 0-87842-025-8). Mountain Pr.
Bockris, J. O'M., ed. Electrochemistry of Cleaner Environments. LC 72-179762. 296p. 1972. 39.50x (ISBN 0-306-30560-7, Plenum Pr). Plenum Pub.
Boulding, Kenneth E. & Stahr, Elvis J. Economics of Pollution. LC 70-179973. (The Charles C. Moskowitz Lectures). 158p. 1971. 12.50x (ISBN 0-8147-0967-2). NYU Pr.
Bradshaw, A. D. & McNeilly, D. T. Evolution & Pollution. (Studies in Biology: No. 130). 80p. 1981. pap. text ed. 8.95 (ISBN 0-7131-2818-6). E Arnold.
Brock, Neely W. & Gary, Blau, eds. Environmental Exposure From Chemicals, Vol. 2. 192p. 1985. 60.00 (ISBN 0-8493-6166-4). CRC Pr.
Brown, Michael. Laying Waste: The Poisoning of America by Toxic Chemicals. 384p. 1981. pap. 3.95 (ISBN 0-671-45359-9). WSP.
Brown, Richard D. & Ouellette, Robert P. Pollution Control at Electric Power Stations: Comparisons for U. S. & Europe. 113p. 1983. 39.95 (ISBN 0-250-40618-7). Butterworth.
Brown, William H. How to Stop the Corporate Polluters. (Illus.). 1972. pap. 1.50 (ISBN 0-88388-020-2). Bellerophon Bks.
Burk, Janet L. & Hayes, Stephen. Environmental Concerns: A Bibliography of U.S. Government Publications, 1971-1973. 1975. 4.00 (ISBN 0-932826-06-7). New Issues MI.
Burrows, Paul. Economic Theory of Pollution Control. 240p. 1980. 27.50x (ISBN 0-262-02150-1); pap. text ed. 9.95x (ISBN 0-262-52056-7). MIT Pr.
Calabrese, Edward J. Pollutants & High Risk Groups: The Biological Basis of Increased Human Susceptibility to Environmental & Occupational Pollutants. LC 77-13957. (Environmental Science & Technology: Wiley-Interscience Series of Texts & Monographs). 266p. 1977. 58.95 (ISBN 0-471-02940-8, Pub. by Wiley-Inerscience). Wiley.
Calmon, C. & Gold, H. Ion Exchange for Pollution Control, 2 vols. 1979. Vol. 1, 272p. 76.50 (ISBN 0-8493-5153-7); Vol. 2, 288p. 81.50 (ISBN 0-8493-5154-5). CRC Pr.
Cannon, James S. A Clear View: Guide to Industrial Pollution Control. LC 75-15321. (Illus.). 1975. pap. 3.95 (ISBN 0-686-70491-6). INFORM.
Cannon, James S. & Armentrout, Frederick S. Environmental Steel Update: Pollution in the Iron & Steel Industry. Schwartz, Wendy C., ed. LC 77-86496. 1977. pap. 42.00 (ISBN 0-87871-006-X). CEP.
Cardwell, Rick D., et al, eds. Aquatic Toxicology & Hazard Assessment-STP 854: Seventh Symposium. LC 84-70338. (Illus.). 590p. 1985. text ed. 60.00 (ISBN 0-8031-0410-3, 04-854000-16). ASTM.
Chakrabarty, A. M., ed. Biodegradation & Detoxification of Environmental Pollutants. 160p. 1982. 50.00 (ISBN 0-8493-5524-9). CRC Pr.
Chem Systems International Ltd. Reducing Pollution from Selected Energy Transformation Sources. 230p. 1976. 21.00x (ISBN 0-86010-036-7, Pub. by Graham & Trotman England). State Mutual Bk.
Chemical Trends in Wildlife: An International Cooperative Study. (Illus.). 1980. pap. 7.00x (ISBN 9-2641-2105-6). OECD.
Cheremisinoff, Paul N. & Young, Richard C., eds. Air Pollution Control & Design Handbook, Pt. 2. (Pollution Engineering & Technology Ser.: Vol. 2). 1977. 75.00 (ISBN 0-8247-6448-X). Dekker.
Chicorel, Marietta, ed. Chicorel Index to Environment & Ecology, 2 vols. LC 75-306805. (Index Ser.). 1000p. 1974. Set. 250.00 (ISBN 0-934598-21-5). Vol. 16 (ISBN 0-934598-25-8). Vol. 16A (ISBN 0-934598-26-6). Am Lib Pub Co.
Chow, J. K., ed. Industrial Pollution Control. 198p. 1983. pap. text ed. 40.00 (ISBN 0-317-02626-7, I00156). ASME.

Komarov, Boris. The Destruction of Nature in the Soviet Union. Vale, Michel & Hollander, Joe, trs. from Rus. LC 80-5452. Orig. Title: Unichtozhenie Prioroda Obostrenie Ekologicheskogo Krizisa V SSSR. 132p. 1980. 25.00 (ISBN 0-87332-157-X). M E Sharpe.

Kovacs, M., ed. Pollution Control & Conservation. 492p. 1985. 84.95x (ISBN 0-470-27509-X). Halsted Pr.

Kullemberg, Gunnar. Pollutant Transfer & Transport in the Sea, 2 vols. 1982. Vol. I, 240p. 77.00 (ISBN 0-8493-5601-6); Vol. II, 248. 77.00 (ISBN 0-8493-5602-4). CRC Pr.

Levine, Adeline G. Love Canal: Science, Politics, & People. LC 80-8361. 288p. 1982. 26.50x (ISBN 0-669-04034-7); pap. 10.00x (ISBN 0-669-05411-9). Lexington Bks.

Lippmann, Morton & Schlesinger, Richard B. Chemical Contamination in the Human Environment. (Illus.). 1979. text ed. 32.50x (ISBN 0-19-502441-9); pap. text ed. 18.95x (ISBN 0-19-502442-7). Oxford U Pr.

Loero, Guido. Boundary Conditions & Global Management. 1975. 41.00 (ISBN 0-12-455050-9). Acad Pr.

Lu, James C., et al. Leachate from Municipal Landfills: Production & Management. LC 84-22746. (Pollution Technology Review Ser.: No. 119). (Illus.). 453p. 1985. 42.00 (ISBN 0-8155-1021-7). Noyes.

Lund, H. F. Industrial Pollution Control Handbook. 1971. 83.50 (ISBN 0-07-039095-9). McGraw.

McKean, Margaret A. Environmental Protest & Citizen Politics in Japan. LC 80-12991. 300p. 1981. 32.50x (ISBN 0-520-04115-1). U of Cal Pr.

Mahlum, D. D. & Sikov, M. R., eds. Developmental Toxicology of Energy-Related Pollutants: Proceedings. LC 78-606139. (DOE Symposium Ser.). 660p. 1978. pap. 24.50 (ISBN 0-87079-113-3, CONF-771017); microfiche 4.50 (ISBN 0-87079-178-8, CONF-771017). DOE.

Martin, M. H. & Coughtrey, P. J. Biological Monitoring of Heavy Metal Pollution: Land & Air. (Pollution Monitor Ser.: No. 5). (Illus.). x, 468p. 1982. 77.75 (ISBN 0-85334-136-2, I-304-82, Pub. by Elsevier Applied Sci England). Elsevier.

Measurement, Detection & Control of Environmental Pollutants. (Proceedings Ser.). (Illus.). 641p. 1976. pap. 70.00 (ISBN 0-685-77310-8, ISP432, IAEA). Unipub.

Melosi, Martin V., ed. Pollution & Reform in American Cities, 1870-1930. 224p. 1979. text ed. 17.50x (ISBN 0-292-76459-6). U of Tex Pr.

Middlebrooks, E. J. Industrial Pollution Control: Agro-Industries. LC 79-10573. (Environmental Science & Technology Ser.: Vol. 1). 445p. 1979. 75.00x (ISBN 0-471-04779-1, Pub. by Wiley-Interscience). Wiley.

Miller, Christopher & Wood, Christopher. Planning & Pollution: An Examination of the Role of Land Planning in the Protection of Environmental Quality. (Illus.). 1983. text ed. 32.50x (ISBN 0-19-823245-4). Oxford U Pr.

Monsanto Research Corporation. Potential Pollutants from Petrochemical Processes. new ed. LC 74-18577. (Illus.). 1976. pap. 14.95 (ISBN 0-87762-144-6). Technomic.

Moran, Joseph M., et al. An Introduction to Environmental Sciences. 464p. 1973. text ed. 14.95 (ISBN 0-316-58218-2); instructor's manual free (ISBN 0-316-58204-2). Little.

Moriarty, F., ed. Ecotoxicology: The Study of Pollutants in Exosystems. 1983. 36.00 (ISBN 0-12-506760-7). Acad Pr.

Morrisey, T. J., ed. Pollution Control Problems & Related Federal Legislation. 290p. 1974. text ed. 29.50x (ISBN 0-8422-5175-8); pap. text ed. 12.50x (ISBN 0-8422-0418-0). Irvington.

Moscato, M., et al, eds. Pollution: Major Sources for Research, Eighteen Hundred to Nineteen Fifty. 1980. 760.00 (ISBN 0-89093-193-3). U Pubns Amer.

National Research Council Assembly of Life Sciences. Indoor Pollutants. 1981. pap. text ed. 16.25 (ISBN 0-309-03188-5). Natl Acad Pr.

National Research Council, Committee on Medical & Biologic Effects of Environmental Pollutants, Division of Medical Science. Vapor-Phase Organic Pollutants. (Medical & Biologic Effects of Environmental Pollutants Ser.). 411p. 1976. pap. 14.50 (ISBN 0-309-02441-2). Natl Acad Pr.

National Research Council, Division of Medical Sciences, Medical & Biologic Effects of Environmental Pollutants, ed. Ozone & Other Photochemical Oxidants. LC 77-1293. 719p. 1977. 19.50 (ISBN 0-309-02531-1). Natl Acad Pr.

Nriagu, Jerome O. Copper in the Environment, 2 pts. Incl. Pt. 1. Ecological Cycling. LC 79-10875. 522p. 94.00x (ISBN 0-471-04778-3); Pt. 2. Health Effects. LC 79-15062. 489p. 1980. 90.00x (ISBN 0-471-04777-5). (Environmental Science & Technology: Texts & Monographs). 1980 (Pub. by Wiley-Interscience). Wiley.

Nuclear Techniques in Environmental Pollution. (Proceedings Ser.). (Illus.). 810p. (Orig.). 1971. pap. 64.50 (ISBN 92-0-060071-9, ISP268, IAEA). Unipub.

Nurnberg, H. W. & Vigneron, J. Pollutants & Their Ectoxicological Significance. 1985. 74.95 (ISBN 0-471-90509-7). Wiley.

OECD Staff. Control Technology for Nitrogen Oxide Emissions from Stationary Sources. 167p. (Orig.). 1983. pap. 14.00x (ISBN 92-64-12485-3). OECD.

--Costs of Coal Pollution Abatement: Results of an International Symposium. 300p. (Orig.). 1983. pap. text ed. 24.00x (ISBN 92-64-12482-9). OECD.

--Emission Control Costs in the Textile Industry. 180p. (Orig.). 1981. pap. 10.50x (ISBN 92-64-12134-X). OECD.

--Transfrontier Pollution & the Role of States. 202p. (Orig.). 1981. pap. text ed. 12.50x (ISBN 92-64-12197-8). OECD.

Orishimo, Isao. Urbanization & Environmental Quality. (Studies in Applied Regional Science). 192p. 1982. lib. bdg. 24.00 (ISBN 0-89838-080-4). Kluwer-Nijhoff.

Ottaway, J. M. Biochemistry of Pollution. (Studies in Biology: No. 123). 64p. 1980. pap. text ed. 8.95 (ISBN 0-7131-2784-8). E Arnold.

The Petroleum Refining Industry-Energy Saving & Environmental Control. (Energy Technology Review 24; Pollution Technology Review: 39). (Illus.). 374p. 1978. 39.00 (ISBN 0-8155-0694-5). Noyes.

Pickering, W. F. Pollution Evaluation: The Quantitative Aspects. (Environmental Science & Technology Ser.: Vol. 2). 1977. 39.75 (ISBN 0-8247-6621-0). Dekker.

Pipes, W. O. Bacterial Indicators of Pollution. 184p. 1982. 63.00 (ISBN 0-8493-5970-8). CRC Pr.

Pollution: An International Problem for Fisheries. (Fisheries Ser.: No. 4). (Illus.). 85p. (Orig., 2nd Printing 1978). 1971. pap. 4.75 (ISBN 92-5-100376-9, F321, FAO). Unipub.

Pollution Charges in Practice. (Document Ser.). 118p. 1980. 7.50x (ISBN 92-64-12042-4). OECD.

Pollution Control & International Trade. (Studies in International Trade: No. 1). pap. 5.00 (G95, GATT). Unipub.

Pollution: The Neglected Dimensions. (Worldwatch Institute Papers: No. 27). 32p. 1979. pap. 2.95 (ISBN 0-686-94935-8, WW27, WW). Unipub.

Pratt, John W., ed. Statistical & Mathematical Aspects of Pollution Problems. (Statistics Textbooks & Monographs: Vol. 6). 424p. 1974. 59.75 (ISBN 0-8247-6132-4). Dekker.

Rabin, Edward H. & Schwartz, Mortimer D. The Pollution Crisis: Official Documents, 1972-1976, 2 vols. LC 73-37009. 1976. lib. bdg. 46.00 ea. Vol. 1 (ISBN 0-379-00163-2). Vol. 2 (ISBN 0-379-00174-8). Set. 92.00. Oceana.

Raychaudhuri, S. P. & Gupta, D. S., eds. Proceedings of International Symposium on Environmental Pollution & Toxicology. (Progress in Ecology Ser.: Vols. V-VII). 333p. 1980. 39.00 (ISBN 0-88065-181-4, Pub. by Messers Today & Tomorrows Printers & Publishers India). Scholarly Pubns.

Roberts, Marc J., et al. Economic Analysis of Industrial Incentives for Pollution Control: Implications for Water Quality. 1967. pap. 8.30x (ISBN 0-89011-450-1, ECR-101). Abt Bks.

Rondia, D., et al, eds. Mobile Source Emissions Included Polycyclic Organic Species. 1983. lib. bdg. 56.50 (ISBN 90-277-1633-1, Pub. by Reidel Holland). Kluwer Academic.

Rose, J., ed. Technological Injury: The Effect of Technological Advances on Environment Life & Society. 244p. 1969. pap. 37.25 (ISBN 0-677-13645-5). Gordon.

Royston, Michael G. Pollution Prevention Pays. 1979. 30.00 (ISBN 0-08-023597-2); pap. 9.25 (ISBN 0-08-023572-7). Pergamon.

Rudd, Robert L. Environmental Toxicology: A Guide to Information Sources. LC 73-17540. (Man & the Environmrnt Information Guide Ser.: Vol. 7). 1977. 60.00x (ISBN 0-8103-1342-1). Gale.

Satriana, M., ed. New Developments in Flue Gas Desulfurization Technology. LC 81-11045. (Pollution Tech. Rev. 82). (Illus.). 326p. 1982. 45.00 (ISBN 0-8155-0863-8). Noyes.

Saunders, P. J. Estimation of Pollution Damage. 1976. 21.50 (ISBN 0-7190-0629-5, Pub. by Manchester Univ Pr). Longwood Pub Group.

Schlink, Mother Basilea. A Matter of Life & Death. LC 73-10827. 96p. 1973. pap. 1.75 (ISBN 0-87123-359-2, 200359). Bethany Hse.

Singer, S. F., ed. The Changing Global Environment. LC 73-86096. viii, 423p. 1975. lib. bdg. 53.00 (ISBN 90-277-0385-X, Pub. by Reidel Holland); pap. 28.95 (ISBN 90-277-0402-3). Kluwer Academic.

Sittig, Marshall, ed. Priority Toxic Pollutants: Health Impacts & Allowable Limits. LC 80-311. (Environmental Health Review Ser.: No. 1). 370p. 1980. 54.00 (ISBN 0-8155-0797-6). Noyes.

Sobel, Lester A., ed. Jobs, Money & Pollution. 1977. lib. bdg. 17.50x (ISBN 0-87196-281-0). Facts on File.

Sors, Andrew I. & Coleman, David, eds. Pollution Research Index: A Guide to World Research in Environmental Pollution. 2nd ed. 555p. 220.00x (ISBN 0-582-90006-9, Pub. by Longman). Gale.

Storin, Diane. Investigating Air, Land, & Water Pollution. (Illus.). 1975. pap. text ed. 3.20x (ISBN 0-913688-07-X). Pawnee Pub.

Symposium on the Development of Muiti-Media Monitoring of Environmental Pollution: Proceedings. (Special Environmental Reports: No. 15). 532p. 1981. pap. 45.00 (ISBN 92-63-10563-4, W480, WMO). Unipub.

Teja, A. S., ed. Chemical Engineering & the Environment. LC 80-26427. (Critical Reports on Applied Chemistry Ser.: Vol. 13). 100p. 1981. pap. 34.95x (ISBN 0-470-27106-X). Halsted Pr.

Thomas, Vinod. Pollution Control in Sao Paulo, Brazil: Costs, Benefits, & Effects on Industrial Location. (Working Paper: No. 501). 127p. 1981. pap. 5.00 (ISBN 0-686-39753-3, WP-0501). World Bank.

Thomas, William A., ed. Indicators of Environmental Quality. LC 72-86142. (Environmental Science Research Ser.: Vol. 1). 285p. 1972. 45.00x (ISBN 0-306-36301-1, Plenum Pr); pap. 9.95 (ISBN 0-306-20011-2). Plenum Pub.

Tietenberg, T. H. Emissions Trading: An Exercise in Reforming Pollution Policy. LC 84-18335. 238p. 1985. lib. bdg. 22.50 (ISBN 0-915707-12-8). Resources Future.

Timbrell, J. A. Principles of Biochemical Toxicology. 240p. 1985. 30.00x (ISBN 0-85066-221-4); pap. text ed. 18.00x (ISBN 0-85066-319-9). Taylor & Francis.

Tinsley, Ian J. Chemical Concepts in Pollutant Behavior. LC 78-24301. (Environmental Science & Technology Ser.). 265p. 1979. 42.50x (ISBN 0-471-03825-3, Pub. by Wiley-Interscience). Wiley.

Toribara, T. Y., et al, eds. Polluted Rain. LC 80-285. (Environmental Science Research Ser.: Vol. 17). 514p. 1980. 62.50 (ISBN 0-306-40353-6, Plenum Pr). Plenum Pub.

--Environmental Pollutants: Detection & Measurement. LC 78-605. (Environmental Science Research Ser.: Vol. 13). (Illus.). 512p. 1978. 75.00x (ISBN 0-306-36313-5, Plenum Pr). Plenum Pub.

Turk, Amos, et al. Ecology, Pollution & Environment. 1972. pap. text ed. 16.95 (ISBN 0-7216-8925-6, CBS C). SCP.

Turk, Jonathan & Turk, Amos. Environmental Science. 3rd ed. 1984. text ed. 32.95 (ISBN 0-03-058467-1, CBS C); instr's manual 10.95 (ISBN 0-03-058468-X). SCP.

Turner, A. C., et al. The Determination of Environmental Lead Near Works & Roads in Conjunction with the EEC Blood-Level Survey: 1978-9, 1980. 1981. 70.00x (ISBN 0-686-97055-1, Pub. by W Spring England). State Mutual Bk.

Turner, R. Kerry, et al. Environmental Economics: Pollution. 1977. 90.00x (ISBN 0-905440-12-9, Pub. by MCB Pubns). State Mutual Bk.

Tver, David F. Dictionary of Dangerous Pollutants, Ecology & Environment. LC 81-1881. (Illus.). 360p. 1981. 29.95 (ISBN 0-8311-1060-0). Indus Pr.

Versino, B. & Ott, H., eds. Physico-Chemical Behaviour of Atmospheric Pollution. 1982. lib. bdg. 78.00 (ISBN 90-277-1349-9, Pub. by Reidel Holland). Kluwer Academic.

Vesilind, P. Aarne & Peirce, Jeffrey J. Environmental Pollution & Control. 2nd ed. LC 82-48648. (Illus.). 375p. 1983. pap. 16.95 (ISBN 0-250-40619-5). Butterworth.

Waldbott, George L. Health Effects of Environmental Pollutants. 2nd ed. LC 77-26880. (Illus.). 350p. 1978. pap. text ed. 18.95 (ISBN 0-8016-5331-2). Mosby.

Walker, Colin. Environmental Pollution by Chemicals. 1980. pap. text ed. 8.25x (ISBN 0-09-123891-9, Hutchinson U Lib). Humanities.

Wardley-Smith, J., ed. The Prevention of Oil Pollution. 264p. 1979. 33.00x (ISBN 0-86010-129-0, Pub. by Graham & Trotman England). State Mutual Bk.

Weiner, J. S., et al, eds. Production, Pollution, Protection. (The Wykeham Science Ser.: No. 19). 368p. 1977. pap. cancelled (ISBN 0-85109-250-0). Taylor & Francis.

WHO Expert Committee. Geneva, 1973. Health Aspects of Environmental Pollution Control-Planning & Implementation of Nationnal Programmes: Report. (Technical Report Ser.: No. 554). (Also avail. in French & Spanish). 1974. pap. 2.40 (ISBN 92-4-120554-7). World Health.

WHO Study Group, Geneva, 1974. Health Hazards from New Environmental Pollutants: Report. (Technical Report Ser.: No. 586). (Also avail. in french & spanish). 1976. pap. 3.20 (ISBN 92-4-120586-5). World Health.

Wilman, Elizabeth A. External Costs of Coastal Beach Pollution: An Hedonic Approach. LC 84-42690. 208p. (Orig.). 1984. pap. text ed. 15.00 (ISBN 0-915707-08-X). Resources Future.

Witters, Weldon L. & Jones-Witters, Patricia. Environmental Biology: The Human Factor. 2nd ed. LC 75-35412. 1982. perfect bdg. 9.95 (ISBN 0-8403-2812-5). Kendall Hunt.

Wood, C. M., et al. Geography of Northwest England. 150p. 1974. pap. 10.50 (ISBN 0-7190-0564-7, Pub. by Manchester Univ Pr). Longwood Pub Group.

Worf, Douglas L., ed. Biological Monitoring for Environmental Effects. LC 79-2977. 240p. 1980. 28.50x (ISBN 0-669-03306-5). Lexington Bks.

Yapp, W. B. & Smith, M. I. Production, Pollution, Protection. (Wykeham Science Ser.: No. 19). 196p. 1972. 9.95x (ISBN 0-8448-1121-1). Crane-Russak Co.

POLLUTION–CONTROL

see Pollution

POLLUTION–LAWS AND LEGISLATION

Bates, J. H. U. K. Marine Pollution Law. 1984. 85.00 (ISBN 1-850-44028-X). Lloyds London Pr.

Controlling Cross-Media Pollutants. LC 84-23076. (Illus.). 54p. (Orig.). 1984. pap. 7.50 (ISBN 0-89164-088-6). Conservation Foun.

Durant, Robert F. When Government Regulates Itself: EPA, TVA & Pollution Control in the 1970's. LC 84-22058. 224p. 1985. text ed. 18.95x (ISBN 0-87049-458-9). U of Tenn Pr.

Lenz, Matthew, Jr. Environmental Pollution: Liability & Insurance. 60p. (Orig.). 1982. pap. 5.00 (ISBN 0-932387-02-0). Insur Info.

Pollution Control & International Trade. (Studies in International Trade: No. 1). pap. 5.00 (G95, GATT). Unipub.

POLLUTION–PREVENTION

see Pollution

POLLUTION CONTROL DEVICES (MOTOR VEHICLES)

see Motor Vehicles–Pollution Control Devices

POLLUTION CONTROL EQUIPMENT

see also Motor Vehicles–Pollution Control Devices

Atkins, M. H. & Lowe, J. F. Economics of Pollution Control in the Non-Ferrous Metals Industry. (Illus.). 1979. 53.00 (ISBN 0-08-022458-X). Pergamon.

Buonicore, Anthony & Theodore, Louis. Industrial Control Equipment for Gaseous Pollutants, 2 vols. new ed. LC 74-25260. (Uniscience Ser). 1975. Vol. 1, 209p. 17.47 (ISBN 0-87819-067-8); Vol. 2, 168p. 40.00 (ISBN 0-87819-068-6). CRC Pr.

Cross, Frank L., Jr. & Hesketh, Howard E. Handbook for the Operation & Maintenance of Air Pollution Control Equipment. LC 74-33843. 285p. 1975. pap. 14.95x (ISBN 0-87762-160-8). Technomic.

European Directories, ed. The Directory of Pollution Control Equipment Manufacturers in Western Europe. 1985. 100.00x (ISBN 0-686-78879-6, Pub. by European Directories England). State Mutual Bk.

Jensen, L. D. Biofouling Control Procedures. (Pollution Engineering Ser.: Vol. 5). 1977. 39.75 (ISBN 0-8247-6600-8). Dekker.

Kays, William B. Construction of Linings for Reservoirs, Tanks, & Pollution Control Facilties. LC 77-3944. (Wiley Series of Practical Construction Guides). 379p. 1977. 59.95x (ISBN 0-471-02110-5, Pub. by Wiley-Interscience). Wiley.

Leeper, G. W. Managing Heavy Metals on the Land. (Pollution Engineering & Technology Ser: Vol. 6). 1977. 35.00 (ISBN 0-8247-6661-X). Dekker.

Martin, A. E., ed. Emission Control Technology for Industrial Boilers. LC 80-26046. (Pollution Tech. Rev. 74: Energy Tech. Rev. 62). (Illus.). 405p. 1981. 48.00 (ISBN 0-8155-0833-6). Noyes.

Morrisey, T. J., ed. Pollution Control Problems & Related Federal Legislation. 290p. 1974. text ed. 29.50x (ISBN 0-8422-5175-8); pap. text ed. 12.50x (ISBN 0-8422-0418-0). Irvington.

Pollution Charges in Practice. (Document Ser.). 118p. 1980. 7.50x (ISBN 92-64-12042-4). OECD.

Spooner, Philip, et al. Slurry Trench Construction for Pollution Migration Control. LC 84-22747. (Pollution Technology Review Ser.: No. 118). (Illus.). 237p. 1985. 36.00 (ISBN 0-8155-1020-9). Noyes.

BOOKS - SUBJECT INDEX POLYMERS AND POLYMERIZATION

Voight, Randall L. & Franklin, George, Jr. A Reference Guide to Environmental Management, Engineering & Pollution Control Resources. 305p. 1983. pap. 35.00 (ISBN 0-930318-12-9). Intl Res Eval.

POLLUTION EQUIPMENT
see Pollution Control Equipment

POLLUTION OF WATER
see Water–Pollution

POLYA, GEORGE, 1887

Polya, George. George Polya-Collected Papers, 2 vols. Boas, Ralph, ed. 1974. Vol. 1, Singularities Of Analytic Functions. 60.00x (ISBN 0-262-02104-8); Vol. 2, 1975 Location Of Zeros. 50.00x (ISBN 0-262-02103-X). MIT Pr.

Szego, Gabor, et al, eds. Studies in Mathematical Analysis & Related Topics: Essays in Honor of George Polya. 1962. 30.00x (ISBN 0-8047-0140-7). Stanford U Pr.

POLYAMIDES

Campbell, Robert A., et al, eds. Advances in Polyamine Research, Vol. 2. LC 77-83687. 395p. 1978. 59.00 (ISBN 0-89004-194-6). Raven.

High-Modulus Wholly Aromatic Fibers. Black, W. Bruce & Preston, Jack, eds. (Fiber Science Ser.: No. 5). 388p. 1973. 75.00 (ISBN 0-8247-6069-7). Dekker.

Mittal, K. L., ed. Polyimides: Synthesis, Characterization & Applications, 2 vols. 1984. Set. 155.00x (Plenum Pr); Vol. 1, 586p. 89.50x (ISBN 0-306-41670-0); Vol. 2, 564p. 89.50x (ISBN 0-306-41673-5). Plenum Pub.

POLYAMINES

Bachrach, Uriel, et al, eds. Advances in Polyamine Research, Vol. 4. 832p. 1983. text ed. 76.00 (ISBN 0-89004-890-8). Raven.

Caldarera, Claudio M., et al, eds. Advances in Polyamine Research, Vol. 3. 512p. 1981. 79.00 (ISBN 0-89004-621-2). Raven.

Campbell, Robert A., et al, eds. Advances in Polyamine Research, Vol. 1. 300p. 1978. text ed. 50.50 (ISBN 0-89004-189-X). Raven.

Stahmann, Mark A., ed. Polyamino Acids, Polypeptides & Proteins: Proceedings of an International Symposium Held at the University of Wisconsin, 1961. LC 62-12893. pap. 104.00 (ISBN 0-317-29055-X, 2021149). Bks Demand UMI.

Tabor, Herbert & Tabor, Celia W., eds. Methods in Enzymology: Polyamines, Vol. 94. 1983. 60.00 (ISBN 0-12-181994-9). Acad Pr.

POLYBUTENES

Rubin, Isaac D. Poly(One-Butene) Its Preparation & Properties. LC 67-28233. (Polymer Monographs). (Illus.). 138p. 1968. 37.25 (ISBN 0-677-01270-5). Gordon.

POLYCHAETA

Fauchald, Kristian. The Polychaete Worms, Definitions & Keys to the Orders, Families & Genera. (Science Ser.: No. 28). (Illus.). 188p. 1977. 6.00 (ISBN 0-938644-08-4). Nat Hist Mus.

Hartman, O., ed. Polychaeta Errantia of Antarctica. LC 64-60091. (Antarctic Research Ser.: Vol. 3). (Illus.). 131p. 1964. 12.00 (ISBN 0-87590-103-4). Am Geophysical.

--Polychaeta Myzostomidae & Sedentaria of Antarctica. LC 66-61601. (Antarctic Research Ser.: Vol. 7). (Illus.). 158p. 1966. 13.00 (ISBN 0-87590-107-7). Am Geophysical.

Pettibone, Marian H. Some Scale-bearing Polychaetes of Puget Sound & Adjacent Waters. LC 53-6933. (Illus.). 136p. 1953. pap. 10.00x (ISBN 0-295-73936-3). U of Wash Pr.

POLYCHLORINATED BIPHENYLS

Ackerman, D. G., et al. Destruction & Disposal of PCB'S by Thermal & Non-Thermal Methods. LC 82-22312. (Pollution Technology Review Ser.: No. 97). (Illus.). 417p. 1983. 48.00 (ISBN 0-8155-0934-0). Noyes.

The Determination of Polychlorinated Biphenyls in Open Ocean Waters. (Intergovernmental Oceanographic Commission Technical Ser.: No. 26). (Illus.). 48p. 1985. pap. 7.50 (ISBN 92-3-102262-8, U1412, UNESCO). Unipub.

D'Itri. PCB's: Human & Environmental Hazards. 1983. text ed. 49.95 (ISBN 0-250-40598-9). Butterworth.

Eisenreich, S., ed. Physical Behavior of PCBs in the Great Lakes. LC 82-72347. (Illus.). 442p. 1982. 49.95 (ISBN 0-250-40584-9). Butterworth.

Hutzinger, O. & Safe, S. The Chemistry of PCB's. LC 83-13598. 280p. 1983. Repr. of 1974 ed. lib. bdg. 62.00 (ISBN 0-89874-665-5). Krieger.

Hutzinger, O., et al. Chemistry of PCB's. LC 73-88621. (Uniscience Ser). 269p. 1974. 62.00 (ISBN 0-8493-5040-9). CRC Pr.

POLYCYCLIC COMPOUNDS

Bjorseth & Randahl. Handbook of Polycyclic Aromatic. 368p. write for info. (ISBN 0-8247-7442-6). Dekker.

Futoma, David J., et al. Analysis of Polycyclic Aromatic Hydrocarbons in Water Systems. 200p. 1981. 66.00 (ISBN 0-8493-6255-5). CRC Pr.

Gelboin, Harry & Ts'O, Paul O., eds. Polycyclic Hydrocardons & Cancer, Vol. 3. LC 78-17706. 1981. 65.00 (ISBN 0-12-279203-3). Acad Pr.

Gelboin, Harry V., ed. Polycyclic Hydrocarbons & Cancer, 2 vols. Incl. Vol. 1. Environment, Chemistry & Metabolism. 70.00 (ISBN 0-12-279201-7); Vol. 2. Molecular & Cell Biology. 1979. 70.00 (ISBN 0-12-279202-5). 1978. Acad Pr.

Lee, Milton L., et al. Analytical Chemistry of Polycyclic Aromatic Compounds. 1981. 75.50 (ISBN 0-12-440840-0). Acad Pr.

Segal, Daniel. Polycyclic Groups. LC 82-9476. (Cambridge Tracts in Mathematics Ser.: No. 82). 200p. 1983. 52.50 (ISBN 0-521-24146-4). Cambridge U Pr.

POLYELECTROLYTE SOLUTIONS
see Electrolyte Solutions

POLYENES

Brodsky, V. Y. & Uryvaeva, I. V. Genome Multiplication in Growth & Development: Biology of Polyploid & Polytene Cells. (Developmental & Cell Biology Ser.: No. 15). (Illus.). 312p. 1985. 79.50 (ISBN 0-521-25323-3). Cambridge U Pr.

Zechmeister, Laszlo. CIS-Trans Isomeric Carotenoids, Vitamins A & Arylpolyenes. 1962. 41.50 (ISBN 0-12-777850-0). Acad Pr.

POLYESTERS
see also Reinforced Plastics; Textile Fibers, Synthetic

Low Profile - Low Shrink Unstaurated Polyester Compositions. 40p. 1978. 40.00x (ISBN 0-686-44673-9, Pub. by Chandler England). State Mutual Bk.

Meyer, Raymond W. Handbook of Polyester Molding Compounds. 220p. 1985. text ed. 27.50 (ISBN 0-412-00771-1, 9199, Pub. by Chapman & Hall England). Methuen Inc.

POLYETHYLENE

Extrusion of High Density Polyethylenes. 169p. 1982. 78.00 (ISBN 0-317-12671-7). T-C Pubns CA.

Extrusion of Low Density Polyethylenes. 153p. 1982. 78.00 (ISBN 0-317-12672-5). T-C Pubns CA.

Opschoor, A. Conformations of Polyethylene & Polypropylene. 78p. 1970. 23.25x (ISBN 0-677-61220-6). Gordon.

POLYGONS

Boehm, J. & Hertel, E. Polyedergeometrie in n-dimensionalen Raeumen konstanter Kruemmung. (LMW-MA Ser.: No. 70). 288p. 1980. 51.95x (ISBN 0-8176-1160-6). Birkhauser.

Miyazaki, K. An Adventure in Multidimensional Space: The Art & Geometry of Polygons, Polyhedra & Polytopes. 1985. 24.95 (ISBN 0-471-81648-5). Wiley.

POLYGRAPH
see Lie Detectors and Detection

POLYHEDRA
see also Topology

Balinski, M. L. & Hoffman, A. J. Polyhedral Combinatorics, Vol. 8. 234p. 1978. pap. 30.00 (ISBN 0-444-85196-8). Elsevier.

Barnette, David W. Map Coloring, Polyhedra & the Four-Color Problem. (Dolciani Mathematical Expositions Ser.: Vol. 8). 1984. 30.00 (ISBN 0-88385-309-4, 82062783). Math Assn.

Coxeter, H. S., et al. The Fifty-Nine Icosahedra. (Illus.). 30p. 1982. pap. 15.00 (ISBN 0-387-90770-X). Springer-Verlag.

Federico, P. J. Descartes on Polyhedra: A Study of the "De Solidorum Elementis". (Sources in the History of Mathematics & Physical Sciences: Vol. 4). (Illus.). 144p. 1982. 39.50 (ISBN 0-387-90760-2). Springer-Verlag.

Holden, Alan. Shapes, Space, & Symmetry. LC 71-158459. (Illus.). 1971. 26.00x (ISBN 0-231-03549-7); pap. 13.00x (ISBN 0-231-08323-8). Columbia U Pr.

Lalvani, Haresh. Transpolyhedra: Dual Transformations by Explosion-Implosion. LC 77-81420. (Papers in Theoretical Morphology Ser.: Vol. 1). 1977. 14.50 (ISBN 0-686-00073-0); pap. 9.50 (ISBN 0-686-00074-9). H Lalvani.

Miyazaki, K. An Adventure in Multidimensional Space: The Art & Geometry of Polygons, Polyhedra & Polytopes. 1985. 24.95 (ISBN 0-471-81648-5). Wiley.

Ryyskov, S. S. & Baranovskii, E. P. C-Types of N-Dimensional Lattices & Five-Dimensional Primitive Parallellohedra. LC 78-21923. (Proceedings of the Steklov Institute of Mathematics). 1978. 61.00 (ISBN 0-8218-3037-6, STEKLO-137). Am Math.

Steklov Institute of Mathematics, Academy of Sciences, USSR & Stogrin, M. I. Regular Dirichlet-Voronoi Partitions for the Second Triclinic Group: Proceedings. LC 75-23284. (Proceedings of the Steklov Institute of Mathematics: No.123). 116p. 1975. 39.00 (ISBN 0-8218-3023-6, STEKLO-123). Am Math.

Stone, D. A. Stratified Polyhedra. LC 77-187427. (Lecture Notes in Mathematics: Vol. 252). 193p. 1972. pap. 10.00 (ISBN 0-387-05726-9). Springer-Verlag.

Wenninger, Magnus J. Polyhedron Models. LC 69-10200. (Illus.). 1971. 37.50 (ISBN 0-521-06917-3); pap. 15.95 (ISBN 0-521-09859-9). Cambridge U Pr.

Zalgaller, Viktor A. Convex Polyhedra with Regular Faces. LC 69-12505. (Seminars in Mathematics Ser.: Vol. 2). 130p. 1969. 29.50x (ISBN 0-306-18802-3, Consultants). Plenum Pub.

POLYHEDRA–MODELS

Wenninger, Magnus J. Dual Models. LC 82-14767. (Illus.). 208p. 1983. 21.95 (ISBN 0-521-24524-9). Cambridge U Pr.

--Polyhedron Models. LC 69-10200. (Illus.). 1971. 37.50 (ISBN 0-521-06917-3); pap. 15.95 (ISBN 0-521-09859-9). Cambridge U Pr.

POLYMERIZATION
see Polymers and Polymerization

POLYMERS AND POLYMERIZATION
see also Acetal Resins; Condensation Products (Chemistry); Elastomers; Macromolecules; Plastics; Polyamides; Polyesters

Aggarwal, S. L., ed. Block Polymers. LC 74-119054. 339p. 1970. 39.50x (ISBN 0-306-30481-3, Plenum Pr). Plenum Pub.

Aklonis, John J. & MacKnight, William J. Introduction to Polymer Viscoelasticity. 2nd ed. LC 82-17528. 295p. 1983. 39.95x (ISBN 0-471-86729-2, Pub. by Wiley Interscience). Wiley.

Aklonis, John J., et al, eds. Introduction to Polymer Viscoelasticity. 249p. 1972. 34.95 (ISBN 0-471-01860-0). Wiley.

Allara, David L., ed. Stabilization & Degradation of Polymers. Hawkins, Walter L. LC 78-10600. (Advances in Chemistry Ser.: No. 169). 1978. 49.95 (ISBN 0-8412-0381-4). Am Chemical.

Allcock, H. R. Heteroatom Ring Systems & Polymers. 1967. 73.50 (ISBN 0-12-050550-9). Acad Pr.

Allen, ed. Polymers with Unusual Properties. price not set (ISBN 0-471-88172-4). Wiley.

Allen, N. S., ed. Degradation & Stablisation of Polymers. (Illus.). 384p. 1983. 70.50 (ISBN 0-85334-194-X, Pub. by Elsevier Applied Sci England). Elsevier.

Allen, N. S. & Schnabel, W., eds. Photochemistry & Photophysics of Polymers. 440p. 1984. 126.00 (ISBN 0-85334-269-5, I-256-84, Pub. by Elsevier Applied Sci England). Elsevier.

Allock, H. R. & Lampe, F. W. Contemporary Polymer Chemistry. 1981. 45.95 (ISBN 0-13-170258-0). P-H.

Allport, D. C. Block Copolymers. James, W. H., ed. (Illus.). 620p. 1973. 64.75 (ISBN 0-85334-557-0, Pub. by Elsevier Applied Sci England). Elsevier.

American Chemical Society. Emulsion Polymerization: An International Symposium Sponsored by the Division of Polymer Chemistry, Inc. at the 169th Meeting of the American Chemical Society, Philadelphia, Penn., April 8-10, 1975. Piirma, Irja & Gardon, John L., eds. LC 75-44458. (American Chemical Society. ACS: No. 24). (Illus.). pap. 103.80 (ISBN 0-317-09441-6, 2019528). Bks Demand UMI.

American Concrete Institute. Polymers in Concrete. LC 73-86176. (American Concrete Institute Publication Ser.: No. SP-40). (Illus.). pap. 92.00 (ISBN 0-317-10006-8, 2004294). Bks Demand UMI.

--Polymers in Concrete: International Symposium. LC 78-73077. (American Concrete Institute, Publication: SP-58). pap. 106.50 (ISBN 0-317-27232-2, 2025082). Bks Demand UMI.

American Society for Metals. Polymeric Materials: Relationships Between Structure & Mechanical Behavior: Papers Presented at a Seminar of the American Society for Metals. LC 74-20127. pap. 156.50 (ISBN 0-317-09007-0, 2015494). Bks Demand UMI.

Analysis, Networks, Peptides. (Advances in Polymer Science Ser.: Vol. 65). (Illus.). 230p. 1984. 44.00 (ISBN 0-387-13656-8). Springer-Verlag.

Andrade, Joseph D., ed. Surface & Interfacial Aspects of Biomedical Polymers, Vol. 1: Surface Chemistry & Physics. 486p. 1985. 69.50x (ISBN 0-306-41741-3, Plenum Pr). Plenum Pub.

Andre, J., et al, eds. Quantum Theory of Polymers. (NATO Advanced Study Inst. Ser.). 1978. lib. bdg. 45.00 (ISBN 90-277-0870-3, Pub. by Reidel Holland). Kluwer Academic.

Andre, J. M., et al, eds. Recent Advances in the Quantum Theory of Polymers: Proceedings. (Lecture Notes in Physics: Vol. 113). 306p. 1980. pap. 26.00 (ISBN 3-540-09731-7). Springer-Verlag.

Andre, Jean-Marie & Ladik, Janos, eds. Electronic Structure of Polymers & Molecular Crystals. LC 75-12643. (NATO ASI Series B, Physics: Vol. 9). 704p. 1975. 95.00x (ISBN 0-306-35709-7, Plenum Pr). Plenum Pub.

Ansell, M. F. Rodd's Chemistry of Carbon Compounds, Suppl. Vol 3F, (Partial) G. 2nd ed. 1984. 86.75 (ISBN 0-444-42269-2, I-479-83). Elsevier.

Applied Science Publishers Ltd. London, ed. Biodegradation of Polymers & Synthetic Polymers: Sessions of the 3rd International Biodegradation Symposium. (Illus.). 1976. 26.00x (ISBN 0-85334-708-5, Pub. by Applied Science). Burgess-Intl Ideas.

Ash, M. & Ash, I. Encyclopedia of Plastics, Polymers & Resins Vol. 1, A-G. 1981. 75.00 (ISBN 0-8206-0290-6). Chem Pub.

--Encyclopedia of Plastics, Polymers & Resins Vol. 2, H-O. 1982. 75.00 (ISBN 0-8206-0296-5). Chem Pub.

--Encyclopedia of Plastics, Polymers & Resins Vol. 3, P-Z. 1983. 75.00 (ISBN 0-8206-0303-1). Chem Pub.

Astarita, G. & Nicolais, L., eds. Polymer Processing & Properties. 464p. 1984. 69.50x (ISBN 0-306-41728-6, Plenum Pr). Plenum Pub.

Baijal, M. D., ed. Plastics Polymer Science & Technology. (SPE Monograph). (Illus.). 945p. 1982. 172.50 (ISBN 0-686-48131-3, 0815). T-C Pubns CA.

Baijal, Mahendra D., ed. Plastic Polymers Science & Technology. LC 31-13066. (Society of Plastic Engineers Monographs). 945p. 1982. 172.50x (ISBN 0-471-04044-4, Pub. by Wiley-Interscience). Wiley.

Baijal, S. K. Flow Behavior of Polymers in Porous Media. 116p. 1982. 49.95x (ISBN 0-87814-188-X). Pennwell Bks.

Bailey, Frederick E., Jr., ed. Initation of Polymerization. LC 83-2613. (ACS Symposium Ser.: No. 212). 498p. 1983. lib. bdg. 52.95x (ISBN 0-8412-0765-8). Am Chemical.

Bailey, R. T., et al. Molecular Motion in High Polymers. (International Series of Monographs on Chemistry). (Illus.). 1981. text ed. 69.00x (ISBN 0-19-851333-X). Oxford U Pr.

Bailey, William J. & Tsuruta, Teiji, eds. Contemporary Topics in Polymer Science, Vol. 4. 1015p. 1983. 135.00x (ISBN 0-306-41248-9, Plenum Pr). Plenum Pub.

Bark, L. S. & Allen, N. S. Analysis of Polymer Systems. (Illus.). 311p. 1982. 55.50 (ISBN 0-85334-122-2, Pub. by Elsevier Applied Sci England). Elsevier.

Barrett, Keith E. Dispersion Polymerization in Organic Media. LC 74-5491. 322p. 1975. 79.95x (ISBN 0-471-05418-6, Pub. by Wiley-Interscience). Wiley.

Bartenev, G. M. & Lavrentev, V. V. Friction & Wear of Polymers. (Tribilogy Ser.: Vol. 6). 320p. 1981. 74.50 (ISBN 0-444-42000-2). Elsevier.

Bartenev, G. M. & Zuyev, Yu. S. Strength & Failure of Visco-Elastic Materials. 1968. 72.00 (ISBN 0-08-012183-7). Pergamon.

Bassett, ed. Developments in Crystalline Polymers, Vol. 1. 279p. 1982. 64.75 (ISBN 0-85334-116-8, Pub. by Elsevier Applied Sci England). Elsevier.

Bassett, D. C. Principles of Polymer Morphology. (Cambrige Solid State Science Ser.). (Illus.). 220p. 1981. 64.50 (ISBN 0-521-23270-8); pap. 24.95 (ISBN 0-521-29886-5). Cambridge U Pr.

Bassett, D. R. & Hamielac, Alvin E., eds. Emulsion Polymers & Emulsion Polymerization. LC 81-10823. (ACS Symposium Ser.: No. 165). 1981. 59.95 (ISBN 0-8412-0642-2). Am Chemical.

Batista, O. A. Microcrystal Polymer Science. LC 74-13742. (Illus.). 30.00 (ISBN 0-07-004084-2). RSC Pubs.

Batzer, Hans & Lohse, Friedrich. Introduction to Macromolecular Chemistry. 2nd ed. LC 78-6175. 297p. 1979. 58.95x (ISBN 0-471-99645-9, Pub. by Wiley-Interscience). Wiley.

Bely, V. A., et al. Friction & Wear in Polymer-Based Materials. LC 80-41825. (Illus.). 400p. 1982. 110.00 (ISBN 0-08-025444-6). Pergamon.

Biesenberger, J. A. Devolatization of Polymers: Fundamentals - Equipment - Application. LC 83-62610. 350p. 1983. text ed. 28.00 (ISBN 0-02-949170-3, Pub. by Hanser International). Macmillan.

Biesenberger, Joseph A. & Sebastain, Donald H. Principles of Polymerization Engineering. 744p. 1983. 54.50 (ISBN 0-471-08616-9). Wiley.

Bikales, N. M., ed. Water-Soluble Polymers. LC 73-79431. (Polymer Science & Technology Ser.: Vol. 2). 440p. 1973. 65.00x (ISBN 0-306-36402-6, Plenum Pr). Plenum Pub.

Bikales, Norbert M., ed. Mechanical Properties of Polymers. LC 78-172950. 280p. pap. text ed. 18.00 (ISBN 0-471-07234-6). Krieger.

Billingham, N. C. Molar Mass Measurements in Polymer Science. LC 77-2823. 254p. 1977. cloth 59.95x (ISBN 0-470-99125-9). Halsted Pr.

Billmeyer, Fred W., Jr. Textbook of Polymer Science. LC 83-19870. 560p. 1984. 34.95x (ISBN 0-471-03196-8, Pub. by Wiley-Interscience). Wiley.

Bird, Byron R., et al. Dynamics of Polymeric Liquids, 2 vols. Incl. Vol. 1. Fluid Mechanics. 576p. 69.45 (ISBN 0-471-07375-X); Vol. 2. Kinetic Theory. 304p. 69.45x (ISBN 0-471-01596-2). LC 76-15408. 1977. Wiley.

Bishop, Richard B. Practical Polymerization for Polystyrene. LC 75-132666. (Illus.). 480p. 1971. 34.95 (ISBN 0-8436-1200-2). Van Nos Reinhold.

Block, H. Poly (y-Benzyl-L-Glutamate) (Polymer Monographs: Vol. 9). 215p. 1983. 49.00 (ISBN 0-677-05680-X). Gordon.

Blumstein, Alexandre, ed. Liquid Crystalline Order in Polymers. 1978. 56.50 (ISBN 0-12-108650-X). Acad Pr.

--Mesomorphic Order in Polymers & Polymerization in Liquid Crystalline Media. LC 78-9470. (ACS Symposium Ser.: No. 74). 1978. 30.95 (ISBN 0-8412-0419-5). Am Chemical.

Blythe, A. R. Electrical Properties of Polymers. LC 77-85690. (Cambridge Solid State Science Ser.). (Illus.). 201p. 1980. pap. text ed. 15.95 (ISBN 0-521-29825-3). Cambridge U Pr.

--Electrical Properties of Polymers. LC 77-85690. (Solid State Science Ser.). 1979. 57.50 (ISBN 0-521-21902-7). Cambridge U Pr.

Bodor, G., ed. Orientation Effects in Solid Polymers. 432p. 1984. pap. 44.95 (ISBN 0-471-04658-2). Krieger.

Boenig, Herman V. Plasma Science & Technology. LC 81-15200. 304p. 1982. 39.95x (ISBN 0-8014-1356-7). Cornell U Pr.

Boguslavskii, Leonid I. & Vannikov, Anatolii V. Organic Semiconductors & Biopolymers. LC 72-75452. (Monographs in Semiconductor Physics Ser.: Vol. 6). 221p. 1970. 32.50x (ISBN 0-306-30433-3, Plenum Pr). Plenum Pub.

Bohdanecky, M. & Kovar, J. Viscosity of Polymer Solutions. (Polymer Science Library: No. 2). 286p. 1982. 76.75 (ISBN 0-444-42066-5). Elsevier.

Bolker, Henry. Natural & Synthetic Polymers: An Introduction. 712p. 1974. 95.00 (ISBN 0-8247-1060-6). Dekker.

Boor, John, Jr. Ziegler-Natta Catalysts & Polymerizations. 1979. 80.00 (ISBN 0-12-115550-1). Acad Pr.

Boretos, John W. Concise Guide to Biomedical Polymers: Their Design, Fabrication & Molding. (Illus.). 208p. 1973. photocopy ed. 27.50x (ISBN 0-398-02674-2). C C Thomas.

Boyer, R. & Keinath, S., eds. Molecular Motion in Polymers by ESR. (MMI Press Symposium Ser.: Vol. 1). 352p. 1980. lib. bdg. 62.50 (ISBN 3-7186-0012-9). Harwood Academic.

Boyer, Raymond F., ed. Technological Aspects of the Mechanical Behavior of Polymers. LC 74-181576. (Applied Polymer Symposia: No. 24). Repr. of 1974 ed. 23.00 (ISBN 0-8357-9378-8, 2007371). Bks Demand UMI.

Brame, Edward G., Jr., ed. Applications of Polymer Spectroscopy. LC 77-25728. 1978. 55.50 (ISBN 0-12-125450-X). Acad Pr.

Brandrup, Johannes & Immergut, E. H., eds. Polymer Handbook. 2nd ed. LC 74-11381. 1408p. 1975. 89.50x (ISBN 0-471-09804-3, Pub. by Wiley-Interscience). Wiley.

Braun, Dietrich & Cherdron, Harald. Techniques of Polymer Syntheses & Characterization. LC 79-148168. pap. 74.00 (ISBN 0-317-08665-0, 2011967). BKs Demand UMI.

Brown, R. Malcolm, Jr., ed. Cellulose & Other Natural Polymer Systems: Biogenesis, Structure, & Degradation. LC 82-3796. 540p. 1982. text ed. 59.50 (ISBN 0-306-40856-2, Plenum Pr). Plenum Pub.

Brown, R. P. & Reed, B. E., eds. Measurement Techniques for Polymeric Solids. 236p. 1984. 78.00 (ISBN 0-85334-274-1, I-257-84, Pub. by Elsevier Applied Sci England). Elsevier.

Bruck, Stephen D. Blood Compatible Synthetic Polymers: An Introduction. (Illus.). 144p. 1974. 16.75x (ISBN 0-398-02931-8). C C Thomas.

Bruns, W., et al. Monte Carlo Applications in Polymer Science. (Lecture Notes in Chemistry Ser.: Vol. 27). 179p. 1981. pap. 16.20 (ISBN 0-387-11165-4). Springer-Verlag.

Bueche, F. Physical Properties of Polymers. LC 78-27015. 364p. 1979. Repr. of 1962 ed. text ed. 27.50 (ISBN 0-88275-833-0). Krieger.

Burke, John J. & Weiss, Volker, eds. Block & Graft Copolymers. LC 73-12903. (Sagamore Army Materials Research Conference Ser.: Vol. 19). 348p. 1973. 35.00x (ISBN 0-306-34519-6, Plenum Pr). Plenum Pub.

--Characterization of Materials in Research: Ceramics & Polymers. LC 75-5272. (Sagamore Army Materials Research Conference Ser.: Vol. 20). 576p. 1975. 45.00x (ISBN 0-306-34520-X, Plenum Pr). Plenum Pub.

Burns. Polyester Molding Compounds. (Plastics Engineering Ser.: Vol. 2). 304p. 1982. 55.00 (ISBN 0-8247-1280-3). Dekker.

Buscall, R., et al, eds. Science & Technology of Polymer Colloids. (Illus.). 336p. 1985. 57.00 (ISBN 0-85334-312-8, Pub. by Elsevier Applied Sci England). Elsevier.

Butler, George & Kresta, Jiri E., eds. Cyclopolymerization & Polymers with Chain-Ring Structures. LC 82-11331. (ACS Symposium Ser.: No. 195). 454p. 1982. lib. bdg. 49.95x (ISBN 0-8412-0731-3). Am Chemical.

Butt, L. T. & Wright, D. C. Use of Polymers in Chemical Plant Construction. (Illus.). vii, 148p. 1981. 49.95x (ISBN 0-85334-914-2, Pub. by Elsevier Applied Sci England). Elsevier.

--Use of Polymers in Chemical Plant Construction. (Illus.). 156p. 1981. text ed. 28.00 (ISBN 0-85334-914-2, Pub. by Applied Sci England). J K Burgess.

Calvert, R., ed. Polymer Latices & Their Applications. 1980. text ed. 40.00x (ISBN 0-02-949280-7). Macmillan.

Canton, H. J., et al, eds. New Scientific Aspect. LC 61-642. (Advances in Polymer Science: Vol. 20). (Illus.). 200p. 1976. 43.00 (ISBN 0-387-07631-X). Springer-Verlag.

Cantow, H. J., ed. Polydiacetylenes. (Advances in Polymer Science: Fortschritte der Hochpolymeren-Forschung: Vol. 63). (Illus.). 160p. 1984. 40.00 (ISBN 0-387-13414-X). Springer-Verlag.

--Polymer Chemistry. LC 61-642. (Advances in Polymer Science: Vol. 25). (Illus.). 1977. 55.00 (ISBN 0-387-08389-8). Springer-Verlag.

Cantow, H. J., et al. Behavior of Macromolecules. (Advances in Polymer Science Ser.: Vol. 46). (Illus.). 170p. 1982. 42.00 (ISBN 0-387-11640-0). Springer-Verlag.

--Light Scattering from Polymers. (Advances in Polymer Science Ser.: Vol. 48). (Illus.). 167p. 1983. 41.50 (ISBN 0-387-12030-0). Springer-Verlag.

--Polymers: Syntheses, Reactivities, Properties. (Advances in Poymer Science: Vol. 32). (Illus.). 1979. 56.00 (ISBN 0-387-09442-3). Springer-Verlag.

--Unusual Properties of New Polymers. (Advances in Polymer Science: Vol. 50). (Illus.). 149p. 1983. 39.00 (ISBN 0-387-12048-3). Springer-Verlag.

Cantow, H. J., et al, eds. Chemistry. LC 61-642. (Advances in Polymer Science: Vol. 31). (Illus.). 1979. 54.00 (ISBN 0-387-09200-5). Springer-Verlag.

--Polymer Products. (Advances in Polymer Science Ser.: Vol. 39). (Illus.). 230p. 1981. 59.50 (ISBN 0-387-10218-3). Springer-Verlag.

--Polymerization Processes. (Advances in Polymer Sciences Ser.: Vol. 38). (Illus.). 180p. 1981. 48.00 (ISBN 0-387-10217-5). Springer-Verlag.

--Polymerization Reactions. LC 61-642. (Advances in Polymer Science: Vol. 28). (Illus.). 1978. 51.00 (ISBN 0-387-08885-7). Springer-Verlag.

--Specialty Polymers. (Advances in Polymer Science Ser.: Vol. 41). (Illus.). 186p. 1981. 58.00 (ISBN 0-387-10554-9). Springer-Verlag.

--Synthesis & Degradation-Rheology & Extrusion. (Advances in Polymer Science: Vol. 47). (Illus.). 170p. 1982. 39.00 (ISBN 0-387-11774-1). Springer-Verlag.

--Analysis - Reactions - Morphology. (Advances in Polymer Science Ser.: Vol. 71). (Illus.). 220p. 1985. 55.00 (ISBN 0-387-15482-5). Springer-Verlag.

Cantow, H. T., ed. Polymerizations & Polymer Properties. (Advances in Polymer Science Ser.: Vol. 43). (Illus.). 240p. 1982. 52.00 (ISBN 0-387-11048-8). Springer-Verlag.

Cantow, M. J., ed. Polymer Fractionation. 1967. 92.50 (ISBN 0-12-158850-5). Acad Pr.

Carraher, Charles E. & Sheats, John, eds. Organometallic Polymers. 1978. 49.50 (ISBN 0-12-160850-6). Acad Pr.

Carraher, Charles E. & Tsuda, Minoru, eds. Modification of Polymers. LC 79-28259. (ACS Symposium Ser.: No. 121). 1980. 49.95 (ISBN 0-8412-0540-X). Am Chemical.

Carraher, Charles E., Jr. & Gebelein, Charles G., eds. Biological Activities of Polymers. LC 82-3988. (ACS Symposium Ser.: No. 186). 1982. 39.95 (ISBN 0-8412-0719-4). Am Chemical.

Carraher, Charles E., Jr. & Moore, James, eds. Modification of Polymers. 390p. 1983. 57.50x (ISBN 0-306-41387-6, Plenum Pr). Plenum Pub.

Carraher, Charles E., Jr. & Sheats, John E., eds. Advances in Organometallic & Inorganic Polymer Science. (Illus.). 472p. 1982. 67.50 (ISBN 0-8247-1610-8). Dekker.

Carraher, Charles E., Jr. & Sperling, L. H., eds. Polymer Applications of Renewable-Resource Materials. LC 82-10127. (Polymer Science & Technology Ser.: Vol. 17). 484p. 1983. 69.50 (ISBN 0-306-41033-8, Plenum Pr). Plenum Pub.

Casale, A., et al. Advances in Polymer Science: Polymerization, Vol. 17. Cantow, H. J., ed. LC 61-642. (Illus.). 120p. 1975. 35.00 (ISBN 0-387-07111-3). Springer-Verlag.

Casale, Antonio & Porter, Roger S. Polymer Stress Reactions, 2 vols. Vol. 1, 1978. 42.00 (ISBN 0-12-162801-9); Vol. 2, 1979. 65.00 (ISBN 0-12-162802-7). Acad Pr.

Cassidy. Thermally Stable Polymers. 392p. 1980. 65.00 (ISBN 0-8247-6969-4). Dekker.

Cazes. Liquid Chromatography of Polymers & Related Materials, Part III. (Chromatographic Science Ser., Vol. 19). 232p. 1981. 40.00 (ISBN 0-8247-1514-4). Dekker.

Ceausescu, E. Sterospecific Polymerization of Isoprene. (Illus.). 300p. 1983. 60.00 (ISBN 0-08-029987-3). Pergamon.

Ceresa, R. J. Block & Graft Copolymerization, Vol. 1. LC 72-5713. pap. 97.30 (ISBN 0-317-29348-6, 2024001). Bks Demand UMI.

Ceresa, R. J., ed. Block & Graft Copolymerization, 2 vols. LC 72-5713. 402p. 1976. Vol. 2. 89.95x (ISBN 0-471-14228-X, Pub. by Wiley-Interscience). Wiley.

Chang Dae Han. Multiphase Flow in Polymer Processing. LC 80-70598. 1981. 67.50 (ISBN 0-12-322460-8). Acad Pr.

Chapoy, L. L., ed. Recent Advances in Liquid Crystalline Polymers: Proceedings of the European Science Foundation Sixth Polymer Workshop, Lyngby, Denmark, 12-14 September 1983. (Illus.). 352p. 1985. 60.00 (ISBN 0-85334-313-6, Pub. by Elsevier Applied Sci England). Elsevier.

Cherry, B. W. Polymer Surfaces. LC 80-40013. (Cambridge Solid State Science Ser.). (Illus.). 150p. 1981. 42.50 (ISBN 0-521-23082-9); pap. 17.95 (ISBN 0-521-29792-3). Cambridge U Pr.

Chichinadze, A. V., ed. Polymers in Friction Assemblies of Machines & Devices: A Handbook. xii, 280p. 1984. 68.50 (ISBN 0-89864-010-5). Allerton Pr.

Chiellini, E. & Giusti, P., eds. Polymers in Medicine: Biomedical & Pharmacological Applications. 425p. 1983. 57.50x (ISBN 0-306-41360-4, Plenum Pr). Plenum Pub.

Chiellini, E., et al. Initiators - Poly-Reactions - Optical Activity. (Advances in Polymer Science, Fortschritte der Hochpolymerenforschung: Vol. 62). (Illus.). 190p. 1984. 39.00 (ISBN 0-387-13232-5). Springer-Verlag.

Chompff, A. J. & Newman, S., eds. Polymer Networks: Structure & Mechanical Properties. LC 73-163286. 493p. 1971. 69.50 (ISBN 0-306-30544-5, Plenum Pr). Plenum Pub.

Ciardelli, F. & Giusti, P. Structural Order in Polymers: International Symposium on Macromolecules, Florence, Italy, 7-12 September 1980. (IUPAC Symposium Ser.). (Illus.). 260p. 1981. 77.00 (ISBN 0-08-025296-6). Pergamon.

Ciba Foundation. Polymerization in Biological Systems. LC 72-86558. (Ciba Foundation Symposium: New Ser.: No. 13). pap. 80.50 (ISBN 0-317-28314-6, 2022139). Bks Demand UMI.

Ciferri, A. & Krigbaum, W. R., eds. Polymer Liquid Crystals. 394p. 1982. 62.50 (ISBN 0-12-174680-1). Acad Pr.

Ciferri, A. & Ward, I. M., eds. Ultra-High Modulus Polymers. (Illus.). 362p. 1979. 63.00 (ISBN 0-85334-800-6, Pub. by Elsevier Applied Sci England). Elsevier.

Clark, A. F., et al, eds. Nonmetallic Materials & Composites at Low Temperatures One. LC 78-26576. (Cryogenic Materials Ser.). 456p. 1979. 69.50x (ISBN 0-306-40077-4, Plenum Pr). Plenum Pub.

Clark, David T. & Feast, W. J., eds. Polymer Surfaces. LC 77-17426. (Illus.). pap. 114.30 (ISBN 0-317-09334-7, 2022101). Bks Demand UMI.

Cogswell, F. N. Polymer Melt Rheology: A Guide for Industrial Practice. LC 80-41762. 225p. 1981. 53.95x (ISBN 0-470-27102-7). Halsted Pr.

Collins, Edward A., et al. Experiments in Polymer Science. LC 73-650. 530p. 1973. pap. text ed. 32.50 (ISBN 0-471-16585-9, Pub. by Wiley-Interscience). Wiley.

Comyn, J. Polymer Permeability. 1985. 67.50 (ISBN 0-85334-322-5, Pub. by Elsevier Applied Sci England). Elsevier.

Cooper, Anthony R., ed. Polymeric Separation Media. LC 82-3668. (Polymer Science & Technology Ser.: Vol. 16). 285p. 1982. 49.50 (ISBN 0-306-40902-X, Plenum Pr). Plenum Pub.

Cooper, Stuart L. & Estes, Gerald M., eds. Multiphase Polymers. LC 79-10972. (Advances in Chemistry Ser.: No. 176). 1979. 64.95 (ISBN 0-8412-0457-8). Am Chemical.

Coordination Polymerization-a Memorial to Karl Ziegler: Proceedings, American Chemical Symposium, UCLA, Los Angeles, California, April 1974. 1975. 49.50 (ISBN 0-12-172450-6). Acad Pr.

Cotter, Robert J. & Matzner, Markus. Ring-Forming Polymerizations, Pt. A: Carbocyclic & Metallorganic Rings. 1969. 80.00 (ISBN 0-12-191701-0). Acad Pr.

--Ring Forming Polymerizations, Pt. B: Heterocyclic Rings. 1972. Vol. 1. 80.50 (ISBN 0-12-191702-9); Vol. 2. 99.00 (ISBN 0-12-191752-5). Acad Pr.

Cowie, J. M. Polymers: Chemistry & Physics of Modern Materials. (Illus.). 1973. pap. text ed. 27.50x (ISBN 0-7002-0222-6). Intl Ideas.

Cowie, J. M., ed. Alternating Copolymers. (Specialty Polymers Ser.). 294p. 1985. 47.50x (ISBN 0-306-41779-0, Plenumn Pr). Plenum Pub.

Cowley, Alan H., ed. Rings, Clusters, & Polymers of the Main Group Elements. LC 83-15462. (ACS Symposium Ser.: No. 232). 182p. 1983. lib. bdg. 32.95x (ISBN 0-8412-0801-8). Am Chemical.

Crank, John & Park, Geoffrey S., eds. Diffusion in Polymers. 1968. 86.00 (ISBN 0-12-197050-7). Acad Pr.

Craver, Clara D., ed. Polymer Characterization, Spectroscopic, Chromatographic, & Physical Instrumental Methods. LC 82-24496. (Advances in Chemistry Ser.: No. 203). 791p. 1983. lib. bdg. 69.95 (ISBN 0-8412-0700-3). Am Chemical.

Critchley, J. P., et al, eds. Heat-Resistant Polymers: Technologically Useful Materials. 448p. 1983. 65.00x (ISBN 0-306-41058-3, Plenum Pr). Plenum Pub.

Critser, James R., Jr. Antioxidants & Stabilizers for Polymers. Incl. Indexes & Abstracts 1967-1971. 315.00 (ISBN 0-914428-06-3). (Ser. 3-6771B). 1972. Lexington Data Inc.

--Antioxidants & Stabilizers for Polymers. (Ser. 3-72). 185p. 1973. 115.00 (ISBN 0-914428-12-8). Lexington Data.

--Antioxidants & Stabilizers for Polymers. (Ser. 3-73). 136p. 1974. 115.00 (ISBN 0-914428-19-5). Lexington Data.

--Antioxidants & Stabilizers for Polymers. (Ser. 3-74). 1975. 120.00 (ISBN 0-914428-24-1). Lexington Data.

--Antioxidants & Stabilizers for Polymers. (Ser. 3-75). 1976. 120.00 (ISBN 0-914428-34-9). Lexington Data.

--Free Radical Initiators: 1953-1970, Ser. 1B. Incl. Indexes Plus Abstracts & a Survey of the U.S. Market. 247p. 575.00 (ISBN 0-914428-00-4). 1971. Lexington Data Inc.

Culbertson, Bill M. & Pittman, C. U., Jr., eds. New Monomers & Polymers. 450p. 1983. 59.50x (ISBN 0-306-41477-5, Plenum Pr). Plenum Pub.

Davidson, Theodore, ed. Polymers in Electronics. LC 83-25782. (ACS Symposium Ser.: No. 242). 605p. 1984. lib. bdg. 79.95x (ISBN 0-8412-0823-9). Am Chemical.

Davis, A. & Sims, D. Weathering of Polymers. (Illus.). 300p. 1983. 64.75 (ISBN 0-85334-226-1, I-266-83, Pub. by Elsevier Applied Sci England). Elsevier.

Dawkins, J. V., ed. Developments in Polymer Characterization, 4 vols. (Illus.). Vol. 1, 1978. 44.50 (ISBN 0-85334-789-1, Pub. by Elsevier Applied Sci England); Vol. 2, 1980. 53.75 (ISBN 0-85334-909-6); Vol. 3, 1982. 61.00 (ISBN 0-85334-119-2); Vol. 4, 1983. 61.00 (ISBN 0-85334-180-X). Elsevier.

Dawydoff, W. Technical Dictionary of High Polymers: English, French, German, Russian. 1969. 145.00 (ISBN 0-08-013112-3). Pergamon.

De Gennes, Pierre-Gilles. Scaling Concepts in Polymer Physics. LC 78-21314. 319p. 1979. 59.50x (ISBN 0-8014-1203-X). Cornell U Pr.

Dictionary of High Polymer Macromolecule. (Eng. & Chinese.). 54p. 1974. pap. 1.95 (ISBN 0-686-92619-6). French & Eur.

Diehl, P., et al, eds. Natural & Synthetic High Polymers: Lectures Presented at the 7th Colloquium on NMR Spectroscopy. LC 70-94160. (NMR, Basic Principles & Progress: Vol. 4). (Illus.). 1971. 46.10 (ISBN 0-387-05221-6). Springer-Verlag.

Dragutan, A. T., et al. Olefin Metathesis & Ring-Opening Polymerization of Cyclo-Olefins. 400p. 1985. text ed. 64.95 (ISBN 0-471-90267-5, Pub. by Wiley-Interscience). Wiley.

Drobnik, J., et al. Polymers in Medicine. (Advances in Polymer Science Ser.: Vol. 57). (Illus.). 190p. 1984. 44.00 (ISBN 0-387-12796-8). Springer-Verlag.

Dusek, K., ed. Polymer Networks. (Advances in Polymer Science Ser.: Vol. 44). (Illus.). 164p. 1982. 47.00 (ISBN 0-387-11471-8). Springer-Verlag.

Dusek, K., et al, eds. Key Polymers. (Advanced in Polymer Science Ser.: Vol. 70). (Illus.). 240p. 1985. 46.50 (ISBN 0-387-15481-7). Springer-Verlag.

Dwight, David W., et al, eds. Photon, Electron, & Ion Probes of Polymer Structure & Properties. LC 81-10816. (ACS Symposium Ser.: No. 162). 1981. 44.95 (ISBN 0-8412-0639-2). Am Chemical.

Elias. Polymerization of Organized Systems. (Midland Macromolecular Monographs). 240p. 1977. 62.50 (ISBN 0-677-15930-7). Gordon.

Elias, H. G., ed. New Commercial Polymers 1969-1975. 226p. 1977. 32.50 (ISBN 0-677-30950-3). Gordon.

Elias, Hans-Georg & Pethrick, Richard A., eds. Polymer Yearbook. 338p. 1983. 25.00 (ISBN 3-7186-0177-X); pap. 12.00 (ISBN 3-7186-0178-8). Harwood Academic.

Eliseeva, V. I., et al. Emulsion Polymerization & Its Applications in Industry. Teague, Sylvia J., tr. from Rus. LC 81-17477. Orig. Title: Emul'Sionnaya Polimerizatsiya I EE Primenenie V Promyshlenosti. 300p. 1981. 59.50 (ISBN 0-306-10961-1, Consultants). Plenum Pub.

Engel, Lothar, et al. An Atlas of Polymer Damage. (Illus.). 1981. reference 50.00 (ISBN 0-13-050013-5). P-H.

Epton, Roger, ed. Chromatography of Synthetic & Biological Polymers: Column Packings, GPC, GF & Gradient Elution, Vol. 1. LC 77-30672. 368p. 1978. 68.95x (ISBN 0-470-99379-0). Halsted Pr.

--Chromatography of Synthetic & Biological Polymers: Hydrophobic, Ion-Exchange & Affinity Methods, Vol. 2. LC 77-40142. 353p. 1978. 79.95 (ISBN 0-470-26366-0). Halsted Pr.

Erickson, J. L., ed. Orienting Polymers: Proceedings of a Workshop Held at the IMA, University of Minnesota, Minneapolis, March 21-26, 1983. (Lecture Notes in Mathematics Ser.: Vol. 1063). vii, 166p. 1984. pap. 12.00 (ISBN 0-387-13340-2). Springer-Verlag.

Failure in Polymers: Molecular Phenomenological Aspects. (Advances in Polymer Science Ser.: Vol. 27). (Illus.). 1978. 47.00 (ISBN 0-387-08829-6). Springer-Verlag.

Feit, Eugene D. & Wilkins, Cletus, Jr., eds. Polymer Materials for Electronic Applcations. LC 82-1670. (ACS Symposium Ser.: No. 184). 1982. 44.95 (ISBN 0-8412-0715-1). Am Chemical.

Fendler, Janos H. & Fendler, Eleanor J. Catalysis in Micellar & Macromolecular Systems. 1975. 91.50 (ISBN 0-12-252850-6). Acad Pr.

Fenner, R. T. Principles of Polymer Processing. 1980. 35.00 (ISBN 0-8206-0285-X). Chem Pub.

Ferry, John D. Viscoelastic Properties of Polymers. 3rd ed. LC 79-2866. 641p. 1980. 64.50x (ISBN 0-471-04894-1, Pub. by Wiley-Interscience). Wiley.

Feters, L. J., et al. Anionic Polymerization. (Advances in Polymer Science Ser.: Vol.56). (Illus.). 1984. 40.00 (ISBN 0-387-12792-5). Springer-Verlag.

Finch, C. A., ed. Chemistry & Technology of Water-Solutable Polymers. 372p. 1983. 59.50x (ISBN 0-306-41251-9, Plenum Pr). Plenum Pub.

Fitch, Robert M., ed. Polymer Colloids, I. LC 70-153721. 187p. 1971. 39.50 (ISBN 0-306-30536-4, Plenum Pr). Plenum Pub.

--Polymer Colloids, II. LC 80-112. 695p. 1980. 95.00 (ISBN 0-306-40350-1, Plenum Pr). Plenum Pub.

Flory, Paul J. Principles of Polymer Chemistry. (Illus.). 688p. 1953. 44.50x (ISBN 0-8014-0134-8). Cornell U Pr.

Frazer, August H. High Temperature Resistant Polymers. LC 68-21491. pap. 88.00 (ISBN 0-317-09197-2, 2006348). Bks Demand UMI.

Frisch, K. C. & Reegen, S. L., eds. Ring-Opening Polymerization. (Kinetics & Mechanisms of Polymerization Ser: Vol. 2). 1969. 95.00 (ISBN 0-8247-1217-X). Dekker.

Gandini, A. & Cheradame, H. Cationic Polymerization. (Advances in Polymer Science Ser.: Vol. 34, 35). (Illus.). 360p. 1980. 87.00 (ISBN 0-387-10049-0). Springer-Verlag.

Gaylord, Norman. High Polymers Series, Vol. 13, Pt. 3. LC 62-15824. 318p. 1962. 32.00 (ISBN 0-686-81269-7). Krieger.

Gebelein, Charles G., ed. Polymeric Materials & Artificial Organs. LC 84-9297. (ACS Symposium Ser.: No. 256). 208p. 1984. lib. bdg. 36.95x (ISBN 0-8412-0854-9). Am Chemical.

Gebelein, Charles G. & Carraher, Charles E., Jr., eds. Bioactive Polymeric Systems: An Overview. 675p. 1985. 95.00x (ISBN 0-306-41855-X, Plenum Pr). Plenum Pub.

Gebelein, Charles G. & Koblitz, Frank K., eds. Biomedical & Dental Applications of Polymers. LC 80-29429. (Polymer Science & Technology Ser.: Vol. 14). 504p. 1981. 75.00x (ISBN 0-306-40632-2, Plenum Pr). Plenum Pub.

Gebelein, Charles G. & Williams, David J., eds. Polymers in Solar Energy Utilization. LC 83-6367. (Symposium Ser.: No. 220). 519p. 1983. lib. bdg. 59.95 (ISBN 0-8412-0776-3). Am Chemical.

Geil, Philip H. Polymer Single Crystals. LC 63-19663. (Polymer Reviews Ser: Vol. 5). 572p. 1973. Repr. of 1963 ed. text ed. 34.50 (ISBN 0-88275-088-7). Krieger.

Gibson, A. E. Processing of Polymer Composite Materials. 1986. price not set (ISBN 0-08-027617-2); pap. price not set (ISBN 0-08-027616-4). Pergamon.

Gingold, Kurt, tr. from Rus. Soviet Urethane Technology, Vol. 1. (Soviet Progress in Polyurethanes Ser.). Orig. Title: Intez I Fiziko-Khimiia Polimerov, No. 7. (Illus., Orig.). 1972. pap. 19.00 (ISBN 0-87762-069-5). Technomic.

Goddard, E. D. & Vincent, B., eds. Polymer Adsorption & Dispersion Stability. LC 83-25787. (ACS Symposium Ser.: No. 240). 477p. 1984. lib. bdg. 79.95 (ISBN 0-8412-0820-4). Am Chemical.

Goethals, Eric J., ed. Cabonic Polymerization & Related Processes. 1984. 35.00 (ISBN 0-12-287470-6). Acad Pr.

Goldberg, E. P. & Nakajima, A. Biomedical Polymers: Polymeric Materials & Pharmaceuticals for Biomedical Use. LC 80-17691. 1980. 43.50 (ISBN 0-12-287580-X). Acad Pr.

Gordon, M., ed. Liquid Crystal Polymers I. (Advances in Polymer Science, Fortschritte der Hochpolymerenforschung: Vol. 59). (Illus.). 180p. 1984. 41.00 (ISBN 0-387-12818-2). Springer Verlag.

Gordon, M. & Plate, N. A., eds. Liquid Crystal Polymers II-III. (Advances in Polymer Science Ser.: Vol. 60-61). (Illus.). 1984. 54.00 (ISBN 0-387-12994-4). Springer-Verlag.

Grassie, N., ed. Developments in Polymer Degradation, Vol. 3. (Illus.). 319p. 1981. 72.25 (ISBN 0-85334-942-8, Pub. by Elsevier Applied Sci England). Elsevier.

--Developments in Polymer Degradation, Vol. 5. 240p. 1984. 52.00 (ISBN 0-85334-238-5, Pub. by Elsevier Applied Sci England). Elsevier.

--Developments in Polymer Degradation, Vol. 6. 256p. 1985. 54.00 (ISBN 0-85334-337-3, Pub. by Elsevier Applied Sci England). Elsevier.

Grassie, Norman & Scott, Gerald. Polymer Degradation & Stabilization. (Illus.). 200p. 1985. 54.50 (ISBN 0-521-24961-9). Cambridge U Pr.

Greene, Francis T., et al, eds. Quality Assurance of Polymeric Materials & Products: STP 846. LC 83-73514. (Illus.). 145p. 1985. pap. text ed. 24.00 (ISBN 0-8031-0408-1, 04-846000-19). ASTM.

Guillet, James. Polymer Photophysics & Photochemistry: An Introduction to the Study of Photoprocesses in Macromolecules. 391p. 1985. 79.50 (ISBN 0-521-23506-5). Cambridge U Pr.

Hall, C. Polymer Materials. (Illus.). 198p. 1981. 38.00 (ISBN 0-686-48129-1, 0805). T-C Pubns CA.

Hall, I. H., ed. Structures of Crystalline Polymers. 312p. 1984. 64.75 (ISBN 0-85334-236-9, I-523-83, Pub. by Elsevier Applied Sci England). Elsevier.

Ham, G. E., ed. Vinyl Polymerization. (Kinetics & Mechanisms of Polymerization Ser.: Vol. 1, Pts. 1 & 2). 992p. Pt. 1, 1967. 99.75 (ISBN 0-8247-1292-7); Pt. 2, 1969. 99.75 (ISBN 0-8247-1294-3). Dekker.

Han, Paul C. D. Polymer Blends & Composites in Multiphase Systems. LC 83-24362. (Advances in Chemistry Ser.: No. 206). 383p. 1984. lib. bdg. 59.95x (ISBN 0-8412-0783-6). Am Chemical.

Harris, F. W. & Seymour, R. B., eds. Structure-Solubility Relationships in Polymers. 1977. 39.00 (ISBN 0-12-327450-8). Acad Pr.

Haward, R. N., ed. Physics of Glassy Polymers. (Illus.). 620p. 1973. 87.00 (ISBN 0-85334-565-1, Pub. by Elsevier Applied Sci England). Elsevier.

Hawkins, W. L. Polymer Degradation & Stabilization. (Polymers, Properties & Applications Ser.: Vol. 8). (Illus.). 150p. 1984. 40.00 (ISBN 0-387-12851-4). Springer-Verlag.

Hawkins, W. Lincoln, ed. Polymer Stabilization. LC 70-154324. 452p. 1971. 79.50 (ISBN 0-471-36300-6, Pub. by Wiley-Interscience). Wiley.

Hearle, J. S. Polymers & Their Properties: Fundamentals of Structured Mechanics, Vol. 1. 385p. 1982. 104.95 (ISBN 0-470-27302-X). Halsted Pr.

Hebeisch, A. & Guthrie, J. T. The Chemistry & Technology of Cellulose Copolymers. (Polymers - Properties & Applications Ser.: Vol. 4). (Illus.). 340p. 1981. 89.50 (ISBN 0-387-10164-0). Springer-Verlag.

Hemsley, Derek. The Light Microscopy of Synthetic Polymers. (Royal Microscopical Society Microscopy Handbooks Ser.). (Illus.). 1984. pap. 9.95x (ISBN 0-19-856404-X). Oxford U Pr.

Henderson, J. Neil & Bouton, Thomas, eds. Polymerization Reactors & Processes. LC 79-12519. (ACS Symposium Ser.: No. 104). 1979. 34.95 (ISBN 0-8412-0506-X). Am Chemical.

Henrici-Olive, G., et al. Advances in Polymer Science, Vol. 15. Cantow, H. J., ed. LC 61-642. (Illus.). iii, 155p. 1974. 44.90 (ISBN 0-387-06910-0). Springer-Verlag.

High Polymers, Vols. 21-29. 2nd ed. Incl. Vol. 21. Macromolecules in Solution. Morawetz, H., ed. LC 74-26655. 495p. 1975; Vol. 22. Conformation of Macromolecules. Birshstein, T. & Ptitsyn, O., eds. LC 65-26217. 350p. 1966. o.p. (ISBN 0-470-39325-4); Vol. 23. Polymer Chemistry of Synthetic Elastomers. Kennedy, J. P. & Tornquist, E. G., eds. LC 67-13948. 1968-69. Pt.2. 49.50 (ISBN 0-470-39327-0); Vol. 24. Vinyl & Diene Monomers. Leonard, E. C., ed. LC 77-94013. 1970; Vol. 25. Fluoropolymers. Wall, L. A., ed. LC 74-165023. 550p. 1972; Vol. 26. Cyclic Monomers. Frisch, K. C., ed. LC 73-174769. 782p. 1972; Vol. 27. Condensation Monomers. Stille, J. K. & Campbell, T. W., eds. LC 72-1260. 745p. 1972; Vol. 28. Allyl Compounds & Their Polymers. Schildknecht, C. E., ed. LC 72-1363. 1973; Vol. 29. Polymerization Processes. Schildkhecht, C. E., ed. 1977. 76.95 (ISBN 0-471-39381-9). Pub. by Wiley-Interscience). Wiley.

Hilado, Carlos J., ed. Pyrolysis of Polymers, Vol. 13. LC 73-82115. (Fire & Flammability Ser.). (Illus.). 1976. pap. 9.95x (ISBN 0-87762-173-X). Technomic.

Hiltner, Anne, ed. Structure-Property Relationships of Polymeric Solids. 278p. 1983. 42.50x (ISBN 0-306-41461-9, Plenum Pr). Plenum Pub.

Hodge, P. & Sherrington, D. C. Polymer-Supported Reactions in Organic Synthesis. 484p. 1980. 106.95 (ISBN 0-471-27712-6). Wiley.

Hoffmann, M., et al. Polymer Analytics. Stahlberg, H., tr. from Ger. (MMI Press Polymer Monographs: Vol. 3). Date not set. price not set (ISBN 3-7186-0024-2). Harwood Academic.

Holmes-Walker, W. A. Polymer Conversion. (Illus.). 286p. 1975. 42.75 (ISBN 0-85334-604-6, Pub. by Elsevier Applied Sci England). Elsevier.

Horer, O. The Structure of Biopolymers. 1974. 27.00 (ISBN 0-9961003-4-2, Pub. by Abacus England). Heyden.

Hugard, Jean. Encyclopedia of Card Tricks. LC 74-82200. (Illus.). 416p. 1974. pap. 6.95 (ISBN 0-486-21252-1). Dover.

Hummel, Deter O., ed. Proceedings of the European Symposium on Polymer Chemistry. 5th ed. (Illus.). 343p. 1979. pap. 51.80x (ISBN 0-89573-002-2). VCH Pubs.

Hummel, Dieter O. Polymer Spectroscopy. LC 73-90783. (Monographs in Modern Chemistry: Vol. 6). (Illus.). 401p. 1974. 96.90x (ISBN 3-527-25411-0). VCH Pubs.

IFAC Conference, 4th, Ghent, Belgium, June 1980. Instrumentation & Automation in the Paper, Rubber, Plastics & Polymerisation Industries: Proceedings. Van Cauwenberghe, A., ed. LC 80-41889. (IFAC Proceedings Ser.). (Illus.). 550p. 1981. 130.00 (ISBN 0-08-024487-4). Pergamon.

Imahori, K. & Higashimura, T., eds. Progress in Polymer Science, Japan, Vol. 8. LC 72-7446. 244p. 1975. 49.95x (ISBN 0-470-65727-8). Halsted Pr.

Imoto, M., et al. Progress in Polymer Science, Japan, 6 vols. 1974. Set. 133.95x (ISBN 0-470-42692-6). Halsted Pr.

Industrial Developments. (Advances in Polymer Science Ser.: Vol. 51). (Illus.). 230p. 1983. 49.00 (ISBN 0-387-12189-7). Springer-Verlag.

The Infrared Spectra Atlas of Monomers & Polymers. 1981. 295.00 (ISBN 0-8456-0064-8). Sadtler Res.

Inorganic Polymers. 84p. 1982. 78.00 (ISBN 0-317-12683-0, L527). T-C Pubns CA.

Ise, Norio & Tabushi, Iwao, eds. An Introduction to Speciality Polymers. LC 82-22012. (Illus.). 200p. 1983. 44.50 (ISBN 0-521-24536-2). Cambridge U Pr.

Ivin, K. J. Ring-Opening Polymerization, Vols. 1-3. 1984. Set. 277.75 (ISBN 0-85334-211-3, I-220-84). Elsevier.

Ivin, K. J. & Saegusa, T., eds. Ring-Opening Polymerization, Vols. 1-3. 1260p. 1984. Set. 225.00 (ISBN 0-85334-237-7, Pub. by Elsevier Applied Sci England). Elsevier.

Janeschitz-Kriegl, H. Polymer Melt Rheology & Flow Birefringence. (Polymers-Properties & Applications Ser.: Vol. 6). (Illus.). 524p. 1983. 43.00 (ISBN 0-387-11928-0). Springer-Verlag.

Jellinek, H. H., ed. Water Structure at the Water-Polymer Interface. LC 70-189943. 182p. 1972. 39.50x (ISBN 0-306-30589-5, Plenum Pr). Plenum Pub.

Jellink, H. H. Aspects of Degradation & Stabilization of Polymers. 690p. 1978. 149.00 (ISBN 0-444-41563-7). Elsevier.

Jenkins, A. D., ed. Progress in Polymer Science, Vol. 9. (Illus.). 380p. 1984. 132.00 (ISBN 0-08-031734-0). Pergamon.

Jenkins, A. D. & Ledwith, A., eds. Reactivity, Mechanism, & Structure in Polymer Chemistry. LC 73-2786. pap. 157.80 (ISBN 0-317-29339-7, 2024030). Bks Demand UMI.

Jenkins, A. D. & Stannett, V. T., eds. Progress in Polymer Science, Vol. 8. (Illus.). 490p. 1983. 114.00 (ISBN 0-08-031007-9). Pergamon.

--Progress in Polymer Science, Vol. 10. (Illus.). 364p. 1985. 132.00 (ISBN 0-08-032721-4, Pub. by Aberdeen Scotland). Pergamon.

Jenkins, Gwyn M. & Kawamura, K. Polymeric Carbons: Carbon Fibre, Glass & Char. LC 74-16995. pap. 46.50 (ISBN 0-317-29379-6, 2024480). Bks Demand UMI.

Jenkins, R., et al. Properties of Polymers. (Advances in Polymer Sciences: Vol. 36). (Illus.). 150p. 1980. 45.00 (ISBN 0-387-10204-3). Springer-Verlag.

Jones, D. W., ed. Introduction to the Spectroscopy of Biological Polymers. 1977. 59.50 (ISBN 0-12-389250-3). Acad Pr.

Katon, J. E., ed. Organic Semiconducting Polymers. LC 68-54854. (Monographs in Macromolecular Chemistry: Vol. 1). Repr. of 1968 ed. 81.30 (ISBN 0-8357-9089-4, 2055044). Bks Demand UMI.

Kaufman, H. S., ed. Polymeric Materials Special Topics: Vol. 1 Elastomers in Medicine. 75.25 (ISBN 0-677-40055-1). Gordon.

Kaufman, Herman S. & Falcetta, Joseph J., eds. Introduction to Polymer Science & Technology: An SPE Textbook. LC 76-16838. (Society of Plastics Engineers Ser.). 613p. 1977. 39.50x (ISBN 0-471-01493-1, Pub. by Wiley-Interscience). Wiley.

Kausch, E. E., ed. Crazing in Polymers. (Advances in Polymer Science: Vol. 52-53). (Illus.). 390p. 1983. 61.50 (ISBN 0-387-12571-X). Springer-Verlag.

Kausch, H. H. & Zachmann, H. G., eds. Characterization of Polymers in the Solid State II. (Advances in Polymer Science Ser.: Vol. 67). (Illus.). vi, 389p. 1985. 45.00 (ISBN 0-387-13780-7). Springer-Verlag.

--Characterization of the Polymers in the Solid State I. (Advances in Polymer Science Ser.: Vol. 66). (Illus.). 240p. 1985. 45.00 (ISBN 0-387-13779-3). Springer-Verlag.

Kausch, H. Henning, et al, eds. Deformation & Fracture of High Polymers. LC 73-19857. 644p. 1973. 69.50x (ISBN 0-306-30772-3, Plenum Pr). Plenum Pub.

Ke, Bacon, ed. Newer Methods of Polymer Characterization. LC 64-13218. 722p. 1964. text ed. 38.50 (ISBN 0-470-46215-9, Pub. by Wiley). Krieger.

Kelen, Tibor. Polymer Degradation. 224p. 1982. 41.50 (ISBN 0-442-24837-7). Van Nos Reinhold.

Kennedy, J. P., et al. Mechanisms of Polyreactions - Polymer Characterization. (Advances in Polymer Science Ser.: Vol. 21). (Illus.). 1976. 40.00 (ISBN 0-387-07727-8). Springer-Verlag.

Kennedy, Joseph P. & Marechal, Ernest. Carbocationic Polymerization. LC 80-26366. 510p. 1982. 95.50x (ISBN 0-471-01787-6, Pub. by Wiley-Interscience). Wiley.

Kesting, Robert E. Synthesis Polymeric Membrane: A Structural Perspective. 2nd ed. 464p. 1985. 45.00 (ISBN 0-471-80717-6). Wiley.

Kinloch, A. J. & Young, R. J., eds. Fracture Behaviour of Polymers. (Illus.). 471p. 1983. 92.50 (ISBN 0-85334-186-9, I-125-83, Pub. by Elsevier Applied Sci England). Elsevier.

Kirshenbaum, Gerald S. Polymer Science Study Guide. LC 73-80661. 146p. (Orig.). 1973. pap. 26.50 (ISBN 0-677-04515-8). Gordon.

Kissin, Y. V. Isospecific Polymerization of Olefins. (Polymers, Properties & Applications Ser.: Vol. 9). (Illus.). 450p. 1985. 131.00 (ISBN 0-387-96105-4). Springer-Verlag.

Klemper, D. & Frisch, K. C., eds. Polymer Alloys I: Blends, Grafts, & Interpenetrating Networks. LC 77-21559. (Polymer Science & Technology Ser.: Vol. 10). 501p. 1977. 75.00 (ISBN 0-306-36410-7, Plenum Pr). Plenum Pub.

Klempner, D. & Frisch, K. C., eds. Polymer Alloys II: Blends, Blocks, Grafts, & Interpenetrating Networks. LC 79-28487. (Polymer Science & Technology Ser.: Vol. 11). 290p. 1980. 49.50 (ISBN 0-306-40346-3, Plenum Pr). Plenum Pub.

Klempner, Daniel & Frisch, Kurt C., eds. Polymer Alloys III: Blends, Blocks, Grafts, & Interpenetrating Networks. 312p. 1983. 49.50 (ISBN 0-306-41138-5, Plenum Pr). Plenum Pub.

Kline, Donald E. Properties & Processing of Polymers for Engineers. (Illus.). 240p. 1984. 37.95 (ISBN 0-13-731125-7). P-H.

Klopffer, W. Introduction to Polymer Spectroscopy. (Polymers-Properties & Application: Vol. 7). (Illus.). 210p. 1984. 40.00 (ISBN 0-387-12850-6). Springer-Verlag.

Koenig, Jack L. Chemical Microstructure of Polymer Chains. LC 80-15165. 414p. 1980. 63.50x (ISBN 0-471-07725-9, Pub. by Wiley Interscience). Wiley.

Kostelnik, R. J. Polymeric Delivery Systems. (Midland Macromolecular Monographs). 322p. 1978. 62.75 (ISBN 0-677-15940-4). Gordon.

Kresta, J. E., ed. Polymer Additives. (Polymer Science & Technology Ser.: Vol. 26). 418p. 1984. 72.50x (ISBN 0-306-41807-X, Plenum Pr). Plenum Pub.

Kresta, Jiri E. Reaction Injection Molding & Fast Polymerization Reactions. LC 82-12389. (Polymer Science & Technology Ser.: Vol. 18). 310p. 1982. 49.50x (ISBN 0-306-41120-2, Plenum Pr). Plenum Pub.

Kryszewski, Marian, et al, eds. Polymer Blends, Vol. 2: Processing, Morphology & Properties. 298p. 1984. 52.50x (ISBN 0-306-41802-9, Plenum Pr). Plenum Pub.

Kukacka, Lawrence E., ed. Applications of Polymer Concrete. LC 81-67492. (SP-69). 228p. (Orig.). 1981. pap. 41.95 (ISBN 0-686-95240-5). ACI.

Kurata, Michio. Thermodynamics of Polymer Solutions. Fujita, Hiroshi, tr. from Jap. (MMI Press Polymer Monographs: Vol. 1). 306p. 1982. 94.00 (ISBN 3-7186-0023-4). Harwood Academic.

Kuryla, W. C. & Pappa, A. J. Flame Retardancy of Polymeric Materials, Vol. 5. 1979. 65.00 (ISBN 0-8247-6778-0). Dekker.

Kuryla, W. C. & Papa, A. J., eds. Flame Retardancy of Polymeric Materials, Vol. 4. 1978. 65.00 (ISBN 0-8247-6747-0). Dekker.

Labana, ed. Chemistry & Properties of Crosslinked Polymers. 1977. 70.00 (ISBN 0-12-432250-6). Acad Pr.

Labana, S. S. & Dickie, R. A., eds. Characterization of Highly Cross-Linked Polymers. LC 83-25733. (ACS Symposium Ser.: No. 243). 321p. 1984. lib. bdg. 44.95 (ISBN 0-8412-0824-7). Am Chemical.

Ladik, Janos & Andre, Jean-Marie, eds. Quantum Chemistry of Polymers: Solid State Aspects. LC 84-3367. 1984. lib. bdg. 59.00 (ISBN 90-277-1741-9, Pub. by Reidel Holland). Kluwer Academic.

Ledwith, A. & North, A. M., eds. Molecular Behavior & the Development of Polymer Materials. 1975. 65.00x (ISBN 0-412-12400-9, NO. 6175, Pub. by Chapman & Hall). Methuen Inc.

Lee, L. H., ed. Adhesion & Adsorption of Polymers, 2 vols. Incl. Pt. A. 504p. 69.50 (ISBN 0-306-40427-3); Pt. B. 458p. 65.00 (ISBN 0-306-40428-1). LC 80-262. (Polymer Science & Technology Ser.: Vols. 12A & B). 1980 (Plenum Pr). Set. 115.00 (ISBN 0-686-65857-4). Plenum Pub.

Lee, Lieng-Huang, ed. Advances in Polymer Friction & Wear. Incl. Pt. A. 437p (ISBN 0-306-36491-3); Pt. B. 442p (ISBN 0-306-36492-1). LC 74-17059. (Polymer Science & Technology Ser.: Vols. 5A & 5B). 1974. 65.00 ea. (Plenum Pr). Plenum Pub.

Lefkowitz, et al. International Symposium on Phase Transitions in Polymers: Proceedings, Ohio, 1980. 326p. 1980. pap. 250.75x (ISBN 0-677-40325-9). Gordon.

Lenk, R. S. Polymer Rheology. (Illus.). 375p. 1978. 68.50 (ISBN 0-85334-765-4, Pub. by Elsevier Applied Sci England). Elsevier.

Lenz, R. W. & Ciardelli, I., eds. Advances in the Preparation & Properties of Stereo-Regular Polymers. (Nato Advanced Study Institutes Series C: Mathematical & Physical Sciences: No. 51). 1980. lib. bdg. 44.00 (ISBN 90-277-1055-4, Pub. by Rediel Holland). Kluwer Academic.

Lenz, R. W. & Stein, R. S., eds. Structure & Properties of Polymer Films. LC 72-88422. (Polymer Science & Technology Ser.: Vol. 1). 355p. 1973. 52.50x (ISBN 0-306-36401-8, Plenum Pr). Plenum Pub.

Lenz, Robert W. Organic Chemistry of Synthetic High Polymers. LC 66-22057. 837p. 1967. 54.95X (ISBN 0-470-52630-0, Pub. by Wiley-Interscience). Wiley.

Lewin, Menachem & Atlas, S. M. Flame-Retardant Polymeric Materials, Vol. 3. LC 75-26781. 284p. 1982. 42.50x (ISBN 0-306-40868-6, Plenum Pr). Plenum Pub.

Lewin, Menachem, et al, eds. Flame-Retardant Polymeric Materials, Vol. 2. LC 75-26781. (Illus.). 345p. 1978. 59.50x (ISBN 0-306-32212-9, Plenum Pr). Plenum Pub.

Lewis, O. Physical Constants of Linear Homopolymers. (Chemie, Physik and Technologie der Kunstoffe in Einzeldarstellungen: Vol. 12). 1968. 38.50 (ISBN 0-387-04064-1). Springer-Verlag.

Lowry, George G., ed. Markov Chains & Monto Carlo Calculations in Polymer Science. LC 70-84777. (Monographs in Macromolecular Chemistry). pap. 84.50 (ISBN 0-317-08367-8, 2055048). Bks Demand UMI.

McGrath, James E., ed. Anionic Polymerization. LC 81-14911. (ACS Symposium Ser: No. 166). 1981. for info. 57.95rite (ISBN 0-8412-0643-0). Am Chemical.

MacGregor, A. & Greenwood, C. T. Polymers in Nature. LC 79-41787. 391p. 1980. 74.95 (ISBN 0-471-27762-2, Pub. by Wiley-Interscience); pap. write for info. (ISBN 0-471-27794-0). Wiley.

McIntyre, Donald & Gornick, F., eds. Light-Scattering from Dilute Polymer Solutions. (International Science Review Ser.). (Illus.). 332p. 1964. 62.50 (ISBN 0-677-00510-5). Gordon.

McKellar, J. F. & Allen, N. S. Photochemistry of Man Made Polymers. (Illus.). 306p. 1975. 55.50 (ISBN 0-85334-799-9, Pub. by Elsevier Applied Sci England). Elsevier.

Madorsky, S. L. Thermal Degradation of Organic Polymers. LC 74-32347. (Polymer Reviews Ser: Vol. 7). 330p. 1975. Repr. of 1964 ed. 19.50 (ISBN 0-88275-265-0). Krieger.

Manson, John A. & Sperling, Leslie H. Polymer Blends & Composites. LC 75-28174. (Illus.). 513p. 1976. 75.00x (ISBN 0-306-30831-2, Plenum Pr). Plenum Pub.

March, Norman & Tosi, Mario, eds. Polymers, Liquid Crystals & Low-Dimensional Solids. (Physics of Solids & Liquids Ser.). 622p. 1984. 89.50x (ISBN 0-306-41641-7, Plenum Pr). Plenum Pub.

Mark, Herman F., et al, eds. Encyclopedia of Polymer Science & Engineering. 2nd ed. Incl. Vol. 1. A to Amorphous Polymers. 843p (ISBN 0-471-89540-7); Vol. 2. Anionic Polymerization to Cationic Polymerization. 904p (ISBN 0-471-88786-2); Vol. 3. Cellular Materials to Cold Forming (ISBN 0-471-88789-7); Vol. 4. Collagen to Defects (ISBN 0-471-88099-X); Vol. 5. Degradation to Electrical Properties (ISBN 0-471-88098-1). 1985. 200.00x ea. (Pub. by Wiley-Interscience); Set. 3500.00 (ISBN 0-471-86519-2). Wiley.

Marton, L. & Fava, R. A., eds. Methods of Experimental Physics: Polymers Molecular Structure & Dynamics, Vol. 16A. (Crystal structure & morphology pt. 16b). 1980. Pt. A. 70.00 (ISBN 0-12-475916-5); Pt. B. 60.00 (ISBN 0-12-475957-2). Acad Pr.

Martuscelli, Ezio, et al, eds. Polymer Blends: Processing, Morphology & Properties. LC 80-22862. 522p. 1981. 75.00 (ISBN 0-306-40578-4, Plenum Pr). Plenum Pub.

Mathias, Lon J. & Carraher, Charles E., Jr., eds. Crown Ethers & Phase Transfer Catalysis in Polymer Science. (Polymer Science & Technology Ser.: Vol. 24). 436p. 1984. 59.50x (ISBN 0-306-41462-7, Plenum Pr). Plenum Pub.

Mathur, N. K., et al. Polymers As Aids in Organic Chemistry. LC 79-52789. 1980. 37.50 (ISBN 0-12-479850-0). Acad Pr.

Matthews, G. A. Polymer Mixing Technology. (Illus.). 280p. 1982. 50.00 (ISBN 0-85334-133-8, Pub. by Elsevier Applied Sci England). Elsevier.

Meltzer, Yale L. Water-Soluble Polymers: Developments since 1978. LC 80-26174. (Chemical Technology Review Ser.: 181). (Illus.). 608p. 1981. 54.00 (ISBN 0-8155-0834-4). Noyes.

Mengoli, G., et al. Electronic Phenomena in Polymer Science. (Advances in Polymer Science Ser.: Vol. 33). (Illus.). 1979. 56.00 (ISBN 0-387-09456-3). Springer-Verlag.

Middleman, Stanley. Flow of High Polymers: Continuum & Molecular Rheology. LC 67-29460. 246p. 1968. 39.50x (ISBN 0-470-60235-X, Pub. by Wiley-Interscience). Wiley.

--Fundamentals of Polymer Processing. 1977. text ed. 45.00 (ISBN 0-07-041851-9). McGraw.

Millich, Frank & Carraher, Charles E. Interfacial Synthesis: Vol. 1, Fundamentals. 1977. 85.00 (ISBN 0-8247-6372-6). Dekker.

Mittal, K. L., ed. Adhesion Aspects of Polymeric Coatings. 670p. 1983. 85.00x (ISBN 0-306-41250-0, Plenum Pr). Plenum Pub.

--Physiochemical Aspects of Polymer Surfaces, Vol. 1. 610p. 1983. 85.00 (ISBN 0-306-41189-X, Plenum Pr). Plenum Pub.

--Physiochemical Aspects of Polymer Surfaces, Vol. 2. 652p. 1983. 89.50 (ISBN 0-306-41190-3, Plenum Pr). Plenum Pub.

Molau, Gunther E., ed. Colloidal & Morphological Behavior of Block & Graft Copolymers. LC 72-148414. 327p. 1971. 42.50x (ISBN 0-306-30527-5, Plenum Pr). Plenum Pub.

Moore, J. A., ed. Macromolecular Syntheses Collective, Vol. 1. LC 63-18627. (Macromolecular Syntheses Ser.). 710p. 1977. 56.95 (ISBN 0-471-61451-3, Pub by Wiley-Interscience). Wiley.

Morawetz, Herbert. Macromolecules in Solution. 2ND ed. LC 83-11991. (High Polymers Ser.: Vol. 21). 1983. Repr. of 1975 ed. text ed. 46.00 (ISBN 0-89874-659-0). Krieger.

--Polymers: The Origins & Growth of a Science. 320p. 1985. 47.50 (ISBN 0-471-89638-1). Wiley.

Mort, J. Electronic Properties of Polymers. Pfister, G., ed. LC 82-2814. 336p. 1982. 51.95x (ISBN 0-471-07696-1, Pub. by Wiley-Interscience). Wiley.

Morton, Maurice, ed. Anionic Polymerization. LC 82-11627. 268p. 1983. 44.00 (ISBN 0-12-508080-8). Acad Pr.

Murakami, K. & Ono, K. Chemorheology of Polymers. (Polymer Science Library: Vol. 1). 216p. 1980. 51.00 (ISBN 0-444-41831-8). Elsevier.

Neiman, M. B. Aging & Stabilization of Polymers. LC 64-23249. 1965. 45.00x (ISBN 0-306-10699-X, Consultants). Plenum Pub.

Nielsen, L. E. Mechanical Properties of Polymers & Composites, Vol. 1. 272p. 1974. 69.75 (ISBN 0-8247-6183-9). Dekker.

Nielsen, Lawrence E. Mechanical Properties of Polymers & Composites, Vol. 2. 320p. 1974. pap. 69.75 (ISBN 0-8247-7210-5). Dekker.

Noshay, Allen & McGrath, James E. Block Polymers. 1977. 69.00 (ISBN 0-12-521750-1). Acad Pr.

O'Konski, Chester, ed. Molecular Electro-Optics, Pt. 2. (Electro-Optics Ser.: Vol. 1). 1978. 85.00 (ISBN 0-8247-6402-1). Dekker.

--Molecular Electro-Optics: Theory & Method, Pt. 1. (Electro-Optics Ser.: Vol. 1). 1976. 95.00 (ISBN 0-8247-6395-5). Dekker.

Olabisi, Olagoka & Robeson, Lloyd. Polymer-Polymer Miscibility. 1979. 49.00 (ISBN 0-12-525050-9). Acad Pr.

Oudar, Jacques. Physics & Chemistry of Surfaces. (Illus.). 1975. 42.50x (ISBN 0-216-90020-4). Intl Ideas.

Pae, K. D., et al. Advances in Polymer Science & Engineering. LC 72-88423. 350p. 1972. 45.00x (ISBN 0-306-30713-8, Plenum Pr). Plenum Pub.

Painter, Paul C., et al. The Theory of Vibrational Spectroscopy & Its Applications to Polymeric Materials. LC 81-12969. 530p. 1982. 74.95x (ISBN 0-471-09346-7, Pub. by Wiley-Interscience). Wiley.

Parker, D. R. Polymer Chemistry. (Illus.). 251p. 1971. 24.00 (ISBN 0-85334-571-6, Pub. by Elsevier Applied Sci England). Elsevier.

Pasika, Wallace M., ed. Carbon Thirteen NMR in Polymer Science. LC 79-13384. (ACS Symposium Ser.: No. 103). 1979. 34.95 (ISBN 0-8412-0505-1). Am Chemical.

Paul, D. R. & Newman, Seymour, eds. Polymer Blends, Vols. 1 & 2. 1978. Vol. 1. 66.00 (ISBN 0-12-546801-6); Vol. 2. 64.50 (ISBN 0-12-546802-4). Acad Pr.

Paul, Donald R. & Harris, F. W., eds. Controlled Release Polymeric Formulations: Symposium at the 171st Meeting of the American Chemical Society. LC 76-29016. (American Chemical Society ACS Symposium Ser.: No. 33). pap. 81.80 (ISBN 0-317-08997-8, 2015234). Bks Demand UMI.

Pearce, E. M. & Schaefgen, J. R., eds. Contemporary Topics in Polymer Science, Vol. 2. LC 77-21311. 324p. 1977. 49.50x (ISBN 0-306-36262-7, Plenum Pr). Plenum Pub.

Pearson, J. R. Mechanics of Polymer Processing. (Illus.). 678p. 1985. 112.50 (ISBN 0-85334-308-X, Pub. by Elsevier Applied Sci England). Elsevier.

Pearson, J. R. & Richardson, S. M., eds. Computational Analysis of Polymer Processing. (Illus.). 343p. 1983. 66.75 (ISBN 0-85334-188-5, I-100-83, Pub. by Elsevier Applied Sci England). Elsevier.

Penczek, S., et al. Cationic Ring-Opening Polymerization. (Advances in Polymer Science Ser.: Vols. 68 & 69). (Illus.). 300p. 1985. 66.00 (ISBN 0-387-13781-5). Springer-Verlag.

Perepechko, I. I. Introduction to Polymer Physics. 266p. 1981. 7.00 (ISBN 0-8285-2093-3, Pub. by Mir Pubs USSR). Imported Pubns.

--Low-Temperature Properties of Polymers. 272p. 1981. 44.00 (ISBN 0-08-025301-6). Pergamon.

Pethrick, R. A. & Richards, R. W. Static & Dynamic Properties of the Polymeric Solid State. 1982. 56.50 (ISBN 90-277-1481-9, Pub. by Reidel Holland). Kluwer Academic.

Pethrick, Richard A. Polymer Yearbook. 2nd ed. 420p. 1985. text ed. 50.00 (ISBN 3-7186-0274-1); pap. text ed. 20.00 (ISBN 3-7186-0276-8). Harwood Academic.

Pham, Quang Tho, et al. Proton & Carbon NMR Spectra of Polymers, Vol. 2. 439p. 1983. text ed. 134.95x (ISBN 0-471-26263-3, Pub. by Wiley-Interscience). Wiley.

Pham, Quange T., et al. Proton & Carbon NMR Spectra of Polymers, Vol. 3. 1984. 125.00 (ISBN 0-471-90394-9). Wiley.

Phillips, David, ed. Polymer Photophysics: Luminescence, Energy Migration & Molecular Motion in Synthetic Polymers. 250p. 1985. 59.95 (ISBN 0-412-16510-4, NO. 9309, Pub. by Chapman & Hall England). Methuen Inc.

Physical Chemistry. (Advances in Polymer Science: Vol. 30). (Illus.). 1979. 56.00 (ISBN 0-387-09199-8). Springer-Verlag.

Piirma, Irja, ed. Emulsion Polymerization. LC 81-17626. 1982. 59.50 (ISBN 0-12-556420-1). Acad Pr.

Pinkus, A. G., ed. Malcolm Dole Symposium: Commemorating the 80th Birthday of Professor Malcolm Dole. 275p. 1984. pap. 39.95 (ISBN 0-471-81336-2). Wiley.

Platzer, Norbert A., ed. Copolymers, Polyblends & Composites. LC 75-17726. (Advances in Chemistry Ser.: No. 142). 1975. 39.95 (ISBN 0-8412-0214-1). Am Chemical.

Poland, D. & Scheraga, H. A. Theory of Helix Coil Transitions in Biopolymers. (Molecular Biology). 1970. 75.00 (ISBN 0-12-559550-6). Acad Pr.

Polymer Membranes. (Advances in Polymer Science Ser.: Vol. 64). (Illus.). 150p. 1985. 32.00 (ISBN 0-387-13483-2). Springer-Verlag.

Polymer Radiation Curing: Epoxies, Phenolics, Fluorocarbons, & Silicones, 1970-Oct. 1984. 168p. 1984. 78.00 (ISBN 0-686-48324-3, LS122). T-C Pubns CA.

Polymer Radiation Curing: Polyolefins & Acrylics, 1970-Sept. 1984. 198p. 1984. 78.00 (ISBN 0-686-48327-8, LS123). T-C Pubns CA.

Polymer Radiation Curing: Styrene & Vinyls, 1970-Oct. 1983. 161p. 1983. 78.00 (ISBN 0-686-48329-4, LS124). T-C Pubns CA.

Polymerization Reactions. Incl. Stable Organic Cation Salts: Ion Pair Equilibria & Use in Cationic Polymerization. Ledwith, A. & Sherrington, D. C.; The Cationic Isomerization: Polymerization of Three-Methyl-One-Butene & Four-Methyl-One-Penene. Kennedy, J. P. & Johnston, J. E.; Grafting on Polyamides. Mano, E. B. & Coutinho, F. M.; Rigid Rods & the Characterization of Polyisozyanides. Millich, F. (Advances in Polymer Science: Vol. 19). (Illus.). 150p. 1975. 42.00 (ISBN 0-387-07460-0). Springer-Verlag.

Poppel & Penniman. Wet End Paper Mill Chemistry: The Role of Electrokinetics. 480p. 1985. price not set (ISBN 0-8247-7439-6). Dekker.

Powell, P. C. Engineering with Polymers. LC 83-7180. 1983. 59.95 (ISBN 0-412-24160-9, NO. 6825, Pub. by Chapman & Hall); pap. 25.00 (ISBN 0-412-24170-6, NO. 6826). Methuen Inc.

Price, Charles C. & Vandenberg, Edwin J., eds. Coordination Polymerization. LC 82-19081. (Polymer Science & Technology Ser.: Vol. 19). 342p. 1983. 52.50x (ISBN 0-306-41139-3, Plenum Pr). Plenum Pub.

Provder, Theodore, ed. Computer Applications in Applied Polymer Science. LC 82-13735. (ACS Symposium Ser.: No. 197). 467p. 1982. lib. bdg. 49.95x (ISBN 0-8412-0733-X). Am Chemical.

Quirk, Roderic P., ed. Transition Metal Catalyzed Polymerizations: Alkenes & Dienes. LC 82-15787. (MMI Press Symposium: Vol. 4). (Illus.). 874p. 1983. 2 pt. set 164.00; pt. A o.p. 89.50; pt. B 84.50 (ISBN 0-317-04170-3). Harwood Academic.

R. H. Chandler Ltd., ed. Per-Compounds & Per-Salts in Polymer Process. 165p. 1980. 169.00x (ISBN 0-686-78862-1, Pub. by Chandler England). State Mutual Bk.

Rabek, Jan F. Experimental Methods in Polymer Chemistry: Physical Principles & Applications. LC 79-40511. 861p. 1980. 205.00 (ISBN 0-471-27604-9, Pub. by Wiley-Interscience). Wiley.

Ranby, B. & Rabek, J. ESR Spectroscopy in Polymer Research. (Polymers-Properties & Applications Ser: Vol. 1). 1977. 73.00 (ISBN 0-387-08151-8). Springer-Verlag.

Ranby, B. & Rabek, J. F., eds. Singlet Oxygen: Reactions with Organic Compounds & Polymers. LC 77-2793. 1978. 76.95x (ISBN 0-471-99535-5, Pub. by Wiley-Interscience). Wiley.

Ranby, Bengt G. & Rabek, J. F. Photodegradation, Photo-Oxidation, & Photostabilization of Polymers: Principles & Applications. LC 74-2498. pap. 111.20 (ISBN 0-317-09017-8, 2016183). Bks Demand UMI.

Randall, James C. Polymer Sequence Determinations from Plus One Plus Three C NMR. 1977. 37.50 (ISBN 0-12-578050-8). Acad Pr.

Ray, N. H. Inorganic Polymers. 1978. 35.00 (ISBN 0-12-583550-7). Acad Pr.

Reactions. (Advances in Polymer Science Ser.: Vol. 58). (Illus.). 145p. 1984. 34.00 (ISBN 0-387-12793-3). Springer-Verlag.

Read, Brian E. & Dean, Gregory D. Determination of Dynamic Properties of Polymers & Composites. LC 78-12690. 207p. 1978. 84.95x (ISBN 0-470-26543-4). Halsted Pr.

Wrinch, Dorothy. Chemical Aspects of Polypeptide Chain Structures & the Cycol Theory. 200p. 1965. 19.50 (ISBN 0-306-30211-X, Plenum Pr). Plenum Pub.

POLYPS

see Coelenterata; Polyzoa

POLYSACCHARIDES

see also Cellulose; Starch; Sugars

American Chemical Society,164th National Meeting. Biogenesis of Plant Cell Wall Polysaccharides: Proceedings. Loewus, Frank, ed. 1973. 94.00 (ISBN 0-12-455350-8). Acad Pr.

Anderson, Laurens & Unger, Frank M., eds. Bacterial Lipopolysacharides: Structure, Synthesis, & Biological Activities. LC 83-158282. (ACS Symposium Ser.: No. 231). 325p. 1983. lib. bdg. 44.95x (ISBN 0-8412-0800-X). Am Chemical.

Aspinall, G. O., ed. The Polysaccharides, Vol. 1. (Molecular Biology Ser.). 330p. 1982. 55.00 (ISBN 0-12-065601-9). Acad Pr.

--The Polysaccharides, Vol. 2. LC 82-6689. (Molecular Biology Ser.). 1983. 70.00 (ISBN 0-12-065602-7). Acad Pr.

--The Polysaccharides, Vol. 3. (Molecular Biology Ser.). 1985. 85.00 (ISBN 0-12-065603-5). Acad Pr.

Blanshard, J. M. & Mitchell, J. R. Polysaccharides in Food. new ed. LC 79-40370. (Studies in the Agricultural & Food Sciences). (Illus.). 1979. text ed. 99.95 (ISBN 0-408-10618-2). Butterworth.

Brant, David A., ed. Solution Properties of Polysaccharides. LC 81-236. (ACS Symposium Ser.: No. 150). 1981. 57.95 (ISBN 0-8412-0609-0). Am Chemical.

Cleveland Symposium on Macromolecules, 1st, Case Western Reserve Univ., Oct. 1976. Proceedings. Walton, A. G., ed. 310p. 1977. 64.00 (ISBN 0-444-41561-0). Elsevier.

Colwell, Rita, et al, eds. Biotechnology of Marine Polysaccharides. LC 84-25221. (Illus.). 550p. 1985. 79.95 (ISBN 0-89116-433-2). Hemisphere Pub.

Crescenzi, V., et al, eds. New Developments in Industrial Polysaccharides. 396p. 1985. text ed. 58.00 (ISBN 2-88124-032-1). Gordon.

Rees, D. A. Polysaccharide Shapes. (Outline Studies in Biology). 1977. pap. 6.95 (ISBN 0-412-13030-0, NO. 6233, Pub. by Chapman & Hall). Methuen Inc.

Rudbach, B. & Baker, R., eds. Immunology of Bacterial Polysaccharides. LC 78-31961. (Developments in Immunology Ser.: Vol. 2). 158p. 1979. 45.50 (ISBN 0-444-00315-0, Biomedical Pr). Elsevier.

Sandford, Paul A. & Laskin, Allen, eds. Extracellular Microbial Polysaccharides. LC 77-6368. (ACS Symposium Ser: No. 45). 1977. 29.95 (ISBN 0-8412-0372-5). Am Chemical.

Sandford, Paul A. & Matsuda, K., eds. Fungal Polysaccharides. LC 80-10639. (ACS Symposium Ser.: No. 126). 1980. 33.95 (ISBN 0-8412-0555-8). Am Chemical.

Stoddart, R. W. Polysaccharide Metabolism. 224p. 1980. 35.00x (ISBN 0-85664-807-8, Pub. by Croom Helm England). State Mutual Bk.

Stoddart, R. W., ed. The Biosynthesis of Polysaccharides. 350p. 1984. 44.50 (ISBN 0-02-948750-1). Macmillan.

POLYSTOMIDAE

Stunkard, Horace W. Studies on North American Polystomidae Aspidogastridae & Paramphistomidae. (Illus.). Repr. of 1917 ed. 12.00 (ISBN 0-384-58730-5). Johnson Repr.

POLYTHENE

see Polyethylene

POLYTOPES

Bronosted, A. An Introduction to Convex Polytopes. (Graduate Texts in Mathematics: Vol. 90). (Illus.). 160p. 1983. 33.00 (ISBN 0-387-90722-X). Springer-Verlag.

Coxeter, H. S. Regular Polytopes. (Illus.). 321p. 1973. pap. 7.95 (ISBN 0-486-61480-8). Dover.

Coxeter, Harold S. Regular Complex Polytopes. LC 73-75855. (Illus.). 208p. 1975. 62.50 (ISBN 0-521-20125-X). Cambridge U Pr.

Grunbaum, Branko. Convex Polytopes. LC 67-20423. (Pure & Applied Mathematics (Wiley) Ser.: Vol. 16). pap. 117.50 (ISBN 0-317-08683-9, 2022541). Bks Demand UMI.

Miyazaki, K. An Adventure in Multidimensional Space: The Art & Geometry of Polygons, Polyhedra & Polytopes. 1985. 24.95 (ISBN 0-471-81648-5). Wiley.

POLYURETHANES

see Urethanes

POLYVINYL ALCOHOL

Pritchard, John G. Poly(Vinyl Alcohol) (Polymer Monographs). (Illus.). 152p. 1970. 37.25x (ISBN 0-677-01670-0). Gordon.

POLYVINYL CHLORIDE

Burgess, R. H. Manufacture & Processing of PVC. 300p. 1982. text ed. 40.00x (ISBN 0-02-949150-9). Macmillan.

Burgess, R. H., ed. Manufacture & Processing of PVC. (Illus.). 276p. 1982. 44.00 (ISBN 0-686-48127-5, 1905). T-C Pubns CA.

Gomez. Engineering with Rigid PVC. (Plastics Engineering Ser.). 544p. 1984. 69.75 (ISBN 0-8247-7080-3). Dekker.

Guyot, A., ed. International Symposium on Polyvinylchloride, 2nd: Proceedings. LC 77-73904. 1977. text ed. 48.00 (ISBN 0-08-021203-4). Pergamon.

Koleske, J. V. & Wartman, L. H. Poly(Vinyl Chloride) (Polymer Monographs). 124p. 1969. 27.95 (ISBN 0-677-01690-5). Gordon.

Nass, Leonard, ed. Encyclopedia of PVC, Vol. 3. 1977. 125.00 (ISBN 0-8247-6471-4). Dekker.

PVC: Formulation, Compounding & Processing. 171p. 1984. 28.00 (ISBN 0-938648-19-5, 1508). T-C Pubns CA.

Sarvetnick, Harold A. Polyvinyl Chloride. LC 77-689. (Plastics Applications Ser.). (Illus.). 268p. 1977. Repr. of 1969 ed. 19.50 (ISBN 0-88275-532-3). Krieger.

Wessling, R. A., ed. Polyvinylidene Chloride. (Polymer Monographs). 212p. 1977. 33.75x (ISBN 0-677-01700-6). Gordon.

Whelan, A. & Craft, J. L., eds. Developments in PVC Production & Processing, Vol. 1. (Illus.). 231p. 1977. 33.50 (ISBN 0-85334-741-7, Pub. by Elsevier Applied Sci England). Elsevier.

POLYZOA

Brown, David A. The Tertiary Cheilostomatous Polyzoa of New Zealand. (Illus.). 406p. 1952. 42.00x (ISBN 0-565-00064-0, Pub. by Brit Mus Nat Hist England). Sabbot-Natural Hist Bks.

Busk, George. Catalogue of the Marine Polyzoa in the British Museum, 1852-75, 3 Pts in One. (Illus.). 1966. Repr. of 1875 ed. 48.00 (ISBN 0-384-06731-X). Johnson Repr.

Larwood, G. P. & Abbott, M. B., eds. Advances in Bryozoology. (Systematics Association Special Volume Ser.). 1979. 77.00 (ISBN 0-12-437450-6). Acad Pr.

Moore, Raymond C., ed. Treatise on Invertebrate Paleontology, Part G: Bryozoa. LC 53-12913. 1953. 16.00 (ISBN 0-8137-3007-4). Geol Soc.

Mundy, S. P. A Key to the British & European Freshwater Bryozoans. 1980. 20.00x (ISBN 0-900386-39-8, Pub. by Freshwater Bio). State Mutual Bk.

Woollacott, Robert M. & Zimmer, Russell L., eds. The Biology of Bryozoans. 1977. 71.50 (ISBN 0-12-763150-X). Acad Pr.

POMOLOGY

see Fruit; Fruit-Culture

POND ECOLOGY

Elementary Science Study. Pond Water. 2nd ed. 1975. tchr's guide 12.56 (ISBN 0-07-018586-7). McGraw.

Hobbie, J. E., ed. Limnology of Tundra Ponds: Barrow, Alaska. LC 80-26373. (US-IBP Synthesis Ser.: Vol. 13). 514p. 1980. 38.50 (ISBN 0-87933-386-3). Van Nos Reinhold.

Kabisch, Klaus & Hemmerling, Joachim. Ponds & Pools: Oases in the Landscape. (Illus.). 261p. 1983. 14.95 (ISBN 0-668-05674-6, 5674). Arco.

Thompson, Gerald, et al. The Pond. LC 83-17574. (Oxford Scientific Films). (Illus.). 256p. 1984. 25.00 (ISBN 0-262-20049-X). MIT Pr.

POND LIFE

see Fresh-Water Biology

PONIES

Campbell, Judith. Four Ponies. 9.50 (ISBN 0-392-09902-0, SpS). Sportshelf.

Edwards, Elwyn H. The Larousse Guide to Horses & Ponies of the World. LC 77-71167. (The Larousse Guide Bks.). (Illus.). 1979. pap. 7.95 (ISBN 0-88332-121-1). Larousse.

Edwards, Elwyn H., ed. A Standard Guide to Horse & Pony Breeds. LC 79-23921. (Illus.). 352p. 1980. 24.95 (ISBN 0-07-019035-6). McGraw.

Henschel, Georgie. The Illustrated Guide to Horses & Ponies. LC 81-68189. 192p. 1982. 16.95 (ISBN 0-668-05353-4, 5353). Arco.

Hope, C. E. The Perfect Pony Owner. 14.50x (ISBN 0-273-40165-3, SpS). Sportshelf.

Hulme, Susan. Native Ponies of the British Isles. 200p. 1981. 15.50 (ISBN 0-904558-86-X). Saiga.

Kidd, Jane. An Illustrated Guide to Horse & Pony Care. LC 81-68162. 240p. 1982. 9.95 (ISBN 0-668-05368-2, 5368). Arco.

Murphy, Genevieve. Young Pony Rider's Companion. 14.50x (ISBN 0-392-13108-0, SpS). Sportshelf.

Tottenham, Katharine. Horse & Pony Breeding Explained. LC 78-9001. (Horseman's Handbook Ser.). (Illus.). 1979. pap. 3.95 (ISBN 0-668-04584-1). Arco.

Wheatley, George. Pony Riders Book. 1970. 10.00x (ISBN 0-87556-407-0). Saifer.

PONTCHARTRAIN BASIN

Saucier, Roger T. Recent Geomorphic History of the Pontchartrain Basin. LC 63-22267. (Coastal Studies: Vol. 9). (Illus.). Repr. of 1963 ed. 26.30 (ISBN 0-8357-9391-5, 2051665). Bks Demand UMI.

POODLES

see Dogs–Breeds–Poodles

POPLAR

Poplars & Willows. (Forestry Ser.: No. 10). 360p. 1980. 40.00 (ISBN 92-5-100500-1, F2046, FAO). Unipub.

Poplars in Forestry & Land Use. (Forestry & Forest Products Studies: No. 12). (Orig.). 1965. pap. 17.00 (ISBN 0-685-09399-9, F324, FAO). Unipub.

POPULAR AUTOMOBILE

see Automobiles, Foreign–Types–Popular

POPULATION–STATISTICS

Chapman, D. G. & Gallucci, V. F., eds. Quantitative Population Dynamics. (Statistical Ecology Ser.). 290p. 1981. 30.00 (ISBN 0-89974-010-3). Intl Co-Op.

Chen, Kuan-I. World Population Growth & Living Standards. 8.95x (ISBN 0-317-18410-5). New Coll U Pr.

Committee on National Statistics, National Research Council. Estimating Population & Income of Small Areas. 1981. pap. text ed. 14.25 (ISBN 0-309-03096-X). Natl Acad Pr.

Green, Rodney. Forecasting with Computer Models: Econometric, Population, & Energy Forecasting. LC 84-15934. 320p. 1985. 29.95 (ISBN 0-03-063788-0); pap. 12.95 (ISBN 0-03-063787-2). Praeger.

Impagliazzo, J. Deterministic Aspects in Mathematical Demography. (Biomathematics: Vol. 13). (Illus.). 200p. 1985. 34.00 (ISBN 0-387-13616-9). Springer-Verlag.

Keyfitz, Nathan C. Introduction to the Mathematics of Population - with Revisions. LC 76-17718. 496p. 1977. 28.95 (ISBN 0-201-03649-5). Addison-Wesley.

Levin, Simon, ed. Population Biology. LC 83-21389. (Proceedings of Symposia in Applied Mathematics: Vol. 30). 102p. 1983. 27.00 (ISBN 0-8218-0083-3, PSAPM 30); pap. 21.00. Am Math.

Masnick, George & Pitkin, John. The Changing Population of States & Regions: Analysis & Projections, 1970-2000. (Illus.). 250p. (Orig.). 1982. pap. 12.00 (ISBN 0-943142-01-6). St Local Inter.

POPULATION BIOLOGY

Cook, L. M., ed. Case Studies in Population Biology. LC 84-19451. 1985. text ed. 35.00 (ISBN 0-7190-1740-8, Pub. by Manchester Univ Pr). Longwood Pub Group.

Hedrick, Philip W. Population Biology: The Evolution & Ecology of Populations. 464p. 1984. text ed. write for info (ISBN 0-86720-043-X). Jones & Bartlett.

Kingsland, Sharon E. Modeling Nature: Episodes in the History of Population Ecology. LC 85-1414. (Science & Its Conceptual Foundations Ser.). (Illus.). 280p. 1985. 27.50 (ISBN 0-226-43726-4). U of Chicago Pr.

May, R. M., ed. Exploitation of Marine Communities. (Dahlem Workshop Reports Ser.: Vol. 32). (Illus.). 370p. 1984. 20.00 (ISBN 0-387-15028-5). Springer-Verlag.

Waltman, Paul. Competition Models in Population Biology. LC 83-50665. (CBMS-NSF Regional Conference Ser.: No. 45). v, 77p. 1983. pap. text ed. 12.50 (ISBN 0-89871-188-6). Soc Indus-Appl Math.

Woehrmann, K. & Loschcke, V., eds. Population Biology & Evolution. (Proceedings in Life Sciences Ser.). (Illus.). 300p. 1984. 44.00 (ISBN 0-387-13278-3). Springer Verlag.

POPULATION GENETICS

Akin, E. The Geometry of Population Genetics. (Lecture Notes in Biomathematics: Vol. 31). 205p. 1979. pap. 18.00 (ISBN 0-387-09711-2). Springer-Verlag.

Ammerman, Albert J. & Cavalli-Sforza, L. L. The Neolithic Transition & the Genetics of Populations in Europe. LC 84-42587. (Illus.). 196p. 1984. text ed. 25.00x (ISBN 0-691-08357-6). Princeton U Pr.

Ayala, F. Evolutionary & Population Genetics: A Primer. 1982. text ed. 21.95. Addison-Wesley.

Berryman, Alan A. Population Systems: A General Introduction. LC 80-26167. 237p. 1981. 18.95x (ISBN 0-306-40589-X, Plenum Pr). Plenum Pub.

Cannings, C. & Thompson, E. A. Genealogical & Genetic Structure. LC 81-6100. (Cambridge Studies in Mathematical Biology: No. 3). (Illus.). 150p. 1981. 42.50 (ISBN 0-521-23946-X); pap. 16.95 (ISBN 0-521-28363-9). Cambridge U Pr.

C. C. Li. First Course in Population Genetics. (Illus.). 1976. pap. 14.95x (ISBN 0-910286-42-6). Boxwood.

Chakravarti, Aravinda. Human Population Genetics. 1984. 39.50 (ISBN 0-442-21745-5). Van Nos Reinhold.

Cook, L. M. Population Genetics: Outline Studies in Biology. 1976. pap. 6.95 (ISBN 0-412-13930-8, NO. 6064, Pub. by Chapman & Hall). Methuen Inc.

Crow, James F. & Kimura, Motoo. An Introduction to Population Genetics Theory. LC 78-103913. 1970. text ed. 21.95x (ISBN 0-8087-2901-2). Burgess.

Dawson, Peter S. & King, Charles E. Population Biology: Retrospect & Prospect. 240p. 1983. 29.50 (ISBN 0-231-05252-9). Columbia U Pr.

Dobzhansky, Theodosius. Dobzhansky's Genetics of Natural Populations: I-XLIII. Lewontin, R. C., et al, eds. 1024p. 1982. 60.00x (ISBN 0-231-05132-8). Columbia U Pr.

--Genetic Diversity & Human Equality. LC 73-76262. 1973. pap. 3.95x (ISBN 0-465-09710-3, TB-5075). Basic.

--Genetics of the Evolutionary Process. LC 72-127363. 505p. 1971. 40.00x (ISBN 0-231-02837-7); pap. 17.00x (ISBN 0-231-08306-8). Columbia U Pr.

Edwards, A. W. Foundations of Mathematical Genetics. LC 76-9168. (Illus.). 1977. 37.50 (ISBN 0-521-21325-8). Cambridge U Pr.

Eriksson, A. W., et al, eds. Population Structure & Genetic Disorders: Proceedings of the 7th Sigfred Juselius Foundation Symposia. LC 80-40143. 1981. 132.00 (ISBN 0-12-241450-0). Acad Pr.

Feldman, Marc & Christiansen, Fred B. Population Genetics. (Illus.). 150p. 1985. pap. text ed. 14.95 (ISBN 0-86542-307-5). Blackwell Sci.

Gale, J. S. Population Genetics. LC 80-12675. (Tertiary Level Biology Ser.). 189p. 1980. 58.95x (ISBN 0-470-26970-7); pap. text ed. 34.95x (ISBN 0-470-26969-3). Halsted Pr.

Hartl, Daniel L. A Primer of Population Genetics. LC 80-23009. (Illus.). 175p. (Orig.). 1981. pap. text ed. 12.50x (ISBN 0-87893-271-2). Sinauer Assoc.

Hedrick, Philip W. Genetics of Populations. 629p. 1983. text ed. write for info. (ISBN 0-86720-011-1). Jones & Bartlett.

Jacquard, Albert. Genetics of Human Populations. Yermanos, D. M., tr. from Fr. LC 77-83065. Tr. of Genetique des Populations humaines. (Illus.). 1978. text ed. 10.50x (ISBN 0-87735-421-9). Freeman Cooper.

Kimura, Motoo & Ohta, Tomoko. Theoretical Aspects of Population Genetics. LC 75-155963. (Monographs in Population Biology: No. 4). 1971. pap. 10.00x (ISBN 0-691-08098-4). Princeton U Pr.

Lasker, G. W. Surnames & Genetic Structure. (Cambridge Studies in Biological Anthropology). 150p. 1985. 24.95 (ISBN 0-521-30285-4). Cambridge U Pr.

Lerner, I. Michael. Genetic Homeostasis. 1970. pap. 4.50 (ISBN 0-486-62506-0). Dover.

Levins, Richard. Evolution in Changing Environments: Some Theoretical Explorations. LC 68-20871. (Monographs in Population Biology: No. 2). (Illus.). 1968. pap. 9.95 (ISBN 0-691-08062-3). Princeton U Pr.

Lewontin, R. C. The Genetic Basis of Evolutionary Change. LC 73-19786. (Biological Ser.: Vol. 25). 346p. 1974. pap. 16.00x (ISBN 0-231-08318-1). Columbia U Pr.

Li, Wen-Hsiung, ed. Stochastic Models in Population Genetics. (Benchmark Papers in Genetics: Vol. 7). 1977. 64.50 (ISBN 0-12-786955-7). Acad Pr.

Malecot, Gustave. The Mathematics of Heredity. Yermanos, D. M., tr. from Fr. LC 69-12603. (Illus.). 88p. 1969. text ed. 17.50x (ISBN 0-7167-0678-4). W H Freeman.

Mani, G. S., ed. Evolutionary Dynamics of Genetic Diversity: Proceedings of a Symposium Held in Manchester, England, March 29-30, 1983. (Lecture Notes in Biomathematics: Vol. 53). vii, 312p. 1984. pap. 19.00 (ISBN 0-387-12903-0). Springer-Verlag.

Manwell, Clyde & Baker, C. M. Molecular Biology & the Origin of Species: Heterosis, Protein Polymorphism, & Animal Breeding. LC 70-103299. (Biology Ser). (Illus.). 446p. 1970. 20.00x (ISBN 0-295-95065-X). U of Wash Pr.

Maruyama, T. Stochastic Problems in Population Genetics. LC 77-24644. (Lecture Notes in Biomathematics: Vol. 17). (Illus.). 1977. pap. text ed. 18.00 (ISBN 0-387-08349-9). Springer-Verlag.

Mather, K. Genetical Structures of Populations. 1973. 16.95x (ISBN 0-412-12140-9, NO. 6191, Pub. by Chapman & Hall). Methuen Inc.

Mettler, Lawrence E. & Gregg, Thomas G. Population Genetics & Evolution. LC 69-16809. (Foundations of Modern Genetics Ser). (Illus.). 1969. pap. 17.95x ref. ed. (ISBN 0-13-685289-0). P-H.

Milkman, Roger, ed. Experimental Population Genetics. (Benchmark Papers in Genetics: Vol. 13). 416p. 1983. 45.95 (ISBN 0-87933-100-3). Van Nos Reinhold.

Morton, Newton E., ed. Genetic Structure of Populations. (Population Genetics Monographs: No. 3). 1974. text ed. 22.00x (ISBN 0-8248-0326-4). UH Pr.

Pilot Study on Conservation of Animal Genetic Resources. 60p. 1975. pap. 7.50 (ISBN 0-685-57609-4, F1062, FAO). Unipub.

Pirchner, Franz. Population Genetics in Animal Breeding. Frape, D. L., tr. from Ger. 408p. 1983. 52.50x (ISBN 0-306-41201-2). Plenum Pub.

Provine, William. Origins of Theoretical Population Genetics. LC 73-153711. (History of Science & Medicine Ser.). 1971. 18.00x (ISBN 0-226-68465-2). U of Chicago Pr.

Roughgarden, Jonathan. Theory of Population Genetics & Evolutionary Ecology: An Introduction. 1979. text ed. write for info. (ISBN 0-02-403180-1). Macmillan.

Salzano, Francisco M. & Freire-Maia, Newton. Problems in Human Biology: A Study of Brazilian Populations. LC 76-83524. 203p. 1970. text ed. 11.95x (ISBN 0-8143-1397-3). Wayne St U Pr.

Schonewald-Cox, et al. Genetics & Conservation: A Reference for Managing Wild Animal & Plant Populations. 1983. 26.95 (ISBN 0-8053-7764-6). Benjamin-Cummings.

Smith, J. Maynard. The Evolution of Sex. LC 77-85689. (Illus.). 1978. 42.50 (ISBN 0-521-21887-X); pap. 13.95x (ISBN 0-521-29302-2). Cambridge U Pr.

Spiess, Eliot B. Genes in Populations. LC 77-3990. 780p. 1977. text ed. 45.50 (ISBN 0-471-81612-4); solutions manual 11.95 (ISBN 0-471-03720-6). Wiley.

Wallace, Bruce. Basic Population Genetics. LC 80-39504. (Illus.). 736p. 1981. 32.00x (ISBN 0-231-05042-9). Columbia U Pr.

--Topics in Population Genetics. 1968. 24.95x (ISBN 0-393-09813-3). Norton.

Weiss, K. M. & Ballonoff, P. A., eds. Demographic Genetics. LC 75-31580. (Benchmark Papers in Genetics: Vol. 3). 414p. 1975. 61.50 (ISBN 0-12-787745-2). Acad Pr.

Wills, Christopher. Genetic Variability. (Illus.). 1981. text ed. 64.00x (ISBN 0-19-857570-X). Oxford U Pr.

Wilson, Edward O. & Bossert, William H. Primer of Population Biology. LC 73-155365. (Illus.). 192p. (Orig.). 1971. pap. text ed. 7.95x (ISBN 0-87893-926-1). Sinauer Assoc.

Zoological Society of London - 26th Symposium. Variation in Mammalian Populations. Berry, R. J. & Southern, H. N., eds. 1971. 63.50 (ISBN 0-12-613326-3). Acad Pr.

POPULATIONS, ANIMAL

see Animal Populations

POPULATIONS, BIRD

see Bird Populations

POPULATIONS, FISH

see Fish Populations

PORCELAIN–COLLECTORS AND COLLECTING

Denker, Ellen & Denker, Bert. The Main Street Pocket Guide to North American Pottery & Porcelain. rev. ed. (Illus.). 256p. 1985. pap. 7.95 (ISBN 0-915590-79-4). Main Street.

Donahue, Lou A. Noritake Collectibles. (Illus.). pap. 5.95 (ISBN 0-87069-282-8); price guide 1.50 (ISBN 0-87069-290-9). Wallace-Homestead.

Godden, G. A. Ridgeway Porcelains. (Illus.). 1985. 59.50 (ISBN 0-907462-65-0). Antique Collect.

Milboun, M. & Milboun, E. Understanding Miniature British Pottery & Porcelain. (Illus.). 184p. 1985. 29.50 (ISBN 0-907462-30-8). Apollo.

PORIFERA

see Sponges

PORK

Ali, Shahrazad. How Not to Eat Pork: Or Life Without the Pig. LC 85-70171. (Illus.). 120p. (Orig.). 1985. pap. 5.95 (ISBN 0-933405-00-6). Civilized Pubns.

Jul, Mogens & Zeuthen, Peter. Quality of Pig Meat: Progress of Food & Nutrition Science. (Vol. 4, No. 6). 80p. 1981. 22.00 (ISBN 0-08-026831-5). Pergamon.

PORK INDUSTRY AND TRADE

Devendra, Canagasaby & Fuller, M. F. Pig Production in the Tropics. (Oxford Tropical Handbooks Ser.). (Illus.). 1979. text ed. 32.50x (ISBN 0-19-859474-7). Oxford U Pr.

Jul, Mogens & Zeuthen, Peter. Quality of Pig Meat: Progress of Food & Nutrition Science. (Vol. 4, No. 6). 80p. 1981. 22.00 (ISBN 0-08-026831-5). Pergamon.

POROSITY

see also Permeability

Lowell, S. & Shields, J. E. Powder Surface Area & Porosity. 2nd ed. (Powder Technology Ser.). 230p. 1984. 50.00 (ISBN 0-412-25240-6, NO. 9012, Pub. by Chapman & Hall England). Methuen Inc.

Nunge, Richard J. Flow Through Porous Media. LC 78-146798. 248p. 1970. 15.95 (ISBN 0-8412-0111-0). Am Chemical.

POROUS MATERIALS

Johnson, D. L. & Sen, P. N., eds. Physics & Chemistry of Porous Media: Schlumberger-Doll Research, 1983. LC 83-73640. (AIP Conference Proceedings: No. 107). 223p. 1984. lib. bdg. 37.50 (ISBN 0-88318-306-4). Am Inst Physics.

Marle, Charles. Multiphase Flow in Porous Media. LC 79-56345. 356p. (Orig.). 1981. pap. 29.95x (ISBN 0-87201-569-6). Gulf Pub.

PORPHYRIN AND PORPHYRIN COMPOUNDS

see also Phthalocyanins

Adler, Alan D., ed. Biological Role of Porphyrins & Related Structures. (Annals of the New York Academy of Sciences: Vol. 244). 694p. 1975. 60.00x (ISBN 0-89072-758-9). NY Acad Sci.

Cubeddu, R. & Andreoni, A., eds. Porphyrins in Tumor Phototherapy. 450p. 1984. 67.50x (ISBN 0-306-41630-1, Plenum Pr). Plenum Pub.

Doiron, Daniel R. & Gomer, Charles J. Porphyrin Localization & Treatment of Tumors. (Progress in Clinical & Biological Research Ser.: Vol. 170). 908p. 1984. 98.00 (ISBN 0-8451-5020-0). A R Liss.

Dolphin, David, ed. The Porphyrins. Incl. Vol. 1, Pt. A. 1978. 78.00 (ISBN 0-12-220101-9); Physical Chemistry. 1978. Vol. 3, Pt. A. 90.00 (ISBN 0-12-220103-5); Vol. 4, Pt. B, 1979. 65.00 (ISBN 0-12-220104-3); Vol. 5, Pt. C. 77.50 (ISBN 0-12-220105-1). LC 77-14197. 1978-79. Acad Pr.

--The Porphyrins: Biochemistry, Vol. 6, Pt. A. 1979. 95.00 (ISBN 0-12-220106-X); o.p. 83.50 set. Acad Pr.

--The Porphyrins Vol. 7: Biochemistry Part B. 1979. 69.50 (ISBN 0-12-220107-8). Acad Pr.

Kessel, David & Dougherty, Thomas J., eds. Porphyrin Photosensitization. LC 82-19001. (Advances in Experimental Medicine & Biology Ser.: Vol. 160). 304p. 1983. 49.50 (ISBN 0-306-41193-8, Plenum Pr). Plenum Pub.

Lever, A. B. & Gray, H. B., eds. Iron Porphyrins. (Physical Bioinorganic Chemistry Ser.). 256p. 1982. Pt. 1. 47.95 (ISBN 0-201-05816-2); Pt. 2. 51.95 (ISBN 0-201-05817-0). Addison-Wesley.

Vernon, Leo P. & Seely, G. R. Chlorophylls: Physical, Chemical & Biological Properties. 1966. 92.50 (ISBN 0-12-718650-6). Acad Pr.

PORPOISES

see also Dolphins

Ellis, Richard. Dolphins & Porpoises. LC 82-47823. 1982. 25.00 (ISBN 0-394-51800-4). Knopf.

Heintzelman, Donald. A World Guide to Whales, Dolphins & Porpoises. LC 80-20823. 176p. 1981. pap. 9.95 (ISBN 0-8329-3230-2, Pub. by Winchester Pr). New Century.

Katona, Steve & Richardson, David. A Field Guide to the Whales, Porpoises, & Seals of the Gulf of Maine & Eastern Canada: Cape Cod to Labrador. (Illus.). 224p. 1983. 22.95 (ISBN 0-684-17901-6, ScribT); pap. 13.95 (ISBN 0-684-17902-4). Scribner.

Norris, Kenneth S. The Porpoise Watcher. LC 74-1329. (Illus.). 250p. 1974. 7.95 (ISBN 0-393-06385-2). Norton.

Norris, Kenneth S., ed. Whales, Dolphins, & Porpoises. (Library Reprint Ser.). 1978. 64.00x (ISBN 0-520-03283-7). U of Cal Pr.

Truitt, Deborah, ed. Dolphins & Porpoises: A Comprehensive, Annotated Bibliography of the Smaller Cetacea. LC 73-19803. 584p. 1974. 90.00x (ISBN 0-8103-0966-1). Gale.

PORSCHE (AUTOMOBILE)

see Automobiles, Foreign–Types–Porsche

PORT WINE

Simon, Andre L. All about Port. (All about Wines: Vol. 3). pap. 7.50 (ISBN 0-87559-181-7). Shalom.

PORTABLE COMPUTERS

Balmer, James E. & Moes, Matthijs. The Portable Computer Book. 400p. 1984. 19.95 (ISBN 0-912003-36-7). Bk Co.

Berner, Jeffrey. The Executive's Guide to Portable Computers. 224p. (Orig.). 1984. pap. 9.95 (ISBN 0-345-31700-9). Ballantine.

Cole, Jim. Ninety-Nine Tips & Tricks for the New Pocket Computers. 128p. (Orig.). 1982. pap. 7.95 (ISBN 0-86668-019-5). ARCsoft.

--One Hundred One Pocket Computer Programming Tips & Tricks. (Illus.). 128p. (Orig.). 1982. pap. 7.95 (ISBN 0-86668-004-7). ARCsoft.

--Pocket Computer Programming Made Easy. (Illus.). 128p. (Orig.). 1982. pap. 8.95 (ISBN 0-86668-009-8). ARCsoft.

--Thirty-Five Practical Programs for the Casio Pocket Computer. (Illus.). 96p. Date not set. 8.95 (ISBN 0-86668-014-4). ARCsoft.

Craig, John C. One Hundred Nineteen Practical Programs for the TRS-80 Pocket Computer. (Illus.). 308p. 1982. 15.95 (ISBN 0-8306-0061-2); pap. 10.25 (ISBN 0-8306-1350-1, 1350). TAB Bks.

Faulk, Ed. Computer in Your Pocket. 160p. 1983. pap. 14.95 (ISBN 0-88190-070-2, BO070). Datamost.

Friedman, Herb. Supercharging the IBM PC Portable. 244p. 1985. pap. 15.95 (ISBN 0-13-875790-9). P H.

Hohenstein, C L. Using Programmable Calculators for Business. LC 81-3065. 296p. 1982. pap. 10.95 (ISBN 0-471-08551-0, Pub. by Wiley Pr). Wiley.

Inman, Don & Conlan, Jim. Problem-Solving on the TRS-80 Pocket Computer. LC 81-10358. (Self-Teaching Guide Ser.). 255p. 1982. pap. text ed. 9.95 (ISBN 0-471-09270-3, Pub. by Wiley Pr). Wiley.

Librach, Hank. Pocket Computer Primer. 96p. 1982. 17.95 (ISBN 0-13-683862-6); pap. 9.95 (ISBN 0-13-683854-5). P-H.

Market Intelligence Research Company Staff. Portable Computer Markets, 1984-1990. 250p. Date not set. pap. text ed. 795.00x (ISBN 0-317-19551-4). Market Res Co.

Marter, Melvin L. Handheld Calculator Programs for Engineering Design. (Illus.). 448p. 1983. 37.95 (ISBN 0-07-040642-1). McGraw.

Mullish, Henry & Kestenbaum, Richard. Financial Analysis by Calculator: Problem-Solving Techniques With Applications. (Illus.). 157p. 1982. 17.95 (ISBN 0-13-316018-1); pap. 8.95 (ISBN 0-13-316000-9). P-H.

--Pocket Computing Power! Basic Programming & Applications. (Illus.). 175p. 1984. pap. text ed. 12.45 (ISBN 0-06-044659-5, HarpC). Har-Row.

Saks, Mark. The Calculator Cookbook: Maximizing the Computational Power of Your Hand-Held Calculator. 286p. 1983. 22.95 (ISBN 0-13-110395-4); pap. 10.95 (ISBN 0-13-110387-3). P-H.

Spikell, Mark A. & Snover, Stephen. Brain Ticklers: Timex-Sinclair 1000 Version. (Illus.). 208p. 1984. 13.95 (ISBN 0-13-081050-9); pap. 7.95 (ISBN 0-13-081000-2). P-H.

Weber Systems Inc. Staff. Sanyo MBC 775 Portable User's Handbook. 330p. (Orig.). 1985. pap. 17.95 (ISBN 0-317-19100-4). Weber Systems.

Witt, Howard. Navigation with a Micro-Computer. 1983. pap. text ed. 14.95 (ISBN 0-87567-082-2). Entelek.

Zehna, Peter & Barr, Don. Statistics by Calculator. 1983. 13.95 (ISBN 0-13-844811-6, Spec). P-H.

PORTABLE POWER TOOLS

see Power Tools

PORTALS

see Doors and Doorways

PORTER, RUFUS, 1792-1884

Lipman, Jean. Rufus Porter Rediscovered. (Illus.). 224p. 1980. 7.98 (ISBN 0-517-54115-7, C N Potter). Crown.

PORTLAND CEMENT

Bye, G. C. Portland Cement: Composition, Production & Properties. (The Pergamon Materials Engineering Practice Ser.). (Illus.). 156p. 1983. 20.00 (ISBN 0-08-029965-2); pap. 11.50 (ISBN 0-08-029964-4). Pergamon.

Further Laboratory Studies of Portland Pozzolan Cements. 1976. pap. 2.00 (ISBN 0-89312-161-4, RD041T). Portland Cement.

Lesley, Robert W., et al. History of the Portland Cement Industry in the United States. LC 72-5061. (Technology & Society Ser.). (Illus.). 346p. 1972. Repr. of 1924 ed. 21.00 (ISBN 0-405-04712-6). Ayer Co Pubs.

Popovics, Sandor, ed. Fundamentals of Portland Cement Concrete - A Quantitative Approach: Fresh Concrete, Vol. 1. LC 81-2796. 477p. 1982. 65.50x (ISBN 0-471-86217-7, Pub. by Wiley-Interscience). Wiley.

Soroka, I. Portland Cement Paste & Concrete. 1980. 48.00 (ISBN 0-8206-0281-7). Chem Pub.

POSITION ANALYSIS

see Topology

POSITIVE ELECTRONS

see Positrons

POSITIVE IONS

see Cations

POSITIVE RAYS

see Molecular Beams

POSITRON ANNIHILATION

Bayley, Barrington J. Annihilation Factor. 144p. 1980. 11.95 (ISBN 0-8052-8018-9, Pub. by Allison & Busby England); pap. 4.95 (ISBN 0-8052-8017-0, Pub. by Allison & Busby England). Schocken.

Coleman, P. G. & Sharma, S. C., eds. Positron Annihilation: Proceedings of the Sixth International Conference on Positron Annihilation, the University of Texas at Arlington, April 3-7, 1982. 1016p. 1983. 132.00 (ISBN 0-444-86534-9, North Holland). Elsevier.

Hautojaervi, P., ed. Positrons in Solids. LC 79-1191. (Topics in Current Physics: Vol. 12). (Illus.). 1979. 38.00 (ISBN 0-387-09271-4). Springer-Verlag.

Kramer, G. Theory of Jets in Electron: Position Annihilation. (Springer Tracts in Modern Physics: Vol. 102). (Illus.). 106p. 1984. 29.00 (ISBN 0-387-13068-3). Springer-Verlag.

POSITRONS

see also Electrons; Neutrons; Positron Annihilation; Protons

Burns, M. L. & Harding, A. K., eds. Positron-Electron Pairs in Astrophysics: AIP Conference Proceeding Center, Goddard Space Flight Center, 1983, No. 101. LC 83-71926. 447p. 1983. lib. bdg. 38.50 (ISBN 0-88318-200-9). Am Inst Physics.

Green, James & Lee, John. Positronium Chemistry. 1964. 35.00 (ISBN 0-12-298650-4). Acad Pr.

Hautojaervi, P., ed. Positrons in Solids. LC 79-1191. (Topics in Current Physics: Vol. 12). (Illus.). 1979. 38.00 (ISBN 0-387-09271-4). Springer-Verlag.

Humberston, John W. & McDowell, M. R., eds. Positron Scattering in Gases. (NATO ASI Series B, Physics: Vol. 107). 240p. 1984. 42.50x (ISBN 0-306-41634-4, Plenum Pr). Plenum Pub.

International Commission on Radiation Units & Measurements. Stopping Powers for Electrons & Positrons. LC 84-12780. (Report Ser.: No. 37). 268p. 1984. pap. text ed. 24.00 (ISBN 0-913394-31-9). Intl Comm Rad Meas.

POTASH

British Sulphur Corporation Ltd, ed. World Survey of Potash Resources. 3rd ed. (Illus.). 290p. 1979. 312.50x (ISBN 0-902777-42-4). Intl Pubns Serv.

McKercher, R. M., ed. Potash Mining Processing Transportation: Proceedings of the International Potash Technology Conference, Saskatoon, Saskatchewan, Canada, October 3-5, 1983. (Illus.). 887p. 1983. 165.00 (ISBN 0-08-025401-2). Pergamon.

POTASSIUM

Aitken, F. C. Sodium & Potassium in Nutrition of Mammals. 296p. 1976. cloth 50.00x (ISBN 0-85198-370-7, Pub. by CAB Bks England). State Mutual Bk.

Case, David B., et al. Advances in Potassium Suplementation. write for info. (ISBN 0-911741-06-2). Advanced Thera Comm.

Graley, A. M. & Nicolls, K. D. Sampling in Surveys of Exchangeable Potassium in Soils. 1980. 20.00x (ISBN 0-643-02486-7, Pub. by CSJRO Australia). State Mutual Bk.

Interrelationships Between Potassium & Magnesium Absorption by Oats. (Agricultural Reseach Reports: No. 642). 1964. pap. 7.25 (ISBN 90-220-0103-2, PDC163, PUDOC). Unipub.

Kaddar, T., et al. The Vital Role of Potassium Fertilizers in Tropical Agriculture: The Present Position, Future Potential & Constraints to Progress. Roth, E. N. & Frederick, E. D., eds. (Technical Bulletin Ser.: T-29). (Illus.). 15p. (Orig.). 1984. pap. text ed. 4.00 (ISBN 0-88090-051-2). Intl Fertilizer.

Kilmer, V. J., et al, eds. The Role of Potassium in Agriculture. (Illus.). 1968. 7.50 (ISBN 0-89118-003-6). Am Soc Agron.

POTASSIUM-ARGON DATING

Dalrymple, G. Brent & Lanphere, Marvin A. Potassium-Argon Dating: Principles, Techniques & Applications to Geochronology. LC 71-84047. (Geology Ser.). (Illus.). 258p. 1969. text ed. 30.95 (ISBN 0-7167-0241-X). W H Freeman.

POTATO STARCH

see Starch

POTATOES

Bourke, P. Austin. Forecasting from Weather Data of Potato Blight & Other Plant Diseases & Pests. (Technical Note Ser.). 1955. pap. 4.00 (ISBN 0-685-22304-3, W4, WMO). Unipub.

Correll, Donovan S. The Potato & Its Wild Relatives: Section Tuberarium of the Genus Solanum. (Illus.). 606p. 1962. lib. bdg. 20.00x (ISBN 0-934454-93-0). Lubrecht & Cramer.

De Bokx, ed. Viruses of Potatoes & Seed-Potato Production. 232p. 1971. 17.50 (ISBN 90-220-0358-2, PDC100, PUDOC). Unipub.

FAO-IAEA-WHO Expert Committee. Geneva, 1969. Wholesomeness of Irradiated Food with Special Reference to Wheat, Potatoes & Onions: Report. (Technical Report Ser.: No. 451). (Also avail. in French & Spanish). 1970. pap. 2.00 (ISBN 92-4-120451-6). World Health.

Harris, P. M., ed. The Potato Crop: The Scientific Basis for Improvement. 1978. 79.95x (ISBN 0-412-12830-6, NO. 6143, Pub. by Chapman & Hall). Methuen Inc.

Hooker, W. J. Compendium of Potato Diseases. LC 80-85459. (Illus.). 125p. 1981. saddle stitched 17.00 (ISBN 0-89054-027-6). Am Phytopathol Soc.

Keijbets, M. J. Pectic Substances in the Cell Wall & the Intercellular Cohesion of Potato Tuber Tissue During Cooking. (Agricultural Research Reports: No. 827). (Illus.). viii, 161p. 1975. pap. 22.00 (ISBN 90-220-0536-4, PDC64, PUDOC). Unipub.

Laufer, Berthold. The American Plant Migration, Vol.1: The Potato. (Field Museum of Natural History). (Illus.). 1938. 11.00 (ISBN 0-527-01888-0). Kraus Repr.

Poultry Industry. (IES Committee Reports Ser.). 1970. member 2.25 (ISBN 0-686-96198-6, CP-36); non-member 4.50 (ISBN 0-686-99729-8). Illum Eng.
Recommended International Code of Practice for Poultry Processing. (CAC-RCP Ser.: No. 14-1976). 13p. 1977. pap. 7.50 (ISBN 92-5-100545-1, F1447, FAO). Unipub.
Saiga Editors. Bantams. (Orig.). 1981. pap. 2.75 (ISBN 0-86230-006-1). Saiga.
Sastry, N. S. & Thomas, C. K. Farm Animal Mangement & Poultry Production. 2nd ed. (Illus.). xv, 539p. 1982. text ed. 35.00x (ISBN 0-7069-1730-8, Pub by Vikas India). Advent NY.

POULTRY NUTRITION
see Poultry–Feeding and Feeds

POULTRY TRADE
see Poultry Industry

POWDER METALLURGY
see also Ceramic Metals; Heat Resistant Alloys; Metal Powders; Sintering

American Society for Metals. Source Book on Powder Metallurgy: A Comprehensive Collection of Oustanding Articles from the Periodical & Reference Literature. Bradbury, Samuel, ed. LC 78-24466. pap. 109.80 (ISBN 0-317-26758-2, 2024348). Bks Demand UMI.
Bork, B. A., ed. Researchers in Powder Metallurgy, Vol. 1. Michalewicz, Z. S., tr. from Rus. LC 66-15306. pap. 39.00 (ISBN 0-317-10429-2, 2020675). Bks Demand UMI.
Borok, B. A., ed. Researches in Powder Metallurgy, Vols. 1 & 2. Incl. Vol. 1. 148p. 1966 (ISBN 0-306-10774-0); Vol. 2. 126p. 1972 (ISBN 0-306-10775-9). LC 66-15306. 39.50x ea. (Consultants). Plenum Pub.
Burke, John J. & Weiss, Volker, eds. Powder Metallurgy for High-Performance Applications. LC 72-5215. (Sagamore Army Materials Research Conference Ser.: Vol. 18). 413p. 1972. 35.00x (ISBN 0-306-34518-8, Plenum Pr). Plenum Pub.
Feeby, C. L. & Ullrich, W. J., eds. Powder Metallurgy in Defense Technology, Vol. 6. 224p. 1985. pap. 52.00 (ISBN 0-918404-62-2). Am Powder Metal.
Gessinger, G. H. Powder Metallurgy of Superalloys. (Monographs in Materials). 330p. 1984. text ed. 69.95 (ISBN 0-408-11033-3). Butterworth.
Harris, S. T. The Technology of Powder Coatings. 304p. 1981. 159.00x (ISBN 0-901994-93-6, Pub. by Portcullio Pr). State Mutual Bk.
Hausner, H. H. & Mal, M. K. Handbook of Powder Metallurgy. 2nd ed. (Illus.). 1982. 85.00 (ISBN 0-8206-0301-5). Chem Pub.
Hausner, H. H. & Taubenblat, P. W., eds. Ferrous & Non-Ferrous P-M Materials. (Modern Developments in Powder Metallurgy: Vol. 10). 42.50 (ISBN 0-918404-39-8). Metal Powder.
--Modern Developments in Powder Metallurgy: Vols. 9, 10, 11, 3 vols. 1977. 120.00x (ISBN 0-918404-41-X). Metal Powder.
--P-M Principles & Production Processes. (Modern Developments in Powder Metallurgy: Vol. 9). 1977. 42.50x (ISBN 0-918404-38-X). Metal Powder.
--P-M Special Materials & Applications. (Modern Developments in Powder Metallurgy: Vol. 11). 1977. 42.50x (ISBN 0-918404-40-1). Metal Powder.
Hausner, H. H., et al, eds. Ferrous & Non-Ferrous Materials. Antes, H. W. (Modern Developments in Powder Metallurgy Ser.: Vol. 13). 608p. 1981. 45.00 (ISBN 0-918404-52-5). Metal Powder.
--Modern Developments in Powder Metallurgy, Vols. 12, 13, 14. 2176p. 1981. Set. 150.00 (ISBN 0-918404-54-1). Metal Powder.
--Principles & Processes. (Modern Developments in Powder Metallurgy Ser.: Vol. 12). 944p. 1981. 80.00 (ISBN 0-918404-51-7). Metal Powder.
--Special Materials. LC 66-5483. (Modern Developments in Powder Metallurgy: Vol. 14). 624p. 1981. 50.00 (ISBN 0-918404-53-3). Metal Powder.
Hausner, Henry H., ed. Modern Developments in Powder Metallurgy: Proceedings of the 1965 International Powder Metallurgy Conference. LC 61-65760. (Illus.). Vol. 1. pap. 103.00 (ISBN 0-317-10894-8, 2019401); Vol. 2. pap. 91.50 (ISBN 0-317-10895-6). Bks Demand UMI.
--New Types of Metal Powders: Proceedings of a Symposium, Cleveland, Ohio, October 24, 1963. LC 64-18802. (Metallurgical Society Conferences: Vol. 23). pap. 44.30 (ISBN 0-317-10381-4, 2001511). Bks Demand UMI.
Hausner, Henry H., et al, eds. New Methods for the Consolidation of Metal Powders. LC 66-22786. (Perspectives in Powder Metallurgy: Fundamentals, Methods & Applications Ser.: Vol. 1). pap. 65.80 (ISBN 0-317-10824-7, 2019406). Bks Demand UMI.
International Powder Technology & Bulk Solids Conference, 1975. POWTECH Seventy-Five: Proceedings of the Third International Powder Technology & Bulk Solids Conference. (Powder Technology Publication Ser.: No. 6). pap. 23.50 (ISBN 0-317-26490-7, 2024038). Bks Demand UMI.
International Powder Technology & Bulk Solids Conference Staff. POWTECH Seventy-One: Proceedings of POWTECH '71. Goldberg, A. S., ed. (Powder Technology Publication Ser.: No. 1). pap. 69.30 (ISBN 0-317-26655-1, 2024036). Bks Demand UMI.
International Powder Technology & Bulk Solids Exhibition & Conference (1973: Harrogate, Eng.) Staff. POWTECH Seventy-Three Papers-Particulate Matter: Special POWTECH 73 Issue. Goldberg, A. S., ed. (Powder Technology Publication Ser.: No. 2). pap. 27.50 (ISBN 0-317-26663-2, 2024037). Bks Demand UMI.
Klare, Erhard, ed. Powder Metallurgy: Applications, Advantages & Limitations. 1983. 51.00 (ISBN 0-87170-154-5). ASM.
Kuhn, Howard A. & Lawley, Alan, eds. Powder Metallurgy Processing: New Techniques & Analyses. 1978. 51.00 (ISBN 0-12-428450-7). Acad Pr.
Kunkel, Robert N. Tooling Design for Powder Metallurgy Parts. (Prepared Courses of Instruction Ser.). pap. 42.00 (ISBN 0-317-27675-1, 2024168). Bks Demand UMI.
Lenel, Fritz V. Powder Metallurgy: Principles & Applications. LC 80-81830. (Illus.). 608p. 1980. 55.00 (ISBN 0-918404-48-7). Metal Powder.
Mocarski, S. & Pietrocini, T., eds. Progress in Powder Metallurgy, 1977: Proceedings, Vol. 33. Incl. Progress in Powder Metallurgy: Proceedings, National Powder Metallurgy Conference, Los Angeles & Cincinatti, 1978 & 1979. Cebulak, W. et al., ed. (Vols. 34 & 35). (Illus., Orig.). 1980. pap. 56.00 (ISBN 0-918404-49-5); Progress in Powder Metallurgy: Annual Conference Proceedings, 1983. Nayar, H. et al., ed. (Vol. 39). 696p. 1984. pap. 75.00 (ISBN 0-918404-61-4); Progress in Powder Metallurgy. Capus, Joseph & Dyke, Donald L., eds. (Vol. 37). 417p. (Orig.). 1982. pap. 60.00 (ISBN 0-918404-56-8). 1977. 42.00x (ISBN 0-918404-43-6). Metal Powder.
MPIF Standard No. 35, Materials Standard for P-M Structure Parts, 1984-1985. rev. ed. pap. 5.00 (ISBN 0-318-04233-9). Metal Powder.
Physical Metallurgy: Part 1: Chapters 1-13; Part 2: Chapters 14-30, 2 pts. 3rd, rev. ed. 2050p. 1984. Set. 185.00 (ISBN 0-444-86628-0, I-005-83, North-Holland); Pt. 1. write for info. (ISBN 0-444-86786-4); Pt. 2. write for info. (ISBN 0-444-86787-2). Elsevier.
Plastics & Passenger Cars. 1984. 30.00 (ISBN 0-89883-337-X, SP566). Soc Auto Engineers.
Powder Metallurgy Science. LC 84-60862. 279p. 1984. 35.00 (ISBN 0-918404-60-6). Metal Powder.
Taubenblat, Pierre W. Copper Base Powder Metallurgy. LC 80-81464. (New Perspectives in Powder Metallurgy Ser.: Vol. 7). (Illus.). 232p. 1980. 42.00 (ISBN 0-918404-47-9). Metal Powder.
Wendon, G. W. Aluminium & Bronze Flake Powders. 1982. 159.00x (ISBN 0-686-81701-X, Pub. by Electrochemical Scotland). State Mutual Bk.
Who's Who in Powder Metallurgy, 1985. rev. ed. LC 76-642022. 1985. pap. 50.00 (ISBN 0-918404-63-0). Am Powder Metal.
Yaverbaum, L. H., ed. Technology of Metal Powders: Recent Developments. LC 80-31. (Chemical Technology Review: No. 153). (Illus.). 400p. 1980. 45.00 (ISBN 0-8155-0794-1). Noyes.

POWDERED MILK
see Milk, Dried

POWDERS
see also Crystals; Metal Powders; Powder Metallurgy

Beddow, J. K. & Meloy, T. P., eds. Testing & Characterization of Powders & Fire Particles. (Powder Advisory Centre Publication Ser. (POWTECH)). 176p. 1979. 57.95 (ISBN 0-471-25602-1, Wiley Heyden). Wiley.
Lowell, S. & Shields, J. E. Powder Surface Area & Porosity. 2nd ed. (Powder Technology Ser.). 230p. 1984. 50.00 (ISBN 0-412-25240-6, NO. 9012, Pub. by Chapman & Hall England). Methuen Inc.
Zimon, A. D. Adhesion of Dust & Powder. LC 69-12547. 424p. 1969. 47.50x (ISBN 0-306-30391-4, Plenum Pr). Plenum Pub.

POWELL, JOHN WESLEY, 1834-1902

Rusho, W. L. Powell's Canyon Voyage. LC 70-64908. (Wild & Woolly West Ser., No. 11). (Illus., Orig.). 1969. 8.00 (ISBN 0-910584-86-9); pap. 2.00 (ISBN 0-910584-12-5). Filter.
Stegner, Wallace. Beyond the Hundredth Meridian: John Wesley Powell & the Second Opening of the West. LC 81-23090. (Illus.). xxvi, 458p. 1982. ltd. ed. 50.00 (ISBN 0-8032-4133-X); pap. 12.50 (ISBN 0-8032-9128-0, BB 798, Bison). U of Nebr Pr.

POWELLIZED TIMBER
see Wood–Preservation

POWER (MECHANICS)
see also Electric Power; Energy Storage; Force and Energy; Machinery; Power Resources; Power Transmission; Steam; Water-Power; Wind Power

Association of Energy Engineers. New Directions in Energy Technology. LC 84-81176. 500p. 1984. text ed. 45.00 (ISBN 0-915586-87-8); pap. text ed. 30.00 (ISBN 0-915586-88-6). Fairmont Pr.
Auer, P. L., ed. Advances in Energy Systems & Technology. LC 78-4795. 1979. Vol. 1. 65.00 (ISBN 0-12-014901-X); Vol. 2. 50.00 (ISBN 0-12-014902-8). Acad Pr.
Auer, Peter L., ed. Advances in Energy Systems & Technology, Vol. 3. 308p. 1982. 55.00 (ISBN 0-12-014903-6). Acad Pr.
Au-Yang, M. K. & Moody, F. J., eds. Interactive-Fluid-Structural Dynamic Problems in Power Engineering. (PVP Ser.: vol. 46). 177p. 1981. 30.00 (ISBN 0-686-34516-9, H00182). ASME.
Bains, G. S., et al. Power Systems Protection. 515p. 1981. 30.00x (ISBN 0-86125-205-5, Pub. by Orient Longman India). State Mutual Bk.
Bohm & MacDonald. Power: Mechanics of Energy Control. 2nd ed. 1983. 18.64 (ISBN 0-87345-256-9). McKnight.
Bose, N. K. Adjustable Speed AC Drive Systems. LC 80-27789. 449p. 1981. 39.95 (ISBN 0-471-09395-5, Pub. by Wiley-Interscience); pap. 25.95 (ISBN 0-471-09396-3, Pub. by Wiley-Interscience). Wiley.
Bostick, W. H., et al, eds. Energy Storage, Compression, & Switching, Vol. 1. LC 75-42405. 537p. 1976. 75.00x (ISBN 0-306-30892-4, Plenum Pr). Plenum Pub.
Bradley, W. B., et al, eds. Emerging Energy Technologies: 1978. 1978. 20.00 (ISBN 0-685-66797-9, G00141). ASME.
Carty, Tony & Smith, Alexander M. Power & Maneuverability. 1978. text ed. 18.75x (ISBN 0-905470-04-4). Humanities.
Chin, G. Y., ed. Advances in Power Technology. 1982. 80.00 (ISBN 0-87170-142-1). ASM.
Coal Fired MHD Power Generation, Vol. 1. 300p. (Orig.). 1981. pap. text ed. 37.50x (ISBN 0-85825-162-0, Pub. by Inst Engineering Australia). Brookfield Pub Co.
Committee on Power Plant Siting. Engineering for Resolution of the Energy-Environment Dilemma. LC 79-186370. (Illus.). 1972. pap. 12.25 (ISBN 0-309-01943-5). Natl Acad Pr.
Considine, Douglas M. Energy Technology Handbook. 1977. 82.50 (ISBN 0-07-012430-2). McGraw.
Counihan, Martin. A Dictionary of Energy. (Illus.). 200p. 1981. 16.95x (ISBN 0-7100-0847-3). Routledge & Kegan.
Culp, Archie W. Principles of Energy Conversion. (Illus.). 1979. text ed. 42.00 (ISBN 0-07-014892-9). McGraw.
Development in Power System Protection. (IEE Conference Publication: No. 185). (Illus.). 303p. 1980. softcover 62.50 (ISBN 0-85296-220-7). Inst Elect Eng.
Diamant, R. M. Energy Conservation Equipment. 156p. 1984. 29.50 (ISBN 0-89397-190-1). Nichols Pub.
Duffy, Joseph. Power: Prime Mover of Technology. rev. ed. 1972. text ed. 21.97 (ISBN 0-87345-420-0). McKnight.
Ford, K. W., et al, eds. Efficient Use of Energy: A Physics Perspective. LC 75-18227. (AIP Conference Proceedings Ser.: No. 25). 305p. 1975. 20.00 (ISBN 0-88318-124-X). Am Inst Physics.
Geckinli, N. C. & Yavus, D., eds. Discrete Fourier Transformation & Its Applications to Power Spectra Estimation. (Studies in Electrical & Electronic Engineering: No. 8). 340p. 1983. 78.75 (ISBN 0-444-41713-3). Elsevier.
Gottlieb, Irving M. Power Control with Solid State Devices. 1985. text ed. 24.95 (ISBN 0-8359-5592-3). Reston.
Graf, Rudolf F. & Graf, Calvin R. Emergency Lighting & Power Projects. LC 84-8865. (Illus.). 304p. (Orig.). 1985. 18.95 (ISBN 0-8306-0788-9); pap. cancelled (1788). TAB Bks.
Grannis, Gary E. Modern Power Mechanics. LC 78-12106. 1979. scp 26.56 (ISBN 0-672-97130-5); pap. 12.04 scp student's manual (ISBN 0-672-97132-1); scp instructor's guide 3.67 (ISBN 0-672-97131-3). Bobbs.
Haywood, R. W. Analysis of Engineering Cycles. 3rd ed. LC 79-41225. (Illus.). 320p. 1980. 53.00 (ISBN 0-08-025441-1); pap. text ed. 15.75 (ISBN 0-08-025440-3). Pergamon.
Hill, Richard F. Energy Technology Conference Proceedings Series Vols. 1-10, 8 Vols. (Illus.). Set. pap. 325.00 (ISBN 0-686-38761-9). Gov Insts.
Hill, Richard F., ed. Energy Technology VII: Expanding Supplies & Conservation. LC 80-66431. (Illus.). 1581p. 1980. pap. text ed. 45.00 (ISBN 0-86587-006-3). Gov Insts.
--Energy Technology XI: Applications & Economics. (Illus.). 1520p. 1984. pap. 58.00 (ISBN 0-86587-012-8). Gov Insts.
Hodge, B. K. Analysis & Design of Energy Systems. LC 84-11568. (Illus.). 320p. 1985. text ed. 30.95 (ISBN 0-13-032814-6). P-H.
Hunt, V. Daniel. Energy Dictionary. 1979. 28.95 (ISBN 0-442-27395-9); pap. 16.95 (ISBN 0-442-23787-1). Van Nos Reinhold.
--Handbook of Energy Technology: Trends & Perspectives. 992p. 1981. 64.95 (ISBN 0-442-22555-5). Van Nos Reinhold.
Institute for Power System. Handbook of Mechanical Power Drives. 2nd ed. 600p. 1982. 190.00x (ISBN 0-85461-067-7, Pub. by Trade & Tech). State Mutual Bk.
Instrumentation for Energy Source Technology. LC 80-118477. 75p. 1980. pap. text ed. 6.00x (ISBN 0-87664-480-9). Instru Soc.
Instrumentation in the Power Industry, Vol. 27: Proceedings of the Power Instrumentation Symposium, 27th. LC 62-52679. 192p. 1984. pap. text ed. 40.00x (ISBN 0-87664-837-5). Instru Soc.
ISA Power Instrumentation Symposium. Instrumentation in the Power Industry, Vol. 23: Proceedings of the 23rd Power Instrumentation Symposium. LC 62-52679. 150p. 1980. pap. text ed. 30.00x (ISBN 0-87664-476-0). Instru Soc.
Isaacs, Alan, ed. The Multilingual Energy Dictionary. 288p. 1981. 22.50 (ISBN 0-87196-430-9). Facts on File.
Kenward, M. Potential Energy. LC 75-36174. (Illus.). 256p. 1976. pap. 12.95 (ISBN 0-521-29056-2). Cambridge U Pr.
Knight, U. G. Power Systems Engineering & Mathematics. 304p. 1975. pap. 29.00 (ISBN 0-08-018294-1). Pergamon.
Kovach, E. G., ed. Technology of Efficient Energy Utilization: Report, Nato Science Committee Conference, les Arcs, France, Oct. 1973. LC 74-19839. 82p. 1974. pap. text ed. 10.75 (ISBN 0-08-018314-X). Pergamon.
MacDonald, Angus J. Power: Mechanics of Energy Control. 1970. text ed. 15.96 (ISBN 0-87345-486-3); mechanical control man. 7.32 (ISBN 0-87345-484-7); fluid control man. 7.32 (ISBN 0-87345-488-X); electric control man. 7.32 (ISBN 0-87345-487-1); optional experiments 7.32 (ISBN 0-87345-489-8); wkbk. & tests 4.67 (ISBN 0-87345-498-7); tchr's guide 46.67 (ISBN 0-87345-497-9); lab manual set 28.00 (ISBN 0-685-04238-3). McKnight.
McKnight Staff Members & Miller, Wilbur R. Power Mechanics. LC 78-53394. (Basic Industrial Arts Ser.). (Illus.). 1978. 7.28 (ISBN 0-87345-798-6); softbound 5.28 (ISBN 0-87345-790-0). McKnight.
Metz, Karen S. Information Sources in Power Engineering. LC 75-32096. 114p. 1976. lib. bdg. 29.95 (ISBN 0-8371-8538-6, MPE/). Greenwood.
Miller, Robert H. Power System Operation. 2nd ed. LC 82-24959. (Illus.). 224p. 1983. 33.50 (ISBN 0-07-041975-2). McGraw.
Mitchell, J. W. Energy Engineering. LC 82-19977. 236p. 1983. 41.95x (ISBN 0-471-08772-6, Pub. by Wiley-Interscience). Wiley.
Moran, Michael. Availability Analysis: A Guide to Efficient Energy Use. (Illus.). 304p. 1982. 55.00 (ISBN 0-13-054874-X). P-H.
Mott-Smith, Morton. Concept of Energy Simply Explained. Orig. Title: Story of Energy, Il. 1934. pap. 3.95 (ISBN 0-486-21071-5). Dover.
Palz, W. & Schnell, W. Wind Energy. 1983. lib. bdg. 32.50 (ISBN 90-2771-603-X, Pub. by Reidel Holland). Kluwer Academic.
Power Instrumentation Symposium. Instrumentation in the Power Industry, Vol. 24: Proceedings of the 24th Power Instrumentation Symposium. LC 62-52679. 200p. 1981. pap. text ed. 35.00x (ISBN 0-87664-520-1). Instru Soc.
--Instrumentation in the Power Industry, Vol. 26: Proceedings of the Power Instrumentation Symposium. LC 62-52679. 248p. 1983. pap. text ed. 40.00x (ISBN 0-87664-770-0). Instru Soc.
Ray, G. F. & Uhlmann, L. The Innovation Process in the Energy Industry. LC 78-17064. (National Institute of Economic & Social Research, Occasional Papers Ser.: No. 30). 1979. 27.95 (ISBN 0-521-22371-7). Cambridge U Pr.
Romer, Robert H. Energy: An Introduction to Physics. LC 75-35591. (Illus.). 628p. 1976. 27.95x (ISBN 0-7167-0357-2); tchr's guide avail. W H Freeman.
Slesser, Malcolm. The Dictionary of Energy. LC 82-10252. 1983. 29.95 (ISBN 0-8052-3816-6). Schocken.
Stein, Charles, ed. Critical Materials Problems in Energy Production. 1976. 70.00 (ISBN 0-12-665050-0). Acad Pr.

Association of Energy Engineers. Advances in Energy Utilization Technology. 1982. text ed. 45.00 (ISBN 0-915586-62-2); pap. text ed. 30.00 (ISBN 0-915586-61-4). Fairmont Pr.
--Energy Audit Source Book. 1982. text ed. 28.00 (ISBN 0-915586-42-8). Fairmont Pr.
Auer, Peter, ed. Energy & the Developing Nations: Proceedings of the Electric Power Research Institute (EPRI) Workshop on Energy & the Developing Nations, Hoover Institution, Stanford University, March 18-20, 1980. LC 80-29586. (Pergamon Policy Studies on Energy). (Illus.). 528p. 1981. 65.00 (ISBN 0-08-027527-3). Pergamon.
Auer, Peter L. & Douglas, David, eds. Advances in Energy Systems & Technology, Vol. 4. (Serial Publication Ser.). 1983. 55.00 (ISBN 0-12-014904-4). Acad Pr.
Axel, Helen, ed. Regional Perspectives on Energy Issues. (Report Ser.: No. 825). (Illus.). vii, 63p. (Orig.). 1982. pap. 75.00 (ISBN 0-8237-0264-2); pap. 15.00 member. Conference Bd.
Axelrod, Regina S., ed. Environment, Energy, & Public Policy: Conflict & Resolution. LC 79-3523. (Conflict & Resolution). (Illus.). 1981. 26.00x (ISBN 0-669-03460-6). Lexington Bks.
Bach, Wilfrid, et al, eds. Interactions of Energy & Climate. 568p. 1980. lib. bdg. 58.00 (ISBN 90-277-1179-8, Pub. by Reidel Holland); pap. 26.50 (ISBN 90-277-1177-1, Pub. by Reidel Holland). Kluwer Academic.
Bagotzky, V. S. & Sjundin, A. M. Chemical Power Sources. LC 80-40832. 1981. 67.50 (ISBN 0-12-072650-5). Acad Pr.
Balachandran, Sarojini, ed. Energy Statistics: A Guide to Information Sources. LC 80-13338. (Natural World Information Guide Ser.: Vol. 1). 272p. 1980. 60.00x (ISBN 0-8103-1419-3). Gale.
Banks, Ferdinand E. Resources & Energy: An Economic Analysis. LC 81-47967. 368p. 1983. 36.50x (ISBN 0-669-05203-5). Lexington Bks.
Barker, Michael. Studies in Renewable Resource Policy, 2 vols. 1981. pap. write for info. (ISBN 0-934842-74-4). Coun State Plan.
Barker, T. S. & Brailovsky, Vladimiro, eds. Oil or Industry: Energy, Industrialization & Economic Policy in Canada, Mexico, Norway, the Netherlands & the United Kingdom. LC 81-67884. 1981. 55.00 (ISBN 0-12-078620-6). Acad Pr.
Barnhill, Herschel J. From Surplus to Substitution: Energy in Texas. (Texas History Ser.). (Illus.). 45p. (Orig.). 1983. pap. text ed. 1.95x (ISBN 0-89641-118-4). American Pr.
Battelle Columbus Laboratories. Solar Energy Employment & Requirements: 1978-1983. 200p. 1981. pap. 29.50x (ISBN 0-89934-102-0, V.065). Solar Energy Info.
Bauly, J. A. & Bauly, C. B., eds. World Energy Directory. 2nd ed. 600p. 1985. 180.00x (ISBN 0-317-31613-3, Pub. by Longman). Gale.
--World Energy Directory: A Guide to Organizations & Research Activities in Non-Atomic Energy. 600p. 1981. 210.00x (ISBN 0-582-90011-5, Pub. by Longman). Gale.
Bemis, Virginia. Energy Guide: A Directory of Information Resources. LC 77-10470. (Reference Library of Social Science: Vol. 43). 1977. lib. bdg. 33.00 (ISBN 0-8240-9870-6). Garland Pub.
Benemann, John R. Biofuels: A Survey. 106p. 1980. pap. 19.95x (ISBN 0-89934-006-7, B045). Solar Energy Info.
Berg, Larry L., et al, eds. The United States & World Energy Sources. LC 81-21171. 320p. 1982. 39.95 (ISBN 0-03-059807-9). Praeger.
Berrie, T. W. Power System Economics. (IEE Power Engineering Ser.: No. 5). 288p. 1983. pap. 69.00 (ISBN 0-906048-88-5, P0005, Pub. by Peregrinus England). Inst Elect Eng.
Bickford, J. P. & Mullineux, N. Computation of Power-System Transients. (IEE Monograph Ser.: No. 18). 186p. 1980. pap. 32.00 (ISBN 0-906048-35-4). Inst Elect Eng.
Biogas & Other Rural Energy Resources Workshop. Workshop on Biogas & Other Rural Energy Resources: Proceedings, Roving Seminar on Rural Energy Development, Held at Bangkok, Manila, Tehran & Jakarta. (Energy Resources Development Ser.: No. 19). 152p. 1979. pap. text ed. 10.00 (ISBN 0-686-71072-X, UN79/2F10, UN). Unipub.
Bisio, Attilio. Encyclopedia of Energy Technology. 4000p. 1983. Set. 350.00x (ISBN 0-471-89039-1, Pub. by Wiley-Interscience). Wiley.
Blair, Peter D., et al. Geothermal Energy: Prospects for Energy Production. LC 81-13139. (Alternate Energy Ser.). 184p. 1982. 36.95x (ISBN 0-471-08063-2, Pub. by Wiley-Interscience). Wiley.
Bocknis, J. O'M. Energy Options Real Economics & the Solar-Hydrogen System. 442p. 1980. cancelled (ISBN 0-85066-204-4). Taylor & Francis.
Bockris, J. O. Energy: The Solar Hydrogen Alternative. LC 75-19125. 365p. 1975. 44.95x (ISBN 0-470-08429-4). Halsted Pr.
Bohi, Douglas R. Analyzing Demand Behavior: A Study of Energy Elasticities. LC 81-47616. (Resources for the Future: Economics of Natural Resources Ser.). 192p. 1981. text ed. 19.50x (ISBN 0-8018-2705-1). Johns Hopkins.
Bohi, Douglas R. & Quandt, William B. Energy Security in the Nineteen Eighties: Economic & Political Perspectives. 67p. 1984. pap. 6.95 (ISBN 0-8157-1001-1). Brookings.
Bohi, Douglas R. & Toman, Michael A. Analyzing Nonrenewable Resource Supply. LC 83-43264. 180p. 1984. lib. bdg. 25.00x (ISBN 0-915707-05-5); pap. text ed. 10.00x (ISBN 0-915707-06-3). Resources Future.
Bohm, Robert A., et al, eds. Toward an Efficient Energy Future: Proceedings of the III International Energy Symposium III-May 23-27, 1982. Energy, Environment, & Resources Center,the University of Tennessee. (International Energy Symposia Ser.). 352p. 1983. prof. ref. 39.95 (ISBN 0-88410-878-3). Ballinger Pub.
--World Energy Production & Productivity: Proceedings of the International Energy Symposium I-October 14, 1980. Energy, Environment, & Resource Center, the University of Tennessee. (International Energy Symposia Ser.). 448p. 1981. prof ref 28.50x (ISBN 0-88410-649-7). Ballinger Pub.
Booth, Don & Booth, Jonathan. Sun-Earth Buffering & Superinsulation. LC 83-72283. (Illus.). 1983. 19.95 (ISBN 0-9604422-4-3); pap. 12.95 (ISBN 0-9604422-3-5). Comm Builders.
Bossong, Ken. A Guide to Community Energy Self-Reliance, Vol. 1. (Illus.). 70p. (Orig.). 1981. pap. 3.25 (ISBN 0-89988-023-1). Citizens Energy.
Boyt & Copperfield. Alternative Sources of Energy, Wind, Hydro, No. 55. 56p. (Orig.). 1982. pap. 3.50 (ISBN 0-917328-45-0). ASEI.
Breslow, N. E. & Whittemore, A. S., eds. Energy & Health. LC 79-63265. (SIAM-SIMS Conference Ser.: No. 6). xii, 340p. 1979. pap. text ed. 18.00 (ISBN 0-89871-000-6). Soc Indus-Appl Math.
Bridwell, Rodger W. High Tech Investing: How to Profit from the Explosive New Growth in Companies in the 80's. LC 82-40358. 83p. 1983. 19.75 (ISBN 0-8129-1033-8). Times Bks.
Brin, Andre. Energy & the Oceans. 164p. 1981. 40.00x (ISBN 0-86103-024-9, Pub. by Westbury House). State Mutual Bk.
Brown, Harry L., ed. Energy Analysis of One Hundred Eight Industrial Processes. LC 84-48572. (Illus.). 313p. 1985. 39.00 (ISBN 0-915586-93-2). Fairmont Pr.
Bruchey, Stuart, ed. Energy in the American Economy, 52 bks, Vols. 1-28. (Illus.). 1979. Set. lib. bdg. 1202.00x (ISBN 0-405-11957-7). Ayer Co Pubs.
Bryant, Raymond C. & McGorray, J. J., eds. Managing Energy for Industry. (Illus.). 277p. 1983. 38.00 (ISBN 0-86587-108-6). Gov Insts.
Buck, L. E. & Goodwin, L. M. Alternative Energy: The Federal Role. 700p. 1982. 80.00 (ISBN 0-07-008730-X). Mcgraw.
Burby, Raymond & Bell, A. Fleming, eds. Energy & the Community. LC 78-15760. 160p. 1979. prof ref 27.50 (ISBN 0-88410-083-9). Ballinger Pub.
Burton, Dudley J. The Goverance of Energy: Problems, Prospects & Underlying Issues. LC 79-89507. 426p. 1980. 35.95x (ISBN 0-03-055981-2). Praeger.
Business Communications Staff. The Energy Revolution: 1980 Energy Conference Proceedings Fourth Annual International Conference on Energy. 1981. 75.00 (ISBN 0-89336-289-1). BCC.
Calzonetti, Frank J. & Eckert, Mark. Finding a Place for Energy: Siting Coal Conversion Facilities. Knight, C. Gregory, ed. LC 81-69236. (Resource Publications in Geography Ser.). (Orig.). 1981. pap. 5.00 (ISBN 0-89291-147-6). Assn Am Geographers.
Capellos, C. & Walker, R. F., eds. Fast Reactions in Energetic Systems. 759p. 1981. 89.50 (ISBN 90-277-1299-9, Pub. by Reidel Holland). Kluwer Academic.
Carruthers J. Bruce II, Business Info. Display, Inc. The Energy Decade: Nineteen Seventy to Nineteen Eighty. LC 81-22884. 558p. 1982. prof ref 150.00 (ISBN 0-88410-873-2). Ballinger Pub.
Carter, Anne P., ed. Energy & the Environment: A Structural Analysis. LC 74-15447. (Illus.). 280p. 1976. 25.00x (ISBN 0-87451-112-7). U Pr of New Eng.
Casper, Barry M. & Wellstone, Paul D. Powerline: The First Battle of America's Energy War. LC 80-25903. (Illus.). 328p. 1981. lib. bdg. 20.00x (ISBN 0-87023-320-3); pap. 9.95 (ISBN 0-87023-321-1). U of Mass Pr.
Cecelski, Elizabeth, et al. Household Energy & the Poor in the Third World: Domestic Energy Consumption for Low-Income Groups in Development Areas. LC 79-4863. (Resources for the Future Ser.). 1979. 6.75x (ISBN 0-8018-2283-1). Johns Hopkins.
Center for Study of the American Experience, ed. Energy in America: Fifteen Views. 285p. 1980. 22.50 (ISBN 0-88474-103-6). Transaction Bks.
Central Intelligence Agency. CIA Energy Information Reprint Series, 5 vols. Bereny, J. A., ed. Incl. Vol. I. The International Energy Situation: Outlook to 1985; Vol. 2. Prospects for Soviet Oil Production; Vol. 3. Prospects for Soviet Oil Production: A Supplemental Analysis; Vol. 4. China: Oil Production Prospects; Vol. 5. World Petroleum Outlook. 189p. 1979. Set. pap. 54.00x (ISBN 0-89934-000-8, V-050). Solar Energy Info.
Chapman, Duane. Energy Resources & Energy Corporations. LC 82-74022. (Illus.). 368p. 1983. 19.95x (ISBN 0-8014-1305-2). Cornell U Pr.
Chase, Andrew, ed. The Use & Processing of Renewable Resources: Chemical Engineering Challenge of the Future. LC 81-12682. (AIChE Symposium: Vol. 77). 141p. 1981. pap. 32.00 (ISBN 0-8169-0205-4, S-207); pap. 17.00 members (ISBN 0-686-47542-9). Am Inst Chem Eng.
Chateau, B. & Lapillone, B. Energy Demand: Facts & Trends. (Topics in Energy Ser.). (Illus.). 280p. 1982. 41.00 (ISBN 0-387-81675-5). Springer-Verlag.
Cheremisinoff, et al. Alternative Sources of Energy Transportation: Biomass Overview, No. 48, Mar.-Apr. 81. Marier, Donald, et al, eds. 60p. (Orig.). 1981. pap. 3.50 (ISBN 0-917328-38-8). ASEI.
Chigier, Norman A. Energy, Combustion & Environment. (Illus.). 689p. 1981. text ed. 55.00 (ISBN 0-07-010766-1). McGraw.
Chilton, Craig. H Two: Unlimited Energy Forever. (Illus., Orig.). 1982. pap. 3.95 (ISBN 0-933638-04-3). Xanadu Ent.
Choe, Boum Jone & Lambertini, Adrain. Global Energy Prospects. (Working Paper: No. 489). 50p. 1981. 5.00 (ISBN 0-686-36153-9, WP-0489). World Bank.
Christensen, John W. Energy, Resources & Environment. 224p. 1981. pap. text ed. 12.95 (ISBN 0-8403-2473-1); lab manual 6.95 (ISBN 0-8403-2575-4). Kendall-Hunt.
Christian, S. D. & Zuckerman, J. J. Energy & the Chemical Sciences. 34.00 (ISBN 0-08-022094-0). Pergamon.
Clark, Peter & Landfield, Judy. Natural Energy Workbook Two. rev. & expanded ed. (Illus.). 1976. pap. text ed. 3.95 (ISBN 0-917198-01-8). Visual Purple.
Clarke, Robin, ed. More than Enough: An Optimistic Assessment of World Energy. (Sextant Ser.: No. 1). 182p. 1982. pap. 18.00 (ISBN 92-3-101986-4, U1206, UNESCO). Unipub.
Cleveland, Harlan, ed. Energy Futures of Developing Countries: The Neglected Victims of the Energy Crisis. LC 80-10702. 104p. 1980. 33.95x (ISBN 0-03-058669-0). Praeger.
Collins, D. H., ed. Power Sources Five: Research & Development in Non-Mechanical Electrical Power Sources. 1975. 96.00 (ISBN 0-12-181450-5). Acad Pr.
--Power Sources Six. (Power Sources Ser.). 1978. 97.50 (ISBN 0-12-181452-1). Acad Pr.
Commerce Clearing House & United States Federal Energy Regulatory Commission. Federal Energy Regulatory Commission Reporter. LC 84-153382. Date not set. price not set. Commerce.
Committee on Nuclear & Alternative Energy Sources. Alternative Energy Demand Futures to 2010. 281p. 1979. pap. 10.50 (ISBN 0-309-02939-2). Natl Acad Pr.
Committee on Nuclear & Alternative Energy Systems. Domestic Potential of Solar & Other Renewable Energy Sources. 1979. pap. 8.50 (ISBN 0-309-02927-9). Natl Acad Pr.
--U. S. Energy Supply Prospects to 2010. 1979. pap. 9.25 (ISBN 0-309-02936-8). Natl Acad Pr.
Committee on Private Sector Participation in Government Energy RD&D Planning. Private Sector Participation in Federal Energy RD&D Planning. 1978. pap. 7.95 (ISBN 0-309-02783-7). Natl Acad Pr.
Commoner, Barry & Boksenbaum, Howard, eds. Energy & Human Welfare: Alternative Technologies for Power Production, Vol. 2. LC 75-8987. 1975. 14.95 (ISBN 0-02-468430-9). Macmillan Info.
Commoner, Barry, et al, eds. Energy & Human Welfare: A Critical Analysis, 3 vols. 1975. 40.00 set (ISBN 0-02-468410-4). Macmillan Info.
Computer Strategies Staff. The Oil & Gas Computer Handbook. 150p. 1983. looseleaf 45.00x (ISBN 0-913505-16-1). Computer Strat.
Congressional Office of Technology Assessment. The Direct Use of Coal: Prospects & Problems of Production & Combustion. 432p. 1981. prof ref. 35.00x (ISBN 0-88410-648-9). Ballinger Pub.
--Energy from Biological Processes: Technical & Environmental Analyses. 248p. 1981. prof ref 35.00x (ISBN 0-88410-647-0). Ballinger Pub.
Congressional Quarterly Inc. Energy Issues: New Directions & Goals. LC 82-2523. (Editorial Research Reports Ser.). 204p. 1982. pap. 9.25 (ISBN 0-87187-234-X). Congr Quarterly.
Connolly, John S. Photochemical Conversion & Storage of Solar Energy. LC 81-12853. 1981. 55.00 (ISBN 0-12-185880-4). Acad Pr.
Considine, Douglas M. Energy Technology Handbook. 1977. 82.50 (ISBN 0-07-012430-2). McGraw.
Constans, Jacques A. Marine Sources of Energy. (Pergamon Policy Studies). (Illus.). 1980. 33.00 (ISBN 0-08-023897-1). Pergamon.
Cook, Earl. Energy: The Ultimate Resource? Natoli, Salvatore J., ed. LC 77-87402. (Resource Papers for College Geography). (Illus.). 1978. pap. 4.00 (ISBN 0-89291-127-1). Assn Am Geographers.
--Man, Energy, Society. LC 75-33774. (Illus.). 478p. 1976. text ed. 25.95 (ISBN 0-7167-0725-X); pap. text ed. 13.95 (ISBN 0-7167-0724-1). W H Freeman.
Copulos, Milton. Energy Perspectives. LC 78-56073. 1978. 6.95 (ISBN 0-686-63839-5). Heritage Found.
Cortese, Charles F., ed. The Social Impacts of Energy Development in the West. 1985. text ed. 24.95x (ISBN 0-8290-0235-9). Irvington.
Cose, Ellis. Decentralizing Energy Decision: The Rebirth of Community Power. LC 83-14686. 135p. 1983. softcover 17.50x (ISBN 0-86531-801-8). Westview.
Cottrell, William F. Energy & Society: The Relation Between Energy, Social Change & Economic Development. LC 75-100152. Repr. of 1955 ed. lib. bdg. 21.75x (ISBN 0-8371-3679-2, COES). Greenwood.
Counihan, Martin. A Dictionary of Energy. (Illus.). 200p. 1981. 16.95x (ISBN 0-7100-0847-3). Routledge & Kegan.
Crabbe, David & McBride, Richard, eds. The World Energy Book: An A-Z, Atlas, & Statistical Sourcebook. (Illus.). 1979. pap. 12.50x (ISBN 0-262-53036-8). MIT Pr.
Craig, Paul P., ed. Energy Decentralization. Levine, Mark D. (AAAS Selected Symposium 72). 175p. 1982. lib. bdg. 21.00x (ISBN 0-86531-407-1). Westview.
Crawley, Gerald M. Energy. (Illus.). 320p. 1975. text ed. write for info. (ISBN 0-02-325580-3, 32558). Macmillan.
Critser, James R., Jr. Energy Systems: Solar, Water, Wind, Geothermal. (Ser. 11-80). 1982. 150.00 (ISBN 0-914428-83-7). Lexington Data.
--Energy Systems: Solar, Wind, Water, Geothermal. (Ser. 11-78). 1979. 135.00 (ISBN 0-914428-58-6). Lexington Data.
--Energy Systems: Solar, Wind, Water, Geothermal. (Ser. 11-79). 1981. 140.00 (ISBN 0-914428-70-5). Lexington Data.
--Energy Systems: Solar, Wind, Water, Geothermal. (Ser. 11-77). 1978. 130.00 (ISBN 0-914428-47-0). Lexington Data.
--Energy Systems: Solar, Wind, Water, Geothermal. (Ser. 11-82). 1983. 150.00 (ISBN 0-88178-001-4). Lexington Data.
--Energy Systems: Solar, Wind, Water Geothermal. (Ser.11-81). 204p. 1983. 150.00 (ISBN 0-88178-000-6). Lexington Data.
Crowley, Maureen, ed. Energy: Sources of Print & Nonprint Materials. LC 79-26574. (Neal-Schuman Sourcebook Ser.). 341p. 1980. 35.00 (ISBN 0-918212-16-2). Neal-Schuman.
Crump, Ralph W., ed. The Design Connection: Energy & Technology in Architecture. Harms, Martin J. (Preston Thomas Memorial Series in Architecture). 144p. 1981. 23.95 (ISBN 0-442-23125-3). Van Nos Reinhold.
Csaki, F. & Anszky, K. Power Electronics. 1980. Repr. of 1975 ed. 50.50 (ISBN 0-9960004-9-6, Pub. by Akademiai Kaido Hungary). Heyden.
Cuff, David J. & Young, William J. The United States Energy Atlas. (Illus.). 1980. 85.00 (ISBN 0-02-691250-3). Free Pr.
Culp, Archie W. Principles of Energy Conversion. (Illus.). 1979. text ed. 42.00 (ISBN 0-07-014892-9). McGraw.
Curran, Samuel C. & Curran, John S. Energy & Human Needs. LC 79-16728. 330p. 1979. 32.95x (ISBN 0-470-26818-2). Halsted Pr.
Daniels, Keith W. Old-Time Alternate Energy. (Illus.). 160p. 1983. pap. 6.95 (ISBN 0-934646-14-7). TX S & S Pr.
Darmstadter, Joel, et al. Energy Today & Tomorrow: Living with Uncertainty, A Book From Resources For The Future. 1983. pap. 13.95 (ISBN 0-13-277632-4). P-H.

Health Impacts of Different Sources of Energy: Proceedings of a Symposium Held at Nashville, June 22-26 1981 Jointly Organized by WHO, UNEP, and IAEA. (Proceedings Ser.). (Illus.). 701p. 1982. pap. 83.75 (ISBN 92-0-010182-8, ISP594, IAEA). Unipub.
Healy, Timothy & Houle, Paul. Energy & Society. 2nd ed. 480p. 1983. pap. text ed. 18.75x (ISBN 0-87835-132-9). Boyd & Fraser.
Hellman, Caroline J. C. & Hellman, Richard. The Competitive Economics of Nuclear & Coal Power. LC 82-47500. 208p. 1982. 26.50x (ISBN 0-669-05533-6). Lexington Bks.
Herman, Stewart W., et al. Energy Futures: Industry & the New Technologies. LC 76-30324. 1977. pap. 11.95 (ISBN 0-88410-617-9). INFORM.
Higgins, Judith H. Energy: A Multimedia Guide for Children & Young Adults. LC 78-15611. (Selection Guide Ser.: No. 2). 195p. 1979. text ed. 22.95 (ISBN 0-87436-266-0). Neal-Schuman.
Hill, Philip G. Power Generation: Resources, Hazards, Technology & Costs. LC 76-54739. 1977. 40.00x (ISBN 0-262-08091-5). MIT Pr.
Hill, Richard F., ed. Energy Technology IV: Confronting Reality. (Illus.). 484p. 1977. pap. text ed. 30.00 (ISBN 0-86587-003-9). Gov Insts.
--Energy Technology VI: Achievements in Perspective. LC 78-55582. 1152p. 1979. pap. text ed. 38.00 (ISBN 0-86587-005-5). Gov Insts.
--Energy Technology VII: Expanding Supplies & Conservation. LC 80-66431. (Illus.). 1581p. 1980. pap. text ed. 45.00 (ISBN 0-86587-006-3). Gov Insts.
--Energy Technology XI: Applications & Economics. (Illus.). 1520p. 1984. pap. 58.00 (ISBN 0-86587-012-8). Gov Insts.
Hollander, Jack M., et al, eds. Annual Review of Energy, Vol. 3. (Illus.). 1978. text ed. 20.00 (ISBN 0-8243-2303-3). Annual Reviews.
--Annual Review of Energy, Vol. 4. (Illus.). 1979. text ed. 20.00 (ISBN 0-8243-2304-1). Annual Reviews.
--Annual Review of Energy, Vol. 5. (Illus.). 1980. text ed. 20.00 (ISBN 0-8243-2305-X). Annual Reviews.
--Annual Review of Energy, Vol. 6. (Illus.). 1981. text ed. 20.00 (ISBN 0-8243-2306-8). Annual Reviews.
Holloway, Milton L., ed. Texas National Energy Modeling Project: An Experience in Large-Scale Model Transfer & Evaluation. 1980. 21.50 (ISBN 0-12-352950-6). Acad Pr.
Holmes, J. D., et al, eds. Wind Engineering 1983: Proceedings of the 6th International Conference on Wind Engineering, Gold Coast, Australia, March 21-25 & Auckland, New Zealand, April 6-7, 1983, 3 vols. (Studies in Wind Engineering & Industrial Aerodynamics: Vol. 3). 1400p. 1984. Repr. Set. 296.50 (ISBN 0-444-42344-3, I-246-84). Elsevier.
Homerding, Gail L. Data Inputs for Projection of Alternative Energy Impact Scenarios: For the Following Counties: Garfield, Mesa, Moffat, Rio Blanco, Routt. 292p. 1979. 25.00 (ISBN 0-686-64179-5). U CO Busn Res Div.
Hottel, H. C. & Howard, J. B. New Energy Technology - Some Facts & Assessments. 384p. 1972. pap. 6.95x (ISBN 0-262-58019-5). MIT Pr.
Howell, Yvonne & Miller, Harry. Selling the Solar Home-California Edition. 93p. 1980. pap. 15.00x (ISBN 0-89934-081-4, R.005). Solar Energy Info.
Hsieh, Kitty, ed. Energy: A Scientific, Technical & Socio-Economic Bibliography. (OSU Press Bibliographic Ser: No. 12). 102p. 1976. pap. 4.95x (ISBN 0-87071-132-6). Oreg St U Pr.
--Energy Reference Sources. (Bibliographic Ser: No. 10). 54p. 1975. pap. 3.95x (ISBN 0-87071-130-X). Oreg St U Pr.
Hu, David. Cogeneration. 1984. text ed. 39.95 (ISBN 0-8359-0771-6). Reston.
Hughart, David P. Prospects for Traditional & Non-Conventional Energy Sources in Developing Countries. (Working Paper: No. 346). ii, 132p. 1979. 5.00 (ISBN 0-686-36159-8, WP-0346). World Bank.
Humpage, W. Derek. Z-Transform Electromagnetic Transient Analysis in High-Voltage Networks. (IEE Power Engineering Ser.: No. 3). 264p. 1982. pap. 65.00 (ISBN 0-906048-79-6, P0003, Pub. by Peregrinus England). Inst Elect Eng.
Hunt, V. Daniel. Energy Dictionary. 1979. 28.95 (ISBN 0-442-27395-9); pap. 16.95 (ISBN 0-442-23787-1). Van Nos Reinhold.
--Handbook of Energy Technology: Trends & Perspectives. 992p. 1981. 64.95 (ISBN 0-442-22555-5). Van Nos Reinhold.
Hyde, Margaret O. Energy: The New Look. 128p. 1981. 9.95 (ISBN 0-07-031552-3). McGraw.
IES Energy Management Committee. IES Recommended Procedure for Lighting Power Limit Determination. (Lighting Energy Management Ser.). (Illus., Orig.). 12.00 (ISBN 0-87995-012-9, IES LEM-1); 7.00 (ISBN 0-686-46680-2). Illum Eng.
IFAC Symposium, New Delhi, India, Aug. 1979. Computer Applications in Large Scale Power Systems: Proceedings, 3 vols. Subramanyam, B. R., ed. (Illus.). 1100p. 1982. Set. 225.00 (ISBN 0-08-024450-5). Pergamon.
IFAC Symposium, Pretoria, South Africa, Sept. 1980. Automatic Control in Power Generation, Distribution & Protection: Proceedings. Herbst, J. F., ed. LC 80-40912. 550p. 1981. 115.00 (ISBN 0-08-026709-2). Pergamon.
Improved Techniques for the Extraction of Primary Forms of Energy. 275p. 1982. 99.00x (ISBN 0-686-45862-1, Pub. by Order Dept Graham Trotman England). State Mutual Bk.
Inall, E. K., ed. High Power High Energy Pulse Production & Application: The Proceedings of an Australian-US Seminar on Energy Storage, Compression, & Switching. LC 78-74553. (Illus.). 1979. text ed. 29.50 (ISBN 0-7081-0311-1, 0530, Pub. by ANUP Australia). Australia N U P.
INFOTERRA Directory of Sources of Information on New & Renewable Sources of Energy. 252p. 1982. pap. 40.00 (ISBN 0-686-95392-4, UNEP068, UNEP). Unipub.
Inglis, David R. Wind Power & Other Energy Options. LC 78-9102. (Illus.). 1978. 16.00 (ISBN 0-472-09303-7); pap. 9.95 (ISBN 0-472-06303-0). U of Mich Pr.
Institution of Chemical Engineers, Research Committee Working Party. Materials & Energy Resources. 68p. 1981. 42.00x (ISBN 0-85295-012-8, Pub. by Inst Chem Eng England). State Mutual Bk.
Instrumentation in the Power Industry, Vol. 25: Proceedings of the 25th Power Instrumentation Symposium. LC 62-52679. 292p. 1982. pap. text ed. 25.00x (ISBN 0-87664-698-4). Instru Soc.
International Conference on Alternative Energy Sources, 3rd, Miami Beach, Alternative Energy Sources Three: Proceedings, 9 Vols. Veziroglu, T. Nejat, ed. LC 82-9181. (Illus.). 4157p. 1983. Set. text ed. 597.00 (ISBN 0-89116-226-7). Hemisphere Pub.
International Conference on Reliability of Power Supply Systems (1977: London) International Conference on Reliability of Power Supply Systems, 21-23 February 1977: Organised by the Power & Control & Automation Divisions of the Institution of Electrical. (Institution of Electrical Engineers Conference Publications Ser.: No. 148). (Illus.). pap. 44.00 (ISBN 0-317-09402-5, 2013557). Bks Demand UMI.
International Electric Energy Conference, 1980. 358p. (Orig.). 1980. pap. text ed. 45.00x (ISBN 0-85825-137-X, Pub. by Inst Engineering Australia). Brookfield Pub Co.
International Project for Soft Energy Paths Network. Tools for the Soft Path. (Illus.). 288p. (Orig.). 1982. pap. 11.95 (ISBN 0-686-83030-X). Brick Hse Pub.
International Science & Technology, Inc. Report on the Potential Use of Small Dams to Produce Power for Low-Income Communities. Allen, Mary M., ed. (Illus.). 1979. 15.00 (ISBN 0-936130-02-4). Intl Sci Tech.
Ion, D. C. Availability of World Energy Resources: First Supplement. 112p. (Orig.). 1976. pap. 12.00x (ISBN 0-87201-908-X). Gulf Pub.
Isaacs, Alan, ed. The Multilingual Energy Dictionary. 288p. 1981. 22.50 (ISBN 0-87196-430-9). Facts on File.
Isacson, Orjan & Rideout, Edward. Energy Systems Handbook. 300p. (Orig.). 1981. pap. 9.95 (ISBN 0-89182-042-6). Charles River Bks.
An Issues Paper: Contributed by the Energy Study Group of the Goals, Processes & Indicators of the Development Project, UNU. 1981. pap. 5.00 (ISBN 92-808-0322-0, TUNU145, UNU). Unipub.
Jager, Jill. Climate & Energy Systems: A Review of Their Interactions. LC 82-21925. 231p. 1983. 42.95x (ISBN 0-471-90114-8, Pub. by Wiley-Interscience). Wiley.
Jaques Cattell Press, ed. Energy Research Programs Directory. 444p. 1980. 75.00 (ISBN 0-8352-1242-4). Bowker.
Jon, D. C. Availability of World Energy Resources. 248p. 1980. 33.00x (ISBN 0-86010-193-2, Pub. by Graham & Trotman England). State Mutual Bk.
Kaliaguine, S. & Mahay, A., eds. Catalysis on the Energy Scene: Proceedings of the Canadian Symposium on Catalysis, 9th, Quebec, P. Q., Sept. 30-Oct. 3, 1984. (Studies in Surface Science & Catalysis: Vol. 19). 602p. 1984. 105.75 (ISBN 0-444-42402-4). Elsevier.
Kamrany, Nake M. U. S. Options for Energy Independence. LC 81-48394. 208p. 1982. 22.50x (ISBN 0-669-05361-9). Lexington Bks.
Kaplan, Seymour. Energy, Economics, & the Environment. (Illus.). 448p. 1983. 42.00 (ISBN 0-07-033286-X). McGraw.
Kaufman, Alvin, ed. Energy, Man & Civilization. 224p. 1980. pap. 20.00x (ISBN 0-939204-11-8, 79-20). Eng Found.
Kaupp, A. Gasification of Rice Hulls: Theory & Praxis. 330p. 1984. pap. 27.00 (ISBN 3-528-02002-4, Pub. by Vieweg & Sohn Germany). Heyden.
Kavrakoglu, Ibbrahim, ed. Mathematical Modeling of Energy Systems. (NATO Advanced Study Institute Ser.: Applied Science, No. 37). 490p. 1980. 55.00x (ISBN 90-286-0690-4). Sijthoff & Noordhoff.
Keeny, Spurgeon M., Jr. Nuclear Power Issues & Choices. LC 77-693. 1977. pap. 16.50 prof ref (ISBN 0-88410-065-0). Ballinger Pub.
Kenward, M. Potential Energy. LC 75-36174. (Illus.). 256p. 1976. pap. 12.95 (ISBN 0-521-29056-2). Cambridge U Pr.
Khouja, W. The Challenge of Energy. LC 81-12435. (Energy Resources & Policies of the Middle East & N. Africa Ser.). (Illus.). 176p. (Orig.). 1982. pap. text ed. 11.95x (ISBN 0-582-78335-6, 81-12435). Longman.
Kikuchi. Power Line Radiation. 1983. lib. bdg. 41.50 (ISBN 90-277-1541-6, Pub. by Reidel Holland). Kluwer Academic.
Kilpatrick, F. & Matchett, D., eds. Water & Energy: Technical & Policy Issues. LC 82-71351. 668p. 1982. pap. 52.00x (ISBN 0-87262-308-4). Am Soc Civil Eng.
Kranzberg, Melvin, et al, eds. Energy & the Way We Live. LC 79-25054. (Illus.). 520p. 1980. lib. bdg. 20.00x (ISBN 0-87835-092-6); pap. text ed. 15.00x (ISBN 0-87835-084-5); study guide 3.75x (ISBN 0-87835-089-6); pap. text bd. with study guide 16.25x (ISBN 0-87835-068-3); article bk. 5.00x (ISBN 0-87835-090-X); source bk. 5.00x (ISBN 0-87835-091-8). Boyd & Fraser.
Kraushaar, Jack J. & Ristinen, Robert A. Energy & Problems of a Technical Society. LC 84-3566. 480p. 1984. 26.50 (ISBN 0-471-86243-6); instrs'. manual avail. (ISBN 0-471-80206-9). Wiley.
Krenz, Jerrold H. Energy: Conversion & Utilization. 2nd ed. 1984. text ed. 39.17 scp (ISBN 0-205-08021-9, 328021); write for info. (ISBN 0-205-08022-7). Allyn.
Kursunglu, Behram N. & Perlmutter, Arnold, eds. Energy for Developed & Developing Countries. LC 81-48092. 224p. 1983. 30.00x (ISBN 0-669-05274-4). Lexington Bks.
Kursunoglu, Behram & Perlmutter, Arnold, eds. Directions in Energy Policy: A Comprehensive Approach to Energy Resource Decision-Making. LC 79-21524. 544p. 1980. prof ref 40.00 (ISBN 0-88410-089-8). Ballinger Pub.
Kursunoglu, Behram, et al, eds. A Global View of Energy. LC 81-47525. 352p. 1982. 39.50x (ISBN 0-669-04647-7). Lexington Bks.
Kursunoglu, Behram N. Global Energy Assessment & Outlook. 610p. 1984. pap. text ed. 170.00 (ISBN 3-7186-0224-5). Harwood Academic.
Kydes, A. S., et al, eds. Energy Modeling & Simulation: Proceedings of the IMACS World Congress on Systems Simulation & Scientific Computation, Tenth, Montreal, Canada, 8-13 Aug., 1982. (IMACS Transactions on Scientific Computation Ser.: Vol. IV). 394p. 1983. 55.25 (ISBN 0-444-86610-8, North Holland). Elsevier.
Laird, Melvin R. Energy - A Crisis in Public Policy. 1977. pap. 2.25 (ISBN 0-8447-3255-9). Am Enterprise.
Landsberg, Hans H. & Dukert, Joseph M. High Energy Costs-Uneven, Unfair, Unavoidable? (Resources for the Future Ser.). 120p. 1981. text ed. 12.50x (ISBN 0-8018-2781-7); pap. 4.95x (ISBN 0-8018-2782-5). Johns Hopkins.
Landsberg, Hans H., et al. Energy & the Social Sciences: An Examination of Research Needs. LC 74-16949. (Resources for the Future, RFF Working Paper: EN-3). pap. 160.00 (ISBN 0-317-26469-9, 2023804). Bks Demand UMI.
Lax, Peter D., ed. Mathematical Aspects of Production & Distribution of Energy. LC 77-7174. (Proceedings of Symposia in Applied Mathematics Ser.: No. 21). 137p. 1979. pap. 18.00 with corrections (ISBN 0-8218-0121-X, PSAPM-21). Am Math.
Lee, Kaiman, ed. Energy Film List. 1977. pap. text ed. 4.50x (ISBN 0-915250-25-X). Environ Design.
Leon, George D. Energy Forever: Power for Today & Tomorrow. LC 81-20547. (How-It-Works Ser.). (Illus.). 160p. 1981. 12.95 (ISBN 0-668-05206-6, 5206). Arco.
Leonard, Ellen M., ed. Wood Burning for Power Production. 135p. pap. 19.95x (ISBN 0-89934-048-2, B048-PP). Solar Energy Info.
Lindsay, R. Bruce. The Control of Energy. (Benchmark Papers in Energy: Vol. 6). 1977. 63.00 (ISBN 0-12-786962-X). Acad Pr.
Liscom, W., ed. The Energy Decade: 1970-1980. (World Energy Industry Information Services Ser.). (Illus.). 1982. 125.00 (ISBN 0-88410-873-2). Busn Info.
Littlefield, Charles W. Man, Minerals, & Masters. (Illus.). 172p. 1980. pap. 7.00 (ISBN 0-89540-059-6, SB-059). Sun Pub.
Lockwood, Robert M. Energy & Man. LC 75-36368. (Public Affairs Radio Ser.). 100p. 1975. pap. 4.00 (ISBN 0-87755-253-3). Bureau Busn UT.
Lucas, N. J. Local Energy Centres. (Illus.). 216p. 1978. 40.75 (ISBN 0-85334-782-4, Pub. by Applied Sci England). Elsevier.
McAuliffe, Charles A. Hydrogen & Energy. LC 80-66847. 112p. 1980. 12.95x (ISBN 0-87201-372-3). Gulf Pub.
McCarl, Henry N., et al. Bibliography on Energy Economics. (Public Administration Ser.: Bibliography P-903). 93p. 1982. pap. 14.25 (ISBN 0-88066-141-0). Vance Biblios.
McCormick, Michael E. Ocean Wave Energy Conversion. LC 81-494. (Alternate Energy Ser.). 233p. 1981. 47.50x (ISBN 0-471-08543-X, Pub. by Wiley-Interscience). Wiley.
McDonald, Stephen L. The Leasing of Federal Lands for Fossil Fuels Production. LC 78-23437. 1979. 17.50x (ISBN 0-8018-2194-0). Johns Hopkins.
McGown, Linda B. & Bockris, John O'M. How to Obtain Abundant Clean Energy. LC 79-24468. 275p. 1980. 18.95x (ISBN 0-306-40399-4, Plenum Pr). Plenum Pub.
McGraw-Hill Editors. McGraw-Hill Encyclopedia of Energy. 2nd ed. Parker, Sybil P., ed. LC 80-18078. (Illus.). 856p. 1980. 57.50 (ISBN 0-07-045268-7). McGraw.
McGuigan, Dermot. Harnessing the Wind for Home Energy. LC 77-17916. (Illus.). 1978. lib. bdg. 9.95 o. p. (ISBN 0-88266-118-3); pap. 6.95 (ISBN 0-88266-117-5). Garden Way Pub.
MacLean, Douglas & Brown, Peter G., eds. Energy & the Future. LC 82-18609. (Illus.). 218p. 1983. text ed. 37.50x (ISBN 0-8476-7149-6); pap. text ed. 18.50x (ISBN 0-8476-7225-5). Rowman.
McMullan, J. R., et al. Energy Resources. (Resource & Environmental Science Ser.). 177p. 1978. pap. text ed. 11.95x (ISBN 0-470-99377-4). Halsted Pr.
McVeigh, J. C. Energy Around the World: An Introduction to Energy Studies: Global Resources, Needs, Utilization. (Illus.). 253p. 1984. 35.00 (ISBN 0-08-031649-2); pap. 15.00 (ISBN 0-08-031650-6). Pergamon.
Manassah, Jamal T., ed. Alternate Energy Sources. 1981. Pt. A. 69.50 (ISBN 0-12-467101-2); Pt. B. 65.00 (ISBN 0-12-467102-0). Acad Pr.
Mangone, G. J., ed. Energy Policies of the World. 1976-79. Vol. 1. 39.25 (ISBN 0-444-00196-4); Vol. 2. 39.25 (ISBN 0-444-00206-5); Vol. 3. 39.25 (ISBN 0-444-00351-7). Elsevier.
Manne, Alan S. & Kim, Sehun. Energy, International Trade, & Economic Growth. (Working Paper: No. 474). 30p. 1981. pap. 3.00 (ISBN 0-686-39764-9, WP-0474). World Bank.
Marier, Donald & Stoiaken, Larry, eds. Alternative Sources of Energy-Hydro, No. 76. (Orig.). 1985. pap. price not set (ISBN 0-917328-66-3). ASEI.
Marier, Donald, et al, eds. Alternative Sources of Energy Wind & Ocean Power. (No. 50). 60p. (Orig.). 1981. pap. 3.50 (ISBN 0-917328-40-X). ASEI.
Marston, Edwin H. The Dynamic Environment: Water, Transportation, & Energy. LC 74-82346. pap. 108.00 (ISBN 0-317-10809-3, 2012461). Bks Demand UMI.
Materials Aspects of World Energy Needs. 1980. 15.50 (ISBN 0-309-03042-0). Natl Acad Pr.
Merriam, Robert L. The Energy Crisis. (Illus.). 7p. (Orig.). 1974. pap. 2.00 (ISBN 0-686-32494-3). R L Merriam.
Merrick, David & Marshall, Richard. Energy: Present & Future Options, Vol. 1. LC 80-41416. 340p. 1981. 63.95x (ISBN 0-471-27922-6, Pub. by Wiley-Interscience). Wiley.
Merrick, David, ed. Energy-Present & Future Options, Vol. 2. 350p. 1984. text ed. 65.00x (ISBN 0-471-90416-3, Pub. by Wiley Interscience). Wiley.
Messel, Harry, ed. Energy for Survival. (Illus.). 368p. 1979. 20.00 (ISBN 0-08-024794-6); pap. 15.00 (ISBN 0-08-024791-1). Pergamon.
Methane Digesters for Fuel Gas & Fertilizer. (Illus.). 1973. pap. text ed. 4.00 (ISBN 0-9600984-2-9). L J Fry.
Metzger, Norman. Energy: The Continuing Crisis. LC 76-18270. (Illus.). 1977. 14.37i (ISBN 0-690-01161-X). T Y Crowell.
Meyers, Robert A. Handbook of Energy Technology & Economics. LC 82-8477. 1089p. 1982. 79.95x (ISBN 0-471-08209-0, Pub. by Wiley-Interscience). Wiley.

Miami International Conference on Alternative Energy Sources, 2nd, Miami Beach. Alternative Energy Sources Two: Proceedings. Veziroglu, T. Nejat, ed. LC 80-25788. (Illus.). 4171p. 1981. Set. text ed. 650.00 (ISBN 0-89116-208-9). Hemisphere Pub.

Military & Aerospace Power Supply Market. 271p. 1982. 1200.00 (ISBN 0-86621-011-3, A1080). Frost & Sullivan.

Millard, Reed & Science Book Associates Editors. Energy: New Shapes-New Careers. LC 82-12433. (Illus.). 192p. 1982. PLB 9.79g (ISBN 0-671-42478-5). Messner.

Miller, David H. Energy at the Surface of the Earth: An Introduction to the Energetics of Ecosystems. (International Geophysics Ser.). 1981. 59.50 (ISBN 0-12-497150-4); student ed. 30.00 (ISBN 0-12-497152-0). Acad Pr.

Miller, E. Willard & Miller, Ruby M. Economic, Political & Regional Aspects of the World's Energy Problems. (Public Administration Ser.: Bibliography P-360). 99p. 1979. pap. 10.50 (ISBN 0-88066-038-4). Vance Biblios.

Miller, G. Tyler, Jr. Energy & Environment: The Four Energy Crises. 2nd ed. 208p. 1980. pap. text ed. write for info. (ISBN 0-534-00836-4). Wadsworth Pub.

Miller, Richard K. Energy Conservation Marketing Handbook. 1982. text ed. 42.50 (ISBN 0-915586-65-7). Fairmont Pr.

Mitsch, W. J., et al. Energy & Ecological Modelling: Proceedings of the International Symposium, Louisville, Ky, April 20-23, 1981. (Developments in Environmental Modelling Ser.: Vol. 1). 848p. 1982. 136.25 (ISBN 0-444-99731-8). Elsevier.

Moavenzadeh, F. & Geltner, D. Transportation, Energy & Economic Development: A Dilemma in the Developing World. (Energy Research Ser.: Vol. 5). 530p. 1984. 102.00 (ISBN 0-444-42338-9, I-247-84). Elsevier.

Mobil Corporation. The Clock Is Running. 1983. 14.95 (ISBN 0-671-43459-4). S&S.

Mobilizing Renewable Energy Technology in Developing Countries: Strengthening Local Capabilities & Research. 52p. 1981. 5.00 (ISBN 0-686-36154-7, EN-8101). World Bank.

Morgan, Robert P. & Iceman, Larry J. Renewable Resource Utilization for Development. (PPS on International Development Ser.). 325p. 1981. 43.00 (ISBN 0-08-026338-0). Pergamon.

Morgan, W. B. & Ross, R. P., eds. Rural Energy Systems in the Humid Tropics: Proceedings of the First Workshop of the United Nations University Rural Energy Systems Project, Ife, Nigeria, 10-12 Aug. 1978. 56p. 1980. pap. 8.50 (ISBN 92-808-0093-0, TUNU088, UNU). Unipub.

Morgenthaler, George W. & Silver, Aaron N., eds. Energy Delta, Supply vs. Demand. (Science & Technology Ser: Vol. 35). 604p. 1975. lib. bdg. 35.00x (ISBN 0-87703-070-7, Pub. by Am Astronaut); pap. 25.00x (ISBN 0-87703-082-0). Univelt Inc.

Moroney, John R., ed. Advances in the Economics of Energy & Resources, Vol. 3. 300p. 1980. 45.00 (ISBN 0-89232-175-X). Jai Pr.

Morris, David. Self-Reliant Cities: Energy & the Transformation of Urban America. LC 81-18301. (Illus.). 256p. 1982. 19.95 (ISBN 0-87156-296-0); pap. 8.95 (ISBN 0-87156-309-6). Sierra.

Morrison, Denton E. Energy II: A Bibliography of 1975-1976 Social Science & Related Literature. (Reference Library of Social Science: Vol. 42). (Lc 76-052702). 1977. lib. bdg. 33.00 (ISBN 0-8240-9871-4). Garland Pub.

Morrison, James. The Complete Energy Savings Handbook for Home Owners. (P-BN 5108 Ser.). 288p. (Orig.). 1979. pap. 2.25i (ISBN 0-06-465108-8). Har-Row.

Mott-Smith, Morton. The Concept of Energy Simply Explained. LC 63-19496. 1964. lib. bdg. 10.50x (ISBN 0-88307-626-8). Gannon.

Murdock, Steve H. & Leistritz, F. Larry. Energy Development in the Western United States: Impact on Rural Areas. LC 79-18478. 384p. 1979. 44.95x (ISBN 0-03-051351-0). Praeger.

Musgrove, Peter J., ed. Wind Energy Conversion, 1984. (Illus.). 460p. 1985. 59.50 (ISBN 0-521-26899-0). Cambridge U Pr.

Mustoe, Julian E. An Atlas of Renewable Energy Resources: In the United Kingdom & North America. LC 83-10301. 202p. 1984. 79.95x (ISBN 0-471-10293-8, Pub. by Wiley-Interscience). Wiley.

Naill, Roger F. Managing the Energy Transition: A System Dynamics Search for Alternatives to Oil & Gas. LC 76-52752. prof ref 27.50 (ISBN 0-88410-608-X). Ballinger Pub.

Napolitano, L. G. Space & Energy. 90.00 (ISBN 0-08-021053-8). Pergamon.

National Academy of Sciences. Energy Use: The Human Dimension. (Illus.). 256p. 1984. text ed. 28.95 (ISBN 0-7167-1620-8); pap. 15.95 (ISBN 0-7167-1621-6). W H Freeman.

NATO Economic Directorate, ed. CMEA: Energy Nineteen Eighty to Nineteen Ninety. (NATO Colloquia). 337p. 1982. 45.00 (ISBN 0-89250-341-6). Orient Res Partners.

Nelson, Robert H. The Making of Federal Coal Policy. (Duke Press Policy Studies). (Illus.). 250p. 1983. 32.50 (ISBN 0-8223-0497-X). Duke.

Nesbit, William, ed. World Energy: Will There Be Enough in 2020? (Decisionmakers Bookshelf: Vol. 6). (Illus.). 88p. (Orig.). 1979. pap. 2.50 (ISBN 0-931032-06-7). Edison Electric.

Neufeld, M. Lynne & Cornog, Martha. Energy & Environment Information Resource Guide. 1982. 12.50 (ISBN 0-942308-15-8). NFAIS.

New Sources of Energy: Proceedings of a United Nations Conference, Vols. 1-7. Incl. Vol. 1. General Sessions. (Reprinted 1976). Repr. of 1979 ed. pap. 14.50 (ISBN 0-686-93409-1, UN63/1/2); Vols. 2 & 3. Geothermal Energy, 2 Pts. (Reprinted 1976). Pt. 1. pap. 21.50 (ISBN 0-686-93410-5, UN63/1/36); Pt. 2. pap. 24.00 (ISBN 0-686-99111-7, UN63/1/37); Vols. 4-6. Solar Energy, 3 Pts. Repr. of 1974 ed. Pt. 1. pap. 24.00 (ISBN 0-686-93412-1, UN63/1/38); Pt. 2. pap. 19.00 (ISBN 0-686-99112-5, UN63/1/39); Pt. 3. pap. 19.00 (ISBN 0-686-99113-3, UN63/1/40); Vol. 7. Wind Power. Repr. of 1974 ed. pap. 19.00 (ISBN 0-686-93415-6, UN63/1/41). (Eng. & Fr., UN). Unipub.

Newcomb, Richard. Future Resources: Their Geostatistical Appraisal. 179p. 1982. 7.50 (ISBN 0-937058-13-0). West Va U Pr.

Newman, Joseph W. The Energy Machine of Joseph Newman: An Invention Whose Time Has Come. Soule, Evan R., Jr., ed. (Illus.). 287p. 1985. 38.45 (ISBN 0-9613835-1-8). J Newman Pub.

Noll, Edward. Wind-Solar Energy for Radiocommunications & Low-Power Electrical Systems. 2nd ed. LC 81-51552. (Illus.). 264p. 1981. pap. 12.95 (ISBN 0-672-21827-5). Sams.

Nordhaus. The Efficient Use of Energy Resources. LC 79-64225. 1979. 25.00x (ISBN 0-300-02284-0). Yale U Pr.

Nordhaus, W. D. & Goldstein, R., eds. International Studies of the Demand for Energy: Selected Papers Presented at a Conference Held by the Institute for Applied Systems Analysis, Schloss Laxenburg, Austria. (Contributions to Economic Analysis: Vol. 120). 340p. 1978. 51.00 (ISBN 0-444-85079-1, North-Holland). Elsevier.

North Eastern Regional Antipollution Conference, 6th, 1975, et al. Energy from Solid Waste Utilization-(Proceedings of Anerac '75 Conference. Barnett, Stanley M. & Sussman, Donald, eds. LC 75-43007. (Illus.). 350p. 1976. pap. 9.95 (ISBN 0-87762-190-X). Technomic.

Oak Ridge Associated Universities. Industrial Energy Use Data Book. 1981. lib. bdg. 88.00 (ISBN 0-8240-7299-5). Garland Pub.

OAO Corp. for U. S. Department of Energy. Biomass Energy Systems Program Summary 1980. 220p. 1981. pap. 29.50x (ISBN 0-89934-103-9, B.022). Solar Energy Info.

Ocean Energy Resources: Presented at the Energy Technology Conference, Houston, Texas, Sept. 18-23, 1977. LC 77-82206. (American Society of Mechanical Engineers. Ocean Engineering Division Ser.: Vol. 4). (Illus.). pap. 27.50 (ISBN 0-317-09776-8, 2016806). Bks Demand UMI.

Oddy, Ray, et al, eds. World Energy Book: A-Z Atlas & Statistical Source Book. LC 78-50805. 259p. 1978. 35.00x (ISBN 0-89397-032-8). Nichols Pub.

Odum, Howard T. & Odum, Elisabeth C. Energy Basis for Man & Nature. 2nd ed. (Illus.). 352p. 1981. text ed. 22.50 (ISBN 0-07-047511-3); pap. text ed. 22.50 (ISBN 0-07-047510-5, C). McGraw.

OECD. Energy Research, Development & Demonstration in the IEA Countries, 1983. 180p. (Orig.). 1984. pap. 22.00X (ISBN 92-64-12627-9). OECD.

--Energy Statistics & Main Historical Series, 1982-1983. (Eng. & Fr.). 145p. (Orig.). 1985. pap. 20.00x (ISBN 92-64-02672-X). OECD.

OECD & IEA, eds. A Group Strategy for Energy Research, Development & Demonstration. 97p. (Orig.). 1980. pap. 8.00x (ISBN 9-2641-2124-2). OECD.

OECD Staff. Employment in the Public Sector. 79p. (Orig.). 1982. pap. 7.25 (ISBN 92-64-12319-9). OECD.

--Energy Policies & Programmes of IEA Countries, 1981 Review. 300p. 1982. pap. 20.00x (ISBN 92-64-12335-0). OECD.

--Energy Research Development & Demonstration in the IEA Countries: Review of National Programmes, 1982. 196p. (Orig.). 1983. pap. 22.00x (ISBN 92-64-12518-3). OECD.

--Energy Statistics 1971-1981. 640p. (Orig.). 1983. pap. text ed. 60.00x (ISBN 92-64-02415-8). OECD.

OECD Staff & IEA Staff. Energy Research, Development & Demonstration in the IEA Countries, 1981 Review of National Programmes. 157p. (Orig.). 1982. pap. 17.00x (ISBN 92-64-12383-0). OECD.

--World Energy Outlook. (Illus.). 500p. (Orig.). 1982. pap. 45.00 (ISBN 92-64-12360-1). OECD.

Oil Daily Editors & Hoffman, Cheryl. Congress on Energy. 1985. 45.00 (ISBN 0-317-18577-2). Oil Daily.

Oppenheimer, Ernest J. Natural Gas: The New Energy Leader. rev. ed. 188p. 1982. pap. 10.00 (ISBN 0-9603982-3-6). Pen & Podium.

--A Realistic Approach to U. S. Energy Independence. (Orig.). 1980. pap. 5.00 (ISBN 0-9603982-0-1). Pen & Podium.

Orlando, Joseph A. Cogeneration Technology Handbook. (Illus.). 178p. 1984. pap. 38.00 (ISBN 0-86587-067-5). Gov Insts.

The Other Energy Crisis: Firewood. (Worldwatch Institute Papers: No. 1). 22p. 1975. pap. 2.95 (ISBN 0-686-94937-4, WW1, WW). Unipub.

Owen, William F. & Culp, Wesner, Clup, Inc. Energy in Wastewater Treatment. (Illus.). 368p. 1982. 45.00 (ISBN 0-13-277665-0). P-H.

Oxford Energy Seminar, First & Mabro, Robert. World Energy; Issues & Policies: Proceedings. 1980. 44.00x (ISBN 0-19-920119-6). Oxford U Pr.

Palz, W. & Pirrwitz, D. Energy from Biomass. 1984. lib. bdg. 54.50 (ISBN 90-277-1700-1, Pub. by Reidel Holland). Kluwer Academic.

Patrick, Dale R. & Fardo, Stephen W. Energy Management & Conservation. (Illus.). 304p. 1982. 30.95 (ISBN 0-13-277657-X). P-H.

Patterson, Walter C. & Griffin, Richard F. Fluidized Bed Energy Technology: Coming to a Boil. LC 78-60484. (Orig.). 1978. pap. 25.00 (ISBN 0-918780-10-1). INFORM.

Penner, S. S. New Sources of Oil & Gas: Gases from Coal, Liquid Fuels from Coal, Shale, Tar Sands, & Heavy Oil Sources. (Illus.). 120p. 1982. 28.00 (ISBN 0-08-029335-2). Pergamon.

Penner, S. S. & Icerman, L. Energy II-Non-Nuclear Energy Technologies, Vol. II. (Illus.). 888p. 1984. 77.00 (ISBN 0-08-031943-2); pap. 29.95 (ISBN 0-08-031942-4). Pergamon.

Perrine, Richard L. & Ernst, W. G., eds. Energy: For Ourselves & Our Posterity. (Rubey Ser.: Vol. III). (Illus.). 640p. 1986. text ed. 37.95 (ISBN 0-13-277278-7). P-H.

Petersohn, Henry H. Computer Failure & Energy Shortages: Effects of Power Problems on Computer Operations. LC 78-10861. 1979. text ed. 25.00 (ISBN 0-89321-250-4). Tech Pr Inc.

Pettit, Rhonda, ed. A Kentucky Energy Resource Utilization Program: Annual Report, July 1, 1982-June 30, 1983. (Illus.). 121p. 1984. pap. text ed. write for info. (ISBN 0-86607-024-9, IMMR84/095). KY Ctr Energy Res.

--A Kentucky Energy Resource Utilization Program: Annual Report, 1979-1980. 115p. (Orig.). 1980. pap. 10.00 (ISBN 0-86607-003-6). KY Ctr Energy Res.

--A Kentucky Energy Resource Utilization Program: Annual Report, 1980-1981. 120p. 1981. pap. 10.00 (ISBN 0-86607-005-2). KY Ctr Energy Res.

--A Kentucky Energy Resource Utilization Program: Proceedings of the Annual Report, July 1, 1982-June 30, 1983. (Illus.). 121p. 1984. pap. text ed. write for info. (ISBN 0-86607-024-9, IMMR84-095). KY Ctr Energy Res.

Phillips, Owen. The Last Chance Energy Book. 160p. 1980. pap. 4.95 (ISBN 0-07-049800-8). McGraw.

Pindyck, Robert S. The Structure of World Energy Demand. (Illus.). 1979. 27.50x (ISBN 0-262-16074-9). MIT Pr.

Pindyke, Robert S., ed. Advances in the Economics of Energy & Resources, Vol. 1. 310p. 1979. 42.50 (ISBN 0-89232-078-8). Jai Pr.

--Advances in the Economics of Energy & Resources, Vol. 2. 250p. 1979. 42.50 (ISBN 0-89232-079-6). Jai Pr.

Plummer, James L., ed. Energy Vulnerability. 488p. 1982. prof ref 39.95x (ISBN 0-88410-871-6). Ballinger Pub.

Pluta, Joseph E., ed. The Energy Picture: Problems & Prospects. LC 80-68659. 185p. 1980. pap. 6.00 (ISBN 0-87755-243-6). Bureau Busn UT.

Power System Protection, Vol. II. (Illus.). 352p. 1981. 79.00 (ISBN 0-906048-53-2). Inst Elect Eng.

Power System Protection, Vol. III. (Illus.). 450p. 1981. 79.00 (ISBN 0-906048-54-0). Inst Elect Eng.

Power System Protection Principles & Components, Vol. 1. (Illus.). 544p. 1981. 88.00 (ISBN 0-906048-47-8). Inst Elect Eng.

PRC Energy Analysis Co. Design, Installation & Operation of Small, Stand-Alone Photovoltaic Powersystems: Applications Seminar Handbook. 353p. 1981. pap. 39.50x (ISBN 0-89934-092-X, P-041). Solar Energy Info.

Prenis, John, ed. Energybook, No. 1: Natural Sources & Backyard Applications. LC 74-84854. (Illus.). 117p. (Orig.). 1975. lib. bdg. 15.90 (ISBN 0-914294-22-9); pap. 7.95 (ISBN 0-914294-21-0). Running Pr.

--Energybook, No. 2: More Natural Sources & Backyard Applications. LC 74-84854. (Illus.). 128p. (Orig.). 1977. lib. bdg. 15.90 (ISBN 0-914294-50-4); pap. 5.00 (ISBN 0-914294-51-2). Running Pr.

Promoting Small Power Production: Implementing Section 210 of PURPA, Center for Renewable Resources, Solar Lobby & Others. 49p. 1981. 3.00 (ISBN 0-937446-04-1, 200). Ctr Renew Resources.

Pryde, Philip R. Nonconventional Energy Resources. LC 82-21827. (Environmental Science & Technology Series of Texts & Monographs). 270p. 1983. 35.95 (ISBN 0-471-86807-8, Pub. by Wiley-Interscience). Wiley.

Public Service Co. of New Mexico for U. S. Department of Energy. Technical & Economic Assessment of Solar Hybrid Repowering: Final Report. 450p. 1981. pap. 49.50x (ISBN 0-89934-083-0, T-044). Solar Energy Info.

Purcell, John. From Hand Ax to Laser: Man's Growing Mastery of Energy. LC 81-16389. (Illus.). 320p. 1983. 16.95 (ISBN 0-8149-0885-3). Vanguard.

Raytheon Service Co. for U. S. Department of Energy. Wind Energy Systems Program Summary Nineteen Eighty. 230p. 1981. pap. 24.50x (ISBN 0-89934-108-X, W-040). Solar Energy Info.

Report of the Fourth Session of the Sub-Committee on Management of Resources within the Limits of National Jurisdiction: Dakar, Senegal, 8-11 June 1982. (Fisheries Reports: No. 272). (Eng. & Fr.). 40p. 1983. pap. text ed. 7.50 (ISBN 92-5-101321-7, F2437, FAO). Unipub.

Report on the United Nations Conference on New & Renewable Sources of Energy, Nairobi, 10-21 August 1981. 126p. 1981. pap. 11.00 (ISBN 0-686-79015-4, UN81/1/24, UN). Unipub.

Residential Energy Audit Manual. 500p. 1981. text ed. 27.50 (ISBN 0-915586-54-1); pap. text ed. 11.95 (ISBN 0-915586-53-3). Fairmont Pr.

Rey, L. & Behrens, C., eds. Arctic Energy Resources: Proceedings of the Conference Held in Oslo, Norway, September 22-24, 1982. (Energy Research Ser.: Vol. 2). 376p. 1983. 78.75 (ISBN 0-444-42218-8). Elsevier.

Reynoldson, George. Let's Reach for the Sun: Thirty Original Solar & Earth Sheltered Home Designs. rev. ed. (Illus.). 144p. 1981. pap. 12.95 (ISBN 0-9603570-1-7). Space-Time.

Rhodes, F. M., ed. Power Up for the Recovery: Industrial Power Conference 1983. 104p. 1983. pap. text ed. 25.00 (ISBN 0-317-02641-0, I00159). ASME.

Ridgeway, James & Conner, Bettina. New Energy: Understanding the Crisis & a Guide to An Alternative Energy System. LC 74-16669. (Institute for Policy Studies Ser.). 228p. 1975. 9.95x (ISBN 0-8070-0504-5). Beacon Pr.

Ritchie, James D. Sourcebook of Farm Energy Alternatives. 384p. 1983. 34.50 (ISBN 0-07-052951-5). McGraw.

Roberts, F. S., ed. Energy: Mathematics & Models. LC 75-41915. (SIAM-SIMS Conference Ser.: No. 3). xxiv, 276p. 1976. pap. text ed. 24.00 (ISBN 0-89871-029-4). Soc Indus-Appl Math.

Robinson, J. S., ed. Chlorine Production Processes: Recent & Energy Saving Developments. LC 81-2361. (Chemical Technology Review: No. 185, Energy Technology Review: No. 64). (Illus.). 388p. 1981. 48.00 (ISBN 0-8155-0842-5). Noyes.

Romer, Robert H. Energy Facts & Figures. LC 84-16278. 72p. (Orig.). 1985. pap. 8.95 (ISBN 0-931691-17-6). Spring St Pr.

Rose, Dan. Energy Transition & the Local Community: A Theory of Society Applied to Hazleton, Pennsylvania. LC 80-52808. (Illus.). 256p. 1981. 25.00x (ISBN 0-8122-7792-9). U of Pa Pr.

Rosenbaum, Walter A. Energy, Politics & Public Policy. LC 80-29273. 229p. 1981. 9.95 (ISBN 0-87187-166-1). Congr Quarterly.

Ross, D. Energy from the Waves. 2nd rev. ed. LC 80-41076. (Illus.). 160p. 1981. 24.00 (ISBN 0-08-026715-7); pap. 10.00 (ISBN 0-08-026716-5). Pergamon.

Ross, Marc H. & Williams, Robert H. Our Energy-Regaining Control. (Illus.). 320p. 1980. 26.50 (ISBN 0-07-053894-8). McGraw.

Rouse, Robert S. & Smith, Robert O. Energy: Resource, Slave, Pollutant; a Physical Science Text. 1975. write for info. (ISBN 0-02-404000-2). Macmillan.

Rudman, Jack. Supervisor (Power Distributor) (Career Examination Ser.: C-423). (Cloth bdg. avail. on request). pap. 12.00 (ISBN 0-8373-0423-7). Natl Learning.

St. Clair, A. E., et al, eds. Energy Resources of Texas. (Illus.). 1976. Repr. 5.00 (ISBN 0-686-36614-X). Bur Econ Geology.

Willrich, Mason. Energy & World Politics. LC 75-12058. 1975. 10.00 (ISBN 0-02-935520-6). Free Pr.

The Working Group Meeting on Efficiency & Conservation in the Use of Energy: Proceedings. (Energy Resources Development Ser.: No. 22). 131p. 1981. pap. 11.00 (ISBN 0-686-78456-1, UN802F12, UN). Unipub.

World Dictionary of Energy Information, Vol. 3: North America. 420p. 1984. 95.00 (583-X). Facts on File.

World Energy Conference, ed. Energy Terminology: A Multi-Lingual Glossary. 275p. 1983. 100.00 (ISBN 0-08-029314-X, B110); pap. 40.00 (ISBN 0-08-029315-8). Pergamon.

World Energy Supplies: 1964-1978. Incl. 1950-1974. 45.00 (UN76/17/5); 1965-1968. (Eng. & Fr.). pap. 3.00 (ISBN 0-686-93507-1, UN70/17/19); 1966-1969. (Eng. & Fr.). pap. 3.00 (ISBN 0-686-93508-X, UN71/17/14); 1968-1971. pap. 9.00 (ISBN 0-686-93509-8, UN73/17/10); 1969-1972. pap. 9.00 (ISBN 0-686-93510-1, UN74/17/7); 1970-1973. pap. 12.00 (ISBN 0-686-93511-X, UN75/17/13); 1971-1975. pap. 17.00 (ISBN 0-686-93512-8, UN77/17/4); 1972-1976. pap. 17.00 (ISBN 0-686-93513-6, UN78/17/7); 1973-1978. pap. 20.00 (ISBN 0-686-93514-4, UN79/17/13). UN). Unipub.

World Hydrogen Energy Conference Papers, 4th, California, USA, 13-17 June 1982 & Veziroglu, T. N. Hydrogen: Today, Tomorrow & Beyond. 132p. 1983. pap. 50.00 (ISBN 0-08-031139-3). Pergamon.

Wright, A. & Newberry, P. G. Electric Fuses. (IEE Power Engineering Ser.: No. 2). 208p. 1982. pap. 26.00 (ISBN 0-906048-78-8, P0002, Pub. by Peregrinus England). Inst Elect Eng.

Yanarella, Ernest J. & Yanarella, Ann-Marie. Energy & the Social Sciences: A Bibliographic Guide to the Literature. (WVSS on Energy & Nat'l Resources Ser.). 350p. 1982. 28.00x (ISBN 0-86531-304-0). Westview.

Yannacone, Victor J., Jr. The Energy Crisis: Danger & Opportunity. LC 74-948. 300p. 1974. pap. text ed. 18.95 (ISBN 0-8299-0013-6). West Pub.

Yearbook of World Energy Statistics, 1979. 60.00 (ISBN 0-686-75224-4, E/F.80.XVII.7). UN.

Yearbook of World Energy Statistics 1980. (Eng. & Fr.). 896p. 1982. 60.00 (ISBN 0-686-81945-4, UN81/17/10, UN). Unipub.

Yearbook of World Energy Supplies 1970-1979. 60.00 (ISBN 0-686-84911-6, E/F.80.XVII.7). UN.

Yearbook of World Energy Supplies 1980. 60.00 (ISBN 0-686-84913-2, E/F.81.XVII.10). UN.

Youngquist, Walter. Energy Resources for the Future: Syllabus. 1977. pap. text ed. 8.50 (ISBN 0-89420-009-7, 231040); cassette recordings 196.75 (ISBN 0-89420-144-1, 231000). Natl Book.

Yuan, S. W., ed. Energy, Resources & Environment: Proceedings of the First U. S.-China Conference. (Illus.). 560p. 1982. pap. 94.00 (ISBN 0-08-029396-4). Pergamon.

Zimmer, Michael, ed. Cogeneration: Current Prospects & Future Opportunities. 3rd. ed. 310p. 1983. Wkbk. 48.00 (ISBN 0-86587-112-4). Gov Insts.

Zimmer, Michael J., ed. Cogeneration: Current Prospects & Future Opportunities. 4th ed. (Illus.). 216p. 1984. 3-ring binder 56.00 (ISBN 0-86587-069-1). Gov Insts.

Zimmer, Michael J. & Heavner, Martin L., eds. Cogeneration in California. (Illus.). 304p. 1983. 3-ring binder 68.00 (ISBN 0-86587-116-7). Gov Insts.

POWER RESOURCES–YEARBOOKS

United Nations. Yearbook of World Energy Statistics 1980-Annuaire Des Statistiques Mondiales De l'Energie 1980. (Fr. & Eng., Illus.). 1982. 60.00x (ISBN 0-8002-3308-5). Intl Pubns Serv.

POWER RESOURCES–ASIA

Asian Development Bank Staff. Asian Energy Problems. LC 81-84610. 304p. 1982. 39.95x (ISBN 0-03-061566-6). Praeger.

Pauker, G. Y., ed. Energy Efficiency & Conservation in the Asia-Pacific Region: Proceedings of the Fouth Workshop, Honolulu, Hawaii, June 2-5, 1981. 200p. 1983. pap. 25.00 (ISBN 0-08-030532-6). Pergamon.

Yager, Joseph A. Energy Balance in Northeast Asia. LC 84-45276. 249p. 1984. 28.95 (ISBN 0-8157-9672-2); pap. 10.95 (ISBN 0-8157-9671-4). Brookings.

POWER RESOURCES–AUSTRALIA

Clark, R. D. Australian Renewable Energy Resources Index, Nos. 1-3. (Microfiche only). 1978. 9.00 (C052, CSIRO). Unipub.

Clark, Robert D., ed. Australian Renewable Energy Resources Index: Issue No. 1. 1979. pap. 7.00x (ISBN 0-686-24273-4, Pub. by CSIRO). Intl Spec Bk.

Electric Energy, Nineteen Eighty-One. 140p. (Orig.). 1981. pap. text ed. 37.50x (ISBN 0-85814-167-1, Pub. by Inst Engineering Australia). Brookfield Pub Co.

Energy Australia. 160p. (Orig.). 1979. pap. text ed. 18.00x (ISBN 0-85825-121-3, Pub. by Inst Engineering Australia). Brookfield Pub Co.

Morse, R. N. & Cooper, P. I. Status of Solar Energy Utilization in Australia for Industrial, Commercial & Domestic Purposes: A State-of-the-Art Report as of Mid-1974. 45p. (2nd Printing 1980). 1974. pap. 6.00 (ISBN 0-643-01120-X, C029, CSIRO). Unipub.

Saddler, Hugh. Energy in Australia. 215p. 1981. text ed. 19.95x (ISBN 0-86861-298-7). Allen Unwin.

Salt, H. Performance of Three Australian Solar Hot Water Systems. 25p. 1976. pap. 6.00 (ISBN 0-643-01951-0, C023, CSIRO). Unipub.

POWER RESOURCES–CHINA–1949-

Taylor, Robert P. Rural Energy Development in China. LC 81-48250. (Resources for the Future Research Paper). 284p. 1982. pap. text ed. 10.50x (ISBN 0-8018-2822-8). Johns Hopkins.

POWER RESOURCES–EUROPE

Chingari, et al. Renewable Energy Systems Market & Analysis in Italy, Spain & Greece. 220p. 1981. pap. 39.50x (ISBN 0-89934-147-0, I071). Solar Energy Info.

Commission of the European Communities, Brussels, Belgium. Energy Research & Development Programme, 2 vols. in one. 1979. lib. bdg. 121.00 (ISBN 90-247-2220-9, Pub. by Martinus Nijhoff Netherlands). Kluwer Academic.

Ray, George F. & Robinson, Colin. European Energy Prospects to Nineteen Ninety. 1982. 295.00x (ISBN 0-686-92042-2, Pub. by Graham & Trotman England). State Mutual Bk.

Starr, Michael R. & Palz, W. Photovoltaic Power for Europe. 1983. PLB 32.50 (ISBN 90-277-1556-4, Pub. by Reidel Holland). Kluwer Academic.

United Nations Economic Commission for Europe, Geneva, Switzerland, ed. Environment & Energy: Environmental Aspects of Energy Production & Use with Particular Reference to New Technologies. LC 79-40550. 1979. 25.00 (ISBN 0-08-024468-8). Pergamon.

POWER RESOURCES–GREAT BRITAIN

Basu, Dipak R. Future Energy Policies for the U. K. 164p. 1981. text ed. 40.50x (ISBN 0-333-31277-5, Pub. by Macmillan England). Humanities.

Bending, Richard & Eden, Richard. U. K. Energy: Structure, Prospects & Policies. (Illus.). 320p. 1985. 49.50 (ISBN 0-521-26708-0). Cambridge U Pr.

Buchan, John. The Thirty-Nine Steps & the Power House. 213p. 1981. 15.00x (ISBN 0-85158-049-1, Pub. by Blackwood & Sons England). State Mutual Bk.

Facing the Energy Future: Does Britain Need New Energy Institutions? 1981. 49.00x (ISBN 0-686-45737-4, Pub. by Pubns Clerk Royal England). State Mutual Bk.

Hannah, Leslie. Engineers, Managers & Politicians: The First Fifteen Years of Nationalized Electricity Supply in Britain. LC 82-15203. (History of Technology Ser.). 350p. 1982. 34.50x (ISBN 0-8018-2862-7). Johns Hopkins.

Institutions & Energy Conversation. 76p. 1982. 30.00x (ISBN 0-900628-28-6, Pub. by Pubns Clerk Royal England). State Mutual Bk.

Leach, Gerald, et al. A Low Energy Strategy for the United Kingdom. (Illus., Orig.). 1979. pap. text ed. 19.25x (ISBN 0-905927-20-6). Humanities.

Littlechild, S. C. & Vaidya, K. G. Energy Strategies for the UK. 256p. 1982. text ed. 29.95x (ISBN 0-04-339029-3). Allen Unwin.

Pearce, D. W., et al. Decision Making for Energy Futures: A Case Study on the Windscale Inquiry into the Reprocessing of Spent Oxide Fuels. 1979. text ed. 26.50x (ISBN 0-333-27438-5). Humanities.

Twidell, John, ed. Guidebook for Small Wind-Energy Conversion Systems. 200p. Date not set. price not set (ISBN 0-521-26898-2). Cambridge U Pr.

POWER RESOURCES–INDIA

Hart, David. Nuclear Power in India: A Comparative Analysis. 192p. 1983. text ed. 24.00x (ISBN 0-04-338101-4). Allen Unwin.

POWER RESOURCES–LATIN AMERICA

Szekely, Francisco, ed. Energy Alternatives in Latin America. (Natural Resources & the Environment Ser.: Vol. 9). (Illus.). 180p. 1983. 19.50 (ISBN 0-907567-16-9, TYP109, TYP); pap. 12.50 (ISBN 0-907567-17-7, TYP136). Unipub.

POWER RESOURCES–MEXICO

Wionczek, Miguel S. & El Mallakh, Ragaei. Mexico's Energy Resources: Toward a Policy of Diversification. (Replica Edition Ser.). 240p. 1984. softcover 24.00x (ISBN 0-86531-835-2). Westview.

POWER RESOURCES–SOVIET UNION

Campbell, Robert W. Soviet Energy Technologies: Planning, Policy, Research & Development. LC 80-7562. 288p. 1980. 25.00x (ISBN 0-253-15965-2). Ind U Pr.

Dienes, Leslie & Shabad, Theodore. The Soviet Energy System: Resource Use & Policies. LC 78-20814. (Scripta Series in Geography). 298p. 1979. 21.95x (ISBN 0-470-26629-5). Halsted Pr.

Hodgkins, Jordan A. Soviet Power. LC 75-31801. 190p. 1976. Repr. of 1961 ed. lib. bdg. 22.50 (ISBN 0-8371-8491-6, HOSP). Greenwood.

Wilson, David & Drayton, Geoffrey. Soviet Oil & Gas to 1990. (Economist Intelligence Unit Special Ser.). (Illus.). 208p. 1982. text ed. 25.00 (ISBN 0-89011-581-8). Abt Bks.

POWER SERIES

Berndt, Bruce C., et al. Chapter Nine of Ramanujan's Second Notebook: Infinite Series Identities, Transformations, & Evaluations, Vol. 23. LC 83-11803. (Contemporary Mathematics Ser.: No. 23). 84p. 1983. pap. 17.00 (ISBN 0-8218-5024-5). Am Math.

Edrei, A., et al. Zeros of Sections of Power Series. (Lecture Notes in Mathematics Ser.: Vol. 1002). 115p. 1983. pap. 10.00 (ISBN 0-387-12318-0). Springer Verlag.

Grabiner, Sandy. Derivations & Automorphisms of Banach Algebras of Power Series. LC 74-7124. (Memoirs: No. 146). 124p. 1974. pap. 11.00 (ISBN 0-8218-1846-5, MEMO-146). Am Math.

Happ, H. H. Piecewise Methods & Applications to Power Systems. LC 79-901. (Systems Engineering & Analysis Ser.). 405p. 1980. 56.95x (ISBN 0-471-35131-8, Pub. by Wiley-Interscience). Wiley.

POWER TOOLS

see also Radial Saws

Cristoforo, R. J. The Complete Book of Stationary Power Tool Techniques. (Popular Science Ser.). (Illus.). 480p. 1985. 31.95 (ISBN 0-317-31387-8). Rodale Pr Inc.

DeCristoforo, R. J. Power Tool Woodworking for Everyone. rev. ed. LC 83-22995. (Illus.). 360p. 1983. 31.95 (ISBN 0-8359-5567-2). Shopsmith.

Graf, Rudolf F. & Whalen, George J. The TAB Handbook of Hand & Power Tools. (Illus.). 512p. (Orig.). 1984. 26.95 (ISBN 0-8306-0638-6, 1638); pap. 17.95 (ISBN 0-8306-1638-1). TAB Bks.

Hall, Walter. Barnacle Parp's Guide to Garden & Yard Power Tools: Selection, Maintenance & Repair. Wallace, Dan, ed. LC 82-20527. (Illus.). 254p. 1983. 18.95 (ISBN 0-87857-446-8, 14-012-0). Rodale Pr Inc.

Hilts, Len & Hedden, Jay. The DREMEL Guide to Compact Power Tools. (Illus.). 266p. 1981. pap. write for info. (ISBN 0-9606512-0-9). DREMEL.

Irvin, D. Power Tool Maintenance. 1971. 33.45 (ISBN 0-07-032050-0). McGraw.

Jones, Peter. Power Tools, Jigs, Holddowns & Extensions. (Illus.). 416p. 1983. 24.95 (ISBN 0-13-687384-7); pap. 14.95 (ISBN 0-13-687376-6). P-H.

Kitchen, Harry T. Handtools for the Electronic Workshop. 128p. 1980. 10.00x (ISBN 0-85242-475-2, Pub. by K Dickson). State Mutual Bk.

McDonnell. The Use of Portable Power Tools. LC 77-85761. 1979. pap. 11.80 (ISBN 0-8273-1100-1); instructor's guide 3.00 (ISBN 0-8273-1101-X). Delmar.

Tools & Their Uses: The Proper Use & Maintenance of Power Tools. 1984. lib. bdg. 79.95 (ISBN 0-87700-552-4). Revisionist Pr.

POWER TRANSISTORS

Baliga, B. J. & Chen, D. Y., eds. Power Transistors: Device Design & Applications. LC 84-19747. 1984. 51.95 (ISBN 0-87942-181-9, PC01750). Inst Electrical.

POWER TRANSMISSION

see also Electric Lines; Electric Power Distribution; Gearing; Machinery; Oil Hydraulic Machinery; Shafting; Water-Power Electric Plants

Abbott, Sheldon L. Automotive Power Trains. LC 77-73274. 256p. 1978. pap. text ed. 17.00 (ISBN 0-02-810130-8); instrs'. manual 3.20 (ISBN 0-02-810140-5). Glencoe.

Basic Academics, 10 Modules. (Illus.). 940p. 1982. Set. spiral bdg. 100.00x (ISBN 0-87683-224-9); instr's. manual 150.00x (ISBN 0-87683-235-4); lesson plans 35.00x (ISBN 0-87683-246-X). G P Courseware.

Basic Mechanical Power Transmission. (Principles of Steam Generation Ser.: Module 3). (Illus.). 50p. 1982. spiral bdg. 10.00x (ISBN 0-87683-253-2); instr's. manual 15.00x (ISBN 0-87683-274-5). G P Courseware.

Bucksch, Herbert. Getriebe-Worterbuch. (Ger. & Eng., Dictionary of Transmissions). 1976. 132.00 (ISBN 0-686-56477-4, M-7423, Pub. by Bauverlag). French & Eur.

Cook, V. Analysis of Distance Protection. Date not set. 39.95 (ISBN 0-471-90749-9). Wiley.

Matick, Richard E. Transmission Lines for Digital & Communications Networks: An Introduction to Transmission Lines, High-Frequency & High-Speed Pulse Characteristics & Applications. LC 68-30561. pap. 95.50 (ISBN 0-317-09847-0, 2052038). Bks Demand UMI.

OECD Staff. District Heating & Combined Heat & Power Systems: A Technology Review. 306p. 1983. pap. 34.00x (ISBN 92-64-12538-8). OECD.

Palz, W., ed. Photovoltaic Power Generation. 1984. lib. bdg. 42.00 (ISBN 90-277-1725-7, Pub. by Reidel Holland). Kluwer Academic.

Papadakis, Constantine & Scarton, Henry, eds. Fluid Transients & Acoustics in the Power Industry: Presented at the Winter Annual Meeting of the American Society of Mechanical Engineers, San Francisco, California, December 10-15, 1978. LC 78-60044. (Illus.). pap. 91.50 (ISBN 0-317-11149-3, 2013875). Bks Demand UMI.

Patton, W. Mechanical Power Transmission. 1979. 25.95 (ISBN 0-13-569905-3). P-H.

Severns, Rudy & Armijos, Jack, eds. Mospower Applications Handbook. (Illus.). 512p. 1985. 20.00 (ISBN 0-930519-00-0). Siliconix Inc.

Trade & Technical Press Editors. Handbook of Mechanical Power Drives. 777p. 1977. 96.00x (ISBN 0-85461-064-2, Pub by Trade & Tech England). Brookfield Pub Co.

Transmission Equipment. (Principles of Steam Generation Ser.: Module 18). (Illus.). 60p. 1982. spiral bdg. 10.00x (ISBN 0-87683-268-0); instr's. manual 15.00x (ISBN 0-87683-289-3). G P Courseware.

Uninterruptible Power Systems. 1983. 15.00 (ISBN 0-318-18030-8, PE 1-1983). Natl Elec Mfrs.

Woerterbuch der Kraftuebertragungselemente. (Ger., Eng., Fr., Span., Dutch, Swed., Ital. & Finnish., Dictionary of Power Transmission Elements). 1976. 32.00 (ISBN 3-7830-0104-8, M-6985). French & Eur.

Wood, Peter. Switching Power Converters. LC 84-21277. 462p. 1984. Repr. of 1981 ed. lib. bdg. 32.50 (ISBN 0-89874-779-1). Krieger.

POWER TRANSMISSION, ELECTRIC

see Electric Power Transmission

PRAIRIE-DOGS

Clark, Timothy W. Ecology & Ethology of the White-Tailed Prairie Dog (Cynomys Lecurus) 97p. 1978. 8.75 (ISBN 0-89326-009-6). Milwaukee Pub Mus.

Pizzimenti, John J. Evolution of the Prairie Dog Genus Cynomys. (Occasional Papers: No. 39). 73p. 1975. pap. 4.00 (ISBN 0-317-04900-3). U of KS Mus Nat Hist.

Smith, Ronald E. Natural History of the Prairie Dog in Kansas. (Miscellaneous Publications Ser.: No. 49). 39p. 1967. pap. 2.25 (ISBN 0-317-04939-9). U of KS Mus Nat Hist.

PRAIRIES

see also Pampas; Steppes; Tundras

Costello, David F. The Prairie World. (Illus.). 1980. pap. 8.95 (ISBN 0-8166-0938-1). U of Minn Pr.

Curry-Lindahl, Kai. Wildlife of the Prairies & Plains. LC 80-27927. (Wildlife Habitat Ser.). (Illus.). 232p. 1981. 19.95 (ISBN 0-8109-1766-1). Abrams.

Duncan, Patricia D. Tallgrass Prairie: The Inland Sea. LC 78-60177. (Illus.). 1979. 20.00 (ISBN 0-913504-44-0). Lowell Pr.

Risser, P. G. The True Prairie Ecosystem. LC 79-19857. (The US-IBP Synthesis Ser.: Vol. 16). 544p. 1981. 34.50 (ISBN 0-87933-361-8). Van Nos Reinhold.

PRE-CAMBRIAN PERIOD

see Geology, Stratigraphic–Pre-Cambrian

PRECAST CONCRETE CONSTRUCTION

Acoustical Properties of Precast Concrete. 22p. pap. 5.00 (ISBN 0-686-39936-6, JR-198). Prestressed Concrete.

Beton. Precast Concrete Connection Details: Part 1-Structural Design manual. 1981. 87.00 (ISBN 0-9960095-3-1, Pub. by Beton Bks W Germany). Heyden.

--Precast Concrete Connection Details: Part 2-Floor Connections. 1978. 71.00 (ISBN 0-9960095-4-X, Pub. by Beton Bks W Germany). Heyden.

Bruce, Alfred & Sandbank, Harold. The History of Prefabrication. LC 72-5038. (Technology & Society Ser.). (Illus.). 80p. 1972. Repr. of 1944 ed. 20.00 (ISBN 0-405-04691-X). Ayer Co Pubs.

Collins, F. Thomas. Manual of Tilt up Construction. 6th ed. (Illus.). 1965. 15.00 (ISBN 0-910846-01-4). Know How.

Connections in Precast Concrete Structures: Strength of Corbels. (PCI Journal Reprints Ser.). 45p. pap. 7.00 (JR31). Prestressed Concrete.

Considerations in the Design & Construction of Precast Concrete Diaphragms for Earthquake Loads. (PCI Journal Reprints Ser.). 20p. pap. 6.00 (ISBN 0-686-40157-3, JR255). Prestressed Concrete.

Dyachenko, P. & Mirotvorsky, S. Precast Reinforced Concrete. (Russian Monographs). 240p. 1969. 69.50 (ISBN 0-677-20780-8). Gordon.

Fire Tests of Joints Between Precast Concrete Wall Panels: Effects of Various Joint Treatments. 1976. pap. 2.50 (ISBN 0-89312-160-6, RD039B). Portland Cement.

Giant Precast Silo for Storing Fertilizers Built in Mexican Port. (PCI Journal Reprints Ser.). 13p. pap. 5.00 (ISBN 0-686-40160-3, JR260). Prestressed Concrete.

Haas, A. M. Precast Concrete: Design & Applications. (Illus.). 160p. 1983. 59.25 (ISBN 0-85334-197-4, I-342-83, Pub. by Elsevier Applied Sci England). Elsevier.

Koncz, T. Manual of Precast Concrete Construction, Vol. 1: Principles, Roof & Floor Units; Wall Panels. 2nd ed. Van Amerongen, C., tr. from Ger. (Illus.). 298p. 1976. 65.00x (ISBN 3-7625-0310-9). Intl Pubns Serv.

--Manual of Precast Concrete Construction, Vol. 2: Industrial Shed-Type & Low-Rise Buildings; Special Structures. Van Amerongen, C., tr. from Ger. (Illus.). 427p. 1971. 67.50x (ISBN 3-7625-0420-2). Intl Pubns Serv.

--Manual of Precast Concrete Construction, Vol. 3: Multi-Storey Industrial & Administrative Buildings; School, University & Residential Buildings. Van Amerongen, C., tr. from Ger. (Illus.). 378p. 1978. 65.00x (ISBN 3-7625-0974-3). Intl Pubns Serv.

Recommended Practice for Precast Post-Tensioned Segmental Construction. 52p. pap. 8.00 (JR-252). Prestressed Concrete.

Sigalov, E. E. & Strongin, S. G. Reinforced Concrete. Kline, S., tr. (Illus.). 396p. 1963. 87.95x (ISBN 0-677-20500-7). Gordon.

The State of the Art Report on Seismic Resistance of Prestressed & Precast Concrete Structures. (PCI Journal Reprints Ser.). 52p. pap. 7.00 (JR194). Prestressed Concrete.

Use of Precast Components in Masonry Building Construction. pap. 4.00 (ISBN 0-686-94355-4, UN72/4/4, UN). Unipub.

Waddell, Joseph J. Precast Concrete: Handling & Erection. (Monograph: No. 8). 1974. 26.75 (ISBN 0-685-85142-7, M-8) (ISBN 0-685-85143-5). ACI.

PRECIOUS METALS

see also Gold; Silver

Beamish, F. E. & Van Loon, J. C. Analysis of Metals: Overview & Selected Methods. 1977. 49.50 (ISBN 0-12-083950-4). Acad Pr.

Bernstein, Jacob. An Investor's Guide to Using Cycles in the Precious Metals & Copper. LC 84-19561. 224p. 1985. 34.95x (ISBN 0-471-88746-3, Pub. by Wiley-Interscience). Wiley.

Bugbee, Edward E. A Textbook of Fire Assaying. 3rd ed. Raese, Jon W., ed. LC 81-17021. (Illus.). 314p. 1981. Repr. of 1940 ed. text ed. 16.80 (ISBN 0-918062-47-0). Colo Sch Mines.

Cavelti, Peter C. New Profits in Gold, Silver, & Strategic Metals: A Complete Investment Guide. 1984. 15.95 (ISBN 0-07-010288-0). McGraw.

Del Mar, Alexander. History of the Precious Metals. 2nd rev ed. LC 68-18230. Repr. of 1902 ed. 37.50x (ISBN 0-678-00475-7). Kelley.

--A History of the Precious Metals from Earliest Times to the Present. 2nd ed. LC 68-58460. (Research & Source Ser.: No. 324). 1969. Repr. of 1902 ed. 23.50 (ISBN 0-8337-0828-7). B Franklin.

El Guindy, M. I., ed. Precious Metals 1982: Proceedings of the 6th International Precious Metals Institute Conference, Newport Beach, California, June 7-11, 1982. 600p. 1983. 140.00 (ISBN 0-08-025396-2). Pergamon.

Grimwade, M. F. Introduction to Precious Metals. (Illus.). 128p. 1985. pap. text ed. 15.95 (ISBN 0-408-01451-2). Butterworth.

Ivosevic, Stanley W. Gold & Silver Handbook: On Geology, Exploration, Production, Economics of Large Tonnage, Low Grade Deposits. (Illus.). 217p. (Orig.). 1984. pap. 29.50 (ISBN 0-9611352-3-9). S W Ivosevic.

Jacob, William. Historical Inquiry into the Production & Consumption of the Precious Metals, 2 Vols. LC 68-22374. Repr. of 1831 ed. 75.00x (ISBN 0-678-00382-3). Kelley.

Kudryk, V. & Corrigan, D. A., eds. Precious Metals: Mining, Extraction, & Processing: Proceedings, AIME Annual Meeting, Los Angeles, 1984. LC 83-63270. (Illus.). 621p. 1984. 42.00 (ISBN 0-89520-469-X); members 28.00; student members 15.00. Metal Soc.

McGachie, R. O., ed. Precious Metals: Proceedings of the Fourth International Precious Metals Conference, Toronto Canada, June 3-5, 1980. 400p. 1981. 55.00 (ISBN 0-08-025369-5). Pergamon.

McQuiston, Frank W., Jr. & Shoemaker, Robert S. Gold & Silver Cyanidation Plant Practice, Vol. 2. (Illus.). 263p. 1981. 39.00x (ISBN 0-89520-281-6). Soc Mining Eng.

Practical Hydromet 'Eighty-Four: Proceedings of the Seventh Annual Symposium on Uranium & Precious Metals. (Illus.). 126p. 1984. pap. 28.00x (ISBN 0-89520-423-1). Soc Mining Eng.

Precious Metals. (Slide Ser.). 40.00 (ISBN 0-686-23292-5). Natl Recycling.

Reese, David A. Precious Metals 1983: Proceedings of the 7th IPMI Conference, San Francisco - June 1983. LC 84-14803. 224p. 1984. 72.00 (ISBN 0-08-025402-0). Pergamon.

Richards, John F., ed. Precious Metals in the Later Medieval & Early Modern Worlds. LC 82-73059. (Illus.). 502p. 1983. 39.95 (ISBN 0-89089-224-5). Carolina Acad Pr.

Robbins, Peter & Lee, Douglas. Guide to Precious Metals & Their Markets. 250p. 1979. 42.50 (ISBN 0-89397-063-8). Nichols Pub.

Smith, Ernest. Working in Precious Metals. 414p. 1981. 35.00x (ISBN 0-7198-0032-3, Pub. by Northwood Bks). State Mutual Bk.

Zysk, E. D., ed. Precious Metals Two: Proceedings of the 5th International Precious Metals Conference, Providence, R. I., June 1982. LC 82-942871. (Illus.). 460p. 1982. 72.00 (ISBN 0-08-025392-X, A145, E130). Pergamon.

PRECIOUS STONES

Here are entered works of mineralogical or technological interest. Works on engraved stones and jewels from the point of view of antiquities or art are entered under Gems.

see also names of precious stones, e.g. Diamonds, Emeralds

Anderson, Basil W. Gem Testing. (Illus.). 1959. 13.95 (ISBN 0-87523-082-2). Emerson.

Anderson, Frank J. Riches of the Earth. (Illus.). 224p. 1981. 24.95 (ISBN 0-8317-7739-7, Rutledge Pr). Smith Pubs.

Arem, Joel E. Color Encyclopedia of Gemstones. (Illus.). 1977. 42.50 (ISBN 0-442-20333-0). Van Nos Reinhold.

--Gemology. write for info. (ISBN 0-442-25632-9). Van Nos Reinhold.

Bauer, Max. Precious Stones, 2 vols. (Illus.). Set. 32.00 (ISBN 0-8446-1608-7). Peter Smith.

--Precious Stones: A Popular Account of Their Characters, Occurence & Applications. Spencer, L. J., tr. LC 69-12082. (Illus.). 1969. 52.50 (ISBN 0-8048-0489-3). C E Tuttle.

--Precious Stones: A Popular Account of Their Characters, Occurrence & Applications with an Introduction to Their Determination with an Appendix on Pearls & Coral, 2 Vols. Spencer, L. J., tr. (Illus.). 1968. Vol. 1. pap. 6.95 (ISBN 0-486-21910-0); Vol. 2. pap. 7.95 (ISBN 0-486-21911-9). Dover.

Beckwith, John A. Gem Minerals of Idaho. LC 70-150817. (Illus., Orig.). 1972. pap. 5.95 enlarged ed. (ISBN 0-87004-228-9). Caxton.

Boyle, Robert. Origine & Virtues of Gems. LC 78-181434. (Contributions to the History of Geology Ser: Vol. 7). 1972. Repr. of 1672 ed. 22.95x (ISBN 0-02-841710-0). Hafner.

Caley, Earle R. & Richards, John C. Theophrastus on Stones. 248p. 1956. 6.00 (ISBN 0-8142-0033-8). Ohio St U Pr.

Coates, Donald R., ed. Glacial Gemorphology: Binghampton Symposia in Geomorphology. (International Ser.: No. 5). (Illus.). 304p. 1981. text ed. 35.00x (ISBN 0-04-551045-8). Allen Unwin.

Frank, Claudia. Enzyklopaedie der Minerale und Edelsteine. (Ger.). 304p. 1977. 80.00 (ISBN 3-451-17622-X, M-7058). French & Eur.

Greenbaum, Walter W. The Gemstone Identifier. LC 82-4074. (Illus.). 196p. 1982. 13.95 (ISBN 0-668-05387-9); pap. 7.95 (ISBN 0-668-05391-7). Arco.

Isaacs, Thelma. Gemstones, Crystals & Healing. 156p. (Orig.). 1982. 14.00 (ISBN 0-934852-97-9); pap. 8.00 (ISBN 0-934852-52-9). Lorien Hse.

Jones, William. History & Mystery of Precious Stones. 75.00 (ISBN 0-8490-0312-1). Gordon Pr.

Liddicoat, Richard T., Jr. Handbook of Gemstone Identification. 11th ed. (Illus.). 1981. 22.75 (ISBN 0-87311-006-4). Gemological.

MacFall, Russell P. Minerals & Gems. LC 74-28082. (Illus.). 256p. 1975. 17.50i (ISBN 0-690-00687-X). T Y Crowell.

Morisawa, Marie, ed. Fluvial Gemorphology: Binghamton Symposia in Geomorphology. (International Ser.: No. 4). 304p. 1981. text ed. 25.00x (ISBN 0-04-551046-6); pap. text ed. 6.75 (ISBN 0-04-371060-3). Allen Unwin.

Pearl, Richard M. Garnet: Gem & Mineral. 1975. pap. 1.00 (ISBN 0-940566-04-4). R M Pearl Bks.

Saha, N. N. Precious Stone That Heal. 249p. 1980. 14.95x (ISBN 0-317-07703-1, Pub. by Allied Pubs India). Asia Bk Corp.

Schumann, Walter. Stones & Minerals: Minerals, Precious Stones, Rocks, Ores. (Illus.). 226p. 1985. 6.98 (ISBN 0-8069-5526-0). Sterling.

Shipley, Robert M. Dictionary of Gems & Gemology. 6th ed. 1974. 7.50 (ISBN 0-87311-007-2). Gemological.

Sinkankas, J. Emerald & Other Beryls. 700p. 1981. text ed. 40.00 (ISBN 0-8019-7114-4). Chilton.

Sinkankas, John. Prospecting for Gemstones & Minerals. rev. ed. 398p. 1970. pap. 12.95 (ISBN 0-442-27620-6). Van Nos Reinhold.

Van Landingham, Sam L. Geology of World Gem Deposits. 1985. 46.50 (ISBN 0-442-28840-9). Van Nos Reinhold.

Vargas, Glenn & Vargas, Martha. Descriptions of Gem Materials. 2nd ed. LC 79-65857. (Illus.). 160p. 1979. 10.00 (ISBN 0-917646-04-5). Glenn Vargas.

PRECIOUS STONES–NORTH AMERICA

Glover, S. L. Origin & Occurrance of Gem Stones in Washington. (Shorey Prospecting Ser.). 32p. 1975. pap. 2.95 (ISBN 0-8466-0001-3). Shorey.

Kunz, George F. Gems & Precious Stones of North America. 1967. pap. 8.95 (ISBN 0-486-21855-4). Dover.

Strong, Mary F. Desert Gem Trails. 2nd rev. ed. 1971. pap. 2.50 (ISBN 0-910652-15-5). Gembooks.

Zeitner, June C. Midwest Gem Trails Field Guide. 80p. 1964. pap. 2.50 (ISBN 0-910652-00-7). Gembooks.

PRECIOUS STONES, ARTIFICIAL

Elwell, Dennis. Man-Made Gemstones. LC 78-41291. 191p. 1979. 74.95x (ISBN 0-470-26606-6). Halsted Pr.

Yaverbaum, L. H., ed. Synthetic Gems-Production Techniques. LC 79-24960. (Chemical Technology Review Ser.: No. 149). (Illus.). 353p. 1980. 39.00 (ISBN 0-8155-0788-7). Noyes.

PRECIPITATION (CHEMISTRY)

see also Electrostatic Precipitation

Engelmann, R. J. & Slinn, W. G., eds. Precipitation Scavenging (1970) Proceedings. LC 70-609397. (AEC Symposium Ser.). 508p. 1970. pap. 20.75 (CONF-700601); microfiche 4.50 (ISBN 0-87079-308-X, CONF-700601). DOE.

Hales, J. P., Jr., ed. Precipitation Chemistry, Vol. 2. 200p. 1982. 39.00 (ISBN 0-08-028782-4). Pergamon.

Martin, J. W. Precipitation Hardening. LC 67-31505. 1968. text ed. 26.00 (ISBN 0-08-012731-2); pap. text ed. 11.75 (ISBN 0-08-012730-4). Pergamon.

Russell, K. C. & Aaronson, H. I., eds. Precipitation Processes in Solids: Proceedings of a Symposium Sponsored by the TMS-AIME Heat Treatment Committee at the 1976 TMS Fall Meeting at Niagara Falls, New York, September 20-21. LC 78-66760. pap. 81.00 (ISBN 0-317-10468-3, 2022769). Bks Demand UMI.

Semonin, Richard W. & Beadle, Robert W., eds. Precipitation Scavenging (1974) Proceedings. LC 76-53788. (ERDA Symposium Ser.). 856p. 1977. pap. 29.50 (ISBN 0-87079-309-8, CONF-741003); microfiche 4.50 (ISBN 0-87079-310-1, CONF-741003). DOE.

Statistical Treatment of Environmental Isotope Data in Precipitation. (Technical Reports Ser.: No. 206). (Illus.). 276p. 1981. pap. 32.50 (ISBN 92-0-145081-8, IDC206, IAEA). Unipub.

Walton, Alan G. The Formation & Properties of Precipitates. LC 79-13594. (Chemical Analysis Ser.: Vol. 23). 244p. 1979. Repr. of 1967 ed. lib. bdg. 14.50 (ISBN 0-88275-990-6). Krieger.

PRECIPITATION HARDENING

see also Hardness; Metals–Heat Treatment; Strengthening Mechanisms in Solids

Speich, Gilbert R. & Clark, John B., eds. Precipitation from Iron-Based Alloys: Preceedings of a Symposium, Cleveland Ohio, October 21, 1963. LC 65-18397. (Metallurgical Society Conferences: Vol. 28). pap. 105.00 (ISBN 0-317-10433-0, 2001516). Bks Demand UMI.

PRECIPITATION (METEOROLOGY)

see also Hail; Rain and Rainfall; Snow

Durham, Jack L. & Teasley, John I., eds. Chemistry of Particles, Fogs & Rains. (Acid Precipitation Ser.: Vol. 2). 288p. 1984. text ed. 32.50 (ISBN 0-250-40567-9). Butterworth.

Environmental Isotope Data: Part 4: World Survey of Isotope Concentration in Precipitation (1968-1969) (Technical Reports Ser.: No. 147). (Illus.). 434p. (Orig.). 1973. pap. 29.25 (ISBN 92-0-145173-3, IDC147, IAEA). Unipub.

Environmental Isotope Data: Part 5: World Survey of Isotope Concentration in Precipitation (1970-1971) (Technical Reports Ser.: No. 165). (Illus.). 309p. 1975. pap. 24.75 (ISBN 92-0-145075-3, IDC165, IAEA). Unipub.

Goldsmith, P., ed. Tropospheric Chemistry with Emphasis on Sulphur & Nitrogen Cycles & the Chemistry of Clouds & Precipitation: A Selection of Papers from the Fifth International Conference of the Commission on Atmospheric Chemistry & Global Pollution. (Illus.). 467p. 1985. 91.00 (ISBN 0-08-031448-1, Pub. by P P L). Pergamon.

Hayden, Bruce P. A Virginia Precipitation Atlas. LC 79-12087. (Illus.). 143p. 1979. 20.00x (ISBN 0-8139-0788-8). U Pr of Va.

Hendray, George & Teasley, John I., eds. Early Biotic Responses to Advancing Lake Acidification. (Acid Precipitation Ser.: Vol. 6). 192p. 1984. text ed. 32.50 (ISBN 0-250-40571-7). Butterworth.

Middleton, William E. A History of the Theories of Rain & Other Forms of Precipitation. LC 66-15982. (The Watts History of Science Library Ser.). pap. 57.80 (ISBN 0-317-26524-5, 2024059). Bks Demand UMI.

Pruppacher, Hans R. & Klett, James D. Microphysics of Atmospheric Clouds & Precipitation. 1978. lib. bdg. 45.00 (ISBN 90-277-0515-1, Pub. by Reidel Holland). Kluwer Academic.

--Microphysics of Clouds & Precipitation. 730p. 1980. pap. 19.95 (ISBN 90-277-1106-2, Pub. by Reidel Holland). Kluwer Academic.

Sevruk, B. & Geiger, H. Selection of Distribution Types for Extremes of Precipitation. (Operational Hydrology Reports: No. 15). 64p. 1981. pap. 6.00 (ISBN 92-63-10560-X, W495, WMO). Unipub.

PRECISION CASTING

Ammen, C. W. Lost Wax Investment Casting. LC 76-8598. 1977. pap. 9.25 (ISBN 0-8306-6725-3, 725). TAB Bks.

Sopcak, James E. Handbook of Lost Wax or Investment Casting. Maclachlan, D. F., ed. (Illus.). 1969. pap. 2.50 (ISBN 0-910652-11-2). Gembooks.

PRECISION OF MEASUREMENT

see Physical Measurements

PREDATION (BIOLOGY)

see also Parasitism; Predatory Animals

Craighead, John J. & Craighead, Frank C., Jr. Hawks, Owls & Wildlife. LC 74-81670. 1969. pap. 7.95 (ISBN 0-486-22123-7). Dover.

Curio, E. The Ethnology of Predation. (Illus.). 1976. 45.00 (ISBN 0-387-07720-0). Springer-Verlag.

Errington, Paul L. Of Predation & Life. facsimile ed. (Illus.). 1967. pap. 12.75x (ISBN 0-8138-2325-0). Iowa St U Pr.

Fransz, H. G. The Functional Response to Prey Density in an Acarine System. New ed. (Simulation Monographs). 143p. 1974. pap. 16.00 (ISBN 90-220-0509-7, PDC37, PUDOC). Unipub.

Markowitz, Hal & Stevens, Victor, eds. Behavior of Captive Wild Animals. LC 77-18156. (Illus.). 320p. 1978. text ed. 24.95x (ISBN 0-88229-385-0). Nelson-Hall.

Ohguchi, Osamu. Prey Density & Selection Against Oddity by Three-Spined Sticklebacks. (Advances in Ethology Ser.: Vol. 23). (Illus.). 80p. (Orig.). 1981. pap. text ed. 22.00 (ISBN 0-686-30706-2). Parey Sci Pubs.

Taylor, R. J. Predation. (Population & Community Biology Ser.). (Illus.). 176p. 1984. text ed. 39.95 (ISBN 0-412-25060-8, 6770, Pub. by Chapman & Hall England); pap. text ed. 17.95 (ISBN 0-412-26120-0, 6771). Methuen Inc.

Teleki, Geza. Predatory Behavior Among Wild Chimpanzees. LC 70-124442. (Illus.). 232p. 1973. 28.50 (ISBN 0-8387-7747-3). Bucknell U Pr.

Zaret, Thomas M. Predation & Freshwater Communities. LC 80-5399. (Illus.). 208p. 1980. text ed. 21.50x (ISBN 0-300-02349-9). Yale U Pr.

PREDATORY ANIMALS

see also Birds of Prey;
also names of carnivorous animals

Blair, Gerry. Predator Caller's Companion. LC 81-497. 280p. 1981. 18.95 (ISBN 0-8329-3362-7, Pub. by Winchester Pr). New Century.

Capstick, Peter H. Maneaters. (Illus.). 200p. 1981. 17.95 (ISBN 0-8227-3023-5). Petersen Pub.

Gaafar, S. M., et al. Parasites, Pests & Predators. (World Animal Science Ser.: Vol. B2). Date not set. write for info. (ISBN 0-444-42175-0). Elsevier.

Halstead, Bruce W. Atlas of Dangerous Aquatic Animals of the World. LC 84-70417. (Illus.). 400p. 1986. 75.00 (ISBN 0-87850-045-6). Darwin Pr.

Kruuk, Hans. The Spotted Hyena: A Study of Predation & Social Behavior. LC 70-175304. (Wildlife Behavior & Ecology Ser). 368p. 1972. 27.50x (ISBN 0-226-45507-6). U of Chicago Pr.

PREFABRICATED BUILDINGS

see Buildings, Prefabricated

PREFABRICATED CONCRETE CONSTRUCTION

see Precast Concrete Construction

PREGNANCY

see also Ovum Implantation

Albertini, A. & Crosignani, P. G., eds. Progress in Perinatal Medicine: Biochemical & Biophysical Diagnostic Procedures. (International Congress Ser.: Vol. 614). 308p. 1984. 63.50 (ISBN 0-444-90370-4, I-456-83, Excerpta Medica). Elsevier.

Pressure Vessels: Division 2-Alternative Rules. (Boiler & Pressure Vessel Code Ser.: Sec. 8). 1980. 110.00 (ISBN 0-685-76826-0, P00082); pap. 150.00 loose-leaf (ISBN 0-685-76827-9, V00082). ASME.
Proposed Standard for Acoustic Emission Examinations During Application of Pressure. 1975. pap. text ed. 2.50 (ISBN 0-685-62574-5, E00096). ASME.
Pugh, C. E. & Wei, B. C., eds. Advances in Design & Analysis Methodology for Pressure Vessels & Piping. (PVP Ser.: Vol. 56). 142p. 1982. 34.00 (H00213). ASME.
Recommended Rules for Care & Operation of Heating Boilers. (Boiler & Pressure Vessel Code Ser.: Sec. 6). 1980. 35.00 (ISBN 0-685-76820-1, P00060); pap. 45.00 loose-leaf (ISBN 0-685-76821-X, V00060). ASME.
Roberts, R., ed. Pressure Vessel & Piping: Design & Analysis - A Decade of Progress: Materials & Fabrication, Vol. 3. 1976. text ed. 50.00 (ISBN 0-685-68906-9, G00100). ASME.
Rules for Inservice Inspection of Nuclear Power Plant Components: Division 1. (Boiler & Pressure Vessel Code Ser.: Sec. XI). 1980. 80.00 (ISBN 0-685-76832-5, P00111); pap. 105.00 loose-leaf (ISBN 0-685-76833-3, V00111). ASME.
Safety Standard for Pressure Vessels for Human Occupancy: American National Standard PVHO 1-1981. (Bk. No. A00092). 1977. 20.00 (ISBN 0-685-46851-8). ASME.
Sangdahl & Semchyshen, eds. Application of Two & One Quarter Cr-1Mo Steel for Thick-Wall Pressure Vessels-STP 755. 473p. 1982. 45.00 (ISBN 0-8031-0741-2, 04-755000-02). ASTM.
Schaefer, A. O., ed. Current Evaluation of Two & a Quarter Chrome One Molybdenum Steel in Pressure Vessels & Piping. 119p. 1972. pap. text ed. 9.50 (ISBN 0-685-28682-7, G00025). ASME.
Schneider, R. W. & Rodabaugh, E. C., eds. Stress Indices & Stress Intensification Factors of Pressure Vessel & Piping Components. (PVP Ser.: Vol. 50). 1164p. 1981. 30.00 (ISBN 0-686-34508-8, H00186). ASME.
Semchyshen, M. Advanced Materials for Pressure Vessel Service with Hydrogen at High Temperature & Pressures. (MPC-18). 288p. 1982. 50.00 (H00227). ASME.
Singh, Krishna & Soler, Alan. Mechanical Design of Heat Exchangers & Pressure Vessel Components. (Illus.). 1100p. 1984. 95.00 (ISBN 0-916877-00-0); incl. software user guide, examples & magnetic tape 2500.00 (ISBN 0-916877-01-9). Arcturus Pubs.
Sluzalis, L. I. & Dempsey, P. E., eds. Performance of Pressure Vessels with Clad & Overlayed Stainless Steel Linings. (MPC Ser.: Vol. 16). 72p. 1981. 20.00 (ISBN 0-686-34501-0, H00205). ASME.
Sundararajan, C., ed. Reliability & Safety of Pressure Components. (PVP Ser.: Vol. 62). 254p. 1982. 50.00 (H00219). ASME.
Thielsch, Helmut. Defects & Failures in Pressure Vessels & Piping. LC 75-15675. 464p. 1977. Repr. of 1965 ed. 32.50 (ISBN 0-88275-308-8). Krieger.
Tuba, I. S. & Wright, W. B., eds. Pressure Vessel & Piping 1972 Computer Programs Verification: An Aid to Developers & Users. LC 72-94235. (Illus.). pap. 49.80 (ISBN 0-317-08488-7, 2016906). Bks Demand UMI.
Waite, H. H., ed. Pressure Vessels & Piping: Design & Analysis - A Decade of Progress: Quality Assurance - Applications - Components, Vol. 4. 1976. text ed. 50.00 (ISBN 0-685-72346-1, G00101). ASME.
Welding & Brazing Qualifications. (Boiler & Pressure Vessel Code Ser.: Sec. 9). 1980. 60.00 (ISBN 0-685-76828-7, P00090); pap. 185.00 loose-leaf (ISBN 0-685-76829-5, V00090). ASME.
Widera, G. E. O., ed. Pressure Vessel Design. (PVP: Vol. 57). 217p. 1982. 44.00 (H00214). ASME.
Zamrik, S. Y. & Dietrich, D., eds. Pressure Vessels & Piping: Design Technology, 1982-A Decade of Progress. 647p. 1982. 85.00 (G00213). ASME.

PRESSURIZED WATER REACTORS

Energy Technology Conference (1977: Houston, TX) Dynamic Analysis of Pressure Vessel & Piping Components: Presented at the Energy Technology Conference, Houston, Texas, September 18-23, 1977. Sundararajan, C., ed. LC 77-82209. (Illus.). pap. 28.30 (ISBN 0-317-09157-3, 2017309). Bks Demand UMI.
Tong, L. S. & Weisman, Joel. Thermal Analysis of Pressurized Water Reactors. LC 77-119001. (ANS Monographs). 320p. 1983. Repr. of 1970 ed. 24.00 (ISBN 0-89448-005-7, 300015). Am Nuclear Soc.
--Thermal Analysis of Pressurized Water Reactors. 2nd, rev., reprint ed. Wallin, Diane, ed. LC 79-54237. (Monograph). 1979. 39.50 (ISBN 0-89448-019-7, 300015). Am Nuclear Soc.

PRESTRESSED CONCRETE

Allen, A. H. An Introduction to Prestressed Concrete. (Educational Ser.). (Illus.). 1978. pap. 17.50x (ISBN 0-7210-1090-3). Scholium Intl.
American Concrete Institute. Bibliography on Prestressed Concrete. 2nd ed. (American Concrete Institute. Bibliography: No. 1). pap. 26.50 (ISBN 0-317-10001-7, 2004254). Bks Demand UMI.
American Society of Civil Engineers, compiled By. Fatigue Life of Prestressed Concrete Beams. 96p. 1977. pap. 7.00x (ISBN 0-87262-094-8). Am Soc Civil Eng.
Applications of Stay-in-Place Prestressed Bridge Deck Panels. (PCI Journal Reprints Ser.). 8p. pap. 4.00 (ISBN 0-686-40119-0, JR211). Prestressed Concrete.
Auxiliary Reinforcement in Concrete Connections. (PCI Journal Reprints Ser.). 22p. pap. 4.00 (ISBN 0-686-40037-2, JR105). Prestressed Concrete.
The Beginnings of Prestressed Concrete in Canada. (PCI Journal Reprints Ser.). 28p. pap. 6.00 (ISBN 0-686-40123-9, JR215). Prestressed Concrete.
Behavior of Prestressed Concrete Structures During the Alaskan Earthquake. (PCI Journal Reprints Ser.). 12p. pap. 5.00 (ISBN 0-686-39978-1, JR32). Prestressed Concrete.
Bright Office Building, Dallas, Texas. (PCI Journal Reprints Ser.). 7p. pap. 4.00 (ISBN 0-686-40148-4, JR244). Prestressed Concrete.
Bruggeling, Ir A. Prestressed Concrete for the Storage of Liquefied Gas. Van Amerongen, C., tr. from Dutch. (Viewpoint Ser.). (Illus.). 111p. 1981. pap. text ed. 49.50x (ISBN 0-7210-1187-X, Pub. by C&CA London). Scholium Intl.
Color, Form & Texture. 16p. pap. 3.50 (ISBN 0-686-39910-2, PR-21). Prestressed Concrete.
Computer Graphics: A Powerful New Tool for the Prestressed Concrete Industry. (PCI Journal Reprints Ser.). 13p. pap. 5.00 (ISBN 0-686-40141-7, JR237). Prestressed Concrete.
Creep & Shrinkage Characterization for Analyzing Prestressed Concrete Structures. (PCI Journal Reprints Ser.). 37p. pap. 7.00 (ISBN 0-686-40129-8, JR225). Prestressed Concrete.
Design & Construction of Giant Precast Prestressed LNG Storage Tanks at Staten Island. (PCI Journal Reprints Ser.). 16p. pap. 5.00 (ISBN 0-686-40079-8, JR159). Prestressed Concrete.
Design Guide Plant Cast Precast & Prestressed Concrete. softcover 35.00x (ISBN 0-937040-17-7). Prestressed Concrete.
Design of Partially Prestressed Flexural Members, Reader Comments. (PCI Journal Reprints Ser.). 14p. pap. 5.00 (ISBN 0-686-40107-7, JR189A). Prestressed Concrete.
Elastic Stability of Flanges of Typical Prestressed Single Tees. (PCI Journal Reprints Ser.). 13p. pap. 5.00 (ISBN 0-686-39992-7, JR43). Prestressed Concrete.
Fire Provisions to Model Building Codes Related to Prestressed Concrete Use. (PCI Journal Reprints Ser.). 69p. pap. 8.00 (ISBN 0-686-40074-7, JR153). Prestressed Concrete.
Garas, F. K. & Armer, G. S. T., eds. Reinforced & Prestressed Microconcrete Models. (Illus.). 400p. 1981. text ed. 60.00x (ISBN 0-86095-880-9). Longman.
Gerwick, Ben C., Jr. & Peters, V. P., eds. Russian-English Dictionary of Prestressed Concrete & Concrete Construction. (Rus. & Eng.). 120p. 1966. 38.50 (ISBN 0-677-00260-2). Gordon.
Guide Specification for Prestressed Concrete Poles. 14p. pap. 5.00 (ISBN 0-686-39964-1, JR-257). Prestressed Concrete.
Guyon, Y. Limit-State Design of Prestressed Concrete, Vol. 2: The Design of the Member. Turner, F. H., tr. from Fr. LC 72-2655. 469p. 1974. 69.95x (ISBN 0-470-33791-5). Halsted Pr.
--Limit State Design of Prestressed Concrete Vol. 2: The Design of the Member, V. (Illus.). 469p. 1974. 57.50 (ISBN 0-85334-601-1, Pub. by Elsevier Applied Sci England). Elsevier.
High Strength Concrete. (PCI Journal Reprints Ser.). 20p. pap. 5.00 (ISBN 0-686-40032-1, JR100). Prestressed Concrete.
Jones, Peter. Concrete & Masonry: A Complete Handbook of Materials & Methods. (Illus.). 416p. 1984. 24.95 (ISBN 0-13-167197-9); pap. 14.95 (ISBN 0-13-167189-8). P-H.
Kong, F. & Evans, R. Reinforced & Prestressed Concrete. 2nd. ed. 1984. pap. 24.50 (ISBN 0-442-30751-9). Van Nos Reinhold.
Leonhardt, Fritz. Prestressed Concrete Design & Construction. 2nd ed. Amerongen, C. V., tr. (Illus.). 75.00 (ISBN 0-8044-4584-2). Ungar.
Libby, James R. Modern Prestressed Concrete. 3rd ed. 1984. 47.50 (ISBN 0-442-25942-5). Van Nos Reinhold.
Lin, T. Y. & Kelly, J. W., eds. Prestressed Concrete Buildings. (Illus.). 334p. 1962. 64.95 (ISBN 0-677-10310-7). Gordon.
Load-Bearing Wall Panels: Design & Application. (PCI Journal Reprints Ser.). 16p. pap. 5.00 (ISBN 0-686-40039-9, JR106). Prestressed Concrete.
Manual for Quality Control for Plants & Production of Architectural Precast Concrete. 25.00x (ISBN 0-937040-06-1, MNL-117-77). Prestressed Concrete.
Nilson, A. H. Design of Prestressed Concrete. 526p. 1978. 45.50 (ISBN 0-471-02034-6). Wiley.
PCI Design for Fire Resistance of Precast Prestressed Concrete. softcover 11.00x (ISBN 0-937040-08-8, MNL-124-77). Prestressed Concrete.
PCI Design Handbook: Precast Prestressed Concrete. 2nd ed. 380p. 1978. 50.00x (ISBN 0-937040-12-6, MNL-120-78). Prestressed Concrete.
PCI Membership Directory. 87p. write for info. softcover (ISBN 0-937040-13-4, SP-M); pap. 5.00 ea., first copy free, members. Prestressed Concrete.
PCI Safety & Loss Prevention Manual. loose leaf 60.00x (ISBN 0-937040-03-7, SLP-100-73). Prestressed Concrete.
Precast Prestressed Concrete Short Span Bridges Spans to 100 Feet. 1980. loose leaf 20.00x (ISBN 0-937040-16-9, SSB-1-81). Prestressed Concrete.
Prestressed Concrete Materials, Fabrication & Inspection. (Civil-Structural Inspection Ser.: Module 29-6). (Illus.). 34p. 1979. spiral bdg. 60.00x (ISBN 0-87683-121-8). G P Courseware.
Reflections on the Beginnings of Prestressed Concrete in America. 1981. soft cover 30.00x (ISBN 0-937040-18-5, JR-H-81). Prestressed Concrete.
Sawko, F., ed. Developments in Prestressed Concrete, 2 vols. (Illus.). 1978. Vol. 1. 48.00 (ISBN 0-85334-790-5, Pub. by Elsevier Applied Sci England); Vol. 2. 29.75 (ISBN 0-85334-811-1). Elsevier.
Serviceability-Based Design of Partially Prestressed Beams. (PCI Journal Reprints Ser.). 47p. pap. 8.00 (JR209). Prestressed Concrete.
Some Recent Corrosion Embrittlement Failures of Prestressing Systems in the U. S. (PCI Journal Reprints Ser.). 20p. pap. 6.00 (ISBN 0-686-40158-1, JR256). Prestressed Concrete.
Splicing of Precast Prestressed Concrete Piles: Pt. 1-Review & Performance of Splices, Pt. 2-Tests & Analysis of Cement-Dowel Splice. (PCI Journal Reprints Ser.). 56p. pap. 8.00 (ISBN 0-686-40067-4). Prestressed Concrete.
The State of the Art Report on Seismic Resistance of Prestressed & Precast Concrete Structures. (PCI Journal Reprints Ser.). 52p. pap. 7.00 (JR194). Prestressed Concrete.
Thurlimann, Bruno. Torsional Strength of Reinforced & Prestressed Concrete Beams: CEB Approach. (IBA Ser.: No. 92). 27p. 1979. pap. text ed. 13.95x (ISBN 0-8176-1125-8). Birkhauser.
Thverlimann, Bruno. Shear Strength of Reinforced & Prestressed Concrete Beams: CEB Approach. (IBA Ser.: No. 93). 23p. 1979. pap. text ed. 12.95x (ISBN 0-8176-1131-2). Birkhauser.
The Use of Prestressed Concrete & Epoxies to Expedite Construction of 1-87. (PCI Journal Reprints Ser.). 16p. pap. 5.00 (ISBN 0-686-39993-5, JR45). Prestressed Concrete.
Wilby, C. B. Post-Tension Prestressed Concrete. (Illus.). 265p. 1981. 48.00 (ISBN 0-85334-944-4, Pub. by Elsevier Applied Sci England). Elsevier.

PRESTRESSED CONCRETE CONSTRUCTION

Abeles, P W. & Bardham Roy, B K. Prestressed Concrete Designer's Handbook. 3rd ed. (Illus.). 550p. 1981. text ed. 45.00 (ISBN 0-7210-1227-2, Pub. by Viewpoint). Scholium Intl.
Bachmann, Hugo. Partial Prestressing of Concrete Structures. (IBA Ser.: No. 95). 20p. 1979. pap. text ed. 9.95x (ISBN 0-8176-1150-9). Birkhauser.
Connections for Precast Prestressed Concrete Buildings Including Earthquake Resistance. 1982. ring bd. 30.00 (ISBN 0-937040-20-7, TR2-82). Prestressed Concrete.
Design Considerations for a Precast Prestressed Apartment Building. 228p. softcover 20.00x (ISBN 0-937040-09-6, SP-DC). Prestressed Concrete.
Design of Load-Bearing Wall Panels. softcover 9.00x (ISBN 0-937040-14-2, JR-154). Prestressed Concrete.
Energy-Efficient Accelerated Curing of Concrete. 1982. ring bd. 36.00 (ISBN 0-937040-19-3, TR-1-82). Prestressed Concrete.
Fire Endurance of Prestressed Concrete Double-Tee Wall Assemblies. (PCI Journal Reprints Ser.). (Illus.). 11p. pap. 5.00 (ISBN 0-686-40046-1, JR115). Prestressed Concrete.
Fundamentals of Prestressed Concrete Design. softcover 9.00x (ISBN 0-937040-02-9, MNL-115-68). Prestressed Concrete.
Gerwick, Ben C., Jr. & Peters, V. P., eds. Russian-English Dictionary of Prestressed Concrete & Concrete Construction. (Rus. & Eng.). 120p. 1966. 38.50 (ISBN 0-677-00260-2). Gordon.
Jones, L. L. Ultimate Load Analysis of Reinforced & Prestressed Concrete Structures. LC 65-28355. 1965. 12.00 (ISBN 0-8044-4475-7). Ungar.
LaGuardia Airport Runway Extension Program. (PCI Journal Reprints). 6p. pap. 4.00 (ISBN 0-686-39987-0, JR40). Prestressed Concrete.
Leonhardt, F. Prestressed Concrete-Design & Construction. 2nd rev. ed. (Illus.). 57.25x (ISBN 3-4330-0435-8). Adlers Foreign Bks.
Leonhardt, Fritz. Prestressed Concrete Design & Construction. 2nd ed. Amerongen, C. V., tr. (Illus.). 75.00 (ISBN 0-8044-4584-2). Ungar.
Lin, T. Y. & Burns, Ned H. Design of Prestressed Concrete Structures. 3rd ed. LC 80-20619. 646p. 1981. text ed. 47.00x (ISBN 0-471-01898-8); tchrs' ed. avail. (ISBN 0-471-08788-2). Wiley.
Lin, T. Y. & Kelly, J. W., eds. Prestressed Concrete Buildings. (Illus.). 334p. 1962. 64.95 (ISBN 0-677-10310-7). Gordon.
PCI Architectural Precast Concrete. (Illus.). 20.00x (ISBN 0-937040-01-0, MNL-122-73). Prestressed Concrete.
PCI Architectural Precast Concrete Drafting Handbook. 25.00 (ISBN 0-13-044602-5, MNL-119). Prestressed Concrete.
PCI Journal Twenty-Five Year Index. 250p. 1982. 30.00 (ISBN 0-937040-21-5, JR-1-82). Prestressed Concrete.
PCI Manual for Structural Design of Architectural Precast Concrete. 448p. 50.00x (ISBN 0-937040-07-X, MNL-121-77). members 25.00. Prestressed Concrete.
PCI Manual on Design of Connections for Precast Prestressed Concrete. softcover 2.00 (ISBN 0-937040-00-2, MNL-123-73). Prestressed Concrete.
Podolny, Walter & Muller, Jean M. Construction & Design of Prestressed Concrete Segmental Bridges. LC 81-13025. (Wiley Ser. of Practical Construction Guides). 561p. 1982. 82.50x (ISBN 0-471-05658-8, Pub. by Wiley Interscience). Wiley.
Precast Segmental Box Girder Bridge Manual. 124p. 1978. softcover 12.00x (ISBN 0-937040-11-8, PSB-78). Prestressed Concrete.
Prestressed Concrete for Buildings. (PCI Journal Reprints Ser.). 48p. pap. 7.00 (JR177). Prestressed Concrete.
Prestressed Concrete Foundations & Ground Anchors. softcover 10.00 (ISBN 0-686-14597-6, PGA-1-75). Prestressed Concrete.
Prestressed Concrete Ocean Structures & Ships. softcover 8.00x (ISBN 0-937040-04-5, OS-75). Prestressed Concrete.
Prestressed Concrete Piling Interaction Diagrams. softcover, ring-bound 30.00x (ISBN 0-937040-10-X, JR-187A). Prestressed Concrete.
Ramaswamy, G. S. Modern Prestressed Concrete Design. (Illus.). 1976. pap. text ed. 25.00x (ISBN 0-8464-0639-X); pap. 17.50 (ISBN 0-686-77190-7). Beekman Pubs.
Simplified Thermal Design of Building Envelopes for Use with Ashrae Standard 90-75. softcover 1.80 (ISBN 0-937040-15-0, JR-179). Prestressed Concrete.

PRIESTLEY, JOSEPH, 1733-1804

Aykroyd, Wallace R. Three Philosophers: Lavoisier, Priestley & Cavendish. LC 77-98808. Repr. of 1935 ed. lib. bdg. 18.75 (ISBN 0-8371-2890-0, AYTB). Greenwood.
Day, Alan E. J. B. Priestley: An Annotated Bibliography. LC 78-68251. (Garland Reference Library of the Humanities). 350p. 1980. lib. bdg. 48.00 (ISBN 0-8240-9798-X). Garland Pub.
Holt, Anne. Life of Joseph Priestley. Repr. of 1931 ed. lib. bdg. 15.00 (ISBN 0-8371-4240-7, HOJP). Greenwood.
Kieft, Lester & Willeford, Bennett R., Jr., eds. Joseph Priestley: Scientist, Theologian, & Metaphysician. LC 77-92577. 120p. 1979. 15.00 (ISBN 0-8387-2202-4). Bucknell U Pr.
Orange, A. D. Joseph Priestly. (Clarendon Biography Ser.). (Illus.). 1974. pap. 3.50 (ISBN 0-912728-71-X). Newbury Bks.
--Joseph Priestly. (Lifelines Ser.: No. 31). (Illus., Orig.). 1983. pap. 3.50 (ISBN 0-85263-252-5, 3, Pub. by Shire Pubns England). Seven Hills Bks.
Priestley, Joseph. Memoirs of Dr. Joseph Priestley, to the Year 1795, Written by Himself, with a Continuation,... LC 78-3422. 1978. Repr. of 1806 ed. lib. bdg. 60.00 (ISBN 0-527-72730-X). Kraus Repr.
Smith, Edgar F. Priestley in America: Seventeen Hundred Ninety-Four to Eighteen Four. Cohen, I. Bernard, ed. LC 79-8408. (Three Centuries of Science in America Ser.). 1980. Repr. of 1920 ed. lib. bdg. 16.00x (ISBN 0-405-12557-7). Ayer Co Pubs.

Thorpe, Thomas E. Joseph Priestly. LC 70-177458. (English Men of Science: No. 3). 230p. 1976. Repr. of 1906 ed. 21.00 (ISBN 0-404-07893-1). AMS Pr.

PRIMARY BATTERIES

see Electric Batteries

PRIMARY PRODUCTIVITY (BIOLOGY)

Charles-Edwards, D. A. The Mathematics of Photosynthesis & Productivity. LC 81-66387. (Experimental Botany Ser.). 1982. 29.50 (ISBN 0-12-170580-3). Acad Pr.

Hickling, C. F. Water As a Productive Environment. LC 75-4394. 200p. 1975. 25.00 (ISBN 0-312-85680-6). St Martin.

Jones, Gareth E. Vegetation Productivity. LC 78-40985. (Topics in Applied Geography Ser.). pap. 28.00 (ISBN 0-317-20789-X, 2025270). Bks Demand UMI.

Lieth, H. & Whittaker, R. H., eds. Primary Productivity of the Biosphere. LC 74-26627. (Ecological Studies: Vol. 14). (Illus.). 350p. 1975. 53.00 (ISBN 0-387-07083-4). Springer-Verlag.

Lieth, Helmut F., ed. Patterns of Primary Production in the Biosphere. LC 78-18691. (Benchmark Papers in Ecology: Vol. 8). 342p. 1978. 47.95 (ISBN 0-87933-327-8). Van Nos Reinhold.

Steeman, Nielson E. Marine Photosynthesis. LC 74-29691. (Oceanography Ser.: Vol. 13). 142p. 1975. 57.50 (ISBN 0-444-41320-0). Elsevier.

Tieszen, L L., ed. Vegetation & Production Ecology of an Alaskan Arctic Tundra. LC 78-14039. (Ecological Studies: Vol. 29). (Illus.). 1979. 49.00 (ISBN 0-387-90325-9). Springer-Verlag.

PRIMATES

see also Apes; Lemurs; Man; Monkeys; Physical Anthropology

Ankel-Simons, Friderun. A Survey of Living Primates & Their Anatomy. 288p. 1983. pap. text ed. write for info. (ISBN 0-02-303500-5). Macmillan.

Armstrong, Este & Falk, Dean, eds. Primate Brain Evolution: Methods & Concepts. LC 81-21150. 346p. 1982. text ed. 42.50 (ISBN 0-306-40914-3, Plenum Pr). Plenum Pub.

Ashton, E. H. & Holmes, R. L., eds. Perspectives in Primate Biology. (Symposia of the Zoological Society of London Ser.: No. 46). 1981. 68.50 (ISBN 0-12-613346-8). Acad Pr.

Balner, Hans & Van Rood, J. J., eds. Transplantation Genetics of Primates. LC 72-1131. (Illus.). 148p. 1972. 56.00 (ISBN 0-8089-0770-0, 790395). Grune.

Board on Agriculture & Renewable Resources. Nutrient Requirements of Non-Human Primates. 83p. 1978. pap. 6.50 (ISBN 0-309-02786-1). Natl Acad Pr.

Bourne, Geoffrey H., ed. Non-Human Primates & Medical Research. 1973. 70.00 (ISBN 0-12-119150-8). Acad Pr.

Bowden, Douglas M. Aging in Nonhuman Primates. (Primate Behavior & Development Ser.). 1979. 32.50 (ISBN 0-442-20734-4). Van Nos Reinhold.

Chiarelli, A. B. Taxonomic Atlas of Living Primates. 1972. 67.50 (ISBN 0-12-172550-2). Acad Pr.

Chiarelli, A. B., ed. Perspectives in Primate Biology. LC 74-10968. (Advances in Behavioral Biology Ser.: Vol. 9). 333p. 1974. 45.00x (ISBN 0-306-37909-0, Plenum Pr). Plenum Pub.

Chiarelli, A. B. & Corruscini, R. S., eds. Primate Evolutionary Biology: Selected Papers - Proceedings, Pt. A. (Illus.). 150p. 1981. 29.00 (ISBN 0-387-11023-2). Springer-Verlag.

Chiarelli, Brunetto, et al, eds. Comparative Karyology of Primates. (World Anthropology Ser.). text ed. 26.40x (ISBN 9-0279-7840-9). Mouton.

Chivers, David C., ed. Recent Advances in Primatology, Vols. 1-4. Vol. 1, 1978. 85.50 (ISBN 0-12-173301-7); Vol. 2, 1978. 56.00 (ISBN 0-12-173302-5); Vol. 3, 1978. 66.50 (ISBN 0-12-173303-3); Vol. 4, 1978. 44.00 (ISBN 0-12-173304-1). Acad Pr.

Chivers, David J., ed. Malayan Forest Primates: Ten Years' Study in a Tropical Rain Forest. LC 80-25181. 388p. 1980. 49.50x (ISBN 0-306-40626-8, Plenum Pr). Plenum Pub.

Ciochon, Russell L. & Fleagle, John G. Primate Evolution & Human Origins. (Illus.). 401p. 1985. pap. text ed. 34.95x (ISBN 0-8053-2240-X, 32240). Benjamin-Cummings.

Clark, W. E. History of the Primates. 5th ed. (Illus.). 1966. pap. 1.25 (ISBN 0-226-10936-4, P227, Phoen). U of Chicago Pr.

Connolly, Cornelius J. External Morphology of the Primate Brain. (Illus.). 386p. 1950. photocopy ed. 36.50x (ISBN 0-398-04230-6). C C Thomas.

Cramer, D. L. Craniofacial Morphology of Pan Paniscus. Szalay, F. S., ed. (Contributions to Primatology: Vol. 10). (Illus.). 1977. 20.50 (ISBN 3-8055-2391-2). S Karger.

Demes, B. Biomechanics of the Primate Skull Base. (Advances in Anatomy, Embryology & Cell Biology Ser.: Vol. 94). (Illus.). 70p. 1985. pap. 22.00 (ISBN 0-387-15290-3). Springer-Verlag.

Elliot, Daniel G. A Review of the Primates, 3 vols. LC 78-72714. Repr. of 1913 ed. Set. 225.00 (ISBN 0-404-18284-4). Vol. 1 (ISBN 0-404-18285-2). Vol. 2 (ISBN 0-404-18286-0). Vol. 3 (ISBN 0-404-18287-9). AMS Pr.

Erwin, Joe & Dukelow, Richard W. Comparative Primate Biology, Vol. 3: Reproduction & Development. 430p. 1985. write for info. (ISBN 0-8451-4003-5). A R Liss.

Erwin, Joe & Mitchell, G. Comparative Primate Biology, Vol. 2A: Behavior & Ecology, Vol. 2A. (CPB Ser.). 596p. 1985. write for info. (ISBN 0-8451-4001-9). A R Liss.

Erwin, Joe & Swindler, Daris R. Comparative Primate Biology, Vol. 1: Systematics, Evolution & Anatomy. 754p. 1985. write for info. (ISBN 0-8451-4000-0). A R Liss.

Fiennes, R. N., ed. Pathology of Simian Primates, 2 pts. Incl. Pt. 1. General Pathology. 84.75 (ISBN 3-8055-1307-0); Pt. 2. Infectious & Parasitic Diseases. 70.75 (ISBN 3-8055-1308-9). (Illus.). 1972. Set. 139.75 (ISBN 3-8055-1329-1). S Karger.

Forbes, Henry O. A Handbook to the Primates, 2 vols. LC 78-72715. Repr. of 1894 ed. Set. 84.50 (ISBN 0-404-18288-7). Vol. 1 (ISBN 0-404-18289-5). Vol. 2 (ISBN 0-404-18290-9). AMS Pr.

Gavan, James A. A Classification of the Order Primates. new ed. Feldman, Lawrence H., ed. & pref. by. LC 75-319248. (Museum Briefs Ser: No. 16). (Orig.). 1975. pap. text ed. 1.90x (ISBN 0-913134-15-5). Mus Anthro Mo.

Gidley, James W. Paleocene Primates of the Fort Union, with Discussion of Relationships of Eocene Primates. Bd. with The Fort Union of the Crazy Mountain Field, Montana, & Its Mammalian Faunas. Simpson, George G. Repr. of 1937 ed. LC 78-72717. 42.50 (ISBN 0-404-18292-5). AMS Pr.

Goodwin, William J. & Augustine, James, eds. Primate Research. LC 76-14940. 127p. 1976. 29.50x (ISBN 0-306-34506-4, Plenum Pr). Plenum Pub.

Gregory, William K. The Structure & Relationships of Notharctus, an American Eocene Primate. LC 78-72719. Repr. of 1920 ed. 47.50 (ISBN 0-404-18294-1). AMS Pr.

--Studies on the Evolution of the Primates. Bd. with The Dentition of Dryopithecus & the Origin of Man. Gegory, William K. LC 78-72720. 67.50 (ISBN 0-404-18295-X). AMS Pr.

Gregory, William K., et al. Original Descriptions of Siwalik Primates Collected Mostly by American Expeditions, Reprinted from Various Sources. LC 78-72724. 1980. 26.50 (ISBN 0-404-18299-2). AMS Pr.

--Studies of Early Fossil Primates in North America. LC 78-72713. 1980. Repr. 34.50 (ISBN 0-404-18283-6). AMS Pr.

Hafez, E. S. Comparative Reproducton of Nonhuman Primates. (Illus.). 572p. 1971. photocopy ed. 58.50x (ISBN 0-398-02302-6). C C Thomas.

Harris, Robert S., ed. Feeding & Nutrition of Nonhuman Primates. 1970. 55.00 (ISBN 0-12-327360-9). Acad Pr.

Harrison, R. M., ed. Endoscopy in Primates & Other Experimental Animals. (Journal of Medical Primatology: Vol. 5, No. 2). (Illus.). 1976. 13.00 (ISBN 3-8055-2428-5). S Karger.

Harrisson, Barbara. Conservation of Nonhuman Primates in Nineteen Seventy. (Primates in Medicine: Vol. 5). 1971. 12.00 (ISBN 3-8055-1243-0). S Karger.

Hearn, J. P., ed. Reproduction in New World Primates: Animal Models for Medical Research. (Illus.). 350p. 1982. text ed. 55.00 (ISBN 0-85200-407-9, Pub. by MTP Pr England). Kluwer Academic.

Hooton, Earnest A. Man's Poor Relations. (Landmarks in Anthropology Ser). Repr. of 1942 ed. 37.00 (ISBN 0-384-24230-8). Johnson Repr.

Huser, H. J. Atlas of Comparative Primate Hematology. 1970. 74.50 (ISBN 0-12-362750-8). Acad Pr.

Institute for Laboratory Animal Resources. Neotropical Primates: Field Studies & Conservation. Thorington, Richard, Jr. & Heltne, Paul, eds. (Illus.). 1976. pap. 11.75 (ISBN 0-309-02442-0). Natl Acad Pr.

International Congress of Primatology, 5th, Nagoya, Japan, August 21-24, 1974. Contemporary Primatology: Proceedings. Kondo, S., et al, eds. (Illus.). x, 522p. 1975. 121.50 (ISBN 3-8055-2165-0). S Karger.

International Congress of Primatology, 4th, August 1972, Portland. Primatology: Proceedings, 4 vols. Montagna, W., ed. Incl. Vol 1. Precultural Primate Behavior. Menzel, E. W., ed. 200p. 49.00 (ISBN 3-8055-1494-8); Vol 2. Primate Reproductive Behavior. Phoenix, C. H., ed. 200p. 24.75 (ISBN 3-8055-1495-6); Vol 3. Craniofacial Biology of Primates. Zingesel, M. R., ed. 180p. 49.00 (ISBN 3-8055-1496-4); Vol. 4. Nonhuman Primates & Human Diseases. McNulty, W. P., Jr., ed. 180p. 29.00 (ISBN 3-8055-1497-2). 1973. Set. 136.25 (ISBN 3-8055-1498-0). S Karger.

International Congress of Primatology, 3rd, Zurich, 1970. Primatology: Proceedings, 3 vols. Incl. Vol. 1. Taxonomy, Anatomy, Reproduction. Biegert, J. & Leutenegger, W., eds. (Illus.). xvi, 278p. 40.50 (ISBN 3-8055-1244-9); Vol. 2. Neurobiology, Immunology, Cytology. Biegert, J. & Leutenegger, W., eds. (Illus.). x, 245p. 38.50 (ISBN 3-8055-1245-7); Vol. 3. Behavior. Kummer, H., ed. (Illus.). x, 191p. 30.00 (ISBN 3-8055-1246-5). 1971. Set. 108.75 (ISBN 3-8055-1247-3). S Karger.

International Symposium on Breeding Non-Human Primates for Laboratory Use, Berne, 1971. Breeding Primates: Proceedings. Beveridge, W. I., ed. (Illus.). 300p. 1972. 27.50 (ISBN 3-8055-1369-0). S Karger.

Kalter, S. S. The Baboon: Microbiology, Clinical Chemistry & Some Hematological Aspects. (Primates in Medicine: Vol. 8). (Illus.). 1973. 30.75 (ISBN 3-8055-1442-5). S Karger.

Kavanagh, Michael. A Complete Guide to Monkeys, Apes & Other Primates. (Illus.). 224p. 1984. 19.95 (ISBN 0-670-43543-0). Viking.

Kratochvil, C., ed. Chimpanzee: Immunological Specificities of Blood. (Primates in Medicine: Vol. 6). 150p. 1972. 25.25 (ISBN 3-8055-1389-5). S Karger.

Luckett, P., ed. Reproductive Biology of the Primates. (Contributions to Primatology: Vol. 3). 284p. 1974. pap. 55.00 (ISBN 3-8055-1671-1). S Karger.

Luckett, W. P. & Szalay, Frederick S., eds. Phylogeny of the Primates: A Multidisciplinary Approach. LC 75-30714. (Illus.). 497p. 1975. 65.00x (ISBN 0-306-30852-5, Plenum Pr.). Plenum Pub.

McGuire, M. T., ed. The St. Kitts Vervet. (Contributions to Primatology: Vol. 1). 202p. 1974. 24.00 (ISBN 3-8055-1692-4). S Karger.

MacPhee, R. D. Auditory Regions of Primates & Eutherian Insectivores. (Contributions to Primatology Series: Vol. 18). (Illus.). xvi, 288p. 1981. pap. 28.25 (ISBN 3-8055-1963-X). S Karger.

Major, C. I., et al. Papers on the Subfossil Primates of Madagascar, Reprinted from Various Sources. LC 78-72722. 1980. 105.00 (ISBN 0-404-18301-8). AMS Pr.

Moynihan, Martin. The New World Primates: Adaptive Radiation & the Evolution of Social Behavior, Languages, & Intelligence. LC 75-3467. 1976. 29.00 (ISBN 0-691-08168-9). Princeton U Pr.

Murphy, G. P., ed. Transplantation in Primates. (Primates in Medicine: Vol. 7). 1972. 25.25 (ISBN 3-8055-1408-5). S Karger.

Napier, J. R. Primates & Their Adaptations. rev. ed. Head, J. J., ed. LC 76-29380. (Carolina Biology Readers Ser.). (Illus.). 16p. 1977. pap. 1.60 (ISBN 0-89278-228-5, 45-9628). Carolina Biological.

Napier, J. R. & Napier, P. H. The Natural History of the Primates. (Illus.). 250p. 1985. 25.00 (ISBN 0-262-14039-X). MIT Pr.

Napier, P. H. Catalogue of Primates in the British Museum (Natural History) & Elsewhere in the British Isles, Part 2: Family Cercopithecidae, Subfamily Cercopthecinae. 203p. 1981. pap. 54.00x (ISBN 0-565-00815-3). Sabbot-Natural Hist Bks.

--Catalogue of Primates in the British Museum (Natural History) & Elsewhere in the British Isles: Part 2; Family Cercopithecidae, Subfamily Cercopithecinae. 214p. 1981. 100.00x (Pub. by Brit Mus Pubns England). State Mutual Bk.

--Catalogue of Primates in the British Museum (Natural History) & Elsewhere in the British Isles, Part 3: Family Cercopithecidae Subfamily Colobinae. 175p. 1985. 70.00x (ISBN 0-565-00894-3, Pub. by Brit Mus Nat Hist England). Sabbot-Natural Hist Bks.

Noback, C. R. & Montagna, W., eds. The Primate Brain. LC 73-95612. (Advances in Primatology: Vol. 1). pap. 81.30 (ISBN 0-317-26292-0, 2055692). Bks Demand UMI.

Noback, Charles R., ed. Sensory Systems of Primates. LC 78-15383. (Advances in Primatology Ser.). (Illus.). 221p. 1978. 37.50x (ISBN 0-306-31127-5, Plenum Pr). Plenum Pub.

Novy, Miles J. & Resko, John A. Fetal Endocrinology. LC 81-19038. (ORPRC Symposium on Primate Reproductive Biology Ser.: Vol. 1). 1981. 49.50 (ISBN 0-12-522601-2). Acad Pr.

Osborn, Henry F., et al. Major Papers on Early Primate, Compiled from the Publications of the American Museum of Natural History: 1902 to 1940. LC 78-72712. 1980. 55.50 (ISBN 0-404-18282-8). AMS Pr.

Osman, William C. Evolutionary Biology of the Primates. 1973. 37.00 (ISBN 0-12-528750-X). Acad Pr.

Pilgrim, C. E. New Siwalik Primates: Their Bearing on the Question of Evolution of Man & the Anthropoidea. Bd. with A Sivapithecus Palate. LC 77-86436. (India Geological Survey. Records of the Geological Survey of India: Vol. 45). Repr. of 1915 ed. 15.00 (ISBN 0-404-16675-X). AMS Pr.

Reichenbach, Heinrich G. Die Vollstandigste Naturgeschicte der Affen. LC 78-72725. Repr. of 1863 ed. 72.50 (ISBN 0-404-18298-4). AMS Pr.

Richard, Alison F. Primate Ecology & Social Organization. Head, J. J., ed. LC 80-66617. (Carolina Biology Readers Ser.). (Illus.). 16p. 1982. pap. 1.60 (ISBN 0-89278-308-7, 45-9708). Carolina Biological.

--Primates in Nature. LC 84-18802. (Illus.). 558p. 1985. 27.95 (ISBN 0-7167-1487-6); pap. 17.95 (ISBN 0-7167-1647-X). W H Freeman.

Rodman, Peter S., ed. Adapations for Foraging in Nonhuman Primates: Contributions to an Organismal Biology of Prosimians, Monkeys, & Apes. 1984. 37.00 (ISBN 0-231-05226-X, King's Crown Paperbacks); pap. 19.00 (ISBN 0-231-05227-8). Columbia U Pr.

Sebeok, Thomas A. & Umiker-Sebeok, D. J., eds. Speaking of Apes: A Critical Anthology of Two-Way Communication with Man. LC 79-17714. (Illus.). 500p. 1980. 39.50x (ISBN 0-306-40279-3, Plenum Pr). Plenum Pub.

Seligsohn, D. Analysis of Species-Specific Molar Adaptations in Strepsirhine Primates. (Contributions to Primatology: Vol. 11). (Illus.). 1977. 131.75 (ISBN 3-8055-2634-2). S Karger.

Simons, Elwyn L. Primate Evolution: An Introduction to Man's Place in Nature. (Illus.). 352p. 1972. pap. text ed. write for info. (ISBN 0-02-410680-1). Macmillan.

Socha, Wladyslaw & Ruffie, Jacques. Blood Groups of Primates: Theory, Practice, Evolutionary Meaning. (Monographs in Primatology: Vol. 3). 488p. 1983. 56.00 (ISBN 0-8451-3402-7). A R Liss.

Steklis, H. & Kling, A., eds. Hormones, Drugs & Social Behavior in Primates. 384p. 1983. 45.00 (ISBN 0-89335-168-7). SP Med & Sci Bks.

Stern, J. T., Jr. Functional Myology of the Hip & Thigh of Cebid Monkeys & Its Implications for the Evolution of Erect Posture. (Bibliotheca Primatologica: No. 14). 1971. pap. 33.25 (ISBN 3-8055-1212-0). S Karger.

Sussman, Robert W. Primate Ecology: Problem Oriented Field Studies. LC 78-17828. 596p. 1979. text ed. 30.95 (ISBN 0-394-34409-X). Random.

Swindler, Daris. Dentition of Living Primates. 1976. 59.00 (ISBN 0-12-679250-X). Acad Pr.

Swindler, Daris R. & Wood, Charles D. Atlas of Primate Gross Anatomy. LC 81-19350. 384p. 1982. Repr. of 1973 ed. lib. bdg. 39.50 (ISBN 0-89874-321-4). Krieger.

Szalay, F. S., ed. Approaches to Primate Paleobiology. (Contributions to Primatology: Vol. 5). (Illus.). 250p. 1975. pap. 64.00 (ISBN 3-8055-1747-5). S Karger.

Szalay, Frederick S. & Delson, Eric. Evolutionary History of the Primates. LC 78-20051. 1980. 49.50 (ISBN 0-12-680150-9). Acad Pr.

Taub, David. Primate Paternalism. (Behavioral Science Ser.). (Illus.). 464p. 1984. 44.00 (ISBN 0-442-27217-0). Van Nos Reinhold.

Terborgh, John. Five New World Primates: A Study in Comparative Ecology. LC 83-42596. (Monographs in Behavior & Ecology). (Illus.). 260p. 1984. 40.00x (ISBN 0-691-08337-1); pap. text ed. 13.50x (ISBN 0-691-08338-X). Princeton U Pr.

Watts, Elizabeth S. Nonhuman Primate Models for Human Growth & Development. (MP Ser.: Vol. 6). 328p. 1985. 46.00 (ISBN 0-8451-3405-1). A R Liss.

Wolfheim, Jaclyn H. Primates of the World: Distribution, Abundance & Conservation. LC 82-13464. (Illus.). 854p. 1983. 57.50x (ISBN 0-295-95899-5). U of Wash Pr.

PRIMATES–BEHAVIOR

Akins, F. R., et al. Behavioral Development of Nonhuman Primates: An Abstracted Bibliography. LC 79-26700. 314p. 1980. 85.00x (ISBN 0-306-65189-0, IFI Plenum). Plenum Pub.

Altman, Stuart A. Social Communication Among the Primates. LC 65-25120. (Midway Reprints Ser.). (Illus.). xiv, 392p. 1982. pap. text ed. 18.00x (ISBN 0-226-01597-1). U of Chicago Pr.

Bell, Robert W. & Smotherman, William F., eds. Maternal Influences & Early Behavior. LC 78-17074. (Illus.). 465p. 1980. text ed. 60.00 (ISBN 0-89335-059-1). SP Med & Sci Bks.

Bowden, Douglas M. Aging in Nonhuman Primates. (Primate Behavior & Development Ser.). 1979. 32.50 (ISBN 0-442-20734-4). Van Nos Reinhold.

Bramblett, Claud A. Patterns of Primate Behavior. (Illus.). 320p. 1985. pap. text ed. 13.95x (ISBN 0-88133-144-9). Waveland Pr.

Bromley, Lynn. Monkeys, Apes & Other Primates. (Illus.). 64p. 1981. pap. 3.95 (ISBN 0-686-80426-0). Bellerophon Bks.

Carpenter, C. R. Naturalistic Behavior of Nonhuman Primates. LC 64-15065. (Illus.). 1964. 27.50x (ISBN 0-271-73084-6). Pa St U Pr.

Carpenter, C. R., ed. Behavioral Regulators of Behavior in Primates. LC 72-3602. (Illus.). 303p. 1974. 30.00 (ISBN 0-8387-1099-9). Bucknell U Pr.

Chalmers, Neil. Social Behavior in Primates. (Contemporary Biology Ser.). (Illus.). 264p. 1979. pap. text ed. 21.50 (ISBN 0-8391-1453-X). Univ Park.

Charles-Dominique, P., et al. Nocturnal Malagasy Primates: Ecology, Physiology & Behavior. LC 89-6799. (Communication & Behavior: an Interdisciplinary Ser.). 1980. 39.50 (ISBN 0-12-169350-3). Acad Pr.

Chiarelli, A. B. & Corruscini, R. S., eds. Primate Behavior & Sociobiology: Selected Papers - Proceedings, Pt. B. (Proceedings in Life Sciences Ser.). (Illus.). 230p. 1981. 36.00 (ISBN 0-387-11024-0). Springer-Verlag.

Chivers, D. J., et al. The Siamang in Malaya: A Field Study of a Primate in Tropical Rain Forest. Hofer, H. & Schultz, A. H., eds. (Contributions to Primatology: Vol. 4). (Illus.). 250p. 1974. 73.25 (ISBN 3-8055-1668-1). S Karger.

Clutton-Brock, T. H., ed. Primate Ecology: Studies of Feeding & Ranging Behavior in Lemurs, Monkeys & Apes. 1977. 75.00 (ISBN 0-12-176850-3). Acad Pr.

Erwin, Joseph, et al. Captivity & Behavior: Primates in Breeding Colonies, Laboratories, & Zoos. (Primate Behavior & Development Ser.). 1979. 39.95 (ISBN 0-442-22329-3). Van Nos Reinhold.

Fedigan, L. M. A Study of Roles in the Arashiyama West Troop of Japanese Monkeys (Macaca Fuscata) Szalay, F. S., ed. (Contributions to Primatology: Vol. 9). (Illus.). 116p. 1976. 21.00 (ISBN 3-8055-2334-3). S Karger.

Fedigan, Linda M. Primate Paradigms: Sex Roles & Social Bonds. (Illus.). 1982. (ISBN 0-920792-03-0); pap. write for info. Eden Pr.

Fobes, James & King, James, eds. Primate Behavior. (Communication & Behavior Ser.). 385p. 1982. 35.00 (ISBN 0-12-261320-1). Acad Pr.

Harre, Rom & Reynolds, Vernon, eds. The Meaning of Primate Signals. LC 83-23219. (Studies in Emotion & Social Interaction). 224p. 1984. 39.50 (ISBN 0-521-25944-4). Cambridge U Pr.

Hinde, Robert A., ed. Primate Social Relationships. LC 83-12023. (Illus.). 400p. 1983. text ed. 45.00x (ISBN 0-87893-275-5); pap. text ed. 25.00x (ISBN 0-87893-276-3). Sinauer Assoc.

Holloway, Ralph. Primate Aggression, Territoriality & Zenophobia: A Comparative Perspective. 1974. 72.00 (ISBN 0-12-352850-X). Acad Pr.

International Congress of Primatology, 3rd, Zurich, 1970. Primatology: Proceedings, 3 vols. Incl. Vol. 1. Taxonomy, Anatomy, Reproduction. Biegert, J. & Leutenegger, W., eds. (Illus.). xvi, 278p. 40.50 (ISBN 3-8055-1244-9); Vol. 2. Neurobiology, Immunology, Cytology. Biegert, J. & Leutenegger, W., eds. (Illus.). x, 245p. 38.50 (ISBN 3-8055-1245-7); Vol. 3. Behavior. Kummer, H., ed. (Illus.). x, 191p. 30.00 (ISBN 3-8055-1246-5). 1971. Set. 108.75 (ISBN 3-8055-1247-3). S Karger.

Jarrard, Leonard E., ed. Cognitive Processes of Nonhuman Primates. 1971. 42.00 (ISBN 0-12-380850-2). Acad Pr.

Jolly, Alison. The Evolution of Primate Behavior. 2nd ed. (The Macmillan Series in Physical Anthropology). 416p. 1985. text ed. write for info. (ISBN 0-02-361140-5). Macmillan.

Kummer, Hans. Social Organization of Hamadryas Baboons: A Field Study. LC 67-25082. 1968. 16.00x (ISBN 0-226-46171-8). U of Chicago Pr.

Kurland, J. A. Kin Selection in the Japanese Monkey. Szalay, F. S., ed. (Contributions to Primatology: Vol. 11). (Illus.). 1977. 27.25 (ISBN 3-8055-2633-4). S Karger.

Loy, J. D., et al. The Behavior of Gonadectomized Rhesus Monkeys. (Contributions to Primatology: Vol. 20). (Illus.). viii, 144p. 1983. 28.25 (ISBN 3-8055-3795-6). S Karger.

Michael, Richard P. & Crook, John H., eds. Comparative Ecology & Behaviour of Primates. 1973. 99.50 (ISBN 0-12-493450-1). Acad Pr.

Mitchell, G. Behavioral Sex Differences in Non-Human Primates. (Primate Behavior & Development Ser.). 1979. 34.50 (ISBN 0-442-24594-7). Van Nos Reinhold.

--Human Sex Differences: A Primatologist's Perspective. 256p. 1981. 24.50 (ISBN 0-442-23865-7). Van Nos Reinhold.

Omark, Donald, et al. Dominance Relations: An Ethological View of Human Conflict & Social Interactions. LC 79-14352. 528p. 1980. lib. bdg. 63.00 (ISBN 0-8240-7048-8). Garland Pub.

Primate Behavior & Social Ecology. (Illus.). 200p. 1984. pap. 22.95 (ISBN 0-412-23220-0, 6894, Pub. by Chapman & Hall England). Methuen Inc.

Roonwal, M. L. & Mohnot, S. M. Primates of South Asia: Ecology, Sociobiology, & Behavior. 1977. 27.50x (ISBN 0-674-70485-1). Harvard U Pr.

Rosenblum, Leonard A., ed. Primate Behavior: Developments in Field & Laboratory Research, 4 vols. Vol. 2, 1971. 60.00 (ISBN 0-12-534002-8); Vol. 3, 1974. 55.00 (ISBN 0-12-534003-6); Vol. 4, 1975. 75.00 (ISBN 0-12-534004-4). Acad Pr.

Ruppenthal, G. C., ed. Nursery Care of Nonhuman Primates. LC 78-322018. (Advances in Primatology Ser.). 349p. 1979. 55.00x (ISBN 0-306-40150-9, Plenum Pr). Plenum Pub.

Schrier, Allan M., et al, eds. Behavior of Non-Human Primates: Modern Research Trends. Vol. 1, 1965. 48.00 (ISBN 0-12-629101-2); Vol. 2, 45.00 (ISBN 0-12-629102-0); Vol. 3, 1971. 45.00 (ISBN 0-12-629103-9); Vol. 4, 1971. 45.00 (ISBN 0-12-629104-7). Acad Pr.

Shafton, Anthony. Conditions of Awareness: Subjective Factors in the Social Adaptations of Man & Other Primates. LC 76-26201. 1976. pap. 10.00 (ISBN 0-9601130-1-0). Riverstone.

Smith, Euclid O. Social Plays in Primates. 1978. 39.00 (ISBN 0-12-652750-4). Acad Pr.

Snowdon, Charles T., et al, eds. Primate Communication. LC 82-1219. 472p. 1983. 42.50 (ISBN 0-521-24690-3). Cambridge U Pr.

PRIMATES AS LABORATORY ANIMALS

Bourne, Geoffrey H., ed. Non-Human Primates & Medical Research. 1973. 70.00 (ISBN 0-12-119150-8). Acad Pr.

Conference on Experimental Medicine & Surgery in Primates, 2nd, New York, 1969. Medical Primatology, 1970: Proceedings. Goldsmith, E. I. & Moor-Jankowski, J., eds. 1971. 119.25 (ISBN 3-8055-1227-9). S Karger.

National Research Council Institute of Laboratory Animal Resources. Primate Population Ecology. 1981. pap. text ed. 14.50 (ISBN 0-309-03179-6). Natl Acad Pr.

Whitney, Robert A., Jr., et al. Laboratory Primate Handbook. 1973. 34.50 (ISBN 0-12-747450-1). Acad Pr.

PRIME NUMBERS

see Numbers, Prime

PRINT MAKING

see Prints–Technique

PRINTED CIRCUITS

see also Electronic Circuits

Bishop Graphics, Inc. The Design & Drafting of Printed Circuits. 1979. 47.95 (ISBN 0-07-005430-4). McGraw.

Business Communications Staff. Rigid & Flexible Printed Circuit Boards. 1985. pap. 1750.00 (ISBN 0-89336-451-7, GO67R). BCC.

Clark, Raymond H. Handbook of Printed Circuit Manufacturing. 1984. 49.50 (ISBN 0-442-21610-6). Van Nos Reinhold.

Coombs, Clyde F. Printed Circuits Handbook. 1979. 48.50 (ISBN 0-07-012608-9). McGraw.

DeForest, W. S. Photoresist: Materials & Processes. 1975. 46.50 (ISBN 0-07-016230-1). McGraw.

Goldberg, Joel. How to Make Printed Circuit Boards. LC 79-18137. (Electro-Skills Ser.). (Illus.). 1980. pap. 7.05 (ISBN 0-07-023634-8). McGraw.

Hamilton, Charles. A Guide to Printed Circuit Board Design. (Illus.). 104p. (Orig.). 1984. pap. text ed. 19.95 (ISBN 0-408-01398-2). Butterworth.

Heiserman, Russell L. Printed Circuit Boards. 146p. 1983. pap. 15.95 (ISBN 0-471-86177-4). Wiley.

Kirkpatrick, James M. Electronic Drafting & Printed Circuit Board Design. LC 84-14929. 288p. 1985. pap. text ed. 24.00 (ISBN 0-8273-2315-8); instr's. guide 4.00 (ISBN 0-8273-2316-6). Delmar.

Kosloff, Albert. Screen Printing Electronic Circuits. (Illus.). 1980. 12.95 (ISBN 0-911380-49-3). Signs of Times.

Leonida, G. Handbook of Printed Circuit Design Manufacture, Components & Assembly. 700p. 1980. 165.00 (ISBN 0-901150-08-8, Pub. by Electrochemical Scotland). State Mutual Bk.

Lindsey, Darry. The Design & Drafting of Printed Circuits. 2nd ed. (Illus.). 400p. 1983. 48.95 (ISBN 0-07-037844-4). McGraw.

Lindsey, Darryl. The Design & Drafting of Printed Circuits. rev ed. LC 81-69173. (Illus.). 1982. 44.95 (ISBN 0-9601748-1-8, 10001). Bishop Graphics.

Lund, Preben. Generation of Precision Artwork for Printed Circuit Boards. LC 77-12388. 353p. 1978. 69.95x (ISBN 0-471-99587-8, Pub. by Wiley-Interscience). Wiley.

Market Intelligence Research Company Staff. Printed Circuit Board ATE Markets. 125p. pap. text ed. 695.00 (ISBN 0-317-19567-0). Market Res Co.

Printed Circuit Board Technology. 173p. 32.00 (ISBN 0-938648-09-8). T-C Pubns CA.

Shemilt, H. R. Printed Circuit Troubleshooting. 105p. 1980. 135.00x (ISBN 0-901150-03-7, Pub. by Electrochemical Scotland). State Mutual Bk.

Sikonowiz, Walter. Designing & Creating Printed Circuits. (Illus.). 164p. (Orig.). 1981. pap. 8.95 (ISBN 0-8104-0964-X). Hayden.

White, Donald R. EMI Control in the Design of Printed Circuit Boards & Backplanes. 3rd ed. Price, Edward R., ed. LC 81-52618. 1982. text ed. 22.00 (ISBN 0-932263-12-7). White Consult.

PRINTERS

see also Printing

Baker, Elizabeth F. Displacement of Men by Machines: Effects of Technological Change in Commerical Printing. Stein, Leon, ed. LC 77-70481. (Work Ser.). (Illus.). 1977. Repr. of 1933 ed. lib. bdg. 26.50x (ISBN 0-405-10155-4). Ayer Co Pubs.

Bates, Albert C. The Work of Hartford's First Printer. 16p. 1925. pap. 1.00 (ISBN 0-940748-47-9). Conn Hist Soc.

Bristol, Roger P. Supplement to Charles Evans' American Bibliography. LC 73-94761. (Bibliographical Society Ser). 640p. 1970. 40.00x (ISBN 0-8139-0287-8). U Pr of Va.

Cosenza, Mario E., ed. Biographical & Bibliographical Dictionary of the Italian Printers & of Foreign Printers in Italy from the Introduction of the Art of Printing into Italy to 1800. 1968. lib. bdg. 100.00 (ISBN 0-8161-0766-1, Hall Library). G K Hall.

Cusick, Suzanne G. Valerio Dorico: Music Printer in Sixteenth Century Rome. Buelow, George, ed. LC 81-4745. (Studies in Musicology: No. 43). 330p. 1981. 49.95 (ISBN 0-8357-1173-0). UMI Res Pr.

Demeter, Richard L. Primer, Presses, & Composing Sticks: Women Printers of the Colonial Period. 1979. 7.50 (ISBN 0-682-49195-0, University). Exposition Pr FL.

Knight, Charles. Old Printer & the Modern Press. LC 71-148340. Repr. of 1854 ed. 22.45 (ISBN 0-404-08838-4). AMS Pr.

Plomer, Henry R. Wynkyn de Worde & His Contemporaries from the Death of Caxton to 1535. LC 77-2719. Repr. of 1925 ed. lib. bdg. 35.00 (ISBN 0-8414-6829-X). Folcroft.

Rogers, Theresa F. & Friedman, Nathalie S. Printers Face Automation: The Impact of Technology on Work & Retirement among Skilled Craftsmen. LC 79-3047. 208p. 1980. 26.50x (ISBN 0-669-03310-3). Lexington Bks.

Rudman, Jack. Printer. (Career Examination Ser.: C-C16). (Cloth bdg. avail. on request). pap. 10.00 (ISBN 0-8373-0616-7). Natl Learning.

Sale, William M. Samuel Richardson: Master Printer. LC 77-22446. (Cornell Studies in English: No.37). (Illus.). 1978. Repr. of 1950 ed. lib. bdg. 27.50x (ISBN 0-8371-9732-5, SASR). Greenwood.

Ward, Robert E. Prince of Dublin Printers: The Letters of George Faulkner. LC 71-160053. 160p. 1972. 15.00x (ISBN 0-8131-1258-3). U Pr of Ky.

PRINTERS (DATA PROCESSING SYSTEMS)

Bridges, David & Naylor, Helen. The Commodore Disk & Printer Handbook. (Illus.). 192p. 1984. pap. 14.95 (ISBN 0-946576-23-8, Pub. by Phoenix Pub). David & Charles.

Condon, M. A. Office System Printer: A Practical Evaluation Guide. 100p. 1982. pap. 14.20 (ISBN 0-471-89413-3). Wiley.

Hogan, Thom. All about Computer Printers. cancelled 19.95 (ISBN 0-89303-305-7). Brady Comm.

Kater, D. A. & Kater, R. L. Getting the Most out of Your Epson Printer. 240p. 1985. 17.95 (ISBN 0-07-033385-8). McGraw.

Ledin, Victor. How to Buy & Use a Printer. 1984. pap. 3.50 (ISBN 0-88284-315-X). Alfred Pub.

Nath, Sanjiva K., et al. Buyer's Guide to Computer Printers. (Illus.). 192p. (Orig.). 1985. 17.95 (ISBN 0-8306-0872-9, 1872); pap. 12.95 (ISBN 0-8306-1872-4). TAB Bks.

Pirisino, Jim. Minute Manual for the Dot Matrix Printer. 1985. pap. 12.95 (ISBN 0-913131-04-0). Minuteware.

Weber Systems, Inc. Epson Printer User's Handbook. 280p. 1985. pap. 9.95 (ISBN 0-345-31842-0). Ballantine.

Weber Systems, Inc. Staff. Okidata Printer User's Handbook. LC 84-29172. (WSI's User's Handbooks to Personal Computers Ser.). 300p. (Orig.). 1985. pap. 15.95 (ISBN 0-938862-19-7). Weber Systems.

PRINTING

Adams, J. Michael & Faux, David D. Printing Technology. 2nd ed. 1982. text ed. write for info. (ISBN 0-534-01016-4, Breton Pubs). Wadsworth Pub.

Bodoni, Giambattista. Manuale Typografia, 2 Vols. 1960. 200.00x (ISBN 0-87556-035-0). Saifer.

DeLuca, J. Practical Problems in Mathematics for Printers. LC 76-3942. 1976. pap. 6.00 (ISBN 0-8273-1280-6); instructor's guide 1.75 (ISBN 0-8273-1286-5). Delmar.

De Vinne, Theodore L. Manual of Printing Office Practice. Lew, Irving, ed. (Bibliographical Reprint Ser.). 1980. Repr. of 1926 ed. text ed. 25.00 ltd. ed. (ISBN 0-89782-003-7). Battery Pk.

Durrant, W. R., et al. Machine Printing. (Library of Printing Technology). 1977. 17.95 (ISBN 0-8038-4671-1). Hastings.

Fairley, M. C. Safety, Health & Welfare in the Printing Industry. 1969. pap. 5.75 (ISBN 0-08-013033-X). Pergamon.

Fontana, John M. Thank Gutenberg for Shakespeare & Ben Franklin. 24p. 1964. pap. 1.25 (ISBN 0-685-26780-6). J M Fontana.

Glassman, Alex, ed. Printing Fundamentals. 1983. write for info (ISBN 0-89852-045-2). TAPPI.

Gordon's Print Price Annual, 1981. 900p. 1980. 235.00 (ISBN 0-931036-06-2). Martin Gordon.

International Congress on Advances in Non-Impact Printing Staff. The Second International Congress on Advances in Non-Impact Printing Technologies: Advance Printing of Paper Summaries. pap. 77.50 (ISBN 0-317-29115-7, 2025037). Bks Demand UMI.

Jackson, Holbrook. Printing of Books. LC 70-134100. (Essay Index Reprint Ser.). 1939. 24.50 (ISBN 0-8369-1931-9). Ayer Co Pubs.

Knight, Charles. Old Printer & the Modern Press. LC 71-148340. Repr. of 1854 ed. 22.45 (ISBN 0-404-08838-4). AMS Pr.

Lawson, Alexander S. Printing Types: An Introduction. LC 70-136232. 160p. 1974. pap. 6.95x (ISBN 0-8070-6659-1, BP474). Beacon Pr.

McLuhan, H. Marshall. Gutenberg Galaxy: The Making of Typographic Man. LC 62-4860. 1962. pap. 10.95 (ISBN 0-8020-6041-2). U of Toronto Pr.

Mecher, Daniel. Planning for Better Imposition. LC 76-102070. 1977. 26.95 (ISBN 0-912920-55-6). North Am Pub Co.

Moore, John W. Historical, Biographical & Miscellaneous Gatherings in the Form of Disconnected Notes Relative to Printers, Printing, Publishing, & Editing of Books, Newspapers, Magazines & Other Literary Productions. 1886. 30.50 (ISBN 0-8337-2450-9). B Franklin.

Morison, S. & Jackson, H. A. Brief Survey of Printing. 59.95 (ISBN 0-87968-788-6). Gordon Pr.

Munsell, Joel. The Typographical Miscellany, Historical & Practical. LC 72-83618. (Illus.). 268p. 1972. Repr. of 1850 ed. 21.00 (ISBN 0-8337-2482-7). B Franklin.

Pottinger, David. Printers & Printing. facsimile ed. LC 70-175709. (Select Bibliographies Reprint Ser). Repr. of 1941 ed. 15.00 (ISBN 0-8369-6624-4). Ayer Co Pubs.

Printing. 1981. text ed. 7.95 (ISBN 0-686-65133-2, 63931); pap. text ed. 5.95 (ISBN 0-686-65134-0, 63958). Natl Textbk.

Ricketts, Charles. A Defense of the Revival of Printing. 160p. 1978. 25.00 (ISBN 0-685-27171-4). Battery Pk.

Rudman, Jack. General Printing. (Occupational Competency Examination Ser.: OCE-20). (Cloth bdg. avail. on request). pap. 13.95 (ISBN 0-8373-5720-9). Natl Learning.

--Journeyman in the Printing Crafts. (Career Examination Ser.: C-410). (Cloth bdg. avail. on request). pap. 12.00 (ISBN 0-8373-0410-5). Natl Learning.

Ruggles, Philip K. Printing Estimating. LC 79-13008. 1979. text ed. write for info. (ISBN 0-534-00747-3, Breton Pubs). Wadsworth Pub.

Simon, Herbert. Introduction to Printing: The Craft of Letterpress. (Illus.). 128p. 1980. pap. 7.50 (ISBN 0-571-11528-4). Faber & Faber.

Small Printing Houses & Modern Technology. (Monographs on Communication Technology & Utilization: No. 6). (Illus.). 80p. 1981. pap. 6.25 (ISBN 92-3-101637-7, U1145, UNESCO). Unipub.

Tripartite Technical Meeting for the Printing & Allied Trades, 2nd, Geneva, 1981. Report One. International Labour Office, ed. iii, 143p. (Orig.). 1981. pap. 10.00 (ISBN 92-2-102691-4). Intl Labour Office.

White, William. Laser Printing. 1983. write for info. (ISBN 0-935506-16-0). Carnegie Pr.

Wooldridge, D. Letter Assembly in Printing. (Library of Printing Technology). 1972. 18.95 (ISBN 0-8038-4274-0). Hastings.

PRINTING–BIBLIOGRAPHY

Bigmore, F. C. A Bibliography of Printing. 1982. 75.00x (ISBN 0-87556-157-8). Saifer.

Bigmore, F. C. & Wyman, C. W. A Bibliography of Printing with Notes & Illustrations, 3 vols. in one. (Illus.). xxii, 976p. 1978. Repr. of 1880 ed. 75.00 (ISBN 0-900470-01-1). Oak Knoll.

Cosenza, Mario E., ed. Biographical & Bibliographical Dictionary of the Italian Printers & of Foreign Printers in Italy from the Introduction of the Art of Printing into Italy to 1800. 1968. lib. bdg. 100.00 (ISBN 0-8161-0766-1, Hall Library). G K Hall.

International Directory of Private Presses (Letterpresses), Second. Westreich, Budd, ed. (Illus.). 132p. (Orig.). 1980. pap. 12.00 (ISBN 0-936300-01-9); pap. 12.00 (ISBN 0-686-36903-3). Pr Arden Park.

McMurtie, Douglas C. Invention of Printing: A Bibliography. LC 71-153487. 1971. Repr. of 1942 ed. lib. bdg. 32.00 (ISBN 0-8337-2342-1). B Franklin.

Newberry Library - Chicago. Dictionary Catalogue of the History of Printing from the John M. Wing Foundation, 6 Vols. 1961. Set. lib. bdg. 595.00 (ISBN 0-8161-0587-1, Hall Library). G K Hall.

--Dictionary Catalogue of the History of Printing from the John M. Wing Foundation, First Supplement, 3 vols. 1970. Set. lib. bdg. 330.00 (ISBN 0-8161-0809-9, Hall Library). G K Hall.

Quast, Emilie. An Index & Bibliography to Douglas C. McMurtrie's, "A History of Printing in the United States". LC 74-5200. 1975. 11.00 (ISBN 0-8337-2341-3). B Franklin.

Selected Bibliography: Screen Printing. 37p. 1976. pap. 10.00 (ISBN 0-317-14992-X). Tech & Ed Ctr Graph Arts RIT.

Walker, W. C., et al. Print Quality Evaluation: A Bibliography. Ray, C. T. & Fetsko, J. M., eds. (TAPPI PRESS Reports Ser.). 63p. 1973. pap. 19.95 (ISBN 0-89852-350-8, 01-01-R050). TAPPI.

Watkins, George T. Bibliography of Printing in America. Lew, Irving, ed. (Bibliographical Reprint Ser.). 1962. pap. 15.00 ltd. ed. (ISBN 0-89782-002-9). Battery Pk.

Weiner, Jack, et al. Paper & Its Relation to Printing. 2nd ed, suppl. 1 ed. LC 62-51039. (Bibliographic Ser.: No. 164, Supplement 2). 1973. pap. 24.00 (ISBN 0-87010-005-X). Inst Paper Chem.

PRINTING–COMPOSITION

see Type-Setting

PRINTING–DATA PROCESSING

CES Industries, Inc. Ed-Lab Eighty Experiment Manual: Printer Interfacing. (Illus., Orig.). 1983. write for info. (ISBN 0-86711-033-3). CES Industries.

Computer Strategies. The Printer's Computer Handbook. 150p. 1984. looseleaf 45.00x (ISBN 0-913505-17-X). Computer Strat.

Durbin, Harold C. Printing & Computer Terminology. LC 80-65655. 206p. (Orig.). 1980. pap. 9.50 (ISBN 0-936786-00-0); pap. text ed. 8.50 (ISBN 0-936786-01-9). Durbin Assoc.

How to Establish Standards for Computer-Assisted Keyboarding Operations. 30.00 (ISBN 0-318-02613-9). Print Indus Am.

International Resource Development Inc. Microcomputer Printers. 174p. 1984. 1650.00x (ISBN 0-88694-589-5). Intl Res Dev.

Kleper, Michael L. Typesetting by Microcomputer. (Illus.). 1982. pap. 10.00 (ISBN 0-930904-04-4). Graphic Dimensions.

National Association of Printers & Lithographers Forms Control Program. (Illus.). 76p. 50.00 (ISBN 0-318-14966-4, P112); first copy new members free; additional copies 25.00 (ISBN 0-318-14967-2). NAPL.

A Primer on Data Communications. 30.00 (ISBN 0-318-02627-9). Print Indus Am.

Rasberry, Leslie. Computer Age Copyfitting. LC 77-83812. (Illus.). 1978. pap. 8.95 (ISBN 0-910158-26-6). Art Dir.

PRINTING–DICTIONARIES

American Dictionary of Printing & Bookmaking. LC 70-135172. 1971. Repr. of 1894 ed. lib. bdg. 29.00 (ISBN 0-8337-0059-6). B Franklin.

Durbin, Harold C. Printing & Computer Terminology. LC 80-65655. 206p. (Orig.). 1980. pap. 9.50 (ISBN 0-936786-00-0); pap. text ed. 8.50 (ISBN 0-936786-01-9). Durbin Assoc.

Friday, Wm. Quick Printing Encyclopedia. LC 82-144544. (Illus.). 509p. 1982. 49.50 (ISBN 0-934432-10-4). Prudential Pub Co.

Glaister, Geoffrey. Glaister's Glossary of the Book: Terms Used in Paper-Making, Printing, Bookbinding, & Publishing. LC 76-47975. 1979. 75.00 (ISBN 0-520-03364-7). U of Cal Pr.

Goodstein, David & Newhouse, Rosalyn, eds. Glossary of Typesetting, Computer, & Communications Terms. 65p. 20.00 (ISBN 0-318-17397-2); members 10.00 (ISBN 0-318-17398-0). Print Indus Am.

Isaacs, Alan, ed. The Multilingual Dictionary of Printing & Publishing. 336p. 1981. 22.50 (ISBN 0-87196-444-9). Facts on File.

Jacobi, Charles T. The Printers' Vocabulary. LC 68-30613. 1975. Repr. of 1888 ed. 35.00x (ISBN 0-8103-3309-0). Gale.

Mintz, Patricia. Dictionary of Graphic Arts Terms: A Communication Tool for People Who Buy Type & Printing. 328p. 1981. 21.95 (ISBN 0-442-26711-8). Van Nos Reinhold.

Moth, Axel. Technical Terms Used in Bibliographies & by the Book & Printing Trades. LC 77-6172. 1977. Repr. of 1917 ed. lib. bdg. 30.00 (ISBN 0-89341-153-1). Longwood Pub Group.

Pasko, W W., ed. American Dictionary of Printing & Bookmaking. LC 66-27215. 1967. Repr. of 1894 ed. 50.00x (ISBN 0-8103-3345-7). Gale.

Reilly, Elizabeth C. Dictionary of Colonial American Printers' Ornaments & Illustrations. LC 75-5023. (Illus.). xxxvi, 514p. 1975. 50.00x (ISBN 0-912296-06-2, Dist. by U Pr of Va). Am Antiquarian.

Savage, William. Dictionary of the Art of Printing. 1965. Repr. of 1841 ed. 32.00 (ISBN 0-8337-3128-9). B Franklin.

PRINTING–FACSIMILIES

see Printing–Specimens

PRINTING–HISTORY

Annenberg, Maurice, intro. by. A Typographical Journey Through the Inland Printer 1883-1900. LC 77-89269. casebound 45.00 (ISBN 0-916526-04-6). Maran Pub.

Benedikz, Benedickt S. Early Printing in Iceland. Clair, Colin, ed. (Spread of Printing Ser.: No. 1). (Illus.). 1969. pap. 9.75 (ISBN 0-8390-0018-9). Abner Schram Ltd.

Blades, William. Books in Chains & Other Bibliographical Papers. LC 68-30610. 1968. Repr. of 1892 ed. 35.00x (ISBN 0-8103-3298-1). Gale.

Bloy, Colin. History of Printing Ink. 148p. 1980. 40.00x (ISBN 0-85331-314-8, Pub. by Lund Humphries England). State Mutual Bk.

Bloy, Colin H. A History of Printing Ink, Balls & Rollers: 1440-1850. (Illus.). 147p. 1980. 19.95 (ISBN 0-913720-07-0, Sandstone). Beil.

Borchardt, D. H. Early Printing in Australia. Clair, Colin, ed. LC 76-78404. (Spread of Printing Ser). (Illus., Orig.). 1969. pap. 9.75 (ISBN 0-8390-0024-3). Abner Schram Ltd.

Boutin, Otto J. A Catfish in the Bodoni: The Golden Age of Tramp Printer's. LC 70-141186. (Illus.). 1971. 4.00 (ISBN 0-87839-004-9). North Star.

Brightly, Charles. The Method of Founding Stereotype as Practised by Charles Brightly. Bidwell, John, ed. (Nineteenth Century Book Arts & Printing History Ser.). 36.00 (ISBN 0-8240-3883-5). Garland Pub.

Bristol, Roger P. Supplement to Charles Evans' American Bibliography. LC 73-94761. (Bibliographical Society Ser). 640p. 1970. 40.00x (ISBN 0-8139-0287-8). U Pr of Va.

Carter, Thomas F. The Invention of Printing in China & Its Spread Westward. 2nd ed. LC 55-5418. pap. 79.80 (ISBN 0-317-10535-3, 2012408). Bks Demand UMI.

Chappell, Warren. A Short History of the Printed Word. LC 79-90409. (Nonpareil Bks.). (Illus.). 288p. 1980. pap. 9.95 (ISBN 0-87923-312-5). Godine.

Chibbett, D. G. The History of Japanese Printing & Book Illustration. LC 76-9362. (Illus.). 264p. 1977. 65.00 (ISBN 0-87011-288-0). Kodansha.

Clair, Colin. Early Printing in Malta. (Spread of Printing Ser.: No. 2). (Illus.). 1969. pap. 9.75 (ISBN 0-8390-0017-0). Abner Schram Ltd.

Cotton, Henry. The Typographical Gazetteer. LC 76-159922. 222p. 1975. Repr. of 1825 ed. 40.00x (ISBN 0-8103-4121-2). Gale.

De Graaf, H. J. Early Printing in Indonesia. Clair, Colin, ed. LC 75-78401. (Spread of Printing Ser). (Illus., Orig.). 1969. pap. 9.75 (ISBN 0-8390-0020-0). Abner Schram Ltd.

Delen. Histoire De la Gravure Dans les Anciens Pays-Bas et Dans les Provinces Belges, Jusgn'a la Fin du Des Origines Siezieme Siecle, 3 vols. in one. LC 73-127252. (Graphic Art Ser.). 1971. Repr. of 1931 ed. lib. bdg. 175.00 (ISBN 0-306-71114-1). Da Capo.

Demeter, Richard L. Primer, Presses, & Composing Sticks: Women Printers of the Colonial Period. 1979. 7.50 (ISBN 0-682-49195-0, University). Exposition Pr FL.

DeVinne, Theodore L. Invention of Printing. LC 68-17971. 1969. Repr. of 1876 ed. 48.00x (ISBN 0-8103-3302-3). Gale.

Dix, Ernest R. Printing in Dublin Prior to 1601. 2nd ed. LC 75-132674. 1971. Repr. of 1932 ed. lib. bdg. 14.50 (ISBN 0-8337-0874-0). B Franklin.

Duff, E. Gordon. Early English Printing: A Series of Facsimilies of All the Types Used in England During the 15th Century. 1969. Repr. of 1896 ed. 23.50 (ISBN 0-8337-0947-X). B Franklin.

Dyer, Alan. James Parker, Colonial Printer: 1715-1770. LC 80-52545. 441p. 1982. 32.50x (ISBN 0-87875-202-1). Whitston Pub.

Eisenstein, Elizabeth. The Printing Press As an Agent of Change, 2 vols. LC 77-91083. 1979. Vol. 1. 67.50 (ISBN 0-521-21967-1); Vol. 2. 47.50 (ISBN 0-521-21969-8); Set. 99.00 (ISBN 0-521-22044-0). Cambridge U Pr.

English Restoration Bookbindings. 1981. 45.00x (ISBN 0-7141-0362-4, Pub. by Brit Lib England); pap. 25.00x (ISBN 0-686-72510-7). State Mutual Bk.

Follett, Frederick. History of the Press in Western New York: From the Beginning to the Middle of the Nineteenth Century. LC 73-6520. (Illus.). 80p. 1973. Repr. of 1920 ed. 8.50 (ISBN 0-916346-03-X). Harbor Hill Bks.

Fournier, Pierre S. & Carter, Harry. Fournier on Typefounding. new ed. LC 78-150161. (Illus.). 412p. 1973. lib. bdg. 25.50 (ISBN 0-8337-1224-1). B Franklin.

Goff, Frederick R. Early Printing in Georgetown (Potomak) 1789-1800. 28p. 1958. pap. 3.00x (ISBN 0-912296-24-0, Dist. by U Pr of Va). Am Antiquarian.

Goudy, Frederic W. Alphabet & Elements of Lettering. rev. ed. 13.00 (ISBN 0-8446-2145-5). Peter Smith.

Goudy, Frederick W. Alphabet & Elements of Lettering. (Illus.). 1922. pap. 4.95 (ISBN 0-486-20792-7). Dover.

Green, Ralph. Works of Ralph Green. LC 81-51378. 112p. 1981. Repr. of 1955 ed. 24.95 (ISBN 0-932606-01-6). Ye Olde Print.

Hatery, Lowell H. & Bush, George P. Technological Change in Printing & Publishing. LC 77-176224. 275p. 1973. 13.75 (ISBN 0-87671-503-X). Lomond.

History of the Bureau of Engraving & Printing. (Illus.). 1978. Repr. of 1963 ed. lib. bdg. 25.00 (ISBN 0-915262-18-5). S J Durst.

Jaggard, William. Printing: Its Birth & Growth. LC 77-94591. 1979. Repr. of 1908 ed. lib. bdg. 15.00 (ISBN 0-89341-184-1). Longwood Pub Group.

John M. Wing Foundation, Newberry Library. Dictionary Catalogue of the History of Printing from the John M. Wing Foundation, Second Supplement. 1981. lib. bdg. 455.00 (ISBN 0-8161-0326-7, Hall Library). G K Hall.

Kelly, Rob R. American Wood Type: Eighteen Twenty-Eight to Nineteen Hundred. (Quality Paperbacks Ser.). 1977. pap. 8.95 (ISBN 0-306-80059-4). Da Capo.

Kennard, J. Some Early Printers & Their Colophons. 1976. lib. bdg. 59.95 (ISBN 0-8490-2626-1). Gordon Pr.

Lohf, Kenneth A., intro. by. Columbia University Libraries, The History of Printing from Its Beginnings to 1930: The Subject Catalogue of the American Type Founders Company Library in the Columbia University Libraries, 4 vols. LC 80-13377. 1980. Set. lib. bdg. 390.00 (ISBN 0-527-18763-1). Kraus Intl.

Lowman, Al. Printing Arts in Texas. 1981. 29.50 (ISBN 0-686-73811-X). Jenkins.

McLean, Ruari. Modern Book Design: From William Morris to the Present Day. (Illus.). 1959. 3.40x (ISBN 0-19-519593-0). Oxford U Pr.

Macmillan, Fiona. Early Printing in New Zealand. Clair, Colin, ed. LC 73-78406. (Spread of Printing Ser). (Illus., Orig.). 1969. pap. 9.75 (ISBN 0-8390-0021-9). Abner Schram Ltd.

McMurtie, Douglas C. Invention of Printing: A Bibliography. LC 71-153487. 1971. Repr. of 1942 ed. lib. bdg. 32.00 (ISBN 0-8337-2342-1). B Franklin.

McMurtrie, Douglas C. Book: The Story of Printing & Bookmaking. 3rd ed. (Illus.). 1943. 60.00x (ISBN 0-19-500011-0). Oxford U Pr.

Miller, C. William. Benjamin Franklin's Philadelphia Printing: A Descriptive Bibliography. LC 72-83464. (Memoirs Ser.: Vol. 102). 1974. 50.00 (ISBN 0-87169-102-7). Am Philos.

Moore, John W. Historical, Biographical & Miscellaneous Gatherings in the Form of Disconnected Notes Relative to Printers, Printing, Publishing, & Editing of Books, Newspapers, Magazines & Other Literary Productions. 1886. 30.50 (ISBN 0-8337-2450-9). B Franklin.

Moran, James. Fit to Be Styled a Typographer. (Illus.). 66p. 34.50 (ISBN 0-913720-10-0, Sandstone); pap. 19.50 (ISBN 0-913720-11-9). Beil.

Morgan, Charlotte E. Origin & History of the New York Employing Printers' Association. LC 68-58608. (Columbia University. Studies in the Social Sciences: No. 319). Repr. of 1930 ed. 15.00 (ISBN 0-404-51319-0). AMS Pr.

Morison, Stanley, et al. Politics & Script: Aspects of Authority & Freedom in the Development of Graeco-Latin Script from the Sixth Century B. C. to the Twentieth Century A. D. Barker, Nicolas, ed. (Illus.). 361p. 38.50x (ISBN 0-906795-26-5). U Pr of Va.

Munsell, Joel. The Typographical Miscellany, Historical & Practical. LC 72-83618. (Illus.). 268p. 1972. Repr. of 1850 ed. 21.00 (ISBN 0-8337-2482-7). B Franklin.

Needham, Joseph & Tsuen-Hsuin, Tsien. Science & Civilization in China: Chemistry & Chemical Technology Part 1: Paper & Printing, Vol. 5. (Illus.). 485p. 1985. 89.50 (ISBN 0-521-08690-6). Cambridge U Pr.

Newberry Library - Chicago. Dictionary Catalogue of the History of Printing from the John M. Wing Foundation, 6 Vols. 1961. Set. lib. bdg. 595.00 (ISBN 0-8161-0587-1, Hall Library). G K Hall.

--Dictionary Catalogue of the History of Printing from the John M. Wing Foundation, First Supplement, 3 vols. 1970. Set. lib. bdg. 330.00 (ISBN 0-8161-0809-9, Hall Library). G K Hall.

Norton, F. J. Descriptive Catalogue of Printing in Spain & Portugal, 1501-1520. LC 76-11062. 1978. 275.00 (ISBN 0-521-21136-0). Cambridge U Pr.

Norton, Frederick J. Printing in Spain, 1501-1520: With a Note on the Early Editions of the "Celestina". LC 65-19156. (Sandars Lectures Ser.: 1963). pap. 60.50 (ISBN 0-317-10580-9, 2022464). Bks Demand UMI.

Oldendow, Knud. Early Printing in Greenland. Clair, Colin, ed. LC 71-78399. (Spread of Printing Ser). (Illus., Orig.). 1969. pap. 9.75 (ISBN 0-8390-0023-5). Abner Schram Ltd.

Palmer, Samuel. A General History of Printing: From the First Invention of It in the City of Mentz, to Its Propagation & Progress Thru' Most of the Kingdoms of Europe: Particularly the Introduction & Success of It Here in England. LC 75-80258. (Bibliography & Reference Ser.: No. 447). 400p. 1972. Repr. of 1733 ed. lib. bdg. 25.50 (ISBN 0-8337-2662-5). B Franklin.

Pasko, W W., ed. American Dictionary of Printing & Bookmaking. LC 66-27215. 1967. Repr. of 1894 ed. 50.00x (ISBN 0-8103-3345-7). Gale.

Plomer, H. R. English Printers' Ornaments. (Research & Source Works Ser: No. 146). 1968. Repr. of 1924 ed. 22.50 (ISBN 0-8337-2786-9). B Franklin.

Plomer, Henry R. English Printing, Fourteen Seventy-Six to Nineteen Hundred. Pollard, Alfred W., ed. 1979. Repr. of 1916 ed. lib. bdg. 39.50 (ISBN 0-8414-6850-8). Folcroft.

--English Printing Fourteen Seventy-Six to Nineteen Hundred. 360p. 1980. Repr. of 1916 ed. lib. bdg. 35.00 (ISBN 0-8482-5576-3). Norwood Edns.

Quast, Emilie. An Index & Bibliography to Douglas C. McMurtrie's, "A History of Printing in the United States". LC 74-5200. 1975. 11.00 (ISBN 0-8337-2341-3). B Franklin.

Rhodes, Dennis E. Early Printing in India, Pakistan, Burma & Ceylon. Clair, Colin, ed. LC 70-78405. (Spread of Printing Ser). (Illus., Orig.). 1969. pap. 9.75 (ISBN 0-8390-0022-7). Abner Schram Ltd.

Ringwalt, J. Luther & Bidwell, John, eds. American Encyclopaedia of Printing. LC 78-74411. (Nineteenth-Century Book Arts & Printing History Ser.: Vol. 21). (Illus.). 1980. lib. bdg. 80.00 (ISBN 0-8240-3895-9). Garland Pub.

Risk, R. T. Erhard Ratdolt, Master Printer. 64p. 1982. 50.00x (ISBN 0-930126-10-6). Typographeum.

Roden, Robert F. Cambridge Press, Sixteen Thirty-Eight to Sixteen Ninety-Two: A History of the First Printing Press Established in English America. (Illus.). 1967. Repr. of 1905 ed. 21.00 (ISBN 0-8337-3041-X). B Franklin.

Sale, William M. Samuel Richardson: Master Printer. LC 77-22446. (Cornell Studies in English: No.37). (Illus.). 1978. Repr. of 1950 ed. lib. bdg. 27.50x (ISBN 0-8371-9732-5, SASR). Greenwood.

Seidensticker, O. First Century of German Printing in America, 1728-1830. 1893. 25.00 (ISBN 0-527-81100-9). Kraus Repr.

Silver, Rollo G. Aprons Instead of Uniforms: The Practice of Printing, 1776-1787. 1977. pap. 5.00x (ISBN 0-912296-19-4, Dist. by U Pr of Va). Am Antiquarian.

Smith, Anne H. Early Printing in South Africa. Clair, Colin, ed. (Spread of Printing Ser., No. 4). (Illus.). 1969. pap. 18.00 (ISBN 0-8390-0025-1). Abner Schram Ltd.

Thomas, Isaiah. The History of Printing in America, 2 vols. Incl. viii, 713p. pap. 52.00 (ISBN 0-384-60177-4). lxxxvii, 423p. Repr. of 1874 ed. 35.00 (ISBN 0-384-60176-6). Johnson Repr.

Thompson, John S. History of Composing Machines: A Complete Record of the Art of Composing Type by Machinery. LC 72-5077. (Technology & Society Ser.). (Illus.). 590p. 1972. Repr. of 1904 ed. 18.00 (ISBN 0-405-04726-6). Ayer Co Pubs.
Thompson, Lawrence S. & Woodbridge, Hensley C. Printing in Colonial Spanish America. LC 75-8384. 1976. 12.50x (ISBN 0-87875-076-2). Whitston Pub.
Tousaint, Auguste. Early Printing in Mauritius, Reunion, Madagascar & the Saychelles. Clair, Colin, ed. (Spread of Printing Ser.: No. 3). (Illus.). 1969. pap. 9.75 (ISBN 0-8390-0019-7). Abner Schram Ltd.
Twitchett, Denis. Printing & Publishing in Medieval China. LC 82-60317. (Illus.). 96p. 1983. pap. 14.50 (ISBN 0-913720-08-9). Beil.
--Printing & Publishing in Medieval China. 48p. 1980. 27.00x (ISBN 0-85331-440-3, Pub. by Lund Humphries England). State Mutual Bk.
Willett, Ralph. A Memoir on the Origin of Printing. Lew, Irving, ed. (Bibliographical Reprint Ser.). 1980. Repr. of 1820 ed. ltd. ed. 25.00 (ISBN 0-89782-032-0). Battery Pk.
Willoughby, Edwin E. The Printing of the First Folio of Shakespeare. 1979. Repr. of 1932 ed. lib. bdg. 16.50 (ISBN 0-8495-5717-8). Arden Lib.
Winckler, Paul A., ed. History of Books & Printing: A Guide to Information Sources. LC 79-13006. (Books, Publishing & Libraries Information Guide Ser.: Vol. 2). 1979. 60.00x (ISBN 0-8103-1408-8). Gale.
Winship, George P. Cambridge Press, Sixteen Thirty-Eight to Sixteen Ninety-Two. facs. ed. LC 68-57346. (Essay Index Reprint Ser). 1945. 22.50 (ISBN 0-8369-1004-4). Ayer Co Pubs.
--Gutenberg to Plantin: An Outline of the Early History of Printing (1450-1600) (Bibliography & Reference Ser.: No. 172). 1968. Repr. of 1926 ed. 20.50 (ISBN 0-8337-3818-6). B Franklin.
Wroth, Lawrence C. A History of Printing in Colonial Maryland, 1686-1776. LC 75-31142. 1976. Repr. of 1922 ed. 28.50 (ISBN 0-404-13614-1). AMS Pr.

PRINTING–LAYOUT AND TYPOGRAPHY

see also Book Design; Type and Type-Founding

Adams, Thomas F. Typographia: Or the Printers Instructor. LC 78-7449. (Nineteenth Century Bookarts & Printing Ser.). 295p. 1980. lib. bdg. 33.00 (ISBN 0-8240-3893-2). Garland Pub.
Berry, Turner W. & Johnson, A. F. Catalogue of Specimens of Printing Types by English & Scottish Printers & Founders 1665-1830. LC 78-74404. (Nineteenth-Century Book Arts & Printing History Ser.: Vol. 12). 1980. lib. bdg. 46.00 (ISBN 0-8240-3886-X). Garland Pub.
Blumenthal, Joseph. Typographic Years: A Printer's Journey Through a Half Century. LC 82-71904. (Illus.). 153p. 26.50 (ISBN 0-913720-38-0). Beil.
Boston Public Library. Typography & Design. 10.00 (ISBN 0-685-60072-6). Boston Public Lib.
Carter, Rob, et al. Typographic Design: Form & Communication. LC 85-667. (Illus.). 262p. 1985. pap. 35.00 (ISBN 0-442-26166-7). Van Nos Reinhold.
Chappell, Warren. A Short History of the Printed Word. LC 79-90409. (Nonpareil Bks.). (Illus.). 288p. 1980. pap. 9.95 (ISBN 0-87923-312-5). Godine.
Chaundy, Theodore W., et al. The Printing of Mathematics: Aids for Authors & Editions & Rules for Compositors & Readers at the University Press, Oxford. pap. 29.80 (ISBN 0-317-10261-3, 2051896). Bks Demand UMI.
Craig, James. Designing with Type. rev. ed. Meyer, Susan, ed. (Illus.). 1980. 22.50 (ISBN 0-8230-1321-9). Watson-Guptill.
Demoney, Jerry & Meyer, Susan E. Pasteups & Mechanicals: A Step-by-Step Guide to Preparing Art for Reproduction. (Illus.). 176p. 1982. 22.50 (ISBN 0-8230-3924-2). Watson-Guptill.
De Vinne, Theodore L. Manual of Printing Office Practice. (Bibliographical Reprint Ser.). 52p. 1978. 25.00 (ISBN 0-685-27169-2). Battery Pk.
Donahue, Bud. The Language of Layout. LC 78-6949. (Art & Design Ser.). 1978. 19.95 (ISBN 0-13-522953-7, Spec); pap. 11.95 (ISBN 0-13-522961-8). P-H.
Ernest-Moriarty, Sandra B. The ABC'S of Typography: A Practical Guide to the Art & Science of Typography. rev. ed. LC 77-80333. 188p. 1984. text ed. 12.50 (ISBN 0-317-14819-2); pap. text ed. 8.95 (ISBN 0-317-14820-6). Art Dir.
Goudy, Frederic W. Goudy's Type Designs: His Story & Specimens. 2nd ed. LC 77-14886. (Treasures of Typography Ser: Vol. II). (Illus.). 1978. 14.95 (ISBN 0-918142-05-9); pap. 9.95 (ISBN 0-918142-04-0). Myriade.
--Typologia: Studies in Type Design & Type Making with Comments on the Invention of Typography, the First Types, Legibility & Fine Printing. 1978. 28.50x (ISBN 0-520-03308-6); pap. 3.95 (ISBN 0-520-03278-0, CAL 334). U of Cal Pr.
Jones, Ted. Direct Silkscreen Printing & Painting: New Directions - Versatile Approaches. Jones, Evelyn, ed. (Illus.). 1980. pap. write for info. (ISBN 0-916928-05-5). New Dimen Studio.
Kleper, Michael L. Illustrated Dictionary of Typographic Communication. (Illus.). 208p. (Orig.). 1983. pap. text ed. 19.00 (ISBN 0-89938-008-5). Tech & Ed Ctr Graph Arts RIT.
--The Illustrated Dictionary of Typographic Communication. (Illus.). 200p. 1983. pap. 19.00 (ISBN 0-930904-03-6). Graphic Dimensions.
Legros, Lucien & Grant, John C. Typographical Printing-Surfaces: The Technology & Mechanism of Their Production. Bidwell, John, ed. LC 78-74403. (Nineteenth-Century Book Arts & Printing History Ser.: Vol. 16). (Illus.). 1980. lib. bdg. 94.00 (ISBN 0-8240-3890-8). Garland Pub.
Lennon, Tom, ed. The Thirteenth, Fourteenth, & Fifteenth Publication Design Annual. (Illus.). 700p. 1982. 39.95 (ISBN 0-937414-24-7). R Silver.
McLean, Ruari. The Thames & Hudson Manual of Typography. (Illus.). 192p. 1980. 18.95 (ISBN 0-500-67022-6). Thames Hudson.
Minshull, Ruth. The Secrets of Making Layouts for Quick Printing. (Illus.). 34p. (Orig.). 1982. pap. 3.98 (ISBN 0-937922-06-4). SAA Pub.
Neurath, Otto. Graphic Communication Through Isotype. 48p. 1981. 25.00x (ISBN 0-7049-0480-2, Pub. by Dept Typography England). State Mutual Bk.
Pedersen, Martin. Typography Five. (Illus.). 216p. 1984. 27.50 (ISBN 0-8230-5539-6). Watson-Guptill.
Pettis, Ruth. The Goudy Presence at Konglomerati Press. (Illus.). 1977. pap. 6.00 (ISBN 0-686-98152-9). Konglomerati.
Photography & Layout for Reproduction. (Illus.). 1978. pap. 5.50 (ISBN 0-87985-218-6, Q-74). Eastman Kodak.
Rasberry, Leslie. Computer Age Copyfitting. LC 77-83812. (Illus.). 1978. pap. 8.95 (ISBN 0-910158-26-6). Art Dir.
Resource Systems International. Layout Procedures & Techniques. 1982. pap. text ed. 15.00 (ISBN 0-8359-3955-3). Reston.
Romano, Frank. Practical Typography from A to Z. 176p. non-members 28.50 (ISBN 0-318-03257-0); members 15.00 (ISBN 0-318-03258-9). Print Indus Am.
Rosen, Ben. Type & Typography. rev. ed. 461p. 1976. pap. 16.95 (ISBN 0-442-27020-8). Van Nos Reinhold.
Ruder, Emil. Typography: A Manual of Design. rev. ed. (Illus.). 220p. (Orig.). 1981. pap. 12.95 (ISBN 0-8038-7223-2). Hastings.
Solo, Julie. Decorative & Display Numbers: Seven Hundred Thirty-Nine Complete Fonts. (Lettering, Calligraphy, Typography Ser.). 104p. 1985. pap. 4.50 (ISBN 0-486-24787-2). Dover.
Swann, Cal. Techniques of Typography. (Illus.). 96p. 1982. pap. 12.00 (ISBN 0-913720-40-2). Beil.
Type Directors Club. Typography Three: The Annual of the Type Director's Club. New ed. (Illus.). 1982. 27.50 (ISBN 0-8230-5537-X). Watson-Guptill.
--Typography Two: The Annual of the Type Directors Club. (Illus.). 216p. 1981. 25.00 (ISBN 0-8230-5536-1). Watson-Guptill.
Zapf, Hermann. Manuale Typographicum. 1970. pap. 7.95 (ISBN 0-262-74004-4). MIT Pr.
--Typographic Variations. 2nd ed. LC 77-80032. (Treasures of Typography Ser.: Vol. I). (Illus.). 1977. pap. 9.95 (ISBN 0-918142-00-8). Myriade.

PRINTING–SPECIMENS

see also Type and Type-Founding

Biegeleisen, J. I. Handbook of Type Faces & Lettering. 4th ed. LC 81-19111. (Illus.). 272p. 1982. pap. 14.95 (ISBN 0-668-05420-4, 5420). Arco.
Biegeleisen, Jacob I. Book of One Hundred Type Face Alphabets. 1974. 10.00 (ISBN 0-911380-03-5). Signs of Times.
Duff, E. Gordon. Early English Printing: A Series of Facsimilies of All the Types Used in England During the 15th Century. 1969. Repr. of 1896 ed. 23.50 (ISBN 0-8337-0947-X). B Franklin.
Fournier, Pierre S. & Carter, Harry. Fournier on Typefounding. new ed. LC 78-150161. (Illus.). 412p. 1973. lib. bdg. 25.50 (ISBN 0-8337-1224-1). B Franklin.
Gates, David. Type. 208p. 1973. 18.50 (ISBN 0-8230-5522-1). Watson-Guptill.
Lambert, Frederick. Letter Forms. 1968. 25.00 (ISBN 0-7206-4890-4). Dufour.
Lieberman, J. Ben. Type & Typefaces. 2nd ed. LC 77-24401. (Treasures of Typography Ser.: Vol. I). (Illus.). 1978. 14.95 (ISBN 0-918142-01-6); pap. 9.95 (ISBN 0-918142-02-4). Myriade.
Longyear, William. Type & Lettering. 4th ed. (Illus.). 176p. 1966. spiral bdg. 14.95 (ISBN 0-8230-5526-4). Watson-Guptill.
More Morgan No. 2. 64p. pap. 9.95 (ISBN 0-87100-204-3, 2202). Morgan.
Plomer, H. R. English Printers' Ornaments. (Research & Source Works Ser: No. 146). 1968. Repr. of 1924 ed. 22.50 (ISBN 0-8337-2786-9). B Franklin.
The Type Specimen Book. 648p. 1974. pap. 19.95 (ISBN 0-442-27915-9). Van Nos Reinhold.

PRINTING–STYLE MANUALS

Treweek, Chris & Zeitlyn, Jonathan. The Alternative Printing Handbook. (Illus.). 112p. 1984. pap. 8.95 (ISBN 0-14-046509-X). Penguin.

PRINTING, OFFSET

see Offset Printing

PRINTING, PRACTICAL

see also Handpress

Burke, Clifford. Printing It! (Illus.). 128p. 1974. pap. 4.95 (ISBN 0-914728-03-2). Wingbow Pr.
Clowes, William. A Guide to Printing, an Introduction for Print Buyers. LC 73-717. (Illus.). 134p. 1973. Repr. of 1963 ed. lib. bdg. 24.75x (ISBN 0-8371-6786-8, CLGP). Greenwood.
Demoney, Jerry & Meyer, Susan E. Pasteups & Mechanicals: A Step-by-Step Guide to Preparing Art for Reproduction. (Illus.). 176p. 1982. 22.50 (ISBN 0-8230-3924-2). Watson-Guptill.
Field, Janet N., et al, eds. Graphic Arts Manual. LC 79-6549. (Illus.). 650p. 1980. lib. bdg. 65.00 (ISBN 0-405-12941-6). Ayer Co Pubs.
Gross, Edmund J. One Hundred-One Ways to Save Money on All Your Printing. (Illus.). 1971. pap. 12.00 (ISBN 0-912256-02-8). Halls of Ivy.
Hansburg, Henry. Experimental Study of the Effect of the Use of the Print Shop in the Improvement of Spelling, Reading, & Visual Perception. LC 74-176837. (Columbia University. Teachers College. Contributions to Education: No. 776). Repr. of 1939 ed. 22.50 (ISBN 0-404-55776-7). AMS Pr.
Hills, Philip J., ed. Trends in Information Transfer. LC 82-3021. vii, 191p. 1982. 25.00 (ISBN 0-313-23600-3, HIT/). Greenwood.
Hird, Kenneth F. Paste-up for Graphic Arts Production. (Illus.). 352p. 1982. pap. text ed. 24.95 (ISBN 0-13-652875-9). P-H.
Hurlburt, Allen. Layout. (Illus.). 160p. 1977. 19.95 (ISBN 0-8230-2655-8). Watson-Guptill.
Karsnitz, John R. Graphic Arts Technology. LC 83-15187. 416p. 1984. text ed. 26.00 (ISBN 0-8273-1828-6); instr's guide 8.00 (ISBN 0-8273-1829-4). Delmar.
Polk, Ralph W. & Polk, Edwin. Practice of Printing. rev. ed. (Illus.). 1971. text ed. 18.12 (ISBN 0-02-665410-5). Bennett IL.
Ryan, Peter A. Preparation of Manuscripts. 1975. pap. 4.00x (ISBN 0-522-83728-X, Pub. by Melbourne U Pr). Intl Spec Bk.
Sutter, Jan. Slinging Ink: A Practical Guide to Producing Booklets, Newspapers, & Ephemeral Publications. LC 82-15179. (Illus.). 168p. 1982. pap. 7.95 (ISBN 0-86576-037-3). W Kaufmann.

PRINTING, TEXTILE

see Textile Printing

PRINTING AS A TRADE

Printing Trades Blue Book: New York Metropolitan Edition 1985. 900p. 1985. pap. 65.00 (ISBN 0-910880-22-0). Lewis.

PRINTING INDUSTRY

Baker, Elizabeth F. Displacement of Men by Machines: Effects of Technological Change in Commerical Printing. Stein, Leon, ed. LC 77-70481. (Work Ser.). (Illus.). 1977. Repr. of 1933 ed. lib. bdg. 26.50x (ISBN 0-405-10155-4). Ayer Co Pubs.
Business Communications Staff. Inks & Printing Chemicals: New Developments. 1982. 975.00 (ISBN 0-89336-212-3, C-025). BCC.
Cameron, Clive A. Going Metric with the U. S. Printing Industry. 125p. 1972. pap. 11.00 (ISBN 0-317-14996-2). Tech & Ed Ctr Graph Arts RIT.
Chappell, Warren. A Short History of the Printed Word. LC 79-90409. (Nonpareil Bks.). (Illus.). 288p. 1980. pap. 9.95 (ISBN 0-87923-312-5). Godine.
Data Base Management for Photocomposition. 15.00 (ISBN 0-318-02624-4). Print Indus Am.
First Printers & Their Books: An Exhibition Catalogue. (Illus.). 1940. pap. 3.00 (ISBN 0-911132-05-8). Phila Free Lib.
Jacobs, Marvin. How to Establish a Cold Typesetting Department & Train Operating Personnel. LC 74-15718. 1974. 21.00 (ISBN 0-912920-35-1). North Am Pub Co.
Knittel, Patricia, ed. Selected Bibliography: Quality Control, Vol. II. 85p. (Orig.). 1982. pap. 15.00 (ISBN 0-89938-007-7). Tech & Ed Ctr Graph Arts RIT.
Miller, Richard K. Noise Control Solutions for Printing & Publishing. (Illus.). 77p. 1981. pap. text ed. 45.00 (ISBN 0-89671-026-2). SEAI Tech Pubns.
Morgan, Charlotte E. Origin & History of the New York Employing Printers' Association. LC 68-58608. (Columbia University. Studies in the Social Sciences: No. 319). Repr. of 1930 ed. 15.00 (ISBN 0-404-51319-0). AMS Pr.
Palmer, Peggy, ed. An American Original: The Story of Kwik-Kopy Printing. (Illus.). 139p. 1980. text ed. 8.95 (ISBN 0-918464-29-3); pap. text ed. 2.95 (ISBN 0-918464-30-7). D Armstrong.
A Primer on Data Communications. 30.00 (ISBN 0-318-02627-9). Print Indus Am.
Printing & Graphics Industry. (UNIDO Guides to Information Sources: No. 14). pap. 4.00 (ISBN 0-686-93282-X, UNID135, UN). Unipub.
Printing & Reprography Conference Proceedings (Joint with Testing) 196p. 1979. soft cover 4.95 (ISBN 0-686-98531-1, 01-05-1079). TAPPI.
Printing & Reprography Conference Papers (Joint with Testing) 225p. 1977. soft cover 4.95 (ISBN 0-686-98533-8, 01-05-1077). TAPPI.
Printing & Reprography Conference Proceedings. 94p. 1978. soft cover 4.95 (ISBN 0-686-98532-X, 01-05-1078). TAPPI.
Printing Trades Blue Book: Southeastern Edition 1985-86. pap. 65.00 (ISBN 0-910880-25-5). Lewis.
Rogers, Theresa F. & Friedman, Nathalie S. Printers Face Automation: The Impact of Technology on Work & Retirement among Skilled Craftsmen. LC 79-3047. 208p. 1980. 26.50x (ISBN 0-669-03310-3). Lexington Bks.
Second Tripartite Technical Meeting for the Printing & Allied Trades, Geneva, 1981. Technological Developments & Their Implications for Employment in the Printing & Allied Trade, with Particular Reference to Developing Countries, Report III. International Labour Office, ed. 46p. (Orig.). 1981. pap. 5.70 (ISBN 92-2-102693-0). Intl Labour Office.
Second Tripartite Technical Meeting for the Printing & Allied Trades, Geneva 1981. Training & Retraining Needs in the Printing & Allied Trades, Report II. International Labour Office, ed. ii, 100p. (Orig.). 1981. pap. 8.55 (ISBN 92-2-102692-2). Intl Labour Office.
Silver, Gerald A. Printing Estimating. LC 70-112001. pap. 40.00 (ISBN 0-317-10639-2, 2011151). Bks Demand UMI.
--Printing Estimating: Forms Book. pap. 20.00 (ISBN 0-317-10888-3, 2013558). Bks Demand UMI.
Testing Conference (Joint with Printing & Reprography) Proceedings. 196p. 1979. pap. 38.95 (ISBN 0-686-43249-5, 01 05 1079). TAPPI.
Testing Conference (Joint with Printing & Reprography) Proceedings. 225p. 1977. pap. 28.95 (ISBN 0-686-43250-9, 01 05 1077). TAPPI.
Tract, Sam. A Planned Approach for Penetrating the High Speed Copying Market for Instant & Small Commercial Printers. (Illus.). 100p. 1984. 3-ring binder 79.95 (ISBN 0-930579-01-1). S Tract Advert.

PRINTING INK

Bissett, D. E., et al, eds. The Printing Ink Manual. 3rd ed. Leach, R. H. & Williams, C. H. (Illus.). 480p. 1984. 49.50 (ISBN 0-442-30600-8). Van Nos Reinhold.
Bloy, Colin. History of Printing Ink. 148p. 1980. 40.00x (ISBN 0-85331-314-8, Pub. by Lund Humphries England). State Mutual Bk.
Bloy, Colin H. A History of Printing Ink, Balls & Rollers: 1440-1850. (Illus.). 147p. 1980. 19.95 (ISBN 0-913720-07-0, Sandstone). Beil.
Business Communications Staff. Inks & Printing Chemicals: New Developments. 1982. 975.00 (ISBN 0-89336-212-3, C-025). BCC.
Duffy, J. I. Printing Inks: Developments Since 1975. LC 79-16231. (Chemical Technology Review Ser.: No. 139). (Illus.). 1980. 42.00 (ISBN 0-8155-0772-0). Noyes.
Flick, Ernest W. Printing Ink Formulations. LC 84-22636. 184p. 1985. 36.00 (ISBN 0-8155-1014-4). Noyes.
Knittel, Patricia, ed. Selected Bibliography: Printing Inks, Vol. I. (Orig.). 1982. pap. 15.00 (ISBN 0-89938-010-7). Tech & Ed Ctr Graph Arts RIT.

PRINTING MACHINERY AND SUPPLIES

see also Linotype; Printing Plates; Type-Setting Machines

Hatery, Lowell H. & Bush, George P. Technological Change in Printing & Publishing. LC 77-176224. 275p. 1973. 13.75 (ISBN 0-87671-503-X). Lomond.

PRINTING PLATES

Hunnisett, Basil. Steel-Engraved Book Illustration in England. LC 79-92108. (Illus.). 288p. 1980. 40.00 (ISBN 0-87923-322-2). Godine.

PRINTING PRESS

see also Handpress

Comparato, Frank E. Chronicles of Genius & Folly: R. Hoe & Company & the Printing Press As a Service to Democracy. (Illus.). 846p. 1979. 39.95 (ISBN 0-911437-00-2); 24.95 (ISBN 0-911437-10-X). Labyrinthos.
Eisenstein, Elizabeth. The Printing Press As an Agent of Change, 2 vols. in 1. LC 77-91083. 852p. 1980. pap. 22.95 (ISBN 0-521-29955-1). Cambridge U Pr.
Moran, James. Printing Presses: History & Development from the Fifteenth Century to Modern Times. (Illus.). 1973. 48.50x (ISBN 0-520-02245-9); pap. 7.95 (ISBN 0-520-02904-6). U of Cal Pr.
Sterne, Harold E. Catalogue of Nineteenth Century Printing Presses. LC 78-63314. (Illus.). 384p. 1978. 19.95 (ISBN 0-932606-00-8). Ye Olde Print.

PRINTMAKING
see Prints–Technique

PRINTS–TECHNIQUE
Berry, C. & Ferguson, J. G. Chapter Six - Discharge, Resist & Special Styles. 75.00x (ISBN 0-686-98198-7, Pub. by Soc Dyers & Colour); pap. 50.00x (ISBN 0-686-98199-5). State Mutual Bk.
Daniels, Harvey. Printmaking. LC 77-146054. (Illus.). 1972. 25.00 (ISBN 0-670-57757-X, Studio). Viking.
Eppink, Norman R. One Hundred & One Prints: The History & Techniques of Printmaking. (Illus.). 272p. 1972. 32.50 (ISBN 0-8061-0915-7); pap. 14.95 (ISBN 0-8061-1181-X). U of Okla Pr.
Erickson, Janet D. & Sproul, Adelaide. Print Making Without a Press. LC 65-19672. pap. 30.80 (ISBN 0-317-10485-3, 2007245). Bks Demand UMI.
Gleadow, R. F. Chapter One - Engraved-Roller Printing. 75.00x (ISBN 0-686-98193-6, Pub. by Soc Dyers & Colour). State Mutual Bk.
Goldman, Judith. American Prints: Process & Proofs. LC 81-47244. (Icon Editions Ser.). (Illus.). 176p. 1979. 24.04i (ISBN 0-06-433261-6, HarpT). Har-Row.
Griffiths, Antony. Prints & Printmaking: An Introduction to the History & Techniques. 152p. 1981. text ed. 18.00 (ISBN 0-394-32673-3, KnopfC). Knopf.
Gutjahr, H. Chapter Five - Direct Print Coloration. 75.00x (ISBN 0-686-98200-2, Pub. by Soc Dyers & Colour); pap. 50.00x (ISBN 0-686-98201-0). State Mutual Bk.
Hawkyard, C. J. Chapter Two - Screen Printing. 75.00x (ISBN 0-686-98194-4, Pub. by Soc Dyers & Colour); pap. 50.00x (ISBN 0-686-98195-2). State Mutual Bk.
Hayter, Stanley W. New Ways of Gravure. rev ed. (Illus.). 304p. 1981. pap. 18.95 (ISBN 0-8230-3174-8). Watson-Guptill.
Jones, F. Chapter Three - Transfer Printing. 75.00x (ISBN 0-686-98205-3, Pub. by Soc Dyers & Colour); pap. 50.00x (ISBN 0-686-98206-1). State Mutual Bk.
Maxwell, W. & Unger. Printmaking: A Beginning Handbook. 1977. (Spec); pap. 9.95 (ISBN 0-13-710681-5, Spec). P-H.
Miles, L. W. Chapter Seven - The Production & Properties of Printing Pastes. 75.00x (ISBN 0-686-98196-0, Pub. by Soc Dyers & Colour); pap. 50.00x (ISBN 0-686-98197-9). State Mutual Bk.
Romberg, Jenean. Let's Discover Printing. (Arts & Crafts Discovery Units Ser). (Illus.). 1974. pap. 7.40x (ISBN 0-87628-527-2). Ctr Appl Res.
Ross, John & Romano, Clare. The Complete Printmaker. LC 72-77151. (Illus.). 1972. 35.00 (ISBN 0-02-927370-6). Free Pr.
--The Complete Relief Print. LC 74-2694. 1974. pap. text ed. 14.95 (ISBN 0-02-927390-0). Free Pr.
Sacilotto, Deli. Photographic Printmaking Techniques. (Illus.). 216p. 1982. 25.00 (ISBN 0-8230-4006-2). Watson-Guptill.
Saff, Donald & Sacilotto, Deli. Printmaking: History & Process. LC 76-54995. 1978. text ed. 27.95 (ISBN 0-03-085663-9, HoltC). HR&W.
Takahashi, Seiichiro. Traditional Woodblock Prints of Japan. LC 74-162683. (Heibonsha Survey of Japanese Art Ser). (Illus.). 176p. 1972. 17.50 (ISBN 0-8348-1002-6). Weatherhill.
Wenniger, Mary A. Collagraph Printmaking. (Illus.). 184p. 1980. pap. 12.50 (ISBN 0-8230-0666-2). Watson-Guptill.

PRIVATE AIRPLANES
see Airplanes, Private

PRIVATE RADIOTELEPHONE
see Citizens Band Radio

PROBABILITIES
see also Correlation (Statistics); Decomposition (Mathematics); Distribution (Probability Theory); Error Functions; Errors, Theory Of; Frequency Curves; Games of Chance (Mathematics); Integrals, Multiple; Law of Large Numbers; Least Squares; Mathematical Statistics; Reliability (Engineering); Sampling (Statistics); Statistical Communication Theory; Stochastic Processes; Time-Series Analysis
Agresti, Alan. Analysis of Ordinal Categorical Data. LC 83-23535. (Probability & Mathematical Statistics-Applied Probablity & Statistics Section Ser.: 1-346). 287p. 1984. 35.95x (ISBN 0-471-89055-3, Pub. by Wiley-Interscience). Wiley.
Aivazjan, S. A., et al. Twenty-Two Papers on Statistics & Probability. LC 61-9803. (Selected Translations in Mathematical Statistics & Probability Ser.: Vol. 6). 1966. 35.00 (ISBN 0-8218-1456-7, STAPRO-6). Am Math.
Aksomaitis, A., et al. Twenty-Nine Papers on Statistics & Probability. LC 61-9803. (Selected Translations in Mathematical Statistics & Probability Ser.: Vol. 9). 1971. 37.00 (ISBN 0-8218-1459-1, STAPRO-9). Am Math.
Alder, Henry L. & Roessler, Edward B. Introduction to Probability & Statistics. 6th ed. LC 76-13643. (Illus.). 426p. 1977. text ed. 26.95 (ISBN 0-7167-0467-6); answer book avail. W H Freeman.
Aldrich, John H. & Nelson, Forrest D. Linear Probability, Logit, & Probit Models. LC 84-51766. 95p. 1984. pap. 5.00 (ISBN 0-8039-2133-0). Sage.
Aleskjavicene, A., et al. Twenty-Four Papers on Statistics & Probability. LC 61-9803. (Selected Translations in Mathematical Statistics & Probability Ser.: Vol. 7). 1968. 37.00 (ISBN 0-8218-1457-5, STAPRO-7). Am Math.
--Twenty-Two Papers on Statistics & Probability. (Selected Translations in Mathematical Statistics & Probability: Vol. 11). 1973. 33.00 (ISBN 0-8218-1461-3, STAPRO-11). Am Math.
Ambarcumjan, G. A., et al. Thirty-Five Papers on Statistics & Probability. LC 61-9803. (Selected Translations in Mathematical Statistics & Probability Ser.: Vol. 4). 1963. 32.00 (ISBN 0-8218-1454-0, STAPRO-4). Am Math.
Anderberg, Michael R. Cluster Analysis for Applications. (Probability & Mathematical Statistics: Vol. 19). 1973. 45.00 (ISBN 0-12-057650-3). Acad Pr.
Anderson, I., ed. Surveys in Combinatorics, 1985. (London Mathematical Society Lecture Note Ser.: No. 103). 180p. 1985. pap. 18.95 (ISBN 0-521-31524-7). Cambridge U Pr.
Anderson, Sharon, et al. Statistical Methods for Comparative Studies: Techniques for Bias Reduction. LC 79-27220. (Wiley Series in Probability & Mathematical Statistics: Applied Probability & Statistics). 289p. 1980. 38.95x (ISBN 0-471-04838-0, Pub. by Wiley-Interscience). Wiley.
Andreev, A. E., et al. Twelve Papers on Function Theory, Probability, & Differential Equations. LC 51-5559. (Translations Ser.: No. 2, Vol. 8). 1957. 43.00 (ISBN 0-8218-1708-6, TRANS 2-8). Am Math.
Ang, A. H. & Tang, W. H. Probability Concepts in Engineering Planning & Design, Vol. 1. LC 75-5892. 409p. 1975. text ed. 44.50x (ISBN 0-471-03200-X). Wiley.
Ang, Alfredo H-S & Tang, Wilson H. Probability Concepts in Engineering Planning & Design, Vol. II. LC 75-5892. 562p. 1984. text ed. 42.50 (ISBN 0-471-03201-8). Wiley.
Anosov, D. V., et al. Twenty-Four Papers on Statistics & Probability: Twenty-Four Papers Statistics & Probability. LC 61-9803. (Selected Translations in Mathematical Statistics & Probability: Vol. 14). 296p. 1978. 38.00 (ISBN 0-8218-1464-8, STAPRO-14); institutional members 28.50; individual members 19.00. Am Math.
Arato, M., et al. Thirty-Two Papers on Statistics & Probability. LC 61-9803. (Selected Translations in Mathematical Statistics & Probability Ser.: Vol. 10). 1972. 36.00 (ISBN 0-8218-1460-5, STAPRO-10). Am Math.
Ash, Robert B. Real Analysis & Probability. (Probability & Mathematical Statistics Ser.). 476p. 1972. 22.50i (ISBN 0-12-065201-3). solutions to problems 2.50i (ISBN 0-12-065240-4). Acad Pr.
Asmussen, Soren & Hering, Heinrich. Branching Processes. (Progress in Probability & Statistics Ser.: Vol. 3). 468p. 1983. text ed. 34.95 (ISBN 0-8176-3122-4). Birkhauser.
Axelrad, D. R. Foundations of the Probabilistic Mechanics of Discrete Media. (Foundations & Philosophy of Science & Technology Ser.). (Illus.). 200p. 1984. 28.00 (ISBN 0-08-025234-6). Pergamon.
Ayer, Alfred J. Probability & Evidence. LC 71-185572. (John Dewey Lecture Ser). 144p. 1979. 19.50x (ISBN 0-231-03650-7); pap. 10.00x (ISBN 0-231-04767-3). Columbia U Pr.
Azema, J. & Yor, M., eds. Seminaire de Probabilites XIX 1983-84. (Lecture Notes in Mathematics: Vol. 1123). (Eng. & Fr.). iv, 504p. 1985. pap. 32.80 (ISBN 0-387-15230-X). Springer-Verlag.
Barlow, Richard & Proschan, Frank. Statistical Theory of Reliability & Life Testing: Probability Models. LC 81-51480. 1981. Repr. of 1975 ed. text ed. 27.50 (ISBN 0-9606764-0-6). To Begin With.
Barr, Donald R. & Zehna, Peter W. Probability: Modeling Uncertainty. (Illus.). 480p. 1983. text ed. 30.95 (ISBN 0-201-10798-8); solution manual 2.00 (ISBN 0-201-10799-6). Addison-Wesley.
Barra, Jean-Rene. Mathematical Basis of Statistics. Hernach, L., tr. LC 80-519. (Probability & Mathematical Statistical Ser.). 1981. 49.50 (ISBN 0-12-079240-0). Acad Pr.
Bartholomew, D. J. Stochastic Models for Social Processes. 3rd ed. (Wiley Ser. in Probability & Mathematical Statistics: Applied Probability & Statistics Section). 365p. 1982. 57.95x (ISBN 0-471-28040-2, Pub. by Wiley-Interscience). Wiley.
Bartlett, M. S. Probability, Statistics & Time: A Collection of Essays. (Monographs on Applied Probability & Statistics). 1975. 17.95x (ISBN 0-412-14150-7, NO. 6029, Pub. by Chapman & Hall England); pap. 12.95x (ISBN 0-412-22260-4, NO. 2964). Methuen Inc.
Bates, Grace E. Probability. (Orig.). 1965. pap. 6.95 (ISBN 0-201-00405-4). Addison-Wesley.
Bauer, H. Probability Theory & Elements of Measure Theory. (Probability & Mathematical Statistics Ser.). 1981. 79.50 (ISBN 0-12-082820-0). Acad Pr.
Beals, Richard, et al, eds. Conference on Modern Analysis & Probability. LC 84-484. (Contemporary Mathematics Ser.: No. 26). 432p. 1984. pap. 34.00 (ISBN 0-8218-5030-X). Am Math.
Beaumaont, G. P. Introductory Applied Probability. LC 83-10700. (Mathematics & Its Applications, Ellis Horwood Ser.). 235p. 1983. 58.95x (ISBN 0-470-27481-6). Halsted Pr.
Beck, A., ed. Probability in Banach Spaces III: Proceedings. (Lecture Notes in Mathematics Ser.: Vol. 860). 329p. 1981. pap. 20.00 (ISBN 0-387-10822-X). Springer-Verlag.
--Probability in Banach Spaces Two. (Lecture Notes in Mathematics Ser.: Vol. 709). 1979. pap. 17.00 (ISBN 0-387-09242-0). Springer-Verlag.
Behara, M., et al, eds. Probability & Information Theory 2. LC 75-406171. (Lecture Notes in Mathematics: Vol. 296). v, 223p. 1973. pap. 14.00 (ISBN 0-387-06211-4). Springer-Verlag.
Bendat, Julius S. Principles & Applications of Random Noise Theory. rev. ed. LC 77-7225. 456p. 1977. Repr. of 1958 ed. lib. bdg. 26.00 (ISBN 0-88275-556-0). Krieger.
Bensoussan, A., et al. Asymptotic Analysis for Periodic Structures. (Studies in Mathematics & Its Applications Ser.: Vol. 5). 700p. 1978. 70.25 (ISBN 0-444-85172-0, North-Holland). Elsevier.
Berger, James O. & Wolpert, Robert L. The Likelihood Principle. Gupta, Shanti S., ed. LC 84-48467. (IMS Lecture Notes-Monograph: Vol. 6). 206p. 1984. pap. 25.00 (ISBN 0-940600-06-4). Inst Math.
Berman, D. L., et al. Nineteen Papers on Statistics & Probability. LC 61-9803. (Selected Translations on Mathematical Statistics & Probability Ser: Vol. 5). 1965. 30.00 (ISBN 0-8218-1455-9, STAPRO-5). Am Math.
Bertrand, Joseph. Calcul Des Probabilites. 2nd ed. LC 78-113114. (Fr.). 389p. 1972. text ed. 13.95 (ISBN 0-8284-0262-0). Chelsea Pub.
Beyer, William H. Handbook of Tables for Probability & Statistics, CRC. 2nd ed. (Handbook Ser.). 1968. 46.00 (ISBN 0-8493-0692-2). CRC Pr.
Bharucha & Reid, eds. Approximate Solutions of Random Equations. (Series in Probability & Applied Mathematics: Vol. 3). 256p. 1979. 61.00 (ISBN 0-444-00344-4, North Holland). Elsevier.
Bharucha-Reid, A. T., ed. Probabilistic Analysis & Related Topics, Vol. 2. 1979. 45.00 (ISBN 0-12-095602-0). Acad Pr.
--Probabilistic Analysis & Related Topics, Vol. 3. LC 78-106053. 166p. 1983. 47.00 (ISBN 0-12-095603-9). Acad Pr.
Bharucha-Reid, Albert T., ed. Probabilistic Analysis in Applied Mathematics, 4 vols. Vol. 1 1968. 68.50 (ISBN 0-12-095701-9); Vol. 2 1970. 59.50 (ISBN 0-12-095702-7); Vol. 3 1973. 77.00 (ISBN 0-12-095703-5). Acad Pr.
Bhat, B. R. Modern Probability Theory: An Introductory Text. 1981. 15.95 (ISBN 0-470-27039-X). Halsted Pr.
Bickel, Peter J. & Doksum, Kjell, eds. A Festschrift for Erich L. Lehmann. (Wadsworth Statistics-Probability Ser.). 461p. 1982. write for info. (ISBN 0-534-98044-9). Wadsworth Pub.
Billingsley, Patrick. Probability & Measure. LC 78-25632. (Probability & Mathematical Statistics Ser.). 515p. 1979. 41.95x (ISBN 0-471-03173-9, Pub. by Wiley-Interscience). Wiley.
Bismut, Jean-Michel. Theorie probabiliste du controle des diffusions. LC 75-41602. (Memoirs: No. 167). 130p. 1976. pap. 14.00 (ISBN 0-8218-1867-8, MEMO-167). Am Math.
Blake, Ian F. Introduction to Applied Probability. LC 78-11360. 528p. 1979. text ed. 47.00x (ISBN 0-471-03210-7). Wiley.
Blohincev, D. I., et al. Probability & Physical Problems. (Translations Ser.: No. 1, Vol. 11). 1962. 24.00 (ISBN 0-8218-1611-X, TRANS 1-11). Am Math.
Bloomfield, Peter & Steiger, William, eds. Applications of Least Absolute Deviations. (Progress in Probability & Statistics Ser.: Vol. 6). 400p. 1983. 24.95 (ISBN 0-8176-3157-7). Birkhauser.
Boole, George. Investigation of the Laws of Thought. 16.00 (ISBN 0-8446-1699-0). Peter Smith.
--Laws of Thought. 1953. pap. 7.95 (ISBN 0-486-60028-9). Dover.
--Logical Works, 2 Vols. Incl. Vol. 1. Studies in Logic & Probability. 500p. 29.95x (ISBN 0-87548-038-1); Vol. 2. Laws of Thought. xvi, 464p. 29.95x (ISBN 0-87548-039-X). 1952. Open Court.
Borovkov, A. A., ed. Advances in Probability: Limit Theorems & Related Problems. 500p. 1984. pap. 48.00 (ISBN 0-387-90945-1). Springer-Verlag.
Borovkov, A. A., et al. Nineteen Papers on Statistics & Probability. LC 61-9803. (Selected Translations on Mathematical Statistics & Probability Ser.: Vol. 2). 1962. 23.00 (ISBN 0-8218-1452-4, STAPRO-2). Am Math.
Borowkow, A. A. Wahrscheinlichkeitstheorie. (Mathematische Reihe Ser.: No. 53). (Ger.). 264p. 1976. 32.95 (ISBN 0-8176-0788-9). Birkhauser.
Braendli, H. Stochastische Fehler Prozesse und Treffwahrscheinlichkeitein. (Ger., Illus.). 206p. 1972. 50.95x (ISBN 0-8176-0655-6). Birkhauser.
--Die Theories des Mehrfach-Schusses. (Ger., Illus.). 200p. 1950. 29.95x (ISBN 0-8176-0042-6). Birkhauser.
Brandt, S. Statistical & Computational Methods in Data Analysis. 2nd, rev. ed. 416p. 1976. 51.00 (ISBN 0-7204-0334-0, North Holland); pap. 28.00 (ISBN 0-444-86615-9). Elsevier.
Breipohl, Arthur M. Probabilistic System Analysis: An Introduction to Probabilistic Models, Decisions & Applications of Random Processes. LC 77-94920. 352p. 1970. 43.50 (ISBN 0-471-10181-8). Wiley.
Brewer, K. R. & Hanif, M. Sampling with Unequal Probabilities. (Lecture Notes in Statistics Ser.: Vol. 15). (Illus.). 164p. 1982. pap. 15.00 (ISBN 0-387-90807-2). Springer-Verlag.
Bunke, H. & Bunke, O., eds. Statistical Inference in Linear Models, Vol. 1. (Probability & Mathematical Statistics Applied Probability & Statistics Section Ser.: 1-345). 400p. 1985. 54.95x (ISBN 0-471-10334-9, Pub. by Wiley-Interscience). Wiley.
Burington, Richard S. & May, Donald C., Jr. Handbook of Probability & Statistics with Tables. 2nd ed. 1970. 36.50 (ISBN 0-07-009030-0). McGraw.
Cajar, H. Billingsley Dimension in Probability Spaces. (Lecture Notes in Mathematics Ser.: Vol. 892). 106p. 1981. pap. 12.00 (ISBN 0-387-11164-6). Springer-Verlag.
Canavos, George C. Applied Probability & Statistical Methods. 1984. text ed. 29.95 (ISBN 0-316-12778-7); solutions manual avail. (ISBN 0-316-12779-5). Little.
Carnegie-Mellon University & DeGroot, Morris H. Probability & Statistics. 2nd ed. LC 84-6269. 644p. 1985. text ed. write for info. (ISBN 0-201-11366-X). Addison-Wesley.
Cerkasov, I. D., et al. Eighteen Papers on Statistics & Probability. LC 61-9803. (Selected Translations on Mathematical Statistics & Probability Ser.: Vol. 3). 1963. 29.00 (ISBN 0-8218-1453-2, STAPRO-3). Am Math.
Chao & Woyczynski. Probability Theory & Harmonic Analysis. (Pure & Applied Mathematics Ser.). 320p. 1986. price not set (ISBN 0-8247-7473-6). Dekker.
Cheriton, David R. Thoth System: Multi-Process Structuring & Probability. (Operating & Programming Systems Ser.: Vol. 8). 191p. 1982. 47.00 (ISBN 0-444-00701-6, North-Holland). Elsevier.
Chuaqui, Rolando. Analysis, Geometry & Probability. (Lecture Notes in Pure & Applied Mathematics Ser.). 352p. 1985. 65.00 (ISBN 0-8247-7419-1). Dekker.
Chung, K. L. Elementary Probability Theory with Stochastic Processes. (Undergraduate Texts in Mathematics Ser.). (Illus.). 1979. 19.80 (ISBN 0-387-90362-3). Springer-Verlag.

Chung, Kai L. A Course in Probability Theory. 2nd ed. (Probability & Mathematical Statistics: A Series of Monographs & Textbooks). 1974. 25.00i (ISBN 0-12-174650-X). Acad Pr.

Clarke, A. B. & Disney, R. L. Probability & Random Processes for Engineers & Scientists. 1970. 45.45 (ISBN 0-471-15980-8). Wiley.

Clarke, A. Bruce & Disney, Ralph L. Probability & Random Processes: A First Course with Applications. (Probability & Mathematical Statistics Ser.). 324p. 1985. 32.95 (ISBN 0-471-08535-9). Wiley.

Conference, 5th, Oberwolfach, Germany, Jan. 29 - Feb. 4, 1978. Probability Measures on Groups: Proceedings. Heyer, H., ed. (Lecture Notes in Mathematics: Vol. 706). 1979. pap. 22.00 (ISBN 0-387-09124-6). Springer-Verlag.

Cook, R. D. & Weisberg, S. Residuals & Influence in Regression. (Monographs on Statistics & Applied Probability). 200p. 1982. 28.95 (ISBN 0-412-24280-X, NO. 6718, Pub. by Chapman & Hall). Methuen Inc.

--Residuals & Influence in Regression. 200p. 1982. 60.00x (ISBN 0-412-24280-X, Pub. by Chapman & Hall England). State Mutual Bk.

Crabill, Delmar. Probability Theory: An Introduction. LC 83-10345. 304p. (Orig.). 1983. pap. text ed. 14.25 (ISBN 0-8191-3332-9). U Pr of Amer.

Cramer, Harold. Elements of Probability Theory & Some of Its Applications. 2nd ed. LC 73-90331. 282p. 1973. pap. text ed. 12.50 (ISBN 0-88275-144-1). Krieger.

Csorgo, M. & Revesz, P. Strong Aproximations in Probability & Statistics. LC 79-57112. (Probability & Mathematical Statistics Ser.). 1981. 44.50 (ISBN 0-12-198540-7). Acad Pr.

Culanovski, I. V., et al. Twenty-Five Papers on Statistics & Probability. LC 61-9803. (Selected Translations in Mathematical Statistics & Probability Ser.: Vol. 1). 1961. 37.00 (ISBN 0-8218-1451-6, STAPRO-1). Am Math.

Czuber, Eman. Wahrscheinlichkeitsrechnung & 'ihre Anwendung Auf Fehlerausgleichung, Statistik & Lebensversicherung, 2 Vols. (Bibliotheca Mathematica Teubneriana Ser.: Nos. 23 & 24). (Ger). 1969. Repr. of 1938 ed. Set. 60.00 (ISBN 0-384-10585-8). Johnson Repr.

Danin, D. Probabilities of the Quantum World. Glebov, oles & Kisin, Vitaly, trs. 270p. 1983. 6.95 (ISBN 0-8285-2739-3, Pub. by Mir Pubs USSR). Imported Pubns.

Davenport, W. Probability & Random Processes: An Introduction for Applied Scientists & Engineers. 1970. 49.00 (ISBN 0-07-015440-6). McGraw.

David, Florence N. Games, Gods & Gambling: The Origins & History of Probability & Statistical Ideas from the Earliest Times to the Newtonian Era. (Illus.). 1962. pap. 14.25x (ISBN 0-02-843710-1). Hafner.

Davison, Mark L. Multidimensional Scaling. LC 82-17403. (Probability & Mathematical Statistics: Applied Probability & Statistic Section Ser.). 242p. 1983. 29.95 (ISBN 0-471-86417-X, Pub. by Wiley-Interscience). Wiley.

Degroot, Morris. Probability & Statistics. LC 74-19691. (Behavioral Science Quantitative Methods Ser). (Illus.). 624p. 1975. text ed. 27.95 (ISBN 0-201-01503-X); sol. manual 7.95 (ISBN 0-201-01509-9). Addison-Wesley.

Dellacherie, C. & Meyer, P. A. Probabilities & Potential. (North Holland Mathematical Studies: No. 29). 190p. 1979. 42.75 (ISBN 0-7204-0701-X, North-Holland). Elsevier.

De Moivre, A. Doctrine of Chances or, a Method of Calculating the Probabilities of Events in Play. 257p. 1967. Repr. of 1738 ed. 45.00x (ISBN 0-7146-1058-5, BHA-01058, F Cass Co). Biblio Dist.

De Morgan, Augustus. An Essay on Probabilities. LC 80-2119. (Development of Science Ser.). (Illus.). lib. bdg. 30.00x (ISBN 0-405-13885-7). Ayer Co Pubs.

Devore, Jay. Probability & Statistics for Engineering & the Physical Sciences. LC 81-21744. (Statistics Ser.). (Illus.). 700p. 1982. pap. text ed. 28.50 pub net (ISBN 0-8185-0514-1). Brooks-Cole.

Disney, R. & Ott, T., eds. Applied Probability--Computer Science: The Interface, 2 Vols. (Progress in Computer Science Ser.). 1982. text ed. 39.95x ea. Vol. 2, 532pp (ISBN 0-8176-3067-8). Vol. 3, 514pp (ISBN 0-8176-3093-7). Birkhauser.

Ditlevsen, Ove. Uncertainty Modeling: With Applications to Multidimensional Civil Engineering. (Illus.). 448p. 1981. text ed. 80.00 (ISBN 0-07-017046-0). McGraw.

Dobrushin & Sinai. Multicomponent Random Systems. (Advances in Probability Ser.: Vol. 6). 84.50 (ISBN 0-8247-6831-0). Dekker.

Dodge, Y. Analysis of Experiments with Missing Data. (Probability & Mathematical Statistics Ser.). 492p. 1985. write for info. (ISBN 0-471-88736-6). Wiley.

Drake, Alvin W. Fundamentals of Applied Probability Theory. (Illus.). 1967. text ed. 48.00 (ISBN 0-07-017815-1). McGraw.

Dudewicz, Edward J. Introduction to Statistics & Probability. LC 75-26827. (American Sciences Press Ser. in Mathematical & Management Sciences: Vol. 1). 1976. text ed. 29.95 (ISBN 0-03-086688-X). Am Sciences Pr.

--Solutions in Statistics & Probability. LC 80-68285. (The American Sciences Press Ser. in Mathematical & Management Sciences: Vol. 3). 1980. pap. text ed. 24.95 (ISBN 0-935950-00-1). Am Sciences Pr.

Dudley, R. M., et al. Ecole d'Ete de Probabilities de Saint-Flour XII, 1982. (Lecture Notes in Mathematics Ser.: Vol. 1097). x, 396p. 1984. pap. 22.50 (ISBN 0-387-13897-8). Springer-Verlag.

Dugue, D., ed. Analytical Methods in Probability Theory: Proceedings. (Lecture Notes in Mathematics Ser.: Vol. 861). 183p. 1981. pap. 14.00 (ISBN 0-387-10823-8). Springer-Verlag.

Durran, J. H. Statistics & Probability. LC 70-96086. (School Mathematics Project Handbks). 1970. text ed. 27.95 (ISBN 0-521-06933-5). Cambridge U Pr.

Dynkin, E. B., et al. Eleven Papers on Analysis, Probability & Topology. LC 51-5559. (Translations, Ser.: No. 2, Vol. 12). 1966. Repr. of 1959 ed. 27.00 (ISBN 0-8218-1712-4, TRANS 2-12). Am Math.

Ecole de'Ete De Probabilites De Saint-Flour, 4th, 1974. Proceedings. Fernique, X. M., et al, eds. LC 75-25522. (Lecture Notes in Mathematics: Vol. 480). 293p. 1975. pap. 18.30 (ISBN 0-387-07396-5). Springer-Verlag.

Elandt-Johnson, Regina C. & Johnson, Norman L. Survival Models & Data Analysis. LC 79-22836. (Wiley Series in Probability & Mathematical Statistics: Applied Probability & Statistics). 457p. 1980. 48.95x (ISBN 0-471-03174-7, Pub. by Wiley-Interscience). Wiley.

Encyclopedia of Mathematics & Its Applications: Integral Geometry & Geometric Probability, Vol. 1. 1984. 42.50 (ISBN 0-317-14404-9, 30221-8). Cambridge U Pr.

Ewart, Park J., et al. Probability for Statistical Decision Making. (Illus.). 400p. 1974. ref. ed. 28.95 (ISBN 0-13-711614-4). P-H.

Fabian, Vaclav & Hannan, James. Introduction to Probability & Mathematical Statistics. LC 84-12998. (Wiley Series in Probability & Mathematical Statistics: 1-345). 448p. 1985. text ed. 42.95 (ISBN 0-471-25023-6, Pub. by Wiley Interscience). Wiley.

Feinsilver, P. J. Special Functions, Probability Semigroups, & Hamiltonian Flows. (Lecture Notes in Mathematics Ser.: Vol. 696). 1978. pap. 14.00 (ISBN 0-387-09100-9). Springer-Verlag.

Feller, William. Introduction to Probability Theory & Its Applications, Vol. 1. 3rd ed. LC 68-11708. (Probability & Mathematical Statistics Ser.). 509p. 1968. 43.50x (ISBN 0-471-25708-7). Wiley.

--An Introduction to Probability Theory & Its Applications, Vol. 2. 2nd ed. LC 57-10805. (Probability & Mathematical Statistics Ser.). 669p. 1971. 46.00x (ISBN 0-471-25709-5). Wiley.

Fine, Terrence L. Theories of Probability: An Examination of Foundations. 1973. 42.50 (ISBN 0-12-256450-2). Acad Pr.

Fisher, Ronald A. Statistical Methods & Scientific Inference. rev. ed. 1973. 14.95x (ISBN 0-02-844740-9). Hafner.

Fisz, Marek. Probability Theory & Mathematical Statistics. 3rd ed. LC 80-12455. 696p. 1980. Repr. of 1963 ed. lib. bdg. 39.50 (ISBN 0-89874-179-3). Krieger.

Fleiss, Joseph L. Statistical Methods for Rates & Proportions. 2nd ed. LC 80-26382. (Probability & Statistics Ser.: Applied Probability & Statistics). 321p. 1981. 37.50x (ISBN 0-471-06428-9, Pub. by Wiley-Interscience). Wiley.

Fortet, R. Elements of Probability Theory. 544p. 1977. 113.50 (ISBN 0-677-02110-0). Gordon.

Fox, John. Linear Statistical Models & Related Methods: With Applications to Social Research. LC 83-23278. (Probability & Mathematical Statistics Ser.: 1-346). 496p. 1984. 39.95x (ISBN 0-471-09913-9, NO. 1-346, Pub. by Wiley-Interscience). Wiley.

Frey, Gerhard, ed. Bela Juhos: Selected Papers. Foulkes, Paul, tr. LC 76-17019. (Vienna Circle Collection Ser: No. 7). 1976. lib. bdg. 55.00 (ISBN 90-277-0686-7, Pub. by Reidel Holland); pap. 28.95 (ISBN 90-277-0687-5). Kluwer Academic.

Frieden, B. R. Probability, Statistical Optics, & Data Analysis. (Series in Information Sciences: Vol. 10). (Illus.). 404p. 1983. 42.00 (ISBN 0-387-11769-5). Springer-Verlag.

Frodesen, A. G., et al. Probability & Statistics in Particle Physics. 1979. 39.00x (ISBN 8-2000-1906-3, Dist. by Columbia U Pr). Universitet.

Furstenberg, H. Stationary Processes & Prediction Theory. (Annals of Mathematics Studies, Vol. 44). (Orig.). 1960. pap. 32.00x (ISBN 0-691-08041-0). Princeton U Pr.

Galambos, J. & Kotz, S. Characterizations of Probability Distributions: A Unified Approach with an Emphasis on Exponential & Related Models. (Lecture Notes in Mathematics: Vol. 675). 1978. pap. 15.00 (ISBN 0-387-08933-0). Springer-Verlag.

Galambos, Janos. Introductory Probability Theory. (Statistics: Textbooks & Monographs Ser.). 256p. 1984. 25.00 (ISBN 0-8247-7179-6). Dekker.

Gani, J. & Rohatgi, V. K., eds. Contributions to Probability: A Collection of Papers Dedicated to Eugene Lukacs. LC 80-768. 1981. 55.00 (ISBN 0-12-274460-8). Acad Pr.

Gleason, Andrew M. Elementary Course in Probability for the Cryptanalyst. (Orig.). pap. 24.80 (ISBN 0-89412-072-7). Aegean Park Pr.

Gnedenko, B. The Theory of Probability. 392p. 1978. 8.45 (ISBN 0-8285-0748-1, Pub. by Mir Pubs USSR). Imported Pubns.

Gnedenko, B. V. Theory of Probability. Yankovsky, George, tr. from Russian. 392p. 1969. 17.00x (ISBN 0-8464-0922-4). Beekman Pubs.

--The Theory of Probability & the Elements of Statistics. 5th ed. Seckler, Bernard, tr. from Rus. LC 61-13496. 529p. 1985. pap. text ed. 9.95 (ISBN 0-8284-1132-8, 132). Chelsea Pub.

Gnedenko, Boris V. & Khinchin, Alexander Y. Elementary Introduction to the Theory of Probability. 5th ed. Boron, Leon F., tr. 1961. pap. text ed. 4.50 (ISBN 0-486-60155-2). Dover.

Golberg, Michael A. An Introduction to Probability Theory with Statistical Applications. (Mathematical Concepts in Science & Engineering Ser.: Vol. 29). 674p. 1984. 69.50x (ISBN 0-306-41645-X, Plenum Pr). Plenum Pub.

Good, I. J. Good Thinking: The Foundations of Probability & Its Applications. (Illus.). 351p. 1983. 35.00x (ISBN 0-8166-1141-6); pap. 14.95x (ISBN 0-8166-1142-4). U of Minn Pr.

Grandell, J. Doubly Stochastic Poisson Processes. (Lecture Notes in Mathematics: Vol. 529). 1976. soft cover 17.00 (ISBN 0-387-07795-2). Springer-Verlag.

Grenander, Ulf. Abstract Inference. LC 80-22016. (Wiley Series in Probability & Mathematical Statistics-Probability & Mathematical Statistics Section). 526p. 1981. 44.95x (ISBN 0-471-08267-8, Pub. by Wiley Interscience). Wiley.

Grimmett, Geoffrey & Stirzaker, David. Probability & Random Processes. (Illus.). 1982. pap. 24.95x (ISBN 0-19-853185-0). Oxford U Pr.

Groenvald. Introduction to Probability & Statistics Using BASIC. (Statistics; Textbooks & Monographs: Vol. 26). 1979. 35.00 (ISBN 0-8247-6543-5). Dekker.

Grossman, W. & Pflug, G., eds. Probability & Statistical Inference. 1982. lib. bdg. 49.50 (ISBN 90-277-1427-4, Pub. by Reidel Holland). Kluwer Academic.

Guttorp. Statistics Inference for Branching Processes. (Probability & Mathematical Ser.). 1986. price not set (ISBN 0-471-82291-4). Wiley.

Gyires, B. Analytic Function Methods in Probability Theory. (Colloquia Mathematica Societatis Janos Bolyoi Ser.: Vol. 21). 379p. 1979. 85.00 (ISBN 0-444-85333-2, North Holland). Elsevier.

Hacking, Ian. The Emergence of Probability: A Philosophical Study of Early Ideas about Probability, Induction, & Statistical Inference. 219p. 1984. pap. 12.95 (ISBN 0-521-31803-3). Cambridge U Pr.

Hacking, Ian M. The Emergence of Probability. LC 74-82224. 216p. 1975. 37.50 (ISBN 0-521-20460-7). Cambridge U Pr.

Hackworth, Robert D. & Howland, Joseph. Introductory College Mathematics: Probability. LC 75-23624. 80p. 1976. pap. text ed. 9.95 (ISBN 0-7216-4417-1). HR&W.

Haight, Frank A. Applied Probability. LC 81-4690. (Mathematical Concepts & Methods in Science & Engineering Ser.: Vol. 23). 302p. 1981. 45.00x (ISBN 0-306-40699-3, Plenum Pr). Plenum Pub.

Halmos, P. R. Lectures on Ergodic Theory. LC 60-8964. 8.95 (ISBN 0-8284-0142-X). Chelsea Pub.

Hamming, Richard W. Methods of Mathematics Applied to Calculus, Probability & Statistics. (Series in Computational Math). (Illus.). 688p. 1985. text ed. 39.95 (ISBN 0-13-578899-4). P-H.

Hand, D. J. Discrimination & Classification. LC 81-13045. (Wiley Ser. in Probability & Mathematical Statistics). 218p. 1981. 44.95x (ISBN 0-471-28048-8, Pub. by Wiley Interscience). Wiley.

Harper, W. L. & Hooker, C. A., eds. Foundations of Probability Theory Statistical Inference & Statistical Theories of Science: Proceedings, 3 vols. Incl. Vol. 1. Foundations & Philosophy of Epistemic Applications of Probability Theory. LC 75-34354. lib. bdg. 55.00 (ISBN 90-277-0616-6); pap. 28.95 (ISBN 90-277-0617-4); Vol. 2. Foundations & Philosophy of Statistical Inference. LC 75-38667. lib. bdg. 68.50 (ISBN 90-277-0618-2); pap. 37.00 (ISBN 90-277-0619-0); Vol. 3. Foundations & Philosophy of Statistical Theories in the Physical Sciences. LC 75-33879. lib. bdg. 39.50 (ISBN 90-277-0620-4); pap. 24.00 (ISBN 90-277-0621-2). (Western Ontatio Ser.: No. 6). 1976. 147.50 set (ISBN 90-277-0614-X, Pub. by Reidel Holland); pap. 79.00 set (ISBN 90-277-0615-8). Kluwer Academic.

--Workshop on Probability & Statistics: Proceedings, 3 vols. (Western Ontario Ser: No. 6). 1975. Set. 147.50 (ISBN 90-277-0614-X); Set. pap. 79.00 (ISBN 90-277-0615-8); Vol. 1. 55.00 (ISBN 90-277-0616-6); Vol. 1. pap. 29.00 (ISBN 90-277-0617-4); Vol. 2. 68.50 (ISBN 90-277-0618-2); Vol. 2. pap. 37.00 (ISBN 90-277-0619-0); Vol. 3. 39.50 (ISBN 90-277-0620-4); Vol. 3. pap. 24.00 (ISBN 90-277-0621-2, Pub. by Reidel Holland). Kluwer Academic.

Hausner, Melvin. Elementary Probability Theory. LC 77-813. 318p. 1977. 10.95x (ISBN 0-306-20026-0, Rosetta). Plenum Pub.

Heron House Editors. The Odds of Virtually Everything. 1981. pap. 3.95 (ISBN 0-89083-874-7). Zebra.

Hersch, Joseph & Rota, Gian-Carlo, eds. George Polya - Collected Papers: Probability; Combinatories; Teaching & Learning in Mathematics, Vol. IV. (Mathematicians of Our Time Ser.: No. 23). 676p. 1984. 65.00 (ISBN 0-262-16097-8). MIT Pr.

Hettmansperger, Thomas P. Statistical Inference Based on Ranks. LC 83-23519. (Probability & Mathematical Statistics Applied Probability & Statictics Sections Ser.). 323p. 1984. 37.50x (ISBN 0-471-88474-X, 1-345, Pub. by Wiley-Interscience). Wiley.

Heyer, H. Probability Measures on Locally Compact Groups. (Ergebnisse der Mathematik und ihrer Grenzgbiete: Vol. 94). 1977. 78.00 (ISBN 0-387-08332-4). Springer-Verlag.

Heyer, H., ed. Probability Measures on Groups VII: Proceedings of a Conference Held in Oberwolfach, 24-30 April 1983. (Lecture Notes in Mathematics Ser.: Vol. 1064). x, 588p. 1984. pap. 30.00 (ISBN 0-387-13341-0). Springer-Verlag.

Heyer, Herbert, ed. Probability Measures on Groups, Oberwolfach, Federal Republic of Germany, 1981: Proceedings. (Lecture Notes in Mathematics Ser.: Vol. 928). 477p. 1982. pap. 25.00 (ISBN 0-387-11501-3). Springer-Verlag.

Hines, William W. & Montgomery, Douglas C. Probability & Statistics in Engineering & Management Science. 2nd ed. LC 79-26257. 634p. 1980. text ed. 41.50 (ISBN 0-471-04759-7); solutions manual avail. (ISBN 0-471-05006-7). Wiley.

Hochberg, et al. Multiple Comparisons. (Probability & Mathematical Statistics Ser.). 1986. price not set (ISBN 0-471-82222-1). Wiley.

Hodges, J. L., Jr. & Lehmann, E. L. Basic Concepts of Probability & Statistics. rev. ed. 2nd ed. LC 72-104973. 1970. text ed. 26.00x (ISBN 0-8162-4004-3); ans. bk. 6.00x (ISBN 0-8162-4024-8). Holden-Day.

Hogben, Lancelot. Statistical Theory. rev. ed. (Illus.). 1968. 15.00x (ISBN 0-393-06305-4). Norton.

Hogg, Robert V. & Tanis, Elliot A. Probability & Statistical Inference. 2nd ed. 500p. 1983. text ed. write for info. (ISBN 0-02-355730-3). Macmillan.

Horwich, Paul. Probability & Evidence. LC 81-18144. (Cambridge Studies in Philosophy). 160p. 1982. 29.95 (ISBN 0-521-23758-0). Cambridge U Pr.

Hume, Beryl. An Introduction to Probability & Statistics. 3rd ed. 1969. pap. 11.00x (ISBN 0-85564-030-8, Pub. by U of W Austral Pr); supplement 1.00. Intl Spec Bk.

Hunter, Jeffrey J. Mathematical Techniques of Applied Probability, Vol. 1: Discrete Time Models: Basic Theory. 518p. 1983. 35.00 (ISBN 0-12-361801-0). Acad Pr.

--Mathematical Techniques of Applied Probability, Vol. 2: Discrete Time Models: Techniques & Applications. (Operations Research & Industrial Engineering Ser.). 1983. 37.50 (ISBN 0-12-361802-9). Acad Pr.

International Congress for Logic, Methodology, & Philosophy of Science, 4th, Bucharest, Sept. 1971. Logic, Language & Probability: Proceedings. Bogdan, R. J. & Niiniluoto, I., eds. LC 72-95892. (Synthese Library: No. 51). 316p. 1973. lib. bdg. 45.00 (ISBN 90-277-0312-4, Pub. by Reidel Holland). Kluwer Academic.

Robinson, Enders A. Probability Theory & Applications. (Illus.). 420p. 1985. 39.00 (ISBN 0-934634-90-4). Intl Human Res.
Rohatgi, V. K. Statistical Inference. LC 83-21848. (Probability & Mathematical Statistics Ser.). 940p. 1984. 44.95x (ISBN 0-471-87126-5, 1-346, Pub. by Wiley-Interscience). Wiley.
Rohatgi, Vijay K. An Introduction to Probability Theory & Mathematical Statistics. LC 75-14378. (Series in Probability & Mathematical Statistics: Probability & Mathematical Statistics Section). 684p. 1976. 46.95 (ISBN 0-471-73135-8, Pub by Wiley-Interscience). Wiley.
Rosenblatt, Murray, ed. Studies in Probability Theory. new ed. LC 78-71935. (MAA Studies in Mathematics: Vol. 18). 211p. 1979. 21.00 (ISBN 0-88385-118-0). Math Assn.
Rosenkrantz, R. D. E. T. Jaynes: Papers on Probability, Statistics & Statistical Physics. 1983. lib. bdg. 49.50 (ISBN 90-277-1448-7, Pub. by Reidel Holland). Kluwer Academic.
Rosenkrantz, Roger D. Foundations & Applications of Inductive Probability. xiv, 326p. (Orig.). 1981. lib. bdg. 29.00x (ISBN 0-917930-23-1); pap. text ed. 15.00x (ISBN 0-917930-03-7). Ridgeview.
Ross & Tukey. Index to Statistics & Probability: Locations & Authors, Vol. 5. LC 72-86075. 1973. 94.00 (ISBN 0-88274-004-0). R & D Pr.
--Index to Statistics & Probability: Permuted Titles, Vols. 3 & 4. LC 72-86075. 1975. Set. 137.00 (ISBN 0-686-15779-6). R & D Pr.
Ross, Sheldon. A First Course in Probability. 400p. 1984. text ed. write for info. (ISBN 0-02-403910-1). Macmillan.
Ross, Sheldon M. Introduction to Probability Models. 3rd ed. 1985. text ed. 28.00i (ISBN 0-12-598463-4). Acad Pr.
Rota, Gian-Carlo, ed. Studies in Probability & Ergodic Theory: Advances in Mathematics Supplementary Studies, Vol. 2. 1978. 75.00 (ISBN 0-12-599102-9). Acad Pr.
Rowntree, Derek. Probability Without Tears. 196p. 1984. 7.95 (ISBN 0-684-17994-6, ScribT). Scribner.
--Probability Without Tears. 169p. 1984. pap. text ed. price not set (ISBN 0-02-404100-9, Pub. by Scribner). Macmillan.
Rozanov, Y. A. Probability Theory: A Concise Course. rev. ed. Silverman, Richard A., tr. from Russian. LC 77-78592. 1977. pap. text ed. 4.00 (ISBN 0-486-63544-9). Dover.
Scheaffer, R. L. & Mendenhall, Wm. Introduction to Probability: Theory & Applications. LC 75-3562. 1975. text ed. 14.95x (ISBN 0-87872-084-7, Duxbury Pr). PWS Pubs.
Schweizer, B. & Sklar, A. Probabilistic Metric Spaces. (Probability & Applied Mathematics Ser.: Vol. 5). 276p. 1982. 46.25 (ISBN 0-444-00666-4, North-Holland). Elsevier.
Seal, Hilary L. Survival Probabilities: The Goal of Risk Theory. LC 78-8599. (Probability & Mathematical Statistics Ser.). 103p. 1978. 53.95 (ISBN 0-471-99683-1, Pub. by Wiley-Interscience). Wiley.
Seminaire De Probabilites, 9th, Universite De Strasbourg. Proceedings. Meyer, P. A., ed. (Lecture Notes in Mathematics: Vol. 465). 598p. 1975. pap. 26.00 (ISBN 0-387-07178-4). Springer-Verlag.
Sen, Pranab Kumar. Sequential Nonparametrics: Invariance Principles & Statistical Inference. LC 81-4432. (Probability & Mathematical Statistics Ser.). 421p. 1981. 53.50x (ISBN 0-471-06013-5, Pub. by Wiley-Interscience). Wiley.
Shiryayev, A. N. Probability: Graduate Texts in Mathematics, Vol. 95. Boas, R. P., tr. from Rus. (Springer Series in Soviet Mathematics). (Illus.). 500p. 1984. 48.00 (ISBN 0-387-90898-6). Springer-Verlag.
Shooman, Martin L. Probabilistic Reliability: An Engineering Approach. rev. ed. 1986. lib. bdg. price not set (ISBN 0-89874-883-6). Krieger.
Shorack, G. R. & Wellner, J. A. Empirical Processes with Applications to Statistics. (Probability & Mathematical Statistics Ser.). 1985. 50.00 (ISBN 0-471-86725-X). Wiley.
Solomon, Herbert. Geometric Probability. (CBMS-NSF Regional Conference Ser.: No. 28). vi, 174p. (Orig.). 1978. pap. text ed. 21.00 (ISBN 0-89871-025-1). Soc Indus-Appl Math.
Soong, T. T. Probabilistic Modeling & Analysis in Science & Engineering. LC 81-19686. 384p. 1981. text ed. 42.50 (ISBN 0-471-08061-6); solutions manual avail. (ISBN 0-471-08575-8); tchr's. manual avail. (ISBN 0-471-08983-4). Wiley.
Spiegel, Murray R. Probability & Statistics. 304p. (Orig.). 1975. pap. text ed. 9.95 (ISBN 0-07-060220-4). McGraw.
Srinivasan, S. K. & Subramanian, R. Probabilistic Analysis of Redundant Systems. (Lecture Notes in Economics & Mathematical Systems Ser.: Vol. 175). (Illus.). 356p. 1980. pap. 33.00 (ISBN 3-540-09736-8). Springer-Verlag.
Steen, Frederick H. Elements of Probability & Mathematical Statistics. 512p. 1982. text ed. write for info. (ISBN 0-87872-299-8, 6075, Duxbury Pr). PWS Pubs.
Steklov Institute of Mathematics, Academy of Sciences, U S S R. Theoretical Problems of Mathematical Statistics: Proceedings. Linnik, Ju V., ed. LC 72-5245. (Proceedings of the Steklov Institute of Mathematics: No. 111). 320p. 1971. 55.00 (ISBN 0-8218-3011-2, STEKLO-111). Am Math.
Strait, Peggy T. First Course in Probability & Statistics with Applications. 581p. 1983. text ed. 29.95 (ISBN 0-15-527520-8, HC); solutions manual avail. (ISBN 0-15-527521-6). HarbraceJ.
Stroock, D. W. An Introduction to the Theory of Large Deviations. (Universitext Ser.). 195p. 1984. pap. 18.00 (ISBN 0-387-96021-X). Springer-Verlag.
Subrahmaniam. A Primer in Probability. (Statistics; Textbooks & Monographs Ser.: Vol. 28). 1979. 29.75 (ISBN 0-8247-6836-1). Dekker.
Sudakov, N. Geometric Problems in the Theory of Infinite-Dimensional Probability Distributions. LC 79-11640. (Proceedings of the Steklov Institute of Mathematics: No. 141). 1979. 57.00 (ISBN 0-8218-3041-4, STEKLO-141). Am Math.
Sveshnikov, A. A. Problems in Probability Theory, Mathematical Statistics & Theory of Random Functions. Silverman, Richard A., tr. from Russian. 1979. pap. text ed. 8.50 (ISBN 0-486-63717-4). Dover.
Symposium in Applied Mathematics, New York, 1957. Applied Probability: Proceedings. MacColl, L. A., ed. LC 50-1183. (Proceedings of Symposia in Applied Mathematics: Vol. 7). 1957. 21.00 (ISBN 0-8218-1307-2, PSAPM-7). Am Math.
Symposium On Probability Methods In Analysis, Loutraki, Greece, 1966. Proceedings. (Lecture Notes in Mathematics: Vol. 31). 1967. pap. 18.30 (ISBN 0-387-03902-3). Springer-Verlag.
Tawadros, Milad A. Basic Statistics & Probability for Business & Economic Decisions. 2nd ed. 1979. text ed. 20.95 (ISBN 0-8403-2094-9). Kendall-Hunt.
Taylor, Robert L., et al. Limit Theorems for Sums of Exchangeable Random Variables. (Probability & Statistics Ser.). 150p. 1985. 19.95x (ISBN 0-8476-7435-5). Rowman & Allanheld.
Thomas, John B. An Introduction to Applied Probability & Random Processes. LC 80-15349. (Illus.). 352p. 1981. Repr. of 1971 ed. lib. bdg. 26.50 (ISBN 0-89874-232-3). Krieger.
Thorp, Edward O. Elementary Probability. LC 75-45419. 162p. Repr. of 1977 ed. 11.50 (ISBN 0-88275-389-4). Krieger.
Tjur, Tue. Probability Based on Random Measures. LC 80-40503. (Wiley Series in Probability & Mathematical Statistics). 232p. 1980. 71.95x (ISBN 0-471-27824-6, Pub. by Wiley-Interscience). Wiley.
Todhunter, Isaac. History of the Mathematical Theory of Probability. LC 51-146. 1949. 17.95 (ISBN 0-8284-0057-1). Chelsea Pub.
Tong, Y. L. & Gupta, Shanti S., eds. Inequalities in Statistics & Probability. LC 83-12975. (IMS Lecture Notes-Monograph Ser.: Vol. 5). x, 253p. 1984. pap. 25.00 (ISBN 0-940600-04-8). Inst Math.
Trivedi, Kishar S. Probability & Statistics with Reliability, Queuing & Computer Science Applications. (Illus.). 672p. 1982. text ed. 41.95 (ISBN 0-13-711564-4). P-H.
Tukey. Index to Statistics & Probability: Citation Index, Vol. 2. LC 72-86075. 1973. 109.00 (ISBN 0-88274-001-6). R & D Pr.
--Index to Statistics & Probability: Index to Minimum Abbreviations, Vol. 6. LC 72-86075. 1979. 60.00 (ISBN 0-88274-005-9). R & D Pr.
U. S. S. R. Symposium on Probability Theory, 2nd, Japan, Aug. 2-9, 1972. Proceedings. Maruyama, G. & Prokhorov, Y. V., eds. (Lecture Notes in Mathematics: Vol. 330). (Illus.). vi, 550p. 1973. pap. 26.00 (ISBN 0-387-06358-7). Springer-Verlag.
Ullman, Neil R. Elementary Statistics: An Applied Approach. LC 77-10828. 372p. 1978. 31.00 (ISBN 0-471-02105-9). wkbk & study guide 13.95 (ISBN 0-471-03209-3). Wiley.
Upton, Graham J. The Analysis of Cross-Tabulated Data. LC 78-4210. (Probability & Mathematical Statistics: Applied Section Ser.). 148p. 1978. 57.95x (ISBN 0-471-99659-9, Pub. by Wiley-Interscience). Wiley.
Vajda, S. Probabilistic Programming. (Probability & Mathematical Statistics Ser.). 1972. 37.00 (ISBN 0-12-710150-0). Acad Pr.
Wald, Abraham. Selected Papers in Statistics & Probability. 1955. 45.00x (ISBN 0-8047-0493-7). Stanford U Pr.
Walpole, Ronald E. Student's Solutions Manual to Accompany Probability & Statistics for Engineers & Scientists. 3rd ed. 124p. 1985. 7.95 (ISBN 0-02-424190-3). Macmillan.
Walpole, Ronald E. & Myers, Raymond H. Probability & Statistics for Engineers & Scientists. 3rd ed. 650p. 1985. text ed. write for info. (ISBN 0-02-424170-9). Macmillan.
Watkins, Susan. Conversations with Seth, Vol. 2. 617p. 1981. 12.95 (ISBN 0-13-172049-X). P-H.
Weaver, Warren. Lady Luck: The Theory of Probability. (Popular Science Ser.). (Illus.). 384p. 1982. pap. 6.00 (ISBN 0-486-24342-7). Dover.
Weron, A., ed. Probability Theory an Vector Spaces II: Proceedings. (Lecture Notes in Mathematics Ser.: Vol. 828). 324p. 1980. pap. 23.00 (ISBN 0-387-10253-1). Springer-Verlag.
--Probability Theory on Vector Spaces: Proceedings, Trzebieszowice, Poland, September 1977. (Lecture Notes in Mathematics Ser.: Vol. 656). 1978. pap. 17.00 (ISBN 0-387-08846-6). Springer-Verlag.
Whittle, P. Probability. LC 76-863. 239p. 1976. pap. 24.95x (ISBN 0-471-01657-8, Pub. by Wiley-Interscience). Wiley.
Whitworth, William A. Choice & Chance with One Thousand Exercises. 5th ed. 1965. Repr. of 1901 ed. 8.95x (ISBN 0-02-854750-0). Hafner.
Williams, Frederick & Holstein, J. E. Introduction to Probability. 1967. text ed. 3.00x spiral bdg (ISBN 0-87543-061-9). Lucas.
Wilson, Colin & Grant, John, eds. Directory of Possibilities. (Illus.). 224p. 1981. 14.95 (ISBN 0-8317-2382-3, Rutledge Pr); pap. 9.95 (ISBN 0-8317-2383-1). Smith Pubs.
Wonnacott, Thomas H. & Wonnacott, Ronald J. Regression: A Second Course in Statistics. (Probability & Mathematical Statistics: Applied & Probability & Statistics). 556p. 1981. 43.50 (ISBN 0-471-95974-X). Wiley.
Woodward, P. M. Information & Probability Theory, with Applications to Radar. LC 80-70175. (Artech Radar Library). (Illus.). 128p. 1980. Repr. of 1953 ed. 22.00 (ISBN 0-89006-103-3). Artech Hse.
Yaglom, A. M. & Yaglom, I. M. Probability & Information. 1983. lib. bdg. 69.00 (ISBN 0-318-00432-1, Pub. by Reidel Holland). Kluwer Academic.

PROBABILITIES–PROGRAMMED INSTRUCTION

Dixon, John R. A Programmed Introduction to Probability. LC 78-25984. 420p. 1979. pap. text ed. 18.50 (ISBN 0-88275-825-X). Krieger.
Rahman, N. A. Exercises in Probability & Statistics. 2nd ed. 1983. 35.00 (ISBN 0-02-850760-6). Macmillan.

PROBES (ELECTRONIC INSTRUMENTS)

Andersen, C. A., ed. Microprobe Analysis. LC 72-8837. 586p. 1973. 43.00 (ISBN 0-471-02835-5). Krieger.
Beddard, G. S. & West, M. A., eds. Flourescent Probes. 1981. 43.00 (ISBN 0-12-084680-2). Acad Pr.
Birks, L. S. Electron Probe Microanalysis. 2nd ed. LC 79-9773. 204p. 1979. Repr. of 1971 ed. lib. bdg. 21.50 (ISBN 0-88275-952-3). Krieger.
CES Industries, Inc. Ed-Lab Eighty Experiment Manual: Thermal Probe Sensor. (Illus., Orig.). 1983. write for info. (ISBN 0-86711-041-4). CES Industries.
Earle, K. M. & Tousimis, A. J., eds. X-Ray & Electron Probe Analysis in Biomedical Research. LC 68-13392. 103p. 1969. 29.50x (ISBN 0-306-39303-4, Plenum Pr). Plenum Pub.
Heinrich, Kurt F. Electron Beam X-Ray Microanalysis. 608p. 1980. 44.50 (ISBN 0-442-23286-1). Van Nos Reinhold.
Reed, J. J. Electron Microprobe Analysis. LC 74-94356. (Monographs on Physics). (Illus.). 350p. 1975. 69.50 (ISBN 0-521-20466-6). Cambridge U Pr.
Scott, V. D. & Love, G. Quantitative Electron-Probe Microanalysis. LC 83-18366. 343p. 1983. 48.95x (ISBN 0-470-27510-3). Halsted Pr.

PROBLEM OF MANY BODIES

see also Perturbation (Astronomy)

Brout, R. & Carruthers, P. Lectures on the Many-Electron Problem. 214p. 1969. 57.75 (ISBN 0-677-02470-3). Gordon.
Caianiello, E. R., ed. The Many-Body Problem, Vol. 2. (Spring Lectures, 1963). 1964. 32.00 (ISBN 0-12-154574-1). Acad Pr.
Conference on Numerical Solution of Ordinary Differential Equations. Proceedings. Bettis, D. G., ed. LC 73-20914. (Lecture Notes in Mathematics Ser.: Vol. 362). viii, 490p. 1974. pap. 22.00 (ISBN 0-387-06602-0). Springer-Verlag.
Danos, M., et al. Methods in Relativistic Nuclear Physics. 308p. 1984. 74.00 (ISBN 0-444-86317-6, North-Holland). Elsevier.
Garrido, L. M., et al, eds. Irreversibility in the Many-Body Problem. LC 72-87519. 470p. 1972. 65.00x (ISBN 0-306-30711-1, Plenum Pr). Plenum Pub.
Inkson, John C. Many-Body Theory of Solids: An Introduction. 324p. 1983. 29.50x (ISBN 0-306-41326-4, Plenum Pr). Plenum Pub.
International University Courses on Nuclear Physics, 11th, Schladming, Austria, 1972. Elementary Particle Physics (Multiparticle Aspects) Proceedings. Urban, P., ed. LC 72-87907. (Acta Physica Austriaca: Suppl. 9). (Illus.). ix, 909p. 1972. 116.90 (ISBN 0-387-81103-6). Springer-Verlag.
Khilmi, G. F. Qualitative Methods in the Many-Body Problem. (Russian Tracts on the Physical Sciences Ser.). (Illus.). 130p. 1961. 34.75 (ISBN 0-677-20120-6). Gordon.
Kimmel, H. & Ristig, M. L., eds. Recent Progress in Many-Body Theories: Proceedings of the Third International Conference on Recent Progress in Many-Body Theories held at Odenthal-Altenburg, Germany, August 29-Sept. 3, 1983. (Lecture Notes in Physics Ser.: Vol. 198). ix, 422p. 1984. pap. 22.00 (ISBN 0-387-12924-3). Springer Verlag.
Kirzhnits, D. A. Field Theoretical Methods in Many-Body Systems. Meadows, A. J., tr. 1967. 72.00 (ISBN 0-08-011779-1). Pergamon.
Kramer. Groups, Systems & Many Body Physics. (Clustering Phenomena in Nuclei Ser.: Vol. 1). 1979. 80.00 (ISBN 0-9940012-7-4). Heyden.
Langreth, David & Suhl, Harry, eds. Many-Body Phenomena at Surfaces. 1984. 39.50 (ISBN 0-12-436560-4). Acad Pr.
Lindgren, I. & Morrison, J. Atomic Many-Body Theory. (Springer Series in Chemical Physics: Vol. 13). (Illus.). 490p. 1982. 54.00 (ISBN 0-387-10504-2). Springer Verlag.
Marciniak, Andrzej. Numerical Solutions of the N-Body Problem. 1985. lib. bdg. 39.50 (ISBN 90-277-2058-4, Pub. by Reidel Holland). Kluwer Academic.
Meeron, E., ed. The Physics of Many-Particle Systems. (Many-Body Problem: Current Research & Reviews Ser.). 698p. 1966. 130.75 (ISBN 0-677-10330-1). Gordon.
Mills, R. L. Propagators for Many-Particle Systems. 140p. 1969. 40.50x (ISBN 0-677-02040-6). Gordon.
Morrison, Harry, ed. Quantum Theory of Many-Particle Systems. (International Science Review Ser.). (Illus.). 360p. 1962. 46.25 (ISBN 0-677-00550-4). Gordon.
Morse, Philip M., et al. Nuclear, Particle & Many Body Physics, 2 vols. 1972. Vol. 1. 78.00 (ISBN 0-12-508201-0); Vol. 2. 70.00 (ISBN 0-12-508202-9). Acad Pr.
Moshinsky, M. Group Theory & the Many-Body Problem. 188p. 1968. 37.25 (ISBN 0-677-01740-5, DMP). Gordon.
--Harmonic Oscillator in Modern Physics: From Atoms to Quarks. (Documents on Modern Physics Ser.). 100p. 1969. 31.25x (ISBN 0-677-02450-9). Gordon.
Pines, David. Many-Body Problem. (Frontiers in Physics Ser.: No. 6). (Illus.). 1973. pap. 30.95 (ISBN 0-8053-7901-0). Benjamin-Cummings.
Ring, P. & Schuck, P. The Nuclear Many-Body Problem. (Texts & Monographs in Physics). (Illus.). 800p. 1980. 33.00 (ISBN 0-387-09820-8). Springer-Verlag.
Schultz, Theodore D. Quantum Field Theory & the Many-Body Problem. (Many-Body Problem: Current Research & Reviews Ser.). 158p. 1964. 33.75 (ISBN 0-677-01130-X). Gordon.
Sigal, I. M. Scattering Theory for Many-Body Quantum Mechanical Systems. (Lecture Notes in Mathematics: Vol. 1011). 132p. 1983. pap. 10.00 (ISBN 0-387-12672-4). Springer-Verlag.
Torrens, Ian M. Interatomic Potentials. 1972. 58.50 (ISBN 0-12-695850-5). Acad Pr.
Vlasov, A. A. Many-Particle Theory & Its Application to Plasma. (Russian Monographs). (Illus.). 418p. 1961. 78.75x (ISBN 0-677-20330-6). Gordon.
Zabolitzky, J. G., et al, eds. Recent Progress in Many-Body Theories: Proceedings. (Lecture Notes in Physics Ser.: Vol. 142). 479p. 1981. pap. 30.00 (ISBN 0-387-10710-X). Springer-Verlag.

PROBLEM OF N-BODIES

see Problem of Many Bodies

PROBLEM OF THREE BODIES

see also Satellites

CISM (International Center for Mechanical Sciences), Dept. for General Mechanics, 1973. The General & Restricted Problems of Three Bodies. Szebehely, V., ed. (CISM International Centre for Mechanical Sciences Ser.: No. 170). (Illus.). 53p. 1974. pap. 6.20 (ISBN 0-387-81264-4). Springer-Verlag.
Schmid, E. W. & Ziegelmann, H. The Quantum Mechanical Three-Body Problem. 222p. 1974. text ed. 47.00 (ISBN 0-08-018240-2). Pergamon.

PROBLEM SOLVING

see also GASP (Computer Program Language)

Anderson, Barry F. The Complete Thinker: A Handbook of Techniques for Creative & Critical Problem Solving. (Illus.). 224p. 1980. (Spec); pap. 4.95 (ISBN 0-13-164582-X). P-H.
Andriole, Stephen J. Handbook of Problem Solving. (Illus.). 327p. 1983. text ed. 25.00 (ISBN 0-89433-186-8). Petrocelli.

Baugh, James R. Solution Training: Overcoming Blocks in Problem Solving. LC 79-20717. 256p. 1980. 9.95 (ISBN 0-88289-246-0). Pelican.

Bear, George G. & Callahan, Carolyn M. On the Nose: Fostering Creativity, Problem Solving & Social Reasoning. (Orig.). 1984. pap. 12.95 (ISBN 0-936386-23-1). Creative Learning.

Binko, C. A., et al. The Ortho Problem Solver. Smith, Michael D., ed. LC 82-82093. (Illus.). 1024p. 1982. 149.95 (ISBN 0-89721-008-5). Ortho.

Birkhoff, Garrett & Scheonstadt, Arthur. Elliptic Problem Solvers, No. II: Symposium. 1984. 44.00 (ISBN 0-12-100560-7). Acad Pr.

Borck, Leslie E. & Fawcett, Stephen B. Learning Counseling & Problem-Solving Skills. LC 82-2916. 160p. (Orig.). 1982. text ed. 26.00 (ISBN 0-917724-30-5, B30); pap. text ed. 13.95 (ISBN 0-917724-35-6, B35). Haworth Pr.

Bowles. Microcomputer Problem Solving Using Pascal. 2nd ed. 500p. 1984. 17.95 (ISBN 0-387-90822-6). Springer-Verlag.

Burger, Henry G. Wordtree: A Transitive Cladistic for Solving Physical & Social Problems. LC 84-13007. 380p. 1984. 149.00 (ISBN 0-936312-00-9). Wordtree.

Cassel, Don. BASIC & Problem Solving Made Easy. 1985. pap. text ed. 18.95 (ISBN 0-8359-0402-4); tchr's. manual avail. (ISBN 0-8359-0403-2). Reston.

Cinnamon, Kenneth M. & Matulef, Norman J., eds. Creative Problem Solving. LC 82-52727. (Applied Skills Training Ser.: Vol. 2). 155p. 1979. looseleaf binder 79.95 (ISBN 0-89889-001-2). Univ Assocs.

Daily, Benjamin W. Ability of High School Pupils to Select Essential Data in Solving Problems. LC 73-176704. (Columbia University. Teachers College. Contributions to Education: No. 190). Repr. of 1925 ed. 22.50 (ISBN 0-404-55190-4). AMS Pr.

Davis, Don D. Induced Task Competence & Effects on Problem Solving Behavior. (Illus.). 52p. (Orig.). 1980. pap. text ed. 3.00 (ISBN 0-907152-00-7). Prytaneum Pr.

Dillman, Richard W. Introduction to Problem Solving with BASIC. 1983. pap. text ed. 20.95 (ISBN 0-03-061981-5). HR&W.

Dubisch, Roy. Basic Mathematics with Hand-Held Calculator. LC 78-57267. 1979. text ed. 29.95 (ISBN 0-8053-2341-4); instr's guide 4.95 (ISBN 0-8053-2344-9). Benjamin-Cummings.

Eden, C. & Jones, S. Messing about in Problems: A Practical Approach. (Frontiers of Operational Research & Applied Systems Analysis Ser.: Vol. 1). (Illus.). 130p. 1983. 22.00 (ISBN 0-08-029961-X); pap. 10.95 (ISBN 0-08-029960-1). Pergamon.

Edgar, William J. The Problem Solver's Guide to Logic. LC 82-20285. 106p. (Orig.). 1983. pap. text ed. 7.50 (ISBN 0-8191-2876-7). U Pr of Amer.

Epstein, R. L. Degrees of Unsolvability: Structure & Theory. (Lecture Notes in Mathematics: Vol. 759). 240p. 1980. pap. 20.00 (ISBN 0-387-09710-4). Springer-Verlag.

Haberman, R. Mathematical Models: Mechanical Vibrations, Population, Dynamics & Traffic Flow, An Introduction to Applied Mathematics. 1977. 39.95 (ISBN 0-13-561738-3). P-H.

Haley, Jay. Problem Solving Therapy: New Strategies for Effective Family Therapy. 275p. 1984. pap. 6.95x (ISBN 0-06-090583-2, TB1991, Torch). Har-Row.

Hill, Claire C. Problem Solving: Learning & Teaching. (Illus.). 143p. 1979. 26.50x (ISBN 0-89397-069-7). Nichols Pub.

Inman, Don & Conlan, Jim. Problem-Solving on the TRS-80 Pocket Computer. LC 81-10358. (Self-Teaching Guide Ser.). 255p. 1982. pap. text ed. 9.95 (ISBN 0-471-09270-3, Pub. by Wiley Pr). Wiley.

Isaksen, Scott G. & Treffinger, Donald J. Creative Problem-Solving: The Basic Course. (Illus.). 215p. 1985. notebook 18.95 (ISBN 0-943456-05-3). Bearly Ltd.

Johnson, Mildred. How to Solve Word Problems in Algebra: A Solved Problem Approach. (Orig.). 1976. pap. 4.95 (ISBN 0-07-032620-7). McGraw.

Jourbain, Robert L. Programmer's Problem Solver for the IBM PC, XT & AT. (Illus.). 320p. 1985. pap. 22.95 (ISBN 0-89303-787-7). Brady Comm.

Kleinmuntz, Benjamin, ed. Problem Solving: Research, Method & Theory. LC 74-14881. (Carnegie-Mellon University Cognition Ser.). 416p. 1975. Repr. of 1966 ed. 24.50 (ISBN 0-88275-219-7). Krieger.

Koffman, Elliot B. Problem Solving & Structured Programming in Pascal. 2nd ed. LC 84-16811. 1985. text ed. 23.95 (ISBN 0-201-11736-3). Addison-Wesley.

Koffman, Elliot B. & Friedman, Frank L. Problem Solving in Structured BASIC-Plus & Vax-II BASIC. LC 83-2566. (Illus.). 448p. 1984. pap. 23.95 (ISBN 0-201-10344-3); instr's. manual 10.00. Addison-Wesley.

Korf, Richard E. Learning to Solve Problems by Searching for Macro-Operators. (Research Notes in Artificial Intelligence Ser.: No. 5). 160p. 1985. pap. text ed. 19.50 (ISBN 0-273-08690-1). Pitman Pub MA.

Lev, B. & Weiss, H. J. Introduction to Mathematical Programming: Quantitative Tools for Decision Making. 290p. 1981. 31.75 (ISBN 0-444-00591-9, North-Holland). Elsevier.

Lewis. Problem-Solving Principles for Ada Programmers: Applied Logic, Psychology, & Grit. 1983. 10.95 (ISBN 0-8104-5211-1, 5211). Hayden.

Lyles, Richard I. Practical Management Problem Solving & Decision Making. 224p. 1982. 21.95 (ISBN 0-442-25889-5). Van Nos Reinhold.

Miller, Lawrence H. Programming & Problem Solving: A Second Course with Pascal. 624p. 1986. text ed. write for info. (ISBN 0-201-05531-7). Addison-Wesley.

Morris, Janet. How to Develop Problem Solving Using a Calculator. LC 81-9569. (Illus.). 40p. 1981. pap. 4.00 (ISBN 0-87353-175-2). NCTM.

National Council of Teachers of Mathematics. Problem Solving in School Mathematics, 1980 Yearbook. LC 79-27145. (Illus.). 241p. 1980. 14.50 (ISBN 0-87353-162-0). NCTM.

Newell, Allen & Simon, Herbert. Human Problem Solving. LC 79-152528. (Illus.). 1972. 37.95 (ISBN 0-13-445403-0). P-H.

Newman, D. J. A Problem Seminar. (Problem Books in Mathematics). 113p. 1982. 17.00 (ISBN 0-387-90765-3). Springer-Verlag.

Nilsson, Nils J. Problem-Solving Methods in Artificial Intelligence. 1971. text ed. 50.95 (ISBN 0-07-046573-8). McGraw.

Noller, Ruth B. & Mauthe, Ernest. Scratching the Surface of Creative Problem Solving. (Illus.). 1977. 2.50 (ISBN 0-914634-39-9). DOK Pubs.

Overholt, James L., et al. Math Problem Solving for Grades 4 Through 8. 428p. 1984. pap. 28.22 (ISBN 0-205-08024-3, EDP 238024). Allyn.

Pearl, Judea. Heuristics: Partially Informed Strategies for Computer Problem Solving. (Artificial Intelligence Ser.). (Illus.). 400p. 1983. 41.95 (ISBN 0-201-05594-5). Addison-Wesley.

Peters, Lawrence J. Software Design: Methods & Techniques. LC 80-50609. 248p. (Orig.). 1981. pap. 27.00 (ISBN 0-917072-19-7). Yourdon.

Polya, George. Mathematical Discovery: On Understanding, Learning, & Teaching Problem Solving. LC 81-1063. 432p. 1981. text ed. 29.50 (ISBN 0-471-08975-3). Wiley.

Polya, Gyorgy. Mathematical Discovery on Understanding, Learning & Teaching Problem Solving, 2 vols. LC 62-8784. 216p. 1962. Vol. 1. 31.45x (ISBN 0-471-69333-2). Wiley.

Problem Solving & Decision Making. 1982. 50.00x (ISBN 0-904951-31-6, Pub. by Bristol Poly). State Mutual Bk.

Raaheim, Kjell. Problem Solving & Intelligence. 1974. pap. 9.00x (ISBN 8-200-08976-2, Dist. by Columbia U Pr). Universitet.

Raphael, Bertram. The Thinking Computer: Mind Inside Matter. LC 75-30839. (Psychology Ser.). (Illus.). 322p. 1976. pap. text ed. 13.95x (ISBN 0-7167-0723-3). W H Freeman.

Rowe, Helga A. Problem Solving & Intelligence. 314p. 1985. text ed. 39.95 (ISBN 0-89859-347-6). L Erlbaum Assocs.

Rubinstein, Mashe F. Patterns of Problem Solving. LC 74-20721. (Illus.). 640p. 1975. text ed. 34.95 ref. ed. (ISBN 0-13-654251-4). P-H.

Rubinstein, Moshe & Pfeiffer, Kenneth. Concepts in Problem Solving. (Illus.). 1980. pap. text ed. 23.95 (ISBN 0-13-166603-7). P-H.

Scandura, Joseph M., et al. Problem Solving: A Structural-Process with Instructional Implications. 1977. 47.50 (ISBN 0-12-620650-3). Acad Pr.

Schoenfeld, Alan H. Mathematical Problem Solving. Monograph ed. Date not set. 58.00 (ISBN 0-12-628870-4); pap. 29.95 (ISBN 0-12-628871-2). Acad Pr.

Serway, Raymond. Concepts in Problem Solving for General Physics, Vol. 1. 1975. pap. text ed. 18.95 (ISBN 0-7216-8065-8, CBS C). SCP.

--Concepts in Problem Solving for General Physics, Vol. 2. 1975. pap. text ed. 18.95 (ISBN 0-7216-8066-6, CBS C). SCP.

Shortt, Joseph & Wilson, Thomas C. Problem Solving & the Computer: A Structured Concept with PL 1 (PLC) 2nd ed. 1979. pap. text ed. 22.95 (ISBN 0-201-06916-4). Addison-Wesley.

Smith, Sanderson M. Mastering Multiple-Choice Mathematics Tests: Algebra, Geometry, Trigonometry. LC 81-20675. (Illus.). 224p. (Orig.). 1982. pap. 6.95 (ISBN 0-668-05409-3). Arco.

Souviney, Randall. Solving Problems Kids Care About. (Illus.). 1981. pap. 11.95 (ISBN 0-673-16534-5). Scott F.

Van Gundy, Arthur B. Techniques of Structured Problem Solving. 320p. 1981. 21.95 (ISBN 0-442-21223-2). Van Nos Reinhold.

Walberg, Franette. Puzzle Thinking: Steps to Logical Thinking & Problem Solving. (Illus.). 1980. 6.95 (ISBN 0-89168-027-6); 6.95 tchr's ed. L Erlbaum Assocs.

Walker, Henry M. Problems for Computer Solution Using BASIC. 189p. (Orig.). 1980. pap. text ed. 16.95 (ISBN 0-316-91834-2). Little.

Whimbey, Arthur & Lochhead, Jack. Problem Solving & Comprehension. 3rd, rev. ed. 350p. 1982. pap. 10.95 (ISBN 0-89168-048-9). L Erlbaum Assocs.

Whimbey, Arthur & Lockhead, Jack. Beyond Problem Solving & Comprehension. (Illus.). 398p. 1984. pap. text ed. 14.95 (ISBN 0-89168-051-9). L Erlbaum Assocs.

Whitten, Kenneth W. & Gailey, Kenneth D. Problem Solving in General Chemistry. 2nd ed. 1984. pap. text ed. 13.95x (ISBN 0-03-063576-4). SCP.

Wickelgren, Wayne E. How to Solve Problems: Elements of a Theory of Problems & Problem Solving. LC 73-15787. (Psychology Ser.). (Illus.). 262p. 1974. pap. text ed. 10.95 (ISBN 0-7167-0845-0). W H Freeman.

PROBLEM SOLVING–DATA PROCESSING

Behforooz, Ali & Holoien, Martin O. Problem Solving & Structured Programming with Pascal. 350p. 1984. pap. write for info. Wadsworth Pub.

Bowles. Microcomputer Problem Solving Using Pascal. 2nd ed. 500p. 1984. 17.95 (ISBN 0-387-90822-6). Springer-Verlag.

Carmony, Lowell A., et al. Problem Solving in Apple Pascal: Teacher's Guide & Solution Manual. 1984. 15.00 (ISBN 0-88175-021-2). Computer Sci.

Dennis, Terry L. Apple Pascal: A Problem-Solving Approach. (Illus.). 400p. 1985. pap. text ed. 16.95 (ISBN 0-314-85228-X). West Pub.

Dunlop, David L. & Sigmund, Thomas F. Problem Solving with a Programmable Calculator: Puzzles, Games, & Simulations with Math & Science Applications. (Illus.). 227p. 1982. 19.95 (ISBN 0-13-721340-9); pap. 10.95 (ISBN 0-13-721332-8). P-H.

Etter, D. M. Problem Solving Software Supplement to "Problem Solving with Structured FORTRAN 77". 1984. pap. 10.00 (ISBN 0-8053-2526-3). Benjamin Cummings.

--Problem Solving with Structured FORTRAN 77. 1984. 24.95 (ISBN 0-8053-2522-0); instr's. manual 5.95 (ISBN 0-8053-2523-9); software supplement package 50.00 (ISBN 0-8053-2524-7). Benjamin-Cummings.

Friedman, Frank & Koffman, Elliot. Problem Solving & Structured Programming in WATFIV. LC 81-20598. (Illus.). 480p. 1982. pap. text ed. 23.95 (ISBN 0-201-10482-2). Addison-Wesley.

Gause, Don C. & Weinberg, Gerald M. Are Your Lights On? How to Figure Out What the Problem Really Is. 157p. (Orig.). 1982. text ed. 16.95 (ISBN 0-316-30522-7); pap. text ed. 7.95 (ISBN 0-316-30521-9). Little.

Grams, Ralph Raymond. Problem Solving, Systems Analysis, & Medicine. (Illus.). 244p. 1972. Set. 31.00x (ISBN 0-398-02298-4); companion volume - Systems Analysis wkbk. incl. (ISBN 0-398-02566-5). C C Thomas.

Gustavson, Frances & Sackson, Marian. Problem Solving & BASIC: A Modular Approach. LC 78-21904. 335p. 1979. pap. text ed. 17.95 (ISBN 0-574-21240-X, 13-4240); instr's guide avail. (ISBN 0-574-21241-8, 13-4241). SRA.

Harrow, Keith. Problem Solving Using PL-1 & PL-C. (Illus.). 464p. 1984. pap. text ed. 21.95 (ISBN 0-13-711796-5). P-H.

Hayes, John R. The Complete Problem Solver. LC 81-3295. 1981. 19.50 (ISBN 0-89168-028-4). L Erlbaum Assocs.

Horabin, Ivan & Lewis, Brian. Algorithms. Langdon, Danny G., ed. LC 78-2307. (Instructional Design Library). (Illus.). 80p. 1978. 19.95 (ISBN 0-87778-106-0). Educ Tech Pubns.

Kieburtz, Richard B. Structured Programming & Problem Solving with Pascal. (Illus.). 1978. pap. 21.95 (ISBN 0-13-854869-2). P-H.

Koffman, Elliot B. & Friedman, Frank L. Problem Solving & Structured Programming in BASIC. LC 78-65355. 1979. pap. text ed. 23.95 (ISBN 0-201-03888-9). Addison-Wesley.

Lewis, William E. Problem-Solving Principles for BASIC Programmers: Applied Logic, Psychology & Grit. (Problem-Solving Principles Ser.). 166p. 1981. pap. 10.95 (ISBN 0-8104-5200-6). Hayden.

--Problem-Solving Principles for FORTRAN Programmers: Applied Logic, Psychology & Grit. (Problem-Solving Principles Ser.). 177p. pap. 10.95 (ISBN 0-8104-5430-0). Hayden.

--Problem-Solving Principles for Pascal Programmers: Applied Logic, Psychology & Grit. 179p. pap. 10.95 (ISBN 0-8104-5767-9). Hayden.

--Problem-Solving Principles for Programmers: Applied Logic, Psychology & Grit. 163p. (Orig.). 1981. pap. 11.95 (ISBN 0-8104-5138-7). Hayden.

Mitchell, William. Prelude to Programming: Problem Solving & Algorithms. 1984. text ed. 22.95 (ISBN 0-8359-5614-8); pap. text ed. 16.95 (ISBN 0-8359-5627-X). Reston.

Molloy, James F. & Curtin, Dennis P. Business Problem Solving: A 1-2-3 Business User's Guide. (Illus.). 176p. 1984. pap. 19.50 (ISBN 0-930764-85-4); software on floppy disk o.p. 29.95. Van Nos Reinhold.

Mullish, Henry & Kestenbaum, Richard. Financial Analysis by Calculator: Problem-Solving Techniques With Applications. (Illus.). 157p. 1982. 17.95 (ISBN 0-13-316018-1); pap. 8.95 (ISBN 0-13-316000-9). P-H.

Nash, John C. Effective Scientific Problem Solving with Small Computers. (Illus.). 272p. 19.95 (ISBN 0-8359-1594-8). Reston.

O'Dell, Jerry W. BASIC Statistics: An Introduction to Problem Solving with Your Personal Computer. LC 84-8804. (Illus.). 462p. (Orig.). 1984. 21.95 (ISBN 0-8306-0759-5); pap. 15.95 (ISBN 0-8306-1759-0, 1759). TAB Bks.

Rudwick, Bernard. Solving Management Problems: A Systems Approach to Planning & Control. LC 78-23266. (Systems Engineering & Analysis Ser.). 496p. 1979. 53.50x (ISBN 0-471-04246-3, Pub. by Wiley-Interscience). Wiley.

Sage, Edwin R. Problem Solving with the Computer. (Illus.). 244p. (Orig.). 1969. pap. 14.95 (ISBN 0-87567-030-X). Entelek.

Shortt, Joseph & Wilson, Thomas C. Problem Solving & the Computer: A Structured Concept with PL 1 (PLC) 2nd ed. 1979. pap. text ed. 22.95 (ISBN 0-201-06916-4). Addison-Wesley.

Spencer, Donald. Problems for Computer Solution. 2nd ed. 128p. 1979. pap. 7.95 (ISBN 0-8104-5191-3). Hayden.

Spikell, Mark A. & Snover, Stephen. Mathematical Problem-Solving with the Microcomputer: Timex-Sinclair 1000 Version. 205p. 1984. 16.95 (ISBN 0-13-561853-3). P-H.

Thomas, Rick. Discover BASIC: A Student's Guide to Problem Solving in BASIC. 1983. 5.95. Sterling Swift.

Weber Systems, Inc. Staff. TK! Solver User's Handbook. LC 84-50836. (WSI's User's Handbooks to Personal Computers Ser.). 300p. 1984. pap. 14.95 (ISBN 0-938862-32-4). Weber Systems.

Younis, Toby. MacBusiness-Solving Problems with Your Macintosh. LC 84-16424. (Illus.). 256p. (Orig.). 1984. 19.95 (ISBN 0-8306-0841-9); pap. 14.95 (ISBN 0-8306-1841-4, 1841). TAB Bks.

PROBLEMS, FAMOUS (IN GEOMETRY)

see Geometry–Problems, Famous

PROCESS CONTROL

see also Chemical Process Control

Abrams, Halle, et al, eds. Optimization of Processing, Properties, & Service Performance Through Microstructural Control - STP 792. LC 82-71748. 341p. 1983. text ed. 37.95 (ISBN 0-8031-0240-2, 04-792000-28). ASTM.

American Society of Mechanical Engineers. Control of Manufacturing Processes & Robotic Systems. 292p. 1983. 50.00 (ISBN 0-317-06828-8, H00279). ASME.

Andrew, William G. & Williams, H. B. Applied Instrumentation in the Process Industries, Vol. 1: A Survey. 2nd ed. LC 79-9418. 407p. 1979. 45.95x (ISBN 0-87201-382-0). Gulf Pub.

Arthur. New Concepts & Practices in Activated Sludge Process Control. LC 81-69767. (Activated Sludge Process Control Ser.). 125p. 1982. 34.95 (ISBN 0-250-40528-8). Butterworth.

Blaschke, W. S. & McGill, J. The Control of Industrial Processes by Digital Techniques: The Organization, Design & Construction of Digital Control Systems. 186p. 1976. 53.25 (ISBN 0-444-41493-2). Elsevier.

Buckley, Page S. Techniques of Process Control. LC 78-10782. 316p. 1979. Repr. of 1964 ed. lib. bdg. 27.50 (ISBN 0-88275-777-6). Krieger.

Control Valve Capacity Test Procedure: ISA Standard S75.02. LC 81-174761. 20p. 1981. pap. text ed. 16.00x (ISBN 0-87664-510-4). Instru Soc.

Control Valve Sizing Equations: An ANSI Approved Standard ISA-S75.01. 12p. 1977. pap. text ed. 10.00 (ISBN 0-87664-400-0). Instru Soc.

Deming, W. E. Quality, Productivity, & Competitive Position. LC 82-61320. (Illus.). 373p. (Orig.). 1982. pap. text ed. 45.00 (ISBN 0-911379-00-2). Ctr Adv Eng Stud.

De Vries, W. R. & Dornfield, D. A., eds. Inspection & Quality Control in Manufacturing Systems. (PED Ser.: Vol. 6). 1982. 24.00 (H00249). ASME.

Driskell, Leslie R. Control Valve Selection & Sizing: An Independent Learning Module of the Instrument Society of America. LC 82-48157. 520p. 1983. text ed. 59.95x (ISBN 0-87664-628-3). Instru Soc.

Eacho, E. M., et al. Process Measurement Fundamentals, 3 vols. (Illus.). 1981. Set. 154.00x (ISBN 0-87683-000-9); Vol. 1; 177p. looseleaf 60.00x (ISBN 0-87683-001-7); Vol. 2; 29p. looseleaf 47.00x (ISBN 0-87683-002-5); Vol. 3; 175p. looseleaf lab manuals 47.00x (ISBN 0-317-11887-0); looseleaf lesson plans 1250.00x (ISBN 0-87683-004-1). G P Courseware.

Garside, Robin. Intrinsically Safe Instrumentation: A Guide. rev. & enl. ed. LC 83-12982. 224p. 1983. pap. text ed. 29.95x (ISBN 0-87664-728-X). Instru Soc.

Ghose, T. K., et al, eds. Mass Transfer & Process Control. LC 72-152360. (Advances in Biochemical Engineering Ser.: Vol. 13). (Illus.). 1979. 57.00 (ISBN 0-387-09468-7). Springer-Verlag.

Guess, Vincent C. Manufacturing Control System User's Guide. (Illus.). 32p. (Orig.). 1982. pap. 10.00 (ISBN 0-940964-03-1). PSE.

Hardt, D. E., ed. Measurement & Control for Batch Manufacturing. 195p. 1982. 40.00 (H00244). ASME.

Harriott, Peter. Process Control. LC 81-18558. 392p. 1983. Repr. of 1964 ed. text ed. 29.50 (ISBN 0-89874-399-0). Krieger.

Himmelblau, David M. Process Analysis by Statistical Methods. (Illus.). 463p. 1970. pap. text ed. 29.95 (ISBN 0-88408-140-0). Sterling Swift.

Holland, R. C. Microcomputers for Process Control. (Pergamon Materials Engineering Practice Ser.). (Illus.). 204p. 1983. 25.00 (ISBN 0-08-029957-1); pap. 12.00 (ISBN 0-08-029956-3). Pergamon.

Howarth, R. J. & Powers, D. W., Jr. Process Instrumentation & Control Fundamentals. (Illus.). 380p. 1976. looseleaf 95.00x (ISBN 0-87683-323-7); Lesson Plans 395.00x (ISBN 0-87683-324-5). G P Courseware.

IFAC-IFIP Symposium, 3rd, MANUFACONT '80, Budapest, Hungary, Oct. 1980. Control Problems & Devices in Manufacturing Technology: Proceedings. Ellis, T. M., ed. (IFAC Proceedings Ser.). 375p. 1981. 77.00 (ISBN 0-08-026720-3). Pergamon.

IFAC International Symposium, 4th, Fredericton, NB, Canada, July 1977. Multivariable Technological Systems: Proceedings. Atherton, D. P., ed. 666p. 1978. text ed. 140.00 (ISBN 0-08-022010-X). Pergamon.

Ingraham, Thomas R., ed. Continuous Processing & Process Control: Proceedings of a Symposium, Philadelphia, Pennsylvania, December 5-8, 1966. LC 68-21964. (Metallurgical Society Conferences: Vol. 49). pap. 140.30 (ISBN 0-317-10626-0, 2001536). Bks Demand UMI.

Instrument Society of America. Dynamic Response Testing of Process Control Instrumentation Standard. (ISA Standard Ser.: No. S26). 1975. pap. text ed. 16.00x (ISBN 0-87664-349-7). Instru Soc.

International Conference on Flexible Manufacturing Systems, Brighton, UK, Oct. 1982. Flexible Manufacturing Systems 1: Proceedings. iv, 520p. 1983. 85.00 (ISBN 0-444-86591-8, I-152-83, North Holland). Elsevier.

International Federation of Automatic Control & Akashi, H. Process Control: Proceedings. (Control Science & Technology Ser.: Vol. 5). 443p. 110.00 (ISBN 0-08-028717-4). Pergamon.

Intrinsically Safe Apparatus & Associated Apparatus for Use in Class I, II, III, Division I Hazardous Locations. (Forty Ser.). 1978. pap. 9.50 (ISBN 0-685-58098-9, 493). Natl Fire Prot.

Jerald, J. P. & Powers, D. W. Process Control Fundamentals, 3 vols. (Illus.). 1981. Set. 154.00x (ISBN 0-87683-005-X); Vol. 1; 157p. looseleaf 60.00x (ISBN 0-87683-006-8); Vol. 2; 306p. looseleaf 47.00x (ISBN 0-87683-007-6); Vol. 3, 313p. 47.00x (ISBN 0-87683-008-4); lesson plans 1250.00x (ISBN 0-87683-009-2). G P Courseware.

Job Titles & Skills Used in the Instrumentation & Process Control Industries. LC 81-86194. 40p. 1981. pap. text ed. 10.00 (ISBN 0-87664-661-5). Instru Soc.

Johnson, Curtis D. Process Control Instrumentation Technology. 2nd ed. LC 81-10488. (Electronic Technology Ser.). 497p. 1982. 31.95 (ISBN 0-471-05789-4); solutions manual avail. (ISBN 0-471-86317-3). Wiley.

Lees, Frank P. Loss Prevention in the Process Industry, 2 vols. new ed. 1980. 299.95 set (ISBN 0-408-10604-2); Vol. 1. 159.95 (ISBN 0-408-10697-2); Vol. 2. 159.95 (ISBN 0-408-10698-0). Butterworth.

Manka, Dan. Automated Stream Analysis for Process Control, Vol. 2. LC 82-8822. 1984. 59.00 (ISBN 0-12-469002-5). Acad Pr.

Manka, Dan, ed. Automated Stream Analysis for Process Control, Vol. 1. LC 82-8822. 336p. 1982. 44.00 (ISBN 0-12-469001-7). Acad Pr.

Moore, Ralph L. The Dynamic Analysis of Automatic Process Control. 276p. 1985. pap. 10.00 instr. guide (ISBN 0-87664-817-0); pap. 34.95 student guide (ISBN 0-87664-818-9). Instru Soc.

Murrill, Paul W. Fundamentals of Process Control Theory. LC 80-84764. (An Independent Learning Module of the Instrument Society of America). 256p. 1981. text ed. 39.95x (ISBN 0-87664-507-4). Instru Soc.

Norden, K. Elis. Electronic Weighing in Industrial Processes. (Illus.). 290p. 1984. text ed. 55.00x (ISBN 0-246-12168-8, Pub. by Granada England). Sheridan.

Patrick, Dale R. & Fardo, Stephen W. Industrial Process Control Systems. (Illus.). 208p. 1985. text ed. 29.95 (ISBN 0-13-462987-6). P-H.

Process Control Equipment. 1983. 495.00 (ISBN 0-318-01946-9). Busn Trend.

Process Controls. (Welding Inspection Ser.: Module 28-6). (Illus.). 44p. 1979. spiral bdg. 7.00x (ISBN 0-87683-110-2). G P Courseware.

PROMECON, Vol. 1: Proceedings of the International Process Measurement & Control Conference, London. LC 81-81490. 200p. 1981. pap. text ed. 36.00x (ISBN 0-87664-530-9). Instru Soc.

Rao, Natti S. Designing Machines & Dies for Polymer Processing with Computer Programs: Fortran & Basic. (Illus.). 208p. 1981. 32.00 (ISBN 0-686-48155-0, 1907). T-C Pubns CA.

Ray, W. Harmon. Advanced Process Control. (Chemical Engineering Ser.). (Illus.). 1980. text ed. 44.00 (ISBN 0-07-051250-7). McGraw.

Rose, L. M. Application of Mathematical Modelling to Process Development & Design. (Illus.). 364p. 1974. 52.00 (ISBN 0-85334-584-8, Pub. by Elsevier Applied Sci England). Elsevier.

Rudd, Dale F. & Watson, Charles C. Strategy of Process Engineering. LC 67-31212. 466p. 1968. 57.00 (ISBN 0-471-74455-7). Wiley.

Shinskey, F. G. PH & pIon: Control in Process & Waste Streams. LC 73-7853. (Environmental Science & Technology Ser.). 259p. 1973. 47.95 (ISBN 0-471-78640-3, Pub. by Wiley-Interscience). Wiley.

--Process Control Systems. 2nd ed. 1979. 42.95 (ISBN 0-07-056891-X). McGraw.

Specification Forms for Process Measurement & Control Instruments, Primary Elements & Control Valves: ISA Standard S20. 72p. 1981. pap. text ed. 24.00x (ISBN 0-87664-347-0). Instru Soc.

Statistical Process Control, 11 papers. 88p. 1983. pap. 30.00 (ISBN 0-89883-318-3, SP547). Soc Auto Engineers.

Technical Association of the Pulp & Paper Industry. Process Technology: A Compilation of Recent Engineering Conference Papers on Process Control & Simulation. pap. 48.00 (ISBN 0-317-28031-7, 2025565). Bks Demand UMI.

Tuning & Control Loop Performance. LC 82-48558. (ISA Monograph: No. 4). 244p. 1983. text ed. 34.95x (ISBN 0-87664-694-1). Instru Soc.

Tyner, Mack & May, Frank P. Process Engineering Control. LC 67-21681. (Illus.). Repr. of 1968 ed. 90.90 (ISBN 0-8357-9962-X, 2012441). Bks Demand UMI.

Waller, Michael H. Measurement & Control of Paper Stock Consistency. LC 82-48598. (ISA Monograph: No. 5). 132p. 1983. pap. text ed. 24.95x (ISBN 0-87664-634-8). Instru Soc.

Weber, Thomas W. An Introduction to Process Dynamics & Control. LC 73-2678. 434p. 1973. 51.95x (ISBN 0-471-92330-3, Pub. by Wiley-Interscience). Wiley.

Yang Wen-Jei & Masabuchi, M. Dynamics for Process & System Control. 456p. 1970. 87.95x (ISBN 0-677-01830-4). Gordon.

Zoss, Leslie M. Applied Instrumentation in the Process Industries, Vol. 4: Control Systems: Theory, Troubleshooting & Design. LC 72-94067. 174p. 1979. 45.95x (ISBN 0-87201-391-X). Gulf Pub.

PROCESS CONTROL–DATA PROCESSING

Arthur. Application of On-Line Analytical Instrumentation to Process Control. LC 82-70694. (Activated Sludge Process Control Ser.). 222p. 1982. 39.95 (ISBN 0-250-40539-3). Butterworth.

Auslander, David & Sagues, Paul. Microprocessors for Measurement & Control. 310p. (Orig.). 1981. pap. 15.99 (ISBN 0-07-931057-5, 57-5). Osborne-McGraw.

Bibbero, Robert J. Microprocessors in Industrial Control: An Independent Learning Module of the Instrument Society of America. LC 82-48556. 256p. 1983. text ed. 39.95x (ISBN 0-87664-624-0, I624-0). Instru Soc.

Buckley, Page S. Techniques of Process Control. LC 78-10782. 316p. 1979. Repr. of 1964 ed. lib. bdg. 27.50 (ISBN 0-88275-777-6). Krieger.

Deshpande, Pradeep B. & Ash, Raymond H. Elements of Computer Process Control with Advanced Control Applications. LC 80-82117. 424p. 1981. text ed. 47.95x (ISBN 0-87664-449-3). Instru Soc.

Deshpande, Pradeep B. & Ash, Raymond H., eds. Elements of Computer Process Control with Advanced Control Applications. (Illus.). 400p. 1983. 47.95 (ISBN 0-13-264093-7). P-H.

Ginn, Peter L. Introduction to Process Control & Digital Minicomputers. LC 82-6036. 292p. 1982. 29.95x (ISBN 0-87201-180-1). Gulf Pub.

Harriott, Peter. Process Control. LC 81-18558. 392p. 1983. Repr. of 1964 ed. text ed. 29.50 (ISBN 0-89874-399-0). Krieger.

Hunter, Ronald P. Automated Process Control Systems: Concepts & Hardware. (Illus.). 1978. ref. ed. 27.95 (ISBN 0-13-054502-3). P-H.

IFAC-IFIP Conference, 6th, Dusseldorf, BRD, Oct. 1980. Digital Computer Applications to Process Control: Proceedings. Isermann, R. & Kaltenecker, H., eds. LC 80-41343. (IFAC Proceedings). 550p. 1981. 110.00 (ISBN 0-08-026749-1). Pergamon.

Johnson, Curtis D. Microprocessor-Based Process Control. rev. ed. (Illus.). 448p. 1984. text ed. 31.95 (ISBN 0-13-580654-2). P-H.

Kingham, E. G., et al, eds. Real Time Data Handling & Process Control, II. 386p. 1984. 57.75 (ISBN 0-444-86846-1, North-Holland). Elsevier.

Kochhar, A. K. Development of Computer-Based Production Systems. LC 79-902. 274p. 1979. 58.95x (ISBN 0-470-26693-7). Halsted Pr.

Koren, Yoram. Computer Control of Manufacturing Systems. (Illus.). 352p. 1983. text ed. 42.00 (ISBN 0-07-035341-7). McGraw.

Lenk, John D. Handbook of Microcomputer Based Instrumentation & Controls. (Illus.). 384p. 1984. 27.95 (ISBN 0-13-380519-0). P-H.

Man & Computer in Process Control. 306p. 1981. 50.00x (ISBN 0-686-75388-7, Pub. by Inst Chem Eng England). State Mutual Bk.

Mellichamp, Duncan A., ed. Real Time Computing: With Applications to Data Acquisition & Control. 469p. 1983. 44.50 (ISBN 0-442-21372-7). Van Nos Reinhold.

Potvin, Jean G. Applied Process Control Instrumentation. 1985. text ed. 29.95 (ISBN 0-8359-9238-1). Reston.

Rembold, Ulrich, et al, eds. Computers in Manufacturing. (Manufacturing Engineering & Material Processing Ser.: Vol. 1). (Illus.). 592p. 1977. pap. 95.00 (ISBN 0-8247-1821-6). Dekker.

Schleip, W. & Schleip, R. Planning & Control in Management: The German RPS System. 80p. 1971. 14.00 (ISBN 0-901223-12-3, NS003). Inst Elect Eng.

Statistical Process Control, 11 papers. 88p. 1983. pap. 30.00 (ISBN 0-89883-318-3, SP547). Soc Auto Engineers.

Umbers, I. G. CRT-TV Displays in the Control of Process Plant: A Review of Applications & Human Factors Design Criteria, 1976. 1981. 30.00x (ISBN 0-686-97052-7, Pub. by W Spring England). State Mutual Bk.

Wells, G. L. & Robson, P. M. Computation for Process Engineers. 1974. 37.50x (ISBN 0-249-44126-8). Intl Ideas.

Yang Wen-Jei & Masabuchi, M. Dynamics for Process & System Control. 456p. 1970. 87.95x (ISBN 0-677-01830-4). Gordon.

PROCESS ENGINEERING
see Production Engineering

PROCESS ENGINEERING (MANUFACTURES)
see Manufacturing Processes

PROCESS PLANNING
see Production Planning

PROCESSES, INFINITE
see also Fractions, Continued; Inequalities (Mathematics); Series

Gardiner, A. Infinite Processes: Background to Analysis. (Illus.). 304p. 1982. 33.00 (ISBN 0-387-90605-3). Springer-Verlag.

Knopp, Konrad. Infinite Sequences & Series. Bagemihl, Frederick, tr. 1956. pap. text ed. 4.25 (ISBN 0-486-60153-6). Dover.

Peter, Rozsa. Playing with Infinity: Mathematical Explorations & Excursions. Dienes, Z. P., tr. (Illus.). 10.25 (ISBN 0-8446-5235-0). Peter Smith.

PROCESSES, IRREVERSIBLE
see Irreversible Processes

PROCESSING, LIST (ELECTRONIC COMPUTERS)
see List Processing (Electronic Computers)

PROCESSING (LIBRARIES)

Bloomberg, Marty & Evans, G. Edward. Introduction to Technical Services for Library Technicians. (Library Science Text). 417p. 1985. text ed. 30.00 (ISBN 0-87287-486-9); pap. text ed. 20.00 (ISBN 0-87287-497-4). Libs Unl.

Cortez, Edwin M. Contracts, RFP's & Other Procurement Documents for Library Automation. LC 82-48493. 1984. write for info. (ISBN 0-669-06158-1). Lexington Bks.

PROCESSING, INDUSTRIAL
see Manufacturing Processes

PROCESSING, PHOTOGRAPHIC
see Photography–Processing

PROCESSING, SIGNAL
see Signal Processing

PROCESSING, TEXT (COMPUTER SCIENCE)
see Text Processing (Computer Science)

PRO-DOS (COMPUTER OPERATING SYSTEM)

Burdick, John & Weiser, Peter B. ProDOS Quick & Simple: For the Apple II Family. 288p. 1985. pap. 19.95 (ISBN 0-673-18077-8). Scott F.

Keeler, Graham. Apple Prodos Disk-File Handling. 300p. 1985. pap. 14.95 (ISBN 0-13-038829-7). P-H.

Little, Gary B. Apple ProDOS: Advanced Features for Programmers. (Illus.). 352p. 1985. pap. 17.95 (ISBN 0-89303-441-X). Brady Comm.

PRODUCER GAS
see Gas and Oil Engines; Gas Manufacture and Works

PRODUCT DIVERSIFICATION
see Diversification in Industry

PRODUCTION ENGINEERING
see also Assembly-Line Methods; Manufactures; Manufacturing Processes; Materials Handling; Production Planning

Alting. Manufacturing Engineering Processes. (Manufacturing Engineering & Materials Processing Ser.: Vol. 7). 384p. 1982. 49.50 (ISBN 0-8247-1528-4). Dekker.

American Society of Tool & Manufacturing Engineers, Non-Traditional Machining Processes Subdivision. Non-Traditional Machining Processes. Springborn, R. K., ed. LC 67-17078. (American Society of Tool & Manufacturing Engineers Data Ser.). pap. 47.50 (ISBN 0-317-11170-1, 2051198). Bks Demand UMI.

American Society of Tool & Manufacturing Engineers. Pneumatic Controls for Industrial Application: A Practical & Comprehensive Presentation of Pneumatic Control System Fundamentals, Control Devices, Associated Facilities, & Application Circuitry for Manual, Semiautomatic, & Automatic Industrial Operations. Wilson, Frank W., ed. LC 65-13379. (Manufacturing Data Ser.). pap. 43.50 (ISBN 0-317-27763-4, 2024178). Bks Demand UMI.

Andrew, William G. & Williams, H. B. Applied Instrumentation in the Process Industries, Vol. 3: Engineering Data & Resource Material. 2nd ed. LC 79-9418. 520p. 1982. 45.95x (ISBN 0-87201-384-7). Gulf Pub.

Austin, James E. Agroindustrial Project Analysis. LC 80-550. (World Bank Ser.). (Illus.). 224p. 1981. text ed. 20.00x (ISBN 0-8018-2412-5); pap. text ed. 7.50x (ISBN 0-8018-2413-3). Johns Hopkins.

Azadivar, Farhad. Design & Engineering of Production Systems. 630p. 1984. text ed. 28.95x (ISBN 0-910554-43-9). Engineering.

Azbel, David. Heat Transfer Applications in Process Engineering. LC 84-14781. (Illus.). 584p. 1985. 39.00 (ISBN 0-8155-0996-0). Noyes.

Bailey, Anne M., ed. The Asiatic Mode of Production: Science & Politics. (Illus.). 1981. pap. 15.95x (ISBN 0-7100-0738-8). Routledge & Kegan.

Barnes, Louis B. Organizational Systems & Engineering Groups: A Comparative Study of Two Technical Groups in Industry. LC 60-13102. pap. 52.50 (ISBN 0-317-10897-2, 2002208). Bks Demand UMI.

Bilotta. Electrical Connection in Electronic Assemblies. (Manufacturing Engineering Ser.). 328p. 1985. price not set (ISBN 0-8247-7319-5). Dekker.

Blackburn, Phil, et al. Technology, Economic Growth & the Labour Process. LC 84-22849. 272p. 1985. 29.95 (ISBN 0-312-79001-5). St Martin.

Bloch, H. P. & Geitner, F. K. Machinery Failure Analysis & Troubleshooting. LC 83-10731. (Practical Machinery Management for Process Plants Ser.: Vol. 2). 656p. 1983. 69.95x (ISBN 0-87201-872-5). Gulf Pub.

Brannan, Carl. Process Systems Development. LC 76-1680. (The Process Engineer's Pocket Handbook Ser.: Vol. 2). 102p. (Orig.). 1983. pap. 9.95x (ISBN 0-87201-713-3). Gulf Pub.

Silver, E. & Peterson, R. Decision Systems for Inventory Management & Production Planning. 2nd ed. (Management Ser.). 722p. 1985. 31.95 (ISBN 0-471-86782-9). Wiley.
Skinner, Wickham & Chakraborty, Kishore. The Impact of New Technology: People & Organizations in Manufacturing & Allied Industries. (Work in America Institute Studies in Productivity: Vol. 18). (Orig.). 1982. pap. 35.00 (ISBN 0-08-029499-5). Pergamon.
Society of Manufacturing Engineers. Fabtech 1985: Proceedings. 1985. write for info. (ISBN 0-87263-200-8). SME.
--Manufacturing Engineering Transaction, Vol. 4. LC 76-646280. pap. 111.30 (ISBN 0-317-27733-2, 2024174). Bks Demand UMI.
Sorge, Arndt & Hartmann, Gert. Microelectronics & Manpower in Manufacturing. 178p. 1983. text ed. 39.90x (ISBN 0-566-00603-0). Gower Pub Co.
Tien Chien Chang & Wysk, Richard A. An Introduction to Automated Process Planning Systems. (Illus.). 352p. 1985. text ed. 35.95 (ISBN 0-13-478140-6). P-H.
Wendle, Bruce C., ed. Engineering Guide to Plastics Plant Layout & Machine Selection. LC 78-54239. 1978. pap. 9.95 (ISBN 0-87762-250-7). Technomic.
Wight, Oliver W. The Executive's Guide to Successful MRP II. 121p. 1982. 20.00 (ISBN 0-939246-00-7). O W Ltd.
--Manufacturing Resource Planning: MRP II Unlocking America's Productivity Potential. 518p. 1981. 35.00 (ISBN 0-939246-03-1). O W Ltd.

PRODUCTION STANDARDS
see also Time and Motion Study; Work Measurement
Blake, R. & Mouton, J. Productivity: The Human Side. 1982. pap. 5.95 (ISBN 0-317-31399-1). AMACOM.
Chorafas, Dimitris N. Office Automation: The Productivity Challenge. (Illus.). 304p. 1982. text ed. 36.95 (ISBN 0-13-631028-1). P-H.
Society of Manufacturing Engineers. Inspection, Gaging & Testing. (Productivity Equipment Ser.). 1984. 47.00 (ISBN 0-87263-170-2). SME.
White, T. Kenneth. The Technical Connection: The How To's of Time Management for the Technical Manager. LC 81-11476. 203p. 1981. 29.95 (ISBN 0-471-94034-8, Pub. by Ronald Pr). Wiley.

PRODUCTS, ANIMAL
see Animal Products

PRODUCTS, BIOLOGICAL
see Biological Products

PRODUCTS, COAL-TAR
see Coal-Tar Products

PRODUCTS, DAIRY
see Dairy Products

PRODUCTS, FARINACEOUS
see Starch

PRODUCTS, MANUFACTURED
see Manufactures

PRODUCTS, NEW
see New Products

PRODUCTS, WASTE
see Waste Products

PROGESTERONE
Bardin, C. Wayne, et al, eds. Progesterone & Progestins. (Illus.). 480p. 1983. text ed. 90.00 (ISBN 0-89004-769-3). Raven.
Campio, L., et al, eds. Role of Medroxyprogesterone in Endocrine-Related Tumors, Vol. 2. 230p. 1983. text ed. 32.00 (ISBN 0-89004-865-7). Raven.
Dalton. Premenstrual Syndrome & Progesterone Therapy. 2nd ed. 1984. 27.50 (ISBN 0-8151-2266-7). Year Bk Med.
Ganten, D. & Pfaff, D., eds. Action of Progesterone on the Brain. (Current Topics in Neuroendocrinology Ser.: Vol. 5). (Illus.). 235p. 1985. 39.00 (ISBN 0-387-13433-6). Springer-Verlag.
Gurpide, Erlio, ed. Biochemical Actions of Progesterone & Progestins, Vol. 286. (Annals of the New York Academy of Sciences.). 449p. 1977. 43.00x (ISBN 0-89072-032-0). NY Acad Sci.

PROGRAMMABLE CALCULATORS
Abramson, J. H. & Peritz, E. Calculator Programs for the Health Sciences. (Illus.). 1983. text ed. 42.50x (ISBN 0-19-503187-3); pap. text ed. 24.95x (ISBN 0-19-503188-1). Oxford U Pr.
Allen, J. L. & Medley, M. W., Jr. Microwave Circuit Design Using Programmable Calculators. (Illus.). 279p. 1980. 54.00 (ISBN 0-89006-089-4). Artech Hse.
Aronofsky, Julius S., et al. Programmable Calculators Business Applications. 203p. 1978. pap. 11.95 (ISBN 0-317-06593-9). Tex Instr Inc.
Ballantyne, E. J., Jr., et al, eds. Manual of Geophysical Hand-Calculator Programs TI & HP Volumes. 1981. TI Vol. looseleaf 50.00 (ISBN 0-931830-20-6); HP Vol. 50.00 (ISBN 0-931830-17-6); Set, TI & HP. 90.00 (ISBN 0-317-12576-1). Soc Exploration.
Barnes, John E. & Waring, Alan J. Pocket Programmable Calculators in Biochemistry. LC 79-2547. 363p. 1980. 47.50x (ISBN 0-471-06434-3, Pub. by Wiley-Interscience); pap. 29.95 (ISBN 0-471-04713-9). Wiley.
Bitter, Gary G. & Mikesell, Jeraldi L. Activities Handbook for Teaching with the Hand Held Calculator. 1979. text ed. 28.57 scp (ISBN 0-205-06713-1, 236713). Allyn.
Burns, C. S. & Parks, T. W. DFT-FFT & Convolution Alogrithms. (Illus.). 232p. 1985. pap. 22.50 (ISBN 0-317-27322-1, LCB8481). Tex Instr Inc.
Chemical Engineering Magazine. Calculator Programs for Chemical Engineers, Vol. 1. (Chemical Engineering Ser.). 304p. 1981. 34.95 (ISBN 0-07-010793-9). McGraw.
--Calculator Programs for Chemical Engineers, Vol 2. 300p. 1984. 37.50 (ISBN 0-07-010849-8). McGraw.
Christman, J. R. Physics Problems for Programmable Calculators. Incl. Wave Mechanics, Optics & Modern Physics. 609p. 1982 (ISBN 0-471-86062-X); Mechanics & Electromagnetism. 299p. 1981 (ISBN 0-471-08212-0). pap. 15.95 (ISBN 0-317-31547-1). Wiley.
Clarke, Frank H. Calculator Programming for Chemistry & the Life Sciences. LC 81-15046. 1981. 33.00 (ISBN 0-12-175320-4). Acad Pr.
Dearing, John, ed. Calculator Tips & Routines: Especially for the HP-41C 41CV. LC 81-90355. 136p. 1981. 15.00 (ISBN 0-942358-00-7). Corvallis Software.
Dunlop, David L. & Sigmund, Thomas F. Problem Solving with a Programmable Calculator: Puzzles, Games, & Simulations with Math & Science Applications. (Illus.). 227p. 1982. 19.95 (ISBN 0-13-721340-9); pap. 10.95 (ISBN 0-13-721332-8). P-H.
Engelsohn, Harold S. Programming Programmable Calculators. (Computer Programming Ser.). 1978. pap. 12.95 (ISBN 0-8104-5105-0). Hayden.
Greynolds, Elbert B. Financial Analysis Using Calculators. (Calculating & Computing Bks.). 472p. 1980. pap. 20.95 (ISBN 0-317-27321-3, LCB4531). Tex Instr Inc.
Harvard Computation Laboratory. A Manual of Operation for the Automatic Sequence Controlled Calculator, 1945. (Charles Babbage Institute Reprint Ser.). 585p. 1985. Repr. of 1946 ed. text ed. 50.00x (ISBN 0-262-01084-4). MIT Pr.
--Proceedings of a Symposium on Large Scale Digital Calculating Machinery 1948. (Charles Babbage Institute Reprint Ser.: No. 8). 340p. 1985. Repr. of 1948 ed. text ed. 35.00x (ISBN 0-262-08152-0). MIT Pr.
Henrici, Peter. The Essentials of Numerical Analysis with Pocket Calculator Demonstrations. LC 81-10468. 409p. 1982. text ed. 38.50 (ISBN 0-471-05904-8); avail. solns. manual (ISBN 0-471-09704-7). Wiley.
Hohenstein, C L. Using Programmable Calculators for Business. LC 81-3065. 296p. 1982. pap. 10.95 (ISBN 0-471-08551-0, Pub. by Wiley Pr). Wiley.
Jagannath, S. Calculator Programs for the Hydrocarbon Processing Industries, 2 vols. LC 80-18679. Vol. 1, 230 p. 1980. 29.95x (ISBN 0-87201-091-0); Vol. 2, 420 p. 1982. 39.95x (ISBN 0-87201-092-9). Gulf Pub.
Kolb, William M. Curve Fitting for Programmable Calculators. 3rd ed. LC 83-51845. (Illus.). 158p. 1984. 12.95 (ISBN 0-943494-02-8). Syntec Inc.
Meck, H. R. Scientific Analysis for Programmable Calculators. (Illus.). 160p. 1981. 15.95 (ISBN 0-13-796417-X, Spec); pap. 7.95 (ISBN 0-13-796409-9). P-H.
Mohler, Lee & Hoffman, Dean G. Mathematical Recreations for the Programmable Calculator. 336p. 1983. pap. 17.50 (ISBN 0-317-00359-3). Hayden.
Moschytz, G. S. & Horn, Paul. Active Filter Design Handbook: For Use with Programmable Pocket Calculators & Minicomputers. LC 80-40845. 316p. 1981. 53.95x (ISBN 0-471-27850-5, Pub. by Wiley-Interscience). Wiley.
Mullish, Henry & Kochan, Stephen. Programmable Pocket Calculators. 264p. 1980. pap. 10.95 (ISBN 0-8104-5175-1). Hayden.
Murdock, Bruce K. Handbook of Electronic Design & Analysis Procedures Using Programmable Calculators. (Electrical-Computer Science & Engineering Ser.). 1979. 36.50 (ISBN 0-442-26137-3). Van Nos Reinhold.
Patterson, G. A. Engine Thermodynamics with a Pocket Calculator. 2nd ed. 149p. 1983. 14.95 (ISBN 0-917410-07-6). Basic Sci Pr.
Seckler, Bernard. The Programmable Hand Calculator: A Teacher's Tool for Mathematics Classroom Lectures. 207p. (Orig.). 1982. handbk. 15.00 (ISBN 0-686-36869-X). Sigma Pr NY.
Slocum, Jonah. Celestial Navigation with a Pocket Calculator. 2nd ed. (Illus.). 148p. 1982. pap. text ed. 14.95 (ISBN 0-917410-06-8). Basic Sci Pr.
Smith, Jon M. Financial Analysis & Business Decisions on the Pocket Calculator. LC 75-39752. (Systems & Controls for Financial Management Ser.: No. 1-357). 317p. 1976. 41.95x (ISBN 0-471-80184-4, Pub. by Wiley-Interscience). Wiley.
Snover, Stephen & Spikell, Mark. How to Program Your Programmable Calculator. 1983. 8.95 (ISBN 0-13-429357-6, Spec). P-H.
--Programming the TI-55 Slide Rule Calculator. 117p. 1982. 15.95 (ISBN 0-13-729921-4); pap. 7.95 (ISBN 0-13-729913-3). P-H.
Texas Instruments. Sourcebook for Programmable Calculators. 1979. 32.50 (ISBN 0-07-063746-6). McGraw.
Texas Instruments Learning Center Staff & Rensselaer Polytechnic Institute Staff. Sourcebook for Programmable Calculators. LC 78-57030. (Illus.). 416p. 1978. 32.50 (ISBN 0-317-06594-7). Tex Instr Inc.
Weir, Maurice D. Calculator Clout: Programming Methods for Your Programmable. (Illus.). 256p. 1981. text ed. 17.95 (ISBN 0-13-110411-X, Spec); pap. text ed. 8.95 (ISBN 0-13-110403-9, Spec). P-H.
--Calculus by Calculator: Solving Single-Variable Calculus Problems with the Programmable Calculator. (Illus.). 387p. 1982. 22.95 (ISBN 0-13-111930-3); pap. 15.95 (ISBN 0-13-111922-2). P-H.
Yue, David. Perspective Drawings by Programmable Calculator: A Method with Graphic Arts. (Illus.). 220p. 1984. 28.45 (ISBN 0-442-29035-7). Van Nos Reinhold.

PROGRAMMING (ELECTRONIC COMPUTERS)
see also Coding Theory; Computer Programming Management; Computer Programs; Data Tapes; Electronic Analog Computers–Programming; Electronic Digital Computers; Integer Programming; Microcomputers–Programming; Programming Languages (Electronic Computers); Punched Card Systems;
also names of specific computers, e.g. IBM 1620
Abbott, J. On-Line Programming: A Management Guide. 64p. 1981. pap. 18.60 (ISBN 0-471-89415-X). Wiley.
Abelson, H. & Sussman, G. Structure & Interpretation of Computer Programs. (MH-MIT Press Ser.). 1984. 32.50 (ISBN 0-07-000422-6). McGraw.
Adams, James M. Data Processing: An Introduction. LC 81-66793. (Data Processing Ser.). (Illus.). 253p. 1982. text ed. 14.60 (ISBN 0-8273-1616-X); tchr's. guide 5.25 (ISBN 0-8273-1617-8). Delmar.
Adler, Howard. One Hundred One Programming Tips & Tricks for the VIC-20 & Commodore 64. 128p. 1983. 8.95 (ISBN 0-86668-030-6). ARCsoft.
Agarwal, Krishna K. Programming with Structured Flowcharts. 142p. 1984. pap. 12.00 (ISBN 0-89433-226-0). Petrocelli.
Ageloff, Roy & Mojena, Richard. Applied BASIC Programming. 464p. 1980. pap. text ed. write for info (ISBN 0-534-00808-9). Wadsworth Pub.
Aho, Alfred V. & Ullman, Jeffrey D. Theory of Parsing, Translation, & Compiling, Vol. 2 Compiling. (Illus.). 471p. 1973. ref. ed. 40.95 (ISBN 0-13-914564-8). P-H.
Al-Sarraf, Hassan S. Programming with BASIC. (Arabic.). 200p. 1985. pap. 13.00 (ISBN 0-471-80970-5). Wiley.
Andriole, Stephen J., ed. Software Development Tools: A Source Book. (Illus.). 240p. 1986. text ed. 29.95 (ISBN 0-89433-272-4). Petrocelli.
Anstis, Stuart. Write Your Own Apple Games. (Illus.). 174p. 1983. 12.95 (ISBN 0-916688-49-6, 2W). Creative Comp.
Arato, M. & Varga, L., eds. Mathematical Models in Computer Science. 1982. 39.50 (ISBN 0-9960072-0-2, Pub. by Akademiai Kaido Hungary). Heyden.
Arjani, K. A. Structured Programming Flowcharts. 1978. pap. text ed. 6.95 (ISBN 0-89669-000-8). Collegium Bk Pubs.
Aron, Joel D. Program Development Process, Pt. I: The Individual Programmer. (IBM Systems Programming Ser.). (Illus.). 280p. 1974. text ed. 27.95 (ISBN 0-201-14451-4). Addison-Wesley.
--The Program Development Process: Pt. II: The Programming Team. LC 74-2847. (Illus.). 704p. 1983. text ed. 32.95 (ISBN 0-201-14463-8). Addison-Wesley.
Arthur, Lowell J. Programmer Productivity: Myths, Methods & Murphy's Law & Murphology-A Guide for Managers, Analysts & Programmers. LC 82-13417. 288p. 1983. 26.95 (ISBN 0-471-86434-X, Pub. by Wiley-Interscience). Wiley.
Ashcroft, J., et al. Programming with FORTRAN 77. 304p. 1981. pap. 18.50x (ISBN 0-246-11573-4, Pub. by Granada England). Sheridan.
Ashley. Command Level Programming Using Maps & Files, Vol. 2. (Data Processing Training Ser.). 1984. pap. write for info. (ISBN 0-471-82365-1). Wiley.
Astesiano, E. & Boehm, C., eds. CAAP 1981 Trees in Algebra & Programming: Proceedings. (Lecture Notes in Computer Science Ser: Vol. 112). 364p. 1981. pap. 22.00 (ISBN 0-387-10828-9). Springer-Verlag.
Augenstein, Moshe & Tenenbaum, Aaron. Data Structures & PL-1 Programming. (Illus.). 1979. text ed. 34.95 (ISBN 0-13-197731-8); exercise manual 10.95 (ISBN 0-13-197756-3). P-H.
Automated Education Center. A Computation Model with Data Flow Sequencing. 19.00 (ISBN 0-403-04457-X). Scholarly.
--Management Guide to Computer Programming. 1969. 25.00 (ISBN 0-403-04472-3). Scholarly.
--Management Systems & Programming. LC 78-79912. 17.50 (ISBN 0-403-04474-X). Scholarly.
Avant-Garde Creations. The Creativity Life Dynamic Book. (Illus.). 84p. 1980. pap. 9.95 (ISBN 0-930182-07-3); pkg. including book, 2 drawing cards & program disk 24.95 (ISBN 0-930182-08-1). Avant Garde Pub.
Avriel, Mordecai, ed. Advances in Geometric Programming. LC 79-20806. (Mathematical Concepts & Methods in Science & Engineering Ser.: Vol. 21). 470p. 1980. 55.00x (ISBN 0-306-40381-1, Plenum Pr). Plenum Pub.
Baase, Sara. VAX-11 Assembly Language Programming. (Computer Science Ser.). (Illus.). 416p. 1983. text ed. 29.95 (ISBN 0-13-940957-2). P-H.
Baber, Robert L. Software Reflected: The Socially Responsible Programming of Computers. 192p. 1982. 29.95 (ISBN 0-444-86372-9). Elsevier.
Barden, William, Jr. How to Program Microcomputers. LC 77-77412. 256p. 1978. pap. 11.95 (ISBN 0-672-21459-8, 21459). Sams.
--TRS-80 Assembly Language Subroutines. (Illus.). 282p. 1982. pap. 18.95 (ISBN 0-13-931188-2). P-H.
Barnes. Programming in Ada. 300p. (Orig.). 1983. pap. 21.95 (ISBN 0-201-13799-2). Addison-Wesley.
Barron, D. W. & Bishop, J. M. Advanced Programming: A Practical Course. (Wiley Series in Computing: 1-320). 277p. 1984. 24.95x (ISBN 0-471-90319-1). Wiley.
Barron, Jonathan C. BASIC Programming Using Structured Modules. 1984. text ed. 20.95 (ISBN 0-03-059241-0). HR&W.
Beck, Leland. System Software: An Introduction to Systems Programming. 496p. 1985. text ed. 33.95 (ISBN 0-201-10950-6). Addison-Wesley.
Beil, Don. The DIF File: For Users of VisiCalc & Other Software. 1983. 16.95 (ISBN 0-8359-1305-8). Reston.
Bell, D. H., et al. Parallel Programming: A Bibliography. Willis, N., ed. (Mongraphs in Informatics (British Computer Society)). 64p. 1983. 19.95x (ISBN 0-471-26277-3, 1601). Wiley.
Bellman, R. Dynamic Programming. (Rand Corporation Research Studies). 1957. 45.00x (ISBN 0-691-07951-X). Princeton U Pr.
Birtwistle, Graham M. & Dahl, Ole-Johan. Simula Begin. 391p. 1979. pap. text ed. 29.50x (ISBN 91-44-06212-5, Pub. by Chartwell-Bratt England). Brookfield Pub Co.
Bjorner, D., ed. Formal Description of Programming Concepts, II. 456p. 1983. 55.50 (ISBN 0-444-86619-1, I-173-83, North Holland). Elsevier.
Bock, R. Darrell & Yates, George R. Multiqual II: Log-linear Analysis of Nominal or Ordinal Qualitative Data by the Method of Maximum Likelihood. 1983. pap. 4.00 (ISBN 0-89498-008-4). Sci Ware.
Bohl, Marilyn. Tools for Structured Design. LC 77-13704. 1978. pap. text ed. 12.95 (ISBN 0-574-21170-5, 13-4170). SRA.
Borgerson, M. J. Advanced BASIC Programming Set. (General Trade Books). 1985. incl. disk 22.90 (ISBN 0-471-89547-4). Wiley.
Bosworth, Bruce. Business Programming Projects with BASIC. 256p. 1984. pap. text ed. 17.95 (ISBN 0-574-21480-1, 13-4480); tchr's ed. (ISBN 0-574-21481-X, 13-4481). SRA.
Brady, J. M. The Theory of Computer Science: A Programming Approach. 1977. pap. 9.95 (ISBN 0-412-15040-9, NO. 6040, Pub. by Chapman & Hall). Methuen Inc.
Brenan, Kathleen M. & Mandell, Steven L. Introduction to Computers & BASIC Programming. (Illus.). 409p. 1983. text ed. 20.95 (ISBN 0-314-78551-5); tchrs.' manual avail. (ISBN 0-314-81042-0). West Pub.
Bridges, George. One Hundred One Programming Tips & Tricks for IBM PCjr. 136p. 1984. 8.95 (ISBN 0-86668-038-1). ARCsoft.
Brown & Sampson. Program Debugging. LC 72-12417. (Computer Monograph Ser.: Vol. 18). 1973. 32.50 (ISBN 0-444-19565-3). Elsevier.

Buerger, E. Woerterbuch Datenerfassung-Programmierung. (Eng., Ger., Fr. & Rus., Dictionary of Data Processing & Programming). 1976. 56.00 (ISBN 3-87144-265-8, M-6967). French & Eur.

Buerger, Ing E., ed. Data Processing Programming: Datenerfassung Programmiering. (Eng., Ger., Fr., Rus.). 1978. 55.00x (ISBN 3-87144-264-X). Adlers Foreign Bks.

Buhler. P-Stat User's Manual. 1985. text ed. write for info. (ISBN 0-87150-838-9, 36G2200, Duxbury Pr). PWS Pubs.

Burge, William H. Recursive Programming Techniques. LC 74-28812. (IBM Systems Programming Ser.). (Illus.). 280p. 1975. text ed. 28.95 (ISBN 0-201-14450-6). Addison-Wesley.

Burger, E., ed. Technical Dictionary of Automatization & Programming: English, French, German, Russian, Slovene. (Eng., Fr., Ger., Rus. & Slovene.). 479p. 1976. 95.00 (ISBN 0-686-92330-8, M-9889). French & Eur.

Campbell, John L. & Zimmerman, Lance. Programming the Apple II & IIe: A Structured Approach. rev. & enl. ed. LC 83-21441. (Illus.). 464p. 1984. pap. 19.95 (ISBN 0-89303-779-6); diskette 30.00 (ISBN 0-89303-780-X); bk. & diskette 49.95 (ISBN 0-89303-777-X). Brady Comm.

Carter, L. R. & Huzan, E. Learn Computer Programming with the Commodore VIC-20. 1983. pap. 5.95 (ISBN 0-679-10537-9). Mckay.

--Teach Yourself Computer Programming with the Commodore 64. 192p. 1983. pap. 6.95 (ISBN 0-679-10538-7). McKay.

Case, Albert F., Jr. Information Systems Development: Principles of Software Engineering & Computer-Aided Software Engineering. (Illus.). 240p. 1986. text ed. 30.00 (ISBN 0-13-464520-0). P-H.

Cassel, Don. The Structured Alternative: Programming Style, Debugging & Verification. 1982. text ed. 25.95 (ISBN 0-8359-7084-1); solutions manual avail. free (ISBN 0-8359-7085-X). Reston.

CES Industries. Ed-Lab Eight Hundred Exercise Manual: Programming for Ohm's Law, Unit 1. (Illus., Orig.). 1982. write for info. (ISBN 0-86711-029-5). CES Industries.

CES Industries, Inc. Ed-Lab Eight Hundred Experiment & Exercise Manual: Programming in BASIC. Rev. ed. (Illus.). 1983. write for info. (ISBN 0-86711-029-5). CES Industries.

--Ed-Lab Experiment Manual: CES 211 Breadboard Lab Manual. (Illus.). 1983. write for info. (ISBN 0-86711-066-X). CES Industries.

CES Industries, Inc. & Nesenoff, Norman. Ed-Lab Eighty Experiment Manual: EPROM Programming. (Illus.). 1983. write for info. (ISBN 0-86711-038-4). CES Industries.

Chambers, John M. Computational Methods for Data Analysis. LC 77-9493. (Wiley Ser. in Probability & Mathematical Statistics: Applied Section). 268p. 1977. 34.95 (ISBN 0-471-02772-3, Pub. by Wiley-Interscience). Wiley.

Chandy, K. & Yeh, Raymond T., eds. Current Trends in Programming Methodology: Software Modeling, Vol. 3. (Illus.). 1978. ref. 34.95 (ISBN 0-13-195727-9). P-H.

Chantler, A. Programming Techniques & Practice. 250p. 1981. pap. 22.95 (ISBN 0-471-89422-2). Wiley.

Charlesworth, A. S. & Fletcher, J. R. Systematic Analog Computer Programming. 2nd ed. 1975. 19.50x (ISBN 0-8464-0905-4). Beekman Pubs.

Chattergy, Rahul & Pooch, Udo W. Top-Down, Modular Programming in FORTRAN with WATFIV. 217p. (Orig.). 1980. pap. 16.95 (ISBN 0-316-13826-6). Little.

Cheifetz, et al. Logic & Set Theory: With an Introduction to Computer Programming. 2nd ed. LC 76-126359. 1983. 19.75x (ISBN 0-916060-05-5). Math Alternatives.

Cheriton, David R. Thoth System: Multi-Process Structuring & Probability. (Operating & Programming Systems Ser.: Vol. 8). 191p. 1982. 47.00 (ISBN 0-444-00701-6, North-Holland). Elsevier.

Chorafas, Dimitrius N. Control Systems Functions & Programming Approaches, 2 Vols. (Mathematics in Science & Engineering: Vol. 27A & B). 1966. Vol. A. 76.00 (ISBN 0-12-174061-7); Vol. B. 63.00 (ISBN 0-12-174062-5). Acad Pr.

Cichanowski, Gerald W. Macro Eleven Programming & PDP Eleven Organization. LC 82-11498. 248p. 1982. pap. text ed. 12.95x (ISBN 0-910554-38-2). Engineering.

CIP Group, ed. The Munich Project CIP. (Lecture Notes in Computer Science Ser.: Vol. 183). (Illus.). xi, 275p. 1985. pap. 16.60 (ISBN 0-387-15187-7). Springer-Verlag.

Clark, K. & Tarnbund, S. A. Logic Programming. 1982. 37.50 (ISBN 0-12-175520-7). Acad Pr.

Clark, Ron. One Hundred One Color Computer Programming Tips & Tricks. 128p. (Orig.). 1982. pap. 7.95 (ISBN 0-86668-007-1). ARCsoft.

Claybrook, Billy G. File Management Techniques. 247p. 1983. text ed. 28.95 (ISBN 0-471-04596-9). Assn Inform & Image Mgmt.

Cluley, J. C. Programming for Minicomputers. LC 77-83270. (Computer Systems Engineering Ser.). 288p. 1978. 19.50x (ISBN 0-8448-1259-5). Crane-Russak Co.

Coan, D. R. Programming Standards, 2 vols. National Computing Centre Ltd. & National Computing Centre Ltd., eds. Incl. Vol. 1. Documentation. write for info. (ISBN 0-685-30481-7); Vol. 2. Techniques. 180p. 1972. 47.50x (ISBN 0-85012-071-3). 240p. 1973. Intl Pubns Serv.

Coffron, James W. Programming the 8086-8088. LC 83-50228. (Illus.). 311p. 1983. pap. 15.95 (ISBN 0-89588-120-9). SYBEX.

Cole, J. W. Perry. ANSI FORTRAN IV with FORTRAN 77 Extensions: A Sructured Programming Approach. 2nd ed. 720p. 1983. pap. write for info. (ISBN 0-697-08172-9); instr's. manual avail. (ISBN 0-697-08177-X). Wm C Brown.

Cole, Jim. Ninety-Nine Tips & Tricks for the New Pocket Computers. 128p. (Orig.). 1982. pap. 7.95 (ISBN 0-86668-019-5). ARCsoft.

--One Hundred One Pocket Computer Programming Tips & Tricks. (Illus.). 128p. (Orig.). 1982. pap. 7.95 (ISBN 0-86668-004-7). ARCsoft.

--Pocket Computer Programming Made Easy. (Illus.). 128p. (Orig.). 1982. pap. 8.95 (ISBN 0-86668-009-8). ARCsoft.

Collin, Raeto C. Programming the Commodore 64. COMPUTE Editors, ed. 609p. (Orig.). 1985. pap. 19.95 (ISBN 0-942386-50-7). Compute Pubns.

Collin, W. G. Introducing Computer Programming. LC 73-89965. 330p. 1979. 15.00x (ISBN 0-85012-210-4). Intl Pubns Serv.

Constable, R. L., et al. An Introduction to the Pl-CV2 Programming Logic. (Lecture Notes in Computer Science: Vol. 135). 292p. 1982. pap. 20.00 (ISBN 0-387-11492-0). Springer-Verlag.

Constable, Robert L. & O'Donnell, Michael J. A Programming Logic: With an Introduction to the PL-CV Verifier. 1978. text ed. 24.95 (ISBN 0-316-15316-8). Little.

Conway, Richard. A Primer on Disciplined Programming: Using PL-1, PL-CS, & PL-CT. (Orig.). 1978. pap. text ed. 16.95 (ISBN 0-316-15426-1). Little.

Conway, Richard & Gries, David. An Introduction to Programming: A Structured Approach Using PL-1 & PL-C. 3rd ed. 728p. 1978. pap. text ed. 24.95 (ISBN 0-316-15414-8). Little.

--Primer on Structured Programming: Using PL-1, PL-C & PL-CT. (Orig.). 1976. pap. text ed. 16.95 (ISBN 0-316-15425-3). Little.

Crawford, Rudd A., Jr. & Copp, David H. Introduction to Computer Programming. 1969. pap. 8.88 (ISBN 0-395-02252-5). HM.

Creative Programming Inc., Staff. Creative Programming: All Stars Level II. rev. ed. (All Stars Ser.). (Illus.). 41p. 1983. wkbk. 9.95 (ISBN 0-912079-06-1, 1002). Creat Prog Inc.

--Creative Programming: Apple II, IIe, Vol. I. (Illus.). 74p. 1983. spiral wkbk 9.95 (ISBN 0-912079-02-9). Creat Prog Inc.

--Creative Programming: Apple II, IIe, Vol. II. 66p. 1983. spiral wkbk. 9.95 (ISBN 0-912079-21-5, 202). Creat Prog Inc.

--Creative Programming: Commodore 64, Vol. III. 80p. (Orig.). 1983. 9.95 (ISBN 0-912079-15-0). Creat Prog Inc.

--Creative Programming: Commodore 64, Vol. I. (Illus.). 75p. (Orig.). 1983. spiral wkbk. 9.95 (ISBN 0-912079-13-4, 901). Creat Prog Inc.

--Creative Programming: Teacher Resource Book, Commodore 64. 130p. 1983. pap. 19.95 (ISBN 0-912079-23-1). Creat Prog Inc.

--Creative Programming: Texas Instruments Professional, Vol. I. 75p. (Orig.). 1983. wkbk. 9.95 (ISBN 0-912079-10-X, 501). Creat Prog Inc.

--Creative Programming: TRS-80, Vol. IV. rev. ed. 1983. spiral 9.95 (ISBN 0-912079-12-6, 104). Creat Prog Inc.

Crookall, Philip. Computer Programming for Real Beginners: Simplified & Self-Taught. LC 84-12292. 96p. 1984. pap. 5.95 (ISBN 0-668-06130-8, 6130-8). Arco.

CSIRO Research Programs: 1979-80. 533p. 1980. pap. 18.00 (ISBN 0-686-71826-7, C033, CSIRO). Unipub.

Daniel, Rudolph M. Timex-Sinclair 2068 Programmer's Guide. (Illus.). 176p. pap. cancelled (ISBN 0-89303-897-0). Brady Comm.

DeLorm, R. T. & Kersten, L. CALCOMP Programming for Digital Plotters. 234p. 1976. pap. 11.95x (ISBN 0-8032-6550-6). U of Nebr Pr.

Dembrinski, P., ed. Mathematical Foundation of Computer Science: Proceedings. (Lecture Notes in Computer Science Ser.: Vol. 88). 723p. 1980. pap. 42.00 (ISBN 0-387-10027-X). Springer-Verlag.

Dezani-Ciancaglini, M. & Montanari, U., eds. International Symposium on Programming, Turin 1982: Proceedings. (Lecture Notes in Computer Science Ser.: Vol. 137). 406p. 1982. pap. 24.00 (ISBN 0-387-11494-7). Springer-Verlag.

Diaz, J. & Ramos, I., eds. Formalization of Programming Concepts: Proceedings. (Lecture Notes in Computer Sciences Ser.: Vol. 107). 478p. 1981. pap. 26.50 (ISBN 0-387-10699-5). Springer-Verlag.

Dickson, G. W. & Smith, H. R. Introduction to FORTRAN IV Programming: A Self-Paced Approach. LC 74-189809. 1972. pap. text ed. 17.95 (ISBN 0-03-088088-2, HoltC). HR&W.

Dictionary of Computer Programming & Data Processing. 386p. 1976. 90.00x (ISBN 0-686-44722-0, Pub. by Collets). State Mutual Bk.

Diehr, George, et al. BASIC Programming for the VAX & PDP-11. LC 83-21689. 473p. 1984. pap. text ed. 23.50 (ISBN 0-471-86817-5); write for info. tchr's. ed. (ISBN 0-471-80224-7). Wiley.

Dijkstra, E. W. A Primer of ALGOL 60 Programming: Together with Report on the Algorithmic Language ALGOL 60. 1962. 29.50 (ISBN 0-12-216250-1). Acad Pr.

Dodd, K. N. Computer Programming & Languages. LC 70-80822. 148p. 1969. 9.95x (ISBN 0-306-30660-3, Plenum Pr). Plenum Pub.

Drury, Donald W. The Art of Computer Programming. (Illus.). 312p. (Orig.). 1982. o.p 16.95 (ISBN 0-8306-0455-3); pap. 10.95 (ISBN 0-8306-1455-9, 1455). TAB Bks.

East, Mary Lou & East, Fred B., eds. Programmers' Handbook of Computer Printer Commands. 1985. pap. 39.95 (ISBN 0-932065-00-7). Cardinal Pt.

Edwards, John B. & Owens, David H. Analysis & Control of Multipass Process. (Control Theory & Applications Ser.). 298p. 1982. 54.95x (ISBN 0-471-10163-X, Pub. by Res Studies). Wiley.

Ehrig, H., et al, eds. Formal Methods & Software Development. (Lecture Notes in Computer Science Ser.: Vol. 186). xiv, 455p. 1985. pap. 25.10 (ISBN 0-387-15199-0). Springer-Verlag.

--Mathematical Foundations of Software Development. (Lecture Notes in Computer Science: Vol. 185). xiv, 418p. 1985. pap. 22.80 (ISBN 0-387-15198-2). Springer-Verlag.

El-Asfouri, Souhail & Johnson, Olin. Computer Organization & Programming: Vax-II. LC 83-3699. (Computer Science Ser.). (Illus.). 544p. 1984. 31.95 (ISBN 0-201-10425-3). Addison-Wesley.

Emmerichs, Jack. The Programmer's Toolbox. LC 84-3196. 418p. 1984. pap. 19.95 (ISBN 0-88056-303-6); incl. disk 39.95 (ISBN 0-88056-229-3). Dilithium Pr.

Engelfriet, J. Simple Program Schemes & Formal Languages. (Lecture Notes in Computer Science Ser.: Vol. 20). vii, 254p. 1974. pap. 18.00 (ISBN 0-387-06953-4). Springer-Verlag.

Erlewine, Michael. Manual of Computer Programming for Astrologers. 224p. 1980. 13.95 (ISBN 0-86690-099-3, 1184-03). Am Fed Astrologers.

Ernst, M. & Steigert, W. Programming with Assembler Language ASS 300. 316p. 1980. 41.95 (ISBN 0-471-25671-4, Wiley Heyden). Wiley.

Even, S. & Kariv, O., eds. Automata, Languages, & Programming. (Lecture Notes in Computer Sciences Ser.: Vol. 115). 552p. 1981. pap. 29.00 (ISBN 0-387-10843-2). Springer-Verlag.

Falk, J. E. & Fiacco, A. V. Mathematical Programming with Parameters & Multi-Level Constraints. 100p. 1981. pap. 42.00 (ISBN 0-08-023621-9). Pergamon.

Federighi, Francis & Reilly, Edward D. Weighting for Baudot & Other Problems for You & Your Computer. (Illus.). 1978. 9.95 (ISBN 0-89529-061-8). Avery Pub.

Fernandez, Judi N. & Ashley, Ruth. Introduction to Computer Programming. LC 83-16726. (Data Processing Training Ser.: 1-615). 301p. 1984. 49.95x (ISBN 0-471-87024-2). Wiley.

Fiacco. Mathematical Programming with Data Perturbations, Pt. II. (Lecture Notes in Pure & Applied Mathematics Ser.). 210p. 1983. 39.75 (ISBN 0-8247-1789-9). Dekker.

Fox, Michael. Ninety-Nine Programming Tips & Tricks for the IBM Personal Computer. 128p. 1984. 8.95 (ISBN 0-86668-046-2). ARCsoft.

Freund, Rudolf, et al. SAS for Linear Models: A Guide to the ANOVA & GLM Procedures. (SAS Series in Statistical Applications: Vol. 1). (Illus.). 231p. (Orig.). 1981. pap. 14.95 (ISBN 0-917382-31-5). SAS Inst.

Fugate, James K. Programming Tools for the IBM PC: Screen Design, Code Generator & High Memory Access. (Illus.). 272p. 1985. pap. 19.95 (ISBN 0-89303-784-2); diskette 30.00 (ISBN 0-89303-785-0). Brady Comm.

Fuori, William M. & Gaughran, Stephen J. Structured COBOL Programming. (Illus.). 544p. 1984. pap. text ed. 25.95 (ISBN 0-13-854430-1). P-H.

Furrer, F. Fehlerkorrigierende Block-Codierung fuer die Datenuebertragung. (LHI Ser.: No. 36). 1981. 75.95x (ISBN 0-8176-0975-X). Birkhauser.

Gamelin, Theodore W. & Greene, Robert E. Introduction to Topology. 1983. text ed. 35.95 (ISBN 0-03-062476-2, CBS C). SCP.

Garey, Michael R. & Johnson, David S. Computers & Intractability: A Guide to the Theory of NP-Completeness. LC 78-12361. (Mathematical Sciences Ser.). (Illus.). 338p. 1979. pap. text ed. 17.95 (ISBN 0-7167-1045-5). W H Freeman.

Gear, C. W. Computer Organization & Programming. 4th ed. (Computer Science Ser.). 432p. 1985. 39.95 (ISBN 0-07-023049-8). McGraw.

Gear, C. William. Introduction to Computers, Structured Programming, & Applications. 1978. Module P: Programming & Languages. 11.95 (ISBN 0-574-21187-X, 13-4187); Module A: Applications & Algorithms In Computer Science. 11.95 (ISBN 0-574-21188-8, 13-4188); Module A: Applications & Algorithms in Science & Engineering. 11.95 (ISBN 0-574-21189-6, 13-4189); Module A: Applications & Algorithms in Business. 11.95 (ISBN 0-574-21190-X, 13-4190); Module C: Computers & Systems. 11.95 (ISBN 0-574-21191-8, 13-4191); FORTRAN & WATFIV Manual. 7.95 (ISBN 0-574-21192-6, 13-4192); Pascal Manual. 7.95 (ISBN 0-574-21193-4, 13-4193); PL/1 & PL/C Manual. 7.95 (ISBN 0-574-21194-2); Basic Manual 7.95. SRA.

Geary, R. C. & Spencer, J. E. Elements of Linear Programing Economics Application. 2nd, rev. ed. (Griffins Statistical Monograph Ser.: No. 15). 1973. pap. 13.00x (ISBN 0-02-845230-5). Hafner.

Geyer, R. F. & Zouwen, J. van der, eds. Sociocybernetics, Vols. 1 & 2. 1978. Vol. 1. pap. 17.00 (ISBN 90-207-0854-6, Pub. by Martinus Nijhoff Netherlands); Vol. 2. pap. 17.00 (ISBN 90-207-0855-4). Kluwer Academic.

Girault, C. & Reisig, W., eds. Application & Theory of Petri Nets-Strassbourg 1980 & Bad Honneff 1981: Proceedings. (Informatik-Fachberichte: Vol. 52). 337p. 1982. pap. 16.70 (ISBN 0-387-11189-1). Springer-Verlag.

Goldberg, Robert & Lorin, Harold. Economics of Information Processing: Vol. 2, Operation Programming & Software Models. LC 81-11429. 185p. 1982. 30.95 (ISBN 0-471-09767-5, Pub. by Wiley Interscience). Assn Inform & Image Mgmt.

Goldblatt, R. Axiomatising the Logic of Computer Programming. (Lecture Notes in Computer Science Ser.: Vol. 130). 304p. 1982. pap. 20.00 (ISBN 0-387-11210-3). Springer-Verlag.

Goodman, R. E., ed. Annual Review in Automatic Programming, Vols. 1, 4. Incl. Vol. 1. 1960 (ISBN 0-08-009217-9); Vol. 2. 1961 (ISBN 0-08-009333-7); Vol. 3. 1963 (ISBN 0-08-009763-4); Vol. 4. rev. ed. 1964 (ISBN 0-08-010857-1). 56.00 ea. Pergamon.

Graham, Neill. Introduction to Computer Science: A Structured Approach. 2nd ed. (Illus.). 568p. 1982. text ed. 29.95 (ISBN 0-314-63243-3). West Pub.

Grishman, Ralph. Assembly Language Programming for Control Data 6000 & Cyber Ser. (Illus.). 248p. 1981. 15.00x (ISBN 0-917448-04-9). Algorithmics.

--Assembly Language Programming for the Control Data 6000 Series & the Cyber Series. Date not set. pap. 15.00 (ISBN 0-686-46118-5). Algorithmics.

Haendler, W., ed. CONPAR Eighty-One Conference on Analysing Problem Classes & Programming for Parallel Computing: Proceedings. (Lecture Notes in Computer Science Ser.: Vol. 111). (Illus.). 508p. 1981. pap. 29.00 (ISBN 0-387-10827-0). Springer-Verlag.

Hailpern, R. T. Verifying Concurrent Processes Using Temporal Logic. (Lecture Notes in Computer Science: Vol. 129). 208p. 1982. pap. 16.00 (ISBN 0-387-11205-7). Springer-Verlag.

Halliwell, J. Practical Programming Principles. (Illus.). 200p. 1982. pap. 30.00 (ISBN 0-85012-337-2). Intl Pubns Serv.

Halliwell, J. D. & Littlewood, G. Practical Programming Principles. 200p. 1982. pap. 25.15 (ISBN 0-471-89420-6). Wiley.

Halpern, M., et al, eds. Annual Review in Automatic Programming. Incl. Vol. 5, Pt. 1. Data Structures & Their Representation in Storage. D'Imperio, A. LC 60-12884. 1970; Vol. 5, Pt. 2. Generalized File Processing. McGee, W. C. 1970; Vol. 6, Pt. 1. Some Studies in Machine Learning Using the Game of Checkers 2. Samuel, A. L. 1969. pap. 15.50 (ISBN 0-08-006575-9); Vol. 6, Pt. 2. A Survey of Macro Processors: A Machine-Independent Assembly Language for Systems Programs. Brown, P. J. & Colouris, G. F. 1969. pap. 15.50 (ISBN 0-08-006586-4); Vol. 6, Pt. 3. On the Formal Description of PL-1. Lucas, P. & Walk, K. 1970. pap. 15.50 (ISBN 0-08-006689-5); Vol. 6, Pt. 4. Joss Two: Design Philosophy. Smith, J. W. 1970. pap. 15.50 (ISBN 0-08-006694-1); Vol. 6, Pt. 5. A New Approach to Optimization of Sequencing Decisions. Shapiro, R. M. & Saint, H. 1970. pap. 15.50 (ISBN 0-08-016336-X); Vol. 7, Pt. 1. Tutorial on Data-Base Organization. Smith, J. W. 1972. pap. 15.50 (ISBN 0-08-016947-3); Vol. 7, Pt. 2. Incremental Complication & Conversational Interpretation. Bertrand, M. & Griffiths, M. M. pap. 15.50 (ISBN 0-08-017049-8); Vol. 7, Pt. 3. Introduction to Algol 68: Automatic Theorem Proving Based on Resolution. Bekis, A. 1973. pap. 15.50 (ISBN 0-08-017128-1); Vol. 7, Pt. 4. Survey of Extensible Programming Language. Solnsteff, N. & Yezerski, A. 1973. pap. 15.50 (ISBN 0-08-017145-1); Vol. 7, Pt. 5. 1975. pap. 15.50 (ISBN 0-08-017881-2); Vol. 7 Complete. 1974. pap. text ed. 49.00 (ISBN 0-08-017806-5). LC 60-12884. pap. write for info. Pergamon.

Hansen, Per B. Programming a Personal Computer. (Illus.). 400p. 1983. 25.00 (ISBN 0-13-730267-3); pap. 18.95 (ISBN 0-13-730283-5). P-H.

Hanson, Jay, et al. Advanced Programmer's Guide Featuring dBASE III & dBASE II. 664p. (Orig.). 1984. pap. 28.95 (ISBN 0-912677-05-8). Ashton-Tate Bks.

Harms, Edward & Zabinski, Michael P. Introduction to APL & Computer Programming. LC 76-20587. 1977. pap. text ed. 29.45 (ISBN 0-471-35201-2); write for info tchr's manual (ISBN 0-471-01940-2). Wiley.

Harrington, Steven. Computer Graphics: A Programming Approach. Vastyan, James E., ed. (Illus.). 480p. 1983. text ed. 33.95 (ISBN 0-07-026751-0). McGraw.

Harrison, Malcolm C. Data Structures & Programming. 1973. text ed. 23.80x (ISBN 0-673-05964-2). Scott F.

Hart, Jack, et al. Cross Reference Utility (CRF) A Programming Aid for the IBM Personal Computer. (Illus.). 192p. 1983. pap. 29.95 (ISBN 0-13-194746-X, Spec). P-H.

Hartling, John. Introduction to Computer Programming: A Problem Solving Approach. 468p. 1983. 25.00 (ISBN 0-932376-21-5, EY-00010-DP). Digital Pr.

Hartnell, Tim. How to Program Your Commodore 64: If You've Never Programmed a Computer Before. 114p. 1984. 6.95 (ISBN 0-345-31663-0). Ballantine.

--How to Program Your MSX Computer. (Orig.). 1985. pap. 7.95 (ISBN 0-345-32691-1). Ballantine.

Harvey, Brian. Computer Science LOGO Style: Introduction to Programming. (Illus.). 260p. (Orig.). 1985. pap. 19.95 (ISBN 0-262-58072-1). MIT Pr.

Hawryszkiewycz, Igor. Database Analysis & Design. 416p. 1984. pap. text ed. 33.95 (ISBN 0-574-21485-2, 13-4485); avail. (ISBN 0-574-21486-0, 13-4486). SRA.

Helwig, Jane T. & SAS Institute Inc. Eine Einfuehrung in das SAS. Frenzel, G., tr. from Eng. (Ger., Illus.). 97p. (Orig.). 1981. pap. 9.95 (ISBN 0-917382-25-0). SAS Inst.

Henderson, Peter. Functional Programming. (Ser. in Computer Science). (Illus.). 1980. text ed. 42.95 (ISBN 0-13-331579-7). P-H.

Henley, E., ed. Stoichiometry. (Computer Programs for Chemical Engineering Education Ser.). 1972. pap. 13.95 (ISBN 0-88408-028-5). Sterling Swift.

Hill, MaryAnn, ed. BMDP User's Digest: BMDP Statistical Software, Inc. rev. ed. 157p. 1982. text ed. 6.00 (ISBN 0-935386-02-5). BMDP Stat.

Hockney, R. W. & Jesshope, C. R. Parallel Computers: Architecture, Programming & Algorithms. 1981. 49.00 (ISBN 0-9960022-8-6, Pub. by A Hilger England); pap. 18.00 (ISBN 0-9960025-5-3). Heyden.

Holmes, B. J. BASIC Programming. 350p. 1982. 37.00x (ISBN 0-905435-25-7, Pub. by DP Pubns). State Mutual Bk.

Holtz, Frederick. Using & Programming the Macintosh, with 32 Ready-to-Run Programs. (Illus.). 256p. (Orig.). 16.95 (ISBN 0-8306-0840-0, 1840); pap. 12.50 (ISBN 0-8306-1840-6). TAB Bks.

How to Get the Most from Your Chess Computer. pap. 9.95 (ISBN 0-686-79080-4). R H M Pr.

Hsaio, David K. Systems Programming: Concepts of Operating & Data Base Systems. LC 74-30699. (Illus.). 352p. 1975. text ed. 31.95 (ISBN 0-201-02950-2). Addison-Wesley.

Hume & Holt. Structured Programming Using PL-1 SP-K. 2nd ed. 1980. pap. text ed. 19.95 (ISBN 0-8359-7131-7); text ed. 21.95 O.P. (ISBN 0-8359-7133-3). Reston.

Hwang, C. Jinshing & Ho, Thomas. Structured Programming in BASIC-PLUS & BASIC PLUS-2: Including VAX-11 BASIC Compatability. LC 83-10259. 492p. 1984. pap. text ed. 28.45 (ISBN 0-471-06338-X). Wiley.

IEEE Standard 828-1983: IEEE Standard for Software Configuration Mangement Plans. 1983. 6.50 (ISBN 0-317-03957-1, SHO9068). IEEE.

IMS-VS DB-DC Online Programming Using MFS & DL-I. 310p. 1985. perfect bdg. 29.95 (ISBN 0-9611810-2-8). D L Shyh Yuan.

IMS-VS DL-I Programming with COBOL Examples. 300p. 1985. perfect bdg. 29.95 (ISBN 0-9611810-3-6). D L Shyh Yuan.

Ingevaldsson, Leif. Jackson Structured Programming: A Practical Method of Program Design. 194p. (Orig.). 1979. pap. text ed. 19.95x (ISBN 0-317-02803-0, Pub. by Chartwell-Bratt England). Brookfield Pub Co.

International Symposium on Theoretical Programming. Proceedings. Ershov, A., ed. (Lectures Notes in Computer Science: Vol. 5). vi, 407p. 1974. pap. 21.00 (ISBN 0-387-06720-5). Springer-Verlag.

Iyengar, N. R. & Gupta, S. K. Programming Methods in Structural Design. 248p. 1982. pap. 32.95x (ISBN 0-470-27298-8). Halsted Pr.

Jackson, Peter & Goode, Peter. Business Programming on Your Spectrum. 157p. 1984. pap. 13.95 (ISBN 0-946576-05-X, Pub. by Phoenix Pub). David & Charles.

Jacobs, Zeney P., et al. Computer Programming in the BASIC Language. 1978. pap. text ed. 15.72 (ISBN 0-205-05836-1, 2058367); tchrs.' guide 9.32 (ISBN 0-205-05837-X, 2058375). Allyn.

Jensen, Craig. The Craft of Computer Programming. 448p. (Orig.). 1985. pap. 12.50 (ISBN 0-446-38147-0). Warner Bks.

Jensen, Paul A. & Barnes, J. Wesley. Network Flow Programming. LC 79-26939. (Industrial Engineering Ser.). 408p. 1980. text ed. 47.45x (ISBN 0-471-04471-7); solutions manual avail. (ISBN 0-471-06063-1). Wiley.

Johannesson, Goran. Programmable Control Systems. 136p. 1985. pap. text ed. 22.50x (ISBN 0-86238-046-4, Pub. by Chartwell-Bratt England). Brookfield Pub Co.

Johnston, Howard. Learning to Program. (Illus.). 464p. 1985. pap. text ed. 19.95 (ISBN 0-13-527754-X). P-H.

Jones, C. Programming Productivity. 480p. 1985. 38.95 (ISBN 0-07-032811-0). McGraw.

Jones, Capers. Programming Productivity: Issues for the Eighties. (Tutorial Texts Ser.). 440p. 1981. 36.00 (ISBN 0-8186-0391-7, Q391); 24.00. IEEE Comp Soc.

Jones, William B. Programming Concepts: A Second Course. (Illus.). 336p. 1982. text ed. 25.95 (ISBN 0-13-729970-2). P-H.

Kanter, Jerome. Taming Your Computer. 1981. 17.95 (ISBN 0-13-884403-8); pap. 8.95 (ISBN 0-13-884395-3). P-H.

Kapp, Dan & Leben, Joseph F. IMS Programming Techniques: A Guide to Using DL-1. (Illus.). 320p. 1983. 19.95 (ISBN 0-442-80505-5). Van Nos Reinhold.

Katzan, Harry, Jr. Computer Systems Organization & Programming. LC 75-23320. (Computer Science Ser.). (Illus.). 416p. 1976. text ed. 28.95 (ISBN 0-574-21080-6, 13-4080). SRA.

Keegel, John C. The Language of Computer Programming in English. (English for Careers Ser.). 1976. pap. 4.25 (ISBN 0-88345-257-X, 18503). Regents Pub.

Kemeny, John G. & Kurtz, Thomas E. BASIC Programming. 3rd ed. LC 79-20683. 334p. 1980. pap. text ed. 26.45x (ISBN 0-471-01863-5); solutions manual avail. (ISBN 0-471-07830-1). Wiley.

Kenah, Lawrence J. & Bate, Simon F. VAX-VMS Internals & Data Structures. 750p. 1984. 55.00 (ISBN 0-932376-52-5, EY-00014-DP). Digital Pr.

Kitsz, Dennis B. The Custom TRS-80 & Other Mysteries. (TRS-80 Information Ser.). (Illus.). 336p. (Orig.). 1982. pap. 29.95 (ISBN 0-936200-02-2). Blue Cat.

Knuth, Donald E. Art of Computer Programming: Semi-Numerical Algorithms, Vol. 2. 2nd ed. 1981. text ed. 36.95 (ISBN 0-201-03822-6). Addison-Wesley.

--The Art of Computer Programming, Vol. 3: Sorting & Searching. 1973. 35.95 (ISBN 0-201-03803-X). Addison-Wesley.

--Tex. (Computer Science Ser.). 512p. 1985. text ed. 25.95 (ISBN 0-201-13447-0). Addison-Wesley.

Kochan, Stephen G. Programming in C. 384p. pap. 18.95 (6261). Hayden.

Kolbin, Vyacheslav V. Stochastic Programming. Grigoryev, Igor P., tr. (Theory & Decision Library: No. 14). 1977. lib. bdg. 34.00 (ISBN 90-277-0750-2, Pub. by Reidel Holland). Kluwer Academic.

Kovacs. Combinatorial Methods of Discrete Programming. 29.00 (ISBN 0-9960070-6-7). Heyden.

Kuehni, Rolf G. Computer Colorant Formulation. LC 75-9018. 144p. 1975. 24.00x (ISBN 0-669-03335-9). Lexington Bks.

Kuenberger, David G. Linear & Nonlinear Programming. (Illus.). 480p. 1984. 36.95 (ISBN 0-201-15794-2). Addison-Wesley.

Kwong, Yat-Sang. On Reductions & Livelocks in Asynchronous Parallel Computation. Stone, Harold, ed. LC 82-6888. (Computer Science: Systems Programming Ser.: No. 7). 120p. 1982. 34.95 (ISBN 0-8357-1342-3). UMI Res Pr.

Lamie. Pascal Programming. 1986. pap. price not set (ISBN 0-471-82308-2). Wiley.

Lamie, Edward L. PL-1 Programming. 352p. 1981. pap. text ed. write for info. (ISBN 0-534-01067-9). Wadsworth Pub.

--PL-1 Programming. 330p. 1982. pap. write for info. Wadsworth Pub.

Lasdon, Leon S. Optimization Theory for Large Systems. (Illus.). 1970. write for info (ISBN 0-02-367800-3). Macmillan.

Laviana, Kenneth J. Basic C.N.C. Programming. Cormier, E. D., ed. 115p. 1983. pap. text ed. 19.95 (ISBN 0-912227-00-1). C E Pub.

Ledgard, Henry, et al. From Baker Street to Binary: An Introduction to Computers & Computer Programming with Sherlock Holmes. 288p. 1983. pap. 10.95 (ISBN 0-07-036983-6, BYTE Bks). McGraw.

Lee, Iva H. Data Entry: Concepts & Exercises. LC 81-11403. 355p. 1982. text ed. 26.95 (ISBN 0-471-08605-3); 22.95 (ISBN 0-471-86584-2). Wiley.

Leemon, Sheldon. Mapping the Commodore 64. 268p. (Orig.). 1984. pap. 14.95 (ISBN 0-942386-23-X). Compute Pubns.

Leeson, Marjorie. Basic Concepts in Data Processing. 2nd ed. 550p. 1980. pap. text ed. write for info. (ISBN 0-697-08134-6); project manual avail. (ISBN 0-697-08135-4); instr's. manual avail. (ISBN 0-697-08163-X). Wm C Brown.

Leeson, Marjorie M. Programming Logic. 320p. 1983. pap. text ed. 19.95 (ISBN 0-574-21420-8, 13-4420); instr's. guide avail. (ISBN 0-574-21421-6, 13-4421). SRA.

Lewis, John B. Analysis of Linear Dynamic Systems. (Illus.). 880p. 1977. 32.95 (ISBN 0-916460-20-7). Matrix Pub.

Lewis, T. G. Using the IBM Personal Computer. 1982. text ed. 19.95 O.P. (ISBN 0-8359-8140-1); pap. text ed. 16.95 (ISBN 0-8359-8138-X). Reston.

Lewis, William E. Problem-Solving Principles for Programmers: Applied Logic, Psychology & Grit. 163p. (Orig.). 1981. pap. 11.95 (ISBN 0-8104-5138-7). Hayden.

Li, Ching Chun. Analysis of Unbalanced Data: A Pre-Program Introduction. LC 82-4253. (Illus.). 160p. 1983. 22.95 (ISBN 0-521-24749-7). Cambridge U Pr.

Libes, Sol, ed. Programmer's Guide to CP-M. 200p. 1983. pap. 12.95 (ISBN 0-916688-37-2, 14C). Creative Comp.

Liffick, Blaise, ed. Simulation: Programming Techniques. LC 78-8649. 1979. pap. 12.95 (ISBN 0-07-037826-6, BYTE Bks). McGraw.

Liffick, Blaise W. Bits & Pieces. (Orig.). 1980. pap. 9.95 (ISBN 0-07-037828-2, BYTE Bks). McGraw.

Ling, Robert F. & Roberts, Harry V. IDA: A User's Guide to the IDA Interactive Data Analysis & Forecasting System. 1981. 17.95 (ISBN 0-07-037906-8). McGraw.

Linger, R. C., et al. Structured Programming: Theory & Practice. LC 78-18641. 1979. text ed. 34.95 (ISBN 0-201-14461-1). Addison-Wesley.

Linz, Peter. Programming Concepts & Problem Solving: An Introduction to Computer Science Using Pascal. 1983. 31.95 (ISBN 0-8053-5710-6); Instr's guide with transparency masters. 4.95 (ISBN 0-8053-5711-4). Benjamin-Cummings.

Lloyd, J. W. Foundations of Logic Programming. (Symbolic Computation, Artificial Intelligence Ser.). x, 124p. 1984. 17.00 (ISBN 0-387-13299-6). Springer-Verlag.

Logsdon, Thomas S. BASIC Programming with Structure & Style. (Orig.). 1985. pap. text ed. 21.00 (ISBN 0-87835-808-0); instr's manual 8.00 (ISBN 0-87835-809-9); transparency masters. avail. (ISBN 0-87835-177-9). Boyd & Fraser.

Logsdon, Tom. Programming in BASIC with Applications. LC 77-75504. 417p. 1977. pap. 24.95 (ISBN 0-88236-180-5). Anaheim Pub Co.

Lohmuller, Keith. Introduction to Business Programming & Systems Analysis. (Illus.). 238p. (Orig.). 1983. 18.95 (ISBN 0-8306-0437-5, 1437); pap. 13.50 (ISBN 0-8306-1437-0). TAB Bks.

Longworth, G. Standards in Programming. (Illus.). 206p. 1981. text ed. 110.00x (ISBN 0-85012-341-0). Intl Pubns Serv.

--Standards in Programming. 206p. 1981. pap. 109.25 (ISBN 0-471-89428-1). Wiley.

Ma, Cynthia S. & Seeborg, Irmtraud. Programming in BASIC. 1978. pap. text ed. 9.50 (ISBN 0-8403-1926-6). Kendall-Hunt.

McCarroll, John D. Computer-Aided Part Programming for Numerical Control: An Industry Study. (Illus.). 152p. 1976. 12.00 (ISBN 0-938654-02-0, CAPP). Indus Dev Inst Sci.

McKeown, Patrick G. Structured Programming Using FORTRAN 77. 482p. 1985. pap. text ed. 20.95 (ISBN 0-15-584411-3, HC). HarBraceJ.

--Structured Programming Using WATFIV. 405p. 1985. pap. text ed. 19.95 (ISBN 0-15-584414-8, HC). HarBraceJ.

McQuillin, R., ed. Computer Programming Directory, 1974. 2nd ed. 1973. 25.00 (ISBN 0-02-468940-8). Macmillan.

Mandell, Steven L. Introduction to BASIC Programming. 2nd ed. LC 84-17393. (Illus.). 176p. 1984. pap. text ed. 11.95 (ISBN 0-314-85263-8). West Pub.

Manna, Z. Lectures on the Logic of Computer Programming. LC 79-93153. (CBMS-NSF Regional Conference Ser.: No. 31). iv, 49p. 1980. pap. text ed. 9.00 (ISBN 0-89871-164-9). Soc Indus-Appl Math.

Mansfield, Richard. Machine Language for Beginners. 350p. pap. 14.95 (ISBN 0-942386-11-6). Compute Pubns.

Marcellus, Daniel. Systems Programming for Small Computers. 1983. text ed. 28.95 (ISBN 0-13-881664-6); pap. text ed. 18.95 (ISBN 0-13-881656-5). P-H.

Marlin, C. D. Coroutines. (Lecture Notes in Computer Science Ser.: Vol. 95). (Illus.). 246p. 1980. pap. 20.00 (ISBN 0-387-10256-6). Springer-Verlag.

Marty, R. PISA Programming System for Interactive Production of Application Software. (Informatik-Fachberichte Ser.). 297p. 1981. pap. 15.00 (ISBN 0-387-10825-4). Springer-Verlag.

Mason, Russell E. Basic, Intermediate Systematic Substitution Training, Set-IS. 1973. Tape 3, t-10, t-11. pap. 25.00x incl. Clinical Applications, Brief Outlines 2, Feeling Training (ISBN 0-89533-016-4). F I Comm.

Mazur, Ken, ed. The Creative TRS-80. (The Creative Ser.). (Illus.). 408p. 1983. pap. 15.95 (ISBN 0-916688-36-4, 18Y). Creative Comp.

Mendelson, Bert. A First Course in Programming with Pascal. 385p. 1982. scp 28.15 (ISBN 0-205-07823-0, 207823). Allyn.

Merchant, Michael J. Applied FORTRAN Programming with Standard FORTRAN, WATFOR, WATFIV & Structured WATFIV. 544p. pap. write for info (ISBN 0-534-00497-0). Wadsworth Pub.

Merkle, Ralph C. Secrecy, Authentication & Public Key Systems. Stone, Harold, ed. LC 82-17611. (Computer Science Systems Programming Ser.: No. 18). 112p. 1982. 34.95 (ISBN 0-8357-1384-9). UMI Res Pr.

Metzner, John R. & Barnes, B. H., eds. Generalized Decision Table Programming. 1977. 35.00 (ISBN 0-12-492050-0). Acad Pr.

Mili, A. An Introduction to Program Verification. 312p. 1985. 37.95 (ISBN 0-442-26322-8). Van Nos Reinhold.

Miller, Larry & Viands, Leon. Introduction to CICS Programming. 1983. 24.95 (ISBN 0-13-479212-2, Spec). P-H.

Mitchell, William. Prelude to Programming: Problem Solving & Algorithms. 1984. text ed. 22.95 (ISBN 0-8359-5614-8); pap. text ed. 16.95 (ISBN 0-8359-5627-X). Reston.

Monolithic Memories, Inc. Technical Staff. Designing with Programmable Array Logic. 2nd ed. 680p. 1983. pap. text ed. 35.95 (ISBN 0-07-042723-2). McGraw.

Moriber, Harry A. Structured BASIC Programming. 512p. 1984. Additional supplements may be obtained from publisher. pap. text ed. 20.95 (ISBN 0-675-20106-3). Merrill.

Moser. Programming Proverbs for Pascal Students. 1985. pap. price not set (ISBN 0-471-82309-0). Wiley.

Mosier, Glenda D. Business Programming Concepts. (Illus.). 160p. (Orig.). 1984. pap. 9.75x (ISBN 0-9606666-3-X). Greenfield Pubns.

Motil, John. Programming Principles: An Introduction. 1983. pap. 29.89 (ISBN 0-205-08005-7, 208005); write for info. solutions manual (ISBN 0-205-08006-5, 208006). Allyn.

Skok, W. Systems & Programming Exercises in Data Processing. 128p. 1982. 30.00x (ISBN 0-905435-30-3, Pub. by DP Pubns). State Mutual Bk.

Smedley, Dan. Programming the PL-1 Way. (Illus.). 300p. 1982. 15.95 (ISBN 0-8306-0092-2); pap. 9.95 (ISBN 0-8306-1414-1, 1414). TAB Bks.

Smith, Robert E. & Johnson, Dora E. FORTRAN Autotester: A Self-Training Course Designed to Emancipate the Scientist & Engineer from the Need for the Professional Programmer. LC 63-827. pap. 48.00 (ISBN 0-317-09144-1, 2016483). Bks Demand UMI.

Smith, Robert L. A Tutorial for Using the TERAK-RT-11. 136p. 1982. pap. text ed. 7.95 (ISBN 0-8403-2697-1). Kendall-Hunt.

Software Packages, G-032. 1980. 875.00 (ISBN 0-89336-159-3). BCC.

Solomon, Eric. Games Programming. LC 83-26292. (Illus.). 250p. 1984. pap. 14.95 (ISBN 0-521-27110-X). Cambridge U Pr.

Sondak, Norman & Hatch, Richard. Using BASIC on the CYBER. 272p. 1982. pap. text ed. 20.95 (ISBN 0-574-21395-3, 13-4395); instr. guide avail. (ISBN 0-574-21396-1, 13-4396). SRA.

Southern, Bob. Structured Programming in Macro-II. 192p. 1984. pap. 21.00 (ISBN 0-932376-85-1, EY-00032-DP). Digital Pr.

Spencer, Donald. Problems for Computer Solution. 2nd ed. 128p. 1979. pap. 7.95 (ISBN 0-8104-5191-3). Hayden.

Sprague, Ralph H., Jr. & McNurlin, Barbara C. Information Systems Management in Practice. (Illus.). 512p. 1986. text ed. 29.95 (ISBN 0-13-464934-6). P-H.

Stankovic, John A. Structured Systems & Their Performance Improvement through Vertical Migration. Stone, Harold S., ed. LC 82-2772. (Computer Science Ser.: Systems Programming: No. 1). 152p. 1982. 39.95 (ISBN 0-8357-1325-3). UMI Res Pr.

Starkey, J. Denbigh & Ross, Rockford. Fundamental Programming & Problem Solving in Pascal. International ed. 625p. 1984. 17.00 (ISBN 0-314-77810-1). West Pub.

Startz, Richard. Eighty Eighty-Seven Applications & Programming for the IBM PC & Other PCs. LC 83-12216. (Illus.). 288p. 1983. pap. 24.95 (ISBN 0-89303-420-7); diskette 30.00 (ISBN 0-89303-421-5); bk. & diskette 54.95 (ISBN 0-89303-425-8). Brady Comm.

Staugaard, Andrew C., Jr. Microcomputer Programming & Interfacing, 6801, 68701 & 6803. LC 80-51716. 352p. 1980. pap. 14.95 (ISBN 0-672-21726-0, 21726). Sams.

Steffy, Wilbert & Darby, Daniel R. Computer-Generated Time Standards: A Methodology. (Illus.). 78p. 1980. 12.00 (ISBN 0-938654-13-6, CGTS). Indus Dev Inst Sci.

Steffy, Wilbert, et al. Computer Ratio Analysis: An Aid to Decision Making. (Illus.). 63p. 12.00 (ISBN 0-938654-14-4, CRA). Indus Dev Inst Sci.

Steklov Institute of Mathematics, Academy of Sciences, U S S R, No. 96. Automatic Programming, Numerical Methods & Functional Analysis: Proceedings. Faddeeva, V. N., ed. (Proceedings of the Steklov Institute of Mathematics: No. 96). 1970. 47.00 (ISBN 0-8218-1896-1, STEKLO-96). Am Math.

Stephens, David. A Programmer's Guide to Video Display Terminals. 335p. (Orig.). 1985. pap. 30.00 (ISBN 0-936158-01-8). Atlan Pub Corp.

Swann, Gloria H. Increasing Programmer's Production Through Logic Development. (Illus.). 1979. text ed. 13.50 (ISBN 0-89433-065-9). Petrocelli.

--Top Down Structured Design Techniques. LC 77-27092. (PBI Series for Computer & Data Processing Professionals). 1978. text ed. 15.00 (ISBN 0-89433-094-2); pap. 11.50 (ISBN 0-89433-019-5). Petrocelli.

Taitt, Kathy. Creative Programming Series. 1981. 9.95 (ISBN 0-318-01179-4). NEC Home Elect.

Titus, Christopher A. TEA: 8080-8085 Co-Resident Editor-Assembler. LC 79-65751. 256p. 1979. pap. 11.95 (ISBN 0-672-21628-0, 21628). Sams.

Titus, Jonathan & Larsen, David. Eighty-Eighty-Five-A Cookbook. LC 80-50054. 352p. 1980. pap. 15.95 (ISBN 0-672-21697-3, 21697). Sams.

Tobias, J. M., ed. Language Design & Programming Methodology: Proceedings. (Lecture Notes in Computer Science Ser.: Vol. 79). 255p. 1980. pap. 20.00 (ISBN 0-387-09745-7). Springer-Verlag.

Tremblay, Jean-Paul & Bunt, Richard B. An Introduction to Computer Science: An Algorithmic Approach, Short Edition. Stewart, Charles E., ed. (Illus.). 432p. 1980. text ed. 33.95 (ISBN 0-07-065167-1). McGraw.

Triance, J. M. COBOL Programming. 180p. 1981. pap. 22.95 (ISBN 0-471-89495-8). Wiley.

Underkoffler, Milton. Introduction to Structured Programming with Pascal. 376p. 1983. pap. text ed. write for info. (ISBN 0-87150-394-8, 8040). PWS Pubs.

--Introduction to Structured Programming with PL-1 & PL-C. 1980. write for info. (ISBN 0-87150-292-5, 2302, Prindle). PWS Pubs.

Van Canegham, Michel & Warren, David D. Logic Programming & Its Applications. Hobbs, Jerry R., ed. LC 85-6214. (Ablex Series in Artificial Intelligence: Vol. 2). 328p. 1985. text ed. 35.00 (ISBN 0-89391-232-8). Ablex Pub.

Van Horn, Royal. Computer Programming for Kids & Other Beginners: Radio Shack Color Computer. (Orig.). 1983. pap. text ed. 10.95 (ISBN 0-88408-163-X). Sterling Swift.

--Computer Programming for Kids & Other Beginners: TRS-80 Model III. (Orig.). 1983. pap. text ed. 10.95 (ISBN 0-88408-162-1). Sterling Swift.

Wadman, Ted & Coffin, Chris. An Easy Course in Programming the HP-11C & HP-15C. (Easy Course Ser.). (Illus.). pap. 18.00 (ISBN 0-931011-02-7). Grapevine Pubns.

Wallis. Programming Technology. (Infotech Computer State of the Arts Reports Ser.). 429p. 1982. 445.00 (ISBN 0-08-028565-1). Pergamon.

Walonick, David S. A Library of Subroutines for the IBM Personal Computer. 117p. 1984. pap. 19.95 (ISBN 0-673-15965-5); diskette 25.00 (ISBN 0-673-18076-X). Scott F.

Ward, Terry A. Applied Programming Techniques in C. 368p. 1985. pap. 19.95 (ISBN 0-673-18050-6). Scott F.

Watts, Harris. The Programme-Maker's Handbook or Goodbye Totter TV. (Illus.). 230p. (Orig.). 1982. pap. text ed. 12.50x (ISBN 0-9507582-0-5). Kumarian Pr.

Webb, J. T. Coral 66 Programming. 1978. 19.50x (ISBN 0-85012-193-0). Intl Pubns Serv.

Wedekind, H. Structural Database Programming. (Illus.). 1977. pap. 19.00x (ISBN 3-446-12371-7). Adlers Foreign Bks.

Weinberg, Gerald M. The Psychology of Computer Programming. (Illus.). 304p. 1971. 16.95 (ISBN 0-442-29264-3). Van Nos Reinhold.

Weinman, David & Kursham, Barbara. VAX BASIC. 1982. text ed. 22.95 (ISBN 0-8359-8239-4); pap. text ed. 17.95 (ISBN 0-8359-8238-6). Reston.

Weinstein, Cheryl & Harris, Carol. Computer Programming for Young Children: A Step-by-Step Guide for Teachers & Parents. 1983. pap. 12.95 (ISBN 0-936386-21-5). Creative Learning.

Weizenbaum, Joseph. Computer Power & Human Reason: From Judgment to Calculation. LC 75-19305. (Illus.). 300p. 1976. pap. text ed. 12.95x (ISBN 0-7167-0463-3). W H Freeman.

Welland, R. COBAL: Programming Pocket Guides. spiral bdg. 6.95 (ISBN 0-201-07750-7, 07750). Addison-Wesley.

--Decision Tables & Computer Programming. 1982. 34.95 (ISBN 0-471-26193-9). Wiley.

Welsh, J. & McKeag, R. M. Structured Systems Programming. (Ser. in Computer Science). (Illus.). 1980. text ed. 32.50 (ISBN 0-13-854562-6). P-H.

West, Raeto. Programming the VIC-20. 1984. pap. 24.95 (ISBN 0-942386-52-3). Compute Pubns.

White, D. J. Dynamic Programming. LC 69-13418. (Illus.). pap. 48.50 (ISBN 0-317-10704-6, 2016296). Bks Demand UMI.

White, Fred. One Hundred One Apple Computer Programming Tips & Tricks. 128p. (Orig.). 1982. pap. 8.95 (ISBN 0-86668-015-2). ARCsoft.

Whittle, Francis J. A Guide to DOS-VSE. 128p. 1985. pap. text ed. price not set (ISBN 0-89787-410-2). Gorsuch Scarisbrick.

Willis, Jerry, et al. Things to Do with Your Osborne Computers. 1983. pap. 3.95 (ISBN 0-451-12852-4, Sig). NAL.

Willoughby, Ralph A., ed. Stiff Differential Systems. LC 74-6300. (IBM Research Symposia Ser). 323p. 1974. 49.50x (ISBN 0-306-30797-9, Plenum Pr). Plenum Pub.

Wirth, N. Programming in Modula-2. (Illus.). 176p. 1982. 13.95 (ISBN 0-387-11674-5). Springer-Verlag.

Wnorowski, Thomas. Master Your Model-200 in 1-Hour. LC 85-71091. (Orig.). 1985. pap. text ed. 19.95 (ISBN 0-931543-02-9). IM Pr.

Wolfe, Philip & Koelling, C. Patrick. BASIC Engineering Science & Business Programs for the Apple II & IIe. 352p. 1984. pap. 19.95 (ISBN 0-89303-284-0); bk. & diskette 44.95 (ISBN 0-89303-290-5); diskette 25.00 (ISBN 0-89303-288-3). Brady Comm.

Wood, David B. A Practical Guide to Machine Language Programming on the Timex-Sinclair 1000 & 5000. (Illus.). 252p. 1984. pap. cancelled (ISBN 0-89303-763-X). Brady Comm.

Wood, Derick. Paradigms & Programming with Pascal. LC 82-19714. 425p. 1984. text ed. 27.95 (ISBN 0-914894-45-5). Computer Sci.

Wright, G. G. & Evans, D. Commercial Computer Programming. LC 74-80128. 208p. cancelled (ISBN 0-85012-113-2). Intl Pubns Serv.

Yeh, R., ed. Current Trends in Programming Methodology: Program Validation, Vol. 2. 1978. 34.95 (ISBN 0-13-195719-8). P-H.

Yeh, Raymond T., ed. Current Trends in Programming Methodology: Data Structuring, Vol. 4. (Illus.). 1978. ref. 34.95 (ISBN 0-13-195735-X). P-H.

--Current Trends in Programming Methodology: Software Specification & Design, Vol. 1. (Illus.). 1977. 34.95 (ISBN 0-13-195701-5). P-H.

Zaks, Rodnay. Programming the Z80. 3rd rev. ed. LC 81-51131. (Illus.). 624p. pap. 19.95 (ISBN 0-89588-069-5, C280). SYBEX.

Zammit. MACRO Eleven Programming. 170p. 1984. 19.00 (ISBN 0-9903001-4-5, Pub. by A Hilger England). Heyden.

PROGRAMMING (ELECTRONIC COMPUTERS)–ABILITY TESTING

Chandrasekaran, B. & Radicchi, S., eds. Computer Program Testing. 362p. 1981. 42.75 (ISBN 0-444-86292-7, North-Holland). Elsevier.

Gehringer, Edward F. Capability Architectures & Small Objects. Stone, Harold, ed. LC 82-6905. (Computer Science: Systems Programming Ser.: No. 10). 240p. 1982. 44.95 (ISBN 0-8357-1347-4). UMI Res Pr.

National Computing Centre Ltd., ed. Program Testing Aids. (Factfinder Ser: No. 8). 60p. (Orig.). 1972. pap. 10.00x (ISBN 0-85012-054-3). Intl Pubns Serv.

PROGRAMMING (ELECTRONIC COMPUTERS)–VOCATIONAL GUIDANCE

National Computing Centre. Working with Computers: A Guide to Jobs & Careers. 3rd ed. (Illus.). 75p. (Orig.). 1982. pap. 8.50x (ISBN 0-85012-359-3). Intl Pubns Serv.

PROGRAMMING (MATHEMATICS)

see also Dynamic Programming; Linear Programming

Abadie, J., ed. Integer & Non-Linear Programming. 544p. 1970. 85.00 (ISBN 0-7204-2036-9). Elsevier.

Arrow, Kenneth J., et al. Studies in Linear & Non-Linear Programming. (Illus.). 1958. pap. 18.50x (ISBN 0-8047-0562-3). Stanford U Pr.

Avriel, M. & Dembo, R. S., eds. Engineering Optimization. (Mathematical Programming Ser.: Vol. 11). 207p. 1980. pap. 42.75 (ISBN 0-444-85399-5, North Holland). Elsevier.

Balinski, M. L. & Lamarechal, C. Mathematical Programming in Use. 196p. 1978. pap. 30.00 (ISBN 0-444-85195-X). Elsevier.

Bellman, Richard E. Adaptive Control Processes: A Guided Tour. (Rand Corporation Research Studies). 1961. 45.00 (ISBN 0-691-07901-3). Princeton U Pr.

Beltrami, E. J. Algorithmic Approach to Nonlinear Analysis & Optimization. (Mathematics in Science & Engineering Ser.: Vol. 63). 1970. 55.00 (ISBN 0-12-085560-7). Acad Pr.

Broy, M. & Schmidt, G., eds. Theoretical Foundations of Programming Methodology. 1982. lib. bdg. 78.50 (ISBN 90-277-1460-6, Pub. by Reidel Holland); pap. 39.50 (ISBN 90-277-1462-2). Kluwer Academic.

Carsberg, Bryan V. Introduction to Mathematical Programming for Accountants. LC 71-95609. 1969. lib. bdg. 17.50x (ISBN 0-678-06006-1). Kelley.

Claycombe, William W. & Sullivan, William G. Foundations of Mathematical Programming. (Illus.). 304p. 1975. 24.95 (ISBN 0-87909-282-3). Reston.

Colloquium on Mathematics & Cybernetics in the Economy, Berlin, 1964. Pseudo-Boolean Programming & Applications. Ivanescu, P. L., ed. (Lecture Notes in Mathematics: Vol. 9). 1965. pap. 10.70 (ISBN 0-387-03352-1). Springer-Verlag.

Craven, B. D. Mathematical Programming & Control Theory. (Mathematics Ser.). 1978. pap. 15.95 (ISBN 0-412-15500-1, NO. 6070, Pub. by Chapman & Hall). Methuen Inc.

De Bakker, M. Mathematical Theory of Program Correctness. 1980. 44.95 (ISBN 0-13-562132-1). P-H.

Dolcetta, I. C., et al, eds. Recent Mathematical Methods in Dynamic Programming. (Lecture Notes in Mathematics: Vol. 1119). vi, 202p. 1985. pap. 14.40 (ISBN 0-387-15217-2). Springer-Verlag.

European Meeting of the Institute of Management Sciences & of the Econometric Institute, Warsaw, 1966. Pseudo-Boolean Methods for Bivalent Programming. Ivanescu, P. L. & Rudeanu, S., eds. (Lecture Notes in Mathematics: Vol. 23). 1966. pap. 10.70 (ISBN 0-387-03606-7). Springer-Verlag.

Faddeeva, V. N., ed. Automatic Programming & Numerical Methods of Analysis. LC 76-37618. (Seminars in Mathematics Ser.: Vol. 18). 1972. 25.00x (ISBN 0-306-18818-X, Consultants). Plenum Pub.

Fox, Richard L. Optimization Methods for Engineering Design. LC 78-127891. (Engineering Ser). 1971. 31.95 (ISBN 0-201-02078-5). Addison-Wesley.

Gallagher, R. H. Optimum Structural Design: Theory & Applications. LC 72-8600. (Numerical Methods in Engineering Ser.). 358p. 1973. 69.95x (ISBN 0-471-29050-5, Pub. by Wiley-Interscience). Wiley.

Gersting, Judith L. Mathematical Structures for Computer Science. LC 82-2550. (Illus.). 432p. 1982. text ed. 28.95 (ISBN 0-7167-1305-5); solutions manual avail. W H Freeman.

Goffin, J. L. & Rousseau, J. M., eds. Applications. (Mathematical Programming Studies: Vol. 20). 218p. 1982. 27.75 (ISBN 0-444-86478-4, I-341-82, North-Holland). Elsevier.

Gottfried, Byron S. & Weisman, Joel. Introduction to Optimization Theory. (Illus.). 592p. 1973. ref. ed. 34.95 (ISBN 0-13-491472-4). P-H.

Holzman. Mathematical Programming for Operations Researchers. (Industrial Engineering Ser.: Vol. 6). 392p. 1981. 55.00 (ISBN 0-8247-1499-7). Dekker.

Huard, P., ed. Point-to-Set Maps & Mathematical Programming. LC 78-23304. (Mathemartical Programming Studies: Vol. 10). 190p. 1979. 34.00 (ISBN 0-444-85243-3, North Holland). Elsevier.

Karwan, M. H., et al. Redundancy in Mathematical Programming: A State-of-the-Art Survey. (Lecture Notes in Economics & Mathematical Systems: Vol. 206). (Illus.). 286p. 1983. pap. 21.00 (ISBN 0-387-11552-8). Springer-Verlag.

Kolman, Bernard & Busby, Robert C. Discrete Mathematical Structures for Computer Science. (Illus.). 512p. 1984. text ed. 30.95 (ISBN 0-13-215418-8). P-H.

Korte, B. & Ritter, K., eds. Mathematical Programming At Oberwolfach II. (Mathematical Programming Studies: Vol. 22). 1985. 33.50 (ISBN 0-444-87691-X). Elsevier.

Kuhn, H. W., ed. Proceedings of the Princeton Symposium on Mathematical Programming. 1971. 42.50 (ISBN 0-691-08088-7). Princeton U Pr.

Kunzi, Hans P., et al. Numerical Methods of Mathematical Optimization with ALGOL & FORTRAN Programs. LC 68-18673. (Computer Science & Applied Mathematics Ser). 1968. 45.00 (ISBN 0-12-428850-2). Acad Pr.

Lange, Oskar. Optimal Decisions. 304p. 1972. text ed. 37.00 (ISBN 0-08-016053-0). Pergamon.

Lasdon, Leon S. Optimization Theory for Large Systems. (Illus.). 1970. write for info. (ISBN 0-02-367800-3). Macmillan.

Lev, B. & Weiss, H. J. Introduction to Mathematical Programming: Quantitative Tools for Decision Making. 290p. 1981. 31.75 (ISBN 0-444-00591-9, North-Holland). Elsevier.

McMillan, Claude. Mathematical Programming. LC 74-23273. (Wiley Management & Administration Ser.). Repr. of 1975 ed. 120.00 (ISBN 0-8357-9931-X, 2017000). Bks Demand UMI.

Manna, Z. Lectures on the Logic of Computer Programming. LC 79-93153. (CBMS-NSF Regional Conference Ser.: No. 31). iv, 49p. 1980. pap. text ed. 9.00 (ISBN 0-89871-164-9). Soc Indus-Appl Math.

Mathematics of the Decision Sciences Part I. Dantzig, G. B. & Veinott, A. F., Jr., eds. LC 62-21481. 429p. 1970. Repr. of 1968 ed. with corrections 41.00 (ISBN 0-8218-1111-8, LAM-11). Am Math.

Messina, P. C. & Murli, A., eds. Problems & Methodolgies in Mathematical Software Production, Sorrento, Italy 1980: Proceedings. (Lecture Notes in Computer Sciences: Vol. 142). 271p. 1982. pap. 14.50 (ISBN 0-387-11603-6). Springer-Verlag.

Mitra, G. Theory & Application of Mathematical Programming. 1977. 41.00 (ISBN 0-12-500450-8). Acad Pr.

Mulvey, J. M. Evaluating Mathematical Programming Techniques, Boulder, Colorado. (Lecture Notes in Economics & Mathematical Systems Ser.: Vol. 199). (Illus.). 379p. 1982. pap. 29.00 (ISBN 0-387-11495-5). Springer-Verlag.

Nemirovskii, A. S. Problem Complexity & Method Efficiency in Optimization. LC 82-11065. 388p. 1983. 53.95 (ISBN 0-471-10345-4, Pub. by Wiley-Interscience). Wiley.

Pfaffenberger, Roger C. & Walker, David A. Mathematical Programming for Economics & Business. (Illus.). 462p. 1976. text ed. 20.95x (ISBN 0-8138-1055-8). Iowa St U Pr.

Prekopa. Studies on Mathematical Programming. (Mathematical Method Operations Research Ser.: Vol. 1). 1979. 21.00 (ISBN 0-9960014-0-9, Pub. by Akademiai Kaido Hungary). Heyden.

Martin, James. Fourth Generation Languages, Vol. I. (Illus.). 432p. 1985. pap. text ed. 39.95 (ISBN 0-13-329673-3). P-H.

Maurer, H. A., ed. Automata, Languages & Programming: Sixth Colloquium. (Lecture Notes in Computer Science Ser.: Vol. 71). 1979. pap. 39.00 (ISBN 0-387-09510-1). Springer-Verlag.

Mayer, John S. IBM PC Survivor's Manual: A Primer for the IBM Personal Computer. 35p. (Orig.). 1982. pap. 11.95 (ISBN 0-9609092-0-6). Mayer Assocs.

Mesa Research. The Lisa Connection. 1984. pap. 19.95 (ISBN 0-8359-4088-8). Reston.

Metcalf, Chris & Sugiyama, Marc. Compute's Beginner's Guide to Machine Language on the the IBM PC & PCjr. Compute!, ed. (Orig.). 1985. pap. 14.95 (ISBN 0-942386-83-3). Compute Pubns.

Microtrend Inc. C Language on the IBM PC. 1984. 14.95. P-H.

Milne, R. & Strachey, C. The Theory of Programming Language Semantics, 2 vols. 1976. Set. 88.00x (ISBN 0-412-14260-0, NO. 6320, Pub. by Chapman & Hall). Methuen Inc.

Moder, J., et al. Project Management with CPM, PERT & PRECEDENCE Diagramming. 3rd ed. 464p. 1983. 27.50 (ISBN 0-442-25415-6). Van Nos Reinhold.

MUMPS Development Committee. American National Standard for Information Systems - Programming Language MUMPS: Programming. 1984. 17.00 (ISBN 0-918118-30-1). MUMPS.

MUMPS Users' Group Meeting. Proceedings. Faulkner, Judith R., ed. 1979. 15.00 (ISBN 0-918118-06-9). MUMPS.

MUMPS Users' Group Meeting, 1973. Proceedings. Zimmerman, Joan, ed. 9.00 (ISBN 0-918118-00-X). MUMPS.

MUMPS Users' Group Meeting, 1974. Proceedings. Zimmerman, Joan, ed. 9.00 (ISBN 0-918118-01-8). MUMPS.

MUMPS Users' Group Meeting, 1975. Proceedings. Zimmerman, Joan, ed. 15.00 (ISBN 0-918118-02-6). MUMPS.

Mumps Users' Group Meeting, 1978. Proceedings. Zimmerman, Pat, ed. 1978. pap. 15.00 (ISBN 0-918118-05-0). MUMPS.

National Computing Centre. High-Level Languages for Microprocessor Projects. Taylor, David & Morgan, Lyndon, eds. (Illus.). 279p. (Orig.). 1980. pap. 37.50x (ISBN 0-85012-233-3). Intl Pubns Serv.

Newey, M. C., ed. Programming Language Systems. new ed. Wolfendale, G. L. LC 78-60544. (Orig.). 1978. pap. text ed. 15.75 (ISBN 0-7081-0493-2, Pub. by ANUP Australia). Australia N U P.

Nicholls, John E. Structure & Design of Programming Languages. LC 74-12801. (IBM Systems Programming Ser.). (Illus.). 592p. 1975. text ed. 36.95 (ISBN 0-201-14454-9). Addison-Wesley.

Nie, Norman H., et al. SCSS: A User's Guide to the SCSS Conversational System. (Illus.). 592p. 1980. text ed. 35.95 (ISBN 0-07-046538-X); pap. text ed. 20.95 (ISBN 0-07-046533-9). McGraw.

Nivat, Maurice & Reynolds, John C., eds. Algebraic Methods in Semantics. (Illus.). 425p. 1985. write for info. Cambridge U Pr.

O'Donnell, M. J. Computing in Systems Described by Equations. LC 77-25999. (Lecture Notes in Computer Science: Vol. 58). 1977. pap. text ed. 14.00 (ISBN 0-387-08531-9). Springer-Verlag.

O'Donnell, Michael J. Equational Logic As a Programming Language. (Foundations of Computing Ser.). (Illus.). 250p. 1985. text ed. 25.00x (ISBN 0-262-15028-X). MIT Pr.

Ollengren, A. Definition of Programming Languages. 1975. 55.00 (ISBN 0-12-525750-3). Acad Pr.

Organick, Elliot I., et al. Programming Language Structure. (Computer Science & Applied Mathematics Ser.). 1978. text ed. 24.00i (ISBN 0-12-528260-5). Acad Pr.

Orr, Kenneth T. Structured Systems Development. LC 77-88593. (Illus.). 192p. (Orig.). 1977. 23.00 (ISBN 0-917072-08-1); pap. 18.50 (ISBN 0-917072-06-5). Yourdon.

Pagen, Frank G. Formal Specifications of Programming Language: A Panoramic Primer. (Illus.). 256p. 1981. text ed. 27.95 (ISBN 0-13-329052-2). P-H.

Paul, M. & Robinet, B., eds. International Symposium on Programming: Sixth Colloquium, Toulouse, April 17-19, 1984 Proceedings. (Lecture Notes in Computer Science Ser.: Vol. 167). vi, 262p. 1984. pap. 16.50 (ISBN 0-387-12925-1). Springer-Verlag.

Peterson, W. Wesley. Introduction to Programming Languages. 1974. 28.95 (ISBN 0-13-493486-5). P-H.

Piloty, R., et al. CONLAN Report. (Lecture Notes in Computer Science: Vol. 151). 174p. 1983. pap. 12.00 (ISBN 0-387-12275-3). Springer-Verlag.

Pratt, Terrence W. Programming Languages: Design & Implementation. 2nd ed. (Illus.). 624p. 1984. text ed. 32.95 (ISBN 0-13-730580-X). P-H.

Pritsker, Alan A. Introduction to Simulation & Slam II. 2nd ed. LC 84-9104. 612p. 1984. text ed. 29.50x (ISBN 0-470-20087-1). Halsted Pr.

Reid, K. Relationship Between Numerical Computation & Programming Language. 378p. 1982. 32.00 (ISBN 0-444-86377-X, North-Holland). Elsevier.

Reijns, G. L. & Dagless, E. L., eds. Concurrent Languages in Distributed Systems-Hardware Supported Implementation: Proceedings of the WG 10.3 Workshop Held in Bristol, UK, 26-28 March 1984. 164p. 1985. 31.50 (ISBN 0-444-87635-9, North-Holland). Elsevier.

Research & Education Association Staff. Handbook & Guide for Comparing & Selecting Languages. (Illus.). 128p. 1985. 8.95 (ISBN 0-87891-561-3). Res & Educ.

Richards, M. & Whitby-Strevens, C. BCPL-The Language & Its Compiler. LC 77-71098. (Illus.). 1981. pap. 12.95 (ISBN 0-521-28681-6). Cambridge U Pr.

Rosen, Robert. Apple Machine Language. 256p. pap. 20.45 (ISBN 0-03-063336-2). HR&W.

Rothmeier, Jeffrey, ed. Proceedings: MUMPS Users' Group Meeting. 1976. 15.00 (ISBN 0-918118-03-4). MUMPS.

Rudall, B. H. & Corns, T. N. Computers & Literature: A Practical Guide. (Computer Language Programmes Ser.). 12.00 (ISBN 0-9901004-6-4, Pub. by Abacus England). Heyden.

Salomaa, A. & Steinby, M., eds. Automata, Languages & Programming. (Lecture Notes in Computer Science Ser.: Vol. 52). 1977. pap. 28.00 (ISBN 0-387-08342-1). Springer-Verlag.

SAS Institute Inc., ed. SAS Applications Guide, 1980 Edition. (Illus.). 204p. (Orig.). 1980. pap. 9.95 (ISBN 0-917382-16-1). SAS Inst.

Schneider, Hans J. Problem Oriented Programming Languages. 151p. 1984. 23.95x (ISBN 0-471-90111-3, Pub. by Wiley-Interscience). Wiley.

Shannon, Terry. Introduction to Vax-VMS. Cavanaugh, Robin, ed. (Illus.). 312p. (Orig.). 1985. 19.95 (ISBN 0-9614729-0-1). Prof Press PA.

Simpson, D., ed. Job Control Languages: Past, Present, & Future. LC 74-80130. 120p. 1974. pap. 22.50x (ISBN 0-85012-119-1). Intl Pubns Serv.

Snook, T., et al. Report on the Programming Language PLZ-SYS. (Illus.). 1978. pap. 11.00 (ISBN 0-387-90374-7). Springer-Verlag.

Southworth, R. & De Leeuw, S. Digital Computation & Numerical Methods. 1965. text ed. 45.00 (ISBN 0-07-059799-5). McGraw.

Spencer, Donald D. Introduction to Information Processing. 3rd ed. 650p. 1981. text ed. 26.95 (ISBN 0-675-08073-8); basic supplement 4.95 (ISBN 0-675-09917-X). Additional supplements maybe obtained from publisher. Merrill.

Sprack-Jones, Karen & Wilks, Yorick. Automatic Natural Language Parsing. LC 83-8601. 208p. 1983. 44.95x (ISBN 0-470-27460-3); pap. 24.95 (ISBN 0-470-20165-7). Halsted Pr.

Stabley, Don H. Logical Programming with System 360. LC 75-96047. 579p. 1970. 45.50 (ISBN 0-471-81945-X); supplementary materials avail. (ISBN 0-471-02856-8). Wiley.

--System 360 Assembler Language. LC 67-30037. 129p. 1967. pap. 25.50x (ISBN 0-471-81950-6, Pub. by Wiley-Interscience). Wiley.

Stein, Jean. Jazz-Five Easy Pieces. 200p. (Orig.). 1985. pap. 17.95 (ISBN 0-07-881111-2). Osborne-McGraw.

Stiegler, Marc & Hansen, Bob. Programming Languages Featuring the IBM-PC. (Orig.). 1984. pap. 9.95 (ISBN 0-671-55929-X, Pub. by Baen Books). PB.

Taylor, Charles F., Jr. The Master Handbook of High-Level Microcomputer Languages. 256p. (Orig.). 1984. 21.95 (ISBN 0-8306-0733-1); pap. 15.50 (ISBN 0-8306-1733-7, 1733). TAB Bks.

Tennant, Harry. Natural Language Processing. (Illus.). 1981. 17.50 (ISBN 0-89433-100-0). Petrocelli.

Tennent, R. Principles of Programming Languages. 1981. 32.95 (ISBN 0-13-709873-1). P-H.

Tobias, J. M., ed. Language Design & Programming Methodology: Proceedings. (Lecture Notes in Computer Science Ser.: Vol. 79). 255p. 1980. pap. 20.00 (ISBN 0-387-09745-7). Springer-Verlag.

Tootill, Alan & Barrow, David. Sixty-Five Hundred Two Machine Code for Humans. 170p. 1985. pap. 12.95 (ISBN 0-13-811340-8). P H.

Tou, Julius. Software Engineering, Vols. 1-2. 1971. Vol. 1. 61.00 (ISBN 0-12-696201-4); Vol. 2. 61.00 (ISBN 0-12-696202-2). Acad Pr.

Truitt, Thomas D. & Mindlin, Stuart B. Introduction to Non-Procedural Language. 544p. 1983. pap. 29.95 (ISBN 0-07-065301-1, BYTE Bks). McGraw.

Tucker, A. B. Programmimg Languages. 2nd ed. (Computer Science Ser.). 915p. 36.95 (ISBN 0-07-065416-6). McGraw.

Tucker, Allen B., Jr. Programming Languages. (Computer Science Ser.). (Illus.). 1978. text ed. 36.95 (ISBN 0-07-065415-8). McGraw.

Uehara, T. & Barbacci, M., eds. Computer Hardware Description Languages & Their Applications. 244p. 1984. 38.50 (ISBN 0-444-86633-7, North Holland). Elsevier.

Volkstorf, Charles. Handbook of Efficiency Techniques. 1985. 16.00 (ISBN 0-918118-31-X). MUMPS.

Wadge, William W. & Ashcroft, Edward A. Lucid, the Dataflow Programming Language. (APIC Studies in Data Processing). 1985. 39.50 (ISBN 0-12-729650-6). Acad Pr.

Wallach, Y. Study & Compilation of Computer Languages. new ed. LC 73-89202. (Mathematics & Its Applications Ser.). 624p. 1974. 129.50 (ISBN 0-677-04010-5). Gordon.

Walters, Richard F., ed. A MUMPS Primer. rev. ed. 1983. pap. 15.00 (ISBN 0-918118-24-7). MUMPS.

Warme, Paul. BASEX. LC 79-775. 1979. pap. 9.95 (ISBN 0-07-068290-9, BYTE Bks). McGraw.

Wasserman, Anthony I. Programming Language Design. (Tutorial Texts Ser.). 527p. 1980. 30.00 (ISBN 0-8186-0312-7, Q312); members 18.00. IEEE Comp Soc.

Watts, Lisa & Wharton, Mike. Machine Code for Beginners. (Computer Bks.). (Illus.). 48p. 1984. 8.95 (ISBN 0-86020-736-6, Usborne-Hayes); PLB 12.95 (ISBN 0-88110-170-2, Usborne-Hayes); pap. 5.95 (ISBN 0-86020-735-8, Usborne-Hayes). EDC.

Wegner, P. An Introduction to Symbolic Programming. (Griffin's Statistical Monographs: No. 1). 219p. 1966. pap. 8.95x (ISBN 0-85264-129-X). Lubrecht & Cramer.

Wells, Timothy. A Structured Approach to Building Programs: COBOL, Vol. 2. (Orig.). 1985. pap. text ed. write for info. (ISBN 0-917072-44-8). Yourdon.

Werum, W. & Windauer, H. Introduction to Pearl Process & Experiment Automation of Realtime Language. 1982. 16.50 (ISBN 0-9940018-4-3, Pub. by Vieweg & Sohn Germany). Heyden.

Wexelblat, Richard L., ed. History of Programming Languages. LC 80-518. (ACM Monograph Ser.). 1981. 49.50 (ISBN 0-12-745040-8). Acad Pr.

Wheatley, Jon. Language & Rules. LC 70-95011. (Janua Linguarum, Ser. Minor: No. 80). (Orig.). 1970. pap. text ed. 5.60x (ISBN 0-686-22416-7). Mouton.

Williams, J. H. & Fisher, D. A., eds. Design & Implementation of Programming Languages: Proceedings of a DoD Sponsored Workshop, Ithaca, Oct., 1976. (Lecture Notes in Computer Science: Vol. 54). 1977. pap. text ed. 26.00 (ISBN 0-387-08360-X). Springer-Verlag.

Williams, Stephanie. Humans & Machines. DiPietro, Robert, ed. LC 84-20359. (Delaware Symposia on Language Studies Ser.). 308p. 1985. text ed. 37.50 (ISBN 0-89391-272-7). Ablex Pub.

Willis, Deborrah & Willis, Jerry. How to Use TeloFacts. (Illus.). 120p. 1983. pap. 9.95 (ISBN 0-88056-116-5); incl. disk 49.95 (ISBN 0-88056-174-2); TeloFacts 2 for the Apple. incl. disk 199.95 (ISBN 0-88056-176-9). Dilithium Pr.

Wood, D. Grammar & L Formas: An Introduction. (Lecture Notes in Computer Science: Vol. 91). 314p. 1980. pap. 23.00 (ISBN 0-387-10233-7). Springer-Verlag.

Young, S. J. Real Time Language Design & Development. (Computers & Their Applications Ser.). 352p. 1982. 85.95 (ISBN 0-470-27343-7). Halsted Pr.

Yourdon, Edward. Managing the Structured Techniques. 2nd ed. LC 79-63254. 280p. (Orig.). 1979. pap. 27.00 (ISBN 0-917072-15-4). Yourdon.

Zapolin, Richard E., ed. Proceedings: MUMPS Users' Group Meeting. 1977. 15.00 (ISBN 0-918118-04-2). MUMPS.

Zimmerman, Joan & Salander, eds. Introduction to Standard MUMPS. rev. ed. 1984. pap. 15.00 (ISBN 0-918118-27-1). MUMPS.

PROGRAMMING MANAGEMENT (ELECTRONIC COMPUTERS)

see Computer Programming Management

PROGRAMS, COMPUTER

see Computer Programs

PROJECT ACE

see Automatic Checkout Equipment

PROJECT APOLLO

American Astronautical Society. Post Apollo Space Exploration, 2 Vols. (Advances in Astronautical Ser.: Vol. 20). 1966. Set. 85.00x (ISBN 0-87703-022-7, Pub. by Am Astronaut). Univelt Inc.

Gray, Mike. Angle of Attack. Date not set. 15.95 (ISBN 0-393-01892-X). Norton.

Hallion, Richard P. & Crouch, Tom D., eds. Apollo: Ten Years Since Tranquillity Base. LC 79-10271. (Illus.). 174p. 1979. 19.95x (ISBN 0-87474-506-3); pap. 19.95x (ISBN 0-87474-505-5). Smithsonian.

Irwin, James B., Jr. & Emerson, W. A. Un Astronauta y la Lumbrera de la Noche. 176p. 1981. Repr. of 1978 ed. 4.25 (ISBN 0-311-01066-0). Casa Bautista.

Lee, Chester M., ed. Apollo Soyuz Mission Report. LC 57-43769. (Advances in the Astronautical Sciences Ser.: Vol. 34). (Illus.). 1977. lib. bdg. 35.00x (ISBN 0-87703-089-8, Pub. by Univelt Inc). Univelt Inc.

Levinson, A. A., ed. Apollo Eleven Lunar Science Conference, Jan., 1970: Proceedings, 3 vols. Incl. Vol. 1. Minerology & Petrology; Vol. 2. Chemical & Isotope Analysis; Vol. 3. Physical Properties. LC 72-119485. c, 2000p. 1971. Set. 305.00 (ISBN 0-08-016392-0). Pergamon.

Steinhoff, Ernst A., ed. The Eagle Has Returned, Pt. 2. New ed. (Science & Technology Ser.: Vol. 45). (Illus.). 1977. 35.00x (ISBN 0-87703-092-8, Pub. by Am Astronaut). Univelt Inc.

PROJECT NETWORKS

see Network Analysis (Planning)

PROJECT VANGUARD

Green, Constance & Lomask, Milton. Vanguard: A History. LC 70-606624. (Illus.). 309p. 1971. text ed. 19.95x (ISBN 0-87474-112-2). Smithsonian.

PROJECTILES

see also Ammunition; Ballistics; Bombs; Cartridges; Guided Missiles; Rockets (Aeronautics); Rockets (Ordnance)

Socffern, J. Projectile Weapons of War & Explosive Compounds. 318p. 1984. Repr. of 1858 ed. 37.00x (ISBN 0-85546-164-0, Pub. by Richmond Pub England). State Mutual Bk.

PROJECTION

see also Geometrical Drawing; Geometry, Descriptive; Map-Projection; Mechanical Drawing; Orthographic Projection

Rosenfeld, B. A. Stereographic Projection. 53p. 1977. pap. 1.95 (ISBN 0-8285-0745-7, Pub. by Mir Pubs USSR). Imported Pubns.

PROJECTIVE DIFFERENTIAL GEOMETRY

see Geometry, Differential–Projective

PROJECTIVE GEOMETRY

see Geometry, Projective

PROLOG (COMPUTER PROGRAM LANGUAGE)

Campbell, John A., ed. Implementation of Prolog. (Artificial Intelligence Ser.: I-381). 391p. 1984. text ed. 74.95x (ISBN 0-470-20044-8); pap. text ed. 29.95x (ISBN 0-470-20045-6). Halsted Pr.

Clark, Keith L. & McCabe, Frank. Micro-Prolog: Programming in Logic. 1984. pap. 16.95 (ISBN 0-13-581264-X). P-H.

Clocksin, W. F. & Mellish, C. S. Programming in Prolog. 279p. 1982. pap. 16.95 (ISBN 0-387-11046-1). Springer-Verlag.

--Programming in Prolog. 2nd ed. xv, 297p. 1984. pap. 17.95 (ISBN 0-387-15011-0). Springer-Verlag.

Dahl. Prolog for Programmers. 1985. pap. price not set (ISBN 0-471-82495-X). Wiley.

Ennals, Richard. Beginning Micro-PROLOG. (Hands On! Computer Bks.). 212p. (Orig.). 1984. pap. 15.34 (ISBN 0-06-669000-5). Har-Row.

Kluzniak, Feliks & Szpakowicz, Stanislaw. Prolog for Programmers. 1985. 47.50 (ISBN 0-12-416520-6). Acad Pr.

Li, Deyi. A PROLOG Database System. LC 83-26896. 207p. 1984. text ed. 44.95x (ISBN 0-471-90429-5). Wiley.

PROMETHIUM

Wheelwright, James. Promethium Technology. (ANS Monographs). 416p. 1973. 22.50 (ISBN 0-89448-002-2, 300006). Am Nuclear Soc.

PRONGHORN ANTELOPE

Caton, John D. The Antelope & Deer of America: A Scientific Treatise upon the Natural History, Habits, Affinities & Capacity for Domestication of the Antilocapra & Cervidae of North America. LC 73-17896. (Natural Sciences in America Ser.). (Illus.). 428p. 1974. Repr. 30.00x (ISBN 0-405-05723-7). Ayer Co Pubs.

Yoakum, James D. & Spalinger, Donald E., eds. American Pronghorn Antelope. LC 79-89207. (Illus.). 244p. (Orig.). 1979. pap. 5.00 (ISBN 0-933564-05-8). Wildlife Soc.

PROOF THEORY

Bittinger, M. L. Logic, Proof, & Sets. 2nd ed. LC 81-14913. 144p. 1982. pap. text ed. 8.95 (ISBN 0-201-10384-2). Addison-Wesley.

Boolos, G. The Unprovability of Consistency. LC 77-85710. (Illus.). 1979. 37.50 (ISBN 0-521-21879-9). Cambridge U Pr.

Hallerberg, Arthur E. Mathematical Proof: An Elementary Approach. (Orig.). 1974. pap. 5.95x (ISBN 0-02-845690-4). Hafner.

Lay, Steven R. Analysis: An Introduction to Proof. (Illus.). 304p. 1986. text ed. 29.95 (ISBN 0-13-032996-7). P-H.

Luckhardt, H. Extensional Goedel Functional Interpretation: A Consistency Proof of Classical Analysis. LC 72-96046. (Lecture Notes in Mathematics: Vol. 306). 161p. 1973. pap. 12.00 (ISBN 0-387-06119-3). Springer-Verlag.

Norman, Edward & Barr, Murray. Logic, Proof, & Mathematical Structures. cancelled (ISBN 0-8130-0739-9). U Presses Fla.

Proof Theory Symposium, Kiel, 1974. Proof Theory Symposium, Keil 1974: Proceedings. Muller, G. H. & Diller, J., eds. (Lecture Notes in Mathematics: Vol. 500). 1976. pap. 21.00 (ISBN 0-387-07533-X). Springer-Verlag.

Schuette, K. Proof Theory. Crossley, J. N., tr. from Ger. LC 76-45768. (Grundlehren der Mathematischen Wissenschaften Ser.: Vol. 225). 1977. 49.00 (ISBN 3-540-07911-4). Springer-Verlag.

Szabo, M. E. Algebra of Proofs. (Studies in Logic & the Foundations of Mathematics: Vol. 88). 298p. 1978. 55.50 (ISBN 0-7204-2286-8, North-Holland). Elsevier.

Takeuti, G. Proof Theory. LC 75-23164. (Studies in Logic & the Foundations of Mathematics: Vol. 81). 372p. 1975. 64.00 (ISBN 0-444-10492-5, North-Holland). Elsevier.

PROPAGATION OF PLANTS

see Plant Propagation

PROPANE

Brightman, Robert. One-Hundred One Practical Uses for Propane Torches. (Illus.). 1978. pap. 5.95 (ISBN 0-8306-1030-8, 1030). TAB Bks.

Carley, Larry W. Propane Conversion of Cars, Trucks & RVs. (Illus.). 224p. 1982. 14.95 (ISBN 0-8306-3103-8); pap. 9.95 (ISBN 0-8306-2103-2, 2103). TAB Bks.

Huyduk, A. S. Propane, Butane & 2-Methylpropane. 100.01 (ISBN 0-08-029202-X). Pergamon.

Mother Earth News Staff. How to Convert Your Vehicle to Propane. Hoffman, Robert, ed. 50p. (Orig.). 1981. pap. 7.50 (ISBN 0-938432-01-X). Mother Earth.

PROPELLANTS

Boyars, Carl & Klager, Karl, eds. Propellants Manufacture, Hazards, & Testing. LC 75-87208. (Advances in Chemistry Ser.: No. 88). 1969. 34.95 (ISBN 0-8412-0089-0). Am Chemical.

PROPELLERS

May, E. R. The Theory & Practice of Controllable Pitch Propellors. (Marine Engineering Practice Ser.: Vol. 2, Pt. 13). 1979. pap. 6.00x (ISBN 0-900976-62-4, Pub. by. Inst Marine Eng). Intl Spec Bk.

Stanton, John R. Theory & Practice of Propellers for Auxiliary Sailboats. LC 75-31778. (Illus.). 79p. 1975. pap. 4.00 (ISBN 0-87033-213-9). Cornell Maritime.

Woodward, John B. Marine Shaft Alignment Calculations. (Michigan Marine Engineering Ser.). 60p. (Orig.). 1985. pap. text ed. 5.00 (ISBN 0-931781-00-0). Jenning Pr.

PROPELLERS, AERIAL

Bent, R. & McKinley, J. Aircraft Powerplants. 5th ed. 608p. 1985. 28.95 (ISBN 0-07-004797-9). McGraw.

Bent, Ralph D. & McKinley, James L. Aircraft Powerplants. 4th ed. Orig. Title: Powerplants for Aerospace Vehicles. (Illus.). 1978. 30.20 (ISBN 0-07-004792-8). McGraw.

Delp, Frank. Aircraft Propellers & Controls. (Aviation Technician Training Course Ser.). (Illus.). 156p. 1979. pap. text ed. 6.95 (ISBN 0-89100-097-6, EA-APC). Aviation Maintenance.

Welch, William A. Lightplane Propeller Design, Selection, Maintenance & Repair. (Modern Aviation Ser.). (Illus.). 1979. 8.95 (ISBN 0-8306-9765-9, 2269). TAB Bks.

PROPERTIES OF MATTER

see Matter–Properties

PROPOSAL WRITING IN RESEARCH

Public Management Institute. Grantspro. 65p. 1984. manual, incl. diskette 200.00x (ISBN 0-916664-39-2). Public Management.

PROSE, COMPUTER

see Computer Prose

PROSPECTING

see also Assaying; Geochemical Prospecting; Mine Surveying; Mine Valuation; Mineralogy, Determinative; Petroleum–Geology

Ansari, Mary B. & Amaral, Anne. Gold & Silver Prospecting Books in Print. 23p. (Orig.). 1984. pap. 4.50 (ISBN 0-318-03520-0). Sierra NV Chapter.

Borehole Logging for Uranium Exploration: A Manual. (Technical Reports Ser.: No. 212). (Illus.). 279p. 1982. pap. 33.50 (ISBN 92-0-145082-6, IDC212, IAEA). Unipub.

Bowie, S. H., et al, eds. Uranium Prospecting Handbook. 346p. 1977. pap. text ed. 49.00x (ISBN 0-900488-15-8). IMM North Am.

Challa, Krishna. Investment & Returns in Exploration & the Impact on the Supply of Oil & Natural Gas Reserves. Bruchey, Stuart, ed. LC 78-22667. (Energy in the American Economy Ser.). (Illus.). 1979. lib. bdg. 16.00x (ISBN 0-405-11971-2). Ayer Co Pubs.

Copp, Henry N. Manual for the Use of Prospectors on the Mineral Lands of the U. S. 5th ed. Bruchey, Stuart, ed. LC 78-53538. (Development of Public Lands Law in the U. S. Ser.). 1979. Repr. of 1897 ed. lib. bdg. 13.00x (ISBN 0-405-11371-4). Ayer Co Pubs.

Curtis, Doris M., et al. How to (Try to) Find on Oil Field. 94p. 1981. 23.95x (ISBN 0-87814-166-9). Pennwell Bks.

Dahlberg, E. C. Applied Hydrodynamics in Petroleum Exploration. (Illus.). 161p. 1982. pap. 24.00 (ISBN 0-387-90677-0). Springer-Verlag.

Davidson, Martin J. & Gottlieb, Benjamin M., eds. Unconventional Methods in Exploration for Petroleum & Natural Gas, No. III. LC 83-8653. (Illus.). 282p. 1984. 50.00 (ISBN 0-87074-188-8). SMU Press.

Harbaugh, John W., et al. Probability Methods in Oil Exploration. LC 76-50631. 269p. 1977. 42.95 (ISBN 0-471-35129-6, Pub. by Wiley-Interscience). Wiley.

Jones, M. J., ed. Prospecting in Areas of Glacial Terrain. 138p. (Orig.). 1973. pap. text ed. 40.25x (ISBN 0-900488-19-0). IMM North Am.

--Prospecting in Areas of Glaciated Terrain 1975. 154p. (Orig.). 1975. pap. text ed. 46.00x (ISBN 0-900488-29-8). IMM North Am.

Lacy, Willard C., ed. Mineral Exploration. LC 82-969. (Benchmark Papers in Geology Ser.: Vol. 70). 434p. 1983. 52.00 (ISBN 0-87933-425-8). Van Nos Reinhold.

Lagal, Roy. Detector Owner's Field Manual. rev. ed. Nelson, Bettye, ed. LC 75-44706. (Illus.). 236p. (Orig.). 1982. pap. 8.95 (ISBN 0-915920-43-3). Ram Pub.

Malyuga, Dmitrii P. Biogeochemical Methods of Prospecting. LC 64-17203. 205p. 1964. 32.50 (ISBN 0-306-10682-5, Consultants). Plenum Pub.

Megill, R. E. Long Range Exploration Planning. 96p. 1985. 33.95 (ISBN 0-87814-286-X). PennWell Bks.

Moody, Graham B. Petroleum Exploration Handbook: A Practical Manual Summarizing the Application of Earth Sciences to Petroleum Exploration. (Illus.). 1961. 75.00 (ISBN 0-07-042867-0). McGraw.

North, Oliver S. Mineral Exploration, Mining, & Processing Patents, 1980. (Illus.). 135p. 1982. 35.00x (ISBN 0-89520-294-8). Soc Mining Eng.

Nuclear Techniques for Mineral Exploration & Exploitation. (Panel Proceedings Ser.). (Illus., Orig.). 1971. pap. 15.50 (ISBN 92-0-041071-5, ISP279, IAEA). Unipub.

Petralia, Joseph F. Gold! Gold! Gold!-A Beginners Handbook & Recreational Guide: How to Prospect for Gold, Vol. 4. 2nd ed. LC 81-126200. (Illus.). 112p. (Orig.). 1982. 10.95 (ISBN 0-9605890-2-3); pap. 6.95 (ISBN 0-9605890-3-1). Sierra Trading.

Prospecting in Areas of Glaciated Terrain 1977. 140p. 1977. pap. text ed. 54.75x (ISBN 0-900488-38-7). IMM North Am.

Prospecting in Areas of Glaciated Terrain 1979. 110p. 1979. pap. text ed. 57.50x (ISBN 0-900488-46-8). IMM North Am.

Prospecting in Areas of Glaciated Terrain 1984, No. 6. (Prospecting in Areas of Glaciated Terrain Ser.). 232p. (Orig.). 1984. pap. text ed. 43.25x (ISBN 0-900488-74-3). IMM North Am.

Savinskii, Igor D. Probability Tables for Locating Elliptical Underground Masses with a Rectangular Grid. LC 65-20212. 110p. 1965. 45.00x (ISBN 0-306-65112-2, IFI Plenum). Plenum Pub.

Silver, Burr A. Subsurface Exploration Stratigraphy. 45.00 (ISBN 0-318-02024-6). IED Pub Hse.

Spooner, Robert D. Response of Natural Gas & Crude Oil Exploration & Discovery to Economic Incentives. Bruchey, Stuart, ed. LC 78-22749. (Energy in the American Economy Ser.). (Illus.). 1979. lib. bdg. 21.00x (ISBN 0-405-12014-1). Ayer Co Pubs.

Steinart, R. Prospecting in Alaska. facs. ed. (Shorey Prospecting Ser.). 28p. pap. 3.95 (ISBN 0-8466-0038-2, S38). Shorey.

Stone, Gregory. Prospecting for Lode Gold. (Illus.). 48p. 1975. pap. 5.95 (ISBN 0-8059-2192-3). Dorrance.

Takken, Suzanne. Petroleum Exploration Handbook. 24.00 (ISBN 0-318-01993-0). IED Pub Hse.

Wallace, A. F. Land Cruising & Prospecting. (Illus.). 175p. pap. 3.50 (ISBN 0-936622-14-8). A R Harding Pub.

PROSPECTING–GEOPHYSICAL METHODS

see also Electric Prospecting; Radioactive Prospecting; Seismic Prospecting

Badley, Michael. Practical Seismic Interpretation. (Illus.). 269p. 1985. 62.00 (ISBN 0-934634-88-2). Intl Human Res.

Borehole Geophysics Applied to Metallic Mineral Prospecting. pap. 4.95 (SSC9, SSC). Unipub.

Dobrin, Milton. Introduction to Geophysical Prospecting. 3rd ed. LC 75-37603. 1976. text ed. 44.95 (ISBN 0-07-017195-5). McGraw.

Geyer, Richard A., ed. CRC Handbook of Geophysical Exploration at Sea. 464p. 1983. 86.50 (ISBN 0-8493-0222-6). CRC Pr.

Howarth, R. J., ed. Statistics & Data Analysis in Geochemical Prospecting. (Handbook of Exploration Geochemistry Ser.: Vol. 2). 438p. 1983. 100.00 (ISBN 0-444-42038-X). Elsevier.

Koefoed, O. Geosounding Principles: Resistivity Sounding Measurements, Vol. 1. LC 79-14798. (Methods in Geochemistry & Geophysics Ser.: Vol. 14A). 272p. 1979. 70.25 (ISBN 0-444-41704-4). Elsevier.

Sittig, Marshall, ed. Geophysical & Geochemical Techniques for Exploration of Hydrocarbons & Minerals. LC 79-24469. (Energy Technology Review Ser.: No. 52). (Illus.). 300p. 1980. 40.00 (ISBN 0-8155-0782-8). Noyes.

Spradley, L. Harold. Surveying & Navigation in Seismic Exploration. (Illus.). 300p. 1985. text ed. 54.00 (ISBN 0-934634-87-4). Intl Human Res.

Whiteley, Robert J. Geophysical Case Study of the Woodlawn Orebody, New South Wales,Australia. LC 79-42637. (Illus.). xviii, 592p. 1981. 110.00 (ISBN 0-08-023996-X). Pergamon.

Zhigach, K. F., ed. Industrial & Exploratory Geophysical Prospecting. LC 62-15541. 136p. 1963. 30.00 (ISBN 0-306-10542-X, Consultants). Plenum Pub.

Zhigach, Kuzma F. Industrial & Exploratory Geophysical Prospecting. Zhigach, K. F., ed. LC 62-15541. pap. 35.50 (ISBN 0-317-27213-6, 2024711). Bks Demand UMI.

PROSTAGLANDIN

Bennett, Alan. Prostaglandins & the Gut, Vol. 1. 1977. 14.40 (ISBN 0-904406-49-0). Eden Pr.

Berti, F. & Velo, G. P., eds. The Prostaglandin System: Endoperoxides, Prostacyclin & Thromboxanes. LC 80-28197. (NATO ASI Series A, Life Sciences: Vol. 36). 437p. 1981. 49.50x (ISBN 0-306-40645-4, Plenum Pr). Plenum Pub.

Berti, F., et al, eds. Prostaglandins & Thromboxanes. LC 77-5364. (NATO ASI Series A, Life Sciences: Vol. 13). 458p. 1977. 59.50x (ISBN 0-306-35613-9, Plenum Pr). Plenum Pub.

Bindra, Jasjit S. Prostaglandin Synthesis. 1977. 60.00 (ISBN 0-12-099460-7). Acad Pr.

Braquet, P., et al, eds. Prostaglandins & Membrane Ion Transport. (Advances in Ion Transport Regulation Ser.). (Illus.). 430p. 1985. text ed. 59.50 (ISBN 0-88167-052-9). Raven.

Cohen, Max, ed. Biological Protection with Prostaglandins, Vol. I. 320p. 1985. price not set (ISBN 0-8493-5962-7). CRC Pr.

Conn, H. L., et al. Prostaglandins, Lipids: New Developments in Artheriosclerosis. 152p. 1981. 44.00 (ISBN 0-444-00566-8, Biomedical Pr). Elsevier.

Crabbe, Pierre, ed. Prostaglandin Research. (Organic Chemistry Ser.). 1977. 65.00 (ISBN 0-12-194660-6). Acad Pr.

Dunn, Michael J. & Patrono, Carlo, eds. Prostaglandins & the Kidney: Biochemistry, Physiology, Pharmacology, & Clinical Applications. 438p. 1983. 49.50 (ISBN 0-306-41054-0, Plenum Med Bk). Plenum Pub.

First International Conference on Prostaglandins & Cancer, Washington, DC, August 30-September 2, 1981. Prostaglandins & Cancer: Proceedings. Powles, Trevor J., et al, eds. LC 82-86. (Prostaglandins & Related Lipids: Vol. 2). 876p. 1982. 84.00 (ISBN 0-8451-2101-4). A R Liss.

Forster, Werner, et al. Prostaglandins & Thromboxins: Proceedings of the Third International Symposium on Prostaglandins & Thromboxanes in the Cardiovascular System, Hale-Salle, GDR, 5-7 May 1980. LC 80-41802. (Illus.). 500p. 1981. 80.00 (ISBN 0-08-027369-6). Pergamon.

Frolich, J. C., ed. Methods in Prostaglandin Research. LC 78-66346. (Advances in Prostaglandin & Thromboxane Research Ser.: Vol. 5). 256p. 1978. 42.00 (ISBN 0-89004-204-7). Raven.

Galli, Claudio, et al, eds. Phospholipases & Prostaglandins. LC 77-87457. (Advances in Prostaglandin & Thromboxane Research Ser.: Vol. 3). 218p. 1978. 40.00 (ISBN 0-89004-201-2). Raven.

Gerrard. Prostaglandins & Blood Cell Function. (Hematology Ser.). 280p. 1985. 65.00 (ISBN 0-8247-7259-8). Dekker.

Greenberg, et al. Prostaglandins. (Modern Pharmacology-Toxicology Ser.: Vol. 21). 440p. 1982. 65.00 (ISBN 0-8247-1682-5). Dekker.

Hayaishi, Osamu & Yamamoto, Shozo, eds. Advances in Prostaglandin, Thromboxane, & Leukotriene Research, Vol. 15. 1985. text ed. 54.00 (ISBN 0-88167-113-4). Raven.

Herman, Arnold, et al, eds. Cardiovascular Pharmacology of the Prostaglandins. 472p. 1982. text ed. 79.00 (ISBN 0-89004-629-8). Raven.

Holman, R. J., ed. Progress in Lipid Research: Golden Jubilee International Conference, Minnesota, USA, May 4-7 1980, Vol. 20. (Illus.). 968p. 1982. 150.00 (ISBN 0-08-028011-0, H115, H125). Pergamon.

Hornstra, G. Dietary Fats, Prostanoids & Arterial Thrombosis. 1983. 48.00 (ISBN 90-247-2667-0, Pub. by Martinus Nijhoff Netherlands). Kluwer Academic.

Horton, E. W. Prostaglandins. (Monographs on Endocrinology: Vol. 7). (Illus.). 235p. 1972. 30.00 (ISBN 0-387-05571-1). Springer-Verlag.

Horton, R. & Dunn, M. J., eds. Prostaglandins & the Kidney. (Journal: Mineral & Electrolyte Metabolism: Vol. 6, No. 1-2). (Illus.). 104p. 1981. pap. 30.00 (ISBN 3-8055-3406-X). S Karger.

Knoll. Symposium on Prostaglandins: 1974, Vol. 2. 15.00 (ISBN 0-9960007-5-5, Pub. by Akademiai Kaido Hungary). Heyden.

Lewis, G. P. The Role of Prostaglandins in Inflammation. 179p. 1976. 60.00 (ISBN 3-456-80270-6, Pub. by Holdan Bk Ltd UK). State Mutual Bk.

Pace-Asciak, C. & Granstrom, E., eds. Prostaglandins & Related Substances. (New Comprehensive Biochemistry Ser.: Vol. 5). 255p. 1983. 49.75 (ISBN 0-444-80517-6, I-380-83, Biomedical Pr). Elsevier.

Poyser, Norman L. Prostaglandins in Reproduction. (Prostaglandins Research Studies). 260p. 1981. 57.95 (ISBN 0-471-09986-4, Pub. by Res Stud Pr). Wiley.

Prostaglandin Biosynthesis. (Landmark Ser.). 1979. 27.50x (ISBN 0-8422-4116-7). Irvington.

Prostaglandins & Reproduction. (Landmark Ser.). 1979. 22.50x (ISBN 0-8422-4109-4). Irvington.

Ramwell, Peter, ed. Prostaglandin Synthetase Inhibitors: New Clinical Applications Proceedings. LC 80-36705. (Prostaglandins & Related Lipids Ser.: Vol. 1). 438p. 1980. 45.00x (ISBN 0-8451-2100-6). A R Liss.

--The Prostaglandins, Vol. 2. (Illus.). 362p. 1974. 55.00x (ISBN 0-306-37792-6, Plenum Pr). Plenum Pub.

Ramwell, Peter W., ed. The Prostaglandins, Vol. 1. LC 72-76858. 418p. 1972. 55.00x (ISBN 0-306-37791-8, Plenum Pr). Plenum Pub.

--The Prostaglandins, Vol. 3. 371p. 1977. 55.00x (ISBN 0-306-37793-4, Plenum Pr). Plenum Pub.

Ramwell, Peter W. & Pharriss, B. B., eds. Prostaglandins in Cellular Biology. LC 78-188715. 537p. 1972. 52.50x (ISBN 0-306-36201-5, Plenum Pr). Plenum Pub.

Roberts, S. M. & Scheinmann, F., eds. Chemistry, Biochemistry & Pharmacology of Prostanoids. 1979. text ed. 105.00 (ISBN 0-08-023799-1). Pergamon.

--New Synthetic Routes to Prostaglandins & Thromboxanes. LC 81-68962. 1982. 59.50 (ISBN 0-12-589620-4). Acad Pr.

Robinson, H. Prostaglandin Synthetase Inhibitors. Vane, J. E., ed. 1974. 31.00 (ISBN 0-7204-7529-5, North Holland). Elsevier.

Samuelsson, B. & Paoletti, R., eds. Advances in Prostaglandin & Thromboxane Research, 2 vols. LC 75-14588. 1976. Vol. 1, 522 p. 74.50 (ISBN 0-89004-050-8); Vol. 2, 535 p. 77.00 (ISBN 0-89004-074-5). Raven.

Samuelsson, Bengt, et al, eds. Advances in Prostaglandin & Thromboxane Research: Fourth International Prostaglandin Conference, Washington, D. C, Vols. 6-8. 1980. Set. text ed. 240.00 (ISBN 0-89004-452-X); text ed. 84.00 ea. Vol. 6, 646 p. Vol. 7, 656 p (ISBN 0-89004-513-5). Vol. 8, 693 p (ISBN 0-89004-514-3). Raven.

Schroer, K., ed. Prostaglandins & Other Eicosanoids in the Cardiovascular System. (Illus.). xiv, 570p. 1985. pap. 70.25 (ISBN 3-8055-4007-8). S Karger.

Serneri, Gian G. N., et al, eds. Platelets, Prostaglandins & the Cardiovascular System. (Advances in Prostaglandin, Thromboxane, & Leukotriene Research Ser.: Vol. 13). (Illus.). 422p. 1985. text ed. 29.50 (ISBN 0-88167-062-6). Raven.

Sparks, Richard M. & Shalita, Richard A. Prostaglandin Abstracts: A Guide to the Literature, 1906-1970. Incl. Vol. 1. 497p. 1974 (ISBN 0-306-67011-9); Vol. 2. 451p. 1975 (ISBN 0-306-67012-7). LC 73-21780. 85.00x ea. (IFI Plenum). Plenum Pub.

Szantay. Synthesis of Prostaglandins. 1978. 18.50 (ISBN 0-9960003-3-X, Pub. by Akademiai Kaido Hungary). Heyden.

Toppozada, M., et al, eds. Prostaglandin & Fertility Regulation. (Advances in Reproductive Health Care Ser.). 1984. lib. bdg. 72.00 (ISBN 0-85200-804-X, Pub. by MTP Pr England). Kluwer Academic.

Von Euler, Ulf S. & Eliasson, Rune, eds. Prostaglandins. 1968. 41.50 (ISBN 0-12-724950-8). Acad Pr.

Wallach, Donald P., et al. Prostaglandins I: Basic Physiology, Vol. 1. (Illus.). 220p. 1973. text ed. 29.00x (ISBN 0-8422-7047-7). Irvington.
Wu. Prostaglandins in Clinical Medicine. 1982. 62.95 (ISBN 0-8151-9609-1). Year Bk Med.

PROTEACEAE

George, Alex. Proteaceae: Introduction to Proteaceae of Western Australia. (Illus.). 1985. 19.95 (ISBN 0-88192-051-7, Dist. by Intl Spec Bk). Timber.

PROTECTION OF BIRDS

see Birds, Protection Of

PROTECTION OF ENVIRONMENT

see Environmental Protection

PROTECTION OF GAME

see Game Protection

PROTECTION OF NATURE

see Nature Conservation

PROTECTION OF PLANTS

see Plants, Protection Of

PROTECTION OF WILDLIFE CONSERVATION

see Wildlife Conservation

PROTECTIVE CLOTHING

see Clothing, Protective

PROTECTIVE COATINGS

see also Corrosion and Anti-Corrosives; Diffusion Coatings; Gums and Resins; Lacquer and Lacquering; Paint; Paper Coatings; Plastic Films; Polyethylene; Vapor-Plating

Acrylic Powder Coatings. 59p. 1977. 40.00x (ISBN 0-686-44642-9, Pub. by Chandler England). State Mutual Bk.
American Society for Materials & Testing. Manual of Coating Work for Light-Water Nuclear Power Primary Containment & Other Safety-Related Facilities, 1st ed. (Illus.). 201p. 1979. 57.50x (ISBN 0-8031-0394-8, 03-401079-14). ASTM.
Antifouling Coatings: Marine Applications, 1970-Jan. 1984. 127p. 1984. 78.00 (ISBN 0-686-48282-4, LS110). T-C Pubns CA.
Aqueous Powder Coatings. (Bibliographies in Point Technology Ser.: No. 37). 47p. 1982. 70.00x (ISBN 0-686-44660-7, Pub. by Chandler England). State Mutual Bk.
Ash, M. & Ash, I. Formulary of Paints & Other Coatings Vol. 2. 1982. 35.00 (ISBN 0-8206-0292-2). Chem Pub.
Bayer, R., ed. Selection & Use of Wear Tests for Coatings - STP 769. 179p. 1982. 21.00 (ISBN 0-8031-0710-2, 04-769000-29). ASTM.
Berger & Wint, eds. New Concepts for Coating Protection of Steel Structures - STP 841. 135p. 1984. 28.00 (ISBN 0-8031-0236-4, 04-841000-14). ASTM.
Biestek, T. & Weber, J. Electrolytic & Chemical Conversion Coatings. 434p. 1981. 85.00x (ISBN 0-901994-78-2, Pub. by Portcullio Pr). State Mutual Bk.
Burns, Robert M. & Bradley, William W. Protective Coatings for Metals. 3rd ed. LC 67-20826. (ACS Monograph: No. 163). 1967. 53.95 (ISBN 0-8412-0285-0). Am Chemical.
Business Communications Staff. Industrial Coatings: New Trends, Markets. 1982. 950.00 (ISBN 0-89336-221-2, C-017). BCC.
Coatings: Plastics & Elastomers as Protective Coatings. 155p. 1984. 78.00 (ISBN 0-317-12670-9). T-C Pubns CA.
Coil Coating Review, Nineteen Seventy to Nineteen Seventy-Six. 55p. 1977. 40.00x (ISBN 0-686-44661-5, Pub. by Chandler England). State Mutual Bk.
Epoxy Power Coatings. 55p. 1973. 40.00x (ISBN 0-686-44666-6, Pub. by Chandler England). State Mutual Bk.
Fitzwater, J. Water Borne Coatings Buyer's Guide. 28p. 1984. pap. text ed. 25.00 (ISBN 0-318-01980-9). Tech Marketing.
Flick, Ernest W. Contemporary Industrial Coatings: Environmentally Safe Formulations. LC 85-4905. (Illus.). 333p. 1985. 48.00 (ISBN 0-8155-1025-X). Noyes.
Fraunhofer, J. A., et al. Protective Paint Coatings for Metals. 118p. 1981. 40.00x (ISBN 0-901994-89-8, Pub. by Portcullio Pr). State Mutual Bk.
Gardon, J. L. & Prane, J. W., eds. Non-Polluting Coatings & Coating Processes. LC 72-97719. 272p. 1973. 42.50x (ISBN 0-306-30729-4, Plenum Pr). Plenum Pub.
Gillies, M. T., ed. Coatings Technology Annual-First Edition. 354p. 1978. 40.00 (ISBN 0-8155-0705-4). Noyes.
--Powder Coatings: Recent Developments. LC 80-26426. (Chemical Tech. Rev.: 183). (Illus.). 326p. 1981. 48.00 (ISBN 0-8155-0836-0). Noyes.
Haken, J. K. Gas Chromatography of Coating Materials. 352p. 1974. 85.00 (ISBN 0-8247-6123-5). Dekker.
Hausner, H. H. Coatings of High-Temperature Materials. LC 65-12156. 296p. 1966. 32.50x (ISBN 0-306-30210-1, Plenum Pr). Plenum Pub.
Heitkamp, A. H., Jr. Water Borne Coatings Buyer's Guide, 1981. 32p. 1981. pap. text ed. 25.00 (ISBN 0-936840-03-X). Tech Marketing.
--Water Borne Coatings Buyer's Guide, 1982. 35p. (Orig.). 1982. pap. text ed. 25.00 (ISBN 0-936840-07-2). Tech Marketing.
High Solids Coatings. 86p. 1982. 60.00x (ISBN 0-686-44668-2, Pub. by Chandler England). State Mutual Bk.
Huges, J. F. Electrostatic Powder Coating. (Electrical & Electronic Engineering Ser.). 1984. 34.95 (ISBN 0-471-90569-0). Wiley.
Jilek, Josef. Powder Coatings Buyer's Guide, 1982. 28p. (Orig.). 1981. pap. text ed. 20.00 (ISBN 0-936840-02-1). Tech Marketing.
Kutzelnigg, A. Testing Metallic Coatings. 1981. 69.00x (ISBN 0-85218-008-X, Pub. by Portcullio Pr). State Mutual Bk.
Leidheiser, Henry, Jr., ed. Corrosion Control by Coatings. LC 79-3990. (Illus.). 1979. lib. bdg. 48.00 (ISBN 0-89500-018-0). Sci Pr.
Lieblich, Jerome H., ed. Protective Finish Collection, 2 vols. 764p. Set. loose-leaf 97.95x (ISBN 0-912702-14-1, PFC). Global Eng.
Lieff, Morris & Stumpf, S. M., eds. Fire Resistive Coatings: The Need for Standards. LC 83-71335. (Special Technical Publications: No. 826). 162p. 1984. pap. text ed. 22.00 (ISBN 0-8031-0214-3, 04-826000-31). ASTM.
Manufacture of Organic Coatings. (Thirty Ser). 1971. pap. 2.00 (ISBN 0-685-58107-1, 35). Natl Fire Prot.
Muller, G. & Jarrett, G. D. Plating on Plastics. 206p. 1981. 49.00x (ISBN 0-85218-038-1, Pub. by Portcullio Pr). State Mutual Bk.
Myers, R. R. & Long, J. S., eds. Film-Forming Compositions, Pt. 1. (Treatise on Coatings Ser.: Vol. 1). 1967. 175.00 (ISBN 0-8247-1471-7). Dekker.
--Film-Forming Compositions, Pt. 2. (Treatise on Coatings Ser.: Vol. 1). 1968. 175.00 (ISBN 0-8247-1472-5). Dekker.
--Film-Forming Compositions, Pt. 3. (Treatise on Coatings Ser.: Vol. 1). 1972. 175.00 (ISBN 0-8247-1476-8). Dekker.
--Formulations, Pt. 1, Vol. 4. (Treatise on Coatings Ser.: Vol. 4). 600p. 1975. 175.00 (ISBN 0-8247-1477-6). Dekker.
Myers, Raymond & Long, J. S., eds. Characterization of Coatings, Pt. 2: Physical Techniques. (Treatise on Coatings Ser: Vol. 2). 1976. 175.00 (ISBN 0-8247-1474-1). Dekker.
Myers, Raymond R. & Long, J. S., eds. Characterization of Coatings: Physical Techniques, Vol. 2, Pt.2. pap. 160.00 (ISBN 0-317-08360-0, 2055321). Bks Demand UMI.
Occasione, John F., et al. Atmospheric Corrosion Investigations of Aluminum-Coated, Zinc-Coated. & Copper-Bearing Steel Wire & Wire Products: A Twenty-Year Report. LC 83-73647. (Special Technical Publications Ser.: No. 585A). (Illus.). 53p. 1984. pap. text ed. 14.00 (ISBN 0-8031-0205-4, 04-585010-02). ASTM.
Oil & Colour Chemists' Association of Australia. Surface Coatings, Vol. 1: Raw Materials & Their Usage. 2nd ed. LC 83-7262. 388p. 1983. 59.95 (ISBN 0-412-25660-6, NO. 6860, Pub. by Chapman & Hall). Methuen Inc.
Paints & Coatings. 1984. 595.00 (ISBN 0-318-04170-7). Busn Trend.
Pappas, S. Peter & Winslow, F. H., eds. Photodegradation & Photostabilization of Coatings. LC 81-467. (ACS Symposium Ser: No. 151). 1981. 39.95 (ISBN 0-8412-0611-2). Am Chemical.
Parfitt & Patsis. Organic Coatings: Science & Technology, Vol. 7. 360p. 1984. 75.00 (ISBN 0-8247-7242-3). Dekker.
Parfitt, G. D., ed. Advances in Organic Coatings Science & Technology: Proceedings of the Fifth Conference 1979, Vol. 3. 300p. 1980. 55.00 (ISBN 0-87762-299-X). Technomic.
Parfitt, G. D. & Patsis, A. V., eds. Advances in Organic Coatings Science & Technology: Proceedings of the Third Conference, Vol. 1. LC 78-66106. 261p. 1979. 55.00 (ISBN 0-87762-265-5). Technomic.
--Advances in Organic Coatings Science & Technology: Proceedings of the Fourth Conference, Vol. 2. LC 79-64141. 294p. 1979. 55.00 (ISBN 0-87762-273-6). Technomic.
--Advances in Organic Coatings Science & Technology: Proceedings of the Sixth Conference, Vol. 4. 431p. 1982. 55.00 (ISBN 0-87762-314-7). Technomic.
Permanence of Organic Coatings - STP 781. 132p. 1982. pap. 15.95 (ISBN 0-8031-0827-3, 04-781000-14). ASTM.
Plog, H. & Crosby, C. E. Coating Thickness Measurement. 131p. 1971. 50.00x (ISBN 0-85218-036-5, Pub. by Portcullio Pr). State Mutual Bk.
Polyster Powder Coatings. 51p. 1976. 40.00x (ISBN 0-686-44691-7, Pub. by Chandler England). State Mutual Bk.
Protective Coating Inspection Fundamentals. (Mechanical Inspection Ser.: Module 30-6). (Illus.). 54p. 1979. spiral 7.00x (ISBN 0-87683-128-5). G P Courseware.
Report on Powder Coating. 162p. 1976. 140.00x (ISBN 0-686-44701-8, Pub. by Chandler England). State Mutual Bk.
Samsonov, G. V., ed. Protective Coatings on Metals, Vol. 1. LC 69-12517. (Illus.). 129p. 1969. 37.50x (ISBN 0-306-18321-8, Consultants). Plenum Pub.
--Protective Coatings on Metals, Vol. 2. LC 69-12517. 212p. 1970. 37.50x (ISBN 0-306-18322-6, Consultants). Plenum Pub.
--Protective Coatings on Metals, Vol. 3. LC 69-12517. 202p. 1971. 37.50x (ISBN 0-306-18323-4, Consultants). Plenum Pub.
--Protective Coatings on Metals, Vol. 4. LC 69-12517. 227p. 1972. 37.50x (ISBN 0-306-18324-2, Consultants). Plenum Pub.
--Protective Coatings on Metals, Vol. 5. LC 69-12517. (Illus.). 275p. 1974. 40.00x (ISBN 0-306-18325-0, Consultants). Plenum Pub.
Selected ASTM Standards for Fence Materials & Products. 181p. 1984. 15.00 (ISBN 0-8031-0824-9, 03-601483-02). ASTM.
Society of Manufacturing Engineers. User's Guide to Powder Coating. 1985. write for info. (ISBN 0-87263-195-8). SME.
Strafford, K. N., et al, eds. Coatings & Surface Treatment for Corrosion & Wear Resistance. (Applied Science & Industrial Technology Ser.). 362p. 1984. text ed. 79.95x (ISBN 0-470-20090-1). Halsted Pr.
Technology Marketing Corporation Staff Editors, ed. Radiation Curing Buyer's Guide, 1981, Vol. 3. 48p. 1981. pap. text ed. 22.00 (ISBN 0-936840-05-6). Tech Marketing.
Technology Marketing Corporation Staff Editors. Radiation Curing Buyer's Guide, 1982, Vol. 4. 50p. 1982. pap. text ed. 22.00 (ISBN 0-936840-06-4). Tech Marketing.
Toropov, N. A. Heat-Resistant Coatings. LC 66-20322. 167p. 1967. 35.00x (ISBN 0-306-10781-3, Consultants). Plenum Pub.
Williams, David J., ed. Nonlinear Optical Properties of Organic & Polymeric Materials. LC 83-15514. (ACS Symoposium Ser.: No. 233). 251p. 1983. lib. bdg. 39.95 (ISBN 0-8412-0802-6). Am Chemical.
Yeates, R. L. Electropainting. 2nd ed. 278p. 1981. 60.00x (ISBN 0-686-87183-9, Pub. by Portcullio Pr). State Mutual Bk.

PROTEIDS

see Proteins

PROTEIN BIOSYNTHESIS

Abraham, Abraham K., et al, eds. Protein Synthesis. LC 83-26463. (Experimental Biology & Medicine Ser.). 480p. 1984. 59.50 (ISBN 0-89603-060-1). Humana.
Anfinsen, C. B., ed. Aspects of Protein Biosynthesis, Pt. A. 1970. 72.00 (ISBN 0-12-058701-7). Acad Pr.
Bermek, E., ed. Mechanisms of Protein Synthesis: Structure-Function Relations, Control Mechanisms, & Evolutionary Aspects. (Proceedings in Life Sciences Ser.). (Illus.). 250p. 1984. 25.00 (ISBN 0-387-13653-3). Springer-Verlag.
Bogorad, L. & Weil, J. H., eds. Nucleic Acids & Protein Synthesis in Plants. LC 77-23267. (NATO ASI Series A, Life Sciences: Vol. 12). 429p. 1977. 55.00x (ISBN 0-306-35612-0, Plenum Pr). Plenum Pub.
Business Communications Staff. Processed Protein. 1985. pap. 1250.00 (ISBN 0-89336-447-9, GA-043R). BCC.
Clark, B. F. The Genetic Code & Protein Biosynthesis. 2nd ed. (Studies in Biology: No. 83). 80p. 1984. pap. text ed. 8.95 (ISBN 0-7131-2887-9). E Arnold.
Cold Spring Harbor Symposia on Quantitative Biology: The Mechanism of Protein Synthesis, Vol. 34. LC 34-8174. (Illus.). 879p. 1970. 44.00x (ISBN 0-87969-033-X). Cold Spring Harbor.
Critser, James R., Jr. Proteins-Peptides: Preparations & Applications. (Ser. 15-84). 182p. 1985. 125.00 (ISBN 0-88178-024-3). Lexington Data.
Dayhoff, M. O., ed. Atlas of Protein Sequence & Structure, Vol. 5, Suppl. No. 1. LC 65-29342. 1973. pap. 5.00 (ISBN 0-912466-04-9). Natl Biomedical.
Dingley, Fay, et al. Fidelity of Protein Synthesis & Transfer RNA During Aging. LC 74-5496. 174p. 1975. text ed. 34.50x (ISBN 0-8422-7220-8). Irvington.
Florini, James R., et al, eds. Rates of Protein Synthesis During Aging. 253p. 1974. text ed. 34.50x (ISBN 0-8422-7221-6). Irvington.
Gething, Mary J., ed. Protein Transport & Secretion. (Current Communications in Molecular Biology Ser.). 220p. (Orig.). 1985. pap. 30.00 (ISBN 0-87969-183-2). Cold Spring Harbor.
Gordon, J., et al, eds. Protein Phosphorylation & Bio-Regulation. (Illus.). x, 234p. 1980. 35.00 (ISBN 3-8055-1168-X). S Karger.
Jackson, R. J. Protein Biosynthesis. Head, J. J., ed. LC 76-29379. (Carolina Biology Readers Ser.). (Illus.). 32p. 1978. pap. 2.00 (ISBN 0-89278-286-2, 45-9686). Carolina Biological.
Kedrovskii, B. V. The Cytology of the Protein Synthesis in an Animal Cell. (Life Sciences Ser.). (Illus.). 474p. 1965. 90.25 (ISBN 0-677-20110-9). Gordon.
Kenney, F. T., et al. Gene Expression & Its Regulation. LC 72-90334. (Basic Life Sciences Ser.: Vol. 1). 588p. 1973. 57.50x (ISBN 0-306-36501-4, Plenum Pr). Plenum Pub.
Knauf, Philip A., ed. Current Topics in Membranes & Transport: Membrane Protein Biosynthesis & Turnover. (Serial Publication). 1985. 89.00 (ISBN 0-12-153324-7). Acad Pr.
Koch, Gebhard & Richter, Dietmar. Biosynthesis, Modification & Processing of Cellular & Viral Polyproteins. 1980. 43.50 (ISBN 0-12-417560-0). Acad Pr.
Kroon, A. M. & Saccone, C., eds. The Biogenesis of Mitochondria: Transcriptional, Translational & Genetic Aspects, Proceedings. 1974. 65.00 (ISBN 0-12-426750-5). Acad Pr.
Medvedev, Zhores A. Protein Biosynthesis & Problems of Heredity Development & Aging. LC 67-71423. pap. 151.50 (ISBN 0-317-28826-1, 2020702). Bks Demand UMI.
Moldave, Kivie, ed. RNA & Protein Synthesis. (Selected Methods in Enzymology Ser.). 1981. 34.50 (ISBN 0-12-504180-2). Acad Pr.
Niederman, Robert A., ed. Molecular Biology & Protein Synthesis. LC 76-13388. (Benchmark Papers in Microbiology Ser.: Vol. 10). 1976. 66.00 (ISBN 0-12-787130-6). Acad Pr.
Nover, L., ed. Heat Shock Response of Eukaryotic Cells. (Illus.). 130p. 1984. pap. 12.50 (ISBN 0-387-13640-1). Springer-Verlag.
Oberley, Larry W., ed. Superoxide Dismutase, Vols. I, & II. 1982. Vol. I, 168pp. 55.00 (ISBN 0-8493-6240-7); Vol. II, 192pp. 55.00 (ISBN 0-8493-6241-5). CRC Pr.
Offord, R. E. & Dibello, C., eds. Semisynthetic Peptides & Proteins. 1978. 49.50 (ISBN 0-12-524350-2). Acad Pr.
Oxender, Dale. Protein Transport & Secretion. LC 84-7880. (UCLA Symposia on Molecular & Cellular Biology, New Ser.: Vol. 15). 422p. 1984. 78.00 (ISBN 0-8451-2614-8). A R Liss.
Perez-Bercoff, R., ed. Protein Biosynthesis in Eukaryotes. LC 81-22720. (NATO ASI Series A, Life Sciences: Vol. 41). 519p. 1982. text ed. 65.00 (ISBN 0-306-40893-7, Plenum Pr). Plenum Pub.
Protein-Ligand Interactions Symposium, Univ. of Konstanz, Germany, Sep, 1974. Proceedings. Blauer, Gideon & Sund, Horst, eds. 1975. 72.00x (ISBN 3-11-004881-7). De Gruyter.
Roberts, S., et al, eds. Mechanisms, Regulation & Special Functions of Protein Synthesis in the Brain. (Developments in Neuro-Science Ser.: Vol. 2). 1978. 84.75 (ISBN 0-444-80030-1, Biomedical Pr). Elsevier.
Rosnay, Joel de. Journey to Life. 48p. 1984. 12.95 (ISBN 0-531-09838-9). Watts.
San Pietro, Anthony, et al, eds. Regulatory Mechanisms for Protein Synthesis in Mammalian Cells. 1968. 65.00 (ISBN 0-12-618960-9). Acad Pr.
Spirin, Alexander S. Ribosome Structure & Protein Biosynthesis. (Illus.). 416p. 1985. text ed. 29.95x (ISBN 0-8053-8390-5). Benjamin-Cummings.
Vazquez, D. Inhibitors of Protein Biosynthesis. (Molecular Biology, Biochemistry, & Biophysics: Vol. 30). (Illus.). 1979. 39.00 (ISBN 0-387-09188-2). Springer-Verlag.
Wainwright, S. D. Control Mechanisms & Protein Synthesis. LC 72-2348. (Molecular Biology Ser.). pap. 106.40 (ISBN 0-8357-9062-2, 2015441). Bks Demand UMI.
Zimmerman, Morris, et al, eds. Percursor Processing in the Biosynthesis of Proteins. LC 80-16863. (Annals of the New Yok Academy of Sciences: Vol. 343). 449p. 1980. 81.00x (ISBN 0-89766-073-0). NY Acad Sci.

PROTEIN METABOLISM

see also Protein Biosynthesis

Board on Agriculture & Renewable Resources, National Research Council. Genetic Improvement of Seed Proteins. LC 76-17097. 1976. pap. 16.75 (ISBN 0-309-02421-8). Natl Acad Pr.
Chibnall, Albert C. Protein Metabolism in the Plant. 1939. 39.50x (ISBN 0-685-69795-9); pap. 19.50x (ISBN 0-685-69796-7). Elliots Bks.
Ciba Foundation. Protein Turnover. LC 72-96519. (Ciba Foundation Symposium: New Ser.: No. 9). pap. 81.80 (ISBN 0-317-28310-3, 2022141). Bks Demand UMI.
Durand, P. & O'Brien, J. S., eds. Genetic Errors of Glycoprotein Metabolism. (Illus.). 220p. 1982. 35.50 (ISBN 0-387-12066-1). Springer-Verlag.
Florkin, M. & Neuberger, A., eds. Comprehensive Biochemistry, Vol. 19B, Pt. 1: Part 1: Protein Metabolism, Vol.19B. 528p. 1980. 101.50 (ISBN 0-444-80171-5, Biomedical Pr). Elsevier.
Florkin, M. & Stotz, E., eds. Comprehensive Biochemistry: Amino Acids Metabolism & Sulphur Metabolism, Vol. 19A. 482p. 1981. 103.50 (ISBN 0-444-80257-6, Biomedical Pr). Elsevier.

Florkin, M., et al, eds. Comprehensive Biochemistry, Vol. 19B, Pt. 2: Protein Metabolism. 514p. 1982. 74.50 (ISBN 0-444-80346-7, Biomedical Pr). Elsevier.

Gething, Mary J., ed. Protein Transport & Secretion. (Current Communications in Molecular Biology Ser.). 220p. (Orig.). 1985. pap. 30.00 (ISBN 0-87969-183-2). Cold Spring Harbor.

Hermens, W. T. Quantification of Circulating Proteins. 1983. 44.00 (ISBN 90-247-2755-3, Pub. by Martinus Nijhoff Netherlands). Kluwer Academic.

International Society for Cell Biology. Use of Radioautography in Investigating Protein Synthesis, Proceedings. Leblond, C. P. & Warren, K. B., eds. (Vol. 4). 1966. 67.50 (ISBN 0-12-611904-X). Acad Pr.

Khairallah, Edward A., et al. Intracellular & Protein Catabolism. LC 85-4304. (Progress in Clinical & Biological Research Ser.: Vol. 180). 750p. 1985. 98.00 (ISBN 0-8451-5030-8). A R Liss.

Koblet, H., et al. Physiology & Pathophysiology of Plasma Protein Metabolism. 240p. 1965. 50.00 (ISBN 3-456-00107-X, Pub. by Holdan Bk Ltd UK). State Mutual Bk.

Koch, Gebhard & Richter, Dietmar. Biosynthesis, Modification & Processing of Cellular & Viral Polyproteins. 1980. 43.50 (ISBN 0-12-417560-0). Acad Pr.

Lajtha, Abel, ed. Protein Metabolism of the Nervous System. LC 74-85373. 732p. 1970. 65.00x (ISBN 0-306-30418-X, Plenum Pr). Plenum Pub.

--Protein Metabolism of the Nervous System. LC 74-85373. pap. 160.00 (ISBN 0-317-30347-3, 2024718). Bks Demand UMI.

Means, Anthony R. & O'Malley, Bert W. Methods in Enzymology: Hormone Action: Calmodulin & Calcium-Binding Proteins, Vol. 102, Pt. G. 1983. 47.50 (ISBN 0-12-182002-5). Acad Pr.

Munro, Hamish N. & Allison, J. B., eds. Mammalian Protein Metabolism, 4 vols. 1964-70. Vol. 1. 83.50 (ISBN 0-12-510601-7); Vol. 2. 83.50 (ISBN 0-12-510602-5); Vol. 3. 81.00 (ISBN 0-12-510603-3); Vol. 4. 94.00 (ISBN 0-12-510604-1). Acad Pr.

Palladin, A. V., et al, eds. Protein Metabolism of the Brain. LC 77-2307. (Studies in Science Ser.: Life Sciences). (Illus.). 346p. 1977. 49.50 (ISBN 0-306-10922-0, Consultants). Plenum Pub.

Pierce, John G., ed. Proteins & Peptides Hormones. LC 82-6159. (Benchmark Papers in Biochemistry: Vol. 4). 459p. 1982. 62.00 (ISBN 0-87933-417-7). Van Nos Reinhold.

Poglazov, Boris F. Structure & Functions of Contractile Proteins. 1966. 62.00 (ISBN 0-12-559150-0). Acad Pr.

Rothschild, Marcus A. & Waldmann, Thomas, eds. Plasma Protein Metabolism: Regulation of Synthesis, Distribution & Degradation. 1970. 72.00 (ISBN 0-12-598750-1). Acad Pr.

Schimke, Robert T. & Katunuma, Nobuhiko, eds. Intracellular Protein Turnover. 1975. 45.00 (ISBN 0-12-625550-4). Acad Pr.

Tschesche, H., ed. Modern Methods in Protein Chemistry: Review Articles. LC 83-14009. x, 464p. 1983. 76.00x (ISBN 3-11-009514-9). De Gruyter.

Turk, Vito, et al, eds. Intracellular Protein Catabolism II. LC 77-72034. 380p. 1977. 45.00x (ISBN 0-306-31037-6, Plenum Pr). Plenum Pub.

PROTEIN SYNTHESIS

see Protein Biosynthesis

PROTEINS

see also Protein Metabolism

also various protein groups and bodies, e.g. Peptones, Casein

Adelman, Richard C. & Roth, George S., eds. Altered Proteins & Aging. 192p. 1983. 49.50 (ISBN 0-8493-5812-4). CRC Pr.

Adelman, Richard C., et al. Enzyme Induction in Aging & Protein Synthesis. LC 74-6131. 172p. 1974. text ed. 21.50x (ISBN 0-8422-7222-4). Irvington.

Advances in Protein Chemistry. Incl. Vol. 29. 1975. 75.00 (ISBN 0-12-034229-4); Vol. 30. 1976. 75.00 (ISBN 0-12-034230-8). (Serial Publication). Acad Pr.

Advances in Protein Chemistry. Incl. Vol. 1. 1945. 75.00 (ISBN 0-12-034201-4); Vol. 2. Anson, M. L., et al, eds. 1944. 75.00 (ISBN 0-12-034202-2); Vols. 3-4. 1947-48. 85.00. Vol. 3 (ISBN 0-12-034203-0). Vol. 4 (ISBN 0-12-034204-9); Vol. 5. 1949. 75.00 (ISBN 0-12-034205-7); Vol. 6. 1951. 85.00 (ISBN 0-12-034206-5); Vol. 7. 1952. 75.00 (ISBN 0-12-034207-3); Vols. 8-9. 1953-54. 85.00. Vol. 8 (ISBN 0-12-034208-1). Vol.9. 85.00 (ISBN 0-12-034209-X); Vol. 10. 1955. 75.00 (ISBN 0-12-034210-3); Vol. 11. 1956. 90.00 (ISBN 0-12-034211-1); Vol. 12. 1957. 90.00 (ISBN 0-12-034212-X); Vol. 13. 1958. 85.00 (ISBN 0-12-034213-8); Vol. 14. 1959. 85.00 (ISBN 0-12-034214-6); Vol. 15. 1961. 75.00 (ISBN 0-12-034215-4); Vol. 16. 1962. 85.00 (ISBN 0-12-034216-2); Vol. 17. 1963. 75.00 (ISBN 0-12-034217-0); Vol. 18. 1964. 75.00 (ISBN 0-12-034218-9); Vol. 19. 1964. 75.00 (ISBN 0-12-034219-7); Vol. 20. 1965. 75.00 (ISBN 0-12-034220-0), 2 vols. 75.00 ea. Vol. 21, 1966 (ISBN 0-12-034221-9). Vol. 22, 1967 (ISBN 0-12-034222-7); Vol. 23. 1968. 75.00 (ISBN 0-12-034223-5); Vol. 24. 1970. 85.00 (ISBN 0-12-034224-3); Vol. 25. 1971. 75.00 (ISBN 0-12-034225-1); Vol. 26. 1972. 75.00 (ISBN 0-12-034226-X); Vol. 27. 1973. 85.00 (ISBN 0-12-034227-8); Vol. 28. 1974. 85.00 (ISBN 0-12-034228-6); Vol. 31. 1977. 75.00 (ISBN 0-12-034231-6); lib ed. o.p. 90.00 (ISBN 0-12-034278-2). LC 44-8853. Vols 1-26. Acad Pr.

Advances in Protein Chemistry, Vol. 35. 396p. 1982. 60.00 (ISBN 0-12-034235-9). Acad Pr.

Advances in Protein Chemistry, Vol. 36. 1984. 52.00 (ISBN 0-12-034236-7). Acad Pr.

Albertini, A., et al, eds. Ferritins & Isoferritins As Biochemical Markers: Proceedings of the Advanced Course on Ferritins & Isoferritins Held in Milan, May 17, 1984. (Symposia of the Giovanni Lorenzini Foundation Ser.: Vol. 19). 208p. 1984. 40.50 (ISBN 0-444-80607-5). Elsevier.

Alexander, P., et al, eds. A Laboratory Manual of Analytical Methods of Protein Chemistry (Including Polypeptides, Vols. 2-5. Incl. Vol. 2. Composition, Structure & Reactivity of Protein. 1960. lib. bdg. 16.50 (ISBN 0-08-011398-2); Vol. 3. Determination of the Size & Shape of Protein in Molecules. 1961; Vol. 4. Protein Analysis. 1965; Vol. 5. 1968. 18.00 (ISBN 0-08-012677-4). Pergamon.

Allen, Robert C., et al. Gel Electrophoresis & Isoelectric Focusing of Proteins: Selected Techniques. LC 84-12694. (Illus.). xiii, 255p. 1984. 39.95 (ISBN 3-11-007853-8). De Gruyter.

Allen, Robert C., et al, eds. Marker Proteins in Inflammation: Proceedings of the Symposium; Lyon, France, April 22-25, 1981. Suskind, Robert M. (Illus.). 608p. 1982. 74.00 (ISBN 3-11-008625-5). De Gruyter.

Althaus, F., et al, eds. ADP-Ribosylation of Proteins. (Proceedings in Life Sciences Ser.). (Illus.). 585p. 1985. 89.50 (ISBN 0-387-15598-8). Springer Verlag.

Altschul, Aaron & Wilcke, Harold L., eds. New Protein Foods, Vol. 5: Seed Storage Proteins. (Food Science & Technology Ser.). 1985. 94.50 (ISBN 0-12-054805-4). Acad Pr.

Altschul, Aaron A., ed. New Protein Foods. (Food Science & Technology Ser.). 1974. Vol. 1A, 1974. 85.00 (ISBN 0-12-054801-1); Vol. 2B 1976. 70.00 (ISBN 0-12-054802-X). Acad Pr.

--New Protein Foods Vol. 4. LC 72-12188. (Food Science & Technology Ser.). 1981. Pt. B. 65.00 (ISBN 0-12-054804-6). Acad Pr.

Altschul, Aaron M. & Wilcke, Harold L., eds. New Protein Foods Vol. 3, Animal Protein Supplies, Part A. (Food Science & Technology Ser.). 1978. 75.00 (ISBN 0-12-054803-8). Acad Pr.

Anfinsen, C. B., et al, eds. Advances in Protein Chemistry, Vol. 34. (Serial Publication Ser.). 1981. 60.00 (ISBN 0-12-034234-0). Acad Pr.

Asquith, R. S., ed. Chemistry of Natural Protein Fibers. LC 76-52636. (Illus.). 417p. 1977. 65.00x (ISBN 0-306-30898-3, Plenum Pr). Plenum Pub.

Atassi, M. Z. & Benjamini, E., eds. Immunobiology of Proteins & Peptides II. (Advances in Experimental Medicine & Biology: Vol. 150). 238p. 1982. 35.00x (ISBN 0-306-41110-5, Plenum Pr). Plenum Pub.

Atassi, M. Z. & Stavitsky, A. B., eds. Immunobiology of Proteins & Peptides I. LC 78-5083. (Advances in Experimental Medicine & Biology Ser.: Vol. 98). 523p. 1978. 59.50x (ISBN 0-306-32698-1, Plenum Pr). Plenum Pub.

Augustyniak, J., ed. Biological Implications of Protein-Nucleic Acid Interactions. 668p. 1981. 81.00 (ISBN 0-444-80292-4). Elsevier.

Azzi, A., et al, eds. Membrane Proteins: A Laboratory Manual. (Illus.). 250p. 1981. pap. 22.50 (ISBN 0-387-10749-5). Springer-Verlag.

Beier, H. M. & Karlson, P., eds. Proteins & Steroids in Early Pregnancy. (Illus.). 346p. 1981. pap. 42.00 (ISBN 0-387-10457-7). Springer Verlag.

Benesch, Reinhold, et al. Sulfur in Proteins. 1959. 81.00 (ISBN 0-12-088150-0). Acad Pr.

Bezkorovainy, Anatoly. Basic Protein Chemistry. (Illus.). 248p. 1971. photocopy ed. 24.50x (ISBN 0-398-00151-0). C C Thomas.

Bigwood, E. J., ed. Protein & Amino Acid Functions. 536p. 1972. text ed. 155.00 (ISBN 0-08-016464-1). Pergamon.

Biochemical Societies of France, Great Britain, Italy, & the Netherlands. Joint Meeting, Venice, 1976. Phosphorylated Proteins & Related Enzymes: Proceedings. 128p. 1977. 10.00 (ISBN 0-904147-45-2). IRL Pr.

Birr, C., ed. Methods of Peptide & Protein Sequence Analysis: Proceedings of the International Conference on Solid Phase, 3rd, Heidelberg, October 1-4, 1979. 532p. 1980. 92.00 (ISBN 0-444-80218-5, Biomedical Pr). Elsevier.

Bisswanger, Hans & Schmincke-Ott, Eva, eds. Multifunctional Proteins. LC 79-16055. 333p. 1980. 84.50 (ISBN 0-471-04270-6, Pub. by Wiley-Interscience). Wiley.

Bjerrum, O. J., ed. Electroimmunochemical Analysis of Membrane Proteins. xiv, 476p. 1983. 106.50 (ISBN 0-444-80461-7, I-158-83, Biomedical Pr). Elsevier.

Blackburn, Stanley. Protein Sequence Determination: Methods & Techniques. LC 77-13046. pap. 75.30 (ISBN 0-317-08354-6, 2055410). Bks Demand UMI.

Block, Richard J. & Bolling, Diana. The Amino Acid Composition of Proteins & Foods: Analytical Methods & Results. 2nd ed. (Illus.). 584p. 1951. 48.50x (ISBN 0-398-04210-1). C C Thomas.

Block, Richard J. & Weiss, Kathryn W. Amino Acid Handbook: Methods & Results of Protein Analysis. (Illus.). 384p. 1956. 32.50x (ISBN 0-398-04211-X). C C Thomas.

Blout, E. R., et al. Peptides, Polypeptides & Proteins. LC 74-22202. 656p. 1974. 38.00 (ISBN 0-471-08387-9). Krieger.

Blundell, T. L. & Johnson, Louise. Protein Crystallography. (Molecular Biology Ser.). 1976. 87.50 (ISBN 0-12-108350-0). Acad Pr.

Bodwell, C. E. Evaluation of Proteins for Humans. (Illus.). 1977. lib. bdg. 56.50 (ISBN 0-87055-215-5). AVI.

Bodwell, C. E. & Adkins, J. S. Protein Quality in Humans: Assessment & in Vitro Estimation. (Illus.). 1981. lib. bdg. 56.50 (ISBN 0-87055-388-7). AVI.

Bog-Hansen, T. C. & Spengler, G. A. Lectins: Biology, Biochemistry, Clinical Biochemistry, Vol.3. (Proceedings of the Fifth Lectin Meeting Bern, May 31-June 5,1982 Ser.). (Illus.). 708p. 1983. 98.00 (ISBN 3-11-009504-1). De Gruyter.

Bohak, Zvi & Sharon, Nathan, eds. Biotechnological Application of Proteins & Enzymes. 1977. 65.00 (ISBN 0-12-110950-X). Acad Pr.

Bradshaw, Ralph A., et al, eds. Proteins in Biology & Medicine. 1983. 41.00 (ISBN 0-12-124580-2). Acad Pr.

Bunting, E. S., ed. Production & Utilisation of Protein in Oilseed Crops. 390p. 1981. 52.00 (ISBN 90-247-2532-1, Pub. by Martinus Nijhoff Netherlands). Kluwer Academic.

Catsimpoolas, N. N., ed. Physical Aspects of Protein Interactions. (Developments in Biochemistry Ser.: Vol. 3). 308p. 1979. 68.50 (ISBN 0-444-00304-5, Biomedical Pr). Elsevier.

Catsimpoolas, Nicholas, ed. Methods of Protein Separation, Vol. 1. LC 75-17684. (Biological Separations Ser.). (Illus.). 282p. 1975. 35.00x (ISBN 0-306-34601-X, Plenum Pr). Plenum Pub.

--Methods of Protein Separation, Vol. 2. LC 75-17684. (Biological Separations Ser.). (Illus.). 344p. 1976. 39.50x (ISBN 0-306-34602-8, Plenum Pr). Plenum Pub.

Celis, Julio E. & Bravo, R. Two-Dimensional Gel Electrophoresis of Proteins: Methods & Applications. LC 83-5022. 1984. 69.50 (ISBN 0-12-164720-X). Acad Pr.

Chance, Britton, et al, eds. Hemes & Hemoproteins. 1967. 80.00 (ISBN 0-12-167856-3). Acad Pr.

Chang, T. M., ed. Biomedical Applications of Immobilized Enzymes & Proteins, 2 vols. Incl. Vol. 1. 448p. 1977. 49.50x (ISBN 0-306-34311-8); Vol. 2. LC 76-56231. 379p. 1977. 49.50x (ISBN 0-306-34312-6). (Illus., Plenum Pr). Plenum Pub.

Cherry, John P., ed. Food Protein Deterioration: Mechanisms & Functionality. LC 82-20739. (ACS Symposium Ser.: No. 206). 444p. 1982. lib. bdg. 49.95x (ISBN 0-8412-0751-8). Am Chemical.

--Protein Functionality in Foods. LC 81-97. (ACS Symposium Ser.: No. 147). 1981. 44.95 (ISBN 0-8412-0605-8). Am Chemical.

Choh Hao Li, ed. Hormonal Proteins & Peptides: Gonadotropic Hormones, Vol. XI. LC 82-22770. 1983. 47.50 (ISBN 0-12-447211-7). Acad Pr.

--Hormonal Proteins & Peptides: Prolactin, Vol. 8. LC 80-11061. 1980. 44.00 (ISBN 0-12-447208-7). Acad Pr.

Ciba Foundation. Molecular Interactions & Activity in Proteins. LC 78-14500. (Ciba Foundation Symposium, New Ser.: 60). pap. 71.80 (ISBN 0-317-29766-X, 2022184). Bks Demand UMI.

--Protein Degradation in Health & Disease. (Ciba Symposium Ser.: No. 75). 1980. 76.75 (ISBN 0-444-90148-5). Elsevier.

Clementi, Enrico & Sarma, Ramaswamy, eds. Structure & Dynamics of Nucleic Acids & Proteins. (Illus.). 600p. 1983. text ed. 49.00 (ISBN 0-940030-04-7). Adenine Pr.

Cleveland Symposium on Macromolecules, 1st, Case Western Reserve Univ., Oct. 1976. Proceedings. Walton, A. G., ed. 310p. 1977. 64.00 (ISBN 0-444-41561-0). Elsevier.

Coffey, S. Rodd's Chemistry of Carbon Compounds, Vol. 4, Pt. J: Proteins. Date not set. price not set (ISBN 0-685-84873-6). Elsevier.

Cohen, Elias. Recognition Proteins, Receptors, & Probes: Invertebrates. LC 84-7878. (Progress in Clinical & Biological Research Ser.: Vol. 157). 228p. 1984. 38.00 (ISBN 0-8451-5007-3). A R Liss.

Cohen, P., ed. Recently Discovered Systems of Enzyme Regulation by Reversible Posphorylation. (Molecular Aspects of Cell Regulation Ser.: Vol. 1). 274p. 1980. 69.00 (ISBN 0-444-80226-6, Biomedical Pr). Elsevier.

Colowick, Sidney & Cunningham, Leon, eds. Methods in Enzymology: Structural & Contractile Proteins: Extracellular Matrix, Vol. 82, Pt. A. 1982. 75.00 (ISBN 0-12-181982-5). Acad Pr.

Colowick, Sidney P. & Frederiksen, D. W., eds. Methods in Enzymology: Structural & Contractile Proteins-The Contractile Apparatus & the Cytoskeleton, Vol. 85. 774p. 1982. 75.00 (ISBN 0-12-181985-X). Acad Pr.

Corbin, Jackie D. & Hardman, Joel D., eds. Methods in Enzymology: Hormone Action: Protein Kinases, Vol. 99, Pt F. 1983. 55.00 (ISBN 0-12-181999-X). Acad Pr.

Cordy, Don. The Protein Book. LC 75-44132. (Illus.). 86p. (Orig.). 1976. 10.95 (ISBN 0-87961-045-X); pap. 4.95 (ISBN 0-87961-044-1). Naturegraph.

Creighton. Proteins. LC 83-19541. (Illus.). 515p. 1984. 36.95 (ISBN 0-7167-1566-X). W H Freeman.

Crewther, W. G., ed. Fibrous Proteins. 414p. 1968. 55.00x (ISBN 0-306-30665-4, Plenum Pr). Plenum Pub.

Croft, L. R. Handbook of Protein Sequence Analysis: A Compilation of Amino Acid Sequences of Proteins. LC 79-41487. 644p. 1980. 137.95 (ISBN 0-471-27703-7). Wiley.

--Introduction to Protein Sequence Analysis. LC 79-41488. 157p. 1980. pap. 21.95 (ISBN 0-471-27710-X). Wiley.

Darbre, A. & Waterfield, M. D. Practical Protein Biochemistry: A Handbook. 1985. write for info. (ISBN 0-471-90673-5). Wiley.

Davis, P., ed. Single Cell Protein. 1975. 47.00 (ISBN 0-12-206550-6). Acad Pr.

Dayhoff, M. O., ed. Atlas of Protein Sequence & Structure, Vol. 5, Suppl. No. 2. LC 65-29342. 1976. 15.00 (ISBN 0-912466-05-7). Natl Biomedical.

--Atlas of Protein Sequence & Structure, Vol. 5, Suppl. No. 1. LC 65-29342. 1973. pap. 5.00 (ISBN 0-912466-04-9). Natl Biomedical.

--Atlas of Protein Sequence & Structure, Vol. 5, Suppl. No. 3. LC 65-29342. 1979. pap. 25.00 (ISBN 0-912466-07-3). Natl Biomedical.

Dayhoff, M. O., et al. Protein Segment Dictionary 78. LC 76-28614. 1978. pap. 99.00 (ISBN 0-912466-08-1). Natl Biomedical.

De Bernard, B., et al, eds. Calcium-Binding Proteins, 1983. (Developments in Biochemistry Ser.: Vol. 25). 472p. 1983. 94.00 (ISBN 0-444-80537-0, I-450-83, Biomedical Pr). Elsevier.

Devenyi, T. & Gergely, J. Amino Acid Peptides & Proteins. 1974. 56.00 (ISBN 0-444-41127-5). Elsevier.

Dickerson, Richard E. & Geis, Irving. The Structure & Action of Proteins. LC 69-11112. 1969. pap. text ed. 21.95 (ISBN 0-8053-2391-0). Benjamin-Cummings.

Dubach, U. & Schmidt, U. Diagnostic Significance of Enzymes & Proteins in Urine. 385p. 1979. 65.00 (ISBN 3-456-80689-2, Pub. by Holdan Bk Ltd UK). State Mutual Bk.

Dudley, J. W., ed. Seventy Generations of Selection for Oil & Protein in Maize. 1974. 10.00 (ISBN 0-89118-502-X). Crop Sci Soc Am.

Edsall, John T., et al, eds. Advances in Protein Chemistry, Vol. 33. LC 44-8853. (Serial Publication Ser.). 1979. 55.00 (ISBN 0-12-034233-2). Acad Pr.

Elmore, D. T. Peptides & Proteins. LC 68-21392. (Cambridge Chemistry Texts Ser). (Illus.). 1968. 32.50 (ISBN 0-521-07107-0); pap. 9.95x (ISBN 0-521-09535-2). Cambridge U Pr.

Fasman, Gerald D. Handbook of Biochemistry & Molecular Biology, CRC: Proteins Section, 3 vols. 3rd ed. LC 75-29514. (Handbook Ser.). 1976. Vol. 1, 427 Pgs. 66.00 (ISBN 0-87819-504-1); Vol. 2, 790p. 86.50 (ISBN 0-87819-505-X); Vol. 3, 633p. 76.50 (ISBN 0-87819-510-6). CRC Pr.

Feeney, Robert E. & Whitaker, John R., eds. Food Proteins: Improvement Through Chemical & Enzymatic Modification. LC 77-7550. (Advances in Chemistry Ser.: No. 160). 1977. 29.95 (ISBN 0-8412-0339-3). Am Chemical.

--Modification of Proteins: Food, Nutritional & Pharmacological Aspects. LC 82-1702. (Advances In Chemistry: No. 198). 402p. 1982. lib. bdg. 59.95 (ISBN 0-8412-0610-4). Am Chemical.

Fennema, Owen, ed. Proteins at Low Temperatures. LC 79-16561. (Advances in Chemistry Ser.: No. 180). 1979. 39.95 (ISBN 0-8412-0484-5). Am Chemical.

Ferranti, M. P. & Fiechter, A., eds. Production & Feeding of Single-Cell Protein: Proceedings of the COST Workshop, Zurich, Switzerland, April 13-15, 1983. (Illus.). 216p. 1983. 37.00 (ISBN 0-85334-243-1, I-337-83, Pub. by Elsevier Applied Sci England). Elsevier.

Flodin, N. W. Vitamin-Trace Mineral-Protein Interactions, Vol. 2. Horrobin, D. F., ed. (Annual Research Reviews). 1980. 30.00 (ISBN 0-88831-062-5, Dist. by Pergamon). Eden Pr.

Flodin, Nestor W. Vitamin-Trace Mineral-Protein Interactions. (Annual Research Reviews Ser.: Vol. 4). 386p. 1981. 38.00 (ISBN 0-88831-114-1). Eden Pr.

Fowden, Leslie & Miflin, B. J., eds. Seed Storage Proteins. (Philosophical Transactions of The Royal Society of London: Ser. B, Vol. 304). (Illus.). 137p. 1984. Repr. lib. bdg. 52.00x (ISBN 0-85403-225-8, Pub. by Royal Soc London). Scholium Intl.

Fox, J. L., et al, eds. Protein Structure & Evolution. 1976. 85.00 (ISBN 0-8247-6386-6). Dekker.

Fox, P. F. & Condon, J. J., eds. Food Proteins. (Illus.). xi, 361p. 1982. 76.00 (ISBN 0-85334-143-5, Pub. by Elsevier Applied Sci England). Elsevier.

Freedman, Robert & Hawkins, H. G., eds. The Enzymology of Post-Translational Modification of Proteins, Vol. I. (Molecular Biology Ser.). 1981. 96.00 (ISBN 0-12-266501-5). Acad Pr.

Freidman, Mendel, ed. Nutritional Improvement of Food & Feed Proteins. LC 78-17278. (Advances in Experimental Medicine & Biology Ser.: Vol. 105). 894p. 1978. 95.00x (ISBN 0-306-40026-X, Plenum Pr). Plenum Pub.

Frieden, Carl & Nichol, Lawrence. Protein-Protein Interactions. LC 80-29424. 403p. 1981. 71.50x (ISBN 0-471-04979-4, Pub. by Wiley-Interscience). Wiley.

Friedman, Mendel, ed. Protein-Metal Interactions. LC 74-13406. (Advances in Experimental Medicine & Biology Ser.: Vol. 48). 702p. 1974. 82.50x (ISBN 0-306-39048-5, Plenum Pr). Plenum Pub.

--Protein Nutritional Quality of Foods & Feeds, Pt. 1: Assay Methods-Biological, Biochemical, & Chemical. (Nutrition & Clinical Nutrition Ser.: Vol. 1). 648p. 1975. 95.00 (ISBN 0-8247-6278-9). Dekker.

Galesloot, T. E. & Tinbergen, B. J., eds. Milk Proteins '84: Proceedings of the International Congress on Milk Proteins, Luxemburg, 7-11 May 1984. 325p. 1985. pap. 60.75 (ISBN 90-220-0860-6, PDC279, Pudoc). Unipub.

Galveston Chapter, Society for Neuroscience, Galveston, TX, Feb.-March, 1981. Proteins in the Nervous System: Structure & Function: Proceedings. Haber, Bernard, et al, eds. LC 81-20903. (Progress in Clinical and Biological Research Ser.: Vol. 79). 322p. 1982. 48.00 (ISBN 0-8451-0079-3). A R Liss.

George, James N., et al, eds. Platelet Membrane Glycoproteins. 412p. 1985. 59.50x (ISBN 0-306-41857-6, Plenum Pr). Plenum Pub.

Ghelis, Charis & Yon, Jeannine. Protein Folding. (Molecular Biology Ser.). 556p. 1982. 74.50 (ISBN 0-12-281520-3). Acad Pr.

Glazer, A. N., et al, eds. Chemical Modification of Proteins. LC 74-84210. (Laboratory Techniques in Biochemistry & Molecular Biology: Vol. 4, Pt. 1). 205p. 1975. pap. 17.50 (ISBN 0-444-10811-X, North-Holland). Elsevier.

Goldberg, I. Single Cell Protein. (Biotechnology Monographs: Vol. 1). (Illus.). 260p. 1985. 49.50 (ISBN 0-387-15308-X). Springer-Verlag.

Goldstein, Irwin J., ed. Carbohydrate-Protein Interaction. LC 78-25788. (ACS Symposium Ser.: No. 88). 1979. 26.95 (ISBN 0-8412-0466-7). Am Chemical.

Goldstein, Lester & Prescott, David N., eds. Cell Biology: Vol. IV, a Comprehensive Treatise, Gene Expression: Translation & the Behavior of Proteins. 1980. 65.00 (ISBN 0-12-289504-5). Acad Pr.

Goodman, Murray, ed. Peptides, Polypeptides, & Proteins: Interactions & Their Biological Implications, Vol. 22. 588p. 1983. text ed. 47.50x (ISBN 0-471-88679-3, Pub. by Wiley-Interscience). Wiley.

Grant, R. A., ed. Applied Protein Chemistry. (Illus.). 332p. 1980. 52.00 (ISBN 0-85334-865-0, Pub. by Elsevier Applied Sci England). Elsevier.

Gutcho, M. Textured Protein Products. LC 77-85662. (Food Technology Review Ser.: No. 44). (Illus.). 1978. 39.00 (ISBN 0-8155-0681-3). Noyes.

Hager, Lowell P., ed. Chemistry & Functions of Colicins. 1973. 33.00 (ISBN 0-12-313550-8). Acad Pr.

Harris, J. Electron Microscopy of Proteins: Vol. 4: Macromolecular Structure & Function. 1984. 65.00 (ISBN 0-12-327604-7). Acad Pr.

Harris, James R., ed. Electron Microscopy of Protein, 2 vols. 1981. Vol. 1. 75.00 (ISBN 0-12-327601-2); Vol. 2. 61.50 (ISBN 0-12-327602-0). Acad Pr.

Harrison, Pauline M. Metalloprotiens: Metal Proteins With Non-Redox Roles, Pt. 2. (Topics in Molecular & Structural Biology Ser.: Vol. 7). 339p. 1985. lib. bdg. 66.00 (ISBN 0-89573-211-4, Pub. by Macmillan Pr UK). VCH Pubs.

Harrison, Pauline M., ed. Metalloprotiens: Metal Protiens With Redox Roles, Pt. 1. (Topics in Molecular & Structural Biology Ser.: Vol. 6). 256p. 1985. lib. bdg. 55.00 (ISBN 0-89573-210-6, Pub. by Macmillan Pr UK). VCH Pubs.

Haschemeyer, Rudolph & Haschemeyer, Audrey H. Proteins: A Guide to Study by Physical & Chemical Methods. LC 72-13134. 445p. 1973. 47.50x (ISBN 0-471-35850-9, Pub. by Wiley-Interscience). Wiley.

Hearn. Peptide & Protein Reviews, Vol. 2. 336p. 1983. 52.50 (ISBN 0-8247-7135-4). Dekker.

Hearn, Milton & T. W. Hearn, Etal, eds. High Performance Liquid Chromatography of Proteins & Peptides: Proceedings of First International Symposium. 1983. 35.00 (ISBN 0-12-335780-2). Acad Pr.

Hearn, Milton W., ed. Peptide & Protein Reviews, Vol. 4. (Illus.). 256p. 1984. 52.50 (ISBN 0-8247-7292-X). Dekker.

Hirai, Hidematsu & Alpert, Elliot, eds. Carcinofetal Proteins: Biology & Chemistry, Vol. 259. (Annals of the New York Academy of Sciences). 452p. 1975. 54.50x (ISBN 0-89072-013-4). NY Acad Sci.

Hnilica, Lubomir S. Chromsomal Nonhistone Proteins: Volume II-Immunology. 280p. 1983. 79.00 (ISBN 0-8493-5512-5). CRC Pr.

Hnilica, Lubomir S., ed. Chromosomal Nonhistone Proteins: Structural Association, Vol. IV. 320p. 1984. 92.00 (ISBN 0-8493-5514-1). CRC Pr.

--Chromosomal Nonhistone Proteins: Vol. I Biology. 208p. 1983. 67.00 (ISBN 0-8493-5511-7). CRC Pr.

Holmes, K. C. & Blow, D. M. The Use of X-Ray Diffraction in the Study of Protein & Nucleic Acid Structure. rev. ed. Glick, D., ed. LC 79-20293. 1979. lib. bdg. 11.50 (ISBN 0-89874-046-0). Krieger.

Hudson, B. J., ed. Developments in Food Proteins, Vol. 1. (Illus.). 339p. 1982. 70.50 (ISBN 0-85334-987-8, Pub. by Elsevier Applied Sci England). Elsevier.

--Developments in Food Proteins, Vol. 3. (Illus.). 288p. 1984. 45.00 (ISBN 0-85334-271-7, I-260-84, Pub. by Elsevier Applied Sci England). Elsevier.

Huijing, F. & Lee, E. Y., eds. Protein Phosphorylation in Control Mechanisms. (Miami Winter Symposia: No. 5). 1973. 49.50 (ISBN 0-12-360950-X). Acad Pr.

Hulse, J. H. & Laing, E. M. Nutritive Value of Triticale Protein. 183p. 1974. pap. 20.00 casebound (ISBN 0-88936-025-1, IDRC21, IDRC). Unipub.

Inglett, George E. Seed Proteins Symposium. (Illus.). 1972. text ed. 50.00 (ISBN 0-87055-117-5). AVI.

Ivatt, Raymond J., ed. The Biology of Glycoproteins. 443p. 1984. 59.50x (ISBN 0-306-41596-8, Plenum Pr). Plenum Pub.

Jakubke, Hans-Dieter & Jeschkeit, Hans. Aminoacids, Peptides & Proteins: An Introduction. 1st English ed. Cotterell, G. P. & Jones, J. H., trs. LC 77-23945. 336p. 1978. 49.95x (ISBN 0-470-99279-4). Halsted Pr.

James, J. & Tas, J. Histochemical Protein Staining Methods. (Royal Microscopy Handbooks Ser.). (Illus.). 1984. pap. 9.95x (ISBN 0-19-856406-6). Oxford U Pr.

Jirgensons, B. Optical Activities of Proteins & Other Macromolecules. rev. ed. (Molecular Biology, Biochemistry & Biophysics Ser.: Vol. 5). (Illus.). 199p. 1973. 41.00 (ISBN 0-387-06340-4). Springer-Verlag.

Johns, E. W., ed. The HMG Chromosomal Proteins. 1982. 41.50 (ISBN 0-12-386050-4). Acad Pr.

Johnson, B. Connor, ed. Postranslational Covalent Modification of Proteins: MS Repro Symposium. 1983. 40.00 (ISBN 0-12-387560-9). Acad Pr.

Jost, Patricia C. & Griffith, O. Hayes. Lipid-Protein Interactions, Vol. 1. 338p. 1982. 86.50x (ISBN 0-471-06457-2, Pub. by Wiley-Interscience). Wiley.

--Lipid-Protein Interactions, Vol. 2. LC 81-16157. 307p. 1982. 80.50x (ISBN 0-471-06456-4, Pub. by Wiley-Interscience). Wiley.

Kaegi, J., ed. Metallothionein Proceedings. (Experientia Supplementum: No. 34). 378p. 1979. 56.95x (ISBN 0-8176-1036-7). Birkhauser.

Kaivarainen, Alex I. Solvent-Dependent Flexibility of Proteins & Principles of Their Function. 1984. lib. bdg. 58.00 (ISBN 0-318-00436-4, Pub. by Reidel Holland). Kluwer Academic.

Katunuma, N., et al, eds. Proteinase Inhibitors. 350p. 1983. 49.00 (ISBN 0-387-12770-4). Springer-Verlag.

Kerese, Istvan, ed. Methods of Protein Analysis. (Series in Analytic Chemistry). 371p. 1984. 82.95x (ISBN 0-470-27497-2, 1-118). Wiley.

King, Jonathan, ed. Protein & Nucleic Acids Structure. 1984. text ed. 29.95 (ISBN 0-8053-5403-4). Benjamin-Cummings.

Kirkwood, John G. Proteins. Scatchard, G., ed. (Documents on Modern Physics Ser.). 376p. (Orig.). 1967. 73.00 (ISBN 0-677-00360-9). Gordon.

Kirschenbaum, D. M. Atlas of Protein Spectra in the Ultraviolet & Visible Regions. Incl. Vol. 1. 302p. 1972. 65.00x (ISBN 0-306-65159-9); Vol. 2. 637p. 1974. 85.00x (ISBN 0-306-67302-9). LC 77-183566 (IFI Plenum). Plenum pub.

Klopper, A. I. & Chard, T., eds. Placental Proteins. (Illus.). 1979. pap. 41.00 (ISBN 0-387-09406-7). Springer-Verlag.

Kritchevsky, David & Gibney, Michael J., eds. Animal & Vegetable Proteins in Lipid Metabolism & Atherosclerosis. LC 82-23961. (Current Topics in Nutrition & Disease Ser.: Vol. 8). 190p. 1983. 32.00 (ISBN 0-8451-1607-X). A R Liss.

Lapanje, Savo. Physicochemical Aspects of Protein Denaturation. LC 78-1919. 346p. 1978. text ed. 40.50 (ISBN 0-471-03409-6). Krieger.

Lasztity, R. The Chemistry of Cereal Proteins. 216p. 1984. 65.00 (ISBN 0-8493-5140-5). CRC Pr.

Laver, W. Graeme & Air, Gillian M., eds. Immune Recognition of Protein Antigens. (Current Communications in Molecular Biology Ser.). 206p. (Orig.). 1985. pap. 30.00 (ISBN 0-87969-185-9). Cold Spring Harbor.

Leach, Sidney J., ed. Physical Principles & Techniques of Protein Chemistry. (Molecular Biology Ser.). Pt. A, 1969. 86.50 (ISBN 0-12-440101-5); Pt. B, 1971. 81.00 (ISBN 0-12-440102-3); Pt. C, 1973. 95.00 (ISBN 0-12-440103-1); Set. o. p. 215.00. Acad Pr.

Lehmann, F. G., ed. Carcino-Embryonic Proteins: Chemistry, Biology, Clinical Application, 2 vols. 1979. Set. 183.00 (ISBN 0-444-80097-2, North Holland); Vol. 1. 135.75 (ISBN 0-444-80095-6); Vol. 2. 135.75 (ISBN 0-444-80096-4). Elsevier.

Li, Choh H., ed. Hormonal Proteins & Peptides, 7 vols. Incl. Vol. 1. 1973. 49.50 (ISBN 0-12-447201-X); Vol. 2. 1973. 59.50 (ISBN 0-12-447202-8); Vol. 3. 1975. 67.50 (ISBN 0-12-447203-6); Vol. 4. 1977. 49.50 (ISBN 0-12-447204-4); Vol. 5. Lipotropin & Related Peptides. 1978. 47.50 (ISBN 0-12-447205-2); Vol. 6. Thyroid Hormones. 1978. 71.50 (ISBN 0-12-447206-0); Vol. 7. Hypothalmic Hormones. 1979. 49.50 (ISBN 0-12-447207-9). LC 78-5444. Acad Pr.

--Versatility of Proteins. 1979. 49.50 (ISBN 0-12-447750-X). Acad Pr.

Liu, T. Y., et al, eds. Frontiers in Biochemical & Biophysical Studies of Proteins & Membranes: Proceedings of the International Conference on Frontiers in Biochemical & Biophysical Studies of Macromolecules, University of Hawaii, Honolulu, Aug. 6-8, 1982. 1983. 100.00 (ISBN 0-444-00822-5, Biomedical Pr). Elsevier.

--Chemical Synthesis & Sequencing of Peptides & Proteins. (Developments in Biochemistry Ser.: Vol. 17). 1981. 68.50 (ISBN 0-444-00623-0, Biomedical Pr). Elsevier.

Lo, T. B., et al, eds. Biochemical & Biophysical Studies of Proteins & Nucleic Acids. Li. 1984. 75.00 (ISBN 0-444-00911-6). Elsevier.

Lottspeich, F. & Henschen, A., eds. High Performance Liquid Chromatography in Protein & Peptide Chemistry. (Illus.). 1982. 58.00x (ISBN 3-11-008542-9). De Gruyter.

Lowe, G. The Cysteine Proteinases. 1976. pap. text ed. 14.00 (ISBN 0-08-020471-6). Pergamon.

Lundblad, Roger L. & Noyes, Claudia M. Chemical Reagents for Protein Modification, Vol. I. 192p. 1984. 59.00 (ISBN 0-8493-5086-7). CRC Pr.

McCann & Dhindsa. Role of Peptides & Proteins in the Control of Reproduction. 370p. 1983. 75.00 (ISBN 0-444-00737-7, Biomedical Pr). Elsevier.

McPherson, Alexander. Preparation & Analysis of Protein Crystals. LC 81-16442. 371p. 1982. 57.95x (ISBN 0-471-08524-3, Pub. by Wiley-Interscience). Wiley.

Maltz, M. A., ed. Protein Food Supplements: Recent Advances. LC 81-38327. (Food Tech. Rev. 54). (Illus.). 404p. 1982. 48.00 (ISBN 0-8155-0865-4). Noyes.

Manwell, Clyde & Baker, C. M. Molecular Biology & the Origin of Species: Heterosis, Protein Polymorphism, & Animal Breeding. LC 70-103299. (Biology Ser). (Illus.). 446p. 1970. 20.00x (ISBN 0-295-95065-X). U of Wash Pr.

Matsubara, Hiroshi & Yamanaka, Tateo. Evolution of Protein Molecules. 1979. 44.00x (ISBN 0-89955-130-0, Pub. by Japan Sci Soc Japan). Intl Spec Bk.

Mihalyi, Elemer. Application of Proteolytic Enzymes to Protein Structure Studies. LC 72-87570. (Uniscience Ser). 1978. Vol. 1. 83.00 (ISBN 0-8493-5189-8). CRC Pr.

--Application of Proteolytic Enzymes to Protein Structure Studies, Vol. 2. 2nd ed. 310p. 1978. 72.50 (ISBN 0-8493-5190-1). CRC Pr.

Needleman, S. B., ed. Advanced Methods in Protein Sequence Determination. LC 77-22808. (Molecular Biology, Biochemistry & Biophysics: Vol. 25). (Illus.). 1977. 38.00 (ISBN 0-387-08368-5). Springer-Verlag.

--Protein Sequence Determination: A Sourcebook of Methods & Techniques. 2nd rev. & enl. ed. (Molecular Biology, Biochemistry & Biophysics Ser.: Vol. 8). (Illus.). 370p. 1975. 63.00 (ISBN 0-387-07256-X). Springer-Verlag.

Nei, Masatoshi & Koehn, Richard K., eds. Evolution of Genes & Proteins. LC 83-477. (Illus.). 380p. 1983. 42.00x (ISBN 0-87893-603-3); pap. 25.00x (ISBN 0-87893-604-1). Sinauer Assoc.

Neurath, H[illegible] ed. Proteins: Composition, Structur[illegible] Function, 3 vols. 2nd ed. Incl. Vol. 4. [illegible]. 71.50 (ISBN 0-12-516264-2); Vol. 5. Mettaloproteins. 1970. 41.50 (ISBN 0-12-516265-0); Vol. 3 o.p. 1965. 48.50 (ISBN 0-12-516263-4). Acad Pr.

Neurath, Hans & Hill, Robert, eds. The Protein, Vol. 5. 736p. 1982. 78.50 (ISBN 0-12-516305-3). Acad Pr.

Neurath, Hans & Hill, Robert L., eds. The Proteins, Vol. 4. 3rd ed. 1979. 63.00 (ISBN 0-12-516304-5). Acad Pr.

New Approaches to Breeding for Improved Plant Protein. (Panel Proceedings Ser.): (Illus.). 193p. 1969. pap. 14.50 (ISBN 92-0-111069-3, ISP212, IAEA). Unipub.

Odell, William D. & Daughaday, William H. Principles of Competitive Protein Binding Assays. (Illus.). 1971. 27.50 (ISBN 0-397-58083-5, 65-71426, Lippincott Medical). Lippincott.

Offord, R. E. Semisynthetic Proteins. LC 79-40521. 235p. 1980. 79.95x (ISBN 0-471-27615-4, Pub. by Wiley-Interscience). Wiley.

Oosawa, Fumio & Asakura, Sho. Thermodynamics of the Polymerization of Protein. 1976. 39.00 (ISBN 0-12-527050-X). Acad Pr.

Osterman, L. A. Methods of Protein & Nucleic Acid Research: Electrophoresis, Isoelectric Focusing, Ultracentrifugation, Vol. 1. (Illus.). 370p. 1984. 59.00 (ISBN 0-387-12735-6). Springer-Verlag.

--Methods of Protein & Nucleic Acid Research: Immunoelectrophoresis - Application of Radioisotopes. (Illus.). 220p. 1984. 38.00 (ISBN 0-387-13094-2). Springer-Verlag.

Oxford, Geoffrey S. Protein Polymorphism. Rollinson, David, ed. (Systematic Association Special Ser.: Vol. 24). 1984. 70.00 (ISBN 0-12-531780-8). Acad Pr.

Paik, Woon Ki & Kim, Sangduk. Protein Methylation. LC 79-19557. 300p. 1980. 64.95 (ISBN 0-471-04867-4). Krieger.

Pariser, E. R., et al. Fish Protein Concentrate: Panacea for Protein Malnutrition? LC 77-28112. (International Nutrition Policy Ser.: NO. 3). 1978. text ed. 35.00x (ISBN 0-262-16069-2). MIT Pr.

Parry, David, ed. Fibrous Proteins: Scientific, Industrial & Medical Aspects, Vol. 1. LC 79-41004. 1980. 57.50 (ISBN 0-12-545701-4). Acad Pr.

--Fibrous Proteins: Scientific, Industrial & Medical Aspects, Vol. 2. 1980. 44.00 (ISBN 0-12-545702-2). Acad Pr.

Peeters, H., ed. Protides of the Biological Fluids: Proceedings, Colloquium on Protides of the Biological Fluids, 26th. LC 58-5908. (Illus.). 1979. text ed. 165.00 (ISBN 0-08-023182-9). Pergamon.

Kreir, Julius P., ed. Parasitic Protozoa: Gregarines, Haemogregarines, Coccida, Plasmodia, & Haemoproteids, Vol. 3. LC 76-13041. 1977. 82.00 (ISBN 0-12-426003-9). Acad Pr.

Laybourn-Parry, Johanna. A Functional Biology of Free-Living Protozoa. (Illus.). 224p. 1984. pap. text ed. 13.95x (ISBN 0-520-05340-0). U of Cal Pr.

--A Functional Biology of Free-Living Protozoa. LC 84-2569. (Illus.). 224p. 1985. text ed. 27.50x (ISBN 0-520-05339-7); pap. 14.95x. U of Cal Pr.

Levandowsky, M. & Hunter, S. H., eds. Biochemistry & Physiology of Protozoa, Vol. 4. 2nd ed. 1983. 69.50 (ISBN 0-12-444604-3). Acad Pr.

Levandowsky, Michael, ed. Biochemistry & Physiology of Protozoa, Vol. 1. 2nd ed. LC 78-20045. 1979. 65.00 (ISBN 0-12-444601-9). Acad Pr.

Levandowsky, Michael & Hutner, S. H., eds. Biochemistry & Physiology of Protozoa, Vol. 2. 2nd ed. 1979. 65.00 (ISBN 0-12-444602-7). Acad Pr.

--Biochemistry & Physiology of Protozoa, Vol. 3. 2nd ed. LC 79-2045. 1980. 60.00 (ISBN 0-12-444603-5). Acad Pr.

Poag, C. Wylie. Ecologic Atlas of Benthic Foraminifera of the Gulf of Mexico. LC 81-3720. 192p. 1981. 29.50 (ISBN 0-87933-900-4). Van Nos Reinhold.

Scholtyseck, E. Fine Structure of Parasitic Protozoa: An Atlas of Micrographs, Drawings & Diagrams. (Illus.). 1979. pap. 45.00 (ISBN 0-387-09010-X). Springer-Verlag.

Sleigh, M. The Biology of Protozoa. (Contemporary Biology Ser). 324p. 1973. pap. text ed. 18.50 (ISBN 0-7131-2410-5). Univ Park.

Thompson, D'Arcy W. Bibliography of Protozoa, Sponges Coelenterata & Worms. LC 77-6993. 1977. Repr. of 1885 ed. lib. bdg. 30.00 (ISBN 0-89341-139-6). Longwood Pub Group.

Tibbs, John F. The Aulacanthidae (Radiolaria: Phaeodaria) of the Antarctic Seas: Paper 2 in Biology of the Antarctic Seas V. Pawson, David L., ed. (Antarctic Research Ser: Vol. 23). 45p. 1976. pap. 19.25 (ISBN 0-87590-126-3). Am Geophysical.

PROTOZOA, PATHOGENIC

Curds, Colin R. British & Other Freshwater Ciliated Protozoa: Part 1. LC 81-15541. (Synopses of the British Fauna Ser.: No. 22). 150p. 1982. 59.50 (ISBN 0-521-24257-6). Cambridge U Pr.

Gutteridge, W. E. & Coombs, G. H. The Biochemistry of Parasitic Protozoa: An Introductory Text. (Illus.). 184p. 1977. pap. text ed. 21.00 (ISBN 0-8391-0886-9). Univ Park.

Weinman, David & Ristic, Miodrag. Infectious Blood Diseases of Man & Animals, 2 Vols. LC 68-18685. 1968. Vol. 1. 89.50 (ISBN 0-12-742501-2); Vol. 2. 95.00 (ISBN 0-12-742502-0). Acad Pr.

PROTOZOOLOGY

Adam, K. M., et al. Medical & Veterinary Protozoology. rev. ed. 1980. 50.00 (ISBN 0-443-00764-0). Churchill.

Chen, T. T., ed. Research in Protozoology, Vol. 4. 1972. 76.00 (ISBN 0-08-016437-4). Pergamon.

Gillies, R. R. Gillies & Dodds Bacteriology Illustrated. 5th ed. LC 82-23595. (Illus.). 224p. (Orig.). 1984. pap. text ed. 28.00 (ISBN 0-443-02809-5). Churchill.

International Congress of Protozoology, 5th. Proceedings. Hutner, S. H., ed. (Illus.). 222p. 1979. pap. text ed. 19.00 (ISBN 0-935868-00-3). Allen Pr.

Kudo, Richard R. Protozoology. 5th ed. (Illus.). 1188p. 1977. 33.75x (ISBN 0-398-01058-7). C C Thomas.

Levine, Norman D. Veterinary Protozoology. (Illus.). 414p. 1985. text ed. 39.50x (ISBN 0-8138-1861-3). Iowa St U Pr.

Ludvik, J., ed. Progress in Protozoology. (Illus.). 1964. 98.50 (ISBN 0-12-459450-6). Acad Pr.

Raikov, I. B. The Protozoan Nucleus: Morphology & Evolution. Bobrov, N. & Verkhovsteva, M., trs. (Cell Biology Monographs: Vol. 9). (Illus.). 450p. 1982. 118.00 (ISBN 0-387-81678-X). Springer-Verlag.

PRUNING

Bailey, Liberty H. Pruning Manual. Christopher, E. P., rev. by. 1954. 15.95 (ISBN 0-02-525420-0). Macmillan.

Brickell, Christopher. Step-by-Step Guide to Pruning. 1979. pap. 7.95 (ISBN 0-671-24831-6, Fireside). S&S.

Grounds, Roger, ed. Practical Pruning. LC 77-70395. (Illus.). 1978. pap. 3.95 (ISBN 0-8120-0797-2). Barron.

Hammett, K. R. Plant Training, Pruning & Tree Surgery. (Illus.). 68p. 1983. 10.50 (ISBN 0-7153-6409-X). David & Charles.

Ortho Books Editorial Staff. All about Pruning. LC 78-57891. (Illus.). 1979. pap. 5.95 (ISBN 0-917102-73-8). Ortho.

Pruning Shade Trees & Practicing Tree Surgery. facs. ed. (Shorey Lost Arts Ser.). 52p. pap. 2.95 (ISBN 0-8466-6041-5, U41). Shorey.

Rudman, Jack. Climber & Pruner. (Career Examination Ser.: C-148). (Cloth bdg. avail. on request). pap. 10.00 (ISBN 0-8373-0148-3). Natl Learning.

--Tree Trimmer. (Career Examination Ser.: C-1526). (Cloth bdg. avail. on request). pap. 8.00 (ISBN 0-8373-1526-3). Natl Learning.

Steffek, Edwin F. The Pruning Manual. rev. ed. 1974. pap. 3.95 (ISBN 0-316-81213-7). Little.

PSELAPHIDAE

Park, O. Pselaphidae of Oceania, with Special Reference to the Fiji Islands. (BMB). pap. 10.00 (ISBN 0-527-02315-9). Kraus Repr.

PSEUDOMONAS

Palleroni, N. J. The Pseudomonas Group. 88p. 1979. 39.00x (ISBN 0-904095-28-2, Pub. by Meadowfield Pr England). State Mutual Bk.

PSEUDORABIES VIRUS

Kaplan, A. S. Herpes Simplex & Pseudorabies Viruses. (Virology Monographs: Vol. 5). (Illus.). 1969. 21.00 (ISBN 0-387-80932-5). Springer-Verlag.

PSYCHOBIOLOGY

see also Psychology, Physiological

Bell, R. W., et al, eds. Developmental Psychobiology & Clinical Neuropsychology. (Interfaces in Psychology Ser.: No. 1). 133p. 1984. 24.95 (ISBN 0-89672-120-5); pap. 14.95 (ISBN 0-89672-119-1). Tex Tech Pr.

Biology Colloquium, 32nd, Oregon State University, 1971. The Biology of Behavior: Proceedings. Kiger, John A., Jr., ed. LC 52-19235. (Illus.). 1972. 9.95x (ISBN 0-87071-171-7). Oreg St U Pr.

Cohen, Sanford I. & Ross, Robert. Handbook of Clinical Psychobiology & Pathology, Vol. 1. LC 80-14321. (Clinical & Community Psychology Ser.). 480p. 1983. text ed. 39.95 (ISBN 0-89116-173-2). Hemisphere Pub.

--Handbook of Clinical Psychobiology & Pathology, Vol. 2. LC 80-14321. (Clinical & Communty Psychology Ser.). 384p. 1983. 49.95 (ISBN 0-89116-174-0). Hemisphere Pub.

Davidson, Richard J. & Davidson, Julian M., eds. Psychobiology of Consciousness. LC 79-316. 508p. 1980. 39.50x (ISBN 0-306-40138-X, Plenum Pr). Plenum Pub.

East, Edward M., ed. Biology in Human Affairs. LC 72-313. (Essay Index Reprint Ser.). Repr. of 1931 ed. 23.50 (ISBN 0-8369-2790-7). Ayer Co Pubs.

Ernst, Franklin H., Jr. Transactional Analysis in Psychobiology: From Prince to Frog to Principle. 1981. pap. 9.50 (ISBN 0-916944-36-0). Addresso'set.

Gaito, John. Molecular Psychobiology: A Chemical Approach to Learning & Other Behavior. (Illus.). 280p. 1966. 24.50x (ISBN 0-398-00635-0). C C Thomas.

Gazzaniga, Michael S. & Blakemore, Colin, eds. Handbook of Psychobiology. 1975. 57.50 (ISBN 0-12-278656-4). Acad Pr.

Gershon, E. S., et al, eds. Genetic Research Strategies in Psychobiology & Psychiatry. (Psychobiology & Psychopathology Ser.: Vol. 1). 1981. 38.50x (ISBN 0-910286-84-1). Boxwood.

Gershon, Elliot S., et al, eds. The Impact of Biology on Modern Psychiatry. LC 76-49665. (Illus.). 288p. 1977. 39.50x (ISBN 0-306-31000-7, Plenum Pr). Plenum Pub.

Greenfield, Norman S. & Lewis, William C., eds. Psychoanalysis & Current Biological Thought. LC 64-7725. 1965. pap. 97.50 (ISBN 0-317-08160-8, 2021133). Bks Demand UMI.

Grenell, Robert & Gabay, Sabit, eds. Biological Foundations of Psychiatry, 2 vols. LC 74-15664. 1976. 63.00 ea.; Vol. 1, 613pgs. (ISBN 0-911216-96-0); Vol. 2, 477 Pgs. (ISBN 0-89004-126-1). Raven.

Groves, Philip M. & Schlesinger, Kurt. Introduction to Biological Psychology. 2nd ed. 752p. 1982. text ed. write for info. (ISBN 0-697-06644-4); instrs. manual avail. (ISBN 0-697-06646-0); study guide avail. (ISBN 0-697-06645-2); transparencies avail. (ISBN 0-697-06653-3). Wm C Brown.

Habig, Robert L., ed. The Brain, Biochemistry & Behavior. 360p. 1984. 35.00 (ISBN 0-915274-22-1); members 25.00. Am Assn Clinical Chem.

Holliday, Laurel. The Violent Sex: Male Psychobiology & the Evolution of Consciousness. LC 78-7344. (Illus.). 1978. pap. 4.95 (ISBN 0-931458-01-3). Bluestocking.

Kalat, James W. & Norton, Thomas J., eds. From Brains to Behavior. 1973. 39.50x (ISBN 0-8422-5115-4). Irvington.

Levy, S. M., ed. Biological Mediators of Behavior & Disease: Neoplasma. 260p. 1982. 59.95 (ISBN 0-444-00708-3, Biomedical Pr). Elsevier.

Lewis, Dorothy O., ed. Vulnerabilities to Delinquency. 343p. 1981. text ed. 37.95 (ISBN 0-89335-136-9). SP Med & Sci Bks.

Mogenson, Gordon J. The Neurobiology of Behavior: An Introduction. LC 77-18283. 334p. 1977. 14.95x (ISBN 0-470-99341-3). Halsted Pr.

Monnier, M. & Meulders, M., eds. Psycho-Neurobiology. (Functions of the Nervous System Ser.: Vol. 4). 716p. 1983. 195.75 (ISBN 0-444-80469-2, I-365-83, Biomedical Pr). Elsevier.

Morozov, P. V., ed. Research on the Viral Hypothesis of Mental Disorders. (Advances in Biological Psychiatry: Vol. 12). (Illus.). x, 178p. 1983. pap. 38.75 (ISBN 3-8055-3706-9). S Karger.

Mortis, Joseph, ed. Recent Advances in Biological Psychiatry, 2 vols. LC 58-14190. Vol. 6, 1963. pap. 71.00 (ISBN 0-317-10483-7, 2003369); Vol. 7, 1964. pap. 78.00 (ISBN 0-317-10484-5). Bks Demand UMI.

Myslobodsky, Michael, ed. Hemisyndromes: Psychobiology, Neurology, Psychiatry. LC 83-2823. 1983. 55.00 (ISBN 0-12-512460-0). Acad Pr.

Pirke, K. M. & Ploog, D., eds. The Psychobiology of Anorexia Nervosa. (Illus.). 200p. 1984. 29.50 (ISBN 0-387-13196-5). Springer-Verlag.

Reynierse, James H., ed. Current Issues in Animal Learning: A Colloquium. LC 78-98389. viii, 394p. 1970. 27.50x (ISBN 0-8032-0744-1). U of Nebr Pr.

Reynolds, Vernon. The Biology of Human Action. 2nd ed. LC 80-11856. (Illus.). 303p. 1980. pap. text ed. 14.95x (ISBN 0-7167-1240-7). W H Freeman.

Riesen, A. H. & Thompson, R. F. Advances in Psychobiology, Vol. 3. LC 70-178148. Repr. of 1976 ed. 96.80 (ISBN 0-8357-9831-3, 2015177). Bks Demand UMI.

Robinson, Daniel N. & Utall, William R. Foundations of Psychobiology. 384p. 1983. text ed. write for info. (ISBN 0-02-402460-0). Macmillan.

Serafetinides, E. A., ed. Methods of Biobehavioral Research. (Seminars in Psychiatry Ser.). 240p. 1979. 34.50 (ISBN 0-8089-1173-2, 793999). Grune.

Serban, George & Kling, Arthur, eds. Animal Models in Human Psychobiology. LC 75-40449. (Illus.). 311p. 1976. 39.50x (ISBN 0-306-30864-9, Plenum Pr). Plenum Pub.

Sprague, James & Epstein, Alan, eds. Progress in Psychobiology & Physiological Psychology, Vol. 8. LC 66-29640. 1979. 55.00 (ISBN 0-12-542108-7). Acad Pr.

Sprague, James M. & Epstein, Alan N., eds. Progress in Psychobiology & Physiological Psychology, Vol. 9. 1980. 49.50 (ISBN 0-12-542109-5). Acad Pr.

Stanley-Jones, D. Kybernetics of Mind & Brain. 192p. 1970. 19.50x (ISBN 0-398-01833-2). C C Thomas.

Stratton, Peter. Psychobiology of the Human Newborn. LC 81-14756. (Developmental Psychology & Its Applications Ser.). 456p. 1982. 63.95 (ISBN 0-471-10093-5, Pub. by Wiley-Interscience). Wiley.

Sulloway, Frank J. Freud, Biologist of the Mind: Beyond the Psychoanalytic Legend. LC 79-7343. 1983. pap. 13.95 (ISBN 0-465-02560-9, CN5095). Basic.

Teyler. A Primer of Psychobiology. 2nd ed. LC 83-20642. (Illus.). 181p. 1984. 15.95 (ISBN 0-7167-1459-0); pap. 8.95 (ISBN 0-7167-1460-4). W H Freeman.

Teyler, Timothy J. A Primer of Psychobiology: Brain & Behavior. LC 74-20989. (Psychology Ser.). (Illus.). 143p. 1975. text ed. 17.95x (ISBN 0-7167-0749-7); pap. text ed. 8.95x (ISBN 0-7167-0748-9); tchr's manual avail. W H Freeman.

Usdin, Earl & Mandell, Arnold J., eds. Biochemistry of Mental Disorders: New Vistas. (Modern Pharmacology - Toxicology Ser.: Vol. 13). 1978. 85.00 (ISBN 0-8247-6504-4). Dekker.

Uttal, W. R. The Psychobiology of Mind. 816p. 1978. 45.00x (ISBN 0-89859-497-9); text ed. 36.00. L Erlbaum Assocs.

Uttal, William R. The Psychobiology of Mind. 785p. 1978. 29.95x (ISBN 0-470-26316-4). Halsted Pr.

Van Praag. Handbook of Biological Psychiatry, Pt. 3. (Experimental & Clinical Psychology Ser.: Vol. 1). 400p. 1980. 75.00 (ISBN 0-8247-6965-1). Dekker.

Van Praag, et al. Handbook of Biological Psychiatry: Brain Mechanisms & Abnormal Behavior - Phychophysiology, Pt. 2. (Experimental & Clinical Psychology Ser.: Vol. 1). 544p. 1980. 85.00 (ISBN 0-8247-6892-2). Dekker.

Wender, Paul H. & Klein, Donald F. Mind, Mood, & Medicine: A Guide to the New Biopsychiatry. 1982. pap. 7.95 (ISBN 0-452-00601-5, Mer). NAL.

Whalen, Richard E., et al, eds. Neural Control of Behavior. 1970. 59.50 (ISBN 0-12-745050-5). Acad Pr.

PSYCHOLOGY–DATA PROCESSING

Apter, Michael J. & Westby, George. The Computer in Psychology. LC 72-5711. 309p. 1973. 48.95x (ISBN 0-471-03260-3, Pub. by Wiley-Interscience). Wiley.

Automated Education Center. Data Processing for Guidance & Counseling Handbook. LC 67-22802. 19.00 (ISBN 0-403-04462-6). Scholarly.

Bailey, Daniel E., ed. Computer Science in Social & Behavioral Science Education. LC 77-25087. (Illus.). 520p. 1978. 32.95 (ISBN 0-87778-101-X). Educ Tech Pubns.

Bird, R. The Computer in Experimental Psychology. LC 80-41610. (Computers & People Ser.). 256p. 1981. 47.50 (ISBN 0-12-099760-6). Acad Pr.

Colby, K. M. Artificial Paranoia: A Computer Simulation of Paranoid Processes. 1975. pap. text ed. 10.75 (ISBN 0-08-018161-9). Pergamon.

Creamer, Lyle R. Computer Applications in Psychology. 1984. velo plastic Bdg. 17.50 (ISBN 0-318-02994-4). L R Creamer.

Heise, David R. Computer-Assisted Analysis of Social Action: Use of Program INTERACT & SURVEY.UNC75. LC 78-8724. (Technical Papers Ser: No. 3). 154p. 1978. pap. text ed. 5.00 (ISBN 0-89143-086-5). U NC Inst Res Soc Sci.

Krug, Samuel E., ed. Psychware: A Reference Guide to Computer-Based Products for Behavioral Assessment in Psychology, Education & Business. LC 84-16461. 816p. 1984. 65.00x (ISBN 0-9611286-5-8, Pub. by Test Corp Am). Westport Pubs.

Mayzner, Mark S. & Dolan, Terrence R. Minicomputers in Sensory & Information Processing Research. LC 78-15762. 280p. 1978. 18.00x (ISBN 0-470-26488-8). Halsted Pr.

Mayzner, Mark S. & Dolan, Terrence R., eds. Minicomputers in Sensory & Information-Processing Research. 288p. 1978. text ed. 29.95x (ISBN 0-89859-478-2). L Erlbaum Assocs.

Nadler, David A. Feedback & Organization Development: Using Data-Based Methods. (Illus.). 1977. pap. text ed. 10.95 (ISBN 0-201-05006-4). Addison-Wesley.

Romanczyk, Raymond G. Clinical Utilization of Microcomputer Technology. (Psychology Practitioner Guidebks.). 128p. 1985. 17.50 (ISBN 0-08-031946-7, Pub. by PPI); pap. 9.95 (ISBN 0-08-031945-9). Pergamon.

Schank, Roger C. & Colby, Kenneth M., eds. Computer Models of Thought & Language. LC 73-11064. (Psychology Ser.). (Illus.). 454p. 1973. text ed. 35.95x (ISBN 0-7167-0834-5). W H Freeman.

Schwartz, Marc D., ed. Using Computers in Clinical Practice: Psychotherapy & Mental Health Applications. LC 83-18648. 510p. 1984. text ed. 34.95 (ISBN 0-86656-208-7, B208). Haworth Pr.

PSYCHOLOGY, GENETIC

see Genetic Psychology

PSYCHOLOGY, PHYSIOLOGICAL

see also Brain–Localization of Functions; Color Vision; Human Engineering; Hypnotism; Psychometrics; Senses and Sensation; Space Perception

Adam, G., ed. Biology of Memory. LC 73-154700. 250p. 1971. 29.50x (ISBN 0-306-30535-6, Plenum Pr). Plenum Pub.

Altman, Joseph. Organic Foundations of Animal Behavior. LC 65-18350. (Illus.). 1966. text ed. 37.50x (ISBN 0-03-052230-7); pap. text ed. 14.95x (ISBN 0-89197-871-2). Irvington.

American Health Research Institute, Ltd. Psycho-Physiological Disorders: General & Medical Research Subject Directory with Bibliography. Bartone, John C., ed. LC 82-72012. 236p. 1982. 39.95 (ISBN 0-941864-40-5); pap. 29.95 (ISBN 0-941864-41-3). ABBE Pubs Assn.

Andreassi, John L. Psychophysiology: Human Behavior & Physiological Response. 1980. pap. 15.95x (ISBN 0-19-502581-4). Oxford U Pr.

Applewhite, Philip B. Molecular Gods: How Molecules Determine Our Behavior. LC 80-22834. (Illus.). 288p. 1981. 10.95 (ISBN 0-13-599530-2). P-H.

Baird, John C. & Noma, Elliot. Fundamentals of Scaling & Psychophysics. LC 78-6011. (Behavior Ser.). 287p. 1978. 42.95x (ISBN 0-471-04169-6, Pub. by Wiley-Interscience). Wiley.

Biokinesiology Institute. Muscle Testing Your Way to Health Using Emotions, Nutrition & Massage. (Illus.). 116p. (Orig.). 1982. pap. 5.95 (ISBN 0-937216-07-0). Biokinesiology Institute.

Blakemore, Colin. Mechanics of the Mind. LC 76-53515. (BBC Reith Lectures: 1976). 1977. 52.50 (ISBN 0-521-21559-5); pap. 13.95 (ISBN 0-521-29185-2). Cambridge U Pr.

Blundell, John. Physiological Psychology. (Essential Psychology Ser.). 1975. pap. 4.95x (ISBN 0-416-81950-8, NO. 2610). Methuen Inc.

PSYCHOMETRICS

see also Decision-Making–Mathematical Models; Factor Analysis

Myers, Jerome L. Fundamentals of Experimental Design. 3rd ed. 1979. text ed. 33.95 (ISBN 0-205-06615-1). Allyn.

Oltman, Debra. Weinberg, Schumaker & Oltman's Statistics: An Intuitive Approach, Study Guide. 4th ed. 250p. (Orig.). 1982. pap. text ed. 7.25 pub net (ISBN 0-8185-0442-0). Brooks-Cole.

Pagano, Robert R. Understanding Statistics in the Behavioral Sciences. (Illus.). 592p. 1981. text ed. 27.95 (ISBN 0-8299-0316-X); student guide avail. (ISBN 0-8299-0341-0). West Pub.

Pedagogical Seminary: (Selections) Hall, G. Stanley, ed. (Contributions to the History of Psychology Ser.: Pt. B, Vol. VI, Psychometric & Educational Psychology). 1983. 30.00 (ISBN 0-89093-320-0). U Pubns Amer.

Porter, Joseph H. & Hamm, Robert J. Statistics: Applications for the Behavioral Sciences. (Psychology Ser.). 425p. 1985. text ed. 20.00 (pub net) (ISBN 0-534-05154-5). Brooks-Cole.

Prunkl, Peter R. The Psychological Testing Workbook. 1979. 12.80 (ISBN 0-918296-13-7). Inst Personality & Ability.

Psychological Statistics, 7 Vols. Set. 25.50x (ISBN 0-86589-014-5); 3.80x ea. Vol. 1, Units 1-3 (ISBN 0-86589-015-3). Vol. 2, Units 4-5 (ISBN 0-86589-016-1). Vol. 3, Units 6-7 (ISBN 0-86589-017-X). Vol. 4, Units 8-9 (ISBN 0-86589-018-8). Vol. 5, Units 10-11 (ISBN 0-86589-019-6). Vol. 6, Units 12-13 (ISBN 0-86589-020-X). Vol. 7, Units 14-15 (ISBN 0-86589-021-8). Individual Learn.

Ramsay, James O. Multiscale II: Four Programs for Multidimensional Scaling by the Method of Maximum Likelihood. pap. 14.00 (ISBN 0-89498-002-5). Sci Ware.

Reynolds, Cecil R. & Brown, Robert T., eds. Perspectives on Bias in Mental Testing. (Perspectives on Individual Differences Ser.). 593p. 1984. 50.00x (ISBN 0-306-41529-1, Plenum Pr). Plenum Pub.

Scandura, Joseph M., et al. Problem Solving: A Structural-Process with Instructional Implications. 1977. 47.50 (ISBN 0-12-620650-3). Acad Pr.

Scheaffer, Richard & McClave, James. Statistics for Engineers. 480p. 1982. text ed. write for info. (ISBN 0-87872-298-X, 6950, Duxbury Pr). PWS Pubs.

Schmiedeck, Raoul A. The Personal Sphere Model. 240p. 1978. text ed. 34.50 (ISBN 0-8089-1093-0, 793915); scoring template kit 14.00 (ISBN 0-8089-1136-8, 793916). Grune.

Slater, P., ed. The Measurement of Intrapersonal Space by Grid Techniques: Explorations of Intrapersonal Space, Vol. 1. LC 76-8908. 258p. 1976. 63.95x (ISBN 0-471-01360-9, Pub. by Wiley-Interscience). Wiley.

Sprinthall, Richard. Basic Statistical Analysis. LC 81-14858. (Psychology-Behavioral Statistics Ser.). (Illus.). 479p. Date not set. pap. text ed. 17.95 (ISBN 0-394-35053-7). Random.

Standards for Educational & Psychological Testing. LC 85-71493. 96p. (Orig.). 1985. pap. 23.00 (ISBN 0-912704-95-0). Am Psychol.

Thorndike, Robert L. Applied Psychometrics. LC 81-81699. 1982. 34.50 (ISBN 0-395-30077-0). HM.

Torgerson, Warren S. Theory & Methods of Scaling. LC 58-10812. 1958. pap. 118.50 (ISBN 0-317-08170-5, 2020339). Bks Demand UMI.

VanDerKamp, Leo J., et al, eds. Psychometrics for Educational Debates. LC 79-4308. 337p. 1980. 76.95x (ISBN 0-471-27596-4, Pub. by Wiley-Interscience). Wiley.

Ward, Eric F. Beginning Statistics for Psychology Students. 4th ed. 1985. pap. text ed. price not set. TIS Inc.

Whaley, Donald L. Psychological Testing & the Philosophy of Measurement. 58p. 1973. pap. text ed. 7.00 (ISBN 0-917472-08-X). F Fournies.

Woodyard, Ella. The Effect of Time Upon Variability. LC 70-177624. (Columbia University. Teachers College. Contributions to Education: No. 216). Repr. of 1926 ed. 17.50 (ISBN 0-404-55216-1). AMS Pr.

Yaremko, Robert M., et al. Reference Handbook of Research & Statistical Methods in Psychology: For Students & Professionals. 335p. 1982. pap. text ed. 10.53I (ISBN 0-06-047332-0, HarpC). Har-Row.

Zoltano, Rosalie F. Psychological Tests: International Survey with Research Subject Index & Bibliography. LC 82-72016. 152p. 1983. 29.95 (ISBN 0-941864-48-0); pap. 21.95 (ISBN 0-941864-49-9). ABBE Pubs Assn.

PSYCHOPHYSICS

see Psychology, Physiological

PSYCHOPHYSIOLOGY

see Psychology, Physiological

PTERIDINES

Blair, J. A., ed. Chemistry & Biology of Pteridines: Pteridines & Folic Acid Derivatives. LC 83-7666. xxxvi, 1070p. 1983. 128.00x (ISBN 3-11-008560-7). De Gruyter.

Curtius, H. C., et al, eds. Biochemical & Clinical Aspects of Pteridines, Vol. 2 - Cancer, Immunology, Metabolic Diseases: Proceedings, Second Winter Workshop on Pterdines, March 6-9, 1983, St. Christopher, Arlberg, Austria. LC 83-24079. xv, 435p. 1984. 87.00x (ISBN 3-11-009813-X). De Gruyter.

Hurst, ed. An Introduction to Chemistry & Biochemistry of Pyrimidines, Purines & Pteridines. LC 79-40736. 266p. 1980. 64.95 (ISBN 0-471-27647-2, Pub. by Wiley-Interscience). Wiley.

Kisliuk, R. L. & Brown, G. M., eds. The Chemistry & Biology of Pteridines. (Developments in Biochemistry Ser.: Vol. 4). 714p. 1979. 71.00 (ISBN 0-444-00305-3, Biomedical Pr). Elsevier.

Pfleiderer, W., et al, eds. Biochemical & Clinical Aspects of Pteridines: Vol. 3, Proceedings of Third Winter Workshop on Pteridines, Feb. 1984. LC 84-17661. (Illus.). xii, 514p. 1984. 99.50x (ISBN 3-11-010163-7). De Gruyter.

Pfleiderer, Wolfgang, ed. Chemistry & Biology of Pteridines: Proceedings of the 5th International Symposium, Held at the University, of Konstanz, Germany,April,1975. viii, 949p. 1975. 76.00x (ISBN 3-11-005928-2). De Gruyter.

Wachter, H. & Curtius, H. C., eds. Biochemical & Clinical Aspects of Pteridines, Vol. 1. (Illus.). 373p. 1982. 68.00x (ISBN 3-11-008984-X). De Gruyter.

PTERIDOPHYTA

see also Ferns

Bir, S. S. Pteridophytes: Some Aspects of Their Structure & Morphology. (Aspects of Plant Sciences Ser.: Vol. III). 170p. 1980. 15.00 (ISBN 0-88065-064-8, Pub. by Messers Today & Tomorrows Printers & Publishers India). Scholarly Pubns.

Clute, Willard N. The Fern-Collector's Guide. (Shorey Lost Arts Ser.). (Illus.). 52p. pap. 3.95 (ISBN 0-8466-6026-1, U26). Shorey.

Grillos, Steve J. Ferns & Fern Allies of California. (California Natural History Guides: No. 16). (Illus., Rita Whittmore). 1966. pap. 2.65 (ISBN 0-520-00519-8). U of Cal Pr.

Kurata, Satoru & Nakaike, Toshiyuki, eds. Illustrations of Pteridophytes of Japan, Vol. 1. 628p. 1979. 60.00x (ISBN 0-86008-269-5, Pub. by U of Tokyo Japan). Columbia U Pr.

--Illustrations of Pteridophytes of Japan, Vol. 2. 648p. 1981. 65.00x (ISBN 0-86008-289-X, Pub. by U of Tokyo Japan). Columbia U Pr.

--Illustrations of Pteridophytes of Japan, Vol. 3. 728p. 1983. 70.00x (ISBN 0-86008-333-0, Pub. by U of Tokyo Japan). Columbia U Pr.

Love, A. Cytotaxonimical Atlas of the Pteridophyta, Vol. 3. (Cytotaxonomical Atlases Ser.: Vol. 3). 1977. 52.50 (ISBN 3-7682-1103-7). Lubrecht & Cramer.

Page, C. N. The Ferns of Britain & Ireland. LC 82-1126. (Illus.). 450p. 1983. 82.50 (ISBN 0-521-23213-9). Cambridge U Pr.

Pascher, A. Suesswasserflora von Suedeuropa, Vol. 24: Pteridophyta und Antophyta, Part 2- Saururaceae bis Asteraceae. Ettl, H., et al, eds. (Illus.). 540p. 1981. lib. bdg. 59.35 (ISBN 3-437-30341-4). Lubrecht & Cramer.

Petrik-Ott, A. J. The Pteridophytes of Kansas, Nebraska, South Dakota & North Dakota, U. S. A. Nova Hedwigia Beiheft, No. 61. 1979. lib. bdg. 30.00 (ISBN 3-7682-5461-5). Lubrecht & Cramer.

Rashid, A. An Introduction to Pteridophyta. 1976. 20.00x (ISBN 0-7069-0447-8, Pub. by Vikas India). Advent NY.

--Introduction to Pteridophyta. 1976. 10.50 (ISBN 0-7069-0447-8). Intl Bk Dist.

Rydberg, Per A. Flora of the Prairies & Plains of Central North America. (Illus.). 1965. Repr. of 1932 ed. 23.95x (ISBN 0-02-851240-5). Hafner.

Smith, Allan R. Pteridophytes. Breedlove, Dennis E., ed. (Flora of Chiapas Ser.: Pt. 2). (Illus.). 370p. (Orig.). 1981. pap. 30.00 (ISBN 0-940228-01-7). Calif Acad Sci.

Sporne, K. R. Morphology of Pteridophytes: The Structure of Ferns & Allied Plants. 4th ed. 1975. pap. text ed. 13.75x (ISBN 0-09-123861-7, Hutchinson U Lib). Humanities.

Toshiyuki, Nakaike. Enumeratio Pteridophytarum Japonicarum. 1975. 42.50x (ISBN 0-86008-135-4, Pub. by U of Tokyo Japan). Columbia U Pr.

Verdoorn, Fr., ed. Manual of Pteridology. (Illus.). 1967. Repr. of 1938 ed. 39.10 (ISBN 90-6123-093-4). Lubrecht & Cramer.

PUBLIC ADMINISTRATION–DATA PROCESSING

Bernstein, Samuel J., ed. Computers in Public Administration: An International Perspective. 450p. 1976. text ed. 54.00 (ISBN 0-08-017869-3). Pergamon.

Bloch, Carolyn C. Federal Energy Information Sources & Data Bases. LC 79-15543. 1979. 24.00 (ISBN 0-8155-0764-X). Noyes.

Bolek, Raymond W., et al. Touche Ross Government Executives' Guide to Selecting a Small Computer. LC 84-4726. 244p. 1984. 49.95 (ISBN 0-13-925611-3, Busn). P-H.

DeGrolier, Eric. The Organization of Information Systems for Government & Public Administration. (Documentation, Libraries & Archives: Studies & Research: No. 8). (Illus.). 163p. 1979. pap. 10.00 (ISBN 92-3-101595-8, U919, UNESCO). Unipub.

Dery, David. Computers in Welfare: The MIS-Match. LC 81-224. (Managing Information Ser.: Vol. 3). (Illus.). 264p. 1981. 25.00 (ISBN 0-8039-1610-8). Sage.

Enger, Norman & Bassler, Richard. Computer Systems & Public Administrators. 1976. pap. 12.50 (ISBN 0-916580-01-6). College Readings.

Kraus, H., ed. The Impact of New Technologies on Information Systems in Public Administration in the 80's. 420p. 1984. 57.50 (ISBN 0-444-86725-2, North-Holland). Elsevier.

Lee, Kaiman. Integrated Municipal Information System. LC 74-184835. 52p. 1974. 12.00x (ISBN 0-915250-12-8). Environ Design.

Ottensmann, J. R. Using Personal Computers in Public Agencies. 208p. 1985. pap. 24.95 (ISBN 0-471-80706-0). Wiley.

Pipe, G. R. & Veenhius, A. A. National Planning for Informatics in Developing Countries: Proceedings of a Conference Held in Baghdad, 1975. 1976. 59.75 (ISBN 0-7204-0392-8, North-Holland). Elsevier.

Pitt, D. C. & Smith, Brian. The Computer Revolution in Public Administration. 224p. 1984. 24.50x (ISBN 0-7108-0747-3, Pub. by Salem Hse Ltd). Merrimack Pub Cir.

Stevens, John M. & McGowan, Robert P. Information Systems & Public Management. 302p. 1985. 38.95 (ISBN 0-03-004447-2). Praeger.

Westin, Alan F., ed. Information Technology in a Democracy. LC 72-143233. (Studies in Technology & Society). 1971. 27.50x (ISBN 0-674-45435-9). Harvard U Pr.

PUBLISHERS AND PUBLISHING–DATA PROCESSING

Botein, Michael & Pearce, Alan. Videotex & Electronic Publishing: A Legal, Regulatory & Economic Analysis. 56p. (Orig.). 1982. pap. text ed. write for info. Comm Media.

Business Communications Staff. Electronic Commercial Publishing. 1984. 1750.00 (ISBN 0-89336-413-4, G-087). BCC.

Carter, Nancy M. & Cullen, John B. The Computerization of Newspaper Organizations: The Impact of Technology on Organizational Structuring. (Illus.). 146p. (Orig.). 1983. lib. bdg. 22.25 (ISBN 0-8191-3378-7); pap. text ed. 9.75 (ISBN 0-8191-3379-5). U Pr of Amer.

Collier, Harry, et al, eds. Electronic Publishing Review: The International Journal of the Transfer of Published Information via Videotex & Online Media. 1984. per year 66.00 (ISBN 0-317-00229-5). Learned Info.

Deighton, Suzan, et al, eds. Computers & Information Processing World Index. 626p. 1984. lib. bdg. 85.00 (ISBN 0-89774-116-1, Co-Pub. with Gower Pub. Co). Oryx Pr.

EUSIDIC: Database Guide 1983. 1983. 50.00 (ISBN 0-317-00238-4). Learned Info.

Information Sources: 1983-84. 1983. 25.00 (ISBN 0-317-00233-3). Learned Info.

International Resource Development Inc. In-Plant Printing in the Age of Corporate Electronic Publishing. 264p. 1984. 985.00x (ISBN 0-88694-613-1). Intl Res Dev.

Moghdam, Dineh. Computers in Newspaper Publishing: User Oriented Systems. (Books in Library & Information Science Ser.: Vol. 22). 1978. 45.00 (ISBN 0-8247-6620-2). Dekker.

Monitor: Online & Electronic Publishing Industry Analytical Review. one year subscription 200.00 (ISBN 0-686-81699-4). Learned Info.

Optical Discs for Office Automation & Electronic Publishing. (Reports Ser.: No. 191). 171p. 1982. 1285.00x (ISBN 0-88694-191-1). Intl Res Dev.

Roth, Stephen. The Computer Edge: Microcomputer Trends-Uses in Publishing. 288p. 1985. 24.95 (ISBN 0-8352-1924-0). Bowker.

Spigai, Frances & Sommer, Peter. A Guide to Electronic Publishing: Opportunities in Online & Viewdata Services. LC 81-20787. (Communications Library). 163p. 1982. spiral professional 95.00 (ISBN 0-914236-87-3, 410-BW). Knowledge Indus.

Van Der Haan, A. & Winters, A. A., eds. The Use of Information in a Changing World: Proceedings of the FID Congress, 42nd, the Hague, Netherlands, Sept. 24-27, 1984. 470p. 1984. 52.00 (ISBN 0-444-87554-9, I-301-84, North Holland). Elsevier.

PUBLISHING, ELECTRONIC

see Electronic Publishing

PUFFBALLS

Kreisel, Hans. Die Lycoperdaceae Der DDR. 1973. Repr. of 1962 ed. 10.50 (ISBN 3-7682-0852-4). Lubrecht & Cramer.

PUFFINS

Lockley, Ronald M. Puffins. 7.50 (ISBN 0-8159-6511-7). Devin.

PUG-DOGS

see Dogs–Breeds–Pug-Dogs

PULLMAN CARS

see Railroads–Cars

PULPWOOD

Atchinson, Joseph E. Nonwood Plant Fiber Pulping Progress Report. LC 82-80290. (No. 13). 148p. 1983. pap. 48.95 (ISBN 0-89852-404-0, 01 01 R104). TAPPI.

Atchison, Joseph E. Nonwood Plant Fiber Pulping, Progress Report, No. 10. (TAPPI PRESS Reports). (Illus.). 125p. 1979. pap. 38.95 (ISBN 0-89852-381-8, 01-01-R081). TAPPI.

Casey, James P. Pulp & Paper: Chemistry & Chemical Technology, 4 vols. 3rd ed. 1983. Set. 305.00 (ISBN 0-471-88186-4, Pub. by Wiley-Interscience). Wiley.

Casey, James P., ed. Pulp & Paper: Chemistry & Chemical Technology, 2 vols. 3rd ed. LC 79-13435. 820p. 1980. Vol. 1, 820 p. 96.50 (ISBN 0-471-03175-5, Pub. by Wiley-Interscience); Vol. 2, 625 p. 91.00 (ISBN 0-471-03176-3). Wiley.

Halpern, M. G., ed. Pulp Mill Processes: Developments since 1977. LC 81-16782. (Pollution Technology Review 85; Chemical Technology Review: No. 198). (Illus.). 371p. 1982. 48.00 (ISBN 0-8155-0871-9). Noyes.

International Pulp Bleaching Conference: Proceedings. 223p. 1982. pap. 44.95 (ISBN 0-686-43244-4, 01 05 1282). TAPPI.

International Sulfite Pulping Conference: Proceedings. 223p. 1982. pap. 44.95 (ISBN 0-686-43245-2, 01 05 1782). TAPPI.

Navarro, Jaime. Evaluation of Mixed Tropical Hardwoods for Pulp & Paper Manufacture. (Illus.). 160p. 1976. pap. 11.00 (ISBN 92-5-100041-7, F776, FAO). Unipub.

New Mining Methods: Thermomechanical Pulping A Panel Dicussion. 55p. 1975. soft cover 4.95 (ISBN 0-686-98534-6, 01-05-0615). TAPPI.

Pearce, J. Kenneth & Stenzel, George. Logging & Pulpwood Production. 452p. 1972. 37.50x (ISBN 0-471-06839-X, Pub. by Wiley-Interscience). Wiley.

Phillips, F. H. The Pulping & Papermaking Potential of Tropical Hardwoods, Vol. 1. 1980. 20.00x (ISBN 0-643-00339-8, Pub. by CSJRO). State Mutual Bk.

Pulping & Paper-Making Properties of Fast Growing Plantation Wood Species, 2 Vols. (Forestry Papers: Nos. 19-1 & 19-2). 886p. 1980. pap. 62.50 set (ISBN 0-686-68193-2, F1969, FAO). Vol. 1, 486p (ISBN 92-5-100865-5). Vol. 2, 400p (ISBN 92-5-100866-3). Unipub.

Pulping Conference: Proceedings. Incl. Pulping Conference Proceedings. TAPPI PRESS Proceedings. 375p. 1979. 38.95 (01-05-0679); Pulping Conference Proceedings. (TAPPI PRESS Proceedings). 512p. 1980. 43.95 (01-05-0680). 514p. 1982. pap. 44.95 (ISBN 0-686-43246-0, 01 05 0682). TAPPI.

Saltman, David. Pulp & Paper Primer. 1983. pap. 8.45 (ISBN 0-89852-410-5); pap. 5.66 members. TAPPI.

Stenzel, George, et al. Logging & Pulpwood Production. 2nd ed. 368p. 1985. 34.95 (ISBN 0-471-86822-1). Wiley.

Technical Association of the Pulp & Paper Industry. Pulping Conference: 1984, Proceedings of the Technical Association of the Pulp & Paper Industry, Hyatt Regency, San Francisco, Ca., November 12-14. Bk. 1. pap. 43.30 (ISBN 0-317-20767-9, 2024786); Bk. 2. pap. 75.00 (ISBN 0-317-20768-7); Bk. 3. pap. 45.00 (ISBN 0-317-20769-5). Bks Demand UMI.

Weiner, Jack & Pollock, Vera. Nonsulfur Pulping. LC 76-57830. (Bibliographic Ser.: No. 275). 1977. pap. 23.00 (ISBN 0-87010-050-5). Inst Paper Chem.

World Pulp & Paper Demand, Supply & Trade: Selected Papers of an Expert Consultation held in Tunis, Sept. 1977, 2 Vols. (Forestry Papers: No. 4-1 & 4-2). (Eng., Fr. & Span., Illus.). 1977. Vol. 1. pap. 22.25 (ISBN 92-5-100505-2, F1434, FAO); Vol. 2. pap. 16.25 (ISBN 92-5-100532-X, F1432). Unipub.

PULSARS

Greenstein, George. Frozen Star. 227p. 1984. 16.95 (ISBN 0-88191-011-2). Freundlich.

Irvine, J. M. Neutron Stars. (Oxford Studies in Physics). (Illus.). text ed. 39.50x (ISBN 0-19-851460-3). Oxford U Pr.

Lenchek, Allen M. Physics of Pulsars. (Topics in Astrophysics & Space Physics Ser.). 184p. 1972. 44.00x (ISBN 0-677-14295-1). Gordon.

Manchester, Richard N. & Taylor, Joseph H. Pulsars. LC 77-4206. (Astronomy & Astrophysics Ser.). (Illus.). 281p. 1977. text ed. 39.95x (ISBN 0-7167-0358-0). W H Freeman.

Sieber, W. & Wielebinski, W. R., eds. Pulsars. xvi, 474p. 1981. 60.50 (ISBN 90-277-1280-8, Pub. by Reidel Holland); pap. 28.95 (ISBN 90-277-1282-4). Kluwer Academic.

PULSE CIRCUITS

see also Pulse Generators

Barna, Arpad. High Speed Pulse Circuits. LC 76-121904. pap. 45.30 (ISBN 0-317-08633-2, 2007370). Bks Demand UMI.

Bell, David A. Solid State Pulse Circuits. 2nd ed. (Illus.). 432p. 1981. 30.95 (ISBN 0-8359-7057-4). Reston.

CES Industries, Inc. Staff. Ed-Lab Six Hundred & Fifty Experiment Manual: Pulses & Waveshaping, Bk.V. (Ed-Lab 650 Experiment Manual Ser.). (Illus.). 1982. lab manual 11.50 (ISBN 0-86711-052-X). CES Industries.

Hughes, Richard S. Selected Video & Pulse Circuitry. LC 74-136725. 153p. 1969. 19.00 (ISBN 0-403-04506-1). Scholarly.

Metzger, G. & Vabre, J. P. Transmission Lines with Pulse Excitation. (Electrical Science Ser). (Fr). 1969. 60.00 (ISBN 0-12-493050-6). Acad Pr.

Millman, Jacob & Taub, H. Pulse, Digital & Switching Waveforms. 1965. text ed. 49.95 (ISBN 0-07-042386-5). McGraw.

Mitchell, Brinton B. Semiconductor Pulse Circuits with Experiments. 1970. text ed. 37.95 (ISBN 0-03-083036-2, HoltC). HR&W.

Swearer, Harvey F. Pulse & Switching Circuits. LC 84-904. 256p. 1984. Repr. of 1970 ed. text ed. 17.50 (ISBN 0-89874-739-2). Krieger.

Tocci, Ronald J. Fundamentals of Pulse & Digital Circuits. 2nd ed. (Electronics Technology Ser.). 1977. text ed. 23.95 (ISBN 0-675-08492-X). Merrill.

Veatch, H. C. Pulse & Switching Circuit Action. 1971. text ed. 31.00 (ISBN 0-07-067386-1). McGraw.

PULSE-CODE MODULATION

Barbier, Maurice G. Pulse Coding. LC 82-80776. (Short Course Handbooks). (Illus.). 89p. (Orig.). 1982. text ed. 26.00 (ISBN 0-934634-52-1); pap. 16.00 (ISBN 0-934634-40-8). Intl Human Res.

PULSE FAMILY

see Legumes

PULSE GENERATORS

Carr, Joseph J. The Complete Handbook of Amplifiers, Oscillators & Multivibrators. (Illus.). 364p. 1981. pap. 11.50 (ISBN 0-8306-1230-0, 1230). TAB Bks.

PULSE TECHNIQUES (ELECTRONICS)

see also Exploding Wire Phenomena; Pulse Circuits; Radar

Barton, David K. Pulse Compression. LC 74-82597. (Radars: Vol. 3). pap. 59.30 (ISBN 0-317-27659-X, 2025060). Bks Demand UMI.

Coekin, J. A. High Speed Pulse Technique. Hammond, P., ed. 263p. 1975. pap. text ed. 14.50 (ISBN 0-08-018773-0). Pergamon.

Frungel, Frank. High Speed Pulse Technology, 4 vols. Incl. Vol. 1. Capacitor Discharges, Magneto-Hydrodynamics, X-Rays, Ultrasonics. 1965. 83.00 (ISBN 0-12-269001-X); Vol. 2. Optical Pulses, Lasers, Measuring Techniques. 1965. 77.00 (ISBN 0-12-269002-8); Vol. 3. 1976. 83.00 (ISBN 0-12-269003-6); Vol. 4. 1980. 66.00 (ISBN 0-12-269004-4). Acad Pr.

Meiling, W. & Stary, F. Nanosecond Pulse Techniques. 430p. 1969. 119.25 (ISBN 0-677-61490-X). Gordon.

Rhodes, Donald. Introduction to Monopulse Radar. (Illus.). 199p. 1980. Repr. of 1959 ed. 22.00 (ISBN 0-89006-091-6). Artech Hse.

Windsor, C. G. Pulsed Neutron Scattering. 400p. 1981. 89.95x (ISBN 0-470-27131-0, PH-25 16). Halsted Pr.

PULSED CIRCUITS

see Pulse Circuits

PULSED REACTORS

Pikaev, Aleksefi K. Pulse Radiolysis of Water & Aqueous Solutions. Hart, Edwin J., ed. LC 66-14343. (Illus.). pap. 77.80 (ISBN 0-317-09468-8, 2055226). Bks Demand UMI.

Pulsed Neutron Research, 2 vols. (Proceedings Ser.). (Illus.). 1615p. 1965. Vol. 1. 37.25 (ISBN 92-0-030765-5, ISP104-1, IAEA); Vol. 2. 50.25 (ISBN 92-0-030865-1, ISP 104-2). Unipub.

Research Applications of Nuclear Pulsed Systems. (Panel Proceedings Ser.). (Illus.). 234p. 1967. pap. 16.25 (ISBN 92-0-151067-5, ISP144, IAEA). Unipub.

Shabalin, E. P. Fast Pulsed & Burst Reactors: A Comprehensive Account of the Physics of Both Single Burst & Repetitively Pulsed Reactors. (Illus.). 1979. 80.00 (ISBN 0-08-022708-2). Pergamon.

PULVERIZERS

see Milling Machinery

PUMAS

see also Panthers

Brock, Stanley E. More About Leemo. (Illus.). 1968. 7.95 (ISBN 0-8008-5350-4). Taplinger.

PUMPERS, FIRE-DEPARTMENT

see Fire-Engines

PUMPING MACHINERY

see also Centrifugal Pumps; Heat Pumps; Oil Hydraulic Machinery; Sucker Rods

American National Standard for Vertical Turbine Pumps - Line Shaft & Submersible Types: E101-77. rev. ed. (AWWA Standards). (Illus.). 56p. 1977. pap. text ed. 9.60 (ISBN 0-89867-163-9). Am Water Wks Assn.

Black, Perry O. Pumps. 3rd ed. 464p. 1977. 10.95 (ISBN 0-672-23292-8). Audel.

Bonnington, S. T. & King, A. L., eds. Jet Pumps & Ejectors: A State of the Art Review & Bibliography. 2nd ed. (BHRA Fluid Engineering Ser.: Vol. 1). 1977. pap. 40.50x (ISBN 0-900983-63-9, Dist. by Air Science Co.). BHRA Fluid.

British Pumps Manufacturers Association, 6th Technical Conference. Proceedings. 270p. 1979. pap. 54.00x (ISBN 0-906085-27-6, Dist. by Air Science Co.). BHRA Fluid.

Chermisinoff, Nicholas P. Fluid Flow: Pumps, Pipes & Channels. LC 81-68034. (Illus.). 702p. 1981. 45.00 (ISBN 0-250-40432-X). Butterworth.

Collier, S. L. Mud Pump Handbook. LC 82-20743. 242p. 1983. 31.95x (ISBN 0-87201-568-8). Gulf Pub.

Crawford. Marine & Offshore Pumping & Piping Systems. 1981. text ed. 54.95 (ISBN 0-408-00548-3). Butterworth.

European Directories, ed. Directory of Pump, Valve & Compressor Manufacturers in Western Europe. 1985. 100.00x (ISBN 0-686-78876-1, Pub. by European Directories England). State Mutual Bk.

Europump Terminology: Pump Names. (Eng. Ger. Ital. Fr. Span.). 300p. 1983. text ed. 90.50 (ISBN 0-85461-089-8). Brookfield Pub Co.

Fong, J. T. & Tashjian, B. J., eds. Inservice Data Reporting & Analysis, PVP-PB-32. (Pressure Vessel & Piping Division Ser.). 1978. 30.00 (ISBN 0-685-66802-9, H00137). ASME.

Hays, Dick & Allen, Bill. Windmills & Pumps of the Southwest. (Illus.). 120p. 1983. pap. 7.95 (ISBN 0-89015-394-9). Eakin Pubns.

Hicks, Tyler G. Pump Operation & Maintenance. LC 81-20890. 328p. 1983. Repr. of 1958 ed. 32.95 (ISBN 0-89874-409-1). Krieger.

Holland, F. A. & Chapman, F. S. Pumping of Liquids. LC 66-29034. 414p. 1966. 23.50 (ISBN 0-442-15118-7). Krieger.

Improving Pump & Well Efficiency. (Illus.). 168p. (AWWA Handbooks-General) 19.50 (ISBN 0-686-44877-4). Am Water Wks Assn.

Institute for Power System. Europump Terminology: Pump Applications. 900p. 1982. 210.00x. State Mutual Bk.

--Pumping Manual. 5th ed. 800p. 1979. 95.00x (ISBN 0-85461-063-4). State Mutual Bk.

Jet Pumps & Ejectors & Gas Lift Techniques, 2nd Symposium. Proceedings. 1975. pap. 54.00x (ISBN 0-900983-43-4, Dist. by Air Science Co.). BHRA Fluid.

Karassik, I. J. & Krutzch, W. C. Pump Handbook. 2nd ed. 1376p. 1985. for info. 84.50 (ISBN 0-07-033302-5). McGraw.

Kovacik, J., ed. Pumps, a Workbook for Engineers: Presented at the Energy-Sources Technology Conference & Exhibition, Houston, Texas, January 19-21, 1981. LC 81-111446. pap. 25.00 (ISBN 0-317-10868-9, 2015731). Bks Demand UMI.

Liljestrand, Walter. Centrifugal Pumps & Piping Systems. LC 83-161604. (Mud Equipment Manual Ser.: No. 4). 192p. (Orig.). 1983. pap. 29.95x (ISBN 0-87201-616-1). Gulf Pub.

McCabe, Robert E., et al. Metering Pump Handbook. (Illus.). 300p. 1984. text ed. 29.95 (ISBN 0-8311-1157-7). Indus Pr.

Operation & Maintenance of Steam Fire Pumps. (Twenty Ser.). 1963. pap. 2.00 (ISBN 0-685-58118-7, 21). Natl Fire Prot.

Pacey, Arnold, compiled by. Hand-Pump Maintenance in the Context of Community Well Projects. rev. ed. (Illus.). 43p. (Orig.). 1980. pap. 4.00x (ISBN 0-903031-70-1, Pub. by Intermediate Tech England). Intermediate Tech.

Pollak, F. Pump Users' Handbook. 2nd ed. LC 80-83759. 214p. 1980. 19.95x (ISBN 0-87201-770-2). Gulf Pub.

--Pump Users' Handbook. 2nd ed. 250p. 1982. 75.00x (ISBN 0-85461-070-7, Pub. by Trade & Tech). State Mutual Bk.

Portable Pumping Units for Fire Department Service. (Ten Ser.). 1959. pap. 2.00 (ISBN 0-685-58121-7, 191). Natl Fire Prot.

Poynton. Metering Pumps. (Chemical Industries Ser.). 216p. 1983. 29.75 (ISBN 0-8247-1759-7). Dekker.

Prosser. Bibliography with Abstracts on Pump Sumps & Intakes. 1978. pap. 21.00x (ISBN 0-900983-70-1, Dist. by Air Science Co). BHRA Fluid.

Prosser, M. J. The Hydraulic Design of Pump Sumps & Intakes. (Illus.). 1977. pap. 32.00x (ISBN 0-86017-027-6, Dist. by Air Science Co.). BHRA Fluid.

Pulsafeeder, Inc. & Chemical Engineering Magazine Staff. Proportioning Pumps. 300p. 1981. cancelled (ISBN 0-07-050929-8). McGraw.

Pump Costs. 1977. pap. 43.00x (ISBN 0-900983-68-X, Dist. by Air Science Co.). BHRA Fluid.

Pump Functional Testing. (Mechanical Inspection Ser.: Module 30-2). (Illus.). 50p. 1979. spiral bdg. 7.00x (ISBN 0-87683-124-2). G P Courseware.

Pump Inspection. (Mechanical Inspection Ser.: Module 30-1). (Illus.). 44p. 1979. spiral bdg. 7.00x (ISBN 0-87683-123-4). G P Courseware.

Pumping Manual. 6th ed. 800p. 1982. 175.00x (ISBN 0-686-86772-6, Pub. by Trade & Tech). State Mutual Bk.

Pumping Manual. 7th ed. LC 83-82524. 650p. 1984. 59.95x (ISBN 0-87201-751-6). Gulf Pub.

Pumps & Compressors. 1984. 595.00 (ISBN 0-686-38424-5, A210). Busn Trend.

Pumps for Progress. 1975. pap. 32.00x (ISBN 0-900983-42-6, Dist. by Air Science Co.). BHRA Fluid.

Pumps: The Developing Needs. 1982. 125.00x (ISBN 0-686-91581-X, Pub. by BHRA Fluid England). State Mutual Bk.

Rudman, Jack. Senior Pump Operator. (Career Examination Ser.: C-2951). (Cloth bdg. avail. on request). pap. 12.00 (ISBN 0-8373-2951-5). Natl Learning.

Sharp, Donald & Graham, Michael, eds. Village Handpump Technology: Research & Evaluation in Asia. (Eng., Fr. & Span.). 72p. 1983. pap. 7.50 (ISBN 0-88936-360-9, IDRC204, IDRC). Unipub.

Standards for Pump Makers & Users. 1973. pap. 25.00x (ISBN 0-685-85163-X, Dist. by Air Science Co.). BHRA Fluid.

Stepanoff, A. J. Centrifugal & Axial Flow Pumps: Theory, Design & Application. 2nd ed. LC 57-10815. 462p. 1957. 61.50x (ISBN 0-471-82137-3, Pub. by Wiley-Interscience). Wiley.

Stepanoff, Alexey J. Pumps & Blowers. LC 75-11894. 324p. 1978. Repr. of 1965 ed. 19.50 (ISBN 0-88275-306-1). Krieger.

Sterling. Pumping Systems. 74p. 1981. 45.00x (ISBN 0-900976-43-8, Pub. by Marine Mgmt England). State Mutual Bk.

Sterling, L. Pumping Systems & Their Auxiliary Equipment. (Illus.). 1976. pap. 10.00x (ISBN 0-900976-43-8, Pub. by Inst Marine Eng). Intl Spec Bk.

Stewart, Harry L. & Philbin, Tom. Pumps. 4th ed. LC 83-22380. 1984. 14.95 (ISBN 0-672-23400-9). Audel.

Swindell, John G. Rudimentary Treatise on Well-Digging, Boring & Pumpwork, Eighteen Forty-Nine. (Illus.). 88p. pap. 12.50. Saifer.

Symposium on Jet Pumps & Ejectors, 1st. Proceedings. 1972. 39.00x (ISBN 0-686-71056-8). BHRA Fluid.

Technical Conference of the BPMA in Conjunction with BHRA, 7th. Pumps: The Developing Needs. Stephens, H. S. & Hanson, J. A., eds. (Illus.). 250p. 1981. pap. 62.00x (ISBN 0-906085-52-7). BHRA Fluid.

Trade & Technical Press Editors. Europump Terminology: Pump Applications. 900p. 1978. 107.00x (ISBN 0-85461-071-5, Pub by Trade & Tech England). Brookfield Pub Co.

--Pump Users' Handbook. 2nd ed. 250p. 32.50x (ISBN 0-85461-070-7, Pub by Trade & Tech England). Brookfield Pub Co.

--Pumping Data, Vol. 2. 140p. 1964. 16.00x (ISBN 0-85461-015-4, Pub by Trade & Tech England). Brookfield Pub Co.

--Pumping Data, Vol. 3. 84p. 1969. 16.00x (ISBN 0-85461-033-2, Pub by Trade & Tech England). Brookfield Pub Co.

--Pumping Manual. 6th ed. 800p. 1979. 110.00 (ISBN 0-85461-063-4, Pub by Trade & Tech England). Brookfield Pub Co.

Trade & Technical Pr.Ltd., ed. Europump Terminology: Pump Applications. 750p. 1981. 120.00x (ISBN 0-686-79319-6, Pub. by Trade & Tech). State Mutual Bk.

Tucker, Allen E., ed. Pumps, Motor Power Units & Reservoirs, Vol. C. rev. ed. (Fluid Power Standards 1984 Ser.). (Illus.). 1984. 56.00 (ISBN 0-942220-73-0); Set. write for info. Natl Fluid Power.

Walker, Rodger. Pump Selection: A Consulting Engineer's Manual. new ed. LC 72-88891. (Illus.). 128p. 1979. 19.95 (ISBN 0-250-40005-7). Butterworth.

Warring, R. H. Pumps, Selection, Systems & Applications. 1969. 30.00x (ISBN 0-85461-079-0, Pub. by Trade & Technical England). Brookfield Pub Co.

--Pumps: Selection, Systems, & Applications. 2nd ed. LC 83-82095. 280p. 1984. 49.95x (ISBN 0-87201-736-2). Gulf Pub.

Watt, Simon B. A Manual on the Automatic Hydraulic Ram for Pumping Water. rev. ed. (Illus.). 40p. 1978. pap. 7.75x (ISBN 0-903031-15-9, Pub. by Intermediate Tech England). Intermediate Tech.

PUMPING STATIONS

see also Water-Supply

Bartlett, R. E. Pumping Stations for Water & Sewage. (Illus.). 150p. 1974. 26.00 (ISBN 0-85334-577-5, Pub. by Elsevier Applied Sci England). Elsevier.

Rudman, Jack. Pump Station Operator. (Career Examination Ser.: C-2442). (Cloth bdg. avail. on request). pap. 10.00 (ISBN 0-8373-2442-4). Natl Learning.

Walker, Rodger. Pump Selection: A Consulting Engineer's Manual. new ed. LC 72-88891. (Illus.). 128p. 1979. 19.95 (ISBN 0-250-40005-7). Butterworth.

Water Pollution Control Federation. Design of Wastewater & Stormwater Pumping Stations ('80) Manual of Practice, Facilities & Development-4, No. 4. 146p. Date not set. pap. 16.00 (ISBN 0-943244-20-X). Water Pollution.

PUMPS

see Pumping Machinery

PUMPS, CENTRIFUGAL

see Centrifugal Pumps

PUNCHED CARD SYSTEMS

see also Accounting Machines; Machine Accounting

Blum, J. & Blum, E. Keypunch, Keytape & Keydisc. 210p. 1975. 33.75 (ISBN 0-677-03950-6). Gordon.

Clow, C. A. & MacDonald, R. D. Punched-Card Data Processing System. 2nd ed. 1975. 9.00 (ISBN 0-07-011424-2). McGraw.

Corcoran, Wayne A. & Istvan, Donald F. Audit & the Punched Card: An Introduction. 1961. pap. text ed. 2.00x (ISBN 0-87776-101-9, R101). Ohio St U Admin Sci.

Eckert, W. J. Punched Card Methods in Scientific Computation. 1984. 25.00x (ISBN 0-262-05030-7). MIT Pr.

Keys, William J. & Powell, Carl. Handbook of Modern Keypunch Operation. (Illus.). 1970. pap. text ed. 14.50 scp (ISBN 0-06-384500-8, HarpC). Har-Row.

Pactor, P. & Kargilis, G. Card-Punch Machine Operation, Bk. 1. 1967. text ed. 16.25 (ISBN 0-07-048031-1). McGraw.

--Card-Punch Machine Operation, Bk. 2. 1973. text ed. 16.25 (ISBN 0-07-048032-X). McGraw.

Rosenblatt, Jules. Key Punch. 1969. scp wkbk. 15.12 (ISBN 0-672-96027-3); scp wkbk. & kit 46.59 (ISBN 0-672-96029-X). Bobbs.

Rudman, Jack. Alphabetic Key Punch Operator, IBM. (Career Examination Ser.: C-13). (Cloth bdg. avail. on request). pap. 10.00 (ISBN 0-8373-1924-2). Natl Learning.

--Card Punch-Key Punch Operator (Alphabetic) (Career Examination Ser.: C-124). (Cloth bdg. avail. on request). pap. 10.00 (ISBN 0-8373-0124-6). Natl Learning.

--Card Punch Operator. (Career Examination Ser.: C-125). (Cloth bdg. avail. on request). pap. 10.00 (ISBN 0-8373-0125-4). Natl Learning.

--Chief Key Punch Operator. (Career Examination Ser.). (Cloth bdg. avail. on request). 1976. pap. 12.00 (ISBN 0-8373-2104-2). Natl Learning.

--Key Punch Operator. (Career Examination Ser.: C-420). (Cloth bdg. avail. on request). pap. 10.00 (ISBN 0-8373-0420-2). Natl Learning.

--Senior Key Punch Operator. (Career Examination Ser.: C-717). (Cloth bdg. avail. on request). pap. 12.00 (ISBN 0-8373-0717-1). Natl Learning.

--Tabulator Operator. (Career Examination Ser.: C-800). (Cloth bdg. avail. on request). pap. 10.0000429502x (ISBN 0-8373-0800-3). Natl Learning.

Stutz, Frederick P. Using the Keypunch & Other Punched Card Equipment. 1973. 5.35x (ISBN 0-916304-07-8). SDSU Press.

PUNCHED TAPES

see Data Tapes

PUNCHING MACHINERY

see also Dies (Metal-Working); Taps and Dies

Paquin, J. R. Die Design Fundamentals. LC 62-19251. (Illus.). 1962. 23.95 (ISBN 0-8311-1010-4); wkbk. o.p. 7.00 (ISBN 0-8311-1011-2). Indus Pr.

PUPIL (EYE)

Alexandridis, E. The Pupil. Telger, T., tr. from Ger. (Illus.). 115p. 1985. 29.90 (ISBN 0-387-96109-7). Springer-Verlag.

PURE FOOD

see Food Adulteration and Inspection

PURIFICATION OF WATER

see Water–Purification

PURINES

Ciba Foundation. Purine & Pyrimidine Metabolism. LC 76-52420. (Ciba Foundation Symposium, New Ser.: 48). pap. 95.30 (ISBN 0-317-29779-1, 2022174). Bks Demand UMI.

De Bruyn, Chris, et al, eds. Purine Metabolism in Man IVA: Clinical & Therapeutic Aspects. (Advances in Experimental Medicine & Biology Ser.: Vol. 165A). 544p. 1983. 75.00x (ISBN 0-306-41363-9, Plenum Pr). Plenum Pub.

De Bruyn, Chris H., et al, eds. Purine Metabolism in Man IVB: Biochemical, Immunological, & Cancer Research. (Advances in Experimental Medicine & Biology Ser.: Vol. 165B). 509p. 1983. 69.50x (ISBN 0-306-41364-7, Plenum Pr). Plenum Pub.

Florkin, M. & Stotz, E., eds. Comprehensive Biochemistry: Amino Acids Metabolism & Sulphur Metabolism, Vol. 19A. 482p. 1981. 103.50 (ISBN 0-444-80257-6, Biomedical Pr). Elsevier.

Hurst, ed. An Introduction to Chemistry & Biochemistry of Pyrimidines, Purines & Pteridines. LC 79-40736. 266p. 1980. 64.95 (ISBN 0-471-27647-2, Pub. by Wiley-Interscience). Wiley.

Jerusalem Symposia on Quantum Chemistry & Biochemistry, Vol. 4. The Purines. Bergmann, E. D. & Pullman, B., eds. 1972. 78.00 (ISBN 0-12-091060-8). Acad Pr.

Lister, J. H. & Brown, D. J., eds. Fused Pyrimidines: Purines, Vol. 24, Pt. 2. LC 68-4274. 655p. 1971. 78.00 (ISBN 0-471-38205-1). Krieger.

Muller, Mathias M., ed. Purine Metabolism in Man IIB: Physiology, Pharmacology & Clinical Aspects. LC 76-62591. (Advances in Experimental Medicine & Biology Ser.: Vol. 76B). 395p. 1977. 52.50x (ISBN 0-306-39090-6, Plenum Pr). Plenum Pub.

Muller, Mathias M., et al, eds. Purine Metabolism in Man IIA: Regulation of Pathways & Enzyme Defects. (Advances in Experimental Medicine & Biology Ser.: Vol. 76A). 663p. 1977. 75.00x (ISBN 0-306-39089-2, Plenum Pr). Plenum Pub.

Rapado, A., et al, eds. Purine Metabolism in Man IIIA: Clinical & Therapeutic Aspects, Pt. A. (Advances in Experimental Medicine & Biology Ser.: Vol. 122A). 481p. 1980. 62.50x (ISBN 0-306-40310-2, Plenum Pr). Plenum Pub.

--Purine Metabolism in Man IIIB: Biochemical, Immunological, & Cancer Research, Pt. B. (Advances in Experimental Medicine & Biology Ser.: Vol. 122B). 482p. 1980. 62.50 (ISBN 0-306-40311-0, Plenum Pr). Plenum Pub.

Roy-Burman, P. Analogues of Nucleic Acid Components: Mechanisms of Action. LC 75-96737. (Recent Results in Cancer Research: Vol. 25). 1970. 21.00 (ISBN 0-387-04990-8). Springer-Verlag.

Sperling, Oded, et al, eds. Purine Metabolism in Man IA: Enzymes & Metabolic Pathways. (Advances in Experimental Medicine & Biology Ser.: Vol. 41A). 402p. 1974. 52.50x (ISBN 0-306-39095-7, Plenum Pr). Plenum Pub.

--Purine Metabolism in Man IB: Biochemistry & Pharmacology of Uric Acid Metabolism. (Advances in Experimental Medicine & Biology Ser.: Vol. 41B). 498p. 1974. 59.50x (ISBN 0-306-39096-5, Plenum Pr). Plenum Pub.

PURPLE MARTIN

Layton, R. B. The Purple Martin. LC 71-92883. (Illus.). 192p. 1969. pap. 6.95x (ISBN 0-912542-01-2). Nature Bks Pubs.

PURPLE MEDIC

see Alfalfa

PYRAZOLONES

Barlin, G. B. Chemistry of Heterocyclic Compounds: Pyrazines - A Series of Monographs, Vol. 41. 712p. 1982. 193.50 (ISBN 0-471-38119-5, Pub. by Wiley-Interscience). Wiley.

PYRENOMYCETES

Ellis, Job B. & Everhart, Benjamin M. North American Pyrenomycetes. (Illus.). 1892. 50.00 (ISBN 0-384-14265-6). Johnson Repr.

Wehmeyer, Lewis E. The Pyrenomycetous Fungi. (Mycologia Memoir: No. 6). 1975. text ed. 28.00 (ISBN 3-7682-0967-9). Lubrecht & Cramer.

PYRHELIOMETER

Third International Pyrheliometer Comparisons: Davos & Locarno, Sept. 1970, Final Report. (Illus.). iv, 224p. (Orig.). 1973. pap. 25.00 (ISBN 0-685-40084-0, W136, WMO). Unipub.

PYRIDAZINE

Castle, Raymond N., ed. Pyridazines, Vol. 28. LC 72-13270. (Hetercyclic Compounds Ser.). 905p. 1973. 109.00 (ISBN 0-471-38213-2). Krieger.

PYRIDINE

Abramovitch, R. A., ed. Chemistry of Heterocyclic Compounds. LC 73-9800. (A Series of Monographs Pyridine & Its Derivitives: Vol. 14, Pt. 1). 451p. 1974. 59.00 (ISBN 0-471-37913-1). Krieger.

--Chemistry of Heterocyclic Compounds. LC 73-9800. (A Series of Monographs Pyridine & Its Derivitives: Vol. 14, Pt. 3). 1249p. 1974. 105.00 (ISBN 0-471-37915-8). Krieger.

Everse, Johannes, et al, eds. The Pyridine Nucleotide Coenzymes. 416p. 1982. 60.00 (ISBN 0-12-244750-6). Acad Pr.

Klingsberg, E., ed. Pyridine & Its Derivatives, Vol. 14, Pt. 4. 711p. 1964. 255.95x (ISBN 0-470-38016-0, Pub. by Wiley-Interscience). Wiley.

Newkome, George R., ed. Pyridine & Its Derivatives, Vol. 14, Pt. 5. LC 59-103038. (Chemistry of Heterocyclic Compounds: A Series of Monographs: 1-079). 714p. 1985. 175.00 (ISBN 0-471-05072-5, 1-079, Pub. by Wiley-Interscience). Wiley.

Sund, Horst, ed. Pyridine Nucleotide: Dependent Dehydrogenases. 513p. 1977. text ed. 66.00x (ISBN 3-11007-091-X). De Gruyter.

PYRIDOXINE

Dolphin, D., et al. Pyridoxal Phosphate: Chemical, Biochemical & Medical Aspects, 2 vols. 1985. Vol. 1, Pt. A. 150.00 (ISBN 0-471-09785-3); Vol. 1, Pt. B. 200.00 (ISBN 0-471-09783-7). Wiley.

PYRIMIDINES

Brown, D. J. The Pyrimidines: Supplement 2. (Chemistry of Hetercyclic Compounds Monographs). 1184p. 1985. 225.00 (ISBN 0-471-02745-6). Wiley.

Ciba Foundation. Purine & Pyrimidine Metabolism. LC 76-52420. (Ciba Foundation Symposium, New Ser.: 48). pap. 95.30 (ISBN 0-317-29779-1, 2022174). Bks Demand UMI.

Florkin, M. & Stotz, E., eds. Comprehensive Biochemistry: Amino Acids Metabolism & Sulphur Metabolism, Vol. 19A. 482p. 1981. 103.50 (ISBN 0-444-80257-6, Biomedical Pr). Elsevier.

Hurst, ed. An Introduction to Chemistry & Biochemistry of Pyrimidines, Purines & Pteridines. LC 79-40736. 266p. 1980. 64.95 (ISBN 0-471-27647-2, Pub. by Wiley-Interscience). Wiley.

Lister, J. H. & Brown, D. J., eds. Fused Pyrimidines: Purines, Vol. 24, Pt. 2. LC 68-4274. 655p. 1971. 78.00 (ISBN 0-471-38205-1). Krieger.

Roy-Burman, P. Analogues of Nucleic Acid Components: Mechanisms of Action. LC 75-96737. (Recent Results in Cancer Research: Vol. 25). 1970. 21.00 (ISBN 0-387-04990-8). Springer-Verlag.

PYRO- AND PIEZO-ELECTRICITY

see also Ferroelectricity; Oscillators, Crystal

Anan'eva, A. A., et al. Ceramic Acoustic Detectors. LC 65-11334. 122p. 1965. 35.00x (ISBN 0-306-10702-3, Consultants). Plenum Pub.

Business Communications Staff. Piezo Electricity, GB-064. 1983. 1250.00 (ISBN 0-89336-324-3). BCC.

Gagnepain, J. J. & Meeker, Thrygve R., eds. Piezoelectricity. (Ferroelectrics Ser.: Vols. 40, Nos. 3-4; 41; & 42, Nos. 1-2). 782p. 1982. 315.00 (ISBN 0-677-16415-7). Gordon.

Galletti, P. M., et al. Proceedings of the First International Symposium on Peizoelectricity in Biomaterials & Biomedical Devices. 318p. 1984. text ed. 85.00 (ISBN 0-677-40485-9). Gordon.

Herbert, J. M. Ferroelectric Transducers & Sensors. (Electrocomponent Science Monographs). 464p. 1982. 49.50 (ISBN 0-677-05910-8). Gordon.

Lang, Sidney B. Sourcebook of Pyroelectricity. (Ferroelectricity & Related Phenomena Ser.). 578p. 1974. 121.50 (ISBN 0-677-01580-1). Gordon.

Lu, C. & Czanderna, A. W., eds. Applications of Piezoelectric Quartz Crystal Microbalances. (Methods & Phenomena Ser.: No. 7). 394p. 1984. 100.00 (ISBN 0-444-42277-3, I-072-84). Elsevier.

Taylor, G. W., et al, eds. Piezoelectricity. (Ferroelectricity & Related Phenomena Ser.: Vol. 4). 418p. 1985. text ed. 84.00 (ISBN 0-677-16660-5). Gordon.

Tiersten, H. F. Linear Piezoelectric Plate Vibrations: Elements of the Linear Theory of Piezoelectricity & the Vibrations of Piezoelectric Plates. LC 69-14562. (Illus.). 212p. 1969. 39.50x (ISBN 0-306-30376-0, Plenum Pr). Plenum Pub.

--Linear Piezoelectric Plate Vibrations: Elements of the Linear Theory of Piezoelectricity & the Vibrations of Piezoelectric Plates. LC 69-14562. pap. 56.80 (ISBN 0-317-27880-0, 2055794). Bks Demand UMI.

PYROCERAMICS

Randeraat, J. Van & Setterington, R. E., eds. Piezoelectric Ceramics. 2nd ed. (Mullard Publications Ser.). (Illus.). 211p. 1974. text ed. 29.50x (ISBN 0-901232-75-0). Scholium Intl.

PYROMETERS AND PYROMETRY

Ulmer, G. C., ed. Research Techniques for High Pressure & High Temperature. (Illus.). 384p. 1971. 25.00 (ISBN 0-387-05594-0). Springer-Verlag.

PYROTECHNICS

see Fireworks

PYRRHOPHYTA

Loeblich, Alfred R., Jr. & Loeblich, Alfred R., 3rd. Index to the Genera, Subgenera, & Sections of the Pyrrophyta. (Studies in Tropical Oceanography Ser: No. 3). 1966. 2.50x (ISBN 0-87024-084-6). U Miami Marine.

PYRROL

Jones, R. A. & Bean, G. P. The Chemistry of Pyrroles. 1977. 85.50 (ISBN 0-12-389840-4). Acad Pr.

PYTHAGORAS, d. 497 B.C.

Dacier, Andre. The Life of Pythagoras. 208p. 1981. cloth 22.50 (ISBN 0-87728-286-2). Weiser.

Diogenes, Laertius. La Vie De Pythagore De Diogene Laerce. Vlastos, Gregory, ed. LC 78-19342. (Morals & Law in Ancient Greece Ser.). 1979. Repr. of 1922 ed. lib. bdg. 21.00x (ISBN 0-405-11537-7). Ayer Co Pubs.

Gorman, Peter. Pythagoras: A Life. 1978. 19.95 (ISBN 0-7100-0006-5). Routledge & Kegan.

Levin, Flora R. The Harmonics of Nicomachus & the Pythagorean Tradition. (American Philological Association, American Classical Studies). 1975. pap. 7.50 (ISBN 0-89130-241-7, 400401). Scholars Pr GA.

Oliver, George. The Pythagorean Triangle. LC 75-16015. (Secret Doctrine Reference Ser). 250p. 1975. Repr. of 1875 ed. 12.00 (ISBN 0-913510-17-3). Wizards.

Philip, James A. Pythagoras & Early Pythagoreanism. LC 66-9226. (Phoenix Series Supplement: Supplementary Vol. 7). pap. 58.00 (ISBN 0-317-08752-5, 2014340). Bks Demand UMi.

Raven, J. E. Pythagoreans & Eleatics. 196p. 12.50 (ISBN 0-89005-367-7). Ares.

Skyrme, Raymond. Ruben Dario & the Pythagorean Tradition. LC 75-11675. (University of Florida Latin American Monographs: No. 15). viii, 107p. 1975. 8.50 (ISBN 0-8130-0382-2). U Presses Fla.

Stanley, Thomas. Pythagoras. 15.00 (ISBN 0-89314-408-8). Philos Res.

Swetz, Frank J. & Kao, T. I. Was Pythagoras Chinese? LC 76-41806. (Illus.). 71p. 1977. pap. 4.95 (ISBN 0-271-01238-2). NCTM.

Taylor, Thomas. Pythagorean Precepts. 1983. pap. 5.95 (ISBN 0-916411-00-1, Pub. by Alexandrian Pr). Holmes pub.

--The Theoretic Arithmetic of the Pythagoreans. 248p. (Orig.). 1983. pap. 12.50 (ISBN 0-87728-558-6). Weiser.

PYTHAGOREAN PROPOSITION

Beaulieu, Victor A. The Reconstruction of Pythagoras' System on the Vibrational Theory of Numbers: The Essential Library of the Great Philosophers. (Illus.). 91p. 1983. Repr. of 1905 ed. 117.45 (ISBN 0-89920-050-8). Am Inst Psych.

Loomis, Elisha S. The Pythagorean Proposition. (Classics in Mathematics Education Ser.: Vol. 1). (Illus.). 306p. 1968. 11.00 (ISBN 0-87353-036-5). NCTM.

Q

Q-DEVICES

see Q-Machines

Q-MACHINES

Motley, R. W. Q Machines. 1975. 47.00 (ISBN 0-12-508650-4). Acad Pr.

QUADPACK (COMPUTER PROGRAMS)

Piessens, R., et al. Quadpack: A Subroutine Package for Automatic Integration. (Springer Series in Computational Mathematics: Vol. 1). (Illus.). 301p. 1983. pap. 24.00 (ISBN 0-387-12553-1). Springer-Verlag.

QUADRATIC EQUATIONS

see Equations, Quadratic

QUADRATIC FORMS

see Forms, Quadratic

QUADRATURE, MECHANICAL

see Numerical Integration

QUADRUMANA

see Primates

QUAILS

Dickey, Charley. Quail Hunting. (Illus.). 112p. pap. 3.95 (ISBN 0-88317-057-4). Stoeger Pub Co.

Johnsgard, Paul A. Grouse & Quails of North America. LC 77-181596. (Illus.). xx, 533p. 1973. 35.00 (ISBN 0-8032-0810-3). U of Nebr Pr.

Leopold, A. Starker. The California Quail. LC 76-48003. (Illus.). 1978. 16.95 (ISBN 0-520-03362-0). U of Cal Pr.

Roseberry, John L. & Klimstra, Willard D. Population Ecology of the Bobwhite. LC 83-2481. (Illus.). 282p. 1983. 25.00x (ISBN 0-8093-1116-X). S Ill U Pr.

Stanger, Margaret A. That Quail, Robert. 1983. pap. 2.25 (ISBN 0-449-20388-3, Crest). Fawcett.

QUALITATIVE ANALYSIS

see Chemistry, Analytic–Qualitative

QUALITY CONTROL

see also Process Control;

also names of specific industries, e.g. Food Industry

Auditing for Quality Assurance. (Quality Assurance Practices Ser.: Module 31-7). (Illus.). 44p. 1979. spiral bdg. 7.00x (ISBN 0-87683-138-2). G P Courseware.

Besterfield, Dale H. Quality Control: A Practical Approach. (Illus.). 1979. ref. 29.95 (ISBN 0-13-745232-2). P-H.

Burr. Elementary Statistical Quality Control. (Statistics; Textbooks & Monograph Ser.: Vol. 25). 1978. 29.75 (ISBN 0-8247-6686-5). Dekker.

Burr, Irving. Statistical Quality Control Methods. (Statistics: Textbooks & Monographs: Vol. 16). 1976. 49.75 (ISBN 0-8247-6344-0). Dekker.

Caplan, Frank. The Quality System: A Sourcebook for Managers & Engineers. LC 80-969. 256p. 1980. 38.50 (ISBN 0-8019-6972-7). Chilton.

Caplen, R. H. A Practical Approach to Quality Control. 4th ed. 326p. 1983. pap. text ed. 17.00x (ISBN 0-09-147451-5, Pub. by Busn Bks England). Brookfield Pub Co.

Case, Kenneth E. & Jones, Lynn L. Profit Through Quality: Quality Assurance Programs for Manufacturers. 1978. pap. text ed. 15.00 (ISBN 0-89806-005-2); pap. text ed. 9.00 members. Inst Indus Eng.

Caves, Richard E. & Roberts, Marc J., eds. Regulating the Product: Quality & Variety. LC 74-18123. 256p. 1975. prof ref 27.50 (ISBN 0-88410-272-6). Ballinger Pub.

Certification & Qualification of Quality Control Inspectors. (Quality Assurance Practices Ser.: Module 31-6). 26p. 1979. spiral bdg. 6.00x (ISBN 0-87683-137-4). G P Courseware.

Charbonneau, Harvey C. & Webster, Gordon L. Industrial Quality Control. (Illus.). 1978. ref. 27.95 (ISBN 0-13-464255-4). P-H.

Crosby, Philip B. Quality Is Free: The Art of Making Quality Certain. 1980. pap. 3.95 (ISBN 0-451-62247-2, ME2247, Ment). NAL.

DataMyte Corporation. DataMyte Handbook: A Practical Guide to Computerized Data Acquisition for Statistical Process Control. 2nd ed. Houston, Jerry, ed. 530p. 1985. pap. 30.00 (ISBN 0-930345-01-0). DataMyte Corp.

Deming, W. E. Quality, Productivity, & Competitive Position. LC 82-61320. (Illus.). 373p. (Orig.). 1982. pap. text ed. 45.00 (ISBN 0-911379-00-2). Ctr Adv Eng Stud.

Dewar, Donald L. Quality Circle Leader Manual & Instructional Guide. (Quality Circle Member Manual: Quality Circle Handbook Ser.). 248p. 1980. pap. 16.00 (ISBN 0-937670-02-2). Quality Circle.

--Quality Circle Member Manual. (Quality Circle Handbook & Quality Circle Leader Manual & Instructional Guide Ser.). (Illus.). 268p. (Orig.). 1980. pap. 11.00 (ISBN 0-937670-01-4). Quality Circle.

--The Quality Circle: What You Should Know about It. (Illus.). 29p. 1980. pap. 0.75 (ISBN 0-937670-04-9). Quality Circle.

--Quality Circles: Answers to One Hundred Frequently Asked Questions. rev. ed. (Illus.). 1980. pap. 4.25 (ISBN 0-937670-00-6). Quality Circle.

Dhillon. Quality Control, Reliability, & Engineering Design. (Industrial Engineering Ser.). 392p. 1985. 49.50 (ISBN 0-8247-7278-4). Dekker.

Didactic Systems Staff. Managing the Quality Control Function. 1970. pap. 24.90 (ISBN 0-89401-065-4); pap. 21.50 two or more (ISBN 0-685-78142-9). Didactic Syst.

Donabedian, Avedis. The Criteria & Standards of Quality, Vol. II. LC 81-6873. (Explorations in Quality Assessment & Monitoring Ser.). (Illus.). 522p. 1981. text ed. 30.00x (ISBN 0-914904-67-1); pap. text ed. 25.00x (ISBN 0-914904-68-X). Health Admin Pr.

Drury, C. G., ed. Human Reliability in Quality Control. Fox, J. G. LC 75-11695. (Illus.). 250p. 1975. 33.00x (ISBN 0-85066-088-2). Taylor & Francis.

Educational Research Council of America. Quality Control Engineer. rev. ed. Ferris, Theodore N. & Marchak, John P., eds. (Real People at Work Ser: E). (Illus.). 36p. 1976. pap. text ed. 2.70 (ISBN 0-89247-039-9, 9319). Changing Times.

Goldberg, Harold. Extending the Limits of Reliability Theory. LC 81-4534. 263p. 1981. 42.95 (ISBN 0-471-07799-2, Pub. by Wiley Interscience). Wiley.

Grant, Eugene L. & Leavenworth, Richard. Statistical Quality Control. 5th ed. (Industrial Engineering & Management Science Ser.). (Illus.). 1979. text ed. 44.95 (ISBN 0-07-024114-7). McGraw.

Sadlej, Joanna. Semi-Empirical Methods of Quantum Chemistry. (Ellis Horwood Series in Chemical Science: 1-449). 416p. 1985. 89.95x (ISBN 0-470-27547-2). Halsted Pr.
Schaefer, Henry F., III. Quantum Chemistry: The Development of AB Initio Methods in Molecular Electronic Structure Theory. 1984. 29.95x (ISBN 0-19-855183-5). Oxford U Pr.
Sinanoglu, Oktay, ed. Modern Quantum Chemistry, 3 Vols. (Istanbul Lectures). 1965. Vol. 1. 63.00 (ISBN 0-12-645001-3); Vol. 2. 63.00 (ISBN 0-12-645002-1); Vol. 3. 63.00 (ISBN 0-12-645003-X). Acad Pr.
Society for Industrial & Applied Mathematical - American Mathematical Society Symposia - New York - April, 1974. Mathematical Aspects of Chemical & Biochemical Problems & Quantum Chemistry: Proceedings. Cohen, Donald S, ed. LC 74-26990. (SIAM-AMS Proceedings Ser.: Vol. 8). 1974. 33.00 (ISBN 0-8218-1328-5, SIAMS-8). Am Math.
Szabo, Attila & Ostlund, Neil S. Modern Quantum Chemistry: Introduction to Advanced Structure Theory. LC 81-71955. 1982. 49.50 (ISBN 0-02-949710-8). Macmillan.
Third International Congress of Quantum Chemistry, Kyoto, Japan, October 29 - Nov. 3, 1979. Horizons of Quantum Chemistry: Proceedings. Fukui, Kenichi & Pullman, Bernard, eds. (International Congresses of Quantum Chemistry Ser.). 296p. 1980. lib. bdg. 39.50 (ISBN 90-277-1105-4, Pub. by Reidel Holland). Kluwer Academic.
Ulstrup, J. Charge Transfer Process in Condensed Media. (Lecture Notes in Chemistry: Vol. 10). 1979. pap. 24.00 (ISBN 0-387-09520-9). Springer-Verlag.
Veselov, M. G., ed. Methods of Quantum Chemistry. Scripta Technica, tr. 1966. 47.00 (ISBN 0-12-719450-9). Acad Pr.
Weinstein, Harel & Green, Jack P., eds. Quantum Chemistry in Biomedical Sciences, Vol. 367. 552p. 1981. 108.00x (ISBN 0-89766-121-4); pap. 108.00x (ISBN 0-89766-122-2). NY Acad Sci.
Williams, A. F. A Theoretical Approach to Inorganic Chemistry. (Illus.). 1979. 60.00 (ISBN 0-387-09073-8). Springer-Verlag.
Zahradnik, R. & Carsky, P. Organic Quantum Chemistry Problems. LC 75-186258. 222p. 1973. 32.50 (ISBN 0-306-30516-X, Plenum Pr); pap. 8.95 (ISBN 0-306-20003-1). Plenum Pub.
Zahradnik, Rudolf & Carsky, Petr. Organic Quantum Chemistry Problems. LC 73-12931. 222p. 1973. pap. 8.95x (ISBN 0-306-20003-1, Rosetta). Plenum Pub.
Zimmerman, Howard E. Quantum Mechanics for Organic Chemists. 1975. 29.50 (ISBN 0-12-781650-X); pap. 19.50 (ISBN 0-12-781651-8). Acad Pr.

QUANTUM DYNAMICS
see Quantum Theory

QUANTUM ELECTRODYNAMICS
see also Quantum Electronics

Barut, A. O., ed. Foundations of Radiation Theory & Quantum Electrodynamics. LC 79-25715. (Illus.). 230p. 1980. 35.00x (ISBN 0-306-40277-7, Plenum Pr). Plenum Pub.
--Quantum Electrodynamics & Quantum Optics. (NATO ASI Ser. B, Physics: Vol. 110). 482p. 1984. 75.00x (ISBN 0-306-41730-8, Plenum Pr). Plenum Pub.
Bialyniccy-Birula, J. Quantum Electrodynamics. LC 74-4473. 541p. 1975. text ed. 52.00 (ISBN 0-08-017188-5). Pergamon.
Craig, David P. & Thirunamachandran, T. Molecular Quantum Electrodynamics. 1984. 58.00 (ISBN 0-12-195080-8). Acad Pr.
Detlovs, V. K., et al. Nine Papers on Logic & Quantum Electrodynamics. American Mathematical Society, tr. LC 51-5559. (Translations Ser.: No. 2, Vol. 23). 1963. 27.00 (ISBN 0-8218-1723-X, TRANS 2-23). Am Math.
Dittrich, W. & Reuter, M. Effective Lagrangians in Quantum Electrodynamics. (Lecture Notes in Physics: Vol. 220). v, 244p. 1985. pap. 14.60 (ISBN 0-387-15182-6). Springer-Verlag.
Feynman, Richard P. Quantum Electrodynamics. LC 61-18179. (Frontiers in Physics Ser.: No. 3). (Illus.). 1961. pap. 24.95 (ISBN 0-8053-2501-8). Benjamin-Cummings.
Graeff, G., et al, eds. Present Status & Aims of Quantum Electrodynamics: Proceedings. (Lecture Notes in Physics Ser.: Vol. 143). 302p. 1981. pap. 22.00 (ISBN 0-387-10847-5). Springer-Verlag.
Greiner, W., ed. Quantum Electrodynamics of Strong Fields. (NATO ASI Series B, Physics: Vol. 80). 912p. 1982. 125.00 (ISBN 0-306-41010-9, Plenum Pr). Plenum Pub.
Gupta, S. N. Quantum Electrodynamics. 238p. 1977. 56.75 (ISBN 0-677-04240-X). Gordon.
Healy, W. P. Non-Relativistic Quantum Electrodynamics. 1983. 39.50 (ISBN 0-12-335720-9). Acad Pr.
Hoyle, Fred & Narlikar, J. V. Action at a Distance in Physics & Cosmology. LC 74-4158. (Astronomy & Astrophysics Ser.). (Illus.). 266p. 1974. text ed. 38.95 (ISBN 0-7167-0346-7). W H Freeman.
Jauch, J. M. & Rohrlich, F. The Theory of Photons & Electrons: Second Corrected Printing. 2nd rev. ed. LC 75-8890. (Texts & Monographs in Physics). (Illus.). 533p. 1976. 28.00 (ISBN 0-387-07295-0). Springer-Verlag.
Landau, et al. Quantum Electrodynamics. 2nd ed. (Course of Theoretical Physics Ser.: Vol. 4). (Illus.). 550p. 1982. 76.00 (ISBN 0-08-026503-0); pap. 29.50 (ISBN 0-08-026504-9). Pergamon.
Roy, R. R. & Reed, R. D. Interactions of Photons & Leptons with Matter. LC 68-23487. 1969. 61.00 (ISBN 0-12-601350-0). Acad Pr.
Schwinger, Julian, ed. Selected Papers on Quantum Electrodynamics. 1958. pap. text ed. 8.50 (ISBN 0-486-60444-6). Dover.
Urban, P. Topics in Applied Quantum Electrodynamics. LC 71-98304. (Illus.). 1970. 40.20 (ISBN 0-387-80962-7). Springer-Verlag.
Vlasov, A. A. Many-Particle Theory & Its Application to Plasma. (Russian Monographs). (Illus.). 418p. 1961. 78.75x (ISBN 0-677-20330-6). Gordon.

QUANTUM ELECTRONICS
see also Masers

Basov, N. G., ed. Lasers & Their Applications in Physical Research. LC 78-13582. (P. N. Lebedev Physics Institute Ser.: Vol. 91). (Illus.). 234p. 1979. 65.00x (ISBN 0-306-10949-2, Consultants). Plenum Pub.
--Material & Apparatus in Quantum Radiophysics. LC 80-21931. (The Lebedev Physics Institute Ser.: Vol. 98). (Illus.). 171p. 1981. 65.00 (ISBN 0-306-10964-6, Consultants). Plenum Pub.
Bockris, J. O. & Khan, S. U. Quantum Electrochemistry. LC 78-11167. 538p. 1978. 69.50 (ISBN 0-306-31143-7, Plenum Pr). Plenum Pub.
Cohen, Marvin M. Introduction to the Quantum Theory of Semiconductors. LC 79-123485. (Illus.). 310p. 1972. 57.75 (ISBN 0-677-02980-2). Gordon.
Corney, Alan. Atomic & Laser Spectroscopy. (Illus.). 1977. text ed. 32.50x (ISBN 0-19-851138-8). Oxford U Pr.
Feld, Michael S., et al, eds. Fundamental & Applied Laser Physics: Proceedings. LC 73-392. Repr. of 1973 ed. 120.00 (ISBN 0-8357-9896-8, 2012431). Bks Demand UMI.
Fisher, Robert A. Optical Phase Conjugation. (Quantum Electronics Princples & Applications Ser.). 612p. 1983. 59.50 (ISBN 0-12-257740-X). Acad Pr.
Goodwin, D. W., ed. Advances in Quantum Electronics. Vol. 1, 1970. 55.00 (ISBN 0-12-035001-7); Vol. 2, 1974. 60.00 (ISBN 0-12-035002-5); Vol. 3, 1975. 85.00 (ISBN 0-12-035003-3). Acad Pr.
Gubanov, Alexsandr I. Quantum Electron Theory of Amorphous Conductors. LC 65-10526. 277p. 1965. 35.00x (ISBN 0-306-10703-1, Consultants). Plenum Pub.
Hershberger, W. D. Topics in Solid State & Quantum Electronics. LC 75-169163. 522p. 1972. 39.50 (ISBN 0-471-37350-8). Krieger.
Jacobs, S. F. & Sargent, M., eds. Physics of Quantum Electronics: Free-Electron Generators of Coherent Radiation, 2 vols. 1982. Vol. 8. text ed. 46.95 (ISBN 0-201-05688-7); Vol. 9. text ed. 39.95 (ISBN 0-201-05689-5). Addison-Wesley.
Knight, P. L., ed. Quantum Electronics & Electro-Optics: Proceedings of the Fifth National Quantum Electronics Conference. 456p. 1983. 59.95 (ISBN 0-471-10278-4). Wiley.
Louisell, William H. Radiation & Noise in Quantum Electronics. LC 76-56801. 318p. 1977. Repr. of 1964 ed. lib. bdg. 17.50 (ISBN 0-88275-503-X). Krieger.
Marcuse, D. Principles of Quantum Electronics. LC 79-8857. 1980. 38.50 (ISBN 0-12-471050-6). Acad Pr.
Moss, T. S. & Stenholm, S. Progress in Quantum Electronics, Vol. 6, Complete. (Illus.). 292p. 1981. 80.00 (ISBN 0-08-028387-X). Pergamon.
Ratner, A. M. Spectral, Spatial, & Temporal Properties of Lasers. LC 76-167677. (Optical Physics & Engineering Ser.). 220p. 1972. 42.50x (ISBN 0-306-30542-9, Plenum Pr). Plenum Pub.
Sanders, J. H. & Stenholm, S., eds. Progress in Quantum Electronics, Vols. 1-4. Incl. Vol. 1, Pt. 1. Parametric Processes. 1969. pap. text ed. 15.50 (ISBN 0-08-006632-1); Vol. 1, Pt. 2. Light Propagation & Light Shifts in Optical Pumping Experiments. 1970. pap. text ed. 15.50 (ISBN 0-08-006795-6); Vol. 1, Pt. 3. Non-Resonant Feedback in Lasers. 1970. pap. text ed. 15.50 (ISBN 0-08-015645-2); Vol. 1, Pt. 4. Semiclassical Theory of the Gas Laser. 1971. pap. text ed. 15.50 (ISBN 0-08-016409-9); Vol. 1, Pt. 5. Laser Lines in Atomic Species. 1971. pap. text ed. 15.50 (ISBN 0-08-016652-0); Vol. 1 (complete) 1971. text ed. 76.00 (ISBN 0-08-016776-4); Vol. 2, Pt. 1. Photon Counting & Photon Statistics. 1972. pap. text ed. 15.50 (ISBN 0-08-016865-5); Vol. 2, Pt. 2. Nonlinear Spectroscopy of Molecules. 1972. pap. text ed. 15.50 (ISBN 0-08-016880-9); Vol. 2, Pt. 3. Collision Broadening of Spectral Lines by Neutral Atoms. 1972. pap. text ed. 15.50 (ISBN 0-08-016881-7); Vol. 2, Pt. 4. Quantum Theory of Josephson Radiation. 1973. pap. text ed. 15.50 (ISBN 0-08-017743-3); Vol. 2 (complete) 1974. text ed. 76.00 (ISBN 0-08-017818-9); Vol. 3, Pt. 1. Three-Level Gas System & Their Interaction with Radiation. 1974. text ed. 76.00 (ISBN 0-08-017765-4); Vol. 3, Pt. 2. Mode-Locking of Lasers. 1974. pap. text ed. 15.50 (ISBN 0-08-017852-9); Vol. 3, Pt. 3. Quantum Theory of the Laser. 1974. pap. text ed. 15.50 (ISBN 0-08-017923-1); Vol. 3 (complete) 1975. text ed. 76.00; Vol. 4, Pt. 1. Self-Focusing: Experimental & Theory. 1975; Vol. 4, Pt. 2. Nonlinear Narrow Optical Resonance by Laser Radiation. 1975; Vol. 4, Pt. 3. Far Infrared Generation by Optical Mixing. 1976; Vol. 4 (complete) 1977. pap. text ed. o.p. (ISBN 0-08-019462-1). pap. write for info. Pergamon.
Skobel'tsyn, D. V., ed. Quantum Electronics & Paramagnetic Resonance. LC 73-120026. (P. N. Lebedev Physics Institute Ser.: Vol. 49). 148p. 1971. 30.00x (ISBN 0-306-10853-4, Consultants). Plenum Pub.
--Quantum Electronics in Lasers & Masers, Pt. 1. LC 68-13059. (P. N. Lebedev Physics Institute Ser.: Vol. 31). (Illus.). 161p. 1968. 32.50x (ISBN 0-306-10800-3, Consultants). Plenum Pub.
--Quantum Electronics in Lasers & Masers, Pt. 2. LC 68-13059. (P. N. Lebedev Physics Institute Ser.: Vol. 52). 306p. 1972. 42.50x (ISBN 0-306-10866-6, Consultants). Plenum Pub.
Townes, C. H. & Miles, P. A., eds. Quantum Electronics & Coherent Light. (Italian Physical Society Ser.: Course 31). 1965. 80.00 (ISBN 0-12-368831-0). Acad Pr.
Yariv, Amnon. Introduction to Optical Electronics. 2nd ed. LC 76-11773. 1976. text ed. 39.95 (ISBN 0-03-089892-7, HoltC). HR&W.
--Quantum Electronics. 2nd ed. LC 75-1392. 570p. 1975. 49.50x (ISBN 0-471-97176-6). Wiley.

QUANTUM FIELD THEORY
see also Algebra of Currents; Polarons; Quantum Electrodynamics; S-Matrix Theory

Abrikosov, A. A. & Gorkov, L. P. Methods of Quantum Field Theory in Statistical Physics. Silverman, Richard, tr. from Rus. 368p. 1975. pap. 7.00 (ISBN 0-486-63228-8). Dover.
Azcarraga, J. A., ed. Topics in Quantum Field Theory & Gauge Theories: Proceedings of the VIII International Seminar on Theoretical Physics, Held by GIFT in Salamanca, June 13-19, 1977. (Lecture Notes in Physics Ser.: Vol. 77). 1978. pap. 20.00 (ISBN 0-387-08841-5). Springer-Verlag.
Berger, C., ed. Photon-Photon Collisions. (Lecture Notes in Physics Ser.: Vol. 191). 417p. 1983. pap. 22.00 (ISBN 0-387-12691-0). Springer-Verlag.
Birrell, N. D. & Davies, P. C. Quantum Fields in Curved Space. LC 81-3851. (Cambridge Monographs on Mathematical Physics: No. 7). (Illus.). 340p. 1982. 57.50 (ISBN 0-521-23385-2). Cambridge U Pr.
--Quantum Fields in Curved Space. (Cambridge Monographs in Mathematical Physics). 360p. 1984. pap. 27.95 (ISBN 0-521-27858-9). Cambridge U Pr.
Bjorken, James D. & Drell, S. D. Relativistic Quantum Fields. (International Pure & Applied Physics Ser.). 1965. text ed. 44.95 (ISBN 0-07-005494-0). McGraw.
Bogoliubov, N. N. & Shirkov, D. V. Introduction to the Theory of Quantized Fields. 3rd ed. LC 79-17919. 616p. 1980. 83.50 (ISBN 0-471-04223-4, Pub. by Wiley-Interscience). Wiley.
Bogolubov, Nikolai N., et al. Introduction to Axiomatic Quantum Field Theory. Fulling, Stephen & Popova, Ludmila G., trs. from Rus. LC 72-5554. (Mathematical Physics Monographs: No. 18). 700p. 1975. text ed. 71.95 (ISBN 0-8053-0982-9). Benjamin-Cummings.
Caianiello, Eduardo R., ed. Renormalization & Invariance in Quantum Field Theory. LC 74-8902. (Nato ASI Series B, Physics: Vol. 5). 404p. 1974. 59.50x (ISBN 0-306-35705-4, Plenum Pr). Plenum Pub.
Craigie, N. S., et al, eds. Monopoles in Quantum Field Theory: Proceedings of the Monopole Meeting, Trieste, Italy, Dec. 11-15, 1981. xxi, 440p. 1982. 49.00x (ISBN 9971-950-28-6, Pub. by World Sci Singapore); pap. 21.00x (ISBN 9971-950-29-4, Pub. by World Sci Singapore). Taylor & Francis.
Dal Cin, Mario, et al, eds. Fundamental Interactions at High Energy Three: Tracts in Mathematics & Natural Sciences, 5 vols. Incl. Vol. 1. Nonpolynomial Lagrangians Renormalization & Gravity. Salam, Abdus. 156p. 41.75 (ISBN 0-677-12050-8); Vol. 2. Broken Scale Variance & the Light Cone. Gell-Mann, M. & Wilson, K. 158p. 45.25 (ISBN 0-677-12060-5); Vol. 3. Invited Papers. Hamermesh, M. 166p. 44.25 (ISBN 0-677-12070-2); Vol. 4. Troubles in the External Field Problem for Invariant Wave Equations. Wightman, A. S. 76p. 30.25 (ISBN 0-677-12080-X); Vol. 5. Multiperipheral Dynamics. Chew, G. 90p. 30.25 (ISBN 0-677-12090-7). LC 79-85472. (Illus.). 646p. 1971. Set. 169.75 (ISBN 0-677-12100-8). Gordon.
Danos, M., et al. Methods in Relativistic Nuclear Physics. 308p. 1984. 74.00 (ISBN 0-444-86317-6, North-Holland). Elsevier.
Davis, W. R. Classical Fields, Particles & the Theory of Relativity. 418p. 1970. 79.75 (ISBN 0-677-02570-X). Gordon.
Deser, Stanley, et al, eds. Lectures on Elementary Particles & Quantum Field Theory, 2 vols. 1971. Vol. 1. pap. 11.50x (ISBN 0-262-54013-4). MIT Pr.
DeWitt, Bryce S. Dynamical Theory of Groups & Fields. (Documents on Modern Physics Ser.). 258p. 1965. pap. 69.50 (ISBN 0-677-00985-2). Gordon.
DeWitt, C. & Stora, R. Les Houches Lectures: 1970, Statistical Mechanics & Quantum Field Theory. 568p. 1971. 150.25 (ISBN 0-677-13330-8). Gordon.
Feynman, Richard P. Theory of Fundamental Processes. (Frontiers in Physics Ser.: No. 4). (Illus.). 1961. pap. 31.95 (ISBN 0-8053-2507-7). Benjamin-Cummings.
Garbaczewski, P. Classical & Quantum Field Theory of Exactly Soluble Nonlinear Systems. 280p. 1984. 37.00x (ISBN 9971-966-55-7, Pub. by World Sci Singapore). Taylor & Francis.
Gourdin, M. Langrangian Formalism & Symmetry Laws. (Documents on Modern Physics Ser.). 108p. 1969. 27.95 (ISBN 0-677-30070-0). Gordon.
Hadlock, Charles. Field Theory & Its Classical Problems. LC 78-71937. (Carus Mathematical Monograph: No. 19). 339p. 1979. 24.00 (ISBN 0-88385-020-6). Math Assn.
Haken, H., ed. Quantum Field Theory of Solids. 330p. 1983. pap. 32.00 (ISBN 0-444-86737-6, North-Holland). Elsevier.
Ingraham, R. L. Renormalization in Quantum Field Theory with a Cut-Off. 196p. 1967. 57.75x (ISBN 0-677-01410-4). Gordon.
International Conference on Mathematical Problems of Quantum Field Theory & Quantum Statistics. Axiomatic Quantum Field Theory Statistics I. Vladimirov, ed. LC 78-6757. (Steklov Institute of Mathematics, Proceedings: No. 135). 1978. 78.00 (ISBN 0-8218-3035-X, STEKLO135). Am Math.
Itzykson, C. & Zuber, J. B. Quantum Field Theory. 1980. 72.95 (ISBN 0-07-032071-3). McGraw.
Jackiw, Roman, et al, eds. Shelter Island: Proceedings of the 1983 Shelter Island Conference on Quantum Field Theory & the Fundamental Problems of Physics, No. II. Witten, Edward. (Illus.). 428p. 1985. text ed. 37.50x (ISBN 0-262-10031-2). MIT Pr.
Julve, J. & Ramon-Medrano, M., eds. Non-Perturbative Aspects of Quantum Field Theory: Proceedings of the XII International GIFT Seminar, Sant Feliu de Guixols, Spain, June 1-5, 1981. iv, 260p. 1982. 35.00x (ISBN 9971-950-34-0, Pub. by World Sci Singapore); pap. 18.00x (ISBN 9971-950-35-9, Pub. by World Sci Singapore). Taylor & Francis.
Kerner, Edward H. Theory of Action-at-a-Distance in Relativistic Particle Dynamics. (International Science Review Ser.). 232p. 1972. 64.95 (ISBN 0-677-13990-X). Gordon.
Kirzhnits, D. A. Field Theoretical Methods in Many-Body Systems. Meadows, A. J., tr. 1967. 72.00 (ISBN 0-08-011779-1). Pergamon.
Levy, M. & Mitter, P., eds. New Developments in Quantum Field Theory & Statistical Mechanics: Cargese 1976. LC 77-8847. (NATO ASI Series B, Physics: Vol. 26). 483p. 1977. 75.00x (ISBN 0-306-35726-7, Plenum Pr). Plenum Pub.
Mandi. Quantum Field Theory. 354p. 1984. pap. 34.95 (ISBN 0-471-90650-6). Wiley.

Manoukian, Edward B. Remoralization. (Pure & Applied Mathematics Ser.). 1983. 39.50 (ISBN 0-12-469450-0). Acad Pr.

Milton, K. & Samuel, M., eds. Workshop on Non-Perturbative Quantum Chromodynamics: Oklahoma State University March, 1983. (Progress in Physics Ser.: Vol. 7). 400p. 1983. 24.95 (ISBN 0-8176-3127-5). Birkhauser.

Morrison, Harry, ed. Quantum Theory of Many-Particle Systems. (International Science Review Ser.). (Illus.). 360p. 1962. 46.25 (ISBN 0-677-00550-4). Gordon.

Nash, C. Relativistic Quantum Fields. 1979. 49.50 (ISBN 0-12-514350-8). Acad Pr.

Novozhilov, Y. V. & Tulub, A. V. The Method of Functionals in the Quantum Theory of Fields. (Russian Tracts on the Physical Sciences Ser.). 90p. 1961. 20.95x (ISBN 0-677-20410-8). Gordon.

Rajaraman, R. Solitions & Instantions: An Introduction to Solitions & Instantions in Quantum Field Theory. 412p. 1982. 87.25 (ISBN 0-444-86229-3, North-Holland). Elsevier.

Ryder, Lewis H. Quantum Field Theory. (Illus.). 350p. 1985. pap. 74.50 (ISBN 0-521-23764-5). Cambridge U Pr.

Schultz, Theodore D. Quantum Field Theory & the Many-Body Problem. (Many-Body Problem: Current Research & Reviews Ser.). 158p. 1964. 33.75 (ISBN 0-677-01130-X). Gordon.

Simon, Barry. P(Phi) 2 Euclidean (Quantum) Field Theory. (Princeton Series in Physics). 450p. 1974. 52.50 (ISBN 0-691-08143-3); pap. 14.50 (ISBN 0-691-08144-1). Princeton U Pr.

Skobel'tsyn, D. V., ed. Quantum Field Theory & Hydrodynamics. LC 66-12629. (P. N. Lebedev Physics Institute Ser.: Vol. 29). 271p. 1967. 32.50x (ISBN 0-306-10768-6, Consultants). Plenum Pub.

Speer, Eugene E. Generalized Feynman Amplitudes. (Annals of Mathematics Studies: No. 62). 1969. 22.00 (ISBN 0-691-08066-6). Princeton U Pr.

Streit, L., ed. Many Degrees of Freedom in Field Theory. LC 77-29217. (NATO ASI Series B, Physics: Vol. 30). 255p. 1978. 45.00x (ISBN 0-306-35730-5, Plenum Pr). Plenum Pub.

--Quantum Fields: Algebras, Processes. (Illus.). 144p. 1980. 48.00 (ISBN 0-387-81607-0). Springer-Verlag.

Takahashi, Y. An Introduction to Field Quantization. 1969. 37.00 (ISBN 0-08-012824-6). Pergamon.

Todorov, I. T. Analytic Properties of Feynman Diagrams in Quantum Field Theory. Risk, Clifford, tr. 168p. 1971. 32.00 (ISBN 0-08-016544-3). Pergamon.

Velo, G. & Wightman, A., eds. Constructive Quantum Field Theory. (Lecture Notes in Physics: Vol. 25). (Illus.). 331p. 1973. pap. 18.30 (ISBN 0-387-06608-X). Springer-Verlag.

Visconti, A. Quantum Field Theory, Vol. 1. LC 66-18237. 1969. 44.00 (ISBN 0-08-011821-6). Pergamon.

Wigner, Eugene P., ed. Dispersion Relations & Their Connection with Causality. (Italian Physical Society Ser.: Course 29). 1964. 75.00 (ISBN 0-12-368829-9). Acad Pr.

QUANTUM LIQUIDS
see also Liquid Helium

Feenberg, E. Theory of Quantum Fluids. (Pure & Applied Physics Ser.: Vol. 31). 1969. 61.50 (ISBN 0-12-250850-5). Acad Pr.

Trickey, S. B., et al, eds. Quantum Fluids & Solids. LC 77-21307. 473p. 1977. 69.50 (ISBN 0-306-31079-1, Plenum Pr). Plenum Pub.

Wiser, N. & Amit, D. J., eds. Quantum Fluids. 624p. 1970. 164.25x (ISBN 0-677-13700-1). Gordon.

QUANTUM MECHANICAL AMPLIFIERS
see Masers

QUANTUM MECHANICAL TUNNELING
see Tunneling (Physics)

QUANTUM MECHANICS
see Quantum Theory

QUANTUM OPTICS

Barut, A. O., ed. Quantum Electrodynamics & Quantum Optics. (NATO ASI Ser. B, Physics: Vol. 110). 482p. 1984. 75.00x (ISBN 0-306-41730-8, Plenum Pr). Plenum Pub.

Bekefi, George. Principles of Laser Plasmas. LC 76-28311. 736p. 1976. 76.95x (ISBN 0-471-06345-2, Pub. by Wiley-Interscience). Wiley.

Bonifacio, R. & Lugiato, L. A., eds. Dissipative Systems in Quantum Optics. (Topics in Current Physics Ser.: Vol. 27). (Illus.). 160p. 1982. 23.00 (ISBN 0-387-11062-3). Springer-Verlag.

Bowden, Charles M., et al, eds. Optical Bistability. LC 81-2559. 626p. 1981. 89.50x (ISBN 0-306-40722-1, Plenum Pr). Plenum Pub.

Claro, F., ed. Nonlinear Phenomena in Physics. (Springer Proceedings in Physics: Vol. 3). (Illus.). ix, 441p. 1985. 35.00 (ISBN 0-387-15273-3). Springer-Verlag.

Engelbrecht, C. A., ed. Quantum Optics-Cathedral Peak, South Africa 1981: Proceedings. (Lecture Notes in Physics: Vol. 155). 329p. 1982. pap. 22.00 (ISBN 0-387-11498-X). Springer-Verlag.

Glauber, R. J., ed. Quantum Optics. (Italian Physical Society: Course 42). 1970. 105.00 (ISBN 0-12-368842-6). Acad Pr.

Goldin, Edwin. Waves & Photons: An Introduction to Quantum Optics. LC 82-10991. (Pure & Applied Optics Ser.). 211p. 1982. 29.95x (ISBN 0-471-08592-8, Pub. by Wiley-Interscience). Wiley.

Knight, P. L. & Allen, L. Concepts of Quantum Optics. (Illus.). 226p. 1983. 30.00 (ISBN 0-08-029150-3); pap. 16.00 (ISBN 0-08-029160-0). Pergamon.

Mandel, L. & Wolf, E., eds. Coherence & Quantum Optics III. LC 73-76700. 913p. 1973. 115.00x (ISBN 0-306-30731-6, Plenum Pr). Plenum Pub.

--Coherence & Quantum Optics IV. LC 78-15470. 1027p. 1978. 135.00x (ISBN 0-306-40038-3, Plenum Pr). Plenum Pub.

--Coherence & Quantum Optics, Vol. V. 1246p. 1984. 150.00x (ISBN 0-306-41517-8, Plenum Pr). Plenum Pub.

Nussenzveig, H. M. Introduction to Quantum Optics. LC 72-80356. (Documents on Modern Physics Ser.). 260p. 1973. 69.50x (ISBN 0-677-03900-X). Gordon.

Perina, Jan. Quantum Statistics of Linear & Nonlinear Optical Phenomena. 1984. lib. bdg. 54.00 (ISBN 90-277-1512-2, Pub. by Reidel Holland). Kluwer Academic.

QUANTUM STATISTICS
see also Fermi Surfaces; Matrix Mechanics; Quantum Liquids; Quantum Theory; Statistical Mechanics; Superfluidity; Wave Mechanics

Alonso, Marcelo & Finn, Edward J. Fundamental University Physics, 2 vols. 2nd ed. Incl. Vol. 1. Mechanics. 1979. text ed. 17.95 (ISBN 0-201-00076-8); Vol. 2. Fields & Waves. 1983. text ed. 19.95 (ISBN 0-201-00077-6). 1980. Addison-Wesley.

Bogoliubov, N. N. Lectures on Quantum Statistics, 2 vols. 252p. 1970. Vol. 1. 69.50 (ISBN 0-677-20030-7); Vol. 2. 48.50 (ISBN 0-677-20570-8). Gordon.

Bogolubov, N. N. & Bogolubov, N. N., Jr. Introduction to Quantum Statistical Mechanics. viii, 300p. 1982. 33.00x (ISBN 9971-950-31-6, Pub. by World Sci Singapore); pap. 19.00x (ISBN 9971-950-04-9, Pub. by World Sci Singapore). Taylor & Francis.

Bratteli, O. & Robinson, D. W., eds. Operators Algebra & Quantum Statistical Mechanics, Vol. II: Equilibrium States; Models. (Texts & Monographs in Physics Ser.). 496p. 1979. 51.00 (ISBN 0-387-09187-4). Springer-Verlag.

Fujita, Shigeji. Introduction to Non-Equilibrium Quantum Statistical Mechanics. LC 82-23209. 178p. 1983. Repr. of 1966 ed. lib. bdg. 14.50 (ISBN 0-89874-593-4). Krieger.

Hurt, Norman & Hermann, R. Quantum Statistical Mechanics & Lie Group Harmonic Analysis, Pt. A. LC 80-13949. (Lie Groups; History, Frontiers & Applications: Vol. 10). 250p. 1980. text ed. 36.00 (ISBN 0-915692-30-9, 991600118). Math Sci Pr.

International Conference on Mathematical Problems of Quantum Field Theory & Quantum Statistics. Axiomatic Quantum Field Theory Statistics I. Vladimirov, ed. LC 78-6757. (Steklov Institute of Mathematics, Proceedings: No. 135). 1978. 78.00 (ISBN 0-8218-3035-X, STEKLO135). Am Math.

Jajte, R. Strong Limit Theorems in Non-Commutative Probability. (Lecture Notes in Mathematics Ser.: Vol. 1110). vi, 152p. 1985. pap. 12.00 (ISBN 0-387-13915-X). Springer-Verlag.

Jancel, R. Foundations of Classical & Quantum Statistical Mechanics. 1969. 59.00 (ISBN 0-08-012823-8). Pergamon.

Kalos, Malvin H., ed. Monte Carlo Methods in Quantum Problems. 1984. lib. bdg. 43.00 (ISBN 90-277-1755-9, Pub. by Reidel Holland). Kluwer Academic.

Khinchin, A. I. Analytical Foundations of Physical Statistics. (Russian Monographs & Texts on the Physical Sciences). 64p. 1961. 24.50 (ISBN 0-677-20140-0). Gordon.

Khinchin, Aleksander Y. Mathematical Foundations of Quantum Statistics. LC 60-11147. 1960. 20.00x (ISBN 0-910670-05-6). Graylock.

Kirkwood, John G. Quantum Statistics & Cooperative Phenomena, Vol. 1. Stillinger, F., ed. (Documents on Modern Physics Ser.). 192p. 1965. 46.25 (ISBN 0-677-00370-6). Gordon.

Louisell, William H. Quantum Statistical Properties of Radiation. LC 73-547. (Pure & Applied Optics Ser.). 528p. 1973. 69.95x (ISBN 0-471-54785-9, Pub. by Wiley-Interscience). Wiley.

Mintz, Stephan & Widmayer, Susan M., eds. Quantum Statistical Mechanics in the Natural Sciences. LC 74-9553. (Studies in the Natural Sciences Ser.: Vol. 4). 503p. 75.00 (ISBN 0-306-36904-4, Plenum Pr). Plenum Pub.

Resnick, Robert. Basic Concepts in Relativity & Early Quantum Theory. 244p. 1972. pap. 21.45 (ISBN 0-471-71703-7). Wiley.

Seiler, Erhard. Gauge Theories as a Problem of Constructive Quantum Field Theory & Statistical Mechanics. (Lecture Notes in Physics Ser.: Vol. 159). 192p. 1982. 12.00 (ISBN 0-387-11559-5). Springer-Verlag.

Trickey, Samuel B., et al, eds. Quantum Statistics & the Many-Body Problem. LC 75-25547. 288p. 1975. 49.50 (ISBN 0-306-30887-8, Plenum Pr). Plenum Pub.

QUANTUM THEORY
see also Angular Momentum (Nuclear Physics); Atomic Theory; Causality (Physics); Chemistry, Physical and Theoretical; Energy-Band Theory of Solids; Exciton Theory; Force and Energy; Isobaric Spin; Moessbauer Effect; Molecular Dynamics; Neutrons; Perturbation (Quantum Dynamics); Phonons; Problem of Many Bodies; Quantum Chemistry; Quantum Electrodynamics; Quantum Field Theory; Quantum Optics; Radiation; Raman Effect; Regge Trajectories; Relativity (Physics); Relaxation (Nuclear Physics); Statistical Thermodynamics; Thermodynamics; Wave Mechanics

Accardi, L. & Frigerio, A., eds. Quantum Probability & Applications to the Quantum Theory of Irreversible Processes: Proceedings of the International Workshop Held at Villa Mondragone, Italy, Sept. 6-11, 1982. (Lecture Notes in Mathematics Ser.: Vol. 1055). vi, 411p. 1984. 21.50 (ISBN 0-387-12915-4). Springer-Verlag.

Adams, E. D. & Ihas, G. G., eds. Quantum Fluids & Solids, 1983: AIP Conference Proceedings No. 103, Sanibel Island, Florida. LC 83-72240. 512p. 1983. lib. bdg. 39.75 (ISBN 0-88318-202-5). Am Inst Physics.

Agarwal, G. S. Quantum-Statistical Theories of Spontaneous Emission & Their Relation to Other Approaches. LC 25-9130. (Tracts in Modern Physics Ser.: Vol. 70). 140p. 1974. 45.50 (ISBN 0-387-06630-6). Springer-Verlag.

Albeverio, S., et al, eds. Stochastic Processes in Quantum Theory & Statistical Physics: Proceedings, Marseille, France, 1981. (Lecture Notes in Physics Ser.: Vol. 173). 337p. 1982. pap. 19.00 (ISBN 0-387-11956-6). Springer-Verlag.

Alonso, Marcelo & Valk, Henry. Quantum Mechanics: Principles & Applications. 1986. Repr. of 1973 ed. lib. bdg. price not set (ISBN 0-89874-894-1). Krieger.

Amrein, W. O. Non-Relativistic Quantum Dynamics. viii, 237p. 1981. pap. 34.50 (ISBN 90-277-1324-3, Pub. by Reidell Holland). Kluwer Academic.

Anderson, Elmer. Modern Physics & Quantum Mechanics. 1971. text ed. 35.95 (ISBN 0-7216-1220-2, CBS C). SCP.

Atkins, P. W. Molecular Quantum Mechanics. 2nd ed. (Illus.). 1983. pap. 27.95x (ISBN 0-19-855170-3). Oxford U Pr.

--Molecular Quantum Mechanics: Solutions Manual. (Illus.). 1983. pap. 14.95x (ISBN 0-19-855180-0). Oxford U Pr.

Atwood, W. B. & Bjorken, J. D. Lectures on Lepton Nucleon Scattering & Quantum Chromo-Dynamics. (Progress in Physics Ser.: Vol. 4). 1982. 34.95 (ISBN 0-8176-3079-1). Birkhauser.

Audi, Michael. The Interpretation of Quantum Mechanics. LC 73-78663. pap. 53.50 (ISBN 0-317-08073-3, 2019953). Bks Demand UMI.

Bargmann, V., ed. Group Representations in Mathematics & Physics: Battelle Seattle 1969 Rencontres. LC 75-146233. (Lecture Notes in Physics: Vol. 6). 1970. pap. 18.30 (ISBN 0-387-05310-7). Springer-Verlag.

Barklon, L. I., et al. Eighteen Papers on Analysis & Quantum Mechanics. LC 51-5559. (Translations Ser.: No. 2, Vol. 91). 1970. 38.00 (ISBN 0-8218-1791-4, TRANS 2-91). Am Math.

Barut, A. O., ed. Quantum Theory, Groups, Fields & Particles. 1983. lib. bdg. 45.50 (ISBN 90-277-1552-1, Pub. by Reidel Holland). Kluwer Academic.

Becker, Richard. Electromagnetic Fields & Interactions. (Illus.). 864p. 1982. pap. 12.50 (ISBN 0-486-64290-9). Dover.

Belinfante, F. J. Measurements of Time Reversal in Objective Quantum Theory. 1975. text ed. 22.00 (ISBN 0-08-018152-X). Pergamon.

Beltrametti, E. & Van Fraassen, Bas C., eds. Current Issues in Quantum Logic. LC 80-29505. (Ettore Majorana International Science Series Physical Sciences: Vol. 8). 502p. 1981. 79.50x (ISBN 0-306-40652-7, Plenum Pr). Plenum Pub.

Bennett, W. R., Jr. Atomic Gas Laser Transition Data: A Critical Evaluation. LC 79-22073. 300p. 1979. 95.00x (ISBN 0-306-65187-4, IFI Plenum). Plenum Pub.

Berezin, F. A. Method of Second Quantization. (Pure and Applied Physics Ser.: Vol. 24). 1966. 47.50 (ISBN 0-12-089450-5). Acad Pr.

Bestor, Arthur. Educational Wastelands: The Retreat from Learning in Our Public Schools. 2nd ed. LC 85-1014. 288p. 1985. 19.95x (ISBN 0-252-01226-7). U of Ill Pr.

Bethe, Hans A. & Jackiw, Roman W. Intermediate Quantum Mechanics. 2nd ed. LC 68-24363. (Lecture Notes & Supplements in Physics Ser.: No. 9). 1968. pap. 34.95 (ISBN 0-8053-0755-9, Adv Bk Prog). Benjamin-Cummings.

Bethe, Hans A. & Salpeter, Edwin E. Quantum Mechanics of One- & Two-Electron Atoms. LC 76-30829. 382p. 1977. pap. 10.95x (ISBN 0-306-20022-8, Plenum Pr). Plenum Pub.

--Quantum Mechanics of One- & Two-Electron Atoms. LC 76-30829. 382p. 1977. pap. 10.95x (ISBN 0-306-20022-8). Plenum Pub.

Biedenharn, C., ed. Quantum Theory of Angular Momentum: A Collection of Reprints & Original Papers. (Perspectives in Physics Ser.). (Illus., Orig.). 1965. pap. 44.00 (ISBN 0-12-096056-7). Acad Pr.

Biedenharn, L. C. & Louck, J. D. Encyclopedia of Mathematics & Its Applications: The Racah-Wigner Algebra in Quantum Theory, Vol. 9. 1984. 59.50 (ISBN 0-521-30229-3). Cambridge U Pr.

Biedenhern, L. C. & Louck, J. D. Encyclopedia of Mathematics & Its Applications: Angular Momentum in Quantum Physics, Vol. 8. 1984. 69.50 (ISBN 0-521-30228-5). Cambridge U Pr.

Bitter, Francis & Medicus, Heinrich A. Fields & Particles: An Introduction to Electromagnetic Wave Phenomena & Quantum Physics. LC 72-87209. pap. 160.00 (ISBN 0-317-08584-0, 2007763). Bks Demand UMI.

Bjorken, James D. & Drell, S. D. Relativistic Quantum Mechanics. (International Series in Pure & Applied Physics). 1964. text ed. 40.95 (ISBN 0-07-005493-2). McGraw.

Blinder, S. M. Foundations of Quantum Dynamics. 1974. 42.00 (ISBN 0-12-106050-0). Acad Pr.

Blokhintsev, D. I. The Philosophy of Quantum Mechanics. LC 68-22439. 132p. 1968. lib. bdg. 24.00 (ISBN 90-277-0105-9, Pub. by Reidel Holland). Kluwer Academic.

--Quantum Mechanics. (Russian Monographs & Texts on the Physical Sciences). 552p. 1966. 115.50 (ISBN 0-677-60080-1). Gordon.

--Quantum Mechanics. Sykes, J. B. & Kearsley, M. J., trs. from Rus. 535p. 1964. lib. bdg. 39.50 (ISBN 90-277-0104-0, Pub. by Reidel Holland). Kluwer Academic.

Bohm, A. Quantum Mechanics. (Texts & Monographs in Physics). (Illus.). 1979. 39.00 (ISBN 0-387-08862-8). Springer-Verlag.

Bohm, David. Quantum Theory. 1951. ref. ed. 42.95 (ISBN 0-13-747873-9). P-H.

--Wholeness & the Implicate Order. 240p. (Orig.). 1983. pap. 6.95 (ISBN 0-7448-0000-5, Ark Paperbacks). Routledge & Kegan.

Bohr, Niels. Niels Bohr Collected Works, Vol. 3: The Correspondence 1918-1923, Vol. 3. Nielsen, J. Rud, ed. 1976. 136.25 (ISBN 0-7204-1803-8, North-Holland). Elsevier.

--Niels Bohr, Collected Works, Vol. 5: The Emergence of Quantum Mechanics, 1924-1926. Stolzenberg, K. & Rudinger, E., eds. 600p. 1985. 92.75 (ISBN 0-444-86501-2, North-Holland). Elsevier.

Brandt, S. & Dahmen, H. D. The Picture Book of Quantum Mechanics. 320p. 1985. 26.95 (ISBN 0-471-81776-7). Wiley.

Bratteli, O. & Robinson, D. W. Operator Algebras & Quantum Statistical Mechanics: Vol I: C & W-Algebras. Symmerty Groups. Decomposition of States. (Texts & Monographs in Physics). 1979. 47.50 (ISBN 0-387-09187-4). Springer-Verlag.

Bruter, C. P., et al, eds. Bifurcation Theory, Mechanics & Physics. 1983. lib. bdg. 58.00 (ISBN 90-2771-631-5, Pub. by Reidel Holland). Kluwer Academic.

Bub, J. The Interpretation of Quantum Mechanics. (Western Ontario Ser.: No. 3). ix, 155p. 1974. lib. bdg. 26.00 (ISBN 90-277-0465-1, Pub. by Reidel Holland); pap. text ed. 16.00 (ISBN 90-277-0466-X, Pub. by Reidel Holland). Kluwer Academic.

Buettgenbach, S. Hyperfine Structure in 4d- & 5d-Shell Atoms. (Springer Tracts in Modern Physics Ser.: Vol. 96). (Illus.). 97p. 1982. 23.00 (ISBN 0-387-11740-7). Springer-Verlag.

Bunge, M., ed. Studies in the Foundations, Methodology & Philosophy of Science, 4 vols. Incl. Vol. 1. Delaware Seminar in the Foundations of Physics. (Illus.); Vol. 2. Quantum Theory & Reality. 1967. 28.00 (ISBN 0-387-03993-7); Vol. 3, Pt. 1. The Search for System. (Illus.). xii, 536p. 1967. 54.50 (ISBN 0-387-03994-5); Vol. 3, Pt. 2. The Search for Truth. (Illus.). viii, 374p. 1967. 47.00 (ISBN 0-387-03995-3); Vol. 4. Problems in the Foundations of Physics. (Illus.). 1971. 28.00 (ISBN 0-387-05490-1). LC 71-163433. Springer-Verlag.

Burt, Philip B. Quantum Mechanics & Nonlinear Waves: Physics. (Monographs & Tracts Ser.). 331p. 1981. 82.50 (ISBN 3-7186-0072-2). Harwood Academic Pubs.
Caianiello, Eduardo R., ed. Renormalization & Invariance in Quantum Field Theory. LC 74-8902. (Nato ASI Series B, Physics: Vol. 5). 404p. 1974. 59.50x (ISBN 0-306-35705-4, Plenum Pr). Plenum Pub.
Calais, Jean-Louis, et al, eds. Quantum Science: Methods & Structure. LC 76-21354. 595p. 1976. 85.00 (ISBN 0-306-30968-8, Plenum Pr). Plenum Pub.
Callaway, Joseph, ed. Quantum Theory of the Solid State. 1976. 29.00 (ISBN 0-12-155256-X). Acad Pr.
Cassels, J. M. Basic Quantum Mechanics. 2nd ed. (Illus.). 206p. 1982. pap. text ed. 17.00x (ISBN 0-333-31768-8). Scholium Intl.
Cassinelli, Gianni. Encyclopedia of Mathematics & Its Applications: The Logic of Quantum Mechanics, Vol. 15. 1984. 37.50 (ISBN 0-317-14391-3, 30235-8). Cambridge U Pr.
Castell, L., et al. Quantum Theory & the Structures of Time & Space, 2 vols. LC 77-83924. 252p. 1977. pap. text ed. 14.00x ea. Vol. 1 (ISBN 0-916672-95-6). Vol. 2 (ISBN 0-916672-96-4). Allanheld.
Chadan, K. & Sabatier, P. C. Inverse Problems in Quantum Scattering Theory. (Texts & Monographs in Physics). (Illus.). 1977. 49.00 (ISBN 0-387-08092-9). Springer-Verlag.
Charles, Pavel. Open Quantum Systems & Feynman Integrals. 376p. 1984. 64.00 (ISBN 90-277-1678-1, Pub. by Reidel Holland). Kluwer Academic.
Chesnut, D. B. Finite Groups & Quantum Theory. LC 81-19351. 270p. 1982. Repr. of 1974 ed. lib. bdg. 26.50 (ISBN 0-89874-468-7). Krieger.
Christensen, S. M. Quantum Theory of Gravity. 500p. 1984. 54.00 (ISBN 0-9960042-1-1, Pub. by A Hilger England). Heyden.
Cini, M. Introduction a la Mecanique des Particules. (Cours & Documents de Mathematiques & de Physique Ser.). (Fr.). 364p. 1972. 93.75 (ISBN 0-677-50380-6). Gordon.
Clark, H. A First Course in Quantum Mechanics. rev. ed. 1982. 12.95 (ISBN 0-442-30173-1). Van Nos Reinhold.
Cohen-Tannoudji, Claude, et al. Quantum Mechanics, 2 vols. LC 76-5874. 1977. Vol. 1. 48.95 (ISBN 0-471-16432-1, Pub. by Wiley-Interscience); 43.95 (ISBN 0-471-16434-8); Vol. 1 898pp. pap. 41.50 (ISBN 0-471-16433-X); Vol. 2 626pp. pap. 37.50 (ISBN 0-471-16435-6). Wiley.
Colodny, Robert G., ed. From Quarks to Quasars: Philosophical Problems of Modern Physics. LC 84-29456. (Pittsburgh Series in Philosophy of Science). (Illus.). 496p. 1986. 50.00x (ISBN 0-8229-3515-5). U of Pittsburgh Pr.
--Paradigms & Paradoxes: The Philosophical Challenge of the Quantum Domain. LC 79-158189. (Philosophy of Science Ser). 1972. 39.95x (ISBN 0-8229-3235-0). U of Pittsburgh Pr.
Condon, Edward U. & Shortley, George H. Theory of Atomic Spectra. (Orig.). 1935. pap. 37.50 (ISBN 0-521-09209-4). Cambridge U Pr.
Constantinescu, F. & Magyari, E. Problems in Quantum Mechanics. 1971. text ed. 28.00 (ISBN 0-08-019008-1). Pergamon.
Creutz, Michael. Quarks, Gluons & Lattices. (Monographs on Mathematical Physics). (Illus.). 175p. 1985. pap. 12.95 (ISBN 0-521-31535-2). Cambridge U Pr.
Cropper, William H. Quantum Physicists & an Introduction to Their Physics. (Illus.). 270p. 1970. pap. 9.95x (ISBN 0-19-500861-8). Oxford U Pr.
Daudel, Raymond, et al, eds. Quantum Theory of Chemical Reactions: Solvent Effect, Reaction Mechanisms, Photochemical Processes, Vol. 11. 340p. 1980. PLB 42.00 (ISBN 90-277-1182-8, Pub. by Reidel Holland). Kluwer Academic.
Davies, E. B., ed. Quantum Theory of Open Systems. 1976. 37.00 (ISBN 0-12-206150-0). Acad Pr.
Davies, P. C. Quantum Mechanics. (Student Physics Ser.). 12800p. (Orig.). 1984. pap. text ed. 9.95x (ISBN 0-7100-9962-2). Routledge & Kegan.
Davydov, A. S. Biology & Quantum Mechanics. Oliver, D., tr. LC 81-15833. (International Series on Natural Philosophy: Vol. 109). (Illus.). 250p. 1981. 50.00 (ISBN 0-08-026392-5). Pergamon.
--Quantum Mechanics, Vol. 1. 2nd ed. Ter Haar, D., tr. 760p. 1976. 25.00 (ISBN 0-08-020437-6); text ed. 76.00 (ISBN 0-08-020438-4). Pergamon.
De Broglie, Louis. Revolution in Physics: A Non-Mathematical Survey of Quanta. Niemeyer, Ralph W., tr. LC 76-95113. Repr. of 1953 ed. lib. bdg. 18.75x (ISBN 0-8371-2582-0, BRRP). Greenwood.
D'Espagnat, B., ed. Foundations of Quantum Mechanics. (Italian Physical Society Ser.: Course 49). 1972. 86.00 (ISBN 0-12-368849-3). Acad Pr.
Dewitt, B. S. & Graham, N., eds. The Many Worlds of Interpretation of Quantum Mechanics: A Fundamental Exposition. (Princeton Series in Physics). 250p. 1973. 32.00 (ISBN 0-691-08126-3); pap. text ed. 13.50 (ISBN 0-691-08131-X). Princeton U Pr.
Dicke, Robert H. & Wittke, J. P. Introduction to Quantum Mechanics. 1960. 30.95 (ISBN 0-201-01510-2). Addison-Wesley.
Dirac, P. The Development of Quantum Theory: J. Robert Oppenheimer Memorial Prize Acceptance Speech. 76p. 1971. 22.00 (ISBN 0-677-02970-5). Gordon.
Dirac, P. A. The Principles of Quantum Mechanics. 4th ed. (International Series of Monographs on Physics). 1958. pap. text ed. 19.95x (ISBN 0-19-852011-5). Oxford U Pr.
Dreizler, Reiner M. & Da Providencia, Joo, eds. Density Functional Methods in Physics. (NATO ASI Series B Physics: Vol. 123). 542p. 1985. 85.00x (ISBN 0-306-41926-2, Plenum Pr). Plenum Pub.
Duff, M. J. & Isham, C. J., eds. Quantum Structure of Space & Time: Proceedings of the Nuffield Workshop, Imperial College, London, August 3-21, 1981. LC 82-9732. 420p. 1983. 52.50 (ISBN 0-521-24732-2). Cambridge U Pr.
Duffey, George H. A Development of Quantum Mechanics. 1983. lib. bdg. 60.00 (ISBN 90-277-1587-4, Pub. by Reidel Holland). Kluwer Academic.
Duke, D. W. & Owens, J. F., eds. Perturbative Quantum Chromodynamics: Tallahassee, 1981. (AIP Conference Proceedings: No. 74). 477p. 1981. lib. bdg. 34.75 (ISBN 0-88318-173-8). Am Inst Physics.
Economou, E. N. Green's Functions in Quantum Physics. (Springer Series in Solid-State Sciences: Vol. 7). (Illus.). 336p. (Second Corrected & Updated Edition). 1983. 22.00 (ISBN 0-387-12266-4). Springer-Verlag.
Edmonds, A. R. Angular Momentum in Quantum Mechanics. rev. ed. (Investigations in Physics, No. 4). 1968. 22.00x (ISBN 0-691-07912-9). Princeton U Pr.
Einstein, Albert & Infeld, Leopold. Evolution of Physics. 1967. pap. 9.95 (ISBN 0-671-20156-5, Touchstone Bks). S&S.
Eisberg, R. & Resnick, R. Quantum Physics: Of Atoms, Molecules, Solids, Nuclei & Particles. 2nd ed. 848p. 1985. 38.50 (ISBN 0-471-87373-X). Wiley.
Eisberg, Robert & Resnick, Robert. Quantum Physics of Atoms, Molecules, Solids, Nuclei & Particles. LC 74-1195. 791p. 1974. text ed. 45.45x (ISBN 0-471-23464-8); avail. solutions (ISBN 0-471-05438-0). Wiley.
Eisberg, Robert M. Fundamentals of Modern Physics. LC 61-6770. (Illus.). 729p. 1961. 45.45x (ISBN 0-471-23463-X). Wiley.
Eisele, John. Modern Quantum Mechanics with Applications to Elementary Particle Physics: An Introduction to Contemporary Physical Thinking. LC 69-19102. Repr. of 1969 ed. 105.90 (ISBN 0-8357-9936-0, 2051240). Bks Demand UMI.
Erf, Robert K. Speckle Metrology. (Quantum Electronics Ser.). 1978. 62.50 (ISBN 0-12-241360-1). Acad Pr.
Faddeev, L. D. & Slavnov, A. A. Gauge Fields: Introduction to Quantum Theory. 1981. 51.95 (ISBN 0-8053-9016-2). Benjamin-Cummings.
Fano, U. & Fano, L. Physics of Atoms & Molecules: An Introduction to the Structure of Matter. LC 76-184808. 456p. 1973. text ed. 35.00x (ISBN 0-226-23782-6). U of Chicago Pr.
Faris, W. G. Self-Adjoint Operators. (Lecture Notes in Mathematics Ser.: Vol. 433). vii, 115p. 1975. pap. 13.00 (ISBN 0-387-07030-3). Springer-Verlag.
Feenberg, Eugene & Pake, George E. Notes on the Quantum Theory of Angular Momentum. LC 59-13223. pap. 20.00 (ISBN 0-317-07876-3, 2000789). Bks Demand UMI.
Fermi, Enrico. Notes on Quantum Mechanics. LC 64-9447. 1962. pap. 5.00x (ISBN 0-226-24361-3). U of Chicago Pr.
Feyman, P & Hibbs, A. R. Quantum Mechanics & Path Integrals. (International Earth & Planetary Sciences Ser). 1965. text ed. 45.95 (ISBN 0-07-020650-3). McGraw.
Feynman, Richard P. Theory of Fundamental Processes. (Frontiers in Physics Ser.: No. 4). (Illus.). 1961. pap. 31.95 (ISBN 0-8053-2507-7). Benjamin-Cummings.
Fluegge, S. Practical Quantum Mechanics. LC 74-23732. (Illus.). xiv, 623p. 1974. pap. 26.00 (ISBN 0-387-07050-8). Springer-Verlag.
--Practical Quantum Mechanics One. rev. ed. (Die Grundlehren der Mathematischen Wissenschaften: Vol. 177). 1971. 52.00 (ISBN 0-387-05276-3). Springer-Verlag.
--Practical Quantum Mechanics Two. rev. ed. (Grundlehren der Mathematischen Wissenschaften: Vol. 178). 1971. 49.60 (ISBN 0-387-05277-1). Springer-Verlag.
Fock, V. Fundamentals of Quantum Mechanics. 375p. 1978. 8.45 (ISBN 0-8285-5197-9, Pub. by Mir Pubs USSR). Imported Pubns.
Fonda, L. & Ghirardi, G. C. Symmetry Principles in Quantum Physics. (Theoretical Physics Ser: Vol. 1). 1970. 45.00 (ISBN 0-8247-1213-7). Dekker.
French, A. P. & Taylor, Edwin F. Introduction to Quantum Physics. (M. I. T. Introductory Physics Ser.). (Illus.). 500p. 1978. pap. text ed. 18.95x (ISBN 0-393-09106-6). Norton.
Fromhold, A. T. Quantum Mechanics for Applied Physics & Engineering. LC 80-19001. 1981. 34.50 (ISBN 0-12-269150-4). Acad Pr.
Fronteau, J., et al, eds. Hadronic Mechanics: Proceedings of the Institute for Basic Research, Harvard Grounds, Cambridge, MA August 2-6, 1983. 290p. 1984. pap. text ed. 70.00x (ISBN 0-911767-11-8). Hadronic Pr Inc.
Gamow, George. Thirty Years that Shook Physics: The Story of Quantum Theory. 240p. 1985. pap. 4.95 (ISBN 0-486-24895-X). Dover.
Gasiorowicz, Stephen G. Quantum Physics. LC 73-22376. 514p. 1974. text ed. 47.95 (ISBN 0-471-29280-X). Wiley.
Gervais, J. L. & Jacob, M., eds. Non-Linear & Collective Phenomena in Quantum Physics. vii, 514p. 1983. 60.00x (ISBN 9971-950-64-2, Pub. by World Sci Singapore); pap. 28.00x (ISBN 9971-950-65-0, Pub. by World Sci Singapore). Taylor & Francis.
Gillespie, Daniel T. A Quantum Mechanics Primer: An Elementary Introduction to the Formal Theory of Non-Relativistic Quantum Mechanics. LC 74-3107. 137p. (Orig.). 1973. pap. text ed. 21.95x (ISBN 0-470-29912-6). Halsted Pr.
Glimm, J. & Jaffe, A. Quantum Physics: A Functional Integral Point of View. (Illus.). 416p. 1981. 28.00 (ISBN 0-387-90551-0); pap. 19.50 (ISBN 0-387-90562-6). Springer-Verlag.
Gloeckle, W. The Quantum Mechanical Few-Body Problem. (Texts & Monographs in Physics). (Illus.). 220p. 1983. 32.00 (ISBN 0-387-12587-6). Springer-Verlag.
Greiner, W., et al. Quantum Electrodynamics of Strong Fields. (Texts & Monographs in Physics). (Illus.). 610p. 1985. 43.00 (ISBN 0-387-13404-2). Springer-Verlag.
Gribbin, John. In Search of Schrodinger's Cat: Quantum Physics & Reality. 320p. 1984. pap. 9.95 (ISBN 0-553-34253-3). Bantam.
Gudder. Stochastic Methods in Quantum Mechanics. (Probability & Applied Mathematics Ser.: Vol. 1). 220p. 1979. 39.50 (ISBN 0-444-00299-5, North Holland). Elsevier.
Gunton, J. D. & Droz, M. Introduction to the Theory of Metastable & Unstable States. (Lecture Notes in Physics: Vol. 183). 140p. 1983. 9.00 (ISBN 0-387-12306-7). Springer-Verlag.
Gustafson, Karl E. & Reinhardt, William P., eds. Quantum Mechanics in Mathematics, Chemistry, & Physics. LC 81-5846. 512p. 1981. 75.00x (ISBN 0-306-40737-X, Plenum Pr). Plenum Pub.
Hahlbohm, Hans-Dieter & Lubbig, Heinz, eds. SQUID: Superconducting Quantum Interference Devices & Their Applications. 724p. 1980. 88.00 (ISBN 3-11-008063-X). De Gruyter.
Haken, H. & Wolf, H. C. Atomic & Quantum Physics: An Introduction to the Fundamentals of Experiment & Theory. Brewer, W. D., tr. from Ger. (Illus.). 415p. 1984. 29.00 (ISBN 0-387-13137-X). Springer Verlag.
Hall, D. O., et al. Biomass for Energy in the Developing Countries: Current Role-Potential-Problems-Prospects. (Illus.). 200p. 1982. 20.00 (ISBN 0-08-028689-5). Pergamon.
Hameka, Hendrik F. Quantum Chemistry. LC 81-3430. 387p. 1981. 42.95 (ISBN 0-471-09223-1, Pub. by Wiley-Interscience). Wiley.
Hanna, Melvin W. Quantum Mechanics in Chemistry. 3rd ed. 1981. pap. text ed. 18.95 (ISBN 0-8053-3705-9, 33705); student solutions manual o.p. 9.95 (ISBN 0-8053-3707-5). Benjamin-Cummings.
Hartkaemper, A. & Neumann, H., eds. Foundations of Quantum Mechanics & Ordered Linear Spaces. LC 74-2859. (Lecture Notes in Physics: Vol. 29). vi, 355p. 1974. pap. 18.00 (ISBN 0-387-06725-6). Springer-Verlag.
Heine, V. Group Theory in Quantum Mechanics. 1963. 35.00 (ISBN 0-08-009242-X). Pergamon.
Heisenberg, Werner. Philosophical Problems of Quantum Physics. LC 79-89842. Orig. Title: Philosophic Problems of Nuclear Science. 1979. 16.00 (ISBN 0-918024-14-5); pap. text ed. 10.00 (ISBN 0-918024-15-3). Ox Bow.
--Physical Principles of the Quantum Theory. 1930. pap. text ed. 4.00 (ISBN 0-486-60113-7). Dover.
--Physics & Philosophy: The Revolution in Modern Science. (World Perspectives Ser.). pap. 5.95xi (ISBN 0-06-130549-9, TB549, Torch). Har-Row.
Hermann, Robert. Topics in the Mathematics of Quantum Mechanics. (Interdisciplinary Mathematics Ser: No. 6). 250p. 1973. 21.00 (ISBN 0-915692-05-8, 991600231). Math Sci Pr.
Hoffman, Banesh. The Strange Story of the Quantum. 2nd ed. 14.50 (ISBN 0-8446-0702-9). Peter Smith.
Hoffmann, Banesh. Strange Story of the Quantum. 1959. pap. text ed. 4.95 (ISBN 0-486-20518-5). Dover.
Holevo, A. S. Probablistic & Statistical Aspects of Quantum Theory. (Series In Statistics & Probability: Vol. 1). 316p. 1982. 85.00 (ISBN 0-444-86333-8, I-290-82, North Holland). Elsevier.
Hooker, C. A., ed. Contemporary Research in the Foundations & Philosophy of Quantum Theory. LC 72-83377. (Western Ontario Ser: No. 2). (Illus.). 385p. 1973. lib. bdg. 55.00 (ISBN 90-277-0271-3, Pub. by Reidel Holland); pap. text ed. 29.50 (ISBN 90-277-0338-8, Pub. by Reidel Holland). Kluwer Academic.
--The Logico-Algebraic Approach to Quantum Mechanics, Vol. I: Historical Evolution. LC 75-8737. (Western Ontario Ser: No. 5). 607p. 1975. lib. bdg. 92.00 (ISBN 90-277-0567-4, Pub. by Reidel Holland); pap. 34.00 (ISBN 90-277-0613-1). Kluwer Academic.
Hooker, Clifford A., ed. Physical Theory As Logico-Operational Structure. (Western Ontario Ser.: No. 7). 1978. lib. bdg. 50.00 (ISBN 90-277-0711-1, Pub. by Reidel Holland). Kluwer Academic.
Hubner, Kurt. Critique of Scientific Reason. Dixon, Paul R., Jr. & Dixon, Hollis M., trs. LC 82-23690. 296p. 1983. lib. bdg. 27.50x (ISBN 0-226-35708-2). U of Chicago Pr.
Iagolnitzer, D., ed. Complex Analysis, Microbial Calculus & Relativistic Quantum Theory. (Lecture Notes in Physics: Vol. 126). 502p. 1980. pap. 38.00 (ISBN 0-387-09996-4). Springer-Verlag.
International Symposium "Fifty Years Schroedinger Equation", Vienna, June 10-12, 1976. The Schroedinger Equation: Proceedings. Thirring, W. & Urban, P., eds. (Acta Physica Austriaca Supplementum: 17). (Illus.). 1977. 39.00 (ISBN 0-387-81437-X). Springer-Verlag.
Isham, C. J., et al, eds. Quantum Gravity: An Oxford Symposium. (Illus.). 1975. 54.00x (ISBN 0-19-851943-5). Oxford U Pr.
Jammer, Max. The Philosophy of Quantum Mechanics: The Interpretations of Quantum Mechanics in Historical Perspective. LC 74-13030. 536p. 1974. 47.95x (ISBN 0-471-43958-4, Pub. by Wiley-Interscience). Wiley.
Jancewicz, Bernard & Lukierski, Jerzy, eds. Quantum Theory of Particles & Fields: Birthday Volume Dedicated to Jan Lopuszanski. 292p. 32.00x (ISBN 9971-950-77-4, Pub. by World Sci Singapore). Taylor & Francis.
Jauch, Josef M. Are Quanta Real? A Galilean Dialogue. LC 72-79907. (Illus.). pap. 22.50 (ISBN 0-8357-9196-3, 2055191). Bks Demand UMI.
Joachain, C. J., ed. Quantum Collision Theory, Pts. 1 & 2. rev. ed. 710p. 1984. pap. 32.00 (ISBN 0-444-86773-2). Elsevier.
Jordan, T. F. Quantum Mechanics in Simple Matrix Form. 272p. 1985. pap. 19.95 (ISBN 0-471-81751-1). Wiley.
Jordan, Thomas F. Linear Operators for Quantum Mechanics. 144p. (Orig.). 1979. pap. text ed. 8.00 (ISBN 0-9602762-0-3). T F Jordan.
Jost, R. Local Quantum Theory. (Italian Physical Society: Course 45). 1970. 70.00 (ISBN 0-12-368845-0). Acad Pr.
Kaempffer, F. A. Concepts in Quantum Mechanics. (Pure & Applied Physics: Vol. 18). 1964. 43.50 (ISBN 0-12-394150-4). Acad Pr.
Kalckar, J. & Rudinger, E., eds. Niels Bohr, Collected Works, Vol. 6: Foundations of Quantum Physics 1, (1926-1932) 600p. 1985. 129.75 (ISBN 0-444-86712-0, North-Holland). Elsevier.
Kittel, Charles. Quantum Theory of Solids. LC 63-20633. 435p. 1963. 44.50x (ISBN 0-471-49025-3). Wiley.
--Quantum Theory of Solids. rev. ed. 1985. pap. write for info. (ISBN 0-471-82563-8). Wiley.
Koga, Toyoki. Foundations of Quantum Physics. LC 80-54503. (Illus.). 208p. (Orig.). 1981. 40.00; pap. 20.00 (ISBN 0-9606114-0-1). Wood & Jones.
Kramer, P. & Saraceno, M. Geometry of the Time-Dependent Variation Principle in Quantum Mechanics. (Lecture Notes in Physics Ser.: Vol. 140). 98p. 1981. pap. 12.00 (ISBN 0-387-10579-4). Springer-Verlag.

Van Der Waerden, B. L., ed. Sources of Quantum Mechanics. pap. text ed. 6.95 (ISBN 0-486-61881-1). Dover.

Van Vleck, John H. Theory of Electric & Magnetic Susceptibilities. (International Series of Monographs on Physics). (Illus.). 1932. pap. 42.50x (ISBN 0-19-851243-0). Oxford U Pr.

Voelkel, A. H. Fields, Particles & Currents. LC 77-23001. (Lecture Notes in Physics: Vol. 66). 1977. pap. text ed. 22.00 (ISBN 0-387-08347-2). Springer-Verlag.

Von Neumann, John. Mathematical Foundations of Quantum Mechanics. (Investigations in Physics Ser.: Vol. 2). 1955. pap. 37.50 (ISBN 0-691-08003-8). Princeton U Pr.

Wallace-Garden, R. Modern Logic & Quantum Mechanics. 178p. 1983. 35.00 (ISBN 0-9960027-3-1, Pub. by A. Hilger England). Heyden.

Weyl, Hermann. Theory of Groups & Quantum Mechanics. 1950. pap. text ed. 7.00 (ISBN 0-486-60269-9). Dover.

Wheeler, J. A. & Zurek, W. H., eds. Quantum Theory & Measurement. 1982. 78.00 (ISBN 0-691-08315-0); pap. 21.50 (ISBN 0-691-08316-9). Princeton U Pr.

Wieder, Sol. The Foundations of Quantum Theory. 1973. 27.00 (ISBN 0-12-749050-7). Acad Pr.

Wolf, Fred A. Star Wave: Mind, Consciousness, & Quantum Physics. (Illus.). 400p. 1985. 19.95 (ISBN 0-02-630860-6). Macmillan.

--Taking the Quantum Leap: The New Physics for Nonscientists. LC 80-8353. (Illus.). 272p. 1981. pap. 10.53i (ISBN 0-06-250981-0, CN-4022, HarpR). Har-Row.

Yariv, Amnon. An Introduction to Theory & Applications of Quantum Mechanics. LC 81-16007. 300p. 1982. 36.50x (ISBN 0-471-06053-4). Wiley.

Yndurain, F. J. Quantum Chromodynamics: An Introduction to the Theory of Quarks & Gluons. (Texts & Monographs in Physics). (Illus.). 227p. 1983. 33.00 (ISBN 0-387-11752-0). Springer-Verlag.

Yourgrau, Wolfgang & Mandelstam, Stanley. Variational Principles in Dynamics & Quantum Theory. 3rd ed. LC 78-73521. 1979. pap. text ed. 4.50 (ISBN 0-486-63773-5). Dover.

Yourgrau, Wolfgang & Merwe, Alwyn Van Der, eds. Perspectives in Quantum Theory. LC 78-74119. 1979. pap. text ed. 6.50 (ISBN 0-486-63778-6). Dover.

Ziman, John M. Elements of Advanced Quantum Theory. LC 69-16290. (Illus.). 1969. 42.50 (ISBN 0-521-07458-4); pap. 18.95 (ISBN 0-521-09949-8). Cambridge U Pr.

QUANTUM THEORY–HISTORY–SOURCES

Gamow, George. Thirty Years that Shook Physics: The Story of Quantum Theory. 240p. 1985. pap. 4.95 (ISBN 0-486-24895-X). Dover.

Hendry, John. The Creation of Quantum Mechanics & the Bohr-Pauli Dialogue. 1984. lib. bdg. 34.50 (ISBN 0-318-00442-9, Pub. by Reidel Holland). Kluwer Academic.

Hermann, A. & Meyenn, K. V., eds. Wolfgang Pauli: Scientific Correspondence with Bohr, Einstein, Heisenberg, Vol. I: 1919-1929. (Sources in the History of Mathematics & Physical Sciences Ser.: Vol. 2). (Illus.). 1979. 110.00 (ISBN 0-387-08962-4). Springer-Verlag.

Kuhn, Thomas S. Black-Body Theory & the Quantum Discontinuity, 1894-1912. LC 77-19022. 1978. 26.50x (ISBN 0-19-502383-8). Oxford U Pr.

Kuhn, Thomas S., et al. Sources for History of Quantum Physics: An Inventory & Report. LC 66-26634. pap. 47.50 (ISBN 0-317-29439-3, 2024291). Bks Demand UMI.

Van Der Waerden, B. L. Sources of Quantum Mechanics. 9.00 (ISBN 0-8446-3103-5). Peter Smith.

Van Der Waerden, B. L., ed. Sources of Quantum Mechanics. pap. text ed. 6.95 (ISBN 0-486-61881-1). Dover.

QUARANTINE, PLANT

see Plant Quarantine

QUARKS

Anisovich, V. V., et al. Quark Model & High Energy Collisions. 280p. 1984. 35.00x (ISBN 9971-966-68-9, Pub. by World Sci Singapore). Taylor & Francis.

Bleuler, k., ed. Quarks & Nuclear Structure: Proceedings of the Klaus Erkelenz Symposium, 3rd Held at Bad Honnef June 13-16, 1983. (Lecture Notes in Physics Ser.: Vol. 197). viii, 414p. 1984. pap. 22.00 (ISBN 0-387-12922-7). Springer Verlag.

Boal, David H. & Woloshyn, Richard M., eds. Short-Distance Phenomena in Nuclear Physics. (NATO ASI Series B, Physics: Vol. 104). 438p. 1983. 62.50x (ISBN 0-306-41494-5, Plenum Pr). Plenum Pub.

Cahn, Robert N., ed. Annihilation: New Quarks & Leptons. (The Annual Reviews Special Collections Program.). 1984. 29.95 (ISBN 0-8053-1610-8). Benjamin Cummings.

Chand, Ramesh, ed. Symmetries & Quark Models. 420p. 1970. 80.95 (ISBN 0-677-13880-6). Gordon.

Close, F. E. Introduction to Quarks & Partons. LC 78-54530. 1979. 55.00 (ISBN 0-12-175150-3); pap. 29.00, 1980 (ISBN 0-12-175152-X). Acad Pr.

Commins, Eugene D. & Bucksbaum, Philip H. Weak Interactions of Leptons & Quarks. LC 82-4452. (Illus.). 674p. 1983. 72.50 (ISBN 0-521-23092-6); pap. 29.95 (ISBN 0-521-27370-6). Cambridge U Pr.

Creutz, Michael. Quarks, Gluons & Lattices. (Monographs on Mathematical Physics). (Illus.). 175p. 1985. pap. 12.95 (ISBN 0-521-31535-2). Cambridge U Pr.

Fries, D. E. & Zeitnitz, B., eds. Quarks & Nuclear Forces. (Tracts in Modern Physics Ser.: Vol. 100). (Illus.). 223p. 1982. 38.00 (ISBN 0-387-11717-2). Springer-Verlag.

Fritzsch, Harald. Quarks: The Stuff of Matter. LC 82-72395. (Illus.). 1983. 19.00 (ISBN 0-465-06781-6). Basic.

Halzen, Francis & Martin, Alan D. Quarks & Leptones: An Introductory Course in Modern Particle Physics. LC 83-14649. 396p. 1984. text ed. 35.50x (ISBN 0-471-88741-2). Wiley.

Huang, K. Quarks, Leptons & Gauge Fields. x, 282p. 1982. 35.00x (ISBN 9971-950-03-0, Pub. by World Sci Singapore). Taylor & Francis.

Jacob, M. & Satz, H., eds. Quark Matter Formation & Heavy Ion Collisions: Proceedings of the Bielefeld Workshop, May 10-14, 1982. v, 586p. 1982. 60.00x (ISBN 9971-950-46-4, Pub. by World Sci Singapore); pap. 26.00x (ISBN 9971-950-47-2, Pub. by World Sci Singpore). Taylor & Francis.

Kajantie, K., ed. Quark Matter Eighty-Four. (Lecture Notes in Physics Ser.: Vol. 221). vi, 305p. 1985. pap. 20.50 (ISBN 0-387-15183-4). Springer-Verlag.

Levy, Maurice, et al, eds. Quarks & Leptons: Cargese 1979. LC 80-25583. (NATO ASI Series B, Physics: Vol. 61). 736p. 1981. 110.00 (ISBN 0-306-40560-1, Plenum Pr). Plenum Pub.

McCusker, Brian. The Quest for Quarks. LC 83-7459. (Illus.). 160p. 1984. 14.95 (ISBN 0-521-24850-7). Cambridge U Pr.

Morpurgo, G., ed. Quarks & Hadronic Structure. LC 76-47490. 328p. 1977. 52.50 (ISBN 0-306-38141-9, Plenum Pr). Plenum Pub.

Nambu, Y. Quarks: Frontiers in Elementary Particle Physics. 250p. 1985. 33.00x (ISBN 9971-966-65-4, Pub. by World Sci Singapore); pap. 19.00x (ISBN 9971-966-66-2, Pub. by World Sci Singapore). Taylor & Francis.

Okun, L. B. Leptons & Quarks. 362p. 1983. 70.25 (ISBN 0-444-86002-9, North-Holland). Elsevier.

--Leptons & Quarks. (Personal Library: Vol. 2). 362p. 1985. pap. 24.95 (ISBN 0-444-86924-7, North-Holland). Elsevier.

Pickering, Andrew. Construction Quarks: A Sociological History of Particle Physics. LC 84-235. (Illus.). 488p. 1984. lib. bdg. 30.00x (ISBN 0-226-66798-7). U of Chicago Pr.

Satz, H., ed. Statistical Mechanics of Quarks & Hadrons: Proceedings of the International Symposium, University of Bieleveld, France, Aug., 1980. 480p. 1981. 74.50 (ISBN 0-444-86227-7, North-Holland). Elsevier.

Urban, P., ed. Quarks & Leptons As Fundamental Particles. (Acta Physica Austriaca Supplemetum Ser.: No. 21). (Illus.). 720p. 1979. 88.00 (ISBN 0-387-81564-3). Springer-Verlag.

Weise, W. Quarks & Nuclei. (International Review of Nuclear Physics Ser.: Vol. 1). 620p. 1984. 60.00x (ISBN 9971-966-61-1, Pub. by World Sci Singapore); pap. 33.00x (ISBN 9971-966-62-X, Pub. by World Sci Singapore). Taylor & Francis.

QUARRIES AND QUARRYING

see also Blasting;

also specific materials quarried, e.g. Limestone, Sandstone

Building Material Manufactures & Quarring. 1985. 150.00x (ISBN 0-317-07194-7, Pub. by Jordan & Sons UK). State Mutual Bk.

Lester, D. Quarrying & Rockbreaking: The Operation & Maintenance of Mobile Plants. 117p. 1984. pap. text ed. 15.00x (ISBN 0-903031-80-9). Brookfield Pub Co.

Lester, David. Quarrying & Rockbreaking: The Operation & Maintenance of Mobile Processing Plants. (Illus.). 117p. 1981. 14.50x (ISBN 0-903031-80-9, Pub. by Intermediate Tech England). Intermediate Tech.

Sanders, Scott R. Stone Country. LC 84-43154. (Illus.). 256p. 1985. 24.95 (ISBN 0-253-18515-7). Ind U Pr.

Sinclair, John. Quarrying, Opencast & Alluvial Mining. (Illus.). 375p. 1969. 50.00 (ISBN 0-444-20040-1, Pub. by Elsevier Applied Sci England). Elsevier.

Surface Mining & Quarrying. 449p. (Orig.). 1983. pap. text ed. 69.95x (ISBN 0-900488-66-2). Imm North Am.

QUARTER HORSE

Denhardt, Robert M. Foundation Sires of the American Quarter Horse. LC 75-40956. 1976. 19.95 (ISBN 0-8061-1337-5). U of Okla Pr.

--The King Ranch Quarter Horses: And Something of the Ranch & the Men That Bred Them. LC 73-123340. (Illus.). 1978. Repr. of 1970 ed. 26.95 (ISBN 0-8061-0924-6). U of Okla Pr.

--Quarter Horses: A Story of Two Centuries. (Illus.). 1967. 16.95 (ISBN 0-8061-0753-7). U of Okla Pr.

--The Quarter Running Horse: America's Oldest Breed. LC 78-21381. 1979. 27.95 (ISBN 0-8061-1500-9). U of Okla Pr.

Mattson, Paul R. Fifty-One Top Quarter Horses: A Pedigree Study. 1980. pap. 9.95 (ISBN 0-686-28067-9). PRESCOB.

Nye, Nelson C. Speed & the Quarter Horse: A Payload of Sprinters. LC 73-140120. (Illus.). 1973. 17.95 (ISBN 0-87004-220-3). Caxton.

Porter, Willard. How to Enjoy Your Quarter Horse. 1974. pap. 3.00 (ISBN 0-87980-280-4). Wilshire.

QUARTIC EQUATIONS

see Equations, Quartic

QUARTZ

see also Oscillators, Crystal

Quartz Crystals: Gems of Poetry. 1969. 9.25 (ISBN 0-912314-04-4). Academy Santa Clara.

QUARTZ OSCILLATORS

see Oscillators, Crystal

QUASARS

Asimov, Isaac. Quasar, Quasar, Burning Bright. LC 77-82613. (Illus.). 1978. 7.95 (ISBN 0-385-13464-9). Doubleday.

Burbidge, Geoffrey & Burbidge, Margaret. Quasi-Stellar Objects. LC 67-17457. (Illus.). 253p. 1967. 20.95 (ISBN 0-7167-0321-1). W H Freeman.

Douglas, G., et al. Quasars & High Energy Astronomy. 504p. 1969. 144.50 (ISBN 0-677-11520-2). Gordon.

Hazard, C. & Mitton, S., eds. Active Galactic Nuclei. LC 78-67426. 1979. 49.50 (ISBN 0-521-22494-2). Cambridge U Pr.

Kaufmann, William J., III. Galaxies & Quasars. LC 79-10570. (Illus.). 226p. 1979. text ed. 21.95 (ISBN 0-7167-1133-8); pap. text ed. 10.95 (ISBN 0-7167-1134-6). W H Freeman.

Shipman, Harry L. Black Holes, Quasars, & the Universe. 2nd ed. (Illus.). 1980. 14.95 (ISBN 0-395-28499-6); text ed. 20.95 (ISBN 0-395-29302-2). HM.

QUATERNARY PERIOD

see Geology, Stratigraphic–Quaternary

QUATERNIONS

see also Ausdehnungslehre; Numbers, Complex; Vector Analysis

Hamilton, William R. Elements of Quaternions, 2 Vols. 3rd ed. Joly, Charles J., ed. LC 68-54711. 1969. Repr. of 1901 ed. Set. 65.00 (ISBN 0-8284-0219-1). Chelsea Pub.

Kyrala, A. Theoretical Physics: Applications of Vectors, Matrices, Tensors & Quaternions. LC 67-12810. (Studies in Physics & Chemistry: No. 5). pap. 93.00 (ISBN 0-317-08733-9, 2051978). Bks Demand UMI.

QUEEN BEES

see Bee Culture

QUERCUS

see Oak

QUETELET, LAMBERT ADOLPHE JACQUES, 1796-1874

Hankins, Frank H. Adolphe Quetelet As Statistician. LC 74-76680. (Columbia University. Studies in the Social Sciences: No. 84). Repr. of 1908 ed. 14.50 (ISBN 0-404-51084-1). AMS Pr.

Lottin, Joseph. Quetelet, Statisticien et Sociologue. (Research & Source Works Ser.: No. 270). 1969. Repr. of 1912 ed. 32.00 (ISBN 0-8337-2150-X). B Franklin.

QUEUING THEORY

Beckmann, Petr. Elementary Queue Theory & Telephone Traffic. 1976. 7.75 (ISBN 0-686-98072-7). Telecom Lib.

Borovkov, A. A. Asymptotic Methods in Queuing Theory. LC 83-12557. (Probability & Mathematical Statistics-Probability & Mathematical Statistics: 1-345). 276p. 1984. 47.95x (ISBN 0-471-90286-1, Pub. by Wiley-Interscience). Wiley.

--Stochastic Processes in Queueing Theory. LC 75-43242. (Applications of Math Ser.: Vol. 4). (Illus.). 1976. pap. 46.00 (ISBN 0-387-90161-2). Springer-Verlag.

Bremaud, P. Point Processes & Queues: Martingale Dynamics. (Springer Series in Statistics). (Illus.). 352p. 1981. 44.00 (ISBN 0-387-90536-7). Springer-Verlag.

Cohen, J. Single Server Queue. 2nd ed. (Applied Mathematics & Mechanics Ser.: Vol. 8). 694p. 1982. 89.50 (ISBN 0-444-85452-5, North-Holland). Elsevier.

Conolly, Brian. Lecture Notes in Queueing Systems. LC 75-7788. 176p. 1975. pap. 19.95x (ISBN 0-470-16857-9). Halsted Pr.

Cooper. Introduction to Queuing Theory. 2nd ed. 348p. 1980. 30.50 (ISBN 0-444-00379-7, North-Holland). Elsevier.

Cox, D. R. & Smith, W. L. Queues: Receptors & Recognition Series B. Incl. Vol. 13. Receptor Regulation. 59.95 (2245); Vol. 12. Purinergic Receptors. 63.00 (2142); Vol. 11. Membrane Receptors. 49.95 (2156); Vol. 10. Neurotransmitter Receptors, Part 2: Biogenic Amines. 49.95 (49.95); Vol. 9. Neurotransmitter Receptors, Part 1: Amino Acids, Peptides & Benzodiazepines. 49.95 (NO.6456); Vol. 8. Virus Receptors, Part 2: Animal Viruses. 43.00 (NO.6413); Vol. 7. Virus Receptors, Part 1: Bacterial Viruses. 43.00 (NO.6416); Vol. 6. Bacterial Adherence. 69.95 (6453); Vol. 5. Taxis & Behavior. 63.00 (NO.6452); Vol. 4. Specificity of Embryological Interactions. 49.95 (NO.6118); Vol. 3. Microbial Interactions. 49.95 (NO.6236); Vol. 2. Intercellular Junctions & Synapses. 53.00 (NO.6107); Vol. 1. The Specificity & Action of Animal, Bacterial & Plant Toxins. 63.00 (NO. 6078). Pub. by Chapman & Hall England). Methuen Inc.

Disney, R. & Ott, T., eds. Applied Probability--Computer Science: The Interface, 2 Vols. (Progress in Computer Science Ser.). 1982. text ed. 39.95x ea. Vol. 2, 532pp (ISBN 0-8176-3067-8). Vol. 3, 514pp (ISBN 0-8176-3093-7). Birkhauser.

Everling, W. Exercises in Computer Systems Analysis. (Lecture Notes in Computer Science: Vol. 35). viii, 184p. 1975. pap. 15.00 (ISBN 0-387-07401-5). Springer-Verlag.

Franken, Peter, et al. Queues & Point Processes. (Probability & Mathematical Statistics Ser.). 208p. 1982. 32.95x (ISBN 0-471-10074-9, Pub. by Wiley-Interscience). Wiley.

Giffen, Walter C. Queueing: Basic Theory & Application. LC 76-44996. (Grid Industrial Engineering Ser.). Repr. of 1978 ed. 92.50 (ISBN 0-8357-9144-0, 2015244). Bks Demand UMI.

Gross, D. & Harris, C. M. Fundamentals of Queueing Theory. 2nd ed. (Probability & Mathematical Statistics Ser.). 640p. 1985. 42.95 (ISBN 0-471-89067-7). Wiley.

Gross, Donald & Harris, Carl M. Fundamentals of Queueing Theory. (Wiley Series in Probability & Mathematical Statistics-Applied Probability & Statistics Section). 556p. 1974. 45.95x (ISBN 0-471-32812-X). Wiley.

Iglehart, D. L. & Shedler, G. S. Regenerative Simulation of Response Times in Network of Queues. (Lecture Notes in Control & Information Sciences: Vol. 26). 204p. 1980. pap. 19.00 (ISBN 0-387-09942-5). Springer-Verlag.

Jaiswal, N. K. Priority Queues. (Mathematics in Science & Engineering Ser.: Vol. 50). 1968. 65.00 (ISBN 0-12-380050-1). Acad Pr.

Jleinrock, Leonard & Gail, Richard. Queuing Systems, Solutions Manual: Theory, No. 1. LC 82-80907. 226p. (Orig.). 1982. pap. text ed. 19.50 (ISBN 0-942948-00-9). Tech Trans Inst.

Kleinrock, Leonard. Queueing Systems, 2 vols. Incl. Vol. 1. Theory. 417p. 41.50x (ISBN 0-471-49110-1); Vol. 2. Computer Applications. 549p. 45.95x (ISBN 0-471-49111-X). LC 44-9846. 417p. 1975-76 (Pub. by Wiley-Interscience). Wiley.

Klimow, Gennadi P. & Konig, Dieter. Bedienungsprozesse. (Mathematische Reihe: No. 68). (Ger., Illus.). 256p. 1976. 43.95x (ISBN 0-8176-1049-9). Birkhauser.

Nair, Sreekantan S. On Certain Priority Queues. LC 78-132638. 171p. 1969. 22.00 (ISBN 0-403-04521-5). Scholarly.

Newell, G. F. Approximate Behavior of Tendem Queues. (Lecture Notes in Economics & Mathematical Systems: Vol. 171). 1979. pap. 24.00 (ISBN 0-387-09552-7). Springer-Verlag.

--The M-M Service System with Ranked Servers in Heavy Traffic. (Lecture Notes in Economics & Mathematical Systems Ser.: Vol. 231). xi, 126p. 1984. 11.00 (ISBN 0-387-13377-1). Springer-Verlag.

Srivastava, H. M. & Kashyap, B. R. Special Functions in Queuing Theory: & Related Stochastic Processes. LC 81-17683. 1982. 42.50 (ISBN 0-12-660650-1). Acad Pr.

Stoyan, Dietrich & Daley, Daryl J., eds. Comparison Methods for Queues & Other Stochastic Models. LC 81-16365. (Probability & Mathematical Statistics Applied Section Ser.). 217p. 1983. text ed. 39.95x (ISBN 0-471-10122-2, Pub. by Wiley-Interscience). Wiley.

Takacs, Lajos. Introduction to the Theory of Queues. LC 82-973. (University Texts in the Mathematical Sciences). x, 268p. 1982. Repr. of 1962 ed. lib. bdg. 37.50x (ISBN 0-313-23357-8, TAIN). Greenwood.

Van Doorn, E. A. Stochastic Monotonicity & Queuing Applications of Birth-Death Processes. (Lecture Notes in Statistics Ser.: Vol. 4). 118p. 1981. pap. 12.00 (ISBN 0-387-90547-2). Springer-Verlag.

White, John A., et al. Analysis of Queueing Systems. (Industrial Engineering & Operations Research Ser.). 1975. 69.50 (ISBN 0-12-746950-8). Acad Pr.

QUEUING THEORY–TABLES

Hillier, F. S., et al. Queueing Tables & Graphs. (Publications in Operations Research Ser.: Vol. 3). 232p. 1981. 43.25 (ISBN 0-444-00582-X, North-Holland). Elsevier.

QUICKSILVER

see Mercury

QUINONE

Pedersen, Jens A., ed. HB of EPR Spectra from Natural & Synthetic Quinones & Quinols. 392p. 1985. 70.00 (ISBN 0-8493-2955-8). CRC Pr.

Trumpower, Bernard L., ed. Function of Quinones in Energy Conserving Systems. 1982. 74.50 (ISBN 0-12-701280-X). Acad Pr.

QUIPU

see also Abacus

Ascher, Marcia & Ascher, Robert. Code of the Quipu: A Study of Media, Mathematics, & Culture. (Illus.). 176p. 1981. pap. 8.95 (ISBN 0-472-06325-1). U of Mich Pr.

R

RABBITS

see also Hares

Arrington, L. R. & Kelley, Kathleen C. Domestic Rabbit Biology & Production. LC 76-10173. 1976. 10.00 (ISBN 0-8130-0537-X). U Presses Fla.

Baker, Rollin H. A New Cottontail (Sylvilagus Floridanus) from Northeastern Mexico. (Museum Ser.: Vol. 7, No. 13). 4p. 1955. pap. 1.25 (ISBN 0-317-04952-6). U of KS Mus Nat Hist.

Bennett, Bob. Raising Rabbits Successfully. (Illus.). 192p. (Orig.). 1984. pap. 8.95 (ISBN 0-913589-03-9). Williamson Pub Co.

--The T.F.H. Book of Pet Rabbits. (Illus.). 80p. 1982. 6.95 (ISBN 0-87666-815-5, HP-014). TFH Pubns.

Bennett, Robert. Raising Rabbits the Modern Way. LC 75-31601. (Illus.). 156p. 1975. pap. 7.95 (ISBN 0-88266-067-5). Garden Way Pub.

Brown, Meg. Exhibition & Pet Rabbits. 1981. 14.00 (ISBN 0-904558-24-X). Saiga.

--Exhibition & Pet Rabbits. 2nd ed. (Illus.). 240p. 1982. 15.50 (ISBN 0-86230-050-9). Triplegate.

Casady, R. B. & Jawin, P. B. Commerical Rabbit Raising. (Shorey Lost Arts Ser.). (Illus.). 69p. pap. 3.95 (ISBN 0-8466-6054-7, U54). Shorey.

Committee On Animal Nutrition. Nutrient Requirements of Rabbits. rev. 7th ed. LC 77-6318. 1977. pap. 5.95 (ISBN 0-309-02607-5). Natl Acad Pr.

Craigie, E. Horne. Laboratory Guide to the Anatomy of the Rabbit. 2nd ed. LC 70-358625. (Illus.). 1966. pap. 8.50x (ISBN 0-8020-2038-0). U of Toronto Pr.

Cumpsty, Denise. Book of the Netherland Dwarf. 186p. 1984. 13.50 (ISBN 0-904558-45-2). Saiga.

Faivre, Milton I. How to Raise Rabbits for Fun & Profit. LC 73-81277. 244p. 1973. 21.95x (ISBN 0-911012-47-8); pap. 11.95 (ISBN 0-88229-493-8). Nelson-Hall.

Hackenbroch, M. H. Die Wirkung der Dosierten Distraktion auf das Ellenbogengelenk des Kaninchens. (Acta Anatomica: Vol. 96, Suppl. 63-1). (Illus.). 1977. 17.50 (ISBN 3-8055-2643-1). S Karger.

Hall, Raymond E. & Kelson, Keith R. Comments on the Taxonomy & Geographic Distribution of Some North American Rabbits. (Museum Ser.: Vol. 5, No. 5). 10p. 1951. pap. 1.25 (ISBN 0-317-05064-8). U of KS Mus Nat Hist.

Hirschhorn, Howard. All about Rabbits. (Illus.). 96p. (Orig.). 1974. 4.95 (ISBN 0-87666-760-4, M-543). TFH Pubns.

Janes, Donald W. Home Ranges & Movements of the Eastern Cottontail in Kansas. (Museum Ser.: Vol. 10, No.7). 20p. 1959. pap. 1.25 (ISBN 0-317-04829-5). U of KS Mus Nat Hist.

Kaissling, B. & Kriz, W. Structural Analysis of the Rabbit Kidney. (Advances in Anatomy, Embryology & Cell Biology: Vol. 56). (Illus.). 1979. pap. 33.00 (ISBN 0-387-09145-9). Springer-Verlag.

Kaplan, Harold M. & Timmons, Edward H. The Rabbit: A Model for the Principles of Mammalian Physiology & Surgery. LC 78-67878. 1979. 29.50 (ISBN 0-12-397450-X). Acad Pr.

Lockley, R. M. The Private Life of the Rabbit. (Illus.). 1975. pap. 3.95 (ISBN 0-380-00447-X, 38224). Avon.

Lord, Rexford Jr. The Cottontail Rabbit in Illinois. LC 63-7977. (Illus.). 112p. 1963. 5.00x (ISBN 0-8093-0080-X). S Ill U Pr.

Paradise, Paul R. Rabbits. (Illus.). 1979. 4.95 (ISBN 0-87666-924-0, KW-021). TFH Pubns.

Sawin, Paul. Rabbit Raising. (Illus.). 83p. pap. 2.00 (ISBN 0-936622-18-0). A R Harding Pub.

Smith, Guy N. Ratting & Rabbiting for Amateur Gamekeepers. 196p. 1979. 13.50 (ISBN 0-904558-64-9). Saiga.

Thear, Katie. Practical Rabbit Keeping. (Concorde Country Bks.). (Illus.). 95p. 1981. pap. 7.95x (ISBN 0-8464-1214-4). Beekman Pubs.

Urban, Ivan & Philippe, Richard. A Stereotaxic Atlas of the New Zealand Rabbit's Brain. (Illus.). 92p. 1972. photocopy ed. 12.75x (ISBN 0-398-02431-6). C C Thomas.

Weisbroth, Stephen H., et al, eds. The Biology of the Laboratory Rabbit. 1974. 85.00 (ISBN 0-12-742150-5). Acad Pr.

Wingerd, Bruce D. Human Anatomy & Rabbit Dissection. LC 83-24395. (Illus.). 144p. 1985. pap. text ed. 18.95x (ISBN 0-8018-3209-8). Johns Hopkins.

RACCOONS

Aal, Katharyn M. The Raccoon Book. LC 82-7831. (Illus.). 88p. 1982. pap. 5.95 (ISBN 0-935526-05-6). McBooks Pr.

RACE

Benedict, Ruth. Race: Science & Politics. 206p. 1982. Repr. of 1950 ed. lib. bdg. 27.50 (ISBN 0-313-23597-X, BENR). Greenwood.

Coon, Carleton S., et al. Races: A Study of the Problems of Race Formation in Man. LC 80-24479. (American Lecture Ser.: No. 77). (Illus.). xiv, 153p. 1981. Repr. of 1950 ed. lib. bdg. 19.75x (ISBN 0-313-22878-7, CORA). Greenwood.

George, Wesley C. The Biology of the Race Problem. 72p. 1979. pap. 2.00x (ISBN 0-911038-76-0, 132). Noontide.

Gobineau, A. de. The Moral & Intellectual Diversity of Races. Rosenberg, Charles, ed. LC 83-48534. (The History of Hereditarian Thought Ser.). 512p. 1984. Repr. of 1856 ed. lib. bdg. 60.00 (ISBN 0-317-14533-9). Garland Pub.

Huntington, Ellsworth. The Character of Races: Influenced by Physical Environment, Natural Selection & Historical Development. Grob, Gerald, ed. LC 76-46082. (Anti-Movements in America). 1977. lib. bdg. 31.00x (ISBN 0-405-09955-X). Ayer Co Pubs.

King, James C. The Biology of Race. rev. ed. LC 81-1345. (Illus.). 220p. 1982. 18.95 (ISBN 0-520-04223-9); pap. 6.95 (ISBN 0-520-04224-7, CAL 539). U of Cal Pr.

Molnar, Stephen. Human Variation: Races, Types & Ethnic Groups. 2nd ed. (Illus.). 304p. 1983. pap. 20.95 (ISBN 0-13-447664-6). P-H.

Osborne, Richard H., ed. The Biological & Social Meaning of Race. LC 75-150652. (Psychology Ser). (Illus.). 182p. 1971. text ed. 20.95x (ISBN 0-7167-0935-X). W H Freeman.

RACING AUTOMOBILES

see Automobiles, Racing

RACING PIGEONS

see Pigeons

RADAR

see also Pulse Techniques (Electronics); Radar Meteorology; Shielding (Electricity)

Bachman, Christian G. Radar Targets. LC 81-48003. 256p. 1982. 31.50x (ISBN 0-669-05232-9). Lexington Bks.

Bagshaw, W. Worked Examples in Relative Radar Plotting. 91p. 1979. 15.00x (ISBN 0-85174-330-7). Sheridan.

Barton, David K. Monopulse Radar. LC 74-82597. (Radars: Vol. 1). pap. 85.80 (ISBN 0-317-27665-4, 2025059). Bks Demand UMI.

--Radar Resolution & Multipath Effects. LC 74-82597. (Radars Ser.: Vol. 4). pap. 94.00 (ISBN 0-317-27647-6, 2025061). Bks Demand UMI.

--Radar Systems Analysis. LC 76-45811. (Artech Radar Library). 1976. Repr. of 1964 ed. 48.00x (ISBN 0-89006-043-6). Artech Hse.

--Radars, Vol. 7: CW & Doppler Radar. LC 78-24055. (Artech Radar Library). 1979. pap. 25.00 (ISBN 0-89006-075-4). Artech Hse.

Barton, David K. & Ward, Harold R. Handbook of Radar Measurement. 425p. 1984. text ed. 55.00 (ISBN 0-89006-155-6). Artech Hse.

Barton, David K., ed. Radars: Radar Clutter, Vol. 5. LC 74-82597. (Artech Radar Library). 1975. pap. 25.00 (ISBN 0-89006-034-7). Artech Hse.

--Radars: The Radar Equation, Vol. 2. 2nd ed. LC 74-82597. (Artech Radar Library). 1975. pap. 25.00 (ISBN 0-89006-031-2). Artech Hse.

Basalov, F. A. & Ostrovityanov, R. V. Statistical Theory of Extended Radar Targets. Barton, William F. & Barton, David K., trs. from Rus. Orig. Title: Statisticheskaya Teoriya Radiolokatsii Protyazhennyz Tselei. 200p. 1984. text ed. 65.00 (ISBN 0-89006-144-0). Artech Hse.

Battan, Louis J. Radar Observation of the Atmosphere. rev. ed. (Illus.). 1981. pap. 18.00x (ISBN 0-226-03921-8). U of Chicago Pr.

Berkowitz, Raymond S. Modern Radar: Analysis, Evaluation & System Design. LC 65-21446. pap. 160.00 (ISBN 0-317-09180-8, 2017411). Bks Demand UMI.

Blake, Lamont V. Radar Range-Performance Analysis. LC 76-16318. (Illus.). 480p. 1980. 43.00x (ISBN 0-669-00781-1). Lexington Bks.

Bole, A. G. & Jones, K. D. Automatic Radar Plotting Aids Manual. LC 81-71212. (Illus.). 150p. 1982. text ed. 16.00x (ISBN 0-87033-285-6). Cornell Maritime.

Brookner, Eli, ed. Radar Technology. LC 77-13055. (Artech Radar Library). (Illus.). 1977. 54.00x (ISBN 0-89006-021-5). Artech Hse.

Burger, William. Radar Observer's Handbook. 7th ed. 350p. 1983. pap. 35.00x (ISBN 0-85174-443-5). Sheridan.

Carpentier, Michael H. Radars-New Concepts. rev. ed. LC 66-27987. 282p. 1968. 80.95 (ISBN 0-677-01760-X). Gordon.

Clarke, J. Advances in Radar Techniques. (Electromagnetic Waves Ser.: No. 20). 1985. 72.00 (ISBN 0-86341-021-9). Inst Electrical.

Cook, Charles E. & Bernfeld, Marvin. Radar Signals: An Introduction to Theory & Application. (Electrical Science Ser.). 1967. 85.00 (ISBN 0-12-186750-1). Acad Pr.

Crispin, J. W., Jr. & Siegel, K. M., eds. Methods of Radar Cross Section Analysis. (Electrical Science Ser). 1968. 90.00 (ISBN 0-12-197750-1). Acad Pr.

Currie, Nicholas C. Techniques of Radar Reflectivity Measurement. LC 83-72777. (Radar Ser.). (Illus.). 500p. 1983. 72.00 (ISBN 0-89006-131-9). Artech Hse.

DiFranco, J. V. & Rubin, W. L. Radar Detection. (Illus.). 654p. 1980. Repr. of 1968 ed. text ed. 61.00 (ISBN 0-89006-092-4). Artech Hse.

Ewell, George W. Radar Transmitters: Systems, Modulators & Devices. (Illus.). 300p. 1982. 32.50 (ISBN 0-07-019843-8). McGraw.

Gerlach, Albert A. Theory & Applications of Statistical Wave-Period Processing, 3 Vols. 1434p. 1970. 352.50 (ISBN 0-677-02510-6). Gordon.

Haykin, S. S., ed. Detection & Estimation: Applications to Radar. LC 75-33340. (Benchmark Papers in Electrical Engineering & Computer Science Ser.: Vol. 13). 1976. 65.00 (ISBN 0-12-786648-5). Acad Pr.

Hovanessian, S. A. Radar Detection & Tracking Systems. LC 73-81238. 1973. 30.00 (ISBN 0-89006-018-5). Artech Hse.

Hovanessian, Shahan A. Radar System Design & Analysis. 400p. 1984. text ed. 66.00 (ISBN 0-89006-147-5). Artech Hse.

Hovanessian, Shahen A. Introduction to Synthetic Array & Imaging Radar. LC 79-27922. (Illus.). 1980. 43.00x (ISBN 0-89006-082-7). Artech Hse.

Johnston, Stephen L. Radar Electronic Counter-Countermeasures. LC 85-4298. 560p. 1985. pap. 47.50 (ISBN 0-89874-850-X). Krieger.

Johnston, Stephen L., ed. Millimeter Wave Radar. (Illus.). 673p. 1980. pap. 54.00 (ISBN 0-89006-095-9). Artech Hse.

--Radar Electronic Counter-Countermeasures. LC 79-18873. (Artech Radar Library Ser.). pap. 139.50 (ISBN 0-317-27643-3, 2025062). Bks Demand UMI.

Kahriles, Peter J. Electronic Scanning Radar Systems (ESRS) Design Handbook. LC 75-43051. (Illus.). pap. 99.00 (ISBN 0-317-08762-2, 2010500). Bks Demand UMI.

Kassam, S. A. & Thomas, J. B., eds. Nonparametric Detection: Theory & Applications. LC 79-22557. (Benchmark Papers in Electrical Engineering & Computer Science Ser.: Vol. 23). 349p. 1980. 57.95 (ISBN 0-87933-359-6). Van Nos Reinhold.

Knott, E. F., et al. Radar Cross Section. 1985. text ed. 60.00 (ISBN 0-89006-174-2). Artech Hse.

Kock, Winton E. Radar, Sonar & Holography: An Introduction. 1973. 28.00 (ISBN 0-12-417450-7). Acad Pr.

Kovaly, John J., ed. Synthetic Aperture Radar. LC 76-42314. (Artech Radar Library). 1976. 42.00 (ISBN 0-89006-056-8). Artech Hse.

Long, Maurice W. Radar Reflectivity of Land & Sea. 2nd ed. LC 75-13435. (Radar Ser.). (Illus.). 400p. 1983. Repr. of 1975 ed. 50.00 (ISBN 0-89006-130-0). Artech Hse.

Maksimov, M. V., et al. Radar Anti-Jamming Techniques. LC 79-22562. (Artech Radar Library). Orig. Title: Zaschita Ot Radiopomenkh. 1979. 39.00 (ISBN 0-89006-078-9). Artech Hse.

Meeks, M. Littleton. Radar Propagation at Low Altitudes. (Artech Radar Library). (Illus.). 250p. 1982. 32.00 (ISBN 0-89006-118-1). Artech Hse.

Mensa, Dean L. High Resolution Radar Imaging. LC 81-71048. (Radar Library). (Illus.). 200p. 1982. 44.00 (ISBN 0-89006-109-2). Artech Hse.

Meyer, Daniel P. & Mayer, Herbert A. Radar Target Detection: Handbook of Theory & Practice. (Electrical Science Ser.). 1973. 76.50 (ISBN 0-12-492850-1). Acad Pr.

Military Groundbased & Shipbased Radar Market. 371p. 1984. 1475.00 (ISBN 0-86621-247-7, A1318). Frost & Sullivan.

Military Intrusion Detection Market (U.S.) 1985. write for info. (ISBN 0-86621-364-3, A1448). Frost & Sullivan.

Mitchell, Richard L. Radar Signal Simulation. LC 75-31380. (Artech Radar Library Ser.). pap. 56.00 (ISBN 0-317-27681-6, 2025054). Bks Demand UMI.

Musha, T., et al, eds. Noise & Clutter Rejection in Radars & Imaging Sensors, 1984: Proceedings of the 1984 International Symposium Held in Tokyo, Japan, October 22-24, 1984. 750p. 1985. 125.00 (ISBN 0-444-87674-X, North-Holland). Elsevier.

Nathanson, Fred E. Radar Design Principles: Signal Processing & the Environment. (Illus.). 1969. 65.95 (ISBN 0-07-046047-7). McGraw.

Nichols, Robert E., Jr. Police Radar: A Guide to Basic Understanding. 76p. 1982. 13.75x (ISBN 0-398-04573-9). C C Thomas.

Ostroff, E. D., et al. Solid State Radar Transmitters. 1985. text ed. 50.00 (ISBN 0-89006-169-6). Artech Hse.

Page, Robert M. The Origin of Radar. LC 78-25844. (Illus.). 1979. Repr. of 1962 ed. lib. bdg. 24.75x (ISBN 0-313-20781-X, PAOR). Greenwood.

Radar Cross Section Lectures. (Illus.). 130p. 1984. 19.50 (ISBN 0-317-36853-2). AIAA.

Radar Observer Manual. 5th ed. (Illus.). 130p. 1983. pap. text ed. 14.55 (ISBN 0-934114-42-0, BK-112). Marine Educ.

Radar 82. (IEE Conference Publication Ser.: No. 216). 512p. 1982. pap. 116.00 (ISBN 0-85296-268-1, IC216). Inst Elect Eng.

Rasmakhnin, M. Radar Made Easy. 136p. 1977. pap. 1.95 (ISBN 0-8285-0832-1, Pub. by Mir Pubs USSR). Imported Pubns.

Rhodes, Donald. Introduction to Monopulse Radar. (Illus.). 199p. 1980. Repr. of 1959 ed. 22.00 (ISBN 0-89006-091-6). Artech Hse.

Rihaczek, August W. Principles of High-Resolution Radar. 505p. 1985. Repr. of 1977 ed. 35.95 (ISBN 0-932146-11-2). Peninsula CA.

Ruck, George T., et al. Radar Cross Section Handbook. LC 68-26774. 949p. 1970. 115.00x (ISBN 0-306-30343-4, Plenum Pr). Plenum Pub.

Schleher, D. C., ed. MTI Radars. (Artech Radar Librry). (Illus.). 1978. 30.00x (ISBN 0-89006-060-6). Artech Hse.

Sites, Michael J. Coded Frequency Shift Keyed Sequences with Applications to Low Data Rate Communication & Radar. LC 75-136728. 107p. 1969. 19.00 (ISBN 0-403-04540-1). Scholarly.

Skolnik, Merrill I. Introduction to Radar Systems. 2nd ed. (Electrical Engineering Ser.). (Illus.). 1980. text ed. 47.95x (ISBN 0-07-057909-1). McGraw.

--Radar Handbook. 1970. 89.50 (ISBN 0-07-057908-3). McGraw.

Toomay, John C. Radar Principles for the Non-Specialist. (Engineering Ser.). 173p. 1982. 23.00 (ISBN 0-534-97943-2). Lifetime Learn.

Tzannes, Nicolaos S. Communication & Radar Systems. (Illus.). 464p. 1985. text ed. 38.95 (ISBN 0-13-153545-5). P-H.

Van Wyck, Samuel M. & Carpenter, Max H. The Radar Book. (Illus.). x, 96p. (Orig.). 1984. pap. text ed. 17.50 (ISBN 0-87033-326-7). Cornell Maritime.

Veley. Semiconductors & Electronic Communications Made Easy. (Illus.). 322p. 1982. o.p 15.95 (ISBN 0-8306-0052-3); pap. 8.95 (ISBN 0-8306-1435-4). TAB Bks.

Wiley, Richard G. Electronic Intelligence: The Analysis of Radar Signals. (Artech House Radar Library). (Illus.). 234p. 1982. 50.00 (ISBN 0-89006-124-6). Artech Hse.

--Electronic Intelligence: The Interception of Radar Signals. 250p. 1985. text ed. 55.00 (ISBN 0-89006-138-6). Artech Hse.

Woodward, P. M. Information & Probability Theory, with Applications to Radar. LC 80-70175. (Artech Radar Library). (Illus.). 128p. 1980. Repr. of 1953 ed. 22.00 (ISBN 0-89006-103-3). Artech Hse.

RADAR–ANTENNAS

see also Radar Telescope

Hansen, R. C., ed. Significant Phased Array Papers. LC 73-81240. (Artech Radar Library). (Illus.). 288p. 1973. pap. 13.00 (ISBN 0-89006-019-3). Artech Hse.

Law, Preston. Shipboard Antennas. (Artech Radar Library). (Illus.). 400p. 1982. 61.00 (ISBN 0-89006-123-8). Artech Hse.

Oliner, Arthur A. & Knittel, George H., eds. Phased Array Antennas. LC 73-189392. (Artech Radar Library). (Illus.). 380p. 1972. 13.00 (ISBN 0-89006-010-X). Artech Hse.

RADAR–DATA PROCESSING

Haykin, S., ed. Array Processing. LC 79-11772. (Benchmark Papers in Electrical Engineering & Computer Science: Vol. 22). 362p. 1979. 59.50 (ISBN 0-87933-351-0). Van Nos Reinhold.

Schleher, D. Curtis, ed. Automatic Detection & Radar Data Processing. LC 80-17165. (Artech Radar Library Ser.). pap. 160.00 (ISBN 0-317-27639-5, 2025063). Bks Demand UMI.

Skillman, William. Radar Calculations Using the TI-59 Programmable Calculator. (Illus.). 350p. 1983. 53.00 (ISBN 0-89006-112-2). Artech Hse.

Skillman, William. A. Radar Calculations Using Personal Computers. 150p. 1984. text ed. 50.00 (ISBN 0-89006-141-6); write for info. Artech Hse.

RADAR IN NAVIGATION

AGARD-NATO. Radar Techniques for Detection Tracking & Navigation. (Agardographs Ser.: No. 100). (Illus.). 616p. 1966. 164.25 (ISBN 0-677-11030-8). Gordon.

Bagshaw, W. Worked Examples in Relative Radar Plotting. 1981. 45.00x (ISBN 0-85174-330-7, Pub. by Brown, Son & Ferguson). State Mutual Bk.

Burger, William. Radar Observer's Handbook. 1981. 60.00x (ISBN 0-85174-314-5, Pub. by Nautical England). State Mutual Bk.

Carpenter, Max H. & Waldo, Wayne M. Real Time Method of Radar Plotting. (Illus.). 48p. 1975. pap. 10.50x (ISBN 0-87033-204-X). Cornell Maritime.

Friedman, Norman. Naval Radar. 240p. 1981. 75.00x (ISBN 0-85177-238-2, Pub. by Conway Maritime England). State Mutual Bk.

Law, Preston. Shipboard Antennas. (Artech Radar Library). (Illus.). 400p. 1982. 61.00 (ISBN 0-89006-123-8). Artech Hse.

Quilter, E. S. Searoom Handbook with Radar Anti-Collision Tables. LC 76-240. 177p. 1976. spiral 15.00x (ISBN 0-87033-221-X). Cornell Maritime.

Radar Observer Manual. 5th ed. (Illus.). 130p. 1983. pap. text ed. 14.55 (ISBN 0-934114-42-0, BK-112). Marine Educ.

Sonnenberg, G. J. Radar & Electronic Navigation. 5th ed. LC 77-30476. 1978. 57.50 (ISBN 0-408-00272-7). Butterworth.

Wilkes, Kenneth. Radio & Radar in Sail & Power Boats. 120p. 1980. 15.00x (ISBN 0-245-53191-2, Pub. by Nautical England). State Mutual Bk.

Wylie, F. J. The Use of Radar at Sea. 5th ed. LC 76-12012. 1978. 19.95 (ISBN 0-87021-965-0). Naval Inst Pr.

RADAR METEOROLOGY

NATO Advanced Study Institute, Goslar, 1975. Atmospheric Effects on Radar Target Identification & Imaging: Proceedings. Jeske, H., ed. (Mathematical & Physical Sciences Ser: No. 27). 1976. lib. bdg. 53.00 (ISBN 90-277-0769-3, Pub. by Reidel Holland). Kluwer Academic.

Rishbeth, H., ed. EISCAT Science: Results from the First Year's Operation of the European Incoherent Scatter Radar: Papers from the EISCAT Workshop, Aussois, France, 5-8 September 1983. 184p. 1984. pap. 66.00 (ISBN 0-08-031440-6). Pergamon.

RADAR TELESCOPE

Mar, James W., ed. Structures Technology for Large Radio & Radar Telescope Systems. 1969. 47.50x (ISBN 0-262-13046-7). MIT Pr.

RADIAL SAWS

Scharff, Robert. Getting the Most Out of Your Radial Arm Saw. 1981. 9.95 (ISBN 0-8359-2457-2). Reston.

RADIATA

see Coelenterata; Echinodermata; Polyzoa

RADIATION

see also Beta Rays; Bremsstrahlung; Collisions (Nuclear Physics); Cosmic Rays; Doppler Effect; Electromagnetic Waves; Electronic Apparatus and Appliances, Effect of Radiation on; Extraterrestrial Radiation; Food, Effect of Radiation on; Gamma Rays; Heat–Radiation and Absorption; Insects, Effect of Radiation on; Invariant Imbedding; Irradiation; Light; Luminescence; Moessbauer Effect; Polarization (Nuclear Physics); Quantum Electrodynamics; Quantum Theory; Radiation Sterilization; Radiative Transfer; Radioactivity; Radiology; Radium; Scattering (Physics); Shielding (Radiation); Sound; Spectrum Analysis; Transport Theory; Van Allen Radiation Belts; X-Rays

Aberg, T., et al. Corpuscles & Radiation in Matter I. (Encyclopedia of Physics: Vol. 31). (Illus.). 670p. 1982. 131.20 (ISBN 0-387-11313-4). Springer-Verlag.

Advances in Physical & Biological Radiation Detectors. (Proceedings Ser.). (Illus.). 742p. (Orig.). 1972. pap. 59.25 (ISBN 92-0-020171-7, ISP269, IAEA). Unipub.

Anderson. Absorption of Ionizing Radiation. (Illus.). 448p. 1984. text ed. 49.50 (ISBN 0-8391-1821-X, 19860). Univ Park.

Atomic Industrial Forum Staff. Radiation Education Notebook. (Public Affairs & Information Program: General). 1983. 15.00 (ISBN 0-318-02249-4). Atomic Indus Forum.

--Radiation Issues for the Nuclear Industry: Set of Papers from AIF Conference on Radiation. (Technical & Economic Reports: Radiation Protection & Environmental Considerations). 1982. 150.00 (ISBN 0-318-02244-3). Atomic Indus Forum.

Bartone, John C., II. Microwaves & Radiation: Medical Analysis Index with Research Bibliography. LC 85-47580. 150p. 1985. 29.95 (ISBN 0-88164-334-3); pap. 21.95 (ISBN 0-88164-335-1). ABBE Pubs Assn.

Barut, A. O., ed. Foundations of Radiation Theory & Quantum Electrodynamics. LC 79-25715. (Illus.). 230p. 1980. 35.00x (ISBN 0-306-40277-7, Plenum Pr). Plenum Pub.

Basov, N. G., ed. Synchrotron Radiation. LC 76-54915. (P. N. Lebedev Physics Institute Ser.: Vol. 80). (Illus.). 224p. 1976. 65.00 (ISBN 0-306-10932-8, Consultants). Plenum Pub.

Biological Effects of Low-Level Radiation: Proceedings of a Symposium, Venice, 11-15 April 1983, IAEA & WHO. 685p. 1983. pap. 107.25 (ISBN 92-0-010183-6, ISP646, IAEA). Unipub.

Bryant, T. H. E. & Lovell, J. MCQs in Radiological Physics. LC 82-4478. 135p. 1983. pap. text ed. 11.00 (ISBN 0-443-02225-9). Churchill.

Clemmensen, Jane. Nonionizing Radiation: A Case for Federal Standards. (Illus.). 1984. pap. 7.50 (ISBN 0-911302-51-4). San Francisco Pr.

Crile, George. The Phenomena of Life: A Radio-Electric Interpretation. Rowland, Amy, ed. (Illus.). 379p. 1985. Repr. of 1936 ed. lib. bdg. 50.00 (ISBN 0-89987-193-3). Darby Bks.

Dereniak, E. L. & Crowe, D. G. Optical Radiation Detectors. LC 84-7356. (Pure & Applied Optics Ser. (1-349)). 300p. 1984. text ed. 42.50x (ISBN 0-471-89797-3, Pub. by Wiley-Interscience). Wiley.

Duplan, J. F. & Chapiro, A., eds. Advances in Radiation Research: Physics & Chemistry, 2 vols, Pt. 1. LC 72-92724. 1973. Set, 668p. 134.25 (ISBN 0-677-15780-0); Vol. 1, 360p. 79.75 (ISBN 0-677-30640-7); Vol. 2, 308p. 69.50 (ISBN 0-677-30650-4). Gordon.

Ebert, M. & Howard, A., eds. Current Topics in Radiation Research, Vol. 11. 1979. 85.00 (ISBN 0-444-85183-6, North Holland). Elsevier.

--Current Topics in Radiation Research, Vol. 13. 1978. 55.50 (ISBN 0-444-85164-X, North-Holland). Elsevier.

Eckert, Martin D. & Bramesco, Norton J. Radiation: All You Need to Know to Stop Worrying...or Start. LC 80-6137. (Illus.). 256p. (Orig.). 1981. pap. 4.95 (ISBN 0-394-74650-3, V-650, Vin). Random.

Fontana, Peter. Atomic Radiative Processes. (Pure & Applied Physics Ser.). 1982. 35.00 (ISBN 0-12-262020-8). Acad Pr.

Gaillard, A. W. & Ritter, W. Tutorials in ERP Research: Endogenous Components. (Advances in Psychology: Vol. 10). 448p. 1983. 59.75 (ISBN 0-444-86551-9, North-Holland). Elsevier.

Gesell, Thomas F., et al, eds. Natural Radiation Environment III: Proceedings, 2 vols. LC 80-607130. (DOE Symposium Ser.). 1789p. 1980. Set. pap. 52.75 (ISBN 0-87079-129-X, CONF-780422); microfiche 4.50 (ISBN 0-87079-458-2, CONF-780422). DOE.

Gloyna, E. F. & Ledbetter, J. O. Principles of Radiological Health. (Environmental Health Engineering Textbk Ser: Vol. 1). 1969. 34.25 (ISBN 0-8247-1250-1). Dekker.

Gusev, N. G. & Dimitriev, P. P. Quantum Radiation of Radioactive Nuclides. new ed. 1979. text ed. 165.00 (ISBN 0-08-023058-X). Pergamon.

Hall, Eric J. Radiation & Life. 1984. 19.50 (ISBN 0-08-028819-7). Pergamon.

Handling of Radiation Accidents. Incl. Handling of Radiation Accidents: 1977. (Proceedings Ser.: No. 2). (Illus.). 593p. 1978. pap. 59.25 (ISBN 92-0-020077-X, ISP463, IAEA). (Proceedings Ser.). (Eng., Fr & Rus., Illus.). 710p. (Orig.). 1969. pap. 53.75 (ISBN 92-0-020269-1, ISP229, IAEA). Unipub.

Harm, Walter. Biological Effects of Ultraviolet Radiation. LC 77-88677. (IUPAB Biophysics Ser.: No. 1). (Illus.). 1980. 44.50 (ISBN 0-521-22121-8); pap. 15.95 (ISBN 0-521-29362-6). Cambridge U Pr.

Heitler, W. The Quantum Theory of Radiation. (Physics Ser.). 430p. 1984. pap. 8.95 (ISBN 0-486-64558-4). Dover.

Howell, John R. Catalog of Radiation Configuration Factors. (Illus.). 248p. 1982. 17.95 (ISBN 0-07-030606-0). McGraw.

Hubbard, L. Ron. All about Radiation. 11.00 (ISBN 0-686-30790-9). Church Scient NY.

Hurst, G. S. & Turner, J. E. Elementary Radiation Physics. LC 80-23962. 202p. 1981. Repr. of 1970 ed. text ed. 15.50 (ISBN 0-89874-249-8). Krieger.

Industrial Application of Radioisotopes & Radiation Technology: Proceedings of an International Conference on Industrial Application of Radioisotopes & Radiation Technology Organized by the International Atomic Energy Agency & Held in Grenoble, France, 28 Sept. to 2 Oct. 1981. (Proceedings Ser.). 595p. 1983. pap. 75.75 (ISBN 92-0-060082-4, ISP598, IAEA). Unipub.

Industrial Uses of Large Radiation Sources, 2 vols. (Proceedings Ser.). (Illus.). 422p. Vol.1. pap. 21.50 (ISBN 92-0-060263-0, ISP75/1, IAEA); Vol. 2. pap. 16.25 (ISBN 92-0-060363-7, ISP75/2). Unipub.

Interaction of Radiation with Condensed Matter, 2 vols. (Proceedings Ser.). (Illus.). pap. 53.00 (ISBN 92-0-130377-7, ISP443/1, IAEA); pap. 53.00 (ISBN 92-0-130477-3, ISP443/2). Unipub.

International Commission on Radiation Units & Measurements. The Dosimetry of Pulsed Radiation. LC 82-82417. 1982. 16.00 (ISBN 0-913394-28-9). Intl Comm Rad Meas.

International Commission on Radiological Protection. Assessment of Internal Contamination Resulting from Recurrent or Prolonged Uptakes. (ICRP Publication Ser.: No. 10a). 1971. pap. 9.25 (ISBN 0-08-016772-1). Pergamon.

--Protection Against Electro Radiation. (ICRP Publication Ser.: No. 4). 1964. pap. 25.00 (ISBN 0-08-029779-X). Pergamon.

International Seminar, Imperial College of Science & Technology, UK & Williams. Finite Element Methods in Radiation Physics: Proceedings. Goddard, A. J., ed. 160p. 1981. pap. 41.00 (ISBN 0-08-028694-1). Pergamon.

Ionizing Radiation: Levels & Effects, 2 Vols. Set. pap. 20.00 (ISBN 0-686-94497-6, UN); Vol. 1: Levels. pap. 11.00 (ISBN 0-686-99374-8, UN72/9/17); Vol. 2: Effects. pap. 11.00 (ISBN 0-686-99375-6, UN72/9/18). Unipub.

Ionizing Radiation: Levels & Effects, 2 vols. 448p. 1982. 12.50x (ISBN 0-8002-3321-2). Intl Pubns Serv.

Ionizing Radiation: Sources & Biological Effects. 773p. 1983. pap. text ed. 63.00 (ISBN 0-686-46327-7, UN82/9/8, UN). Unipub.

Ionizing Radiation: Sources & Biological Effects. 773p. 1982. 63.00x (ISBN 0-8002-3313-1). Intl Pubns Serv.

Isotopes & Radiation in Soil Organic-Matter Studies. (Proceedings Ser.). (Eng., Fr., Rus. & Span., Illus.). 584p. (Orig.). 1968. pap. 36.00 (ISBN 92-0-010368-5, ISP190, IAEA). Unipub.

Johnson, Everett R. Radiation-Induced Decomposition of Inorganic Molecular Ions. 154p. 1970. 46.25 (ISBN 0-677-02650-1). Gordon.

Joint EAEA-WHO Expert Committee. Medical Uses of Ionizing Radiation & Radioisotopes. (Technical Report Ser: No. 492). 56p. 1972. pap. 1.60 (ISBN 92-4-120492-3, 1346). World Health.

Kangro, H. History of Planck's Radiation Law. 300p. 1976. cancelled (ISBN 0-85066-063-7). Taylor & Francis.

Kunz, C., ed. Synchrotron Radiation: Techniques & Applications. LC 78-24275. (Topics in Current Physics: Vol. 10). (Illus.). 1979. 52.00 (ISBN 0-387-09149-1). Springer-Verlag.

Lacey, Jim & Keough, Allen H. Radiation Curing. (Illus.). 96p. 1980. 30.00 (ISBN 0-938648-15-2, 2004). T-C Pubns CA.

--Radiation Curing: A Discussion of Advantages, Features & Applications. LC 80-52815. (Illus.). 89p. (Orig.). 1980. pap. text ed. 8.50 (ISBN 0-87263-060-9). SME.

L'Annuziata, Michael F. & Legg, Joe, eds. Isotopes & Radiation in Agricultural Sciences: Animals, Plants, Food & the Environment, Vol. 2. 1984. 75.00 (ISBN 0-12-436602-3). Acad Pr.

Lapp, Ralph & Andrews, Howard. Nuclear Radiation Physics. 4th ed. (Illus.). 1972. 35.95 (ISBN 0-13-625988-X). P-H.

Large Radiation Sources for Industrial Processes. (Proceedings Ser.). (Illus.). 696p. (Orig.). 1970. pap. 50.25 (ISBN 92-0-060069-7, ISP236, IAEA). Unipub.

Large Radiation Sources in Industry. Vol. 1. pap. 18.00 (ISBN 92-0-060060-3, ISP12-1, IAEA); Vol. 2. pap. 18.00 (ISBN 92-0-060160-X, ISP12-2). Unipub.

Lawrence, J. H., et al. Radioisotopes & Radiation: Recent Advances in Medicine, Agriculture, & Industry. (Illus.). 12.00 (ISBN 0-8446-0765-7). Peter Smith.

Lawrence, John H., et al. Radioisotopes & Radiation: Recent Advances in Medicine, Agriculture, & Industry. LC 69-20423. 1969. lib. bdg. 11.50x (ISBN 0-88307-645-4). Gannon.

Louisell, William H. Quantum Statistical Properties of Radiation. LC 73-547. (Pure & Applied Optics Ser.). 528p. 1973. 69.95x (ISBN 0-471-54785-9, Pub. by Wiley-Interscience). Wiley.

Luckey, T. D. Hormesis with Ionizing Radiation. 232p. 1980. 66.00 (ISBN 0-8493-5841-8). CRC Pr.

McCormac, B. M. Radiation Trapped in the Earth's Magnetic Field. 908p. 1966. 90.25x (ISBN 0-677-01210-1). Gordon.

McLean, F. C. & Budy, A. M. Radiation, Isotopes, & Bone. (Atomic Energy Commission Monographs). 1964. 14.50 (ISBN 0-12-484950-4). Acad Pr.

Marion, Jerry & Heald, Mark A. Classical Electromagnetic Radiation. 2nd ed. 1980. 26.00i (ISBN 0-12-472257-1); solutions manual 2.50i (ISBN 0-12-472258-X). Acad Pr.

Markovic, V., ed. Radiation Processing: Fourth International Meeting on Radiation Processing, Dubrovnik, Yugoslavia, October 1982, 2 vols. 980p. 1983. Set. 140.00 (ISBN 0-08-029162-7). Pergamon.

Marshall, Walter. Nuclear Power Technology, Vol. 3: Nuclear Radiation. (Illus.). 1983. 65.00x (ISBN 0-19-851959-1). Oxford U Pr.

Mayneord, W. V. & Clark, R. H. Carcinogenesis & Radiation Risk: A Biomathematical Reconnaissance. 1980. 40.00x (ISBN 0-686-69940-8, Pub. by Brit Inst Radiology England). State Mutual Bk.

Medicus & Hubbard, L. Ron. All about Radiation. LRH Personal Compilations Bureau, ed. 1957. 21.34 (ISBN 0-88404-062-3). Bridge Pubns Inc.

Mihalas, Dimitri & Mihalas, Barbara W. Foundations of Radiation Hydrodynamics. (Illus.). 1984. 75.00x (ISBN 0-19-503437-6). Oxford U Pr.

Natural Background Radiation in the United States. LC 75-13474. (NCRP Reports Ser.: No. 45). 1975. 9.00 (ISBN 0-913392-27-8). NCRP Pubns.

NCRP. Evaluation of Occupational & Environmental Exposures to Radon & Radon Daughters in the United States. LC 84-4756. (NCRP Report Ser.: No. 78). 204p. 1984. pap. text ed. 15.00 (ISBN 0-913392-68-5). Natl Coun Radiation.

--Exposures from the Uranium Series with Emphasis on Radon & Its Daughters. LC 84-3420. (NCRP Report Ser.: No. 77). 131p. 1984. pap. text ed. 12.00 (ISBN 0-913392-67-7). Natl Coun Radiation.

--Iodine-129: Evaluation of Releases from Nuclear Power Generation. LC 83-23145. (NCRP Report Ser.: No. 75). 74p. 1983. pap. text ed. 10.00 (ISBN 0-913392-65-0). Natl Coun Radiation.

--Radiological Assessment: Predicting the Transport, Bioaccumulation, & Uptake by Man of Radionuclides Released to the Environment. LC 84-4773. (NCRP Report Ser.: No. 76). 300p. 1984. pap. text ed. 17.00 (ISBN 0-913392-66-9). Natl Coun Radiation.

Nikitina, T. S., et al, eds. Effect of Ionizing Radiation on High Polymers. (Russian Tracts on the Physical Sciences Ser.). (Illus.). 96p. 1963. 27.95x (ISBN 0-677-20480-9). Gordon.

Nuclear Radiation in Warfare. 150p. 1981. 21.00 (ISBN 0-85066-217-6). Taylor & Francis.

Occupational Radiation Exposure in Nuclear Fuel Cycle Facilities. (Proceedings Ser.). (Illus.). 640p. 1980. pap. 89.50 (ISBN 92-0-020080-X, ISP527, IAEA). Unipub.

Olesen, Henning L. Radiation Effects on Electronic Systems. LC 65-22183. 230p. 1966. 32.50x (ISBN 0-306-30228-4, Plenum Pr). Plenum Pub.

Orton, Colin G., ed. Progress in Medical Radiation Physics, Vol. 1. 401p. 1982. 55.00x (ISBN 0-306-40713-2, Plenum Pr). Plenum Pub.

Panati, Charles & Hudson, Michael. The Silent Intruder: Surviving the Radiation Age. 224p. 1981. 9.95. HM.

Piesinger, Gregory H. Nuclear Radiation: What It Is, How to Detect It, How to Protect Yourself from It. LC 80-24001. (Illus.). 127p. (Orig.). 1980. pap. 9.95 (ISBN 0-937224-00-6). Dyco Inc.

Poch, David. Radiation Alert. LC 83-45160. (Illus.). 192p. 1985. pap. 9.95 (ISBN 0-385-19029-8). Doubleday.

Pollard, Ernest C. Radiation: One Story of the M. I. T. Radiation Lab. 1940-1945. (Illus.). 197p. 1982. pap. 8.00 (ISBN 0-9612798-1-8). Woodburn Pr.

Purington, Robert & Patterson, Wade. Handling Radiation Emergencies. McKinnon, G. P. & Dean, A. E., eds. LC 76-54461. 1977. pap. 8.75 (ISBN 0-87765-089-6). Natl Fire Prot.

Radiation Damage & Sulphydryl Compounds. (Panel Proceedings Ser.). (Illus.). 191p. 1969. pap. 14.50 (ISBN 92-0-011169-6, ISP221, IAEA). Unipub.

Radiation Engineering in the Academic Curriculum: Study Group Meeting, Haifa, Aug. 27-Sept. 4, 1973. (Panel Proceedings Ser.). (Illus.). 362p. 1975. pap. 33.00 (ISBN 92-0-161075-0, ISP372, IAEA). Unipub.

Radiation Experiment in the Vicinity of Barbados: Final Report, NSF Grant Ga. 12603. 100p. 1970. pap. 5.00x (ISBN 0-299-97027-2). U of Wis Pr.

Radiation Exposure from Consumer Products & Miscellaneous Sources. LC 77-85462. (NCRP Reports Ser.: No. 56). 1977. 8.00 (ISBN 0-913392-38-3). NCRP Pubns.

Radiation Including Satellite Techniques: WMO-IUGG Symposium Bergen, 1968. (Technical Note Ser.: No. 104). (Illus.). 556p. 1970. pap. 50.00 (ISBN 0-685-04922-1, W74, WMO). Unipub.

The Control of Exposure of the Public to Ionizing Radiation in the Event of Accident or Attack. LC 82-81909. 1982. 20.00 (ISBN 0-913392-58-8). NCRP Pubns.

Effects of Radiation on Meiotic Systems. (Panel Proceedings Ser.). (Illus.). 223p. 1968. pap. 16.25 (ISBN 92-0-111168-1, ISP173, IAEA). Unipub.

Fajardo, Luis F. Pathology of Radiation Injury. LC 82-15373. (Masson Monographs in Diagnostic Pathology: Vol. 6). (Illus.). 300p. 1982. 69.50 (ISBN 0-89352-182-5). Masson Pub.

Friedman, Milton, ed. The Biological & Clinical Basis of Radiosensitivity. (Illus.). 592p. 1974. photocopy ed. 62.75x (ISBN 0-398-02951-2). C C Thomas.

Gofman, John W. Radiation & Human Health: A Comprehensive Investigation of the Evidence Relating Low-Level Radiation to Cancer & Other Diseases. LC 80-26484. (Illus.). 928p. 1981. 29.95 (ISBN 0-87156-275-8). Sierra.

Grosch, Daniel S. & Hopwood, Larry E. Biological Effects of Radiation. 2nd ed. LC 79-51677. 1979. 41.50 (ISBN 0-12-304150-3). Acad Pr.

Harm, Walter. Biological Effects of Ultraviolet Radiation. LC 77-88677. (IUPAB Biophysics Ser.: No. 1). (Illus.). 1980. 44.50 (ISBN 0-521-22121-8); pap. 15.95 (ISBN 0-521-29362-6). Cambridge U Pr.

Health Impacts of Different Sources of Energy: Proceedings of a Symposium Held at Nashville, June 22-26 1981 Jointly Organized by WHO, UNEP, and IAEA. (Proceedings Ser.). (Illus.). 701p. 1982. pap. 83.75 (ISBN 92-0-010182-8, ISP594, IAEA). Unipub.

Hubner, K. F. & Fry, S. A., eds. Medical Basis for Radiation Accident Preparedness. 546p. 1980. 74.50 (ISBN 0-444-00431-9, Biomedical Pr). Elsevier.

Hurley, Patrick M. Living with Nuclear Radiation. 136p. 1982. 18.50 (ISBN 0-472-09339-8); pap. 10.95 (ISBN 0-472-06339-1). U of Mich Pr.

Illinger, Karl H., ed. Biological Effects of Nonionizing Radiation. LC 81-2652. (ACS Symposium Ser.: No. 157). 1981. 39.95 (ISBN 0-8412-0634-1). Am Chemical.

International Atomic Energy Agency & World Health Organization. Diagnosis & Treatment of Acute Radiation Injury: Proceedings. (Eng, Fr, & Rus., Illus.). 425p. 1961. 10.80 (ISBN 92-4-156024-X). World Health.

International Symposium on Biological Aspects of Radiation Protection - Kyoto, Japan - 1969. Proceedings. Hug, O. & Sugahara, T., eds. 1971. 54.00 (ISBN 0-387-05325-5). Springer-Verlag.

Isotope & Radiation Research on Animal Diseases & Their Vectors. (Proceedings Ser.). (Illus.). 468p. 1980. pap. 66.50 (ISBN 92-0-010080-5, ISP525, IAEA). Unipub.

Kalia, R. K. & Vashishta, P., eds. Melting, Localization & Chaos. 302p. 1982. 75.75 (ISBN 0-444-00695-8, North-Holland). Elsevier.

Lanzl, Lawrence H., et al. Radiation Accidents & Emergencies in Medicine, Research, & Industry. (Illus.). 352p. 1965. 34.50x (ISBN 0-398-01079-X). C C Thomas.

Late Biological Effects of Ionizing Radiation, 2 vols. 1979. pap. 51.25 (ISBN 0-685-94884-6, ISP489-1, IAEA); pap. 53.75 (ISBN 92-0-010778-8, ISP489-2). Unipub.

Leone. Ionizing Radiation & Immune Processes. 532p. 1962. 142.50 (ISBN 0-677-10300-X). Gordon.

Lindop, Patricia J. & Sacher, G. A., eds. Radiation & Aging. 1966. 32.50x (ISBN 0-89563-020-6). Intl Ideas.

Methodology for Assessing Impacts of Radioactivity on Aquatic Ecosystems. (Technical Reports Ser.: No. 190). 1979. pap. 60.00 (ISBN 92-0-125379-6, IDC190, IAEA). Unipub.

National Research Council Assembly of Life Sciences. Federal Research on the Biological & Health Effects of Ionizing Radiation. 169p. 1981. pap. text ed. 12.50 (ISBN 0-309-03190-7). Natl Acad Pr.

NCRP. Evaluation of Occupational & Environmental Exposures to Radon & Radon Daughters in the United States. LC 84-4756. (NCRP Report Ser.: No. 78). 204p. 1984. pap. text ed. 15.00 (ISBN 0-913392-68-5). Natl Coun Radiation.

--Exposures from the Uranium Series with Emphasis on Radon & Its Daughters. LC 84-3420. (NCRP Report Ser.: No. 77). 131p. 1984. pap. text ed. 12.00 (ISBN 0-913392-67-7). Natl Coun Radiation.

Peyton, Mary F., ed. Biological Effects of Microwave Radiation. LC 61-11807. 333p. 1961. 35.00x (ISBN 0-306-30113-X, Plenum Pr). Plenum Pub.

Radiation-Induced Cancer. (Proceedings Ser.). (Illus.). 498p. 1969. pap. 35.75 (ISBN 92-0-010269-7, ISP228, IAEA). Unipub.

Radiological Assessment: Predicting the Transport, Bioaccumulation, & Uptake by Man of Radionuclides Released to the Environment. (NCRP Report Ser.: No. 76). 1984. 17.00 (ISBN 0-913392-66-9). NCRP Pubns.

Risk Evaluation for Protection of the Public in Radiation Accidents. (Safety Ser.: No. 21). 78p. 1967. pap. 7.00 (ISBN 92-0-123267-5, ISP124, IAEA). Unipub.

Saenger, Eugene L. & AEC Technical Information Center. Medical Aspects of Radiation Accidents. 376p. 1963. 29.50 (ISBN 0-87079-268-7, TID-18867); microfiche 4.50 (ISBN 0-87079-388-8, TID-18867). DOE.

Sankaranarayanan, K. Genetic Effects of Ionizing Radiation in Multicellular Eukaryotes & the Assessment of Genetic Radiation Hazards in Man. 385p. 1982. 81.00 (ISBN 0-444-80379-3, Biomedical Pr). Elsevier.

Shimanovskaya, K. & Shiman, Alexander. Radiation Injury of Bone: Bone Injuries Following Radiation Therapy of Tumors. Haigh, Basil, tr. (Illus.). 300p. 1983. 40.00 (ISBN 0-08-028821-9). Pergamon.

Shore, Bernard & Hatch, Frederick, eds. Biological Implications of the Nuclear Age: Proceedings. LC 74-603800. (AEC Symposium Ser.). 334p. 1969. pap. 16.25 (ISBN 0-87079-150-8, CONF-690303); microfiche 4.50 (ISBN 0-87079-151-6, CONF-690303). DOE.

Sibley, C. Bruce. Surviving Doomsday. 1977. 10.00x (ISBN 0-686-87233-9, Pub. by Shaw & Sons). State Mutual Bkq.

Sikov, Melvin R. & Mahlum, D. Dennis, eds. Radiation Biology of the Fetal & Juvenile Mammal: Proceedings. LC 74-603748. (AEC Symposium Ser.). 1026p. 1969. pap. 33.75 (ISBN 0-87079-318-7, CONF-690501); microfiche 4.50 (ISBN 0-87079-319-5, CONF-690501). DOE.

Some Physical, Dosimetry & Biomedical Aspects of Californium. (Panel Proceedings Ser.). (Illus.). 278p. 1977. pap. 31.50 (ISBN 92-0-111476-1, ISP418, IAEA). Unipub.

Sowby, F. D., ed. Principles for Limiting Exposure of the Public to Natural Sources of Radiation. (ICRP Publication Ser.: No. 39). 20p. 1984. pap. 17.00 (ISBN 0-08-031503-8). Pergamon.

Steel, G. G., et al. Biological Basis of Radiotherapy. 1983. 59.75 (ISBN 0-444-80511-7). Elsevier.

Sternglass, Ernest. Secret Fallout: Low-Level Radiation from Hiroshima to Three-Mile Island. rev. ed. (McGraw-Hill Paperbacks Ser.). 300p. (Orig.). 1981. pap. 5.95 (ISBN 0-07-061242-0). McGraw.

Taliaferro, William H., et al. Radiation & Immune Mechanisms. (Atomic Energy Commission Monographs). (Illus.). 1964. 17.00 (ISBN 0-12-682450-9). Acad Pr.

Van Bekkum, O. & De Vries, H. Radiation Chimeras. 1967. 73.50 (ISBN 0-12-710350-3). Acad Pr.

Van Cleave, Charles & AEC Technical Information Center. Late Somatic Effects of Ionizing Radiation. LC 68-62106. 310p. 1968. pap. 15.75 (ISBN 0-87079-253-9, TID-24310); microfiche 4.50 (ISBN 0-87079-254-7, TID-24310). DOE.

Yuhas, John M., et al, eds. Biology of Radiation Carcinogenesis. LC 74-14486. 371p. 1976. 50.50 (ISBN 0-89004-010-9). Raven.

Zirkle, Raymond E., ed. Biological Effects of External X & Gamma Radiation, Part 2. AEC Technical Information Center. (National Nuclear Energy Ser.: Vol. 22C). 487p. 1956. pap. 35.50 (ISBN 0-87079-146-X, TID-5220); microfilm 10.00 (ISBN 0-87079-147-8, TID-5220). DOE.

RADIATION–SAFETY MEASURES

see also Radiation Protective Agents

Advances in Radiation Protection Monitoring. (Proceedings Ser.). (Illus.). 778p. 1980. pap. 99.25 (ISBN 92-0-020279-9, ISP494, IAEA). Unipub.

Atomic Industrial Forum Staff. Radiation Issues for the Nuclear Industry: Set of Papers from AIF Conference on Radiation. (Technical & Economic Reports: Radiation Protection & Environmental Considerations). 1982. 150.00 (ISBN 0-318-02244-3). Atomic Indus Forum.

Basic Radiation Protection Criteria. LC 78-134693. (NCRP Reports Ser.: No. 39). 1971. 8.00 (ISBN 0-913392-21-9). NCRP Pubns.

Braestrup, Carl B. & Wyckoff, Harold O. Radiation Protection. (Illus.). 382p. 1958. 32.50x (ISBN 0-398-04219-5). C C Thomas.

Brodsky, Allen. Handbook of Radiation Measurement & Protection, CRC: Selection A-General Scientific & Engineering Information, 2 vols. Vol. 1, 1979 720 Pgs. 86.50 (ISBN 0-8493-3756-9); Vol. 2, Oct 1982, 736 Pgs. 94.00 (ISBN 0-8493-3757-7). CRC Pr.

Brodsky, Allen & Klement, eds. Handbook of Radiation Measurement & Protection: Section B, Vol. III. 496p. 1982. 74.50 (ISBN 0-8493-3768-2). CRC Pr.

Cember, H. Introduction to Health Physics. 2nd ed. 1969. 60.00 (ISBN 0-08-030129-0). Pergamon.

Clark, Linda. Are You Radioactive? LC 73-76155. 128p. 1973. pap. 5.95 (ISBN 0-8159-5013-6). Devin.

Control & Removal of Radioactive Contamination in Laboratories. (NCRP Reports Ser.: No. 8). 1951. 6.00 (ISBN 0-913392-00-6). NCRP Pubns.

The Dose Limitation System in the Nuclear Fuel Cycle & in Radiation Protection: Proceedings of the International Symposium on the Application of the Dose Limitation System in Nuclear Fuel Cycle Facilities & Other Radiation Practices Sponsored by International Atomic Energy Agency, World Health Organization, OECD Nuclear Energy Agency, International Commission on Radiological Protection & Held in Madrid, 19-23 October 1981. (Proceedings Ser.). (Illus.). 675p. 1983. pap. 84.75 (ISBN 92-0-020182-2, ISP599, IAEA). Unipub.

Ebert, H., et al, eds. Radiation Protection Optimization-Present Experience & Methods: Proceedings of the European Scientific Seminar, Luxembourg, Oct. 1979. LC 80-41671. (Illus.). 330p. 1981. 55.00 (ISBN 0-08-027291-6). Pergamon.

Eisenberg, ed. Radiation Protection: A Systematic Approach to Safety: Proceedings of the 5th Congress of the International Radiation Protection Society, March 1980, Jerusalem, 2 vols. (Illus.). 1055p. 1980. Set. 200.00 (ISBN 0-08-025912-X). Pergamon.

Food & Agriculture Organization of the U.N., et al. Protection of the Public in the Event of Radiation Accidents: Proceedings. (Eng, Fr, & Rus., Illus.). 370p. 1965. 14.40 (ISBN 92-4-156025-8). World Health.

Friedell, Hymer L. Radiation Protection: Concepts & Trade Offs. 7.00 (ISBN 0-686-30848-4). NCRP Pubns.

General Guide on Protection Against Ionising Radiations. (Illus.). 1963. 2.85 (ISBN 92-2-100946-7). Intl Labour Office.

Gloyna, E. F. & Ledbetter, J. O. Principles of Radiological Health. (Environmental Health Engineering Textbk Ser: Vol. 1). 1969. 34.25 (ISBN 0-8247-1250-1). Dekker.

Gollnick, Daniel A. Basic Radiation Protection Technology. (Illus.). 454p. 1983. text ed. 42.00 (ISBN 0-916339-01-7); pap. text ed. 33.00 (ISBN 0-916339-00-9). Pacific Rad.

--Radiation Protection Technology: Student Manual, a Self-Study Course. 195p. 1984. wkbk. 175.00 (ISBN 0-916339-02-5). Pacific Rad.

ICRP. Protection Against Ionizing Radiation from External Sources Used in Medicine. (ICRP Publication: No. 33). 74p. 1982. 25.00 (ISBN 0-08-029779-X). Pergamon.

Inhalation Risks from Radioactive Contaminants. (Technical Reports Ser.: No. 142). (Illus.). 146p. (Orig.). 1973. pap. 14.25 (ISBN 92-0-125073-8, IDC142, IAEA). Unipub.

Instrumentation & Monitoring Methods for Radiation Protection. LC 78-62094. (NCRP Reports Ser.: No. 57). 1978. 8.00 (ISBN 0-913392-40-5). NCRP Pubns.

International Commission on Radiation Units and Measurements. Radiation Protection Instrumentation & Its Application. LC 70-177297. (Illus.). v, 60p. 1971. 12.00 (ISBN 0-913394-38-6). Intl Comm Rad Meas.

International Commission on Radiological Protection. Protection Against Electro Radiation. (ICRP Publication Ser.: No. 4). 1964. pap. 25.00 (ISBN 0-08-029779-X). Pergamon.

--Protection of the Patient in Radionuclide Investigations. (ICRP Publication Ser.: No. 17). 1971. pap. 10.00 (ISBN 0-08-016773-X). Pergamon.

--Radiation Protection in Schools for Pupils up to the Age of 18 Years. (ICRP Publication Ser: No. 13). 1970. pap. 8.50 (ISBN 0-08-016356-4). Pergamon.

Kamath, P. R. Environmental Radiation Surveillance Laboratory: A Guide to Design, Layout, Staff & Equipment Requirements. (Also avail. in French). 1970. 2.80 (ISBN 92-4-154012-5). World Health.

Keil, A. A. Radiation Control. 256p. 1960. pap. 4.75 (ISBN 0-685-46052-5, SPP-4). Natl Fire Prot.

Kiefer, H. & Maushart, R. Radiation Protection Measurement. Friese, Ralf, tr. LC 70-133884. 576p. 1972. Pergamon.

Klement, Alfred W., Jr., ed. CRC Handbook of Environmental Radiation. 496p. 1982. 90.00 (ISBN 0-8493-3761-5). CRC Pr.

Medical Supervision of Radiation Workers. (Safety Ser.: No. 25). (Illus., Orig.). 1968. pap. 10.00 (ISBN 92-0-123068-0, ISP201, IAEA). Unipub.

Medical X-Ray & Gamma Ray Protection for Energies up to 10 MeV: Equipment Design & Use. LC 68-19236. (NCRP Reports Ser.: No. 33). 1968. 7.00 (ISBN 0-913392-15-4). NCRP Pubns.

Morgan, K. Z. & Turner, J. E. Principles of Radiation Protection. LC 67-22415. 640p. 1973. Repr. of 1967 ed. 34.50 (ISBN 0-88275-128-X). Krieger.

NCRP. Neutron Contamination from Medical Electron Accelerators. LC 84-19848. (NCRP Report Ser.: No. 79). 128p. 1984. pap. text ed. 14.00 (ISBN 0-913392-70-7). Natl Coun Radiation.

--Protection in Nuclear Medicine & Ultrasound Diagnostic Procedures in Children. LC 83-61834. (NCRP Report Ser.: No. 73). 81p. 1983. pap. text ed. 10.00 (ISBN 0-913392-63-4). Natl Coun Radiation.

--Radiation Protection & Measurement for Low-Voltage Neutron Generators. LC 83-62802. (NCRP Report Ser.: No. 72). 80p. 1983. pap. text ed. 10.00 (ISBN 0-913392-61-8). Natl Coun Radiation.

Norwood, W. Daggett. Health Protection of Radiation Workers. (Illus.). 468p. 1975. 50.75x (ISBN 0-398-03291-2). C C Thomas.

Operational Radiation Safety Program. LC 79-62918. (NCRP Reports Ser.: No. 59). 1978. 8.00 (ISBN 0-913392-43-X). NCRP Pubns.

Paterson, H. Wade & Thomas, Ralph H. Accelerator Health Physics. 1973. 59.50 (ISBN 0-12-547150-5). Acad Pr.

Planning for the Handling of Radiation Accidents. (Safety Ser.: No. 32). 91p. 1970. pap. 9.25 (ISBN 92-0-123269-1, ISP227, IAEA). Unipub.

Protection Against Neutron Radiation. LC 73-138550. (NCRP Reports Ser.: No. 38). 1971. 9.00 (ISBN 0-913392-20-0). NCRP Pubns.

Protection Against Radiation from Brachytherapy Sources. LC 67-190610. (NCRP Reports Ser.: No. 40). 1972. 8.00 (ISBN 0-913392-22-7). NCRP Pubns.

Protection of the Thyroid Gland in the Event of Releases of Radioiodine. LC 77-82607. (NCRP Reports Ser.: No. 55). 1977. 9.00 (ISBN 0-913392-37-5). NCRP Pubns.

The Provision of Radiological Protection Services. (Safety Ser.: No. 13). (Illus.). 82p. 1965. pap. 7.75 (ISBN 92-0-123365-5, ISP94, IAEA). Unipub.

Purington, Robert & Patterson, Wade. Handling Radiation Emergencies. McKinnon, G. P. & Dean, A. E., eds. LC 76-54461. 1977. pap. 8.75 (ISBN 0-87765-089-6). Natl Fire Prot.

Quantitative Risk in Standards Setting: Proceedings of 16th Annual Meeting. 1981. 15.00 (ISBN 0-318-02042-4). NCRP Pubns.

Radiation Damage in Reactor Materials: 1969, 2 vols. (Proceedings Ser.). (Illus.). 1071p. (Vol. 1). 1969. Vol. 1. pap. 34.25 (ISBN 92-0-030069-3, ISP230-1, IAEA); Vol. 2. pap. 45.00 (ISBN 92-0-030169-X, # ISP 230-2). Unipub.

Radiation Protection. rev. ed. (Illus.). 184p. 1981. Set. training materials 2900.00x (ISBN 0-87683-172-2); 60.00x (ISBN 0-87683-173-0); lesson plans 1875.00x (ISBN 0-87683-174-9); transparencies 500.00x (ISBN 0-87683-176-5); question bank 1175.00x. G P Courseware.

Radiation Protection & Measurements for Low-Voltage Neutron Generators. (NCRP Report Ser.: No. 72). 1984. 10.00 (ISBN 0-913392-61-8). NCRP Pubns.

Radiation Protection & New Medical Diagnostic Approaches: Proceedings of the 18th Annual Meeting. 1983. 16.00 (ISBN 0-318-02044-0). NCRP Pubns.

Radiation Protection Design Guidelines for Zero Point One to One Hundred MeV Particle Accelerator Facilities. LC 76-52067. (NCRP Reports Ser.: No. 51). 1977. 9.00 (ISBN 0-913392-33-2). NCRP Pubns.

Radiation Protection for Medical & Allied Health Personnel. LC 76-19728. (NCRP Reports Ser.: No. 48). 1976. 9.00 (ISBN 0-913392-30-8). NCRP Pubns.

Radiation Protection in Educational Institutions. LC 66-25710. (NCRP Reports Ser.: No. 32). 1966. 7.00 (ISBN 0-913392-14-6). NCRP Pubns.

Radiation Protection in Mining & Milling of Uranium & Thorium. 1976. 19.95 (ISBN 92-2-101504-1). Intl Labour Office.

Radiation Protection in Veterinary Medicine. LC 77-121706. (NCRP Reports Ser.: No. 36). 1970. 8.00 (ISBN 0-913392-18-9). NCRP Pubns.

Radiation Protection of Workers in Mining & Milling of Radioactive Ores. (Safety Ser.: No. 26). 108p. 1983. pap. 15.00 (ISBN 92-0-123683-2, ISP637, IAEA). Unipub.

Radiation Protection Progress Reports, 1978. (Commission of the European Communities Symposium Ser.). 870p. 1979. 94.75 (ISBN 3-7186-0011-0). Harwood Academic.

Radiation Protection Progress Reports, 1980. (Commission of the European Communities Symposium Ser.). 1358p. 1981. 198.00 (ISBN 3-7186-0062-5). Harwood Academic.

International Commission on Radiation Units & Measurement. Radiation Dosimetry: Electron Beams with Energies Between One & Fifty Mev. LC 84-12763. (ICRU Report Ser.: No. 35). 154p. 1984. pap. text ed. 23.00 (ISBN 0-913394-29-7). Intl Comm Rad Meas.

Kartha. Dosimetry Workbook. 1982. 22.50 (ISBN 0-8151-4983-2). Year Bk Med.

Kase, Kenneth R. & Nelson, Walter R. Concepts of Radiation Dosimetry. LC 78-5705. (Illus.). 232p. 1978. 30.00 (ISBN 0-08-023162-4); pap. 14.75 (ISBN 0-08-023161-6). Pergamon.

Klement, Alfred W., Jr., ed. CRC Handbook of Environmental Radiation. 496p. 1982. 90.00 (ISBN 0-8493-3761-5). CRC Pr.

Kondratyev, K. Ya. & Fedorova, M. P. Radiation Regime of Inclined Surfaces. (Technical Note Ser.: No. 152). 1977. pap. 18.00 (ISBN 92-63-10467-0, W380, WMO). Unipub.

Lovell, S. An Introduction to Radiation Dosimetry. LC 78-67261. (Techniques of Measurement in Medicine Ser.: No. 4). (Illus.). 1979. 27.95 (ISBN 0-521-22436-5); pap. 8.95x (ISBN 0-521-29497-5). Cambridge U Pr.

McLaughlin, W. L., ed. Trends in Radiation Dosimetry. (Illus.). 320p. 1983. pap. 25.00 (ISBN 0-08-029143-0). Pergamon.

Mahesk, K. & Vij, D. R. Techniques of Radiation Dosimetry. 500p. 1985. text ed. 29.95x (ISBN 0-470-20052-9). Halsted Pr.

Measurement of Absorbed Dose of Neutrons & Mixtures of Neutrons & Gamma - Rays. (NCRP Reports Ser.: No. 25). 1961. 6.00 (ISBN 0-913392-08-1). NCRP Pubns.

Monitoring of Radioactive Effluents from Nuclear Facilities. (Proceedings Ser.). (Illus.). 610p. 1978. pap. 70.00 (ISBN 92-0-020078-8, ISP466, IAEA). Unipub.

National & International Standardization of Radiation Dosimetry, 2 vols. (Proceedings Ser.). 1979. pap. 56.50 (ISBN 92-0-010478-9, ISP471-1, IAEA); pap. 40.50 (ISBN 92-0-010578-5, 471-2). Unipub.

Nelson, Walter R. & Jenkins, T. M., eds. Computer Techniques in Shielding & Dosimetry. LC 79-20872. (Ettore Majorana International Science Ser., Physical Sciences: Vol. 3). 530p. 1980. 79.50x (ISBN 0-306-40307-2, Plenum Pr). Plenum Pub.

Neutron Dosimetry, 2 Vols. (Proceedings Ser.). 1268p. (Vol. 1 - 653p., Vol. 2 - 615p.). Vol.1. pap. 32.25 (ISBN 92-0-010063-5, ISP69-1, IAEA); Vol.2. pap. 32.25 (ISBN 92-0-010163-1, ISP69-2). Unipub.

Oberhofer. Applied Thermoluminescence Dosimetry. 1981. 87.50 (ISBN 0-9960021-7-0, Pub. by Inst Physics England). Heyden.

OECD-Nuclear Energy Agency. Dosimetry Aspects of Exposure to Radon & Thoron Daughter Products. 120p. 1983. pap. 16.00x (ISBN 92-64-12520-5). OECD.

Profio, A. Edward. Radiation Shielding & Dosimetry. LC 78-15649. 1979. 58.95x (ISBN 0-471-04329-X, Pub. by Wiley-Interscience). Wiley.

Radiological Surveillance of Airborne Contaminants in the Working Environment. (Safety Ser.: No. 49). (Illus.). 138p. 1980. pap. 22.75 (ISBN 92-0-623279-7, ISP484, IAEA). Unipub.

Solid-State Dosimetry. (Bibliographical Ser.: No. 23). 143p. 1967. pap. (ISBN 92-0-114067-3, ISP138, IAEA). Unipub.

Some Physical, Dosimetry & Biomedical Aspects of Californium. (Panel Proceedings Ser.). (Illus.). 278p. 1977. pap. 31.50 (ISBN 92-0-111476-1, ISP418, IAEA). Unipub.

Standardization of Radiation Dosimetry in the Soviet Union, France, the United Kingdom, the Federal Republic of Germany & Czechoslavakia. (Illus.). 101p. (Orig.). 1973. pap. 8.25 (ISBN 92-0-117073-4, ISTR4, IAEA). Unipub.

Thomas, Ralph H. & Perez-Mendez, Victor, eds. Advances in Radiation Protection & Dosimetry. LC 80-20218. (Ettore Majorana International Science Ser., Life Sciences: Vol. 2). 667p. 1980. 95.00x (ISBN 0-306-40468-0, Plenum Pr). Plenum Pub.

Wachsmann, F. & Drexler, G. Graphs & Tables for Use in Radiology. 2nd. rev. enlarged ed. 1976. 29.00 (ISBN 0-387-07809-6). Springer-Verlag.

RADIATION ECOLOGY
see Radioecology

RADIATION FIELD PHOTOGRAPHY
see Kirlian Photography

RADIATION GENETICS
see Radiogenetics

RADIATION IMMUNOLOGY

Bizollon, C. A., ed. Monoclonal Antibodies & New Trends in Immunoassays: Proceedings of the 6th International Symposium on Radioimmunology Held in Lyon, France, 12-14 April, 1984. 310p. 1984. 59.25 (ISBN 0-444-80619-9). Elsevier.

--Physiological Peptides & New Trends in Radioimmunology. 370p. 1981. 59.25 (ISBN 0-444-80358-0, Biomedical Pr). Elsevier.

Burcheil, Scott W., et al, eds. Tumor Imaging: The Radioimmunochemical Detection of Cancer. (Illus.). 272p. 1981. 43.50x (ISBN 0-89352-156-6). Masson Pub.

Burchiel, S. W. & Rhodes, B. A., eds. Radioimmunoimaging & Radioimmunotherapy. 416p. 1983. 95.00 (ISBN 0-444-00806-3, Biomedical Pr). Elsevier.

International Congress of Chemotherapy, 12th, Florence, Italy. Current Chemotherapy & Immunotherapy: Proceedings, 2 Vols. Periti, Piero & Grassi, Giuliana G., eds. 1606p. 1982. Set. text ed. 97.00 (ISBN 0-914826-39-5). Am Soc Microbio.

Jaffe, Bernard & Behrman, Harold, eds. Methods of Radioimmunoassay. 1974. 48.00 (ISBN 0-12-379250-9). Acad Pr.

Radiation & the Control of Immune Response. (Panel Proceedings Ser.). (Illus.). 126p. 1968. pap. 9.25 (ISBN 92-0-011168-8, ISP175, IAEA). Unipub.

Radioimmunoassay & Related Procedures in Medicine. (Illus.). 471p. (Orig.). 1974. pap. 39.50 ea. (ISBN 0-686-77040-4, ISP350-1, IAEA); Vol. 1. pap. (ISBN 92-0-010274-3); Vol. 2. pap. (ISBN 92-0-010374-X, ISP350-2). Unipub.

Simmons, Ivor L. & Ewing, Galen W., eds. Methods in Radioimmunoassay, Toxicology & Related Areas. LC 74-23819. 183p. 1974. 45.00x (ISBN 0-306-39307-7, Plenum Pr). Plenum Pub.

Taliaferro, William H., et al. Radiation & Immune Mechanisms. (Atomic Energy Commission Monographs). (Illus.). 1964. 17.00 (ISBN 0-12-682450-9). Acad Pr.

RADIATION LOGGING (OIL WELLS)
see Oil Well Logging, Radiation

RADIATION MUTAGENESIS
see Radiogenetics

RADIATION PROTECTION
see Radiation–Safety Measures

RADIATION PROTECTIVE AGENTS
see also Radiation–Safety Measures

Brodsky, Allen. Handbook of Radiation Measurement & Protection, CRC: Selection A-General Scientific & Engineering Information, 2 vols. Vol. 1, 1979 720 Pgs. 86.50 (ISBN 0-8493-3756-9); Vol. 2, Oct 1982, 736 Pgs. 94.00 (ISBN 0-8493-3757-7). CRC Pr.

Commercial Portable Gauges for Radiometric Determination of the Density & Moisture Content of Building Materials. (Technical Reports Ser.: No. 130). (Illus.). 210p. (Orig.). 1972. pap. 20.50 (ISBN 92-0-165071-X, IDC130, IAEA). Unipub.

Handbook on Calibration of Radiation Protection Monitoring Instruments. (Technical Reports Ser.: No. 133). (Illus.). 93p. (Orig.). 1972. pap. 9.50 (ISBN 92-0-125071-1, IDC133, IAEA). Unipub.

International Commission on Radiological Protection. Radiation Protection in Schools for Pupils up to the Age of 18 Years. (ICRP Publication Ser: No. 13). 1970. pap. 8.50 (ISBN 0-08-016356-4). Pergamon.

Manual of Industrial Radiation Protection, 6 pts. Incl. Pt 1. Convention & Recommendation Concerning the Protection of Workers Against Ionising Radiations. 1963; Pt 2. Model Code of Safety Regulations (Ionising Radiations) 1965; Pt 3. General Guide on Protection Against Ionising Radiations. (Illus.). 1963; Pt 4. Guide on Protection Against Ionising Radiations in Industrial Radiography & Fluoroscopy. (Illus.). 1965; Pt 5. Guide on Protection Against Ionising Radiations in the Application of Luminous Compounds. (Illus.). 1964; Pt 6. Radiation Protection in the Mining & Milling of Radioactive Ores. 1968. Intl Labour Office.

Manual on Radiation Protection in Hospitals & General Practice. Incl. Vol. 1. Basic Protection Requirements. Braestrup, C. B. & Vikterlof, K. J. 1974. 4.80 (ISBN 92-4-154038-9); Vol. 2. Unsealed Sources. Frost, D. & Jammet, H. 1975. 9.60 (ISBN 92-4-154039-7); Vol. 3. X-Ray Diagnosis. Keane, B. E. & Tikhonov, K. B. 1975. 7.20 (ISBN 92-4-154040-0). (Also avail. in French). World Health.

Physical, Chemical, & Biological Properties of Radiocerium Relevant to Radiation Protection Guidelines. LC 79-84485. (NCRP Reports Ser.: No. 60). 1978. 9.00 (ISBN 0-913392-44-8). NCRP Pubns.

Radiation Protection Progress Reports, 1978. (Commission of the European Communities Symposium Ser.). 870p. 1979. 94.75 (ISBN 3-7186-0011-0). Harwood Academic.

Seuss, Michael J., ed. Nonionizing Radiation Protection. (WHO Regional Publications, European Series: No.10). viii, 267p. 1982. 14.50 (ISBN 92-890-1101-7). World Health.

Sowby, F. D., ed. Principles of Monitoring for the Radiation Protection of the Public. (ICRP Publication Ser.: No. 43). (Illus.). 20p. 1984. pap. 22.00 (ISBN 0-08-032335-9). Pergamon.

Taylor, Lauriston S. Radiation Protection Standards. (Monotopic Reprint Ser.). 112p. 1971. 22.95 (ISBN 0-8493-0111-4). CRC Pr.

RADIATION SHIELDING
see Shielding (Radiation)

RADIATION STERILIZATION

Inactivation of Peroxidase, Pectinesterase & Alkaline Phosphatase in Polymers as a Model for Irradiation of Dried Foodstuffs. (Agricultural Research Reports: No. 113). 1972. pap. 4.00 (ISBN 90-220-0383-3, PDC188, PUDOC). Unipub.

Mann, H. K. Radiation Sterilization of Plastic Medical Devices: Seminar under the Auspices of the University of Lowell, Mass., March 1979. 128p. 1980. pap. 23.00 (ISBN 0-08-025067-X). Pergamon.

Manual on Radiation Sterilization of Medical & Biological Materials. (Technical Reports Ser.: No. 149). (Illus.). 327p. (Orig.). 1974. pap. 26.50 (ISBN 92-0-115073-3, IDC149, IAEA). Unipub.

Preservation of Fruit & Vegetables by Radiation. (Panel Proceedings Ser.). (Illus.). 152p. 1968. pap. 10.00 (ISBN 92-0-111068-5, ISP149, IAEA). Unipub.

Radiosterilization of Medical Products, Pharmaceuticals & Bioproducts. (Technical Reports Ser.: No. 72). (Illus.). 94p. 1967. pap. 9.00 (ISBN 92-0-115067-9, IDC72, IAEA). Unipub.

Radiosterilization of Medical Products. (Proceedings Ser.). (Eng., Fr., Rus. & Span., Illus.). 458p. 1967. pap. 27.25 (ISBN 92-0-010367-7, ISP157, IAEA). Unipub.

Sterilization & Preservation of Biological Tissues by Ionizing Radiation. (Panel Proceedings Ser.). (Illus.). 127p. (Orig.). 1970. pap. 9.75 (ISBN 92-0-111370-6, ISP247, IAEA). Unipub.

Symposium on Ionizing Radiation for Sterilization of Medical Products & Biological Tissues, Bombay, Dec 9-13, 1974. Radiosterilization of Medical Products, 1974: Proceedings. (Proceedings Ser.). (Illus.). 541p. 1975. pap. 49.00 (ISBN 92-0-010475-4, ISP383, IAEA). Unipub.

RADIATION THERAPY
see Radiotherapy

RADIATIVE TRANSFER
see also Heat–Radiation and Absorption

Bolle, H. J., ed. Radiation in the Atmosphere: Proceedings. LC 77-5205. (Illus.). 1977. lib. bdg. 62.00 (ISBN 0-89500-002-4). Sci Pr.

Chandrasekhar, Subrahmanyan. Radiative Transfer. (Illus.). 1960. pap. 7.95 (ISBN 0-486-60590-6). Dover.

Penner, S. S. & Olfe, Daniel B. Radiation & Reentry. LC 67-22773. (Reentry Physics Ser.). 1968. 86.50 (ISBN 0-12-550450-0). Acad Pr.

Pomraning, G. C., et al. Theoretical & Computational Radiation Hydrodynamics: Vol. 1, Radiation-Hydrodynamics Theoretical Considerations. LC 70-135085. 228p. 1969. 20.00 (ISBN 0-403-04529-0). Scholarly.

Swihart, Thomas L. Radiation Transfer & Stellar Atmospheres. (Astronomy & Astrophysics Ser.: Vol. 12). 142p. 1981. 38.00 (ISBN 0-912918-18-7, 0018). Pachart Pub Hse.

Van De Hulst, H. C. Multiple Light Scattering: Tables, Formulas & Applications, Vol.1. LC 79-51687. 1980. 41.50 (ISBN 0-12-710701-0). Acad Pr.

RADICALS (CHEMISTRY)

Armstrong, Donald, et al, eds. Free Radicals in Molecular Biology, Aging, & Disease. (Aging Ser.: vol 27). 432p. 1984. text ed. 76.50 (ISBN 0-88167-048-0). Raven.

Bass, Arnold M. & Broida, H. P., eds. Formation & Trapping of Free Radicals. (Illus.). 1960. 72.00 (ISBN 0-12-080350-X). Acad Pr.

Berndt, A. Magnetic Properties of Free Radicals: Part D 1: Organic Anion Radicals. (Landolt-Boernstein Ser.: Group II Vol. 9). (Illus.). 920p. 1980. 411.60 (ISBN 0-387-08884-9). Springer-Verlag.

Blois, M. S., ed. Symposium on Free Radicals in Biological Systems. 1961. 75.00 (ISBN 0-12-107550-8). Acad Pr.

Borden, Weston T. Diradicals. LC 82-8604. 343p. 1982. 49.50 (ISBN 0-471-08661-4, Pub. by Wiley-Interscience). Wiley.

Buchachenko, Anatoli L. Stable Radicals. LC 65-11336. 180p. 1965. 32.50x (ISBN 0-306-10729-5, Consultants). Plenum Pub.

Critser, James R., Jr. Free Radical Initiators (1972) (Ser. 1-72). 1975. 55.00 (ISBN 0-914428-27-6). Lexington Data.

--Free Radical Initiators (1973) (Ser. No. 1-73). 86p. 1975. 55.00 (ISBN 0-914428-31-4). Lexington Data.

Davies, D. I. & Parrott, M. J. Free Radicals in Organic Synthesis. (Reactivity & Structure: Vol. 7). 1978. 37.00 (ISBN 0-387-08723-0). Springer-Verlag.

Fischer, H. & Hellwege, K. H., eds. Magnetic Properties of Free Radicals: Organic Cation Radicals & Polyradicals. (Landolt-Bernstein Ser. Group II: Vol. 9, Pt. 2). 380p. 1980. 197.40 (ISBN 0-387-09666-3). Springer-Verlag.

Floyd, Robert A., ed. Free Radicals & Cancer. (Illus.). 552p. 1982. 75.00 (ISBN 0-8247-1551-9). Dekker.

Halliwell, Barry & Gutteridge, John M. Free Radicals in Biology & Medicine. (Illus.). 1985. 45.00 (ISBN 0-19-854137-6). Oxford U Pr.

Hay, J. M. Reactive Free Radicals. 1974. 34.00 (ISBN 0-12-333550-7). Acad Pr.

Hudlicky, Milos. Chemistry of Organic Fluorine Compounds. LC 73-14377. 903p. 1976. text ed. 172.95x (ISBN 0-470-41835-4). Halsted Pr.

Huyser, Earl S. Free-Radical Chain Reactions. LC 77-106013. pap. 99.30 (ISBN 0-317-08639-1, 2011873). Bks Demand UMI.

Institute of Physical Chemistry, Uppsala. Fifth International Symposium on Free Radicals. 854p. 1961. 160.75 (ISBN 0-677-10180-5). Gordon.

Kochi, Jay K., ed. Free Radicals, 2 Vols. LC 72-6105. (Reactive Intermediates in Organic Chemistry Ser). 906p. 1973. Vol. 2. 97.50 (ISBN 0-471-49702-9, Pub by Wiley-Interscience). Wiley.

Mc Manus, Samuel P., ed. Organic Reactive Intermediates. (Organic Chemistry Ser.). 1973. 67.00 (ISBN 0-12-485450-8). Acad Pr.

Nonhebel, D. C. & Tedder, J. M. Radicals. LC 78-54721. (Cambridge Texts in Chemistry & Biochemistry Ser.). (Illus.). 1979. 42.50 (ISBN 0-521-22004-1); pap. 18.95x (ISBN 0-521-29332-4). Cambridge U Pr.

Nonhebel, D. C. & Walton, J. C. Free-Radical Chemistry. LC 73-97887. (Illus.). 600p. 1973. 110.00 (ISBN 0-521-20149-7). Cambridge U Pr.

Petrakis, L. & Grandy, D. W. Free Radicals in Coals & Synthetic Fuels. (Coal Science & Technology Ser.: No. 5). 274p. 1983. 66.00 (ISBN 0-444-42237-4, I-306-83). Elsevier.

Pryor, William. Free Radicals in Biology, Vol. 5. LC 75-13080. 1982. 54.50 (ISBN 0-12-566505-9). Acad Pr.

Pryor, William A. Free Radicals. LC 64-8731. (McGraw-Hill Series in Advanced Chemistry). pap. 91.50 (ISBN 0-317-08742-8, 2003757). Bks Demand UMI.

--Free Radicals in Biology, Vol. 6. 1984. 75.00 (ISBN 0-12-566506-7). Acad Pr.

--Frontiers of Free Radical Chemistry. LC 80-19007. 1980. 44.00 (ISBN 0-12-566550-4). Acad Pr.

Pryor, William A., ed. Free Radicals in Biology, 3 vols. Vol. 1. 1976. 65.00 (ISBN 0-12-566501-6); Vol. 2. 1976. 65.00 (ISBN 0-12-566502-4); Vol. 3. 1977. 67.50 (ISBN 0-12-566503-2). Acad Pr.

--Organic Free Radicals. LC 78-1672. (ACS Symposium Ser.: No. 69). 1978. 47.95 (ISBN 0-8412-0421-7). Am Chemical.

Root, John W., ed. Fluorine-Containing Free Radicals. LC 77-26667. (ACS Symposium Ser.: No. 66). 1978. 23.95 (ISBN 0-8412-0399-7). Am Chemical.

Rozantsev, E. G. Free Nitroxyl Radicals. LC 69-12541. 249p. 1970. 34.50x (ISBN 0-306-30396-5, Plenum Pr). Plenum Pub.

Starks, Charles. Free Radical Telomerization. 1974. 66.00 (ISBN 0-12-663650-8). Acad Pr.

Williams, G. H., ed. Advances in Free Radical Chemistry, 4 vols. Vol. 2, 1967. 85.00 (ISBN 0-12-017002-7); Vol. 3, 1969. 85.00 (ISBN 0-12-017003-5); Vol. 4, 1972. 85.00 (ISBN 0-12-017004-3); Vol. 5, 1975. 85.00 (ISBN 0-12-017005-1). Acad Pr.

RADIO
see also Electro-Acoustics; Modulation (Electronics); Morse Code; Oscillators, Electric; Radar; Sound–Recording and Reproducing also subdivision Radio Equipment under subjects, e.g. Automobiles–Radio Equipment; and headings beginning with the word Radio, e.g. Radio Frequency Modulation; Radio In Navigation

Aitken, Hugh G. Syntony & Spark-the Origins of Radio Technology. LC 75-34247. (Science, Culture & Society Ser.). cancelled (ISBN 0-8357-9989-1, 2051289). Bks Demand UMI.

Arnheim, Rudolf. Radio. LC 73-161151. (History of Broadcasting: Radio to Television Ser). (Illus.). 1971. Repr. of 1936 ed. 25.50 (ISBN 0-405-03570-5). Ayer Co Pubs.

Bartone, John C., II. Radio & Radio Waves: Medical Research Index with Reference Bibliography. LC 85-47571. 150p. 1985. 29.95 (ISBN 0-88164-316-5); pap. 21.95 (ISBN 0-88164-317-3). ABBE Pubs Assn.

Beitman, Morris N. Most-Often-Needed Nineteen Twenty-Six-Nineteen Thirty-Eight Radio Diagrams. pap. 9.95 (ISBN 0-914126-12-1). Vintage Radio.

Blake, George C. History of Radio Telegraphy & Telephony. LC 74-4667. (Telecommunications Ser). (Illus.). 425p. 1974. Repr. of 1928 ed. 35.50 (ISBN 0-405-06034-3). Ayer Co Pubs.

Busby, Linda J. & Parker, Donald L. The Art & Science of Radio. 1984. text ed. 21.00 (ISBN 0-205-08049-9, 488049). Allyn.

Hall, M. P. Effects of the Troposphere on Radio Communication. (Electromagnetic Waves Ser.). (Illus.). 1980. 56.00 (ISBN 0-906048-25-7). Inst Elect Eng.

Transmission Lost Companion for Satellite, Fiber Optics Microwave, Radio Communications. 145p. 695.00 (ISBN 0-317-17614-5, FSI122, Pub. by Future Syst Inc). Monegon Ltd.

Valentich, Joseph H. Short Range Radio Telemetry for Rotating Instrumentation. LC 77-78670. 192p. 1977. text ed. 32.00x (ISBN 0-87664-358-6). Instru Soc.

RADIO, AUTOMOBILE

see Automobiles–Radio Equipment

RADIO, CITIZENS BAND

see Citizens Band Radio

RADIO, SHORT WAVE

see also Citizens Band Radio; Microwaves

Bennett, Hank & Helms, Harry L. The Complete Shortwave Listener's Handbook. 2nd ed. LC 80-14325. (Illus.). 308p. 1980. pap. 13.95 (ISBN 0-8306-1255-6, 1255). TAB Bks.

Dexter, Gerry L. Shortwave Listening Today: Modern Guide to Shortwave Listening. (Illus.). 160p. (Orig.). 1984. pap. 9.95 (ISBN 0-317-13513-9). Universal Elect.

Haslach, Robert D. Netherlands World Broadcasting. LC 83-62843. (Illus., Orig.). 1984. pap. 19.95 (ISBN 0-914021-00-1); pap. 9.99. L Miller Pub.

MacHarg, Kenneth D. Tune in the World: The Listener's Guide to Intenational Shortwave Radio. LC 83-62842. (Illus.). 110p. 1983. pap. 9.99 (ISBN 0-914021-01-X). L Miller Pub.

Miller, Larry & MacHarg, Kenneth D. The Shortwave Book. 1984. 9.99 (ISBN 0-914021-02-8). L Miller Pub.

Overbeck, Wayne & Steffen, James. Computer Programs for Ham Radio. 224p. pap. 12.95 (0657). Hayden.

Van Voorhis, S. N., ed. Microwave Receivers. (Illus.). 9.00 (ISBN 0-8446-3106-X). Peter Smith.

RADIO, SHORT WAVE–TRANSMITTERS AND TRANSMISSION

Chabak, Michael. Speedx Reference Guide to the Utilities. 237p. (Orig.). 1985. pap. 11.75 looseleaf (ISBN 0-934705-05-4). Speedx.

Frost, Jens. World Radio & TV Handbook 1980. 34th ed. 1980. pap. 19.50 (ISBN 0-8230-5906-5). Watson-Guptill.

Wiesner. Telegraph & Data Transmission over Shortwave Radio Links: Fundamental Principles & Networks Paper. 199p. 1984. pap. 21.95 (ISBN 0-471-90599-2). Wiley.

RADIO, SINGLE-SIDEBAND

Collins Radio Company. Amateur Single Sideband. LC 77-71665. (Illus.). 1977. pap. text ed. 4.95 (ISBN 0-918232-05-8, HR-SSB). Comm Tech.

Graves, Frederick. Mariner's Guide to Single Sideband. (Illus.). 108p. (Orig.). 1982. pap. 9.95. Stephens Eng Assocs.

--Mariner's Guide to Single Sideband. (Illus.). 112p. 1985. pap. 11.95 (ISBN 0-911677-00-3). Stephens Eng Assocs.

RADIO ANTENNAS

see Radio–Antennas

RADIO ASTRONOMY

see also Interstellar Communication; Radio Telescope

Aarons, Jules, ed. Solar System Radio Astronomy. LC 65-14086. 416p. 1965. 39.50x (ISBN 0-306-30192-X, Plenum Pr). Plenum Pub.

Bracewell, Ronald N., ed. Paris Symposium on Radio Astronomy. (Illus.). 1959. 50.00x (ISBN 0-8047-0571-2). Stanford U Pr.

Edge, David O. & Mulkay, Michael J. Astronomy Transformed: The Emergence of Radio Astronomy in Britain. LC 76-13532. (Science, Culture & Society Ser.). pap. 124.50 (ISBN 0-317-27975-0, 2055755). Bks Demand UMI.

Hey, James S. The Evolution of Radio Astronomy. LC 73-80636. 224p. 1973. text ed. 17.50 o.p (ISBN 0-88202-027-7, Sci Hist); pap. text ed. 8.95 (ISBN 0-88202-030-7, Sci Hist). Watson Pub Intl.

I.A.U. Symposium, No. 60, Maroochydore, Queensland, September 3-7, 1973. Galactic Radio Astronomy: Proceedings. Kerr, F. J. & Simonson, S. C., eds. LC 74-81939. (I.A.U. Symposia: No. 60). 654p. 1974. lib. bdg. 103.00 (ISBN 90-277-0501-1, Pub. by Reidel Holland); pap. 79.00 (ISBN 90-277-0502-X, Pub. by Reidel Holland). Kluwer Academic.

Jauncey, D. L., ed. Radio Astronomy & Cosmology. (Symposium of the International Astronomical Union: No. 74). 1977. lib. bdg. 50.00 (ISBN 90-277-0838-X, Pub. by Reidel Holland); pap. 26.00 (ISBN 90-277-0839-8, Pub. by Reidel Holland). Kluwer Academic.

Kruger, Albrecht, ed. Introduction to Solar Radio Astronomy & Radio Physics. (Geophysics & Astrophysics Monographs: No. 16). 1979. lib. bdg. 50.00 (ISBN 90-277-0957-2, Pub. by Reidel Holland); pap. 23.50 (ISBN 90-277-0997-1, Pub. by Reidel Holland). Kluwer Academic.

Kuzmin, A. D. & Salomonovich, A. E. Radioastronomical Methods of Antenna Measurements. (Electrical Science Monographs). 1967. 49.50 (ISBN 0-12-431150-4). Acad Pr.

Pacholczyk, A. G. A Handbook of Radio Sources, Vol. 1. (Astronomy & Astrophysics Ser. Reference Works in Astronomy: Vol. 5). (Illus.). 1978. 38.00x (ISBN 0-912918-20-9). Pachart Pub Hse.

Pulsating Stars, Vols. 1 & 2. 1969-70. 25.00x ea. (Plenum Pr). Vol. 1 (ISBN 0-306-30401-5). Vol. 2 (ISBN 0-306-37092-1). Plenum Pub.

Skobel'tsyn, D. V., ed. Radio Astronomy: Instruments & Observations. LC 70-129264. (P. N. Lebedev Physics Institute Ser.: Vol. 47). 184p. 1971. 35.00x (ISBN 0-306-10845-3, Consultants). Plenum Pub.

Smith, F. G. Pulsars. LC 75-44569. (Cambridge Monographs on Physics). (Illus.). 1977. 49.50 (ISBN 0-521-21241-3). Cambridge U Pr.

Sullivan, W., III. Classics in Radio Astronomy. 1982. 59.50 (ISBN 90-277-1356-1, Pub. by Reidel Holland). Kluwer Academic.

Sullivan, W. T., ed. The Early Years of Radio Astronomy: Reflections Fifty Years after Jansky's Discovery. LC 83-23227. 440p. 1984. 39.50 (ISBN 0-521-25485-X). Cambridge U Pr.

Van Schooneveld, Cornelis, ed. Image Formation from Coherence Functions in Astronomy. (Astrophysics & Space Science Library: No. 76). 1979. lib. bdg. 39.50 (ISBN 90-277-0987-4, Pub. by Reidel Holland). Kluwer Academic.

Verschuur, G. L. The Invisible Universe: The Story of Radio Astronomy. LC 73-22202. (Heidelberg Science Library: Vol. 20). (Illus.). 160p. 1974. pap. 12.95 (ISBN 0-387-90078-0). Springer-Verlag.

RADIO BROADCASTING

see also Radio–Transmitters and Transmission; Radio Stations; Television Broadcasting

Alcorn, Samuel R. The World Is Yours-Enjoy Listening to International Radio. 64p. 1984. pap. 2.95 (ISBN 0-914542-14-1). Gilfer.

Arnheim, Rudolf. Radio: The Psychology of an Art of Sound. LC 73-164504. (Cinema Ser). 1972. Repr. of 1936 ed. lib. bdg. 35.00 (ISBN 0-306-70291-6). Da Capo.

Bash, Dick. Novice Class: Amateur Radio Operator Test Guide. Rev., 3rd ed. Bash, Richard M., ed. (Illus.). 104p. 1984. pap. 9.95 (ISBN 0-938408-13-5). Bash Educ Serv.

Becker, Judith, et al. Fine-Tuning: An NCCB Report on Noncommercial Radio. 1980. pap. 5.00 (ISBN 0-9603466-4-3). T R A C.

Broadcasting from Space. (Reports & Papers on Mass Communication: No. 60). 65p. (Orig.). 1970. pap. 5.00 (ISBN 92-3-100857-9, U60, UNESCO). Unipub.

Browne, Donald R. International Radio Broadcasting: The Limits of the Limitless Medium. LC 81-22707. 384p. 1982. 34.95 (ISBN 0-03-059619-X). Praeger.

Chester, Giraud, et al. Television & Radio. 5th ed. (Illus.). 1978. ref. ed. 30.95 (ISBN 0-13-902981-8). P-H.

Diamant, Lincoln, ed. The Broadcast Communications Dictionary. 2nd, rev., enl. ed. 1978. 10.95 (ISBN 0-8038-0788-0). Hastings.

Dikshit, Kiranmani A., et al. Rural Radio: Programme Format. (Monographs on Communication Technology & Utilization: No. 5). 94p. 1979. pap. 5.00 (ISBN 92-3-101616-4, U893, UNESCO). Unipub.

Eastman, Susan Tyler & Klein, Robert. Strategies in Broadcast & Cable Promotion: Commercial Television, Radio, Cable, Pay Television, Public Television. 352p. 1982. pap. text ed. write for info. (ISBN 0-534-01156-X). Wadsworth Pub.

Fletcher, James, ed. Handbook of Radio & T V Broadcasting. 352p. 1981. 32.50 (ISBN 0-442-22417-6). Van Nos Reinhold.

Hasling, John. The Fundamentals of Radio Broadcasting. (Illus.). 1980. pap. text ed. 21.95x (ISBN 0-07-026992-0). McGraw.

Head, Sydney W., et al. Broadcasting in America. 4th ed. LC 81-83274. 1982. 25.95 (ISBN 0-395-28657-3); instr's. manual 1.50 (ISBN 0-395-28658-1); study guide 9.50 (ISBN 0-395-29624-2). HM.

Limburg, Val E. Workbook for Mass Communication & Society. 144p. 1982. pap. text ed. 8.45 (ISBN 0-8403-2641-6). Kendall-Hunt.

McLeish, Robert. The Technique of Radio Production. (Library of Communication Techniques Ser.). (Illus.). 1978. 24.95 (ISBN 0-240-51008-9). Focal Pr.

Matthews, Arthur C. Radio Production Handbook: A Beginner's Guide to Broadcasting & Cablecasting. Zapel, Arthur L. & Meyer, Sheila, eds. LC 82-60762. (Illus.). 225p. (Orig.). 1982. pap. text ed. 9.95 (ISBN 0-916260-19-4). Meriwether Pub.

O'Donnell, Lewis B., et al. Modern Radio Production. 320p. 1985. pap. write for info. (ISBN 0-534-05064-6). Wadsworth Pub.

Oringel, Robert S. Audio Control Handbook: For Radio & Television Broadcasting. 5th rev. & enl. ed. (Communication Arts Bks.). (Illus.). 380p. 1983. pap. text ed. 14.95 (ISBN 0-8038-0550-0). Hastings.

Redfern, Barrie. Local Radio. (Media Manual Ser.). (Illus.). 1978. pap. 14.95 (ISBN 0-240-50980-3). Focal Pr.

Robinson, Thomas P. Radio Networks & the Federal Government. Sterling, Christopher H., ed. LC 78-21735. (Dissertations in Broadcasting Ser.). 1979. Repr. of 1943 ed. lib. bdg. 21.00x (ISBN 0-405-11772-8). Ayer Co Pubs.

Steiner, Peter O. Workable Competition in the Radio Broadcasting Industry. new ed. Sterling, Christopher H., ed. LC 78-21741. (Dissertations in Broadcasting Ser.). (Illus.). 1979. lib. bdg. 32.50x (ISBN 0-405-11777-9). Ayer Co Pubs.

Sterling, Christopher H., ed. The Radio Industry: The Story of Its Development. LC 74-4687. (Telecommunications Ser). (Illus.). 344p. 1974. Repr. of 1928 ed. 23.00x (ISBN 0-405-06055-6). Ayer Co Pubs.

RADIO BROADCASTING–HISTORY

Harlow, Alvin. Old Wires & New Waves. LC 70-161145. (History of Broadcasting: Radio to Television Ser). 1971. Repr. of 1936 ed. 36.00 (ISBN 0-405-03566-7). Ayer Co Pubs.

Hill, Jonathan. The Cat's Whisker. 1981. 27.00x (ISBN 0-905368-46-0, Pub. by Jupiter England). State Mutual Bk.

MacDonald, J. Fred. Don't Touch That Dial. LC 79-87700. 408p. 1979. 25.95x (ISBN 0-88229-528-4); pap. 12.95x (ISBN 0-88229-673-6). Nelson-Hall.

MacFarland, David T. Development of the Top Forty Radio Format. Sterling, Christopher H., ed. LC 78-21726. (Dissertations in Broadcasting Ser.). (Illus.). 1979. lib. bdg. 44.00x (ISBN 0-405-11765-5). Ayer Co Pubs.

Schwarzlose, Richard A. The American Wire Service. new ed. Sterling, Christopher H., ed. LC 78-21738. (Dissertations in Broadcasting Ser.). (Illus.). 1979. lib. bdg. 34.50x (ISBN 0-405-11774-4). Ayer Co Pubs.

RADIO CIRCUITS

Cuthbert, Thomas R., Jr. Circuit Design Using Personal Computers. LC 82-16015. 494p. 1983. 45.95x (ISBN 0-471-87700-X, Pub. by Wiley-Interscience). Wiley.

Seventy-Three Magazine Editors. Master Handbook of Ham Radio Circuits. Traister, Robert J., ed. 1978. 12.95 (ISBN 0-8306-7801-8); pap. 8.95 (ISBN 0-8306-6801-2, 801). TAB Bks.

Solid State Design for the Radio Amateur. 7.00 (ISBN 0-87259-201-4). Am Radio.

RADIO CONTROL

see also Citizens Band Radio; Models and Modelmaking–Radio Control Systems

Burkinshaw, Bill. Introducing Radio Control Model Aircraft. (Illus.). 96p. 1983. pap. 9.95 (ISBN 0-85242-801-4). Aztex.

Marks, Fred M. Getting the Most from Radio Control Systems. Angle, Burr, ed. LC 80-81430. (Illus.). 88p. (Orig.). 1980. pap. 8.95 (ISBN 0-89024-550-9). Kalmbach.

Radio Broadcasting Research Project. Studies in the Control of Radio, Nos. 1-6. LC 79-161174. (History of Broadcasting: Radio to Television Ser). 1971. Repr. of 1948 ed. 29.00 (ISBN 0-405-03581-0). Ayer Co Pubs.

Schroder, Jack E. How to Build & Fly Radio Control Gliders. Angle, Burr, ed. (Illus., Orig.). 1980. pap. 4.00 (ISBN 0-89024-549-5). Kalmbach.

Smeed, Vic. Introducing Radio Control Model Boats. (Illus.). 96p. 1983. pap. 9.95 (ISBN 0-85242-803-0). Aztex.

RADIO ELEMENTS

see Radioactive Substances

RADIO EQUIPMENT, AUTOMOBILE

see Automobiles–Radio Equipment

RADIO FREQUENCY

see also Radio Frequency Modulation; Radio Waves

American Radio Relay League. Radio Frequency Interference. 1984. 3.00 (ISBN 0-87259-425-4). Am Radio.

Barnett, Richard, ed. Scanner Master Connecticut & Rhode Island Guide: Code & Unit Manual. (Scanner Master Frequency Guides Ser.: No. 3). 96p. 1983. 9.95 (ISBN 0-939430-02-9). Scanner Master.

--Scanner Master Connecticut & Rhode Island Guide: Frequency Manual. (Scanner Master Frequency Guides Ser.: No. 2). (Illus.). 96p. 1983. 9.95 (ISBN 0-939430-01-0). Scanner Master.

Barnett, Richard & Soomre, Edward, eds. Scanner Master Massachusetts Guide. 2nd ed. (Frequency Guides Ser.: No. 9). (Illus.). 1985. write for info. (ISBN 0-939430-08-8). Scanner Master.

--Scanner Master New England Guide. (Frequency Guides Ser.: No. 10). (Illus.). 1985. write for info. (ISBN 0-939430-09-6). Scanner Master.

Cody, William J., Jr. & White, William. Software Manual for the Elementary Functions. (Illus.). 288p. 1980. text ed. 29.95 (ISBN 0-13-822064-6). P-H.

Grandolfo, M., et al, eds. Biological Effects & Dosimetry of Nonionizing Radiation: Radiofrequency & Microwave Energies. (NATO ASI Series A, Life Sciences: Vol. 49). 682p. 1982. 89.50x (ISBN 0-306-41017-6, Plenum Pr). Plenum Pub.

Hayward, W. H. Introduction to Radio Frequency Design. (Illus.). 384p. 1982. 34.95 (ISBN 0-13-494021-0). P-H.

Prelinger, Rich, ed. Scanner Master New York Metro-Northeast Jersey Guide. (Scanner Master Frequency Guide Ser.: No. 4). (Illus.). 160p. 1983. 12.95 (ISBN 0-939430-03-7). Scanner Master.

Prelinger, Richard, ed. Monitor America. (Scanner Master Frequency Guide Ser.: No. 8). (Illus.). 608p. 1985. 14.95 (ISBN 0-939430-07-X). Scanner Master.

Radiofrequency Electromagnetic Fields: Properties, Quantities, & Units, Biophysical Interaction, & Measurements, No. 67. LC 80-82007. 1981. 10.00 (ISBN 0-913392-52-9). NCRP Pubns.

Silverman, Warren, ed. Scanner Master Metropolitan New York Guide. (Frequency Guides Ser.: No. 11). (Illus.). 1985. write for info. (ISBN 0-939430-10-X). Scanner Master.

Skomal, Edward N. & Smith, Albert A., Jr. Measuring the Radio Frequency Environment. (Illus.). 384p. 1985. 42.50 (ISBN 0-442-28184-6). Van Nos Reinhold.

RADIO FREQUENCY MODULATION

see also Radio, Short Wave

American Radio Relay League. FM & Repeaters for the Radio Amateur. LC 72-96087. pap. 5.00 (ISBN 0-87259-454-8). Am Radio.

Klapper, Jacob, ed. Selected Papers on Frequency Modulation. (Illus.). 16.50 (ISBN 0-8446-0166-7). Peter Smith.

Neely, Daniel K. Technicians Guide to Servicing Two-Way FM Radio. (Illus.). 1978. 14.95 (ISBN 0-13-898635-5, Parker). P-H.

Tibbs, Christopher E. & Johnstone, C. C. Frequency Modulation Engineering. 2nd, rev. ed. pap. 113.00 (ISBN 0-317-10016-5, 2016625). Bks Demand UMI.

RADIO FREQUENCY SPECTROSCOPY

see also Microwave Spectroscopy

Das, T. P. & Hahn, E. L. Nuclear Quadrupole Resonance Spectroscopy. (Solid State Physics: Suppl. 1). 1958. 56.00 (ISBN 0-12-607761-4). Acad Pr.

Gozzini, A., ed. Topics of Radiofrequency Spectroscopy. (Italian Physical Society: Course 17). 1962. 75.00 (ISBN 0-12-368817-5). Acad Pr.

Jansky, Donald M. Spectrum Management Techniques. White, Donald R., ed. LC 76-52508. (Illus.). 187p. 1977. text ed. 32.00 (ISBN 0-932263-11-9). White Consult.

RADIO IN AERONAUTICS

Andrews, Samuel J. & Gifford, E. H. Man & the Incarnation: The Study of Philippians 2 & Psalm 110. 1981. lib. bdg. 15.00 (ISBN 0-86524-078-7, 9510). Klock & Klock.

Doberstein, Dick. Communications Made Easy for Pilots. (Illus.). 78p. 1980. pap. text ed. 5.95x (ISBN 0-685-55702-2, Simplified). Aviation.

Illman, Paul E. & Pouzar, Jay F. The Pilot's Radio Communications Handbook. LC 84-8515. (Illus.). 224p. (Orig.). 1984. pap. 11.95 (ISBN 0-8306-2365-5, 2365). TAB Bks.

Kneitel, Tom. Air-Scan: Guide to Aeronautical Communications. 4th ed. (Illus.). 120p. 1984. pap. 10.95 (ISBN 0-939780-03-8). CRB Res.

Powell, J. Aircraft Radio Systems. (Aerospace Engineering Ser.). 416p. 1981. text ed. 80.00 (ISBN 0-273-08444-5). Pitman Pub MA.

Taylor & Parmar. Ground Studies for Pilots, Vol. 1: Radio Aids. 3rd ed. 208p. 1979. 22.50x (ISBN 0-246-11169-0, Pub. by Granada England). Sheridan.

RADIO IN NAVIGATION

see also Radar in Navigation

Hancock, Harry E. Wireless at Sea: The First Fifty Years. LC 74-7683. (Telecommunications Ser). (Illus.). 233p. 1974. Repr. of 1950 ed. 25.50x (ISBN 0-405-06048-3). Ayer Co Pubs.

Robinson, Jan & Fowler, Cheryl A., eds. Ship to Shore. (Illus.). 350p. 1983. 11.95 (ISBN 0-9612686-0-3). Ship-Shore.

Wedlake, G. E. SOS: The Story of Radio Communications. LC 73-91529. (Illus.). 240p. 1974. 14.50x (ISBN 0-8448-0270-0). Crane-Russak Co.

Wilkes, Kenneth. Radio & Radar in Sail & Power Boats. 120p. 1980. 15.00x (ISBN 0-245-53191-2, Pub. by Nautical England). State Mutual Bk.

RADIO INTERFERENCE

see Radio–Interference

Disposal of Radioactive Wastes into Marine & Fresh Waters. (Bibliographical Ser.: No. 5). 365p. 1962. pap. 7.00 (ISBN 92-0-024062-3, ISP215, IAEA). Unipub.

Disposal of Radioactive Wastes into Rivers, Lakes & Estuaries. (Safety Ser.: No. 36). (Illus.). 77p. (Orig.). 1971. pap. 9.75 (ISBN 92-0-123171-7, ISP283, IAEA). Unipub.

Disposal of Radioactive Wastes into the Ground. (Proceedings Ser.). (Illus.). 666p. (Orig.). 1967. pap. 43.00 (ISBN 92-0-020267-5, ISP156, IAEA). Unipub.

Dix, O. R. & Jackson, M. P. Lithology, Microstructures, Fluid Inclusions, & Geochemistry of Rock Salt & of the Cap-Rock Contact in Oakwood Dome East Texas: Significance for Nuclear Waste Storage. (Report of Investigations: RI 120). (Illus.). 59p. 1982. 3.00 (ISBN 0-318-03261-9). Bur Econ Geology.

Dlouhy, Z. Disposal of Radioactive Wastes. (Studies in Environmental Science: Vol. 15). 246p. 1982. 59.75 (ISBN 0-444-99724-5). Elsevier.

DOE Technical Information Center. Radioactive Waste Management: Low-Level Radioactive Waste: A Bibliography Covering January Through December 1982. 144p. 1983. pap. 14.50 (ISBN 0-87079-502-3, DOE/TIC-3387 (SUPPL. 1)); microfiche 4.50 (ISBN 0-87079-503-1, DOE/TIC-3387 (SUPPL. 1)). DOE.

--Radioactive Waste Management: Nuclear Fuel Cycle Reprocessing: A Bibliography. 248p. 1982. pap. 16.25 (ISBN 0-87079-506-6, DOE/TIC-3396); microfiche 4.50 (ISBN 0-87079-507-4, DOE/TIC-3396). DOE.

--Radioactive Waste Management: Waste Isolation: A Bibliography. 295p. 1982. pap. 17.50 (ISBN 0-87079-504-X, DOE/TIC-3388); microfiche 4.50 (ISBN 0-87079-505-8, DOE/TIC-3388). DOE.

Duffy, J. I., ed. Treatment, Recovery, & Disposal Processes for Radioactive Wastes: Recent Advances. LC 82-22260. (Pollution Technology Review No.95, Chemical Technology Review No. 216). (Illus.). 287p. 1983. 39.00 (ISBN 0-8155-0922-7). Noyes.

Economics in Managing Radioactive Wastes. (Technical Reports Ser.: No. 83). 86p. (Orig.). 1968. pap. 6.25 (ISBN 92-0-125168-8, IDC83, IAEA). Unipub.

Emelity, L. A. Operation & Control of Ion-Exchange Processes for Treatment of Radioactive Wastes. (Technical Reports Ser.: No. 78). (Illus.). 145p. 1967. pap. 10.00 (ISBN 92-0-125067-3, IDC78, IAEA). Unipub.

Environmental Assessment Methodologies for Sea Dumping of Radioactive Wastes: Recommendations. (Safety Ser.: No. 65). 42p. 1985. pap. 9.75 (ISBN 92-0-623084-0, ISP681, IAEA). Unipub.

Grover, J. R. Management of Plutonium Contaminated Waste. (Radioactive Waste Management Ser.: Vol. III). 196p. 1982. 30.00 (ISBN 3-7186-0110-9). Harwood Academic.

Grover, John. Review of Waste Management Organizations. (Radioactive Waste Management & the Nuclear Fuel Cycle Ser. (Special Journal Issue)). 116p. 1984. pap. text ed. 28.00 (ISBN 3-7186-0202-4). Harwood Academic.

Guide to the Safe Handling of Radioactive Wastes at Nuclear Power Plants. (Technical Reports Ser.: No. 198). (Illus.). 84p. 1980. pap. 15.50 (ISBN 92-0-125080-0, IDC198, IAEA). Unipub.

Handling & Storage of High-Level Radioactive Liquid Wastes - Required Cooling. (Technical Reports Ser.: No. 191). (Illus.). 116p. 1979. pap. 20.75 (ISBN 92-0-125479-2, IDC191, IAEA). Unipub.

Hebel, W. & Cottone, G., eds. Methods of Krypton-85 Management, Vol. 10. (Radioactive Waste Management Ser.). (Illus.). 304p. 1984. 34.50 (ISBN 3-7186-0167-2). Harwood Academic.

Jackson, Thomas, ed. Nuclear Waste Management: The Ocean Alternative-Edited Proceedings of a Public Policy Forum Sponsored by the Oceanic Society in the GeorgetownUniversity Law Center, DC, February 6, 1980. (Pergamon Policy Studies on Energy). (Illus.). 100p. 1981. 19.25 (ISBN 0-08-027204-5). Pergamon.

Jantzen, C. M., et al, eds. Scientific Basis for Nuclear Waste Management VIII, Vol. 44. LC 85-5023. 1985. text ed. 55.00 (ISBN 0-931837-09-X). Materials Res.

Johansson, Thomas B. & Steen, Peter. Radioactive Waste from Nuclear Power Plants. LC 80-6052. (Illus.). 1981. 16.95 (ISBN 0-520-04199-2). U of Cal Pr.

Kasperson, Roger E. & Berberian, Mimi, eds. Equity Issues in Radioactive Waste Management. LC 81-18702. 416p. 1983. text ed. 35.00 (ISBN 0-89946-055-0). Oelgeschlager.

Krissher, W. & Simon, R. A., eds. Testing, Evaluation & Shallow Land Burial of Low & Medium Radioactive Waste Forms. (Radioactive Waste Management Ser.: Vol. 13). 239p. 1984. 38.00 (ISBN 3-7186-0206-7). Harwood Academic.

League of Women Voters Education Fund. A Nuclear Waste Primer. (Illus.). 63p. 1982. pap. 3.00 (ISBN 0-89959-253-8, 391). LWV US.

Lindblom, U. E. & Gnirk, P. F. Nuclear Waste Disposal: Can We Rely on Bedrock? 80p. 1981. 19.75 (ISBN 0-08-027608-3); pap. 10.50 (ISBN 0-08-027595-8). Pergamon.

McCarthy, G. J., ed. Scientific Basis for Nuclear Waste Management, Vol. 1. LC 79-12440. 581p. 1979. 69.50x (ISBN 0-306-40181-9, Plenum Pr) Plenum Pub.

McLaren, Lynda H., ed. Radioactive Waste Management: High-Level Radioactive Wastes: A Bibliography, Supplement 1. 349p. 1984. pap. 19.75 (ISBN 0-87079-528-7, DOE/TIC-3389); microfiche 4.50 (ISBN 0-87079-529-5, DOE/TIC-3389). DOE.

--Radioactive Waste Management: Nuclear Fuel Cycle: A Bibliography, Supplement 1. 138p. 1984. pap. 11.50 (ISBN 0-87079-532-5, DOE/TIC-3396); microfiche 4.50 (ISBN 0-87079-533-3, DOE/TIC-3396). DOE.

--Radioactive Waste Management: Spent Fuel Storage: A Bibliography. 152p. 1984. pap. 11.75 (ISBN 0-87079-534-1, DOE/TIC-3395-S1); microfiche 4.50 (ISBN 0-87079-535-X, DOE/TIC-3395-S1). DOE.

McVay, G. L. Scientific Basis for Nuclear Waste Management VII: Proceedings for the 7th International Symposium on the Scientific Basis for Nuclear Waste Management, Boston, MA, Nov. 14-17, 1983, Vol. 26. (Material Research Society Symposia Ser.: Vol. 26). 1121p. 1984. 110.00 (ISBN 0-444-00906-X, North Holland). Elsevier.

Management of Gaseous Wastes from Nuclear Facilities. (Proceedings Ser.). (Illus.). 701p. 1981. pap. 84.25 (ISBN 92-0-020380-9, ISP561, IAEA). Unipub.

Management of Low & Intermediate Level Radioactive Wastes. (Illus.). 814p. (Orig.). 1971. pap. 56.00 (ISBN 92-0-020170-9, ISP264, IAEA). Unipub.

Management of Radioactive Wastes from the Nuclear Fuel Cycle, 2 vols. 1981. pap. 78.75 set (ISBN 92-0-020276-4, ISP433, IAEA); Vol. 1. pap. 40.00 (ISBN 92-0-020376-0, ISP433/1); Vol. 2. pap. 41.75 (ISP433/2). Unipub.

Management of Tritium at Nuclear Facilities. (Technical Reports Ser.: No. 234). 62p. (Orig.). 1984. pap. 13.00 (ISBN 92-0-125084-3, IDC234, IAEA). Unipub.

Management of Wastes from the Mining & Milling of Uranium & Thorium Ores: A Code of Practice & Guide to the Code. (Safety Ser.: No. 44). (Illus.). 60p. 1977. pap. 9.75 (ISBN 92-0-123276-4, ISP457, IAEA). Unipub.

Medvedev, Zhores A. Nuclear Disaster in the Urals. LC 80-10894. (Illus.). 224p. 1980. pap. 2.95 (ISBN 0-394-74445-4, Vin). Random.

Miles, Edward L., et al. Nuclear Waste Disposal under the Seabed: Assessing the Policy Issues, No. 22. LC 85-80007. (Policy Papers in International Affairs). (Illus.). xii, 112p. 1985. pap. 7.50x (ISBN 0-87725-522-9). U of Cal Intl St.

Miller, E. Willard & Miller, Ruby M. Environmental Hazards-Radioactive Materials & Wastes: A Bibliography. (Public Administration Ser.: Bibliography P-1616). 67p. 1985. pap. 9.75 (ISBN 0-89028-266-8). Vance Biblios.

Milnes, A. G. Geology & Radwaste. Date not set. 60.00 (ISBN 0-12-498070-8); pap. 39.95 (ISBN 0-12-498071-6). Acad Pr.

Moore, John G., ed. Scientific Basis for Nuclear Waste Management, Vol. 3. LC 81-10663. 650p. 1981. 69.50x (ISBN 0-306-40803-1, Plenum Pr) Plenum Pub.

Murdock, Steve H. & Leistritz, F. Larry. Nuclear Waste: Socioeconomic Dimensions of Long-Term Storage. LC 83-60130. (Special Studies in Science, Technology, & Public Policy-Society). 343p. 1983. 28.50x (ISBN 0-86531-447-0). Westview.

National Research Council. Social & Economic Aspects of Radioactive Waste Disposal. 175p. 1984. pap. 14.50 (ISBN 0-309-03444-2). Natl Acad Pr.

Navratil, James D. & Schulz, W. W. Actinide Recovery From Waste & Low Grade Sources. (Radioactive Waste Management Ser.: Vol. VI). 350p. 1982. 68.00 (ISBN 3-7186-0105-2). Harwood Academic.

Northrup, Clyde J., Jr., et al, eds. Scientific Basis for Nuclear Waste Management, Vol. 2. LC 79-12440. 955p. 1980. 95.00x (ISBN 0-306-40550-4, Plenum Pr) Plenum Pub.

Nuclear Safety Associates-Impell Corporation Staff. Methodologies for Classification of Low-Level Radioactive Wastes from Nuclear Power Plants: AIF-NESP-027. (National Environmental Studies Project: NESP Reports). 1983. 50.00 (ISBN 0-318-02235-4). Atomic Indus Forum.

Nuclear Waste Management: The Ocean Alternative. 124p. 1981. 14.50 (ISBN 0-08-027204-5). Oceanic Soc Stamford.

OECD Nuclear Energy Agency. Regulation Governing the Transport of Radioactive Materials. 202p. (Orig.). 1981. pap. 21.00x (ISBN 92-64-12158-7). OECD.

OECD Staff. Geological Disposal of Radioactive Waste: Geochemical Processes. 144p. (Orig.). 1983. pap. 14.00 (ISBN 92-64-12385-7). OECD.

--Seabed Disposal of High-Level Radioactive Waste: Nuclear Energy Agency. 246p. (Orig.). 1984. pap. 28.00x (ISBN 92-64-12576-0). OECD.

Organization for Economic Research & Development Staff. Geological Disposal of Radioactive Waste: An Overview of the Current Status of Understanding & Development. 116p. (Orig.). 1984. pap. 20.00x (ISBN 92-64-12587-6). OECD.

Park, Kilho P., et al, eds. Wastes in the Ocean: Radioactive Wastes & the Ocean, Vol. 3. (Environmental Science & Technology Texts & Monographs: No. 1-121). 522p. 1983. 85.00 (ISBN 0-471-09770-5, Pub. by Wiley Interscience). Wiley.

Practices in the Treatment of Low & Intermediate-Level Radioactive Wastes. (Proceedings Ser.). (Illus.). 952p. 1966. pap. 48.00 (ISBN 92-0-020166-0, ISP116, IAEA). Unipub.

Radioactive Waste Disposal in the Ocean. (NCRP Reports Ser.: No. 16). 1954. 6.00 (ISBN 0-913392-05-7). NCRP Pubns.

Radioactive Waste Disposal into the Ground. (Safety Ser.: No. 15). (Illus.). 111p. 1965. pap. 9.00 (ISBN 92-0-123565-8, ISP103, IAEA). Unipub.

Recommendations for the Disposal of Carbon-Fourteen Wastes. (NCRP Reports Ser.: No. 12). 1953. 6.00 (ISBN 0-913392-03-0). NCRP Pubns.

Recommendations for Waste Disposal of Phosphorus - Thirty-Two & Iodine - One Thirty-One for Medical Users. (NCRP Reports Ser.: No. 9). 1951. 6.00 (ISBN 0-913392-01-4). NCRP Pubns.

Research & Development of Radioactive Waste Management & Storage. (Radioactive Waste Management Ser.: Vol. 12). 406p. 1983. text ed. 60.00 (ISBN 3-7186-0191-5). Harwood Academic.

Resnikoff, Marvin. The Next Nuclear Gamble: Transportation & Storage of Nuclear Waste. 378p. 1985. 29.95 (ISBN 0-88738-095-6). Transaction Bks.

Rochlin, Gene I. Plutonium, Power, & Politics: International Arrangements for the Disposition of Spent Nuclear Fuel. LC 78-68833. 1979. 36.50x (ISBN 0-520-03887-8). U of Cal Pr.

Roy. Radioactive Waste Disposal: The Waste Package, Vol. 1. (Radioactive Waste Disposal Ser.: No. 1). (Illus.). 256p. 1982. 30.00 (ISBN 0-08-027541-9, A145). Pergamon.

Safety Analysis Methodologies for Radioactive Waste Repositories in Shallow Ground: Procedures & Data. (Safety Ser.: No. 64). 53p. (Orig.). 1984. pap. 11.75 (ISBN 92-0-123484-8, ISP656, IAEA). Unipub.

Safety Assessment for the Underground Disposal of Radioactive Wastes. (Safety Ser.: No. 56). 46p. 1982. pap. 9.00 (ISBN 92-0-623181-2, ISP590, IAEA). Unipub.

Separation, Storage & Disposal of Krypton-85. (Technical Reports Ser.: No. 199). (Illus.). 66p. 1980. pap. 13.25 (ISBN 92-0-125180-7, IDC199, IAEA). Unipub.

Shallow Ground Disposal of Radioactive Wastes: A Guidebook. (Safety Ser.: No. 53). 52p. 1981. pap. 10.75 (ISBN 92-0-123281-0, ISP578, IAEA). Unipub.

Shapiro, Fred C. Radwaste: A Reporter's Investigation of Nuclear Waste Disposal. LC 81-40238. 288p. 1981. 14.50 (ISBN 0-394-51159-X). Random.

Simon, R. & Orlowski, S., eds. Radioactive Waste Management & Disposal. (Commission of the European Communities Symposium Ser.). 706p. 1980. 115.50 (ISBN 3-7186-0056-0). Harwood Academic.

Site Investigations, Design, Construction, Operation, Shutdown & Surveillance of Repositories for Low & Intermediate Level Radioactive Wastes in Rock Cavities. (Safety Ser.: No. 62). 95p. (Orig.). 1984. pap. 18.50 (ISBN 92-0-123284-5, ISP659, IAEA). Unipub.

Site Investigations, Design, Construction, Operation, Shutdown & Surveillance of Repositories for Low- & Intermediate-Level Radioactive Wastes in Rock Cavities. (Safety Ser.: No. 62). 92p. 1984. pap. 18.50 (ISBN 92-0-123284-5, ISP659, IAEA). Unipub.

Site Investigations for Repositories for Solid Radioactive Wastes in Shallow Ground. (Technical Reports Ser.: No. 216). (Illus.). 89p. 1982. pap. 15.50 (ISBN 92-0-125382-6, IDC216, IAEA). Unipub.

Site Selection Factors for Repositories of Solid High-Level & Alpha Bearing Wastes in Geological Formations. (Illus.). 64p. 1978. pap. 10.75 (ISBN 92-0-125177-7, IDC177, IAEA). Unipub.

Standardization of Radioactive Waste Categories. (Technical Reports Ser.: No. 101). (Illus., Orig.). 1970. pap. 6.25 (ISBN 92-0-125070-3, IDC101, IAEA). Unipub.

Stewart, Donald C. Data for Radioactive Waste Management & Nuclear Applications. 304p. 1985. 54.50 (ISBN 0-471-88627-0). Wiley.

Storage Tanks for Liquid Radioactive Wastes: Their Design & Use. (Technical Reports Ser.: No. 135). (Illus.). 55p. (Orig.). 1972. pap. 7.75 (ISBN 92-0-125072-X, IDC135, IAEA). Unipub.

Straub, C. W. Public Health Implications of Radioactive Waste Releases. 61p. 1970. pap. 3.60 (ISBN 92-4-156006-1, 597). World Health.

Underground Disposal of Radioactive Wastes: Basic Guidance. (Safety Ser.: No. 54). 56p. 1981. pap. 10.75 (ISBN 92-0-123381-7, ISP579, IAEA). Unipub.

Underground Disposal of Radioactive Wastes: Proceedings, 2 Vols. (Proceedings Ser.). 1980. pap. 85.00 (ISBN 92-0-020180-6, ISP528 1, IAEA); pap. 85.00 (ISBN 92-0-020280-2, ISP528 2). Unipub.

Use of Argillaceous Materials for the Isolation of Radioactive Waste. 290p. 1980. 17.00x (ISBN 92-64-02050-0). OECD.

Use of Local Minerals in the Treatment of Radioactive Waste. (Technical Reports Ser.: No. 136). (Illus.). 128p. (Orig.). 1973. pap. 13.25 (ISBN 92-0-125172-6, IDC136, IAEA). Unipub.

Vance, Mary. Radioactive Waste Disposal: A Bibliography. (Public Administration Ser.: P-1676). 102p. 1985. pap. 15.00 (ISBN 0-89028-386-9). Vance Biblios.

Walker, Charles A., et al, eds. Too Hot to Handle? Social & Policy Issues in the Management of Radioactive Wastes. LC 82-20000. (Fastback Ser.: No. 26). 240p. 1983. text ed. 21.50x (ISBN 0-300-02899-7); pap. 5.95x (ISBN 0-300-02993-4). Yale U Pr.

Waste Isolation Systems Panel, Board on Radioactive Waste Management, National Research Council. A Study of the Isolation System for Geologic Disposal of Radioactive Wastes. 1983. pap. text ed. 24.95 (ISBN 0-309-03384-5). Natl Acad Pr.

Willrich, Mason & Lester, Richard K. Radioactive Waste: Management & Regulation. LC 77-80228. 1977. 17.95 (ISBN 0-02-934560-X). Free Pr.

RADIOACTIVE WASTES

see also Radioactive Waste Disposal

American Society of Civil Engineers, compiled by. Nuclear Facilities Siting. LC 82-73507. 64p. 1982. pap. 11.75x (ISBN 0-87262-344-0). Am Soc Civil Eng.

--Nuclear Waste Management. LC 82-73506. 52p. 1982. pap. 11.75x (ISBN 0-87262-343-2). Am Soc Civil Eng.

Brookins, D. G., ed. Scientific Basis for Nuclear Waste Management, VI. (Materials Research Society Symposia Proceedings Ser.: Vol. 15). 808p 1983. 104.00 (ISBN 0-444-00780-6, North Holland). Elsevier.

Carley-Macauly, K. W., ed. Radioactive Waste: Advanced Management Methods for Medium-Active Liquid Waste. (Radioactive Waste Management Ser.). 352p. 1981. 79.25 (ISBN 3-7186-0060-9). Harwood Academic.

Characteristics of Solidified High-Level Waste Products. (Technical Reports Ser.). (Illus.). 1979. pap. 19.75 (ISBN 92-0-125079-7, IDC187, IAEA). Unipub.

De Marsily, G., et al, eds. Predictive Geology with Emphasis on Nuclear-Waste Disposal: Proceedings of Papers Presented at Sessions Sponsored by the International Association for Mathematical Geology at the 26th International Geological Congress in Paris, July 1980. (Computers & Geology Ser.: Vol. 4). (Illus.). 222p. 1981. 39.00 (ISBN 0-08-026246-5). Pergamon.

Development of Regulatory Procedures for the Disposal of Solid Radioactive Waste in Deep, Continental Formations. (Safety Ser.: No. 51). 26p. 1980. pap. 7.25 (ISBN 92-0-123080-X, ISP540, IAEA). Unipub.

DOE Technical Information Center. Radioactive Waste Management: Airborne Radioactive Effluents: Releases & Processing: A Bibliography. 244p. 1982. pap. 16.00 (ISBN 0-87079-479-5, DOE/TIC-3397); microfiche 4.50 (ISBN 0-87079-480-9, DOE/TIC-3397). DOE.

--Radioactive Waste Management: Decontamination & Decommissioning: Bibliography. 126p. 1982. pap. 13.00 (ISBN 0-87079-484-1, DOE/TIC-3391); microfiche 4.50 (ISBN 0-87079-485-X, DOE/TIC-3391). DOE.

--Radioactive Waste Management: Formerly Utilized Sites-Remedial Action: A Bibliography. 47p. 1982. pap. 8.50 (ISBN 0-87079-486-8, DOE/TIC-3392); microfiche 4.50 (ISBN 0-87079-487-6, DOE/TIC-3392). DOE.

--Radioactive Waste Management: High-Level Radioactive Wastes: A Bibliography. 246p. 1982. pap. 16.25 (ISBN 0-87079-475-2, DOE/TIC-3389); microfiche 4.50 (ISBN 0-87079-476-0, DOE/TIC-3389). DOE.

--Radioactive Waste Management: Radioactive Waste Inventories & Projections: A Bibliography. 18p. 1982. pap. 7.00 (ISBN 0-87079-490-6, DOE/TIC-3394); microfiche 4.50 (ISBN 0-87079-491-4, DOE/TIC-3394). DOE.

--Radioactive Waste Management: Spent Fuel Storage: A Bibliography. 154p. 1982. pap. 12.00 (ISBN 0-87079-477-9, DOE/TIC-3395); microfiche 4.50 (ISBN 0-87079-478-7, DOE/TIC-3395). DOE.

--Radioactive Waste Management: Transuranic Wastes: A Bibliography. 136p. 1982. pap. 14.50 (ISBN 0-87079-481-7, DOE/TIC-3390); microfiche 4.50 (ISBN 0-87079-482-5, DOE/TIC-3390). DOE.

--Radioactive Waste Management: Uranium Mill Tailings: A Bibliography. 105p. 1982. pap. 13.00 (ISBN 0-87079-492-2, DOE/TIC-3393); microfiche 4.50 (ISBN 0-87079-493-0, DOE/TIC-3393). DOE.

--Radioactive Waste Processing & Disposal: A Bibliography Covering January 1981 Through December 1981. 855p. 1982. pap. 33.50 (ISBN 0-87079-395-0, DOE/TIC-3311-S11); microfiche 4.50 (ISBN 0-87079-460-4, DOE/TIC-3311-S11). DOE.

--Radioactive Waste Processing & Disposal: A Bibliography Covering January 1982 Through December 1982. 1122p. 1983. pap. 40.00 (ISBN 0-87079-508-2, DOE/TIC-311-S12); microfiche 4.50 (ISBN 0-87079-509-0, DOE/TIC-3311-S12). DOE.

Fried, Sherman, ed. Radioactive Waste in Geologic Storage. LC 79-9754. (ACS Symposium Ser.: No. 100). 1979. 39.95 (ISBN 0-8412-0498-5). Am Chemical.

Heckman, Richard A. & Minichino, Camille. Nuclear Waste Management Abstracts. LC 81-19868. (IFI Data Base Library). 104p. 1982. text ed. 55.00x (ISBN 0-306-65202-1, Plenum Pr). Plenum Pub.

High Level Nuclear Waste from Past to Present: Policy & Prophecy. 1980. 3.25 (ISBN 0-686-29373-8). Tech Info Proj.

Hyde, Margaret O. Everyone's Trash Problem: Nuclear Wastes. LC 78-23859. 1979. 9.95 (ISBN 0-07-031551-5). McGraw.

Jensen, B. S. Migration Phenomena of Radionuclides into the Geosphere: A Critical Review of the Available Information. (Radioactive Waste Management Ser.). 200p. 1982. 25.50 (ISBN 3-7186-0120-6). Harwood Academic.

League of Women Voters. The Nuclear Waste Primer. 96p. (Orig.). 1985. 11.95 (ISBN 0-8052-6007-2, Pub. by N Lyons Bks); pap. 5.95 (ISBN 0-8052-6006-4, Pub. by N Lyons Bks). Schocken.

League of Women Voters Education Fund. A Nuclear Waste Primer. (Illus.). 63p. 1982. pap. 3.00 (ISBN 0-89959-253-8, 391). LWV US.

Lipschutz, Ronnie. Radioactive Waste: Politics, Technology & Risk. LC 79-19649. 272p. 1980. prof ref 26.50x (ISBN 0-88410-621-7). Ballinger Pub.

Machi, S., ed. Radiation Processing for Environmental Conservation. 202p. 1985. pap. 27.50 (ISBN 0-08-031435-X). Pergamon.

Management of Radioactive Wastes at Nuclear Power Plants. (Safety Ser.: No. 28). (Illus.). 225p. 1968. pap. 16.50 (ISBN 92-0-123268-3, ISP208, IAEA). Unipub.

The Management of Radioactive Wastes Produced by Radioisotope Users. (Safety Ser.: No. 12). 58p. (Fr. & Rus. eds. also avail.). 1965. pap. 6.25 (ISBN 92-0-123265-9, ISP87, IAEA). Unipub.

The Management of Radioactive Wastes Produced by Radioisotope Users: Technical Addendum. (Safety Ser.: No. 19). (Illus.). 81p. (Fr. ed. also avail.). 1966. pap. 7.75 (ISBN 92-0-123366-3, ISP119, IAEA). Unipub.

Management of Wastes from Uranium Mining & Milling. (Proceedings Ser.). (Illus.). 735p. 1983. pap. 92.50 (ISBN 92-0-020282-9, ISP622, IAEA). Unipub.

Milnes, A. G. Geology & Radwaste. Date not set. 60.00 (ISBN 0-12-498070-8); pap. 39.95 (ISBN 0-12-498071-6). Acad Pr.

Mineral & Energy Resources Board. Radioactive Wastes at the Hanford Reservation. 1978. pap. 9.95 (ISBN 0-309-02745-4). Natl Acad Pr.

Moghissl, A. A., et al, eds. Nuclear Power Waste Technology. (Bk. No. G00132). 1978. 40.00 (ISBN 0-685-37571-4). ASME.

Moore, John G., ed. Scientific Basis for Nuclear Waste Management, Vol. 3. LC 81-10663. 650p. 1981. 69.50x (ISBN 0-306-40803-1, Plenum Pr). Plenum Pub.

Murdock, Steve H. & Leistritz, F. Larry. Nuclear Waste: Socioeconomic Dimensions of Long-Term Storage. LC 83-60130. (Special Studies in Science, Technology, & Public Policy-Society). 343p. 1983. 28.50x (ISBN 0-86531-447-0). Westview.

Murray, Raymond L. Understanding Radioactive Waste. Powell, Judith A., ed. (Illus.). 128p. 1982. pap. 10.00 (ISBN 0-935470-12-3). Battelle.

--Understanding Radioactive Waste. 2nd ed. Powell, Judith A., ed. (Illus.). 128p. 1983. pap. 10.00 (ISBN 0-935470-19-0). Battelle.

Near-Field Phenomena in Geologic Repositories for Radioactive Waste. (Eng. & Fr., Orig.). 1982. pap. 24.50x (ISBN 92-64-02236-8). OECD.

OECD-NEA. Long-Term Management of Radioactive Waste: Legal Administrative & Financial Aspects. 136p. (Orig.). 1984. pap. 14.00X (ISBN 92-64-12622-8). OECD.

--Radiological Significance & Management of Tritium, Carbon-14, Krypton-85, Iodine-129, Arising from the Nuclear Fuel Cycle. (Illus.). 222p. (Orig.). 1980. pap. text ed. 19.00x (ISBN 92-64-12083-1, 66-80-06-1) (ISBN 92-64-12083-1). OECD.

OECD Staff. Geological Disposal of Radioactive Waste in SITU Experiments in Granite. (Orig.). 1983. pap. 20.00 (ISBN 92-64-02416-6). OECD.

--Radionuclide Release Scenarios for Geologic Repositories. 233p. (Orig.). 1981. pap. 15.00x (ISBN 92-64-02172-8). OECD.

Plumb, G. R., ed. Nuclear Waste Reprocessing. (Illus.). 72p. 1984. pap. 40.00 (ISBN 0-08-031509-7). Pergamon.

Radioiodine Removal in Nuclear Facilities: Methods & Techniques for Normal & Emergency Situations. (Technical Reports Ser.: No. 201). (Illus.). 98p. 1981. pap. 17.25 (ISBN 92-0-125280-3, IDC201, IAEA). Unipub.

Shrum, Wesley. Organized Technology: Networks & Innovation in Technical Systems. (Science & Society: A Purdue University Series in Science, Technology, & Human Values). (Illus.). 304p. 1985. pap. 4.50 (ISBN 0-911198-74-1). Purdue U Pr.

Symposium, Stockholm, Sweden, June 2-5, 1975. Combined Effects of Radioactive Chemical & Thermal Releases to the Environment: Proceedings. (Proceedings Ser.). (Illus.). 358p. 1976. pap. 33.00 (ISBN 92-0-020275-6, ISP404, IAEA). Unipub.

Topp. Scientific Basis for Nuclear Waste Management. (Materials Research Society Symposia Ser.: Vol. 6). 768p. 1982. 112.50 (ISBN 0-444-00699-0, North-Holland). Elsevier.

Treatment of Low- & Intermediate-Level Liquid Radioactive Wastes. (Technical Reports Ser.: No. 236). (Illus.). 145p. 1985. pap. 26.50 (ISBN 92-0-125184-X, IDC236, IAEA). Unipub.

Treatment of Low & Intermediate-Level Solid Radioactive Wastes. (Technical Reports Ser.: No. 223). (Illus.). 93p. 1983. pap. 18.50 (ISBN 92-0-125183-1, IDC223, IAEA). Unipub.

Williams, Frederick C. & Deese, David A., eds. Nuclear Nonproliferation: The Spent Fuel Problem. (Pergamon Policy Studies). 1980. 35.00 (ISBN 0-08-023887-4). Pergamon.

RADIOACTIVITY

see also Autoradiography; Beta Rays; Carbon–Isotopes; Cosmic Rays; Electrons; Fluorescence; Helium; Ionization of Gases; Nuclear Geophysics; Nuclear Physics; Plutonium; Radioactive Contamination of Food; Radioactive Substances; Radioactive Tracers; Radiobiology; Radiochemistry; Radiography; Radiotherapy; Radium; Tracers (Chemistry); Transmutation (Chemistry); Transplutonium Elements; Transuranium Elements; X-Rays

Adams, John A. & Lowder, Wayne M., eds. Natural Radiation Environment. LC 64-12256. (Illus.). 1964. 35.00x (ISBN 0-226-00596-8). U of Chicago Pr.

Assessment of Airborne Radioactivity. (Illus., Orig.). 1967. pap. 50.25 (ISBN 92-0-020367-1, ISP159, IAEA). Unipub.

Badash, Lawrence. Radioactivity in America: Growth & Decay of a Science. LC 78-20525. 1979. text ed. 27.50x (ISBN 0-8018-2187-8). Johns Hopkins.

Curie, Marie. Radioactive Substances: A Translation from the French of the Classical Thesis Presented to the Faculty of Sciences in Paris. LC 79-139128. (Illus.). 1971. Repr. of 1961 ed. lib. bdg. 18.75x (ISBN 0-8371-5744-7, CURS). Greenwood.

Edelmann, A., ed. Radioactivity for Pharmaceutical & Allied Research Laboratories. 1960. 52.50 (ISBN 0-12-230850-6). Acad Pr.

Environmental Radioactivity: Proceedings of the 19th Annual Meetings. 1984. 17.00 (ISBN 0-318-02045-9). NCRP Pubns.

Horner, Jack K. Natural Radioactivity in Water Supplies. (Westview Studies in Water Policy & Management). 325p. 1985. pap. 27.50x (ISBN 0-8133-0050-9). Westview.

Hutchinson, J. M. & Mann, W. B., eds. Metrology Needs in the Measurement of Environmental Radioactivity: Seminar Sponsered by the International Committee for Radionuclide Metrology. (Illus.). 1980. pap. 39.00 (ISBN 0-08-022943-3). Pergamon.

Jenkins, E. N. & Lewis, I. Radioactivity: A Science in Its Historical & Social Context. LC 78-11959. (Wykeham Science Ser.: No. 52). 197p. 1979. pap. 13.50x (ISBN 0-8448-1371-0). Crane-Russak Co.

Kathren, Ronald L. Radioactivity in the Environment. LC 84-3838. 368p. 1984. text ed. 66.00 (ISBN 3-7186-0203-2). Harwood Academic.

Lapp, Ralph E. The Radiation Controversy. 2nd ed. LC 78-83841. (Illus.). 1979. pap. 2.95 ea. (ISBN 0-9603716-0-5). Reddy Comm.

Lenoble, Jacqueline, ed. Radiative Transfer in Scattering & Absorbing Atmospheres: Standard Computational Procedures. 1985. write for info. (ISBN 0-937194-05-0). A Deepak Pub.

Lipschutz, Ronnie. Radioactive Waste: Politics, Technology & Risk. LC 79-19649. 272p. 1980. prof ref 26.50x (ISBN 0-88410-621-7). Ballinger Pub.

Miller, Dudley G. Radioactivity & Radiation Detection. LC 70-146446. (Illus.). 122p. 1972. 35.75x (ISBN 0-677-01490-2). Gordon.

National Council on Radiation Protection. A Handbook of Radioactivity Measurement Procedures. 2nd ed. LC 84-25423. (NCRP Report Ser.: No. 58). 600p. 1985. text ed. 22.00 (ISBN 0-913392-71-5). Natl Coun Radiation.

Nesmeyanov, A. N. Guide to Practical Radio Chemistry, Vol. 2. 446p. 1984. 9.00 (ISBN 0-8285-2888-8, Pub. by Mir Pubs USSR). Imported Pubns.

Pfotzer, G., et al. Time Pattern of Ionizing Radiation in Balloon Altitudes in High Latitudes, 2 Pts in 1. 1962. pap. 8.90 (ISBN 0-387-02880-3). Springer-Verlag.

Radioactivite. (Technical Reports Ser.: No. 47). (Fr. & Rus.). 131p. 1965. pap. (ISBN 92-0-235065-5, STI/DOC/10/47, IAEA). Unipub.

Rutherford, Ernest & Boltwood, Bertram B. Rutherford & Boltwood: Letters on Radioactivity. Badash, Lawrence, ed. LC 78-81411. (Yale Studies in the History of Science & Medicine Ser.: No. 4). (Illus.). pap. 100.50 (ISBN 0-8357-9490-3, 2016787). Bks Demand UMI.

Stewart, Donald C. Handling Radioactivity: A Practical Approach for Scientists & Engineers. LC 80-19258. 282p. 1981. 49.50 (ISBN 0-471-04557-8, Pub. by Wiley-Interscience). Wiley.

RADIOACTIVITY–INSTRUMENTS

see also Nuclear Counters; Radioactivity–Measurement

Directory of Whole-Body Radioactivity Monitors. (Technical Directories). (Illus.). 1034p. (Orig.). 1970. pap. 80.75 (ISBN 92-0-112070-2, ISP213, IAEA). Unipub.

International Commission on Radiation Units and Measurements. Radiation Protection Instrumentation & Its Application. LC 70-177297. (Illus.). v, 60p. 1971. 12.00 (ISBN 0-913394-38-6). Intl Comm Rad Meas.

RADIOACTIVITY–MEASUREMENT

see also Neutrons–Measurement; Radioactivation Analysis; Radioactive Dating; Radioactive Prospecting; Radioactivity–Instruments; Radioisotope Scanning

Akimov, Yu K. Scintillation Counters in High Energy Physics. 1965. 49.00 (ISBN 0-12-047450-6). Acad Pr.

Institute of Physics. Radiation Measurements in Nuclear Power 1966. (Institute of Physics Conference Ser.: No. 2). 1967. 55.00 (ISBN 0-9960028-1-2, Pub. by Inst Physics England). Heyden.

International Commission on Radiation Units and Measurements. Linear Energy Transfer. LC 72-113962. (Illus.). viii, 51p. 1970. 10.00 (ISBN 0-913394-34-3). Intl Comm Rad Meas.

International Commission on Radiation Units & Measurements. Measurement of Low-Level Radioactivity. LC 71-186876. (Illus.). v, 66p. 1972. 12.00 (ISBN 0-913394-40-8). Intl Comm Rad Meas.

International Commission on Radiation Units and Measurements. Neutron Fluence, Neutron Spectra & Kerma. LC 75-97639. (Illus.). viii, 57p. 1969. 9.00 (ISBN 0-913394-31-9). Intl Comm Rad Meas.

Kiefer, H. & Maushart, R. Radiation Protection Measurement. Friese, Ralf, tr. LC 70-133884. 576p. 1972. Pergamon.

Mann, W. B. & Ayres, R. L., eds. Radioactivity & Its Measurement. 2nd ed. LC 79-40881. (Illus.). 1980. 48.00 (ISBN 0-08-025028-9); pap. 14.50 (ISBN 0-08-025027-0). Pergamon.

Methods of Low-Level Counting & Spectrometry: Proceedings of an International Symposium on Methods of Low-Level Counting & Spectrometry Organized by the International Atomic Energy & Held in Berlin (West), 6-10 April 1981. (Proceedings Ser.). (Illus.). 563p. 1982. pap. 66.50 (ISBN 92-0-030081-2, ISP592, IAEA). Unipub.

Mitchell, I. V. & Barfoot, K. M. Particle-Induced X-Ray Emission Analysis: Application to Analytical Problems. (Nuclear Science Applications Ser.). 63p. 1981. 15.50 (ISBN 3-7186-0085-4). Harwood Academic.

Particle Size Analysis in Estimating the Significance of Airborne Contamination. (Technical Reports Ser.: No. 179). (Illus.). 234p. 1978. pap. 30.25 (ISBN 92-0-125078-9, IDC179, IAEA). Unipub.

Rapid Methods for Measuring Radioactivity in the Environment. (Proceedings Ser.). (Illus.). 967p. (Orig.). 1972. pap. 71.50 (ISBN 92-0-020371-X, ISP289, IAEA). Unipub.

Traceability & Quality Control in the Measurement of Environmental Radioactivity: Seminar Sponsored by the International Committee for Radionuclide Metrology in Braunschweig, June 18-19, 1979. 80p. 1980. pap. 15.00 (ISBN 0-08-026253-8). Pergamon.

Tritium Measurement Techniques. LC 76-16301. (NCRP Reports Ser.: No. 47). 1976. 9.00 (ISBN 0-913392-29-4). NCRP Pubns.

Wang, Chih H. & Willis, David L. Radiotracer Methodology in the Biological Environmental & Physical Sciences. (Illus.). 512p. 1975. 40.95 (ISBN 0-13-752212-6). P-H.

RADIOACTIVITY–PHYSIOLOGICAL EFFECT

see also Nuclear Medicine

Assessment of Radioactive Contamination in Man. (Proceedings Ser.). (Illus.). 698p. (Orig.). 1972. pap. 51.25 (ISBN 92-0-020072-9, ISP290, IAEA). Unipub.

Brill, A. B., et al. Low-Level Radiation Effects: A Fact Book. 2nd ed. Bigler, Rodney E., ed. LC 82-16937. 156p. 1982. looseleaf incl. 1985 updates 32.00 (ISBN 0-932004-23-7); Updates 1985; 80p. Insert Package 10.00 (ISBN 0-317-19594-8). Soc Nuclear Med.

CISM (International Center for Mechanical Sciences), Dept. for Mechanics of Deformable Bodies, Univ. of Vienna, 1970. Radiation Damage. Schmid, E. & Lintner, K., eds. Incl. Behavior of Insonated Metals. (CISM Pubns. Ser.: No. 64). (Illus.). 88p. 1973. pap. 10.60 (ISBN 0-387-81124-9). Springer-Verlag.

Jenkins, E. N. Radioactivity: A Science in Its Historical & Social Context. (The Wykeman Ser.: No. 48). 200p. 1979. pap. cancelled (ISBN 0-85109-730-8). Taylor & Francis.

Manual on Early Medical Treatment of Possible Radiation Injury: With an Appendix on Sodium Burns. (Safety Ser.: No. 47). 142p. 1978. pap. 17.50 (ISBN 92-0-123278-0, ISP506, IAEA). Unipub.

Trenn, T. J., ed. Radioactivity & Atomic Theory. 536p. 1975. cancelled (ISBN 0-85066-077-7). Taylor & Francis.

RADIOACTIVITY–SAFETY MEASURES

see also Atomic Bomb–Safety Measures; Radioactive Decontamination; Radioactive Waste Disposal; Shielding (Radiation)

Control & Removal of Radioactive Contamination in Laboratories. (NCRP Reports Ser.: No. 8). 1951. 6.00 (ISBN 0-913392-00-6). NCRP Pubns.

International Commission on Radiological Protection. Radiation Protection - Recommendations of the ICRP. 2nd ed. (ICRP Publication Ser.: No. 26). 1966. pap. 15.75 (ISBN 0-08-021511-4). Pergamon.

--Reference Man. (ICRP Publication Ser: No. 23). 1975. 89.00 (ISBN 0-08-017024-2). Pergamon.

Kiefer, H. & Maushart, R. Radiation Protection Measurement. Friese, Ralf, tr. LC 70-133884. 576p. 1972. Pergamon.

Management of Persons Accidentally Contaminated with Radionuclides. LC 79-91648. (NCRP Reports Ser.: No. 65). 1980. 10.00 (ISBN 0-913392-49-9). NCRP Pubns.

Sharpe, A. G. & Emeleus, H. J., eds. Advances in Inorganic Chemistry & Radiochemistry, Vol. 26. (Serial Publication Ser.). 1983. 64.50 (ISBN 0-12-023626-5). Acad Pr.

RADIOECOLOGY

see also Radioactive Pollution

Assembly of Mathematical & Physical Sciences, National Research Council. Long-Term Worldwide Effects of Multiple Nuclear-Weapons Detonations. LC 75-29733. xvi, 213p. 1975. pap. 14.95 (ISBN 0-309-02418-8). Natl Acad Pr.

Clubb, Jerome M. Ecological Data in Comparative Research: Report on a First International Data Confrontation Seminar. (Reports & Papers in the Social Sciences: No. 25). 37p. 1970. pap. 5.00 (ISBN 92-3-100845-5, U174, UNESCO). Unipub.

Effluent & Environmental Radiation Surveillance, STP 698. 374p. 1980. 36.50x (ISBN 0-8031-0329-8, 04-698000-35). ASTM.

Eichholz, Geoffrey G. Environmental Aspects of Nuclear Power. LC 84-27759. (Illus.). 704p. 1985. 47.50 (ISBN 0-87371-017-7). Lewis Pubs Inc.

Eisenbud, Merril. Environmental Radioactivity. 2nd ed. (Environmental Science: An Interdisciplinary Monograph). 1973. 75.00 (ISBN 0-12-235150-9). Acad Pr.

Environmental Isotope Data: Part 2: World Survey of Isotope Concentration in Precipitation (1964-1965) (Technical Reports Ser.: No. 117). (Illus.). 403p. (Orig.). 1970. pap. 27.25 (ISBN 92-0-145070-2, IDC117, IAEA). Unipub.

Environmental Radiation Measurements. LC 76-51565. (NCRP Reports Ser.: No. 50). 1976. 9.00 (ISBN 0-913392-32-4). NCRP Pubns.

Klechkovskii, V. M., et al. Radioecology. LC 73-4697. 371p. 1973. 72.95x (ISBN 0-470-49035-7). Halsted Pr.

Klement, A. W. & Schultz, V., eds. Freshwater & Terrestrial Radioecology: A Selected Bibliography. LC 80-22169. 587p. 1980. 48.50 (ISBN 0-87933-389-8). Van Nos Reinhold.

Kulikov, N. V. & Molchanova, I. V. Continental Radioecology: Soil & Freshwater Ecosystems. Pavlov, V. P., tr. from Rus. 174p. 1982. 29.50x (ISBN 0-306-40494-X, Plenum Pr). Plenum Pub.

Kuo-Nan Liou, ed. An Introduction to Atmospheric Radiation. LC 80-769. (International Geophysics Ser.). 1980. 37.50 (ISBN 0-12-451450-2). Acad Pr.

Maximum Permissible Body Burdens & Maximum Permissible Concentrations of Radionuclides in Air & in Water for Occupational Exposures. (NCRP Reports Ser.: No. 22). 1959. 6.00 (ISBN 0-913392-06-5). NCRP Pubns.

NEA Seminar, 3rd, Tokyo, Oct. 1-5 1979. Marine Radioecology: Proceedings. 418p. 1980. 21.50x (ISBN 92-64-02053-5). OECD.

Nuclear Power, the Environment, & Man. (Illus.). 195p. 1982. pap. 16.00 (ISBN 92-0-129082-9, ISP635, IAEA). Unipub.

Radiation for a Clean Environment: Proceedings. (Proceedings Ser.). (Illus.). 672p. 1976. pap. 67.25 (ISBN 92-0-060075-1, ISP402, IAEA). Unipub.

Rapid Methods for Measuring Radioactivity in the Environment. (Proceedings Ser.). (Illus.). 967p. (Orig.). 1972. pap. 71.50 (ISBN 92-0-020371-X, ISP289, IAEA). Unipub.

Rudolph, Thomas D., ed. The Enterprise, Wisconsin, Radiation Forest: Preirradiation Ecological Studies, Pt. 1. ERDA Technical Information Center. LC 74-600049. 155p. 1974. pap. 12.00 (TID-26113-PT. 1); microfiche 4.50 (ISBN 0-87079-193-1, TID-26113-PT. 1). DOE.

Schultz, Vincent & Whicker, F. Ward. Radioecological Techniques. LC 81-22706. 309p. 1982. text ed. 37.50 (ISBN 0-306-40797-3, Plenum Pr). Plenum Pub.

Schultz, Vincent & Whicker, F. W., eds. Radioecology: Nuclear Energy & the Environment, Vols. I & II. 1982. Vol. I, 224p. 74.50 (ISBN 0-8493-5353-X); Vol. II, 240p. 74.50 (ISBN 0-8493-5354-8). CRC Pr.

The Study of Radiation in a Tropical Atmosphere: Final Report. 100p. 1970. pap. 5.00x (ISBN 0-299-97028-0). U of Wis Pr.

Symposium on Radioecology, Oregon State University, May 12-14, 1975. Radioecology & Energy Resources: Proceedings. Cushing, C. E., Jr., ed. (Ecological Society of America Special Publications Ser.: No. 1). 1976. 58.00 (ISBN 0-12-786290-0). Acad Pr.

Zavitkovski, J., ed. The Enterprise, Wisconsin, Radiation Forest: Radioecological Studies, Pt. 2. ERDA Technical Information Center. LC 76-30437. 220p. 1977. pap. 13.50 (ISBN 0-87079-102-8, TID-26113-P2); microfiche 4.50 (ISBN 0-87079-194-X, TID-26113-P2). DOE.

RADIOFREQUENCY SPECTROSCOPY

see Radio Frequency Spectroscopy

RADIOGENETICS

Crow, James F. How Well Can We Assess Genetic Risk? Not Very. 1981. 9.00 (ISBN 0-913392-56-1). NCRP Pubns.

Evans, H. J., et al, eds. Human Radiation Cytogenetics. 1967. 17.00 (ISBN 0-444-10188-8, North-Holland). Elsevier.

Genetical Aspects of Radiosensitivity: Mechanisms of Repair. (Panel Proceedings Ser.). (Illus.). 175p. 1966. pap. 10.75 (ISBN 92-0-111266-1, ISP130, IAEA). Unipub.

RADIOGRAPHIC EXAMINATION OF MATERIALS

see Radiography, Industrial

RADIOGRAPHY

see also Autoradiography; Microradiography; Radiography, Medical; X-Ray Photogrammetry; X-Rays

Anderson, D. H. Compartmental Modeling & Tracer Kinetics. (Lecture Notes in Biomathematics: Vol. 50). 302p. 1983. pap. 20.00 (ISBN 0-387-12303-2). Springer-Verlag.

Ballinger, Philip W. Merrill's Atlas of Radiographic Positions & Radiologic Procedures, 3 Vols. 5th ed. (Illus.). 950p. 1982. text ed. 99.95 (ISBN 0-8016-3408-3). Mosby.

Barrett, H. H. Radiological Imaging, Vol. I: The Theory of Image Formation, Detection, & Processing. Swindell, W., ed. LC 80-69416. 1981. 55.00 (ISBN 0-12-079601-5). Acad Pr.

Bell, G. & Finlay, D. Basic Radiographic Positioning & Anatomy. (Illus.). 270p. Date not set. price not set (Pub. by Bailliere-Tindall). Saunders.

British Nuclear Energy Society, ed. Radiography with Neutrons. 167p. 1975. 80.00x (ISBN 0-7277-0019-7, Pub. by Brit Nuclear England). State Mutual Bk.

Bryant, Lawrence E. & McIntire, Paul, eds. Radiography & Radiation Testing. 2nd ed. (Nondestructive Testing Handbook). (Illus.). 925p. 1984. 99.95 (ISBN 0-931403-00-6, 128). Am Soc Nondestructive.

Capp, M. Paul. Digital Radiographic Imaging. (Illus.). 500p. Date not set. price not set (ISBN 0-7216-1117-6). Saunders.

Carroll, Quinn B. Fuchs's Principles of Radiographic Exposure, Processing & Quality Control. 3rd ed. (Illus.). 394p. 1985. 29.75x (ISBN 0-398-05081-3); lab manual 12.75x (ISBN 0-398-05082-1); instr's. manual 9.75x (ISBN 0-398-05117-8). C C Thomas.

Combined Meeting Program & Abstracts: 32nd Annual Denver X-ray Conference & the ACA Summer Meeting, 1983. 1983. pap. 5.00 (ISBN 0-317-01198-7). Polycrystal Bk Serv.

Curtis, Christopher, et al. Whole-Body Autoradiography. (Biological Techniques Ser.). 1981. 35.00 (ISBN 0-12-199660-3). Acad Pr.

Donohue, Daniel P. An Analysis of Radiographic Quality: Lab Manual & Workbook. 2nd ed. (Illus.). 378p. 1984. pap. text ed. 19.00 (ISBN 0-8391-1988-7, 20885). Univ Park.

Edwards, Cris, et al. Radiation Protection for Dental Radiographers. LC 84-42910. (Illus.). 300p. (Orig.). 1984. pap. text ed. 14.95x (ISBN 0-940122-16-2, MAP-12). Multi Media CO.

Ely, R. V., ed. Microfocal Radiography. LC 80-40653. 1981. 69.50 (ISBN 0-12-238140-8). Acad Pr.

Felix, R., et al. Contrast Media in Digital Radiography. (Current Clinical Practice Ser.: Vol. 12). 1984. 77.00 (ISBN 0-444-90365-8, I-489-83). Elsevier.

Fundamentals of Radiography, Module 26-5. (Nondestructive Examination Techniques I Ser.). (Illus.). 84p. 1979. spiral bdg. 9.00x (ISBN 0-87683-094-7). G P Courseware.

Goodman, Lawrence R. & Putnam, C. The Radiographic Evaluation of the Intensive Care Unit Patient. LC 78-50186. Date not set. write for info. (ISBN 0-87527-172-3). Green.

Harvey, Andrea & Geisler, Linda. Radiographers: Laboratory Manual for Students. 248p. 1984. 24.50 (ISBN 0-916973-01-8). Burnell Co.

Hiss, Stephen S. Understanding Radiography. 2nd ed. (Illus.). 536p. 1983. 34.75x (ISBN 0-398-04774-X); spiral study guide 16.75x (ISBN 0-398-04775-8). C C Thomas.

Kreel, Louis. Clark's Positioning in Radiography, Vol. 1. 10th ed. (Illus.). 500p. 1980. 49.95 (ISBN 0-8151-5190-X). Year Bk Med.

Krinitzsky, E. L. Radiography in the Earth Sciences & Soil Mechanics. LC 75-207539. (Monographs in Geoscience Ser.). 157p. 1970. 29.50x (ISBN 0-306-30448-1, Plenum Pr). Plenum Pub.

Lambrecht, R. M. & Eckelman, W. C., eds. Animal Models in Radiotracer Design. (Illus.). 260p. 1983. 36.00 (ISBN 0-387-90878-1). Springer-Verlag.

Lawson, Elizabeth. Radiography & Radiotherapy: Seeing Through You. 136p. 1982. 30.00x (ISBN 0-85225-759-7, Pub. by Careers Con England). State Mutual Bk.

McKears & Owen. Surgical Anatomy for Radiographers. 124p. 1979. pap. 12.50 (ISBN 0-7236-0511-4). PSG Pub Co.

Maurer, Edward L. Practical Applied Roentgenology. 212p. 1983. text ed. 39.50 (ISBN 0-683-05650-6). Williams & Wilkins.

Miller, R. Radiographic Contrast Agents. Miller, R., ed. (Illus.). 544p. 1977. text ed. 53.00 (ISBN 0-8391-1117-7). Univ Park.

Myers, Patricia A. An Introduction to Radiographic Technique. LC 79-25032. 128p. 1980. 17.95 (ISBN 0-03-056654-1). Praeger.

Practical Applications of Neutron Radiography & Gaging - STP 586. 330p. 1976. 25.50 (ISBN 0-8031-0535-5, 04-586000-22). ASTM.

Radiographic Specifications & Code Requirements. (Nondestructive Examination Techniques Ser.: No. I: Module 26-7). (Illus.). 40p. 1979. spiral bdg. 7.00x (ISBN 0-87683-096-3). G P Courseware.

Radiography Inspection. (Nondestructive Examination Techniques Ser.: No. I: Module 26-6). (Illus.). 52p. 1979. spiral bdg. 7.00x (ISBN 0-87683-095-5). G P Courseware.

Roberts, T. R. Radiochromatography: The Chromatography & Electrophoresis of Radiolabelled Compounds. (Journal of Chromatography Library: Vol. 14). 174p. 1978. 49.00 (ISBN 0-444-41656-0). Elsevier.

Snopek, Albert M. Fundamentals of Special Radiographic Procedures. (Illus.). 352p. 1975. text ed. 34.00 (ISBN 0-07-059515-1). McGraw.

--Fundamentals of Special Radiographic Procedures. 2nd ed. (Illus.). 350p. 1984. write for info. (ISBN 0-7216-1293-8). Saunders.

Sweeney, Richard J. Radiographic Artifacts: Their Cause & Control. (Illus.). 263p. 1983. text ed. 31.75 (ISBN 0-397-50554-X, 65-07081, Lippincott Medical). Lippincott.

Takahashi, S. & Sakuma, S. Magnification Radiography. (Illus.). 160p. 1975. text ed. 48.00 (ISBN 0-387-07238-1). Springer-Verlag.

Zimmer, Emil A. Artifacts, & Handling & Processing Faults on X-Ray Films. (Illus.). 67p. 1960. 29.00 (ISBN 0-8089-0554-6, 794968). Grune.

RADIOGRAPHY, INDUSTRIAL

see also Radiography; Radioisotopes–Industrial Applications

Engineering Industry Training Board, ed. Training for Industrial Site Radiography, 14 vols. Incl. Vol. 1. Introduction to Radiography; Vol. 2. Ionizing Radiations; Vol. 4. Image Formation; Vol. 5. Safety; Vol. 6. X-Ray Equipment; Vol. 7. Gamma-Ray Equipment; Vol. 8. Exposure; Vol. 9. Operations; Vol. 10. Pipe-Crawler Equipment. 69.95. (Illus.). 1977. Set. 42.50x (ISBN 0-89563-025-7). Intl Ideas.

Halmshaw, R. Industrial Radiology: Theory & Practice. (Illus.). xii, 329p. 1982. 64.75 (ISBN 0-85334-105-2, Pub. by Elsevier Applied Sci England). Elsevier.

International Labour Office. Guidelines for the Use of ILO International Classification of Radiographs of Pneumoconioses. rev. ed. (Occupational Safety & Health Ser.: No. 22). (Orig.). 1984. pap. 3.40 (ISBN 92-2-102463-6). Intl Labour Office.

Radiation Safety Training Criteria for Industrial Radiography. LC 78-61401. (NCRP Reports Ser.: No. 61). 1978. 8.00 (ISBN 0-913392-45-6). NCRP Pubns.

Radiography in Modern Industry, No. W-37. 4th rev. ed. (Illus.). 170p. 1980. 15.00 (ISBN 0-87985-257-7). Eastman Kodak.

Rumyantsev, S. Industrial Radiology. (Russian Monographs Ser.). 280p. 1969. 75.25 (ISBN 0-677-20850-2). Gordon.

RADIOGRAPHY, MEDICAL

see also Tomography

also subdivision Radiography under names of organs e.g. Brain–Radiography

Bell, Roy. One Thousand & One Questions about Radiologic Technology, Vol. 3. LC 80-137150. (Illus.). 192p. 1983. pap. text ed. 10.50 (ISBN 0-8391-1957-7, 20559). Univ Park.

--Self-Assessment Tests for the Practicing Radiographer. 208p. 1984. pap. text ed. 12.00 (ISBN 0-8391-2079-6, 22055). Univ Park.

Bloom, William L., Jr., et al. Medical Radiographic Technic. 3rd ed. (Illus.). 368p. 1979. photocopy ed. 37.75x (ISBN 0-398-00171-5). C C Thomas.

Brody, William R. Digital Radiography. (Illus.). 240p. 1984. text ed. 40.50 (ISBN 0-89004-242-X). Raven.

Bull, Sheila. Skeletal Radiography. (Illus.). 224p. 1985. pap. text ed. 27.95 (ISBN 0-407-00278-2). Butterworth.

Cottrall, M. B. Fundamentals of Clinical Radionuclide Imaging. 1982. 25.00x (ISBN 0-686-92013-9, Pub. by Brit Inst Radiology England). State Mutual Bk.

Goldman, Myer & Cope, David. A Radiographic Index. 7th ed. (Illus.). 112p. 1982. pap. text ed. 10.00 (ISBN 0-7236-0660-9). PSG Pub Co.

Hay, G. A. & Hughes, D. First Year Physics for Radiographers. 3rd ed. (Illus.). 343p. 1984. pap. 19.95 (ISBN 0-7216-0811-6, Pub. by Bailliere-Tindall). Saunders.

Heuck, F. H., ed. Radiological Functional Analysis of the Vascular System: Contrast Media-Methods - Results. (Illus.). 296p. 1983. 50.00 (ISBN 0-387-12185-4). Springer-Verlag.

Jacobi, Charles A. & Paris, Don Q. Textbook of Radiologic Technology. 6th ed. LC 76-41715. (Illus.). 559p. 1977. text ed. 28.95 (ISBN 0-8016-2385-5). Mosby.

James, A. Everett, Jr., et al. Digital Image Processing in Radiology. 278p. 1984. 57.00 (ISBN 0-683-04355-2). Williams & Wilkins.

Kaemmer. Comprehensive Review of Radiography. (Red Book Ser.). 400p. Date not set. price not set (ISBN 0-471-80817-2). Wiley.

Kelsey, Charles A. Radiation Safety for Laboratory Technicians. Gardner, Alvin F., ed. (Allied Health Professions Monographs). 42p. 1983. 5.00 (ISBN 0-87527-319-X). Green.

Kreel, Louis. Clark's Positioning in Radiography, Vol. 2. 1981. 49.95 (ISBN 0-8151-5191-8). Year Bk Med.

Lauer, Gary. Principles & Practices of the College-Based Radiography Program. Gardner, Alvin F., ed. (Allied Health Professions Monograph). 280p. 1984. 37.50 (ISBN 0-87527-310-6). Green.

Lawson, Elizabeth. Radiography & Radiotherapy: Seeing Through You. 136p. 1982. 30.00x (ISBN 0-85225-759-7, Pub. by Careers Con England). State Mutual Bk.

Mettler, Fred A., Jr. & Moseley, Robert D., eds. Medical Effects of Ionizing Radiation. 304p. 1985. 59.50 (ISBN 0-8089-1704-8, 792896). Grune.

Rothschild, Marcus A. Abdominal Organ Imaging. LC 78-55281. (Illus.). 212p. 1979. 25.50 (ISBN 0-88416-193-5). PSG Pub Co.

Seeram, Euclid. X-Ray Imaging Equipment: An Introduction. (Illus.). 610p. 1985. 44.50x (ISBN 0-398-05078-3). C C Thomas.

RADIOIMMUNOASSAY

Albertini, ed. Radioimmunoassay of Hormones, Proteins & Enzymes. (International Congress Ser.: Vol. 528). 1981. 61.00 (ISBN 0-444-90173-6). Elsevier.

Albertini, A., et al, eds. Cost-Benefit & Predictive Value of Radioimmunoassay. (Symposia of the Giovanni Lorenzini Foundation Ser.: Vol. 18). 270p. 1984. 62.00 (ISBN 0-444-80618-0). Elsevier.

Bloom, Stephen R. & Long, R. G. Radioimmunoassay of Gut Regulatory Peptides. 256p. 1982. 35.95 (ISBN 0-03-062116-X). Praeger.

Bowie, Lemuel J. Automated Instrumentation for Radioimmunoassay. 224p. 1980. 69.00 (ISBN 0-8493-5747-0). CRC Pr.

Chard, T. An Introduction to Radioimmunoassay & Related Techniques. 2nd, rev. & enl. ed. (Laboratory Techniques in Biochemistry & Molecular Biology Ser.: Vol. 6, Pt. 2). 284p. 1982. 72.25 (ISBN 0-444-80420-X, Biomedical Pr); pap. 27.75 (ISBN 0-444-80424-2). Elsevier.

FAO & IAEA. Laboratory Training Manual on Radioimmunoassay in Animal Reproduction. (Technical Report Ser.: No. 233). 269p. (Orig.). 1984. pap. text ed. 45.00 (ISBN 92-0-115084-9, IDC233, IAEA). Unipub.

Parratt, David, et al. Radioimmunoassay of Antibody: And Its Clinical Applications. LC 81-12939. 234p. 1982. 41.95x (ISBN 0-471-10061-7, Pub. by Wiley-Interscience). Wiley.

Pasternak, Charles A., ed. Radioimmunoassay in Clinical Biochemistry. LC 76-675546. pap. 79.30 (ISBN 0-317-29335-4, 2024025). Bks Demand UMI.

Radioimmunoassay & Related Procedures in Medicine 1982. (Illus.). 825p. 1983. pap. 104.00 (ISBN 92-0-010482-7, ISP625, IAEA). Unipub.

Yalow, Rosalyn S., ed. Radioimmunoassay. LC 83-8594. (Benchmark Papers In Microbiology: Vol. 20). 416p. 1983. 49.95 (ISBN 0-87933-109-7). Van Nos Reinhold.

RADIOIMMUNOLOGY

see Radiation Immunology

RADIOISOTOPE LABORATORIES

Chase, Grafton D. & Rabinowitz, Joseph L. Principles of Radioisotope Methodology. 3rd ed. LC 66-19903. 1967. text ed. 37.95x (ISBN 0-8087-0308-0). Burgess.

Manual on Safety Aspects of the Design & Equipment of Hot Laboratories. (Safety Ser.: No. 30). (Illus.). 102p. 1969. pap. 10.75 (ISBN 92-0-123069-9, ISP169, IAEA). Unipub.

RADIOISOTOPE SCANNING

Bulcke, J. A. & Baert, A. L. Clinical & Radiological Aspects of Myopathies: CT Scanning-EMG-Radio-Isotopes. (Illus.). 187p. 1982. 58.00 (ISBN 0-387-11443-2). Springer-Verlag.

Carey, James E., et al, eds. CRC Manual of Nuclear Medicine Procedures. 248p. 1983. 39.50 (ISBN 0-8493-0708-2). CRC Pr.

Feinendegen, L. E. Tritium Labeled Molecules in Biology & Medicine. (Atomic Energy Commision Monographs). 1967. 29.50 (ISBN 0-12-251550-1). Acad Pr.

Johnston, Gerald & Jones, A. E. Atlas of Gallium - 67 Scintigraphy: A New Method of Radioisotope Diagnosis. LC 73-18375. 232p. 1974. 32.50x (ISBN 0-306-30769-3, Plenum Pr). Plenum Pub.

Kniseley, Ralph M. & Andrews, Gould A., eds. Progress in Medical Radioisotope Scanning: Proceedings. (AEC Symposium Ser.). 539p. 1963. microfiche 4.50 (ISBN 0-87079-314-4, TID-7673). DOE.

Medical Radioisotope Scanning: 1964, 2 vols. (Proceedings Ser.). 1964. Vol. 1. pap. 30.75 (ISBN 92-0-010264-6, ISP82-1, IAEA); Vol. 2. pap. 26.25 (ISBN 92-0-010364-2, ISP82-2). Unipub.

Serafini, Aldo, ed. Nuclear Cardiology: Principles & Methods. LC 76-39783. (Topics in Cardiovascular Disease Ser.). (Illus.). 264p. 1977. 35.00x (ISBN 0-306-30952-1, Plenum Med. Bk.). Plenum Pub.

Silberstein, E. B. & McAfee, J. G. Differential Diagnosis in Nuclear Medicine. 336p. 1984. 35.00 (ISBN 0-07-057530-4). McGraw.

A Survey of Images of a Phanton Produced by Radioisotope Scanners & Cameras 1976. 1980. 16.00x (ISBN 0-686-69959-9, Pub. by Brit Inst Radiology). State Mutual Bk.

RADIOISOTOPES

see also Radioactive Tracers; Radioisotope Laboratories; Radioisotope Scanning; Radiotherapy;
also subdivision Isotopes under names of elements, e.g. Carbon–Isotopes

Barnes, W. E., ed. Basic Physics of Radiotracers. 1983. Vol. I, 216p. 67.00 (ISBN 0-8493-6001-3); Vol. II, 176p. 56.00 (ISBN 0-8493-6002-1). CRC Pr.

A Basic Toxicity Classification of Radionuclides. (Technical Reports Ser.: No. 15). 39p. 1963. pap. 6.25 (ISBN 0-686-93176-9, IDC15, IAEA). Unipub.

Chackett, K. Radionuclide Technology. 1981. 42.50 (ISBN 0-442-30170-7); pap. 19.95 (ISBN 0-442-30171-5). Van Nos Reinhold.

Clinical Uses of Whole-Body Counting. (Panel Proceedings Ser.). (Illus.). 291p. (Orig.). 1966. pap. 16.00 (ISBN 92-0-111066-9, ISP122, IAEA). Unipub.

Contemporary Equipment for Work with Radioactive Isotopes. LC 59-14767. 1959. 30.00x (ISBN 0-306-10517-9, Consultants). Plenum Pub.

The Efficient Importation & Distribution of Radioisotopes. (Technical Reports Ser.: No. 19). (Eng., Fr. & Span.). 21p. 1963. pap. 6.25 (ISBN 92-0-155063-4, IDC19, IAEA). Unipub.

Eichholz, Geoffrey G., ed. Radioisotope Engineering. LC 77-142891. (Illus.). pap. 106.80 (ISBN 0-317-07974-3, 2055012). Bks Demand UMI.

Environmental Behaviour of Radionuclides Released in the Nuclear Industry. (Proceedings Ser.). (Eng., Fr. & Rus., Illus.). 749p. (Orig.). 1974. pap. 66.50 (ISBN 92-0-020473-2, ISP345, IAEA). Unipub.

Environmental Migration of Long-Lived Radionuclides: Proceeding of an International Symposium of Migration in the Terrestial Environment on Long-Lived Radionuclides from the Nuclear Fuel Cycle Organized by the International Atomic Energy Agency, the Commission of the European Communities & the OECD Nuclear Energy Action Agency, Knoxville, USA, July 27-31, 1981. (Proceedings Ser.). (Illus.). 830p. 1982. pap. 105.00 (ISBN 92-0-020082-6, ISP597, IAEA). Unipub.

Genetic Models & Parameters for Assessing the Environmental Transfer of Radionuclides from Routine Releases: Exposures of Critical Groups. (Safety Ser.: No. 57). (Illus.). 96p. 1983. pap. text ed. 16.00 (ISBN 92-0-123582-8, ISP611, IAEA). Unipub.

Goswitz, Francis A., et al, eds. Clinical Uses of Radionuclides: Critical Comparison with Other Techniques: Proceedings. LC 72-660271. (AEC Symposium Ser.). 718p. 1972. 26.00 (ISBN 0-87079-002-1, CONF-711101); microfiche 4.50 (ISBN 0-87079-164-8, CONF-711101). DOE.

Guide to the Safe Design, Construction & Use of Radioisotopic Power Generators for Certain Land & Sea Applications. (Safety Ser.: No. 33). 31p. (Orig.). 1970. pap. 6.25 (ISBN 92-0-123070-2, ISP246, IAEA). Unipub.

Hayes, Raymond L., et al, eds. Radioisotopes in Medicine - In Vitro Studies: Proceedings. LC 68-60071. (AEC Symposium Ser.). 753p. 1968. pap. 26.75 (ISBN 0-87079-327-6, CONF-671111); microfiche 4.50 (ISBN 0-87079-328-4, CONF-671111). DOE.

Helus, Frank, ed. Radionuclides Production, 2 Vols. 1983. Vol. I, 176p. 56.00 (ISBN 0-8493-6003-X); Vol. II, 184. 63.00 (ISBN 0-8493-6004-8). CRC Pr.

Hendee, William R. Radioactive Isotopes in Biological Research. LC 84-3911. 374p. 1984. Repr. of 1973 ed. lib. bdg. 48.50 (ISBN 0-89874-750-3). Krieger.

ICRP. Radionuclide Transformation: Energy & Intensity of Emissions: ICRP Publication. Sowby, F. D., ed. (Illus.). 1200p. 1983. 210.00 (ISBN 0-08-030760-4). Pergamon.

International Commission on Radiation Units & Measurements. Methods of Assessment of Absorbed Dose in Clinical Use of Radionuclides. LC 79-90172. 1979. 14.00 (ISBN 0-913394-26-2). Intl Comm Rad Meas.

Jensen, B. S. Migration Phenomena of Radionuclides into the Geosphere: A Critical Review of the Available Information. (Radioactive Waste Management Ser.). 200p. 1982. 25.50 (ISBN 3-7186-0120-6). Harwood Academic.

Kniseley, Ralph M., et al, eds. Dynamic Clinical Studies with Radioisotopes: Proceedings. (AEC Symposium Ser.). 658p. 1964. pap. 24.50 (ISBN 0-87079-181-8, TID-7678); microfiche 4.50 (ISBN 0-87079-182-6, TID-7678). DOE.

Lawrence, J. H., et al. Radioisotopes & Radiation: Recent Advances in Medicine, Agriculture, & Industry. (Illus.). 12.00 (ISBN 0-8446-0765-7). Peter Smith.

Lawrence, John H., et al. Radioisotopes & Radiation: Recent Advances in Medicine, Agriculture, & Industry. LC 69-20423. 1969. lib. bdg. 11.50x (ISBN 0-88307-645-4). Gannon.

Mann, G. C., et al, eds. Applied Radionuclide Metrology: Proceedings of the International Committee for Radionuclide Metrology Seminar, Geel, Belgium, 16-17 May 1983. (International Journal of Applied Radiation & Isotopes Ser.: Vol. 34, No. 8). 286p. 1983. pap. 25.20 (ISBN 0-08-030271-8). Pergamon.

Manual of Radioisotope Production. (Technical Reports Ser.: No. 63). (Illus.). 446p. 1966. pap. 25.50 (ISBN 92-0-145366-3, IDC63, IAEA). Unipub.

The Migration of Long-Lived Radionuclides in the Geosphere: Proceedings of the Workshop, Brussels 29/31 Jan. 1979. 1979. 17.00x (ISBN 92-64-01925-1). OECD.

Mladjenovic, M. Radioisotope & Radiation Physics: An Introduction. 1973. 60.00 (ISBN 0-12-502350-2). Acad Pr.

NCRP. General Concepts for Dosimetry of Internally Deposited Radionuclides. LC 85-8965. (NCRP Report Ser.: No. 84). 100p. 1985. pap. text ed. write for info. (ISBN 0-913392-77-4). NCRP Pubns.

--Radiological Assessment: Predicting the Transport, Bioaccumulation, & Uptake by Man of Radionuclides Released to the Environment. LC 84-4773. (NCRP Report Ser.: No. 76). 300p. 1984. pap. text ed. 17.00 (ISBN 0-913392-66-9). Natl Coun Radiation.

Production & Use of Short Lived Radioisotopes From Reactors, 2 Vols. (Proceedings Ser.). (Illus.). 706p. (Vol. 1). Vol. 1. pap. 21.50 (ISBN 92-0-060063-8, ISP64-1, IAEA); Vol. 2. pap. 18.00 (ISBN 92-0-060163-4, ISP64-2). Unipub.

Radioisotope Production & Quality Control. (Technical Reports Ser.: No. 128). (Illus.). 969p. (Orig.). 1971. pap. 66.00 (ISBN 92-0-145171-7, IDC128, IAEA). Unipub.

Radioisotopes in the Pulp & Paper Industry. (Panel Proceedings Ser.). (Illus.). 117p. 1968. pap. 9.25 (ISBN 92-0-161068-8, ISP202, IAEA). Unipub.

Root, John W. & Krohn, Kenneth A., eds. Short-Lived Radionuclides in Chemistry & Biology. LC 81-19148. (Advances in Chemistry Ser.: No. 197). 1982. 72.95 (ISBN 0-8412-0603-1). Am Chemical.

Symposium. Isotope Ratios as Pollutant Source & Behavior Indicators: Proceedings. (Proceedings Ser.). (Illus.). 489p. 1975. pap. 49.25 (ISBN 92-0-010375-8, ISP382, IAEA). Unipub.

Transuranium Nuclides in the Enviroment: Proceedings. (Proceedings Ser.). (Illus.). 724p. 1976. pap. 78.75 (ISBN 92-0-020076-1, ISP410, IAEA). Unipub.

Wegst, Audrey V., et al. Radioisotopes in Biology & Medicine: Introductory Principles & Techniques. 1964. pap. 6.85 (ISBN 0-87506-031-5, 87506-031-5). Campus.

Welch, Michael J., ed. Radiopharmaceuticals & Other Compounds Labelled with Short-Lived Radionuclides. LC 76-26764. 1977. pap. text ed. 44.00 (ISBN 0-08-021344-8). Pergamon.

Ziegler, Charles A., ed. Applications of Low-Energy X & Gamma Rays. LC 78-141897. (Illus.). 478p. 1971. 106.50x (ISBN 0-677-14640-X). Gordon.

RADIOISOTOPES–DECAY

see also Beta Decay

Biological Effects of Transmutation & Decay of Incorporated Radioisotopes. (Panel Proceedings Ser.). (Illus.). 244p. (Orig.). 1968. pap. 15.25 (ISBN 92-0-011268-4, ISP183, IAEA). Unipub.

Kocher, David C. & DOE Technical Information Center. Radioactive Decay Data Tables. LC 81-607800. 227p. 1981. pap. 13.75 (ISBN 0-87079-124-9, DOE/TIC-11026); microfiche 4.50 (ISBN 0-87079-496-5, DOE/TIC-11026). DOE.

RADIOISOTOPES–INDUSTRIAL APPLICATIONS

see also Radiography, Industrial; Radioisotopes in Hydrology

All-Union Scientific & Technical Conference on the Application of Isotopes. Application of Radioactive Isotopes in the Food & Fishing Industries & in Agriculture, Vol. 2. 94p. 1959. 35.00x (ISBN 0-306-17022-1, Consultants). Plenum Pub.

Industrial Application of Radioisotopes & Radiation Technology: Proceedings of an International Conference on Industrial Application of Radioisotopes & Radiation Technology Organized by the International Atomic Energy Agency & Held in Grenoble, France, 28 Sept. to 2 Oct. 1981. (Proceedings Ser.). 595p. 1983. pap. 75.75 (ISBN 92-0-060082-4, ISP598, IAEA). Unipub.

Radiation & Radioisotopes for Industrial Microorganisms. 1971. pap. 27.00 (ISBN 92-0-010371-5, ISP287, IAEA). Unipub.

Radioisotope Applications in Industry. pap. 7.25 (ISBN 92-0-162063-2, ISP70, IAEA). Unipub.

Radioisotope Tracers in Industry & Geophysics. (Proceedings Ser.). (Illus.). 710p. 1967. pap. 45.00 (ISBN 92-0-060067-0, ISP142, IAEA). Unipub.

Radioisotopes in the Pulp & Paper Industry. (Panel Proceedings Ser.). (Illus.). 117p. 1968. pap. 9.25 (ISBN 92-0-161068-8, ISP202, IAEA). Unipub.

RADIOISOTOPES–LABORATORY MANUALS

Faires, R. A. & Boswell, G. G. Radioisotope Lab Techniques. 4th ed. LC 80-41045. 272p. 1980. text ed. 49.95 (ISBN 0-408-70940-5). Butterworth.

RADIOISOTOPES–PHYSIOLOGICAL EFFECT

see also Radioisotopes in the Body

The Biological Implications of Radionuclides Released from Nuclear Industries: Proceedings of Symposium Vienna 26-30 March 1979, 2 Vols. 923p. 1979. Vol. 1. pap. 67.25 (ISBN 92-0-010479-7, ISP522 1, IAEA); Vol. 2. pap. 62.00 (ISBN 92-0-010579-3, ISP522 2). Unipub.

International Commission on Radiological Protection. Alkaline Earth Metabolism in Adult Man. (ICRP Publication Ser: No. 20). 1973. pap. 15.25 (ISBN 0-08-017191-5). Pergamon.

Management of Persons Accidentally Contaminated with Radionuclides. LC 79-91648. (NCRP Reports Ser.: No. 65). 1980. 10.00 (ISBN 0-913392-49-9). NCRP Pubns.

Maximum Permissible Body Burdens & Maximum Permissible Concentrations of Radionuclides in Air & in Water for Occupational Exposures. (NCRP Reports Ser.: No. 22). 1959. 6.00 (ISBN 0-913392-06-5). NCRP Pubns.

Radioisotopes in Animal Nutrition & Physiology. (Proceedings Ser.). (Illus.). 884p. 1965. pap. 27.00 (ISBN 92-0-010065-1, ISP90, IAEA). Unipub.

RADIOISOTOPES IN AGRICULTURE

see also Radioisotopes in Dairying; Soils, Radioactive Substances in

All-Union Scientific & Technical Conference on the Application of Isotopes. Application of Radioactive Isotopes in the Food & Fishing Industries & in Agriculture, Vol. 2. 94p. 1959. 35.00x (ISBN 0-306-17022-1, Consultants). Plenum Pub.

Isotopes & Radiation in Soil Organic-Matter Studies. (Proceedings Ser.). (Eng., Fr., Rus. & Span., Illus.). 584p. (Orig.). 1968. pap. 36.00 (ISBN 92-0-010368-5, ISP190, IAEA). Unipub.

Radiation & Radioisotopes Applied to Insects of Agricultural Importance. (Proceedings Ser.). (Illus.). 508p. 1963. 25.25 (ISBN 92-0-010263-8, ISP74, IAEA). Unipub.

Radiotracer Studies of Chemical Residues in Food & Agriculture. (Panel Proceedings Ser.). (Illus.). 167p. (Orig.). 1973. pap. 14.50 (ISBN 92-0-111272-6, ISP332, IAEA). Unipub.

Seed Protein Improvement in Cereals & Grain Legumes: Proceedings of Symposium, Neuherburg 4-8 Sept. 1978, 2 Vols. 1979. pap. 59.25 (ISBN 92-0-010079-1, ISP496-1, IAEA); pap. 65.50 (ISBN 92-0-010179-8, ISP496-2). Unipub.

Selection in Mutation Breeding. (Panel Proceedings Ser.). (Illus.). 180p. 1985. pap. 29.00 (ISBN 92-0-111284-X, ISP665, IAEA). Unipub.

RADIOISOTOPES IN BIOLOGY

Feinendegen, L. E. & Tisljarlentulis, G., eds. Molecular & Microdistribution of Radioisotopes & Biological Consequences: Proceedings Held in Julich, Federal Republic of Germany, October 1975. (Current Topics in Radiator Research Ser.: Vol. 12). 1978. Repr. 138.50 (ISBN 0-444-85142-9, North-Holland). Elsevier.

Hendee, William R. Radioactive Isotopes in Biological Research. LC 84-3911. 374p. 1984. Repr. of 1973 ed. lib. bdg. 48.50 (ISBN 0-89874-750-3). Krieger.

Radioisotope Sample Measurement Techniques in Medicine & Biology. (Proceedings Ser.). 724p. 1965. pap. 38.50 (ISBN 92-0-010165-8, ISP106, IAEA). Unipub.

RADIOISOTOPES IN DAIRYING

Radioisotopes & Radiation in Dairy Science & Technology. (Proceedings Ser.). (Illus.). 259p. 1966. pap. 14.50 (ISBN 92-0-010266-2, ISP135, IAEA). Unipub.

RADIOISOTOPES IN ENTOMOLOGY

Laboratory Training Manual on the Use of Isotopes & Radiation in Entomology. 2nd ed. (Technical Reports Ser.: No. 61). (Illus.). 274p. 1977. pap. 31.50 (ISBN 92-0-115177-2, IDC61, IAEA). Unipub.

Radiation & Radioisotopes Applied to Insects of Agricultural Importance. (Proceedings Ser.). (Illus.). 508p. 1963. 25.25 (ISBN 92-0-010263-8, ISP74, IAEA). Unipub.

Radioisotopes & Ionizing Radiations in Entomology: 1961-1963. (Bibliographical Ser.: No. 15). 565p. 1965. pap. (ISBN 92-0-014065-3, STI/PUB/21/15, IAEA). Unipub.

Radioisotopes & Ionizing Radiations in Entomology: 1964-1965. (Bibliographical Ser.: No. 24). 454p. 1976. pap. write for info. (ISBN 92-0-014067-X, STI/PUB/21/24, IAEA). Unipub.

Radioisotopes & Ionizing Radiations in Entomology: 1966-1967. (Bibliographical Ser.: No. 36). 818p. 1969. pap. write for info. (ISBN 92-0-014069-6, STI/PUB/21/36, IAEA). Unipub.

Radioisotopes in the Detection of Pesticide Residues. (Panel Proceedings Ser.). (Illus.). 116p. 1966. pap. 7.25 (ISBN 92-0-111166-5, ISP123, IAEA). Unipub.

RADIOISOTOPES IN HYDROLOGY

Application of Isotope Techniques in Hydrology. (Technical Reports Ser.: No. 11). (Illus.). 31p. (Orig.). 1962. pap. 6.25 (ISBN 92-0-145062-1, IDC11, IAEA). Unipub.

Gaspar, E. & Oncescu, M. Radioactive Tracers in Hydrology. (Developments in Hydrology Ser.: Vol. 1). 342p. 1972. 76.75 (ISBN 0-444-40986-6). Elsevier.

Guide to the Safe Handling of Radioisotopes in Hydrology. (Safety Ser.: No. 20). (Illus.). 638p. 1966. pap. 6.25 (ISBN 92-0-020176-8, ISP131, IAEA). Unipub.

Isotopes in Hydrology. (Proceedings Ser.). (Eng., Fr. & Rus., Illus.). 740p. (Orig.). 1967. pap. 43.25 (ISBN 92-0-040067-1, ISP141, IAEA). Unipub.

Manipulation des Radioisotopes en Hydrologie. (Safety Ser.: No. 20). 40p. (Eng. ed. also avail.). 1967. pap. write for info. (ISBN 92-0-223567-8, IAEA). Unipub.

Maximum Permissible Body Burdens & Maximum Permissible Concentrations of Radionuclides in Air & in Water for Occupational Exposures. (NCRP Reports Ser.: No. 22). 1959. 6.00 (ISBN 0-913392-06-5). NCRP Pubns.

Methods of Surveying & Monitoring Marine Radioactivity. (Safety Ser.: No. 11). 95p. 1962. pap. 7.75 (ISBN 92-0-123165-2, ISP86, IAEA). Unipub.

Perry, Eugene C., Jr. & Montgomery, Carla W., eds. Isotope Studies of Hydrologic Processes. LC 82-3431. (Illus.). 118p. 1982. 25.00 (ISBN 0-87580-082-3). N Ill U Pr.

Radioisotopes in Hydrology. (Proceedings Ser.). (Illus.). 459p. 1963. 21.00 (ISBN 92-0-040063-9, ISP71, IAEA). Unipub.

Reference Methods for Marine Radioactivity Studies - 2. (Technical Reports Ser.: No. 169). (Illus.). 240p. 1975. pap. 27.00 (ISBN 92-0-125275-7, IDC169, IAEA). Unipub.

Stable Isotope Hydrology: Deutrium & Oxygen-18 in the Water Cycle. (Technical Reports Ser.: No. 210). (Illus.). 339p. 1981. pap. 42.50 (ISBN 92-0-145281-0, IDC210, IAEA). Unipub.

Tritium & Other Environmental Isotopes in the Hydrological Cycle. (Technical Reports Ser.: No. 73). (Illus.). 83p. 1967. pap. 7.75 (ISBN 92-0-145067-2, IDC73, IAEA). Unipub.

RADIOISOTOPES IN MICROBIOLOGY

All-Union Scientific & Technical Conference on the Application of Isotopes. Application of Radioactive Isotopes in Microbiology, Vol. 2. 28p. 1959. 17.50x (ISBN 0-306-17023-X, Consultants). Plenum Pub.

RADIOISOTOPES IN SOIL PHYSICS

Francis, C. W. Radiostrontium Movement in Soils & Uptake in Plants. LC 78-19051. (DOE Critical Review Ser.). 139p. 1978. pap. 11.50 (ISBN 0-87079-110-9, TID-27564); microfiche 4.50 (ISBN 0-87079-332-2, TID-27564). DOE.

Soil-Moisture & Irrigation Studies. (Panel Proceedings Ser.). 1966. pap. 7.25 (ISBN 92-0-011067-3, ISP133, IAEA). Unipub.

Tracer Techniques in Sediment Transport. (Technical Reports Ser.: No. 145). (Illus.). 234p. (Orig.). 1973. pap. 22.00 (ISBN 92-0-145073-7, IDC145, IAEA). Unipub.

RADIOISOTOPES IN THE BODY

Cloutier, Roger J., et al, eds. Medical Radionuclides: Radiation Dose & Effects, Proceedings. LC 70-606556. (AEC Symposium Ser.). 528p. 1970. pap. 21.25 (ISBN 0-87079-269-5, CONF-691212); microfiche 4.50 (ISBN 0-87079-270-9, CONF-691212). DOE.

Eckelman, W. C., ed. Technetium Ninety-Nine-M: Generators, Chemistry, & Preparation of Radiopharmaceuticals. (Illus.). 168p. 1983. 25.00 (ISBN 0-08-029144-9). Pergamon.

ICRP. Limits for Intakes of Radionuclides by Workers, 7 vols. Sowby, F. D., ed. (ICRP Publications: No. 30). 2500p. 1982. 405.00 (ISBN 0-08-028863-4). Pergamon.

Radioisotope Techniques in the Study of Protein Metabolism. (Technical Reports Ser.: No. 45). 1965. pap. 17.25 (ISBN 92-0-115165-9, IDC45, IAEA). Unipub.

Sowby, F. D., ed. Limits for Intakes of Radionuclides by Workers: ICRP Publication No. 30, Part 3. (Annals of the ICRP Ser.: Vol. 5, Nos. 2-3). 128p. 1982. 28.00 (ISBN 0-08-026834-X). Pergamon.

Tritium & Other Radionuclide Labled Organic Compounds Incorporated in Genetic Material. LC 79-84486. (NCRP Reports Ser.: No. 63). 1979. 10.00 (ISBN 0-913392-47-2). NCRP Pubns.

RADIOLARIA, FOSSIL

Catalogue of Planktonic Foraminifera, 6 vols. 1976. Set. 600.00 (ISBN 0-686-84238-3). Am Mus Natl Hist.

RADIOLOGICAL DECONTAMINATION

see Radioactive Decontamination

RADIOLOGICAL PHYSICS

see Radiology

RADIOLOGY

see also Radiation; Radiography

Amiel, M. & Moreau, J. F., eds. Contrast Media in Radiology, Appraisal & Prospects, Lyon 1981: Proceedings. (Illus.). 370p. 1982. 32.50 (ISBN 0-387-11534-X). Springer-Verlag.

Anderson, O. R. Radiolaria. (Illus.). 350p. 1983. 65.00 (ISBN 0-387-90832-3). Springer-Verlag.

Armstrong, Peter. Critical Problems in Diagnostic Radiology. (Illus.). 304p. 1983. text ed. 38.75 (ISBN 0-397-50496-9, 65-06406, Lippincott Medical). Lippincott.

Baert, A. L., et al. Frontier in European Radiology, Vol. 2. (Illus.). 110p. 1982. 32.00 (ISBN 0-387-11349-5). Springer-Verlag.

Baert, A. L., et al, eds. Frontiers in European Radiology, Vol. 1. (Illus.). 170p. 1982. 42.00 (ISBN 0-387-10753-3). Springer-Verlag.

Ballinger, Philip W. Merrill's Atlas of Radiographic Positions & Radiologic Procedures, 3 Vols. 5th ed. (Illus.). 950p. 1982. text ed. 99.95 (ISBN 0-8016-3408-3). Mosby.

Barnes, Broda O. & Barnes, Charlotte W. Heart Attack Rareness in Thyroid-Treated Patients. 104p. 1972. 12.75x (ISBN 0-398-02519-3). C C Thomas.

Barrett, H. H. & Swindell, W. Radiological Imaging: The Theory of Formation & Detection & Processing, Vol. 2. LC 80-69416. (Biophysics & Bioengineering Ser.). 1981. 55.00 (ISBN 0-12-079602-3). Acad Pr.

Bell. One Thousand & One Questions about Radiologic Technology, Vol. 2. (Illus.). 192p. 1982. pap. text ed. 10.50 (ISBN 0-8391-1774-4). Univ Park.

Bell, Roy. One Thousand & One Questions About Radiologic Technology, Vol. 1. 192p. (Orig.). 1980. pap. text ed. 10.50 (ISBN 0-8391-1607-1). Univ Park.

Bloomfield, J. A. Introduction to Organ Imaging. (Medical Outline Ser.). 1984. pap. text ed. write for info. (ISBN 0-87488-072-6). Med Exam.

Bouchard, Eric. Radiology Management: An Introduction. LC 82-22355. (Illus.). 310p. (Orig.). 1983. pap. 18.95X (ISBN 0-940122-04-9). Multi Media CO.

Bradley, William G., Jr., et al. Magnetic Resonance Imaging of the Brain, Head & Neck: A Text-Atlas. 144p. 1985. 65.00 (ISBN 0-87189-094-1). Aspen Systems.

Brogdon, Byron G. Opinions, Comments & Reflections on Radiology. LC 82-82972. (Illus.). 249p. 1982. 14.95 (ISBN 0-939442-01-9). Brentwood Pub.

Bushong, Stewart. Radiologic Science Workbook & Laboratory Manual. 2nd ed. (Illus.). 260p. 1981. pap. text ed. 13.95 (ISBN 0-8016-0927-5). Mosby.

Bushong, Stewart C. Radiologic Science for Technologists: Physics, Biology & Protection. 2nd ed. LC 80-19. (Illus.). 504p. 1980. 29.95 (ISBN 0-8016-0928-3). Mosby.

--Radiologic Science for Technologists: Physics, Biology, & Protection. 3rd ed. (Illus.). 560p. 1984. pap. text ed. 31.95 (ISBN 0-8016-0933-X). Mosby.

Chapman, Stephen & Nakielny, Richard. A Guide to Radiological Procedures. 1981. pap. text ed. 17.95x (ISBN 0-7216-0712-8, Bailliere-Tindall). Saunders.

Colombetti, L. Radiotracers in Biology & Medicine, Vol. I. 447p. 1982. write for info. (ISBN 0-8493-6027-7). CRC Pr.

Crawford, O. William & Gautot, Henri J., eds. X-Ray Technology Examination Review Book, Vol. 2. 3rd ed. 1973. pap. 13.25 (ISBN 0-87488-442-X). Med Exam.

Critser, James R., Jr. Radiological Equipment. (Ser. 10R-82). 1983. 80.00 (ISBN 0-88178-007-3). Lexington Data.

DeAngelis, Robert. Radiologic Science Workbook. 256p. 1982. 17.95 (ISBN 0-03-060619-5). Praeger.

Donner, M. W. & Heuck, F., eds. Radiology Today. A Multinational Series, Vol. 1. (Illus.). 431p. 1981. 79.50 (ISBN 0-387-10099-7). Springer-Verlag.

Donner, M. W. & Heuck, F. H., eds. Radiology Today, Vol. 2. (Illus.). 420p. 1983. 69.00 (ISBN 0-387-11754-7). Springer-Verlag.

Etter, Lewis E. Glossary of Words & Phrases Used in Radiology, Nuclear Medicine & Ultrasound. 2nd ed. 384p. 1970. 33.50x (ISBN 0-398-00526-5). C C Thomas.

Evans, K. T. & Knight, B. Forensic Radiology. (Illus.). 160p. 1981. text ed. 34.25 (ISBN 0-632-00587-4, B 1614-X). Mosby.

Frankel, Robert. Radiation Protection for Radiologic Technologists. (Illus.). 1976. text ed. 27.95 (ISBN 0-07-021875-7). McGraw.

Frommer, Herbert H. Radiology in Dental Practice. LC 81-38411. (Illus.). 303p. 1981. text ed. 34.95 (ISBN 0-8016-1709-X). Mosby.

Glasser, Otto. Doctor W. C. Rontgen. 2nd ed. (Illus.). 192p. 1972. 20.25x (ISBN 0-398-02196-1). C C Thomas.

Goodman, Lawrence R. & Putnam, Charles E. Intensive Care Radiology: Imaging of the Critically Ill. 2nd ed. (Saunders Monographs in Clinical Radiology: Vol. 20). (Illus.). 352p. 1983. 47.50 (ISBN 0-7216-4166-0). Saunders.

Goodwin, Paul H. & Hinkley, Edith. Physical Foundations of Radiology. LC 70-106337. pap. 102.30 (ISBN 0-317-08404-6, 2006252). Bks Demand UMI.

Gosink, Barbara B. & Squire, Lucy F. Diagnostic Radiology. 2nd ed. (Series of Exercises in Diagnostic Radiology: Vol. 8). (Illus.). 220p. 1981. text ed. 17.95 (ISBN 0-7216-4175-X). Saunders.

Graham, Billie J. & Thomas, William N. An Introduction to Physics for Radiologic Technologist. LC 74-12911. pap. 64.80 (ISBN 0-317-08967-6, 2015279). Bks Demand UMI.

Gurley, LaVerne T. & Callaway, William J. Introduction to Radiologic Technology. LC 81-82005. (Illus.). 300p. (Orig.). 1982. pap. 16.95x (ISBN 0-940122-02-2). Multi Media CO.

Halmshaw, R. Industrial Radiology Techniques. (Wykeham Science Ser.: No. 3). 278p. 1971. pap. write for info. (ISBN 0-85109-210-1). Taylor & Francis.

Hazzard, D. G. & Litz, M. L. Biological Effects & Characterizations of Ultrasound Sources: Papers Presented at the "Proceedings of the Symposium of Biological Effects & Characterizations of Ultrasound Sources". (Illus.). 215p. 1979. text ed. 42.00 (ISBN 0-7194-0021-X, Pub by Castle Hse England). J K Burgess.

Hendee, William R., et al. Radiologic Physics, Equipment, & Quality Control. LC 77-204. pap. 75.30 (ISBN 0-317-26174-6, 2024265). Bks Demand UMI.

Herlinger, Hans. Clinical Radiology of the Liver, Pts. A & B. (Diagnostic Radiology Ser.: Vol. 1). (Illus.). 1224p. 1983. 295.00 set (ISBN 0-8247-1069-X). Vol. A. 542 p. Vol. B 656 p. Dekker.

International Commission on Radiological Protection. Assessment of Internal Contamination Resulting from Recurrent or Prolonged Uptakes. (ICRP Publication Ser.: No. 10a). 1971. pap. 9.25 (ISBN 0-08-016772-1). Pergamon.

Jacob, Alphons & Jackson, Herbert L. Dictionary of Radiologic Terminology. 107p. 1982. 27.50 (ISBN 0-87527-216-9). Green.

Johns, Harold E. & Cunningham, John R. The Physics of Radiology. 4th ed. (Illus.). 816p. 1983. 49.50x (ISBN 0-398-04669-7). C C Thomas.

Kirchner, Sandra G., et al. Emergency Radiology of the Shoulder, Arm & Hand. LC 81-52309. (Advanced Exercises in Diagnostic Radiology Ser.: Vol. 15). (Illus.). 153p. 1981. pap. text ed. 20.95 (ISBN 0-7216-5457-6). Saunders.

Leopold, Lynn A. Radiology at the University of Pennsylvania: 1890-1975. LC 81-40557. (Illus.). 200p. 1982. 37.50x (ISBN 0-8122-7820-8). U of Pa Pr.

Meschan, Isadore. An Atlas of Anatomy Basic to Radiology. LC 73-89936. (Illus.). 1120p. 1975. text ed. 37.00 ea.; text ed. 71.00 single vol. (ISBN 0-7216-6310-9). Vol. 1 (ISBN 0-7216-6308-7). Vol. 2 (ISBN 0-7216-6309-5). Saunders.

Muhr, C. & Bergstrom, K. Frontiers in European Radiology, Vol. 3. (Illus.). 140p. 1984. 33.60 (ISBN 0-387-11446-7). Springer-Verlag.

Myers, Patricia A. A Glossary for Radiologic Technologists. LC 80-20917. 206p. 1981. 29.95 (ISBN 0-03-057584-2). Praeger.

Neuder, Gustav F. & Ullrich, Heinz M. Dictionary of Radiological Engineering. 1979. pap. text ed. 24.80 (ISBN 3-11-007807-4). De Gruyter.

Orton, Colin G., et al, eds. Radiological Physics Examination Review Book, Vol. 1. 2nd ed. 1978. spiral bdg. 18.00 (ISBN 0-87488-486-1). Med Exam.

Osborn, Royce R. A Professional Approach to Radiology Administration. (Illus.). 228p. 1980. 30.75x (ISBN 0-398-04097-4). C C Thomas.

Powell, N. W. Handbook for Radiologic Technologists & Special Procedures Nurses in Radiology. (Illus.). 104p. 1974. 14.75x (ISBN 0-398-03066-9). C C Thomas.

Radiologic Quality Control Manual. 1983. pap. text ed. 39.95 (ISBN 0-8359-6366-7). Reston.

Radiological Assessment: Predicting the Transport, Bioaccumulation, & Uptake by Man of Radionuclides Released to the Environment. (NCRP Report Ser.: No. 76). 1984. 17.00 (ISBN 0-913392-66-9). NCRP Pubns.

Sarwar, Mohammad, et al. Basic Neuroradiology. (Illus.). 820p. 1983. 95.00 (ISBN 0-87527-230-4). Green.

Shapiro, Jerome H. & Hipona, Florencio A. Radiology. 2nd ed. (Medical Examination Review Bk.: Vol. 17). 1972. spiral bdg. 20.50 (ISBN 0-87488-117-X). Med Exam.

Stefani, S. & Hubbard, Lincoln B. Mathematics for Technologists in Radiology, Nuclear Medicine & Radiation Therapy. LC 78-32110. (Illus.). 240p. 1979. pap. text ed. 14.95 (ISBN 0-8016-4762-2). Mosby.

Veiga-Pires, ed. Intervention Radiology. (International Congress Ser.: Vol. 522). 414p. 1981. 79.75 (ISBN 0-444-90165-5, Excerpta Medica). Elsevier.

Wilkins, R. A. & Viamonte, M. Interventional Radiology. (Illus.). 512p. 1982. text ed. 59.95 (ISBN 0-632-00769-9, B 5256-1). Mosby.

Wilks, Robin J. Principles of Radiological Physics. (Illus.). 528p. 1981. pap. text ed. 43.75 (ISBN 0-443-02035-3). Churchill.

Wood, Raymond G. Computers in Radiotherapy. (Medical Computing Ser.). 171p. 1981. 64.95x (ISBN 0-471-09994-5, Pub. by Res Stud Pr). Wiley.

RADIOLOGY, MEDICAL

see also Nuclear Medicine; Radiography, Medical; Radiotherapy

Ando. Comprehensive Atlas of Maxillofacial Radiology. 1985. price not set (ISBN 0-912791-17-9). Ishiyaku Euro.

Barton, John P. & Von Der Hardt, Peter. Neutron Radiography. 1983. lib. bdg. 126.00 (ISBN 90-2771-528-9, Pub. by Reidel Holland). Kluwer Academic.

Bell, Roy. One Thousand & One Questions about Radiologic Technology, Vol. 4. 1985. pap. text ed. 12.00 (ISBN 0-8391-2086-9, 22144). Univ Park.

Berk, Robert N. & Lasser, Elliott C. Radiology of the Ileocecal Area. LC 74-11684. (Saunders Monographs in Clinical Radiology: Vol. 5). pap. 85.50 (ISBN 0-317-08646-4, 2012284). Bks Demand UMI.

Bernard, Raymond. The Danger We All Face: Suppressed Truth about Radiation. 62p. pap. 4.95 (ISBN 0-88697-045-8). Life Science.

Bontrager, Kenneth L. & Anthony, Barry T. Textbook of Radiographic Positioning & Related Anatomy. LC 81-82006. (Illus.). 560p. (Orig.). 1982. text ed. 49.95x (ISBN 0-940122-01-4). Multi Media CO.

Bryant, T. H. E. & Lovell, J. MCQs in Radiological Physics. LC 82-4478. 135p. 1983. pap. text ed. 11.00 (ISBN 0-443-02225-9). Churchill.

Bushong, Stewart. Radiologic Science Workbook & Laboratory Manual. 2nd ed. (Illus.). 260p. 1981. pap. text ed. 13.95 (ISBN 0-8016-0927-5). Mosby.

Bushong, Stewart C. Radiologic Science for Technologists: Physics, Biology & Protection. 2nd ed. LC 80-19. (Illus.). 504p. 1980. 29.95 (ISBN 0-8016-0928-3). Mosby.

--Radiologic Science for Technologists: Physics, Biology, & Protection. 3rd ed. (Illus.). 560p. 1984. pap. text ed. 31.95 (ISBN 0-8016-0933-X). Mosby.

Critser, James R., Jr. Radiological Equipment. (Ser. 10R-83). 88p. 1984. 80.00 (ISBN 0-88178-018-9). Lexington Data.

--Radiological Equipment. (Ser. 10R-84). 1984. 90.00 (ISBN 0-88178-055-3). Lexington Data.

Curry, Thomas S., III, et al. Christensen's Introduction to the Physics of Diagnostic Radiology. 3rd ed. LC 84-3951. (Illus.). 515p. 1984. text ed. 30.00 (ISBN 0-8121-0918-X). Lea & Febiger.

Duplan, J. F. & Chapiro, A., eds. Advances in Radiation Research: Biology & Medicine, 3 vols, Pt. 2. LC 72-92724. 1973. Set, 1564p. 249.75 (ISBN 0-677-15770-3); Vol. 1, 490p. 90.25 (ISBN 0-677-30880-9); Vol. 2, 540p. 97.25 (ISBN 0-677-30890-6); Vol. 3, 534p. 97.25 (ISBN 0-677-30900-7). Gordon.

Durakovic, Asaf. Nuclear Medicine Technologist's Handbook. 1985. 32.50 (ISBN 0-87527-311-4). Green.

Elyaderani, Morteza, et al. Invasive Uroradiology: A Manual of Diagnostic & Therapeutic Techniques. (Illus.). 224p. 1984. 40.00 (ISBN 0-669-07537-X, Collamore). Heath.

Gofman, John W. & O'Connor, Egan. X-Rays: Health Effects of Common Exams. LC 84-23527. (Illus.). 456p. 1985. 25.00 (ISBN 0-87156-838-1). Sierra.

Goldman, Amy B., ed. Procedures in Skeletal Radiology. 720p. 1984. 99.50 (ISBN 0-8089-1655-6, 7916-41). Grune.

Goldman, M. A Guide to the X-Ray Department. 100p. 1978. pap. 10.50 (ISBN 0-7236-0493-2). PSG Pub Co.

Greaney, Richard B. & Gerber, Frederic H. Scintigraphic Review of the Hip. 1985. 22.50 (ISBN 0-87527-269-X). Green.

Greenfield, George B. & Hubbard, Lincoln B. Computers in Radiology. (Illus.). 200p. 1984. text ed. 30.00 (ISBN 0-443-08349-5). Churchill.

Hendee, William R. The Selection & Performance of Radiologic Equipment. 400p. 1985. 48.50 (ISBN 0-683-03958-X). Williams & Wilkins.

Hunter, Tim B. The Computer in Radiology. 1985. price not set (ISBN 0-87189-235-9). Aspen Systems.

Ishikawa, Tohru. Clinical Applications of Dynamic CT Scanning. Date not set. 42.50. Green.

Jackson, Herbert L. Mathematics of Radiology & Nuclear Medicine. LC 70-107201. (Illus.). 180p. 1971. 12.00 (ISBN 0-87527-019-0). Green.

Jackson, Stewart M. & Johnson, Ann. Radiation Oncology. 1985. 37.50 (ISBN 0-87527-334-3). Green.

Jacobson, Alex & Caufield, Page, eds. Introduction to Radiographic Cephalometry. LC 84-27838. (Illus.). 137p. 1985. write for info. (ISBN 0-8121-0963-5). Lea & Febiger.

Johns, Harold E. & Cunningham, John R. The Physics of Radiology. 4th ed. (Illus.). 816p. 1983. 49.50x (ISBN 0-398-04669-7). C C Thomas.

Kieffer, Stephen A. & Heitzman, E. Robert. Atlas of Cross-Sectional Anatomy: Computed Tomography, Ultrasound, Radiography, Gross Anatomy. (Illus.). 1979. text ed. 70.00x (ISBN 0-06-141152-3, 14-11529, Harper Medical). Lippincott.

Lasjaunias, P., et al, eds. Frontiers in European Radiology, Vol. 4. (Illus.). 165p. 1984. 30.20 (ISBN 0-387-13410-7). Springer-Verlag.

Lemke, H. U., et al, eds. Computer Assisted Radiology - Computergestutzte Radiologie. (Eng. & Ger., Illus.). 750p. 1985. 39.00 (ISBN 0-387-15520-1). Springer Verlag.

Meredith & Massey. Fundamental Physics of Radiology. 3rd ed. 718p. 1979. 41.50 (ISBN 0-7236-0450-9). PSG Pub Co.

Nahum, Henri & Fekete, Francois. Radiology of the Postoperative Digestive Tract. Oestreich, Alan E., tr. from Fr. LC 79-73738. (Illus.). 160p. 1979. 39.50x (ISBN 0-89352-027-6). Masson Pub.

NCRP. Induction of Thyroid Cancer by Ionizing Radiation. (NCRP Report Ser.: No. 80). 70p. 1985. pap. text ed. 13.00 (ISBN 0-913392-72-3). Natl Coun Radiation.

Orton, Colin G., ed. Progress in Medical Radiation Physics, Vol. 1. 401p. 1982. 55.00x (ISBN 0-306-40713-2, Plenum Pr). Plenum Pub.

Parker. Introduction to Radiology. LC 65-7347. 1984. 27.50 (ISBN 0-397-52112-X, Lippincott Medical). Lippincott.

Radiation Protection in Pediatric Radiology: NCRP Report 68. LC 81-80187. 1981. 11.00 (ISBN 0-913392-54-5). NCRP Pubns.

Robertson, William W. & Hirsh, Guy. Portable X-Ray Techniques Used in Orthopaedic Practice. Date not set. 27.50. Green.

Sorgen, Richard A. & Russo, Robert D., Jr. Abdominal C.T. For Resident & Clinician. 108p. 1982. 39.50 (ISBN 0-87527-289-4). Green.

Sutton, David. Textbook of Radiology & Imaging. 3rd ed. 1981. text ed. 149.00 i vol. set (ISBN 0-443-01700-X); text ed. 175.00 2 vol. set (ISBN 0-443-02371-9). Churchill.

The Use of Computers in Therapeutic Radiology: International Conference, 1966. 1980. 16.00x (ISBN 0-686-69961-0, Pub. by Brit Inst Radiology). State Mutual Bk.

Van Der Plaats, G. J. Medical X-Ray Techniques in Diagnostic Radiology. 1979. lib. bdg. 79.50 (ISBN 90-247-2155-5, Pub by Martinus Nijhoff Netherlands). Kluwer Academic.

Wachsmann, F. & Drexler, G. Graphs & Tables for Use in Radiology. 2nd. rev. enlarged ed. 1976. 29.00 (ISBN 0-387-07809-6). Springer-Verlag.

Wegst, Audrey V., et al. Radioisotopes in Biology & Medicine: Introductory Principles & Techniques. 1964. pap. 6.85 (ISBN 0-87506-031-5, 87506-031-5). Campus.

Weinstein, James B., et al. Pocket Atlas of Normal CT Anatomy. (Illus.). 88p. 1985. pap. text ed. 14.00 (ISBN 0-88167-070-7). Raven.

Wicke, Lothar. Atlas of Radiologic Anatomy. 3rd ed. (Illus.). 248p. 1982. text ed. 19.50 (ISBN 0-8067-2113-8). Urban & S.

RADIOLOGY–DATA PROCESSING

Hunter, Tim B. The Computer in Radiology. 1985. price not set (ISBN 0-87189-235-9). Aspen Systems.

RADIOLYSIS

see Radiation Chemistry

RADIOMETRIC ANALYSIS

see Radioactivation Analysis

RADIONUCLIDES

see Radioisotopes

RADIOPHARMACEUTICALS

Andrews, Gould A., et al, eds. Radioactive Pharmaceuticals: Proceedings. LC 66-60068. (AEC Symposium Ser.). 702p. 1966. pap. 25.50 (ISBN 0-87079-325-X, CONF-651111); microfiche 4.50 (ISBN 0-87079-326-8, CONF-651111). DOE.

Bacq, Z. M. Sulfur Containing Radio-Protective Agents. 344p. 1975. text ed. 110.00 (ISBN 0-08-016298-3). Pergamon.

Balaban, A., et al. Labelled Compounds & Radiopharmaceuticals Applied in Nuclear Medicine. 1985. 110.00 (ISBN 0-471-90458-9). Wiley.

Cox, P. H. Progress in Radiopharmacology 3. 1983. 44.00 (ISBN 90-247-2768-5, Pub. by Martinus Nijhoff Netherlands). Kluwer Academic.

Cox, Peter H. & King, Christine M. Radiopharmacy & Radiopharmacology Yearbook. 392p. 1985. text ed. 47.00 (ISBN 2-88124-114-X); pap. text ed. 18.00 (ISBN 2-88124-113-1). Gordon.

Heindel, Ned D., et al, eds. The Chemistry of Radiopharmaceuticals. LC 77-94827. (Cancer Management Ser.: Vol. 3). (Illus.). 304p. 1978. 45.50x (ISBN 0-89352-019-5). Masson Pub.

Rothschild, Marcus A. Abdominal Organ Imaging. LC 78-55281. (Illus.). 212p. 1979. 25.50 (ISBN 0-88416-193-5). PSG Pub Co.

Saha, G. B. Fundamentals of Nuclear Pharmacy. 2nd ed. (Illus.). xxi, 287p. 1984. 31.00 (ISBN 0-387-90882-X). Springer-Verlag.

Sovak, M., ed. Radiocontrast Agents. (Handbook of Experimental Pharmacology: Vol. 73). (Illus.). 640p. 1984. 178.00 (ISBN 0-387-13107-8). Springer-Verlag.

Theobald, A. E., ed. Radiopharmaceuticals & Radiopharmacy Practice. 250p. 1985. 44.00x (ISBN 0-85066-318-0). Taylor & Francis.

Tubis, Manuel & Wolf, Walter, eds. Radiopharmacy. LC 75-28385. 911p. 1976. 124.95 (ISBN 0-471-89227-0, Pub. by Wiley-Interscience). Wiley.

Welch, Michael J., ed. Radiopharmaceuticals & Other Compounds Labelled with Short-Lived Radionuclides. LC 76-26764. 1977. pap. text ed. 44.00 (ISBN 0-08-021344-8). Pergamon.

RADIOTELEPHONE

see also Mobile Radio Stations

Block, Richard A., ed. Radiotelephone Operator. (Illus.). 52p. 1984. pap. 6.00 (ISBN 0-934114-56-0, BK-111). Marine Educ.

Rudman, Jack. Radio Telephone Operator. (Career Examination Ser.: C-2883). (Cloth bdg. avail. on request). pap. 10.00 (ISBN 0-8373-2883-7). Natl Learning.

Shrader, Robert L. & Boyce, Jefferson C. Practice Tests for Radiotelephone Licenses. 1977. pap. text ed. 16.00 (ISBN 0-07-057130-9). McGraw.

Weagant, Warren. Tests-Answers for FCC General Radio-Telephone Operator License. 8th ed. 192p. 1981. pap. write for info. (ISBN 0-933132-07-7). Command Prods.

RADIOTHERAPY

see also Gamma Rays; Radiation–Dosage; Radium

Amendola, B. E. & Amendola, M. A., eds. Radiation Oncology. 350p. 1984. 56.50 (ISBN 0-444-00846-2, Biomedical Pr). Elsevier.

Christiansen, W. N. & Hogbom, J. A. Radiotelescopes. 2nd ed. (Monographs in Physics). (Illus.). 250p. 1985. 59.50 (ISBN 0-521-26209-7). Cambridge U Pr.

Computer Calculation of Dose Distribution in Radiotherapy. (Technical Reports Ser.: No. 57). (Illus.). 215p. pap. 15.00 (ISBN 92-0-115166-7, IDC57, IAEA). Unipub.

Computers in Radiotherapy: 1968 2nd International Conference. 1980. 9.00x (ISBN 0-686-69946-7, Pub. by Brit Inst Radiology England). State Mutual Bk.

Computers in the Control of Treatment Units: Applications of Modern Technology in Radiotherapy. 1980. 10.00x (ISBN 0-686-69945-9, Pub. by Brit Inst Radiology England). State Mutual Bk.

DuBoulay, G. H., ed. Considerations about the Use of Computers in Radiodiagnostic Departments. 1980. 50.00x (ISBN 0-686-69947-5, Pub. by Brit Inst Radiology England). State Mutual Bk.

Easson, E. C. & Pointon, R. C., eds. The Radiotherapy of Malignant Disease. (Illus.). 500p. 1985. 69.00 (ISBN 0-387-13104-3). Springer-Verlag.

Friedman, Milton, ed. The Biological & Clinical Basis of Radiosensitivity. (Illus.). 592p. 1974. photocopy ed. 62.75x (ISBN 0-398-02951-2). C C Thomas.

Hornback, Ned B. Self-Assessment of Current Knowledge in Therapeutic Radiology. 3rd ed. 1984. pap. text ed. write for info (ISBN 0-87488-394-6). Med Exam.

Johari, Om, et al, eds. Ultrastructural Effects of Radiation on Tissues & Cells. Bhatt, Sudha A. (Illus.). 172p. (Orig.). 1983. pap. text ed. 18.00 (ISBN 0-931288-29-0). Scanning Electron.

Jonckheer, M. H. & Deconinck, F., eds. X-Ray Fluorescent Scanning of the Thyroid. 1983. lib. bdg. 39.50 (ISBN 0-89838-561-X, Pub. by Martinus Nijhoff Netherlands). Kluwer Academic.

Klevenhagen, S. C. Physics of Electron Beam Therapy. (Medical Physics Handbook 13). 200p. 1985. 29.00 (ISBN 0-85274-781-0, Pub. by A Hilger Techo Hse UK). Heyden.

Lacey, Jim & Keough, Allen H. Radiation Curing: A Discussion of Advantages, Features & Applications. LC 80-52815. pap. 24.30 (ISBN 0-317-10943-X, 2019120). Bks Demand UMI.

Levitt, Seymour H. & Tapley, Norah, eds. Technological Basis of Radiation Therapy: Practical Clinical Applications. LC 83-9889. (Illus.). 336p. 1984. text ed. 45.00 (ISBN 0-8121-0898-1). Lea & Febiger.

Medical X-Ray & Gamma Ray Protection for Energies up to 10 MeV: Equipment Design & Use. LC 68-19236. (NCRP Reports Ser.: No. 33). 1968. 7.00 (ISBN 0-913392-15-4). NCRP Pubns.

Pizzarello, Donald J., ed. Radiation Biology. 312p. 1982. 85.00 (ISBN 0-8493-6011-0). CRC Pr.

Protection Against Radiation from Brachytherapy Sources. LC 67-190610. (NCRP Reports Ser.: No. 40). 1972. 8.00 (ISBN 0-913392-22-7). NCRP Pubns.

Raju, M. R. & Raju, M. Bapi. Heavy Particple Radiotherapy. LC 79-27459. 1980. 49.50 (ISBN 0-12-576250-X). Acad Pr.

Shinoda, Gunji K., et al, eds. X-Ray Optics & Microanalysis: Proceedings of the Sixth International Conference. 908p. 1972. 100.00x (ISBN 0-86008-077-3, Pub. by U of Tokyo Japan). Columbia U Pr.

Sowby, F. D., ed. Protection of the Patient in Radiation Therapy. (ICRP Publication Ser.: No. 44). (Illus.). 60p. 1985. pap. 22.00 (ISBN 0-08-032336-7). Pergamon.

Specification of Gamm - Ray Brachytherapy Sources. LC 73-94306. (NCEBP Reports Ser.: No. 41). 1974. 7.00 (ISBN 0-913392-23-5). NCRP Pubns.

Structural Shielding Design & Evaluation for Medical Use of X-Rays & Gamma - Rays of Energies up to Ter Mev. LC 76-22969. (NCRP Reports Ser.: No. 49). 1976. 8.00 (ISBN 0-913392-31-6); adjunct to nCRP report no. 49 12.00 (ISBN 0-686-30845-X). NCRP Pubns.

Stryker, John A. Radiation Oncology. (Medical Outline Ser.). 1984. pap. text ed. write for info (ISBN 0-87488-589-2). Med Exam.

Stryker, John A., et al. Radiation Therapy Technology Examination Review. 2nd ed. LC 84-9151. 1984. pap. text ed. write for info. (ISBN 0-87488-366-0). Med Exam.

Torpie, Richard J., et al. Radiation Therapy & Thanatology. 194p. 1984. 21.75x (ISBN 0-398-04885-1). C C Thomas.

Tretter, Patricia & Kutscher, Lillian G. Psychological Aspects of Radiation Therapy: The Patient, the Family & the Staff. 19.00 (ISBN 0-405-13096-1). Ayer Co Pubs.

Upton, Arthur C. Radiation Injury: Effects, Principles, & Perspectives. LC 69-17672. pap. 34.00 (ISBN 0-317-07735-X, 2019988). Bks Demand UMI.

Zuppinger, A., et al, eds. High Energy Electrons in Radiation Therapy. (Illus.). 130p. 1980. pap. 28.40 (ISBN 0-387-10188-8). Springer-Verlag.

RADIUM

see also Radioactivity; Radiography; Radiotherapy

Curie, Marie. Radioactive Substances: A Translation from the French of the Classical Thesis Presented to the Faculty of Sciences in Paris. LC 79-139128. (Illus.). 1971. Repr. of 1961 ed. lib. bdg. 18.75x (ISBN 0-8371-5744-7, CURS). Greenwood.

Selman, Joseph. Fundamentals of X-Ray & Radium Physics. 7th ed. (Illus.). 728p. 1985. 29.75x (ISBN 0-398-05065-1). C C Thomas.

Vdovenko, V. M. & Dubasov, Yu V. Analytical Chemistry of Radium. Mandel, N., tr. from Rus. LC 74-30131. (Analytical Chemistry of Elements Ser.). 198p. 1925. 58.95x (ISBN 0-470-90488-7). Halsted Pr.

RADON

Deans, Stanley R. The Radon Transform & Some of Its Applications. LC 83-1125. 289p. 1983. 37.95x (ISBN 0-471-89804-X, Pub. by Wiley-Interscience). Wiley.

Helgason, Sigurdur. The Radon Transform. (Progress in Mathematics Ser.: No. 5). 186p. 1980. pap. 17.50x (ISBN 0-8176-3006-6). Birkhauser.

Radon in Uranium Mining: Proceedings, Washington D.C., Sept. 4-7, 1973. (Proceedings Ser.). (Illus.). 173p. 1975. pap. 18.00 (ISBN 92-0-041075-8, ISP391, IAEA). Unipub.

Thomas, Erik. The Lebesgue-Nikodym Theorem for Vector Valued Radon Measures. LC 73-22198. (Memoirs: No. 139). 101p. 1974. pap. 10.00 (ISBN 0-8218-1839-2, MEMO-139). Am Math.

RAFINESQUE, CONSTANTINE SAMUELS, 1783-1840

Rafinesque: Autobiography & Lives, 3 vols. in one. original Anthology ed. Sterling, Keir B., ed. LC 77-83130. (Biologists & Their World Ser.). (Illus.). 1978. lib. bdg. 52.00x (ISBN 0-405-10723-4). Ayer Co Pubs.

RAILROAD CAR BRAKES

see Railroads–Brakes

RAILROAD CONSTRUCTION

see Railroads–Construction; Railroad Engineering

RAILROAD ENGINEERING

see also Railroads–Construction; Railroads–Surveying

Bhattacharjee, P. K. & Basu, A. K. A Textbook of Railway Engineering. 188p. 1981. 20.00x (ISBN 0-86125-285-3, Pub. by Orient Longman India). State Mutual Bk.

Fastenrath, Fritz, ed. Railroad Track; Theory & Practice: Material Properties, Cross Sections, Welding & Treatment. Grant, Walter, tr. from Ger. LC 80-5340. (Illus.). 1980. 85.00 (ISBN 0-8044-4231-2). Ungar.

Fiennes, G. F. I Tried to Run a Railway. text ed. 17.50x (ISBN 0-392-07972-0, SpS). Sportshelf.

Guins, S. G. & Tack, C. E., eds. Anthology of Rail Vehicle Dynamics: Freight Car Impact, Vol. I. Incl. Anthology of Rail Vehicle Dynamics: Effects of Train Action & Rail Car Vibration, Vol. II. Tack, C. E. & Guins, S. G., eds. 270p. 1972. pap. text ed. 25.00 (H00365); Anthology of Rail Vehicle Dynamics: Axles, Wheels & Rail - Wheel Interaction, Vol. III. Guins, S. G. & Tack, C. E., eds. 361p. 1973. pap. text ed. 30.00 (H00066). 175p. 1971. pap. text ed. 20.00 (ISBN 0-685-78338-3, H00064). ASME.

Hay, William H. Railroad Engineering. 2nd ed. LC 81-23117. 758p. 1982. 55.95x (ISBN 0-471-36400-2, Pub. by Wiley-Interscience). Wiley.

Railway Engineering Symposium: Upgrading of Australia's Rail Transport Systems. 235p. 1983. pap. text ed. 15.00x (ISBN 0-85825-203-1, Pub. by Inst Engineering Australia). Brookfield Pub Co.

Rhodes, R. G. & Mulhall, B. E. Magnetic Levitation for Rail Transport. (Monographs on Cryogenics). 1981. 29.95x (ISBN 0-19-854802-8). Oxford U Pr.

Rudman, Jack. Railroad Equipment Inspector. (Career Examination Ser.: C-210). (Cloth bdg. avail. on request). pap. 12.00 (ISBN 0-8373-0210-2). Natl Learning.

--Railroad Track & Structure Inspector. (Career Examination Ser.: C-209). (Cloth bdg. avail. on request). pap. 12.00 (ISBN 0-8373-0209-9). Natl Learning.

Schlomann, A. Illustrierte Technische Woerterbucher: Eisenbahnmaschinenwesen, Vol. 6. (Ger., Eng., Fr., Rus., Span. & Ital., Dictionary of Railway Engineering). 1909. pap. 9.95 (ISBN 0-686-56486-3, M-7473, Pub. by R. Oldenbourg). French & Eur.

--Illustrierte Technische Woerterbucher: Eisenbahnbau und Betrieb, Vol. 5. (Ger., Eng., Fr., Rus., Span. & Ital., Dictionary of Railway engineering). 1909. pap. 9.95 (ISBN 0-686-56485-5, M-7472, Pub. by R. Oldenbourg). French & Eur.

Sperandeo, Andy. The Model Railroad Layout Wiring Guide. Hayden, Bob, ed. (Illus., Orig.). 1985. pap. price not set (ISBN 0-89024-060-4). Kalmbach.

RAILROAD ENGINEERS

see Locomotive Engineers

RAILROAD MODELS

see Railroads–Models

RAILROADS

see also Locomotives; Mine Railroads; Railroads, Cable; Subways

also names of individual railroads

Aldcroft, D. H. & Mort, D. Rail & Sea Transport. 280p. 1981. 39.00 (ISBN 0-08-026105-1). Pergamon.

Allen, Cecil J. Modern Railways: Their Engineering, Equipment & Operation. LC 72-9045. (Illus.). 307p. 1973. Repr. of 1959 ed. lib. bdg. 24.75x (ISBN 0-8371-6565-2, ALMR). Greenwood.

Alston, Liviu L. Railways & Energy. 94p. pap. 3.00 (ISBN 0-318-02821-2, WP0634). World Bank.

Bezilla, Michael. Electric Traction on the Pennsylvania Railroad, 1895-1968. LC 79-65858. (Illus.). 1980. 24.90x (ISBN 0-271-00241-7). Pa St U Pr.

Born, Erhard. Lexikon Fuer Eisenbahnfreunde. (Ger.). 1977. pap. 39.95 (ISBN 3-7658-0238-7, M-7200). French & Eur.

Carter, Ernest. Let's Look at Trains. 9.50x (ISBN 0-392-08037-0, SpS). Sportshelf.

Cockle, George R. Union Pacific Forties...on the Move. LC 81-65096. (Overland Railbook Ser.). (Illus.). 208p. 1985. pap. 23.50 (ISBN 0-916160-10-6). G R Cockle.

Cummings, O. R. Berkshire Street Railway. (Transportation Bulletin: No. 79). (Illus.). 1972. 7.50 (ISBN 0-910506-15-9). De Vito.

Donovan, Frank & Henry, Seth. Headlights & Markers. LC 68-8776. (Illus.). 1968. 17.95 (ISBN 0-87095-006-1). Golden West.

Dorin, Patrick C. Commuter Railroads. encore ed. LC 72-113615. 1970. 9.95 (ISBN 0-87564-507-0). Superior Pub.

Freeman, Allen G. Railways: Past, Present, & Future. LC 82-60816. (Illus.). 304p. 1982. 40.00 (ISBN 0-688-00636-1). Morrow.

Furlow, Malcolm. HO Narrow Gauge Railroad You Can Build. (Illus.). 60p. (Orig.). 1984. pap. 7.95 (ISBN 0-89024-058-2). Kalmbach.

Heavyside, G. T. Narrow Gauge into the Eighties. LC 79-56067. (Illus.). 96p. 1980. 16.95 (ISBN 0-7153-7979-8). David & Charles.

Heseltine, Charles D. Bangor Street Railway. (Illus.). 1976. 6.00 (ISBN 0-910506-17-5). De Vito.

Jacobs, H. W. Betterment Briefs: A Collection of Published Papers on Organized Industrial Efficiency. 2nd ed. (Management History Ser.: No. 80). (Illus.). 271p. 1975. Repr. of 1909 ed. 22.50 (ISBN 0-87960-108-6). Hive Pub.

Jane's World Railways, 1977. 79.50x (ISBN 0-531-03268-X). Key Bk Serv.

Jane's World Railways, 1979-1980. 109.95 (ISBN 0-531-03906-4). Key Bk Serv.

Jensen, Larry. The Movie Railroads. (Illus.). 256p. 1981. 34.95 (ISBN 0-933506-05-8). Darwin Pubns.

Kerr, Arnold D. & Kornhauser, Alain L., eds. Productivity in Railroads: Proceedings of a Symposium Held at Princeton University, July, 1977. (Pergamon Policy Studies). 1980. 26.00 (ISBN 0-08-023871-8). Pergamon.

Marshall, John. Rail Facts & Feats. (Illus.). 252p. 1980. 19.95 (ISBN 0-900424-56-7, Pub by Guinness Superlatives England). Sterling.

Martin, Ed. Stamford Street Railroad Co. (Transportation Bulletin Ser.: No. 83). (Illus.). 1978. 9.00 (ISBN 0-910506-19-1). De Vito.

Nock, O. S., ed. World Atlas of Railways. (Illus.). 1978. 10.95 (ISBN 0-8317-9500-X, Mayflower Bks). Smith Pubs.

Payne, P. L. Rubber & Railways. 246p. 1961. 40.00x (ISBN 0-85323-482-5, Pub. by Liverpool Univ England). State Mutual Bk.

Rail Steel: Developments Processing & Use - STP 644. 488p. 1978. 45.00 (ISBN 0-8031-0545-2, 04-644000-01). ASTM.

Rail Talk. pap. 5.95 (ISBN 0-686-75196-5). Chatham Pub CA.

Ranger, Dan. Pacific Coast Shay. LC 64-8046. 112p. 16.95 (ISBN 0-87095-022-3). Golden West.

Shaw, Frederic. Little Railways of the World. LC 58-59719. (Illus.). 1958. 14.95 (ISBN 0-8310-7007-2). Howell-North.

Showalter, Dennis E. Railroads & Rifles: Soldiers, Technology & Unification of Germany. (Illus.). 267p. 1975. 17.50 (ISBN 0-208-01505-1, Archon). Shoe String.

Taber, Thomas T. Delaware, Lackawana & Western Railroad in the Twentieth Century, Vol. 2. (Illus.). 1981. 30.00 (ISBN 0-9603398-3-3). T T Taber.

Wagner, Jack R. The Last Whistle. LC 74-83756. (Illus.). 136p. 1974. 17.50 (ISBN 0-8310-7107-9). Howell-North.

RAILROADS–AUTOMATION

Barwell, F. T. Automation & Control in Transport. 2nd rev. ed. LC 82-18981. 400p. 1983. 66.00 (ISBN 0-08-026712-2). Pergamon.

RAILROADS–BRAKES

Wright, Roy V., ed. Freight Car Construction Details, Underframes & Brakes: Pt. 5. (Train Shed Ser.: No. 77). (Illus.). 1979. pap. 4.50 (ISBN 0-87962-081-1). N K Gregg.

RAILROADS–BUILDINGS AND STRUCTURES

see also Railroads–Repair Shops

Berg, Walter G. Buildings & Structures of American Railroads, Pt. 5. (Train Shed Cyclopedia Ser: No. 33). (Illus.). 72p. 1975. pap. 4.95 (ISBN 0-912318-64-3). N K Gregg.

--Buildings & Structures of American Railroads, Pt. 6. (Train Shed Cyclopedia Ser: No. 38). (Illus.). 72p. 1975. pap. 4.95 (ISBN 0-912318-69-4). N K Gregg.

Berg, Walter G., ed. Building & Structures of American Railroads, Pt. 4. (Train Shed Cyclopedia Ser., No. 24). (Illus.). 1974. pap. 4.95 (ISBN 0-912318-54-6). N K Gregg.

Pompidou, Centre G., ed. All Stations: A Journey Through 150 Years of Railway History. (Illus.). 1981. 19.95 (ISBN 0-500-01255-5). Thames Hudson.

Thorne, Peter. Thirty-Four New Electronic Projects for Model Railroaders. Angle, Burr, ed. 80p. 1982. 10.95 (ISBN 0-89024-039-6). Kalmbach.

RAILROADS–CARS

see also Electric Railroads–Cars

Big Boy. pap. 14.50 (ISBN 0-685-83313-5). Chatham Pub CA.

Cars, Scales and Gates from the 1909 BUDA Catalog. (Train Shed Cyclopedia Ser: No. 28). (Illus.). 80p. 1975. pap. 5.50 (ISBN 0-912318-59-7). N K Gregg.

Chesley, Alan B., illus. Cabin Cars of the Pennsylvania & Long Island Railroads. LC 82-81756. (Caboose Data Bk.: No. 2). (Illus.). 64p. 1982. pap. 12.98 (ISBN 0-934088-08-X). NJ Intl Inc.

Crump, Spencer. Rail Car, Locomotive & Trolley Builders: An All-Time Directory. Date not set. write for info. (ISBN 0-87046-032-3, Pub. by Trans-Anglo). Interurban.

Custom Brass Second Edition Catalogue. (Illus.). 48p. 1980. pap. 6.95 (ISBN 0-934088-05-5). NJ Intl Inc.

Dixon, Thomas W., Jr. Chesapeake & Ohio H7 Series. LC 79-51795. (Classic Power Ser.: No. 1). (Illus.). 53p. 1979. pap. 6.95 (ISBN 0-934088-00-4). NJ Intl Inc.

Dressler, Thomas. The First Northerns: Northern Pacific A Class 4-8-4. LC 80-85076. (Classic Power Ser.: No. 4). (Illus.). 100p. 1981. pap. 12.95 (ISBN 0-934088-03-9). NJ Intl Inc.

--USRA 2-8-8-2 Series. rev. & exp. ed. LC 80-81576. (Classic Power Ser.: No. 3). (Illus.). 150p. 1985. pap. 18.95 (ISBN 0-934088-02-0). NJ Intl Inc.

Electric Locomotives & Motor Cars: Part 5. (Train Shed Ser.: No. 78). (Illus.). 1979. pap. 4.50 (ISBN 0-87962-077-3). N K Gregg.

Forney, Matthias, ed. The Car Builder's Dictionary. (Illus.). 544p. 1971. Repr. of 1879 ed. lib. bdg. 14.95 buckram (ISBN 0-912318-16-3). N K Gregg.

Forney, Matthias N. The Railroad Car Builders Pictorial Dictionary. (Illus.). 13.25 (ISBN 0-8446-5187-7). Peter Smith.

Freight & Passenger Cars, Shops & Terminals of the Late 1940's & 1950's: Part 2. (Train Shed Ser.: No. 79). (Illus.). 1979. pap. 4.95 (ISBN 0-87962-082-X). N K Gregg.

Freight & Passenger Cars, Shops & Terminals, 40's & 50's: Pt. 4. (Train Shed Ser.: No. 90). (Illus.). 1980. pap. 4.95 (ISBN 0-87962-093-5). N K Gregg.

Garg, Vijay K., et al. Dynamics of Railway Vehicle Systems. LC 83-21475. (Monograph). 1984. 69.50 (ISBN 0-12-275950-8). Acad Pr.

Harley, E. T. Pennsy Q Class. LC 82-81755. (Classic Power Ser.: No. 5). (Illus.). 88p. 1982. pap. 15.95 (ISBN 0-934088-09-8). NJ Intl Inc.

Husband, Joseph. History of the Pullman Car. LC 74-13857. (Illus.). 161p. 1974. Repr. of 1917 ed. 15.00 (ISBN 0-912382-16-3). Black Letter.

--The Story of the Pullman Car. LC 72-5055. (Technology & Society Ser.). (Illus.). 238p. 1972. Repr. of 1917 ed. 21.00 (ISBN 0-405-04707-X). Ayer Co Pubs.

Kichenside, Geoffrey. One Hundred Fifty Years of Railway Carriages. LC 81-65962. (Illus.). 96p. 1981. 16.95 (ISBN 0-7153-8196-2). David & Charles.

Moyar, Gerald J. & Pilkey, Walter D., eds. Advanced Techniques, Proceedings of a Conference Held in Chicago, Sept. 27-28, 1978. LC 78-1678. 484p. 1978. 65.00 (ISBN 0-08-022153-X). Pergamon.

PCC, Car That Fought Back. (Illus.). 29.95 (ISBN 0-686-75191-4). Chatham Pub CA.

Rail Motor Cars Nineteen Nineteen to Nineteen Twenty. (Train Shed Cyclopedia Ser: No. 30). (Illus.). 64p. 1975. pap. 4.50 (ISBN 0-912318-61-9). N K Gregg.

Rowland, Don. British Railways Wagons. (Illus.). 160p. 1985. 27.50 (ISBN 0-7153-8183-0). David & Charles.

Simmons-Boardman Publishing Corp. Car & Locomotive Cyclopedia, 1984. 5th ed. LC 84-50897. (The Car & Locomotive Cyclopedia of American Practices Ser.). 1000p. 1984. 69.95 (ISBN 0-911382-01-1). Simmons Boardman.

Tufnell, Roger. The British Railcar: AEC to HST. (Illus.). 96p. 1984. 17.95 (ISBN 0-7153-8529-1). David & Charles.

Voss, William. Freight Cars, 1892, from Railway Car Construction. (Train Shed Cyclopedia Ser: No. 29). (Illus.). 80p. 1975. pap. 5.50 (ISBN 0-912318-60-0). N K Gregg.

--Passenger Cars from Railway Car Construction, 1892. (Train Shed Cyclopedia Ser: No. 39). (Illus.). 80p. 1976. pap. 5.50 (ISBN 0-912318-70-8). N K Gregg.

Wait, John C., ed. Freight & Passenger Cars from the 1898 Car Builder's Dictionary: Part 1, No. 55. (Train Shed Ser.). (Illus.). 1977. pap. 4.50 (ISBN 0-912318-90-2). N K Gregg.

--Freight & Passenger Cars from the 1898 Car Builder's Dictionary: Part 2, No. 57. (Train Shed Ser.). (Illus.). 1977. pap. 4.50 (ISBN 0-912318-92-9). N K Gregg.

--Freight & Passenger Cars from the 1898 Car Builder's Dictionary: Part 3, No. 59. (Train Shed Ser.). (Illus.). 1977. pap. 4.50 (ISBN 0-912318-94-5). N K Gregg.

Weld, Louis D. Private Freight Cars & American Railways. LC 70-76679. (Columbia University. Studies in the Social Sciences: No. 81). Repr. of 1908 ed. 17.50 (ISBN 0-404-51081-7). AMS Pr.

Wright, Roy V., ed. Boilers: Part Three. (Train Shed Ser.: No. 82). (Illus.). 1979. pap. 4.95 (ISBN 0-87962-085-4). N K Gregg.

--Cabooses & Freight Car Construction Details: Part 4. (Train Shed Ser.: No. 75). (Illus.). 1978. pap. 4.50 (ISBN 0-87962-080-3). N K Gregg.

--Car Builder's Cyclopedia, 1925: Major Pages, Part 2. (Train Shed Ser.: No. 62). (Illus.). 1977. pap. 4.50 (ISBN 0-912318-97-X). N K Gregg.

--Car Builder's Cyclopedia, 1925: Major Pages, Part 1. (Train Shed Ser.: No. 61). (Illus.). 1977. pap. 4.50 (ISBN 0-912318-96-1). N K Gregg.

--Car Builder's Cyclopedia, 1925: Major Pages, Part 3. (Train Shed Ser.: No. 63). (Illus.). 1977. pap. 4.50 (ISBN 0-912318-98-8). N K Gregg.

--Car Builder's Cyclopedia, 1925: Major Pages, Part 4. (Train Shed Ser.: No. 65). (Illus.). 1978. pap. 4.50 (ISBN 0-87962-067-6). N K Gregg.

--Cow Catchers, Cabs & Fittings Plus Tenders: Part 4. (Train Shed Ser.: No. 76). (Illus.). 1978. pap. 4.50 (ISBN 0-87962-076-5). N K Gregg.

--Frames Cylinders & Valve Gears: Part 5. (Train Shed Ser.: No. 87). (Illus.). 1979. pap. 4.95 (ISBN 0-87962-090-0). N K Gregg.

--Freight & Passenger Cars: Shops & Terminals, Pt. 3. (Train Shed Ser.: No. 85). (Illus.). 1979. pap. 4.95 (ISBN 0-87962-088-9). N K Gregg.

--Freight Car Construction Details: Industrial & Export Cars, Pt. 7. (Train Shed Ser.: No. 83). (Illus.). 1979. pap. 4.95 (ISBN 0-87962-086-2). N K Gregg.

--Freight Car Construction Details, Safety Appliances & Trucks: Pt. 6. (Train Shed Ser.: No. 81). (Illus.). 1979. pap. 4.95 (ISBN 0-87962-084-6). N K Gregg.

--Freight Car Construction Details, Underframes & Brakes: Pt. 5. (Train Shed Ser.: No. 77). (Illus.). 1979. pap. 4.50 (ISBN 0-87962-081-1). N K Gregg.

--Freight Cars from the 1919 Car Builder's Dictionary, Pt. 1. (Train Shed Cyclopedia Ser: No. 35). (Illus.). 80p. 1975. pap. 5.50 (ISBN 0-912318-66-X). N K Gregg.

--Freight Cars from the 1919 Car Builder's Dictionary, Pt. 2. (Train Shed Cyclodedia Ser: No. 36). (Illus.). 80p. 1975. pap. 5.50 (ISBN 0-912318-67-8). N K Gregg.

--Gondolas & Hoppers: Part 2. (Train Shed Cyclopedia: No. 70). (Illus.). 1978. pap. 4.50 (ISBN 0-87962-072-2). N K Gregg.

--Hoppers, Tanks, Containers Cars & Cabooses: Part 3. (Train Shed Ser.: No. 71). (Illus.). 1978. pap. 4.50 (ISBN 0-87962-073-0). N K Gregg.

--Locos of the Forties & Fifties: Part 2. (Train Shed Ser.: No. 80). (Illus.). 1979. pap. 4.95 (ISBN 0-87962-083-8). N K Gregg.

--Motor Cars & Passenger Construction Details: Part 8. (Train Shed Ser.: No. 86). (Illus.). 1979. pap. 4.95 (ISBN 0-87962-089-7). N K Gregg.

--Motor Passenger Cars & Construction Details: Part 5. (Train Shed Ser.: No. 67). (Illus.). 1978. pap. 4.50 (ISBN 0-87962-069-2). N K Gregg.

--Passenger Cars from the 1943 Car Builder's Cyclopedia. 16th ed. (Train Shed Cyclopedia Ser., No. 21). (Illus.). 1974. pap. 4.50 (ISBN 0-912318-51-1). N K Gregg.

--Passenger Cars from the 1999 Car Builder's Dictionary. (Train Shed Cyclopedia Ser: No. 42). (Illus.). 1976. pap. 3.00 (ISBN 0-912318-73-2). N K Gregg.

--Passenger Construction Details & Interior Fittings: Part 9. (Train Shed Ser.: No. 88). (Illus.). 1979. pap. 4.95 (ISBN 0-87962-091-9). N K Gregg.

--Passenger Details, Trucks & Industrials: Part 6. (Train Shed Ser.: No. 68). (Illus.). 1978. pap. 4.50 (ISBN 0-87962-070-6). N K Gregg.

--Pistons & Trucks: Part Six. (Train Shed Ser.: No. 89). (Illus.). 1980. pap. 4.95 (ISBN 0-87962-092-7). N K Gregg.

--Railway Service Cars 1928-1943. (Train Shed Cyclopedia Ser, No. 26). (Illus.). 1974. pap. 4.95 (ISBN 0-912318-56-2). N K Gregg.

--Smoke Boxes & Stokers: Part 4. (Train Shed Ser.: No. 84). (Illus.). 1979. pap. 4.95 (ISBN 0-87962-087-0). N K Gregg.

--Smoke Boxes, Stokers, Valve Gears & Trucks: Part 3. (Train Ser.: No. 74). (Illus.). 1978. pap. 4.50 (ISBN 0-87962-075-7). N K Gregg.

RAILROADS–CONSTRUCTION

see also Railroads–Surveying; Tunnels and Tunneling

Berg, Walter G. Buildings & Structures of American Railroads, Pt. 2. 9th ed. (Train Shed Cyclopedia Ser., No. 13). (Illus.). 1973. pap. 4.95 (ISBN 0-912318-42-2). N K Gregg.

--Buildings & Structures of American Railroads, Pt. 3. 9th ed. (Train Shed Cyclopedia Ser., No. 19). (Illus.). 1974. pap. 4.50 (ISBN 0-912318-48-1). N K Gregg.

Fulton, Robert L. Epic of the Overland: An Account of the Building of the Central & Union Pacific Railroad. LC 54-3213. 109p. 1982. lib. bdg. 44.95x (ISBN 0-89370-713-9). Borgo Pr.

Helmers, Dow. Historic Alpine Tunnel. (Illus.). 208p. 1978. write for info.; pap. 14.95 (ISBN 0-937080-02-0). Century One.

Kyner, J. H. End of the Track: Biography of Western Pioneer Railroad Builder. 12.00 (ISBN 0-8446-2416-0). Peter Smith.

Williams, F. S. Our Iron Roads: Vol. 1; History & Construction. 272p. 1984. 35.00x (ISBN 0-905418-88-3, Pub. by Gresham England). State Mutual Bk.

RAILROADS–DICTIONARIES

English-Chinese Dictionary of Railway Terms. (Eng. & Chinese.). 1025p. 1977. 17.95 (ISBN 0-686-92493-2, M-9559). French & Eur.

Forney, Matthias, ed. The Car Builder's Dictionary. (Illus.). 544p. 1971. Repr. of 1879 ed. lib. bdg. 14.95 buckram (ISBN 0-912318-16-3). N K Gregg.

Forney, Matthias N. The Railroad Car Builders Pictorial Dictionary. (Illus.). 13.25 (ISBN 0-8446-5187-7). Peter Smith.

Simmons-Boardman Publishing Corp. Railway Age's Comprehensive Railroad Dictionary. abr. ed. LC 83-51791. 162p. 1984. 17.95 (ISBN 0-911382-00-3). Simmons Boardman.

Wait, John C., ed. Freight & Passenger Cars from the 1898 Car Builder's Dictionary: Part 1, No. 55. (Train Shed Ser.). (Illus.). 1977. pap. 4.50 (ISBN 0-912318-90-2). N K Gregg.

--Freight & Passenger Cars from the 1898 Car Builder's Dictionary: Part 2, No. 57. (Train Shed Ser.). (Illus.). 1977. pap. 4.50 (ISBN 0-912318-92-9). N K Gregg.

Wright, Roy V., ed. Freight Cars from the 1919 Car Builder's Dictionary, Pt. 2. (Train Shed Cyclodedia Ser: No. 36). (Illus.). 80p. 1975. pap. 5.50 (ISBN 0-912318-67-8). N K Gregg.

--Passenger Cars from the 1999 Car Builder's Dictionary. (Train Shed Cyclopedia Ser: No. 42). (Illus.). 1976. pap. 3.00 (ISBN 0-912318-73-2). N K Gregg.

RAILROADS–ENGINEERING

see Railroad Engineering

RAILROADS–FREIGHT CARS

see Railroads–Cars

RAILROADS–HISTORY

Baer, Christopher T. Canals & Railroads of the Mid-Atlantic States, 1800-1860. 80p. 1981. pap. 15.00x (ISBN 0-914650-19-X). Eleutherian Mills-Hagley.

Cars, Scales and Gates from the 1909 BUDA Catalog. (Train Shed Cyclopedia Ser: No. 28). (Illus.). 80p. 1975. pap. 5.50 (ISBN 0-912318-59-7). N K Gregg.

Chesnutt, N. P. Southern Union. LC 79-87779. 1979. 14.00 (ISBN 0-930208-07-2). Mangan Bks.

Clifford, Howard. Western Rail Guide. (Illus.). 168p. 1983. pap. 9.95 (ISBN 0-87564-540-2). Superior Pub.

Cockman, F. G. Discovering Preserved Railways. (Discovering Ser.: No. 253). (Illus., Orig.). 1983. pap. 2.95 (ISBN 0-85263-723-3, 3381119, Pub. by Shire Pubns England). Seven Hills Bks.

Collias, Joe G. Mopac Power. (Illus.). 352p. 1980. 35.00 (ISBN 0-8310-7117-6). Howell-North.

Condit, Carl W. The Port of New York: A History of the Rail & Therminal System from the Grand Central Electrification to the Present, Vol. 2. LC 79-16850. 384p. 40.00x (ISBN 0-226-11461-9). U of Chicago Pr.

Cookridge, E. H. The Orient Express: The Life & Time of the World's Most Famous Train. 1978. 12.95 (ISBN 0-394-41176-5). Random.

Course, Edwin. Railways Then & Now. 1979. 21.00 (ISBN 0-7134-0533-3, Pub. by Batsford England). David & Charles.

Eatwell, David & Cooper-Smith, John H. Live Steam: Locomotives & Lines Today. (Illus.). 120p. 1980. 19.95 (ISBN 0-7134-2079-0, Pub. by Batsford England). David & Charles.

Foss, Charles R. Evening Before the Diesel: A History of the Grand Trunk Western Railroad. (Illus.). 1980. 49.95 (ISBN 0-87108-552-6). Pruett.

Freight & Passenger Cars, Shops & Terminals of the Late 1940's & 1950's: Part 2. (Train Shed Ser.: No. 79). (Illus.). 1979. pap. 4.95 (ISBN 0-87962-082-X). N K Gregg.

Freight & Passenger Cars, Shops & Terminals, 40's & 50's: Pt. 4. (Train Shed Ser.: No. 90). (Illus.). 1980. pap. 4.95 (ISBN 0-87962-093-5). N K Gregg.

Harder, Klaus P. Environmental Factors of Early Railroads: A Comparative Study of Massachusetts & the German States of Baden & the Pfalz Before 1870. Bruchey, Stuart, ed. LC 80-2808. (Dissertations in European Economic History II). (Illus.). 1981. lib. bdg. 38.50x (ISBN 0-405-13992-6). Ayer Co Pubs.

Jewell, Donald V. Southern Pacific Motive Power Annual, 1977-1980. LC 80-66138. (Illus.). 88p. 1981. 15.00 (ISBN 0-89685-009-9). Chatham Pub CA.

Jones, Robert C. Two Feet Between the Rails: The Early Years, Vol. 1. Collman, Russ, ed. (Illus.). 416p. 1979. 45.00 (ISBN 0-913582-17-4). Sundance.

Kellett, John R. The Impact of Railways on Victorian Cities. (Studies in Social History). (Illus.). 1979. pap. 12.50 (ISBN 0-8020-6383-7). U of Toronto Pr.

Lehigh Valley Railroad. 30.00 (ISBN 0-686-70722-2). Chatham Pub CA.

Murdock, Dick. Hogheads & Highballs: Railroad Lore & Humor. 2nd ed. Murdock, Jayne, ed. LC 79-89177. (Illus.). 64p. (Orig.). 1979. pap. 5.00 (ISBN 0-932916-04-X). May Murdock.

Patterson, E. M. The County Donegal Railways. new ed. (Illus.). 176p. 1982. 17.50 (ISBN 0-7153-8167-9). David & Charles.

Pompidou, Centre G., ed. All Stations: A Journey Through 150 Years of Railway History. (Illus.). 1981. 19.95 (ISBN 0-500-01255-5). Thames Hudson.

Taylor, William L. A Productive Monopoly: The Effect of Railroad Control on New England Coastal Steamship Lines, 1870-1916. LC 70-111457. (Illus.). 339p. 1970. 27.50x (ISBN 0-87057-123-0). U Pr of New Eng.

White, John H., Jr. The John Bull: 150 Years a Locomotive. LC 81-607054. (Illus.). 136p. (Orig.). 1981. pap. 6.95 (ISBN 0-87474-961-1). Smithsonian.

Wright, Roy V., ed. Frames Cylinders & Valve Gears: Part 5. (Train Shed Ser.: No. 87). (Illus.). 1979. pap. 4.95 (ISBN 0-87962-090-0). N K Gregg.

--Locos of the Forties & Fifties: Part 2. (Train Shed Ser.: No. 80). (Illus.). 1979. pap. 4.95 (ISBN 0-87962-083-8). N K Gregg.

--Motor Cars & Passenger Construction Details: Part 8. (Train Shed Ser.: No. 86). (Illus.). 1979. pap. 4.95 (ISBN 0-87962-089-7). N K Gregg.

--Passenger Construction Details & Interior Fittings: Part 9. (Train Shed Ser.: No. 88). (Illus.). 1979. pap. 4.95 (ISBN 0-87962-091-9). N K Gregg.

--Pistons & Trucks: Part Six. (Train Shed Ser.: No. 89). (Illus.). 1980. pap. 4.95 (ISBN 0-87962-092-7). N K Gregg.

RAILROADS–MAINTENANCE AND REPAIR

see also Railroads–Repair Shops; Railroads–Snow Protection and Removal

Simmons-Boardman Publishing Corp. Car & Locomotive Cyclopedia, 1984. 5th ed. LC 84-50897. (The Car & Locomotive Cyclopedia of American Practices Ser.). 1000p. 1984. 69.95 (ISBN 0-911382-01-1). Simmons Boardman.

RAILROADS–MANAGEMENT

Anderson, W. L. Railroad Track Briefs for the Plant Engineer. (Illus.). 1979. 10.00 (ISBN 0-682-49448-8). Exposition Pr FL.

Chandler, Alfred D., ed. The Railroads: Pioneers in Modern Management, an Original Anthology. LC 79-7528. (History of Management Thought & Practice Ser.). 1980. lib. bdg. 28.50x (ISBN 0-405-12312-4). Ayer Co Pubs.

Shaw, Robert B. History of Railroad Accidents, Safety Precautions & Operating Practices. 1978. 10.00 (ISBN 0-686-10935-X). Northern Pr.

RAILROADS–MODELS

Anderson, Willard V., ed. Easy-to-Build Model Railroad Structures. (Illus.). 96p. (Orig.). 1958. pap. 4.50 (ISBN 0-89024-514-2). Kalmbach.

Armstrong, John H. Eighteen Tailor-Made Model Railroad Track Plans. Hayden, Bob, ed. (Illus.). 80p. (Orig.). 1984. pap. 10.95 (ISBN 0-89024-040-X). Kalmbach.

Bradley, Maurice. Buildings for Model Railways. (Illus.). 96p. 1983. 14.95 (ISBN 0-7153-8343-4). David & Charles.

Bradshaw, John. Greenberg's Guide to Kusan, AMT, & Auburn Trains. Greenberg, Linda, ed. 1985. pap. write for info. (ISBN 0-89778-073-6). Greenberg Pub Co.

Carstens, Harold H. Lionel Standard Gauge Era. LC 64-56883. (Carstens Hobby Bks.: C-13). 1974. pap. 3.00 (ISBN 0-911868-13-5). Carstens Pubns.

--Traction Planbook. 2nd ed. (Carstens Hobby Bks.: C-16). (Illus.). 1969. pap. 6.00 (ISBN 0-911868-16-X). Carstens Pubns.

Carstens, Harold H., ed. Circus Trains & Modelling. LC 75-8473. (Rail-Craft Library: C-29). (Illus.). 1975. pap. 3.00 (ISBN 0-911868-29-1). Carstens Pubns.

Chubb, Bruce. Computers in Model Railroading. Hayden, Bob, ed. (Illus., Orig.). 1985. pap. price not set (ISBN 0-89024-077-9). Kalmbach.

Curren, Art. Kitbashing Model Railroad Structures. (Illus., Orig.). 1985. pap. price not set (ISBN 0-89024-059-0). Kalmbach.

Dolzall, Gary & Dolzall, Stephen. Diesel From Eddystone: The Story of Baldwin Diesel Locomotives. Hayden, Bob, ed. (Illus.). 152p. (Orig.). 1984. pap. 18.95 (ISBN 0-89024-052-3). Kalmbach.

Easy-to-Build Model Railroad Freight Cars. LC 73-131060. (Illus.). 100p. 1971. pap. 3.00 (ISBN 0-89024-520-7). Kalmbach.

Frary, Dave. How to Build Realistic Model Railroad Scenery. Hayden, Bob, ed. (Illus.). 100p. (Orig.). 1981. pap. 8.95 (ISBN 0-89024-037-X). Kalmbach.

Garrison, Paul. All about N Gauge Model Railroading. (Illus.). 240p. (Orig.). 1982. pap. 11.95 (ISBN 0-8306-1387-0, 1387). TAB Bks.

--One Hundred One Model Railroad Layouts. (Illus.). 160p. (Orig.). 1983. 17.95 (ISBN 0-8306-0514-2, 1514); pap. 11.50 (ISBN 0-8306-1514-8). TAB Bks.

Gorkill, W. A. A Beginner's Guide to Railway Modeling. (Illus.). 64p. 1982. 9.95 (ISBN 0-7153-8127-X). David & Charles.

Greenberg, Bruce C. Greenberg's Guide to American Flyer: Prewar 0 & Standard. (Orig.). 1986. pap. 35.00 (ISBN 0-89778-014-0, 6411). Greenberg Pub Co.

Greenberg, Bruce C., ed. Greenberg's Lionel Catalogues, Vol. 1: Nineteen Twenty-Three to Nineteen Thirty-Two. (Illus.). 490p. 1982. text ed. 95.00 (ISBN 0-89778-011-6). Greenberg Pub Co.

--Greenberg's Lionel Catalogues, Vol. 2: Nineteen Thirty-Three to Forty-Two. (Illus.). 516p. 1982. text ed. 95.00 (ISBN 0-89778-012-4). Greenberg Pub Co.

Hayden, Bob, ed. Model Railroader Cyclopedia, Vol. III: Freight Equipment. (Illus.). 224p. (Orig.). 1986. pap. 36.00. Kalmbach.

--Scratchbuilding & Kitbashing Model Railroad Stations. LC 77-86282. 1978. pap. 4.95 (ISBN 0-89024-533-9). Kalmbach.

--Track Planning Ideas from Model Railroader. LC 80-84022. (Illus.). 96p. (Orig.). 1981. pap. 5.95 (ISBN 0-89024-555-X). Kalmbach.

Klein, Maury D. K-1 Operating 0 & 0-27 Trains: A Comprehensive Guide to the Design, Construction & Operation of a Layout for Lionel Trains. rev. ed. (Illus.). 245p. 1984. pap. 7.50 (ISBN 0-934580-02-2). MDK Inc.

Klein, Maury D., ed. Complete Service Manual for American Flyer Trains. (Illus.). 402p. 1978. lib. bdg. 25.00 sewn (ISBN 0-934580-06-5, K-3). MDK Inc.

--Complete Service Manual for Lionel Trains. (Illus.). 1979. Repr. of 1978 ed. lib. bdg. 16.00 (ISBN 0-934580-04-9, K-2). MDK Inc.

Kramer & Krause. Lehigh & New England. (Carstens Hobby Bks.: No. C41). 1981. pap. 9.95 (ISBN 0-911868-41-0). Carstens Pubns.

Krause & Crist. Susquehanna: NYS&W. (Carstens Hobby Bks.: No. C38). (Illus.). 1980. pap. 12.00 (ISBN 0-911868-38-0). Carstens Pubns.

Krause & Grenard. East Broad Top. (Carstens Hobby Bks: No. C40). 1980. pap. 9.95 (ISBN 0-911868-40-2). Carstens Pubns.

--Steam in the Alleghenies: Western Maryland. (Carstens Hobby Bks.: No. C37). (Illus.). 1981. pap. 9.95 (ISBN 0-911868-37-2). Carstens Pubns.

Larson, Russ. N Scale Primer. LC 73-84417. (Illus.). 104p. 1974. pap. 7.50 (ISBN 0-89024-521-5). Kalmbach.

Larson, Russ, ed. N Scale Model Railroad Track Plans. LC 71-107073. (Illus.). 44p. 1969. pap. 4.50 (ISBN 0-89024-509-6). Kalmbach.

Levy, A. A Century of Model Trains. 2nd, dual language ed. (Eng & Ger., Illus.). 208p. 1974. 45.00 (ISBN 0-911868-02-X). Carstens Pubns.

McComas, Tom & Tuohy, James. Lionel: A Collectors Guide & History, Vol. IV:1970-1980. 138p. 1980. 24.95 (ISBN 0-937522-00-7). TM Prods.

McDuffie, Al. Greenberg's Guide to Ives. Greenberg, Bruce C., ed. (Orig.). 1984. 40.00 (ISBN 0-89778-013-2). Greenberg Pub Co.

Mallerich, Dallas. Greenberg's Guide to N Gauge. 112p. (Orig.). 1981. pap. 15.95 (ISBN 0-89778-007-8). Greenberg Pub Co.

Mallery, Paul. Design Handbook for Model Railroads. (Illus.). 1979. pap. 6.95 (ISBN 0-911868-31-3). Carstens Pubns.

--Electrical Handbook for Model Railroads, Vol. 1. (Carstens Hobby Bks.: C-21). 1971. pap. 4.95 (ISBN 0-911868-21-6). Carstens Pubns.

--Electrical Handbook for Model Railroads, Vol. 2. rev. ed. (Carstens Hobby Bks.). 1982. pap. 8.95 (ISBN 0-911868-43-7). Carstens Pubns.

Olson, John. Building an H-O Railroad with Personality: The Jerome & Southwestern. Hayden, Bob, ed. (Illus.). 68p. (Orig.). 1983. pap. 6.95 (ISBN 0-89024-042-6). Kalmbach.

Quinby. Interurban Interlude. (Illus.). 1969. 12.00 (ISBN 0-911868-76-3). Carstens Pubns.

Ruocchio, Albert C. & Klein, Maury D. Track Layout & Accessory Manual for Lionel Trains. (Illus.). 1979. pap. 3.00 saddle-stitched (ISBN 0-934580-08-1, K-4). MDK Inc.

Schafer, Mike, ed. Classic Articles from Model Railroader. LC 79-90508. 80p. (Orig.). 1979. pap. 4.50 (ISBN 0-89024-545-2). Kalmbach.

Schafer, Mike, ed. & intro. by. More Railroads You Can Model. LC 77-86274. (Illus.). 1978. pap. 5.50 (ISBN 0-89024-534-7). Kalmbach.

Schafer, Mike, ed. Traction Guidebook for Model Railroaders. LC 74-76225. (Illus.). 120p. (Orig.). 1974. pap. 4.00 (ISBN 0-89024-522-3). Kalmbach.

Schleicher, Robert, ed. & illus. The Best of Model Railroading Track Plans. LC 83-82161. (Illus.). 96p. 1983. pap. text ed. 6.50 (ISBN 0-9612692-0-0). Eastwood Pub Co.

Shantar, Stan. Greenberg's Operating & Repair Manual for Lionel-Fundimensions Trains: 1970-1978. Greenberg, Linda, ed. LC 78-74525. (Illus.). 1978. pap. 5.95 (ISBN 0-89778-070-1). Greenberg Pub Co.

Smeed, Vic. Complete Railway Modelling. LC 82-73546. 192p. 1983. pap. 14.95 (ISBN 0-8019-7367-8). Chilton.

Smeed, Vic, ed. Complete Railway Modelling. 192p. 1982. 60.00x (ISBN 0-85223-196-2, Pub. by Ebury Pr England). State Mutual Bk.

Thorne, Peter J. Practical Electronic Projects for Model Railroaders. LC 74-82041. (Illus.). 80p. (Orig.). 1974. pap. 7.50 (ISBN 0-89024-523-1). Kalmbach.

Wesolowski, Wayne. Model Railroad Structures. (Illus.). 230p. 1984. pap. 9.95 (ISBN 0-911868-48-8, C48). Carstens Pubns.

Westcott, Linn. How to Build Model Railroad Benchwork. Hayden, Bob, ed. LC 79-89760. (Orig.). 1979. pap. 5.50 (ISBN 0-89024-542-8). Kalmbach.

--How to Wire Your Model Railroad. 5th ed. (Illus.). 88p. 1959. pap. 5.95 (ISBN 0-89024-511-8). Kalmbach.

Willard, Ken. Eight Easy Projects for Half-A Engines. Angle, Burr, ed. (Illus.). 48p. (Orig.). 1985. pap. 6.95 (ISBN 0-89024-055-8). Kalmbach.

RAILROADS–OPERATION

see Railroads–Management

RAILROADS–REPAIR SHOPS

Jacobs, H. W. Betterment Briefs: A Collection of Published Papers on Organized Industrial Efficiency. 2nd ed. (Management History Ser.: No. 80). (Illus.). 271p. 1975. Repr. of 1909 ed. 22.50 (ISBN 0-87960-108-6). Hive Pub.

RAILROADS–SAFETY APPLIANCES

see also Railroads–Brakes; Railroads–Signaling

Oehler, K. Entwicklungsgeschichte der elektrischen Eisenbahnsicherungstechnik in der Schweiz. 200p. 1981. 28.95x (ISBN 0-8176-1233-5). Birkhauser.

Shaw, Robert B. History of Railroad Accidents, Safety Precautions & Operating Practices. 1978. 10.00 (ISBN 0-686-10935-X). Northern Pr.

RAILROADS–SIGNALING

see also Railroads–Safety Appliances; Signals and Signaling

Adams, B. B. & Hitt, Rodney, eds. Signals & Signal Symbols from the 1911 Railway Signal Dictionary. 2nd ed. (Train Shed Cyclopedia Ser, No. 27). (Illus.). pap. 2.50 (ISBN 0-912318-57-0). N K Gregg.

Oehler, K. Entwicklungsgeschichte der elektrischen Eisenbahnsicherungstechnik in der Schweiz. 200p. 1981. 28.95x (ISBN 0-8176-1233-5). Birkhauser.

RAILROADS–SNOW PROTECTION AND REMOVAL

Parkes, G. Richard. Railway Snowfighting Equipment Methods. 17.50x (ISBN 0-392-08846-0, SpS). Sportshelf.

RAILROADS–SURVEYING

Hickerson, Thomas F. Route Location & Design. 5th ed. (Illus.). 1967. text ed. 44.00 (ISBN 0-07-028680-9). McGraw.

RAILROADS–SWITCHES

see Railroads–Construction

RAILROADS–TRAINS

Beebe, Lucius. Overland Limited. LC 63-22352. (Illus.). 1963. 15.00 (ISBN 0-8310-7038-2). Howell-North.

Beebe, Lucius & Clegg, Charles. The Trains We Rode, 2 Vols. LC 65-25208. 30.00 ea. Vol. 1 (ISBN 0-8310-7054-4). Vol. 2 (ISBN 0-8310-7058-7). Howell-North.

Carstens, Harold H. Traction Planbook. 2nd ed. (Carstens Hobby Bks.: C-16). (Illus.). 1969. pap. 6.00 (ISBN 0-911868-16-X). Carstens Pubns.

Cookridge, E. H. The Orient Express: The Life & Time of the World's Most Famous Train. 1978. 12.95 (ISBN 0-394-41176-5). Random.

Deere & Company. Power Trains: Compact Equipment. (Funadamentals of Service Compact Equipment Ser.). (Illus.). 104p. 1983. pap. text ed. 8.80 (ISBN 0-86691-030-1); wkbk. 3.80 (ISBN 0-86691-033-6). Deere & Co.

Electric Locomotives & Motor Cars: Part 5. (Train Shed Ser.: No. 78). (Illus.). 1979. pap. 4.50 (ISBN 0-87962-077-3). N K Gregg.

Morgan, David P., ed. I Like Trains. LC 80-84023. (Illus.). 104p. (Orig.). 1981. 6.50 (ISBN 0-89024-553-3). Kalmbach.

Nock, O. S. Standard Gauge Great Western Four-Four-Zero's, Vol. 1. 1977. 16.95 (ISBN 0-7153-7411-7). David & Charles.

Our GM Scrap Book. 10.95 (ISBN 0-685-83364-X). Chatham Pub CA.

Reed, Robert. The Streamline Era. LC 75-12995. (Illus.). 300p. 1975. 32.95 (ISBN 0-87095-053-3). Golden West.

Stoffels, Wolfgang. Turbotrains. 124p. 1983. 25.95 (ISBN 0-8176-1172-X). Birkhauser.

Thiessen, Frank & Davis, Dales. Automotive Power Trains. 1984. text ed. 27.95 (ISBN 0-8359-0345-1); pap. text ed. 20.95 (ISBN 0-8359-0344-3). Reston.

Webster, J. Automotive Power Trains. (Illus.). 1982. 12.95 (ISBN 0-8269-0250-2). Am Technical.

Williams, Guy R. The World of Modern Trains. (Illus.). 256p. 1970. 19.95 (ISBN 0-233-96227-1). Andre Deutsch.

Wright, Roy V., ed. Cabooses & Freight Car Construction Details: Part 4. (Train Shed Ser.: No. 75). (Illus.). 1978. pap. 4.50 (ISBN 0-87962-080-3). N K Gregg.

--Cow Catchers, Cabs & Fittings Plus Tenders: Part 4. (Train Shed Ser.: No. 76). (Illus.). 1978. pap. 4.50 (ISBN 0-87962-076-5). N K Gregg.

--Freight Car Construction Details, Underframes & Brakes: Pt. 5. (Train Shed Ser.: No. 77). (Illus.). 1979. pap. 4.50 (ISBN 0-87962-081-1). N K Gregg.

--Smoke Boxes, Stokers, Valve Gears & Trucks: Part 3. (Train Ser.: No. 74). (Illus.). 1978. pap. 4.50 (ISBN 0-87962-075-7). N K Gregg.

RAILROADS–TURNOUTS

see Railroads–Construction

RAILROADS–CANADA

Keefer, T. C. Philosophy of Railroads. LC 72-163835. (Social History of Canada Ser.). 1972. pap. 6.50 (ISBN 0-8020-6157-5). U of Toronto Pr.

Leggett, Robert F. Railways of Canada. (Illus.). 255p. (Orig.). 1983. pap. 9.95 (ISBN 0-88894-269-9, Pub. by Salem Hse Ltd). Merrimack Pub Cir.

RAILROADS–GREAT BRITAIN

Allan, Cecil J. Nineteen Forty-Eight British Railway Locomotives, Comb. Vol. 10.00x (ISBN 0-392-08815-0, SpS). Sportshelf.

Awdry, W. V. & Cook, Chris, eds. A Guide to the Steam Railways of Great Britain. 312p. 1983. 19.95 (ISBN 0-7207-1417-6, Pub. by Michael Joseph). Merrimack Pub Cir.

Bailey, M. R. British Railway Headcodes. pap. 4.00x (ISBN 0-392-15733-0, SpS). Sportshelf.

Baughan, Peter E. Chester & Holyhead Railway: The Main Line up 1880, Vol. 1. (Railway History Ser.). (Illus.). 17.95 (ISBN 0-7153-5617-8). David & Charles.

--Railways of Wharfedale. LC 76-91236. (Illus.). 1969. 19.95x (ISBN 0-678-05650-1). Kelley.

Baxter, Robert. Baxter's Britrail Guide. LC 72-83184. 1985. 9.95 (ISBN 0-913384-06-2). Rail-Europe-Baxter.

Bonner, G. A. British Transport Law by Road & Rail. 1974. 11.50 (ISBN 0-7153-6000-0). David & Charles.

Bradshaw, George. Bradshaw's July 1938 Railway Guide. LC 68-24743. (Illus.). Repr. of 1938 ed. 50.00x (ISBN 0-678-05750-8). Kelley.

British Railways Diesel Locomotives. pap. 4.00x (ISBN 0-392-08717-0, SpS). Sportshelf.

Brown, Alex. Making Books Work. 13.50x (ISBN 0-392-16526-0, ABC). Sportshelf.

Crossing, William. Crossing's Guide to Dartmoor. 2nd ed. (Illus.). 529p. 1965. 13.50 (ISBN 0-7153-4017-4, Pub. by Batsford, England). David & Charles.

Donaghy, Thomas J. Liverpool & Manchester Railway Operations 1831-1845. (Illus.). 184p. 1973. 7.95 (ISBN 0-7153-5705-0). David & Charles.

Eatwell, David & Cooper-Smith, John H. Return to Steam: Steam Tours on British Rail from Nineteen Sixty-Nine. 1978. 17.95 (ISBN 0-7134-0864-2, Pub. by Batsford England). David & Charles.

Essery, R. J., et al. British Goods Wagon. LC 73-95620. (Illus.). 1970. lib. bdg. 17.95x (ISBN 0-678-05664-1). Kelley.

Farr, Grahame. West Country Passenger Steamers. LC 67-103343. (Illus.). 1967. 24.95x (ISBN 0-678-05656-0). Kelley.

Glover, John. London's Railways Today. LC 80-70293. (Illus.). 96p. 1981. 17.50 (ISBN 0-7153-8070-2). David & Charles.

Hamilton, James A. Britain's Greatest Rail Disaster: The Quintinshill Blaze of 1915. LC 76-448378. (Illus.). 1969. lib. bdg. 12.95x (ISBN 0-678-06018-5). Kelley.

London Transport Locomotives & Rolling Stock. pap. 5.00x (ISBN 0-392-08782-0, SpS). Sportshelf.

Morgan, John S. British Independent Light Railways. LC 79-56060. 96p. 1980. 17.95 (ISBN 0-7153-7933-X). David & Charles.

Page, James. Forgotten Railways: South Wales. LC 79-51099. (Illus.). 1979. 19.95 (ISBN 0-7153-7734-5). David & Charles.

Quayle, H. I. & Jenkins, S. C. Branch Lines into the Eighties. LC 79-56065. (Illus.). 96p. 1980. 16.95 (ISBN 0-7153-7980-1). David & Charles.

Ronald, D. W. & Carter, R. J. The Longmoor Military Railway. 1974. 19.95 (ISBN 0-7153-6357-3). David & Charles.

Siviter, Roger. Steam Specials: British Rail's Return to Steam. LC 81-65960. (Illus.). 96p. 1981. 14.95 (ISBN 0-7153-8126-1). David & Charles.

Thomas, David. Country Railway. LC 76-20128. 1976. 14.95 (ISBN 0-7153-7285-8). David & Charles.

Thomas, John. Gretna: Britain's Worst Railway Disaster. LC 75-77873. 1969. 12.95x (ISBN 0-678-05538-6). Kelley.

--The North British Railway. LC 70-469296. (Illus.). 1975. 17.95 (ISBN 0-7153-4697-0). Vol. 2. David & Charles.

Tuplin, William A. British Steam since Nineteen Hundred. LC 69-12249. (Illus.). 1968. 17.95x (ISBN 0-678-05637-4). Kelley.

Webb, Brian & Duncan, John. AC Electric Locomotives of the British Rail. (Illus.). 1979. 17.95 (ISBN 0-7153-7663-2). David & Charles.

Whishaw, Francis. Railways of Great Britain & Ireland. LC 68-56390. (Illus.). Repr. of 1842 ed. 45.00x (ISBN 0-678-05629-3). Kelley.

Whitehouse, P. B. & Snell, J. B. Narrow Gauge Railways of the British Isles. (Illus.). 176p. 1984. 24.00 (ISBN 0-7153-8520-8). David & Charles.

RAILROADS–GREAT BRITAIN–HISTORY

Allen, David. Diesels in the North East. 112p. 30.00x (ISBN 0-86093-262-1, Pub. by ORPC Ltd UK). State Mutual Bk.

--Diesels Nationwide, Vol. 3. 128p. 30.00x (ISBN 0-86093-113-7, Pub. by ORPC Ltd UK). State Mutual Bk.

Allen, Jan. Diesels in East Anglia. 80p. 30.00x (ISBN 0-86093-105-6, Pub. by ORPC Ltd UK). State Mutual Bk.

Bowen Cooke, C. J. British Locomotives, Eighteen Ninety-Four. 396p. 1980. 35.00x (ISBN 0-905418-72-7, Pub. by Gresham England). State Mutual Bk.

British Railways Steam Locomotives. pap. 4.00x (ISBN 0-392-08894-0, SpS). Sportshelf.

Brooks, David. The Railway Navvy. (Illus.). 216p. 1983. 21.00 (ISBN 0-7153-8449-X). David & Charles.

Carter, Ernest. British Steam Locomotives. pap. 7.50x (ISBN 0-392-08880-0, SpS). Sportshelf.

Cartwright, Ralph & Russell, R. T. The Welshpool & Lanfair Light Railway. LC 80-70290. (Illus.). 208p. 1981. 16.95 (ISBN 0-7153-8151-2). David & Charles.

Cockman, F. G. British Railways' Steam Locomotives. (History in Camera Ser.). (Illus.). 64p. (Orig.). 1980. pap. 6.95 (ISBN 0-85263-531-1, Pub. by Shire Pubns England). Seven Hills Bks.

Gordon, D. I. Regional History of the Railway of Great Britain, Vol. 5. 1976. 19.95 (ISBN 0-7153-7431-1). David & Charles.

Hoole, Ken & Hoole, Ken. The North East Railway Book. LC 79-52364. (Illus.). 1979. 14.95 (ISBN 0-7153-7683-7). David & Charles.

Hume, John R. & Johnston, Colin. Glasgow Stations. 1979. 19.95 (ISBN 0-7153-7569-5). David & Charles.

Jenkinson, David. The Power of the Royal Scots. 128p. pap. text ed. 35.00 (ISBN 0-86093-175-7, ORPC Ltd UK). State Mutual Bk.

Joby, R. S. The Railway Builders: Victorian Railway Contractors. (Illus.). 200p. 1983. 19.95 (ISBN 0-7153-7959-3). David & Charles.
Johnston, Hank. Short Line to Paradise. (Trans-Anglo Ser.: No. 222). (Illus.). 96p. 1976. 8.95 (ISBN 0-87046-022-6, Pub. by Trans-Anglo). Interurban.
Joy, David. A Regional History of the Railways of Great Britain: Vol. 14: The Lake Counties. (Illus.). 240p. 1983. 23.50x (ISBN 0-946537-00-3). David & Charles.
Judge, Colin. Diesels Nationwide, Vol. 2. 128p. 30.00x (ISBN 0-86093-068-8, Pub. by ORPC Ltd UK). State Mutual Bk.
Judge, Colin W. Diesels Nationwide, Vol. 4. 128p. 30.00x (ISBN 0-86093-114-5, Pub. by ORPC Ltd UK). State Mutual Bk.
Kennedy, Rex. Diesels & Electrics on Shed: London Midland Region, Vol. 1. 80p. 30.00x (ISBN 0-86093-035-1, Pub. by ORPC Ltd UK). State Mutual Bk.
--Diesels & Electrics on Shed: Western Region, Vol. 3. 104p. 30.00x (ISBN 0-86093-042-4, Pub. by ORPC Ltd UK). State Mutual Bk.
Lambert, Anthony J. Nineteenth Century Railway History Through the Illustrated London News. (Illus.). 128p. 1984. 27.00 (ISBN 0-7153-8521-6). David & Charles.
Leleux, Robin. A Regional History of the Railways of Great Britain: The East Midlands, Vol. 9. (Illus.). 248p. 1984. 24.00 (ISBN 0-946537-06-2). David & Charles.
Marsden, C. J. The Power of the Electro-Diesels. 112p. 30.00x (ISBN 0-86093-065-3, Pub. by ORPC Ltd UK). State Mutual Bk.
Marsden, Colin. Thirty-Five Years of Main Line Diesel Traction. 176p. 35.00x (ISBN 0-86093-171-4, Pub. by ORPC Ltd UK). State Mutual Bk.
Nicolle, B. B. R. Electrics: Midland Region, No. 3. 32p. 20.00x (ISBN 0-86093-056-4, Pub. by ORPC Ltd UK). State Mutual Bk.
Nock, O. S. The Last Years of British Railways Steam: Reflections Ten Years After. 1978. 15.95 (ISBN 0-7153-7583-0). David & Charles.
--Standard Gauge Great Western Four-Four-Zero's: 1904-1965, Vol. 2. LC 78-62486. (Illus.). 1978. 16.95 (ISBN 0-7153-7684-5). David & Charles.
Ransome-Wallis, P. The Last Steam Locomotive of British Railways. 27.50x (ISBN 0-392-15392-0, SpS). Sportshelf.
Rowledge, P. Engines of the L. M. S. Built Nineteen Twenty-Three to Nineteen Fifty-One. 152p. 20.00x (ISBN 0-902888-59-5, Pub. by ORPC Ltd UK). State Mutual Bk.
Russell, J. H. A Pictorial Record of Great Western Absorbed Engines. 288p. 60.00x (ISBN 0-902888-74-9, Pub. by ORPC Ltd UK). State Mutual Bk.
Shephard, David. A Brush with Steam. (Illus.). 232p. 1983. 24.00 (ISBN 0-7153-8157-1). David & Charles.
Siviter, Roger. Diesels & Semaphores. 128p. 45.00x (ISBN 0-86093-345-8, Pub. by ORPC Ltd UK). State Mutual Bk.
Somerville, Christopher. Walking Old Railways. LC 78-74078. 1979. 17.50 (ISBN 0-7153-7681-0). David & Charles.
Spence, Jeoffry. Surviving Steam Railways. 1979. pap. 5.50 (ISBN 0-7134-0641-0, Pub. by Batsford England). David & Charles.
Summers, A. W. Engines Good & Bad. 96p. 29.00x (ISBN 0-86093-326-1, Pub. by ORPC Ltd UK). State Mutual Bk.
Talbot, E. A Pictorial Record of British Railway Standard Steam Locomotives. 160p. 45.00x (ISBN 0-86093-158-7, Pub. by ORPC Ltd Uk). State Mutual Bk.
Turner, Keith. North Wales Tramways. LC 79-74089. 1979. 17.95 (ISBN 0-7153-7769-8). David & Charles.
Vaughan, J. A. M. & Marsden, C. J. The Power of the 56's. 128p. 30.00x (ISBN 0-86093-150-1, Pub. by ORPC Ltd UK). State Mutual Bk.
Vaughan, John. Double-Headed Diesels Nationwide. 112p. 30.00x (ISBN 0-86093-081-5, Pub. by ORPC Ltd UK). State Mutual Bk.
Vaughn, John A. The Power of the H. S. T.'s. 120p. 30.00x (ISBN 0-86093-186-2, Pub. by ORPC Ltd UK). State Mutual Bk.
Walton, Peter. Diesels over the Settle to Carlisle Route. 120p. 30.00x (ISBN 0-86093-119-6, Pub. by ORPC Ltd UK). State Mutual Bk.
Whitely, J. S. & Marrison, G. W. Power of the A1s, A2s, & A3s. 112p. 35.00 (ISBN 0-86093-133-1, Pub. by ORPC Ltd UK). State Mutual Bk.
Whitely, J. S. & Morrison, G. W. The Power of the BR Standard Pacifics. 112p. 35.00x (ISBN 0-86093-067-X, Pub. by ORPC Ltd UK). State Mutual Bk.
Williams, F. S. Our Iron Roads: Vol. 1; History & Construction. 272p. 1984. 35.00x (ISBN 0-905418-88-3, Pub. by Gresham England). State Mutual Bk.

RAILROADS–IRELAND

Nock, O. S. Irish Steam. (Illus.). 176p. 1982. 17.50 (ISBN 0-7153-7961-5). David & Charles.
Whishaw, Francis. Railways of Great Britain & Ireland. LC 68-56390. (Illus.). Repr. of 1842 ed. 45.00x (ISBN 0-678-05629-3). Kelley.

RAILROADS–JAPAN

Straszak, A. & Tuch, R., eds. The Shinkansen High-Speed Rail Network of Japan: Proceedings of a IIASA Conference, June 27-30 1977. (IIASA Proceedings Ser.: Vol. 7). 1980. 155.00 (ISBN 0-08-024444-0). Pergamon.

RAILROADS–UNITED STATES

Ball, Don, Jr. America's Railroads: The Second Generation. (Illus.). 224p. 1980. 44.95 (ISBN 0-393-01416-9). Norton.
--Railroads. (Illus.). 1985. 37.50 (ISBN 0-393-02236-6). Norton.
Berg, Walter G. Buildings & Structures of American Railroads, Pt. 2. 9th ed. (Train Shed Cyclopedia Ser., No. 13). (Illus.). 1973. pap. 4.95 (ISBN 0-912318-42-2). N K Gregg.
--Buildings & Structures of American Railroads, Pt. 3. 9th ed. (Train Shed Cyclopedia Ser., No. 19). (Illus.). 1974. pap. 4.50 (ISBN 0-912318-48-1). N K Gregg.
Bezilla, Michael. Electric Traction on the Pennsylvania Railroad, 1895-1968. LC 79-65858. (Illus.). 1980. 24.90x (ISBN 0-271-00241-7). Pa St U Pr.
Central Electric Railfans' Association. Indiana Railroad System: Bulletin No. 91. (Illus.). 72p. 1975. pap. 5.00 (ISBN 0-915348-92-6). Central Electric.
Choda, Kelly. Thirty Pound Rails. LC 57-17961. (Wild & Woolly West Ser., No. 1). (Illus., Orig.). 1956. 8.00 (ISBN 0-910584-90-7); pap. 1.50 (ISBN 0-910584-01-X). Filter.
Collias, Joe G. The Last of Steam. LC 60-14067. (Illus.). 1960. 25.00 (ISBN 0-8310-7018-8). Howell-North.
DeNevi, Don. Tragic Train "the City of San Francisco" Development & Historic Wreck of a Streamliner. LC 77-3499. (Illus.). 1977. 19.95 (ISBN 0-87564-525-9). Superior Pub.
Facts & Arguments in Favour of Adopting Railways in Preference to Canals, in the State of Pennsylvania. 4th ed. LC 78-112543. (Rise of Urban America). 1970. Repr. of 1825 ed. 9.00 (ISBN 0-405-02452-5). Ayer Co Pubs.
Fisher, John S. A Builder of the West: The Life of General William Jackson Palmer. Bruchey, Stuart, ed. LC 80-1306. (Railroads Ser.). (Illus.). 1981. Repr. of 1939 ed. lib. bdg. 35.00x (ISBN 0-405-13775-3). Ayer Co Pubs.
Herring, James M. The Problem of Weak Railroads. Bruchey, Stuart, ed. LC 80-1316. (Railroads Ser.). 1981. Repr. of 1929 ed. lib. bdg. 15.00x (ISBN 0-405-13788-5). Ayer Co Pubs.
Hofsommer, Don L., ed. Railroads in the West. (Illus.). 118p. 1978. pap. text ed. 9.95x (ISBN 0-89745-002-7). Sunflower U Pr.
Hofsommer, Donovan L. KATY Northwest: The Story of a Branch Line Railroad. (Illus.). 1976. 26.95 (ISBN 0-87108-086-9). Pruett.
Hubbard, Freeman. Encyclopedia of North American Railroading. (Illus.). 448p. 1982. 59.95 (ISBN 0-07-030828-4). McGraw.
McClelland, Allen. Virginian & Ohio Railroad. (Illus.). 104p. 1984. pap. 19.95 (ISBN 0-911868-47-X, C47). Carstens Pubns.
Milwaukee Rails. 26.95 (ISBN 0-686-75189-2). Chatham Pub CA.
Olson, Sherry H. Depletion Myth: A History of Railroad Use of Timber. LC 70-148940. 1971. 16.50x (ISBN 0-674-19820-4). Harvard U Pr.
Pearson, A. J. The Railways & the Nation. 13.50 (ISBN 0-392-15604-0, SpS). Sportshelf.
Pushkarev, Boris S., et al. Urban Rail in America: An Exploration of Criteria for Fixed-Guideway Transit. LC 81-47293. (Illus.). 320p. 1982. 27.50x (ISBN 0-253-37555-X). Ind U Pr.
Railroads of Arizona, Vol. 2. 35.00 (ISBN 0-686-75192-2). Chatham Pub CA.
Railroads of Hawaii. 22.95 (ISBN 0-686-75193-0). Chatham Pub CA.
Rails in the Northwest. pap. 9.50 (ISBN 0-686-75195-7). Chatham Pub CA.
Roaring U 50's. pap. 10.95 (ISBN 0-686-75200-7). Chatham Pub CA.
Route of the Warbonnets. 22.95 (ISBN 0-686-75198-1). Chatham Pub CA.
South Pacific Coast. 34.95 (ISBN 0-686-75205-8). Chatham Pub CA.
Southern California & the Pacific Electric. 9.95 (ISBN 0-686-75202-3). Chatham Pub CA.
The Sp 4300 4-8-2's. 30.00 (ISBN 0-686-75209-0). Chatham Pub CA.
Steam & Thunder in the Timber. 60.00 (ISBN 0-686-75206-6). Chatham Pub CA.
Tanner, Henry S. Description of the Canals & Railroads of the United States. LC 68-27678. (Illus.). Repr. of 1840 ed. 27.50x (ISBN 0-678-00595-8). Kelley.
Trains or Northern New England. 8.95 (ISBN 0-686-75210-4). Chatham Pub CA.
Zlatkovich, Charles P. Texas Railroads: A Record of Construction & Abandonment. (Research Monograph). 100p. (Orig.). 1981. pap. 10.00 (ISBN 0-87755-248-7); 10.00. Bureau Busn UT.

RAILROADS–UNITED STATES–HISTORY

Adams, Charles F., Jr. Railroads: Their Origin & Problems. Bruchey, Stuart, ed. LC 80-1294. (Railroads Ser.). 1981. Repr. of 1878 ed. lib. bdg. 20.00x (ISBN 0-405-13764-8). Ayer Co Pubs.
Best, Gerald M. Ships & Narrow Gauge Rails: The Story of the Pacific Coast Company. LC 64-19122. (Illus.). 155p. 1981. Repr. of 1964 ed. 15.00 (ISBN 0-8310-7042-0). Howell-North.
Bezilla, Michael. Electric Traction on the Pennsylvania Railroad, 1895-1968. LC 79-65858. (Illus.). 1980. 24.90x (ISBN 0-271-00241-7). Pa St U Pr.
Carr, Hobart C. Early History of Iowa Railroads. Bruchey, Stuart, ed. LC 80-1277. (Railroads Ser.). 1981. lib. bdg. 15.00x (ISBN 0-405-13752-4). Ayer Co Pubs.
Carter, Warren B. Locomotives of the Jersey Central 1-999. rev. ed. (Illus.). 105p. (Orig.). 1978. pap. 7.50 (ISBN 0-941652-02-5). Railroadians.
Cary, John W. The Organization & History of the Chicago, Milwaukee & St. Paul Railway Company. Bruchey, Stuart, ed. LC 80-1296. (Railroads Ser.). 1981. Repr. of 1893 ed. lib. bdg. 35.00x (ISBN 0-405-13766-4). Ayer Co Pubs.
Cherington, Charles R. The Regulation of Railroad Abandonments. Bruchey, Stuart, ed. LC 80-1299. (Railroads Ser.). (Illus.). 1981. Repr. of 1948 ed. lib. bdg. 25.00x (ISBN 0-405-13769-9). Ayer Co Pubs.
Coach Cabbage & Caboose. 39.95 (ISBN 0-686-70716-8). Chatham Pub CA.
Condit, Carl W. The Pioneer Stage of Railroad Electrification. LC 77-76428. (Transactions Ser.: Vol. 67, Pt. 7). 1977. pap. 6.00 (ISBN 0-87169-677-0). Am Philos.
Crippen, Waldo. The Kansas Pacific Railroad: A Cross Section of an Age of Railroad Building. Bruchey, Stuart, ed. LC 80-1278. (Railroads Ser.). 1981. lib. bdg. 12.00x (ISBN 0-405-13753-2). Ayer Co Pubs.
Digerness, David S. The Mineral Belt: Old South Park-Across the Great Divide, Vol. 2. (Illus.). 416p. 49.00 (ISBN 0-913582-21-2). Sundance.
Dorin, Patrick C. Amtrak Trains & Travel. LC 79-22566. (Illus.). 1980. 19.95 (ISBN 0-87564-533-X). Superior Pub.
--The Chesapeake & Ohio Railway: George Washington's Railroad. (Illus.). 256p. 1981. 24.95 (ISBN 0-87564-537-2). Superior Pub.
Douglas, George H. Rail City: Chicago, U. S. A. LC 81-6361. (Illus.). 288p. 1981. 27.50 (ISBN 0-8310-7150-8). Howell-North.
Drury, George. The Train-Watcher's Guide to North American Railroads. Hayden, Bob, ed. (Illus.). 230p. (Orig.). 1983. pap. 10.95 (ISBN 0-89024-061-2). Kalmbach.
Facts & Arguments in Favour of Adopting Railways in Preference to Canals, in the State of Pennsylvania. 4th ed. LC 78-112543. (Rise of Urban America). 1970. Repr. of 1825 ed. 9.00 (ISBN 0-405-02452-5). Ayer Co Pubs.
Greever, William S. Arid Domain. Bruchey, Stuart, ed. LC 78-56663. (Management of Public Lands in the U. S. Ser.). (Illus.). 1979. Repr. of 1954 ed. lib. bdg. 16.00x (ISBN 0-405-11334-X). Ayer Co Pubs.
Grosfield, Byron. Buckaroos & Boxcars. (Illus.). 1981. pap. 6.50 (ISBN 0-686-79549-0). McGlynn.
Hanson, Erle C. East Shore & Suburban Railway. LC 77-11120. (Illus.). 34p. 1978. 4.95 (ISBN 0-87095-073-8). Golden West.
Harder, Klaus P. Environmental Factors of Early Railroads: A Comparative Study of Massachusetts & the German States of Baden & the Pfalz Before 1870. Bruchey, Stuart, ed. LC 80-2808. (Dissertations in European Economic History II). (Illus.). 1981. lib. bdg. 38.50x (ISBN 0-405-13992-6). Ayer Co Pubs.
Heilich, Frederick W., III. The History of the Blairstown Railway. LC 81-53048. (Illus.). 96p. (Orig.). 1981. pap. 12.00 (ISBN 0-941652-04-1). Railroadians.
Henry Huntington & the Pacific Electric. 10.00 (ISBN 0-686-70717-6). Chatham Pub CA.
Hetch Hetchy & Its Dam Railroad. 25.00 (ISBN 0-685-83341-0). Chatham Pub CA.
Hochschild, Harold K. Adirondack Steamboats on Raquette & Blue Mountain Lakes. (Illus.). 33p. 1962. pap. 3.95 (ISBN 0-8156-8025-2, Pub. by Adirondack Museum). Syracuse U Pr.
Hollander, Jacob H. The Cincinnati Southern Railway: A Study in Municipal Activity. LC 78-63826. (Johns Hopkins University. Studies in the Social Sciences. Twelfth Ser. 1894: 1). Repr. of 1894 ed. 11.50 (ISBN 0-404-61087-0). AMS Pr.
Kennan, George. Misrepresentation in Railroad Affairs. Bruchey, Stuart, ed. LC 80-1323. (Railroads Ser.). 1981. Repr. of 1916 ed. lib. bdg. 12.00x (ISBN 0-405-13798-2). Ayer Co Pubs.
Key System Album. 17.95 (ISBN 0-686-70719-2). Chatham Pub CA.
Last of the Three-Foot Loggers. 15.95 (ISBN 0-686-70721-4). Chatham Pub CA.
Lucas, Walter A. The History of the New York, Susquehanna & Western Railroad. 2nd ed. (Illus.). 195p. 1980. pap. 15.00 (ISBN 0-941652-03-3). Railroadians.
Matthews, Fred. Northern California Railroads: The Silver Age, Vol. I. (Illus.). 224p. 1984. pap. 45.00 (ISBN 0-913582-33-6). Sundance.
New England Diesels. 28.95 (ISBN 0-686-70727-3). Chatham Pub CA.
Ogburn, Charlton. Railroads: The Great American Adventure. LC 76-693. (Special Publications Ser.: No. 11). (Illus.). 1977. lib. bdg. 8.50 (ISBN 0-87044-194-9). Natl Geog.
Poor, Henry V. History of the Railroads & Canals of the United States. LC 68-56564. Repr. of 1860 ed. 50.00x (ISBN 0-678-00665-2). Kelley.
Red Trains Remembered. 16.95 (ISBN 0-686-75199-X). Chatham Pub CA.
Reisdorff, James J. Locomotive Sixty-Nine: From Alaska to Nebraska. (Illus.). 28p. 1984. pap. 3.00 (ISBN 0-9609568-2-4). South Platte.
Ripley, John W. & Richmond, Robert W., eds. The Santa Fe in Topeka. (Illus.). 1979. pap. 6.95 (ISBN 0-685-96284-9). Shawnee County Hist.
Robinson, John R. The Octopus: A History of the Construction, Conspriracies, Extortions, Robberies & Villainous Acts of Subsidized Railroads. Bruchey, Stuart, ed. LC 80-1340. (Railroads Ser.). 1981. Repr. of 1894 ed. lib. bdg. 12.00x (ISBN 0-405-13812-1). Ayer Co Pubs.
Shank, W. H., ed. Welch Report, Allegheny Portage RR, 1833. 1979. 1.50 (ISBN 0-933788-23-1). Am Canal & Transport.
Smith, Philip R. Improved Surface Transportation & Nebraska's Population Distribution, 1860-1960. Bruchey, Stuart, ed. LC 80-1289. (Railroads Ser.). (Illus.). 1981. lib. bdg. 30.00x (ISBN 0-405-13760-5). Ayer Co Pubs.
Southern Pacific Motive Power Annual, 1966-67. (Illus.). 10.35 (ISBN 0-89685-001-3). Chatham Pub CA.
Southern Pacific Motive Power Annual, 1967-68. (Illus.). 10.35 (ISBN 0-89685-002-1). Chatham Pub CA.
Southern Pacific Motive Power Annual, 1968-69. (Illus.). pap. 10.35 soft cover (ISBN 0-89685-003-X). Chatham Pub CA.
Southern Pacific Motive Power Annual, 1970. (Illus.). 10.35 (ISBN 0-89685-004-8). Chatham Pub CA.
Staff, Virgil. D-Day on the Western Pacific. Sebree, Mac, ed. LC 82-1051. (Special Ser. 81). (Illus.). 224p. 1982. 29.95 (ISBN 0-916374-51-3). Interurban.
Streamline Era. 29.95 (ISBN 0-685-83399-2). Chatham Pub CA.
Taylor, George & Neu, Irene D. The American Railroad Network, Eighteen Sixty-One to Eighteen Ninety. Bruchey, Stuart, ed. LC 80-1350. (Railroads Ser.). 1981. Repr. of 1956 ed. lib. bdg. 15.00x (ISBN 0-405-13819-9). Ayer Co Pubs.
They Felled the Redwoods. (Illus.). 19.95 (ISBN 0-686-70734-6). Chatham Pub CA.
Villard, Henry. The Early History of Transportation in Oregon. Bruchey, Stuart, ed. LC 80-1348. (Railroads Ser.). 1981. Repr. of 1944 ed. lib. bdg. 12.00x (ISBN 0-405-13820-2). Ayer Co Pubs.
Westhaeffer, Paul J. History of the Cumberland Valley Railroad. LC 79-178. (Illus.). 1979. 21.50 (ISBN 0-933954-00-X). Natl Rail Hist Soc DC Chap.
Wilson, Robert S. Trolley Trails Through the West: Northern California. (Trolley Trails Through the West Ser.: Vol. 7). (Illus.). 1979. pap. 5.00 (ISBN 0-934944-07-5). Wilson Bros.

RAILROADS, CABLE

Schultz, Russell E. A Milwaukee Transport Era: The Trackless Trolley Years. Sebree, Mac, ed. (Interurbans Special Ser.: 74). (Illus.). 160p. (Orig.). 1980. pap. 13.95 (ISBN 0-916374-43-2). Interurban.
Smith, J. Bucknall & Hilton, George W. A Treatise Upon Cable or Rope Traction As Applied to the Working of Street & Other Railways. LC 76-53131. (Illus.). 1978. Repr. 14.50 (ISBN 0-913896-08-X). Owlswick Pr.

RAILROADS, FUNICULAR

see Railroads, Cable

RAILROADS, INDUSTRIAL

see also Logging Railroads

California Central Coast Railways. (Illus.). 44.95 (ISBN 0-686-75183-3). Chatham Pub CA.

RAILROADS, LOGGING

see Logging Railroads

RAILROADS, MINE

see Mine Railroads

RAILROADS, NARROW-GAGE
see also Logging Railroads
Beebe, Lucius & Clegg, Charles. Narrow Gauge in the Rockies. LC 58-5789. (Illus.). 1958. 20.00 (ISBN 0-8310-7003-X). Howell-North.
Best, G. M. Mexican Narrow Gauge. LC 68-57487. (Illus.). 14.95 (ISBN 0-8310-7073-0). Howell-North.
Choda, Kelly. Thirty Pound Rails. LC 57-17961. (Wild & Woolly West Ser., No. 1). (Illus., Orig.). 1956. 8.00 (ISBN 0-910584-90-7); pap. 1.50 (ISBN 0-910584-01-X). Filter.
Dean, Ian. Industrial Narrow Gauge Railways. (Shire Album Ser.: No. 145). (Orig.). 1985. pap. 3.50 (ISBN 0-85263-752-7, Pub. by Shire Pubns England). Seven Hills Bks.
Grenard, Ross B. Requiem for the Narrow Gauge. 125p. 1984. 24.95 (ISBN 0-912113-13-8); pap. 12.95 (ISBN 0-912113-12-X). Railhead Pubns.
Krause, John. The American Narrow-Gauge. LC 78-12544. (Illus.). 256p. 1978. 30.95 (ISBN 0-87095-059-2). Golden West.
Mexican Narrow Gauge. 14.95 (ISBN 0-685-83350-X). Chatham Pub CA.
Moody, Linwood W. The Maine Two-Footers. LC 59-12774. (Illus.). 1959. 14.95 (ISBN 0-8310-7010-2). Howell-North.
Patterson, Edward M. History of the Narrow-Gauge Railways of North West Ireland Pt. 1. 2nd ed. LC 69-12548. (Illus.). 1969. 17.95x (ISBN 0-678-05620-X). Kelley.
Price, Brick. Modeling Narrow Gauge Railroads. LC 83-43301. 272p. (Orig.). 1985. pap. 17.95 (ISBN 0-8019-7293-0). Chilton.
Turner, Susan. The Padarn & Penrhyn Railways. LC 74-76199. (Railway History Ser). (Illus.). 168p. 1975. 14.95 (ISBN 0-7153-6547-9). David & Charles.

RAILROADS, UNDERGROUND
see Subways

RAIN AND RAINFALL
see also Acid Rain; Dendrochronology; Droughts; Floods; Meteorology; Moisture; Rain-Making; Runoff; Snow; Storms
Campbell, S., ed. Sampling & Analysis of Rain - STP 823. 96p. 1984. pap. 18.00 (ISBN 0-8031-0266-6, 04-823000-17). ASTM.
Harremoes, P., ed. Rainfall As the Basis for Urban Run-off Design & Analysis: Proceedings of a Specialised Seminar Held in Copenhagen, Denmark, 24-26 August, 1983. (Illus.). 370p. 1984. pap. 80.00 (ISBN 0-08-031506-2). Pergamon.
Hutchinson, C. F., et al, eds. Rainfall Collection for Agriculture in Arid & Semiarid Regions: Proceedings of a Workshop Hosted by the University of Arizona, U. S. A, & the Chapingo Postgraduate College, Mexico. Garduno, M. Anaya. 97p. 1981. 39.00x (ISBN 0-85198-486-X, Pub. by CAB Bks England). State Mutual Bk.
Middleton, William E. A History of the Theories of Rain & Other Forms of Precipitation. LC 66-15982. (The Watts History of Science Library Ser.). pap. 57.80 (ISBN 0-317-26524-5, 2024059). Bks Demand UMI.
Overton, D. E. & Meadows, M. E. Stormwater Modeling. 1976. 49.50 (ISBN 0-12-531550-3). Acad Pr.
Parde, Maurice. Beziehungen Zwischen Niederschlag und Abfluss Bei Grossen Sommer Hochwassern. pap. 10.00 (ISBN 0-384-44780-5). Johnson Repr.
Singh, Vijay P., ed. Rainfall-Runoff Relationship. LC 81-71290. 1982. 36.00 (ISBN 0-918334-45-4). WRP.
--Statistical Analysis of Rainfall & Runoff. LC 81-71289. 1982. 36.00 (ISBN 0-918334-44-6). WRP.
Toribara, T. Y., et al, eds. Polluted Rain. LC 80-285. (Environmental Science Research Ser.: Vol. 17). 514p. 1980. 62.50 (ISBN 0-306-40353-6, Plenum Pr). Plenum Pub.
Udden, Johan A. On the Cyclonic Destruction of Rainfall. LC 6-19923. (Augustana College Library Publication Ser.: No. 4). 21p. 1905. pap. 1.00 (ISBN 0-910182-02-7). Augustana Coll.

RAIN FORESTS
Allen, Paul H. The Rain Forests of Golfo Dulce. LC 77-76150. (Illus.). 1956. 30.00x (ISBN 0-8047-0955-6). Stanford U Pr.
Conversion of Tropical Moist Forests. 1980. 13.95 (ISBN 0-309-02945-7). Natl Acad Pr.
Fearnside, Philip M. Human Carrying Capacity of the Brazillian Rainforest. 352p. 1985. 35.00x (ISBN 0-231-06104-8). Columbia U Pr.
Hall, J. B. & Swaine, M. D. Distribution & Ecology of Vascular Plants in a Tropical Rain Forest. (Geobotany Ser.: Vol. I). 392p. 1981. 112.00 (ISBN 90-6193-681-0, Pub. by Junk Pubs Netherlands). Kluwer Academic.
Halle, F., et al. Tropical Trees & Forests: An Architectural Analysis. 1978. 82.00 (ISBN 0-387-08494-0). Springer-Verlag.
Hanify & Blencowe. Guide to the HOH Rain Forest. LC 77-10569. (Illus.). 1977. pap. 1.95 (ISBN 0-87564-627-1). Superior Pub.
Lanly, Jean-Paul. Tropical Forest Resources. (Forestry Papers: No. 30). (Eng., Fr. & Span.). 117p. 1982. pap. 8.75 (ISBN 0-925101-87-7, F2287, FAO). Unipub.
Leigh, Egbert G., Jr., et al, eds. The Ecology of a Tropical Forest: Seasonal Rhythms & Long Term Changes. LC 82-600181. (Illus.). 468p. 1983. pap. text ed. 25.00 (ISBN 0-87474-601-9). Smithsonian.
Maberlev, D. J. Tropical Rain Forest Ecology. (Tertiary Level Biology Ser.). 170p. 1983. 38.00 (ISBN 0-412-00431-3, NO. 5058); pap. 18.95 (ISBN 0-412-00441-0, NO. 5059). Methuen Inc.
Meggers, Betty J., et al. Tropical Forest Ecosystems in Africa & South America: A Comparative Review. LC 72-8342. (Illus.). 350p. 1973. pap. 15.00x (ISBN 0-87474-125-4). Smithsonian.
Poore, Duncan. Ecological Guidelines for Development in Tropical Rain Forests. (Illus.). 39p. 1976. pap. 10.00 (ISBN 2-88032-000-3, IUCN71, IUCN). Unipub.
Richards, Paul W. Tropical Rain Forest. LC 79-50507. (Illus.). 1952. 85.00 (ISBN 0-521-06079-6); pap. 29.95 (ISBN 0-521-29658-7). Cambridge U Pr.
Roth, I. Stratification of Tropical Forests as seen in Leaf Structure. (Task for Vegetation Science). 1984. lib. bdg. 115.00 (ISBN 90-6193-946-1, Pub. by Junk Pubs Netherlands). Kluwer Academic.
Smith, Nigel J. Rainforest Corridors: The Transamazon Colonization Scheme. LC 81-7478. 200p. 1982. 27.50x (ISBN 0-520-04497-5). U of Cal Pr.
Sutton, S. L., et al. Tropical Rain Forest: Ecology & Management. (Illus.). 512p. 1984. 57.00x (ISBN 0-632-01142-4). Blackwell Sci.
Synnott, T. J. A Manual of Permanent Plot Procedures for Tropical Rain Forests. 1979. 30.00x (ISBN 0-85074-031-2, Pub. by For Lib Comm England). State Mutual Bk.
--Tropical Rain Forest Silviculture: A Research Project Report. 1980. 30.00x (ISBN 0-85074-050-9, Pub. by For Lib Comm England). State Mutual Bk.
Tropical Forest Ecosystems: A State of Knowledge Report Prepared by UNESCO-UNEP-FAO. (Natural Resources Research Ser.: No. 14). (Illus.). 683p. 1978. 67.00 (ISBN 92-3-101591-5, U874, UNESCO). Unipub.
Whitmore, T. C. Change with Time & the Role of Cyclones in Tropical Rain Forest On Kolombangara, Solomon Islands. 1974. 30.00x (ISBN 0-85074-021-5, Pub. by For Lib Comm England). State Mutual Bk.
--Tropical Rain Forests of the Far East. 2nd ed. (Illus.). 1984. 64.50x (ISBN 0-19-854136-8). Oxford U Pr.

RAIN-MAKING
Humphreys, William J. Rain Making & Other Weather Vagaries. LC 77-10228. Repr. of 1926 ed. 16.50 (ISBN 0-404-16208-8). AMS Pr.
Maybank, J. The Scientific Planning & Organization of Precipitation Enhancement Experiments, with Particular Attention to Agricultural Needs. (Technical Note Ser.: No. 154). (Illus.). 1978. pap. 10.00 (ISBN 92-63-10478-6, W377, WMO). Unipub.
Spence, Clark C. The Rainmakers: American "Pluviculture" to World War II. LC 79-26022. x, 175p. 1980. 15.95x (ISBN 0-8032-4117-8). U of Nebr Pr.
Weisbecker, Leo. Snowpack, Cloud-Seeding, & the Colorado River: A Technology Assessment of Weather Modification. LC 74-15900. 1974. 11.95x (ISBN 0-8061-1225-5); pap. 5.95x (ISBN 0-8061-1226-3). U of Okla Pr.

RAINBOW
see also Reflection (Optics); Refraction
Corliss, William R. Rare Halos, Mirages, Anomalous Rainbows, & Related Electromagnetic Phenomena. (Catalog of Geophysical Anomalies Ser.). (Illus.). 244p. 1984. 12.95 (ISBN 0-915554-12-7). Sourcebook.
Greenler, Robert. Rainbows, Halos & Glories. LC 80-143722. (Illus.). 304p. 1980. 32.50 (ISBN 0-521-23605-3). Cambridge U Pr.
Klika, Thom. Rainbows. LC 78-21416. (Illus.). 1979. pap. 7.95 (ISBN 0-312-66294-7). St Martin.

RAMAN EFFECT
see also Raman Spectroscopy
Anderson, Anthony, ed. The Raman Effect, Vol. 1. LC 77-134788. pap. 104.00 (ISBN 0-317-08513-1, 2055067). Bks Demand UMI.
Basov, N. G., ed. Stimulated Raman Scattering. Adashko, J. George, tr. LC 82-18238. (Proceedings (Trudy) of the Lebedev Physics Institute: Vol. 99). 144p. 1982. 55.00x (ISBN 0-306-10968-9, Consultants Bureau). Plenum Pub.
Cardona, M., ed. Light Scattering in Solids I. 2nd ed. (Topics in Applied Physics Ser.: Vol. 8). (Illus.). 363p. 1983. pap. 32.00 (ISBN 0-387-11913-2). Springer-Verlag.
Koningstein, J. A. Introduction to the Theory of the Raman Effect. LC 72-77876. 166p. 1972. lib. bdg. 29.00 (ISBN 90-277-0234-9, Pub. by Reidel Holland); pap. 18.50 (ISBN 90-277-0276-4, Pub. by Reidel Holland). Kluwer Academic.
Pockrand, I. Surface Enhanced Raman Vibrational Studies at Solid-Gas Interfaces. (Springer Tracts in Modern Physics: Vol. 104). (Illus.). 160p. 1984. 29.50 (ISBN 0-387-13416-6). Springer-Verlag.

RAMAN SPECTROSCOPY
see also Molecular Spectra
Brame, Edward G. & Grasselli, Jeannette, eds. Infrared & Raman Spectroscopy, Pt. B. (Practical Spectroscopy Ser.: Vol. 1). 1977. 65.00 (ISBN 0-8247-6526-5). Dekker.
Chang, Richard K. & Furtak, Thomas E., eds. Surface Enhanced Raman Scattering. LC 81-22739. 450p. 1982. text ed. 55.00x (ISBN 0-306-40907-0, Plenum Pr). Plenum Pub.
Clark. Advances in Infared & Raman Spectroscopy, Vol. 9. 1982. 124.95 (ISBN 0-471-26215-3). Wiley.
--Advances in Infrared & Raman Spectroscopy, Vol. 8. 1981. 130.95 (ISBN 0-471-25640-4, Pub. by Wiley Heyden). Wiley.
Clark, R. J. & Hester, R. E. Advances In Infrared & Raman Spectroscopy, Vol. 10. 454p. 1983. 118.00 (ISBN 0-471-26216-1, Pub. by Wiley Heyden). Wiley.
Clark, R. J. & Hester, R. E., eds. Advances in Infrared & Raman Spectroscopy, 5 vols. Vol. 1. 1975 ed. 96.95 (ISBN 0-471-25631-5, Pub. by Wiley Heyden); Vol. 2. 1976 ed. 96.95 (ISBN 0-471-25632-3); Vol. 3. 1977 ed. o.p. 89.95 (ISBN 0-471-25633-1); Vol. 4. 1978 ed. o.p. 121.95 (ISBN 0-471-25634-X). Wiley.
--Advances in Infrared & Raman Spectroscopy, Vol. 5. 404p. 1978. casebound 130.95 (ISBN 0-471-25636-6, Pub. by Wiley Heyden). Wiley.
--Advances in Infrared & Raman Spectroscopy, Vol. 6. (Advances in Infrared & Raman Spectroscopy Ser.). 355p. 1979. 130.95 (ISBN 0-471-25637-4, Pub. by Wiley Heyden). Wiley.
--Advances in Infrared & Raman Spectroscopy, Vol. 7. (Advances in Infrared & Raman Spectroscopy Ser.). 400p. 1980. 129.95 (ISBN 0-471-25639-0, Pub. by Wiley Heyden). Wiley.
--Advances in Infrared & Raman Spectroscopy, Vol. 12. price not set (ISBN 0-471-90674-3). Wiley.
Clark, R. J. H. & Hester, R. E. Advances in Infrared & Raman Spectroscopy, Vol. 11. 383p. 1984. 98.00x (ISBN 0-471-26267-6, Pub. by Wiley Heyden). Wiley.
Eesley, G. L. Coherent Raman Spectroscopy. (Illus.). 150p. 1981. 44.00 (ISBN 0-08-025058-0). Pergamon.
Freeman, Stanley K. Application of Laser Raman Spectroscopy. LC 73-12688. 350p. 1974. 25.00 (ISBN 0-471-27788-6). Krieger.
Grasselli, Jeanette G., et al. Chemical Applications of Raman Spectroscopy. LC 81-1326. 198p. 1981. 45.00 (ISBN 0-471-08541-3, Pub. by Wiley-Interscience). Wiley.
Hallam, Harry E., ed. Vibrational Spectroscopy of Trapped Species: Infrared & Raman Studies of Matrix-Isolated Molecules, Radicals & Ions. LC 72-8601. pap. 110.50 (ISBN 0-317-26652-7, 2024035). Bks Demand UMI.
Harvey, Albert B., ed. Chemical Applications of Nonlinear Raman Spectroscopy. LC 80-69418. 1981. 59.50 (ISBN 0-12-329050-3). Acad Pr.
International Conference on Raman Spectroscopy 8th, 1982, Bordeaux, et al. Raman Spectroscopy: Linear & Nonlinear. Lascombe, Jean & Huong, Pham V., eds. pap. 160.00 (ISBN 0-317-08718-5, 2022542). Bks Demand UMI.
International Conference on Raman Spectroscopy (6th: 1978: Bangalore, India) Raman Spectroscopy: Proceedings of the 6th International Conference on Raman Spectroscopy, Bangalore, India, 4-9 September 1978, 2 vols, Vols. 1 & 2. Schmid, E. D. & Krishnan, R. S., eds. LC 83-131239. Vol. 1 - Invited Lectures. pap. 112.30 (ISBN 0-317-29336-2, 2024026); Vol. 2 - Contributed Papers. pap. 135.50 (ISBN 0-317-29337-0). Bks Demand UMI.
Long, D. A. Raman Spectroscopy. 1977. text ed. 60.95x (ISBN 0-07-038675-7, C). McGraw.
Mathieu, J. P., ed. Advances in Raman Spectorscopy: Proceedings of the Third International Conference on Raman Spectroscopy: University of Reims, France, September, 1972. LC 73-76120. pap. 160.00 (ISBN 0-317-26546-6, 2023996). Bks Demand UMI.
Murphy, W. F., ed. Proceedings of the 7th International Conference on Raman Spectroscopy, Ottawa, Canada, Aug. 4-9, 1980. 710p. 1980. 91.50 (ISBN 0-444-86038-X, North-Holland). Elsevier.
Nakamoto, Kazuo. Infrared & Raman Spectra of Inorganic & Coordination Compounds. 3rd ed. LC 77-15107. 1978. 45.50x (ISBN 0-471-62979-0, Pub. by Wiley-Interscience). Wiley.
--Laboratory Raman Spectroscopy. LC 84-13022. 138p. 1985. 29.95 (ISBN 0-471-81323-0, Pub. by Wiley-Interscience). Wiley.
Person. Vibrational Intensities in Infrared & Raman Spectroscopy. (Studies in Physical & Theoretical Chemistry: Vol. 20). 466p. 1982. 95.75 (ISBN 0-444-42115-7). Elsevier.
Siesler, H. W. & Holland-Moritz, K. Infrared & Raman Spectroscopy of Polymers. (Practical Spectroscopy Ser.: Vol. 4). (Illus.). 400p. 1980. 69.75 (ISBN 0-8247-6935-X). Dekker.
Sterin, K. E., et al. Raman Spectra of Hydrocarbons: A Data Handbook. LC 79-42704. 360p. 1980. 95.00 (ISBN 0-08-023596-4). Pergamon.
Szymanski, Herman A, ed. Raman Spectroscopy, Vol. 1. LC 64-23241. 250p. 1967. 39.50 (ISBN 0-306-37741-1, Plenum Pr). Plenum Pub.
Szymanski, Herman A., ed. Raman Spectroscopy, Vol. 2. LC 64-23241. 221p. 1970. 39.50 (ISBN 0-306-37742-X, Plenum Pr). Plenum Pub.
Theophanides, Theo M., ed. Infrared & Raman Spectroscopy of Biological Molecules. (NATO Advanced Study Institutes Ser.). 1979. lib. bdg. 47.50 (ISBN 90-277-0966-1, Pub. by Reidel Holland). Kluwer Academic.
Tobin, Marvin C. Laser Raman Spectroscopy. LC 80-11511. 184p. 1982. Repr. of 1971 ed. lib. bdg. 25.50 (ISBN 0-89874-159-9). Krieger.
Tu, A. T. Raman Spectroscopy in Biology: Principles & Applications. LC 82-6901. 448p. 1982. text ed. 69.95x (ISBN 0-471-07984-7, Pub. by Wiley-Interscience). Wiley.
Weber, A., ed. Raman Spectroscopy of Gases & Liquids. (Topics in Current Physics Ser.: Vol. 11). (Illus.). 1979. 37.00 (ISBN 0-387-09036-3). Springer-Verlag.

RAMANUJAN, AEJANGAR, SRINIVASA, 1887-1920
Berndt, B. C. Ramanujan's Notebooks, Pt. 1. (Illus.). 430p. 1985. 54.00 (ISBN 0-387-96110-0). Springer-Verlag.
Hardy, Godfrey H. Ramanujan. 3rd ed. LC 59-10268. 1978. 12.95 (ISBN 0-8284-0136-5). Chelsea Pub.

RANA
see Frogs

RANDOM NOISE THEORY
Brown, Robert G. Introduction to Random Signal Analysis & Kalman Filtering. 416p. 1983. text ed. 36.00 (ISBN 0-471-08732-7). Wiley.
Gerlach, Albert A. Theory & Applications of Statistical Wave-Period Processing, 3 Vols. 1434p. 1970. 352.50 (ISBN 0-677-02510-6). Gordon.
Stratonovich, R. L. Topics in the Theory of Random Noise, 2 vols. (Mathematics & Its Applications Ser.). 1963-67. Set. 130.75 (ISBN 0-677-00800-7); Vol. 1, 306p. 75.25x (ISBN 0-677-00780-9); Vol. 2, 344p. 78.75x (ISBN 0-677-00790-6). Gordon.
Uhrig, Robert E. Random Noise Techniques in Nuclear Reactor Systems. LC 71-110558. (Illus.). pap. 95.40 (ISBN 0-317-08879-3, 2012436). Bks Demand UMI.
Van Der Ziel, Aldert. Noise in Measurements. LC 76-12108. 228p. 1976. 40.50x (ISBN 0-471-89895-3, Pub. by Wiley-Interscience). Wiley.
Whalen, A. D. Detection of Signals in Noise. (Electrical Science Ser.). 1971. 55.00 (ISBN 0-12-744850-0). Acad Pr.

RANDOM NUMBERS
see Numbers, Random

RANDOM PROCESSES
see Stochastic Processes
Clarke, A. Bruce & Disney, Ralph L. Probability & Random Processes: A First Course with Applications. (Probability & Mathematical Statistics Ser.). 324p. 1985. 32.95 (ISBN 0-471-08535-9). Wiley.

RANDOM SAMPLING
see also Sampling (Statistics)
Levy, Paul. Random Functions: A Laplacian Random Function Depending on a Point of Hilbert Space. LC 56-8639. (University of California Publications in Statistics Ser.: Vol. 2, No. 10). pap. 20.00 (ISBN 0-317-11008-X, 2021182). Bks Demand UMI.
Steindl, J. Random Processes & the Growth of Firms: A Study of the Pareto Law. 249p. 1965. text ed. 22.00x (ISBN 0-85264-063-3). Lubrecht & Cramer.

RANDOM WALKS (MATHEMATICS)
Barber, M. N. & Ninham, B. W. Random & Restricted Walks: Theory & Applications. (Mathematics & Its Applications Ser.). 190p. 1970. 46.25 (ISBN 0-677-02620-X). Gordon.
Conference, 5th, Oberwolfach, Germany, Jan. 29 - Feb. 4, 1978. Probability Measures on Groups: Proceedings. Heyer, H., ed. (Lecture Notes in Mathematics: Vol. 706). 1979. pap. 22.00 (ISBN 0-387-09124-6). Springer-Verlag.
Hughes, B. D. & Ninham, B. W. The Mathematics & Physics of Disordered Media: Percolation, Random Walk, Modeling & Simulation. (Lecture Notes in Mathematics: Vol. 1035). vii, 431p. 1983. pap. 20.00 (ISBN 0-387-12707-0). Springer-Verlag.

Principles of Random Walk. 2nd ed. LC 75-26883. (Graduate Texts in Mathematics Ser.: Vol. 34). 425p. 1976. 30.95 (ISBN 0-387-90150-7). Springer-Verlag.

Shlesinger, Michael F. & West, Bruce J., eds. Random Walks & Their Applications in the Physical & Biological Sciences: NBS-La Jolla Institute - 1982. LC 84-7028. (AIP Conference Proceedings Ser.: No. 109). 243p. 1984. lib. bdg. 38.75 (ISBN 0-88318-308-0). Am Inst Physics.

RANGE MANAGEMENT

see also Grazing; Livestock; Range Research

Arnold, G. W. & Dudzinski, M. L. Ethology of Free Ranging Domestic Animals. (Developments in Animal & Veterinary Sciences Ser.: Vol. 2). 198p. 1979. 57.50 (ISBN 0-444-41700-1). Elsevier.

Barnes, William C. Western Grazing Grounds & Forest Ranges. Bruchey, Stuart, ed. LC 78-56685. (Management of Public Lands in the U.S. Ser.). (Illus.). 1979. Repr. of 1913 ed. lib. bdg. 26.50x (ISBN 0-405-11317-X). Ayer Co Pubs.

Branson, Farrell A., et al. Rangeland Hydrology. 2nd ed. 352p. 1981. pap. text ed. 15.00 (ISBN 0-8403-2408-1). Kendall-Hunt.

French, N. R., ed. Perspectives in Grassland Ecology: Results & Applications of the US-IBP Grassland Biome Study. LC 78-13971. (Ecological Studies: Vol. 32). (Illus.). 1979. 39.00 (ISBN 0-387-90384-4). Springer-Verlag.

Humphrey, Robert R. Range Ecology. LC 62-20671. pap. 60.00 (2015179). Bks Demand UMI.

Vallentine, John F. Range Development & Improvements. 2nd ed. LC 79-26676. (Illus.). 1980. text ed. 18.95x (ISBN 0-8425-1708-1). Brigham.

Vallentine, John F., ed. U. S.-Canadian Range Management Nineteen Seventy Eight to Nineteen Eighty. 180p. 1981. lib. bdg. 55.00x (ISBN 0-912700-96-3). Oryx Pr.

RANGE RESEARCH

Vallentine, John F. & Sims, Phillip L., eds. Range Science: A Guide to Information Sources. (Natural World Information Guide Ser.: Vol. 2). 250p. 1980. 60.00x (ISBN 0-8103-1420-7). Gale.

RANGES (STOCK)

see Stock-Ranges

RANGIFER

see Caribou; Reindeer

RANK ORDER STATISTICS

Bechhofer, Robert E., et al. Sequential Identification & Ranking Procedures: With Special Reference to Koopman-Darmois Populations. LC 67-28463. (Statistical Research Monographs Ser.: Vol. 3). pap. 109.50 (ISBN 0-317-09299-5, 2019954). Bks Demand UMI.

Bremmer. Tables of Dominant Weight Multiplicites of Simple Life Algebras of Rank Less Than or Equal to 8. (Pure & Applied Mathematics: Monographs & Textbooks). 232p. 1985. 65.00 (ISBN 0-8247-7270-9). Dekker.

RAPE (PLANT)

Appelqvist, L. A. & Ohlson, R., eds. Rapeseed. 391p. 1973. 104.25 (ISBN 0-444-40892-4). Elsevier.

Kramer, J. K. & Saver, F. D., eds. High & Low Erucic Acid Rapeseed Oils: Production, Usage, Chemistry & Toxilogical Evaluation. LC 82-13805. 1983. 79.50 (ISBN 0-12-425080-7). Acad Pr.

RARE ANIMALS

see also Extinct Animals; Rare Birds

Cadieux, Charles. These Are the Endangered. LC 80-54448. (Illus.). 240p. 1981. 16.95 (ISBN 0-913276-35-9). Stone Wall Pr.

Convention on International Trade in Endangered Species of Wild Fauna & Flora, Conference of the Parties, 1st Meeting, Berne, 1976: Proceedings. 554p. 1981. pap. 44.00 (ISBN 0-686-93127-0, IUCN). Unipub.

Convention on International Trade in Endangered Species of Wild Fauna & Flora, Geneva, 1977. Special Working Session of the Conference Parties (CITES) Proceedings. 271p. 1978. pap. 22.50 (ISBN 0-686-74017-3, CIT001, IUCN). Unipub.

Durrell, Gerald. Ark on the Move. 1983. 14.95 (ISBN 0-698-11211-3, Coward). Putnam Pub Group.

Eckholm, Erik. Disappearing Species: The Social Challenge. LC 78-66428. (Worldwatch Papers). 1978. pap. 2.00 (ISBN 0-916468-21-6). Worldwatch Inst.

Ehrlich, Paul & Ehrlich, Anne. Extinction: The Causes & Consequences of the Disappearance of Species. 1981. 16.95 (ISBN 0-394-51312-6). Random.

Emonds, Gerhardt. Guidelines for National Implementation of the Convention on International Trade in Endangered Species of Wild Fauna & Flora. (Environmental Policy & Law Papers: No. 17). 148p. 1981. pap. 12.50 (ISBN 0-686-97536-7, IUCN104, IUCN). Unipub.

Groves, R. H. & Ride, W. D., eds. Species at Risk: Research in Australia. 250p. 1982. 40.00 (ISBN 0-387-11416-5). Springer-Verlag.

Hoage, R. J., ed. Animal Extinctions: What Everyone Should Know. LC 85-8342. (National Zoological Park Symposia for the Public Ser.). (Illus.). 160p. (Orig.). 1985. pap. 9.95 (ISBN 0-87474-521-7, HOAEP). Smithsonian.

Mackal, Roy P. Searching for Hidden Animals. 320p. 1982. 42.00x (ISBN 0-85614-076-7, Pub. by Gentry England). State Mutual Bk.

Nitecki, Matthew H., ed. Extinctions. LC 84-40253. (Illus.). 340p. 1984. lib. bdg. 30.00x (ISBN 0-226-58689-8); pap. 16.00x (ISBN 0-226-58690-1). U of Chicago Pr.

Norton, Bryan G., ed. The Preservation of Species: The Value of Biological Diversity. (Center for Philosophy & Public Policy, University of Maryland Ser.). 272p. 1986. text ed. 29.50 (ISBN 0-691-08389-4). Princeton U Pr.

Ono, Dana R., et al. Vanishing Fishes of North America. LC 82-62896. (Illus.). 268p. 1983. 29.95 (ISBN 0-913276-43-X). Stone Wall Pr.

Pritchard, P. C. & Marquez, Rene. Kemp's Ridley Turtle or Atlantic Ridley, (Lepidochelys kempi) (Illus.). 30p. 1973. pap. 8.00 (ISBN 2-88032-020-8, IUCN10, IUCN). Unipub.

Pritchard, Peter C., ed. Rare & Endangered Biota of Florida. Incl. Vol. One. Mammals. Layne, James N., ed. xx, 52p. 1979. pap. 5.00 (ISBN 0-8130-0617-1); Vol. Two. Birds. Kale, Herbert W., ed. xix, 121p. 1979. pap. 7.00 (ISBN 0-8130-0618-X); Vol. Three. Amphibians & Reptiles. McDiarmid, Roy W., ed. xxii, 74p. 1979. pap. 5.50 (ISBN 0-8130-0619-8); Vol. Four. Fishes. Gilbert, Carter R., ed. xviii, 58p. 1979. pap. 5.00 (ISBN 0-8130-0620-1); Vol. 5. Plants. Ward, Daniel B., ed. 1980. pap. 10.50 (ISBN 0-8130-0638-4); Vol. 6. Invertebrates. Franz, Richard, ed. LC 78-12121. 1982. pap. 7.50 (ISBN 0-8130-0725-9). LC 78-12121. U Presses Fla.

Thornback, Jane & Jenkins, Martin, eds. The IUCN Mammal Red Data Book, Part 1: Threatened Mammalian Taxa of the Americas & the Australasian Zoogeographic Region. 560p. 1982. 20.00 (ISBN 2-88032-600-1, IUCN106, IUCN). Unipub.

Threatened Deer. (Illus.). 434p. 1978. pap. 15.00 (ISBN 2-88032-201-4, IUCN74, IUCN). Unipub.

Whitlock, Ralph. Rare Breeds: The Vulnerable Survivors. LC 80-26342. (Illus.). 160p. 1981. 19.95 (ISBN 0-442-26279-5). Van Nos Reinhold.

Yaffee, Steven L. Prohibitive Policy: Implementing the Federal Endangered Species Act. (American Politics & Public Policy Ser.). 240p. 1982. 27.50x (ISBN 0-262-24024-6). MIT Pr.

RARE BIRDS

Ehrlich, Paul & Ehrlich, Anne. Extinction: The Causes & Consequences of the Disappearance of Species. 1981. 16.95 (ISBN 0-394-51312-6). Random.

Greenway, James C., Jr. Extinct & Vanishing Birds of the World. 2nd ed. (Illus.). 1967. pap. 7.95 (ISBN 0-486-21869-4). Dover.

Heltne, Paul. The Lion Tailed Macaque: Status & Conservation. LC 84-28938. (MP Ser.). 422p. 1985. 58.00 (ISBN 0-8451-3406-X). A R Liss.

King, Warren B. Endangered Birds of the World: The ICBP Bird Red Data Book. LC 81-607796. 624p. 1981. text ed. 19.95x (ISBN 0-87474-584-5); pap. text ed. 8.95x (ISBN 0-87474-583-7). Smithsonian.

Nash, Hugh, et al, eds. The Condor Question: Captive or Forever Free? LC 81-68548. (Illus.). 304p. (Orig.). 1981. pap. 0.95 (ISBN 0-913890-48-0). Brick Hse Pub.

Red Data Book Endangered Birds, Pt. 2. pap. 20.95 (IUCN). Unipub.

Ripley, S. Dillon. A Naturalist's Adventure in Nepal: Search for the Spiny Babbler. (Illus.). 301p. 1981. Repr. of 1953 ed. 15.00 (ISBN 0-87474-810-0). Smithsonian.

--Rails of the World: A Monograph of the Family Rallidae. Portfolio ed. LC 83-81671. (Illus.). 32p. 1984. 40.00x (ISBN 0-87474-804-6, RIPR). Smithsonian.

Roberson, Don. Rare Birds of the West Coast of North America. LC 80-51054. (Illus.). 548p. 1980. 24.95 (ISBN 0-9605352-0-9). Woodcock.

Temple, Stanley, ed. Endangered Birds: Management Techniques for Preserving Threatened Species. (Illus.). 488p. 1978. 19.50x (ISBN 0-299-07520-6). U of Wis Pr.

Whitlock, Ralph. Birds at Risk. 230p. 1981. text ed. 30.50x (ISBN 0-239-00207-5, Pub. by Moonraker). Humanities.

Zeleny, Lawrence. The Bluebird: How You Can Help Its Fight for Survival. LC 74-22832. (Midland Bks.: No. 212). (Illus.). 192p. 1976. pap. 7.95 (ISBN 0-253-20212-4). Ind U Pr.

RARE EARTH METALS

see Earths, Rare

RARE EARTHS

see Earths, Rare

RARE GASES

see Gases, Rare

RARE METALS

see Nonferrous Metals

RARE PLANTS

Dierschke, Hartmut. Internationale Vereinigung Fuer Vegetationskunde: Berichte der Internationalen Symposien: Syntaxonomie (1980) (Ger., Illus.). 614p. 1981. lib. bdg. 56.00x (ISBN 3-7682-1309-9). Lubrecht & Cramer.

Emonds, Gerhardt. Guidelines for National Implementation of the Convention on International Trade in Endangered Species of Wild Fauna & Flora. (Environmental Policy & Law Papers: No. 17). 148p. 1981. pap. 12.50 (ISBN 0-686-97536-7, IUCN104, IUCN). Unipub.

Gomez-Campo, C., ed. Plant Conservation in the Mediterranean Area. (Geobotany Ser.). 1985. lib. bdg. 67.50 (ISBN 90-6193-523-7, Pub. by Junk Pubs Netherlands). Kluwer Academic.

Morse, L. E. & Henifin, M. S., eds. Rare Plant Conservation: Geographical Data Organization. 377p. 1981. pap. 25.00x (ISBN 0-89327-223-X). NY Botanical.

Synge, H., ed. Biological Aspects of Rare Plant Conservation. LC 80-42067. 592p. 1981. 89.95 (ISBN 0-471-28004-6, Pub. by Wiley-Interscience). Wiley.

Ward, Daniel B. & Pritchard, Peter C., eds. Plants. LC 78-12121. (Rare & Endangered Biota of Florida Ser.: Vol. 5). 1979. pap. 10.50 (ISBN 0-8130-0638-4). U Presses Fla.

RASPAIL, FRANCOIS VINCENT, 1794-1878

Weiner, Dora B. Raspail, Scientist & Reformer. LC 68-19761. (Illus.). 1968. 34.00x (ISBN 0-231-03059-2). Columbia U Pr.

RAT

see Rats

RATIO ANALYSIS

Churchill, Stuart W. The Interpretation & Use of Rate Data: The Rate Concept. rev. ed. LC 78-23365. (Illus.). 510p. 1982. pap. text ed. 32.50 (ISBN 0-89116-234-8); solution manual 5.95 (ISBN 0-89116-260-7). Hemisphere Pub.

Gupta, L. C. Financial Ratios for Monitoring Corporate Sickness: Towards a More Systematic Approach. (Illus.). 1983. 16.95x (ISBN 0-19-561513-1). Oxford U Pr.

Mott, Sheryl S. Ratio Analysis Workbook. Andover, James J., ed. LC 84-18977. 256p. 1984. wkbk. 22.95 (ISBN 0-934914-57-5). NACM.

Steffy, Wilbert, et al. Computer Ratio Analysis: An Aid to Decision Making. (Illus.). 63p. 12.00 (ISBN 0-938654-14-4, CRA). Indus Dev Inst Sci.

RATIO AND PROPORTION

Hart, Kathleen M. Ratio: Children's Strategies & Errors. 128p. 1984. 20.00 (ISBN 0-7005-0637-3). Taylor & Francis.

Oresme, Nicole, ed. De proportionibus proportionum. Grant, Edward, tr. Bd. with Ad pauca respicientes. (Medieval Science Publications Ser.). (Illus.). 488p. 1966. 50.00x (ISBN 0-299-04000-3). U of Wis Pr.

RATIONAL GAMES (MATHEMATICS)

see Games of Strategy (Mathematics)

RATIONAL NUMBERS

see Numbers, Rational

RATS

see also Wood-Rats

Altman, J. & Bayer, S. A. The Development of the Rat Spinal Chord. (Advances in Anatomy, Embryology & Cell Biology Ser.: Vol. 58). (Illus.). 160p. 1984. pap. 25.00 (ISBN 0-387-13119-1). Springer-Verlag.

Baer, Melvyn J., et al. The Postnatal Development of the Rat Skull. LC 81-19837. 1983. text ed. 125.00x (ISBN 0-472-10011-4). U of Mich Pr.

Baker, Henry J., et al, eds. The Laboratory Rat. LC 79-51688. (American College of Laboratory Animal Medicine Ser.). Vol. 1: Biology & Diseases 1979. 67.50 (ISBN 0-12-074901-7); Vol. 2: Research Applications 1980. 63.00 (ISBN 0-12-074902-5). Acad Pr.

Barnett, S. A. The Rat: A Study in Behavior. 3rd, rev. ed. LC 74-33509. xiv, 318p. 1976. lib. bdg. 22.00x (ISBN 0-226-03740-1); pap. 11.00x (ISBN 0-226-03742-8). U of Chicago Pr.

Bohensky, Fred. Photo Manual & Dissection Guide of the Rat. (Avery's Anatomy Ser.). (Illus.). 140p. (Orig.). 1985. lab manual 6.95 (ISBN 0-89529-213-0). Avery Pub.

Brody, Elizabeth G. Genetic Basis at Spontaneous Activity in the Albino Rat. (Comparative Psychology Monographs). 1942. pap. 5.00 (ISBN 0-527-24924-6). Kraus Repr.

Burckhardt-Stuker, Ruth. Versuche zur Experimentellen Alalgetika-Abhaengigkeit bei der Ratte. (European University Studies: No. 6, Vol. 107). (Ger.). 284p. 1983. 26.85 (ISBN 3-261-03277-4). P Lang Pubs.

Castaing, D., et al. Hepatic & Portal Surgery in the Rat. (Illus.). 184p. 1980. 41.50x (ISBN 0-89352-101-9). Masson Pub.

Chan-Palay, V. Cerebellar Dentate Nucleus: With Applications to the Terrestrinal Planets & Meteorites. LC 76-46462. 1977. 132.00 (ISBN 0-387-07958-0). Springer-Verlag.

Chiasson, Robert B. Laboratory Anatomy of the White Rat. 4th ed. (Laboratory Anatomy Ser.). 112p. 1980. wire coil write for info. (ISBN 0-697-04644-3). Wm C Brown.

Costoff, Allen. Ultrastructure of Rat Adenohypophysis: Correlation with Function. 1973. 49.00 (ISBN 0-12-191550-6). Acad Pr.

Craigie, Edward H. Craigie's Neuroanatomy of the Rat. rev. ed. Zeman, Wolfgang & Innes, James R., eds. 1963. 52.00 (ISBN 0-12-195450-1). Acad Pr.

Elwood, R. W., ed. Parental Behaviour of Rodents. LC 82-8625. 296p. 1983. text ed. 53.95x (ISBN 0-471-10252-0, Pub. by Wiley-Interscience). Wiley.

Farris, Edmond J. & Griffith, John Q., Jr., eds. Rat in Laboratory Investigation. 2nd ed. (Illus.). 1963. Repr. of 1949 ed. 50.00h (ISBN 0-02-844550-3). Hafner.

Felix, H., et al. Dynamic Morphology of Leukemia Cells: A Comparative Study by Scanning Electron Microscopy & Microcinematography. (Illus.). 1978. 63.00 (ISBN 0-387-08495-9). Springer-Verlag.

Fox, Susan. Rats. (Illus.). 96p. 1984. 4.95 (ISBN 0-87666-933-X, KW-128). TFH Pubns.

Greaves, P. & Faccini, J. M. Rat Histopathology. 260p. 1984. 52.00 (ISBN 0-444-90364-X). Elsevier.

Greene, Eunice G. Anatomy of the Rat. (Illus.). 1971. Repr. of 1935 ed. 75.00x (ISBN 0-02-845440-5). Hafner.

Hamilton, Leonard W., ed. Basic Limbic System Anatomy of the Rat. LC 76-46401. (Illus.). 167p. 1976. 25.00x (ISBN 0-306-30925-4, Plenum Pr). Plenum Pub.

Hendrickson, Robert. More Cunning Than Man: A Social History of Rats & Men. LC 82-48512. 288p. 1983. 19.95 (ISBN 0-8128-2894-1). Stein & Day.

Jones, William. Rats, Mice, & Cockroaches: The Dilemma & Solutions. LC 81-90323. (Illus.). 104p. (Orig.). 1982. pap. 13.95 (ISBN 0-9607272-0-5). Ramico Pubns.

Knox, W. E. Enzyme Patterns in Fetal, Adult & Neo-Plastic Rat Tissues. 2nd ed. 1976. 29.50 (ISBN 3-8055-2357-2). S Karger.

Konig, Joachim & Klippell, Renate A. The Rat Brain: A Stereoetaxic Atlas of the Forebrain & the Lower Parts of the Brain Stem. LC 63-21368. (Illus.). 168p. 1974. Repr. of 1963 ed. 22.50 (ISBN 0-88275-034-8). Krieger.

Lambert, Rene. Surgery of the Digestive System in the Rat. Julien, Brian, tr. (Illus.). 520p. 1965. photocopy ed. 50.50x (ISBN 0-398-01076-5). C C Thomas.

McClenaghan, Leroy R. & Gaines, Michael S. Reproduction in Marginal Populations of the Hispid Cotton Rat (Sigmodon Hispidus) in Northern Kansas. (Occasional Papers: Vol. 74). 16p. 1978. pap. 1.25 (ISBN 0-317-04888-0). U of KS Mus Nat Hist.

Miller, G. S., Jr. Characters & Probable History of the Hawaiian Rat. Bd. with Ectoparasites of Some Polynesian and Malaysian Rats of the Genus Rattus. Ewing, H. E. pap. 8.00 (ISBN 0-527-02117-2). Kraus Repr.

Moojen, Joao. Speciation in the Brazilian Spiny Rats: Genus Proechimys (Family Echimyidae) (Museum Ser.: Vol. 1, No. 19). 106p. 1948. pap. 5.50 (ISBN 0-317-04890-2). U of KS Mus Nat Hist.

Newberne, Paul M. & Butler, W. H., eds. Rat Hepatic Neoplasia. 1978. text ed. 45.00x (ISBN 0-262-14029-2). MIT Pr.

Nitschke, Werner. Acoustic Behavior in the Rat: Research Theory & Applications. LC 82-11270. 204p. 1982. 29.95 (ISBN 0-03-061973-4). Praeger.

Olds, R. J. A Colour Atlas of the Rat: Dissection Guide. LC 78-24742. 112p. 1979. text ed. 17.95x (ISBN 0-470-26647-3). Halsted Pr.

Paxinos, G. & Watson, C. The Rat Brain in Stereotoxic Coordinates. 1983. 41.00 (ISBN 0-12-547620-5). Acad Pr.

Paxinos, George, ed. The Rat Nervous System: Forebrain & Midbrain, Vol. 1. Date not set. price not set (ISBN 0-12-547631-0). Acad Pr.

--The Rat Nervous System: Hindbrain & Spinal Cord, Vol. 2. Date not set. price not set (ISBN 0-12-547632-9). Acad Pr.

Pefaur, Jaime E. & Hoffmann, Robert S. Studies of Small Mammal Populations at Three Sites on the Northern Great Plains. (Occasional Papers: No. 37). 27p. 1975. pap. 1.75 (ISBN 0-317-04887-X). U of KS Mus Nat Hist.

Pellegrino, L. J., et al. Stereotaxic Atlas of the Rat Brain. 2nd ed. LC 79-9438. 279p. 1979. 29.50x (ISBN 0-306-40269-6, Plenum Pr). Plenum Pub.

BOOKS - SUBJECT INDEX REARRANGEMENTS (CHEMISTRY)

Raedler, A. & Sievers, J. The Development of the Visual System of the Albino Rat. (Advances in Anatomy, Embryology & Cellbiology Ser.: Vol. 50, Pt. 3). (Illus.). 100p. 1975. pap. 28.40 (ISBN 0-387-07079-6). Springer-Verlag.
Sherwood, Nancy & Timiras, Paola. A Stereotaxic Atlas of the Developing Rat Brain. LC 70-103674. (Fr. & Ger., Illus.). 1970. 70.00x (ISBN 0-520-01656-4). U of Cal Pr.
Svendgaard, N. A., et al. Regenerative Properties of Central Monoamine Neurons: Studies in the Adult Rat Using Cerebral Iris Implants As Targets. (Advances in Anatomy, Embroyology, & Cell Biology Ser.: Vol. 51, Pt. 4). (Illus.). 70p. (Orig.). 1975. pap. 34.30 (ISBN 0-387-07299-3). Springer-Verlag.
Thompson, Samuel, et al. The Adrenal Medulla of Rats: Comparative Physiology, Histology, & Pathology. (Illus.). 124p. 1981. photocopy ed. 20.75x (ISBN 0-398-04091-5). C C Thomas.
Thorpe, Darwin R. Rat: A Dissection Guide in Color. (Illus.). 1968. pap. 6.95 (ISBN 0-87484-132-1). Mayfield Pub.
Waynforth, H. B. Experimental & Surgical Techniques in the Rat. LC 79-41548. 1980. 36.50 (ISBN 0-12-738850-8). Acad Pr.
Zinsser, Hans. Rats, Lice & History: The Biography of Bacillus. 320p. 1984. pap. 6.70i (ISBN 0-316-98896-0). Little.

RATTLESNAKES

Armstrong, Barry L. & Murphy, James B. The Natural History of Mexican Rattlesnakes. Wiley, E. O. & Collins, Joseph T., eds. (U of KS Museum of Nat. Hist. Special Publication: No. 5). (Illus.). 88p. (Orig.). 1979. pap. 6.00 (ISBN 0-89338-010-5). U of KS Mus Nat Hist.
Dobie, J. Frank. Rattlesnakes. 1965. 14.45 (ISBN 0-316-18799-2). Little.
Ipsen, D. C. Rattlesnakes & Scientists. (Illus.). 111p. 1970. 6.95x (ISBN 0-8464-1179-2). Beekman Pubs.
Klauber, Laurence M. Rattlesnakes: Their Habits, Life Histories, & Influence on Mankind. abr. ed. LC 80-16660. (Illus.). 400p. 1982. 19.95 (ISBN 0-520-04038-4); pap. 8.95 (ISBN 0-520-04039-2, CAL 652). U of Cal Pr.
--Rattlesnakes: Their Habits, Life Histories & Influence on Mankind, 2 vols. 2nd ed. LC 78-188573. (Illus.). 1973. Boxed Set. 80.00 (ISBN 0-520-01775-7). U of Cal Pr.
Murphy, James B. & Armstrong, Barry L. Maintenance of Rattlesnakes in Captivity. (Special Publication Ser.: No.3). (Illus.). 55p. 1978. pap. 3.00 (ISBN 0-89338-006-7). U of KS Mus Nat Hist.

RAW FOOD

see Food, Raw

RAW MATERIALS

see also Farm Produce; Forest Products

Agricultural Raw Materials: Competition with Synthetic Substitutes. (Economic & Social Development Papers: No. 48). (Illus.). 62p. 1985. pap. 7.50 (ISBN 92-5-102138-4, F2672, FAO). Unipub.
Backstrand, G. Resources, Society & Future. 1980. 47.00 (ISBN 0-08-023266-3); pap. 18.00 (ISBN 0-08-023267-1). Pergamon.
Banks, Ferdinand E. Resources & Energy: An Economic Analysis. LC 81-47967. 368p. 1983. 36.50x (ISBN 0-669-05203-5). Lexington Bks.
Bennett, Merrill K. International Commodity Stockpiling As an Economic Stabilizer. LC 69-10070. 1969. Repr. of 1949 ed. lib. bdg. 15.00 (ISBN 0-8371-0308-8, BECS). Greenwood.
Committee on Contingency Plans for Chromium Utilization, National Research Council. Contingency Plans for Chromium Utilization. LC 77-95193. (Illus.). 1978. 11.95 (ISBN 0-309-02737-3). Natl Acad Pr.
Harmon, Elmer M. Commodity Reserve Currency. LC 68-59258. (Columbia University Studies in the Social Sciences: No. 599). Repr. of 1959 ed. 15.00 (ISBN 0-404-51599-1). AMS Pr.
Hurstfield, J. The Control of Raw Materials. 1982. 53.00 (ISBN 0-527-35763-4). Kraus Intl.
Killough, Hugh B. & Killough, Lucy W. Raw Materials of Industrialism. LC 79-137951. (Economic Thought, History & Challenge Ser). 1971. Repr. of 1929 ed. 25.50x (ISBN 0-8046-1453-9, Pub. Kennikat). Assoc Faculty Pr.
Kingsman, B. G. Raw Materials Purchasing: An Operational Research Approach. (Frontiers of Operational Research & Applied Systems Analysis Ser.: Vol. 4). (Illus.). 376p. 1985. 45.00 (ISBN 0-08-029976-8); pap. 32.00 (ISBN 0-08-029975-X). Pergamon.
Page, Talbot. Conservation & Economic Efficiency: An Approach to Materials Policy. LC 76-22846. (Resources for the Future Ser). 288p. 1977. 21.50x (ISBN 0-8018-1904-0); pap. 8.95x (ISBN 0-8018-1951-2). Johns Hopkins.
Stpierre, L. E. & Brown, G. R. Future Sources of Organic Raw Materials (CHEMRAWN II) 62.00 (ISBN 0-08-022390-7). Pergamon.
Wu, Y. L. Raw Material Supply in a Multipolar World. 2nd ed. (Strategy Papers Ser.: No. 34). 112p. 1980. pap. 4.95x (ISBN 0-8448-1339-7). Crane-Russak Co.

RAYLEIGH, JOHN WILLIAM STRUTT, BARON, 1842-1919

Strutt, Robert J. Life of John William Strutt, Third Baron Rayleigh, O. M., F. R. S. (Illus.). 468p. 1968. 35.00x (ISBN 0-299-04690-7). U of Wis Pr.

RAYON

Turbak, Albin F., ed. Solvent Spun Rayon, Modified Cellulose Fibers & Derivatives. LC 77-12220. (ACS Symposium Ser.: No. 58). 1977. 26.95 (ISBN 0-8412-0388-1). Am Chemical.

RAYS (FISHES)

Tinker, Spencer W. & DuLuca, Charles J. Sharks & Rays: A Handbook of the Sharks & Rays of Hawaii & the Central Pacific Ocean. LC 73-77578. 1973. 7.25 (ISBN 0-8048-1082-6). C E Tuttle.

RAYS, INFRA-RED

see Infra-Red Rays

RAYS, INVISIBLE

see Spectrum, Infra-Red; Spectrum, Ultra-Violet

RAYS, ROENTGEN

see X-Rays

RAYS, ULTRA-VIOLET

see Ultra-Violet Rays

REACTANCE AMPLIFIERS

see Parametric Amplifiers

REACTION, CONDITIONS AND LAWS OF (CHEMISTRY)

Jennings, K. R. & Cundall, R. B., eds. Progress in Reaction Kinetics, Vol. 10 Complete. 402p. 1981. 91.00 (ISBN 0-08-027155-3). Pergamon.
Murthy, S. B., ed. Turbulent Mixing in Nonreactive & Reactive Flows. LC 75-22329. 464p. 1975. 69.50x (ISBN 0-306-30874-6, Plenum Pr). Plenum Pub.

REACTION RATE (CHEMISTRY)

see Chemical Reaction, Rate Of

REACTIONS, CHEMICAL

see Chemical Reactions

REACTIVITY (CHEMISTRY)

see also Chemical Affinity

Abramovitch, R. A., ed. Reactive Intermediates, Vol. 2. LC 79-344. 614p. 1982. 79.50x (ISBN 0-306-40594-6, Plenum Pr). Plenum Pub.
Chin, Chen-An & Song, Pill-Soon. Reactivity Indices for Biomolecules. (Graduate Studies: No. 24). (Illus.). 176p. 1981. 33.00 (ISBN 0-89672-093-4); pap. 20.00 (ISBN 0-89672-092-6). Tex Tech Pr.
Daudel, R. Quantum Theory of Chemical Reactivity. LC 73-75762. 1973. lib. bdg. 31.50 (ISBN 90-277-0265-9, Pub. by Reidel Holland); pap. 24.00 (ISBN 90-277-0420-1). Kluwer Academic.
Fisher, H., et al. Electronic Structure of Organic Compounds. (Topics in Current Chemistry: Vol. 24). 1971. pap. 18.90 (ISBN 0-387-05540-1). Springer-Verlag.
Klopman, Gilles, ed. Chemical Reactivity & Reaction Paths. LC 73-17325. 382p. 1974. 29.50 (ISBN 0-471-49355-4). Krieger.
Koptyug, V. A. Contemporary Problems in Carbonium Ion Chemistry III Arenium Ions: Structure & Reactivity. (Topics in Current Chemistry, Fortschritte der Chemischen Forschung: Vol. 122). (Illus.). 270p. 1984. 45.50 (ISBN 0-387-13043-8). Springer-Verlag.
Wood, John, et al, eds. Reactivity of Solids. LC 77-785. (Illus.). 810p. 1977. 95.00x (ISBN 0-306-31021-X, Plenum Pr). Plenum Pub.

REACTOR FUEL ELEMENTS

see Nuclear Fuel Elements

REACTOR FUEL REPROCESSING

Analytical Methods in Nuclear Fuel Cycle. (Proceedings Ser.). (Illus.). 586p. (Orig.). 1973. pap. 50.25 (ISBN 92-0-050072-2, ISP291, IAEA). Unipub.
Chayes, Abraham & Lewis, W. Bennett, eds. International Arrangements for Nuclear Fuel Reprocessing. LC 76-52961. 280p. 1976. prof ref 27.50 (ISBN 0-88410-052-9). Ballinger Pub.
DOE Technical Information Center. Radioactive Waste Management: Spent Fuel Storage: A Bibliography. 154p. 1982. pap. 12.00 (ISBN 0-87079-477-9, DOE/TIC-3395); microfiche 4.50 (ISBN 0-87079-478-7, DOE/TIC-3395). DOE.
Lyon, William S., ed. Analytical Chemistry in Nuclear Fuel Reprocessing. LC 77-16721. (Illus.). 1978. lib. bdg. 35.00 (ISBN 0-89500-006-7). Sci Pr.
Storage of Water Reactor Spent Fuel in Water Pools. (Technical Reports Ser.: No. 218). (Illus.). 143p. 1983. pap. 21.75 (ISBN 92-0-155182-7, IDC218, IAEA). Unipub.
Wymer, Raymond G. & Vondra, Benedict L., Jr., eds. Light Water Reactor Nuclear Fuel Cycle. 272p. 1981. 77.00 (ISBN 0-8493-5687-3). CRC Pr.

REACTOR FUELS

see Nuclear Fuels

REACTORS (NUCLEAR PHYSICS)

see Nuclear Reactors

REACTORS, BREEDER

see Breeder Reactors

REACTORS, CHEMICAL

see Chemical Reactors

REACTORS, GAS COOLED

see Gas Cooled Reactors

REACTORS, ORGANIC COOLED

see Organic Cooled Reactors

REACTORS, PULSED

see Pulsed Reactors

READER-PRINTERS (MICROPHOTOGRAPHY)

Association for Information & Image Management. Uniform Product Disclosure for Roll Film Readers: AIIM MS27-1982. (Standards & Recommended Practices Ser.). 4p. 1982. pap. 6.00 (ISBN 0-89258-078-X, M027); pap. 5.25 member. Assn Inform & Image Mgmt.

READERS–SCIENCE

Bloomer, Richard H. Reading Comprehension for Scientists. 228p. 1963. 16.50x (ISBN 0-398-00172-3). C C Thomas.
Constant, Constantine. Earth Science: Intermediate Level. 1972. wkbk. ed. 9.00 (ISBN 0-87720-154-4). AMSCO Sch.
Kilgour, O. F. Introduction to Science for Catering & Homecraft Students. 1976. pap. 12.50 (ISBN 0-434-91057-0, Pub. by W Heinemann Ltd). David & Charles.
Lander, Eleanor. Science & Technology: A Reader. 176p. 1983. pap. text ed. 8.95 (ISBN 0-88377-257-4). Newbury Hse.
Mould, J. Albert & Geffner, Saul L. Review Text in General Science. 2nd ed. 1974. pap. text ed. 7.67 (ISBN 0-87720-001-7). AMSCO Sch.
Saslow, Joan M. & Mongillo, John F. English in Context: Reading Comprehension for Science & Technology, Bk. III. (Illus.). 192p. 1986. pap. text ed. 9.95 (ISBN 0-13-280041-1). P-H.
Weber, R. L. More Random Walks in Science: An Anthology. 1982. 19.50 (ISBN 0-9960024-0-5, Pub. by A Hilger England). Heyden.
Weber, R. L. & Mendoza, E. A Random Walk in Science: An Anthology. 1973. 16.50 (ISBN 0-9960025-4-5, Pub. by A Hilger England). Heyden.
Weisler, Jules. Physical Science: Intermediate Level. 1971. wkbk. 9.08 (ISBN 0-87720-009-2). AMSCO Sch.
--Review Text in Physical Science: Intermediate Level. 1970. pap. text ed. 7.92 (ISBN 0-87720-007-6). AMSCO Sch.

READY-RECKONERS

see also Addition; Mathematics–Tables, etc.; Multiplication
also subdivision Tables and Ready-Reckoners under various subjects, e.g. Lumber Trade–Tables and Ready-Reckoners

Locke, Flora M. Math Shortcuts. LC 72-5775. (Self-Teaching Guides Ser.). 166p. 1972. pap. 6.95 (ISBN 0-471-54328-4, Pub. by Wiley Pr). Wiley.
McKeown, G. P. & Rayward-Smith, V. J. Mathematics for Computing. 428p. 1982. pap. 29.95 (ISBN 0-470-27268-6). Halsted Pr.
Meyers, Lester. High-Speed Math. 2nd ed. LC 74-23585. 556p. 1975. Repr. of 1957 ed. 29.50 (ISBN 0-88275-240-5). Krieger.
Pocket Estimator. 1982. pap. 6.00 (ISBN 0-911592-40-7); pap. 5.00. Natl Assn Home.

REAGENTS, CHEMICAL

see Chemical Tests and Reagents

REAL ESTATE BUSINESS–DATA PROCESSING

Bechhoefer, Ina S., ed. Guide to Real Estate & Mortgage Banking Software, 2 vols. 1200p. 1985. Set. 115.00 (ISBN 0-917935-02-0). Real Est Sol.
Benedict, Howard M., et al. Calculator Techniques for Real Estate. LC 77-11252. 1977. 14.95 (ISBN 0-913652-10-5). Realtors Natl.
Church, Albert M. & Gustafson, Robert H. Statistics & Computers in the Appraisal Process. 160p. 1976. pap. 15.00 (ISBN 0-88329-006-5). Intl Assess.
Computer Strategies. The Real Estate Agency Computer Handbook. 150p. 1983. looseleaf 45.00x (ISBN 0-913505-18-8). Computer Strat.
Gonzales, Laurence. Computers for Realtors: User Friendly Guides. 144p. 1984. 6.95 (ISBN 0-345-31477-8). Ballantine.
--User Friendly Guides: Computers for Realtors. 144p. (Orig.). 1984. pap. 6.95 (ISBN 0-345-31477-8). Ballantine.
Halligan, Joseph. Real Estate: Softwhere. 2nd ed. Winther, Richard, ed. (Software Directories Ser.: Vol. 2). (Orig.). 1985. pap. 29.95 (ISBN 0-918451-71-X). Moore Data.
Huges, Patricia & Ochi, Kaz. The Power of VisiCalc Real Estate. 166p. 1982. pap. 14.95 (ISBN 0-13-687350-2). P-H.
Institute of Real Estate Management & National Association of Realtors. Real Estate Software Guidelines: Property Management. LC 83-83110. (Real Estate Software Guidelines Ser.). (Illus.). 145p. 1984. looseleaf 29.95 (ISBN 0-912104-75-9). Inst Real Estate.
Irwin, R. Computerizing Your Real Estate Office. 192p. 1985. 19.95 (ISBN 0-07-032116-7). McGraw.
Jaffe, Austin J. Analyzing Real Estate Decisions Using Lotus 1-2-3. 1985. pap. text ed. 17.95 (ISBN 0-8359-9192-X); software 99.95 (ISBN 0-8359-9193-8). Reston.
Longman Financial Services Publishing Staff. Financial Services Software Directory-the Buyer's Guide, Summer Supplement (1984) 220p. (Orig.). 1984. pap. 45.00 (ISBN 0-88462-515-X, 1972-03, Real Estate Ed). Longman USA.
--Investor's Guide to Software. 1985 ed. 260p. (Orig.). pap. 14.95 (ISBN 0-88462-512-5, 1972-02, Pub. by Longman Fin Serv Pub). Longman USA.
Reade, Christopher B. Real Estate Guide to Microcomputers. (Guides to Microcomputing Ser.). (Illus.). 300p. Date not set. pap. 27.95 (ISBN 0-88462-606-7, 1302-02, Pub. by Longman Fin. Serv. Pub.). Longman USA.

REAL NUMBERS

see Numbers, Real

REAL-TIME DATA PROCESSING

see also on-Line Data Processing

Blackman, Maurice. Design of Real Time Applications. Authur Andersen & Co., ed. LC 74-26960. 265p. 1975. 59.95 (ISBN 0-471-07770-4, Pub. by Wiley-Interscience). Wiley.
Bull, G. M., ed. Real-Time Programming, 1983: Proceedings of the IFAC-IFIP Workshop, 12th, Hertford, UK, March 1983. 100p. 1983. 26.00 (ISBN 0-08-030568-7). Pergamon.
Foster, C. C. Real Time Programming: Neglected Topics. 1981. 9.95 (ISBN 0-201-01937-X). Addison-Wesley.
Freedman, A. L. & Lees, R. A. Real-Time Computer Systems. LC 76-22844. (Computer Systems Engineering Ser.). 277p. 1977. 27.50x (ISBN 0-8448-1003-7). Crane-Russak Co.
Glass, Robert. Real-Time Software. (Illus.). 464p. 1984. text ed. 26.95 (ISBN 0-13-767103-2). P-H.
IFAC Conference, Guadalajara City, Mexico, Jan. 1983. Real Time Digital Control Applications: Proceedings. Alonso-Conchiero, A., ed. (IFAC Proceedings Ser.). 800p. 1984. 169.00 (ISBN 0-08-029980-6). Pergamon.
IFAC-IFIP Workshop, Leibnitz, Austria, 1980. Real Time Programming, 1980: Proceedings. Haase, V. H., ed. LC 80-49720. (IFAC Proceedings Ser.). 150p. 1980. 47.00 (ISBN 0-08-027305-X). Pergamon.
IFAC-IFIP Workshop, Mariehamn-Aland, Finland, 1978. Real Time Programming, 1978: Proceedings. Cronhjort, B., ed. (IFAC Proceedings). (Illus.). 138p. 1979. 35.00 (ISBN 0-08-024492-0). Pergamon.
Martin, J. Design of Real Time Computer Systems. 1967. ref. ed. 40.00 (ISBN 0-13-201400-9). P-H.
Martin, James. Design of Man-Computer Dialogues. (Illus.). 496p. 1973. ref. ed. 42.50 (ISBN 0-13-201251-0). P-H.
Martin, James T. Programming Real-Time Computer Systems. (Illus.). 1965. ed. 38.95ref. (ISBN 0-13-730507-9). P-H.
Mellichamp, Duncan A., ed. Real Time Computing: With Applications to Data Acquisition & Control. 469p. 1983. 44.50 (ISBN 0-442-21372-7). Van Nos Reinhold.
Meyer, H., ed. Real-Time Data Handling & Process Control. (First European Symposium, Berlin, Germany, 1979). 786p. 1980. 95.75 (ISBN 0-444-85468-1, North-Holland). Elsevier.
Onoe, Morio, et al, eds. Real-Time Medical Image Processing. LC 80-23779. 257p. 1980. 45.00x (ISBN 0-306-40551-2, Plenum Pr). Plenum Pub.
--Real-Time-Parallel Computing: Imaging Analysis. LC 80-28025. 424p. 1981. 59.50x (ISBN 0-306-40639-X, Plenum Pr). Plenum Pub.
Savitzky, Stephen R. Real-Time Microprocessor Systems. (Illus.). 416p. 1985. 47.50 (ISBN 0-442-28048-3). Van Nos Reinhold.
Strock, O. J. Telemetry Computer Systems: An Introduction. LC 82-49001. 380p. 1983. text ed. 44.95x (ISBN 0-87664-711-5). Instru Soc.
Ward, Paul T. & Mellor, Stephen J. Structured Development for Real-Time Systems: Design Techniques, Vol. 3. (Orig.). 1985. pap. text ed. 28.95 (ISBN 0-917072-53-7). Yourdon.
--Structured Development for Real Time Systems: Essential Modeling Techniques, Vol. 2. 144p. (Orig.). 1985. pap. text ed. 28.95 (ISBN 0-917072-52-9). Yourdon.
--Structured Development for Real-Time Systems, Vol. 1: Introduction & Tools. LC 85-50815. (Illus.). 160p. (Orig.). 1985. pap. 28.95 (ISBN 0-917072-51-0). Yourdon.

REARRANGEMENTS (CHEMISTRY)

Maitland, Geoffrey C., et al. Intermolecular Forces: Their Origin & Determination. (International Series of Monographs in Chemistry). (Illus.). 1981. 79.00x (ISBN 0-19-855611-X). Oxford U Pr.

Stevens, T. S. & Watts, W. E. Selected Molecular Rearrangements. LC 75-5927. 222p. (Orig.). 1972. 19.95 (ISBN 0-442-07983-4). Krieger.

REASONING

see also Induction (Logic); Logic

Barnett, Peter. Tools of Thought: The Practical Foundations of Formal Reasoning. 310p. 1981. 18.95x (ISBN 0-87073-655-8); pap. text ed. 9.95x (ISBN 0-87073-656-6). Schenkman Bks Inc.

Bear, George G. & Callahan, Carolyn M. On the Nose: Fostering Creativity, Problem Solving & Social Reasoning. (Orig.). 1984. pap. 12.95 (ISBN 0-936386-23-1). Creative Learning.

Bosanquet, Bernard. Implication & Linear Inference. LC 20-20435. 1968. Repr. of 1920 ed. 15.00 (ISBN 0-527-10012-9). Kraus Repr.

Bundy, Alan. The Computer Modeling of Mathematical Reasoning. 1984. 17.00 (ISBN 0-12-141252-0). Acad Pr.

Cederblom, Jerry & Paulsen, David. Critical Reasoning. 2nd ed. 272p. 1985. pap. text ed. write for info. (ISBN 0-534-05616-4). Wadsworth Pub.

Dummett, Michael & Minio, Robert. Elements of Intuitionism. (Oxford Logic Guides Ser.). 1977. text ed. 39.95x (ISBN 0-19-853158-3). Oxford U Pr.

Faust, David. The Limits of Scientific Reasoning. LC 84-5172. 220p. 1984. 25.00x (ISBN 0-8166-1356-7); pap. 12.95 (ISBN 0-8166-1359-1). U of Minn pr.

Finocchiaro, Maurice A. Galileo & the Art of Reasoning: Rhetorical Foundations of Logic & Scientific Method. (Philosophy of Science Studies: No. 61). 463p. 1980. lib. bdg. 42.00 (ISBN 90-277-1094-5, Pub. by Reidel Holland); pap. 21.00 (ISBN 90-277-1095-3). Kluwer Academic.

Gupta, M. M., et al, eds. Approximate Reasoning in Expert Systems. 840p. 1985. 92.75 (ISBN 0-444-87808-4, North-Holland). Elsevier.

Horstmann, Rolf-Peter, et al, eds. Transcendental Arguments & Science. (Synthese Library: No. 133). 1979. lib. bdg. 34.00 (ISBN 90-277-0963-7, Pub. by Reidel Holland); pap. 16.00 (ISBN 90-277-0964-5). Kluwer Academic.

Nickerson, Raymond S. Reflections on Reasoning. 200p. 1985. text ed. 19.95; pap. 9.95 (ISBN 0-89859-763-3). L Erlbaum Assocs.

Smith. Statistical Reasoning. 1985. 34.30 (ISBN 0-205-08295-5, 168295). Allyn.

Smullyan, Raymond. Five Thousand B.C. & Other Philosophical Fantasies. 192p. 1984. pap. 5.95 (ISBN 0-312-29517-0). St Martin.

Toulmin, Stephen. Uses of Argument. 1958-1964. pap. 11.95 (ISBN 0-521-09230-2). Cambridge U Pr.

RECLAMATION OF LAND

see also Drainage; Irrigation; Marshes; Sand Dunes; Shore Protection

Berkman, Richard L. & Viscusi, W. Kip. Damming the West: The Report on the Bureau of Reclamation. LC 72-77707. (Ralph Nader Study Group Reports). 286p. 1973. 12.95 (ISBN 0-670-25460-6, Grossman). Viking.

Brookings Institution, Washington, D. C. Institute for Government Research. The U. S. Reclamation Service: Its History, Activities & Organization. LC 72-3015. (Service Monographs of the U.S. Government: No. 2). Repr. of 1919 ed. 24.50 (ISBN 0-404-57102-6). AMS Pr.

Butterworth Staff, ed. Land Conservation & Development Commission Decisions (LCDC) Selected Decisions, 1974-1979, 3 vols. 1984. Set. write for info.; Individual vols. 40.00 (ISBN 0-317-12918-X). Butterworth Legal Pubs.

Chase, Stuart. Rich Land, Poor Land. LC 70-92612. (Illus.). Repr. of 1936 ed. 26.50 (ISBN 0-404-01478-X). AMS Pr.

DeVore, R. William & Graves, Donald H., eds. Nineteen Eighty-Four Symposium on Surface Mining, Hydrology, Sedimentology & Reclamation: Proceedings. LC 83-60966. (Illus.). 492p. (Orig.). 1984. pap. 45.00 (ISBN 0-89779-062-6, UKY BU136). OES Pubns.

De Vore, R. William & Graves, Donald H., eds. Proceedings, 1983 Symposium on Surface Mining, Hydrology, Sedimentology & Reclamation. LC 83-60966. (Illus.). 554p. (Orig.). 1983. pap. 45.00 (ISBN 0-89779-058-8, UKY BU 133). OES Pubns.

Hutnik, Russell & Davis, Grant, eds. Ecology & Reclamation of Devastated Land, 2 Vols. LC 76-122849. (Illus.). 1070p. 1973. Vol. 1, 552p. 98.25x (ISBN 0-677-15580-8); Vol. 2, 518p. 98.25x (ISBN 0-677-15590-5); Set. 175.75x (ISBN 0-677-15600-6). Gordon.

Jenkins, Hal. A Valley Renewed: The History of the Muskingum Watershed Conservancy District. LC 76-28950. 206p. 1976. 15.00x (ISBN 0-87338-194-7); pap. 5.75x (ISBN 0-87338-195-5). Kent St U Pr.

Kleinfeld, Judith, et al. Land Claims & Native Manpower: Staffing Regional & Village Corporations under Alaska Native Claims Settlement Act of 1971. LC 73-620103. (Institute of Social & Economic Research Ser.: No. 36). 60p. 1973. pap. 2.00x (ISBN 0-295-95307-1). U of Wash Pr.

Korthals-Altes, J. Sir Cornelius Vermuyden: The Lifework of a Great Anglo-Dutchman in Land-Reclamation & Drainage, with Some Notes by the Author on the Present Condition of Drainage in England & a Resume of the Drainage Legislation in Holland. Wilkins, Mira, ed. LC 76-29751. (European Business Ser.). (Illus.). 1977. Repr. of 1925 ed. lib. bdg. 23.50 (ISBN 0-405-09767-0). Ayer Co Pubs.

Lampen, Dorothy. Economic & Social Aspects of Federal Reclamation. LC 78-64135. (Johns Hopkins University. Studies in the Social Sciences. Forty-Eighth Ser. 1930: 1). Repr. of 1930 ed. 16.00 (ISBN 0-404-61247-4). AMS Pr.

--Economic & Social Aspects of Federal Reclamation. Bruchey, Stuart, ed. LC 78-56686. (Management of Public Lands in the U. S. Ser.). (Illus.). 1979. Repr. of 1930 ed. lib. bdg. 12.00x (ISBN 0-405-11338-2). Ayer Co Pubs.

Land-Water Classification. (Ecological Land Classification Ser.: No. 5). 1979. pap. 8.50 (ISBN 0-660-10039-8, SSC124, SSC). Unipub.

Law, Dennis L. Mind-Land Rehabilitation. 1984. 26.50 (ISBN 0-442-25987-5). Van Nos Reinhold.

Longobardi, Cesare. Land-Reclamation in Italy: Rural Revival in the Building of a Nation. LC 78-180410. (Illus.). Repr. of 1936 ed. 27.50 (ISBN 0-404-56134-9). AMS Pr.

Mosburg, Lewis G. Handbook on Basic Land Management. 1978. 36.00 (ISBN 0-89419-027-X). Inst Energy.

People for Open Space. Endangered Harvest: The Future of Bay Area Farmland. (Orig.). 1980. pap. 5.00 (ISBN 0-9605262-0-X). PFOS.

Schaller, Frank W. & Sutton, Paul, eds. Reclamation of Drastically Disturbed Lands. 1978. 21.50 (ISBN 0-89118-052-4). Am Soc Agron.

Sendlein, L. V. & Yazicigil, H., eds. Surface Mining Environmental Monitoring & Reclamation Handbook. 750p. 1983. 89.75 (ISBN 0-444-00791-1, Excerpta Medica). Elsevier.

Smardon, Richard C., ed. The Future of Wetlands: Assessing Visual-Cultural Values. LC 78-72316. (Illus.). 240p. 1983. text ed. 39.50x (ISBN 0-86598-020-9). Allanheld.

Smith, M. A. Contaminated Land: Reclamation & Treatment. (NATO-Challenges of Modern Society Ser.). 456p. 1985. 65.00x (ISBN 0-306-41928-9, Plenum Pr). Plenum Pub.

Sopper, William E. & Seaker, Eileen M. Land Reclamation & Biomass Production Using Municipal Wastewater & Sludge. LC 82-80452. (Illus.). 544p. 1982. 30.00x (ISBN 0-271-00314-6). Pa St U Pr.

Taylor, Paul S. Essays on Land, Water & the Law in California: An Original Anthology. Bruchey, Stuart, ed. LC 78-7083. (Development of Public Land Law in the U. S. Ser.). 1979. lib. bdg. 40.00x (ISBN 0-405-11394-3). Ayer Co Pubs.

Teele, Ray P. The Economics of Land Reclamation in the United States. Bruchey, Stuart, ed. LC 78-56683. (Management of Public Lands in the U. S. Ser.). (Illus.). 1979. Repr. of 1927 ed. lib. bdg. 25.50x (ISBN 0-405-11355-2). Ayer Co Pubs.

Thames, John, ed. Reclamation & Use of Disturbed Land in the Southwest. LC 76-17133. Repr. of 1977 ed. 71.50 (ISBN 0-8357-9623-X, 2055250). Bks Demand UMI.

Wiener, Daniel P., et al. Reclaiming the West: The Coal Industry & Surface-Mined Lands. LC 80-81777. 1980. pap. 20.00x (ISBN 0-918780-16-0). INFORM.

Williams, M. The Making of the South Australian Landscape: A Study in the Historical Geography of South Australia. 1974. 69.50 (ISBN 0-12-785955-1). Acad Pr.

Woodard, Robert. Basic Land Management. 752p. 1983. 50.00 (ISBN 0-89419-281-7). Inst Energy.

RECONNAISSANCE, PHOTOGRAPHIC

see Photographic Reconnaissance Systems

RECORDER (PHYSICAL INSTRUMENTS)

see Recording Instruments

RECORDING INSTRUMENTS

see also Information Display Systems

Business Communications Staff. Magnetic Recording Equipment-Tapes, 1977-85. 1983. 1250.00 (ISBN 0-89336-377-4, G-073). BCC.

Hoagland, Albert A. Digital Magnetic Recording. LC 82-23203. 164p. 1983. Repr. of 1963 ed. lib. bdg. 9.50 (ISBN 0-89874-591-8). Krieger.

Keene, Sherman. Practical Techniques for the Recording Engineer. 2nd ed. LC 81-148444. (Illus.). 1981. text ed. 29.75 (ISBN 0-942080-00-9); tchr's. manual 45.00 (ISBN 0-942080-03-3); students wkbk. 7.75 (ISBN 0-942080-04-1); (ISBN 0-942080-05-X). SKE Pub.

RECOVERY OF NATURAL RESOURCES

see Recycling (Waste, etc.)

RECREATION RESEARCH

Recreation Planning & Development, 2 Vols. 775p. 1979. pap. 56.50x (ISBN 0-87262-200-2). Am Soc Civil Eng.

RECTIFICATION OF SPIRITS

see Distillation

RECTIFIERS, ELECTRIC CURRENT

see Electric Current Rectifiers

RECURSIVE FUNCTIONS

see also Machine Theory

Berger, Robert. Undecidability of the Domino Problem. LC 52-42839. (Memoirs: No. 66). 72p. 1966. pap. 9.00 (ISBN 0-8218-1266-1, MEMO-66). Am Math.

Brainerd, Walter S. & Landweber, Lawrence H. Theory of Computation. LC 73-12950. 336p. 1974. 41.50x (ISBN 0-471-09585-0). Wiley.

Butts, Robert E. & Hintikka, Jaakko, eds. Logic, Foundations of Mathematics & Computability Theory. (Western Ontario Ser: No. 9). 1977. lib. bdg. 53.00 (ISBN 90-277-0708-1, Pub. by Reidel Holland). Kluwer Academic.

Cutland, N. J. Computability: An Introduction to Recursive Function Theory. LC 79-51823. 1980. 62.50 (ISBN 0-521-22384-9); pap. 19.95 (ISBN 0-521-29465-7). Cambridge U Pr.

Davis, M., ed. The Undecidable: Basic Papers on Undecidable Propositions, Unsolvable Problems & Computable Functions. LC 65-3996. 440p. 1965. 36.50 (ISBN 0-911216-01-4). Raven.

Davis, Martin. Computability & Unsolvability. (Mathematics Ser.). 288p. 1983. pap. 6.50 (ISBN 0-486-61471-9). Dover.

Eilenberg, Samuel & Elgot, Calvin. Recursiveness. 1970. 22.50 (ISBN 0-12-234050-7). Acad Pr.

Fenstad, J. E., et al, eds. Generalized Recursion Theory II: Proceedings of the 1977 Oslo Symposium. (Studies in Logic: Vol. 94). 354p. 1978. 68.00 (ISBN 0-444-85163-1, Biomedical Pr). Elsevier.

Fitting, M. Fundamentals of Generalized Recursion Theory. (Studies in Logic & the Foundations of Mathematics: Vol. 105). 308p. 1982. 64.00 (ISBN 0-444-86171-8, North-Holland). Elsevier.

Hermes, Hans. Enumerability, Decidability, Computability: An Introduction to the Theory of Recursive Functions. 2nd ed. Hermann, G. T. & Plassmann, O., trs. (Grundlehren der Mathematischen Wissenschaften: Vol. 127). (Illus.). 1969. 30.00 (ISBN 0-387-04501-5). Springer-Verlag.

Jones, Neil D. Computability Theory. (ACM Monograph Ser). 1973. 45.00 (ISBN 0-12-390050-6). Acad Pr.

Kleene, S. C. Formalized Recursive Functionals & Formalized Realizability. LC 52-42839. (Memoirs: No. 89). 106p. 1969. pap. 10.00 (ISBN 0-8218-1289-0, MEMO-89). Am Math.

Ljung, Lennart & Soderston, Tonsten. Theory & Practice of Recursive Identification. Willsky, Alan S., ed. (The MIT Press Signal Processing, Optimization, & Control Ser.). (Illus.). 544p. 1983. 55.00x (ISBN 0-262-12095-X). MIT Pr.

McNaughton, Robert. Elementary Computability, Formal Languages & Automata. (Illus.). 464p. 1982. text ed. 28.95 (ISBN 0-13-253500-9). P-H.

Moldestad, J. Computations in Higher Types. LC 77-1375. (Lecture Notes in Mathematics Ser: Vol. 574). 1977. pap. 18.00 (ISBN 0-387-08132-1). Springer-Verlag.

Montague. Abstracts & Recursion Theory. (Studies in Logic). Date not set. price not set (ISBN 0-444-86159-9, North-Holland). Elsevier.

Normann, D. Recursion on the Countable Functionals. (Lecture Notes in Mathematics: Vol. 811). 191p. 1980. pap. 15.00 (ISBN 0-387-10019-9). Springer-Verlag.

Rose, H. E. Subrecursion: Functions & Hierarchies. (Oxford Logic Guides). 1984. 35.00x (ISBN 0-19-853189-3). Oxford U Pr.

Sacks, Gerald. Degrees of Unsolvability. (Annals of Mathematics Studies: No. 55). (Orig.). 1963. pap. 22.00 (ISBN 0-691-07941-2). Princeton U Pr.

Salomaa, Arto. Encyclopedia of Mathematics & Its Applications, Vol. 25: Computation & Automata. (Illus.). 336p. 1984. 39.50 (ISBN 0-521-30245-5). Cambridge U Pr.

Wimp, J. Computation with Recurrence Relations. (Applicable Mathematics Ser.). 240p. 1984. text ed. 50.00 (ISBN 0-273-08508-5). Pitman Pub MA.

Yasuhara, Ann. Recursive Function Theory & Logic. (Computer Science & Applied Mathematics Ser.). 1971. 66.50 (ISBN 0-12-768950-8). Acad Pr.

RECURSIVE PROGRAMMING

Barron, D. W. Recursive Techniques in Programming. 2nd ed. (Computer Monograph Series: Vol. 3). 1974. text ed. 24.75 (ISBN 0-444-19524-6). Elsevier.

Burge, William H. Recursive Programming Techniques. LC 74-28812. (IBM Systems Programming Ser.). (Illus.). 280p. 1975. text ed. 28.95 (ISBN 0-201-14450-6). Addison-Wesley.

Gecseg, F., ed. Fundamentals of Computation Theory: Proceedings. (Lecture Notes in Computer Science: Vol. 117). 471p. 1981. pap. 26.50 (ISBN 0-387-10854-8). Springer-Verlag.

Miernyk, William H. Elements of Input-Output Analysis. (Orig.). 1965. pap. text ed. 7.00 (ISBN 0-394-30393-8, RanC). Random.

RECYCLING (WASTE, ETC.)

Here are entered works on the processing of waste paper, cans, bottles, etc. Works on the recycling or reuse of specific materials are entered under Wood Waste, Agricultural wastes, etc. Works on reclaiming and reusing equipment or parts are entered under Salvage (Waste, etc.).

see also Energy Conservation; Salvage (Waste, etc.); Waste Products

America's Renewable Resource Potential. (SAF Convention Proceedings Ser. -1975). (Illus.). 503p. (Orig.). 1976. pap. 7.00 (ISBN 0-939970-02-3). Soc Am Foresters.

Barton, Allan F. Resource Recovery & Recycling. LC 78-13601. (Environmental Science & Technology Ser.). 418p. 1979. 72.50x (ISBN 0-471-02773-1, Pub. by Wiley-Interscience). Wiley.

Bendersky, David, et al. Resource Recovery Processing Equipment. LC 82-7882. (Pollution Technology Rev. 93). (Illus.). 417p. 1983. 42.00 (ISBN 0-8155-0911-1). Noyes.

Berkowitz, Joan B., et al, eds. Unit Operations for Treatment of Hazardous Industrial Wastes. LC 78-62520. (Pollution Technology Review: No. 47). (Illus.). 920p. 1979. 42.00 (ISBN 0-8155-0717-8). Noyes.

Bewick, Michael W., ed. Handbook of Organic Waste Conversion. (Van Nostrand Reinhold Environmental Engineering Ser.). 432p. 1980. 29.95 (ISBN 0-442-20679-8). Van Nos Reinhold.

Bibliotheca Press Research Division. Recycling for Living, Fun & Profit. 52p. 1981. pap. text ed. 5.00 (ISBN 0-939476-29-0, Pub. by Biblio Pr GA). Prosperity & Profits.

Bibliotheca Press Research Project. Selected Topics on Creative Ways to Recycle. (A Recycling Ser.). 1983. text ed. 29.95 (ISBN 0-939476-88-6, Pub. by Biblio Pr GA); pap. text ed. 15.95 (ISBN 0-939476-89-4). Prosperity & Profits.

Brown, Michael D. Resource Recovery Project Studies. (Illus.). 169p. 1983. 39.95 (ISBN 0-250-40611-X). Butterworth.

Bruce, A. M. Sewage Sludge Stabilisation & Disinfection. (Water & Waste Water Technology Ser.: No. 1-714). 624p. 1984. text ed. 69.95x (ISBN 0-470-20080-4). Halsted Pr.

Bruce, A. M. & Connor, E. S., eds. Stabilisation, Disinfection & Odour Control in Sewage Sludge Treatment. 200p. 1984. text ed. 59.95x (ISBN 0-470-20033-2). Halsted Pr.

Burlace, C. J. & Whalley, L. Waste Plastics & Their Potential for Recycle, 1977. 1981. 40.00x (ISBN 0-686-97166-3, Pub. by W Spring England). State Mutual Bk.

Center for Self-Sufficiency Research Division. Center for Self Sufficiency Catalog of Recycled Business Books. 12p. 1984. pap. 1.00 (ISBN 0-910811-81-4, Pub. by Center Self Suff). Prosperity & Profits.

Center for Self-Sufficiency Research Division. Recycled Craft Books: Center for Self Sufficiency Catalog. 15p. 1985. pap. 1.00 (ISBN 0-910811-82-2, Pub. by Center Self Suff). Prosperity & Profits.

Center for Self-Sufficiency Research Division. Recycling: A Bibliography. 16p. 1984. pap. 1.00 (ISBN 0-910811-91-1, Pub. by Center Self Suff). Prosperity & Profits.

China: Recycling of Organic Wastes in Agriculture: Report of a FAO-UNDP Tour to the People's Republic of China, April 28 - May 24, 1981. (Soils Bulletins: No. 40). (Eng., Fr. & Span.). 122p. (3rd printing 1981). 1977. pap. 9.00 (ISBN 92-5-100524-9, F1405, FAO). Unipub.

Cliatt, Mary J. & Shaw, Jean M. Junk Treasures: A Sourcebook for Using Recycled Materials with Children. (Illus.). 256p. 1981. pap. text ed. 15.95 (ISBN 0-13-512608-8). P-H.

Committee on Mineral Resources & the Environment, National Research Council. Resource Recovery from Municipal Solid Wastes: Mineral Resources & the Environment Supplementary Report. 432p. 1975. pap. 10.75 (ISBN 0-309-02422-6). Natl Acad Pr.

Daniels, Keith W., compiled by. Recycling & Repairing, Nineteen Twelve to Nineteen Forty Eight. (Illus.). 290p. (Orig.). 1978. pap. 9.95 (ISBN 0-937468-00-2). Lost Data.

Data Notes Publishing Staff. Paper Recycling: Data Notes. LC 83-90731. 30p. 1983. pap. text ed. 9.95 (ISBN 0-911569-41-3, Pub. by Data Notes). Prosperity & Profits.

Easterling, Ronald E., intro. by. Reuse of Disposables. (Illus.). 104p. (Orig.). 1983. pap. text ed. 35.00 (ISBN 0-910275-27-0). Assn Adv Med Instrs.

Energy Conservation Through Waste Utilization: Proceedings of 1978 National Waste Processing Conference. 500p. 1978. 90.00 (ISBN 0-685-92280-4, I00119). ASME.

Environmental Resources Ltd. The Economics of Recycling. 167p. 1978. 19.00x (ISBN 0-86010-123-1, Pub. by Graham & Trotman England). State Mutual Bk.

Europool. Secondary Materials in Domestic Refuse As Energy Sources. 80p. 1977. 16.50x (ISBN 0-86010-064-2, Pub. by Graham & Trotman England). State Mutual Bk.

Europool Limited. The Disposal & Recycling of Scrap Metal from Cars & Large Household Apparatus. 164p. 1978. 90.00x (ISBN 0-86010-154-1, Pub. by Graham & Trotman England). State Mutual Bk.

Fahm, Lattee A. The Waste of Nations: The Economic Utilization of Human Waste in Agriculture. LC 79-88260. (LandMark Studies). (Illus.). 188p. 1980. text ed. 28.50x (ISBN 0-916672-28-X). Allanheld.

Gillies, M. T., ed. Potable Water from Wastewater. LC 81-1886. (Pollution Technology Review: No. 76). (Illus.). 305p. 1981. 42.00 (ISBN 0-8155-0845-X). Noyes.

Goldstein, Jerome. Recycling: How to Re-Use Wastes in Home, Industry & Society. LC 78-20983. (Illus.). 1979. 14.95x (ISBN 0-8052-3706-2). Schocken.

Grayson, Martin, ed. Recycling, Fuel & Resource Recovery: Economic & Environmental Factors. LC 84-7516. (Encyclopedia Reprint Ser.). 232p. 1984. text ed. 39.95x (ISBN 0-471-81175-0). Wiley.

Hayes, Denis. Repairs, Reuse, Recycling: First Steps Toward a Sustainable Society. LC 78-64455. (Worldwatch Papers). 1978. pap. 2.00 (ISBN 0-916468-22-4). Worldwatch Inst.

Henstock, M. & Bever, M. B., eds. New & Better Uses of Secondary Resources: Proceedings of the Second Recycling World Congress, Philippine International Conventional Center, Manila, March 1979. 278p. 1980. pap. 52.00 (ISBN 0-08-026245-7). Pergamon.

Henstock, M. E. Recycling & Disposal of Solid Waste. LC 75-4235. 223p. 1975. pap. 41.00 (ISBN 0-08-019685-3). Pergamon.

Henstock, M. E., ed. Reutilization of Waste Materials: Selected Papers from the Third Recycling World Congress, Basle, Switzerland, 29 September-1 October 1980. 80p. 1981. pap. 26.00 (ISBN 0-08-028743-3). Pergamon.

Henstock, M. E. & Biddulph, M. W., eds. Solid Waste As a Resource. LC 77-24726. 1978. text ed. 31.00 (ISBN 0-08-021571-8). Pergamon.

Holmes, John R. Refuse Recycling & Recovery: A Review of the State of the Art. LC 80-42145. (Institution of Environmental Science Ser.). 200p. 1981. 45.95 (ISBN 0-471-27902-1, Pub. by Wiley-Interscience); pap. 23.95x (ISBN 0-471-27903-X). Wiley.

Horacek, Robert G. Deinking by Washing. Corwin, Harold E., ed. (Recycling of Papermaking Fibers Ser.). (Illus.). 33p. 1983. pap. 19.95 (ISBN 0-89852-409-1). TAPPI.

Jabs, Carolyn. Re-Uses: Two-Thousand One Hundred & Thirty-Three Ways to Recycle & Re-Use the Things You Ordinarily Throw Away. 1982. 18.95 (ISBN 0-517-54663-9). Crown.

Jackson, F. R. Recycling & Reclaiming of Municipal Solid Wastes 1975. LC 74-25026. (Pollution Technology Review Ser: No. 17). 342p. 1975. 24.00 (ISBN 0-8155-0560-4). Noyes.

Kiang. Waste Energy Utilization Technology. (Energy, Power & Environment Ser.: Vol. 9). 264p. 1981. 39.75 (ISBN 0-8247-1173-4). Dekker.

Kiang, Yen-Hsiung & Metry, Amir. Hazardous Waste Processing Technology. LC 81-69070. (Illus.). 549p. 1982. text ed. 49.95 (ISBN 0-250-40411-7). Butterworth.

Kut, David & Hare, Gerard. Waste Recycling for Energy Conservation. LC 81-80645. 326p. 1981. 59.95x (ISBN 0-470-27178-7). Halsted Pr.

McCarthy, Gregory J. & Lauf, Robert J., eds. Fly Ash Coal & Conversion By-Products: Characterization, Utilization & Disposal I, Vol. 43. LC 85-7248. 1985. text ed. 30.00 (ISBN 0-931837-08-1). Materials Res.

Martin, A. E., ed. Small-Scale Resource Recovery Systems. LC 81-18944. (Pollution Technology Review: No. 89). (Illus.). 364p. 1982. 42.00 (ISBN 0-8155-0885-9). Noyes.

Mason, Billy. Directory of Recyclable Wastes. (Illus.). 1976. pap. text ed. 9.95 (ISBN 0-942140-01-X). Kelso.

Mason, Billy, ed. Directory of Recycable Wastes, Bk. 2. (Orig.). 1981. pap. 9.95 (ISBN 0-942140-00-1). Kelso.

Moo-Young, M., et al, eds. Waste Treatment & Utilization: Theory & Practice of Waste Management Two, Proceedings. (Illus.). 587p. 1981. 105.00 (ISBN 0-08-024012-7). Pergamon.

National Waste Processing Conference, 1976. From Waste to Resource Through Processsing, with Supplement: Proceedings. 585p. 1976. pap. text ed. 90.00 (ISBN 0-685-68904-2, 1X0096). ASME.

OECD. Beverage Containers: Re-Use or Re-Cycling. 159p. (Orig.). 1978. pap. 9.00x (ISBN 92-64-11792-X). OECD.

OECD Staff. Household Waste: Separate Collection & Recycling. 142p. (Orig.). 1983. pap. 14.50x (ISBN 92-64-12387-3). OECD.

Page, Talbot. Conservation & Economic Efficiency: An Approach to Materials Policy. LC 76-22846. (Resources for the Future Ser). 288p. 1977. 21.50x (ISBN 0-8018-1904-0); pap. 8.95x (ISBN 0-8018-1951-2). Johns Hopkins.

Plaut, Thomas & Steiker, Gene. Characteristics of Wastepaper Markets & Trends in Scrap Paper Recycling, Prices, Demand & Availability: A National & Regional Overview. (Discussion Paper Ser.: No. 103). 1978. pap. 3.25 (ISBN 0-686-32269-X). Regional Sci Res Inst.

Recovery of Metals from Shredding Operations & Wire & Cable Chopping. (Illus.). 7.50 (ISBN 0-317-06750-8). Natl Recycling.

Recycling Consort Division Staff. Aluminum Recycling: A Correspondence Course Workbook. 20p. 1984. pap. text ed. 11.95 (ISBN 0-318-01195-6, Pub. by Consortium). Prosperity & Profits.

Recycling Research Division Staff. Fly Ash: A Correspondence Course Workbook. 18p. 1984. pap. text ed. 11.95 (ISBN 0-318-01194-8, Pub. by Recycling Resort). Prosperity & Profits.

--Paper Recycling: A Correspondence Course. 16p. 1984. pap. text ed. 11.95 (ISBN 0-318-01188-3, Pub. by Recycling Consort). Prosperity & Profits.

--Silver Recycling: A Correspondence Course. 10p. 1984. pap. text ed. 11.95 (ISBN 0-318-01189-1, Pub. by Recycling Consort). Prosperity & Profits.

Repairs, Reuse, Recycling: First Steps Toward a Sustainable Society. (Worldwatch Institute Papers: No. 23). 45p. 1978. pap. 2.95 (ISBN 0-686-94930-7, WW23, WW). Unipub.

Resource Recovery & Utilization, STP592. 212p. 1975. 20.00 (ISBN 0-8031-0558-4, 04-592000-41). ASTM.

Scentouri. Rubber Recycling: A Correspondence Course Workbook. 15p. 1984. pap. text ed. 11.95 (ISBN 0-318-01196-4, Pub. by Scentouri). Prosperity & Profits.

Schuler, Michael. The Utilization & Recycle of Agricultural Wastes & Residues. 304p. 1980. 82.00 (ISBN 0-8493-5569-9). CRC Pr.

Sengupta, Subrata & Wong, Kau-Fui V., eds. Resource Recovery from Solid Wastes: Proceedings of a Conference in Miami Beach, Florida, May 10-12, 1982. LC 82-18145. 600p. 1982. 105.00 (ISBN 0-08-028825-1, A125). Pergamon.

Sittig, Marshall. Metal & Inorganic Waste Reclaiming Encyclopedia. LC 80-21669. (Pollution Tech. Rev. 70; Chem. Tech. Rev. 175). (Illus.). 591p. (Orig.). 1981. 54.00 (ISBN 0-8155-0823-9). Noyes.

--Organic & Polymer Waste Reclaiming Encyclopedia. LC 80-26007. (Chem. Tech. Rev. 180: Pollution Tech. Rev. 73). (Illus.). 512p. 1981. 54.00 (ISBN 0-8155-0832-8). Noyes.

Smith, Paul I. Recycling Waste. 1976. text ed. 22.50x (ISBN 0-87936-011-9). Scholium Intl.

Technical Association of the Pulp & Paper Industry. Recycling: Reuse of Waste Resources: Presented At the TAPPI Empire State Section, Annual Spring Conference, June 9-10, 1972. LC 74-153924. (Technical Association of the Pulp & Paper Industry CA Report Ser.: No. 45). pap. 27.30 (ISBN 0-317-29317-6, 2022355). Bks Demand UMI.

Tin Cans & Trash Recovery: Saving Energy Through Utilizing Municipal Ferrous Waste. 1980. pap. 2.00 (ISBN 0-686-29241-3). Tech Info Proj.

Update Publicare Research. Recycling Update: Packet of Back Issues. LC 83-80431. 35p. 1983. pap. text ed. 4.00 (ISBN 0-686-38894-1, Pub. by Update Pub Co). Prosperity & Profits.

Vesiland, P., et al. Unit Operations in Resource Recovery Engineering. (Illus.). 1980. text ed. 45.00 (ISBN 0-13-937953-3). P-H.

Vogler, Jon. Work from Waste: Recycling Wastes to Create Employment. (Illus.). 396p. (Orig.). 1981. pap. 14.75x (ISBN 0-903031-79-5, Pub. by Intermediate Tech England). Intermediate Tech.

Waste Paper Recovery: Economic Aspects & Environmental Impacts. 1979. 8.50x (ISBN 92-64-11910-8). OECD.

Weiers, Werner & Fischer, Roland. The Disposal & Utilization of Abatoir Waste in the European Communities. 148p. 1978. 33.00x (ISBN 0-86010-073-1, Pub. by Graham & Trotman England). State Mutual Bk.

RECYCLING OF WASTE PRODUCTS

see Salvage (Waste, etc.)

RED DEER

Clutton-Brock, T. H. & Guinness, F. E. Red Deer: Behavior & Ecology of Two Sexes. LC 81-22025. (Wildlife Behavior & Ecology (WBE)). (Illus.). 1982. lib. bdg. 40.00x (ISBN 0-226-11056-7); pap. 14.00x (ISBN 0-226-11057-5). U of Chicago Pr.

RED FOX

Lloyd, H. G. The Red Fox. (Illus.). 320p. 1980. 40.00 (ISBN 0-7134-1190-2, Pub. by Batsford England). David & Charles.

Stanley, William C. Habit of the Red Fox in Northeastern Kansas. (Miscellaneous Publications Ser.: No. 34). 31p. 1963. pap. 1.75 (ISBN 0-317-04947-X). U of KS Mus Nat Hist.

Zimen, E., ed. The Red Fox: Symposium on Behavior & Ecology. (Biogeographica Ser.: Vol. 18). 286p. 1980. lib. bdg. 73.50 (ISBN 9-0619-3219-X, Pub. by Junk Pubs Netherlands). Kluwer Academic.

REDOX REACTION

see Oxidation-Reduction Reaction

REDUCTION, CHEMICAL

see also Oxidation-Reduction Reaction

Augustine, R. L., ed. Reduction. (Techniques & Applications in Organic Synthesis Ser.: Vol. 2). 1968. 65.00 (ISBN 0-8247-1026-6). Dekker.

Doyle, M. P. & West, C. T., eds. Stereoselective Reductions. (Benchmark Papers in Organic Chemistry: Vol. 6). 1976. 71.00 (ISBN 0-12-786368-0). Acad Pr.

Gaylord, Norman G. Reduction with Complex Metal Hydrides. LC 55-8227. (Illus.). 1062p. 1956. text ed. 45.00 (ISBN 0-470-29436-1, Pub. by Wiley). Krieger.

Hudlicky, M. Reductions in Organic Chemistry. LC 84-3768. (Ellis Horwood Series in Chemical Science). 300p. 1984. 45.00x (ISBN 0-470-20018-9). Halsted Pr.

Primas, H. Chemistry, Quantum Mechanics & Reductionism. 2nd ed. 451p. 1983. 35.00 (ISBN 0-387-12838-7). Springer-Verlag.

Vincent, A. Oxidation & Reduction in Inorganic & Analytical Chemistry: A Programmed Introduction. 1985. write for info. (ISBN 0-471-90698-0). Wiley.

REDUCTION DIVISION (GENETICS)

see Meiosis

REDWOOD

Becking, Rudolf W. A Pocket Flora of the Redwood Forest. (Illus.). 262p. (Orig.). 1982. pap. 15.00 (ISBN 0-933280-02-5). Island CA.

Carranco, Lynwood. The Redwood Lumber Industry. (Illus.). 218p. 35.95 (ISBN 0-87095-084-3). Golden West.

Carranco, Lynwood & Labbe, John. Logging the Redwoods. LC 72-80989. (Illus.). 144p. 1975. boxed 17.95 (ISBN 0-87004-236-X). Caxton.

Johnston, Hank. They Felled the Redwoods: A Saga of Rails and Flumes in the High Sierra. 3rd rev. ed. LC 78-104874. (Illus.). 1966. 19.95 (ISBN 0-87046-003-X, Pub. by Trans-Anglo). Interurban.

Oandasan, William. A Branch of California Redwood. 62p. 1980. pap. 5.00 (ISBN 0-935626-03-4). U Cal AISC.

Schrepfer, Susan R. The Fight to Save the Redwoods: A History of Environmental Reform, 1917-1978. LC 81-69828. (Illus.). 296p. 1983. 25.00x (ISBN 0-299-08850-2). U of Wis Pr.

REEFS

see also Coral Reefs and Islands

D'Itri, Frank M. Artificial Reefs: U. S. & Japan. (Illus.). 489p. 1985. 49.95 (ISBN 0-87371-010-X). Lewis Pubs Inc.

James, N. P. & Ginsburg, R. N. The Seaward Margin of Belize Barrier & Atoll Reefs. (International Association of Sedimentologists & the Societas Internationalis Limnologiae Symposium Proceedings Ser.: No. 3). 191p. 1980. pap. 52.95x (ISBN 0-470-26928-6). Halsted Pr.

Pollock, J. B. Fringing & Fossil Reefs of Oahu. (BMB). Repr. of 1928 ed. 11.00 (ISBN 0-527-02161-X). Kraus Repr.

Rezak, R., et al. Reefs & Banks of the North Western Gulf of Mexico: Their Geological, Physical & Biological Dynamics. 320p. 1985. 49.95 (ISBN 0-471-89379-X). Wiley.

Third International Coral Reef Symposium: Proceedings, 1977, 2 Vols. 1300p. 1977. 60.00 set (ISBN 0-930050-03-7). Vol. 1 (ISBN 0-930050-01-0). Vol. 2 (ISBN 0-930050-02-9). Univ Miami A R C.

RE-ENTRY PROBLEMS (ASTRONAUTICS)

see Space Vehicles–Atmospheric Entry

REFERENCE GROUPS

Bressoud, David M. Analytic & Combinatorial Generalizations of the Rogers-Ramanujan Identities. LC 79-27622. (Memoirs Ser.: Vol. 227). 54p. 1980. pap. 9.00 (ISBN 0-8218-2227-6, MEMO-227). Am Math.

REFLECTANCE SPECTROSCOPY

Kortuem, G. Reflectance Spectroscopy: Principles, Methods, Applications. Lohr, J. E., tr. LC 79-86181. (Illus.). 1969. 54.00 (ISBN 0-387-04587-2). Springer-Verlag.

REFLECTION (OPTICS)

see also Light–Scattering

Elmer, William B. The Optical Design of Reflectors. 2nd ed. LC 79-14206. (Wiley Series in Pure & Applied Optics). 290p. 1980. 42.50x (ISBN 0-471-05310-4, Pub. by Wiley-Interscience). Wiley.

--The Optical Design of Reflectors: Condensed Extracts of Book for Engineer's Manuals & Technical Classrooms. (Illus.). 1977. pap. 4.70x (ISBN 0-9601028-2-5). Elmer.

Method of Reflectometry. (Measurement & Testing Guides Ser.). 1974. 4.50 (ISBN 0-686-96299-0, LM-44); members 2.25 (ISBN 0-686-99758-1). Illum Eng.

REFLECTION SPECTROSCOPY

see Reflectance Spectroscopy

REFLECTOMETER

see also Reflectance Spectroscopy

Method of Reflectometry. (Measurement & Testing Guides Ser.). 1974. 4.50 (ISBN 0-686-96299-0, LM-44); members 2.25 (ISBN 0-686-99758-1). Illum Eng.

REFLEX CAMERAS

see Single-Lens Reflex Cameras

REFLEXES

Bender, Miriam. Bender-Purdue Reflex Test & Training Manual. 1974. pap. 16.00x includes manual & recording forms (ISBN 0-87879-137-X). Acad Therapy.

Capute, Arnold J., et al. Primitive Reflex Profile. LC 77-27294. (Illus.). 114p. 1977. text ed. 21.00 (ISBN 0-8391-1181-9). Univ Park.

Carter, Mildred. Hand Reflexology: Key to Perfect Health. 1975. 12.95 (ISBN 0-13-383612-6, Reward); pap. 4.95 (ISBN 0-13-383604-5). P-H.

--Helping Yourself with Foot Reflexology. Orig. Title: Helping Yourself to Vibrant Health Through Secrets of Foot Reflexology. (Illus.). 1969. 10.95 (ISBN 0-13-386680-7, Reward); pap. 4.95 (ISBN 0-13-386532-0). P-H.

Desmedt, John E., ed. Motor Control Mechanisms in Health & Disease: Advances in Neurology, Vol. 39. (Illus.). 1224p. 1983. 163.00 (ISBN 0-89004-723-5). Raven.

Fiorentino, Mary R. Reflex Testing Methods for Evaluating CNS Development. 2nd ed. (Illus.). 72p. 1981. 15.75x (ISBN 0-398-02584-3). C C Thomas.

Kunz, Kevin & Kunz, Barbara. The Complete Guide to Foot Reflexology. Shoemaker, Ken, ed. 150p. 1982. 16.95 (ISBN 0-686-97525-1, Spectrum); pap. 8.95 (ISBN 0-13-160580-1, Spectrum). P-H.

--Hand & Foot ReflexologyReflexology: A Self-Help Guide. 1984. pap. 8.95 (ISBN 0-9606070-1-3). RRP.

Sechenov, Ivan M. Reflexes of the Brain. 1965. pap. 6.95x (ISBN 0-262-69006-3). MIT Pr.

REFORESTATION

see also Forests and Forestry; Tree Planting

Bollinger, William H., et al. Project Design & Recommendations for Watershed Reforestation & Fuelwood Development in Sri Lanka. (Illus.). 122p. 1979. pap. 15.00 (ISBN 0-936130-03-2). Intl Sci Tech.

REFRACTION

see also Light–Scattering

Abrams, J. D. Duke-Elder's Practice of Refraction. 9th ed. (Illus.). 1978. text ed. 35.00 (ISBN 0-443-01478-7). Churchill.

Middleton, Thomas H. Light Refractions. LC 75-38232. 184p. 1976. 7.95 (ISBN 0-930454-00-6). Verbatim Bks.

Tarasov, L. V. & Tarasov, A. N. Discussions on Refraction of Light. 239p. 1985. pap. 3.95 (ISBN 0-8285-2885-3, Pub. by Mir Pubs USSR). Imported Pubns.

REFRACTORIES

see Refractory Materials

REFRACTORY MATERIALS

see also Ceramic Fibers; Refractory Transition Metal Compounds; Vapor-Plating

Alper, A. M., ed. High Temperature Oxides. Incl. Part 1. Magnesia, Lime & Chrome Refractories. 1970 (ISBN 0-12-053301-4); Part 2. Oxides of Rare Earths, Titanium, Zirconium, Hafnium, Niobium & Tantalum. 1970 (ISBN 0-12-053302-2); Part 3. MgO Al2O3, BeO Ceramics. 1970 (ISBN 0-12-053303-0); Part 4. Refractory Glasses, Glass-Ceramics & Ceramics. 1971 (ISBN 0-12-053304-9). 72.00 ea. Acad Pr.

British Ceramic Research Association Symposium. Special Ceramics: Proceedings, 3 vols. Popper, P., ed. Incl. Vol. 1. 1961. 55.00 (ISBN 0-12-561650-3); Vol. 2. 1963; Vol. 3. 1966. Acad Pr.

Chesters, J. H. Refractories for Iron & Steelmaking. 502p. 1974. text ed. 30.00x (ISBN 0-900497-89-0, Metals Soc). Brookfield Pub Co.
--Refractories: Production & Properties. 562p. (Orig.). 1973. pap. text ed. 50.00x (ISBN 0-900497-84-X, Metals Soc). Brookfield Pub Co.
Duffy, J. I., ed. Refractory Materials: Developments Since 1977. LC 80-21945. (Chemical Technology Review: No. 178). (Illus.). 367p. 1981. 42.00 (ISBN 0-8155-0827-1). Noyes.
Frankhouser, William L., et al. Gasless Combustion Synthesis of Refractory Compounds. LC 84-22640. (Illus.). 152p. 1985. 24.00 (ISBN 0-8155-1015-2). Noyes.
Gilchrist, J. D. Fuel, Furnaces & Refractories. 2nd ed. 1977. text ed. 37.00 (ISBN 0-08-020430-9); pap. text ed. 12.75 (ISBN 0-08-020429-5). Pergamon.
Gwyther, D. N. Heat Transfer Fuels & Refractories Fluid Flow in Furnace Technology. 146p. 1985. pap. text ed. write for info. (ISBN 0-901462-25-X, Metals Soc). Brookfield Pub Co.
Hausner, H. H. & Bowman, M. G. Fundamentals of Refractory Compounds. 325p. 1968. 35.00x (ISBN 0-306-30319-1, Plenum Pr). Plenum Pub.
Matkovick, V. I., ed. Boron & Refractory Borides. LC 77-5056. 1977. 120.00 (ISBN 0-387-08181-X). Springer-Verlag.
Otte, H. M. & Locke, S. R., eds. Materials Science Research Series, Vol. 2. LC 63-17645. 319p. 1965. 39.50x (ISBN 0-306-38502-3, Plenum Pr). Plenum Pub.
Pincus, Alexis G. Refractories in the Glass Industry. LC 78-55364. (Provessing in the Glass Industry Ser.). 280p. 1980. 24.95 (ISBN 0-911993-09-6). Ashlee Pub Co.
Samsonov, G. V. & Kislyi, P. S. High-Temperature Non-Metallic Thermocouples & Sheaths. LC 65-26628. 133p. 1967. 29.50x (ISBN 0-306-10765-1, Consultants). Plenum Pub.
Samsonov, G. V., ed. Refractory Carbides. LC 73-83892. (Studies in Soviet Science-Physical Sciences Ser.). 461p. 1974. 55.00x (ISBN 0-306-10900-X, Consultants). Plenum Pub.
Storms, Edmund K. Refractory Carbides. 1967. 65.00 (ISBN 0-12-672850-X). Acad Pr.
Toropov, N. A. Heat-Resistant Coatings. LC 66-20322. 167p. 1967. 35.00x (ISBN 0-306-10781-3, Consultants). Plenum Pub.
Toropov, N. A., ed. Chemistry of High Temperature Materials. LC 74-79891. (Illus.). 237p. 1969. 35.00x (ISBN 0-306-10820-8, Consultants). Plenum Pub.

REFRACTORY MATERIALS–TABLES, CALCULATIONS, ETC.

Samsonov, Gregory & Vinitskii, I. M. Handbook of Refractory Compounds. LC 79-17968. 567p. 1980. 95.00x (ISBN 0-306-65181-5, IFI Plenum). Plenum Pub.

REFRACTORY METALS

see Heat Resistant Alloys

REFRACTORY TRANSITION METAL COMPOUNDS

Chesters, J. H. Refractories for Iron & Steelmaking. 502p. 1974. text ed. 30.00x (ISBN 0-900497-89-0, Metals Soc). Brookfield Pub Co.
Douglas, Bodie & Saito, Yoshihiko, eds. Stereochemistry of Optically Active Transition Metal Compounds. LC 80-10816. (ACS Symposium Ser.: No. 119). 1980. 44.95 (ISBN 0-8412-0538-8). Am Chemical.
Hausner, H. H. Coatings of High-Temperature Materials. LC 65-12156. 296p. 1966. 32.50x (ISBN 0-306-30210-1, Plenum Pr). Plenum Pub.
Samsonov, G. V., ed. Refractory Transition Metal Compounds: High Temperature Cermets. 1964. 56.00 (ISBN 0-12-617550-0). Acad Pr.
Vahldiek, F. W. & Mersol, S. A., eds. Anisotropy in Single-Crystal Refractory Compounds, 2 Vols. LC 68-20273. 898p. 1968. Vol. 1, 405p. 45.00x (ISBN 0-306-37038-7, Plenum Pr); Vol. 2, 493p. 45.00x (ISBN 0-306-37039-5). Plenum Pub.

REFRIGERANTS–TABLES, CALCULATIONS, ETC.

Bogart, Marcel J. Ammonia Absorption Refrigeration in Industrial Processes. LC 81-197. 474p. 1981. 75.00x (ISBN 0-87201-027-9). Gulf Pub.

REFRIGERATION AND REFRIGERATING MACHINERY

see also Air Conditioning; Cold Storage; Compressors; Cooling-Towers; Freeze-Drying; Heat Exchangers; Refrigerants–Tables, Calculations, etc.; Thermoelectric Cooling

Abd-El-Wahed. Refrigeration & Conditioning Dictionary. (Eng., Fr., Ger. & Arabic.). 395p. 1979. 45.00 (ISBN 0-686-97399-2, M-9756). French & Eur.
Air Conditioning & Refrigeration Institute. Refrigeration & Air Conditioning. (Illus.). 1979. 32.95 (ISBN 0-13-770164-0). P-H.
Althouse, Andrew & Turnquist, C. H. Modern Refrigeration & Air Conditioning. LC 81-20002. (Illus.). 1012p. 1982. text ed. 26.00x (ISBN 0-87006-340-5); lab manual 5.28x (ISBN 0-87006-422-3). Goodheart.
Anderson, Edwin P. Refrigeration: Home & Commercial. 2nd ed. LC 83-22379. 1984. 16.95 (ISBN 0-672-23396-7). Audel.
Anderson, Edwin P. & Miller, Rex. Refrigeration: Home & Commercial. LC 83-22379. 736p. 1984. 16.95 (ISBN 0-672-23396-7). G K Hall.
Application of Infrared Sensing Devices to the Assessment of Building Heat Loss Characteristics, ANSI-ASHRAE Standard 101-1981. (ASHRAE Standards Ser.). 1983. pap. text ed. 14.00 (ISBN 0-910110-27-1). Am Heat Ref & Air Eng.
Applied Technical Dictionary: Air Conditioning & Refrigeration. (Eng., Ger., Fr., Rus. & Slovak.). 69.00x (ISBN 0-569-08534-9, Pub. by Collets). State Mutual Bk.
ASTM Standards on Engine Coolants (D-15) 5th ed. 152p. 1980. pap. 12.75x (ISBN 0-8031-0282-8, 03-415080-12). ASTM.
B C C Cryogenic Equipment Guide. 28p. 1981. Repr. of 1979 ed. 60.00x (ISBN 0-686-75386-0, Pub. by Inst Chem Eng England). State Mutual Bk.
Betts, D. S. Refrigeration & Thermometry Below One Kelvin. LC 75-34695. (Illus.). 304p. 1976. 29.50x (ISBN 0-8448-0853-9). Crane-Russak Co.
--Refrigeration & Thermometry Below One Kelvin. 40.00x (ISBN 0-686-97021-7, Pub. by Scottish Academic Pr Scotland). State Mutual Bk.
Bogart, Marcel J. Ammonia Absorption Refrigeration in Industrial Processes. LC 81-197. 474p. 1981. 75.00x (ISBN 0-87201-027-9). Gulf Pub.
Booth, K. M., ed. Dictionary of Refrigeration & Air Conditioning. 315p. 1971. 27.75 (ISBN 0-444-20069-X, Pub. by Elsevier Applied Sci England). Elsevier.
Brady, C., et al, eds. Industrial-Commercial Refrigeration Maintenance. (Illus.). 226p. 1982. spiral bdg. 45.00x (ISBN 0-85083-528-3). Intl Ideas.
Clark, A. F., ed. Advances in Cryogenic Engineering, Vol. 30. 1020p. 1984. 95.00x (ISBN 0-306-41704-9, Plenum Pr). Plenum Pub.
Cryogenics Safety Manual: A Guide to Good Practice. 136p. 1981. 54.00x (ISBN 0-686-75393-3, Pub. by Inst Chem Eng England). State Mutual Bk.
Department of Energy. Solar Heating & Cooling: Commercial Buildings Demonstration Project Summaries. 1978. pap. 14.95x (ISBN 0-930978-35-8, H-021). Solar Energy Info.
--Solar Heating & Cooling: Research & Development Project Summaries. pap. 14.95x (ISBN 0-930978-36-6, H-009). Solar Energy Info.
Design & Operation of Cold Stores in Developing Countries. (Agricultural Services Bulletin Ser.: No. 19/2). 80p. 1985. pap. 7.50 (ISBN 92-5-101373-X, F2691 5071, FAO). Unipub.
Doolin, James H. La Biblia Doolin Para el Tecnico Reparador. 500p. 1973. 35.00 (ISBN 0-914626-01-9). Doolco Inc.
--Commercial Refrigeration. 72p. 1982. pap. 15.00 (ISBN 0-914626-08-6). Doolco Inc.
--Doolin's Trouble Shooters Bible. 500p. 1963. 35.00 (ISBN 0-914626-00-0). Doolco Inc.
--Frost Free & Conventional Refrigerators. 70p. 1982. pap. 15.00 (ISBN 0-914626-09-4). Doolco Inc.
--Residential Cooling, 2 pts. 1982. pap. 15.00 ea. Pt. 1: 50p (ISBN 0-914626-04-3). Pt. 2: 91p (ISBN 0-914626-05-1). Doolco Inc.
Doring, G. & Rudolphi. Tiefkuhl Lexikon. (Ger.). 239p. 10.95 (ISBN 3-87150-020-8, M-7666, Pub. by Deutscher Fachverlag). French & Eur.
Dossat, Roy J. Principles of Refrigeration. 2nd ed. LC 78-2938. 603p. 1978. text ed. 35.95x (ISBN 0-471-03550-5); solutions manual 8.00 (ISBN 0-471-03771-0). Wiley.
Eastop, Thomas D. & Gasiorek, Janus M. Air Conditioning Through Worked Examples, with Chapters 7 & 8 on Duct Sizing & Fans. LC 73-441904. pap. 91.00 (ISBN 0-317-10833-6). Bks Demand UMI.
Elonka, Stephen M. & Minich, Quaid W. Standard Refrigeration & Air Conditioning Questions & Answers. 3rd ed. (Illus.). 416p. 1983. 36.95 (ISBN 0-07-019317-7). McGraw.
Engine Coolant Testing: State of the Art, STP 705. 374p. 1980. 32.50x (ISBN 0-8031-0331-X, 04-705000-12). ASTM.
Fast, R. W., ed. Advances in Cryogenic Engineering, Vol. 29. 1072p. 1984. 95.00x (ISBN 0-306-41703-0, Plenum Pr). Plenum Pub.
Frederking, T. H., et al, eds. Cryogenic Processes & Equipment, Nineteen Eighty-Two. LC 83-11414. (AIChE Symposium: Vol. 79). 143p. 1983. pap. 40.00 (ISBN 0-8169-0249-6); pap. 20.00 members (ISBN 0-317-03720-X). Am Inst Chem Eng.
Furgerson, W. F. Conserving Energy in Refrigeration. Gyftopoulos, Elias P. & Cohen, Karen C., eds. (Industrial Energy-Conservation Manuals: No. 12). 144p. 1982. loose-leaf 20.00x (ISBN 0-262-06080-9). MIT Pr.
Geist, Carl. New Ways to Solve Your Refrigeration & Air Conditioning Service Problems. LC 72-87832. (Illus.). 256p. 1972. 15.95 (ISBN 0-912524-07-3). Busn News.
Goliber, Paul F. Refrigeration Servicing. LC 75-6064. 91p. 1976. pap. 8.40 (ISBN 0-8273-1005-6). Delmar.
Gosling, C. T. Applied Air Conditioning & Refrigeration. 2nd ed. (Illus.). 410p. 1980. 44.50 (ISBN 0-85334-877-4, Pub. by Elsevier Applied Sci England). Elsevier.
Gosney, W. B. Principles of Refrigeration. LC 80-42210. (Illus.). 700p. 1982. 105.00 (ISBN 0-521-23671-1). Cambridge U Pr.
Hallowell, Elliott R. Cold & Freezer Storage Manual. 2nd ed. (Illus.). 1980. text ed. 39.50 (ISBN 0-87055-366-6). AVI.
Heating, Air Conditioning & Refrigeration. 1984. 650.00 (ISBN 0-318-03908-7). Busn Trend.
International Institute of Refrigeration. Low Temperatures & Electric Power. Van Iherbeek, A., ed. 1971. 79.00 (ISBN 0-08-016370-X). Pergamon.
International Symposium on Cooling Systems. Proceedings. 1975. pap. 32.00x (ISBN 0-900983-41-8, Dist. by Air Science Co.). BHRA Fluid.
Jennings, Burgess H. Environmental Engineering: Analysis & Practice. 765p. 1970. text ed. 34.75 scp (ISBN 0-7002-2259-6, HarpC); solution manual avail. Har-Row.
Kissell, Thomas. Motors, Controls & Circuits for Air Conditioning & Refrigeration Systems. 1984. text ed. 26.95 (ISBN 0-8359-4666-5). Reston.
Lamere, Bernard. Guide to Home Air Conditioners & Refrigeration Equipment. (Illus., Orig.). 1963. pap. 6.50 (ISBN 0-8104-0294-7). Hayden.
Langley, Bill. Basic Refrigeration. 416p. 1982. text ed. 25.95 (ISBN 0-8359-0417-2); solutions manual avail. (ISBN 0-8359-0418-0). Reston.
Langley, Billy. Air Conditioning & Refrigeration Trouble-Shooting Handbook. (Illus.). 650p. 1980. text ed. 35.95 (ISBN 0-8359-0204-8). Reston.
Langley, Billy C. Control Systems for Air Conditioning & Refrigeration. (Illus.). 192p. 1985. text ed. 24.95 (ISBN 0-13-171679-4). P-H.
--Electric Controls for Refrigeration & Air Conditioning. 1974. 29.95 (ISBN 0-13-247072-1); pap. 23.95 ref. ed. (ISBN 0-13-247064-0). P-H.
--Electricity for Refrigeration & Air Conditioning. text ed. 24.95 (ISBN 0-8359-1601-4); pap. text ed. 19.95 (ISBN 0-8359-1600-6); solutions manual avail. (ISBN 0-8359-1791-6). Reston.
--Refrigeration & Air Conditioning. 2nd ed. 1982. text ed. 29.95 (ISBN 0-8359-6617-8); lab manual avail. (ISBN 0-8359-6619-4); instrs' avail. (ISBN 0-8359-6618-6). Reston.
Londahl, Goran. Refrigerated Storage in Fisheries. (Fisheries Technical Papers: No. 214). 82p. 1981. pap. 7.50 (ISBN 92-5-101116-8, F2230, FAO). Unipub.
Long, Wayne. Refrigeration & Air Conditioning: Operation & Analysis Servicing. 832p. 1985. text ed. 31.95 scp (ISBN 0-672-97994-2); scp instr's guide 7.33 (ISBN 0-672-97995-0). Bobbs.
Mahoney, Edward. Electricity for Air Conditioning & Refrigeration. (Illus.). 1980. text ed. 24.95 (ISBN 0-8359-1620-0); pap. text ed. 19.95 (ISBN 0-8359-1619-7); free instrs' manual (ISBN 0-8359-1621-9). Reston.
--Readings & Interpreting Diagrams in Air Conditioning & Refrigeration. 1983. text ed. 24.95 (ISBN 0-8359-6483-3); pap. text ed. 18.95 (ISBN 0-8359-6482-5); instr's. manual avail. (ISBN 0-8359-6484-1). Reston.
Meacock, M. H. Refrigeration Processes: A Practical Handbook on the Physical Properties of Refrigerants & Their Applications. (International Series in Heating, Ventilation & Refrigeration: Vol. 12). 1979. 48.00 (ISBN 0-08-024211-1); pap. 18.75 (ISBN 0-08-024234-0). Pergamon.
Merritt, John. Refrigeration on Fishing Vessels. 2nd ed. (Illus.). 164p. 1979. pap. 20.50 (ISBN 0-85238-095-X, FN24, Pub. by FNB). Unipub.
Merritt, John H. Refrigeration on Fishing Vessels. 1978. 40.00 (ISBN 0-685-63449-3). State Mutual Bk.
Method of Testing Dessicants for Refrigerant Drying, ASHRAE Standard 35-1983. (ASHRAE Standards Ser.). 6p. 1983. pap. text ed. 12.00 (ISBN 0-318-00446-1). Am Heat Ref & Air Eng.
Method of Testing Dynamic Characteristics of Propeller Fans-Aerodynamically Excited Fan Vibrations & Critical Speeds, ASHRAE Standard 87.1-1983. (ASHRAE Standards Ser.). 30p. 1983. pap. text ed. 14.00 (ISBN 0-910110-30-1). Am Heat Ref & Air Eng.
Method of Testing Open Refrigerator for Food Stores, ASHRAE Standard ANSI-ASHRAE 72-1983. (ASHRAE Standards Ser.). 13p. 1983. pap. text ed. 14.00 (ISBN 0-910110-29-8). Am Heat Ref & Air Eng.
Miller, Rex. Refrigeration & Air-Conditioning Technology. 1983. text ed. 20.92 (ISBN 0-02-665540-3); student ed. 5.32 (ISBN 0-02-665560-8); tchr's. ed. 5.32 (ISBN 0-02-665550-0). Bennett IL.
Morris, W. D. Heat Transfer & Fluid Flow in Rotating Coolant Channels, Vol. 2. (Mechanical Engineering Ser.). 248p. 1982. 48.95 (ISBN 0-471-10121-4, Pub. by Res Stud Pr). Wiley.
Munton, R. & Stott, J. R. Refrigeration at Sea. 2nd ed. (Illus.). 238p. 1978. 52.00 (ISBN 0-85334-766-2, Pub. by Elsevier Applied Sci England). Elsevier.
Nouveau Dictionnaire International du Froid. (Fr., Eng., Ger., Rus., Span. & It.). 300p. (New International Dictionary of Refrigeration). 1970. 135.00 (ISBN 0-686-56738-2, M-6432). French & Eur.
Olivo & Marsh. Principles of Refrigeration. LC 76-14089. 1979. o. p. 21.60 (ISBN 0-8273-1014-5); pap. text ed. 18.60 (ISBN 0-8273-1003-X). Delmar.
Palmquist, Roland. Refrigeration & Air Conditioning Library, 2 vols. (Illus.). 1977. Set. 21.95 (ISBN 0-672-23305-3); vol. I, air conditioning 10.95, home & commercial (ISBN 0-672-23288-X); vol. II refrigeration:home & commercial, 656pgs. 12.95 (ISBN 0-672-23286-3). Audel.
--Refrigeration & Air Conditioning Library, 2 vols. (Illus.). 1984. Set. 20.50 (ISBN 0-672-23411-4); Vol. 1, Air Conditioning: Home & Commercial. 14.95 (ISBN 0-672-23397-5); Vol. 2, Refrigeration: Home & Commercial. 16.95 (ISBN 0-672-23397-5). Audel.
Pita, Edward G. Refrigeration Principles & Systems: An Energy Approach. LC 83-21780. 148p. 1984. text ed. 29.95 (ISBN 0-471-87611-9); write for info tchrs ed (ISBN 0-471-89758-2); pap. 12.95 study guide (ISBN 0-471-80546-7). Wiley.
Reed, G. H. Refrigeration. LC 74-15129. (Illus.). 1969. 12.95 (ISBN 0-8306-0295-X). TAB Bks.
--Refrigeration: A Practical Manual for Apprentices. 3rd ed. (Illus.). 153p. 1974. 15.00 (ISBN 0-85334-605-4, Pub. by Elsevier Applied Sci England). Elsevier.
Reed, G. H., ed. Refrigeration: A Practical Manual for Mechanics. 2nd Ed. ed. (Illus.). 232p. 1981. 27.75 (ISBN 0-85334-964-9, Pub. by Elsevier Applied Sci England). Elsevier.
Refrigeration & Air Conditioning. (Equipment Planning Guides: No. 14). 1978. pap. 25.50 (ISBN 92-2-101895-4, ILO96, ILO). Unipub.
Rosenberg, M. B. English-Russian Dictionary of Refrigerating & Cryogenic Engineering. (Eng. & Rus.). 467p. 1978. Leatherette 15.95 (ISBN 0-686-92382-0, M-9063). French & Eur.
Rozenberg, M. B. English-Russian Dictionary of Refrigeration & Low Temperature Technology. 2nd, rev. ed. 80.00 (ISBN 0-08-024737-7). Pergamon.
Rudman, Jack. Air Conditioning & Refrigeration. (Occupational Competency Examination Ser.: OCE-1). (Cloth bdg. avail. on request). pap. 13.95 (ISBN 0-8373-5701-2). Natl Learning.
--Refrigerating Machine Mechanic. (Career Examination Ser.: C-1451). (Cloth bdg. avail. on request). pap. 10.00 (ISBN 0-8373-1451-8). Natl Learning.
--Refrigerating Machine Operator. (Career Examination Ser.: C-670). (Cloth bdg. avail. on request). pap. 10.00 (ISBN 0-8373-0670-1). Natl Learning.
Sabin, A. Ross, ed. Refrigeration, Pt. I. (Illus.). 144p. 1974. 20.00 (ISBN 0-938336-01-0). Whirlpool.
--Refrigeration, Pt. II. (Illus.). 208p. 1974. 20.00 (ISBN 0-938336-02-9). Whirlpool.
Schneider, Raymond K. Systematic Commercial Refrigeration Service. LC 78-14464. (Illus.). 192p. 1979. 15.95x (ISBN 0-912524-18-9). Busn News.
Sealed Glass Tube Method to Test the Chemical Stability of Material for Use Within Refrigerant Systems, ASHRAE Standard ANSI-ASHRAE 97-1983. (ASHRAE Standards Ser.). 1983. pap. text ed. 14.00 (ISBN 0-910110-31-X). Am Heat Ref & Air Eng.
Sergeev, G. B. & Batyuk, V. A. Cryochemistry. 298p. 1981. 12.00 (ISBN 0-8285-2159-X, Pub. by Mir Pubs USSR). Imported Pubns.
Severns, William H. & Fellows, Julian R. Air Conditioning & Refrigeration. LC 58-7908. (Illus.). pap. 144.30 (ISBN 0-317-10907-3, 2019289). Bks Demand UMI.

Simplified Energy Analysis Using the Modified Bin Method. (Illus.). 472p. 1984. pap. text ed. 40.00 nonmember price (ISBN 0-910110-39-5); pap. text ed. 20.00 member price (ISBN 0-318-01915-9). Am Heat Ref & Air Eng.

Stoecker, W. F. Using SI Units (Standard International Metric) in Heating, Air Conditioning, & Refrigeration. LC 74-26697. (Illus.). 1975. 7.50 (ISBN 0-912524-12-X). Busn News.

Stoecker, W. F. & Jones, J. W. Refrigeration & Air Conditioning. 2nd ed. 464p. 1982. 44.00x (ISBN 0-07-061619-1). McGraw.

Technical Dictionary: Refrigeration & Air Conditioning. (Eng., Fr., Ger. & Arabic.). 1979. 35.00x (ISBN 0-686-44746-8, Pub. by Collets). State Mutual Bk.

Timmerhaus, K. D. & Snyder, H. A., eds. Advances in Cryogenic Engineering, Vol. 25. LC 57-35598. (Illus.). 868p. 1980. 85.00x (ISBN 0-306-40504-0, Plenum Pr). Plenum Pub.

Tressler, Donald K., et al. Freezing Preservation of Foods, 4 vols. 4th ed. Incl. Vol. 1. Principles of Refrigeration; Equipment for Freezing & Transporting Food. 50.00 (ISBN 0-87055-044-6); Vol. 2. Factors Affecting Quality in Frozen Foods. 55.00 (ISBN 0-87055-045-4); Vol. 3. Commercial Freezing Operations; Fresh Foods; Vol. 4. Freezing of Precooked & Prepared Foods. (Illus.). 1968. AVI.

Trott, A. R. Refrigeration & Air Conditioning. 304p. 1981. 39.50 (ISBN 0-07-084543-3). McGraw.

Turner, F. H. Concrete & Cryogenics. (Viewpoint Publication Ser.). (Illus.). 125p. 1979. pap. text ed. 35.00x (ISBN 0-7210-1124-1, Pub by C&CA London). Scholium Intl.

Walker, Graham. Cryocoolers, Part 1: Fundamentals. (The International Cryogenics Monograph). 355p. 1983. 55.50x (ISBN 0-306-40715-9, Plenum Press). Plenum Pub.

Zurick, Timothy. Air Conditioning, Heating & Refrigeration Dictionary. LC 77-10318. 1977. sewn lexotone 5.95 (ISBN 0-912524-16-2). Busn News.

REFRIGERATION AND REFRIGERATING MACHINERY–HISTORY

Jones, Joseph C., Jr. American Ice Boxes. LC 81-85407. (Illus.). 106p. (Orig.). 1981. pap. 7.95 (ISBN 0-9607572-0-1). Jobeco Bks.

Sherlock, V. M. The Fever Man: A Biography of Dr. John Gorrie. LC 82-81065. 152p. 17.00 (ISBN 0-9610620-0-2). Medallion Pr.

REFRIGERATION AND REFRIGERATING MACHINERY–VOCATIONAL GUIDANCE

Budzik, Richard. Opportunities in Refrigeration & Air Conditioning. (VGM Career Bks.). (Illus.). 160p. 1983. 7.95 (ISBN 0-8442-6624-8, 6624-8, Passport Bks.); pap. 5.95 (ISBN 0-8442-6626-4, 6626-4). Natl Textbk.

Cooper, William B. Licensed Operator's Key to Refrigeration. LC 74-14660. (Illus.). 1975. 14.95 (ISBN 0-912524-11-1). Busn News.

Harfenist, Sylvan. Refrigeration License Manual. 2nd ed. LC 74-24888. (Illus.). 1975. pap. 12.00 (ISBN 0-668-02726-6). Arco.

REFUGES, WILDLIFE

see Wildlife Refuges

REFUSE AND REFUSE DISPOSAL

see also Factory and Trade Waste; Incinerators; Pollution; Radioactive Waste Disposal; Refuse As Fuel; Sewage Disposal; Street Cleaning; Water–Pollution

Ackerman, D. G., et al. Destruction & Disposal of PCB'S by Thermal & Non-Thermal Methods. LC 82-22312. (Pollution Technology Review Ser.: No. 97). (Illus.). 417p. 1983. 48.00 (ISBN 0-8155-0934-0). Noyes.

Brown, F. Lee & Lebeck, A. O. Cars, Cans, & Dumps: Solutions for Rural Residuals. (Resources for the Future Ser). 222p. 1976. 17.50x (ISBN 0-8018-1797-8). Johns Hopkins.

Brune, John. Resonant Rubbish. 3.50 (ISBN 0-913714-66-6). Legacy Bks.

Cointreau, Sandra J. Environmental Management of Urban Solid Wastes in Developing Countries: A Project Guide. (Urban Development Technical Paper: No. 5). 214p. 1982. pap. 5.00 (ISBN 0-8213-0063-6). World Bank.

Cole, Leslie. Waste Management in the States. LC 82-147343. pap. 20.00 (ISBN 0-317-10672-4, 2020427). Bks Demand UMI.

Composting of Municipal Residues & Sludges. (Illus.). 1977. 10.00x (ISBN 0-686-26015-5, CO7); softcover 5.00x (ISBN 0-686-26016-3). Info Transfer.

Curi, K. Treatment & Disposal of Liquid & Solid Industrial Wastes: Proceedings of the Third Turkish-German Environmental Engineering Symposium, Istanbul, July 1979. LC 80-40993. (Illus.). 515p. 1980. 96.00 (ISBN 0-08-023999-4). Pergamon.

Dickinson, D., ed. Practical Waste Treatment & Disposal. (Illus.). 214p. 1974. 39.00 (ISBN 0-85334-580-5, Pub. by Elsevier Applied Sci England). Elsevier.

Disposal of Oil & Debris Resulting from a Spill Cleanup Operation, STP 703. 158p. 1980. soft cover 15.75x (ISBN 0-8031-0324-7, 04-703000-16). ASTM.

Disposal of Residues on Land. (Illus.). 1977. 5.00x (ISBN 0-686-26026-0, RL7); softcover 5.00x (ISBN 0-686-26027-9). Info Transfer.

Duedall, I. W., et al. Wastes in the Ocean: Industrial & Sewage Wastes in the Ocean, Vol. 1. (Environmental Science & Technology Ser.). 431p. 1983. 69.95 (ISBN 0-471-09772-1); Set. 180.00 (ISBN 0-471-82054-7). Wiley.

Ellis, H. M., et al. Problems in Community Wastes Management. (Public Health Papers Ser: No. 38). 89p. 1969. pap. 2.80 (ISBN 92-4-130038-8, 1352). World Health.

Environmental Impact Analysis Research Council at the Chicago National Convention, Oct. 1978. Appropriate Technology in Water Supply & Waste Disposal. American Society of Civil Engineers, ed. 280p. 1979. pap. 17.00x (ISBN 0-87262-148-0). Am Soc Civil Eng.

Everett, L. G., et al. Vadose Zone Monitoring for Hazardous Waste Sites. LC 84-16509. (Pollution Technology Review Ser.: No. 112). (Illus.). 358p. 1985. 36.00 (ISBN 0-8155-1000-4). Noyes.

Fair, Gordon M. & Okun, Daniel A. Water & Wastewater Engineering, 2 vols. LC 66-16139. Vol. 1, Water Supply & Wastewater Removal. pap. 128.00 (ISBN 0-317-11201-5, 2055401); Vol. 2, Water Purification & Wastewater Treatment & Disposal. pap. 160.00 (ISBN 0-317-11202-3). Bks Demand UMI.

Flintoff, F. & Millard, R. Public Cleansing. (Illus.). 475p. 1969. 44.50 (ISBN 0-85334-004-8, Pub. by Elsevier Applied Sci England). Elsevier.

Francis, Chester & Auerbach, Stanley I., eds. Environment & Solid Wastes: Characterization, Treatment, & Disposal. LC 82-71528. (Illus.). 450p. 1983. 49.95 (ISBN 0-250-40583-0). Butterworth.

Gilbert, Jane. Efforts at Intermunicipal Cooperation for Solid Waste Disposal: Why They Fail. (Discussion Paper Ser.: No. 68). 1973. pap. 4.50 (ISBN 0-686-32234-7). Regional Sci Res Inst.

Gotaas, H. B. Composting: Sanitary Disposal & Reclamation of Organic Wastes. (Monograph Ser: No. 31). (Eng. & Fr., Illus.). 205p. 1956. 14.00 (ISBN 92-4-140031-5). World Health.

Grisham, J. W., ed. Health Aspects of the Disposal of Waste Chemicals. 560p. 1985. 85.00 (ISBN 0-08-033159-9, Pub by PPI). Pergamon.

Hagerty, D. Joseph, et al. Solid Waste Management. LC 73-10281. (Van Nostrand Reinhold Environmental Engineering Ser.). pap. 79.00 (ISBN 0-317-11224-4, 2014903). Bks Demand UMI.

Hazardous Material Risk Assessment, Disposal & Management. (Illus.). 1979. 20.00 (ISBN 0-318-01363-0). Hazardous Mat Control.

Hazardous Wastes & Environmental Emergencies: Management-Prevention-Cleanup-Control. (Illus.). 1984. text ed. 45.00 (ISBN 0-318-01361-4). Hazardous Mat Control.

Henstock. Disposal & Recovers of Municipal Solid Waste. 1983. text ed. 59.95 (ISBN 0-408-01174-2). Butterworth.

Henstock, M. E. Recycling & Disposal of Solid Waste. LC 75-4235. 223p. 1975. pap. 41.00 (ISBN 0-08-019685-3). Pergamon.

Hickman, H. L., Jr., et al. Thermal Conversion Systems for Municipal Solid Waste. LC 84-16496. (Pollution Technology Review Ser.: No. 113). (Illus.). 746p. 1985. 56.00 (ISBN 0-8155-1001-2). Noyes.

Holmes, John R., ed. Practical Waste Management. LC 82-8633. 565p. 1983. 74.95 (ISBN 0-471-10491-4, Pub. by Wiley-Interscience). Wiley.

IRE Research Staff. Solid Waste-Resource Recovery Management. (Swm-1ser). 1978. 175.00 (ISBN 0-930318-06-4). Intl Res Eval.

Kester, D. R., et al. Wastes in the Ocean: Deep-Sea Waste Disposal, Vol. 5. (Environmental Science & Technology Ser.). 432p. 1984. 26.50 (ISBN 0-471-89331-5). Wiley.

Ketchum, Bostwick H., et al, eds. Ocean Dumping of Industrial Wastes. (Marine Science Ser.: Vol. 12). 536p. 1981. 79.50x (ISBN 0-306-40653-5, Plenum Pr). Plenum Pub.

Loehr, Raymond. Agricultural Waste Management. 1974. 85.00 (ISBN 0-12-455250-1). Acad Pr.

Mantell, Charles L. Solid Wastes: Origin, Collection, Processing & Disposal. LC 74-26930. 1152p. 1975. 106.95x (ISBN 0-471-56777-9, Pub by Wiley-Interscience). Wiley.

Maurice, S. Charles & Smithson, Charles W. Pollution in America: The Trouble with Trash. Pejovich, Steve & Dethloff, Henry, eds. (Series on Public Issues: No. 7). (Illus.). 27p. (Orig.). 1984. pap. 2.00 (ISBN 0-86599-017-4). Ctr Educ Res.

Melosi, Martin V. Garbage in the Cities: Refuse, Reform, & the Environment, 1880-1980. LC 81-40399. (Environmental History Ser.: No. 4). (Illus.). 286p. 1982. 21.50x (ISBN 0-89096-119-0). Tex A&M Univ Pr.

Milazzo, G., ed. Energetics & Technology of Biological Elimination of Wastes. (Studies in Enviornmental Science: Vol. 9). 252p. 1981. 59.75 (ISBN 0-444-41900-4). Elsevier.

National Research Council Board on Ocean Science & Policy. Disposal of Industrial & Domestic Wastes: Land & Sea Alternatives. 210p. 1984. pap. 16.50 (ISBN 0-309-03484-1). Natl Acad Pr.

National Research Council Commission on Natural Resources. Disposal of Excess Spoil from Coal Mining. 1981. pap. text ed. 11.00 (ISBN 0-309-03197-4). Natl Acad Pr.

National Research Council Committee on Ocean Waste Transportation. Ocean Disposal Systems for Sewage Sludge & Effluent. 126p. 1984. pap. 13.95 (ISBN 0-309-03490-6). Natl Acad Pr.

National Waste Processing Conference - Meeting the Challenge: Proceedings, 1982. 1982. 100.00 (I00150). ASME.

Parr, James F., et al, eds. Land Treatment of Hazardous Wastes. LC 82-14402. (Illus.). 422p. 1983. 45.00 (ISBN 0-8155-0926-X, Noyes Pubns). Noyes.

Pavoni, Joseph, et al. Handbook of Solid Waste Disposal: Materials & Energy Recovery. LC 74-26777. 566p. 1975. 37.50 (ISBN 0-442-23027-3). Krieger.

Rail Transport of Solid Wastes. (Special Reports Ser: No. 40). 150p. 1970. 10.00 (ISBN 0-917084-10-1). Am Public Works.

Reed, Alexander W. Ocean Waste Disposal Practices. LC 75-15205. (Pollution Technology Review No. 23; Ocean Technology Review No. 4). (Illus.). 336p. 1976. 24.00 (ISBN 0-8155-0591-4). Noyes.

Remini, William C., ed. Evaluation of Current Developments in Municipal Waste Treatment: Proceedings. LC 77-10538. (ERDA Symposium Ser.). 128p. 1977. pap. 11.25 (ISBN 0-87079-201-6, CONF-770108); microfiche 4.50 (ISBN 0-87079-205-9, CONF-770108). DOE.

Rimberg, D. Municipal Solid Waste Management. LC 75-24766. (Pollution Technology Review Ser.: No. 26). (Illus.). 381p. 1976. 24.00 (ISBN 0-8155-0596-5). Noyes.

Rogoshewski, P., et al. Remedial Action Technology for Waste Disposal Sites. LC 83-7282. (Pollution Technology Review Ser.: No. 101). (Illus.). 497p. 1983. 36.00 (ISBN 0-8155-0947-2). Noyes.

Rubel, Fred N. Incineration of Solid Wastes. LC 74-77723. (Pollution Technology Review Ser: No. 13). (Illus.). 246p. 1975. 24.00 (ISBN 0-8155-0551-5). Noyes.

Savas, E. Steven. Decision-Related Research on the Organization of Service Delivery Systems in Metropolitan Areas: Solid Waste Management. LC 79-83822. 1979. codebook write for info. (ISBN 0-89138-982-2). ICPSR.

Sittig, Marshall. Incineration of Industrial Hazardous Wastes & Sludges. LC 79-21252. (Pollution Technology Review: No. 63). (Illus.). 348p. 1980. 48.00 (ISBN 0-8155-0774-7). Noyes.

--Landfill Disposal of Hazardous Wastes & Sludges. LC 79-20359. (Pollution Technology Review: No. 62). (Illus.). 369p. 1980. 48.00 (ISBN 0-8155-0773-9). Noyes.

Sobetzer, John G. & Corson, Lynn A. Solid Waste Management in Michigan: A Guide for Local Government & Citizens. LC 82-620009. 1982. 5.00 (ISBN 0-941872-35-1). MSU Comm Dev.

Solid Waste Collection Practice. 1975. 28.00x (ISBN 0-917084-00-4). Am Public Works.

State of California. Health Aspects of Wastewater Recharge: A State-of-the-Art Review. LC 78-69808. (Illus.). 1978. Repr. 26.00 (ISBN 0-912394-18-8). Water Info.

Steiker, Gene. A Framework for Evaluating the Economic Effects of Regional Solid Waste Systems. (Discussion Paper Ser.: No. 72). 1974. pap. 4.50 (ISBN 0-686-32238-X). Regional Sci Res Inst.

Stephenson, J. W., et al, eds. Incinerator & Solid Waste Technology, 1962-1975. 415p. 1975. pap. text ed. 60.00 (ISBN 0-685-62568-0, I00092). ASME.

Stevens, Barbara J. Handbook of Municipal Waste Management Systems: Planning & Practice. (Environmental Engineering Ser.). 320p. 1980. 32.50 (ISBN 0-442-23362-0). Van Nos Reinhold.

Tchobanoglous, George, et al. Solid Wastes: Engineering Principles & Management Issues. (Illus.). 1977. text ed. 48.00 (ISBN 0-07-063235-9). McGraw.

Techniques for the Solidification of High-Level Waste. (Technical Reports Ser.: No. 176). (Illus.). 1978. pap. 18.50 (ISBN 92-0-125077-0, IDC176, IAEA). Unipub.

Thermodynamic Data for Waste Incineration: Bk. No. H00141. 1979. 30.00 (ISBN 0-685-95761-6). ASME.

United Nations Environment Programme & Moo-Young, M. Biotechnology & Waste Treatment: Proceedings of a Workshop Sponsored by the United Nations Environment Programme Held at the University of Waterloo, Canada, 27-31 July, 1981. 84p. 1982. 36.00 (ISBN 0-08-028784-0). Pergamon.

U. S. Works Progress Administration. Annotated Bibliography on Incineration, Carbonization & Reduction of Garbage, Rubbish & Sewage Sludge. LC 70-168706. (Bibliography & Reference Ser.: No. 430). 1971. Repr. of 1939 ed. lib. bdg. 22.50 (ISBN 0-8337-3947-6). B Franklin.

Wagner, E. G. & Lanoix, J. N. Excreta Disposal for Rural Areas & Small Communities. (Monograph Ser: No. 39). (Eng, Fr, & Span.). 187p. 1958. 11.20 (ISBN 92-4-140039-0). World Health.

WHO Expert Committee. Dubendorf, 1971. Solid Wastes Disposal & Control: Report. (Technical Report Ser.: No. 484). (Also avail. in French & Spanish). 1971. pap. 2.00 (ISBN 92-4-120484-2). World Health.

REFUSE AS FUEL

see also Biomass Energy

Barton, Allan F. Resource Recovery & Recycling. LC 78-13601. (Environmental Science & Technology Ser.). 418p. 1979. 72.50x (ISBN 0-471-02773-1, Pub. by Wiley-Interscience). Wiley.

Cherimisinoff, Paul N. & Morresi, Angelo. Energy from Solid Wastes. (Pollution Engineering & Technology Ser.: Vol. 1). 1976. 85.00 (ISBN 0-8247-6454-4). Dekker.

Conference of ASME, 1976. Present Status & Research Needs in Energy Recovery from Wastes: Proceedings. Matula, Richard A., ed. 1977. pap. text ed. 35.00 (ISBN 0-685-81974-4, H00091). ASME.

De Renzo, D. J., ed. European Technology for Obtaining Energy from Solid Waste. LC 78-61896. (Energy Technology Review No. 34: Pollution Technology Review No. 54). (Illus.). 281p. 1978. 39.00 (ISBN 0-8155-0730-5). Noyes.

Domino, F. A., ed. Energy from Solid Waste-Recent Developments. LC 79-84428. (Energy Tech. Rev. No. 42, Pollution Tech. Rev. No. 56). (Illus.). 321p. 1979. 36.00 (ISBN 0-8155-0750-X). Noyes.

Energy from Biomass & Wastes Symposium, 7th. 1417p. 1983. 100.00 (ISBN 0-910091-02-1). Inst Gas Tech.

Gasser, J. K. Composting of Agricultural & Other Wastes: Proceedings of a Seminar Organized by the Commission of the European Communities, Oxford, England, 19-22, March, 1984. 336p. 1985. 57.00 (ISBN 0-85334-357-8, Pub. by Elsevier Applied Sci England). Elsevier.

Hasselriis, Floyd. Refuse-Derived Fuel Processing. LC 83-12968. (Vol. 4). 400p. 1984. 39.95 (ISBN 0-250-40314-5). Butterworth.

Hobson, P. N., et al. Methane Production from Agricultural & Domestic Wastes. LC 81-5048. (Energy from Wastes Ser.). 269p. 1981. 54.95x (ISBN 0-470-27154-X). Halsted Pr.

Institute of Gas Technology. Energy from Biomass & Wastes Symposium, 8th. xii, 1529p. 1984. 100.00 (ISBN 0-910091-50-1). Inst Gas Tech.

OAO Corp. for U. S. Department of Energy. Biomass Energy Systems Program Summary 1980. 220p. 1981. pap. 29.50x (ISBN 0-89934-103-9, B.022). Solar Energy Info.

Parker, C. & Roberts, T., eds. Energy from Waste: An Evaluation of Conversion Technologies. 232p. 1985. 42.00 (ISBN 0-85334-352-7, Pub. by Elsevier Applied Sci England). Elsevier.

Pearce, D. W., et al. Decision Making for Energy Futures: A Case Study on the Windscale Inquiry into the Reprocessing of Spent Oxide Fuels. 1979. text ed. 26.50x (ISBN 0-333-27438-5). Humanities.

Porteous, Andrew. Refuse Derived Fuels. LC 81-80593. (Energy from Wastes Ser.). 137p. 1981. 34.95x (ISBN 0-470-27170-1). Halsted Pr.

Robinson, J. S., ed. Fuels from Biomass: Technology & Feasibility. LC 80-23488. (Energy Tech. Re. 61; Chem. Tech. Rev. 176). (Illus.). 377p. 1981. 48.00 (ISBN 0-8155-0824-7). Noyes.

Veal, F. J. Methane from Sorted Domestic Refuse: An Economic Assessment, 1977. 1981. 40.00x (ISBN 0-686-97114-0, Pub. by W Spring England). State Mutual Bk.

--Methane from Sorted Domestic Refuse: A Re-appraisal, 1979. 1982. 40.00x (ISBN 0-686-97117-5, Pub. by W Spring England). State Mutual Bk.

REFUSE INCINERATORS

see Incinerators

REGENERATION (BIOLOGY)

see also Cells

Egar, Margaret, et al. Regeneration in Lower Vertebrates & Invertebrates, 3 vols, Vol. 2. LC 72-8249. 1973. 24.50x (ISBN 0-8422-7051-5). Irvington.

Eichler, Victor, et al. Regeneration in Lower Vertebrates & Invertebrates, 3 vols, Vol. 3. LC 72-8249. 1972. 24.50x (ISBN 0-8422-7052-3). Irvington.

Fausto, Nelson, et al. Liver Regeneration, No. 2. LC 72-13504. (Illus.). 220p. 1973. text ed. 24.00x (ISBN 0-8422-7080-9). Irvington.

Goss, Richard J. Principles of Regeneration. 1969. 51.00 (ISBN 0-12-293050-9). Acad Pr.

Kaup, Ludger & Kaup, Burchard. Holomorphic Functions of Several Variables: An Introduction to the Fundamental Theory. Bridgeland, Michael, tr. LC 83-10120. (Studies in Mathematics: No. 3). xvi, 350p. 1983. 49.95x (ISBN 3-11-004150-2). De Gruyter.

Kempczinski, R. F., et al. Organ & Tissue Regeneration in Mammals II. new ed. LC 72-13503. 157p. 1973. text ed. 25.50x (ISBN 0-8422-7059-0). Irvington.

Leevy, Carroll M. Liver Regeneration in Man. (Illus.). 128p. 1973. 18.50x (ISBN 0-398-02776-5). C C Thomas.

Liozner, L. D., ed. Organ Regeneration: A Study of Developmental Biology in Mammals. LC 74-20709. (Studies in Soviet Science - Life Sciences). (Illus.). 339p. 1974. 45.00x (ISBN 0-306-10903-4, Consultants). Plenum Pub.

McMinn, R. M. Tissue Repair. LC 68-23489. 1969. 68.00 (ISBN 0-12-485950-X). Acad Pr.

Malkin, Leonard I., et al. Liver Regeneration, No. 1. (Illus.). 200p. 1973. text ed. 24.00x (ISBN 0-8422-7079-5). Irvington.

Nettesheim, P., et al. Organ & Tissue Regeneration in Mammals I. LC 72-13503. 167p. 1972. text ed. 27.50x (ISBN 0-8422-7048-5). Irvington.

Ord, Margery G. & Stocken, Lloyd A. Cell & Tissue Regeneration: A Biochemical Approach. LC 84-3536. (Cell Biology; a Series of Monographs: 1570). 221p. 1984. 42.50x (ISBN 0-471-86248-7, Pub. by Wiley-Interscience). Wiley.

Polezhaev, L. V. Loss & Restoration of Regenerative Capacity in Tissues & Organs of Animals. Carlson, Bruce M., tr. LC 71-160029. 1972. 22.50x (ISBN 0-674-53920-6). Harvard U Pr.

--Organ Regeneration in Animals: Recovery of Organ Regeneration Ability in Animals. (Illus.). 200p. 1972. photocopy ed. 24.50x (ISBN 0-398-02381-6). C C Thomas.

Seil, Frederick J., ed. Nerve, Organ, & Tissue Regeneration: Research Perspectives. (Symposium). 1983. 39.50 (ISBN 0-12-635120-1). Acad Pr.

Svendgaard, N. A., et al. Regenerative Properties of Central Monoamine Neurons: Studies in the Adult Rat Using Cerebral Iris Implants As Targets. (Advances in Anatomy, Embryology, & Cell Biology Ser.: Vol. 51, Pt. 4). (Illus.). 70p. (Orig.). 1975. pap. 34.30 (ISBN 0-387-07299-3). Springer-Verlag.

Turner, James E., et al. Regeneration in Lower Vertebrates & Invertebrates, 3 vols, Vol. 1. LC 72-8249. 1973. 24.50x (ISBN 0-8422-7046-9). Irvington.

Zeleny, Charles. Studies on the Factors Controlling the Rate of Regeneration. (Illus.). Repr. of 1916 ed. 12.00 (ISBN 0-384-70850-1). Johnson Repr.

REGGE TRAJECTORIES

Collins, P. D. An Introduction to Regge Theory & High-Energy Physics. LC 76-2233. (Cambridge Monographs on Mathematical Physics). (Illus.). 1977. 125.00 (ISBN 0-521-21245-6). Cambridge U Pr.

Collins, P. D. & Squires, E. J. Regge Poles in Particle Physics. (Springer Tracts in Modern Physics: Vol. 45). 1968. 58.50 (ISBN 0-387-04339-X). Springer-Verlag.

REGRESSION ANALYSIS

see also Correlation (Statistics)

Allen, David M. & Cady, Foster B. Analyzing Experimental Data by Regression. (Research Methods Ser.). (Illus.). 394p. 1982. 31.00 (ISBN 0-534-97963-7). Lifetime Learn.

--Analyzing Experimental Data by Regression. 394p. 1982. 31.00 (ISBN 0-534-97963-7). Van Nos Reinhold.

Andrews, Frank M., et al. Multiple Classification Analysis: A Report on a Computer Program for Multiple Regression Using Categorical Predictors. rev. ed. LC 73-620206. 105p. 1973. cloth 12.00x (ISBN 0-87944-148-8); pap. 8.00x (ISBN 0-87944-055-4). Inst Soc Res.

Barlow, R. E., et al. Statistical Inference Under Order Restrictions: The Theory & Application of Isotonic Regression. LC 74-39231. (Probability & Statistics Ser.). (Illus.). 388p. 1972. 74.95x (ISBN 0-471-04970-0, Pub. by Wiley-Interscience). Wiley.

Belsley, David A., et al. Regression Diagnostics: Identifying Influential Data & Sources of Collinearity. LC 79-19876. (Ser. in Probability & Mathematical Statistics: Applied Probability & Statistics). 292p. 1980. 36.95x (ISBN 0-471-05856-4, Pub. by Wiley-Interscience). Wiley.

Berry, William & Feldman, Stanley. Multiple Regression in Practice. 1985. 5.00 (ISBN 0-8039-2054-7). Sage.

Bibby, John & Toutenburg, Helge. Prediction & Improved Estimation in Linear Models. (Probability & Mathematical Statistics Tracts on Probability & Statistic Section). 188p. 1977. 42.95x (ISBN 0-471-01656-X, Pub. by Wiley-Interscience). Wiley.

Boyce, David E., et al. A Computer Program for Optimal Regression Analysis. (Discussion Paper Ser.: No. 28). 1969. pap. 5.75 (ISBN 0-686-32197-9). Regional Sci Res Inst.

Breiman, Leo, et al. Classification & Regression Trees. LC 83-19708. (Statistics-Probability Ser.). 358p. 1983. write for info (ISBN 0-534-98053-8); pap. write for info (ISBN 0-534-98054-6). Wadsworth Pub.

Brook. Applied Regression Analysis & Experimental Design. (Statistics: Monographs & Textbooks). 264p. 1985. 39.75 (ISBN 0-8247-7252-0). Dekker.

Chatterjee, Samprit & Price, Bertram. Regression Analysis by Example. LC 77-24510. (Probability & Mathematical Statistics Ser.: Applied Probability Section). 228p. 1977. 31.95 (ISBN 0-471-01521-0, Pub. by Wiley-Interscience). Wiley.

Cook, R. D. & Weisberg, S. Residuals & Influence in Regression. 200p. 1982. 60.00x (ISBN 0-412-24280-X, Pub. by Chapman & Hall England). State Mutual Bk.

Dasso, Jerome. Computerized Assessment Administration. LC 73-83136. 1974. 14.00 (ISBN 0-88329-001-4). Intl Assess.

Draper, Norman R. & Smith, Harry. Applied Regression Analysis. 2nd ed. LC 80-17951. (Probability & Mathematical Statistics Ser.). 709p. 1981. 36.95x (ISBN 0-471-02995-5). Wiley.

Dunn, Olive J. & Clark, Virginia A. Applied Statistics: Analysis of Variance & Regression. LC 73-13683. (Probability & Mathematical Statistics Ser.). 387p. 1974. 35.50x (ISBN 0-471-22700-5, Pub. by Wiley-Interscience). Wiley.

Edwards, Allen L. An Introduction to Linear Regression & Correlation. LC 75-38811. (Illus.). 213p. 1976. pap. text ed. 11.95 (ISBN 0-7167-0561-3). W H Freeman.

--Multiple Regression & the Analysis of Variance & Covariance. 2nd ed. LC 84-25915. (Illus.). 221p. 1985. text ed. 19.95 (ISBN 0-7167-1703-4); pap. text ed. 12.95 (ISBN 0-7167-1704-2). W H Freeman.

Fedorov, V. V. Theory of Optimal Experiments. (Probability & Mathematical Statistics Ser.). 1972. 67.00 (ISBN 0-12-250750-9). Acad Pr.

Freund, R. & Minton, P. Regression Methods. (Statistics Ser.: Vol. 30). 1979. 29.75 (ISBN 0-8247-6647-4). Dekker.

Fuller, Wayne A. Introduction to Statistical Time Series. LC 76-6954. (Probability & Mathematical Statistics Ser.). 470p. 1976. 47.50x (ISBN 0-471-28715-6, Pub. by Wiley-Interscience). Wiley.

Gunst, R. F. & Mason, R. L. Regression Analysis & Its Application: A Data Oriented Approach. (Statistics: Textbooks & Monographs Ser.: Vol. 34). 49.75 (ISBN 0-8247-6993-7). Dekker.

Hilton, Gordon. Intermediate Politometrics. LC 75-43733. 336p. 1976. 26.00x (ISBN 0-231-03783-X). Columbia U Pr.

Huang, David S. Regression & Econometric Methods. LC 80-12646. 288p. 1980. Repr. of 1970 ed. lib. bdg. 21.50 (ISBN 0-89874-181-5). Krieger.

Johansen, S. Functional Relations, Random Coefficients & Nonlinear Regression with Application to Kinetic Data. (Lecture Notes in Statistics Ser.: Vol. 22). viii, 126p. 1984. 13.00 (ISBN 0-387-90968-0). Springer-Verlag.

Kelly, Francis J., et al. Research Design in the Behavioral Sciences: Multiple Regression Approach. LC 69-15324. 367p. 1969. 6.00x (ISBN 0-8093-0341-8). S Ill U Pr.

Kleinbaum & Kupper. Applied Regression Analysis & Other Multivariate Methods. LC 77-22327. 1978. write for info. (ISBN 0-87150-355-7, Duxbury Pr). PWS Pubs.

Lewis, Ernest L. & Mouw, John T. The Use of Contrast Coefficients: Supplement to McNeil, Kelly, & McNeil, "Testing Research Hypotheses Using Multiple Linear Regression". LC 77-16406. 80p. 1978. pap. text ed. 2.95x (ISBN 0-8093-0868-1). S Ill U Pr.

Lewis-Beck, Michael S. Applied Regression: An Introduction. LC 80-5821. (Quantitative Applications in the Social Sciences Ser.: No. 22). (Illus.). 79p. 1980. pap. 5.00 (ISBN 0-8039-1494-6). Sage.

McNeil, Judy & McNeil, Keith. Manual of Program DPLINEAR: For Use with McNeil, Kelly, McNeil "Testing Research Hypotheses Using Multiple Linear Regression". LC 74-25176. 53p. 1975. pap. text ed. 1.95x (ISBN 0-8093-0729-4). S Ill U Pr.

McNeil, Keith, et al. Testing Research Hypotheses Using Multiple Linear Regression. LC 75-6639. 600p. 1975. pap. text ed. 7.95x (ISBN 0-8093-0755-3). S Ill U Pr.

Merrill, Arthur A. Fitting Linear & Curvilinear Regression Lines with a Pocket Calculator. 1978. pap. 3.00 (ISBN 0-911894-40-3). Analysis.

Nicholls, D. F. & Quinn, B. G. Random Coefficient Autoregressive Models: An Introduction. (Lecture Notes in Statistics: Vol. 11). (Illus.). 154p. 1982. pap. 14.00 (ISBN 0-387-90766-1). Springer-Verlag.

Plackett, R. L. Principles of Regression Analysis. LC 60-50875. pap. 46.00 (ISBN 0-317-09179-4, 2051613). Bks Demand UMI.

Ratkowsky. Nonlinear Regression Modeling. (Monographs & Textbooks in Statistics). 232p. 1983. 39.75 (ISBN 0-8247-1907-7). Dekker.

Sadler, D. R. Numerical Methods for Nonlinear Regression. 1975. 15.25x (ISBN 0-7022-0964-3). U of Queensland Pr.

Seber, G. A. Linear Regression Analysis. (Wiley Ser. in Probability & Mathematical Statistics). 465p. 1977. 51.50x (ISBN 0-471-01967-4, Pub by Wiley-Interscience). Wiley.

Weisberg, S. Applied Linear Regression. LC 80-10378. (Probability & Mathematical Statistics: Applied Probability & Statistics Section). 283p. 1980. 34.95x (ISBN 0-471-04419-9, Pub. by Wiley-Interscience). Wiley.

Younger, MarySue. First Course in Linear Regression. 2nd ed. 1985. text ed. write for info. (ISBN 0-87150-865-6, 36G5030, Duxbury Pr). PWS Pubs.

REGULAR FUNCTIONS

see Analytic Functions

REGULATORS

see Voltage Regulators

REICHENBACH, HANS, 1891-1953

Salmon, Wesley C., ed. Hans Reichenbach: Logical Empiricist. (Synthese Library: No. 132). 1979. lib. bdg. 39.50 (ISBN 90-277-0958-0, Pub. by Reidel Holland). Kluwer Academic.

REINCARNATION

Cranston, Sylvia & Williams, Carey. Reincarnation: A New Horizon in Science, Religion & Society. 1984. 16.95 (ISBN 0-517-55496-8, Harmony). Crown.

Fox, Emmet. Power Through Constructive Thinking. 1940. 9.95i (ISBN 0-06-062930-4, HarpR). Har-Row.

Montgomery, Ruth. Threshold to Tomorrow. 256p. 1983. 13.95 (ISBN 0-399-12759-3, Putnam). Putnam Pub Group.

Stevenson, Ian. Twenty Cases Suggestive of Reincarnation. LC 79-93627. 396p. 1980. pap. 7.95 (ISBN 0-8139-0872-8). U Pr of Va.

Williston, Glenn & Johnstone, Judith. Soul Search: Spiritual Growth Through a Knowledge of Past Lifetimes. 256p. (Orig.). 1983. pap. 9.95 (ISBN 0-85500-161-5, Turnstone Pr). Sterling.

REINDEER

see also Caribou

Georgeson, C. C. Reindeer & Caribou. facs. ed. (Shorey Historical Ser.). (Illus.). 24p. pap. 2.95 (ISBN 0-8466-0159-1, S159). Shorey.

Hadwen, Seymour. Reindeer in Alaska. facs. ed. (Shorey Historical Ser.). (Illus.). 104p. pap. 6.95 (ISBN 0-8466-0168-0, S168). Shorey.

Hatt, Gudmund. Notes on Reindeer Nomadism. LC 20-5783. (American Anthro. Association Memoirs). 1919. pap. 15.00 (ISBN 0-527-00525-8). Kraus Repr.

Ingold, Tim. Hunters, Pastoralists & Ranchers. LC 78-73243. (Cambridge Studies in Social Anthropology: No. 28). (Illus.). 1980. 39.50 (ISBN 0-521-22588-4). Cambridge U Pr.

Laufer, Berthold. Reindeer & Its Domestication. LC 18-12075. (Amer Anthro Assn Memoirs). 1917. pap. 15.00 (ISBN 0-527-00517-7). Kraus Repr.

Reynolds, S. H. Pleistocene Red Deer, Reindeer & Roe. pap. 10.00 (ISBN 0-384-50440-X). Johnson Repr.

REINFORCED CONCRETE

American Concrete Institute Staff. Shear in Reinforced Concrete. LC 73-94112. (American Concrete Institute, Publication Ser.: SP-42). (Illus.). Vol. 1. pap. 108.30 (ISBN 0-317-10241-9); Vol. 2. pap. 131.00 (ISBN 0-317-10242-7). Bks Demand UMI.

American Society of Civil Engineers. Flexural Mechanics of Reinforced Concrete: Proceedings of the International Symposium, Miami, Fla., Nov. 10-12, 1964. LC 66-402. (Illus.). pap. 150.00 (ISBN 0-317-10957-X, 2002788). Bks Demand UMI.

Boughton, Brian. Reinforced Concrete Detailer's Manual. 2nd ed. (Illus.). 136p. 1971. text ed. 14.95x (ISBN 0-8464-0788-4). Beekman Pubs.

Chen, W. F. Plasticity in Reinforced Concrete. (Illus.). 576p. 1982. text ed. 46.95 (ISBN 0-07-010687-8). McGraw.

Florin, Gustav. Interpretation of Shear & Bond in Reinforced Concrete. (Structural Engineering Ser.: Vol. 1). (Illus.). 86p. 1980. pap. 24.00x (ISBN 0-87849-033-7). Trans Tech.

Fordyce, Wodehouse & Fordyce, M. W. GRC in Buildings. 1983. text ed. 39.95 (ISBN 0-408-00395-2). Butterworth.

Garas, F. K. & Armer, G. S. T., eds. Reinforced & Prestressed Microconcrete Models. (Illus.). 400p. 1981. text ed. 60.00x (ISBN 0-86095-880-9). Longman.

Glass Fiber Reinforced Concrete Products: Properties & Applications. (PCI Journal Reprints Ser.). 28p. pap. 6.00 (ISBN 0-686-40108-5, JR190). Prestressed Concrete.

Guide Specification for Glass Fiber Reinforced Concrete Panels. 14p. pap. 4.00 (ISBN 0-686-39961-7, SPC-120-82). Prestressed Concrete.

Hannant, D. J. Fibre Cements & Fibre Concretes. 219p. 1978. 59.95 (ISBN 0-471-99620-3, Pub. by Wiley-Interscience). Wiley.

Hsu, T. Torsion of Reinforced Concrete. 1984. 46.50 (ISBN 0-442-26401-1). VAn Nos Reinhold.

Kemp, Emory L. & Wang, Jah-Chi. Behavior & Design Criteria for Bond in Reinforced Concrete: Report for Distribution to the Reinforced Concrete Research Council of the American Society of Civil Engineers. pap. 114.00 (ISBN 0-317-10734-8, 2022638). Bks Demand UMI.

Kong, F. & Evans, R. Reinforced & Prestressed Concrete. 2nd. ed. 1984. pap. 24.50 (ISBN 0-442-30751-9). Van Nos Reinhold.

Nawy, Edward G. Reinforced Concrete: A Fundamental Approach. (Illus.). 688p. 1985. text ed. 40.95 (ISBN 0-13-771643-5). P-H.

--Simplified Reinforced Concrete. (Illus.). 320p. 1986. text ed. 29.95 (ISBN 0-317-29670-1). P-H.

Nishkin, V. S. Thermal Stresses in a Composite Cylinder with an Arbitrary Temperature Distribution Along Its Length. 119p. 1966. 49.50x (ISBN 0-306-65116-5, IFI Plenum). Plenum Pub.

Parker, Harry. Simplified Design of Reinforced Concrete. 5th ed. Ambrose, James, ed. LC 84-10462. 250p. 1984. text ed. 30.95x (ISBN 0-471-80349-9, Pub. by Wiley-Interscience). Wiley.

Schneider, R. & Dickey, W. Reinforced Masonry Design. 1980. 50.00 (ISBN 0-13-771733-4). P-H.

Schwer, L. E., ed. Nonlinear Numerical Analysis of Reinforced Concrete. 1982. 30.00 (H00242). ASME.

Taylor, R. Composite Reinforced Concrete. 126p. 1979. 22.50x (ISBN 0-7277-0077-4). Am Soc Civil Eng.

Vance, Mary. Reinforced Concrete: A Bibliography. (Architecture Ser.: Bibliography A 838). 48p. 1982. pap. 7.50 (ISBN 0-88066-248-4). Vance Biblios.

REINFORCED CONCRETE BEAMS

see Concrete Beams

REINFORCED CONCRETE BOATS

see Concrete Boats

REINFORCED CONCRETE CONSTRUCTION

see also Precast Concrete Construction; Prestressed Concrete Construction

ACI Committee Staff. Building Code Requirements for Reinforced Concrete: ACI 318-83. 1983. 31.00 (ISBN 0-317-17423-1). ACI.

ACI Committee 224. Causes, Mechanism, & Control of Cracking in Concrete. (Bibliography: No. 9). 1971. pap. 36.25 (ISBN 0-685-85148-6, B-9). ACI.

ACI Committee 318. Building Code Requirements for Reinforced Concrete: ACI 318-77 ANSI A89.1-1972. 102p. 1977. 27.50 (ISBN 0-685-03451-8, 318-77). ACI.

--Building Code Requirements for Reinforced Concrete: ACI 318-71 ANSI A89.1-1972. 78p. 1971. 23.00 (ISBN 0-685-85075-7, 318-71). ACI.

--Building Code Requirements for Reinforced Concrete SI Metric Edition: ACI 318-71. 1975. 23.00 (ISBN 0-685-85081-1, 318-7 SI). ACI.

--Commentary on Building Code Requirements for Reinforced Concrete: ACI 318R-77. 132p. 1977. 27.50 (ISBN 0-685-03453-4, 318-77C) (ISBN 0-685-03454-2). ACI.

ACI Committee 340. Design Handbook in Accordance with the Strength Design Method of ACI 318-77: Columns, Vol. 2. 1978. binder 55.50 (ISBN 0-685-85093-5, SP-17A78). ACI.

Baikov, V. & Sigalov, E. Reinforced Concrete Structures, 2 vols. 664p. 1981. 14.50 (ISBN 0-8285-1975-7, Pub. by Mir Pubs USSR). Imported Pubns.

Barker, John A. Reinforced Concrete Detailing. 2nd ed. (Illus.). 1981. 98.00x (ISBN 0-19-859523-9). Oxford U Pr.

Westfall, Richard S. Science & Religion in Seventeenth-Century England. 1973. pap. 4.95 (ISBN 0-472-06190-9, 190, AA). U of Mich Pr.
White, Lynn, Jr. Medieval Religion & Technology: Collected Essays. LC 77-83113. (Center for Medieval & Renaissance Studies, UCLA: No. 13). 1978. 39.50x (ISBN 0-520-03566-6). U of Cal Pr.
Wonderly, Daniel E. God's Time-Records in Ancient Sediments: Evidences of Long Time Spans in Earth's History. LC 77-85681. (Illus.). 258p. (Orig.). 1977. pap. 7.00 (ISBN 0-930402-01-4). Crystal MI.

RELIGION AND SCIENCE–HISTORY OF CONTROVERSY

Carmell, Aryeh & Domb, Cyril, eds. Challenge. 1978. 13.95 (ISBN 0-87306-174-8); pap. 7.95 (ISBN 0-87306-165-9). Feldheim.
Carus, Paul. The Religion of Science. 3rd ed. 145p. 6.95 (ISBN 0-912050-68-3). Open Court.
Cosslett, Tess. Science & Religion in the Nineteenth Century. LC 83-7505. (Cambridge English Prose Texts Ser.). 225p. 1984. 39.50 (ISBN 0-521-24402-1); pap. 14.95 (ISBN 0-521-28668-9). Cambridge U Pr.
Custance, Arthur C. Science & Faith, Vol. 8. 9.95 (ISBN 0-310-23031-4). Zondervan.
Dillenberger, John. Protestant Thought & Natural Science: A Historical Interpretation. LC 77-7200. 1977. Repr. of 1960 ed. lib. bdg. 22.75x (ISBN 0-8371-9670-1, DIPT). Greenwood.
Gebler, Karl Von. Galileo Galilei & the Roman Curia from Authentic Sources. Sturge, Jane, tr. LC 76-1124. 1977. Repr. of 1897 ed. lib. bdg. 28.50x (ISBN 0-915172-11-9). Richwood Pub.
Greene, John C. Darwin & the Modern World View. LC 61-15489. (Rockwell Lectures Ser.). 152p. 1973. pap. text ed. 4.95x (ISBN 0-8071-0062-5). La State U Pr.
Haber, Francis C. The Age of the World: Moses to Darwin. LC 77-13854. 1978. Repr. of 1959 ed. lib. bdg. 22.00x (ISBN 0-8371-9898-4, HAAW). Greenwood.
Hovenkamp, Herbert. Science & Religion in America, 1800-1860. LC 78-53332. 1978. 25.00x (ISBN 0-8122-7748-1). U of Pa Pr.
Kappeler, Max. Metaphysics & Science in Christian Science. (Orig.). 1985. pap. 3.50 (ISBN 0-942958-11-X). Kappeler Inst Pub.
Lau, Dicksen T. The New Religion & Relativity. LC 83-62038. 138p. (Orig.). 1983. pap. 5.95 (ISBN 0-9612000-0-6). Magnolia Bks.
Nelkin, Dorothy. The Creation Controversy: Science or Scripture in the Schools? LC 83-45954. 242p. 1984. pap. 9.95x (ISBN 0-8070-3155-0, BP 675). Beacon Pr.
Raven, Charles E. Natural Religion & Christian Theology: First & Second Series, 2 vols. LC 77-27176. (Gifford Lectures: 1951-52). Repr. of 1953 ed. Set. 37.50 (ISBN 0-404-60540-0). AMS Pr.
Russell, Bertrand. Religion & Science. 1961. pap. 8.95 (ISBN 0-19-500228-8, GB). Oxford U Pr.
Shapiro, Barbara J. John Wilkins, 1614-1672: An Intellectual Biography. LC 73-84042. 1969. 40.00x (ISBN 0-520-01396-4). U of Cal Pr.
Simpson, James Y. Landmarks in the Struggle Between Science & Religion. LC 75-118549. 1971. Repr. of 1925 ed. 24.50x (ISBN 0-8046-1174-2, Pub. by Kennikat). Assoc Faculty Pr.
White, Andrew D. History of the Warfare of Science with Theology in Christendon, 2 Vols. Set. 26.50 (ISBN 0-8446-3170-1). Peter Smith.
White, Edward A. Science & Religion in American Thought. LC 68-54307. (Stanford University. Stanford Studies in History, Economics, & Poltical Science: No. 8). Repr. of 1952 ed. 17.50 (ISBN 0-404-50972-X). AMS Pr.

REMANENT MAGNETISM
see Paleomagnetism

REMODELING OF BUILDINGS
see Buildings–Repair and Reconstruction

REMODELING OF DWELLINGS
see Dwellings–Remodeling

REMOTE CONTROL
see also Electronic Control; Guidance Systems (Flight); Photoelectric Cells; Radio Control; Space Vehicles–Guidance Systems; Synchros

CES Industries, Inc. Ed-Lab Eighty Experiment Manual: Touch Sensor. (Illus., Orig.). 1983. write for info. (ISBN 0-86711-040-6). CES Industries.
Cunningham, John E. & Horn, Delton T. Handbook of Remote Control & Automation Techniques. 2nd ed. (Illus.). 350p. 1984. 21.95 (ISBN 0-8306-0777-3); pap. 13.95 (ISBN 0-8306-1777-9, 1777). TAB Bks.
Freedy, Amos, et al. The Application of a Theoretical Learning Model to a Remote Handling Control System. LC 73-141073. 104p. 1970. 19.00 (ISBN 0-403-04501-0). Mgmt Info Serv.
Young, R. E. Supervisory Remote Control Systems. (IEE Control Engineering Ser.: No. 4). (Illus.). 192p. 1977. 42.00 (ISBN 0-901223-94-8, CE004). Inst Elect Eng.

REMOTE SENSING

Allan, Thomas D. Satellite Microwave Remote Sensing. (Marine Science Ser.). 526p. 1983. 110.00x (ISBN 0-470-27397-6). Halsted Pr.
Application of Remote Sensing Techniques for Improving Desert Locust Survey & Control. (Illus.). 92p. 1977. pap. 10.50 (ISBN 92-5-100112-X, F721, FAO). Unipub.
Applications of Remote Sensing to Hydrology. 52p. (Joint WMO-UNESCO Publication). 1979. pap. 10.00 (ISBN 92-63-10513-8, W453, WMO). Unipub.
ASCE Conference, Aerospace Division, 1980. Civil Engineering Applications of Remote Sensing. Kiefer, Ralph W., ed. LC 80-67879. 199p. 1980. pap. 19.50x (ISBN 0-87262-253-3). Am Soc Civil Eng.
Barrett, E. C. & Curtis, L. R. Introduction to Environmental Remote Sensing. 2nd ed. (Illus.). 300p. 1982. 60.00x (ISBN 0-412-23080-1, NO. 6734, Pub. by Chapman & Hall); pap. 31.00x (ISBN 0-412-23090-9, NO. 6735). Methuen Inc.
Bernstein, R., ed. Digital Image Processing for Remote Sensing. LC 77-94520. 1978. 49.85 (ISBN 0-87942-105-3, PC01024). Inst Electrical.
Bryan, M. Leonard, ed. Remote Sensing of Earth Resources: A Guide to Information Sources. LC 79-22792. (Geography & Travel Information Guide Ser.: Vol. 1). (Illus.). 188p. 1979. 60.00x (ISBN 0-8103-1413-4). Gale.
Business Communications Staff. Electronic Sensors. 1983. 1250.00 (ISBN 0-89336-354-5, G-076). BCC.
CES Industries, Inc. Ed-Lab Eight Hundred Experiment Manual: Contactor Sensor Operation. (Illus., Orig.). 1983. write for info. (ISBN 0-86711-048-1). CES Industries.
--Ed-Lab Eight Hundred Experiment Manual: Infra-Red Sensor. (Illus., Orig.). 1983. write for info. (ISBN 0-86711-047-3). CES Industries.
--Ed-Lab Eight Hundred Experiment Manual: Photocell Sensor. (Illus., Orig.). 1983. write for info. (ISBN 0-86711-049-X). CES Industries.
--Ed-Lab Eighty Experiment Manual: Photocell Sensor. (Illus., Orig.). 1983. write for info. (ISBN 0-86711-036-8). CES Industries.
Cheung, Peter, et al, eds. Theory, Design, & Biomedical Application of Solid State Chemical Sensors. (Uniscience Ser.). 320p. 1978. 84.00 (ISBN 0-8493-5375-0). CRC Pr.
CISM (International Center for Mechanical Sciences) Fluidic Sensors & Some Large Scale Devices. Jacobs, B. E., ed. (CISM Intl. Centre for Mechanical Sciences, Courses & Lectures: No. 52). (Illus.). 41p. 1974. pap. 6.70 (ISBN 0-387-81228-8). Springer-Verlag.
Clough, D. J. & Morley, L. W., eds. Earth Observation Systems for Resource Management & Environmental Control. LC 77-13989. (NATO Conference Series II, Systems Science: Vol. 4). 487p. 1977. 69.50x (ISBN 0-306-32844-5, Plenum Pr). Plenum Pub.
Colwell, Robert N., ed. Manual of Remote Sensing, 2 vols. 2nd ed. LC 83-6055. 2724p. 1983. Set. (106.00 member) 132.00 (ISBN 0-937294-52-7). Vol. I (ISBN 0-937294-41-1). Vol. II (ISBN 0-937294-42-X). ASP & RS.
Complete Index to "Photogrammetric Engineering & Remote Sensing", Vol. I-XLV, 1934-1979. 288p. 1980. pap. 17.00 (ISBN 0-937294-16-0); pap. 9.50 member. ASP & RS.
Conference on Remotely Manned Systems, 2nd, June 1975. Robots & Manipulator Systems: Papers, 2 pts. Heer, E., ed. LC 77-73105. 336p. 1977. pap. text ed. 32.00 ea. Pt. 1 (ISBN 0-08-021727-3). Pt. 2 (ISBN 0-08-022681-7). Pergamon.
Cracknell, A. P. Remote Sensing in Meteorology Oceanography & Hydrology. LC 81-4151. (Environmental Sciences Ser.). 542p. 1981. 112.95x (ISBN 0-470-27183-3). Halsted Pr.
Curran, Paul. Principles of Remote Sensing. (Illus.). 260p. 1984. text ed. 24.95 (ISBN 0-582-30097-5). Longman.
Deepak, Adarsh, ed. Inversion Methods in Atmospheric Remote Sounding. 1977. 57.50 (ISBN 0-12-208450-0). Acad Pr.
--Remote Sensing of Atmospheres & Oceans. LC 80-18881. 1980. 55.00 (ISBN 0-12-208460-8). Acad Pr.
Deepak, Adarsh & Rao, K. R., eds. Applications of Remote Sensing for Rice Production. (Illus.). 1985. 49.00 (ISBN 0-937194-03-4). A Deepak Pub.
De Loor, G. P., ed. Radar Remote Sensing. (Remote Sensing Reviews Ser.: Vol. 1, No. 1). 185p. 1984. 47.50 (ISBN 3-7186-0132-X). Harwood Academic.
Egan. Photometry & Polarization in Remote Sensing. 480p. 1985. 68.00 (ISBN 0-444-00892-6). Elsevier.
Estes, John E. & Senger, Leslie W. Remote Sensing: Techniques for Environmental Analysis. LC 73-8601. 340p. 1975. 33.45x (ISBN 0-471-24595-X). Wiley.
Ginsberg, Irving W. Fundamentals of Electro-Optical Remote Sensing. (Orig.). 1986. write for info. (ISBN 0-89464-003-8). Krieger.
Hall, Dorothy & Martinec, Jaroslav. Remoting Sensing of Ice & Snow. 200p. 1985. 49.95 (ISBN 0-412-25910-9, 9536). Methuen Inc.
Harper, Dorothy. Eye in the Sky: Introduction to Remote Sensing. 2nd ed. 252p. 1983. pap. text ed. 18.50x (ISBN 0-919868-17-7, Pub. by Multisci Pubns Ltd). Brookfield Pub Co.
Henderson, A. Sellers, ed. Satellite Sensing of a Cloudy Atmosphere: Observing the Third Planet. (Illus.). 336p. 1984. 40.00x (ISBN 0-85066-254-0). Taylor & Francis.
Henderson, F. B. & Rock, B. N., eds. Frontiers for Geological Remote Sensing from Space: Report of the Fourth Geosat Workshop. 88p. 1984. 26.00 (ISBN 0-937294-50-0). ASP & RS.
Holz, Robert K. The Surveillant Science: Remote Sensing of the Environment. 2nd ed. LC 84-7508. 413p. 1984. pap. text ed. 21.95x (ISBN 0-471-08638-X). Wiley.
Hord, Michael. Digital Image Processing of Remotely Sensed Data. (Notes & Reports in Computer Science & Applied Mathematics Ser.). 221p. 1982. 29.50 (ISBN 0-12-355620-1). Acad Pr.
Industrial Sensor Directory. 140p. 1983. 35.00 (ISBN 0-910747-04-0). Tech Data TX.
Janata, Jiri & Huber, Robert J., eds. Solid State Chemical Sensors. Date not set. 49.50 (ISBN 0-12-380210-5). Acad Pr.
Johannsen, Chris J. & Sanders, James L., eds. Remote Sensing for Resource Management. LC 82-16740. (Illus.). 688p. 1982. text ed. 45.00 (ISBN 0-935734-08-2). Soil Conservation.
Kahle, A. B., et al, eds. Sessions on Remote Sensing 1980. (Advances in Space Research: Vol. 1, No. 10). (Illus.). 314p. 1981. pap. 44.00 (ISBN 0-08-028388-8). Pergamon.
Kennie. Remote Sensing in Civil Engineering. 1985. 75.00 (ISBN 0-470-20135-5). Wiley.
Kong, Jin A., et al. Theory of Microwave Remote Sensing. LC 84-17397. 400p. 1985. text ed. 45.00x (ISBN 0-471-88860-5, Pub. by Wiley-Interscience). Wiley.
Lavigne, D. M., et al. Remote Sensing & Ecosystem Management. (Norsk Polarinstitutt Skrifter: Vol. 166). (Illus.). 51p. 1980. pap. 5.00x (ISBN 0-686-69914-9, Dist. by Columbia U Pr). Universitet.
LeBlond, Robert. Remote Sensing & Development: Report on IDRC-Supported Projects in the Sudan, Bolivia, Tanzania, Bangldesh & Mali. 24p. 1982. pap. 7.50 (ISBN 0-88936-302-1, IDRC174, IDRC). Unipub.
Lillesand, Thomas M. & Kiefer, Ralph W. Remote Sensing & Image Interpretation. LC 78-27846. 612p. 1979. text ed. 41.95x (ISBN 0-471-02609-3). Wiley.
Lo, R. E., ed. Earth Observation & Remote Sensing by Satellites: Proceedings of the Symposium on Earth Observation & Remote Sensing by Satellites, Hannover, West Germany, 21 May 1982. 56p. 1983. pap. 41.25 (ISBN 0-08-031152-0). Pergamon.
Measures, Raymond M. Laser Remote Sensing: Fundamentals & Applications. LC 83-10379. 510p. 1983. 48.50x (ISBN 0-471-08193-0, Wiley-Interscience). Wiley.
Meier, Mark. Remote Sensing of Snow & Ice. (Technical Papers in Hydrology: No. 19). (Illus.). 54p. (A Contribution to the International Hydrological Programme). 1979. pap. 7.50 (ISBN 92-3-101730-6, U976, UNESCO). Unipub.
Mooradian, A. & Killinger, D. K. Optical & Laser Remote Sensing. (Springer Ser. in Optical Sciences: Vol. 39). (Illus.). 383p. 1983. 37.00 (ISBN 0-387-12170-6). Springer-Verlag.
Morain, Stanley A., pref. by. Thermosense II: Proceedings. 264p. 1979. pap. 14.00 (ISBN 0-937294-17-9); pap. 10.00 members. ASP & RS.
Multilingual Dictionary of Remote Sensing & Photogrammetry. 368p. 1984. 34.00 (ISBN 0-937294-46-2); members 24.00. ASP & RS.
Nihoul, J. C., ed. Remote Sensing of Shelf Sea Hydrodynamics: Proceedings of the International Liege Colloquium on Ocean Hydrodynamics, 15th, May 2-6, 1983. (Oceanography Ser.: No. 38). 354p. 1984. 69.25 (ISBN 0-444-42314-1). Elsevier.
Norton, Harry N. Sensor & Analyzer Handbook. (Illus.). 608p. 1982. 39.95 (ISBN 0-13-806760-0). P-H.
Pouquet, J. Earth's Science in the Age of the Satellite. LC 73-94454. Orig. Title: Les Sciences De la Terre a L'heure Des Satellites. 190p. 1974. lib. bdg. 34.25 (ISBN 90-277-0437-6). Kluwer Academic.
Renewable Resources Management: Applications of Remote Sensing - RNRF Symposium. 760p. 1984. pap. 42.00 (ISBN 0-937294-51-9). ASP & RS.
Report of the Second International Training Course in Remote Sensing Applications for Agriculture: Rome, 1977. (Miscellaneous Documents Ser.). 93p. 1978. pap. 7.50 (ISBN 92-5-100425-0, F1316, FAO). Unipub.
Richason, Benjamin F. Introduction to Remote Sensing of the Environment. (National Council for Geography Education Pacesetter Ser.). (Illus.). 1978. text ed. 32.95 (ISBN 0-8403-2834-6). Kendall-Hunt.
Sabins, Floyd F., Jr. Remote Sensing: Principles & Interpretation. LC 77-27595. (Earth Sciences Ser.). (Illus.). 426p. 1978. text ed. 41.95x (ISBN 0-7167-0023-9). W H Freeman.
Schanda, E., ed. Remote Sensing for Environmental Sciences. (Ecological Studies: Vol. 18). (Illus.). 370p. 1976. 45.00 (ISBN 0-387-07465-1). Springer-Verlag.
Sensor Design Using Computer Tools, Los Angeles, Calif., Jan. 1982. Sensor Design Using Computer Tools: Proceedings. Jamieson, John A., ed. (SPIE Seminar Proceedings: Vol. 327). 208p. 1982. 40.00 (ISBN 0-89252-362-X); 34.00, members (ISBN 0-317-34759-4). SPIE.
Siegal, B. S. & Gillespie, A. R. Remote Sensing in Geology. 702p. 1980. text ed. 61.95 (ISBN 0-471-79052-4). Wiley.
Slater, Philip N. Remote Sensing: Optics & Optical Systems. (Illus.). 450p. 1980. text ed. 49.95 (ISBN 0-201-07250-5). Addison-Wesley.
Survey of the Profession: Photogrammetry, Surveying, Mapping, Remote Sensing. 1982. pap. 35.00 (ISBN 0-937294-40-3); pap. 25.00 members. ASP & RS.
Swain, Philip H. & Davis, Shirley M. Remote Sensing: The Quantitative Approach. (Illus.). 1978. text ed. 58.00 (ISBN 0-07-062576-X). McGraw.
Thomson, Keith P., et al, eds. Remote Sensing & Water Resources Management. (American Water Resources Association Proceedings: No. 17). pap. 111.30 (ISBN 0-317-11249-X, 2017815). Bks Demand UMI.
Townshend, J. R., ed. Terrain Analysis & Remote Sensing. (Illus.). 240p. (Orig.). 1981. text ed. 45.00x (ISBN 0-04-551036-9); pap. text ed. 24.95x (ISBN 0-04-551037-7). Allen Unwin.
Transborder Data Flows: Transnational Corporations & Remote-Sensing Data. (Centre on Transnational Corporations). (Illus.). 74p. 1985. pap. 8.50 (UN84/2A11, UN). Unipub.
Twomey, S. Introduction to the Mathematics of Inversion in Remote Sensing & Indirect Measurements. (Developments in Geomathematics Ser.: Vol. 3). 244p. 1977. 85.00 (ISBN 0-444-41547-5, North Holland). Elsevier.
Vernberg, F John & Diemer, Ferdinand P., eds. Processes in Marine Remote Sensing. LC 81-16214. (The Belle W.Baruch Library in Marine Science: No. 12). (Illus.). 560p. 1981. lib. bdg. 39.95x (ISBN 0-87249-411-X). U of SC Pr.
Veziroglu, T. Nejat, ed. Remote Sensing: Energy Related Studies. LC 75-23018. 491p. 1975. 39.50x (ISBN 0-470-90665-0). Halsted Pr.
Wade, J. E., et al. Wind Power Potential: A Prospector's Handbook of Remote Sensing Techniques. 329p. (Orig.). 1984. pap. text ed. 65.00 (ISBN 0-88016-034-9). Windbks.
Watson, Ken & Regan, Robert D., eds. Geophysics Reprint Series: No. 3, Remote Sensing. 581p. 1983. text ed. 50.00 (ISBN 0-317-12580-X). Soc Exploration.
--Remote Sensing, No. 3. (Geophysics Reprint Ser.). 581p. 1983. pap. 40.00 members (ISBN 0-931830-23-0); pap. 50.00 non-members (ISBN 0-317-06796-6). Soc Exploration.
Zuev, V. E. & Naats, I. E. Inverse Problems of Lidar Sensing of the Atmosphere. (Springer Ser. in Optical Sciences: Vol. 29). (Illus.). 260p. 1983. 44.00 (ISBN 0-387-10913-7). Springer-Verlag.

REMOTE TERRAIN SENSING
see Remote Sensing

REMSEN, IRA, 1846-1927

Getman, Frederick H. The Life of Ira Remsen. Cohen, I. Bernard, ed. LC 79-7962. (Three Centuries of Science in America Ser.). (Illus.). 1980. Repr. of 1940 ed. lib. bdg. 16.00x (ISBN 0-405-12543-7). Ayer Co Pubs.
Roberts, Millard F. History of Remsen: Seventeen Eighty-Nine to Nineteen Eighty-One. 2nd ed. LC 84-52801. 453p. 1985. 15.00 (ISBN 0-317-19605-7). L M Licht.

RENAULT (AUTOMOBILE)
see Automobiles, Foreign–Types–Renault

REPAIRING
see also Automatic Checkout Equipment; Buildings–Repair and Reconstruction;
also subdivision Repairing under various subjects, e.g. Jewelry–Repairing

Daniels, Keith W., compiled by. Recycling & Repairing, Nineteen Twelve to Nineteen Forty Eight. (Illus.). 290p. (Orig.). 1978. pap. 9.95 (ISBN 0-937468-00-2). Lost Data.
Johnson, L. How to Restore & Repair Practically Everything. 208p. 19.95 (ISBN 0-07-032607-X). McGraw.

Nueckel, Susan, ed. A Selected Guide to Make-It, Fix-It, Do-It-Yourself Books. LC 72-82609. (Selected Guide Ser.). 300p. 1973. 14.50 (ISBN 0-8303-0125-9); pap. 6.50 (ISBN 0-8303-0123-2). Fleet.

Reader's Digest Editors. Fix-It-Yourself Manual. LC 77-73634. (Illus.). 480p. 1977. 21.95 (ISBN 0-89577-040-7, Pub. by RD Assn). Random.

Rudman, Jack. Repair Aide. (Career Examination Ser.: C-1453). (Cloth bdg. avail. on request). pap. 8.00 (ISBN 0-8373-1453-4). Natl Learning.

--Repair Crew Chief. (Career Examination Ser.: C-1454). (Cloth bdg. avail. on request). pap. 10.00 (ISBN 0-8373-1453-4). Natl Learning.

Schultz, Morton J. How to Fix It. (Illus.). 1978. pap. 4.95 (ISBN 0-07-055649-0). McGraw.

REPEATER STATIONS

see Radio Relay Systems

REPLACEMENT REACTIONS

see Substitution Reactions

REPORTS, SCIENTIFIC

see Technical Reports

REPORTS, TECHNICAL

see Technical Reports

REPRESENTATIONS OF GROUPS

Arad, Z. & Herzog, M., eds. Products of Conjugacy Classes in Groups. (Lecture Notes in Mathematics: Vol. 1112). v, 244p. 1985. pap. 14.40 (ISBN 0-387-13916-8). Springer-Verlag.

Auslander, Louis & Moore, C. C. Unitary Representations of Solvable Lie Groups. LC 52-42839. (Memoirs: No. 62). 199p. 1971. pap. 12.00 (ISBN 0-8218-1262-9, MEMO-62). Am Math.

Bargmann, V., ed. Group Representations in Mathematics & Physics: Battelle Seattle 1969 Rencontres. LC 75-146233. (Lecture Notes in Physics: Vol. 6). 1970. pap. 18.30 (ISBN 0-387-05310-7). Springer-Verlag.

Basov, N. G., ed. Problems in the General Theory of Relativity & the Theory of Group Representations. LC 78-12612. (P. N. Lebedev Physics Institutes Ser.: Vol. 96). (Illus.). 193p. 1979. 55.00 (ISBN 0-306-10951-4, Consultants). Plenum Pub.

Berkowitz, Leonard, ed. Group Processes. 1978. 23.50 (ISBN 0-12-091840-4). Acad Pr.

Brezin, Jonathan. Unitary Representation Theory for Solvable Lie Groups. LC 52-42839. (Memoirs: No. 79). 122p. 1968. pap. 9.00 (ISBN 0-8218-1279-3, MEMO-79). Am Math.

Brocker, T. & Dieck, Tom T. Representations of Compact Lie Groups. (Graduate Texts in Mathematics Ser.: Vol. 98). (Illus.). x, 313p. 1985. 39.00 (ISBN 0-387-13678-9). Springer-Verlag.

Carmelli, Moshe & Malin, Shimon. Representations of the Rotation & Lorentz Groups: An Introduction. (Lecture Notes in Pure & Applied Mathematics Ser.: Vol. 16). 1976. 35.00 (ISBN 0-8247-6449-8). Dekker.

Dornhoff, L. Group Representation Theory, Pt. A: Ordinary Representation Theory. (Pure & Applied Mathematics Ser: Vol. 7). 362p. 1971. 45.00 (ISBN 0-8247-1147-5). Dekker.

--Group Representation Theory, Pt. B: Modular Representation Theory. (Pure & Applied Mathematics Ser: Vol. 7). 280p. 1972. 45.00 (ISBN 0-8247-1148-3). Dekker.

Gelbart, Stephen S. Automorphic Forms & Adele Groups. (Annals of Mathematics Studies: No. 83). 280p. 1975. 26.50x (ISBN 0-691-08156-5). Princeton U Pr.

Gelfand, I. M. Representation Theory: Selected Papers. LC 82-4440. (London Mathematical Society Lecture Notes Ser. 69). 330p. 1982. pap. 34.50 (ISBN 0-521-28981-5). Cambridge U Pr.

Gordon, Robert. Representation Theory of Algebras. (Lecture Notes in Pure & Applied Math Ser.: Vol. 37). 1978. 65.00 (ISBN 0-8247-6714-4). Dekker.

Hill, Victor E. Groups, Representations & Characters. LC 75-43362. 1976. text ed. 16.95x (ISBN 0-02-846790-6). Hafner.

Increst. Operator Algebras & Group Representations, Vols. 1 & 2. (Monogrphs & Studies in Mathematics: Nos. 17 & 18). 592p. 1983. text ed. 49.95 vol. 1 (ISBN 0-273-08604-9); text ed. 49.95 vol. 2 (ISBN 0-273-08605-7). Pitman Pub MA.

James, G. D. Representations of General Linear Groups. (London Mathematical Society Lecture Note Ser.: No. 94). 160p. 1984. pap. 19.95 (ISBN 0-521-26981-4). Cambridge U Pr.

Johnson, D. J. Topics in the Theory of Group Presentations. (London Mathematical Society Lecture Note Ser.: No. 42). (Illus.). 230p. (Orig.). 1980. pap. 34.50x (ISBN 0-521-23108-6). Cambridge U Pr.

Keown, R. An Introduction to Group Representation Theory. (Mathematics in Science & Engineering Ser.). 1975. 59.50 (ISBN 0-12-404250-3). Acad Pr.

Kerber, A. Representations of Permutation Groups, Part 1: Representations of Wreath Products & Applications to the Representations Theory of Symmetric & Alternating Groups. LC 72-183956. (Lecture Notes in Mathematics: Vol. 240). viii, 192p. 1971. pap. 10.00 (ISBN 0-387-05693-9). Springer-Verlag.

Kirillov, A. A. Elements of the Theory of Representations. Hewitt, E., tr. from Rus. (Grundlehren der Mathematischen Wissenschaften: Vol. 220). (Illus.). 256p. 1976. 52.00 (ISBN 0-387-07476-7). Springer-Verlag.

Knutson, D. Lambda-Rings & the Representation Theory of the Symmetric Group. LC 73-75663. (Lecture Notes in Mathematics: Vol. 308). iv, 203p. 1973. pap. 14.00 (ISBN 0-387-06184-3). Springer-Verlag.

Kramer. Groups, Systems & Many Body Physics. (Clustering Phenomena in Nuclei Ser.: Vol. 1). 1979. 80.00 (ISBN 0-9940012-7-4). Heyden.

Langlands, R. Base Change for GL (2) LC 79-28820. (Annals of Mathematics Studies: No. 96). 225p. 1980. 27.00x (ISBN 0-691-08263-4); pap. 12.00 (ISBN 0-691-08272-3). Princeton U Pr.

Lusztig, George. The Discrete Series Representations of the General Linear Groups Over a Finite Field. (Annals of Mathematics Studies: No. 81). 150p. 1974. 15.00 (ISBN 0-691-08154-9). Princeton U Pr.

Mackey, G. W. Unitary Group Representations. (Mathematics Lecture Note Ser.: No. 55). 1978. pap. 36.95 (ISBN 0-8053-6703-9). Benjamin-Cummings.

Naimark, M. A. Theory of Group Representations. (Illus.). 576p. 1982. 68.00 (ISBN 0-387-90602-9). Springer-Verlag.

Narayana. Combinatorics, Representation Theory & Statistical Methods in Groups: Young Day Proceedings. (Lecture Notes in Pure & Applied Mathematics Ser.: Vol. 57). 192p. 1980. 37.50 (ISBN 0-8247-6937-6). Dekker.

Reiner, I., ed. Representation Theory of Finite Groups & Related Topics: Proceedings of the Symposia in Pure Mathematics-Madison, Wis.-1970. LC 79-165201. (Vol. 21). 1971. 29.00 (ISBN 0-8218-1421-4, PSPUM-21). Am Math.

Roggenkamp, K. W. Lattices Over Orders 2. new ed. LC 71-108334. (Lecture Notes in Mathematics: Vol. 142). 1970. pap. 18.30 (ISBN 0-387-04931-2). Springer-Verlag.

Roggenkamp, K. W. & Huber-Dyson, V. Lattices Over Orders 1. (Lecture Notes in Mathematics: Vol. 115). 1970. pap. 18.30 (ISBN 0-387-04904-5). Springer-Verlag.

Seminar on Periodic Maps. Proceedings. (Lecture Notes in Mathematics: Vol. 46). 1967. pap. 10.70 (ISBN 0-387-03917-1). Springer-Verlag.

Silberger, A. J. PGL-2, Over the P-Adics: Its Representations, Spherical Functions, & Fourier Analysis. LC 70-139951. (Lecture Notes in Mathematics: Vol. 166). 1970. pap. 14.00 (ISBN 0-387-05193-7). Springer-Verlag.

Stein, Elias M. Analytic Continuation of Group Representatives. LC 73-151591. (Yale Mathematical Monographs: No. 2). Repr. of 1971 ed. 15.00 (ISBN 0-8357-1679-1, 2016791). Bks Demand UMI.

Steklov Institute of Mathematics, Academy of Science, U. S. S. R., No. 80. Algebraic Number Theory & Representations: Proceedings. Faddeev, D. K., ed. (Proceedings of the Steklov Institute of Mathematics). 1968. 49.00 (ISBN 0-8218-1880-5, STEKLO-80). Am Math.

Stratila, S. V. & Voiculescu, D. V. Representations of AF-Algebras & of the Group U (Infinity) (Lecture Notes in Mathematics: Vol. 486). ix, 169p. 1975. pap. 14.00 (ISBN 0-387-07403-1). Springer-Verlag.

Vilenkin, N. Ja. Special Functions & the Theory of Group Representations. Rev. ed. LC 68-19438. (Translations of Mathematical Monographs: Vol. 22). 613p. 1983. pap. 53.00 (ISBN 0-8218-1572-5, MMONO-22). Am Math.

Wolf, J. A. Unitary Representations of Maximal Parabolic Subgroups of the Classical Groups. LC 76-44397. (Memoirs: No. 180). 193p. 1976. pap. 15.00 (ISBN 0-8218-2180-6, MEMO-180). Am Math.

Zelobenko, D. P. Compact Lie Groups & Their Representations. LC 73-17185. (Translations of Mathematical Monographs: Vol. 40). 448p. 1983. pap. 45.00 (ISBN 0-8218-1590-3, MMONO-40). Am Math.

REPRODUCTION

see also Cells; Embryology; Fertilization (Biology); Fetus; Generative Organs; Genetics; Plants–Reproduction; Pregnancy; Spontaneous Generation

Abel, Ernest L., compiled by. Alcohol & Reproduction: A Bibliography. LC 82-6202. ix, 219p. 1982. lib. bdg. 29.95 (ISBN 0-313-23474-4, AAR/). Greenwood.

Adiyodi, K. G. & Adiyodi, Rita G. Reproductive Biology of Invertebrates, Oogenesis, Oviposition & Oosorption, Vol. 1. LC 81-16355. 770p. 1983. 117.95 (ISBN 0-471-10128-1, Pub. by Wiley-Interscience). Wiley.

Adler, Norman T., ed. Neuroendocrinology of Reproduction: Physiology & Behavior. LC 80-28245. 576p. 1981. 42.00x (ISBN 0-306-40600-4, Plenum Pr); pap. 18.95x (ISBN 0-306-40611-X). Plenum Pub.

Ageing & Reproduction. 122p. 1970. 35.00x (ISBN 0-686-45131-7, Pub. by Biochemical England). State Mutual Bk.

Ansell, I. D. Atlas of Male Reproductive System Pathological. (Current Histopathology Ser.). 1985. lib. bdg. 77.00 (ISBN 0-85200-327-7, Pub. by MTP Pr England). Kluwer Academic.

Aristotle. Generation of Animals. (Loeb Classical Library: No. 366). 1943. 12.50x (ISBN 0-674-99403-5). Harvard U Pr.

Ashley Montagu, M. F. The Reproductive Development of the Female: A Study in the Comparative Physiology of the Adolescent Organism. 3rd ed. LC 78-55285. (Illus.). 252p. 1979. 26.00 (ISBN 0-88416-218-4). PSG Pub Co.

Austin, C. R. & Short, R. V., eds. Artificial Control of Reproduction. LC 70-185569. (Reproduction in Mammals Ser.: Bk. 5). (Illus.). 1973. 32.50 (ISBN 0-521-08505-5); pap. 9.95 (ISBN 0-521-09713-4). Cambridge U Pr.

--The Evolution of Reproduction. LC 76-8170. (Reproduction in Mammals Ser.: Bk. 6). (Illus.). 1975. pap. 9.95 (ISBN 0-521-29085-6). Cambridge U Pr.

--Hormonal Control of Reproduction. 2nd ed. LC 81-18060. (Reproduction of Mammals Ser.: No. 3). 170p. 1984. 42.50 (ISBN 0-521-25637-2); pap. 16.95 (ISBN 0-521-27594-6). Cambridge U Pr.

--Reproductive Fitness. (Reproduction in Mammals Ser.: Bk. 4). (Illus.). 225p. 1985. 39.50 (ISBN 0-521-26649-1); pap. 14.95 (ISBN 0-521-31984-6). Cambridge U Pr.

--Reproductive Patterns. LC 78-189597. (Reproduction in Mammals Ser.: Bk. 4). (Illus.). 120p. 1973. 32.50 (ISBN 0-521-08578-0); pap. 9.95 (ISBN 0-521-09616-2). Cambridge U Pr.

Balazs, Andras, et al. Reproduction & Aging. 331p. 1974. text ed. 29.50x (ISBN 0-8422-7159-7). Irvington.

Balin, H. & Glasser, S., eds. Reproductive Biology. 1973. 74.50 (ISBN 0-444-15004-8, Excerpta Medica). Elsevier.

Bellina, Joseph H. & Wilson, Josleen. You Can Have a Baby: Everything You Need to Know about Fertility. (Illus.). 1985. 18.95 (ISBN 0-517-55619-7). Crown.

Beltsville Symposia in Agricultural Research, ed. Animal Reproduction, No. 3. LC 78-65535. (Beltsville Symposia in Agricultural Research). (Illus.). 434p. 1979. 42.95 (ISBN 0-470-26672-4). Halsted Pr.

Biology Colloquium, 22nd, Oregon State University, 1961. Physiology of Reproduction: Proceedings. Hisaw, Frederick L., Jr., ed. LC 52-19235. (Illus.). 1963. 9.95x (ISBN 0-87071-161-X). Oreg St U Pr.

Biology of Reproduction in Mammals. 540p. 1969. 39.00x (ISBN 0-686-45134-1, Pub. by Biochemical England). State Mutual Bk.

Blackwelder, Richard E. & Shepherd, Benjamin A., eds. Diversity of Animal Reproduction. 152p. 1981. 59.00 (ISBN 0-8493-6355-1). CRC Pr.

Blerkom, Jonathan Van & Motta, Pietro. The Cellular Basis of Mammalian Reproduction. LC 78-10230. (Illus.). 263p. 1979. text ed. 42.00 (ISBN 0-8067-2041-7). Urban & S.

Boyarsky, Saul & Polakoski, Kenneth, eds. Goals in Male Reproductive Research: Proceedings of Conference on Future Goals in Reproductive Medicine & Surgery, 20 September, 1979, Bethesda, Md. 144p. 1981. 33.00 (ISBN 0-08-025910-3). Pergamon.

Buffalo Reproduction & Artificial Insemination: Proceedings of the Seminar Sponsored by SIDA-Govt. of India, held at the National Dairy Research Institute, Karnal, India, Dec. 4-15, 1978. (Animal Production & Health Papers: No. 13). 370p. 1979. pap. 26.50 (ISBN 92-5-100743-8, F2086, FAO). Unipub.

Christiansen, J. Reproduction in the Dog & Cat. (Illus.). 225p. Date not set. pap. price not set (Pub. by Bailliere-Tindall). Saunders.

Circulation & Reproduction Phenomena. 192p. 1970. 35.00x (ISBN 0-686-45135-X, Pub. by Biochemical England). State Mutual Bk.

Clark, W. H. & Adams, T. S., eds. Advances in Invertebrate Reproduction. (Developments in Endocrinology Ser.: Vol. 11). 400p. 1981. 68.50 (ISBN 0-444-00594-3, Biomedical Pr). Elsevier.

Clarke, J. R., ed. Oxford Reviews of Reproductive Biology, Vol. 6. (Illus.). 356p. 1984. text ed. 79.00x (ISBN 0-19-857539-4). Oxford U Pr.

Cleland, John & Hobcraft, John. Reproductive Change in Developing Countries. (Illus.). 320p. 1985. 24.95x (ISBN 0-19-828465-9). Oxford U Pr.

Clymer, R. Swinburne. Mystery of Sex: Race Regeneration. 273p. 1950. 7.95 (ISBN 0-932785-32-8). Philos Pub.

Comparative Aspects of Reproduction in Chiroptera (Bats) 1979. 32.00x (ISBN 0-686-45136-8, Pub. by Biochemical England). State Mutual Bk.

Council for Science & Society. Human Procreation: Ethical Aspects of the New Techniques. (Illus.). 1984. pap. 5.95x (ISBN 0-19-857608-0). Oxford U Pr.

Courot, M., ed. The Male in Farm Animal Reproduction. (Current Topics in Veterinary Medicine Ser.). 1985. lib. bdg. 69.50 (ISBN 0-89838-682-9, Pub. by Martinus Nijhoff Netherlands). Kluwer Academic.

Coutinho, Elsimar M. & Fuchs, Fritz, eds. Physiology & Genetics of Reproduction. LC 74-17494. (Basic Life Sciences: Vol. 4A & 4B). (Illus.). 464p. 1974. Set. Part A 52.50x (ISBN 0-306-36591-X, Plenum Pr); Part B 59.50x (ISBN 0-306-36592-8). Plenum Pub.

Crawley, Lawrence, et al. Reproduction, Sex, & Preparation for Marriage. 2nd ed. (Illus.). 256p. 1973. pap. 18.95 (ISBN 0-13-773937-0). P-H.

Crighton, D. B., ed. Immunological Aspects of Reproduction in Mammals. (Nottingham Easter School Ser.: No. 38). 448p. 1984. text ed. 135.00 (ISBN 0-408-10865-7). Butterworth.

Cross, Hansell F. All about Sex & Reproduction in a Nutshell: A Short Reference of Biological Facts. 1983. 10.00 (ISBN 0-533-05302-1). Vantage.

DeNicola, Alejandro F. & Blaquier, Jorge A. Physiopathology of Hypophysial Disturbances & Diseases of Reproduction. LC 82-15219. (Progress in Clinical & Biological Research Ser.: Vol. 87). 352p. 1982. 36.00 (ISBN 0-8451-0087-4). A R Liss.

Diczfalusy, E., ed. Pharmacology of Reproduction, Vol. 2. LC 67-19416. 1968. 37.00 (ISBN 0-08-012368-6). Pergamon.

Doty, Richard L., ed. Mammalian Olfaction: Reproducive Processes, & Behavior. 1976. 55.00 (ISBN 0-12-221250-9). Acad Pr.

Dukelow, W. Richard, et al. Laparoscopic Techniques in Studies of Reproductive Physiology. 1977. text ed. 32.50x (ISBN 0-8422-7232-1). Irvington.

Ebling, F. J. & Henderson, I. W., eds. Biological & Clinical Aspects of Reproduction. (International Congress Ser.: No. 394). 1976. 107.75 (ISBN 90-219-0324-5, Excerpta Medica). Elsevier.

Edinin, M. & Johnson, M. H., eds. Immunobiology of Gametes. LC 76-49952. (Clinical & Experimental Immunoreproduction Ser.: No. 4). (Illus.). 1977. 69.50 (ISBN 0-521-21441-6). Cambridge U Pr.

Edqvist, Lars-Eric & Kindahl, Hans. Prostaglandins in Animal Reproduction, Vol II. (Developments in Animal & Veterinary Sciences Ser.: Vol. 13). 1984. 67.50 (ISBN 0-444-42294-3, I-049-84). Elsevier.

Effects of Pharmacologically Active Substances on Sexual Function. 124p. 1968. 35.00x (ISBN 0-686-45140-6, Pub. by Biochemical England). State Mutual Bk.

Engels, W. Advances in Invertebrate Reproduction. 1984. 92.50 (ISBN 0-444-80568-0, I-183-84). Elsevier.

The Environment & Reproduction in Mammals & Birds. 628p. 1973. 60.00x (ISBN 0-686-45143-0, Pub. by Biochemical England). State Mutual Bk.

Equine Reproduction. 776p. 1975. 100.00x (ISBN 0-686-45144-9, Pub. by Biochemical England). State Mutual Bk.

Equine Reproduction II. 652p. 1979. 100.00x (ISBN 0-906545-03-X, Pub. by Biochemical England). State Mutual Bk.

Farley, John. Gametes & Spores: Ideas about Sexual Reproduction, 1750-1914. LC 82-87. (Illus.). 312p. 1982. text ed. 27.50x (ISBN 0-8018-2738-8). Johns Hopkins.

Finn, C. A., ed. Oxford Reviews of Reproductive Biology, Vol. 2. (Illus.). 1980. text ed. 79.00x (ISBN 0-19-857535-1). Oxford U Pr.

--Oxford Reviews of Reproductive Biology, Vol. 3. (Illus.). 1981. text ed. 79.00x (ISBN 0-19-857536-X). Oxford U Pr.

--Oxford Reviews of Reproductive Biology, Vol. 4. (Illus.). 1982. cloth 79.00x (ISBN 0-19-857537-8). Oxford U Pr.

Fitch, Henry S. Reproductive Cycles in Tropical Reptiles. (Occasional Papers: No. 96). 53p. 1982. 3.25 (ISBN 0-317-04861-9). U of KS Mus Nat Hist.

Flerko, B., et al, eds. Reproduction & Development: Proceedings of the 28th International Congress of Physiological Sciences, Budapest, 1980. LC 80-41877. (Advances in Physiological Sciences: Vol. 15). (Illus.). 200p. 1981. 28.00 (ISBN 0-08-027336-X). Pergamon.

Frajese, G., et al, eds. Oligozoospermia: Recent Progress in Andrology. 496p. 1981. text ed. 70.50 (ISBN 0-89004-589-5). Raven.

Frajese, Gaetano, ed. Proceedings of the First International Symposium on Reproduction. (Serono Symposia Publications Ser.). Date not set. text ed. price not set. Raven.

Franchimont, P. & Channing, C. P., eds. Intragonadal Regulation of Reproduction. LC 81-66365. 1981. 55.00 (ISBN 0-12-265280-0). Acad Pr.

Fraser, Andrew F. Reproductive Behaviour in Ungulates. 1968. 39.00 (ISBN 0-12-266450-7). Acad Pr.

Garcia, Celso-Ramon & Rosenfeld, David L. Human Fertility: The Regulation of Reproduction. LC 76-15411. (Illus.). 163p. 1977. pap. text ed. 15.00x (ISBN 0-8036-3910-4). Davis Co.

Gebbie, Donald A. Reproductive Anthropology: Descent Through Woman. LC 80-42013. 321p. 1981. 54.95x (ISBN 0-471-27985-4, Pub. by Wiley-Interscience). Wiley.

Genetics & Reproduction. 124p. 1972. 35.00x (ISBN 0-686-45150-3, Pub. by Biochemical England). State Mutual Bk.

Giese, Arthur C. & Pearse, John S., eds. Reproduction of Marine Invertebrates: Molluscs: Pelecypods & Lesser Classes, Vol. 5. LC 72-84365. 1979. 70.00 (ISBN 0-12-282505-5). Acad Pr.

Giese, Pearse. Reproduction of Marine Invertebrates: Entoprocts: Lesser Callomates. 1975. Vol. 2. 80.50. Acad Pr.

Gilmore, Desmond. Environmental Factors in Mammal Reproduction. (Illus.). 340p. 1981. text ed. 53.50 (ISBN 0-8391-1656-X). Univ Park.

Gleicher, Norbert. Reproductive Immunology. LC 81-11812. (Progress in Clinical & Biological Research Ser.: Vol. 70). 510p. 1981. 86.00 (ISBN 0-8451-0070-X). A R Liss.

Greep, Roy O., ed. Reproductive Physiology IV. (International Review of Physiology Ser.: Vol. 27). (Illus.). 352p. 1983. text ed. 49.50 (ISBN 0-8391-1555-5, 14206). Univ Park.

Greep, Roy O. & Koblinsky, Majorie A., eds. Frontiers in Reproduction & Fertility Control. 1977. 55.00x (ISBN 0-262-07068-5). MIT Pr.

Hafez, E. S. Comparative Reproducton of Nonhuman Primates. (Illus.). 572p. 1971. photocopy ed. 58.50x (ISBN 0-398-02302-6). C C Thomas.

Hafez, E. S. & Kenemans, P. An Atlas of Human Reproduction: By Scanning Electron Microscopy. 300p. 1982. text ed. 60.00 (ISBN 0-85200-411-7, Pub. by MTP Pr England). Kluwer Academic.

Hamilton, David & Naftolin, Frederick, eds. Basic Reproductive Medicine, Vol. 1: Basic & Development of Reproduction. (Illus.). 176p. 1981. text ed. 30.00x (ISBN 0-262-08089-3); pap. text ed. 13.75x (ISBN 0-262-58045-4). MIT Pr.

--Basic Reproductive Medicine, Vol. 2: Reproductive Function in Men. (Illus.). 336p. 1982. text ed. 32.50x (ISBN 0-262-08102-4); pap. text ed. 16.50x (ISBN 0-262-58046-2). MIT Pr.

Harrison, Richard J. Reproduction & Man. (Contemporary Science Library). (Illus.). 1971. pap. 1.65x (ISBN 0-393-00581-X, Norton Lib). Norton.

Hearn, J. P., ed. Reproduction in New World Primates: Animal Models for Medical Research. (Illus.). 350p. 1982. text ed. 55.00 (ISBN 0-85200-407-9, Pub. by MTP Pr England). Kluwer Academic.

Hogarth, Peter J. Biology of Reproduction. (Tertiary Level Biology Ser.). 189p. 1982. 23.95x (ISBN 0-470-27348-8). Halsted Pr.

Holmes, R. L. Reproduction & Environment. (Contemporary Science Library). (Illus.). 1971. pap. 1.65x (ISBN 0-393-00588-7, Norton Lib). Norton.

Hrdy, Sarah B. The Langurs of Abu: Female & Male Strategies of Reproduction. (Illus.). 1977. 22.50x (ISBN 0-674-51057-7); pap. 8.95x (ISBN 0-674-51058-5). Harvard U Pr.

Hubinont, P. O., ed. Ontogeny of Bonding Attachment. (Progress in Reproductive Biology & Medicine: Vo. 11). (Illus.). vi, 178p. 1984. 61.75 (ISBN 3-8055-3862-6). S Karger.

Hunter, R. H. Physiology & Technology of Reproduction in Female Domestic Animals. 1981. 60.00 (ISBN 0-12-361950-5). Acad Pr.

International Conference on Comparative Aspects of Reproductive Failure - Dartmouth - 1966. Proceedings. Benirschke, K., ed. (Illus.). 1967. 58.50 (ISBN 0-387-03751-9). Springer-Verlag.

International Congress of Primatology, 3rd, Zurich, 1970. Primatology: Proceedings, 3 vols. Incl. Vol. 1. Taxonomy, Anatomy, Reproduction. Biegert, J. & Leutenegger, W., eds. (Illus.). xvi, 278p. 40.50 (ISBN 3-8055-1244-9); Vol. 2. Neurobiology, Immunology, Cytology. Biegert, J. & Leutenegger, W., eds. (Illus.). x, 245p. 38.50 (ISBN 3-8055-1245-7); Vol. 3. Behavior. Kummer, H., ed. (Illus.). x, 191p. 30.00 (ISBN 3-8055-1246-5). 1971. Set. 108.75 (ISBN 3-8055-1247-3). S Karger.

International Planned Parenthood Federation, ed. Immunology & Reproduction. 1969. 14.00x (ISBN 0-686-87110-3, Pub. by Intl Planned Parent). State Mutual Bk.

International Symposium on Aging Gametes, Seattle, June 1973. Aging Gametes-Their Biology & Pathology: Proceedings. Blandeau, R. J., ed. (Illus.). xii, 415p. 1975. 51.25 (ISBN 3-8055-1842-0). S Karger.

Jagiello, Georgiana & Vogel, Henry J., eds. Bioregulators of Reproduction. LC 81-7906. (P&S Biomedical Sciences Ser.). 1981. 71.50 (ISBN 0-12-379980-5). Acad Pr.

Jones, Richard E. Human Reproduction & Sexual Behavior. (Illus.). 608p. 1984. pap. 28.95 (ISBN 0-13-447524-0). P-H.

Lange, Oskar & Banasinski, A. Theory of Reproduction & Accumulation. 1969. 32.00 (ISBN 0-08-012256-6). Pergamon.

LaVal, Richard K. & Fitch, Henry S. Structure Movements & Reproduction in Three Costa Rican Bat Communities. (Occasional Papers: No. 69). 28p. 1977. pap. 1.75 (ISBN 0-317-04875-9). U of KS Mus Nat Hist.

Lein, Allen. The Cycling Female: Her Menstrual Rhythm. LC 78-23675. (Illus.). 135p. 1979. pap. text ed. 11.95 (ISBN 0-7167-1038-2). W H Freeman.

Lindsay, D. R. & Pearce, D. T., eds. Reproduction in Sheep. 427p. 1985. 79.50 (ISBN 0-521-30659-0). Cambridge U Pr.

Lloyd, Charles W., ed. Recent Progress in the Endocrinology of Reproduction: Proceedings. 1959. 71.50 (ISBN 0-12-453450-3). Acad Pr.

Lockey, James E., et al. Reproduction: The New Frontier in Occupational & Environmental Health Research. LC 84-7871. (Progress in Clinical & Biological Research Ser.: Vol. 160). 628p. 1984. 68.00 (ISBN 0-8451-5010-3). A R Liss.

Luckett, P., ed. Reproductive Biology of the Primates. (Contributions to Primatology: Vol. 3). 284p. 1974. pap. 55.00 (ISBN 3-8055-1671-1). S Karger.

McCann & Dhindsa. Role of Peptides & Proteins in the Control of Reproduction. 370p. 1983. 75.00 (ISBN 0-444-00737-7, Biomedical Pr). Elsevier.

McClenaghan, Leroy R. & Gaines, Michael S. Reproduction in Marginal Populations of the Hispid Cotton Rat (Sigmodon Hispidus) in Northern Kansas. (Occasional Papers: Vol. 74). 16p. 1978. pap. 1.25 (ISBN 0-317-04888-0). U of KS Mus Nat Hist.

McKerns, Kenneth W., ed. Reproductive Processes & Contraception. LC 80-20744. (Biochemical Endocrinology Ser.). 756p. 1981. 79.50x (ISBN 0-306-40534-2, Plenum Pr). Plenum Pub.

McLaren, A. Advances in Reproductive Physiology, Vols. 1-5. Incl. Vol. 1. 1966 (ISBN 0-12-036601-0); Vol. 2. 1967; Vol. 3. 1968 (ISBN 0-12-036603-7); Vol. 4. 1969 (ISBN 0-12-036604-5); Vol. 5. Bishop, Marcus, ed. 1971. 70.00 ea. (ISBN 0-12-036605-3). 70.00 ea. Acad Pr.

Mahesh, V. B. & Muldoon, T. G., eds. Functional Correlates of Hormone Receptors in Reproduction. (Developments in Endocrinology Ser.: Vol. 12). 594p. 1981. 122.00 (ISBN 0-444-00604-4, Biomedical Pr). Elsevier.

Mahler, Fred. Alternative Ways of Life: An Approach from the Viewpoint of the Reproductive-Change Theory: Project on Goals, Processes, and Indicators of Development. 18p. 1982. pap. 5.00 (ISBN 92-808-0451-0, TUNU199, UNU). Unipub.

Mann, T. & Lutwak-Mann, C. Male Reproductive Function & Semen. (Illus.). 498p. 1981. 89.50 (ISBN 0-387-10383-X). Springer-Verlag.

Mariner, James L. Human Reproduction & Development. (Illus.). 155p. (Orig.). 1979. pap. text ed. 4.95x (ISBN 0-88334-118-2). Ind Sch Pr.

Mattison, Donald R., ed. Reproductive Toxicology. LC 83-927. (Progress in Clinical & Biological Research Ser.: Vol. 117). 408p. 1983. 58.00 (ISBN 0-8451-0117-X). A R Liss.

Montagna, William & Sadler, William A., eds. Reproductive Behavior. LC 74-14728. (Advances in Behavioral Biology Ser.: Vol. 11). 384p. 1974. 49.50x (ISBN 0-306-37911-2, Plenum Pr). Plenum Pub.

Morris, Desmond. Patterns of Reproductive Behavior. (Illus.). 528p. 1980. 12.95 (ISBN 0-224-61795-8, Pub. by Jonathan Cape). Merrimack Pub Cir.

Mosher, William D., et al. Reproductive Impairments Among Married Couples: United States. (Series Twenty Three: No. 11). 55p. 1982. pap. text ed. 1.75 (ISBN 0-8406-0252-9). Natl Ctr Health Stats.

Mosley, W. H., ed. Nutrition & Human Reproduction. LC 77-28738. 526p. 1978. 65.00x (ISBN 0-306-31122-4, Plenum Pr). Plenum Pub.

Nalbandov, A. V. Reproductive Physiology of Mammals & Birds: The Comparative Physiology of Domestic & Laboratory Animals & Man. 3rd ed. LC 75-25890. (Animal Science Ser.). (Illus.). 334p. 1976. 29.95x (ISBN 0-7167-0843-4). W H Freeman.

Negro-Vilar, Andres, ed. Male Reproduction & Fertility. 406p. 1983. text ed. 98.00 (ISBN 0-89004-746-4). Raven.

Nieschlag, E., ed. Hormone Assays in Reproductive Medicine. (Hormone Research: Vol. 9, No. 6). (Illus.). 1978. pap. 13.25 (ISBN 3-8055-2975-9). S Karger.

Nisbet, Ian C. & Karch, Nathan J. Chemical Hazards to Human Reproduction. LC 82-14441. (Illus.). 245p. 1983. 28.00 (ISBN 0-8155-0931-6). Noyes.

Novy, Miles J. & Resko, John A. Fetal Endocrinology. LC 81-19038. (ORPRC Symposium on Primate Reproductive Biology Ser.: Vol. 1). 1981. 49.50 (ISBN 0-12-522601-2). Acad Pr.

Ochiai, K., et al, eds. Endocrine Correlates of Reproduction. (Illus.). xii, 320p. 1984. 37.50 (ISBN 0-387-13514-6). Springer-Verlag.

Paige, Karen E., et al. The Female Reproductive Cycle: An Annotated Bibliography. (Women's Studies). 624p. 1985. lib. bdg. 75.00 (ISBN 0-8161-8343-0). G K Hall.

Pancheri, P., et al, eds. Endorphins, Neuroregulators & Behavior in Human Reproduction. (Current Clinical Practice Ser.: Vol. 26). 1985. 87.00 (ISBN 0-444-90403-4). Elsevier.

Pincus, Gregory, ed. Control of Fertility. 1965. 52.50 (ISBN 0-12-557056-2). Acad Pr.

Pope John Center Staff. Technological Powers & the Person: Nuclear Energy & Reproductive Technology. Lossing, Larry D. & Bayer, Edward J., eds. (Illus.). 370p. (Orig.). 1983. pap. 15.95 (ISBN 0-935372-12-1). Pope John Ctr.

Poyser, Norman L. Prostaglandins in Reproduction. (Prostaglandins Research Studies). 260p. 1981. 57.95 (ISBN 0-471-09986-4, Pub. by Res Stud Pr). Wiley.

Price, D. Porter. Cattle Reproduction Primer. 1986. price not set (ISBN 0-9606246-5-1). SW Sci Pub.

Reid, Duncan E., et al. Principles & Management of Human Reproduction. LC 70-118593. (Illus.). Repr. of 1972 ed. 120.00 (2016678). Bks Demand UMI.

Reiter, R. J., ed. The Pineal & Reproduction. (Progress in Reproductive Biology: Vol. 4). (Illus.). 1978. 50.75 (ISBN 3-8055-2815-9). S Karger.

Reiter, R. J. & Follett, B. K., eds. Seasonal Reproduction in Higher Vertebrates. (Progress in Reproductive Biology: Vol. 5). (Illus.). vi, 222p. 1980. 66.00 (ISBN 3-8055-0246-X). S Karger.

Rele, J. R. Fertility Analysis Through Extension of Stable Population Concepts & Stochastic Model of Human Reproduction. LC 76-5422. (Population Monograph Ser.: No. 11). 1976. Repr. lib. bdg. 35.00 (ISBN 0-8371-8826-1, REFA). Greenwood.

Rickart, Eric A. Reproduction Growth & Development in Two Species of Cloud Forest Peromycus from Southern Mexico. (Occasional Papers: No. 67). 22p. 1977. pap. 1.25 (ISBN 0-317-04907-0). U of Ks Mus Nat Hist.

Rowlands, J. W., et al. Equine Reproduction, No. III. 1982. 179.00x (ISBN 0-906545-08-0, Pub. by Journals Repro England). State Mutual Bk.

Salisbury, G. W., et al. Physiology of Reproduction & Artificial Insemination of Cattle. 2nd ed. LC 77-13598. (Animal Science Ser.). (Illus.). 798p. 1978. text ed. 43.95x (ISBN 0-7167-0025-5). W H Freeman.

Schwaner, Terry D. Reproductive Biology of Lizards on the American Samoan Islands. (Occasional Papers: No. 86). 53p. 1980. 3.00 (ISBN 0-317-04887-2). U of KS Mus Nat Hist.

Scott, James & Jones, Warren R., eds. Immunology of Human Reproduction. 498p. 1976. 69.00 (ISBN 0-8089-0954-1, 793945). Grune.

Segal, Sheldon J., et al. The Regulation of Mammalian Reproduction. (Illus.). 614p. 1973. photocopy ed. 59.75x (ISBN 0-398-02405-7). C C Thomas.

Serio, Mario & Martini, Luciano, eds. Animal Models in Human Reproduction. 500p. 1980. text ed. 64.50 (ISBN 0-89004-522-4). Raven.

Shulman, Sidney, et al, eds. Immunological Factors in Human Reproduction. (Serono Symposia Ser.: No. 45). 1982. 44.00 (ISBN 0-12-640780-0). Acad Pr.

Shulman, Sidney S. Reproduction & Antibody Response. LC 75-2388. (Uniscience Ser.). 150p. 1975. 48.00 (ISBN 0-87819-059-7). CRC Pr.

Silver, Rae, intro. by. Hormones & Reproductive Behavior: Readings from Scientific American. LC 79-1192. (Illus.). 181p. 1979. text ed. 20.95x (ISBN 0-7167-1093-5); pap. text ed. 11.95x (ISBN 0-7167-1094-3). W H Freeman.

Smith, Robert L. Sperm Competition & the Evolution of Animal Mating Systems. 1984. 41.00 (ISBN 0-12-652570-6). Acad Pr.

Society For The Study Of Developmental Biology - 24th Symposium. Reproduction: Molecular, Subcellular & Cellular. Locke, M., ed. 1966. 63.00 (ISBN 0-12-454174-7). Acad Pr.

Sorensen, A. M., Jr. Repro Lab: A Laboratory Manual for Animal Reproduction. 4th ed. (Illus.). 151p. 1979. pap. text ed. 7.95x (ISBN 0-89641-011-0). American Pr.

Sorensen, Anton M., Jr. Animal Reproduction: Principles & Practice. Zappa, C. Robert, ed. (Agriculture Sciences Ser.). (Illus.). 1979. text ed. 42.95 (ISBN 0-07-059670-0). McGraw.

Stancyk, Stephen E., ed. Reproductive Ecology of Marine Invertebrates. LC 79-13841. (Belle W. Baruch Library in Marine Science Ser.). xvi, 284p. 1979. lib. bdg. 39.95x (ISBN 0-87249-379-2). U of SC Pr.

Steinbergen. Reproductive Biology & Medicine. Date not set. write for info. (ISBN 0-444-00834-9). Elsevier.

Symond, Zuspan. Clinical & Diagnostic Procedures in Gynecology Reproduction Medicine. 1984. Pt. A, 500 pg. 55.00 (ISBN 0-8247-7031-5); Pt. B, 488 pg. 55.00 (ISBN 0-8247-1778-3). Dekker.

Taylor, Howard C., ed. Human Reproduction: Lectures in Physiology, Population, & Family Planning. Incl. Vol. 1. Physiology. 160p. spiral 165.00x (ISBN 0-262-20034-1); pap. 14.00x (ISBN 0-262-70011-5); Vol. 2. Population. 160p. spiral 165.00x (ISBN 0-262-20035-X); pap. 14.00x (ISBN 0-262-70012-3); Vol. 3. Family Planning. 250p. spiral 165.00x (ISBN 0-262-20036-8); pap. 14.00x (ISBN 0-262-70013-1). 1976. Set. text ed. 450.00x incl. 500 color transparencies (ISBN 0-262-20037-6). MIT Pr.

Tienhoven, Ari Van. Reproductive Physiology of Vertebrates. 2nd ed. (Illus.). 560p. 1982. 49.50x (ISBN 0-8014-1281-1). Cornell U Pr.

Toder, V. & Beer, A. E., eds. Immunology & Immunopathology of Reproduction. (Contributions to Gynecology & Obstetics: Vol. 14). (Illus.). viii, 180p. 1985. 52.50 (ISBN 3-8055-4059-0). S Karger.

Tokei. Essays on the Asiatic Mode of Reproduction. 1979. 13.00 (ISBN 0-9960013-9-5, Pub. by Akademiai Kaido Hungary). Heyden.

Vaitukaitis. Clinical Reproductive Neuroendocrinology. (Current Endocrinology Ser.: Vol. 5). 238p. 1982. 48.00 (ISBN 0-444-00657-5, Biomedical Pr). Elsevier.

Van Blerkom, Jonathan & Motta, Pietro, eds. Ultrastructure of Reproduction Gametogenesis, Fertilization & Embryogenesis. (Electron Microscopy in Biology & Medicine). 1983. lib. bdg. 74.00 (ISBN 0-89838-572-5, Pub. by Martinus Nijhoff Netherlands). Kluwer Academic.

Vandenbergh, John G., ed. Pheromones & Reproduction in Mammals. LC 82-22776. 1983. 41.50 (ISBN 0-12-710780-0). Acad Pr.

Vokaer, R. & De Bock, G., eds. Sexual Endocrinology: Proceedings of the Fondation pour la recherche en endocrinologie sexuelle et la reproduction humaine. 252p. 1975. text ed. 52.00 (ISBN 0-08-018170-8). Pergamon.

Wegmann, Thomas C. & Gill, Thomas J., III, eds. Immunology of Reproduction. (Illus.). 1983. text ed. 49.50x (ISBN 0-19-503096-6). Oxford U Pr.

Whitfield, Philip. The Animal Family: The Fascinating Variety of Parenthood, from the Courtship Displays to the Day the Children Leave Home. (Illus.). 1980. 21.95 (ISBN 0-393-01304-9). Norton.

WHO Scientific Group. Geneva, 1968. Biological Components of Human Reproduction; Studies of Their Variations in Population Groups: Report. (Technical Report Ser.: No. 435). (Also avail. in French & Spanish). 1969. pap. 2.00 (ISBN 92-4-120435-4). World Health.

WHO Scientific Group. Geneva, 1972. Reproductive Function in the Human Male: Report. (Technical Report Ser.: No. 520). (Also avail. in French & Spanish). 1973. pap. 1.60 (ISBN 92-4-120520-2). World Health.

Yen, Samuel S. & Jaffe, Robert B. Reproductive Endocrinology: Physiology, Pathophysiology & Clinical Management. 2nd ed. (Illus.). Date not set. price not set (ISBN 0-7216-9630-9). Saunders.

Bernstein, Ilene N. & Freeman, Howard E. Academic & Entreprenurial Research: The Consequences of Diversity in Federal Evaluation Studies. LC 74-83208. 108p. 1975. text ed. 9.95x (ISBN 0-87154-109-2). Russell Sage.

Beveridge, William I. Art of Scientific Investigation. 1960. pap. 3.95 (ISBN 0-394-70129-1, V129, Vin). Random.

Bloom, Martin. Research in the Human Services. 710p. 1986. text ed. price not set (ISBN 0-02-311040-6). Macmillan.

Braybrooke, Susan, ed. Design for Research: Principles of Laboratories. 1985. 25.00 (ISBN 0-471-06260-X). Wiley.

Broad, William & Wade, Nicholas. Betrayers of the Truth: Fraud & Deceit in the Halls of Science. 256p. 1983. pap. 6.95 (ISBN 0-671-49549-6, Touchstone). S&S.

Bromberg, Joan L. Fusion: Science, Politics & the Invention of a New Energy Source. (Illus.). 376p. 1985. 40.00x (ISBN 0-262-02180-3); pap. 9.95 (ISBN 0-262-52106-7). MIT Pr.

Brown, George H. And Part of Which I Was - Recollections of a Research Engineer. LC 82-72256. (Illus.). 342p. 1982. 20.00 (ISBN 0-9612524-0-5). Angus Cupar.

Brown, Richard D. National Environmental Policiea & Research Programs. LC 83-50572. 165p. 1983. pap. 25.00 (ISBN 0-87762-330-9). Technomic.

Bush, George P. & Hattery, Lowell H., eds. Teamwork in Research. 1953. 4.00 (ISBN 0-87419-007-X). U Pr of Wash.

Cannon, Walter B. The Way of an Investigator. 1945. 30.00 (ISBN 0-8274-4190-8). R West.

Centre National de la Recherce Scientifique, ed. Annuaire Francais de Droit International: 1981, Vol. XXVII (1981) LC 57-28515. (Fr.). 1206p. 1982. cancelled (ISBN 2-222-03121-4). Intl Pubns Serv.

Columbia University. Quarter Century of Learning, 1904-1929. facs. ed. LC 68-58780. (Essay Index Reprint Ser). 1931. 21.50 (ISBN 0-8369-1028-1). Ayer Co Pubs.

Committee on Science, Engineering & Public Policy. Research Briefing 1983. 92p. 1983. pap. text ed. 8.50 (ISBN 0-309-03437-X). Natl Acad Pr.

Coyle, William. Research Papers. 6th ed. 240p. (Orig.). 1985. pap. text ed. 8.48scp (ISBN 0-672-61637-8). Bobbs.

Crowl, Thomas K. Fundamentals of Research: A Practical Guide for Educators & Special Educators. (Illus.). 275p. 1986. text ed. 26.95x (ISBN 0-942280-13-X). Pub Horizons.

CSIRO Published Papers: Subject Index (1916-1968, 16 Vols. (Complete to 1968). 1978. pap. 72.00 (ISBN 0-643-02114-0, C054, CSIRO). Unipub.

Dixon, Diana & Hills, Philip. Talking about Your Research. 1981. 25.00x (ISBN 0-906083-19-2, Pub. by Primary Com England). State Mutual Bk.

Epton, S. R., et al, eds. Managing Interdisciplinary Research. 245p. 1985. 29.95 (ISBN 0-471-90317-5, Pub. by Wiley-Interscience). Wiley.

Farkas. Sociology of Science & Research. 1980. 51.00 (ISBN 0-9960016-7-0, Pub. by Akademiai Kaido Hungary). Heyden.

Ferre, John P. Merrill Guide to the Research Paper. 1983. pap. text ed. 9.95 (ISBN 0-675-20029-6). Additional supplements may be obtained from publisher. Merrill.

Fisher, Ronald A. Statistical Methods for Research Workers. 14th ed. (Illus.). 1973. 19.95x (ISBN 0-02-844730-1). Hafner.

Forti, Augusto. Research & Human Needs: A Search for a New Development Paradigm. (Illus.). 176p. 1981. 33.00 (ISBN 0-08-027417-X). Pergamon.

Friedman, Lawrence M., et al. Fundamentals of Clinical Trials. 2nd ed. 236p. 1981. 29.00 (ISBN 0-88416-296-6). PSG Pub Co.

Gamow, George, et al. Science in Progress, Eighth Series. facsimile ed. Baitsell, George A., ed. LC 78-37534. (Essay Index Reprint Ser). Repr. of 1953 ed. 33.00 (ISBN 0-8369-2533-5). Ayer Co Pubs.

Glasser, Alan. Research & Development Management. (Illus.). 384p. 1982. 32.95 (ISBN 0-13-774091-3). P-H.

Gonseth, Ferdinand. Time & Method: An Essay on the Methodology of Research. Guggenheimer, Eva H., tr. (Illus.). 468p. 1972. 39.75x (ISBN 0-398-02297-6). C C Thomas.

Gordon, Michael. The Evaluation of Research Papers by Primary Journals in the U. K. 76p. 1978. 25.00x (ISBN 0-906083-03-6, Pub. by Primary Com England). State Mutual Bk.

Granstrand, Ove. Technology, Management & Marketing. LC 82-16804. 300p. 1982. 25.00x (ISBN 0-312-79007-4). St Martin.

Hagstrom, Warren O. Scientific Community. LC 74-18379. (Arcturus Books Paperbacks). 319p. 1975. pap. 4.25 (ISBN 0-8093-0720-0). S Ill U Pr.

Hale, George E. National Academies & the Progress of Research. Cohen, I. Bernard, ed. LC 79-7965. (Three Centuries of Science in America Ser.). 1980. Repr. of 1915 ed. lib. bdg. 14.00x (ISBN 0-405-12546-1). Ayer Co Pubs.

Hauer, Mary, et al. Books, Libraries, & Research. 1983. pap. text ed. 13.95 (ISBN 0-8403-3067-7, 40306701). Kendall-Hunt.

Hawkins, C. & Sorgi, M., eds. Research. (Illus.). 195p. 1985. pap. 18.00 (ISBN 0-387-13992-3). Springer-Verlag.

Hook, Sidney, et al, eds. The Ethics of Teaching & Scientific Research. LC 76-56902. 212p. 1977. 14.95 (ISBN 0-87975-068-5). Prometheus Bks.

Horowitz, Lois. Knowing Where to Look: The Ultimate Guide to Research. 368p. 1984. 16.95 (ISBN 0-89879-159-6). Writers Digest.

Huck, Schuyler W., et al. Reading Statistics & Research. 1974. pap. text ed. 13.95 scp (ISBN 0-06-042976-3, HarpC). Har-Row.

Husserl, Edmund. Logische Untersuchungen, 3 Vols. (Ger.). 1968. Repr. of 1913 ed. Set. 38.00x (ISBN 3-4847-0118-8). Adlers Foreign Bks.

Igor, Boy. And Yet it Moves: The Realization & Suppression of Science & Technology. (Illus.). 144p. (Orig.). 1985. pap. 4.00 (ISBN 0-934727-00-7). Zamisdat Pr.

Information Gatekeepers, Inc. The Second Viewtext Exposition VT'82. 1981. 125.00 (ISBN 0-686-38471-7). Info Gatekeepers.

Institute of Petroleum. Methods for Analysis & Testing, Vol. 1, Pt. 1. 1982. 145.00x (ISBN 0-471-26146-7, Pub. by Wiley Heyden). Wiley.

Jacob, Herbert. Using Published Data: Errors & Remedies. LC 84-50250. 63p. 1984. pap. 5.00 (ISBN 0-8039-2299-X). Sage.

Jewett, Frank B., et al. Science in Progress, Fifth Series. facsimile ed. Baitsell, George A, ed. LC 78-37534. (Essay Index Reprint Ser). Repr. of 1947 ed. 35.50 (ISBN 0-8369-2530-0). Ayer Co Pubs.

Kendrew, J. & Shelley, J. Priorities in Research. (International Congress Ser.: Vol. 615). 1984. 59.75 (ISBN 0-444-90333-X, I-181-84). Elsevier.

Kesselman-Turkel, Judi & Peterson, Franklynn. Research Shortcuts. 120p. 1982. pap. 2.95 (ISBN 0-8092-5749-1). Contemp Bks.

Kinnon, Collette M., ed. New Horizons of Human Knowledge: A Series of Public Talks Given at UNESCO. (Illus.). 98p. 1981. pap. 15.00 (ISBN 92-3-101903-1, U1196, UNESCO). Unipub.

Kone, Eugene H. & Jordan, Helene J., eds. The Greatest Adventure: Basic Research That Shapes Our Lives. LC 73-83747. (Illus.). 304p. 1974. 9.80x (ISBN 0-87470-018-3). Rockefeller.

Kruzas, Anthony T. & Gill, Kay, eds. International Research Centers: Supplement, 2 issues. 250p. 1984. pap. 200.00x (ISBN 0-8103-0468-6). Gale.

Landman, Uzi, ed. Statistical Mechanics & Statistical Methods in Theory & Applications. LC 77-22526. 814p. 1977. 115.00x (ISBN 0-306-31077-5, Plenum Pr). Plenum Pub.

Lang, Gerhard & Heiss, George D. A Practical Guide to Research Methods. 3rd ed. LC 83-23343. 206p. (Orig.). 1984. lib. bdg. 27.50 (ISBN 0-8191-3725-1); pap. text ed. 17.75 (ISBN 0-8191-3726-X). U Pr of Amer.

Langfitt, Thomas W., et al, eds. Partners in the Research Enterprise: University-Corporate Relations in Science & Technology. LC 83-3508. (Illus.). 224p. 1983. 35.00x (ISBN 0-8122-7893-3); pap. 14.95x (ISBN 0-8122-1150-2). U of Pa Pr.

Lawler, Edward E., III, et al. Doing Research That Is Useful for Theory & Practice. LC 84-43092. (Management Series & Social & Behavioral Science). 1985. text ed. 24.95x (ISBN 0-87589-649-9). Jossey-Bass.

Lawrence, Ernest O. Science in Progress, First Series. facsimile ed. Baitsell, George A., ed. LC 78-37534. (Essay Index Reprint Ser). Repr. of 1939 ed. 36.00 (ISBN 0-8369-2526-2). Ayer Co Pubs.

Leedy, Paul D. How to Read Research & Understand It. 1981. write for info. (ISBN 0-02-369250-2). Macmillan.

Lemaine, G., et al. Strategies et Choix dans la Recherche. (Maison des Sciences de l'Homme, Paris, Publications: No. 5). 1977. pap. 8.80x (ISBN 0-686-25775-8). Mouton.

Light, Richard J., ed. Evaluation Studies Review Annual, No. 8. 672p. 1983. 40.00 (ISBN 0-8039-1987-5). Sage.

Lindberg, John. Routines for Research: A Handbook of Basic Library Skills. LC 82-15962. 172p. 1983. lib. bdg. 23.50 (ISBN 0-8191-2750-7); pap. text ed. 11.25 (ISBN 0-8191-2751-5). U Pr of Amer.

Lindsley, Karen B., ed. Cave Research Foundation Annual Report: 1984. (Illus.). 60p. (Orig.). 1985. pap. 6.00 (ISBN 0-939748-17-7). Cave Bks MO.

Lipetz, Ben-Ami. Guide to Case Studies of Scientific Activity. LC 65-23580. 1965. 20.00x (ISBN 0-910788-02-2). Intermedia.

--Measurement of Efficiency of Scientific Research. LC 65-23581. 1965. 20.00x (ISBN 0-910788-01-4). Intermedia.

Lothrop, Warren C. Paradoxes in Research Administration. 1959. pap. 2.00 (ISBN 0-87744-051-4). Mich St U Pr.

Manten, A. A. & Timman, T., eds. Information Policy & Scientific Research. 170p. 1983. 40.50 (ISBN 0-444-86611-6, I-170-83). Elsevier.

Martin, Brian. The Bias of Science. LC 79-670595. 100p. (Orig.). 1979. pap. 6.00x (ISBN 0-909509-13-1, Pub. by Soc Res Sci Australia). Intl Spec Bk.

Mattessich, Richard. Instrumental Reasoning & Systems Methodology. (Theory & Decision Library: No. 15). xvii, 396p. 1980. lib. bdg. 44.75 (ISBN 90-277-0837-1); pap. 19.95 (ISBN 90-277-1081-3). Kluwer Academic.

Meyer, Gerd. Strukturinterne und Umstrukturierende Neuerungen Dargestellt Am Beispiel der Forschung. (VHS-V Ser.: Vol. 5). (Ger.). 339p. 1982. 28.95 (ISBN 3-261-04998-7). P Lang Pubs.

Miles, Walter R., et al. Science in Progress, Fourth Series. facsimile ed. Baitsell, George A., ed. LC 78-37534. (Essay Index Reprint Ser). Repr. of 1945 ed. 42.00 (ISBN 0-8369-2529-7). Ayer Co Pubs.

Miller, Howard S. Dollars for Research: Science & Its Patrons in Nineteenth-Century America. LC 71-103291. (Illus.). 276p. 1970. 20.00x (ISBN 0-295-95058-7). U of Wash Pr.

Miller, Mara. Where to Go for What: How to Research, Organize & Present Your Information. (Illus.). 240p. 1981. 11.95 (ISBN 0-13-957217-1, Spec); pap. 5.95 (ISBN 0-13-957209-0). P-H.

Milliken, George A. & Johnson, Dallas E. Analysis of Messy Data: Designed Experiments, Vol. I. LC 84-839. (Research Methods Ser.). 600p. 1984. 45.00 (ISBN 0-534-02713-X, Dist. by Van Nos Reinhold). Lifetime Learn.

Milliken, William G., pref. by. Directory of Research, Development & Testing Facilities in Michigan. 132p. (Orig.). 1981. pap. 12.00x (ISBN 0-938654-29-2). Indus Dev Inst Sci.

Mtewa, Mekki, ed. Science, Technology & Development: Options & Policies. LC 82-42546. (Illus.). 254p. (Orig.). 1982. lib. bdg. 25.50 (ISBN 0-8191-2533-4); pap. text ed. 13.25 (ISBN 0-8191-2534-2). U Pr of Amer.

Naess, Arne. The Pluralist & Possibilist Aspect of the Scientific Enterprise. 1972. 30.00x (ISBN 8-200-04609-5, Dist. by Columbia U Pr). Universitet.

Nelkin, Dorothy. Science As Intellectual Property: Who Controls Scientific Research. (AAAS Series on Issues in Science & Technology). 130p. 1983. text ed. 15.95 (ISBN 0-317-05124-5); pap. text ed. 7.95 (ISBN 0-02-949090-1). Macmillan.

--Science As Intellectual Property: Who Controls Scientific Research. (AAAS Series on Issues in Science & Technology). 130p. 1983. text ed. 15.95 (ISBN 0-02-949080-4); pap. text ed. 7.95. Free Pr.

Newman, A. A., ed. Photographic Techniques in Scientific Research, Vol. 3. 1979. 90.00 (ISBN 0-12-517963-4). Acad Pr.

Norman, Colin. The God That Limps: Science & Technology in the Eighties. 1981. 14.95 (ISBN 0-393-01504-1); pap. 6.95 (ISBN 0-393-30026-9). Norton.

Osburn, Charles B. Academic Research & Library Resources: Changing Patterns in America. LC 78-20017. (New Directions in Librarianship: No. 3). (Illus.). 1979. lib. bdg. 27.50 (ISBN 0-313-20722-4, OAR/). Greenwood.

Patten, Bradley M., et al. Science in Progress, Seventh Series. facsimile ed. Baitsell, George A., ed. LC 78-37534. (Essay Index Reprint Ser). Repr. of 1951 ed. 40.00 (ISBN 0-8369-2532-7). Ayer Co Pubs.

Pelz, Donald C. & Andrews, Frank M. Scientists in Organizations: Productive Climates for Research & Development. rev. ed. LC 76-620038. 400p. 1976. 18.00x (ISBN 0-87944-208-5). Inst Soc Res.

Petty, Clayton. Research Techniques in the Rat. (Illus.). 382p. 1982. 36.75x (ISBN 0-398-04595-X). C C Thomas.

Phillips, Don I. & Shen, Benjamin S., eds. Research in the Age of the Steady-State University. (AAAS Selected Symposium 60 Ser.). 130p. 1982. lib. bdg. 19.00x (ISBN 0-86531-380-6). Westview.

Posavac, Emil J. & Carey, Raymond G. Program Evaluation: Methods & Case Studies. 2nd ed. (Illus.). 368p. 1985. text ed. 28.95 (ISBN 0-13-729484-0). P-H.

Rabier, Jacques-Rene & Inglehart, Ronald. Euro-Barometer 10-A: Scientific Priorities in the European Community, October-November 1978. LC 81-84734. 1981. write for info. codebook (ISBN 0-89138-944-X). ICPSR.

Research in British Universities, Polytechnics & Colleges: Physical Sciences, Vol. 1. 1982. 75.00x (ISBN 0-904654-23-0, Pub. by Brit Lib England). State Mutual Bk.

Ritterbush, Philip C., ed. Scientific Institutions of the Future. LC 72-3811. (Prometheus Paperback Ser). 164p. 1972. pap. 3.95 (ISBN 0-87491-502-3). Acropolis.

Rivers, W. Finding Facts: Interviewing, Observing, Using Reference Sources. 1975. pap. 13.95 (ISBN 0-13-316364-4). P-H.

Ross, Robert. Research: An Introduction. pap. 5.95 (ISBN 0-06-460141-2, CO 141, COS). B&N NY.

Rowe, Mary B., ed. What Research Says to the Science Teacher, Vol. 1. Incl. What Research Says to the Science Teacher, Vol. 2. Rowe, Mary B., ed. (Orig.). 1979. pap. 6.00 (ISBN 0-87355-013-7); What Research Says to the Science Teacher, Vol. 3. Harms, Norris C. & Yager, Robert E., eds. (Orig.). 1981. pap. 7.50 (ISBN 0-87355-018-8); What Research Says to the Science Teacher, Vol. 4. Yager, Robert E., ed. 107p. 1982. pap. 8.00. 1978. pap. 5.00 (ISBN 0-87355-009-9). Natl Sci Tchrs.

Rudman, Jack. Director of Research & Evaluation. (Career Examination Ser.: C-2891). (Cloth bdg. avail. on request). pap. 14.00 (ISBN 0-8373-2891-8). Natl learning.

--Research Worker. (Career Examination Ser.: C-546). (Cloth bdg. avail. on request). pap. 10.00 (ISBN 0-8373-0546-2). Natl Learning.

Science Policy & Organization of Research in Norway. (Science Policy Studies & Documents). (Orig.). 1966. pap. 5.00 (ISBN 92-3-100621-5, U574, UNESCO). Unipub.

Science Policy Research & Teaching Units: Europe & North America, 1967-1970. 378p. (Orig.). 1971. pap. 8.25 (ISBN 92-3-000891-5, U582, UNESCO). Unipub.

Shapley, Harlow, et al. Science in Progress, Third Series. facsimile ed. Baitsell, George A., ed. LC 78-37534. (Essay Index Reprint Ser). Repr. of 1942 ed. 33.00 (ISBN 0-8369-2528-9). Ayer Co Pubs.

Sharpe, R. S., ed. Research Techniques in Non-Destructive Testing, Vol. 6. 1983. 59.50 (ISBN 0-12-639056-8). Acad Pr.

Shelly, M. W. & Glatt, E., eds. The Research Society. 564p. 1968. 92.50x (ISBN 0-677-11540-7). Gordon.

Sindermann, Carl J. The Joy of Science: Excellence & Its Rewards. 256p. 1985. (full discount avail.) 16.95 (ISBN 0-306-42035-X, Pub. by Plenum Pr). Plenum Pub.

Sipe, H. Craig & Farmer, Walter A. A Summary of Research in Science Education 1980. 503p. 1982. 26.95x (ISBN 0-471-87028-5, Pub. by Wiley Interscience). Wiley.

Smith, Robert V. Graduate Research: A Guide for Students in the Sciences. 175p. 1984. 21.95 (ISBN 0-89495-037-1); pap. 14.95 (ISBN 0-89495-038-X). ISI Pr.

Smyth, H. D., et al. Science in Progress, Sixth Series. facsimile ed. Baitsell, George A., ed. LC 78-37534. (Essay Index Reprint Ser). Repr. of 1949 ed. 34.50 (ISBN 0-8369-2531-9). Ayer Co Pubs.

Snyder, Laurence H., et al. Science in Progress, Ninth Series. facsimile ed. Baitsell, George A., ed. LC 78-37534. (Essay Index Reprint Ser). Repr. of 1955 ed. 33.00 (ISBN 0-8369-2534-3). Ayer Co Pubs.

Stadler, L. J., et al. Science in Progress, Second Series. facsimile ed. Baitsell, George A., ed. LC 78-37534. (Essay Index Reprint Ser). Repr. of 1940 ed. 35.50 (ISBN 0-8369-2527-0). Ayer Co Pubs.

Steele, Harold C. How to Motivate & Direct Students in Science Research. LC 70-112288. 1970. 6.95 (ISBN 0-87397-013-6). Strode.

Stepan, Nancy. The Idea of Race in Science: Great Britain 1800-1960. 230p. 1982. lib. bdg. 27.50 (ISBN 0-208-01972-3). Shoe String.

Struening, Elmer L. & Brewer, Marilynn B., eds. Handbook of Evaluation Research. 448p. 1983. pap. 17.95 (ISBN 0-8039-2162-4). Sage.

Stuart, Harold C. Center, the Group under Observation, Sources of Information & Studies in Progress. (SRCD M). 1939. 21.00 (ISBN 0-527-01508-3). Kraus Repr.

Technical Insights, Inc. Staff. Annual Report on Research & Development: 1984-the Year That Was; 1985-the Year to Come. LC 83-644912. 350p. 1985. 315.00 (ISBN 0-317-14657-2). Tech Insights.

Terleckyj, Nestor E., ed. The State of Science & Research: Some New Indicators. (Illus.). 200p. 1977. 22.00 (ISBN 0-89158-124-3). Natl Planning.

Trumbull, Richard. Research & Its Management: A Perspective & Critique. 1984. 12.95 (ISBN 0-533-05942-9). Vantage.

Tullock, Gordon. The Organization of Inquiry. LC 66-26026. pap. 60.50 (ISBN 0-317-26871-6, 2023461). Bks Demand UMI.

Tyndall, John. The Scientific Use of Man's Imagination. (Illus.). 181p. 1977. 43.15 (ISBN 0-89266-326-X). Am Classical Coll Pr.

Grant, Malcolm A., et al. Geothermal Reservoir Engineering. LC 82-4105. (Energy Science & Technology Ser.). 1983. 49.50 (ISBN 0-12-295620-6). Acad Pr.

Green, Gordon G. & Eiker, Earl E., eds. Accomplishments & Impacts of Reservoirs. 238p. 1983. pap. 24.00x (ISBN 0-87262-382-3). Am Soc Civil Eng.

Greene, J. R. The Creation of Quabbin Reservoir: Death of the Swift River Valley. 2nd. Ed ed. (Illus.). 123p. 1982. pap. 9.95 (ISBN 0-9609404-0-5). J R Greene.

Gunnison, D., ed. Microbial Processes in Reservoirs. (Developments in Hydrobiology Ser.). 1985. lib. bdg. 52.50 (ISBN 90-6193-525-3, Pub. by Junk Pub Netherlands). Kluwer-Academic.

Henderson-Sellers, B. Engineering Limnology. LC 84-1765. 500p. 1984. text ed. 65.95 (ISBN 0-273-08539-5). Pitman Pub MA.

Hollo, R., et al. HP-41CV Reservoir Economics & Engineering Manual. LC 83-12690. 280p. 1983. 49.95x (ISBN 0-87201-357-X); magnetic cards, manual 325.00 (ISBN 0-87201-351-0). Gulf Pub.

Institution of Civil Engineers Staff, ed. Floods & Reservoir Safety: An Engineering Guide. 64p. 1978. pap. 10.00x (ISBN 0-7277-0033-2). Am Soc Civil Eng.

Kays, William B. Construction of Linings for Reservoirs, Tanks, & Pollution Control Facilties. LC 77-3944. (Wiley Series of Practical Construction Guides). 379p. 1977. 59.95x (ISBN 0-471-02110-5, Pub. by Wiley-Interscience). Wiley.

McCoy, R. L. PETROCALC (TM) 1: Reservoir Engineering & Formation Evaluation. LC 82-24233. (PETROCALC (TM) Software for Petroleum Engineers Ser.). 144p. 1983. 29.95x (ISBN 0-87201-553-X); disk 200.00x (ISBN 0-87201-554-8). Gulf Pub.

--PETROCALC (TM) 3: Reservoir Economics & Evaluation. LC 84-558. (PETROCALC (TM) TM Software for Petroleum Engineers Ser.). 1984. incl. disk 395.00x (ISBN 0-87201-729-X). Gulf Pub.

Matson, Tim. Earth Ponds: The Country Pond Maker's Guide. (Illus.). 104p. 1982. pap. 10.95 (ISBN 0-914378-86-4). Countryman.

Nelson, R. A. Geologic Analysis of Naturally Fractured Reservoirs. (Illus.). 256p. 1985. 39.95x (ISBN 0-87201-575-0). Gulf Pub.

New York City Reservoirs in the Catskill Mountains. pap. 2.00 (ISBN 0-686-31388-7). Outdoor Pubns.

Recommendations Concerning Reservoirs. 1967. pap. 5.00 (ISBN 92-3-100664-9, U520, UNESCO). Unipub.

Reiss, L. H. Reservoir Engineering Aspects of Fractured Formations. LC 80-82728. 112p. (Orig.). 1981. pap. 18.95x (ISBN 0-87201-303-0). Gulf Pub.

Report of the Man-Made Lakes Stock Assessment Working Group: Jinji, Uganda, 1970. (Fisheries Reports: No. 87). 13p. 1970. pap. 7.50 (ISBN 0-686-93051-7, F1688, FAO). Unipub.

Taub, Frieda B., ed. Lakes & Reservoirs. (Ecosystems of the World Ser.: Vol. 23). 350p. 1984. 200.00 (ISBN 0-444-42059-2, I-487-83). Elsevier.

Timmerman, E. H. Practical Reservoir Engineering, Vol. 2. 367p. 1982. 71.95x (ISBN 0-87814-181-2). Pennwell Bks.

Toebes, G. H. & Sheppard, A., eds. Reservoir Systems Operations. LC 81-70788. 601p. 1981. pap. 40.00x (ISBN 0-87262-288-6). Am Soc Civil Eng.

Wahlstrom, E. Dams: Dam Foundations & Reservoir Sites. 1974. 59.75 (ISBN 0-444-41236-0). Elsevier.

RESERVOIRS–MATHEMATICAL MODELS

Aziz, K. & Settari, A. Petroleum Reservoir Simulation. (Illus.). 475p. 1979. 89.00 (ISBN 0-85334-787-5, Pub. by Elsevier Applied Sci England). Elsevier.

Ewing, R. E., ed. The Mathematics of Reservoir Simulation. LC 83-51501. (Frontiers in Applied Mathematics: No. 1). (Illus.). xii, 186p. 1984. text ed. 24.50 (ISBN 0-89871-192-4). Soc Indus-Appl Math.

Gessford, John E. The Use of Reservoir Water for Hydroelectric Power Generation. Bruchey, Stuart, ed. LC 78-22684. (Energy in the American Economy Ser.). (Illus.). 1979. lib. bdg. 12.00x (ISBN 0-405-11987-9). Ayer Co Pubs.

RESIDENTIAL CONSTRUCTION

see House Construction

RESIDUAL STRESSES

see also Stress Corrosion

Kanazawa, Takeshi & Kobayashi, A. S., eds. Significance of Defects in Welded Structures: Proceedings of the Japan-U. S. Seminar, 1973, Tokyo. 413p. 1974. 45.00x (ISBN 0-86008-114-1, Pub. by U of Tokyo Japan). Columbia U Pr.

VandeWalle, L. J. Residual Stress for Designers & Metallurgists. 1981. 51.00 (ISBN 0-87170-106-5). ASM.

RESIDUE ARITHMETIC

see Modular Arithmetic

RESIDUES OF AGRICULTURAL CHEMICALS

see Spraying and Dusting Residues in Agriculture

RESINOGRAPHY

Rochow, Theodore G. & Rochow, Eugene G. Resinography: An Introduction to the Definition, Identification, & Recognition of Resins, Polymers, Plastics, & Fibers. LC 75-34208. (Illus.). 193p. 1976. 35.00x (ISBN 0-306-30863-0, Plenum Pr). Plenum Pub.

RESINS

see Gums and Resins

RESISTANCE OF MATERIALS

see Strength of Materials

RESISTANCE OF PLANTS TO DISEASE

see Plants–Disease and Pest Resistance

RESISTANCE WELDING

see Electric Welding

RESONANCE

see also Electron Paramagnetic Resonance; Nuclear Magnetic Resonance; Quantum Electronics

Albeverio, S., et al, eds. Resonances Models & Phenomena. (Lecture Notes in Physics Ser.: Vol. 211). vi, 359p. 1984. pap. 21.00 (ISBN 0-387-13880-3). Springer-Verlag.

Braginsky, V. B., et al. Systems with Small Dissipation. Gliner, Erast, tr. (Illus.). 152p. 1985. lib. bdg. 28.00x (ISBN 0-226-07072-7); pap. 12.00x (ISBN 0-226-07073-5). U of Chicago Pr.

Di Bartolo, Baldassare & Powell, Richard C. Phonons & Resonances in Solids. LC 75-35691. (Illus.). pap. 133.30 (ISBN 0-317-09219-7, 2012430). Bks Demand UMI.

Needham, Joseph & Gwei-Djen, Lu. Trans-Pacific Echoes & Resonances: Listening Once Again. 120p. 1985. 18.00x (ISBN 9971-950-86-3, Pub. by World Sci Singapore). Taylor & Francis.

Rousseau, D., ed. Structural & Resonance Techniques in Biological Research. LC 54-11056. (Physical Techniques in Biology & Medicine Ser.). 1984. 69.00 (ISBN 0-12-599320-X). Acad Pr.

Symposium, University of Sao Paulo, 1969. Periodic Orbits, Stability & Resonances: Proceedings. Giacaglia, G. E., ed. LC 74-124848. 530p. 1970. lib. bdg. 50.00 (ISBN 90-277-0170-9, Pub. by Reidel Holland). Kluwer Academic.

Waseda, Y. Novel Application of Anomalous (Resonance) X-ray Scattering for Structural Characterization of Disordered Materials. (Lecture Notes in Physics Ser.: Vol. 204). vi, 183p. 1984. pap. 11.00 (ISBN 0-387-13359-3). Springer-Verlag.

RESONANCE, MAGNETIC

see Magnetic Resonance

RESOURCE RECOVERY

see Recycling (Waste, etc.)

RESPIRATION

see also Anoxemia; Respiratory Organs

Bouhuys, Arend, ed. The Physiology of Breathing: A Textbook for Medical Students. LC 76-46724. (Illus.). 368p. 1977. 30.00 (ISBN 0-8089-0984-3, 790647). Grune.

Cherniack, Reuben M. Pulmonary Function Testing. LC 77-75533. (Illus.). 1977. pap. text ed. 12.50 (ISBN 0-7216-2528-2). Saunders.

Davis, Joan & Mason, Celestine. Intensive Care of the Respiratory. 1986. cancelled (ISBN 0-442-22006-5). Van Nos Reinhold.

Dempsey, Jerome A. & Reed, Charles E., eds. Muscular Exercise & the Lung. (Illus.). 416p. 1977. 50.00x (ISBN 0-299-07220-7). U of Wis Pr.

Diamond, John. Speech, Language & the Power of Breath in Behavioral Kinesiology. (Behavioral Kinesiology Ser.). 85p. 1983. pap. 47.50 (ISBN 0-911238-77-8). B of A.

Fitzgerald, Robert S., et al, eds. The Regulation of Respiration During Sleep & Anesthesia. LC 78-6658. (Advances in Experimental Medicine & Biology Ser.: Vol. 99). 460p. 1978. 59.50x (ISBN 0-306-32699-X, Plenum Pr). Plenum Pub.

Furley, David J. & Wilkie, J. S., eds. Galen: On Respiration & the Arteries, an Edition with English Translation & Commentary of De Usu Respirationis, an in Arteriis Natura Sanguis Contineatur, De Usu Pulsum, & De Causis Respirationis. LC 81-47130. 300p. 1983. 30.00x (ISBN 0-691-08286-3). Princeton U Pr.

Gel'man, N. S., et al. Respiration & Phosphorylation of Bacteria. LC 66-26220. 238p. 1967. 32.50x (ISBN 0-306-30296-9, Plenum Pr). Plenum Pub.

Griscom, John H. Uses & Abuses of Air: Showing Its Influence in Sustaining Life & Producing Disease. LC 79-125743. (American Environmental Studies). 1970. Repr. of 1854 ed. 17.00 (ISBN 0-405-02668-4). Ayer Co Pubs.

Haggard, Howard W. & Greenberg, Leon A. Diet & Physical Efficiency: Influence of Frequency of Meals Upon Physical Efficiency & Industrial Productivity. Stein, Leon, ed. LC 77-70500. (Work Ser.). (Illus.). 1977. lib. bdg. 20.00x (ISBN 0-405-10171-6). Ayer Co Pubs.

Haldane, John S. Organisms & Enviorment as Illustrated by the Physiology of Breathing. 1917. 39.50x (ISBN 0-686-83659-6). Elliots Bks.

Hall, Diana L. Why Do Animals Breathe? Cohen, I. Bernard, ed. LC 80-2089. (Development of Science Ser.). (Illus.). 1981. lib. bdg. 25.00x (ISBN 0-405-13855-5). Ayer Co Pubs.

Hempfing, W. P., ed. Microbial Respiration. LC 78-22097. (Benchmark Papers in Microbiology: Vol. 13). 337p. 1979. 45.95 (ISBN 0-87933-344-8). Van Nos Reinhold.

Hornbein. Regulation of Breathing, 2 pts. (Lung Biology in Health & Disease Ser.: Vol. 17). 1981. Pt. 1. 85.00 (ISBN 0-8247-6607-5); Pt. 2. 99.50 (ISBN 0-8247-1013-4). Dekker.

Ingelstedt, Sven. Studies on the Conditioning of Air in the Respiratory Tract. 1956. 12.00 (ISBN 0-384-25735-6). Johnson Repr.

Kelsey, Neal. Respiratory Therapy Review: A Workbook & Study Guide. 2nd ed. LC 81-14170. (Illus.). 402p. 1982. pap. text ed. 25.95 (ISBN 0-8016-2638-2). Mosby.

Kryger, Meir H. Pathophysiology of Respiration. LC 81-2113. (Wiley Ser. in Pathophysiology). 352p. 1981. pap. text ed. 19.95 (ISBN 0-471-05923-4, Pub. by Wiley Med). Wiley.

McLaughlin, Arthur J., Jr. Organization & Management for Respiratory Therapists. LC 78-1577. (Illus.). 160p. 1979. pap. text ed. 12.50 (ISBN 0-8016-3311-7). Mosby.

Nakamura, Takashi. Oriental Breathing Therapy. LC 79-91515. (Illus.). 160p. 1981. pap. 11.50 (ISBN 0-87040-478-4). Japan Pubns USA.

Nicholls, Peter. The Biology of Oxygen. Head, J. J., ed. LC 81-67981. (Carolina Biology Readers Ser.). (Illus.). 16p. 1982. pap. 1.60 (ISBN 0-89278-300-1, 45-9700). Carolina Biological.

Nunn, J. F. Applied Respiratory Physiology. 2nd ed. 1977. 69.95 (ISBN 0-407-00060-7). Butterworth.

Pallot, David J. Control of Respiration. 1983. 39.50x (ISBN 0-19-520439-5). Oxford U Pr.

Piiper, J., ed. Respiratory Function in Birds, Adult & Embryonic: Proceedings, Satellite of the 27th International Congress of Physiological Sciences, Paris 1977. (Proceedings in Life Sciences). (Illus.). 1978. 38.00 (ISBN 0-387-08645-5). Springer-Verlag.

Rama, Swami, et al. Science of Breath-a Practical Guide. LC 79-65517. (Illus.). 166p. 1979. 8.95 (ISBN 0-89389-059-6); pap. 6.95 (ISBN 0-89389-057-X). Himalayan Pubs.

Randall, D. J., et al. The Evolution of Air Breathing in Vertebrates. LC 80-462. (Illus.). 176p. 1981. 34.50 (ISBN 0-521-22259-1). Cambridge U Pr.

Rau. Respiratory Therapy Pharmacology. 2nd ed. 1984. 24.95 (ISBN 0-8151-7076-9). Year Bk Med.

Saunders & Sullivan. Sleep & Breathing. (Lung Biology in Health & Disease Ser.). 640p. 1984. 75.00 (ISBN 0-8247-7064-1). Dekker.

Schlaefke, M. E., et al, eds. Central Neurone Environment & the Control Systems of Breathing & Circulation. (Proceedings in Life Sciences Ser.). 275p. 1983. 37.00 (ISBN 0-387-11671-0). Springer-Verlag.

Snider, Gordon L. Clinical Pulmonary Medicine. 1981. 34.50 (ISBN 0-316-80218-2). Little.

Societas Europaea Physiologiae Clinicae Respiratoriae & Gesellschaft fuer Lungen und Atmungsforschung, Bochum, 1969. Chronic Inflammation of the Bronchi: Proceedings. Ulmer, W. T., ed. (Progress in Respiration Research: Vol. 6). 1971. 68.25 (ISBN 3-8055-1189-2). S Karger.

Speads, Carola H. Breathing: The ABC's. LC 77-11537. (Illus.). 1978. 12.45i (ISBN 0-06-013996-X, HarpT). Har-Row.

Stough, Carl & Stough, Reece. Dr. Breath: The Story of Breathing Coordination. LC 81-82800. 255p. 1981. Repr. of 1970 ed. 14.95 (ISBN 0-940830-00-0). Stough Inst.

Traver, Gayle A., ed. Respiratory Nursing: The Science & Art. LC 81-16285. 474p. 1982. 28.00 (ISBN 0-471-04539-X, Pub. by Wiley Med). Wiley.

West, John B., ed. Bioengineering Aspects of the Lung. (Lung Biology & Health Ser.: Vol. 3). 1977. 89.75 (ISBN 0-8247-6378-5). Dekker.

Widdicombe, J., ed. Respiratory Physiology, Vol. II. 1977. 35.50 (ISBN 0-8391-1063-4). Univ Park.

Witschi, Hanspeter & Nettesheim, Paul. Mechanisms in Respiratory Toxicology, 2 Vols. 288p. 1981. Vol. I, 240p. 86.00 (ISBN 0-8493-5689-X); Vol. II 240p. 81.00 (ISBN 0-8493-5690-3). CRC Pr.

Wood & Lenfant. Evolution of Respiratory Processes. LC 79-4051. (Lung Biology in Health & Disease Ser.: Vol. 13). 1979. 69.75 (ISBN 0-8247-6793-4). Dekker.

Zagelbaum, Gary L. & Pare, J A. Manual of Acute Respiratory Care. (Little, Brown Spiral Manual Ser.). 1982. 16.95 (ISBN 0-316-98467-1). Little.

RESPIRATION OF PLANTS

see Plants–Respiration

RESPIRATORY ORGANS

see also Lungs; Respiration

Blodgett, Diane E., ed. Manual of Respiratory Care Procedures. (Illus.). 239p. 1980. pap. text ed. 13.75 (ISBN 0-397-50434-9, 65-05614, Lippincott Medical). Lippincott.

Brain, et al. Respiratory Defense Mechanisms, Pt. 2. (Lung Biology in Health & Disease Ser.: Vol. 5). 1977. 99.50 (ISBN 0-8247-6532-X). Dekker.

--Respiratory Defense Mechanisms, Pt. 1. (Lung Biology in Health & Disease Ser.: Vol. 5). 1977. 75.00 (ISBN 0-8247-6381-5). Dekker.

Brainard, C. A. & Wirth, M. Respiratory Care: National Board Review. (Illus.). 512p. 1984. pap. 24.95 (ISBN 0-89303-816-4). Brady Comm.

Dejours, Pierre, ed. Principles of Comparative Respiratory Physiology. 2nd ed. LC 74-25821. 251p. 1981. 32.50 (ISBN 0-444-80279-7, North-Holland). Elsevier.

Drage, Charles, ed. Respiratory Medicine for Primary Care Physicians. LC 82-6870. 222p. 1983. 33.00 (ISBN 0-12-788165-4). Acad Pr.

Forgacs, Paul. Problems in Respiratory Medicine. Fry, J., et al, eds. LC 81-68106. (Problems in Practice Ser.: Vol. 2). (Illus.). 158p. 1982. text ed. 20.00x (ISBN 0-8036-3684-9). Davis Co.

Goldberg, Kathy E. & Mason, Joan E., eds. Respiratory Emergencies. (Nursing Now Ser.). (Illus.). 128p. 1984. text ed. 13.95 (ISBN 0-916730-80-8). Springhouse Corp.

Gong, Henry, Jr. & Drage, Charles W., eds. The Respiratory System: A Core Curriculum. (Illus.). 400p. 1982. 28.95x (ISBN 0-8385-8280-X). ACC.

Harper, Rosalind W. A Guide to Respiratory Care: Physiology & Clinical Applications. (Illus.). 361p. 1982. pap. text ed. 26.00 (ISBN 0-397-54243-7, 64-02002, Lippincott Nursing). Lippincott.

Herzog, H., ed. Ketotifen in the Prophylactic Treatment of Bronchial Asthma. (Journal: Respiration: Vol. 39). (Illus.). 54p. 1980. pap. 17.25 (ISBN 3-8055-1171-X). S Karger.

Hirnle, Robert W. Clinical Simulations in Neonatal Respiratory Therapy. LC 81-13134. 316p. 1982. pap. 18.95 (ISBN 0-471-08266-X, Pub. by Wiley Medical). Wiley.

Ingwersen, Ulla. Respiratory Physical Therapy & Pulmonary Care. LC 76-27094. pap. 44.00 (ISBN 0-317-07783-X, 2017410). Bks Demand UMI.

Netter, Frank, illus. Respiratory System, Vol. 7. (Medical Illustrations Ser.). (Illus.). 1979. 52.50x (ISBN 0-914168-09-6). CIBA Med.

Petty, Thomas L., ed. Intensive & Rehabilitative Respiratory Care: A Practical Approach to the Management of Acute & Chronic Respiratory Failure. 3rd ed. LC 81-23630. (Illus.). 464p. 1982. text ed. 22.50 (ISBN 0-8121-0764-0). Lea & Febiger.

Prakash, O. Applied Physiology in Clinical Respiratory Care. 1982. 76.00 (ISBN 90-247-2662-X, Pub. by Martinus Nijhoff Netherlands). Kluwer Academic.

Respiratory System. (Medical Ser.). (Illus.). 52p. 1983. pap. text ed. 9.95 (ISBN 0-935920-12-9). Natl Pub Black Hills.

Sawyer, Kenneth C. Management of Foreign Bodies in the Food & Air Passages. (Illus.). 208p. 1967. photocopy ed. 19.75x (ISBN 0-398-01653-4). C C Thomas.

Slonim, N. Balfour. Respiratory Physiology. 4th ed. LC 81-11055. (Illus.). 301p. 1981. pap. text ed. 19.95 (ISBN 0-8016-4668-5). Mosby.

Teresinski, Michael F. & Cheremisinoff, Paul N. Industrial Respiratory Protection. LC 82-72859. (Illus.). 349p. 1983. 39.95 (ISBN 0-250-40587-3). Butterworth.

Thacker, E. Winifred. Postural Drainage & Respiratory Control. 3rd ed. (Illus.). 1971. 12.95 (ISBN 0-8151-8779-3). Year Bk Med.

Weibel, Ewald R. The Pathway for Oxygen. (Illus.). 320p. 1984. text ed. 27.50t (ISBN 0-674-65791-8); pap. text ed. 17.50t (ISBN 0-674-65790-X). Harvard U Pr.

Widdicombe, John & Davies, Andrew. Respiratory Physiology. (Illus.). 128p. 1984. pap. text ed. 15.50 (ISBN 0-8391-2020-6, 21288). Univ Park.

RESTORATION OF BUILDINGS

see Architecture–Conservation and Restoration

RESTRAINT OF ANIMALS

see Animals, Treatment Of

RETAINING WALLS

Newman, Morton. Standard Cantilever Retaining Walls. LC 81-14248. 670p. 1981. Repr. of 1976 ed. lib. bdg. 42.50 (ISBN 0-89874-389-3). Krieger.

Reimbert, M. & Reimbert, A. Retaining Walls, Anchorages & Sheet Piling: Part1. LC 74-77789. (Series on Rock & Soil Mechanics). Orig. Title: Murs De Soutenements. (Illus.). 284p. 1974. 40.00x (ISBN 0-87849-009-4). Trans Tech.

RETICULO-ENDOTHELIAL SYSTEM

see also Histoplasmosis; Macrophages

Bellanti, Joseph A. & Herscowitz, Herbert B., eds. The Reticuloendothelial System: A Comprehensive Treatise: Vol. 6: Immunology. (Immunology Ser.). 337p. 1984. 55.00x (ISBN 0-306-41421-X, Plenum Pr). Plenum Pub.

Carr, Ian & Daems, W. T., eds. The Reticuloendothalial System--A Comprehensive Treatise, Vol. 1: Morphology. (Illus.). 818p. 1980. 69.50x (ISBN 0-306-40291-2, Plenum Pr). Plenum Pub.

Heller, John H., ed. Reticuloendothelial Structure & Function. LC 60-9817. Repr. of 1960 ed. 91.80 (ISBN 0-8357-9976-X, 2012566). Bks Demand UMI.

Reichard, Sherwood M. & Filkens, James P., eds. The Reticuloendothelial System: A Comprehensive Treatise, Vol. 7A. (Physiology Ser.). 436p. 59.50x (ISBN 0-306-41422-8, 00497076, Plenum Pr). Plenum Pub.

Sbarra, Anthony J. & Strauss, Robert, eds. Reticuloendothelial System--A Comprehensive Treatise: Biochemistry & Metabolism. 456p. 1980. 55.00x (ISBN 0-306-40292-0, Plenum Pr). Plenum Pub.

RETINA

see also Color Vision

Ali, M. A. & Anctil, M. Retinas of Fishes: An Atlas. LC 76-22204. (Illus.). 1976. 71.00 (ISBN 0-387-07840-1). Springer-Verlag.

Bazan, N. G. & Lolley, R. N., eds. Neurochemistry of the Retina: Proceedings of the International Symposium on the Neurochemistry of the Retina, 28 August - 1 September 1979, Athens, Greece. (Illus.). 584p. 1980. 105.00 (ISBN 0-08-025485-3). Pergamon.

Bonnet, Mireille. Microsurgery of Retinal Detachment. (Illus.). 1980. text ed. 33.00x (ISBN 0-89352-067-5). Masson Pub.

Chignell, A. H. Retinal Detachment Surgery. (Illus.). 1980. 40.00 (ISBN 0-387-09475-X). Springer-Verlag.

Corboy, J. M. The Retinoscopy Book: A Manual for Beginners. rev. ed. LC 79-65451. 143p. 1979. text ed. 19.50 (ISBN 0-913590-67-3). Slack Inc.

Drujan, Boris D. & Laufer, Miguel, eds. The S-Potential. LC 82-20394. (Progress in Clinical & Biological Research Ser.: Vol. 113). 364p. 1982. 60.00 (ISBN 0-8451-0113-7). A R Liss.

Granit, Ragnar. Sensory Mechanisms of the Retina. (Illus.). 1963. Repr. of 1947 ed. 17.95x (ISBN 0-02-845410-3). Hafner.

Gruen, Gerd. The Development of the Vertebrate Retina: A Comparative Survey. (Advances in Anatomy, Embryology, & Cell Biology Ser.: Vol. 78). (Illus.). 130p. 1982. pap. 26.00 (ISBN 0-387-11770-9). Springer-Verlag.

Hilfer, S. R. & Sheffield, J. B., eds. Molecular & Cellular Basis of Visual Acuity. (Cell & Developmental Biology of the Eye). (Illus.). 210p. 1984. 37.00 (ISBN 0-387-90964-8). Springer-Verlag.

Orfanos, C. E. & Schuppli, R., eds. Workshop on Oral Retinoids in Dermatology Held on the 15th International Congress of Dermatology, Mexico City, October 1977. 1978. pap. 11.25 (ISBN 3-8055-2950-3). S Karger.

Osborne, N. O. & Chader, G. J., eds. Progress in Retinal Research, Vol. 1. (Illus.). 245p. 1982. 79.00 (ISBN 0-08-028901-0). Pergamon.

Ramon Y Cajal, Santiago. Structure of the Retina. Thorpe, Sylvia A., tr. (Illus.). 224p. 1972. 23.50x (ISBN 0-398-02385-9). C C Thomas.

Rand, Gertrude. The Factors That Influence the Sensitivity of the Retina to Color. Bd. with Learning in Dementia Praecox. Boring, E. G. Repr. of 1913 ed; An Experiment in Linear Space Perception. Maxfield, F. N. Repr. of 1913 ed; The Form Board Test. Sylvester, R. H. Repr. of 1913 ed; The Influence of Stimulus Duration on Reaction Time. Wells, G. R. Repr. of 1913 ed. (Psychology Monographs General & Applied: Vol. 15). pap. 36.00 (ISBN 0-317-15615-2). Kraus Repr.

Ratliff, Floyd, ed. Studies on Excitation & Inhibition in the Retina. LC 73-89539. (Illus.). 688p. 1974. 17.50x (ISBN 0-87470-044-2). Rockefeller.

Rodieck, R. W. The Vertebrate Retina: Principles of Structure & Function. LC 79-190434. (Biology Ser.). (Illus.). 1044p. 1973. text ed. 69.95x (ISBN 0-7167-0696-2). W H Freeman.

Van Buren, J. M. The Retinal Ganglion Cell Layer: A Physiological Anatomical Correlation in Man & Primates of the Normal Topographical Anatomy of the Retinal Ganglion Cell Layer & Its Alterations with Lesions of the Visual Pathways. (Illus.). 160p. 1963. photocopy ed. 16.00x (ISBN 0-398-04422-8). C C Thomas.

Vogel, M. Postnatal Development of the Cat's Retina. (Advances in Anatomy, Embryology, & Cell Biology: Vol. 54, Pt. 4). (Illus.). 1978. pap. 23.00 (ISBN 0-387-08799-0). Springer-Verlag.

Wagner, H. J. Cell Types & Connectivity Patterns in Mosaic Retinas. (Advances in Anatomy, Embryology & Cell Biology: Vol. 55, Pt. 3). (Illus.). 1978. pap. 31.00 (ISBN 0-387-09013-4). Springer-Verlag.

Zinn, Keith M. & Marmor, Michael F., eds. The Retinal Pigment Epithelium. (Illus.). 531p. 1979. text ed. 45.00x (ISBN 0-674-76684-9). Harvard U Pr.

RETOUCHING (PHOTOGRAPHY)

see Photography–Retouching

RETRIEVERS

see also Dogs–Breeds, subdivided to specific types of retrievers, e.g. Dogs–Breeds–Labrador Dogs

Kersley, J. A. Training the Retriever: A Manual. LC 77-165561. (Illus.). 208p. 1985. 13.95 (ISBN 0-87605-774-1). Howell Bk.

Wolters, Richard A. Water Dog. 1964. 12.50 (ISBN 0-525-23021-1, 01214-360). Dutton.

REUSABLE SPACE VEHICLES

Bowers, P. Rockwell Space Shuttle: Minigraph 10. write for info (ISBN 0-942548-15-9). Aerofax.

Deutsche Gesellschaft Fur Luft und Raumfahrt. Utilization of Space Shuttle & Spacelab: Proceedings of an International Meeting Held in Bonn, 1976. (Illus.). 1976. pap. 30.00x (ISBN 3-88135-034-9). Univelt Inc.

Greene, Lawrence P., ed. Space-Enhancing Technological Leadership. LC 57-43769. (Advances in the Astronautical Sciences Ser.: Vol. 44). (Illus.). 630p. 1981. lib. bdg. 65.00x (ISBN 0-87703-147-9, Pub. by Am Astronaut); pap. text ed. 50.00x (ISBN 0-87703-148-7); Microfiche Supplement 5.00x (ISBN 0-87703-164-9). Univelt Inc.

Joels, Kerry M. & Kennedy, Gregory P. The Space Shuttle Operators' Manual. Kennedy, Gregory P., designed by. (Orig.). 1982. pap. 9.95 (ISBN 0-345-30321-0). Ballantine.

Kaplan, Marshall H. Space Shuttle: America's Wings to the Future. 2nd ed. 216p. 1982. 19.95 (ISBN 0-8168-8451-X). Aero.

Shuttle Environment & Operations. 85.00 (ISBN 0-317-06661-7). AIAA.

Space Shuttle. 1985. 35.00 (ISBN 0-87263-171-0). SME.

Space Shuttle: Dawn of an Era, Vol 41. 1980. Part 1, 452pp. 45.00x (ISBN 0-87703-111-8, Pub. by Am Astronaut); Part 2, 502pp. 55.00x (ISBN 0-87703-113-4); microfiche suppl. 5.00x (ISBN 0-87703-136-3). Univelt Inc.

Stockton, William & Wilford, John N. Space-Liner: The New York Times Report on the Columbia's Voyage. 183p. 1981. 12.50 (ISBN 0-8129-0979-8). Times Bks.

Torres, George. The Space Shuttle: A Quantum Leap. (Illus.). 1984. cancelled (ISBN 0-8283-1976-6). Branden Pub Co.

REVEGETATION

see also Reforestation

Lewis, Roy R., III, ed. Creation & Restoration of Coastal Plant Communities. 232p. 1982. 69.50 (ISBN 0-8493-6573-2). CRC Pr.

Thames, John, ed. Reclamation & Use of Disturbed Land in the Southwest. LC 76-17133. Repr. of 1977 ed. 71.50 (ISBN 0-8357-9623-X, 2055250). Bks Demand UMI.

REVOLVERS

see also Colt Revolver

Askins, Charles. Askins on Pistols & Revolvers. Bryant, Ted & Askins, Bill, eds. 144p. 1980. text ed. 25.00 (ISBN 0-935998-22-5); pap. 8.95 (ISBN 0-935998-21-7). Natl Rifle Assn.

Dougan, John C. Know Your Ruger Single Action Revolvers: 1953-1963. Amber, John T., ed. (Know Your Gun Ser.). (Illus.). 192p. 1981. 35.00 (ISBN 0-941540-05-7). Blacksmith Corp.

Hogg, Ian V. Revolvers. (Illus.). 1984. 12.95 (ISBN 0-85368-674-2, Arms & Armour Pr). Sterling.

Lewis, Jack. Gun Digest Book of Single Action Revolvers. LC 82-72295. (Illus.). 256p. (Orig.). 1982. pap. 11.95 (ISBN 0-910676-48-8). DBI.

Millard, J. T. A Handbook on the Primary Identification of Revolvers & Semi-Automatic Pistols. (Illus.). 168p. 1974. pap. 10.25x (ISBN 0-398-03081-2). C C Thomas.

Munnell, J. C. A Blacksmith Guide to Ruger Rimfire Revolvers. (Illus.). 56p. 1982. pap. 7.50 (ISBN 0-941540-07-3). Blacksmith Corp.

Myatt, F. An Illustrated Guide to Pistols & Revolvers. LC 80-70974. (Illus.). 160p. 1981. 9.95 (ISBN 0-668-05233-3, 5233). Arco.

Nonte, George C., Jr. Revolver Guide. (Illus.). 288p. pap. 10.95 (ISBN 0-88317-094-9). Stoeger Pub Co.

Report of Board on Tests of Revolvers & Automatic Pistols 1907. (Illus.). pap. 3.50 (ISBN 0-686-20763-7). Sand Pond.

Ross, H. W. A Blacksmith Guide to Ruger Flattops & Super Blackhawks. (Illus.). 96p. 1982. pap. 9.95 (ISBN 0-941540-08-1). Blacksmith Corp.

Seaton, Lionel, tr. Famous Auto Pistols & Revolvers, Vol. II. (Illus.). 1979. 6.95 (ISBN 0-89149-030-2). Jolex.

Williams, Mason. The Sporting Use of the Handgun. (Illus.). 288p. 1979. 14.75x (ISBN 0-398-03850-3). C C Thomas.

Wood, J. B. Gun Digest Book of Firearms Assembly - Disassembly: Pt. II: Revolvers. LC 79-54271. (Illus.). 320p. 1979. pap. 12.95 (ISBN 0-695-81316-1). DBI.

REVOLVING CANNON

see Machine Guns

REVOLVING SYSTEMS

see Rotational Motion

RHEOLOGY

see also Colloids; Deformations (Mechanics); Elasticity; Materials–Creep; Plasticity; Non-Newtonian Fluids; Viscosity

Billington, E. W. & Tate, A. The Physics of Deformation & Flow. (Illus.). 720p. 1981. text ed. 72.00 (ISBN 0-07-005285-9). McGraw.

Cantow, H. J., et al, eds. Synthesis & Degradation-Rheology & Extrusion. (Advances in Polymer Science: Vol. 47). (Illus.). 170p. 1982. 39.00 (ISBN 0-387-11774-1). Springer-Verlag.

Davenport, T. C., ed. Rheology of Lubricants. (Illus.). 148p. 1973. 22.25 (ISBN 0-85334-473-6, Pub. by Elsevier Applied Sci England). Elsevier.

Dealy, John M. Rheometers for Molten Plastics: A Practical Guide to Testing & Property Measurement. 300p. 1981. 39.50 (ISBN 0-442-21874-5). Van Nos Reinhold.

Drilling Mud & Cement Slurry Rheology Manual. 152p. 1982. 80.00x (ISBN 2-7108-0373-9, Pub. by Order Dept Graham Trotman England). State Mutual Bk.

Eirich, Frederick R., ed. Rheology: Theory & Applications, 5 vols. 1956-1969. Vol. 1. 1956. 95.00 (ISBN 0-12-234301-8); Vol. 2. 1958. 90.00 (ISBN 0-12-234302-6); Vol. 3. 1959. 90.00 (ISBN 0-12-234303-4); Vol. 4. 1967. 95.00 (ISBN 0-12-234304-2); Vol. 5. 1970. 95.00 (ISBN 0-12-234305-0). Acad Pr.

Gross, D. R. & Hwang, N. H. The Rheology of Blood, Blood Vessels & Associated Tissues. (NATO Advanced Study, Applied Science Ser.: No. 41). 382p. 1981. 42.50 (ISBN 90-286-0950-4). Sijthoff & Noordhoff.

Gross, D. R. & Hwang, N. H. C., eds. The Rheology of Blood Vessels & Associated Tissues. 1981. lib. bdg. 42.50 (ISBN 90-286-0950-4, Pub. Martinus Nijhoff Netherlands). Kluwer Academic.

Handbook of Rheology for Drilling Fluids & Cement Slurries. 152p. 1982. 90.00x (ISBN 2-7108-0373-9, Pub. by Graham & Trotman England). State Mutual Bk.

Harris, John. Rheology & Non-Newtonian Flow. LC 76-49635. pap. 94.00 (ISBN 0-317-27686-7, 2025217). Bks Demand UMI.

Hull, Harry H. Addendum to an Approach to Rheology Through Multivariable Thermodynamics. 24p. 1982. pap. 4.00x (ISBN 0-686-83764-9). Hull.

--An Approach to Rheology Through Multi-Variable Thermodynamics. 192p. 1982. text ed. 28.00 (ISBN 0-9606118-2-7). Hull.

Hutton, J. F., et al, eds. Theoretical Rheology. (Illus.). xvi, 377p. 1975. 52.00 (ISBN 0-85334-638-0, Pub. by Elsevier Applied Sci England). Elsevier.

International Symposium on Rheology & Soil Mechanics. Proceedings. Sirieys, P. M. & Kravtchenko, J., eds. (Eng. & Fr., Illus.). 1966. 92.10 (ISBN 0-387-03652-0). Springer-Verlag.

Janeschitz-Kriegl, H. Polymer Melt Rheology & Flow Birefringence. (Polymers-Properties & Applications Ser.: Vol. 6). (Illus.). 524p. 1983. 43.00 (ISBN 0-387-11928-0). Springer-Verlag.

Keedwell, M. J., ed. Rheology & Soil Mechanics. (Illus.). 340p. 1984. 57.00 (ISBN 0-85334-285-7, Pub. by Elsevier Applied Sci England). Elsevier.

May, Clayton A., ed. Chemorheology of Thermosetting Polymers. LC 83-12280. (ACS Symposium Ser.: No. 227). 325p. 1983. lib. bdg. 44.95x (ISBN 0-8412-0794-1). Am Chemical.

Middleman, Stanley. Flow of High Polymers: Continuum & Molecular Rheology. LC 67-29460. 246p. 1968. 39.50x (ISBN 0-470-60235-X, Pub. by Wiley-Interscience). Wiley.

Murakami, K. & Ono, K. Chemorheology of Polymers. (Polymer Science Library: Vol. 1). 216p. 1980. 51.00 (ISBN 0-444-41831-8). Elsevier.

Sherman, P. Industrial Rheology. 1970. 73.50 (ISBN 0-12-639950-6). Acad Pr.

Sherman, P., ed. Food Texture & Rheology. 1979. 62.00 (ISBN 0-12-639960-3). Acad Pr.

Sobotka, Z. Rheology of Materials & Engineering Structures. (Rheology Ser.: Vol. 2). 1984. 120.50 (ISBN 0-444-99621-4). Elsevier.

Tanner, Roger I. Engineering Rheology. (Oxford Engineering Science Ser.). (Illus.). 368p. 1985. 65.00 (ISBN 0-19-856144-X). Oxford U Pr.

Vinogradov, G. V. & Malkin, A. Y. Rheology of Polymers. (Illus.). 468p. 1980. 64.00 (ISBN 0-387-09778-3). Springer-Verlag.

Vyalov, S. S. Rheological Fundamentals of Soil Mechanics. (Developments in Geotechnical Engineering Ser.: Vol. 36). Date not set. write for info. (ISBN 0-444-42223-4). Elsevier.

Whorlow, R. W. Rheological Techniques. LC 79-40992. (Physics in Medicine & Biology Ser.). 447p. 1980. 104.95 (ISBN 0-470-26736-4). Halsted Pr.

RHEOLOGY (BIOLOGY)

Bauer, R. D. & Busse, R., eds. The Arterial System: Dynamics, Control Theory & Regulation. (Illus.). 1978. pap. 30.00 (ISBN 0-387-08897-0). Springer-Verlag.

Fung, Y. C. Biomechanics: Mechanical Properties of Living Tissues. (Illus.). 400p. 1981. 34.50 (ISBN 0-387-90472-7). Springer-Verlag.

Gabelnick, Henry L. & Litt, Mitchell. Rheology of Biological Systems. (Illus.). 320p. 1973. 24.50x (ISBN 0-398-02589-4). C C Thomas.

Hull, Harry H. Approach to Rheology Through Multivariable Thermodynamics. 158p. 1981. pap. 16.00 (ISBN 0-9606118-0-0); addendum 4.00 (ISBN 0-9606118-3-5). Hull.

Hwang, N. H. & Gross, D. R., eds. Biorheology: Physics of Biological Tissues, No. 41. (NATO Advanced Study Institute Series of Applied Science). 382p. 1981. 42.50x (ISBN 90-286-0950-4). Sijthoff & Noordhoff.

Messmer, K. & Hammersen, F., eds. White Cell Rheology & Inflammation. (Mikrozirkulation in Forschung und Klinik; Progress in Applied Microcirculation Ser.: Vol. 7). (Illus.). x, 124p. 1985. pap. 28.75 (ISBN 3-8055-4040-X). S Karger.

Miller, W., et al, eds. Die Lumboischialgie. (Fortbildungskurse fuer Rheumatologie: Vol. 6). (Illus.). xii, 264p. 1982. pap. 30.75 (ISBN 3-8055-2207-X). S Karger.

RHESUS MONKEY

Bleier, Ruth. The Hypothalmus of the Rhesus Monkey: A Cytoarchitectonic Atlas. LC 84-40146. (Illus.). 136p. 1984. text ed. 50.00x (ISBN 0-299-09890-7). U of Wis Pr.

Chan-Palay, V. Cerebellar Dentate Nucleus: With Applications to the Terrestrinal Planets & Meteorites. LC 76-46462. 1977. 132.00 (ISBN 0-387-07958-0). Springer-Verlag.

Davis, Roger T. & Leathers, Charles W. Behavior & Pathology of Aging in Rhesus Monkeys. LC 85-5255. (MP Ser.: Vol. 8). 326p. 1985. write for info. (ISBN 0-8451-3407-8). A R Liss.

Loy, J. D., et al. The Behavior of Gonadectomized Rhesus Monkeys. (Contributions to Primatology: Vol. 20). (Illus.). viii, 144p. 1983. 28.25 (ISBN 3-8055-3795-6). S Karger.

Manocha, S. L., et al. Macaca Mulatta Enzyme Histochemistry of the Nervous System. 1970. 60.00 (ISBN 0-12-469350-4). Acad Pr.

Szebenyi, Emil. Atlas of Macaca Mulatta. LC 79-78611. (Illus.). 307p. 1969. 55.00 (ISBN 0-8386-7347-3). Fairleigh Dickinson.

Valerio, D. A., et al. Macaca Mulatta: Management of a Laboratory Breeding Colony. 1969. pap. 24.50 (ISBN 0-12-710056-3). Acad Pr.

RHINENCEPHALON

Moulton, D. G., ed. Methods in Olfactory Research. 1975. 81.00 (ISBN 0-12-508950-3). Acad Pr.

Valverde-Garcia, Facundo. Studies on the Piriform Lobe. LC 65-16689. (Illus.). 1965. 10.00x (ISBN 0-674-85200-1). Harvard U Pr.

RHINOCEROS

Alexander, Scott. Advanced Rhinocerology. 9th ed. LC 81-51912. (Illus.). 128p. (Orig.). 1981. pap. 4.95 (ISBN 0-937382-01-9). Rhinos Pr.

Elephants & Rhinos in Africa: A Time for Decision. (Illus.). 36p. 1982. pap. 10.00 (ISBN 2-88032-208-1, IUCN113, IUCN). Unipub.

Martin, Esmond B. The International Trade in Rhinoceros Products. (Illus.). 83p. 1980. pap. 7.50 (ISBN 2-88032-203-0, IUCN86, IUCN). Unipub.

Rookmaaker, L. C., ed. Bibliography of the Rhinoceros: An Analysis of the Literature on the Recent Rhinoceroses in Culture, History & Biology. 312p. 1983. lib. bdg. 25.00 (ISBN 90-6191-261-X, Pub. by Balkema RSA). IPS.

Schenkel, R. & Schenkel-Hulliger, L. Ecology & Behavior of the Black Rhinoceros (Diceros Bicornis L.) A Field Study. (Mammalia Depicta Ser.: Vol. 5). (Illus.). 100p. (Orig.). 1969. pap. text ed. 16.50 (ISBN 3-4900-6918-8). Parey Sci Pubs.

Stumpke, Harald. The Snouters: Form & Life of the Rhinogrades. Chadwick, Leigh, tr. LC 81-10429. (Illus.). 118p. 1981. 4.95 (ISBN 0-226-77895-9, Phoen). U of Chicago Pr.

RHINOLOPHUS

see Bats

RHIZOCTONIA SOLANI

Parmeter, J. R., ed. Rhizoctonia Solani: Biology & Pathology. LC 69-16510. (Illus.). 1970. 46.50x (ISBN 0-520-01497-9). U of Cal Pr.

RHIZOPODA

Cash, J. & Hopkinson, J. British Freshwater Rhizopoda & Heliozoa, 5 Vols. 1905-21. Set. 92.00 (ISBN 0-384-07835-4). Johnson Repr.

RHODESIAN RIDGEBACK (DOG)

see Dogs–Breeds–Rhodesian Ridgeback

RHODIUM

Dickson, Ronald S. Organometallic Chemistry of Rhodium & Tridium. (Organometallic Chemistry Ser.). 1983. 85.00 (ISBN 0-12-215480-0). Acad Pr.

RHODODENDRON

Clarke, J. Harold. Getting Started with Rhododendrons & Azaleas. LC 82-16995. (Illus.). 268p. 1982. pap. 14.95 (ISBN 0-917304-30-6). Timber.

Cox, P. Larger Species of Rhododendrons. 1981. 49.00 (ISBN 0-7134-1747-1, Pub. by Batsford England). David & Charles.

Cox, Peter. Dwarf Rhododendrons. (Illus.). 296p. 1973. 17.95 (ISBN 0-02-528560-2). Macmillan.

Davidian, H. H. Rhododendron Species: The Lepidotes, Vol. I. LC 81-23232. (Illus.). 470p. 1982. cloth 59.95 (ISBN 0-917304-71-3). Timber.

Galle, Fred & Fell, Derek. All about Azaleas, Camellias & Rhododendrons. Beley, Jim, ed. LC 85-70879. (Illus.). 96p. (Orig.). 1985. pap. 5.95 (ISBN 0-89721-064-6). Ortho.

Leach, David G. Rhododendrons of the World. (Illus.). 1961. 50.00 (ISBN 0-684-10351-6, ScribT). Scribner.

Luteyn, James L. & O'Brien, Mary E., eds. Contributions Toward a Classification of Rhododendron. LC 79-27378. (Illus.). 340p. 1980. pap. 22.00x (ISBN 0-89327-221-3). NY Botanical.

Rhododendron Handbook 1980. 1982. 40.00x (ISBN 0-906603-18-8, Pub. by RHS Ent England). State Mutual Bk.

Rhododendrons & Their Relatives. 2.25 (ISBN 0-686-21158-8). Bklyn Botanic.

Sunset Editors. Azaleas, Rhododendrons, Camellias. LC 81-82866. (Illus.). 96p. 1982. pap. 4.95 (ISBN 0-376-03020-8, Sunset Bks). Sunset-Lane.

Wade, L. Keith. Phenology of Cultivated Rhododendrons in Lower Mainland of British Columbia. (Illus.). 225p. (Orig.). 1979. pap. 8.25 (ISBN 0-89955-412-1, Pub. by U BC Pr Canada). Intl Spec Bk.

West, Franklin H., et al. Hybrids & Hybridizers: Rhododendrons & Azaleas for Eastern North America. Livingston, Philip A., ed. LC 77-16822. (Illus.). 1978. 30.00 (ISBN 0-915180-04-9). Harrowood Bks.

Young, Judy & Chong, Lu-Sheng, trs. from Chinese. Rhododendrons of China. LC 80-68082. 1980. 18.00 (ISBN 0-8323-0373-9). Binford.

RHODOPHYCEAE

Dixon, Bashford. Biology of the Rhodophyta. (University Reviews of Botany: No. 4). (Illus.). 285p. 1977. pap. text ed. 17.50x (ISBN 3-87429-124-3). Lubrecht & Cramer.

Marine Algae of New Zealand, Vol. 3. Incl. Pt. 1. Bangiophycidate & Florideophycidate. Chapman, V. J. 14.00 (ISBN 3-7682-0591-6); Pt. 2. Florideophycidae: Rhodymeniales. Chapman, V. J. & Dromgoole, F. I. 8.00 (ISBN 3-7682-0592-4). (Illus.). 1970. Lubrecht & Cramer.

Romagnesi, H. & Gilles, G. Les Rhodophylles des Forets Cotieres du Gabon et de la Cote d'ivoire. (Nova Hedwigia Beiheft: No. 59). (Illus.). lib. bdg. 87.50 (ISBN 3-7682-5459-3). Lubrecht & Cramer.

RHOPALOCERA

see Butterflies

RHYNCHONELLA, FOSSIL

Ager, D. V. The Liassic Rhynchonellidae, Pt. 1. 12.00 (ISBN 0-384-00470-9). Johnson Repr.

Pettit, N. E. Rhynchonellidae of the British Chalk, 2 Pts. Repr. of 1950 ed. Set. 18.00 (ISBN 0-384-46080-1). Johnson Repr.

RHYNCHOTA

see Hemiptera

RIBONUCLEASE

Egami, F. & Nakamura, K. Microbial Ribonucleases. LC 68-8784. (Molecular Biology, Bichemistry, & Biophysics Ser.: Vol. 6). 1969. 25.00 (ISBN 0-387-04657-7). Springer-Verlag.

RIBONUCLEIC ACID

Agris, Paul F. The Modified Nucleosides of Transfer RNA: A Bibliography of Biochemical & Biophysical Studies From 1970-1979. LC 80-81197. 220p. 1980. 32.00 (ISBN 0-8451-0207-9). A R Liss.

Agris, Paul F. & Kopper, Randall A. The Modified Nucleosides of Transfer RNA, II: A Laboratory Manual of Genetic Analysis, Identification, & Sequence Determination. LC 80-81197. 320p. 1983. 38.00 (ISBN 0-8451-0225-7). A R Liss.

Altman, Sidney, ed. Transfer RNA. (MIT Press Cell Monograph Ser.: No. 2). 1978. text ed. 47.50x (ISBN 0-262-01056-9). MIT Pr.

Becker, Yechiel, ed. Viral Messenger RNA. (Developments in Molecular Virology Ser.). 1985. lib. bdg. 62.50 (ISBN 0-89838-706-X, Pub. by Martinus Nijhoff Netherlands). Kluwer Academic.

Brownlee, G. G. Determination of Sequences in RNA. (Laboratory Techniques in Biochemistry & Molecular Biology Ser.: Vol. 3, No. 1). 1973. Repr. 21.75 (ISBN 0-444-10102-0, North-Hollnd). Elsevier.

Dubois-Dalco, M., et al. Assembly of Enveloped RNA Viruses. Kingsbury, D. W., ed. (Illus.). 250p. 1984. 49.50 (ISBN 0-387-81802-2). Springer-Verlag.

Fink, Mary A., ed. Immune RNA in Neoplasia. 1976. 49.50 (ISBN 0-12-256940-7). Acad Pr.

Guthrie, G., et al. M R N A: Current Research, 2 vols. (Illus.). 220p. 1972. Vol. 1. text ed. 27.50x (ISBN 0-8422-7049-3); Vol. 2. text ed. 27.50x (ISBN 0-8422-7050-7). Irvington.

Kenney, F. T., et al. Gene Expression & Its Regulation. LC 72-90334. (Basic Life Sciences Ser.: Vol. 1). 588p. 1973. 57.50x (ISBN 0-306-36501-4, Plenum Pr). Plenum Pub.

Losick, R. & Chamberlin, M., eds. RNA Polymerase. LC 76-17182. (Monograph: Vol. 6). (Illus.). 899p. 1976. 72.50x (ISBN 0-87969-115-8). Cold Spring Harbor.

Moldave, Kivie, ed. RNA & Protein Synthesis. (Selected Methods in Enzymology Ser.). 1981. 34.50 (ISBN 0-12-504180-2). Acad Pr.

Osawa, S., et al, eds. Genetics & Evolution of RNA Polymerase & RNA Ribosomes. 670p. 1981. 108.50 (ISBN 0-444-80288-6, Biomedical Pr). Elsevier.

Replication of DNA & RNA. (The Landmark Ser.). 1979. 22.50x (ISBN 0-8422-4124-8). Irvington.

Sarin, Prem S. & Gallo, Robert C., eds. Inhibitors of DNA & RNA Polymerases. (International Encyclopedia of Pharmacology & Therapeutics Ser.: Section 103). (Illus.). 1980. 81.00 (ISBN 0-08-024932-9). Pergamon.

Schimmel, Paul, ed. Transfer RNA: Structure, Properties & Recognition. Soll, Dieter & Abelson, John. LC 79-17143. (Monograph: No. 9A). (Illus.). 584p. 1979. 82.50x (ISBN 0-87969-128-X). Cold Spring Harbor.

Science Press. Role of RNA in Development & Reproduction. 932p. 1981. 67.50 (ISBN 0-442-20090-0). Van Nos Reinhold.

Sirlin, J. L. Biology of RNA. 1972. 72.00 (ISBN 0-12-646950-4). Acad Pr.

Stephenson, John R., ed. Molecular Biology of RNA Tumor Viruses. LC 79-29668. (Molecular Biology Ser.). 1980. 65.00 (ISBN 0-12-666050-6). Acad Pr.

Stewart, P. R. & Letham, D. S., eds. The Ribonucleic Acids. 2nd ed. LC 77-4899. 1977. 33.00 (ISBN 0-387-90281-3). Springer-Verlag.

Venkstern, Tat'kilana. The Primary Structure of Transfer RNA. Madison, James T., ed. LC 79-186259. pap. 78.30 (ISBN 0-317-30346-5, 2024717). Bks Demand UMI.

Venkstern, Tat'Yana. The Primary Structure of Transfer RNA. LC 79-186259. 306p. 1973. 39.50x (ISBN 0-306-30577-1, Plenum Pr). Plenum Pub.

Weissmann, Sherman M., ed. Methods for DNA & RNA Sequencing. LC 82-22261. 480p. 1983. 46.95 (ISBN 0-03-059174-0). Praeger.

Zinder, Norton D., ed. RNA Phages. LC 75-4319. (Monograph: Vol. 5). (Illus.). 448p. 1975. 49.50x (ISBN 0-87969-109-3). Cold Spring Harbor.

RIBONUCLEOPROTEINS

see Nucleoproteins

RIBOSOMES

Attardi, Guiseppe, et al. Animal Ribosomes: Experimental Studies of the Last Five Years. 200p. 1972. text ed. 22.50x (ISBN 0-8422-7012-4). Irvington.

Bielka, Heinz, ed. The Eukaryotic Ribosome. (Illus.). 320p. 1982. 35.00 (ISBN 0-387-11059-3). Springer-Verlag.

Hadjiolov, A. A. The Nucleolus Ribosome Boigenesis. (Cell Biology Monographs: Vol. 12). (Illus.). 290p. 1984. 49.00 (ISBN 0-387-81790-5). Springer-Verlag.

Masayasu Nomura, et al, eds. Ribosomes. LC 74-83791. (Monograph: Vol. 4). (Illus.). 942p. 1974. 79.00x (ISBN 0-87969-110-7). Cold Spring Harbor.

Osawa, S., et al, eds. Genetics & Evolution of RNA Polymerase & RNA Ribosomes. 670p. 1981. 108.50 (ISBN 0-444-80288-6, Biomedical Pr). Elsevier.

Spirin, Alexander S. Ribosome Structure & Protein Biosynthesis. (Illus.). 416p. 1985. text ed. 29.95x (ISBN 0-8053-8390-5). Benjamin-Cummings.

RICE

Chandler, Robert F., Jr. Rice in the Tropics: A Guide to Development of National Programs. (IADS Development-Oriented Literature Ser.). 1979. lib. bdg. 24.50x (ISBN 0-89158-361-0). Westview.

Early Senescence of Rice & Drechslera Oryzae in the Wagenigen Polder. (Agricultural Research Reports). 1977. pap. 14.00 (ISBN 90-220-0621-2, PDC108, PUDOC). Unipub.

The Economic Transformation of Family Rice-Farming in Surinam. (Agricultural Research Reports: No. 718). 67p. 1969. pap. 7.00 (ISBN 0-686-93156-4, PDC176, PUDOC). Unipub.

Esmay, Merle L., et al. Rice Postproduction Technology in the Tropics. LC 79-15428. (An East-West Center Book). (Illus.). 146p. (Orig.). 1979. pap. text ed. 8.00x (ISBN 0-8248-0638-7). UH Pr.

FAO Rice Report. Incl. 1963. pap. 4.50 (ISBN 0-685-48245-6, F157); 1964. pap. 4.50 (ISBN 0-685-48246-4, F158); 1965. pap. 4.50 (ISBN 0-685-48247-2, F159, FAO); 1966. pap. 4.50 (ISBN 0-685-48248-0, F160); 1967. pap. 4.50 (ISBN 0-685-48249-9, F161); 1969. pap. 4.50 (F162); 1970. pap. 4.50 (F163); 1971. pap. 4.50 (F164); 1972. 39p. 1973. pap. 4.50 (F165); 1973-1974. 32p. 1974. pap. 4.50 (F166); 1974-1975. 27p. 1975. pap. 4.75 (F167). (Commodity Reports). (Illus., Orig., FAO). Unipub.

Freeman, J. D. Iban Agriculture: A Report on the Shifting Cultivation of Hill Rice by the Iban of Sarawak. LC 77-86974. Repr. of 1955 ed. 25.00 (ISBN 0-404-16709-8). AMS Pr.

Garibaldi, F. Rice Parboiling. (Agricultural Services Bulletins: No. 56). (Illus.). 73p. 1985. pap. 7.50 (ISBN 92-5-101400-0, F2671, FAO). Unipub.

--Rice Testing - Methods & Equipment. (Agricultural Services Bulletins: No. 18). 55p. (3rd Printing 1979). 1973. pap. 7.50 (ISBN 92-5-100739-X, F1897, FAO). Unipub.

Grist, Donald H. Rice. 5th ed. LC 73-90193. (Tropical Agriculture Ser.). (Illus.). 1975. pap. 30.00x (ISBN 0-582-46033-6). Longman.

The History & Future of Rice Cultivation in Hokkaido. 15p. 1980. pap. 5.00 (ISBN 92-808-0100-7, TUNU057, UNU). Unipub.

Isotope Studies on Rice Fertilization. (Technical Reports Ser.: No. 181). (Illus.). 134p. 1978. pap. 19.00 (ISBN 92-0-115078-4, IDC181, IAEA). Unipub.

Kawaguchi, Keizaburo & Kyuma, Kazutake. Paddy Soils in Tropical Asia: Their Material Nature & Fertility. (Center for Southeast Asian Studies, Kyoto University). (Illus.). 1978. text ed. 20.00x (ISBN 0-8248-0570-4); pap. text ed. 12.00x (ISBN 0-8248-0571-2). UH Pr.

Luh, Bor S. Rice: Production & Utilization. (Illus.). 1980. lib. bdg. 65.00 (ISBN 0-87055-332-1). AVI.

Matsushima, Seizo. High-Yielding Rice Cultivation: A Method for Maximizing Rice Yield Through "Ideal Plants". (Illus.). 1976. 32.50x (ISBN 0-86008-164-8, Pub. by Japan Sci Soc). Intl Spec Bk.

Report of the Fourteenth Session of the International Rice Commission. 29p. 1978. pap. 7.50 (ISBN 92-5-100322-X, F1233, FAO). Unipub.

Research & Breeding for Mechanical Culture of Rice in Surinam. 309p. 1967. 37.75 (ISBN 0-686-51210-3, PDC79, PUDOC). Unipub.

Rice Fertilization. (Technical Reports Ser.: No. 108). (Illus.). 177p. (Orig.). 1970. pap. 14.75 (ISBN 92-0-115270-1, IDC108, IAEA). Unipub.

Rice Milling in Developing Countries. (Commodity Bulletins: No. 45). (Orig.). 1969. pap. 4.50 (ISBN 0-685-09404-9, F414, FAO). Unipub.

Robertson, G. W. Rice & Weather. (Technical Note Ser.: No. 144). (Illus.). 40p. (CAGM Rapporteur on Meteorological Factors Affecting Rice Production). 1975. pap. 12.00 (ISBN 92-63-10423-9, W188, WMO). Unipub.

The Role of Traditional Water Management in Modern Paddy Cultivation in Sri Lanka. (Project on the Sharing of Traditional Technology). 78p. 1981. pap. 5.00 (ISBN 0-686-94207-8, TUNU153, UNU). Unipub.

Scheltema, W. Puddling Against Dry Plowing for Lowland Rice Culture in Surinam: Effect on Soil & Plant, & Interaction with Irrigation & Nitrogen Dressing. (Agricultural Research Reports: No. 828). (Dutch & Eng., Illus.). viii, 241p. 1975. pap. 28.00 (ISBN 90-220-0538-0, PDC76, PUDOC). Unipub.

Subbarao, K. Rice Marketing System & Compulsory Levies in Andhra Pradesh: A Study of Public Intervention in Food Grain Marketing, India. 1979. 12.00x (ISBN 0-8364-0365-7). South Asia Bks.

Tsunoda, S. & Takahashi, N., eds. Biology of Rice. (Developments in Crop Science Ser.: Vol. 7). 300p. 1984. 61.00 (ISBN 0-444-99615-X, I-142-84). Elsevier.

Upland Rice. Rev. ed. (Better Farming Ser.: No. 20). 30p. 1977. pap. 7.50 (ISBN 92-5-100621-0, F78, FAO). Unipub.

Venkataraman, G. Blue-Green Algae for Rice Production. (Soils Bulletins: No. 46). 110p. 1981. pap. 8.00 (ISBN 92-5-101107-9, F2215, FAO). Unipub.

Venketaraman, G. S., et al. Algal Biofertilizers & Rice Cultivation. 83p. 1972. 8.00 (ISBN 0-88065-202-0, Pub. by Messers Today & Tomorrows Printers & Publishers India). Scholarly Pubns.

Wet Paddy or Swamp Rice. Rev. ed. (Better Farming Ser.: No. 21). 40p. 1977. pap. 7.50 (ISBN 92-5-100622-9, F79, FAO). Unipub.

RICE–DISEASES AND PESTS

Characterization & Ecological Aspects of Rice Yellow Mottle Virus in Kenya. (Agricultural Research Reports: No. 829). 1974. pap. 28.00 (ISBN 90-220-0540-2, PDC19, PUDOC). Unipub.

Flint, Mary L., et al, eds. Integrated Pest Management for Rice. LC 82-73445. (Illus.). 85p. (Orig.). 1983. pap. text ed. 15.00x (ISBN 0-931876-61-3, 3280). Ag & Nat Res.

Guidelines for Integrated Control of Rice Insect Pests. (Plant Production & Protection Papers: No. 14). (Eng., Fr. & Span.). 123p. 1979. pap. 9.00 (ISBN 92-5-100705-5, F1858, FAO). Unipub.

Mather, T. H. Environmental Management for Vector Control in Rice Fields. (Irrigation & Drainage Papers: No. 41). (Illus.). 152p. 1985. pap. 12.00 (ISBN 92-5-102104-X, F2665, FAO). Unipub.

RICE BREEDING

Chatterjee, Maiti. Rice Production Technology Manual. 139p. 1981. 19.00x (ISBN 0-686-76661-X, Pub. by Oxford & IBH India). State Mutual Bk.

De Datta, Surajit K. Principles & Practices of Rice Production. LC 80-28941. 618p. 1981. 49.95x (ISBN 0-471-08074-8, Pub. by Wiley-Interscience). Wiley.

Deepak, Adarsh & Rao, K. R., eds. Applications of Remote Sensing for Rice Production. (Illus.). 1985. 49.00 (ISBN 0-937194-03-4). A Deepak Pub.

Equipment for Rice Production. (Agricultural Development Papers: No. 84). pap. 8.00 (F125, FAO). Unipub.

Esmay, Merle L., et al. Rice Postproduction Technology in the Tropics. LC 79-15428. (An East-West Center Book). (Illus.). 146p. (Orig.). 1979. pap. text ed. 8.00x (ISBN 0-8248-0638-7). UH Pr.

Matsushima, Seizo. Rice Cultivation for the Million. 350p. 1980. 35.00x (ISBN 0-89955-203-X, Pub. by Japan Sci Soc Japan). Intl Spec Bk.

Response of Rice to Fertilizer. pap. 4.50 (F413, FAO). Unipub.

Rice Breeding with Induced Mutations. (Technical Reports Ser.: No. 86). (Illus.). 155p. 1968. pap. 13.00 (ISBN 92-0-115068-7, IDC86, IAEA). Unipub.

Rice Breeding with Induced Mutations - 2. (Technical Reports Ser.: No. 102). (Illus.). 124p. (Orig.). 1970. pap. 13.00 (ISBN 92-0-115070-9, IDC102, IAEA). Unipub.

Rice Breeding with Induced Mutations - 3. (Technical Reports Ser.: No. 131). (Illus.). 198p. (Orig.). 1972. pap. 18.50 (ISBN 92-0-115271-X, IDC131, IAEA). Unipub.

Rice Development & Rainfed Rice Production. (Plant Production & Protection Papers: No. 41). 109p. 1982. pap. 8.00 (ISBN 92-5-101310-1, F2406, FAO). Unipub.

Silver, W. S. & Schroder, E. C., eds. Practical Application of Azolla for Rice Production. (Development in Plant & Soil Sciences). 1984. lib. bdg. 35.00 (ISBN 90-247-3068-6, Pub. by Martinus Nijhoff Netherlands). Kluwer-Academic.

Technology Diffusion Among Asian Rice Farmers: Report of a Study Meeting. 171p. 1983. pap. 14.75 (ISBN 92-833-1475-1, APO103, APO). Unipub.

Wang, Jaw-Kai & Hagan, Ross E. Irrigated Rice Production Systems. (Tropical Agriculture Ser.). 1980. 42.00x (ISBN 0-89158-486-2). Westview.

RICKOVER, HYMAN GEORGE

Polmar, Norman & Allen, Thomas P. Rickover: Controversy & Genius. LC 81-14327. (Illus.). 745p. 1982. 20.75 (ISBN 0-671-24615-1). Nautical & Aviation.

RIEMANN SPACE

see Spaces, Generalized

RIEMANN SURFACES

Accola, R. D. Riemann Surfaces, Theta Functions, & Abelian Automorphisms Groups. LC 75-25928. (Lecture Notes in Mathematics: Vol. 483). iii, 105p. 1975. pap. text ed. 13.00 (ISBN 0-387-07398-1). Springer-Verlag.

Ahlfors, Lars, et al, eds. Advances in the Theory of Riemann Surfaces. LC 72-121729. (Annals of Mathematics Studies: No. 66). 1971. 35.00x (ISBN 0-691-08081-X). Princeton U Pr.

Alling, N. L. & Greenleaf, N. Foundation of the Theory of Klein Surfaces. LC 73-172693. (Lecture Notes in Mathematics: Vol. 219). ix, 117p. 1971. pap. 11.00 (ISBN 0-387-05577-0). Springer-Verlag.

Beardon, Alan. A Primer on Riemann Surfaces. LC 82-4439. (London Mathematical Society Lecture Note Ser.: No. 78). 150p. 1984. pap. 24.95 (ISBN 0-521-27104-5). Cambridge U Pr.

Cohn, Harvey. Conformal Mapping on Riemann Surfaces. (Illus.). 352p. 1980. pap. text ed. 7.50 (ISBN 0-486-64025-6). Dover.

Farkas, H. M. & Kra, I. Riemann Surfaces. (Graduate Texts in Mathematics). (Illus.). 350p. 1980. pap. 35.00 (ISBN 0-387-90465-4). Springer-Verlag.

Forster, O. Lectures on Riemann Surfaces. (Graduate Texts in Mathematics Ser.: Vol. 81). (Illus.). 254p. 1981. 41.00 (ISBN 0-387-90617-7). Springer-Verlag.

Greenberg, Leon, ed. Discontinuous Groups & Reimann Surfaces. LC 73-16783. (Annals of Mathematics Studies: No. 79). 450p. 1974. text ed. 38.00 (ISBN 0-691-08138-7). Princeton U Pr.

Greene, Robert E. Isometric Embeddings of Riemannian & Pseudo Riemannian Manifolds. LC 52-42839. (Memoirs: No. 97). 63p. 1970. pap. 9.00 (ISBN 0-8218-1297-1, MEMO-97). Am Math.

Gunning, R. C. Riemann Surfaces & Generalized Theta Functions. (Illus.). 1976. 31.00 (ISBN 0-387-07744-8). Springer-Verlag.

Gunning, Robert C. Lectures on Vector Bundles Over Riemann Surfaces. (Mathematical Notes Ser.: No. 6). (Orig.). 1967. pap. 25.00 (ISBN 0-691-07998-6). Princeton U Pr.

Hasumi, M. Hardy Classes on Infinitely Connected Riemann Surfaces. (Lecture Notes in Mathematics: Vol. 1027). 280p. 1983. pap. 15.00 (ISBN 0-387-12729-1). Springer Verlag.

Heins, M. Hardy Classes on Riemann Surfaces. LC 75-84833. (Lecture Notes in Mathematics: Vol. 98). (Orig.). 1969. pap. 10.70 (ISBN 0-387-04617-8). Springer-Verlag.

Krushkal', Samuel L. Quasiconformal Mappings & Riemann Surfaces. LC 79-995. (Scripta Series in Mathematics). 319p. 1979. 27.95x (ISBN 0-470-26695-3). Halsted Pr.

McShane, E. J. Riemann-Type Integral that Includes Lebesgue-Stieltjes, Bochner & Stochastic Integrals. LC 52-42839. (Memoirs: No. 88). 54p. 1979. pap. 10.00 (ISBN 0-8218-1288-2, MEMO-88). Am Math.

Nevanlinna, R. Analytic Functions. Emig, P., tr. (Grundlehren der Mathematischen Wissenschaften: Vol. 162). (Illus.). 1970. 47.00 (ISBN 0-387-04834-0). Springer-Verlag.

Sario, L. & Nakai, M. Classification Theory of Riemann Surfaces. LC 76-96693. (Die Grundlehren der Mathematischen Wissenschaften: Vol. 164). (Illus.). 1970. 61.00 (ISBN 0-387-04836-7). Springer-Verlag.

Springer, George. Introduction to Riemann Surfaces. 2nd ed. LC 80-67978. (Illus.). viii, 309p. 1981. text ed. 15.95 (ISBN 0-8284-0313-9). Chelsea Pub.

RIEMANNIAN GEOMETRY

see Geometry, Riemannian

RIEMANNIAN MANIFOLDS

Azencott, R. & Wilson, E. N. Homogenous Manifolds with Negative Curvature II. LC 76-44403. (Memoirs: No. 178). 102p. 1976. pap. 13.00 (ISBN 0-8218-2178-4, MEMO178). Am Math.

Blair, D. E. Contact Manifold in Riemannian Geometry. (Lecture Notes in Mathematics Ser: Vol. 509). 1976. pap. 13.00 (ISBN 0-387-07626-3). Springer-Verlag.

Boothby, William M. An Introduction to Differentiable Manifolds & Riemannian Geometry. (Pure & Applied Mathematics Ser.). 1986. price not set (ISBN 0-12-116052-1). Acad Pr.

Cheeger, J. & Ebin, D. G. Comparison Theorems in Riemannian Geometry. LC 74-83725. (Mathematical Library: Vol. 9). 174p. 1975. 47.00 (ISBN 0-444-10764-9, North-Holland). Elsevier.

Conner, P. E. Neumann's Problem for Differential Forms on Riemannian Manifolds. LC 52-42839. (Memoirs Ser.: No. 20). 58p. 1979. pap. 10.00 (ISBN 0-8218-1220-3, MEMO-20). Am Math.

D'Atri, J. E. & Ziller, W. Naturally Reductive Metrics & Einstein Metrics on Compact Lie Groups. LC 79-7. (Memoirs Ser.: No. 215). 72p. 1982. pap. 13.00 (ISBN 0-8218-2215-2). Am Math.

Ivic, A. The Riemann Zeta-Function. (Pure & Applied Mathematics Ser.). 336p. 1985. 49.95 (ISBN 0-471-80634-X). Wiley.

Klingenberg, Wilhelm. Closed Geodesics on Riemannian Manifolds. LC 83-5979. (CBMS Regional Conference Series in Mathematics, Vol. 53). 79p. 1983. pap. 13.00 (ISBN 0-8218-0703-X). Am Math.

Morse, Marston. Global Variational Analysis: Weierstrass Integrals on a Riemannian Manifold. LC 76-836. (Mathematical Notes: No. 16). 264p. 1976. pap. 26.50 (ISBN 0-691-08181-6). Princeton U Pr.

Mostow, G. D. Strong Rigidity of Locally Symmetric Spaces. (Annals of Mathematics Studies: No. 78). 220p. 1974. 22.50x (ISBN 0-691-08136-0). Princeton U Pr.

Namba, M. Families of Meromorphic Functions on Compact Riemann Surfaces. (Lecture Notes in Mathematics: Vol. 767). 284p. 1979. pap. 20.00 (ISBN 0-387-09722-8). Springer-Verlag.

Pitts, John T. Existence & Regularity of Minimal Surfaces on Riemannian Manifolds. LC 81-47150. (Mathematical Notes: No. 27). 192p. (Orig.). 1981. pap. 17.00 (ISBN 0-691-08290-1). Princeton U Pr.

Sario, L., et al. Classification Theory of Riemannian Manifolds. LC 77-22197. (Lecture Notes in Mathematics: Vol. 605). 1977. pap. text ed. 26.00 (ISBN 0-387-08358-8). Springer-Verlag.

Steklov Institute of Mathematics, Academy of Sciences, U.S.S.R. Geodesic Flows on Closed Riemann Manifolds with Negative Curvature: Proceedings. Anosov, D. V., ed. (Proceedings of the Steklov Institute of Mathematics: No. 90). 1969. 58.00 (ISBN 0-8218-1890-2, STEKLO-90). Am Math.

Toth. Harmonic & Minimal Maps with Applications in Geometry & Physics. 1984. 70.00 (ISBN 0-470-20127-4). Wiley.

Tricerri, F. & Vanhecke, L. Homogeneous Structure on Riemannian Manifolds. LC 83-2097. (London Mathematical Society Lecture Note Ser.: No. 83). 130p. 1983. pap. 22.95 (ISBN 0-521-27489-3). Cambridge U Pr.

RIEMANNIAN SPACE

see Riemannian Manifolds

RIFLES

see also Sharps Rifle; Winchester Rifle

Beard, Ross E., Jr. Carbine: The Story of David Marshall Williams. LC 76-20847. 1977. ltd ed, signed 15.00 (ISBN 0-87844-047-X). Sandlapper Pub Co.

Buchele, William & Shumway, George. Recreating the American Longrifle. 4th ed. LC 83-601511. (Gunmaker Ser.). (Illus.). 175p. 1983. casebound 27.50 (ISBN 0-87387-085-9); pap. 20.00. Shumway.

Davis, Henry. A Forgotten Heritage: The Story of the Early American Rifle. 1976. Repr. of 1941 ed. 9.95 (ISBN 0-88227-008-7). Gun Room.

DeHaas, Frank. Bolt Action Rifles. Rev. ed. LC 73-16310000005. 448p. 1984. pap. 14.95 (ISBN 0-910676-69-0). DBI.

Edsall, James. The Golden Age of Single Shot Rifles. 2.75 (ISBN 0-913150-29-0). Pioneer Pr.

--The Revolver Rifles. 2.50 (ISBN 0-913150-30-4). Pioneer Pr.

Fremantle, T. F. The Book of the Rifle. (Library Classics Ser.). (Illus.). 576p. 1985. Repr. of 1901 ed. 54.00 (ISBN 0-935632-26-3). Wolfe Pub Co.

Grant, James J. More Single Shot Rifles. (Illus.). 25.00 (ISBN 0-88227-006-0). Gun Room.

--Single-Shot Rifles. 25.00 (ISBN 0-88227-017-6). Gun Room.

Haas, Frank de. Mr. Single Shot's Gunsmithing-Idea Book. (Illus.). 176p. (Orig.). 1983. 18.95 (ISBN 0-8306-0111-2); pap. 13.50 (ISBN 0-8306-1511-3, 1511). TAB Bks.

Hanson. The Plains Rifle. 19.95 (ISBN 0-88227-015-X). Gun Room.

Harriger, Russell. Longrifles of Pennsylvania: Jefferson, Clarion & Elk Counties, Vol. 1. LC 83-51452. (Illus.). 256p. 1984. 40.00 (ISBN 0-87387-087-5). Shumway.

Hoffschmidt, E. J. Know Your M-1 Garand Rifles. (Know Your Gun Ser.). (Illus.). 80p. (Orig.). 1976. pap. 5.95 (ISBN 0-941540-02-2). Blacksmith Corp.

Kindig, Joe, Jr. Thoughts on the Kentucky Rifle in its Golden Age. 2nd, Annotated ed. LC 81-52790. (Illus.). 562p. 1983. casebound 75.00 (ISBN 0-87387-084-0). Shumway.

McAulay, John D. Carbines of the Civil War, 1861-1865. 1981. 7.95 (ISBN 0-913150-45-2). Pioneer Pr.

McNaugher, Thomas L. The M-Sixteen Controversies: Military Organizations & Weapons Acquisition. LC 83-24574. 220p. 1984. 29.95 (ISBN 0-03-063632-9). Praeger.

Mallory, Franklin B. & Olson, Ludwig. The Krag Rifle Story. LC 79-65973. 224p. 1980. 20.00 (ISBN 0-9603306-0-7). Springfield Res Serv.

Myatt, F. An Illustrated Guide to Rifles & Automatic Weapons. LC 80-70977. (Illustrated Military Guides Ser.). (Illus.). 160p. 1981. 9.95 (ISBN 0-668-05229-5, 5229). Arco.

O'Connor, Jack. The Hunting Rifle. (Illus.). 320p. pap. 7.95 (ISBN 0-88317-054-X). Stoeger Pub Co.

--The Rifle Book. 3rd, Rev. ed. (Illus.). 1978. o. p. 13.95 (ISBN 0-394-41314-8); pap. 13.95 (ISBN 0-394-73458-0). Knopf.

Olson, John. John Olson's Book of the Rifle. LC 73-20849. (Illus.). 1974. pap. 6.95 (ISBN 0-87955-413-4); pap. 6.95 (ISBN 0-89149-025-6). Jolex.

Ottenson, Stuart. Benchrest Actions & Triggers. Wolfe, Dave, ed. 61p. 1983. pap. 8.50 (ISBN 0-935632-12-3). Wolfe Pub Co.

Otteson, Stuart. The Bolt Action: A Design Analysis. LC 83-60432. 1976. pap. write for info. (Pub. by Winchester Pr). New Century.

Page, Warren. The Accurate Rifle. (Illus.). 256p. pap. 8.95 (ISBN 0-88317-023-X). Stoeger Pub Co.

Petzal, David. Twenty-Two Caliber Rifle. LC 72-79360. (Illus.). 1973. 12.95 (ISBN 0-8329-0778-2, Pub. by Winchester Pr). New Century.

Rywell, Martin. American Antique Rifles. 2.00 (ISBN 0-913150-05-3). Pioneer Pr.

Shelsby, Earl, ed. NRA Gunsmithing Guide: Updated. rev. ed. (Illus.). 336p. (Orig.). 1980. pap. text ed. 11.95 (ISBN 0-935998-47-0). Natl Rifle Assn.

Shumway, George. Pennsylvania Longrifles of Note. LC 77-506. (Illus.). 63p. 1977. pap. 7.50 (ISBN 0-87387-077-8). Shumway.

Steindler, R. A. Rifle Guide. (Illus.). 304p. pap. 9.95 (ISBN 0-88317-092-2). Stoeger Pub Co.

Taylor. African Rifles & Cartridges. 21.95 (ISBN 0-88227-013-3). Gun Room.

U. S. Rifle Caliber .30 Model 1903. 2.00 (ISBN 0-913150-16-9). Pioneer Pr.

U. S. Rifle Model 1866 Springfield. 1.75 (ISBN 0-913150-14-2). Pioneer Pr.

U. S. Rifle Model 1870 Remington. 1.75 (ISBN 0-913150-15-0). Pioneer Pr.

Whelen, Townsend. The Hunting Rifle. 464p. 1984. Repr. of 1924 ed. 39.00 (ISBN 0-935632-13-1). Wolfe Pub Co.

Womack, Lester. The Commercial Mauser 'ninety-Eight Sporting Rifle. Angevine, Jay B., Jr., ed. (Illus.). 72p. 1981. 20.00 (ISBN 0-9605530-0-2). Womack Assoc.

Wood, J. B. Gun Digest Book of Firearms Assembly - Disassembly: Pt. IV: Centerfire Rifles. LC 79-54271. (Illus.). 288p. 1980. pap. 12.95 (ISBN 0-686-73998-1). DBI.

--Gun Digest Book of Firearms Assembly - Disassembly: Pt. III: Rimfire Rifles, Part III. LC 79-54271. (Illus.). 288p. 1980. pap. 12.95 (ISBN 0-695-81419-2). DBI.

The World's Assault Rifles. 19.95 (ISBN 0-686-15932-2). TBN Ent.

RIFTS (GEOLOGY)

Quennell, Albert M., ed. Continental Rifts. (Benchmark Papers in Geology: Vol. 90). (Illus.). 352p. 1985. 44.50 (ISBN 0-442-27661-3). Van Nos Reinhold.

--Rift Valley: Afro-Arabian. (Benchmark Papers in Geology: Vol. 60). 419p. 1982. 52.95 (ISBN 0-87933-383-9). Van Nos Reinhold.

RIGID DYNAMICS

see Dynamics, Rigid

RING FORMATION (CHEMISTRY)

Boschke, F. L., ed. Inorganic Ring Systems. (Topics in Current Chemistry Ser.: Vol. 102). (Illus.). 240p. 1982. 43.00 (ISBN 0-387-11345-2). Springer-Verlag.

Cotter, Robert J. & Matzner, Markus. Ring-Forming Polymerizations, Pt. A: Carbocyclic & Metallorganic Rings. 1969. 80.00 (ISBN 0-12-191701-0). Acad Pr.

Cowley, Alan H., ed. Rings, Clusters, & Polymers of the Main Group Elements. LC 83-15462. (ACS Symposium Ser.: No. 232). 182p. 1983. lib. bdg. 32.95x (ISBN 0-8412-0801-8). Am Chemical.

Keehn, Philip & Rosenfeld, Stuart M., eds. Cyclophanes, 2 Vols. (Organic Chemistry Ser.). 1983. Vol. 1. 65.00 (ISBN 0-12-403001-7); Vol. 2. 60.00 (ISBN 0-12-403002-5). Acad Pr.

Ulrich, Henri. Cycloaddition Reactions of Heterocumulenses. (Organic Chemistry Ser.: Vol. 9). 1967. 75.00 (ISBN 0-12-708250-6). Acad Pr.

Van Oystaeyen, F., ed. Methods in Ring Theory. 1984. lib. bdg. 74.00 (ISBN 90-277-1743-5, Pub. by Reidel Holland). Kluwer Academic.

RINGS (ALGEBRA)

see also Associative Rings; Fields, Algebraic; Ideals (Algebra); Measure Theory; Modules (Algebra); Topological Algebras

Arnold, David M. Finite Rank Torsion Free Abolian Groups & Rings. (Lecture Notes in Mathematics Ser.: Vol. 931). 191p. 1982. pap. 13.00 (ISBN 0-387-11557-9). Springer-Verlag.

Atiyah, Michael F. & Macdonald, I. G. Introduction to Commutative Algebra. 1969. text ed. 24.95 (ISBN 0-201-00361-9). Addison-Wesley.

Behrens, Ernst-August. Ring Theory. (Pure & Applied Mathematics Ser.: Vol. 44). 1972. 66.00 (ISBN 0-12-085250-0). Acad Pr.

Benson, D. J. Modular Representation Theory: New Trends & Methods. (Lecture Notes in Mathematics Ser.: Vol. 1081). xi, 231p. 1984. pap. 13.50 (ISBN 0-387-13389-5). Springer-Verlag.

Bhattacharya, P. B. & Jain, S. K. First Course in Rings, Fields & Vector Spaces. 238p. 1977. cloth 14.95x (ISBN 0-470-99047-3, 76-55303). Halsted Pr.

Bican, et al. Rings, Modules, & Preradicals. 264p. 1982. 45.00 (ISBN 0-8247-1568-3). Dekker.

Bjork, J. E. Rings of Differential Operators. (Mathematical Library: Vol. 21). 360p. 1979. 66.00 (ISBN 0-444-85292-1, North Holland). Elsevier.

Borceux, F. & Van Den Bossche, G. Algebra in a Localic Topos with Applications to Ring Theory. (Lecture Notes in Mathematics Ser.: Vol. 1038). 240p. 1983. pap. 13.00 (ISBN 0-387-12711-9). Springer Verlag.

Brumfield, Gregory W. Partially Ordered Rings & Semi-Algebraic Geometry. (London Mathematical Society Lecture Note Ser.: No. 37). 1980. pap. 29.95 (ISBN 0-521-22845-X). Cambridge U Pr.

Chatters, A. W. & Hajarnavis, C. R. Rings with Chain Conditions. LC 80-19315. (Research Notes in Mathematics Ser.: No. 44). 198p. (Orig.). 1980. pap. text ed. 23.95 (ISBN 0-273-08446-1). Pitman Pub MA.

Cohn, P. M. Free Rings & Their Relations. (London Mathematical Society Monographs). 1972. 69.50 (ISBN 0-12-179150-5). Acad Pr.

Dauns, John & Hofmann, Karl. Representation of Rings by Sections. LC 52-42839. (Memoirs: No. 83). 180p. 1983. pap. 10.00 (ISBN 0-8218-1283-1, MEMO-83). Am Math.

Dobbs, D. E. Cech Cohomological Dimensions for Commutative Rings. LC 78-131545. (Lecture Notes in Mathematics: Vol. 147). 1970. pap. 11.00 (ISBN 0-387-04936-3). Springer-Verlag.

Evans, E. G. & Griffiths, P. Syzygies. (London Mathematical Society Lecture Note Ser.: No. 106). 160p. Date not set. pap. price not set. (ISBN 0-521-31411-9). Cambridge U Pr.

Faith, C. Algebra I: Rings, Modules, & Categories. LC 72-96724. (Die Grundlehren der Mathematischen Wissenschaften: Vol. 190). (Illus.). xxiii, 565p. 1973. 54.00 (ISBN 0-387-05551-7). Springer-Verlag.

Faith, Carl. Injective Modules & Injective Quotient Rings. (Lecture Notes in Pure & Applied Mathematics Ser.: Vol. 72). (Illus.). 120p. 1982. 25.00 (ISBN 0-8247-1632-9). Dekker.

Feigelstock, Shalom. Additive Groups of Rings. (Research Notes in Mathematics Ser.: No. 83). 218p. 1983. pap. text ed. 16.95 (ISBN 0-273-08591-3). Pitman Pub MA.

Fleury, P. J., ed. Advances in Non-Communicative Ring-Theory, Plattsburg, 1981. (Lecture Notes in Mathematics: Vol. 951). 142p. 1982. pap. 11.00 (ISBN 0-387-11597-8). Springer-Verlag.

Gelfand, Israel M., et al. Commutative Normed Rings. LC 61-15024. 1964. 14.95 (ISBN 0-8284-0170-5). Chelsea Pub.

Goodearl, K. R. Singular Torsion & the Splitting Properties. LC 72-4344. (Memoirs: No. 124). 89p. 1972. pap. 10.00 (ISBN 0-8218-1824-4, MEMO-124). Am Math.

--Von Neumann Regular Rings. (Monographs & Studies: Vol. 4). 388p. 1979. text ed. 59.95 (ISBN 0-686-91967-X). Pitman Pub MA.

Goodearl, K. R., et al. Affine Representations of Grothendieck Groups & Applications to Rickart C-Algebras & Aleph O-Continuous Regular Rings. LC 80-17018. (Memoirs: No. 234). 163p. 1980. pap. 9.00 (ISBN 0-8218-2234-9). Am Math.

Goodearl, Kenneth R. Ring Theory: Nonsingular Rings & Modules. (Lecture Notes in Pure & Applied Mathematics: Vol.33). 224p. 1976. 49.75 (ISBN 0-8247-6354-8). Dekker.

Gordon, Robert. Ring Theory. 1972. 65.00 (ISBN 0-12-291350-7). Acad Pr.

Haley, D. K. Equational Compactness in Rings with Applications to the Theory of Topological Rings. Dold, A. & Eckmann, B., eds. (Lecture Notes in Mathematics: Vol. 745). 1979. pap. 14.00 (ISBN 0-387-09548-9). Springer-Verlag.

Harrison, D. K. Finite & Infinite Primes for Rings & Fields. LC 52-42839. (Memoirs: No. 68). 62p. 1966. pap. 9.00 (ISBN 0-8218-1268-8, MEMO-68). Am Math.

Herstein, I. N. Noncommutative Rings. (Carus Monograph: No. 15). 199p. 1968. 16.50 (ISBN 0-88385-015-X, CAM-15); members 14.00. Math Assn.

--Rings with Involution. LC 76-27861. (Chicago Lectures in Mathematics). 1976. pap. text ed. 8.00x (ISBN 0-226-32806-6). U of Chicago Pr.

--Topics in Ring Theory. LC 69-17035. (Chicago Lectures in Mathematics Ser). 1969. pap. text ed. 6.00x (ISBN 0-226-32802-3). U of Chicago Pr.

Hofmann, K. H. Lectures on the Applications of Sheaves to Ring Theory: Tulane University Ring & Operator Theory Year, 1970-71, Vol. 3. (Lecture Notes in Mathematics: Vol. 248). 315p. 1971. pap. 13.00 (ISBN 0-387-05714-5). Springer-Verlag.

Hofmann, K. H. & Luikkonen, J., eds. Recent Advances in the Representation Theory of Rings & C-Algebras by Continuous Sections. LC 74-11237. (Memoirs: No. 148). 182p. 1974. pap. 12.00 (ISBN 0-8218-1848-1, MEMO-148). Am Math.

International Conference, Kent State U., April 4-5, 1975. Noncommutative Ring Theory: Papers. Cozzens, J. H., et al, eds. (Lecture Notes in Mathematics: Vol. 545). 1976. 17.00 (ISBN 0-387-07985-8). Springer-Verlag.

Jacobson, Nathan. Structure of Rings. rev. ed. LC 63-21795. (Colloquium Pbns. Ser.: Vol. 37). 299p. 1984. Repr. 24.00 (ISBN 0-8218-1037-5, COLL-37). Am Math.

--Theory of Rings. LC 43-15310. (Mathematical Surveys Ser.: No. 2). 151p. 1982. pap. 30.00 (ISBN 0-8218-1502-4, SURV-2). Am Math.

Jain, S. R., ed. Ring Theory, Vol. 25. (Lecture Notes in Pure & Applied Mathematics). 1977. 45.00 (ISBN 0-8247-6577-X). Dekker.

Jategaonkar, A. V. Left Principal Ideal Rings. LC 74-114015. (Lecture Notes in Mathematics: Vol. 123). 1970. pap. 10.70 (ISBN 0-387-04912-6). Springer-Verlag.

Jerison, M. & Gillman, L. Rings of Continuous Functions. Gehring, F. W. & Moore, C. C., eds. LC 76-20442. (Graduate Texts in Mathematics: Vol. 43). xi, 300p. 1960. 28.00 (ISBN 0-387-90198-1). Springer-Verlag.

Kaplansky, Irving. Commutative Rings. rev. ed. LC 74-5732. 192p. 1974. text ed. 12.00x (ISBN 0-226-42454-5). U of Chicago Pr.

--Fields & Rings. rev. 2nd ed. LC 72-78251. (Chicago Lectures in Mathematics Ser). 224p. 1972. text ed. 12.50x (ISBN 0-226-42450-2); pap. text ed. 9.00x (ISBN 0-226-42451-0). U of Chicago Pr.

Kochman, Stanley O. The Symplectic Cobordism Ring I. LC 79-27872. 206p. 1980. paper 13.00 (ISBN 0-8218-2228-4, MEMO-228). Am Math.

Kruse, Robert L. & Price, David T. Nilpotent Rings. (Notes on Mathematics & Its Applications Ser.). 136p. 1969. 37.25 (ISBN 0-677-02230-1). Gordon.

McCoy, Neal H. The Theory of Rings. LC 72-11558. xxi, 161p. 1972. Repr. of 1964 ed. text ed. 9.50 (ISBN 0-8284-0266-3). Chelsea Pub.

McDonald, Bernard, ed. Ring Theory & Algebra Three. (Pure & Applied Mathematics Ser.: Vol. 55). (Illus.). 448p. 1980. 64.75 (ISBN 0-8247-1158-0). Dekker.

McDonald, Bernard R., et al, eds. Ring Theory: Proceedings of the Oklahoma Conference. (Lecture Notes in Pure & Applied Mathematics Ser: Vol. 7). 264p. 1974. 45.00 (ISBN 0-8247-6162-6). Dekker.

May, J. P. E-Zero-Zero Ring Spaces & F-Zero-Zero Ring Spectra. (Lecture Notes in Mathematics Ser: Vol. 577). 1977. pap. 18.00 (ISBN 0-387-08136-4). Springer-Verlag.

Montgomery, S. Fixed Rings of Finite Automorphism Groups of Associative Rings. (Lectures Notes in Mathematics Ser.: Vol. 818). 126p. 1980. pap. 13.00 (ISBN 0-387-10232-9). Springer-Verlag.

Nastasescu, C. Graded & Filtered Rings & Modules. (Lecture Notes in Mathematics: Vol. 758). 148p. 1979. pap. 16.00 (ISBN 0-387-09708-2). Springer-Verlag.

Newman, Morris. Integral Matrices. (Pure & Applied Mathematics Ser.: Vol. 45). 1972. 49.50 (ISBN 0-12-517850-6). Acad Pr.

Orzech, Morris & Small, Charles. The Brauer Group of Commutative Rings. (Pure & Applied Mathematics Ser.: Vol. 11). 200p. 1975. 35.00 (ISBN 0-8247-6261-4). Dekker.

Osofsky, Barbara L. Homological Dimensions of Modules. LC 72-6826. (CBMS Regional Conference Series in Mathematics: No. 12). 89p. 1979. pap. 10.00 (ISBN 0-8218-1662-4, CBMS-12). Am Math.

Oystaeyen, F. M. & Verschcoren, A. H., eds. Brauer Groups in Ring Theory & Algebraic Geometry, Antwerp 1981. (Lecture Notes in Mathematics: Vol. 917). 300p. 1982. pap. 20.00 (ISBN 0-387-11216-2). Springer-Verlag.

Passi, I. B. Group Rings & Their Augmentation Ideals. (Lecture Notes in Mathematics Ser.: Vol. 715). 1979. pap. 13.00 (ISBN 0-387-09254-4). Springer-Verlag.

Passman, Donald S. The Algebraic Structure of Group Rings. LC 84-15403. 750p. 1985. Repr. of 1977 ed. lib. bdg. 59.95 (ISBN 0-89874-789-9). Krieger.

Passman, R. D. Infinite Group Rings. (Pure & Applied Mathematics Ser: Vol. 6). 1971. 35.00 (ISBN 0-8247-1523-3). Dekker.

Petrich, M. Lectures in Rings & Semigroups. (Lecture Notes in Mathematics: Vol. 380). viii, 182p. 1974. pap. 13.00 (ISBN 0-387-06730-2). Springer-Verlag.

Pierce, Richard S. Modules Over Commutative Regular Rings. LC 52-42839. (Memoirs Ser.: No. 70). 112p. 1976. pap. 13.00 (ISBN 0-8218-1270-X, MEMO-70). Am Math.

Pilz, G. Near Rings: The Theory & Its Application. (Mathematics Studies: Vol. 23). 1983. 59.75 (ISBN 0-7204-0566-1, I-154-83, North-Holland). Elsevier.

Pleskin, W., ed. Group Rings of Finite Groups over p-adic Integers. (Lecture Notes in Mathematics: Vol. 1026). 151p. 1983. pap. 12.00 (ISBN 0-387-12728-3). Springer Verlag.

Popescu, N. Abelian Categories with Applications to Rings & Modules. (London Mathematical Society Monographs). 1973. 75.00 (ISBN 0-12-561550-7). Acad Pr.

Procesi, Claudio. Rings with Polynomial Identities. (Pure & Applied Mathematics Ser: Vol. 17). 202p. 1973. 39.75 (ISBN 0-8247-6015-8). Dekker.

Ratliff, L. J., Jr. Chain Conjectures in Ring Theory: An Exposition of Conjectures on Catenary Chains. (Lecture Notes in Mathematics: Vol. 647). 1978. pap. 10.00 (ISBN 0-387-08758-3). Springer-Verlag.

Reiner, I. Maximal Orders. (London Mathematical Society Monographs). 1975. 70.00 (ISBN 0-12-586650-X). Acad Pr.

Ring Theory Conference, 2d: 1975: University of Oklahoma. Ring Theory II: Proceedings of the Second Oklahoma Conference. McDonald, Bernard R. & Morris, Robert A., eds. LC 76-55134. (Lecture Notes in Pure & Applied Mathematics: Vol. 26). pap. 78.80 (ISBN 0-317-08349-X, 2017693). Bks Demand UMI.

Rowen, Louis H. Polynomial Identities in Ring Theory. (Pure & Applied Mathematics Ser.). 1980. 57.50 (ISBN 0-12-599850-3). Acad Pr.

Sally, Judith. Numbers of Generators of Ideals of Local Rings. (Lecture Notes in Pure & Applied Math Ser.: Vol. 35). 1978. 29.75 (ISBN 0-8247-6645-8). Dekker.

Schofield, A. H. Representations of Rings over Skew Fields. (London Mathematical Society Lecture Note Ser.: No. 92). (Illus.). 240p. 1985. pap. 27.95 (ISBN 0-521-27853-8). Cambridge U Pr.

Small, Lance W. Reviews in Ring Theory. LC 81-10770. 250.00 (ISBN 0-8218-0215-1, REVRING). Am Math.

Szasz, Ferenc. Radicals of Rings. LC 79-40509. 288p. 1981. 48.95x (ISBN 0-471-27583-2, Pub. by Wiley-Interscience). Wiley.

Tachikawa, H. QF-Three & QF-One Rings. Ringel, C. M., ed. (Lecture Notes in Mathematics: Vol. 351). 172p. 1973. pap. 14.00 (ISBN 0-387-06501-6). Springer-Verlag.

Van Oystaeyen. Ring Theory. (Lecture Notes in Pure & Applied Mathematics Ser.: Vol. 40). 1978. 39.75 (ISBN 0-8247-6814-0). Dekker.

Van Oystaeyen, F. Ring Theory. (Lecture Notes in Pure & Applied Ser.: Vol. 51). 1979. 95.00 (ISBN 0-8247-6854-X). Dekker.

Van Oystaeyen, F. & Verschoren, A. Relative Invariants of Rings: The Commutative Theory. (Pure & Applied Mathematics: A Series of Monographs & Textbooks: Vol. 79). 272p. 1983. 42.50 (ISBN 0-8247-7043-9). Dekker.

--Relative Invariants of Rings: The Noncommutative Theory. (Pure & Applied Mathematics: A Series of Monographs & Textbooks: Vol. 86). (Illus.). 312p. 1984. 59.75 (ISBN 0-8247-7281-4). Dekker.

Van Oystaeyen, F., ed. Ring Theory, Antwerp Nineteen-Eighty: Prooceedings. (Lecture Notes in Mathematics Ser.: Vol. 825). 209p. 1980. pap. 17.00 (ISBN 0-387-10246-9). Springer-Verlag.

Vovsi, S. M. Triangular Products of Group Representations & Their Applications. (Progress in Mathematics Ser.: No. 17). 150p. 1982. text ed. 15.00x (ISBN 0-8176-3062-7). Birkhauser.

RINGS OF OPERATORS

see Von Neumann Algebras

RIPPLES

Chuang, Shen-lun. Investigation of Impact of Rigid & Elastic Bodies with Water. LC 70-139810. 124p. 1970. 25.00 (ISBN 0-403-04489-8). Scholarly.

RITTENHOUSE, DAVID, 1732-1796

Hindle, Brooke. David Rittenhouse. Cohen, I. Bernard, ed. LC 79-3120. (Three Centuries of Science in America Ser.). 1980. Repr. of 1964 ed. lib. bdg. 34.50x (ISBN 0-405-12569-0). Ayer Co Pubs.

Hindle, Brooke & Cohen, I. Bernard, eds. The Scientific Writings of David Rittenhouse: An Original Authology. LC 79-7987. (Three Centuries of Science in America Ser.). (Illus.). 1980. lib. bdg. 45.00x (ISBN 0-405-12568-2). Ayer Co Pubs.

RIVER DISCHARGE MEASUREMENTS

see Stream Measurements

RIVERS

see also Dams; Deltas; Erosion; Estuaries; Floods; Hydraulic Engineering; Hydrography; Thermal Pollution of Rivers, Lakes, etc.; Water–Pollution; Water-Power; Watersheds

also names of specific Rivers, or Rivers and Valleys, e.g. Mississippi River, Rhine River and Valley

Allen, Charles. A Mountain in Tibet: The Search for Mount Kailas & the Sources of the Great Rivers of Asia. (Illus.). 256p. 1982. 27.50 (ISBN 0-233-97281-1). Andre Deutsch.

Ariyoshi, Sawako. The River Ki. Tahara, Mildred, tr. from Japanese. LC 79-66240. 243p. 1982. pap. 5.25 (ISBN 0-87011-514-6). Kodansha.

Barnes, R. S. Estuarine Biology. 2nd ed. (Studies in Biology: No. 49). 80p. 1984. pap. text ed. 8.95 (ISBN 0-7131-2905-0). E Arnold.

Biggs, Howard. The River Medway. 160p. 1982. 30.00 (ISBN 0-86138-005-3, Pub. by Terence Dalton England). State Mutual Bk.

Brydon, Norman F. The Passaic River: Past, Present, Future. (Illus.). 400p. 1974. 30.00x (ISBN 0-8135-0770-7). Rutgers U Pr.

Burmeister, Walter F. Appalachian Waters 4: Southeastern U. S. Rivers. LC 74-80983. 1975. pap. 10.00 (ISBN 0-912660-22-8). Appalachian Bks.

Canter, L. W. River Water Quality Monitoring. (Illus.). 230p. 1985. 28.00 (ISBN 0-87371-011-8). Lewis Pubs Inc.

Cawley, Margaret & Cawley, James. Exploring the Little Rivers of New Jersey. 3rd rev. ed. 1971. pap. 8.95 (ISBN 0-8135-0685-9). Rutgers U Pr.

Childe, Vere G. The Danube in Prehistory. LC 75-41055. (BCL Ser.: No. I). Repr. of 1929 ed. 40.00 (ISBN 0-404-14520-5). AMS Pr.

Clark, William. Sing Peace to Cedar River. Brunelle, Jim, ed. (Illus.). 240p. 1983. pap. 10.95 (ISBN 0-930096-41-X). G Gannett.

Cunge, J. A. & Holley, F. M. Practical Aspects of Computational River Hydraulics. LC 79-25810. (Water Resources Engineering Ser.). 420p. 1981. text ed. 82.95 (ISBN 0-273-08442-9). Pitman Pub MA.

Discharge of Selected Rivers of the World. Incl. Vol. 1. General & Regime Characteristics of Stations Selected. 70p. 1969. pap. 9.25 (ISBN 92-3-001164-9, U165); Vol. 2. Monthly & Annual Discharges Recorded at Various Selected Stations (From Start of Observations up to 1964) 194p. 1971. pap. 12.50 (ISBN 92-3-000847-8, U166); Vol. 3, Pt. 1. Mean Monthly & Extreme Discharges (1965-1969) 98p. 1971; Vol. 3, Pt. 2. Mean Monthly & Extreme Discharges (1969-1972) 214p. 1974. pap. 13.25 (ISBN 92-3-001178-9, U168); Vol. 3, Pt. 3. Mean Monthly & Extreme Discharges (1972-1975) 123p. 1979. pap. 9.25 (ISBN 92-3-001569-5, U916). (Studies & Reports in Hydrology: No. 5). (Eng., Fr., Span. & Rus., Orig., UNESCO). Unipub.

Dzulynski, Stanislaw & Sanders, John. Current Marks on Firm Mud Bottoms. (Connecticut Academy of Arts & Sciences Transaction: Vol. 42). 96p. 1962. pap. 9.50 (ISBN 0-208-01107-2). Shoe String.

Footner, Hulbert. Rivers of the Eastern Shore. (Illus.). 381p. 1979. Repr. of 1944 ed. 14.95 (ISBN 0-87033-092-6). Tidewater.

Francis, Austin. Catskill Rivers. LC 83-4164. (Illus.). 224p. 1983. 24.95 (ISBN 0-8329-0282-9, Pub. by Winchester Pr). New Century.

Greeson, Phillip E., ed. River-Quality Assessments: Proceedings of a Symposium Held in Tucson, Arizona, November 2-3, 1977. LC 79-87721. pap. 49.80 (ISBN 0-317-11245-7, 2017814). Bks Demand UMI.

Hey, R. D., et al. Gravel-Bed Rivers: Fluvial Processes, Engineering & Management. LC 81-16390. 875p. 1982. 112.00x (ISBN 0-471-10139-7, Pub. by Wiley-Interscience). Wiley.

Isaac, P. C. River Management. (Illus.). 258p. 1967. 29.75 (ISBN 0-85334-460-4, Pub. by Elsevier Applied Sci England). Elsevier.

Jansen, P. P., et al. Principles of River Engineering: The Non-Tidal Alluvial River. LC 79-40141. (Water Resources Engineering Ser.). 509p. 1979. text ed. 139.95 (ISBN 0-273-01139-1). Pitman Pub MA.

Jarvis, R. & Woldenberg, M. River Networks. 1984. 56.95 (ISBN 0-87933-106-2). Van Nos Reinhold.

Kabir, Humayun. Men & Rivers. 1981. 2.75x (ISBN 0-8364-0702-4, Pub. by Sargam India). South Asia Bks.

Kissack, Keith. The River Wye. (Illus.). 1979. 20.00x (ISBN 0-900963-79-4, Pub. by Terence Dalton England). State Mutual Bk.

Knighton, D. Fluvial Forms & Processes. 224p. 1984. pap. text ed. 16.95 (ISBN 0-7131-6405-0). E Arnold.

Large, R. G. The Skeena: River of Destiny. (Illus.). 208p. 1981. pap. 8.95 (ISBN 0-88826-091-1). Superior Pub.

Lewin, John, ed. British Rivers. (Illus.). 228p. 1981. text ed. 60.00x (ISBN 0-04-551047-4). Allen Unwin.

McCaffrey, M. Stanislaus. The Dolores: Guide & Reference Book. LC 81-5922. 96p. (Orig.). pap. cancelled (ISBN 0-87108-578-X). Pruett.

May, George W. Down Illinois Rivers. (Illus.). 400p. 1981. 16.00x (ISBN 0-9605566-5-6). G W May.

Messel, H., ed. Surveys of Tidal River Systems in the Northern Territory & Their Crocodile Populations, 7 vols. Incl. Tidal Waterways of Castlereagh Bay & Hutchinson & Cadell Straits: Bennett, Darbitla, Djigaglia Djabura, Ngandadauda Creeks & the Glyde & Woolen Rivers. (Monograph: No. 9). 23.25 (ISBN 0-08-024801-2); Tidal Waterways of Buckingham & Ulundurwi Bays: Buckingham, Kalarwoi, Warawuruwoi & Kurala Rivers & Slippery Creek. (Monograph: No. 10). 18.00 (ISBN 0-08-024802-0); Tidal Waterways of Arnhem Bay: Darwarunga, Habgood, Baralminer, Gobalpa, Coromuro, Cato, Peter John & Burungbirinung Rivers. (Monograph: No. 11). 21.50 (ISBN 0-08-024803-9); Tidal Waterways on the South-Western Coast of the Gulf of Carpentaria: Limmen Bight Towns, Roper, Phelp & Wilson Rivers; Nayarnpi, Wungguliyanga, Painnyilatya, Mangkurdurrungku & Yiwapa Creeks. (Monograph: No. 12). 17.00 (ISBN 0-08-024804-7); Tidal Waterways on the Southern Coast of the Gulf of Carpentaria: Calvert, Robinson, Wearyan & McArthur Rivers & Some Intervening Creeks. (Monograph: No. 13). 19.00 (ISBN 0-08-024805-5); Tidal Waterways of the Van Diemen Gulf: Ilamary; River, Iwalg, Saltwater & Minimini: Creeks & Coastal Arms on Cobourg Peninsula. Resurveys of the Alligator Region Rivers. (Monograph: No. 14). 20.00 (ISBN 0-08-024806-3); Some River & Creek Systems on the West Coast of Cape York Peninsula in the Gulf of Carpentaria: Nassau, Staaten & Gilbert Rivers & Duck Creek. (Monograph: No. 16). write for info. (ISBN 0-08-024807-1). (Illus.). 1980. write for info. Pergamon.

Morisawa, Marie. Rivers. (Illus.). text ed. 35.00 (ISBN 0-582-48981-4); pap. text ed. 27.95x (ISBN 0-582-48982-2). Longman.

Ogden, John. Yorkshire's River Aire. (Illus.). 1979. 30.00x (ISBN 0-900963-55-7, Pub. by Terence Dalton England). State Mutual Bk.

--Yorkshire's River Derwent. (Illus.). 1979. 25.00x (ISBN 0-900963-42-5, Pub. by Terence Dalton England). State Mutual Bk.

Organizing Committee of the Symposium. River Sedimentation: Proceedings of the Second International Symposium, 11-16 October, 1983, Nanjing, China, 2 vols. 1658p. 1985. Vol. 1. 72.00 (ISBN 0-8133-0253-6); Vol. 2. 80.00 (ISBN 0-8133-0275-7); Set. 140.00 (ISBN 0-317-20866-7). Westview.

Osgood, Charles G. Spenser's English Rivers. LC 77-22473. 1920. lib. bdg. 8.50 (ISBN 0-8414-6542-8). Folcroft.

Parker, Rowland. The Common Stream. (Illus.). 252p. 1981. pap. 5.95 (ISBN 0-586-08253-0, Pub. by Granada England). Academy Chi Pubs.

Patterson, R. M. Dangerous River. (Illus.). 272p. pap. 7.95 (ISBN 0-686-74142-0). Superior Pub.

Peter, P. Canal & River Levees. (Developments in Geotechnical Engineering Ser.: Vol. 29). 540p. 1982. 104.25 (ISBN 0-444-99726-1). Elsevier.

Petts, Geoffrey E. Rivers. (Sources & Methods in Geography Ser.). (Illus.). 216p. (Orig.). 1983. pap. text ed. 16.50 (ISBN 0-408-11070-8). Butterworth.

Richards, Keith. Rivers: Form & Process in Alluvial Channels. 272p. 1982. 38.00x (ISBN 0-416-74900-3, NO. 3738); pap. 18.95 (ISBN 0-416-74910-0, NO. 3739). Methuen Inc.

River Quality: The Nineteen Eighty Survey & Future Outlook. 40p. 1981. 35.00x (ISBN 0-901090-36-0, Pub. by Natl Water England). State Mutual Bk.

River Training & Bank Protection. (Water Resources Development Ser.: No. 4). pap. 2.00 (ISBN 0-686-92889-X, UN53/2F6, UN). Unipub.

Rivers & Lakes. LC 84-24463. (Planet Earth Ser.). 1985. lib. bdg. 19.94 (ISBN 0-8094-4509-3, Pub. by Time-Life). Silver.

Robinson, Keith & Lehman, Fred. South Fork of the American River: From Chili Bar Dam to Salmon Falls Road. (Whitewater Ser.). (Illus.). 1982. pap. 3.95 (ISBN 0-941838-00-5). Lore Unlim.

--Stanislaus River: From Camp Nine to Parrots Ferry. (Whitewater Ser.). (Illus.). 1982. pap. 3.95 (ISBN 0-941838-01-3). Lore Unlim.

--Tuolumne River: From Lumsden Bridge to Ward's Ferry. (Whitewater Ser.). (Illus.). 1982. pap. 3.95 (ISBN 0-941838-02-1). Lore Unlim.

Russell, Richard J. River & Delta Morphology. LC 67-29343. (Louisiana State University Studies, Coastal Studies Ser.: No. 20). pap. 20.00 (ISBN 0-317-29938-7, 2051688). Bks Demand UMI.

Russell, Ronald. Rivers. 1978. 7.50 (ISBN 0-7153-7473-7). David & Charles.

Rzoska, Julian. On the Nature of Rivers: With Case Stories of the Nile, Zaire, & Amazon. 1978. pap. 10.50 (ISBN 90-6193-589-X, Pub. by Junk Pubs Netherlands). Kluwer Academic.

Schumm, S. River Morphology. 1982. pap. 45.95 (ISBN 0-87933-001-5). Van Nos Reinhold.

Applying Robotics in the Aerospace Industry, 17 papers. 59.50 (ISBN 0-317-07143-2, 815). SME.
ASME Winter Annual Meeting, Phoenix, Ariz., Nov. 1982. Robotics Research & Advanced Applications. Book, Wayne J., ed. 287p. 1982. 50.00 (H00236). ASME.
Ayres, Robert U. & Miller, Steven M. Robotics: Applications & Social Implications. LC 82-13881. 368p. 1982. prof ref 32.50x (ISBN 0-88410-891-0). Ballinger Pub.
--Robotics: Applications & Social Implications. 339p. 1983. text ed. 32.50scp (ISBN 0-88410-891-0, HarpC). Har-Row.
Behavioral Objectives in Aviation Automated Systems Symposium. 378p. 1982. pap. 45.00 (ISBN 0-89883-079-6, P114). Soc Auto Engineers.
Berger, Phil. The State-of-the-Art Robot Catalog: Robots for Fun, Show, Personal & Home Use & Industry. LC 83-20838. (Illus.). 148p. 1984. pap. 12.95 (ISBN 0-396-08361-7). Dodd.
Berk, A. A. Practical Robotics & Interfacing for the Spectrum. (Illus.). 160p. (Orig.). 1984. pap. 13.95 (ISBN 0-246-12576-4, Pub. by Granada England). Sheridan.
Bonney, M. & Yong, Y. F., eds. Robot Safety. 300p. 1985. 40.00x (ISBN 0-903608-69-3, Pub. by IFS Pubns UK). Air Sci Co.
Bortz, A. Robotics: A Decision-Makers Guide. 1986. cancelled. Van Nos Reinhold.
Brady, M., et al, eds. Robotics & Artificial Intelligence. (NATO ASI Ser.: Series F: No. 11). xviii, 694p. 1984. 62.50 (ISBN 0-387-12888-3). Springer-Verlag.
Brady, Michael & Paul, Richard, eds. International Symposium of Robotics Research. LC 83-25592. (Artificial Intelligence Ser.). (Illus.). 600p. 1984. text ed. 65.00x (ISBN 0-262-02207-9). MIT Pr.
--Robotics Research: First International Symposium. 1984. 65.00x (ISBN 0-262-02207-9). MIT Pr.
British Robot Association Members' Handbook, 1982-83. 236p. 1983. pap. write for info. (ISBN 0-903608-38-3, Pub. by IFSPUBS). Scholium Intl.
British Robot Association: Proceedings of the 8th Annual Conference. 1985. 80.00x (ISBN 0-903608-87-1, Pub. by IFS Pubns UK). Air Sci Co.
Brock, T. E., ed. British Robot Association Annual Conference, 7th: Proceedings of the Conference, Cambridge, UK, 14-16 May, 1984. 300p. 1984. 53.75 (ISBN 0-444-87532-8, Pub. by North Holland). Elsevier.
Burton, Phillip E. The Dictionary of Robotics. 1984. write for info. Garland Pub.
Canadian CAD-CAM & Robotics: Conference Proceedings. 2nd ed. 200p. 1983. pap. 25.00 (ISBN 0-87263-119-2). ASME.
Cardoza, Anne & Vlk, Suzee J. Robotics. (Illus.). 160p. 1985. 16.95 (ISBN 0-8306-0858-3, 1858); pap. 10.95 (ISBN 0-8306-1858-9). TAB Bks.
CES Industries, Inc. Ed-Lab Eight Hundred Experiment Manual: Robotics Interfacing. (Illus., Orig.). 1983. write for info. (ISBN 0-86711-046-5). CES Industries.
CES Industries, Inc. & Nesenoff, Norman. Ed-Lab Eighty Experiment Manual: Robotics Interfacing. (Illus., Orig.). 1983. write for info. (ISBN 0-86711-034-1). CES Industries.
Chacko, George K. Robotics-Artificial Intelligence-Productivity. (Illus.). 360p. 1985. text ed. 39.95 (ISBN 0-89433-228-7). Petrocelli.
--Robotics-Artificial Intelligence-Productivity: Japan & the USA. (Illus.). 340p. 1985. 39.95 (ISBN 0-317-31197-2). Van Nos Reinhold.
Chin, F. Automation & Robots: A Selected Bibliography of Books. (Public Administration Ser.: Bibliography P-969). 19p. 1982. 3.00 (P-969). Vance Biblios.
Computers in Engineering, 1982, 4 Vols. Incl. Vol. 1. Computer-Aided Design, Manufacturing, & Simulation. 351p (G00215); Vol. 2. Robots & Robotics. 261p (G00216); Vol. 3. Mesh Generation, Finite Elements, Computers in Structural Optimization, Computers in the Engineering Workplace, Computers in Energy Systems, Personal Computing. 273p (G00217); Process Control, State-of-the-Art Printing Technology, Software Engineering & Management, Statistical Modeling & Reliability Techniques, Computers in Education. 305p (G00218). 1982. Set. 200.00 (ISBN 0-317-07007-X, G00219); 60.00 ea. ASME.
Corbeil, Richard L., Sr. Tele-Robotics: The New Medium for Marketing, Sales, & Politics: An Innovative Breakthrough in Communications & Target Marketing. (Illus.). 112p. 1984. 10.00 (ISBN 0-682-40137-4). Exposition Pr FL.
Craig, John J. Introduction to Robotics: Mechanics & Control. 1985. 35.95. Addison-Wesley.
Critchlow, Arthur J. Introduction to Robotics. 550p. 1986. text ed. price not set lab manual & instrs.' manual (ISBN 0-02-325590-0). Macmillan.
Cutkosky, Mark R. Robotic Grasping & Fine Manipulation. 1985. lib. bdg. 29.95 (ISBN 0-89838-200-9). Kluwer Academic.
Danthine, Andre & Geradin, Michel, eds. Advanced Software in Robotics: Proceedings of an International Meeting, Liege, Belgium, May 1983. x, 370p. 1984. 48.00 (ISBN 0-444-86814-3, I-533-83, North Holland). Elsevier.
Derek, Kelly. A Layman's Introduction to Robotics. (Illus.). 220p. 1985. 27.95 (ISBN 0-317-28908-X). Petrocelli.
Designing Your Product for Robotics. 52p. 1982. pap. 15.00 (ISBN 0-89883-288-8, SP517). Soc Auto Engineers.
Developments in Mechanized, Automated & Robotic Welding: Proceedings. 320p. 1981. 62.00 (ISBN 0-317-05231-4, Pub. by IFSPUBS). Scholium Intl.
Displays, Electronics, & Sensor Technology. 215p. 1984. pap. 50.00 (ISBN 0-89883-336-1, SP565). Soc Auto Engineers.
Dwivedi, S. N., ed. Robotics & Factories of the Future. 650p. 1985. 50.00 (ISBN 0-387-15015-3). Springer-Verlag.
Electronic Displays & Information Systems. 128p. 1981. pap. 38.00 (ISBN 0-89883-060-5, P92). Soc Auto Engineers.
Electronic Displays, Information Systems, & On-Board Electronics. 164p. 1982. pap. 38.00 (ISBN 0-89883-068-0, P103). Soc Auto Engineers.
Engelberger, J. Robotics in Practice. 1983. pap. 24.95 (ISBN 0-317-31400-9). AMACOM.
Engelberger, Joseph F. Robotics in Practice: Management & Applications of Robotics In Industry. LC 80-66866. (Illus.). 1981. 44.95 (ISBN 0-8144-5645-6); pap. 24.95 (ISBN 0-8144-7587-6). AMACOM.
Fisher, Edward L., ed. Robotics & Industrial Engineering: Selected Readings. 268p. 1983. pap. 34.95 (ISBN 0-89806-045-1). Inst Indus Eng.
Flora, Philip C., ed. International Robotics Industry Directory, 1984. 4th ed. (Illus.). 348p. 1984. pap. 35.00 (ISBN 0-444-86890-9). Tech Data Corp.
Garoogian, Andrew. Robotics, Nineteen Sixty to Nineteen Eighty-Three: An Annotated Bibliography. LC 84-1763. (CompuBibs Ser.: No. 1). 119p. 1984. pap. 16.50x (ISBN 0-914791-03-6). Vantage Info.
Gevarter, William B. Artificial Intelligence & Robotics: Five Overviews (Robotics, Expert Systems, Computer Vision, Computer-Based Natural Language Processing & Artificial Inteligence) LC 84-70998. (Robotics & Artificial Intelligence Applications Ser.: Vols. 1-5C). 696p. 1984. lib. bdg. 99.50x (ISBN 0-89934-227-2, BT918). Business Technology Bks.
--Intelligent Machines: An Introductory Perspective of Artificial Intelligence & Robotics. LC 84-22326. (Illus.). 240p. 1985. text ed. 33.95 (ISBN 0-13-468810-4). P-H.
--Robotics: An Overview. LC 83-70567. (Robotics & Artificial Intelligence Applications Ser.: Vol. 1). 110p. 1984. pap. 24.50x (ISBN 0-89934-176-4, BT-001). Business Technology Bks.
Goldberg, Joel. Electronic Servicing of Robotic Equipment. LC 84-8198. (Illus.). 224p. 1985. text ed. 27.95 (ISBN 0-13-252131-8). P-H.
Goldman, Ron. Design of An Interactive Manipulator Programming Environment. Stone, Harold, ed. LC 84-28091. (Computer Science; Artificial Intelligence Ser.: No. 16). 158p. 1985. 44.95 (ISBN 0-8357-1616-3). UMI Res Pr.
Gomersall, A. & Farmer, P. Robotics. (Illus.). 200p. 1984. 45.00 (ISBN 0-387-15010-2). Springer-Verlag.
Gomersall, Alan & Farmer, Penny, eds. Robotics Bibliography: 1970-1981. 230p. 1982. text ed. 68.00x (ISBN 0-903608-19-7, Pub by IFSPUBS). Scholium Intl.
Groover, M. P. & Weiss, M. Industrial Robotics: Technology, Programming & Applications. (CAD-CAM Robotics & Computer Vision Ser.). 480p. 1986. price not set (ISBN 0-07-024989-X). McGraw.
Hackwood, S. & Beni, G. Recent Advances in Robotics. 426p. 1985. 32.50 (ISBN 0-471-88383-2). Wiley.
Hanafusa, Hideo & Inoue, Hirochika, eds. Robotics Research: Second International Symposium. (Artificial Intelligence Ser.). (Illus.). 500p. 1985. text ed. 50.00x (ISBN 0-262-08151-2). MIT Pr.
Hardt, D. E. & Book, W. J., eds. Control of Manufacturing Processes & Robotic Systems. 144p. 1983. 30.00 (ISBN 0-317-06646-3, H00278). ASME.
Hawk, Gerald L. & Strimaitis, Janet R., eds. Advances in Laboratory Automation-Robotics, 1984. (Illus.). 360p. 1984. 45.00 (ISBN 0-931565-00-6). Zymark Corp.
Heath Company Staff. Robotics & Industrial Electronics. (Illus.). 730p. 1983. pap. text ed. 29.95 (ISBN 0-87119-094-X, EB-1801); tchr's. ed. 9.95 (ISBN 0-87119-096-6); lab manual 14.95 (ISBN 0-87119-095-8). HeathKit-Zenith Ed.
Heath, Larry. Fundamentals of Robotics: Theory & Applications. 1984. text ed. 32.95 (ISBN 0-8359-2189-1). Reston.
Helmers, Carl, ed. Robotics Age: In the Beginning. 241p. 1983. pap. 16.95 (ISBN 0-8104-6325-3). Hayden.
Hoekstra. Robotics & Automated Systems. 1985. text ed. 22.35 (ISBN 0-538-33650-1, IE65). SW Pub.
Holland, John M. Basic Robotic Concepts. LC 83-60173. (Blacksburg Continuing Education Ser.). 272p. 1983. pap. text ed. 19.95 (ISBN 0-672-21952-2). Sams.
Hollingum, J. Machine Vision. (Illus.). 100p. 1984. pap. 19.50 (ISBN 0-387-13837-4). Springer-Verlag.
Hunt, H. Allan & Hunt, Timothy L. Human Resource Implications of Robotics. LC 83-6201. 208p. 1983. text ed. 21.95 (ISBN 0-88099-009-0); pap. text ed. 14.95 (ISBN 0-88099-008-2). W E Upjohn.
Industrial & Personal Robotics. 1984. 3 ring bdg. 145.00 (ISBN 0-317-20437-8). Optosonic Pr.
International Computers in Engineering Conference & Exhibit, 1983. Computers in Engineering: Papers, 3 Vols. Incl. Vol. 1. Computer-Aided Design, Manufacturing, & Simulation, 55 papers. Cokonis, T. J., ed. 357p. 70.00 (GOO230); Vol. 2. Robotics Theory & Applications; Computers in Education, 47 papers. Ruoff, C. F. & Shoup, T. E., eds. 320p. 70.00 (GOO231); Vol. 3. Computer Software & Applications, 44 papers. Dietrich, D. E., ed. 263p. 70.00 (GOO232). 1983. Set. 180.00 (GOO233). ASME.
International Conference on Advanced Robotics, Tokyo, Japan, Sept. 1983. Proceedings. Robotics Society of Japan, ed. 466p. 1983. pap. 150.00x (ISBN 0-903608-61-8). Scholium Intl.
International Conference on Automotive Electronics, 3rd: Proceedings. 354p. 1981. pap. 50.00 (ISBN 0-85298-477-4, P102). Soc Auto Engineers.
International Congress on Transportation & Electronics, Convergence '82: Proceedings. 265p. 1982. pap. 38.00 (ISBN 0-89883-076-1, P111). Soc Auto Engineers.
International Resource Development Inc. Personal Robot Market. 255p. 1984. 1650.00x (ISBN 0-88694-615-8). Intl Res Dev.
Japan Industrial Robot Association. The Robotics Industry of Japan: Today & Tomorrow. 592p. 1982. pap. 525.00 (ISBN 0-13-782102-6). P-H.
The Japanese Automobile Industry: Model & Challenge for the Future? 147p. 1981. pap. 15.00 (ISBN 0-939512-08-4, P95). Soc Auto Engineers.
Japanese Industrial Robot Association, ed. The Specifications & Applications of Industrial Robots in Japan 1984. (Illus.). 780p. 1984. softbound 125.00x (ISBN 0-87936-016-X). Scholium Intl.
Jones. World According to Robo the Robot. 1985. 12.95 (ISBN 0-8104-6331-8). Hayden.
Jones, Paul, ed. Robotics for Safety & Profit. (Illus.). 78p. 1981. 20.00 (ISBN 0-9608316-0-6). P-P Pubns.
Kafrissen, Edward & Stephans, Mark. Industrial Robots & Robotics. 396p. 1984. 30.95 (ISBN 0-317-18044-4). Robot Inst Am.
Kafrissen, Edward & Stephen, Mark. Industrial Robotics & Robotics. LC 83-17723. 396p. 1984. text ed. 28.95 (ISBN 0-8359-3071-8). Reston.
Kaplinsky, Raphael. Automation. (Illus.). 224p. 1984. pap. text ed. 18.95 (ISBN 0-582-90203-7). Longman.
Kelly, Derek. A Layman's Guide to Robotics. 1985. 29.95 (ISBN 0-89433-265-1). Petrocelli.
Knight, Timothy. Probots & People: The Age of the Personal Robot. (Illus.). 144p. 1984. 9.95 (ISBN 0-317-12664-4). McGraw.
Knittel, Patricia. Selected Bibliography: Robotics, Vol. 1. 14p. 1983. pap. 15.00 (ISBN 0-89938-012-3). Tech & Ed Ctr Graph Arts RIT.
Korein, James U. A Geometric Investigation of Reach. (Association for Computing Machinery Distinguished Dissertation Award Ser.). (Illus.). 210p. 1985. text ed. 30.00x (ISBN 0-262-11104-7). MIT Pr.
Lane, K. A., ed. Machine Tools, 1984: Proceedings of the International Conference, Birmingham, UK, 26-28 June 1984. 650p. 1984. 87.00 (ISBN 0-444-87542-5, North Holland). Elsevier.
Lasers in Metalworking: A Summary & Forecast. 165p. 1983. pap. 80.00 (ISBN 0-317-05222-5). Elsevier.
Lee, C. George, et al. Robotics. 2nd ed. 630p. 1985. 45.00 (ISBN 0-8186-0658-4); prepub. 29.00 (ISBN 0-317-31796-2). IEEE Comp Soc.
Lee, C. S. G., et al. Tutorial on Robotics. (Tutorial Texts Ser.). 573p. 1983. 39.00 (ISBN 0-8186-0515-4). IEEE Comp Soc.
Lee, Mary P. & Lee, Richard S. Exploring Careers in Robotics. (Careers in Depth Ser.). 144p. 1984. lib. bdg. 8.97 (ISBN 0-8239-0620-5). Rosen Group.
L'Hote, Francois, et al. Robot Technology: Robot Components & Systems, Vol. 4. (Illus.). 352p. 1984. text ed. 41.95 (ISBN 0-13-782160-3). P-H.
McDonald, A. C. Robotics Design & Maintenance. 1985. text ed. 29.95 (ISBN 0-8359-6688-7); instr's. manual avail. (ISBN 0-8359-6689-5). Reston.
Machine Vision for Robotics & Automated Inspection: Technical Report for Engineers & Managers, 3 Vols. Incl. Vol. 1. Fundamentals; Vol. 2. Applications; Vol. 3. Manufacturers-Systems. 1984. Set. 185.00 (ISBN 0-89671-046-7). SEAI Tech Pubns.
McLuckie, John D. The Robotics Workbook. 1985. pap. text ed. 4.95 wkbk. (ISBN 0-538-33670-6, IE67). SW Pub.
Malcolm, Douglas R., Jr. Robotics: An Introduction. 1985. text ed. write for info. (ISBN 0-534-04752-1). Breton Pubs.
Masterson, James & Poe, Elmer. Robotics. 1984. text ed. 27.95 (ISBN 0-8359-6692-5). Reston.
Miller, Robert J., ed. Robotics: Future Factories, Future Workers. (Annals: Vol. 470). 224p. 1983. 15.00 (ISBN 0-317-06457-6); pap. 7.95 (ISBN 0-317-06458-4). Am Acad Pol Soc Sci.
Minsky, Marvin. Robotics. LC 84-24390. (Illus.). 384p. 1985. 19.95 (ISBN 0-385-19414-5, Anchor Pr). Doubleday.
Morecki, A., ed. Robotics & Manipulators: Theory & Practice. 36p. 1983. pap. 9.20 (ISBN 0-08-030530-X, 11). Pergamon.
Mortimer, J. & Rooks, B., eds. Decade of Robotics: Special Tenth Anniversary Issue of the Industrial Robot Magazine. (Illus.). 168p. 1983. pap. 34.00 (ISBN 0-387-12545-0). Springer-Verlag.
National Bureau of Standards, Automation Technology Branch. Robotics & Artificial Intelligence: A Glossary. B-T Books, ed. LC 83-73203. 137p. 1984. Repr. of 1982 ed. 34.50x (ISBN 0-89934-186-1, BT-906). Business Technology Bks.
Nof, Shimon Y. Handbook of Industrial Robotics. 1408p. 1985. 76.95 (ISBN 0-471-89684-5). Wiley.
OECD Staff. Micro-Electronics, Robotics, & Jobs. (ICCP Ser.: No. 7). 265p. (Orig.). 1983. pap. 25.00x (ISBN 92-64-12384-9). OECD.
Parent, Michel & Laurgeau, Claude. Robot Technology: Logic & Programming, Vol. 5. (Illus.). 192p. 1985. text ed. 41.95 (ISBN 0-13-782178-6). P-H.
Paul, J. K., ed. High Technology International Trade & Competition: Robotics, Computers, Telecommunications, Semiconductors. LC 84-5916. (Illus.). 394p. 1984. 42.00 (ISBN 0-8155-0988-X). Noyes.
Penning, D. Robotics: Present & Future. 1986. cancelled. Van Nos Reinhold.
Pentland, Alex. From Pixels to Predicates. Hobbs, Jerry R., ed. (Ablex Series in Artificial Intelligence: Vol. 3). 320p. 1985. text ed. 35.00 (ISBN 0-89391-237-9). Ablex Pub.
Petit, Jean-Pierre. Run, Robot, Run: Artificial Intelligence & Robotics. Stewart, Ian, tr. from Fr. (The Adventures of Archibald Higgins Ser.). (Illus.). 76p. 1985. pap. 7.95 (ISBN 0-86576-083-7). W Kaufmann.
Petrocelli Books Editorial Staff. The Future of the Semiconductors Computer, Robotics & Telecommunication: A Source Book. (Illus.). 300p. 1984. text ed. 49.95 (ISBN 0-89433-259-7). Petrocelli.
Plander, I., ed. Artificial Intelligence & Information-Control Systems of Robots: Proceedings of the International Conference on Artificial Intelligence & Information-Control Systems of Robots, Smolenice, 3rd, Czechoslovakia, June 11-15, 1984. 402p. 1984. 55.75 (ISBN 0-444-87533-6, Pub. by North Holland). Elsevier.
Proceedings of the Fourth BRA Annual Conference. 253p. 1981. pap. 54.00x (ISBN 0-903608-17-0, Pub. by IFSPUBS). Scholium Intl.
Pugh, A., ed. Robotic Technology. (IEE Control Engineering Ser.: No. 23). 168p. 1983. 40.00 (ISBN 0-86341-004-9). Inst Elect Eng.
Ranky, P. & Ho, C. Y. Robot Modelling: Control & Applications with Software. 380p. 1985. 45.00 (Pub. by IFS Pubns UK). Air Sci Co.
Ra'nky, P. G. & Ho, C. Y. Robot Modelling. 380p. 1985. 45.00 (ISBN 0-387-15373-X). Springer-Verlag.
Rathmill, K., ed. Robotic Assembly. (International Trends in Manufacturing Technology Ser.). 350p. 1985. 39.50 (ISBN 0-387-15483-3). Springer-Verlag.
Rathmill, K., et al, eds. Robot Technology & Applications. (Illus.). 203p. 1985. 31.00 (ISBN 0-387-13960-5). Springer-Verlag.

Morecki, A. & Kedzior, K., eds. Theory & Practice of Robots & Manipulators: Proceedings of the Second CISM-IFTOMM International Symposium, Warsaw, September, 1976. 500p. 1978. 102.25 (ISBN 0-444-99812-8). Elsevier.
Morgan, C. Using Robots. 250p. 1984. 38.00 (ISBN 0-387-12584-1). Springer Verlag.
Mori, Masahiro. The Buddha in the Robot: A Robot Engineer's Thoughts on Science & Religion. Friedrich, Ralph, ed. Terry, Charles S., tr. 192p. 1981. pap. 5.95 (ISBN 4-333-01002-0, Pub. by Kosei Publishing Co). C E Tuttle.
Osborne, David M. Robots, 2 Vols. Incl. Bk. 1. Robots, An Introduction to Basic Concepts & Applications; Bk. 2. The Application of Robots to Practical Work. 1984. Bk. 1. 29.95 (ISBN 0-910853-00-2); Bk. 2. 27.50 (ISBN 0-910853-02-9); softcover 19.95 ea. (ISBN 0-910853-03-7). Midwest Sci-Tech.
Owen, Tony. Assembly with Robots. (Illus.). 224p. 1985. text ed. 29.95 (ISBN 0-13-049578-6). P-H.
Pattis, Richard E. Karel the Robot: A Gentle Introduction to the Art of Programming. LC 80-26748. 106p. 1981. pap. text ed. 10.95 (ISBN 0-471-08928-1). Wiley.
Paul, Richard P. Robot Manipulators: Mathematics, Programming, & Control. (MIT Press Artificial Intelligence Ser.). (Illus.). 279p. 1981. text ed. 34.50x (ISBN 0-262-16082-X). MIT Pr.
Proceedings of the Fourth BRA Annual Conference. 253p. 1981. pap. 54.00x (ISBN 0-903608-17-0, Pub. by IFSPUBS). Scholium Intl.
Pugh, A., ed. Robot Vision. (International Trends in Manufacturing Technology). 356p. 1983. 49.50 (ISBN 0-387-12073-4). Springer-Verlag.
--Robot Vision & Sensory Controls IV: Proceedings of the 4th International Conference, London, UK, 9-11 October, 1984. 540p. 1985. 111.00 (ISBN 0-444-87626-X, North-Holland). Elsevier.
Raibert, Marc. Legged Robots That Balance. (Artificial Intelligence Ser.). (Illus.). 275p. 1985. text ed. 30.00x (ISBN 0-262-18117-7). MIT Pr.
RIA Robot Safety Seminar Proceedings & Proposed Safety Standard. 79p. 1985. pap. text ed. 34.00 (ISBN 0-317-18021-5). Robot Inst Am.
Robillard, Mark J. Advanced Robot Systems. LC 84-50184. (Illus.). 216p. 1984. pap. 15.95 (ISBN 0-672-22166-7). Sams.
The Robot Exhibit: History Fantasy & Reality. (Illus.). 64p. 1984. 10.00 (ISBN 0-88321-052-5). AM Craft.
The Robot Industry of Japan: Today & Tomorrow. 581p. 1982. pap. 650.00 (ISBN 0-317-05227-6). SME.
Robot News Update, 6 papers. 1983. 21.00 (ISBN 0-317-07144-0, 757). SME.
Robot Vision & Sensory Controls: Proceedings of the 3rd International Conference, Cambridge, MA., Nov. 1983, 2 Vols. Incl. Vol. 1. Sensor Applications & Systems (ISBN 0-903608-51-0); Vol. 2. Sensor Research (ISBN 0-903608-59-6). 103p. 80.00 ea. (ISBN 0-317-05230-6); Set. 136.00. SME.
Robots Eight, Detroit, Mich., June 1984. Robots Eight Conference Proceedings, 2 Vols. Incl. Vol. I. Applications for Today; Vol. II. Future Considerations. 1800p. 1984. Set. 113.00 (ISBN 0-318-01664-8); 67.00 ea. Robot Inst Am.
Rony, Peter R. & Rony, Karl E. Introduction to Robot Programming. 1984. pap. text ed. 24.95 (ISBN 0-8359-3266-4). Reston.
Rooks, B., ed. Robot Vision & Sensory Controls 3: Proceedings of the 3rd International Conference, Held in Cambridge, MA, Nov. 6-10, 1983. 700p. 1984. 98.00 (ISBN 0-444-86872-0). Elsevier.
Sadamoto, Kuni. Robots in the Japanese Economy. (Illus.). 280p. 1981. 65.00x (ISBN 0-89955-344-3, Pub. by Survey Japan). Intl Spec BK.
Society of Manufacturing Engineers. Robots: Proceedings, 2 vols, No. 8. 1984. Set. 110.00 (ISBN 0-87263-147-8). SME.
--Robots: Proceedings, 2 vols, No. 9. 1985. Set. 110.00 (ISBN 0-87263-189-3). SME.
Sturridge, Helen, et al. The Arco Book of Electronics. LC 84-2868. (Illus.). 140p. 1984. 11.95 (ISBN 0-668-06154-5, 6154-5). Arco.
Susnjara, Ken. A Manager's Guide to Industrial Robots. LC 83-4512. (A Spectrum Bk.). (Illus.). 192p. 1983. 16.95 (ISBN 0-13-549881-3); pap. 8.95 (ISBN 0-13-549873-2). P-H.
Thring, Meredith W. Robots & Telechirs. LC 83-10685. (Engineering Science Ser.). 298p. 1983. 54.95x (ISBN 0-470-27465-4); pap. 34.95 (ISBN 0-470-20174-6). Halsted Pr.
Todd, D. J. Walking Machines: A Introduction to Legged Robots. (Advanced Industrial Technology Ser.). 240p. 1985. text ed. 39.50 (ISBN 0-412-01131-X, 9661, Pub. by Chapman & Hall England). Methuen Inc.
U. S. Robot Market. 420p. 1983. 1375.00 (ISBN 0-86621-084-9). Frost & Sullivan.
Warnecke, H. J. & Schraft, R. D. Industrial Robots: Application Experience. (Eng.). 298p. 1982. pap. text ed. 56.00x softbound (ISBN 0-903608-21-9, Pub by IFSPUBS). Scholium Intl.
Warring, R. H. Robots & Robotology. (Illus.). 128p. (Orig.). 1984. 13.95 (ISBN 0-8306-0673-4); pap. 8.25 (ISBN 0-8306-1673-X, 1673). TAB Bks.
Wojcikiewicz, Karl & Johnson, Ron. Robot Applications. LC 84-12757. (Illus.). 600p. 1984. 99.95 (ISBN 0-87119-055-9); pap. text ed. 19.95 (ISBN 0-317-14618-1); tchr's. ed. 9.95 (ISBN 0-87119-108-3); 10.95 (ISBN 0-87119-056-7). Heathkit-Zenith Ed.
Working Robots. 168p. 1984. pap. 12.95 (ISBN 0-317-05866-5). Hayden.
Zimmerman, Howard. Robots. LC 79-63382. 1979. pap. 7.95 (ISBN 0-931064-12-0). Starlog Group.

ROBOTS–PROGRAMMING

Vukobratovic, M. & Potkonjak, V. Scientific Fundamentals of Robotics 6. (Communications & Control Engineering Ser.). (Illus.). xiii, 305p. 1985. 42.00 (ISBN 0-387-13074-8). Springer-Verlag.

ROBOTS, INDUSTRIAL

Asfahl, C. Ray. Robots & Manufacturing Automation. 490p. 1985. 32.95 (ISBN 0-471-80212-3). Wiley.
Behavioral Objectives in Aviation Automated Systems Symposium. 378p. 1982. pap. 45.00 (ISBN 0-89883-079-6, P114). Soc Auto Engineers.
Bereny, Justin A., ed. Industrial Robots: A Survey of Domestic & Foreign Patents (1969-1983) LC 85-71672. (Robotics & Artificial Intelligence Applications Ser.: Vol. 6). 250p. (Orig.). 1985. pap. 89.50x (ISBN 0-89934-230-2, BT021). Business Technology Bks.
Bonney, M. & Yong, Y. F., eds. Robot Safety. 300p. 1985. 40.00x (ISBN 0-903608-69-3, Pub. by IFS Pubns UK). Air Sci Co.
--Robot Safety. (International Trends in Manufacturing Technology Ser.). 300p. 1985. 39.50 (ISBN 0-387-15484-1). Springer-Verlag.
Business Communications Staff. New Directions in Robots for Manufacturing, G-053. 1982. 975.00 (ISBN 0-89336-219-0). BCC.
Cugy, Andre & Page, Kogan. Industrial Robot Specifications. Ioannou, Adrian, ed. LC 84-14660. 367p. 1984. text ed. 175.00 (ISBN 0-8144-7628-7). Amacom.
Developments in Mechanized, Automated & Robotic Welding: Proceedings. 320p. 1981. 62.00 (ISBN 0-317-05231-4, Pub. by IFSPUBS). Scholium Intl.
Engelberger, Joseph F. Robotics in Practice: Management & Applications of Robotics In Industry. LC 80-66866. (Illus.). 1981. 44.95 (ISBN 0-8144-5645-6); pap. 24.95 (ISBN 0-8144-7587-6). AMACOM.
Fourteenth International Symposium on Industrial Robots, 14th: Proceedings. 1984. lib. bdg. 110.00x (ISBN 0-903608-75-8, Pub. by IFS Pubns UK). Air Sci Co.
Gardner, Keith, ed. Systems & Technology for Advanced Manufacturing. 270p. 1983. 32.00 (749). SME.
Hunt, Daniel V. Industrial Robotics Handbook. (Illus.). 432p. 1983. 34.00 (ISBN 0-8311-1148-8). Indus Pr.
Industrial Robots. (Productivity Equipment Ser.). (Illus.). 416p. 1983. pap. 38.00 (ISBN 0-87263-097-8). Robot Inst Am.
Industrial Robots: A Delphi Forecast of Markets & Technology. LC 82-50754. 232p. 1982. 65.00 (ISBN 0-87263-087-0). SME.
Industrial Robots: A Summary & Forecast. 150p. 1982. 10.00 (ISBN 0-918989-01-9). Tech Tran Consult.
Industrial Robots from A to Z: Programmed Learning Course, 2 vols. Set. 195.00 (ISBN 0-317-07078-9, MGI II). SME.
Industrial Robots, Human Factors: Technical Paper Set, 7 papers. 1982. pap. 24.50 (708). SME.
Industrial Robots Symposium, 14th International: Proceedings. 738p. 1984. 126.00 (ISBN 0-317-18023-1). Robot Inst Am.
International Conference on Industrial Robot Technology, 3rd, Univ. Nottingham, Eng., Mar. 1976 & International Symposium on Industrial Robots, 6th, Univ. Nottingham, Eng., Mar. 1976. First Joint Robots Conference: Proceedings. Brock, T. E., ed. 530p. 1977. softbound 75.00x (ISBN 0-685-89046-5). Scholium Intl.
International Conference on Industrial Robot Technology, 1st, Univ. of Nottingham, Mar. 1973. Proceedings. 322p. 1977. softbound 30.00x (ISBN 0-685-89047-3). Scholium Intl.
International Robot Conference & Exhibition, 1st, Long Beach, Calif., June 1983. InteRobot Eighty-Three: Proceedings. (Illus.). 1983. 75.00 (ISBN 0-317-01310-6). Tech Data Corp.
International Symposium Industrial Robots: Proceedings on Industrial Robot Technology, Stuttgart, W. Germany, 1978, 2 Vols. 1024p. 120.00. Scholium Intl.
International Symposium on Industrial Robots, 10th, Milan, Italy, 1980 & International Conference on Industrial Robot Technology, 5th, Milan, Italy, 1980. Industrial Robots: Proceedings. (Illus.). 686p. 1982. text ed. 110.00x (Pub. by IFSPUBS). Scholium Intl.
International Symposium on Industrial Robots: Proceedings, 13th, Robots 7, Chicago, April 1983, 2 vols. Incl. Vol. I. Applications Worldwide. xxii, 970p (RIA(07)); Vol. II. Future Directions. xxii, 880p (RIA(08)). 1800p. 1983. Set. pap. 98.00 (ISBN 0-87263-114-1, RIA(09)); pap. 59.00 ea. SME.
International Symposium on Industrial Robots, 12th, Paris, June 9-11 1982. Proceedings. x, 540p. 1982. 101.00 (ISBN 0-444-86471-7, North Holland). Elsevier.
Japan Industrial Robot Association. The Robotics Industry of Japan: Today & Tomorrow. 592p. 1982. pap. 525.00 (ISBN 0-13-782102-6). P-H.
The Japanese Automobile Industry: Model & Challenge for the Future? 147p. 1981. pap. 15.00 (ISBN 0-939512-08-4, P95). Soc Auto Engineers.
Japanese Industrial Robot Association, ed. The Specifications & Applications of Industrial Robots in Japan 1984. (Illus.). 780p. 1984. softbound 125.00x (ISBN 0-87936-016-X). Scholium Intl.
Jira & Sobim, eds. Industrial Robots: Proceedings of the 11th International Symposium on Industrial Robots, Tokyo, Japan, Oct. 1982. 852p. 1981. 118.00x. Scholium Intl.
Kafrissen, Edward & Stephans, Mark. Industrial Robots & Robotics. 396p. 1984. 30.95 (ISBN 0-317-18044-4). Robot Inst Am.
Kafrissen, Edward & Stephen, Mark. Industrial Robotics & Robotics. LC 83-17723. 396p. 1984. text ed. 28.95 (ISBN 0-8359-3071-8). Reston.
Katzan, Harry, Jr. A Manager's Guide to Productivity, Quality Circles & Industrial Robots. (Illus.). 160p. 1985. 27.95 (ISBN 0-442-24823-7). Van Nos Reinhold.
Lammineur, P. & Cornillie, O. Industrial Robots, Vol. 2. (EPO Applied Technology Ser.: Vol. 2). (Illus.). 164p. 1984. 50.00 (ISBN 0-08-031143-1). Pergamon.
Light Assembly Robots Market in Europe. 320p. 1985. 1950.00 (ISBN 0-86621-684-7). Frost & Sullivan.
Machining Centers. 333p. 1983. pap. 36.00 (765). SME.
Miller, Richard K. Robots in Industry: Applications for Assembly. 2nd ed. (Illus.). 210p. 1984. pap. text ed. 125.00 (ISBN 0-89671-054-8). SEAI Tech Pubns.
--Robots in Industry: Applications for Foundries. 2nd ed. (Illus.). 190p. 1984. pap. text ed. 125.00 (ISBN 0-89671-055-6). SEAI Tech Pubns.
--Robots in Industry: Applications for the Electronics Industry. (Illus.). 190p. 1984. pap. text ed. 125.00 (ISBN 0-89671-049-1). SEAI Tech Pubns.
--Robots in Industry: Applications for the Plastics Industry. 2nd ed. 180p. 1984. pap. text ed. 125.00 (ISBN 0-89671-053-X). SEAI Tech Pubns.
--Robots in Industry: General Applications. 2nd ed. (Illus.). 219p. 1984. pap. text ed. 125.00 (ISBN 0-89671-056-4). SEAI Tech Pubns.
--Three-D Vision Applications for Industry. (Illus.). 160p. 1984. pap. text ed. 190.00 (ISBN 0-89671-060-2). SEAI Tech Pubns.
Miller, Richard R. Robots in Industry: Applications for Metal Fabrication. 2nd ed. (Illus.). 226p. 1984. pap. text ed. 125.00 (ISBN 0-89671-057-2). SEAI Tech Pubns.
Mortimer, J. & Rooks, B., eds. Decade of Robotics: Special Tenth Anniversary Issue of the Industrial Robot Magazine. (Illus.). 168p. 1983. pap. 34.00 (ISBN 0-387-12545-0). Springer-Verlag.
Nof, Shimon Y. Handbook of Industrial Robotics. 1408p. 1985. 76.95 (ISBN 0-471-89684-5). Wiley.
OECD Staff. Industrial Robots: Their Role in Manufacturing Industry. (Orig.). 1983. pap. 9.75x (ISBN 92-64-12486-1). OECD.
Owen, A. E. Flexible Assembly Systems: Assembly by Robots & Computerized Integrated Systems. 230p. 1984. 42.50x (ISBN 0-306-41527-5). Plenum Pub.
Popov, E. P., ed. Modern Robot Engineering. Pasechnik, Grigory, tr. from Rus. (Advances in Science & Technology in the USSR: Technology Ser.). 198p. 1982. pap. 5.95 (ISBN 0-8285-2338-X, Pub. by Mir Pubs USSR). Imported Pubns.
Pugh, A., ed. Robot Vision. (International Trends in Manufacturing Technology). 356p. 1983. 49.50 (ISBN 0-387-12073-4). Springer-Verlag.
--Robot Vision & Sensory Controls IV: Proceedings of the 4th International Conference, London, UK, 9-11 October, 1984. 540p. 1985. 111.00 (ISBN 0-444-87626-X, North-Holland). Elsevier.
Ranky, P. & Ho, C. Y. Robot Modelling: Control & Applications with Software. 380p. 1985. 45.00 (Pub. by IFS Pubns UK). Air Sci Co.
Report on Industrial Robots in Japan. 50.00 (ISBN 0-317-05991-2). Tech Data TX.
The Robot Industry of Japan: Today & Tomorrow. 581p. 1982. pap. 650.00 (ISBN 0-317-05227-6). SME.
Robot Market Explosion. (Reports Ser.: No. 196). 151p. 1982. 1285.00x (ISBN 0-88694-196-2). Intl Res Dev.
Robotics & CAD-CAM Market Place, 1985: A Worldwide Guide to Information Sources. 242p. 1985. 49.95 (ISBN 0-8352-1820-1). Bowker.
Robotics & the Factory of the Future, 16 papers. 1982. pap. 30.00 (P117). Soc Auto Engineers.
Robots in Automobile Industy: Proceedings of the 2nd International Conference. 1985. 67.00x (ISBN 0-317-19986-2, Pub by IFS Pubns UK). Air Sci Co.
Rooks, B., ed. Robot Vision & Sensory Controls 3: Proceedings of the 3rd International Conference, Held in Cambridge, MA, Nov. 6-10, 1983. 700p. 1984. 98.00 (ISBN 0-444-86872-0). Elsevier.
Seireg, Ali, ed. Advances in Computer Technology, 2 vols. Incl. Vol. I. Industry; Energy; Robots & Manipulators; Mini & Micro Software; Application & Design. 480p (H00173); Vol. II. Microprocessor; Automotive Development; Systems; Data Base; Finite Elements; Graphics; Education; Manufacturing; Management; Language Standards; Personal Computing. 492p (H00174). 1980. text ed. 60.00 ea. (ISBN 0-317-02542-2). ASME.
Sensors & Actuators: New Approaches. 1984. pap. 35.00 (ISBN 0-89883-338-8, SP567). Soc Auto Engineers.
Sensors & Actuators, 1983, 10 papers. 92p. 1983. pap. 25.00 (ISBN 0-89883-307-8, SP536). Soc Auto Engineers.
Snyder, Wesley E. Industrial Robots: Computer Interfacing & Control. (Industrial Robots Ser.). (Illus.). 288p. 1985. text ed. 33.95 (ISBN 0-13-463159-5). P-H.
Society of Manufacturing Engineers. Industrial Robots. 2nd ed. (Productivity Equipment Ser.). 1985. 47.00 (ISBN 0-87263-181-8). SME.
--Industrial Robots: Robots, Accessories, Components, Vision Systems, Control Systems, Consultants. LC 82-61731. pap. 106.00 (ISBN 0-317-30170-5, 1015352). Bks Demand UMI.
A Survey of Industrial Robots. 2nd ed. 143.00 (ISBN 0-686-31442-5). C I M Systems.
Susnjara, Ken. A Manager's Guide to Industrial Robots. LC 83-4512. (A Spectrum Bk.). (Illus.). 192p. 1983. 16.95 (ISBN 0-13-549881-3); pap. 8.95 (ISBN 0-13-549873-2). P-H.
--A Manager's Guide to Industrial Robots. 186p. 1982. pap. text ed. 9.95 (ISBN 0-317-18020-7). Robot Inst Am.
Tanner, W. R., ed. Industrial Robots: Applications. 2nd ed. 484p. 1981. 39.00 (ISBN 0-686-48153-4, 2003). T-C Pubns CA.
--Industrial Robots: Fundamentals. 2nd ed. 446p. 1981. 39.00 (ISBN 0-686-48152-6, 2002). T-C Pubns CA.
Tanner, William R., ed. Industrial Robots. 1st ed. LC 78-71001. (Illus.). Vol. 1, Fundamentals. pap. 73.30 (ISBN 0-317-10953-7, 2019118); Vol. 2, Applications. pap. 74.30 (ISBN 0-317-10954-5). Bks Demand UMI.
--Industrial Robots. LC 78-71001. (Manufacturing Update Ser.). Vol. 1. pap. 73.30 (ISBN 0-317-27722-7, 2024173); Vol. 2. pap. 74.30 (ISBN 0-317-27723-5). Bks Demand UMI.
Tech Tran Corporation Staff. Industrial Robots: A Summary & Forecast. 2nd ed. 247p. 1983. spiral bound 50.00 (ISBN 0-918989-04-3). Tech Tran Consult.
Technical Insights Inc. Robots in Industry: Applications for Assembly. LC 82-9926. 212p. 1984. 125.00 (ISBN 0-89671-039-4). Tech Insights.
--Robots in Industry: Applications for Foundries. LC 82-99924. 180p. 1984. 125.00 (ISBN 0-89671-055-6). Tech Insights.
--Robots in Industry: Applications for the Electronics Industry. 196p. 1983. 125.00 (ISBN 0-89671-049-1). Tech Insights.
--Robots in Industry: Applications for the Plastics Industry. LC 82-99928. 163p. 1984. 125.00 (ISBN 0-89671-041-6). Tech Insights.
--Robots in Industry: General Applications. LC 82-99925. 219p. 1984. 125.00 (ISBN 0-89671-056-4). Tech Insights.
Tenth Conference on Production Research & Technology: Proceedings, 32 papers. 240p. 1983. pap. 38.00 (ISBN 0-89883-087-7, P128). Soc Auto Engineers.

Thirteenth ISIR Robots 7: Proceedings, 2 Vols. Incl. Vol. 1. Applications Worldwide. 990p. pap. 59.00 (723); Vol. 2. Future Directions. 902p. pap. 59.00 (724). 1800p. 1983. pap. 98.00 (725). SME.

Thring, Meredith W. Robots & Telechirs. LC 83-10685. (Engineering Science Ser.). 298p. 1983. 54.95x (ISBN 0-470-27465-4); pap. 34.95 (ISBN 0-470-20174-6). Halsted Pr.

Vukobratovic, M. & Potkonjak, V. Scientific Fundamentals of Robotics 6. (Communications & Control Engineering Ser.). (Illus.). xiii, 305p. 1985. 42.00 (ISBN 0-387-13074-8). Springer-Verlag.

Warnecke, H. J. & Schraft, R. D. Industrial Robots: Application Experience. (Eng.). 298p. 1982. pap. text ed. 56.00x softbound (ISBN 0-903608-21-9, Pub by IFSPUBS). Scholium Intl.

Warring, R. H. Robots & Robotology. (Illus.). 128p. (Orig.). 1984. 13.95 (ISBN 0-8306-0673-4); pap. 8.25 (ISBN 0-8306-1673-X, 1673). TAB Bks.

Weston, R. H. Robot Systems & Their Industrial Applications. 290p. 1984. cancelled (ISBN 0-246-12202-1, Pub. by Granada England). Sheridan.

Woods, W. A., et al, eds. Japan's Industrial Robots. Massie, A. 99p. 1982. 48.00 (ISBN 0-318-00452-6, Pub. by Intl QC Forum). Media Intl Promo.

ROCHESTER INSTITUTE OF TECHNOLOGY

Gordon, Dane R. Rochester Institute of Technology: Industrial Development & Educational Innovation in a American City. LC 82-6389. (Illus.). 450p. 1982. fine binding 89.95 (ISBN 0-88946-150-3). E Mellen.

ROCK COLLECTING

see Mineralogy–Collectors and Collecting

ROCK-CRYSTAL

see Quartz

ROCK FISH

see Striped Bass

ROCK-FLINT

see Chert

ROCK MECHANICS

see also Engineering Geology; Marine Geotechnique; Soil Mechanics

American Society for Testing & Materials. Testing Techniques for Rock Mechanics. LC 66-24783. (American Society for Testing & Materials Ser.: Special Technical Publication, No. 402). pap. 76.00 (ISBN 0-317-11253-8, 2001129). Bks Demand UMI.

American Society of Civil Engineers, compiled by. New Horizons in Rock Mechanics. 795p. 1973. 25.00x (ISBN 0-87262-050-6). Am Soc Civil Eng.

Assonyi, Cs. & Richter, R. The Continuum Theory of Rock Mechanics. Balkay, B., tr. from Hungarian. (Rock & Soil Mechanics Ser.). (Illus.). 1979. 58.00x (ISBN 0-87849-027-2). Trans Tech.

ASTM Committee D-18 on Soil & Rock. Laterally Loaded Deep Foundations: Analysis & Performance. Langer, J. A., et al, eds. LC 83-72942. (Special Technical Publication Ser.: No. 835). 250p. 1984. text ed. 34.00 (ISBN 0-8031-0207-0, 04-835000-38). ASTM.

Baar, C. A. Applied Salt Rock Mechanics, Vol. 1: The In-Situ Behavior of Salt Rocks. (Developments in Geotechnical Engineering Ser.: Vol. 16A). 296p. 1977. 68.00 (ISBN 0-444-41500-9). Elsevier.

Brady, B. H. & Brown, E. T. Rock Mechanics: For Underground Mining. (Illus.). 550p. 1985. text ed. 60.00x (ISBN 0-04-622004-6); pap. text ed. 29.95x (ISBN 0-04-622005-4). Allen Unwin.

Brand, E. W. & Brenner, R. P., eds. Soft Clay Engineering. (Developments in Geotechnical Engineering Ser.: Vol. 20). 780p. 1982. 134.00 (ISBN 0-444-41784-2). Elsevier.

Brown, E. T., ed. Rock Characterization, Testing & Monitoring: ISRM Suggested Methods. LC 80-49711. 200p. 1981. pap. 22.00 (ISBN 0-08-027309-2). Pergamon.

Busch, Daniel A. & Link, David A. Exploration Methods for Sandstone Reservoirs. (Illus.). 300p. 1985. cancelled 49.50x (ISBN 0-87201-237-9). Gulf Pub.

Carter, M. Geotechnical Engineering Handbook. (Illus.). 244p. 1982. 35.00 (ISBN 0-412-00341-4, NO. 5041, Chapman & Hall). Methuen Inc.

Cernica, John N. Geotechnical Engineering. 1982. text ed. 40.95 (ISBN 0-03-059182-1). HR&W.

Cook, N. G. Problems in Rock Mechanics. (Illus.). 1985. 19.95x (ISBN 0-412-24110-2, NO. 6750, Pub. by Chapman & Hall). Methuen Inc.

Division of Earth Sciences. Rock-Mechanics Research in the U. S. (Illus.). 1966. pap. 5.25 (ISBN 0-309-01466-2). Natl Acad Pr.

Dowding, Charles H. & Singh, Madan M., eds. Rock Mechanics in Productivity & Production. LC 84-70738. (Twenty-Fifth Symposium on Rock Mechanics Ser.). (Illus.). 1222p. 1984. 50.00x (ISBN 0-89520-424-X, 424-X). Soc Mining Eng.

Drnevich & Gray, eds. Acoustic Emissions in Geotechnical Engineering Practice - STP 750. 218p. 1981. 25.00 (ISBN 0-8031-0788-9, 04-750000-38). ASTM.

Dunn, Irving S., et al. Fundamentals of Geotechnical Analysis. LC 79-13583. 414p. 1980. text ed. 42.50x (ISBN 0-471-03698-6); solutions manual avail. (ISBN 0-471-04997-2). Wiley.

Dunnicliff, John & Deere, Don U., eds. Judgement in Geotechnical Engineering: The Professional Legacy of Ralph B. Peck. LC 83-23261. 332p. 1984. 49.95x (ISBN 0-471-89767-1, Pub. by Wiley-Interscience). Wiley.

Ewert, F. K. Rock Grouting. (Illus.). 420p. 1985. 65.00 (ISBN 0-387-15252-0). Springer-Verlag.

Goodman, Richard. Methods of Geological Engineering in Discontinuous Rocks. LC 75-42152. (Illus.). 1975. text ed. 35.00 (ISBN 0-8299-0066-7). West Pub.

Goodman, Richard & Gen-Hua Shi. Block Theory & Its Application to Block Engineering. LC 84-3348. (Illus.). 336p. 1985. text ed. 55.95 (ISBN 0-13-078189-4). P-H.

Goodman, Richard E. Rock Mechanics. LC 80-13155. 478p. 1980. text ed. 47.75x (ISBN 0-471-04129-7). Wiley.

Goodman, Richard E. & Hueze, Francios E., eds. Issues in Rock Mechanics: Twenty-Third Symposium. LC 82-71989. (Illus.). 1133p. 1982. 45.00x (ISBN 0-89520-297-2). Soc Mining Eng.

Gray, Kenneth E., ed. Basic & Applied Rock Mechanics: Proceedings of the Symposium on Rock Mechanics, 10th, University of Texas at Austin, 1968. LC 74-161923. pap. 160.00 (ISBN 0-317-08700-2, 2012663). Bks Demand UMI.

Habib, Pierre. An Outline of Soil & Rock Mechanics. LC 82-17677. 145p. 1983. 32.50 (ISBN 0-521-24461-7); pap. 11.95 (ISBN 0-521-28704-9). Cambridge U Pr.

Hancock, P. L., ed. Multiple Deformation in Ductile & Brittle Rocks: A Selection of Papers Presented at the International Conference on Multiple Deformation & Foliation Development, Bemagui, NSW, Australia, 4-10 Feb. 1984. 242p. 1985. pap. 49.50 (ISBN 0-08-031419-8, Pub by PPL). Pergamon.

Heard, H. C., et al, eds. Flow & Fracture of Rocks. LC 72-91609. (Geophysical Monograph Ser.: Vol. 16). (Illus.). 352p. 1972. 23.00 (ISBN 0-87590-016-X). Am Geophysical.

Hoek, E. & Bray, J. W. Rock Slope Engineering. 3rd ed. 360p. 1981. pap. text ed. 43.25x (ISBN 0-900488-57-3). IMM North Am.

Hoek, E. & Brown, E. T. Underground Excavations in Rock. 532p. 1980. text ed. 69.00x (ISBN 0-900488-54-9); pap. text ed. 43.25x (ISBN 0-900488-55-7). IMM North Am.

Hoek, E. & Imperial College of Science & Technology, Rock Mechanics Section. KWIC Index of Rock Mechanics Literature: Pt. 1, 1870-1968. 1977. text ed. 195.00 (ISBN 0-08-022063-0). Pergamon.

Hunt, R. E. Geotechnical Engineering Practices. 531p. 1985. price not set (ISBN 0-07-031310-5). McGraw.

Illes, J. H., ed. Mechanism of Graben Formation. (Developments in Geotechtonics Ser.: Vol. 17). 266p. 1981. Repr. 64.00 (ISBN 0-444-41956-X). Elsevier.

International Society for Rock Mechanics, 3rd Congress. Advances in Rock Mechanics: Reports of Current Reasearch. xxxii, 1505p. 1974. Vol. 2, Pts. A & B. 35.25 (ISBN 0-309-02246-0); Vol. 3: Events & Discussions 1979 216pg. pap. 10.25 (ISBN 0-309-02944-9). Natl Acad Pr.

International Society for Rock Mechanics. ISRM List of Members, 1980. 250p. 1981. pap. 40.00 (ISBN 0-08-027587-7). Pergamon.

Jaeger, C. Rock Mechanics & Engineering. 2nd ed. LC 77-85700. (Illus.). 1979. 105.00 (ISBN 0-521-21898-5). Cambridge U Pr.

Jaeger, J. C. & Cook, N. G. Fundamentals of Rock Mechanics. 3rd ed. 1979. 27.95 (ISBN 0-412-22010-5, NO. 6337, Pub. by Chapman & Hall). Methuen Inc.

Jenkins, J. P. & Brown, E. T., eds. KWIC Index of Rock Mechanics Literature: Pt. 2, 1969-1976. LC 79-40980. 742p. 1979. 195.00 (ISBN 0-08-022065-7). Pergamon.

Jenkins, J. P. & Smith, A. M., eds. Thesaurus of Rock & Soil Mechanics Terms. 72p. 1984. pap. 15.00 (ISBN 0-08-031632-8). Pergamon.

Jumikis, Alfreds R. Rock Mechanics. 2nd ed. LC 83-80617. 614p. 1983. 58.00x (ISBN 0-87201-785-0). Gulf Pub.

Kovaco, W. & Holtz, R. Introduction to Geotechnical Engineering. 1981. 15.95 (ISBN 0-13-484394-0). P-H.

Lester, David. Quarrying & Rockbreaking: The Operation & Maintenance of Mobile Processing Plants. (Illus.). 117p. 1981. 14.50x (ISBN 0-903031-80-9, Pub. by Intermediate Tech England). Intermediate Tech.

Monicard, R. Properties of Reservoir Rocks: Core Analysis. LC 79-56347. 168p. 1980. 24.95x (ISBN 0-87201-765-6). Gulf Pub.

Mueller, L., ed. Rock Mechanics. (CISM Pubns. (International Center for Mechanical Sciences) Causes & Lectures: Vol. 165). (Illus.). 390p. 1982. pap. 34.90 (ISBN 0-387-81301-2). Springer-Verlag.

Norwegian Institute of Rock Schach Blasting Techniques. Rock Bolting: A Practical Handbook Describing All Aspects of Rock Bolts & Their Application in Rock Engineering. 1979. 16.25 (ISBN 0-08-022503-9). Pergamon.

Obert, Leonard & Durall, Wilbur I. Rock Mechanics & the Design of Structures in Rock. LC 66-26753. 1ap. pap. 160.00 (ISBN 0-317-28074-0, 2055766). Bks Demand UMI.

Pincus, Howard J. & Hoskins, Earl R., eds. Measurement of Rock Properties at Elevated Pressures & Temperatures-STP 869. LC 84-24558. (Illus.). 162p. 1985. text ed. 30.00 (ISBN 0-8031-0237-2, 04-869000-38). ASTM.

Priest, Stephen D. Hemispehrical Projection Methods in Rock Mechanics. (Illus.). 128p. 1984. pap. text ed. 14.95x (ISBN 0-04-622007-0). Allen Unwin.

Roberts, A. Applied Geotechnology: A Text for Students & Engineers on Rock Excavation & Related Topics. (Illus.). 416p. 1982. 55.00 (ISBN 0-08-024015-1); pap. 25.00 (ISBN 0-08-024014-3). Pergamon.

Rock Mechanics Symposium Participants. Stability of Rock Slopes: Proceedings of the Symposium on Rock Mechanics, 13th, University of Illinois, Urbana, August 30-September 1, 1971. Cording, Edward J., ed. LC 76-380975. (Illus.). pap. 160.00 (ISBN 0-317-08305-8, 2019553). Bks Demand UMI.

Rossmanith, H. P., ed. Rock Fracture Mechanics. (CISM International Centre for Mechanical Sciences. Courses & Lectures Ser.: No. 275). 484p. 1983. pap. 36.00 (ISBN 0-387-81747-6). Springer Verlag.

Scheidegger, A. E., ed. Tectonic Stresses in the Alpine-Mediterranean Region: Proceedings. (Rock Mechanics Supplementum: Vol. 9). (Illus.). 270p. 1980. pap. 75.60 (ISBN 0-387-81578-3). Springer-Verlag.

Sikarskie, D. L., ed. Rock Mechanics Symposium: Proceedings, Vol. 3. 130p. 1973. pap. text ed. 12.50 (ISBN 0-685-38865-4, I00012). ASME.

Stagg, K. G. & Zienkiewicz, O. C., eds. Rock Mechanics in Engineering Practice. LC 68-9674. (Numerical Methods in Engineering Ser.). 442p. 1968. 54.95 (ISBN 0-471-81965-4, Pub. by Wiley-Interscience). Wiley.

Stephansson, O. & Jones, M. J., eds. Application of Rock Mechanics to Cut & Fill Mining. 376p. (Orig.). 1981. pap. text ed. 132.25x (ISBN 0-900488-60-3). IMM North Am.

Symposium on Rock Mechanics. Applications of Rock Mechanics: Proceedings - 15th Symposium on Rock Mechanics Held at the State Game Lodge, Custer State Park, South Dakota, Sept. 17-19, 1973. LC 78-307544. (Symposium on Rock Mechanics Proceedings Ser.: Vol. 15). (Illus.). pap. 160.00 (ISBN 0-317-08315-5, 2019534). Bks Demand UMI.

Symposium on Rock Mechanics, 11th., University of California, Berkeley, 1969. Rock Mechanics-Theory & Practice: Proceedings. Somerton, Wilbur H., ed. LC 73-103203. (Illus.). pap. 160.00 (ISBN 0-317-10996-0, 2004326). Bks Demand UMI.

Symposium on Rock Mechanics(16th, 1975, University of Minnesota) Design Methods in Rock Mechanics: Proceedings - 16th Symposium on Rock Mechanics, Sept. 22-24, 1975. Fairhurst, Charles & Crouch, Steven L., eds. (Illus.). pap. 106.80 (ISBN 0-317-08309-0, 2019540). Bks Demand UMI.

Symposium on Underground Rock Chambers. Underground Rock Chambers: Symposium held during the ASCE National Meeting on Water Resources Engineering, Phoenix, Arizona, Jan. 13-14, 1971. LC 78-322140. pap. 151.50 (ISBN 0-317-08299-X, 2019554). Bks Demand UMI.

Treagus, S. H., ed. Strain Patterns in Rocks. 250p. 1983. 44.00 (ISBN 0-08-030273-4, 2302). Pergamon.

Turchaninov, I. A., et al. Principles of Rock Mechanics. Hustrulid, William A., ed. Peabody, A. L., tr. from Rus. LC 79-67433. (Illus.). 493p. 1979. 45.00x (ISBN 0-918990-06-8). Terraspace.

Vutukuri, V. S., et al. Handbook on Mechanical Properties of Rocks: Testing Techniques & Results, Vol. 1. LC 74-82971. (Series on Rock & Soil Mechanics). (Illus.). 300p. 1974. pap. text ed. 65.00x (ISBN 0-87849-010-8). Trans Tech.

--Handbook on Mechanical Properties of Rocks, Vol. 2. LC 74-82971. (Rock & Soil Mechanics Ser.). (Illus.). 350p. 1977. text ed. 65.00x (ISBN 0-87849-021-3). Trans Tech.

ROCK SHELTERS

see Caves

ROCKET ENGINES

see also Rockets (Aeronautics)

Hill, Philip G. & Peterson, C. R. Mechanics & Thermodynamics of Propulsion. 1965. 41.95 (ISBN 0-201-02838-7). Addison-Wesley.

Irvine, Jerry. Optimizing Performance Through Motor Selection & Design Concepts. (Ace Information Report Ser.: No. 6). 1984. 3.95 (ISBN 0-912468-04-1). CA Rocketry.

Irving, Jerry & Kline, Korey. Motor Installation: Clustering & Staging. (Ace Information Report Ser.: Nos. 1-3). 1984. 1.99 (ISBN 0-912468-01-7). CA Rocketry.

Penner, S. S. Chemical Rocket Propulsion & Combustion Research. (Illus.). 170p. 1962. 45.25x (ISBN 0-677-00710-8). Gordon.

Sutton, George A. & Ross, Donald M. Rocket Propulsion Elements: An Introduction to the Engineering of Rockets. 4th ed. LC 75-29197. 557p. 1976. 52.95x (ISBN 0-471-83836-5, Pub. by Wiley-Interscience). Wiley.

ROCKET FLIGHT

see Space Flight

ROCKET MOTORS, LIQUID PROPELLANT

see Liquid Propellant Rockets

ROCKET ORDNANCE

see Rockets (Ordnance)

ROCKET PLANES

see also X-Fifteen (Rocket Aircraft)

Oates, Gordon C. Aerothermodynamics of Gas Turbines & Rocket Propulsion. LC 84-11152. (Illus.). 412p. 1984. 45.00 (ISBN 0-915928-87-6). AIAA.

Sanger, E. & Bredt, J. Rocket Drive for Long Range Bombers. Hamermesh, M., tr. 1944. pap. 3.95 (ISBN 0-910266-21-2). Bk Page.

ROCKET PROJECTILES

see Rockets (Ordnance)

ROCKET PROPULSION (AIRPLANES)

see Rocket Planes

ROCKET SHIPS

see Space Ships

ROCKETRY

see also Ballistic Missiles; Guided Missiles; Rocket Planes; Rockets (Aeronautics); Rockets (Ordnance); Space Ships; Space Vehicles; Space Vehicles–Propulsion Systems;

also names of particular types and uses of rockets, e.g. Nuclear Rockets and Atmosphere, Upper–Rocket Observations

Bland, William M., Jr. The History of Rocket Technology: Essays on Research, Development, & Utility. Emme, Eugene M., ed. LC 64-17625. pap. 82.80 (ISBN 0-317-09294-4, 2001337). Bks Demand UMI.

Carton, D. S., et al, eds. Rocket Propulsion Technology. LC 61-15168. 374p. 1961. 32.50x (ISBN 0-306-30149-0, Plenum Pr). Plenum Pub.

Humphreys, B. J. Steam Rockets. 120p. 1972. pap. 7.95 (ISBN 0-912468-08-4). CA Rocketry.

Humphreys, B. J., Jr. Amateurs & Rockets, Vol. 1. 1970. 9.95 (ISBN 0-912468-00-9). CA Rocketry.

Irvine, Jerry. Boosted Dart Technology. (Ace Information Report Ser.: No. 5). 1984. 4.95 (ISBN 0-912468-03-3). CA Rocketry.

--Ground Support Equipment. (Ace Information Report Ser.: No. 7). 1984. 2.50 (ISBN 0-912468-05-X). CA Rocketry.

--High Power Construction Techniques. (Ace Information Report Ser.: No. 8). 1984. 4.95 (ISBN 0-912468-06-8). CA Rocketry.

--Optimizing Performance Through Motor Selection & Design Concepts. (Ace Information Report Ser.: No. 6). 1984. 3.95 (ISBN 0-912468-04-1). CA Rocketry.

Irvine, Jerry & Kline, Korey. Ace Fugue Shroud Method. (Ace Information Report Ser.: No. 4). 1984. 1.50 (ISBN 0-912468-02-5). CA Rocketry.

Irvine, Jerry, ed. Rocketcon Eighty-Five Proceedings. 1985. 25.00 (ISBN 0-912468-18-1). CA Rocketry.

--Rocketcon Eighty-Four Proceedings. 1985. 25.00 (ISBN 0-912468-17-3). CA Rocketry.

Ordway, Frederick I., III & Sharpe, Mitchell R. The Rocket Team. (Illus.). 496p. 1982. pap. 9.95 (ISBN 0-262-65013-4). MIT Pr.

Rogers, Charles E. Aerotech Mach Busters Guide. 1984. 9.95 (ISBN 0-912468-09-2). CA Rocketry.

--Near-Orbital Rocket: Multi-Stage Capable Altitude Prediction, Drag, Center of Pressure, Plotting Agive Nose Cones. 1983. write for info. (ISBN 0-912468-14-9). CA Rocketry.

--Sub & Supersonic Experimental Rocket Computer Programs: Fourth Order Range-Kutta, Altitude Prediction, Drag, Center of Pressure. 1983. 49.00 (ISBN 0-912468-13-0). CA Rocketry.

Teleflite Corporation. Building Your Own Rocket Motors. Incl. The Incredible Five Cent Sugar Rocket. Teleflite Corporation. pap. 5.00 incl. Microsond One (ISBN 0-317-29266-8); The Microsond One. Teleflite Corporation. pap. 2.00 (ISBN 0-317-29267-6); The Homemade Hydrogen Report. Teleflite Corporation. pap. 5.00 (ISBN 0-317-29268-4). (Illus.). 148p. (Orig.). 1983. pap. 21.95 (ISBN 0-930387-00-7). Teleflite Corp.

ROCKETRY–DICTIONARIES

Konarski, M. M. Russian-English Dictionary of Modern Terms in Aeronautics & Rocketry. (Rus. & Eng.). 1962. 97.00 (ISBN 0-08-009658-1). Pergamon.

ROCKETRY–HISTORY

Stoiko, Michael. Pioneers of Rocketry. 11.95 (ISBN 0-89190-722-X, Pub. by Am Repr). Amereon Ltd.

Winter, Frank H. Prelude to the Space Age: The Rocket Societies: 1924-1940. LC 81-607883. (Illus.). 207p. (Orig.). 1983. pap. text ed. 15.00x (ISBN 0-87474-963-8). Smithsonian.

ROCKETS (AERONAUTICS)

see also Atmosphere, Upper–Rocket Observations; Ballistic Missiles; Guided Missiles; Ion Rockets; Jet Propulsion; Liquid Propellant Rockets; Nuclear Rockets; Project Vanguard; Rocket Engines; Rocket Planes; Rockets (Ordnance); Space Ships

American Society for Testing & Materials. Symposium on Recent Developments in Nondestructive Testing of Missiles & Rockets. (American Society for Testing & Materials. Special Technical Publication Ser.: No. 350). pap. 30.30 (ISBN 0-317-09141-7, 2000116). Bks Demand UMI.

Bland, William M., Jr. The History of Rocket Technology: Essays on Research, Development, & Utility. Emme, Eugene M., ed. LC 64-17625. pap. 82.80 (ISBN 0-317-09294-4, 2001337). Bks Demand UMI.

Code for Unmanned Rockets: 1982. 1982. 8.00 (ISBN 0-317-07396-6, NFPA 1122). Natl Fire Prot.

Cornelisse, J. W., et al. Rocket Propulsion & Spaceflight Dynamics. LC 78-40059. (Aerospace Engineering Ser.). 505p. 1979. text ed. 89.95 (ISBN 0-273-01141-3). Pitman Pub MA.

Eames, James P. Turbine & Jet-Propelled Aircraft Powerplants. (Illus.). 1954. 5.25 (ISBN 0-910354-06-5). Chartwell.

Irvine, Jerry & Rogers, Charles E. U. S. Rockets Flight Sheet Guide. 1984. 9.95 (ISBN 0-912468-10-6). CA Rocketry.

Kennedy, Gregory P., compiled by. Rockets, Missiles, & Spacecraft of the National Air & Space Museum, Smithsonian Institution. LC 83-600049. (Illus.). 165p. 1983. pap. 6.50 (ISBN 0-87474-571-3). Smithsonian.

Penner, S. S. Chemical Rocket Propulsion & Combustion Research. (Illus.). 170p. 1962. 45.25x (ISBN 0-677-00710-8). Gordon.

Sixth Sounding Rocket. 1982. 50.00 (ISBN 0-317-06667-6). AIAA.

ROCKETS (AERONAUTICS)–FUEL

Malone, Hugh E. The Analysis of Rocket Propellants. (Analysis of Organic Materials Ser.). 1977. 39.00 (ISBN 0-12-466750-3). Acad Pr.

ROCKETS (AERONAUTICS)–MODELS

Banks, Michael. Countdown: The Complete Guide to Model Rocketry. (Illus.). 224p. (Orig.). 1985. pap. 16.95 (ISBN 0-8306-1991-7, 1991). TAB Bks.

--Second Stage Advanced Model Rocketry. Angle, Burr, ed. (Illus., Orig.). 1985. pap. 8.50 (ISBN 0-89024-057-4). Kalmbach.

Cannon, Robert L. & Banks, Michael A. The Rocket Book: A Guide to Building & Launching Model Rockets for Teachers & Students Of the Space Age. (Illus.). 240p. 1985. 22.95 (ISBN 0-13-782251-0); pap. 12.95 (ISBN 0-13-782244-8). P-H.

Code for Model Rocketry. (Forty Ser.). 1968. pap. 2.00 (ISBN 0-685-58101-2, 41L). Natl Fire Prot.

Goodman, Howard A. Planpak Number 83131: Model Rocket Launch Panel. (Illus.). 24p. (Orig.). 1984. pap. text ed. 3.95 (ISBN 0-914465-00-7, 83131). S S J Pubns.

Malawicki, Douglas J. & Schwenn, Donald C. Model Rockets from Design to Launch. 1976. pap. text ed. 8.00 (ISBN 0-912468-16-5); tchrs'. ed. 10.00 (ISBN 0-912468-15-7). CA Rocketry.

Pratt, Douglas R. Basics of Model Rocketry. Angle, Burr, ed. LC 80-84580. (Illus., Orig.). 1981. pap. 6.50 (ISBN 0-89024-557-6). Kalmbach.

Rogers, Charles E. Model Rocket Computer Programs: Malewicki Closed-Form Altitude, Coefficient of Drag & Center of Pressure. 1983. 29.00 (ISBN 0-912468-12-2). CA Rocketry.

Schleicher, Robert. The ETV Model Book: How to Make & Fly Space & Special Effects Models. LC 78-14626. 1979. 13.95 (ISBN 0-8019-6800-3); pap. 7.95 (ISBN 0-8019-6801-1, 6801). Chilton.

Stine, G. Harry. Handbook of Model Rocketry. 5th ed. LC 82-8913. (Illus.). 352p. 1983. lib. bdg. 16.95 (ISBN 0-668-05358-5); pap. 10.95 (ISBN 0-668-05360-7). Arco.

ROCKETS (AERONAUTICS)–MOTORS

see Rocket Engines

ROCKETS (ORDNANCE)

see also Guided Missiles; Rockets (Aeronautics); V-Two Rocket

Morey, Loren. The Power Rockets. (Illus.). 197p. 28.00x (ISBN 0-89126-110-9). MA AH Pub.

Ryan, J. W. Guns, Mortars & Rockets. (Brassey's Battlefield Weapons Systems & Technology: Vol. 2). (Illus.). 236p. 1982. 26.00 (ISBN 0-08-028324-1, P110); pap. 13.00 (ISBN 0-08-028325-X). Pergamon.

ROCKETS, ATOMIC POWERED

see Nuclear Rockets

ROCKFISH

see Striped Bass

ROCKS

see also Crystallography; Geochemistry; Geology; Mineralogy; Petrology; Rock Mechanics
also varieties of rock, e.g. Granite, Limestone

Allan, David & Brown, Vinson. An Illustrated Guide to Common Rocks & Their Minerals. rev. 2nd ed. LC 76-7372. (Illus.). 60p. (Orig.). 1976. pap. 3.00 (ISBN 0-87961-054-9). Naturegraph.

Audubon Society & Chesterman, Charles W. The Audubon Society Field Guide to North American Rocks & Minerals. LC 78-54893. (Illus.). 1979. 13.50 (ISBN 0-394-50269-8). Knopf.

Augustithis, S. S. Atlas of the Textural Patterns of Granites, Gneisses & Associated Rock Types. 378p. 1973. 113.00 (ISBN 0-444-40977-7). Elsevier.

Barker, F., ed. Trondhjemites, Dacites, & Related Rocks. LC 78-24338. (Developments in Petrology Ser.: Vol. 6). 660p. 1979. 76.75 (ISBN 0-444-41765-6). Elsevier.

Bates, Robert L. Geology of the Industrial Rocks & Minerals. LC 69-15364. (Illus.). 1969. pap. 8.50 (ISBN 0-486-62213-4). Dover.

Bates, Robert L. & Jackson, Julie. Our Modern Stone Age. LC 81-17219. (Illus.). 150p. (Orig.). 1981. 18.95 (ISBN 0-86576-027-6). W Kaufmann.

Bisdom, E. B. Submicroscopy of Soils & Weathered Rocks: First Workshop of the International Working Group on Submicroscopy of Undisturbed Soil Materials, Wageningen, The Netherlands, 1980. (Eng. & Fr.). 320p. 1981. 45.25 (ISBN 90-220-0777-4, PDC235, Pudoc). Unipub.

Bishop, A. C., et al. Catalogue of the Rock Collections in the British Museum (Natural History). 2nd ed. 148p. 1984. pap. text ed. 36.00x (ISBN 0-565-00875-7, Pub by Brit Mus Nat Hist England). Sabbot-Natural Hist Bks.

Buchanan, D. L. & Jones, M. J., eds. Sulphide Deposits in Mafic & Ultramafic Rocks: Proceedings of Nickel Sulphide Field Conference III, Western Australia, 1982. (Orig.). 1984. pap. text ed. 78.00x (ISBN 0-900488-71-9). Imm North Am.

Carmichael, R. CRC Handbook of Physical Properties of Rocks, Vol. I. 416p. 1981. 71.50 (ISBN 0-8493-0226-9). CRC Pr.

Carmichael, Robert S., ed. CRC Handbook of Physical Properties of Rocks, Vol. III. 360p. 1984. 60.00 (ISBN 0-8493-0228-5). CRC Pr.

Conference on Rock Engineering for Foundations & Slopes, University of Colorado. Rock Engineering for Foundations & Slopes: Proceedings of a Specialty Conference, University of Colorado, Boulder, Colorado, August 15-18, 1976, 2 vols. LC 77-368041. Vol. 1. pap. 112.30 (ISBN 0-317-10584-1, 2019552); Vol. 2. pap. 67.50 (ISBN 0-317-10585-X). Bks Demand UMI.

Craw, Julia & French, Bernada. Family Fun with Rocks. pap. 1.00 (ISBN 0-910652-16-3). Gembooks.

Croucher, Ronald & Woolley, Alan R. Fossils, Minerals & Rocks: Collection & Preservation. LC 82-1282. (Illus.). 64p. 1982. 7.95 (ISBN 0-521-24736-5, Copublished with the British Museum). Cambridge U Pr.

Deer, William A., et al. Introduction to Rock Forming Minerals. 528p. 1966. pap. 29.95x (ISBN 0-470-20516-4). Halsted Pr.

Desautels, Paul E. Rocks & Minerals. LC 73-91134. (Collector's Series: No. 1). (Illus.). 160p. 1982. 3.95 (ISBN 0-448-04088-3, G&D). Putnam Pub Group.

Dietrich, R. V. Stones: Their Collection, Identification, & Uses. LC 79-24760. (Geology Ser.). (Illus.). 145p. 1980. pap. text ed. 11.95 (ISBN 0-7167-1139-7). W H Freeman.

Dietrich, R. V. & Wicander, E. Reed. Minerals, Rock & Fossils. LC 82-20220. (Self-Teaching Guides Ser.). 212p. 1983. pap. text ed. 9.95 (ISBN 0-471-89883-X, Pub. by Wiley Pr). Wiley.

Dunning & Hammons. Let's Talk About Rocks. 3.95 (ISBN 0-87505-125-1). Borden.

Farmer, I. W. Engineering Behavior of Rocks. LC 82-20853. 213p. 1983. 43.00 (ISBN 0-412-25280-5, NO. 6842, Pub. by Chapman & Hall); pap. 21.00 (ISBN 0-412-13980-4, NO. 6781). Methuen Inc.

Grandy, James. Guide to Eastern Rocks & Minerals. (Illus.). 40p. pap. 3.50 (ISBN 0-88839-105-6). Hancock House.

Gronberg, Margaret & Nutting, Linda. Rock Hunting in Texas: Where to Go & How to Get There. (Illus.). 128p. (Orig.). 1986. pap. 9.95x (ISBN 0-88415-786-5, Lone Star Bks). Gulf Pub.

Hamilton, et al. Larousse Guide to Minerals, Rocks & Fossils. LC 77-71167. 1977. 15.95 (ISBN 0-88332-079-7, 8095); pap. 9.95 (ISBN 0-88332-078-9, 8094). Larousse.

Harder, Herrmann. Lexikon Fuer Mineralien - und Gesteins Freunde. (Ger.). 1977. 25.00 (ISBN 3-7658-0253-0, M-7198). French & Eur.

Hellwege, K. H., ed. Physical Properties of Rocks. (Landolt-Boernstein Ser.: Group V, Vol. 1, Subvol. b). (Illus.). 610p. 1982. 389.30 (ISBN 0-387-11070-4). Springer-Verlag.

Holmyard, E. J. & Mandeville, D. C., eds. Avicennae De Congelatione et Conglutinatione Lapidum. LC 79-8593. 96p. Repr. of 1927 ed. 19.50 (ISBN 0-404-18447-2). AMS Pr.

Jackson, Bob. The Rockhound's Guide to Washington, Vol. IV. (Illus.). 50p. (Orig.). 1985. pap. 3.95 (ISBN 0-918499-07-0). Jackson Mtn.

Kirkaldy, J. F. Minerals & Rocks. (Illus.). 192p. 1982. 12.95 (ISBN 0-7137-0783-6, Pub. by Blandford Pr England). Sterling.

Lama, R. D. & Vutukuri, V. S. Handbook on Mechanical Properties of Rocks, Vol. III. (Rock & Soil Mechanics Ser.). (Illus.). 1978. 65.00x (ISBN 0-87849-022-1). Trans Tech.

--Handbook on Mechanical Properties of Rocks, Vol. IV. (Rock & Soil Mechanics Ser.). (Illus.). 1978. 65.00x (ISBN 0-87849-023-X). Trans Tech.

La Pointe, P. R. & Hudson, J. A., eds. Characterization & Interpretation of Rock Mass Joint Patterns. (Special Paper Ser.: No. 199). (Illus.). 45p. 1985. 10.50 (ISBN 0-8137-2199-7). Geol Soc.

Leet, Lewis D. Vibrations from Blasting Rock. LC 60-10037. Repr. of 1960 ed. 37.50 (ISBN 0-8357-9183-1, 2017747). Bks Demand UMI.

Lefond, Stanley J., ed. Industrial Minerals & Rocks: (Nonmetallics Other Than Fuels) rev., 4th ed. LC 73-85689. (Seeley W. Mudd Ser.). pap. 160.00 (ISBN 0-317-29747-3, 2017421). Bks Demand UMI.

Mitchell, Richard S. Dictionary of Rocks. (Illus.). 240p. 1985. 29.95 (ISBN 0-442-26328-7). Van Nos Reinhold.

Mondadori, ed. Simon & Schuster's Guide to Rocks & Minerals. pap. 10.95 (ISBN 0-671-24417-5). S&S.

Mottana, A., et al. Guia de Minerales y Rocas. (Span.). 608p. 1980. leatherette 44.95 (ISBN 84-253-1234-5, S-36342). French & Eur.

Niggli, Paul. Rocks & Mineral Deposits. Parker, Robert L., tr. LC 53-8082. (Geology Texts Ser.). pap. 71.50 (ISBN 0-317-29240-4, 2055547). Bks Demand UMI.

O'Reilly, W. Rock & Mineral Magnetism. LC 83-20012. 224p. 1984. 45.00x (ISBN 0-412-00401-1, NO. 5049). Methuen Inc.

Parkhomenko, E. I. Electrical Properties of Rocks. LC 67-10311. 314p. 1967. 45.00x (ISBN 0-306-30267-5, Plenum Pr). Plenum Pub.

Poindexter, O. F., et al. Rocks & Minerals of Michigan. (Illus.). 49p. (Orig.). 1971. pap. 3.95 (ISBN 0-910726-73-6). Hillsdale Educ.

Pough, Frederick H. A Field Guide to Rocks & Minerals. 4th ed. (Peterson Field Guide Ser.). 1976. 17.95 (ISBN 0-395-24047-6); pap. 12.95 (ISBN 0-395-24049-2). HM.

Ramsay, John G. Folding & Fracturing of Rocks. (International Ser. in Earth & Planetary Sciences). (Illus.). 1967. text ed. 66.95 (ISBN 0-07-051170-5). McGraw.

Raymond, Loren A., ed. Melanges: Their Nature, Origin, & Significance. (Special Paper Ser.: No. 198). (Illus.). 175p. 1985. 22.00 (ISBN 0-8137-2198-9). Geol Soc.

Schumann, Walter. Stones & Minerals: Minerals, Precious Stones, Rocks, Ores. (Illus.). 226p. 1985. 6.98 (ISBN 0-8069-5526-0). Sterling.

Shackley, Myra. Rocks & Man. (Illus.). 160p. 1982. pap. text ed. 9.95x (ISBN 0-04-913019-6). Allen Unwin.

Stacey, F. D. & Banerjee, S. K. Physical Principles of Rock Magnetism. LC 72-87965. (Developments in Solid Earth Geophysics Ser.: Vol. 5). 224p. 1974. 59.75 (ISBN 0-444-41084-8, X1973). Elsevier.

Studies in Standard Samples of Silicate Rocks & Minerals: Edition of Usable Values, Pt. 4. 1974. pap. 3.70 (SSC77, SSC). Unipub.

Techter, David. Stereogram Book of Rocks, Minerals & Gems. 64p. (Orig.). 1970. pap. text ed. 6.95 (ISBN 0-8331-1701-7). Hubbard Sci.

Titkov, Nikolai I., et al. Electrochemical Induration of Weak Rocks. LC 60-13950. pap. 20.00 (ISBN 0-317-10409-8, 2020647). Bks Demand UMI.

Watson, Janet. Rocks & Minerals. 2nd rev. ed. (Introducing Geology Ser.). (Illus.). pap. text ed. 5.95x (ISBN 0-04-551031-8). Allen Unwin.

ROCKS–AGE

see Geological Time; Geology, Stratigraphic

ROCKS–ANALYSIS

Argenheister, G., ed. Physical Properties of Rocks. (Landolt-Boernstein Ser.: Group V. Vol. 1, Subvol. a). (Illus.). 390p. 1982. 286.70 (ISBN 0-387-10333-3). Springer-Verlag.

Augustithis, S. S. Atlas of the Textural Patterns of Basic & Ultrabasic Rocks & Their Genetic Significance. 1979. 102.00x (ISBN 3-11-006571-1). De Gruyter.

Austrian Society for Geomechanics, 18th Colloquium. Stability of Rock Slopes & Underground Excavations. Mueller, L., ed. (Illus.). 1970. 33.70 (ISBN 0-387-80958-9). Springer-Verlag.

Baidyuk, Bronislav V. Mechanical Properties of Rocks at High Temperatures & Pressures. LC 65-25221. 75p. 1967. 25.00x (ISBN 0-306-10778-3, Consultants). Plenum Pub.

Brown, E. T., ed. Rock Characterization, Testing & Monitoring: ISRM Suggested Methods. LC 80-49711. 200p. 1981. pap. 22.00 (ISBN 0-08-027309-2). Pergamon.

Clark, George B. Geotechnical Centrifuges for Model Studies & Physical Property Testing of Rock & Rock Structures. Raese, Jon W., ed. LC 81-21614. (Colorado School of Mines Quarterly Ser.: Vol. 76, No. 4). (Illus.). 63p. 1982. pap. text ed. 12.00 (ISBN 0-686-79746-9). Colo Sch Mines.

Field Testing & Instrumentation of Rock, STP 554. 188p. 1974. 18.75 (ISBN 0-8031-0350-6, 04-554000-38). ASTM.

Jeffery, P. G. & Hutchison, D. Chemical Methods of Rock Analysis. 3rd ed. (Pergamon Series in Analytical Chemistry: Vol. 4). (Illus.). xv, 385p. 1981. 58.00 (ISBN 0-08-023806-8). Pergamon.

Johnson, Wesley M. & Maxwell, John A. Rock & Mineral Analysis, Vol.27. 2nd ed. LC 81-1659. (Chemical Analysis Ser.). 489p. 1981. 80.00x (ISBN 0-471-02743-X, Pub. by Wiley-Interscience). Wiley.

Low-Flow, Low-Permeability Measurements in Largely Impermeable Rocks. 1979. 16.00x (ISBN 92-64-01955-3). OECD.

Moorhouse, Walter W. Study of Rocks in Thin Section. 1959. text ed. 36.95 scp (ISBN 0-06-044610-2, HarpC). Har-Row.

Reeves, R. D. & Brooks, R. R. Trace Element Analysis of Geological Materials: Vol. 51. LC 78-8064. (Chemical Analysis: Monographs on Analytical Chemistry & Its Applications). 421p. 1979. 69.00 (ISBN 0-471-71338-4, Pub. by Wiley-Interscience). Wiley.

Solomin, G. A. Methods of Determining eH & pH in Sedimentary Rocks. LC 65-11958. 56p. 1965. 20.00x (ISBN 0-306-10700-7, Consultants). Plenum Pub.

ROCKS–CLASSIFICATION AND NOMENCLATURE

Elsevier's Mineral & Rock Table. Lof, P., compiled by. 1982. 13.00 (ISBN 0-444-42081-9). Elsevier.

Kimbler, Frank S. & Narsavage, Robert J., Jr. New Mexico Rocks & Minerals Guide. LC 81-5350. (Illus.). 76p. (Orig.). 1981. pap. 8.95 (ISBN 0-913270-97-0). Sunstone Pr.

Sampling of Soil & Rock: A Symposium Presented at the Seventy-Third Annual Meeting, Toronto, Ont., Canada, June 21-26, 1970. LC 75-137453. (American Society for Testing & Materials: No. 483). pap. 49.80 (ISBN 0-317-07983-2, 2015508). Bks Demand UMI.

Schumann, Walter. Minerals & Rocks. LC 79-301701. (Nature Guides Ser.). (Illus.). 144p. 1979. pap. 5.95 (ISBN 0-7011-2362-1, Pub. by Chatto & Windus). Merrimack Pub Cir.

Thorpe, R. S., ed. Andesites: Orogenic Andesites & Related Rocks. LC 80-42307. 237p. 1982. 124.95x (ISBN 0-471-28034-8, Pub. by Wiley-Interscience). Wiley.

ROCKS, CARBONATE

see also Carbonatites; Limestone

Bardossy, G. Karst Bauxites: Bauxite Deposits on Carbonate Rocks. (Developments in Economic Geology Ser.: Vol. 14). 442p. 1982. 83.00 (ISBN 0-444-99727-X). Elsevier.

WHO Study Group. Geneva, 1974. Ecology & Control of Rodents of Public Health Importance: Report. (Technical Report Ser.: No. 571). (Also avail. in French & Spanish). 1975. pap. 3.20 (ISBN 92-4-120571-7). World Health.

Williams, G. M. Cytochemical Markers in Rodent Hepatocarcinogenesis. (Lectures in Toxicology: No. 17). (Illus.). 1983. 60.00 (ISBN 0-08-029786-2). Pergamon.

Wilson, Robert W. Additional Remains of the Multituberculate Genus Eucosmodon. (Museum Ser.: Vol. 9, No.6). 7p. 1956. 1.25 (ISBN 0-317-04819-8). U of KS Mus Nat Hist.

Wood, Albert E. The Oligocene Rodents of North America, Vol. 70, Pt. 5. 1980. 8.00 (ISBN 0-87169-705-X). Am Philos.

Young, Allen M. Seasonal Adult Emergences of Cicadas (Homoptera: Cicadidae) in Northwestern Costa Rica. 29p. 1980. 3.00 (ISBN 0-89326-067-3). Milwaukee Pub Mus.

RODENTS AS CARRIERS OF DISEASE

Jones, T. C., et al, eds. Respiratory System. (Monographs on Pathology of Laboratory Animals). (Illus.). 320p. 1985. 86.00 (ISBN 0-387-13521-9). Springer-Verlag.

Procedures to Investigate Arthropod-Borne & Rodent Borne Illness. 93p. 2.00 (ISBN 0-318-17809-5); bulk rates avail. Intl Assn Milk.

U. S. Environmental Protection Agency, ed. Federal Insecticide, Fungicide, & Rodenticide Act: Compliance-Enforcement Guidance Manual. (Illus.). 512p. 1984. pap. 64.00 (ISBN 0-86587-032-2). Gov Insts.

RODS

see Bars (Engineering)

ROEBLING, JOHN AUGUSTUS, 1805-1869

Sayenga, Donald. Ellet & Roebling: Their Friendship & Rivalry. 1983. 4.00 (ISBN 0-933788-42-8). Am Canal & Transport.

Schuyler, Hamilton. Roeblings: A Century of Engineers, Bridge-Builders & Industrialists. LC 77-175582. Repr. of 1931 ed. 29.50 (ISBN 0-404-05625-3). AMS Pr.

ROENTGEN RAYS

see X-Rays

ROENTGENOGRAMS

see X-Rays

ROLLER BEARINGS

see also Ball-Bearings

Din Standards for Balland Roller Bearings. 522.00 (ISBN 0-686-28174-8, 10059-4/24). Heyden.

Dowson, Duncan & Higginson, Gordon R. Elasto-Hydrodynamics Lubrication: SI Edition. 2nd ed. 1977. o,p, 35.00 (ISBN 0-08-021303-0); pap. 15.50 (ISBN 0-08-021302-2). Pergamon.

Hoo, J., ed. Rolling Contact Fatigue Testing of Bearing Steels - STP 771. 422p. 1982. 43.95 (ISBN 0-8031-0712-9, 04-771000-02). ASTM.

ROLLING (METAL-WORK)

Flat Rolling: A Comparison of Rolling Mill Types. 206p. 1979. text ed. 20.00x (ISBN 0-904357-24-4, Metals Soc). Brookfield Pub Co.

Roberts, William L. Cold Rolling of Steel. (Manufacturing Engineering & Materials Processing Ser.: Vol. 2). (Illus.). 808p. 1978. 99.75 (ISBN 0-8247-6780-2). Dekker.

--Hot Rolling of Steel. (Manufacturing Engineering Ser.: Vol. 10). (Illus.). 1024p. 1983. 75.00 (ISBN 0-8247-1345-1). Dekker.

Severdenko, V. P., et al, eds. Ultrasonic Rolling & Drawing of Metals. LC 73-188920. 206p. 1972. 35.00x (ISBN 0-306-10872-0, Consultants). Plenum Pub.

Tselikov, A. I. Theory of Lengthwise Rolling. 342p. 1981. 10.00 (ISBN 0-8285-2181-6, Pub. by Mir Pubs USSR). Imported Pubns.

ROLLING CONTACT

see also Bearings (Machinery); Cams; Gearing

Browne, A. L. The General Problem of Rolling Contact. Tsai, N. T., ed. (AMD: Vol. 40). 170p. 1980. 28.00 (ISBN 0-686-69852-5, G00173). ASME.

Harris, Tedric A. Rolling Bearing Analysis. 2nd ed. LC 83-23481. 565p. 1984. 74.95x (ISBN 0-471-79979-3, Pub. by Wiley-Interscience). Wiley.

ROLLING-MILLS

see also Rolling (Metal-Work)

Flat Rolling: A Comparison of Rolling Mill Types. 206p. 1979. text ed. 20.00x (ISBN 0-904357-24-4, Metals Soc). Brookfield Pub Co.

ROLLING-STOCK

see Locomotives

ROLLS ROYCE (AUTOMOBILE)

see Automobiles, Foreign–Types–Rolls Royce

ROMANOFF, ALEXIS LAWRENCE, 1892-

Colebrook, C. Spider, Egg, & Microcosm: Three Men & Three Worlds of Science. LC 55-9287. 1955. 8.00 (ISBN 0-9600476-1-1). E Kinkead.

ROOF-TRUSSES

see Roofs; Trusses

ROOFS

see also Domes

Alcock, N. W. Cruck Construction: An Introduction & Catalogue. (CBA Research Reports Ser.: No. 42). 180p. 1981. pap. text ed. 24.50x (ISBN 0-906780-11-X, Pub. by Coun Brit Archaeology). Humanities.

Badzinski, Stanley, Jr. Roof Framing. (Illus.). 1976. 12.95 (ISBN 0-13-782466-1); student ed. 12.95. P-H.

Brann, Donald R. Roofing Simplified. LC 81-65487. 176p. 1983. pap. 6.95 (ISBN 0-87733-896-5). Easi-Bild.

--Roofing Simplified. rev. ed. LC 71-99939. 1977. lib. bdg. 5.95 (ISBN 0-87733-096-4). Easi-Bild.

--Roofing Simplified. LC 71-99939. 1979. pap. 5.95 (ISBN 0-87733-696-2). Easi-Bild.

Fearn, Jacqueline. Thatch & Thatching. (Shire Album Ser.: No. 16). (Illus.). 32p. 1985. pap. 3.50 (ISBN 0-85263-337-8, Pub. by Shire Pubns England). Seven Hills Bks.

Goss, Ralph. Roofing Ready Reckoner for Timber Roofs of Any Span or Pitch. 2nd ed. 75p. 1979. pap. text ed. 11.25x (ISBN 0-258-96690-4, Pub. by Granada England). Brookfield Pub Co.

Griffin, C. W. AIA: Manual of Built-Up Roof Systems. 2nd ed. 1982. 44.50 (ISBN 0-07-024783-8). McGraw.

Gross, Marshall. Roof Framing. 480p. (Orig.). 1984. pap. 19.50 (ISBN 0-910460-40-X). Craftsman.

Gumpertz, W., ed. Single-Ply Roofing Technology- STP 790. 120p. 1982. pap. 14.25 (ISBN 0-8031-0778-1, 04-790000-10). ASTM.

Long Span Roof Structures. LC 81-69226. 365p. 1981. pap. 24.50x (ISBN 0-87262-287-8). Am Soc Civil Eng.

Meyers, Donald L. Modern Roofing: Care & Repair. Horowitz, Shirley M., ed. LC 81-66574. (Illus.). 144p. (Orig.). 1981. 19.95 (ISBN 0-932944-33-7); pap. 6.95 (ISBN 0-932944-34-5). Creative Homeowner.

Parker, Harry & Ambrose, James. Simplified Design of Roof Trusses Architects & Builders. 3rd ed. LC 81-19800. 301p. 1982. 32.50x (ISBN 0-471-07722-4, Pub. by Wiley-Interscience). Wiley.

Performance Approach in Determining Required Levels of Insulation in Concrete Roof Systems. (PCI Journal Reprints Ser.). 16p. pap. 6.00 (ISBN 0-686-40153-0, JR250). Prestressed Concrete.

Pracht, Klaus. Modern Oriels on Roofs & Facades. (Illus.). 160p. 1984. 35.00 (ISBN 0-442-27286-3). Van Nos Reinhold.

Roof Coverings. (Two Hundred Ser.). 1970. pap. 2.00 (ISBN 0-685-58164-0, 203). Natl Fire Prot.

Roofing Systems, STP 603. 148p. 1976. pap. 14.75 (ISBN 0-8031-0559-2, 04-603000-10). ASTM.

Roofs & Siding. LC 77-90094. (Home Repair & Improvement Ser.). (Illus.). 1978. lib. bdg. 15.94 (ISBN 0-8094-2391-X, Pub. by Time-Life). Silver.

Rudman, Jack. Foreman Roofer. (Career Examination Ser.: C-1416). (Cloth bdg. avail. on request). pap. 10.00 (ISBN 0-8373-1416-X). Natl Learning.

--Roofer. (Career Examination Ser.: C-677). (Cloth bdg. avail. on request). pap. 8.00 (ISBN 0-8373-0677-9). Natl Learning.

Siegele, H. H. Roof Framing. rev. ed. LC 74-25285. (A Home Craftsman Bk.). (Illus.). 176p. 1980. pap. 7.95 (ISBN 0-8069-8626-3). Sterling.

Single Ply Roofing. 1983. 25.00 (ISBN 0-318-01492-0, 11065). Indus Fabrics.

Sunset Editors. Patio Roofs: How to Build. 3rd ed. LC 73-89579. (Illus.). 80p. 1974. pap. 3.95 (ISBN 0-376-01455-5, Sunset Bks.). Sunset-Lane.

--Roofing & Siding. LC 80-53487. (Illus.). 120p. 1981. pap. 5.95 (ISBN 0-376-01491-1, Sunset Bks). Sunset-Lane.

Szabo, K. & Kollar, L. Structural Design of Cable-Suspended Roofs. (Series in Engineering Science: Civil Engineering: 1-467). 242p. 1984. 74.95x (ISBN 0-470-27188-4). Halsted Pr.

Wass, Alonzo & Saunders. Residential Roof Framing. (Illus.). 268p. 1980. text ed. 22.95 (ISBN 0-8359-6655-0). Reston.

Watson, John A. Commercial Roofing Systems. 1984. text ed. 26.95 (ISBN 0-8359-0857-7). Reston.

--Roofing Systems: Materials & Applications. (Illus.). 1979. text ed. 23.95 (ISBN 0-8359-6687-9). Reston.

Williams, Benjamin. Rafter Length Manual. (Illus.). 1979. pap. 10.75 (ISBN 0-910460-67-1). Craftsman.

ROOFS, SHELL

see also Roofs, Suspension

Billington, D. P. Thin Shell Concrete Structures. 1965. 42.50 (ISBN 0-07-005271-9). McGraw.

Design of Barrel Shell Roofs. 28p. 1954. pap. 1.55 (ISBN 0-89312-054-5, IS082D). Portland Cement.

Elias, Z. M. Cylindrical Shell Roof Design. 1972. pap. 11.95x (ISBN 0-8156-6036-7, Am U Beirut). Syracuse U Pr.

Fischer, L. Theory & Practice of Shell Structures. (Illus.). 1968. 76.00x (ISBN 3-4330-0127-8). Adlers Foreign Bks.

Litle, William A. Reliability of Shell Buckling Predictions. (Press Research Monographs: No. 25). 1964. 25.00x (ISBN 0-262-12013-5). MIT Pr.

Ramaswamy, G. S. Design & Construction of Concrete Shell Roofs. rev. ed. LC 81-19299. 758p. 1984. lib. bdg. 59.50 (ISBN 0-89874-001-0). Krieger.

Wilby, C. B. & Khwaja, I. Concrete Shell Roofs. LC 77-391. 327p. 1977. 74.95x (ISBN 0-470-99088-0). Halsted Pr.

ROOFS, SUSPENSION

Krishna, P. Cable-Suspended Roofs. 1978. 38.50 (ISBN 0-07-035504-5). McGraw.

ROOMS, CLEAN

see Clean Rooms

ROOTS (BOTANY)

Arkin, G. F. & Taylor, H. M., eds. Modifying the Root Environment to Reduce Crop Stress. LC 81-69116. 420p. 1981. text ed. 34.50 (ISBN 0-916150-40-2); text ed. 24.95 members. Am Soc Ag Eng.

Bergersen, F. J. Root Nodules of Legumes: Structure & Functions. LC 83-185046. (Botanical Research Studies Press). 164p. 1982. 37.95x (ISBN 0-471-10456-6, Pub. by Res Stud Pr). Wiley.

Boehm, W. Methods of Studying Root Systems. LC 79-9706. (Ecological Studies: Vol. 33). (Illus.). 1979. 45.00 (ISBN 0-387-09329-X). Springer-Verlag.

Carston, Rachel. Devil's Claw Root & Other. 1981. pap. 8.95x (ISBN 0-317-06967-5, Regent House). B of A.

Cooper, A. J. Root Temperature & Plant Growth. 73p. 1973. 30.00x (ISBN 0-85198-271-9, Pub. by CAB Bks England). State Mutual Bk.

Elliott, Douglas. Roots: An Underground Botany. LC 75-46234. (Illus.). 160p. 1976. pap. 7.95 (ISBN 0-85699-132-5). Chatham Pr.

Foster, R. C., et al. Ultrastructure of the Root-Soil Interface. (Illus.). 157p. 1983. 36.00 (ISBN 0-89054-051-9). Am Phytopathol Soc.

Garrett, S. D. Pathogenic Root-Infecting Fungi. LC 72-10024. (Illus.). 1970. 52.50 (ISBN 0-521-07786-9). Cambridge U Pr.

Krupa, S. V., ed. Ecology of Root Pathogens. Dommergues, Y. R., tr. (Developments in Agricultural & Managed-Forest Ecology: Vol. 5). 282p. 1979. 81.00 (ISBN 0-444-41639-0). Elsevier.

Methods for the Examination of Root System & Roots. 1971. pap. 11.75 (ISBN 90-220-0324-8, PDC127, PUDOC). Unipub.

Miller, Robert H. Root Anatomy & Morphology: A Guide to the Literature. viii, 271p. 1974. 22.50 (ISBN 0-208-01452-7, Archon). Shoe String.

Plucknett, Donald L. Small-Scale Processing & Storage of Tropical Root Crops. (Tropical Agriculture Ser.). 1979. lib. bdg. 39.00x (ISBN 0-89158-471-4). Westview.

Root Activity Patterns of Some Tree Crops. (Technical Reports Ser.: No. 170). (Illus.). 154p. 1976. pap. 16.00 (ISBN 92-0-115175-6, IDC170, IAEA). Unipub.

Roots & Tubers. (Better Farming Ser.: No. 16). 58p. 1977. pap. 7.50 (ISBN 92-5-100155-3, F74, FAO). Unipub.

Torrey, John G. & Clarkson, D., eds. The Development & Function of Roots. 1975. 97.00 (ISBN 0-12-695750-9). Acad Pr.

Zolo, Don. Legion of Roots. 180p. 1982. pap. 3.95 (ISBN 0-9608852-0-X). General Means.

ROPE

see also Cordage; Knots and Splices

Day, Cyrus L. Art of Knotting & Splicing. 3rd rev. ed. LC 55-10028. (Illus.). 225p. 1970. 18.95 (ISBN 0-87021-083-1). Naval Inst Pr.

Grainger, Stuart E. Creative Ropecraft. (Illus.). 1977. 12.95 (ISBN 0-393-08746-8). Norton.

Wheelock, Walt. Ropes, Knots & Slings for Climbers. rev. ed. (Illus.). 1982. wrappers 1.50 (ISBN 0-910856-00-1). La Siesta.

ROSES

Albera, A. E. Making Roses Behave. (Illus.). 1960. spiral bdg. 2.50 (ISBN 0-87505-244-4). Borden.

Beckett, Kenneth A. The Garden Library: Roses. Dorling Kindersley Ltd., ed. 96p. 1984. pap. 4.95 (ISBN 0-345-30906-5). Ballantine.

Browne, Roland A. The Rose-Lover's Guide: A Practical Handbook for Rose Gardening. LC 73-92067. (Illus.). 256p. 1983. pap. 9.95 (ISBN 0-689-70642-1, 291). Atheneum.

Crepin, F. Primitiae Monographiae Rosarum: Meteriaux Pour Servir a L'Histoire Des Roses, 6 pts. in 1 vol. 1972. Repr. of 1882 ed. 35.00 (ISBN 3-7682-0759-5). Lubrecht & Cramer.

Curtis, Henry. Beauties of the Rose. facsimile ed. (Illus.). 120p. 1981. 65.00 (ISBN 0-936736-00-3). Sweetbrier.

Earle, Alice M. Sun Dials & Roses of Yesterday. LC 79-75790. 1969. Repr. of 1902 ed. 45.00x (ISBN 0-8103-3830-0). Gale.

Ellwanger, H. B. The Rose. (Old Roses Ser.). Repr. of 1882 ed. text ed. 19.50 (ISBN 0-930576-15-2). E M Coleman Ent.

Gault, S. M. & Synge, P. M. Dictionary of Roses. 191p. 22.95 (ISBN 0-7181-0911-2, Pub. by Michael Joseph). Merrimack Pub Cir.

Gault, S. Millar & Synge, Patrick M. The Dictionary of Roses in Colour. (Illus.). 192p. 1985. pap. 14.95 (ISBN 0-7181-2182-1, Pub. by Michael Joseph). Merrimack Pub Cir.

Gibson, Michael. Growing Roses. (Illus.). 200p. 1984. 18.95 (ISBN 0-917304-92-6). Timber.

Gregory, Tony. The Pocket Encyclopedia of Modern Roses. (Illus.). 192p. 1984. 9.95 (ISBN 0-7137-1261-9, Pub. by Blandford Pr England). Sterling.

Harkness, Jack. Roses. 290p. 1978. 40.00x (ISBN 0-460-04328-5, Pub. by J M Dent England). State Mutual Bk.

Hessayon, D. G. & Wheatcroft, Harry. Be Your Own Rose Expert. 35p. 1977. pap. 2.50 (ISBN 0-8119-0358-3). Fell.

Horst, Kenneth R. Compendium of Rose Diseases. (Illus.). 50p. 1983. pap. text ed. 17.00 (ISBN 0-89054-052-7). Am Phytopathol Soc.

Krussmann, Gerd. The Complete Book of Roses. LC 81-16611. Orig. Title: Rosen, Rosen, Rosen. 436p. 1981. 50.00 (ISBN 0-917304-64-0). Timber.

Lindley, John. Rosarum Monographia: Or a Botanical History of Roses. (Old Roses Ser.). (Illus.). Repr. of 1820 ed. text ed. 27.50 (ISBN 0-930576-16-0). E M Coleman Ent.

MacGregor, John C. A Portfolio of Rose Hips. (Illus.). 20p. 1981. 35.00x (ISBN 0-936736-01-1); pap. 25.00 (ISBN 0-936736-02-X). Sweetbrier.

Mechlin, Stuart, ed. The Rose. (Illus.). 1979. 17.95 (ISBN 0-8317-7498-3, Mayflower Bks). Smith Pubs.

Ortho Books Staff, ed. All about Roses. LC 76-29248. 1977. pap. 5.95 (ISBN 0-917102-23-1). Ortho.

Roses. 2.25 (ISBN 0-686-21143-X). Bklyn Botanic.

Shrub Roses of Today. rev. ed. 242p. 1981. 40.00x (ISBN 0-460-04177-0, Pub. by J M Dent England). State Mutual Bk.

Thomas, Graham S. Climbing Roses Old & New. 208p. 1981. 40.00 (ISBN 0-460-04346-3, Pub. by J M Dent). State Mutual Bk.

--Climbing Roses: Old & New. new ed. (Illus.). 204p. 1983. text ed. 21.95x (ISBN 0-460-04604-7, BKA 04826, Pub by J. M. Dent England). Biblio Dist.

--Shrub Roses of Today. Rev. ed. (Illus.). 242p. 1980. 22.50x (ISBN 0-460-04533-4, Pub. by J M Dent England). Biblio Dist.

Tillotson, Will. Roses of Yesterday & Today. Stemler, Dorothy, ed. (Illus.). 88p. 1980. pap. 5.00 (ISBN 0-936736-03-8). Sweetbrier.

ROSIN

see Gums and Resins

ROTARY CONVERTERS

Regulatory Compliances for Converters: Seminar Notes. 42p. 1981. soft bound 19.95 (ISBN 0-686-92624-2). TAPPI.

Richardson, Robert M. Synchronous Packet Radio Using the Software Approach: AX.25 Protocal, Vol. 2. Belvins, T. F., ed. 280p. 1984. 22.00x (ISBN 0-940972-08-5). Richcraft Eng.

ROTARY ENGINES

American Society of Mechanical Engineers. Loss Prevention of Rotating Machinery: Papers Presented at ASME Petroleum Division Conference, Houston, Texas, September 1971. LC 71-187881. pap. 20.00 (ISBN 0-317-11090-X, 2011328). Bks Demand UMI.

ROTATARIA

see Rotifera

ROTATING MASSES OF FLUID

Greenspan, H. P. Theory of Rotating Fluids. LC 68-12058. (Cambridge Monographs on Mechanics & Applied Mathematics). (Illus.). 1968. text ed. 57.50 (ISBN 0-521-05147-9). Cambridge U Pr.

Roberts, P. H. & Soward, A. M., eds. Rotating Fluids in Geophysics. 1979. 55.00 (ISBN 0-12-589650-6). Acad Pr.

ROTATING SYSTEMS

see Rotational Motion

ROTATION OF THE EARTH

see Earth–Rotation

ROTATION OF THE PLANE OF POLARIZATION

see Polarization (Light)

ROTATION SPECTRA

see Molecular Rotation

ROTATIONAL MOTION

see also Gyroscope; Orbits; Rotors

Anderson, R. T., et al. Large Rotating Machine Winding. (Illus.). 201p. 1981. Repr. of 1969 ed. spiral 52.50x (ISBN 0-89563-049-4). Intl Ideas.

CISM (International Center for Mechanical Sciences), Dept for General Mechanics, Dubrovnik, 1971. Rotational Dynamics of Orbiting Gyrostats: Proceedings. Roberson, R., et al, eds. (CISM Pubns. Ser.: No. 102). (Illus.). 208p. 1974. pap. 23.10 (ISBN 0-387-81198-2). Springer-Verlag.

Molin, Y. N., et al. Spin Exchange: Principles & Applications in Chemistry & Biology. (Springer Series in Chemical Physics: Vol. 8). (Illus.). 242p. 1980. 48.00 (ISBN 0-387-10095-4). Springer-Verlag.

Mukunda, N., et al. Relativistic Models of Extended Hadrons Obeying a Mas-Spin Trajectory Constraint. (Lecture Notes in Physics: Vol. 165). 163p. 1982. pap. 11.00 (ISBN 0-387-11586-2). Springer-Verlag.

Richardson, Donald. Rotating Electric Machines & Transformers. 2nd ed. 1982. text ed. 32.95 (ISBN 0-8359-6750-6); instrs'. manual avail. (ISBN 0-8359-6751-4). Reston.

Walker, Jearl. Roundabout: A Scientific American Reader. LC 85-4358. (Illus.). 80p. 1985. text ed. 19.95 (ISBN 0-7167-1724-7); pap. text ed. 10.95 (ISBN 0-7167-1725-5). W H Freeman.

ROTATIONAL MOTION (RIGID DYNAMICS)

see also Top

CISM (International Center for Mechanical Sciences) Gyrodynamics. Magnus, K., ed. (CISM Intl. Centre for Mechanical Science, Courses & Lectures Ser.: No. 53). (Illus.). x, 280p. 1974. pap. 15.40 (ISBN 0-387-81229-6). Springer-Verlag.

Euromech 38 Colloquium, Louvain-la-Neuve, Belgium, 3-5 September, 1973. Gyrodynamics: Proceedings. Willems, P. Y., ed. (Illus.). 300p. 1974. 28.40 (ISBN 0-387-06776-0). Springer-Verlag.

Large Rotating Machine Winding. 55.00x (ISBN 0-85083-045-1, Pub. by Engineering Ind). State Mutual Bk.

ROTIFERA

Ahlstrom, Elbert H. A Quantitative Study of Rotatoria in Terwilliger's Pond, Put-in Bay, Ohio. 1934. 1.00 (ISBN 0-86727-029-2). Ohio Bio Survey.

Harring, H. K. & Myers, F. J. The Rotifer Fauna of Wisconsin. (Illus.). 1973. Repr. of 1927 ed. 56.00 (ISBN 3-7682-0820-6). Lubrecht & Cramer.

ROTORS

Adams, M. L., Jr., ed. Rotor Dynamical Instability. (AMD Ser.: Vol. 55). 100p. 1983. pap. text ed. 24.00 (ISBN 0-317-02645-3, G00227). ASME.

Burke, J. J. & Weiss, V., eds. Application of Fracture Mechanics to Design. LC 78-14819. (Sagamore Army Materials Research Conference Proceedings Ser.: Vol. 22). 347p. 1978. 55.00x (ISBN 0-306-40040-5, Plenum Pr). Plenum Pub.

Dimaragonas, A. D., et al. Analytical Methods in Rotor Dynamics. (Illus.). 217p. 1983. 55.50 (ISBN 0-85334-199-0, Pub. by Elsevier Applied Sci England). Elsevier.

Eshleman, R. L. Critical Speeds & Response of Flexible Rotor Systems. LC 72-92595. (Flexible Rotor-Bearing System Dynamics Ser.: Vol. 1). (Illus.). pap. 20.00 (ISBN 0-317-11108-6, 2011592). Bks Demand UMI.

Fluid Film Bearing Committee of the Lubrication Division. Topics in Fluid Film Bearing & Rotor Bearing Systems Design & Optimization: Presented at the Design Engineering Conference, Chicago, Ill., April 17-20, 1978. Rohde, S. M., et al, eds. LC 78-52526. pap. 70.00 (ISBN 0-317-11248-1, 2017648). Bks Demand UMI.

Jaffee, R. I., ed. Rotor Forgings for Turbines & Generators: Proceedings of an International Workshop by Electric Power Research Institute, Palo Alto, California, U. S. A., September 14-17, 1980. LC 82-5358. (Illus.). 932p. 1982. 165.00 (ISBN 0-08-029373-5, A115). Pergamon.

Kushul', Mikhail Y. Self-Induced Oscillations of Rotors. LC 64-19440. 124p. 1964. 32.50x (ISBN 0-306-10693-0, Consultants); 32.50 (ISBN 0-686-66517-1). Plenum Pub.

Kushulb, Mikhail Y. The Self-induced Oscillations of Rotors. LC 64-19440. pap. 32.30 (ISBN 0-317-28008-2, 2055802). Bks Demand UMI.

Mahrenholtz, O, ed. Dynamics of Rotors: Stability & System Identification. (CISM International Centre for Mechanical Sciences: Vol. 273). (Illus.). vi, 511p. 1985. pap. 37.40 (ISBN 0-387-81846-4). Springer-Verlag.

Rieger, N. F. Unbalance Response & Balancing of Flexible Rotors in Bearings. LC 72-92595. (Flexible Rotor-Bearing System Dynamics Ser.: Vol. 2). (Illus.). pap. 20.00 (ISBN 0-317-11118-3, 2012305). Bks Demand UMI.

Symposium of International Union of Theoretical & Applied Mechanics, Lyngby, Denmark, Aug. 1974. Dynamics of Rotors: Proceedings. Niordson, F. I., ed. (Illus.). xii, 564p. 1975. 52.00 (ISBN 0-387-07384-1). Springer-Verlag.

Tondl, Ales. Some Problems of Rotor Dynamics. Gonda, Jan, ed. Dolan, Pavel, tr. from Czech. LC 66-72920. pap. 108.50 (ISBN 0-317-26203-3, 2052128). Bks Demand UMI.

ROTTWEILER (DOG)

see Dogs–Breeds–Rottweiler

RPG (COMPUTER PROGRAM LANGUAGE)

Bux, William E. & Cunningham, Edward G. RPG & RPG II Programming: Applied Fundamentals. (Illus.). 1979. pap. text ed. 23.95 (ISBN 0-13-783423-3). P-H.

Carson, Kelton. Simplified Computer Programming: Including the Easy RPG Way. LC 73-90739. (Illus.). 240p. 1974. pap. 8.95 (ISBN 0-8306-3676-5, 676). TAB Bks.

Cormier, Robert & Paquette, Laurence. RPG II Programming: A Building Block Approach. 206p. 1982. pap. write for info. Wadsworth Pub.

--RPG Two Programming: A Building Block Approach. 224p. 1981. pap. text ed. write for info. (ISBN 0-534-01018-0). Wadsworth Pub.

Couger, J. Daniel & McFadden, Fred R. First Course in Data Processing with BASIC, COBOL, FORTRAN & RPG. 3rd ed. LC 83-17032. (Wiley Series in Computers & Information Processing Systems for Business: 1-661). 682p. 1984. text ed. 28.95 (ISBN 0-471-86946-5); write for info. tchr's ed. (ISBN 0-471-86952-X); pap. 15.95 student wkbk (ISBN 0-471-86951-1); write for info. tests (ISBN 0-471-88531-2); write for info. slides (ISBN 0-471-88493-6). Wiley.

Essick, Edward. RPG-II Programming. 354p. 1981. pap. text ed. 20.95 (ISBN 0-574-21315-5, 13-4315); instr's. guide avail. (ISBN 0-574-21316-3, 13-4316). SRA.

Essick, Edward L. RPG for System 360 & System 370. (Orig.). 1973. pap. text ed. 20.95 scp (ISBN 0-06-382625-9, HarpC). Har-Row.

Feingold, Carl. RPG II Programming. 720p. 1982. pap. text ed. write for info. (ISBN 0-697-08150-8); instrs.' manual avail. (ISBN 0-697-08152-4). Wm C Brown.

Fisher, Robert A. An Introduction to RPG: RPG II Programming. LC 74-9537. 393p. 1975. pap. 36.50x (ISBN 0-471-26001-0). Wiley.

Introduction to RPG II. (Computer Literacy Ser.). pap. 19.95 (ISBN 0-318-04027-1). Sperry Comp Syst.

Minkema, Douglas D. & Carter, Gerald L. RPG II Programming. 2nd ed. (RPG II Programming-Advanced Topics Ser.). 1977. pap. text ed. 17.50 (ISBN 0-9610582-2-6). Apollo Com.

--RPG II Programming Teacher's Guide. 175p. text ed. 55.00 (ISBN 0-9610582-5-0). Apollo Com.

Minkema, Douglas D. & Pasquini, Mark T. RPG II Programming Advanced Topics. (RPG II Programming-Advanced Topics Ser.). 187p. 1977. pap. text ed. 14.50 (ISBN 0-9610582-3-4). Apollo Com.

--RPG II Programming-Advanced Topics Teacher's Guide. 210p. text ed. 55.00 (ISBN 0-9610582-6-9). Apollo Com.

Murach, Mike. System-Three-Sixty RPG. LC 70-178830. (Illus.). 297p. 1972. pap. text ed. 20.95 (ISBN 0-574-16097-3, 13-1415); instr's guide avail. (ISBN 0-574-16128-7, 13-1416); transparency masters avail. (ISBN 0-574-16129-5, 13-1417). SRA.

Myers, Stanley. RPG II & RPG III with Business Applications. 1983. text ed. 26.95 (ISBN 0-8359-6753-0); write for info. solution manual O.P. Reston.

Myers, Stanley E. RPG II with Business Applications. (Illus.). 1979. text ed. 26.95 (ISBN 0-8359-6303-9); instrs'. manual avail. (ISBN 0-8359-6304-7). Reston.

Seeds, Harice L. Programming RPG II. LC 79-127669. 454p. 1971. pap. 28.95 (ISBN 0-471-77113-9). Wiley.

Shelly, Gary B. & Cashman, Thomas J. Computer Programming RPG II. LC 76-19352. 560p. 1976. pap. text ed. 24.95 (ISBN 0-88236-226-7). Anaheim Pub Co.

Stern, Nancy, et al. RPG II & RPG III Programming. LC 83-12536. 680p. 1984. pap. text ed. 28.45x (ISBN 0-471-87625-9). Wiley.

Warnecke, H. J. & Schraft, R. D. Industrial Robots: Application Experience. (Eng.). 298p. 1982. pap. text ed. 56.00x softbound (ISBN 0-903608-21-9, Pub by IFSPUBS). Scholium Intl.

RT-11 (COMPUTER OPERATING SYSTEM)

Beaumont, David, et al. Working with RT-II. (Illus.). 150p. 1984. pap. 24.00 (ISBN 0-932376-31-2, EY-00021-DP). Digital Pr.

RUBBER

see also Elastomers

Bartenev, G. M. & Zuyev, Yu. S. Strength & Failure of Visco-Elastic Materials. 1968. 72.00 (ISBN 0-08-012183-7). Pergamon.

Brown, R. P. Physical Testing of Rubbers. (Illus.). 327p. 1979. 44.50 (ISBN 0-85334-788-3, Pub. by Elsevier Applied Sci England). Elsevier.

Brydson, J. A., ed. Developments with Natural Rubber. (Illus.). 148p. 1967. 16.75 (ISBN 0-85334-062-5, Pub. by Elsevier Applied Sci England). Elsevier.

Data Notes Publishing Staff. Rubber Recycling: Data Notes. 30p. 1983. pap. text ed. 4.95 (ISBN 0-911569-43-X, Pub. by Data Notes). Prosperity & Profits.

Davis, A. & Sims, D. Weathering of Polymers. (Illus.). 300p. 1983. 64.75 (ISBN 0-85334-226-1, I-266-83, Pub. by Elsevier Applied Sci England). Elsevier.

Duck, E. W. Plastics & Rubbers. 1972. 10.00 (ISBN 0-8022-2076-2). Philos Lib.

Dunn, A. S. Rubber & Rubber Elasticity, No. 48. (Journal of Polymer Science: Polymer Symposia). 232p. 1974. pap. 15.00 (ISBN 0-685-88107-5, Pub. by Wiley). Krieger.

Eirich, Frederick R., ed. Science & Technology of Rubber. 1978. 78.00 (ISBN 0-12-234360-3). Acad Pr.

Evans, C. W., ed. Developments in Rubber & Rubber Composites, Vol. 1. (Illus.). 184p. 1980. 33.50 (ISBN 0-85334-892-8, Pub. by Elsevier Applied Sci England). Elsevier.

--Developments in Rubber & Rubber Composites, Vol. 2. (Illus.). 183p. 1983. 44.50 (ISBN 0-85334-173-7, I-460-82, Pub. by Elsevier Applied Sci England). Elsevier.

Glossary of Terms Relating to Rubber & Rubber Technology. 122p. 1972. pap. 10.00 (ISBN 0-8031-0101-5, STP184A). ASTM.

The Goodyear Story. LC 82-73862. 1983. write for info (ISBN 0-87502-116-6). Benjamin Co.

Heinisch, K. F. Dictionary of Rubber. (Illus.). 545p. 1974. 52.00 (ISBN 0-85334-568-6, Pub. by Elsevier Applied Sci England). Elsevier.

Institute of Rubber, 1969. International Conference: Proceedings. 628p. 1969. 143.50 (ISBN 0-677-61210-9). Gordon.

Maclaren, W. A. Rubber, Tea & Cacao with Special Sections on Coffee, Spices & Tobacco. 1980. lib. bdg. 75.00 (ISBN 0-8490-3110-9). Gordon Pr.

Mark, James E. & Lal, Joginder, eds. Elastomers & Rubber Elasticity. LC 82-11320. (ACS Symposium Ser.: No. 193). 576p. 1982. lib. bdg. 59.95x (ISBN 0-8412-0729-1). Am Chemical.

Mold Release Agents for Rubbers & Plastics, 1973-Jan. 1983. 162p. 1983. 78.00 (ISBN 0-686-48316-2, LS130). T-C Pubns CA.

Morrell, S. H., ed. Progress in Rubber Technology, Vol. 44. 139p. 1981. 46.25 (ISBN 0-85334-984-3, Pub. by Elsevier Applied Sci England). Elsevier.

Nutt, A. R. Toxic Hazards of Rubber Chemicals. 200p. 1984. 37.50 (ISBN 0-85334-242-3, Pub. by Elsevier Applied Sci England). Elsevier.

Payne, P. L. Rubber & Railways. 246p. 1961. 40.00x (ISBN 0-85323-482-5, Pub. by Liverpool Univ England). State Mutual Bk.

Rubber & Related Products - STP 553: New Methods for Testing & Analyzing. 200p. 1974. 20.25 (ISBN 0-8031-0560-6, 04-55300-20). ASTM.

Rubber Foundation. Elseviers Rubber Dictionary. (Eng., Fr., Span., Ital., Port., Ger., Dutch, Swedish, Indonesian & Japanese.). 1537p. 1959. 191.50 (ISBN 0-444-40499-6). Elsevier.

The Rubber Tree. (Better Farming Ser.: No. 25). 31p. 1977. pap. 7.50 (ISBN 92-5-100156-1, F83, FAO). Unipub.

Scentouri. Rubber Recycling: A Correspondence Course Workbook. 15p. 1984. pap. text ed. 11.95 (ISBN 0-318-01196-4, Pub. by Scentouri). Prosperity & Profits.

Solo, Robert. Across the High Technology Threshold: The Case of Synthetic Rubber. 130p. 1980. Repr. of 1959 ed. lib. bdg. 22.50 (ISBN 0-8482-6222-0). Norwood Edns.

Wake, W. C., et al, eds. Analysis of Rubber & Rubber-Like Polymers. 3rd ed. (Illus.). 340p. 1983. 66.75 (ISBN 0-85334-215-6, Pub. by Elsevier Applied Sci England). Elsevier.

Whelan, A. & Lee, K. S., eds. Developments in Rubber Technology, Vol. 3. (Illus.). 240p. 1982. 61.00 (ISBN 0-85334-135-4, Pub. by Elsevier Applied Sci England). Elsevier.

RUBBER, ARTIFICIAL

Advances in Synthetic Rubbers & Elastomers Science & Technology. LC 79-64141. 334p. 1977. pap. 14.95 (ISBN 0-87762-237-X). Technomic.

Blackley, D. C. Synthetic Rubbers: Their Chemistry & Technology. (Illus.). 372p. 1983. 72.25 (ISBN 0-85334-152-4, I-462-82, Pub. by Elsevier Applied Sci England). Elsevier.

Business Communications Staff. Thermoplastics Elastomers: Rubber Substitutes, P-026N. 1985. 1750.00 (ISBN 0-89336-431-2). BCC.

Fikhtegol'ts, V. S., et al. Ultraviolet Spectra of Elastomers & Rubber Chemicals. LC 66-12889. 170p. 1966. 49.50x (ISBN 0-306-65119-X, IFI Plenum). Plenum Pub.

Information Sources on the Natural & Synthetic Rubber Industry. (UNIDO Guides to Information Sources Ser.: No.34). 108p. 1980. pap. 4.00 (ISBN 0-686-70503-3, UN). Unipub.

RUBBER FOAM

see Foam Rubber

RUBBER INDUSTRY AND TRADE

see also Rubber, Artificial

Allee, et al. Basic Compounding & Processing of Rubber. Long, Harry, ed. (Illus.). xii, 237p. 1985. text ed. 10.00 (ISBN 0-912415-02-9). Rubber Division.

Brydson, J. Rubber Chemistry. (Illus.). 458p. 1978. 89.00 (ISBN 0-85334-779-4, Pub. by Elsevier Applied Sci England). Elsevier.

Evans, C. W. Powdered & Particulate Rubber Technology. (Illus.). 107p. 1978. 24.00 (ISBN 0-85334-773-5, Pub. by Elsevier Applied Sci England). Elsevier.

Freakley, P. K. & Payne, A. R. Theory & Practice of Engineering with Rubber. (Illus.). 666p. 1978. 96.25 (ISBN 0-85334-772-7, Pub. by Elsevier Applied Sci England). Elsevier.

Freakley, Philip K. Rubber Processing & Production Organization. 472p. 1985. 59.50x (ISBN 0-306-41745-6, Plenum Pr). Plenum Pub.

Goering, Theodore J. & D'Silva, Emmanuel H. Natural Rubber. (Illus.). 66p. (Orig.). 1982. pap. text ed. 5.00 (ISBN 0-8213-0045-8). World Bank.

Grilli, Enzo R., et al. The World Rubber Economy: Structure, Changes, & Prospects. LC 80-554. (World Bank Occasional Papers). (Illus.). 224p. 1981. pap. text ed. 10.00x (ISBN 0-8018-2421-4). Johns Hopkins.

IFAC Conference, 4th, Ghent, Belgium, June 1980. Instrumentation & Automation in the Paper, Rubber, Plastics & Polymerisation Industries: Proceedings. Van Cauwenberghe, A., ed. LC 80-41889. (IFAC Proceedings Ser.). (Illus.). 550p. 1981. 130.00 (ISBN 0-08-024487-4). Pergamon.

Information Sources on the Natural & Synthetic Rubber Industry. (UNIDO Guides to Information Sources Ser.: No.34). 108p. 1980. pap. 4.00 (ISBN 0-686-70503-3, UN). Unipub.

International Natural Rubber Agreement: 1979. 27p. 1980. pap. 3.00 (ISBN 0-686-94718-5, UN802D5, UN). Unipub.

Lighting for Manufacturing Rubber Tires. 4.50 (ISBN 0-686-47876-2, CP-35). Illum Eng.

The Maritime Transplantation of National Rubber. pap. 3.00 (ISBN 0-686-94516-6, UN70/2D/11, UN). Unipub.

Miller, Richard K., et al. Noise Control Solutions for the Rubber & Plastics Industry. 45.00 (ISBN 0-686-74624-4). Fairmont Pr.

Morton, Maurice. Rubber Technology. 2nd ed. LC 81-8317. 614p. 1981. Repr. of 1973 ed. 39.50 (ISBN 0-89874-372-9). Krieger.

Nondestructive Test Methods in the Rubber & Plastics Industries, 1983-1984. 50p. 1984. 78.00 (ISBN 0-686-48317-0, LS128). T-C Pubns CA.

Plastic & Rubber Working Machinery. (Machinery Studies). 1980. 350.00 (ISBN 0-686-31531-6). Busn Trend.

Sittig, M. Pollution Control in the Plastics & Rubber Industry. LC 75-2940. (Pollution Technology Review Ser: No. 18). (Illus.). 306p. 1975. 36.00 (ISBN 0-8155-0572-8). Noyes.

Sloane, T. O. Rubber Hand Stamps & the Manipulation of India Rubber. 1985. pap. 6.50 (ISBN 0-917914-28-7). Lindsay Pubns.

Tires & Rubber Products. 1985. 650.00 (ISBN 0-318-04398-X). Busn Trend.

Van Alphen, J. Rubber Chemicals. 2nd & enl. ed. Van Turnhout, C. M., ed. LC 73-81826. (Illus.). 197p. 1973. lib. bdg. 42.00 (ISBN 90-277-0349-3, Pub. by Reidel Holland). Kluwer Academic.

Van Cauwenbergue, A. R., ed. Instrumentation & Automation in the Paper, Rubber, Plastics & Polymerization Industries: Proceedings of the Fifth International IFAC-IMEKO Symposium, Antwerp, Belgium, 11-13 October 1983. (IFAC Proceedings Ser.). 528p. 1984. 120.00 (ISBN 0-08-031112-1). Pergamon.

Wake & Tidd. Analysis of Rubber, 1982. Date not set. price not set. Elsevier.

Whelan, A. & Lee, K. S., eds. Developments in Rubber Technology, Vol. 3. (Illus.). 240p. 1982. 61.00 (ISBN 0-85334-135-4, Pub. by Elsevier Applied Sci England). Elsevier.

Yescombe, E. R. Plastics & Rubbers: World Sources of Information. 512p. 1976. 55.50 (ISBN 0-85334-675-5, Pub. by Elsevier Applied Sci England). Elsevier.

RUBBER-SHEET GEOMETRY

see Topology

RUBBER TIRES

see Tires, Rubber

RUBIDIUM

Gorsini, G. U., ed. Current Trends in Lithium & Rubidium. 1984. lib. bdg. 49.50 (ISBN 0-85200-782-5, Pub. by MTP Pr England). Kluwer Academic.

RUBUS

Royen, P. Van. The Genus Rubus (Rosaceae) in New Guinea. (Monographiae Phanerogamarum). 1969. 17.50 (ISBN 3-7682-0612-2). Lubrecht & C.

Weber, H. E. Die Gattung Rubus L. (Rosaceae) im Nordwestlichen Europa vom Nordwestdeutschen Tiefland bis Skandinavien mit Besonderer Berucksichtigung Schleswig-Holsteins. (Illus.). 1973. 52.50 (ISBN 3-7682-0858-3). Lubrecht & Cramer.

RUFFED GROUSE

see Grouse

RUG AND CARPET INDUSTRY

Wira, ed. Carpet Testing. 1977. 30.00x (ISBN 0-686-87144-8). State Mutual Bk.

RUG MANUFACTURE

see Weaving

RULERS (INSTRUMENTS)

Roberts, Kenneth D. Introduction to Rule Collecting. (Illus.). 22p. (Orig.). 1982. pap. text ed. 2.00 (ISBN 0-913602-52-3). K Roberts.

RUMINANTS

see also Giraffes

Ad Hoc Consultation on the Value of Non-Protein Nitrogen for Ruminants: Report. 1971. pap. 15.00 (F1086, FAO). Unipub.

Andreeva, N. K. Atlas of Helminths (Strongylata) of Domestic Wild Ruminants of Kazakhstan. 206p. 1981. 75.00x (ISBN 0-686-72943-9, Pub. by Oxford & IBH India). State Mutual Bk.

Arnold, G. W. & Dudzinski, M. L. Ethology of Free Ranging Domestic Animals. (Developments in Animal & Veterinary Sciences Ser.: Vol. 2). 198p. 1979. 57.50 (ISBN 0-444-41700-1). Elsevier.

Ashdown. Color Atlas of the Ruminants. (Illus.). 240p. 1983. text ed. 75.00 (ISBN 0-8391-1760-4). Univ Park.

Baker, Frank H. & Miller, Mason E. Emerging Technology & Management for Ruminants. (International Stockmen's School Proceedings, 1985 Ser.). 450p. 1985. 40.00x (ISBN 0-8133-0120-3). Westview.

Butler, John E., ed. The Ruminant Immune System. LC 80-29702. (Advances in Experimental Medicine & Biology Ser.: Vol. 137). 915p. 1981. 95.00x (ISBN 0-306-40641-1, Plenum Pr). Plenum Pub.

Church, D. C. Digestive Physiology & Nutrition of Ruminants: Digestive Physiology, Vol. 1. 1976. text ed. 22.00x (ISBN 0-9601586-4-2). O & B Bks.

Church, D. C., ed. Digestive Physiology & Nutrition of Ruminants: Nutrition, Vol. 2. 2nd ed. 1979. text ed. 27.50x (ISBN 0-9601586-5-0). O & B Bks.

Loosli, J. K. & McDonald, I. Nonprotein Nitrogen in the Nutrition of Ruminants. (Agricultural Planning Studies: No. 75). 94p. (2nd Printing 1976). 1968. pap. 13.25 (ISBN 92-5-101563-5, F299, FAO). Unipub.

Research Co-Ordination Meeting & Panel. Tracer Studies on Non-Protein Nitrogen for Ruminants, 2: Proceedings. (Illus.). 208p. 1975. pap. 21.75 (ISBN 92-0-111175-4, ISP302-1, IAEA). Unipub.

Ruminant Nutrition: Selected Articles from the World Animal Review. (Animal Production & Health Papers: No. 12). 165p. 1978. pap. 12.00 (ISBN 92-5-100650-4, F1889, FAO). Unipub.

Scaramuzzi, R. J. & Lincoln, D. W., eds. Reproductive Endocrinology of Domestic Ruminants. 270p. 95.00x (ISBN 0-906545-06-4, Pub. by Journals Repro England). State Mutual Bk.

Use of Tritiated Water in Studies of Production & Adaption in Ruminants: Five-Year Research Co-ordination Programme Organized by the Joint FAO-IAEA Division of Atomic Energy in Food and Agriculture. (Panel Proceedings Ser.). (Illus.). 218p. 1982. pap. 28.75 (ISBN 92-0-111082-0, ISP576, IAEA). Unipub.

Van Soest, Peter J. Nutritional Ecology of the Ruminant. LC 81-83655. 375p. 1982. 32.00x (ISBN 0-9601586-0-X). O & B Bks.

RUNNING, ANIMAL

see Animal Locomotion

RUN OFF

see Runoff

RUNOFF

see also Drainage; Erosion; Rain and Rainfall; Water Storage; Water-Supply

De Vore, R. William & Huffsey, R. R., eds. International Symposium on Urban Storm Runoff: Proceedings 1979. LC 79-66289. (Illus.). 365p. (Orig.). 1979. pap. 33.50 (ISBN 0-89779-020-0, UKY BU118). OES Pubns.

Harremoes, P., ed. Rainfall As the Basis for Urban Run-off Design & Analysis: Proceedings of a Specialised Seminar Held in Copenhagen, Denmark, 24-26 August, 1983. (Illus.). 370p. 1984. pap. 80.00 (ISBN 0-08-031506-2). Pergamon.

Singh, Vijay P., ed. Rainfall-Runoff Relationship. LC 81-71290. 1982. 36.00 (ISBN 0-918334-45-4). WRP.

--Statistical Analysis of Rainfall & Runoff. LC 81-71289. 1982. 36.00 (ISBN 0-918334-44-6). WRP.

Stephenson, D. Stormwater Hydrology & Drainage. (Developments in Water Science: Vol. 14). 276p. 1981. 59.75 (ISBN 0-444-41998-5). Elsevier.

RUNOFF–MATHEMATICAL MODELS

Modeling Urban Run-off: A Qualislinear Approach. (Agricultural Research Reports: No. 874). 1978. pap. 14.00 (ISBN 90-220-0665-4, PDC139, PUDOC). Unipub.

Overton, D. E. & Meadows, M. E. Stormwater Modeling. 1976. 49.50 (ISBN 0-12-531550-3). Acad Pr.

RURAL SEWERAGE

see Sewerage, Rural

RURAL WATER-SUPPLY

see Water-Supply, Rural

RUSSELL, BERTRAND RUSSELL, 3RD EARL, 1872-1970

Eames, Elizabeth R. Bertrand Russell's Theory of Knowledge. LC 77-78529. 1969. 6.00 (ISBN 0-8076-0509-3). Braziller.

Grattan-Guinness, I., ed. Dear Russell-Dear Jourdain: A Commentary on Russall's Logic Based on His Correspondence with Philip Jourdain. LC 77-9431. 234p. 1977. 19.00x (ISBN 0-231-04460-7). Columbia U Pr.

Kilmister, C. W. Russell. LC 84-18050. 1984. 27.50 (ISBN 0-312-69613-2). St Martin.

Klemke, E. D., ed. Essays on Bertrand Russell. LC 71-100379. 469p. 1970. pap. 8.95x (ISBN 0-252-00167-2). U of Ill Pr.

Perry, L., ed. Bertrand Russell, A. S. Neill, Homer Lane, W. H. Kilpatrick: Four Progressive Educators. 1968. pap. text ed. 1.95x (ISBN 0-02-975150-0). Macmillan.

Roberts, George W., ed. Bertrand Russell: The Memorial Volumes, Vol. 1. (Muirhead Library of Philosophy Ser.). 1979. text ed. 50.00x (ISBN 0-391-00717-3). Humanities.

Russell, Bertrand. Autobiography of Bertrand Russell. (Unwin Paperbacks Ser.). 1978. pap. 7.95 (ISBN 0-04-921022-X). Allen Unwin.

--Autobiography of Bertrand Russell: Vol. 1, 1872-1914. 1967. 17.95 (ISBN 0-04-921003-3). Allen Unwin.

--Autobiography of Bertrand Russell: Vol. 2, 1914-1944. 1968. 17.95 (ISBN 0-04-921009-2). Allen Unwin.

--Autobiography of Bertrand Russell Vol. 3: 1944-1967. 232p. 1981. Repr. of 1970 ed. 17.95 (ISBN 0-04-921010-6). Allen Unwin.

--My Philosophical Development. (Unwin Paperbacks Ser.). 1975. pap. 3.95 (ISBN 0-04-192030-9). Allen Unwin.

Sainsbury, Mark. Russell. (The Arguments of the Philosophers Ser.). 1979. 36.00x (ISBN 0-7100-0155-X); pap. 14.95 (ISBN 0-7102-0536-8). Routledge & Kegan.

RUSSELL, HARRY LUMEN, 1866-1954

Beardsley, Edward H. Harry L. Russell & Agricultural Science in Wisconsin. (Illus.). 252p. 1969. 25.00x (ISBN 0-299-05470-5). U of Wis Pr.

--Harry L. Russell & Agricultural Science in Wisconsin. LC 77-84950. pap. 67.30 (ISBN 0-317-28985-3, 2023728). Bks Demand UMI.

RUSSIAN LANGUAGE–TECHNICAL RUSSIAN

Condoyannis, George E. Scientific Russian. LC 77-16615. 238p. 1978. pap. 10.50 (ISBN 0-88275-643-5). Krieger.

Croxton, Clive A. Russian for the Scientist & Mathematician. LC 83-10209. 210p. 1984. 34.95x (ISBN 0-471-90260-8, Pub. by Wiley-Interscience). Wiley.

Gould, S. H. Russian for the Mathematician. LC 72-76762. (Illus.). 224p. 1972. pap. 21.00 (ISBN 0-387-05811-7). Springer-Verlag.

Mitrokhina, V. I. & Motovilova, O. G. Russian for Scientists. 349p. 1981. 10.00 (ISBN 0-8285-2171-9, Pub. by Rus Lang Pubs USSR). Imported Pubns.

RUSSIAN SCIENCE

see Science, Russian

RUSSIAN WOLFHOUND

see Dogs–Breeds–Russian Wolfhound

RUST

see Corrosion and Anti-Corrosives; Steel–Corrosion

RUSTLESS COATINGS

see Corrosion and Anti-Corrosives

RUSTS (FUNGI)

Bushnell, William R. & Roelfs, Alan P. The Cereal Rusts: Vol. 1: Origins, Specificity, Structure & Physiology. LC 83-15035. 1984. 70.00 (ISBN 0-12-148401-7). Acad Pr.

Cummins, G. B. & Hiratsuka, Y. Illustrated Genera of Rust Fungi. rev. ed. LC 83-72397. (Illus.). 152p. 1983. spiral bound 16.00 (ISBN 0-89054-058-6). Am Phytopathol Soc.

Cummins, George B. Rust Fungi on Legumes & Composites in North America. LC 78-60541. 426p. 1978. pap. 14.95x (ISBN 0-8165-0653-1). U of Ariz Pr.

Littlefield, Larry J. & Heath, Michele C. Ultrastructure of Rust Fungi. LC 78-22530. 1979. 45.00 (ISBN 0-12-452650-0). Acad Pr.

Marshall, Rush P. Control of Cedar-Apple Rust on Red Cedar. 1941. pap. 34.50x (ISBN 0-686-51364-9). Elliots Bks.

Roebbelen, Gerhard & Sharp, Eugene L. Mode of Inheritance, Interaction & Application of Genes Conditioning Resistance to Yellow Rust. (Advances in Plant Breeding Ser.: Vol. 9). (Illus.). 88p. (Orig.). 1978. pap. text ed. 25.00 (ISBN 3-489-71110-6). Parey Sci Pubs.

Scott, K. J. & Chakravorty, A. K., eds. The Rust Fungi. 1982. 59.00 (ISBN 0-12-633520-6). Acad Pr.

RUTHENIUM

Seddon, Elaine A. & Seddon, Kenneth R. Chemistry of Ruthenium. (Topics in Inorganic Chemistry Ser.: Vol. 19). 1374p. 1984. 240.75 (ISBN 0-444-42375-3, I-255-84). Elsevier.

RUTHERFORD, ERNEST RUTHERFORD, BARON, 1871-1937

Andrade, E. N. Rutherford & the Nature of the Atom. (Illus.). 11.25 (ISBN 0-8446-2053-X). Peter Smith.

Birks, J. B. & Birks, J. B., eds. Proceedings of the Rutherford Jubilee International Conference-Manchester, 1962. 90.00 (ISBN 0-12-101162-3). Acad Pr.

Shea, William R. & Bunge, M. A., eds. Rutherford & Physics at the Turn of the Century. 1979. 20.00x (ISBN 0-88202-184-2). Watson Pub Intl.

Wilson, David. Rutherford: Simple Genius. (Illus.). 625p. 1983. 27.50x (ISBN 0-262-23115-8). MIT Pr.

RX (COMPUTER PROGRAMS)

Blum, R. L. Discovery & Representation of Causal Relationships from a Large Time-Oriented Clinical Database: The RX Project. (Lecture Notes in Medical Informatics Ser.: Vol. 19). 242p. 1982. pap. 20.00 (ISBN 0-387-11962-0). Springer-Verlag.

RYE SMUT

see Ergot

RYE WHISKEY

see Whiskey

S

S-MATRIX THEORY

Deif, A. S. Advanced Matrix Theory for Scientists & Engineers. 256p. 1982. 39.95x (ISBN 0-470-27316-X). Halsted Pr.

Eden, Richard & Landshoff, D. I. The Analytic S-Matrix. LC 66-13387. pap. 73.80 (ISBN 0-317-08713-4, 2022447). Bks Demand UMI.

Kay, I. & Moses, H. Inverse Scattering Papers. (LIE Groups: History Frontiers & Applications Ser.: No. 12). 305p. 1982. 30.00 (ISBN 0-915692-32-5, 991600029). Math Sci Pr.

Wigner, Eugene P., ed. Dispersion Relations & Their Connection with Causality. (Italian Physical Society Ser.: Course 29). 1964. 75.00 (ISBN 0-12-368829-9). Acad Pr.

SABRE (JET FIGHTER PLANES)

Davis, Larry. F-86 Sabre in Action. (Aircraft in Action Ser.). (Illus.). 1984. pap. 4.95 (ISBN 0-89747-032-X, 1033). Squad Sig Pubns.

SACCHARIDES

Academy Forum, National Academy of Sciences. Sweeteners: Issues & Uncertainties. LC 75-29990. vi, 259p. 1975. pap. 9.50 (ISBN 0-309-02407-2). Natl Acad Pr.

Farrell, A. S. Mono & Disaccharides in Water. 1986. 100.00x (ISBN 0-08-023919-6). Pergamon.

Marshall, J. John, ed. Mechanisms of Saccharide Polymerization & Depolymerization. LC 80-16155. 1980. 44.00 (ISBN 0-12-474150-9). Acad Pr.

SADDLERY

see also Harness Making and Trade

Beatie, Russel H. Saddles. LC 79-6708. (Illus.). 408p. 1981. 39.50 (ISBN 0-8061-1584-X). U of Okla Pr.

Davis, Sidney A. The Saddler. (Illus.). 64p. (Orig.). 1980. pap. 6.50 (ISBN 0-85263-527-3, Pub. by Shire Pubns England). Seven Hills Bks.

Edwards, E. H. Saddlery. (Illus.). 9.95 (ISBN 0-85131-151-2, BL2405, Dist. by Miller). J A Allen.

Edwards, E. Hartley. Saddlery. 200p. 1981. 30.00x (ISBN 0-85131-151-2, Pub. by Allen & Co). State Mutual Bk.

Grant, Bruce & Rice, Lee M. How to Make Cowboy Horse Gear. 2nd ed. LC 56-10884. (Illus.). 192p. 1956. pap. 6.50 (ISBN 0-87033-034-9). Cornell Maritime.

Hasluck, Paul N. Saddlery & Harness Making. (Illus.). 9.95 (ISBN 0-85131-148-2, BL6610, Dist. by Miller). J A Allen.

--Saddlery & Harness Making. 160p. 1981. 30.00x (ISBN 0-85131-148-2, Pub. by Allen & Co). State Mutual Bk.

Jones, Dave. Making & Repairing Western Saddles. LC 81-19106. (Illus.). 160p. 1982. 14.95 (ISBN 0-668-04906-5). Arco.

Sheilds, J. H. To Handmake a Saddle. (Illus.). 10.00 (ISBN 0-87556-618-9). Saifer.

Shields, J. H. To Handmake a Saddle. (Illus.). pap. 6.95 (ISBN 0-85131-222-5, NL51, Dist. by Miller). J A Allen.

Steffen, Randy. United States Military Saddles, 1812-1943. LC 72-9268. (Illus.). 1973. 14.95 (ISBN 0-8061-1074-0). U of Okla Pr.

Tuke, Diana R. Stitch by Stitch: A Guide to Equine Saddles. (Illus.). Repr. write for info. (ISBN 0-85131-049-4, NL51, Dist. by Miller). J A Allen.

SAFES

Hobbs, A. C. Construction of Locks & Safes. Tomlinson, Charles, ed. (Illus.). vi, 212p. 1982. Repr. of 1868 ed. 20.00 (ISBN 0-87556-126-8); stiff wrappers 15.00 (ISBN 0-686-82966-2). Saifer.

Tobias, Marc W. Locks, Safes, & Security: A Handbook for Law Enforcement Personnel. (Illus.). 352p. 1971. photocopy ed. 35.50x (ISBN 0-398-02155-4). C C Thomas.

SAFETY, INDUSTRIAL

see Industrial Safety

SAFETY EDUCATION

see also Traffic Safety

Albers, Vernon M. How to Use Woodworking Tools Effectively & Safely. (Illus.). 190p. 1974. 8.95 (ISBN 0-498-01851-2). A S Barnes.

Corporate Aviation Safety Seminar (29th: 1984: Montreal, Canada) Staff. Advancing Safety Through Effective Communication (Proceedings) of the 29th Annual Meeting April 1-3, 1984, Le Bonaventure Westin Hotel, Montreal, Canada. pap. 56.00 (ISBN 0-317-26834-1, 2023492). Bks Demand UMI.

The Driver & Home Safety Manual. 64p. 1982. 4.80 (ISBN 0-87912-128-9, 330.59). Natl Safety Coun.

Hendrick, Kingsley. Improving Employee Safety & Health Performance: A Managerial Guide. 1982. 37.50 (ISBN 0-8240-7269-3). Garland Pub.

Petersen, Dan. Safety Management: A Human Approach. LC 74-32008. (Illus.). 395p. 1975. 25.50x (ISBN 0-913690-04-X). Aloray.

SAFETY ENGINEERING

see Industrial Safety

SAILBOATS

Barnes, Howard. Backyard Boatyard. LC 81-81417. (Illus.). 144p. 1982. pap. 10.95 (ISBN 0-87742-144-7). Intl Marine.

Caswell, Christopher. Trailerable Sailboats. (Illus.). 1982. 19.95 (ISBN 0-393-03271-X). Norton.

Damour, Jacques. One Hundred & One Tips & Hints for Your Sailboat. LC 81-84142. 192p. 1982. pap. 2.95 (ISBN 0-86721-070-2). Jove Pubns.

Gibbs, Tony. Advanced Sailing. LC 74-83575. (Illus.). 1978. 8.95 (ISBN 0-312-00630-6); pap. 6.95 (ISBN 0-312-00631-4). St Martin.

--The Coastal Cruiser. (Illus.). 1981. 24.95 (ISBN 0-393-03267-1). Norton.

Gougeon, M. & Knog, T. Evolution of Modern Sailboat Design. 1974. pap. 6.95 (ISBN 0-02-001400-7, Collier). Macmillan.

Hankinson, Ken. Rigging Small Sailboats. LC 72-97327. (Illus.). pap. 6.50 (ISBN 0-686-05389-3). Glen-L Marine.

Leavens, John, ed. The Catboat Book. LC 73-88648. 168p. 1973. 20.00 (ISBN 0-87742-034-3). Intl Marine.

Lenski, Lois. Little Sailboat. Date not set. 5.25 (ISBN 0-8098-1002-6). McKay.

Meisel, Tony, ed. Under Sail: Equipment for the Serious Sailor. LC 81-14259. (Illus.). 192p. 1982. 24.95 (ISBN 0-02-583940-3). Macmillan.

Rosenow, Frank. Sailing Craft. (Illus.). 128p. 1982. 15.95 (ISBN 0-914814-33-8). Sail Bks.

Schult, Joachim. Curious Yachting Inventions. LC 74-1526. (Illus.). 139p. 1974. 14.95 (ISBN 0-8008-2104-1). Taplinger.

Spurr, Daniel. Spurr's Boatbook: Upgrading the Cruising Sailboat. LC 83-18404. (Illus.). 352p. 1984. 29.95 (ISBN 0-915160-57-9). Seven Seas.

Stephenson, Edward P., ed. The Sailboat Owner's Equipment Catalogue. (Illus.). 256p. 1982. pap. 13.95 (ISBN 0-312-69674-4). St Martin.

Taylor, George. Build Your Sailing Cruiser. 152p. 1982. 39.00x (ISBN 0-333-32047-6, Pub. by Nautical England). State Mutual Bk.

SAILING SHIPS

see also Clipper-Ships; Sailboats

Allen, Oliver. The Windjammers. Time-Life Books, ed. (The Seafarers Ser.). 1979. 13.95 (ISBN 0-8094-2703-6). Time-Life.

Allen, Oliver E. The Windjammers. LC 78-10819. (The Seafarers Ser.). (Illus.). 1979. lib. bdg. 21.27 (ISBN 0-8094-2704-4, Pub. by Time-Life). Silver.

American Neptune Pictorial Supplements, Vol. 15 Whaling Vessels. 1973. pap. 3.50 (ISBN 0-87577-102-5). Peabody Mus Salem.

Anderson, Romola & Anderson, R. C. The Sailing Ship: Six Thousand Years of History. LC 79-177507. 22.00 (ISBN 0-405-08205-3). Ayer Co Pubs.

Chapelle, Howard I. American Small Sailing Craft. (Illus.). 1951. 26.95 (ISBN 0-393-03143-8). Norton.

Davis, Charles G. Rigs of the Nine Principal Types of American Sailing Vessels. (Illus.). pap. 0.95 (ISBN 0-87577-028-2). Peabody Mus Salem.

De Groot, Irene & Vorstman, Robert. Sailing Ships. 280p. 1981. 75.00x (ISBN 0-86092-052-6, Pub. by Fraser Bks). State Mutual Bk.

Haw, Frank & Buckley, Raymond. Oregon Saltwater Fishing Guide. 2nd ed. Jones, Stan, ed. (Illus.). 200p. pap. 6.95 (ISBN 0-939936-03-8). Jones Pub.

O'Farrell, R. C. Seafood Fishing for Amateur & Professional. 1978. 25.00 (ISBN 0-685-63452-3). State Mutual Bk.

Sosin, Mark & Kreh, Lefty. Fishing the Flats. LC 82-20158. (Illus.). 160p. 1983. 16.95 (ISBN 0-8329-0278-0, Pub. by Winchester Pr); pap. 9.95 (ISBN 0-8329-0280-2, Pub. by Winshester Pr). New Century.

SALTS

see also Fused Salts

Bohme, H. & Viehe, H. G. Imminium Salts in Organic Chemistry. LC 76-16155. (Advances in Organic Chemistry Ser.: Vol. 9, Pt. 2). 238p. 1979. 145.00 (ISBN 0-471-90693-X, Pub. by Wiley-Interscience). Wiley.

Bohme, H. & Viehe, H. G., eds. Iminium Salts in Organic Chemistry. LC 76-16155. (Advances in Organic Chemistry Ser: Vol. 9, Pt. 1). 631p. 1976. 127.00 (ISBN 0-471-90692-1, Pub. by Wiley-Interscience). Wiley.

De Langre, Jacques. Seasalt's Hidden Power: The Scientific Proof Finding & Identifying & Usage Manual. 1984. pap. 3.00 (ISBN 0-916508-35-8). Happiness Pr.

Schlitt, W. Joseph, ed. Salts & Brines Nineteen Eighty-Five. LC 84-52557. (Illus.). 209p. 1985. pap. 40.00 (ISBN 0-89520-434-7, 434-7). Soc Mining Eng.

Solymosi, F. Structure & Stability of Salts of Halogen Oxyacids in the Solid Phase. LC 75-19287. 116.80 (ISBN 0-8357-9985-9, 2016157). Bks Demand UMI.

Sonnenfeld, Peter. Brine & Evaporities: Depositional Environments of Precipitates in Hypersaline Brines. 1984. 75.00 (ISBN 0-12-654780-7). Acad Pr.

SALTS, FUSED

see Fused Salts

SALVAGE

Baptist, C. N. Salvage Operations. 160p. 1979. 19.50x (ISBN 0-540-07378-4). Sheridan.

Beham, Hervey. Salvagers. 211p. 1980. 30.00x (ISBN 0-686-78989-X, Pub. by Essex County England). State Mutual Bk.

Brady, Edward M. Marine Salvage Operations. LC 59-12836. (Illus.). 250p. 1960. 12.00x (ISBN 0-87033-051-9). Cornell Maritime.

Cayford, John E. Underwater Work: A Manual of Scuba Commercial Salvage & Construction Operations. 2nd ed. LC 66-28081. (Illus.). 271p. 1966. 13.50x (ISBN 0-87033-129-9). Cornell Maritime.

Milazzo, Giulio, ed. Staedtekonferenz Ueber Abfallbeseitigung: Conference on Urban Waste Disposal. (Eng. Fr. Ger. & Ital.). 700p. 1983. write for info (ISBN 0-8176-1282-3). Birkhauser.

Salvaging Operations. (Six Hundred Ser). 1964. pap. 2.00 (ISBN 0-685-58209-4, 604). Natl Fire Prot.

Thompson, Frank E., Jr. Diving, Cutting & Welding in Underwater Salvage Operations. LC 70-92687. (Illus.). 1944. pap. 4.00x (ISBN 0-87033-139-6). Cornell Maritime.

SALVAGE (WASTE, ETC.)

Here are entered works on reclaiming and reusing equipment or parts. Works on the processing of waste paper, cans, bottles, etc. are entered under Recycling (waste, etc.).

see also Recycling (Waste, etc.)

Allen, Peter, ed. Hazardous Waste Management. 300p. 1984. pap. 985.00 (ISBN 0-931634-41-5). FIND-SVP.

American Society of Mechanical Engineers. Combustion Fundamentals for Waste Incineration. LC 74-19743. pap. 56.00 (ISBN 0-317-27801-0, 2024182). Bks Demand UMI.

ASCE Conference on Environmental Engineering, New York, July, 1980. The Hazardous Waste Dilemma: Issues & Solutions. Saukin, Walter, ed. LC 81-65627. 334p. 1981. pap. 24.75x (ISBN 0-87262-266-5). Am Soc Civil Eng.

Curi, Kriton. Appropriate Waste Management for Developing Countries: Proceedings of the First International Symposium on Environmental Technology for Developing Countries held in Istanbul, Turkey, July 7-14, 1982. 690p. 1985. 95.00x (ISBN 0-306-41909-2, Plenum Pr). Plenum Pub.

Data Notes Publishing Staff. Aluminum Recycling: Data Notes. LC 83-90732. 30p. 1983. pap. text ed. 4.95 (ISBN 0-911569-40-5, Pub. by Data Notes). Prosperity & Profits.

--Automobile Recycling: Data Notes. LC 83-90735. 30p. pap. text ed. 4.95 (ISBN 0-911569-50-2, Pub. by Data Notes). Prosperity & Profits.

--Equipment Recycling: Data Notes. LC 83-90736. 30p. 1983. pap. text ed. 4.95 (ISBN 0-911569-48-0, Pub. by Data Notes). Prosperity & Profits.

--Furniture Recycling: Data Notes. 30p. 1983. pap. 4.95 (ISBN 0-911569-45-6, Pub. by Data Notes). Prosperity & Profits.

--Kitchen Recycling: Data Notes. LC 83-90733. 35p. 1983. pap. text ed. 9.95 (ISBN 0-911569-51-0, Pub. by Data Notes). Prosperity & Profits.

--Rubber Recycling: Data Notes. 30p. 1983. pap. text ed. 4.95 (ISBN 0-911569-43-X, Pub. by Data Notes). Prosperity & Profits.

--Shelter Recycling: Data Notes. 30p. 1983. pap. text ed. 9.95 (ISBN 0-911569-46-4, Pub. by Data Notes). Prosperity & Profits.

--U. S. Directory of Places to Locate Recyclable Scrap. 60p. 1983. text ed. 19.95 (ISBN 0-911569-14-6, Pub. by Data Notes). Prosperity & Profits.

The Growth Role for Fabrics in Solid Waste Management. 96p. 1980. 50.00 (ISBN 0-318-01477-7, 10035). Indus Fabrics.

Holmes, John R. Practical Waste Management in Developing Countries. LC 84-22070. 1985. write for info. (ISBN 0-471-90641-7). Wiley.

Howell, Fred G., et al, eds. Mineral Cycling in Southeastern Ecosystems: Proceedings. LC 75-33463. (ERDA Symposium Ser.). 920p. 1975. pap. 31.00 (ISBN 0-87079-022-6, CONF-740513); microfiche 4.50 (ISBN 0-87079-276-8, CONF-740513). DOE.

IFSTA Committee. Salvage & Overhaul. 7th ed. Carlson, Gene P. & England, David, eds. (Illus.). 246p. 1985. pap. text ed. 12.00 (ISBN 0-87939-058-1). Intl Fire Serv.

Lester, James P. & Bowman, Ann, eds. The Politics of Hazardous Waste Management. (Duke Press Policy Studies). 318p. (Orig.). 1984. text ed. 32.75 (ISBN 0-8223-0507-0); pap. text ed. 12.75 (ISBN 0-8223-0523-2). Duke.

Marx, Wesley. Waste. LC 79-137805. (Man & His Environment Ser.). pap. 47.30 (ISBN 0-317-11223-6, 2013235). Bks Demand UMI.

Moo-Young, M., et al, eds. Waste Treatment & Utilization: Theory & Practice of Waste Management Two, Proceedings. (Illus.). 587p. 1981. 105.00 (ISBN 0-08-024012-7). Pergamon.

North Eastern Regional Antipollution Conference, 6th, 1975, et al. Energy from Solid Waste Utilization-(Proceedings of Anerac '75 Conference. Barnett, Stanley M. & Sussman, Donald, eds. LC 75-43007. (Illus.). 350p. 1976. pap. 9.95 (ISBN 0-87762-190-X). Technomic.

OECD. Economic Instruments in Solid Waste Management. 193p. (Orig.). 1981. pap. text ed. 8.00x (ISBN 92-64-12227-3). OECD.

Pratt, Alan, ed. Directory of Waste Disposal & Recovery. 232p. 1978. 60.00x (ISBN 0-686-99829-4, Pub. by Graham & Trotman England). State Mutual Bk.

Reid, George H. Boatmen's Guide to Light Salvage. LC 78-27593. (Illus.). 78p. 1979. pap. 6.00 (ISBN 0-87033-248-1). Cornell Maritime.

Sawyer, James W. Automotive Scrap Recycling: Processes, Prices, & Prospects. LC 74-3101. (Resources for the Future Ser.). (Illus.). 160p. 1974. 14.00x (ISBN 0-8018-1620-3). Johns Hopkins.

Technical Association of the Pulp & Paper Industry. Recycling: Reuse of Waste Resources: Presented At the TAPPI Empire State Section, Annual Spring Conference, June 9-10, 1972. LC 74-153924. (Technical Association of the Pulp & Paper Industry CA Report Ser.: No. 45). pap. 27.30 (ISBN 0-317-29317-6, 2022355). Bks Demand UMI.

Use of Agriculture & Industrial Wastes in Low-Cost Construction. pap. 5.00 (ISBN 0-686-94353-8, UN76/4/10, UN). Unipub.

Voight, Randall L. Waste Management & Resources Recovery Information Database. 1979. 1250.00 (ISBN 0-930318-07-2); quarterly updates 125.00 (ISBN 0-686-77211-3). Intl Res Eval.

Waste & Water Management Systems. 52p. 1976. 35.00 (ISBN 0-318-01547-1, 22030). Indus Fabrics.

Wilson, David C. Waste Management: Planning, Evaluation & Technologies. (Illus.). 1981. text ed. 98.00x (ISBN 0-19-859001-6). Oxford U Pr.

Woolfe, Jeremy, ed. Waste Management. viii, 277p. 1981. 44.50 (ISBN 90-277-1338-3, Pub. by Reidel Holland). Kluwer Academic.

SAMOYED (DOG)

see Dogs–Breeds–Samoyed

SAMPLING (STATISTICS)

see also Biometry; Errors, Theory Of; Mathematical Statistics; Numbers, Random; Probabilities; Quality Control

Arkin, Herbert. Sampling Methods for the Auditor: An Advanced Treatment. LC 81-2735. (Illus.). 288p. 1982. 32.95 (ISBN 0-07-002194-5). McGraw.

Barnett, Vic. Elements of Sampling Theory. 152p. 1975. pap. text ed. 12.50x (ISBN 0-8448-0614-5). Crane-Russak Co.

Bean, Judy A. Distribution & Properties of Variance Estimators for Complex Multistage Probability Samples. LC 74-16356. (Data Evaluation & Methods Research Ser. 2: No. 65). 70p. 1975. pap. 1.25 (ISBN 0-8406-0029-1). Natl Ctr Health Stats.

Board, R. G. & Lovelock, D. W., eds. Sampling: Microbiological Monitoring of Environments. (Society for Applied Bacteriology Technical Ser.: No. 7). 1973. 45.00 (ISBN 0-12-108250-4). Acad Pr.

Bracken, Jerome & Schliefer, Arthur. Tables for Normal Sampling with Unknown Variances: The Student Distribution & Economically Optimal Sampling Plans. LC 64-13716. pap. 52.00 (ISBN 0-317-08675-8, 2002196). Bks Demand UMI.

Brewer, K. R. & Hanif, M. Sampling with Unequal Probabilities. (Lecture Notes in Statistics Ser.: Vol. 15). (Illus.). 164p. 1982. pap. 15.00 (ISBN 0-387-90807-2). Springer-Verlag.

Cassel, Claes-Magnus, et al. Foundations of Inference in Survey Sampling. LC 77-5114. (Probability & Mathematical Statistics Ser., Probability & Statistics Section). 192p. 1977. 41.95 (ISBN 0-471-02563-1, Pub. by Wiley-Interscience). Wiley.

Cochran, William G. Sampling Techniques. 3rd ed. LC 77-728. (Probability & Mathematical Statistics Ser.). 428p. 1977. text ed. 38.45 (ISBN 0-471-16240-X). Wiley.

Cornish, et al. Sampling Systems for Process Analyzers. 1981. 99.95 (ISBN 0-408-00261-1). Butterworth.

Daniel, Wayne W., ed. Collecting Sensitive Data by Randomized Response: An Annotated Bibliography. LC 79-12210. (Research Monograph: No. 85). 1979. spiral bdg. 15.00 (ISBN 0-88406-127-2). Ga St U Busn Pub.

Deming, William E. Some Theory of Sampling. 602p. 1984. pap. 14.95 (ISBN 0-486-64684-X). Dover.

Dodge, Harold F. & Romig, Harry G. Sampling Inspection Tables: Single & Double Sampling. 2nd ed. LC 59-6763. (Ser. in Probability & Mathematical Statistics). (Illus.). 224p. 1959. 40.95 (ISBN 0-471-21747-6, Pub. by Wiley-Interscience). Wiley.

Efron, B. The Jackknife, the Bootstrap & Other Resampling Plans. LC 81-84708. (CBMS-NSF Regional Conference Ser.: No. 38). vii, 92p. 1982. pap. text ed. 14.00 (ISBN 0-89871-179-7). Soc Indus Appl Math.

Green, Roger H. Sampling Design & Statistical Methods for Environmental Biologists. LC 78-24422. 257p. 1979. 32.50x (ISBN 0-471-03901-2). Wiley.

Guenther, William C. Scientific Sampling for Statistical Quality Control. LC 77-72042. (Griffin Statistical Monographs: No. 37). 1977. 16.25 (ISBN 0-02-845560-6). Macmillan.

Guy, Dan M. An Introduction to Statistical Sampling in Auditing. LC 80-17279. (Wiley Series in Accounting & Information Systems). 229p. 1981. text ed. 27.45 (ISBN 0-471-04232-3); tchrs manual avail. (ISBN 0-471-09092-1). Wiley.

Hald, A. Statistical Theory of Sampling Inspection by Attributes. (Probability & Mathematical Statistics Ser.). 1981. 84.00 (ISBN 0-12-318350-2). Acad Pr.

Hansen, M. H., et al. Sample Survey Methods & Theory, 2 Vols. LC 53-8112. (Wiley Series in Probability & Mathematical Statistics). 1953. Vol. 1: Methods & Applications. 55.50x (ISBN 0-471-34914-3); Vol. 2: Theory. 51.50x (ISBN 0-471-34947-X, Pub. by Wiley-Interscience). Wiley.

Krewski, D., et al, eds. Current Topics in Survey Sampling. 1981. 35.00 (ISBN 0-12-426280-5). Acad Pr.

McRae, T. W. Statistical Sampling for Audit & Control. LC 73-19329. 279p. 1974. 58.95x (ISBN 0-471-58991-8, Pub. by Wiley-Interscience). Wiley.

Mardia, K. V. Statistics & Directional Data. (Probability & Mathematical Statistics Ser.: Vol. 13). 1972. 67.50 (ISBN 0-12-471150-2). Acad Pr.

Nisselson, Harold, et al. Incomplete Data in Sample Surveys: Treatise, 2 vols. 1983. Vol. 1. 55.00 (ISBN 0-12-363901-8); Vol. 2. 55.00 (ISBN 0-12-363902-6). Acad Pr.

Odeh, Robert E. & Fox, Martin. Sample Size Choice: Charts for Experiments with Linear Models. (Statistics: Textbooks & Monographs Ser.: Vol. 14). 208p. 1975. pap. 45.00 (ISBN 0-8247-7213-X). Dekker.

Patil, G. P. Random Counts in Scientific Work, 3 vols. Incl. Vol. 1. Random Counts in Models & Structures. 276p. 1970 (ISBN 0-271-00114-3); Vol. 2. Random Counts in Biomedical & Social Sciences. 232p. 1970 (ISBN 0-271-00115-1); Vol. 3. Random Counts in Physical Science, Geoscience, & Business. 215p. 1970 (ISBN 0-271-00116-X). LC 73-114351. (Illus.). 22.50x ea. Pa St U Pr.

Sample Surveys of Current Interest, 2 Pts. Twelfth Report. pap. 12.00 (ISBN 0-686-94413-5, UN73/17/5, UN); Thirteenth Report. pap. 15.00 (ISBN 0-686-99363-2, UN79/17/2). Unipub.

Scheaffer, Richard L. & Mendenhall, William. Elementary Survey Sampling. 2nd ed. LC 78-188866. 1979. text ed. write for info. (ISBN 0-87150-384-0, Duxbury Pr). PWS Pubs.

Scott, Chris, et al. Sampling for Monitoring & Evaluation. LC 85-12019. write for info. (ISBN 0-8213-0535-2). World Bank.

Steindl, J. Random Processes & the Growth of Firms: A Study of the Pareto Law. 249p. 1965. text ed. 22.00x (ISBN 0-85264-063-3). Lubrecht & Cramer.

Sudman, Seymour. Applied Sampling. (Quantitative Studies in Social Relations). 1976. 24.00 (ISBN 0-12-675750-X). Acad Pr.

Vanasse, Robert W. Statistical Sampling for Auditing & Accounting Decisions: A Simulation. 2nd ed. 1976. text ed. 13.50 (ISBN 0-07-066851-5). McGraw.

Warwick, Donald P. & Lininger, Charles A. The Sample Survey: Theory & Practice. (Illus.). 384p. 1975. pap. text ed. 20.95 (ISBN 0-07-068395-6). McGraw.

Williams, Bill. A Sampler on Sampling. LC 77-23839. (Probability & Mathematical Statistics Ser.). 254p. 1978. 30.95x (ISBN 0-471-03036-8, Pub. by Wiley-Interscience). Wiley.

Yates, Frank. Sampling Methods for Censuses & Surveys. 4th ed. 450p. 1980. 55.00 (ISBN 0-02-855510-4). Macmillan.

SANCTUARIES, WILDLIFE

see Wildlife Refuges

SAND

see also Particles

Garner, L. E. Sand Resources of Texas Gulf Coast. (Report of Investigations: RI 60). (Illus.). 85p. 1967. 1.50 (ISBN 0-318-03161-2). Bur Econ Geology.

Pettijohn, F. J., et al. Sand & Sandstone. LC 79-168605. 1973. pap. 29.50 (ISBN 0-387-90071-3). Springer-Verlag.

Romanova, Mariya A. Air Survey of Sand Deposits by Spectral Luminance. LC 63-21214. 158p. 1964. 35.00x (ISBN 0-306-10672-8, Consultants). Plenum Pub.

Stide, A. H. Offshore Tidal Sands: Processes & Deposits. (Illus.). 1982. 55.00 (ISBN 0-412-12970-1, NO. 6657, Pub. by Chapman & Hall). Methuen Inc.

SAND DUNES

Bagnold, R. A. Physics of Blown Sand & Desert Dunes. 1941. 43.00 (ISBN 0-412-10270-6, NO. 6020, Pub. by Chapman & Hall). Methuen Inc.

Ranwell, D. S. Ecology of Salt Marshes & Sand Dunes. (Illus.). 1972. 34.00 (ISBN 0-412-10500-4, NO.6305, Pub. by Chapman & Hall). Methuen Inc.

Sand Dune Management in Australia 1983: Perth, Western Australia, November 25-27, 81. 32p. (Orig.). 1983. text ed. 12.00x (ISBN 0-85825-191-4, Pub. by Inst Engineering Australia). Brookfield Pub Co.

Trimble, Stephen A., et al. Great Sand Dunes: The Shape of the Wind. Bullard, Jean & Watkins, Christina, eds. (Popular Ser.: No. 16). (Illus.). 32p. 1975. pap. 1.90 (ISBN 0-911408-34-7). SW Pks Mnmts.

SANDPIPERS

Johnsgard, Paul A. The Plovers, Sandpipers, & Snipes of the World. LC 80-22712. (Illus.). xviii, 541p. 1981. 45.00 (ISBN 0-8032-2553-9). U of Nebr Pr.

SANDSTONE

Berg, Robert R. Reservior Sandstones. (Illus.). 576p. 1986. text ed. 34.95 (ISBN 0-13-774373-4). P-H.

Busch, Daniel A. & Link, David A. Exploration Methods for Sandstone Reservoirs. (Illus.). 300p. 1985. cancelled 49.50x (ISBN 0-87201-237-9). Gulf Pub.

Galloway, W. E., et al. Depositional Framework, Hydrostratigraphy & Uranium Mineralization of the Oakville Sandstone (Miocene), Texas Coastal Plain. (Report of Investigations Ser.: RI 113). (Illus.). 51p. 1982. 2.50 (ISBN 0-318-03245-7). Bur Econ Geology.

McGowen, J. H. & Groat, C. G. Van Horn Sandstone, West Texas: An Alluvial Fan Model for Mineral Exploration. (RI 72). (Illus.). 57p. 1982. Repr. of 1971 ed. 2.50 (ISBN 0-318-03173-6). Bur Econ Geology.

Morton, R. A., et al. Continuity & Internal Properties of Gulf Coast Sandstones & Their Implications for Geopressured Fluid Production. (Report of Investigations Ser.: RI 132). (Illus.). 70p. 1983. 3.00 (ISBN 0-318-03287-2). Bur Econ Geology.

Pettijohn, F. J., et al. Sand & Sandstone. LC 79-168605. 1973. pap. 29.50 (ISBN 0-387-90071-3). Springer-Verlag.

Wallace, David R. Idle Weeds: The Life of a Sandstone Ridge. LC 79-21447. (Illus.). 192p. 1980. 12.95 (ISBN 0-87156-271-5). Sierra.

Jansky, Donald M. World Atlas of Satellites. LC 83-71123. (Telecommunications Ser.). (Illus.). 1983. 48.00 (ISBN 0-89006-117-3). Artech Hse.
King-Hele, D. G., et al. The Rae Table of Earth Satellites Nineteen Fifty-Seven to Nineteen Eighty-Two. 2nd ed. 751p. 1983. 79.95 (ISBN 0-471-87909-6, Pub. by Wiley-Interscience). Wiley.
King-Hele, Desmond. Observing Earth Satellites. LC 82-20083. (Illus.). 184p. 1983. 15.95 (ISBN 0-442-24877-6). Van Nos Reinhold.
Majus, J. & Spaniol, O., eds. Data Networks with Satelites. (Informatik-Fachberichte: Vol. 67). 251p. 1983. pap. 14.50 (ISBN 0-387-12311-3). Springer-Verlag.
Philipps Publishing Staff. The Satellite Directory, 1985. 1100p. 1985. 197.00 (ISBN 0-317-27802-9). Knowledge Indus.
Royal Aircraft Establishment. Table of Earth Satellites, Nineteen Fifty Seven to Nineteen Eighty. 680p. 75.00x (ISBN 0-87196-599-2). Facts on File.
Szebehely, Victor, ed. Dynamics of Planets & Satellites & Theories of Their Motion. (Astrophysics & Space Science Library: No. 72). 1978. lib. bdg. 47.50 (ISBN 90-277-0869-X, Pub. by Martinus Nijhoff Netherlands). Kluwer Academic.
Van Allen, James A. Scientific Uses of Earth Satellites. LC 56-11813. pap. 81.50 (ISBN 0-317-07811-9, 2055659). Bks Demand UMI.
Vinnichenko, N. K. & Gorelik, A. G., eds. Advances in Satellite Meteorology, Vol. 2. Levi, M., tr. from Rus. 148p. 1974. text ed. 39.95x (ISBN 0-470-90836-X). Halsted Pr.

SATELLITES, ARTIFICIAL
see Artificial Satellites

SATURN (PLANET)
Alexander, Arthur F. The Planet Saturn: A History of Observation, Theory & Discovery. 16.50 (ISBN 0-8446-5728-X). Peter Smith.
Brush, Stephen G., ed. Maxwell on Saturn's Rings: James Clerk Maxwell's Unpublished Manuscripts & Letters on the Stability of Saturn's Rings. Everitt, C. W., et al. 240p. 1983. text ed. 27.50x (ISBN 0-262-13190-0). MIT Pr.
Dubois, Marie-Marguerite. Dictionnaire Moderne Saturne: Francais-Anglais, Anglais-Francais. 10th ed. (Fr. & Eng.). 1552p. 1972. 29.95 (ISBN 0-686-57126-6, M-6174). French & Eur.
Gehrels, Tom & Matthews, Mildred S., eds. Saturn. LC 84-2517. 968p. 1984. 37.50x (ISBN 0-8165-0829-1). U of Ariz Pr.
Hunt, Garry & Moore, Patrick. Saturn. (The Rand Mcnally Library of Astronomical Atlases for Amateur & Professional Observers). (Illus.). 96p. 1982. 16.95 (ISBN 0-528-81545-8). Rand.
Washburn, Mark. Distant Encounters: The Exploration of Jupiter & Saturn. LC 82-47659. (Illus.). 288p. 1983. pap. 12.95 (ISBN 0-15-626108-1, Harv). HarBraceJ.

SAUCERS, FLYING
see Flying Saucers

SAULT SAINTE MARIE CANAL
Dickinson, John N. To Build a Canal: Sault Ste. Marie, 1853-1854 & After. LC 80-27693. (Illus.). 222p. 1981. 21.50 (ISBN 0-8142-0309-4). Ohio St U Pr.
Osborn, Chase. The Soo-Scenes in & About Sault Ste. Marie Michigan in 1887. (Illus.). 46p. 1983. pap. 5.00 (ISBN 0-912382-30-9). Black Letter.

SAWMILLS
Business Management Clinic for Sawmill Operators, Sawmill & Plywood Clinic, Portland, Oregon, March 1979. Business Management for Sawmill Operators: Proceedings. LC 79-89293. (A Forest Industries Bk.). (Illus.). 1979. pap. 30.00 (ISBN 0-87930-112-0). Miller Freeman.
Computer Automation for Sawmill Profit. 116p. 1984. 18.00 (ISBN 0-8403-3259-9). Forest Prod.
Electronics in the Sawmill Workshop, 1st, Sawmill & Plywood Clinic, Portland, Oregon, March, 1979. Electronics in the Sawmill: Proceedings. LC 79-53861. (A Forest Industries Bk.). (Illus.). 1979. pap. 35.00 (ISBN 0-87930-113-9). Miller Freeman.
French, Robert D., ed. Sawmill Techniques for Southeast Asia: Proceedings of 2nd Southeast Asia Sawmill Seminar, Manila, 1977, Vol. 2. LC 75-27386. (A Forest Industries Book). (Illus.). 174p. 1978. pap. 35.00 (ISBN 0-87930-105-8). Miller Freeman.
Lhuede, E. P. & Davern, W. A. Noise Levels in Australian Sawmills. 1980. 20.00x (ISBN 0-643-00348-7, Pub. by CSJRO Australia). State Mutual Bk.
Ninth Sawmill Clinic, Portland, Oregon, March, 1979. Modern Sawmill Techniques: Proceedings, Vol. 9. LC 73-88045. (Sawmill Clinic Library: (A Forest Industies Bk)). (Illus.). 1979. pap. 30.00 (ISBN 0-87930-114-7). Miller Freeman.
North American Sawmill & Panel Clinic, Portland, Oregon, March 1980, & Miller Freeman Publications, Inc. Modern Sawmill & Panel Techniques: Vol. 1: Proceedings. LC 80-82375. (A Forest Industries Bk.). (Illus.). 156p. 1980. pap. 45.00 (ISBN 0-87930-086-8). Miller Freeman.
Sawmill Clinic, 5th, Portland, Oregon, March 1975. Modern Sawmill Techniques Vol. 5: Proceedings. White, Vernon S., ed. LC 73-88045. (Sawmill Clinic Library: A Forest Industries Bk.). (Illus.). 400p. 1975. 35.00 (ISBN 0-87930-047-7). Miller Freeman.
Sawmill Clinic, 6th, Portland, Oregon, March 1976. Modern Sawmill Techniques Vol. 6: Proceedings. White, Vernon S., ed. LC 73-88045. (Sawmill Clinic Library: A Forest Industries Bk.). (Illus.). 304p. 1976. 35.00 (ISBN 0-87930-052-3). Miller Freeman.
Small & Medium Sawmills in Developing Countries: A Guide for Their Planning and Establishment. (Forestry Papers: No. 28). (Eng. & Span.). 160p. 1981. pap. 11.75 (ISBN 92-5-101155-9, F2272, FAO). Unipub.
Williston, Ed M. Lumber Manufacturing: The Design & Operation of Sawmills & Planer Mills. LC 76-6718. (A Forest Industries Book). (Illus.). 1976. 32.50 (ISBN 0-87930-054-X). Miller Freeman.
Williston, Ed M., ed. Small Log Sawmills: Profitable Product Selection, Process Design & Operation. LC 80-84893. (A Forest Industries Bk.). (Illus.). 368p. 1981. 52.50 (ISBN 0-87930-091-4); pap. 42.50. Miller Freeman.

SAWS
see also Band Saws; Jig Saws
America Pulpwood Association. Chain Saw Manual. Modified ed. 118p. 1980. pap. text ed. 6.25x (ISBN 0-8134-2133-0). Interstate.
Safe Design & Use of Chain Saws: An ILO Code of Practice. 72p. 1978. pap. 8.75 (ISBN 92-2-101927-6, ILO90, ILO). Unipub.
Scharff, Robert. Getting the Most Out of Your Table Saw. 1981. 9.95 (ISBN 0-8359-2461-0). Reston.
--Your Chain Saw. 1981. 10.95 (ISBN 0-8359-9494-5). Reston.
Thomas, et al. Safe Chain Saw Design. (Illus.). 1983. 39.95 (ISBN 0-938830-02-3). Inst Product.
Williston, Ed M. Saws: Design, Selection, Operation, Maintenance. LC 77-93351. (A Forest Industries Book). (Illus.). 288p. 1978. pap. 32.50 (ISBN 0-87930-073-6). Miller Freeman.

SCAFFOLDING
Grant, Murray. Scaffold Falsework Design to BS 5975. (Viewpoint Publication Ser.). (Illus.). 1982. pap. text ed. 17.95x (ISBN 0-86310-005-8). Scholium Intl.
Rossnagel, W. E. Handbook of Rigging: In Construction & Industrial Operations. 3rd ed. 1964. 42.50 (ISBN 0-07-053940-5). McGraw.

SCALAR FIELD THEORY
Gohberg, I., et al. Matrices & Indefinite Scalar Products. (Operator Theory Ser.: Vol. 8). 302p. 1983. text ed. 39.95 (ISBN 3-7643-1527-X). Birkhauser.

SCALE-INSECTS
Ferris, Gordon F. Atlas of the Scale Insects of North America, 7 vols. in 6. Incl. Vol. 1. The Diaspididae. Pt. 1. 40.00 (ISBN 0-404-08501-6); Vols. 2 & 3. The Diaspididae. Pts. 2 & 3. 75.00 (ISBN 0-404-08502-4); Vol. 4. The Diaspididae. Pt. 4, with Index to Pts. 1-4. 40.00 (ISBN 0-404-08503-2); Vol. 5. The Pseudococcidae. Pt. 1. 40.00 (ISBN 0-404-08504-0); Vol. 6. The Pseudococcidae. Pt. 2, with Index to Pts. 1-2. 40.00 (ISBN 0-404-08505-9); Vol. 7. The Families Aclerdidae, Asterolecaniidae Conchaspididae, Dactylopiidae & Lacciferidae, with Index. 40.00 (ISBN 0-404-08506-7). (Illus.). Repr. of 1955 ed. Set. 275.00 (ISBN 0-404-08500-8). AMS Pr.

SCALLOPS
Broon, M. J. Synopsis of Biological Data on Scallops: Chlamys (Aequipecten) Opercularis (Linaeus) Argopecten Irradians (Lamarck) Argopecten Gibbus (Linnaeus) (Fisheries Synopses: No. 114). (Illus.). 44p. 1976. pap. 7.50 (ISBN 92-5-100213-4, F846, FAO). Unipub.
Fishing News Books Ltd. Staff, ed. Scallops & the Diver-Fisherman. 144p. 1981. 40.00x (ISBN 0-85238-114-X, Pub. by Fishing News England). State Mutual Bk.
Scallop & Queen Fisheries in the British Isles. 141p. 1983. pap. text ed. 16.75 (ISBN 0-85238-128-X, FN104, FNB). Unipub.

SCANDIUM
Borisenko, Leonid F. Scandium: Its Geochemistry & Mineralogy. LC 62-15551. pap. 20.50 (ISBN 0-317-10633-3, 2003358). Bks Demand UMI.
Horovitz, C. T., et al. Scandium: Its Occurence, Chemistry, Physics, Metallurgy, Biology & Technology. 1975. 95.00 (ISBN 0-12-355850-6). Acad Pr.

SCARABAEOIDEA
Ritcher, Paul O. White Grubs & Their Allies. LC 66-63008. (Studies in Entomology Ser: No. 4). (Illus.). 216p. 1966. 19.95x (ISBN 0-87071-054-0). Oreg St U Pr.

SCATTERING (MATHEMATICS)
Baumgartel, Hellmut & Wollenberg, Manfred. Mathematical Scattering Theory. (Operator Theory: Advances & Applications, Vol. 9). 1983. text ed. 44.95 (ISBN 3-7643-1519-9). Birkhauser.
Bednar, J. Bee, et al, eds. Conference on Inverse Scattering: Theory & Application. LC 83-51381. x, 290p. 1983. text ed. 26.50 (ISBN 0-89871-190-8). Soc Indus-Appl Math.

SCATTERING (PHYSICS)
see also Potential Scattering; S-Matrix Theory
Agranovich, Z. S. & Marchenko, V. A. Inverse Problem of Scattering Theory. Seckler, B. D., tr. (Russian Monographs and Texts on the Physical Sciences Ser.). 304p. 1963. 80.95 (ISBN 0-677-20010-2). Gordon.
AIP Conference. Pi-Pi Scattering-1973: AIP Conference Proceedings, No. 13. Williams, D. K. & Hagopian, V., eds. LC 73-81704. 361p. 1973. 14.00 (ISBN 0-88318-112-6). Am Inst Physics.
AIP Conference Proceedings No. 89, Argonne National Laboratory, 1981. Neutron Scattering: Proceedings. Faber, John, Jr., ed. LC 82-73094. 397p. 1982. lib. bdg. 35.50 (ISBN 0-88318-188-6). Am Inst Physics.
Austin, S. M., ed. The Two-Body Force in Nuclei. Crawley, G. M. LC 72-76009. 390p. 1972. 55.00x (ISBN 0-306-30598-4, Plenum Pr). Plenum Pub.
Barut, Asim O., ed. Scattering Theory: Aspects of Scattering Processes in Atomic, Nuclear, & Particle Physics. 440p. 1969. 119.25 (ISBN 0-677-12730-8). Gordon.
Bayvel, L. P. & Jones, A. R. Electromagnetic Scattering & Its Applications. (Illus.). 1981. 63.00 (ISBN 0-85334-955-X, Pub. by Elsevier Applied Sci England). Elsevier.
Bendow, B. & Langeler, B. Polariton - Mediated Light Scattering & Electronic Structure of Noble Metals. (Springer Tracts in Modern Physics Ser.: Vol. 82). (Illus.). 1978. 33.00 (ISBN 0-387-08814-8). Springer-Verlag.
Bransden, B. H. Atomic Collision Theory. 2nd ed. (Illus.). 500p. 1970. text ed. 39.95 (ISBN 0-8053-1181-5). Benjamin-Cummings.
Brink, D. M. Semi-Classical Methods for Nucleus-Nucleus Scattering. (Cambridge Monographs on Mathematical Physics). 300p. Date not set. price not set. (ISBN 0-521-23940-0). Cambridge U Pr.
Burke, P. G. & Moiseiwitsch, B. L., eds. Atomic Processes & Applications. 1976. 76.75 (ISBN 0-7204-0444-4, North-Holland). Elsevier.
Chen, Sow-Hsin, et al, eds. Scattering Techniques Applied to Supramolecular & Non-Equilibrium Systems. LC 81-13767. (NATO ASI Series B, Physics: Vol. 73). 942p. 1981. text ed. 125.00x (ISBN 0-306-40828-7, Plenum Pr). Plenum Pub.
Chow, P. L., et al, eds. Multiple Scattering & Waves in Random Media. 286p. 1981. 42.75 (ISBN 0-444-86280-3, North-Holland). Elsevier.
Colton, David & Kress, Rainer. Integral Equation Methods in Scattering Theory. LC 82-21870. (Pure & Applied Mathematics Ser.). 271p. 1983. 43.50x (ISBN 0-471-86420-X, Pub. by Wiley-Interscience). Wiley.
Comper, W. D., et al. Solar Energy Phase Transfer Catalysis Transport Processes. (Advances in Polymer Sciences: Vol. 55). (Illus.). 170p. 1984. 41.00 (ISBN 0-387-12592-2). Springer-Verlag.
DaSanto, J. A., ed. Mathematical Methods & Applications of Scattering Theory: Proceedings. (Lecture Notes in Physics Ser.: Vol. 130). 331p. 1980. pap. 26.00 (ISBN 0-387-10023-7). Springer-Verlag.
Eu, B. C. Semiclassical Theories of Molecular Scattering. (Springer Series in Chemical Physics: Vol. 26). (Illus.). 240p. 1984. 32.00 (ISBN 0-387-12410-1). Springer-Verlag.
Geltman, Sydney. Topics in Atomic Collision Theory. (Pure & Applied Physics Ser: Vol. 32). 1969. 67.50 (ISBN 0-12-279650-0). Acad Pr.
Goodman, Frank O & Wachman, Harold Y. Dynamics of Gas-Surface Scattering. 1976. 76.00 (ISBN 0-12-290450-8). Acad Pr.
Hamlin, R. C., ed. New Crystallographic Detectors & the Workshop on Crystallographic Detectors at the Nat. Bureau of Standards, Wash. D. C. (Transactions of the American Crystallographic Association Ser.: Vol. 18). 179p. 1982. pap. 15.00 (ISBN 0-686-45036-1). Polycrystal Bk Serv.
Henderson, Douglas, ed. Theoretical Chemistry: Theory of Scattering: Papers in Honor of Henry Eyring, Vol. 6B. (Serial Publications). 1981. 58.50 (ISBN 0-12-681907-6). Acad Pr.
Hoehler, G. Elastic & Charge Exchange: Scattering of Elementary Particles, Subvol. B: Pion Nucleon Scattering. (Landolt-Boernstein Ser.: Group 1, Vol. 9, Suppl. B, Part 1). (Illus.). 420p. 1982. 226.60 (ISBN 0-387-09694-9). Springer-Verlag.
Kerker, Milton. Scattering of Light & Other Electromagnetic Radiation. (Physical Chemistry Ser.: Vol. 16). 1969. 94.50 (ISBN 0-12-404550-2). Acad Pr.
Kocinski, J. & Wojtczak, L. Critical Scattering Theory: An Introduction. (Phase Transition Phenomena Ser.: Vol. 1). 228p. 1979. 57.50 (ISBN 0-444-99795-4). Elsevier.
Lax, Peter D. & Phillips, Ralph S. Scattering Theory. (Pure & Applied Mathematics Ser.,: Vol. 26). 1967. 66.00 (ISBN 0-12-440050-7). Acad Pr.
Lenoble, Jacqueline, ed. Radiative Transfer in Scattering & Absorbing Atmospheres: Standard Computational Procedures. 1985. write for info. (ISBN 0-937194-05-0). A Deepak Pub.
Martin, A. & Cheung, F. Analyticity Properties & Bounds of Scattering Amplitudes. (Documents on Modern Physics Ser.). 142p. 1970. 42.95 (ISBN 0-677-02290-5). Gordon.
Newton, R. G. Scattering Theory of Waves & Particles. 2nd ed. (Texts & Monographs in Physics). 800p. 1982. 51.00 (ISBN 0-387-10950-1). Springer-Verlag.
Niekisch, E. A. Springer Tracts in Modern Physics, Vol. 61. Hoehler, G., ed. LC 25-9130. (Illus.). 200p. 1972. 44.30 (ISBN 0-387-05739-0). Springer-Verlag.
Nikolic, M., ed. Analysis of Scattering & Decay. (Documents on Modern Physics Ser.). 344p. (Orig.). 1968. 66.00x (ISBN 0-677-12810-X). Gordon.
Novikov, S., et al. Theory of Solitons: The Inverse Scattering Method. Zakharov, V. E., ed. (Contemporary Soviet Mathematics Ser.). 272p. 1984. 49.50x (ISBN 0-306-10977-8, Plenum Pr). Plenum Pub.
Panter, Philip F. Communication Systems Design: Line-of-Sight & Tropo-Scatter Systems. LC 82-7. 1982. Repr. of 1972 ed. 37.50 (ISBN 0-89874-360-5). Krieger.
Reed, Michael & Simon, Barry. Methods of Modern Mathematical Physics, 4 vols. Incl. Vol. 1. Functional Analysis. 1972; Vol. 2. Fourier Analysis Self-Adjointness. 1975. 39.50 (ISBN 0-12-585002-6); Vol. 3. Scattering Theory. 1979. 46.50 (ISBN 0-12-585003-4); Vol. 4. 1978. 39.50 (ISBN 0-12-585004-2). Acad Pr.
Rodberg, L. S. & Thaler, R. M. Introduction to the Quantum Theory of Scattering. (Pure & Applied Physics: Vol. 26). 1967. 45.00 (ISBN 0-12-591950-6). Acad Pr.
Ross, Marc. Quantum Scattering Theory: Selected Papers. LC 63-16622. pap. 75.00 (ISBN 0-317-08058-X, 2055227). Bks Demand UMI.
Rowell, R. L. & Stein, R. S., eds. Electromagnetic Scattering. 862p. 1967. 163.25 (ISBN 0-677-11920-8). Gordon.
Schopper, H. Elastic & Charge Exchange Scattering of Elementary Particles: Nucleon Nucleon & Kaon Nucleon Scattering. (Landolt-Boernstein: Group I, Vol. 9). (Illus.). 750p. 1980. 273.00 (ISBN 0-387-09382-6). Springer-Verlag.
Schopper, H., ed. Elastic & Charge Exchange Scattering of Elementary Particles: Pion Nucleon Scattering-Methods & Results of Phenomenological Analyses. (Landolt-Boernstein-New Series. Group I: Vol. 9, Subvol. B, Pt. 2). (Illus.). 610p. 1983. 396.90 (ISBN 0-387-11282-0). Springer-Verlag.
Simon, Barry. Quantum Mechanics for Hamiltonians Defined As Quadratic Forms. LC 73-146648. (Princeton Series in Physics). 1971. 26.00x (ISBN 0-691-08090-9). Princeton U Pr.
Sitenko, A. G. Lectures in Scattering Theory. Shepherd, P. J., ed. & tr. 280p. 1971. text ed. 41.00 (ISBN 0-08-016574-5). Pergamon.
Squires, G. L. Introduction to the Theory of Thermal Neutron Scattering. LC 77-85682. (Illus.). 1978. 67.50 (ISBN 0-521-21884-5). Cambridge U Pr.
Steklov Institute of Mathematics, Academy of Sciences, U S S R, No. 97. Milne Problem with Anisotropic Scattering: Proceedings. Maslennikov, M. Y., ed. (Proceedings of the Steklov Institute of Mathematics: No. 97). 1969. 43.00 (ISBN 0-8218-1897-X, STEKLO-97). Am Math.
Van De Hulst, H. C. Multiple Light Scattering: Tables, Formulas & Applications, Vol.1. LC 79-51687. 1980. 41.50 (ISBN 0-12-710701-0). Acad Pr.
Wilcox, C. H. Scattering Theory for the d'Alembert Wave Equation in Exterior Domains. (Lecture Notes in Mathematics Ser.: Vol. 442). iii, 184p. 1975. pap. 14.00 (ISBN 0-387-07144-X). Springer-Verlag.

SCATTERING MATRIX
see S-Matrix Theory

SCATTERING OF LIGHT
see Light-Scattering

SCATTERING OF PARTICLES
see Scattering (Physics)
SCELOPORUS
Blair, W. Frank. The Rusty Lizard: A Population Study. LC 59-8122. pap. 47.80 (ISBN 0-317-29262-5, 2055521). Bks Demand UMI.
SCHNAUZERS
see Dogs–Breeds–Schnauzer
SCHOOL LUNCHROOMS, CAFETERIAS, ETC.
Deacon, Gene E. Kid Tested Menus with Kitchen & Lunchroom Techniques for Day Care Centers. LC 81-90547. (Illus.). 120p. (Orig.). 1981. pap. 10.00 (ISBN 0-941790-01-0). Gold Crest.
Dow, Clista. Lunchroom Waste: A Study of "How Much & How Come". Smith, Linda H., ed. 1978. pap. 4.95 (ISBN 0-936386-04-5). Creative Learning.
Rudman, Jack. School Lunch Manager. (Career Examination Ser.: C-703). (Cloth bdg. avail. on request). pap. 10.00 (ISBN 0-8373-0703-1). Natl Learning.
SCIENCE
see also Astronomy; Bacteriology; Biology; Botany; Chemistry; Crystallography; Geology; Life Sciences; Mathematics; Meteorology; Mineralogy; Natural History; Paleontology; Petrology; Physics; Physiology; Space Sciences; Television in Science; Zoology
also headings beginning with the word Scientific
Abbot, Charles G. Adventures in the World of Science. 1958. 8.50 (ISBN 0-8183-0226-7). Pub Aff Pr.
Abdel-Malek, Anouar & Blue, Gregory, eds. Science & Technology in the Transformation of the World. 497p. 1982. 36.25 (ISBN 92-808-0339-5, TUNU193, UNU). Unipub.
Ackerson, et al. Gateways to Science. 4th ed. 1982. write for info. laboratory bks. McGraw.
Ailes, Catherine P. & Rushing, Francis W. The Science Race: Training & Utilization of Scientists & Engineers, U. S. & U. S. S. R. LC 81-17516. 280p. 1982. 28.50x (ISBN 0-8448-1407-5). Crane-Russak Co.
Aristotelian Society For The Systematic Study Of Philosophy. Problems of Science & Philosophy: Proceedings, Supplementary Vol. 2. 15.00 (ISBN 0-384-47981-2); pap. 10.00 (ISBN 0-384-47982-0). Johnson Repr.
Asimov, Isaac. Asimov's New Guide to Science. rev. ed. LC 83-46093. (Illus.). 940p. 1984. 29.95 (ISBN 0-465-00473-3). Basic.
--Life & Time. LC 78-62644. 1978. 9.95 (ISBN 0-385-14645-0). Doubleday.
--The Road to Infinity. 256p. 1981. pap. 2.75 (ISBN 0-380-54155-6, 54155-6, Discus). Avon.
--View from a Height. 1975. pap. 2.25 (ISBN 0-380-00356-2, 45336-3, Discus). Avon.
Atkins, Kenneth R., et al. Essentials of Physical Science. LC 77-12507. 546p. 1978. text ed. 35.95 (ISBN 0-471-03617-X); study guide 13.45 (ISBN 0-471-03551-3); avail. tchrs. manual (ISBN 0-471-03552-1). Wiley.
Augros, Robert M. & Staeuciu, George. The New Story of Science. LC 84-43228. 1984. pap. 6.95 (ISBN 0-89526-833-7). Regnery Gateway.
Barmark, Jan, ed. Perspectives in Metascience. (Regiae Societatis-Interdisciplinaria: No. 2). 199p. 1980. text ed. 21.50x (ISBN 91-85252-21-2). Humanities.
Barnes, Barry. About Science. 208p. 1985. 24.95x (ISBN 0-631-14157-X); pap. 8.95 (ISBN 0-631-14158-8). Basil Blackwell.
Barnes, Barry & Edge, David, eds. Science in Context: Readings in the Sociology of Science. 384p. (Orig.). 1982. pap. text ed. 10.95x (ISBN 0-262-52076-1). MIT Pr.
Barton, Ralph. Science in Rhyme Without Reason. 59.95 (ISBN 0-8490-1000-4). Gordon Pr.
Bartone, Mary R. Television in Medicine & Science: Subject Analysis & Research Guide with Bibliography. LC 83-45546. 152p. 1984. 29.95 (ISBN 0-88164-088-3); pap. 21.95 (ISBN 0-88164-089-1). ABBE Pubs Assn.
Bavink, Bernhard. The Natural Sciences. LC 74-26248. (History, Philosophy & Sociology of Science Ser). 1975. Repr. of 1932 ed. 53.00x (ISBN 0-405-06578-7). Ayer Co Pubs.
Belloli, Robert C. Contemporary Physical Science: Our Impact on Our World. (Illus.). 1978. write for info. (ISBN 0-02-308070-1). Macmillan.
Bernstein, Jeremy. Experiencing Science. LC 77-20415. 1978. 12.50 (ISBN 0-465-02185-9). Basic.
Blackwelder, Sheila K. Science for All Seasons. (Human Science Ser.). (Illus.). 272p. 1980. 11.95 (ISBN 0-13-795286-4, Spec); pap. 5.95 (ISBN 0-13-795278-3). P-H.
Blackwell, Richard J., compiled by. A Bibliography of the Philosophy of Science; Nineteen Forty-Five to Nineteen Eighty-One. LC 83-5671. xvii, 585p. 1983. lib. bdg. 75.00 (ISBN 0-313-23124-9, BLB/). Greenwood.
Blinn, Walter C., ed. Search for Explanation: Studies in Natural Science Vol. 3. (Illus.). 409p. 1969. text ed. 9.75x (ISBN 0-87013-132-X). Mich St U Pr.
Bliven, Bruce. Men Who Make the Future. facs. ed. LC 70-111816. (Essay Index Reprint Ser). 1942. 21.50 (ISBN 0-8369-1643-3). Ayer Co Pubs.
Boas, George. Challenge of Science. LC 65-23907. (John Danz Lecture Ser.). 116p. 1965. 10.00x (ISBN 0-295-73735-2). U of Wash Pr.
Bodington, Stephen. Science & Social Action. 192p. 1980. 14.00x (ISBN 0-8052-8027-8, Pub. by Allison & Busby England); pap. 7.95 (ISBN 0-8052-8026-X, Pub. by Allison & Busby England). Schocken.
Boltzmann, Ludwig. Wissenschaftliche Abhandlungen, 3 Vols. Hasenohrl, Fritz, ed. LC 66-26524. (Ger). 1969. Set. 99.50 (ISBN 0-8284-0215-9). Chelsea Pub.
Booth, Verne H. & Bloom, Mortimer. Physical Science: A Study of Matter & Energy. 3rd ed. (Illus.). 800p. 1972. text ed. write for info. (ISBN 0-02-312280-3, 31228). Macmillan.
Box, G. E. & Leonard, Chien-Fu-Wu, eds. Scientific Inference: Data Analysis & Robustiness (Symposium) LC 82-22755. 1983. 24.00 (ISBN 0-12-121160-6). Acad Pr.
Brannigan, Augustine. The Social Basis of Scientific Discoveries. 228p. 1981. 29.95 (ISBN 0-521-23695-9); pap. 11.95 (ISBN 0-521-28163-6). Cambridge U Pr.
Bronwell, Arthur B. Science & Technology in the World of the Future. LC 74-114914. 1970. 22.50 (ISBN 0-471-10594-5, Pub. by Wiley). Krieger.
Brooks, Bearl. Beginning Science. (Science Ser.). 24p. 1979. 5.00 (ISBN 0-8209-0139-3, S-1). ESP.
Bryson, Lyman, ed. Science & Freedom. facsimile ed. LC 71-156620. (Essay Index Reprint Ser). Repr. of 1947 ed. 18.00 (ISBN 0-8369-2385-5). Ayer Co Pubs.
Bueche, Fred. Physical Science. LC 73-182927. (Illus.). 1972. 21.95x (ISBN 0-87901-019-3). Worth.
Building Basic Skills in Science. (Building Basic Skills Ser.). 158p. 1982. pap. 5.88 (ISBN 0-8092-5973-7). Contemp Bks.
Burke, John G. The Uses of Science in the Age of Newton. LC 83-1223. (UCLA Clark Library Professorship: No. 8). 226p. 1984. text ed. 22.50x (ISBN 0-520-04970-5). U of Cal Pr.
Burkett, J., ed. Directory of Scientific Directories: A World Guide to Scientific Directories Including Medicine, Agriculture, Engineering, Manufacturing, & Industrial Directories. 3rd ed. LC 79-40288. 649p. 95.00x (ISBN 0-582-90150-2, Pub. by Longman). Gale.
Busch, Lawrence, ed. Science & Agricultural Development. LC 81-65005. 198p. 1981. text ed. 31.50x (ISBN 0-86598-022-5). Allanheld.
Bush, Vannevar. Endless Horizons. LC 74-26253. (History, Philosophy & Sociology of Science Ser). 1975. Repr. 19.00x (ISBN 0-405-06581-7). Ayer Co Pubs.
Butler, Samuel. Essays on Life, Art & Science. Streatfeild, R. A., ed. LC 77-95333. 1970. Repr. of 1908 ed. 26.00 (ISBN 0-8046-1345-1, Pub. by Kennikat). Assoc Faculty Pr.
Buzzati-Traverso, Adriano A. The Scientific Enterprise, Today & Tomorrow. (Illus.). 439p. 1978. 59.50 (ISBN 92-3-101268-1, U865, UNESCO). Unipub.
Cain, Sandra G. & Evans, Jack M. Sciencing: An Involvement Approach to Elementary Science Methods. 1979. 17.95 (ISBN 0-675-08364-8). Merrill.
Callister, W. D. Materials Science & Engineering: An Introduction. 602p. 1985. 34.95 (ISBN 0-471-08145-0). Wiley.
Campbell, Norman R. What Is Science? 1921. pap. 4.50 (ISBN 0-486-60043-2). Dover.
Carona, Philip. Basic Science Skills. (Pre-GED Basic Skills Ser.). 1979. pap. 5.95 (ISBN 0-07-010138-8). McGraw.
--Power Skills in Science. 1979. pap. 4.95 (ISBN 0-07-010134-5). McGraw.
Caullery, Maurice. Universities & Scientific Life in the United States. LC 74-26257. (History, Philosophy & Sociology of Science Ser). 1975. Repr. of 1922 ed. 24.50x (ISBN 0-405-06585-X). Ayer Co Pubs.
Cavalieri, Liebe F. The Double-Edged Helix: Genetic Engineering in the Real World. Anshen, Ruth N., ed. LC 84-17890. (Convergence Ser.). 208p. 1984. pap. 9.95 (ISBN 0-03-000998-7). Praeger.
Chalmers, A. F. What Is This Thing Called Science? An Assessment of the Nature & Status of Science & Its Methods. 1976. pap. text ed. 12.25x (ISBN 0-7022-1341-1). Humanities.
Chigier, Norman A. & Stern, Edward A., eds. Collective Phenomena & the Applications of Physics to Other Fields of Science. 491p. 1976. pap. text ed. 25.00x (ISBN 0-916088-01-4). Brain Res.
Ciencia Interamericana: Vol. 17, Nos. 3-4. (Edicion en homenaje al Bicentenario de los Estados Unidos). 1977. pap. 1.00 (ISBN 0-685-80053-9). OAS.
Cohen, I. Bernard. The Newtonian Revolution: With Illustrations of the Transformation of Scientific Ideas. LC 79-18637. (Illus.). 404p. 1983. pap. 17.95 (ISBN 0-521-27380-3). Cambridge U Pr.
Cohn, Alfred E. Medicine, Science & Art. (Essay Index Reprint Ser.). 1982. Repr. of 1931 ed. lib. bdg. 15.50 (ISBN 0-8290-0840-3). Irvington.
Coker, William C., ed. Studies in Science. LC 77-39098. (Essay Index Reprint Ser.). (University of North Carolina sesquicentennial publications). Repr. of 1946 ed. 40.00 (ISBN 0-8369-2683-8). Ayer Co Pubs.
Conference On The Scientific Spirit And Democratic Faith - 3rd. Science for Democracy. facs. ed. LC 70-121459. (Essay Index Reprint Ser.). 1946. 18.00 (ISBN 0-8369-1793-6). Ayer Co Pubs.
Conference On The Scientific Spirit And Democratic Faith-1st-New York-1943. Scientific Spirit & Democratic Faith. facs. ed. LC 72-121457. (Essay Index Reprint Ser). 1944. 14.00 (ISBN 0-8369-1872-X). Ayer Co Pubs.
Congressional Quarterly Inc. Advances in Science. LC 78-25601. (Editorial Research Reports). 188p. 1979. pap. 7.95 (ISBN 0-87187-142-4). Congr Quarterly.
Cook, Thomas & Campbell, Donald T. Quasi-Experimentation. 1979. pap. 22.95 (ISBN 0-395-30790-2). HM.
Cooper, Theodore W. Functionality: A Revelation for Science. LC 83-51463. (Illus.). 562p. 1984. tchr's ed 55.00 (ISBN 0-915428-05-9). Technicon Pubs.
Corcoran, Eileen L. Meeting Basic Competencies in Practical Science & Health: A Workstudy Book to Improve Daily Living Skills. (Illus.). 1985. 3.00x (ISBN 0-88323-210-3, 237); tchr's. answer key avail. (ISBN 0-88323-154-9, 245). Richards Pub.
Crowther, James G. Founders of British Science: John Wilkins, Robert Boyle, John Ray, Christopher Wren, Robert Hooke, Isaac Newton. LC 82-2954. (Illus.). xii, 296p. 1982. Repr. of 1960 ed. lib. bdg. 42.50x (ISBN 0-313-23540-6, CRFO). GreenWood.
Dana, Edward S., et al, eds. A Century of Science in America. LC 72-94344. (The American Scientific Community, 1790-1920 Ser.). 1973. Repr. of 1918 ed. lib. bdg. 34.00 (ISBN 0-8420-1654-6). Scholarly Res Inc.
Daniels, George H., ed. Nineteenth-Century American Science: A Reappraisal. LC 79-186547. 292p. 1972. text ed. 17.95x (ISBN 0-8101-0381-8). Northwestern U Pr.
Dempsey, Michael W., ed. Illustrated Fact Book of Science. LC 82-16412. (Illus.). 236p. 1983. 9.95 (ISBN 0-668-05729-7, 5729). Arco.
Dietz, David. Science in Hawaii. (Illus.). 1968. 0.50 (ISBN 0-941200-03-5). Aquarius.
Dixon, Robert. Physical Science: A Dynamic Approach. (Illus.). 1979. 30.95 (ISBN 0-13-669820-4). P-H.
Dixon, Robert T. Physical Science: A Dynamic Approach. 2nd ed. (Illus.). 480p. 1986. text ed. 29.95 (ISBN 0-13-669847-6). P-H.
Dotterer, Ray H. Philosophy by Way of the Sciences: An Introductory Textbook. (Select Bibliographies Reprint Ser). Repr. of 1929 ed. 26.50 (ISBN 0-8369-6642-2). Ayer Co Pubs.
Durbin, Paul T., ed. A Guide to the Culture of Science, Technology, & Medicine. 784p. 1984. 19.95x (ISBN 0-02-907890-3). Free pr.
Earman, John, ed. Testing Scientific Theories. (Minnesota Studies in the Philosophy of Science: Vol. X). (Illus.). 384p. 1984. 39.50x (ISBN 0-8166-1158-0); pap. 16.95x (ISBN 0-8166-1159-9). U of Minn Pr.
Eddington, Arthur S. Science & the Unseen World. 1979. Repr. of 1929 ed. lib. bdg. 10.00 (ISBN 0-8414-4004-2). Folcroft.
Eisemon, Thomas O. The Science Profession in the Third World: Studies from India & Kenya. Altbach, Philip G., ed. LC 82-7662. (Special Studies in Comparative Education). 186p. 1982. 23.95 (ISBN 0-03-062023-6). Praeger.
Elkana, Yehuda, et al, eds. Toward a Metric of Science: The Advent of Science Indicators. LC 77-24513. (Science, Culture & Society Ser.). 1978. 38.50x (ISBN 0-471-98435-3, Pub. by Wiley-Interscience). Wiley.
Esbozo del Desarrollo Industrial de America Latina y de Sus Principales Implicaciones Sobre el Sistema Cientifico y Tecnologico. (Estudios Sobre el Desarrollo Cientifico y Tecnologico: No. 14). (Span.). 1973. pap. 1.00 (ISBN 0-8270-5945-0). OAS.
Esquema de Analisis De los Recursos Humanos Cientifico-Tecnologicos. (Estudios Sobre el Desarrollo Cientifico y Tecnologico: No. 8). (Span.). 1972. pap. 1.00 (ISBN 0-8270-5940-X). OAS.
European Sources of Science & Technology. 5th ed. 500p. 1981. 190.00x (ISBN 0-582-90108-1, Pub. by Longman). Gale.
Falls, William R. Investigations in the College Physical Sciences. 1977. pap. text ed. 10.95 (ISBN 0-8403-1752-2). Kendall-Hunt.
Faulkenstein, Dezmon A. Faulkenstein's Theories Are Loose on the Earth. 1982. 7.95 (ISBN 0-533-04690-4). Vantage.
Fetzer, James. Scientific Knowledge. 1982. lib. bdg. 49.50 (ISBN 90-277-1335-9, Pub. by Reidel Netherlands); pap. text ed. 14.95 (ISBN 90-277-1336-7, Pub. by Reidel Holland). Kluwer Academic.
The Freedom of Science: An Original Anthology. LC 74-25150. (History, Philosophy & Sociology of Science Ser.). 1975. Repr. 15.00x (ISBN 0-405-06636-8). Ayer Co Pubs.
Fuller, R. Buckminster. Operating Manual for Spaceship Earth. 1978. pap. 8.95 (ISBN 0-525-47433-1, 0869-260). Dutton.
Futuyma, Douglas. Science On Trial. 1982. 16.00 (ISBN 0-394-52371-7); pap. 7.95 (ISBN 0-394-70679-X). Pantheon.
Gabel, Dorothy. Introductory Science Skills. 470p. (Orig.). 1984. pap. text ed. 12.95x (ISBN 0-88133-122-8). Waveland Pr.
Garbedian, H. Gordon. Major Mysteries of Science. 306p. 1981. Repr. of 1933 ed. lib. bdg. 40.00 (ISBN 0-89984-240-2). Century Bookbindery.
Gardner, Martin. Fads & Fallacies. LC 57-14907. lib. bdg. 13.50x (ISBN 0-88307-102-9). Gannon.
--Fads & Fallacies in the Name of Science. 2nd ed. Orig. Title: In the Name of Science. 363p. 1957. pap. 4.95 (ISBN 0-486-20394-8). Dover.
--Science: Good, Bad & Bogus. 432p. 1983. pap. 3.95 (ISBN 0-380-61754-4, 61754-4, Discus). Avon.
General Science Index: Vol. 1-5, 1978-79 to 1980-83. LC 79-2592. (Sold on service basis). 1980. write for info. Wilson.
Gibbons, Michael & Gummett, Philip, eds. Science, Technology & Society Today. LC 83-20639. 192p. 1984. 16.00 (ISBN 0-7190-1090-X, Pub. by Manchester Univ Pr); pap. 7.50 (ISBN 0-7190-0878-6). Longwood Pub Group.
Gibson, William C., compiled by. Excitement & Fascination of Science, Vol. 1. 1965. text ed. 6.50 (ISBN 0-8243-1602-9). Annual Reviews.
--The Excitement & Fascination of Science, Vol. 2. LC 65-29005. 1978. text ed. 12.00 (ISBN 0-8243-2601-6); pap. text ed. 10.00 (ISBN 0-8243-2602-4). Annual Reviews.
Gjertsen, Derek. Classics of Science: A Study of Twelve Enduring Scientific Works. LC 83-27539. 384p. 1984. text ed. 24.95x (ISBN 0-936508-09-4); pap. text ed. 12.95x (ISBN 0-936508-12-4). Barber Pr.
Goldberg, Edward D., ed. North Sea Science: Papers Presented at the NATO Science Committee Conference, November 1971. (Illus.). 420p. 1973. 40.00x (ISBN 0-262-07056-1). MIT Pr.
Goldstein, Martin & Goldstein, Inge F. How We Know: An Exploration of the Scientific Process. LC 77-20510. (Illus.). 375p. 1978. 18.95x (ISBN 0-306-31069-4, Plenum Pr). Plenum Pub.
Goran, Morris. Can Science Be Saved? LC 81-121. 94p. 1981. perfect bound 9.95 (ISBN 0-88247-593-2). R & E Pubs.
Grandy, Richard E., ed. Theories & Observation in Science. vii, 184p. 1980. lib. bdg. 24.00x (ISBN 0-917930-39-8); pap. 8.50x (ISBN 0-917930-19-3). Ridgeview.
Gray, George W. Science at War. LC 72-4531. (Essay Index Reprint Ser.). Repr. of 1943 ed. 20.00 (ISBN 0-8369-2944-6). Ayer Co Pubs.
Gruenfeld, Joseph. Science & Values. 210p. (Orig.). 1973. pap. 22.00x (ISBN 90-6032-016-6, Pub. by B R Gruener). Benjamins North AM.
Gruner, Rolf. Theory & Power: On the Character of Modern Science. 1977. pap. text ed. 17.75x (ISBN 90-6032-087-5). Humanities.
Guide to American Scientific & Technical Directories. 2nd ed. 350p. 1975. 25.00 (ISBN 0-686-62442-4). B Klein Pubns.
Hacking, Ian. Representing & Intervening: Introductory Topics in the Philosophy of Natural Science. LC 83-5132. 272p. 1983. 39.50 (ISBN 0-521-23829-3); pap. 12.95 (ISBN 0-521-28246-2). Cambridge U Pr.
Hagerstrand, T., ed. The Identification of Progress in Learning. (Illus.). 200p. 1985. 39.50 (ISBN 0-521-30087-8). Cambridge U Pr.
Halpern, Richard P. Physical Science. (Illus.). 313p. (Orig.). 1983. pap. 5.95 (ISBN 0-06-460195-1, COS CO 195). B&N NY.
Hanson, Norwood R. Perception & Discovery: An Introduction to Scientific Inquiry. Humphreys, Willard C., ed. LC 75-95161. (Illus.). 435p. 1969. pap. text ed. 12.00x (ISBN 0-87735-510-X). Freeman Cooper.
Harrington, John W. Discovering Science. LC 80-80721. (Illus.). 144p. 1981. pap. text ed. 12.95 (ISBN 0-395-25527-9). HM.

Harrison, James, ed. Science Now. LC 84-6437. (Illus.). 192p. 1984. 21.95 (ISBN 0-668-06209-6, 6209). Arco.

Haskell, Edward, ed. Full Circle: The Moral Force of Unified Science. LC 72-84271. (Current Topics of Contemporary Thought Ser.). (Illus.). 270p. (Orig.). 1972. 57.75 (ISBN 0-677-12480-5). Gordon.

Hesse, Mary. Structure of Scientific Inference. LC 73-85373. 1974. 44.00x (ISBN 0-520-02582-2). U of Cal Pr.

Hinman, Frank. Impact of the New Physics. LC 60-15956. 1961. 5.00 (ISBN 0-8022-0725-1). Philos Lib.

Hoagland, Hudson. Reflections on Science & Human Affairs. 100p. 1974. text ed. 9.50x (ISBN 0-87073-814-3). Schenkman Bks Inc.

Hobson, E. W. The Domain of Natural Science. 9.25 (ISBN 0-8446-2260-5). Peter Smith.

Hobson, Ernest W. The Domain of Natural Science. LC 77-27210. (Gifford Lectures: 1921-22). Repr. of 1923 ed. 24.50 (ISBN 0-404-60467-6). AMS Pr.

--The Domain of Natural Science. LC 68-24653. (Orig.). 1969. pap. 4.95 (ISBN 0-486-21966-6). Dover.

Holmes, Neal J. & Leake, John B. Gateways to Science Webstermaster Activities, Level 1. 4th ed. (Gateways to Science Ser.). 43p. 1982. pap. text ed. 47.52 (ISBN 0-07-029851-3). McGraw.

--Gateways to Science Webstermaster Activities, Level 2. 4th ed. (Gateways to Science Ser.). 43p. 1983. pap. text ed. 47.52s (ISBN 0-07-029852-1). McGraw.

--Gateways to Science Webstermaster Activities, Level 4. 4th ed. (Gateways to Science Ser.). 89p. 1983. pap. text ed. 47.52s (ISBN 0-07-029854-8). McGraw.

House, John. The Wonders of Science. (Science Ser.). 24p. 1977. wkbk. 5.00 (ISBN 0-8209-0155-5, S-17). ESP.

House, Peggy A. Interactions of Science & Mathematics. (Illus.). 185p. 1982. pap. 7.50 (ISBN 0-686-94079-2). NCTM.

Hull, Thomas G. & Jones, Tom. Scientific Exhibits. (Illus.). 144p. 1961. photocopy ed. 14.75x (ISBN 0-398-00884-1). C C Thomas.

Igor, Boy. And Yet it Moves: The Realization & Suppression of Science & Technology. (Illus.). 144p. (Orig.). 1985. pap. 4.00 (ISBN 0-934727-00-7). Zamisdat Pr.

Institute of National Science & Chinese Academy of Science. Ancient China's Technology & Science. (China Knowledge Ser.). (Illus.). 632p. (Orig.). 1983. 16.95 (ISBN 0-8351-1235-7); pap. 9.95 (ISBN 0-8351-1001-X). China Bks.

International Conference on the Unity of the Sciences, 5th, Washington, D. C., Nov. 26-28, 1976. The Search for Absolute Values: Proceedings-Harmony among the Sciences, 2 vols. LC 77-77448. 1060p. 1977. Set. casebd. smythesewn 32.50 (ISBN 0-89226-005-X); Set. pap. 12.50 (ISBN 0-89226-006-8). ICF Pr.

An Introduction to Policy Analysis in Science & Technology. (Science Policy Studies & Documents: No. 46). (Illus.). 93p. (2nd Printing 1982). 1979. pap. 5.00 (ISBN 92-3-101725-X, U955, UNESCO). Unipub.

Jachim, Anton G. Science Policy Making in the United States & the Batavia Accelerator. LC 74-26633. 220p. 1975. 9.95x (ISBN 0-8093-0674-3). S Ill U Pr.

Jacobson, Jerry. The Secret of Life: Perspectivism in Science. 1983. 10.00 (ISBN 0-8022-2400-8). Philos Lib.

Jacobson, Willard & Bergman, Abby. Science for Children: A Book for Teachers. (Illus.). 1980. text ed. 28.95 (ISBN 0-13-794784-4). P-H.

Jessen, Joel. The IMPERATIVE STEP: The Step from Metaphysics to Science. 113p. 1972. pap. 7.00 (ISBN 0-942958-04-7). Kappeler Inst Pub.

Jordan, H. & Kone, E., eds. The Scientific Endeavor. LC 65-18302. (Illus.). 340p. 1965. 6.00x (ISBN 0-87470-004-3); pap. 3.50x. Rockefeller.

Justus, Fred. Everyday Science. (Science Ser.). 24p. 1977. wkbk. 5.00 (ISBN 0-8209-0141-5, S-3). ESP.

--Our World of Science. (Science Ser.). 24p. 1980. wkbk. 5.00 (ISBN 0-8209-0147-4, S-9). ESP.

--Science Facts Puzzles. (Puzzles Ser.). 24p. 1980. wkbk. 5.00 (ISBN 0-8209-0298-5, PU-12). ESP.

Kahn, Robert & Nestler, Herbert. Power Skills in Science II. 1978. pap. 4.95 (ISBN 0-07-033194-4). McGraw.

Kahndike, Jennie M. Toxicology I in Health, Science & Medicine: Research Reference Analysis with Bibliography. LC 84-45989. 150p. 1985. 29.95 (ISBN 0-88164-300-9); pap. 21.95 (ISBN 0-88164-301-7). ABBE Pubs Assn.

Kauchak, Donald P. & Eggen, Paul. Exploring Science in the Elementary School. 1980. pap. 21.50 (ISBN 0-395-30643-4); Instr's. manual 1.00 (ISBN 0-395-30644-2). HM.

Kilgour, O. F. Introduction to Science for Catering & Homecraft Students. 3rd ed. (Illus.). 1976. pap. text ed. 21.00x. Intl Ideas.

Kintsch, W. Method & Tactics in Cognitive Science. 336p. 1984. 29.95 (ISBN 0-89859-327-1). L Erlbaum Assocs.

Klein, Randolph Shipley, ed. Science & Society in Early America: Essays in Honor of Whitfield J. Bell, Jr. 300p. 1985. 30.00 (ISBN 0-317-36902-4). Am Philos.

Kondratov, A. The Riddles of Three Oceans. 267p. 1974. 4.45 (ISBN 0-8285-0833-X, Pub. by Progress Pubs USSR). Imported Pubns.

Kone, Eugene H. & Jordan, Helene J., eds. The Greatest Adventure: Basic Research That Shapes Our Lives. LC 73-83747. (Illus.). 304p. 1974. 9.80x (ISBN 0-87470-018-3). Rockefeller.

Korchin, Florence G. Science in the Marketplace. Woolf, Robert, ed. (Illus.). 280p. 1984. pap. text ed. 13.95x spiral bd. (ISBN 0-9611318-0-2); lab manual incl. Tiger Pubn.

Korzybski, Alfred. Science & Sanity: An Introduction to Non-Aristotelian Systems & General Semantics. 4th ed. LC 58-6260. 806p. 1980. 23.50x (ISBN 0-937298-01-8). Inst Gen Seman.

Krauskopf, Konrad B. & Beiser, Arthur. Fundamentals of Physical Science. 6th ed. LC 76-152006. (Illus.). 1971. text ed. 34.95 (ISBN 0-07-035440-5, C). McGraw.

Kursunoglu, Behram & Perlmutter, Arnold, eds. Studies in the Natural Sciences, Vols. 1-2 & 6-9. Incl. Vol. 1, Impact of Basic Research on Technology. LC 73-82141. 1973. 49.50x (ISBN 0-306-36901-X); Vol. 2, Fundamental Interactions in Physics. LC 73-84002. 1973. 65.00x (ISBN 0-306-36902-8); Vol. 6, Progress in the Neurosciences. LC 74-10822. 1974. 25.00x (ISBN 0-306-36906-0); Vol. 7, Topics in Energy & Resources. LC 74-14644. 1974. 39.50x (ISBN 0-306-36907-9); Vol. 8, Progress in Lasers & Laser Fusion. LC 75-16375. 1975. 65.00x (ISBN 0-306-36908-7); Vol. 9, Theories & Experiments in High Energy Physics. LC 75-16281. 1975. 75.00x (ISBN 0-306-36909-5). LC 73-82141 (Plenum Pr). Plenum Pub.

Lambert, Jill. Scientific & Technical Journals. 191p. 1985. lib. bdg. 19.00 (ISBN 0-85157-375-4, Pub. by Bingley England). Shoe String.

Lambright, W. Henry. Presidential Management of Science & Technology: The Johnson Presidency. (Johnson Presidency Ser.). 238p. 1985. text ed. 25.00x (ISBN 0-292-76494-4). U of Tex Pr.

Lankester, Edwin R. Science from an Easy Chair, Second Series. facs. ed. LC 79-152185. (Essay Index Reprint Ser). 1913. 21.50 (ISBN 0-8369-2210-7). Ayer Co Pubs.

Learner, Howard. White Paper on Science Museums. 53p. (Orig.). 1979. pap. 2.50 (ISBN 0-89329-025-4). Ctr Sci Public.

Lenihan. Science in Action. 1979. 22.00 (ISBN 0-9960018-8-3, Pub. by A Hilger England). Heyden.

Lenihan, J. & Fleming, J. B. Science in Action. 1983. pap. 8.50 (ISBN 0-9960027-1-5, Pub. by A Hilger England). Heyden.

Lewart, Cass. Science & Engineering Sourcebook. LC 82-80269. (Illus.). 96p. (Orig.). 1982. pap. 9.95 (ISBN 0-942412-02-8); Pre-recorded cass. 8.95 (ISBN 0-686-98227-4). Micro Text Pubs.

Linking Science Education to the Rural Environment: Some Experiences. 77p. 1980. pap. 7.00 (ISBN 0-686-63001-7, UB83, UB). Unipub.

Lipscombe, Joan & Williams, Bill. Are Science & Technology Neutral? (Science in a Social Context Ser.). 1979. pap. 4.95 (ISBN 0-408-71312-7). Butterworth.

Lovelock, J. E. Gala: A New Look at Life on Earth. (Illus.). 1979. 17.95x (ISBN 0-19-217665-X). Oxford U Pr.

McConnell, R. B., ed. Art, Science & Human Progress. LC 83-4936. (Illus.). 192p. 1983. text ed. 25.00x (ISBN 0-87663-428-5). Universe.

McGill, Ormond. Science Magic: One Hundred One Experiments You Can Do. (Illus.). 164p. 1984. lib. bdg. 11.95 (ISBN 0-668-05849-8); pap. 7.95 (ISBN 0-668-05853-6). Arco.

Malinowsky, H. Robert. Science & Engineering Literature for Media Centers & School Libraries. lib. bdg. cancelled (ISBN 0-87287-428-1). Libs Unl.

Mansfield, Richard S. & Busse, Thomas V. The Psychology of Creativity & Discovery: Scientists & Their Work. LC 80-29219. 164p. 1981. 19.95x (ISBN 0-88229-653-1). Nelson-Hall.

Martin, Paul D. Science: It's Changing Your World. Crump, Donald J., ed. (Books for World Explorers Series 6: No. 3). (Illus.). 104p. 1985. 6.95 (ISBN 0-87044-516-2); lib. bdg. 8.50 (ISBN 0-87044-521-9). Natl Geog.

Maxwell, Nicholas. From Knowledge to Wisdom: A Revolution in the Aims & Methods of Science. 256p. 1984. 24.95x (ISBN 0-631-13602-9). Basil Blackwell.

Messel, H., ed. Science Update. (Illus.). 336p. 1983. pap. 18.00 (ISBN 0-08-029842-7, 02/32:9, 17/47:2,10). Pergamon.

Method for Priority Determination in Science & Technology. (Science Policy Studies & Documents: No. 40). 108p. 1977. pap. 5.00 (ISBN 92-3-101485-4, U841, UNESCO). Unipub.

Mirsky, Leon, ed. Transversal Theory. (Mathematics in Science & Engineering Ser.: Vol. 75). 1971. 65.00 (ISBN 0-12-498550-5). Acad Pr.

Mitroff, Ian. The Subjective Side of Science. (The Systems Inquiry Ser.). 328p. 1983. pap. 14.95x (ISBN 0-914105-21-3). Intersystems Pubns.

Monroe, James & Jackson, Bonnie. Physical Science: An Inquiry Approach. LC 76-51749. pap. 155.80 (ISBN 0-317-28117-8, 2022507). Bks Demand UMI.

Moravcsik, Michael J. How to Grow Science. LC 80-17469. (Illus.). 224p. (Orig.). 1980. text ed. 12.50x (ISBN 0-87663-344-0). Universe.

Morgan, Robert P., et al. Science & Technology for Development: The Role of U. S. Universities. (Policy Studies). (Illus.). 1979. 56.00 (ISBN 0-08-025107-2). Pergamon.

Nader, Claire & Zahlan, A. B., eds. Science & Technology in Developing Countries. LC 69-16284. (Illus.). 1969. 67.50 (ISBN 0-521-07380-4). Cambridge U Pr.

Nalimov, V. V. The Faces of Science. Colodny, Robert G., ed. LC 81-6654. (Illus.). 297p. 1981. 22.50 (ISBN 0-89495-010-X). ISI Pr.

National Academy of Sciences. Frontiers in Science & Technology. LC 83-1574. (Illus.). 240p. 1983. text ed. 32.95 (ISBN 0-7167-1516-3); pap. text ed. 16.95 (ISBN 0-7167-1517-1). W H Freeman.

National Research Council Commission on Human Resources Staff. Science for Non-Specialists: The College Years. 130p. 1982. pap. text ed. 9.95 (ISBN 0-309-03231-8). Natl Acad Pr.

National Research Council National Academy of Sciences & Committee on Science & Public Policy. Peer Review in the National Science Foundation: Phase Two of a Study. 1981. pap. text ed. 8.75 (ISBN 0-309-03182-6). Natl Acad Pr.

Nayar, B. K., ed. Science & Development. 234p. 1981. 25.00x (ISBN 0-86125-251-9, Pub. by Orient Longman India). State Mutual Bk.

Noble, David. America by Design: Science, Technology & the Rise of Corporate Capitalism. 1977. 17.95 (ISBN 0-394-49983-2). Knopf.

Nova: Adventures in Science. LC 82-16306. (Illus.). 288p. 1982. 27.95 (ISBN 0-201-05358-6); pap. 14.95 (ISBN 0-201-05359-4). Addison-Wesley.

Ollard, E. A. Elementary Science. 128p. 1981. 40.00x (ISBN 0-686-87217-7, Pub. by Portcullio Pr). State Mutual Bk.

Only One Science. 7.50 (ISBN 0-318-18090-1, NSB 80-1). NSF.

Orr, J. B., et al. What Science Stands For. LC 72-134157. (Essay Index Reprint Ser). 1937. 12.00 (ISBN 0-8369-1938-6). Ayer Co Pubs.

Osler, William. Science & Immortality. Repr. of 1904 ed. 15.00 (ISBN 0-686-19869-7). Ridgeway Bks.

Passmore, John. Science & Its Critics. (Mason Welch Gross Lecture Ser). 1978. 15.00x (ISBN 0-8135-0852-5). Rutgers U Pr.

Patty, Catherrine. Basic Skills Science Workbook: Grade 4. (Basic Skills Workbooks). 32p. 1982. wkbk. 0.99 (ISBN 0-8209-0403-1, SW-E). ESP.

Payne & Falls. Physical Science Principles & Applications: A Student Study Guide. 184p. 1984. pap. text ed. 10.95 (ISBN 0-8403-3248-3). Kendall-Hunt.

Payne, Charles A. & Falls, William R. Modern Physical Science: A Student Study Guide. 1976. pap. text ed. 7.95 (ISBN 0-8403-1364-0). Kendall-Hunt.

Peacocke, A. R. The Sciences & Theology in the Twentiety Century. (Oxford International Symposia Ser.). 320p. 1981. 25.00x (ISBN 0-85362-188-8). Routledge & Kegan.

Peet, Louise J. Science Fundamentals: A Background for Household Equipment. LC 71-137093. (Illus.). 132p. 1972. pap. 5.50x (ISBN 0-8138-0835-9). Iowa St U Pr.

Petzow, G. R., et al, eds. Microstructural Science, Vol. 9. 446p. 1981. 88.00 (ISBN 0-444-00633-8). Elsevier.

Physical Science for Non-Science Students: An Approach to Physical Science. 416p. 1974. pap. 32.50x (ISBN 0-471-68922-X). Wiley.

Physics Survey Committee. Physics in Perspective: The Nature of Physics and the Subfields of Physics (Student Edition) (Illus.). 368p. 1973. pap. 8.50 (ISBN 0-309-02118-9). Natl Acad Pr.

Pingree, David. Census of the Exact Sciences in Sanskrit. LC 70-115882. (Memoirs Ser.: Vols. 81, 86, & 111). 1970. pap. 10.00 Ser. A, Vol. 1 (ISBN 0-87169-081-0); pap. 12.00 Ser. A, Vol. 2 (ISBN 0-87169-086-1); pap. 15.00 Ser. A, Vol. 3 (ISBN 0-87169-111-6). Am Philos.

Pitre, B. G., et al. Introductory Science One: A Modern Approach. 124p. 1981. 29.00x (ISBN 0-86125-507-0, Pub. by Orient Longman India). State Mutual Bk.

--Introductory Science Three: A Modern Approach. 162p. 1981. 29.00 (ISBN 0-86125-509-7, Pub. by Orient Longman India). State Mutual Bk.

--Introductory Science Two: A Modern Approach. 122p. 1981. 29.00x (ISBN 0-86125-508-9, Pub. by Orient Longman India). State Mutual Bk.

Planck, Max. Where Is Science Going? Murphy, James, tr. from Ger. LC 80-84974. 224p. 1981. 20.00 (ISBN 0-918024-21-8); pap. text ed. 10.00 (ISBN 0-918024-22-6). Ox Bow.

Platt, John R. The Excitement of Science. LC 74-2556. 174p. 1974. Repr. of 1962 ed. lib. bdg. 18.75x (ISBN 0-8371-7402-3, PLES). Greenwood.

Poincare, H. The Foundations of Science: Science & Hypothesis, the Value of Science, Science & Method. Halstead, George B., tr. from Fr. LC 81-48682. 568p. 1982. lib. bdg. 33.50 (ISBN 0-8191-2318-8); pap. text ed. 20.75 (ISBN 0-8191-2319-6). U Pr of Amer.

Pollard, A. B. & Schofield, C. W. Basic Physical Science for Technicians. (Illus.). 1977. pap. 16.95x (ISBN 0-7131-3384-8). Intl Ideas.

Pollock, M., ed. Common Denominators in Art & Science. 220p. 1983. 27.00 (ISBN 0-08-028457-4). Pergamon.

Poppy, Willard J. & Wilson, Leland L. Exploring the Physical Sciences. 2nd ed. (Illus.). 464p. 1973. text ed. 30.95 (ISBN 0-13-297457-6); study guide o.p. 2.95 (ISBN 0-13-297531-9). P-H.

Preer, James R., et al. Integrated Sciences. 1983. coil bdg. 6.95 (ISBN 0-88252-055-5). Paladin Hse.

Price, Derek D. Science Since Babylon. enl. ed. 1975. pap. 7.95x (ISBN 0-300-01798-7). Yale U Pr.

Prior, Moody E. Science & the Humanities. LC 62-13293. Repr. of 1962 ed. 25.90 (ISBN 0-8357-9470-9, 2015306). Bks Demand UMI.

Radimersky, George W. German Science Reader: An Analytical Approach to Translation Problems. LC 50-8071. pap. 63.30 (ISBN 0-317-09358-4, 2012533). Bks Demand UMI.

Radner, Michael & Radner, Daisie. Science & Unreason. 128p. 1982. pap. text ed. write for info. (ISBN 0-534-01153-5). Wadsworth Pub.

Reed, Evelyn. Sexism & Science. LC 77-92144. (Illus.). 1977. cloth 20.00 (ISBN 0-87348-540-8). Path Pr NY.

Regan. Evoked Potentials in Science & Medicine. 2nd ed. 1985. write for info. (ISBN 0-471-82332-5). Wiley.

Reingold, Nathan, ed. The Sciences in the American Context: New Perspectives. LC 79-607059. 399p. 1979. pap. text ed. 9.95x (ISBN 0-87474-797-X). Smithsonian.

Rektorys, Karel. Variational Methods in Mathematics, Science & Engineering. Basch, Michael, tr. from Czech. 572p. 1980. lib. bdg. 34.00 (ISBN 90-277-0561-5, Pub. by Reidel Holland). Kluwer Academic.

Report of the Fourth Session of the Tropical Experiment Board. (GARP Special Reports: No. 9). (Illus.). 1973. pap. 14.00 (ISBN 0-685-39013-6, W320, WMO). Unipub.

Rescher, Nicholas. Scientific Explanation. LC 71-80675. 1970. 14.95 (ISBN 0-02-926330-1). Free Pr.

Rheingold, Howard & Levine, Howard. Talking Tech: A Conversational Guide to Science & Technology. LC 82-21537. (Illus.). 324p. 1983. pap. 6.70 (ISBN 0-688-01603-0, Quill NY). Morrow.

Roberts, Archibald E. The Most Secret Science. 200p. 1984. pap. 12.00 (ISBN 0-934120-08-0). Betsy Ross Pr.

Rossini, Frederick D. Fundamental Measures & Constants for Science & Technology. LC 74-14759. 142p. 1974. text ed. 34.50 (ISBN 0-8493-5079-4). Krieger.

Rota, Gian-Carlo & Reynolds, Mark, eds. Science, Computers, & People: From the Tree of Mathematics, Stanislaw Ulam. (Illus.). 1985. 14.95 (ISBN 0-8176-3276-X). Birkhauser.

Russell, Bertrand. Scientific Outlook. 1962. pap. 6.95 (ISBN 0-393-00137-7, Norton Lib). Norton.

Sagan, Carl. Broca's Brain: Reflections on the Romance of Science. LC 78-21810. (Illus.). 1979. 14.95 (ISBN 0-394-50169-1). Random.

Salam, Abdus. Pakistan-American Institute of Science & Technology (PAISTECH), University of Maryland, Proceedings. Zubairi, M. Yameen, ed. 1984. write for info. (ISBN 0-930895-03-7). Byron Daven Pubs.

First International Seminar on Science & Technology in the Transformation of the World: A Report of Proceedings, Belgrade, Yugoslavia, Oct. 1979. 112p. 1980. pap. 10.00 (ISBN 92-808-0196-1, TUNU117, UNU). Unipub.
Friedman, Sharon M., et al. Scientists & Journalists: Reporting Science as News. 352p. 24.95x (ISBN 0-02-910750-4). Free Pr.
Gardner, Martin, ed. Great Essays in Science. (Great American Thinkers Ser). 1970. pap. write for info. WSP.
The Gear-Box of Priorities: Positions. 15p. 1981. pap. 5.00 (ISBN 92-808-0168-6, TUNU126, UNU). Unipub.
Gordon, Bonnie, ed. Songs from Unsung Worlds: Science In Poetry. 250p. 1985. 14.95 (ISBN 0-8176-3236-0); pap. 11.95 (ISBN 0-8176-3296-4). Birkhauser.
Goulden, Clyde E., ed. The Changing Scenes in the Natural Sciences 1776-1976. (Special Publication: No. 12). 362p. 1977. 27.00 (ISBN 0-910006-39-3). Acad Nat Sci Phila.
Gutting, Gary, ed. Paradigms & Revolutions: Appraisals & Applications of Thomas Kuhn's Philosophy of Science. LC 80-20745. 256p. 1980. text ed. 18.95 (ISBN 0-268-01542-2); pap. text ed. 9.95 (ISBN 0-268-01543-0). U of Notre Dame Pr.
Haldane, John B. Possible Worlds: And Other Papers. facsimile ed. LC 75-167351. (Essay Index Reprint Ser). Repr. of 1928 ed. 18.00 (ISBN 0-8369-2452-5). Ayer Co Pubs.
--Science & Human Life. facs. ed. LC 72-142638. (Essay Index Reprint Ser.). 1933. 17.00 (ISBN 0-8369-2161-5). Ayer Co Pubs.
Halliwell, James Orchard & Wright, Thomas. Letters of the Historical Society of Science from the Reign of Elizabeth to Charles II. 1965. 22.50x (ISBN 0-8464-0562-8). Beekman Pubs.
Harrison, James, ed. Scientists As Writers. 1965. pap. 5.95x (ISBN 0-262-58004-7). MIT Pr.
Herschel, John F. Preliminary Discourse on the Study of Natural Philosophy. 1967. Repr. of 1830 ed. Facsimile Ed. 25.00 (ISBN 0-384-22690-6). Johnson Repr.
Hildebrand, Joel H. Science in the Making. LC 84-25250. (Bempton Lectures in America Ser.: No. 9). viii, 116p. 1985. Repr. of 1957 ed. lib. bdg. 29.75x (ISBN 0-313-24737-4, HISC). Greenwood.
Hlawiczka, Paul. Gyrotropic Waveguides. 1982. 34.00 (ISBN 0-12-349940-2). Acad Pr.
Holton, G. The Scientific Imagination. LC 76-47196. (Illus.). 1978. 47.50 (ISBN 0-521-21700-8); pap. 13.95 (ISBN 0-521-29237-9). Cambridge U Pr.
Hooke, Robert. Posthumous Works. (Sources of Science Ser., No. 73). 1969. Repr. of 1705 ed. 40.00 (ISBN 0-384-24165-4). Johnson Repr.
Houston, W. V., et al. Scientists Look at Our World. LC 71-142694. (Essay Index Reprint Ser.). Repr. of 1952 ed. 15.00 (ISBN 0-8369-2859-8). Ayer Co Pubs.
Hoyle, Fred. Of Men & Galaxies. LC 64-25266. (Jessie & John Danz Lecture Ser.). 83p. 1964. 10.00x (ISBN 0-295-73859-6). U of Wash Pr.
Hubble, Edwin. The Nature of Science, & Other Lectures. LC 77-14173. 1977. Repr. of 1954 ed. lib. bdg. 18.75x (ISBN 0-8371-9841-0, HUNS). Greenwood.
Humayun, Kabir. Science, Democracy, & Islam: And Other Essays. LC 80-2195. Repr. of 1955 ed. 20.00 (ISBN 0-404-18967-9). AMS Pr.
Hunken, Jorie & Madama, John. Ladybugs & Lettuce Leaves. Hale, Dorinda & Hackman, Sandra, eds. (Illus.). 84p. 1982. pap. text ed. 6.95 (ISBN 0-89329-096-3); tchr's manual 105 pgs. 8.00 (ISBN 0-89329-097-1). Ctr Sci Public.
Hutchinson, George E. Itinerant Ivory Tower. LC 71-117812. (Essay Index Reprint Ser). 1953. 21.50 (ISBN 0-8369-1712-X). Ayer Co Pubs.
Huxley, Thomas H. Autobiography & Essays. Matthews, Brander, ed. LC 20-195. 1969. Repr. of 1919 ed. 21.00 (ISBN 0-527-43850-2). Kraus Repr.
--Collected Essays, 9 Vols. LC 68-57614. (Illus.). 1969. Repr. of 1902 ed. Set. lib. bdg. 138.75x (ISBN 0-8371-0491-2, HUCE). Greenwood.
--Critiques & Addresses. LC 72-3358. (Essay Index Reprint Ser.). Repr. of 1873 ed. 15.50 (ISBN 0-8369-2908-X). Ayer Co Pubs.
International Carnahan Conference. Security Through Science & Engineering: Proceedings. Jackson, J. S. & De Vore, R. William, eds. LC 82-646157. (Illus.). 277p. (Orig.). 1983. pap. 33.50 (ISBN 0-89779-057-X, UKY BU 132). OES Pubns.
International Conference on the Unity of Sciences, 9th, Miami Beach, Nov. 27-30, 1980. Absolute Values & the Search for the Peace of Mankind: Proceedings, 2 vols. LC 81-85132. 1202p. 1981. Set. casebound 33.00 (ISBN 0-89226-014-9); Set. pap. 17.50 (ISBN 0-89226-013-0). ICF Pr.
International Conference on the Unity of the Sciences, 10th, Seoul, Nov. 9-13,1981. The Search for Absolute Values & the Creation of the New World: Proceedings, 2 vols. LC 82-83958. 1458p. 1982. Set. casebound 40.00 (ISBN 0-89226-017-3); Set. pap. 25.00 (ISBN 0-89226-018-1). ICF Pr.
Jarrett, Henry, et al. Science & Resources: Prospects & Implications of Technological Advance. LC 77-23132. (Resources for the Future, Inc.). (Illus.). 1977. Repr. of 1959 ed. lib. bdg. 22.50x (ISBN 0-8371-9470-9, JASR). Greenwood.
Jeans, James H. The Mysterious Universe. LC 75-41156. Repr. of 1933 ed. 14.50 (ISBN 0-404-14742-9). AMS Pr.
Jones, Howard M., et al. Shape of Likelihood: Relevance & the University. Littleton, Taylor, ed. LC 73-135709. (Franklin Lectures in the Sciences & Humanities Second Ser.). 100p. 1971. 9.95 (ISBN 0-8173-6642-3). U of Ala Pr.
Kac, M., et al. Discrete Thoughts: Essays on Mathematics, Science, & Philosophy. 1985. write for info. (ISBN 0-8176-3285-9). Birkhauser.
Klotz, Irving. Bending Perception to Wish. 1985. write for info. (ISBN 0-8176-2403-1). Birkhauser.
Lankester, Edwin R. Science from an Easy Chair, First Series. facs. ed. LC 79-152185. (Essay Index Reprint Ser). 1910. 24.50 (ISBN 0-8369-2194-1). Ayer Co Pubs.
--Secrets of Earth & Sea. LC 76-93352. (Essay Index Reprint Ser). 1920. 19.00 (ISBN 0-8369-1301-9). Ayer Co Pubs.
Law, Frederick H. Science in Literature. 364p. 1981. Repr. of 1929 ed. lib. bdg. 30.00 (ISBN 0-89987-515-7). Darby Bks.
Lawrence, Ernest O. Centennial of the Sheffield Scientific School. facsimile ed. Baitsell, George A., ed. LC 70-107681. (Essay Index Reprint Ser.). 1959. 21.50 (ISBN 0-8369-1544-5). Ayer Co Pubs.
Lewis, Gilbert N. Anatomy of Science. facsimile ed. LC 75-156680. (Essay Index Reprint Ser.). Repr. of 1926 ed. 18.00 (ISBN 0-8369-2408-8). Ayer Co Pubs.
Lightman, Alan P. Time Travel & Papa Joe's Pipe: Essays on the Human Side of Science. (Illus.). 192p. 1984. 12.95 (ISBN 0-684-18112-6, ScribT). Scribner.
Logic & Foundations of Science, Institute Henri Poincare, Paris, May 1964. E. W. Beth Memorial Colloquium. Destouches, J. L., ed. LC 75-4899. 137p. 1967. 21.00 (ISBN 90-277-0076-1, Pub. by Reidel Holland). Kluwer Academic.
Lubbock, John. Scienthic Lectures. LC 72-4522. (Essay Index Reprint Ser.). Repr. of 1879 ed. 18.00 (ISBN 0-8369-2960-8). Ayer Co Pubs.
Mach, Ernst. Popular Scientific Lectures. 432p. 1985. pap. 10.95 (ISBN 0-87548-440-9). Open Court.
Mandelbaum, Maurice. Philosophy, History, & the Sciences: Selected Critical Essays. LC 83-18721. 336p. 1984. text ed. 28.50x (ISBN 0-8018-3112-1). Johns Hopkins.
Maritain, Jacques. Science & Wisdom. 241p. 1980. Repr. lib. bdg. 25.00 (ISBN 0-89760-540-3). Telegraph Bks.
Marks, John. Science & the Making of the Modern World. xiv, 507p. 1983. pap. text ed. 20.00x (ISBN 0-435-54781-X). Heinemann Ed.
Mathews, Shailer, et al. Contributions of Science to Religion. LC 79-117822. (Essay Index Reprint Ser). 1924. 27.50 (ISBN 0-8369-1763-4). Ayer Co Pubs.
Medawar, P. B. The Limits of Science. LC 83-48841. 124p. 1984. 11.95 (ISBN 0-06-039036-0). Har-Row.
Medawar, Peter. Pluto's Republic: Incorporating "The Art of the Soluble" & "Induction & Intuition in Scientific Thought". (Illus.). 1982. 27.50 (ISBN 0-19-217726-5); pap. 8.95x (ISBN 0-19-283039-2, Galaxy Bks.). Oxford U Pr.
Mellor, David H., ed. Science, Belief & Behavior. LC 79-41614. (Illus.). 240p. 1980. 34.50 (ISBN 0-521-22960-X). Cambridge U Pr.
Millikan, Robert A. Science & Life. LC 76-93360. (Essay Index Reprint Ser). 1924. 14.00 (ISBN 0-8369-1307-8). Ayer Co Pubs.
Mohr, H. Lectures on Structure & Significance of Science. (Illus.). 1977. 28.00 (ISBN 0-387-08091-0). Springer-Verlag.
Morrell, Jack & Thackray, Arnold, eds. Gentlemen of Science: Early Correspondence of the British Association for the Advancement of Science. (Royal Historical Society Camden Fourth Ser.: No. 30). 382p. 1985. 15.00 (ISBN 0-86193-103-3, Pub. by Boydell & Brewer). Longwood Pub Group.
Neyman, Jerzy, ed. The Heritage of Copernicus: Theories: "Pleasing to the Mind". 1974. pap. 14.95x (ISBN 0-262-64016-3). MIT Pr.
Parr, Leslie, ed. Science of the Times, 1: A New York Times Survey. Date not set. 16.95 (ISBN 0-405-19030-1, 703). Ayer Co Pubs.
Phillips, Venia T. Minutes & Correspondence of the Academy of Natural Sciences of Philadelphia: 1812-1924, Microfilm Publication Guide. Phillips, Maurice E., ed. (Special Publication: No. 7). 92p. (Orig.). 1967. pap. 7.50 (ISBN 0-910006-35-0). Acad Nat Sci Phila.
Philosophy of Science Association, 1972. Boston Studies in the Philosophy of Science, Vol. 20: Proceedings. Schaffner, K. & Cohen, R. S., eds. LC 72-624169. (Synthese Library: Vol. 64). 1974. lib. bdg. 53.00 (ISBN 90-277-0408-2, Pub. by Reidel Holland); pap. text ed. 29.00 (ISBN 90-277-0409-0). Kluwer Academic.
Planck, Max K. Scientific Autobiography & Other Papers. Gaynor, Frank, tr. 1968. Repr. of 1949 ed. lib. bdg. 18.75x (ISBN 0-8371-0194-8, PLAP). Greenwood.
Points of View. facs. ed. LC 78-76910. (Essay Index Reprint Ser.). 1930. 10.25 (ISBN 0-8369-0026-X). Ayer Co Pubs.
Polanyi, Michael. Science, Faith & Society. 1964. pap. 4.95 (ISBN 0-226-67290-5, P155, Phoen). U of Chicago Pr.
Rabinowitch, V. & Rabinowitch, E., eds. Views on Science, Technology & Development. LC 74-32201. 300p. 1975. text ed. 44.00 (ISBN 0-08-018241-0). Pergamon.
Reichenbach, Hans. Modern Philosophy of Science: Selected Essays. Reichenbach, Maria, ed. LC 81-13344. ix, 214p. 1982. Repr. of 1959 ed. lib. bdg. 24.75x (ISBN 0-313-23274-1, REMD). Greenwood.
Rescher, N., et al, eds. Essays in Honor of Carl G. Hempel: A Tribute on the Occasion of His Sixty-Fifth Birthday. (Synthese Library: No.24). 272p. 1969. 29.50 (ISBN 90-277-0085-0, Pub. by Reidel Holland); pap. 22.00 (ISBN 90-277-0409-0, Pub. by Reidel Holland). Kluwer Academic.
Rescher, Nicholas. Reason & Rationality in Natural Science: A Group of Essays. 228p. (Orig.). 1985. lib. bdg. 23.75 (ISBN 0-8191-4763-X, Co-Pub. by Ctr for Philosophy of Science); pap. 12.25 (ISBN 0-8191-4764-8). U Pr of Amer.
Reynolds, Neil B. & Manning, Ellis L., eds. Excursions in Science. LC 72-1237. (Essay Index Reprint Ser.). Repr. of 1939 ed. 19.50 (ISBN 0-8369-2857-1). Ayer Co Pubs.
Robert Anton Wilson: Right Where You Are Sitting Now. LC 82-4084. 192p. 1982. pap. 7.95 (ISBN 0-915904-65-9). And-Or Pr.
Robertson, C. Grant, et al. Humanism & Technology & Other Essays. facs. ed. LC 68-22099. (Essay Index Reprint Ser). 1924. 14.00 (ISBN 0-8369-0553-9). Ayer Co Pubs.
Rosenthal-Schneider, Ilse. Reality & Scientific Truth: Discussions with Einstein, Von Laue, & Planck. Braun, Thomas, ed. LC 80-13950. (Illus.). 150p. 1980. 13.95 (ISBN 0-8143-1650-6). Wayne St U Pr.
Royal Society. Selected Lectures, 3 Vols. 1968-1970. Vol. 1. 39.50 (ISBN 0-12-573650-9); Vol. 2. 39.50 (ISBN 0-12-573652-5); Vol. 3. 39.50 (ISBN 0-12-573653-3). Acad Pr.
Russell, Edward J. Science & Modern Life. facsimile ed. LC 70-117833. (Essay Index Reprint Ser). Repr. of 1955 ed. 14.00 (ISBN 0-8369-2440-1). Ayer Co Pubs.
Sakharov. Collected Scientific Works. 240p. 1982. 27.50 (ISBN 0-8247-1714-7). Dekker.
Science To-Day & To-Morrow, Comp. from a Series of Lectures Delivered at Morley College. facs. ed. LC 67-30231. (Essay Index Reprint Ser). 1932. 13.00 (ISBN 0-8369-0857-0). Ayer Co Pubs.
Scientific Lectures Presented at the Eighth World Meteorological Congress: Geneva, May 1979. (Eng. & Fr.). 112p. 1981. pap. 11.00 (ISBN 92-63-00568-0, W501, WMO). Unipub.
Senechal, Marjorie, ed. Structures of Matter & Patterns of Science. 200p. 1980. text ed. 18.50x (ISBN 0-87073-908-5); pap. text ed. 8.95x o. p. (ISBN 0-87073-909-3). Schenkman Bks Inc.
Seward, Albert C., ed. Science & the Nation, Essays by Cambridge Graduates. facs. ed. LC 67-26780. (Essay Index Reprint Ser). 1917. 18.00 (ISBN 0-8369-0864-3). Ayer Co Pubs.
Seydel, J. K., ed. & intro. by. QSAR & Strategies in the Design of Bioactive Compounds. (Illus.). 466p. 1985. 62.50 (ISBN 0-89573-433-8). VCH Pubs.
Shafer, W. H., ed. Masters Theses in the Pure & Applied Sciences Accepted by Colleges & Universities of the United States & Canada: Thesis Year 1980, Vol. 25. LC 58-62673. 316p. 1982. 85.00x (ISBN 0-306-40991-7, Plenum Pr). Plenum Pub.
Spacy, Jacques, et al. Science for Development: An Essay on the Origin & Organization of National Science Policies. 224p. (Orig.). 1971. pap. 7.50 (ISBN 92-3-100893-5, U572, UNESCO). Unipub.
Speaking of Science: Proceedings of the Royal Institution, Vol. 51. 176p. 1979. pap. cancelled (ISBN 0-85066-186-2). Taylor & Francis.
Speaking of Science Seventy-Seven: Proceedings of the Royal Institution, Vol. 50. 300p. 1978. cancelled (ISBN 0-85066-135-8). Taylor & Francis.
Steinhardt, Jacinto. Science & the Modern World. LC 66-19930. 225p. 1966. 29.50x (ISBN 0-306-30239-X, Plenum Pr). Plenum Pub.
Sullivan, J. W. N. Aspects of Science. 238p. 1981. Repr. of 1926 ed. lib. bdg. 35.00 (ISBN 0-89984-420-0). Century Bookbindery.
Synge, John L. Science: Sense & Nonsense. LC 72-8534. (Essay Index Reprint Ser.). 1972. Repr. of 1951 ed. 17.00 (ISBN 0-8369-7332-1). Ayer Co Pubs.
Thomas, Henry & Thomas, Dana L. Living Adventures in Science. facsimile ed. LC 77-167428. (Essay Index Reprint Ser). Repr. of 1954 ed. 20.00 (ISBN 0-8369-2573-4). Ayer Co Pubs.
Thomson, John A. Riddles of Science. facsimile ed. LC 77-152218. (Essay Index Reprint Ser). Repr. of 1932 ed. 21.50 (ISBN 0-8369-2257-3). Ayer Co Pubs.
Truesdell, C. An Idiot's Fugitive Essays on Science: Methods, Criticism, Training, Circumstances. (Illus.). 640p. 1984. 58.00 (ISBN 0-387-90703-3); pap. 24.00 (ISBN 0-387-91221-5). Springer-Verlag.
Tykodi, Ralph J., ed. The Taste of Science. LC 75-25480. 130p. 1975. pap. 4.95x (ISBN 0-87762-183-7). Technomic.
UNA-USA National Policy Panel. Science & Technology in an Era of Independence. LC 74-29459. (Illus.). 1975. pap. text ed. 2.00x (ISBN 0-934654-12-3). UNA-USA.
Vavoulis, Alexander & Colver, A. Wayne, eds. Science & Society: Selected Essays. LC 66-15005. 1966. pap. text ed. 7.50x (ISBN 0-8162-9172-1). Holden-Day.
Velikhov, E. P., et al, eds. Science, Technology & the Future: Soviet Scientists Analysis of the Problems of & Prospects for the Development of Science & Technology & Their Role in Society. LC 79-40113. (Illus.). 480p. 1980. 43.00 (ISBN 0-08-024743-1). Pergamon.
Von Baer, Karl E. Reden Gehalten in Wissenschaftlichen Versammlungen und Kleinere Aufsatze Vermischten Inhalts, 3 vols. in two. Sterling, Keir B., ed. LC 77-81114. (Biologists & Their World Ser.). (Ger.). 1978. Repr. of 1876 ed. Set. lib. bdg. 93.00x (ISBN 0-405-10700-5); lib. bdg. 46.50x ea. Vol. 1 (ISBN 0-405-10701-3). Vol. 2 (ISBN 0-405-10702-1). Ayer Co Pubs.
Von Humboldt, Alexander. Aspects of Nature in Different Lands & Different Climates. Sabine, Mrs., tr. LC 70-99251. 1970. Repr. of 1850 ed. 32.00 (ISBN 0-404-03385-7). AMS Pr.
Weissmann, Gerald. The Woods Hole Cantata: Essays on Science & Society. 224p. 1985. 14.95 (ISBN 0-396-08618-7). Dodd.
Whitehead, Alfred N. Essays in Science & Philosophy. LC 68-21332. (Illus.). 1968. Repr. of 1947 ed. lib. bdg. 37.50x (ISBN 0-8371-0268-5, WHES). Greenwood.
--Science & the Modern World. LC 67-2244. 1967. pap. 9.95x (ISBN 0-02-935190-1). Free Pr.
Wigner, Eugene P. Symmetries & Reflections: Scientific Essays of Eugene P. Wigner. LC 77-18149. (Illus.). 1978. Repr. of 1967 ed. lib. bdg. 32.50 (ISBN 0-313-20107-2, WISY). Greenwood.
Wilber, Ken, ed. The Holographic Paradigm & Other Paradoxes: Exploring the Leading Edge of Science. LC 82-50277. 300p. 1982. pap. 8.95 (ISBN 0-394-71237-4). Shambhala Pubns.
Williams, Charles W. Direction: The Essential Dimension. 1960. 8.95 (ISBN 0-8315-0003-4). Speller.
Young, Arthur M. The Foundations of Science: The Missing Parameter. (Broadside Editions Ser.). (Illus.). 1985. pap. 3.95 (ISBN 0-931191-03-3). Rob Briggs.
Young, Louise B. & Trainor, William T., eds. Science & Public Policy. LC 70-83742. (Illus.). 626p. 1971. lib. bdg. 22.50 (ISBN 0-379-00332-5). Oceana.

SCIENCE–AUTHORSHIP
see Technical Writing

SCIENCE–BIBLIOGRAPHY

Alsmeyer, D. & Atkins, A. G., eds. Guide to Science & Technology in the Asia Pacific Area. 540p. 150.00x (ISBN 0-582-90100-6, Pub. by Longman). Gale.
American Health Research Institute Staff. International Cooperation in Medicine & Science: Subject Analysis Index with Research Bibliography. LC 85-47585. 150p. 1985. 29.95 (ISBN 0-88164-344-0); pap. 21.95 (ISBN 0-88164-345-9). ABBE Pubs Assn.
A Bibliography of Recommendations (ISO, BS, NEN, ANSI) for the Preparation of Scientific Publications. 1977. pap. 4.00 (ISBN 90-220-0390-6, PUDOC138, PUDOC). Unipub.
Black, George W., Jr. American Science & Technology: A Bicentennial Bibliography. LC 78-15820. 172p. 1979. 15.95x (ISBN 0-8093-0898-3). S Ill U Pr.

Boland, Bill, et al, eds. Annals Index. (Annals of The New York Academy of Sciences Ser.: Vol. 391). 154p. 1982. lib. bdg. 30.00x (ISBN 0-89766-172-9); pap. 30.00x (ISBN 0-89766-173-7). NY Acad Sci.

Cohan, Leonard, ed. Readers Advisory Service: Selected Topical Booklists, Vol. 10. 1983. 115.00 (ISBN 0-685-79403-2). Sci Assoc Intl.

Committee On Data For Science And Technology Of The International Council Of Scientific Unions. International Compendium of Numerical Data Projects. 1969. 38.00 (ISBN 0-387-04570-8). Springer-Verlag.

Dibner, Bern. Heralds of Science. 1969. pap. 7.95x (ISBN 0-262-54004-5). MIT Pr.

Directory of Japanese Scientific Periodicals. 3rd ed. LC 68-5037. 1976. 57.50x (ISBN 0-8002-0761-0). Intl Pubns Serv.

Hahn, Roger. Bibliography of Quantitative Studies on Science & Its History. LC 79-65637. (Berkeley Papers in History of Science: No. 3). (Orig.). 1980. pap. 5.00x (ISBN 0-918102-04-9). U Cal Hist Sci Tech.

Hall, W. H. SFBRI: Science Book Review Index, Vol. 15. 80p. 1985. lib. bdg. 19.95x (ISBN 0-89370-570-5). Borgo Pr.

International Catalogue of Scientific Literature, 1901-1914, 238 vols. in 32. Incl. Section A-Mathematics. 67.00 (ISBN 0-685-23269-7); Section B-Mechanics. 42.00 (ISBN 0-685-23270-0); Section C-Physics, 2 vols. Set. 125.00 (ISBN 0-685-23271-9); Section D-Chemistry, 4 vols. Set. 300.00 (ISBN 0-685-23272-7); Section E-Astronomy. 75.00 (ISBN 0-685-23273-5); Section F-Meterology. 75.00 (ISBN 0-685-23274-3); Section G-Mineralogy. 75.00 (ISBN 0-685-23275-1); Section H-Geology. 80.00 (ISBN 0-685-23276-X); Section J-Geography. 90.00 (ISBN 0-685-23277-8); Section K-Paleontology. 67.00 (ISBN 0-685-23278-6); Section L-General Biology. 42.00 (ISBN 0-685-23279-4); Section M-Botany, 3 vols. Set. 250.00 (ISBN 0-685-23280-8); Section N-Zoology, 5 vols. Set. 400.00 (ISBN 0-685-23281-6); Section 0-Human Anatomy. 75.00 (ISBN 0-685-23282-4); Section P-Anthropology, 2 vols. Set. 125.00 (ISBN 0-685-23283-2); Section Q-Physiology, 4 vols. Set. 350.00 (ISBN 0-685-23284-0); Section R-Bacteriology, 2 vols. Set. 175.00 (ISBN 0-685-23285-9). 1902-1919. Repr. of 1902 ed. Set. 1985.00 (ISBN 0-685-23268-9). Johnson Repr.

Jaques Cattell Press, ed. American Men & Women of Science Cumulative Index: Vols. 1-14. 1983p. 125.00x (ISBN 0-8352-1238-6). Bowker.

--American Men & Women of Science: Physical & Biological Sciences, 7 vols. 15th ed. 7010p. 1982. Set. 495.00 (ISBN 0-8352-1413-3); 85.00 ea. Bowker.

John Crerar Library. List of Books on the History of Science. Josephson, A. G., ed. 1911. 48.00 (ISBN 0-527-46300-0); supplement dec. 1916 20.00 (ISBN 0-527-46310-8). Kraus Repr.

Jones, E. G., ed. Guide to Science & Technology in Eastern Europe: A Reference Guide to Science & Technology in Eastern Europe. (Illus.). 320p. 150.00x (ISBN 0-582-90101-4, Pub. by Longman). Gale.

Malinowsky, H. Robert & Richardson, Jeanne M. Science & Engineering Literature: A Guide to Reference Sources. 3rd ed. LC 80-21290. (Library Science Text). 342p. 1980. lib. bdg. 33.00x (ISBN 0-87287-230-0); pap. text ed. 21.00 (ISBN 0-87287-245-9). Libs Unl.

Mieli, Aldo. Science Arabe & Son Role Dans l'Evolution Scientifique Mondiale. (Medieval Studies Reprint Ser.). (Fr.). Repr. of 1938 ed. lib. bdg. 44.00x (ISBN 0-697-00044-3). Irvington.

Northeastern University - Dodge Library, Boston. Selective Bibliography in Science & Engineering. 1964. 78.00 (ISBN 0-8161-0701-7, Hall Library). G K Hall.

Office for History of Science & Technology. William Henry Bragg & William Lawrence Bragg: A Bibliography of Their Non-Technical Writings. LC 77-94209. (Berkeley Papers in History of Science: No. 2). 1978. pap. 5.00x (ISBN 0-918102-01-4). U Cal Hist Sci Tech.

Pelletier, Paul. Prominent Scientists: An Index to Collective Biographies. 311p. 1980. 34.95 (ISBN 0-918212-41-3). Neal-Schuman.

Pure & Applied Science Books, 1876-1982, 6 vols. 7784p. 1982. Set. 300.00x (ISBN 0-8352-1437-0). Bowker.

Renyi-Vamos, F. & Balogh, F. Titles from the Hungarian Academy of Sciences. 1981. 59.00x (ISBN 0-569-08544-6, Pub. by Collet's). State Mutual Bk.

Reuss, Jeremias D. Repertorium Commentationuma Societatibus Litterariis Editarum Secundum Disciplinarum Ordinem, 16 vols. 1962. 550.00 (ISBN 0-8337-2966-7). B Franklin.

A Scientific American Book: Bibliography. LC 84-21099. 1985. write for info. (ISBN 0-7167-1711-5); pap. write for info. (ISBN 0-7167-1712-3). W H Freeman.

Scientific American, Inc. Scientific American Cumulative Index 1948-1978. 1979. 45.00 (ISBN 0-89454-002-5). Scientific Am Inc.

Scientific & Technical Books & Serials in Print 1985, 3 vols. 1984. 120.00 (ISBN 0-8352-1860-0). Bowker.

Shafer, W. H., ed. Masters Theses in the Pure & Applied Sciences Accepted by Colleges & Universities of the United States & Canada: Vol. 22: Thesis Year 1977. LC 58-62673. 320p. 1978. 85.00x (ISBN 0-306-40059-6, Plenum Pr). Plenum Pub.

Shur, Shimon, et al. The Kibbutz: A Bibliography of Scientific & Professional Publications in English. (Kibbutz, Communal Society, & Alternative Social Policy Ser.). 103p. 1981. lib. bdg. 22.50 (ISBN 0-8482-6402-9). Norwood Edns.

Stillwell, Margaret B. The Awakening Interest in Science During the First Century of Printing, 1450-1550. LC 78-114982. 399p. 1970. 25.00x (ISBN 0-8139-0935-X, Biographical Soc. of Amer.). U Pr of Va.

Thorndike, Lynn & Kibre, Pearl, eds. A Catalogue of Incipits of Mediaeval Scientific Writings in Latin. rev. & enl. ed. 1963. 35.00x (ISBN 0-910956-11-1). Medieval Acad.

Whitrow, M., ed. ISIS Cumulative Bibliography, 1913-1965, 2 vols. LC 72-186272. 1976. Vol. 3, Subjects 772pg. 85.00 (ISBN 0-7201-0296-0); Vols. 1-2, Personalities & Institutions, 1971 1527 pg. 127.00 (ISBN 0-7201-0183-2). Mansell.

Whitrow, Magda. ISIS Cumulative Bibliography, 1913-1965: Volumes 4 & 5, Civilizations & Periods. 1100p. 1982. 212.00 (ISBN 0-7201-0549-8). Mansell.

Wolff, Kathryn & Storey, Jill, eds. AAAS Science Book List Supplement. LC 78-6540. 457p. 1978. casebd. 16.50 (ISBN 0-87168-218-4). AAAS.

Young, Thomas. Course of Lectures on Natural Philosophy & the Mechanical Arts, 2 Vols. LC 7-31708. Repr. of 1807 ed. Set. 135.00 (ISBN 0-384-70408-5); Vol. 1. 75.00 (ISBN 0-384-70406-9); Vol. 2. 65.00 (ISBN 0-384-70407-7). Johnson Repr.

SCIENCE–BIBLIOGRAPHY–CATALOGS

Academy of Natural Sciences of Philadelphia. Catalog of the Library of the Academy of Natural Sciences of Philadelphia, 16 vols. 1972. Set. lib. bdg. 1595.00 (ISBN 0-8161-0946-X, Hall Library). G K Hall.

Aluri, Rao & Robinson, Judith. A Guide to U. S. Government Scientific & Technical Resources. 259p. 1983. lib. bdg. 23.50 (ISBN 0-87287-377-3). Libs Unl.

Catalog of the Atmospheric Sciences Collection in the Library & Information Services Division, National Oceanic & Atmospheric Administration. 1978. lib. bdg. 2185.00 (ISBN 0-8161-0240-6, Hall Library). G K Hall.

Roller, Duane & Goodman, Marcia M. Catalogue of the History of Science: Collections of the University of Oklahoma Libraries, 2 vols. LC 76-381954. 1212p. 1976. Set. 212.00x (ISBN 0-7201-0452-1). Mansell.

Scientific & Technical Books & Serials in Print 1986, 3 vols. 4100p. 1985. 149.95 (ISBN 0-8352-2083-4). Bowker.

Silverstein, Theodore, ed. Medieval Latin Scientific Writings in the Barberini Collection: A Provisional Catalogue. LC 58-5492. Repr. of 1957 ed. 29.50 (ISBN 0-8357-9648-5, 2016981). Bks Demand UMI.

SCIENCE–CLASSIFICATION

see Classification of Sciences

SCIENCE–COLLECTED WORKS

Brode, Wallace R., ed. Science in Progress, Fourteenth Series. LC 78-37534. (Essay Index Reprint Ser.). 1972. Repr. of 1964 ed. 21.00 (ISBN 0-8369-7274-0). Ayer Co Pubs.

--Science in Progress, Twelfth Series. LC 78-37534. (Essay Index Reprint Ser). 1972. Repr. of 1962 ed. 23.00 (ISBN 0-8369-7275-9). Ayer Co Pubs.

Cardano, Girolamo. Opera Omnia, 10 vols. Repr. of 1663 ed. 34.50 ea.; Set. 445.00 (ISBN 0-384-07500-2). Johnson Repr.

Cohen, Morris R. & Drabkin, Israel E. Source Book in Greek Science. LC 58-12979. (Source Books in the History of the Sciences Ser). (Illus.). 1948. text ed. 35.00x (ISBN 0-674-82320-6). Harvard U Pr.

Davy, Norman. British Scientific Literature in the 17th Century. LC 71-105777. 1970. Repr. of 1953 ed. 21.00x (ISBN 0-8046-0947-0, Pub. by Kennikat). Assoc Faculty Pr.

Gamow, George, et al. Science in Progress, Eighth Series. facsimile ed. Baitsell, George A., ed. LC 78-37534. (Essay Index Reprint Ser). Repr. of 1953 ed. 33.00 (ISBN 0-8369-2533-5). Ayer Co Pubs.

Gardner, Martin, ed. The Sacred Beetle & Other Great Essays in Science. LC 84-42795. 427p. 1984. 22.95 (ISBN 0-87975-257-2). Prometheus Bks.

Gibbs, J. Willard. Scientific Papers, 2 vols. Set. 21.50 (ISBN 0-8446-2127-7). Peter Smith.

History, Philosophy & Sociology of Science, 60 vols. 1975. 1476.00 (ISBN 0-405-06575-2). Ayer Co Pubs.

Jewett, Frank B., et al. Science in Progress, Fifth Series. facsimile ed. Baitsell, George A, ed. LC 78-37534. (Essay Index Reprint Ser). Repr. of 1947 ed. 35.50 (ISBN 0-8369-2530-0). Ayer Co Pubs.

Jones, Howard M. & Cohen, I. Bernard. A Treasury of Scientific Prose: A Nineteenth Century Anthology. LC 76-49816. (Illus.). 1977. Repr. of 1963 ed. lib. bdg. 24.75x (ISBN 0-8371-9363-X, JOTS). Greenwood.

Korzybski, Alfred. Selections from Science & Sanity. 306p. 1972. pap. 9.50. Inst Gen Seman.

Lawrence, Ernest O. Science in Progress, First Series. facsimile ed. Baitsell, George A., ed. LC 78-37534. (Essay Index Reprint Ser). Repr. of 1939 ed. 36.00 (ISBN 0-8369-2526-2). Ayer Co Pubs.

Miles, Walter R., et al. Science in Progress, Fourth Series. facsimile ed. Baitsell, George A., ed. LC 78-37534. (Essay Index Reprint Ser). Repr. of 1945 ed. 42.00 (ISBN 0-8369-2529-7). Ayer Co Pubs.

Neurath, Otto, et al, eds. Foundations of the Unity of Science: Toward an International Encyclopedia of Unified Science. LC 56-553. (Foundations of the Unity of Science Ser: Vols. 1 & 2). 1955. Vol. 1. 25.00x (ISBN 0-226-57586-1); Vol. 2. 25.00x (ISBN 0-226-57588-8). U of Chicago Pr.

Patten, Bradley M., et al. Science in Progress, Seventh Series. facsimile ed. Baitsell, George A., ed. LC 78-37534. (Essay Index Reprint Ser). Repr. of 1951 ed. 40.00 (ISBN 0-8369-2532-7). Ayer Co Pubs.

Phillips, Venia T. & Phillips, Maurice E. Guide to the Manuscript Collections in the Academy of Natural Sciences of Philadelphia. (Special Publication: No. 5). (Illus.). 553p. 1963. lib. bdg. 15.00 (ISBN 0-910006-33-4). Acad Nat Sci Phila.

Radical Science Collective, ed. Radical Science. 204p. 1984. text ed. 29.00x (ISBN 0-391-03112-0, Pub. by Free Assn UK); pap. text ed. 12.00x (ISBN 0-391-03111-2). Humanities.

Rumford, Benjamin T. Collected Works of Count Rumford, 5 vols. Brown, Sanborn C., ed. Incl. Vol. 1. Nature of Heat. (Illus.). xiv, 507p. 1968 (ISBN 0-674-13951-8); Vol. 2. Practical Applications of Heat. (Illus.). x, 533p. 1969 (ISBN 0-674-13952-6); Vol. 3. Devices & Techniques. (Illus.). x, 514p. 1969; Vol. 4. Light & Armament. (Illus.). viii, 511p. 1970 (ISBN 0-674-13954-2); Vol. 5. Public Institutions. (Illus.). xii, 524p. 1970 (ISBN 0-674-13955-0). LC 68-17633. 30.00x ea. (Belknap Pr). Harvard U Pr.

Runes, Dagobert D. Treasury of World Science. (Quality Paperback: No. 108). 978p. (Orig.). 1962. pap. 4.95 (ISBN 0-8226-0108-7). Littlefield.

Scheele, K. W. Collected Papers. Dobbin, Leonard, tr. Repr. of 1931 ed. 22.00 (ISBN 0-527-79750-2). Kraus Repr.

Science in Progress. LC 78-37534. (Eleventh Ser). 1972. Repr. of 1960 ed. 28.25 (ISBN 0-8369-7241-4). Ayer Co Pubs.

The Sciences Today. new ed. Adler, Mortimer J., ed. LC 75-4350. (The Great Ideas Anthologies Ser). (Illus.). 564p. 1976. 15.00x (ISBN 0-405-07173-6). Ayer Co Pubs.

Shafer, Wade H., ed. Masters Theses in the Pure & Applied Sciences: Accepted by Colleges & Universities of the United States & Canada, Vol. 27. 340p. 1984. 85.00x (ISBN 0-306-41661-1, Plenum Pr). Plenum Pub.

Shapley, Harlow, et al. Science in Progress, Third Series. facsimile ed. Baitsell, George A., ed. LC 78-37534. (Essay Index Reprint Ser). Repr. of 1942 ed. 33.00 (ISBN 0-8369-2528-9). Ayer Co Pubs.

Smyth, H. D., et al. Science in Progress, Sixth Series. facsimile ed. Baitsell, George A., ed. LC 78-37534. (Essay Index Reprint Ser). Repr. of 1949 ed. 34.50 (ISBN 0-8369-2531-9). Ayer Co Pubs.

Snyder, Laurence H., et al. Science in Progress, Ninth Series. facsimile ed. Baitsell, George A., ed. LC 78-37534. (Essay Index Reprint Ser). Repr. of 1955 ed. 33.00 (ISBN 0-8369-2534-3). Ayer Co Pubs.

Stadler, L. J., et al. Science in Progress, Second Series. facsimile ed. Baitsell, George A., ed. LC 78-37534. (Essay Index Reprint Ser). Repr. of 1940 ed. 35.50 (ISBN 0-8369-2527-0). Ayer Co Pubs.

University Of California - Members Of The Faculties. Science in the University. facs. ed. LC 68-20331. (Essay Index Reprint Ser). 1944. 20.00 (ISBN 0-8369-0856-2). Ayer Co Pubs.

Volta, Alessandro G. Opere, 7 vols. (Sources of Science Ser.). Repr. of 1929 ed. Set. 315.00 (ISBN 0-384-64900-9). Johnson Repr.

Von Helmholtz, Hermann. Selected Writings of Hermann Von Helmholtz. Kahl, Russell, ed. LC 70-105503. (Illus.). 1971. 37.50x (ISBN 0-8195-4039-0). Wesleyan U Pr.

Waterman, Alan T., et al. Science in Progress, Thirteenth Series. Brode, Wallace R., ed. LC 78-37534. (Essay Index Reprint Ser.). 1972. Repr. of 1963 ed. 22.00 (ISBN 0-8369-7240-6). Ayer Co Pubs.

Wells, H. G. Early Writings in Science & Science Fiction. Philmus, Robert M. & Hughes, David, eds. LC 73-91673. 1975. 29.50x (ISBN 0-520-02679-9). U of Cal Pr.

Young, Thomas. Course of Lectures on Natural Philosophy & the Mechanical Arts, 2 Vols. LC 7-31708. Repr. of 1807 ed. Set. 135.00 (ISBN 0-384-70408-5); Vol. 1. 75.00 (ISBN 0-384-70406-9); Vol. 2. 65.00 (ISBN 0-384-70407-7). Johnson Repr.

--Miscellaneous Works of the Late Thomas Young, 3 vols. Repr. of 1855 ed. Set. 125.00 (ISBN 0-384-40420-0). Johnson Repr.

SCIENCE–DATA PROCESSING

Abraham, F. & Tiller, W. A., eds. An Introduction to Computer Simulation in Applied Science. LC 72-83047. 220p. 1972. 29.50 (ISBN 0-306-30579-8, Plenum Pr). Plenum Pub.

Abraham, Farid F. & Tiller, William A., eds. An Introduction to Computer Simulation in Applied Science. LC 72-83047. pap. 58.30 (ISBN 0-317-30342-2, 2024714). Bks Demand UMI.

Annino, R. & Driver, R. Personal Computers in Scientific & Engineering Applications. 1985. 39.95 (ISBN 0-471-79978-5). Wiley.

Ascher & Russell, eds. Numerical Boundary Value ODE's. (Progress in Scientific Computing: No. 6). 1985. text ed. write for info. (ISBN 0-8176-3302-2). Birkhauser.

Bajpai, Avi C. FORTRAN & Algol: A Programmed Course for Students of Science & Technology. LC 73-5712. pap. 51.90 (ISBN 0-317-08899-8, 2013981). Bks Demand UMI.

Barnaal, Dennis. Analog & Digital Electronics for Scientific Application. 1982. text ed. write for info. (ISBN 0-534-01044-X, Breton Pubs). Wadsworth Pub.

--Digital & Microprocessor Electronics for Scientific Application. 1982. pap. text ed. write for info. (ISBN 0-534-01043-1, Breton Pubs). Wadsworth Pub.

Beech, G., ed. Computer Assisted Learning in Science Education. LC 78-40566. 1979. pap. text ed. 50.00 (ISBN 0-08-023010-5). Pergamon.

Brenan, J. P., et al, eds. Computers in Botanical Collections. LC 75-9386. 226p. 1975. 39.50x (ISBN 0-306-30847-9, Plenum Pr). Plenum Pub.

Bures, Jan & Krekule, Ivan. Practical Guide to Computer Applications in Neurosciences. 398p. 1983. 54.95 (ISBN 0-471-10012-9, Pub. by Wiley-Interscience). Wiley.

Carr, Joseph J. Sixty-Eight Scientific & Engineering Programs for the Apple II & IIe. 1984. 19.95 (ISBN 0-8359-6920-7). Reston.

Carr, Joseph L. Sixty-Eight Scientific & Engineering Programs for the IBM PC & PC XT. 1984. 19.95 (ISBN 0-8359-6921-5). Reston.

Chapman, J. R. Computers in Mass Spectrometry. 1978. 49.50 (ISBN 0-12-168750-3). Acad Pr.

Chi, Joseph. CADSES: Computer Aided Design of Scientific & Engineering Systems. 268p. (Orig.). 1984. pap. text ed. 24.95 (ISBN 0-930945-01-8). HCP Systems.

Cooper, J. W. Introduction to Pascal for Scientists. LC 80-28452. 260p. 1981. 28.95x (ISBN 0-471-08785-8, Pub. by Wiley-Interscience). Wiley.

Cozby, Paul C. Using Computers in the Behavioral Sciences. 1984. 9.95 (ISBN 0-87484-714-1). Mayfield Pub.

Crandall, Richard E. Pascal Applications for the Sciences. LC 82-24832. (Self-Teaching Guides). 224p. 1983. pap. text ed. 16.95 (ISBN 0-471-87242-3, 1-581). Wiley.

Deighton, S., ed. Microprocessor Applications in Science & Medicine, 1977-1978: Bibliography. 1979. 28.00 (ISBN 0-85296-448-X). Inst Elect Eng.

Diehl, P., et al. Computer Assistance in the Analysis of High-Resolution NMR Spectra. (NMR Basic Principles & Progress: Vol. 6). (Illus.). 100p. 1972. 24.00 (ISBN 0-387-05532-0). Springer-Verlag.

Ellington, H. I., et al. Games & Simulations in Science Education. 180p. 1981. 27.50x (ISBN 0-89397-093-X). Nichols Pub.

Fernbach, S. & Taub, A., eds. Computers & Their Role in the Physical Sciences. 638p. 1970. 113.50 (ISBN 0-677-14030-4). Gordon.

Field, Paul E. & Davies, John A. Computer Interfacing Techniques in Science. LC 84-26714. 224p. 1985. pap. 12.95 (ISBN 0-673-18112-X). Scott F.

Fleming, George. Computer Simulation Techniques in Hydrology. (Environmental Science Ser.). 352p. 1975. 42.50 (ISBN 0-444-00157-3). Elsevier.

Flora, Philip C. International Engineering-Scientific Software Directory. (Illus., Orig.). Date not set. pap. text ed. 35.00 (ISBN 0-910747-05-9). Tech Data TX.

Friend, J. N. Science Data. 4th ed. 120p. 1960. 10.00x (ISBN 0-85264-090-0, Pub. by Griffin England). State Mutual Bk.

Gibson, Glenn A. & Liu, Yu-Cheng. Microcomputers for Engineers & Scientists. (Illus.). 1980. text ed. 38.95 (ISBN 0-13-580886-3). P-H.

Gilder, Jules H. IBM Programs in Science & Engineering. 256p. pap. 16.95 (6356). Hayden.

Glaeser, P. S., ed. Data for Science & Technology: Proceedings of the International CODATA Conference, Eighth, Jachranka, Poland, 4-7 Oct., 1982. 350p. 1983. 49.00 (ISBN 0-444-86668-X, I-460-83, North Holland). Elsevier.

Glowinski & Lions, eds. Computing Methods in Applied Sciences & Engineering. 724p. 1980. 70.25 (ISBN 0-444-86008-8, North-Holland). Elsevier.

Glowinski, R. & Lions, J. L. Computing Methods in Applied Sciences & Engineering, VI. 1984. 74.00 (ISBN 0-444-87597-2). Elsevier.

Goffman, William & Warren, Kenneth. Scientific Information Systems & the Principle of Selectivity. LC 80-49. 202p. 1980. 31.95 (ISBN 0-03-056081-0). Praeger.

Hubin, Wilbert N. BASIC Programming for Scientists & Engineers. LC 77-21343. (Illus.). 1978. pap. 21.95 ref. ed. (ISBN 0-13-066480-4). P-H.

Jones, A. & Weinstock, H. Computer-Based Science Instruction. 376p. 1978. 37.50x (ISBN 90-286-0248-8). Sijthoff & Noordhoff.

Keilis-Borok, V. I., ed. Computational Seismology. LC 76-140827. 227p. 1972. 45.00 (ISBN 0-306-10861-5, Consultants). Plenum Pub.

Korn, Granino A. Microprocessors & Small Digital Computer Systems: For Engineers & Scientists. LC 77-492. 1977. 49.95 (ISBN 0-07-035367-0). McGraw.

Kulisch, Ulrich W. & Miranker, Willard L., eds. A New Approach to Scientific Computation (Symposium) (Notes & Reports in Computer Science & Applied Mathematics Ser.). 1983. 44.00 (ISBN 0-12-428660-7). Acad Pr.

Lengenfelder, Helga. Libraries, Information Centers & Databases in Science & Technology: A World Guide. 561p. 1985. 100.00x (ISBN 3-598-10533-9). K G Saur.

Lewart, Cass. Science & Engineering Programs for the IBM PC. (Illus.). 150p. 1983. 18.95 (ISBN 0-13-794925-1). P-H.

--Science & Engineering Programs for the PCjr. 200p. 1985. pap. 14.95 (ISBN 0-13-794942-1); incl. disk 29.95 (ISBN 0-13-794975-8). P-H.

--Science & Engineering Programs for the Tandy 2000. 1984. pap. 14.95 cancelled (ISBN 0-13-795089-6). P-H.

--Science & Engineering Sourcebook. 96p. 1982. 17.95 (ISBN 0-13-795229-5); pap. 9.95 (ISBN 0-13-795211-2). P-H.

Lewart, Cass R. Science & Engineering Programs for the IBM PC. (Illus.). 240p. 1984. incl. diskette 39.95 (ISBN 0-13-794934-0). P-H.

--Scientific & Engineering Sourcebook: Professional Programs for the Timex Sinclair 1000. LC 82-62818. (Illus.). 120p. (Orig.). 1983. 14.95 (ISBN 0-07-037444-9, Byte Bks). McGraw.

Lindsay, Robert, ed. Computer Analysis of Neuronal Structures. LC 76-50605. (Illus.). 226p. 1977. 39.50x (ISBN 0-306-30964-5, Plenum Pr). Plenum Pub.

McKenzie, J., et al, eds. Interactive Computer Graphics in Science Teaching. LC 78-40598. (Computers & Their Applications Ser.). 247p. 1978. 42.95x (ISBN 0-470-26419-5). Halsted Pr.

Meck, H. R. Scientific Analysis for Programmable Calculators. (Illus.). 160p. 1981. 15.95 (ISBN 0-13-796417-X, Spec); pap. 7.95 (ISBN 0-13-796409-9). P-H.

Mikhailov, A. I., et al. Scientific Communications & Informatics. Burger, Robert H., tr. LC 83-81012. xxxi, 402p. 1984. text ed. 55.50 (ISBN 0-87815-046-3). Info Resources.

Miller, Alan R. BASIC Programs for Scientists & Engineers. LC 81-84003. (Scientists & Engineers Ser.: No. 2). (Illus.). 318p. 1981. pap. 16.95 (ISBN 0-89588-073-3, B240). SYBEX.

--FORTRAN Programs for Scientists & Engineers. LC 82-80263. (Scientists & Engineers Ser.: No. 3). (Illus.). 280p. 1982. pap. 16.95 (ISBN 0-89588-082-2, F440). SYBEX.

--Pascal Programs for Scientists & Engineers. LC 81-51128. (Scientists & Engineers Ser.: No. 1). (Illus.). 374p. 1981. pap. 17.95 (ISBN 0-89588-058-X, P340). SYBEX.

Murrill, Paul W. & Smith, Cecil L. FORTRAN IV Programming for Engineers & Scientists. 2nd ed. LC 73-1689. (Illus.). 322p. 1973. pap. text ed. 6.50 scp (ISBN 0-352-03700-8, HarpC); scp solution manual 6.95 (ISBN 0-352-03700-8). Har-Row.

Nakamura, Shoichiro. Computational Methods in Engineering & Science. LC 85-9737. 472p. 1986. Repr. of 1977 ed. lib. bdg. price not set (ISBN 0-89874-867-4). Krieger.

Paker, Y. Minicomputers: A Reference Book for Engineers, Scientists & Managers. 1980. 59.00 (ISBN 0-9961005-0-4, 996100504, Pub. by Abacus England). Heyden.

Palmer, Ian R. Data Base Systems: A Practical Reference. 320p. 1975. pap. text ed. 24.50 (ISBN 0-89435-010-2). QED Info Sci.

Reynolds, L. & Simmonds, D. Presentation of Data in Science. rev. ed. 1982. 37.00 (ISBN 90-247-2398-1, Pub. by Martinus Nijhoff Netherlands). Kluwer Academic.

Reynolds, Linda & Simmonds, Doig. Presentation of Data in Science. 223p. 1984. lib. bdg. 32.50 (ISBN 90-247-2398-1, Pub. by Martinus Nijhoff Netherlands); pap. text ed. 24.00 (ISBN 90-247-3054-6, Pub. by Martinus Nijhoff Netherlands). Kluwer Academic.

Rodrigue, Garry. Parallel Computations, Vol. 1. (Computational Techniques Ser.). 1982. 66.00 (ISBN 0-12-592101-2). Acad Pr.

Rossmassler, S. A. & Watson, D. G., eds. Data Handling for Science & Technology: An Overview & Sourcebook. xvi, 184p. 1980. 35.00 (ISBN 0-444-86012-6, North-Holland). Elsevier.

Ruckdeschel, Fred. BASIC Scientific Subroutines, 2 vols. 1981. Vol. 1. 27.95 (ISBN 0-07-054201-5); Vol. 2. 27.95 (ISBN 0-07-054202-3). McGraw.

Rumble, J. R. & Hampel, V. E. Database Management in Science Technology. 1984. 45.00 (ISBN 0-444-86865-8, I-085-84). Elsevier.

Scientific & Engineering Software Guide. 287p. 1984. 19.95 (ISBN 0-317-04403-6). Micro Info.

Severin, Ranier. Commodore 64 for Scientists & Engineers. Dykema, Greg, tr. from Ger. 250p. 1984. pap. text ed. 19.95 (ISBN 0-916439-09-7). Abacus Soft.

Shanahan, William F. Essential Math, Science, & Computer Terms for College Freshmen. LC 79-3323. (Illus.). 1981. pap. 5.95 (ISBN 0-671-18435-0). Monarch Pr.

Siler, William & Lindberg, Donald A., eds. Computers in Life Science Research. LC 75-34075. (Illus.). 272p. 1975. 45.00x (ISBN 0-306-34502-1, Plenum Pr). Plenum Pub.

Sloman, Aaron. The Computer Revolution in Philosophy: Philosophy, Science & Models of Mind. (Harvester Studies in Cognitive Science). 1978. text ed. 27.75x (ISBN 0-391-00830-7); pap. text ed. 16.00x (ISBN 0-391-00831-5). Humanities.

Smardzewski, R. R. Microprocessor Programming & Applications for Scientists & Engineers. LC 84-13759. (Data Handling in Science & Technology Ser.: Vol. 1). 1984. 36.50 (ISBN 0-444-42407-5). Elsevier.

Stepleman, R. S., ed. Scientific Computing: Applications of Mathematics & Computing to the Physical Sciences. 364p. 1983. 51.00 (ISBN 0-444-86607-8). Elsevier.

Streeter, Donald N. The Scientific Process & the Computer. LC 73-21744. pap. 120.00 (ISBN 0-317-08515-8, 2007078). Bks Demand UMI.

Talcott Mountain Science Center. Byte by Byte: Microcomputer Programs for the Middle School Science Classroom. 12.95 (643). Creative Learning.

--Discovering Science on Your ADAM, with 25 Programs. (Illus.). 176p. (Orig.). 1984. 15.95 (ISBN 0-8306-0780-3); pap. 9.95 (ISBN 0-8306-1780-9, 1780). TAB Bks.

Thompson, William J. Computing in Applied Science. LC 83-21625. 325p. 1984. text ed. 28.50 (ISBN 0-471-09355-6). Wiley.

Trost, Stanley R. & Pomernacki, Charles. VisiCalc for Science & Engineering. LC 83-60045. (Illus.). 203p. 1983. pap. 15.95 (ISBN 0-89588-096-2). SYBEX.

Williams. Computer-Readable Databases, a Directory & Data Source Book: Science, Technology & Medicine. 4th ed. Date not set. write for info. (ISBN 0-444-87613-8). Elsevier.

Wolfe, Philip & Koelling, C. Patrick. Basic Engineering & Scientific Programs for the IBM PC. LC 83-7100. (Illus.). 356p. 1983. pap. text ed. 21.95 (ISBN 0-89303-330-8); bk. & diskette 46.95 (ISBN 0-89303-331-6); 25.00 (ISBN 0-89303-333-2). Brady Comm.

Yuen, C. K. & Fraser, D. Digital Spectral Analysis. 1979. 12.00x (ISBN 0-643-02419-0, Pub. by CSIRO). Intl Spec Bk.

--Digital Spectral Analysis. (Applicable Mathematics Ser.). 168p. 1979. pap. text ed. 24.95 (ISBN 0-273-08439-9). Pitman Pub MA.

SCIENCE–DICTIONARIES

Alford, M. H. & Alford, V. L. Russian-English Scientific & Technical Dictionary, 2 vols. LC 73-88348. (Rus. & Eng.). 1970. Set. 60.00 (ISBN 0-08-012227-2). Pergamon.

Asimov, Isaac. Enciclopedia Biografica De Ciencia y Tecnologia. 2nd ed. (Espn.). 800p. 1974. 47.95 (ISBN 84-292-7004-3, S-50544). French & Eur.

Ballentyne, D. W. & Lovett, D. R. Dictionary of Named Effects & Laws in Chemistry, Physics & Mathematics. 4th ed. 1980. 19.95x (ISBN 0-412-22390-2, NO. 6780, Pub. by Chapman & Hall England). Methuen Inc.

Beadnell, Charles M. Encyclopaedic Dictionary of Science & War. LC 74-164093. 1971. Repr. of 1943 ed. 43.00x (ISBN 0-8103-3753-3). Gale.

Bordes, Gerard. La Grande Encyclopedie Alpha des Sciences et des Techniques, 20 vols. (Fr.). 1976. Set. 1225.00 (ISBN 0-686-57311-0, M-6290). French & Eur.

Braun, Edmund. Wissenschaftstheoretisches Lexikon. (Ger.). 1977. 79.95 (ISBN 3-222-10953-2, M-7688, Pub. by Styria). French & Eur.

Butler, Neville, et al. Enciclopedia de la Vida, 5 vols. 6th ed. (Espn.). 2100p. 1978. Set. leather 175.00 (ISBN 84-02-00346-X, S-50570). French & Eur.

Bynum, William F., et al, eds. Dictionary of the History of Science. LC 81-47116. (Illus.). 528p. 1981. 50.00 (ISBN 0-691-08287-1); pap. 12.95 (ISBN 0-691-02384-0). Princeton U Pr.

Carpovich, Eugene A. Russian-English Atomic Dictionary: Physics, Mathematics, Nucleonics. rev. ed. 2nd ed. LC 57-8256. (Rus. & Eng.). 1959. 15.00 (ISBN 0-911484-00-0). Tech Dict.

Chu-Chi, W. English-Chinese Dictionary of Physical Terms. (Eng. & Chinese.). 218p. 1973. leatherette 25.00 (ISBN 0-686-92350-2, M-9258). French & Eur.

Clarke, Donald. How It Works: The Illustrated Science & Invention Encyclopedia. 3rd ed. (Illus.). 3440p. 1983. lib. bdg. 324.95x (ISBN 0-686-39381-3). M Cavendish Corp.

Concise Science Dictionary. (Illus.). 1985. 22.50 (ISBN 0-19-211593-6). Oxford U Pr.

Considine, Douglas M. Van Nostrand's Scientific Encyclopedia. 6th ed. (Illus.). 3100p. 1984. 2 vol. ed. 139.50 (ISBN 0-442-25164-5); 1 vol. ed. 107.50 (ISBN 0-442-25161-0). Van Nos Reinhold.

Considine, Douglas M., ed. Van Nostrand's Scientific Encyclopedia. 6th ed. (Illus.). 3100p. 1982. One volume. 107.50 (ISBN 0-442-25161-0); Two volume set. 139.50 (ISBN 0-442-25164-5). Van Nos Reinhold.

Cook, J. Gordon. Science for Everyman Encylopedia. 643p. 1964. 40.00x (ISBN 0-900541-51-2, Pub. by Meadowfield Pr England). State Mutual Bk.

Czerni & Skrzynka. Polish-English Dictionary of Science & Technology. (Pol. & Eng.). 754p. 1976. 95.00x (ISBN 0-686-44737-9, Pub. by Collets). State Mutual Bk.

Czerni, S. & Skrzynska, M. Polish Concise Technology Dictionary: Polish-English. 5th ed. 846p. 1983. 50.00x (ISBN 0-89918-537-1). Vanous.

--Polish Science & Technology Dictionary: English-Polish. 6th ed. (Pol. & Eng.). 910p. 1982. 50.00x (ISBN 0-89918-536-3, P536). Vanous.

Czerni, Sergiusz & Skrzynska, Maria, eds. English-Polish Dictionary of Science & Technology. 5th ed. 1976. 36.00x (ISBN 0-686-23574-6). Intl Learn Syst.

--Polish-English Dictionary of Science & Technology. 3rd ed. (Pol. & Eng.). 1976. 30.00x (ISBN 0-686-19981-2). Intl Learn Syst.

--Polish-English, English-Polish Dictionary of Science & Technology, 2 Vols. rev. & enl. ed. 1755p. Set. 85.00 (ISBN 0-318-04724-1, Pub. by Wydawnictwa Poland). Heinman.

Daintith, John. A Dictionary of Physical Sciences. LC 76-41039. (Illus.). 1977. 25.00x (ISBN 0-87663-723-3, Pica Pr). Universe.

Daintith, John, ed. A Dictionary of Physical Sciences. (A Helix Bk.: No. 379). (Illus.). 340p. 1983. pap. 9.95 (ISBN 0-8226-0379-9). Rowman & Allanheld.

De la Cierva, Patronato J. Diccionario Ruso-Espanol de la Ciencia y la Tecnica. 2nd ed. (Span.). 700p. 1972. 50.00 (ISBN 84-237-0407-6, S-50249). French & Eur.

DeVries, Louis & Hochman, Stanley. French-English Science & Technology Dictionary. 4th ed. (Fr. & Eng.). 1976. 39.95 (ISBN 0-07-016629-3). McGraw.

DeVries, Louis & Jacolev, Leon. German-English Science Dictionary. 4th ed. (Ger. & Eng.). 1978. 37.95 (ISBN 0-07-016602-1). McGraw.

Dictionary of Science & Technology. (Eng. & Chinese.). 469p. 1973. 14.95 (ISBN 0-686-92348-0, M-9261). French & Eur.

Dictionary of Science & Technology. (Eng. & Chinese.). 1689p. 1978. 9.95 (ISBN 0-686-92375-8, M-9560). French & Eur.

Dictionary of Science & Technology: Eng. & Chinese. (Chinese.). 713p. 1979. pap. 5.95 (ISBN 0-686-92552-1, M-9587). French & Eur.

Dorian, A. F. Dictionary of Science & Technology: English-German. 2nd., rev. ed. 1402p. 1978. 138.50 (ISBN 0-444-41649-8). Elsevier.

--Dictionary of Science & Technology: German-English. 2nd ed. 1120p. 1981. 121.50 (ISBN 0-444-41997-7). Elsevier.

Dorian, A. F., ed. Dictionary of Science & Technology, 2 Vols. 1979. Vol. I: Eng. & Fr. 138.50 (ISBN 0-444-41829-6); Vol. II: Fr. & Eng. 138.50 (ISBN 0-444-41911-X). Elsevier.

Enciclopedia De la Ciencia y De la Tecnica, 6 vols. 3rd ed. (Espn.). 3055p. 1977. Set. leather 320.00 (ISBN 84-85185-10-2, S-50566). French & Eur.

Enciclopedia de la Ciencia y de la Tecnica, 8 vols. 5th ed. (Espn.). 3055p. 1977. Set. leather 320.00 (ISBN 84-7060-483-X, S-50567). French & Eur.

Enciclopedia De la Ciencia y De la Tecnica, 4 vols. (Espn.). 1344p. 1978. Set. 64.00 (ISBN 84-278-0549-7, S-50543). French & Eur.

Enciclopedia Italiana di Scienze, Lettere ed Arti, (Treccani, 41 vols. (It). 1928-1961. Set. 3685.00 (ISBN 0-8277-3018-7). Pergamon.

Enciclopedia Salvat de las Ciencias, 20 vols. (Espn.). 7840p. 1968. Set. 600.00 (ISBN 84-7137-227-4, S-12298). French & Eur.

Encyclopedie Internationale Des Sciences et Des Techniques, 11 vols. (Fr.). Set. 850.00 (ISBN 0-686-57161-4, M-6220). French & Eur.

Encyclopedie Scientifique et Technique, 5 vols. (Fr.). 2480p. 1975. Set. 495.00 (ISBN 0-686-57166-5, M-6233). French & Eur.

Encyclopedie Thematique Weber: Vol. 5, La Science 1. (Fr.). 59.95 (ISBN 0-686-57171-1, M-6238). French & Eur.

Encyclopedie Thematique Weber: Vol. 6, La Science 2. (Fr.). 59.95 (ISBN 0-686-57172-X, M-6239). French & Eur.

English-Chinese Dictionary of Scientific & Technology Abreviations. (Eng. & Chinese.). 587p. 1979. pap. 9.95 (ISBN 0-686-97363-1, M-9250). French & Eur.

English-Polish Dictionary of Science & Technology. 4th ed. (Eng. & Pol.). 892p. 90.00x (ISBN 0-569-08263-3, Pub. by Collets). State Mutual Bk.

Fachlexikon ABC Technik und Naturwissenschaft, Vols. 1 & 2. (Ger.). 1970. Set. leatherette 55.00 (ISBN 3-87144-004-3, M-7384). French & Eur.

Flood, W. E. Scientific Words: Their Structure & Meaning. LC 74-6707. 220p. 1974. Repr. of 1960 ed. lib. bdg. 22.50x (ISBN 0-8371-7541-0, FLOW). Greenwood.

Godman, A. & Payne, E. M. F. Longman Dictionary of Scientific Usage. (Illus.). 1979. pap. text ed. 15.95x (ISBN 0-582-52587-X). Longman.

Grolier Incorporated. Encyclopedia Science Supplement, 1984. Kondo, Herbert, ed. LC 64-7603. (Illus.). 1982. write for info. (ISBN 0-7172-1514-8). Grolier Ed Corp.

Halbauer, S. Russisch-Deutsches Woerterbuch Fuer Naturwissenschaftler und Ingenieure. (Ger. & Rus.). 170p. 1971. 9.95 (ISBN 0-686-56466-9, M-7607, Pub. by M. Hueber). French & Eur.

Hyman, Charles J., ed. Dictionary of Physics & Allied Sciences: German-English. LC 77-6949. (Ger. & Eng.). 1978. 30.00 (ISBN 0-8044-4433-1). Ungar.

Idlin, Ralph, ed. Dictionary of Physics & Allied Sciences: English-German. LC 77-6950. (Eng. & Ger.). 1978. 30.00 (ISBN 0-8044-4435-8). Ungar.

Illustrated Science & Invention Encyclopedia: How It Works, 23 vols. 1982. 183.54 (ISBN 0-87475-801-7). Stuttman.

Insight: The Illustrated Encyclopedia of Science & the Future. (Illus.). 2752p. 1983. lib. bdg. 179.95x (ISBN 0-86307-069-8). M Cavendish Corp.

Japanese-Chinese Science & Technology Dictionary. (Japanese & Chinese.). 175p. 1976. 19.95 (ISBN 0-686-92480-0, M-9260). French & Eur.

Jerrard, H. G. & McNeill, D. B. Diccionario de Unidades Cientificas. 3rd ed. (Span.). 216p. 1974. pap. 11.95 (ISBN 0-686-57367-6, S-50215). French & Eur.

Jouffroy, A. Dictionnaire des Inventions et Decouvertes Anciennes et Modernes, 2 vols. Migne, J. P., ed. (Nouvelle Encyclopedie Theologique Ser.: Vols. 35-36). (Fr.). 1424p. Repr. of 1860 ed. lib. bdg. 181.00x (ISBN 0-89241-277-1). Caratzas.

Judge, Harry, et al, eds. Oxford Illustrated Encyclopedia: The Physical World, Vol. 1. (Illus.). 384p. 1985. 35.00 (ISBN 0-19-869129-7). Oxford U Pr.

Khatib, Ahmed. English-Arabic Dictionary of Scientific & Technical Terms. (Illus.). 1983. 48.00x (ISBN 0-86685-075-9). Intl Bk Ctr.

Lapedes, D. Dizionario Enciclopedico Scientifico e Tecnico: Inglese-Italiano, Italiano-Inglese. (Eng. & Ital.). 2122p. 1980. Leatherette 175.00 (ISBN 0-686-92540-8, M-9201). French & Eur.

Lucas, David. First Science Dictionary: English with Arabic Glossary. 9.95x (ISBN 0-86685-077-5). Intl Bk Ctr.

McGraw-Hill Editors. Dictionary of Science & Engineering. 960p. 1984. 36.00 (ISBN 0-07-045483-3). McGraw.

--McGraw-Hill Encyclopedia of Science & Technology, 15 vols. 5th ed. (Illus.). 12715p. 1982. Set. 1100.00 (ISBN 0-07-079280-1). McGraw.

McGraw-Hill Editors & Parker, Sybil, eds. McGraw-Hill Concise Encyclopedia of Science & Technology. LC 83-26794. (Illus.). 2065p. 1984. 95.00 (ISBN 0-07-045482-5). Mcgraw.

McGraw-Hill Editors & Parker, Sybil P., eds. McGraw Hill Dictionary of Earth Sciences. 3rd ed. 856p. 1984. 36.00 (ISBN 0-07-045252-0). McGraw.

Malgorn, Guy. Spanish-English, English-Spanish Technical Dictionary, 2 Vols. 2nd ed. Rodriguez, Maria R. & Armisen, Pedro, trs. from Fr. (Orig.). 1985. Set. pap. 35.00 (ISBN 0-318-04723-3, Pub. by Paraninfo Spain). Span.-Eng., xxiv-570p (ISBN 84-283-1354-7). Eng.-Span., xxiv-606p (ISBN 84-283-0923-X). Heinman.

Mingot, Tomas De Galiana. Pequeno Larousse de ciencias y tecnicas. new ed. (Span.). 1056p. 1975. 26.95 (ISBN 0-685-55467-8, 21115). Larousse.

Mullen, William B. Dictionary of Scientific Word Elements. LC 69-20141. (Quality Paperback: No. 102). 146p. (Orig.). 1969. pap. 2.95 (ISBN 0-8226-0102-8). Littlefield.

Neurath, Otto, et al. Encyclopedia & Unified Science. (Foundations of the Unity of Science Ser.: Vol. 1, No. 1). (Orig.). 1938. pap. 1.85x (ISBN 0-226-57576-4, P400). U of Chicago Pr.

Neurath, Otto, et al, eds. Foundations of the Unity of Science: Toward an International Encyclopedia of Unified Science. LC 56-553. (Foundations of the Unity of Science Ser: Vols. 1 & 2). 1955. Vol. 1. 25.00x (ISBN 0-226-57586-1); Vol. 2. 25.00x (ISBN 0-226-57588-8). U of Chicago Pr.

O'Bannon, Loran S. Dictionary of Ceramic Science & Engineering. 350p. 1983. 45.00x (ISBN 0-306-41324-8, Plenum Pr). Plenum Pub.

Radcliffe, Stanley. Learn Scientific German. 165p. 1978. 30.00x (ISBN 0-906515-16-5, Pub. by Bristol Classical Pr). State Mutual Bk.

Ruffo, Sandro. Enciclopedia Monografica de Ciencias Naturales, 5 vols. (Espn.). 2500p. 1974. Set. 170.00 (ISBN 84-03-40999-0, S-50568). French & Eur.

Technisch Wissenschaftliches Taschenwoerterbuch. (Ger.). 408p. (Technical Scientific Dictionary). 32.00 (ISBN 3-87749-014-X, M-7643, Pub. by Georg Siemens Verlagsbuchhandlung). French & Eur.

Thines, Georges & Lempereur, Agnes. Dictionnaire General des Sciences Humaines. (Fr.). 1000p. 1975. 135.00 (ISBN 0-686-57231-9, M-6532). French & Eur.

Ubarov, Chapman. Diccionario de Ciencias. (Span.). 226p. 1970. 12.25 (ISBN 84-237-0299-5, S-50245). French & Eur.

Yule, John-David. Concise Encyclopedia of the Sciences. 600p. 1981. 29.95 (ISBN 0-87196-491-0). Facts on File.

Yule, John-David, ed. Concise Encyclopedia of the Sciences. 590p. 1982. pap. 18.95 (ISBN 0-442-29208-2). Van Nos Reinhold.

Zamoyska, H. Multilingual Student's Dictionary of Basic Terms Used in Chemistry, Mathematics, Physics & Allied Fields. 1978. 49.00x (ISBN 0-686-44734-4, Pub. by Collets). State Mutual Bk.

Zimmerman, M. G. Russian-English Scientific & Technical Dictionary of Useful Combinations & Expressions. (Rus. & Eng.). 27.50 (ISBN 0-87559-119-1); thumb indexed 32.50 (ISBN 0-87559-140-X). Shalom.

Zimmerman, Mikhail. Russian-English Translators Dictionary: A Guide to Scientific & Technical Usage. 2nd ed. LC 83-10229. 544p. 1984. 59.95 (ISBN 0-471-90218-7, Pub. by Wiley-Interscience). Wiley.

Zimmerman, Mikhail G. Russian-English Translators Dictionary: A Guide to Scientific & Technical Usage. LC 67-19391. (Rus. & Eng.). 295p. 1967. 32.50x (ISBN 0-306-30300-0, Plenum Pr). Plenum Pub.

SCIENCE–EARLY WORKS TO 1800

see also Science, Ancient; Science, Medieval

Cardano, Girolamo. Opera Omnia, 10 vols. Repr. of 1663 ed. 34.50 ea.; Set. 445.00 (ISBN 0-384-07500-2). Johnson Repr.

Clayton, John. Reverend John Clayton: A Parson with a Scientific Mind. Berkeley, Edmund & Berkeley, Dorothy S., eds. LC 65-23459. (Virginia Historical Document: No. 6). (Illus.). 1965. 15.00x (ISBN 0-8139-0067-0). U Pr of Va.

Cohen, Morris R. & Drabkin, Israel E. Source Book in Greek Science. LC 58-12979. (Source Books in the History of the Sciences Ser). (Illus.). 1948. text ed. 35.00x (ISBN 0-674-82320-6). Harvard U Pr.

Grant, Edward. A Source Book in Medieval Science. LC 70-183977. (Source Books in the History of Science Ser). 896p. 1974. text ed. 45.00x (ISBN 0-674-82360-5). Harvard U Pr.

Hooke, Robert. Posthumous Works. (Illus.). 518p. 1971. Repr. of 1775 ed. 65.00x (ISBN 0-7146-1600-1, F Cass Co). Biblio Dist.

King, David A. A Catalogue of the Scientific Manuscripts in the Egyptian National Library, Pt. 1. (Catalogs Ser.: Vol. 2). (Arabic.). 830p. 1981. pap. 40.00 (ISBN 0-686-84036-4, Am Res Ctr Egypt Publications Ser.). Undena Pubns.

Lanfranco Of Milan. Lanfrank's Science of Cirurgie. Fleischhacker, R. V., ed. (EETS, OS Ser.: No. 102). 25.00 (ISBN 0-527-00103-1). Kraus Repr.

Ray, John. The Wisdom of God Manifested in the Works of the Creation: Heavenly Bodies, Elements, Meteors, Fossils, Vegetables, Animals. Egerton, Frank N., 3rd, ed. LC 77-74250. (History of Ecology Ser.). 1978. Repr. of 1717 ed. lib. bdg. 40.00x (ISBN 0-405-10419-7). Ayer Co Pubs.

Renaissance Books of Science, from the Collection of Albert E. Lownes. LC 70-123866. (Illus.). 123p. 1970. pap. 12.50x (ISBN 0-87451-985-3). U Pr of New Eng.

Rohault, Jacques. A System of Natural Philosophy, 2 Vols. (Sources of Science, House Ser.: No. 50). Repr. of 1723 ed. Set. 65.00 (ISBN 0-384-51760-9). Johnson Repr.

Sherley, Thomas. A Philosophical Essay: Declaring the Probable Causes Whence Stones Are Produced in the Greater World. Albritton, Claude C., Jr., ed. LC 77-6541. (History of Geology Ser.). 1978. Repr. of 1672 ed. lib. bdg. 17.00x (ISBN 0-405-10460-X). Ayer Co Pubs.

Shirley, John & Hoeniger, F. David, eds. Science & the Arts in the Renaissance. LC 82-49312. (Illus.). 224p. 1985. 32.50 (ISBN 0-918016-69-X). Folger Bks.

Stearns, Raymond P. Science in the British Colonies of America. LC 78-122915. (Illus.). 780p. 1970. 35.00x (ISBN 0-252-00120-6). U of Ill Pr.

SCIENCE–EXAMINATIONS, QUESTIONS, ETC.

Anderson, Fred A. Scoring High on Medical & Health Sciences Exams. 48p. (Orig.). 1983. pap. 5.95 (ISBN 0-939570-02-5). Skills Improvement.

Buros, Oscar K., ed. Science Tests & Reviews. LC 75-8114. xxiii, 296p. 1975. 25.00x (ISBN 0-910674-21-3). U of Nebr Pr.

Diamond, Harriet & Dutwin, Physsil. The Science Test. rev. ed. (GED Ser.). 202p. 1985. pap. 6.85 (ISBN 0-8092-5586-3). Contemp Bks.

Ford, Brian J. One Hundred & One More Questions about Science. (Illus.). 128p. 1984. 12.95 (ISBN 0-241-11246-X, Pub. by Hamish Hamilton England). David & Charles.

Goldwyn, Martin. You'd Better Believe It! (Illus.). 256p. 1982. pap. 5.95 (ISBN 0-8065-0792-6). Citadel Pr.

Katz, Irvin W. MCAT Science Review. LC 83-11948. 288p. 1983. pap. 8.95 (ISBN 0-668-05745-9, 5745). Arco.

MacKay, A. L. The Harvest of a Quiet Eye: A Selection of Scientific Questions. 1977. 22.50 (ISBN 0-9960026-0-X, Pub. by A Hilger England); pap. 10.00 (ISBN 0-9960025-9-6). Heyden.

Nathan, Harold D. GED Science Test Preparation Guide: High School Equivalency Examination. (Cliffs Test Preparation Ser.). 164p. (Orig.). 1980. pap. 3.95 (ISBN 0-8220-2010-6). Cliffs.

Rudman, Jack. Biology & General Science. (National Teachers Examination Ser.: NT-3). (Cloth bdg. avail. on request). pap. 11.95 (ISBN 0-8373-8413-3). Natl Learning.

--Biology & General Science - Sr. H.S. (Teachers License Examination Ser.: T-4). (Cloth bdg. avail. on request). pap. 13.95 (ISBN 0-8373-8004-9). Natl Learning.

--Chemistry & General Sciences - Sr. H.S. (Teachers License Examination Ser.: T-6). (Cloth bdg. avail. on request). pap. 13.95 (ISBN 0-686-66502-3). Natl Learning.

--Chemistry, Physics & General Science. (National Teachers Examination Ser.: NT-7). (Cloth bdg. avail. on request). pap. 11.95 (ISBN 0-8373-8417-6). Natl Learning.

--Earth Science & General Science - Sr. H.S. (Teachers License Examination Ser.: T-14). (Cloth bdg. avail. on request). pap. 13.95 (ISBN 0-8373-8014-6). Natl Learning.

--General Science-Jr. H.S. (Teachers License Examination Ser.: T-22). (Cloth bdg. avail. on request). pap. 13.95 (ISBN 0-8373-8022-7). Natl Learning.

--Laboratory Specialist - Jr. H.S. (Teachers License Examination Ser.: T-33). (Cloth bdg. avail. on request). pap. 13.95 (ISBN 0-8373-8033-2). Natl Learning.

--Laboratory Specialist (Physical Sciences) Sr. H.S. (Teachers License Examination Ser.: T-35). (Cloth bdg. avail. on request). pap. 13.95 (ISBN 0-8373-8035-9). Natl Learning.

--Natural Sciences. (College-Level Examination Ser.: ATS-9D). (Cloth bdg. avail. on request). pap. 9.95 (ISBN 0-8373-5009-3). Natl Learning.

--Physics & General Science - Sr. H.S. (Teachers License Examination Ser.: T-46). (Cloth bdg. avail. on request). pap. 13.95 (ISBN 0-8373-8046-4). Natl Learning.

--Professional Careers in the Natural Sciences. (Career Examination Ser.: C-2386). (Cloth bdg. avail. on request). pap. 10.00 (ISBN 0-8373-2386-X). Natl Learning.

--Science & Mathematics. (National Teachers Examination Ser.: NC-5). (Cloth bdg. avail. on request). pap. 11.95 (ISBN 0-8373-8405-2). Natl Learning.

--Technical Aide in Science & Engineering. (Career Examination Ser.: C-829). (Cloth bdg. avail. on request). pap. 10.00 (ISBN 0-8373-0829-1). Natl Learning.

Schenk, Brian, ed. The Cambridge Program for the GED Science Test. (GED Preparation Ser.). (Illus.). 224p. (Orig.). 1981. pap. 6.66 (ISBN 0-8428-9389-X); Cambridge Exercise Book for the Science Test. wkbk. 3.93 (ISBN 0-8428-9395-4). Cambridge Bk.

Wall, Janet, compiled by. Compendium of Standardized Science Tests. rev. ed. 1981. pap. 7.00 (ISBN 0-87355-021-8). Natl Sci Tchrs.

SCIENCE–EXHIBITIONS

Decker, Fred W. Science Travel Guide: The Guide to Technological Expositions, Museums, Landmarks, & Science Originals. 1971. pap. 1.95X (ISBN 0-88246-017-X). Oreg St U Bkstrs.

Science & Technology Division, Akron-Summit County Public Library, ed. Science Fair Project Index: Nineteen Seventy-Three to Nineteen Eighty. LC 83-3353. 729p. 1983. 47.50 (ISBN 0-8108-1605-9). Scarecrow.

SCIENCE–EXPERIMENTS

see also Experimental Design

Anderson, O. Roger. The Experience of Science: A New Perspective for Laboratory Teaching. LC 75-37967. 1976. pap. text ed. 8.95x (ISBN 0-8077-2489-0). Tchrs Coll.

Brown, Robert. Three Hundred Thirty-Three More Science Tricks & Experiments. (Illus.). 208p. 1984. 15.95 (ISBN 0-8306-0835-4); pap. 10.95 (ISBN 0-8306-1835-X, 1835). TAB Bks.

--Three Hundred Thirty-Three Science Tricks & Experiments. (Illus.). 208p. (Orig.). 1984. 15.95 (ISBN 0-8306-0825-7); pap. 9.95 (ISBN 0-8306-1825-2, 1825). TAB Bks.

Conant, James B., et al. Harvard Case Histories in Experimental Science, 2 Vols. Roller, Duane & Roller, Duane H., eds. LC 57-12843. (Illus.). 1957. Set. 40.00x (ISBN 0-674-37400-2). Harvard U Pr.

DeVito, Alfred & Krockover, Gerald H. Creative Sciencing: A Practical Approach. 2nd ed. (Illus.). 262p. 1980. text ed. 17.95 (ISBN 0-316-18159-5); tchr's manual avail. (ISBN 0-316-18162-5). Little.

Engelhardt, Tristram H., Jr. & Caplan, Arthur, eds. Scientific Controversies: Case Studies in the Resolution & Closure of Disputes in Sciences & Technology. 704p. Date not set. price not set. (ISBN 0-521-25565-1). Cambridge U Pr.

Gardner, Martin. Entertaining Science Experiments with Everyday Objects. Orig. Title: Science Puzzlers. (Illus.). 128p. 1981. pap. 2.50 (ISBN 0-486-24201-3). Dover.

--Entertaining Science Experiments with Everyday Objects. (Illus.). 13.50 (ISBN 0-8446-5888-X). Peter Smith.

Harre, Rom. Great Scientific Experiments: Twenty Experiments That Changed Our View of the World. (Illus.). 1983. pap. 8.95 (ISBN 0-19-286036-4, GB 733, GB). Oxford U Pr.

--Great Scientific Experiments: Twenty Experiments That Changed Our View of the World. (Illus.). 1981. 17.95 (ISBN 0-19-520436-0). Oxford U Pr.

Marson, Ron. Metric Measuring Thirty-Five. LC 81-90446. (Science with Simple Things Ser.: No. 35). (Illus.). 80p. 1984. pap. 13.95 tchr's ed. (ISBN 0-941008-35-5). Tops Learning.

Science & Technology Division, Akron-Summit County Public Library, ed. Science Fair Project Index: Nineteen Seventy-Three to Nineteen Eighty. LC 83-3353. 729p. 1983. 47.50 (ISBN 0-8108-1605-9). Scarecrow.

SCIENCE–FELLOWSHIPS

see Science–Scholarships, Fellowships, etc.

SCIENCE–HISTORY

see also Science, Ancient; Science, Medieval

Abro, A. The Evolution of Scientific Thought: From Newton to Einstein. 2nd ed. (Illus.). 481p. 1950. pap. 7.50 (ISBN 0-486-20002-7). Dover.

Achinstein, Peter & Hannaway, Owen, eds. Observation, Experiment, & Hypothesis in Modern Physical Science. 1985. 37.50 (ISBN 0-262-01083-6). MIT Pr.

Al-Daffa, A. A. A Brief Exposition of Arabic & Islamic Scientific Heritage: Arabic Edition. LC 78-31087. 256p. 1979. 14.50 (ISBN 0-471-05348-1). Wiley.

Alford, C. Fred. Science & the Revenge of Nature: Marcuse & Habermas. LC 85-627. 208p. 1983. 24.50 (ISBN 0-8130-0817-4). U Presses Fla.

Anikin, Andrei V. A Science In Its Youth. Cook, K. M., tr. from Rus. LC 78-31568. 389p. 1979. pap. 3.50 (ISBN 0-7178-0503-4). Intl Pubs Co.

Anton, John P., ed. Science & the Sciences in Plato. LC 78-13418. 1980. 25.00x (ISBN 0-88206-301-4). Caravan Bks.

Ashley Montagu, M. F., ed. Studies & Essays in the History of Science & Learning. LC 74-26275. (History, Philosophy & Sociology of Science Ser). (Illus.). 1975. Repr. of 1944 ed. 47.50x (ISBN 0-405-06603-1). Ayer Co Pubs.

Babbage, C. Reflections on the Decline of Science in England & on Some of Its Causes. 256p. 1971. Repr. of 1830 ed. 25.00x (ISBN 0-7165-1578-4, BBA 02134, Pub. by Irish Academic Pr Ireland). Biblio Dist.

Badash, Lawrence. Kapitza, Rutherford & the Kremlin. LC 84-11822. (Illus.). 144p. 1985. 20.00x (ISBN 0-300-01465-1). Yale U Pr.

Barnett, H. G. Qualitative Science. LC 82-90249. 1983. 15.00 (ISBN 0-533-05373-0). Vantage.

Bedini, Silvio A. At the Sign of the Compass & Quadrant: The Life & Times of Anthony Lamb. LC 83-73281. (Translations Ser.: Vol. 74, pt. 1). 84p. 1984. 12.00 (ISBN 0-87169-741-6). Am Philos.

Bennett, Adrian A. John Fryer: The Introduction of Western Science & Technology into Nineteenth-Century China. LC 68-4092. (East Asian Monograph Ser.: No. 24). 1967. pap. 11.00x (ISBN 0-674-47650-6). Harvard U Pr.

Berman, Morris. Social Change & Scientific Organization: The Royal Instutution, Seventeen Ninety-Nine to Eighteen Forty-Four. LC 77-79702. (Illus.). 249p. 1978. 34.95x (ISBN 0-8014-1093-2). Cornell U Pr.

Bernal, J. D. Science in History, 4 vols. Incl. Vol. 1. The Emergence of Science. pap. 8.95x (ISBN 0-262-52020-6); Vol. 2. The Scientific & Industrial Revolution. pap. 8.95x (ISBN 0-262-52021-4); Vol. 3. The Natural Sciences in Our Time. pap. 8.95x (ISBN 0-262-52022-2); Vol. 4. The Social Sciences: a Conclusion. pap. 8.95x (ISBN 0-262-52023-0). 1971. Set. pap. 30.00x (ISBN 0-262-02142-0). MIT Pr.

Bernhard, C. G. & Crawford, E., eds. Science, Technology & Society in the Time of Alfred Nobel: Proceedings of a Nobel Symposium held at Bjorkborn, Karlskoga, Sweden, August 17-22, 1981. LC 82-11254. (Illus.). 440p. 1982. 65.00 (ISBN 0-08-027939-2). Pergamon.

Bezkorovainy, Anatoly. Science & Medicine in Imperial Russia. (Illus.). 271p. 1980. soft cover, spiral bdg. 12.00 (ISBN 0-9607600-0-8). Bezkorovainy.

Boas, Marie. Scientific Renaissance, 1450-1630. (Illus.). pap. 7.95xi (ISBN 0-06-130583-9, TB583, Torch). Har-Row.

Bochner, Salomon. Role of Mathematics in the Rise of Science. 1966. 37.50x (ISBN 0-691-08028-3); pap. 10.50 (ISBN 0-691-02371-9). Princeton U Pr.

British Association For The Advancement Of Science. March of Science: A First Quinquennial Review 1931-1935. facs. ed. LC 68-55841. (Essay Index Reprint Ser). 1937. 17.00 (ISBN 0-8369-0254-8). Ayer Co Pubs.

Brockway, Lucile H. Science & Colonial Expansion: The Role of the British Royal Botanic Gardens. LC 79-51669. (Studies in Social Discontinuity). 1979. 29.50 (ISBN 0-12-134150-X). Acad Pr.

Brown, Harcourt. Scientific Organizations in Seventeenth Century France, 1620-1680. LC 66-27046. 1967. Repr. of 1934 ed. 8.50x (ISBN 0-8462-0974-8). Russell.

Buchdahl, G. Fine Structure History of Science: Lessons for Methodology. pap. 14.75 (ISBN 0-08-028930-4). Pergamon.

Bullough, Vern L., ed. The Scientific Revolution. LC 77-21207. (European Problem Studies). 136p. 1978. pap. text ed. 5.95 (ISBN 0-88275-635-4). Krieger.

Burke, John G. The Uses of Science in the Age of Newton. LC 83-1223. (UCLA Clark Library Professorship: No. 8). 226p. 1984. text ed. 22.50x (ISBN 0-520-04970-5). U of Cal Pr.

Butterfield, Herbert. Origins of Modern Science. rev. ed. 1965. pap. text ed. 10.95x (ISBN 0-02-905070-7). Free Pr.

Butts, Robert E. Kant & the Double Government Methodology. 1984. lib. bdg. 43.00 (ISBN 90-277-1760-5, Pub. by Reidel Holland). Kluwer Academic.

Bynum, William F., et al, eds. Dictionary of the History of Science. LC 81-47116. (Illus.). 528p. 1981. 50.00 (ISBN 0-691-08287-1); pap. 12.95 (ISBN 0-691-02384-0). Princeton U Pr.

Casimir, Hendrik B. Haphazard Reality: Half A Century of Science. LC 83-48112. 368p. 1984. pap. 7.64i (ISBN 0-06-091104-2, CN 1104, CN). Har-Row.

Caverni, Raffaello. Storia Del Metodo Sperimentale in Italia, 6 vols. xxii, 3478p. 1972. Repr. of 1891 ed. 300.00 (ISBN 0-384-07965-2). Johnson Repr.
Charleton, Walter. Physiologia Epicuro-Gassendo-Charltoniana; or, a Fabrick of Science Natural Upon the Hypothesis of Atoms. 1967. Repr. of 1654 ed. 50.00 (ISBN 0-384-08535-0). Johnson Repr.
Clagett, Marshall, ed. Critical Problems in the History of Science. LC 59-5304. pap. 108.20 (ISBN 0-8357-9773-2, 2015357). Bks Demand UMI.
Cohen, I. Bernard. Album of Science: From Leonardo to Lavoisier, 1450-1800. LC 80-15542. (Illus.). 1980. 55.00 (ISBN 0-684-15377-7, ScribR). Scribner.
--Revolution in Science. (Illus.). 704p. 1985. 25.00 (ISBN 0-674-76777-2, Belknap Pr). Harvard U Pr.
Cohen, I. Bernard, ed. The Development of Science Series, 63 vols. 1981. Set. lib. bdg. 2004.00x (ISBN 0-405-13850-4). Ayer Co Pubs.
Conant, James B., et al. Harvard Case Histories in Experimental Science, 2 Vols. Roller, Duane & Roller, Duane H., eds. LC 57-12843. (Illus.). 1957. Set. 40.00x (ISBN 0-674-37400-2). Harvard U Pr.
Cooter, Roger. The Cultural Meaning of Popular Science: Phrenology & the Organization of Consent in Nineteenth Century Britain. (History of Medicine Ser.). (Illus.). 448p. 1985. 37.50 (ISBN 0-521-22743-7). Cambridge U Pr.
Crawford, Elisabeth. The Beginnings of the Nobel Institution: The Science Prizes 1901-1950. 300p. 1984. 34.50 (ISBN 0-521-26584-3). Cambridge U Pr.
Crombie, A. C. Augustine to Galileo. (Illus.). 1979. text ed. 25.00x (ISBN 0-674-05273-0). Harvard U Pr.
Cutts, Edward L. Science & Characters of the Middle Ages. 552p. 1981. Repr. of 1926 ed. lib. bdg. 40.00 (ISBN 0-8495-0876-2). Arden Lib.
Dampier, William C. History of Science. 1965. pap. 21.95 (ISBN 0-521-09366-X, 366). Cambridge U Pr.
Daniels, George H. American Science in the Age of Jackson. LC 67-28710. 282p. 1968. 29.00x (ISBN 0-231-03073-8). Columbia U Pr.
Darwin, Charles. Metaphysics, Materialism, & the Evolution of the Mind: Early Writings of Charles Darwin. LC 80-15763. 1980. pap. 6.95x (ISBN 0-226-13659-0, P906, Phoen). U of Chicago Pr.
Dauben, Joseph W. & Sexton, Virginia S., eds. History & Philosophy of Science: Selected Papers, Vol. 412. 1983. 33.00x (ISBN 0-89766-217-2); pap. 33.00x (ISBN 0-89766-218-0). NY Acad Sci.
Daumas, ed. Histoire Generale des Techniques, 3 tomes. Incl. Tome I. Les Origines de la Civilisation Technique. 66.80 (ISBN 0-685-35926-3); Tome II. Les Premieres Etapes du Machinsisme. 66.80 (ISBN 0-685-35927-1); Tome III. L' Expansion du Machinisme. 66.80 (ISBN 0-685-35928-X). French & Eur.
Daumas, Maurice. Histoire de la Science. (Historique Ser.). write for info. French & Eur.
Debus, A. G. Man & Nature in the Renaissance. LC 77-91085. (Cambridge History of Science Ser.). (Illus.). 1978. 29.95 (ISBN 0-521-21972-8); pap. 10.95 (ISBN 0-521-29328-6). Cambridge U Pr.
Dingle, Herbert. Scientific Adventure. facs. ed. LC 71-121462. (Essay Index Reprint Ser). 1953. 24.50 (ISBN 0-8369-1749-9). Ayer Co Pubs.
Downs, Robert B. Landmarks in Science: Hippocrates to Carson. LC 82-154. 305p. 1982. lib. bdg. 23.50 (ISBN 0-87287-295-5). Libs Unl.
Durbin, Paul T., ed. A Guide to the Culture of Science, Technology, & Medicine. LC 79-7582. 1980. 65.00 (ISBN 0-02-907820-2). Free Pr.
Eastwood, Bruce. Directory of Audio-Visual Sources: History of Science, Medicine & Technology. 160p. 1979. 20.00 (ISBN 0-88202-185-0). Watson Pub Intl.
Elkana, Yahuda, et al, eds. Debates on the Decline of Science: An Original Anthology. LC 74-25148. (History, Philosophy & Sociology of Science Ser). 1975. Repr. 22.00x (ISBN 0-405-06632-5). Ayer Co Pubs.
Engelhardt, Tristram H., Jr. & Caplan, Arthur, eds. Scientific Controversies: Case Studies in the Resolution & Closure of Disputes in Sciences & Technology. 704p. Date not set. price not set. (ISBN 0-521-25565-1). Cambridge U Pr.
Fernald, L. D. The Hans Legacy: A Story of Science. LC 83-11539. 241p. 1984. text ed. 29.95x (ISBN 0-89859-301-8). L Erlbaum Assocs.
Finocchiaro, Maurice A. History of Science As Explanation. LC 72-3582. 280p. 1973. 15.95x (ISBN 0-8143-1480-5). Wayne St U Pr.
Fleming, Donald & Fish, Joseph. Science & Technology in Providence, 1760-1914: An Essay in the History of Brown University in the Metropolitan Community. LC 52-9555. (Illus.). 54p. 1952. pap. 4.00x (ISBN 0-87057-031-5). U Pr of New Eng.
Gale, George. Theory of Science. (Illus.). 1979. text ed. 28.95 (ISBN 0-07-022680-6). McGraw.
Gascoigne, Robert M. A Historical Catalogue of Scientists & Scientific Books: From the Earliest Times to the Close of the 19th Century. LC 84-48013. (Reference Library of the Humanities). 1200p. 1984. lib. bdg. 150.00 (ISBN 0-8240-8959-6). Garland Pub.
Gillispie, Charles C. Edge of Objectivity: An Essay in the History of Scientific Ideas. 1960. pap. 12.95 (ISBN 0-691-02350-6). Princeton U Pr.
Goldstein, Thomas. Dawn of Modern Science: From the Arabs to Leonardo Da Vinci. 1980. 12.95 (ISBN 0-395-26298-4). HM.
--Dawn of Modern Science: From the Arabs to Leonardo da Vinci. 1982. pap. 7.95 (ISBN 0-395-32132-8). HM.
Gong, Jeh-Tween. Super Unified Theory: The Foundations of Science. LC 84-90325. 104p. 1984. text ed. 35.00 (ISBN 0-916713-01-6); pap. 27.00 (ISBN 0-916713-02-4). Gong Ent.
Greene, John C. American Science in the Age of Jefferson. (Illus.). 1984. pap. text ed. 24.95 (ISBN 0-8138-0102-8). Iowa St U Pr.
Gregory, Richard L. Mind in Science: A History of Explanations in Psychology & Physics. LC 81-7732. (Illus.). 648p. 1981. 34.50 (ISBN 0-521-24307-6). Cambridge U Pr.
Hahn, Roger. Bibliography of Quantitative Studies on Science & Its History. LC 79-65637. (Berkeley Papers in History of Science: No. 3). (Orig.). 1980. pap. 5.00x (ISBN 0-918102-04-9). U Cal Hist Sci Tech.
Hall, A. Rupert. From Galileo to Newton. (Illus.). 380p. 1982. pap. 6.95 (ISBN 0-486-24227-7). Dover.
--The Revolution in Science Fifteen Hundred to Seventeen Fifty. LC 82-8978. 1983. text ed. 18.95x (ISBN 0-582-49133-9). Longman.
Hall, Alfred R. The Scientific Revolution, Fifteen Hundred to Eighteen Hundred: The Formation of the Modern Scientific Attitude. pap. 12.95x (ISBN 0-8070-5093-8, BP 29). Beacon Pr.
Hall, Daniel, et al. The Frustration of Science. LC 74-28502. (History, Philosophy & Sociology of Science Ser). 1975. Repr. 14.00 (ISBN 0-405-06620-1). Ayer Co Pubs.
Haller, Albrecht Von. Tagebuch Seiner Beobachtungen, 2 vols. 774p. Repr. of 1787 ed. 75.00 (ISBN 0-384-21066-X). Johnson Repr.
Hammond, D. B. Stories of Scientific Discovery. facs. ed. LC 74-76901. (Essay Index Reprint Ser). 1923. 17.00 (ISBN 0-8369-0015-4). Ayer Co Pubs.
Hankins, Thomas L. Science & the Enlightenment. (History of Science Ser.). (Illus.). 200p. 1985. 29.95 (ISBN 0-521-24349-1); pap. 9.95 (ISBN 0-521-28619-0). Cambridge U Pr.
Harman, P. M. Energy, Force & Matter: The Conceptual Development of Nineteenth-Century Physics. LC 81-17029. (Cambridge History of Science Ser.). (Illus.). 192p. 1982. pap. 10.95 (ISBN 0-521-28812-6). Cambridge U Pr.
--The Scientific Revolution. (Lancaster Pamphlet Ser.). 48p. 1983. pap. 3.95 (ISBN 0-416-35040-2, NO. 3851). Methuen Inc.
Harre, R. & Eastwood, D. G. The Method of Science. LC 76-116973. (Wykeham Science Ser.: No. 8). 140p. 1970. 9.95x (ISBN 0-8448-1110-6). Crane-Russak Co.
Harre, Rom. Great Scientific Experiments: Twenty Experiments That Changed Our View of the World. (Illus.). 1983. pap. 8.95 (ISBN 0-19-286036-4, GB 733, GB). Oxford U Pr.
Hart, Ivor B. Makers of Science. facs. ed. LC 68-8469. (Essay Index Reprint Ser.). 1923. 16.00 (ISBN 0-8369-0076-6). Ayer Co Pubs.
Heher, J. M., ed. Great Scienctific Adventures One As Reported in the New York Times: Program Guide. 155p. 1981. pap. text ed. 7.95 (ISBN 0-667-00594-3). Microfilming Corp.
Heims, Steve J. John Von Neumann & Norbert Wiener: From Mathematics to the Technologies of Life & Death. 546p. 1980. pap. 11.95 (ISBN 0-262-58056-X). MIT Pr.
Howson, C., ed. Method & Appraisal in the Physical Sciences. LC 75-44580. 280p. 1976. 52.50 (ISBN 0-521-21110-7). Cambridge U Pr.
Hunter, Mark. Fantastic Journeys: Five Great Quests. (Illus.). 1979. 12.95 (ISBN 0-8027-0638-X). Walker & Co.
Hutten, Ernest H. The Origins of Science: An Inquiry into the Foundations of Western Thought. LC 77-13633. 1978. Repr. of 1962 ed. lib. bdg. 27.50x (ISBN 0-313-20003-3, HUOR). Greenwood.
International Congress of Historical Studies (Sciences), 2nd: Rome, 1903, (Atti, 12 vols. in 6. Repr. Set. 420.00 (ISBN 0-317-15410-9). Kraus Repr.
International Congress of Historical Studies (Sciences), 3rd: Berlin, 1908, (Kongress-Tageblatt) Repr. 60.00 (ISBN 0-317-15412-5). Kraus Repr.
International Congress of Historical Studies (Sciences), 4th: London, 1913, (Essays, 2 vols. in 1. Repr. 60.00 (ISBN 0-317-15413-3). Kraus Repr.
International Congress of Historical Studies (Sciences), 5th: Brussels, 1923, (Compte-Rendu) Repr. 60.00 (ISBN 0-317-15414-1). Kraus Repr.
International Congress of Historical Studies (Sciences), 6th: Oslo, 1928, (Resumes) Repr. 41.00 (ISBN 0-317-15416-8). Kraus Repr.
International Congress of Historical Studies (Sciences), 7th: Warsaw, 1933, (Resumes) Repr. 80.00 (ISBN 0-317-15417-6). Kraus Repr.
International Congress of Historical Studies (Sciences), 8th: Zurich, 1938, (Actes, Communications) Repr. 80.00 (ISBN 0-317-15419-2). Kraus Repr.
International Congress of Historical Studies (Sciences), 9th: Paris, 1950, (Rapports, Actes) Repr. 107.00 (ISBN 0-317-15420-6). Kraus Repr.
International Congress of History of Science, University of California, Berkeley, 1985, 2 vols. Incl. Abstracts of Papers Presented in Scientific Sections. 550p (ISBN 0-918102-13-8); Abstracts of Papers Presented in Symposia. 300p (ISBN 0-918102-14-6). LC 85-62072. (Orig.). 1985. pap. 30.00 (ISBN 0-317-31451-3). U Cal Hist Sci Tech.
Jastrow, Joseph, ed. Story of Human Error. facs. ed. LC 67-30219. (Essay Index Reprint Ser). 1936. 18.50 (ISBN 0-8369-0568-7). Ayer Co Pubs.
Jeans, James. The Growth of Physical Science. 364p. 1982. Repr. of 1948 ed. lib. bdg. 30.00 (ISBN 0-89984-906-7). Century Bookbindery.
Jeon, Sang-Woon. Science & Technology in Korea: Traditional Instruments & Techniques. (East Asian Science Ser). 448p. 1974. 35.00x (ISBN 0-262-10014-2). MIT Pr.
Jones, Richard F. Ancients & Moderns: A Study of the Rise of the Scientific Movement in Seventeenth Century England. 2nd ed. 1961. 12.75 (ISBN 0-8446-2340-7). Peter Smith.
--Ancients & Moderns: A Study of the Rise of the Scientific Movement in Seventeenth Century England. 384p. 1982. pap. 6.50 (ISBN 0-486-24414-8). Dover.
Jordan, Pascual. Science & the Course of History. Manheim, Ralph, tr. LC 73-17920. 139p. 1974. Repr. of 1955 ed. lib. bdg. 18.75x (ISBN 0-8371-7280-2, JOSC). Greenwood.
Kearney, Hugh. Science & Change. LC 76-96433. (World University Library Ser.). (Illus., Orig.). 1971. pap. 5.95 (ISBN 0-07-033425-0). McGraw.
Kline, Morris. Mathematics & the Physical World. (Illus.). 496p. 1981. pap. 6.95 (ISBN 0-486-24104-1). Dover.
Klotz, Irving. Bending Perception to Wish. 1985. write for info. (ISBN 0-8176-2403-1). Birkhauser.
Kuhn, Thomas S. The Essential Tension: Selected Studies in Scientific Tradition & Change. LC 77-78069. (Illus.). 1979. lib. bdg. 25.00x (ISBN 0-226-45805-9); pap. 12.00x (ISBN 0-226-45806-7, P831, Phoen). U of Chicago Pr.
--Structure of Scientific Revolutions. 2nd ed. LC 70-107472. (Foundations of the Unity of Science Ser: Vol. 2, No. 2). 1970. pap. 5.95 (ISBN 0-226-45804-0, P411, Phoen). U of Chicago Pr.
--Structure of Scientific Revolutions. 2nd ed. LC 70-107472. (Foundations of the Unity of Science Ser: Vol. 2, No. 2). 1970. 17.50x (ISBN 0-226-45803-2). U of Chicago Pr.
Langford, Jerome J. Galileo, Science & the Church. rev. ed. 1971. pap. 6.95x (ISBN 0-472-06173-9, 173, AA). U of Mich Pr.
Lenard, Philipp. Great Men of Science: A History of Scientific Progress. Hathfield, H. Stanfford, tr. from Ger. 1979. Repr. of 1933 ed. lib. bdg. 40.00 (ISBN 0-89987-500-9). Darby Bks.
Lenard, Philipp E. Great Men of Science. Hatfield, H. Stafford, tr. LC 74-105026. (Essay Index Reprint Ser). 1933. 25.00 (ISBN 0-8369-1614-X). Ayer Co Pubs.
Lloyd, G. E. Early Greek Science: Thales to Aristotle. Finley, M. I., ed. (Ancient Culture & Society Ser). (Illus.). 1974. pap. 4.95x (ISBN 0-393-00583-6). Norton.
McCormmach, Russell, ed. Historical Studies in the Physical Sciences, 4 vols. LC 73-8263. (Illus.). 1975. Vol. 5. 31.00x (ISBN 0-691-08155-7); Vol. 6. 55.00x (ISBN 0-691-08166-2); Vol. 7. 52.00x (ISBN 0-691-08169-7). Princeton U Pr.
McCormmach, Russell K., et al. Historical Studies in the Physical Sciences, Vol. 10. LC 77-75220. (Illus.). 1979. text ed. 28.50x (ISBN 0-8018-2191-6). Johns Hopkins.
Markovits, Andrei S. & Deutsch, Karl W., eds. Fear of Science-Trust in Science: Conditions for Change in the Climate of Opinion. LC 80-13131. 288p. 1980. text ed. 35.00 (ISBN 0-89946-038-0). Oelgeschlager.
Marks, John. Science & the Making of the Modern World. xiv, 507p. 1983. pap. text ed. 20.00x (ISBN 0-435-54781-X). Heinemann Ed.
Mason, Stephen F. History of the Sciences. Orig. Title: Main Currents of Scientific Thought. 1962. pap. 7.95 (ISBN 0-02-093400-9, Collier). Macmillan.
Mathias, Peter, ed. Science & Society, 1600-1900. (Illus.). 176p. 1972. 32.50 (ISBN 0-521-08375-3). Cambridge U Pr.
May, John G., compiled by. Historical Studies in the Physical Sciences: A Subject Index to Vols. 1-10. LC 84-51371. 50p. (Orig.). 1984. pap. 3.50 (ISBN 0-918102-11-1). U Cal Hist Sci Tech.
Medvedev, Zhores A. Soviet Science. 1978. 15.95 (ISBN 0-393-06435-2). Norton.
Menard, Henry W. Science: Growth & Change. LC 77-156138. (Illus.). xiv, 215p. 1971. 12.50x (ISBN 0-674-79280-7). Harvard U Pr.
Mendelsohn, Everett & Nowotny, Helga, eds. Science Between Utopia & Dystopia, 1984. (Sociology of the Sciences Yearbook: No. 8). 310p. 1984. 46.00 (ISBN 90-277-1719-2, Pub. by Reidel Holland); pap. text ed. 24.00 (ISBN 90-277-1721-4). Kluwer Academic.
Merz, John T. History of European Thought in the Nineteenth Century, 4 Vols. 16.50 ea. (ISBN 0-8446-2579-5). Peter Smith.
Meyerson, Emile. The Relativistic Deduction: Epistemological Implications of the Theory of Relativity with a Review by Albert Einstein. Sipfle, David A. & Sipfle, Mary A., trs. 290p. 1984. lib. bdg. 49.00 (ISBN 90-277-1699-4, Pub. by Reidel Holland). Kluwer Academic.
Middleton, W. E. Knowles. The Experimenters: A Study of the Accademia del Cimento. LC 77-142816. (It., Illus.). pap. 81.90 (ISBN 0-8357-9271-4, 2015692). Bks Demand UMI.
Mieli, Aldo. Science Arabe & Son Role Dans l'Evolution Scientifique Mondiale. (Medieval Studies Reprint Ser.). (Fr.). Repr. of 1938 ed. lib. bdg. 44.00x (ISBN 0-697-00044-3). Irvington.
Miller, Samuel. Brief Retrospect of the Eighteenth Century, 2 Vols. LC 70-132812. 1970. Repr. of 1803 ed. Set. 54.50 (ISBN 0-8337-2395-2). B Franklin.
Moore, G. H. Zermelo's Axiom of Choice: Its Origin, Development & Influence. (Studies in the History of Mathematics & physical Sciences: Vol. 8). 352p. 1982. 43.00 (ISBN 0-387-90670-3). Springer-Verlag.
Morrell, Jack & Thackray, Arnold, eds. Gentlemen of Science: Early Correspondence of the British Association for the Advancement of Science. (Royal Historical Society Camden Fourth Ser.: No. 30). 382p. 1985. 15.00 (ISBN 0-86193-103-3, Pub. by Boydell & Brewer). Longwood Pub Group.
Mouy, Paul. Le Developpment de la Physique Cartesienne 1646-1712 (the Development of Cartesian Physics) Cohen, I. Bernard, ed. LC 80-2138. (Development of Science Ser.). 1981. Repr. of 1934 ed. lib. bdg. 30.00 (ISBN 0-405-13893-8). Ayer Co Pubs.
Nachmansohn, D. German-Jewish Pioneers in Science, 1900-1933. LC 79-10550. (Illus.). 1979. 38.00 (ISBN 0-387-90402-6). Springer-Verlag.
Nagel, Ernest. Teleology Revisited & Other Essays in the Philosophy & History of Science. 368p. 1979. 30.00x (ISBN 0-231-04504-2); pap. 15.00x (ISBN 0-231-04505-0). Columbia U Pr.
National Academy of Sciences, Washington, DC & True, Frederick W. A History of the First Half-Century of the National Academy of Sciences, 1863-1913, Vol. 1. 24.50 (ISBN 0-405-12698-0). Ayer Co Pubs.
National Academy of Sciences, Washington, DC Staff & True, Frederick W. A History of the First, Half-Century of the National Academy of Sciences, 1863-1913, Vol. 2. 24.50 (ISBN 0-405-12699-9). Ayer Co Pubs.
Needham, Joseph. Science & Civilization in China, 5 vols. Incl. Vol. 1. Introductory Orientations. 1954. 65.00 (ISBN 0-521-05799-X); Vol. 2. History of Scientific Thought. 110.00 (ISBN 0-521-05800-7); Vol. 3. Mathematics & the Sciences of the Heavens & the Earth. 160.00 (ISBN 0-521-05801-5); Vol. 4. Physics & Physical Technology, 3 pts; Pt. 1. Physics. 1962. 90.00 (ISBN 0-521-05802-3); Pt. 2. Mechanical Engineering. 125.00 (ISBN 0-521-05803-1); Pt. 3. Engineering & Nautics. 1970. 160.00 (ISBN 0-521-07060-0); Vol. 5, Pt. 4. Spagyrical Discovery & Invention. 500p. 135.00 (ISBN 0-521-08573-X). Cambridge U Pr.

Needham, Joseph & Pagel, Walter, eds. Background to Modern Science. LC 74-26281. (History, Philosophy & Sociology of Science Ser.). 1975. Repr. 19.00x (ISBN 0-405-06608-2). Ayer Co Pubs.

Nicolson, Marjorie H. Pepys' Diary & the New Science. LC 65-26012. (Illus.). 198p. 1965. 14.95 (ISBN 0-8139-0188-X). U Pr of Va.

Norman, Ruth. Future World, Vol. 3. 525p. (Orig.). 1986. pap. 12.95 (ISBN 0-932642-85-3). Unarius.

--The Grand Design of Life for Man, Vol. 2. 590p. text ed. cancelled (ISBN 0-932642-82-9). Unarius.

Nowotny, Helga & Rose, Hilary, eds. Countermovements in the Sciences. (Sociology of the Sciences Ser.: No. 3). 1979. lib. bdg. 34.00 (ISBN 90-277-0971-8, Pub. by Reidel Holland); pap. 15.95 (ISBN 90-277-0972-6, Pub. by Reidel Holland). Kluwer Academic.

Olson, Richard. Science Deified & Science Defied: The Historical Significance of Science in Western Culture from the Bronze Age to the Beginnings of the Modern Era ca. 3500 B.C. to ca. A.D. 1640. LC 82-40093. (Illus.). 375p. 1983. 35.00x (ISBN 0-520-04621-8); pap. 9.95 (ISBN 0-520-04716-8). U of Cal Pr.

Owen, George E. The Universe of the Mind. LC 76-125674. (Seminar in the History of Ideas Ser: No. 4). (Illus.). 368p. 1971. 30.00x (ISBN 0-8018-1131-7); pap. 8.50x (ISBN 0-8018-1179-1). Johns Hopkins.

Pandit, G. L. The Structure & Growth of Scientific Knowledge. 1983. 39.50 (ISBN 90-277-1434-7, Pub. by Reidel Holland). Kluwer Academic.

Paradis, James & Postlewait, Thomas, eds. Victorian Science & Victorian Values: Literary Perspectives. 375p. 1985. text ed. 30.00 (ISBN 0-8135-1106-2); pap. text ed. 14.00 (ISBN 0-8135-1107-0). Rutgers U Pr.

Paul, Harry W. The Rise of the Science Empire in France, Eighteen Sixty to Nineteen Thirty Nine: From Knowledge to Power. 480p. Date not set. price not set. (ISBN 0-521-26504-5). Cambridge U Pr.

--The Sorcerer's Apprentice: The French Scientist's Image of German Science, 1840-1919. LC 77-178986. (University of Florida Social Sciences Monographs: No. 44). 86p. 1972. pap. 3.50 (ISBN 0-8130-0347-4). U Presses Fla.

Peacocke, A. R., ed. The Sciences & Theology in the Twentieth Century. LC 81-14771. 309p. 1982. 25.00 (ISBN 0-268-01704-2). U of Notre Dame Pr.

Pennsylvania University Bicentennial Conference. Studies in the History of Science. Speiser, E. A. & Neugebauer, Otto, eds. LC 68-26202. Repr. of 1941 ed. 17.50x (ISBN 0-8046-0358-8, Pub. by Kennikat). Assoc Faculty Pr.

Pledge, H. T. Science Since Fifteen-Hundred: A Short History of Mathematics, Physics, Chemistry, Biology. 11.75 (ISBN 0-8446-0850-5). Peter Smith.

Price, Derek D. Science Since Babylon. enl. ed. 1975. pap. 7.95x (ISBN 0-300-01798-7). Yale U Pr.

Reichenbach, Hans. From Copernicus to Einstein. Winn, Ralph B., tr. (Illus.). 1980. Repr. of 1942 ed. 2.25 (ISBN 0-486-23940-3). Dover.

Richter, Maurice N., Jr. The Autonomy of Science: An Historical Comparative Analysis. LC 80-23534. 188p. 1981. text ed. 15.50 (ISBN 0-87073-381-8); pap. text ed. 8.95 (ISBN 0-87073-382-6). Schenkman Bks Inc.

Rider, Robin E. & Lowood, Henry E., eds. Guide to Sources in Northern California for History of Science & Technology. (Berkeley Papers in History of Science: Vol. x). (Illus.). 193p. (Orig.). 1985. pap. text ed. 12.00 (ISBN 0-918102-12-X). U Cal Hist Sci Tech.

Ritterbush, Philip. Overtures to Biology: Speculations of Eighteenth Century Naturalists. 1964. 59.50x (ISBN 0-685-69859-9). Elliots Bks.

Robinson, Gloria, ed. Preludes to Genetics. 15.00x (ISBN 0-87291-127-6). Coronado Pr.

Roller, Duane & Goodman, Marcia M. Catalogue of the History of Science: Collections of the University of Oklahoma Libraries, 2 vols. LC 76-381954. 1212p. 1976. Set. 212.00x (ISBN 0-7201-0452-1). Mansell.

Roller, Duane H., ed. Perspectives in the History of Science & Technology. LC 77-144163. (Illus.). pap. text ed. 10.95x (ISBN 0-8061-1144-5). U of Okla Pr.

Ronan, Colin A. Science: Its History & Development among the World's Cultures. (Illus.). 528p. 1983. 29.95 (ISBN 0-87196-745-6). Facts on File.

--Science: Its History & Development among the World's Cultures. 528p. 1985. pap. 14.95 (ISBN 0-8160-1165-6). Facts on File.

Rosen, Edward. Copernicus & the Scientific Revolution. LC 83-9380. (Anvil Ser.). 224p. (Orig.). 1984. pap. text ed. 6.95 (ISBN 0-89874-573-X). Krieger.

Rosenkrantz, Roger D. Inference, Method & Decision. (Synthese Library: No. 115). 1977. lib. bdg. 34.00 (ISBN 90-277-0817-7, Pub. by Reidel Holland); pap. 16.00 (ISBN 90-277-0818-5). Kluwer Academic.

Rousseau, G. S. & Porter, R., eds. The Ferment of Knowledge: Studies in the Historiography of Eighteenth-Century Science. LC 80-40001. 550p. 1980. 54.50 (ISBN 0-521-22599-X). Cambridge U Pr.

Sarton, George. Ancient Science & Modern Civilization. LC 54-10992. vi, 112p. 1964. pap. 2.95x (ISBN 0-8032-5228-5, BB 302, Bison). U of Nebr Pr.

--Introduction to the History of Science, 5 vols. Incl. Vol. 1. From Homer to Omar Khayyam. Repr. of 1927 ed; Vol. 2. From Rabbi Ben Ezra to Roger Bacon, 2 prs. Repr. of 1931 ed; Vol. 3, Pt. 1. First Half of the 14th Century. Repr. of 1947 ed; Vol. 3, Pt. 2. Second Half of the 14th Century. Repr. of 1948 ed. LC 74-22012. 1975. Set. 275.00 (ISBN 0-88275-172-7). Krieger.

--Life of Science: Essays in the History of Civilization. facsimile ed. LC 70-167410. (Essay Index Reprint Ser). Repr. of 1948 ed. 16.00 (ISBN 0-8369-2472-X). Ayer Co Pubs.

--Six Wings: Men of Science in the Renaissance. LC 56-11998. (Illus.). 336p. 1957. 19.50x (ISBN 0-253-35275-4). Ind U Pr.

Schmitt, Charles A. Studies in Renaissance Philosophy & Science. 342p. 1981. 70.00x (ISBN 0-86078-093-7, Pub. by Variorum). State Mutual Bk.

Schneer, Cecil J. The Evolution of Physical Science: Major Ideas from Earliest Times to the Present. 416p. 1984. pap. text ed. 13.50 (ISBN 0-8191-3790-1). U Pr of Amer.

Shapere, Dudley. Reason & the Search for Knowledge. (Orig.). 1984. pap. text ed. 19.95 (ISBN 90-277-1641-2, Pub. by Reidel Holland). Kluwer Academic.

Shorr, Philip. Science & Superstition in the Eighteenth Century: A Study of the Treatment of Science in Two Encyclopedias of 1725-1750. LC 33-3916. (Columbia University. Studies in the Social Sciences: No. 364). Repr. of 1932 ed. 10.00 (ISBN 0-404-51364-6). AMS Pr.

Sil. Manuscripts of the Dibner Collection: Manuscripts in the History of Science & Technology in the Smithsonian Institution Libraries. LC 85-11576. (Illus.). 176p. 1985. 35.00x (ISBN 0-88135-025-7). Watson Pub Intl.

Silliman, Benjamin. A Journal of Travels in England, Holland, & Scotland, & of Two Passages over the Atlantic in the Years 1805 & 1806, 2 vols. 2nd ed. Cohen, I. Bernard, ed. LC 79-7990. (Three Centuries of Science in America Ser.). (Illus.). 1980. Repr. of 1812 ed. lib. bdg. 62.00x (ISBN 0-405-12572-0); lib. bdg. 30.50x ea. Vol. 1 (ISBN 0-405-12614-X). Vol. 2 (ISBN 0-405-12573-9). Ayer Co Pubs.

--A Visit to Europe in Eighteen Fifty-One, 2 vols. Cohen, I. Bernard, ed. LC 79-8406. (Three Centuries in Science in America Ser.). (Illus.). 1980. Repr. of 1856 ed. lib. bdg. 75.00x (ISBN 0-405-12574-7); lib. bdg. 37.50x ea. Vol. 1 (ISBN 0-405-12684-0). Vol. 2 (ISBN 0-405-12575-5). Ayer Co Pubs.

Singer, Charles. Short History of Scientific Ideas to 1900. (Oxford Paperback Ser.). 1959. pap. 9.95x (ISBN 0-19-881049-0). Oxford U Pr.

Singer, Charles, ed. Studies in the History & Method of Science, 2 vols. in one. LC 74-26291. (History, Philosophy & Sociology of Science Ser). (Illus.). 1975. Repr. 64.00x (ISBN 0-405-06617-1). Ayer Co Pubs.

Somerville, Mary. On the Connexion of the Physical Sciences. 7th ed. LC 74-26296. (History, Philosophy & Sociology of Science Ser). 1975. Repr. 38.50x (ISBN 0-405-06621-X). Ayer Co Pubs.

Stableford, Brian M. The Mysteries of Modern Science. (Quality Paperback Ser.: No. 360). 270p. 1980. pap. 4.95 (ISBN 0-8226-0360-8). Littlefield.

Stegmuller, Wolfgang, ed. Collected Papers on Epistemology, Philosophy of Science & History of Philosophy, 2 vols. new ed. (Synthese Library: No. 101). 1976. Vol. 1. lib. bdg. 37.00 (ISBN 90-277-0642-5, Pub. by Reidel Holland); Vol. 2. lib. bdg. 39.50 (ISBN 90-277-0643-3); Set. lib. bdg. 76.00 (ISBN 90-277-0767-7). Kluwer Academic.

Stepan, Nancy. Beginnings of Brazilian Science. (Illus.). 225p. 1981. pap. 6.95 (ISBN 0-88202-032-3, Sci Hist). Watson Pub Intl.

Stillwell, Margaret B. The Awakening Interest in Science During the First Century of Printing, 1450 to 1550. 399p. 1970. 25.00 (ISBN 0-686-31070-5). Biblio Soc Am.

Stuewer, Roger H., ed. Historical & Philosophical Perspectives of Science. LC 57-12861. (Minnesota Studies in the Philosophy of Science Ser.: Vol. 5). pap. 101.00 (ISBN 0-317-28158-5, 2055963). Bks Demand UMI.

Sullivan, J. W. Limitations of Science. LC 77-122072. Repr. of 1930 ed. 27.50x (ISBN 0-678-03172-X). Kelley.

Swenson, Lloyd S. Genesis of Relativity. (Studies in the History of Science: No. 1). (Illus.). 1978. lib. bdg. 29.00 (ISBN 0-89102-101-9). B Franklin.

Taton, ed. Histoire Generale des Sciences, 3 tomes. Incl. Tome I. La Science Antique et Medievale, des Origines a 1450. 14.95 (ISBN 0-685-35930-1); Tome II. La Science Moderne, de 1450 a 1800; Tome III. La Science Contemporaine, 2 pts. 32.50 ea. French & Eur.

Taylor, F. Sherwood. Short History of Science & Scientific Thought. (Illus.). 1963. pap. 8.95x (ISBN 0-393-00140-7). Norton.

Teich, M. & Young, R., eds. Changing Perspectives in the History of Science: Essays in Honor of John Needham. LC 72-96576. 480p. 1973. lib. bdg. 26.00 (ISBN 90-277-0328-0, Pub. by Reidel Holland). Kluwer Academic.

Thorndike, Lynn. A History of Magic & Experimental Science, 8 vols. Incl. Vols. 1 & 2. The First Thirteen Centuries. 1923. Vol. 1. (ISBN 0-231-08794-2); Vol. 2. (ISBN 0-231-08795-0); Vols. 3 & 4. Fourteenth & Fifteenth Centuries. Vol. 3. (ISBN 0-231-08796-9); Vol. 4. (ISBN 0-231-08797-7); Vols. 5 & 6. The Sixteenth Century. 1941. Vol. 5. (ISBN 0-231-08798-5); Vol. 6. (ISBN 0-231-08799-3); Vols. 7 & 8. The Eighteenth Century. 1958. Vol. 7. (ISBN 0-231-08800-0); Vol. 8. (ISBN 0-231-08801-9). LC 23-2984. 70.00x ea. Columbia U Pr.

Tierney, Brian, et al. Enlightenment. 3rd ed. 1968. pap. text ed. 1.95 (ISBN 0-394-32057-3, RanC). Random.

Toulmin, Stephen & Goodfield, June. The Architecture of Matter. LC 81-71397. (Phoenix Ser.). 398p. 1982. pap. 11.95 (ISBN 0-226-80840-8). U of Chicago Pr.

Toynbee, Arnold. Lectures on the Industrial Revolution of the Eighteenth Century in England: Popular Addresses, Notes & Other Fragments. 282p. 1982. Repr. of 1908 ed. lib. bdg. 40.00 (ISBN 0-89984-470-7). Century Bookbindery.

Trefil, James S. Physics As a Liberal Art. LC 77-6729. 1978. text ed. 20.00 (ISBN 0-08-019863-5). Pergamon.

Ullmann-Margalit, E., ed. The Kaleidoscope of Science, Vol. 1. (Israel Colloquium Studies in History, Philosophy & Sociology of Science: Vol. 1). 255p. 1985. text ed. 21.95x (ISBN 0-391-03242-9). Humanities.

Underwood, E. Ashworth, ed. Science, Medicine, & History, 2 vols. LC 74-26300. (History, Philosophy & Sociology of Science Ser). (Illus.). 1975. Repr. Set. 99.00x (ISBN 0-405-06624-4); 49.50x ea. Vol. 1 (ISBN 0-405-06640-6). Vol. 2 (ISBN 0-405-06641-4). Ayer Co Pubs.

Vickers, Brian, ed. Occult & Scientific Mentalities in the Renaissance. LC 83-15116. 350p. 1984. 39.50 (ISBN 0-521-25879-0). Cambridge U Pr.

Vucinich, Alexander S. Science in Russian Culture: A History to 1860. 1963. 32.50x (ISBN 0-8047-0157-1). Stanford U Pr.

Waheed, K. A. Islam & the Origin of Modern Science. pap. 1.25 (ISBN 0-686-18451-3). Kazi Pubns.

Weart, Spencer. Scientists in Power. LC 78-21670. (Illus.). 1979. text ed. 22.50x (ISBN 0-674-79515-6). Harvard U Pr.

Webster, Charles. The Great Instauration: Science, Medicine & Reform 1626-1660. LC 76-4550. 630p. 1976. text ed. 45.00x (ISBN 0-8419-0267-4). Holmes & Meier.

Westfall, R. S. The Construction of Modern Science. LC 77-84001. (History of Science Ser.). (Illus.). 1978. 34.50 (ISBN 0-521-21863-2); pap. 10.95 (ISBN 0-521-29295-6). Cambridge U Pr.

Westfall, Richard S. Science & Religion in Seventeenth-Century England. 1973. pap. 4.95 (ISBN 0-472-06190-9, 190, AA). U of Mich Pr.

Whewell, William. History of the Inductive Sciences, 3 vols. Repr. of 1967 ed. 85.00x set (ISBN 0-7146-1149-2, F Cass Co). Biblio Dist.

--Selected Writings on the History of Science. Elkana, Yehuda, ed. (Classics of British Historical Literature Ser.). 452p. 1984. lib. bdg. 35.00x (ISBN 0-226-89433-9); pap. 15.00x (ISBN 0-226-89434-7). U of Chicago Pr.

White, Andrew D. History of the Warfare of Science with Theology in Christendon, 2 Vols. Set. 26.50 (ISBN 0-8446-3170-1). Peter Smith.

Wightman, William P. The Growth of Scientific Ideas. (Illus.). 495p. 1974. Repr. of 1966 ed. lib. bdg. 37.50 (ISBN 0-8371-7484-8, WISI). Greenwood.

Williams, L. Pearce & Steffens, Henry J. The History of Science in Western Civilization: Modern Science 1700-1900, Vol. III. LC 77-18484. 1978. pap. text ed. 16.50 (ISBN 0-8191-0333-0). U Pr of Amer.

Wilson, Grove. Human Side of Science. LC 72-1286. (Essay Index Reprint Ser.). Repr. of 1929 ed. 25.00 (ISBN 0-8369-2877-6). Ayer Co Pubs.

Woolf, Harry, ed. The Analytic Spirit: Essays in the History of Science. LC 80-69841. (Illus.). 368p. 1981. 34.50x (ISBN 0-8014-1350-8). Cornell U Pr.

Yerkes, Robert M., ed. New World of Science. facs. ed. LC 68-58818. (Essay Index Reprint Ser). 1920. 27.50 (ISBN 0-8369-1166-0). Ayer Co Pubs.

Zloczower, A. Career Opportunities & the Growth of Scientific Discovery in Ninteenth Century Germany, with Special Reference to the Development of Physiology. Cohen, I. Bernard, ed. LC 80-2095. (Development of Science Ser.). (Illus.). 1981. lib. bdg. 12.00x (ISBN 0-405-13860-1). Ayer Co Pubs.

SCIENCE–HISTORY–MUSEUMS

see Science Museums

SCIENCE–HISTORY–UNITED STATES

Adams, John Q. Report of the Secretary of State Upon Weights & Measures: Prepared in Obedience to a Resolution of the House of Representatives of the Fourteenth of December, 1819. Cohen, I. Bernard, ed. LC 79-7945. (Three Centuries of Science in America Ser.). 1980. Repr. of 1821 ed. lib. bdg. 23.00x (ISBN 0-405-12526-7). Ayer Co Pubs.

Badash, Lawrence & Broida, H. P., eds. Reminiscences of Los Alamos: 1943-1945. (Studies in the History of Modern Science: No. 5). 180p. 1980. lib. bdg. 26.50 (ISBN 90-277-1097-X); pap. 9.95 (ISBN 90-277-1098-8). Kluwer Academic.

Beard, Charles A., ed. Century of Progress. facs. ed. LC 79-128205. (Essay Index Reprint Ser). 1932. 27.50 (ISBN 0-8369-1903-3). Ayer Co Pubs.

Beaver, Donald D. The American Scientific Community, 1800 to 1860: A Statistical Historical Study. Zuckerman, Harriet & Merton, Robert K., eds. LC 79-8973. (Dissertations on Sociology Ser.). 1980. lib. bdg. 33.50x (ISBN 0-405-12950-5). Ayer Co Pubs.

Black, George W., Jr. American Science & Technology: A Bicentennial Bibliography. LC 78-15820. 172p. 1979. 15.95x (ISBN 0-8093-0898-3). S Ill U Pr.

Buck, P. American Science & Modern China, 1876-1936. LC 79-19190. (Illus.). 1980. 34.50 (ISBN 0-521-22744-5). Cambridge U Pr.

Caullery, Maurice J. Universities & Scientific Life in the United States. LC 72-94312. (The American Scientific Community, 1790-1920 Ser.). 1973. Repr. of 1922 ed. lib. bdg. 28.00 (ISBN 0-8420-1677-5). Scholarly Res Inc.

Cohen, I. Bernard, ed. Thomas Jefferson & the Sciences: An Original Anthology. LC 79-7970. (Three Centuries of Science in America Ser.). (Illus.). 1980. 57.50x (ISBN 0-405-12552-6). Ayer Co Pubs.

--Three Centuries of Science in America Series, 66 bks. (Illus.). 1980. Set. lib. bdg. 2939.000.00x (ISBN 0-405-12525-9). Ayer Co Pubs.

Daniels, George H., ed. Nineteenth-Century American Science: A Reappraisal. LC 79-186547. 292p. 1972. text ed. 17.95x (ISBN 0-8101-0381-8). Northwestern U Pr.

Dupree, A. Hunter. Science in the Federal Government: A History of Policies & Activities to 1940. Cohen, I. Bernard, ed. LC 79-7959. (Three Centuries of Science in America Ser.). (Illus.). 1980. Repr. of 1957 ed. lib. bdg. 39.00x (ISBN 0-405-12540-2). Ayer Co Pubs.

Ellicott, Andrew. The Journal of Andrew Ellicott. Cohen, I. Bernard, ed. LC 79-7960. (Three Centuries of Science in America Ser.). (Illus.). 1980. Repr. of 1803 ed. lib. bdg. 39.00x (ISBN 0-405-12541-0). Ayer Co Pubs.

Jaffe, Bernard. Men of Science in America: The Story of American Science Told Through the Lives & Achievements of Twenty Outstanding Men from Earliest Colonial Times to the Present Day. rev. ed. Cohen, I. Bernard, ed. LC 79-7968. (Three Centuries of Science in America Ser.). (Illus.). 1980. Repr. of 1958 ed. lib. bdg. 62.00x (ISBN 0-405-12551-8). Ayer Co Pubs.

Ketner, Kenneth, ed. Proceedings: C. S. Peirce Bicentennial International Congress. (Graduate Studies, Texas Tech Univ.: No. 23). 400p. (Orig.). 1981. 75.00 (ISBN 0-89672-075-6); pap. 50.00 (ISBN 0-89672-074-8). Tex Tech Pr.

Kevles, Daniel J. The Physicists. 1978. 15.95 (ISBN 0-394-46631-4). Knopf.

Kohlstedt, Sally G. The Formation of the American Scientific Community: The American Association for the Advancement of Science, 1848-1860. (Illus.). 320p. 1976. 22.50x (ISBN 0-252-00419-1). U of Ill Pr.

Laudan, Larry. Progress & Its Problems: Towards a Theory of Scientific Growth. LC 76-24586. 1977. 23.00x (ISBN 0-520-03330-2); pap. 7.95x (ISBN 0-520-03721-9). U of Cal Pr.

McRae, Robert. The Problem of the Unity of the Sciences: Bacon to Kant. LC 62-2304. pap. 40.00 (ISBN 0-317-08188-8, 2014318). Bks Demand UMI.

Parkinson, Claire L. Breakthroughs: A Chronology of Great Achievements in Science & Mathematics. (Reference Books in Science). 1985. lib. bdg. 29.95 (ISBN 0-8161-8706-1). G K Hall.

Reingold, Nathan. Science in Nineteenth Century America. 1979. Repr. of 1964 ed. lib. bdg. 19.50x (ISBN 0-374-96778-4). Octagon.

Reingold, Nathan, ed. The New American State Papers: Science & Technology Subject Set, 14 vols. LC 72-95578. 1973. Set. lib. bdg. 800.00 (ISBN 0-8420-1575-2). Scholarly Res Inc.

--The Papers of Joseph Henry: The Princeton Years, January 1838-1840, Vol. 4. LC 72-2005. (The Papers of Joseph Henry Ser.). (Illus.). 475p. 1981. text ed. 35.00x (ISBN 0-87474-792-9). Smithsonian.

--The Papers of Joseph Henry, Vol. 5: The Princeton Years, January 1841-December 1843. LC 72-2005. (The Joseph Henry Papers). (Illus.). 500p. 1985. 45.00x (ISBN 0-87474-793-7, REP5). Smithsonian.

--Science in Nineteenth-Century America: A Documentary History. LC 85-1021. xii, 340p. 1985. pap. text ed. 12.50x (ISBN 0-226-70947-7). U of Chicago Pr.

Reingold, Nathan & Reingold, Ida H., eds. Science in America: A Documentary History, 1900-1939. LC 81-2584. 1982. 37.50x (ISBN 0-226-70946-9). U of Chicago Pr.

Rossiter, Margaret W. Women Scientists in America: Struggles & Strategies to 1940. 1984. pap. 10.95 (ISBN 0-8018-2509-1). Johns Hopkins.

Schlagel, Richard H. From Myth to the Modern Mind: A Study of the Origins & Growth of Scientific Thought: Volume I: Animism to Archimedes. LC 84-23361. (American University Studies V (Philosophy): Vol. 12). 283p. 1985. text ed. 30.00 (ISBN 0-8204-0219-2). P Lang Pubs.

Shute, Michael. The Scientific Work of John Winthrop: An Original Anthology. Cohen, I. Bernard, ed. LC 79-8005. (Three Centuries of Science in America Ser.). (Illus.). 1980. lib. bdg. 23.00x (ISBN 0-405-12593-3). Ayer Co Pubs.

True, Frederick & Cohen, I. Bernard, eds. The Semi-Centennial Anniversary of the National Academy of Sciences: & a History of the First Half-Century of the National Academy of Sciences, 2 vols. 1863-1913. LC 79-7977. (Three Centuries of Science in America Ser.). (Illus.). 1980. Repr. of 1913 ed. Set. lib. bdg. 49.00x (ISBN 0-405-12560-7). Ayer Co Pubs.

SCIENCE–INFORMATION SERVICES

see also Communication in Science

Archenhold, W. F., et al. School Science Laboratories: A Handbook of Design, Management & Organization. 303p. 1980. 35.00x (ISBN 0-7195-3436-4, Pub. by Murray Pubs England). State Mutual Bk.

Chen, Ching-Chih, ed. Scientific & Technical Information Sources. 1977. 50.00x (ISBN 0-262-03062-4). MIT Pr.

Committee On Data For Science And Technology Of The International Council Of Scientific Unions. International Compendium of Numerical Data Projects. 1969. 38.00 (ISBN 0-387-04570-8). Springer-Verlag.

Garvey, William D. Communication: The Essence of Science Facilitating Information Exchange Among Librarians, Scientists, Engineers, & Students. 1979. pap. text ed. 19.50 (ISBN 0-08-023344-9). Pergamon.

Glaeser, P. S., ed. Data for Science & Technology: Proceedings of the 7th International CODATA Conference, Kyoto, Japan, 8-11 October 1980. (Illus.). 638p. 1981. 165.00 (ISBN 0-08-026201-5); pap. 46.00 (ISBN 0-08-026203-1). Pergamon.

Herner, Saul. A Brief Guide to Sources of Scientific & Technical Information. 2nd ed. LC 80-81087. (Illus.). xi, 160p. 1980. lexotone soft cover 15.00 (ISBN 0-87815-031-5). Info Resources.

Inose, H., ed. Scientific Information Systems in Japan. 260p. 1981. 59.75 (ISBN 0-444-86151-3, North-Holland). Elsevier.

Meadows, A. J., ed. Development of Science Publishing in Europe. 272p. 1981. 42.75 (ISBN 0-444-41915-2). Elsevier.

Mount, Ellis, ed. Serving End-Users in Sci-Tech Libraries. LC 84-10789. (Science & Technology Libraries: Vol. 5, No. 1). 122p. 1984. text ed. 19.95 (ISBN 0-86656-327-X, B327). Haworth Pr.

Uhlig, Ronald P., et al. The Office of the Future. (Monograph Series of the International Council for Computer Communications: Vol. 1). 379p. 1980. 40.00 (ISBN 0-444-85336-7); pap. 25.00 (ISBN 0-444-86060-6). Elsevier.

Williams, Martha E., ed. Annual Review of Information Science & Technology, 1978, Vol. 13. LC 66-25096. 386p. 1978. 45.00 (ISBN 0-914236-21-0, 306-BW). Knowledge Indus.

SCIENCE–INTERNATIONAL COOPERATION

see also Exchanges, Literary and Scientific

Ailes, Catherine P. & Pardee, Arthur E., Jr. Cooperation in Science & Technology: An Evaluation of the U. S.-Soviet Agreement. (WVSS in Science, Technology & Society Ser.). 300p. 1985. pap. 26.00x (ISBN 0-8133-0204-8). Westview.

American Health Research Institute Staff. International Cooperation in Medicine & Science: Subject Analysis Index with Research Bibliography. LC 85-47585. 150p. 1985. 29.95 (ISBN 0-88164-344-0); pap. 21.95 (ISBN 0-88164-345-9). ABBE Pubs Assn.

Hayes, William C., Jr., ed. Space: New Opportunities for International Ventures. (Science & Technology Ser.: Vol. 49). 300p. 1980. lib. bdg. 35.00x (ISBN 0-87703-124-X, Pub. by Am Astronaut); pap. text ed. 25.00 (ISBN 0-87703-125-8). Univelt Inc.

Kelley, Harold H., et al. Close Relationships. LC 82-25128. 572p. 1983. 29.95 (ISBN 0-7167-1442-6); pap. text ed. 19.95 (ISBN 0-7167-1443-4). W H Freeman.

Measurement of Scientific & Technological Activities. (Statistical Reports & Studies: No. 15). 63p. 1969. pap. 5.00 (ISBN 92-3-100759-9, U377, UNESCO). Unipub.

OAS General Secretariat Department of Scientific & Technological Affairs. Los Organismos Centrales De Politica Cientifica y Tecnologica En America Latina. (Estudios Sobre el Desarrollo Cientifico y Tecnologico: No. 38). 124p. 1980. 4.00 (ISBN 0-8270-1192-X). OAS.

Report of the First Session of the Joint Scientific Committee for GARP: Amsterdam, 26 March-3 April 1980. 140p. 1980. pap. 25.00 (ISBN 0-686-70050-3, W474, WMO). Unipub.

Ritterberger, Volker, ed. Science & Technology in a Changing International Order: The United Nations Conference on Science & Technology for Development. (Special Studies in Social, Political, & Economic Development). 200p. 1982. lib. bdg. 32.00x (ISBN 0-86531-146-3). Westview.

Science & Technology for Development: Proposals for the Second United Nations Development Decade. pap. 1.50 (ISBN 0-686-94411-9, UN70/1/23, UN). Unipub.

Wilson, Thomas W., Jr. Science, Technology & Development: The Politics of Modernization. LC 79-53795. (Headline Ser.: No. 245). (Illus., Orig.). 1979. pap. 3.00 (ISBN 0-87124-055-6). Foreign Policy.

Wool, Harry. The Transits of Venus. Cohen, I. Bernard, ed. LC 80-2150. (Development of Science Ser.). (Illus.). 1981. lib. bdg. 25.00x (ISBN 0-405-13959-4). Ayer Co Pubs.

SCIENCE–LABORATORY MANUALS

Kapili, Pascual H. & Calvero, Teofidez E. Improvising Science Equipment: A Handbook. (Illus.). 1978. pap. text ed. 8.25x (ISBN 0-686-23914-8, Pub. by New Day Pub). Cellar.

Lange, Erwin F. Laboratory Exercises in Physical Science. 3rd ed. (Illus.). 1970. pap. text ed. 6.95x (ISBN 0-87015-185-1). Pacific Bks.

Marek, Edmund A & Lewis, Melanie. Laboratory Investigations for General Science, Pt. 2. (Illus.). 101p. 1982. pap. text ed. 5.95x (ISBN 0-89641-078-1). American Pr.

Postl, Anton. Laboratory Experiments in Physical Science. 1978. 12.95 (ISBN 0-88246-089-7). Oreg St U Bkstrs.

Schmid, M. & Murphy, M. Introducing Science Concepts in the Laboratory. 2nd ed. 1978. text ed. 6.00 (ISBN 0-13-477380-2). P-H.

SCIENCE–LANGUAGE

see also Science–Terminology

Andrews, Stephen P. Primary Synopsis of Universology & Alwato: The New Scientific Universal Language. Stern, Madeleine B., ed. 1971. 12.50x (ISBN 0-87730-007-0). M&S Pr.

Huckin, Thomas & Olsen, Leslie. English for Science & Technology: A Handbook for Non-Native Speakers. (Illus.). 576p. 1983. 24.95 (ISBN 0-07-030821-7). McGraw.

Johansson, Stig. Some Aspects of the Vocabulary of Learned & Scientific English. (Goteborg Studies in English: No. 42). (Illus.). 1978. pap. text ed. 14.50x (ISBN 91-7346-050-8). Humanities.

Purvis, Keith. Read & Note: English Study Skills for Science Students. 1977. pap. text ed. 3.95x (ISBN 0-435-28717-6); tchr's. ed. 7.95x (ISBN 0-435-28718-4). Heinemann Ed.

SCIENCE–METHODOLOGY

see also Classification of Sciences; Communication in Science; Experimental Design; Logic; Stereology

Achinstein, Peter & Hannaway, Owen, eds. Observation, Experiment, & Hypothesis in Modern Physical Science. 1985. 37.50 (ISBN 0-262-01083-6). MIT Pr.

Ackoff, Russell L. Scientific Method: Optimizing Applied Research Decisions. LC 83-12060. 476p. 1984. Repr. of 1962 ed. text ed. 34.50 (ISBN 0-89874-661-2). Krieger.

Aliotta, Antonio. The Idealistic Reaction Against Science. McCaskill, Agnes, tr. from It. LC 74-26246. (History, Philosophy & Sociology of Science Ser). 1975. Repr. of 1914 ed. 37.50x (ISBN 0-405-06576-0). Ayer Co Pubs.

Bacon, Francis. The Advancement of Learning. Kitchin, G. W., ed. (Rowman & Littlefield University Library). 246p. 1973. 13.00x (ISBN 0-87471-664-0); pap. 7.50x (ISBN 0-87471-665-9). Rowman.

--New Organon & Related Writings. Anderson, Fulton H., ed. LC 60-11682. 1960. pap. 9.63 scp (ISBN 0-672-60289-X, LLA97). Bobbs.

--Two Books...of the Proficience & Advancement of Learning. LC 70-25525. (English Experience Ser.: No. 218). 236p. Repr. of 1605 ed. 39.00 (ISBN 90-221-0218-1). Walter J Johnson.

Balderston, Jack, et al. Modern Management Techniques in Engineers & R & D. 320p. 1984. 39.95 (ISBN 0-442-26436-4). Van Nos Reinhold.

Boldrini, M. Scientific Truth & Statistical Method. 1971. 20.25 (ISBN 0-02-841610-4). Hafner.

Brady, Donald. Logic of the Scientific Method. LC 73-15697. 92p. 1973. pap. text ed. 6.95x (ISBN 0-8422-0361-3). Irvington.

Bross. Scientific Strategies. (Statistics: Textbooks & Monographs: Vol. 35). 1981. 29.75 (ISBN 0-8247-1273-0). Dekker.

Bunge, M. Method, Model & Matter. LC 72-86102. (Synthese Library: No. 44). 196p. 1973. lib. bdg. 26.00 (ISBN 90-277-0252-7, Pub. by Reidel Holland). Kluwer Academic.

Bunge, M., ed. & pref. by. The Methodological Unity of Science. LC 73-83554. (Theory & Decision Library Ser: No. 3). 1973. lib. bdg. 39.50 (ISBN 90-277-0354-X, Pub. by Reidel Holland); pap. 24.00 (ISBN 90-277-0404-X, Pub. by Reidel Holland). Kluwer Academic.

Bunge, M., ed. Studies in the Foundations, Methodology & Philosophy of Science, 4 vols. Incl. Vol. 1. Delaware Seminar in the Foundations of Physics. (Illus.); Vol. 2. Quantum Theory & Reality. 1967. 28.00 (ISBN 0-387-03993-7); Vol. 3, Pt. 1. The Search for System. (Illus.). xii, 536p. 1967. 54.50 (ISBN 0-387-03994-5); Vol. 3, Pt. 2. The Search for Truth. (Illus.). viii, 374p. 1967. 47.00 (ISBN 0-387-03995-3); Vol. 4. Problems in the Foundations of Physics. (Illus.). 1971. 28.00 (ISBN 0-387-05490-1). LC 71-163433. Springer-Verlag.

Carmichael, R. D. The Logic of Discovery. LC 74-26255. (History, Philosophy & Sociology of Science Ser). 1975. Repr. 22.00x (ISBN 0-405-06583-3). Ayer Co Pubs.

Cochran, William G. Planning & Analysis of Observational Studies. LC 83-6461. 174p. 1983. 23.95x (ISBN 0-471-88719-6). Wiley.

Coffey, Peter. Science of Logic, Vol. 2. 15.00 ea. (ISBN 0-8446-1120-4). Peter Smith.

D'Abro, A. Evolution of Scientific Thought from Newton to Einstein. 15.50 (ISBN 0-8446-1937-X). Peter Smith.

De Rosnay, Joel. The Macroscope: A New World Scientific System. Edwards, Robert I., tr. LC 76-5122. (Illus.). 1979. 15.95i (ISBN 0-06-011029-5, HarpT). Har-Row.

Descartes, Rene. Discours De la Methode. (Illus.). 1965. pap. 4.50 (ISBN 0-685-11145-8). French & Eur.

--Discours de la Methode: Avec: Extraits de la Dioptrique, des Meteores, du Mond, de Homme, de Lettres et de la Vie de Descartes par Baillet. 254p. 1966. 4.50 (ISBN 0-686-55669-0). French & Eur.

--Discourse on Method. 2nd ed. Lafleur, Laurence J., tr. LC 60-13395. (Orig.). 1956. pap. 3.56 scp (ISBN 0-672-60180-X, LLA19). Bobbs.

--Discourse on Method & Other Writings. Wollaston, tr. (Classics Ser.). (Orig.). 1968. pap. 3.95 (ISBN 0-14-044206-5). Penguin.

Feyerabend, Paul K. Philosophical Papers: Realism, Rationalism & Scientific Method, Vol. 1. 367p. 1985. pap. 13.95 (ISBN 0-521-31642-1). Cambridge U Pr.

Ford, et al. Tools, Methods & Languages for Scientific & Engineering Computation. 1984. 59.25 (ISBN 0-444-87570-0). Elsevier.

Frey, Gerhard, ed. Bela Juhos: Selected Papers. Foulkes, Paul, tr. LC 76-17019. (Vienna Circle Collection Ser: No. 7). 1976. lib. bdg. 55.00 (ISBN 90-277-0686-7, Pub. by Reidel Holland); pap. 28.95 (ISBN 90-277-0687-5). Kluwer Academic.

Ghiselin, Michael. The Triumph of the Darwinian Method. LC 84-4491. x, 288p. 1984. pap. 9.95x (ISBN 0-226-29024-7). U of Chicago Pr.

Giere, Ronald N. Understanding Scientific Reasoning. 2nd ed. LC 83-22562. 1984. pap. text ed. 19.95 (ISBN 0-03-063068-1, HoltC). HR&W.

Giere, Ronald N. & Westfall, Richard S., eds. Foundations of Scientific Method: The Nineteenth Century. LC 72-79910. pap. 59.70 (ISBN 0-8357-9213-7, 2055202). Bks Demand UMI.

Glymour, Clark. Theory & Evidence. LC 79-3209. 352p. 1980. 38.00x (ISBN 0-691-07240-X); pap. 15.00x LPE (ISBN 0-691-10077-2). Princeton U Pr.

Groth, Alexander J. Progress & Chaos. LC 83-17549. (Eng.). 242p. 1984. pap. text ed. 9.50 (ISBN 0-89874-677-9). Krieger.

Handy, Rollo & Harwood, E. C. Useful Procedures of Inquiry. LC 72-93865. (Orig.). 1973. 12.50x (ISBN 0-913610-00-3). Behavioral Mass.

Harre, R. The Method of Science. (The Wykeham Science Ser.: No. 8). 140p. 1970. pap. cancelled (ISBN 0-85109-090-7). Taylor & Francis.

Harre, R. & Eastwood, D. G. The Method of Science. LC 76-116973. (Wykeham Science Ser.: No. 8). 140p. 1970. 9.95x (ISBN 0-8448-1110-6). Crane-Russak Co.

Harre, Rom. Great Scientific Experiments: Twenty Experiments That Changed Our View of the World. (Illus.). 1983. pap. 8.95 (ISBN 0-19-286036-4, GB 733, GB). Oxford U Pr.

Harris, Errol E. Hypothesis & Perception: The Roots of Scientific Method. (Muirhead Library of Philosophy). 1970. text ed. 19.00x (ISBN 0-391-00014-4). Humanities.

Hilpinen, Risto, ed. Scientific Rationality: Studies in the Foundations of Science & Ethics. (Philosophical Studies in Philosophy: No. 21). 247p. 1980. lib. bdg. 45.00 (ISBN 90-277-1112-7, Pub. by Reidel Holland). Kluwer Academic.

Hooke, Robert. Introduction to Scientific Inference. LC 75-28676. (Illus.). 101p. 1976. Repr. of 1963 ed. lib. bdg. 18.75 (ISBN 0-8371-8470-3, HOIS). Greenwood.

Howson, C., ed. Method & Appraisal in the Physical Sciences. LC 75-44580. 280p. 1976. 52.50 (ISBN 0-521-21110-7). Cambridge U Pr.

Hubner, Kurt. Critique of Scientific Reason. Dixon, Paul R. & Dixon, Hollis M., trs. LC 82-23690. (Illus.). xii, 284p. 1985. pap. 9.95 (ISBN 0-226-35709-0). U of Chicago Pr.

Jeffreys, Harold. Scientific Inference. 3rd ed. LC 71-179159. (Illus.). 280p. 1973. 52.50 (ISBN 0-521-08446-6). Cambridge U Pr.

Killeffer, David H. How Did You Think of That: An Introduction to the Scientific Method. LC 73-75724. (Chemistry in Action Ser.). 153p. 1973. pap. 4.95 (ISBN 0-8412-0163-3). Am Chemical.

Korner, Stephan. Experience & Theory. 1966. text ed. 19.75x (ISBN 0-7100-3628-0). Humanities.

Lastrucci, Carlo. Scientific Approach. 272p. 1967. 11.25 (ISBN 0-87073-042-8). Schenkman Bks Inc.

Lenzen, Victor F. Procedures of Empirical Science. LC 71-131570. (Foundations of the Unity of Science Ser: Vol. 1, No. 5). 1938. pap. 1.95x (ISBN 0-226-57580-2, P404, Phoen). U of Chicago Pr.

LeShan, Lawrence & Margenau, Henry. Einstein's Space & Van Gogh's Sky: Physical Reality & Beyond. 288p. 1983. pap. 6.95 (ISBN 0-02-093180-8). Macmillan.

Levi, Isaac. Gambling with Truth: An Essay on Induction & the Aims of Science. 264p. 1974. pap. 5.95x (ISBN 0-262-62026-X). MIT Pr.

Lowinger, Armand. Methodology of Pierre Duhem. Repr. of 1941 ed. 10.00 (ISBN 0-404-04058-6). AMS Pr.

Lunetta, Vincent N. & Novick, Shimshon. Inquiring & Problem Solving in the Physical Sciences: A Sourcebook. 224p. 1982. text ed. 16.95 (ISBN 0-8403-2631-9). Kendall-Hunt.

McCain, Garvin & Segal, Erwin M. The Game of Science. 4th ed. LC 81-6170. 200p. (Orig.). 1981. pap. text ed. 10.75 pub net (ISBN 0-8185-0482-X). Brooks-Cole.

Mannoia, V. James, Jr. What Is Science? An Introduction to the Structure & Methodology of Science. LC 79-47988. (Illus.). 149p. 1980. pap. text ed. 7.50 (ISBN 0-8191-0989-4). U Pr of Amer.

Medawar, Peter B. Induction & Intuition in Scientific Thought. LC 69-17272. (Memoirs Ser.: Vol. 75). 1980. 5.00 (ISBN 0-87169-075-6). Am Philos.

Mill, J. S. John Stuart Mill's Philosophy of Scientific Method. (Library of Classics Ser.: No. 12). 1950. pap. text ed. 8.95x (ISBN 0-02-849250-1). Hafner.

Morris, Richard. Dismantling the Universe: The Nature of Scientific Discovery. 224p. 1983. 14.95 (ISBN 0-671-45239-8). S&S.

--Dismantling the Universe: The Nature of Scientific Discovery. 224p. 1984. pap. 6.95 (ISBN 0-671-52818-1, Touchstone Bks). S&S.

Polya, George. Mathematical Methods in Science. Lax, Anneli, ed. LC 76-25863. (New Mathematical Library: No. 26). 234p. pap. 10.00 (ISBN 0-88385-626-3). Math Assn.

Popper, Karl R. Conjectures & Refutations: The Growth of Scientific Knowledge. 1968. pap. 8.95xi (ISBN 0-06-131376-9, TB1376, Torch). Har-Row.
--Logic of Scientific Discovery. rev. ed. pap. 9.50xi (ISBN 0-06-130576-6, TB576, Torch). Har-Row.
Potter, Merle C. Mathematical Methods in the Physical Sciences. (Illus.). 1978. ref. ed. 38.95 (ISBN 0-13-561134-2). P-H.
Przelecki, Marian, et al, eds. Formal Methods in the Methodology of Empirical Sciences. new ed. (Synthese Library: No. 103). 1976. lib. bdg. 55.00 (ISBN 90-277-0698-0, Pub. by Reidel Holland). Kluwer Academic.
Rowland, John. Mysteries of Science. LC 78-105035. (Essay Index Reprint Ser). 1957. 19.00 (ISBN 0-8369-1624-7). Ayer Co Pubs.
Russell, Bertrand. Mathematics, Metaphysics & the Power of the Scientific Method, 2 vols. (Illus.). 225p. 1985. Repr. Set. 187.75 (ISBN 0-89901-215-9). Found Class Reprints.
Simon, Herbert A. Models of Discovery. LC 77-8930. (Boston Studies in the Philosophy of Science: No. 54). 1977. lib. bdg. 55.00 (ISBN 90-277-0812-6, Pub. by Reidel Holland); pap. 14.00 (ISBN 90-277-0970-X). Kluwer Academic.
Sindermann, Carl J. Winning the Games Scientists Play. LC 82-12225. (Illus.). 304p. 1982. (full discount avail.) 15.95 (ISBN 0-306-41075-3, Plenum Pr). Plenum Pub.
Singer, Charles, ed. Studies in the History & Method of Science, 2 vols. in one. LC 74-26291. (History, Philosophy & Sociology of Science Ser). (Illus.). 1975. Repr. 64.00x (ISBN 0-405-06617-1). Ayer Co Pubs.
Statistical Distributions in Scientific Work. 1981. 3 volume set 156.00 (ISBN 0-686-33364-0, Pub. by Reidel Holland); Vol. 4, Models, Structures & Characterizations, xxii, 456p. 59.00 (ISBN 90-277-1332-4); Vol. 6 Applications In Physical, Social & Life Sciences, xxii, 439p. 59.00 (ISBN 90-277-1333-2); 59.00 (ISBN 90-277-1334-0). Kluwer Academic.
Suppes, P. Studies in the Methodology & Foundations of Science: Selected Papers, 1951-1969. (Synthese Library: No. 22). 473p. 1969. lib. bdg. 45.00 (ISBN 90-277-0020-6, Pub. by Reidel Holland). Kluwer Academic.
Symposium, Brussels. Information & Prediction in Science: Proceedings. Dockx, S. & Bernays, P., eds. 1965. 63.00 (ISBN 0-12-219050-5). Acad Pr.
Thompson, Richard L. Mechanistic & Nonmechanistic Science. (Illus.). 264p. (Orig.). 1982. pap. 8.00 (ISBN 0-89647-014-8). Bala Bks.
Tweney, Ryan D., et al, eds. On Scientific Thinking. 496p. 1981. 42.00x (ISBN 0-231-04814-9); pap. 18.00x (ISBN 0-231-04815-7). Columbia U Pr.
Tyndall, John. The Art of Physical Investigation & the Scientific Use of Man's Imagination. (Illus.). 1979. Repr. of 1898 ed. 47.75 (ISBN 0-89901-001-6). Found Class Reprints.
Van't Hoff, J. H. Imagination in Science. (Molecular Biology, Biophysics & Biochemistry Ser.: Vol. 1). 1967. pap. 10.00 (ISBN 0-387-03933-3). Springer-Verlag.
Wartofsky, Marx W., ed. Models. (Boston Studies in the Philosophy of Science: No. 1, Vol. 2). 1979. lib. bdg. 37.00 (ISBN 90-277-0736-7, Pub. by Reidel Holland); pap. 16.00 (ISBN 90-277-0947-5). Kluwer Academic.
Weimer, W. B. Notes on the Methodology of Scientific Research. 272p. 1979. 29.95x (ISBN 0-89859-498-7). L Erlbaum Assocs.
Woolf, Harry, ed. The Analytic Spirit: Essays in the History of Science. LC 80-69841. (Illus.). 368p. 1981. 34.50x (ISBN 0-8014-1350-8). Cornell U Pr.

SCIENCE–MISCELLANEA

Asimov, Isaac. Fact & Fancy. (Illus.). 208p. 1972. pap. 1.25 (ISBN 0-380-01174-3, 10306). Avon.
Einstein, Xavier. Trivia Mania: Science & Nature. 1984. pap. 2.50 (ISBN 0-317-05599-2). Zebra.
Ford, Brian J. One Hundred & One Questions about Science. (Illus.). 128p. 1984. 12.95 (ISBN 0-241-10992-2, Pub. by Hamish Hamilton England). David & Charles.
Goldstein, Martin & Goldstein, Inge. The Experience of Science: An Interdisciplinary Approach. 424p. 1984. 22.50x (ISBN 0-306-41538-0, Plenum Pr). Plenum Pub.
Goldwyn, Martin M. You'd Better Believe It. 1979. 10.00 (ISBN 0-8065-0672-5). Citadel Pr.
Harris, Sidney. What's So Funny about Science? Cartoons from American Scientist. LC 77-82638. (Illus.). 128p. 1977. 8.95x (ISBN 0-913232-39-4); pap. 5.95 (ISBN 0-913232-42-4). W Kaufmann.
Houwink, R., ed. Odd Book of Data. 1965. 8.50 (ISBN 0-444-40299-3). Elsevier.
Larson, Dewey B. The Neglected Facts of Science. 140p. 1982. 9.00 (ISBN 0-913138-09-6); pap. 7.50 (ISBN 0-913138-10-X). North Pacific.
Lemaine, Gerard. Perspectives on the Emergence of Scientific Disciplines. 1977. text ed. 20.00x (ISBN 9-0279-7743-7). Mouton.
Silverstone, Roger. Framing Science: The Making of a BBC Documentary. 250p. 1985. 24.95x (ISBN 0-85170-164-7, Pub. by British Film Inst England); pap. 14.95x (ISBN 0-85170-165-5). U of Ill Pr.
Ziman, John M. Puzzles, Problems & Enigmas: Occasional Pieces on the Human Aspects of Science. LC 80-42112. 256p. 1981. 29.95 (ISBN 0-521-23659-2). Cambridge U Pr.

SCIENCE–MORAL ASPECTS

see Science and Ethics

SCIENCE–NOMENCLATURE

see also subdivision Nomenclature under the various natural sciences, e.g. Botany–Nomenclature; Zoology–Nomenclature

Shipp, James F. Russian-English Index to Scientific Apparatus Nomenclature. 2nd ed. 92p. 1983. pap. text ed. 8.50 (ISBN 0-917564-15-4). Wychwood Pr.

SCIENCE–NOTATION

Lapidus, Leon & Pinder, George F. Numerical Solution of Partial Differential Equations in Science & Engineering. LC 81-16491. 677p. 1982. 51.95x (ISBN 0-471-09866-3, Pub. by Wiley-Interscience). Wiley.

SCIENCE–OUTLINES, SYLLABI, ETC.

Holmes, N. J., et al. Gateways to Science, 6 Levels. 4th ed. Incl. Level 1. 192p. text ed. 9.84 (ISBN 0-07-029821-1); Level 2. 192p. text ed. 10.36 (ISBN 0-07-029822-X); Level 3. 320p. text ed. 11.08 (ISBN 0-07-029823-8); Level 4. 368p. text ed. 12.28 (ISBN 0-07-029824-6); Level 5. 384p. text ed. 13.00 (ISBN 0-07-029825-4); Level 6. 432p. text ed. 13.40 (ISBN 0-07-029826-2). 1983. McGraw.

SCIENCE–PERIODICALS

Annals Index, 1978-1979, Vol. 351. (Annals of the New York Academy of Sciences). 90p. 1980. 23.00x (ISBN 0-89766-091-9); pap. 23.00x (ISBN 0-89766-092-7). NY Acad Sci.
Balachandran, Sarojini. Directory of Publishing Sources: The Researcher's Guide to Journals in Engineering & Technology. 386p. 1982. 39.95 (ISBN 0-471-09200-2, Pub. by Wiley-Interscience). Wiley.
Bolton, Henry C. Catalogue of Scientific & Technical Periodicals. 1665-1895. 2nd ed. Repr. of 1897 ed. 72.00 (ISBN 0-384-04985-0). Johnson Repr.
Bowen, D. Q., ed. Quaternary Science Reviews, Vol. 2. (Illus.). 328p. 1984. 96.00 (ISBN 0-08-031736-7). Pergamon.
British Library Staff. Abstracting & Indexing Periodicals in the Science Reference Library. 3rd ed. (Orig.). 1985. pap. 7.50 (ISBN 0-7123-0716-8, Pub. by British Lib). Longwood Pub Group.
Center for Research Libraries. Scientific & Technical Journals Listing, 1981. 142p. (Orig.). 1981. pap. text ed. 10.00 (ISBN 0-932486-24-X); members free. Ctr Res Lib.
Center for Research Libraries, ed. Monograph Catalog: The Center for Research Libraries Catalog, 5 vols. 1979. 332.00 set (ISBN 0-932486-13-4). Ctr Research Lib.
Ciencia Interamericana. (Span., Illus.). 71p. 1981. pap. 1.00 (ISBN 0-686-75079-9). OAS.
Gascoigne, Robert M. A Historical Catalogue of Scientific Periodicals, 1665-1900. LC 84-48863. 200p. 1985. lib. bdg. 27.00 (ISBN 0-8240-8752-6). Garland Pub.
Kyang, R. Periodicals Current in Mainland China Held by the Science Reference Library. 2nd ed. 91p. (Orig.). 1984. pap. 6.75 (ISBN 0-7123-0711-7, Pub. by British Lib). Longwood Pub Group.
Mason, P. C. Classified Directory of Japanese Periodicals: Engineering & Industrial Chemistry. 230p. 1984. 90.00x (ISBN 0-85142-044-3, Pub. by Aslib England). State Mutual Bk.
Michaelis, Anthony R., ed. Interdisciplinary Science Reviews Essay Ennual: Volume 5, 1981. pap. 87.50 (ISBN 0-317-28354-5, 2022543). Bks Demand UMI.
Provisional World List of Periodicals Dealing with Science & Technology Policies: 1973. (Science Policy Studies & Documents: No. 33). 112p. 1974. pap. 6.00 (ISBN 92-3-101189-8, U500, UNESCO). Unipub.
Yannarella, Philip A. & Aluri, Rao. U. S. Government Scientific & Technical Periodicals. LC 75-38740. 271p. 1976. 15.00 (ISBN 0-8108-0888-9). Scarecrow.

SCIENCE–PHILOSOPHY

see also Naturalism

Achinstein, Peter. Concepts of Science: A Philosophical Analysis. LC 68-15451. 279p. 1968. pap. 8.95x (ISBN 0-8018-1273-9). Johns Hopkins.
Achinstein, Peter & Hannaway, Owen, eds. Observation, Experiment, & Hypothesis in Modern Physical Science. 1985. 37.50 (ISBN 0-262-01083-6). MIT Pr.
Agassi, Joseph & Cohen, Robert, eds. Scientific Philosophy Today. 1982. lib. bdg. 69.50 (ISBN 90-277-1262-X, Pub. by Reidel Netherlands); pap. text ed. 34.50 (ISBN 90-277-1263-8, Pub. by Reidel Holland). Kluwer Academic.
Alford, C. Fred. Science & the Revenge of Nature: Marcuse & Habermas. LC 85-627. 208p. 1983. 24.50 (ISBN 0-8130-0817-4). U Presses Fla.
American Academy of Arts and Sciences, Boston. Science & the Modern Mind: A Symposium. facsimile ed. Gerald, Holton, ed. LC 70-167304. (Essay Index Reprint Ser). Repr. of 1958 ed. 12.00 (ISBN 0-8369-2446-0). Ayer Co Pubs.
American Association for the Advancement of Science, Section, L, 1949. Boston Studies in the Philosophy of Science, Vol. 11: Philosophical Foundations of Science, Proceedings. Seeger, R. J. & Cohen, R. S., eds. LC 73-83555. (Synthese Library: No. 58). 545p. 1974. 66.00 (ISBN 90-277-0390-6, Pub. by Reidel Holland); pap. 34.00 (ISBN 90-277-0376-0). Kluwer Academic.
American Catholic Philosophical Association. Philosophy & the Experimental Sciences: Proceedings, Vol. 26. 1952. 18.00 (ISBN 0-384-46400-9). Johnson Repr.
Amsterdamski, Stefan. Between Experience & Metaphysics: Philosophical Problems of the Evolution of Science. Michalowski, P., tr. from Pol. LC 75-2184. (Boston Studies in the Philosophy of Science: No. 35). xviii, 193p. 1975. lib. bdg. 29.00 (ISBN 90-277-0568-2, Pub. by Reidel Holland); pap. 16.00 (ISBN 90-277-0580-1). Kluwer Academic.
Anton, John P., ed. Science & the Sciences in Plato. LC 78-13418. 1980. 25.00x (ISBN 0-88206-301-4). Caravan Bks.
Arber, Agnes. The Mind & the Eye. (Cambridge Science Classics Ser.). 150p. 1985. pap. 16.95 (ISBN 0-521-31331-7). Cambridge U Pr.
Arbib, Michael A. In Search of the Person: Philosophical Explorations in Cognitive Science. LC 85-14152. 160p. (Orig.). 1985. lib. bdg. 20.00x (ISBN 0-87023-499-4); pap. 9.95 (ISBN 0-87023-500-1). U of Mass Pr.
Aronson, Jerrold R. A Realist Philosophy of Science. LC 82-22956. 278p. 1984. 25.00 (ISBN 0-312-66474-5). St Martin.
Asquith, Peter D. & Giere, Ronald, eds. PSA 1980, 2 Vols. 1980. Vol. I. 9.50 (ISBN 0-917586-14-X); pap. 7.50 (ISBN 0-917586-13-1); Vol. II, 678P. 1982. 23.75 (ISBN 0-917586-16-6). Philos Sci Assn.
Asquith, Peter D. & Kyburg, Henry E., Jr., eds. Current Research in Philosophy of Science. LC 78-61267. 533p. 1979. 12.50 (ISBN 0-917586-08-5); pap. 10.50 (ISBN 0-917586-07-7). Philos Sci Assn.
Asquith, Peter D. & Nickles, Thomas, eds. PSA 1982, 2 Vols. 414p. 1982. Vol. I. 21.00 (ISBN 0-917586-18-2); pap. 19.00 (ISBN 0-917586-17-4); Vol. II, 730P. 1983. 25.00 (ISBN 0-917586-19-0). Philos Sci Assn.
Ayres, C. E. Science-the False Messiah. Bd. with Holier Than Thou; The Way of the Righteous. LC 71-130660. Repr. of 1927 ed. 37.50x (ISBN 0-678-00774-8). Kelley.
Barnett, H. G. Qualitative Science. LC 82-90249. 1983. 15.00 (ISBN 0-533-05373-0). Vantage.
Benjamin, A. Corne. Science, Technology & Human Values. LC 65-10698. 306p. 1965. 22.00x (ISBN 0-8262-0035-4). U of Mo Pr.
Beth, E. W. Science a Road to Wisdom: Collected Philosophical Studies. Wesly, Peter, tr. from Dutch. 123p. 1968. lib. bdg. 21.00 (ISBN 90-277-0003-6, Pub. by Reidel Holland). Kluwer Academic.
Bhaskar, Roy. A Realist Theory of Science. 2nd ed. 258p. 1978. text ed. 28.00x (ISBN 0-391-00576-6); pap. text ed. 16.50x (ISBN 0-391-00577-4). Humanities.
Bonevac, Daniel A. Reduction in the Abstract Sciences. 184p. 1982. 18.50 (ISBN 0-915145-14-6). Hackett Pub.
Bornstein, Marc H., ed. Psychology & Its Allied Disciplines: Psychology & the Natural Sciences, Vol. III. 1984. pap. 24.95 (ISBN 0-89859-322-0). L Erlbaum Assocs.
Bradley, J. Mach's Philosophy of Science. (Illus.). 226p. 1971. 65.00 (ISBN 0-485-11124-1, Pub. by Athlone Pr Ltd). Longwood Pub Group.
Branick, Vincent P. Wonder in a Technical World: An Introduction to the Method & Writers of Philosophy. LC 80-67205. 256p. 1980. lib. bdg. 12.25 (ISBN 0-8191-1248-8). U Pr of Amer.
Bridges, Horace J. Taking the Name of Science in Vain. facs. ed. LC 72-86734. (Essay Index Reprint Ser). 1928. 18.00 (ISBN 0-8369-1168-7). Ayer Co Pubs.
Bridgman, Percy W. Philosophical Writings of Percy William Bridgman: An Original Anthology, 2 vols. in 1. Cohen, I. Bernard, ed. LC 79-7952. (Three Centuries of Science in America Ser.). 1980. lib. bdg. 19.00x (ISBN 0-405-12532-1). Ayer Co Pubs.
Brittan, Gordon G., Jr. Kant's Theory of Science. LC 77-85531. 1978. 25.00 (ISBN 0-691-07221-3). Princeton U Pr.
Broad, Charles D. Scientific Thought. (Quality Paperback: No. 208). 555p. 1959. pap. 4.95 (ISBN 0-8226-0208-3). Littlefield.
Brody, Boruch. Readings in the Philosophy of Science. LC 71-98091. (Philosophy Ser). 1970. text ed. 33.95 (ISBN 0-13-760702-4). P-H.
Bronowski, J. The Common Sense of Science. LC 53-9924. 1978. pap. 4.95 (ISBN 0-674-14651-4). Harvard U Pr.
Bronowski, Jacob. The Origins of Knowledge & Imagination. LC 77-13209. (Silliman Lectures Ser.). 1978. 17.50x (ISBN 0-300-02192-5); pap. 5.95x (ISBN 0-300-02409-6). Yale U Pr.
--Science & Human Values. pap. 4.95xi (ISBN 0-06-130505-7, TB505, Torch). Har-Row.
Brown, Harold I. Perception, Theory & Commitment: A New Philosophy of Science. LC 76-22991. 1979. pap. 7.50x (ISBN 0-226-07618-0, P812, Phoen). U of Chicago Pr.
--Perception, Theory & Commitment: The New Philosophy of Science. LC 76-22991. (Illus.). 1977. 19.95 (ISBN 0-913750-13-1). Precedent Pub.
Bukharin, Nikolai. Science at the Crossroads. new ed. 228p. 1971. 28.50x (ISBN 0-7146-2868-9, F Cass Co). Biblio Dist.
Bunge, M. Method, Model & Matter. LC 72-86102. (Synthese Library: No. 44). 196p. 1973. lib. bdg. 26.00 (ISBN 90-277-0252-7, Pub. by Reidel Holland). Kluwer Academic.
Bunge, M., ed. & pref. by. The Methodological Unity of Science. LC 73-83554. (Theory & Decision Library Ser: No. 3). 1973. lib. bdg. 39.50 (ISBN 90-277-0354-X, Pub. by Reidel Holland); pap. 24.00 (ISBN 90-277-0404-X, Pub. by Reidel Holland). Kluwer Academic.
Burks, Arthur W. Chance, Cause, Reason: An Inquiry into the Nature of Scientific Evidence. LC 74-11617. 1979. pap. 12.50x (ISBN 0-226-08088-9, P836, Phoen). U of Chicago Pr.
Burtt, Edwin A. Metaphysical Foundations of Modern Physical Science. 2nd ed. (International Library of Psychology, Philosophy & Scientific Method). 1967. text ed. 29.00x (ISBN 0-7100-3032-0); pap. text ed. 9.45x (ISBN 0-391-01633-4). Humanities.
Butterfield, Herbert. Origins of Modern Science. rev. ed. 1965. pap. text ed. 10.95x (ISBN 0-02-905070-7). Free Pr.
Butts, Robert E. Kant & the Double Government Methodology. 1984. lib. bdg. 43.00 (ISBN 90-277-1760-5, Pub. by Reidel Holland). Kluwer Academic.
Butts, Robert E. & Hintikka, Jaakko, eds. Foundational Problems in the Special Sciences. (Western Ontario Ser: No. 10). 1977. lib. bdg. 53.00 (ISBN 90-277-0710-3, Pub. by Reidel Holland). Kluwer Academic.
--Historical & Philosophical Dimensions of Logic, Methodology & Philosophy of Science. (Western Ontario Ser: No. 12). 1977. lib. bdg. 56.00 (ISBN 90-277-0831-2, Pub. by Reidel Holland). Kluwer Academic.
Capek, M. Bergson & Modern Physics: A Re-Interpretation & Re-Evaluation. LC 79-146967. (Synthese Library: No. 37). 414p. 1971. 42.00 (ISBN 90-277-0186-5, Pub. by Reidel Holland). Kluwer Academic.
Carnap, Rudolf & Gardner, Martin, eds. Introduction to the Philosophy of Science. LC 66-16499. pap. 8.95x (ISBN 0-465-09517-8, TB-5018). Basic.
Causey, Robert L. Unity of Science. (Synthese Library: No. 109). 1977. lib. bdg. 34.00 (ISBN 90-277-0779-0, Pub. by Reidel Holland). Kluwer Academic.
Cazenave, ed. Science & Consciousness: Two Views of the Universe. Hall, A. & Callender, E., trs. (Illus.). 550p. 1984. 70.00 (ISBN 0-08-028127-3, 0720, 2601, 3505, 3506). Pergamon.
Chalmers, Alan. What Is This Thing Called Science? (Paperbacks Ser.). 179p. 1985. pap. 8.95 (ISBN 0-7022-1831-6). U of Queensland Pr.
Chant, Colin & Fauvel, John. Darwin to Einstein: Historical Studies in Science & Belief. (Illus.). 352p. 1981. text ed. 27.00x (ISBN 0-582-49156-8). Longman.
Chiara, M. L., ed. Italian Studies in the Philosophy of Science. Fawcett, Carolyn, tr. (Boston Studies in the Philosophy of Science: No. 47). 525p. 1980. lib. bdg. 73.50 (ISBN 90-277-0735-9, Pub. by Reidel Holland); pap. 34.00 (ISBN 90-277-1073-2, Pub. by Reidel Holland). Kluwer Academic.
Churchland, P. M. Scientific Realism & the Plasticity of Mind. LC 78-73240. (Cambridge Studies in Philosophy). (Illus.). 1979. 29.95 (ISBN 0-521-22632-5). Cambridge U Pr.
Churchman, C. West. Design of Inquiring Systems, Basic Concepts in Systems Analysis. LC 72-174810. 1972. 18.50x (ISBN 0-465-01608-1). Basic.

Ciba Foundation. Civilization & Science in Conflict or Collaboration? LC 77-188826. (Ciba Foundation Symposium - New Ser.: No. 1). pap. 59.30 (ISBN 0-317-28331-6, 2022134). Bks Demand UMI.

Clarke, Desmond M. Descartes' Philosophy of Science. LC 82-82082. 224p. 1982. text ed. 22.50x (ISBN 0-271-00325-1). Pa St U Pr.

Clements, Tad S. Science & Man: The Philosophy of Scientifc Humanism. (American Lecture Philosophy). 168p. 1968. 14.75x (ISBN 0-398-00316-5). C C Thomas.

Cohen, Morris R. Reason & Nature. 1978. pap. 7.50 (ISBN 0-486-23633-1). Dover.

--Reason & Nature: An Essay on the Meaning of Scientific Method. 469p. 1985. Repr. of 1931 ed. lib. bdg. 65.00 (ISBN 0-8414-1996-5). Folcroft.

Cohen, Robert & Wartofsky, Marx. Language, Logic & Method. 1983. 69.50 (ISBN 90-277-0725-1, Pub. by Reidel Holland). Kluwer Academic.

Cohen, Robert S. & Wartofsky, Marx. Epistemology, Methodology, & the Social Sciences. 1983. lib. bdg. 48.00 (ISBN 90-277-1454-1, Pub. by Reidel Holland). Kluwer Academic.

--Hegel & the Sciences. 1984. lib. bdg. 61.50 (ISBN 90-277-0726-X, Pub. by Reidel Holland). Kluwer Academic.

Cole, K. C. Sympathetic Vibrations: Reflections on Physics As a Way of Life. LC 84-60547. (Illus.). 288p. 1984. 16.95 (ISBN 0-688-03968-5). Morrow.

Collingwood, Robin G. Idea of Nature. 1960. pap. 7.95 (ISBN 0-19-500217-2, GB). Oxford U Pr.

Colloquium for Philosophy of Science, Boston, 1966-1969. Boston Studies in the Philosophy of Science: Proceedings, Vol. 5. Cohen, R. S. & Wartofsky, M. W., eds. (Synthese Library: No. 19). 482p. 1969. 42.00 (ISBN 90-277-0015-X, Pub. by Reidel Holland). Kluwer Academic.

Colloquium for the Philosophy of Science, Boston, 1961-1962. Boston Studies in the Philosophy of Science: Proceedings, Vol. 1. Wartofsky, M. W., ed. (Synthese Library: No. 6). 212p. 1963. 24.00 (ISBN 90-277-0021-4, Pub. by Reidel Holland). Kluwer Academic.

Colloquium for the Philosophy of Science, Boston, 1966-68. Boston Studies in the Philosophy of Science: Proceedings, Vol. 4. Cohen, R. S. & Wartofsky, M. W, eds. (Synthese Library: No. 18). 537p. 1969. 45.00 (ISBN 90-277-0014-1, Pub. by Reidel Holland). Kluwer Academic.

Colloquium for the Philosophy of Sciences, Boston, 1969-72. Boston Studies in the Philosophy of Science, Vol. 14: Methodological & Historical Essays in the Natural & Social Sciences, Proceedings. Cohen, R. S. & Wartofsky, M. W., eds. LC 73-83558. (Synthese Library: No.60). 405p. 1974. 48.50 (ISBN 90-277-0392-2, Pub. by Reidel Holland); pap. 26.00 (ISBN 90-277-0378-7). Kluwer Academic.

Colloquium in the Philosophy of Science, Salzburg, 1969. Induction, Physics, & Ethics: Proceedings. Weingartner, P. & Zecha, G., eds. LC 78-118137. (Synthese Library: No. 31). 382p. 1970. lib. bdg. 39.50 (ISBN 90-277-0158-X, Pub. by Reidel Holland). Kluwer Academic.

Colodny, Robert G., ed. Beyond the Edge of Certainty: Essays in Contemporary Science & Philosophy. LC 83-1162. (CPS Publications in Philosophy of Science Ser.). (Illus.). 298p. 1983. text ed. 26.75 (ISBN 0-8191-3057-5); pap. text ed. 14.00 (ISBN 0-8191-3058-3). U Pr of Amer.

--Frontiers of Science & Philosophy. LC 61-9401. (Philosophy of Science Ser.). 1962. 26.95x (ISBN 0-8229-3100-1). U of Pittsburgh Pr.

--Frontiers of Science & Philosophy. LC 83-1212. (SPS Publications in Philosophy of Science Ser.). (Illus.). 296p. 1983. text ed. 26.75 (ISBN 0-8191-3060-5); pap. text ed. 14.00 (ISBN 0-8191-3061-3). U Pr of Amer.

Commins, Saxe D. & Linscott, Robert N., eds. Man & the Universe: The Philosophers of Science. pap. 0.75 (ISBN 0-671-47078-7). WSP.

Curtin, Deane W. The Aesthetic Dimension of Science. LC 81-19243. 1982. 12.50 (ISBN 0-8022-2393-1). Philos Lib.

Dart, Francis. Teaching Science as a Second Culture. Ives, Kenneth, ed. (Illus.). 60p. 1983. pap. 4.00 (ISBN 0-89670-009-7). Progresiv Pub.

De Forto, Rocco Z. Philosophy in Medicine, Science & Health: Subject Analysis Index with Reference Bibliography. LC 84-47864. 150p. 1985. 29.95 (ISBN 0-88164-402-1); pap. 21.95 (ISBN 0-88164-403-X). ABBE Pubs Assn.

Denbigh, K. G. An Inventive Universe. LC 75-13561. 220p. 1975. 8.95 (ISBN 0-8076-0802-5). Braziller.

Depew, David J. & Weber, Bruce H., eds. Evolution at a Crossroads: The New Biology & the New Philosophy of Science. 288p. 1985. text ed. 25.00x (ISBN 0-262-04079-4). MIT Pr.

Dilworth, Craig. Scientific Progress: A Study Concerning the Nature of the Relation Between Successive Scientific Theories. 160p. 1982. 29.95 (ISBN 90-277-1311-1, Pub. by Reidel Holland). Kluwer Academic.

Dingle, Herbert. Scientific Adventure. facs. ed. LC 71-121462. (Essay Index Reprint Ser). 1953. 24.50 (ISBN 0-8369-1749-9). Ayer Co Pubs.

Domson, Charles & Cohen, I. Bernard, eds. Nicolas Fatio De Duillier & the Prophets of Paris. LC 80-2086. (Development of Science Ser.). (Illus.). 1981. lib. bdg. 15.00 (ISBN 0-405-13852-0). Ayer Co Pubs.

Dotterer, Ray H. Philosophy by Way of the Sciences: An Introductory Textbook. (Select Bibliographies Reprint Ser). Repr. of 1929 ed. 26.50 (ISBN 0-8369-6642-2). Ayer Co Pubs.

--Philosophy by Way of the Sciences: An Introductory Textbook. 484p. Repr. of 1929 ed. lib. bdg. 23.00 (ISBN 0-8290-0823-3). Irvington.

Dubos, Reme. Celebrations of Life. 276p. 1982. pap. 5.95 (ISBN 0-07-017894-1). McGraw.

Durbin, Paul T., ed. A Guide to the Culture of Science, Technology, & Medicine. LC 79-7582. 1980. 65.00 (ISBN 0-02-907820-2). Free Pr.

Eccles, John C. Facing Reality: Philosophical Adventures by a Brain Scientist. LC 76-121064. (Heidelberg Science Library: Vol. 13). (Illus.). 1970. pap. 15.00 (ISBN 0-387-90014-4). Springer-Verlag.

Edel, Abraham. Science & the Structure of Ethics. LC 61-8082. (Foundations of the Unity of Science Ser: Vol. 2, No. 3). 1961. pap. 2.25x (ISBN 0-226-57593-4, P412, Phoen). U of Chicago Pr.

Eisele, Carolyn & Martin, Richard M., eds. Studies in the Scientific & Mathematical Philosophy of Charles S. Pierce: Essays by Carolyn Eisele. (Studies in Philosophy). 1979. text ed. 38.40x (ISBN 90-279-7808-5). Mouton.

Elkana, Yehuda, ed. The Interaction Between Science & Philosophy: Sambursky Festschrift. 1972. text ed. 18.00x (ISBN 0-391-00255-4). Humanities.

Elvee, Richard Q., ed. Mind in Nature: New Concepts of Mind in Science & Philosophy; The Nobel Conference XVII. LC 82-48155. 176p. (Orig.). 1983. pap. 7.64i (ISBN 0-06-250285-9, CN4046, HarpR). Har-Row.

Engels, Frederick. Dialectics of Nature. 399p. 1940. 7.50 (ISBN 0-7178-0049-0); pap. 3.50 (ISBN 0-7178-0048-2). Intl Pubs Co.

Eurich, Nell. Science in Utopia: A Mighty Design. LC 67-14339. pap. 65.40 (ISBN 0-317-09457-2, 2017014). Bks Demand UMI.

E.W. Beth Memorial Colloquium, Paris, 1964. Logic & Foundations of Science: Proceedings. Destouches, J. L., ed. 137p. 1967. lib. bdg. 21.00 (ISBN 90-277-0076-1, Pub. by Reidel Holland). Kluwer Academic.

Faust, David. The Limits of Scientific Reasoning. LC 84-5172. 220p. 1984. 25.00x (ISBN 0-8166-1356-7); pap. 12.95 (ISBN 0-8166-1359-1). U of Minn pr.

Feigl, Herbert & Scriven, M., eds. Foundations of Science & the Concepts of Psychology & Psychoanalysis. LC 56-11610. (Studies in the Philosophy of Science: Vol. 1). 1956. 22.50x (ISBN 0-8166-0122-4). U of Minn Pr.

Fetzer, James S. Sociobiology & Epistemology. 1985. lib. bdg. 39.50 (ISBN 90-277-2005-3, Pub. by Reidel Holland); pap. text ed. 14.95 (ISBN 90-277-2006-1). Kluwer Academic.

Feyerabend, Paul. Against Method. (Illus.). 1978. pap. 7.95 (ISBN 0-8052-7008-6, Pub by NLB). Schocken.

Finocchiaro, Maurice A. History of Science As Explanation. LC 72-3582. 280p. 1973. 15.95x (ISBN 0-8143-1480-5). Wayne St U Pr.

Fisher, Alden L. & Murray, George B., eds. Philosophy & Science As Modes of Knowing: Selected Essays. LC 69-18680. (Orig.). 1969. pap. text ed. 7.95x (ISBN 0-89197-340-0). Irvington.

Floistad, Guttorm. Contemporary Philosophy: A New Survey, (Philosophy of Science, Vol. II. 1982. 78.50 (ISBN 90-247-2518-6, Pub. by Martinus Nijhoff Netherlands). Kluwer Academic.

Frank, Philipp. Modern Science & Its Philosophy. LC 74-26263. (History, Philosophy & Sociology of Science Ser). 1975. Repr. 27.00x (ISBN 0-405-06591-4). Ayer Co Pubs.

Frey, Gerhard, ed. Bela Juhos: Selected Papers. Foulkes, Paul, tr. LC 76-17019. (Vienna Circle Collection Ser: No. 7). 1976. lib. bdg. 55.00 (ISBN 90-277-0686-7, Pub. by Reidel Holland); pap. 28.95 (ISBN 90-277-0687-5). Kluwer Academic.

Freyhofer, Horst H. The Vitalism of Hans Driesch: The Success & Decline of a Scientific Theory. (European University Studies: Series 20, Philosophy: Vol. 83). 250p. 1982. 24.20 (ISBN 3-8204-5703-8). P Lang Pubs.

Gadol, E. T., ed. Rationality & Sciences: A Memorial Volume for Moritz Schlick. (Illus.). 228p. 1982. 26.00 (ISBN 0-387-81721-2). Springer-Verlag.

Gale, George. Theory of Science. (Illus.). 1979. text ed. 28.95 (ISBN 0-07-022680-6). McGraw.

Giedymin, Jerzy. Science & Convention: Essays on the Origin & Significance of the Conventionalist Philosophy of Science. (Foundations & Philosophy of Science & Technology Ser.). 260p. 1981. 33.00 (ISBN 0-08-025790-9). Pergamon.

Giere, Ronald N. & Westfall, Richard S., eds. Foundations of Scientific Method: The Nineteenth Century. LC 72-79910. pap. 59.70 (ISBN 0-8357-9213-7, 2055202). Bks Demand UMI.

Gilbert, G. N. & Mulkay, Michael. Opening Pandora's Box: A Sociological Analysis of Scientists' Discourse. LC 83-5338. 1984. 37.50 (ISBN 0-521-25418-3); pap. 12.95 (ISBN 0-521-27430-3). Cambridge U Pr.

Gillispie, Charles C. Edge of Objectivity: An Essay in the History of Scientific Ideas. 1960. pap. 12.95 (ISBN 0-691-02350-6). Princeton U Pr.

Gingerich, Owen, ed. The Nature of Scientific Discovery. LC 74-18374. (Illus.). 616p. 1975. 25.00x (ISBN 0-87474-148-3). Smithsonian.

Goodman, Nelson. Fact, Fiction & Forecast. 4th ed. 176p. 1983. text ed. 10.00x (ISBN 0-674-29070-4); pap. text ed. 4.95x (ISBN 0-674-29071-2). Harvard U Pr.

--The Structure of Appearance: Boston Studies in the Philosophy of Science LIII. (Synthese Library: No. 107). 1977. lib. bdg. 42.00 (ISBN 90-277-0773-1, Pub. by Reidel Holland); pap. 11.00 (ISBN 90-277-0774-X). Kluwer Academic.

Gregg, J. R. & Harris, F. T., eds. Form & Strategy in Science: Studies Dedicated to Joseph Henry Woodger on His 70th Birthday. 476p. 1964. lib. bdg. 39.50 (ISBN 90-277-0018-4, Pub. by Reidel Holland). Kluwer Academic.

Gregory, Richard L. Mind in Science: A History of Explanations in Psychology & Physics. LC 81-7732. (Illus.). 648p. 1981. 34.50 (ISBN 0-521-24307-6). Cambridge U Pr.

Griffin, David R. & Cobb, John B., Jr., eds. Mind in Nature: Essays on the Interface of Science & Philosophy. 1977. pap. text ed. 10.25 (ISBN 0-8191-0157-5). U Pr of Amer.

Grof, Stanislav, ed. Ancient Wisdom & Modern Science. 360p. 1984. 34.50x (ISBN 0-87395-848-9); pap. 10.95x (ISBN 0-87395-849-7). State U NY Pr.

Grover, Sonja C. Toward a Psychology of the Scientist: Implications of Psychological Research for Contemporary Philosophy of Science. LC 80-6092. 102p. (Orig.). lib. bdg. 18.25 (ISBN 0-8191-1574-6); pap. text ed. 8.50 (ISBN 0-8191-1575-4). U Pr of Amer.

Grunfeld, Joseph. Changing Rational Standards: A Survey of Modern Philosophy of Science. 184p. 1986. lib. bdg. 22.50 (ISBN 0-8191-4972-1); pap. text ed. 10.50 (ISBN 0-8191-4973-X). U Pr of Amer.

--Science & Values. 210p. 1980. text ed. 23.50x (ISBN 90-6032-018-2). Humanities.

Gustav, Bergmann. Philosophy of Science. LC 77-5439. 181p. lib. bdg. 71.50x (ISBN 0-8371-9623-X, BEPH). Greenwood.

Hacking, Ian. Scientific Revolutions. (Oxford Readings in Philosphy Ser.). 1981. pap. text ed. 7.95x (ISBN 0-19-875051-X). Oxford U Pr.

Haldane, J. B. Daedalus or Science & the Future. 27.50 (ISBN 0-686-17006-7). Quaker City.

Haldane, John B. Marxist Philosophy & the Sciences. LC 78-86757. (Essay Index Reprint Ser). 1939. 15.00 (ISBN 0-8369-1137-7). Ayer Co Pubs.

Haldane, John S. The Sciences & Philosophy. LC 77-27199. (Gifford Lectures: 1927-28). Repr. of 1927 ed. 24.50 (ISBN 0-404-60479-X). AMS Pr.

Hanson, Norwood R. Patterns of Discovery: An Enquiry into the Conceptual Foundations of Science. 1958-1965. 49.50 (ISBN 0-521-05197-5); pap. 13.95 (ISBN 0-521-09261-2). Cambridge U Pr.

Harding, S. G. Can Theories Be Refuted? Essays on the Duhem-Quine Thesis. LC 75-28339. (Synthese Library: No. 81). 366p. 1976. 58.00 (ISBN 90-277-0629-8, Pub. by Reidel Holland); pap. 25.00 (ISBN 90-277-0630-1). Kluwer Academic.

Harre, H. R. Philosophies of Science: An Introductory Survey. 1972. pap. 6.95x (ISBN 0-19-888056-1, OPB). Oxford U Pr.

Harre, R. Matter & Method. 1979. lib. bdg. 22.00x (ISBN 0-917930-28-2); pap. text ed. 6.00x (ISBN 0-917930-08-8). Ridgeview.

Harre, Rom. Principles of Scientific Thinking. LC 78-126074. 1970. 22.50x (ISBN 0-226-31708-0). U of Chicago Pr.

Harris, Errol E. The Foundations of Metaphysics in Science. LC 83-3502. 510p. 1983. pap. text ed. 20.75 (ISBN 0-8191-3169-5). U Pr of Amer.

Haskell, Edward, ed. Full Circle: The Moral Force of Unified Science. LC 72-84271. (Current Topics of Contemporary Thought Ser.). (Illus.). 270p. (Orig.). 1972. 57.75 (ISBN 0-677-12480-5). Gordon.

Healey, Richard. Reduction, Time & Reality: Studies in the Philosophy of the Natural Sciences. 208p. 1981. 34.50 (ISBN 0-521-23708-4). Cambridge U Pr.

Heelan, Patrick A. Space-Perception & the Philosophy of Science. LC 82-4842. (Illus.). 300p. 1983. 30.00x (ISBN 0-520-04611-0). U of Cal Pr.

Heisenberg, Werner. Physicist's Conception of Nature. Pomerans, Arnold J., tr. Repr. of 1958 ed. lib. bdg. 18.75 (ISBN 0-8371-3107-3, HECN). Greenwood.

--Tradition in Science. 160p. (Orig.). 1983. pap. 10.95 (ISBN 0-8164-2488-8, Pub. by Seabury). Winston Pr.

Heller, M., et al, eds. Philosophy in Science, Vol. 1. 191p. 1983. 28.00 (ISBN 0-88126-641-8). Pachart Pub Hse.

Helmholtz, H. von. Boston Studies in the Philosophy of Science, Vol. 37: Epistemological Writings, a New Selection. Cohen, R. S. & Elkana, Y., eds. Cohen, R. S. & Elkana, Y., trs. (Synthese Library: No. 79). 215p. 1976. 31.50 (ISBN 90-277-0290-X, Pub. by Reidel Holland); pap. 16.00 (ISBN 90-277-0582-8). Kluwer Academic.

Hempel, Carl. Philosophy of Natural Science. (Orig.). 1966. pap. 12.95x ref. ed. (ISBN 0-13-663823-6). P-H.

Hempel, Carl G. Aspects of Scientific Explanation. LC 65-15441. 1970. pap. text ed. 14.95 (ISBN 0-02-914340-3). Free Pr.

--Fundamentals of Concept Formation in Empirical Science. (Foundations of the Unity of Science Ser: Vol. 2, No. 7). 1952. pap. 2.25x (ISBN 0-226-57597-7, P416, Phoen). U of Chicago Pr.

Hempel, Carl G. & Putnam, Hilary. Methodology, Epistemology, & Philosophy of Science. 1983. lib. bdg. 69.50 (ISBN 90-277-1646-3, Pub. by Reidel Holland). Kluwer Academic.

Henderson, Lawrence J. Order of Nature. facs. ed. LC 70-150186. (Select Bibliographies Reprint Ser). 1917. 18.00 (ISBN 0-8369-5699-0). Ayer Co Pubs.

Holbrook, Bruce. The Stone Monkey: An Alternative Chinese-Scientific Reality. LC 81-11063. 1981. 15.00 (ISBN 0-688-00665-5); pap. 7.95 (ISBN 0-688-00732-5, Quill). Morrow.

Holton, G. The Scientific Imagination. LC 76-47196. (Illus.). 1978. 47.50 (ISBN 0-521-21700-8); pap. 13.95 (ISBN 0-521-29237-9). Cambridge U Pr.

Home, R. W., ed. Science under Scrutiny. 1983. lib. bdg. 36.00 (ISBN 90-277-1602-1, Pub. by Reidel Holland). Kluwer Academic.

Horstmann, Rolf-Peter, et al, eds. Transcendental Arguments & Science. (Synthese Library: No. 133). 1979. lib. bdg. 34.00 (ISBN 90-277-0963-7, Pub. by Reidel Holland); pap. 16.00 (ISBN 90-277-0964-5). Kluwer Academic.

Hoyle, Fred. Of Men & Galaxies. LC 64-25266. (Jessie & John Danz Lecture Ser.). 83p. 1964. 10.00x (ISBN 0-295-73859-6). U of Wash Pr.

Hubner, Kurt. Critique of Scientific Reason. Dixon, Paul R., Jr. & Dixon, Hollis M., trs. LC 82-23690. 296p. 1983. lib. bdg. 27.50x (ISBN 0-226-35708-2). U of Chicago Pr.

Husserl, Edmund. Crisis of European Sciences & Transcendental Phenomenology: An Introduction to Phenomenological Philosophy. Carr, David, tr. LC 77-82511. (Studies in Phenomenology & Existential Philosophy Ser). 1970. 24.95 (ISBN 0-8101-0255-2); pap. 11.95 (ISBN 0-8101-0458-X). Northwestern U Pr.

Hutten, Ernest H. The Origins of Science: An Inquiry into the Foundations of Western Thought. LC 77-13633. 1978. Repr. of 1962 ed. lib. bdg. 27.50x (ISBN 0-313-20003-3, HUOR). Greenwood.

Inge, W. R. Science & Ultimate Truth. 1978. lib. bdg. 8.50 (ISBN 0-8495-2603-5). Arden Lib.

International Colloquium on Philosophy, Science Theology in the Middle Ages, 1st, 1973. The Cultural Context of Medieval Learning: Proceedings, No.76. Murdock, John E. & Sylla, Edith D., eds. (Synthese Library: Boston Studies in the Philosophy of Science 26). ix, 540p. (Orig.). 1975. 68.50 (ISBN 90-277-0560-7, Pub. by Reidel Holland); pap. 39.50 (ISBN 90-277-0587-9, Pub. by Reidel Holland). Kluwer Academic.

Powers, Jonathan. Philosophy & the New Physics. (Methuens Ideas Ser.). (Illus.). 150p. 1982. pap. 8.50x (ISBN 0-416-73480-4, NO. 3795). Methuen Inc.

PSA 1976, Vol. 2. LC 72-624169. 618p. 1977. pap. 6.25 (ISBN 0-917586-03-4). Philos Sci Assn.

PSA 1978, 2 vols. LC 72-624169. 9.00x (ISBN 0-917586-06-9); pap. 6.00 (ISBN 0-917586-05-0); Vol. II, 478P. 22.50 (ISBN 0-917586-10-7). Philos Sci Assn.

Pubek, Ronald E. The Metaphysical Imperative: A Critique of the Modern Approach to Science. LC 82-40244. 166p. (Orig.). 1983. lib. bdg. 23.50 (ISBN 0-8191-2663-2); pap. text ed. 11.00 (ISBN 0-8191-2664-0). U Pr of Amer.

Radnitzky, Gerard & Anderson, Gunnar, eds. The Structure & Development of Science. (Boston Studies in the Philosophy of Science, No. LIX: Synthese Library: No. 136). 1979. lib. bdg. 39.50 (ISBN 90-277-0994-7, Pub. by Reidel Holland); pap. 15.80 (ISBN 90-277-0995-5). Kluwer Academic.

Ravetz, Jerome R. Scientific Knowledge & Its Social Problems. 1971. pap. 9.95 (ISBN 0-19-519721-6, 388, GB). Oxford U Pr.

Reichenbach, Hans. Modern Philosophy of Science: Selected Essays. Reichenbach, Maria, ed. LC 81-13344. ix, 214p. 1982. Repr. of 1959 ed. lib. bdg. 24.75x (ISBN 0-313-23274-1, REMD). Greenwood.

Rescher, Nicholas. The Limits of Science. LC 84-184. (Pittsburg Series in Philosophy & History of Science). 260p. 1985. 29.95x (ISBN 0-520-05180-7). U of Cal Pr.

--Peirce's Philosophy of Science: Critical Studies in His Theory of Induction & Scientific Method. LC 77-82479. 1979. pap. text ed. 4.95x (ISBN 0-268-01527-9). U of Notre Dame Pr.

--Scientific Progress: A Philosophical Essay on the Economics of Research in Natural Science. LC 77-74544. 1977. 26.95x (ISBN 0-8229-1128-0). U of Pittsburgh Pr.

Rescher, Nicholas, ed. The Limits of Lawfulness: Studies on the Scope & Nature of Scientific Knowledge. LC 83-6872. (CPS Publications in Philosophy of Science). 120p. (Orig.). 1983. lib. bdg. 21.50 (ISBN 0-8191-3176-8, Co-pub. by Ctr Philo Sci); pap. text ed. 9.25 (ISBN 0-8191-3177-6). U Pr of Amer.

--Scientific Explanation & Understanding: Essays on Reasoning & Rationality. LC 83-14815. (CPS Publications in Philosophy of Science). 156p. (Orig.). 1983. lib. bdg. 22.50 (ISBN 0-8191-3465-1); pap. text ed. 10.25 (ISBN 0-8191-3466-X). U Pr of Amer.

Richards, Stewart. Philosophy & Sociology of Science: An Introduction. LC 83-18833. 224p. 1984. 20.00x (ISBN 0-8052-3884-0). Schocken.

Richter, Maurice N., Jr. Science As a Cultural Process. 160p. 1972. pap. text ed. 7.95 (ISBN 0-87073-073-8). Schenkman Bks Inc.

Rocha e Silva, Mauricio. Rational Frontiers of Science. LC 82-46. 1982. pap. 7.50 (ISBN 0-89874-190-4). Krieger.

Romanyshyn, Robert D. Psychological Life: From Science to Metaphor. (Illus.). 227p. 1982. text ed. 19.95x (ISBN 0-292-76473-1). U of Tex Pr.

Romey, Bill. Confluent Education in Science. LC 75-36718. (Illus.). 121p. 1976. pap. text ed. 3.95 (ISBN 0-915492-01-6). Ash Lad Pr.

Rossi, Paolo. The Dark Abyss of Time: The History of the Earth & the History of Nations from Hooke to Vico. Cochrane, Lydia G., tr. LC 84-8481. 352p. 1985. 35.00x (ISBN 0-226-72835-8). U of Chicago Pr.

Rowland, John. Mysteries of Science. LC 78-105035. (Essay Index Reprint Ser). 1957. 19.00 (ISBN 0-8369-1624-7). Ayer Co Pubs.

Rubinstein, Robert A., et al. Science As Cognitive Process: Toward an Empirical Philosophy of Science. LC 83-14730. 208p. 1984. 19.95x (ISBN 0-8122-7911-5). U of Pa Pr.

Ruse, Michael. The Philosophy of Biology. 231p. 1973. pap. text ed. 9.45x (ISBN 0-09-115220-8, Hutchinson U Lib). Humanities.

Russell, Bertrand. Icarus or the Future of Science. 1977. Repr. of 1924 ed. lib. bdg. 17.50 (ISBN 0-8492-2310-5). R West.

--Impact of Science on Society. LC 68-54290. Repr. of 1953 ed. 15.00 (ISBN 0-404-05466-8). AMS Pr.

Rychlak, Joseph F. A Philosophy of Science for Personality Theory. 2nd ed. LC 80-15614. 528p. 1981. 28.75 (ISBN 0-88275-889-6). Krieger.

Salmon, Merrilee H. Philosophy & Archaeology. (Studies in Archaeology Ser.). 1982. 21.00 (ISBN 0-12-615650-6). Acad Pr.

Salmon, Wesley C. The Foundations of Scientific Inference. LC 67-21649. 1967. pap. 5.95x (ISBN 0-8229-5118-5). U of Pittsburgh Pr.

--Space, Time, & Motion: A Philosophical Introduction. 2nd rev. ed. LC 80-18423. (Illus.). 160p. 1981. pap. 8.95x (ISBN 0-8166-1004-5). U of Minn Pr.

Santayana, George. Reason in Science: "The Life of Reason", Vol. 5. 320p. 1983. pap. 6.00 (ISBN 0-486-24439-3). Dover.

Schafer, Wolf, ed. Finalization in Science. 1983. lib. bdg. 59.00 (ISBN 90-277-1549-1, Pub. by Reidel Holland). Kluwer Academic.

Scheffler, Israel. The Anatomy of Inquiry: Philosophical Studies in the Theory of Science. LC 81-85415. 390p. 1981. lib. bdg. 19.50 (ISBN 0-915144-97-2); pap. text ed. 9.95 (ISBN 0-915144-98-0). Hackett Pub.

--Science & Subjectivity. 2nd ed. LC 81-85414. 178p. 1982. lib. bdg. 17.50 (ISBN 0-915145-31-6); pap. text ed. 6.95 (ISBN 0-915145-30-8). Hackett Pub.

Schlagel, Richard H. From Myth to the Modern Mind: A Study of the Origins & Growth of Scientific Thought: Volume I: Animism to Archimedes. LC 84-23361. (American University Studies V (Philosophy): Vol. 12). 283p. 1985. text ed. 30.00 (ISBN 0-8204-0219-2). P Lang Pubs.

Schwartz, Richard B. Samuel Johnson & the New Science. 198p. 1971. 27.50x (ISBN 0-299-06010-1). U of Wis Pr.

Science, Philosophy & Religion. 559p. Date not set. Repr. of 1942 ed. lib. bdg. 85.00 (ISBN 0-8492-3208-2). R West.

Scientific Thought: Some Underlying Concepts, Methods & Procedures. LC 72-79987. 252p. (Co-published with Mouton, The Hague). 1972. 24.25 (ISBN 92-3-101023-9, U589, UNESCO). Unipub.

Scientific Thought: Some Underlying Concepts, Methods & Procedures. (New Babylon, Studies in the Social Sciences: No. 9). (Illus.). 1972. 19.20x (ISBN 90-2797-145-5). Mouton.

Shapere, Dudley. Reason & the Search for Knowledge. (Orig.). 1984. pap. text ed. 19.95 (ISBN 90-277-1641-2, Pub. by Reidel Holland). Kluwer Academic.

Shea, William R., ed. Basic Issues in the Philosophy of Science. LC 76-22198. 1976. pap. text ed. 7.95 (ISBN 0-88202-160-5). Watson Pub Intl.

Sheehan, H. Marxism & the Philosophy of Science- A Critical History: Vol. 1: The First Hundred Years. 446p. 1985. text ed. 35.45x (ISBN 0-391-02998-3). Humanities.

Shelp, Earl E. The Clinical Encounter. 1984. lib. bdg. 39.50 (ISBN 90-277-1593-9, Pub. by Reidel Holland). Kluwer Academic.

Sherburne, Donald W., ed. A Key to Whitehead's "Process & Reality". LC 81-11661. 264p. 1981. pap. 8.50x (ISBN 0-226-75293-3). U of Chicago Pr.

Simms, James R. Measure of Knowledge. LC 71-118312. 1970. 8.75 (ISBN 0-8022-2347-8). Philos Lib.

Simon, Herbert A. Models of Discovery. LC 77-8930. (Boston Studies in the Philosophy of Science: No. 54). 1977. lib. bdg. 55.00 (ISBN 90-277-0812-6, Pub. by Reidel Holland); pap. 14.00 (ISBN 90-277-0970-X). Kluwer Academic.

Singer, Charles. Short History of Scientific Ideas to 1900. (Oxford Paperback Ser.). 1959. pap. 9.95x (ISBN 0-19-881049-0). Oxford U Pr.

Siu, Ralph G. Tao of Science: An Essay on Western Knowledge & Eastern Wisdom. (Illus.). 1958. pap. 7.95 (ISBN 0-262-69004-7). MIT Pr.

Sklar, Lawrence. Philosophy & Spacetime Physics. LC 84-24128. 1985. 25.00x (ISBN 0-520-05374-5). U of Cal Pr.

Slaatte, Howard A. Modern Science & the Human Condition. LC 81-40185. 230p. 1981. pap. text ed. 11.75 (ISBN 0-8191-1586-X); lib. bdg. 22.50 (ISBN 0-8191-1676-9). U Pr of Amer.

Smellie, William. The Philosophy of Natural History, 2 vols. LC 78-67541. Repr. 125.00 set (ISBN 0-404-17230-X). AMS Pr.

Smith, Peter. Realism & the Progress of Science. LC 81-6151. (Cambridge Studies in Philosophy). 160p. 1982. 22.95 (ISBN 0-521-23937-0). Cambridge U Pr.

Smith, Wolfgang. Cosmos & Transcendence: Breaking Through the Barriers of Scientific Belief. 168p. (Orig.). 1984. pap. 8.95 (ISBN 0-89385-028-4). Sugden.

Smullyan, Raymond. Five Thousand B.C. & Other Philosophical Fantasies. 192p. 1984. pap. 5.95 (ISBN 0-312-29517-0). St Martin.

Sosa, Ernest, ed. The Philosophy of Nicholas Rescher: Discussion & Replies. (Philosophical Studies in Philosophy: No. 15). 1979. lib. bdg. 26.00 (ISBN 90-277-0962-9, Pub. by Reidel Holland). Kluwer Academic.

Sparrow, Carroll M. Voyages & Cargoes. 1947. 3.00 (ISBN 0-685-09018-3). Dietz.

Spector, Marshall. Concepts of Reduction in Physical Science. LC 78-5441. (Philosophical Monographs: Second Annual Ser.). 126p. 1978. 24.95 (ISBN 0-87722-131-6); pap. 14.95 (ISBN 0-87722-127-8). Temple U Pr.

--Methodological Foundations of Relativistic Mechanics. 224p. 1973. pap. 8.95x (ISBN 0-268-00488-9). U of Notre Dame Pr.

Stanesby, Derek. Science, Reason & Religion. 210p. 1985. 29.95 (ISBN 0-7099-3360-6, Pub. by Croom Helm Ltd). Longwood Pub Group.

Stegmueller, W. The Structuralist View of Theories: A Possible Analogue. 1979. pap. 20.00 (ISBN 0-387-09460-1). Springer-Verlag.

Stegmuller, Wolfgang, ed. Collected Papers on Epistemology, Philosophy of Science & History of Philosophy, 2 vols. new ed. (Synthese Library: No. 101). 1976. Vol. 1. lib. bdg. 37.00 (ISBN 90-277-0642-5, Pub. by Reidel Holland); Vol. 2. lib. bdg. 39.50 (ISBN 90-277-0643-3); Set. lib. bdg. 76.00 (ISBN 90-277-0767-7). Kluwer Academic.

Stenhouse, David. Active Philosophy in Education & Science. 240p. 1984. text ed. 28.50x (ISBN 0-04-370141-8); pap. text ed. 9.95x (ISBN 0-04-370142-6). Allen Unwin.

Stern, Alfred. Problemas Filosoficos de la Ciencia. LC 76-22489. (Coleccion Mente y Palabra). (Span.). 1976. 6.25 (ISBN 0-8477-2813-7); pap. 5.00 (ISBN 0-8477-2814-5). U of PR Pr.

Stockman, Norman. Antipositivistic Theories of the Sciences. 1983. lib. bdg. 49.95 (ISBN 90-277-1567-X, Pub. by Reidel Holland). Kluwer Academic.

Stove, David. Popper & after: Four Modern Irrationalists. 192p. 1982. 19.25 (ISBN 0-08-026792-0); pap. 10.50 (ISBN 0-08-026791-2). Pergamon.

Stuewer, Roger H., ed. Historical & Philosophical Perspectives of Science. LC 57-12861. (Minnesota Studies in the Philosophy of Science Ser.: Vol. 5). pap. 101.00 (ISBN 0-317-28158-5, 2055963). Bks Demand UMI.

Suppe, Frederick, ed. The Structure of Scientific Theories. 2nd ed. LC 72-89604. (Illus.). 832p. 1977. 35.00x (ISBN 0-252-00655-0); pap. 14.50 (ISBN 0-252-00634-8). U of Ill Pr.

Tavanec, P. V., ed. Problems of the Logic of Scientific Knowledge. (Synthese Library: No. 25). 429p. 1970. lib. bdg. 58.00 (ISBN 90-277-0087-7, Pub. by Reidel Holland). Kluwer Academic.

Tennant, Frederick R. Philosophy of the Sciences or the Relations Between the Departments of Knowledge. Repr. of 1932 ed. lib. bdg. 15.00x (ISBN 0-8371-4353-5, TEPS). Greenwood.

Tillich, Paul. The System of the Sciences According to Objects & Methods. LC 80-67078. Orig. Title: Das System der Wissenschaften nach Gegenstanden und Methoden. 288p. 1981. 22.50 (ISBN 0-686-76167-7). Bucknell U Pr.

Tondl, L. Boston Studies in the Philosophy of Science, Vol. 10: Scientific Procedures. Short, David, tr. from Czech. LC 72-77880. (Synthese Library: No. 47). 268p. 1973. 34.00 (ISBN 90-277-0147-4, Pub. by Reidel Holland); pap. 18.50 (ISBN 90-277-0323-X). Kluwer Academic.

Toulmin, Stephen. Foresight & Understanding: An Enquiry into the Aims of Science. pap. 4.95xi (ISBN 0-06-130564-2, TB564, Torch). Har-Row.

Toulmin, Stephen E. Foresight & Understanding: An Enquiry into the Aims of Science. LC 81-13446. 115p. 1982. Repr. of 1961 ed. lib. bdg. 22.50x (ISBN 0-313-23345-4, TOFO). Greenwood.

Tudor, Andrew. Beyond Empiricism: Philosophy of Science in Sociology. (Monographs in Social Theory). 224p. (Orig.). 1982. pap. 9.95x (ISBN 0-7100-0925-9). Routledge & Kegan.

Tuomela, Raimo. Human Action & Its Explanation. (Synthese Library: No. 116). 1977. lib. bdg. 55.00 (ISBN 90-277-0824-X, Pub. by Reidel Holland). Kluwer Academic.

Tuomela, Raimo, ed. Dispositions. (Synthese Library: No. 113). 1977. lib. bdg. 50.00 (ISBN 90-277-0810-X, Pub. by Reidel Holland). Kluwer Academic.

Turchin, Valentin F. The Phenomenon of Science. Frentz, Brand, tr. from Russian. LC 77-4330. 1977. 36.00x (ISBN 0-231-03983-2). Columbia U Pr.

Turner, Merle B. Philosophy & the Science of Behavior, Including Psychology & the Philosophy of Science. LC 66-25267. (Century Psychology Ser.). (Illus.). 1967. 36.50x (ISBN 0-89197-341-9); pap. text ed. 9.95x (ISBN 0-89197-342-7). Irvington.

Tweney, Ryan D., et al, eds. On Scientific Thinking. 496p. 1981. 42.00x (ISBN 0-231-04814-9); pap. 18.00x (ISBN 0-231-04815-7). Columbia U Pr.

UNESCO Colloqium, 10th Anniversary of the Death of Albert Einstein & Teilhard De Charden. Science & Synthesis: An International Colloquium Organized by UNESCO on the Tenth Anniversary of the Death of Albert Einstein & Teilhard De Chardin. Crook, B. M., tr. LC 77-143044. 1971. 29.00 (ISBN 0-387-05344-1). Springer-Verlag.

VanFrassen, B. C. The Scientific Image. (Clarendon Library of Logic & Philosophy Ser.). 1980. text ed. 45.00x (ISBN 0-19-824424-X); 14.95x (ISBN 0-19-824427-4). Oxford U Pr.

Verharen, Charles C. Rationality in Philosophy & Science. LC 83-40046. 176p. 1983. lib. bdg. 24.75 (ISBN 0-8191-3297-7); pap. text ed. 11.25 (ISBN 0-8191-3298-5). U Pr of Amer.

Voegelin, Eric. Science, Politics & Gnosticism. LC 68-14367. 128p. 4.95 (ISBN 0-89526-964-3). Regnery-Gateway.

Wallace, William A. From a Realist Point of View: Essays on the Philosophy of Science. 352p. 1983. lib. bdg. 27.00 (ISBN 0-8191-3445-7); pap. text ed. 15.25 (ISBN 0-8191-3446-5). U Pr of Amer.

Wartofsky, Marx W., ed. Models. (Boston Studies in the Philosophy of Science: No. 1, Vol. 2). 1979. lib. bdg. 37.00 (ISBN 90-277-0736-7, Pub. by Reidel Holland); pap. 16.00 (ISBN 90-277-0947-5). Kluwer Academic.

Watkins, John. Science & Scepticism. LC 84-42555. (Illus.). 450p. 1984. text ed. 44.00x (ISBN 0-691-07294-9); pap. 14.50x (ISBN 0-691-10171-X). Princeton U Pr.

Weingartner, et al. Proceedings of the Seventh International Congress of Logic, Methodology & Philosophy of Science. (Studies in Logic: Vol. 115). Date not set. price not set (ISBN 0-444-87656-1). Elsevier.

Weiss, John, ed. The Origins of Modern Consciousness. LC 65-10145. (Waynebooks Ser: No. 18). (Orig.). 1965. pap. 4.95x (ISBN 0-8143-1261-6). Wayne St U Pr.

Wellmuth, John. Nature & Origins of Scientism. (Aquinas Lecture). 1944. 7.95 (ISBN 0-87462-108-9). Marquette.

Westfall, Richard S. Science & Religion in Seventeenth-Century England. 1973. pap. 4.95 (ISBN 0-472-06190-9, 190, AA). U of Mich Pr.

Whewell, William. On the Philosophy of Discovery: Chapters Historical & Critical. 1971. Repr. of 1860 ed. lib. bdg. 32.00 (ISBN 0-8337-3764-3). B Franklin.

--Philosophy of the Inductive Sciences, 2 vols. 1967. Repr. of 1847 ed. 95.00x (ISBN 0-7146-1156-5, BHA-01156, F Cass Co). Biblio Dist.

--The Philosophy of the Inductive Sciences, 2 Vols. 2nd facsimile ed. Repr. of 1847 ed. Set. 62.00 (ISBN 0-384-67940-4). Johnson Repr.

Whitehead, Alfred N. Concept of Nature. pap. 11.95 (ISBN 0-521-09245-0). Cambridge U Pr.

--Nature & Life. LC 34-9604. (Illus.). 1969. Repr. of 1934 ed. lib. bdg. 18.75 (ISBN 0-8371-0751-2, WHNL). Greenwood.

--A Philosopher Looks at Science. (Reprints in Philosophy Ser.). lib. bdg. 32.50x (ISBN 0-697-00211-X); pap. 9.95x (ISBN 0-89197-883-6). Irvington.

Whitley, Richard. The Intellectual & Social Organization of the Sciences. 1984. 34.95x (ISBN 0-19-827248-0). Oxford U Pr.

Whyte, Lancelot L. Accent on Form: An Anticipation of the Science of Tomorrow. LC 72-10702. 198p. 1973. Repr. of 1954 ed. lib. bdg. 22.50 (ISBN 0-8371-6622-5, WHAF). Greenwood.

Wickham, Harvey. Unrealists. LC 78-105051. (Essay Index Reprint Ser). 1930. 19.00 (ISBN 0-8369-1736-7). Ayer Co Pubs.

--Unrealists. LC 73-105851. (Essay & General Literature Index Reprint Ser). 1971. Repr. of 1931 ed. 22.00x (ISBN 0-8046-1338-9, Pub by Kennikat). Assoc Faculty Pr.

Wickramsinghe, Chandra. Fundamental Studies & the Future of Science. LC 84-107333. 392p. 1984. text ed. 41.50x (ISBN 0-906449-57-X, Pub. by U of Coll Cardiff UK). Humanities.

Wojcicki, Ryszard. Topics in the Formal Methodology of Empirical Sciences. Jansen, Ewa, tr. from Polish. (Synthese Library: No. 135). 1980. lib. bdg. 50.00 (ISBN 90-277-1004-X, Publ by Reidel Holland). Kluwer Academic.

Wolman, Benjamin. Logic of Science in Psychoanalysis. 353p. 1984. 35.00x (ISBN 0-231-05744-X). Columbia U Pr.

Young, Arthur M. Which Way Out? And Other Essays. (Illus.). 206p. (Orig.). 1980. 14.95 (ISBN 0-9609850-1-8). Rob Briggs.

Ziman, John. An Introduction to Science Studies: The Philosophical & Social Aspects of Science & Technology. (Illus.). 208p. 1985. 22.95 (ISBN 0-521-25988-6). Cambridge U Pr.

Ziman, John M. Reliable Knowledge. LC 78-3792. (Illus.). 1979. 29.95 (ISBN 0-521-22087-4). Cambridge U Pr.

Zimmermann, Robert E. Aesthetic, 2 vols. (Ger). Repr. of 1858 ed. 95.00 (ISBN 0-685-02113-0). Johnson Repr.

Zinov'ev, A. A. Boston Studies in the Philosophy of Science, Vol 9: Foundations of the Logical Theory of Scientific Knowledge (Complex Logic) Blakeley, T. J., tr. from Russ. LC 74-135109. (Synthese Library: No. 46). 301p. 1973. 38.00 (ISBN 90-277-0193-8, Pub. by Reidel Holland); pap. 23.00 (ISBN 90-277-0324-8). Kluwer Academic.

Zumbach, Clark. The Transcendent Science: Kant's Conception of Biological Methodology. 1984. lib. bdg. 32.00 (ISBN 90-247-2904-1, Pub. by Martinus Nijhoff Netherlands). Kluwer Academic.

Brewer, Waldo L. Factors Affecting Student Achievement & Change in a Physical Science Survey Course. LC 70-176691. (Columbia University. Teachers College. Contributions to Education Ser.: No. 868). Repr. of 1943 ed. 22.50 (ISBN 0-404-55868-2). AMS Pr.
Butts, D. P. A Summary of Research in Science Education 1979. 130p. 1981. pap. 28.95 (ISBN 0-471-86587-7). Wiley.
Cain, Sandra E. & Evans, Jack M. Sciencing: An Involvement Approach to Elementary Science Methods. 350p. 1984. pap. text ed. 16.95 (ISBN 0-675-20055-5). Additional supplements may be obtained from publisher. Merrill.
Carin, Arthur & Sund, Robert. Teaching Modern Science. 4th ed. 336p. 1984. pap. 18.95 (ISBN 0-675-20221-3). Merrill.
--Teaching Science Through Discovery. 5th ed. 512p. 1984. 25.95 (ISBN 0-675-20387-2). Additional supplements may be obtained from publisher. Merrill.
Carin, Arthur A. & Sund, Robert B. Teaching Modern Science. 3rd ed. (Elementary Education Ser.: No. C22). 352p. 1980. pap. text ed. 17.95 (ISBN 0-675-08193-9). Merrill.
Case Studies in Science Education. Incl. Vol. 1. The Case Reports (SE 78-741); Vol. 2. Design, Overview, & General Findings (SE78-7411). 11.00 (ISBN 0-318-18101-0). NSF.
Committee on Science, Engineering, & Public Policy, Offices of Public Sector AAAS, ed. Guide to Education in Science, Engineering, & Public Policy. 91p. 1985. pap. text ed. 3.00 ea (ISBN 0-87168-271-0). AAAS.
Curtis, Francis D. Some Values Derived from Extensive Reading of General Science. LC 75-177601. (Columbia University. Teachers College. Contributions to Education: No. 163). Repr. of 1924 ed. 22.50 (ISBN 0-404-55163-7). AMS Pr.
Cusimano, Vincent J. & Halpern, Stephen. Contemporary Issues in Science: Course Manual. 139p. (Orig.). 1982. pap. text ed. 15.95 (ISBN 0-914639-25-0). SI Cont Ed Inc.
--Contemporary Issues in Science: Implementation Manual. 98p. (Orig.). 1982. pap. text ed. 15.95 (ISBN 0-914639-26-9). SI Cont Ed Inc.
Danilov, Victor J. Science & Technology Centers. (Illus.). 416p. 1982. 50.00x (ISBN 0-262-04068-9). MIT Pr.
Dart, Francis. Teaching Science as a Second Culture. Ives, Kenneth, ed. (Illus.). 60p. 1983. pap. 4.00 (ISBN 0-89670-009-7). Progresiv Pub.
Doran, Rodney L. Basic Measurement & Evaluation of Science Instruction. (Illus., Orig.). 1980. pap. 5.00 (ISBN 0-87355-016-1). Natl Sci Tchrs.
Drew, David E. Strengthening Academic Science. LC 85-6471. 300p. 1985. write for info. (ISBN 0-03-071574-1). Praeger.
Elementary Science Study. Drops, Streams, & Containers. 1971. tchr's. guide 20.20 (ISBN 0-07-017692-2). McGraw.
--Earthworms. 1971. tchr's. guide 13.80 (ISBN 0-07-017707-4). McGraw.
Elmer, Marilyn. Science for Christian Schools, Five. (Science for Christian Schools Ser.). (Illus.). 212p. 1977. text ed. 11.95 (ISBN 0-89084-032-6); tchr's. ed. 25.50 (ISBN 0-89084-038-5). Bob Jones Univ Pr.
Farmer, Walter A. & Farrell, Margaret A. Systematic Instruction in Science for the Middle & High School Years. LC 79-4252. (Illus.). 1980. pap. text ed. 17.30 (ISBN 0-201-02435-7, Sch Div). Addison-Wesley.
Forte, Imogene & MacKenzie, Joy. Creative Science Experiences for the Young Child. rev. ed. (Illus.). 176p. 1983. pap. text ed. 8.95 (ISBN 0-86530-056-9, IP-056). Incentive Pubns.
Frey, Karl, et al, eds. Research in Science Education in Europe: Report of a Cooperative Study & a European Contact Workshop Organised by the Council of Europe & the Institute for Science Education, FRG (Kiel) 394p. 1977. pap. text ed. 18.50 (ISBN 90-265-0266-4, Pub. by Swets & Zeitlinger Netherlands). Hogrefe Intl.
Gabel, Dorothy L. & Kagan, Martin H. A Summary of Research in Science Education 1978. 578p. 1980. pap. 23.95x (ISBN 0-471-08869-2, Pub. by Ronald Pr). Wiley.
Gastel, Barbara. Presenting Science to the Public. (Professional Writing Ser.). (Illus.). 146p. 1983. 17.95 (ISBN 0-89495-028-2); pap. 11.95 (ISBN 0-89495-029-0). ISI Pr.
Glass, Hiram B. Science & Liberal Education. LC 60-8285. (Davis Washington Mitchell Lectures). pap. 31.80 (ISBN 0-317-09391-6, 2003383). Bks Demand UMI.
Goldstein, Amy J. & Granade, Charles, eds. Graduate Programs in the Physical Sciences & Mathematics 1986. 20th ed. (Annual Guides to Graduate Study Ser.). 650p. (Orig.). 1985. pap. 22.95 (ISBN 0-87866-345-2). Petersons Guides.
Gomathi Krishnamachari & Kakar, I. B. Discovering Science, 2 bks. 205p. (Orig.). 1983. Bk. 1. pap. text ed. 3.95x (ISBN 0-86131-410-7); Bk. 2. pap. text ed. 3.95x (ISBN 0-86131-411-5). Apt Bks.
Good, Ronald G. How Children Learn Science: Conceptual Development & Implications for Teaching. (Illus.). 1977. text ed. write for info. (ISBN 0-02-344640-4). Macmillan.
Goodfield, June. Reflections on Science & the Media. LC 81-66420. 113p. 1981. 9.00x (ISBN 0-87168-252-4). AAAS.
Goodlad, J. S. Science for Non-Scientists. 1973. 14.50x (ISBN 0-19-858209-9). Oxford U Pr.
Guralnick, Stanley M. Science & the Ante-Bellum American College. LC 75-12219. (Memoirs Ser: Vol. 109). 1975. pap. 5.00 (ISBN 0-87169-109-4). Am Philos.
Harbeck, Mary, ed. The Second Sourcebook for Science Supervisors. rev. ed. 1976. pap. 5.00 (ISBN 0-87355-004-8). Natl Sci Tchrs.
HM Study Skills Group. Science Study Skills Teachers Guide. 1983. pap. 7.50 (ISBN 0-88210-151-X). Natl Assn Principals.
Holmes, N. J., et al. People, Concepts & Processes Series. Incl. Level 1. text ed. 9.64 (ISBN 0-07-029501-8); Level 2. text ed. 10.08 (ISBN 0-07-029502-6); Level 3. text ed. 11.32 (ISBN 0-07-029503-4); Level 4; Level 5; Level 6. 1974. McGraw.
Hornberger, Theodore. Scientific Thought in the American College 1638-1800. 1968. lib. bdg. 14.50x (ISBN 0-374-93952-7). Octagon.
Hounshell, Paul B. & Trollinger, Ira R. Games for the Science Classroom: An Annotated Bibliography. 1977. pap. 7.00 (ISBN 0-87355-006-4). Natl Sci Tchrs.
Howard, Frederick T. Complexity of Mental Processes in Science Testing. LC 79-178800. (Columbia University. Teachers College. Contributions to Education: No. 879). Repr. of 1943 ed. 22.50 (ISBN 0-404-55879-8). AMS Pr.
Huxley, T. H. Science & Education: Essays. (Educational Ser.). 1910. Repr. 25.00 (ISBN 0-8482-4424-9). Norwood Edns.
Jones, A. & Weinstock, H. Computer-Based Science Instruction. 376p. 1978. 37.50x (ISBN 90-286-0248-8). Sijthoff & Noordhoff.
Kahle, Jane B. Double Dilemma: Minorities & Women in Science Education. LC 81-84383. (Illus.). 181p. (Orig.). 1982. pap. 5.95 (ISBN 0-931682-13-4). Purdue Univ.
Kailath, Thomas, ed. Modern Signal Processing: Proceedings of the Arab School on Science & Technology. LC 84-19289. (Illus.). 440p. 1985. text ed. 79.95 (ISBN 0-89116-386-7). Hemisphere Pub.
Kapili, Pascual H. & Calvero, Teofidez E. Improvising Science Equipment: A Handbook. (Illus.). 1978. pap. text ed. 8.25x (ISBN 0-686-23914-8, Pub. by New Day Pub). Cellar.
Korol, Alexander G. Soviet Education for Science & Technology. LC 73-9212. 513p. 1974. Repr. of 1957 ed. lib. bdg. 45.00x (ISBN 0-8371-6978-X, KOSE). Greenwood.
Kwong Lee Dow. Teaching Science in Australian Schools. Selleck, R. J., ed. (The Second Century in Australian Education Ser.). (Illus.). 120p. 1971. pap. 8.50x (ISBN 0-522-84014-0, Pub. by Melbourne U Pr). Intl Spec Bk.
Lange, Erwin F. Laboratory Exercises in Physical Science. 3rd ed. (Illus.). 1970. pap. text ed. 6.95x (ISBN 0-87015-185-1). Pacific Bks.
Lankford, T. Randall. Integrated Science for Health Students. 3rd ed. 1984. text ed. 28.95 (ISBN 0-8359-3106-4); instr's manual avail. (ISBN 0-8359-3101-3). Reston.
Linking Science Education to Real Life: Curriculum Design, Development & Implementation. (Asian Programme of Educational Innovation For Development). 90p. 1981. pap. 7.00 (ISBN 0-686-69639-5, UB90, UB). Unipub.
Loiry, William S. Winning with Science: The Complete Guide to Science Research & Programs for Students. 1985. 14.95 (ISBN 0-9607654-7-6); pap. 9.95 (ISBN 0-9607654-8-4). Loiry Pubs Hse.
MacKay, Donald M. Science & the Quest for Meaning. LC 81-17504. pap. 21.80 (ISBN 0-317-30150-0, 2025333). Bks Demand UMI.
Martin, Michael. Concepts of Science Education: A Philosophical Analysis. 184p. 1985. pap. text ed. 9.75 (ISBN 0-8191-4479-7). U Pr of Amer.
Martin, Ralph E., Jr. The Credibility Principle & Teacher Attitudes Toward Science. LC 83-49429. (American University Studies XIV (Education): Vol. 3). 250p. (Orig.). 1984. pap. text ed. 20.55 (ISBN 0-8204-0101-3). P Lang Pubs.
National Board on Graduate Education. Science Development: An Evaluation Study. 1975. pap. 9.50 (ISBN 0-309-02329-7). Natl Acad Pr.
National Convocation on Precollege Education in Math & Science, National Academy of Sciences. Science & Mathematics in the Schools: Report of a Convocation. 32p. 1982. pap. text ed. 2.00 (ISBN 0-309-03330-6). Natl Acad Pr.
National Research Council. Indicators of Precollege Education in Science & Mathematics: A Preliminary Review. 212p. 1985. pap. text ed. 16.50 (ISBN 0-309-03536-8). Natl Acad Pr.
New Trends in Integrated Science Teaching, 5 vols. Incl. Vol. 1. 1969-1970; Vol. 2. 1973. 239p. pap. 15.00 (ISBN 92-3-101114-6, U418); Vol. 3. Education of Teachers. Richmond, P. E., ed. (Illus.). 240p. 1974. pap. 18.00 (ISBN 92-3-101190-1, U419); Vol. 4. 1977. 199p. pap. 14.50 (ISBN 92-3-101440-4, U420); Vol. 5. 1979. Reay, Judith, ed. (Illus.). 238p. pap. 17.00 (ISBN 92-3-101757-8, U1073). (Teaching of Basic Sciences Ser., UNESCO). Unipub.
New Trends in the Utilization of Educational Technology for Science Education. (Illus.). 248p. (Orig.). 1975. pap. 13.25 (ISBN 92-3-101143-X, U428, UNESCO). Unipub.
New UNESCO Source Book for Science Teaching. (Illus.). 270p. (Orig., 3rd Printing 1979). 1973. pap. 13.50 (ISBN 92-3-101058-1, U430, UNESCO). Unipub.
Newman, Michele M. & McRae, Madelyn A., eds. Films in the Sciences: Reviews & Recommendations. LC 80-67466. (AAAS Reference Sourcebook Ser.: Vol. 4). 186p. 1980. text ed. 14.00x (ISBN 0-686-72330-9). AAAS.
Nichols, Herbert L., Jr. Science Blundering: An Outsider's View. LC 84-6140. (Illus.). 128p. 1984. 15.00 (ISBN 0-911040-18-8). North Castle.
NSTA Handbook, 1982-1983. 5.00 (ISBN 0-686-84081-X). Natl Sci Tchrs.
Ogborn, J. M., ed. Individual Study in Undergraduate Science. 1977. pap. text ed. 24.50x (ISBN 0-435-69580-0). Heinemann Ed.
--Practical Work in Undergraduate Science. (H.E.L.P. Ser.). 1977. pap. text ed. 24.50x (ISBN 0-435-69582-7). Heinemann Ed.
--Small Group Teaching in Undergraduate Science. (H.E.L.P. Ser.). 1977. pap. text ed. 24.50x (ISBN 0-435-69581-9). Heinemann Ed.
--Students' Reactions to Undergraduate Science. (H.E.L.P. Ser.). 1977. pap. text ed. 24.50x (ISBN 0-435-69583-5). Heinemann Ed.
Olson, J. K., ed. Innovation in the Science Curriculum. 192p. 1982. 23.50 (ISBN 0-89397-127-8). Nichols Pub.
Olstad, Roger G. & Haury, David L. A Summary of Research in Science Education, 1984. (Science Education Ser.: Vol. 68, No. 3). 363p. 1984. pap. text ed. 23.95x (ISBN 0-471-81740-6). Wiley.
Ormerod, M. B. & Duckworth, D. Pupils' Attitude Toward Science: A Review of Research. 160p. 1975. 12.00x (ISBN 0-85633-077-9, Pub. by NFER Nelson UK). Taylor & Francis.
Philadelphia Suburban School Study Council Group C. Science: Suggestions for Teaching. 1958. pap. 2.50x (ISBN 0-8134-0495-9, 495). Interstate.
Planning for Science Teaching Improvements in Asian Schools. Repr. of 1970 ed. 2.75 (ISBN 0-685-27882-4, UB46, UB). Unipub.
Rabat Seminar, 1962. The Teaching of Sciences in African Universities: Report. (The Development of Higher Education Ser.). 112p. 1964. pap. 5.00 (ISBN 0-686-94191-8, U659, UNESCO). Unipub.
Rider, Robin E. & Lowood, Henry E., eds. Guide to Sources in Northern California for History of Science & Technology. (Berkeley Papers in History of Science: Vol. x). (Illus.). 193p. (Orig.). 1985. pap. text ed. 12.00 (ISBN 0-918102-12-X). U Cal Hist Sci Tech.
Rostoker, W. & Domagala, R. A Study Aid for Introductory Materials Science & Engineering. 1974. spiral bdg. 6.80x (ISBN 0-87563-070-7). Stipes.
Rowe, Mary B. Education in the Eighties: Science. 184p. 1982. 17.95 (ISBN 0-8106-3162-8); pap. 11.95 (ISBN 0-8106-3161-X). NEA.
Saint-Martin, Monique De. Les Fonctions Sociales de L'enseignement Scientifique. (Cahiers Du Centre De Sociologie Europeenne: No. 8). (Illus.). 1971. pap. 10.40x (ISBN 90-2796-915-9). Mouton.
Schmidt, Victor E. & Rockcastle, Verne N. Teaching Science with Every Day Things. 2nd ed. (Illus.). 224p. 1982. pap. 21.95 (ISBN 0-07-055355-6). McGraw.
Schwab, Joseph J. Science, Curriculum, & Liberal Education: Selected Essays. Westbury, Ian & Wilkof, Neil J., eds. LC 78-5848. (Phoenix Ser.). vi, 394p. 1982. pap. 9.95x (ISBN 0-226-74187-7). U of Chicago Pr.
Science & Children Editorial Staff & Bindel, Henry J., Jr., eds. Directory of Science Education Suppliers. 1982. pap. 3.00 (ISBN 0-686-46936-4). Natl Sci Tchrs.
Science in Basic Functional Education: Philosophy, Approaches, Methods, & Materials. (Asian Programme of Educational Innovation for Development Ser.). (Illus.). 1977. pap. 6.75 (ISBN 0-685-77316-7, UB53, UNESCO). Unipub.
Science Policy Research & Teaching Units: Europe & North America, 1967-1970. 378p. (Orig.). 1971. pap. 8.25 (ISBN 92-3-000891-5, U582, UNESCO). Unipub.
Seaborg, Glenn T. Science & Liberal Education in the Space Age. LC 60-1274. (Augustana College Occasional Papers: No. 5). 15p. 1960. pap. 0.50 (ISBN 0-910182-26-4). Augustana Coll.
Shayer, Michael & Adey, Philip. Towards a Science of Science Teaching. (Orig.). 1981. pap. text ed. 12.95x (ISBN 0-435-57825-1). Heinemann Ed.
Sheckles, Mary. Building Children's Science Concepts Through Experience. LC 58-8243. 1958. pap. text ed. 4.25x (ISBN 0-8077-2149-2). Tchrs Coll.
Shymansky, J. A. & Penick, J. E. Journal of Research in Science Teaching, Vol. 20. 136p. 1983. pap. 14.95 (ISBN 0-471-88187-2). Wiley.
Sipe, H. Craig & Farmer, Walter A. A Summary of Research in Science Education 1980. 503p. 1982. 26.95x (ISBN 0-471-87028-5, Pub. by Wiley Interscience). Wiley.
Skolnick, Joan, et al. How To Encourage Girls in Math & Science: Strategies for Parents & Educators. (Illus.). 192p. 1982. 15.95 (ISBN 0-13-405670-1, Spec); pap. 7.95 (ISBN 0-13-405662-0). P-H.
Smith, Robert V. Graduate Research: A Guide for Students in the Sciences. 175p. 1984. 21.95 (ISBN 0-89495-037-1); pap. 14.95 (ISBN 0-89495-038-X). ISI Pr.
Solomon, Joan. Teaching Children in the Laboratory. 156p. 1980. 25.00 (ISBN 0-7099-2304-X, Pub. by Croom Helm Ltd); pap. 9.00 (ISBN 0-7099-2305-8). Longwood Pub Group.
Source Book for Science Teaching. (UNESCO, pub.). pap. 8.00 (UM11, UN). Unipub.
Taylor, Jeremy R. The Science Lecture Room: A Planning Study to Examine the Principles of Location & Design of Lecture Rooms in the Development of University Science Areas. LC 67-24941. pap. 31.80 (ISBN 0-317-27100-8, 2024548). Bks Demand UMI.
Taylor, Paul A. & Gibbs, Ronald K. How Ought Science Be Taught. LC 72-6342. 1972. 29.00x (ISBN 0-8422-5018-2); pap. text ed. 8.50x (ISBN 0-8422-0153-X). Irvington.
Tcherikover, Victor A. Teaching of Science. Incl. The Teaching of Science As Enquiry. Schwab, Joseph J. (Inglis Lectures Ser: 1961); Science in the Elementary School. Brandwein, Paul F. (The Burton Lectures Ser: 1961). LC 62-8184. vi, 152p. 1961. 8.95x (ISBN 0-674-87046-8). Harvard U Pr.
Thompson, William P. Orientation in Science. LC 82-20189. 480p. (Orig.). 1983. lib. bdg. 32.25 (ISBN 0-8191-2885-6); pap. text ed. 18.75 (ISBN 0-8191-2886-4). U Pr of Amer.
Ticotsky, Alan. Who Says You Can't Teach Science? 1985. pap. 7.95 (ISBN 0-673-18107-3). Scott F.
Tiner, John H. Science Bulletin Board Ideas. pap. 5.95 (ISBN 0-89137-614-3). Quality Pubns.
Turner, Dorothy M. History of Science Teaching in England. Cohen, I. Bernard, ed. LC 80-2148. (Development of Science Ser.). (Illus.). 1981. lib. bdg. 20.00x (ISBN 0-405-13955-1). Ayer Co Pubs.
UNESCO Handbook for Science Teachers. 208p. (Co-published with Heinemann Educational Books, London; and Unipub, New York). 1980. pap. 14.95 (ISBN 92-3-101666-0, U1029, UNESCO). Unipub.
Van De Voort, Alice M. The Teaching of Science in Normal Schools & Teachers Colleges. LC 75-177679. (Columbia University. Teachers College. Contributions to Education: No. 287). Repr. of 1927 ed. 17.50 (ISBN 0-404-55287-0). AMS Pr.
Voss, B. E. A Summary of Research in Science Education 1981. 424p. 1983. pap. 19.95 (ISBN 0-471-88199-6). Wiley.
Waters, Eugene A. A Study of the Application of an Educational Theory to Science Instruction. LC 76-177663. (Columbia University. Teachers College. Contributions to Education: No. 864). Repr. of 1942 ed. 17.50 (ISBN 0-404-55864-X). AMS Pr.
Wilson, R. W. Useful Addresses for Science Teachers: A Guide to Curriculum Development. 2nd ed. 1974. pap. 29.95x (ISBN 0-7131-1828-8). Intl Ideas.
Wolfinger, Donna M. Teaching Science in the Elementary School: Content, Process & Attitude. 1984. text ed. 24.95 (ISBN 0-316-95101-3); tchrs manual avail. (ISBN 0-316-95102-1). Little.

BOOKS - SUBJECT INDEX SCIENCE, ANCIENT

Ziman, John M. Teaching & Learning About Science & Society. LC 80-40326. (Illus.). 148p. 1980. 27.95 (ISBN 0-521-23221-X). Cambridge U Pr.

SCIENCE–STUDY AND TEACHING (ELEMENTARY)

Aarons, Trudy & Koelsch, Francine. One Hundred & One Science Activities. 156p. (Orig.). 1981. pap. text ed. 11.95 (ISBN 0-88450-879-X, 7221-B). Communication Skill.
Activities for the Young Scientist. 1984. 7.00 (ISBN 0-939418-80-0). Ferguson-Florissant.
Allen, Dorothea. Elementary Science Activities for Every Month of the School Year. LC 81-9503. 258p. 1981. 17.50 (ISBN 0-13-259952-X, Parker). P-H.
Basic Skills Science Workbook: Grade 8. (Basic Skills Workbooks). 32p. 1982. wkbk. 0.99 (ISBN 0-8209-0407-4, SW-I). ESP.
Carmichael, Viola S. Science Experiences for Young Children. Reed, R., ed. LC 81-85434. (Orig.). 1982. pap. 6.95 (ISBN 0-88247-633-5). R & E Pubs.
Cohen, et al. Teaching Science As a Decision Making Process. 296p. 1984. pap. text ed. 14.50 (ISBN 0-8403-3402-8). Kendall-Hunt.
Collette, Alfred T. & Chiapetta, Eugene L. Science Instruction in the Middle & Secondary Schools. (Illus.). 592p. 1984. text ed. 24.95 (ISBN 0-8016-1095-8). Mosby.
Crescimbeni, Joseph. Science Enrichment Activities for the Elementary School. LC 80-28026. 272p. 1981. 24.95x (ISBN 0-13-794693-7, Parker). P-H.
Downs, Gary E. & Gerlovich, Jack A., eds. Science Safety for Elementary Teachers. (Illus.). 102p. 1983. pap. text ed. 8.95x (ISBN 0-8138-1641-6). Iowa St U PR.
Esler & Esler. Teaching Elementary Science. 4th ed. 1984. write for info. (ISBN 0-534-03408-X). Wadsworth Pub.
Gega. Science in Elementary Education. 5th ed. 1985. pap. price not set (ISBN 0-471-82565-4). Wiley.
Harlem, Wynne. New Trends in Primary School Science Education, Vol. 1. 220p. 1982. pap. text ed. 17.00 (ISBN 92-3-102034-X, U1291, UNESCO). Unipub.
Hayes, Marilyn. Basic Skills Social Studies Workbook: Grade 5. (Basic Skills Workbooks). 32p. 1982. wkbk. 0.99 (ISBN 0-8209-0400-7, SSW-F). ESP.
Holler, Kathy. Seasons. (Science Ser.). 24p. 1982. wkbk. 5.00 (ISBN 0-8209-0163-6, S-25). ESP.
House, John. The Wonders of Science. (Science Ser.). 24p. 1977. wkbk. 5.00 (ISBN 0-8209-0155-5, S-17). ESP.
Houston, Jack. Basic Skills Science Workbook: Grade 3. (Basic Skills Workbooks). 32p. 1982. wkbk. 0.99 (ISBN 0-8209-0402-3, SW-D). ESP.
--Basic Skills Science Workbook: Grade 5. (Basic Skills Workbooks). 32p. 1982. wkbk. 0.99 (ISBN 0-8209-0404-X, SW-F). ESP.
--Basic Skills Science Workbook: Grade 6. (Basic Skills Workbooks). 32p. 1982. wkbk. 0.99 (ISBN 0-8209-0405-8, SW-G). ESP.
--Basic Skills Science Workbook: Grade 7. (Basic Skills Workbooks). 32p. 1982. wkbk. 0.99 (ISBN 0-8209-0406-6, SW-H). ESP.
--Jumbo Science Yearbook: Grade 6. (Jumbo Science Ser.). 96p. 1979. 14.00 (ISBN 0-8209-0027-3, JSY 6). ESP.
--Jumbo Science Yearbook: Grade 7. (Jumbo Science Ser.). 96p. 1981. 14.00 (ISBN 0-8209-0028-1, JSY 7). ESP.
--Jumbo Science Yearbook: Grade 8. (Jumbo Science Ser.). 96p. 1982. 14.00 (ISBN 0-8209-0029-X, JSY 8). ESP.
Iatridis, Mary D. Teaching Science to Young Children: A Resource Book. LC 84-48879. 150p. 1985. lib. bdg. 20.00 (ISBN 0-8240-8747-X). Garland Pub.
Justus, Fred. Science Adventures. (Science Ser.). 24p. 1977. wkbk. 5.00 (ISBN 0-8209-0142-3, S-4). ESP.
--Science Facts. (Science Ser.). 24p. 1978. wkbk. 5.00 (ISBN 0-8209-0144-X, S-6). ESP.
--Science Goals. (Science Ser.). 24p. 1980. wkbk. 5.00 (ISBN 0-8209-0143-1, S-5). ESP.
--The Science World. (Science Ser.). 24p. 1978. wkbk. 5.00 (ISBN 0-8209-0156-3, S-18). ESP.
Kapili, Pascual H. & Calvero, Teofidez E. Improvising Science Equipment: A Handbook. (Illus.). 1978. pap. text ed. 8.25x (ISBN 0-686-23914-8, Pub. by New Day Pub). Cellar.
Levenson, Elaine. Teaching Children about Science: Ideas & Activities Every Teacher & Parent Can Use. (Illus.). 272p. 1985. pap. 14.95 (ISBN 0-13-891730-2). P-H.
Osborne, Roger & Freyberg, Peter. Learning in Science: The Implications of Children's Science. LC 84-27915. viii, 198p. (Orig.). 1985. pap. text ed. 12.00x (ISBN 0-435-57260-1). Heinemann Ed.
Padilla, Michael J., ed. Science & the Early Adolescent. 144p. 1982. 6.00 (ISBN 0-686-84080-1). Natl Sci Tchrs.
Patty, Catherine. Jumbo Science Yearbook: Grade 4. (Jumbo Science Ser.). 96p. 1978. 14.00 (ISBN 0-8209-0025-7, JSY 4). ESP.
Phan Hoc Sink. I Find Out About Science: Grade 1. (Vietnamese.). 1976. pap. text ed. 6.00 (ISBN 0-15-599242-2). Ctr Appl Ling.
Roeper, Annemarie & McLeod, Marion. Physical Science for Young Children: A Guide for the Teacher. 1984. 6.00 (ISBN 0-317-17325-1). Trillium Pr.
Shoemaker, Lois M. Natural Science Education in the German Elementary School. LC 77-177788. (Columbia University. Teachers College. Contributions to Education Ser.: No. 445). Repr. of 1930 ed. 22.50 (ISBN 0-404-55445-8). AMS Pr.
Showell, Romola. Practical Primary Science: A Source Book for Teachers. (Ward Lock Educational Ser.). 29.00x (ISBN 0-7062-4240-8, Pub. by Ward Lock Educational England). State Mutual Bk.
--Teaching Science to Infants. (Ward Lock Educational Ser.). 29.00x (ISBN 0-7062-3847-8, Pub. by Ward Lock Educational England). State Mutual Bk.
Wheeler, Gerald & Kirkpatrick, Larry. Physics: Building a World View. (Illus.). 576p. 1983. prof. ref. 26.95 (ISBN 0-13-672204-0). P-H.

SCIENCE–STUDY AND TEACHING (SECONDARY)

Carey, Helen, ed. Playing with Energy. 106p. (Orig.). 1981. pap. 5.00 (ISBN 0-87355-020-X). Natl Sci Tchrs.
Collette, Alfred T. & Chiapetta, Eugene L. Science Instruction in the Middle & Secondary Schools. (Illus.). 592p. 1984. text ed. 24.95 (ISBN 0-8016-1095-8). Mosby.
Everote, Warren P. Agricultural Science to Serve Youth: Outcomes of a Course in Experimental Science for Secondary-School Students. LC 72-176760. (Columbia University. Teachers College. Contributions to Education: No. 901). Repr. of 1943 ed. 22.50 (ISBN 0-404-55901-8). AMS Pr.
Farmer, Walter A. & Farrell, Margaret A. Systematic Instruction in Science for the Middle & High School Years. LC 79-4252. (Illus.). 1980. pap. text ed. 17.30 (ISBN 0-201-02435-7, Sch Div). Addison-Wesley.
Hellweg, Susan A. & Falcione, Raymond L. Internships in the Communication Arts & Sciences. 72p. 1985. pap. text ed. 4.95x (ISBN 0-89787-320-3). Gorsuch Scarisbrick.
Kapili, Pascual H. & Calvero, Teofidez E. Improvising Science Equipment: A Handbook. (Illus.). 1978. pap. text ed. 8.25x (ISBN 0-686-23914-8, Pub. by New Day Pub). Cellar.
Smith, Norman F. How Fast Do Your Oysters Grow: Investigate & Discover Through Science Project. LC 82-60649. (Illus.). 128p. 1982. PLB 9.79g (ISBN 0-671-42629-X). Messner.

SCIENCE–TABLES, ETC.

LeFax Pub. Co. Editors. Conversion Tables. (Lefax Data Bks.: No. 630). (Illus.). looseleaf bdg. 3.00 (ISBN 0-685-14129-2); pap. 2.50 (ISBN 0-685-14130-6). LeFax.
Powell, Russell H., ed. Handbooks & Tables in Science & Technology. 2nd ed. LC 82-19842. 384p. 1983. 55.00x (ISBN 0-89774-039-4). Oryx Pr.

SCIENCE–TERMINOLOGY

Biddle, Wayne. Coming to Terms: Lexicon for the Science Watcher. LC 80-54198. (Illus.). 128p. 1981. 8.95 (ISBN 0-670-33092-2). Viking.
Brown, Roland W. Composition of Scientific Words. 882p. 1979. Repr. of 1956 ed. lib. bdg. 65.00 (ISBN 0-89987-050-3). Darby Bks.
--Composition of Scientific Words. LC 78-14717. 882p. 1978. Repr. of 1956 ed. 19.95x (ISBN 0-87474-286-2). Smithsonian.
Brunner, Theodore F. & Berkowitz, Luci. The Elements of Scientific & Specialized Terminology. 1967. spiral bdg. 12.95x (ISBN 0-8087-0235-1). Burgess.
Godman, Arthur. Barnes & Noble Thesaurus of Science. (Illus.). 256p. 1983. 13.41i (ISBN 0-06-015176-5, EH 580); pap. 6.68i (ISBN 0-06-463580-5, EH 580). B&N NY.
Markov, A. S., et al. Dictionary of Scientific & Technical Terminology. 1984. lib. bdg. 34.50 (ISBN 0-318-01661-3, Pub. by Martinus Nijhoff Netherlands). Kluwer Academic.
Purvis, Keith. Read & Note: English Study Skills for Science Students. 1977. pap. text ed. 3.95x (ISBN 0-435-28717-6); tchr's. ed. 7.95x (ISBN 0-435-28718-4). Heinemann Ed.
Radcliffe, Stanley. Scientific German: Translation Passages. 1979. 20.00x (ISBN 0-906515-48-3, Pub. by Bristol Classical Pr). State Mutual Bk.
Rheingold, Howard & Levine, Howard. Talking Tech: A Conversational Guide to Science & Technology. LC 81-14130. (Illus.). 320p. 1982. 13.50 (ISBN 0-688-00783-X). Morrow.
Sahai, Hardeo & Berrios, Jose. A Dictionary of Statistical, Scientific & Technical Terms: English-Spanish, Spanish-English. Smith, Richard A. & Heise, Jeanne, eds. (Spanish Ser.). (Eng. & Span.). 143p. 1981. write for info. (ISBN 8-4534-0004-0, Pub. by Wadsworth Internacional Iberoamerica). Wadsworth Pub.
Science & Technology for Development. 784p. 1979. pap. 26.00 (UN79115, UN). Unipub.
Steffanides, George F. The Scientist's Thesaurus: A Treasury of the Stockwords of Science. 4th ed. 156p. 1978. pap. 3.00 (ISBN 0-9600114-0-4). Steffanides.

SCIENCE–VOCATIONAL GUIDANCE

Conference on Scientific Management, 1st. Addresses & Discussions at the Conference on Scientific Management: Proceedings. LC 72-90030. (Management History Ser.: No. 9). 399p. Repr. of 1912 ed. 22.50 (ISBN 0-87960-014-4). Hive Pub.
Easton, Thomas A. Careers in Science. LC 83-73707. 1984. 12.25 (ISBN 0-87094-476-2); pap. 9.95 (ISBN 0-87094-546-7). Dow Jones-Irwin.
Educational Research Council of America. Solar Cell Scientist. Ferris, Theodore N. & Marchak, John P., eds. (Real People at Work Ser.: S). (Illus.). 36p. 1977. 2.70 (ISBN 0-89247-143-3, 9634). Changing Times.
Eiduson, Bernice T. & Beckman, Linda, eds. Science As a Career Choice: Theoretical & Empirical Studies. LC 72-83833. 752p. 1973. 25.00x (ISBN 0-87154-230-7). Russell Sage.
Engineering, Science & Computer Jobs 1986. 7th ed. 900p. 1985. pap. 15.95 (ISBN 0-87866-348-7). Petersons Guides.
Glaser, Barney G. Organizational Scientists: Their Professional Careers. LC 68-25515. 1964. 22.50x (ISBN 0-672-51186-X); pap. text ed. 9.95x (ISBN 0-89197-872-0). Irvington.
Humphreys, Sheila M., ed. Women & Minorities in Science: Strategies for Increasing Participation. (Selected Symposium: No. 66). 225p. 1982. lib. bdg. 26.00x. Westview.
Krohn, Roger G. Social Shaping of Science: Institutions, Ideology, & Careers in Science. LC 75-90792. (Contributions in Sociology: No. 4). (Illus.). 1971. lib. bdg. 29.95 (ISBN 0-8371-1852-2, KRS/). Greenwood.
La Follette, Marcel C., ed. Quality in Science. 250p. 1982. 30.00x (ISBN 0-262-12099-2); pap. 12.50x (ISBN 0-262-62040-5). MIT Pr.
Medawar, P. B. Advice to a Young Scientist. LC 79-1676. (Sloan Foundation Bk.). 1979. 13.41i (ISBN 0-06-013029-6, HarpT). Har-Row.
Nagle, Robert & Chasek, Judith. Careers Related to Science Program Supplement. Picker, Erica, ed. LC 77-730363. 1977. 2.25 (ISBN 0-87453-050-4). Denoyer.
Olsson, David L. & Raphael, Harold J. Opportunities in Packaging Science. (VGM Career Bks.). (Illus.). 160p. 1983. 7.95 (ISBN 0-317-03478-2, 6587-4, Passport Bks.); pap. 5.95 (ISBN 0-317-03479-0, 6587-0). Natl Textbk.
Science in the Marketplace. rev. ed. text ed. 20.00 (ISBN 0-317-27064-8); tchr's. manual & lab package avail. Tiger Pubn.
Shaw, Mildred. On Becoming a Personal Scientist: Interactive Computer Elicitation of Personal Models of the World. LC 78-73891. 1980. 65.00 (ISBN 0-12-639280-3). Acad Pr.
Stearner, S. Phyllis. Able Scientists-Disabled Persons: Careers in the Sciences. LC 84-60396. (Illus.). 80p. 1984. pap. 12.95 (ISBN 0-916655-00-8). J R Assocs.
Vetter, Betty, ed. Opportunities in Science & Engineering. 94p. 1984. 15.00 (ISBN 0-318-17827-3). Sci Manpower.

SCIENCE–YEARBOOKS

Briggs, Winslow R., et al, eds. Annual Review of Plant Physiology, Vol. 24. LC 51-1660. (Illus.). 1973. text ed. 20.00 (ISBN 0-8243-0624-4). Annual Reviews.
Bunch, Bryan, ed. The Science Almanac 1985-1986. LC 84-20405. 576p. 1984. 19.95 (ISBN 0-385-19321-1, Anchor Pr); pap. 12.95 (ISBN 0-385-19320-3, Anchor Pr). Doubleday.
Calhoun, David. Yearbook of Science & the Future 1984. 448p. 1983. write for info. Ency Brit Inc.
--Yearbook of Science & the Future 1984: 1985. 448p. 1984. write for info. Ency Brit Inc.
Calhoun, David, ed. Yearbook of Science & the Future, 1983. 448p. 1982. write for info. (ISBN 0-85229-384-4). Ency Brit Inc.
Carnegie Institution of Washington Year Book, Vol. 76. Incl. Vol. 76. (Illus.). 1977. 16.50 (ISBN 0-87279-649-3); (Illus.). 1978. 16.50 (ISBN 0-87279-650-7); Vol. 78. (Illus.). 1979. 16.50 (ISBN 0-87279-653-1); Vol. 79. (Illus.). 1980. 16.50 (ISBN 0-87279-653-1); Vol. 80. (Illus.). 784p. 1981. 16.50 (ISBN 0-87279-654-X); Vol. 81. (Illus.). 786p. 1982. 16.50 (ISBN 0-87279-655-8); Vol. 82. (Illus.). 789p. 1983. 16.50 (ISBN 0-87279-657-4); (Illus.). 195p. 1984. 7.00 (ISBN 0-87279-658-2). (Illus.). 1977. 16.50 (ISBN 0-87279-649-3). Carnegie Inst.
Houston, Jack. Jumbo Science Yearbook: Grade 3. (Jumbo Science Ser.). 96p. 1978. 14.00 (ISBN 0-8209-0024-9, JSY 3). ESP.
--Jumbo Science Yearbook: Grade 5. (Jumbo Science Ser.). 96p. 1979. 14.00 (ISBN 0-8209-0026-5, JSY 5). ESP.
McGraw-Hill, ed. McGraw-Hill Yearbook of Science & Technology 1984. (Illus.). 520p. 1983. 46.00 (ISBN 0-07-045492-2). McGraw.
McGraw-Hill Editors. Yearbook of Science & Technology, 1985. 335p. 1984. 50.00 (ISBN 0-07-045366-7). McGraw.
--Yearbook of Science & Technology, 1986. 528p. 1985. write for info. (ISBN 0-07-046181-3). McGraw.
Popular Science Books Editors. Popular Science Do-It-Yourself Yearbook 2. 1983. 19.95 (ISBN 0-442-27489-0). Van Nos Reinhold.
Schwarz, Richard, ed. Internationales Jahrbuch Fuer Interdisziplinere Forschung: Wissenschaft Als Interdisziplinaeres Problem, Vol. 2. new ed. (Ger.). xvi, 316p. 1975. 41.20x (ISBN 3-11-005897-9). De Gruyter.
Science Indicators 1982. 9.50 (ISBN 0-318-18091-X). NSF.

SCIENCE, AFRICAN

Alexander, E. Curtis. Cheikh Anta Diop: An African Scientist. LC 84-81324. (Pan African Internationalist Handbook Ser.). 84p. (Orig.). 1984. pap. 6.95 (ISBN 0-938818-07-4). ECA Assoc.
Worthington, Edgar B. Science in Africa: A Review of Scientific Research Relating to Tropical & Southern Africa. LC 70-89013. Repr. of 1938 ed. 37.50x (ISBN 0-8371-1740-2, WOS&). Greenwood.

SCIENCE, ANCIENT

see also Science–History

Aristotle. Aristotle's Physics. Hope, Richard, tr. LC 61-5498. xiv, 242p. 1961. pap. 6.25x (ISBN 0-8032-5093-2, BB 122, Bison). U of Nebr Pr.
--Aristotles's Physics, Bks. 1 & 2. Charlton, W., ed. (Clarendon Aristotle Ser.). 1970. 12.95x (ISBN 0-19-872026-2). Oxford U Pr.
Barnes, Jonathan, et al, eds. Science & Speculation. LC 82-4221. (Studies in Hellinistic Theory & Practice). 352p. 1983. 47.50 (ISBN 0-521-24689-X). Cambridge U Pr.
Chattopadhyaya, Debiprasad. Science & Society in Ancient India. (Philosophical Currents Ser.: No. 22). 1978. text ed. 34.75x (ISBN 90-6032-098-0). Humanities.
Clagett, Marshall. Greek Science in Antiquity. facs. ed. LC 77-142615. (Essay Index Reprint Ser.). 1955. 17.00 (ISBN 0-8369-2150-X). Ayer Co Pubs.
Claggett, Marshall. Greek Science in Antiquity. 1963. pap. 2.50 (ISBN 0-02-091880-1, Collier). Macmillan.
Fritz, Kurt Von. Grundprobleme der Geschichte der antiken Wissenschaft. 759p. 1971. 55.60x (ISBN 3-11-001805-5). De Gruyter.
Heidel, William A. Heroic Age of Science. LC 79-155101. Repr. of 1933 ed. 19.00 (ISBN 0-404-03234-6). AMS Pr.
Holbrook, Bruce. The Stone Monkey: An Alternative Chinese-Scientific Reality. LC 81-11063. 1981. 15.00 (ISBN 0-688-00665-5); pap. 7.95 (ISBN 0-688-00732-5, Quill). Morrow.
Kotb, Yusef S. Science & Science Education in Egyptian Society. LC 79-176944. (Columbia University. Teachers College. Contributions to Education: No. 967). Repr. of 1951 ed. 22.50 (ISBN 0-404-55967-0). AMS Pr.
Lawn, Brian, ed. The Prose Salernitan Questions: An Anonymous Collection Dealing with Science & Medicine Written by an Englishman Circa 1200, with an Appendix of Ten Related Collections. (British Academy: Auctores Britannici Medii Aevi: Vol. V). 1979. 89.00x (ISBN 0-19-725978-2). Oxford U Pr.
Lloyd, G. E. Greek Science After Aristotle. LC 72-11959. (Ancient Culture & Society Ser.). (Illus.). 208p. 1973. pap. 5.95x (ISBN 0-393-00780-4). Norton.
Lloyd, Geoffrey E. Magic, Reason & Experience: Studies in the Origin & Development of Greek Science. LC 78-25710. (Illus.). 1979. 62.50 (ISBN 0-521-22373-3); pap. 19.95 (ISBN 0-521-29641-2). Cambridge U Pr.
Murdoch, John E. Album of Science, Vol. 1: Antiquity & the Middle Ages. LC 84-1400. (Illus.). 375p. 1984. 63.00 (ISBN 0-684-15496-X, ScribR). Scribner.
O'Leary, D. L. How Greek Science Passed to the Arabs. 196p. 1979. 12.50 (ISBN 0-89005-282-4). Ares.
Reymond, Arnold. History of the Sciences in Greco-Roman Antiquity. Bray, Ruth G. De, tr. LC 63-18046. 1963. 10.00x (ISBN 0-8196-0128-4). Biblo.
Solmsen, Friedrich. Aristotle's System of the Physical World. Repr. of 1960 ed. 37.00 (ISBN 0-384-56596-4). Johnson Repr.

Stahl, William H. Roman Science: Origins, Development, & Influence to the Later Middle Ages. LC 78-5597. 1978. Repr. of 1962 ed. lib. bdg. 37.50 (ISBN 0-313-20473-X, STRO). Greenwood.

SCIENCE, APPLIED
see Technology

SCIENCE, ARAB

Al-Daffa, A. A. A Brief Exposition of Arabic & Islamic Scientific Heritage: Arabic Edition. LC 78-31087. 256p. 1979. 14.50 (ISBN 0-471-05348-1). Wiley.

King, David A. Catalogue of the Scientific Manuscripts in the Egyptian National Library, Pt. 1. (Catalogs Ser.: Vol. 2). (Arabic.). 830p. 1981. pap. 40.00 (ISBN 0-686-84036-4, Am Res Ctr Egypt Publications Ser.). Undena Pubns.

O'Leary, D. L. How Greek Science Passed to the Arabs. 196p. 1979. 12.50 (ISBN 0-89005-282-4). Ares.

Stroyls, John J. & Al-Daffa, Ali A. Studies on the Exact Sciences in Medieval Islam. 247p. 1984. 39.95x (ISBN 0-471-90320-5, Pub. by Wiley Interscience). Wiley.

Zahlan, A. B. Science & Science Policy in the Arab World. LC 79-3380. 1980. 26.00x (ISBN 0-312-70232-9). St Martin.

SCIENCE, AUSTRALIAN

Crump, Ian A., ed. Scientific & Technical Research Centres in Australia. new ed. 1977. 11.00x (ISBN 0-643-00145-X, Pub. by CSIRO); pap. 7.25x (ISBN 0-643-00140-9, Pub. by CSIRO). Intl Spec Bk.

SCIENCE, BRITISH

Berman, Morris. Social Change & Scientific Organization: The Royal Instutution, Seventeen Ninety-Nine to Eighteen Forty-Four. LC 77-79702. (Illus.). 249p. 1978. 34.95x (ISBN 0-8014-1093-2). Cornell U Pr.

Brockway, Lucile H. Science & Colonial Expansion: The Role of the British Royal Botanic Gardens. LC 79-51669. (Studies in Social Discontinuity). 1979. 29.50 (ISBN 0-12-134150-X). Acad Pr.

Cardwell, D. S. The Organization of Science in England. 2nd ed. 1972. pap. text ed. 10.00x (ISBN 0-435-54154-4). Heinemann Ed.

Cooter, Roger. The Cultural Meaning of Popular Science: Phrenology & the Organization of Consent in Nineteenth Century Britain. (History of Medicine Ser.). (Illus.). 448p. 1985. 37.50 (ISBN 0-521-22743-7). Cambridge U Pr.

Cosslett, Tess. The Scientific Movement & Victorian Literature. LC 82-10284. 1983. 22.50x (ISBN 0-312-70298-1). St Martin.

Curds, Colin R. British & Other Freshwater Ciliated Protozoa: Part 1. LC 81-15541. (Synopses of the British Fauna Ser.: No. 22). 150p. 1982. 59.50 (ISBN 0-521-24257-6). Cambridge U Pr.

Gaston, Jerry. Originality & Competition in Science: A Study of the British High Energy Physics Community. LC 73-81313. 1973. 16.00x (ISBN 0-226-28429-8). U of Chicago Pr.

Haines, George, 4th. Essays on German Influence upon English Education & Science, 1850-1919. (Connecticut College Monograph: No. 9). xi, 188p. 1969. 17.50 (ISBN 0-208-00762-8, Archon). Shoe String.

Hall, Marie B. All Scientists Now: The Royal Society in the Nineteenth Century. (Illus.). 272p. 1985. 49.50 (ISBN 0-521-26746-3). Cambridge U Pr.

Hunter, Michael. Science & Society in Restoration England. LC 80-41071. 224p. 1981. 47.50 (ISBN 0-521-22866-2); pap. 15.95 (ISBN 0-521-29685-4). Cambridge U Pr.

Inkster, Ian & Morrell, Jack. Metropolis & Province: Science in British Culture 1780-1850. LC 82-40354. 328p. 1983. 30.00x (ISBN 0-8122-7855-0). U of Pa Pr.

McDonald, Philip B. English & Science. 1979. Repr. of 1929 ed. lib. bdg. 20.00 (ISBN 0-8495-3515-8). Arden Lib.

Macreary, S. E., ed. Guide to Science & Technology in the U. K. (Illus.). 431p. 1971. 67.50x (ISBN 0-85280-270-6). Intl Pubns Serv.

Merton, Robert K. Science, Technology & Society in Seventeenth Century England. 1978. pap. text ed. 7.45x. Humanities.

Morrell, Jack & Thackray, Arnold. Gentlemen of Science: Early Years of the British Association for the Advancement of Science. (Illus.). 1981. pap. 14.95x (ISBN 0-19-520396-8). Oxford U Pr.

Raven, Charles E. English Naturalists from Neckam to Ray: A Study of the Making of the Modern World. LC 47-12381. 1968. Repr. of 1947 ed. 27.00 (ISBN 0-527-74100-0). Kraus Repr.

Russell, Colin. Science & Social Change in Britain, 1700-1900. LC 83-11021. (Illus.). 260p. 1983. 25.00 (ISBN 0-312-70239-6). St Martin.

Todd, Ruthven. Tracks in the Snow. Studies in English Science & Art: William Blake, Henry Fuseli, John Martin. 133p. 1980. Repr. of 1946 ed. lib. bdg. 22.50 (ISBN 0-8495-5152-8). Arden Lib.

Turner, Dorothy M. History of Science Teaching in England. Cohen, I. Bernard, ed. LC 80-2148. (Development of Science Ser.). (Illus.). 1981. lib. bdg. 20.00x (ISBN 0-405-13955-1). Ayer Co Pubs.

SCIENCE, CANADIAN

Cordell, Arthur J. & Gilmour, James, eds. The Role & Function of Government Laboratories & the Transfer of Technology to the Manufacturing Sector. (Science Council of Canada Background Studies: No. 35). 1976. pap. 12.00 (ISBN 0-685-77314-0, SSC72, SSC). Unipub.

Gordon, J. K., ed. Canada's Role in Science & Technology for Development: Proceedings of a Symposium Held at the Ontario Science Centre, Toronto, Canada, 10-13 May 1979. 136p. 1979. pap. 5.00 (ISBN 0-88936-230-0, IDRC141, IDRC). Unipub.

Meilicke, Carl A. & Storch, Janet L., eds. Perspectives on Canadian Health & Social Services Policy: History & Emerging Trends. LC 80-12118. (Illus.). 534p. 1980. text ed. 38.95x (ISBN 0-914904-42-6). Health Admin Pr.

SCIENCE, CHINESE

Chang Shu-Ting. The Chinese Mushroom (Volvariella volvacea) Morphology, Cytology, Genetics, Nutrition, & Cultivation. (Illus.). 118p. 1972. 12.50x (ISBN 0-295-95743-3, Pub by Chinese Univ Hong Kong). U of Wash Pr.

Clarke, Basil, ed. Chinese Science & the West. 1984. 30.00x (ISBN 0-686-45585-1, Pub. by Nile & Mackenzie Ltd England). State Mutual Bk.

Current Topics in Chinese Science: Section A: Physics. 498p. 1984. pap. text ed. 54.00 (ISBN 0-677-06220-6). Gordon.

Current Topics in Chinese Science, Section A: Physics, Vol. 3. 496p. 1985. pap. text ed. 58.00 (ISBN 0-677-40375-5). Gordon.

Current Topics in Chinese Science: Section B: Chemistry, Vol. 3. 575p. 1984. pap. text ed. 68.00 (ISBN 0-677-40385-2). Gordon.

Current Topics in Chinese Science: Section C: Mathematics. 493p. 1984. pap. 25.00 (ISBN 0-317-11705-X). Gordon.

Current Topics in Chinese Science, Section C: Mathematics, Vol. 3. 880p. 1985. pap. text ed. 98.00 (ISBN 0-677-40405-0). Gordon.

Current Topics in Chinese Science: Section D: Biology. 560p. 1984. pap. text ed. 63.00 (ISBN 0-677-06250-8). Gordon.

Current Topics in Chinese Science, Section D: Biology, Vol. 3. 506p. 1985. pap. text ed. 60.00 (ISBN 0-677-40415-8). Gordon.

Current Topics in Chinese Science: Section E: Astronomy. 220p. 1984. pap. text ed. 24.00 (ISBN 0-677-06260-5). Gordon.

Current Topics in Chinese Science, Section E: Astronomy, Vol. 3. 220p. 1985. pap. text ed. 26.00 (ISBN 0-677-40425-5). Gordon.

Current Topics in Chinese Science: Section F: Earth Science. 785p. 1984. pap. text ed. 88.00 (ISBN 0-677-06270-2). Gordon.

Current Topics in Chinese Science, Section F: Earth Science, Vol. 3. 916p. 1985. pap. text ed. 96.00 (ISBN 0-677-40435-2). Gordon.

Current Topics in Chinese Science: Section G: Medical Science. 265p. 1984. pap. text ed. 28.00 (ISBN 0-677-06705-4). Gordon.

Current Topics in Chinese Science, Section G: Medical Science, Vol. 3. 902p. 1985. pap. text ed. 95.00 (ISBN 0-677-40455-7). Gordon.

Dean, Genevieve C. Science & Technology in the Development of Modern China: An Annotated Bibliography. LC 74-76296. 279p. 1974. 32.00x (ISBN 0-7201-0376-2). Mansell.

Furth, Charlotte. Ting Wen-Chiang: Science & China's New Culture. LC 78-95920. (East Asian Ser: No. 42). 1970. text ed. 20.00x (ISBN 0-674-89270-4). Harvard U Pr.

Gould, Sidney H. Sciences in Communist China: A Symposium Presented at the New York Meeting of the American Association for Advanced Science. LC 74-7534. 872p. 1975. Repr. of 1961 ed. lib. bdg. 47.50x (ISBN 0-8371-7583-6, GOSC). Greenwood.

Hu, Shiu-Ying. An Enumeration of Chinese Materia Medica. LC 81-10843. 312p. 1981. 24.00x (ISBN 0-295-95744-1, Pub by Chinese Univ Hong Kong). U of Wash Pr.

Joseph Needham's Contribution to the History of Science & Technology in China. 30p. 1981. pap. 5.00 (ISBN 92-808-0187-2, TUNU139, UNU). Unipub.

Needham, Joseph. Science in Traditional China. (Illus.). 144p. 1982. text ed. 12.50x (ISBN 0-674-79438-9); pap. 4.95 (ISBN 0-674-79439-7). Harvard U Pr.

Needham, Joseph & Tsuen-Hsuin, Tsien. Science & Civilization in China: Chemistry & Chemical Technology Part 1: Paper & Printing, Vol. 5. (Illus.). 485p. 1985. 89.50 (ISBN 0-521-08690-6). Cambridge U Pr.

Ngok, Lee & Chi-keung, Leung, eds. Cultural Change & Science & Medicine, 4 vols, Vol. 4. (China: Development & Challenge--Proceedings of the Fifth Leverhulme Conference Ser.). 370p. (Orig.). 1981. pap. text ed. 25.00x (ISBN 0-566-04019-0, Pub. by Centre Asian Stud). Gower Pub Co.

Orleans, Leo A., ed. Science in Contemporary China. LC 79-65178. 640p. 1980. 40.00x (ISBN 0-8047-1078-3). Stanford U Pr.

Qian, Wen-Yuan. The Great Inertia: Scientific Stagnation in Traditional China. LC 84-14217. 156p. 1985. 27.50 (ISBN 0-7099-2104-7, Pub. by Croom Helm Ltd). Longwood Pub Group.

Ridley, Charles P. China's Scientific Policies. 1976. pap. 4.25 (ISBN 0-8447-3222-2). Am Enterprise.

Ronan, Colin, ed. The Shorter Science & Civilisation in China, Vol. 2. 400p. 1985. pap. 19.95 (ISBN 0-521-31536-0). Cambridge U Pr.

--The Shorter Science & Civilisation in China, Vol. 3. 280p. Date not set. price not set (ISBN 0-521-25272-5); pap. price not set (ISBN 0-521-31560-3). Cambridge U Pr.

Ronan, Colin A. Shorter Science & Civilisation in China, Vol. 1. LC 77-82513. (Illus.). 1978. 39.50 (ISBN 0-521-21821-7). Cambridge U Pr.

--Shorter Science & Civilization in China, Vol. 2. LC 77-82513. (Illus.). 250p. 1982. 39.50 (ISBN 0-521-23582-0). Cambridge U Pr.

Sigurdson, Jon S. Technology & Science in the People's Republic of China. 1980. 35.00 (ISBN 0-08-024288-X) (ISBN 0-686-66170-2). Pergamon.

Sivin, Nathan, ed. Science & Technology in East Asia. (Illus.). 1977. 15.00 (ISBN 0-88202-162-1, Sci Hist); pap. 8.95 (ISBN 0-88202-161-3). Watson Pub Intl.

World Sci Singapore, ed. Thirty Years' Review of China's Science & Technology, 1949-1979. viii, 314p. 1982. 60.00x (ISBN 9971-950-48-0, Pub. by World Sci Singapore). Taylor & Francis.

Xu Liangying & Fan Dianian. Science & Socialist Construction in China. Perrolle, Pierre M., ed. Hsu, John C., tr. from Chinese. LC 81-23250. 230p. 1982. 35.00 (ISBN 0-87332-189-8). M E Sharpe.

SCIENCE, COMMUNICATION IN
see Communication in Science

SCIENCE, FRENCH

Anderson, Wilda C. Between the Library & the Laboratory: The Language of Chemistry in Eighteenth-Century France. LC 84-47942. 1985. text ed. 22.50x (ISBN 0-8018-3229-2). Johns Hopkins.

Caullery, Maurice. French Science & Its Principle Discoveries since the Seventeenth Century. LC 74-26256. (History, Philosophy & Sociology of Science Ser). (Illus.). 1975. Repr. of 1934 ed. 20.00x (ISBN 0-405-06584-1). Ayer Co Pubs.

Coleman, William & Cohen, I. Bernard, eds. French Views of German Science. LC 80-2106. (Development of Science Ser.). (Illus.). 1981. lib. bdg. 45.00x (ISBN 0-405-13871-7). Ayer Co Pubs.

Crosland, Maurice P. Society of Arcueil: A View of French Science at the Time of Napoleon First. LC 67-4884. (Illus.). 1967. 32.50x (ISBN 0-674-81555-6). Harvard U Pr.

Hahn, Roger. The Anatomy of a Scientific Institution: The Paris Academy of Sciences, 1666-1803. LC 70-130795. (Illus.). 1971. 44.00x (ISBN 0-520-01818-4). U of Cal Pr.

Montessori. Pedagogie Scientifique, 3 tomes. Set. 49.95 (ISBN 0-685-33998-X). French & Eur.

Nye, Mary J. Science in the Provinces: Scientific Communities & Provincial Leadership in France, 1860-1930. 1986. 32.50x (ISBN 0-520-05561-6). U of Cal Pr.

Paul, Harry W. The Rise of the Science Empire in France, Eighteen Sixty to Nineteen Thirty Nine: From Knowledge to Power. 480p. Date not set. price not set. (ISBN 0-521-26504-5). Cambridge U Pr.

--The Sorcerer's Apprentice: The French Scientist's Image of German Science, 1840-1919. LC 77-178986. (University of Florida Social Sciences Monographs: No. 44). 86p. 1972. pap. 3.50 (ISBN 0-8130-0347-4). U Presses Fla.

SCIENCE, GERMAN

Coleman, William & Cohen, I. Bernard, eds. French Views of German Science. LC 80-2106. (Development of Science Ser.). (Illus.). 1981. lib. bdg. 45.00x (ISBN 0-405-13871-7). Ayer Co Pubs.

Hufbauer, Karl. The Formation of the Chemical Community (1720-1795) LC 81-2988. 288p. 1982. 45.00x (ISBN 0-520-04318-9); pap. 14.95x (ISBN 0-520-04415-0, CAMPUS 299). U of Cal Pr.

Nachmansohn, D. German-Jewish Pioneers in Science, 1900-1933. LC 79-10550. (Illus.). 1979. 38.00 (ISBN 0-387-90402-6). Springer-Verlag.

Nisbet, H. B. Goethe & the Scientific Tradition. (Publications of the Institute of Germanic Studies: Vol. 14). 83p. 1972. text ed. 15.25x (ISBN 0-85457-050-0, Pub. by Inst Germanic UK). Humanities.

Petit, Gabriel, et al, eds. Les Allemands et la Science. LC 80-2141. (Develpoment of Science Ser.). (Illus.). 1981. lib. bdg. 35.00x (ISBN 0-405-13896-2). Ayer Co Pubs.

Zloczower, A. Career Opportunities & the Growth of Scientific Discovery in Ninteenth Century Germany, with Special Reference to the Development of Physiology. Cohen, I. Bernard, ed. LC 80-2095. (Development of Science Ser.). (Illus.). 1981. lib. bdg. 12.00x (ISBN 0-405-13860-1). Ayer Co Pubs.

SCIENCE, GREEK
see Science, Ancient

SCIENCE, HUNGARIAN

Erdey-Gruz, Tibor & Kulcsar, Kalman, eds. Science & Scholarship in Hungary. 2nd ed. 1975. 16.95x (ISBN 0-8464-0816-3). Beekman Pubs.

Renyi-Vamos, F. & Balogh, F. Titles from the Hungarian Academy of Sciences. 1981. 59.00x (ISBN 0-569-08544-6, Pub. by Collet's). State Mutual Bk.

SCIENCE, INDIC

Chattopadhyaya, Debiprasad. Science & Society in Ancient India. (Philosophical Currents Ser.: No. 22). 1978. text ed. 34.75x (ISBN 90-6032-098-0). Humanities.

Gupta, S. P. Modern India & Progress in Science & Technology. 166p. 1979. 15.95x (ISBN 0-7069-0743-4, Pub by Vikas India). Advent NY.

Jaggi, O P. History of Science & Technology in India. 2500p. 1982. 675.00 (ISBN 0-317-14273-9, Pub. by Holdan Bk Ltd UK). State Mutual Bk.

Morehouse, Ward, ed. Science & the Human Condition in India & Pakistan. LC 68-56606. (Illus.). 252p. 1968. 7.50x (ISBN 0-87470-010-8). Rockefeller.

Nanda, B. R. Science & Technology in India. 1977. 11.00x (ISBN 0-7069-0475-3). Intl Bk Dist.

Nanda, B. R., ed. Science & Technology in India. 1978. 9.00x (ISBN 0-8364-0170-0). South Asia Bks.

Rangarao, B. V. & Chaubey, N. P., eds. Social Perspective of Development of Science & Technology in India. 1983. 22.00x (ISBN 0-8364-0931-0, Pub. by Heritage India). South Asia Bks.

Satyaprakash. Indian Science Index, 1976. 1978. 32.50x (ISBN 0-8364-0421-1). South Asia Bks.

Satyaprakash, ed. Indian Science Index, 1975. 1976. 12.50x (ISBN 0-88386-937-3). South Asia Bks.

SCIENCE, JAPANESE

Gibson, Robert W., Jr. & Kunkel, Barbara K. Japanese Scientific & Technical Literature: A Subject Guide. LC 80-39693. (Illus.). xv, 560p. 1981. lib. bdg. 75.00 (ISBN 0-313-22929-5, GJS/). Greenwood.

Inose, H., ed. Scientific Information Systems in Japan. 260p. 1981. 59.75 (ISBN 0-444-86151-3, North-Holland). Elsevier.

Kimura, Shigeru. Japan's Science Edge: How the Cult of Anti-Science Thought in America Limits U. S. Scientific & Technological Progress. LC 85-5331. (Illus.). 172p. (Orig.). 1985. lib. bdg. 19.75 (ISBN 0-8191-4645-5, Pub. by Woodrow Wilson Intl Ctr); pap. text ed. 7.95 (ISBN 0-8191-4646-3, Pub. by Woodrow Wilson Intl Ctr). U Pr of Amer.

Science & Technology in the History of Modern Japan: Imitation or Endogenous Creativity? 22p. 1981. pap. 5.00 (ISBN 92-808-0185-6, TUNU134, UNU). Unipub.

Sivin, Nathan, ed. Science & Technology in East Asia. (Illus.). 1977. 15.00 (ISBN 0-88202-162-1, Sci Hist); pap. 8.95 (ISBN 0-88202-161-3). Watson Pub Intl.

SCIENCE, LATIN AMERICAN

Ciencia Interamericana: Vol. 17, Nos. 3-4. (Edicion en homenaje al Bicentenario de los Estados Unidos). 1977. pap. 1.00 (ISBN 0-685-80053-9). OAS.

Forbush, Scott E & Casaverde, Mateo. Equatorial Electrojet in Peru. LC 62-51815. (Carnegie Institution of Washington Publication Ser.: No. 620). pap. 35.30 (ISBN 0-317-08543-3, 2007905). Bks Demand UMI.

OAS General Secretariat Department of Scientific & Technological Affairs. Los Organismos Centrales De Politica Cientifica y Tecnologica En America Latina. (Estudios Sobre el Desarrollo Cientifico y Tecnologico: No. 38). 124p. 1980. 4.00 (ISBN 0-8270-1192-X). OAS.

Sagasti, Francisco R. Technology, Planning & Self-Reliant Development: A Latin American View. LC 78-26010. (Praeger Special Studies). 202p. 1979. 35.95 (ISBN 0-03-047221-0). Praeger.

Science & Technology in Latin America. 1983. pap. text ed. 85.00x (ISBN 0-582-90057-3). Gale.

Statistics on Science & Technology in Latin America: 1976. 1977. pap. 5.00 (ISBN 92-3-101336-X, U632, UNESCO). Unipub.
Stepan, Nancy. Beginnings of Brazilian Science. (Illus.). 225p. 1981. pap. 6.95 (ISBN 0-88202-032-3, Sci Hist). Watson Pub Intl.

SCIENCE, MEDIEVAL

see also Science–History

Allbutt, Thomas C. Science & Medieval Thought. LC 75-23673. Repr. of 1901 ed. 19.50 (ISBN 0-404-13226-X). AMS Pr.
Bartholomaeus, Anglicus. Medieval Lore. Steele, R., ed. LC 66-23970. (Medieval Library). Repr. of 1926 ed. 18.50 (ISBN 0-8154-0016-0). Cooper Sq.
Buridan, Jean. Iohannis Buridan, Quaestiones Super Libris Quattuor De Caelo et Mundo. Moody, Ernest A., ed. (Mediaeval Academy of America Publications). 1942. 25.00 (ISBN 0-527-01704-3). Kraus Repr.
Campbell, Anna M. Black Death & Men of Learning. LC 31-29792. Repr. of 1931 ed. 18.50 (ISBN 0-404-01368-6). AMS Pr.
Clagett, Marshall. Giovanni Marliani & Late Medieval Physics. LC 70-181929. (Columbia University Studies in the Social Sciences: No. 483). Repr. of 1941 ed. 12.50 (ISBN 0-404-51483-9). AMS Pr.
Dales, Richard C. The Scientific Achievement of the Middle Ages. (Middle Ages Ser.). (Illus.). 1973. text ed. 20.00 (ISBN 0-8122-7673-6); pap. text ed. 8.95x (ISBN 0-8122-1057-3). U of Pa Pr.
Fox, George G. Medieval Sciences in the Works of John Gower. LC 65-21089. (Studies in Poetry, No. 38). 1969. Repr. of 1931 ed. lib. bdg. 49.95x (ISBN 0-8383-0553-9). Haskell.
Franklin, Allan. The Principle of Inertia in the Middle Ages. LC 76-10515. 100p. (Orig.). 1976. pap. 7.95x (ISBN 0-87081-069-3). Colo Assoc.
Grant, Edward. Studies in Medieval Science & Natural Philosophy. 378p. 1981. 70.00x (ISBN 0-86078-089-9, Pub. by Variorum). State Mutual Bk.
Grant, Edward, ed. Nicole Oresme & the Kinematics of Circular Motion: Tractatus De Commensurabilitate Vel Incommensurabilitate Motuum Celi. Grant, Edward, tr. LC 79-133238. (Medieval Science Ser). (Illus.). 438p. 1971. 50.00x (ISBN 0-299-05830-1). U of Wis Pr.
International Colloquium on Philosophy, Science, & Theology in the Middle Ages, 1st, Boston, Sept. 1973. Boston Studies in the Philosophy of Science, Vol. 26: The Cultural Context of Medieval Learning, Proceedings. Murdoch, J. E. & Sylla, E. D., eds. LC 75-24997. (Synthese Library: No. 76). 566p. 1975. 68.50 (ISBN 90-277-0560-7, Pub. by Reidel Holland); pap. 39.50 (ISBN 90-277-0587-9). Kluwer Academic.
Kren, Claudia. Medieval Science & Technology: A Selected, Annotated Bibliography. Multhauf, Robert & Wells, Ellen, eds. LC 84-48012. (Bibliographies on the History of Science & Technology Ser.). 400p. 1985. lib. bdg. 53.00 (ISBN 0-8240-8969-3). Garland Pub.
Langford, Jerome J. Galileo, Science & the Church. rev. ed. 1971. pap. 6.95x (ISBN 0-472-06173-9, 173, AA). U of Mich Pr.
Lindberg, David C., ed. Science in the Middle Ages. LC 78-5367. (Chicago History of Science & Medicine Ser.). (Illus.). 1979. lib. bdg. 40.00x o. s. i. (ISBN 0-226-48232-4); pap. 9.95x (ISBN 0-226-48233-2, P870, Phoen). U of Chicago Pr.
Long, Pamela O., intro. by. Science & Technology in Medieval Society. (Annals of The New York Academy of Sciences Ser.: Vol. 441). 224p. 1984. lib. bdg. 50.00x (ISBN 0-89766-276-8); pap. 50.00x (ISBN 0-89766-277-6). NY Acad Sci.
Machaut's World: Science & Art in the Fourteenth Century, Vol. 314. (Annals of the New York Academy of Sciences). 1978. 32.00x (ISBN 0-89072-079-7); pap. 32.00x (ISBN 0-89072-072-X). NY Acad Sci.
Murdoch, John E. Album of Science, Vol. 1: Antiquity & the Middle Ages. LC 84-1400. (Illus.). 375p. 1984. 63.00 (ISBN 0-684-15496-X, ScribR). Scribner.
Stahl, William H. Roman Science: Origins, Development, & Influence to the Later Middle Ages. LC 78-5597. 1978. Repr. of 1962 ed. lib. bdg. 37.50 (ISBN 0-313-20473-X, STRO). Greenwood.
Steneck, Nicholas H. Science & Creation in the Middle Ages: Henry of Langenstein (d. 1397) on Genesis. LC 75-19881. 256p. 1976. text ed. 14.95x (ISBN 0-268-01672-0). U of Notre Dame Pr.
--Science & Creation in the Middle Ages: Henry of Langenstein (D. 1397) on Genesis. LC 75-19881. 1977. pap. 7.95x (ISBN 0-268-01691-7). U of Notre Dame Pr.
Stroyls, John J. & Al-Daffa, Ali A. Studies on the Exact Sciences in Medieval Islam. 247p. 1984. 39.95x (ISBN 0-471-90320-5, Pub. by Wiley Interscience). Wiley.
Weisheipl, James A. Development of Physical Theory in the Middle Ages. 1971. pap. 3.95 (ISBN 0-472-06181-X, 181, AA). U of Mich Pr.

SCIENCE, PAKISTANI

Morehouse, Ward, ed. Science & the Human Condition in India & Pakistan. LC 68-56606. (Illus.). 252p. 1968. 7.50x (ISBN 0-87470-010-8). Rockefeller.

SCIENCE, POLISH

Walentynowicz, Bohdan. Polish Contributions to the Science. 1983. lib. bdg. 63.00 (ISBN 90-277-1233-6, Pub. by Reidel Holland). Kluwer Academic.

SCIENCE, PRIMITIVE

see Science, Ancient

SCIENCE, ROMAN

see Science, Ancient

SCIENCE, RUSSIAN

Badash, Lawrence. Kapitza, Rutherford & the Kremlin. LC 84-11822. (Illus.). 144p. 1985. 20.00x (ISBN 0-300-01465-1). Yale U Pr.
Boss, Valentine. Newton & Russia: The Early Influence, 1698-1796. LC 73-188352. (Russian Research Center Studies: No. 69). (Illus.). 563p. 1972. 22.50x (ISBN 0-674-62275-8). Harvard U Pr.
Johnson, Nicholas L. Handbook of Soviet Lunar & Planetary Exploration. (Science & Technology Ser.: Vol. 47). 276p. 1979. lib. bdg. 35.00x (ISBN 0-87703-130-4); pap. text ed. 25.00x (ISBN 0-87703-131-2). Univelt Inc.
Khalatnikov, I. M., ed. Physics Reviews, Vol. 1. (Soviet Scientific Reviews Ser.: Section A). 322p. 1979. lib. bdg. 170.00 (ISBN 3-7186-0004-8). Harwood Academic.
--Physics Reviews, Vol. 2. (Soviet Scientific Reviews Ser.: Section A). 496p. 1980. lib. bdg. 170.00 (ISBN 3-7186-0017-X). Harwood Academic.
Kramish, Arnold. Atomic Energy in the Soviet Union. LC 59-14724. pap. 61.50 (ISBN 0-317-08466-6, 2002903). Bks Demand UMI.
Lewis, Robert. Science & Industrialization in U. S. S. R. LC 79-1380. 211p. 1979. text ed. 34.50x (ISBN 0-8419-0494-4). Holmes & Meier.
Medvedev, Zhores A. Soviet Science. 1978. 15.95 (ISBN 0-393-06435-2). Norton.
National Council of American Soviet Friendship. Science in Soviet Russia. LC 74-25151. (History, Philosophy & Sociology of Science Ser). 1975. Repr. 16.00x (ISBN 0-405-06635-X). Ayer Co Pubs.
Skulachev, V. P., ed. Biology Reviews, Vol. 2. (Soviet Scientific Reviews Ser.: Section D). 400p. 1981. 170.00 (ISBN 3-7186-0058-7). Harwood Academic.
Vol'Pin, E., ed. Chemistry Reviews, Vol. 2. (Soviet Scientific Reviews Ser.: Section B). 480p. 1980. 170.00 (ISBN 3-7186-0018-8). Harwood Academic.
Vol'Pin, M. E., ed. Chemistry Reviews, Vol. 3. (Soviet Scientific Reviews Ser.: Section B). 307p. 1981. 170.00 (ISBN 3-7186-0057-9). Harwood Academic.
Vucinich, Alexander. Empire of Knowledge: Academy of Sciences of the U.S.S.R., 1917-1970. 02/1984 ed. LC 83-3484. 24.95 (ISBN 0-520-04871-7). U of Cal Pr.

SCIENCE AND CIVILIZATION

Here are entered works on the role of science in the history and development of civilization.

Afanasyev, V. G. Scientific & Technological Revolution: Its Impact on Management & Education. 320p. 1975. 4.25 (ISBN 0-8285-0435-0, Pub. by Progress Pubs USSR). Imported Pubns.
Albergotti, J. Clifton. Mighty Is the Charm: Lectures on Science, Literature, & the Arts. LC 81-40158. (Illus.). 248p. (Orig.). 1982. lib. bdg. 26.00 (ISBN 0-8191-2207-6); pap. text ed. 12.25 (ISBN 0-8191-2208-4). U Pr of Amer.
Allen, Jonathan, ed. March Fourth: Scientists, Students & Society. 1970. pap. 4.95x (ISBN 0-262-51008-1). MIT Pr.
Amey, Peter. The Scientific Revolution. Yapp, Malcolm, et al, eds. (World History Ser.). (Illus.). 1980. lib. bdg. 6.95 (ISBN 0-89908-132-0); pap. text ed. 2.45 (ISBN 0-89908-107-X). Greenhaven.
Barber, Bernard. Science & the Social Order. LC 78-1569. 228p. 1978. Repr. of 1952 ed. lib. bdg. 32.50 (ISBN 0-313-20356-3, BASSO). Greenwood.
Barber, Bernard & Hirsch, Walter, eds. The Sociology of Science. LC 78-5937. viii, 662p. 1978. Repr. of 1962 ed. lib. bdg. 55.00 (ISBN 0-313-20403-9, BASOS). Greenwood.
Ben-David, Joseph. The Scientist's Role in Society: A Comparative Study with a New Introduction. LC 84-2758. 236p. 1984. 20.00x (ISBN 0-226-04227-8); pap. text ed. 8.95x (ISBN 0-226-04221-9). U of Chicago Pr.
Bennett, Jesse Lee. The Diffusion of Science. LC 74-26250. (History, Philosophy & Sociology of Science Ser). 1975. Repr. 17.00x (ISBN 0-405-06580-9). Ayer Co Pubs.
Berkner, L. V. The Scientific Age. LC 75-16841. 137p. 1975. Repr. of 1964 ed. lib. bdg. 22.50x (ISBN 0-8371-8263-8, BESAG). Greenwood.
Bernal, J. D. The Social Function of Science. 482p. 1980. Repr. lib. bdg. 40.00 (ISBN 0-8492-3754-8). R West.
Blume, Stuart S. Toward a Political Sociology of Science. LC 73-5291. 1974. text ed. 18.95 (ISBN 0-02-904350-6). Free Pr.
Bronowski, Jacob. Magic, Science, & Civilization. LC 78-1660. (Bampton Lectures in America Ser.: No. 20). 88p. 1978. 15.00x (ISBN 0-231-04484-4); pap. 8.00 (ISBN 0-231-04485-2). Columbia U Pr.
--Science & Human Values. rev. & enl. ed. Bd. with The Abacus & the Rose. (Illus.). 142p. 1972. pap. 3.37i (ISBN 0-06-080269-3, P269, PL). Har-Row.
Carovillano, Robert L. & Skehan, James W., eds. Science & the Future of Man. 1st u.s. ed. 1971. 22.50x (ISBN 0-262-03031-4). MIT Pr.
Charles, Cheryl & Samples, Bob, eds. Science & Society: Knowing, Teaching, Learning. LC 78-70847. (Bulletin Ser.: No. 57). 1978. pap. 6.95 (ISBN 0-87986-021-9, 498-15274). Nat Coun Soc Studies.
Crosson, Frederick J., ed. Science & Contemporary Society. 1967. 15.95x (ISBN 0-268-00247-9). U of Notre Dame Pr.
Cushing, James T., et al, eds. Science & Reality. LC 84-40360. 240p. 1984. text ed. 21.95 (ISBN 0-268-01714-X, 85-17146); pap. text ed. 11.95 (ISBN 0-268-01715-8, 85-17153). U of Notre Dame Pr.
Danzin, A. Science & the Second Renaissance of Europe. 1979. pap. text ed. 27.00 (ISBN 0-08-022442-3). Pergamon.
Datt, S. C. & Srivastava, S. B. Foundation Course: Science & Society. 242p. 1985. pap. text ed. 10.95x (ISBN 0-7069-2669-2, Pub. by Vikas India). Advent NY.
Day, Stacey B., ed. Image of Science & Society. (Biosciences Communications: Vol. 3, No. 1). 1977. 8.25 (ISBN 3-8055-2690-3). S Karger.
Dubos, Rene J. Reason Awake: Science for Man. LC 70-111327. 280p. 1970. 26.00x (ISBN 0-231-03181-5); pap. 11.00x (ISBN 0-231-08629-6). Columbia U Pr.
Elkana, Yehuda, et al, eds. Science, Internationalism & War: An Original Anthology. LC 74-25185. (History, Philosophy & Sociology of Science Ser). 1975. Repr. 16.00x (ISBN 0-405-06633-3). Ayer Co Pubs.
Farson, Richard E., ed. Science & Human Affairs. LC 64-18925. (Orig.). 1965. pap. 4.95x (ISBN 0-8314-0006-4). Sci & Behavior.
Gebhardt, Eike, ed. Science As Behavior: Sociological Approaches to the Sciences. 576p. 1982. 29.95 (ISBN 0-8264-0015-9); pap. 12.95 (ISBN 0-8264-0024-8). Continuum.
Gore, G. The Scientific Basis of National Progress, Including That of Morality. 218p. 1970. Repr. of 1882 ed. 26.00x (ISBN 0-7146-2407-1, BHA-02407, F Cass Co). Biblio Dist.
Grof, Stanislav. East & West: Ancient Wisdom & Modern Science. (Broadside Ser.). 30p. 1985. pap. 2.95 (ISBN 0-931191-00-9). Rob Briggs.
Haldane, J. B. Science & Everyday Life. LC 74-26267. (History, Philosophy & Sociology of Science Ser). 1975. Repr. 25.50x (ISBN 0-405-06595-7). Ayer Co Pubs.
Hanen, Marsha P., et al, eds. Science, Pseudo-Science & Society. 303p. 1980. pap. text ed. 14.25x (ISBN 0-88920-100-5, Pub. by Wilfrid Laurier U Pr Canada). Humanities.
Harre, Rom. Great Scientific Experiments: Twenty Experiments That Changed Our View of the World. (Illus.). 1981. 17.95 (ISBN 0-19-520436-0). Oxford U Pr.
Harris, Henry, ed. Scientific Models & Man. 1979. text ed. 18.95x (ISBN 0-19-857168-2). Oxford U Pr.
Hemily, P. W. & Ozdas, M. N., eds. Science & Future Choice, 2 vols. Incl. Vol. 1. Building on Scientific Achievement. 45.00x (ISBN 0-19-858162-9); Vol. 2. Technological Challenge for Social Changes. 49.50x (ISBN 0-19-858169-6). 1979. Oxford U Pr.
Holton, G. The Scientific Imagination. LC 76-47196. (Illus.). 1978. 47.50 (ISBN 0-521-21700-8); pap. 13.95 (ISBN 0-521-29237-9). Cambridge U Pr.
Home, R. W., ed. Science under Scrutiny. 1983. lib. bdg. 36.00 (ISBN 90-277-1602-1, Pub. by Reidel Holland). Kluwer Academic.
Hoover, Dwight W. & Koumoulides, John T., eds. Science & History. (Conspectus of History Ser.). (Orig.). 1982. pap. 4.95 (ISBN 0-937994-02-2). Ball State Univ.
Huxley, Julian S. Science & Social Needs. Repr. of 1935 ed. 22.00 (ISBN 0-527-43820-0). Kraus Repr.
International Colloquium on Science, Technology & Society, Vienna, 1979. Science, Technology & Society-Needs, Challenges & Limitations: Proceedings. Standke, Klaus-Heinrich, ed. (Pergamon Policy Studies on International Development). 656p. 1980. 110.00 (ISBN 0-08-025947-2). Pergamon.
Isselbacher, Kurt J., ed. Medicine, Science & Society: Symposia Celebrating the Harvard Medical School Bicentennial. 736p. 1984. text ed. 75.00 (ISBN 0-471-88882-6, Pub. by Wiley Med.). Wiley.
Jacquard, Albert. Endangered by Science? Moriarty, Mary, tr. 232p. 1985. 20.00x. Columbia U Pr.
Jordan, Pascual. Science & the Course of History. Manheim, Ralph, tr. LC 73-17920. 139p. 1974. Repr. of 1955 ed. lib. bdg. 18.75x (ISBN 0-8371-7280-2, JOSC). Greenwood.
Kaplan, Norman, ed. Science & Society. LC 74-26271. (History, Philosophy & Sociology of Science Ser). 1975. Repr. 46.50x (ISBN 0-405-06599-X). Ayer Co Pubs.
Kropotkin, Peter. Modern Science & Anarchism. 1980. lib. bdg. 49.95 (ISBN 0-8490-3125-7). Gordon Pr.
Layton, E. T., et al, eds. The Dynamics of Science & Technology. (Sociology of the Sciences Ser.: No. 2). 1978. lib. bdg. 36.50 (ISBN 90-277-0880-0, Pub. by Reidel Holland); pap. text ed. 18.50 (ISBN 90-277-0881-9). Kluwer Academic.
Layton, Edwin T., Jr., ed. Technology & Social Change in America. (Higham-Perkins Ser). 181p. 1973. scp 12.50 (ISBN 0-06-043881-9, HarpC). Har-Row.
Leicester Conference, 1976. Public Understanding of Science & Technology: Proceedings, Leicester Conference, 1976. 160p. 1980. pap. 21.00x (ISBN 0-942776-00-3, Pub by I.C.P.). Pub Ctr Cult Res.
Leiss, William. The Domination of Nature. LC 75-188358. 1972. 6.95 (ISBN 0-8076-0646-4). Braziller.
Lindsay, Robert B. The Role of Science in Civilization. LC 73-3234. (Illus.). 318p. 1973. Repr. of 1963 ed. lib. bdg. 20.50x (ISBN 0-8371-6837-6, LIRS). Greenwood.
Lynchburg College Faculty Staff, ed. Science, Technology & Society. LC 81-71947. (Classical Selections on Great Issues, Symposium Readings: Series 2, Vol. 2). 468p. 1982. lib. bdg. 21.50 (ISBN 0-8191-2297-1); pap. text ed. 9.00 (ISBN 0-8191-2298-X). U Pr of Amer.
McGucken, William. Scientists, Society: The Social Relations of Science Movement in Great Britain, 1931-1947. LC 83-8320. 395p. 1984. 22.50x (ISBN 0-8142-0351-5). Ohio St U Pr.
Marvin, Francis S., ed. Recent Developments in European Thought. LC 71-111851. (Essay Index Reprint Ser.). 1920. 19.00 (ISBN 0-8369-1619-0). Ayer Co Pubs.
Mayor, F., ed. Scientific Research & Social Goals: Toward a New Development Model. 248p. 1982. 39.00 (ISBN 0-08-028118-4). Pergamon.
Mee, A. J. Science Two Thousand, Bk. I. (Orig.). 1981. pap. text ed. 7.50x (ISBN 0-435-57566-X). Heinemann Ed.
Mendelsohn, Everett & Nowotny, Helga, eds. Science Between Utopia & Dystopia, 1984. (Sociology of the Sciences Yearbook: No. 8). 310p. 1984. 46.00 (ISBN 90-277-1719-2, Pub. by Reidel Holland); pap. text ed. 24.00 (ISBN 90-277-1721-4). Kluwer Academic.
Merton, Robert K. The Sociology of Science. Storer, Norman W., ed. LC 72-97623. 1973. 30.00x (ISBN 0-226-52091-9). U of Chicago Pr.
Millikan, Robert A. Science & the New Civilization. facsimile ed. LC 76-142671. (Essay Index Reprint Ser). Repr. of 1930 ed. 18.00 (ISBN 0-8369-2418-5). Ayer Co Pubs.
Monod, Jacques. Chance & Necessity. 1972. pap. 3.95 (ISBN 0-394-71825-9, Vin). Random.
Montgomery, David. Imperial Science & National Survival. LC 80-70692. 1981. 2.50x (ISBN 0-87081-094-4). Colo Assoc.
Moulton, Forest R., ed. The World & Man As Science Sees Them. 1937. 30.00 (ISBN 0-8495-6272-4). Arden Lib.
Nabseth, L. & Ray, G. F. Diffusion of New Technology. (National Institute of Economic & Social Research Economic & Social Studies: No. 29). (Illus.). 300p. 1974. 42.50 (ISBN 0-521-20430-5). Cambridge U Pr.
Nakayama, Shigeru & Dusenberry, Jerry. Academic & Scientific Traditions in China, Japan, & the West. 251p. 1984. 24.50x (ISBN 0-86008-339-X, Pub. by U of Tokyo Japan). Columbia U Pr.
National Academy of Sciences. Science & Technology: A Five-Year Outlook. LC 79-15862. (Illus.). 544p. 1979. pap. 13.95x (ISBN 0-7167-1141-9). W H Freeman.
OECD Staff. Assessing the Impacts of Technology on Society. 80p. (Orig.). 1983. pap. 9.00x (ISBN 92-64-12409-8). OECD.
On the Edge of a Razor Blade: The New Historical Blocs & Socio-Cultural Alternatives in Europe. 33p. 1980. pap. 5.00 (ISBN 92-808-0169-4, TUNU111, UNU). Unipub.

Paradis, James & Postlewait, Thomas, eds. Victorian Science & Victorian Values: Literary Perspectives. LC 80-29513. 362p. 1981. 72.00x (ISBN 0-89766-109-5, VOL. 360); pap. 72.00x. NY Acad Sci.

Pecujlic, Miroslav, et al, eds. Science & Technology in the Transformation of the World. LC 83-40706. 174p. 1984. 19.95 (ISBN 0-312-70265-5). St Martin.

Peterson, Dean F. Man, Science & Society. 6p. 1971. pap. 2.00 (ISBN 0-87421-042-9). Utah St U Pr.

Peterson, Rita W. & Butts, David. Science & Society. 1983. text ed. 23.95 (ISBN 0-675-20022-9). Additional supplements may be obtained from publisher. Merrill.

The Project of Socio-Cultural Development Alternatives in a Changing World: Report on the Formative Stage (May 1978 - Dec. 1979) 160p. 1980. pap. 13.50 (ISBN 92-808-0167-8, TUNU116, UNU). Unipub.

Rabinowitch, Eugene I. The Dawn of a New Age: Reflections on Science & Human Affairs. LC 63-20898. pap. 85.00 (ISBN 0-317-09265-0, 2020150). Bks Demand UMI.

Restivo, Sal. The Social Relations of Physics, Mysticism & Mathematics. 1983. lib. bdg. 49.50 (ISBN 90-277-1536-X, Pub. by Reidel Holland). Kluwer Academic.

Restructuring a Framework for Assessment of Science & Technology as a Driving Power for Social Development: A Biosocial Approach. 22p. 1981. pap. 5.00 (ISBN 92-808-0179-1, TUNU130, UNU). Unipub.

Rosenberg, Charles E. No Other Gods: On Science & American Social Thought. LC 75-36942. 288p. 1976. pap. 7.95x (ISBN 0-8018-2097-9). Johns Hopkins.

Ross, Ralph. Symbols & Civilization: Science, Religion, Morals, Art. LC 62-21848. 1963. pap. 3.25 (ISBN 0-15-687605-1, Harv). HarBraceJ.

Russell, Bertrand. The Impact of Science on Society. (Unwin Paperbacks). 1976. pap. 3.95 (ISBN 0-04-300063-0). Allen Unwin.

Schooler, D. Science, Scientists & Public Policy. LC 70-122274. 1971. pap. text ed. 4.50 (ISBN 0-02-928010-9). Free Pr.

Science & Technology As an Organic Part of Contemporary Culture. 12p. 1980. pap. 5.00 (ISBN 92-808-0186-4, TUNU124, UNU). Unipub.

Science & the Making of Contemporary Civilization. 25p. 1980. pap. 5.00 (ISBN 92-808-0177-5, TUNU110, UNU). Unipub.

Science Education Assoc. London. Science in Society. Lewis, John L., ed. 1981. complete pack 100.00x (ISBN 0-686-79369-2, 00407); tchrs. manual 20.00x (ISBN 0-435-54043-2); Omnibus reader's pack 36.00x (ISBN 0-435-54042-4). Heinemann Ed.

Science, Technology, & Politics in a Changing World. 9p. 1980. pap. 5.00 (ISBN 92-808-0243-7, TUNU123, UNU). Unipub.

Symposium on Science & Technology in Kuwait, May 1978. Proceedings. Behbehani, et al, eds. LC 81-12403. (Illus.). 288p. 1982. text ed. 65.00x (ISBN 0-582-78325-9). Longman.

Szent-Gyorgyi, Albert. Crazy Ape. LC 75-118313. 1970. 3.95 (ISBN 0-8022-2348-6). Philos Lib.

--What Next. LC 73-136016. 1971. 5.00 (ISBN 0-8022-2045-2). Philos Lib.

Thornton, Jesse E., compiled by. Science & Social Change. LC 72-357. (Essay Index Reprint Ser.). Repr. of 1939 ed. 29.00 (ISBN 0-8369-2830-X). Ayer Co Pubs.

Toda, Masanao. Man, Robot & Society. 224p. 1981. lib. bdg. 20.00 (ISBN 0-89838-060-X). Kluwer-Nijhoff.

Toward a Clearer Definition of the Role of Science & Technology in Transformation. 31p. 1981. pap. 5.00 (ISBN 92-808-0181-3, TUNU136, UNU). Unipub.

Trotsky, Leon. Problems of Everyday Life: And Other Writings on Culture & Science. Fidler, G. R., et al, trs. LC 79-186693. 352p. 1973. 25.00 (ISBN 0-913460-14-1, Dist. by Path Pr NY); pap. 7.95 (ISBN 0-913460-15-X, Dist. by Path Pr NY). Monad Pr.

Vavoulis, Alexander & Colver, A. Wayne, eds. Science & Society: Selected Essays. LC 66-15005. 1966. pap. text ed. 7.50x (ISBN 0-8162-9172-1). Holden-Day.

Warshofsky, Fred, ed. Twenty-First Century: The New Age of Exploration, Vol. 1. (Twentyfirst Century Ser). (Illus.). 1969. 10.95 (ISBN 0-670-73582-5). Viking.

Weisskopf, Victor F. Knowledge & Wonder: The Natural World As Man Knows It. 2nd ed. (Illus.). 1979. pap. 6.95 (ISBN 0-262-73052-9). MIT Pr.

Whitley, Richard, ed. Social Processes of Scientific Development. 1974. 24.50x (ISBN 0-7100-7705-X). Routledge & Kegan.

Wightman, W. P. Science in a Renaissance Society. 1972. (Hutchinson U Lib); pap. text ed. 6.50x (ISBN 0-09-111651-1). Humanities.

Woodruff, Lorande L., ed. Development of the Sciences: Second Series. 1941. 49.50x (ISBN 0-686-83526-3). Elliots Bks.

Yuan, Luke C. & Wu, Chien-Shiung, eds. Elementary Particles: Science, Technology & Society. 1971. 73.50 (ISBN 0-12-774850-4). Acad Pr.

SCIENCE AND ETHICS

Allen, Jonathan, ed. March Fourth: Scientists, Students & Society. 1970. pap. 4.95x (ISBN 0-262-51008-1). MIT Pr.

Becker, Lawrence C. On Justifying Moral Judgements. (International Library of Philosophy & Scientific Method). 199p. 1973. text ed. 20.45x (ISBN 0-7100-7524-3, Pub. by Routledge Kegan Paul England). Humanities.

Cattell, Raymond B. A New Morality from Science: Beyondism. 1973. 42.00 (ISBN 0-08-016956-2). Pergamon.

Conference on Science & Values. Science & Values: Patterns of Tradition & Change. Thackray, Arnold & Mendelsohn, Everett, eds. 1974. text ed. 11.50x (ISBN 0-391-00234-1). Humanities.

Diener, Edward & Crandall, Rick. Ethics in Social & Behavioral Research. LC 78-8881. 1978. lib. bdg. 20.00x (ISBN 0-226-14823-8). U of Chicago Pr.

Engelhardt, H. Tristram, Jr. & Callahan, Daniel, eds. Morals, Science & Sociality. LC 78-14481. (The Foundations of Ethics & Its Relationships to Sciences: Vol. III). 1978. pap. 7.95 (ISBN 0-916558-03-7). Hastings Ctr Inst Soc.

Glass, Hiram B. Science & Ethical Values. LC 81-13170. ix, 101p. 1981. Repr. of 1965 ed. lib. bdg. 22.50x (ISBN 0-313-23141-9, GLSE). Greenwood.

Gore, G. The Scientific Basis of National Progress, Including That of Morality. 218p. 1970. Repr. of 1882 ed. 26.00x (ISBN 0-7146-2407-1, BHA-02407, F Cass Co). Biblio Dist.

Graham, Loren R. Between Science & Values. 448p. 1981. 24.00 (ISBN 0-231-05192-1); pap. 12.50x (ISBN 0-231-05193-X). Columbia U Pr.

Haller, R., ed. Science & Ethics. (Grazer Philosophische Studien: Vol. 12-13). 298p. 1981. text ed. 32.75x (ISBN 90-6203-913-8, Pub. by Rodopi Holland). Humanities.

Hill, A. V. The Ethical Dilemma of Science. LC 60-13207. 416p. 1960. 10.00x (ISBN 0-87470-001-9). Rockefeller.

Holton, Gerald & Morison, Robert S., eds. Limits of Scientific Inquiry. 1979. 19.95x (ISBN 0-393-01212-3); pap. 5.95x (ISBN 0-393-95056-5). Norton.

International Conference on the Unity of the Sciences, 2nd, Tokyo, Nov. 18-21, 1973. Modern Science & Moral Values: Proceedings. LC 75-306280. 608p. 1974. casebound smythesewn 20.00x (ISBN 0-89226-000-9). ICF Pr.

Kass, Leon R. Toward a More Natural Science: Biology & Human Affairs. (Illus.). 359p. 1985. 23.50 (ISBN 0-02-918340-5). Free Pr.

Lakoff, Sanford A., ed. Science & Ethical Responsibility. 1980. pap. text ed. 31.95 (ISBN 0-201-03993-1). Addison-Wesley.

Lappe, Marc & Morison, Robert S., eds. Ethical & Scientific Issues Posed by Human Uses of Molecular Genetics, Vol. 265. (Annals of the New York Academy of Sciences). 208p. 1976. 26.00x (ISBN 0-89072-019-3). NY Acad Sci.

Lowrance, William W. Science & Human Values. 265p. 1985. 24.95x (ISBN 0-19-503605-0). Oxford U Pr.

McCormick, Richard A. How Brave a New World: Dilemmas in Bioethics. LC 80-921. 456p. 1981. 15.95 (ISBN 0-385-17179-X). Doubleday.

Margenau, Henry. Ethics & Science. LC 77-8684. 314p. 1979. Repr. of 1964 ed. 20.50 (ISBN 0-88275-577-3). Krieger.

Reagan, Charles E. Ethics for Scientific Researchers. 2nd ed. 184p. 1971. 20.75x (ISBN 0-398-01558-9). C C Thomas.

Santilli, Ruggero M. Ethical Probe on Einstein's Followers in the U. S. A. An Insider's View. 345p. 1985. pap. 20.00 (ISBN 0-931753-00-7). Alpha Pub Trust.

Sardar, Ziauddin, ed. The Touch of Midas: Science, Values & the Environment in Islam & the West. LC 83-22262. 253p. 1984. 35.00 (ISBN 0-7190-0974-X, Pub. by Manchester Univ Pr). Longwood Pub Group.

Shannon, Thomas. Bioethics. rev. ed. LC 76-18054. 646p. 1980. pap. 14.95 (ISBN 0-8091-1970-6). Paulist Pr.

Shrader-Frechette, Kristin S. Science Policy, Ethics, & Economic Methodology. 1985. lib. bdg. 39.50 (ISBN 90-277-1806-7, Pub. by Reidel Holland); pap. text ed. 19.50 (ISBN 90-277-1845-8, Pub. by Reidel Holland). Kluwer Academic.

Singer, Peter. The Expanding Circle: Ethics and Sociobiology. 190p. 1981. 10.95 (ISBN 0-374-15112-1). FS&G.

Szent-Gyorgyi, Albert. Crazy Ape. LC 75-118313. 1970. 3.95 (ISBN 0-8022-2348-6). Philos Lib.

Teichler-Zallen, Doris & Clements, Colleen D. Science & Morality: New Directions in Bioethics. LC 80-8926. 320p. 1982. 29.00x (ISBN 0-669-04406-7); pap. text ed. 12.00x (ISBN 0-669-09808-6). Lexington Bks.

Walters, Leroy, ed. Bibliography of Bioethics, Vol. 7. 375p. 1981. 55.00 (ISBN 0-02-933770-4). Free Pr.

SCIENCE AND LAW

Areen, Judith, et al. Law, Science & Medicine. LC 84-8181. (University Casebook Ser.). 1494p. 1984. text ed. 34.50 (ISBN 0-88277-179-5). Foundation Pr.

Blank, Robert H. Redefining Human Life: Reproductive Technologies & Social Policy. (Special Studies in Science, Technology, & Public Policy-Society). 280p. 1983. lib. bdg. 27.00x (ISBN 0-86531-665-1). Westview.

Channels, Noreen L. Social Science Methods in the Legal Process. LC 84-11527. (Illus.). 286p. 1985. 39.95x (ISBN 0-86598-013-6). Rowman & Allanheld.

Cohen, Morris L. & Ronen, Naomi, eds. Law & Science: A Selected Bibliography. rev. ed. 155p. 1980. 25.00x (ISBN 0-262-03073-X). MIT Pr.

Imwinkelried, Edward J., ed. Scientific & Expert Evidence. 2nd ed. 1353p. 1981. text ed. 45.00 (ISBN 0-686-76237-1, C3-1168). PLI.

Nyhart, J. D. & Carrow, Milton M., eds. Law & Science in Collaboration: Resolving Regulatory Issues of Science & Technology. LC 81-47689. 320p. 1983. 30.00x (ISBN 0-669-04907-7). Lexington Bks.

Peczenik, Aleksander, et al. Theory of Legal Science. 1984. lib. bdg. 74.00 (ISBN 90-277-1834-2, Pub. by Reidel Holland). Kluwer Academic.

Schmandt, Jurgen. Policy Analysis & Science Policy. (Working Paper Ser.: No. 18). 63p. 1981. pap. 3.00 (ISBN 0-318-00172-1). LBJ Sch Pub Aff.

Shrader-Frechette, Kristin S. Science Policy, Ethics, & Economic Methodology. 1985. lib. bdg. 39.50 (ISBN 90-277-1806-7, Pub. by Reidel Holland); pap. text ed. 19.50 (ISBN 90-277-1845-8, Pub. by Reidel Holland). Kluwer Academic.

Smith, Gordon B., et al, eds. Soviet & East European Law & the Scientific-Technical Revolution. (Pergamon Policy Studies on International Politics). (Illus.). 330p. 1981. 37.00 (ISBN 0-08-027195-2). Pergamon.

Thomas, William A., ed. Science & Law. LC 83-1209. (A Westview Special Study). (Illus.). 168p. 1983. 17.50x (ISBN 0-86531-442-X). Westview.

SCIENCE AND SPACE

see Space Sciences

SCIENCE AND STATE

see also Research and Development Contracts; State Encouragement of Science, Literature, and Art; Technology and State

Ames, Mary E. Outcome Uncertain: Science & the Political Process. 1982. pap. 3.50 (ISBN 0-380-59535-4, 59535-4, Discus). Avon.

Averch, Harvey A. A Strategic Analysis of Science & Technology Policy. LC 84-47961. 232p. 1985. text ed. 20.00x (ISBN 0-8018-2467-2). Johns Hopkins.

Barfield, Claude. Science Policy From Ford to Reagan: Change & Continuity. 1983. 13.95 (ISBN 0-8447-3495-0); pap. 5.95 (ISBN 0-8447-3494-2). Am Enterprise.

Behrman, Daniel. Science & Technology in Development: A UNESCO Approach. (Illus.). 104p. 1979. pap. 5.25 (ISBN 92-3-101726-8, U947, UNESCO). Unipub.

Blume, Stuart S. Perspectives in the Sociology of Science. LC 76-30827. 1977. 56.95 (ISBN 0-471-99480-4, Pub. by Wiley-Interscience). Wiley.

Bogdanor, Vernon, ed. Science & Politics: The Herbert Spencer Lectures, 1982. (Illus.). 1984. 16.95x (ISBN 0-19-857605-6). Oxford U Pr.

Brooks, Douglas L. America Looks to the Sea: Ocean Use & the National Interest. 266p. 1984. write for info. (ISBN 0-86720-250-5). Jones & Bartlett.

Budworth. Public Science Private View. 1981. 24.00 (ISBN 0-9960021-3-8, Pub. by Inst Physics England); pap. 13.00 (ISBN 0-9960021-4-6, Pub. by Inst Physics England). Heyden.

Burger, Edward J., Jr. Science at the White House: A Political Liability. LC 80-81425. 208p. 1981. text ed. 19.00x (ISBN 0-8018-2433-8). Johns Hopkins.

Bush, Vannevar. Science the Endless Frontier: A Report to the President. Cohen, I. Bernard, ed. LC 79-7953. (Three Cneturies of Science in America Ser.). 1980. Repr. of 1945 ed. lib. bdg. 16.00x (ISBN 0-405-12534-8). Ayer Co Pubs.

Cole, Leonard A. Politics & the Restraint of Science. LC 83-2992. (Illus.). 200p. 1983. 17.95 (ISBN 0-86598-125-6). Rowman & Allanheld.

Committee on Science, Engineering & Public Policy. Strengthening the Government-University Partnership in Science. 188p. 1983. 14.50 (ISBN 0-309-03380-2). Natl Acad Pr.

Cushing, James T., et al, eds. Science & Reality. LC 84-40360. 240p. 1984. text ed. 21.95 (ISBN 0-268-01714-X, 85-17146); pap. text ed. 11.95 (ISBN 0-268-01715-8, 85-17153). U of Notre Dame Pr.

Daly, D. J. & Globerman, S. Tariff & Science Policies: Applications of a Model of Nationalism. LC 76-24911. (Ontario Economic Council Research Studies). (Illus.). 1976. pap. 7.50 (ISBN 0-8020-3338-5). U of Toronto Pr.

Doern, G. Bruce. Science & Politics in Canada. LC 79-180255. pap. 63.00 (ISBN 0-317-26055-3, 2023842). Bks Demand UMI.

Dupree, A. Hunter. Science in the Federal Government: A History of Policies & Activities to 1940. Cohen, I. Bernard, ed. LC 79-7959. (Three Centuries of Science in America Ser.). (Illus.). 1980. Repr. of 1957 ed. lib. bdg. 39.00x (ISBN 0-405-12540-2). Ayer Co Pubs.

Geison, Gerald, ed. Professions & the French State: 1700-1900. LC 83-14700. 352p. 1984. 35.00x (ISBN 0-8122-7912-3). U of Pa Pr.

Golden, William T., et al, eds. Science Advice to the President. LC 79-28743. (Pergamon Policy Studies). 268p. 1980. 55.00 (ISBN 0-08-025963-4). Pergamon.

Goonatilake, Susantha. Aborted Discovery: Science & Creativity in the Third World. (Third World Studies). 201p. 1984. pap. 9.25 (ISBN 0-86232-089-5, Pub. by Zed Pr England). Biblio Dist.

Gummett, Philip. Science & Technology Policy in the 1980's & Beyond. 275p. 1984. pap. text ed. 32.00 (ISBN 0-582-90200-2). Gale.

Gusman, Sam, et al. Public Policy for Chemicals: National & International Issues. LC 80-68965. 152p. (Orig.). 1980. pap. 8.50 (ISBN 0-89164-062-2). Conservation Foun.

Haas, Ernst B., et al. Scientists & World Order: The Uses of Technical Knowledge in International Organizations. LC 76-47981. 1978. 32.50x (ISBN 0-520-03341-8). U of Cal Pr.

Hailsham, Quintin M. Science & Politics. LC 73-16740. 110p. 1974. Repr. of 1963 ed. lib. bdg. 24.75x (ISBN 0-8371-7227-6, HASC). Greenwood.

Hall, Harry S. Congressional Attitudes Toward Science & Scientists: A Study of Legislative Reactions to Atomic Energy & the Political Participation of Scientists. Bruchey, Stuart, ed. LC 78-22687. (Energy in the American Economy Ser.). 1979. lib. bdg. 32.50x (ISBN 0-405-11990-9). Ayer Co Pubs.

Holton, G. & Blanpied, W., eds. Science & Its Public: The Changing Relationship. LC 75-41391. (Boston Studies in the Philosophy of Science: No. 33). 330p. 1975. lib. bdg. 37.00 (ISBN 90-277-0657-3, Pub. by Reidel Holland); pap. 17.50 (ISBN 90-277-0658-1). Kluwer Academic.

Human Goals & Science Policy. (Science Council of Canada Background Studies: No. 38). 1977. pap. 7.40 (ISBN 0-685-80155-1, SSC48, SSC). Unipub.

Islamic Science. 1982. 90.00x (ISBN 0-905035-02-X, Pub. by Scorp Pubns England). State Mutual Bk.

Jachim, Anton G. Science Policy Making in the United States & the Batavia Accelerator. LC 74-26633. 220p. 1975. 9.95x (ISBN 0-8093-0674-3). S Ill U Pr.

Killian, James R., Jr. Sputnik, Scientists, & Eisenhower: A Memoir of the First Special Assistant to the President for Science & Technology. LC 77-21560. 1977. 30.00x (ISBN 0-262-11066-0); pap. 9.95 (1982) (ISBN 0-262-61035-3). MIT Pr.

Kistiakowsky, George B. A Scientist at the White House. 1976. 27.50x (ISBN 0-674-79496-6). Harvard U Pr.

Krohn, Roger G. Social Shaping of Science: Institutions, Ideology, & Careers in Science. LC 75-90792. (Contributions in Sociology: No. 4). (Illus.). 1971. lib. bdg. 29.95 (ISBN 0-8371-1852-2, KRS/). Greenwood.

Kuehn, Thomas J. & Porter, Alan L. Science, Technology & National Policy. (Illus.). 608p. 1980. 39.95x (ISBN 0-8014-1343-5); pap. 12.95x (ISBN 0-8014-9876-7). Cornell U Pr.

Manning, Thomas G. Government in Science: The U. S. Geological Survey, 1867-1894. LC 67-17851. (Illus.). 272p. 1967. 20.00x (ISBN 0-8131-1142-0). U Pr of Ky.

Manten, A. A. & Timman, T., eds. Information Policy & Scientific Research. 170p. 1983. 40.50 (ISBN 0-444-86611-6, I-170-83). Elsevier.

Mathias, Peter, ed. Science & Society, 1600-1900. (Illus.). 176p. 1972. 32.50 (ISBN 0-521-08375-3). Cambridge U Pr.

Turner, Gerard L'E. Nineteenth-Century Scientific Instruments. LC 83-48656. (Illus.). 340p. 1984. 60.00 (ISBN 0-520-05160-2). U of Cal Pr.
Ward, F. A. A Catalogue of European Scientific Instruments in the Department of Medieval & Later Antiquities of the British Museum. 176p. 1981. 150.00x (ISBN 0-7141-1345-X, Pub. by Brit Mus Pubns England). State Mutual Bk.

SCIENTIFIC ASSOCIATIONS
see Scientific Societies
SCIENTIFIC COMMUNICATIONS
see Communication in Science
SCIENTIFIC EDUCATION
see Science–Study and Teaching
SCIENTIFIC ERRORS
see Errors, Scientific
SCIENTIFIC EXPEDITIONS
see also names of regions explored, e.g. Africa, Central

An Account of a Geographical & Astronomical Expedition to the Northern Par ts of Russia. 420p. 1984. Repr. of 1802 ed. 42.00x (ISBN 0-85546-172-1, Pub. by Richmond Pub England). State Mutual Bk.
Adams, Richard & Lockley, Ronald. Voyage Through the Antarctic. LC 82-48484. (Illus.). 160p. 1982. 13.95 (ISBN 0-394-52858-1). Knopf.
Andrews, Roy C. Ends of the Earth. LC 78-164078. (Towers Bks). (Illus.). x, 355p. 1972. Repr. of 1929 ed. 40.00x (ISBN 0-8103-3923-4). Gale.
Atkins, John. Voyage to Guinea, Brazil & the West Indies in H.M.S. "Swallow" & "Weymouth". 258p. 1970. Repr. of 1735 ed. 27.50x (ISBN 0-7146-1787-3, F Cass Co). Biblio Dist.
Byrd, Richard E. Discovery: The Story of the Second Byrd Antarctic Expedition. facsimile ed. LC 71-37874. (Select Bibliographies Reprint Ser). Repr. of 1935 ed. 36.00 (ISBN 0-8369-6711-9). Ayer Co Pubs.
Durrell, Gerald. Ark on the Move. 1983. 14.95 (ISBN 0-698-11211-3, Coward). Putnam Pub Group.
Dyer, Ira & Chryssostomidis, C., eds. Arctic Technology & Policy. LC 83-18403. (Illus.). 281p. 1984. text ed. 79.95 (ISBN 0-89116-361-1). Hemisphere Pub.
Engstrand, Iris W. Spanish Scientists in the New World: The Eighteenth-Century Expeditions. LC 80-50863. (Illus.). 234p. 1981. 27.50x (ISBN 0-295-95764-6). U of Wash Pr.
Furse, Chris. Elephant Island: An Antarctic Expedition. 264p. 1981. 35.00x (ISBN 0-904614-02-6, Pub. by Nelson Ltd). State Mutual Bk.
GEOSECS Atlantic Expedition Atlases. Vol. 1. 31.00 (ISBN 0-318-18095-2); Vol. 2. 34.00 (ISBN 0-318-18096-0). NSF.
GEOSECS Indian Ocean Expedition. Vol. 5. 17.00 (ISBN 0-318-18099-5). NSF.
GEOSECS Indian Ocean Expedition Atlases. Vol. 6. 36.00 (ISBN 0-318-18098-7). NSF.
GEOSECS Pacific Expedition Atlases. Vol. 4. 39.00 (ISBN 0-318-18097-9). NSF.
Geotzmann, William H. & Sloan, Kay. Looking Far North: The Harriman Expedition to Alaska, 1899. LC 82-61034. 1983. pap. 9.95 (ISBN 0-691-00591-5). Princeton U Pr.
Heyerdahl, Thor. The Tigris Expedition: In Search of Our Beginnings. (Illus.). 1982. pap. 7.95 (ISBN 0-452-25358-6, Z5358, Plume). NAL.
Holub, Emil. Seven Years in South Africa: Travels, Researches, & Hunting Adventures, Between the Diamong-Fields & the Zambesi, 1827-79, 2 Vols. LC 2-14174. 1971. Repr. of 1881 ed. Set. 80.00 (ISBN 0-384-24073-9, L158). Johnson Repr.
Humboldt, Alexander Von. Personal Narrative of Travels to the Equinoctial Regions of America During the Years 1799-1804, 3 Vols. Ross, Thomasina, tr. LC 69-13241. 1969. Repr. of 1851 ed. 60.00 (ISBN 0-405-08642-3, Blom Pubns). Ayer Co Pubs.
MacCreagh, Gordon. White Waters & Black. LC 85-8745. (Illus.). 422p. 1985. pap. 14.95 (ISBN 0-226-50016-0). U of Chicago Pr.
Nansen, Fridtjof, ed. Norwegian North Polar Expedition 1893-96: Scientific Results, 6 Vols. LC 68-55205. (Illus.). 1968. Repr. of 1906 ed. Set. lib. bdg. 187.00x (ISBN 0-8371-3852-3, NANO). Greenwood.
Narbeth, Colin. Admiral Seymour's Expedition & Taku Forts 1900. 1980. 35.00x (ISBN 0-902633-69-4, Pub. by Picton England). State Mutual Bk.
Neider, Charles. Beyond Cape Horn: Travels in the Antarctic. LC 80-13220. (Illus.). 400p. 1980. 16.95 (ISBN 0-87156-233-2). Sierra.
Scoresby, William, Jr. The Eighteen Hundred & Six Log Book Concerning the Arctic Voyage of Captain William Scoresby, Sr. 40p. 1982. 60.00x (ISBN 0-686-44543-0, Pub. by Caedmon of Whitby). State Mutual Bk.
Serpa Pinto, Alexandre A. How I Crossed Africa, from the Atlantic to the Indian Ocean, Through Unknown Countries, 2 vols. Elwes, Alfred, tr. LC 5-15665. Repr. of 1881 ed. Set. 95.00 (ISBN 0-384-54880-6). Johnson Repr.
Von Humboldt, Alexander & Bonpland, Aime. Personal Narrative of Travels to the Equinoctial Regions of America During the Years 1799-1804, 7 Vols. in 6 Pts. Williams, Helen M., tr. LC 1-20782. Repr. of 1829 ed. Set. 215.00 (ISBN 0-404-03440-3). AMS Pr.
Wood, Robert D. The Voyage of the Water Witch: A Scientific Expedition to Paraguay & the La Plata Region (1853-1856) LC 85-50095. (Illus.). 114p. 1985. pap. 10.00x (ISBN 0-911437-15-0). Labyrinthos.

SCIENTIFIC FRENCH
see French Language–Technical French
SCIENTIFIC ILLUSTRATION
see also Biological Illustration; Technical Illustration

Clarke, Carl D. Illustration, Its Technique & Application to the Sciences. 2nd ed. (Illus.). 258p. 1949. 25.00 (ISBN 0-685-25473-9). Standard Arts.
Dillon, Brian D., ed. The Student's Guide to Archaeological Illustrating. rev. ed. (Archaeological Research Tools Ser.: Vol. 1). (Illus.). 154p. Date not set. pap. 8.50x (ISBN 0-917956-38-9). UCLA Arch.
Jastrzebski, Zbigniew T. Scientific Illustration: A Guide for the Beginning Artist. (Illus.). 336p. 1985. 49.95 (ISBN 0-13-795949-4); pap. 22.95 (ISBN 0-13-795931-1). P H.
Ridgway, John L. Scientific Illustration. (Illus.). 1938. 15.00x (ISBN 0-8047-0996-3). Stanford U Pr.
Speed, Harold. The Practice & Science of Drawing. 3rd ed. (Illus.). 11.25 (ISBN 0-8446-4638-5). Peter Smith.
Wood, Phyllis. Scientific Illustration: A Guide to Biological, Zoological, & Medical Rendering Techniques, Design, Printing, & Display. 152p. 1982. pap. 14.95 (ISBN 0-442-29307-0). Van Nos Reinhold.

SCIENTIFIC INSTITUTIONS
see Scientific Societies
SCIENTIFIC INSTRUMENTS
see Scientific Apparatus and Instruments
SCIENTIFIC JOURNALISM
see Journalism, Scientific
SCIENTIFIC LIBRARIES
see also Information Storage and Retrieval Systems–Science

Evans, A. J., et al. Education & Training of Users of Scientific & Technical Information: UNISIST Guide for Teachers. (Illus.). 143p. (2nd Printing 1982). 1977. pap. 10.50 (ISBN 92-3-101452-8, U746, UNESCO). Unipub.
Mount, Ellis. University Science & Engineering Libraries. 2nd ed. LC 84-6530. (Contributions in Librarianship & Information Science Ser.: No. 49). (Illus.). x, 303p. 1985. lib. bdg. 35.00 (ISBN 0-313-23949-5, MOU/). Greenwood.
Mount, Ellis, ed. Cataloging & Indexing in Sci-Tech Libraries. (Science & Technology Libraries: Vol. 2, No. 3). 86p. 1982. pap. text ed. 15.00 (ISBN 0-86656-204-4, B204). Haworth Pr.
--Current Awareness Services in Sci-Tech Libraries. (Science & Technology Libraries Ser.: Vol. 2, No. 1). 80p. 1982. pap. 15.00 (ISBN 0-86656-113-7, B113). Haworth Pr.
--Data Manipualtion in Sci-Tech Libraries. LC 85-5569. (Science & Technology Libraries: Vol. 5, No. 4). 144p. 1985. text ed. 19.95 (ISBN 0-86656-441-1). Haworth Pr.
--Document Delivery for Sci-Tech Libraries. (Science & Technology Libraries: Vol. 2, No. 4). 127p. 1982. pap. text ed. 15.00 (ISBN 0-86656-200-1, B200). Haworth Pr.
--Fee-Based Services in Sci-Tech Libraries. LC 84-19186. (Science & Technology Libraries: Vol. 5, No. 2). 120p. 1985. text ed. 19.95 (ISBN 0-86656-326-1). Haworth Pr.
--Online vs. Manual Searching in Sci-Tech Libraries. (Science & Technology Libraries: Vol. 3, No. 1). 83p. 1982. pap. text ed. 15.00 (ISBN 0-86656-203-6, B203). Haworth Pr.
--Planning Facilities for Science & Technology Libraries. LC 83-8570. (Science & Technology Libraries: Vol. 3, No. 4). 121p. 1983. text ed. 19.95 (ISBN 0-86656-237-0, B237). Haworth Pr.
--Role of Maps in Sci-Tech Libraries. LC 84-27919. (Science & Technology Libraries: Vol. 5, No. 3). 136p. 1985. text ed. 17.95 (ISBN 0-86656-395-4). Haworth Pr.
--Role of Patents in Sci-Tech Libraries. LC 82-2885. (Science & Technology Libraries Ser.: Vol. 2, No. 2). 97p. 1982. 25.00 (ISBN 0-86656-114-5, B114). Haworth Pr.
--Role of Translations in Sci-Tech Libraries. LC 82-23353. (Science & Technology Libraries: Vol. 3, No. 2). 94p. 1983. 20.00 (ISBN 0-86656-217-6, B217). Haworth Pr.
--Sci-Tech Libraries in Museums & Aquariums. (Science & Technology Libraries: Vol. 6, Nos. 1-2). 200p. text ed. write for info. (ISBN 0-86656-484-5). Haworth Pr.
--Scientific & Technical Libraries in the Seventies: A Guide to Information Sources. (Books, Publishing & Libraries Information Guide Ser.: Vol. 4). 300p. 1980. 60.00x (ISBN 0-8103-1483-5). Gale.
--Training of Sci-Tech Librarians & Library Users. LC 81-6975. (Science & Technology Libraries: Vol. 1, No. 3). 72p. 1981. pap. text ed. 15.00 (ISBN 0-917724-75-5, B75). Haworth Pr.
Sherrod, John & Hodina, Alfred, eds. Reader in Science Information. LC 72-97713. 403p. 1973. 28.50 (ISBN 0-313-24046-9, ZRN/). Greenwood.
Strauss, L., et al. Scientific & Technical Libraries: Their Organization & Administration. LC 83-22256. 462p. 1985. Repr. of 1964 ed. write for info. (ISBN 0-89874-698-1). Krieger.

SCIENTIFIC LITERATURE
see also Science–Bibliography

A Bibliography of Recommendations (ISO, BS, NEN, ANSI) for the Preparation of Scientific Publications. 1977. pap. 4.00 (ISBN 90-220-0390-6, PDC138, PUDOC). Unipub.
Bishop, Claude T. How to Edit a Scientific Journal. (The Professional Editing & Publishing Ser.). 138p. 1984. 21.95 (ISBN 0-89495-033-9); pap. 14.95 (ISBN 0-89495-034-7). ISI Pr.
Grogan, Denis. Science & Technology: An Introduction to the Literature. 4th ed. 400p. 1982. 27.50 (ISBN 0-85157-315-0, Pub. by Bingley England); pap. 18.50 (Pub. by Bingley England). Shoe String.
Harnad, Stevan, ed. Peer Commentary on Peer Review: A Case Study in Scientific Quality Control. LC 82-19860. 80p. 1983. pap. 13.95 (ISBN 0-521-27306-4). Cambridge U Pr.
Hoijer, Dorothy J. A Bibliographic Guide to Neuroenzyme Literature. LC 72-102211. pap. 82.50 (ISBN 0-317-27111-3, 2024704). Bks Demand UMI.
Loosjes, T. P. On Documentation of Scientific Literature. 2nd ed. 187p. 1973. 17.50 (ISBN 0-408-70429-2). Shoe String.
Science Literature Indicators Study, 1975: Update of NFAIS-75-1. 75p. 1977. 15.00 (ISBN 0-942308-10-7). NFAIS.
Stephens, James. Francis Bacon & the Style of Science. LC 74-33514. xii, 188p. 1975. lib. bdg. 13.00x (ISBN 0-226-77260-8). U of Chicago Pr.
Turley, Raymond. Understanding the Structure of Scientific & Technical Literature: A Case-Study Approach. 173p. 1983. 16.00 (ISBN 0-85157-368-1, Pub. by Bingley England). Shoe String.

SCIENTIFIC LITERATURE SEARCHING
see Information Storage and Retrieval Systems–Science
SCIENTIFIC METHOD
see Science–Methodology
SCIENTIFIC RECREATIONS
see also Mathematical Recreations

Goldstein, Martin & Goldstein, Inge. How We Know: An Exploration of the Scientific Process. LC 80-39869. (Da Capo Quality Paperbacks Ser.). (Illus.). 376p. 1981. pap. 8.95 (ISBN 0-306-80140-X). Da Capo.
Perelman, Ya. Problemas y Experimentos Recreativos. (Span.). 423p. 1975. 8.95 (ISBN 0-8285-1698-7, Pub. by Mir Pubs USSR). Imported Pubns.
Vlasov, L. & Trifonov, D. Quimica Recreativa. (Span.). 349p. 1972. 5.45 (ISBN 0-8285-1470-4, Pub. by Mir Pubs USSR). Imported Pubns.
Ward, Alan. Tricks with Science, Words & Numbers. (Illus.). 96p. 1983. 14.95 (ISBN 0-7134-3653-0, Pub. by Batsford England). David & Charles.

SCIENTIFIC REPORTS
see Technical Reports
SCIENTIFIC RESEARCH
see Research
SCIENTIFIC RESEARCH AS A PROFESSION
see Research As a Profession
SCIENTIFIC RUSSIAN
see Russian Language–Technical Russian
SCIENTIFIC SATELLITES

Astrophysics & Space Science. The Scientific Satellite Programmed During the International Magnetospheric Study: Proceedings, Vol. 57. Knott, K. & Battrick, B., eds. LC 75-44353. 1976. lib. bdg. 58.00 (ISBN 90-277-0688-3, Pub. by Reidel Holland). Kluwer Academic.
Henderson, A. Sellers, ed. Satellite Sensing of a Cloudy Atmosphere: Observing the Third Planet. (Illus.). 336p. 1984. 40.00x (ISBN 0-85066-254-0). Taylor & Francis.
Houghton, J. T., et al, eds. The Study of the Ocean & the Land Surface from Satellites. (Philosophical Transactions of Royal Society: Series A, Vol. 309). (Illus.). 222p. 1984. Repr. text ed. 76.00x (ISBN 0-85403-211-8, Pub. by Royal Soc London). Scholium Intl.
Lala, P., ed. Satellite Perturbations & Orbital Determination. (Advances in Space Research: Vol. 1, No. 6). (Illus.). 95p. 1981. pap. 13.25 (ISBN 0-08-028380-2). Pergamon.
Measurements from Satellite Platforms. Incl. Annual Scientific Report on NAS5-11542, 1968-69. 1970. pap. 10.00x (ISBN 0-299-97030-2); Annual Scientific Report on NAS5-11542, 1969-70. 1971. pap. 7.50x (ISBN 0-299-97037-X); Annual Scientific Report on NAS5-11542, 1970-71. 1972. pap. 10.00x (ISBN 0-299-97041-8); Annual Scientific Report on NAS5-11542, 1971-72. 1972. pap. 7.50x (ISBN 0-299-97049-3); Annual Scientific Report on NAS5-21798, 1972-73. 1974. pap. 15.00x (ISBN 0-299-97052-3); Annual Scientific Report on NAS5-21798,1973-74. 1975. pap. 5.00x (ISBN 0-299-97055-8). pap. U of Wis Pr.
Multidisciplinary Studies of the Social, Economic, & Political Impact Resulting from Recent Advances in Satellite Meteorology, 6 vols. 1975. Vol. 1. pap. 15.00x (ISBN 0-299-97035-3); Vol. 2. pap. 15.00x (ISBN 0-299-97036-1); Vol. 3. pap. 10.00x (ISBN 0-299-97046-9); Vol. 4. pap. 10.00x (ISBN 0-299-97047-7); Vol. 5. pap. 10.00x (ISBN 0-299-97051-5); Vol. 6. pap. 10.00x (ISBN 0-299-97057-4). U of Wis Pr.
Robinson. Satellite Oceanography: An Introduction for Oceanographers & Remote-Sensing Scientist. (Marine Science Ser.). 1985. 59.95 (ISBN 0-470-20148-7). Wiley.
Satellites in Meteorology, Oceanography & Hydrology. (Eng., Fr., Span. & Rus.). 56p. 1982. pap. 5.00 (ISBN 92-63-10585-5, W533, WMO). Unipub.
Tanczer, T., ed. First FGGE Results from Satellites. (Advances in Space Research: Vol. 1, No. 4). (Illus.). 331p. 1981. pap. 44.00 (ISBN 0-08-027160-X). Pergamon.

SCIENTIFIC SOCIETIES
see also Learned Institutions and Societies; Science–Societies, etc.

American Council of Learned Societies, ed. Concise Dictionary of Scientific Biography. 1981. 70.00 (ISBN 0-684-16650-X, ScribR). Scribner.
Archibald, Raymond C. A Semicentennial History of the American Mathematical Society: Eighteen Hundred Eighty-Eight to Nineteen Hundred Thirty-Eight; with Biographies & Bibliographies Odents, 2 vols. Cohen, I. Bernard, ed. LC 79-7947. (Three Centuries of Science in America Ser.). (Illus.). 1980. Repr. of 1938 ed. Set. lib. bdg. 55.00x (ISBN 0-405-12528-3). Ayer Co Pubs.
Boehm, George A. & Groner, Alex. The Battelle Story: Science in the Service of Mankind. LC 81-14875. (Illus.). 170p. 1982. 10.00 (ISBN 0-935470-10-7). Battelle.
Brown, Harcourt. Scientific Organizations in Seventeenth Century France, 1620-1680. LC 66-27046. 1967. Repr. of 1934 ed. 8.50x (ISBN 0-8462-0974-8). Russell.
Camerini-Davalos, Rafael A., et al, eds. Atherogenesis, Vol. 275. (Annals of the New York Academy of Sciences). 1976. 47.00x (ISBN 0-89072-054-1). NY Acad Sci.
Crump, I. A. Australian Scientific Societies & Professional Associations. (3 microfiches). 1978. pap. 13.75 (ISBN 0-686-71823-2, C034, CSIRO). Unipub.
--Scientific & Technical Research Centres in Australia. 224p. 1981. pap. 9.00 (ISBN 0-686-71844-5, C036, CSIRO). Unipub.
Day, Stacey B., ed. What Is a Scientist? Memorial Issue for Professor Oscar Bodansky. (Biosciences Communications: Vol. 4, No. 5). 1978. pap. 8.25 (ISBN 3-8055-2967-8). S Karger.
Hilton, Ronald. The Scientific Institutions of Latin America. 804p. 1970. 12.00 (ISBN 0-912098-08-2). Cal Inst Intl St.
Kyed, James M. & Matarazzo, James M. Scientific, Engineering, & Medical Societies Publications in Print, 1980-81. 4th ed. 626p. 1981. 65.00x (ISBN 0-8352-1403-6). Bowker.
Lo, R. E., ed. Earth Observation & Remote Sensing by Satellites: Proceedings of the Symposium on Earth Observation & Remote Sensing by Satellites, Hannover, West Germany, 21 May 1982. 56p. 1983. pap. 41.25 (ISBN 0-08-031152-0). Pergamon.
Ornstein, Martha. The Role of Scientific Societies in the Seventeenth Century. LC 74-26282. (History, Philosophy & Sociology of Science Ser). 1975. Repr. 35.50x (ISBN 0-405-06609-0). Ayer Co Pubs.
Ritterbush, Philip C., ed. Scientific Institutions of the Future. LC 72-3811. (Prometheus Paperback Ser). 164p. 1972. pap. 3.95 (ISBN 0-87491-502-3). Acropolis.
Verrel, Barbara & Opitz, Helmut, eds. World Guide to Scientific Associations & Learned Societies. 947p. 1984. lib. bdg. 112.00 (ISBN 3-598-20522-8). K G Saur.
Watkins, Ralph J., ed. Directory of Selected Scientific Institutions in Mainland China. LC 76-138410. (Publications Ser.: No. 96). 1971. 19.50x (ISBN 0-8179-1961-9). Hoover Inst Pr.
Young, Margaret L., ed. Scientific & Technical Organizations & Agencies Directory. 1000p. 1985. 140.00x (ISBN 0-8103-2100-9). Gale.

SCIENTIFIC VOYAGES

see Scientific Expeditions

SCIENTIFIC WRITING

see Technical Writing

SCIENTISTS

see also Astronomers; Biologists; Botanists; Chemists; Ecologists; Geologists; Mathematicians; Naturalists; Ornithologists; Paleontologists; Physicists; Science–Vocational Guidance; Science Teachers; Women Scientists; Zoologists

Ahlfors, Lars V. Lars Valerian Ahlfors: Collected Papers, 2 Vols. 544p. 1982. text ed. 65.00X ea. Vol. 1 (ISBN 0-8176-3075-9). Vol. 2 (ISBN 0-8176-3076-7). Set. text ed. 130.00x (ISBN 0-8176-3077-5). Birkhauser.

Aris, Rutherford & Davis, H. Ted, eds. Springs of Scientific Creativity: Essays on Founders of Modern Science. LC 82-23715. (Illus.). 352p. 1983. 32.50x (ISBN 0-8166-1087-8). U of Minn Pr.

Arther, Richard O. The Scientific Investigator. (Illus.). 248p. 1976. photocopy ed. 19.75x (ISBN 0-398-00055-7). C C Thomas.

Badash, Lawrence. Kapitza, Rutherford & the Kremlin. LC 84-11822. (Illus.). 144p. 1985. 20.00x (ISBN 0-300-01465-1). Yale U Pr.

Badaway, M. K. Achieving Excellence in Managing Technical Professionals. 1986. price not set (ISBN 0-442-20480-9). Van Nos Reinhold.

Badawy, Michael K. Developing Managerial Skills in Engineers & Scientists. (Managerial Skill Development in Engineering & Science Ser.). 480p. 1982. 31.50 (ISBN 0-442-20481-7). Van Nos Reinhold.

Bedini, Silvio A. Thinkers & Tinkers: Early American Men of Science. (Illus.). 519p. 1983. Repr. of 1975 ed. 21.00 (ISBN 0-910845-19-0, 901). Landmark Ent.

Ben-David, Joseph. The Scientist's Role in Society: A Comparative Study with a New Introduction. LC 84-2758. 236p. 1984. 20.00x (ISBN 0-226-04227-8); pap. text ed. 8.95x (ISBN 0-226-04221-9). U. of Chicago Pr.

Beyerchen, Alan D. Scientists under Hitler: Politics & the Physics Community in the Third Reich. LC 77-2167. (Illus.). 1981. 33.00x (ISBN 0-300-01830-4); pap. 9.95x (ISBN 0-300-02758-3, Y-404). Yale U Pr.

Breeden, James O. Joseph Jones, M.D. Scientist of the Old South. LC 73-80462. (Illus.). 320p. 1975. 28.00x (ISBN 0-8131-1296-6). U Pr of Ky.

Bridges, Thomas C. & Tiltman, Hubert H. Master Minds of Modern Science. facs. ed. LC 68-57307. (Essay Index Reprint Ser.). 1931. 18.00 (ISBN 0-8369-0064-2). Ayer Co Pubs.

Broad, William & Wade, Nicholas. Betrayers of the Truth: Fraud & Deceit in the Halls of Science. 256p. 1983. pap. 6.95 (ISBN 0-671-49549-6, Touchstone). S&S.

Carwell, Hattie. Blacks in Science: Astrophysicist to Zoologist. (Illus.). 96p. 1977. 6.50 (ISBN 0-682-48911-5). Exposition Pr FL.

Cranefield, Paul F., ed. Two Great Scientists of the Nineteenth Century: Correspondence of Emil Du Bois-Reymond & Carl Ludwig. Ayed, Sabine L., tr. from Ger. LC 79-24140. 204p. 1982. text ed. 17.50x (ISBN 0-8018-2351-X). Johns Hopkins.

Crowther, James G. Famous American Men of Science. facs. ed. LC 69-18925. (Essay Index Reprint Ser). 1937. 27.50 (ISBN 0-8369-0040-5). Ayer Co Pubs.

--Founders of British Science: John Wilkins, Robert Boyle, John Ray, Christopher Wren, Robert Hooke, Isaac Newton. LC 82-2954. (Illus.). xii, 296p. 1982. Repr. of 1960 ed. lib. bdg. 42.50x (ISBN 0-313-23540-6, CRFO). GreenWood.

D. J. B. Copp. Register of Consulting Scientists. 6th ed. 100p. 1984. 27.00 (ISBN 0-9903000-0-5, Pub. by A Hilger England). Heyden.

Darmstaedter, Ludwig. Naturforscher und Erfinder. (Illus.). 1926. 16.00 (ISBN 0-384-10840-7). Johnson Repr.

De Kruif, Paul. Hunger Fighters. LC 67-32084. 1967. pap. 0.95 (ISBN 0-15-642430-4, Harv). HarBraceJ.

Dougherty, David E. From Technical Professional to Corporate Manager: A Guide to Career Transition. LC 84-7236. 279p. 1984. 19.95 (ISBN 0-471-80707-9, Pub. by Wiley-Interscience). Wiley.

Dyson, Freeman. Disturbing the Universe: A Life in Science. LC 78-20665. (Sloan Foundation Bk.). 1979. 12.95i (ISBN 0-06-011108-9, HarpT). Har-Row.

Eakin, Richard M. Great Scientists Speak Again. LC 74-22960. (Illus.). 128p. 1982. 12.95 (ISBN 0-520-04768-0). U. of Cal Pr.

Engstrand, Iris W. Spanish Scientists in the New World: The Eighteenth-Century Expeditions. LC 80-50863. (Illus.). 234p. 1981. 27.50x (ISBN 0-295-95764-6). U. of Wash Pr.

Fierz, Markus, ed. Girolamo Cardano (1501-1576) Physician, Natural Philosopher, Mathematician, Astrologer & Interpreter of Dreams. Niman, Helga, tr. from Ger. 242p. 1983. 29.95x (ISBN 0-8176-3057-0). Birkhauser.

Galton, Francis. Memories of My Life. LC 72-1639. Repr. of 1908 ed. 25.00 (ISBN 0-404-08128-2). AMS Pr.

Gellhorn, Walter. Security, Loyalty & Science. Repr. of 1950 ed. 27.00 (ISBN 0-384-18000-0). Johnson Repr.

George, William H. The Scientist in Action: A Scientific Study of His Methods. LC 74-26264. (History, Philosophy & Sociology of Science Ser). 1975. Repr. 27.50x (ISBN 0-405-06592-2). Ayer Co Pubs.

Gibson, Charles R. Heroes of the Scientific World. facs. ed. LC 79-117794. (Essay Index Reprint Ser.). 1913. 21.50 (ISBN 0-8369-1653-0). Ayer Co Pubs.

Gilpin, Robert G., Jr. American Scientists & Nuclear Weapons Policy. 1962. 35.00x (ISBN 0-691-07501-8). Princeton U Pr.

Goldman, Martin. The Demon in the Aether: The Story of James Clerk Maxwell, the Father of Modern Science. 320p. 1983. 30.00 (ISBN 0-9960042-2-X, Pub. by A Hilger England). Heyden.

Grazia, Alfred de. Cosmic Heretics: A Personal History of Attempts to Establish & Resist Theories of Quantavolution & Catastrophe in the Natural & Human Sciences, 1962-1983. (Quantavolution Ser.). 396p. 1984. pap. 23.00X (ISBN 0-940268-08-6). Metron Pubns.

Guinagh, Kevin. Inspired Amateurs. facs. ed. LC 67-26746. (Essay Index Reprint Ser). 1937. 18.00 (ISBN 0-8369-0500-8). Ayer Co Pubs.

Gumpert, Martin. Trail-Blazers of Science: Life Stories of Some Half-Forgotten Pioneers of Modern Research. facs. ed. Shuman, Edwin L., tr. LC 68-29212. (Essay Index Reprint Ser). 1968. Repr. of 1936 ed. 18.00 (ISBN 0-8369-0501-6). Ayer Co Pubs.

Gvishiani, D. M., et al. Scientific Intelligentsia in the U. S. S. R. Structure & Dynamics of Personnel. Sayers, Jane, tr. from Russ. 1976. 12.95x (ISBN 0-8464-0820-1). Beekman Pubs.

Hagstrom, Warren O. Scientific Community. LC 74-18379. (Arcturus Books Paperbacks). 319p. 1975. pap. 4.25 (ISBN 0-8093-0720-0). S Ill U Pr.

Hammond, D. B. Stories of Scientific Discovery. facs. ed. LC 74-76901. (Essay Index Reprint Ser). 1923. 17.00 (ISBN 0-8369-0015-4). Ayer Co Pubs.

Hart, Ivor B. Makers of Science. facs. ed. LC 68-8469. (Essay Index Reprint Ser.). 1923. 16.00 (ISBN 0-8369-0076-6). Ayer Co Pubs.

Ho, Ching-Ju. Personnel Studies of Scientists in the United States. LC 76-176867. (Columbia University. Teachers College. Contributions to Education: No. 298). Repr. of 1928 ed. 22.50 (ISBN 0-404-55298-6). AMS Pr.

Hoskin, Michael. Mind of the Scientist: Imaginary Conversations with Galileo, Newton, Herschel, Darwin, & Pasteur. LC 72-164020. (Illus.). 1972. 7.95 (ISBN 0-8008-5248-6). Taplinger.

Ireland, Norma O. Index to Scientists of the World from Ancient to Modern Times: Biographies & Portraits. LC 62-13662. (The Useful Reference Ser. of Library Bks: Vol. 90). 1962. lib. bdg. 13.00x (ISBN 0-87305-090-8). Faxon.

Johnson, Diane. Edwin Broun Fred: Scientist, Administrator, Gentleman. (Illus.). 192p. 1974. 20.00x (ISBN 0-299-06580-4). U. of Wis Pr.

Kornhauser, William. Scientists in Industry: Conflict & Accommodation. LC 82-1001. (A Publication of the Institute of Industrial Relations Ser.). xii, 230p. 1982. Repr. of 1962 ed. lib. bdg. 32.50x (ISBN 0-313-23491-4, KOSC). Greenwood.

Lane, Henry H. Henry Higgins Lane (1878-1965) Biographical Data. (Miscellaneous Publications Ser.: No. 48). 8p. 1967. 1.25 (ISBN 0-317-04777-9). U. of KS Mus Nat Hist.

Leidecker, Kurt F. Scientific German by the Method of Discovery. 1947. 10.95x (ISBN 0-913298-67-0). S F Vanni.

Lenard, Philipp E. Great Men of Science. Hatfield, H. Stafford, tr. LC 74-105026. (Essay Index Reprint Ser.). 1933. 25.00 (ISBN 0-8369-1614-X). Ayer Co Pubs.

McGraw-Hill. Modern Scientists & Engineers, 3 vols. 1980. 135.00 (ISBN 0-07-045266-0). McGraw.

Mahoney, Michael J. The Scientist As Subject: The Psychological Imperative. LC 76-5878. 264p. 1976. prof ref 19.50 (ISBN 0-88410-505-9); pap. text ed. 14.95 prof ref (ISBN 0-88410-514-8). Ballinger Pub.

Medawar, P. B. Advice to a Young Scientist. LC 79-1676. 128p. 1981. pap. 5.72i (ISBN 0-06-090810-6, CN 810, CN). Har-Row.

Miller, Howard S. Dollars for Research: Science & Its Patrons in Nineteenth-Century America. LC 71-103291. (Illus.). 276p. 1970. 20.00x (ISBN 0-295-95058-7). U. of Wash Pr.

Neressian, Nancy J. Faraday to Einstein: Constructing Meaning in Scientific Theories. 1984. lib. bdg. 38.00 (ISBN 90-247-2997-1, Pub. by Martinus Nijhoff Netherlands). Kluwer Academic.

O'Brien, Charles F. Sir William Dawson: A Life in Science & Religion. LC 71-153381. (Memoirs Ser.: Vol. 84). 1971. pap. 7.00 (ISBN 0-87169-084-5). Am Philos.

Pelz, Donald C. & Andrews, Frank M. Scientists in Organizations: Productive Climates for Research & Development. rev. ed. LC 76-620038. 400p. 1976. 18.00x (ISBN 0-87944-208-5). Inst Soc Res.

Proceedings of the Association of Orthodox Jewish Scientists, Vol. 6. 1982. pap. 8.95 (ISBN 0-87306-225-6). Feldheim.

Proctor, Richard A. Wages & Wants of Science-Workers. 270p. 1970. Repr. of 1876 ed. 28.50x (ISBN 0-7146-1627-3, F Cass Co). Biblio Dist.

Pupin, Michael. From Immigrant to Inventor. Cohen, I. Bernard, ed. LC 79-7983. (Three Centuries of Science in America Ser.). (Illus.). 1980. Repr. of 1930 ed. lib. bdg. 34.50x (ISBN 0-405-12565-8). Ayer Co Pubs.

Raistrick, Arthur. Quakers in Science & Industry. LC 68-18641. (Illus.). Repr. of 1950 ed. 35.00x (ISBN 0-678-05622-6). Kelley.

Reichenbach, Hans. From Copernicus to Einstein. Winn, Ralph B., tr. 10.25 (ISBN 0-8446-5805-7). Peter Smith.

Roe, Anne. The Making of a Scientist. LC 73-15059. 244p. 1974. Repr. of 1953 ed. lib. bdg. 22.50x (ISBN 0-8371-7151-2, ROMS). Greenwood.

Rotblat, J., ed. Scientists, the Arms Race & Disarmament. 325p. 1982. 24.95x. Taylor & Francis.

Sarton, George. Six Wings: Men of Science in the Renaissance. LC 56-11998. (Illus.). 336p. 1957. 19.50x (ISBN 0-253-35275-4). Ind U Pr.

Sas, Louis F., ed. Grands Savants Francais: Lectures Scientifiques. (Fr.,., Illus., Orig.). 1961. pap. text ed. 3.95x (ISBN 0-89197-189-0). Irvington.

Scientific Manpower Commission. Guide to Data on Scientists & Engineers. 288p. 1984. write for info. Sci Manpower.

Selected Works of Joel Asaph Allen. LC 73-17843. (Natural Sciences in America Ser.). (Illus.). 976p. 1974. Repr. 49.00x (ISBN 0-405-05765-2). Ayer Co Pubs.

Selye, Hans. From Dream to Discovery. LC 74-26290. (History, Philosophy & Sociology of Science Ser). 1975. Repr. 32.00x (ISBN 0-405-06616-3). Ayer Co Pubs.

Shapiro, Stanley J. Exploring Careers in Science. (Careers in Depth Ser.). (Illus.). 140p. 1983. lib. bdg. 8.97 (ISBN 0-8239-0535-7). Rosen Group.

Shipp, James F. Russian-English Dictionary of Surnames: Important Names from Science & Technology. (Rus. & Eng.). xvi, 317p. (Orig.). 1981. pap. text ed. 18.50x (ISBN 0-917564-10-3). Wychwood Pr.

Shute, Michael. The Scientific Work of John Winthrop: An Original Anthology. Cohen, I. Bernard, ed. LC 79-8005. (Three Centuries of Science in America Ser.). (Illus.). 1980. lib. bdg. 23.00x (ISBN 0-405-12593-3). Ayer Co Pubs.

Simpson. Introductory Electronics for Scientists & Engineers. 2nd ed. 1985. write for info. (ISBN 0-205-08377-3, 738377). Allyn.

Sindermann, Carl J. The Joy of Science: Excellence & Its Rewards. 256p. 1985. (full discount avail.) 16.95 (ISBN 0-306-42035-X, Pub. by Plenum Pr). Plenum Pub.

--Winning the Games Scientists Play. LC 82-12225. (Illus.). 304p. 1982. (full discount avail.) 15.95 (ISBN 0-306-41075-3, Plenum Pr). Plenum Pub.

Spencer, Baldwin. Spencer's Last Journey, Being the Journal of an Expedition to Tierra Del Fuego. LC 76-44790. Repr. of 1931 ed. 27.50 (ISBN 0-404-15972-9). AMS Pr.

Strong, C. L. Projects for the Amateur Scientist. pap. 7.95 (ISBN 0-671-20747-4, Fireside). S&S.

Teller, Edward. Reluctant Revolutionary. LC 64-25274. 85p. 1964. 8.00x (ISBN 0-8262-0032-X). U. of Mo Pr.

Teller, Edward, et al. Education of the Scientist in a Free Society. Drought, A. Bernard, ed. 1959. pap. 7.95 (ISBN 0-87462-412-6). Marquette.

Theodorides, J., ed. Un Grand Medecin et Biologiste Cashmir - Joseph Davaine. 1969. pap. 50.00 (ISBN 0-08-012366-X). Pergamon.

Thomas, Henry & Thomas, Dana L. Living Adventures in Science. facsimile ed. LC 77-167428. (Essay Index Reprint Ser). Repr. of 1954 ed. 20.00 (ISBN 0-8369-2573-4). Ayer Co Pubs.

Turkevich, John. Soviet Men of Science. Blanshei, J., et al, eds. LC 75-19267. 441p. 1975. Repr. of 1963 ed. lib. bdg. 45.00x (ISBN 0-8371-8246-8, TUSM). Greenwood.

Van Sertima, Ivan. Blacks In Science: Ancient & Modern. 300p. (Orig.). 1983. pap. 14.95x (ISBN 0-87855-941-8). Transaction Bks.

Velikovsky, et al. Scientists Confront Scientists Who Confront Velikovsky. 2nd ed. Greenberg, Lewis M., et al, eds. (Illus., Orig.). pap. 5.00x (ISBN 0-917994-06-X). Kronos Pr.

Visher, Stephen S. Scientists Starred 1903-1943 in American Men of Science. LC 74-26301. (History, Philosophy & Sociology of Science Ser). 1975. Repr. 42.00x (ISBN 0-405-06625-2). Ayer Co Pubs.

Walsh, James J. Catholic Churchmen in Science, First Ser. facs. ed. LC 68-16985. (Essay Index Reprint Ser). 1906. 19.00 (ISBN 0-8369-0971-2). Ayer Co Pubs.

--Catholic Churchmen in Science, Second Ser. facs. ed. LC 67-22126. (Essay Index Reprint Ser.). 1909. 19.00 (ISBN 0-8369-1387-6). Ayer Co Pubs.

--Catholic Churchmen in Science. Third Ser. facs. ed. LC 67-22126. (Essay Index Reprint Ser). 1917. 19.00 (ISBN 0-8369-0972-0). Ayer Co Pubs.

Watson, David L. Scientists Are Human. LC 74-26305. (History, Philosophy & Sociology of Science Ser). 1975. Repr. 24.50x (ISBN 0-405-06629-5). Ayer Co Pubs.

Weber, Robert L. Pioneers of Science: Nobel Prize Winners in Physics. Lenihan, J. M., ed. 285p. 1980. 23.00 (ISBN 0-9960020-1-4, Pub. by A Hilger England). Heyden.

White, John A. Values & Scientists. 88p. (Orig.). 1984. lib. bdg. 19.00 (ISBN 0-8191-3584-4); pap. text ed. 7.50 (ISBN 0-8191-3585-2). U Pr of Amer.

Wilson, Grove. Great Men of Science: Their Lives & Discoveries. 397p. 1981. Repr. of 1929 ed. lib. bdg. 30.00 (ISBN 0-89760-923-9). Telegraph Bks.

Young, Thomas. Miscellaneous Works of the Late Thomas Young, 3 vols. Repr. of 1855 ed. Set. 125.00 (ISBN 0-384-40420-0). Johnson Repr.

Zuckerman, Harriet. Scientific Elite: Nobel Laureates in the United States. LC 76-26444. (Illus.). 1979. 14.95 (ISBN 0-02-935760-8); pap. text ed. 7.95 (ISBN 0-02-935880-9). Free Pr.

SCIENTISTS–BIOGRAPHY

Abbott, David, ed. The Biographical Dictionary of Scientists: Astronomers. LC 84-9236. (The Biographical Dictionary of Scientists Ser.). 210p. 1984. 18.95x (ISBN 0-911745-80-7). P Bedrick Bks.

--The Biographical Dictionary of Scientists: Biologists. LC 84-10972. (The Biographical Dictionary of Scientists Ser.). 188p. 1984. 18.95x (ISBN 0-911745-82-3). P Bedrick Bks.

--The Biographical Dictionary of Scientists: Chemists. LC 84-9284. (The Biographical Dictionary of Scientists Ser.). 210p. 1984. 18.95x (ISBN 0-911745-81-5). P Bedrick Bks.

--The Biographical Dictionary of Scientists: Physicists. LC 84-9211. (The Biographical Dictionary of Scientists Ser.). 220p. 1984. 18.95x (ISBN 0-911745-79-3). P Bedrick Bks.

Alexander, E. Curtis. Cheikh Anta Diop: An African Scientist. LC 84-81324. (Pan African Internationalist Handbook Ser.). 84p. (Orig.). 1984. pap. 6.95 (ISBN 0-938818-07-4). ECA Assoc.

American Council of Learned Societies, ed. Concise Dictionary of Scientific Biography. 1981. 70.00 (ISBN 0-684-16650-X, ScribR). Scribner.

Asimov, Isaac. Asimov's Biographical Encyclopedia of Science & Technology. 2nd. rev. ed. LC 81-47861. (Illus.). 984p. 1982. 29.95 (ISBN 0-385-17771-2). Doubleday.

Baumler, Ernest. Paul Ehrlich, Scientist for Life: A Biography. Edwards, Grant, tr. from Ger. 304p. 1984. text ed. 39.50x (ISBN 0-8419-0837-0). Holmes & Meier.

Bellman, Richard. Eye of the Hurricane: An Autobiography. 300p. 1984. 33.00x (ISBN 9971-966-00-X, Pub. by World Sci Singapore); pap. 17.00x (ISBN 9971-966-01-8). Taylor & Francis.

Box, Joan F. R. A. Fisher: The Life of a Scientist. LC 78-1668. (Probability & Mathematical Statistics Ser.). 512p. 1978. 45.50x (ISBN 0-471-09300-9, Pub. by Wiley-Interscience). Wiley.

Brown, Percy. American Martyrs to Science Through the Roentgen Rays. (Illus.). 276p. 1936. photocopy ed. 27.50x (ISBN 0-398-04223-3). C C Thomas.

Butzer, P. L. & Feher, F., eds. E. B. Christoffel: The Influence of His Work in Mathematics & the Physical Sciences. (Illus.). 656p. 1981. 52.95x (ISBN 0-8176-1162-2). Birkhauser.

Crowther, James G. Famous American Men of Science. facs. ed. LC 69-18925. (Essay Index Reprint Ser). 1937. 27.50 (ISBN 0-8369-0040-5). Ayer Co Pubs.

Defries, Amelia D. Pioneers of Science. facs. ed. LC 74-117782. (Essay Index Reprint Ser). 1928. 17.00 (ISBN 0-8369-1646-8). Ayer Co Pubs.

Downs, Robert B. Landmarks in Science: Hippocrates to Carson. LC 82-154. 305p. 1982. lib. bdg. 23.50 (ISBN 0-87287-295-5). Libs Unl.

Dunlap, Orrin E. Radio's One Hundred Men of Science. facs. ed. LC 70-128235. (Essay Index Reprint Ser). 1944. 25.00 (ISBN 0-8369-1916-5). Ayer Co Pubs.
Dyson, Freeman. Disturbing the Universe. LC 78-20665. 304p. 1981. pap. 6.68 (ISBN 0-06-090771-1, CN 771, CN). Har-Row.
--Innenansichten: Erinnerungen in die Zukunft. Zehnder, Jeanette, tr. from Eng. (Science & Society Ser.: No. 38). Orig. Title: Disturbing the Universe. (Ger.). 288p. 1981. 19.95 (ISBN 0-8176-1200-9). Birkhauser.
Elliott, Clark A. Biographical Dictionary of American Science: The Seventeenth Through the Nineteenth Centuries. LC 78-4292. 1979. lib. bdg. 60.50x (ISBN 0-313-20419-5, EAS/). Greenwood.
Feldman, Anthony & Ford, Peter. Scientists & Inventors. (Horizons of Knowledge Ser.). (Illus.). 1979. 24.95 (ISBN 0-87196-410-4). Facts on File.
Force, James E. William Whiston: Honest Newtonian. (Illus.). 240p. 1985. 37.50 (ISBN 0-521-26590-8). Cambridge U Pr.
Gillispie, Charles C., ed. Dictionary of Scientific Biography, Supple. I, Vol. 15. LC 69-18090. 1978. 55.00 (ISBN 0-684-14779-3, ScribR). Scribner.
--Dictionary of Scientific Biography: Compact Edition, 8 vols. LC 69-18090. 1970-1980. Set. text ed. 750.00 (ISBN 0-684-16962-2, ScribR); text ed. 80.00 ea. Scribner.
Green, Joseph R., ed. English Men of Science, 7 vols. Repr. of 1908 ed. Set. 125.45 (ISBN 0-404-07890-7). AMS Pr.
Henderson, James S., et al. A Notable Career in Finding Out. LC 77-160731. (Illus.). 48p. 1971. 5.00x (ISBN 0-87470-016-7). Rockefeller.
Hodges, Andrew. Alan Turing: The Enigma. 608p. 1984. pap. 10.95 (ISBN 0-671-52809-2, Touchstone Bks). S&S.
Howard, John E. Musings & Reminiscences of A Pseudo-Scientist. 1985. 6.00 (ISBN 0-682-40260-5). Exposition Pr FL.
Hsiao, T. C., ed. Who's Who in Computer Education & Research: U. S. Edition. U. S. ed. LC 74-18169. 330p. 1975. 35.00x (ISBN 0-912291-01-X). Sci & Tech Pr.
Johnson, Kenneth R. The Fulcanelli Phenomenon. 334p. 1981. 35.00x (ISBN 0-85978-051-1, Pub. by Spearman England). State Mutual Bk.
Jordon, David S., ed. Leading American Men of Science. LC 72-94315. (The American Scientific Community, 1790-1920 Ser.). (Illus.). 1973. Repr. of 1910 ed. lib. bdg. 37.00 (ISBN 0-8420-1674-0). Scholarly Res Inc.
Kueschner's Deutscher Gelehrtenkalender 1982, 3 vols. 14th ed. 1982. Set. 180.00x (ISBN 3-11-008558-5). De Gruyter.
Lambe, John. A Briefe Description of the Notorious Life of J. Lambe. LC 76-57394. (English Experience Ser.: No. 811). 1977. Repr. of 1628 ed. lib. bdg. 3.50 (ISBN 90-221-0811-2). Walter J Johnson.
Lenard, Philipp. Great Men of Science: A History of Scientific Progress. Hathfield, H. Stanfford, tr. from Ger. 1979. Repr. of 1933 ed. lib. bdg. 40.00 (ISBN 0-89987-500-9). Darby Bks.
Lipset, David. Gregory Bateson: The Legacy of a Scientist. LC 81-70493. 372p. 1982. pap. 12.95x (ISBN 0-8070-4663-9, BP 637). Beacon Pr.
McPhee, John. The Curve of Binding Energy. 224p. 1974. 10.95 (ISBN 0-374-13373-5); pap. 4.95 (ISBN 0-374-51598-0). FS&G.
Manning, Kenneth R. Black Apollo of Science: The Life of Ernest Everett Just. (Illus.). 1983. 29.95 (ISBN 0-19-503299-3); pap. 8.95 (ISBN 0-19-503498-8, GB770, Galaxy Bks.). Oxford U Pr.
Metchnikoff, Olga. Life of Elie Metchnikoff. LC 72-7248. (Select Bibliographies Reprint Ser.). 1972. Repr. of 1921 ed. 22.00 (ISBN 0-8369-6949-9). Ayer Co Pubs.
Millikan, Robert A. The Autobiography of Robert A. Millikan. Cohen, I. Bernard, ed. LC 79-7975. (Three Centuries of Science in America Ser.). (Illus.). 1980. Repr. of 1950 ed. lib. bdg. 26.50x (ISBN 0-405-12558-5). Ayer Co Pubs.
Moulton, Forest R. & Schifferes, Justus J., eds. The Autobiography of Science. 748p. 1980. 25.00x (ISBN 0-7195-0979-3, Pub. by Murray Pubs England). State Mutual Bk.
Muller, Herbert J. The Uses of the Past: Profiles of Former Scientists. 408p. 1985. pap. 11.95 (ISBN 0-8052-0783-X). Schocken.
National Academy of Sciences. Biographical Memoirs, Vol. 44. xii, 370p. 1974. 10.00 (ISBN 0-309-02238-X). Natl Acad Pr.
--Biographical Memoirs, Vol. 45. vii, 465p. 1974. 10.00 (ISBN 0-309-02239-8). Natl Acad Pr.
--Biographical Memoirs, Vol. 50. 416p. 1979. text ed. 10.00 (ISBN 0-309-02549-4). Natl Acad Pr.
--Biographical Memoirs, Vol. 51. 418p. 1980. text ed. 10.00 (ISBN 0-309-02888-4). Natl Acad Pr.
--Biographical Memoirs, Vol. 52. 495p. 1980. text ed. 10.00 (ISBN 0-309-03099-4). Natl Acad Pr.
--Biographical Memoirs, Vol. 53. 400p. 1982. text ed. 10.00 (ISBN 0-309-03287-3). Natl Acad Pr.
--Biographical Memoirs, Vol. 54. 418p. 1983. text ed. 13.00 (ISBN 0-309-03391-8). Natl Acad Pr.
Osterbrock, Donald E. James E. Keeler, Pioneer American Astrophysicist: And the Early Development of American Astrophysics. (Illus.). 420p. 1985. 39.50 (ISBN 0-521-26582-7). Cambridge U Pr.
Paul, Charles B. Science & Immortality: The Eloges of the Paris Academy of Sciences (1699-1791) LC 80-17208. 250p. 1980. 24.50x (ISBN 0-520-03986-6). U of Cal Pr.
Pelletier, Paul A. Prominent Scientists: An Index to Collective Biographies. 2nd ed. 400p. 1985. lib. bdg. 34.95 (ISBN 0-918212-78-2). Neal-Schuman.
Putilov, B. Nikolai Miklouho-Maclay: Traveller, Scientist, & Humanist. 239p. 1982. 6.95 (ISBN 0-8285-2351-7, Pub. by Progress Pubs USSR). Imported Pubns.
Rossi, Aldo. A Scientific Autobiography. Venuti, Lawrence, tr. from Ital. (Illus.). 128p. 1981. pap. 9.95 (ISBN 0-262-68041-6). MIT Pr.
Santilli, Ruggero M. Il Grande Grido: Ethical Probe on Einstein Followers in the U. S. A.-An Insider's View. (Illus.). 356p. 1984. 19.95 (ISBN 0-931753-00-7). Alpha Pub Trust.
Shine, Ian B. & Wrobel, Sylvia. Thomas Hunt Morgan: Pioneer of Genetics. LC 76-40551. (Illus.). 188p. 1976. 15.00x (ISBN 0-8131-0095-X). U Pr of Ky.
Stamp, Tom & Stamp, Cordelia. William Scoresby, Arctic Scientist. 1981. 35.00x (ISBN 0-686-98238-X, Pub. by Caedmon of Whitby). State Mutual Bk.
Stenzel, Franz. Cleveland Rockwell: Scientist & Artist, Eighteen Thirty-Seven to Nineteen Hundred Seven. LC 72-80732. (Illus.). 158p. 1972. pap. 9.95 (ISBN 0-87595-037-X). Oreg Hist Soc.
Tidcombe, Marianne. The Bookbindings of T. J. Cobden-Sanderson: A Study in His Work, 1884-1893, Based on His Time Book in the British Library. (Illus.). 420p. 1984. 90.00 (ISBN 0-7123-0027-9, Pub. by British Lib). Longwood Pub Group.
Urdang Assoc., ed. Biographical Encyclopedia of Scientists. 936p. 1981. lib. bdg. 80.00 (ISBN 0-87196-396-5). Facts on File.
Van Iterson, G. & Den Dooren, L. E. Martinus Willem Beijerinck: His Life & Work. 1983. 45.00x (ISBN 0-910239-02-9). Sci Tech Inc.
Who's Who in Frontier Science & Technology. 2nd, rev. ed. 800p. 1985. 94.00x (ISBN 0-8379-5702-8). Marquis.
Who's Who in Science in Europe. 4th ed. 2500p. 1984. Set. 500.00 (ISBN 0-582-90109-X). Taylor & Francis.
Who's Who of British Scientists 1980-81. 650p. 1981. 75.00x (ISBN 0-312-87433-2). St Martin.
Williams, Trevor I., ed. A Biographical Dictionary of Scientists. 3rd ed. 674p. 1982. 29.95x (ISBN 0-470-27326-7). Halsted Pr.
Wilson, Grove. Human Side of Science. LC 72-1286. (Essay Index Reprint Ser.). Repr. of 1929 ed. 25.00 (ISBN 0-8369-2877-6). Ayer Co Pubs.
Youmans, William J. & Sterling, Keir B., eds. Pioneers of Science in America: Sketches of Their Lives & Scientific Work. rev. ed. LC 77-83845. (Biologists & Their World Ser.). (Illus.). 1978. Repr. of 1896 ed. lib. bdg. 46.50x (ISBN 0-405-10743-9). Ayer Co Pubs.

SCIENTISTS–CORRESPONDENCE, REMINISCENCES, ETC.

Abrahams, Harold J. & Savin, Marion B., eds. Selections from the Scientific Correspondence of Elihu Thomson. 1971. 35.00x (ISBN 0-262-01034-8). MIT Pr.
Barrett, Eric C. & Fisher, David, eds. Scientists Who Believe: Twenty-One Tell Their Own Stories. 1984. pap. 4.50 (ISBN 0-8024-7634-1). Moody.
Bradley, James. Miscellaneous Works & Correspondence of James Bradley & Supplement. Rigaud, Stephen P., ed. Repr. of 1832 ed. 84.00 (ISBN 0-686-86229-5). Johnson Repr.
Chargaff, Erwin. Heraclitean Fire: Sketches from a Life before Nature. LC 77-95216. 252p. 1978. 14.00x (ISBN 0-87470-029-9). Rockefeller.
Clarke, Arthur C. Ascent to Orbit: A Scientific Autobiography. LC 83-26039. 226p. 1984. text ed. 21.50 (ISBN 0-471-87910-X). Wiley.
Haskins, Caryl P., ed. The Search for Understanding: Selected Writings of Scientists of the Carnegie Institution. (Illus.). 330p. 1967. 5.00 (ISBN 0-87279-954-9). Carnegie Inst.
Kistiakowsky, George B. A Scientist at the White House. 1976. 27.50x (ISBN 0-674-79496-6). Harvard U Pr.
Krebs, Hans. Reminiscences & Reflections. (Illus.). 1982. 21.95x (ISBN 0-19-854702-1). Oxford U Pr.
Madden, Charles F., ed. Talks with Scientists. LC 68-10730. 224p. 1968. 5.85x (ISBN 0-8093-0298-5). S Ill U Pr.
Meyenn, K. V., ed. Wolfgang Pauli: Scientific Correspondence with Bohr, Einstein, Heisenberg a. o. Part II: 1930-1939. (Sources in the History of Mathematics & Physical Sciences Ser.: Vol. 6). 800p. 1985. 110.00 (ISBN 0-387-13609-6). Springer-Verlag.
Newton, Isaac. Correspondence of Isaac Newton, 4 vols. Turnbull, H. W. & Scott, J. F., eds. 1961. 74.50 ea.; Vol. 1. (ISBN 0-521-05812-0); Vol. 2. (ISBN 0-521-05813-9); Vol. 4. (ISBN 0-521-05815-5). Cambridge U Pr.
--The Correspondence, Seventeen Hundred Nine to Seventeen Thirteen, Vol. 5. Hall, A. R. & Tilling, Laura, eds. 1975. 110.00 (ISBN 0-521-08721-X). Cambridge U Pr.
Priestley, Joseph. Memoirs of Dr. Joseph Priestley, to the Year 1795, Written by Himself, with a Continuation,... LC 78-3422. 1978. Repr. of 1806 ed. lib. bdg. 60.00 (ISBN 0-527-72730-X). Kraus Repr.
Spencer, Baldwin. Spencer's Scientific Correspondence with Sir J. G. Frazer & Others. Marett, R. R. & Penniman, T. K., eds. LC 76-44792. Repr. of 1932 ed. 19.50 (ISBN 0-404-15973-7). AMS Pr.
Tarbell, D. Stanley & Tarbell, Ann T., eds. Roger Adams: Scientist & Statesman. LC 81-17625. 1981. 13.95x (ISBN 0-8412-0598-1); pap. 9.95. Am Chemical.
Weintraub, Pamela, ed. The Omni Interviews. LC 83-26501. 336p. 1984. 17.95 (ISBN 0-89919-215-7); pap. 9.95 (ISBN 0-89919-269-6). Ticknor & Fields.

SCIENTISTS–DIRECTORIES

Arnett, Ross H., Jr., ed. The Naturalists' Directory & Almanac: International Supplement, 1980-1981. 43rd ed. 310p. (Orig.). 1980. pap. 5.00x (ISBN 0-916846-11-3). Flora & Fauna.
International Directory of Marine Scientists, 1977. 1978. pap. 21.75 (ISBN 92-5-000367-6, F1311, FAO). Unipub.
Jaques Cattell Press, ed. American Men & Women of Science: Physical & Biological Sciences, 7 vols. 15th ed. 7010p. 1982. Set. 495.00 (ISBN 0-8352-1413-3); 85.00 ea. Bowker.
Lewis, Mary J., ed. Directory of North American Fisheries Scientists. 450p. 1984. pap. text ed. 30.00 (ISBN 0-913235-18-0). Am Fisheries Soc.
The Naturalist's Directory. 43rd ed. 1978. 12.95 (ISBN 0-916846-02-4). World Natural Hist.
Varley, Allen, ed. Who's Who in Ocean & Freshwater Science. LC 79-301729. pap. 84.00 (ISBN 0-317-27839-8, 2025251). Bks Demand UMI.
Who's Who in Science in Europe, 4 vols. 3rd ed. LC 74-165291. 2500p. 1978. Set. 600.00x (ISBN 0-85280-211-0). Intl Pubns Serv.
Young, M. E., ed. International Directory of Conchologists, 1982-83. LC 73-91404. 1982-83. 5.00 (ISBN 0-915792-06-3). Shell Cab.

SCIENTISTS–EMPLOYMENT

Guidelines to Professional Employment for Engineers & Scientists. 1978. 1.00x (ISBN 0-87615-162-4, 511-78). AAES.
Kipp, E. M. People Aspects of Research & Development Management: Attracting & Retaining R & D Personnel. 116p. 1967. 37.25 (ISBN 0-677-40040-3). Gordon.
Schmidt, Terry D. Managing Your Career Success: Practical Strategies for Engineers, Scientists & Technical Managers. 216p. 1982. 20.95 (ISBN 0-534-97948-3); pap. 12.95, 1983 (ISBN 0-534-02993-0). Lifetime Learn.

SCIENTISTS–PSYCHOLOGY

Eslea, Brian. Fathering the Unthinkable: Masculinity, Scientists & the Nuclear Arms Race. 230p. (Orig.). 1983. pap. 8.95 (ISBN 0-86104-391-X, Pub by Pluto Pr). Longwood Pub Group.
Grover, Sonja C. Toward a Psychology of the Scientist: Implications of Psychological Research for Contemporary Philosophy of Science. LC 80-6092. 102p. (Orig.). lib. bdg. 18.25 (ISBN 0-8191-1574-6); pap. text ed. 8.50 (ISBN 0-8191-1575-4). U Pr of Amer.
Hilts, Philip. Scientific Temperaments. 1982. 15.95 (ISBN 0-671-22533-2). S&S.
Maslow, Abraham H. Psychology of Science: A Reconnaissance. LC 66-11479. 190p. 1966. pap. 3.95 (ISBN 0-89526-972-4). Regnery-Gateway.

SCINTILLATION COUNTERS

Akimov, Yu K. Scintillation Counters in High Energy Physics. 1965. 49.00 (ISBN 0-12-047450-6). Acad Pr.
Horrocks, D. L., ed. Organic Scintillators. LC 68-23113. 422p. 1968. 119.25 (ISBN 0-677-12860-6). Gordon.
Horrocks, Donald L. & Peng, Chin-Tzu, eds. Organic Scintillators & Liquid Scintillation Counting. LC 77-137625. 1971. 73.50 (ISBN 0-12-356250-3). Acad Pr.
Kobayashi, Yutaka & Maudsley, David V. Biological Applications of Liquid Scintillation Counting. 1974. 44.00 (ISBN 0-12-417250-4). Acad Pr.
Peng, Chin-Tzu, et al. Liquid Scintillation Counting: Recent Applications & Development, Vol. 2: Two Sample Preparation & Applications. LC 80-10906. 1980. 45.00 (ISBN 0-12-549902-7). Acad Pr.
Peng, Chin-Tzu, et al, eds. Liquid Scintillation Counting: Recent Applications & Development, Vol. 1: Physical Aspects. LC 80-10906. 1980. 39.50 (ISBN 0-12-549901-9). Acad Pr.
Scintillation Detectors. (Advanced Health Physics Training Ser.). (Illus.). 170p. 1983. Set. training materials 1700.00x (ISBN 0-87683-192-7); looseleaf materials 45.00x (ISBN 0-87683-193-5); lesson plans 1250.00x (ISBN 0-87683-194-3); transparencies 250.00x (ISBN 0-87683-195-1); question bank 625.00x (ISBN 0-87683-196-X). G P Courseware.
Symposium on Liquid Scintillation Counting. Liquid Scintillation Counting: Proceedings of a Symposium on Liquid Scintillation Counting, Bath, England, September 13-16, 1977, Vol. 5. Crook, M. A. & Johnson, P., eds. pap. 29.00 (ISBN 0-317-29406-7, 2024011). Bks Demand UMI.

SCINTILLATION SPECTROMETRY

Calhoun, Thomas O. Henry Vaughan: The Achievement of Silex Scintillans. LC 79-51851. 272p. 1981. 25.00 (ISBN 0-87413-165-0). U Delaware Pr.
Mandell, Charles H. Scintillation Camera Lung Imaging: An Anatomic Atlas & Guide. LC 76-16057. 208p. 1976. 70.50 (ISBN 0-8089-0960-6, 792660). Grune.
Noujaim, A. A., et al, eds. Liquid Scintillation: Science & Technology. 1976. 45.00 (ISBN 0-12-522350-1). Acad Pr.
Shafroth, Stephen, ed. Scintillation Spectroscopy of Gamma Radiation. 454p. 1967. 85.75x (ISBN 0-677-11070-7). Gordon.

SCORPIONS

Francke, Oscar F. Systematic Revision of Diplocentrid Scorpions (Diplocentridae) from Circum - Caribbean Lands. (Special Publications: No. 14). (Illus.). 92p. (Orig.). 1978. pap. 7.00 (ISBN 0-89672-062-4). Tex Tech Pr.
Van Der Hammen, L. A Berlese, Acari Myriopoda et Scorpiones Eighteen Eighty-Two to Nineteen Three, 12 vols. 4616p. 1980. Set. 315.00 (ISBN 90-6193-603-9, Pub. by Junk Pubs Netherlands). Kluwer Academic.
Wills, L. J. The British Triassic Scorpions, Pts. 1 & 2. Repr. of 1947 ed. Set. 22.00 (ISBN 0-384-68650-8). Johnson Repr.

SCOTCH WHISKEY

see Whiskey

SCOTTISH TERRIERS

see Dogs–Breeds–Scottish Terriers

SCREEN PROCESS PRINTING

Hawkyard, C. J. Chapter Two - Screen Printing. 75.00x (ISBN 0-686-98194-4, Pub. by Soc Dyers & Colour); pap. 50.00x (ISBN 0-686-98195-2). State Mutual Bk.
Kosloff, Albert. Ceramic Screen Printing. 3rd ed. (Illus.). 141p. 1984. 18.95 (ISBN 0-911380-63-9). Signs of Times.
--Screen Printing Electronic Circuits. (Illus.). 1980. 12.95 (ISBN 0-911380-49-3). Signs of Times.
Selected Bibliography: Screen Printing. 37p. 1976. pap. 10.00 (ISBN 0-317-14992-X). Tech & Ed Ctr Graph Arts RIT.
Swerdlow, Robert M. The Step-by-Step Guide to Screen Process Printing. (Illus.). 192p. 1985. text ed. 21.95 (ISBN 0-13-846949-0); pap. 17.95 (ISBN 0-13-846956-3). P-H.

SCREW-CUTTING MACHINES

see also Taps and Dies

Cleeve, Martin. Screwcutting in the Lathe. (Workshop Practice Ser.: No. 3). (Illus.). 128p. 1985. pap. 9.95 (ISBN 0-85242-838-3, Pub. by Argus). Aztex.

SCREW PROPELLERS

see Propellers

SCREW-THREADS

Bradley, Ian. Screw Threads & Twist Drills. (Illus.). 112p. 1985. pap. 6.95 (ISBN 0-317-14788-9, Pub. by Argus). Aztex.
Din Standards for Screw Threads. 808.00 (ISBN 0-686-28183-7, 10702-4/45). Heyden.
Lieblich, Jerome H., ed. Screw Thread Standards for Federal Services. 582p. 1978. loose-leaf 64.95x (ISBN 0-912702-11-7, FED-STD-H28). Global Eng.
Screw Threads & Gaskets for Fire Hose Connections. (Ten Ser). 1974. pap. 2.00 (ISBN 0-685-58131-4, 194). Natl Fire Prot.
Sidders, Peter. A Guide to World Screw Threads. LC 71-185990. (Illus.). 292p. 1972. 24.00 (ISBN 0-8311-1092-9). Indus Pr.

Seymour, Raymond B., ed. Plastic Mortars, Sealants, & Caulking Compounds. LC 79-19752. (ACS Symposium Ser.: No. 113). 1979. 29.95 (ISBN 0-8412-0523-X). Am Chemical.

Warring, R. H. Seals & Sealing. 272p. 1981. 79.50x (ISBN 0-85461-072-3, Pub by Trade & Tech England). Brookfield Pub Co.

SEALING-WAX

see also Sealing Compounds

King, Edwin J. The Seals of the Order of St. John of Jerusalem. LC 78-63355. (The Crusades & Military Orders: Second Ser.). (Illus.). Repr. of 1932 ed. 24.50 (ISBN 0-404-16248-7). AMS Pr.

SEALS (ANIMALS)

see also Pinnipedia; Sealing

Bailey, Alfred M. The Hawaiian Monk Seal. (Museum Pictorial Ser.: No. 7). 1949. pap. 1.10 (ISBN 0-916278-36-0). Denver Mus Natl Hist.

Bonner, W. Nigel. Seals & Man: A Study of Interactions. LC 81-69684. (Illus.). 184p. (Orig.). 1982. pap. 9.95x (ISBN 0-295-95890-1, Pub. by Wash Sea Grant). U of Wash Pr.

Hewer, H. R. British Seals. LC 74-105. (New Naturalist Ser). (Illus.). 231p. 1974. 14.95 (ISBN 0-8008-1056-2). Taplinger.

International Conference on the Mediterranean Monk Seal, 1st, Rhodes, Greece, 1978. The Mediterranean Monk Seal: Proceedings. Ronald, K. & Duguy, R., eds. LC 79-41227. (UNEP Technical Ser.: Vol. 1). (Illus.). 250p. 1979. 28.00 (ISBN 0-08-025654-6); pap. 17.25 (ISBN 0-08-025655-4). Pergamon.

Katona, Steve & Richardson, David. A Field Guide to the Whales, Porpoises, & Seals of the Gulf of Maine & Eastern Canada: Cape Cod to Labrador. (Illus.). 224p. 1983. 22.95 (ISBN 0-684-17901-6, ScribT); pap. 13.95 (ISBN 0-684-17902-4). Scribner.

Kooyman, Gerald L. Weddell Seal: Consummate Diver. LC 80-18794. (Illus.). 176p. 1981. 44.50 (ISBN 0-521-23657-6). Cambridge U Pr.

Lockley, R. M. Grey Seal, Common Seal. (Illus.). 1966. 9.50 (ISBN 0-8079-0060-5). October.

Lockley, Ronald M. Saga of the Grey Seal. 8.50 (ISBN 0-8159-6801-9). Devin.

The Mediterranean Monk Seal: Proceedings of the First International Conference, Rhodes, Greece, 2-5 May 1978, Vol. 1. (UNEP Technical Ser.). 182p. 1981. pap. 23.00 (ISBN 0-08-025655-4, PERG23, PERGAM). Unipub.

Peterson, Richard S. & Bartholomew, George A. The Natural History & Behavior of the California Sea Lion. (ASM Special Publication Ser.: No. 1). (Illus.). ix, 79p. 1967. 6.00 (ISBN 0-943612-00-4). Am Soc Mammalogists.

SEALS. (Illus.). 1973. pap. 12.00 (ISBN 2-88032-028-3, IUCN40, IUCN). Unipub.

Watson, Paul & Rogers, Warren. Sea Shepherd: One Man's Crusade for Whales & Seals. (Illus.). 1981. 14.95 (ISBN 0-393-01499-1). Norton.

SEAMANSHIP

see also Knots and Splices; Navigation

Armstrong, M. C. Practical Ship Handling. 112p. 1980. 19.50x (ISBN 0-85174-387-0). Sheridan.

Blair, Carvel H. Seamanship: A Handbook for Oceanographers. LC 76-56349. (Illus.). 238p. 1977. 9.00x (ISBN 0-87033-228-7). Cornell Maritime.

Chamier, John. Safety & Seamanship. 1979. 14.95x (ISBN 0-8464-0067-7). Beekman Pubs.

Chapman, Charles F. & Maloney, E. S. Chapman Piloting, Seamanship & Small Boat Handling. 55th ed. 640p. 1981. 19.95 (ISBN 0-87851-809-6); deluxe ed. 24.95 (ISBN 0-87851-810-X). Hearst Bks.

Clissold, Peter. Basic Seamanship. 1981. 20.00x (ISBN 0-85174-368-4, Pub. by Nautical England). State Mutual Bk.

--Basic Seamanship. 6th ed. 353p. 1975. pap. 11.50x (ISBN 0-85174-255-6). Sheridan.

Cockcroft, A. N. Nicholl's Seamanship & Nautical Knowledge. 1981. 45.00x (ISBN 0-85174-362-5, Pub. by Nautical England). State Mutual Bk.

Cockroft, A. N., ed. Nicholls's Seamanship & Nautical Knowledge. 24th ed. 443p. 1979. 26.50x (ISBN 0-85174-362-5). Sheridan.

Derrett, D. R. Ship Stability for Master & Mates. 3rd rev. ed. 1972. 30.00 (ISBN 0-540-01403-6). Heinman.

Dodge, D. O. & Kyriss, S. E. Seamanship: Fundamentals for the Deck Officer. 2nd ed. LC 80-5684. (Fundamentals of Naval Science: Vol. 2). 272p. 1981. text ed. 16.95x (ISBN 0-87021-613-9). Naval Inst Pr.

Forsberg, Gerald. Brown's Pocket-Book for Seamen. 1981. 50.00x (ISBN 0-85174-391-9, Pub. by Brown Son Ferguson). State Mutual Bk.

Gallagher, Robert E. Byron's Journal of His Circumnavigation, 1764-1766. 230p. 1964. 20.00x (ISBN 0-686-79455-9, Pub. by Hakluyt Soc England). State Mutual Bk.

Henderson, Richard. Sail & Power. 3rd ed. LC 78-62059. (Illus.). 325p. 1979. 19.95 (ISBN 0-87021-577-9); pap. 15.50x (ISBN 0-87021-578-7). Naval Inst Pr.

Hourigan, Patrick W. A Manual of Seamanship for the Officer of the Deck, Ship Under Sail Alone: The 1903 Edition. LC 79-93029. 148p. 1980. 8.95 (ISBN 0-87021-361-X). Naval Inst Pr.

James, Richard & Plant, Richard M. Study Guide to the Multiple Choice Examinations for Chief Mate & Master. 2nd ed ed. LC 82-2441. 686p. 1982. 28.50x (ISBN 0-87033-288-0). Cornell Maritime.

--Study Guide to the Multiple Choice Examinations for Third & Second Mates. 4th ed ed. LC 82-2438. 1982. pap. 24.50x (ISBN 0-87033-289-9). Cornell Maritime.

Jarman, Colin & Beavis, Bill. Modern Rope Seamanship. LC 76-20290. (Illus.). 1979. 16.95 (ISBN 0-87742-074-2). Intl Marine.

Kemp, J. F. & Young, P. Ship Stability: Notes & Examples. 2nd ed. (Kemp & Young Ser.). 132p. 1971. pap. 9.95x (ISBN 0-540-00361-1). Sheridan.

Kemp, John. Seamanship Notes. 4th ed. (Kemp & Young Ser.). (Illus.). 100p. (Orig.). 1983. pap. text ed. 9.95x (ISBN 0-540-07357-1, Pub. by Stanford Maritime). Sheridan.

Kemp, John F. Ocean Navigator (Reed's) 1977. 3rd ed. (Illus.). 45.00 (ISBN 0-900335-47-5). Heinman.

Ludins, George H. Seamanship for New Skippers. (Illus.). 1980. pap. 5.95 (ISBN 0-916224-54-6). Banyan Bks.

MacEwen, W. A. Blue Book of Questions & Answers for Third Mates. 2nd ed. LC 65-25384. (Illus.). 190p. 1965. pap. 7.50x (ISBN 0-87033-008-X). Cornell Maritime.

Miller, A. G., rev. by. Boatswain's Manual. 4th ed. 316p. 1984. 26.50x (ISBN 0-85174-475-3). Sheridan.

Milligan, John E. The Amateur Pilot. LC 81-19419. (Illus.). 134p. 1982. pap. 7.50 (ISBN 0-87033-280-5). Cornell Maritime.

Mort, S. W. Bluewater Seamanship. 1981. 75.00x (ISBN 0-85174-403-6, Pub. by Nautical England). State Mutual Bk.

--Bluewater Seamanship. 93p. 1981. 16.50x (ISBN 0-85174-403-6). Sheridan.

Nares, J. G. Seamanship, Eighteen Sixty-Two. 368p. 1984. 30.00x (ISBN 0-905418-37-9, Pub. by Gresham England). State Mutual Bk.

Paasch, Henri. Dictionnaire Anglais-Francais et Francais-Anglais des Termes et Locutions Maritimes. 2nd ed. (Fr. & Eng.). 320p. 1974. pap. 23.50 (ISBN 0-686-57065-0, M-6437). French & Eur.

Prince, W. Bartlett. Pilot - Take Charge. 2nd ed. 94p. 1970. 4.50x (ISBN 0-85174-139-8). Sheridan.

Rousmaniere, John. The Annapolis Book of Seamanship. (Illus.). 352p. 1983. 24.95 (ISBN 0-671-24687-9). S&S.

Rudman, Jack. Special Rigger. (Career Examination Ser.: C-750). (Cloth bdg. avail. on request). pap. 10.00 (ISBN 0-8373-0750-3). Natl Learning.

Sailing & Seamanship. 4th ed. LC 76-29794. (Illus.). 243p. 1983. pap. text ed. 8.00 (ISBN 0-930028-02-3). US Coast Guard.

Sanders, R. E. Practice of Ocean Rescue. 260p. 1977. 13.50x (ISBN 0-85174-294-7). Sheridan.

Simpson, A. Nautical Knowledge for Fishermen. 217p. 1979. pap. 13.50x (ISBN 0-85174-368-4). Sheridan.

Smith, Harvey G. The Arts of the Sailor. (Everyday Handbook Ser.). pap. 3.95 (ISBN 0-06-463482-5, EH 482, EH). B&N NY.

Tate, William H. A Mariner's Supplement for the Nineteen Eighty-One Inland Rules of the Road. LC 74-80004. (Illus.). 32p. 1981. pap. 0.95x (ISBN 0-87021-386-5). Naval Inst Pr.

United States Coast Guard Auxiliary. Boating Skills & Seamanship. 9th ed. LC 74-164688. (Illus.). 252p. 1984. pap. text ed. 8.00 (ISBN 0-930028-00-7). US Coast Guard.

Van Dorn, William G. Oceanography & Seamanship: A Guide for Ocean Cruising. LC 73-15377. (Illus.). 550p. 1974. 22.50 (ISBN 0-396-06888-X). Dodd.

Walliser, Blair. New Basic Seamanship & Safe Boat Handling. 1985. pap. 11.95 (ISBN 0-385-23074-5). Doubleday.

Zee, Thomas E. Able Seaman & Lifeboatman: All Grades. rev. "F" ed. Block, Richard A. & Hall, Daniel W., eds. (Illus.). 623p. 1983. pap. 32.00 (ISBN 0-934114-40-4, BK-105). Marine Educ.

SEAMEN

Here are entered works on naval seamen in general. Works on members of the Armed Forces, including naval seamen, are entered under the heading Soldiers.

see also Pilots and Pilotage

also United States–Navy, and similar headings

Bonwick, G. Automation on Shipboard. 1969. 35.00 (ISBN 0-312-06195-1). St Martin.

Crawford, William P. Mariner's Weather. (Illus.). 1979. 22.95 (ISBN 0-393-03221-3). Norton.

Dodge, D. O. & Kyriss, S. E. Seamanship: Fundamentals for the Deck Officer. 2nd ed. LC 80-5684. (Fundamentals of Naval Science: Vol. 2). 272p. 1981. text ed. 16.95x (ISBN 0-87021-613-9). Naval Inst Pr.

SEAPLANES

see also Amphibian Planes

Allward, Maurice. An Illustrated History of Seaplanes & Flying Boats. (Illus.). 1980. cancelled (ISBN 0-904978-54-0). Transatlantic.

Andrews, C. F. & Morgan, E. B. Supermarine Aircraft since Nineteen Fourteen. (Illus.). 352p. 1981. 29.95 (ISBN 0-370-10018-2, Pub. by the Bodley Head). Merrimack Pub Cir.

Braybrook, Roy. British Aerospace Harrier & Sea Harrier. (Illus.). 192p. 1984. 19.95 (ISBN 0-85045-561-8, Pub. by Osprey England). Motorbooks Intl.

British Flying Boats: A Pictorial Survey. 96p. 1981. 25.00x (ISBN 0-85153-137-7, Pub. by D B Barton England). State Mutual Bk.

D. Bradford Barton Ltd., ed. American Flying Boats: A Pictorial Survey. 1981. 25.00x (ISBN 0-686-97136-1, Pub. by D B Barton England). State Mutual Bk.

--British Float Planes: A Pictorial Survey. 96p. 1981. 25.00x (ISBN 0-85153-255-1, Pub. by D B Barton England). State Mutual Bk.

Frey, Jay J. How to Fly Floats: Seaplane Flying. (Illus.). 1972. pap. 3.00 (ISBN 0-911721-71-1, Pub. by Edo-Aire). Aviation.

Kinsey, Gordon. Seaplanes-Felixstowe. (Illus.). 1979. 20.00 (ISBN 0-900963-89-1, Pub. by Terence Dalton England). State Mutual Bk.

Knott, Richard C. The American Flying Boat. LC 79-84247. 262p. 1979. 31.95 (ISBN 0-87021-070-X). Naval Inst Pr.

Palmer, H. R. The Seaplanes. LC 65-16861. (Famous Aircraft Ser.). 52p. 1980. 6.95 (ISBN 0-8168-5649-4). Aero.

World Float Planes Military & Civil from 1905 to the Present Day: A Pictorial Survey. 96p. 1981. 25.00x (ISBN 0-85153-254-3, Pub. by D B Barton England). State Mutual Bk.

World Flying Boats: A Pictorial Survey. 96p. 1981. 25.00x (ISBN 0-85153-191-1, Pub. by D B Barton England). State Mutual Bk.

SEASHORE

see also Beaches; Coast Changes; Coasts; Sand Dunes; Shore Lines

Barrett & Yonge. Collins Pocket Guide to the Seashore. 29.95 (ISBN 0-00-219321-3, Collins Pub England). Greene.

Costello, David F. The Seashore World. LC 79-7641. (Illus.). 256p. 1980. 14.37i (ISBN 0-690-01235-7). Har-Row.

Crowder, William. Seashore Life Between the Tides. (Illus.). 12.00 (ISBN 0-8446-5173-7). Peter Smith.

Schwartz, M. L., ed. The Encyclopedia of Beaches & Coastal Environments. (Encyclopedia of Earth Sciences Ser.: Vol. XV). 940p. 1982. 95.00 (ISBN 0-87933-213-1). Van Nos Reinhold.

Swenson, Allan. Secrets of a Seashore. (Secret of Ser.). (Illus.). 80p. 1981. 6.95 (ISBN 0-930096-27-4); pap. 5.95 (ISBN 0-930096-28-2). G Gannett.

Trefil, James. A Scientist at the Seashore. LC 84-14112. (Illus.). 208p. 1985. 16.95 (ISBN 0-684-18235-1, ScribT). Scribner.

Voss, Gilbert L. Seashore Life of Florida & the Caribbean. rev. ed. LC 80-20172. (Illus.). 199p. 1980. pap. 8.95 (ISBN 0-916224-58-9). Banyan Bks.

SEASHORE BIOLOGY

see also Coastal Flora; Shore Birds

Audubon Society & Meinkoth, Norman A. The Audubon Society Field Guide to North American Seashore Creatures. LC 81-80828. (Illus.). 1981. 13.50 (ISBN 0-394-51993-0). Knopf.

Berrill, N. J. & Berrill, Jacquelyn. One Thousand & One Questions Answered About the Seashore. LC 76-12889. (The One Thousand & One Questions Ser.). (Illus.). 305p. 1976. pap. 4.95 (ISBN 0-486-23366-9). Dover.

Brafield, Alan E. Life in Sandy Shores. (Studies in Biology: No. 89). 64p. 1978. pap. text ed. 8.95 (ISBN 0-7131-2682-5). E Arnold.

Costello, David F. The Seashore World. LC 79-7641. (Illus.). 256p. 1980. 14.37i (ISBN 0-690-01235-7). Har-Row.

Coulombe, Deborah. The Seaside Naturalist: A Guide to Nature at the Seashore. 256p. 1984. 19.95 (ISBN 0-13-797259-8); pap. 12.95 (ISBN 0-13-797242-3). P-H.

Harris, Cricket. Seashore Life. (Orig.). pap. 3.95 (ISBN 0-8200-0205-4). Great Outdoors.

Hay, John. Sandy Shore. LC 68-18991. (Illus.). 1968. 8.95 (ISBN 0-85699-006-X). Chatham Pr.

Hedgpeth, Joel W. Introduction to Seashore Life of the San Francisco Bay Region & the Coast of Northern California. (California Natural History Guides: No. 9). (Illus.). 1962. pap. 2.95 (ISBN 0-520-00544-9). U of Cal Pr.

Hinton, Sam. Seashore Life of Southern California. LC 69-14343. (California Natural History Guides: No. 26). (Illus.). 1969. 14.95x (ISBN 0-520-02993-3); pap. 3.95 (ISBN 0-520-01470-7). U of Cal Pr.

Johnson, Myrtle E. & Snook, H. J. Seashore Animals of the Pacific Coast. (Illus.). 16.50 (ISBN 0-8446-2336-9). Peter Smith.

Pietschmann, V. Hawaiian Shore Fishes. (BMB). Repr. of 1938 ed. 12.00 (ISBN 0-527-02264-0). Kraus Repr.

Smith, Lynwood. Common Seashore Life of the Pacific Northwest. (Illus.). 66p. 1962. 10.95 (ISBN 0-911010-65-3). pap. 4.95 (ISBN 0-911010-64-5). Naturegraph.

Snively, Gloria. Exploring the Seashore: A Guide to the Shore Birds & Intertidal Plants & Animals of British Columbia, Washington & Oregon. LC 78-63412. (Illus.). 240p. 1978. pap. 11.95 (ISBN 0-916076-24-5). Writing.

Southward, Alan J. Life on the Sea-Shore. LC 65-8401. (Illus.). 1965. 8.95x (ISBN 0-674-53351-8). Harvard U Pr.

SEASHORE BIOLOGY–GREAT BRITAIN

Campbell, A. C. The Larousse Guide to the Seashore & Shallow Seas of Britain & Europe. LC 80-82755. (Larousse Nature Guides Ser.). (Illus.). 320p. (Orig.). 1981. 10.95 (ISBN 0-88332-251-X, 8068). Larousse.

SEASHORE ECOLOGY

Bannink, B. A., ed. Integration of Ecological Aspects in Coastal Engineering Projects: Proceedings of a Symposium held in Rotterdam, the Netherlands, June 6-10, 1983, 2 vols, Vol. 16:1-4. LC 83-25745. (Illus.). 800p. 1984. Set. pap. 160.00 (ISBN 0-08-031036-2). Pergamon.

Barbour, Michael G., et al. Coastal Ecology: Bodega Head. LC 70-173902. (Illus.). 1974. 30.00x (ISBN 0-520-02147-9). U of Cal Pr.

Bird, C. F. & Ongkosongo, Otto S. Environmental Changes on the Coasts of Indonesia. 52p. 1981. pap. 10.00 (ISBN 92-808-0197-X, TUNU128, UNU). Unipub.

Boaden, P. J. & Seed, R. An Introduction to Coastal Ecology. (Illus.). 192p. 1985. 39.95 (ISBN 0-412-01021-6, 9442); pap. 19.95 (ISBN 0-412-01031-3, 9443). Methuen Inc.

Boaden, P. S. & Seed, R. An Introduction to Coastal Ecology. (Tertiary Level Biology Ser.). 192p. 1985. text ed. 39.95 (ISBN 0-412-01021-6, Pub. by Chapman & Hall); pap. text ed. 19.95 (ISBN 0-412-01031-3, Pub. by Chapman & Hall). Methuen Inc.

Jefferies, R. L. & Davy, A. J., eds. Ecological Processes in Coastal Environments: Nineteenth Symposium of the British Ecological Society. 684p. 1979. 114.95 (ISBN 0-470-26741-0). Halsted Pr.

Jenkins, Morton. Seashore Studies. (Practical Ecology Ser.). (Illus.). 104p. 1983. pap. text ed. 8.50x (ISBN 0-04-574019-4). Allen Unwin.

Kremer, J. & Nixon, S. W. A Coastal Marine Ecosystem: Simulation & Analysis. LC 77-22785. (Ecological Studies: Vol. 24). (Illus.). 1977. 46.00 (ISBN 0-387-08365-0). Springer-Verlag.

Livingston, R. J., ed. Ecological Processes in Coastal & Marine Systems. LC 79-12388. (Marine Science Ser.: Vol. 10). 560p. 1979. 79.50x (ISBN 0-306-40318-8, Plenum Pr). Plenum Pub.

Mann, K. H. Ecology of Coastal Waters: A Systems Approach. LC 81-40321. (Studies in Ecology: Vol. 8). (Illus.). 300p. 1981. pap. 18.00x (ISBN 0-520-04734-6). U of Cal Pr.

Perkins, Bob F. Deltaic Sedimentation on the Louisiana Coast. 1982. 10.00. SEPM.

Symposium on Inland Waterways for Navigation, Flood Control & Water Diversions. Inland Waterways for Navigation, Flood Control & Water Diversions: Third Annual Symposium of the Waterways, Harbors & Coastal Engineering Division of ASCE, Colorado State University, Fort Collins, Colorado, August 10-12, 1976, 2 vols. Vol. 1. pap. 160.00 (ISBN 0-317-28778-8, 2017762); Vol. 2. pap. 160.00 (ISBN 0-317-28779-6). Bks Demand UMI.

Wilman, Elizabeth A. External Costs of Coastal Beach Pollution: An Hedonic Approach. LC 84-42690. 208p. (Orig.). 1984. pap. text ed. 15.00 (ISBN 0-915707-08-X). Resources Future.

SEASONS

see also names of seasons

Teale, Edwin W. Journey into Summer. (The American Seasons Ser.). (Illus.). 1981. pap. 8.95 (ISBN 0-396-07957-1). Dodd.

SEATS

see Chairs

SEAWATER

see also Underwater Acoustics

Bidwell, Joseph P. & Spotte, Stephen. Artificial Seawaters: Formulas & Methods. 360p. 1985. write for info. (ISBN 0-86720-057-X). Jones & Bartlett.

Delyannis, A. E. & Delyannis, E. E. Seawater & Desalting, Vol. 1. 180p. 1980. 39.00 (ISBN 0-387-10206-X). Springer-Verlag.

Parsons, Y., et al. A Manual of Chemical & Biological Methods for Seawater Analysis. (Illus.). 144p. 1984. 19.50 (ISBN 0-08-030288-2); pap. 8.95 (ISBN 0-08-030287-4). Pergamon.

A Practical Handbook of Seawater Analysis. 2nd ed. pap. 18.75 (SSC70, SSC). Unipub.

BOOKS - SUBJECT INDEX

SEDIMENTATION AND DEPOSITION

Scott, Jeanette, ed. Desalination of Seawater by Reverse Osmosis. LC 80-26421. (Pollution Tech. Rev.: No. 75). 431p. 1981. 39.00 (ISBN 0-8155-0837-9). Noyes.

SEAWEED

see also Marine Algae

Bird, Carolyn J. & Ragan, Mark A., eds. Proceedings of the Eleventh International Seaweed Symposium. (Developments in Hydrobiology Ser.). 1985. lib. bdg. 128.50 (ISBN 90-6193-773-6, Pub. by Junk Pubs Netherlands). Kluwer Academic.

Chapman, A. R. Biology of Seaweeds. (Illus.). 160p. 1979. pap. text ed. 15.00 (ISBN 0-8391-1340-4). Univ Park.

Cheney, Daniel P. & Mumford, Thomas M., Jr. Shellfish & Seaweed Harvests of Puget Sound. (A Puget Sound Bk.). (Illus.). 144p. (Orig.). 1984. pap. 8.95 (ISBN 0-295-95990-8, Pub. by Wash Sea Grant). U of Wash Pr.

Dixon, Peter S. & Irvine, Linda M. Seaweeds of the British Isles; Vol. 1, Rhodophyta: Pt. 1, Introduction, Nemeliales, Gigartinales. (Illus.). 1977. pap. 31.00x (ISBN 0-565-00781-5, Pub. by Brit Mus Nat Hist). Sabbot-Natural Hist Bks.

Guiry, M. D. A Consensus & Bibliography of Irish Seaweeds. (Bibliotheca Phycologica Ser.: No. 44). 1979. pap. text ed. 14.00x (ISBN 3-7682-1209-2). Lubrecht & Cramer.

Irvine, Linda M. Seaweeds of the British Isles, Vol. 1: Rhodophyta: Part 2A, Cryptonemiales (sensu-stricto), Palmariales Rhodymeniales. (Illus.). xii, 115p. 1983. pap. 30.00x (ISBN 0-565-00871-4, Pub. by Brit Mus Nat Hist). Sabbot-Natural Hist Bks.

Jensen, A. & Stein, J. R., eds. Seaweed: Ninth International Symposium. LC 77-18657. (Illus.). 1979. lib. bdg. 62.00 (ISBN 0-89500-010-5). Sci Pr.

Khan, M. Fundamentals of Phycology. 1978. pap. 11.50x (ISBN 0-89955-281-1, Pub. by Intl Bk Dist). Intl Spec Bk.

Lee, Thomas F. The Seaweed Handbook: An Illustrated Guide to Seaweeds from North Carolina to the Arctic. LC 77-6966. (Illus.). 1977. case 20.00x (ISBN 0-913352-04-7). Mariners Boston.

Levring, Tore, ed. Tenth International Seaweed Symposium. (Illus.). 780p. 1981. 78.00 (ISBN 3-11-008389-2). De Gruyter.

Lobban, Christopher S. & Wynne, Michael J., eds. The Biology of Seaweeds. LC 81-69858. (Illus.). 784p. 1982. 87.50x (ISBN 0-520-04585-8). U of Cal Pr.

Lobban, Christopher S., et al. The Physiological Ecology of Seaweeds. (Illus.). 300p. 1985. 44.50 (ISBN 0-521-26508-8). Cambridge U Pr.

Ruprecht, F. J. Phycologia Ochotiensis. Tange des ochotskischen Meeres, (from Middendorff's Sibirische Reise) (Illus.). 1978. Repr. of 1851 ed. lib. bdg. 52.50 (ISBN 3-7682-1184-3). Lubrecht & Cramer.

Sorensen, L. O. A Guide To the Seaweeds of South Padre Island, Texaas. 123p. 1979. pap. text ed. 8.95x (ISBN 0-89787-101-4). Gorsuch Scarisbrick.

Stein, Janet, ed. Handbook of Phycological Methods. (Illus.). 512p. 1973. 59.50 (ISBN 0-521-20049-0); pap. 21.95 (ISBN 0-521-29747-8). Cambridge U Pr.

Trainor, F. R. Introductory Phycology. LC 77-26663. 525p. 1978. text ed. 39.95 (ISBN 0-471-88190-2). Wiley.

SECOND HOMES

Home Planners. Two Hundred Twenty-three Vacation Homes. (Illus.). 176p. 1982. pap. 4.25 (ISBN 0-918894-30-1). Home Planners.

Miller, Rex. Residential Electrical Wiring. (Illus.). 300p. 1981. text ed. 14.24 (ISBN 0-02-665620-5); student guide 5.32 (ISBN 0-02-665640-X); tchr's. ed. 5.32 (ISBN 0-02-665630-2). Bennett IL.

Time-Life Books Editors. Cabins & Cottages. (Home Repair & Improvement). (Illus.). 1979. 11.95 (ISBN 0-8094-2410-X). Time-Life.

U. S. Dept. of Agriculture. Vacation Homes & Cabins: 16 Complete Plans. 14.50 (ISBN 0-8446-5674-7). Peter Smith.

SECONDARY BATTERIES

see Storage Batteries

SECRETION

see also Glands; Hormones; Neurosecretion; also names of secretions, e.g. Bile, Perspiration, Urine

Duncan, C. J. & Hopkins, C. R., eds. Secretory Mechanisms. LC 79-10003. (Society for Experimental Biology Symposium: No. 33). (Illus.). 1980. 82.50 (ISBN 0-521-22684-8). Cambridge U Pr.

Gregory, R. A. & Petersen, O. H., eds. The Control of Secretion: Proceedings. (Royal Society of London Ser.). (Illus.). 193p. 1982. text ed. 74.00x (ISBN 0-85403-179-0, Pub. by Royal Soc London). Scholium Intl.

Poisner, A. M. & Trifaro, J. M., eds. The Electrophysiology of the Secretory Cell: The Secretory Process, Vol. 2. 312p. 1985. 83.50 (ISBN 0-444-80599-0). Elsevier.

--Secretory Granule. (Secretory Process Ser.: Vol. 1). 416p. 1982. 113.00 (ISBN 0-444-80383-1, Biomedical Pr). Elsevier.

Rubin, Ronald. Calcium & the Secretory Process. LC 74-10557. (Illus.). 204p. 1974. 29.50x (ISBN 0-306-30778-2, Plenum Pr). Plenum Pub.

Suzuki, T. Physiology of Adrenocortical Secretion. (Frontiers of Hormone Research: Vol. 11). (Illus.). viii, 216p. 1983. 56.25 (ISBN 3-8055-3644-5). S Karger.

SECURITY SYSTEMS

see also Eavesdropping

Anderson. Bank Security. 1981. text ed. 29.95 (ISBN 0-409-95038-6). Butterworth.

Barnard, Robert L. Intrusion Detection Systems. 300p. 1981. text ed. 24.95 (ISBN 0-409-95026-2). Butterworth.

Bose, Keith W. Video Security Systems. 2nd ed. 210p. 1982. 19.95 (ISBN 0-409-95057-2). Butterworth.

Business Communications Staff. Security Alarm Systems. 1985. pap. 1250.00 (ISBN 0-89336-437-1, G-046N). BCC.

Cole, Richard B. The Application of Security Systems & Hardware. 272p. 1970. photocopy ed. 27.95x (ISBN 0-398-00332-7). C C Thomas.

Cunningham, John E. Security Electronics. 3rd ed. LC 82-51040. 264p. 1983. pap. 13.95 (ISBN 0-672-21953-0). Sams.

DeVore, R. William & Jackson, J. S., eds. Carnahan Conference on Security Technology, 1985: Proceedings. (Illus.). 181p. 1985. pap. 22.50 (ISBN 0-89779-061-8, UKY BU137). OES Pubns.

De Vore, R. William & Jackson, J. S., eds. Security Through Science & Engineering: Proceedings, Third International Conference. LC 80-83300. (Illus.). 313p. 1980. pap. 33.50 (ISBN 0-89779-042-1, UKYBU122). OES Pubns.

Fak, V., ed. Security: IFIP-SEC '83. 290p. 1984. 39.00 (ISBN 0-444-86669-8, North-Holland). Elsevier.

Green, Gion. Introduction to Security. 3rd ed. 1981. text ed. 22.95 (ISBN 0-409-95036-X); instr's manual avail. Butterworth.

Guarino, Vincent J. Everyman's Guide to Better Home Security. (Illus.). 136p. 1981. pap. 7.95 (ISBN 0-87364-217-1). Paladin Pr.

Healy, Richard J. Design for Security. 2nd ed. 280p. 1983. 41.95 (ISBN 0-471-06429-7, Pub. by Wiley Interscience). Wiley.

Hofmeister, Richard & Prince, David. Security Dictionary. LC 83-61093. 8.95 (ISBN 0-672-22020-2). Sams.

LaMont, M. Dean. Understanding Electronic Security Systems. Luecke, Gerald, ed. LC 82-50800. (Understanding Ser.). (Illus.). 128p. (Orig.). 1979. pap. 9.95 (ISBN 0-89512-105-0, LCB 7201). Tex Instr Inc.

Nonte, George C., Jr. To Stop a Thief: The Complete Guide to House, Apartment & Property Protection. (Illus.). 244p. pap. 4.95 (ISBN 0-88317-028-0). Stoeger Pub Co.

Nye, J. Michael. Who, What & Where in Communications Security. 130p. 1981. 200.00 (ISBN 0-686-98046-8). Telecom Lib.

Poyner, Barry. Design Against Crime: Beyond Defensible Space. LC 83-7454. (Illus.). 118p. 1983. text ed. 29.95 (ISBN 0-408-01230-7). Butterworth.

Purpura, Philip. Security & Loss Prevention. LC 83-10044. 512p. 1983. text ed. 22.95 (ISBN 0-409-95075-0). Butterworth.

Schnabolk, Charles. Physical Security: Practices & Technology. 388p. text ed. 22.95 (ISBN 0-686-40710-5). Butterworth.

Tobias, Marc W. Locks, Safes, & Security: A Handbook for Law Enforcement Personnel. (Illus.). 352p. 1971. photocopy ed. 35.50x (ISBN 0-398-02155-4). C C Thomas.

Traister, John E. Design & Application of Security-Fire-Alarm Systems. (Illus.). 176p. 1981. 21.00 (ISBN 0-07-065114-0). McGraw.

Trimmer. Understanding & Servicing Alarms. 1981. text ed. 22.95 (ISBN 0-409-95045-9). Butterworth.

Walker. Electronic Security Systems. 1983. pap. text ed. 29.95 (ISBN 0-408-01160-2). Butterworth.

Wanat, Guy, et al. Supervisory Techniques for the Security Professional. 160p. 1981. text ed. 22.95 (ISBN 0-409-95035-1). Butterworth.

Waters, Tony. Home Protection. 99p. 1982. pap. text ed. 9.95 (ISBN 0-408-00576-9). Butterworth.

SEDIMENT TRANSPORT

see also Channels (Hydraulic Engineering)

Bogardi, John L. Sediment Transport in Alluvial Streams. 68.00 (ISBN 9-6305-1826-0). WRP.

Graf, W. H. Hydraulics of Sediment Transport. LC 79-128788. 513p. 1984. 45.00 (ISBN 0-918334-81-0). WRP.

International Symposium, 1983. Proceedings, 1983 International Symposium on Urban Hydrology, Hydraulics & Sediment Control. De Vore, R. William, ed. LC 83-60965. (Illus.). 531p. (Orig.). 1983. pap. 33.50 (ISBN 0-89779-056-1, UKY BU 131). OES Pubns.

Meyer, R. E. & Meyer, R. E., eds. Waves on Beaches & Resulting Sediment Transport. 1972. 26.50 (ISBN 0-12-493250-9). Acad Pr.

Raudkivi, A. J. Loose Boundary Hydraulics. 2nd ed. Francis, J. D., ed. 326p. 1976. text ed. 44.00 (ISBN 0-08-018772-2); pap. text ed. 25.00 (ISBN 0-08-018771-4). Pergamon.

Shen, H. W., ed. Applications of Stochastic Processes to Sediment Transport: Sedimentation Process in Rivers & Coastal Environments. Kikkawa, H. LC 79-67693. 1979. 32.00 (ISBN 0-918334-31-4). WRP.

Simons, Daryl B. & Senturk, Fuat. Sediment Transport Technology. LC 76-19737. 1977. 40.00 (ISBN 0-918334-14-4). WRP.

Statham, Ian. Earth Surface Sediment Transport. (Contemporary Problems in Geography Ser.). (Illus.). 1977. 26.50x (ISBN 0-19-874076-X); pap. 10.95x (ISBN 0-19-874077-8). Oxford U Pr.

Stelczer, K. Bed-Load Transport: Theory & Practice. LC 80-54288. 1981. 22.00 (ISBN 0-918334-39-X). WRP.

Tanner, William F., ed. Shorelines Past & Present, 3 vols. 745p. 1980. pap. 50.00 (ISBN 0-686-83996-X). FSU Geology.

Thornton, Wendy A., ed. Hydrotransport Bibliography. 1970. text ed. 24.00x (ISBN 0-900983-09-4, Dist. by Air Science Co.). BHRA Fluid.

Yalin, Mehmet S. Mechanics of Sediment Transport. 2nd ed. 1977. text ed. 62.00 (ISBN 0-08-021162-3). Pergamon.

SEDIMENTARY ROCKS

see Rocks, Sedimentary

SEDIMENTARY STRUCTURES

Allen, J. R. Sedimentary Structures, 2 Vols. (Developments in Sedimentology Ser.: Vol. 30B). 594p. 1982. Vol. 1. 110.75 (ISBN 0-444-41935-7); Vol. 2. 110.75 (ISBN 0-444-41945-4). Elsevier.

--Sedimentary Structures: Their Character & Physical Basis, Pts. A & B. (Developments in Sedimentology Ser.: Vol. 30). 1984. pap. 57.50 (ISBN 0-444-42232-3). Elsevier.

Bernard, H. A. & LeBlanc, R. J., Sr. Recent Sediments of Southeast Texas - a Field Guide to the Brazos Alluvial & Deltaic Plains & the Galveston Barrier Island Complex: Resume of the Quaternary Geology of the Northwestern Gulf of Mexico Province. (Guidebook Ser.: GB 11). 132p. 1970. Repr. 7.00 (ISBN 0-686-29319-3). Bur Econ Geology.

Bloom, Barbara H. Index to the Journal of Sedimentary Petrology, Volumes 1-26, 1931-1956. (Society of Economic Paleontologists & Mineralogists, Special Publication: No. 6). pap. 20.00 (ISBN 0-317-27107-5, 2024733). Bks Demand UMI.

Bouma, Arnold H. Methods for the Study of Sedimentary Structures. LC 78-11914. 476p. 1979. Repr. of 1969 ed. lib. bdg. 29.50 (ISBN 0-88275-760-1). Krieger.

Collinson, J D. & Thompson, D B. Sedimentary Structuress. (Illus.). 240p. 1982. text ed. 40.00x (ISBN 0-04-552017-8); pap. text ed. 17.95x (ISBN 0-04-552018-6). Allen Unwin.

Conybeare, C. E. Lithostratigraphic Analysis of Sedimentary Basins. LC 79-6951. 1979. 59.50 (ISBN 0-12-186050-7). Acad Pr.

Davis, R. A., Jr., ed. Coastal Sedimentary Environments. 2nd, rev. ed. (Illus.). xvii, 716p. 1985. 39.80 (ISBN 0-387-96097-X). Springer-Verlag.

Dott, Robert H. & Shaver, Robert H., eds. Modern & Ancient Geosynclinal Sedimentation: Proceedings of a Symposium Dedicated to Marshall Key & Held at Madison, Wisconsin, 1972. LC 74-175858. (Society of Economic Paleontologists & Mineralogists, Special Publication: No. 19). pap. 97.30 (ISBN 0-317-27152-0, 2024742). Bks Demand UMI.

Durand, B., ed. Thermal Phenomena in Sedimentary Basins. LC 84-73154. (Illus.). 400p. (Orig.). 1985. pap. 76.95x (ISBN 0-87201-865-2). Gulf Pub.

McKee, Edwin D. Sedimentary Structures in Dunes of the Namib Desert, South West Africa. (Special Paper Ser.: No. 188). (Illus.). 1982. 8.00 (ISBN 0-8137-2188-1). Geol Soc.

Monty, C., ed. Phanerozoic Stromatolites: Case Histories. (Illus.). 249p. 1981. 55.00 (ISBN 0-387-10474-7). Springer-Verlag.

Reineck, H. E. & Singh, I. B. Depositional Sedimentary Environments-with Reference to Terrigenous Classics. (Illus.). 439p. 1974. 31.50 (ISBN 0-387-10189-6). Springer-Verlag.

Royal Society of London. The Evolution of Sedimentary Basins: Proceedings of a Royal Society Discussion Meeting held on 3 & 4 June 1981. Kent, Peter & McKenzie, D. P., eds. (Illus.). 338p. 1982. text ed. 112.00x (ISBN 0-85403-184-7, Pub. by Royal Soc London). Scholium Intl.

SEDIMENTATION ANALYSIS

Bouma, Arnold H. Methods for the Study of Sedimentary Structures. LC 78-11914. 476p. 1979. Repr. of 1969 ed. lib. bdg. 29.50 (ISBN 0-88275-760-1). Krieger.

De Vore, R. William & Graves, Donald H., eds. Proceedings, 1983 Symposium on Surface Mining, Hydrology, Sedimentology & Reclamation. LC 83-60966. (Illus.). 554p. (Orig.). 1983. pap. 45.00 (ISBN 0-89779-058-8, UKY BU 133). OES Pubns.

Friedman, Gerald M. & Sanders, John E. Principles of Sedimentology. LC 78-5355. 792p. 1978. text ed. 47.50 (ISBN 0-471-75245-2). Wiley.

Fujita, H. Mathematical Theory of Sedimentation Analysis. (Physical Chemistry: Vol. 11). 1962. 75.00 (ISBN 0-12-269750-2). Acad Pr.

Gill, Dan & Merriam, Daniel F. Geomathematical & Petrophysical Studies in Sedimentology, an International Symposium: Proceedings of Papers Presented at Sessions Sponsored by the International Association for Mathematical Geology at the Tenth International Congress on Sedimentology in Jerusalem, July 1979. (Computers & Geology Ser.: Vol. 3). (Illus.). 285p. 1979. 48.00 (ISBN 0-08-023832-7). Pergamon.

Harms, John C., et al. Depostitional Environments as Interpreted from Primary Sedimentary Structures & Stratification Sequences. LC 76-350871. (Society of Economic Paleontologists & Mineralogists, Short Course Ser.: No. 2). pap. 41.30 (ISBN 0-317-27142-3, 2024748). Bks Demand UMI.

Jopling, Alan V. & McDonald, Barrie C., eds. Glaciofluvial & Glaciolacustrine Sedimentation. LC 76-350111. (Society of Economic Paloeontologists & Mineralogists, Special Publication: No. 23). pap. 81.00 (ISBN 0-317-27146-6). Bks Demand UMI.

Larsen, G. & Chilingar, G. V., eds. Diagenesis in Sediments & Sedimentary Rocks, Vol. 1. (Developments in Sedimentology Ser.: Vol. 25A). 580p. 1979. 74.50 (ISBN 0-444-41657-9). Elsevier.

Merriam, D. F., ed. Mathematical Models of Sedimentary Processes. LC 72-78629. (Computer Applications in the Earth Sciences Ser.). 271p. 1972. 45.00x (ISBN 0-306-30701-4, Plenum Pr). Plenum Pub.

Methodology for Biomass Determinations & Microbial Activities in Sediments, STP 673. 199p. 1979. 22.50x (ISBN 0-8031-0511-8, 04-673000-16). ASTM.

Miall, A. D. Principles of Sedimentary Basin Analysis. (Illus.). 550p. 1984. 39.00 (ISBN 0-387-90941-9). Springer-Verlag.

Morgan, James P. & Shaver, Robert H., eds. Deltaic Sedimentation: Modern & Ancient. LC 72-191407. (Society of Economic Paleontologists & Mineralogists, Special Publication: No. 15). pap. 83.00 (ISBN 0-317-27153-9, 2024740). Bks Demand UMI.

Whalley, W. Brian. Scanning Electron Microscopy in the Study of Sediments. 400p. 1980. pap. 29.50x (ISBN 0-86094-017-9, Pub. by GEO Abstracts England). State Mutual Bk.

Williams, J. W. Ultracentrifugation of Macromolecules: Modern Topics. 1973. 33.00 (ISBN 0-12-755160-3). Acad Pr.

SEDIMENTATION AND DEPOSITION

see also Erosion; Flocculation; Marine Sediments; Rocks, Sedimentary

Aigner, T. Storm Depositional Systems. (Lecture Notes in Earth Sciences: Vol. 3). vii, 174p. 1985. pap. 14.50 (ISBN 0-387-15231-8). Springer-Verlag.

Allen, J. R. Experiments in Physical Sedimentology. 64p. (Orig.). 1985. pap. text ed. 7.95x (ISBN 0-04-551066-0). Allen Unwin.

Allen, John R. Physical Processes of Sedimentation: An Introduction. (Earth Science Ser.). (Illus.). 1970. pap. text ed. 11.95x (ISBN 0-04-551014-8). Allen Unwin.

--Principles of Physical Sedimentology. (Illus.). 400p. 1985. text ed. 40.00x (ISBN 0-04-551095-4); pap. text ed. 24.95x (ISBN 0-04-551096-2). Allen Unwin.

Asquith, George B. Subsurface Carbonate Depositional Models. 121p. 1979. 39.95x (ISBN 0-87814-104-9). Pennwell Bks.

Ballance, Peter F. & Reading, Harold G., eds. Sedimentation of Oblique-Slip Mobile Zones. (International Association of Sedimentologists & the Societ As Internationalis Limnological Symposium). 265p. 1980. pap. 69.95x (ISBN 0-470-26927-8). Halsted Pr.

Bayer, U. & Seilacher, A., eds. Sedimentary & Evolutionary Cycles. (Lecture Notes in Earth Sciences: Vol. 1). vi, 465p. 1985. pap. 29.50 (ISBN 0-387-13982-6). Springer-Verlag.

Brenchley, P. J. & Williams, B. P., eds. Sedimentology: Recent Developments & Applied Aspects. (Illus.). 320p. 1985. text ed. 60.00 (ISBN 0-632-01192-0); pap. 30.00 (ISBN 0-632-01418-0). Blackwell Pubns.
Brown, L. F., et al. Pennsylvanian Depositional Systems in North-Central Texas: A Guide for Interpreting Terrigenous Clastic Facies in a Cratonic Basin. (Guidebook Ser.: GB 14). (Illus.). 122p. 1973. Repr. 4.00 (ISBN 0-686-29322-3). Bur Econ Geology.
Caughey, C. A. Depositional Systems in the Paluxy Formation (Lower Cretaceous), Northeast Texas: Oil, Gas, & Ground-Water Resources. (GC 77-8). (Illus.). 59p. 1977. Repr. 2.50 (ISBN 0-686-29327-4, GC 77-8). Bur Econ Geology.
Christiansson, Carl. Soil Erosion & Sedimentation in Semi-Arid Tanzania: Studies of Environmental Change & Ecological Imbalance. 208p. 1983. pap. text ed. 24.50x (ISBN 0-8419-9743-8, Africana). Holmes & Meier.
Creer, K. M., et al, eds. Geomagnetism of Baked Clays & Recent Sediments. 324p. 1983. 53.25 (ISBN 0-444-42231-5, I-268-83). Elsevier.
DeVore, R. William & Graves, Donald H. Nineteen Eighty-Five Symposium on Surface Mining, Hydrology, Sedimentology & Reclamation: Proceedings. LC 83-60966. (Illus.). 600p. (Orig.). 1985. text ed. 45.00 (ISBN 0-89779-064-2, UKY BU139). OES Pubns.
DeVore, R. William & Huffsey, R. Nineteen Eighty-Five International Symposium on Urban Hydrology, Hydraulic & Infrastructures & Water Quality Control: Proceedings. (Illus.). 335p. (Orig.). 1985. pap. 33.50 (ISBN 0-89779-063-4, UKY BU138). OES Pubns.
DeVore, R. William & Graves, Donald H., eds. Nineteen Eighty-Four Symposium on Surface Mining, Hydrology, Sedimentology & Reclamation: Proceedings. LC 83-60966. (Illus.). 492p. (Orig.). 1984. pap. 45.00 (ISBN 0-89779-062-6, UKY BU136). OES Pubns.
De Vore, R. William & Huffsey, R., eds. Nineteen Eighty-Four International Symposium on Urban Hydrology, Hydrolics & Sediment Control: Proceedings. LC 83-60965. (Illus.). 284p. (Orig.). 1984. pap. 33.50 (ISBN 0-89779-060-X, UKY BU135). OES Pubns.
De Vore, R. William & Wood, Don J., eds. Proceedings 1981 International Symposium on Urban Hydrology, Hydraulics & Sediment Control. LC 81-82243. (Illus.). 473p. (Orig.). 1981. pap. 33.50 (ISBN 0-89779-047-2, UKY BU125). OES Pubns.
Duff, Peter, et al. Cyclic Sedimentation. (Developments in Sedimentology Ser.: Vol. 10). 280p. 1967. 81.00 (ISBN 0-444-40183-0). Elsevier.
Dutton, S. P. Depositional Systems & Hydrocarbon Resource Potential of the Pennsylvanian System, Palo Duro & Dalhart Basins, Texas Panhandle. (Illus.). 49p. 1980. 1.50 (ISBN 0-318-03136-1, GC80-8). Bur Econ Geology.
Dutton, S. P., et al. Geology & Geohydrology of the Palo Duro Basin, Texas Panhandle: A Report on the Progress of Nuclear Waste Isolation Feasibility Studies (1978) (Geological Circular Ser.: 79-1). (Illus.). 99p. 1979. 2.50 (ISBN 0-686-29328-2, GC 79-1). Bur Econ Geology.
Erxleben, A. W. Depositional Systems in the Canyon Group (Pennsylvanian System), North-Central Texas. (Report of Investigations Ser.: RI 82). (Illus.). 76p. 1980. Repr. of 1975 ed. 4.00 (ISBN 0-318-03216-3). Bur Econ Geology.
Evenson, Edward B., et al, eds. Tills & Related Deposits: Proceedings of the INQUA Symposia on the Genesis & Lithology of Quaternary Deposits, USA 1981, Argentina 1982. 1983. lib. bdg. 45.00 (ISBN 90-6191-511-2, Pub. by Balkema RSA). IPS.
Freytet, P. & Plaziat, J. Continental Carbonate Sedimentation & Pedogenesis: Late Cretaceous & Early Tertiary of Southern France. (Contributions to Sedimentology Ser.: No. 12). (Illus.). 213p. 1982. pap. text ed. 49.60x (ISBN 3-510-57012-X). Lubrecht & Cramer.
Galloway, W. E. Terrigenous Elastic Depositional Systems. (Illus.). 420p. 1983. 41.00 (ISBN 0-387-90827-7). Springer-Verlag.
Galloway, W. E. & Brown, L. F., Jr. Depositional Systems & Shelf-Slope Relationships in Upper Pennsylvanian Rocks, North-Central Texas. (Report of Investigations Ser.: RI 75). (Illus.). 62p. 1981. Repr. of 1972 ed. 3.00 (ISBN 0-318-03182-5). Bur Econ Geology.
Galloway, W. E., et al. Depositional & Ground-Water Flow Systems in the Exploration for Uranium: Syllabus for Research Colloquium Held in Austin, 1978. (Illus.). 267p. 1979. 6.00 (ISBN 0-318-03374-7). Bur Econ Geology.
Garde, R. J. & Ranga-Raju, K. G. Mechanics of Sediment Transportation & Alluvial Stream Problems. 2nd ed. 1985. 34.95 (ISBN 0-470-20109-6). Halsted Pr.
Gentile, Richard J. Influence of Structural Movement on Sedimentation During the Pennsylvanian Period in Western Missouri. LC 74-4528. 108p. 1968. 10.00x (ISBN 0-8262-7619-9). U of Mo Pr.
Ginsburg, R. N., ed. Tidal Deposits: A Case Book of Recent Examples & Fossil Counterparts. LC 75-28228. (Illus.). xiii, 421p. 1975. 52.00 (ISBN 0-387-06823-6). Springer-Verlag.
Ginsburg, Robert N., ed. Evolving Concepts in Sedimentology. LC 72-4016. (The John Hopkins University Studies in Geology: No. 21). pap. 51.00 (ISBN 0-317-28475-4, 2020737). Bks Demand UMI.
Golterman, H. L., ed. Interactions Between Sediments & Fresh Water. (Illus.). 1977. pap. 52.00 (ISBN 90-220-0632-8, PDC47, PUDOC). Unipub.
Greenwood, B. & Davis, R. A., Jr., eds. Hydrodynamics & Sedimentation in Wave-Dominated Coastal Environments. (Developments in Sedimentology Ser.: No. 39). 474p. 1984. 96.50 (ISBN 0-444-42400-8). Elsevier.
Gulf Publishing Co. Evaporite Deposits. LC 81-82357. 266p. 1981. 54.95x (ISBN 0-87201-277-8). Gulf Pub.
Hakanson, L. & Jansson, M. Principles of Lake Sedimentology. (Illus.). 320p. 1983. 41.00 (ISBN 0-387-12645-7). Springer-Verlag.
Iijima, A. & Hein, J. R., eds. Siliceous Deposits in the Pacific Region. (Developments in Sedimentology Ser.: No. 36). 472p. 1982. 85.00 (ISBN 0-686-84505-6). Elsevier.
International Symposium, 1983. Proceedings, 1983 International Symposium on Urban Hydrology, Hydraulics & Sediment Control. De Vore, R. William, ed. LC 83-60965. (Illus.). 531p. (Orig.). 1983. pap. 33.50 (ISBN 0-89779-056-1, UKY BU 131). OES Pubns.
Krumbein, William C. & Sloss, L. L. Stratigraphy & Sedimentation. 2nd ed. LC 61-11422. (Illus.). 660p. 1963. 35.95 (ISBN 0-7167-0219-3). W H Freeman.
Laronne, Jonathan & Mosley, M. Paul, eds. Erosion & Sediment Yield. LC 81-6456. (Benchmark Papers in Geology: Vol. 63). 400p. 1982. 48.95 (ISBN 0-87933-409-6). Van Nos Reinhold.
Leeder, M R. Sedimentology: Process & Product. (Illus.). 528p. 1982. text ed. 50.00x (ISBN 0-04-551053-9); pap. text ed. 24.95x (ISBN 0-04-551054-7). Allen Unwin.
Leggett, Jeremy K., ed. Trench-Forearc Geology: Sedimentation & Tectonics on Modern & Ancient Active Plate Margins. (Illus.). 582p. 1982. text ed. 90.00x (ISBN 0-632-00708-7). Blackwell Pubns.
Lewis, D. Practical Sedimentation. 1984. 22.95 (ISBN 0-87933-443-6). Van Nos Reinhold.
McBride, E. F. Sedimentary Petrology & History of the Haymond Formation (Pennsylvanian), Marathon Basin, Texas. (Report of Investigations Ser.: RI 57). 101p. 1966. 2.50 (ISBN 0-686-29339-8). Bur Econ Geology.
McGowen, J. H., et al. Geochemistry of Bottom Sediments, Matagorda Bay System, Texas. (Illus.). 64p. 1979. 1.50 (ISBN 0-686-29329-0, GC 79-2). Bur Econ Geology.
--Depositional Framework of the Lower Dockum Group (Triassic), Texas Panhandle. (Report of Investigations Ser.: RI 97). (Illus.). 60p. 1979. 2.00 (ISBN 0-318-03233-3). Bur Econ Geology.
McGowen, M. K. & Lopez, C. M. Depositional Systems in the Nacatoch Formation (Upper Cretaceous), Northeast Texas & Southwest Arkansas. (Report of Investigations Ser.: RI 137). (Illus.). 59p. 1983. 2.00 (ISBN 0-318-03297-X). Bur Econ Geology.
Matter, Albert & Tucker, Maurice E., eds. Modern & Ancient Lake Sediments. (International Association of Sedimentologists & the Societas Internationalis Limnologiae Symposium Proceding Ser.). 290p. 1979. 39.95x (ISBN 0-470-26571-X). Halsted Pr.
Maynard, J. B. Geochemistry of Sedimentary Ore Deposits. (Illus.). 305p. 1983. 32.00 (ISBN 0-387-90783-1). Springer-Verlag.
Measurement of River Sediments. (Operational Hydrology Reports: No. 16). 61p. 1981. pap. 7.00 (ISBN 92-63-10561-8, W506, WMO). Unipub.
Morton, R. A. & McGowen, J. H. Modern Depositional Environments of the Texas Coast. (Guidebook Ser.: GB 20). (Illus.). 167p. 1983. Repr. of 1980 ed. 4.50 (ISBN 0-318-03129-9). Bur Econ Geology.
Nittrouer, C. A., ed. Sedimentary Dynamics of Continential Shelves. (Developments in Sedementology Ser.: Vol. 32). 450p. 1981. 76.50 (ISBN 0-444-41962-4). Elsevier.
Organizing Committee of the Symposium. River Sedimentation: Proceedings of the Second International Symposium, 11-16 October, 1983, Nanjing, China, 2 vols. 1658p. 1985. Vol. 1. 72.00 (ISBN 0-8133-0253-6); Vol. 2. 80.00 (ISBN 0-8133-0275-7); Set. 140.00 (ISBN 0-317-20866-7). Westview.
Parker, A. & Sellwood, B. W., eds. Sediment Diagenesis. pap. text ed. 24.50 (ISBN 90-277-1874-1, Pub. by Reidel Holland). Kluwer Academic.
Pettijohn, F. J. Sedimentary Rocks. 3rd ed. 736p. 1975. text ed. 40.50 scp (ISBN 0-06-045191-2, HarpC). Har-Row.
Potter, P. E. & Pettijohn, F. J. Paleocurrents & Basin Analysis. 2nd ed. LC 76-30293. (Illus.). 1977. 39.00 (ISBN 0-387-07952-1). Springer-Verlag.
Presley, M. W. & McGillis, K. A. Coastal Evaporite & Tidal-Flat Sediments of the Upper Clear Fork & Glorieta Formations, Texas Panhandle. (Report of Investigations Ser.: RI 115). (Illus.). 50p. 1982. 2.00 (ISBN 0-318-03248-1). Bur Econ Geology.
Reading. Sedimentary Environments. 2nd ed. Date not set. write for info. (ISBN 0-444-00861-6). Elsevier.
Reading, H. G. Sedimentary Environments & Facies. 2nd ed. (Illus.). 680p. 1985. pap. text ed. 39.95x (ISBN 0-632-01223-4). Blackwell Pubns.
Reading, H. G., ed. Sedimentary Environments & Facies. 558p. 1979. pap. 35.25 (ISBN 0-444-00293-6). Elsevier.
Reijers, T. J. & Hsu, K. J. Manual of Carbonate Sedimentology. Date not set. price not set (ISBN 0-12-584840-4). Acad Pr.
Residential Erosion & Sediment Control: Objectives, Principles & Design Considerations. 64p. 1978. pap. 10.00x (ISBN 0-87262-133-2). Am Soc Civil Eng.
Residential Erosion & Sediment Control: Objectives, Principles & Design Considerations. (Cost Effective Residential Development Standards Ser.). (Illus.). 63p. 1979. pap. 12.50 (ISBN 0-86718-036-6); pap. 10.00 members. Natl Assn Home.
Residential Erosion & Sediment Control: Objectives, Principles & Design Considerations. LC 78-63632. (Illus.). 63p. 1978. pap. 12.50 (ISBN 0-87420-584-0, E09); pap. 10.00 members. Urban Land.
Rieke, H. H. & Chilingarian, G. V. Compaction of Argillaceous Sediments. LC 74-190682. (Developments in Sedimentology Ser.: Vol. 16). 424p. 1974. 74.50 (ISBN 0-444-41054-6). Elsevier.
Schwarzacher, W. Sedimentation Models & Quantitative Stratigraphy. 384p. 1975. 85.00 (ISBN 0-444-41302-2). Elsevier.
Sedimentation Engineering. (Manual & Report on Engineering Practice Ser.: No. 54). 761p. 1975. 39.00x (ISBN 0-87262-001-8). Am Soc Civil Eng.
Singer, A. & Galan, E., eds. Palygorskite-Sepiolite: Occurrences, Genesis & Uses. (Developments in Sedimentology Ser.: Vol. 37). 352p. 1984. 54.00 (ISBN 0-444-42337-0, I-145-84). Elsevier.
Sly, Peter G. Sediment-Freshwater Interaction. 1982. text ed. 125.00 (ISBN 90-6193-760-4, Pub. by Junk Pubs Netherlands). Kluwer Academic.
Smith, G. E. Depositional Systems, San Angelo Formation (Permian), North Texas: Facies Control of Red-Bed Copper Mineralization. (Report of Investigations Ser.: RI 80). (Illus.). 74p. 1974. Repr. 3.00 (ISBN 0-318-03206-6). Bur Econ Geology.
Solis, R. F. Upper Tertiary & Quaternary Depositional Systems, Central Coastal Plain, Texas: Regional Geology of the Coastal Aquifer & Potential Liquid-Waste Repositories. (Illus.). 89p. 1981. 3.00 (ISBN 0-318-03239-2). Bur Econ Geology.
Stanley, D. J. & Kelling, G., eds. Sedimentation in Submarine Canyons, Fans & Trenches. LC 77-19163. 395p. 1978. 63.95 (ISBN 0-87933-313-8). Van Nos Reinhold.
Svedberg, Theodor & Pedersen, Kai O. The Ultracentrifuge. Repr. of 1940 ed. 49.00 (ISBN 0-384-58890-5). Johnson Repr.
Swift, D. J. & Palmer, Harold D., eds. Coastal Sedimentation. LC 78-18696. (Benchmark Papers in Geology: Vol. 42). 339p. 1978. 49.95 (ISBN 0-87933-330-8). Van Nos Reinhold.
Thompson, D. M. Atoka Group (Lower-Middle Pennsylvanian), Northern Fort Worth Basin, Texas: Terrigenous Depositional Systems, Diagenesis, Reservoir Distribution, & Quality. (Report of Investigations Ser.: RI 125). (Illus.). 62p. 1982. 2.50 (ISBN 0-318-03270-8). Bur Econ Geology.
Weimer, R. J., et al. Tectonic Influence on Sedimentation, Early Cretaceous, East Flank Powder River Basin, Wyoming & South Dakota. Raese, Jon & Goldberg, J. H., eds. LC 82-17894. (Colorado School of Mines Quarterly: Vol. 77, No. 4). (Illus.). 61p. 1983. pap. text ed. 12.00 (ISBN 0-686-82131-9). Colo Sch Mines.
White, W. A., et al. Submerged Lands of Texas, Corpus Christi Area: Sediments, Geochemistry, Benthic Macroinvertebrates, & Associated Wetlands. (Submerged Lands Ser.). (Illus.). 154p. 1983. 9.50 (ISBN 0-318-03338-0). Bur Econ Geology.
Wilson, R. C. Residual Deposits: Surface Related Weathering Processes & Materials. (Illus.). 262p. 1983. text ed. 50.00x (ISBN 0-632-01072-X). Blackwell Pubns.
Winker, C. D., et al. Depositional Setting, Structural Style, & Sandstone Distribution in Three Geopressured Geothermal Areas, Texas Gulf Coast. (Report of Investigations Ser.: RI 134). (Illus.). 60p. 1983. 2.50 (ISBN 0-318-03292-9). Bur Econ Geology.

SEDIMENTS (GEOLOGY)

see also Clay; Marine Sediments; Sand; Sedimentary Structures

Bricker, Owen P., et al. Seminar on Organism-Sediment Interrelationships, 1971. (Bermuda Biological Station Special Pubn.: No. 9). (Illus.). ii, 171p. 1971. pap. 9.00 (ISBN 0-917642-09-0). Bermuda Bio.
Briggs. Sources & Methods in Geography: Sediments. 1977. 13.50 (ISBN 0-408-70815-8). Butterworth.
Brookfield, M. E. & Ahlbrandt, T. A., eds. Eolian Sediments & Processes. (Developments in Sedimentology Ser.: No. 38). 660p. 1983. 78.75 (ISBN 0-444-42233-1, I-310-83). Elsevier.
Bryant, Vaughn M. & Holloway, Richard G., eds. Pollen Records of Late Quaternary North American Sediments. (Illus.). 350p. 1985. 35.00 (ISBN 0-931871-01-8). Am Assn Strat.
Cowgill, et al. History of Laguna De Petenixil: A Small Lake in Northern Guatemala. (Connecticut Academy of Arts Sciences Memoirs Ser.: Vol. 17). (Illus.). 126p. 1966. pap. 15.00 (ISBN 0-208-00784-9). Shoe String.
Fairbridge, R. W. & Bourgeois, J., eds. The Encyclopedia of Sedimentology. LC 78-18259. (Encyclopedia of Earth Sciences Ser.: Vol. VI). 901p. 1978. 98.00 (ISBN 0-87933-152-6). Van Nos Reinhold.
Friedman, G. M. & Johnson, K. G. Exercises in Sedimentology. 208p. 1982. pap. 16.95 (ISBN 0-471-87453-1). Wiley.
Fuechtbauer, Hans. Sediments & Sedimentary Rocks 1. (Sedimentary Petrology Ser.: Pt. 2). (Illus.). 464p. 1974. lib. bdg. 36.50 (ISBN 3-510-65007-7). Lubrecht & Cramer.
Ginsburg, R. N. & Garrett, Peter. Seminar on Organism-Sediment Interrelations 1968. (Bermuda Biological Station Special Pubn.: No. 2). (Illus.). ii, 154p. 1969. pap. 7.00 (ISBN 0-917642-02-3). Bermuda Bio.
Ginsburg, Robert N. & Stanley, Steven M. Seminar on Organism-Sediment Interrelationships, 1969. (Bermuda Biological Station Special Pubn.: No. 6). (Illus.). iv, 110p. 1970. pap. 6.00 (ISBN 0-917642-06-6). Bermuda Bio.
Golterman, H. L., ed. Interactions Between Sediments & Fresh Water. 1977. pap. 34.00 (ISBN 90-6193-563-6, Pub. by Junk Pubs. Netherlands). Kluwer Academic.
Goudie, A. S. & Pye, K., eds. Chemical Sediments & Geomorphology. 1983. 58.00 (ISBN 0-12-293480-6). Acad Pr.
Kennett, James P., ed. Magnetic Stratigraphy of Sediments. LC 79-13662. (Benchmark Papers in Geology Ser.: Vol. 54). 464p. 1980. 48.50 (ISBN 0-87933-354-5). Van Nos Reinhold.
King, E. A., ed. Chondrules & Their Origins. 375p. 1984. 33.00x (ISBN 0-942862-01-5). Lunar & Planet Inst.
Larsen, G. & Chilingar, G. V., eds. Diagenesis in Sediments & Sedimentary Rocks, Vol. 2. (Developments in Sedimentology Ser.: Vol. 25B). 572p. 1983. 117.00 (ISBN 0-444-42013-4). Elsevier.
Liddell, W. D. & Ohlhorst, S. L. Modern & Ancient Carbonate Environments of Jamaica. Ginsburg, Robert N., ed. (Sedimenta Series-Sedimenta X). (Illus.). 100p. (Orig.). 1984. pap. 12.00 (ISBN 0-932981-09-7). Univ Miami CSL.
Luepke, Gretchen, ed. Stability of Heavy Minerals in Sediments. 1984. 36.50 (ISBN 0-442-25925-5). Van Nos Reinhold.
Lugn, Alvin L. Sedimentation in the Mississippi River between Davenport, Iowa, & Cairo, Illinois. LC 28-14418. (Augustana College Library Publication Ser.: No. 11). 104p. 1927. pap. 1.00 (ISBN 0-910182-08-6). Augustana Coll.
Mackenzie, Fred T., et al. Seminar on Organism-Sediment Interrelationships, 1970. (Bermuda Biological Station Special Pubn.: No. 7). (Illus.). iv, 170p. pap. 9.00 (ISBN 0-917642-07-4). Bermuda Bio.
Natland, Manley L., et al. A System of Stages for Correlation of Magallanes Basin Sediments. LC 74-75964. (Geological Society of America Memoir Ser.: No. 139). pap. 50.00 (ISBN 0-317-28976-4, 2023735). Bks Demand UMI.
Purser, B. H., ed. The Persian Gulf. LC 72-97023. (Illus.). viii, 471p. 1973. 55.00 (ISBN 0-387-06156-8). Springer-Verlag.
Reading, H. G. Sedimentary Environments & Facies. 2nd ed. (Illus.). 680p. 1985. pap. text ed. 39.95x (ISBN 0-632-01223-4). Blackwell Pubns.

Bath, Markus. Introduction to Seismology. (Wissenschaft und Kultur Band: No. 27). (Illus.). 428p. 1979. 31.95 (ISBN 0-8176-0956-3). Birkhauser.

Ben-Menahem, A. & Singh, S. Seismic Waves & Sources. (Illus.). 1000p. 1981. 99.00 (ISBN 0-387-90506-5). Springer-Verlag.

Berkhout, A. J. Seismic Migration: Imaging of Acoustic Energy by Wave Field Extrapolation; A Theoretical Aspect. 2nd rev. & enl. ed. (Developments in Solid Earth Geophysics Ser.: Vol. 14A). 352p. 1983. 59.50 (ISBN 0-444-42130-0). Elsevier.

Bessonova, E. N., et al. Investigation of the Mechanism of Earthquakes. LC 60-9255. (Soviet Research in Geophysics Ser.: Trudy No. 40). 1960. 34.50x (ISBN 0-306-10625-6, Consultants). Plenum Pub.

Bolt, Bruce A. Nuclear Explosions & Earthquakes: The Parted Veil. LC 75-28295. (Illus.). 309p. 1976. text ed. 26.95 (ISBN 0-7167-0276-2). W H Freeman.

Bullen, K. E. An Introduction to the Theory of Seismology. 3rd ed. LC 79-7707. (Illus.). 1979. 52.50 (ISBN 0-521-04367-0); pap. 17.95x (ISBN 0-521-29686-2). Cambridge U Pr.

Bullen, K. E. & Bolt, B. A. An Introduction to the Theory of Seismology. 4th ed. (Illus.). 470p. Date not set. price not set (ISBN 0-521-23980-X); pap. price not set (ISBN 0-521-28389-2). Cambridge U Pr.

Byerlee, J. D. & Wyss, M. Rock Friction & Earthquake Prediction. (Contributions to Current Research in Geophysics: No. 6). (Illus.). 413p. 1978. 70.95x (ISBN 0-8176-1018-9). Birkhauser.

Committee on Seismology, ed. Global Earthquake Monitoring: Its Uses, Potentials, & Support Requirements. LC 77-5219. 1977. pap. text ed. 7.75 (ISBN 0-309-02608-3). Natl Acad Pr.

Datta, S. K., ed. Earthquake Ground Motion & Its Effects On Structures. (AMD Ser.: Vol. 53). 197p. 1982. 40.00 (H00241). ASME.

Davison, Charles. The Founders of Seismology. Albritton, Claude C., Jr., ed. LC 77-6518. (History of Geology Ser.). 1978. Repr. of 1927 ed. lib. bdg. 18.00 (ISBN 0-405-10441-3). Ayer Co Pubs.

De Silva, Clarence W. Dynamic Testing & Seismic Qualification Practice. LC 80-8879. 416p. 1982. 48.50x (ISBN 0-669-04393-1). Lexington Bks.

Earthquake Prediction: Proceedings of the International Symposium on Earthquake Prediction. 995p. pap. 135.00 (ISBN 92-3-101883-3, U1441, UNESCO). Unipub.

Fitch, Albert A. Seismic Reflection Interpretation. (Geo-Exploration Monographs: Ser. 1, No. 8). (Illus.). 1976. text ed. 27.30x (ISBN 0-686-31719-X). Lubrecht & Cramer.

Galperin, E. I. The Polarization Method of Seismic Studies. 1983. lib. bdg. 58.00 (ISBN 90-277-1555-6, Pub. by Reidel Holland). Kluwer Academic.

Giese, P., et al, eds. Explosion Seismology in Central Europe: Data & Results. 1976. 86.20 (ISBN 0-387-07764-2). Springer-Verlag.

Kanai, Kiyoshi. Engineering Seismology. 251p. 1983. 34.50x (ISBN 0-86008-326-8, Pub. by U of Tokyo Japan). Columbia U Pr.

Karnik, V. Seismicity of the European Area, Part 1. 364p. 1969. lib. bdg. 45.00 (ISBN 90-277-0121-0, Pub. by Reidel Holland). Kluwer Academic.

--Seismicity of the European Area, Part 2. LC 78-468652. (Illus.). 218p. 1971. lib. bdg. 60.50 (ISBN 90-277-0179-2, Pub. by Reidel Holland). Kluwer Academic.

Keilis-Borok, V. I., ed. Computational Seismology. LC 76-140827. 227p. 1972. 45.00 (ISBN 0-306-10861-5, Consultants). Plenum Pub.

Lin, C. & Au-Yang, M. K., eds. Seismic Analysis of Power Plant Systems & Components. (PUP Ser.: Vol. 73). 200p. 1983. pap. text ed. 44.00 (ISBN 0-317-02647-X, H00259). ASME.

Lindeburg, Michael R. Seismic Design for the Professional Engineering Examination. 3rd ed. LC 80-81796. (Engineering Review Manual Ser.). (Illus.). 104p. 1980. 13.95 (ISBN 0-932276-32-6). Prof Engine.

McDonald, John A. & Gardner, G. H. Seismic Studies in Physical Modeling: Physical Modeling. LC 82-81374. (Illus.). 258p. 1983. text ed. 54.00 (ISBN 0-934634-39-4). Intl Human Res.

Macinante, Joseph A. Seismic Mountings for Vibration Isolation. LC 83-21860. 304p. 1984. 39.95x (ISBN 0-471-87084-6, Pub. by Wiley-Interscience). Wiley.

McQuillin, R., et al. An Introduction to Seismic Interpretation. 2nd ed. LC 84-80958. (Illus.). 256p. 1985. 44.95x (ISBN 0-87201-774-5); pap. text ed. 22.95x (ISBN 0-87201-773-7). Gulf Pub.

Medvedev, Sergei V. Problems of Engineering Seismology. LC 63-17635. 112p. 1963. 32.50x (ISBN 0-306-10576-4, Consultants). Plenum Pub.

Mendel, Jerry M. Optimal Seismic Deconvolution: An Estimation Based Approach. LC 82-22739. (Monograph). 1983. 39.50 (ISBN 0-12-490780-6). Acad Pr.

Murauchi, Sadanori, compiled by. Seismic Reflection Profiles in the Western Pacific, 1965-74. 232p. 1977. 37.50x (ISBN 0-86008-193-1, Pub. by U of Tokyo Japan). Columbia U Pr.

Myles, Douglas. The Great Waves. (Illus.). 224p. 1985. 16.95 (ISBN 0-07-044237-1). McGraw.

OECD-NEA. Reference Seismic Ground Motions in Nuclear Safety Assessments. (Illus.). 171p. (Orig.). 1980. pap. text ed. 16.00x (ISBN 92-64-12100-5). OECD.

Richter, Charles F. Elementary Seismology. LC 58-5970. (Geology Ser.). (Illus.). 768p. 1958. 39.95x (ISBN 0-7167-0211-8). W H Freeman.

Sadovskii, M. A., ed. Seismic Effects of Underground Explosions. LC 61-17729. 88p. 1962. 27.50x (ISBN 0-306-10601-9, Consultants). Plenum Pub.

Scott, Stanley. Policies for Seismic Safety: Elements of a State Governmental Program. LC 79-19189. (Illus., Orig.). 1979. pap. 5.75x (ISBN 0-87772-268-4). Inst Gov Stud Berk.

Seismic Analysis & Testing of Nuclear Power Plants: A Safety Guide. (Safety Ser.: No. 50-SG-S2). 59p. 1979. pap. 12.25 (ISBN 0-686-65378-5, ISP545, IAEA). Unipub.

Sengbush, Ray L. Seismic Exploration Methods. LC 82-81559. (Illus.). 296p. 1983. text ed. 44.00 (ISBN 0-934634-21-1). Intl Human Res.

Sheriff, R. E. & Geldart, L. P. Exploration Seismology: Data-Processing & Interpretation, Vol. 2. LC 81-18176. (Illus.). 300p. 1984. 32.50 (ISBN 0-521-25064-1). Cambridge U Pr.

Simon, Ruth B. Earthquake Interpretations: A Manual for Reading Seismograms. LC 81-8428. (Illus.). 160p. (Orig.). 1981. pap. text ed. 9.95x (ISBN 0-913232-81-5). W Kaufmann.

Sjogren, Bengt. Shallow Refraction Seismics. 256p. 1984. 49.95 (ISBN 0-412-24210-9, NO. 9171, Pub. by Chapman & Hall). Methuen Inc.

Spradley, L. Harold. Surveying & Navigation in Seismic Exploration. (Illus.). 300p. 1985. text ed. 54.00 (ISBN 0-934634-87-4). Intl Human Res.

Svenson, Arthur G. Earthquakes, Earth Scientists & Seismic-Safety Planning in California. 146p. (Orig.). 1984. lib. bdg. 19.75 (ISBN 0-8191-3735-9); pap. text ed. 9.00 (ISBN 0-8191-3736-7). U Pr of Amer.

Tribolet, J. Seismic Applications of Homomorphic Signal Processing. 1979. 38.95 (ISBN 0-13-779801-6). P-H.

Waters, Kenneth H. Reflection Seismology: A Tool for Energy Resource Exploration. 2nd ed. LC 80-26042. 453p. 1981. 58.50x (ISBN 0-471-08224-4, Pub. by Wiley-Interscience). Wiley.

White, J. E. Underground Sound: Application of Seismic Waves. (Methods in Geochemistry & Geophysics Ser.: Vol. 18). 254p. 1983. 59.75 (ISBN 0-444-42139-4). Elsevier.

Wyss, M., ed. Earthquake Prediction & Seismicity Patterns. (Contributions to Current Research in Geophysics Ser.: No. 8). 240p. 1980. 47.95x (ISBN 0-8176-1122-3). Birkhauser.

Zverev, S. M. Problems in Deep Seismic Sounding. LC 65-26627. 166p. 1967. 32.50x (ISBN 0-306-10783-X, Consultants). Plenum Pub.

SEISMOMETRY

see also Earthquakes; Seismic Prospecting

Aki, Keiiti & Richards, Paul G. Quantitative Seismology: Theory & Methods, Vol. I. LC 79-17434. (Geology Bks.). (Illus.). 573p. 1980. text ed. 47.95 (ISBN 0-7167-1058-7). W H Freeman.

--Quantitative Seismology: Theory & Methods, Vol. II. LC 79-17434. (Geology Bks.). (Illus.). 389p. 1980. text ed. 47.95 (ISBN 0-7167-1059-5). W H Freeman.

Sheriff, Robert E. Seismic Stratigraphy. LC 80-83974. (Illus.). 227p. 1980. text ed. 32.00 (ISBN 0-934634-08-4); pap. 25.00 (ISBN 0-934634-51-3). Intl Human Res.

Yan, M. J., ed. Dynamic & Seismic Analysis of Systems & Components. (PVP Ser.: Vol. 65). 192p. 1982. 44.00 (H00222). ASME.

SELECTION, NATURAL

see Natural Selection

SELECTIVE ABSORPTION

see Absorption Spectra

SELENIUM

Committee on Medical & Biologic Effects of Environmental Pollutants, National Research Council. Selenium. LC 76-40687. (Medical & Biologic Effects of Environmental Pollutants Ser). 203p. 1976. pap. 11.75 (ISBN 0-309-02503-6). Natl Acad Pr.

Gerlach, E., ed. The Physics of Selenium & Tellurium. (Springer Series in Solid State Sciences: Vol.13). (Illus.). 1979. 37.00 (ISBN 0-387-09692-2). Springer-Verlag.

Gutting, Robert. Selenium. 1.39x (ISBN 0-686-29934-5). Cancer Control Soc.

Hogg, D. R. Organic Compounds of Sulphur, Selenium & Tellurium, Vols. 1-5. Incl. Vol. 1. 1969-70 Literature. 1971. 47.00 (ISBN 0-85186-259-4); Vol. 2. 1970-1972 Literature. 1973. 52.00 (ISBN 0-85186-269-1); Vol. 3. 1972-74 Literature. 1975. 63.00 (ISBN 0-85186-279-9); Vol. 4. 1974-76 Literature. 1977. 88.00 (ISBN 0-85186-289-6); Vol. 5. 1979. 98.00 (ISBN 0-85186-620-4, Pub. by Royal Soc Chem London). LC 72-78527. Am Chemical.

Lewis, Alan. Selenium: The Facts about This Essential Element. 2.50x (ISBN 0-7225-0734-8). Cancer Control Soc.

Mills, K. C. Thermodynamic Data for Inorganic Sulphides, Selenides & Tellurides. LC 74-173939. pap. 160.00 (ISBN 0-317-08901-3, 2051842). Bks Demand UMI.

Nicolaou, K. C. & Petasis, N. A. Selenium in Natural Products Synthesis. LC 83-72883. (Illus.). 300p. 1984. 37.50 (ISBN 0-914891-00-6). C I S.

Passwater, Richard. Selenium As Food & Medicine. 1980. 2.95x. Cancer Control Soc.

Passwater, Richard A. Selenium As Food & Medicine. LC 80-82325. 200p. 1981. 10.95 (ISBN 0-87983-237-1); pap. 2.95 (ISBN 0-87983-229-0). Keats.

Patai, S. The Chemistry of Organic Selenium & Tellurium Compounds. 1000p. 1985. price not set (ISBN 0-471-90425-2). Wiley.

Rosenfeld, Irene & Beath, O. A. Selenium. 2nd ed. 1964. 67.00 (ISBN 0-12-597550-3). Acad Pr.

Shamberger, Raymond J. Biochemistry of Selenium. (Biochemistry of the Elements Ser.: Vol. 2). 346p. 1983. 47.50x (ISBN 0-306-41090-7, Plenum Pr). Plenum Pub.

Wilber, Charles G. Selenium: A Potential Environmental Poison & a Necessary Food Constituent. (Illus.). 136p. 1983. 19.50x (ISBN 0-398-04858-4). C C Thomas.

SELENOLOGY

see Moon

SELENOPHOMA

Sprague, Roderick & Johnson, A. G. Species of Selenophoma on North American Grasses. (Studies in Botany Ser: No. 10). (Illus.). 44p. 1950. pap. 4.95x (ISBN 0-87071-020-6). Oreg St U Pr.

SELF-OPTIMIZING SYSTEMS

see Self-Organizing Systems

SELF-ORGANIZING SYSTEMS

see also Adaptation (Biology); Adaptive Control Systems; Artificial Intelligence; Perceptrons

Fu, King-Sun, ed. Pattern Recognition & Machine Learning. LC 77-163287. 343p. 1971. 55.00 (ISBN 0-306-30546-1, Plenum Pr). Plenum Pub.

Nicolis, G. & Prigogine, I. Self-Organization in Non-Equilibrium Systems: From Dissipative Structures to Order Through Fluctuations. LC 76-49019. 491p. 1977. 70.00 (ISBN 0-471-02401-5, Pub. by Wiley-Interscience). Wiley.

SELSYN

see Synchros

SEMIARID REGIONS

see Arid Regions

SEMICONDUCTOR DIODES

see Diodes, Semiconductor

SEMICONDUCTOR NUCLEAR COUNTERS

Semiconductor Nuclear Particle Detectors. (Bibliographical Ser.: No. 8). 95p. 1962. pap. (ISBN 92-0-034262-0, IAEA). Unipub.

SEMICONDUCTORS

see also Diodes; Diodes, Semiconductor; Electric Current Rectifiers; Electroluminescence; Microelectronics; Parametric Amplifiers; Thermistors; Thermoelectric Apparatus and Appliances; Transistors; Tunnel Diodes

also particular semiconducting substances, e.g. Germanium, Silicon; and headings beginning with the word Semiconductor

Abrahams, J. R. & Pridham, G. J. Semiconductor Circuits: Theory, Design & Experiment. 25.00 (ISBN 0-08-011652-3). Pergamon.

Abrikosov, N. K., ed. Semiconductor Materials. LC 62-21587. 139p. 1963. 27.50x (ISBN 0-306-10659-0, Consultants). Plenum Pub.

Abriksov, N. K., et al. Semiconducting Two-Six, Four-Six, & Five-Six Compounds. LC 69-12527. (Monographs in Semiconductor Physics Ser.: Vol. 3). 250p. 1969. 32.50x (ISBN 0-306-30389-2, Plenum Pr). Plenum Pub.

Adler, M. S. & Temple, V. A. Semiconductor Avalanche Breakdown Design Manual. 60p. 1979. 165.00x (ISBN 0-931690-10-2). Genium Pub.

Agajanian, A. H. Semiconducting Devices: A Bibliography of Fabrication Technology, Properties, & Applications. LC 76-42313. 968p. 1976. 135.00x (ISBN 0-306-65166-1, IFI Plenum). Plenum Pub.

AIP Conference Proceedings, No. 20 Yorktown Heights. Tetrahedrally Bonded Amorphous Semiconductors: Proceedings, No. 20. Brodsky, M., et al, eds. LC 74-80145. 369p. 1974. 16.00 (ISBN 0-88318-119-3). Am Inst Physics.

Alfano, R. R. Semiconductors Probed by Ultrafast Laser Spectroscopy, Vol. 1. 1985. 79.50 (ISBN 0-12-049901-0). Acad Pr.

--Semiconductors Probed by Ultrafast Laser Spectroscopy, Vol. 2. 1985. 85.00 (ISBN 0-12-049902-9). Acad Pr.

Allen, Peter, ed. The Semiconductor Industry. 310p. 1984. pap. 985.00 (ISBN 0-931634-40-7). FIND-SVP.

Almazov, A. B. Electronic Properties of Semiconducting Solid Solutions. LC 68-18820. (Illus.). 82p. 1968. 25.00x (ISBN 0-306-10808-9, Consultants). Plenum Pub.

Ambroziak, A. Semiconductor Photoelectric Devices. 344p. 1970. 93.75 (ISBN 0-677-61800-X). Gordon.

Angelo, E. James, Jr. Electronics: BJT's, FET's & Microcircuits. LC 78-6803. 646p. 1979. Repr. of 1969 ed. lib. bdg. 38.50 (ISBN 0-88275-678-8). Krieger.

Anselm, A. Introduction to Semiconductor Theory. (Illus.). 646p. 1982. 42.95 (ISBN 0-13-496034-3). P-H.

Automated Semiconductor Wafer Fabrication Market. 276p. 1984. 1550.00 (ISBN 0-86621-227-2). Frost & Sullivan.

Bajaj, K. K., et al, eds. Spectroscopy of Shallow Centers in Semiconductors: Selected Proceedings of the 1st International Conference, Berkeley, CA, USA, 2-3 Aug. 1984. 120p. 1985. pap. 25.00 (ISBN 0-08-032569-6, Pub. by PPL). Pergamon.

Balkanski, M. & Moss, T. S. Handbook on Semiconductors: Optical Properties of Semiconductors, Vol. 2. 634p. 1980. 125.75 (ISBN 0-444-85273-5, North-Holland). Elsevier.

Barna, Arpad. High Speed Pulse & Digital Techniques. LC 79-26264. 185p. 1980. 29.50x (ISBN 0-471-06062-3, Pub. by Wiley-Interscience). Wiley.

Basov, N. G., ed. Electrical & Optical Properties of Type III-V Semiconductors. LC 77-26132. (P. N. Lebedev Physics Institute Ser.: Vol. 89). (Illus.). 126p. 1977. pap. 55.00x (ISBN 0-306-10944-1, Consultants). Plenum Pub.

--Exciton & Domain Luminescence of Semiconductors. LC 79-14567. (P. N. Levedev Physics Institute Ser.: Vol. 97). (Illus.). 119p. 1979. 55.00 (ISBN 0-306-10958-1, Consultants). Plenum Pub.

--Optical Properties of Semiconductors. LC 75-37609. (P. N. Lebedev Physics Institute Ser.: Vol. 75). (Illus.). 181p. 1976. 55.00x (ISBN 0-306-10916-6, Consultants). Plenum Pub.

Bauer, G., et al, eds. Two-Dimensional Systems, Heterostructures & Superlattices: Proceedings of the International Winterschool Mauterndorf, Austria, Feb. 26-Mar. 2, 1984. (Springer Series in Solid-State Sciences: Vol. 53). (Illus.). 290p. 1984. 29.50 (ISBN 0-387-13584-7). Springer-Verlag.

Baum, V. A. Semiconductor Solar Energy Converters. LC 69-17884. 222p. 1969. 35.00x (ISBN 0-306-10830-5, Consultants). Plenum Pub.

Beleznay, F., et al, eds. New Developments in Semiconductor Physics: Proceedings. (Lecture Notes in Physics: Vol. 122). (Illus.). 276p. 1980. pap. 23.00 (ISBN 0-387-09988-3). Springer-Verlag.

Bell, David A. Electronic Devices & Circuits. 2nd ed. (Illus.). 480p. 1979. 28.95 (ISBN 0-8359-1634-0); students manual avail. (ISBN 0-8359-1635-9). Reston.

--Solid State Pulse Circuits. 2nd ed. (Illus.). 432p. 1981. 30.95 (ISBN 0-8359-7057-4). Reston.

Benda, Hansjochen. Introduction to the Basic Principles of Semiconductors. (Siemens Programmed Instruction Ser.: 1). pap. 20.00 (ISBN 0-317-26185-1, 2052078). Bks Demand UMI.

Berger, L. I. & Prochukhan, V. D. Ternary Diamond-Like Semiconductors. LC 69-17903. 114p. 1969. 30.00x (ISBN 0-306-10833-X, Consultants). Plenum Pub.

Berlin, Howard M. Guide to CMOS Basics, Circuits, & Experiments. LC 79-67128. 224p. 1979. pap. 9.95 (ISBN 0-672-21654-X). Sams.

Bir, G. L. & Pikus, G. E. Symmetry & Strain-Induces Effects in Semiconductors. 484p. 1974. 94.95 (ISBN 0-470-07321-7). Halsted Pr.

Boguslavskii, Leonid I. & Vannikov, Anatolii V. Organic Semiconductors & Biopolymers. LC 72-75452. (Monographs in Semiconductor Physics Ser.: Vol. 6). 221p. 1970. 32.50x (ISBN 0-306-30433-3, Plenum Pr). Plenum Pub.

Bonch-Bruevich, et al. Domain Electrical Instabilities in Semiconductors. (Studies in Soviet Science: Physical Sciences Ser.). (Illus.). 400p. 1975. 55.00 (ISBN 0-306-10911-5, Consultants). Plenum Pub.

Borisova, Z. U. Glassy Semiconductors. Adashko, J. George, tr. from Rus. LC 81-17734. 516p. 1981. 85.00x (ISBN 0-306-40609-8, Plenum Pr). Plenum Pub.

King, Richard A. IBM PC-DOS Handbook. LC 83-61387. (Illus.). 296p. 1983. pap. 16.95 (ISBN 0-89588-103-9). SYBEX.
Kingston, R. H., ed. Semiconductor Surface Physics. LC 60-14439. 1957. 20.00x (ISBN 0-8122-7113-0). U of Pa Pr.
Kiselev, V. F. & Krylov, O. V. Adsorption Processes on Semiconductor & Dielectric Surfaces I. (Springer Series in Chemical Physics: Vol. 32). (Illus.). 295p. Date not set. 43.50 (ISBN 0-387-12416-0). Springer-Verlag.
Klinger, M. I. Problems of Linear Electron Transport Theory in Semiconductors. LC 78-40821. 1979. text ed. 175.00 (ISBN 0-08-018224-0). Pergamon.
Kovacs, F. High-Frequency Application of Semiconductor Devices. (Studies in Electrical & Electronic Engineering: Vol. 5). 392p. 1981. 74.50 (ISBN 0-444-99756-3). Elsevier.
Kressel, H., ed. Characterization of Epitaxial Semiconductor Films. (Methods & Phenomena Ser.: Vol. 2). 216p. 1976. Repr. 57.50 (ISBN 0-444-41438-X). Elsevier.
--Semiconductor Devices for Optical Communication. 2nd, updated ed. (Topics in Applied Physics Ser.: Vol. 39). (Illus.). 325p. 1982. pap. 27.00 (ISBN 0-387-11348-7). Springer-Verlag.
Kubat, M. Power Semiconductors. 550p. 1984. 39.00 (ISBN 0-387-12569-8). Springer-Verlag.
Kurata, Mamoru. Numerical Analysis for Semiconductor Devices. LC 80-8374. 288p. 1982. 33.00x (ISBN 0-669-04043-6). Lexington Bks.
Kutasov, B. A., et al, eds. Thermoelectric Properties of Semiconductors. LC 64-21683. 109p. 1964. 25.00x (ISBN 0-306-10675-2, Consultants). Plenum Pub.
Lampert, M. A. & Mark, P. Current Injections in Solids. (Electrical Science Ser). 1970. 80.00 (ISBN 0-12-435350-9). Acad Pr.
Lancaster, Gordon. Electron Spin Resonance in Semiconductors. LC 67-21450. (Monographs on Electron Spin Resonance Ser.). 152p. 1967. 24.50x (ISBN 0-306-30307-8, Plenum Pr). Plenum Pub.
Landsberg, P. T. & Willoughby, A. F, eds. Recombination in Semiconductors: Selected Proceedings of the International Conference Held at the University of Southampton, England. 30 August - 1st September 1978. 1979. 57.00 (ISBN 0-08-024226-X). Pergamon.
Landwehr, G., ed. Application of High Magnetic Fields in Semiconductor Physics: Proceedings, Grenoble, France, 1982. (Lecture Notes in Physics Ser.: Vol. 177). 552p. 1983. pap. 31.00 (ISBN 0-387-11996-5). Springer-Verlag.
Lannoo, M. & Bourgoin, J. Point Defects in Semiconductors I. (Springer Ser. in Solid-State Sciences: Vol. 22). (Illus.). 260p. 1981. 37.00 (ISBN 0-387-10518-2). Springer-Verlag.
Larrabee, Robert D. Neutron Transmutation of Semiconductor Materials. 326p. 1984. 75.00x (ISBN 0-306-41504-6, Plenum Pr). Plenum Pub.
Lattice Defects in Semiconductors 1974: Freiburg. (Institute of Physics Conference Ser.: No. 23). 1974. 75.00 (ISBN 0-9960030-2-9, Pub. by Inst Physics England). Heyden.
Laude, Lucien D., ed. Cohesive Properties of Semi-Conductors under Laser Irradiation. 1983. lib. bdg. 87.00 (ISBN 90-2472-857-6, Pub. by Martinus Nijhoff Netherlands). Kluwer Academic.
Leamy, H. J., et al, eds. Grain Boundaries in Semiconductors. Seager. (Materials Research Society Symposia Proceedings Ser.: Vol. 5). 418p. 1982. 76.50 (ISBN 0-444-00697-4, North-Holland). Elsevier.
Levin, Alexander A. Solid State Quantum Chemistry: The Chemical Bond & Energy Bands in Tetrahedral Semiconductors. 1977. text ed. 43.95x (ISBN 0-07-037435-X). McGraw.
Lindmayer, Joseph, et al. Fundamentals of Semiconductor Devices. LC 76-16765. 506p. 1979. Repr. of 1965 ed. 34.00 (ISBN 0-88275-424-6). Krieger.
McKelvey, John P. Solid State & Semiconductor Physics. LC 81-19390. 526p. 1982. Repr. of 1966 ed. 29.50 (ISBN 0-89874-396-6). Krieger.
Madelung, O., ed. Semiconductors: Physics of Group IV Elements & IL-V Compounds. (Landolt-Boernstein Ser.: Group III, Vol. 17, Pt. a). (Illus.). 670p. 1982. 499.30 (ISBN 0-387-10610-3). Springer-Verlag.
Malvino, A. P. Semiconductor Circuit Approximations: An Introduction to Transistors & Integrated Circuits; Experiments for Semiconductor Circuit Approximations. 4th ed. 128p. 1985. 31.95 (ISBN 0-07-039898-4); pap. 13.95 (ISBN 0-07-039899-2). McGraw.
Market Intelligence Research Company Staff. Semiconductor Automatic Test Equipment Markets. 125p. Date not set. pap. text ed. 595.00 (ISBN 0-317-19552-2). Market Res Co.
Masuda, Kohzoh & Silver, Marvin, eds. Energy & Charge Transfer in Organic Semiconductors. LC 74-7112. 200p. 1974. 39.50x (ISBN 0-306-30803-7, Plenum Pr). Plenum Pub.
Mayer, J. W., et al. Ion Implantation. 1970. 59.50 (ISBN 0-12-480850-6). Acad Pr.
Meese, J. M., ed. Neutron Transmutation Doping in Semiconductors. LC 79-395. 381p. 1979. 59.50x (ISBN 0-306-40155-X, Plenum Pr). Plenum Pub.
Meier, H. Organic Semiconductors: Dark & Photoconductivity of Organic Solids. LC 74-76846. (Monographs in Modern Chemistry: Vol. 2). (Illus.). 676p. 1974. 81.20x (ISBN 3-527-25438-2). VCH Pubs.
Melen, R. & Buss, D. Charged Coupled Devices: Technology & Applications. LC 76-20887. (IEEE Press Reprint Ser.). 415p. 1977. 34.95 (ISBN 0-471-02570-4). Wiley.
Melen, Roger & Buss, Dennis, eds. Charge-Coupled Devices: Technology & Applications. LC 76-20887. 1977. 36.35 (ISBN 0-87942-083-9, PC00802). Inst Electrical.
Metal Semiconductor Contracts: Manchester 1974. (Institute of Physics Conference Ser.: No. 22). 1974. 65.00 (ISBN 0-9960030-1-0, Pub. by Inst Physics England). Heyden.
Microscopy of Semiconducting Materials 1981. (Reports on Progress in Physics Ser.: No. 60). 1981. 75.00 (ISBN 0-9960039-6-7, Pub. by Inst Physics England). Heyden.
Military Gallium Arsenide Semiconductor Market (U.S.) 1985. write for info. (ISBN 0-86621-423-2, A1498). Frost & Sullivan.
Military Semiconductor Market. 207p. 1984. 1750.00 (ISBN 0-86621-206-X). Frost & Sullivan.
Milne, A. D. Mos Devices: Design & Manufacture. LC 83-110. 186p. 1985. 21.95x (ISBN 0-470-27421-2). Halsted Pr.
Milnes, A. G. Semiconductor Devices & Integrated Electronics. 1008p. 1980. 28.50 (ISBN 0-442-23660-3). Van Nos Reinhold.
--Semiconductor Devices & Integrated Electronics. 1008p. 1983. pap. 19.95 (ISBN 0-442-26217-5). Van Nos Reinhold.
Morgan, R. A. Plasma Etching in Semiconductor Fabrication: Plasma Technology, Vol. 1. 1985. 72.25 (ISBN 0-444-42419-9). Elsevier.
Mortenson, Kenneth E. & Borrego, Jose M., eds. Design, Performance & Application of Microwave Semiconductor Control Components. LC 70-189394. (Modern Frontiers in Applied Science Ser.). (Illus.). 290p. 1972. pap. 12.00x (ISBN 0-89006-009-6). Artech Hse.
Morton, R. M. One Hundred & Ten Semiconductor Projects for the Home Constructor. (Illus.). 1969. pap. 8.45 (ISBN 0-592-02864-X, NB 10, Pub. by Newnes-Butterworth). Hayden.
Muller, Richard S. & Kamins, Theodore I. Device Electronics for Integrated Circuits. LC 77-1332. 1977. 40.50 (ISBN 0-471-62364-4); solutions avail. (ISBN 0-471-03042-2). Wiley.
Murr, L. Solid State Electronics. (Electrical Engineering & Electronics Ser.: Vol. 4). 1978. 34.50 (ISBN 0-8247-6676-8). Dekker.
Myamlin, Viktor & Pleskov, Yurii V. Electrochemistry of Semiconductors. LC 66-12887. pap. 113.00 (ISBN 0-317-27893-2, 2055790). Bks Demand UMI.
Myamlin, Viktor A. & Pleskov, Yu. V. Electrochemistry of Semiconductors. LC 66-12887. 430p. 1967. 65.00x (ISBN 0-306-30275-6, Plenum Pr). Plenum Pub.
Myuller, Rudolf L. Electrical Conductivity of Vitreous Substances. LC 74-128508. 197p. 1971. 35.00x (ISBN 0-306-10847-X, Consultants). Plenum Pub.
Nag, B. R. Electron Transport in Compound Semiconductors. (Springer Ser. in Solid-State Sciences: Vol. 11). (Illus.). 470p. 1980. 56.00 (ISBN 3-540-09845-3). Springer-Verlag.
Nagaoka, Y. & Fukuyama, H., eds. Anderson Localization, Kyoto, Japan, 1981: Proceedings. (Springer Series in Solid-State Sciences: Vol. 39). (Illus.). 225p. 1982. 37.00 (ISBN 0-387-11518-8). Springer-Verlag.
Nagev, E., ed. Physics of Magnetic Semiconductors. 388p. 1983. 11.95 (ISBN 0-8285-5123-5, Pub. by Mir Pubs USSR). Imported Pubns.
Narayan, J. & Yan, T. Y, eds. Defects in Semiconductors. (Materials Research Society Symposia Proceedings Ser.: Vol. 2). 538p. 1981. 85.00 (ISBN 0-444-00596-X, North-Holland). Elsevier.
Nasledov, Dmitrii N. & Goryunova, N. A., eds. Soviet Research in New Semiconductor Materials. Tybulewicz, A., tr. LC 65-11956. pap. 31.50 (ISBN 0-317-09195-6, 2020668). Bks Demand UMI.
Nicollian, E. H. & Brews, J. R. MOS (Metal Oxide Semiconductor) Physics & Technology. LC 81-7607. 906p. 1982. 88.50x (ISBN 0-471-08500-6, Pub. by Wiley-Interscience). Wiley.
Nishizawa, J., ed. Semiconductor Technologies: Japan Annual Reviews in Electronics, Computers & Telecommunications. (Jarect Ser.: Vol. 13). 1985. 95.00 (ISBN 0-444-87504-2). Elsevier.
Nowogrodzki, M., ed. Advanced III-V Semiconductor Materials Technology Assessment. LC 83-22132. (Chemical Technology Review Ser.: 225). (Illus.). 220p. 1984. 32.00 (ISBN 0-8155-0974-X). Noyes.
Nozik, Arthur J., ed. Photoeffects at Semiconductor-Electrolyte Interfaces. LC 80-27773. (Symposium Ser.: No. 146). 1981. 44.95 (ISBN 0-8412-0604-X). Am Chemical.
OAS General Secretariat Department of Scientific & Technological Affairs. Semiconductors. 2nd ed. (Serie De Fisica (Monograph on Physics): No. 6). 63p. 1980. Repr. text ed. 3.50 (ISBN 0-8270-1068-0). OAS.
OECD. The Semiconductor Industry: Trade Related Issues. (Orig.). 1985. pap. 19.00x (ISBN 92-64-12687-2). OECD.
Okimoto, Daniel I., et al, eds. Competitive Edge: The Semiconductor Industry in the U. S. & Japan. LC 83-40107. (ISIS Studies in International Policy). xviii, 275p. 1984. 27.50x (ISBN 0-8047-1225-5). Stanford U Pr.
Pankove, Jacques I. Optical Processes in Semiconductors. 2nd ed. LC 75-16756. (Illus.). 448p. 1976. pap. text ed. 8.50 (ISBN 0-486-60275-3). Dover.
Pantelides, Sokrates T. Deep Centers in Semiconductors: A State-of-the-Art Approach. 772p. 1985. text ed. 95.00 (ISBN 2-88124-109-3). Gordon.
Paul, J. K., ed. High Technology International Trade & Competition: Robotics, Computers, Telecommunications, Semiconductors. LC 84-5916. (Illus.). 394p. 1984. 42.00 (ISBN 0-8155-0988-X). Noyes.
Paul, W. & Moss, T. S., eds. Handbook on Semiconductors: Band Theory & Transport Properties, Vol. 1. 842p. 1982. 157.50 (ISBN 0-444-85346-4, North-Holland). Elsevier.
Petrocelli Books Editorial Staff. The Future of the Semiconductors Computer, Robotics & Telecommunication: A Source Book. (Illus.). 300p. 1984. text ed. 49.95 (ISBN 0-89433-259-7). Petrocelli.
Phillips, J. C. Bonds & Bands in Semiconductors. (Materials, Science & Technology Ser.). 1973. 69.00 (ISBN 0-12-553350-0). Acad Pr.
Physics of Semiconductors: Edinburgh 1978. (Institute of Physics Conference Ser.: No. 43). 1979. 87.50 (ISBN 0-9960032-3-1, Pub. by Inst Physics England). Heyden.
Pilkuhn, M., ed. High Excitation & Short Pulse Phenomena: Proceedings of the IUPAP Semiconductor Symposium, 3rd, 26 July, 1984, Trieste, Italy. 606p. 1985. 74.00 (ISBN 0-444-86931-X, North-Holland). Elsevier.
Poate, John M. & Mayer, James W. Laser Annealing of Semiconductors. 1982. 67.00 (ISBN 0-12-558820-8). Acad Pr.
Power Semiconductor Market. 236p. 1984. 1450.00 (ISBN 0-86621-237-X). Frost & Sullivan.
Prince, Betty & Due-Gundersen, Gunnar. Semiconductor Memories. LC 82-24804. 201p. 1983. 23.95x (ISBN 0-471-90146-6, Pub. by Wiley-Interscience). Wiley.
Rabii, S. Physics of Four-Six Compounds & Alloys. 264p. 1974. 69.50x (ISBN 0-677-05070-4). Gordon.
Radiation Damage & Defects in Semiconductors: Reading 1972. (Institute of Physics Conference Ser.: No. 16). 1972. 60.00 (ISBN 0-9960029-5-2, Pub. by Inst Physics England). Heyden.
Radiation Effects in Semiconductors: 1976. (Institute of Physics Conference Ser.: No. 31). 1977. 75.00 (ISBN 0-9960031-0-X, Pub. by Inst Physics England). Heyden.
Rauluskiewicz, J., et al. Physics of Narrow Gap Semiconductors. (Proceedings). 1978. 85.00 (ISBN 0-444-99801-2). Elsevier.
Ravi, K. V. Imperfections & Impurities in Semiconductor Silicon. LC 80-21978. 379p. 1981. 54.50x (ISBN 0-471-07817-4, Pub. by Wiley-Interscience). Wiley.
Ridley, B. K. Quantum Processes in Semiconductors. (Illus.). 1982. 49.00x (ISBN 0-19-851150-7). Oxford U Pr.
Roggwiller, P. & Sittig, Roland, eds. Semiconductor Devices for Power Conditioning. LC 82-16167. (Brown Boveri Symposia Ser.). 384p. 1982. 55.00x (ISBN 0-306-41131-8, Plenum Pr). Plenum Pub.
Ryvkin, S. M. & Shmartsev, Y. V., eds. Physics of p-n Junctions & Semiconductor Devices. LC 72-128510. 366p. 1971. 45.00x (ISBN 0-306-10846-1, Consultants). Plenum Pub.
Ryvkin, Solomon M. Photoelectric Effects in Semiconductors. LC 64-25832. 402p. 1964. 45.00x (ISBN 0-306-10684-1, Consultants). Plenum Pub.
Saleh, Adel A. Theory of Resistive Mixers. 1971. 27.50x (ISBN 0-262-19093-1). MIT Pr.
Schulz, M. J. & Pensl, G., eds. Insulating Films on Semiconductors: Proceedings. (Springer Series in Electrophsyics: Vol. 7). (Illus.). 312p. 1981. 32.00 (ISBN 0-387-11021-6). Springer Verlag.
Seeger, K. Semiconductor Physics: An Introduction. 2nd ed. (Springer Series in Solid-State Sciences: Vol. 40). (Illus.). 510p. 1982. 42.00 (ISBN 0-387-11421-1). Springer-Verlag.
Seidman, Arthur H. & Waintraub, Jack L. Electronics: Devices, Discrete & Integrated Circuits. (Electronics Technology Ser.). 1977. text ed. 31.95 (ISBN 0-675-08494-6). Additional supplements may be obtained from publisher. Merrill.
Selberherr, S. Analysis & Simulation of Semiconductor Devices. (Illus.). 300p. 1984. 54.00 (ISBN 0-387-81800-6). Springer-Verlag.
Self Study Books in Electrical & Semiconductor Engineering: P3 The Magnetic Field. 1978. pap. 3.95 (ISBN 0-471-25970-5). Wiley.
Semi-Conductor C-028: Crystals, Junctions, Dopants. 1982. 1250.00 (ISBN 0-89336-251-4). BCC.
Semiconductor Chip Protection Act of 1984. 35.00 (ISBN 0-317-29500-4, #CO3298, Law & Business). HarBraceJ.
Semiconductor Detectors. (Advanced Health Physics Training Ser.). (Illus.). 106p. 1983. training materials pkg. 1700.00x (ISBN 0-87683-197-8); looseleaf 45.00x (ISBN 0-87683-198-6); lesson plans 1250.00x (ISBN 0-87683-199-4); transparencies 250.00x (ISBN 0-87683-200-1); question bank 625.00x (ISBN 0-87683-201-X). G P Courseware.
Semiconductors: Subvolume E-Physics of Non-Tetrahodrally Bonded Elements & Binary Compounds I. (Landolt-Boernstein, New Series-Group III: Vol. 17). (Illus.). 410p. 1983. 361.60 (ISBN 0-387-11780-6). Springer-Verlag.
SEMINEX Technical Seminar & Exhibition, London, England, March 26-30, 1979. Semiconductor & Microprocesor Technology 1979: Selected Papers. Dummer, G. W. A., ed. (Illus.). 252p. 1980. pap. 55.00 (ISBN 0-08-026134-5). Pergamon.
Seraphin, B. O., ed. Solar Energy Conversion: Solid-State Physics Aspects. (Topics in Applied Physics: Vol. 31). (Illus.). 1979. 60.00 (ISBN 0-387-09224-2). Springer-Verlag.
Severns, Rudy & Armijos, Jack, eds. Mospower Applications Handbook. (Illus.). 512p. 1985. 20.00 (ISBN 0-930519-00-0). Siliconix Inc.
Seymour, J. Electronic Devices & Components. LC 80-28112. 504p. 1981. pap. 32.95x (ISBN 0-470-27108-6). Halsted Pr.
Sharma, B. L., ed. Metal-Semiconductor Schottky Barrier Junctions & Their Applications. 386p. 1984. 52.50x (ISBN 0-306-41521-6, Plenum Pr). Plenum Pub.
Shaw, D., ed. Atomic Diffusion in Semiconductors. LC 74-178779. 607p. 1973. 89.50x (ISBN 0-306-30455-4, Plenum Pr). Plenum Pub.
Shaw, M. P., et al. The Gunn-Hilsum Effect. LC 76-45995. 1979. 37.50 (ISBN 0-12-638350-2). Acad Pr.
Shklovskii, B. I. & Efros, A. L. Electronic Properties of Doped Semiconductors. (Springer Series in Solid-State Sciences: Vol. 45). (Illus.). 350p. 1984. 49.00 (ISBN 0-387-12995-2). Springer-Verlag.
Shmartsev, Yu T., et al. Refractory Semiconductor Materials. LC 65-27346. 103p. 1966. 24.50x (ISBN 0-306-10747-3, Consultants). Plenum Pub.
Shuey, R. T. Semi-Conducting Ore Minerals. (Developments in Economic Geology Ser: Vol. 4). 415p. 1975. 66.00 (ISBN 0-444-41357-X). Elsevier.
Simon, J. & Andre, J. J. Molecular Semiconductors. Lehn, J. M. & Rees, C. W., eds. (Illus.). 350p. 1985. 59.00 (ISBN 0-387-13754-8). Springer-Verlag.
Sirota, N. N., ed. Chemical Bonds in Semiconductors & Solids. LC 66-17188. 293p. 1968. 32.50x (ISBN 0-306-10779-1, Consultants). Plenum Pub.
--Chemical Bonds in Semiconductors & Thermodynamics. LC 66-17188. (Illus.). 293p. 1968. 37.50x (ISBN 0-306-10804-6, Consultants). Plenum Pub.
Skobel'tsyn, D. V., ed. Electrical & Optical Properties of Semiconductors. LC 68-18561. (P. N. Lebedev Physics Institute Ser.: Vol. 37). (Illus.). 196p. 1968. 32.50x (ISBN 0-306-10806-2, Consultants). Plenum Pub.
--Quantum Electronics in Lasers & Masers, Pt. 1. LC 68-13059. (P. N. Lebedev Physics Institute Ser.: Vol. 31). (Illus.). 161p. 1968. 32.50x (ISBN 0-306-10800-3, Consultants). Plenum Pub.
--Surface Properties of Semiconductors & Dynamics of Ionic Crystals. LC 77-136983. (P. N. Lebedev Physics Institute Ser.: Vol. 48). 148p. 1971. 27.50x (ISBN 0-306-10854-2, Consultants). Plenum Pub.

Steklov Institute of Mathematics, Academy of Sciences, U S S R, No. 107. Equations in a Free Semigroup, 1971: Proceedings. Hmelevsky, Ju. I., ed. LC 76-4883. (Proceedings of Symposia in Pure Mathematics: No. 107). 1976. 90.00 (ISBN 0-8218-3007-4, STEKLO-107). Am Math.

VanCasteren, J. A. Generators of Strongly Continuous Semigroups. (Research Notes in Mathematics Ser.: No. 115). 216p. 1985. pap. text ed. 17.95 (ISBN 0-273-08669-3). Pitman Pub Ma.

SEMIMETALS

Willardson. Semiconductors & Semimetals, Vol. 23. 1985. 66.00 (ISBN 0-317-26972-0). Acad Pr.

Willardson & Beer, eds. Semiconductors & Semimetals, Vol. 22: Lightwave Communications Technology, Pt. E. Integrated Optoelectronics. Date not set. price not set (ISBN 0-12-752154-2). Acad Pr.

Willardson, R. K. & Beer, Albert C. Semiconductors & Semimetals, Vol. 21B: Hydrogenated Amorphous Silicon: Optical Properties. 1984. 75.00 (ISBN 0-12-752148-8). Acad Pr.

Willardson, R. K. & Beer, A., eds. Semiconductors & Semimetals: Lightwave Communication Technology: Pt. B, Material Growth Technologies, Vol. 22. 1985. 55.00 (ISBN 0-12-752151-8). Acad Pr.

Willardson, R. K. & Beer, A. C., eds. Semiconductors & Semimetals. Incl. Vol. 1. Physics of III-V Compounds. 1967. 83.00 (ISBN 0-12-752101-1); Vol. 2. Physics of III-V Compounds. 1966. 83.00 (ISBN 0-12-752102-X); Vol. 3. Optical Properties of III-V Compounds. 1967. 83.00 (ISBN 0-12-752103-8); Vol. 4. Physics of III-V Compounds. 1968. 83.00 (ISBN 0-12-752104-6); Vol. 5. Infrared Detectors. 1970. 83.00 (ISBN 0-12-752105-4); Vol. 6. Injection Phenomena. 1970. 83.00 (ISBN 0-12-752106-2); Vol. 7A. Semiconductor Applications & Devices. 1971. 83.00 (ISBN 0-12-752107-0); Vol. 7B. Applications & Devices. 1971. 83.00 (ISBN 0-12-752147-X); Vol. 8. Techniques for Studying Semiconducting Materials. 1972. 83.00 (ISBN 0-12-752108-9); Vol. 9. Modulation Techniques. 1972. 83.00 (ISBN 0-12-752109-7); Vol. 10. 1975. 83.00 (ISBN 0-12-752110-0); Vol. 11. 1976. 30.00 (ISBN 0-12-752111-9); Vol. 12. 1977. 78.00 (ISBN 0-12-752112-7). Acad Pr.

--Semiconductors & Semimetals: Hydrogenated Amorphous Silicon, Pt. C: Electronic & Transport Properties, Vol. 21C. 1984. 74.50 (ISBN 0-12-752149-6). Acad Pr.

--Semiconductors & Semimetals: Hydrogenated Amorphous Silicon, Pt. D: Device Applications, Vol. 21D. 1984. 65.00 (ISBN 0-12-752150-X). Acad Pr.

Willardson, R. K. & Beer, Albert C., eds. Semiconductors & Semimetals, Vol. 20. LC 65-20648. 1984. 77.00 (ISBN 0-12-752120-8). Acad Pr.

Willardson, R. K., et al, eds. Semiconductors & Semimetals: Cadmium Telluride. 1978. Vol. 13. 45.00 (ISBN 0-12-752113-5); Vol. 14. 1979. 49.50 (ISBN 0-12-752114-3). Acad Pr.

Willardson, Robert & Beer, A., eds. Semiconductors & Semimetals, Vol. 16: Defects, HgCd, Se, HgCdO & Te. 1981. 44.00 (ISBN 0-12-752116-X). Acad Pr.

Willardson, Robert & Beer, A. C., eds. Semiconductors & Semimetals: Contacts, Junctions, Emitters, Vol. 15. 1981. 57.50 (ISBN 0-12-752115-1). Acad Pr.

--Semiconductors & Semimetals, Vol. 18: Mercury Cadmium Telluride. 1981. 65.50 (ISBN 0-12-752118-6). Acad Pr.

Willardson, Robert K. & Beer, Albert C., eds. Semiconductors & Semimetals: Deep Levels, Gas Alloys, Photochemistry, Vol. 19. LC 65-26048. 1983. 59.00 (ISBN 0-12-752119-4). Acad Pr.

SEMI-PRECIOUS STONES

see Precious Stones

SEMIQUINONE

see Quinone

SEMPERVIVUM

Praeger, R. L. An Account of the Sempervivum Group. 1967. pap. 14.00 (ISBN 3-7682-0445-6). Lubrecht & Cramer.

SENSATION

see Senses and Sensation

SENSE DATA

Basic Principles of Sensory Evaluation - STP 433. 110p. 1968. pap. 5.75 (ISBN 0-8031-0784-6, 04-433000-36). ASTM.

Correlation of Subjective-Objective Methods in the Study of Odors & Taste, STP 440. 112p. 1968. pap. 5.75 (ISBN 0-8031-0017-5, 04-440000-36). ASTM.

Manual on Sensory Testing Methods- STP 434. 82p. 1968. pap. 4.25 (ISBN 0-8031-0018-3, 04-434000-36). ASTM.

SENSE-ORGANS

see also Chemoreceptors; Senses and Sensation; also names of sense organs, e.g. Ear, Eye, Nose

Cold Spring Harbor Symposia on Quantitative Biology: Sensory Receptors, Vol. 30. LC 34-8174. (Illus.). 663p. 1966. 38.00x (ISBN 0-87969-029-1). Cold Spring Harbor.

Hayes, A. Wallace, ed. Toxicology of the Eye, Ear, & Other Special Senses. (Target Organ Toxicology Ser.). 268p. 1985. text ed. 56.50 (ISBN 0-89004-840-1). Raven.

Laverack, M. S. & Cosens, D. J., eds. Sense Organs. (Illus.). 394p. 1982. 85.00x (ISBN 0-216-91094-3). Intl Ideas.

Neff, William D., ed. Contributions to Sensory Physiology, 5 vols. Incl. Vol. 1. 1965 (ISBN 0-12-151801-9); Vol. 2. 1967 (ISBN 0-12-151802-7); Vol. 3. 1969 (ISBN 0-12-151803-5); Vol. 4. 1970 (ISBN 0-12-151804-3); Vol. 5. 1971 (ISBN 0-12-151805-1). 65.00 ea. Acad Pr.

Porter, R., ed. Studies in Neurophysiology. LC 87-51674. (Illus.). 1978. 115.00 (ISBN 0-521-22019-X). Cambridge U Pr.

Sensory Processes, 2 Pts. (Handbook of Physiology Section 1: The Nervous System, Vol. III). 1244p. 1984. 275.00 (ISBN 0-683-01108-1). Am Physiological.

Zoological Society Of London - 23rd Symposium. Invertebrate Receptors. Newall, ed. 1968. 54.00 (ISBN 0-12-613323-9). Acad Pr.

Zotterman, Yngve, ed. Sensory Functions of the Skin with Special Reference to Man. LC 76-20572. 1976. text ed. 89.00 (ISBN 0-08-021208-5). Pergamon.

SENSES AND SENSATION

see also Hearing; Sense Data; Sense-Organs; Space Perception; Taste; Vision

Amerine, Maynard A., et al. Principles of Sensory Evaluation of Food. (Food and Science Technology Monographs). 1965. 75.00 (ISBN 0-12-056150-6). Acad Pr.

Ammon, Jeanne E. & Etzel, Mary E. Sensorimotor Organization in Reach & Prehension: A Developmental Model. 1977. pap. 2.50 (ISBN 0-912452-19-6). Am Phys Therapy Assn.

Autrum, H., et al, eds. Handbook of Sensory Physiology, 8 vols. Incl. Vol. 1. Principles of Receptor Physiology. Loewenstein, W. R., ed. 1971. 76.00 (ISBN 0-387-05144-9); Vol. 2. Somatosensory System. Iggo, A., ed. 1973. 158.00 (ISBN 0-387-05941-5); Vol. 3, Pt. 1. Enteroceptors. Neil, E., ed. 1972. 39.50 (ISBN 0-387-05523-1); Vol. 3, Pt. 2. Muscle Receptors. Hunt, C. C., et al. 1974. 78.00 (ISBN 0-387-06891-0); Vol. 4. Chemical Sense. Beidler, L. M., ed. 1971. Pt. 1 Olfaction. 63.00 (ISBN 0-387-05291-7); Pt. 2. Taste. 58.00 (ISBN 0-387-05501-0); Vol. 5, Pt. 1. Auditory System. 152.00 (ISBN 0-387-06676-4); Vol. 6, Pt. 1. Vestibular System. Kornhuber, H. H., ed. 148.00 (ISBN 0-387-06889-9); Vol. 7, Pt. 1. Photochemistry of Vision. Dartnall, H. J., ed. 1972. 93.00 (ISBN 0-387-05145-7); Vol. 7, Pt. 2. Physiology of Photoreceptor Organs. Fuortes, M. G., ed. 1972. 115.00 (ISBN 0-387-05743-9); Vol. 7, Pts. 3A & 3B. Central Processing of Vision Information. Jung, R., ed. LC 70-190496. 1973. Pt. A. 149.00 (ISBN 0-387-05769-2); Pt. B. 137.00 (ISBN 0-387-06056-1). Pt. B; Vol. 7, Pt. 4. Visual Psychophysics. Jameson, D. & Hurvich, L. M., eds. 1972. 125.00 (ISBN 0-387-05146-5); Vol. 8. Perception. Teuber, H. L., ed. 155.00 (ISBN 0-387-08300-6). Springer-Verlag.

Bach-Y-Rita, Paul & Collins, C. C., eds. Brain Mechanisms in Sensory Substitution. 1972. 40.00 (ISBN 0-12-071040-4). Acad Pr.

Barlow, H. B. & Mollon, J. D., eds. The Senses. LC 81-17007. (Cambridge Texts in the Physiological Sciences Ser.: No. 3). (Illus.). 400p. 1982. 67.50 (ISBN 0-521-24474-9); pap. 22.95 (ISBN 0-521-28714-6). Cambridge U Pr.

Bosma, James F. Third Symposium on Oral Sensation & Perception: The Mouth of the Infant. (Illus.). 484p. 1972. 58.75x (ISBN 0-398-02238-0). C C Thomas.

Burton, Maurice. The Sixth Sense of Animals. LC 72-6622. (Illus.). 192p. 1973. 7.95 (ISBN 0-8008-7232-0). Taplinger.

Burtt, E. T. & Pringle, A. The Senses of Animals. LC 73-77794. (Wykeham Science Ser.: No. 26). 168p. 1974. 9.95x (ISBN 0-8448-1153-X). Crane-Russak Co.

Colombetti, Giuliano & Lenci, Francesco, eds. Membranes & Sensory Transduction. 375p. 1984. 52.50x (ISBN 0-306-41439-2, Plenum Pr). Plenum Pub.

Colombetti, Giuliano, et al, eds. Sensory Perception & Transduction in Aneural Organisms. (NATO ASI Series A, UFE Sciences: Vol. 89). 338p. 1985. 52.50x (ISBN 0-306-42000-7, Plenum Pr). Plenum Pub.

Coren, Stanley, et al. Sensation & Perception. 2nd ed. 1984. 22.00i (ISBN 0-12-188555-0); pap. 5.00i instr's. manual (ISBN 0-12-188556-9). Acad Pr.

Correia, Manning J. & Perachio, Adrian A. Contemporary Sensory Neurobiology. LC 85-142. (Progress in Clinical & Biological Research Ser.: Vol. 176). 372p. 1985. 58.00 (ISBN 0-8451-5026-X). A R Liss.

Dawson, W. W. & Enoch, J. M., eds. Foundations of Sensory Science. (Illus.). 615p. 1984. 108.00 (ISBN 0-387-12967-7). Springer Verlag.

Dubner, Ronald & Kawamura, Yojiro, eds. Oral-Facial Sensory & Motor Mechanisms. LC 75-135617. 384p. 1971. 32.50x (ISBN 0-306-50018-3, Plenum Pr). Plenum Pub.

The Five Senses. 1982. 1.00 (ISBN 0-939418-45-2). Ferguson-Florissant.

Galun, Rachel, et al, eds. Sensory Physiology & Behavior. LC 75-14130. (Advances in Behavioral Biology Ser.: Vol. 15). 367p. 1975. 49.50x (ISBN 0-306-37915-5, Plenum Pr). Plenum Pub.

Geldard, Frank A. Human Senses. 2nd ed. LC 72-37432. 584p. 1972. text ed. 50.45x (ISBN 0-471-29570-1). Wiley.

Gibson, James J. The Senses Considered as Perceptual Systems. (Illus.). 336p. 1983. pap. text ed. 15.95x (ISBN 0-88133-062-0). Waveland Pr.

Goldstein, E. Bruce. Sensation & Perception. 2nd ed. 481p. 1984. text ed. write for info. (ISBN 0-534-03035-1). Wadsworth Pub.

Granit, Ragnar. Receptors & Sensory Perception. LC 75-14597. (Mrs. Hepsa Ely Silliman Memorial Lectures). (Illus.). 369p. 1975. Repr. of 1955 ed. lib. bdg. 24.75x (ISBN 0-8371-8213-1, GRRS). Greenwood.

Grastyan, E. & Molnar, P., eds. Sensory Functions: Proceedings of the 28th International Congress of Physiological Sciences, Budapest, 1980. LC 80-41852. (Advances in Physiological Sciences). (Illus.). 350p. 1981. 44.00 (ISBN 0-08-027337-8). Pergamon.

Guidelines for the Selection & Training of Censory Panel Members - STP 758. 35p. 1981. pap. 7.25 (ISBN 0-8031-0783-8, 04-758000-36). ASTM.

Hudson, William H. A Hind in Richmond Park. Repr. of 1923 ed. 35.00 (ISBN 0-404-03413-6). AMS Pr.

Jacobson, M., ed. Development of Sensory Systems. (Handbook of Sensory Physiology: Vol. 9). (Illus.). 1978. 135.00 (ISBN 0-387-08632-3). Springer-Verlag.

Kaufman, Lloyd. Perception: The World Transformed. (Illus.). 1979. 29.95x (ISBN 0-19-502464-8). Oxford U Pr.

Kuznicki & Rutkiewic, eds. Selected Sensory Methods Problems & Approaches to Measuring Hedonics - STP 773. 113p. 1982. pap. 11.95 (ISBN 0-8031-0782-X, 04-773000-36). ASTM.

Lloyd, Geoffrey E. & Owen, G. E., eds. Aristotle on Mind & the Senses. LC 77-9389. (Classical Studies). 1978. 44.50 (ISBN 0-521-21669-9). Cambridge U Pr.

Lobb, Nancy. The Five Senses. (Science in Action Ser.). (Illus.). 48p. 1982. pap. text ed. 2.85 (ISBN 0-915510-75-8). Janus Bks.

Ludel, Jacqueline. Introduction to Sensory Processes. LC 77-16785. (Psychology Ser.). (Illus.). 401p. 1978. pap. text ed. 15.95x (ISBN 0-7167-0031-X). W H Freeman.

McBurney, D. & Collings. Introduction to Sensation-Perception. (Experimental Psychology Ser.). 1977. O.P. 26.95 (ISBN 0-13-496000-9). P-H.

McBurney, Donald H. & Collings, Virginia B. Introduction to Sensation-Perception. 2nd ed. (Illus.). 368p. 1984. text ed. 28.95 (ISBN 0-13-496019-X). P-H.

Masterton, R. Bruce, ed. Handbook of Behavioral Neurobiology, Vol. 1: Sensory Integration. new ed. LC 78-17238. 600p. 1978. 55.00x (ISBN 0-306-35191-9, Plenum Pr). Plenum Pub.

Mayer, Melanie J. & Hooper, K. S. Sensory Perception Laboratory Manual. 333p. 1982. pap. 17.95 (ISBN 0-471-09276-2); write for info tchr's manual (ISBN 0-471-87679-8). Wiley.

Montagu, Ashley. Touching: The Human Significance of the Skin. LC 75-151290. (Illus.). 1971. 25.00x (ISBN 0-231-03488-1). Columbia U Pr.

Moskowitz, H. R. & Scharf, B., eds. Sensation & Measurement: Papers in Honor of S. S. Stevens. LC 74-77966. 550p. 1974. lib. bdg. 74.00 (ISBN 90-277-0474-0, Pub. by Reidel Holland). Kluwer Academic.

Neff, William D. Contributions to Sensory Physiology, Vol. 8. (Serial Publication). 1984. 44.00 (ISBN 0-12-151808-6). Acad Pr.

Neff, William D., ed. Contributions to Sensory Physiology, 5 vols. Incl. Vol. 1. 1965 (ISBN 0-12-151801-9); Vol. 2. 1967 (ISBN 0-12-151802-7); Vol. 3. 1969 (ISBN 0-12-151803-5); Vol. 4. 1970 (ISBN 0-12-151804-3); Vol. 5. 1971 (ISBN 0-12-151805-1). 65.00 ea. Acad Pr.

Ordy, J. Mark & Brizzee, Kenneth, eds. Sensory Systems & Communication in the Elderly. LC 79-65426. (Aging Ser.: Vol. 10). 334p. 1979. text ed. 46.00 (ISBN 0-89004-235-7). Raven.

Ottoson, D., et al, eds. Progress in Sensory Physiology, Vol. 1. (Illus.). 160p. 1981. 39.00 (ISBN 0-387-08413-4). Springer-Verlag.

Rincover, Arnold. How to Use Sensory Extinction. 34p. 1981. 6.00 (ISBN 0-89079-062-0). Pro Ed.

Schiff, William & Foulke, Emerson, eds. Tactual Perception: A Sourcebook. LC 81-10172. (Illus.). 500p. 1982. 44.50 (ISBN 0-521-24095-6). Cambridge U Pr.

Schiffman, Harvey R. Sensation & Perception: An Integrated Approach. 540p. 1982. 33.50 (ISBN 0-471-08208-2). Wiley.

Schmidt, Robert F., ed. Fundamentals of Sensory Physiology. 2nd, rev. ed. Biederman-Thorson, M. A., tr. (Springer Study Edition Ser.). (Illus.). 286p. 1981. pap. 22.00 (ISBN 0-387-10349-X). Springer-Verlag.

Sensory Evaluation of Appearance of Materials-STP 545. 194p. 1973. 19.75 (ISBN 0-8031-0564-9, 04-545000-36). ASTM.

Spillmann, Lothar & Wooten, Bill, eds. Sensory Experience, Adaptation & Perception: Festschrift for Ivo Kohler. 796p. 1983. text ed. 74.95x (ISBN 0-89859-218-6). L Erlbaum Assocs.

Tamar, Henry. Principles of Sensory Physiology. (Illus.). 408p. 1972. photocopy ed. 39.50x (ISBN 0-398-02209-7). C C Thomas.

Vinnikov, Y. A. Sensory Reception: Cytology, Molecular Mechanisms & Evolution. LC 74-412. (Molecular Biology, Biochemistry & Biophysics Ser.: Vol. 17). (Illus.). x, 392p. 1974. 71.00 (ISBN 0-387-06674-8). Springer-Verlag.

Von Bekesy, George. Sensory Inhibition. LC 66-17713. 1967. 29.00x (ISBN 0-691-08612-5); pap. text ed. 7.95 (ISBN 0-691-02453-7). Princeton U Pr.

Wenzel, Bernice M. & Zeigler, H. Philip, eds. Tonic Functions of Sensory Systems, Vol. 290. (Annals of the New York Academy of Sciences Ser.). 435p. 1977. 52.00x (ISBN 0-89072-036-3). NY Acad Sci.

Zuckerman, Marvin, ed. Biological Bases for Sensation Seeking, Impulsivity & Anxiety. 288p. 1983. text ed. 29.95x (ISBN 0-89859-255-0). L Erlbaum Assocs.

SENSES AND SENSATION–DATA PROCESSING

Brock, ed. Robot Vision & Sensory Control: Proceedings of the Second International Conference, Stuttgart, BRD, Nov. 1982. iv, 388p. 1983. 85.00 (ISBN 0-444-86548-9, North-Holland). Elsevier.

Carnegie Symposium on Cognition, Eighth Annual. Visual Information Processing: Proceedings. Chase, William G., ed. 1973. 49.50 (ISBN 0-12-170150-6). Acad Pr.

Reichardt, W., ed. Processing of Optical Data by Organisms & by Machines. (Italian Physical Society: Course No. 43). 1970. 95.00 (ISBN 0-12-368843-4). Acad Pr.

Schumaker, Robert A., et al. Study for Applying Computer-Generated Images to Visual Stimulation. LC 74-131394. 142p. 1969. 19.00 (ISBN 0-403-04536-3). Scholarly.

Shaw, M. L., ed. Recent Advances in Personal Construct Technology. (Computers & People Ser.). 1981. 39.00 (ISBN 0-12-639260-9). Acad Pr.

Stone, Jonathan. Parallel Processing in the Visual Systems: The Classification of Retinal Ganglion Cells & Its Impact on the Neurobiology of Vision. (Perspectives in Vision Research Ser.). 430p. 1983. 55.00x (ISBN 0-306-41220-9, Plenum Pr). Plenum Pub.

SENSING, REMOTE

see Remote Sensing

SENSITOMETRY, PHOTOGRAPHIC

see Photographic Sensitometry

SEPARATION (TECHNOLOGY)

see also Adsorption; Chromatographic Analysis; Crystallization; Diffusion; Distillation; Electrophoresis; Emulsions; Extraction (Chemistry); Flotation; Fluidization; Isotope Separation; Membranes (Technology); Osmosis; Precipitation (Chemistry); Separators (Machines)

Bhatia, Mahesh V. & Cheremisinoff, Paul N. Solids Separation & Mixing. LC 79-63114. (Process Equipment Ser.: Vol. 1). 303p. 1979. 35.00 (ISBN 0-87762-272-8). Technomic.

Brian, P. L. Staged Cascades in Chemical Processing. (International Series in the Physical & Chemical Engineering Sciences). (Illus.). 272p. 1972. ref. ed. 38.95 (ISBN 0-13-840280-9). P-H.

Business Communications Staff. Gas Separation. 1985. pap. 1950.00 (ISBN 0-89336-422-3, C-062). BCC.

Chemical Engineering Magazine. Separation Techniques I: Liquid-Liquid Systems. (Chemical Engineering Book). 384p. 1980. 39.50 (ISBN 0-07-010711-4). McGraw.

--Separation Techniques II: Gas-Liquid-Solid Systems. (Chemical Engineering Book). 400p. 1980. 35.00 (ISBN 0-07-010717-3). McGraw.

Freeman, Mark P. & FitzPatrick, Joseph A., eds. Theory, Practice & Process Principles for Physical Separation. LC 81-68949. 750p. 1981. pap. 50.00 (ISBN 0-8169-0204-6, P-32); pap. 40.00 members (ISBN 0-317-03776-5). Am Inst Chem Eng.

Gerritsen, Theo, ed. Modern Separation of Macromolecules & Particles. LC 69-14292. (Progress in Separation & Purification Ser.: Vol. 2). (Illus.). pap. 65.50 (ISBN 0-317-09353-3, 2011958). Bks Demand UMI.

Grushka, E. New Developments in Separation Methods. 1976. 49.75 (ISBN 0-8247-6411-0). Dekker.

Henley, Ernest J. & Seader, J. D. Equilibrium-Stage Separation Operations in Chemical Engineering. LC 80-13293. 742p. 1981. text ed. 54.95 (ISBN 0-471-37108-4, Pub. by Wiley-Interscience). Wiley.

Holland, C. Fundamentals & Modeling of Separation Processes: Absorption, Distillation, Evaporation & Extraction. (International Ser. in Physical & Chemical Engineering Science). (Illus.). 464p. 1975. 44.95 (ISBN 0-13-344390-6). P-H.

Karger, Barry L., et al. Introduction to Separation Science. LC 73-4016. 586p. 1973. 39.50x (ISBN 0-471-45860-0, Pub. by Wiley-Interscience). Wiley.

King, C. Judson. Separation Processes. 2nd ed. (Chemical Engineering Ser.). (Illus.). 1979. text ed. 44.00 (ISBN 0-07-034612-7). McGraw.

Lemlich, Robert. Adsorptive Bubble Separation Techniques. 1972. 71.50 (ISBN 0-12-443350-2). Acad Pr.

LeRoith, Derek, et al, eds. Purification of Fermentation Products: Applications to Large-Scale Processes. LC 84-24316. (ACS Symposium Ser.: No. 271). 198p. 1985. lib. bdg. 44.95x (ISBN 0-8412-0890-5). Am Chemical.

The Less-Common Means of Separation: Proceedings, No. 12, Birmingham, April 1963. 128p. 1981. 30.00x (ISBN 0-85295-084-5, Pub. by Inst Chem Eng England). State Mutual Bk.

Li, Norman N. Recent Developments in Separation Science, Vols. VI & VII. 1981. Vol. VI, 208p. 71.50 (ISBN 0-8493-5487-0); Vol. VII, 224p. 76.50 (ISBN 0-8493-5488-9). CRC Pr.

--Recent Developments in Separation Science, Vol. 5. 288p. 1979. 71.50 (ISBN 0-8493-5485-4). CRC Pr.

Li, Norman N., ed. Recent Developments in Separation Science, 5 vols. LC 72-88417. (Uniscience Ser.). Vol. 1, 229 Pgs. 61.00 (ISBN 0-8493-5029-8); Vol. 2, 1972, 292p. 66.00 (ISBN 0-8493-5030-1); Vol. 3A, 1977, 224p. 62.00 (ISBN 0-8493-5481-1); Vol. 3B, 1977, 200p. 56.00 (ISBN 0-8493-5482-X); Vol. 4, 1978, 248p. 65.00 (ISBN 0-8493-5483-8). CRC Pr.

Marinsky, Jacob A. & Marcus, Yizhok, eds. Ion Exchange & Solvent Extraction, Vol. 5. 294p. 1973. 65.00 (ISBN 0-8247-6061-1). Dekker.

Miller, James M. Separation Methods in Chemical Analysis. LC 74-13781. 309p. 1975. 45.00x (ISBN 0-471-60490-9, Pub. by Wiley-Interscience). Wiley.

Parsonage, P. Commercial Application of Solids Separation Using Paramagnetic Liquids: Economic & Technical Considerations, 1978. 1981. 69.00x (ISBN 0-686-97046-2, Pub. by W Spring England). State Mutual Bk.

--Design & Testing of Paramagnetic Liquid Separation Systems, 1978. 1981. 69.00x (ISBN 0-686-97054-3, Pub. by W Spring England). State Mutual Bk.

Pratt, Henry R. Countercurrent Separation Processes. 537p. 1967. 76.75 (ISBN 0-444-40461-9). Elsevier.

Solids Separation Processes: Proceedings, Dublin, 1980. (Symposium Ser.: No. 59). 650p. 1981. 139.00x (ISBN 0-85295-121-3, Pub. by Inst Chem Eng England). State Mutual Bk.

Svarovsky, Ladislav. Solid-Liquid Separation. 2nd ed. 1981. text ed. 79.95 (ISBN 0-408-70943-X). Butterworth.

Wakeman, R. J., ed. Progress in Filtration & Separation, Vol. 1. 346p. 1979. 72.50 (ISBN 0-444-41819-9). Elsevier.

--Progress in Filtration & Separation, Vol. 2. 306p. 1981. 72.50 (ISBN 0-444-42006-1). Elsevier.

Weissberger, Arnold & Hsu, Hsien-Wen. Separations by Centrifugal Phenomena. LC 81-4991. (Techniques of Chemistry Ser.: Vol. 16). 466p. 1981. 78.50x (ISBN 0-471-05564-6, Pub. by Wiley-Interscience). Wiley.

SEPARATORS (MACHINES)

see also Centrifuges; Filters and Filtration

Stephens, H. S. & Priestley, G., eds. Papers Presented at the International Conference on Hydrocyclones. (Illus.). 247p. (Orig.). 1980. pap. 69.00x (ISBN 0-906085-48-9). BHRA Fluid.

Storch, O. Industrial Separators for Gas Cleaning. LC 78-10916. (Chemical Engineering Monographs: Vol. 6). 388p. 1979. 66.00 (ISBN 0-444-99808-X). Elsevier.

SEPTAL REGION (BRAIN)

see Septum (Brain)

SEPTUM (BRAIN)

DeFrance, Jon F., ed. The Septal Nuclei. LC 76-43348. (Advances in Behavioral Biology Ser.: Vol. 20). 550p. 1976. 65.00x (ISBN 0-306-37920-1, Plenum Pr). Plenum Pub.

SEQUENCE, FIBONACCI

see Fibonacci Numbers

SEQUENCE SPACES

Kamthan. Sequence Spaces & Theory. (Lecture Notes in Pure & Applied Mathematics Ser.: Vol. 65). 1981. 65.00 (ISBN 0-8247-1224-2). Dekker.

Ruckle, W. H. Sequence Spaces. LC 80-22969. (Research Notes in Mathematics Ser.: No. 49). 224p. (Orig.). 1981. pap. text ed. 27.50 (ISBN 0-273-08507-7). Pitman Pub MA.

SEQUENCES (MATHEMATICS)

see also Series; Summability Theory

French, S. Sequencing & Scheduling: An Introduction to the Mathematics of the Job-Shop. (Mathematics & Its Applications Ser.). 245p. pap. 37.95 (ISBN 0-470-27456-5). Halsted Pr.

Gelfand, S. I., et al. Sequences & Combinatorial Problems. (Pocket Mathematical Library). 92p. 1968. 24.50 (ISBN 0-677-20730-1). Gordon.

Grosswald, E., ed. Representations of Integers As Sums of Squares. (Illus.). 200p. 1985. 45.00 (ISBN 0-387-96126-7). Springer-Verlag.

Halberstam, H. & Roth, K. Sequences. 293p. 1983. Repr. of 1966 ed. 31.00 (ISBN 0-387-90801-3). Springer-Verlag.

Kuipers, Lauwerens & Niederreiter, H. Uniform Distribution of Sequences. LC 73-20497. (Pure & Applied Mathematics (Wiley) Ser.). pap. 101.00 (ISBN 0-317-08710-X, 2055524). Bks Demand UMI.

Narkiewicz, W. Uniform Distribution of Sequences of Integers in Residue Classes. (Lecture Notes in Mathematics Ser.: Vol. 1087). vii, 125p. 1984. pap. 10.00 (ISBN 0-387-13872-2). Springer-Verlag.

Sloane, N. J. A Handbook of Integer Sequences. 1973. 31.00 (ISBN 0-12-648550-X). Acad Pr.

Stout, William F. Almost Sure Convergence. 1974. 69.00 (ISBN 0-12-672750-3). Acad Pr.

Whitehead. Design & Analysis of Sequential Clinical Trials. (Mathematics & Its Applications Ser.). 272p. 1983. pap. 27.95 (ISBN 0-470-20138-X). Wiley.

Whitehead, John. Design & Analysis of Sequential Clinical Trials. (Mathematics & Its Applications Ser.). 272p. 1983. 69.95x (ISBN 0-470-27355-0). Halsted Pr.

Wimp, Jet. Sequence Transformations & Their Applications. LC 80-68564. (Mathematics in Science & Engineering Ser.). 1981. 49.50 (ISBN 0-12-757940-0). Acad Pr.

SEQUENTIAL ANALYSIS

Bechhofer, Robert E., et al. Sequential Identification & Ranking Procedures: With Special Reference to Koopman-Darmois Populations. LC 67-28463. (Statistical Research Monographs Ser.: Vol. 3). pap. 109.50 (ISBN 0-317-09299-5, 2019954). Bks Demand UMI.

Chernoff, Herman. Sequential Analysis & Optimal Design. (CBMS-NSF Regional Conference Ser.: No. 8). (Illus.). v, 119p. (Orig.). 1972. pap. text ed. 12.00 (ISBN 0-89871-006-5). Soc Indus-Appl Math.

Proctor, Michael & Abell, Peter. Sequence Analysis. 133p. 1985. text ed. 32.95x (ISBN 0-566-00686-3). Gower Pub Co.

Rapoport, Amnon, et al. Response Models for Detection of Change. (Theory & Decision Library: No. 18). 1979. lib. bdg. 30.00 (ISBN 90-277-0934-3, Pub. by Reidel Holland). Kluwer Academic.

Sankoff, David & Kruskal, Joseph P. Time Warps, String Edits & Macromolecules: The Theory & Practice of Sequence Comparison. LC 83-11874. (Illus.). 400p. 1983. 32.95 (ISBN 0-201-07809-0). Addison-Wesley.

Sen, Pranab K. Theory & Applications of Sequential Nonparametrics. LC 84-52332. (CBMS-NSF Regional Conference Ser.: No. 49). v, 100p. 1985. pap. text ed. 15.50 (ISBN 0-89871-051-0). Soc Indus-Appl Math.

Shiryayev, A. N. Optimal Stopping Rules. Aries, A. B., tr. from Rus. LC 77-11198. (Applications of Mathematics: Vol. 8). (Illus.). 1978. 36.00 (ISBN 0-387-90256-2). Springer-Verlag.

Sirjaev, A. N. Statistical Sequential Analysis. LC 73-445. (Translations of Mathematical Monographs: Vol. 38). 192p. 1973. 42.00 (ISBN 0-8218-1588-1, MMONO-38). Am Math.

Wald, Abraham. Sequential Analysis. LC 73-85900. 1973. pap. text ed. 6.50 (ISBN 0-486-61579-0). Dover.

Wallach, Y. Alternating Sequential: Parallel Processing. (Lecture Notes in Computer Science: Vol. 127). 327p. 1982. pap. 20.00 (ISBN 0-387-11194-8). Springer-Verlag.

Woodroofe, M. Nonlinear Renewal Theory in Sequential Analysis. LC 81-84856. (CBMS-NSF Regional Conference Ser.: No. 39). v, 119p. 1982. 16.00 (ISBN 0-89871-180-0). Soc Indus Appl Math.

SEQUENTIAL MACHINE THEORY

see also Electronic Digital Computers

Aiserman, Mark A., et al. Logic, Automata & Algorithms. (Mathematics in Science & Engineering Ser). (Rus). 1971. 80.50 (ISBN 0-12-046350-4). Acad Pr.

Bavel, Zamir. Introduction to the Theory of Automata & Sequential Machines. 1983. text ed. 31.95 (ISBN 0-8359-3271-0). Reston.

Brainerd, Walter S. & Landweber, Lawrence H. Theory of Computation. LC 73-12950. 336p. 1974. 41.50x (ISBN 0-471-09585-0). Wiley.

Codd, E. F. Cellular Automata. (ACM Ser). 1968. 37.00 (ISBN 0-12-178850-4). Acad Pr.

Davies, Alan J. The Finite Element Method: A First Approach. (Oxford Applied Mathematics & Computing Science Ser.). (Illus.). 1980. pap. 26.95x (ISBN 0-19-859631-6). Oxford U Pr.

Harrison, M. A. Lectures on Linear Sequential Machines. 1970. 47.50 (ISBN 0-12-327750-7). Acad Pr.

Kamthan. Sequence Spaces & Theory. (Lecture Notes in Pure & Applied Mathematics Ser.: Vol. 65). 1981. 65.00 (ISBN 0-8247-1224-2). Dekker.

Kohavi, Zvi. Switching & Finite Automata Theory. 2nd ed. Feigenbaum & Hamming, eds. (McGraw-Hill Computer Science Ser.). (Illus.). 1978. text ed. 46.95 (ISBN 0-07-035310-7). McGraw.

McNaughton, Robert. Elementary Computability, Formal Languages & Automata. (Illus.). 464p. 1982. text ed. 28.95 (ISBN 0-13-253500-9). P-H.

Martin, Robert L. Studies in Feedback Shift-Register Synthesis of Sequential Machines. (Press Research Monographs: No. 50). 1969. 30.00x (ISBN 0-262-13047-5). MIT Pr.

Montgomery, S. Fixed Rings of Finite Automorphism Groups of Associative Rings. (Lectures Notes in Mathematics Ser.: Vol. 818). 126p. 1980. pap. 13.00 (ISBN 0-387-10232-9). Springer-Verlag.

Paz, Azaria. Introduction to Probabilistic Automata. LC 74-137627. (Computer Science & Applied Mathematics Ser). 1971. 60.00 (ISBN 0-12-547650-7). Acad Pr.

Pessen, D. & Hubl, W. The Design & Application of Programmable Sequence Controllers for Automation Systems. LC 78-40456. pap. 32.00 (ISBN 0-317-07930-1, 2020976). Bks Demand UMI.

Poplasen, Ilija. Computerized Two & Three Dimensional Finite Existents Analysis. 2nd ed. (Illus.). Repr. of 1979 ed. 15.00 (ISBN 0-935352-01-5). MIR PA.

--Computerized Two & Three Dimensional Finite Existents Analysis. 64p. 1982. 15.00 (ISBN 0-935352-09-0). MIR PA.

Tou, Julius T., ed. Applied Automata Theory. LC 68-26634. (Electrical Science Ser.). 1969. 80.00 (ISBN 0-12-696230-8). Acad Pr.

SEQUOIA

Loofbourow, Leon. He Shall Be Like a Tree: An Interpretation of the Seguoias. (Illus.). 1968. pap. 1.50 (ISBN 0-918634-27-X). D M Chase.

SERENGETI NATIONAL PARK

Hayes, Harold. The Last Place on Earth. LC 76-15562. 1977. 10.00 (ISBN 0-8128-2072-X). Stein & Day.

Herlocker, Dennis. Woody Vegetation of the Serengeti National Park. (Kleberg Studies in Natural Resources). (Illus.). 1975. pap. 5.95 (ISBN 0-89096-195-6). Tex A&M Univ Pr.

Jager, T. Soils of the Serengeti Woodlands, Tanzania. 253p. 1982. pap. 29.25 (ISBN 90-220-0775-8, PDC239, Pudoc). Unipub.

Sinclair, A. R. & Norton-Griffiths, M. Serengeti: Dynamics of an Ecosystem. LC 79-10146. (Illus.). 384p. 1979. lib. bdg. 35.00x (ISBN 0-226-76028-6). U of Chicago Pr.

SERICULTURE

see also Silkworms

Charlsey, Simon. Culture & Sericulture: Social Anthropology & Development in a South Indian Livestock Industry. (Studies in Anthropology). 1982. 35.00 (ISBN 0-12-169380-5). Acad Pr.

Mulberry Cultivation: Sericulture Manual, Vol. 1. (Agricultural Services Bulletins: No. 15/1). (Eng. & Fr., Illus.). 150p. 1976. pap. 17.75 (ISBN 92-5-100419-6, F710, FAO). Unipub.

Sericulture Manual (FAO). Unipub.

Sericulture Manual, 2 Vols. (Agricultural Service Bulletins: No. 15-1 & 15-2). (Eng. & Fr.). 1979. pap. 9.00 (ISBN 92-5-100310-6, F1591, FAO); pap. 8.25 (ISBN 92-5-100172-3, F1326). Unipub.

Serres, Oliver de. The Perfect Use of Silkworms. Geffe, N., tr. LC 72-232. (English Experience Ser.: No. 345). 100p. 1971. Repr. of 1607 ed. 16.00 (ISBN 90-221-0345-5). Walter J Johnson.

SERIES

see also Polynomials; Summability Theory

Ahiezer, N. I., et al. Fifteen Papers on Real & Complex Functions, Series, Differential & Integral Equations. LC 51-5559. (Translations Ser.: No. 2, Vol. 86). 1970. 34.00 (ISBN 0-8218-1786-8, TRANS 2-86). Am Math.

Alenicyn, Ju. E., et al. Fifteen Papers on Series & Functions of Complex Variables. LC 51-5559. (Translations Ser.: No. 2, Vol. 43). 1964. 27.00 (ISBN 0-8218-1743-4, TRANS 2-43). Am Math.

Balasov, L. A., et al. Fourteen Papers on Series & Approximation. LC 51-5559. (Translations Ser.: No. 2, Vol. 77). 1968. 35.00 (ISBN 0-8218-1777-9, TRANS 2-77). Am Math.

Budak, B. M. & Fomin, S. V. Multiple Integrals, Field Theory & Series. 640p. 1978. 18.00 (ISBN 0-8285-2096-8, Pub. by Mir Pubs USSR). Imported Pubns.

Bugrov, Y. S. & Nikolsky, S. M. Differential Equations, Multiple Integrals. (Theory of Functions of a Complex Variable Ser.). 475p. 1983. 9.95 (ISBN 0-8285-2657-5, Pub. by Mir Pubs USSR). Imported Pubns.

Davis, Harold T. Summation of Series. 140p. 1962. 6.00 (ISBN 0-911536-19-1). Trinity U Pr.

Kahane, Jean-Pierre. Some Random Series of Functions. (Cambridge Studies in Advanced Mathematics: No. 5). 250p. 1985. 47.50 (ISBN 0-521-24966-X). Cambridge U Pr.

Mangulis, Visvaldis. Handbook of Series for Scientists & Engineers. 1965. 37.50 (ISBN 0-12-468850-0). Acad Pr.

Pringsheim, Alfred. Vorlesungen Uber Zahlen & Funktionenlehre, 2 Vols. (Bibliotheca Mathematica Teubneriana Ser: Nos. 28-29). (Ger). 1969. Repr. of 1916 ed. Set. 145.00 (ISBN 0-384-47885-9). Johnson Repr.

Steklov Institute of Mathematics, Academy of Sciences, U S S R & Steckin, S. B. Sequences of Convergence for Series: Proceedings. (Proceedings of the Steklov Institute of Mathematics: No. 86). 1967. 25.00 (ISBN 0-8218-1886-4, STEKLO-86). Am Math.

SERIES, DIRICHLET'S

Fukushima, M. Dirichlet Forms & Markov Processes. (North-Holland Mathematical Library: Vol. 23). 196p. 1980. 51.00 (ISBN 0-444-85421-5, North Holland). Elsevier.

Langlands, R. Base Change for GL (2) LC 79-28820. (Annals of Mathematics Studies: No. 96). 225p. 1980. 27.00x (ISBN 0-691-08263-4); pap. 12.00 (ISBN 0-691-08272-3). Princeton U Pr.

Maeda, F. Y. Dirichlet Integrals on Harmonic Spaces. (Lecture Notes in Mathematics: Vol. 803). 180p. 1980. pap. 15.00 (ISBN 0-387-09995-6). Springer-Verlag.

Weil, A. Dirichlet Series & Automorphic Forms. LC 72-151320. (Lecture Notes in Mathematics: Vol. 189). 1971. pap. 15.00 (ISBN 0-387-05382-4). Springer-Verlag.

SERIES, FOURIER

see Fourier Series

SERIES, INFINITE

see also Series, Orthogonal; Tauberian Theorems

Berndt, Bruce C., et al. Chapter Nine of Ramanujan's Second Notebook: Infinite Series Identities, Transformations, & Evaluations, Vol. 23. LC 83-11803. (Contemporary Mathematics Ser.: No. 23). 84p. 1983. pap. 17.00 (ISBN 0-8218-5024-5). Am Math.

Fichtenholz, G. M. Functional Series. (Pocket Mathematical Library). 176p. 1970. 32.50 (ISBN 0-677-20950-9). Gordon.

--Infinite Series: Ramifications. (Pocket Mathematical Library). 138p. 1970. 37.25 (ISBN 0-677-20940-1). Gordon.

--Infinite Series: Rudiments. Silverman, Richard A., tr. from Rus. (Pocket Mathematical Library). 144p. 1970. 37.25 (ISBN 0-677-20930-4). Gordon.

Galambos, J. Representations of Real Numbers by Infinite Series. LC 75-44296. (Lecture Notes in Mathematics: Vol. 502). 1976. pap. 13.00 (ISBN 0-387-07547-X). Springer-Verlag.

Hajnal, A., et al, eds. Finite & Infinite Sets, 2 vols. (Colloquia Mathematica Societatis Janos Bolyai Ser.: No. 37). 902p. 1985. Set. 98.00 (ISBN 0-444-86763-5, North-Holland). Vol. 1 (ISBN 0-444-86893-3). Vol. 2 (ISBN 0-444-86894-1). Elsevier.

Hirschman, Isidore I. Infinite Series. LC 77-13787. (Athena Series, Selected Topics in Mathematics). (Illus.). 1978. Repr. of 1963 ed. lib. bdg. 21.50 (ISBN 0-8371-9897-6, HIIS). Greenwood.

Knopp, Konrad. Infinite Sequences & Series. Bagemihl, Frederick, tr. 1956. pap. text ed. 4.25 (ISBN 0-486-60153-6). Dover.

Rabin, M. Automata on Infinite Objects & Church's Problem. LC 72-6749. (CBMS Regional Conference Series in Mathematics: No. 13). 22p. 1982. 11.00 (ISBN 0-686-93294-3). Am Math.

Walsh, J. L. Interpolation & Approximation by Rational Functions in the Complex Domain. rev. ed. LC 60-3978. (Colloquium Pubns. Ser.: Vol. 20). 406p. 1966. Repr. of 1935 ed. 46.00 (ISBN 0-8218-1020-0, COLL-20). Am Math.

Whittaker, Edmund T. & Watson, George N. A Course of Modern Analysis. 4th ed. 1927. pap. text ed. 29.95 (ISBN 0-521-09189-6). Cambridge U Pr.

SERIES, ORTHOGONAL

see also Functions, Orthogonal

Bari, N. K., et al. Series & Approximation, Vol. 3. (Translations Ser.: No. 1). 1962. 24.00 (ISBN 0-8218-1603-9, TRANS 1-3). Am Math.

Bockarev, S. V. The Method of Averaging in the Theory of Orthogonal Series, & Some Questions in the Theory of Bases. LC 80-26300. (Proceedings of the Steklov Institute of Mathematics: No. 146). 1980. 34.00 (ISBN 0-8218-3045-7). Am Math.

Higgins, J. R. Completeness & Basis Properties of Sets of Special Functions. LC 76-19630. (Cambridge Tracts in Mathematics Ser.: No. 72). (Illus.). 1977. 59.50 (ISBN 0-521-21376-2). Cambridge U Pr.

Olevsky, A. M. Fourier Series with Respect to General Orthogonal Systems, Vol. 86. LC 74-32297. (Ergebnisse der Mathematik und Ihrer Grenzgebiete). 160p. 1975. 48.00 (ISBN 0-387-07103-2). Springer-Verlag.

Steklov Institute of Mathematics, Academy of Sciences, USSR. Limits of Interdeterminacy in Measure of Trigonometric & Orthogonal Series: Proceedings. (Proceedings of the Steklov Institute of Mathematics: No. 99). 1968. 23.00 (ISBN 0-8218-1899-6, STEKLO-99). Am Math.

SERIES, POWER

see Power Series

SERIES, TRIGONOMETRIC

see Fourier Series

SEROLOGY

see also Immunology

Albert, E. D., et al, eds. Histocompatibility Testing, 1984. 820p. 1984. 98.00 (ISBN 0-387-13464-6). Springer-Verlag.

Decary, Francine & Rock, Gail A., eds. Platelet Serology. (Current Studies in Hematology & Blood Transfusion: No. 52). (Illus.). x, 150p. 1986. 41.75 (ISBN 3-8055-4208-9). S Karger.

Hackel, Emanuel & Mallory, Delores, eds. Theoretical Aspects of HLA. (Illus.). 141p. 1982. 22.70 (ISBN 0-914404-71-7). Am Assn Blood.

Hunt, Susan M. Investigation of Serological Evidence: A Manual for Field Investigators. (Illus.). 90p. 1984. 16.75x (ISBN 0-398-04940-8). C C Thomas.

Selwood, Neville & Hedges, Alan. Transplantation Antigens: A Study in Serological Data Analysis. LC 78-5708. Repr. of 1978 ed. 38.30 (ISBN 0-8357-9995-6, 2016180). Bks Demand UMI.

Stansfield. Serology & Immunology. 1981. write for info. (ISBN 0-02-415740-6). Macmillan.

Van Regenmortal, M. H. Serology & Immunochemistry of Plant Viruses. LC 81-17631. 1982. 47.00 (ISBN 0-12-714180-4). Acad Pr.

WHO Sceintific Group, Geneva, 1969. Multipurpose Serological Serveys & WHO Serum Reference Banks: A Report. (Technical Report Ser: No. 454). 95p. 1970. pap. 2.80 (ISBN 92-4-120454-0, 741). World Health.

SEROTONIN

Costa, E., et al, eds. Serotonin, New Vistas: Biochemistry & Behavioral & Clinical Studies. LC 73-91166. (Advances in Biochemical Psychopharmacology Ser.: Vol. 11). 446p. 1974. 45.50 (ISBN 0-911216-69-3). Raven.

--Serotonin, New Vistas: Histochemistry & Pharmacology. LC 73-91165. (Advances in Biochemical Psychopharmacology Ser.: Vol. 10). 345p. 1974. 45.50 (ISBN 0-911216-68-5). Raven.

DeClerck, Fred & Vanhoutte, Paul M., eds. Five-Hydroxytryptamine in Peripheral Reactions. 242p. 1982. text ed. 48.50 (ISBN 0-89004-772-3). Raven.

Erspamer, V., ed. Five-Hydroxytryptamine & Related Indolealkylamines. (Handbook of Experimental Pharmacology: Vol. 19). (Illus.). 1966. 106.00 (ISBN 0-387-03536-2). Springer-Verlag.

Green, Richard A., ed. Neuropharmacology of Serotonin. (Illus.). 300p. 1985. cloth 35.00 (ISBN 0-19-261471-1). Oxford U Pr.

Haber, Bernard, et al, eds. Serotonin: Current Aspects of Neurochemistry & Function. (Advances in Experimental Medicine & Biology Ser.: Vol. 133). 840p. 1981. 89.50x (ISBN 0-306-40579-2, Plenum Pr). Plenum Pub.

Ho, Beng T., et al, eds. Serotonin in Biological Psychiatry: Advances in Biochemical Psychopharmacology, Vol. 34. 352p. 1982. text ed. 43.50 (ISBN 0-89004-803-7). Raven.

Jacoby, J. H. & Lytle, L. D., eds. Serotonin Neurotoxins. (Annals of the New York Academy of Sciences: Vol. 305). 702p. 1978. pap. 68.00x (ISBN 0-89072-061-4). NY Acad Sci.

Knoll. Symposium on Pharmachaminergic & Serotonergic Mechanisms, Vol. 3. 1979. 14.00 (ISBN 0-9960007-6-3, Pub. by Akademiai Kaido Hungary). Heyden.

Menlewicz, J., et al, eds. Serotonin in Affective Disorders. (Advances in Biological Psychiatry: Vol. 14). (Illus.). vi, 90p. 1984. 23.00 (ISBN 3-8055-3898-7). S Karger.

Osborne, Neville V. Biology of Serotonergic Transmission. LC 81-14671. 522p. 1982. 79.95x (ISBN 0-471-10032-3, Pub. by Wiley-Interscience). Wiley.

Reneman, R. S. & Bollinger, A., eds. Serotonin & Microcirculation. (Mikrozirkulation in Forschung und Klinik; Progess in Applied Microcirculation Ser.: Vol. 10). (Illus.). 92p. 1985. pap. 25.75 (ISBN 3-8055-4163-5). S Karger.

Schlossberger, H. G., et al, eds. Progress in Tryptophan & Serotonin Research: Proceedings-Fourth Meeting of the International Study Group for Tryptophan Research (ISTRY) LC 84-1719. xix, 889p. 1984. 96.00x (ISBN 3-11-009760-5). De Gruyter.

Sokoloff, B. Carcinoid & Serotonin. (Recent Results in Cancer Research: Vol. 15). 1968. 21.00 (ISBN 0-387-04306-3). Springer-Verlag.

SERPENTS

see Snakes

SERVICE STATIONS, AUTOMOBILE

see Automobiles–Service Stations

SERVOMECHANISMS

see also Electronic Control; Hydraulic Servomechanisms; Synchros

CES Industries, Inc. Ed-Lab Experiment Manual: CES 303 Synchro-Servo Mechanism. (Illus.). 1981. write for info. (ISBN 0-86711-012-0). CES Industries.

Electro-Craft Corp. DC Motors, Speed Controls, Servo Systems: An Engineering Handbook. 3rd exp. ed. LC 76-56647. 504p. 1977. text ed. 45.00 (ISBN 0-08-021714-1); pap. text ed. 19.50 (ISBN 0-08-021715-X). Pergamon.

Kurman, K. J. Feedback Control: Theory & Design. (Studies in Automation & Control: Vol. 4). 1984. 90.75 (ISBN 0-444-99640-0, I-122-84). Elsevier.

SET THEORY

see also Categories (Mathematics); Functions of Real Variables; Measure Theory; Rings (Algebra)

Adjan, S. I., ed. Mathematical Logic, the Theory of Algorithms & the Theory of Sets: Dedicated to Academician Petr Sergeevic Novikov. LC 77-3359. (Proceedings of the Steklov Institute of Mathematics Ser.: No. 133). 1977. 66.00 (ISBN 0-8218-3033-3, STEKLO 133). Am Math.

Alexandrov, Paul S. Introduction to the Theory of Sets & Functions. write for info. (ISBN 0-685-07980-5). Chelsea Pub.

Auslander, Louis & Markus, Lawrence. Flat Lorentz Three Manifolds. LC 52-42839. (Memoirs: No. 30). 60p. 1959. pap. 11.00 (ISBN 0-8218-1230-0, MEMO-30). Am Math.

Barwise, K. J. Admissible Sets & Structures: An Approach to Definability Theory. (Perspectives in Mathematical Logic Ser.). (Illus.). 400p. 1975. 47.50 (ISBN 0-387-07451-1). Springer-Verlag.

Bell, J. L. Boolean-Valued Models & Independence Proofs in Set Theory. 2nd ed. (Logic Guides Ser.). 1985. 22.95x (ISBN 0-19-853241-5). Oxford U Pr.

Benedetto, J. Harmonic Analysis on Totally Disconnected Sets. LC 77-163741. (Lecture Notes in Mathematics: Vol. 202). 1971. pap. 14.00 (ISBN 0-387-05488-X). Springer-Verlag.

Bittinger, M. L. Logic, Proof, & Sets. 2nd ed. LC 81-14913. 144p. 1982. pap. text ed. 8.95 (ISBN 0-201-10384-2). Addison-Wesley.

Cantor, Georg. Contributions to the Founding of the Theory of Transfinite Numbers. Jourdain, Philip E., tr. pap. 4.95 (ISBN 0-486-60045-9). Dover.

--Contributions to the Founding of the Theory of Transfinite Numbers. Jourdain, P. E., tr. ix, 220p. 1952. 19.95 (ISBN 0-87548-157-4). Open Court.

Cech, E. Point Sets. 1969. 65.00 (ISBN 0-12-164850-8). Acad Pr.

Chong, C. T. Techniques of Admissible Recursion Theory. (Lecture Notes in Mathematics Ser.: Vol. 1106). ix, 214p. 1984. pap. 11.00 (ISBN 0-387-13902-8). Springer-Verlag.

Christian, Robert R. Introduction to Logic & Sets. 2nd ed. LC 65-14567. (Blaisdell Books in the Pure & Applied Sciences). pap. 32.00 (ISBN 0-317-08549-2, 2055126). Bks Demand UMI.

Chuaqui, R. B. Axiomatic Set Theory of Classes: Impredicative Theories of Classes. (Mathematics Studies: Vol. 51). 388p. 1981. 59.75 (ISBN 0-444-86178-5, North-Holland). Elsevier.

Clarke, D. A., et al. Foundations of Analysis: With An Introduction to Logic & Set Theory. LC 73-136217. (Century Mathematics Ser.). (Illus., Orig.). 1971. text ed. 19.95x (ISBN 0-89197-171-8). Irvington.

Cohen, Paul J. Set Theory & the Continuum Hypothesis. (Math Lecture Notes Ser.: No. 3). (Orig.). 1966. pap. 28.95 (ISBN 0-8053-2327-9, Adv Bk Prog). Benjamin-Cummings.

Devlin, K. Fundamentals of Contemporary Set Theory. (Universitext Ser.). 1979. pap. 15.00 (ISBN 0-387-90441-7). Springer-Verlag.

Devlin, K. J. Constructibility. (Perspectives in Mathematical Logic Ser.). (Illus.). 425p. 1984. 58.00 (ISBN 0-387-13258-9). Springer-Verlag.

--Sets, Functions & Logic. 90p. 1981. (Pub. by Chapman & Hall England); pap. 7.95x (ISBN 0-412-22670-7, NO. 2048). Methuen Inc.

Devlin, K. J. & Johnsbraten, H. The Souslin Problem. (Lecture Notes in Mathematics Ser.: Vol. 405). vii, 132p. 1974. pap. 13.00 (ISBN 0-387-06860-0). Springer-Verlag.

Drake, Frank R. Set Theory: An Introduction to Large Cardinals. (Studies in Logic & the Foundation of Mathematics Ser: Vol. 76). 352p. 1974. 53.25 (ISBN 0-444-10535-2, North-Holland). Elsevier.

Dubois, Didier & Prade, Henri. Fuzzy Sets & Systems: Theory & Applications. LC 79-6952. (Mathematics in Science & Engineering Ser.). 1980. 75.00 (ISBN 0-12-222750-6). Acad Pr.

Erdos, P., et al, eds. Combinational Set Theory: Partition Relations for Cardinals. (Studies in Logic & the Foundations of Mathematics: Vol. 106). 348p. 1984. 52.00 (ISBN 0-444-86157-2, North Holland). Elsevier.

Faltings, G. & Wustholz, G. Rational Points, Vol. 6. (Aspects of Mathematics Ser.). 1984. write for info. (ISBN 0-9904001-5-8, Pub. by Vieweg & Sohn Germany). Heyden.

Fishburn, Peter C. Interval Orders & Interval Sets: A Study of Partially Ordered Sets. (Wiley Interscience Series in Discrete Mathematics). 215p. 1985. text ed. 33.50x (ISBN 0-471-81284-6, Pub. by Wiley-Interscience). Wiley.

Floret, K. Weekly Compact Sets. (Lecture Notes in Mathematics Ser.: Vol. 801). 123p. 1980. pap. 13.00 (ISBN 0-387-09991-3). Springer-Verlag.

Fraenkel, P., et al. Foundations of Set Theory. 2nd ed. (Studies in Logic: Vol. 67). 1973. 36.25 (ISBN 0-7204-2270-1). Elsevier.

Freiman, G. A. Foundations of a Structural Theory of Set Addition. LC 73-9804. (Translations of Mathematical Monographs Ser.: Vol. 37). 1973. 36.00 (ISBN 0-8218-1587-3, MMONO-37). Am Math.

Frydman, Roman & Phelps, Edmund. Individual Forecasting & Aggregate Outcomes: "Rational Expectations" Examined. LC 83-10165. 256p. 1984. 39.50 (ISBN 0-521-25744-1). Cambridge U Pr.

Gelfand & Walker. Ensemble Modeling. 344p. 1984. 45.00 (ISBN 0-8247-7180-X). Dekker.

Gordon, Carl E. & Hindman, Neil. Elementary Set Theory: Proof Techniques. LC 74-14794. 1975. text ed. 13.95x (ISBN 0-02-845350-6). Hafner.

Grattan-Guinness, I., ed. From the Calculus to Set Theory 1630-1910: An Introductory History. 306p. 1980. pap. text ed. 12.00x (ISBN 0-7156-1625-0, Pub. by Duckworth England). Biblio Dist.

Gupta, M. M., et al, eds. Advances in Fuzzy Set Theory & Applications. 753p. 1979. 106.50 (ISBN 0-444-85372-3, North Holland). Elsevier.

Gut, A. & Schmidt, K. D. Amarts & Set Function Processes. (Lecture Notes in Mathematics: Vol. 1042). 258p. 1983. pap. 15.00 (ISBN 0-387-12867-0). Springer Verlag.

Hallett, Michael. Cantorian Set Theory & Limitation of Size. (Oxford Logic Guides Ser.). 1984. 32.50x (ISBN 0-19-853179-6). Oxford U Pr.

Halmos, P. R. Naive Set Theory. LC 74-10687. (Undergraduate Texts in Mathematics Ser.). 110p. 1974. pap. 19.00 (ISBN 0-387-90092-6). Springer-Verlag.

Hamilton, A. G. Numbers, Sets & Axioms: The Apparatus of Mathematics. LC 82-4206. 250p. 1983. 44.50 (ISBN 0-521-24509-5); pap. 18.95 (ISBN 0-521-28761-8). Cambridge U Pr.

Hausdorff, Felix. Grundzuege der Mengenlehre. (Ger). 1965. 19.95 (ISBN 0-8284-0061-X). Chelsea Pub.

--Set Theory. 2nd ed. LC 57-8493. 14.95 (ISBN 0-8284-0119-5). Chelsea Pub.

Hinman, P. G. Recursion-Theoretic Hierarchies. (Perspectives in Mathematical Logic Ser.). 1978. 57.00 (ISBN 0-387-07904-1). Springer-Verlag.

Hrbacek, Jech. Introduction to Set Theory. 2nd ed. 232p. 1984. 39.75 (ISBN 0-8247-7074-9). Dekker.

Hrbacek, Karel & Jech, Thomas. Introduction to Set Theory. LC 78-2668. (Lecture Notes in Pure & Applied Mathematics Ser.: Vol. 45). Repr. of 1978 ed. 37.30 (ISBN 0-8357-9084-3, 2017853). Bks Demand UMI.

International Colloquium, June 25-July 1, 1973. Infinite & Finite Sets: Proceedings, 3 vols. Hajnal, A., et al, eds. (Colloquia Mathematica Societatis Janos Bolyai Ser.: Vol. 10). 1556p. 1975. Set. 170.25 (ISBN 0-444-10732-0, North-Holland). Elsevier.

Jech, T. & Prikry, K. Ideals Over Uncountable Sets: Application of Almost Disjoint Functions & Generic Ultrapowers. LC 79-5. (Memoirs: No. 214). 71p. 1982. pap. 13.00 (ISBN 0-8218-2214-4). Am Math.

Jensen, R. R. & Prestel, A., eds. Set Theory & Model Theory: Proceedings. (Lecture Notes in Mathematics Ser.: Vol. 872). 174p. 1981. pap. 13.00 (ISBN 0-387-10849-1). Springer-Verlag.

Jiang, Boju. Lectures on Nielsen Fixed Point Theory. LC 82-20756. (Contemporary Mathematics Ser.: Vol. 14). 112p. 1982. pap. 17.00 (ISBN 0-8218-5014-8, CONM/14). Am Math.

Kamke, E. Theory of Sets. Bagemihl, Frederick, tr. 1950. pap. 3.00 (ISBN 0-486-60141-2). Dover.

Kaplansky, Irving. Set Theory & Metric Spaces. 2nd ed. LC 77-7344. 1977. text ed. 9.50 (ISBN 0-8284-0298-1). Chelsea Pub.

Kenyon, Hewitt & Morse, Anthony P. Web Derivatives. LC 73-2858. (Memoirs Ser.: No. 132). 177p. 1973. pap. 11.00 (ISBN 0-8218-1832-5, MEMO-132). Am Math.

Kleinberg, E. M. Infinitary Combinatorics & the Axiom of Determinateness. (Lecture Notes in Mathematics: Vol. 612). 1977. pap. text ed. 14.00 (ISBN 0-387-08440-1). Springer-Verlag.

Kruse, Arthur. Souslinoid & Analytic Sets in a General Setting. LC 52-42839. (Memoirs: No. 86). 127p. 1969. pap. 9.00 (ISBN 0-8218-1286-6, MEMO-86). Am Math.

Kunen, K. Set Theory. (Studies in Logic & the Foundations of Mathematics: Vol. 102). 1984. 27.50 (ISBN 0-444-86839-9, I-013-84). Elsevier.

--Set Theory: An Introduction to Independence Proofs. (Studies in Logic: Vol. 102). 314p. 1981. 40.50 (ISBN 0-444-85401-0, North-Holland). Elsevier.

Kuratowski, K. & Mostawski, A. Set Theory. 2nd ed. LC 74-83731. (Studies in Logic and the Foundations of Mathematics: Vol. 86). 514p. 1976. 68.00 (ISBN 0-7204-0470-3, North-Holland). Elsevier.

Lachlan, A., et al, eds. Set Theory & Hierarchy Theory 5: Bierutowice, Poland 1976. (Lecture Notes in Mathematics: Vol 619). 1977. pap. 22.00 (ISBN 0-387-08521-1). Springer-Verlag.

Landel, Robert D. & Freeland, James R. Aggregate Production Planning: Text & Cases. 1985. pap. 14.95 (ISBN 0-8359-0031-2); Solution's Manual free (ISBN 0-8359-0032-0). Reston.

Levy, A. Basic Set Theory. (Perspectives in Mathematical Logic). 1979. 32.00 (ISBN 0-387-08417-7). Springer-Verlag.

Levy, Azriel. Hierarchy of Formulas in Set Theory. LC 52-42839. (Memoirs: No. 57). 76p. 1974. pap. 13.00 (ISBN 0-8218-1257-2, MEMO-57). Am Math.

Lindahl, L. A. & Poulsen, F. Thin Sets in Harmonic Analysis. (Lecture Notes in Pure & Applied Mathematics Ser.: Vol. 2). 1971. 35.00 (ISBN 0-8247-1317-6). Dekker.

Lipschutz, Seymour. Set Theory & Related Topics. (Orig.). 1964. pap. 7.95 (ISBN 0-07-037986-6). McGraw.

Lopez, Jorge M. & Ross, Kenneth A. Sidon Sets. (Lecture Notes in Pure & Applied Mathematics Ser.: Vol. 13). 208p. 1975. 39.75 (ISBN 0-8247-6289-4). Dekker.

Mansfield, Richard & Weitkamp, Galen. Recursive Aspects of Descriptive Set Theory. (Logic Guides Ser.). 1985. 19.95x (ISBN 0-19-503602-6). Oxford U Pr.

Marek, W. & Srebrny, M., eds. Set Theory & Hierarchy Theory. (Lecture Notes in Mathematics: Vol. 537). 1976. 20.00 (ISBN 0-387-07856-8). Springer-Verlag.

Mathias, A. R. Surveys in Set Theory. LC 83-10106. (London Mathematical Society Lecture Note Ser.: No. 87). 256p. 1983. 29.95 (ISBN 0-521-27733-7). Cambridge U Pr.

Mazet, P. Analytic Sets in Locally Convex Spaces. (Mathematics Studies: Vol. 89). 1984. 38.50 (ISBN 0-444-86867-4, I-088-84, North-Holland). Elsevier.

Monk, J. Donald. Introduction to Set Theory. LC 79-21279. 206p. 1980. Repr. of 1969 ed. lib. bdg. 16.50 (ISBN 0-89874-006-1). Krieger.

Moore, Robert L. Foundations of Point Set Theory. rev. ed. LC 62-8325. (Colloquium Publishers Ser.: Vol. 13). 419p. 1982. pap. 61.00 (ISBN 0-8218-1013-8, COLL-13). Am Math.

BOOKS - SUBJECT INDEX SEWAGE–PURIFICATION

Morse, A. P. A Theory of Sets: Monographs. 2nd ed. (Pure & Applied Mathematics Ser.). Date not set. price not set (ISBN 0-12-507952-4). Acad Pr.
Mueller, G. H. & Scott, D. S., eds. Higher Set Theory: Proceeding, Oberwolfach Germany, April 13-23, 1977. (Lecture Notes in Mathematics Ser.: Vol. 669). 1978. pap. 29.00 (ISBN 0-387-08926-8). Springer-Verlag.
Muller, G. H. & Richter, M. M., eds. Models & Sets, Pt. 1. (Lecture Notes in Mathematics Ser.: Vol. 1103). viii, 484p. 1984. pap. 25.00 (ISBN 0-387-13900-1). Springer-Verlag.
Ortiz, Alejandro & Zierer, Ernesto. Set Theory & Linguistics. (Janua Linguarum, Ser. Minor: No. 70). (Orig.). 1968. pap. text ed. 7.60x (ISBN 90-2790-597-5). Mouton.
Reed, G. M., ed. Set-Theoretic Topology. 1977. 47.50 (ISBN 0-12-584950-8). Acad Pr.
Representation, Comprehension & Communication of Sets: The Role of Number. 32p. 1980. pap. 5.00 (ISBN 92-808-0133-3, TUNU055, UNU). Unipub.
Rival, Ivan, ed. Graphs & Order: The Role of Graphs in the Theory of Ordered Sets & Its Applications. 1985. lib. bdg. 99.00 (ISBN 90-277-1943-8, Pub. by Reidel Holland). Kluwer Academic.
--Ordered Sets. 1982. 99.00 (ISBN 90-277-1396-0, Pub. by Reidel Holland). Kluwer Academic.
Roethel, Louis F. & Weinstein, Abraham. Logic, Sets & Numbers. 3rd ed. 415p. 1983. text ed. write for info. (ISBN 0-534-02687-7). Wadsworth Pub.
Rogers, C. A., et al, eds. Analytic Sets. LC 80-40647. (London Mathematical Society Symposia). 1981. 72.00 (ISBN 0-12-593150-6). Acad Pr.
Rosser, Barkley J. Simplified Independence Proofs: Boolean Valued Models of Set Theory. (Pure & Applied Mathematics Ser: Vol. 31). 1969. 49.50 (ISBN 0-12-598050-7). Acad Pr.
Rudin, M. E. Lectures on Set Theoretic Topology. LC 74-31124. (CBMS Regional Conference Series in Mathematics: No. 23). 76p. 1980. pap. 9.00 (ISBN 0-8218-1673-X, CBMS-23). Am Math.
Rueff, Marcel & Jeger, Max. Sets & Boolean Algebra. Howson, A. G., ed. LC 72-189267. (Mathematical Studies: A Series for Teachers & Students: No. 4). pap. 48.00 (ISBN 0-317-20064-X, 2023329). Bks Demand UMI.
Skolem, Thoralf A. Abstract Set Theory. (Mathematical Lectures Ser.: No. 8). (Orig.). 1962. pap. 2.25x (ISBN 0-268-00000-X). U of Notre Dame Pr.
Steklov Institute of Mathematics, Academy of Sciences, U S S R. Topological Imbeddings in Euclidean Space: Proceedings. Keldys, L. V., ed. (Proceedings of the Steklov Institute of Mathematics: No. 81). 1968. 58.00 (ISBN 0-8218-1881-3, STEKLO-81). Am Math.
Stoll, Robert R. Set Theory & Logic. 474p. 1979. pap. 8.50 (ISBN 0-486-63829-4). Dover.
--Sets, Logic, & Axiomatic Theories. 2nd ed. LC 74-8932. pap. 61.00 (ISBN 0-317-08628-6, 2055554). Bks Demand UMI.
Tammann, Gustav. The States of Aggregation. 1978. Repr. of 1925 ed. lib. bdg. 25.00 (ISBN 0-8492-2733-X). R West.
Ulam, Stanislaw M. Stanislaw Ulam: Sets, Numbers & Universes: Selected Works. Beyer, William, et al, eds. LC 73-21686. 654p. 1974. 60.00x (ISBN 0-262-13094-7). MIT Pr.
Vaidyanathaswamy, R. Set Topology. 2nd ed. LC 60-8968. 14.95 (ISBN 0-8284-0139-X). Chelsea Pub.
Van Dalen, D., et al. Sets: Naive, Axiomatic & Applied. 1978. pap. text ed. 24.00 (ISBN 0-08-023047-4). Pergamon.
Vaught, R. L. Set Theory: An Introduction. 1985. text ed. write for info. (ISBN 0-8176-3238-7). Birkhauser.
Wang, Hao. Logic, Computers & Sets. LC 70-113155. Orig. Title: Survey of Mathematical Logic. 1970. Repr. of 1962 ed. text ed. 24.95 (ISBN 0-8284-0245-0). Chelsea Pub.
Wang, Paul P., ed. Advances in Fuzzy Sets, Possibility Theory, & Applications. 434p. 1983. 55.00x (ISBN 0-306-41390-6, Plenum Pr). Plenum Pub.
Williams, N. H. Combinatorial Set Theory. (Studies in Logic: Vol. 91). 028p. 1977. 42.75 (ISBN 0-7204-0722-2, North-Holland). Elsevier.
Yager, Ronald R., ed. Fuzzy Set & Possibility Theory: Recent Developments. (Illus.). 672p. 1982. 77.00 (ISBN 0-08-026294-5, D110). Pergamon.
You-Feng Lin & Shwu Yeng T. Lin. Set Theory with Applications. 2nd, rev. & expanded ed. LC 80-26583. Orig. Title: Set Theory: an Intuitive Approach. (Illus.). 221p. 1980. pap. text ed. 13.95 (ISBN 0-936166-03-7). Mariner Pub.
Young, William H. & Young, Grace C. Theory of Sets of Points. 2nd ed. LC 75-184793. 330p. 1972. text ed. 19.50 (ISBN 0-8284-0259-0). Chelsea Pub.
Zupan, J. Clustering of Large Data Sets. (Chemometrics Research Studies). 122p. 1982. text ed. 39.95x (ISBN 0-471-10455-8, Pub. by Res Stud Pr). Wiley.

SETON, ERNEST THOMPSON, 1860-1946
Seton, Ernest T. Trail of an Artist-Naturalist: Autobiography of Ernest Thompson Seton. Sterling, Keir B., ed. LC 77-81134. (Biologists & Their World Ser.). (Illus.). 1978. Repr. of 1940 ed. lib. bdg. 36.50x (ISBN 0-405-10734-X). Ayer Co Pubs.
Wadland, John H. Ernest Thompson Seton: Man in Nature & the Progressive Era, 1880-1915. Sterling, Keir B., ed. LC 77-81136. (Biologists & Their World Ser.). (Illus.). 1978. lib. bdg. 43.00x (ISBN 0-405-10736-6). Ayer Co Pubs.
Wiley, Farida A., ed. Ernest Thompson Seton's America. (American Naturalists Ser.). (Illus.). 1975. pap. 9.95 (ISBN 0-85699-121-X). Devin.

SETS (MATHEMATICS)
see Set Theory

SEVERAL COMPLEX VARIABLES, FUNCTIONS OF
see Functions of Several Complex Variables

SEWAGE
Activated Sludge: A Comparison of Oxygen & Air Systems. 118p. 1983. pap. 15.50x (ISBN 0-87262-362-9). Am Soc Civil Eng.
American Society of Civil Engineers & American Water Works Association, eds. Glossary: Water & Wastewater Control Engineering. LC 80-70933. 398p. 1969. 25.00x (ISBN 0-87262-262-2). Am Soc Civil Eng.
American Society of Civil Engineers, compiled by. Wastewater Treatment Plant Design. (Manual & Report on Engineering Practice Ser.: No. 36). 574p. 1977. 20.00x (ISBN 0-87262-213-4). Am Soc Civil Eng.
Anaerobic Sludge Digestion ('68) (Manual of Practice Ser.: No. 16). 60p. Date not set. pap. 8.00 (ISBN 0-943244-13-7). Water Pollution.
Barnes, D., et al, eds. Surveys in Industrial Wastewater Treatment, 2 vols. (Water Resources Engineering Ser.). 700p. 1984. Vol. 1. 64.95 (ISBN 0-273-08586-7); Vol. 2. 44.95 (ISBN 0-273-08588-3). Pitman Pub MA.
Berglund, S., et al, eds. Utilisation of Sewage Sludge on Land: Rates of Application & Long-Term Effects of Metals. 1984. lib. bdg. 39.00 (ISBN 90-277-1701-X, Pub. by Reidel Holland). Kluwer Academic.
BNA's Environmental & Safety Information Services. Sewage Treatment Construction Grants Manual. write for info. BNA.
Committee on a Multimedium Approach to Municipal Sludge Management, National Research Council. Multimedium Management of Municipal Sludge. LC 77-93086. (Analytical Studies for the U. S. Environmental Protection Agency Ser.). (Illus.). 1978. pap. text ed. 9.50 (ISBN 0-309-02733-0). Natl Acad Pr.
Cooper, P. F. & Atkinson, B., eds. Biological Fluidised Bed Treatment of Water & Wastewater. LC 80-41740. 411p. 1981. 106.95 (ISBN 0-470-27112-4). Halsted Pr.
Curds, C. R. & Hawkes, H. A., eds. Ecological Aspects of Used Water Treatment, Vol. 1. 1976. 66.00 (ISBN 0-12-199501-1). Acad Pr.
Davis, R. D. & Hucker, G., eds. Environmental Effects of Organic & Inorganic Contaminants in Sewage Sludge. 1983. lib. bdg. 36.95 (ISBN 90-277-1586-6, Pub. by Reidel Holland). Kluwer Academic.
D'Itri, Frank, et al, eds. Municipal Wastewater in Agriculture. 1982. 55.00 (ISBN 0-12-214880-0). Acad Pr.
D'Itri, Frank M., ed. Wastewater Renovation & Reuse: Proceedings of the International Conference on the Renovation & Reuse of Wastewater Through Aquatic & Terrestrial Systems. LC 76-54588. (Pollution Engineering & Technology: Vol. 3). pap. 120.00 (ISBN 0-317-08391-0, 2055036). Bks Demand UMI.
Drake, R. A. R., ed. Instrumentation & Control of Water & Wastewater Treatment & Transport Systems: Proceedings of the 4th IAWPRC Workshop Held in Houston & Denver, USA, 27 April - 4 May 1985. (Advances in Water Pollution Control Ser.). (Illus.). 766p. 1985. 130.00 (ISBN 0-08-032591-2, Pub. by P P L). Pergamon.
Eckenfelder, W. W. & Englander, A. J. Effluent Variability from Waste Water Treatment Processes & Its Control. 1976. pap. 50.00 (ISBN 0-08-019843-0). Pergamon.
Economic Commission for Europe. Engineering Equipment & Automation Means for Waste-Water Management in ECE Countries: A Report on Prevailing Practices & Recent Experience in Production & Use of Engineering Equipment & Automation Means for Preventing Water Pollution, Pt. 1. 111p. 1985. pap. 12.50 (UN84/2E13 5071, UN). Unipub.
Eikum, A. S. & Seabloom, R. W. Alternative Wastewater Treatment. 1982. 45.00 (ISBN 90-277-1430-4, Pub. by Reidel Holland). Kluwer Academic.
Engineering Equipment & Automation Means for Waste-Water Management in ECE Countries, Pt. 1. 111p. 12.50 (ISBN 0-317-18703-1, E.84.II.E.13). UN.
Escritt, Leonard B. Sewerage & Sewage Treatment: International Practice. LC 83-1300. 450p. 1984. 58.95x (ISBN 0-471-10339-X, Pub. by Wiley-Interscience). Wiley.
Gameson, A. L. Discharge of Sewage from Sea Outfalls. 140.00 (ISBN 0-08-018302-6). Pergamon.
Gravity Sanitary Sewer Design & Construction. (Manual of Practice, Facilities Development: No. 5). 288p. 1982. pap. text ed. 20.00 (ISBN 0-87262-313-0); 15.00. Water Pollution.
Hartigan, John P. & Willeke, Gene E., eds. Land Disposal of Wastewater: An Annotated Bibliography, No. 837. 1975. 5.00 (ISBN 0-686-20362-3). CPL Biblios.
Horvath, I., ed. Modelling in the Technology of Wastewater Treatment. LC 82-22530. (Illus.). 192p. 1984. 40.00 (ISBN 0-08-023978-1). Pergamon.
Hucker, T. W. & Catroux, G. Phosphorus in Sewage Sludge & Animal Waste Slurries. 1982. 39.50 (ISBN 90-277-0317-5, Pub. by Reidel Holland). Kluwer Academic.
Hudson, James F., et al. Pollution-Pricing: Industrial Response to Wastewater Charges. LC 80-8363. 240p. 1981. 29.50x (ISBN 0-669-04033-9). Lexington Bks.
Iskandar, I. K., ed. Modeling Wastewater Renovation: Land Treatment. LC 80-39879. (Environmental Science & Technology: a Wiley-Interscience Series of Texts & Monographs). 802p. 1981. 110.00x (ISBN 0-471-08128-0, Pub. by Wiley-Interscience). Wiley.
Jenkins, S. H. Advanced Treatment & Reclamation of Wastewater. flexi-cover 99.00x (ISBN 0-08-022937-9). Pergamon.
--A Consolidated Approach to Activated Sludge Process Design. flexi-cover 50.00x (ISBN 0-08-019835-X). Pergamon.
--Instrumentation & Control for Water & Wastewater Treatment & Transport Systems. flexi-cover 99.00x (ISBN 0-08-022098-3). Pergamon.
--Kinetics of Wastewater Treatment, Copenhagen, Denmark, June 1979. flexi-cover 47.00x (ISBN 0-08-024855-1). Pergamon.
Junkins, David R. & Deeny, Kevin J. The Activated Sludge Process: Fundamentals of Operation. LC 82-70699. (Illus.). 260p. 1983. 14.95 (ISBN 0-250-40506-7). Butterworth.
Korbitz, William E. Modern Management of Wastewater Utilities. LC 81-2162. (STPM Press Ser.). 264p. 1981. lib. bdg. 40.00 (ISBN 0-8240-7069-0). Garland Pub.
L'Hermite, P. & Ott, H., eds. Characterization, Treatment & Use of Sewage Sludge. xviii, 803p. 1981. 87.00 (ISBN 90-277-1294-8, Pub. by Reidel Holland). Kluwer Academic.
McClelland, Nina I. & Evans, Joe L., eds. Individual Onsite Wastewater Systems, Volume 7: Proceedings of the Seventh National Conference, 1980. LC 76-50983. (Illus.). 355p. 1981. 30.00 (ISBN 0-940006-00-6). Natl Sanit Foun.
Mandt, Mikkel G. & Bell, Bruce A. Oxidation Ditches in Wastewater Treatment. LC 82-70700. (Illus.). 169p. 1982. 39.95 (ISBN 0-250-40430-3). Butterworth.
Meinck, F. & Mohle, K. Dictionary of Water & Sewage Engineering. 2nd rev. ed. (Ger., Eng., Fr., & Ital.). 738p. 1977. 138.50 (ISBN 0-444-99811-X). Elsevier.
National Association of Home Builders. Alternatives to Public Sewer. 105p. 1978. pap. 13.50 (ISBN 0-86718-004-8); pap. 10.00. Natl Assn Home.
--Residential Wastewater Systems. (Illus.). 110p. 1980. pap. 23.00 (ISBN 0-86718-040-4); pap. 17.00 members. Natl Assn Home.
The Operation & Maintenance of Small Sewage Works. 70p. 1981. 25.00x (ISBN 0-904561-76-3, Pub. by Natl Water England). State Mutual Bk.
Owen, William F. & Culp, Wesner, Clup, Inc. Energy in Wastewater Treatment. (Illus.). 368p. 1982. 45.00 (ISBN 0-13-277665-0). P-H.
Pettygrove, G. Stuart & Asano, Takashi. Irrigation with Reclaimed Municipal Wastewater. (Illus.). 518p. 1985. 37.50 (ISBN 0-87371-061-4). Lewis Pubs Inc.
Principles, Methods & Practice, Vol. 1. 164p. 1982. 69.00x (ISBN 0-901090-27-1, Pub. by Natl Water England). State Mutual Bk.
Ramalho, R. S. Solutions Manual for Introduction to Wastewater Treatment Processes. 2nd ed. 1983. 12.50 (ISBN 0-12-576562-2). Acad Pr.
Rantala, P. & Luonsi, A., eds. Anaerobic Treatment of Forest Industry Wastewaters: Proceedings of the First IAWPRC Symposium on Forest Industry Wastewaters, Tampere, Finland, 11-15 June 1984. (Illus.). 326p. 1985. pap. 44.00 (ISBN 0-08-032729-X, Pub. by PPL). Pergamon.
Rudman, Jack. Sewage Plant Operator Trainee. (Career Examination Ser.: C-2281). (Cloth bdg. avail. on request). 1977. pap. 10.00 (ISBN 0-8373-2281-2). Natl Learning.
--Superintendent of Sewers. (Career Examination Ser.: C-2276). (Cloth bdg. avail. on request). 1977. pap. 12.00 (ISBN 0-8373-2276-6). Natl Learning.
Sludge Thickening ('80) (Manual of Practice, Facilities & Development Ser.: No. 1). 154p. Date not set. pap. 16.00 (ISBN 0-943244-18-8). Water Pollution.
Smith, D. W. & Hrudey, S. E., eds. Design of Water & Wastewater Services for Cold Climate Communities: Seminar in Edmonton in June 1980 of the 10th IAWPR Conference. (Illus.). 190p. 1981. 39.00 (ISBN 0-08-029079-5, E140). Pergamon.
Sopper, William E. & Kerr, Sonja N., eds. Utilization of Municipal Sewage Effluent & Sludge on Forest & Disturbed Land. LC 78-15275. (Illus.). 1979. text ed. 30.00x (ISBN 0-271-00205-0). Pa St U Pr.
Steel, E. W. & McGhee, Terence. Water Supply & Sewerage. 5th ed. (Illus.). 1979. text ed. 42.00 (ISBN 0-07-060929-2). McGraw.
Strategies, Technologies & Economics of Waste Water Management in ECE Countries. 77p. 1985. 12.50 (ISBN 0-317-18366-4). UN.
Structured Model of Bacterial Growth & Tests with Activated Sludge in a One-Stage & Two-Stage Chemostat. (Agricultural Research Reports: 886). 1979. pap. 18.00 (ISBN 90-220-0702-2, PDC116, PUDOC). Unipub.
Von Der Emde, W. & Tench, H. B., eds. Design & Operation of Large Wastewater Treatment Plants: Proceedings of a Workshop Held in Vienna, Austria, 19-23 September. (Illus.). 700p. 1985. pap. 132.00 (ISBN 0-08-031733-2). Pergamon.
Wastewater Treatment & Resource Recovery: Report of a Workshop on High-Rate Algae Ponds, Singapore, 27-29 Feb. 1980. 47p. 1980. pap. 7.50 (ISBN 0-88936-260-2, IDRC154, IDRC). Unipub.
Water Pollution Control Federation. Simplified Laboratory Procedures for Wastewater Examination. 56p. pap. 8.00 (ISBN 0-686-30426-8). Water Pollution.
--Sludge Dewatering. (Manual of Practice: 20). (Illus.). 164p. 1983. pap. text ed. 26.00 (ISBN 0-943244-42-0). Water Pollution.
--Wastewater Sampling for Process & Quality Control, 1980: Manual of Practice, Operation & Maintenance-I. 101p. Date not set. pap. 12.00 (ISBN 0-943244-21-8). Water Pollution.
Welch, E. B. Ecological Effects of Waste Water. LC 78-11371. 1980. 47.50 (ISBN 0-521-22495-0); pap. 16.95 (ISBN 0-521-29525-4). Cambridge U Pr.
Winkler, Michael. Biological Treatment of Waste-Water. 301p. 1981. 84.95x (ISBN 0-470-27185-X). Halsted Pr.

SEWAGE–PURIFICATION
Application of Adsorption to Wastewater Treatment. (Illus.). 1981. text ed. 40.00 (ISBN 0-937976-03-2). Enviro Pr.
Application of Chemical Engineering to the Treatment of Sewage: Proceedings, No. 41, York, April 1975. 286p. 1981. 100.00x (ISBN 0-85295-007-1, Pub. by Inst Chem Eng England). State Mutual Bk.
Barnes, D. & Bliss, P. Biological Control of Nitrogen in Wastewater Treatment. 150p. 1983. 35.00 (ISBN 0-419-12350-4, NO. 6765, E & FN Spon). Methuen Inc.
Bruce, A. M. Sewage Sludge Stabilisation & Disinfection. (Water & Waste Water Technology Ser.: No. 1-714). 624p. 1984. text ed. 69.95x (ISBN 0-470-20080-4). Halsted Pr.
Bruce, A. M. & Connor, E. S., eds. Stabilisation, Disinfection & Odour Control in Sewage Sludge Treatment. 200p. 1984. text ed. 59.95x (ISBN 0-470-20033-2). Halsted Pr.
Bruce, A. M. & Havelaar, A. H., eds. Disinfection of Sewage Sludge: Technical, Economic & Microbiological Aspects. 1982. lib. bdg. 34.95 (ISBN 90-277-1502-5, Pub. by Reidel Holland). Kluwer Academic.
Busch, Arthur W. Aerobic Biological Treatment of Waste Waters. LC 70-155639. 418p. 1971. 35.00x (ISBN 0-87201-008-2). Gulf Pub.
Casey, T. J., et al, eds. Methods of Characterization of Sewage Sludge. 164p. 1984. lib. bdg. 29.00 (ISBN 90-277-1782-6, Pub. by Reidel Holland). Kluwer Academic.
Cortinovis, Dan. Controlling Wastewater Treatment Processes. LC 84-61877. (Illus.). 150p. (Orig.). 1984. pap. 14.95 (ISBN 0-918967-00-7). Ridgeline Pr.
Culp, Gordon, et al. Wastewater Reuse & Recycling Technology. LC 80-21778. (Pollution Technology Review Ser.: 72). (Illus.). 838p. 1981. 48.00 (ISBN 0-8155-0829-8). Noyes.
Curds, C. R. & Hawkes, H. A., eds. Ecological Aspects of Used Water Treatment, Vol. 1. 1976. 66.00 (ISBN 0-12-199501-1). Acad Pr.

Cushnie, G. C., Jr. Removal of Metals from Wastewater: Neutralization & Precipitation. LC 83-22142. (Pollution Technology Review Ser.: No. 107). (Illus.). 232p. 1984. 32.00 (ISBN 0-8155-0976-6). Noyes.
De Renzo, D. J., ed. Nitrogen Control & Phosphorus Removal in Sewage Treatment. LC 78-59820. (Pollution Technology Review Ser.: No. 44). 1978. 32.00 (ISBN 0-8155-0711-9). Noyes.
Dinges, W. Ray. Natural Systems for Water Pollution Control. (Environmental Engineering Ser.). 352p. 1981. 28.95 (ISBN 0-442-20166-4). Van Nos Reinhold.
D'Itri, Frank M., ed. Wastewater Renovation & Reuse: Proceedings of the International Conference on the Renovation & Reuse of Wastewater Through Aquatic & Terrestrial Systems. LC 76-54588. (Pollution Engineering & Technology: Vol. 3). pap. 120.00 (ISBN 0-317-08391-0, 2055036). Bks Demand UMI.
Fair, Gordon M. & Okun, Daniel A. Water & Wastewater Engineering, 2 vols. LC 66-16139. Vol. 1, Water Supply & Wastewater Removal. pap. 128.00 (ISBN 0-317-11201-5, 2055401); Vol. 2, Water Purification & Wastewater Treatment & Disposal. pap. 160.00 (ISBN 0-317-11202-3). Bks Demand UMI.
Fochtman, Edward G., et al, eds. Forum on Ozone Disinfection. LC 76-51563. 1977. text ed. 18.00 (ISBN 0-918650-01-1); text ed. 25.00 non-members (ISBN 0-918650-00-3). Intl Ozone.
Fukui, S. & Tanaka, A. Immobilized Biocatalysts-Saccharomyces Yeasts-Wastewater Treatment. (Advances in Biochemical Engineering Biotech 29 Ser.). (Illus.). 160p. 1984. 33.00 (ISBN 0-387-12860-3). Springer-Verlag.
Gibbon, D. L. Aeration of Activated Sludge in Sewage Treatment. LC 74-8138. 126p. 1975. text ed. 28.00 (ISBN 0-08-018156-2). Pergamon.
Grady & Lim. Biological Wastewater Treatment: Theory & Applications. LC 80-20171. (Pollution Engineering & Technology Ser.: Vol. 12). 984p. 1980. 95.00 (ISBN 0-8247-1000-2). Dekker.
Humenick, M. J. Water & Wastewater Treatment: Calculations for Chemistry & Physical Processes. (Pollution Engineering & Technology Ser.: Vol. 4). 1977. pap. 45.00 (ISBN 0-8247-7280-6). Dekker.
Jaag, O., et al, eds. Water Pollution Research: Proceedings of the Second International Conference. 2nd ed. 1966. Set. 245.00 (ISBN 0-08-011438-5). Pergamon.
James, A., ed. Mathematical Models in Water Pollution Control. LC 77-7214. 420p. 1978. 79.95x (ISBN 0-471-99471-5, Pub. by Wiley-Interscience). Wiley.
Jenkins, S. H. Design-Operation Interactions at Large Waste Water Treatment Plants. flexi-cover 50.00 (ISBN 0-08-020901-7). Pergamon.
--Developments in Land Methods of Wastewater Treatment & Utilization. flexi-cover 99.00x (ISBN 0-08-024894-2). Pergamon.
--Treatment of Domestic & Industrial Wastewaters in Large Plants: Proceedings of a Workshop Held in Vienna, Austria, Sept. 1979. (Progress in Water Technology: Vol. 12, Nos. 3 & 5). 550p. 1981. 99.00 (ISBN 0-08-026033-0). Pergamon.
Jenkins, S. H., et al. Practical Experiences of Control & Automation in Wastewater Treatment & Water Resources Management, Vol. 13/8-12. flexi-cover 165.00x (ISBN 0-08-029086-8). Pergamon.
Judkins, Joseph F. & Benefield, Larry D. Process Chemisty for Water & Wastewater Treatment. (Illus.). 528p. 1982. 41.95 (ISBN 0-13-722975-5). P-H.
L'Hermite, P. & Ott, H., eds. Processing & Use of Sewage Sludge. 600p. 1984. lib. bdg. 79.50 (ISBN 90-277-1727-3, Pub. by Reidel Holland). Kluwer Academic.
McWhirter, J. R., ed. Use of High Purity Oxygen in the Activated Sludge Process, 2 vols. (Uniscience Ser.). 1978. Vol. 1, 296p. 66.00 (ISBN 0-8493-5101-4); Vol. 2, 292p. 66.00 (ISBN 0-8493-5102-2). CRC Pr.
Mara, Duncan. Sewage Treatment in Hot Climates. LC 75-23421. 168p. 1976. 48.95x (ISBN 0-471-56784-1, Pub. by Wiley-Interscience). Wiley.
Mattock, G., ed. New Processes of Waste Water Treatment & Recovery. 415p. 1978. 101.95 (ISBN 0-470-26341-5). Halsted Pr.
Middlebrooks, E. Joe. Water Reuse. LC 80-70324. 1982. text ed. 69.95 (ISBN 0-250-40359-5). Butterworth.
On-Site Sewage Treatment: Proceedings of the American Society of Agricultural Engineers, Third National Symposium. LC 82-70361. 352p. (Orig.). 1982. pap. 19.50 (ISBN 0-916150-43-7); members 16.00. Am Soc Ag Eng.
Parker, Homer. Wastewater Systems Engineering. (Illus.). 464p. 1975. 41.95 (ISBN 0-13-945758-5). P-H.
Patterson, James W. Industrial Wastewater Treatment Technology. 2nd ed. 416p. 1985. text ed. 49.95 (ISBN 0-409-90002-8). Butterworth.
Pawlowski, L. Physiochemical Methods for Water & Wastewater Treatment. 1980. 68.00 (ISBN 0-08-024013-5). Pergamon.
Perrich, Jerry R., ed. Activated Carbon Absorption for Wastewater Treatment. 272p. 1981. 82.00 (ISBN 0-8493-5693-8). CRC Pr.
Procedures & Practices in Activated Sludge Process Control. 34.95 (ISBN 0-250-40630-6). Butterworth.
Processing Water-Treatment-Plant Sludge. (AWWA Handbooks - General). (Illus.). 160p. 1974. pap. text ed. 10.80 (ISBN 0-89867-016-0). Am Water Wks Assn.
Ramalho, R. S. Introduction to Wastewater Treatment Processes. 2nd ed. 1983. 59.00 (ISBN 0-12-576560-6). Acad Pr.
Randall, Clifford W. & Benefield, Larry D. Biological Processes Design for Wastewater Treatment. (Environmental Sciences Ser.). (Illus.). 1980. text ed. 35.95 (ISBN 0-13-076406-X). P-H.
Rice, Rip G., ed. First International Symposium on Ozone for Water & Wastewater Treatment. LC 74-28539. (Illus.). 1974. text ed. 15.00 (ISBN 0-918650-03-8); text ed. 20.00 non-members (ISBN 0-918650-04-6). Intl Ozone.
Rich, Linvil G. Low-Maintenance, Mechanically-Simple Wastewater Treatment Systems. (Water Resources & Environmental Engineering). (Illus.). 1980. text ed. 38.95 (ISBN 0-07-052252-9). McGraw.
Rudman, Jack. Senior Sewage Treatment Plant Operator. (Career Examination Ser.: C-1556). (Cloth bdg. avail. on request). pap. 12.00 (ISBN 0-8373-1556-5). Natl Learning.
Saltzberg, Edward R. & Cushnie, George C., Jr. Centralized Waste Treatment of Industrial Wastewater. LC 85-4986. (Illus.). 415p. 1985. 45.00 (ISBN 0-8155-1038-1). Noyes.
Schmidtke, Norbert W. & Smith, Daniel W., eds. Scale-up of Water & Wastewater Treatment Processes. 512p. 1983. text ed. 39.95 (ISBN 0-250-40638-1). Butterworth.
Sundstrom, Donald W. & Klei, Herbert E. Wastewater Treatment. LC 78-13058. (Illus.). 1979. 41.95 (ISBN 0-13-945832-8). P-H.
Von Der Emde, W. & Tench, H. B., eds. Design & Operation of Large Wastewater Treatment Plants: Proceedings of a Workshop Held in Vienna, Austria, 19-23 September. (Illus.). 700p. 1985. pap. 132.00 (ISBN 0-08-031733-2). Pergamon.
Wastewater Treatment & Resource Recovery: Report of a Workshop on High-Rate Algae Ponds, Singapore, 27-29 Feb. 1980. 47p. 1980. pap. 7.50 (ISBN 0-88936-260-2, IDRC154, IDRC). Unipub.
Wastewater Treatment Plant Design ('77) Manual of Practice, No. 8. (Illus.). 550p. 20.00 (ISBN 0-943244-08-0, M0008). Water Pollution.
Water Pollution Control Federation. Aeration in Wastewater Treatment ('71) (Manual of Practice Ser.: No. 5). 96p. 30.00 (ISBN 0-931956-04-8); pap. 11.00 (ISBN 0-943244-05-6); pap. 8.25 members. Water Pollution.
--Chlorination of Wastewater ('76) (Manual of Practice Ser.: No. 4). 112p. 1976. pap. 12.00 (ISBN 0-943244-04-8, M0004); pap. 9.00 members. Water Pollution.
--Design of Wastewater & Stormwater Pumping Stations ('80) Manual of Practice, Facilities & Development-4, No. 4. 146p. Date not set. pap. 16.00 (ISBN 0-943244-20-X). Water Pollution.
White, George C. Disinfection of Wastewater & Water for Reuse. LC 78-18457. 400p. 1978. 27.50 (ISBN 0-442-29405-0). Krieger.
Wilson, F. Design Calculations in Wastewater Treatment. 1980. 35.00x (ISBN 0-419-11690-7, NO. 6535, Pub. by E & FN Spon); pap. 15.95x (ISBN 0-419-11700-8, NO. 6534). Methuen Inc.

SEWAGE DISPOSAL

see also Refuse and Refuse Disposal; Water–Pollution

Acceptable Sludge Disposal Techniques. (Illus.). 1978. softcover 18.00x (ISBN 0-686-26023-6, MSL8). Info Transfer.
American Society of Civil Engineers, compiled By. Financing & Charges for Wastewater Systems. 2nd ed. 120p. 1984. pap. 35.00x (ISBN 0-87262-432-3). Am Soc Civil Eng.
Arceivala. Wastewater Treatment & Disposal. (Pollution Engineering & Technology Ser.: Vol. 15). 920p. 1981. 99.50 (ISBN 0-8247-6973-2). Dekker.
ASCE Urban Water Resources Research Council Conference, Nov. 1976. Guide for Collection, Analysis, & Use of Urban Stormwater Data. 128p. 1977. pap. 5.75x (ISBN 0-87262-077-8). Am Soc Civil Eng.
Bartlett, R. E. Public Health Engineering-Sewarage. 2nd ed. 196p. 1979. 33.50 (ISBN 0-85334-796-4, Pub. by Elsevier Applied Sci England). Elsevier.
Brunner, Calvin R. Design of Sewage Sludge Incineration Systems. LC 80-21916. (Pollution Technology Review Ser.: No. 71). (Illus.). 380p. 1981. 48.00 (ISBN 0-8155-0825-5). Noyes.
Cain, Louis P. Sanitation Strategy for a Lakefront Metropolis: The Case of Chicago. LC 76-14711. 173p. 1978. 15.00 (ISBN 0-87580-064-5). N Ill U Pr.
Canter, Larry W. & Knox, R. C. Effect of Septic Tank Systems on Ground Water Quality. LC 84-23280. (Illus.). 336p. 1985. 29.95 (ISBN 0-87371-012-6). Lewis Pubs Inc.
Chambers, B. & Chambers, E. J. Bulking of Activated Sludge: Preventative & Remedial Methods. 279p. 1982. 74.95x (ISBN 0-470-27299-6). Halsted Pr.
Combined Sewer Separation Using Pressure Sewers. 211p. 1969. pap. 12.00x (ISBN 0-87262-017-4). Am Soc Civil Eng.
Coppa & Avery Consultants Staff. The Design of Sewage Disposal Plants: A Bibliography. (Architecture Ser.: Bibliography A 1320). 1985. pap. 2.00 (ISBN 0-89028-270-6). Vance Biblios.
Dart, M. C. & Jenkins, S. H. Disposal of Sludge to Sea, Vol. 14, No. 3. pap. 40.00x (ISBN 0-08-029093-0). Pergamon.
Design of Municipal Sludge Compost Facilities. (Illus.). 1978. softcover 15.00x (ISBN 0-686-26022-8). Info Transfer.
Disposal of Community Wastewater: Report. (Technical Report Ser.: No. 541). (Also avail. in Fr. & Span.). 1974. pap. 2.40 (ISBN 92-4-120541-5). World Health.
Evans, Joe L. & Waldorf, Lawrence, eds. Individual Onsite Wastewater Systems, Vol. 8: Proceedings of the Eighth National Conference, 1981. LC 76-50983. (Illus.). 325p. 1982. 35.00 (ISBN 0-940006-01-4). Natl Sanit Foun.
Fair, Gordon M., et al. Water & Wastewater Engineering: Water Supply & Wastewater Removal, Vol. 1. LC 66-16139. 489p. 1966. 53.45x (ISBN 0-471-25130-5). Wiley.
Ganczarczyk. Activated Sludge Processes. (Pollution Engineering Ser.). 288p. 1983. 59.75 (ISBN 0-8247-1758-9). Dekker.
Glossary: Water & Wastewater Control Engineering. 2nd ed. (General References Ser.). (Illus.). 456p. 1981. text ed. 25.00 (ISBN 0-89867-263-5). Am Water Wks Assn.
Grava, Sigurd. Urban Planning Aspects of Water Pollution Control. LC 72-87147. (Illus.). 223p. 1969. 30.00x (ISBN 0-231-03280-3). Columbia U Pr.
Hammer, David E. & Kadlec, Robert H. Wetlands Utilization for Management of Community Wastewater: Concepts & Operations in Michigan. (Illus.). 28p. 1980. 12.00 (ISBN 0-938654-28-4). Indus Dev Inst Sci.
Hammer, Mark J. Water & Waste-Water Technology. 2nd ed. 1986. price not set (ISBN 0-471-82961-7). Wiley.
James, R. W. Sewage Sludge Treatment & Disposal. LC 76-17939. (Pollution Technology Review: No. 29). (Illus.). 339p. 1977. 39.00 (ISBN 0-8155-0630-9). Noyes.
Jenkins, S. H. Treatment of Domestic & Industrial Wastewaters in Large Plants: Proceedings of a Workshop Held in Vienna, Austria, Sept. 1979. (Progress in Water Technology: Vol. 12, Nos. 3 & 5). 550p. 1981. 99.00 (ISBN 0-08-026033-0). Pergamon.
Lam, D. C., et al. Effluent Transport & Diffusion Models for the Coastal Zone. (Lecture Notes on Coastal & Estuarine Studies: Vol. 5). (Illus.). 170p. 1984. pap. 19.00 (ISBN 0-387-90928-1). Springer-Verlag.
Management & Disposal of Residues from the Treatment of Industrial Wastewaters. (Illus.). 1975. 5.00xsoftcover (ISBN 0-686-26014-7, 1WW5). Info Transfer.
Meinck, Fritz. Woerterbuch fuer das Wasser und Abwasserfach. 2nd ed. (Ger., Eng., Fr. & Ital., Dictionary of Water and Sewage Disposal Plants). 1977. 128.00 (ISBN 3-486-35352-7, M-6920). French & Eur.
Metcalf & Eddy Inc. Wastewater Engineering: Collection, Treatment, Disposal & Reuse. 2nd ed. Tchobanoglous, George, ed. (Illus.). 1978. text ed. 46.95 (ISBN 0-07-041677-X). McGraw.
Middlebrooks, Joe E., et al. Wastewater Stabilization Lagoon Design, Performance & Upgrading. (Illus.). 320p. 1982. text ed. 45.00x (ISBN 0-02-949500-8). Macmillan.
Municipal Sludge Management. (Illus.). 1974. 5.00x (ISBN 0-686-26020-1, MSL4). Info Transfer.
Municipal Sludge Management & Disposal. (Illus.). 1975. 10.00x (ISBN 0-686-25733-2, MSL5). Info Transfer.
Odor Control for Wastewater Facilities ('79) (Manual of Practice Ser.: No. 22). (Illus.). 70p. Date not set. pap. 8.00 (ISBN 0-943244-17-X). Water Pollution.
Okun, D. A. & Ponghis, G. Community Wastewater Collection & Disposal. (Also avail. in French). 1975. pap. 16.80 (ISBN 92-4-156045-2). World Health.
Operation & Maintenance of Wastewater Collection Systems ('80) (Manual of Practice: No. 7). 95p. Date not set. pap. 12.00 (ISBN 0-943244-07-2). Water Pollution.
Pearson, E. A. & De Fraga Frangipane, E. Marine Pollution & Marine Waste Disposal. 140.00x (ISBN 0-08-019730-2). Pergamon.
Pineo, C. S. & Subrahmanyan, D. V. Community Water Supply & Excreta Disposal Situation in the Developing Countries. (Offset Publication Ser.: No. 15). (Also avail. in French). 1975. pap. 4.80 (ISBN 92-4-170015-7). World Health.
Research Symposia, 53rd Conference, 1980: Proceedings. Date not set. pap. 20.00 (ISBN 0-686-30424-1). Water Pollution.
Rudman, Jack. District Foreman (Sewer Maintenance) (Career Examination Ser.: C-1815). (Cloth bdg. avail. on request). pap. 12.00 (ISBN 0-8373-1815-7). Natl Learning.
--Foreman (Sewer Maintenance) (Career Examination Ser.: C-1816). (Cloth bdg. avail. on request). pap. 10.00 (ISBN 0-8373-1816-5). Natl Learning.
--Senior Sewage Treatment Worker. (Career Examination Ser.: C-791). (Cloth bdg. avail. on request). pap. 12.00 (ISBN 0-8373-0791-0). Natl Learning.
--Sewage Treatment Operator. (Career Examination Ser.: C-1488). (Cloth bdg. avail. on request). pap. 12.00 (ISBN 0-8373-1488-7). Natl Learning.
--Sewage Treatment Operator Trainee. (Career Examination Ser.: C-1489). (Cloth bdg. avail. on request). pap. 10.00 (ISBN 0-8373-1489-5). Natl Learning.
--Sewage Treatment Plant Supervisor. (Career Examination Ser.: C-1490). (Cloth bdg. avail. on request). pap. 12.00 (ISBN 0-8373-1490-9). Natl Learning.
--Sewage Treatment Worker. (Career Examination Ser.: C-734). (Cloth bdg. avail. on request). pap. 10.00 (ISBN 0-8373-0734-1). Natl Learning.
--Sewage Treatment Worker Trainee. (Career Examination Ser.: C-735). (Cloth bdg. avail. on request). pap. 10.00 (ISBN 0-8373-0735-X). Natl Learning.
Scott & Smith. Dictionary of Waste & Water Treatment. 1981. text ed. 49.95 (ISBN 0-408-00495-9). Butterworth.
Tchobanoglous, George, et al, eds. Wastewater Management: A Guide to Information Sources. LC 74-11570. (Man & the Environment Information Guide Ser.: Vol. 2). 260p. 1976. 60.00x (ISBN 0-8103-1338-3). Gale.
Torrey, S., ed. Sludge Disposal by Landspreading Techniques. LC 79-12526. (Pollution Technology Review Ser.: No. 58). (Illus.). 372p. 1979. 36.00 (ISBN 0-8155-0762-3). Noyes.
Trullinger, Robert W. & Warren, George M. Clean Water & Sewage Disposal on the Farm. facs. ed. (Shorey Lost Arts Ser.). 52p. pap. 3.95 (ISBN 0-8466-6036-9, U36). Shorey.
Uniform System for Accounts for Wastewater Utilities ('70) (Manual of Practice Ser.: No. 10). 71p. Date not set. pap. 8.00 (ISBN 0-943244-10-2). Water Pollution.
Vance, Mary. Sewage Disposal: A Bibliography. (Public Administration Ser.: Bibliography P-897). 87p. 1982. pap. 12.75 (ISBN 0-88066-137-2). Vance Biblios.
--Sewage Disposal Plants: A Bibliography. (Public Administration Ser.: Bibliography P-898). 66p. 1982. pap. 9.75 (ISBN 0-88066-138-0). Vance Biblios.
Vesiland. Waste Water Sludge Management & Disposal for the Practicing Engineer. (Illus.). 389p. 1985. 39.95 (ISBN 0-87371-060-6). Lewis Pubs Inc.
Vesilind, P. Aarne. Treatment & Disposal Wastewater Sludges. rev. ed. LC 78-71431. (Illus.). 1979. 39.95 (ISBN 0-250-40290-4). Butterworth.
Von Der Emde, W. & Tench, H. B., eds. Design & Operation of Large Wastewater Treatment Plants: Proceedings of a Workshop Held in Vienna, Austria, 19-23 September. (Illus.). 700p. 1985. pap. 132.00 (ISBN 0-08-031733-2). Pergamon.
Warner, Don L. & Lehr, Jay H. Subsurface Wastewater Injection: The Technology of Injecting Wastewater into Deep Wells for Disposal. LC 81-80736. (Illus.). 344p. 1981. pap. 16.00 (ISBN 0-912722-03-7). Prem Press.
Waste Treatment & Utilization: Theory & Practice of Waste Management Proceedings of the International Symposium Held at the University of Waterloo, Waterloo, Ontario, Canada July 5-7 1978. (Illus.). 574p. 1979. 72.00 (ISBN 0-08-023831-9). Pergamon.

Water Pollution Control Federation. Financing & Charges for Wastewater Systems ('73) (Illus.). 68p. Date not set. pap. 8.00 (ISBN 0-943244-25-0). Water Pollution.

--Instrumentation in Wastewater Treatment Plants ('78) (Manual of Practice Ser.: No. 21). 108p. 1978. pap. 12.00 (ISBN 0-943244-16-1, M0027). Water Pollution.

--Operation of Wastewater Treatment Plants ('76) (Manual of Practice Ser.: No. 11). (Illus.). 536p. Date not set. 30.00 (ISBN 0-943244-11-0); pap. 25.00 (ISBN 0-943244-12-9). Water Pollution.

--Preliminary Treatment for Wastewater Facilities ('80) Manual of Practice, Operation & Maintenance-2, No. 2. 52p. 1980. pap. 6.00 (ISBN 0-943244-22-6); pap. 4.50 members. Water Pollution.

Water Supply & Waste Disposal. 46p. 1980. pap. 3.00 (ISBN 0-686-39678-2). World Bank.

Yehaskel, Albert. Industrial Wastewater Cleanup: Recent Developments. LC 79-12395. (Pollution Technology Review Ser.: No. 57). (Illus.). 1979. 39.00 (ISBN 0-8155-0758-5). Noyes.

SEWERAGE

see also Drainage; Plumbing; Sewage

American Society of Civil Engineers Staff & Water Pollution Control Federation Staff, eds. Existing Sewer Evaluation & Rehabilitation. (Manual & Report on Engineering Practice Ser.: No. 62). 116p. 1983. pap. 18.00x (ISBN 0-87262-389-0). Am Soc Civil Eng.

American Society of Civil Engineers & Water Pollution Control Federation. Gravity Sanitary Sewer Design & Construction. LC 81-69182. (Manual & Report on Engineering Practice Ser.: No. 60). 291p. 1982. 20.00x (ISBN 0-87262-313-0). Am Soc Civil Eng.

Barnes, D. & Wilson, F. Chemistry & Unit Operations in Sewage Treatment. (Illus.). 339p. 1978. 48.00 (ISBN 0-85334-783-2, Pub. by Elsevier Applied Sci England). Elsevier.

Bartlett, Ronald E. Surface Water Sewerage. 2nd ed. LC 80-42202. 147p. 1981. 39.95x (ISBN 0-470-27144-2). Halsted Pr.

Culp, Russell L. & Wesner, George M. Handbook of Advanced Wastewater Treatment. 2nd ed. 1978. 42.50 (ISBN 0-442-21784-6). Van Nos Reinhold.

Design & Construction of Sanitary & Storm Sewers. (Manula & Report on Engineering Practice Ser.: No. 37). 350p. 1969. 17.00x (ISBN 0-87262-214-2). Am Soc Civil Eng.

Design & Construction of Sanitary & Storm Sewers ('69) (Manual of Practice Ser.: No. 9). Date not set. 17.00 (ISBN 0-943244-09-9). Water Pollution.

Eckenfelder, W. & Santhanam, C., eds. Sludge Treatment. (Pollution, Engineering & Technology Ser.: Vol. 14). 1981. 85.00 (ISBN 0-8247-6977-5). Dekker.

Escritt, Leonard B. Sewerage & Sewage Treatment: International Practice. LC 83-1300. 450p. 1984. 58.95x (ISBN 0-471-10339-X, Pub. by Wiley-Interscience). Wiley.

Featherstone, R. E. & James, A., eds. Urban Drainage Systems. 229p. 1982. text ed. 76.95 (ISBN 0-273-08596-4). Pitman Pub MA.

Forster, C. F. Biotechnology & Wastewater Treatment. (Cambridge Studies in Biotechnology: No. 2). (Illus.). 392p. 1985. 59.50 (ISBN 0-521-25723-9). Cambridge U Pr.

Helliwell, P. R., ed. Urban Storm Drainage. LC 78-18235. 728p. 1978. 79.95x (ISBN 0-470-26461-6). Halsted Pr.

Howard, William T. & Hammer, Thomas R. Water-Quality Impacts of Unsewered Housing. (Discussion Paper Ser.: No. 66). 1973. pap. 4.50 (ISBN 0-686-32232-0). Regional Sci Res Inst.

Meinck, Fritz. Woerterbuch fuer das Wasser und Abwasserfach. 2nd ed. (Ger., Eng., Fr. & Ital., Dictionary of Water and Sewage Disposal Plants). 1977. 128.00 (ISBN 3-486-35352-7, M-6920). French & Eur.

Metcalf & Eddy Inc. Wastewater Engineering: Collection, Treatment, Disposal & Reuse. 2nd ed. Tchobanoglous, George, ed. (Illus.). 1978. text ed. 46.95 (ISBN 0-07-041677-X). McGraw.

Metcalf & Eddy, Inc. & Tchobanoglous, George. Wastewater Engineering: Collection & Pumping of Wastewater. (Water Resources & Engineering Ser.). (Illus.). 448p. 1981. text ed. 45.00 (ISBN 0-07-041680-X). McGraw.

The Operation & Maintenance of Small Sewage Works. 70p. 1981. 25.00x (ISBN 0-904561-76-3, Pub. by Natl Water England). State Mutual Bk.

Paints & Protective Coatings for Wastewater Treatment Facilities ('69) (Manual of Practice No. 17). 86p. Date not set. pap. 10.00 (ISBN 0-943244-14-5). Water Pollution.

Principles, Methods & Practice, Vol. 1. 164p. 1982. 69.00x (ISBN 0-901090-27-1, Pub. by Natl Water England). State Mutual Bk.

Rosenkrantz, Barbara G., ed. Sewering the Cities: An Original Anthology. LC 76-40352. (Public Health in America Ser.). (Illus.). 1977. Repr. of 1977 ed. lib. bdg. 20.00x (ISBN 0-405-09879-0). Ayer Co Pubs.

Rudman, Jack. Assistant Director of Maintenance (Sewer District) (Career Examination Ser.: C-2908). (Cloth bdg. avail. on request). pap. 14.00 (ISBN 0-8373-2908-6). Natl Learning.

--Foreman (Highways & Sewers) (Career Examination Ser.: C-2190). (Cloth bdg. avail. on request). pap. 10.00 (ISBN 0-8373-2190-5). Natl Learning.

--Sewage Plant Operator. (Career Examination Ser.: C-2443). (Cloth bdg. avail. on request). pap. 12.00 (ISBN 0-8373-1880-7). Natl Learning.

--Sewer Inspector. (Career Examination Ser.: C-2454). (Cloth bdg. avail. on request). pap. 12.00 (ISBN 0-8373-2454-8). Natl Learning.

--Superintendent of Sewer Service. (Career Examination Ser.: C-2141). (Cloth bdg. avail. on request). 1977. pap. 12.00 (ISBN 0-8373-2141-7). Natl Learning.

--Supervisor (Water & Sewer Systems) (Career Examination Ser.: C-2907). (Cloth bdg. avail. on request). pap. 10.00 (ISBN 0-8373-2907-8). Natl Learning.

Sewer Charges for Wastewater Collection & Treatment. 32p. (Orig.). 1982. pap. text ed. 6.00 (ISBN 0-943244-39-0). Water Pollution.

Sewers for Adoption: A Design & Construction Guide for Developers. 68p. 1982. 29.00x (ISBN 0-901090-38-7, Pub. by Natl Water England). State Mutual Bk.

Steel, E. W. & McGhee, Terence. Water Supply & Sewerage. 5th ed. (Illus.). 1979. text ed. 42.00 (ISBN 0-07-060929-2). McGraw.

Urban Runoff-Quantity & Quality. 278p. 1975. pap. 14.00x (ISBN 0-87262-103-0). Am Soc Civil Eng.

Wanielista, Martin P. Stormwater Management: Quantity & Quality. LC 78-62292. 1978. 59.95 (ISBN 0-250-40261-0). Butterworth.

Water Pollution Control Federation & ASCE. Existing Sewer Evaluation & Rehabilitation. (Manual of Practice, Facilities Development Ser.: 6). (Illus.). 116p. 1983. text ed. 18.00 (ISBN 0-943244-43-9). Water Pollution.

Water Pollution Control Federation. Guidelines for Developing a Wastewater Safety Program. (Manual of Practice, Systems Mgmnt. Ser.: 2). (Illus.). 56p. (Orig.). 1983. pap. text ed. 12.00 (ISBN 0-943244-48-X); 9.00. Water Pollution.

SEWERAGE, RURAL

Pacey, Arnold, compiled by. Rural Sanitation: Planning & Appraisal. (Illus.). 68p. (Orig.). 1980. pap. 7.75x (ISBN 0-903031-72-8, Pub. by Intermediate Tech England). Intermediate Tech.

Watson, M. Rural Sanitation in the Tropics. 1976. lib. bdg. 69.95 (ISBN 0-8490-2548-6). Gordon Pr.

SEWERS

see Sewerage

SEWING

see also Dressmaking

Alderman, Sharon & Wertenberger, Kathryn. Handwoven, Tailormade: A Tandem Guide to Fabric Designing, Weaving, Sewing & Tailoring. LC 82-81683. (Illus.). 147p. 1982. 17.50 (ISBN 0-934026-08-4). Interweave.

Benton, Kitty. Sewing Classic Clothes for Children. 160p. 1981. 19.95 (ISBN 0-87851-204-7). Hearst Bks.

Coleman, A. Creative Sewing Machine. 1981. pap. 12.50 (ISBN 0-7134-3310-8, Pub. by Batsford England). David & Charles.

De Lynn, Eileen. Secrets of How to Have the Latest Pant Styles: Style Pants or Restyle Pants & Save Money. Boyce, D. E., ed. (Illus.). 128p. 1982. 18.95 (ISBN 0-941110-01-X); pap. 14.95 (ISBN 0-941110-00-1). Seagulls Artistic.

Enger, Ronald L. Do It Yourself (At Home) Sewing Machine Care & Repair. (Illus.). 33p. 1978. pap. 3.95 (ISBN 0-685-59470-X). R L Enger.

Goldsworthy, Maureen. Clothes for Disabled People. (Illus.). 120p. 1981. 14.95 (ISBN 0-7134-3929-7, Pub. by Batsford England). David & Charles.

Graef, Judy & Strom, J. Concepts in Clothing. 1976. 21.40 (ISBN 0-07-023889-8). McGraw.

Jones, Frances. Modern Sewing: A Text & Handbook. LC 71-155248. (Illus.). 498p. 1972. text ed. 7.50x (ISBN 0-8134-1300-1, 1300). Interstate.

Kopp, Ernestine & Rolfo, Vittorina. How to Draft Basic Patterns. 3rd. ed. 100p. 1983. text ed. 14.50 (ISBN 0-87005-467-8); designers neckline curve incl. Fairchild.

Ladbury, Ann. Batsford Book of Sewing. 1978. pap. 11.95 (ISBN 0-7134-0199-0, Pub. by Batsford England). David & Charles.

--The Dressmaker's Dictionary. LC 82-8725. (Illus.). 360p. 1983. 19.95 (ISBN 0-668-05653-3, 5653). Arco.

Lawrence, Judy & Yurick, Clotilde. Sew Smart with Ultra Suede Fabric & Other Luxury Suedes. (Illus.). 106p. 1981. pap. 5.95x (ISBN 0-9605860-0-8). Sewing Knits.

McCall's Staff. McCall Pattern Guide to Sewing Power. 184p. 1983. pap. text ed. 9.95 (ISBN 0-8403-3239-4). Kendall-Hunt.

Martensson, Kerstin. Kwik-Sew Method for Easy Sewing. (Illus.). pap. 8.50 (ISBN 0-913212-09-1). Kwik Sew.

Murdoch, Katharine. The Measurement of Certain Elements of Hand Sewing. LC 73-177097. (Columbia University. Teachers College. Contributions to Education Ser.: No. 103). Repr. of 1919 ed. 22.50 (ISBN 0-404-55103-3). AMS Pr.

Oblander, Ruth. Slacks for Perfect Fit: Sew-Fit Method. LC 81-50280. (Illus.). 64p. 1981. pap. 4.00x (ISBN 0-933956-07-X). Sew-Fit.

Oblander, Ruth, et al. The Sew-Fit Manual. LC 77-84538. (Illus.). 1978. 26.00x (ISBN 0-933956-03-7). Sew-Fit.

Popko, Rhonda. The Book of Basic Sewing. (Illus.). 104p. (Orig.). 1981. pap. 4.95 (ISBN 0-8326-2249-4, 7523). Delair.

Reich, Naomi, et al. Essentials of Clothing Construction. 2nd ed. (Illus.). 1978. pap. 18.95 (ISBN 0-13-284398-6). P-H.

Riley, Jean. Bargello Borders. 1974. write for info. Needlemania.

Riley, Patricia. The Skirtmaking Book. 1979. 18.95 (ISBN 0-7134-1641-6, Pub. by Batsford England). David & Charles.

Rudman, Jack. Seamstress. (Career Examination Ser.: C-1619). (Cloth bdg. avail. on request). pap. 8.00 (ISBN 0-8373-1619-7). Natl Learning.

Ruggieri, Lorraine. Woman's Day Book of No-Pattern Sewing. 128p. (Orig.). 1981. pap. 6.95 (ISBN 0-449-90053-3, Columbine). Fawcett.

Sewing Essentials. LC 84-42637. (Illus.). 17.95 (ISBN 0-394-54051-4); pap. 9.95 (ISBN 0-394-72757-6). Random.

Shaeffer, Claire B. The Complete Book of Sewing Shortcuts. LC 81-50981. (Illus.). 256p. 1981. 19.95 (ISBN 0-8069-5432-9). Sterling.

Tuit, Ann. Introducing Pattern Cutting. 1974. pap. text ed. 11.50x (ISBN 0-435-42860-8). Heinemann Ed.

Vogue Sewing Book. rev. ed. 24.95x (ISBN 0-685-70732-6). Wehman.

SEWING-MACHINES

Automating the Sewing Room. 1982. 40.00 (ISBN 0-318-01187-5, 13110). Indus Fabrics.

Head, Carol. Old Sewing Machines. (Shire Album Ser.: No. 84). (Illus.). 32p. pap. 2.95 (ISBN 0-85263-591-5, Pub. by Shire Pubns England). Seven Hills Bks.

Hutchison, Howard. The Complete Handbook of Sewing Machine Repair. (Illus.). 1980. pap. 9.95 (ISBN 0-8306-1163-0, 1163). TAB Bks.

SEX–CAUSE AND DETERMINATION

see also Eugenics; Sex Chromosomes

Amann, Rupert, ed. Prospects for Sexing Mammalian Sperm. LC 82-70138. 1982. pap. text ed. 24.50x (ISBN 0-87081-134-7). Colo Assoc.

Austin, C. R. & Edwards, U. R., eds. Mechanisms of Sex Differentiation in Animals & Man. LC 81-66380. 1981. 89.00 (ISBN 0-12-068540-X). Acad Pr.

Bleier, Ruth. Science & Gender: A Critique of Biology & Its Theories on Women. (Athene Ser.). (Illus.). 250p. 1984. 25.00 (ISBN 0-08-030972-0); pap. 12.50 (ISBN 0-08-030971-2). Pergamon.

Bull, James. Evolution of Sex Determining Mechanisms. 1983. 23.95 (ISBN 0-8053-0400-2). Benjamin-Cummings.

Charnov, E. L. The Theory of Sex Allocation: MPB. 1982. 47.50 (ISBN 0-691-08311-8); pap. 14.95 (ISBN 0-691-08312-6). Princeton U Pr.

Glucksmann, A. Sex Determination & Sexual Dimorphism in Mammals. 174p. 1978. pap. cancelled (ISBN 0-85109-790-1). Taylor & Francis.

--Sexual Dimorphism in Human & Mammalian Biology & Pathology. LC 80-42373. 374p. 1981. 55.00 (ISBN 0-12-286960-5). Acad Pr.

Glucksmann, Alfred & Smith, M. I. Sex Determination & Sexual Dimorphism in Mammals. LC 78-63273. (Wykeham Science Ser.: No. 54). 174p. 1979. pap. 13.50x (ISBN 0-8448-1370-2). Crane-Russak Co.

Lepori, N. G. Sex Differentiation, Hermaphroditism & Intersexuality in Vertebrates Including Man. (Illus.). 372p. 1980. text ed. 49.50x (ISBN 88-212-0747-1, Pub. by Piccin Italy). J K Burgess.

Mittwoch, Ursula. Genetics of Sex Differentiation. 1973. 50.00 (ISBN 0-12-501040-0). Acad Pr.

Money, John & Ehrhardt, Anke A. Man & Woman, Boy & Girl: Differentiation & Dimorphism of Gender Identity from Conception to Maturity. LC 72-4012. (Illus.). 325p. (Orig.). 1973. pap. 8.95x (ISBN 0-8018-1406-5). Johns Hopkins.

O'Donald, Peter. Genetic Models of Sexual Selection. LC 78-73249. (Illus.). 1980. 42.50 (ISBN 0-521-22533-7). Cambridge U Pr.

Ohno, S. Major Sex-Determining Genes. LC 78-10285. (Monographs on Endocrinology: Vol. 11). (Illus.). 1979. 24.00 (ISBN 0-387-08965-9). Springer-Verlag.

Saier, M. H. & Jacobson, G. R. The Molecular Basis of Sex & Differentiation: A Comparative Study of Evolution, Mechanism & Control in Microorganisms. (Illus.). 225p. 1984. pap. 34.50 (ISBN 0-387-96007-4). Springer-Verlag.

Summit, Robert & Bergsma, Daniel, eds. Sex Differentiation & Chromosomal Abnormalities. (Alan R. Liss, Inc. Ser.: Vol. 14, No. 6c). 1978. 61.00 (ISBN 0-686-23951-2). March of Dimes.

Wachtel, Stephen, ed. H-Y Antigen & the Biology of Sex Determination. 304p. 1982. 51.50 (ISBN 0-8089-1514-2, 794715). Grune.

SEX (BIOLOGY)

see also Generative Organs; Reproduction; Sex–Cause and Determination

Avers, Charlotte J. Biology of Sex. LC 74-1021. pap. 73.30 (ISBN 0-317-28753-2, 2055487). Bks Demand UMI.

Brambilla, F. & Bridges. Perspectives in Endocrine Psychobiology. LC 76-27305. Repr. of 1978 ed. 147.50 (ISBN 0-8357-9953-0, 2016160). Bks Demand UMI.

Daly, Martin & Wilson, Margo. Sex, Evolution & Behavior. 2nd ed. 400p. 1983. pap. text ed. write for info. (ISBN 0-87150-767-6, 4511, Pub. by Willard Grant Pr). PWS Pubs.

Dwyer, Joyce M. Human Reproduction: The Female System & the Neonate. LC 76-2580. 209p. 1976. text ed. 7.95x (ISBN 0-8036-2970-2). Davis Co.

Eberhard, William G. Sexual Selection & Animal Genitalia. (Illus.). 288p. 1985. text ed. 25.00x (ISBN 0-674-80283-7). Harvard U Pr.

Effects of Pharmacologically Active Substances on Sexual Function. 124p. 1968. 35.00x (ISBN 0-686-45140-6, Pub. by Biochemical England). State Mutual Bk.

Gallien, Louis E. Bases Cytologiques & Genetiques de la Sexalite, Vol. 1. (Cours & Documents de Biologie Ser.). (Fr.). 406p. 1973. 112.25 (ISBN 0-677-50540-X). Gordon.

Gerrick, David J. Sex at the Cellular Level. (Illus.). 1978. 20.00 (ISBN 0-916750-50-7, CX-15). Dayton Labs.

Ghiselin, Michael T. The Economy of Nature & the Evolution of Sex. LC 73-78554. 1974. 36.50x (ISBN 0-520-02474-5). U of Cal Pr.

Goodman, Madeleine J. & Goodman, Lenn E. The Sexes in the Human Population. (Illus.). 203p. (Orig.). pap. text ed. 16.95x (ISBN 0-917232-12-7). Gee Tee Bee.

Halliday, Tim. Sexual Strategy. LC 82-2607. (Phoenix). (Illus.). 160p. 1982. pap. 12.50 (ISBN 0-226-31387-5). U of Chicago Pr.

Hite, Shere. The Hite Report on Male Sexuality. LC 80-2709. 1129p. 1981. 19.95 (ISBN 0-394-41392-X). Knopf.

Hutchison, J. B., ed. Biological Determinants of Sexual Behavior. LC 76-57753. 822p. 1978. 135.95 (ISBN 0-471-99490-1, Pub by Wiley-Interscience). Wiley.

Jacob, Francois & Wollman, E. Sexuality & the Genetics of Bacteria. rev. ed. 1961. 64.50 (ISBN 0-12-379450-1). Acad Pr.

Kornicker, Louis S. Sexual Dimorphism, Ontogeny, & Functional Morphology of Rutiderma Hartmanni Poulsen, 1965 (Crustacea: Ostracoda) LC 84-600218. (Smithsonian Contributions to Zoology Ser.: No. 408). pap. 20.00 (ISBN 0-317-30425-9, 2024936). Bks Demand UMI.

Langdon-Davies, John. Seeds of Life. 1955. 9.95 (ISBN 0-8159-6808-6). Devin.

Lipshutz, Harold. Sex: Facts, Fantasy, Hogwash, & the Urologic Backwash. (Illus.). 192p. 1984. 10.95 (ISBN 0-8059-2897-9). Dorrance.

Newcombe, F., ed. Human Sexual Dimorphism: Proceedings of the Annual Meeting of the Society for the Study of Human Biology, 24th. (Annals of the Human Biology Ser.: Vol. 24). 350p. 1985. 53.00 (ISBN 0-85066-267-2). Taylor & Francis.

Paulk, Earl. Sex Is God's Idea. 175p. (Orig.). 1985. pap. 5.95 (ISBN 0-917595-04-1). K-Dimension.

Russo, Raymond M., et al. Advanced Textbook of Sexual Development & Disorders in Childhood & Adolescence. (Advanced Textbook Ser.). 1983. pap. text ed. 25.00 (ISBN 0-87488-485-3). Med Exam.

Smith, J. Maynard. The Evolution of Sex. LC 77-85689. (Illus.). 1978. 42.50 (ISBN 0-521-21887-X); pap. 13.95x (ISBN 0-521-29302-2). Cambridge U Pr.

Steen, Edwin B. & Price, James H. Human Sex & Sexuality. 338p. 1977. pap. text ed. write for info. (ISBN 0-02-416260-4). Macmillan.

Vallet, H. Lawrence & Porter, Ian H., eds. Genetic Mechanisms of Sexual Development. LC 78-25762. (Birth Defects Institute Symposium Ser.: No. 7). 1979. 45.00 (ISBN 0-12-710550-6). Acad Pr.

Williams, George C. Sex & Evolution. LC 74-2985. (Monographs in Population Biology: No. 8). 200p. 1974. 27.50x (ISBN 0-691-08147-6); pap. 9.95x (ISBN 0-691-08152-2). Princeton U Pr.

SEX CHROMOSOMES

see also Sex–Cause and Determination

Bull, James. Evolution of Sex Determining Mechanisms. 1983. 23.95 (ISBN 0-8053-0400-2). Benjamin-Cummings.

Mittwoch, Ursula. Genetics of Sex Differentiation. 1973. 50.00 (ISBN 0-12-501040-0). Acad Pr.

--Sex Chromosomes. 1967. 58.50 (ISBN 0-12-501050-8). Acad Pr.

Ohno, S. Major Sex-Determining Genes. LC 78-10285. (Monographs on Endocrinology: Vol. 11). (Illus.). 1979. 24.00 (ISBN 0-387-08965-9). Springer-Verlag.

Robinson, Arthur, et al, eds. Sex Chromosome Aneuploidy: Prospective Studies on Children. LC 78-13921. (Alan R. Liss Ser.: Vol. 15, No. 1). 1979. 38.00 (ISBN 0-8451-1024-1). March of Dimes.

--Sex Chromosome Aneuploidy: Prospective Studies on Children Proceedings. LC 78-13921. (Birth Defects Original Article Ser.: Vol. XV, No. 1). 294p. 1979. 42.00 (ISBN 0-8451-1024-1). A R Liss.

Spectra Publishing Co., Inc. The Fragile X Syndrome. Hagerman, Randi J. & McBogg, Pamela M., eds. (Illus.). 1983. text ed. 26.45 (ISBN 0-915667-00-2); pap. text ed. 16.95 (ISBN 0-915667-01-0). Spectra Pub Co.

Stewart, Donald A., ed. Children with Sex Chromosome Aneuploidy: Follow-up Studies. LC 82-21657. (Birth Defects: Original Article Ser.: Vol. 18, No. 4). 268p. 1982. 54.00 (ISBN 0-8451-1052-7). A R Liss.

Summit, Robert & Bergsma, Daniel, eds. Sex Differentiation & Chromosomal Abnormalities. (Alan R. Liss, Inc. Ser.: Vol. 14, No. 6c). 1978. 61.00 (ISBN 0-686-23951-2). March of Dimes.

SEX DETERMINATION

see Sex–Cause and Determination

SEX DIFFERENTIATION

see Sex–Cause and Determination

SEXUAL ORGANS

see Generative Organs

SHAFTING

see also Power Transmission

Woodward, John B. Marine Shaft Alignment Calculations. (Michigan Marine Engineering Ser.). 60p. (Orig.). 1985. pap. text ed. 5.00 (ISBN 0-931781-00-0). Jenning Pr.

SHARKS

Ashley, Laurence M. & Chiasson, Robert B. Laboratory Anatomy of the Shark. 4th ed. (Laboratory Anatomy Ser.). 80p. 1982. write for info wire coil bdg (ISBN 0-697-04731-8). Wm C Brown.

Bohensky, Fred. Photo Manual & Dissection Guide of the Shark. (Avery's Anatomy Ser.). (Illus.). 144p. (Orig.). 1981. pap. text ed. 7.95 (ISBN 0-89529-140-1). Avery Pub.

Brown, Theo W. Sharks: The Silent Savages. (Illus.). 200p. pap. 5.95 (ISBN 0-88317-085-X). Stoeger Pub Co.

Budker, Paul. The Life of Sharks. LC 71-148462. (Illus.). 222p. 1971. 27.50x (ISBN 0-231-03551-9); pap. 11.00s (ISBN 0-231-08314-9). Columbia U Pr.

Castro, Jose I. The Sharks of North American Waters. LC 82-45892. (W. L. Moody, Jr., Natural History Ser.: No. 5). (Illus.). 194p. (Orig.). 1983. 19.50 (ISBN 0-89096-140-9); pap. 9.95 (ISBN 0-89096-143-3). Tex A&M Univ Pr.

Cousteau, Jacques-Yves & Cousteau, Philippe. Shark: Splendid Savage of the Sea. 1970. 12.95 (ISBN 0-385-06892-1). Doubleday.

Eaton, Theodore H., Jr. Teeth of Edestid Sharks. (Museum Ser.: Vol. 12, No. 8). 16p. 1962. 1.25 (ISBN 0-317-04785-X). U of KS Mus Nat Hist.

Ellis, Richard. The Book of Sharks: A Complete Illustrated Natural History of the Sharks of the World. (Illus.). 256p. 1983. pap. 14.95 (ISBN 0-15-613552-3, Harv). HarBraceJ.

Gans, Carl & Parsons, Thomas S. A Photographic Atlas of Shark Anatomy: The Gross Morphology of Squalas Acanthias. LC 80-24528. (Illus.). 106p. 1981. spiral bnd. 8.00x (ISBN 0-226-28120-5). U of Chicago Pr.

Greenberg, Idaz & Greenberg, Jerry. Sharks & Other Dangerous Sea Creatures. (Illus.). 1981. saddlestiched 4.95x (ISBN 0-913008-09-5). Seahawk Pr.

Helm, Thomas. Shark. 1963. pap. 1.95 (ISBN 0-02-063000-X, Collier). Macmillan.

Kreuzer, Rudolf, et al. Shark Utilization & Marketing. (Eng. & Span.). 187p. 1978. pap. 13.50 (ISBN 92-5-100654-7, F1531, FAO). Unipub.

Lineaweaver, Thomas H., 3rd & Backus, Richard H. Natural History of Sharks. LC 75-109174. (Illus.). 1970. 11.49i (ISBN 0-397-00660-8). Har-Row.

Matthews, Brad. Killer Sharks: The Real Story. 192p. (Orig.). 1976. pap. 1.50 (ISBN 0-532-15190-9). Woodhill.

Moss, Sanford A. Sharks: An Introduction for the Amateur Naturalist. (Illus.). 240p. 1984. 19.95 (ISBN 0-13-808312-6); pap. 10.95 (ISBN 0-13-808304-5). P-H.

Romashko, Sandra D. The Shark: Lord of the Sea. 4th ed. LC 76-150452. (Illus.). 64p. 1984. pap. 3.75 (ISBN 0-89317-001-1). Windward Pub.

Scharp, Hal. Answers to Your Questions About Sharks. LC 79-13420. (Illus.). 1979. 10.95 (ISBN 0-87961-080-8); pap. 4.95 (ISBN 0-87961-079-4). Naturegraph.

Tinker, Spencer W. & DuLuca, Charles J. Sharks & Rays: A Handbook of the Sharks & Rays of Hawaii & the Central Pacific Ocean. LC 73-77578. 1973. 7.25 (ISBN 0-8048-1082-6). C E Tuttle.

Zahuaranec, Bernard J., ed. Shark Repellents from the Sea: New Perspectives. (AAAS Selected Symposium 83). 225p. 1983. 28.00x (ISBN 0-86531-593-0). Westview.

SHARKS–AFRICA

Wallett, Tim. Shark Attack & Treatment of Victims in Southern African Waters. 1980. 25.00x (ISBN 0-686-69986-6, Pub. by Bailey & Swinton South Africa). State Mutual Bk.

SHARPENING OF TOOLS

Bradley, Ian. Sharpening Small Tools. LC 79-91402. (Home Craftsman Bk.). (Illus.). 128p. 1980. pap. 5.95 (ISBN 0-8069-8922-X). Sterling.

Coggin, James K., et al. Manual for Sharpening Hand Woodworking Tools. (Illus.). 1943. pap. 3.35 (ISBN 0-8134-0100-3, 100); 2.50x. Interstate.

Cunningham, Beryl M. & Holtrop, Wm. Woodshop Tool Maintenance. rev. ed. (Illus.). 296p. 1974. pap. text ed. 23.48 (ISBN 0-02-666280-9). Bennett IL.

Davidson, Glenn D. Tool Grinding & Sharpening Handbook. LC 84-24121. (Illus.). 128p. (Orig.). 1985. pap. 6.95 (ISBN 0-8069-7904-6). Sterling.

Geary, Don. How to Sharpen Anything. LC 82-5955. (Illus.). 224p. (Orig.). 1983. o.p 19.95 (ISBN 0-8306-2463-5, 1463); pap. 13.95 (ISBN 0-8306-1463-X). TAB Bks.

SHARPS RIFLE

Manual of Arms for the Sharps Rifle. 1.50 (ISBN 0-913150-33-9). Pioneer Pr.

Rywell, Martin. Sharps Rifle: The Gun That Shaped American Destiny. 160p. 5.00 (ISBN 0-913150-21-5). Pioneer Pr.

SHEAF THEORY

see Sheaves, Theory of

SHEAR (MECHANICS)

American Concrete Institute Staff. Shear in Reinforced Concrete. LC 73-94112. (American Concrete Institute, Publication Ser.: SP-42). (Illus.). Vol. 1. pap. 108.30 (ISBN 0-317-10241-9); Vol. 2. pap. 131.00 (ISBN 0-317-10242-7). Bks Demand UMI.

Bradbury, J. S., et al, eds. Turbulent Shear Flows, Two. (Illus.). 480p. 1980. 78.00 (ISBN 0-387-10067-9). Springer-Verlag.

Bradbury, L. J., et al. Turbulent Shear Flow 3rd: University of California, Selected Papers, 1981. (Illus.). 321p. 1982. 69.00 (ISBN 0-387-11817-9). Springer-Verlag.

Durst, F., et al, eds. Turbulent Shear Flows I: Proceedings of the First International Symposium, Pennsylvania State University, University Park, Pennsylvania, April 18-20, 1977. (Illus.). 1979. 59.00 (ISBN 0-387-09041-X). Springer-Verlag.

Laboratory Shear Strength of Soil- STP 740. 720p. 1981. 54.25 (ISBN 0-8031-0789-7, 04-740000-38). ASTM.

Michel, R., et al, eds. Unsteady Turbulent Shear Flows: Proceedings. (International Union of Theoretical & Applied Mechanics Ser.). 450p. 1981. 44.00 (ISBN 0-387-11099-2). Springer-Verlag.

Peterson, F. & Carmi, S., eds. Three Dimensional Turbulent Shear Flows. 160p. 1982. 30.00 (G00211). ASME.

Shear Stability of Multigrade Oils - IP Fleet Test, DS49-S1. (Data Ser.). 36p. 1974. pap. 4.00x (ISBN 0-8031-0566-5, 05-049001-12). ASTM.

Townsend, A. A. The Structure of Turbulent Shear Flow. 2nd ed. LC 74-14441. (Monographs on Mechanics & Applied Mathematics). 300p. 1975. 95.00 (ISBN 0-521-20710-X). Cambridge U Pr.

SHEAVES, THEORY OF

see also Homology Theory

Fourman, M. P., et al, eds. Applications of Sheaves. (Lecture Notes in Mathematics: Vol. 753). 1979. pap. 45.00 (ISBN 0-387-09564-0). Springer-Verlag.

Grauert, H. Coherent Analytic Sheaves. (Grudlehren der mathematischen Wissenchaften. A Series of Comrehesive Studies in Mathematics: Band 265). 260p. 1984. 36.50 (ISBN 0-387-13178-7). Springer Verlag.

Hartshorne, R. Residues & Duality. (Lecture Notes in Mathematics: Vol. 20). 1966. pap. 21.90 (ISBN 0-387-03603-2). Springer-Verlag.

Hofmann, K. H. Lectures on the Applications of Sheaves to Ring Theory: Tulane University Ring & Operator Theory Year, 1970-71, Vol. 3. (Lecture Notes in Mathematics: Vol. 248). 315p. 1971. pap. 13.00 (ISBN 0-387-05714-5). Springer-Verlag.

Kamber, Franz W. & Tondeur, Philippe. Invariant Differential Operators & Cohomology of Lie Algebra Sheaves. LC 52-42839. (Memoirs: No. 113). 1971. pap. 9.00 (ISBN 0-8218-1813-9, MEMO-113). Am Math.

Siu Yum-Tong & Trautmann, G. GAP-Sheaves & Extension of Coherent Analytic Subsheaves. LC 77-142788. (Lecture Notes in Mathematics: Vol. 172). 1971. pap. 11.00 (ISBN 0-387-05294-1). Springer-Verlag.

Siu, Yum-Tong & Trautmann, Gunther. Deformations of Coherent Analytic Sheaves with Compact Supports. LC 80-26105. (MEMO Ser.: No. 238). 155p. 1981. pap. 12.00 (ISBN 0-8218-2238-1). Am Math.

Strooker, J. R. Introduction to Categories, Homological Algebra & Sheaf Cohomology. LC 77-80849. 1978. 57.50 (ISBN 0-521-21699-0). Cambridge U Pr.

Swan, Richard G. Theory of Sheaves. LC 64-24979. (Chicago Lectures in Mathematics Ser). (Orig.). 1964. 8.00x (ISBN 0-226-78329-4). U of Chicago Pr.

Tennison, B. R. Sheaf Theory. LC 74-31791. (London Mathematical Society Lecture Note Ser.: No. 20). 120p. 1976. pap. 22.95 (ISBN 0-521-20784-3). Cambridge U Pr.

SHEEP

Barlow, Richard M. & Patterson, Deryck S. Border Disease of Sheep: A Virus-Induced Teratogenic Disorder. (Advances in Veterinary Medicine Ser.: Vol. 36). (Illus.). 36p. 1982. pap. text ed. 24.00 (ISBN 0-686-35822-8). Parey Sci Pubs.

Brooke, C. H. & Ryder, M. L. Declining Breeds of Mediterranean Sheep. (Animal Production & Health Papers: No. 8). (Eng. & Fr., Illus.). 68p. 1978. pap. 7.50 (ISBN 92-5-100507-9, F1596, FAO). Unipub.

Carles, A. B. Sheep Production in the Tropics. (Tropical Handbooks). (Illus.). 1983. 31.95x (ISBN 0-19-859449-6). Oxford U Pr.

Carlson, Paul H. Texas Woollybacks: The Range Sheep & Goat Industry. LC 82-40311. (Illus.). 256p. 1982. 19.50 (ISBN 0-89096-133-6). Tex A&M Univ Pr.

Croston, David & Pollot, Geoff. Planned Sheep Production. 256p. (Orig.). 1985. pap. text ed. 22.50x (ISBN 0-00-383033-0, Pub. by Collins England). Sheridan.

Ensminger, M. Eugene. Sheep & Wool Science. 4th ed. LC 73-79612. 1970. text ed. 27.35 (ISBN 0-8134-1113-0); text ed. 20.50x. Interstate.

Fraser, A. F., ed. Reproductive & Developmental Behavior in Sheep: An Anthology from "Applied Animal Ethology". (Developments in Animal & Veterinary Sciences Ser.: Vol. 18). 478p. 1985. 59.25 (ISBN 0-444-42444-X). Elsevier.

Fraser, Allan & Stamp, John. Sheep Husbandry & Diseases. 6th ed. 350p. 1986. 24.00x (ISBN 0-246-11209-3, Pub. by Granada England). Sheridan.

Gerrick, David J. Anatomy of the Sheep Kidney: Clinical Implications. (Illus.). 1978. 20.00 (ISBN 0-916750-04-3). Dayton Labs.

Haresign, William. Sheep Production. (University of Nottingham Easter School of Agriculture Ser.). 92p. 1983. text ed. 130.00 (ISBN 0-408-10844-4). Butterworth.

Hecker, J. F. The Sheep as an Experimental Animal. 1983. 37.50 (ISBN 0-12-336050-1). Acad Pr.

Intensive Sheep Production in the Near East. (Animal Production & Health Paper: No. 40). 67p. 1984. pap. text ed. 7.50 (ISBN 92-5-101399-3, F2530, FAO). Unipub.

Jensen, Rue & Swift, Brinton L. Diseases of Sheep. 2nd ed. LC 81-20701. (Illus.). 330p. 1982. text ed. 35.00 (ISBN 0-8121-0836-1). Lea & Febiger.

Johnston, R. G. Introduction to Sheep Farming. 272p. 1983. pap. 14.00x (ISBN 0-246-11962-4, Pub. by Granada England). Sheridan.

Juergenson, Elwood M. Approved Practices in Sheep Production. 4th ed. (Illus.). 455p. 1981. 19.95 (ISBN 0-8134-2163-2, 2163); text ed. 14.95x. Interstate.

Land, R. B. & Robinson, D. W. Genetics of Reproduction in Sheep. 400p. 1985. text ed. 79.95 (ISBN 0-407-00302-9). Butterworth.

Lindsay, D. R. & Pearce, D. T., eds. Reproduction in Sheep. 427p. 1985. 79.50 (ISBN 0-521-30659-0). Cambridge U Pr.

Mason, I. L. Prolific Tropical Sheep. (Animal Production & Health Papers: No. 17). (Eng., Fr. & Span.). 130p. 1980. pap. 9.50 (ISBN 92-5-100845-0, F2107, FAO). Unipub.

Mason, J. L. Sheep Breeds of the Mediterranean. 215p. 1971. cloth 49.00x (ISBN 0-686-45638-6, Pub. by CAB Bks England). State Mutual Bk.

Maudslay, Robert. Texas Sheepman. facsimile ed. Kupper, Winifred, ed. LC 78-157347. (Select Bibliographies Reprint Ser). Repr. of 1951 ed. 18.00 (ISBN 0-8369-5808-X). Ayer Co Pubs.

May, Neil D. The Anatomy of the Sheep: A Dissection Manual. 3rd ed. (Illus.). 1971. 25.00x (ISBN 0-7022-0691-1). U of Queensland Pr.

Mediterranean Cattle & Sheep in Cross-Breeding: Report of the First FAO Expert Consultation on Breed Evaluation & Crossbreeding, Rome, Italy, March 30-April 1, 1977. (Animal Production & Health Papers: No. 6). (Eng. & Fr.). 42p. 1977. pap. 7.50 (ISBN 92-5-100381-5, F1327, FAO). Unipub.

Midwest Plan Service Staff. Sheep Housing & Equipment Handbook. 3rd ed. LC 81-18842. (Illus.). 116p. 1982. 6.00 (ISBN 0-89373-052-1, MWPS-3). Midwest Plan Serv.

Monson, Gale & Sumner, Lowell, eds. The Desert Bighorn: Its Life History, Ecology, & Management. LC 80-18889. 370p. 1980. 27.50x (ISBN 0-8165-0689-2). U of Ariz Pr.

National Academy of Sciences. Nutrient Requirements of Sheep. 72p. 1975. pap. 7.25 (ISBN 0-309-02212-6). Natl Acad Pr.

Oakley, Bruce & Schafer, Rollie. Neuroanatomy: Dissection of the Sheep Brain. (Illus.). 32p. 1980. pap. text ed. 2.98x (ISBN 0-472-08691-X). U of Mich Pr.

Owen, J. B. Performance Recording in Sheep. 132p. 1971. 39.00x (ISBN 0-85198-020-1, Pub. by CAB Bks England). State Mutual Bk.

Parker, Ronald B. The Sheep Book: A Handbook for the Modern Shepherd. (Illus.). 384p. 1983. 19.95 (ISBN 0-684-17871-0, ScribT). Scribner.

Ponting, Kenneth. Sheep of the World in Color. (Illus.). 132p. 1980. 14.95 (ISBN 0-7137-0941-3, Pub. by Blandford Pr England). Sterling.

Ryder, Michael L. & Stephenson, Stuart K. Wool Growth. LC 66-16694. (Illus.). 1968. 97.50 (ISBN 0-12-605150-X). Acad Pr.

Sheep & Goat Breeding. (Better Farming Ser.: No. 12). 51p. 1977. pap. 7.50 (ISBN 92-5-100152-9, F70, FAO). Unipub.

Simmons, Paula. Raising Sheep the Modern Way. Griffith, Roger, ed. LC 76-44530. (Illus.). 160p. 1976. pap. 7.95 (ISBN 0-88266-093-4). Garden Way Pub.

Speedy, Andrew W. Sheep Production: Science into Practice. LC 79-41352. (Longman Handbooks in Agriculture Ser.). (Illus.). 195p. (Orig.). 1980. pap. text ed. 16.95x (ISBN 0-582-45582-0). Longman.

Taneja, G. C. Sheep Husbandry in India. 168p. 1981. 45.00x (ISBN 0-86131-009-8, Pub. by Orient Longman India). State Mutual Bk.

Trefethen, James, ed. The Wild Sheep in Modern North America. 302p. 1975. pap. 12.00 (ISBN 0-940864-04-5). Boone & Crockett.

Turner, H. Newton & Young, S. S. Quantitative Genetics in Sheep Breeding. 1982. 95.00x (ISBN 0-686-97901-X, Pub. by CSIRO Australia). State Mutual Bk.

SHEEP–AUSTRALIA

Carter, Harold B., ed. The Sheep & Wool Correspondence of Sir Joseph Banks, 1781-1820. (Illus.). xxx, 641p. 1979. 94.00x (ISBN 0-565-00802-1, Pub. by Brit Mus Nat Hist England). Sabbot-Natural Hist Bks.

Donald, A. D., et al. Epidemiology & Control of Gastrointestinal Parasites of Sheep in Australia. 152p. 1982. 30.00x (ISBN 0-643-00301-0, Pub. by CSIRO Australia). State Mutual Bk.

SHEEP–INDIA

Acharya, R. M. Sheep & Goat Breeds of India. (Animal Production & Health Papers: No. 30). 197p. 1982. pap. 14.50 (ISBN 92-5-101212-1, F2340, FAO). Unipub.

Taneja, G. C. Sheep Husbandry in India. cancelled (ISBN 0-8364-0315-0, Orient Longman). South Asia Bks.

SHEET-METAL WORK

see also High Energy Forming; Plate-Metal Work

Bies, John D. Sheet Metal Work. (AUDEL Ser.). 472p. 1985. lib. bdg. 17.95 (ISBN 0-8161-1706-3). G K Hall.

Blandford. The Master Handbook of Sheetmetalwork-with Projects. 378p. 1981. 16.95 (ISBN 0-8306-9644-X); pap. 9.95 (ISBN 0-8306-1257-2, 1257). TAB Bks.

Budzik, Richard S. Practical Sheet Metal Projects-130 Graded Projects with Drawings, Forming Information & Sequences. LC 79-93132. (Illus.). 1979. 24.95 (ISBN 0-912914-06-8). Practical Pubns.

--Precision Sheet Metal Blueprint Reading. LC 75-86373. (Illus.). 127p. 1969. text ed. 17.95 (ISBN 0-912914-11-4); tchr's materials 24.95 (ISBN 0-912914-13-0); wkbk 16.95 (ISBN 0-912914-12-2). Practical Pubns.

--Precision Sheet Metal Mathematics. LC 71-83129. (Illus.). 349p. 1969. text ed. 17.95 (ISBN 0-912914-14-9); instr's guide 24.95 (ISBN 0-912914-16-5); wkbk 19.95 (ISBN 0-912914-15-7). Practical Pubns.
--Precision Sheet Metal Shop Practice. LC 78-97566. (Illus.). 96p. 1969. 13.95 (ISBN 0-912914-17-3); tchrs' materials 24.95 (ISBN 0-912914-19-X); wkbk 17.95 (ISBN 0-912914-18-1). Practical Pubns.
--Precision Sheet Metal Shop Theory. LC 79-77566. (Illus.). 334p. 1969. 17.95 (ISBN 0-912914-08-4); tchrs' materials 24.95 (ISBN 0-912914-10-6); wkbk 19.95 (ISBN 0-912914-09-2). Practical Pubns.
--Sheet Metal Shop Fabrication Projects Including Over Three Hundred Fifty Graded Parts. LC 80-84009. (Illus.). 1980. 19.95 (ISBN 0-912914-07-6). Practical Pubns.
--Sheet Metal Technology. 2nd ed. 1981. scp 19.96 (ISBN 0-672-97360-X); scp instr's. guide 3.67 (ISBN 0-672-97361-8); scp students manual 10.28 (ISBN 0-672-97362-6). Bobbs.
--Short Course in Sheet Metal Shop Theory: Including 25 Practical Projects. LC 79-93131. (Illus.). 1979. 17.95 (ISBN 0-912914-05-X). Practical Pubns.
--Specialty Items Used Today (Sheet Metal) Including Methods of Design & Fabrication & Important Trade Topics. LC 74-79537. (Illus.). 1979. 44.95 (ISBN 0-912914-04-1). Practical Pubns.
Eary, Donald F. & Reed, Edward A. Techniques of Pressworking Sheet Metal: An Engineering Approach to Die Design. 2nd ed. 1974. ref. ed. 39.95 (ISBN 0-13-900696-6). P-H.
International Deep Drawing Research Group. Sheet Metal Forming & Energy Conservation: Proceedings of the Biennial Congress of the International Deep Drawing Research Group, 9th, Ann Arbor, Michigan, U. S. A., October 13-14, 1976. LC 76-27547. (Illus.). pap. 73.00 (ISBN 0-317-10787-9, 2050982). Bks Demand UMI.
Johnston, Philip M. & Liebowitz, Murray. Advanced Sheet Metal Skills. LC 76-14088. 1978. pap. 15.80 (ISBN 0-8273-1239-3); instr's. guide 5.25 (ISBN 0-8273-1240-7). Delmar.
Koistinen, D. P. & Wang, N. M., eds. Mechanics of Sheet Metal Forming: Material Behavior & Deformation Forming. LC 78-21587. (General Motors Research Symposia Ser.). 426p. 1978. 59.50x (ISBN 0-306-40068-5, Plenum Pr). Plenum Pub.
Mathematics for Sheet Metal Fabrication. LC 79-118846. 1970. pap. text ed. 14.00 (ISBN 0-8273-0295-9); instr's. manual 4.20 (ISBN 0-8273-0296-7). Delmar.
Metals Society, ed. Production & Use of Coil-Coated Strip. 184p. (Orig.). 1981. pap. text ed. 60.00x (ISBN 0-904357-37-6, Metals Soc). Brookfield Pub Co.
Meyer, L. A. Sheet Metal Shop Practice. 4th ed. (Illus.). 1976. 16.95 (ISBN 0-8269-1902-2). Am Technical.
Newby, John R., ed. Source Book on Forming of Steel Sheet: A Discriminative Selection of Outstanding Articles from the Periodical & Reference Literature. LC 76-28176. (American Society for Metals. Engineering Bookshelf Ser.). (Illus.). pap. 99.80 (ISBN 0-317-11148-5, 2019498). Bks Demand UMI.
Reid, Hugh B. Sheet Metal Layout Simplified, 3 vols. Vol. 1. 1981. 19.50 (ISBN 0-685-77694-8); Vol. 2. 1981. 19.50 (ISBN 0-685-41577-5); Vol. 3. 1981. 19.50 (ISBN 0-685-41578-3). H B Reid.
Rudman, Jack. Gang Foreman (Structures-Group D) (Sheet Metal) (Career Examination Ser.: C-293). (Cloth bdg. avail. on request). pap. 12.00 (ISBN 0-8373-0293-5). Natl Learning.
--Sheet Metal Fabrication. (Occupational Competency Examination Ser.: OCE-31). (Cloth bdg. avail. on request). 13.95 (ISBN 0-8373-5731-4). Natl Learning.
--Sheet Metal Worker. (Career Examination Ser.: C-736). (Cloth bdg. avail. on request). pap. 12.00 (ISBN 0-8373-0736-8). Natl Learning.
Schumacher, F. Practical Problems in Mathematics for Sheet Metal Technicians. LC 71-74885. 1973. pap. text ed. 7.40 (ISBN 0-8273-0287-8); instructor's guide 3.00 (ISBN 0-8273-0288-6). Delmar.
Sheet Metal Forming & Formability. 406p. 1981. 125.00x (ISBN 0-86108-012-2, Pub. by Portcullio Pr). State Mutual Bk.
Sheet Metal Industries Year Book. 1981. 95.00x (ISBN 0-686-87230-4, Pub. by Portcullio Pr). State Mutual Bk.
Twelfth Automotive Materials Symposium, Detroit, April 29-30, 1985. Computer Modeling of Sheet Metal Forming Processes: Theory, Verification, & Application. Tang, S. C. & Wang, N. M., eds. Metal Soc.
Wakeford, R. E. Sheet Metal Work, No. 8. (Workshop Practics Ser.). (Illus.). 152p. Date not set. pap. 11.95 (ISBN 0-85242-849-9, Pub. by Aztex Corp). Argus Bks.
Watkins, W. Sheet Metal Fabrication. (Illus.). 1971. pap. text ed. 22.30x (ISBN 0-444-20124-6, Pub. by Applied Science). Burgess-Intl Ideas.
--Sheet Metal Fabrication. (Illus.). 263p. 1971. 24.25 (ISBN 0-444-20124-6, Pub. by Applied Sci England). Elsevier.
Wendes, Herbert C. Sheet Metal Estimating Handbook. 250p. 1982. 27.95 (ISBN 0-442-25739-2). Van Nos Reinhold.
Zinngrabe. Sheet Metal Blueprint Reading: For the Building Trades. LC 79-2748. 138p. 1980. 15.20 (ISBN 0-8273-1352-7); instr.'s guide 4.80 (ISBN 0-8273-1353-5). Delmar.
Zinngrabe, C. J. & Schumacher, F. W. Practical Layout for Sheet Metal Shop. LC 75-6063. 1975. pap. text ed. 10.40 (ISBN 0-8273-0224-X); instructor's guide 4.20 (ISBN 0-8273-0225-8). Delmar.
--Sheet Metal Hand Processes. LC 73-2159. 1974. 12.60 (ISBN 0-8273-0220-7); instr.'s guide o.p. 2.20 (ISBN 0-8273-0221-5). Delmar.
Zinngrabe, Claude J. Mathematics for the Sheet Metal Technician. Pt. 1. pap. 38.00 (ISBN 0-317-11095-0, 2004563); Pt. 2. pap. 50.50 (ISBN 0-317-11096-9). Bks Demand UMI.

SHEET-METAL WORK–PATTERN-MAKING

Betterley, Melvin. Sheet Metal Drafting. 2nd ed. (Illus.). 1977. pap. text ed. 26.40 (ISBN 0-07-005126-7). McGraw.
Budzik, Richard S. Fittings Used Today That Require Triangulation Including the Theory of Triangulation. 2nd ed. LC 75-182389. (Illus.). 1982. 19.95 (ISBN 0-912914-21-1). Practical Pubns.
--Today's Forty Most Frequently-Used Fittings. 2nd ed. LC 73-188876. (Illus.). 184p. 1983. 19.95 (ISBN 0-912914-22-X). Practical Pubns.
Daugherty, J. S. & Powell, R. E. Sheet-Metal Pattern Drafting & Shop Problems. rev. ed. 196p. 1975. pap. text ed. 16.88 (ISBN 0-02-665680-9). Bennett IL.
Kaberlein, Joseph J. Air Conditioning Sheet Metal Layout. 3rd ed. 1973. 17.95 (ISBN 0-02-819360-1). Glencoe.
--Short-Cuts for Round Layouts. 3rd ed. 1973. 17.95 (ISBN 0-02-819390-3). Glencoe.
--Triangulation Short-Cut Layouts. 3rd ed. 1973. 17.95 (ISBN 0-02-819410-1). Glencoe.
Meyer, Leo A. Sheet Metal Layout. 2nd ed. (Illus.). 1979. pap. text ed. 24.10 (ISBN 0-07-041731-8). McGraw.
Rabl, S. S. Ship & Aircraft Fairing & Development: For Draftsman & Loftsmen & Sheet Metal Workers. 109p. 1941. spiral bdg. 6.00x (ISBN 0-87033-096-9). Cornell Maritime.

SHEET-METAL WORKING MACHINERY

see also Punching Machinery

Budzik, Richard S. Sheet Metal Shop Fabrication Projects Including Over Three Hundred Fifty Graded Parts. LC 80-84009. (Illus.). 1980. 19.95 (ISBN 0-912914-07-6). Practical Pubns.
Sheet Metal Forming Proceedings. (Illus.). 362p. 1978. 65.00x (ISBN 0-86108-012-2). Intl Pubns Serv.
Zinngrabe, C. J. & Schumacher, F. W. Sheet Metal Machine Processes. LC 73-2160. 1975. pap. text ed. 11.80 (ISBN 0-8273-0222-3); instr.'s guide 3.00 (ISBN 0-8273-0223-1). Delmar.

SHELL MODELS (NUCLEAR PHYSICS)

see Nuclear Shell Theory

SHELL MOLDING (FOUNDING)

Narayanan, R., ed. Shell Structures: Stability & Strength. 360p. 1985. 69.00 (ISBN 0-85334-343-8, Pub. by Elsevier Applied Sci England). Elsevier.

SHELL PARAKEET

see Budgerigars

SHELL ROOFS

see Roofs, Shell

SHELLFISH

see also Crustacea; Mollusks

Barber, Russell J. The Wheeler's Site: A Specialized Shellfish Processing Station on the Merrimack River. (Peabody Museum Monographs: No. 7). (Illus.). 96p. 1983. pap. 10.00x (ISBN 0-87365-907-4). Peabody Harvard.
Boyle, P. R. Molluscs & Man. (Studies in Biology: No. 134). 64p. 1981. pap. text ed. 8.95 (ISBN 0-7131-2824-0). E Arnold.
Cheney, Daniel P. & Mumford, Thomas M., Jr. Shellfish & Seaweed Harvests of Puget Sound. (A Puget Sound Bk.). (Illus.). 144p. (Orig.). 1984. pap. 8.95 (ISBN 0-295-95990-8, Pub. by Wash Sea Grant). U of Wash Pr.
Hocutt, Charles H., et al. Power Plants: Effects on Fish & Shellfish Behavior. 1980. 38.50 (ISBN 0-12-350950-5). Acad Pr.
Murray, Harold D. & Leonard, A. B. Handbook of Unionid Mussels in Kansas. (Miscellaneous Publications: No. 28). 184p. 1962. pap. 8.00 (ISBN 0-686-79811-2). U of KS Mus Nat Hist.
Names of Fishes, Shellfish & Marine Animals. (Terminology Bulletin: No. 38C). (Eng., Lat. & Chinese.). 142p. 1979. pap. 5.70 (ISBN 92-5-000788-4, FAO). Unipub.
Parmalee, Paul W. The Fresh-Water Mussels of Illinois. (Popular Science Ser.: Vol. VIII). (Illus.). 108p. 1967. pap. 3.00 (ISBN 0-89792-029-5). Ill St Museum.
Pownall, Glen. New Zealand Shells and Shellfish. 88p. 1980. (Pub. by Viking Sevenseas New Zealand). Intl Spec Bk.
Recommended International Code of Hygienic Practice for Molluscan Shellfish. (Codex Alimentarius Commission Reports). 22p. 1980. pap. 7.50 (ISBN 92-5-100893-0, F1949, FAO). Unipub.
Robinson, Robert H. The Essential Book of Shellfish. LC 82-184274. (Illus.). 160p. 1983. pap. 6.95 (ISBN 0-89709-040-3). Liberty Pub.
Romashko, Sandra. The Savory Shellfish of North America. LC 77-74610. (Illus.). 1977. pap. 2.95 (ISBN 0-89317-015-1). Windward Pub.
Shellfish. (The Good Cook Ser.). 1982. 14.95 (ISBN 0-8094-2933-0). Time-Life.
Sinderman, C. J. Principal Diseases of Marine Fish & Shellfish. 1970. 71.00 (ISBN 0-12-645850-2). Acad Pr.
Sinderman, Carl J., ed. Disease Diagnosis & Control in North American Marine Aquaculture. (Developments in Aquaculture & Fisheries Science Ser.: Vol. 6). 330p. 1977. 66.00 (ISBN 0-444-00237-5). Elsevier.
Tedone, David. Complete Shellfisherman's Guide. (Illus.). 200p. 1981. pap. 7.95 (ISBN 0-933614-09-8). Peregrine Pr.
Walker, Charlotte. Fish & Shellfish. (Illus.). 160p. 1984. pap. 7.95 (ISBN 0-89586-258-1). H P Bks.
WHO Expert Committee. Geneva, 1973. Fish & Shellfish Hygiene: Report. (Technical Report Ser.: No. 550). (Also avail. in French & Spanish). 1974. pap. 2.40 (ISBN 92-4-120550-4). World Health.

SHELLFISH–BACTERIOLOGY

Greenberg, Arnold E. & Hunt, Daniel A., eds. Laboratory Procedures for the Examination of Seawater & Shellfish. 5th ed. LC 84-24321. 80p. 1984. 15.00 (ISBN 0-87553-119-9). Am Pub Health.

SHELLFISH FISHERIES

see also Lobster Fisheries

Milne, P. H. Fish & Shellfish Farming in Coastal Waters. (Illus.). 208p. 30.00 (ISBN 0-85238-022-4, FN32, FNB). Unipub.
--Fish & Shellfish Farming in Coastal Waters. 1978. 40.00 (ISBN 0-685-63408-6). State Mutual Bk.
Nowak, W. S. The Marketing of Shellfish. (Fisheries Ser.: No. 13). (Illus.). 280p. 22.50 (ISBN 0-85238-010-0, FN59, FAO). Unipub.
--The Marketing of Shellfish. 1978. 25.00 (ISBN 0-685-63433-7). State Mutual Bk.
Waine, Peter R. Culture of Bivalue Molluses. 1978. 20.00 (ISBN 0-685-63398-5). State Mutual Bk.

SHELLS

see also Mollusks

Abbott, Tucker & Dance, Peter. Compendium of Seashells: A Color Guide to More than 4000 of the World's Marine Shells. (Illus.). 400p. 1983. 50.00 (ISBN 0-525-93269-0, 04854-1460). Dutton.
Aiken, D. W. & Fuller, K. J. Living Volute of Africa. 1970. pap. 3.50 (ISBN 0-913792-01-2). Shell Cab.
Andrews, Jean. Texas Shells: A Field Guide. (Elma Dill Russell Spencer Foundation Ser.: No. 11). (Illus.). 201p. 1981. pap. 8.95 (ISBN 0-292-72431-4). U of Tex Pr.
Audubon Society & Rehder, Harrold A. The Audubon Society Field Guide to North American Seashells. LC 80-84239. 1981. 13.50 (ISBN 0-394-51913-2). Knopf.
Bergeron, Eugene. How to Clean Sea Shells. rev. ed. LC 72-12754. (Illus.). 1973. pap. 1.00 (ISBN 0-8200-0206-2). Great Outdoors.
Bertsche, G. Practitioners Shell Model. 1972. 24.50 (ISBN 0-444-10348-1). Elsevier.
Bosch, Donald & Bosch, Eloise. Seashells of Oman. LC 81-14236. (Illus.). 1982. text ed. 35.00x (ISBN 0-582-78309-7). Longman.
Bouchet, Philippe, et al. Seashells of Western Europe. Picton, B. E., tr. from Fr. (Illus.). 1979. 5.95 (ISBN 0-915826-05-4). Am Malacologists.
British Tourist Authority. Shell Book of the Islands of Britain. 198p. 1982. 19.95 (ISBN 0-7112-0087-4, Pub. by B T A). Merrimack Pub Cir.
Brost, Fred B. & Coale, Robert D. Guide to Shell Collecting in the Kwajalein Atoll. LC 78-130418. (Illus.). 1971. pap. 11.00 (ISBN 0-8048-0942-9). C E Tuttle.
Carpenter, Philip P. Catalogue of the Collection of Mazatlan Shells in the British Museum. (Illus.). 576p. Repr. of 1857 ed. 8.00 (ISBN 0-87710-371-2); illustrations 8.00, 110p. (ISBN 0-87710-372-0). Paleo Res.
Carstarphen, Dee. The Conch Book. LC 81-90632. (Illus.). 80p. 1981. pap. 6.95 (ISBN 0-9607544-0-7). Pen & Ink.
Dance, S. P. The Collector's Encyclopedia of Shells. 2nd ed. 1982. 24.95 (ISBN 0-07-015292-6). McGraw.
Dance, S. Peter. The World's Shells. LC 76-16581. (Illus.). 1976. 12.95 (ISBN 0-07-015291-8). McGraw.
Dittmar, Lucy. Caribbean Tropical Nature Guide. (Illus.). 64p. pap. 5.95 (ISBN 0-686-75259-7). Banyan Bks.
Emerson, William K. & Jacobson, Morris K. American Museum of Natural History Guide to Shells. 1976. 8.95 (ISBN 0-394-73048-8). Knopf.
Feinberg, Harold. Simon & Schuster Guide to Shells. (Illus.). 1980. pap. 9.95 (ISBN 0-671-25320-4). S&S.
Feininger, Andreas. Shells: Forms & Designs of the Sea. (Illus.). 128p. 1983. pap. 8.95 (ISBN 0-486-24498-9). Dover.
Gillett, K. & Yaldwyn, J. Australian Seashores in Colour. LC 77-109409. (Illus.). 1970. 5.00 (ISBN 0-8048-0861-9). C E Tuttle.
Greenberg, Jerry. Field Guide to Marine Invertebrates. plastic card 3.95 (ISBN 0-916224-79-1). Banyan Bks.
Greenberg, Jerry & Idaz. The Coral Reef. (Illus.). 64p. pap. 4.95 (ISBN 0-686-75254-6). Banyan Bks.
Greenberg, Margaret & Olds, Nancy J. The Sanibel Shell Guide. LC 82-71090. (Illus.). 117p. (Orig.). 1982. pap. 5.95 (ISBN 0-89305-041-5). Anna Pub.
Hall, Frances W. Shells of the Florida Coast. rev. ed. 1979. pap. 1.95 (ISBN 0-8200-0207-0). Great Outdoors.
Hinton, Alan. Shells of New Guinea & the Central Indo-Pacific. LC 75-15482. (Illus.). 1976. 18.50 (ISBN 0-8048-1166-0). C E Tuttle.
Humfrey, Michael. Sea Shells of the West Indies: A Guide to the Marine Molluscs of the Caribbean. LC 74-20213. (Illus.). 352p. 1975. 19.95 (ISBN 0-8008-7014-X). Taplinger.
Humphrey. The Sea Shells of the West Indies. 24.95 (ISBN 0-00-219252-7, Collins Pub England). Greene.
Jacobson, M. K. & Emerson, W. K. Shells from Cape Cod to Cape May: With Special Reference to the New York City Area. Orig. Title: Shells of the New York City Area. (Illus.). 10.25 (ISBN 0-8446-0155-1). Peter Smith.
Kay, E. Alison. Hawaiian Marine Shells: Reef & Shore Fauna of Hawaii; Section 4 - Mollusca. LC 78-73430. (Special Publication Ser.: 64 (4)). (Illus.). 671p. 1979. 35.00 (ISBN 0-910240-26-4). Bishop Mus.
Keen, A. Myra & McLean, James H. Sea Shells of Tropical West America: Marine Mollusks from Baja California to Peru. 2nd ed. (Illus.). 1971. 47.50 (ISBN 0-8047-0736-7). Stanford U Pr.
Kelburn, Richard & Rippery, Elizabeth. Sea Shells of Southern Africa. (Illus.). 264p. 1982. 49.95 (ISBN 0-86954-094-7, Pub. by Macmillan S Africa). Intl Spec Bk.
Kirtisinghe, Parakrama. Sea Shells of Sri Lanka: Including Forms Scattered Throughout the Indian & Pacific Oceans. LC 77-72607. (Illus.). 1978. 12.50 (ISBN 0-8048-1189-X). C E Tuttle.
McKay, Frances P. Let's Go Shelling. LC 68-3449. (Illus., Orig.). 1967. pap. 1.95 (ISBN 0-8200-0203-8). Great Outdoors.
McLean, James H. Marine Shells of Southern California. (Science Ser.: No. 24). (Illus.). 104p. 1978. 5.00 (ISBN 0-938644-03-3). Nat Hist Mus.
Melvin, A. Gordon. Seashell Parade: Fascinating Facts, Pictures, & Stories. LC 72-96776. (Illus.). 1973. 11.50 (ISBN 0-8048-0971-2). C E Tuttle.
Melvin, A. Gordon & Melvin, Lorna S. One-Thousand World Sea Shells--Rare to Common, with Values. LC 79-65628. (Illus.). 1980. 18.50 (ISBN 0-8048-1221-7). C E Tuttle.
Morris, Percy A. Field Guide to Atlantic Coast Shells. 3rd ed. LC 72-75612. (Illus.). 1973. 15.95 (ISBN 0-395-16809-0); pap. 10.95 (ISBN 0-395-17170-9). HM.
--A Field Guide to Pacific Coast Shells. LC 72-75612. (Peterson Field Guide Ser). 1974. 15.95 (ISBN 0-395-08029-0); pap. 10.95 (ISBN 0-395-18322-7). HM.
Newell, Peter & Newell, Patricia. Seashores. 120p. 1979. 30.00x (ISBN 0-7148-2013-X, Pub. by Phaidon Pr). State Mutual Bk.
Oldroyd, Ida S. The Marine Shells of the West Coast of North America, 4 vols. (Illus.). 1924. Set. 125.00x (ISBN 0-8047-0987-4). Stanford U Pr.
Oliver, A. P. The Larousse Guide to Shells of the World. LC 79-91944. (The Larousse Guide Books). (Illus.). 1980. 15.95 (ISBN 0-88332-107-6); pap. 9.95 (ISBN 0-88332-133-5). Larousse.

Powell, A. W. Shells of New Zealand. 154p. 1982. pap. 42.00x (ISBN 0-7233-0470-X, Pub. by Whitcoulls New Zealand). State Mutual Bk.
Pownall, Glen. New Zealand Shells and Shellfish. 88p. 1980. (Pub. by Viking Sevenseas New Zealand). Intl Spec Bk.
Radwin, George E. & D'Attilio, Anthony. Murex Shells of the World: An Illustrated Guide to the Muricidae. LC 75-7485. (Illus.). 326p. 1976. 38.50 (ISBN 0-8047-0897-5). Stanford U Pr.
Rhyne, Nancy. Carolina Seashells. LC 81-17342. (Illus.). 128p. pap. 4.95 (ISBN 0-914788-53-1). East Woods.
Robinson, Adrian & Millward, Roy. The Shell Book of the British Coast. (Illus.). 496p. (Orig.). 1983. 31.50 (ISBN 0-7153-8150-4). David & Charles.
Romashko, Sandra. The Complete Collector's Guide to Shells & Shelling. LC 81-51067. (Illus.). 112p. (Orig.). 1984. pap. 5.95 (ISBN 0-89317-032-1). Windward Pub.
Romashko, Sandra D. The Shell Book: A Complete Guide to Collecting & Identifying. 5th ed. LC 76-360976. (Illus.). 64p. 1984. pap. 3.95 (ISBN 0-89317-000-3). Windward Pub.
Safer, Jane F. Spirals from the Sea: An Anthropological Look at Shells. (Illus.). 1982. 12.98 (ISBN 0-517-54036-3, C N Potter Bks). Crown.
Safer, William S. Shelling. (Illus.). 64p. 1981. 21.00 (ISBN 0-88014-034-8). Mosaic Pr OH.
Sandved, Kiell & Abbott, R. Tucker. Shells in Color. LC 76-185986. 1973. 18.95 (ISBN 0-670-63968-0). Viking.
Saunders, Graham. Shells. LC 79-823. (Spotter's Guides). (Illus.). 1979. 3.95 (ISBN 0-8317-7768-0, Mayflowerr Bks); pap. 1.95 (ISBN 0-8317-7769-9). Smith Pubs.
Say, Thomas. Conchology. first ed. Abbott, R. T., ed. 32p. Repr. of 1819 ed. 5.00 (ISBN 0-915826-09-7). Am Malacologists.
Sharabati, Doreen. Saudi Arabian Seashells. 1982. 50.00x (ISBN 0-9507641-0-8, Pub. by Cave Pubns England). State Mutual Bk.
Siekman, Lula. Great Outdoors Book of Shells. LC 65-5925. pap. 3.95 (ISBN 0-8200-0202-X). Great Outdoors.
Smythe, Kathleen. Seashells of the Arabian Gulf. (Natural History of the Arabian Gulf Ser.). (Illus.). 180p. 1982. text ed. 18.50x (ISBN 0-04-594001-0). Allen Unwin.
Stix, Hugh & Stix, Marguerite. Shell: Five Hundred Million Years of Inspired Design. LC 68-12922. (Illus.). 1968. 55.00 (ISBN 0-8109-0475-6); pap. 9.95 o. p. (ISBN 0-8109-2098-0). Abrams.
Tebble, Norman. British Bivalve Seashells: A Handbook for Identification. 2nd ed. (Illus.). 212p. 1976. pap. 6.75x (ISBN 0-11-491401-X, Pub. by Brit Mus Nat Hist England). Sabbot-Natural Hist Bks.
Tinker, Spencer W. Pacific Sea-Shells. LC 57-18069. (Illus.). 1957. bds. 7.95 (ISBN 0-8048-0464-8). C E Tuttle.
Vilas, Curtis N. & Vilas, Naomi R. Florida Marine Shells. LC 72-109421. (Illus.). 1970. 17.50 (ISBN 0-8048-0883-X). C E Tuttle.
Wagner, R. J. & Abbott, R. Tucker. Standard Catalog of Shells. new ed. LC 77-88916. (Illus.). 1978. buckram looseleaf 55.00 (ISBN 0-915826-03-8); Supplement 1 looseleaf incl. (ISBN 0-915826-04-6); Supplement 2 incl. (ISBN 0-915826-10-0). Am Malacologists.
--World Size Records, 1985. (Standard Catalog of Shells Ser.). (Illus., Orig.). 1985. pap. 6.00 (ISBN 0-915826-15-1). Am Malacologists.
White, James. Seashells of the Pacific Northwest. LC 73-892391. (Illus.). 1976. 9.95 (ISBN 0-8323-0232-5); pap. 6.50 (ISBN 0-8323-0233-3). Binford.
Young, M. E., ed. International Directory of Conchologists, 1982-83. LC 73-91404. 1982-83. 5.00 (ISBN 0-913792-06-3). Shell Cab.
Zeigler, Rowland F. & Porreca, Humbert E. Olive Shells of the World. LC 78-91609. (Illus.). 1969. 12.95 (ISBN 0-9600668-0-2). Shell Cab.

SHELLS (ENGINEERING)

see also Plates (Engineering); Roofs, Shell; Tanks

Axelrad, E. L. & Emmerling, F. A., eds. Flexible Shells: Theory & Applications. (Illus.). 290p. 1984. 23.00 (ISBN 0-387-13526-X). Springer-Verlag.
Baker, E. H., et al. Structural Analysis of Shells. LC 79-27250. 364p. 1981. Repr. of 1972 ed. lib. bdg. 42.50 (ISBN 0-89874-118-1). Krieger.
Billington, D. P. Thin Shell Concrete Structures. 1965. 42.50 (ISBN 0-07-005271-9). McGraw.
Bushnell, D. Computerized Buckling Analysis of Shells. (Mechanics of Elastic Stability Ser.). 1985. lib. bdg. 85.00 (ISBN 0-318-04125-1, Pub. by Martinus Nijhoff Netherlands). Kluwer Academic.
Calladine, Christopher R. Theory of Shell Structures. LC 82-4255. 700p. 1983. 140.00 (ISBN 0-521-23835-8). Cambridge U Pr.
Chatterjee, B. K. Theory & Design of Concrete Shells. 256p. 1971. 69.50 (ISBN 0-677-61740-2). Gordon.
Design Constants for Interior Cylindrical Concrete Shells. 30p. 1960. pap. 2.00 (ISBN 0-89312-050-2, EB020D). Portland Cement.
Donnell, Lloyd H. Beams, Plates & Shells. (Engineering Societies Monograph Ser.). 1976. text ed. 60.00 (ISBN 0-07-017593-4). McGraw.
Elias, Z. M. Analysis of Axisymmetric Shells by a Mixed Variational Principle. 60p. 1972. pap. text ed. 10.00x (ISBN 0-8156-6037-5, Am U Beirut). Syracuse U Pr.
Fischer, L. Theory & Practice of Shell Structures. (Illus.). 1968. 76.00x (ISBN 3-4330-0127-8). Adlers Foreign Bks.
Fluegge, W. Stresses in Shells. 2nd ed. LC 74-183604. (Illus.). 525p. 1973. 38.00 (ISBN 0-387-05322-0). Springer-Verlag.
Gibson, J. E. Thin Shells: Computing & Theory. (International Series in Structure & Solid Body Mechanics). (Illus.). 1980. 47.00 (ISBN 0-08-023275-2); pap. 18.00 (ISBN 0-08-024204-9). Pergamon.
Gioncu, Victor. Thin Reinforced Concrete Shells: Special Analysis Problems. LC 78-10388. 500p. 1979. 78.95x (ISBN 0-471-99735-8, Pub. by Wiley-Interscience). Wiley.
Gould, Phillip. Finite Element Analysis of Shells of Revolution. (Surveys in Structural Engineering & Structural Mechanics Ser.). 1985. text ed. 34.95 (ISBN 0-273-08654-5). Pitman Pub MA.
Huges, T. J., et al, eds. Nonlinear Finite Element Analysis of Plates & Shells. (AMD Ser.: Vol. 48). 286p. 1981. 40.00 (ISBN 0-686-34480-4, H00198). ASME.
International Union of Theoretical & Applied Mechanics Symposium, 2nd Copenhagen, 1967. Theory of Thin Shells: Proceedings. Niordson, F. I., ed. LC 68-26458. (Illus.). 1969. 67.90 (ISBN 0-387-04735-2). Springer-Verlag.
Kollar, L. & Dulacskai, E. Buckling of Shells for Engineers. LC 83-1697. 303p. 1984. text ed. 49.95x (ISBN 0-471-90328-0, Pub. by Wiley-Interscience). Wiley.
Lukasiewicz, S. Local Loads in Plates & Shells, No. 4. (Mechanics of Surface Structures). 596p. 1979. 85.00x (ISBN 9-0286-0047-7). Sijthoff & Noordhoff.
Mollman, H. Introduction to the Theory of Thin Shells. 180p. 1981. 51.95x (ISBN 0-471-28056-9, Pub. by Wiley-Interscience). Wiley.
Olszak, W. & Sawczuk, A. Inelastic Behavior in Shells. 122p. 1968. 42.95x (ISBN 0-677-61350-4). Gordon.
Ramm, E., ed. Buckling of Shells, Stuttgart, FRG 1982: Proceedings. (Illus.). 672p. 1982. 46.00 (ISBN 0-387-11785-7). Springer-Verlag.
Siekman, Lula. Handbook of Shells. rev. ed. 1981. pap. 2.95 (ISBN 0-8200-0208-9). Great Outdoors.
Sih, G. C., ed. Plates & Shells with Cracks: A Collection of Stress Intensity Factor Solutions for Cracks in Plates & Shells. (Mechanics of Fracture Ser.: No. 3). 352p. 1976. 62.50x (ISBN 90-286-0146-5). Sijthoff & Noordhoff.
Soedel. Vibration of Shells & Plates. (Mechanical Engineering Ser.: Vol. 7). 472p. 1981. 59.75 (ISBN 0-8247-1193-9). Dekker.
Szilard, Rudolph, ed. Hydromechanically Loaded Shells: Proceedings of the 1971 Symposium of the International Association for Shell Structures. LC 72-93559. (Illus.). 943p. 1973. text ed. 60.00x (ISBN 0-8248-0264-0). UH Pr.
Ugural, Ansel C. Stresses in Plates & Shells. (Illus.). 352p. 1981. text ed. 45.00x (ISBN 0-07-065730-0). McGraw.
Wilby, C. B. Design Graphs for Concrete Shell Roofs. (Illus.). xii, 148p. 1980. 37.50x (ISBN 0-85334-899-5). Burgess-Intl Ideas.
Yamaki, N. Elastic Stability of Circular Cylindrical Shells. (North Holland Series in Applied Mathematics: Vol. 27). 1984. 57.75 (ISBN 0-444-86857-7, I-552-83, North-Holland). Elsevier.

SHELLS, ELASTIC

see Elastic Plates and Shells

SHELTERS, AIR RAID

see Air Raid Shelters

SHERRY

Jeffs, Julian. Sherry. (Faber Wine Books Ser.). 320p. 17.95 (ISBN 0-571-18047-7); pap. 8.95 (ISBN 0-571-11799-6). Faber & Faber.
Simon, Andre L. All about Sherry. (All About Wines: Vol. 6). 7.50 (ISBN 0-87559-183-3). Shalom.

SHETLAND SHEEP DOGS

see Dogs–Breeds–Shetland Sheep Dogs

SHIELDING (ELECTRICITY)

Morrison, Ralph. Grounding & Shielding Techniques in Instrumentation. 2nd ed. LC 77-3265. 146p. 1977. 26.95x (ISBN 0-471-02992-0, Pub. by Wiley-Interscience). Wiley.
White, Donald R. Electromagnetic Shielding Materials & Performance. 2nd ed. LC 75-16592. 1980. text ed. 42.00 (ISBN 0-932263-08-9). White Consult.

SHIELDING (RADIATION)

Chilton, Arthur B. & Shultis, Kenneth. Principles of Radiation Shielding. (Illus.). 464p. 1984. 42.95 (ISBN 0-13-709907-X). P-H.
International Conference on Reactor Shielding, 5th. Nuclear Reactor Shielding: Proceedings. Roussin, Robert W., et al, eds. LC 77-10195. 1977. lib. bdg. 87.00 (ISBN 0-89500-005-9). Sci Pr.
Jaeger, R. G., et al, eds. Engineering Compendium on Radiation Shielding: Shielding Materials, Vol. 2. LC 68-19816. (Illus.). 440p. 1975. 180.00 (ISBN 0-387-05075-2). Springer-Verlag.
--Engineering Compendium on Radiation Shielding, Vols. 1 & 3. Incl. Vol. 1: Shielding Fundamentals & Methods. (Illus.). xii, 537p. 1968. 160.10 (ISBN 0-387-04080-3); Vol. 3: Shield Design & Engineering. 1970. 180.00 (ISBN 0-387-05076-0). LC 68-19816. (Illus., Sponsored by the International Atomic Energy Agency, Vienna). Springer-Verlag.
Nelson, Walter R. & Jenkins, T. M., eds. Computer Techniques in Shielding & Dosimetry. LC 79-20872. (Ettore Majorana International Science Ser., Physical Sciences: Vol. 3). 530p. 1980. 79.50x (ISBN 0-306-40307-2, Plenum Pr). Plenum Pub.
Profio, A. Edward. Radiation Shielding & Dosimetry. LC 78-15649. 1979. 58.95x (ISBN 0-471-04329-X, Pub. by Wiley-Interscience). Wiley.
Shimizu, Akinao & Aoki, Katsutada. Application of Invariant Imbedding to Reactor Physics. (Nuclear Science & Technology Ser). 1972. 55.00 (ISBN 0-12-640150-0). Acad Pr.
Structural Shielding Design & Evaluation for Medical Use of X-Rays & Gamma - Rays of Energies up to Ter Mev. LC 76-22969. (NCRP Reports Ser.: No. 49). 1976. 8.00 (ISBN 0-913392-31-6); adjunct to nCRP report no. 49 12.00 (ISBN 0-686-30845-X). NCRP Pubns.

SHIFTING CULTIVATION

Grandstaff, Terry B. Shifting Cultivation in Northern Thailand: Possibilities for Development. (Resource Systems Theory & Methodology Ser.: No. 3). 44p. 1981. pap. 10.00 (ISBN 92-808-0192-9, TUNU120, UNU). Unipub.
Norman, M. J. T. Annual Cropping Systems in the Tropics: An Introduction. LC 79-10625. (Illus.). x, 276p. 1979. text ed. 20.00 (ISBN 0-8130-0632-5). U Presses Fla.
Spencer, Joseph E. Shifting Cultivation in Southeastern Asia. LC 67-63051. (University of California Publications in Geography Ser.: Vol. 19). pap. 64.00 (ISBN 0-317-29507-1, 2021275). Bks Demand UMI.

SHIH TZU (DOG)

see Dogs–Breeds–Shih Tzu

SHIP-BUILDING

see also Boat-Building; Marine Engines; Naval Architecture; Propellers; Sails; Ship Models; Ships, Iron and Steel; Ships, Wooden; Shipyards; Trim (Of Ships); Warships; Yacht-Building also particular types of vessels, e.g. Steamboats, Torpedo-Boats

Abell, Wescott. The Shipwright's Trade. LC 81-71244. (Illus.). 227p. 1982. Repr. of 1949 ed. 16.00 (ISBN 0-87033-284-8). Cornell Maritime.
Baker, Elijah. Introduction to Steel Shipbuilding. 2nd ed. (Illus.). 1953. 34.45 (ISBN 0-07-003359-5). McGraw.
Beattie, D. H. & Somerville, W. M. Ship's Gear: A Review of Deck Machinery. (Marine Engineering Practice Ser.: Vol. 2, Pt. 16). 1979. pap. 9.00x (ISBN 0-900976-78-0, Pub. by Inst Marine Eng). Intl Spec Bk.
Chapelle, Howard I. Boatbuilding. (Illus.). 1941. 25.95 (ISBN 0-393-03113-6). Norton.
Chapman, Frederik H. Architectura Navalis Mercatoria: Facsimile of the Classic Eighteenth Century Treatise on Shipbuilding. 152p. 75.00 (ISBN 0-229-97491-0). Sheridan.
De Feyter, C. A. Industrial Policy & Shipbuilding: Changing Economic Structures in the Low Countries, 1600-1980. 200p. (Orig.). 1982. pap. 19.00x (ISBN 90-6194-323-X). Benjamins North Am.
Desmond, Charles. Wooden Ship-Building. 2nd ed. 232p. pap. 14.95 (ISBN 0-911572-37-6). Vestal.
Evans, J. Harvey, ed. Ship Structural Design Concepts. (Illus.). 837p. 1975. 45.00x (ISBN 0-87033-209-0). Cornell Maritime.
Eyres, D. J. Ship Construction. 2nd ed. (Illus.). 340p. 1978. pap. 22.50x (ISBN 0-434-90556-9). Sheridan.
Freeston, Ewart Co & Kent, Bernard. Modelling Thames Sailing Barges. 96p. 1980. 15.00x (ISBN 0-85177-091-6, Pub. by Cornell England). State Mutual Bk.
Furttenbach, Josef. Ship Building. (Printed Sources of Western Art Ser.). (Ger., Illus.). 150p. 1981. pap. 45.00 slipcase (ISBN 0-915346-62-1). A Wofsy Fine Arts.
Fyson, John, ed. FAO Investigates Ferro-Cement Fishing Crafts. (Illus.). 200p. (Orig.). 1974. pap. 37.25 (ISBN 0-85238-061-5, FN13, FNB). Unipub.
Holms, A. C. Practical Shipbuilding, 2 vols. LC 76-49170. 1977. lib. bdg. 200.00 (ISBN 0-8490-2461-7). Gordon Pr.
Hughes, Owen F. Ship Structural Design: A Rationally-Based, Computer Aided, Optimization Approach. LC 83-1110. (Ocean Engineering Ser.). 566p. 1983. 77.95x (ISBN 0-471-03241-7, 1-194, Pub. by Wiley-Interscience). Wiley.
IFIP-IFAC International Conference, 3rd, Univ. of Strathclyde, Scotland, June 1979. Computer Application in the Automation of Shipyard Operation & Ship Design, III: Proceedings. Kuo, C., et al, eds. (Computer Applications in Shipping & Shipbuilding Ser.: Vol. 6). 385p. 1980. 89.50 (ISBN 0-444-85337-5, North Holland). Elsevier.
International Shipping & Shipbuilding Directory. 1985. 185.00x (ISBN 0-686-27091-6). State Mutual Bk.
IPC Business Press, ed. Directory of Shipowners, Shipbuilders & Marine Engineers. 70.00x (ISBN 0-617-00310-6, Pub. by IPC Busn England). State Mutual Bk.
Kemp, J. F. & Young, P. Ship Construction: Sketches & Notes. 3rd ed. (Kemp & Young Ser.). 136p. 1977. pap. 9.95x (ISBN 0-540-00360-3). Sheridan.
Kuo, Chengi. Computer Methods for Ship Surface Design. LC 73-584131. (Illus.). pap. 58.50 (ISBN 0-317-08222-1, 2010061). Bks Demand UMI.
La Dage, John H. Modern Ships: Elements of Their Design, Construction, & Operation. 2nd ed. LC 65-21747. (Illus.). 389p. 1965. 11.50 (ISBN 0-87033-065-9). Cornell Maritime.
Lavery, Brian. Deane's Doctrine of Naval Architecture 1670. 192p. 1980. 69.50x (ISBN 0-85177-180-7, Pub. by Conway Maritime England). State Mutual Bk.
Lloyd's Marine Equipment Guide, 1982-83. 336p. 1982. 78.00x (ISBN 0-907432-09-3). Intl Pubns Serv.
Lloyd's Maritime Directory, 1983. 2nd ed. 1200p. 1983. 120.00x (ISBN 0-907432-51-4). Intl Pubns Serv.
MacBride, J. D. Handbook of Practical Shipbuilding. lib. bdg. 75.00 (ISBN 0-8490-1932-X). Gordon Pr.
McKay, Richard C. South Street. LC 76-160128. (American History & Americana Ser., No. 47). 1971. lib. bdg. 69.95x (ISBN 0-8383-1280-2). Haskell.
Munro-Smith, R. Elements of Ship Design. 145p. 1981. 50.00x (Pub. by Marine Mgmt England). State Mutual Bk.
Personnel Requirements for an Advanced Shipyard Technology. 1980. 7.95 (ISBN 0-309-02949-X). Natl Acad Pr.
Pursey, H. J. Merchant Ship Construction. 1981. 40.00x (ISBN 0-85174-144-4, Pub. by Nautical England). State Mutual Bk.
--Merchant Ship Construction. 7th ed. 217p. 1983. 26.50x (ISBN 0-85174-454-0). Sheridan.
Rogers, D. F., ed. Computer Applications in the Automation of Shipyard Operation & Ship Design, Vol. 4. (Computer Applications in Shipping & Shipbuilding: Vol. 9). 356p. 1982. 53.25 (ISBN 0-444-86408-3, I-300-82, North-Holland). Elsevier.
Safety & Health in Shipbuilding & Ship Repairing. (An IRO Code of Practice Ser.: No. 27). 1984. 15.70 (ISBN 92-2-101199-2). Intl Labour Office.
Slack, Kenneth E. In the Wake of the Spray. 275p. 1981. Repr. of 1966 ed. 17.50 (ISBN 0-911378-38-3). Sheridan.
Taggart, Robert, ed. Ship Design & Construction. 3rd ed. (Illus.). 748p. 1980. 75.00 (ISBN 0-9603048-0-0); members 55.00. Soc Naval Arch.
Taylor, D. A. Merchant Ship Construction. 2nd ed. (Illus.). 240p. 1985. pap. text ed. 24.95 (ISBN 0-408-01535-7). Butterworth.
U. S. Navy, Bureau of Ships, ed. Wood: A Manual for Its Use As a Shipbuilding Material. LC 82-74415. (Illus.). 418p. 1983. 22.00 (ISBN 0-9610602-0-4); pap. 19.00 (ISBN 0-9610602-1-2). Teaparty Bks.
Vlietstra, J. Ship Operations Automation III. (Computer Applications in Shipping & Shipbuilding Ser.: Vol. 7). 336p. 1980. 66.00 (ISBN 0-444-86033-9, North-Holland). Elsevier.
Walker, Fred. Steel Ship Building. (Shire Album Ser.: No. 73). (Illus.). 32p. (Orig.). 1981. pap. 2.95 (ISBN 0-85263-569-9, Pub. by Shire Pubns England). Seven Hills Bks.
Walton, Thomas & Baxter, B. Know Your Own Ship, Construction, Stability Etc. 28th. ed. 373p. 1970. text ed. 19.95x (ISBN 0-85264-151-6). Lubrecht & Cramer.
White, G. W. Elementary Beam Theory & the Ship Girder. 124p. 1979. 15.00x (ISBN 0-540-07352-0). Sheridan.

Whall, W. B. The Romance of Navigation. LC 72-83272. (Illus.). Repr. of 1930 ed. 22.00 (ISBN 0-405-09061-7). Ayer Co Pubs.

Worcester, G. R. Junks & Sampans of the Yangtze. LC 68-54115. (Illus.). 626p. 1971. 62.95 (ISBN 0-87021-335-0). Naval Inst Pr.

SHIPS–AUTOMATION

Bonwick, G. Automation on Shipboard. 1969. 35.00 (ISBN 0-312-06195-1). St Martin.

Datz, I. Mortimer. Power Transmission & Automation for Ships & Submersibles. (Illus.). 190p. 45.00 (ISBN 0-85238-074-7, FN23, FNB). Unipub.

Volta, E., ed. Ship Operation Automation, IV. (Computer Applications in Shipping: Vol. 10). 316p. 1983. 47.00 (ISBN 0-444-86572-1, North-Holland). Elsevier.

SHIPS–CARGO

see also Cargo Handling

Garoche, Pierre. Dictionary of Commodities Carried by Ship. 366p. 1952. pap. 10.00x (ISBN 0-87033-019-5). Cornell Maritime.

McDonald, W. F. Notes on the Problems of Cargo Ventilation. (Technical Note Ser.: No. 17). 38p. 1957. pap. 7.00 (ISBN 0-685-22329-9, W11, WMO). Unipub.

Sauerbier, Charles L. Marine Cargo Operations. (Materials Handling & Packaging Ser.). 548p. 1956. 49.95x (ISBN 0-471-75504-4, Pub. by Wiley-Interscience). Wiley.

Thomas, R. E. & Thomas, O. O. Stowage: The Properties & Stowage of Cargoes. 1981. 70.00x (ISBN 0-85174-000-6, Pub. by Nautical England). State Mutual Bk.

SHIPS–CONSTRUCTION

see Ship-Building

SHIPS–CORROSION

Chandler, K. A. Marine & Offshore Corrosion. 2nd ed. 432p. 1985. text ed. 79.95 (ISBN 0-408-01175-0). Butterworth.

Corrosion in the Marine Environment: A Joint Conference Held on 8-9 Nov. 1973. (Illus.). 104p. 1975. pap. 21.00x (ISBN 0-900976-34-9, Pub. by Inst Marine Eng). Intl Spec Bk.

Deere, Derek H., ed. Corrosion in Marine Environment International Sourcebook I: Ship Painting & Corrosion. LC 76-15600. 259p. 1977. 74.95x (ISBN 0-470-15203-6). Halsted Pr.

Schumacher, M. M., ed. Seawater Corrosion Handbook. LC 78-70745. (Illus.). 494p. 1979. 36.00 (ISBN 0-8155-0736-4). Noyes.

SHIPS–FIRES AND FIRE PREVENTION

Fire Protection of Vessels During Construction, Repair, & Layup. (Three Hundred Ser.). 1970. pap. 2.00 (ISBN 0-685-58059-8, 312). Natl Fire Prot.

Marine Publications Intl. Ltd., ed. Ships Firefighting Manual. 1981. 50.00x (ISBN 0-906314-03-8, Pub. by Marine Pubns Intl England). State Mutual Bk.

National Academy of Sciences. Ships. LC 77-79218. (Fire Safety Aspects of Polymeric Materials: Vol. 9). 236p. 1980. 19.00 (ISBN 0-87762-230-2). Technomic.

Royal Institution of Naval Architects & Institute of Marine Engineering, eds. Prevention & Control of Fires in Ships. (Illus.). 1976. 15.00x (ISBN 0-89955-400-8, Pub. by Inst Marine Eng). Intl Spec Bk.

Rushbrook, F. Fire Aboard: The Problems of Prevention & Control in Ships, Port Installations & Offshore Structures. 2nd ed. (Illus.). 1979. 75.00 (ISBN 0-686-77984-3). Heinman.

Rushbrook, Frank. Fire Aboard. 1981. 70.00x (ISBN 0-85174-331-5, Pub. by Nautical England). State Mutual Bk.

--Fire Aboard: The Problems of Prevention & Control in Ships, Port Installations & Offshore Structures. 2nd ed. 638p. 1979. 65.00x (ISBN 0-85174-331-5). Sheridan.

SHIPS–HYDRODYNAMICS

see also Stability of Ships

Bishop, R. E. & Price, W. G. Hydroelasticity of Ships. LC 78-67297. 1980. 105.00 (ISBN 0-521-22328-8). Cambridge U Pr.

Newman, John N. Marine Hydrodynamics. 1977. 35.00x (ISBN 0-262-14026-8). MIT Pr.

SHIPS–MAINTENANCE AND REPAIR

see also Damage Control (Warships)

Berendsen, A. M. Ship Painting Manual. (Illus.). 1975. 45.00 (ISBN 90-228-1951-5). Heinman.

Control of Gas Hazards on Vessels to Be Repaired. (Three Hundred Ser). 1972. pap. 2.00 (ISBN 0-685-58057-1, 306). Natl Fire Prot.

Norris, A. Operation of Machinery in Ships: Steam Turbines Boilers & Auxiliary Plant. (Practice Ser.: Vol. 2, Pt. 15). 1979. 9.00x (ISBN 0-900976-80-2, Pub. by Inst Marine Eng). Intl Spec Bk.

Shields, S., et al. Ship Maintenance: A Quantitative Approach. (Illus.). 1976. pap. 19.50x (ISBN 0-900976-51-9, Pub. by Inst Marine Eng). Intl Spec Bk.

Stanford, Peter. The Ships That Brought Us So Far. (Illus.). pap. 2.00 (ISBN 0-686-15903-9). Sea Hist Pr.

SHIPS–RADIO

see Radio in Navigation

SHIPS–RECOGNITION

Greenway, Ambrose. Soviet Merchant Ships. Mason, Kenneth, ed. 226p. 1982. 49.00x (ISBN 0-85937-253-7, Pub. by Mason England). State Mutual Bk.

Moore, John E., ed. Jane's Fighting Ships 1976-77. LC 75-15172. 1976. 79.50 (ISBN 0-934636-03-6). Key Bk Serv.

SHIPS, CARGO

see Cargo Ships

SHIPS, ELECTRICITY ON

see Electricity on Ships

SHIPS, IRON AND STEEL

Baker, Elijah. Introduction to Steel Shipbuilding. 2nd ed. (Illus.). 1953. 34.45 (ISBN 0-07-003359-5). McGraw.

Emmerson, George S. SS Great Eastern: The Greatest Iron Ship. LC 80-69345. (Illus.). 216p. 1981. 18.95 (ISBN 0-7153-8054-0). David & Charles.

Heal, D. Iron & Steel-Shipbuilding. (Reviews of UK Statistical Sources Ser.: Vol. 16). 209p. 1984. 35.00 (ISBN 0-08-030191-6). Pergamon.

Nicholson, Ian. Small Steel Craft. (Illus.). 206p. 1971. 19.95x (ISBN 0-8464-1137-7). Beekman Pubs.

Stanford, Peter. The Ships That Brought Us So Far. (Illus.). pap. 2.00 (ISBN 0-686-15903-9). Sea Hist Pr.

Walker, Fred. Steel Ship Building. (Shire Album Ser.: No. 73). (Illus.). 32p. (Orig.). 1981. pap. 2.95 (ISBN 0-85263-569-9, Pub. by Shire Pubns England). Seven Hills Bks.

SHIPS, WOODEN

Brewington, M. V. Shipcarvers of North America. LC 79-187020. (Illus.). 190p. 1972. pap. 4.95 (ISBN 0-486-22168-7). Dover.

Leavitt, John F. The Charles W. Morgan. LC 73-83835. (Illus.). 131p. 1973. 14.00 (ISBN 0-913372-09-9). Mystic Seaport.

Stanford, Peter. The Ships That Brought Us So Far. (Illus.). pap. 2.00 (ISBN 0-686-15903-9). Sea Hist Pr.

U. S. Navy, Bureau of Ships, ed. Wood: A Manual for Its Use As a Shipbuilding Material. LC 82-74415. (Illus.). 418p. 1983. 22.00 (ISBN 0-9610602-0-4); pap. 19.00 (ISBN 0-9610602-1-2). Teaparty Bks.

Wooden Shipbuilding & Small Craft Preservation. (Illus.). 104p. (Orig.). 1976. pap. 6.50 (ISBN 0-89133-045-3). Preservation Pr.

SHIP'S STABILITY

see Stability of Ships

SHIPYARDS

Pollard, Sidney & Robertson, Paul. British Shipbuilding Industry Eighteen Seventy to Nineteen Fourteen. LC 78-12500. (Studies in Business History: No. 30). 1979. 20.00x (ISBN 0-674-08287-7). Harvard U Pr.

SHOCK (MECHANICS)

see also Blast Effect; Shock Tubes; Shock Waves

Buchsbaum, Frank & Freudenstein, Ferdinand. Vibration & Shock Mount Handbook. (Illus.). 144p. 1984. pap. 3.75 (ISBN 0-318-01513-7). Stock Drive.

Harris, Cyril M. & Crede, Charles E. Shock & Vibration Control Handbook. 2nd ed. 1976. 63.00 (ISBN 0-07-026799-5). McGraw.

Meyer, Richard E., ed. Transonic, Shock, & Multidimensional Flows: Advances in Scientific Computing. (Mathematics Research Center Symposium Ser.). 1982. 30.00 (ISBN 0-12-493280-0). Acad Pr.

Morrow, Charles T. Shock & Vibration Engineering. LC 63-7556. pap. 101.00 (ISBN 0-317-08532-8, 2011956). Bks Demand UMI.

Reiff, D. D., ed. Component Support Snubbers: Design, Application & Testing. (PVP: No. 42). 130p. 1980. 10.00 (ISBN 0-686-69844-4, H00169). ASME.

Tustin, Wayne, et al. Vibration & Shock Test Fixture Design. 1971. text ed. write for info. Tustin Inst.

SHOCK TUBES

Ahlborn, Boye, et al, eds. Shock Tube & Shock Wave Research: Proceedings of the Eleventh International Symposium on Shock Tubes & Waves. LC 77-20168. (Illus.). 670p. 1978. 60.00x (ISBN 0-295-95582-1). U of Wash Pr.

International Shock Tube Symposium, 9th, Stanford Univ., 1973. Recent Developments in Shock Tube Research: Proceedings. Bershader, Daniel & Griffith, Wayland, eds. LC 73-80624. (Illus.). 848p. 1973. 48.50x (ISBN 0-8047-0842-8). Stanford U Pr.

SHOCK WAVES

see also Blast Effect; Shock Tubes; Underground Nuclear Explosions

Ahlborn, Boye, et al, eds. Shock Tube & Shock Wave Research: Proceedings of the Eleventh International Symposium on Shock Tubes & Waves. LC 77-20168. (Illus.). 670p. 1978. 60.00x (ISBN 0-295-95582-1). U of Wash Pr.

Burke, John J. & Weiss, Volker, eds. Shock Waves & the Mechanical Properties of Solids. (Sagamore Army Materials Research Conference Ser.: Vol. 17). 427p. 1971. 35.00x (ISBN 0-306-34517-X, Plenum Pr). Plenum Pub.

Caldirola, P. & Knoepfel, H., eds. Physics of High Energy Density. (Italian Physical Society: Course 48). 1971. 80.00 (ISBN 0-12-368848-5). Acad Pr.

CISM (International Center for Mechanical Sciences) Lectures on the Theory of Exothermic Flows Behind Shock Waves. Cherny, G. G., ed. (CISM Intl. Centre for Mechanical Sciences, Courses & Lectures Ser.: No. 36). (Illus.). 143p. 1974. pap. 18.90 (ISBN 3-211-81168-0). Springer-Verlag.

Greene, Edward F. & Toennies, J. Peter. Chemical Reactions in Shock Waves. 1964. 56.00 (ISBN 0-12-299850-2). Acad Pr.

Hesaaraki, Mahmud. Structure of Shock Waves in Magnetohydrodynamics. LC 84-3085. (Memoirs: No. 302). 98p. 1984. pap. 10.00 (ISBN 0-8218-2303-5). Am Math.

Kirkwood, John G. Shock & Detonation Waves. Wood, W. W., ed. LC 68-7145. (Documents on Modern Physics Ser.). (Illus.). 142p. 1967. 40.50 (ISBN 0-677-00380-3). Gordon.

Lax, P. D. Hyperbolic Systems of Conservation Laws & the Mathematical Theory of Shock Waves. (CBMS-NSF Regional Conference Ser.: No. 11). v, 48p. 1973. pap. text ed. 8.00 (ISBN 0-89871-177-0). Soc Indus-Appl Math.

Lifshitz. Shock Waves in Chemistry. 400p. 1981. 75.00 (ISBN 0-8247-1331-1). Dekker.

Liu, Tai-Ping. Admissible Solutions of Hyperbolic Conservation Laws: Memoirs of the Arms. LC 80-28506. (Memoirs Ser.: No. 240). 78p. 1981. pap. 9.00 (ISBN 0-8218-2240-3). Am Math.

Majda, Andrew. The Existence of Multi-Dimensional Shock Fronts. LC 83-3725. (Memoirs of the American Mathematical Society: No. 281). 94p. 1983. pap. 10.00 (ISBN 0-8218-2281-0). Am Math.

--The Stability of Multi-Dimensional Shock Fronts. LC 82-20636. (Memoirs Ser.: No. 275). 96p. paper 9.00 (ISBN 0-8218-2275-6, MEMO/275). Am Math.

Meyers, Mare A. & Murr, Lawrence E., eds. Shock Waves & High-Strain-Rate Phenomena in Metals: Concepts & Applications. LC 80-27395. 1116p. 1981. 130.00x (ISBN 0-306-40633-0, Plenum Pr). Plenum Pub.

Morawetz, C. S. Lectures on Nonlinear Waves & Shocks. (Tata Institute Lectures on Mathematics Ser.). 137p. 1982. pap. 10.00 (ISBN 0-387-10830-0). Springer-Verlag.

Morris, Charles E., ed. Los Alamos Shock Wave Profile Data. LC 81-70654. (Los Alamos Scientific Laboratory Series on Dynamic Material Properties). 512p. 1982. 44.00x (ISBN 0-520-04013-9). U of Cal Pr.

Nellis, W. J., et al, eds. Shock Waves in Condensed Matter: 1981 (Menlo Park) LC 82-70014. (AIP Conference Proceedings: No. 78). 715p. 1982. lib. bdg. 43.00 (ISBN 0-88318-177-0). Am Inst Physics.

Predvoditelev, A. S., ed. Physics of Heat Exchange & Gas Dynamics. LC 62-12858. 99p. 1963. 25.00x (ISBN 0-306-10574-8, Consultants). Plenum Pub.

Propagation of Shock Waves in Solids: Presented at the Applied Mechanics Conference, Salt Lake City, Utah, June 14-17, 1976. LC 76-12662. (American Soceity of Mechanical Engineers, Applied Mechanics Division: Vol. 17). pap. 30.50 (ISBN 0-317-26673-X, 2024185). Bks Demand UMI.

Smoller, J. Shock Waves & Reaction-Diffusion Equations. (Grundlehren der Mathematischen Wissenschaften: Vol. 258). (Illus.). 581p. 1983. 41.00 (ISBN 0-387-90752-1). Springer-Verlag.

Stupochenko, Y. V., et al. Relaxation in Shock Waves. Lee, R. Shao-Lin, tr. LC 67-21459. (Applied Physics & Engineering Ser.: Vol. 1). (Illus.). 1967. 56.00 (ISBN 0-387-03727-6). Springer-Verlag.

Tidman, D. A. Shock Waves in Collisionless Plasmas. Krali, N. A., ed. LC 74-13711. 187p. (Orig.). 1971. 16.25 (ISBN 0-471-86785-3). Krieger.

Varley, Eric. The Propagation of Shock Waves in Solids: AMD, Vol. 17. 1976. pap. text ed. 16.00 (ISBN 0-685-68905-0, I00102). ASME.

Zel'Dovich, Ya B., et al. Physics of Shock Waves & High Temperature Hydrodynamic Phenomena, 2 Vols. Vol. 1 1966. 76.50 (ISBN 0-12-778701-1); Vol. 2 1967. 76.50 (ISBN 0-12-778702-X). Acad Pr.

SHOE INDUSTRY AND TRADE

see Boots and Shoes–Trade and Manufacture

SHOE REPAIRING

see Boots and Shoes–Repairing

SHOEMAKERS

Melder, Keith. Life & Times in Shoe City: The Shoe Workers of Lynn, an Exhibition at the Essex Institute, Salem. (Illus.). 56p. 1979. pap. 2.00 (ISBN 0-88389-101-8). Essex Inst.

SHOES

see Boots and Shoes

SHOOTING

Here are entered works on the use of firearms and the technique of shooting. Works on shooting game are entered under the heading Hunting.

see also Ammunition; Ballistics; Explosives; Firearms

Carlisle, G. L. & Stanbury, Percy. Shotgun & Shooter. Rev. ed. 232p. 1981. 35.00x (ISBN 0-686-87325-4, Pub. by Hutchinson). State Mutual Bk.

Marchington, John. Shooting: A Complete Guide for Beginners. (Illus.). 184p. (Orig.). 1982. pap. 6.95 (ISBN 0-571-11932-8). Faber & Faber.

Riling, Ray. Guns & Shooting: A Bibliography. (Illus.). 1981. 75.00 (ISBN 0-9603094-3-8). Ray Riling.

Set Your Sights: A Guide to Handgun Basics. (Illus.). 1982. 1.95 (ISBN 0-916682-34-X). Outdoor Empire.

SHOP MANAGEMENT

see Factory Management

SHOP MATHEMATICS

Anderson, John G. Technical Shop Mathematics. 2nd ed. (Illus.). 500p. 1983. 20.95 (ISBN 0-8311-1145-3); Answer Manual avail. Indus Pr.

Bailey, Frank A. Basic Mathematics for Drafting & Machine Shop. 1977. pap. 9.75x (ISBN 0-673-15066-6). Scott F.

Boyce, John, et al. Mathematics for Technical & Vocational Students. 7th ed. LC 81-2686. 561p. 1982. 26.95 (ISBN 0-471-05182-9); students study guide 10.95 (ISBN 0-471-09266-5). Wiley.

Christopher, John. Introductory Technical Mathematics. (Illus.). 448p. 1982. 26.95 (ISBN 0-13-501635-5). P-H.

Levine, Samuel. Vocational & Technical Mathematics in Action. (Illus., Orig.). 1969. pap. 12.95x (ISBN 0-8104-5717-2); inst. guide & ans. bk. 1.95x (ISBN 0-8104-5719-9); transparencies 102.15 (ISBN 0-8104-8851-5). Hayden.

National Machine Tool Builders Association. Shop Math. (NMTBA Shop Practices Ser.). 140p. 1982. pap. 13.95 (ISBN 0-471-07841-7). Wiley.

Power, Thomas C. Practical Shop Mathematics. (Illus.). 1979. pap. text ed. 24.20 (ISBN 0-07-050591-8). McGraw.

Rudman, Jack. Shop Mathematics. (Career Examination Ser.: CS-36). (Cloth bdg. avail. on request). pap. 6.00 (ISBN 0-8373-3736-4). Natl Learning.

Scharff, Robert. Math for Construction Workshop & the Home. LC 79-91445. (Popular Science Ser.). (Illus.). 608p. 1982. 23.03i (ISBN 0-06-013784-3, HarpT). Har-Row.

Smith, Robert. Mathematics for Machine Technology. (Mathematics Trade Ser.). 288p. 1974. pap. text ed. 13.80 (ISBN 0-8273-1198-2); instructor's guide 4.70 (ISBN 0-8273-1199-0). Delmar.

Vezzani, A. A. & Leuchtman, Alex. Use of the Mechanics' Handbooks. rev. ed. LC 68-59490. 1969. pap. 5.95x (ISBN 0-911168-17-6); ans. bk. 2.95x (ISBN 0-911168-18-4). Prakken.

Wolfe, John H. & Phelps, E. R. Practical Shop Mathematics, Vol. 1: Elementary. 4th ed. 1958. 20.20 (ISBN 0-07-071358-8). McGraw.

SHOP PRACTICE

see Machine-Shop Practice

SHOPS

see Workshops

SHORE BIRDS

see also Sea Birds

Bent, Arthur C. Life Histories of North American Shore Birds, 2 Vols. (Illus.). 1927-29. pap. 7.00 ea.; Vol. 1. pap. (ISBN 0-486-20933-4); Vol. 2. pap. (ISBN 0-486-20934-2). Dover.

--Life Histories of North American Shore Birds, 2 Vols. (Illus.). 13.00 ea. (ISBN 0-8446-1642-7). Peter Smith.

Burger, Joanna & Olla, Bori L., eds. Shorebirds: Breeding Behavior & Populations. (Behavior of Marine Animals Ser.: Vol. 5). 421p. 1984. 59.50x (ISBN 0-306-41590-9, Plenum Pr). Plenum Pub.

--Shorebirds: Migration & Foraging Behavior. (Behavior of Marine Animals Ser.: Vol. 6). 323p. 1984. 49.50x (ISBN 0-306-41591-7, Plenum Pr). Plenum Pub.

Johnsgard, Paul A. North American Game Birds of Upland & Shoreline. LC 74-15274. (Illus.). xxx, 231p. 1975. pap. 8.95 (ISBN 0-8032-5811-9, BB 597, Bison). U of Nebr Pr.

--The Plovers, Sandpipers, & Snipes of the World. LC 80-22712. (Illus.). xviii, 541p. 1981. 45.00 (ISBN 0-8032-2553-9). U of Nebr Pr.

Romashko, Sandra. Birds of the Water, Sea & Shore. LC 77-81169. (Illus.). 1985. pap. 3.95x (ISBN 0-89317-016-X). Windward Pub.

Warren, Michael. Shorelines: Birds at the Water's Edge. LC 84-40104. (Illus.). 128p. 1984. 25.00 (ISBN 0-8129-1133-4). Times Bks.

SHORE EROSION

see Beach Erosion; Coast Changes

SHORE FLORA

see Coastal Flora

SHORE LINES
see also Coast Changes; Coasts; Shore Protection

Brehaut, Roger N. Ecology of Rocky Shores. (Studies in Biology: No. 139). 64p. 1982. pap. text ed. 8.95 (ISBN 0-7131-2839-9). E Arnold.

Heikoff, Joseph M., ed. Shorelines & Beaches in Coastal Management: A Bibliography, No. 876. 1975. 6.50 (ISBN 0-686-20368-2). CPL Biblios.

Kaufman, Wallace & Pilkey, Orrin. The Beaches are Moving: The Drowning of America's Shoreline. (Living with the Shore Ser.). (Illus.). 326p. 1983. pap. 9.75 (ISBN 0-8223-0574-7). Duke.

Leed, Roger, ed. Shorelines Management: The Washington Experience. (Washington Sea Grant Ser.). 184p. 1973. pap. 7.50x (ISBN 0-295-95309-8). U of Wash Pr.

Mills, J. V., ed. Ying Yai Sheng Lan, by Ma Huan: The Overall Survey of the Ocean's Shores, 1433. 393p. 1970. 59.00x (ISBN 0-686-79466-4, Pub. by Hakluyt Soc England). State Mutual Bk.

Nairn, A. E. & Stehli, F. G., eds. Ocean Basins & Margins. Incl. Vol. 1: The South Atlantic. 600p. 1973 (ISBN 0-306-37771-3); Vol. 2: The North Atlantic. 662p. 1974 (ISBN 0-306-37772-1); Vol. 3: The Gulf of Mexico & The Caribbean. 722p. 1975 (ISBN 0-306-37773-X); Vol. 4A: The Eastern Mediterranean. 519p. 1977 (ISBN 0-306-37774-8); Vol. 4B: The Western Mediterranean. 462p. 1978 (ISBN 0-306-37779-9); Vol. 5: The Arctic Ocean. 686p. 1981 (ISBN 0-306-37775-6). LC 72-83046. (Illus.). each 75.00x (Plenum Pr). Plenum Pub.

Weimer, R. J. & Tillman, R. W. Tectonic Influence on Deltaic Shoreline Facies, Fox Hills Sandstone, West-Central Denver Basin. Raese, Jon W., ed. (CSM Professional Contributions Ser.: No. 10). (Illus.). 131p. (Orig.). 1980. pap. 12.00 (ISBN 0-686-63164-1). Colo Sch Mines.

SHORE PROTECTION
see also Beach Erosion; Coast Changes; Coasts; Harbors; Hydraulic Engineering; Reclamation of Land; Sea-Walls; Shore Lines

Bailey, Gilbert E. & Thayer, Paul S. California's Disappearing Coast: A Legislative Challenge. LC 74-170336. (Illus., Orig.). 1971. pap. 3.00x (ISBN 0-87772-083-5). Inst Gov Stud Berk.

Barnes, R. S., ed. The Coastline: A Contribution to Our Understanding of Its Ecology & Physiography in Relation to Land-Use & Management & the Pressures to Which It Is Subject. LC 76-51343. 356p. 1977. 59.95x (ISBN 0-471-99470-7, Pub. by Wiley-Interscience). Wiley.

Bruun, P. Design & Construction of Mounds for Breakwater & Coastal Protection. (Developments in Geotechnical Engineering Ser.: Vol. 37). 1985. 92.75 (ISBN 0-444-42391-5). Elsevier.

Bruun, P. & Mehta, A. J. Stability of Tidal Inlets: Theory & Engineering. (Developments in Geotechnical Engineering Ser.: Vol. 23). 510p. 1978. 76.75 (ISBN 0-444-41728-1). Elsevier.

Doyle, Larry R., et al. Living with the West Florida Shore. (Living with the Shore Ser.). 1984. 24.75 (ISBN 0-8223-0516-X); pap. 11.75 (ISBN 0-8223-0517-8). Duke.

Griggs, Gary B. & Savoy, Lauret E., eds. Living with the California Coast. (Living with the Shore Ser.). (Illus.). 424p. 1985. 27.95 (ISBN 0-8223-0632-8); pap. 14.95 (ISBN 0-8223-0633-6). Duke.

Healy, R., et al. Protecting the Golden Shore: Lessons from the Calif. Coastal Commissions. Healy, Robert G., ed. LC 78-65565. (Orig.). 1978. pap. 7.50 (ISBN 0-89164-052-5). Conservation Found.

Kelley, Joseph, et al. Living with the Louisiana Shore. (Living with the Shore Ser.). (Illus.). 176p. 22.75 (ISBN 0-8223-0518-6); pap. 9.75 (ISBN 0-8223-0519-4). Duke.

Kowalski, T., ed. Floating Breakwater Conference Papers, 1974. (Marine Technical Report Ser.: No. 24). 1974. pap. 5.00 (ISBN 0-938412-10-8). URI MAS.

Mitchell, James K. Community Response to Coastal Erosion: Individual & Collective Adjustments to Hazard on the Atlantic Shore. LC 73-92652. (Research Papers Ser.: No. 156). 209p. 1974. 10.00 (ISBN 0-89065-063-2). U Chicago Dept Geog.

Muir-Wood, A. M. Coastal Hydraulics. 200p. 1979. 57.75x (ISBN 0-677-61680-5). Gordon.

Price, J. H., et al, eds. The Shore Environment, Vol. 2: Ecosystems. (Systematics Association Special Ser.: No. 17). 1981. 98.00 (ISBN 0-12-564702-6). Acad Pr.

Price, J. R., et al, eds. The Shore Environment, Vol. 1: Methods. (Systematics Association Special Ser.: No.17). 1981. 63.00 (ISBN 0-12-564701-8). Acad Pr.

Thorn, R. B. & Simmons, J. C. Sea Defense Works: Design, Construction & Emergency. 2nd ed. (Illus.). 128p. 1971. 11.00 (ISBN 0-8088-7020-3). Davey.

Weimer, R. J. & Tillman, R. W. Tectonic Influence on Deltaic Shoreline Facies, Fox Hills Sandstone, West-Central Denver Basin. Raese, Jon W., ed. (CSM Professional Contributions Ser.: No. 10). (Illus.). 131p. (Orig.). 1980. pap. 12.00 (ISBN 0-686-63164-1). Colo Sch Mines.

Williams, William W. Coastal Changes. LC 75-3873. (Illus.). 220p. 1975. Repr. of 1960 ed. lib. bdg. 16.00x (ISBN 0-8371-8088-0, WICOC). Greenwood.

Wilman, Elizabeth A. External Costs of Coastal Beach Pollution: An Hedonic Approach. LC 84-42690. 208p. (Orig.). 1984. pap. text ed. 15.00 (ISBN 0-915707-08-X). Resources Future.

SHORES, C. W.

Sterling, Keir B., ed. Scientific Publications of Charles Wilkins Short: Original Anthology. LC 77-81125. (Biologists & Their World Ser.). 1978. lib. bdg. 32.00x (ISBN 0-405-10721-8). Ayer Co Pubs.

SHORT TAKE-OFF AND LANDING AIRCRAFT

McCormick, B. W., Jr., ed. Aerodynamics of V-STOL Flight. 1967. 35.00 (ISBN 0-12-482350-5). Acad Pr.

SHORT WAVE RADIO
see Radio, Short Wave

SHORTENINGS
see Oils and Fats, Edible

SHORTHAND

Bales, Peter. The Writing Schoolmaster: Brachygraphie, Orthographie, Calygraphie. LC 70-26226. (English Experience Ser.: No. 194). 122p. 1969. Repr. of 1590 ed. 16.00 (ISBN 90-221-0194-0). Walter J Johnson.

Blanchard, Adele B. Quickscript: The Fast & Simple Shorthand Method. LC 82-67031. 160p. 1982. pap. 5.95 (ISBN 0-668-05572-3, 5572). Arco.

Blum, Walter & Yerian, C. Theo. Personal Shorthand for the Journalist. 176p. (Orig.). 1980. pap. text ed. 8.85 (ISBN 0-89420-214-6, 242032); optional cassettes recordings 237.20 (ISBN 0-89420-225-1, 242000). Natl Book.

Brooks, William A. A B C Shorthand. pap. 1.50 (ISBN 0-87497-049-0). Assoc Bk.

Evans, John C. Shorthand. 1963. pap. 4.76i (ISBN 0-06-463225-3, EH 225, EH). B&N NY.

Geringer, Lauren R. Your Own Shortcut Shorthand. LC 79-55059. (Orig.). 1980. pap. 5.95 (ISBN 0-935020-06-3). Gehry Pr.

Grossman, Jeremy. Quickhand. (Self-Teaching Guides Ser.). 128p. 1976. pap. text ed. 6.95 (ISBN 0-471-32887-1). Wiley.

Kanegis, James. Chemical & Technical Stenography: Anniv. Gregg. 1950. 10.00x (ISBN 0-9600226-1-9). Kanegis.

Kupsh, Joyce, et al. Machine Transcription & Dictation. LC 77-15790. (Word Processing Ser.). 246p. 1978. pap. text ed. 19.95x (ISBN 0-471-02734-0); tchr's. manual avail. (ISBN 0-471-04211-0). Wiley.

Meyer, Lois & Moyer, Ruth. Machine Transcription in Modern Business. 2nd ed. LC 81-4709. 1982. pap. text ed. 19.95 (ISBN 0-471-08260-0); tchr.'s manual avail. (ISBN 0-471-86585-0). Wiley.

Rutan, Al. Rutan Shorthand for Everyone. (Illus.). 88p. (Orig.). 1980. pap. 8.50 (ISBN 0-936222-05-0). Rutan Pub.

Salser, Carl W. & Yerian, C. Theo. Personal Shorthand: Ps-80, Bks. 1 & 2. (Personal Shorthand Cardinal Ser.). 369p. 1981. text ed. 12.85 (ISBN 0-89420-221-9, 241180 TEXT); cassette 625.50 (ISBN 0-89420-167-0, 241000 CASSETTE). Natl Book.

Schatz, A. E. & Funk, B. M. Transcription Skills for Information Processing, Unit 4. 1981. pap. 5.28 text workbook (ISBN 0-07-055203-7). McGraw.

--Transcription Skills for Information Processing, Unit 5. 1981. pap. 5.28 text workbook (ISBN 0-07-055204-5). McGraw.

--Transcription Skills for Information Processing, Unit 6. 1981. pap. 5.28 text workbook (ISBN 0-07-055205-3). McGraw.

--Transcription Skills for Information Processing, Unit 7. 1981. pap. 5.28 text workbook (ISBN 0-07-055206-1). McGraw.

--Transcription Skills for Information Processing, Unit 8. 1981. pap. 5.28 text workbook (ISBN 0-07-055207-X). McGraw.

Smith, E. Ray, et al. Shorthand Speed Building & Transcription in a Modern Office. (Shorthand Ser.: 1-577). 269p. 1983. pap. text ed. 15.95 (ISBN 0-471-86533-8). Wiley.

SRA. Stenospeed for the Legal Secretary. 353p. 1981. pap. text ed. 24.95 (ISBN 0-574-20880-1, 13-3880). SRA.

--Stenospeed for the Medical Secretary. 418p. 1981. pap. text ed. 24.95 (ISBN 0-574-20885-2, 13-3885). SRA.

Sutton, Valerie. Sign Writing Shorthand for Sign Language Stenography. 1982. text ed. 15.00 (ISBN 0-914336-52-5). Ctr Sutton Movement.

Zelter, M. Exploring Shorthand. 96p. 1980. text ed. 5.89x (ISBN 0-7715-0735-6). Forkner.

SHORTHAND–EXAMINATIONS, QUESTIONS, ETC.

Hammer, Hy. Principal Clerk-Principal Stenographer. rev. ed. LC 82-11446. 256p. 1982. pap. 8.00 (ISBN 0-668-05536-7, 5536). Arco.

Hammer, Hy, ed. Test Preparation for Stenographer-Typist. LC 82-11429. 208p. (Orig.). 1982. pap. 8.00 (ISBN 0-668-05535-9, 5535). Arco.

Koch, Harry W. Typist & Stenographer Examinations. 2nd ed. 1976. 6.00 (ISBN 0-913164-63-1). Ken-Bks.

SHORTHAND–EXERCISES FOR DICTATION

Farmer & Anderson. Business Transcription. 192p. 1973. text ed. 11.20x (ISBN 0-7715-0740-2). Forkner.

Gallion, Leona M. & Kavan, C. Bruce. Computer Analyzed Vocabulary-Controlled Dictation Materials for Beginning Gregg Shorthand. 2nd ed. 270p. 1981. pap. text ed. 9.50x (ISBN 0-8134-2210-8). Interstate.

Walsh, John P., et al. Practice Dictation for Computer Shorthand: Theory & Transcription. (Computer Shorthand Ser.). 30p. 1984. pap. 295.00 (ISBN 0-471-80660-9). Wiley.

SHOT-GUNS

Brockway, William R. Recreating the Double Barrell Muzzle-Loading Shotgun. (Illus.). 1985. 27.50 (ISBN 0-87387-090-5); pap. 20.00 (ISBN 0-87387-089-1). Shumway.

Burch, Monte. Shotgunner's Guide. 176p. 1980. 18.95 (ISBN 0-8329-3117-9, Pub. by Winchester Pr). New Century.

Hastings, Macdonald. The Shotgun: A Social History. (Illus.). 224p. 1981. 29.95 (ISBN 0-7153-8062-1). David & Charles.

Laycock, George. Shotgunner's Bible. LC 69-15216. 1969. pap. 4.95 (ISBN 0-385-00978-X). Doubleday.

Lewis, Jack & Mitchell, Jack. Shotgun Digest. 2nd ed. LC 74-80333. 288p. 1980. pap. 11.95 (ISBN 0-910676-13-5). DBI.

McIntosh, Michael. The Best Shotguns Ever Made in America: Seven Vintage Doubles to Shoot & to Treasure. 1981. 17.95 (ISBN 0-684-16825-1, ScribT). Scribner.

Marshall-Ball, Robin. The Sporting Shotgun. 1981. 14.95 (ISBN 0-86230-037-1). Saiga.

--The Sporting Shotgun. (Illus.). 172p. 1982. 23.95 (ISBN 0-913276-38-3). Stone Wall Pr.

O'Connor, Jack. The Shotgun Book. 2nd, Rev. ed. LC 77-92795. (Illus.). 1978. pap. 9.95 (ISBN 0-394-73562-5). Knopf.

Robinson, Roger H. The Police Shotgun Manual. (Illus.). 168p. 1973. 14.75x (ISBN 0-398-02630-0). C C Thomas.

Skillen, Charles R. Combat Shotgun Training. (Illus.). 224p. 1982. 26.75x (ISBN 0-398-04672-7). C C Thomas.

Swearengen, Thomas F. Worlds Fighting Shotguns. (World Weapons Ser.: Vol. IV). 1978. 29.95 (ISBN 0-686-73789-X). TBN Ent.

Thomas, Gough. Shotguns & Cartridges for Game & Clays. 3rd ed. (Illus.). 254p. 1976. 25.00 (ISBN 0-7136-1583-4). Transatlantic.

Wallack, L. R. American Shotgun Design & Performance. LC 77-21886. 1977. 16.95 (ISBN 0-8329-2366-4, Pub. by Winchester Pr). New Century.

Wood, J. B. Gun Digest Book of Firearms Assembly-Disassembly: Part V, Shotguns. LC 79-54271. 288p. 1980. pap. 12.95 (ISBN 0-910676-11-9). DBI.

SHREWS

Choate, Jerry R. Systematics & Zoogeography of Middle American Shrews of the Genus Cryptotis. (Museum Ser.: Vol. 19, No. 3). 123p. 1970. 6.25 (ISBN 0-317-04961-5). U of KS Mus Nat Hist.

Findley, James S. Speciation of the Wandering Shrew. (Museum Ser.: Vol. 9, No. 1). 68p. 1955. pap. 3.75 (ISBN 0-686-80279-9). U of KS Mus Nat Hist.

--Taxonomy & Distribution of Some American Shrews. (Museum Ser.: Vol. 7, No. 14). 6p. 1955. pap. 1.25 (ISBN 0-317-05008-7). U of KS Mus Nat Hist.

Junge, Jane A. & Hoffman, Robert S. An Annotated Key to the Long-Tailed Shrews (Genus Sorex) of the United States & Canada: With Notes on Middle American Sorex. (Occasional Papers: No. 94). 48p. 1981. pap. 3.25 (ISBN 0-317-04860-0). U of KS Mus Nat Hist.

Rathbun, G. B. The Social Structure & Ecology of Elephant-Shrews. (Advances in Ethology Ser.: Vol. 20). (Illus.). 84p. (Orig.). 1979. pap. text ed. 29.50 (ISBN 3-489-60836-4). Parey Sci Pubs.

SHRIKES

Bent, Arthur C. Life Histories of North American Wagtails, Shrikes, Vireos & Their Allies. (Illus.). 1950. pap. 8.95 (ISBN 0-486-21085-5). Dover.

--Life Histories of North American Wagtails, Shrikes, Vireos & Their Allies. (Illus.). 14.00 (ISBN 0-8446-1644-3). Peter Smith.

SHRIMPS

Bliss, Dorothy. Shrimps, Lobster, & Crabs: Their Fascinating Life Story. LC 82-7853. (Illus.). 256p. 1982. 14.95 (ISBN 0-8329-0124-5). New Century.

Chace, Fenner. The Caridean Shrimps (Crustacea Decapoda) of the Albatross Philippine Expedition, 1907-1910, Pt. 2: Families Glyphocrangonidae & Crangonidae. LC 83-600061. (Smithsonian Contributions to Zoology: No. 397). pap. 20.00 (ISBN 0-317-20103-4, 2023164). Bks Demand UMI.

Gulland, John A. & Rothschild, Brian J., eds. Penaeid Shrimps - Their Biology & Management. (Illus.). 308p. 1985. pap. 72.00 (ISBN 0-85238-131-X, FN108, FNB). Unipub.

Headstrom, Richard. All about Lobsters, Crabs, Shrimps, & Their Relatives. (Nature Ser.). 144p. 1985. pap. 3.95 (ISBN 0-486-24795-3). Dover.

On the Volatile Flavour Compounds of Cooked Trassi, a Cured Shrimp Paste Condiment of the Far East. (Agricultural Research Reports: No. 183). 1972. pap. 8.25 (ISBN 90-220-0410-4, PDC190, PUDOC). Unipub.

Recommended International Code of Practice for Shrimps or Prawns. (CAC-RCP Ser.: No. 17-1978). 42p. 1980. pap. 7.50 (ISBN 92-5-100915-5, F1950, FAO). Unipub.

Recommended International Standard for Canned Shrimp or Prawns. pap. 5.50 (F642, FAO). Unipub.

Report on Selective Shrimp Trawls: Expert Consultation Held at the Netherlands, 1973. (Fisheries Reports: No. 139). 71p. 1973. pap. 7.50 (ISBN 0-686-93970-0, F784, FAO). Unipub.

Stock Assessment of Shrimp in the Indian Ocean Area (Bahrain, Iran, Iraq, Kuwait, Oman, Qatar, Saudi Arabia, United Arab Emirates) Report of the Meeting of the Ad Hoc Group of the IOFC Special Working Party on Stock Assessment of Shrimp in the Indian Ocean Area, to Consider the Stocks in the Area Covered by the UNDP-FAO Regional Fishery Survey & Development Project REM-71-278. Doha, Qatar, 26-29 April 1976. (Eng. & Fr.). 28p. pap. 7.50 (ISBN 92-5-100287-8, F840, FAO). Unipub.

Williams, Austin B. Shrimps, Lobsters, & Crabs of the Atlantic Coast. rev. ed. LC 83-600095. (Illus.). 568p. 1984. text ed. 40.00x (ISBN 0-87474-960-3). Smithsonian.

World Scientific Conference on the Biology & Culture of Shrimps & Prawns: Proceedings, Mexico City, 1967, Vol. 1. (Fisheries Reports: No. 57). 75p. 1968. pap. 7.50 (ISBN 0-686-92989-6, F1672, FAO). Unipub.

SHRUBS
see also specific shrubs, e.g. Rhododendron

Adams, William D. Shrubs & Vines for Southern Landscapes. LC 76-15455. (Illus.). 96p. (Orig.). 1979. pap. 6.95x (ISBN 0-88415-804-7, Pub. by Pacesetter Pr). Gulf Pub.

Clay, Horace F. & Hubbard, James C. Tropical Shrubs. LC 77-7363. (Hawaii Garden Ser: No. 2). (Illus.). 312p. 1977. 40.00 (ISBN 0-8248-0466-X). UH Pr.

Eagle, Audrey. Eagle's Trees & Shrubs of New Zealand in Colour. (Illus.). 311p. 1983. Repr. of 1975 ed. 95.00x (ISBN 0-686-84831-4, Pub. by W Collins New Zealand). Intl Spec Bk.

Edwards, Ray. Choosing & Caring for Garden Shrubs. pap. 4.50 (ISBN 0-7153-7902-X). David & Charles.

Elias, T. Shrubs for the Landscape. 1986. cancelled (ISBN 0-442-26405-4). Van Nos Reinhold.

Evenari, M., et al. Hot Deserts & Arid Shrublands, Vols. 12A & B. (Ecosystems of the World Ser.). Date not set. Set. price not set (ISBN 0-444-42297-8). Vol. 12A (ISBN 0-444-42282-X). Vol. 12B (ISBN 0-444-42296-X). Elsevier.

Flowering Shrubs. 2.25 (ISBN 0-686-21139-1). Bklyn Botanic.

Fruit Trees & Shrubs. 2.25 (ISBN 0-686-21159-6). Bklyn Botanic.

Grace, Julie, ed. Trees & Shrubs. (Know Your Garden Ser.). (Illus.). 179p. 1983. Repr. of 1973 ed. 24.95 (ISBN 0-917304-84-5). Timber.

Gupton, Oscar W. & Swope, Fred C. Trees & Shrubs of Virginia. LC 80-21585. (Illus.). 205p. 1981. 10.95 (ISBN 0-8139-0886-8). U Pr of Va.

Hellyer, Arthur. Garden Shrubs. 256p. 1982. 39.00x (ISBN 0-686-97608-8, Pub. by Dent Australia). State Mutual Bk.

--Garden Shrubs. (Illus.). 256p. 1982. 25.00x (ISBN 0-460-04474-5, Pub. by J M Dent England). Biblio Dist.

Howland, Joseph E. How to Select & Care for Shrubs & Hedges. Ortho Books Editorial Staff, ed. LC 80-66346. (Illus.). 96p. (Orig.). 1981. pap. 5.95 (ISBN 0-917102-88-6). Ortho.

Krussmann, Gerd. Manual of Cultivated Broad-leaved Trees & Shrubs, Vol. 1. Epp, Michael, tr. from Ger. Tr. of Handbuch der Laubgeholze. 498p. 1984. 65.00 (ISBN 0-917304-78-0). Timber.

Lamb, Samuel H. Native Trees & Shrubs of the Hawaiian Islands. LC 80-19715. 160p. 1981. pap. 14.95 (ISBN 0-913270-91-1). Sunstone Pr.
Millar Gauult, S. Diccionario Ilustrado En Color De Arbustos. (Span.). 213p. 1978. 48.00 (ISBN 84-252-0695-2, S-50274). French & Eur.
Mooberry, F. M. & Scott, Jane H. Grow Native Shrubs in Your Garden. LC 80-69807. 1980. 4.95x (ISBN 0-940540-01-0). Brandywine Conserv.
Nooteboom, H. P. Revision of the Symplocaceae of the Old World. (Leiden Botanical Ser: No. 1). 1975. lib. bdg. 53.00 (ISBN 90-6021-242-8, Pub. by Leiden Univ Holland). Kluwer Academic.
Northington, David K. Systematic Studies of the Genus Pyrrhopappus (Compositae, Cichorieae) (Special Publications: No. 6). 38p. 1974. pap. 2.00 (ISBN 0-89672-031-4). Tex Tech Pr.
One Hundred Finest Trees & Shrubs. 2.25 (ISBN 0-686-21127-8). Bklyn Botanic.
Petrides, George A. Field Guide to Trees & Shrubs. 1973. 15.95 (ISBN 0-395-13651-2); pap. 10.95 (ISBN 0-395-17579-8). HM.
Pittman, Blair, photos by. The Natural World of the Texas Big Thicket. LC 78-6369. (The Louise Lindsey Merrick Texas Environment Ser.: No. 2). (Illus.). 100p. 1978. 24.95 (ISBN 0-89096-061-5). Tex A&M Univ Pr.
Polunin, Oleg. Trees & Bushes of Europe. (Illus.). 1976. 18.95x (ISBN 0-19-217631-5). Oxford U Pr.
Sapody, C & Toth, I., eds. A Colour Atlas of Flowering Trees & Shrubs. 312p. 1982. 51.00 (Pub. by Akademiai Kiado Hungary). Heyden.
Standley, P. Trees & Shrubs of Mexico, 5 vols. 1976. Set. lib. bdg. 600.00 (ISBN 0-8490-2766-7). Gordon Pr.
Symonds, George W. The Shrub Identification Book. LC 63-7388. 1963. 17.95 (ISBN 0-688-00040-1); pap. 12.95 (ISBN 0-688-05040-9). Morrow.
Tree & Shrub Forms-Their Landscape Use. 2.25 (ISBN 0-686-21157-X). Bklyn Botanic.

SHRUBS–AUSTRALIA

Chippendale, G. M. Eucalypts of the Western Australian Goldfields. 1982. 30.00x (ISBN 0-686-97915-X, Pub. by CSIRO Australia). State Mutual Bk.
Thomas, Graham S. Shrub Roses of Today. Rev. ed. (Illus.). 242p. 1980. 22.50x (ISBN 0-460-04533-4, Pub. by J M Dent England). Biblio Dist.

SHRUBS–GREAT BRITAIN

Harz, Kurt. Trees & Shrubs. (Illus.). 150p. 1981. pap. 5.95 (ISBN 0-7011-2542-X, Pub. by Chatto & Windus). Merrimack Pub Cir.

SHRUBS–UNITED STATES

Billington, Cecil. Shrubs of Michigan. 2nd ed. LC 44-1024. (Bulletin Ser.: No. 20). (Illus.). 339p. 1949. text ed. 10.00x (ISBN 0-87737-005-2). Cranbrook.
Brown, Clair. Louisiana Trees & Shrubs. 1965. 7.50 (ISBN 0-87511-012-6). Claitors.
Dwelley, Marilyn J. Trees & Shrubs of New England. LC 79-52448. (Illus., Orig.). 1980. pap. 12.95 (ISBN 0-89272-064-6). Down East.
Ferris, Roxana S. Native Shrubs of the San Francisco Bay Region. (California Natural History Guides Ser.: No. 24). (Illus.). 1968. pap. 2.85 (ISBN 0-520-00405-1). U of Cal Pr.
Jones, L. R. & Rand, F. V. The Handbook of Vermont Shrubs & Woody Vines. LC 79-84806. pap. 3.95 (ISBN 0-8048-1316-7). C E Tuttle.
Keith, Rebecca M. & Giles, Floyd A. Dwarf Shrubs for the Midwest. LC 80-12867. (Illus.). 179p. 1980. 20.00 (ISBN 0-252-00817-0). U of Ill Pr.
McMinn, Howard E. An Illustrated Manual of California Shrubs. 1939. 40.00x (ISBN 0-520-00847-2). U of Cal Pr.
Muenscher, Walter C. Keys to Woody Plants. 6th, rev. ed. (Illus.). 108p. 1950. 11.95x (ISBN 0-8014-0307-3). Comstock.
Newcomb, Lawrence. Newcomb's Wildflower Guide: An Ingenious New Key System for Quick Positive Field Identification of the Wildflowers, Flowering Shrubs & Vines of Northeastern & North-Central North America. (Illus.). 1977. 18.45i (ISBN 0-316-60441-0). Little.
Perry, Robert C. Trees & Shrubs for Dry California Landscapes. LC 81-81013. (Illus.). 184p. 1981. 32.50 (ISBN 0-9605988-0-4); text ed. 32.50 (ISBN 0-9605988-1-2). Land Design.
Raven, Peter H. Native Shrubs of Southern California. (California Natural History Guides Ser.: No. 15). (Illus.). 1966. pap. 4.95 (ISBN 0-520-01050-7). U of Cal Pr.
Rosendahl, Carl O. Trees & Shrubs of the Upper Midwest. LC 55-8489. 1955. 17.50x (ISBN 0-8166-0118-6). U of Minn Pr.
Stokes, Donald. The Natural History of Wild Shrubs & Vines. LC 80-8219. (Illus.). 256p. 1981. 17.26i (ISBN 0-06-014163-8, HarpT). Har-Row.
Thomas, John H. & Parnell, Dennis R. Native Shrubs of the Sierra Nevada. (Natural History Guides Ser.: No. 34). 1974. 14.95x (ISBN 0-520-02738-8); pap. 5.95 (ISBN 0-520-02538-5). U of Cal Pr.
Wharton, Mary E. & Barbour, Roger W. Trees & Shrubs of Kentucky. LC 73-77257. (Illus.). 592p. 1973. 19.00 (ISBN 0-8131-1294-X). U Pr of Ky.
Wigginton, Brooks E. Trees & Shrubs for the Southeast. LC 63-22479. 304p. 1963. 15.00 (ISBN 0-8203-0189-2). U of Ga Pr.

SI

see Metric System

SIALIC ACID

Gottschalk, Alfred. The Chemistry & Biology of Sialic Acids & Related Substances. LC 60-50363. pap. 33.30 (ISBN 0-317-08958-7, 2050783). Bks Demand UMI.
Rosenberg, Abraham & Schengrund, Cara-Lynne, eds. Biological Roles of Sialic Acid. LC 76-16502. (Illus.). 393p. 1976. 45.00x (ISBN 0-306-30903-3, Plenum Pr). Plenum Pub.
Schauer, R., ed. Sialic Acids: Chemistry, Metabolism, & Function. (Cell Biology Monographs: Vol. 10). (Illus.). 344p. 1982. 79.00 (ISBN 0-387-81707-7). Springer-Verlag.

SIAMESE CAT

Naples, Marge. This Is the Siamese Cat. (Illus.). 1964. 12.95 (ISBN 0-87666-853-8, PS-617). TFH Pubns.
Nelson, Vera M. Siamese Cat Book. 5th ed. (Illus.). 1976. 9.95 (ISBN 0-87666-182-7, AP-4300). TFH Pubns.
Reagan, Ron. Siamese Cats. (Illus.). 127p. 1981. 4.95 (ISBN 0-87666-860-0, KW-062). TFH Pubns.
Van Der Meid, Louise B. Siamese Cats. (Orig.). pap. 2.95 (ISBN 0-87666-183-5, M-509). TFH Pubns.

SIBERIAN HUSKY

see Dogs–Breeds–Siberian Husky

SIDALCEA

Hitchcock, C. Leo & Kruckeberg, A. R. A Study of the Perennial Species of Sidalcea. LC 57-62501. (Publications in Biology Ser.: No. 18). (Illus.). 96p. 1957. pap. 10.00x (ISBN 0-295-73947-9). U of Wash Pr.

SIDEREAL SYSTEM

see Stars

SIGHT

see Vision

SIGNAL FLOWGRAPHS

see Flowgraphs

SIGNAL PROCESSING

Arbel, Arie F. Analog Signal Processing & Instrumentation. (Illus.). 246p. 1984. pap. 24.95 (ISBN 0-521-31866-1). Cambridge U Pr.
Beker, H. J. & Piper, F. C. Secure Speech Communications: A Monograph. (Microelectronics & Signal Processing Ser.). Date not set. 39.50 (ISBN 0-12-084780-9). Acad Pr.
Blahut, Richard E. Fast Algorithms for Digital Signal Processing. 1985. 41.95 (ISBN 0-201-10155-6). Addison-Wesley.
Candy, J. V. Signal Processing: Model Based Approach. 256p. 1986. price not set (ISBN 0-07-009725-9). McGraw.
Cappellini, V. & Constantinides, A. G., eds. Digital Signal Processing-84: Proceedings of the International Conference Held in Florence, Italy, 5-8 September 1984. 886p. 1985. 98.00 (ISBN 0-444-87583-2, North-Holland). Elsevier.
Chen. One Dimensional Digital Signal Processing. (Electrical Engineering & Electronics Ser.: Vol. 9). 1979. 39.75 (ISBN 0-8247-6877-9). Dekker.
Cowan, C. F. & Grant, P. M. Adaptive Filters. (Illus.). 368p. 1985. text ed. 41.95 (ISBN 0-13-004037-1). P-H.
Dudgeon, Dan E. & Mersereau, Russell M. Multidimensional Digital Signal Processing. (Illus.). 448p. 1984. professional 41.95 (ISBN 0-13-604959-1). P-H.
Gerbrands, Jan J., ed. EURASIP Directory 1983: Directory of European Signal Processing Research Institutions. LC 84-15892. 1984. lib. bdg. 59.00 (ISBN 90-277-1824-5, Pub. by Reidel Holland). Kluwer Academic.
Giordano, Arthur A. & Hsu, Frank M. Least Square Estimation with Applications to Digital Signal Processing. 416p. 1985. 44.90 (ISBN 0-471-87857-X, Pub. by Wiley-Interscience). Wiley.
Lynn, Paul A. Introduction to the Analysis & Processing Signals. 19.95 (ISBN 0-672-22253-1). Sams.
Morgan, D. P. Surface-Wave Devices for Signal Processing. (Studies in Electrical & Electronic Engineering Ser.: No. 19). 432p. 1985. 90.75 (ISBN 0-444-42511-X). Elsevier.
Oppenheim, A. Applications of Digital Signal Processing. LC 77-8547. 1978. 37.95 (ISBN 0-13-039115-8). P-H.
Oppenheim, Alan V. & Schafer, Ronald W. Digital Signal Processing. LC 74-17280. (Illus.). 608p. 1975. text ed. 38.95 (ISBN 0-13-214635-5). P-H.
Preston, K. & Onoe, M., eds. Digital Processing of Biomedical Images. LC 76-25538. 457p. 1976. 69.50x (ISBN 0-306-30967-X, Plenum Pr). Plenum Pub.
Quarmby, David. Signal Processor Chips. 192p. 1985. 22.95 (ISBN 0-13-809450-0); pap. 14.95 (ISBN 0-13-809443-8). P H.
Quarmby, David, ed. Signal Processor Chips. 210p. 1984. cancelled (ISBN 0-246-12171-8, Pub. by Granada England). Sheridan.
Rabiner, Lawrence R. & Rader, Charles N., eds. Digital Signal Processing. LC 72-90358. (Illus.). 1972. 17.10 (ISBN 0-87942-018-9, PP00182). Inst Electrical.
Rao, K. Ramamohan, ed. Discrete Transforms & Their Applications. (Benchmark Papers in Electrical Engineering & Computer Science). 368p. 1985. 49.95 (ISBN 0-442-27669-9). Van Nos Reinhold.
Saito, Shuzo & Nakata, Kazuo, eds. Fundamentals of Speech Signal Processing: Monograph. LC 83-9237. Date not set. 59.00 (ISBN 0-12-614880-5). Acad Pr.
Salazar, Andres C., ed. Digital Signal Computers & Processors. LC 77-82295. 1977. 43.65 (ISBN 0-87942-099-5, PC00968). Inst Electrical.
Schussler, H. W., ed. Signal Processing II - Theories & Applications: Proceedings of the EUSIPCO-83 Second European Signal Processing Conference. Erlangen, W. Germany, Sept. 12-16, 1983. 866p. 1984. 86.75 (ISBN 0-444-86743-0, North Holland). Elsevier.
Srinath, M. D. & Rajasekaran, P. K. An Introduction to Statistical Signal Processing with Applications. LC 78-15417. 499p. 1979. 49.95x (ISBN 0-471-04404-0, Pub. by Wiley-Interscience). Wiley.
Weinert, H. L., ed. Reproducing Kernel Hilbert Spaces: Applications in Statistical Signal Processing. LC 82-9332. (Benchmark Papers in Electrical Engineering & Computer Science: Vol. 25). 655p. 1982. 63.50 (ISBN 0-87933-434-7). Van Nos Reinhold.
Widrow, Bernard & Stearns, Samuel D. Adaptive Signal Processing. (Illus.). 528p. 1985. text ed. 42.95 (ISBN 0-13-004029-0). P-H.
Willsky, Alan S. Digital Signal Processing & Control & Estimation Theory: Points of Tangency, Areas of Intersection, & Parallel Directions. 1979. 37.50x (ISBN 0-262-23091-7). MIT Pr.
Young, Thomas V. Linear Systems & Digital Signal Processing. (Illus.). 400p. 1985. text ed. 37.95 (ISBN 0-13-537366-2). P-H.
Yuen, C. K. Microprocessor Systems & Their Application to Signal Processing. 1982. 49.50 (ISBN 0-12-774950-0). Acad Pr.
Yuen, C. K. & Fraser, D. Digital Spectral Analysis. (Applicable Mathematics Ser.). 168p. 1979. pap. text ed. 24.95 (ISBN 0-273-08439-9). Pitman Pub MA.

SIGNAL STORAGE TUBES

see Storage Tubes

SIGNAL THEORY (TELECOMMUNICATION)

see also Coding Theory; Electric Filters; Electronic Noise; Modulation (Electronics); Radio Waves; Waves; Signal Processing

Brown, Robert G. Introduction to Random Signal Analysis & Kalman Filtering. 416p. 1983. text ed. 36.00 (ISBN 0-471-08732-7). Wiley.
Chen, C. H. Nonlinear Maxium Entropy Spectral Analysis Methods for Signal Recognition. LC 82-8630. (Pattern Recognition & Image Processing Research Studies). 170p. 1982. 34.95 (ISBN 0-471-10497-3, Pub by Res Stud Pr). Wiley.
Chen, C. H., ed. Pattern Recognition & Signal Processing, No. 29. (NATO Advanced Study Institute Ser.). 666p. 1978. 46.00x (ISBN 90-286-0978-4). Sijthoff & Noordhoff.
Connor, F. R. Signals. (Introductory Topics in Electronics & Telecommunications Ser.). (Illus.). 1972. pap. text ed. 17.95x (ISBN 0-7131-3262-0). Intl Ideas.
Cruz, Jose B. & Van Valkenburg, M. E. Signals in Linear Circuits. 480p. 1974. text ed. 37.95 (ISBN 0-395-16971-2); instr's. manual 11.50 (ISBN 0-395-17838-X). HM.
Digital Signal Processing Committee, ed. Programs for Digital Signal Processing. LC 79-89028. 1979. 48.85 (ISBN 0-87942-127-4, PC01180); tape version 62.95 (ISBN 0-686-96748-8). Inst Electrical.
Folberth, D. G. & Grobman, W. D., eds. VLSI-Technology & Design. LC 84-15848. 1984. 41.95 (ISBN 0-87942-180-0, PC01743). Inst Electrical.
Franks, L. E., ed. Data Communication: Fundamentals of Baseband Transmission. LC 74-12338. (Benchmark Papers in Electrical Engineering & Computer Science Ser: Vol. 9). 1975. 64.50 (ISBN 0-12-786480-6). Acad Pr.
Frederick, Dean K. & Carlson, A. Bruce. Linear Systems in Communication & Control. LC 71-155118. 575p. 1971. 46.50x (ISBN 0-471-27721-5). Wiley.
Gerlach, Albert A. Theory & Applications of Statistical Wave-Period Processing, 3 Vols. 1434p. 1970. 352.50 (ISBN 0-677-02510-6). Gordon.
Gibson, Jerry D. & Melsa, James L. Introduction to Nonparametric Detection with Applications. (Mathematics in Science & Engineering Ser.). 1975. 70.00 (ISBN 0-12-282150-5). Acad Pr.
Good, I. S. & Osteyee, D. B. Information Weight of Evidence, the Singularity Between Probability Measures & Signal Detection. LC 74-393. (Lecture Notes in Mathematics: Vol. 376). xi, 156p. 1974. pap. 12.00 (ISBN 0-387-06726-4). Springer-Verlag.
Haykin, Simon. Communication Systems. 2nd ed. (Management Ser.). 653p. 1983. 42.50 (ISBN 0-471-09691-1); solution manual avail. (ISBN 0-471-87155-9). Wiley.
Haykin, Simon, et al. Array Signal Processing. (Illus.). 432p. 1984. text ed. 43.95 (ISBN 0-13-046482-1). P-H.
Jayant, N. S. & Noll, P. Digital Coding of Waveforms: Principles & Applications to Speech & Video. (Illus.). 688p. 1984. text ed. 41.95 (ISBN 0-13-211913-7). P-H.
McClellen, Joseph H. & Rader, Charles M. Number Theory in Digital Signal Processing. (Signal Processing Ser.). (Illus.). 1979. ref. 38.95 (ISBN 0-13-627349-1). P-H.
Mitra, S. K. & Ekstrom, M. P., eds. Two-Dimensional Digital Signal Processing. LC 77-25337. (Benchmark Papers in Electrical Engineering & Computer Science: Vol. 20). 400p. 1978. 56.50 (ISBN 0-87933-320-0). Van Nos Reinhold.
Oppenheim, Alan V. & Schafer, Ronald W. Digital Signal Processing. LC 74-17280. (Illus.). 608p. 1975. text ed. 38.95 (ISBN 0-13-214635-5). P-H.
Oppenheim, Alan V., et al. Signals & Systems. (Illus.). 464p. 1982. 38.95 (ISBN 0-13-809731-3). P-H.
Patrick, E. A. & Costello, J. P. Unsupervised Estimation & Processing of Unknown Signals. LC 71-136727. 207p. 1970. 19.00 (ISBN 0-403-04528-2). Scholarly.
Rabiner, Lawrence R. & Gold, Bernard. Theory & Application of Digital Signal Processing. (Illus.). 720p. 1975. ref. ed. 38.95 (ISBN 0-13-914101-4). P-H.
Su, Kendall L. A Collection of Solved Problems in Circuits, Electronics, & Signal Analysis, Vol. 1. 96p. 1980. pap. text ed. 7.95 (ISBN 0-8403-2262-3). Kendall-Hunt.
--A Collection of Solved Problems in Circuits, Electronics & Signal Analysis, Vol. 2. 96p. 1981. pap. text ed. 7.50 (ISBN 0-8403-2486-3). Kendall-Hunt.
Tzafestas, Spyros G., ed. Walsh Functions in Signal & Systems Analysis & Design. (Illus.). 368p. 1985. 59.50 (ISBN 0-442-28298-2). Van Nos Reinhold.
Urkowitz, Harry. Signal Theory & Random Processes. LC 83-70360. (Radar Ser.). (Illus.). 750p. 1983. 72.00 (ISBN 0-89006-121-1). Artech Hse.
VanTrees, Harry L. Detection, Estimation & Modulation Theory, 2 pts. Incl. Pt. 1. Detection, Estimation & Linear Modulation Theory. 697p. 1968. 55.50x (ISBN 0-471-89955-0); Pt. 3. Radar-Sonar Signal Processing & Gaussian Signals in Noise. 626p. 1971. 75.00 (ISBN 0-471-89958-5). LC 67-23331. (Illus.). Wiley.
VLSI Technical Committee Staff. VLSI-Signal Processing. LC 84-82077. 1984. 37.50 (ISBN 0-87942-186-X, PC01800). Inst Electrical.
VSLI Signal Processing. LC 84-82077. 1984. 37.50 (ISBN 0-87942-186-X, PC01800). Inst Electrical.
Whalen, A. D. Detection of Signals in Noise. (Electrical Science Ser.). 1971. 55.00 (ISBN 0-12-744850-0). Acad Pr.
Wilmhurst, T. H. Signal Recovery from Noise in Electronic Instrumentation. (0852747837). 200p. 1985. 32.00 (ISBN 0-9903003-2-3, Pub. by A Hilger England). Heyden.

SIGNALS (INFORMATION THEORY)

see Information Measurement

Arbel, Arie F. Analog Signal Processing & Instrumentation. LC 79-13461. (Illus.). 1980. 87.50 (ISBN 0-521-22469-1). Cambridge U Pr.

SIGNALS AND SIGNALING

see also Military Fireworks; Morse Code; Railroads–Signaling; Sonar

Bellanger, Maurice G. Digital Processing of Signals: Theory & Practice. McMullan, Jean, tr. 336p. 1984. text ed. 49.95x (ISBN 0-471-90318-3, Pub. by Wiley-Interscience). Wiley.
Bjorno, L., ed. Underwater Acoustics & Signal Processing. 1981. 87.00 (ISBN 90-277-1255-7, Pub. by Reidel Holland). Kluwer Academic.
Cappelini, V. & Constantinides, A. G., eds. Digital Signal Processing. 1980. 59.50 (ISBN 0-12-159080-1). Acad Pr.
Carrington, John F. Talking Drums of Africa. LC 70-77195. (Illus.). Repr. of 1949 ed. 19.75 (ISBN 0-8371-1292-3, CDA&, Pub. by Negro U Pr). Greenwood.

Chen, C. H. Seismic Signal Analysis & Discrimination. (Methods in Geochemistry & Geophysics: Vol. 17). 196p. 1983. 53.25 (ISBN 0-444-42136-X). Elsevier.
Chen, C. H., ed. Digital Waveform Processing & Recognition. 224p. 1982. 68.00 (ISBN 0-8493-5777-2). CRC Pr.
Connor, F. R. Signals. 2nd ed. (Introductory Topics in Electronics & Telecommunication). 144p. 1982. pap. text ed. 9.95 (ISBN 0-7131-3458-5). E Arnold.
Friedman, David H. Detection of Signals by Template Matching. LC 78-79301. pap. 20.00 (ISBN 0-317-08131-4, 2003861). Bks Demand UMI.
Report of the Chief Signal Officer, U. S. Signal Corps. LC 74-4671. (Illus.). 544p. 1974. Repr. of 1920 ed. 35.00x (ISBN 0-405-06037-8). Ayer Co Pubs.
Rudman, Jack. Assistant Signal Circuit Engineer. (Career Examination Ser.: C-47). (Cloth bdg. avail. on request). pap. 12.00 (ISBN 0-8373-0047-9). Natl Learning.
--Signal Electrician. (Career Examination Ser.: C-2440). (Cloth bdg. avail. on request). pap. 12.00 (ISBN 0-686-53555-3). Natl Learning.
--Signal Maintainer. (Career Examination Ser.: C-742). (Cloth bdg. avail. on request). pap. 12.00 (ISBN 0-8373-0742-2). Natl Learning.
Russell, J. Sea Signalling Simplified. (Illus.). 84p. 1973. 9.95x (ISBN 0-8464-0826-0). Beekman Pubs.
Russell, P. J. Sea Signalling Simplified. rev. ed. 1977. 5.95 (ISBN 0-8286-0072-4). J De Graff.
Scheips, Paul J. & Sterling, Christopher, eds. Military Signal Communications: An Original Anthology, 2 vols. LC 80-483. (Historical Studies in Telecommunications Ser.). (Illus.). 1980. Set. lib. bdg. 71.50x (ISBN 0-405-13193-3). Ayer Co Pubs.
Travers, Donald J. Precision Signal Handling & Converter-Microprocessor Interface: A Tutorial Presentation. 90p. 1984. pap. text ed. 29.95x (ISBN 0-87664-803-0). Instru Soc.
United States Commission to Consider the Present, Organizations of the Signal Service, Geological Survey, Coast, & Geodetic Survey, & Hydrographic Office. Testimony Before the Joint Commission to Consider the Present Organizations of the Signal Service, Geological Survey, Coast & Geodetic Survey, & the Hydrographic Office of the Navy Department: With a View to Secure Greater Efficiency, Vol. 1. 49.00 (ISBN 0-405-12518-6). Ayer Co Pubs.
Woods, David L. A History of Tactical Communications Techniques. LC 74-4700. (Telecommunications Ser). (Illus.). 310p. 1974. 27.00x (ISBN 0-405-06063-7). Ayer Co Pubs.
Woods, David L. & Sterling, Christopher, eds. Signaling & Communicating at Sea: An Original Anthology. LC 80-484. (Historical Studies in Telecommunications Ser.). (Illus.). 1981. lib. bdg. 73.00x (ISBN 0-405-13195-X). Ayer Co Pubs.
Ziemer, Rodger, et al. Signals & Systems: Continuous & Discrete. 1st ed. 624p. 1983. write for info. (ISBN 0-02-431650-4). Macmillan.

SILANE

Lutwack, Ralph & Morrison, Andrew, eds. Silicon Material Preparation & Economical Wafering Methods. LC 84-5968. (Illus.). 586p. 1984. 54.00 (ISBN 0-8155-0990-1). Noyes.
Plueddemann, Edwin P., ed. Silane Coupling Agents. LC 82-9791. 244p. 1982. 39.50x (ISBN 0-306-40957-7, Plenum Pr). Plenum Pub.

SILICA

see also Quartz

Dunnom, D., ed. Health Effects of Synthetic Silica Particulates-STP 732. 223p. 1981. 24.00 (ISBN 0-8031-0734-X, 04-732000-17). ASTM.
Iler, Ralph K. The Chemistry of Silica: Solubility, Polymerization, Colloid & Surface Properties & Biochemistry. LC 78-23960. 866p. 1979. 115.00 (ISBN 0-471-02404-X, Pub. by Wiley-Interscience). Wiley.
--The Colloid Chemistry of Silica & Silicates. LC 55-1415. pap. 83.80 (ISBN 0-317-09823-3, 2000877). Bks Demand UMI.
Primak, W. The Compacted States of Vitreous Silica. (Studies in Radiation Effects in Solids: Vol. 4). 202p. 1975. 53.50x (ISBN 0-677-03340-0). Gordon.
Sosman, Robert B. The Phases of Silica. LC 65-19405. pap. 100.00 (ISBN 0-317-10761-5, 2050311). Bks Demand UMI.

SILICATES

see also Fullers Earth

Applied Technical Dictionary: Silicate Technology. (Eng., Ger., Fr. & Slovak.). 50.00x (ISBN 0-569-08557-8, Pub. by Collets). State Mutual Bk.
ASTM Committees D-22 & E-34. Definitions for Asbestos & Other Health-Related Silicates - STP 834. Levadie, Benjamin, ed. LC 83-72557. (Illus.). 205p. 1984. pap. text ed. 30.00 (ISBN 0-8031-0209-7, 04-834000-17). ASTM.
Babcock, Clarence L. Silicate Glass Technology Methods. LC 76-30716. (Wiley Series in Pure & Applied Optics). pap. 84.00 (ISBN 0-317-28068-6, 2055768). Bks Demand UMI.
Babushkin, V. I., et al. Thermodynamics of Silicates. Frenkel, B. N. & Terentyev, V. A., trs. from Rus. (Eng., Illus.). 470p. 1985. 98.00 (ISBN 0-387-12750-X). Springer Verlag.
Belov, Nikolai V. Crystal Chemistry of Large-Cation Silicates. LC 63-17642. pap. 42.00 (ISBN 0-317-08935-8, 2003357). Bks Demand UMI.
Bennett, H. & Reed, R. A. Chemical Methods of Silicate Analysis. 1981. 55.00x (Pub. by Brit Ceramic Soc England). State Mutual Bk.
--Chemical Methods of Silicate Analysis: A Handbook. 1972. 47.50 (ISBN 0-12-088740-1). Acad Pr.
Borg, I. Y. & Smith, D. K. Calculated X-Ray Powder Patterns for Silicate Minerals. LC 72-110814. (Geological Society of America Memoir Ser.: No. 122). pap. 160.00 (ISBN 0-317-28991-8, 2023730). Bks Demand UMI.
Eitel, Wilhelm. Silicate Melt Equilibria. Philips, J. G. & Madgwick, T. G., trs. from Ger. LC 51-62230. pap. 31.50 (ISBN 0-317-11176-0, 2050514). Bks Demand UMI.
--Thermochemical Methods in Silicate Investigation. LC 52-3556. pap. 35.00 (ISBN 0-317-08719-3, 2050515). Bks Demand UMI.
Eitel, Wilhelm, ed. Silicate Science: A Treatise, 5 vols. Incl. Vol. 1. Silicate Structures. 1964 (ISBN 0-12-236301-9); Vol. 2. Glasses, Enamels, Slags. 1964 (ISBN 0-12-236302-7); Vol. 3. Dry Silicate Systems. 1966 (ISBN 0-12-236303-5); Vol. 4. Hydrothermal Silical Systems. 1966 (ISBN 0-12-236304-3); Vol. 5. Ceramics & Hydraulic Binders. 1966 (ISBN 0-12-236305-1). 99.00 ea. Acad Pr.
Falcone, James S., Jr., ed. Soluble Silicates. LC 82-115114. (ACS Symposium Ser.: No. 194). 1982. 39.95 (ISBN 0-8412-0730-5). Am Chemical.
Iler, Ralph K. The Chemistry of Silica: Solubility, Polymerization, Colloid & Surface Properties & Biochemistry. LC 78-23960. 866p. 1979. 115.00 (ISBN 0-471-02404-X, Pub. by Wiley-Interscience). Wiley.
--The Colloid Chemistry of Silica & Silicates. LC 55-1415. pap. 83.80 (ISBN 0-317-09823-3, 2000877). Bks Demand UMI.
Lazarev, A. N. Vibrational Spectra & Structure of Silicates. LC 70-136984. 239p. 1972. 42.50x (ISBN 0-306-10856-9, Consultants). Plenum Pub.
Studies in Standard Samples of Silicate Rocks & Minerals: Edition of Usable Values, Pt. 4. 1974. pap. 3.70 (SSC77, SSC). Unipub.
Toropov, N. A. & Barzakovskii, V. P. High-Temperature Chemistry of Silicates & Other Oxide Systems. LC 65-25264. 216p. 1966. 34.50x (ISBN 0-306-10749-X, Consultants). Plenum Pub.

SILICIDES

Aronsson, Bertil & Lundstrohm, Torsten. Borides, Silicides, & Phosphides: A Critical Review of Their Preparation, Properties & Crystal Chemistry. LC 65-8351. pap. 34.50 (ISBN 0-317-08693-6, 2013149). Bks Demand UMI.
Murarka, S. P, ed. Silicides for VLSI Applications. 1983. 21.50 (ISBN 0-12-511220-3). Acad Pr.

SILICON

see also Silica

Aston, S. R. Silicon Geochemistry & Biogeochemistry. 1983. 44.50 (ISBN 0-12-065620-5). Acad Pr.
Beadle, W. E., et al. Quick Reference Manual for Silicon Integrated Circuit Technology. 736p. 1985. 65.00 (ISBN 0-471-81588-8). Wiley.
Bendz, G. & Lindqvist, I., eds. Biochemistry of Silicon & Related Problems. LC 77-29160. 603p. 1978. 75.00x (ISBN 0-306-33710-X, Plenum Pr). Plenum Pub.
Bereshnoi, A. S. Silicon & Its Binary Systems. 283p. 1960. 25.00x (ISBN 0-306-10602-7, Consultants). Plenum Pub.
Boschke, F., ed. Silicon Chemistry One. LC 51-5497. (Topics in Current Chemistry: Vol. 50). (Illus.). 180p. 1974. 33.00 (ISBN 0-387-06714-0). Springer-Verlag.
--Silicon Chemistry Two. LC 51-5497. (Topics in Current Chemistry Ser.: Vol. 51). (Illus.). 140p. 1974. 30.00 (ISBN 0-387-06722-1). Springer-Verlag.
Colvin, Ernest W. Silicon in Organic Synthesis. LC 85-19. 360p. 1985. Repr. of 1981 ed. lib. bdg. write for info. (ISBN 0-89874-843-7). Krieger.
Freyhardt, H. C., ed. Silicon-Chemical Etching. (Crystals-Growth, Properties & Applications Ser.: Vol. 8). (Illus.). 255p. 1982. 57.00 (ISBN 0-387-11862-4). Springer-Verlag.
Grabmaier, J., ed. Silicon. (Crystals-Growth, Properties, & Applications Ser.: Vol. 5). (Illus.). 215p. 1981. 57.00 (ISBN 0-387-10932-3). Springer-Verlag.
Guldberg, Jens, ed. Silicon. LC 81-7305. 515p. 1981. 75.00x (ISBN 0-306-40738-8, Plenum Pr). Plenum Pub.
Gupta, D. C., ed. Silicon Processing- STP 804. LC 82-83529. 559p. 1983. text ed. 60.00 (ISBN 0-8031-0243-7, 04-804000-46). ASTM.
International Symposium on Silicon Materials, Science & Technology (2d: 1973: Chicago) Semiconductor Silicon: 1973 International Symposium. Huff, Howard R. & Burgess, Ronald R., eds. (Illus.). pap. 160.00 (ISBN 0-317-08778-9, 2051088). Bks Demand UMI.
Joannopoulos, J. D. & Lucovsky, G., eds. The Physics of Hydrogenated Amorphous Silicon I. (Topics in Applied Physics: Vol. 55). (Illus.). 320p. 1984. 47.50 (ISBN 0-387-12807-7). Springer Verlag.
Keller & Mulbauer. Floating Zone Silicon. (Preparation & Properties of Solid State Materials Ser.: Vol. 5). 256p. 1981. 49.75 (ISBN 0-8247-1167-X). Dekker.
Kintzinger, J. P. & Marsmann, H. Oxygen-Seventeen & Silicon-Twenty-Nine. (NMR-Basic Principles & Progress Ser.: Vol. 17). (Illus.). 235p. 1981. 50.00 (ISBN 0-387-10414-3). Springer-Verlag.
Lifetime Factors in Silicon- STP 712. 258p. 1980. 23.50x (ISBN 0-8031-0390-5, 04-712000-46). ASTM.
Lutwack, Ralph & Morrison, Andrew, eds. Silicon Material Preparation & Economical Wafering Methods. LC 84-5968. (Illus.). 586p. 1984. 54.00 (ISBN 0-8155-0990-1). Noyes.
Ravi, K. V. Imperfections & Impurities in Semiconductor Silicon. LC 80-21978. 379p. 1981. 54.50x (ISBN 0-471-07817-4, Pub. by Wiley-Interscience). Wiley.
Renmore, C. D. Silicon Chips: The Magical Mineral in Your Telephone, Calculator, Toys, Automobile, Hospital, Air Conditioning, Factory, Furnace, Sewing Machine, & Countless Other Future Inventions. LC 80-24153. (Illus.). 160p. 1980. 8.95 (ISBN 0-8253-0022-3). Beaufort Bks NY.
Simpson, T. L. & Yolcani, B. E., eds. Silicon & Siliceous Structures in Biological Systems. (Illus.). 587p. 1981. 120.00 (ISBN 0-387-90592-8). Springer-Verlag.
Thompson, M. J., et al, eds. Materials Issues in Applications of Amorphous Silicon Technology, Vol. 49. 1985. text ed. 42.00 (ISBN 0-931837-14-6). Materials Res.
Wang, F. F., ed. Impurity Doping Processes in Silicon. (Materials Processing, Theory & Practices: Vol. 2). 644p. 1981. 123.50 (ISBN 0-444-86095-9, North-Holland). Elsevier.

SILICON CARBIDE

Conference on Silicon Carbide, 3rd, 1973. Silicon Carbide: Proceedings. Marshall, R. C. & Faust, John W., Jr., eds. LC 74-2394. (Illus.). 692p. 1974. 29.95x (ISBN 0-87249-315-6). U of SC Pr.
Frantsevich, I. N. Silicon Carbide. LC 69-12512. 276p. 1970. 40.00x (ISBN 0-306-10838-0, Consultants). Plenum Pub.

SILICON COMPOUNDS

see also Organosilicon Compounds

Joannopoulos, J. D. & Lucovsky, G., eds. The Physics of Hydrogenated Amorphous Silicon II. (Topics in Applied Physics Ser.: No. 56). (Illus.). 385p. 1984. 47.50 (ISBN 0-387-12808-5). Springer-Verlag.
Voronkov, M. G., et al. The Siloxane Bond: Physical Properties & Chemical Transformations. LC 78-16675. (Studies in Soviet Science--Physical Sciences Ser.). (Illus.). 505p. 1978. 85.00 (ISBN 0-306-10940-9, Consultants). Plenum Pub.

SILICON ORGANIC COMPOUNDS

see Organosilicon Compounds

SILICONES

Zvyagin, B. B. Electron-Diffraction Analysis of Clay Mineral Structures. LC 65-17783. (Monographs in Geoscience Ser.). 264p. 1967. 42.50x (ISBN 0-306-30273-X, Plenum Pr). Plenum Pub.

SILK

see also Brocade; Rayon

Adams, Carol, et al. Under Control: Life in a Nineteenth Century Silk Factory. LC 83-7500. (Women in History Ser.). 1984. pap. 3.95 (ISBN 0-521-27481-8). Cambridge U pr.
Folk Silkwork Making: Ming, Quig Dynasties. Date not set. price not set (ISBN 0-442-20081-1). Sci Pr.
Jolly, M. S., et al. Non-Mulberry Silks. (Agricultural Services Bulletins: No. 29). 195p. 1979. pap. 12.75 (ISBN 92-5-100347-5, F1856, FAO). Unipub.

SILK, ARTIFICIAL

see Rayon

SILK MANUFACTURE AND TRADE

Kolander, Cheryl. A Silk Worker's Notebook. (Illus.). 168p. 1985. 12.00 (ISBN 0-317-28727-3). Interweave.
May, Florence L. Silk Textiles of Spain: Eighth to Fifteenth Century. (Illus.). 1957. 14.00 (ISBN 0-87535-092-5). Hispanic Soc.

SILKWORMS

Crotch, W. J. A Silkmoth Rearer's Handbook. 165p. 1969. 90.00x (ISBN 0-686-75578-2, Pub. by Amateur Entomol Soc). State Mutual Bk.
The Development & Diffusion of Improved Hybrid Silkworms in Japan: The First Filial Generation. 56p. 1982. pap. 5.00 (ISBN 92-808-0253-4, TUNU177, UNU). Unipub.
Egerton, Frank N., 3rd, ed. Phytopathologlical Classics of the Nineteenth Century: An Original Anthology. LC 77-74246. (History of Ecology Ser.). (Illus.). 1978. lib. bdg. 34.50x (ISBN 0-405-10415-4). Ayer Co Pubs.
Silkworm in Ancient China. Date not set. price not set (ISBN 0-442-20083-8). Sci Pr.

SILLIMAN, BENJAMIN, 1770-1864

Wilson, Leonard G., ed. Benjamin Silliman & His Circle. 1979. 20.00 (ISBN 0-88202-173-7). Watson Pub Intl.

SILOS

Ghali, A. Circular Storage Tanks & Silos. LC 79-12406. 210p. 1979. 37.00x (ISBN 0-419-11500-5, NO.6121, Pub. by E & FN Spon England). Methuen Inc.
Reimbert, M. & Reimbert, A. Silos. (Bulk Materials Handling Ser). (Illus.). 400p. 1976. text ed. 60.00 (ISBN 0-87849-014-0). Trans Tech.

SILT

see Sedimentation and Deposition

SILUNDUM

see Silicon Carbide

SILURIAN PERIOD

see Geology, Stratigraphic–Silurian

SILURIAN PERIOD, LOWER

see Geology, Stratigraphic–Ordovician

SILVER

see also Silver Mines and Mining; Silverwork

Branson, O. T. What You Need to Know about Your Gold & Silver. (Illus.). 56p. (Orig.). 1980. pap. 4.95 (ISBN 0-918080-44-4). Treasure Chest.
Fuerstenau, Maurice C. & Palmer, R. B., eds. Gold, Silver, Uranium & Coal - Geology, Mining, Extraction, & Environment. LC 82-73914. (Illus.). 526p. 1983. pap. text ed. 40.00x (ISBN 0-89520-406-1, 406-1). Soc Mining Eng.
Jastram, Roy W. Silver: The Restless Metal. LC 80-28361. 224p. 1981. 37.50x (ISBN 0-471-03912-8, Pub. by Wiley-Interscience). Wiley.
Kolisko, Eugen & Kolisko, Lily. Silver & Its Connection with the Human Organism. 1978. pap. 3.95x (ISBN 0-906492-10-6, Pub by Kolisko Archives). St George Bk Serv.
Merton, Henry A. Your Gold & Silver: An Easy Guide to Appraising Household Objects, Coins, Heirlooms & Jewelry. (Illus.). 96p. 1981. pap. 5.95 (ISBN 0-02-077410-9, Collier). Macmillan.
Recycling Research Division Staff. Silver Recycling: A Correspondence Course. 10p. 1984. pap. text ed. 11.95 (ISBN 0-318-01189-1, Pub. by Recycling Consort). Prosperity & Profits.

SILVER FOX

see Foxes

SILVER MINES AND MINING

see also Prospecting

Bakewell, P. J. Silver Mining & Society in Colonial Mexico, Zacatecas, 1546-1700. LC 78-158553. (American Latin Studies: No. 15). (Illus.). 1972. 49.50 (ISBN 0-521-08227-7). Cambridge U Pr.
A History of the Comstock Silver Lode & Mines. LC 73-92646. 6.95 (ISBN 0-88394-024-8). Brown Bk.
Moen, Wayne S. Silver Occurrences of Washington. (Bulletin Ser.: No. 69). (Illus.). 188p. 1976. 4.00 (ISBN 0-686-38464-4). Geologic Pubns.
Motten, C. J. Mexican Silver & the Enlightenment. LC 72-120650. 1970. Repr. lib. bdg. 14.00x (ISBN 0-374-95970-6). Octagon.
North American Silver Deposits. LC 83-63353. 1984. 75.50 (ISBN 0-942218-21-3). Minobras.
Schlitt, W. J. & Larson, W. C., eds. Gold & Silver Leaching, Recovery & Economics. LC 81-68558. (Illus.). 148p. 1981. text ed. 20.00x (ISBN 0-89520-289-1). Soc Mining Eng.
Von Mueller, Karl. Silver Refiners Handbook. (Placer Miner's Manual Ser.: Vol. 4). 1984. write for info. (ISBN 0-89316-627-8). Exanimo Pr.

SILVERSMITHING

see Silverwork

SILVERWORK

see also Jewelry; Jewelry Making

Abbey, S. Goldsmith's & Silversmith's Handbook. 2nd rev. ed. (Illus.). 1968. 17.50 (ISBN 0-685-12021-X). Heinman.
Adair, John. Navajo & Pueblo Silversmiths. (Civilization of the American Indian Ser.: No. 25). (Illus.). 1975. Repr. of 1944 ed. 14.95 (ISBN 0-8061-0133-4). U of Okla Pr.
Bovin, Murray. Silversmithing & Art Metal for Schools, Tradesmen, Craftsmen. LC 64-2766. (Illus.). 1977. 16.50 (ISBN 0-910280-04-5); pap. 12.95 (ISBN 0-910280-03-7). Bovin.
Chickering, Elenita C. Arthur J. Stone: Handwrought Silver, 1901-1937. LC 81-68101. (Illus.). 24p. (Orig.). 25.00 (ISBN 0-934552-37-1). Boston Athenaeum.

Choate, Sharr & De May, Bonnie C. Creative Gold & Silversmithing: Jewelry, Decorative Metalcraft. (Arts & Crafts Ser). (Illus.). 1970. pap. 8.95 (ISBN 0-517-52413-9). Crown.
Glover, Elizabeth. The Gold & Silver Wyre-Drawers. (Illus.). 91p. 1979. 47.50x (ISBN 0-8476-3144-3). Rowman.
--The Gold & Silver Wyre-Drawers. 1979. 65.00x (ISBN 0-686-97113-2, Pub. by Phillimore England). State Mutual Bk.
Hawley, Ruth. Omani Silver. LC 77-20799. (Illus.). 1977. pap. text ed. 7.50x (ISBN 0-582-78070-5). Longman.
Hayward, J. F. The Courtauld Silver: An Introduction to the Work of the Courtauld Family of Goldsmiths. (Illus.). 64p. 1975. 22.50x (ISBN 0-85667-018-9, Pub. by Sotheby Pubns England). Biblio Dist.
Kramer, Karl & Kramer, Nora. Coppercraft & Silver Made at Home. 1971. pap. 5.95 (ISBN 0-486-22790-1). Dover.
Loyen, Frances. The Thames & Hudson Manual of Silversmithing: The Constructional Processes. (Illus.). 1980. pap. 10.95 (ISBN 0-500-68021-3). Thames Hudson.
Maryon, Herbert. Metalwork & Enamelling: A Practical Treatise on Gold & Silversmiths' Work & Their Allied Crafts. LC 76-130881. lib. bdg. 13.50x (ISBN 0-88307-195-9). Gannon.
Newell, Edward T. Standard Ptolemaic Silver. LC 80-70056. (Illus.). 1981. Repr. of 1900 ed. softcovered 6.00 (ISBN 0-915262-49-5); supplement incl. S J Durst.
Renwick Gallery. Georg Jensen Silversmithy: Seventy-Seven Artists, Seventy-Five Years. LC 79-607160. (Illus.). 128p. 1980. 20.00x (ISBN 0-87474-800-3); pap. 9.95 (ISBN 0-87474-801-1). Smithsonian.
Seitz & Finegold. Silversmithing (FET) LC 82-70657. 480p. 1983. 35.00 (ISBN 0-8019-7232-9). Chilton.
White, Benjamin. Silver: Its History & Romance. LC 71-174144. (Illus.). xxviii, 325p. 1972. Repr. of 1920 ed. 48.00x (ISBN 0-8103-3930-7). Gale.
Wright, Margaret. Hopi Silver: A Brief History of Hopi Silversmithing. LC 72-76377. (Illus.). 120p. 1973. pap. 8.95 (ISBN 0-87358-097-4). Northland.

SIMPLIFICATION OF WORK
see Methods Engineering

SIMSCRIPT (COMPUTER PROGRAM LANGUAGE)
Pritsker, A. Alan & Rolston, Laurie J. Introduction to Simulation & Slam II, Solutions Manual. 2nd ed. (Illus.). 257p. 1981. 40.00 (ISBN 0-938974-00-9). Systems Pub.
Pritsker, Alan A. Introduction to Simulation & Slam II. 2nd ed. LC 84-9104. 612p. 1984. text ed. 29.50x (ISBN 0-470-20087-1). Halsted Pr.

SIMULA (COMPUTER PROGRAM LANGUAGE)
see also ALGOL (Computer Program Language)
Lamprecht, G. Introduction to Simula 67. 1983. 19.50 (ISBN 0-9940017-2-X, Pub. by Vieweg & Sohn Germany). Heyden.

SIMULATION METHODS
see also Artificial Intelligence; Bionics; Electromechanical Analogies; Mathematical Models; Mathematical Optimization; SIMSCRIPT (Computer Program Language)
Ameling, W., ed. First European Simulation Congress: ESC 83. (Informatik-Fachberichte Ser.: Vol. 71). 653p. 1983. pap. 27.60 (ISBN 0-387-12723-2). Springer Verlag.
Amico, et al. All about Simulation, Ninteen Eighty-Four, Vol. 14. (Norfolk Ser.: No. 1). 30.00 (ISBN 0-317-17124-0). Soc Computer Sim.
Ashour, Said, et al, eds. Computer Simulation in Design Applications. (SCS Simulation Ser.: Vol. 3, No. 1). 1976. 30.00 (ISBN 0-686-36662-X). Soc Computer Sim.
Bain. Statistical Analysis of Reliability & Life Testing Models. (Statistics; Textbooks & Monographs Ser.: Vol. 24). 1978. 49.75 (ISBN 0-8247-6665-2). Dekker.
Bekiroglu, Haluk, ed. Computer Models for Production & Inventory Control, Vol. 12 No. 2. 1984. 30.00 (ISBN 0-318-01063-1). Soc Computer Sim.
--Simulation in Inventory & Production Control. 63p. 1983. softbound 20.00 (ISBN 0-686-42972-9). Soc Computer Sim.
Bernard, James E. An Overview of Simulation in Highway Transportation, Vol. 7. 1977. two book set 30.00 (ISBN 0-318-01053-4). Soc Computer Sim.
Bernard, James E., ed. An Overview of Simulation in Highway Transportation, 2 vols, Pts. 1 & 2. (SCS Simulation Ser.: Vol. 7, Nos. 1 & 2). Set. 30.00 (ISBN 0-686-36672-7). Soc Computer Sim.
Boocock, Sarane S. & Schild, E. O., eds. Simulation Games in Learning. LC 68-21913. 279p. 1978. pap. 14.95 (ISBN 0-8039-1002-9). Sage.
Bryant, Ry & Vaget, Brian W., eds. Simulation in Strongly Typed Languages: Ada, Pascal, Simula... (SCS Simulation Ser.: Vol. 13, No. 2). 1984. 30.00 (ISBN 0-317-05019-2). Soc Computer Sim.
Burden, Ernest. Design Simulation: Use of Photographic & Electronic Media in Design & Presentation. 232p. 1985. text ed. 37.50 (ISBN 0-471-79977-7, Pub. by Wiley-Interscience). Wiley.
Caldwell, D. K. & Gohring, eds. Progress in Simulation, 2 vols. 1972. Vol. 1,382. 106.50 (ISBN 0-677-14890-9); Vol. 2, 380. 101.25 (ISBN 0-677-12490-2). Gordon.
Carroll, John, ed. Computer Simulation in Emergency Planning. (Simulation Series: Vol. 11, No. 2). 1983. 30.00 (ISBN 0-686-38791-0). Soc Computer Sim.
Cash, Kathy. Designing & Using Simulations for Training. (Technical Note Ser.: No. 20). 34p. (Orig.). 1982. pap. 1.50 (ISBN 0-932288-66-9). Ctr Intl Ed U of MA.
Coleman, Thomas G., ed. Computer Simulation of Physiological Systems. 40p. pap. 10.00 (ISBN 0-686-36684-0). Soc Computer Sim.
Computer Models & Application of the Sterile-Male Technique. (Panel Proceedings Ser.). (Illus.). 195p. (Orig.). 1973. pap. 18.00 (ISBN 92-0-111573-3, ISP340, IAEA). Unipub.
Dekker, L. & Savastano, G., eds. Simulation of Systems, 1979. 1170p. 1980. 138.50 (ISBN 0-444-86123-8, North-Holland). Elsevier.
Dent, J. B. & Blackie, M. J. Systems Simulation in Agriculture. (Illus.). 180p. 1979. 31.50 (ISBN 0-85334-827-8, Pub. by Elsevier Applied Sci England). Elsevier.
De Sola Pool, Ithiel, et al. Candidates, Issues & Strategies: A Computer Simulation of the 1960 & 1964 Presidential Elections. 2nd rev. ed. 1965. pap. 5.95x (ISBN 0-262-66003-2). MIT Pr.
Dietzler, Andrew J. Time Sharing Task Control for a Hybrid Computer Simulation Laboratory. LC 75-128003. 172p. 1969. 19.00 (ISBN 0-403-04494-4). Scholarly.
Giloi, W. K. Principles of Continuous System Simulation. (Illus.). 1976. pap. 19.50x (ISBN 3-5190-2336-9). Adlers Foreign Bks.
Gray, Lynton & Waitt, Ian, eds. Perspectives on Academic Gaming & Simulation: Simulation in Management & Business Education, No. 7. 160p. 1982. 35.00 (ISBN 0-89397-139-1). Nichols Pub.
Greenlaw, P. S. & Hottenstein, M. P. Prosim: A Production Management Simulation. 1969. pap. text ed. 14.50 scp (ISBN 0-7002-2224-3, HarpC); instructor's manual avail. (ISBN 0-06-362455-9); scp 360 computer deck 45.95 (ISBN 0-352-07309-8); scp 700-7000 computer deck 23.50 (ISBN 0-352-07310-1). Har-Row.
Gruver, W. A. Simulation & Identification in Biological Science. 160p. 1985. Repr. lib. bdg. 19.95x (ISBN 0-89370-892-5). Borgo Pr.
Heller, M. R., et al. Maritime Simulation. (Illus.). xii, 290p. 1985. 29.50 (ISBN 0-387-15620-8). Springer-Verlag.
Highland, Harold, ed. Winter Simulation Conference Proceedings, 1982. 650p. 1982. 48.00 (ISBN 0-686-38789-9). Soc Computer Sim.
Holtz, Per A. Index to Simulation Literature. 332p. 1982. pap. 38.00. Soc Computer Sim.
Horn, Robert E. & Cleaves, Anne, eds. The Guide to Simulations-Games for Education & Training. 4th ed. LC 79-19823. (Illus.). 692p. 1980. 49.95 (ISBN 0-8039-1375-3). Sage.
Javor, A., ed. Simulation in Research & Development: Proceedings of the IMACS European Simulation Meeting on Simulation in Research & Development Eger, Hungary, 27-30, Aug.; 1984. 266p. 1985. 37.00 (ISBN 0-444-87747-9, North Holland). Elsevier.
Jones, Ken. Simulations: A Handbook for Teachers. 180p. 1980. 27.50x (ISBN 0-89397-090-5). Nichols Pub.
Kaplus. Peripheral Array Processors, Vol. 14. (SCS Series: No. 2). 1984. 30.00 (ISBN 0-317-17125-9). Soc Computer Sim.
Karplus, Walter J., ed. Peripheral Array Processors. (Simulation Ser.: Vol. 11, No. 1). 170p. 1982. 30.00 (ISBN 0-686-38787-2). Soc Computer Sim.
Kydes, A. S., ed. Energy Modeling & Simulation. 394p. 1983. 55.25 (ISBN 0-444-86610-8). Elsevier.
Lehnert, W. G. The Process of Question Answering: Computer Simulation of Cognition. 288p. 1978. text ed. 29.95x (ISBN 0-89859-417-0). L Erlbaum Assocs.
Leventhal, Lance A., ed. Modeling & Simulation on Microcomputers, 1982. 119p. 1982. pap. 20.00 (ISBN 0-686-36686-7). Soc Computer Sim.
Lewis, P. A., et al. Advanced Simulation & Statistics Package. 80p. 1985. pap. 59.95 (ISBN 0-534-05304-1); double-sided disk incl. Wadsworth Pub.
Macaluso, Pat. Learning Simulation Techniques on a Microcomputer Playing Blackjack & Other Monte Carlo Games. (Illus.). 154p. (Orig.). 1983. 16.95 (ISBN 0-8306-0535-5, 1535); pap. 10.95 (ISBN 0-8306-1535-0). TAB Bks.
McLeod, John, ed. Computer Modeling & Simulation: Principles of Good Practice. (SCS Simulation Ser.: Vol. 10, No. 2). 1982. 30.00 (ISBN 0-686-36680-8). Soc Computer Sim.
Megarry, Jacquetta, ed. Aspects of Simulation & Gaming: An Anthology of SAGSET Journal Volumes. 200p. 1977. 34.00 (ISBN 0-85038-075-8). Nichols Pub.
Mihram, G. Arthur. Simulation: Statistical Foundations & Methodology. (Mathematics in Science & Engineering Ser: Vol. 92). 1972. 80.00 (ISBN 0-12-495950-4). Acad Pr.
Modeling & Simulation on Microcomputers: 1983. 1983. softbound 20.00 (ISBN 0-686-38790-2). Soc Computer Sim.
Modeling & Simulation on Microcomputers. 1984. 20.00. Soc Computer Sim.
Nash, P. Systems Modelling & Optimisation. (IEE Control Engineering Ser.: No. 16). 224p. 1981. 47.50 (ISBN 0-906048-63-X, CE016). Inst Elect Eng.
Naylor, Thomas H. Simulation Models in Corporate Planning. LC 78-31258. (Praeger Special Studies). 312p. 1979. 37.95 (ISBN 0-03-047061-7). Praeger.
Naylor, Thomas H., ed. Simulation in Business & Decision Making. (SCS Simulation Ser.: Vol. 9, No. 1). 1981. 30.00 (ISBN 0-318-01052-6). Soc Computer Sim.
Oren, et al. Winter Simulation Conference WSC Proceedings: Orlando, 2 vols. 1980. 48.00 ea. (ISBN 0-317-17117-8). Soc Computer Sim.
Oren, Tuncer I. & Delfosse, Claude M., eds. Winter Simulation Conference, Atlanta GA, December 1981: Proceedings, 2 vols. 1360p. 48.00 ea. Soc Computer Sim.
Patterson, Phillip D., ed. Recent Developments in Urban Gaming. (SCS Simulation Ser.: Vol. 2, No. 2). 1972. 30.00 (ISBN 0-686-36659-X). Soc Computer Sim.
Paulre, B. E., ed. System Dynamics & the Analysis of Change: Proceedings of the 6th International Conference, University of Paris, Dauphine, November, '80. 382p. 1981. 64.00 (ISBN 0-444-86251-X, North-Holland). Elsevier.
Pritsker, A. A. Introduction to Simulation & Slamm II. 612p. 1984. 29.50. Systems Pub.
Pritsker, A. Alan & Rolston, Laurie J. Introduction to Simulation & Slam II, Solutions Manual. 2nd ed. (Illus.). 257p. 1981. 40.00 (ISBN 0-938974-00-9). Systems Pub.
Proceedings of First International Conference in Simulation in Manufacturing. 1985. 85.00x (ISBN 0-903608-84-7, Pub. by IFS Pubns UK). Air Sci Co.
Richalet, J., et al. Identification des Processus par la Methode du Modele. (Theorie Des Systemes Ser.). 378p. 1972. 106.50 (ISBN 0-677-50740-2). Gordon.
Roberts, Nancy & Andersen, David. Introduction to Computer Simulation: The System Dynamics Approach. (Illus.). 1983. text ed. 23.95 (ISBN 0-201-06414-6). Addison-Wesley.
Roberts, Stephen, et al. Winter Simulation Conference: Arlington, 2 vols. (WCS Proceedings Ser.). 1983. Set. 48.00 ea. (ISBN 0-317-17118-6). Soc Computer Sim.
Roberts, Stephen D. & England, William L., eds. Survey of the Application of Simulation to Health Care. (SCS Simulation Ser.: Vol. 10, No. 1). 1981. 30.00 (ISBN 0-686-36678-6). Soc Computer Sim.
Schellenberger, R. & Boseman, G. MANSYM III: A Dynamic Management Simulator with Decision Support System. (Management Ser.). 94p. 1982. pap. text ed. 17.95 (ISBN 0-471-08581-2); write for info. tchrs. manual (ISBN 0-471-86815-9). Wiley.
Shannon, Robert E. Systems Simulation: The Art & Science. (Illus.). 368p. 1975. ref. ed. 32.95 (ISBN 0-13-881839-8). P-H.
Sheppard, et al. Winter Simulations Conference: Dallas. 1984. 75.00 (ISBN 0-911801-04-9). Soc Computer Sim.
Silvern, Leonard C. Systems Engineering of Education: Roles of Feedback & Feedforward During Simulation, No. 18. LC 74-79181. 1974. text ed. 6.00 (ISBN 0-87657-113-5). Ed & Training.
Solomon, Susan L. Simulation of Waiting-Line Systems. (Illus.). 464p. 1983. text ed. 35.98 (ISBN 0-13-810044-6). P-H.
Standridge. Simulation in Health Care Delivery Systems Nineteen Eighty-Four. pap. 20.00 (ISBN 0-911801-02-2). Soc Computer Sim.
Summer Computer Simulation Conference Proceedings, Boston, 2 vols. 1984. Set. 90.00 (ISBN 0-317-17120-8). Soc Computer Sim.
Summer Computer Simulation Conference Proceedings: Vancouver, 2 vols. 1983. Set. 90.00 (ISBN 0-317-17119-4). Soc Computer Sim.
Summer Computer Simulation Conference Proceedings: 1980 (Seattle), 1981 (Washington, D. C.) & 1982 (Denver) 750p. pap. 50.00 ea. Soc Computer Sim.
Summer Computer Simulation Conference, 1982: Proceedings. 678p. 1982. softbound 50.00 (ISBN 0-686-38788-0). Soc Computer Sim.
Sworder, D. D., ed. Systems & Simulation in the Service of Society. (SCS Simulation Ser.: Vol. 1, No. 2). 1971. 30.00 (ISBN 0-686-36655-7). Soc Computer Sim.
Therien, Normand, ed. Simulating the Environment Impact of a Large Hydroelectric Project. (SCS Simulation Ser.: Vol. 9, No. 2). 1981. 30.00 (ISBN 0-686-36677-8). Soc Computer Sim.
Thorelli, Hans B. & Graves, R. L. International Operations Simulation. LC 64-16969. 1964. 17.00 (ISBN 0-02-932540-4). Free Pr.
Ung, Monte, ed. Aerospace Simulation. 1984. 30.00. Soc Computer Sim.
Unger, et al. Simulation Software & Ada. 1984. pap. 20.00 (ISBN 0-911801-03-0). Soc Computer Sim.
Vogt, William G. & Mickle, Marlin H., eds. Modeling & Simulation, Vol. 11: Proceedings of the Annual Pittsburgh Conference on Modeling & Simulation, Pts. 1, 2, 3, & 4. LC 73-85004. 1980. Set. pap. text ed. 149.00x (ISBN 0-87664-652-6); Pt. 1. pap. text ed. 40.00x (ISBN 0-87664-495-7); Pt. 2. pap. text ed. 40.00x (ISBN 0-87664-496-5); Pt. 3. pap. text ed. 40.00x (ISBN 0-87664-497-3); Pt. 4. pap. text ed. 40.00x (ISBN 0-87664-498-1). Instru Soc.
--Modeling & Simulation, Vol. 13: Proceedings of the Annual Pittsburgh Conference on Modeling & Simulation, 4 pts. LC 73-85004. 1744p. 1982. pap. text ed. 40.00 ea. Pt. 1; 512p (ISBN 0-87664-712-3). Pt. 2; 546p (ISBN 0-87664-713-1). Pt. 3; 408p (ISBN 0-87664-714-X). Pt. 4; 368p (ISBN 0-87664-715-8). Set. pap. text ed. 149.00 (ISBN 0-87664-716-6). Instru Soc.
--Modeling & Simulation, Vol. 14: Proceedings of the Annual Pittsburgh Conference on Modeling & Simulation, 4 pts. in 3 bks. LC 73-85004. 1576p. 1983. Set. pap. text ed. 149.00x (ISBN 0-87664-795-6); Pts. 1 & 2. pap. text ed. 55.00x (ISBN 0-87664-792-1); Pt. 3. pap. text ed. 55.00x (ISBN 0-87664-793-X); Pt. 4. pap. text ed. 55.00x (ISBN 0-87664-794-8). Instru Soc.
Vogy, William G. & Mickle, Marlin H., eds. Modeling & Simulation, Vol. 12: Proceedings of the Annual Pittsburgh Conference on Modeling & Simulation, 4 pts. LC 73-85004. 1776p. 1981. Set. pap. text ed. 149.00x (ISBN 0-87664-563-5); pap. text ed. 40.00x ea. Pt. 1 Energy & Environment (ISBN 0-87664-559-7). Pt. 2-Systems, Control & Computers (ISBN 0-87664-560-0). Pt. 3-Socio-economics & Biomedical (ISBN 0-87664-561-9). Pt. 4-General Modeling & Simulation (ISBN 0-87664-562-7). Instru Soc.
Watt, Kenneth E., ed. Simulation of Energy Systems. (SCS Simulation Ser.: Vol. 8, Nos. 1 & 2). 1978. No.1. 30.00 ea. (ISBN 0-911801-00-6); No.2. (ISBN 0-911801-01-4). Soc Computer Sim.
Watts, Elizabeth S. Nonhuman Primate Models for Human Growth & Development. (MP Ser.: Vol. 6). 328p. 1985. 46.00 (ISBN 0-8451-3405-1). A R Liss.
Wheeler, Carol A. & Dalton, Marie. Word Processing Simulations for Electronic Typewriters & Text Editors. LC 81-11630. (Word Processing Ser.). 224p. 1982. pap. 15.95 (ISBN 0-471-08158-2). Wiley.
Winter Simulation Conference Proceedings. Incl. Arlington, 2 vols. Roberts, Stephen. 1983. 48.00 ea.; 1982. Highland, Harold. 650p. 1982. 48.00 (ISBN 0-317-31363-0); Orlando, 2 vols. Oren. 1980p. 75.00 (ISBN 0-911801-04-9). Soc Computer Sim.

SIMULATION PROGRAMMING LANGUAGE
see SIMSCRIPT (Computer Program Language)

SIMULATORS, SPACE
see Space Simulators

SIMULTANEOUS EQUATIONS
see Equations, Simultaneous

SINCLAIR ZX-80 (COMPUTER)
Alcock, Donald. Illustrating Superbasic on the Sinclair QL. (Illus.). 191p. 1985. pap. 11.95 (ISBN 0-521-31517-4). Cambridge U Pr.
Charlton, Mark. The Gateway Guide to the ZX-81 & ZX-80. rev. ed. (Illus.). 176p. 1981. pap. 9.95 (ISBN 0-916688-41-0, 16O). Creative Comp.

SINCLAIR ZX-81 (COMPUTER)
Anbarlian, Harry. An Introduction to VisiCalc Spreadsheeting on the ZX-81 & Timex-Sinclair 1000. 272p. 1983. pap. text ed. 26.95 (ISBN 0-07-001699-2). McGraw.
Baker, Toni. Mastering Machine Code on Your ZX-81. 176p. 1982. 18.41. P-H.

Bradbeer, Robin. Learning to Use the ZX-81 Computer. (Learning to Use Computer Series, A Gower Read-Out Publication). 86p. (Orig.). 1982. pap. text ed. 12.00x (ISBN 0-566-03451-4). Gower Pub Co.

Charlton, Mark. The Gateway Guide to the ZX-81 & ZX-80. rev. ed. (Illus.). 176p. 1981. pap. 9.95 (ISBN 0-916688-41-0, 16O). Creative Comp.

Cyborg Software Systems, Inc., et al. The ZX-80, ZX-81, & Timex-Sinclair 1000 Microcomputers. rev. ed. (Nanos Reference Cards Ser.). (Illus.). 20p. 1982. 5.95 (ISBN 0-915069-13-X). Nanos Sys.

Floegel, Ekkehard. ZX-81 Timex: Programming in BASIC & Machine Language. 139p. 9.95 (ISBN 0-317-05097-4). Elcomp.

--ZX-81 Timex: Programming in BASIC & Machine Language. 139p. 9.95 (ISBN 3-921682-98-3). Blue Cat.

Grant, John & Grant, Catherine. The ZX Programmer's Companion. LC 83-23967. 256p. 1984. pap. 11.95 (ISBN 0-521-27044-8). Cambridge U Pr.

Hartnell, Tim. Getting Acquainted with Your ZX-81. 3rd ed. 120p. 1981. pap. 9.95 (ISBN 0-916688-33-X, 15Y). Creative Comp.

Hergert, Douglas. Your Timex-Sinclair 1000 & ZX-81. LC 82-62360. (Illus.). 159p. 1983. pap. 6.95 (ISBN 0-89588-099-7). SYBEX.

Hurley, Randle. The Sinclair ZX-81. (Illus.). 176p. 1983. 17.95 (ISBN 0-8306-0523-1, 1523). TAB Bks.

Larsen, Sally G., ed. Computers for Kids: Timex-Sinclair 1000 & ZX-81 Edition. 64p. 1983. pap. 5.95 (ISBN 0-916688-32-1, 12S). Creative Comp.

Lien, David A. Learning Timex-Sinclair BASIC for the Timex 1000 & the Sinclair ZX-81. LC 82-73469. (CompuSoft Learning Ser.). (Illus.). 352p. (Orig.). 1983. pap. 14.95 (ISBN 0-932760-15-5). CompuSoft.

Logan, Ian. Understanding Your ZX-81. 1983. write for info. Melbourne Hse.

Maunder, Robert. The ZX-81 Companion. LC 82-73856. 131p. 1981. pap. 9.95 (ISBN 0-916688-26-7, 17P). Creative Comp.

Norman, Robin. Timex-Sinclair 1000 ZX-81 BASIC Book. LC 82-50022. 192p. 1983. pap. 12.95 (ISBN 0-672-21957-3, 21957). Sams.

Page, Edward. One Hundred One Timex-Sinclair 1000 ZX-81 Programming Tips & Tricks. 128p. (Orig.). 1982. pap. 7.95 (ISBN 0-86668-020-9). ARCsoft.

--Thirty-Seven Timex-Sinclair 1000 ZX-81 Computer Programs for Home, School & Office. (Illus.). 96p. (Orig.). 1982. pap. 8.95 (ISBN 0-86668-021-7). ARCsoft.

Schnapp, Russell L. & Stafford, Irvin G. Computer Graphics for the Timex-Sinclair 1000, ZX-81. (Personal Computing Ser.). (Illus.). 128p. 1984. pap. text ed. 13.95 (ISBN 0-13-164278-2); cassette 14.95 (ISBN 0-13-164286-3). P-H.

Sickler, Albert N. Using & Programming the ZX-81 & TS-1000, Including Ready-to-Run Programs. (Illus.). 168p. 1983. 14.95 (ISBN 0-8306-0117-1); pap. 8.95 (ISBN 0-8306-0617-3, 1617). TAB Bks.

Valentine, Roger. What Can I Do with My Timex-Sinclair 1000? Lots! 56 Programs for the Timex-Sinclair 1000 & ZX-81. LC 83-1339. (Wiley Professional Software Ser.). (Illus.). 164p. 1983. pap. 9.95 (ISBN 0-471-88730-7, Pub. by Wiley Pr); program cassette 19.95 (ISBN 0-471-88729-3, Wiley Professional Software). Wiley.

Weber, Jeffrey R. User's Guide to the Timex-Sinclair ZX 81. (WSI's How to Use Your Microcomputer Ser.). 280p. (Orig.). 1984. pap. cancelled. Weber Systems.

SINCLAIR ZX SPECTRUM (COMPUTER)

Anbarlian, H. An Introduction to Vu-Calc Spreadsheeting for the Timex-Sinclair 2000 & the Sinclair ZX Spectrum. 448p. 1983. pap. 27.95 (ISBN 0-07-001698-4, BYTE Bks). McGraw.

Berk, A. A. Practical Robotics & Interfacing for the Spectrum. (Illus.). 160p. (Orig.). 1984. pap. 13.95 (ISBN 0-246-12576-4, Pub. by Granada England). Sheridan.

Bradbeer, Robin. Learning to Use the ZX Spectrum. (Learning to Use Computer Series, A Gower Read-Out Publication). 96p. (Orig.). 1982. pap. text ed. 12.00x (ISBN 0-566-03481-6). Gower Pub Co.

Ewbank, Kay & James, Mike. The Spectrum Gamesmaster. (Illus.). 160p. (Orig.). 1984. pap. 13.95 (ISBN 0-246-12515-2, Pub. by Granada England). Sheridan.

Grant, John & Grant, Catherine. The ZX Programmer's Companion. LC 83-23967. 256p. 1984. pap. 11.95 (ISBN 0-521-27044-8). Cambridge U Pr.

Jackson, Peter & Goode, Peter. Business Programming on Your Spectrum. 157p. 1984. pap. 13.95 (ISBN 0-946576-05-X, Pub. by Phoenix Pub). David & Charles.

Ludinski, G. Brainteasers for the Spectrum 48k. 144p. 1984. pap. 12.95 (ISBN 0-946576-10-6, Pub. by Phoenix Pub). David & Charles.

McLean, Ian, et al. The ZX Spectrum: Your Personal Computer. 1983. 9.95 (ISBN 0-13-985028-7). P-H.

Scott, Allan. The Spectrum Add-On Guide. (Illus.). 160p. (Orig.). 1984. pap. 11.95 (ISBN 0-246-12563-2, Pub. by Granada England). Sheridan.

Vickers, Steven. Pocket Guide: The Sinclair Spectrum. (Pitman Programming Pocket Guides Ser.). 64p. 1984. pap. 6.95 (ISBN 0-273-02075-7). Pitman Pub MA.

SINGLE-LENS REFLEX CAMERAS

Alesse, Craig. Basic Thirty-Five mm Photo Guide. LC 79-54311. (Illus.). 110p. (Orig.). 1980. pap. 9.95 (ISBN 0-936262-00-1). Amherst Media.

H P Books, ed. How to Select & Use Your SLR System. LC 81-82138. 1981. 7.95 (ISBN 0-89586-112-7). H P Bks.

MacDonnell, Kevin. Choosing & Using SLR Lenses. (Illus.). 96p. (Orig.). pap. 5.95 (ISBN 0-317-11639-8, 3600, Pub. by Fountain). Morgan.

Watkins, Derek. SLR Photography. LC 76-54090. 1977. 17.50 (ISBN 0-7153-7301-3). David & Charles.

SINGLE-SIDEBAND RADIO

see Radio, Single-Sideband

SINTERING

Eremenko, Valentin A., et al. Liquid-Phase Sintering. LC 78-107537. 75p. 1970. 25.00x (ISBN 0-306-10839-9, Consultants). Plenum Pub.

Invenson, V. A. Densification of Metal Powders During Sintering. LC 72-94822. (Studies in Soviet Science - Physical Sciences Ser.). 242p. 1973. 45.00x (ISBN 0-306-10881-X, Consultants). Plenum Pub.

Kolar, D., et al, eds. Sintering: Theory & Practice. (Materials Science Monographs: Vol. 14). 654p. 1983. 138.50 (ISBN 0-444-42122-X). Elsevier.

Kuczynski, G., et al, eds. Sintering & Related Phenomena. 904p. 1970. 169.95 (ISBN 0-677-10890-7). Gordon.

Kuczynski, G. C., ed. Sintering & Catalysis. LC 75-35639. (Materials Science Research Ser.: Vol. 10). 522p. 1975. 75.00x (ISBN 0-306-38510-4, Plenum Pr). Plenum Pub.

--Sintering & Related Phenomena. LC 63-17645. (Materials Science Research Ser.: Vol. 6). 463p. 1973. 69.50x (ISBN 0-306-38506-6, Plenum Pr). Plenum Pub.

--Sintering Processes. LC 79-25813. (Materials Sciences Research Ser.: Vol. 13). 585p. 1980. 85.00x (ISBN 0-306-40336-6, Plenum Pr). Plenum Pub.

Kuczynski, G. C., et al, eds. Sintering & Heterogeneous Catalysis. (Materials Science Research Ser.: Vol. 16). 346p. 1984. 55.00x (ISBN 0-306-41666-2, Plenum Pr). Plenum Pub.

Ristic, Momcilo M., ed. Sintering-New Developments. (Materials Science Monographs: Vol. 4). 380p. 1979. 78.75 (ISBN 0-444-41796-6). Elsevier.

Waldron, M. B. & Daniell, B. L. Sintering. LC 79-307614. (Monographs in Powder Science & Technology). pap. 29.50 (ISBN 0-317-10497-7, 2019651). Bks Demand UMI.

SIPHONATA

see Hemiptera

SIPHONOPHORA

Totton, A. K. A Synopsis of the Siphonophora. (Illus.). viii, 231p. 1965. 48.00x (ISBN 0-565-00642-8, Pub. by Brit Mus Nat Hist). Sabbot-Natural Hist Bks.

SIXTY-FIVE HUNDRED AND TWO (MICROPROCESSOR)

Bright, Bob. Pocket Guide: Assembly Language for the 6502. (Pitman Programming Pocket Guides Ser.). 64p. (Orig.). 1984. pap. 6.95 (ISBN 0-273-01990-2). Pitman Pub MA.

De Jong, Marvin. Programming & Interfacing the Sixty-Five Two, with Experiments. LC 79-67130. 416p. 1980. pap. 17.95 (ISBN 0-672-21651-5, 21651). Sams.

Des Jardins, Paul R., et al. Apple II & II Plus Microcomputer, BASIC & 6502. rev. ed. (Nanos Reference Cards Ser.). 16p. 1982. 4.95 (ISBN 0-915069-10-5). Nanos Sys.

--The Sixty-Five Hundred Two Microprocessor. (Nanos Reference Cards Ser.). 16p. (Orig.). 1983. pap. 4.95 (ISBN 0-915069-16-4). Nanos Sys.

Findley, Robert. Software Gourmet Guide & Cookbook: 6502. pap. 13.95 (ISBN 0-8104-6277-X, 6277). Hayden.

Hendrix, Stephen. The Handbook 6502, 65C02, & 65816. 300p. (Orig.). 1985. pap. 17.95 (ISBN 0-317-19101-2). Weber Systems.

Holland, John M. Advanced Sixty-Five Two Interfacing. LC 81-86551. 192p. 1982. pap. 13.95 (ISBN 0-672-21836-4, 21836). Sams.

Hyde, Randy. Using 6502 Assembly Language. (Illus.). 301p. 1981. 19.95 (ISBN 0-88190-003-6, B0003). Datamost.

Leventhal, Lance A. & Saville, Winthrop. Sixty-Five Zero Two Assembly Language Subroutines. 546p. (Orig.). 1979. pap. 17.95 (ISBN 0-07-931059-1, 59-1). Osborne-McGraw.

Roberts, Sam D. How to Program Your Atari in 6502 Machine Language. 106p. 1982. 9.95 (ISBN 0-936200-37-5). Blue Cat.

Scanlon, Leo J. Sixty-Five Two Software Design. LC 79-67131. 272p. 1980. pap. 13.95 (ISBN 0-672-21656-6, 21656). Sams.

Skier, K. Top-Down Assembly Language Programming for Your 6502 Personal Computer. 434p. 1983. pap. 16.95 (CC 07-057863-X). SYBEX.

Windeknecht, Thomas G. Systems Programming 6502. 256p. 1983. pap. text ed. 14.50 (ISBN 0-316-94563-3). Little.

Zaks, Rodnay. Advanced 6502 Programming: Based on 6502 Games, 1980. LC 82-60235. (The Sixty-five Hundred Two Ser.: No. 3). (Illus.). 292p. 1982. pap. 15.95 (ISBN 0-89588-089-X, G402A). SYBEX.

--Programming the 6502. 4th ed. LC 83-61686. (Six Thousand Five Hundred & Two Ser.: No. 1). (Illus.). 408p. 1983. pap. 14.95 (ISBN 0-89588-135-7, C202). SYBEX.

SIZE OF PARTICLES

see Particles

SKELETON

see also Anthropometry; Bone; Bones; Skull
also names of bones, e.g. Clavicle, Humerus

Bass, William M. Human Osteology: A Laboratory & Field Manual of the Human Skeleton. 2nd ed. Evans, David R., ed. LC 77-172091. (Special Publications Ser.: No. 2). (Illus.). 288p. (Orig.). 1971. pap. 9.00 (ISBN 0-943414-07-5). MO Arch Soc.

Fazelas, Gy I & Kosa, F. Forensic Fetal Osteology. 1979. 41.50 (ISBN 0-9960011-9-0, Pub. by Akademiai Kaido Hungary). Heyden.

Goldman, Amy B., ed. Procedures in Skeletal Radiology. 720p. 1984. 99.50 (ISBN 0-8089-1655-6, 7916-41). Grune.

Green, Stuart A. Complications of External Skeletal Fixation: Causes, Prevention & Treatment. (Illus.). 208p. 1981. 32.75x (ISBN 0-398-04482-1). C C Thomas.

Hrdlicka, Ales. The Skeletal Remains of Early Man. 1930. 48.00 (ISBN 0-384-24710-5). Johnson Repr.

Krogman, Wilton M. Human Skeleton in Forensic Medicine. (Illus.). 364p. 1978. 19.75x (ISBN 0-398-01054-4). C C Thomas.

Kunin, Arthur S. & Simons, David J., eds. Skeletal Research: An Experimental Approach, Vol. 2. 1983. 60.00 (ISBN 0-12-429002-7). Acad Pr.

Mears, Dana C. External Skeletal Fixation. (Illus.). 689p. 1983. 93.00 (ISBN 0-683-05900-9). Williams & Wilkins.

Papadatos, Costas J. & Bartsocas, Christos S., eds. Skeletal Dysplasias. LC 82-17277. (Progress in Clinical & Biological Research Ser.: Vol. 104). 572p. 1982. 60.00 (ISBN 0-8451-0104-8). A R Liss.

Roche, A. F., et al. Skeletal Maturity of Children Six to Eleven Years: Racial, Area, & Socioeconomic Differentials. LC 74-18049. (Data from the Health Examination Survey Ser. 11: No. 149). 70p. 1975. pap. 1.75 (ISBN 0-8406-0030-5). Natl Ctr Health Stats.

Roche, Alex F., et al. Skeletal Maturity of Youths 12-17 Years: Racial, Geographic Area, & Socioeconomic Differentials. Shipp, Audrey, ed. (Ser. 11: No. 167). 1978. pap. 2.50 (ISBN 0-8406-0121-2). Natl Ctr Health Stats.

Schlossberg, Leon. Human Skeleton: Functional Model. 1961. incl. with teacher's guide 60.00x (ISBN 0-8018-0577-5). Johns Hopkins.

Shipman, Pat & Walker, Alan. The Human Skeleton. (Illus.). 360p. 1985. 27.50x (ISBN 0-674-41610-4). Harvard U Pr.

Shuttleworth, Frank K. Sexual Maturation & the Skeletal Growth of Girls Age Six to Nineteen. (SRCD M). 1938. pap. 10.00 (ISBN 0-527-01505-9). Kraus Repr.

Simmons, David J. & Kukin, Arthur S., eds. Skeletal Research: An Experimental Approach. 1979. 71.50 (ISBN 0-12-644150-2). Acad Pr.

Stockton, Anita & Torres, Mary R. Human Skeleton: Thirty-Five Inch Functional Scale Model with Instructional Guide. 1985. manual 15.00x (ISBN 0-8018-2970-4); model skeleton 195.00 (ISBN 0-8018-2989-5). Johns Hopkins.

Walter, W. G. Skeletal Muscle Pharmacology. 474p. 1982. 102.25 (ISBN 0-444-90226-0, Excerpta Medica). Elsevier.

Wildenthal, K. Degradative Processes in Heart & Skeletal Muscle. (Research Monographs in Cell & Tissue Physiology: Vol. 3). 462p. 1980. 110.25 (ISBN 0-444-80235-5). Elsevier.

Wolfe, John N., et al. Atlas of Xeroradiographic Anatomy of Normal Skeletal Systems. (Illus.). 208p. 1978. 32.50x (ISBN 0-398-03715-9). C C Thomas.

SKIAGRAPHY

see Radiography

SKIN

Alexander, J. O'Donel. Arthropods & Human Skin. (Illus.). 430p. 1984. 90.00 (ISBN 0-387-13235-X). Springer-Verlag.

Behrendt, Hans & Green, Marvin. Patterns of Skin PH from Birth Through Adolescence: With a Synopsis on Skin Growth. (Illus.). 116p. 1971. 14.75x (ISBN 0-398-00125-1). C C Thomas.

Bernstein, I. A. & Seiji, M., eds. Biochemistry of Normal & Abnormal Epidermal Differentiation. (Current Problems in Dermatology: Vol. 10). (Illus.). x, 442p. 1981. pap. 58.00 (ISBN 3-8055-1915-X). S Karger.

Carruthers, Christopher. Biochemistry of Skin in Health & Disease. (Illus.). 284p. 1962. photocopy ed. 31.75x (ISBN 0-398-00288-6). C C Thomas.

Goldsmith, Lowell A., ed. Biochemistry & Physiology of the Skin, 2 vols. (Illus.). 1983. Set. 150.00x (ISBN 0-19-261253-0). Oxford U Pr.

Jarrett, A., ed. The Physiology & Pathophysiology of the Skin: Vol. 4, The Hair Follicle. 1977. 79.50 (ISBN 0-12-380604-6). Acad Pr.

--The Physiology & Pathophysiology of the Skin: Vol. 5, the Sweat Glands, Skin Permeation, Lymphatics, the Nails. 1979. 66.00 (ISBN 0-12-380605-4). Acad Pr.

Kenshalo, Dan R. The Skin Senses. (Illus.). 656p. 1968. photocopy ed. 69.50x (ISBN 0-398-01005-6). C C Thomas.

Kenshalo, Dan R., ed. Sensory Functions of the Skin of Humans. LC 79-22582. 447p. 1979. 55.00x (ISBN 0-306-40321-8, Plenum Pr). Plenum Pub.

LuBowe, Irwin I. & Huss, Barbara. A Teenage Guide to Healthy Skin & Hair. 224p. 1983. pap. 6.95 (ISBN 0-8290-1159-5). Irvington.

Maibach, H., ed. Skin Microbiology: Relevance to Clinical Infection. Aly, R. 384p. 1981. 44.50 (ISBN 0-387-90528-6). Springer-Verlag.

Mali, J. W., ed. Some Fundamental Approaches in Skin Research. (Current Problems in Dermatology: Vol. 9). (Illus.). viii, 152p. 1981. pap. 41.75 (ISBN 3-8055-3080-3). S Karger.

Marks, R. & Payne, P. A. Bioengineering & the Skin. (Illus.). 320p. 1981. text ed. 59.00 (ISBN 0-85200-314-5, Pub. by MTP Pr England). Kluwer Academic.

Noble, W. C. Microbiology of Human Skin. 433p. 1981. 90.00x (ISBN 0-686-80441-4, Pub. by Lloyd-Luke England). State Mutual Bk.

Sinclair, David. Mechanisms of Cutaneous Sensation. 2nd ed. (Illus.). 1981. pap. text ed. 45.00x (ISBN 0-19-261174-7). Oxford U Pr.

Spearman, R. I. & Riley, P. A., eds. The Skin of Vertebrates. (Linnean Society Symposium Ser.: No. 9). 1981. 99.50 (ISBN 0-12-656950-9). Acad Pr.

Wertelecki, Wladimir & Plato, Chris C., eds. Dermatoglyphics Fifty Years Later. LC 79-2595. (Alan R. Liss Ser.: Vol. 15, No. 6). 1979. 91.00 (ISBN 0-8451-1031-4). March of Dimes.

Zotterman, Yngve, ed. Sensory Functions of the Skin with Special Reference to Man. LC 76-20572. 1976. text ed. 89.00 (ISBN 0-08-021208-5). Pergamon.

SKULL

Here are entered anatomical and pathological works.

see also Craniology; Craniometry; Head

De Beer, Gavin R. The Development of the Vertebrate Skull. (Illus.). xxiv, 730p. 1985. pap. text ed. 22.50x (ISBN 0-226-13960-3); 45.00x (ISBN 0-226-13958-1). U of Chicago Pr.

Demes, B. Biomechanics of the Primate Skull Base. (Advances in Anatomy, Embryology & Cell Biology Ser.: Vol. 94). (Illus.). 70p. 1985. pap. 22.00 (ISBN 0-387-15290-3). Springer-Verlag.

Lang, J. Clinical Anatomy of the Head: Neurocranium, Orbita, Craniocervical Regions. (Illus.). 489p. 1983. 490.00 (ISBN 0-387-11014-3). Springer-Verlag.

Moore, W. J. The Mammalian Skull. (Biological Structure & Function Ser.: No. 8). (Illus.). 400p. 1981. 99.50 (ISBN 0-521-23318-6). Cambridge U Pr.

Waddington, Margaret M. Atlas of the Human Skull. LC 81-66760. (Illus.). 1981. 85.00 (ISBN 0-9914903-6-3). Academy Bks.

Weidenreich, Franz. The Brain & Its Role in the Phylogenetic Transformation of the Human Skull. LC 78-72707. Repr. of 1941 ed. 19.50 (ISBN 0-404-18278-X). AMS Pr.

SKUNKS

Hall, E. Raymond & Dalquest, Walter W. Geographic Range of the Hooded Skunk, Mephitis Macroura, with Description of a New Subspecies from Mexico. (Museum Ser.: Vol. 1, No. 24). 6p. 1950. pap. 1.25 (ISBN 0-317-05023-0). U of KS Mus Nat Hist.

Hume, Charles. Raise & Train Skunks. pap. 3.95 (ISBN 0-87666-223-8, M-527). TFH Pubns.

SKY

see Atmosphere

SKYE TERRIER
see Dogs–Breeds–Skye Terrier
SKYRAIDER (FIGHTER PLANES)
see also Fighter Planes
Rausa, Rosario. Skyraider: The Douglas A-1 "Flying Dump Truck". LC 82-14187. (Illus.). 224p. 1982. 19.95 (ISBN 0-933852-31-2). Nautical & Aviation.
SKYSCRAPERS
Goldberger, Paul. The Skyscraper. LC 81-47480. (Illus.). 224p. 1983. pap. 12.95 (ISBN 0-394-71586-1). Knopf.
Schueller, Wolfgang. High-Rise Building Structures. LC 84-27809. 290p. 1985. Repr. of 1977 ed. lib. bdg. price not set (ISBN 0-89874-835-6). Krieger.
Vance, Mary. Skyscrapers: A Bibliography of Recent Books & Periodicals Articles. (Architecture Ser.: Bibliography A-577). 55p. 1981. pap. 8.25 (ISBN 0-88066-119-4). Vance Biblios.
SLABS, CONCRETE
see Concrete Slabs
SLAG
Physicochemical Properties of Molten Slags & Glasses. 530p. (Orig.). 1983. pap. text ed. 70.00x (ISBN 0-904357-54-6, Pub. by the Metals Society). Brookfield Pub Co.
SLATER, SAMUEL, 1768-1835
White, George S. Memoir of Samuel Slater. LC 66-18322. (Illus.). Repr. of 1836 ed. 37.50x (ISBN 0-678-00218-5). Kelley.
SLAUGHTERING AND SLAUGHTER-HOUSES
Ashbrook, Frank G. Butchering, Processing & Preservation of Meat. (Illus.). 336p. 1955. pap. 9.95 (ISBN 0-442-20377-2). Van Nos Reinhold.
Clarke, Mary W. The Slaughter Ranches & their Makers. (Illus.). 12.95 (ISBN 0-686-70086-4). Jenkins.
SLIDE-RULE
Harris, Charles O. Slide Rule Simplified. 3rd ed. LC 78-183979. pap. 88.00 (ISBN 0-317-08654-5, 2004578). Bks Demand UMI.
Perrine, James O. Slide Rule Handbook. 112p. 1965. 20.95 (ISBN 0-677-01060-5). Gordon.
Schirmacher, Stan L. Slide Rule in a Nutshell. 1960. pap. 1.00x (ISBN 0-686-08956-1). Anozira.
Shuster, Carl N. A Study of the Problems in Teaching the Slide Rule. LC 72-177784. (Columbia University. Teachers College. Contributions to Education: No. 805). Repr. of 1940 ed. 22.50 (ISBN 0-404-55805-4). AMS Pr.
Snover, Stephen & Spikell, Mark. Programming the TI-55 Slide Rule Calculator. 117p. 1982. 15.95 (ISBN 0-13-729921-4); pap. 7.95 (ISBN 0-13-729913-3). P-H.
SLIDES (PHOTOGRAPHY)
Eastman Kodak Company. The Sourcebook-Kodak Ektagraphic Slide Projectors. 3rd ed. Price, A. L., ed. (Illus.). 100p. 1983. pap. text ed. 8.95 (ISBN 0-87985-295-X, S-74). Eastman Kodak.
Gilhuis, Wout. Creative Colour Transparencies. (Illus.). 160p. 1980. text ed. 14.95 (ISBN 0-85242-711-5, 3711). Morgan.
Kueter, Roger A. & Miller, Janeen. Slides. Duane, James E., ed. LC 80-21335. (Instructional Media Library: Vol. 13). (Illus.). 112p. 1981. 19.95 (ISBN 0-87778-173-7). Educ Tech Pubns.
Voogel, E. & Keyzer, P. Two Hundred Slide Tips. (Photo Tips Ser.). (Illus.). 102p. (Orig.). 1980. pap. 4.95 (ISBN 0-85242-502-3, 3471). Morgan.
SLIDES (TRANSPARENCIES)
see Slides (Photography)
SLIDES, LANTERN
see Slides (Photography)
SLIME FUNGI
see Myxomycetes
SLIME MOLDS
see Acrasiales; Myxomycetes
SLOPES (PHYSICAL GEOGRAPHY)
Ahnert, Frank. A General & Comprehensive Theoretical Model of Slope Profile Development. (Occasional Papers in Geography: No. 1). (Illus.). 95p. pap. 2.00 (ISBN 0-686-32710-1). U MD Geography.
Atkinson, J. H. Foundations & Slopes: An Introduction to Applications of Critical State Soil Mechanics. 382p. 1981. pap. 34.95x (ISBN 0-470-27246-5). Halsted Pr.
Bromhead, E. N. The Stability of Slopes. 352p. 1985. text ed. 49.95 (ISBN 0-412-01061-5, 9358, Pub. by Chapman & Hall). Methuen Inc.
--The Stability of Slopes. (Illus.). 352p. 1985. 49.95 (ISBN 0-412-01061-5, 9358). Methuen Inc.
Brunsden, D. Slopes: Form & Process. (The Special Publication of the Institute of British Geographers Ser.: No. 3). 1980. 27.50 (ISBN 0-12-137980-9). Acad Pr.
Carson, M. A. & Kirkby, M. J. Hillslope Form & Process. (Cambridge Geographical Studies). 67.50 (ISBN 0-521-08234-X). Cambridge U Pr.
Chowdhury, R. N. Slope Analysis. (Developments in Geotechnical Engineering Ser.: Vol. 22). 422p. 1978. 83.00 (ISBN 0-444-41724-9). Elsevier.
Haigh, Martin J. Evolution of Slopes on Artificial Landforms, Blaenavon, U. K. LC 78-7267. (Research Papers Ser.: No. 183). (Illus.). 1978. pap. 10.00 (ISBN 0-89065-090-X). U Chicago Dept Geog.
Popov, Igor V. & Kotlov, F. V., eds. The Stability of Slopes. LC 62-12857. 83p. 1963. 25.00x (ISBN 0-306-10657-4, Consultants). Plenum Pub.
Schumm, Stanley A. & Mosley, M. Paul, eds. Slope Morphology. (Benchmark Papers in Geology: Vol. 6). 454p. 1973. 57.95 (ISBN 0-87933-024-4). Van Nos Reinhold.
SLURRY
Baker, P. J. & Jacobs, B. E. Guide to Slurry Pipeline Systems. (Illus.). 58p. (Orig.). 1980. PLB 29.50x (ISBN 0-906085-38-1, Dist. by Air Science Co.). BHRA Fluid.
Drilling Mud & Cement Slurry Rheology Manual. 152p. 1982. 80.00x (ISBN 2-7108-0373-9, Pub. by Order Dept Graham Trotman England). State Mutual Bk.
Gittins, Lavinia. Wear in Slurry Pipelines. (BHRA Information Ser.). (Illus.). 173p. (Orig.). 1980. pap. 41.00x (ISBN 0-906085-45-4). BHRA Fluid.
Hay, E., ed. Slurry Transportation & Pneumatic Handling. 104p. 1983. pap. text ed. 24.00 (ISBN 0-317-03527-4, H00256). ASME.
International Conference on Slurry Transport, 8th: Proceedings. LC 83-61467. (Illus.). 519p. 1983. 75.00 (ISBN 0-932066-08-9). Slurry Tech.
Linderman, Charles W., ed. International Technical Conference on Slurry Transportation, 4th: Proceedings. LC 79-63397. (Illus.). 248p. 1971. pap. 50.00 (ISBN 0-932066-04-6). Slurry Tech.
--International Technical Conference on Slurry Transportation, 5th: Proceedings. 5th ed. LC 80-92621. (Illus.). 296p. (Orig.). 1980. pap. 65.00 (ISBN 0-932066-05-4). Slurry Tech.
Seventh International Technical Conference on Slurry Transportation: Proceedings. LC 82-6012. (Illus.). 454p. 1982. 75.00 (ISBN 0-932066-07-0). Slurry Tech.
Skedgell, David A., ed. International Technical Conference on Slurry Transportation, 6th: Proceedings. LC 81-84303. (Illus.). 400p. (Orig.). 1981. pap. 65.00 (ISBN 0-932066-06-2). Slurry Tech.
Spooner, Philip, et al. Slurry Trench Construction for Pollution Migration Control. LC 84-22747. (Pollution Technology Review Ser.: No. 118). (Illus.). 237p. 1985. 36.00 (ISBN 0-8155-1020-9). Noyes.
Wasp, Edward J., et al. Solid-Liquid Flow Slurry Pipeline Transportation. LC 78-75080. 240p. 1979. 44.95x (ISBN 0-87201-809-1). Gulf Pub.
SMALL BUSINESS–DATA PROCESSING
Baker, Richard H. How to Run Your Business with dBASE II. 26.95 (ISBN 0-8306-0918-0, 1918); pap. 16.95 (ISBN 0-8306-1918-6). TAB Bks.
Beaman, I. R. Small Business Systems for First-Time Users. 180p. 1982. pap. 20.75 (ISBN 0-471-89427-3). Wiley.
Berkery, Michael J. & Bolek, Raymond W. Touche Ross Guide to Selecting a Small Business Computer. LC 84-26528. 337p. 1985. pap. 19.95 (ISBN 0-13-925744-6). P-H.
Blumenthal, Susan. Understanding & Buying a Small Business Computer. LC 81-86553. 160p. 1982. pap. 9.95 (ISBN 0-672-21890-9, 21890). Sams.
Canning, R. G. & Leeper, N. C. So You Are Thinking about a Small Business Computer. 203p. 1982. 22.95 (ISBN 0-13-823625-9); pap. 10.95 (ISBN 0-13-823617-8). P-H.
Christy, Ron & Jones, Billy M. The Complete Information Bank for Entrepreneurs & Small Business Managers. LC 81-70750. (Illus.). 300p. 19.50 (ISBN 0-941958-00-0, Wichita Ctr Entrep SBM). WSU Hist Resources.
Cohen, Jules & McKinney, Catherine S. How to Microcomputerize Your Small Business. (Illus.). 182p. 1983. 18.95 (ISBN 0-13-423897-4); pap. 9.95 (ISBN 0-13-423889-3). P-H.
Contrucci, Peg. The Home Office: How to Set It Up, Operate It, & Make It Pay Off. 300p. 1985. 24.95 (ISBN 0-13-393034-3); pap. 12.95 (ISBN 0-13-393026-2). P-H.
Curry, Jess W., Jr. & Bonner, David M., eds. Up & Running: The Small Business Computer Implementation Cookbook. (Illus.). 150p. 1984. 17.95 (ISBN 0-13-937723-9); pap. 9.95 (ISBN 0-13-937715-8). P-H.
Daniels, Shirley. All You Need to Know about Microcomputers: The Small Business Manager's Advisory. LC 79-64577. (Illus.). 144p. 1979. pap. text ed. 7.95x (ISBN 0-89914-003-3). Third Party Pub.
Eischen, Martha. Does Your Small Business Need a Computer? (Illus.). 168p. 1983. 18.95 (ISBN 0-8306-0224-0, 1624). TAB Bks.
Falk, Howard. Handbook Computer Application for Small or Medium Business. LC 83-70782. 384p. 1983. 19.95 (ISBN 0-8019-7393-7). Chilton.
Gardner, Richard. Micro-Personal-Small Business-Home Computing Directory. 265p. 1985. pap. 29.95 (ISBN 0-933342-05-5). Resources.
Gibson, Glenn A. & Gibson, Mary L. Understanding & Selecting Small Business Computers. (Illus.). 400p. 1986. text ed. 28.95 (ISBN 0-13-937046-3). P-H.
Grieb, William E., Jr. The Small Business Computer Today & Tomorrow. 1984. pap. 6.95 (ISBN 0-671-55907-9, Pub. by Baen Bks). PB.
Hockney, Donald. Personal Computers for the Successful Small Business. 208p. 1984. 15.95 (ISBN 0-02-551870-4). Macmillan.
Holtz, Herman. How to Become a More Successful Consultant with Your Personal Computer. (The Consultant's Library). 150p. (Orig.). 1985. pap. 29.00 (ISBN 0-930686-21-7). Bermont Bks.
Jong, Steven F. Word Processing for Small Business. LC 82-61964. 224p. 1983. pap. 11.95 (ISBN 0-672-21929-8, 21929). Sams.
Kolve, Carolee N. How to Buy (& Survive!) Your First Computer: A Guide for Small Business Success. LC 83-795. (Illus.). 256p. 1983. pap. 14.95 (ISBN 0-07-035130-9, BYTE Bks). McGraw.
Kutten, L. J. Computer Buyer's Protection Guide: How to Protect Your Rights in the Microcomputer Marketplace. 96p. 1983. 19.95 (ISBN 0-13-164195-6); pap. 12.95 (ISBN 0-13-164187-5). P-H.
McGlynn, Daniel R. Personal Computing: Home, Professional, & Small Business Applications. 2nd ed. LC 81-16146. 335p. 1982. pap. 16.95x (ISBN 0-471-86164-2, Pub. by Wiley-Interscience). Wiley.
--Simplified Guide to Small Computers for Business. LC 82-24812. 241p. 1983. pap. 19.50 (ISBN 0-471-86853-1, Pub. by Wiley Interscience). Wiley.
Murray, Jean W. Starting & Operating a Word Processing Service. LC 83-2229. 32p. 1983. pap. 3.50 (ISBN 0-87576-102-X). Pilot Bks.
Rubin, Charles. Appleworks: Boosting your Business with Integrated Software. (Illus.). 288p. (Orig.). 1985. pap. 16.95 (ISBN 0-914845-47-0). Microsoft.
Santoro, Rocco M., et al. Sunbrite Laundry Company: A Computerized Practice Set for a Service Establishment - Apple & IBM Edition. (Career Accounting Ser.). 25p. 1984. pap. 8.95 (ISBN 0-471-80857-1). Wiley.
Schadewald, Robert J. The dBASE Guide for Small Business. 1984. pap. 24.95 (ISBN 0-8359-1245-0). Reston.
Schadewald, Robert J. & Dickey, William. The dBASE II Guide for Small Business. 350p. 1984. pap. 24.95 (ISBN 0-912677-07-4). Ashton-Tate Bks.
Shaw, Donald R. Your Small Business Computer: Evaluating, Selecting, Financing, Installing & Operating the Hardware & Software That Fits. 288p. 1982. 21.95 (ISBN 0-442-27540-4); pap. 10.95 (ISBN 0-442-28137-4). Van Nos Reinhold.
Sippl, Charles & Dahl, Fred. Computer Power for the Small Business. (Illus.). 1979. text ed. 15.95 (ISBN 0-13-165373-3, Spec); pap. text ed. 7.95 (ISBN 0-13-165365-2, Spec). P-H.
Skees, William D. Before You Invest in a Small Business Computer. (Management Ser.). 344p. 1982. 27.50 (ISBN 0-534-97937-8). Lifetime Learn.
Small Business Accounting Software Guide. 340p. 1984. 19.95 (ISBN 0-317-04404-4). Micro Info.
Small Business Software Guide & Handbook Including Vertical Market & Accounting Programs. 1985. Master Volume. 19.95 (ISBN 0-912603-33-X); Apple Volume. 16.95 (ISBN 0-912603-42-9); IBM Volume. 16.95 (ISBN 0-912603-19-4). Micro Info.
Smith, Brian R. & Austin, Daniel J. Word Processing: A Guide for Small Business. LC 82-24914. (Illus.). pap. 9.95 (ISBN 0-86616-021-3). Greene.
Vandeventer, Don. The Small Business Guide to the Commodore 64. Vineyard, Paula, ed. (Illus.). 200p. (Orig.). 1985. pap. 19.95 (ISBN 0-917525-02-7). Work At Home.
Wilcox, Russell E. Computer & Microcomputer Systems for Small Businesses. LC 83-43246. 256p. 1984. lib. bdg. 27.50 (ISBN 0-89774-131-5). Oryx Pr.
SMALL COMPUTERS
see Minicomputers
SMALL MAGELLANIC CLOUDS
see Magellanic Clouds
SMALLTALK 80 (COMPUTER SYSTEM)
Krasner, Glenn. Smalltalk-80: Bits of History, Words of Advice. LC 83-5985. (Computer Science Ser.). (Illus.). 256p. 1983. pap. 23.95 (ISBN 0-201-11669-3). Addison-Wesley.
SMARTWRITER (COMPUTER PROGRAM)
Roth, Pam. The Second Book of Adam: Using SmartWriter. 260p. 1984. pap. 10.95 (ISBN 0-88022-066-X, 111). Que Corp.
SMELL
see also Odors; Olfactory Nerve; Rhinencephalon
Amoore, John E. Molecular Basis of Odor. (Illus.). 216p. 1970. 21.00x (ISBN 0-398-00039-5). C C Thomas.
Bang, Betsy G. Functional Anatomy of the Olfactory System in 23 Orders of Birds. (Acta Anatomica: Suppl. 58, Vol. 79). 1971. pap. 9.50 (ISBN 3-8055-1193-0). S Karger.
Breipohl, W., ed. Olfaction & Endocrine Regulation: Proceedings of the Fourth European Chemoreception Research Organization Mini-Symposium & the Second International Laboratory Workshop on Olfaction, Essen FRG, 1981. 426p. 1982. pap. 35.00 (ISBN 0-904147-35-5). IRL Pr.
Brown, Richard E. & MacDonald, David W., eds. Social Odours in Mammals, 2 vols. (Illus.). 1985. Vol. 1. 60.00x (ISBN 0-19-857546-7); Vol. 2. 45.00x (ISBN 0-19-857617-X). Oxford U Pr.
Denton, Derek A. & Coghlan, John P., eds. Olfaction & Taste, Vol. 5. 1975. 55.50 (ISBN 0-12-209750-5). Acad Pr.
Kashara, Y., et al, eds. Proceedings of the Seventeenth Japanese Symposium on Taste & Smell. (Eng. & Japanese., Illus.). 209p. 1984. pap. 16.00 (ISBN 0-317-17341-3). IRL Pr.
Moulton, D. G., ed. Methods in Olfactory Research. 1975. 81.00 (ISBN 0-12-508950-3). Acad Pr.
Wright, R. H., ed. The Sense of Smell. 248p. 1982. 69.50 (ISBN 0-8493-5232-0). CRC Pr.
Yoshida, Masaaki, ed. Proceedings of the Sixteenth Symposium of the Japanese Association for the Study of Taste & Smell. (Eng. & Japanese., Illus.). 190p. 1982. pap. 16.00 (ISBN 0-317-17342-1). IRL Pr.
SMELTING
see also Electrometallurgy; Metallurgy; Ore-Dressing
Corwin, T. K., et al. International Technology for the Nonferrous Smelting Industry. LC 82-3434. (Chemical Tech. Rev. 205, Pollution Tech Rev. 90). (Illus.). 413p. 1982. 36.00 (ISBN 0-8155-0894-8). Noyes.
Environmental Aspects of Aluminum Smelting: A Technical Review. (Industry Technical Review Ser.: Vol. 3). 167p. 1981. pap. 25.00 (ISBN 92-807-1014-1, UNEP050, UNEP). Unipub.
Fell, James E., Jr. Ores to Metals: The Rocky Mountain Smelting Industry. LC 79-9093. (Illus.). xvi, 341p. 1979. 24.50x (ISBN 0-8032-1951-2). U of Nebr Pr.
Nriagu, Jerome O. Environmental Impacts of Smelters. LC 83-21761. (Advances in Environmental Science & Technology Ser.: 2-010). 608p. 1984. 95.00 (ISBN 0-471-88043-4, Pub. by Wiley-Interscience). Wiley.
Ruddle, R. W. Difficulties Encountered in Smelting in the Lead Blast Furnace. 56p. 1957. 11.50 (ISBN 0-686-38297-8). IMM North Am.
Sohn, H. Y., et al, eds. Advances in Sulfide Smelting: Proceedings, TMS Fall Extractive Meeting, San Francisco, 1983. LC 83-62531. (Illus.). 1143p. 1983. 60.00 (ISBN 0-89520-463-0). Metal Soc.
Sturtevant, Simon. Metallica: Or, the Treatise of New Metallicall Inventions. LC 74-28887. (English Experience Ser.: No. 764). 1975. Repr. of 1612 ed. 9.50 (ISBN 90-221-0764-7). Walter J Johnson.
SMITH CHARTS
Smith, Phillip H. Electronic Applications of the Smith Chart. LC 82-14829. 250p. 1983. Repr. of 1969 ed. lib. bdg. 49.50 (ISBN 0-89874-552-7). Krieger.
SMITHSONIAN INSTITUTION
Alborn, et al. The Popular Smithsonian. 1976. pap. 0.95 (ISBN 0-87972-080-8). Bowling Green Univ.
Baird, S. F., et al. Birds of North America: The Descriptions of Species Based Chiefly on the Collections in the Museum of the Smithsonian Institution, 2 vols. in one. LC 73-17799. (Natural Sciences in America Ser). (Illus.). 1974. 73.00x (ISBN 0-405-05715-6). Ayer Co Pubs.
Baird, Spencer F. Mammals of North America: The Descriptions of Species Based Chiefly on the Collections in the Museum of the Smithsonian Institution. LC 73-17797. (Natural Sciences in America Ser.). (Illus.). 844p. 1974. Repr. 58.50x (ISBN 0-405-05710-5). Ayer Co Pubs.
Dibner, Bern. Heralds of Science. rev. ed. LC 80-25340. (Illus.). 96p. 1981. 14.95 (ISBN 0-88202-191-5); pap. 8.95 (ISBN 0-88202-192-3). Watson Pub Intl.

Goode, George B. The Smithsonian Institution Eighteen Hundred Forty-Six to Eighteen Hundred Ninety-Six: The History of Its First Half Century. Cohen, I. Bernard, ed. LC 79-3119. (Three Centuries of Science in America Ser.). (Illus.). 1980. Repr. of 1897 ed. lib. bdg. 76.00x (ISBN 0-405-12584-4). Ayer Co Pubs.

Hellman, Geoffrey T. The Smithsonian: Octopus on the Mall. LC 77-16190. 1978. Repr. of 1967 ed. lib. bdg. 27.50 (ISBN 0-313-20019-X, HESM). Greenwood.

Hinsley, Curtis M., Jr. Savages & Scientists: The Smithsonian Institution & the Development of American Anthropology 1846-1910. LC 80-20193. (Illus.). 319p. 1981. text ed. 19.95x (ISBN 0-87474-518-7). Smithsonian.

Oehser, Paul H. Sons of Science: The Story of the Smithsonian Institution & Its Leaders. LC 69-10144. (Illus.). 1968. Repr. of 1949 ed. lib. bdg. 18.75 (ISBN 0-8371-0185-9, OESI). Greenwood.

Rhees, William J. An Account of the Smithsonian Institution: Its Founder, Building, Operations, Etc. Cohen, I. Bernard, ed. LC 79-8404. (Three Centuries of Science in America Ser.). (Illus.). 1980. Repr. of 1859 ed. lib. bdg. 12.00x (ISBN 0-405-12582-8). Ayer Co Pubs.

--The Smithsonian Institution: Documents Relative to Its History, 2 vols. Cohen, I. Bernard, ed. LC 79-8405. (Three Centuries of Science in America Ser.). (Illus.). 1980. Set. lib. bdg. 172.00x (ISBN 0-405-12583-6); lib. bdg. 86.00x (ISBN 0-686-65997-X). Vol. 1 (ISBN 0-405-12597-6). Vol. 2 (ISBN 0-405-12599-2). Ayer Co Pubs.

Smithsonian Bks. Smithsonian World. Gallagher, Patricia, ed. 256p. 1984. cancelled (ISBN 0-89599-013-X). Smithsonian Bks.

Smithsonian Experience. LC 77-9213. (Illus.). 256p. 1977. 19.95 (ISBN 0-89599-000-8, Dist. by Norton). Smithsonian Bks.

The Smithsonian Experience. LC 77-9213. (Illus.). 256p. 1981. pap. 9.95 (ISBN 0-89599-008-3). Smithsonian Bks.

Smithsonian Institute. The Smithsonian Experience. (Illus.). 1978. 19.95 (ISBN 0-89599-000-8). Norton.

SMITHSONIAN INSTITUTION–ASTROPHYSICAL OBSERVATORY

Hayes, E. Nelson, ed. Trackers of the Skies. LC 68-28835. (Illus.). 1968. pap. 3.00x (ISBN 0-87299-003-6). Howard Doyle.

SMOG

Gooriah, B. D. & Williams, F. P. The Investigation of Air Pollution: National Survey of Smoke & Sulphur Dioxide--Annual Summary Statistics for the Period 1963-4 to 1977-8, 1979. 1981. 60.00x (ISBN 0-686-97088-8, Pub. by W Spring England). State Mutual Bk.

National Research Council, Division of Medical Sciences, Medical & Biologic Effects of Environmental Pollutants, ed. Ozone & Other Photochemical Oxidants. LC 77-1293. 719p. 1977. 19.50 (ISBN 0-309-02531-1). Natl Acad Pr.

Photochemical Smog: Contribution of Volatile Organic Compounds. 98p. 1982. pap. 9.50 (ISBN 92-64-12297-4). OECD.

SMOG CONTROL DEVICES (MOTOR VEHICLES)

see Motor Vehicles–Pollution Control Devices

SMOKE

see also Combustion; Fume Control; Smog

Committee on Fire Research, National Research Council. Air Quality & Smoke from Urban & Forest Fires. LC 76-8356. (Illus.). 381p. 1976. pap. 11.75 (ISBN 0-309-02500-1). Natl Acad Pr.

--Physiological & Toxicological Aspects of Combustion Products. LC 76-24955. 1976. pap. 9.50 (ISBN 0-309-02521-4). Natl Acad Pr.

Interlaboratory Cooperative Study in the Precision & Accuracy of the Determination of the Relative Density of Black Smoke Using ASTM D 3211, DS 55-S 10. 54p. 1974. pap. 5.00 (ISBN 0-8031-0380-8, 05-055100-17). ASTM.

Smoke & Heat Venting. (Two Hundred Ser). 1968. pap. 6.00 (ISBN 0-685-58165-9, 204). Natl Fire Prot.

Standard Test Method for Measuring the Smoke Generated by Solid Materials. 1974. pap. 2.50 (ISBN 0-685-58190-X, 258-T). Natl Fire Prot.

Teague, Paul E., ed. Smoke & Other Products of Combustion. LC 76-47957. (Illus.). 1977. pap. text ed. 5.00 (ISBN 0-87765-085-3, SPP-41). Natl Fire Prot.

SMOKE PREVENTION

see also Fuel; Furnaces; Incinerators

Butcher, D. G. & Parnell, A. C. Smoke Control in Fire Safety Design. 1979. 42.00x (ISBN 0-419-11190-5, Pub. by E & FN Spon, NO. 6558). Methuen Inc.

SMOOTHING FILTERS (MATHEMATICS)

see Digital Filters (Mathematics)

SNAILS

Baker, H. B. Zonitid Snails from Pacific Islands, 4 pts. in 3 vols. (BMB). Repr. of 1941 ed. Pt. 1. 19.00 (ISBN 0-527-02266-7); Pt. 2. 14.00 (ISBN 0-527-02273-X); Pt. 3. 22.00 (ISBN 0-527-02274-8). Kraus Repr.

Brown, D. S. Freshwater Snails of Africa & Their Medical Importance. 488p. 1980. cancelled (ISBN 0-85066-145-5). Taylor & Francis.

Brown, David S. Freshwater Snails of Africa & Their Medical Importance. LC 81-670043. (Illus.). 450p. 1980. 27.50x (ISBN 0-85066-145-5). Am Malacologists.

Cooke, C. M., Jr. Land Snail Genus Carelia. (BMB Ser.: No. 85). Repr. of 1931 ed. 12.00 (ISBN 0-527-02191-1). Kraus Repr.

Cooke, C. M., Jr. & Kondo, Y. Revision of Tornatellinidae & Achatinellidae. (BMB Ser.: No. 221). Repr. of 1960 ed. 32.00 (ISBN 0-527-02329-9). Kraus Repr.

Davis, George M. The Origin & Evolution of the Gastropod Family Pomatiopsidae, with Emphasis on the Mekong River Triculinae. (Monograph: No. 20). (Illus.). 120p. 1979. pap. 14.00 (ISBN 0-910006-28-8). Acad Nat Sci Phila.

Kerney & Cameron. A Field Guide to the Land Snails of Britain & North West Europe. 29.95 (ISBN 0-00-219676-X, Collins Pub England). Greene.

Neal, M. C. Hawaiian Helicinidae. (BMB Ser.). Repr. of 1934 ed. 12.00 (ISBN 0-527-02231-4). Kraus Repr.

Pilsbry, H. A., et al. Land Snails from Hawaii, Christmas Island & Samoa. (BMB). pap. 8.00 (ISBN 0-527-02153-9). Kraus Repr.

Taft, Celeste. The Shell-Bearing Land Snails of Ohio. 1961. 3.50 (ISBN 0-86727-045-4). Ohio Bio Survey.

Thompson, Fred G. Freshwater Snails of Florida: A Manual for Identification. LC 83-23370. (Illus.). x, 94p. (Orig.). 1985. pap. 19.50 (ISBN 0-8130-0781-X). U Presses Fla.

SNAKE VENOM

Brown, John H. Toxicology & Pharmacology of Venoms from Poisonous Snakes. (Illus.). 208p. 1973. pap. 12.75x (ISBN 0-398-03018-9). C C Thomas.

Lee, C. Y., ed. Snake Venoms. (Handbook of Experimental Pharmacology: Vol. 52). (Illus.). 1979. 259.00 (ISBN 0-387-08709-5). Springer-Verlag.

Tu, Anthony T., ed. Rattlesnake Venoms: Their Actions & Treatment. (Illus.). 416p. 1982. 75.00 (ISBN 0-8247-1691-4). Dekker.

SNAKES

see also Poisonous Snakes;

also particular kinds of snakes, e.g. Rattlesnakes

Allen, Ross. How to Keep Snakes in Captivity. rev. ed. LC 76-184098. pap. 2.95 (ISBN 0-8200-0304-2). Great Outdoors.

Ashton, Ray E., Jr. & Ashton, Patricia S. Handbook of Reptiles & Amphibians of Florida: The Snakes, Vol. 1. LC 81-51066. (Handbook of Reptiles & Amphibians of Florida Ser.). (Illus.). 176p. (Orig.). 1981. pap. 12.95 (ISBN 0-89317-033-X). Windward Pub.

Campbell, Jonathan A. & Ford, Linda S. Phylogenetic Relationships of the Colubrid Snakes of the Genus Adelphicos in the Highlands of Middle America. (Occasional Papers: No. 100). 22p. 1982. 2.25 (ISBN 0-317-04838-4). U of KS Mus Nat Hist.

Campden-Main, Simon M. A Field Guide to the Snakes of South Vietnam. (Illus.). 1983. pap. 9.95 (ISBN 0-9612494-0-4). Herpetological Search.

Clark, Donald R., Jr. Ecological Study of the Worm Snake Carphophis Vermis (Kennicott) (Museum Ser.: Vol. 19, No. 2). 110p. 1970. pap. 5.75 (ISBN 0-686-79836-8). U of KS Mus Nat Hist.

Dixon, James R. The Neotropical Colubrid Snake Genus Liophis. I. The Generic Concept. 40p. 1980. 3.25 (ISBN 0-89326-055-X). Milwaukee Pub Mus.

Duellman, William E. Systematic Status of the Colubrid Snake: Leptodeira Discolor Gunther. (Museum Ser.: Vol. 11, No.1). 9p. 1958. 1.25 (ISBN 0-317-04849-X). U of KS Mus Nat Hist.

--A Taxonomic Study of the Middle American Snake: Pituophis Deppei. (Museum Ser.: Vol. 10, No. 10). 12p. 1960. 1.25 (ISBN 0-317-04847-3). U of KS Mus Nat Hist.

Dunson, W. A. Biology of Sea Snakes. (Illus.). 544p. 1975. 53.50 (ISBN 0-8391-0819-2). Univ Park.

Fitch, Henry S. A Demographic Study of the Ringneck Snake (Diadophis Punctatus) in Kansas. (Miscellaneous Publications Ser.: No. 62). 53p. 1975. pap. 2.75 (ISBN 0-686-80359-0). U of KS Mus Nat Hist.

Fitch, Henry S. & Maslin, T. Paul. Occurrence of the Garter Snake, Thamnophis Sirtalis, in the Great Plains & Rocky Mountains. (Museum Ser.: Vol. 13, No. 5). 20p. 1961. pap. 1.25 (ISBN 0-686-80355-8). U of KS Mus Nat Hist.

Gunther, Albert. Catalogue of Colubrine Snakes in the Collection of the British Museum. xvi, 281p. 1971. Repr. of 1858 ed. 9.00x (ISBN 0-565-00709-2, Pub. by British Mus Nat Hist England). Sabbot-Natural Hist Bks.

Gyi, Ko Ko. A Revision of Colubrid Snakes of the Subfamily Homalopsinae. (Museum Ser.: Vol. 20, No. 2). 177p. 1970. pap. 9.00 (ISBN 0-686-80361-2). U of KS Mus Nat Hist.

Haast, William E. & Anderson, Robert. Complete Guide to Snakes of Florida. (Illus.). 144p. (Orig.). 1981. pap. 8.95 (ISBN 0-940810-00-X). Phoenix FL.

Hardy, Laurence M. & Cole, Charles J. Morphological Variation in a Population of the Snake, Tantilla Gracilis Baird & Girard. (Museum Ser.: Vol. 17, No. 15). 17p. 1968. pap. 1.25 (ISBN 0-686-80362-0). U of KS Mus Nat Hist.

Henderson, R. W. & Binder, M. H. The Ecology & Behavior of Vine Snakes: Anaetulla, Oxybelis, Thelotornis, Uromacer: A Review. 38p. 1980. 3.25 (ISBN 0-89326-063-0). Milwaukee Pub Mus.

Henderson, Robert W. Aggregating Behavior & Exploitation of Subterranean Habitat by Gravid Eastern Mild Snakes (Lampropeltis T. triangulum) 1980. 1.00 (ISBN 0-89326-056-8). Milwaukee Pub Mus.

Introduction of Ophiobolus Graminis Into New Polders & Its Decline. (Agricultural Research Reports: No. 713). 1968. pap. 8.25 (ISBN 90-220-0177-6, XPUDOC, PUDOC). Unipub.

Leetz, Thomas. TFH Book of Snakes. (The T.F.H. Book Ser.). (Illus.). 80p. 1983. 6.95 (ISBN 0-87666-561-X, HP-017). TFH Pubns.

Legler, John M. A New Snake of the Genus Geophis from Chihuahua, Mexico. (Museum Ser.: Vol. 11, No. 4). 8p. 1959. 1.25 (ISBN 0-317-04868-6). U of KS Mus Nat Hist.

Linzey, Donald W. & Clifford, Michael J. Snakes of Virginia. LC 81-12951. (Illus.). 159p. 1981. 15.95x (ISBN 0-8139-0826-4). U Pr of Va.

Logier, E. B. Snakes of Ontario. LC 58-2290. (Illus.). 1958. pap. 8.50 (ISBN 0-8020-6069-2). U of Toronto Pr.

Parker, H. W. Snakes: A Natural History. 2nd ed. LC 76-55850. (Illus.). 112p. 1977. 14.95x (ISBN 0-8014-1095-9); pap. 7.50 (ISBN 0-8014-9164-9). Cornell U Pr.

Parker, Hampton W. Snakes of the World: Their Ways & Means of Living. (Illus.). 191p. 1977. pap. 4.95 (ISBN 0-486-23479-7). Dover.

Parker, William S. & Brown, William S. Comparative Ecology of Two Colubrid Snakes, Masticophis T. Taeniatus & Pituophis Melanolucus Deserticola in Northern Utah. 104p. 1980. 9.95 (ISBN 0-89326-058-4). Milwaukee Pub Mus.

Peters, James A. Dictionary of Herpetology. LC 85-2302. (Illus.). 1964. 16.25x (ISBN 0-02-850230-2). Hafner.

Pinney, Roy. The Snake Book. LC 78-68336. (Illus.). 256p. 1981. 12.95 (ISBN 0-385-13547-5). Doubleday.

Roberts, Mervin F. All about Boas & Other Snakes. (Illus.). 96p. (Orig.). 1975. 6.95 (ISBN 0-87666-763-9, PS-313). TFH Pubns.

Schwaner, Terry D. & Mount, Robert H. Systematic & Ecological Relationships of the Water Snakes Natrix Sipedon & N. Fasciata in Alabama & the Florida Panhandle. (Occasional Papers: No. 45). 44p. 1976. 2.50 (ISBN 0-317-04885-6). U of KS Mus Nat Hist.

Shea, George. Snakes. LC 80-21294. (Creatures Wild & Free Ser.). 1981. 6.95 (ISBN 0-88436-776-2, 35456). EMC.

Simon, Hilda. Easy Identification Guide to North American Snakes. LC 79-55263. (Illus.). 1979. flex. cover 10.95 (ISBN 0-396-07771-4). Dodd.

Smith, M. Monograph of the Sea Snakes. (Illus.). 1964. Repr. of 1926 ed. 14.00 (ISBN 3-7682-0260-7). Lubrecht & Cramer.

Smith, Malcolm A. Reptilia & Amphibia: Serpentes, Vol. 3. 2nd ed. Shipley, A. B., ed. (Fauna of British India Ser.). (Illus.). xii, 583p. 1981. Repr. of 1953 ed. 50.00 (ISBN 0-88065-218-7, Pub. by Messers Today &Tomorrows Printers & Publishers India). Scholarly Pubns.

Snakes of the Catskill Mountains. pap. 1.50 (ISBN 0-686-31390-9). Outdoor Pubns.

Stratton, Richard F. Beginning with Snakes. (Illus.). 96p. pap. 4.95 (ISBN 0-87666-934-8, KW-127). TFH Pubns.

Sweeney, R. C. Snakes of Nyasaland. (Illus.). 1971. Repr. of 1961 ed. 16.74 (ISBN 90-6123-242-2). Lubrecht & Cramer.

Topsell, Edward. The Historie of Serpents; or, the Second Book of Living Creatures. LC 72-6035. (English Experience Ser.: No. 562). 336p. 1973. Repr. of 1608 ed. 58.00 (ISBN 90-221-0562-8). Walter J Johnson.

Varkey, Alexander. Comparative Cranial Myology of North American Natricine Snakes. 76p. 1979. 7.50 (ISBN 0-89326-035-5). Milwaukee Pub Mus.

Visser, John & Chapman, David. Snakes & Snakebite. 1980. 30.00x (ISBN 0-686-69984-X, Pub. by Bailey & Swinton South Africa). State Mutual Bk.

Webb, Robert G. A Review of the Mexican Garter Snake: Thamnophis Cyrtopsis Postremus Smith with Comments on Thamnophis Vicinus Smith. 13p. 1978. 0.75 (ISBN 0-89326-033-9). Milwaukee Pub Mus.

Wilson, Larry D. A Review of the Colubrid Snakes of the Genus Tantilla of Central America. 77p. 1982. 10.00 (ISBN 0-89326-082-7). Milwaukee Pub Mus.

Wilson, Larry D. & Meyer, John R. Snakes of Honduras. 2nd Rev. ed. (Publications in Biology & Geology: No. 6). 159p. 1982. pap. 29.95 (ISBN 0-89326-073-8). Milwaukee Pub Mus.

--Systematics of the Calamarina Group of the Colubrid Snake Genus Tantilla. 1981. 3.25 (ISBN 0-89326-069-X). Milwaukee Pub Mus.

Wright, Albert H. & Wright, Anna A. Handbook of Snakes of the United States & Canada, 2 Vols. (HANH Ser.). (Illus.). 1151p. 1957. 59.50x (ISBN 0-8014-0463-0). Comstock.

SNOBOL (COMPUTER PROGRAM LANGUAGE)

Griswold, Ralph E. The Macro Implementation of SNOBOL4: A Case Study of Machine-Independent Software Development. LC 72-184097. 1972. text ed. 36.95 (ISBN 0-7167-0447-1). W H Freeman.

Griswold, Ralph E. & Griswold, Madge T. A Snobol Four Primer. (Illus.). 128p. 1973. pap. 16.95 (ISBN 0-13-815381-7). P-H.

Griswold, Ralph E., et al. Snobol Four Programming Language. 2nd ed. (Automatic Computation Ser). 1971. pap. 21.95 (ISBN 0-13-815373-6). P-H.

Maurer, W. D. The Programmer's Introduction to SNOBOL. LC 75-26837. (Elsevier Computer Science Library Ser.: No. 3). 142p. 1976. (North Holland); pap. 20.50 (ISBN 0-444-00172-7). Elsevier.

SNOW, CHARLES PERCY, SIR, 1905-

Boytinck, Paul. C. P. Snow: A Reference Guide. 1980. lib. bdg. 28.50 (ISBN 0-8161-8357-0, Hall Reference). G K Hall.

Green, Martin B. Science & the Shabby Curate of Poetry: Essays about the Two Cultures. LC 77-27419. 1978. Repr. of 1964 ed. lib. bdg. 17.00x (ISBN 0-313-20191-9, GRSS). Greenwood.

SNOW

see also Avalanches; Snow Crystals

Colbeck, Samuel C. Dynamics of Snow & Ice Masses. LC 79-17949. 1980. 55.00 (ISBN 0-12-179450-4). Acad Pr.

Dalrymple, Paul, et al. A Year of Snow Accumulation at Plateau Station; Thermal Properties & Heat Transfer Processes of Low-Temperature Snow; Radiative Heat Transfer; Process in Snow & Ice; Papers 1, 2, 3 & 4: Meteorological Studies at Plateau Station, Antarctica. Businger, Joost A., ed. (Antarctic Research Ser.: Vol. 25). (Illus.). 1977. pap. 13.50 (ISBN 0-87590-125-5). Am Geophysical.

Gray, D. M. & Male, D. H., eds. Handbook of Snow: Principles, Processes, Management & Use. (Illus.). 800p. 1981. 66.00 (ISBN 0-08-025375-X); pap. 29.00 (ISBN 0-08-025374-1). Pergamon.

Kirk, Ruth. Snow. LC 77-14997. (Illus.). 1980. pap. 6.20 (ISBN 0-688-08268-8). Quill NY.

Seasonal Snow Cover: A Guide for Measurement, Compilation & Assemblage of Data. (Technical Papers in Hydrology: Vol. 1). (Orig.). 1970. pap. 5.25 (ISBN 92-3-100803-X, U594, UNESCO). Unipub.

U. S. National Committee for the International Hydrological Decade. Advanced Concepts & Techniques in the Study of Snow & Ice Resources. Santeford, H. & Smith, J., eds. x, 789p. 1974. pap. 16.75 (ISBN 0-309-02235-5). Natl Acad Pr.

SNOW CRYSTALS

Antarctic Snow & Ice Studies, I & II, 2 Vols. LC 64-60078. (Antarctic Research Ser. 2 & 16). (Illus.). 277P. Vol. 2. 1964 15.00, (ISBN 0-87590-102-6); 412P. Vol. 16. 1971 32.00, (ISBN 0-87590-116-6). Am Geophysical.

Bentley, W. A. & Humphreys, W. J. Snow Crystals. (Illus.). 1931. pap. 9.95 (ISBN 0-486-20287-9). Dover.

--Snow Crystals. (Illus.). 18.50 (ISBN 0-8446-1660-5). Peter Smith.

LaChapelle, Edward R. Field Guide to Snow Crystals. LC 70-85215. (Illus.). 108p. 1969. pap. 8.95 (ISBN 0-295-95040-4). U of Wash Pr.

SNOW REMOVAL

see also Railroads–Snow Protection and Removal

Managing Snow Removal & Ice Control Programs. (Special Reports Ser: No. 42). 168p. 1974. 15.00x (ISBN 0-917084-09-8). Am Public Works.

Snow Removal & Ice Control in Urban Areas. (Special Reports Ser: No. 30). (Illus.). 128p. 1965. 15.00x (ISBN 0-917084-23-3). Am Public Works.

SNOWFLAKES
see Snow Crystals

SNOWMOBILES

Ainsworth, Fay, ed. Snowmobile Safety & You. (Illus.). 1982. Student Ed. 1.95 (ISBN 0-916682-33-1); Instr. Ed. 2.95 (ISBN 0-916682-32-3). Outdoor Empire.

Chilton's Automotive Editorial Staff. Snowmobiles, Nineteen Sixty-Nine to Nineteen Eighty. (Illus.). 1981. pap. 11.95 (ISBN 0-8019-6978-6). Chilton.

Lund, Morten & Williams, Bea. The Snowmobiler's Bible. LC 73-18519. (Illus.). 192p. 1974. pap. 4.50 (ISBN 0-385-06799-2). Doubleday.

SNOWPLOW EFFECT
see Plasma Dynamics

SOAP AND SOAP TRADE
see also Cleaning Compounds; Detergents, Synthetic

Bramson, Ann. Soap. 2nd ed. LC 75-7286. 1975. pap. 4.95 (ISBN 0-911104-57-7, 073). Workman Pub.

Hobson, Phyllis. Making Homemade Soaps & Candles. LC 74-75461. (Country Skills Library). (Illus.). 48p. 1974. pap. 2.95 (ISBN 0-88266-026-8). Garden Way Pub.

Hunting, Anthony L. Encyclopedia of Shampoo Ingredients. LC 82-90176. 480p. (Orig.). 1983. pap. text ed. 75.00 (ISBN 0-9608752-0-4). Micelle Pr.

McGowan, Ellen A. A Comparative Study of Detergents, with Special Reference to the Teaching of the Subject. LC 75-177025. (Columbia University. Teachers College. Contributions to Education: No. 441). Repr. of 1930 ed. 22.50 (ISBN 0-404-55441-5). AMS Pr.

Mason, Billy. Grandmaw Old Fashion Soap Making. 1978. 5.00 (ISBN 0-942140-04-4). Kelso.

Soap & Detergrent Industry. (UNIDO Guides to Information Sources: No. 24). pap. 4.00 (ISBN 0-686-93278-1, UNID181, UN). Unipub.

SOARING (AERONAUTICS)
see Gliding and Soaring

SOCIAL BEHAVIOR IN ANIMALS

Allee, Warder C. The Social Life of Animals. LC 75-41008. Repr. of 1938 ed. 22.00 (ISBN 0-404-14639-2). AMS Pr.

Banks, Edwin M., ed. Vertebrate Social Organization. LC 76-26571. (Benchmark Papers in Animal Behavior: Vol. 8). 1977. 67.00 (ISBN 0-12-786130-0). Acad Pr.

Brown, Richard E. & MacDonald, David W., eds. Social Odours in Mammals, 2 vols. (Illus.). 1985. Vol. 1. 60.00x (ISBN 0-19-857546-7); Vol. 2. 45.00x (ISBN 0-19-857617-X). Oxford U Pr.

Cohen, Joel E. Casual Groups of Monkeys & Men: Stochastic Models of Elemental Social Systems. LC 73-133215. (Illus.). 1971. 10.00x (ISBN 0-674-09981-8). Harvard U Pr.

Dietz, James M. Ecology & Social Organization of the Maned Wolf (Chrysocyon Brachyurus) LC 83-600292. (Smithsonian Contributions to Zoology: No. 392). pap. 20.00 (ISBN 0-317-19847-5, 2023009). Bks Demand UMI.

Schein, Martin W., ed. Social Hierarchy & Dominance. LC 74-26937. (Benchmark Papers in Animal Behavior, Ser. 3). 401p. 1975. 63.00 (ISBN 0-12-787419-4). Acad Pr.

Shafton, Anthony. Conditions of Awareness: Subjective Factors in the Social Adaptations of Man & Other Primates. LC 76-26201. 1976. pap. 10.00 (ISBN 0-9601130-1-0). Riverstone.

Wilson, Edward O. Sociobiology: The New Synthesis. LC 74-83910. (Illus.). 416p. 1975. 35.00x (ISBN 0-674-81621-8). Harvard U Pr.

SOCIAL INSECTS
see Insect Societies

SOCIAL SCIENCES–DATA PROCESSING

Abelson, Robert B., ed. Using Microcomputers in the Social Studies Classroom. LC 83-14925. (Orig.). 1983. pap. 9.95 (ISBN 0-89994-282-2). Soc Sci Ed.

Andrews, Frank M., et al. A Guide for Selecting Statistical Techniques for Analyzing Social Science Data. 2nd ed. LC 74-620117. 80p. 1981. pap. 8.00x (ISBN 0-87944-274-3). Inst Soc Res.

Aoki, Masanao & Marzollo, Angelo, eds. New Trends in Dynamic System Theory & Economics. LC 78-27701. 1979. 41.50 (ISBN 0-12-058860-9). Acad Pr.

Armor, D. J. & Couch, A. S. Data-Text Primer. LC 78-165564. 1972. pap. text ed. 15.95 (ISBN 0-02-901020-9). Free Pr.

Bailey, Daniel E., ed. Computer Science in Social & Behavioral Science Education. LC 77-25087. (Illus.). 520p. 1978. 32.95 (ISBN 0-87778-101-X). Educ Tech Pubns.

Boguslaw, Robert. Systems Analysis & Social Planning: Human Problems of Post-Industrial Society. 1982. text ed. 29.50x (ISBN 0-8290-0111-5). Irvington.

Bohrnstedt, George W. & Knoke, David. Statistics for Social Data Analysis. LC 81-82889. 530p. 1982. text ed. 27.50 (ISBN 0-87581-275-9). Peacock Pubs.

Brier, Alan, et al. Computers & the Social Sciences. LC 74-12052. 285p. 1974. 30.00x (ISBN 0-231-03914-X); pap. 15.00x (ISBN 0-231-03915-8). Columbia U Pr.

Brownell, Blaine A. Using Microcomputers. 1985. 16.95 (ISBN 0-8039-2291-4). Sage.

Budin, Howard, et al. Using Computers in the Social Studies. (Computers in the Curriculum Ser.: No. 1). 136p. (Orig.). 1986. pap. text ed. 11.95x (ISBN 0-8077-2781-4). Tchrs Coll.

Chartrand, Robert L., ed. Computers in the Service of Society. LC 73-112401. 256p. 1972. 32.00 (ISBN 0-08-016332-7). Pergamon.

Cohen, Louis & Holliday, Michael. Statistics for Social Scientists: An Introductory Text with Computer Programmes in Basic. 382p. 1983. pap. text ed. 20.95 (ISBN 0-06-041321-2, HarpC). Har-Row.

Conrad, Peter & Reinharz, Shulamit, eds. Computers & Qualitative Data: A Special Issue of Qualitative Sociology. 212p. 1984. pap. 16.95 (ISBN 0-89885-218-8). Human Sci Pr.

Davisson, William I. Information Processing. LC 76-109528. 276p. 1970. pap. 12.50x (ISBN 0-306-50010-8, Plenum Pr). Plenum Pub.

Dery, David. Computers in Welfare: The MIS-Match. LC 81-224. (Managing Information Ser.: Vol. 3). (Illus.). 264p. 1981. 25.00 (ISBN 0-8039-1610-8). Sage.

Greenbaum, Joan M. In the Name of Efficiency: Management Theory & Shopfloor Practice in Data Processing Work. 210p. 1979. 27.95 (ISBN 0-87722-151-0). Temple U Pr.

Heise, David R. Computer-Assisted Analysis of Social Action: Use of Program INTERACT & SURVEY.UNC75. LC 78-8724. (Technical Papers Ser: No. 3). 154p. 1978. pap. text ed. 5.00 (ISBN 0-89143-086-5). U NC Inst Res Soc Sci.

Hy, Ronn J. Using the Computer in the Social Sciences: A Nontechnical Approach. LC 77-956. (Illus.). 156p. 1977. 15.00 (ISBN 0-444-00211-1). Elsevier.

Jendrek. Through the Maze: Statistics with Computer Applications. 1984. write for info. (ISBN 0-534-03921-9). Wadsworth Pub.

Klieger, Douglas M. Computer Use for Social Scientists. 350p. 1983. pap. 21.53 scp (ISBN 0-205-07962-8, 207962). Allyn.

Knoke, David & Kuklinski, James H. Network Analysis. (Sage University Papers: Quantitative Applications in the Social Sciences: Vol. 28). 88p. pap. 5.00 (ISBN 0-8039-1914-X). Sage.

Kruskal, Joseph B. & Wish, Myron. Multidimensional Scaling. LC 77-93286. (University Papers Ser.: Quantitative Applications in the Social Sciences, No. 11). 93p. 1978. pap. 5.00 (ISBN 0-8039-0940-3). Sage.

LaPlante, Josephine M. An Introduction to Computer Analysis in the Social Sciences & Business Using SAS. (Learning Packages in the Policy Sciences Ser.: No. 21). (Illus.). 53p. (Orig.). 1981. pap. text ed. 3.50x (ISBN 0-936826-16-9). Pol Stud Assocs.

Law, Henry G. & Snyder, Conrad W., Jr., eds. Research Methods for Multi-Mode Data Analysis. 272p. 1984. 49.95 (ISBN 0-03-062826-1). Praeger.

Lehman, Richard S., ed. Programming for the Social Sciences: Algorithms & FORTRAN 77 Coding. 1985. text ed. write for info. (ISBN 0-89859-588-6). L Erlbaum Assocs.

Madron, Thomas W., et al. Using Microcomputers in Research. 1985. 5.00 (ISBN 0-8039-2457-7). Sage.

Meadows, Donella H. The Electronic Oracle Computer Models & Social Decisions. LC 84-13060. 1985. 39.95 (ISBN 0-471-90558-5). Wiley.

Mochmann, Ekkehard & Muller, Paul J. Data Protection & Social Science Research. 229p. 1982. text ed. 36.50x (ISBN 3-593-32604-3). Irvington.

National Computing Centre Ltd. Computers in the Social Sciences: A Study Guide. Penney, G., ed. LC 74-164433. (Computers & People Ser). 48p. 1973. pap. 10.00x (ISBN 0-85012-095-0). Intl Pubns Serv.

Raben, J. & Marks, G. Data Bases in the Humanities & the Social Sciences. 330p. 1980. 46.75 (ISBN 0-444-86220-X, North-Holland). Elsevier.

Rattenbury, Judith & Pelletier, Paula. Data Processing in the Social Sciences with OSIRIS III. LC 74-620138. 245p. 1974. 15.00x (ISBN 0-87944-163-1); pap. 10.00x (ISBN 0-87944-162-3). Inst Soc Res.

Rattenbury, Judith, et al. Computer Processing of Social Science Data Using OSIRIS IV. 200p. (Orig.). 1984. pap. text ed. 20.00x (ISBN 0-87944-295-6). Inst Soc Res.

Rowe, Beverley & Scheer, Marianne, eds. Computer Software for Social Science Data. 246p. 1977. 25.00x (ISBN 0-900296-55-0, Pub. by Social Sci Res). State Mutual Bk.

Ruggles, Nancy D., ed. Role of the Computer in Economic & Social Research in Latin America. (Other Conferences Ser.: No. 8). 409p. 1975. 20.00 (ISBN 0-87014-260-7, Dist. by Columbia U Pr). Natl Bur Econ Res.

Slavin, Simon, ed. Applying Computers in Social Service & Mental Health Agencies. LC 81-20102. (Administration in Social Work Ser.: Vol. 5, Nos. 3 & 4). 184p. 1982. text ed. 30.00 (ISBN 0-86656-102-1, B102). Haworth Pr.

Sorin, Martin D. Data Entry Without Keypunching: Improved Preparation for Social-Data Analysis. LC 78-24637. 288p. 1982. 23.00x (ISBN 0-669-02803-7). Lexington Bks.

Taylor, James B. Using Microcomputers in Social Agencies. LC 81-1759. (Human Services Guides Ser.: Vol. 19). (Illus.). 219p. 1981. pap. 7.95 (ISBN 0-8039-1617-5). Sage.

Vallee, Jacques, et al. Social, Managerial, & Economic Issues. (Group Communication Through Computers: Vol. 4). 222p. 1978. 15.00 (ISBN 0-318-14421-2, R40). Inst Future.

Vasu, Ellen S. & Palmer, Richard I. An Introduction to Research & the Computer: A Self-Instructional Package. LC 77-28538. (IRSS Technical Papers Ser: No. 1). 37p. 1977. pap. text ed. 3.50 (ISBN 0-89143-085-7). U NC Inst Res Soc Sci.

Williams. Computer-Readable Databases, a Directory & Data Source Book: Business, Law, Humanities & Social Sciences. 4th ed. Date not set. write for info. (ISBN 0-444-87614-6). Elsevier.

SOCIAL SCIENCES–MATHEMATICAL MODELS

Abraham, Ralph & Shaw, Chris. Dynamics: The Geometry of Behavior: Pt. 3, Global Behavior. (Visual Mathematical Ser.). (Illus.). 176p. 1985. pap. 26.00x (ISBN 0-942344-03-0). Aerial Pr.

Adams, William J. Calculus for Business & Social Science. LC 74-5524. 250p. 1975. text ed. 30.75 (ISBN 0-471-00988-1). Wiley.

Ball, M. A. Mathematics in the Social & Life Sciences: Theories, Models & Methods. (Mathematics & Its Applications Ser.). 1985. 49.95 (ISBN 0-470-20191-6). Halsted Pr.

Budnick, F. S. Finite Mathematics with Applications in Management & Social Sciences. 512p. 1985. 29.95 (ISBN 0-07-008861-6). McGraw.

Burghes, D. N. & Wood, A. D. Mathematical Models in the Social Management & Life Sciences. LC 79-40989. (Mathematics & Its Applications Ser.). 287p. 1980. pap. text ed. 28.95x (ISBN 0-470-27073-X). Halsted Pr.

Dwyer, James H. Statistical Models for the Social & Behavioral Sciences. (Illus.). 1983. text ed. 39.95x (ISBN 0-19-503145-8). Oxford U Pr.

Harshbarger, Ronald J. & Reynoldds, James J. Mathematical Applications for Management, Life & Social Studies. 604p. 1981. text ed. 26.95 (ISBN 0-669-03209-3); student solutions guide 3.95 (ISBN 0-669-03211-5); answer key 1.95 (ISBN 0-669-06400-9). Heath.

Huckfeidt, Robert R., et al, eds. Dynamic Modeling: An Introduction. LC 82-42610. (Quantitative Applications in the Social SCiences Ser.: Vol. 27). 1982. pap. 5.00 (ISBN 0-8039-0946-2). Sage.

Katzner, Donald W. Analysis Without Measurement. LC 82-4469. 366p. 1983. 39.50 (ISBN 0-521-24847-7). Cambridge U Pr.

Lial, Margaret L. & Miller, Charles D. Mathematics with Applications in the Management, Natural, & Social Sciences. 3rd ed. 1983. text ed. 27.90x (ISBN 0-673-15793-8). Scott F.

Meadows, Donella H. The Electronic Oracle Computer Models & Social Decisions. LC 84-13060. 1985. 39.95 (ISBN 0-471-90558-5). Wiley.

Mizrahi, Abe & Sullivan, Michael. Finite Mathematics with Applications for Business & Social Sciences. 4th ed. LC 82-17590. 637p. 1983. 33.50 (ISBN 0-471-05398-8); study guide 12.95 (ISBN 0-471-08693-2). Wiley.

Olinick, Michael. Introduction to Mathematical Models in the Social & Life Sciences. LC 77-77758. (Illus.). 1978. text ed. 26.95 (ISBN 0-201-05448-5). Addison-Wesley.

Plewis, Ian. Analysing Change Methods for the Measurement & Explanations of Change in the Social Sciences. 1985. 29.95 (ISBN 0-471-10444-2). Wiley.

Roberts, Fred S. Discrete Mathematical Models with Applications to Social Biological & Environmental Problems. (Illus.). 560p. 1976. Ref. Ed. 39.95 (ISBN 0-13-214171-X). P-H.

--Graph Theory & Its Applications to Problems of Society. LC 78-6277. (CBMS-NSF Regional Conference Ser.: No. 29). v, 122p. (Orig.). 1978. pap. text ed. 17.00 (ISBN 0-89871-026-X). Soc Indus-Appl Math.

Wheeler, Ruric E. & Peeples, W. D., Jr. Finite Mathematics: With Applications to Business & the Social Sciences. LC 80-13916. 550p. 1980. text ed. 24.00 pub net (ISBN 0-8185-0418-8). Brooks-Cole.

Williams. Mathematics with Applications in the Management, Natural & Social Sciences. 1985. 31.52 (ISBN 0-205-07188-0, 567188); instr. manual 7.23 (ISBN 0-205-07189-9, 567189). Allyn.

SOCIAL SCIENCES–STATISTICS

Berger, Louis S. Introductory Statistics: A New Approach for Behavioral Science Students. LC 79-2484. 407p. 1981. text ed. 37.50 (ISBN 0-8236-2775-6). Intl Univs Pr.

Champion, Dean. Basic Statistics for Social Research. 2nd ed. 1981. text ed. write for info. (ISBN 0-02-320600-4). Macmillan.

Cohen & Holliday. Statistics For the Social Sciences. 320p. 1982. text ed. 31.50 (ISBN 0-06-318219-X, Pub. by Har-Row Ltd England); pap. text ed. 18.50 (ISBN 0-06-318220-3, Pub. by Har-Row Ltd England). Har-Row.

Cohen, Louis & Holliday, Michael. Statistics for Social Scientists: An Introductory Text with Computer Programmes in Basic. 382p. 1983. pap. text ed. 20.95 (ISBN 0-06-041321-2, HarpC). Har-Row.

Compendium of Social Statistics: 1977. (Statistical Papers Ser.: No. 4). 1325p. 1980. pap. 35.00 (ISBN 0-686-68947-X, UN80 17 6, UN). Unipub.

Elifson, Kirk W., et al. Fundamentals of Social Statistics. 416p. 1982. text ed. 22.95 (ISBN 0-394-35023-5, RanC); 6.95 (ISBN 0-394-35025-1). Random.

Fuller, M. F. & Lury, D. A. Statistics Workbook for Social Science Students. 250p. 1977. text ed. 30.00x (ISBN 0-86003-016-4, Pub. by Allan Pubs England); pap. text ed. 15.25x (ISBN 0-86003-117-9). Humanities.

Horowitz, Gideon. Sadistic Statistics: An Introduction to Statistics for the Social & Behavioral Sciences. 2nd ed. (Illus.). 170p. 1981. pap. text ed. 10.95 (ISBN 0-89529-135-5). Avery Pub.

Kim, Jae-On & Mueller, Charles. Introduction to Factor Analysis: What It Is & How to Do It. LC 79-103006. (The University Papers Ser.: Quantitive Applications in the Social Sciences No. 13). 79p. 1978. pap. 5.00 (ISBN 0-8039-1165-3). Sage.

Kim, Jae-On & Mueller, Charles W. Factor Analysis: Statistical Methods & Practical Issues. LC 78-64332. (University Papers: Quantitative Applications in the Social Sciences No. 14). 88p. 1978. pap. 5.00 (ISBN 0-8039-1166-1). Sage.

Lutz, Gene M. Understanding Social Statistics. 624p. 1983. text ed. write for info. (ISBN 0-02-372980-5). Macmillan.

McKay, David & Schofield, Norman, eds. Data Analysis & the Social Sciences. LC 83-42529. 291p. 1983. 29.95 (ISBN 0-312-18300-3). St Martin.

Stevens, James P. Applied Multivariate Statistics for Social Sciences. 300p. Date not set. text ed. 45.00 (ISBN 0-89859-568-1). L Erlbaum Assocs.

Watson, George & McGaw, Dickinson. Statistical Inquiry: Elementary Statistics for the Political, Social & Policy Sciences. LC 79-12109. 410p. 1980. text ed. 32.45x (ISBN 0-471-02087-7). Wiley.

Wildt, Albert R. & Vahtola, Olli. Analysis of Covariance. LC 78-64331. (University Papers Ser.: Quantitative Applications in the Social Sciences No. 12). 93p. 1978. pap. 5.00 (ISBN 0-8039-1164-5). Sage.

Wright, Sonia R. Quantitative Methods & Statistics: A Guide to Social Research. LC 79-12570. (Illus.). 1979. 24.00 (ISBN 0-8039-1294-3); pap. 12.00 (ISBN 0-8039-1295-1). Sage.

SOCIAL SCIENCES–STATISTICAL METHODS

Aydelotte, William O., et al, eds. Dimensions of Quantitative Research in History. LC 72-736. (Quantitative Studies in History Ser). 420p. 1972. pap. 18.00 LPE (ISBN 0-691-10045-4, 45). Princeton U Pr.

Duncan, Otis D., et al. Statistical Geography: Problems in Analyzing Areal Data. LC 77-7890. (Illus.). 1977. Repr. of 1961 ed. lib. bdg. 17.75x (ISBN 0-8371-9676-0, DUSG). Greenwood.

Dunn, Edgar S. Social Information Processing & Statistical Systems-Change & Reform. LC 74-5289. pap. 64.00 (ISBN 0-317-10338-5, 2051570). Bks Demand UMI.

Dwyer, James H. Statistical Models for the Social & Behavioral Sciences. (Illus.). 1983. text ed. 39.95x (ISBN 0-19-503145-8). Oxford U Pr.

Edwards, Ward & Newman, J. Robert. Multiattribute Evaluation. (Quantitative Applications in the Social Sciences Ser.: Vol. 26). (Illus.). 96p. 1982. pap. 5.00 (ISBN 0-8039-0095-3). Sage.

SOCIAL SERVICE–DATA PROCESSING

SOCIOBIOLOGY

SOCIOLOGY–MATHEMATICAL MODELS

SOCKETS, ELECTRIC
see Electric Contactors

SODIUM

SODIUM CHLORIDE
see Salt

SODIUM METABOLISM

SOFT DRINK INDUSTRY
see also Beverages

SOFT DRINKS
see Beverages
SOFTCOATED WHEATEN TERRIER
see Dogs–Breeds–Softcoated Wheaten Terrier
SOFTWARE, COMPUTER
see Computer Programs; Programming (Electronic Computers); Programming Languages (Electronic Computers);
also similiar headings
SOIL (ENGINEERING)
see Soil Mechanics
SOIL ABSORPTION
see also Soil Absorption and Adsorption
SOIL ABSORPTION AND ADSORPTION
see also Soil Percolation

SOIL ADSORPTION
see Soil Absorption and Adsorption
SOIL BIOLOGY
see also Earthworms; Soil Ecology; Soil Fauna; Soil Micro-Organisms

SOIL CAPILLARITY

SOIL CHEMISTRY
see also Soil Absorption and Adsorption

Organic Materials & Soil Productivity in the Near East: Papers Presented at the FAO-SIDA Workshop on the Use of Organic Materials for Improving Soil Productivity in the Near East. (Soils Bulletins: No. 45). 336p. (English with an Arabic summary). 1982. pap. 24.00 (ISBN 92-5-001217-9, F2334, FAO). Unipub.

Paul & Ladd. Soil Biochemistry, Vol. 5. (Books on Soils & the Environment). 504p. 1981. 84.75 (ISBN 0-8247-1131-9). Dekker.

Paul, E. A. & McLaren, A. D., eds. Soil Biochemistry, Vol. 4. (Books on Soils & the Environment). 296p. 1975. softcover 65.00 (ISBN 0-8247-7023-4). Dekker.

Shainberg, I. & Shalhevet, J., eds. Soil Salinity under Irrigation. (Ecological Studies; Analysis & Synthesis: Vol. 51). (Illus.). 370p. 1984. 52.00 (ISBN 0-387-13565-0). Springer-Verlag.

Soil Chemistry, Soil Fertility & Soil Clay Mineralogy Commissions of the International Society of Soil Science, 13-18 July 1976, Jerusalem. Agrochemicals in Soils: Selected Papers. Banin, A. & Kafkafi, U., eds. LC 79-41750. 500p. 1980. 94.00 (ISBN 0-08-025914-6). Pergamon.

Sposito, Garrison. The Surface Chemistry of Soils. (Illus.). 234p. 1984. 42.50x (ISBN 0-19-503421-X). Oxford U Pr.

Stucki, J. W. & Banwart, L., eds. Advanced Chemical Methods for Soil & Clay Minerals Reasearch. 488p. 1980. lib. bdg. 58.00 (ISBN 0-686-29003-8, Pub. by Reidel Holland). Kluwer Academic.

Tan. Principles of Soil Chemistry. (Books in Soil & the Environment). 304p. 1982. 34.50 (ISBN 0-8247-1336-2). Dekker.

Van Assche, C., ed. Agro-Ecological Aspects of Soil Disinfestation. (Agro-Ecosystems Ser.: Vol. 1, No. 2). 1974. 18.00 (ISBN 0-686-43414-5). Elsevier.

Vose, Peter B. & Ruschel, Alaides P., eds. Associative N-Two Fixation, Vols. 1 & 2. 1981. Vol. 1, 232 Pgs. 65.00 (ISBN 0-8493-6130-3); Vol. 2, 288 Pgs. 75.00 (ISBN 0-8493-6131-1). CRC Pr.

Wambeke, A. van. Management Properties of Ferralsols. (Soils Bulletins: No. 23). 120p. (2nd Printing 1979). 1980. pap. 8.75 (ISBN 92-5-100754-3, F1165, FAO). Unipub.

Yu, T., ed. Physical Chemistry of Paddy Soils. (Illus.). 1985. 59.50 (ISBN 0-387-13001-2). Springer-Verlag.

SOIL CLASSIFICATION

see Soils–Classification

SOIL COMPACTION

see Soil Stabilization

SOIL CONDITIONERS

see Soil Stabilization

SOIL CONSERVATION

see also Erosion; Soil Erosion

Arakeri, H. R. & Donahue, Roy. Principles of Soil Conservation & Water Management. LC 83-27044. 266p. 1984. 30.50x (ISBN 0-8476-7350-2); tables incl. Rowman & Allanheld.

Archer, Sellers G. Soil Conservation. LC 56-6002. (Illus.). 1969. Repr. of 1956 ed. 16.95x (ISBN 0-8061-0346-9). U of Okla Pr.

Ayres, Quincy C. Soil Erosion & Its Control. LC 72-2832. (Use & Abuse of America's Natural Resources Ser). (Illus.). 382p. 1972. Repr. of 1936 ed. 30.00 (ISBN 0-405-04501-8). Ayer Co Pubs.

Bennett, Hugh H. Soil Conservation. LC 74-125731. (American Environmental Studies). 1970. Repr. of 1939 ed. 51.00 (ISBN 0-405-02656-0). Ayer Co Pubs.

Black, Peter E., ed. Readings in Soil & Water Conservation. 275p. 1974. text ed. 38.50x (ISBN 0-8422-5204-5); pap. text ed. 14.95x (ISBN 0-8422-0452-0). Irvington.

Chakela, Q. K. Soil Erosion & Reservoir Sedimentation in Lesotho. 1981. text ed. 29.50x (ISBN 0-8419-9737-3, Africana). Holmes & Meier.

Christy, Lawrence C. Legislative Principles of Soil Conservation. (Soils Bulletins: No. 15). 73p. (2nd Printing 1977). 1971. pap. 7.50 (ISBN 92-5-100257-6, F1157, FAO). Unipub.

Cocannouer, Joseph. Weeds: Guardians of the Soil. (Illus.). pap. 7.95 (ISBN 0-8159-7205-9). Devin.

Constantinesco, I. Soil Conservation for Developing Countries. (Soils Bulletins: No. 30). (Eng., Fr. & Span., Illus.). 104p. (3rd Printing 1981). 1976. pap. 7.75 (ISBN 92-5-100101-4, F1172, FAO). Unipub.

Cook, Ray L. Soil Management for Conservation & Production. LC 62-8770. (Illus.). 527p. 1962. 40.50 (ISBN 0-471-16995-1). Wiley.

Crosson, Pierre R. & Brubaker, Sterling. Resource & Environmental Effects of U. S. Agriculture. LC 82-47984. (Resources for the Future Ser.). 272p. 1983. pap. 15.00x (ISBN 0-8018-2920-8). Johns Hopkins.

Davies, J., et al. Guide to the Study of Soil Ecology. 1973. text ed. 12.40 (ISBN 0-13-370973-6); pap. text ed. 10.84 (ISBN 0-13-370965-5). P-H.

El-Swaffy, S. A. & Moldenhauer, W. C., eds. Soil Erosion & Conservation. 806p. 35.00 (ISBN 0-935734-11-2). Soil Conservation.

Faulkner, Edward H. Plowman's Folly. 154p. 1943. 10.95 (ISBN 0-8061-0124-5); pap. 5.95 (ISBN 0-8061-1169-0). U of Okla Pr.

Foster, Albert B. & Bosworth, Duane. Approved Practices in Soil Conservation. 5th ed. (Illus.). 470p. 1982. 19.95 (ISBN 0-8134-2170-5, 2170); text ed. 14.95x. Interstate.

Gray, Donald & Leiser, Andrew. Biotechnical Slope Protection: Economic Methods for Earth Support & Erosion Control. 432p. 1982. 28.95 (ISBN 0-442-21222-4). Van Nos Reinhold.

Greenland, D. J. & Lal, R., eds. Soil Conservation & Management in the Humid Tropics. LC 76-8908. 283p. 1977. 84.95 (ISBN 0-471-99473-1, Pub. by Wiley-Interscience). Wiley.

Halcrow, Harold G., et al, eds. Soil Conservation Policies, Institutions, & Incentives. LC 82-699. 330p. 1982. text ed. 6.00 (ISBN 0-935734-06-6). Soil Conservation.

Hudson, Norman. Soil Conservation. 2nd ed. LC 81-66538. (Illus.). 320p. 1981. 27.50x (ISBN 0-8014-1436-9). Cornell U Pr.

--Soil Conservation. LC 76-160152. 1971. 17.50x (ISBN 0-8014-0654-4). Cornell U Pr.

--Soil Conservation. 2nd ed. LC 81-66538. (Illus.). 324p. pap. text ed. 15.95x (ISBN 0-8014-9343-9). Cornell U Pr.

Jacks, Graham V. & Whyte, Robert O. Vanishing Lands: A World Survey of Soil Erosion. LC 72-4280. (World Affairs Ser.: National & International Viewpoints). (Illus.). 384p. 1972. Repr. of 1939 ed. 25.50 (ISBN 0-405-04573-5). Ayer Co Pubs.

Kirkby, M. J. & Morgan, R. P., eds. Soil Erosion: Landscape Systems. (A Series in Geomorphology). 312p. 1981. 79.95x (ISBN 0-471-27802-5, Pub. by Wiley-Interscience). Wiley.

Knuti, Leo L., et al. Profitable Soil Management. 2nd ed. 1970. text ed. 31.52 (ISBN 0-13-729400-X). P-H.

Kohnke, Helmut & Bertrand, A. R. Soil Conservation. (Agricultural Ser.). 1959. text ed. 45.95 (ISBN 0-07-035285-2). McGraw.

Kussow, W. & El-Swaify, S. A., eds. Soil Erosion & Conservation in the Tropics. (ASA Special Publications Ser.). 149p. 1982. pap. 8.50 (ISBN 0-89118-068-0). Am Soc Agron.

Moldenhauer, William C., pref. by. Soil Conservation Policies: An Assessment. LC 80-406. 154p. (Orig.). 1980. pap. 6.50 (ISBN 0-935734-04-X). Soil Conservation.

Morgan, R. P., ed. Soil Conservation: Problems & Prospects. 576p. 1981. 74.95x (ISBN 0-471-27882-3, Pub. by Wiley-Interscience). Wiley.

Oliverio, Jean E. Footprints in the Soil & Reflections on the Water. (Illus.). 1972. 6.00 (ISBN 0-87012-137-5). McClain.

Palmer, Robert G. & Troeh, Frederick R. Introductory Soil Science: Laboratory Manual. 2nd ed. 1977. pap. 7.95x (ISBN 0-8138-1555-X). Iowa St U Pr.

Pritchard, H. Wayne, pref. by. Resource Conservation Glossary. 3rd ed. LC 82-5830. 193p. 1982. pap. 7.00 (ISBN 0-935734-09-0). Soil Conservation.

Residential Erosion & Sediment Control: Objectives, Principles & Design Considerations. 64p. 1978. pap. 10.00x (ISBN 0-87262-133-2). Am Soc Civil Eng.

Residential Erosion & Sediment Control: Objectives, Principles & Design Considerations. LC 78-63632. (Illus.). 63p. 1978. pap. 12.50 (ISBN 0-87420-584-0, E09); pap. 10.00 members. Urban Land.

Rudman, Jack. Soil Conservationist. (Career Examination Ser.: C-1032). (Cloth bdg. avail. on request). pap. 10.00 (ISBN 0-8373-1032-6). Natl Learning.

Schwab, G. O., et al. Elementary Soil & Water Engineering. 2nd ed. LC 76-132224. 316p. 1979. 40.00 (ISBN 0-471-76526-0); Arabic Translation 9.80 (ISBN 0-471-04504-7). Wiley.

Schwab, Glenn O. & Frevert, Richard K. Soil & Water Conservation Engineering. 3rd ed. LC 80-27961. 525p. 1981. 44.00 (ISBN 0-471-03078-3); solutions manual avail. (ISBN 0-471-05018-0). Wiley.

Selby, M. J. Hillslope Materials & Processes. (Illus.). 1982. 46.00x (ISBN 0-19-874126-X); pap. 24.00x (ISBN 0-19-874127-8). Oxford U Pr.

Soil Erosion by Water: Some Measures for Its Control on Cultivated Lands. (Agricultural Development Papers: No. 81). 284p. (2nd Printing 1978). 1965. pap. 21.50 (ISBN 92-5-100474-9, F1478, FAO). Unipub.

Soil Erosion by Wind & Measures for Its Control on Agriculture Lands. (Agricultural Development Papers: No. 71). 88p. 1960. pap. 5.25 (ISBN 92-5-100473-0, F424, FAO). Unipub.

The Soil: How to Conserve the Soil. (Better Farming Ser.: No. 5). (Illus.). 29p. 1976. pap. 7.50 (ISBN 92-5-100144-8, F63, FAO). Unipub.

Sopper, William E. & Kardos, Louis T., eds. Recycling Treated Municipal Wastewater & Sludge Through Forest & Cropland. LC 73-2382. (Illus.). 479p. 1973. 27.50x (ISBN 0-271-01159-9). Pa St U Pr.

Tate & Klein. Soil Reclamation Process. (Books in Soil & Environment Ser.). 432p. 1985. 59.50 (ISBN 0-8247-7286-5). Dekker.

Torrent Control Terminology. (Conservation Guides: No. 6). (Eng., Span., Ital. & Ger.). 165p. 1982. pap. 12.00 (ISBN 92-5-001091-5, F2224, FAO). Unipub.

Toy, Terrence J. Erosion: Research Techniques, Erodibility & Sediment Delivery. 86p. 1980. pap. 4.60x (ISBN 0-86094-000-4, Pub. by GEO Abstracts England). State Mutual Bk.

Traynor, Joe. Ideas in Soil & Plant Nutrition. (Orig.). 1980. pap. 5.00 (ISBN 0-9604704-0-9); pap. text ed. 5.00 (ISBN 0-9604704-0-9). Kovak Bks.

Troeh, Frederick R., et al. Soil & Water Conservation. Troeh, Miriam, ed. (Illus.). 1980. text ed. 34.95 (ISBN 0-13-822155-3). P-H.

Vance, Mary. Soil Conservation: Monographs. (Public Administration Series: Bibliography P-1541). 56p. 1984. pap. 8.25 (ISBN 0-89028-141-6). Vance Biblios.

SOIL CORROSION

Kittrick, J. A., et al, eds. Acid Sulfate Weathering. (SSSA Special Publication Ser.). 242p. 1982. 12.50 (ISBN 0-89118-770-7). Soil Sci Soc Am.

Schmidt, B. L., et al, eds. Determinants of Soil Loss Tolerance. (ASA Special Publication Ser.). 153p. 1982. pap. 8.50 (ISBN 0-89118-071-0). Am Soc Agron.

Zachar, D. Soil Erosion. (Developments in Soil Science Ser.: Vol. 10). 548p. 1982. 93.75 (ISBN 0-444-99725-3). Elsevier.

SOIL ECOLOGY

Agrochemical Residue-Biota Interactions in Soil & Aquatic Ecosystems. (Panel Proceedings Ser.). (Illus.). 305p. 1981. pap. 38.50 (ISBN 92-0-111280-7, ISP548, IAEA). Unipub.

Brown, Allison L. Ecology of Soil Organisms. LC 78-313368. 1978. pap. text ed. 9.95x (ISBN 0-435-60621-2). Heinemann Ed.

Davies, J., et al. Guide to the Study of Soil Ecology. 1973. text ed. 12.40 (ISBN 0-13-370973-6); pap. text ed. 10.84 (ISBN 0-13-370965-5). P-H.

Dickinson, C. H. & Pugh, G. J., eds. Biology of Plant Litter Decomposition, 2 vols. 1974. Vol. 1. 60.00 (ISBN 0-12-215001-5); Vol. 2. 99.00 (ISBN 0-12-215002-3). Acad Pr.

Fitter, A. H., ed. Ecological Interactions in the Soil Environment. (Illus.). 400p. 1985. pap. text ed. 57.00x (ISBN 0-632-01386-9). Blackwell Pubns.

Freckman, Diana W., ed. Nematodes in Soil Ecosystems. (Illus.). 220p. 1982. text ed. 20.00x (ISBN 0-292-75526-0). U of Tex Pr.

Gray. The Ecology of Soil Bacteria. 698p. 1982. 70.00x (ISBN 0-85323-161-3, Pub. by Liverpool Univ England). State Mutual Bk.

Hyams, Edward. Soil & Civilization. 312p. 1980. 15.00x (ISBN 0-7195-3311-2, Pub. by Murray Pubs England). State Mutual Bk.

Jenny, H. The Soil Resource: Origin & Behavior. (Ecological Studies: Vol. 37). (Illus.). 377p. 1980. 32.50 (ISBN 0-387-90543-X). Springer-Verlag.

Penn, Raymond J. Environmental Aspects of Natural Resource Managements: Agriculture & Soils. (Agricultural Services Bulletins: No. 14). (Eng., Fr. & Span.). 39p. (3rd Printing 1975). 1972. pap. 7.50 (ISBN 92-5-101882-0, F709, FAO). Unipub.

Rauschkolb, Roy S. Land Degradation. (Soils Bulletins: No. 13). 117p. (2nd Printing 1977). 1971. pap. 8.00 (ISBN 92-5-100106-5, F1156, FAO). Unipub.

Russell, J. S. & Greacen, E. L. Soil Factors in Crop Production in a Semi-Arid Environment. 1978. text ed. 30.25x (ISBN 0-7022-1303-9). U of Queensland Pr.

Van Assche, C., ed. Agricultural Aspects of Soil Disinfestation: Proceedings of the International Symposium, Louvain, 1973. (Agro-Ecosystems Ser.: Vol. 1, No. 3). 1974. 20.50 (ISBN 0-686-43413-7). Elsevier.

SOIL ENGINEERING

see Soil Mechanics

SOIL EROSION

Batie, Sandra S. Soil Erosion: Crisis in America's Croplands? LC 83-1942. (Illus.). 136p. (Orig.). 1983. pap. 8.50 (ISBN 0-89164-068-1). Conservation Foun.

Black, C. A. Soil-Plant Relationships. LC 83-17509. 800p. 1984. Repr. of 1957 ed. lib. bdg. 55.50 (ISBN 0-89874-675-2). Krieger.

Brown, Lester. Soil Erosion: Quiet Crisis in the World Economy. (Worldwatch Papers Ser.). 1984. pap. 4.00 (ISBN 0-916468-60-7). Worldwatch Inst.

Christiansson, Carl. Soil Erosion & Sedimentation in Semi-Arid Tanzania: Studies of Environmental Change & Ecological Imbalance. 208p. 1983. pap. text ed. 24.50x (ISBN 0-8419-9743-8, Africana). Holmes & Meier.

Clark, Edwin H., II, et al. Eroding Soils: The Off-Farm Impacts. LC 85-9619. (Illus.). 252p. (Orig.). 1985. pap. 15.00 (ISBN 0-89164-086-X). Conservation Foun.

Crosson, Pierre R. & Stout, Anthony T. Productivity Effects of Cropland Erosion in the United States. LC 83-19094. 152p. 1984. pap. text ed. 11.00x (ISBN 0-8018-3207-1). Johns Hopkins.

El-Swaffy, S. A. & Moldenhauer, W. C., eds. Soil Erosion & Conservation. 806p. 35.00 (ISBN 0-935734-11-2). Soil Conservation.

FitzPatrick, E. A. Soils: Their Formation, Classification & Ditribution. LC 82-12669. (Illus.). 384p. 1983. pap. text ed. 23.00x (ISBN 0-582-30116-5). Longman.

Kelley, Hubert W. Keeping the Land Alive: Soil Erosion - Its Causes & Cures. (Soils Bulletins: No. 50). 95p. 1983. pap. text ed. 7.50 (ISBN 92-5-101342-X, F2430, FAO). Unipub.

Kirkby, M. J. & Morgan, R. P., eds. Soil Erosion: Landscape Systems. (A Series in Geomorphology). 312p. 1981. 79.95x (ISBN 0-471-27802-5, Pub. by Wiley-Interscience). Wiley.

SOIL EXHAUSTION

Craven, Avery O. Soil Exhaustion As a Factor in the Agricultural History of Virginia and Maryland, 1606-1860. 1926. 11.50 (ISBN 0-8446-1136-0). Peter Smith.

SOIL FAUNA

see also Earthworms; Insects; Soil Micro-Organisms

Marshall, V. G. Effects of Manures & Fertilizers on Soil Fauna: A Review. 79p. 1977. 40.00x (ISBN 0-85198-384-7, Pub. by CAB Bks England). State Mutual Bk.

SOIL FERTILITY

see also Plant Indicators

Bal, L. Zoological Ripening of Soils. (Agricultural Research Reports: No.850). (Illus.). 382p. 1982. pap. 41.50 (ISBN 90-220-0615-8, PDC240, PUDOC). Unipub.

China: Azolla Propagation & Small Scale Biogas Technology: Report on an FAO-UNDP Study Tour to the Peoples Republic of China, May 21 - June 11, 1978. (Soils Bulletins: No. 41). (Eng., Fr & Span.). 93p. 1978. pap. 7.50 (ISBN 92-5-100721-7, F1631, FAO). Unipub.

Colwell, J. D. Computations for Studies of Soil Fertility & Fertilizer Requirements. 297p. 1978. pap. 60.00x (ISBN 0-85198-437-1, Pub. by CAB Bks England). State Mutual Bk.

Cook, Ray L. Soil Management for Conservation & Production. LC 62-8770. (Illus.). 527p. 1962. 40.50 (ISBN 0-471-16995-1). Wiley.

Curtis, P. E. & Courson, R. L. Outline of Soil Fertility. 1981. spiral bdg. 8.80x (ISBN 0-87563-204-1). Stipes.

Davidescu, D. & Davidescu, V. Evaluation of Fertility by Plant & Soil Analysis. 1982. 69.00 (ISBN 0-9961005-1-2, Pub. by Abacus England). Heyden.

Engelstad, Orvis P., ed. Nutrient Mobility in Soils: Accumulation & Losses. (Illus.). 1970. pap. 3.00 (ISBN 0-89118-759-6). Soil Sci Soc Am.

Foth. Soil Fertility. Date not set. pap. price not set (ISBN 0-471-82507-7). Wiley.

Garrett, S. D. Soil Fungi & Soil Fertility: An Introduction to Soil Mycology. 2nd ed. (Illus.). 150p. 1981. 21.00 (ISBN 0-08-025507-8); pap. 9.50 (ISBN 0-08-025506-X). Pergamon.

Guidelines for the Control of Soil Degradation. 38p. 1984. pap. text ed. 7.50 (ISBN 92-5-101404-3, F2544, FAO). Unipub.

Hauser, G. F. Soil Fertility Investigations on Farmers' Fields. (Soils Bulletins: No. 11). (Eng., Fr. & Span.). 84p. (2nd Printing 1977). 1970. pap. 7.50 (ISBN 92-5-100383-1, F1322, FAO). Unipub.

Jones, Ulysses. Fertilizers & Soil Fertility. 2nd ed. 464p. 1982. text ed. 22.95 (ISBN 0-8359-1962-5); instr's. manual free (ISBN 0-8359-1963-3). Reston.

Pauli, F. W. Soil Fertility: A Biodynamical Approach. (Illus.). 1967. text ed. 23.50 (ISBN 0-9960018-1-6, Pub. by A Hilger England). Heyden.

Soil Fertility in the Great Konya Basin, Turkey. (Agricultural Research Reports: No. 15). 1970. pap. 11.75 (ISBN 90-220-0328-0, PDC183, PUDOC). Unipub.

Thompson, Louis M. & Troeh, Frederick. Soils & Soil Fertility. 4th ed. (Ag Ser.). (Illus.). 1977. text ed. 38.95 (ISBN 0-07-064411-X). McGraw.

Tinsley, J. & Darbyshire, J. F., eds. Biological Processes & Soil Fertility. (Developments in Plant & Soil Sciences). 1984. lib. bdg. 69.00 (ISBN 90-247-2902-5, Pub. by Martinus Nijhoff Netherlands). Kluwer-Academic.

Smith, G. N. Elements of Soil Mechanics for Civil & Mining Engineers. 342p. 1968. 75.25x (ISBN 0-677-61280-X). Gordon.
--Elements of Soil Mechanics for Civil & Mining Engineers. 5th ed. 493p. 1982. pap. text ed. 21.75x (ISBN 0-246-11765-6, Pub. by Granada England). Brookfield Pub Co.
Smith, Geoffrey N. Elements of Soil Mechanics for Civil & Mining Engineers. 4th ed. (Illus.). 370p. 1978. pap. 14.00x (ISBN 0-8464-0368-4). Beekman Pubs.
Smith, M. J. Concise Soil Mechanics. (Illus.). 160p. 1983. pap. text ed. 14.95x (ISBN 0-7121-0361-9). Trans-Atlantic.
Sopher, Charles & Baird, Jack. Soils & Soil Management. 2nd ed. 1981. text ed. 23.95 (ISBN 0-8359-7031-0); instr's. manual free (ISBN 0-8359-7032-9). Reston.
Sowers, George F. Introductory Soil Mechanics & Foundations: Geotechnic Engineering. 4th ed. (Illus.). 1979. text ed. write for info. (ISBN 0-02-413870-3). Macmillan.
Spangler, Merlin G. & Handy, Richard L. Soil Engineering. 4th ed. LC 73-8. 819p. 1982. text ed. 35.50 scp (ISBN 0-7002-2533-1, HarpC); solutions manual avail. (ISBN 0-06-366382-1). Har-Row.
Special Procedures for Testing Soil & Rock for Engineering Purposes- STP 479. 630p. 1970. 15.75 (ISBN 0-8031-0051-5, 04-479000-38). ASTM.
Stamatopoulos, A. C. Soil Improvement by Preloading. (Geotechnical Engineering Ser.). 208p. 1985. 35.95 (ISBN 0-471-81593-4). Wiley.
Storr, Eric D., ed. Expansive Soils. 250p. 1984. pap. text ed. 30.00x (ISBN 0-85825-208-2, Pub. by Inst Engineering Australia). Brookfield Pub Co.
Terzaghi, Karl. Theoretical Soil Mechanics. 510p. 1943. 53.50 (ISBN 0-471-85305-4, Pub. by Wiley-Interscience). Wiley.
Terzaghi, Karl & Peck, R. B. Soil Mechanics in Engineering Practice. 2nd ed. LC 67-17356. 729p. 1967. 49.95x (ISBN 0-471-85273-2, Pub. by Wiley-Interscience). Wiley.
Thorne, Marlowe D. & Thorne, D. Wynne. Soil, Water & Crop Production. (Illus.). 1979. text ed. 22.50 (ISBN 0-87055-281-3). AVI.
Truitt, Marcus M. Soil Mechanics Technology. (Illus.). 384p. 1983. 26.95 (ISBN 0-13-822254-1). P-H.
Tschebotarioff, Gregory P. Foundations, Retaining & Earth Structures: The Art of Design Construction & Its Scientific Basis in Soil Mechanics. 2nd ed. (Illus.). 704p. 1973. 48.50 (ISBN 0-07-065377-1). McGraw.
Underwater Soil Sampling, Testing, & Construction Control: A Symposium Presented at the Seventy-Fourth Annual Meeting, American Society for Testing & Materials, 1971. LC 77-185536. (ASTM Special Technical Publication: 501). pap. 61.80 (ISBN 0-317-26537-7, 2023988). Bks Demand UMI.
Van Wijk, A. L. A Soil Technological Study on Effectuating & Maintaining Adequate Playing Conditions of Grass Sports Fields. (Agricultural Research Reports: No. 903). 138p. 1980. pap. 29.50 (ISBN 90-220-0743-X, PDC220, PUDOC). Unipub.
Vickers, Brain. Laboratory Work in Soil Mechanics. 2nd ed. 170p. 1983. pap. text ed. 19.50x (ISBN 0-246-22819-9, Pub. by Granada England). Brookfield Pub Co.
Vickers, Brian. Laboratory Work in Soil Mechanics. 2nd ed. 192p. 1983. pap. 16.00x (ISBN 0-246-11819-9, Pub. by Granada England). Sheridan.
Visser, A., ed. Elsevier's Dictionary of Soil Mechanics. (Eng., Fr., Dutch, & Ger.). 359p. 1965. 89.50 (ISBN 0-444-40613-1). Elsevier.
Vollmer, Ernst. Encyclopaedia of Hydraulics, Soil & Foundation Engineering. 398p. 1967. 89.50 (ISBN 0-444-40615-8). Elsevier.
Vyalov, S. S. Rheological Fundamentals of Soil Mechanics. (Developments in Geotechnical Engineering Ser.: Vol. 36). Date not set. write for info. (ISBN 0-444-42223-4). Elsevier.
Winterkorn, Hans F. & Fang, F. Y., eds. Foundation Engineering Handbook. 736p. 1975. 54.50 (ISBN 0-442-29564-2). Van Nos Reinhold.
Wray, Warren K. Measuring Engineering Properties of Soil. (Illus.). 240p. 1986. pap. text ed. 26.95 (ISBN 0-13-568577-X). P-H.
Wu, T. H. Soil Dynamics. LC 79-117987. (Illus.). 1977. Repr. text ed. 20.00x (ISBN 0-918498-01-5). T H Wu.
--Soil Mechanics. 2nd ed. LC 75-26633. 440p. 1982. Repr. of 1979 ed. text ed. 30.00x (ISBN 0-918498-02-3). T H Wu.
Zeevaert, Leonardo. Foundation Engineering for Difficult Subsoil Conditions. 2nd ed. 688p. 1982. 44.95 (ISBN 0-442-20169-9). Van Nos Reinhold.

SOIL MICRO-ORGANISMS

Alexander, Martin. Introduction to Soil Microbiology. 2nd ed. LC 77-1319. 467p. 1977. text ed. 38.50 (ISBN 0-471-02179-2); arabic translation avail. Wiley.
--Introduction to Soil Microbiology. 2nd ed. (Arabic.). 573p. 1982. pap. 18.00 (ISBN 0-471-06392-4). Wiley.
Bisdom, E. B. Submicroscopy of Soils & Weathered Rocks: First Workshop of the International Working Group on Submicroscopy of Undisturbed Soil Materials, Wageningen, The Netherlands, 1980. (Eng. & Fr.). 320p. 1981. 45.25 (ISBN 90-220-0777-4, PDC235, Pudoc). Unipub.
Dommerques, Y. & Krupa, S. V. Interactions Between Non-Pathogenic Soil Microorganisms & Plants. (Developments in Agricultural & Managed-Forest Ecology: Vol. 4). 476p. 1978. 117.00 (ISBN 0-444-41638-2). Elsevier.
Domsch, K. L., et al. Compendium of Soil Fungi, 2 vols. LC 80-41403. 1981. Set. 1. 192.00 (ISBN 0-12-220420-4); Vol. 1, 1981. 120.00 (ISBN 0-12-220401-8); Vol. 2, 1984. 55.50 (ISBN 0-12-220402-6). Acad Pr.
Garrett, S. D. Pathogenic Root-Infecting Fungi. LC 72-10024. (Illus.). 1970. 52.50 (ISBN 0-521-07786-9). Cambridge U Pr.
--Soil Fungi & Soil Fertility: An Introduction to Soil Mycology. 2nd ed. (Illus.). 150p. 1981. 21.00 (ISBN 0-08-025507-8); pap. 9.50 (ISBN 0-08-025506-X). Pergamon.
Gilman, Joseph C. A Manual of Soil Fungi. facsimile ed. (Illus.). 1957. pap. 17.50x (ISBN 0-8138-2320-X). Iowa St U Pr.
Gray. The Ecology of Soil Bacteria. 698p. 1982. 70.00x (ISBN 0-85323-161-3, Pub. by Liverpool Univ England). State Mutual Bk.
Griffin, D. M. Ecology of Soil Fungi. LC 72-247. (Illus.). 208p. 1972. text ed. 19.95x (ISBN 0-8156-5035-3). Syracuse U Pr.
Mikola, Peitsa, ed. Tropical Mycorrhiza Research. 1980. 45.00x (ISBN 0-19-854553-3). Oxford U Pr.
Parr, J. F., et al, eds. Water Potential Relations in Soil Microbiology. 151p. 1981. pap. 6.25 (ISBN 0-89118-767-7). Soil Sci Soc Am.
Sillanpaa, Mikko. Micronutrients & the Nutrient Status of Soils. (Soils Bulletins: No. 48). 458p. 1982. 32.75 (ISBN 92-5-101193-1, F2331, FAO). Unipub.
Tsutomu Hattori. Microbial Life in the Soil: An Introduction. (Bks. in Soils & the Environment: Vol. 5). 448p. 1973. 89.75 (ISBN 0-8247-6023-9). Dekker.

SOIL MOISTURE

see also Drainage; Plant-Water Relationships; Soil Capillarity; Soil Percolation

Aitchison, G. D. Moisture Equilibria & Moisture Changes in Soils Beneath Covered Areas. 1982. 59.00x (ISBN 0-686-97906-0, Pub. by CSIRO Australia). State Mutual Bk.
Analog Modeling of Transient Moisture Flow in Unsaturated Soil. (Agricultural Research Reports: No. 894). 54p. 1980. pap. 10.50 (ISBN 90-220-0713-8, PDC151, PUDOC). Unipub.
Greacen, E. L. Soil Water Assessment by the Neutron Method. 1982. 60.00x (ISBN 0-686-97898-6, Pub. by CSIRO Australia). State Mutual Bk.
Handreck, K. A. When Should I Water. 1980. 20.00x (ISBN 0-643-02522-7, Pub. by CSJRO Australia). State Mutual Bk.
Hillel, Daniel. Soil & Water: Physical Principles & Processes. (Physiological Ecology Ser). 1971. 45.00 (ISBN 0-12-348550-9). Acad Pr.
Palmer, Robert G. & Troeh, Frederick R. Introductory Soil Science: Laboratory Manual. 2nd ed. 1977. pap. 7.95x (ISBN 0-8138-1555-X). Iowa St U Pr.
Soil-Moisture & Irrigation Studies. (Panel Proceedings Ser.). 1966. pap. 7.25 (ISBN 92-0-011067-3, ISP133, IAEA). Unipub.
Soil-Moisture & Irrigation Studies - 2. (Panel Proceedings Ser.). (Illus.). 189p. 1973. pap. 14.50 (ISBN 92-0-011073-8, ISP327, IAEA). Unipub.

SOIL MULCHING

see Mulching

SOIL ORGANIC MATTER

see Humus

SOIL PERCOLATION

see also Drainage; Seepage; Soil Capillarity

Cedergren, Harry R. Seepage, Drainage & Flow Nets. 2nd ed. LC 77-3664. 534p. 1977. 60.95 (ISBN 0-471-14179-8, Pub. by Wiley-Interscience). Wiley.
Nielsen, D. R., et al, eds. Soil Water. (Illus.). 1972. 8.50 (ISBN 0-89118-005-2). Am Soc Agron.

SOIL PHYSICS

see also Radioisotopes in Soil Physics; Soil Absorption and Adsorption; Soil Mechanics; Soil Moisture; Soil Percolation

Abriola, L. M. Multiphase Migration of Organic Compounds in a Porous Medium: A Mathematical Model. (Lecture Notes in Engineering Ser.: Vol. 8). (Illus.). viii, 232p. 1984. pap. 15.00 (ISBN 0-387-13694-0). Springer-Verlag.
Baver, Leonard D., et al. Soil Physics. 4th ed. LC 72-5318. 498p. 1972. 37.50x (ISBN 0-471-05974-9). Wiley.
Ghildyal. Soilphysics Theory & Practice. 1985. 39.95 (ISBN 0-470-20125-8). Wiley.
Hanks, R. J. & Ashcroft, G. L. Applied Soil Physics. (Advanced Series in Agricultural Sciences: Vol. 8). (Illus.). 159p. 1983. pap. 21.50 (ISBN 0-387-90927-3). Springer-Verlag.
Hebrew University Conference, Rehovot, Israel. Optimizing the Soil Physical Environment Toward Greater Crop Yields: Proceedings. Hillel, D., ed. 1972. 37.50 (ISBN 0-12-348540-1). Acad Pr.
Hillel, Daniel. Applications of Soil Physics. LC 80-535. 1980. 47.50 (ISBN 0-12-348580-0). Acad Pr.
--Fundamentals of Soil Physics. 1980. 45.00 (ISBN 0-12-348560-6). Acad Pr.
--Introduction to Soil Physics. LC 81-10848. 1982. pap. 27.50 (ISBN 0-12-348520-7). Acad Pr.
--Soil & Water: Physical Principles & Processes. (Physiological Ecology Ser). 1971. 45.00 (ISBN 0-12-348550-9). Acad Pr.
Isotopes & Radiation in Research on Soil-Plant Relationships. (Proceedings Ser.). (Illus.). 660p. pap. 92.25 (ISBN 0-686-65377-7, ISP501, IAEA). Unipub.
Isotopes & Radiation in Soil-Plant Nutrition Studies. (Proceedings Ser.). (Eng., Fr., Rus. & Span., Illus.). 624p. (Orig.). 1965. pap. 32.00 (ISBN 92-0-010265-4, ISP108, IAEA). Unipub.
Jones, J. A. The Nature of Soil Piping: A Review of Research. 300p. 1981. pap. 50.00x (ISBN 0-86094-077-2, Pub. by GEO Abstracts England). State Mutual Bk.
Kezdi, A. Soil Physics: Selected Topics. (Developments in Geotechnical Engineering Ser.: Vol. 25). 160p. 1979. 59.75 (ISBN 0-444-99790-3). Elsevier.
Kirkham, Don & Powers, W. L. Advanced Soil Physics. LC 74-153083. 534p. 1972. 60.00x (ISBN 0-471-48875-5, Pub. by Wiley-Interscience). Wiley.
Kirkham, Don, et al. Advanced Soil Physics. LC 83-23873. 552p. 1984. Repr. of 1972 ed. 52.50 (ISBN 0-89874-721-X). Krieger.
Koorevaar, P., et al. Elements of Soil Physics. (Developments in Soil Science Ser.: Vol. 13). 1983. 29.00 (ISBN 0-444-42242-0, I-392-83). Elsevier.
Laboratory Training Manual on the Use of Isotopes & Radiation in Soil-Plant Relations Research. (Technical Reports Ser.: No. 29). (Illus.). 166p. 1964. pap. 10.00 (ISBN 92-0-115064-4, IDC29, IAEA). Unipub.
Marshall, T. J. & Holmes, J. W. Soil Physics. LC 78-73809. (Illus.). 1980. 90.00 (ISBN 0-521-22622-8); pap. 29.95x (ISBN 0-521-29579-3). Cambridge U Pr.
Oswal, M. C. A Textbook of Soil Physics. (Illus.). vii, 214p. 1983. text ed. 22.50x (ISBN 0-7069-2347-2, Pub. by Vikas India). Advent NY.
Sound Absorption at the Soil Surface. (Agricultural Research Reports: 715). 1969. pap. 14.00 (ISBN 0-686-51211-1, PDC93, PUDOC). Unipub.

SOIL POLLUTION

see also Bacteria, Pathogenic; Sewage Disposal; Soil Micro-Organisms; Soils, Radioactive Substances in

Smith, M. A. Contaminated Land: Reclamation & Treatment. (NATO-Challenges of Modern Society Ser.). 456p. 1985. 65.00x (ISBN 0-306-41928-9, Plenum Pr). Plenum Pub.
Yaron, B., et al, eds. Polluntants in Porous Media: The Unsaturated Zone Between Soil Surface & Groundwater. (Ecological Studies, Analysis & Synthesis: Vol. 47). (Illus.). 330p. 1984. 49.00 (ISBN 0-387-13179-5). Springer-Verlag.

SOIL SCIENCE

see also Agriculture

Aandahl, Andrew R. Soil Teaching Aid. LC 79-12843. (Illus.). xxxii, 140p. 1979. pap. 100.00x with slide carousel (ISBN 0-8032-5902-6); tape cassette 5.00x (ISBN 0-8032-1012-4). U of Nebr Pr.
Balogh, J. & Mahunka, S., eds. Primitive Oribatids of the Palaeartic Region. (Soil Mites of the World Ser.: No. 1). 370p. 1983. 106.50 (ISBN 0-444-99655-9, I-301-83). Elsevier.
Barber, Stanley A. Soil Nutrient Bioavailability: A Mechanistic Approach. LC 83-23331. 398p. 1984. 39.95x (ISBN 0-471-09032-8, Pub. by Wiley-Interscience). Wiley.
Batten, J. W. & Gibson, J. Sullivan. Soils, Their Nature, Classes, Distribution, Uses, & Care. rev. 2nd ed. LC 76-40302. (Illus.). 314p. 1977. 14.50 (ISBN 0-8173-2876-9). U of Ala Pr.
Bisdom, E. B. & Duclox, J., eds. Submicroscopic Studies of Soils. (Developments in Soil Science Ser.: Vol. 12). 352p. 1983. Repr. 79.00 (ISBN 0-444-42195-5, I-308-83). Elsevier.
Boardman, John, ed. Soils & Quarternary Landscape Evolution. 1985. 49.95 (ISBN 0-471-90528-3). Wiley.
Bolt, G. H., ed. Soil Chemistry, Pt. B: Physico-Chemical Models. 2nd, rev. ed. (Developments in Soil Science Ser.: Vol. 5B). 538p. 1982. 76.75 (ISBN 0-444-42060-6). Elsevier.
Bonneau, Maurice & Souchier, B., eds. Constituents & Properties of Soils. LC 81-68957. 1982. 67.00 (ISBN 0-12-114550-6). Acad Pr.
Bowles, J. E. Engineering Properties of Soils & Their Measurement. 3rd ed. 464p. 1985. pap. price not set (ISBN 0-07-006754-6). McGraw.
Buurman, Peter, ed. Podzols: Temperate Regions. (Benchmark Papers in Soil Science). 464p. 1984. 49.50 (ISBN 0-442-21129-5). Van Nos Reinhold.
Doomkamp, J. C., et al, eds. Geology, Geomorphology & Pedology of Bahrain. 443p. 150.00x (ISBN 0-86094-021-7, Pub. by GEO Abstracts England). State Mutual Bk.
Duchaufour, Philippe. Ecological Atlas of Soils of the World. De Kimpe, C. R., tr. from Fr. LC 77-94822. (Illus.). 178p. 1978. 43.00x (ISBN 0-89352-012-8). Masson Pub.
Effect of Seed & Soil Disinfectants on Establishment, Growth & Mutual Relations of White Clover & Grass in Leys. (Agricultural Research Reports: No. 741). 1970. pap. 4.00 (ISBN 90-220-0289-6, PDC180, PUDOC). Unipub.
Emerson, W. W., et al, eds. Modification of Soil Structure. 438p. 1978. 101.95 (ISBN 0-471-99530-4, Pub. by Wiley-Interscience). Wiley.
Erosion & Productivity of Soils Containing Rock Fragments. (Special Publication Ser.). 103p. 1984. 12.00 (ISBN 0-89118-773-1). Soil Sci Soc Am.
Fairbridge, R. W. & Finkl, C. W., Jr., eds. The Encyclopedia of Soil Science: Part 1, Physics, Chemistry, Biology, Fertility, & Technology. LC 78-31233. (Encyclopedia of Earth Sciences Ser.: Vol. XII). 700p. 1979. 81.00 (ISBN 0-87933-176-3). Van Nos Reinhold.
Faniran, A. & Areola, A. The Essentials of Soil Study. LC 79-670194. 1977. 14.50x (ISBN 0-435-95311-7). Heinemann Ed.
Feda, J. Stress in Subsoil & Methods of Final Settlement Calculation. (Developments in Geotechnical Materials Ser.: Vol. 18). 216p. 1978. 53.25 (ISBN 0-444-99800-4). Elsevier.
Finkl, Charles, Jr., ed. Soil Classification. LC 81-6214. (Benchmark Papers in Soil Science: Vol. 1). 416p. 1982. 46.50 (ISBN 0-87933-399-5). Van Nos Reinhold.
Fitter, A. H., ed. Ecological Interactions in the Soil Environment. (Illus.). 400p. 1985. pap. text ed. 57.00x (ISBN 0-632-01386-9). Blackwell Pubns.
FitzPatrick, E. A. Micromorphology of Soils. (Illus.). 330p. 1984. 59.95 (ISBN 0-412-24200-1, 5067, Pub. by Chapman & Hall England). Methuen Inc.
Foster, R. C., et al. Ultrastructure of the Root-Soil Interface. (Illus.). 157p. 1983. 36.00 (ISBN 0-89054-051-9). Am Phytopathol Soc.
Foth, Henry D. Fundamentals of Soil Science. 1977. pap. text ed. 9.50 study guide (ISBN 0-8403-2790-0, 40279001). Kendall-Hunt.
--Fundamentals of Soil Science. 7th ed. LC 83-23383. 435p. 1984. text ed. 35.45 (ISBN 0-471-88926-1). Wiley.
Foth, Henry D., et al. Laboratory Manual for Introductory Soil Science. 6th ed. 224p. 1982. write for info wire coil bdg (ISBN 0-697-05855-7). Wm C Brown.
Fourth Meeting of the East African Sub-Committee for Soil Correlation & Land Evaluation: Arusha, Tanzania, October-November 1980. (World Soil Resources Reports: No. 54). 207p. 1982. pap. text ed. 15.00 (ISBN 92-5-101271-7, F2392, FAO). Unipub.
Frissel, M. J., ed. Cycling of Mineral Nutrients in Agricultural Ecosystems. (Developments in Agricultural & Managed-Forest Ecology Ser.: Vol. 3). 356p. 1978. Repr. 64.00 (ISBN 0-444-41660-9). Elsevier.
Harpstead, Milo I. & Hole, Francis D. Soil Science Simplified. (Illus.). 122p. 1980. pap. text ed. 8.25x (ISBN 0-8138-1515-0). Iowa St U Pr.
Hausenbuiller, R. L. Soil Science: Principles & Practices. 2nd ed. 664p. 1978. text ed. write for info. (ISBN 0-697-05853-0). Wm C Brown.
--Soil Science: Principles & Practices. 3rd ed. 624p. 1985. text ed. write for info. (ISBN 0-697-05856-5); write for info. instr's. manual (ISBN 0-697-05857-3). Wm C Brown.
Hunt, Charles B. Geology of Soils: Their Evolution, Classification, & Uses. LC 71-158739. (Geology Ser.). (Illus.). 344p. 1972. text ed. 37.95 (ISBN 0-7167-0253-3). W H Freeman.
Johnson, Leon J. Introductory Soil Science: A Study Guide & Laboratory Manual. (Illus.). 1979. pap. text ed. write for info. (ISBN 0-02-361120-0). Macmillan.
Jongerius, A. & Rutherford, G. K., eds. Glossary of Soil Micromorphology. (Eng., Fr., Ger., Span. & Rus.). 152p. 1979. 30.50 (ISBN 90-220-0637-9, PDC4, PUDOC). Unipub.
Knapp, B. J. Soil Processes. (Process in Physical Geography Ser.: No. 2). (Illus.). 1979. pap. text ed. 6.95x (ISBN 0-04-631011-8). Allen Unwin.

Landforms & Soils in Eastern Surinam (South America) (Agricultural Research Reports: No. 771). 1972. pap. 18.25 (ISBN 90-220-0381-7, PDC187, PUDOC). Unipub.

Leeper, Geoffrey W. Introduction to Soil Science. 4th ed. 1967. 9.50x (ISBN 0-522-83656-9, Pub. by Melbourne U Pr). Intl Spec Bk.

Liu, Cheng & Evett, Jack. Soil Properties: Testing, Measurement & Evaluation. (Illus.). 224p. 1984. pap. 26.95 (ISBN 0-13-822379-3). P-H.

McRae, S. G. & Burnham, C. P. Land Evaluation. (Monographs on Soil Survey). (Illus.). 1981. 45.00x (ISBN 0-19-854518-5). Oxford U Pr.

Martha, D. J. Agricultural Science Wageningen in Focus. 92p. 1981. 30.00x (ISBN 90-220-0771-5, Pub. by CAB Bks England). State Mutual Bk.

Microstructure & Stability of Two Sandy Loam Soils with Different Soil Management. (Agricultural Research Reports: No. 724). 1969. pap. 7.25 (ISBN 90-220-0190-3, PDC178, PUDOC). Unipub.

Nelson, D. W., et al, eds. Chemical Mobility & Reactivity in Soil Systems. (Special Publication Ser.). 262p. 1983. pap. 12.00 (ISBN 0-89118-771-5). Soil Sci Soc Am.

Nielsen, D. R. & Bouma, J., eds. Soil Spatial Variability: Proceedings of a Workshop of the ISSS & the SSSA, Las Vegas, USA, Nov. 30 - Dec. 1 1984. 243p. 1985. pap. 18.75 (ISBN 90-220-0891-6, PDC296, Pudoc). Unipub.

Olson, Gerald W. Field Guide to Soils & the Environment: A Guide for Teaching & Learning about Soil Surveys & Their Applications. 238p. 1984. 49.00 (ISBN 0-412-25970-2, NO. 5065, Pub. by Chapman & Hall England); pap. 21.00 (ISBN 0-412-25960-5, NO. 5066, Pub. by Chapman & Hall England). Methuen Inc.

--Soils & the Environment: A Guide to Their Applications. 191p. 1982. (Pub by Chapman & Hall England); pap. 17.95x (ISBN 0-412-23760-1, 6587). Methuen Inc.

Paddy Soils: Proceedings. 800p. 1981. 62.00 (ISBN 0-387-10900-5). Springer-Verlag.

Peavy, William. Southern Gardener's Soil Handbook. LC 78-58245. (Illus.). 96p. (Orig.). 1979. pap. 6.95x (ISBN 0-88415-817-9, Pub. by Pacesetter Pr). Gulf Pub.

Peterson, A. G. & Swan, J. B., eds. Universal Soil Loss Equation: Past, Present & Future. 53p. 1979. pap. 3.75 (ISBN 0-89118-766-9). Soil Sci Soc Am.

Pitty, A. F. Geography & Soil Properties. 1979. 15.95 (ISBN 0-416-75380-9, NO. 2374); pap. 15.95x (ISBN 0-416-71540-0, NO. 2375). Methuen Inc.

Plaster, Edward. Soils: Science & Management. LC 85-4486. 352p. 1985. text ed. 29.80 (ISBN 0-8273-2406-5); instrs. guide avail. (ISBN 0-8273-2407-3). Delmar.

Rieger, Samuel, ed. The Genesis & Classification of Cold Soils: Monographs. 206p. 1983. 35.00 (ISBN 0-12-588120-7). Acad Pr.

Rode, A. A. System of Research Methods in Soil Science. (Russ.). 80p. 1981. 30.00x (ISBN 0-686-76670-9, Pub. by Oxford & IBH India). State Mutual Bk.

Russell, E. W. Soil Conditions & Plant Growth. 10th ed. LC 74-168964. (Illus.). 867p. 1974. text ed. 35.00x (ISBN 0-582-44048-3). Longman.

Sabey, B. R. Introductory Experimental Soil Science. 1969. spiral bdg. 5.80x (ISBN 0-87563-025-1). Stipes.

Sanchez, Pedro A. Properties & Management of Soils in the Tropics. LC 76-22761. 618p. 1976. 49.95x (ISBN 0-471-75200-2, Pub. by Wiley-Interscience). Wiley.

Sandy Soils: Report of the FAO-UNDP Seminar on Reclamation & Management of Sandy Soils in the Near East & North Africa, Nicosia, 3-8 Dec. 1973. (Soils Bulletins: No. 25). (Illus.). 251p. 1975. pap. 16.25 (ISBN 92-5-100613-X, F1167, FAO). Unipub.

Schafer, John W. A Guided Independent Study to Soil Science. rev. ed. 1982. coil bdg. 10.95 (ISBN 0-88252-040-7). Paladin Hse.

Schnitzer, M. & Khan, S. U., eds. Soil Organic Matter. (Developments in Soil Science: Vol. 8). 320p. 1978. 78.75 (ISBN 0-444-41610-2). Elsevier.

Silver, W. S. & Schroder, E. C., eds. Practical Application of Azolla for Rice Production. (Development in Plant & Soil Sciences). 1984. lib. bdg. 35.00 (ISBN 90-247-3068-6, Pub. by Martinus Nijhoff Netherlands). Kluwer-Academic.

The Soil: How to Improve the Soil. Rev. ed. (Better Farming Ser.: No. 6). (Illus.). 29p. 1976. pap. 7.50 (ISBN 92-5-100145-6, F64, FAO). Unipub.

Soil Information Systems: Proceedings of the Working Group on Soil Information Systems, Wageningen, The Netherlands, Sept. 1-4, 1975. Bie, S. W., ed. 1977. pap. 12.00 (ISBN 90-220-0592-5, PDC89, PUDOC). Unipub.

Soon, Yoong-Kee. Soil Nutrient Availablitity. (VNR Soil Science Ser.). 368p. 1985. 45.50 (ISBN 0-442-28123-4). Van Nos Reinhold.

Steward, B. A., ed. Advances in Soil Science, Vol. 2. (Illus.). 220p. 1985. 39.50 (ISBN 0-387-96114-3). Springer-Verlag.

Stewart, B. A., ed. Advances in Soil Science, Vol. 1. (Illus.). 375p. 1985. 40.00 (ISBN 0-387-96027-9). Springer-Verlag.

--Advances in Soil Science, Vol. 3. (Illus.). 240p. 1985. 44.50 (ISBN 0-387-96116-X). Springer-Verlag.

Szabolcs, I. Review of Research on Salt-Affected Soils. (Natural Resources Research Ser.: No. 15). (Illus.). 137p. (Bibliography Compiled by G. Varallyay). 1979. pap. 20.25 (ISBN 92-3-101613-X, U972, UNESCO). Unipub.

Uses of Soil Information Systems: Proceedings of the Australian Meeting of the ISSS Working Group on Soil Information Systems, Canberra, 2-4 March, 1976. Moore, Alan W. & Bie, Stein W., eds. 1978. pap. 14.00 (ISBN 90-220-0638-7, PDC98, Pub. by PUDOC). Unipub.

Welch, Charles D. & McCart, Gerald D. An Introduction to Soil Science in the Southeast. (Illus.). xiv, 280p. 1963. 14.95x (ISBN 0-8078-0888-1). U of NC Pr.

White, R. E. Introduction to the Principles & Practice of Soil Science. LC 79-14361. 198p. 1979. pap. 34.95x (ISBN 0-470-26717-8). Halsted Pr.

Wilding, L. P., et al, eds. Pedogenesis & Soil Taxonomy: Pt. 1, Concepts & Interactions. (Developments in Soil Science Ser.: No. 11A). 304p. 1983. 44.25 (ISBN 0-444-42100-9, I-316-83). Elsevier.

--Pedogenesis & Soil Taxonomy: Vol. 2, The Soil Orders. (Developments in Soil Science Ser.: Vol. 11B). 1983. 50.00 (ISBN 0-444-42137-8, I-422-83). Elsevier.

Yaron, B., et al, eds. Polluntants in Porous Media: The Unsaturated Zone Between Soil Surface & Groundwater. (Ecological Studies, Analysis & Synthesis: Vol. 47). (Illus.). 330p. 1984. 49.00 (ISBN 0-387-13179-5). Springer-Verlag.

Yong, Raymond N., ed. Geological Environment & Soil Properties. 453p. 1983. pap. 36.00x (ISBN 0-87262-381-5). Am Soc Civil Eng.

Zeevaert, Leonardo. Foundation Engineering for Difficult Subsoil Conditions. LC 73-4020. (Illus.). pap. 160.00 (ISBN 0-317-11093-4, 2007910). Bks Demand UMI.

SOIL SCIENCE–BIBLIOGRAPHY

Greenwood, L. Larry & Rohrer, Richard L. KWIC Index to the Commonwealth Bureau of Soils Annotated Bibliographies on Soils & Fertilizers. LC 73-621756. (Libraries Bibliography: No. 13). 1974. Repr. 10.00 (ISBN 0-686-20814-5). KSU.

SOIL SCIENCE–LABORATORY MANUALS

Beck, R. H., et al. Introductory Soil Science: A Laboratory Manual. (Illus.). 276p. 1984. 10.80x (ISBN 0-87563-222-X). Stipes.

Butler, Orton C. An Introductory Soils Laboratory Handbook. 1979. 8.00 (ISBN 0-682-49169-1, University). Exposition Pr FL.

Tarjan, Armen C. Check List of Plant & Soil Nematodes: A Nomenclatorial Compilation. LC 60-10226. xiv, 200p. 1960. 8.25 (ISBN 0-8130-0223-0); suppl. 1967 6.75 (ISBN 0-8130-0224-9). U Presses Fla.

SOIL STABILIZATION

see also Drilling Muds

American Society for Testing & Materials. Compaction of Soils. LC 65-18214. (American Society for Testing & Materials: Special Technical Publication, No. 377). pap. 35.30 (ISBN 0-317-10980-4, 2000734). Bks Demand UMI.

Analyses for Soil Structure Interaction Effects for Nuclear Power Plants. 159p. 1979. pap. 13.50x (ISBN 0-87262-183-9). Am Soc Civil Eng.

Building Research Advisory Board - Federal Housing Administration. Criteria for Compacted Fills. 1965. pap. 3.00 (ISBN 0-309-01281-3). Natl Acad Pr.

Chilingarian, G. V. & Wolf, K., eds. Compaction of Coarse-Grained Sediments, 2 pts. LC 73-85220. 550p. 1975-77. Pt. 1. 104.25 (ISBN 0-444-41152-6); Pt. 2. 117.00 (ISBN 0-444-41361-8). Elsevier.

Emerson, W. W., et al, eds. Modification of Soil Structure. 438p. 1978. 101.95 (ISBN 0-471-99530-4, Pub. by Wiley-Interscience). Wiley.

Kezdi, A. Stabilized Earth Roads. (Developments in Geotechnical Engineering Ser.: Vol. 19). 328p. 1979. 74.50 (ISBN 0-444-99786-5). Elsevier.

Mechanisms of Soil Stabilization. 1982. 39.00x (ISBN 0-686-97907-9, Pub. by CSIRO Australia). State Mutual Bk.

Titkov, N. I., et al. Mineral Formation & Structure in the Electrochemical Induration of Weak Rocks. LC 65-20210. 52p. 1965. 25.00x (ISBN 0-306-10734-1, Consultants). Plenum Pub.

SOIL SURVEYS

Brink, A. B. & Partridge, T. C. Soil Survey for Engineering. (Monographs on Soil Survey). (Illus.). 1982. text ed. 74.00x (ISBN 0-19-854537-1); pap. text ed. 21.95x (ISBN 0-19-854583-5). Oxford U Pr.

Butler, B. E. Soil Survey of the Horticultural Soils in the Murrumbidgee Irrigation Areas, New South Wales. 80p. 1981. 25.00x (ISBN 0-643-02432-8, Pub. by CSIRO Australia). State Mutual Bk.

De Gruijter, J. J. Numerical Classification of Soils & Its Application in Survey. (Agricultural Research Reports: No. 855). (Illus.). 1978. pap. 22.00 (ISBN 90-220-0608-5, PDC59, PUDOC). Unipub.

Gousen, Doeko. Aerial Photo Interpretation in Soil Survey. (Soils Bulletins: No. 6). (Eng., Fr. & Span.). 116p. (3rd. Printing 1976). 1967. pap. 8.50 (ISBN 92-5-100105-7, F1151, FAO). Unipub.

Guidelines for Soil Profile Description. 1978. pap. 7.50 (ISBN 92-5-100508-7, F1448, FAO). Unipub.

Hodgson, J. M. Soil Sampling & Soil Description. (Monographs on Soil Survey). (Illus.). 1978. 34.50x (ISBN 0-19-854511-8). Oxford U Pr.

Laboratory Shear Testing of Soils, STP 361. 514p. 1965. 24.50 (ISBN 0-8031-0048-5, 04-361000-38). ASTM.

Land Evaluation in Europe: Report on the Technical Consultation, Nitra, Czechoslovakia, 1-6 Sept. 1975. (Soils Bulletins: No. 29). (Illus.). 123p. 1975. pap. 9.00 (ISBN 0-685-66339-6, F1169, FAO). Unipub.

Landon, J. R. Booker Tropical Soil Manual: A Handbook for Soil Survey & Agricultural Land Evaluuation in the Tropics & Sub-Tropics. (Illus.). 450p. 1984. text ed. 50.00 (ISBN 0-582-46049-2). Longman.

Palmer, Robert G. & Troeh, Frederick R. Introductory Soil Science: Laboratory Manual. 2nd ed. 1977. pap. 7.95x (ISBN 0-8138-1555-X). Iowa St U Pr.

Western, S. Soil Survey Contracts & Quality Control. (Monographs on Soil Survey). (Illus.). 1979. 38.00x (ISBN 0-19-854513-4). Oxford U Pr.

Young, A. Tropical Soils & Soil Survey. LC 75-19573. (Cambridge Geographical Studies: No. 9). 1976. 77.50 (ISBN 0-521-21054-2). Cambridge U Pr.

--Tropical Soils & Soil Survey. LC 75-19573. (Cambridge Geographical Studies: No. 9). 468p. 1980. pap. 19.95 (ISBN 0-521-29768-0). Cambridge U Pr.

Young, Anthony & Dent, David. Soil Survey & Land Evaluation. (Illus.). 304p. 1981. text ed. 35.00x (ISBN 0-04-631013-4); pap. text ed. 17.95x (ISBN 0-04-631014-2). Allen Unwin.

SOIL SURVEYS–GEOPHYSICAL METHODS

see also Prospecting–Geophysical Methods

Greacen, E. L. Soil Water Assessment by the Neutron Method. (Illus.). 140p. 1982. pap. text ed. 17.50 (ISBN 0-643-00414-9, Pub. by CSIRO). Intl Spec Bk.

SOIL TYPES

see Soils–Classification

SOILLESS AGRICULTURE

see Hydroponics

SOILS

see also Agricultural Chemistry; Agricultural Physics; Clay; Compost; Drainage; Fertilizers and Manures; Forest Soils; Frozen Ground; Humus; Irrigation; Mulching; Particles; Reclamation of Land; Sand

also headings beginning with the word Soil

Aandahl, Andrew R. Soils of the Great Plains: Land Use, Crops, & Grasses. LC 81-7435. (Illus.). xvi, 282p. 1982. 28.50x (ISBN 0-8032-1011-6). U of Nebr Pr.

American Society for Testing & Materials. Evaluation of Relative Density & Its Role in Geotechnical Projects Involving Cohesionless Soils. Selig, E. T. & Ladd, R. S., eds. LC 72-90704. pap. 129.00 (ISBN 0-317-26539-3, 2023989). Bks Demand UMI.

Amos, Dan. Soils & Its Uses. 1979. text ed. 15.95 (ISBN 0-8359-7038-8); instrs' manual avail. (ISBN 0-8359-7039-6). Reston.

Armson, K. A. Forest Soils: Properties & Processes. 1977. 27.50 (ISBN 0-8020-2265-0). U of Toronto Pr.

Bear, Firman E. Soils in Relation to Crop Growth. LC 65-23863. 304p. 1977. Repr. of 1965 ed. 19.50 (ISBN 0-88275-927-2). Krieger.

Beeson, Kenneth & Matrone, Gennard. The Soil Factor in Nutrition: Animal & Human. (Nutrition & Clinical Nutrition Ser.: Vol. 2). 1976. 39.75 (ISBN 0-8247-6484-6). Dekker.

Berger, Kermit C. Sun, Soil, & Survival: An Introduction to Soils. LC 72-3608. (Illus.). 371p. pap. 12.95x (ISBN 0-8061-1388-X). U of Okla Pr.

Birkeland, Peter W. Soils & Geomorphology. (Illus.). 1984. text ed. 37.50x (ISBN 0-19-503398-1); pap. 22.95x (ISBN 0-19-503435-X). Oxford U Pr.

Boone, F. R., ed. Experiences with Three Tillage Systems on a Marine Loam Soil II: 1976-1979: A Joint Study of the Westmaas Research Group on New Tillage Systems, Carried Out on the Westmaas Experimental Husbandry Farm. (Agricultural Research Reports: No. 925). (Illus.). 263p. 1985. pap. 28.00 (ISBN 90-220-0855-X, PDC280, Pudoc). Unipub.

Bowles, Joseph E. Engineering Properties of Soils & Their Measurements. 2nd ed. (Illus.). 1978. pap. text ed. 35.95 (ISBN 0-07-006752-X). McGraw.

Bridges, E. M. World Soils. 2nd ed. LC 77-90204. (Illus.). 1979. 32.50 (ISBN 0-521-21956-6); pap. 11.95 (ISBN 0-521-29339-1). Cambridge U Pr.

Bridges, E. M. & Davidson, D. A., eds. Principles & Applications of Soil Geography. LC 80-41509. (Illus.). 320p. 1982. text ed. 15.95x (ISBN 0-582-30014-2). Longman.

Buringh, P. Introduction to the Study of Soils in Tropical & Subtropical Regions. 3rd ed. (Illus.). 146p. (16 full colour page photographs of soil profiles). 1979. pap. 14.00 (ISBN 90-220-0691-3, PDC146, Pudoc). Unipub.

Burns, R. G., ed. Soil Enzymes. 1978. 69.50 (ISBN 0-12-145850-4). Acad Pr.

Buurman, Peter, ed. Podzols: Temperate Regions. (Benchmark Papers in Soil Science). 464p. 1984. 49.50 (ISBN 0-442-21129-5). Van Nos Reinhold.

Capper, P. L., et al. Problems in Engineering Soils. 3rd ed. 1980. 14.95x (ISBN 0-419-11840-3, NO. 2966, Pub. by E & FN Spon). Methuen Inc.

Carter, Vernon G. & Dale, Tom. Topsoil & Civilization. rev. ed. (Illus.). 240p. 1974. 12.95 (ISBN 0-8061-0332-9); pap. 8.95x (ISBN 0-8061-1107-0). U of Okla Pr.

--Topsoil & Civilization. (Illus.). 308p. pap. 8.95 (ISBN 0-8061-1107-0). U of Okla Pr.

Cook, J. Gordon. Your Guide to the Soil. 480p. 1965. 40.00x (ISBN 0-900541-53-9, Pub. by Meadowfield Pr England). State Mutual Bk.

Cook, Ray L. Soil Management for Conservation & Production. LC 62-8770. (Illus.). 527p. 1962. 40.50 (ISBN 0-471-16995-1). Wiley.

Darwin, Charles. Darwin on Earthworms: The Formation of Vegetable Mould Through the Action of Worms. (Illus.). 160p. 1976. 7.95 (ISBN 0-916302-10-5); pap. 5.95 (ISBN 0-916302-06-7). Bookworm Pub.

Division of Soils Commenwealth Scientific & Industrial Research Organization, Australia, ed. Soils: An Australian View Point. 1983. 89.00 (ISBN 0-12-654240-6). Acad Pr.

Donahue, Roy & Miller, John. Soils: An Introduction to Soils & Plant Growth. 5th ed. (Illus.). 656p. 1983. text ed. 34.95 (ISBN 0-13-822288-6). P-H.

Donahue, Roy L., et al. Our Soils & Their Management (Increasing Production Through Environmental Soil & Water Conservation. 5th ed. LC 82-82462. xv, 622p. 1983. 23.00 (ISBN 0-8134-2251-5); text ed. 18.00x. Interstate.

Elliott, L. F. & Stevenson, F. J., eds. Soils for Management of Organic Wastes & Waste Waters. (Illus.). 1977. 17.50 (ISBN 0-89118-049-4). Am Soc Agron.

Faulkner, Edward H. Plowman's Folly. 154p. 1943. 10.95 (ISBN 0-8061-0124-5); pap. 5.95 (ISBN 0-8061-1169-0). U of Okla Pr.

Flegmann, G. W. & George, R. A. Soils & Other Growth Media. 1977. text ed. 13.00 (ISBN 0-87055-240-6). AVI.

Food & Agriculture Organization. Soil Map of the World: Europe, Vol. 5. 199p. 1981. pap. 22.00 (ISBN 0-686-83161-6, M134, UNESCO). Unipub.

Foth, Henry D. & Schafer, John. Soil Geography & Land Use. LC 79-27731. 484p. 1980. text ed. 43.50 (ISBN 0-471-01710-8). Wiley.

Fridland, V. M. Comparative Physiology & Evolution of Vision in Invertebrates C. 1981. 30.00x (ISBN 0-686-76629-6, Pub. by Oxford & IBH India). State Mutual Bk.

Fried, Maurice & Broeshart, Hans. Soil-Plant System in Relation to Inorganic Nutrition. (Atomic Energy Commission Monographs). 1967. 23.50 (ISBN 0-12-268050-2). Acad Pr.

Frissel, M. J. & Reiniger, P. Simulation of Accumulation and Leaching in Soils. 124p. 1975. pap. 7.50 (ISBN 90-220-0530-5, PDC82, PUDOC). Unipub.

Fuller, Wallace H. Management of Southwestern Desert Soils. LC 74-15601. (Illus.). 195p. 1975. pap. 7.50 (ISBN 0-8165-0442-3). U of Ariz Pr.

--Soils of the Desert Southwest. LC 74-79390. (Illus.). 102p. 1975. pap. 4.95 (ISBN 0-8165-0441-5). U of Ariz Pr.

Gaerity, Jack. Bread & Roses from Stone. facs. ed. (Shorey Lost Arts Ser.). 92p. pap. 4.95 (ISBN 0-8466-0126-5, S126). Shorey.

Gerrard, John. Soils & Landforms. (Illus.). 256p. 1981. text ed. 35.00x (ISBN 0-04-551048-2); pap. text ed. 17.95x (ISBN 0-04-551049-0). Allen Unwin.

Gieseking, J. E., ed. Soil Components, Vol. Two: Inorganic Components. (Illus.). 770p. 1974. 102.00 (ISBN 0-387-06862-7). Springer-Verlag.
Goring, Cleve A. & Hamaker, John W., eds. Organic Chemicals in the Soil Environment. LC 71-179384. (Books in Soils & the Environment Ser.: Vol. 1). pap. 114.00 (ISBN 0-317-28661-7, 2055084). Bks Demand UMI.
Hendricks, David M. Arizona Soils. Haney, Richard A., ed. (Illus.). 280p. (Orig.). 1985. pap. 55.00 (ISBN 0-932913-02-4). Univ AZ Agriculture.
Hole, Francis D. Soils of Wisconsin. LC 75-12209. (Illus.). 240p. 1976. 40.00x (ISBN 0-299-06830-7). U of Wis Pr.
Hole, Francis D. & Campbell, James B. Soil Landscape Analysis. LC 83-24418. (Illus.). 214p. 1985. 35.95x (ISBN 0-86598-140-X). Rowman & Allanheld.
ISSS Working Group on Soil Information Systems. Developments in Soil Information Systems: Proceedings of a Working Group Meeting at Varna-Sofia, Bulgaria, May 30-June 4, 1977. Sadovsky, A. D. & Bie, S. W., eds. 119p. 1978. pap. 7.50 (ISBN 0-686-93147-5, PDC107, Pudoc). Unipub.
Jacks, H. V. Soil. 5.00 (ISBN 0-685-28378-X). Philos Lib.
Jumikis, Alfred R. Thermal Geotechnics. 1977. 50.00x (ISBN 0-8135-0824-X). Rutgers U Pr.
Kalpage, F. S. Tropical Soils: Classification, Fertility & Management. LC 75-20866. 300p. 1976. 26.00 (ISBN 0-312-81935-8). St Martin.
Kilmer, Victor J. Handbook of Climate & Soils in Agriculture. 456p. 1982. 94.00 (ISBN 0-8493-3811-5). CRC Pr.
Kilmer, Victor J., ed. Handbook of Soils & Climate in Agriculture. 456p. 1982. 94.00 (ISBN 0-686-84130-1). CRC Pr.
Knuti, Leo L., et al. Profitable Soil Management. 2nd ed. 1970. text ed. 31.52 (ISBN 0-13-729400-X). P-H.
Laacke, R. J., ed. California Forest Soils: A Guide for Professional Foresters & Resource Managers & Planners. LC 79-62985. (Illus., Orig.). 1979. pap. text ed. 5.00x (ISBN 0-931876-32-X, 4094). Ag & Nat Res.
Landon, J. R. Booker Tropical Soil Manual: A Handbook for Soil Survey & Agricultural Land Evaluation in the Tropics & Sub-Tropics. (Illus.). 450p. 1984. text ed. 50.00 (ISBN 0-582-46049-2). Longman.
Mahaney, W. C. Quaternary Soils. (York Ser.). 508p. 1980. pap. 27.60x (ISBN 0-686-27386-9, Pub. by GEO Abstracts England). State Mutual Bk.
Marshall, C. Edmund. The Physical Chemistry & Mineralogy of Soils: Volume 1: Soil Materials. LC 75-22180. 398p. 1975. Repr. of 1964 ed. 22.50 (ISBN 0-88275-351-7). Krieger.
Miska, J. P. Solonetz Soils of the World. 136p. 1975. 30.00x (ISBN 0-85198-345-6, Pub. by CAB Bks England). State Mutual Bk.
Money, D. C. Climate, Soils & Vegatation. 1981. 25.00x (ISBN 0-7231-0769-6, Pub. by Univ Tutorial England). State Mutual Bk.
Moore, A. W., ed. Information Systems for Soil & Related Data: Proceedings of the Second Australian Meeting of the ISSS Working Group on Soil Information Systems, Canberra, Australia, 19-21 February 1980. 161p. 1981. 26.25x (ISBN 90-220-0763-4, Pub. by CAB Bks England). State Mutual Bk.
Palmer, Robert G. & Troeh, Frederick R. Introductory Soil Science: Laboratory Manual. 2nd ed. 1977. pap. 7.95x (ISBN 0-8138-1555-X). Iowa St U Pr.
PCA Soil Primer. 1973. pap. 3.00 (ISBN 0-89312-105-3, EB007S). Portland Cement.
Plaisance, George. Lexique Pedologique Trilingue. (Fr.). 355p. 1958. pap. 22.50 (ISBN 0-686-57082-0, M-6458). French & Eur.
Richards, K., et al, eds. Geomorphology & Soils. (Illus.). 500p. 1985. text ed. 50.00x (ISBN 0-04-551093-8). Allen Unwin.
Rudman, Jack. Soil Scientist. (Career Examination Ser.: C-1033). (Cloth bdg. avail. on request). 10.00 (ISBN 0-8373-1033-4). Natl Learning.
Sanchez, Pedro A. Properties & Management of Soils in the Tropics. LC 76-22761. 618p. 1976. 49.95x (ISBN 0-471-75200-2, Pub. by Wiley-Interscience). Wiley.
Sanglerat, G. Penetrometer & Soil Exploration. (Developments in Geotechnical Engineering Ser.: Vol. 1). 464p. 1972. 72.50 (ISBN 0-444-40976-9). Elsevier.
Schlichtling, E. & Schwertmann, U. Pseudogley & Gley: Genesis & Use of Hydromorphic Soils. (Illus.). 772p. 1973. pap. 88.30x (ISBN 3-527-25449-8). VCH Pubs.
Simpson, Ken. Soil. LC 82-169. (Agriculture Bks.). 1983. pap. text ed. 14.95x (ISBN 0-582-44641-4). Longman.
Singer, Michael J. Soils. 523p. 1986. text ed. price not set. Macmillan.
Smart, Peter & Tovey, N. Keith. Electron Microcopy of Soils & Sediments: Examples. (Illus.). 1981. 70.00x (ISBN 0-19-854515-0). Oxford U Pr.
Soil Map of the World, 10: Australasia. 221p. 1978. pap. text ed. 26.00 (ISBN 0-686-94179-9, M119, UNESCO). Unipub.
Soils. 2.25 (ISBN 0-686-21123-5). Bklyn Botanic.
Soils & Crop Protection Chemicals. (Monograph Ser.: No. 27). 200p. (Orig.). 1984. pap. 32.00x (ISBN 0-901436-80-1, Pub. by B C P C England). Intl Spec Bk.
Soils of Cumra Area, Turkey: Cumra Bolgesinin Topraklari Turkiye. (Agricultural Research Reports: No. 720). 1969. pap. 11.75 (ISBN 90-220-0186-5, PDC177, PUDOC). Unipub.
Sopher, Charles & Baird, Jack. Soils & Soil Management. 2nd ed. 1981. text ed. 23.95 (ISBN 0-8359-7031-0); instr's. manual free (ISBN 0-8359-7032-9). Reston.
Sposito, Garrison. The Thermodynamics of Soil Solutions. (Illus.). 1981. 47.50x (ISBN 0-19-857568-8). Oxford U Pr.
Stevenson. Cycles of Soils. 1985. price not set (ISBN 0-471-82218-3). Wiley.
Stevenson, F. J., ed. Nitrogen in Agricultural Soils. (ASA Monograph: No. 22). 940p. 1982. 30.00 (ISBN 0-89118-070-2). Am Soc Agron.
Trace Elements in Soils & Agriculture. (Soils Bulletins: No. 17). (Eng., Fr. & Span.). 70p. 1972. pap. 7.50 (ISBN 0-686-92718-4, F1159, FAO). Unipub.
Tresemer, David. Transplants in Soil Blocks. (Illus.). 1983. pap. 3.00 (ISBN 0-938670-03-4). By Hand & Foot.
Wambeke, A. van. Management Properties of Ferralsols. (Soils Bulletins: No. 23). 120p. (2nd Printing 1979). 1980. pap. 8.75 (ISBN 92-5-100754-3, F1165, FAO). Unipub.
Young, A. Tropical Soils & Soil Survey. LC 75-19573. (Cambridge Geographical Studies: No. 9). 1976. 77.50 (ISBN 0-521-21054-2). Cambridge U Pr.
--Tropical Soils & Soil Survey. LC 75-19573. (Cambridge Geographical Studies: No. 9). 468p. 1980. pap. 19.95 (ISBN 0-521-29768-0). Cambridge U Pr.

SOILS–ANALYSIS

Andrew, C. S. & Kamprath, E. J. Mineral Nutrition of Legumes in Tropical & Subtropical Soils. 415p. 1978. 36.00 (ISBN 0-643-00311-8, C014, CSIRO). Unipub.
Bresler, E., et al. Saline & Sodic Soils: Principles, Dynamics, Modeling. (Advanced Series in Agricultural Sciences: Vol. 10). (Illus.). 280p. 1982. 51.00 (ISBN 0-387-11120-4). Springer-Verlag.
Brewer, Roy. Fabric & Mineral Analysis of Soils. LC 75-17850. 498p. 1976. Repr. of 1964 ed. 27.50 (ISBN 0-88275-314-2). Krieger.
Burringh, P. Introduction to the Study of Soils in Tropical & Subtropical Regions. 99p. 1981. 52.00x (ISBN 0-686-76649-0, Pub. by Oxford & IBH India). State Mutual Bk.
Clayton, P. M. & Tiller, K. G. A Chemical Method for the Determination of the Heavy Metal Content of Soils in Environmental Studies. 1980. 20.00x (ISBN 0-643-00341-X, Pub. by CSJRO Australia). State Mutual Bk.
Cottenie, A. Soil & Plant Testing As a Basis of Fertilizer Recommendations. (Soils Bulletins: No. 38-2). 120p. 1980. pap. 9.00 (ISBN 92-5-100956-2, F2034, FAO). Unipub.
Davies, Brian E., ed. Applied Soil Trace Elements. LC 79-40640. 482p. 1980. 79.95 (ISBN 0-471-27625-1, Pub. by Wiley-Interscience). Wiley.
De Gruijter, J. J. Numerical Classification of Soils & Its Application in Survey. (Agricultural Research Reports: No. 855). (Illus.). 1978. pap. 22.00 (ISBN 90-220-0608-5, PDC59, PUDOC). Unipub.
Demars & Chaney, eds. Geotechnical Properties, Behavior, & Performance of Calcareous Soils - STP 777. 414p. 1982. 39.00 (ISBN 0-8031-0787-0, 04-777000-38). ASTM.
Determination of Phosphate Status of Soils in Naaldwijk Area for Growing Lettuce in Glasshouses. (Agricultural Research Reports: No. 153). 1971. pap. 4.00 (ISBN 90-220-0347-7, PDC184, PUDOC). Unipub.
Dixon, J. B. & Weed, S. B., eds. Minerals in Soil Environments. 1977. 25.00 (ISBN 0-89118-765-0). Soil Sci Soc Am.
Fridland, V. M. Comparative Physiology & Evolution of Vision in Invertebrates C. 1981. 30.00x (ISBN 0-686-76629-6, Pub. by Oxford & IBH India). State Mutual Bk.
--Soil Combination & Their Genesis. 1981. 60.00x (ISBN 0-686-76666-0, Pub. by Oxford & IBH India). State Mutual Bk.
Frissel, M. J. & Reiniger, P. Simulation of Accumulation & Leaching in Soils. 124p. 1981. 70.00x (ISBN 0-686-76662-8, Pub. by Oxford & IBH India). State Mutual Bk.
Graley, A. M. & Nicolls, K. D. Sampling in Surveys of Exchangeable Potassium in Soils. 1980. 20.00x (ISBN 0-643-02486-7, Pub. by CSJRO Australia). State Mutual Bk.
Guidelines: Land Evaluation for Rainfed Agriculture. (Soils Bulletins: No. 52). 237p. 1984. pap. 18.00 (ISBN 92-5-101455-8, F2639, FAO). Unipub.
Gupta, T. C. & Pahwa, K. N. A Century of Soil Salinity Research in India. 400p. 1981. 72.00x (ISBN 0-686-76627-X, Pub. by Oxford & IBH India). State Mutual Bk.
Handreck, K. A. Organic Matter & Soils. (Discovering Soils Ser.: No. 7). 51p. 1979. pap. 6.00 (ISBN 0-686-71837-2, C047, CSIRO). Unipub.
--What's Wrong with My Soil. (Discovering Soils Ser.: No. 4). 28p. 1979. pap. 6.00 (ISBN 0-686-71849-6, C045, CSIRO). Unipub.
Hauser, G. The Calibration of Soil Tests for Fertilizer Recommendations. (Soils Bulletins: No. 18). 78p. (2nd Printing 1977). 1973. pap. 7.50 (ISBN 92-5-100258-4, F1160, FAO). Unipub.
Henry, C. D. & Kapadia, R. R. Trace Elements in Soils of the South Texas Uranium District: Concentrations, Origin, & Environmental Significance. (Report of Investigations Ser.: RI 101). (Illus.). 52p. 1980. 2.00 (ISBN 0-318-03243-0). Bur Econ Geology.
Jarrett, P. M., ed. Testing of Peats & Organic Soils - STP 820. LC 83-70259. 241p. 1983. text ed. 34.00 (ISBN 0-8031-0254-2, 04-820000-38). ASTM.
Kovacs, William D. & Holtz, Robert D. An Introduction to Geotechnical Engineering. (Illus.). 720p. 1981. text ed. 38.95 (ISBN 0-13-484394-0). P-H.
Lal, R. & Greenland, D. J., eds. Soil Physical Properties & Crop Production in the Tropics. LC 79-40583. 551p. 1979. 137.95x (ISBN 0-471-99757-9, Pub. by Wiley-Interscience). Wiley.
Loveday, J. Methods for Analysis of Irrigated Soils. 208p. 1974. 39.00x (ISBN 0-85198-302-2, Pub. by CAB Bks England). State Mutual Bk.
Moore, A. W. & Cook, B. G., eds. Information Systems for Soil & Related Data: Proceedings of the Second Australian Meeting of the ISSS Working Group on Soil Information Systems, Canberra, Australia, 19-21 February 1980. 161p. 1981. pap. 17.25 (ISBN 90-220-0763-4, PDC221, Pudoc). Unipub.
Peck, T. R., et al, eds. Soil Testing: Correlating & Interpreting the Analytical Results. (Illus.). 1977. 6.00 (ISBN 0-89118-047-8). Am Soc Agron.
--Soil Testing: Correlating & Interpreting the Analytical Results. 117p. 1977. pap. 6.00 (ISBN 0-89118-047-8). Soil Sci Soc Am.
A Provisional Methodology for Soil Degradation Assessment. (Illus.). 84p. 1980. pap. 35.75 (ISBN 92-5-100869-8, F1958, FAO). Unipub.
Sampling of Soil & Rock: A Symposium Presented at the Seventy-Third Annual Meeting, Toronto, Ont., Canada, June 21-26, 1970. LC 75-137453. (American Society for Testing & Materials: No. 483). pap. 49.80 (ISBN 0-317-07983-2, 2015508). Bks Demand UMI.
Smart, P. & Tovey, N. K. Electron Microscopy of Soils & Sediment: Techniques. (Illus.). 1982. 98.00x (ISBN 0-19-857574-2). Oxford U Pr.
Soil & Plant Testing & Analysis: Report of an Expert Consultation, Held in Rome, 13-17 June 1977. (Soils Bulletins: No. 38-1). 251p. 1980. pap. 18.00 (ISBN 92-5-100961-9, F2033, FAO). Unipub.
Soil Nitrogen As Fertilizer or Pollutant. (Panel Proceedings Ser.). (Illus.). 398p. 1980. pap. 56.50 (ISBN 92-0-111080-4, ISP535, IAEA). Unipub.
Soils: An Outline of Their Properties & Management. (Discovering Soils Ser.: No. 1). 40p. 1977. pap. 5.00 (ISBN 0-643-02042-X, C057, CSIRO). Unipub.
Spoil Specimen Preparation for Laboratory Testing- STP 599. 350p. 1976. 35.00 (ISBN 0-8031-0790-0, 04-599000-38). ASTM.
Thornburn, Thomas H. & Bauer, Edward E. Introductory Soil Testing. (Illus.). 1962. pap. 5.60x (ISBN 0-87563-009-X). Stipes.
Townsend, W. N. An Introduction to the Scientific Study of the Soil. 1981. 120.00x (ISBN 0-686-76648-2, Pub. by Oxford & IBH India). State Mutual Bk.
Walsh, L. M. & Beaton, J. D., eds. Soil Testing & Plant Analysis. (Illus.). 471p. 1973. 10.00 (ISBN 0-89118-755-3). Soil Sci Soc Am.
Wilde, S. S., et al. Soil & Plant Analysis for Tree Culture. 172p. 1981. 45.00 (ISBN 0-686-76665-2, Pub. by Oxford & IBH India). State Mutual Bk.

SOILS–BACTERIOLOGY

see Soil Micro-Organisms

SOILS–BIBLIOGRAPHY

see Soil Science–Bibliography

SOILS–CAPILLARITY

see Soil Capillarity

SOILS–CLASSIFICATION

Buol, S. W. Soil Genesis & Classification. 1981. 42.00x (ISBN 0-686-76667-9, Pub. by Oxford & IBH India). State Mutual Bk.
Buol, S. W., et al. Soil Genesis & Classification. 2nd ed. 1980. text ed. 19.50x (ISBN 0-8138-1460-X). Iowa St U Pr.
Butler, B. E. Soil Classification for Soil Survey: Monographs on Soil Survey. (Illus.). 1980. 32.50x (ISBN 0-19-854510-X). Oxford U Pr.
The Canadian System of Soil Classification. 1979. 16.50 (ISBN 0-660-01620-6, SSC112, SSC). Unipub.
FitzPatrick, E. A. Soils: Their Formation, Classification & Ditribution. LC 82-12669. (Illus.). 384p. 1983. pap. text ed. 23.00x (ISBN 0-582-30116-5). Longman.
Fridland, V. M. Soil Combination & Their Genesis. 1981. 60.00x (ISBN 0-686-76666-0, Pub. by Oxford & IBH India). State Mutual Bk.
Greenland, D. J., ed. Characterization of Soils in Relation to Their Classification & Management for Crop Productions. (Illus.). 1981. 84.00x (ISBN 0-19-854538-X). Oxford U Pr.
Head, K. H. Manual of Soil Laboratory Testing: Permeability, Quick Shear Strength & Compressibility Tests, 2 vols. 339p. 1982. Vol. 1. 58.95x (ISBN 0-470-26973-1); Vol. 2. 48.95x (ISBN 0-470-27289-9). Halsted Pr.
The Soil: How the Soil Is Made up. (Better Farming Ser.: No. 4). (Illus.). 37p. 1976. pap. 7.50 (ISBN 92-5-100143-X, F62, FAO). Unipub.
Thompson, Louis M. & Troeh, Frederick. Soils & Soil Fertility. 4th ed. (Ag Ser.). (Illus.). 1977. text ed. 38.95 (ISBN 0-07-064411-X). McGraw.
Usda, et al. Soil Taxonomy: A Basic System of Soil Classification for Making & Interpreting Soil Surveys. (Selected Government Publications Reprint Ser.: 1-698). 768p. 1975. 49.95x (ISBN 0-471-80009-0, Pub. by Wiley-Interscience). Wiley.
Webster, R. Quantitative & Numerical Methods in Soil Classification & Survey. (Monographs on Soil Survey). (Illus.). 1977. 46.00x (ISBN 0-19-854512-6). Oxford U Pr.

SOILS–MAPS

Barker, Raymond J. & McDole, Robert E. Idaho Soils Atlas. LC 82-60201. (Illus.). 148p. 1983. 18.95 (ISBN 0-89301-088-X). U Pr of Idaho.
Soil Map of Europe. 31p. 1965. 41.75 (ISBN 0-685-02466-0, F425, FAO). Unipub.
Soil Map of the World, 1: Legend. 59p. 1975. pap. 31.00 with sheet & text (ISBN 92-3-101125-1, M81, UNESCO). Unipub.
Soil Map of the World, 2: North America. (Illus.). 1976. pap. text ed. 22.00 (ISBN 92-3-101126-X, M83, UNESCO). Unipub.
Soil Map of the World, 3: Mexico & Central America. (Illus.). 1976. pap. text ed. 13.00 (ISBN 92-3-101127-8, M86, UNESCO). Unipub.

SOILS–MECHANICS

see Soil Mechanics

SOILS–RADIOACTIVITY

see Soils, Radioactive Substances in

SOILS–AFRICA

East African Subcommittee for Soil Correlation & Land Evaluation. Report of the Second Meeting of the Eastern African Sub-Committee for Soil Correlation & Land Evaluation: Addis-Ababa, Ethiopia, 25-30 October 1976. (World Soil Resources Reports: No. 47). 131p. 1978. pap. 8.50 (ISBN 92-5-100408-0, F1318, FAO). Unipub.
Fourth Meeting of the West African Subcommittee for Soil Correlation & Land Evaluation: Proceedings, Banjul, Gambia, 20-27 Oct. 1979. (World Soil Resources Reports: No. 53). 124p. 1982. pap. 9.50 (ISBN 92-5-101117-6, F2218, FAO). Unipub.
Jager, T. Soils of the Serengeti Woodlands, Tanzania. 253p. 1982. pap. 29.25 (ISBN 90-220-0775-8, PDC239, Pudoc). Unipub.
Shantz, Homer L. & Marbut, Curtis F. Vegetation & Soils of Africa. LC 70-170848. Repr. of 1923 ed. 19.00 (ISBN 0-404-05953-8). AMS Pr.
Soil Map of the World, 6: Africa. 299p. 1977. pap. 166.50 (ISBN 0-686-94177-2, UNESCO). Unipub.
Third Meeting of the Eastern African Subcommittee for Soil Correlation & Land Evaluation: Lusaka, Zambia, April 18-30, 1978. (World Soil Resources Reports: No. 51). 170p. 1981. pap. 11.25 (ISBN 92-5-100902-3, F2082, FAO). Unipub.

SOILS–AFRICA, WEST

Jones, M. J. & Wild, A. Soils of the West African Savanna. 246p. 1975. 40.00x (ISBN 0-85198-348-0, Pub. by CAB Bks England). State Mutual Bk.

SOILS–ANTARCTIC REGIONS

Tedrow, John C. Soils of the Polar Landscapes. 1977. 65.00x (ISBN 0-8135-0808-8). Rutgers U Pr.

SOILS–ASIA

Highly Calcareous Lacustrine Soils in the Great Konya Basin, Turkey. (Agricultural Research Reports: 752). 1971. pap. 15.00 (ISBN 9-0220-0336-1, PDC39, PUDOC). Unipub.

Kawaguchi, Keizaburo & Kyuma, Kazutake. Paddy Soils in Tropical Asia: Their Material Nature & Fertility. (Center for Southeast Asian Studies, Kyoto University). (Illus.). 1978. text ed. 20.00x (ISBN 0-8248-0570-4); pap. text ed. 12.00x (ISBN 0-8248-0571-2). UH Pr.

Morphology & Geochemistry of Three Clay Soils of a Tropical Costal Plain (Surinam) (Agricultural Research Reports: PDC56). 1970. pap. 4.00 (ISBN 90-220-0194-6, PDC56, PUDOC). Unipub.

Organic Materials & Soil Productivity in the Near East: Papers Presented at the FAO-SIDA Workshop on the Use of Organic Materials for Improving Soil Productivity in the Near East. (Soils Bulletins: No. 45). 336p. (English with an Arabic summary). 1982. pap. 24.00 (ISBN 92-5-001217-9, F2334, FAO). Unipub.

Red Soils in Indonesia. 167p. 1980. pap. 52.75 (ISBN 90-220-0715-4, PDC209, Pudoc). Unipub.

Soil Map of the World, 7: South Asia. 117p. 1977. pap. 55.00 (ISBN 0-686-94176-4, M92, UNESCO). Unipub.

Soil Map of the World, 8: North & Central Asia. 165p. 1978. pap. 232.50 (ISBN 0-686-94175-6, M97, UNESCO). Unipub.

Soil Map of the World, 9: South-East Asia. 149p. 1979. pap. 18.50 (ISBN 0-686-94174-8, M90, UNESCO). Unipub.

Soil Salinity & Alkalinity in the Great Konya Basin, Turkey. (Agricultural Research Reports: 743). 1970. pap. 9.00 (ISBN 90-220-0310-8, PDC92, PUDOC). Unipub.

Soils of the Great Konya Basin, Turkey. (Agricultural Research Reports: 740). (Illus.). 1970. pap. 28.00 (ISBN 90-220-0304-3, PDC90, PUDOC). Unipub.

Soils of the Kucuk Menderes Valley, Turkey. (Agricultural Research Reports: 785). (Illus.). 1972. pap. 40.00 (ISBN 90-220-0421-X, PDC91, PUDOC). Unipub.

SOILS–AUSTRALIA

Butler, B. E. Soil Survey of the Horticultural Soils in the Murrumbidgee Irrigation Areas, New South Wales. 80p. 1981. 25.00x (ISBN 0-643-02432-8, Pub. by CSIRO Australia). State Mutual Bk.

Handreck, K. A. What's Wrong with My Soil. (Discovering Soils Ser.: No. 4). 28p. 1979. pap. 6.00 (ISBN 0-686-71849-6, C045, CSIRO). Unipub.

Lands of the Alligator Rivers Area: Northern Territory. (Land Research Ser.: No. 38). (Illus.). 173p. 1976. pap. 13.50 (ISBN 0-643-00208-1, C019, CSIRO). Unipub.

Murtha, G. G. Soils & Land Use on the Northern Section of the Townsville Costal Plan, North Queensland. (Soils and Land Use Ser.: No. 55). (Illus.). 1977. pap. 7.00x (ISBN 0-643-00156-5, Pub. by CSIRO). Intl Spec Bk.

Northcote, K. H. Description of Australian Soils. 170p. 1982. 40.00x (ISBN 0-643-00139-5, Pub. by CSIRO Australia). State Mutual Bk.

--Descriptions of Australian Soils. 170p. 1978. cloth 40.00x (ISBN 0-643-00264-2, Pub. by CAB Bks England). State Mutual Bk.

Northcote, K. H., et al. A Description of Australian Soils. 170p. 1975. pap. 18.00 (ISBN 0-643-00139-5, C024, CSIRO). Unipub.

--A Description of Australian Soils. (Illus.). 1977. 21.00x (ISBN 0-643-00139-5, Pub. by CSIRO); 59 slides 28.00x (ISBN 0-643-00190-5). Intl Spec Bk.

Oades, J. M. & Lewis, D. G. Red-Brown Earths of Australia. 1982. 40.00x (ISBN 0-686-97899-4, Pub. by CSIRO Australia). State Mutual Bk.

Rentz, D. C. & Balderson, J. Catalogue of Australian Tettigoniidae. 1980. 20.00x (ISBN 0-643-00331-2, Pub. by CSJRO Australia). State Mutual Bk.

Russell, J. S. & Greacen, E. L. Soil Factors in Crop Production in a Semi-Arid Environment. 1978. text ed. 30.25x (ISBN 0-7022-1303-9). U of Queensland Pr.

Soils: Australia's Greatest Resource. (Discovering Soils Ser.: No. 2). 10p. pap. 6.00 (ISBN 0-686-71845-3, C048, CSIRO). Unipub.

When Should I Water. (Discovering Soils Ser.: No. 8). 76p. 1979. pap. text ed. 6.00 (ISBN 0-643-02522-7, C044, CSIRO). Unipub.

Wooldridge, M. J. Simultaneous Dry Bulb & Wet Bulb Temperature Data for Fourteen Australian Locations. 146p. 1980. 25.00 (ISBN 0-643-00343-6, Pub. by CSIRO Australia). State Mutual Bk.

SOILS–CANADA

The Canadian System of Soil Classification. 1979. 16.50 (ISBN 0-660-01620-6, SSC112, SSC). Unipub.

Soils of Canada, 3 vols. (Illus.). 1978. pap. 35.00 set (ISBN 0-660-00502-6, SSC95, SSC). Unipub.

Soils of Canada, 2 vols. (Illus., Report & inventory). 1977. Set. pap. 35.00x (ISBN 0-660-00502-6). Brookfield Pub Co.

SOILS–CHINA

Thorp, James. Geography of the Soils of China. 1976. lib. bdg. 69.95 (ISBN 0-8490-1881-1). Gordon Pr.

SOILS–GREAT BRITAIN

Dimbleby, G. W. The Development of British Heathlands & their Soils. 1962. 45.00x (ISBN 0-686-45495-2, Pub. by For Lib Comm England). State Mutual Bk.

SOILS–INDIA

Gupta, T. C. & Pahwa, K. N. A Century of Soil Salinity Research in India. 400p. 1981. 72.00x (ISBN 0-686-76627-X, Pub. by Oxford & IBH India). State Mutual Bk.

Rajan, S. V. & Rao, H. G. Studies on Soils of India. 425p. 1978. 12.00x (ISBN 0-7069-0568-7, Pub. by Vikas India). Advent Ny.

SOILS–NETHERLANDS

De Bakker, H. Major Soils & Soil Regions in the Netherlands. (Illus.). 1979. lib. bdg. 53.00 (ISBN 9-06193-590-3, Pub. by Junk Pubs Netherlands). Kluwer Academic.

--Major Soils & Soil Regions in the Netherlands. 192p. 105.00x (ISBN 0-686-45853-2, Pub. by CAB Bks England). State Mutual Bk.

Major Soils & Soil Regions in The Netherlands. 1978. pap. 80.00 (ISBN 90-220-0675-1, PDC5, PUDOC) (ISBN 90-6193-590-3). Unipub.

Molybdenum Uptake by Beets in Dutch Soils. (Agricultural Research Reports: No. 775). 1972. pap. 8.25 (ISBN 90-220-0393-0, PDC189, PUDOC). Unipub.

SOILS (ENGINEERING)

see Soil Mechanics

SOILS, RADIOACTIVE SUBSTANCES IN

Campbell, J. A. & Bewick, M. W. Neutron Activation Analysis. 36p. 1978. 40.00x (ISBN 0-85198-438-X, Pub. by CAB Bks England). State Mutual Bk.

Clayton, R. F. Monitoring of Radioactive Contamination on Surfaces. (Technical Reports Ser.: No. 120). (Illus.). 33p. (Orig.). 1970. pap. 7.50 (ISBN 92-0-125570-5, IDC120, IAEA). Unipub.

Isotopes & Radiation in Soil-Plant Nutrition Studies. (Proceedings Ser.). (Eng., Fr., Rus. & Span., Illus.). 624p. (Orig.). 1965. pap. 32.00 (ISBN 92-0-010265-4, ISP108, IAEA). Unipub.

Laboratory Training Manual on the Use of Isotopes & Radiation in Soil-Plant Relations Research. (Technical Reports Ser.: No. 29). (Illus.). 166p. 1964. pap. 10.00 (ISBN 92-0-115064-4, IDC29, IAEA). Unipub.

Milnes, A. G. Geology & Radwaste. Date not set. 60.00 (ISBN 0-12-498070-8); pap. 39.95 (ISBN 0-12-498071-6). Acad Pr.

Smith, P. C., et al. The Use of Nuclear Meters in Soils Investigations. LC 67-13261. (American Society for Testing & Materials Ser.: Special Technical Publication, No. 412). pap. 35.50 (ISBN 0-317-11246-5, 2000938). Bks Demand UMI.

Tracer Manual on Crops & Soils. (Technical Reports Ser.: No. 171). (Illus.). 227p. 1976. pap. 33.00 (ISBN 92-0-115076-8, IDC171, IAEA). Unipub.

Vose, P. B. Introduction to Nuclear Techniques in Agronomy & Plant Biology. (Illus.). 1980. 63.00 (ISBN 0-08-024924-8); pap. 29.00 (ISBN 0-08-024923-X). Pergamon.

SOLANACEAE

D'Arcy, W. G., ed. Solanaceae: Biology & Systematics. (Illus.). 608p. 1985. 60.00x (ISBN 0-231-05780-6). Columbia U Pr.

Heiser, Charles B., Jr. Nightshades: The Paradoxical Plants. LC 70-85798. (Biology Ser.). (Illus.). 200p. 1969. text ed. 12.95 (ISBN 0-7167-0672-5). W H Freeman.

Huber, K. A. Morphologisch und Entwicklungsgeschichtliche Untersuchungen an Blueten und Bluetenstaenden Von Solannaceen und Von Nolana Paradoxa Lindl: Nolanaceae. (Dissertationes Botanicae Ser.: No. 55). (Ger., Illus.). 486p. 1980. pap. text ed. 35.00x (ISBN 3-7682-1268-8). Lubrecht & Cramer.

Van Gastel, A. J. Mutability of the Self-Incompatibility Locus & Identification of the S-Bearing Chromosome in Nicotiana Alata. (Agricultural Research Reports: No. 852). 1976. pap. 5.00 (ISBN 90-220-0603-4, PDC202, PUDOC). Unipub.

SOLANUM

Inbreeding Heterosis Fertility Plasmon Differentiation & Phytophtora - Resistance in Solanum Verrucosum Schlechte & Some Interspecific Crosses in Solanum. (Agricultural Research Reports: No. 748). 1970. pap. 21.50 (ISBN 90-220-0326-4, PDC182, PUDOC). Unipub.

Van Breukelen, E. W. Pseudogamic Production of Dihaploids & Monoploids in Solanum Tuberosum & Some Related Species. (Agricultural Research Reports: No. 908). 129p. 1981. pap. 15.25 (ISBN 90-220-0762-6, PDC227, PUDOC). Unipub.

SOLAR ACTIVITY

see also Auroras; International Years of the Quiet Sun, 1964-1965; Solar Flares; Solar Radiation; Sun-Spots

Bumba, Vaclav & Kleczek, Josip, eds. Basic Mechanisms of Solar Activity. (Symposium of the International Astronomical Union Ser.: Vol. 71). 1976. lib. bdg. 74.00 (ISBN 90-277-0680-8, Pub. by Reidel Holland); pap. 39.50 (ISBN 90-277-0681-6). Kluwer Academic.

ESLAB-ESRIN Symposium, Noordwijk, Netherlands, September 16-19, 1969. Intercorrelated Satellite Observations Related to Solar Events: Proceedings. Manno, V. & Page, D. E., eds. LC 70-179894. (Astrophysics & Space Science Library: No.19). 672p. 1970. lib. bdg. 63.00 (ISBN 9-0277-0128-8, Pub. by Reidel Holland). Kluwer Academic.

European Astronomical Meeting, 1st, Athens, 1972. Solar Activity & Related Interplanetary & Terrestrial Phenomenon: Proceedings, Vol. 1. Xanthakis, J., ed. (Illus.). 200p. 1973. 58.50 (ISBN 0-387-06314-5). Springer-Verlag.

IAU Symposium, No. 35, Budapest, Hungary, Sept. 1967. Structure & Development of Solar Active Regions: Proceedings. Kiepenheuer, K. O., ed. (IAU Symposia). 608p. 1968. lib. bdg. 58.00 (ISBN 90-277-0122-9). Kluwer Academic.

Jones, J. Solar Greenhouse Gardening. 1986. cancelled (ISBN 0-442-24568-8). Van Nos Reinhold.

Kreider, Jan F. Medium & High Temperature Solar Processes. LC 79-51694. (Energy Service & Engineering Ser.). 1979. 55.00 (ISBN 0-12-425980-4). Acad Pr.

McCormac, Billy M. & Seliga, Thomas A., eds. Solar-Terrestrial Influences on Weather & Climate. 1979. lib. bdg. 24.00 (ISBN 90-277-0978-5, Pub. by Reidel Holland). Kluwer Academic.

Zirker, Jack B., ed. Coronal Holes & High Speed Wind Streams. LC 77-84528. (Illus.). 1977. text ed. 22.50x (ISBN 0-87081-109-6). Colo Assoc.

SOLAR AIR CONDITIONING

National Bureau of Standards. Performance Criteria for Solar Heating & Cooling Systems in Commerical Buildings. 215p. 1985. pap. 29.95 (ISBN 0-317-18186-6, H-052). Solar Energy Info.

Sheet Metal & Air Conditioning Contractors' Natl. Assoc. Inc. Staff. Installation Standards for Heating, Air Conditioning & Solar Systems. 5th ed. 150p. 1985. pap. 29.95 (ISBN 0-317-18187-4, H-053). Solar Energy Info.

U. S. Dept. of Commerce, National Bureau of Standards. Test Methods & Standards Development for Active Solar Heating & Cooling Systems. 132p. 1984. pap. 12.95X (H050). Solar Energy Info.

SOLAR BATTERIES

Baum, V. A. Semiconductor Solar Energy Converters. LC 69-17884. 222p. 1969. 35.00x (ISBN 0-306-10830-5, Consultants). Plenum Pub.

Chandra, Suresh. Photoelectrochemical Solar Cells. (Electrocomponent Science Monographs: Vol. 5). 245p. 1985. text ed. 59.00 (ISBN 2-88124-014-3). Gordon.

Chopra, Kasturi L. & Das, Sunhit R. Thin Film Solar Cells. 599p. 1983. 85.00x (ISBN 0-306-41141-5, Plenum Pr). Plenum Pub.

CNES. Solar Cells. (Illus.). 690p. 1971. 163.25 (ISBN 0-677-50450-0). Gordon.

Educational Research Council of America. Solar Cell Scientist. Ferris, Theodore N. & Marchak, John P., eds. (Real People at Work Ser.: S). (Illus.). 36p. 1977. 2.70 (ISBN 0-89247-143-3, 9634). Changing Times.

Fahrenbruch, Alan & Bube, Richard. Fundamentals of Solar Cells. LC 82-13919. 1983. 68.00 (ISBN 0-12-247680-8). Acad Pr.

Fonash, Stephen J. Solar Cell Device Physics. LC 81-14934. (Energy Science & Engineering Ser.: Resources, Technology, Management). 1981. 49.50 (ISBN 0-12-261980-3). Acad Pr.

Green, Martin A. Solar Cells: Operation Principles Technology & Systems Applications. (Illus.). 256p. 1982. 38.95 (ISBN 0-13-822270-3). P-H.

Hu, Chenming & White, Richard M. Solar Cells: From Basic to Advanced Systems. (Series in Electrical Engineering: Power & Energy). (Illus.). 288p. 1983. text ed. 43.95 (ISBN 0-07-030745-8). McGraw.

Johnston, Wilbur D., Jr. Solar Voltaic Cells. (Energy, Power & Environment Ser.: Vol. 7). (Illus.). 224p. 1980. 45.00 (ISBN 0-8247-6992-9). Dekker.

Koltun, M. M. Selective Optical Surfaces for Solar Energy Converters. Siddons, D. P., ed. Chomet, S., tr. from Rus. LC 81-69401. Tr. of Selektivnye Opticheskie Poverkhnosti Preobrazovatelei Solnechnoe Energii. vi, 239p. 1981. 42.50 (ISBN 0-89864-003-2). Allerton Pr.

Laws, Robert J. Solar Cells: What You Always Wanted to Know. LC 82-1510. (Illus.). 128p. 1983. 11.95x (ISBN 0-89490-069-2). Enslow Pubs.

Rabl, Ari. Active Solar Collectors & Their Applications. (Illus.). 500p. 1985. text ed. 59.00x (ISBN 0-19-503546-1). Oxford U Pr.

Seippel, Robert. Photo Voltaics. 1983. text ed. 26.95 (ISBN 0-8359-5538-9). Reston.

Shrum, Wesley. Organized Technology: Networks & Innovation in Technical Systems. (Science & Society: A Purdue University Series in Science, Technology, & Human Values). (Illus.). 304p. 1985. pap. 4.50 (ISBN 0-911198-74-1). Purdue U Pr.

Solar Electric Technologies. Five Year Research Plan, Nineteen Eighty-Four to Nineteen Eighty-Eight: Photovolactics: Electricity from Sunlight. 32p. 1984. pap. 4.95 (P-060). Solar Energy Info.

SOLAR CELLS

see Solar Batteries

SOLAR CORONA

see Sun

SOLAR ECLIPSES

see Eclipses

SOLAR ENERGY

see also Ocean Thermal Power Plants; Solar Engines; Solar Heating

Adams, Tim. Sun World. Hardy, Alice, ed. LC 78-74428. (A-1). 4.00 (ISBN 0-686-24151-7); pap. 2.00 (ISBN 0-686-24152-5). Central FL Voters.

Agnihotri, O. P. & Gupta, B. K. Solar Selective Surfaces. LC 80-17392. (Wiley Alternate Energy Ser.). 215p. 1981. 44.95x (ISBN 0-471-06035-6, Pub. by Wiley-Interscience). Wiley.

AIA Research Corporation. Passive Solar Design: A Short Bibliography for Practitioners. 1979. pap. 6.50x (ISBN 0-89934-040-7, A-007). Solar Energy Info.

--Passive Solar Design: A Survey of Monitored Buildings. 353p. 1979. pap. 39.50x (ISBN 0-930978-85-4, A008). Solar Energy Info.

--Passive Solar Research & Development Project Summaries. 1979. pap. 11.95x (ISBN 0-89934-041-5, A-011). Solar Energy Info.

--A Survey of Passive Solar Buildings. 176p. 1979. pap. 16.50x (ISBN 0-930978-84-6, A-002-PP). Solar Energy Info.

AIA Research Corporation for U. S. Department of Housing & Urban Renewal. A Survey of Passive Solar Homes. 105p. 1981. pap. 14.50x (ISBN 0-89934-026-1, A017). Solar Energy Info.

Allen, James. From Poverty to Power. 184p. 1980. pap. 7.50 (ISBN 0-89540-061-8, SB-061). Sun Pub.

American Institute of Architects. Architect's Handbook of Energy Practice: Active Solar Systems. (Illus.). 58p. 1982. pap. 7.50 (ISBN 0-913962-54-6). Am Inst Arch.

American Society of Mechanical Engineers. Heat Transfer Division. Heat Transfer in Solar Energy Systems: Presented at the Winter Annual Meeting of the American Society of Mechanical Engineers, Atlanta, Georgia, Nov. 27-Dec. 2, 1977. Howell, J. R. & Min, T., eds. LC 77-89012. pap. 35.30 (ISBN 0-317-08530-1, 2051730). Bks Demand UMI.

American Society of Mechanical Engineers. Modeling, Simulation, Testing & Measurements for Solar Energy Systems: Presented at the Winter Annual Meeting of ASME, San Francisco, CA., December 10-15, 1978. Nash, J. M. & Smok, J. T., eds. LC 78-67977. pap. 26.80 (ISBN 0-317-26621-7, 2024183). Bks Demand UMI.

American Solar Energy Society Staff. American Solar Energy Society Membership Directory 1982-83 & Guide to Programs. 120p. 1982. pap. text ed. 45.00x (ISBN 0-89553-049-X). Am Solar Energy.

AMETEK. Solar Energy Handbook: Theory & Application. LC 78-14646. 1979. 18.50x (ISBN 0-8019-6776-7). Chilton.

AMETEK Inc. Power Systems Group. Solar Energy Handbook: Theory & Applications of Solar-Generated Electricity. 2nd ed. LC 81-71091. 1984. 37.50 (ISBN 0-8019-7154-3). Chilton.

Anachem Inc Staff & Sandia National Laboratories. Solar Heating Materials Handbook: Environmental & Safety Considerations for Selection. (Illus.). 286p. 1984. pap. 28.95x (H051). Solar Energy Info.

Anderson, Bruce. The New Solar Home Book. (Illus.). 256p. (Orig.). 1985. pap. 16.95 (ISBN 0-931790-70-0). Brick Hse Pub.

Anderson, Bruce & Riordan, Michael. The Solar Home Book: Heating, Cooling, & Designing with the Sun. LC 76-29494. (Illus.). 298p. 1976. pap. 10.95 (ISBN 0-917352-01-7); pap. 8.50 members. Natl Assn Home.

Anderson, Bruce & Wells, Malcolm. Passive Solar Energy. 1981. pap. 10.95 (ISBN 0-931790-09-3). Brick Hse Pub.

Anderson, Bruce, compiled by. Passive Solar Design Handbook. (Illus.). 752p. 1984. 55.00 (ISBN 0-442-20810-3). Van Nos Reinhold.

Anderson, Edward E. Fundamentals of Solar Thermal Energy Conversion. LC 81-22852 576p. 1983. text ed. 38.95 (ISBN 0-201-00008-3). Addison-Wesley.

Andrassy, Stella. The Solar Cookbook. LC 79-88818. 128p. 1981. pap. 5.95 (ISBN 0-87100-142-X, 2142). Morgan.
Argonne National Laboratory. Thermal Energy Storage: Design & Installation Manual. rev., 2nd ed. 372p. 1983. 54.50x (ISBN 0-89934-009-1, H.929); pap. 39.50x (ISBN 0-89934-010-5, H.029). Solar Energy Info.
Arizona State University Library. Solar Energy Index. 1980. 175.00 (ISBN 0-08-023888-2). Pergamon.
--Solar Energy Index: Supplement I. 250p. 1982. 105.00 (ISBN 0-08-028832-4). Pergamon.
Aronson, E. A., et al. Satellites & Forecasting of Solar Radiation. Bahm, Raymond E., ed. LC 80-70943. (International Solar Energy Society, American Section, Workshop Ser.). 1982. pap. text ed. 32.50x (ISBN 0-89553-026-0). Am Solar Energy.
Artz, Robert J. & Walker, J. Robert. Solar Energy. 1984. text ed. 26.95 (ISBN 0-8359-7017-5); instr's. manual avail. (ISBN 0-8359-7018-3). Reston.
An Assessment of Problems Experienced with Operating Solar Systems in Canada & the Northern United States. (Solar Technical Ser.: No. 1). 73p. 1980. 9.00 (ISBN 0-660-10174-2, SSC139, SSC). Unipub.
ASTM Standards on Solar Energy. 144p. 1981. pap. 9.75 (ISBN 0-8031-0837-0, 03-544081-41). ASTM.
Bachofen, R. & Mislin, H., eds. New Trends in Research & Utilization of Solar Energy Through Biological Systems. (Experientia Supplementum: Vol. 43). 156p. 1982. text ed. 26.95 (ISBN 0-8176-1335-8). Birkhauser.
Baer, Steve. Sunspots. LC 75-20779. 1977. pap. 6.95 (ISBN 0-686-21779-9). Zomeworks Corp.
Bainbridge, David A. The Second Passive Solar Catalog. (Illus.). 110p. (Orig.). 1981. pap. 12.50 (ISBN 0-933490-02-X). Passive Solar.
Balcomb, et al. Passive Solar Design Handbook: Vol. 2, Passive Solar Design Analysis. 428p. 1981. pap. 44.50x (ISBN 0-89934-128-4, A-015). Solar Energy Info.
Balcomb, D., et al. Passive Solar Design Handbook: Passive Solar Design Analysis, Vol. 3. 668p. 1984. pap. 39.50x (ISBN 0-89934-203-5, A-923). Solar Energy Info.
--Passive Solar Design Handbook: Vol. 2, Passive Solar Design Analysis; Vol. 3, Passive Solar Design Analysis (Cont.) 1096p. (Vols. 2 & 3 in one binding). 1983. Repr. of 1982 ed. 89.50x (ISBN 0-89934-201-9, A-922). Solar Energy Info.
Balcomb, J. D., et al. Passive Solar Heating & Cooling: Proceedings of the Conference & Workshop, May 1976, Albuquerque, New Mexico. Keller, M. H., ed. 355p. pap. text ed. cancelled (ISBN 0-89553-108-9). Am Solar Energy.
Barbieri, R. H., et al. Process Heat in California: Applications & Potential for Solar Energy in the Industrial, Agricultural & Commercial Sectors. 1978. pap. 14.95x (ISBN 0-930978-72-2, D-004). Solar Energy Info.
Battelle Columbus Laboratories. Installation of a Modular Photovoltaic Array Field with Low Balance-of-System Costs. Sandia National Labs for U. S. Dept. of Energy, ed. 71p. 1984. pap. 9.95x (P-056). Solar Energy Info.
--Solar Energy Employment & Requirements: 1978-1983. 200p. 1981. pap. 29.50x (ISBN 0-89934-102-0, V.065). Solar Energy Info.
Battelle Northwest Laboratory. Analysis of Federal Incentives Used to Stimulate Energy Production. 416p. 1980. Repr. of 1978 ed. 49.50x (ISBN 0-89934-174-8, V052-PP). Solar Energy Info.
Batts, H. Lewis, Jr. & Tenenbaum, Michael, eds. Proceedings: Great Lakes Solar Greenhouse Conference II Kalamazoo, Michigan, June, 8-9, 1979. (Illus.). xiiii, 137p. (Orig.). 1980. pap. 10.00 (ISBN 0-939294-02-8, SB-416-G7). Beech Leaf.
Beach, Charles & Fordyce, Edward, eds. A Solar World: Proceedings of the Annual Meeting of the International Solar Energy Society, 3 vols. 1977. Set. pap. text ed. 115.00x (ISBN 0-89553-004-X). Am Solar Energy.
Becker, Clarence F. Solar Radiation Availability on Surfaces in the U. S. as Affected by Season, Orientation, Latitude, Altitude, & Cloudiness. Bruchey, Stuart, ed. LC 78-22659. (Energy in the American Economy Ser.). (Illus.). 1979. lib. bdg. 14.00x (ISBN 0-405-11963-1). Ayer Co Pubs.
Behrman, Daniel. Solar Energy: The Awakening Science. 1980. pap. 7.95 (ISBN 0-316-08772-6). Little.
Bereny, Justin A. Survey of the Emerging Solar Energy Industry. De Winter, Francis, ed. LC 77-71664. (Illus.). 405p. 1977. 60.00x (ISBN 0-930978-00-5, V-901); pap. 34.50x (ISBN 0-930978-01-3). Solar Energy Info.
Bloss, W. H. & Grassi, G., eds. E. C. Photovoltaic Solar Energy Conference, 4th. 1982. 96.00 (ISBN 90-277-1463-0, Pub. by Reidel Holland). Kluwer Academic.
Bocknis, J. O'M. Energy Options Real Economics & the Solar-Hydrogen System. 442p. 1980. cancelled (ISBN 0-85066-204-4). Taylor & Francis.
Bockris, John O. Energy Options: Real Economics & the Solar-Hydrogen System. 441p. 1980. 44.95x (ISBN 0-470-26915-4). Halsted Pr.
Boer, Karl W. & Duffie, John A., eds. Advances in Solar Energy: An Annual Review of Research & Development in 1981, Vol. I. (Illus.). 1982. pap. text ed. 95.00x (ISBN 0-89553-040-6). Am Solar Energy.
Booth, Don & Booth, Jonathan. Sun-Earth Buffering & Superinsulation. LC 83-72283. (Illus.). 1983. 19.95 (ISBN 0-9604422-4-3); pap. 12.95 (ISBN 0-9604422-3-5). Comm Builders.
Bossong, Ken. Passive Solar Retrofit for Homeowners & Apartment Dwellers. (Illus.). 80p. (Orig.). 1981. pap. text ed. 6.00 (ISBN 0-89988-068-1). Citizens Energy.
Bossong, Ken & Pilarski, Jan. National Passive Solar Directory. (Illus.). 60p. 1983. pap. text ed. 4.50 (ISBN 0-89988-100-9). Citizens Energy.
Bossong, Ken, et al. Solar Compendium, Vol. 1. (Illus.). 115p. 1980. 6.50 (ISBN 0-89988-013-4). Citizens Energy.
--A Solar Critique: Solar Compendium, Vol. II. 80p. (Orig.). 1981. 5.00 (ISBN 0-89988-070-3). Citizens Energy.
--Solar Energy & Big Business: Solar Compendium, Vol. III. (Illus.). 50p. (Orig.). 1983. pap. text ed. 4.00 (ISBN 0-89988-082-7). Citizens Energy.
Bowen, Arthur, et al. Passive Cooling. 1200p. 1982. pap. text ed. 150.00x (ISBN 0-89553-033-3). Am Solar Energy.
Boyle, Godfrey. Living on the Sun: Harnessing Renewable Energy for an Equitable Society. (Ideas in Progress Ser.). (Illus.). 128p. 1978. (Dist by Scribner); pap. 6.95 (ISBN 0-7145-0862-4). M Boyars.
Brewer, Robert N., et al. Solar Applications in Agriculture. 143p. 1981. 12.95 (ISBN 0-89168-034-9). L Erlbaum Assocs.
Brink, Michael. Solar Energy Sourcebook. 1985. text ed. 32.95 (ISBN 0-8359-7033-7). Reston.
Buckley, Shawn. Sun Up to Sun Down: Understanding Solar Energy. (Illus.). 1979. pap. 6.95 (ISBN 0-07-008790-3). McGraw.
Burg, Nan C. An Annotated Bibliography of Solar Energy Research & Technology Applicable to Community Buildings & Other Non-Residential Construction. 1977. 3.00 (ISBN 0-686-19118-8, 1263). CPL Biblios.
Business Communications Staff. Tapping Solar Markets in Developing Countries. 1980. 800.00 (ISBN 0-89336-274-3, E-041). BCC.
Byers, T. J. Twenty Selected Solar Projects: Making Photovoltaics Work for You. 1984. 19.95 (ISBN 0-13-934779-8); pap. 11.95 (ISBN 0-13-934761-5). P-H.
Calhoun, Elizabeth. Twenty Simple Solar Projects: Fun, Practical, Attractive, Easy-to-Build Projects, Powered by the Sun. (Illus.). 272p. 1983. 16.95 (ISBN 0-87857-476-X). Rodale Pr Inc.
Cambel, A. B, et al, eds. The Solar Energy-Utility Interface. 190p. 1982. pap. 24.00 (ISBN 0-08-028695-X). Pergamon.
Canadian Solar Energy Society. Energex 82 Technical Conference: Proceedings. 1228p. 1983. pap. text ed. 120.00x (ISBN 0-89553-120-8). Am Solar Energy.
Cardon, F., et al, eds. Photovoltaic & Photoelectrochemical Solar Energy Conversion. LC 81-10666. (NATO ASI Series B, Physics: Vol. 69). 436p. 1981. 65.00 (ISBN 0-306-40800-7, Plenum Pr). Plenum Pub.
Center for Self Sufficiency Research Division. Solar Education, Home Plan Kits & Solar Related Companies: A Reference. 100p. 1986. pap. text ed. 6.95 (ISBN 0-910811-35-0, Pub. by Center Self Suff). Prosperity & Profits.
--The Solar Energy Index. LC 83-90710. 100p. 1985. pap. text ed. 6.95 (ISBN 0-910811-11-3, Pub. by Center Self Suff). Prosperity & Profits.
Chauliaguet, Charles, et al. Solar Energy in Buildings. LC 8-27031. 174p. 1979. 42.95 (ISBN 0-471-27570-0, Pub. by Wiley-Interscience). Wiley.
Chingari, et al. Renewable Energy Systems Market & Analysis in Italy, Spain & Greece. 220p. 1981. pap. 39.50x (ISBN 0-89934-147-0, I071). Solar Energy Info.
Clark, E. F. & De Winter, Francis, eds. The Control of Solar Energy Systems for Heating & Cooling. (International Solar Energy Society, American Section, Workshops Ser.). 1978. pap. text ed. 36.00x (ISBN 0-89553-017-1). Am Solar Energy.
Clark, Elizabeth F. & De Winter, Francis, eds. Use of Solar Energy for the Cooling of Buildings. (International Solar Energy Society, American Section, Workshop Ser.). 1978. pap. text ed. 36.00x (ISBN 0-89553-012-0). Am Solar Energy.
Clarke, M. J., et al, eds. Solar Energy Materials. (Structure & Bondigg Ser.: Vol. 49). (Illus.). 182p. 1982. 44.00 (ISBN 0-387-11084-4). Springer-Verlag.
Committee on Nuclear & Alternative Energy Systems. Domestic Potential of Solar & Other Renewable Energy Sources. 1979. pap. 8.50 (ISBN 0-309-02927-9). Natl Acad Pr.
Connolly, John S. Photochemical Conversion & Storage of Solar Energy. LC 81-12853. 1981. 55.00 (ISBN 0-12-185880-4). Acad Pr.
Cook, Jeffrey & Prowler, Donald, eds. Passive Systems Seventy-Eight: A Selection of the Leading Passive Solar Papers of the Year Presented at National Solar Conferences in Philadelphia & Denver. 1978. pap. text ed. 27.00x (ISBN 0-89553-016-3). Am Solar Energy.
Coombs, J., et al. Plants As Solar Collectors: Optimizing Productivity for Energy. 1983. lib. bdg. 32.50 (ISBN 90-277-1625-0, Pub. by Reidel Holland). Kluwer Academic.
Cost-Effective Solar Energy Systems for Commercial & Residential Applications. (Illus.). 254p. (Orig.). 1980. pap. 225.00x (ISBN 0-940520-07-9, M109, Pub. by Future Syst Inc). Monegon Ltd.
Council on Environmental Quality. Solar Energy: Progress & Promise. pap. 9.95x (ISBN 0-930978-41-2, V-021). Solar Energy Info.
Crowley, J. S. & Zimmerman, L. Z. Practical Passive Solar Design: A Guide to Homebuilding & Land Development. 256p. 1983. 37.95 (ISBN 0-07-014769-8). McGraw.
Daniels, Farrington. Direct Use of the Sun's Energy. 1974. pap. 2.50 (ISBN 0-345-29226-X). Ballantine.
--Direct Use of the Sun's Energy. LC 64-20913. 391p. 1983. pap. text ed. 7.95x (ISBN 0-300-02986-1). Yale U Pr.
Daniels, Farrington & Duffie, John A., eds. Solar Energy Research. LC 55-6325. pap. 76.50 (ISBN 0-317-10982-0, 2002069). Bks Demand UMI.
Davidson, Homer L. Thirty Three Photovoltaic Projects. (Illus.). 272p. (Orig.). 1982. 16.95 (ISBN 0-8306-2467-8, 1467); pap. 10.95 (ISBN 0-8306-1467-2). TAB Bks.
Davidson, Joel & Komp, R. J. The Solar Electric Home: A Photovoltaics How-To Handbook. LC 83-70647. (Illus.). 200p. 1983. pap. 11.95 (ISBN 0-937948-04-7). AATEC Pubns.
Den Ouden, C., ed. Thermal Storage of Solar Energy. 378p. 1982. 39.50 (ISBN 90-247-2492-9, Pub. by Martinus Nijhoff Netherlands). Kluwer Academic.
Department of Energy. Photovoltaic Energy Systems: Program Summary. 220p. 1980. pap. 34.95x (ISBN 0-89934-070-9, P-040). Solar Energy Info.
--Solar Energy: A Status Report. pap. 6.95 (ISBN 0-930978-43-9, V-022). Solar Energy Info.
--Solar Heating & Cooling: Commercial Buildings Demonstration Project Summaries. 1978. pap. 14.95x (ISBN 0-930978-35-8, H-021). Solar Energy Info.
--Solar Heating & Cooling: Research & Development Project Summaries. pap. 14.95x (ISBN 0-930978-36-6, H-009). Solar Energy Info.
--Solar Thermal Power Systems: Program Summary. 270p. 1979. pap. 29.95x (ISBN 0-89934-127-6, T-041). Solar Energy Info.
De Winter, F., ed. Sun: Mankind's Future Source of Energy, 3 vols. 1979. text ed. 380.00 (ISBN 0-08-022725-2). Pergamon.
De Winter, Francis. Determination of the Relative Cost Effectiveness of Different Absorption Coatings in the Flat Plate Collector. (Illus.). 48p. 1978. pap. 9.95x (ISBN 0-930978-08-0, H-012). Solar Energy Info.
--Solar Energy & the Flat Plate Collector: An Annotated Bibliography. 31p. 1978. pap. 11.50x (ISBN 0-930978-09-9, H-004). Solar Energy Info.
Dickerson, W. & Cheremisinoff, P., eds. Solar Energy Technology Handbook, Pt. A: Engineering Fundamentals, 2 vols. Incl. Pt. B: Applications, Systems Design & Economics (ISBN 0-8247-6927-9). (Energy, Power & Environment Ser.: Vol. 6). 808p. 1980. 115.00 ea. (ISBN 0-8247-6872-8). Dekker.
Distributed Solar Electricity 1980-2000: Transition from Monopoly to Competition in Electric Power Generation. (Illus.). 165p. (Orig.). 1980. pap. 475.00x (ISBN 0-940520-03-6, M103, Pub. by Future Syst Inc). Monegon Ltd.
Duffie, John A. & Beckman, William A. Solar Energy Thermal Processes. LC 74-12390. 386p. 1974. 44.95 (ISBN 0-471-22371-9, Pub. by Wiley-Interscience). Wiley.
--Solar Engineering of Thermal Processes. LC 80-13297. 762p. 1980. 36.95 (ISBN 0-471-05066-0, Pub. by Wiley-Interscience). Wiley.
Edwards, D. K. Solar Collector Design. rev. ed. LC 78-24684. (Solar Ser.). 68p. (Orig.). 1978. pap. 3.50 (ISBN 0-89168-000-4). L Erlbaum Assocs.
Eggers-Lura, A. Solar Energy in Developing Countries. 1979. 72.00 (ISBN 0-08-023253-1). Pergamon.
Ehrenkrantz Group, et al. Solar Energy Performance History Information Series, Three Volume Set (1-3) Vol. 1 Active Solar Energy Systems; Preliminary Design Practice Manual Based on Field Experience, Vol. 2 Solar Domestic Hot Water; A Reference Manual, Vol. 3 Architectural & Engineering Concerns in Solar System Design, Installation, & Operation. 398p. 1982. pap. 69.50x (ISBN 0-89934-158-6, H-017). Solar Energy Info.
Electric Power Research Institute. Electric Utility Solar Energy Activities. 200p. pap. 18.95x (ISBN 0-930978-21-8, V-019). Solar Energy Info.
Elkington, John. Sun Traps: Energy for a Renewable Future. 408p. 1984. pap. 6.95 (ISBN 0-14-022425-4, Pelican). Penguin.
Energy Information Administration. Solar Collector Manufacturing Activity. Bereny, J. A., ed. 46p. 1980. pap. 9.95x (ISBN 0-930978-12-9, H-024). Solar Energy Info.
Environmental Law Institute. Legal Barriers to Solar Heating & Cooling of Buildings. 368p. 1980. 50.00x (ISBN 0-89499-006-3). Bks Business.
Ericson, Kay. The Solar Jobs Book. LC 80-17886. 220p. 1980. pap. 9.95 (ISBN 0-931790-12-3). Brick Hse Pub.
Farag, Ihab H. & Melsheimer, Stephen S., eds. Fundamentals & Applications of Solar Energy, Pt. II. LC 80-16305. (AIChE Symposium Ser.: Vol. 77). 96p. 1981. pap. 32.00 (ISBN 0-8169-0218-6, S-210); pap. 17.00 members (ISBN 0-686-47540-2). Am Inst Chem Eng.
Farrands, Barry J. Everything You Always Wanted to Know About Solar Energy: But Didn't Know Who to Ask. Sinclair, Dale, ed. LC 80-81372. (Illus.). 425p. (Orig.). 1980. pap. 39.95x (ISBN 0-936982-00-4). Promise Corp.
Federal Energy Administration. Project Independence Blueprint: Final Task Force Report, Solar Energy. 564p. Repr. of 1974 ed. 59.50x (ISBN 0-89934-062-8, V054-PP). Solar Energy Info.
Feldman, Stephen L. & Wirtshafter, Robert M., eds. On the Economics of Solar Energy: The Public Utility Interface. LC 79-5442. 272p. 1980. 31.50x (ISBN 0-669-03449-5). Lexington Bks.
Field, Richard L. The Drapery Solar-Liner. (Solar Energy Ser.: No. 581). (Illus., Orig.). 1978. pap. 3.95 (ISBN 0-931912-12-1). Solpub.
--The Solar Insulator-Insulator TM. (Solar Energy Ser.: No. 580). (Illus., Orig.). 1978. pap. 3.95 (ISBN 0-931912-11-3). Solpub.
Fisk, Marion J. & Anderson, H. William. Introduction to Solar Technology. LC 80-29599. (Engineering Ser.). (Illus.). 640p. 1982. text ed. 28.95 (ISBN 0-201-04713-6); solution manual 1.50 (ISBN 0-201-14591-X). Addison-Wesley.
Flavin, Christopher. Energy & Architecture: The Solar & Conservation Potential. LC 80-54002. (Worldwatch Papers). 1980. pap. 2.00 (ISBN 0-916468-39-9). Worldwatch Inst.
Fleck, Paul A. Solar Energy Handbook, Special California Edition: How to Save Three Thousand Dollars on State Income Taxes with Solar Energy. (Illus.). 1977. pap. 5.95 (ISBN 0-918826-03-9). Time-Wise.
Fleck, Paul A., ed. Solar Energy Handbook. rev. ed. (Illus.). 1976. pap. 4.45 (ISBN 0-918826-01-2). Time-Wise.
Florida Solar Energy Center. Performance Monitoring of Active Solar Energy Systems. Yarosh, Marvin, ed. 327p. 1984. pap. 34.95 (H047). Solar Energy Info.
Frank, Ruth F. Something New Under the Sun, Building Connecticut's First Solar Home. LC 79-22222. (Illus.). 1980. 8.95 (ISBN 0-931790-03-4). Brick Hse Pub.
Franta, G. E., ed. Progress in Solar Energy: Proceedings of the American Section of the International Solar Energy Society, Vol. 6. 1500p. 1984. pap. 135.00x Preprints (ISBN 0-89553-126-7). Am Solar Energy.
Franta, Gregory E. & Glenn, Barbara H., eds. Twenty-Five Years of the Sun at Work: Proceedings of the Annual Meeting of the American Section of the International Solar Energy Society, Phoenix 1980, 2 vols. 1980. Set. pap. 150.00x (ISBN 0-89553-021-X). Am Solar Energy.
Franta, Gregory E. & Haggard, Keith W., eds. Progress in Solar Energy: Vol. 5, The Renewable Challenge. 1985. pap. text ed. 185.00x (ISBN 0-89553-034-1). Am Solar Energy.
Freeman, J. W., ed. Solar Power Satellites: Proceedings of the International Symposium, Toulouse, France, June 1980. 200p. 1981. pap. 39.00 (ISBN 0-08-027592-3). Pergamon.
The Future of Photovoltaic Solar Electricity: The Next 20 Years. 1982. pap. 325.00 (ISBN 0-940520-09-5, Pub. by Future Syst Inc). Monegon Ltd.

Metz, Don. Superhouse: The Next Generation of Passive Solar, Energy Saving Houses. LC 81-13251. (Illus.). 160p. 1981. pap. 12.95 (ISBN 0-88266-258-9). Garden Way Pub.

Metz, William D. & Hammond, Allen L. Solar Energy in America. LC 78-69957. (Science Reports: Vol. 2). 1978. casebound o.p. 18.50x (ISBN 0-87168-301-6); pap. 8.50x (ISBN 0-87168-238-9). AAAS.

Mid-American Solar Energy Complex. Passive Solar Products Catalog. 360p. 1982. pap. 44.50x (ISBN 0-89934-175-6, A-020). Solar Energy Info.

Midwest Plan Service Personnel. Low Temperature & Solar Grain Drying Handbook. 1st ed. (Illus.). 86p. 1980. pap. 5.00 (ISBN 0-89373-048-3, MWPS-22). Midwest Plan Serv.

Minan, John H., ed. Legal Aspects of Solar Energy. Lawrence, William H. 256p. 1981. 28.50x (ISBN 0-669-03761-3). Lexington Bks.

Miskell, Jack T. Solar Hardware Supplies: A Review Analysis, E-036. 1980. 875.00 (ISBN 0-89336-192-5). BCC.

Mitre Corporation for the U. S. Department of Energy. Solar Thermal Repowering. 70p. 1981. pap. 29.50x (ISBN 0-89934-142-X, T-042). Solar Energy Info.

Mitre Corporation for U. S. Department of Energy. Solar Thermal Repowering: Utility-Industry Market Potential in the Southwest. 174p. 1981. pap. 29.50x (ISBN 0-89934-143-8, T-043). Solar Energy Info.

Montgomery, R. H. The Solar Decision Book: Your Guide to Making a Sound Investment. LC 79-762. 1976. pap. text ed. 25.95x. Wiley.

Morris, David. Be Your Own Power Company. (Illus.). 336p. 1983. 15.95 (ISBN 0-87857-477-8); pap. 9.95 (ISBN 0-87857-478-6). Rodale Pr Inc.

Morse, R. N. & Cooper, P. I. Status of Solar Energy Utilization in Australia for Industrial, Commercial & Domestic Purposes: A State-of-the-Art Report as of Mid-1974. 45p. (2nd Printing 1980). 1974. pap. 6.00 (ISBN 0-643-01120-X, C029, CSIRO). Unipub.

Morse, R. N., et al. The Status of Solar Energy Utilization in Australia for Industrial, Commercial & Domestic Purposes. (Illus.). 45p. 1977. pap. 1.50x (ISBN 0-643-01120-X, Pub. by CSIRO). Intl Spec Bk.

Murphy, L. M., ed. Solar Engineering, 1983. 632p. 1983. pap. text ed. 85.00 (ISBN 0-317-02649-6, H00252). ASME.

Murr, Lawrence E., ed. Solar Materials Science. LC 80-18959. 1980. 44.50 (ISBN 0-12-511160-6). Acad Pr.

Myers, John D. Solar Applications in Industry & Commerce. (Illus.). 432p. 1984. text ed. 34.95 (ISBN 0-13-822404-8). P-H.

Nash, J. M. & Thomas, W. B., eds. Modeling, Simulation, Testing, & Measurements for Solar Energy Systems. 1978. 18.00 (ISBN 0-685-66806-1, H00138). ASME.

National Association of Home Builders. Solar Energy for Homes--Current Status. 72p. 1980. pap. 6.75 (ISBN 0-86718-043-9). Natl Assn Home.

National Bureau of Standards. Weathering Performance of Cover Materials for Flat Plate Solar Collectors. 70p. pap. 7.95 (H046). Solar Energy Info.

National Passive Solar Conference. Passive Eighty-One: Proceedings of the National Passive Solar Conference, 6th, Portland, Oregon, 1981. Hayes, John & Kolar, William, eds. LC 81-12741. 1982. pap. text ed. 150.00x (ISBN 0-89553-032-5). Am Solar Energy.

National Passive Solar Conference, 2nd Conference, Philadelphia, 1978. Passive Solar State of the Art: Proceedings, 3 vols. Prowler, Don, ed. LC 78-61242. 1978. Set. pap. text ed. 60.00x (ISBN 0-89553-008-2). Am Solar Energy.

National Passive Solar Conference, 3rd, San Jose, 1979. Proceedings. Miller, Harry, et al, eds. 1979. pap. text ed. 80.00x (ISBN 0-89553-015-5). Am Solar Energy.

National Passive Solar Conference, 4th, Kansas City, 1979. Proceedings. Franta, Gregory E., ed. pap. text ed. 80.00x (ISBN 0-89553-018-X). Am Solar Energy.

National Passive Solar Conference, 5th, Amherst, 1980. Proceedings, 2 vols. Hayes, John & Snyder, Rachel, eds. (Illus.). 1980. Set. pap. text ed. 150.00x (ISBN 0-89553-025-2). Am Solar Energy.

Neff, Thomas L. The Social Costs of Solar Energy: A Study of Photovoltaic Energy Systems. LC 80-23732. (Pergamon Policy Studies on Science & Technology). (Illus.). 110p. 1981. 19.75 (ISBN 0-08-026315-1). Pergamon.

Nentwig, K. Elsevier's Dictionary of Solar Technology: In English, German, French, Spanish & Italian. 214p. 1985. 83.50 (ISBN 0-444-42459-8). Elsevier.

Neville, R. C. Solar Energy Conversion: The Solar Cell. (Studies in Electrical & Electronic Engineering: Vol. 13). 298p. 1978. 70.25 (ISBN 0-444-41712-5). Elsevier.

Newton, Alwin B. & Gilman, Stanley H. Solar Collector Performance Manual. (Illus.). 201p. 1983. pap. text ed. 35.00 (ISBN 0-910110-04-2). Am Heat Ref & Air Eng.

Nicholsen, Niclo. Solar Energy Catalogue. 1977. pap. cancelled (ISBN 0-686-20479-4). Baraka Bk.

Northeast Solar Energy Ctr., for U. S. Dept. of Energy, Boston, MA. Passive Solar Products Directory. 107p. 1982. pap. 19.95x (ISBN 0-89934-173-X, A019). Solar Energy Info.

Ohta, T., ed. Solar-Hydrogen Energy System: An Authoritative Review of Water-Splitting Systems by Solar Beam & Solar Heat; Hydrogen Production, Storage & Utilization. LC 79-40694. (Illus.). 1979. 57.00 (ISBN 0-08-022713-9). Pergamon.

Olgyay, Aladar & Olgyay, Victor. Solar Control & Shading Devices. 1976. pap. 13.50x (ISBN 0-691-02358-1); 40.00 (ISBN 0-691-08186-7). Princeton U Pr.

Orrall, Frank, ed. Solar Active Regions. LC 79-565371. (Skylab Solar Workshop Ser.). 1981. 22.50x (ISBN 0-87081-085-5). Colo Assoc.

Pacific Northwest Laboratory. Export Potential for Photovoltaic Systems. 210p. 1980. pap. 24.95x (ISBN 0-89934-014-8, P039). Solar Energy Info.

Palmiter, Larry & Wheeling, Terry. SUNCODE Documentation & User's Manual. 235p. 1981. ringbinder 35.00 (ISBN 0-934478-29-5). Ecotope.

Palz, W., ed. Solar Energy Data. 1983. lib. bdg. 45.50 (ISBN 90-277-1566-1, Pub. by Reidel Holland). Kluwer Academic.

Palz, W. & Fittipaldi, F., eds. Photovoltaic Solar Energy Conference, Fifth E. C. 1984. lib. bdg. 125.00 (ISBN 90-277-1724-9, Pub. by Reidel Holland). Kluwer Academic.

Palz, W & Steemers, Tc, eds. Solar Houses in Europe: How They Have Worked. LC 80-49715. (Illus.). 320p. 1981. 44.00 (ISBN 0-08-026743-2); pap. 22.00 (ISBN 0-08-026744-0). Pergamon.

Palz, W., et al, eds. First EC Conference on Solar Collectors in Architecture: Integration of Photovoltaic & Thermal Collectors In New & Old Building Structures. 1984. lib. bdg. 48.00 (ISBN 90-277-1784-2, Pub. by Reidel Holland). Kluwer Academic.

Palz, Wolfgang. Third E. C. Photovoltaic Solar Energy Conference. 1982. 81.50 (ISBN 90-277-1230-1, Pub. by Reidel Holland). Kluwer Academic.

Patton, A. R. Solar Energy for Heating & Cooling of Buildings. LC 75-2941. (Energy Technology Review Ser.: No. 7). 328p. 1975. 24.00 (ISBN 0-8155-0579-5). Noyes.

Paul, J. K., ed. Passive Solar Energy Design & Materials. LC 79-83903. (Energy Technology Review Ser.: No. 41). (Illus.). 386p. 1979. 39.00 (ISBN 0-8155-0746-1). Noyes.

Penner, S. S. & Icerman, L. Energy II-Non-Nuclear Energy Technologies, Vol. II. (Illus.). 888p. 1984. 77.00 (ISBN 0-08-031943-2); pap. 29.95 (ISBN 0-08-031942-4). Pergamon.

Porter, George & Hawthorne, William. Solar Energy. (Royal Society Ser.). (Illus.). 167p. 1980. Repr. of 1980 ed. text ed. 46.00x (ISBN 0-85403-131-6, Pub. by Royal Society London). Scholium Intl.

Priest, E. Solar Magnetohydrodynamics. 1982. lib. bdg. 99.00 (ISBN 90-277-1374-X, Pub. by Reidel Holland). Kluwer Academic.

Public Service Co. of New Mexico for U. S. Department of Energy. Technical & Economic Assessment of Solar Hybrid Repowering: Final Report. 450p. 1981. pap. 49.50x (ISBN 0-89934-083-0, T-044). Solar Energy Info.

Pulfrey, David L. Photovoltaic Power Generation. LC 77-18220. 234p. 1978. 24.95 (ISBN 0-442-26640-5). Krieger.

Rapp, Donald. Solar Energy. (Illus.). 576p. 1981. text ed. 40.00 (ISBN 0-13-822213-4). P-H.

Reece, Ray. The Sun Betrayed: A Report on the Corporate Seizure of U. S. Solar Energy Development. LC 79-66992. 234p. 1979. 15.00 (ISBN 0-89608-072-2); pap. 5.50 (ISBN 0-89608-071-4). South End Pr.

Reynoldson, George. Let's Reach for the Sun: Thirty Original Solar & Earth Sheltered Home Designs. rev. ed. (Illus.). 144p. 1981. pap. 12.95 (ISBN 0-9603570-1-7). Space-Time.

Rich, Daniel & Veigel, Jon M., eds. The Solar Energy Transition: Implementation & Policy Implications. 205p. 1983. lib. bdg. 26.00x (ISBN 0-86531-603-1). Westview.

Ritchie, Ralph W. Solar Energy Owner's Guide, No. 1. (Energy & Ecology "Do It" Book). (Illus.). 100p. (Orig.). 1981. pap. 5.00 (ISBN 0-939656-07-8). Studios West.

Robertson, E. E. Bioconversion: Fuels from Biomass. LC 77-84975. (Solar Ser). (Orig.). 1977. pap. text ed. 3.00 (ISBN 0-89168-003-9). L Erlbaum Assocs.

Robertson, Vincent & Robertson, Roin. Alternate Energy-Solar Energy. 1977. pap. 3.95 (ISBN 0-685-59747-4). Alternate Energy.

Rodberg, Leonard & Schacter, Meg. State Conservation & Solar Energy Tax Programs: Incentives or Windfalls? 97p. 1980. 9.95 (ISBN 0-934842-50-7). Coun State Plan.

Rogers, Everett M., et al. Solar Energy Information. LC 81-67755. (International Solar Energy Society, American Section, Workshop Ser.). 1982. pap. text ed. 22.50x (ISBN 0-89553-031-7). Am Solar Energy.

Rose, Harvey. Solar Energy Now. LC 81-70870. 222p. 1982. 29.95 (ISBN 0-250-40537-7). Butterworth.

Rose, Pat R. The Solar Boat Book. LC 80-69217. (Illus.). 266p. (Orig.). 1979. pap. 9.95 (ISBN 0-9604874-0-9). Aqua-Sol Ent.

Sandia Laboratories. Passive Solar Buildings: A Compilation of Data & Results. 70p. 1979. pap. 12.95x (ISBN 0-930978-40-4, A-003). Solar Energy Info.

Sandia Laboratories for the U.S. Department of Energy. Passive Solar Buildings. 285p. 1981. pap. 34.50x (ISBN 0-89934-030-X, A-016). Solar Energy Info.

Sandia National Laboratories for U. S. Dept. of Energy. Design Handbook for Photovoltaic Systems. 296p. 1981. pap. 29.95x (P-054). Solar Energy Info.

Sandia National Laboratories for U. S. Dept. of Energy & Naff, George. Photovoltaic Array Field Optimization & Modularity Study. 318p. 1983. pap. 29.95x (P-055). Solar Energy Info.

Sandia National Laboratories for U. S. Department of Energy. Photovoltaic Array Fields: Development of a Standard Modular Design for Low-Cost Flat-Panels. 194p. 1984. pap. 39.50x (ISBN 0-89934-204-3, P-048). Solar Energy Info.

Sandia National Labs for U. S. Dept. of Energy. Design of a Photovoltaic Central Power Station. 81p. 1984. pap. 10.95x (P-057). Solar Energy Info.

--Design of a Photovoltaic Central Power Station Flat-Plate Array. 243p. 1984. pap. 24.95x (P-058). Solar Energy Info.

Sandis National Labs for U. S. Dept of Energy. Design of a Photovoltaic Central Power Station Concentrator Array. 244p. 1984. pap. 24.95 (P-059). Solar Energy Info.

Sav, G. T. The Dynamic Demand for Energy Stocks: An Analysis of Tax Policy Options for Solar Processes. LC 83-4892. (Contemporary Studies in Energy Analysis & Policy: Vol. 2). 1983. 40.00 (ISBN 0-89232-316-7). Jai Pr.

Sayigh, A. A. Solar Energy Application in Buildings. LC 78-67882. 1979. 65.00 (ISBN 0-12-620860-3). Acad Pr.

Schiffman, Yale M. & D'Alessio, Gregory J. Limits to Solar & Biomass Energy Growth. LC 81-48071. 320p. 1983. 32.00 (ISBN 0-669-05253-1). Lexington Bks.

Schmidt, W. K. & Grunwaldt, H., eds. The Source Region of the Solar Wind. Date not set. lib. bdg. 49.50 (ISBN 90-277-1537-8, Pub. by Reidel Holland). Kluwer Academic.

Schwolsky, Rick & Hayes, John, eds. Solar Business Experience. (Solar Realities Forum: Learning from Experience Ser.). 1982. pap. text ed. 30.00x (ISBN 0-89553-047-3). Am Solar Energy.

Sebald, A. V., ed. Mathematical Models & Simulation in Solar Energy Research for Buildings. 237p. 1980. 33.00 (ISBN 0-08-025453-5). Pergamon.

Secretariat for Futures Studies, Stockholm. Solar vs. Nuclear: The Solar Nuclear Alternative. 1980. 47.00 (ISBN 0-08-024758-X); pap. 18.00 (ISBN 0-08-024759-8). Pergamon.

Seraphin, B. O., ed. Solar Energy Conversion: Solid-State Physics Aspects. (Topics in Applied Physics: Vol. 31). (Illus.). 1979. 60.00 (ISBN 0-387-09224-2). Springer-Verlag.

SERI. A New Prosperity: Building a Sustainable Energy Future the SERI (Solar Conservation Study) LC 81-6089. 454p. (Orig.). 1981. 39.95x (ISBN 0-471-88652-1, Brick Hse Pub.). Wiley.

Shama, Avraham. Marketing Solar Energy Innovations. LC 81-11870. 320p. 1981. 39.95 (ISBN 0-03-058299-7). Praeger.

Shepard, Michael, ed. Solar Remodeling in Northern New Mexico. (Illus.). 110p. (Orig.). 1981. pap. 4.95 (ISBN 0-686-32883-3). NMSEA.

Shewchun, John S. & Curtis, David B. Solar Energy & the Canadian Mining Sector: A Demand Forecast. 60p. (Orig.). 1978. pap. text ed. 4.00x (ISBN 0-686-63137-4, Pub. by Ctr Resource Stud Canada). Brookfield Pub Co.

Shurcliff, W. A. Passive Solar Design Analysis: Simplifying Guide, Vol. 3. pap. 14.95 (A026). Solar Energy Info.

--Simiplifying Guide to the Los Alamos, Vol. 3: Passive Solar Design Analysis. pap. 14.95 (A-026). Solar Energy Info.

Shurcliff, William A. Superinsulated Houses & Double Envelope Houses. 200p. 1981. pap. 14.00 (ISBN 0-931790-18-2); pap. 12.50 members. Natl Assn Home.

Silverstein, Michael. Once & Future Resource: A History of Solar Energy. 1977. pap. text ed. 8.00x (ISBN 0-915250-32-2). Environ Design.

Smith, Dennis E. Solar Fuel: How to Make Automotive Fuel Using Your Own Alcohol Solar Still. LC 80-80971. (Illus.). 96p. (Orig.). 1980. pap. 4.95 (ISBN 0-915216-53-1). Marathon Intl Pub Co.

Smith, Shane. The Bountiful Solar Greenhouse: A Guide to Year-Round Food Production. (Illus.). 224p. (Orig.). 1982. pap. 8.00 (ISBN 0-912528-08-7). John Muir.

Solar Action: Twenty-Seven Communities Boost Renewable Energy Use. 83p. 1981. 5.95 (ISBN 0-937446-03-3, 203). Ctr Renew Resources.

Solar Action: 27 Communities Boost Renewable Energy Use. 1981. pap. 9.00x (ISBN 0-686-84642-7). Am Solar Energy.

Solar Age Magazine, ed. The Solar Age Resource Book: A Complete Guidebook for the Consumer to Harnessing the Power of Solar Energy, in Depth & Up-to-Date. LC 78-74580. (Illus.). 1979. pap. 7.95 (ISBN 0-89696-050-1). SolarVision.

Solar Age Magazine Editors, ed. Solar Age Catalog: A Guide to Solar Energy Knowledge & Materials. LC 77-79117. (Illus.). 1977. pap. 4.50 (ISBN 0-918984-00-9). SolarVision.

Solar Dwelling Designs. LC 80-52592. (Illus.). 144p. 1980. pap. 6.95 (ISBN 0-8069-8674-3). Sterling.

Solar Electric Technologies. Five Year Research Plan, Nineteen Eighty-Four to Nineteen Eighty-Eight: Photovolactics: Electricity from Sunlight. 32p. 1984. pap. 4.95 (P-060). Solar Energy Info.

Solar Electricity: An Economic Approach to Solar Energy. 1978. 35.00 (ISBN 92-3-101427-7, U785, UNESCO). Unipub.

Solar Energy & Conservation Symposium-Workshop, Miami Beach, Florida, 1978. Solar Energy & Conservation: Technology, Commercialization, Utilization: Proceedings. Veziroglu, T. Nejat, ed. LC 79-19526. (Illus.). 2000p. 1980. 325.00 (ISBN 0-08-025551-5). Pergamon.

Solar Energy & the Consumer Loan: California Edition. (Solarcal Seminar Ser.). 100p. 1981. Repr. of 1979 ed. wkbk. ed. 25.00x (ISBN 0-89934-082-2, R.006). Solar Energy Info.

Solar Energy Conversion II: An Update, Selected Lectures. (Illus.). 664p. 1981. 100.00 (ISBN 0-686-78581-9). Pergamon.

Solar Energy: Proceedings of the WMO-UNESCO Symposium, Geneva, 30 Aug.-3 Sept. 1976. (Illus.). lv, 654p. 1977. pap. 50.00 (ISBN 92-63-10477-8, W358, WMO). Unipub.

Solar Energy Research Inst. for the U. S. Dept. of Energy. Passive Solar Performance: Summary of 1981-1982 Class B Results. 257p. 1983. pap. 24.95 (A024). Solar Energy Info.

Solar Energy Research Institute. Annual Review of Solar Energy (Nineteen Seventy-Eight) 166p. 1981. pap. 19.95x (ISBN 0-930978-77-3, V029). Solar Energy Info.

--Fuel from Farms: A Guide to Small-Scale Ethanol Production. 161p. 1980. 34.95x (ISBN 0-89934-050-4, B947-PP); pap. 19.95x (ISBN 0-89934-051-2, B047-PP). Solar Energy Info.

--A New Prosperity: Building a Sustainable Energy Future (Solar Conservation Study) LC 81-6089. 1981. 19.95x (ISBN 0-931790-53-0). Brick Hse Pub.

--Solar Energy Information Locator - Nineteen Eighty. 60p. 1981. pap. 4.95x (ISBN 0-89934-089-X, V.062). Solar Energy Info.

--Solar Thermal Technology Annual Evaluation Report Fiscal Year 1983. 126p. 1984. pap. 12.95x (ISBN 0-317-17139-9, T-045). Solar Energy Info.

Solar Energy Research Institute for U. S. Department of Energy. Photovoltaic Energy Systems Performance Criteria. 183p. 1984. pap. 29.50x (ISBN 0-89934-206-X, P-050). Solar Energy Info.

Solar Energy Timetable. (Worldwatch Institute Papers: No. 19). 40p. 1978. pap. 2.95 (ISBN 0-686-94929-3, WW19, WW). Unipub.

Solar Ponds Promise Energy Bonanza if Problems Can Be Solved. 6p. 1981. 10.00 (ISBN 0-318-01545-5, 22025). Indus Fabrics.

Solar Products Specifications Guide: A Technical Specifications Guide That Continuously Monitors the Developments of Solar Products. (Illus.). 1983. binder-1 year of update service. 125.00 (ISBN 0-686-65545-1). SolarVision.

Solar Systems Code Review Manual. 5.00 (ISBN 0-318-00055-5). Intl Conf Bldg Off.

Southern California Edison Staff, et al. Ten MWe Solar Thermal Central Receiver Pilot Plant. 117p. Date not set. pap. 19.95 (ISBN 0-317-20251-0, T-048). Solar Energy Info.

The Spec Guide: Energy Products Specifications for Conservation, Solar Wind & Photovoltaics. 7th ed. (Illus.). 1985. 49.00 (ISBN 0-317-17142-9). SolarVision.

Spring Hill Center. Solar Energy & Potentials for Minnesota. Hoel, Donna & Ziegenhagen, John, eds. 1978. pap. text ed. 2.50 (ISBN 0-932676-02-2). Spring Hill.

Jones, R. Sunspace Primer Guide for Solar Heating. 1984. 32.50 (ISBN 0-442-24575-0). Van Nos Reinhold.

Keyes, John. The Solar Conspiracy. LC 75-24833. pap. 3.95 (ISBN 0-87100-095-4). Morgan.

Kornher, Steve & Zaugg, Andy. The Complete Handbook of Solar Air Heating Systems: How to Design & Build Efficient, Economical Systems for Heating Your Home. (Illus.). 1983. 17.95 (ISBN 0-87857-442-5). Rodale Pr Inc.

Kreider, Jan & Kreith, Frank. Solar Heating & Cooling: Active & Passive Design. 2nd ed. 496p. 1982. 37.95x (ISBN 0-07-035486-3). McGraw.

Kreider, Jan F. The Solar Heating Design Process: Active & Passive. (Illus.). 432p. 1982. 37.50x (ISBN 0-07-035478-2). McGraw.

Kutscher, Charles F. & Davenport, R. L. Design Approaches for Solar Industrial Process Heat Systems: Nontracking & Line Focus Collector Technologies. (Progress in Solar Energy Ser.). 452p. 1983. pap. text ed. 45.00x (ISBN 0-89553-113-5). Am Solar Energy.

Lawrence Livermore Laboratories. Design Guide for Shallow Solar Ponds. 55p. 1979. pap. 14.95x (ISBN 0-930978-50-1, H-008). Solar Energy Info.

Lebens, Ralph M. Passive Solar Heating Design. LC 80-40255. 234p. 1980. 58.95x (ISBN 0-470-26977-4). Halsted Pr.

Lee, Kaiman & Silverstein, Michael. The Buyer's Book of Solar Water Heaters. 4th ed. LC 79-104450. (Illus.). 1979. 50.00x (ISBN 0-915250-30-6). Environ Design.

Los Alamos Scientific Laboratory, Solar Energy Group & Balcomb, D. Passive Solar Heating & Cooling Conference & Workshop Proceedings, 1976. 355p. 1980. pap. 29.95x (ISBN 0-89934-021-0, A-004). Solar Energy Info.

Lucas, Ted. How to Build a Solar Heater. rev. ed. 1980. pap. 7.95 (ISBN 0-517-54056-8, Michelman Books). Crown.

Lunde, Peter J. Solar Thermal Engineering: Space Heating & Hot Water Systems. LC 79-15389. 612p. 1980. 46.50 (ISBN 0-471-03085-6); solution manual avail. (ISBN 0-471-89177-0). Wiley.

Meltzer, Michael. Passive & Active Solar Heating Technology. (Illus.). 448p. 1985. pap. text ed. 28.95 (ISBN 0-13-653114-8). P-H.

Montgomery, R. H. The Solar Decision Book: A Guide for Heating Your Home with Solar Energy. 328p. 1978. pap. 25.95 (ISBN 0-471-05652-9). Wiley.

National Bureau of Standards. Performance Criteria for Solar Heating & Cooling Systems in Commerical Buildings. 215p. 1985. pap. 29.95 (ISBN 0-317-18186-6, H-052). Solar Energy Info.

Operation Update Series in Solar Heating & Cooling, 8 bks. 1981. Set. 95.00 (ISBN 0-07-079240-2). McGraw.

Photovoltaic System Design. (Illus.). 1982. 59.95 (ISBN 0-918984-04-1). Solarvision.

Plante, Russell H. Solar Domestic Hot Water: A Practical Guide to Installation & Understanding. LC 82-19966. 332p. 1983. text ed. 33.95x (ISBN 0-471-09592-3). Wiley.

Reif, Daniel K. Passive Solar Water Heaters: How to Design & Build a Batch System. 208p. (Orig.). 1983. pap. 12.95 (ISBN 0-931790-39-5). Brick Hse Pub.

--Solar Retrofit: Adding Solar to Your Home. (Illus.). 200p. 1981. pap. 11.95 (ISBN 0-931790-15-8). Brick Hse Pub.

Rentz, Tom W. Low Cost Solar Heaters for Your Home. (Orig.). 1978. pap. 2.95 (ISBN 0-89036-104-5). Hawkes Pub Inc.

Sadler, John M. How to Heat Hot Water Without Going Broke: Build Yourself a Solar Heater with a One Year Payback. (Illus.). 1979. lib. bdg. 11.00 (ISBN 0-930250-05-2); pap. 5.95 (ISBN 0-930250-06-0). J M Sadler.

Salt, H. Performance of Three Australian Solar Hot Water Systems. 25p. 1976. pap. 6.00 (ISBN 0-643-01951-0, C023, CSIRO). Unipub.

Scheller, William G. Solar Heating. LC 80-50049. 160p. 1980. pap. 8.95 (ISBN 0-672-21621-3). Sams.

Schubert, R. & Ryan, L. Fundamentals of Solar Heating. 1981. 35.95 (ISBN 0-13-344457-0). P-H.

Sheet Metal & Air Conditioning Contractors' Natl. Assoc. Inc. Staff. Installation Standards for Heating, Air Conditioning & Solar Systems. 5th ed. 150p. 1985. pap. 29.95 (ISBN 0-317-18187-4, H-053). Solar Energy Info.

Shurcliff, William A. New Inventions in Low-Cost Solar Heating: One Hundred Daring Schemes Tried & Untried. LC 79-50275. (Illus.). 1979. 18.00x (ISBN 0-931790-05-0); pap. 13.95x (ISBN 0-931790-02-6). Brick Hse Pub.

--Solar Heated Buildings of North America: 120 Outstanding Examples. LC 78-57234. (Illus.). 296p. 1978. 14.95 (ISBN 0-931790-01-8). Brick Hse Pub.

Simonson, J. R. Computing Methods in Solar Heating Design. (Illus.). 354p. 1984. text ed. 39.50x (ISBN 0-333-32844-2). Scholium Intl.

Solar Cooling & Heating Forum, Dec. 13-15, 1976, Miami Beach. Solar Cooling & Heating: Architectural, Engineering & Legal Aspects, Proceedings, 3 vols. new ed. Veziroglu, T. N., ed. LC 77-28813. (Illus.). 1066p. 1978. Set. text ed. 250.00 (ISBN 0-89116-165-1). Hemisphere Pub.

Solar Energy Research Institute. Design Approaches for Solar Industrial Process Heat Systems. 423p. 1983. pap. 42.50x (ISBN 0-89934-210-8, D-010). Solar Energy Info.

--A Summary & Assessment of Historical Reliability & Maintainability Data for Solar Hot Water & Space Conditioning Systems. 60p. 1984. pap. 6.95X (H048). Solar Energy Info.

Solar Heating Catalogue, No. 2. 1979. pap. 5.00 (ISBN 0-660-10075-4, SSC133, SSC). Unipub.

The Solar Heating System Construction Manual. 272p. pap. text ed. 19.95 (ISBN 0-8019-7098-9). Chilton.

Solar Water Heating Reprint Series, 4 pubns. Incl. The Solar Heater - Bulletin No. 469. Farrall, A. W. Repr. of 1929 ed; Domestic Solar Water Heating in Florida - Bulletin No. 18. Hawkins, H. M. Repr. of 1947 ed; Use of Solar Energy for Heating Water. Brooks, F. A. Repr. of 1939 ed; Solar Energy & Its Use for Heating Water in California - Bulletin No. 602. Brooks, F. A. Repr. of 1936 ed. 1978. Set. pap. 29.50x (ISBN 0-930978-11-0, H-006). Solar Energy Info.

Steemers, T. C. & Den Ouden, C., eds. Solar Energy Applications to Dwellings. 1983. lib. bdg. 63.00 (ISBN 90-277-1696-X, Pub. by Reidel Holland). Kluwer Academic.

Sunset Editors. Solar Heating & Cooling: Homeowner's Guide. LC 78-53673. (Illus.). 96p. 1978. pap. 5.95 (ISBN 0-376-01524-1, Sunset Bks.). Sunset-Lane.

Szokolay, S. V. Solar Energy & Building. 2nd ed. LC 77-21700. 174p. 1977. 29.95x (ISBN 0-470-99235-2). Halsted Pr.

Turrent, D. & Baker, N. Solar Thermal Energy in Europe. 1983. lib. bdg. 39.50 (ISBN 90-2771-592-0, Pub. by Reidel Holland). Kluwer Academic.

Twitchell, Mary. Solar Projects for Under Five Hundred Dollars. Griffith, Roger, ed. (Illus.). 176p. (Orig.). 1985. pap. 11.95 (ISBN 0-88266-363-1). Garden Way Pub.

U. S. Army Corps of Engineers, Construction Engineering Research Laboratory. Development of a Modular Solar Domestic Hot Water System for the Department of Defense Barracks. 26p. 1984. pap. 3.95X (H049). Solar Energy Info.

U. S. Department of Energy. Solar Energy for Agriculture & Industrial Process Heat: Program Summary. 91p. 1979. pap. 14.95x (ISBN 0-930978-26-9, D-005). Solar Energy Info.

U. S. Dept. of Commerce, National Bureau of Standards. Test Methods & Standards Development for Active Solar Heating & Cooling Systems. 132p. 1984. pap. 12.95X (H050). Solar Energy Info.

Vitro Laboratories. Solar Energy Performance History Information Series, Three Volume Set (4-6) Vol. 4, Performance of Active Solar Space Heating Systems, Comparative Report; Vol. 5, Performance of Solar Hot Water Systems, Comparative Report; Vol. 6, Performance of Active Solar Space Cooling Systems, Comparative Report. 610p. 1983. pap. 79.50x (ISBN 0-89934-200-0, H-045). Solar Energy Info.

Ward, Dan S., et al. How to Solve Materials & Design Problems in Solar Heating & Cooling. LC 81-18928. (Energy Technology Review: No. 77). (Illus.). 298p. 1982. 36.00 (ISBN 0-8155-0889-1). Noyes.

Warkov, Seymour & Meyer, Judith W. Solar Diffusion & Public Incentives. LC 81-47000. (Illus.). 176p. 1982. 22.00 (ISBN 0-669-04510-1). Lexington Bks.

Watson, Donald. Designing & Building a Solar House: Your Place in the Sun. LC 76-53830. (Illus.). 288p. 1977. 14.95 (ISBN 0-88266-086-1). Garden Way Pub.

Whillier, Austin. Solar Energy Collection & Its Utilization for House Heating. Bruchey, Stuart, ed. LC 78-22712. (Energy in the American Economy Ser.). (Illus.). 1979. lib. bdg. 16.00x (ISBN 0-405-12022-2). Ayer Co Pubs.

Williams, J. Richard. Design & Installation of Solar Heating & Hot Water Systems. LC 82-72856. (Illus.). 427p. 1983. 49.95 (ISBN 0-250-40593-8). Butterworth.

--Passive Solar Heating. LC 82-72857. (Illus.). 304p. 1983. 39.95 (ISBN 0-250-40601-2). Butterworth.

Wittgenstein, Herta. Solar Heat for Less. (Illus.). 1978. 6.95 (ISBN 0-685-30207-5). Nautilus Bks.

Yanda, Bill & Fisher, Rick. The Food & Heat Producing Solar Greenhouse. rev. ed. LC 79-91276. (Illus.). 208p. (Orig.). 1980. pap. 8.00 (ISBN 0-912528-20-6). John Muir.

SOLAR HOUSES

AIA Research Corporation. Solar Dwelling Design Concepts. 146p. 1981. pap. 9.95x (ISBN 0-930978-24-2, H-025). Solar Energy Info.

Alward, Ron & Shapiro, Andy. Low-Cost Passive Solar Greenhouses: A Design & Construction Guide. (Illus.). 176p. 1982. pap. 10.95 (ISBN 0-684-17503-7, ScribT). Scribner.

Anderson, Bruce, compiled by. Passive Solar Design Handbook. (Illus.). 752p. 1984. 55.00 (ISBN 0-442-20810-3). Van Nos Reinhold.

Balcomb, J. Douglas, et al. Passive Solar Design Handbook. Jones, R., ed. (Passive Solar Design Handbook Ser.: Vol. 3, 1980). 668p. 1983. pap. text ed. 25.00x (ISBN 0-89553-106-2). Am Solar Energy.

Better Homes & Gardens Editors. Solar Living. (All about Your House Ser.). (Illus.). 160p. 1983. 9.95 (ISBN 0-696-02166-8). BH&G.

Booth, Don, et al. Sun-Earth Buffering & Superinsulation. Wolf, Ray, ed. (Illus.). 232p. 1984. pap. 12.95 (ISBN 0-9604422-3-5). Rodale Pr Inc.

Carriere, Dean & Day, Fraser. Solar Houses for a Cold Climate. (Illus.). 1982. pap. 4.50 Encore (ISBN 0-684-17424-3, ScribT). Scribner.

Cook, Jeffrey. Award-Winning Passive Solar House Designs. Stetson, Fred, ed. (Illus.). 176p. 1983. pap. 14.95 (ISBN 0-88266-313-5). Garden Way Pub.

Crowther, Richard L. Affordable Passive Solar Homes. 188p. 1983. 24.00x (ISBN 0-89553-129-1). Am Solar Energy.

--Affordable Passive Solar Homes. LC 84-5404. (Illus.). 192p. (Orig.). 1984. pap. 24.00 (ISBN 0-916653-00-5, 65300). Sci Tech.

Dawson, Joseph C. Seeking Shelter: How to Find & Finance an Energy-Efficient Home. LC 83-61369. (Illus.). 256p. 1983. 17.95 (ISBN 0-688-00902-6). Morrow.

Dean, Thomas & Hedden, Jay. How to Solarize Your House. (Illus.). 176p. 1982. encore ed. o.p. 5.95 (ISBN 0-684-16295-4, ScribT); pap. 10.95 (ISBN 0-684-17425-1). Scribner.

Ebert, Robert, ed. Solar Design: A Handbook for Solar Homebuilders. 1983. pap. write for info. (ISBN 0-942886-02-X). Periwinkle Pubns.

--Solar Home Plan Book. 1983. pap. 3.95 (ISBN 0-942886-03-8). Periwinkle Pubns.

Geery. Solar Greenhouses: Underground. (Illus.). 416p. 1982. o.p 19.95 (ISBN 0-8306-0069-8); pap. 12.95 (ISBN 0-8306-1272-6, 1272). TAB Bks.

Head, William D. Gardening Under Cover: A Northwest Guide to Solar Greenhouses, Coldframes & Cloches. Stewart, Kay, ed. LC 83-22383. (Illus.). 104p. 1984. pap. 9.95 (ISBN 0-9612716-0-4). Amity Found.

Hibshman, Dan. Your Affordable Solar Home. LC 82-10747. (Tools for Today Ser.). (Illus.). 128p. (Orig.). 1983. pap. 7.95 (ISBN 0-87156-327-4). Sierra.

Installation Guidelines for Solar DHW Systems in One & Two Family Dwellings. 107p. 1980. pap. 5.50 (ISBN 0-318-11795-9). Gov Printing Office.

Klima, Jon. The Solar Controls Book: Fundamentals of Domestic Hot Water & Space Heating Solar Controls, 4 vols. (Illus.). 1982. Set. 39.95 (ISBN 0-940894-04-1); tchr's. guide, solutions manual 5.95 (ISBN 0-940894-05-X). Solar Training.

--The Solar Controls Book: Fundamentals of Domestic Hot Water & Space Heating Solar Controls: Vol. 1: Basic Electrical Principles for the Solar Installer. LC 81-52177. (Illus.). 1981. 14.95 (ISBN 0-940894-00-9). Solar Training.

--The Solar Controls Book: Fundamentals of Domestic Hot Water & Space Heating Solar Controls: Vol. 2: Differential Controls for Domestic Hot Water Systems. LC 81-52177. (Illus.). 1982. 10.95 (ISBN 0-940894-01-7). Solar Training.

--The Solar Controls Book: Fundamentals of Domestic Hot Water & Space Heating Solar Controls: Vol. 3: Advanced Control Systems. LC 81-52177. (Illus.). 1982. 10.95 (ISBN 0-940894-02-5). Solar Training.

--The Solar Controls Book: Fundamentals of Domestic Hot Water & Space Heating Solar Controls: Vol. 4: Interfaces. LC 81-52177. (Illus.). 1982. 10.95 (ISBN 0-940894-03-3). Solar Training.

Lebens, R. Passive Solar Architure in Europe, No. 2. (Illus.). 156p. 1983. pap. text ed. 31.50 (ISBN 0-85139-957-6, Pub. by Architecture Pr England). Humanities.

Lebens, Ralph M., ed. Passive Solar Architecture in Europe. LC 81-6928. 238p. 1981. pap. 26.95x (ISBN 0-470-27266-X). Halsted Pr.

Magee, Tim, et al. A Solar Greenhouse Guide for the Pacific Northwest. 2nd ed. Stewart, Annie & Sassaman, Richard, eds. (Illus.). 91p. 1979. pap. 6.00 (ISBN 0-934478-26-0). Ecotope.

Montgomery, Richard H. & Miles, Walter F. Solar Decision Book of Homes: A Guide to Designing & Remodeling for Solar Heating. LC 81-16397. 332p. 1982. text ed. 29.95 (ISBN 0-471-08280-5); pap. 23.95 (ISBN 0-471-87523-6); tchr's. manual avail. (ISBN 0-471-06319-3). Wiley.

Palz, W. & Steemers, T. C., eds. Solar Energy Applications to Dwellings. 1982. 32.50 (ISBN 90-277-1372-3, Pub. by Reidel Holland). Kluwer Academic.

Palz, W., et al, eds. Solar Collectors in Architecture: Integration of Photovoltaic & Thermal Collectors in New & Old Building Structures. 320p. 1984. 48.00 (ISBN 90-277-1784-2, Pub. by Reidel Holland). Kluwer Academic.

Reif, Daniel K. Solar Retrofit: Adding Solar to Your Home. 199p. 1981. 29.95 (ISBN 0-471-87860-X). Wiley.

Ritchie, Ralph W. Solar Energy Owner's Guide, No. 1. (Energy & Ecology "Do It" Book). (Illus.). 100p. (Orig.). 1981. pap. 5.00 (ISBN 0-939656-07-8). Studios West.

Schepp, Brad & Hastie, Stephen M. The Complete Passive Solar Home Book. (Illus.). 320p. (Orig.). 1985. 24.95 (ISBN 0-8306-0657-2, 1657); pap. 16.95 (ISBN 0-8306-1657-8). TAB Bks.

Schwolsky, Rick & Williams, James. The Builder's Guide to Solar Construction. 352p. 1982. 36.50x (ISBN 0-07-055786-1). McGraw.

Shapiro, Andrew M. The Homeowner's Complete Handbook for Add-On Solar Greenhouses & Sunspaces. 1985. 19.95 (ISBN 0-87857-507-3); pap. 13.95 (ISBN 0-87857-508-1). Rodale Pr Inc.

Shepard, Michael, ed. Solar Remodeling in Northern New Mexico. (Illus.). 110p. (Orig.). 1981. pap. 4.95 (ISBN 0-686-32883-3). NMSEA.

Slurcliff, William A. Super Solar Houses. 140p. 1983. 27.95 (ISBN 0-471-87861-8). Wiley.

Sodha, M. S., et al. Fundamentals of Solar Passive Building. (International Series on Building Environmental Engineering). (Illus.). 200p. 1986. 35.00 (ISBN 0-08-030550-4, Pub. by Aberdeen Scotland). Pergamon.

Sunset Editors, ed. Solar Remodeling. LC 82-81372. (Illus.). 96p. (Orig.). 1982. pap. 5.95 (ISBN 0-376-01535-7, Sunset Bks). Sunset-Lane.

Szokolay, S. V. World Solar Architecture. LC 80-40900. 278p. 1980. 79.95x (ISBN 0-470-27001-2). Halsted Pr.

U. S. Department of Housing & Urban Development in Cooperation with the U. S. Department of Energy. Passive Solar Homes. (Illus.). 284p. (Orig.). 1982. pap. 12.95 (ISBN 0-89696-161-3, An Everest House Book). Dodd.

U. S. Dept. of Housing & Urban Development. Passive Solar Single-Family Homes. 288p. 1982. 19.95x (ISBN 0-87196-674-3). Facts on File.

Watson, Donald. Designing & Building a Solar House. rev. ed. (Illus.). 237p. 1985. pap. 15.95 (ISBN 0-88266-401-8). Garden Way Pub.

--Designing & Building a Solar House. rev. ed. Date not set. price not set. Storey Comm Inc.

Wells, Madeline & Williamson, Jane. So You Want to See A Solar Building? A Tour Guide for Northern New Mexico. (Illus.). 128p. 1982. pap. 6.95 (ISBN 0-942372-04-2). NMSEA.

SOLAR PHYSICS

see Sun

SOLAR POWER

see Solar Energy

SOLAR RADIATION

see also Extraterrestrial Radiation; Ocean-Atmosphere Interaction; Pyrheliometer; Solar Activity; Solar Batteries; Solar Energy; Solar Furnaces; Spectrum, Solar; Sun-Spots; Van Allen Radiation Belts

Becker, Clarence F. Solar Radiation Availability on Surfaces in the U. S. as Affected by Season, Orientation, Latitude, Altitude, & Cloudiness. Bruchey, Stuart, ed. LC 78-22659. (Energy in the American Economy Ser.). (Illus.). 1979. lib. bdg. 14.00x (ISBN 0-405-11963-1). Ayer Co Pubs.

Bolle, H. J., ed. Radiation in the Atmosphere: Proceedings. LC 77-5205. (Illus.). 1977. lib. bdg. 62.00 (ISBN 0-89500-002-4). Sci Pr.

Bray, R. J., et al. The Solar Granulation. 2nd ed. LC 83-1881. (Cambridge Astrophysics Ser.: No. 4). 1984. 54.50 (ISBN 0-521-24714-4). Cambridge U Pr.

Building Research Advisory Board, National Research Council. Solar Radiation Considerations in Building Planning & Design. 1976. pap. 10.25 (ISBN 0-309-02516-8). Natl Acad Pr.

Coulsen, Kinsell L. Solar & Terrestrial Radiation. 1975. 35.75 (ISBN 0-12-192950-7). Acad Pr.

Gerrick, David J. Sunlight: Friend or Foe. 1978. 20.00 (ISBN 0-916750-56-6). Dayton Labs.

Goldberg, B., ed. Solar Radiation Measurements in Developing Countries. 135p. 1983. pap. 23.00 (ISBN 0-08-030547-4). Pergamon.

Hollwich, F. The Influence of Ocular Light Perception on Metabolism in Man & Animal. LC 78-17076. (Topics in Environmental Physiology & Medicine Ser.). (Illus.). 1979. 52.00 (ISBN 0-387-90315-1). Springer-Verlag.

I.A.U. Symposium, No. 68, Buenos Aires, Argentina, June 11-14, 1974. Solar Gamma-X & EUV Radiation: Proceedings. Kane, S. R., ed. LC 75-6545. (I.A.U. Symposia: No. 68). 439p. 1975. 76.00 (ISBN 90-277-0576-3, Pub. by Reidel Holland); pap. 53.00 (ISBN 90-277-0577-1, Pub. by Reidel Holland). Kluwer Academic.

Iqbal, Mohammad. An Introduction to Solar Radiation (Monograph) 416p. 1983. 62.50 (ISBN 0-12-373750-8); pap. 32.00 (ISBN 0-12-373752-4). Acad Pr.

IUA Symposium, College Park, Md., Aug. 7-10, 1979. Radio Physics of the Sun: Proceedings. Gergely, T. E. & Kundu, M. R., eds. (International Astronomical Union Symposium Ser.: No. 86). 472p. 1980. lib. bdg. 60.50 (ISBN 90-277-1120-8, Pub. by Reidel Holland); pap. 29.00 (ISBN 90-277-1121-6, Pub. by Reidel Holland). Kluwer Academic.

Kondratyav, K. Ya. Radiation in the Atmosphere. (International Geophysics Ser.: Vol. 12). 1969. 99.00 (ISBN 0-12-419050-2). Acad Pr.

Lillyquist, Michael J. Sunlight & Health. 272p. 1985. 15.95 (ISBN 0-396-08482-6). Dodd.

McLean, Donald J., ed. Solar Radiophysics. (Illus.). 550p. Date not set. price not set (ISBN 0-521-25409-4). Cambridge U Pr.

Paltridge, G. & Platt, C. Radiative Processes in Meteorology & Climatology. (Developments in Atmospheric Science: Vol. 5). 318p. 1976. 76.75 (ISBN 0-444-41444-4). Elsevier.

Palz, W., ed. Solar Radiation Data. 1982. 24.50 (ISBN 90-277-1387-1, Pub. by Reidel Holland). Kluwer Academic.

Peters, B., ed. Cosmic Rays, Solar Particles & Space Research. (Italian Physical Society: Vol. 19). 1964. 70.00 (ISBN 0-12-368819-1). Acad Pr.

Reifsnyder, William E. & Lull, Howard W. Radiant Energy in Relation to Forests. LC 77-10239. (U. S. Department of Agriculture. Technical Bulletin: 1344). Repr. of 1965 ed. 15.00 (ISBN 0-404-16217-7). AMS Pr.

Solar Radiation Data Directory. 154p. 1983. pap. 8.50 (ISBN 0-318-11830-0). Gov Printing Office.

SOLAR SEA POWER PLANTS

see Ocean Thermal Power Plants

SOLAR SPECTRUM

see Spectrum, Solar

SOLAR SYSTEM

see also Comets; Earth; Ephemerides; Meteors; Moon; Orbits; Planets; Satellites; Sun; also names of individual planets

Aarons, Jules, ed. Solar System Radio Astronomy. LC 65-14086. 416p. 1965. 39.50x (ISBN 0-306-30192-X, Plenum Pr). Plenum Pub.

Airy, George B. Gravitation. rev. ed. 1969. pap. 2.50 (ISBN 0-911014-02-0). Neo Pr.

Alfven, H. & Arrhenius, G. Structure & Evolutionary History of the Solar System. LC 75-29444. (Geophysics & Astrophysics Monographs: No. 5). xvi, 280p. 1975. lib. bdg. 42.00 (ISBN 90-277-0611-5, Pub. by Reidel Holland); pap. 31.50 (ISBN 90-277-0660-3). Kluwer Academic.

Alfven, Hannes. On the Origin of the Solar System. LC 72-9604. (International Series of Monographs on Physics). (Illus.). 194p. 1973. Repr. of 1954 ed. lib. bdg. 82.50 (ISBN 0-8371-6595-4, ALOS). Greenwood.

Asimov, Isaac. The Sun Shines Bright. LC 80-2039. 312p. 1981. 13.95 (ISBN 0-385-17145-5). Doubleday.

Beatty, J. Kelly, et al, eds. The New Solar System. 2nd ed. LC 81-2661. pap. 62.00 (ISBN 0-317-20616-8, 2024570). Bks Demand UMI.

Burnham, Robert, Jr. Burnham's Celestial Handbook: An Observer's Guide to the Universe Beyond the Solar System, Vols. 1 & 2. LC 77-82888. (Illus.). 1978. pap. 9.95. Vol. 1 (ISBN 0-486-23567-X). Vol. 2. pap. 10.95 (ISBN 0-486-23568-8). Dover.

Copernicus, Nicholas. De Revolutionibus Orbium Coelestium. 1965. Repr. of 1543 ed. Facsimile Ed. 50.00 (ISBN 0-384-09806-1). Johnson Repr.

Dermott, S. F. The Origin of the Solar System. LC 77-7547. 668p. 1978. 144.95 (ISBN 0-471-99529-0, Pub. by Wiley-Interscience); pap. 61.95 (ISBN 0-471-27585-9, Pub. by Wiley-Interscience). Wiley.

Dreyer, John L. History of Astronomy from Thales to Kepler. pap. 8.50 (ISBN 0-486-60079-3). Dover.

--History of Astronomy from Thales to Kepler. 15.50 (ISBN 0-8446-1997-3). Peter Smith.

Duncombe, Raynor L., ed. Dynamics of the Solar System. (I. A. U. Symposia Ser.: No. 81). 1979. lib. bdg. 45.00 (ISBN 90-277-0976-9, Pub. by Reidel Holland); pap. 28.95 (ISBN 90-277-0977-7, Pub. by Reidel Holland). Kluwer Academic.

Echaore, Susan D. The Solar System. (Science in Action Ser.). (Illus.). 48p. 1982. pap. text ed. 2.85 (ISBN 0-915510-80-4). Janus Bks.

Elton, Sam. New Model of Solar System. LC 66-18990. 1967. 5.00 (ISBN 0-8022-0450-3). Philos Lib.

European Astronomical Meeting, 1st, Athens, 1972. Solar Activity & Related Interplanetary & Terrestrial Phenomenon: Proceedings, Vol. 1. Xanthakis, J., ed. (Illus.). 200p. 1973. 58.50 (ISBN 0-387-06314-5). Springer-Verlag.

Gehrels, Tom, ed. Protostars & Planets: Studies of Star Formatiand of the Origin of the Solar System. LC 78-10269. pap. 160.00 (ISBN 0-317-07759-7, 2020435). Bks Demand UMI.

Genet, Russell M., ed. Solar System Photometry Handbook. LC 83-21382. (Illus.). 224p. 1983. pap. text ed. 17.95 (ISBN 0-943396-03-4). Willmann-Bell.

Grazia, Alfred de & Milton, Earl R. Solaria Binaria: Origins & History of the Solar System. (Quantavolution Ser.). (Illus.). 292p. 1984. pap. 21.00x (ISBN 0-940268-04-3). Metron Pubns.

Greeley, Ronald. Planetary Landscapes. (Illus.). 256p. 1985. 39.95x (ISBN 0-04-551080-6). Allen Unwin.

Hardy, David A. Atlas of the Solar System. 96p. 1982. 65.00x (ISBN 0-437-06540-5, Pub. by Windmill Pr). State Mutual Bk.

--Atlas of the Solar System. (Illus.). 96p. 1983. 26.50 (ISBN 0-437-06540-5, Pub. by Worlds Work). David & Charles.

Hartmann, William K. Moons & Planets. 2nd ed. 528p. 1983. text ed. write for info. (ISBN 0-534-00719-8). Wadsworth Pub.

Hide, R., et al, eds. Rotation in the Solar System: Proceedings of a Royal Society Discussion Meeting Held March 8-9, 1984. (Illus.). 191p. 1985. lib. bdg. 58.00x (ISBN 0-85403-236-3). Scholium Intl.

Hunt, Garry & Moore, Patrick. Rand McNally Atlas of the Solar System. (Illus.). 464p. 1983. 40.00 (ISBN 0-528-81122-3). Rand.

I.A.U. Symposium No. 65, Torun, Poland, 5-8 September 1973. Exploration of the Planetary System: Proceedings. Woszczyk, A. & Iwaniszewska, C., eds. LC 73-94458. (Symposium of the International Astronomical Union Ser: No. 65). 1974. lib. bdg. 92.00 (ISBN 90-277-0449-X, Pub. by Reidel Holland); pap. text ed. 68.50 (ISBN 90-277-0450-3, Pub. by Reidel Holland). Kluwer Academic.

IAU Symposium, 62nd, Warsaw, Poland, 5-8 September 1973. The Stability of the Solar System & Small Stellar Systems: Proceedings. Kozai, Y., ed. LC 74-76475. (Symposium of the International Astronomical Union: No. 62). 1974. lib. bdg. 37.00 (ISBN 90-277-0458-9, Pub. by Reidel Holland); pap. text ed. 36.85 (ISBN 90-277-0459-7). Kluwer Academic.

Jastrow, R. & Cameron, A. G., eds. Origin of the Solar System: Proceedings. 1963. 49.00 (ISBN 0-12-381150-3). Acad Pr.

Jones, B. W. & Keynes, Milton. The Solar System. (Illus.). 400p. 1984. 40.00 (ISBN 0-08-026496-4); pap. 19.50 (ISBN 0-08-026495-6). Pergamon.

Kaufmann, William J., III. Planets & Moons. LC 78-21156. (Illus.). 219p. 1979. pap. text ed. 10.95 (ISBN 0-7167-1040-4). W H Freeman.

Kennell, C. F., et al, eds. Solar Systems, Plasma Physics, 3 vols. 1979. Set. 223.50 (ISBN 0-444-85268-9, North Holland); Vol. 1. 97.75 (ISBN 0-444-85115-1); Vol. 3. 89.25 (ISBN 0-444-85267-0). Elsevier.

King, J. W. & Newman, W. S. Solar Terrestrial Physics. 1967. 62.00 (ISBN 0-12-407850-8). Acad Pr.

Kivelson, Margaret G. The Solar System: Observations & Interpretations. (Illus.). 448p. 1986. text ed. 43.95 (ISBN 0-13-821927-3). P-H.

Lal, D. Early Solar Systems Processes & the Present Solar System. (Enrico Fermi Summer School Ser.: Vol. 73). 266p. 1980. 57.50 (ISBN 0-444-85458-4, North-Holland). Elsevier.

Lunan, Duncan. Man & the Planets: The Resources of the Solar System. (Illus.). 306p. 1984. 17.95 (ISBN 0-906798-17-5, Pub. by Salem Hse Ltd). Merrimack Pub Cir.

Lunan, Duncan, et al. New Worlds for Old. LC 79-62916. (Illus.). 1979. 12.95 (ISBN 0-688-03486-1). Morrow.

Miller, Ron & Hartmann, William K. The Grand Tour: A Traveler's Guide to the Solar System. LC 80-54620. (Illus.). 192p. 1980. 19.95 (ISBN 0-89480-147-3, 331); pap. 11.95 (ISBN 0-89480-146-5, 447). Workman Pub.

Moore, Patrick. Travellers in Space & Time. LC 83-7401. (Illus.). 192p. 1984. pap. 14.95 (ISBN 0-385-19051-4). Doubleday.

O'Leary, Brian & Beatty, J. Kelly, eds. The New Solar System. (Illus.). 192p. 1981. 22.95 (ISBN 0-933346-26-3). Sky Pub.

--The New Solar System. 2nd ed. 240p. 1982. 24.95 (ISBN 0-933346-36-0); pap. 13.95 (ISBN 0-933346-37-9). Sky Pub.

O'Reilly, W., ed. Magnetism, Planetary Rotation, & Convention in the Solar System: Retrospect & Prospect, Vol. 7. (Geophysical Surveys Ser.: Nos. 1, 2 & 3). 1985. lib. bdg. 49.00 (ISBN 90-277-2050-9, Pub. by Reidel Holland). Kluwer Academic.

Ortner, J. & Maseland, H., eds. Introduction to Solar-Terrestial Relations. 514p. 1965. 132.95 (ISBN 0-677-00650-0). Gordon.

Payne, George. Solar System Astronomy. 1980. text ed. 9.95 wire coil bdg. (ISBN 0-88252-103-9). Paladin Hse.

Preiss, Byron, ed. The Planets. LC 85-47649. (Illus.). 304p. 1985. pap. 24.95 (ISBN 0-553-05109-1). Bantam.

Ransom, C. J. The Age of Velikovsky. LC 76-22381. (Illus.). 1977. 12.95 (ISBN 0-917994-01-9). Kronos Pr.

Rossi, B., ed. Space Exploration & the Solar System. (Italian Physical Society: Course 24). 1964. 65.00 (ISBN 0-12-368824-8). Acad Pr.

Ryan, Peter. Solar System. Pesek, Ludek, tr. (Illus.). 1979. 19.95 (ISBN 0-670-65636-4). Viking.

Scientific American Editors. The Solar System: A Scientific American Book. LC 75-28113. (Illus.). 145p. 1975. pap. text ed. 9.95x (ISBN 0-7167-0550-8). W H Freeman.

Seventeenth Annual Meeting, Seattle, 1971. Outer Solar System, 2 pts. Vagners, Juris, ed. (Advances in the Astronautical Sciences Ser.: Vol. 29). 1971. Pt. 1. lib. bdg. 40.00x (ISBN 0-87703-059-6, Pub. by Am Astronaut); Pt. 2. lib. bdg. 45.00x (ISBN 0-87703-060-X). Univelt Inc.

Skinner, Brian J., ed. The Solar System & Its Strange Objects. LC 81-21156. (The Earth & Its Inhabitants: Selected Readings from American Scientist Ser.). (Illus.). 197p. (Orig.). 1982. pap. 11.95x (ISBN 0-913232-84-X). W Kaufmann.

Smoluchowski, Roman. The Solar System. LC 83-11661. (Scientific American Library). (Illus.). 192p. 1983. 27.95 (ISBN 0-7167-1492-2). W H Freeman.

Stimson, Dorothy. The Gradual Acceptance of the Copernican Theory of the Universe: A Study in the History of Thought. 11.50 (ISBN 0-8446-0270-1). Peter Smith.

Sullivan & Sullivan. Programmed Astronomy: The Solar System. 1972. pap. text ed. 9.00 (ISBN 0-8449-0500-3); tchrs' manual 4.00; test 3.00. Learning Line.

Szebehely, Victor, ed. Stability of the Solar System & Its Minor Natural & Artificial Bodies. (NATO ASI Series C: Mathematical & Physical Science). 1985. lib. bdg. 54.00 (ISBN 0-318-04528-1, Pub. by Reidel Holland). Kluwer-Academic.

Use of Space Systems for Planetary Geology & Geophysics. (Science & Technology Ser.: Vol. 17). 1967. 45.00x (ISBN 0-87703-045-6, Pub. by Am Astronaut); microfiche suppl. 10.00x (ISBN 0-87703-135-5). Univelt Inc.

Whipple, Fred L. Orbiting the Sun: Planets & Satellites of the Solar System. (Illus.). 344p. 20.00 (ISBN 0-674-64125-6). Harvard U Pr.

Whitcomb, John C. Origin of the Solar System. (Biblical & Theological Studies). pap. 1.75 (ISBN 0-8010-9590-5). Baker Bk.

Whitcomb, John C., Jr. Origin of the Solar System. 1964. pap. 1.75 (ISBN 0-87552-537-7). Presby & Reformed.

Wood, John. The Solar System. 1979. pap. 15.95 (ISBN 0-13-822015-8). P-H.

SOLAR WIND

Brandt, John C. Introduction to the Solar Wind. LC 75-89919. (Illus.). 199p. 1970. text ed. 22.95 (ISBN 0-7167-0328-9). W H Freeman.

Federal Energy Administration. Wind Energy Conversion Systems Manufacturing & Sales Activity. Bereny, J. A., ed. 1978. pap. 6.95x (ISBN 0-930978-13-7, W-030). Solar Energy Info.

Hundhausen, A. J. Coronal Expansion & Solar Wind. LC 72-85398. (Physics & Chemistry in Space: Vol. 5). (Illus.). 270p. 1972. 32.00 (ISBN 0-387-05875-3). Springer-Verlag.

Linscott, Bradford S. Large, Horizontal-Axis Wind Turbines. 68p. 1984. pap. 7.95X (W067). Solar Energy Info.

SOLDER AND SOLDERING

see also Alloys; Brazing; Welding

American Welding Society. Soldering Manual, SM. 2nd ed. 160p. 1978. 24.00 (ISBN 0-87171-151-6); member 18.00. Am Welding.

Cain, Tubal. Soldering & Brazing, No. 9. (Workshop Practice Ser.). (Illus.). 136p. Date not set. pap. 11.95 (ISBN 0-85242-845-6, Pub. by Aztex Corp). Argus Bks.

Manko, Howard H. Solders & Soldering. 2nd ed. LC 79-9714. (Illus.). 1980. 36.50 (ISBN 0-07-039897-6). McGraw.

Pascoe, G. Solders & Soldering. 1986. 30.00 (ISBN 0-08-027295-9); pap. 12.00. Pergamon.

Woodgate, Ralph W. The Handbook of Machine Soldering: A Guide for the Soldering of Electronic Printed Wiring Assemblies. LC 82-17540. 224p. 1983. 29.50x (ISBN 0-471-87540-6, Pub. by Wiley Interscience). Wiley.

SOLENOIDS

see also Magnets

Montgomery, D. Bruce. Solenoid Magnet Design: The Magnetic & Mechanical Aspects of Resistive & Superconducting Systems. LC 79-13585. 328p. 1980. Repr. of 1969 ed. lib. bdg. 18.50 (ISBN 0-88275-993-0). Krieger.

SOLES

see Flatfishes

SOLID FILM

see Thin Films

SOLID FUEL REACTORS

see also Boiling Water Reactors; Heavy Water Reactors; Pressurized Water Reactors

Zimmer, Ben A. The Whys Behind Testing Standards for Solid Fuel Burning Appliances. 1981. 3.50 (ISBN 0-686-31891-9, TR 81-4). Society Fire Protect.

SOLID GEOMETRY

see Geometry, Solid

SOLID HELIUM

Wilks, John. Properties of Liquid & Solid Helium. (International Series of Monographs on Physics). 1967. 79.00x (ISBN 0-19-851245-7). Oxford U Pr.

SOLID SOLUTIONS

see Solutions, Solid

SOLID STATE CHEMISTRY

see also Solid State Physics

Adams, David M. Inorganic Solids: An Introduction to Concepts in Solid-State Structural Chemistry. LC 73-16863. pap. 88.00 (ISBN 0-317-09025-9, 2051237). Bks Demand UMI.

Adler, G., ed. Molecular Crystals & Liquid Crystals Special Topics: Proceedings of the Fifth International Symposium on Organic Solid State Chemistry, Brandeis University, June 1978, 2 pts. 632p. 1979. 531.50 (ISBN 0-677-40265-1). Gordon.

Adler, George, ed. Organic Solid State Chemistry. 526p. 1969. 130.75 (ISBN 0-677-13200-X). Gordon.

Berkowitz, B. J. & Scattergood, R. O., eds. Chemistry & Physics of Rapidly Solidified Materials: Proceedings, TMS Fall Meeting, St. Louis, Missouri, 1982. LC 83-61484. (Illus.). 315p. 1983. 45.00 (ISBN 0-89520-460-6). Metal Soc.

Blossey, E. C. & Neckers, D. C., eds. Solid Phase Synthesis. (Benchmark Papers in Organic Chemistry Ser: Vol. 2). 400p. 1975. 66.00 (ISBN 0-12-786165-3). Acad Pr.

Bradley, Charles O. High Pressure Methods in Solid State Research. LC 68-58922. pap. 45.80 (ISBN 0-317-28019-8, 2055799). Bks Demand UMI.

Budnikov, P. P. & Ginstling, A. M. Principles of Solid State Chemistry. Shaw, K., tr. (Illus.). 454p. 1968. 52.00 (ISBN 0-85334-028-5, Pub. by Elsevier Applied Sci England). Elsevier.

Burns, Gerald & Glazer, A. M. Introduction to Space Groups for Solid State Scientists. 1978. 23.00 (ISBN 0-12-145760-5). Acad Pr.

Byrn, Stephen. Solid State Chemistry of Drugs. LC 82-13950. 349p. 1982. 60.00 (ISBN 0-12-148620-6). Acad Pr.

Falicov, L. M., et al, eds. Valence Fluctuations in Solids: Proceedings of the International Conference at Santa Barbara, California, Jan. 27-30, 1981. 466p. 1981. 74.50 (ISBN 0-444-86204-8, North-Holland). Elsevier.

Goodenough, John B. & Whittingham, M. Stanley, eds. Solid State Chemistry of Energy Conversion & Storage: A Symposium Sponsored by the Division of Inorganic Chemistry at the 71st Meeting of the American Chemical Society. LC 77-20011. (Advances in Chemisty Ser.: No. 163). pap. 95.50 (ISBN 0-317-08982-X, 2015231). Bks Demand UMI.

Hardy, J. R. & Karo, A. M. The Lattice Dynamics & Statistics of Alkali Halide Crystals. LC 79-339. 324p. 1979. 49.50x (ISBN 0-306-40221-1, Plenum Pr). Plenum Pub.

Harrison, Walter A. Electronic Structure & the Properties of Solids: The Physics of the Chemical Bond. LC 79-17364. (Illus.). 582p. 1980. text ed. 41.95 (ISBN 0-7167-1000-5); instr's guide avail. (ISBN 0-7167-1220-2). W H Freeman.

Holt, Smith, et al, eds. Solid State Chemistry: A Contemporary Overview. LC 80-17185. (Advances in Chemistry Ser.: No. 186). 1980. 59.95 (ISBN 0-8412-0472-1). Am Chemical.

Janata, Jiri & Huber, Robert J., eds. Solid State Chemical Sensors. Date not set. 49.50 (ISBN 0-12-380210-5). Acad Pr.

Konig, E. & Kremer, S. Magnetism Diagrams for Transition Metal Ions. LC 79-17840. 569p. 1979. 75.00x (ISBN 0-306-40260-2, Plenum Pr). Plenum Pub.

Kroger, F. A. The Chemistry of Imperfect Crystals, Vol. 1. 313p. 1974. 61.75 (ISBN 0-444-10561-1, North-Holland). Elsevier.
Ladd, M. F. Structure & Bonding in Solid State Chemistry. LC 78-41289. (Ellis Horwood Series in Chemical Science). 326p. 1979. 69.95 (ISBN 0-470-26597-3). Halsted Pr.
McCaldin, J. O. & Somorjai, G., eds. Progress in Solid State Chemistry, Vols. 8-10. Incl. Vol. 8. 1973. text ed. 76.00 (ISBN 0-08-017147-8); Vol. 9. 1976. text ed. 76.00 (ISBN 0-08-018067-1); Vol. 10, Pt. 1. pap. text ed. 8.00 (ISBN 0-08-019479-6); Vol. 10, Pt. 2. Heterogeneous Catalysis by Metals. Sinfelt. 1976. pap. text ed. 8.00 (ISBN 0-08-019480-X); Vol. 10, Pt. 3. 1976. pap. text ed. 12.50 (ISBN 0-08-019481-8); Vol. 10, Pt. 4. 1976. pap. text ed. 15.50 (ISBN 0-08-019482-6); Vol. 10 (complete) 1977. text ed. 76.00 (ISBN 0-08-019483-4). LC 63-11362. pap. text ed. write for info. Pergamon.
Madelung, O. Introduction to Solid-State Theory. LC 77-26263. (Springer Ser. in Solid-State Sciences: Vol. 2). (Illus.). 1978. 32.00 (ISBN 0-387-08516-5). Springer-Verlag.
Metselaar, R., et al. Solid State Chemistry, 1982. 852p. 1983. 202.25 (ISBN 0-444-42147-5). Elsevier.
Mixing of Particulate Solids: Second European Symposium. (Symposium Ser.: No. 65). 250p. 1981. 75.00x (ISBN 0-85295-134-5, Pub. by IChemE). State Mutual Bk.
Molecular Crystals & Liquid Crystals Special Topics: Proceedings of the Eighth International Liquid Crystals Conference, Kyoto, Japan, June 30-July 4, 1980, 6 vols. 1955p. 1981. pap. 698.95x (ISBN 0-677-40295-3). Gordon.
NATO Advanced Study Institutes. Electrode Processes in Solid State Ionics: Proceedings. Kleitz, M. & Dupuy, J., eds. LC 75-44113. 1976. lib. bdg. 53.00 (ISBN 90-277-0679-4, Pub. by Reidel Netherlands). Kluwer Academic.
Ploog, K. & Graf, K. Molecular Beam Epitaxy of III-V Compounds: A Comprehensive Bibliography 1958-1983. (Illus.). 235p. 1984. pap. 19.50 (ISBN 0-387-13177-9). Springer-Verlag.
Rosenblatt, G. M. & Worrell, W. L., eds. Progress in Solid State Chemistry, Vol. 13. (Illus.). 376p. 1982. 125.00 (ISBN 0-08-029712-9). Pergamon.
Russell, K. C. & Aaronson, H. I., eds. Precipitation Processes in Solids: Proceedings of a Symposium Sponsored by the TMS-AIME Heat Treatment Committee at the 1976 TMS Fall Meeting at Niagara Falls, New York, September 20-21. LC 78-66760. pap. 81.00 (ISBN 0-317-10468-3, 2022769). Bks Demand UMI.
Schmalzried, Hermann. Solid State Reactions. 2nd ed. (Monographs in Modern Chemistry: Vol. 12). (Illus.). 254p. 1981. cloth 61.30x (ISBN 0-89573-031-6). VCH Pubs.
Solid State Chemistry. 1980. 5.90 (ISBN 0-910362-14-9). Chem Educ.
Structural Problems. (Structure & Bonding Ser.: Vol. 37). (Illus.). 1979. 57.00 (ISBN 0-387-09455-5). Springer-Verlag.
Vanselow, R. & Howe, R., eds. Chemistry & Physics of Solid Surfaces V. (Springer Series in Chemical Physics: Vol. 35). (Illus.). 570p. 1984. 45.50 (ISBN 0-387-13315-1). Springer-Verlag.
West, Anthony. Solid State Chemistry & Its Applications. 734p. 1984. text ed. 67.95x (ISBN 0-471-90377-9). Wiley.
Wolfe, Raymond, ed. Applied Solid State Science: Advances in Materials & Device Research. Incl. Vol. 4. 1974. 85.00 (ISBN 0-12-002904-9); Vol. 5. 1975. 85.00 (ISBN 0-12-002905-7); lib. ed. o.p. 120.00 (ISBN 0-12-002974-X); Vol. 6. 1976. 75.00 (ISBN 0-12-002906-5); lib. ed. o.p. 90.00 (ISBN 0-12-002976-6). (Serial Publication). Acad Pr.
Wood, John, et al, eds. Reactivity of Solids. LC 77-785. (Illus.). 810p. 1977. 95.00x (ISBN 0-306-31021-X, Plenum Pr). Plenum Pub.

SOLID-STATE COUNTERS

see Semiconductor Nuclear Counters

SOLID STATE ELECTRONICS

Barber, Alfred W. Experimenter's Guide to Solid State Electronics Projects. (Illus.). 1980. 17.95 (ISBN 0-13-295451-6, Parker). P-H.
Beach, Donald P. & Lyons, Richard A. Solid State Electronic Amplifiers: An Empirical Approach. 1984. text ed. 28.95 (ISBN 0-8359-6951-7). Reston.
Bradley, C. C. High-Pressure Methods in Solid State Research. 184p. 1969. 15.00x (ISBN 0-306-30693-X, Plenum Pr). Plenum Pub.
Cannon, Don L. Understanding Solid Electronics, Vol. II. Battle, Charles W. & Luecke, Gerald, eds. (Understanding Ser.). (Illus.). 256p. (Orig.). 1985. pap. 14.95 (ISBN 0-89512-183-2). Tex Instr Inc.
Eilenberger, G. Solitons: Mathematical Methods for Physicists. (Springer Series in Solid-State Sciences: Vol. 19). (Illus.). 192p. 1981. 22.00 (ISBN 0-387-10223-X). Springer-Verlag.
Eschenfelder, A. H. Magnetic Bubble Theory. 2nd corrected & updated ed. (Springer Series in Solid-State Sciences: Vol. 14). (Illus.). 364p. 1981. pap. 38.00 (ISBN 0-387-10790-8). Springer-Verlag.
Faber, R. B. Essentials of Solid State Electronics. 735p. 1985. 32.95 (ISBN 0-471-86575-3); lab guide avail. (ISBN 0-471-81492-X). Wiley.
Genn, Robert C. Illustrated Guide to Practical Solid State Circuits...with Experiments & Projects. 335p. 1983. 21.95 (ISBN 0-13-450643-X). P-H.
Genn, Robert C., Jr. Practical Handbook of Solid State Troubleshooting. LC 80-23897. 256p. 1981. 12.95 (ISBN 0-13-691303-2, Parker). P-H.
Goetzberger, A. & Zerbst, M., eds. Solid State Devices Nineteen Eighty-Two: ESSDERC-SSSDT Meeting at Munich, 13-16 September 1982. (Illus.). 201p. 1983. 46.00x (ISBN 3-87664-072-5). VCH Pubs.
Gottlieb, Irving. Solid State High Frequency Power. 1981. text ed. 29.95 (ISBN 0-8359-7048-5). Reston.
Gottlieb, Irving M. Power Control with Solid State Devices. 1985. text ed. 24.95 (ISBN 0-8359-5592-3). Reston.
Grosse, P., ed. Advances in Solid State Physics, Vol. 22. 1982. 56.00 (ISBN 0-9940018-7-8, Pub. by Vieweg & Sohn Germany). Heyden.
Hafford, W. E., et al. Understanding Solid-State Electronics. 4th ed. Luecke, Gerald & Korte, Ben, eds. LC 84-51250. (Understanding Ser.). (Illus.). 276p. 1984. pap. text ed. 14.95 (ISBN 0-89512-162-X, LCB8453). Tex Instr Inc.
Howard W. Sams Engineering Staff. Tube Substitution Handbook. 21st ed. LC 80-13842. 128p. 1980. pap. 4.95 (ISBN 0-672-21746-5). Sams.
Howes, M. J. & Morgan, D. V. Reliability & Degradation: Semiconductor Devices & Circuits. LC 80-42310. (Wiley Series in Solid State Devices & Circuits). 424p. 1981. 63.95x (ISBN 0-471-28028-3, Pub. by Wiley-Interscience). Wiley.
Introduction to Automotive Solid State Electronics. LC 81-52155. 96p. 1981. pap. 9.95 (ISBN 0-672-21825-9). Sams.
Krauss, Herbert L. & Bostian, Charles W. Solid State Radio Engineering. LC 78-27797. 534p. 1980. 42.50 (ISBN 0-471-03018-X); solutions manual avail. (ISBN 0-471-05293-0). Wiley.
Kubo, S. R. & Hanamura, E. E., eds. Relaxation of Elementary Excitations: Proceedings. (Springer Ser. in Solid-State Sciences: Vol. 18). (Illus.). 285p. 1980. 48.00 (ISBN 0-387-10129-2). Springer-Verlag.
Loveday, George C. & Seidman, Arthur H. Troubleshooting Solid State Circuits. LC 80-21954. 110p. 1981. pap. text ed. 13.95 (ISBN 0-471-08371-2). Wiley.
MacDonald, Lorne. Basic Solid State Electronic Circuit Analysis Through Experimentation. 488p. 1981. pap. 16.00x (ISBN 0-911908-12-9). Tech Ed Pr.
--Basic Solid State Electronic Circuit Analysis Through Experimentation. 2nd ed. 488p. 1984. pap. 17.50 (ISBN 0-317-20395-9). Tech Ed Pr.
Mackenroth, Donald R. & Sands, Leo G. Illustrated Encyclopedia of Solid State Circuits & Applications. LC 84-23077. (Illus.). 353p. cancelled 29.95 (ISBN 0-13-450537-9, Busn). P-H.
Maloney, Timothy. Industrial Solid State Electronics. 2nd ed. (Illus.). 624p. 1986. text ed. 34.95 (ISBN 0-13-463423-3). P-H.
Maloney, Timothy J. Industrial Solid State Electronics: Devices & Systems. (Illus.). 1980. text ed. 32.95 (ISBN 0-13-463406-3). P-H.
Matthews, J. I. Experiments in Solid State Electronics. 1972. text ed. 21.60 (ISBN 0-07-040961-7). McGraw.
Mott, Nevill & Davis, E. A. Electronic Processes in Non-Crystalline Materials. 2nd ed. (International Series of Monographs on Physics). (Illus.). 1979. 69.00x (ISBN 0-19-851288-0). Oxford U Pr.
Neudeck, Gerold W. The Bipolar Junction Transistor. LC 81-14977. (Modular Series on Solid State Devices: No. 3). (Illus.). 85p. 1983. pap. 10.95 (ISBN 0-201-05322-5). Addison-Wesley.
--The PN Junction Diode. LC 81-14979. (Modular Series on Solid State Devices: No. 2). (Illus.). 120p. 1983. pap. 10.95 (ISBN 0-201-05321-7). Addison-Wesley.
Pearman, Richard. Solid State Industrial Electronics. 1982. text ed. 32.95 (ISBN 0-8359-7041-8); instrs'. manual avail. (ISBN 0-8359-7042-6). Reston.
Pierret, Robert F. Field Effect Device. LC 81-15035. (Modular Series on Solid State Devices: No. 4). (Illus.). 116p. 1983. pap. 10.95 (ISBN 0-201-05323-3). Addison-Wesley.
Pierret, Robert F. & Neudeck, Gerold W. Modular Series on Solid State Devices: Semiconductor Fundamentals, Vol. I. LC 81-14978. (Electrical Engineering Ser.). (Illus.). 1983. pap. text ed. 10.95 (ISBN 0-201-05320-9); solutions manual 2.50 (ISBN 0-201-05324-1). Addison-Wesley.
Reineker, P., et al, eds. Electronic Excitations & Interaction Processes. (Springer Series in Solid-State Sciences: Vol. 49). (Illus.). 285p. 1983. 32.00 (ISBN 0-387-12843-3). Springer Verlag.
Rhoderick, E. H. Solid State Devices, 1983. (Institute of Physics Conference Ser.: No. 69). 1984. 46.00 (ISBN 0-9903800-1-7, Pub. by A Hilger England). Heyden.
Rockis. Solid State Fundamentals for Electricians. (Illus.). 240p. 1985. 15.95 (ISBN 0-8269-1628-7). Am Technical.
Ruthkowski, George B. Solid State Electronics. 2nd ed. 1980. scp 28.44 (ISBN 0-672-97315-4); scp instructors guide 7.33 (ISBN 0-672-97317-0); scp lab manual 10.28 (ISBN 0-672-97316-2). Bobbs.
Seippel, Robert G. & Nelson, Roger L. Designing Solid-State Power Supplies. LC 74-31519. (Electronics Technician Learning Module Ser.). (Illus.). pap. 21.30 (ISBN 0-317-08825-4, 2011571). Bks Demand UMI.
Sirota, N. N. Solid State Transformations. Gorskii, F. K., ed. Archard, Geoffrey D., tr. from Rus. LC 66-18733. pap. 44.80 (ISBN 0-317-08917-X, 2020673). Bks Demand UMI.
Solid State Devices 1971: Munich. (Institute of Physics Conference Ser.: No. 12). 1971. 49.00 (ISBN 0-9960029-1-X, Pub. by Inst Physics England). Heyden.
Solid State Devices 1972: Lancaster. (Institute of Physics Conference Ser.: No. 15). 1972. 49.00 (ISBN 0-9960029-4-4, Pub. by Inst Physics England). Heyden.
Solid State Devices 1973: Munich. (Institute of Physics Conference Ser.: No. 19). 1973. 49.00 (ISBN 0-9960029-8-7, Pub. by Inst Physics England). Heyden.
Solid State Devices 1974: Nottingham. (Institute of Physics Conference Ser.: No. 25). 1975. 49.00 (ISBN 0-9960030-4-5, Pub. by Inst Physics England). Heyden.
Solid State Devices 1976: Munich. (Institute of Physics Conference Ser.: No. 32). 1977. 49.00 (ISBN 0-9960031-1-8, Pub. by Inst Physics England). Heyden.
Solid State Devices 1977: Brighton. (Institute of Physics Conference Ser.: No. 40). 1978. 49.00 (ISBN 0-9960032-0-7, Pub. by Inst Physics England). Heyden.
Streetman, B. Solid State Electronic Devices. 2nd ed. 1980. 38.95 (ISBN 0-13-822171-5). P-H.
Tarter, Ralph E. Principles of Solid State Power Conversion. 45.00 (ISBN 0-672-22018-0, 22018). Sams.
Tedeschi, F. P. & Taber, M. R. Solid State Electronics. LC 75-27996. 1976. pap. 16.80 (ISBN 0-8273-1171-0); instructor's guide 3.00 (ISBN 0-8273-1172-9). Delmar.
Traister, Robert J. Experimenter's Guide to Solid-State Diodes. (Illus.). 208p. 1984. 21.95 (ISBN 0-13-295444-3). P-H.
--The Experimenter's Guide to Solid-State Diodes. 192p. 1985. pap. 12.95 (ISBN 0-13-295551-2). P-H.
Treusch, J., ed. Advances in Solid State Physics, Vol. 21. 1981. 70.00 (ISBN 0-9940017-6-2, Pub. by Vieweg & Sohn Germany). Heyden.
Van Der Ziel, Aldert. Solid State Physical Electronics. 3rd ed. (Illus.). 544p. 1976. 41.95 (ISBN 0-13-821603-7). P-H.
Weiss, H., ed. Solid State Devices 1979. (Conference Ser.: No.53). 153p. 1980. 49.00 (ISBN 0-9960033-3-9, Pub. by Inst Physics England). Heyden.
Wells, R. Solid State Power Rectifiers. 186p. 1982. text ed. 24.50 (ISBN 0-246-11751-6, Pub. by Granada England). Brookfield Pub Co.
--Solid State Power Rectifiers. 192p. 1982. 20.00x (ISBN 0-246-11751-6, Pub. by Granada England). Sheridan.

SOLID STATE PHYSICS

see also Solid State Chemistry; Solids

Advances in Solid State Physics, Vol. 24. 1984. 56.00 (ISBN 0-9904000-4-2, Pub. by Vieweg & Sohn Germany). Heyden.
Alcacer, Luis, ed. The Physics & Chemistry of Low Dimensional Solids. (NATO Advanced Study Institute Ser. C: Mathematical & Physical Sciences: No. 56). 436p. 1980. lib. bdg. 50.00 (ISBN 90-277-1144-5, Pub. by Reidel Holland). Kluwer Academic.
Ashcroft, Neil W. & Mermin, N. David. Solid State Physics. LC 74-9772. 1976. text ed. 46.95 (ISBN 0-03-083993-9, CBS C). SCP.
Ausloos, M & Elliot, R. J., eds. Magnetic Phase Transitions. (Springer Series in Solid-State Sciences: Vol. 48). (Illus.). 269p. 1983. 32.00 (ISBN 0-387-12842-5). Springer Verlag.
Barisic, S., et al, eds. Quasi One-Dimensional Conductors One. (Lecture Notes in Physics: Vol. 95). 1979. pap. 22.00 (ISBN 0-387-09240-4). Springer-Verlag.
Barone, Antonio & Paterno, Gianfranco. The Physics & Applications of the Josephson Effect. 529p. 1982. 58.95x (ISBN 0-471-01469-9, Pub. by Wiley-Interscience). Wiley.
Barsic, S., ed. Quasi One-Dimensional Conductors Two. (Lecture Notes in Physics: Vol. 96). 1979. pap. 26.00 (ISBN 0-387-09241-2). Springer-Verlag.
Basov, N. G., ed. Exciton & Domain Luminescence of Semiconductors. LC 79-14567. (P. N. Levedev Physics Institute Ser.: Vol. 97). (Illus.). 119p. 1979. 55.00 (ISBN 0-306-10958-1, Consultants). Plenum Pub.
Beck, A., ed. Probability in Banach Spaces III: Proceedings. (Lecture Notes in Mathematics Ser.: Vol. 860). 329p. 1981. pap. 20.00 (ISBN 0-387-10822-X). Springer-Verlag.
Berkowitz, B. J. & Scattergood, R. O., eds. Chemistry & Physics of Rapidly Solidified Materials: Proceedings, TMS Fall Meeting, St. Louis, Missouri, 1982. LC 83-61484. (Illus.). 315p. 1983. 45.00 (ISBN 0-89520-460-6). Metal Soc.
Bindmann. Festkoerperphysik und Elektronische Technik. (Eng. & Ger.). 1104p. (Dictionary of Solid State Physics and Electrical Engineering). 1972. 83.95 (ISBN 3-87097-055-3, M-7410, Pub. by Brandstetter). French & Eur.
Binh, Vu T., ed. Surface Mobilities on Solid Materials: Fundamental Concepts & Applications. (NATO ASI Series B, Physics: Vol. 86). 598p. 1983. 89.50x (ISBN 0-306-41125-3, Plenum Press). Plenum Pub.
Bishop, A. R. & Schneider, T., eds. Solutions & Condensed Matter Physics: Proceedings. rev. ed. (Series in Solid-State Sciences: Vol. 8). (Illus.). 342p. 1978. 35.00 (ISBN 0-387-09138-6). Springer-Verlag.
Blakemore, J. S. Solid State Physics. 506p. Date not set. price not set. (ISBN 0-521-30932-8). Cambridge U Pr.
Blazynski, T. Z. Applied Elasto-Plasticity of Solids. (Illus.). 272p. 1984. text ed. 39.50x (ISBN 0-317-18202-1). Scholium Intl.
Bonse, U. & Rauch, H., eds. Neutron Interferometry. (Illus.). 1979. 59.00x (ISBN 0-19-851947-8). Oxford U Pr.
Braeunlich, P., ed. Thermally Stimulated Relaxation in Solids. (Topics in Applied Physics Ser.: Vol. 37). (Illus.). 1979. 59.00 (ISBN 0-387-09595-0). Springer-Verlag.
Brenig, W. & Manzel, D., eds. Desorption Induced by Electronic Transitions: Diet II. (Surface Sciences Ser.: Vol. 4). (Illus.). ix, 291p. 1985. 32.00 (ISBN 0-387-15593-7). Springer Verlag.
Brown, James. Introductory Solid Mechanics. LC 74-156805. pap. 112.00 (ISBN 0-317-07989-1, 2051225). Bks Demand UMI.
Burns, Gerald. Solid State Physics. Date not set. text ed. price not set (ISBN 0-12-146070-3). Acad Pr.
Burns, Gerald & Glazer, A. M. Introduction to Space Groups for Solid State Scientists. 1978. 23.00 (ISBN 0-12-145760-5). Acad Pr.
Buyers, W. J., ed. Moment Formation in Solids. (NATO ASI Series B, Physics: Vol. 117). 350p. 1984. 49.50x (ISBN 0-306-41834-7, Plenum Pr). Plenum Pub.
Cardona, M. & Guentherodt, G., eds. Light Scattering in Solids II: Basic Concept & Instrumentation. (Topics in Applied Physics Ser.: Vol. 50). (Illus.). 251p. 1982. 48.00 (ISBN 0-387-11380-0). Springer-Verlag.
Chandra, S. Superionic Solids: Principles & Applications. 404p. 1981. 74.50 (ISBN 0-444-86039-8, North-Holland). Elsevier.
Chaney & Putnam, eds. Electronic Properties Research Literature Retrieval Guide 1972-1976, 4 vols. LC 79-16082. 1374p. 1979. Set. 375.00x (ISBN 0-306-68010-6, IFI Plenum). Plenum Pub.
Cochran, J. F. & Haering, R. R., eds. Modern Solid State Physics, Vol. 1: Electrons on Metals. (Simon Fraser Summer School Lectures Ser., 1967). 402p. 1968. 76.50 (ISBN 0-677-12680-8). Gordon.
Coleman, R. V., ed. Solid State Physics. (Methods of Experimental Physics Ser.: Vol. 11). 1974. 90.00 (ISBN 0-12-475911-4). Acad Pr.

SOLID WASTE MANAGEMENT
see Factory and Trade Waste; Refuse and Refuse Disposal; Salvage (Waste, etc.)

SOLIDIFICATION
see also Melting Points; Solid Helium; Solutions, Solid

SOLIDS
see also Crystals; Elastic Solids; Energy-Band Theory of Solids; Exciton Theory; Permeability; Phonons; Solid State Physics; Thin Films; Tunneling (Physics); Zone Melting

Adams, David M. Inorganic Solids: An Introduction to Concepts in Solid-State Structural Chemistry. LC 73-16863. pap. 88.00 (ISBN 0-317-09025-9, 2051237). Bks Demand UMI.

--Inorganic Solids: An Introduction to Concepts in Solid-Stte Structural Chemistry. LC 73-16863. pap. 88.00 (ISBN 0-317-30437-2, 2024928). Bks Demand UMI.

AIP International Conf., Williamsburg, 1976. Structure & Excitation of Amorphous Solids: Proceedings. Lucovsky, G. & Galeener, F. L., eds. LC 76-22279. (AIP Conference Proceedings: No. 31). 1976. 19.50 (ISBN 0-88318-130-4). Am Inst Physics.

Alcacer, Luis, ed. The Physics & Chemistry of Low Dimensional Solids. (NATO Advanced Study Institute Ser. C: Mathematical & Physical Sciences: No. 56). 436p. 1980. lib. bdg. 50.00 (ISBN 90-277-1144-5, Pub. by Reidel Holland). Kluwer Academic.

Amelinckx, S., et al, eds. Solid State Dosimetry. 744p. 1970. 149.25 (ISBN 0-677-13470-3). Gordon.

American Society of Mechanical Engineers. Dynamics of Structured Solids. Hermann, George, ed. LC 68-58743. pap. 28.50 (ISBN 0-317-08722-3, 2016807). Bks Demand UMI.

Andersen, S., et al, eds. Atomic Collisions in Solids: Conference, No. IV. 476p. 1972. 132.95 (ISBN 0-677-04660-X). Gordon.

Anderson, P. W. Concepts in Solids: Lectures on the Theory of Solids. (Frontiers in Physics Ser.: No. 10). 1963. pap. 27.95 (ISBN 0-8053-0229-8). Benjamin-Cummings.

Arifov, Ubai A., ed. Secondary Emission & Structural Properties of Solids. Archard, Geoffrey C., tr. from Russian. LC 78-157931. pap. 38.50 (ISBN 0-317-08295-7, 2020683). Bks Demand UMI.

Axelrad, D. R. Micromechanics of Solids. 1978. 64.00 (ISBN 0-444-99806-3). Elsevier.

Azaroff, Leonid V. Introduction to Solids. LC 75-20462. 474p. 1975. Repr. of 1960 ed. 28.00 (ISBN 0-88275-345-2). Krieger.

Bacon, G. E. Architecture of Solids. LC 81-9762. (Wykeham Science Ser.: No. 58). 138p. 1981. pap. 16.50x (ISBN 0-8448-1397-4). Crane-Russak Co.

Bamford, C. H. & Tipper, C. F. Reactions of Solids with Gases. (Comprehensive Chemical Kinetics Ser.: Vol. 21). 1984. 79.75 (ISBN 0-444-42288-9, I-450-84). Elsevier.

--Simple Processes at the Gas-Solid Interface. (Comprehensive Chemical Kinetics Ser.: Vol. 19). 1984. 135.25 (ISBN 0-444-42287-0, I-147-84). Elsevier.

Bassani, F. & Parravicini, Pastori. Electron States & Optical Transitions in Solids. 312p. 1975. text ed. 52.00 (ISBN 0-08-016846-9). Pergamon.

Bell, James F. Physics of Large Deformation of Crystalline Solids. (Springer Tracts in Natural Philosophy: Vol. 14). (Illus.). 1968. 35.00 (ISBN 0-387-04343-8). Springer-Verlag.

Bhatia, Mahesh V. & Cheremisinoff, Paul N. Solids Separation & Mixing. LC 79-63114. (Process Equipment Ser.: Vol. 1). 303p. 1979. 35.00 (ISBN 0-87762-272-8). Technomic.

Bishay, Adlai, ed. Recent Advances in Science & Technology of Materials, 3 vols. LC 74-17098. 1974. Vol. 1, 419p. 65.00x (ISBN 0-306-37691-1, Plenum Pr); Vol. 2, 449p. 65.00x (ISBN 0-306-37692-X); Vol. 3, 391p. 65.00x (ISBN 0-306-37693-8). Plenum Pub.

Borissov, M., ed. Optical & Acoustic Waves in Solids-Modern Topics: Proceedings of the International School on Condensed Matter Physics, 2nd, Varna, Bulgaria Sept. 23-30, 1982. vi, 484p. 1983. 67.00x (ISBN 9971-950-61-8, Pub. by World Sci Singapore). Taylor & Francis.

Bozzi, Ed. High Solids Coatings Buyer's Guide. 1982. pap. text ed. 21.00 (ISBN 0-936840-01-3). Tech Marketing.

Bube, Richard H. Photoconductivity of Solids. LC 78-1084. 484p. 1978. Repr. of 1960 ed. 28.50 (ISBN 0-88275-660-5). Krieger.

Budnikov, P. P. & Ginstling, A. M. Principles of Solid State Chemistry. 468p. 1970. 119.50 (ISBN 0-677-61250-8). Gordon.

Burgess, R. E., ed. Fluctuation Phenomena in Solids. (Pure & Applied Physics Ser.: Vol. 19). 1964. 79.50 (ISBN 0-12-143650-0). Acad Pr.

Burstein, E., ed. Atomic Structure & Properties of Solid. (Italian Physical Society Ser.: Course 52). 1973. 92.00 (ISBN 0-12-368852-3). Acad Pr.

Burstein, Elias, ed. Tunneling Phenomena in Solids. Lindqvist, S. LC 69-12528. (Illus.). 579p. 1969. 79.50x (ISBN 0-306-30362-0, Plenum Pr). Plenum Pub.

Callaway, Joseph. Electron Energy Bands in Solids. (Solid State Reprint Ser.). 1964. 21.50 (ISBN 0-12-608450-5). Acad Pr.

Cardona, M. Modulation Spectroscopy. (Solid State Physics: Suppl. 11). 1969. 76.00 (ISBN 0-12-607771-1). Acad Pr.

Cardona, M. & Guentherodt, G., eds. Light Scattering in Solids III: Recent Results. (Topics in Applied Physics: Vol. 51). (Illus.). 305p. 1982. 47.00 (ISBN 0-387-11513-7). Springer-Verlag.

Cardona, M. & Ley, L., eds. Photoemission in Solids I: General Principles. LC 78-2503. (Topics in Applied Physics: Vol. 26). (Illus.). 1978. 52.00 (ISBN 0-387-08685-4). Springer-Verlag.

Catlow, C. R. & Mackrodt, W. C., eds. Computer Simulation of Solids. (Lecture Notes in Physics Ser.: Vol. 166). 320p. 1982. pap. 19.00 (ISBN 0-387-11588-9). Springer-Verlag.

Chalmers, B., ed. Progress in Materials Science, Vol. 23. 280p. 1980. 105.00 (ISBN 0-08-024846-2). Pergamon.

Chalmers, Bruce. The Structure & Properties of Solids: An Introduction to Materials Science. 155p. 1982. 25.95x (ISBN 0-471-26214-5, Pub. by Wiley Heyden). Wiley.

CISM (International Center for Mechanical Sciences), Dept. of Mechanics of Solids. Thermodynamics of Materials with Memory. Coleman, B. D., ed. (CISM Pubns. Ser.: No. 73). iii, 47p. 1973. pap. 8.90 (ISBN 0-387-81125-7). Springer Verlag.

Clark, G. M. Structure of Non-Molecular Solids: A Coordinated Polyhedron Approach. (Illus.). 365p. 1972. 50.00 (ISBN 0-85334-544-9, Pub. by Elsevier Applied Sci England). Elsevier.

Crandall, Stephen H., et al. Introduction to the Mechanics of Solids. 2nd ed. (Illus.). 640p. 1972. text ed. 45.00 (ISBN 0-07-013436-7). McGraw.

--An Introduction to the Mechanics of Solids: SI Units. 2nd ed. (Illus.). 1978. text ed. 45.00 (ISBN 0-07-013441-3). McGraw.

Crawford, James H. & Slifkin, Lawrence M., eds. Point Defects in Solids, 3 vols. Incl. Vol. 1, General & Ionic Crystals. 556p. 1972. 75.00x (ISBN 0-306-37511-7); Vol. 2, Semiconductor & Molecular Crystals. 480p. 1975. 75.00 (ISBN 0-306-37512-5); Vol. 3, Defects in Metals. 1978. 37.50x (ISBN 0-306-37513-3). LC 72-183562. (Illus., Plenum Pr). Plenum Pub.

Datz, Sheldon, et al. Atomic Collisions in Solids, 2 vols. Incl. Vol. 1. 502p. 75.00x (ISBN 0-306-38211-3); Vol. 2. 477p. 75.00x (ISBN 0-306-38212-1). LC 74-26825. 1975. price 135.00 set (Plenum Pr). Plenum Pub.

Dawson, Thomas H. Theory & Practice of Solid Mechanics. LC 76-26010. (Illus.). 281p. 1976. 45.00x (ISBN 0-306-30931-9, Plenum Pr). Plenum Pub.

Devreese, J. T., et al, eds. Highly Conducting One Dimensional Solids. LC 78-11396. (Physics of Solids & Liquids Ser.). (Illus.). 435p. 1979. 65.00x (ISBN 0-306-40099-5, Plenum Pr). Plenum Pub.

Di Bartolo, B., ed. Luminescence of Inorganic Solids. LC 78-16681. 720p. 1978. 110.00x (ISBN 0-306-40034-0, Plenum Pr). Plenum Pub.

Division Of Physical Sciences. Research in Solid State Sciences: Opportunities & Relevance to National Needs. LC 8-61848. 1968. pap. 5.75 (ISBN 0-309-01600-2). Natl Acad Pr.

Douglas, R. W. & Ellis, Bryan, eds. Amorphous Materials: Papers Presented to the Third International Conference on the Physics of Non-Crystalline Solids, Sheffield University, September 1970. LC 77-162326. pap. 142.00 (ISBN 0-317-08992-7, 2016152). Bks Demand UMI.

Drauglis, E., et al. Molecular Processes on Solid Surfaces. (Materials Science & Engineering Ser.). 1969. text ed. 77.50 (ISBN 0-07-017827-5). McGraw.

Duke, C. B. Tunneling in Solids. (Solid State Physics, Suppl. 10). 1969. 76.00 (ISBN 0-12-607770-3). Acad Pr.

Ehrenreich, H. & Liebert, L., eds. Solid State Physics: Suppl. No. 14 Liquid Crystals. 1978. 59.50 (ISBN 0-12-607774-6). Acad Pr.

Eisenberg, Martin A. Introduction to the Mechanics of Solids. LC 78-74682. (Illus.). 1980. text ed. 36.95 (ISBN 0-201-01934-5); solutions manual 3.00 (ISBN 0-201-01935-3). Addison-Wesley.

Estructura Electronica de los Solidos. (Serie De Fisica: No. 3). (Span.). 1974. pap. 1.00 (ISBN 0-8270-6160-9). OAS.

Fiermans, L., et al, eds. Electron & Ion Spectroscopy of Solids. LC 78-6171. (NATO ASI Series B, Physics: Vol. 32). 487p. 1978. 75.00x (ISBN 0-306-35732-1, Plenum Pr). Plenum Pub.

Flood, E. A., ed. The Solid-Gas Interface, Vols. 1 & 2. 1967. Vol. 1. 125.00 (ISBN 0-8247-1200-5); Vol. 2. 125.00 (ISBN 0-8247-1201-3). Dekker.

Galasso, F. S. Structure & Properties of Inorganic Solids. LC 70-104123. 1970. 50.00 (ISBN 0-08-006873-1). Pergamon.

Geguzin, Y. E. & Krivoglaz, M. A. Migration of Macroscopic Inclusions in Solids. LC 73-83894. (Studies in Soviet Science - Physical Sciences Ser.). (Illus.). 342p. 1973. 37.50x (ISBN 0-306-10889-5, Consultants). Plenum Pub.

Geller, S., ed. Solid Electrolytes. LC 77-21873. (Topics in Applied Physics: Vol. 21). (Illus.). 1977. 49.00 (ISBN 0-387-08338-3). Springer-Verlag.

Gibbs, Ronald J., ed. Suspended Solids in Water. LC 74-19329. (Marine Science Ser.: Vol. 4). 320p. 1974. 55.00x (ISBN 0-306-35504-3, Plenum Pr). Plenum Pub.

Goldberg, Paul. Luminescence of Inorganic Solids. 1966. 111.00 (ISBN 0-12-287550-8). Acad Pr.

Goldring, Gvirol & Kalish, Rafael. Hyperfine Interactions of Excited Nuclei, 4 vols. LC 78-127883. (Illus.). 1378p. 1971. Set. 377.75 (ISBN 0-677-14600-0); 106.50 ea. Vol. 1, 386p (ISBN 0-677-15120-9). Vol. 2, 400p (ISBN 0-677-15130-6). Vol. 3, 280p (ISBN 0-677-15140-3). Vol. 4, 396p (ISBN 0-677-15150-0). Gordon.

Gregory, J. Solid-Liquid Separation. 363p. 1984. 87.95 (ISBN 0-470-20021-9). Halsted Pr.

Gurtin, Morton E., ed. Phase Transformations & Material Instabilities in Solids. (Mathematics Research Center Symposium Ser.). 1985. 17.00 (ISBN 0-12-309770-3). Acad Pr.

Haken, H., ed. Quantum Field Theory of Solids. 330p. 1983. pap. 32.00 (ISBN 0-444-86737-6, North-Holland). Elsevier.

Hall, H. E. Solid State Physics. LC 73-10743. (Manchester Physics Ser.). 351p. 1974. 57.95x (ISBN 0-471-34280-7); pap. 26.95x (ISBN 0-471-34281-5, Pub. by Wiley-Interscience). Wiley.

Harper, Charles A. Handbook of Thick Film Hybrid Microelectronics: A Practical Sourcebook for Designers, Fabricators & Users. (Classic Handbook Reissue Program Ser.). 1024p. 1974. 69.75 (ISBN 0-07-026680-8). McGraw.

Harrison, Walter A. Solid State Theory. 1980. pap. text ed. 8.95 (ISBN 0-486-63948-7). Dover.

Hautojaervi, P., ed. Positrons in Solids. LC 79-1191. (Topics in Current Physics: Vol. 12). (Illus.). 1979. 38.00 (ISBN 0-387-09271-4). Springer-Verlag.

Hayes, William & Stoneham, A. M. Defects & Defect Processes in Nonmetallic Solids. 400p. 1985. text ed. 46.95x (ISBN 0-471-89791-4, Pub. by Wiley-Interscience). Wiley.

Henderson, B., ed. Defects & Their Structure in Nonmetallic Solids. Hughes, A. E. LC 74-624. (NATO ASI Series B, Physics): Vol. 19). 505p. 1976. 75.00x (ISBN 0-306-35719-4, Plenum Pr). Plenum Pub.

Hildebrand, Joel, et al. Regular & Related Solutions: The Solubility of Gases, Liquids & Solids. LC 79-122670. 238p. 1970. 15.95 (ISBN 0-442-15665-0). Krieger.

Holden, Alan. The Nature of Solids. LC 65-22156. (Illus.). 1968. pap. 14.00x (ISBN 0-231-08591-5). Columbia U Pr.

Hopkins, H. G. & Sewell, M. J., eds. Mechanics of Solids: The Rodney Hill 60th Anniversary Volume. LC 80-40995. (Illus.). 720p. 1982. 110.00 (ISBN 0-08-025443-8). Pergamon.

Horton, G. & Maradudin, A., eds. Dynamical Properties of Solids, Vol. 3: Metals, Superconductors, Magnetic Materials & Liquids. 334p. 1980. 74.50 (ISBN 0-444-85314-6, North-Holland). Elsevier.

--Dynamical Properties of Solids, Vol. 4: Disordered Solids, Optical Properties. 478p. 1980. 93.75 (ISBN 0-444-85315-4, North-Holland). Elsevier.

Horton, G. K. & Maradudin, A. A. Dynamical Properties of Solids, Vols. 1 & 2: Crystalline Solids, 2 vols. 1974-76. Vol. 1, Fundamentals. 147.00 (ISBN 0-444-10536-0, North-Holland); Vol. 2, Applications. 140.50 (ISBN 0-444-10970-6). Elsevier.

Horton, G. K. & Yamada, Y. Lattice Dynamical Properties of Solids, Vol. 5. Date not set. write for info. (ISBN 0-444-86780-5). Elsevier.

Hughes, A. E., et al. Real Solids & Radiation. LC 74-32348. (Wykeham Science Ser.: No. 35). 208p. 1975. 8.60x (ISBN 0-8448-1162-9). Crane-Russak Co.

Institution of Chemical Engineers. Mixing of Particulate Solids. 52.50 (ISBN 0-08-028763-8). Pergamon.

--Solids Separation Processes. 72.00 (ISBN 0-08-028757-3). Pergamon.

International Conference on Light Scattering Spectra of Solids, New York University, New York, 1968. Proceedings. Wright, G. B., ed. (Illus.). 1969. 135.00 (ISBN 0-387-04645-3). Springer-Verlag.

International Symposium on Hydrotransport of Solids in Pipes, 4th. Proceedings. 1977. 54.00x (ISBN 0-900983-56-6). BHRA Fluid.

International Symposium on Hydrotransport of Solids in Pipes, 3rd. Proceedings. 1974. 45.00x (ISBN 0-900983-38-8). BHRA Fluid.

International Symposium on Pneumotransport of Solids in Pipes, 2nd. Proceedings. 1973. 47.00x (ISBN 0-900983-52-3). BHRA Fluid.

International Symposium on Pneumotransport of Solids in Pipes, 1st. Proceedings. 1972. 34.00x (ISBN 0-900983-15-9). BHRA Fluid.

International Union of Theoretical & Applied Mechanics Colloquium, Madrid, 1955. Deformation & Flow of Solids: Proceedings. Grammel, Richard, ed. Tr. of Verformung & Fliessen Des Festokoerpors. (Eng, Ger, Fr. & Span., Illus.). 1956. 34.30 (ISBN 0-387-02095-0). Springer-Verlag.

I.U.T.A.M Symposium on Optical Methods in Mechanics of Solids. Optical Methods in Mechanics of Solids: Proceedings. Lagarde, Alexis, ed. 692p. Date not set. 44.00x (ISBN 90-286-0860-5). Sijthoff & Noordhoff.

Kane, Philip F. & Larrabee, Graydon B., eds. Characterization of Solid Surfaces. LC 73-84000. (Illus.). 670p. 1974. 59.50x (ISBN 0-306-30752-9, Plenum Pr). Plenum Pub.

Kelly, A. Strong Solids. 2nd ed. (Monographs on the Physics & Chemistry of Materials Ser.). (Illus.). 1973. 59.00x (ISBN 0-19-851350-X). Oxford U Pr.

King, D. A. & Woodruff, D. P., eds. Adsorption at Solid Surface. (Chemical Physics of Solid Surface & Heterogeneous Catalysis Ser.: Vol. 2A). 386p. 1983. 119.25 (ISBN 0-444-42026-6). Elsevier.

Kittel, Charles. Quantum Theory of Solids. LC 63-20633. 435p. 1963. 44.50x (ISBN 0-471-49025-3). Wiley.

Klein, M. L. & Venables, J. A., eds. Rare Gas Solids, Vol. 1. 1976. 99.00 (ISBN 0-12-413501-3). Acad Pr.

Kolsky, H. Stress Waves in Solids. 2nd ed. (Illus.). 1963. pap. text ed. 6.95 (ISBN 0-486-61098-5). Dover.

Lampert, M. A. & Mark, P. Current Injections in Solids. (Electrical Science Ser) 1970. 80.00 (ISBN 0-12-435350-9). Acad Pr.

Latanision, R. M. & Fischer, T. E. Advances in Mechanics & Physics of Surfaces, Vol. 1. 262p. 1981. 69.50 (ISBN 3-7186-0026-9). Harwood Academic.

Laznicka, M. Physics of Solid Surfaces. (Studies in Surface Science & Catalysts: Vol. 9). 282p. 1982. 66.00 (ISBN 0-444-99716-4). Elsevier.

Lebon, G. & Perzyna, P., eds. Recent Developments in Thermomechanics of Solids. (CISM-Course & Lectures Ser.: Vol. 262). (Illus.). 415p. 1980. pap. 43.70 (ISBN 0-387-81597-X). Springer-Verlag.

Levy, F. A., ed. Fritz Hulliger: Structural Chemistry of Layer-Type Phases. LC 76-26635. (Physics & Chemistry of Materials with Layered Structures Ser: No. 5). 1976. lib. bdg. 55.00 (ISBN 90-277-0714-6, Pub. by Reidel Holland). Kluwer Academic.

Lifshits, I. Quantum Theory of Solids. 320p. 1982. pap. 8.95 (ISBN 0-8285-2333-9, Pub. by Mir Pubs USSR). Imported Pubns.

Maradudin, A. A. & Nardelli, G. F., eds. Elementary Excitations in Solids: The Cortina Lectures, July 1966, & Selected Lectures from the Conference on Localized Excitations, Milan, July 25-26, 1966. LC 68-26772. pap. 134.00 (ISBN 0-317-30349-X, 2024719). Bks Demand UMI.

March, Norman & Tosi, Mario, eds. Polymers, Liquid Crystals & Low-Dimensional Solids. (Physics of Solids & Liquids Ser.). 622p. 1984. 89.50x (ISBN 0-306-41641-7, Plenum Pr). Plenum Pub.

Mass Transport in Non-Metallic Solids. 1982. 40.00x (ISBN 0-686-44592-9, Pub. by Brit Ceramic Soc England). State Mutual Bk.

Maugin, G. A., ed. The Mechanical Behavior of Electromagnetic Solid Continua. 428p. 1983. 50.00 (ISBN 0-444-86818-6, I-445-83, North Holland). Elsevier.

Mitra, S. S. & Nudelman, S., eds. Far-Infrared Properties of Solids. LC 78-122627. 605p. 1970. 85.00x (ISBN 0-306-30491-0, Plenum Pr). Plenum Pub.

Mitra, Shashanka S., ed. Physics of Structurally Disordered Solids. LC 76-18804. (NATO ASI Series B, Physics: Vol. 20). 791p. 1976. 115.00 (ISBN 0-306-35720-8, Plenum Pr). Plenum Pub.

Miyamoto, Hiroshi, ed. Recent Research on Mechanical Behavior of Solids. 427p. 1979. 45.00 (ISBN 0-86008-247-4, Pub. by U of Tokyo Japan). Columbia U Pr.

Moorjani, K. & Coey, J. M. Disordered Solids. write for info. Elsevier.

Mura, T. Micromechanics of Defects in Solids. 1982. lib. bdg. 98.00 (ISBN 90-247-2560-7, Pub. by Martinus Nijhoff Netherlands). Kluwer Academic.

Nemat-Nasser, S. Variational Methods in the Mechanics of Solids: Proceedings of the UUTAM Symposium, Sept. 11-13, 1978. LC 80-41529. (Illus.). 426p. 1980. 120.00 (ISBN 0-08-024728-8). Pergamon.

SOLUBILITY–TABLES, ETC.

Linke, William F. Seidell's Solubilities: Inorganic & Metal-Organic Compounds, 2 vols. 4th ed. Incl. Vol. 1. A-J. 1486p. 1958; Vol. 2. K-Z. 1914p. 1965 (ISBN 0-8412-0098-X). 44.95 ea. Am Chemical.

Stephen, H., et al. Solubilities of Inorganic & Organic Compounds, 3 vols. LC 79-40319. 7300p. 1979. Set. 1065.00 (ISBN 0-08-023599-9). Pergamon.

SOLUBLE FERMENTS

see Enzymes

SOLUTION (CHEMISTRY)

see also Activity Coefficients; Colloids; Diffusion; Electrolysis; Electrolyte Solutions; Extraction (Chemistry); Ionic Solutions; Ions; Osmosis; Precipitation (Chemistry); Solubility; Solvents; Solvolysis; Suspensions (Chemistry)

Amis, Edward S. & Hinton, James F. Solvent Effects on Chemical Phenomena. 1973. Vol. 1. 83.00 (ISBN 0-12-057301-6). Acad Pr.

Ben-Naim, Arieh. Hydrophobic Interactions. LC 79-510. (Illus.). 319p. 1980. 45.00x (ISBN 0-306-40222-X, Plenum Pr). Plenum Pub.

--Water & Aqueous Solutions: Introduction to a Molecular Theory. LC 74-7325. (Illus.). 474p. 1974. 65.00x (ISBN 0-306-30774-X, Plenum Pr). Plenum Pub.

Bertini, I., et al, eds. Advances in Solution Chemistry. LC 80-28783. 398p. 1981. 65.00x (ISBN 0-306-40638-1, Plenum Pr). Plenum Pub.

Cohen, I. Bernard, ed. Theory of Solutions & Stereo-Chemistry. LC 80-2103. (Development of Science Ser.). (Illus.). 1981. lib. bdg. 35.00x (ISBN 0-405-13868-7). Ayer Co Pubs.

Eisenberg, Henryk. Biological Macromolecules & Polyelectrolytes in Solution. (Monographs on Physical Biochemistry). (Illus.). 1976. 75.00x (ISBN 0-19-854612-2). Oxford U Pr.

Freier, Rolf K. Aqueous Solutions: Data for Inorganic & Organic Compounds, 2 vols. Vol. 1, 1976. 92.00x (ISBN 3-11-001627-3); Vol. 2, 1978. 92.00x (ISBN 3-11-006537-1). De Gruyter.

Gutmann, Viktor. Coordination Chemistry in Non-Aqueous Solutions. LC 68-13490. (Illus.). 1968. 29.50 (ISBN 0-387-80867-1). Springer-Verlag.

Hartley, F. R., et al. Solution Equilibria. LC 79-42956. 361p. 1980. 106.95 (ISBN 0-470-26880-8). Halsted Pr.

Kertes, A. S. & Marcus, Y., eds. Solvent Extraction Research: Proceedings of the 5th International Conference on Solvent Extraction Chemistry, 1968. LC 75-99274. pap. 86.50 (ISBN 0-317-10523-X, 2055150). Bks Demand UMI.

Khamskii, Eugenii. Crystallization from Solutions. LC 72-76425. (Illus.). 106p. 1969. 34.50x (ISBN 0-306-10826-7, Consultants). Plenum Pub.

Kirkwood, John G. Macromolecules. Auer, P. L., ed. (Documents on Modern Physics Ser.). 208p. (Orig.). 1967. 40.50 (ISBN 0-677-00340-4). Gordon.

--Theory of Solutions. Salsburg, Z. W. & Poirier, J., eds. (Documents on Modern Physics Ser.). 316p. (Orig.). 1968. 62.50 (ISBN 0-677-01030-3). Gordon.

Kruus, Peeter. Liquids & Solutions: Structure & Dynamics. 1977. 99.75 (ISBN 0-8247-6427-7). Dekker.

Lonngren, Karl & Scott, Alwyn, eds. Solitons in Action. 1978. 35.00 (ISBN 0-12-455580-2). Acad Pr.

Luck, Werner A. Structure of Water & Aqueous Solutions. (Illus.). 590p. 1974. 67.50x (ISBN 3-527-25588-5). VCH Pubs.

Mittal, K. L., ed. Solution Chemistry of Surfactants, 2 vols. LC 79-15067. 1979. Set. 120.00x (Plenum Pr); Vol. 1, 69.50x (ISBN 0-306-40174-6); Vol. 2, 460p. 69.50x (ISBN 0-306-40175-4). Plenum Pub.

--Surfactants in Solution, 3 Vols. 712p. 1984. 255.00x set (Plenum Pr); Vol. 1, 712p. 95.00x (ISBN 0-306-41483-X); Vol. 2, 718p. 95.00x (ISBN 0-306-41484-8); Vol. 3, 740p. 95.00x (ISBN 0-306-41485-6). Plenum Pub.

Murrell, J. N. & Boucher, E. A. Properties of Liquids & Solutions. LC 81-21921. 288p. 1982. 53.95 (ISBN 0-471-10201-6, Pub. by Wiley-Interscience); pap. text ed. 24.95 (ISBN 0-471-10202-4, Pub. by Wiley-Interscience). Wiley.

Parfitt, Geoffrey D. & Rochester, Colin H., eds. Absorption From Solution at the Solid Liquid Interface. 1983. 79.50 (ISBN 0-12-544980-1). Acad Pr.

Royal Swedish Academy of Sciences, Nobel Symposium, Bjorkborns Herrgard, Karlskoga, Sweden, Sept. 1979. Chemistry & Geochemistry of Solutions at High Temperatures & Pressures: Proceedings. Rickard, David & Wickman, Frans E., eds. (Physics & Chemistry of the Earth Ser., International Ser. in Earth Sciences: Vols. 13 & 37). (Illus.). 600p. 1982. 185.00 (ISBN 0-08-026285-6). Pergamon.

Scatchard, George. Equilibrium in Solutions & Surface & Colloid Chemistry. Scheinberg, I. Herbert, ed. (Commonwealth Fund Ser). (Illus.). 384p. 1976. 30.00x (ISBN 0-674-26025-2). Harvard U Pr.

Shinoda, et al, eds. Principles of Solution & Solubility. (Undergraduate Chemistry a Ser. of Textbooks: Vol. 5). 1978. 34.50 (ISBN 0-8247-6717-9). Dekker.

Taube, H. Electron Transfer Reactions of Complex Ions in Solution. (Current Chemical Concepts Ser.). 1970. 37.50 (ISBN 0-12-683850-X). Acad Pr.

Weber, Walter J., Jr. & Matijevic, Egon, eds. Adsorption from Aqueous Solution. LC 68-59407. (Advances in Chemistry Ser: No. 79). 1968. 19.95 (ISBN 0-8412-0080-7). Am Chemical.

Weissberger, Arnold, et al, eds. Techniques of Chemistry: Vol. 8, Pt. 2, Solutions & Solubilities. LC 75-2331. 512p. 1976. 55.50 (ISBN 0-471-93266-3). Krieger.

SOLUTIONS

Takeno, S, ed. Dynamical Problems in Soliton Systems. (Springer Series in Synergetics: Vol. 30). (Illus.). 310p. 1985. 32.00 (ISBN 0-387-15372-1). Springer-Verlag.

SOLUTIONS, ELECTROLYTE

see Electrolyte Solutions

SOLUTIONS, IONIC

see Ionic Solutions

SOLUTIONS, SOLID

see also Diffusion; Solidification

Aplan, F. F., et al, eds. Solution Mining Symposium, 1974: Proceedings of a Symposium, 103rd AIME Annual Meeting, Dallas, Texas, Feb. 25-27, 1974. LC 73-94005. pap. 119.80 (ISBN 0-317-29727-9, 2017422). Bks Demand UMI.

Collings, E. W. & Gegel, H. L., eds. Physics of Solid Solution Strengthening. LC 75-33368. 306p. 1975. 45.00x (ISBN 0-306-30890-8, Plenum Pr). Plenum Pub.

Mahanty, J. & Ninham, B. W., eds. Dispersion Forces. 1977. 47.50 (ISBN 0-12-465050-3). Acad Pr.

Massalski, T. B., ed. Alloying Behavior & Effects in Concentrated Solid Solutions. LC 65-18398. (Metallurgical Society Conferances Ser.: Vol. 29). pap. 113.80 (ISBN 0-317-10461-6, 2001517). Bks Demand UMI.

Saxena, S. K. Thermodynamics of Rock-Forming Crystalline Solutions. (Minerals, Rocks & Inorganic Materials Ser.: Vol. 8). (Illus.). xii, 188p. 1973. 37.00 (ISBN 0-387-06175-4). Springer-Verlag.

SOLVATION

Amis, Edward S. & Hinton, James F. Solvent Effects on Chemical Phenomena. 1973. Vol. 1. 83.00 (ISBN 0-12-057301-6). Acad Pr.

Burger, K. Solvation: Ionic & Complex Formation in Non-Aqueous Solvents. (Studies in Analytical Chemistry: Vol. 6). 268p. 1983. cloth 61.75 (ISBN 0-444-99697-4). Elsevier.

SOLVENTS

see also Plasticizers; Solvolysis

Amis, Edward S. Solvent Effects on Reaction Rates & Mechanisms. 1966. 73.50 (ISBN 0-12-057350-4). Acad Pr.

Astarita, Gianni, et al. Gas Treating with Chemical Solvents. LC 82-11016. 493p. 1983. 54.95 (ISBN 0-471-05768-1, Pub. by Wiley-Interscience). Wiley.

Coetzee, J. F., ed. Recommended Methods for Purification of Solvents. (International Union of Pure & Applied Chemistry). 1982. 22.00 (ISBN 0-08-022370-2). Pergamon.

Coetzee, Johannes & Ritchie, Calvin D. Solute-Solvent Interactions, Vol. 2. 1976. 85.00 (ISBN 0-8247-6416-1). Dekker.

Cold Cleaning with Halogenated Solvents - STP 403A. 52p. 1981. pap. 7.25 (ISBN 0-8031-0758-7, 04-403010-15). ASTM.

Collings, A. J. & Luxon, S. G. Safe Use of Solvents. 1982. 49.00 (ISBN 0-12-181250-2). Acad Pr.

Covington, A. K. & Dickinson, T., eds. Physical Chemistry of Organic Solvents Systems. LC 72-77042. 823p. 1973. 110.00 (ISBN 0-306-30569-0, Plenum Pr). Plenum Pub.

Flick, Ernest W., ed. Industrial Solvents Handbook, 1985. 3rd ed. LC 84-22637. (Illus.). 650p. 1985. 86.00 (ISBN 0-8155-1010-1). Noyes.

Gutmann, Viktor. Coordination Chemistry in Non-Aqueous Solutions. LC 68-13490. (Illus.). 1968. 29.50 (ISBN 0-387-80867-1). Springer-Verlag.

Infrared Spectra Handbook of Common Organic Solvents. 1983. 295.00 (ISBN 0-8456-0093-1). Sadtler Res.

International Solvent Extraction Conference, Denver, Colorado, August 26th to September 2, 1983: Proceedings. 559p. 1983. pap. 80.00 (ISBN 0-8169-0254-2, P-37); pap. 60.00 members (ISBN 0-317-03770-6). Am Inst Chem Eng.

Kakabadse, G., ed. Solvent Problems in Industry: Papers from the 3rd & 4th European Solvents Symposia, Manchester, UK, 1980 & 1983. (Illus.). 251p. 1985. 45.00 (ISBN 0-85334-304-7, Pub. by Elsevier Applied Sci England). Elsevier.

Lagowski, J. J., ed. Chemistry of Non-Aqueous Solvents, 4 vols. 1966-76. Vol. 1, 1966. 72.00 (ISBN 0-12-433801-1); Vol. 2, 1967. 72.00 (ISBN 0-12-433802-X); Vol. 3, 1970. 72.00 (ISBN 0-12-433803-8); Vol. 4, 1976. 77.00 (ISBN 0-12-433804-6). Acad Pr.

Lo, Teh C., et al. Handbook of Solvent Extraction. LC 82-15957. 1350p. 1983. 129.50x (ISBN 0-471-04164-5, Pub. by Wiley-Interscience). Wiley.

Mamantov, Gleb, ed. Characterization of Solutes in Nonaqueous Solvents. LC 77-212204. 333p. 1977. 52.50x (ISBN 0-306-31108-9, Plenum Pr). Plenum Pub.

Marcus, Y., ed. Solvent Extraction Reviews, Vol. 1. 1971. 65.00 (ISBN 0-8247-1438-5). Dekker.

Marinsky, Jacob A., ed. Ion Exchange & Solvent Extraction, Vol. 8. Marcus, Yizhok. 456p. 1981. 65.00 (ISBN 0-8247-1333-8). Dekker.

Marinsky, Yizhak. Ion Exchange & Solvent Extraction, Vol. 9. 592p. 1985. 85.00 (ISBN 0-8247-7120-6). Dekker.

Scheflan, Leopold & Jacob, Morris B. The Handbook of Solvents. LC 53-8766. 736p. 1973. Repr. of 1953 ed. 45.00 (ISBN 0-88275-130-1). Krieger.

Shinoda, Keozeo, ed. Solvent Properties of Surfactant Solutions. LC 68-1233. (Surfactant Science Ser.: Vol. 2). pap. 93.50 (ISBN 0-317-28559-9, 2055028). Bks Demand UMI.

Tremillon, B. Chemistry in Non-Aoueous Solvents. Corcoran, N., tr. LC 73-86094. 1974. lib. bdg. 41.00 (ISBN 90-277-0389-2, Pub. by Reidel Holland). Kluwer Academic.

SOLVOLYSIS

see also Hydrolysis

Kertes, A. S. & Marcus, Y., eds. Solvent Extraction Research: Proceedings of the 5th International Conference on Solvent Extraction Chemistry, 1968. LC 75-99274. pap. 86.50 (ISBN 0-317-10523-X, 2055150). Bks Demand UMI.

SOMATOLOGY

see Physical Anthropology

SONAR

Amos, D. A Fisherman's Guide to Echo Soundings & Sonar Equipment: Acoustic Fish Detection Instruments. (Marine Bulletin Ser.: No. 41). 68p. 1980. 2.00 (ISBN 0-938412-30-2, P870). URI MAS.

Busnel, R. G. & Fish, J. F., eds. Animal Sonar Systems. LC 79-23074. (NATO ASI Series A, Life Sciences: Vol. 28). 1159p. 1980. 95.00x (ISBN 0-306-40327-7, Plenum Pr). Plenum Pub.

Cox, Albert W. Sonar & Underwater Sound. LC 74-15547. (Illus.). 1975. 24.00x (ISBN 0-669-95935-9). Lexington Bks.

Echo Sounding & Sonar for Fishing: An FAO Fishing Manual. 120p. 1980. pap. 22.50 (ISBN 0-85238-110-7, FN86, FNB). Unipub.

Edgerton, Harold E. Sonar Images. (Illus.). 224p. 1986. pap. text ed. 21.95 (ISBN 0-13-822644-X). P-H.

Gerlach, Albert A. Theory & Applications of Statistical Wave-Period Processing, 3 Vols. 1434p. 1970. 352.50 (ISBN 0-677-02510-6). Gordon.

Kassam, S. A. & Thomas, J. B., eds. Nonparametric Detection: Theory & Applications. LC 79-22557. (Benchmark Papers in Electrical Engineering & Computer Science Ser.: Vol. 23). 349p. 1980. 57.95 (ISBN 0-87933-359-6). Van Nos Reinhold.

Kock, Winton E. Radar, Sonar & Holography: An Introduction. 1973. 28.00 (ISBN 0-12-417450-7). Acad Pr.

Mitson, R. B. Fisheries Sonar. 287p. 1984. 49.95 (ISBN 0-85238-124-7, FN100, FNB). Unipub.

Ol'shevskii, V. V. Statistical Methods in Sonar. LC 78-18196. (Studies in Soviet Science - Physical Sciences Ser.). 262p. 1978. 65.00x (ISBN 0-306-10947-6, Consultants). Plenum Pub.

Tacconi, Giorgio, ed. Aspects of Signal Processing, 2 vols. LC 77-3238. (NATO Advanced Study Institute: C. Math & Phys. Science 33). 1977. lib. bdg. 87.00 set (ISBN 90-277-0798-7, Pub. by Reidel Holland). Kluwer Academic.

Urick, R. J. Sound Propagation in the Sea. 272p. 1982. 23.95 (ISBN 0-932146-08-2). Peninsula CA.

Veley. Semiconductors & Electronic Communications Made Easy. (Illus.). 322p. 1982. o.p 15.95 (ISBN 0-8306-0052-3); pap. 8.95 (ISBN 0-8306-1435-4). TAB Bks.

SONIC BOOM

Wiggins, John H., Jr. Effects of Sonic Boom. 174p. 1969. 32.00 (ISBN 0-9600346-0-9). Wiggins.

SONIC ENGINEERING

see Acoustical Engineering

SONOHOLOGRAPHY

see Acoustic Holography

SONOPTOGRAPHY

see Acoustic Holography

SORGHUM

Chopra, Kuldip R. Technical Guideline for Sorghum & Millet: Seed Production. 110p. 1982. pap. text ed. 8.75 (ISBN 92-5-101259-8, F2377, FAO). Unipub.

Elements of Integrated Control of Sorghum Pests. (Plant Production & Protection Papers: No. 19). (Eng., Fr. & Span., Illus.). 167p. 1979. pap. 12.00 (ISBN 92-5-100884-1, F1943, FAO). Unipub.

Hulse, Joseph, et al. Sorghum & the Millets: Their Composition & Nutritive Value. LC 79-40871. 1980. 184.00 (ISBN 0-12-361350-7). Acad Pr.

Improvement & Production of Maize, Sorghum & Millet, 2 vols. (Plant Production & Protection Papers: Nos. 24-1 & 24-2). 703p. 1980. Set. pap. 51.75 (ISBN 0-686-74540-X, F2129, FAO). Vol. 1, General Principles, 226p (ISBN 92-5-101012-9). Vol. 2, Breeding, Agronomy & Seed Production, 500p (ISBN 92-5-101011-0). Unipub.

Jotwani, M. G. & Young, W. R. Control of Sorghum Shoot Fly. 330p. 1981. 35.00x (ISBN 0-686-76630-X, Pub. by Oxford & IBH India). State Mutual Bk.

Prasad Rao, N. Ganga & House, Leland R. Sorghum in Seventies. 638p. 1981. 80.00x (ISBN 0-686-76668-7, Pub. by Oxford & IBH India). State Mutual Bk.

SOROBAN

see Abacus

SORPTION

see Absorption; Adsorption

SORPTION, SOIL

see Soil Absorption and Adsorption

SORPTION OF GASES

see Gases–Absorption and Adsorption

SORTING (ELECTRONIC COMPUTERS)

Akl, Selim G. Parallel Sorting Algorithms. Date not set. pap. 24.95 (ISBN 0-12-047681-9). Acad Pr.

Lorin, Harold. Sorting & Sort Systems. (Illus.). 480p. 1975. 31.95 (ISBN 0-201-14453-0). Addison-Wesley.

SOUND

see also Absorption of Sound; Acoustical Engineering; Architectural Acoustics; Computer Sound Processing; Echo; Electro-Acoustics; Hearing; Music–Acoustics and Physics; Noise; Ultrasonics; Underwater Acoustics; Vibration

Alkin, Glyn. TV Sound Operations. (Media Manual Ser.). (Illus.). 1975. pap. 14.95 (ISBN 0-240-50865-3). Focal Pr.

Applied Technical Dictionary: Acoustics. 50.00x (ISBN 0-569-08535-7, Pub. by Collets). State Mutual Bk.

Beagley, H. A., ed. Auditory Investigation: The Scientific & Technological Basis. (Illus.). 1979. text ed. 95.00x (ISBN 0-19-857526-2). Oxford U Pr.

Berg, Richard E. & Stork, David G. The Physics of Sound. (Illus.). 416p. 1982. 31.95 (ISBN 0-13-674283-1). P-H.

Bergmann, P. G., et al. Physics of Sound in the Sea, 4 pts. Incl. Pt. 1. Transmission. Bergmann, P. G. & Yaspan, A. 266p. 48.75 (ISBN 0-677-01890-8); Pts. 2 & 3. Reverbreration Bd with Reflection of Sound from Submarines & Surface Vessels. Gerjuoy, E., et al, eds. 218p. 32.50 (ISBN 0-677-01900-9); Pt. 4. Acoustic Properties of Wakes. Wildt, R., ed. 128p. 19.75 (ISBN 0-677-01910-6). (Documents on Modern Physics Ser.). 612p. 1968. Set. 145.75 (ISBN 0-677-01920-3). Gordon.

Blake, William K. Mechanics of Flow-Induced Sound & Vibration, 2 vols. LC 83-3698. (Applied Mathematics & Mechanics Ser.). Date not set. Vol. 1: General Concepts & Elementary Sources. write for info. (ISBN 0-12-103501-8); Vol. 2: Complex Flow-Structure Interactions. write for info. (ISBN 0-12-103502-6). Acad Pr.

Chan, Janis F. Sound. (Science in Action Ser.). (Illus.). 48p. 1982. pap. text ed. 2.85 (ISBN 0-915510-78-2). Janus Bks.

Chapple, M. A Level Physics: Wave Motion-Sound & Light, Vol. 2. 2nd ed. (Illus.). 240p. (Orig.). 1979. pap. text ed. 14.95x (ISBN 0-7121-0155-1, Pub. by Macdonald & Evans England). Trans-Atlantic.

Collison, David. Stage Sound. LC 75-6799. (Illus.). 154p. 1976. text ed. 15.00x (ISBN 0-910482-65-9). Drama Bk.

Dowling, Ann & Williams, John e. Sound & Sources of Sound. LC 82-15687. 321p. 1983. 64.95x (ISBN 0-470-27370-4); pap. 26.95x (ISBN 0-470-27388-7). Halsted Pr.

Graf, Calvin R. Exploring Light, Radio & Sound Energy: With Projects. (Illus.). 240p. (Orig.). 1985. 17.95 (ISBN 0-8306-0758-7, 1758); pap. 10.95 (ISBN 0-8306-1758-2). TAB Bks.

Helmholtz, Hermann L. On the Sensations of Tone. 1954. pap. 9.95 (ISBN 0-486-60753-4). Dover.

Hunt, Frederick V. Origins in Acoustics: The Science of Sound from Antiquity to the Age of Newton. LC 78-5032. (Illus.). 1978. 20.00x (ISBN 0-300-02220-4). Yale U Pr.

Ihde, Don. Listening & Voice: A Phenomenology of Sound. LC 76-8302. (Illus.). x, 188p. 1976. 15.00x (ISBN 0-8214-0201-3, 2-82071); pap. 9.00x (ISBN 0-8214-0563-2, 82-82089). Ohio U Pr.

Johnson-Walker, Kenneth W., et al. The Science of Hi-Fidelity. LC 81-81012. (Illus.). 1981. pap. text ed. 21.95 (ISBN 0-8403-2297-6). Kendall-Hunt.

Leitner, Bernhard. Sound: Space. LC 77-93954. 109p. 1978. pap. 25.00x usa (ISBN 0-8147-4983-6). NYU Pr.

Lloyd, Llewelyn S. Music & Sound. LC 70-107815. (Select Bibliographies Reprint Ser). 1937. 18.00 (ISBN 0-8369-5188-3). Ayer Co Pubs.

--Music & Sound. Repr. of 1937 ed. lib. bdg. 15.00x (ISBN 0-8371-4260-1, LLMS). Greenwood.

Mason, Warren P., ed. Physical Acoustics: Principles & Methods. Incl. Vol. 1A. Methods & Devices. 1964. 80.50 (ISBN 0-12-477901-8); Vol. 1B. Methods & Devices. 1964. 76.50 (ISBN 0-12-477941-7); Vol. 2A. Properties of Gases, Liquids & Solutions. 1965. 80.50 (ISBN 0-12-477902-6); Vol. 2B. Properties of Polymers & Nonlinear Acoustics. 1965. 76.50 (ISBN 0-12-477942-5); Vol. 3A. Applications to the Study of Imperfections & Lattice Dynamics. 1966. 80.50 (ISBN 0-12-477903-4); Vol. 3B. Applications to the Study of Imperfections & Lattice Dynamics. 1965. 73.50 (ISBN 0-12-477943-3); Vol. 4A. Applications to Quantum & Solid State Physics. 1966. 76.50 (ISBN 0-12-477904-2); Vol. 4B. Applications to Quantum & Solid State Physics. 1968. 80.50 (ISBN 0-12-477944-1); Vol. 5. 1969. 76.50 (ISBN 0-12-477905-0); Vol. 6. Thurston, R., ed. 1970. 77.50 (ISBN 0-12-477906-9); Vol. 7. 1970. 77.50 (ISBN 0-12-477907-7); Vol. 8. 1971. 77.50 (ISBN 0-12-477908-5); Vol. 9. 1972. 76.50 (ISBN 0-12-477909-3); Vol. 10. 1973. 82.50 (ISBN 0-12-477910-7); Vol. 13. Thurston, R. N., ed. 1977. 75.00 (ISBN 0-12-477913-1); Vol. 14. Thurston, R. N., ed. 1979. 77.50 (ISBN 0-12-477914-X). Acad Pr.

Nelkon, M. Optics, Waves & Sound. 6th ed. 1973. pap. text ed. 14.50x (ISBN 0-435-68662-3). Heinemann Ed.

Ogden, Robert M. Hearing. LC 73-97562. Repr. of 1924 ed. 19.50 (ISBN 0-404-04812-9). AMS Pr.

--Hearing. LC 75-124248. (Select Bibliographies Reprint Ser.). 1924. 29.00 (ISBN 0-8369-5137-9). Ayer Co Pubs.

Pellegrino, Ronald. The Electronic Arts of Sound & Light. 256p. 1982. 28.50 (ISBN 0-442-26499-2). Van Nos Reinhold.

Pierce, John R. The Science of Musical Sound. LC 82-21427. (Scientific American Library). (Illus.). 242p. 1983. 27.95 (ISBN 0-7167-1508-2). W H Freeman.

Rayleigh, Strutt. Theory of Sound, Vols. I & II. Vol. 1. pap. 8.50 (ISBN 0-486-60292-3); Vol. 2. pap. 8.95 (ISBN 0-486-60293-1). Dover.

Reichardt, L. Dictionary of Technical Acoustics. (Ger., Fr., Rus., Span., Pol. & Hungarian.). 1978. 20.40x (ISBN 0-685-92166-2). Adlers Foreign Bks.

Reichardt, W. Dictionary of Acoustics: English-German-French-Russian-Spanish-Polish-Madarsko-Slovene. (Eng., Ger., Fr., Rus., Span., Pol., Madarsko & Slovene.). 267p. 1978. 95.00 (ISBN 0-686-92601-3, M-9897). French & Eur.

Rossing, Thomas D. Science of Sound: Musical, Electronic, Environmental. LC 80-12028. (Chemistry Ser.). (Illus.). 512p. 1981. text ed. 33.95 (ISBN 0-201-06505-3). Addison-Wesley.

Science of Sound. 10.00 (ISBN 0-685-28377-1). Philos Lib.

Sears, Francis W. Mechanics, Heat, & Sound. 2nd ed. (Illus.). 1950. 23.95 (ISBN 0-201-06905-9). Addison-Wesley.

Skudrzyk, E. J. Foundations of Acoustics, Basic Mathematics & Basic Acoustics. LC 76-161480. (Illus.). 1971. 160.00 (ISBN 0-387-80988-0). Springer-Verlag.

Slawson, Wayne. Sound Color. LC 84-2474. 1985. 30.00x (ISBN 0-520-05185-8). U of Cal Pr.

Stephens, R. W., ed. Sound: In Eight Languages. LC 74-16209. (International Dictionaries of Science & Technology Ser). 853p. 1974. 74.95x (ISBN 0-470-82200-7). Halsted Pr.

Strutt, John W. & Rayleigh, Baron. The Theory of Sound, 2 vols. 2nd rev. & enl. ed. (Illus.). Set. 31.50 (ISBN 0-8446-0871-8). Peter Smith.

Taylor, Sedley. Sound & Music: A Non-Mathematical Treatise on the Physical Constitution of Musical Sounds & Harmony. (Illus.). Repr. of 1873 ed. 24.00 (ISBN 0-384-59641-X). Johnson Repr.

Tyndall, John. Sound. rev. 3rd ed. Repr. of 1903 ed. lib. bdg. 22.50x (ISBN 0-8371-2255-4, TYS). Greenwood.

White, Frederick A. Our Acoustic Environment. LC 75-8888. 524p. (Orig.). 1975. 37.50 (ISBN 0-471-93920-X). Krieger.

SOUND–APPARATUS

see also Loud-Speakers; Magnetic Recorders and Recording; Microphone

Alten. Audio in Media. 2nd ed. 1986. text ed. write for info (ISBN 0-534-06156-7). Wadsworth Pub.

Audio Cassettes: The User Medium. (Illus.). 1978. pap. 5.00 (ISBN 92-3-101468-4, U747, UNESCO). Unipub.

Audio Reference Guide, 1983. 514p. 85.00 (ISBN 0-318-01043-7). Orion Res.

Barber, Alfred W. Handbook of Hi Fi Audio Systems & Projects. 224p. 1981. 18.95 (ISBN 0-686-92208-5, Parker). P-H.

Earl, John. Audio Technicians-Bench Manual. 182p. 1980. 25.00x (ISBN 0-85242-093-5, Pub. by K Dickson). State Mutual Bk.

Gerber, Eduard A. & Ballato, Arthur, eds. Precision Frequency Control, Vol. 1: Acoustic Resonators & Filters. 1985. 69.50 (ISBN 0-12-280601-8). Acad Pr.

Grove, Bob. Behind the Dial. Force, Rich, ed. 57p. (Orig.). 1977. pap. 4.95 (ISBN 0-88006-001-8, BK 7307). Green Pub Inc.

High-Performance Review, Vol. 2: Audio Equipment & Recordings for the Perceptive Listener. (Illus.). 600p. 1983. pap. 26.00x (ISBN 0-88232-083-1, Pub. by High-Performance Review Pub). Delbridge Pub Co.

Horowitz, Mannie. How to Design & Build Audio Amplifiers, Including Digital Circuits. 2nd ed. (Illus.). 350p. (Orig.). 1980. pap. 10.95 (ISBN 0-8306-1206-8, 1206). TAB Bks.

Kinsler, Lawrence E., et al. Fundamentals of Acoustics. 3rd ed. LC 81-7463. 480p. 1982. text ed. 41.50x (ISBN 0-471-02933-5); answers avail. (ISBN 0-471-09743-8). Wiley.

Lenk, John D. Complete Guide to Compact Disc Player (CD) Troubleshooting & Repair. (Illus.). 224p. 1986. text ed. 29.95 (ISBN 0-13-159955-0). P-H.

Professional Sound Blue Book, 1984. 373p. 1984. 35.00 (ISBN 0-318-01260-X). Orion Res.

Professional Sound Blue Book, 1985. 420p. 1985. 89.50 (ISBN 0-932089-01-1). Orion Res.

The Professional Sound Reference Guide, 1983. 325p. 75.00 (ISBN 0-318-01042-9). Orion Res.

Rosenthal, Murray P. How to Select & Use Loudspeakers & Enclosures. LC 79-2359. 1979. pap. 5.50 (ISBN 0-8104-0831-7). Hayden.

Tarumoto, David H., ed. High-Performance Review, Vol. 3: Audio Equipment & Recordings for the Perceptive Listener. (Illus.). 700p. 1984. pap. 26.00x (ISBN 0-88232-093-9). Delbridge Pub Co.

Vick, Bill, et al. Encyclopedia for the TRS-80, Vol. 1. McCarthy, Nan & Crocker, Chris, eds. (Illus.). 269p. (Orig.). 1981. 19.95 (ISBN 0-88006-025-5, EN8101); pap. text ed. 10.95 (ISBN 0-88006-026-3, EN8081). Green Pub Inc.

Wells, Andy J. Audio Servicing: Theory & Practice. (Illus.). 240p. (Orig.). 1980. pap. text ed. 18.55 (ISBN 0-07-069246-7). McGraw.

SOUND–BIBLIOGRAPHY

Drouillard, T. F. Acoustic Emission: A Bibliography with Abstracts. LC 79-268. (IFI Data Base Library). 805p. 1979. 135.00x (ISBN 0-306-65179-3, IFI Plenum). Plenum Pub.

SOUND–INSULATION

see Soundproofing

SOUND–MEASUREMENT

Barkhatov, A. N. Modeling of Sound Propagation in the Sea. LC 74-136985. 91p. 1971. 25.00x (ISBN 0-306-10855-0, Consultants). Plenum Pub.

SOUND–RECORDING AND REPRODUCING

see also High-Fidelity Sound Systems; Magnetic Recorders and Recording; Stereophonic Sound Systems

Alkin, Glyn. Sound Recording & Reproduction. LC 80-41481. (Illus.). 226p. 1981. 16.95 (ISBN 0-240-51070-4). Focal Pr.

Audio Cassettes: The User Medium. (Illus.). 1978. pap. 5.00 (ISBN 92-3-101468-4, U747, UNESCO). Unipub.

Beitman, Hartford. Recorded Sound. (Illus., Orig.). 1981. pap. text ed. 2.00 (ISBN 0-938630-13-X). ARS Enterprises.

Bernstein, Julian L. Audio Systems. LC 78-2563. 424p. 1978. Repr. of 1966 ed. lib. bdg. 24.50 (ISBN 0-88275-668-0). Krieger.

Borwick, John. Sound Recording Practice. 2nd ed. 1980. 55.00x (ISBN 0-19-311920-X). Oxford U Pr.

Eargle, John. Sound Recording. 2nd ed. 320p. 1980. 24.95 (ISBN 0-442-22557-1). Van Nos Reinhold.

Eastman Kodak Company, ed. Sound: Magnetic Sound Recording for Motion Pictures. LC 77-87984. (Illus.). 1977. pap. text ed. 6.25 (ISBN 0-87985-202-X, S-75). Eastman Kodak.

Everest, F. A. How to Build a Small Budget Recording Studio from Scratch: With 12 Tested Designs. LC 79-14398. (Illus.). 1979. pap. 11.95 (ISBN 0-8306-1166-5, 1166). TAB Bks.

Green, Michael L., ed. Audio Equipment. 1978. pap. 1.95 (ISBN 0-89552-018-4). DMR Pubns.

--CB, Carsound & Communication Equipment. 1978. pap. 1.95 (ISBN 0-89552-016-8). DMR Pubns.

Honore, Paul M. A Handbook for Sound Recording. LC 78-69641. 204p. 1980. 14.95 (ISBN 0-498-02232-3). A S Barnes.

Link House Mag., Croydon Ltd., ed. Pro-Audio Yearbook 1984. 1985. 150.00 (ISBN 0-686-97110-8, Pub. by Link Hse Mag England). State Mutual Bk.

McWilliams, Jerry. The Preservation & Restoration of Sound Recordings. LC 79-17173. (Illus.). 1979. pap. text ed. 11.00 (ISBN 0-910050-41-4). AASLH Pr.

Nisbett, Alec. The Technique of the Sound Studio. 4th ed. (Library of Communication Techniques). (Illus.). 560p. 1979. 28.95 (ISBN 0-240-51003-8); pap. text ed. 19.95 (ISBN 0-240-51100-X). Focal Pr.

Oringel, Robert S. Audio Control Handbook: For Radio & Television Broadcasting. 5th rev. & enl. ed. (Communication Arts Bks.). (Illus.). 380p. 1983. pap. text ed. 14.95 (ISBN 0-8038-0550-0). Hastings.

Roys, H. E., ed. Disc Recording & Reproduction. LC 77-17927. (Benchmark Papers in Acoustic Ser.: Vol. 12). 416p. 1978. 48.50 (ISBN 0-87933-309-X). Van Nos Reinhold.

Sams Editiorial Staff. Sound System Engineering. 2nd ed. 1985. 39.95 (ISBN 0-317-29685-X, 21857). Sams.

Tarumoto, David H., ed. High-Performance Review: Audio Equipment & Recordings for the Perceptive Listener, Vol. 4. (Illus.). 700p. 1985. pap. 26.00 (ISBN 0-88232-098-X, Pub. by High-Performance Review Pub). Delbridge Pub co.

--High-Performance Review, Vol. 3: Audio Equipment & Recordings for the Perceptive Listener. (Illus.). 700p. 1984. pap. 26.00x (ISBN 0-88232-093-9). Delbridge Pub Co.

Traylor, Joseph G. Physics of Stereo-Quad Sound. (Illus.). 1977. pap. 10.95x (ISBN 0-8138-0025-0). Iowa St U Pr.

Villchur, Edgar. Reproduction of Sound in High Fidelity & Stereo Phonographs. (Illus.). 1966. pap. text ed. 2.95 (ISBN 0-486-21515-6). Dover.

SOUND, LOCALIZATION OF

Blauert, Jens. Spacial Hearing: The Psycho Physics of Human Sound Localization. 1983. 42.50x (ISBN 0-262-02190-0). MIT Pr.

SOUND ABSORPTION

see Absorption of Sound

SOUND ENGINEERING

see Acoustical Engineering

SOUND HOLOGRAPHY

see Acoustic Holography

SOUND NAVIGATION AND RANGING

see Sonar

SOUND PRESSURE

see also Aerodynamics, Hypersonic; Aerodynamics, Supersonic; Aerodynamics, Transonic; Noise; Shock Waves; Ultrasonics

Acoustic Emission Monitoring of Pressurized Systems - STP 697. 228p. 1979. 26.50x (ISBN 0-8031-0271-2, 04-697000-22). ASTM.

SOUND PROCESSING, COMPUTER

see Computer Sound Processing

SOUND PRODUCTION BY ANIMALS

see also Animal Sounds

Tavolga, William N., ed. Sound Production in Fishes. LC 76-28352. (Benchmark Papers in Animal Behavior: Vol. 9). 1977. 66.00 (ISBN 0-12-787515-8). Acad Pr.

SOUND RECORDING AND REPRODUCING

see Sound–Recording and Reproducing

SOUND-WAVES

see also Doppler Effect; Molecular Acoustics; Phonons; Sound Pressure; Ultrasonic Waves; Underwater Acoustics

Andersen, Neil R. & Zahuranec, Bernard J., eds. Oceanic Sound Scattering Prediction. LC 77-3445. (Marine Science Ser.: Vol. 5). 859p. 1977. 110.00x (ISBN 0-306-35505-1, Plenum Pr). Plenum Pub.

Bass, F. G. & Fuchs, M. Wave Scattering from Statistically Rough Surfaces. LC 77-23113. 1979. text ed. 125.00 (ISBN 0-08-019896-1). Pergamon.

Fry, Dennis B. The Physics of Speech. LC 78-56752. (Textbooks in Linguistics Ser.). (Illus.). 1979. 32.50 (ISBN 0-521-22173-0); pap. 10.95 (ISBN 0-521-29379-0). Cambridge U Pr.

Knabe, Walter E. Theoretical Study of the Generation of Infrasonic Waves in the Atmosphere. LC 70-136105. 105p. 1967-69. 19.00 (ISBN 0-403-04511-8). Scholarly.

Meyer, Erwin & Neumann, Ernst-Georg. Physical & Applied Acoustics: An Introduction. 1972. 29.50 (ISBN 0-12-493150-2). Acad Pr.

Oliner, A. A. Acoustic Surface Waves. LC 77-17957. (Topics in Applied Physics Ser.: Vol. 24). (Illus.). 1978. 64.00 (ISBN 0-387-08575-0). Springer-Verlag.

Sette, D., ed. New Directions in Physical Acoustics: Proceedings. (Enrico Fermi International Summer School of Physics Ser.: No. 63). 534p. 1976. 115.00 (ISBN 0-7204-0489-4, North-Holland). Elsevier.

Wilcox, C. H. Sound Propagation in Stratified Fluids. (Applied Mathematical Sciences Ser.: Vol. 50). ix, 198p. 1984. pap. 19.80 (ISBN 0-387-90986-9). Springer-Verlag.

SOUND-WAVES–INDUSTRIAL APPLICATIONS

see Acoustical Engineering

SOUNDING AND SOUNDINGS

Kaufman, A. A. & Keller, G. V. Frequency & Transient Soundings. (Methods in Geochemistry & Geophysics Ser.: Vol. 16). 686p. 1983. 144.75 (ISBN 0-444-42032-0, I-283-83). Elsevier.

--Magnetotelluric Sounding Method. (Methods in Geochemistry & Geophysics Ser.: Vol. 15). 596p. 1981. 125.75 (ISBN 0-444-41863-6). Elsevier.

Patra, H. P. & Mallick, K. Geosounding Principles: Time Varying Geoelectric Soundings, Vol. 2. (Methods in Geochemistry & Geophysics Ser.: Vol. 14B). 420p. 1980. 83.00 (ISBN 0-444-41811-3). Elsevier.

Sixth Sounding Rocket. 1982. 50.00 (ISBN 0-317-06667-6). AIAA.

SOUNDPROOFING

Purkis, H. J. Building Physics: Acoustics. 1966. 28.00 (ISBN 0-08-011443-1); pap. 12.50 (ISBN 0-08-011442-3). Pergamon.

SOUNDS

Flowers, Ann M. The Big Book of Sounds. 3rd ed. LC 80-81413. 352p. 1980. pap. text ed. 8.75x (ISBN 0-8134-2142-X, 2142). Interstate.

SOUPED UP MOTORS

see Automobiles, Racing–Motors

SOUTHERN PACIFIC RAILROAD

Beebe, Lucius. The Central Pacific & the Southern Pacific Railroads. LC 63-12942. (Illus.). 1963. 35.00 (ISBN 0-8310-7034-X). Howell-North.

Cortani, R. M. Diesels of the Espee: Alco PA's. LC 75-38238. (Illus.). 1975. 22.50 (ISBN 0-89685-034-X). Chatham Pub CA.

DeNevi, Don. Tragic Train "the City of San Francisco" Development & Historic Wreck of a Streamliner. LC 77-3499. (Illus.). 1977. 19.95 (ISBN 0-87564-525-9). Superior Pub.

Duke, Donald. Southern Pacific Steam Locomotives. LC 62-6982. (Illus.). 88p. 13.95 (ISBN 0-87095-012-6). Golden West.

Southern Pacific Motive Power Annual, 1974-1976. (Illus.). 1976. 15.00 (ISBN 0-89685-008-0). Chatham Pub CA.

Southern Pacific Motive Power Annual, 1971. (Illus.). 1971. 12.50 (ISBN 0-89685-005-6). Chatham Pub CA.

Southern Pacific Motive Power Annual, 1972. (Illus.). 1973. 12.50 (ISBN 0-89685-006-4). Chatham Pub CA.

Southern Pacific Motive Power Annual, 1973. (Illus.). 1974. 12.50 (ISBN 0-89685-007-2). Chatham Pub CA.

Southern Pacific Review 1977. 10.00 (ISBN 0-686-75203-1). Chatham Pub CA.

Southern Pacific Review 1980. 14.00 (ISBN 0-686-75204-X). Chatham Pub CA.

Southern Pacific Steam Locomotives. 13.95x (ISBN 0-685-83394-1). Chatham Pub CA.

Strapac, Joseph A. Southern Pacific Review 1978-1979. new ed. (Illus.). 1979. pap. 15.95 (ISBN 0-930742-03-6). Shade Tree.

SOY-BEAN

Caldwell, B. E., ed. Soybeans: Improvement, Production & Uses. (Illus.). 1973. 14.50 (ISBN 0-89118-017-6). Am Soc Agron.

Chen, Philip S. Soybeans for Health & a Longer Life. rev. ed. LC 73-83947. (Pivot Fact Book). 224p. 1974. pap. 1.50 (ISBN 0-87983-061-1). Keats.

Da Mata, F. S. Soya Bean & Weather. (Technical Note Ser.: No. 160). xvi, 64p. 1978. pap. 20.00 (ISBN 92-63-10498-0, W396, WMO). Unipub.

Hinson, K. & Hartwig, E. E. Soybean Production in the Tropics. (Plant Production & Protection Papers: No. 4, Rev. 1). 232p. 1982. pap. 16.75 (ISBN 92-5-101216-4, F2332, FAO). Unipub.

Houck, James P., et al. Soybeans & Their Products: Markets, Models & Policy. LC 72-79099. (Illus.). 278p. 1972. 15.00x (ISBN 0-8166-0659-5). U of Minn Pr.

Leviton, Richard. Tofu, Tempeh, Miso & Other Soyfoods. Passwater, Richard A. & Mindell, Earl R., eds. (Good Health Guide Ser.). 36p. 1982. pap. 0.95 (ISBN 0-87983-284-3). Keats.

Norman, Geoffrey A., ed. Soybean Physiology, Agronomy, & Utilization. 1978. 39.50 (ISBN 0-12-521160-0). Acad Pr.

Scott, Walter O. & Aldrich, Samuel R. Modern Soybean Production. 2nd ed. LC 83-60922. (Illus.). 1983. 24.95. S&A Pubns Inc.

Shurtleff, William & Aoyagi, Akiko. The Book of Tempeh: Professional Edition. LC 78-20185. (Illus.). 248p. Repr. of 1979 ed. 16.95 (ISBN 0-933332-05-X). Soyfoods Center.
--Miso Production: The Book of Miso, Vol. II. rev. ed. LC 76-19599. (Soyfoods Production Ser.: No. 1). (Illus.). 80p. 1979. pap. 14.95 (ISBN 0-933332-00-9). Soyfoods Center.
--Tempeh Production: The Book of Tempeh, Vol. II. LC 79-89281. (Soyfoods Production Ser.: No. 3). (Illus.). 256p. 1980. pap. 24.95 (ISBN 0-933332-02-5). Soyfoods Center.
--Tofu & Soymilk Production: The Book of Tofu, Vol. II. LC 74-31629. (Soyfoods Production Ser.: No. 2). (Illus.). 336p. 1984. 36.95 (ISBN 0-933332-14-9); pap. 29.95 (ISBN 0-933332-13-0). Soyfoods Center.
Sinclair, J. B. & Shurtleff, M. C., eds. Compendium of Soybean Diseases. 2nd ed. (Compendia Ser: 2nd). (Illus.). 64p. 1975. pap. 12.00 saddle stitch (ISBN 0-89054-022-5). Am Phytopathol Soc.
Technology of Production of Edible Flours & Protein Products From Soybean. (Agricultural Services Bulletins: No. 11). (Eng., Fr. & Span.). 158p. 1979. pap. 11.50 (ISBN 92-5-100741-1, F706, FAO). Unipub.
Watanade, Tokuji & Kishi, Asako. The Book of Soybeans: Nature's Miracle Protein. LC 81-80832. (Illus.). 192p. 1982. pap. 12.95 (ISBN 0-686-97678-9). Japan Pubns USA.
Wilcke, Harold L., et al, eds. Soy Protein & Human Nutrition. LC 78-25585. 1979. 41.00 (ISBN 0-12-751450-3). Acad Pr.
Wolf, W. J. & Cowan, J. C. Soybeans As a Food Source. rev. 2nd ed. LC 75-9535. (Monotopic Reprint Ser.). 111p. 1975. 16.95 (ISBN 0-8493-0112-2). CRC Pr.

SPACE, OUTER
see Outer Space

SPACE, RIEMANNIAN
see Riemannian Manifolds

SPACE AND TIME
see also Ether (Of Space); Hyperspace; Relativity (Physics)

Blokhintsev, D. I. Space & Time in the Microworld. Smith, Z., tr. from Rus. LC 72-77871. Orig. Title: Prostranstuo I Uremja V Micromire. 330p. 1973. lib. bdg. 60.50 (ISBN 90-277-0240-3, Pub. by Reidel Holland). Kluwer Academic.
Calder, Nigel. Timescale: An Atlas of the Fourth Dimension. LC 83-47874. (Illus.). 336p. 1983. 19.95 (ISBN 0-670-71571-9). Viking.
Capek, M., ed. Boston Studies in the Philosophy of Science, Vol. 22: The Concepts of Space & Time - Their Structure & Their Development. LC 73-75761. (Synthese Library: No. 74). 564p. 1975. 58.00 (ISBN 90-277-0355-8, Pub. by Reidel Holland); pap. 26.00 (ISBN 90-277-0375-2). Kluwer Academic.
Carlstein, Tommy, et al, eds. Timing Space & Spacing Time, 3 vols. Incl. Vol. I. Making Sense of Time. 150p. 32.95x (ISBN 0-470-26511-6); Vol. II. Human Activity & Time Geography. 286p. 53.95x (ISBN 0-470-26513-2); Vol. III. Time & Regional Dynamics. 120p. 32.95x (ISBN 0-470-26512-4). 1979. Halsted Pr.
Cox, Richard T. Time, Space, & Atoms. LC 33-6773. pap. 42.50 (ISBN 0-317-29503-9, 2055962). Bks Demand UMI.
Davies, P. C. The Physics of Time Asymmetry. LC 74-81536. 1974. 38.50x (ISBN 0-520-02825-2); pap. 6.50x (ISBN 0-520-03247-0). U of Cal Pr.
--Space & Time in the Modern Universe. LC 76-27902. (Illus.). 1977. 37.50 (ISBN 0-521-21445-9); pap. 14.95 (ISBN 0-521-29151-8). Cambridge U Pr.
Earman, John S., et al, eds. Foundations of Space-Time Theories. LC 77-83503. (Studies in the Philosophy of Science: Vol. 8). (Illus.). 1977. 27.50 (ISBN 0-8166-0807-5). U of Minn Pr.
Esposito, F. Paul & Witten, Louis, eds. Asymptotic Structure of Space-Time. LC 77-487. 442p. 1977. 69.50x (ISBN 0-306-31022-8, Plenum Pr). Plenum Pub.
Evans, D. J., ed. Sparsity & Its Applications. 352p. 1985. 39.50 (ISBN 0-521-26272-0). Cambridge U Pr.
Feigl, Herbert & Maxwell, G., eds. Scientific Explanation, Space & Time. LC 57-12861. (Studies in the Philosophy of Science Ser: Vol. 3). 1962. 25.00x (ISBN 0-8166-0266-2). U of Minn Pr.
Ferrara, S., et al, eds. Conformal Algebra in Space - Time & Operator Product Expansion. LC 25-9130. (Springer Tracts in Modern Physics: Vol. 67). iv, 69p. 1973. 22.50 (ISBN 0-387-06216-5). Springer-Verlag.
Friedman, Michael. Foundations of Space-Time Theories: Relativistic Physics & Philosophy of Science. LC 82-61362. 400p. 1983. 35.00 (ISBN 0-691-07239-6). Princeton U Pr.
Gribbin, John. Spacewarps. 224p. 1984. pap. 9.95 (ISBN 0-385-29366-6, Delta). Dell.
Grunbaum, A. Boston Studies in the Philosophy of Science, Vol. 12: Philosophical Problems of Space & Time. 2nd ed. LC 73-75763. (Synthese Library: No. 55). 884p. 1973. 66.00 (ISBN 90-277-0357-4, Pub. by Reidel Holland); pap. 25.00 (ISBN 90-277-0358-2). Kluwer Academic.
Grunbaum, Adolf. Geometry & Chronometry in Philosophical Perspective. LC 68-22363. 1968. 12.50x (ISBN 0-8166-0489-4); pap. 3.45x (ISBN 0-8166-0490-8, MP16). U of Minn Pr.
Hall, Edward T. Hidden Dimension. LC 66-11173. (Illus.). 1966. pap. 4.50 (ISBN 0-385-08476-5, A609, Anch). Doubleday.
Hawking, Steven & Ellis, G. F. The Large Scale Structure of Space-Time. LC 72-93671. (Illus.). 376p. 1973. 72.50 (ISBN 0-521-20016-4); pap. 29.95 (ISBN 0-521-09906-4). Cambridge U Pr.
Hestenes, David. Space-Time Algebra. (Documents on Modern Physics Ser.). 102p. (Orig.). 1966. 28.95x (ISBN 0-677-01390-6). Gordon.
Hinckfuss, Ian. The Existence of Space & Time. (Illus.). 1975. 19.95x (ISBN 0-19-824519-X). Oxford U Pr.
Ives, Herbert E. The Einstein Myth & the Ives Papers. Turner, Dean & Hazelett, Richard, eds. LC 77-78425. 1979. 22.50 (ISBN 0-8159-5823-4). Devin.
Jammer, Max. Concepts of Space: The History of Theories of Space in Physics. 2nd ed. LC 69-18034. 1969. 15.00x (ISBN 0-674-15771-0). Harvard U Pr.
Jaques, Elliott. The Form of Time. LC 81-17510. 252p. 1982. 29.50x (ISBN 0-8448-1394-X). Crane-Russak Co.
Kaufmann, William J., III. Black Holes & Warped Spacetime. LC 79-18059. (Illus.). 221p. 1979. pap. text ed. 10.95 (ISBN 0-7167-1153-2). W H Freeman.
Kramer, D., et al. Exact Solutions of Einstein's Field Equations. (Cambridge Monographs on Mathematical Physics). 400p. 1981. 85.00 (ISBN 0-521-23041-1). Cambridge U Pr.
Marder, L. Time & the Space-Traveller. LC 77-182498. (Illus.). 1972. 15.00x (ISBN 0-8122-7650-7); pap. 7.95x (ISBN 0-8122-1054-9). U of Pa Pr.
Matzner, Richard A. & Shepley, L. C., eds. Spacetime & Geometry: The Alfred Schild Lectures. 199p. 1982. text ed. 37.50x (ISBN 0-292-77567-9). U of Tex Pr.
Mermin, N. David. Space & Time in Special Relativity. LC 67-30052. (Illus.). 1968. pap. text ed. 19.95 (ISBN 0-07-041499-8). McGraw.
Morris, Richard. Time's Arrows: Scientific Attitudes Toward Time in Western Culture. 234p. 1985. 17.95 (ISBN 0-671-50158-5). S&S.
Nerlich, G. The Shape of Space. 260p. 1976. 37.50 (ISBN 0-521-21101-8). Cambridge U Pr.
Ohanian, Hans C. Gravitation & Space Time. new ed. (Illus.). 400p. 1976. text ed. 24.95x (ISBN 0-393-09198-8). Norton.
Park, David. The Image of Eternity: Roots of Time in the Physical World. LC 79-22984. 160p. 1980. lib. bdg. 14.50x (ISBN 0-87023-286-X). U of Mass Pr.
Penrose, Roger & Rindler, Wolfgang. Spinors & Space Time, Vol. 1: Two-Spinor Calculus & Relativistic Fields. 480p. 1984. 89.50 (ISBN 0-521-24527-3). Cambridge U Pr.
--Spinors & Space Time, Vol. 2: Spinor & Twistor Methods in Space-Time Geometry. 400p. Date not set. price not set (ISBN 0-521-25267-9). Cambridge U Pr.
Persinger, Michael A. & Lafreniere, Gyslaine F. Space-Time Transients & Unusual Events. LC 76-12634. 224p. 1977. 20.95x (ISBN 0-88229-334-6). Nelson-Hall.
Philips, Paul. Time-Space Transcendence. LC 84-71711. 72p. (Orig.). 1984. pap. 2.95 (ISBN 0-930149-00-9). Am Parapsy Res.
Prigogine, Ilya. From Being to Becoming: Time & Complexity in the Physical Sciences. LC 79-26774. (Illus.). 272p. 1980. pap. text ed. 15.95x (ISBN 0-7167-1108-7). W H Freeman.
Raine, Derek J. & Heller, Michael. The Science of Space-Time. (Astronomy & Astrophysics Ser.: Vol. 9). (Illus.). 256p. 1981. text ed. 38.00 (ISBN 0-912918-12-8, 0012). Pachart Pub Hse.
Sack, Robert D. Conceptions of Space in Social Thought: A Geographic Perspective. (Illus.). 240p. 1981. 27.50x (ISBN 0-8166-1012-6); pap. 9.95x (ISBN 0-8166-1015-0). U of Minn Pr.
Salmon, Wesley C. Space, Time, & Motion: A Philosophical Introduction. 2nd rev. ed. LC 80-18423. (Illus.). 160p. 1981. pap. 8.95x (ISBN 0-8166-1004-5). U of Minn Pr.
Schrodinger, Erwin. Space-Time Structure. (Illus.). 119p. Date not set. price not set (ISBN 0-521-31520-4). Cambridge U Pr.
Schutz, J. W. Foundations of Special Relativity: Kinematic Axioms for Minkowski Space-Time. (Lecture Notes in Mathematics: Vol. 361). (Illus.). 314p. 1973. pap. 17.00 (ISBN 0-387-06591-1). Springer-Verlag.
Seifert, H. J., ed. Mathematical Aspects of Superspace. 240p. 1984. 39.00 (ISBN 90-277-1805-9, Pub. by Reidel Holland). Kluwer Academic.
Silverman, Sanford L. & Silverman, Martin G. Theory of Relationships. LC 63-13349. 1964. 6.00 (ISBN 0-8022-1571-8). Philos Lib.
Sims, Jean & Connelly, Michael. Time & Space: A Basic Reader. (Illus.). 176p. 1982. pap. text ed. 12.95 (ISBN 0-13-922005-4). P-H.
Sims, Reginald W. & Price, James H., eds. Evolution, Time & Space. 1983. 59.00 (ISBN 0-12-644550-8). Acad Pr.
Sklar, Lawrence. Philosophy & Spacetime Physics. LC 84-24128. 1985. 25.00x (ISBN 0-520-05374-5). U of Cal Pr.
--Space, Time, & Spacetime. 1977. pap. 8.95x (ISBN 0-520-03174-1, CAMPUS164). U of Cal Pr.
Smart, John J., ed. Problems of Space & Time. 1964. pap. 2.95 (ISBN 0-02-067600-X). Macmillan.
Suppes, P., ed. Space, Time & Geometry. LC 73-86097. (Synthese Library: No. 56). 450p. 1973. lib. bdg. 53.00 (ISBN 90-277-0386-8, Pub. by Reidel Holland); pap. text ed. 26.00 (ISBN 90-277-0442-2). Kluwer Academic.
Swinburne, Richard. Space, Time & Causality. 1983. 39.50 (ISBN 90-277-1437-1, Pub. by Reidel Holland). Kluwer Academic.
Taylor, Edwin F. & Wheeler, John A. Spacetime Physics. LC 65-13566. (Physics Ser.). (Illus.). 208p. 1966. pap. text ed. 11.95x (ISBN 0-7167-0336-X); answer book avail. W H Freeman.
Torrance, Thomas F. Space, Time & Incarnation. 1969. pap. 4.95 (ISBN 0-19-520082-9, GB562, GB). Oxford U Pr.
Wald, Robert M. Space, Time & Gravity: The Theory of the Big Bang & Black Holes. LC 77-4038. (Illus.). 1977. 10.95x (ISBN 0-226-87030-8); pap. 5.95 (ISBN 0-226-87031-6). U of Chicago Pr.
Weyl, Hermann. Space, Time, Matter. 1922. pap. text ed. 5.95 (ISBN 0-486-60267-2). Dover.

SPACE BIOLOGY
Here are entered works on the biology of man or other earth life while in outer space. Works on life indigenous to outer space are entered under Life on Other Planets.
see also Life on Other Planets

El-Genk, Mohamed S. & Hoover, Mark D., eds. Space Nuclear Power Systems: The Proceedings on the First Symposium on Space Nuclear Power Systems, 2 Vols. LC 84-16634. 1985. 110.00 (ISBN 0-89464-004-6). Krieger.
Holmquist, R., ed. Life Sciences & Space Research. LC 63-6132. 1977. text ed. 58.00 (ISBN 0-08-021635-8). Pergamon.
Sable, Martin H. Exobiology: A Research Guide. LC 78-7287. xi, 324p. 1978. 17.95 (ISBN 0-931600-00-6). Green Oak Pr.

SPACE CARS
see Space Stations

SPACE CHAMBERS
see Space Simulators

SPACE CHEMISTRY
see Cosmochemistry

SPACE COLONIES

Lovelock, James & Allaby, Michael. The Greening of Mars. 224p. 1985. pap. 3.50 (ISBN 0-446-32967-3). Warner Bks.

SPACE COMMUNICATION
see Interstellar Communication

SPACE COMMUNICATION SYSTEMS
see Astronautics–Communication Systems

SPACE ELECTRONICS
see Astrionics

SPACE ENVIRONMENT
see also Cosmic Rays; Extraterrestrial Radiation; Interstellar Matter; Magnetic Fields (Cosmic Physics); Solar Radiation; Space Simulators

Basic Environmental Problems of Man in Space II, 6th International Symposium, Bonn, Germany, 3-6 November 1980 & Klein, K. E. Proceedings. Hordinsky, J. R., ed. 250p. 1982. pap. 70.00 (ISBN 0-08-028697-6, A140). Pergamon.
Beer, T. & Kucherawy, M. D. The Aerospace Environment. (Wykeham Science Ser.: No. 36). 170p. 1975. 8.60x (ISBN 0-8448-1163-7). Crane-Russak Co.
Berry, Adrian. The Next Ten Thousand Years: A Vision of Man's Future in the Universe. 1975. pap. 2.25 (ISBN 0-451-61601-4, ME1601, Ment). NAL.
Bowen, J. R., et al. Shock Waves, Explosions & Detonations. 45.00 (ISBN 0-915928-76-0). AIAA.
Cosmos Nine-Five-Four: The Occurrence & Nature of Recovered Debris. 60p. 1980. pap. 9.25 (ISBN 0-660-10589-6, SSC155, SSC). Unipub.
Effects of the Space Environment on Materials Symposium: Proceedings, St. Louis MO, 19-21 April 1967. (Science of Advanced Materials & Process Engineering Ser., Vol. 11). 20.00 (ISBN 0-938994-11-5). Soc Adv Material.
Grey, Jerry. Beachheads in Space: A Blueprint for the Future. (Illus.). 288p. 1983. 14.95 (ISBN 0-02-545590-7). Macmillan.
Heppenheimer, T. A. Towards Distant Suns. (Illus.). 1980. pap. 8.95 (ISBN 0-449-90035-5, Columbine). Fawcett.
Hodge, P. W. Interplanetary Dust. 288p. 1981. 44.25 (ISBN 0-677-03620-5). Gordon.
Napolitano, L. G. Space: Mankind's Fourth Environment, Vol. II. pap. 68.00 (ISBN 0-08-029986-5). Pergamon.
Sagan, Carl. Cosmic Connection: An Extraterrestrial Perspective. LC 80-1867. (Illus.). 288p. 1980. pap. 8.95 (ISBN 0-385-17365-2, Anch). Doubleday.
Shuttle Environment & Operations. 85.00 (ISBN 0-317-06661-7). AIAA.
Tobias, Cornelius A. & Todd, Paul, eds. Space Radiation Biology & Related Topics. (US Atomic Energy Commission Monograph Ser.). 1973. 52.25 (ISBN 0-12-691850-3). Acad Pr.
Whicher, Olive. The Idea of Counterspace. (Orig.). 1975. pap. 1.00 (ISBN 0-88010-097-4). Anthroposophic.

SPACE EXPLORATION (ASTRONAUTICS)
see Outer Space–Exploration

SPACE FLIGHT
see also Astrodynamics; Astronautics; Manned Space Flight; Navigation (Astronautics); Rockets (Aeronautics); Space Stations; Space Trajectories

Al'pert, Y. L., et al. Space Physics with Artificial Satellites. LC 64-23253. 240p. 1965. 42.50x (ISBN 0-306-10727-9, Consultants). Plenum Pub.
Baker, David. Conquest: A History of Space Achievements from Science Fiction to the Shuttle. (Illus.). 187p. 1985. pap. 12.95 (ISBN 0-947703-00-4, Pub by Salem Hse Ltd). Merrimack Pub Cir.
--History of Manned Space Flight. LC 81-3101. (Herbert Michelman Bks.). (Illus.). 512p. 1985. 19.95 (ISBN 0-517-54377-X). Crown.
Benford, Timothy & Wilkes, Brian. The Space Program Quiz & Fact Book. LC 84-48816. 240p. 1985. pap. 8.95 (ISBN 0-06-096005-1, PL6005, PL). Har-Row.
--The Space Program Quiz & Fact Book. LC 84-48816. 240p. 1985. 15.34 (ISBN 0-06-015454-3, HarpT). Har-Row.
Bond, A. C. & Faget, M. A. Technologies of Manned Space Flight. 132p. 1965. 38.50 (ISBN 0-677-01250-0). Gordon.
Bryan, C. D. National Air & Space Museum. (Illus.). 1979. 60.00 (ISBN 0-8109-0666-X). Abrams.
Business Communications Staff. Commercial Opportunities in Space, Including Communications Materials, Research. 1984. 1500.00 (ISBN 0-89336-370-7, GB-075). BCC.
Calloway, P. H. Human Ecology in Space Flight, 3 Vols. Incl. Vol. 1. Proceedings of the First Conference. 286p. 1969. 63.95 (ISBN 0-677-65030-2); Vol. 2. Proceedings of the Second Conference. 298p. 1967. 63.95 (ISBN 0-677-65040-X); Vol. 3. Proceedings of the Third Conference. 246p. 1968. 55.00 (ISBN 0-677-65050-7). 830p. 1969. Set. 161.75 (ISBN 0-677-65220-8). Gordon.
Clarke, Arthur C. Voices from the Sky. 1980. pap. 2.50 (ISBN 0-671-82141-5). PB.
Cornelisse, J. W., et al. Rocket Propulsion & Spaceflight Dynamics. LC 78-40059. (Aerospace Engineering Ser.). 505p. 1979. text ed. 89.95 (ISBN 0-273-01141-3). Pitman Pub MA.
Furniss, Tim. Manned Spaceflight Log. (Illus.). 128p. 1983. 10.95 (ISBN 0-86720-631-4). Jane's Pub Inc.
--Space Flight: The Records. (Illus.). 176p. 1985. cancelled (ISBN 0-85112-435-6, Pub. by Guinness Superlatives England); pap. 9.95 (ISBN 0-85112-451-8, Pub. by Guinness Superlatives England). Sterling.
Goddard Memorial Symposium - 5th - 1967. Voyage to the Planets. (Science & Technology Ser.: Vol. 16). 20.00x (ISBN 0-87703-044-8, Pub. by Am Astronaut). Univelt Inc.
Goddard Memorial Symposium- 7th - Washington D. C. - 1969. Reducing Cost of Space Transportation. (Science & Technology Ser.: Vol. 21). (Illus.). 1969. 25.00x (ISBN 0-87703-049-9, Pub. by Am Astronaut). Univelt Inc.
Goldman, Nathan C. Space Commerce: Free Enterprise on the High Frontier. LC 84-16761. 208p. 1985. 25.00 ea. (ISBN 0-88730-003-0). Ballinger Pub.
Jane's Pocket Books. Jane's Pocket Book of Space Exploration. Wilding-White, T. M., ed. (Jane's Pocket Book Ser.). 1977. pap. 5.95 (ISBN 0-02-080660-4, Collier). Macmillan.
Jasentuliyana, N. & Chipman, R., eds. International Space Programmes & Policies: Proceedings of the 2nd United Nations Conference on the Exploration & Peaceful Uses of Outer Space (UNISPACE), Vienna, Austria, August 1982. 1984. 65.00 (ISBN 0-444-87572-7, North-Holland). Elsevier.

Koelle, D. E., ed. Space Systems Economics: Cost Reductions in Space Operations. 60p. Date not set. pap. 45.00 (ISBN 0-08-031656-5). Pergamon.

Krieger, F. J. Behind the Sputniks. 1958. 12.00 (ISBN 0-8183-0152-X). Pub Aff Pr.

Marder, L. Time & the Space-Traveller. LC 77-182498. (Illus.). 1972. 15.00x (ISBN 0-8122-7650-7); pap. 7.95x (ISBN 0-8122-1054-9). U of Pa Pr.

Murray, Bruce C. & Burgess, Eric. Flight to Mercury. LC 76-25017. (Illus.). 162p. 1976. 26.00x (ISBN 0-231-03996-4). Columbia U Pr.

Napolitano, Luigi G. Space Two Thousand. LC 83-8795. 709p. 65.00 (ISBN 0-915928-73-6). AIAA.

Nicolson, Iain. Sputnik to Space Shuttle: The Complete Story of Space Flight. (Illus.). 224p. 1985. pap. 9.95 (ISBN 0-396-08231-9). Dodd.

Out of This World: An Illustrated Guide to Space Technology & Exploration. 128p. 1985. 14.95 (ISBN 0-668-06335-1). Arco.

Petersen, N. V., ed. Space Rendezvous, Rescue, Recovery, 2 Vols. (Advances in the Astronautical Sciences Ser.: Vol. 16). 1963. Pt. 1. 45.00x (ISBN 0-87703-017-0, Pub. by Am Astronaut); Pt. 2. 30.00x (ISBN 0-87703-018-9). Univelt Inc.

Pogue, William R. How Do You Go to the Bathroom in Space? 160p. (Orig.). 1985. pap. 4.95 (ISBN 0-8125-4910-4). Tor Bks.

Segel, Thomas D. Men in Space. LC 75-28519. (Illus.). 225p. 1975. 19.95 (ISBN 0-87364-033-0). Paladin Pr.

Sixteenth Annual Meeting, Anaheim, California, 1970. Space Shuttles & Interplanetary Missions: Proceeding. (Advances in the Astronautical Sciences Ser.: Vol. 28). 1970. 35.00x (ISBN 0-87703-055-3, Pub. by Am Astronaut). Univelt Inc.

Smith, Melvyn. From X-15 to Space Shuttle. (Illus.). 300p. 1986. 20.95 (ISBN 0-85429-480-5, Pub. by G T Foulis Ltd). Interbook.

Space Science Board. Human Factors in Long-Duration Space Flight. LC 70-189063. (Illus.). 288p. 1972. pap. 8.25 (ISBN 0-309-01947-8). Natl Acad Pr.

Steinhoff, E. A., ed. The Eagle Has Returned. (Science & Technology Ser.: Vol. 43). (Illus.). 1976. 30.00x (ISBN 0-87703-086-3, Pub. by Am Astronaut). Univelt Inc.

Stockton, William & Wilford, John N. Space-Liner: The New York Times Report on the Columbia's Voyage. 183p. 1981. 12.50 (ISBN 0-8129-0979-8). Times Bks.

Turnill, Reginald. Jane's Spaceflight Directory. (Illus.). 352p. 1984. 50.00 (ISBN 0-7106-0208-1). Jane's Pub Inc.

Von Braun, Wernher, et al. Space Travel: A History. rev. ed. LC 74-13813. (Illus.). 360p. 1985. 28.80 (ISBN 0-06-181898-4, HarpT). Har-Row.

Weber, Ronald. Seeing Earth: Literary Responses to Space Exploration. LC 84-16567. xiv, 138p. 1985. pap. text ed. 19.95x (ISBN 0-8214-0791-0, 82-85504). Ohio U Pr.

Werz, James R., ed. Spacecraft Attitude Determination & Control. (Astrophysics & Space Science Library: No. 73). 858p. 1980. 52.00 (ISBN 90-277-0959-9, Pub. by Reidel Holland); pap. 29.00 (ISBN 90-277-1204-2). Kluwer Academic.

Zipkin, M A. & Edwards, R. N., eds. Power Systems for Space Flight. LC 63-13306. (Vol. 11). (Illus.). 943p. (J). members 23.50 (ISBN 0-317-36826-5); list 47.00 (ISBN 0-317-36827-3). AIAA.

SPACE FLIGHT–MATHEMATICAL MODELS

Leitmann, George, ed. Optimization Techniques with Applications to Aerospace Systems. (Mathematics in Science & Engineering,: Vol. 5). 1962. 75.00 (ISBN 0-12-442950-5). Acad Pr.

SPACE FLIGHT PROPULSION SYSTEMS

see Space Vehicles–Propulsion Systems

SPACE FLIGHT TO MARS

Boston, Penelope J., ed. The Case for Mars. (Science & Technology Ser.: Vol. 57). 348p. 1984. lib. bdg. 45.00x (ISBN 0-87703-197-5, Pub. by Am Astro Soc); pap. text ed. 25.00x (ISBN 0-87703-198-3). Univelt Inc.

Cooper, Henry S., Jr. The Search for Life on Mars. LC 79-20061. 276p. 1980. 10.95 (ISBN 0-03-046166-9). HR&W.

Morgenthaler, G. W., ed. Exploration of Mars. (Advances in the Astronautical Sciences Ser.: Vol. 15). 1963. 45.00x (ISBN 0-87703-016-2, Pub. by Am Astronaut). Univelt inc.

Oberg, James E. Mission to Mars: Plans & Concepts for the First Manned Landing. 1983. pap. 6.95 (ISBN 0-452-00655-4, Mer). NAL.

Von Braun, Wernher. The Mars Project. LC 52-12407. 100p. 1962. pap. 4.95x (ISBN 0-252-72544-1). U of Ill Pr.

SPACE FLIGHT TO THE MOON

see also Moon–Exploration; Project Apollo

American Astronautical Society. Lunar Flight Problems. Fleisig, R., ed. (Advances in the Astronautical Sciences Ser.: Vol. 18). 1964. 45.00x (ISBN 0-87703-020-0, Pub. by Am Astronaut). Univelt inc.

Hallion, Richard P. & Crouch, Tom D., eds. Apollo: Ten Years Since Tranquillity Base. LC 79-10271. (Illus.). 174p. 1979. 19.95x (ISBN 0-87474-506-3); pap. 19.95x (ISBN 0-87474-505-5). Smithsonian.

Symposium, New York, 1960. Lunar Exploration & Spacecraft Systems: Proceedings. (Special Volumes: Vol. 2). 1960. 15.00x (ISBN 0-87703-001-4, Pub. by Am Astronaut). Univelt Inc.

Symposium on Manned Lunar Flight, Denver, 1961. Manned Lunar Flight. Morgenthaler, G. W. & Jacobs, H., eds. (Advances in the Astronautical Sciences Ser.: Vol. 10). 1963. 35.00x (ISBN 0-87703-011-1, Pub. by Am Astronaut). Univelt Inc.

SPACE FLIGHT TRAINING

see Flight Training

SPACE FRAME STRUCTURES

Space Technology & Heat Transfer Conference, 1970, Los Angeles. Space Systems & Thermal Technology for the 70's. LC 72-17650. pap. 123.30 (ISBN 0-317-10961-8, 2005682). Bks Demand UMI.

Space Technology & Heat Transfer Conference, Los Angeles, 1970. Space Systems & Thermal Technology for the 70's, Pt. 2. LC 72-17650. pap. 101.50 (ISBN 0-317-10230-3, 2013322). Bks Demand UMI.

SPACE LABORATORIES

see Space Stations

SPACE LATTICE (MATHEMATICS)

see Lattice Theory

SPACE MEDICINE

see also Life Support Systems (Space Environment); Manned Space Flight; Weightlessness

Sokov, Vasnil S. Space Flight & Aerospace Medicine: General Survey with Research Subject Directory & Bibliography. LC 82-7225. 140p. 1983. 29.95 (ISBN 0-941864-66-9); pap. 21.95 (ISBN 0-941864-67-7). ABBE Pubs Assn.

SPACE NAVIGATION

see Navigation (Astronautics)

SPACE OF MORE THAN THREE DIMENSIONS

see Hyperspace; Space and Time

SPACE PERCEPTION

Eliot, John & Smith, Ian M. An International Directory of Spatial Tests. 462p. 1983. 198.00x (ISBN 0-7005-0517-2, Pub. by NFER Nelson UK); microfiche 100.00x (ISBN 0-7005-0651-9). Taylor & Francis.

Hall, Edward T. Hidden Dimension. LC 66-11173. (Illus.). 1966. pap. 4.50 (ISBN 0-385-08476-5, A609, Anch). Doubleday.

Howard, Ian P. Human Visual Orientation. LC 80-41689. 697p. 1981. 69.95x (ISBN 0-471-27946-3, Pub. by Wiley-Interscience). Wiley.

Ivins, William M., Jr. Art & Geometry. 1946. pap. 2.95 (ISBN 0-486-20941-5). Dover.

Millman, Howard L. Creating a Safe Space. 1977. pap. text ed. 7.50 (ISBN 0-8191-0284-9). U Pr of Amer.

Slater, P. The Measurement of Intrapersonal Space by Grid Technique: Dimensions of Intrapersonal Space, Vol. 2. 270p. 1977. 60.95x (ISBN 0-471-99450-2). Wiley.

Subtelny, Stephen & Konigsberg, Irwin R., eds. Determinants of Spatial Organization: Symposium of the Society for Developmental Biology, 37th. LC 78-23508. 1979. 39.50 (ISBN 0-12-612983-5). Acad Pr.

Watson, O. Michael. Proxemic Behavior: A Cross-Cultural Study. 1970. text ed. 14.00x (ISBN 0-686-22399-3). Mouton.

SPACE PHOTOGRAPHY

see also Photographic Reconnaissance Systems

Ferris, Timothy. Spaceshots: The Beauty of Nature Beyond Earth. LC 84-42705. (Illus.). 143p. 1984. 24.45 (ISBN 0-394-53890-0). Pantheon.

Sheffield, Charles. Earthwatch: A Survey of the World from Space. LC 81-3676. (Illus.). 160p. 1981. 24.95 (ISBN 0-02-610090-8). Macmillan.

SPACE PROBES

Strong, James. Search for the Solar System: The Role of Unmanned Interplanetary Probes. (Illus.). 1973. 12.95x (ISBN 0-8464-0827-9). Beekman Pubs.

SPACE PROPULSION

see Space Vehicles–Propulsion Systems

SPACE RADIATION

see Extraterrestrial Radiation

SPACE RESCUE OPERATIONS

Baker, David. History of Manned Space Flight. LC 81-3101. (Herbert Michelman Bks.). (Illus.). 512p. 1985. 19.95 (ISBN 0-517-54377-X). Crown.

Bolger, Philip H., ed. Space Rescue & Safety 1974. (Science & Technology Ser.: Vol. 37). (Illus.). 294p. 1975. lib. bdg. 25.00x (ISBN 0-87703-073-1, Pub. by Am Astronaut). Univelt Inc.

--Space Rescue & Safety, 1975. New ed. (Science & Technology Ser: Vol. 41). (Illus.). 1976. lib. bdg. 25.00x (ISBN 0-87703-077-4, Pub. by Am Astronaut). Univelt Inc.

Brown, Jeri W. Space Safety & Rescue: 1979-1981, Vol. 54. (Science & Technology Ser.). (Illus.). 456p. 1983. lib. bdg. 45.00x (ISBN 0-87703-177-0, Pub. by Am Astronaut); pap. text ed. 35.00x (ISBN 0-87703-178-9). Univelt Inc.

SPACE RESEARCH

see Astronautical Research; Outer Space–Exploration; Space Sciences

SPACE ROCKETS

see Space Vehicles

SPACE SCIENCES

see also Astronautics; Astronomy; Cosmic Physics; Cosmochemistry; Ether (Of Space); Geophysics; Outer Space; Space Biology; Space and Time; Space Medicine

Advances in Space Research, Vol. 1, No. 1. pap. 46.00 (ISBN 0-08-027151-0). Pergamon.

Anaejionu, Paul, et al, eds. Space & Society: Challenges & Choices. (Science & Technology Ser.: Vol. 59). (Illus.). 442p. (Orig.). 1984. lib. bdg. 55.00x (ISBN 0-87703-204-1, Pub. by Am Astro Soc); pap. text ed. 35.00x (ISBN 0-87703-205-X). Univelt Inc.

The Application of Space Technology to Development. pap. 2.50 (ISBN 0-686-94707-X, UN72/2A/12, UN). Unipub.

Atreya, S. K. & Caldwell, J. J., eds. Planetary Aeronomy & Astronomy. (Advances in Space Research Ser.: Vol. 1, No.9). (Illus.). 216p. 1981. pap. 31.00 (ISBN 0-08-028385-3). Pergamon.

Avduyevsky, V. S. Scientific Foundations of Space Manufacturing. 173p. 1985. pap. 5.95 (ISBN 0-8285-2949-3, Pub. by Mir Pubs USSR). Imported Pubns.

Bekey, Ivan, ed. Permanent Presence-Making It Work: Twenty-Second Goddard Memorial Symposium, Mar. 15-16, 1984 Greenbelt, MD. (Science & Technology Ser.: Vol. 60). 190p. 1985. 40.00 (ISBN 0-317-27277-2); pap. 30.00 (ISBN 0-317-27278-0). Univelt Inc.

Bewersdorff, A., ed. Materials Science in Space. (Advances in Space Research Ser.: Vol. 1, No. 5). (Illus.). 171p. 1981. pap. 23.00 (ISBN 0-08-027161-8). Pergamon.

Bluth, B. J. & McNeal, S. R., eds. Update on Space, Vol. 1. LC 80-52460. (Illus., Orig.). 1981. pap. 7.95 (ISBN 0-937654-00-0). Natl Behavior.

Bolle, H. J., ed. Remote Sounding of the Atmosphere from Space: Proceedings of the Committee on Space Research, 21st Plenary Meeting, Innsbruck, Austria, 1978. (Illus.). 1979. 69.00 (ISBN 0-08-023419-4). Pergamon.

Brand, Stewart, ed. Space Colonies. 1977. pap. 5.00 (ISBN 0-14-004805-7). Penguin.

Brandt, John C. & Maran, Stephen P., eds. The New Astronomy & Space Science Reader. LC 76-54316. (Illus.). 371p. 1977. text ed. 23.95 (ISBN 0-7167-0350-5); pap. text ed. 12.95 (ISBN 0-7167-0349-1). W H Freeman.

Canan, James. War in Space. LC 81-48032. 192p. 1982. 13.41i (ISBN 0-06-038022-5, HarpT). Har-Row.

Casci, Corrado, ed. Recent Advances in the Aerospace Sciences. 454p. 1985. 55.00x (ISBN 0-306-41079-6, Plenum Pr). Plenum Pub.

Educational Research Council of America. Space Technologist. Ferris, Theodore N. & Marchak, John P., eds. (Real People at Work Ser.: R). (Illus.). 36p. 1977. 2.70- (ISBN 0-89247-138-7, 9629). Changing Times.

Eisner, Will. Signal from Space. Kitchen, Denis, ed. (Illus.). 136p. 1983. pap. 16.95 (ISBN 0-317-00648-7). Kitchen Sink.

Ford, C. Quentin, ed. Space Technology & Earth Problems. (Science & Technology Ser.: Vol. 23). (Illus.). 1970. lib. bdg. 35.00x (ISBN 0-87703-051-0, Pub. by Am Astronaut); microfiche suppl. 20.00x (ISBN 0-87703-134-7). Univelt Inc.

Greve, Tim, et al, eds. The Impact of Space Science on Mankind. LC 76-26652. (Nobel Foundation Symposia Ser.). 125p. 1976. 35.00x (ISBN 0-306-33701-0, Plenum Pr). Plenum Pub.

Hanle, Paul A. & Chamberlain, Von Del, eds. Space Science Comes of Age: Perspectives in the History of the Space Sciences. LC 80-28966. (Illus.). 194p. 1981. 22.50x (ISBN 0-87474-508-X); pap. 12.50x (ISBN 0-87474-507-1). Smithsonian.

Haymes, Robert C. Introduction to Space Science. LC 78-140550. (Space Science Text Ser.). pap. 143.30 (ISBN 0-317-08888-2, 2055127). Bks Demand UMI.

Hechler, Ken. The Endless Space Frontier: A History of the House Committee on Science & Astronautics 1959-1978. Eastman, Albert E., ed. (American Astronautical Society History Ser.: Vol. 4). (Illus.). 460p. (Orig.). 1982. lib. bdg. 45.00x (ISBN 0-87703-157-6, Pub. by Am Astronaut); pap. text ed. 35.00x (ISBN 0-87703-158-4). Univelt Inc.

Hess, W. & Mead, G., eds. Introduction to Space Science. 2nd rev. & enl. ed. 1074p. 1968. 187.25x (ISBN 0-677-01450-3). Gordon.

Holmquist, ed. Life Sciences & Space Research XVIII: Committee on Space Research. 1980. 58.00 (ISBN 0-08-024436-X). Pergamon.

Holmquist, R., ed. Life Sciences & Space Research XVII. (Illus.). 1979. text ed. 58.00 (ISBN 0-08-023416-X). Pergamon.

Hord, R. Michael, ed. HB of Space Technology: Status & Projections. 304p. 1985. 66.00 (ISBN 0-8493-3535-3). CRC Pr.

International Astronomical Union, 10th Colliquium, Cambridge University, 1970. Gravitational N-Body Problem: Proceedings. Lecar, M., ed. LC 72-154740. (Astrophysics & Space Science Library: No. 31). 441p. 1972. lib. bdg. 60.50 (ISBN 90-277-0203-9, Pub. by Reidel Holland). Kluwer Academic.

International Symposium on Solar-Terrestial Physics, Leningrad, 1970. Solar-Terrestrial Physics: Proceedings, 4 vols. Dyer, E. R., ed. LC 78-170337. (Astrophysics & Space Science Library). 914p. 1972. lib. bdg. 113.00 (ISBN 90-277-0209-8, Pub. by Reidel Holland); in 4 Pts., Pt.1: The Sun, Pt 2: The Interplanetary Medium, Pt. 3: The Magnetosphere, Pt. 4: The Upper Atmosphere avail. Kluwer Academic.

Koch-Miramond, L. & Lee, M. A., eds. Particle Acceleration Processes, Shockwaves, Nucleosynthesis & Cosmic Rays: Proceedings of Symposia 6 & 8 & the Joint Sessions 6-8 of the COSPAR Twenty-fifth Plenary Meeting Held in Graz, Austria, 25 June to 7 July 1984. (Illus.). 542p. 1985. pap. 99.00 (ISBN 0-08-032711-7). Pergamon.

Marechal, A. & Courtes, G., eds. Space Optics. 398p. 1974. 101.25 (ISBN 0-677-50680-5). Gordon.

Murashkevich, A. M. & Vladimirov, O. N. English-Russian Aviation & Space Abbreviations Dictionary. (Eng. & Rus.). 622p. 1981. 45.00x (ISBN 0-686-44706-9, Pub. by Collets). State Mutual Bk.

Murchie, Guy. Music of the Spheres: The Material Universe from Atom to Quasar, Simply Explained, 2 vols. (Illus.). 28.00 set (ISBN 0-8446-0815-7). Peter Smith.

Napolitano, L. G., ed. Space, Mankind's Fourth Environment: Selected Proceedings of the XXXII IAF Congress, Rome, September 6-12, 1981. (Astronautical Research Ser.). 450p. 1982. 99.00 (ISBN 0-08-028708-5, A140). Pergamon.

Potegal, Michael, ed. Spatial Abilities: Development & Physiological Foundations. rev. ed. (Developmental Psychology Ser.). 1982. 47.50 (ISBN 0-12-563080-8). Acad Pr.

Riedler, W. & Friedrich, M., eds. Scientific Ballooning -II. (Advances in Space Research: Vol. 1, No. 11). (Illus.). 274p. 1981. pap. 38.00 (ISBN 0-08-028390-X). Pergamon.

Ruekl, A. Maps of Lunar Hemispheres: Views of the Lunar Globe from Six Cardinal Directions in Space. LC 77-179896. (Astrophysics & Space Science Library: No. 33). (Illus.). 24p. 1972. lib. bdg. 37.00 (ISBN 90-277-0221-7, Pub. by Reidel Holland). Kluwer Academic.

Rycroft, Michael J., ed. Space Research, Vols. 13-19. 1977. Vol. 13, 1977. text ed. 105.00 (ISBN 0-08-021787-7); Vol. 14, 1977. text ed. 125.00 (ISBN 0-08-021788-5); Vol. 15, 1977. text ed. 105.00 (ISBN 0-08-021789-3); Vol. 16, 1977. text ed. 105.00 (ISBN 0-08-021795-8); Vol. 17, 1977. text ed. 105.00 (ISBN 0-08-021636-6); Vol. 18, 1978. text ed. 125.00 (ISBN 0-08-022021-5); Vol. 19, 1979. text ed. 125.00 (ISBN 0-08-023417-8). Pergamon.

Shagam, R., et al, eds. Studies in Earth & Space Sciences: A Memoir in Honor of Harry Hammond Hess. LC 76-190172. (Geological Society of America Memoir Ser.: No. 132). pap. 160.00 (ISBN 0-317-29124-6, 2025026). Bks Demand UMI.

Shea, M. A., et al, eds. Study of Travelling Interplanetary Phenomena. (Astrophysics & Space Science Library: No. 71). 1977. lib. bdg. 50.00 (ISBN 90-277-0860-6, Pub. by Reidel Holland). Kluwer Academic.

Space Science Board. Space Research: Directions for the Future. 1966. pap. 8.75 (ISBN 0-309-01403-4). Natl Acad Pr.

Steinhoff, Ernst, ed. Aerospace Research & Development. (Science & Technology Ser.: Vol. 24). (Illus.). 1970. lib. bdg. 40.00x (ISBN 0-87703-052-9, Pub. by Am Astronaut). Univelt Inc.

Syunyaev, R. A. Astrophysics & Space Physics Reviews, Vol. 3. (Soviet Scientific Reviews Ser.: Section E). 450p. 1984. text ed. 170.00 (ISBN 3-7186-0092-7). Harwood Academic.

--Astrophysics & Space Physics Reviews, Vol. 4. (Soviet Scientific Reviews Ser.: Section E). 375p. 1985. text ed. 170.00 (ISBN 3-7186-0125-7). Harwood Academic.

Zuckerberg, Harry, ed. Exploitation of Space for Experimental Research. (Advances in the Astronautical Sciences Ser.: Vol. 24). (Illus.). 1968. 30.00x (ISBN 0-87703-027-8, Pub. by Am Astronaut). Univelt Inc.

SPACE SHIPS

see also Nuclear Rockets; Rocket Planes; Space Stations

Morgenthaler, G. W. & Hollstein, M., eds. Space Shuttle & Spacelab Utilization: Near-Term & Long-Term Benefits for Mankind. LC 57-43769. (Advances in the Astronautical Sciences: Vol. 37, Pt. I.). 1978. lib. bdg. 40.00x (ISBN 0-87703-096-0, Pub. by Am Astronaut). Univelt Inc.

Napolitano, Luigi G. & International Astronautical Congress, 27th, Anaheim, Ca., Oct. 1976. Proceedings. 1978. text ed. 70.00 (ISBN 0-08-021732-X). Pergamon.

Von Braun, Wernher. The Mars Project. LC 52-12407. 100p. 1962. pap. 4.95x (ISBN 0-252-72544-1). U of Ill Pr.

Zimmerman, Howard. Spaceships. enl. ed. 1980. pap. 8.95 (ISBN 0-931064-23-6). Starlog Group.

SPACE SHIPS–PILOTS

see Astronauts

SPACE SHUTTLES

see Reusable Space Vehicles

SPACE SIMULATORS

AGARD-NATO. Fluid Dynamic Aspects of Space Flight, 2 vols. (Agardographs Ser.: No. 87). 1966. Vol. 1, 416p. 119.25 (ISBN 0-677-11560-1); Vol. 2, 362p. 94.95 (ISBN 0-677-11570-9); Set, 778p. 212.75 (ISBN 0-677-11440-0). Gordon.

SPACE STATIONS

Bekey, Ivan, ed. Permanent Presence-Making It Work: Twenty-Second Goddard Memorial Symposium, Mar. 15-16, 1984 Greenbelt, MD. (Science & Technology Ser.: Vol. 60). 190p. 1985. 40.00 (ISBN 0-317-27277-2); pap. 30.00 (ISBN 0-317-27278-0). Univelt Inc.

Burger, Jan J., et al, eds. Atmospheric Physics from Spacelab. (Astrophysics & Space Science Library: No. 61). 1976. lib. bdg. 55.00 (ISBN 90-277-0768-5, Pub. by Reidel Holland). Kluwer Academic.

Carr, G. P. & Montemerlo, M., eds. Aerospace Crew Station Design: Proceedings of a Course Presented by the School of Biomechanics of the Center for Transportation Studies, Amalfi, Italy, 19-22 Oct. 1983. 1984. 57.75 (ISBN 0-444-87569-7, North-Holland). Elsevier.

Deutsche Gesellschaft Fur Luft und Raumfahrt. Utilization of Space Shuttle & Spacelab: Proceedings of an International Meeting Held in Bonn, 1976. (Illus.). 1976. pap. 30.00x (ISBN 3-88135-034-9). Univelt Inc.

Forehlich, Walter. Spacelab: An International Short-Stay Orbiting Laboratory. (NASA EP Ser.: No. 165). 82p. 1983. pap. 7.00 (ISBN 0-318-11750-9). Gov Printing Office.

Gerard, Mireille & Edwards, Pamela W. Space Station: Policy, Planning & Utilization. 30.00 (ISBN 0-915928-80-9). AIAA.

International Astronautical Congress, Tokyo, Japan, September 22-27, 1980 & Napolitano, L. G. Applications of Space Developments II: Selected Papers. 310p. 1981. pap. 70.00 (ISBN 0-08-028676-3). Pergamon.

International Astronautical Congress, New York, October, 18,1968. Manned Laboratories in Space. Singer, S. F., ed. (Astro Physics & Space Science Library: No.16). 133p. 1969. lib. bdg. 26.00 (ISBN 90-277-0140-7, Pub. by Reidel Holland). Kluwer Academic.

Koelle, Dietrich E. & Butler, George V., eds. Shuttle-Spacelab: The New Transportation System & Its Utilization. LC 57-43769. (Advances in the Astronautical Sciences Ser.: Vol. 43). (Illus.). 342p. 1981. lib. bdg. 45.00x (ISBN 0-87703-144-4, Pub. by Am Astronaut); pap. text ed. 35.00x (ISBN 0-87703-146-0). Univelt Inc.

Morgenthaler, G. W. & Hollstein, M., eds. Space Shuttle & Spacelab Utilization: Near-Term & Long-Term Benefits for Mankind. LC 57-43769. (Advances in the Astronautical Sciences: Vol. 37, Pt. I.). 1978. lib. bdg. 40.00x (ISBN 0-87703-096-0, Pub. by Am Astronaut). Univelt Inc.

Napolitano, L. G. Space Stations, Present & Future. 110.00 (ISBN 0-08-020366-3). Pergamon.

Ninth Communication Satelite Systems. 110.00 (ISBN 0-317-06663-3). AIAA.

O'Leary, Brian. Project Space Station. 160p. 1983. 12.95 (ISBN 0-8117-1701-1). Stackpole.

O'Leary, Brian, ed. Space Industrialization, Vols. I & II. 1981. Vol. I, 176. 61.00 (ISBN 0-8493-5890-6); Vol. II, 240p. 78.00 (ISBN 0-8493-5891-4). CRC Pr.

Simpson, T. R. The Space Station: An Idea Whose Time Has Come. LC 84-21253. 1985. 19.95 (ISBN 0-87942-182-7, PC01768). Inst Electrical.

Sixteenth Annual Meeting, Anaheim, California, 1970. Space Stations: Proceeding. (Advances in the Astronautical Sciences Ser.: Vol. 27). 1970. 45.00x (ISBN 0-87703-054-5, Pub. by Am Astronaut). Univelt Inc.

Space Station Task Force National Aeronautics & Space Administration. Space Station Program: Description, Applications & Opportunities. LC 85-4963. (Illus.). 754p. 1985. 67.00 (ISBN 0-8155-1024-1). Noyes.

Stoewer, H. & Bainum, P. M., eds. From Spacelab to Space Station: Fifth DGLR-AAS Symposium, Oct. 3-5, 1984, Hamburg, Gemany. (Advances in the Astronautical Sciences Ser.: Vol. 56). 270p. 1984. 50.00 (ISBN 0-317-27273-X); pap. 40.00 (ISBN 0-317-27274-8). Univelt Inc.

Stoewer, H. & Bainum, Peter M., eds. From Spacelab to Space Station. (Advances in the Astronautical Sciences Ser.: Vol. 56). (Illus.). 270p. (Orig.). 1985. lib. bdg. 50.00 (ISBN 0-87703-209-2, Pub by Am Astro Soc); pap. text ed. 40.00 (ISBN 0-87703-210-6). Univelt Inc.

Waltz, Donald M. Orbit Servicing of Space Systems. (Orig.). 1985. write for info. (ISBN 0-89464-002-X). Krieger.

SPACE STRUCTURES

see Space Frame Structures

SPACE TELECOMMUNICATION

see Interstellar Communication

SPACE-TIMES

see Space and Time

SPACE TRAJECTORIES

see also Artificial Satellites–Orbits; Artificial Satellites–Tracking; Space Vehicles–Atmospheric Entry

Altman, S. P. Orbital Hodograph Analysis. (Science & Technology Ser.: Vol. 3). 1965. 20.00x (ISBN 0-87703-031-6, Pub. by Am Astronaut). Univelt Inc.

Anthony, M. L., ed. Space Flight Mechanics Symposium. (Science & Technology Ser.: Vol. 11). 1966. 45.00 (ISBN 0-87703-039-1, Pub. by Am Astronaut). Univelt Inc.

COSPAR-IAU-IUTAM Symposium, Paris, 1965. Trajectories of Artificial Celestial Bodies As Determined from Observations: Proceedings. Kovalevsky, J., ed. (Illus.). 1966. 52.00 (ISBN 0-387-03681-4). Springer-Verlag.

Helvey, T. C., ed. Space Trajectories. 1960. 53.00 (ISBN 0-12-340450-9). Acad Pr.

Marec, J. P. Optimal Space Trajectories. LC 79-14664. (Studies in Astronautics: Vol. 1). 330p. 1979. 74.50 (ISBN 0-444-41812-1). Elsevier.

Richards, P. B., ed. Recent Developments in Space Flight Mechanics. (Science & Technology Ser.: Vol. 9). 1966. 25.00x (ISBN 0-87703-037-5). Univelt Inc.

Vinh, N. X. Optimal Trajectories in Atmospheric Flight. (Studies in Astronautics: Vol. 2). 402p. 1981. 85.00 (ISBN 0-444-41961-6). Elsevier.

SPACE TRAVEL

see Space Flight

SPACE VEHICLES

see also Artificial Satellites; Astronautics; Reusable Space Vehicles; Space Ships; Space Stations

Aerospace Testing Seminar Proceedings, 2nd, March 1975. LC 62-38584. (Illus.). 332p. 1975. pap. text ed. 15.00 (ISBN 0-915414-41-4). Inst Environ Sci.

AGARD-NATO. Combustion & Propulsion: Colloquium on Energy Sources & Energy Conversion. (Agardographs Ser.: No. 81). 936p. 1967. 236.95 (ISBN 0-677-10560-6). Gordon.

--Fluid Dynamic Aspects of Space Flight, 2 vols. (Agardographs Ser.: No. 87). 1966. Vol. 1, 416p. 119.25 (ISBN 0-677-11560-1); Vol. 2, 362p. 94.95 (ISBN 0-677-11570-9); Set, 778p. 212.75 (ISBN 0-677-11440-0). Gordon.

Bursnall, W. J., et al, eds. Space Shuttle Missions of the 80's. LC 57-43769. (Advances in the Astronautical Sciences Ser.: Vol. 32, Pts. 1 & 2). (Illus.). 1977. lib. bdg. 95.00x set (ISBN 0-87703-120-7, Pub. by Am Astronaut); Pt. 1. lib. bdg. 40.00x (ISBN 0-87703-078-2); Pt. 2. lib. bdg. 55.00x (ISBN 0-87703-087-1); microfiche suppl. 65.00x (ISBN 0-87703-133-9). Univelt Inc.

CISM (International Center for Mechanical Sciences) Dept. of General Mechanics, Dubrovnik, 1971. Dynamics of Flexible Spacecraft. Likins, P. W., et al, eds. (CISM International Centre for Mechanical Sciences Ser.: No. 103). (Illus.). 158p. 1974. pap. 17.40 (ISBN 0-387-81199-0). Springer-Verlag.

Hall, Lawrence B. & Shilling, Charles W., eds. Planetary Quarantine: Principles, Methods & Problems. LC 71-158834. (Illus.). 184p. 1971. 57.75 (ISBN 0-677-15100-4). Gordon.

Jane's Pocket Books. Jane's Pocket Book of Space Exploration. Wilding-White, T. M., ed. (Jane's Pocket Book Ser.). 1977. pap. 5.95 (ISBN 0-02-080660-4, Collier). Macmillan.

Kammermeyer, Karl, ed. Atmosphere in Space Cabins & Closed Environments. LC 66-22190. 271p. 1966. 25.00x (ISBN 0-306-50038-8, Plenum Pr). Plenum Pub.

Kane, T. R., et al. Spacecraft Dynamics. 1983. 55.00 (ISBN 0-07-037843-6). McGraw.

Kaplan, Marshall H. Modern Spacecraft Dynamics & Control. LC 76-14859. 415p. 1976. text ed. 46.50x (ISBN 0-471-45703-5). Wiley.

Kennedy, Gregory P., compiled by. Rockets, Missiles, & Spacecraft of the National Air & Space Museum, Smithsonian Institution. LC 83-600049. (Illus.). 165p. 1983. pap. 6.50 (ISBN 0-87474-571-3). Smithsonian.

Leitmann, George, ed. Optimization Techniques with Applications to Aerospace Systems. (Mathematics in Science & Engineering,: Vol. 5). 1962. 75.00 (ISBN 0-12-442950-5). Acad Pr.

Monograph: Solar & Space Simulation. 60p. 1985. 20.00 (ISBN 0-915414-83-X). Inst Environ Sci.

Napolitano, L. G. A New Era of Space Transportation. 90.00 (ISBN 0-08-021710-9). Pergamon.

Nooshin, ed. Third International Conference on Space Structures. 1056p. 1984. 142.50 (ISBN 0-85334-309-8, Pub. by Elsevier Applied Sci England). Elsevier.

Shuttle Environment & Operations. 85.00 (ISBN 0-317-06661-7). AIAA.

Spacecraft Contamination: Sources & Prevention. LC 84-12401. 333p. 1984. 69.50 (ISBN 0-915928-85-X); members 49.50 (ISBN 0-317-36800-1). AIAA.

Werz, James R., ed. Spacecraft Attitude Determination & Control. (Astrophysics & Space Science Library: No. 73). 858p. 1980. 52.00 (ISBN 90-277-0959-9, Pub. by Reidel Holland); pap. 29.00 (ISBN 90-277-1204-2). Kluwer Academic.

SPACE VEHICLES–ACCIDENTS

see Astronautics–Accidents

SPACE VEHICLES–ATMOSPHERIC ENTRY

Horton, T. E., ed. Thermophysics & Atmospheric Entry. 45.00 (ISBN 0-915928-66-3). AIAA.

Loh, W. H. Re-Entry & Planetary Entry: Physics & Technology, 2 pts. Incl. Pt. 1. Dynamics, Physics, Radiation, Heat Transfer & Ablation. (Illus.). viii, 487p. 1968. 69.00 (ISBN 0-387-04048-X); Pt. 2. Advanced Concepts, Experiments, Guidance Control & Technology. (Illus.). x, 293p. 1968. 46.00 (ISBN 0-387-04049-8). (Applied Physics & Engineering Ser.: Vol. 2). Springer-Verlag.

Petersen, N. V., ed. Space Rendezvous, Rescue, Recovery, 2 Vols. (Advances in the Astronautical Sciences Ser.: Vol. 16). 1963. Pt. 1. 45.00x (ISBN 0-87703-017-0, Pub. by Am Astronaut); Pt. 2. 30.00x (ISBN 0-87703-018-9). Univelt Inc.

Regan, Frank J. Re-Entry Vehicle Dynamics. LC 83-16198. (Illus.). 414p. 1984. 32.00 (ISBN 0-915928-78-7). AIAA.

Thermophysics of Atmospheric Entry. LC 82-6686. (Illus.). 521p. 1982. 55.00 (ISBN 0-317-36806-0); members 35.00 (ISBN 0-317-36807-9). AIAA.

SPACE VEHICLES–BATTERIES

see Solar Batteries

SPACE VEHICLES–DESIGN AND CONSTRUCTION

Bauer, Paul E. & Collicott, Howard E. Entry Vehicle Heating & Thermal Protection Systems: Space Shuttle, Solar Starprobe, Jupiter Galileo Probe. 45.00 (ISBN 0-915928-74-4). AIAA.

Collicott, Howard E. & Bauer, Paul E. Spacecraft Thermal Control, Design & Operation. 45.00 (ISBN 0-915928-75-2). AIAA.

Horton, T. E., ed. Spacecraft Radiative Transfer & Temperature Control. 45.00 (ISBN 0-915928-67-1). AIAA.

SPACE VEHICLES–GUIDANCE SYSTEMS

see also Astronautical Instruments

Guidance & Control. 75.00 (ISBN 0-317-06664-1). AIAA.

SPACE VEHICLES–INSTRUMENTS

see Astronautical Instruments

SPACE VEHICLES–MATERIALS

Application of Composite Materials - STP 524. 191p. 1973. 30.75 (ISBN 0-8031-0115-5, 04-524000-33). ASTM.

Kinslow, R., ed. High-Velocity Impact Phenomena. 1970. 89.50 (ISBN 0-12-408950-X). Acad Pr.

Otte, H. M. & Locke, S. R., eds. Materials Science Research Series, Vol. 2. LC 63-17645. 319p. 1965. 39.50x (ISBN 0-306-38502-3, Plenum Pr). Plenum Pub.

SPACE VEHICLES–MODELS

Oberg, James E., et al. Famous Spaceships of Fact & Fantasy. Edmonson, Harold, ed. LC 78-78249. 1979. pap. 8.50 (ISBN 0-89024-539-8). Kalmbach.

SPACE VEHICLES–NUCLEAR POWER PLANTS

see also Space Vehicles–Propulsion Systems

Angelo, Joseph A., Jr. & Buden, David. Space Nuclear Power. LC 84-16701. 302p. 1985. lib. bdg. 46.50 (ISBN 0-89464-000-3, Pub. by Orbit Book Co). Krieger.

SPACE VEHICLES–PROPULSION SYSTEMS

see also Controlled Fusion; Nuclear Rockets; Rocketry

Alpert, Y. L. The Near-Earth & Interplanetary Plasma: General Properties & Fundamental Theory, Vol. 1. 175p. 1983. 72.50 (ISBN 0-521-24364-5). Cambridge U Pr.

--The Near-Earth & Interplanetary Plasma: Plasma Flow, Plasma Waves & Oscillations, Vol. 2. LC 82-12879. 150p. 1983. 62.50 (ISBN 0-521-24601-6). Cambridge U Pr.

Billman, L. S. Advanced Propulsion Concepts: Fourth Symposium. 314p. 1966. 84.75 (ISBN 0-677-11080-4). Gordon.

Brewer, G. R. Ion Propulsion, Technology & Applications. 550p. 1970. 145.75 (ISBN 0-677-02600-5). Gordon.

Caveny, Leonard H. Orbit-Raising & Maneuvering Propulsion: Research Status & Needs. 72.00 (ISBN 0-915928-82-5). AIAA.

Hill, Philip G. & Peterson, C. R. Mechanics & Thermodynamics of Propulsion. 1965. 41.95 (ISBN 0-201-02838-7). Addison-Wesley.

Robinson, J., ed. Shuttle Propulsion Systems. (AD-05 Ser.). 1982. 24.00 (H00243). ASME.

Usafosr - General Electric Company. Advanced Propulsion Concepts, Third Symposium, Vol. 1. 340p. 1964. 94.95 (ISBN 0-677-10010-8). Gordon.

SPACE VEHICLES–RELIABILITY

Goddard Memorial Symposium, 3rd, Washington D. C., 1965. Scientific Experiments for Manned Orbital Flight: Proceedings. Badgley, P. C., ed. (Science & Technology Ser.: Vol. 4). 1965. 30.00x (ISBN 0-87703-032-4, Pub. by Am Astronaut). Univelt Inc.

Horowitz, P., ed. Manned Space Reliability Symposium. (Science & Technology Ser.: Vol. 1). 1964. 20.00x (ISBN 0-87703-029-4, Pub. by Am Astronaut). Univelt Inc.

SPACE VEHICLES–RESCUE WORK

see Space Rescue Operations

SPACE VEHICLES–TRAJECTORIES

see Space Trajectories

SPACE WEATHER

see Space Environment

SPACECRAFT

see Space Vehicles

SPACECRAFT ACCIDENTS

see Astronautics–Accidents

SPACES, ALGEBRAIC

see Algebraic Spaces

SPACES, FUNCTION

see Function Spaces

SPACES, GENERALIZED

see also Algebras, Linear; Banach Spaces; Geometry, Riemannian; Metric Spaces; Moment Spaces

Bognar, J. & Szoekelalvi-Nagy, J. Indefinite Inner Product Spaces. LC 73-10669. (Ergebnisse der Mathematik und Ihrer Grenzgebiete: Vol. 78). 236p. 1974. 31.00 (ISBN 0-387-06202-5). Springer-Verlag.

Buseman, Herbert H. Metric Methods in Finsler Spaces. (Annals of Mathematics Studies: No. 8). 1942. 18.00 (ISBN 0-527-02724-3). Kraus Repr.

Duren, Peter L. Theory of HP Spaces. LC 74-117092. (Pure & Applied Mathematics Ser.: Vol. 38). 1970. 55.00 (ISBN 0-12-225150-4). Acad Pr.

Marussi, A. Intrinsic Geodesy. Reilly, I, tr. from Ital. (Illus.). 240p. 1985. 56.00 (ISBN 0-387-15133-8). Springer-Verlag.

Naimpally, S. A. & Warrack, B. D. Proximity Spaces. LC 73-118858. (Tracts in Mathematics & Mathematical Physics: No. 59). 1971. 22.95 (ISBN 0-521-07935-7). Cambridge U Pr.

Namioka, Isaac. Partially Ordered Linear Topological Spaces. LC 52-42389. (Memoirs: No. 24). 50p. 1974. pap. 14.00 (ISBN 0-8218-1224-6, MEMO-24). Am Math.

Pogorelov, A. V., ed. Topics in the Theory of Surfaces in Elliptic Space. (Russian Tracts on the Physical Sciences Ser.). (Illus.). 146p. 1962. 45.25x (ISBN 0-677-20400-0). Gordon.

Pyatekskii-Shapiro, I. I. Automorphic Functions & the Geometry of Classical Domains. (Mathematics & Its Applications Ser.). 272p. 1969. 56.75x (ISBN 0-677-20310-1). Gordon.

Schatten, Robert. Norm Ideals of Completely Continuous Operators. (Ergebnisse der Mathematik und Ihrer Grenzebiete: Vol. 27). 1970. Repr. 26.00 (ISBN 0-387-04806-5). Springer-Verlag.

--Theory of Cross-Spaces. (Annals of Math Studies). 1950. pap. 13.00 (ISBN 0-527-02742-1). Kraus Repr.

Schutz, J. W. Foundations of Special Relativity: Kinematic Axioms for Minkowski Space-Time. (Lecture Notes in Mathematics: Vol. 361). (Illus.). 314p. 1973. pap. 17.00 (ISBN 0-387-06591-1). Springer-Verlag.

Ivrii, V. The Precise Spectral Asymptotics for Elliptic Operators Acting in Fiberings over Manifolds with Boundary. (Lecture Notes in Mathematics Ser.: Vol. 1100). v, 225p. 1984. pap. 13.50 (ISBN 0-387-13361-5). Springer-Verlag.
Joergens, K. & Weidmann, J. Spectral Properties of Hamiltonian Operators. LC 72-97678. (Lecture Notes in Mathematics: Vol. 313). 140p. 1973. pap. 12.00 (ISBN 0-387-06151-7). Springer-Verlag.
Kantorovitz, S. Spectral Theory of Banach Space Operators. (Lecture Notes in Mathematics: Vol. 1012). 179p. 1983. pap. 12.00 (ISBN 0-387-12673-2). Springer Verlag.
Knowles, E. W. & Lewis, R. T., eds. Spectral Theory of Differential Operators. (Mathematics Studies: Vol. 55). 384p. 1981. 53.25 (ISBN 0-444-86277-3, North-Holland). Elsevier.
Koopmans, L. H. The Spectral Analysis of Time Series. 1974. 58.50 (ISBN 0-12-419250-5). Acad Pr.
Kromer, Ralph E. Asymptotic Properties of the Autoregressive Spectral Estimator. LC 73-131403. 196p. 1969. 22.00 (ISBN 0-403-04512-6). Scholarly.
Lattes, Robert. Methods of Resolution for Selected Boundary Problems in Mathematical Physics. (Documents on Modern Physics Ser.). 200p. 1969. 57.75x (ISBN 0-677-30060-3). Gordon.
--Quelques Methodes de Resolutions de Problemes aux Limites de la Physique Mathematiques. (Cours & Documents de Mathematiques & de Physique Ser.). 196p. (Orig.). 1967. 57.75x (ISBN 0-677-50060-2). Gordon.
Levitan, B. M. & Sargsjan, I. S. Introduction to Spectral Theory: Selfadjoint Ordinary Differential Operators. LC 75-15565. (Translations of Mathematical Monographs: Vol. 39). 1975. 95.00 (ISBN 0-8218-1589-X, MMONO-39). Am Math.
Lorch, Edgar R. Spectral Theory. LC 62-9824. (University Texts in the Mathematical Sciences Ser.). pap. 42.50 (ISBN 0-317-08657-X, 2051947). Bks Demand UMI.
Nikol'skii, N. K., ed. Spectral Theory of Functions & Operators, II: 1983. LC 80-11102. (Proceedings of the Steklov Institute of Mathematics: Vol. 155). 176p. 1983. pap. text ed. 55.00 (ISBN 0-8218-3072-4, STEKLOV 155). Am Math.
--Spectral Theory of Functions & Operators, 1 pt. LC 80-1102. (Proceedings of the Steklov Institute of Mathematics: No. 130). 1980. 50.00 (ISBN 0-8218-3030-9, STEKLO-130). Am Math.
Plesner, A. I. Spectral Theory of Linear Operators, 2 Vols. Nestell, Merlynd & Gibbs, Alan G., trs. LC 68-20524. 1969. Vol. 1. 18.00 (ISBN 0-8044-4767-5); Vol. 2. 18.00 (ISBN 0-8044-4768-3). Ungar.
Priestley, M. B., ed. Spectral Analysis & the Time Series, 2 Vols. in 1, Vol. 1 & Vol.2. (Probability & Mathematical Statistics Ser.). 1983. 42.50 (ISBN 0-12-564922-3). Acad Pr.
Satto. Spectral Representations of Schroedinger Operators with Long-Range Potentials. (Lecture Notes in Mathematics: Vol. 727). 1979. pap. 14.00 (ISBN 0-387-09514-4). Springer-Verlag.
Smith, C. Ray & Grandy, W. T., Jr., eds. Maximum-Entropy & Bayesian Methods in Inverse Problems. 1985. lib. bdg. 44.50 (ISBN 90-277-2074-6, Pub. by Reidel Holland). Kluwer Academic.
Steklov Institute of Mathematics. Selected Problems of Weighted Approximation & Spectral Analysis: Proceedings. Nikolskii, N. K., ed. LC 76-46375. (Proceeding of the Steklov Institute of Mathematics: No. 120). 1976. 67.00 (ISBN 0-8218-3020-1, STEKLO-120). Am Math.
Stenhagen, Einar, et al, eds. Registry of Mass Spectral Data, 4 Vols. LC 74-910. 3358p. 1974. Set. 615.50 (ISBN 0-471-82115-2, Pub. by Wiley-Interscience). Wiley.
Symposium, Dundee, 1974. Spectral Theory & Differential Equations: Proceedings. Everitt, W. N., ed. LC 75-6605. (Lecture Notes in Mathematics Ser.: Vol. 448). xii, 321p. 1975. pap. 20.00 (ISBN 0-387-07150-4). Springer-Verlag.
Tong, H. Threshold Models in Non-Linear Time Series Analysis. (Lecture Notes in Statistics: Vol. 21). (Illus.). 323p. 1983. pap. 24.00 (ISBN 0-387-90918-4). Springer-Verlag.
Wende, Burkhard, ed. Spectral Line Shapes. 1981. 92.00x (ISBN 3-11-008150-4). De Gruyter.
Xia, Daoxing. Spectral Theory of Hyponormal Operators. (Operator Theory, Advances & Applications: Vol. 10). 256p. 1983. text ed. 29.95 (ISBN 3-7643-1541-5). Birkhauser.
Yadrenko, Mikhail I. Spectral Theory of Random Fields. Balakrishnan, A. V., ed. (Translation Series in Mathematics & Engineering). 272p. 1983. pap. 26.00 (ISBN 0-387-90823-4). Springer-Verlag.

SPECTROCHEMICAL ANALYSIS
see Spectrum Analysis

SPECTROCHEMISTRY
see also Infra-Red Spectrometry; Molecular Spectra

Barrow, Gordon M. Structure of Molecules: An Introduction to Molecular Spectroscopy. (Orig.). 1963. pap. 18.95 (ISBN 0-8053-0521-1). Benjamin-Cummings.
Boumans, Paul W. Theory of Spectrochemical Excitation. LC 66-27686. 383p. 1966. 42.50x (ISBN 0-306-30281-0, Plenum Pr). Plenum Pub.
--Theory of Spectrochemical Excitation. LC 66-27686. pap. 98.50 (ISBN 0-317-27891-6, 2055791). Bks Demand UMI.
Hartmann, H. & Wanczek, K. P. Ion Cyclotron Resonance Spectrometry, Vol. II. (Lecture Notes in Chemistry: Vol. 31). 538p. 1982. pap. 32.80 (ISBN 0-387-11957-4). Springer-Verlag.
Kadish, Karl M., ed. Electrochemical & Spectrochemical Studies of Biological Redox Component. LC 82-11487. (Advances in Chemistry: No. 201). 752p. 1982. lib. bdg. 94.95x (ISBN 0-8412-0661-9). Am Chemical.
Phillips, J. P., et al, eds. Organic Electronic Spectral Data, Vol. 7. LC 60-16428. 1318p. 1971. 62.50 (ISBN 0-471-68798-7). Krieger.
Phillips, John P., et al, eds. Organic Electron Spectral Data, Vol.13. LC 60-16428. 1190p. 1977. 66.00 (ISBN 0-471-03563-7). Krieger.
Scheinmann, F. An Introduction to Spectroscopic Methods for the Identification of Organic Compounds, Vol. 1. LC 76-99991. 1970. 11.95 (ISBN 0-08-006662-3). Pergamon.
--An Introduction to Spectroscopic Methods for the Identification of Organic Compounds, Vol. 2. LC 76-99991. 368p. 1974. text ed. 30.00 (ISBN 0-08-016719-5); pap. text ed. 18.50 (ISBN 0-08-016720-9). Pergamon.

SPECTROGRAPH

Rothenberg, Martin. Programmed Learning Problem Set to Teach the Interpretation of a Class of Speech Spectrograms. (Illus.). 1963. pap. 5.20 (ISBN 0-87506-023-4). Campus.

SPECTROMETER
see also Gamma Ray Spectrometry; Infra-Red Spectrometry; Mass Spectrometry; Scintillation Spectrometry

Boumans, P. W. Line Coincidence Tables for Inductively Coupled Plasma Atomic Emission Spectrometry, 2 vols. LC 80-41344. (Illus.). 941p. 1984. 275.00 set (ISBN 0-08-031404-X). Pergamon.
Cole, Howard, ed. Tables of Wavenumbers for the Calibration of Infrared Spectrometers, Vol. 9. 2nd ed. 1977. text ed. 44.00 (ISBN 0-08-021247-6). Pergamon.
Dean, John A. & Rains, Theodore C., eds. Flame Emission & Atomic Absorption Spectrometry, 2 vols. Incl. Vol. 1. Theory. pap. 114.00 (ISBN 0-317-10435-7); Vol. 2. Components & Techniques. pap. 96.00 (ISBN 0-317-10436-5). LC 76-78830. pap. (2055080). Bks Demand UMI.
Debertin, K. & Mann, W. B. Gamma & X-Ray Spectrometry Techniques & Applications. 25.00 (ISBN 0-08-029159-7). Pergamon.
Hartmann, H. & Wanczek, K. P. Ion Cyclotron Resonance Spectrometry. (Lecture Notes in Chemistry: Vol. 7). (Illus.). 1978. pap. 19.00 (ISBN 0-387-08760-5). Springer-Verlag.
Harwit, Martin & Sloane, J. Neil. Hadamard Transform Optics. LC 78-31096. 1979. 39.50 (ISBN 0-12-330050-9). Acad Pr.
Jenkins. Quantitative X-Ray Spectrometry. 608p. 1981. 85.00 (ISBN 0-8247-1266-8). Dekker.
Market Intelligence Research Company Staff. Analytical Instrument World Markets, 1980-1990. pap. text ed. 695.00x (ISBN 0-317-19558-1). Market Res Co.
Martin, A. E. Infrared Interferometric Spectrometers: A Series of Advances, Vol. 8. (Vibrational Spectra & Structure Ser.). 292p. 1980. 74.50 (ISBN 0-444-41907-1). Elsevier.
Photoelectron Spectrometry. Incl. Photoelectron Spectra of Nonmetallic Solids & Consequences for Quantum Chemistry. Jrgensen, C. K; Fractional Prentage Methods for Ionisation of Open Shells of D & F Electrons. Cox, P. A; X-Ray Photoelectron Spectroscopy: Application to Metals & Alloys. Watson, R. E. & Perlman, M. L.; Ultraviolet Photoelectron Spectroscopy of Gases Adsorbed on Metal Surfaces. Bradshaw, A. M., et al.. (Structure & Bonding: Vol. 24). (Illus.). iv, 170p. 1975. 40.00 (ISBN 0-387-07364-7). Springer-Verlag.
Scharf, W. & Lisieski, W. Amplitude Distribution Spectrometers. (Fundamental Studies in Engineering: Vol. 3). 568p. 1980. 106.50 (ISBN 0-444-99777-6). Elsevier.
Tsalev, D. L. & Zaprianov, Z. K., eds. Atomic Absorption Spectrometry in Occupational & Environmental Health Practice, Vol. I. 264p. 1984. 78.00 (ISBN 0-8493-5603-2). CRC Pr.

SPECTROMETRY, GAMMA RAY
see Gamma Ray Spectrometry

SPECTROMETRY, TIME-OF-FLIGHT
see Time-Of-Flight Mass Spectrometry

SPECTROPHOTOMETRY

Elwell, W. T. & Gidley, J. A. Atomic Absorption Spectrophotometry. 2nd ed. 1966. 21.00 (ISBN 0-08-012063-6). Pergamon.
IES Guide to Spectroradiometric Measurements. 5.50 (LM-58). Illum Eng.
International Astronomical Union Symposium No. 50, Villa Carlos Paz, Argentina, Oct. 18-24, 1971. Spectral Classification & Multicolor Photometry: Proceedings. Fehrenbach, Ch. & Westerlund, B. E., eds. LC 72-87471. 314p. 1973. lib. bdg. 53.00 (ISBN 90-277-0280-2, Pub. by Reidel Holland); pap. text ed. 37.00 (ISBN 90-277-0363-9). Kluwer Academic.
Marczenko, Zygmund. Spectrophotometric Determination of Elements. LC 74-33186. (Ser. in Analytical Chemistry). 643p. 1976. 114.95x (ISBN 0-470-56865-8). Halsted Pr.
Romanova, Mariya A. Air Survey of Sand Deposits by Spectral Luminance. LC 63-21214. 158p. 1964. 35.00x (ISBN 0-306-10672-8, Consultants). Plenum Pub.
Stewart, J. E. Infrared Spectroscopy: Experimental Methods & Techniques. 1970. 99.75 (ISBN 0-8247-1643-4). Dekker.
Sunshine, Irving & Gerber, S. R. Spectrophotometric Analysis of Drugs: Including Atlas of Spectra. (Illus.). 256p. 1963. 25.75x (ISBN 0-398-04420-1). C C Thomas.
Sunshine, Irving, ed. CRC Handbook of Spectrophotometric Data of Drugs. 496p. 1981. 78.00 (ISBN 0-8493-3571-X). CRC Pr.
Weissberger, A. & Rossiter, B. W., eds. Techniques of Chemistry: Optical, Spectroscopic & Radioactivity Methods: Iternferometry, Light Scattering, Microscopy, Microwave & Magnetic Resonance Spectroscopy, Vol. 1, Pt. 3A. 732p. 1972. 60.00 (ISBN 0-471-92729-5). Krieger.

SPECTROSCOPE
see also Spectrograph; Spectrophotometry; Spectrum Analysis

Cummins, H. Z. & Pike, E. R., eds. Photon Correlation & Light Beating Spectroscopy. LC 74-938. (NATO ASI Series B, Physics: Vol. 3). 584p. 1974. 89.50x (ISBN 0-306-35703-8, Plenum Pr). Plenum Pub.
Donini, J. C., ed. Recent Advances in Group Theory & Their Application to Spectroscopy. LC 79-13112. (NATO ASI Series B, Physics: Vol. 43). 704p. 1979. 105.00x (ISBN 0-306-40172-X, Plenum Pr). Plenum Pub.
Eland, J. H. Photoelectron Spectroscopy. (Illus.). 272p. 1984. text ed. 49.95 (ISBN 0-408-71057-8). Butterworth.
Hellwege, K. H. & Hellwege, A. M., eds. Molecular Constants, Mostly from Microwaves, Molecular Beam, & Electron Resonance Spectroscopy. (Landolt-Boernstein, New Series: Group II, Vol. 14). (Illus.). 375p. (Supplement to Volumes II-4 & II-6, Subvolume b). 1983. 242.40 (ISBN 0-387-11857-8). Springer-Verlag.
May, Leopold, ed. Spectroscopic Tricks, Vol. 2. 388p. 1971. 42.50x (ISBN 0-306-30301-9, Plenum Pr). Plenum Pub.
--Spectroscopic Tricks, Vol. 3. LC 67-17377. 400p. 1973. 42.50x (ISBN 0-306-35223-0, Plenum Pr). Plenum Pub.
NATO Advanced Study Institute, 1973. Chemical Spectroscopy & Photochemistry in the Vacuum: Proceedings. Sandorfy, C., et al, eds. LC 73-91209. (NATO Advanced Studies Institute Ser: No. C-8). 1974. lib. bdg. 74.00 (ISBN 90-277-0418-X, Pub. by Reidel Holland). Kluwer Academic.
Parsons, M. L., et al. Atlas of Spectral Interferences in ICP Spectroscopy. LC 79-24222. 654p. 1980. 85.50x (ISBN 0-306-40334-X, Plenum Pr). Plenum Pub.
Tarasov, K. I. The Spectroscope. (Illus.). 1974. 65.00 (ISBN 0-9960017-7-8, Pub. by A Hilger England). Heyden.
Wehry, E. L. Modern Fluorescence Spectroscopy, Vol. 1. LC 75-43827. (Modern Analytical Chemistry Ser.). (Illus.). 238p. 1976. 37.50x (ISBN 0-306-33903-X, Plenum Pr). Plenum Pub.
Wehry, E. L., ed. Modern Fluorescence Spectroscopy, Vol. 2. LC 75-43827. (Modern Analytical Chemistry Ser.). (Illus.). 459p. 1976. 59.50x (ISBN 0-306-33904-8, Plenum Pr). Plenum Pub.

SPECTROSCOPY
see Spectrum Analysis

SPECTROSCOPY, ASTRONOMICAL
see Astronomical Spectroscopy

SPECTROSCOPY, NUCLEAR
see Nuclear Spectroscopy

SPECTROSCOPY, PLASMA
see Plasma Spectroscopy

SPECTROSCOPY, RAMAN
see Raman Spectroscopy

SPECTRUM, ATOMIC
see Atomic Spectra

SPECTRUM, INFRA-RED
see also Heat-Radiation and Absorption; Infra-Red Rays; Infra-Red Spectrometry; Photography, Infra-Red

AIP Conference Proceedings No. 90 Boulder, 1982. Laser Techniques for Extreme Ultraviolet Spectroscopy. McIlrath, T. J. & Freeman, R. R., eds. LC 82-73205. 497p. 1982. lib. bdg. 37.00 (ISBN 0-88318-189-4). Am Inst Physics.
The Atlas of Near Infrared Spectra. 1982. 275.00 (ISBN 0-8456-0062-1). Sadtler Res.
Bellamy, L. J. The Infrared Spectra of Complex Molecules, Vol. 1. 3rd ed. 1975. 39.95x (ISBN 0-412-13850-6, NO. 6033, Pub. by Chapman & Hall). Methuen Inc.
--Infrared Spectra of Complex Molecules, Vol. 2. 2nd ed. 299p. 1980. 39.95 (ISBN 0-412-22350-3, NO. 6333, Pub. by Chapman & Hall England). Methuen Inc.
Brame, E. G. & Grasselli, Jeannette, eds. Infrared & Raman Spectroscopy P & C, Pt. C. (Practical Spectroscopy Ser.: Vol. 1). 1977. 65.00 (ISBN 0-8247-6527-3). Dekker.
Button, Kenneth J., ed. Reviews of Infrared & Millimeter Waves, Vol. 1. 365p. 1983. 55.00x (ISBN 0-306-41260-8, Plenum Pr). Plenum Pub.
Clark, R. J. H. & Hester, R. E. Advances in Infrared & Raman Spectroscopy, Vol. 11. 383p. 1984. 98.00x (ISBN 0-471-26267-6, Pub. by Wiley Heyden). Wiley.
Durig, James R., ed. Analytical Applications of FT-IR to Molecular & Biological Systems. (NATO Advanced Study Institute Ser. C - Mathematical & Physical Sciences: No. 57). 607p. 1980. lib. bdg. 68.50 (ISBN 90-277-1145-3, Pub. by Reidel Holland). Kluwer Academic.
Ferraro, John R. & Basile, Louis J., eds. Fourier Transform Infrared Spectroscopy, Vol. 4. 1985. 74.50 (ISBN 0-12-254104-9). Acad Pr.
Hershenson, Herbert M. Infrared Absorption Spectra, 2 vols. Incl. Index for 1945-57. 1959. 43.50 (ISBN 0-12-343250-2). Acad Pr.
Herzberg, Gerhard. Molecular Spectra & Molecular Structure, 3 vols. Incl. Vol.1. Spectra of Diatomic Molecules. 2nd ed. 1950. 32.50 (ISBN 0-442-03385-0); Vol. 2. Infrared & Raman Spectra of Polyatomic Molecules. 1945. 32.50 (ISBN 0-442-03386-9); Vol. 3. Electronic Spectra & Electronic Structure of Polyatomic Molecules. 1966. 32.50 (ISBN 0-442-03387-7). Van Nos Reinhold.
Hill, R. R. & Rendell, D. A. Interpretation of Infrared Spectra: A Programmed Introduction. 208p. 1975. 34.95 (ISBN 0-471-25771-0, Wiley Heyden). Wiley.
The Infrared Spectra Atlas of Monomers & Polymers. 1981. 295.00 (ISBN 0-8456-0064-8). Sadtler Res.
Infrared Spectra Handbook of Inorganic Compounds. 1984. 295.00 (ISBN 0-8456-0112-1). Sadtler Res.
The Infrared Spectra Handbook of Minerals & Clays. 1982. 265.00 (ISBN 0-8456-0080-X). Sadtler Res.
The Infrared Spectra Handbook of Priority Pollutants & Toxic Chemicals. 1982. 265.00 (ISBN 0-8456-0077-X). Sadtler Res.
The Interpretation of Vapor-Phase Infrared Spectra. Vol. 1 Group Frequency Data. 120.00 (ISBN 0-8456-0092-3); Vol. 2 Corresponding Spectra. 350.00 (ISBN 0-8456-0100-8); Set. 425.00. Sadtler Res.
Moller, Karl & Rothchild, Walter G. Far-Infrared Spectroscopy. LC 70-118624. 818p. 1971. 74.95 (ISBN 0-471-61313-4). Krieger.
Nakamoto, Kazuo. Infrared & Raman Spectra of Inorganic & Coordination Compounds. 3rd ed. LC 77-15107. 1978. 45.50x (ISBN 0-471-62979-0, Pub. by Wiley-Interscience). Wiley.
Nyquist, R. A. & Kegel, R. O. Infrared Spectra of Inorganic Compounds. 1971. 71.00 (ISBN 0-12-523450-3). Acad Pr.
Rao, Chintamani N. Chemical Applications of Infrared Spectroscopy. 1964. 71.50 (ISBN 0-12-580250-1). Acad Pr.
Rao, K. N. Wavelength Standards in the Infrared. 1966. 57.50 (ISBN 0-12-580650-7). Acad Pr.
Royal Society of London. New Techniques in Optical & Infrared Spectroscopy: Proceedings of a Royal Society Discussion Meeting held 21-22 April 1982. Series, G. W. & Thrush, B. A., eds. (Illus.). 221p. 1983. text ed. 65.00x (ISBN 0-85403-195-2, Pub. by Royal Soc London). Scholium Intl.
Sadtler Research Laboratories, Inc. The Sadtler Handbooks. Incl. Sadtler Handbook of Proton NMR Spectra. 295.00 (ISBN 0-8456-0034-6); Sadtler Handbook of Ultraviolet Spectra. 295.00 (ISBN 0-8456-0035-4); Sadtler Handbook of Infrared Spectra. 295.00 (ISBN 0-8456-0033-8). 1978. Set. 690.00 (ISBN 0-685-51844-2). Sadtler Res.
Schultz, G. & Moss, T. S., eds. High-Resolution Infrared & Submillimetre Spectroscopy: A Selection of Papers Presented at a Workshop Held in Bonn, 1977. 1978. pap. text ed. 25.00 (ISBN 0-08-021675-7). Pergamon.
Szymanski, Herman A. & Erickson, Ronald E. Infrared Band Handbook, 2 Vols. 2nd ed. LC 71-123546. 1512p. 1970. Set. 175.00x (ISBN 0-306-65138-6, IFI Plenum). Plenum Pub.

Zhbankov, Rostislav G. Infrared Spectra of Cellulose & Its Derivatives. Stepanov, Academician B., ed. Densham, A. B., tr. from Rus. LC 65-25268. (Illus.). pap. 86.80 (ISBN 0-317-09373-8, 2020674). Bks Demand UMI.

SPECTRUM, MOLECULAR

see Molecular Spectra

SPECTRUM, SOLAR

Drummond, A. J. & Thekaekara, M. P. The Extraterrestrial Solar Spectrum. 1973. pap. text ed. 12.00 (ISBN 0-915414-43-0). Inst Environ Sci.

Symposium, University of Utrecht, 1963. The Solar Spectrum: Proceedings. De Jager, C., ed. (Astrophysics & Space Science Library: No. 1). 417p. 1965. lib. bdg. 39.50 (ISBN 90-277-0119-9, Pub. by Reidel Holland). Kluwer Academic.

SPECTRUM, ULTRA-VIOLET

see also Ultra-Violet Rays

Green, Alex E., ed. The Middle Ultraviolet: Its Science & Technology. LC 66-22839. (Wiley Series in Pure & Applied Optics). pap. 101.50 (ISBN 0-317-09204-9, 2007393). Bks Demand UMI.

Hershenson, Herbert M. Ultraviolet & Visible Absorption Spectra, 3 vols. Incl. Index for 1930-1954. 1956. 46.50 (ISBN 0-12-343265-0). Acad Pr.

Hirayama, Kenzo. Handbook of Ultraviolet & Visible Absorption Spectra of Organic Compounds. LC 66-24948. 645p. 1967. 75.00x (ISBN 0-306-65123-8, IFI Plenum). Plenum Pub.

Jones, M. H. & Woodcock, J. T. Ultraviolet Spectrometry of Flotation Reagents with Special Reference to the Determination of Xanthate in Flotation Liquors. 1980. 50.00x (ISBN 0-900488-20-4, Pub. by Inst Mining England). State Mutual Bk.

Lang, L., ed. Absorption Spectra in the Ultraviolet & Visible Region. Incl. Vols. 3-4. 86.50 ea. Vol. 3, 1963 (ISBN 0-12-436303-2). Vol. 4, 1963 (ISBN 0-12-436304-0); Vol. 5. 1965. 86.50 (ISBN 0-12-436305-9); Vols. 6-12. 86.50 ea. Vol. 6, 1966 (ISBN 0-12-436306-7). Vol. 7, 1967 (ISBN 0-12-436307-5). Vol. 8, 1967 (ISBN 0-12-436308-3). Vol. 9, 1968 (ISBN 0-12-436309-1). Vol. 10, 1968 (ISBN 0-12-436310-5). Vol. 11,1969. (ISBN 0-12-436311-3); Vol. 12, 1970. (ISBN 0-12-436312-1); Index to Volumes. 1969. 47.50 (ISBN 0-12-436356-3); Vols. 13-15. 1970. 86.50 ea. Vol. 13 (ISBN 0-12-436313-X). Vol. 14,1971 (ISBN 0-12-436314-8). Vol. 15 (ISBN 0-12-436315-6); Index to Volumes 11-15. 1971. 47.50 (ISBN 0-12-436357-1); Vols. 16-17. 1972-73. 86.50 ea. Vol. 17 (ISBN 0-12-436317-2). Acad Pr.

Photoelectric Spectrometry Group, England & Institut fuer Spektrochemie und Angewandte Spektroskopie, Germany. U V Atlas of Organic Compounds, 5 vols. 1966-71. Set. 275.00 (ISBN 0-306-68300-8, IFI Plenum); 65.00 ea. Vol. 1 (ISBN 0-306-68301-6). Vol. 2 (ISBN 0-306-68302-4). Vol. 3 (ISBN 0-306-68303-2). Vol. 4 (ISBN 0-306-68304-0). Vol. 5 (ISBN 0-306-68305-9). Plenum Pub.

Samson, James A. Techniques of Vacuum Ultraviolet Spectroscopy. LC 67-19780. 1980. Repr. of 1967 ed. 30.00 (ISBN 0-918626-15-3). VUV Assocs.

Vodar, Boris & Romand, J. Some Aspects of Vacuum Ultraviolet Radiation Physics. LC 73-20163. 1974. text ed. 54.00 (ISBN 0-08-016984-8). Pergamon.

SPECTRUM, ULTRA-VIOLET–BIBLIOGRAPHY

Kirschenbaum, Donald M., ed. Bibliographic Atlas of Protein Spectra in the Ultraviolet & Visible Regions. 522p. 1983. 95.00x (ISBN 0-306-65207-2, IFI-Plenum). Plenum Pub.

SPECTRUM, VIBRATIONAL

see Vibrational Spectra

SPECTRUM ANALYSIS

see also Absorption Spectra; Astronomical Spectroscopy; Atomic Spectra; Electron Paramagnetic Resonance; Gamma Ray Spectrometry; Laser Spectroscopy; Light; Mass Spectrometry; Microwave Spectroscopy; Molecular Spectra; Nuclear Spectroscopy; Radio Frequency Spectroscopy; Raman Spectroscopy; Scintillation Spectrometry; Spectroscope; Spectrum, Solar; Spectrum, Ultra-Violet; Ultra-Violet Rays; X-Ray Spectroscopy;

also subdivision Spectra under subjects, e.g. Iron–Spectra; Neon–Spectra; Stars–Spectra

Abraham, R. J. & Loftus, P. Proton & Carbon-13 Nmr Spectroscopy: An Integrated Approach. 216p. 1978. 29.95 (ISBN 0-471-25576-9, Wiley Heyden). Wiley.

AIP Conference, Philadelphia, April, 1972. Experimental Meson Spectroscopy 1972: Proceedings, No. 8. Kwan-Wu Lai & Rosenfeld, A. H., eds. LC 72-88226. (Illus.). 489p. 1972. 14.00 (ISBN 0-88318-107-X). Am Inst Physics.

Akademiia Nauk SSSR & Institut khimicheskoi fiziki. Atlas of Electron Spin Resonance Spectra: Theoretically Calculated Multicomponent Symmetrical Spectra, Vol. 1. LC 63-21216. pap. 58.30 (ISBN 0-317-09765-2, 2003355). Bks Demand UMI.

Alfano, R. R., ed. Biological Events Proved by Ultrafast Laser Spectroscopy. LC 82-1613. (Quantum Electronics Ser.). 1982. 59.00 (ISBN 0-12-049950-9). Acad Pr.

Alkemade, Cornelis T. & Herrmann, Roland. Fundamentals of Analytical Flame Spectroscopy. LC 79-4376. 442p. 1979. 104.95 (ISBN 0-470-26710-0). Halsted Pr.

American Society for Testing & Materials. Symposium on Spectroscopy. LC 60-9523. (American Society for Testing & Materials, Special Technical Publication: No. 269). pap. 62.80 (ISBN 0-317-09560-9, 2000106). Bks Demand UMI.

Avram, Margareta & Mateescu, Gh. Infrared Spectroscopy: Applications in Organic Chemistry. LC 78-16322. 532p. 1978. Repr. of 1972 ed. lib. bdg. 33.00 (ISBN 0-88275-711-3). Krieger.

Baker, A. J., et al. More Spectroscopic Problems in Organic Chemistry. 2nd ed. 139p. 1975. 35.95 (ISBN 0-471-25591-2, Wiley Heyden). Wiley.

Banks, Richard C., et al. Introductory Problems in Spectroscopy. 1980. 25.95 (ISBN 0-8053-0572-6). Benjamin-Cummings.

Barnes, Austin, et al, eds. Matrix Isolation Spectroscopy. x, 606p. 1981. 69.50 (ISBN 90-277-1328-6, Pub. by Reidel Holland). Kluwer Academic.

Barnes, Ramon M., ed. Emission Spectroscopy. LC 75-30672. 1976. 73.50 (ISBN 0-12-786137-8). Acad Pr.

Bashkin, S., ed. Beam-Foil Spectroscopy. (Topics in Current Physics: Vol. 1). 1976. 42.00 (ISBN 0-387-07914-9). Springer-Verlag.

Bashkin, Stanley, ed. Beam-Foil Spectroscopy, 2 Vols. LC 68-8275. (Illus.). 678p. 1968. Set. 180.50 (ISBN 0-677-12940-8). Gordon.

Bell, J. Ellis, ed. Spectroscopy in Biochemistry, 2 vols. 336p. Vol. 1, May 1981. 82.00 (ISBN 0-8493-5551-6); Vol. 2, April, 1981. 82.00 (ISBN 0-8493-5552-4). CRC Pr.

Bendat, Julius S. & Piersol, Allan G. Engineering Applications of Correction & Spectral Analysis. LC 79-25926. 302p. 1980. 41.95x (ISBN 0-471-05887-4, Pub. by Wiley-Interscience). Wiley.

Berkowitz, Joseph. Photoabsorption, Photoionization & Photoelectron Spectroscopy. (Pure & Applied Physics Ser.). 1979. 59.50 (ISBN 0-12-091650-9). Acad Pr.

Beyer, H. J. & Kleinpoppen, Hans, eds. Progress in Atomic Spectroscopy, Part C. (Physics of Atoms & Molecules Ser.). 625p. 1983. 85.00x (ISBN 0-306-41300-0, Plenum Pr). Plenum Pub.

Bhacca, Norman S. & William, Dudley H. Applications of NMR Spectroscopy in Organic Chemistry: Illustrations from the Steroid Field. LC 64-25659. (Holden-Day Series in Physical Techniques in Chemistry). pap. 52.00 (ISBN 0-317-09053-4, 2016285). Bks Demand UMI.

Birks, L. S. X-Ray Spectrochemical Analysis, Vol. 2. 2nd ed. LC 71-79144. (Illus.). 143p. 1969. text ed. 11.25 (ISBN 0-471-07525-6, Pub. by Wiley). Krieger.

Blackburn, James A., ed. Spectral Analysis: Methods & Techniques. 304p. 1970. 65.00 (ISBN 0-8247-1045-2). Dekker.

Bloembergen, N., ed. Nonlinear Spectroscopy: Proceedings. (Enrico Fermi Internatinal School of Physics Ser.: No. 64). 460p. 1977. 95.75 (ISBN 0-7204-0568-8, North-Holland). Elsevier.

Boschke, F., ed. New Methods in Chemistry. LC 51-5497. (Topics in Current Chemistry Ser.: Vol. 36). (Illus.). 127p. 1973. pap. 23.60 (ISBN 0-387-06098-7). Springer-Verlag.

Boumans, P. W. Atomic Absorption Spectroscopy-Past, Present & Future: To Commemorate the 25th Anniversary of Alan Walsh's Landmark Paper in Spectrochimica Acta. 248p. 1981. pap. 35.00 (ISBN 0-08-026267-8). Pergamon.

Boumans, P. W., et al, eds. A Profile of Current Developments in Atomic Spectroscopy: Dedicated to Kurt Laqua on the Occasion of His 65th Birthday. 400p. 1985. 82.50 (ISBN 0-08-031447-3). Pergamon.

Brame, Edward G., Jr., ed. Applications of Polymer Spectroscopy. LC 77-25728. 1978. 55.50 (ISBN 0-12-125450-X). Acad Pr.

Braterman, P. S., et al. Spectra & Chemical Interactions. LC 67-11280. (Structure & Bonding: Vol. 26). 1976. 36.00 (ISBN 0-387-07591-7). Springer-Verlag.

Bratos, S. & Pick, R. M., eds. Vibrational Spectroscopy of Molecular Liquids & Solids. LC 80-12174. (NATO ASI Series B, Physics: Vol. 56). 475p. 1980. 69.50x (ISBN 0-306-40445-1, Plenum Pr). Plenum Pub.

Breene, R. G., Jr. Theories of Spectral Line Shape. LC 80-20664. 344p. 1981. 50.95x (ISBN 0-471-08361-5, Pub. by Wiley-Interscience). Wiley.

Breitmaier, E. & Voelter, W. Thirteen-C NMR Spectroscopy: Methods & Applications. 2nd ed. (Monographs in Modern Chemistry: Vol. 5). (Illus.). 344p. 1978. 57.70x (ISBN 0-89573-004-9). VCH Pubs.

Breitmaier, Eberhard & Bauer, Gerhard. Thirteen C-NMR Spectroscopy: A Working Manual with Exercises. Cassels, Bruce K., tr. from Ger. (MMI Press Polymer Monographs). 431p. 1984. 108.00 (ISBN 3-7186-0022-6). Harwood Academic.

Breitmeier, E., et al. Thirteen NMR Spectroscopy. (MMI Press Polymer Monograph). 431p. 1984. text ed. 108.00 (ISBN 3-7186-0022-6). Harwood Academic.

Bremser, W., et al. Carbon Thirteen NMR Spectral Data: A Living Comfiche Collection of Reference Material. 3rd ed. 1981. 550.00 (ISBN 3-527-25899-X). VCH Pubs.

--Chemical Shift Ranges in Carbon-13 NMR Spectroscopy. vvii, 891p. 1982. 137.50X (ISBN 0-89573-053-7). VCH Pubs.

Brookman, Alan. The Invisible World. LC 83-60896. (Exploration & Discovery Ser.). 1983. 13.80 (ISBN 0-382-06720-7). Silver.

Brown, S. B. An Introduction to Spectroscopy for Biochemists. LC 79-41632. 1980. 49.50 (ISBN 0-12-137080-1). Acad Pr.

Brundle, C. R. & Baker, A. D. Electron Spectroscopy, Vol. 5. 1984. 75.00 (ISBN 0-12-137805-5). Acad Pr.

Brundle, C. R. & Baker, A. D., eds. Electron Spectroscopy: Theory, Techniques, & Applications. Vol. 1, 1977. 79.00 (ISBN 0-12-137801-2); Vol. 2, 1979. 60.00 (ISBN 0-12-137802-0); Vol. 3, 1979. 63.00 (ISBN 0-12-137803-9). Acad Pr.

Buck, Otto, et al, eds. Electron & Positron Spectroscopies in Material Science & Engineering. (Materials Science Ser.). 1979. 67.50 (ISBN 0-12-139150-7). Acad Pr.

Campbell, I. D. & Dwek, R. A. Biological Spectroscopy: Concepts, Applications & Problems. 1984. 39.95 (ISBN 0-8053-1847-X); pap. 26.95 (ISBN 0-8053-1849-6). Benjamin-Cummings.

Cannon, C. J. The Transfer of Spectral Line Radiation. (Illus.). 650p. 1985. 99.50 (ISBN 0-521-25995-9). Cambridge U Pr.

Cardona, M. Modulation Spectroscopy. (Solid State Physics: Suppl. 11). 1969. 76.00 (ISBN 0-12-607771-1). Acad Pr.

Carrington. Computers for Spectroscopists. LC 74-12526. 275p. 1975. 54.95x (ISBN 0-470-13581-6). Halsted Pr.

Carrington, R. A. Computers for Spectroscopists. LC 74-12526. 275p. 1974. 27.50 (ISBN 0-470-13581-6, Pub. by Wiley). Krieger.

Centre National de la Recherche Scientifique. New Methods of Instrumental Spectroscopy. 210p. 1972. 57.75 (ISBN 0-677-30240-1). Gordon.

Chakrabarti, C. L. Progress in Analytical Atomic Spectroscopy, 2 vols. (Illus.). 282p. 1981. Set. 84.00 (ISBN 0-08-027126-X). Pergamon.

Chamberlain, J. Principles of Interferometric Spectroscopy. LC 78-13206. 347p. 1979. 94.95 (ISBN 0-471-99719-6). Wiley.

Chang, Raymond. Basic Principles of Spectroscopy. LC 77-10971. 314p. 1978. Repr. of 1971 ed. lib. bdg. 21.50 (ISBN 0-88275-613-3). Krieger.

Chen, Sow-Hsin & Yip, Sidney, eds. Spectroscopy in Biology & Chemistry: Neutron, X-Ray, Laser. 1974. 55.00 (ISBN 0-12-170850-0). Acad Pr.

Childers, D. G., ed. Modern Spectrum Analysis. LC 78-55097. 1978. 41.55 (ISBN 0-87942-107-X, PC01040). Inst Electrical.

Chrien, R. E. & Kane, W. R., eds. Neutron-Capture Gamma Ray Spectroscopy. new ed. LC 79-9772. 900p. 1979. 115.00x (ISBN 0-306-40166-5, Plenum Pr). Plenum Pub.

Chu, Wei-Kan, et al. Backscattering Spectroscopy. 1978. 65.00 (ISBN 0-12-173850-7). Acad Pr.

Clarke, Richard H., ed. Triplet State ODMR Spectroscopy: Techniques & Applications to Biophysical Systems. LC 81-10486. 566p. 1982. 67.95x (ISBN 0-471-07988-X, Pub. by Wiley-Interscience). Wiley.

Clerc, J. T., et al. Structural Analysis of Organic Compounds by Combined Application of Spectroscopic Methods. (Studies in Analytical Chemistry: Vol. 1). 288p. 1982. 61.75 (ISBN 0-444-99748-2). Elsevier.

Cline Love, L. J. & Eastwood, Delyle, eds. Advances in Luminescence Spectroscopy - STP 863. LC 84-71320. (Illus.). 129p. 1985. pap. text ed. 26.00 (ISBN 0-8031-0412-X, 04-863000-39). ASTM.

Cohen, I. Bernard, ed. The Wave Theory of Light & Spectra. LC 80-2102. (Development of Science Ser.). (Illus.). 1981. lib. bdg. 35.00x (ISBN 0-405-13867-9). Ayer Co Pubs.

Cohen, Richard L. Applications of Mossbauer Spectroscopy, Vol. 2. 1980. 60.00 (ISBN 0-12-178402-9). Acad Pr.

Comes, F. J. & Muller, A., eds. Spectroscopy in Chemistry & Physics: Modern Trends. (Studies in Physical & Theoretical Chemistry: Vol. 8). 342p. 1980. 81.00 (ISBN 0-444-41856-3). Elsevier.

Compilation of Methods for Emission Spectrochemical Analysis. 7th ed. 1114p. 1982. 49.00 (ISBN 0-8031-0513-4, 03-502082-39). ASTM.

Cooks, R. G, ed. Collision Spectroscopy. LC 77-10761. (Illus.). 459p. 1977. 65.00x (ISBN 0-306-31044-9, Plenum Pr). Plenum Pub.

Cooper, James W. Spectroscopic Techniques for Organic Chemists. LC 79-23952. 1980. 29.50x (ISBN 0-471-05166-7, Pub. by Wiley-Interscience). Wiley.

Coyle, J. D., et al, eds. Interpretation of NMR Spectra: An Introductory Audio Visual Programme. 62p. 1983. 18.95 (ISBN 0-471-26228-5, Pub. by Wiley-Interscience); wkbk. avail. (ISBN 0-471-90369-8). Wiley.

Coyle, John, et al. Interpretation of NMR Spectra: An Introductory Audio-Visual Programme. 1984. pap. write for info. (ISBN 0-471-26227-7). Wiley.

Craver, Clara D., ed. Polymer Characterization: Interdisciplinary Approaches. LC 70-163285. 279p. 1971. 39.50x (ISBN 0-306-30545-3, Plenum Pr). Plenum Pub.

Creswell, Clifford J., et al. Spectral Analysis of Organic Compounds: An Introductory Programmed Text. 2nd ed. LC 72-77099. 1972. pap. 14.95x (ISBN 0-8087-0335-8). Burgess.

Criddle, W. J. & Ellis, G. P. Spectral & Chemical Characterization of Organic Compounds: A Laboratory Handbook. 2nd ed. LC 80-40497. 115p. 1980. 45.95x (ISBN 0-471-27813-0, Pub. by Wiley-Interscience); pap. 21.95 (ISBN 0-471-27812-2). Wiley.

Crooks, J. E. The Spectrum in Chemistry. 1978. pap. 23.50 (ISBN 0-12-195552-4). Acad Pr.

Cundall, R. B., et al, eds. Time-Resolved Fluorescence Spectroscopy in Biochemistry & Biology. (NATO ASI Series A, Life Sciences: Vol. 69). 800p. 1983. 110.00x (ISBN 0-306-41476-7, Plenum Pr). Plenum Pub.

Delgass, William, et al. Spectroscopy in Heterogeneous Catalysis. LC 78-27885. 1979. 49.50 (ISBN 0-12-210150-2). Acad Pr.

Denney, R. C. Dictionary of Spectroscopy. 2nd ed. 208p. 1982. 39.95x (ISBN 0-471-87478-7, Pub. by Wiley-Interscience). Wiley.

Di Bartolo, Baldassare, ed. Spectroscopy of the Excited State. LC 75-38526. (NATO ASI Series B, Physics: Vol. 12). 416p. 1976. 62.50x (ISBN 0-306-35712-7, Plenum Pr). Plenum Pub.

Dixon, Robert C. Spread Spectrum Systems. 2nd ed. 422p. 1984. text ed. 37.50x (ISBN 0-471-88309-3, Wiley-Interscience). Wiley.

Dorio, M. M. & Freed, J. A., eds. Multiple Electron Resonance Spectroscopy. LC 78-27381. (Illus.). 524p. 1979. 69.50x (ISBN 0-306-40123-1, Plenum Pr). Plenum Pub.

Douglas, Bodie & Hollingworth, Charles A. Introduction to Applications of Symmetry to Bonding & Spectra. 1985. 39.00 (ISBN 0-12-221340-8). Acad Pr.

Dunitz, J. D., et al. Inorganic Chemistry & Spectroscopy. (Structure & Bonding: Vol. 36). (Illus.). 1979. 51.00 (ISBN 0-387-09201-3). Springer-Verlag.

Durig, James R., ed. Analytical Applications of FT-IR to Molecular & Biological Systems. (NATO Advanced Study Institute Ser. C. - Mathematical & Physical Sciences: No. 57). 607p. 1980. lib. bdg. 68.50 (ISBN 90-277-1145-3, Pub. by Reidel Holland). Kluwer Academic.

Dyke, S. F., et al. Organic Spectroscopy: An Introduction. 2nd ed. (Illus.). 1979. pap. text ed. 13.95x (ISBN 0-582-45076-4). Longman.

Ebdon, L. & Jackson, K. W., eds. Annual Reports on Analytical Atomic Spectroscopy, Vol. 13. 427p. 1985. 99.00 (ISBN 0-85186-687-5, 99610478X, Pub. by Royal Soc Chem UK). Heyden.

Eisenthal, Kenneth B., ed. Applications of Picosecond Spectroscopy to Chemistry. 384p. 1984. lib. bdg. 59.00 (ISBN 90-277-1788-5, Pub.by Reidel Academic). Kluwer Academic.

Elwell, W. T. & Gidley, J. A. Atomic Absorption Spectrophotometry. 2nd ed. 1966. 21.00 (ISBN 0-08-012063-6). Pergamon.

Engelson, Morris. Modern Spectrum Analyzer Theory & Application. 275p. 1984. text ed. 55.00 (ISBN 0-89006-150-5). Artech Hse.

Engelson, Morris & Telewski, Fred. Spectrum Analyzer Theory & Applications. LC 73-81244. (Modern Frontiers in Applied Science Ser.). pap. 71.80 (ISBN 0-317-30035-0, 2025050). Bks Demand UMI.

European Congress on Molecular Spectroscopy 8th 1965 Denmark. Molecular Spectroscopy. pap. 81.80 (ISBN 0-317-12977-5, 2020713). Bks Demand UMI.

Ferraro, John. Vibrational Spectroscopy at High External Pressures: The Diamond Anvil Cell (Monograph) LC 83-22355. 1984. 59.00 (ISBN 0-12-254160-X). Acad Pr.

Ferraro, John R. & Basile, Louis J., eds. Fourier Transform Infared Spectroscopy, Vol. 3: Techniques Using Fourier Transform Interferometry. 1982. 39.00 (ISBN 0-12-254103-0). Acad Pr.

--Fourier Transform Infrared Spectroscopy, Vol. 4. 1985. 74.50 (ISBN 0-12-254104-9). Acad Pr.

Fitting, Dale & Adler, Laszlo. Ultrasonic Spectral Analysis for Nondestructive Evaluation. LC 80-14991. 364p. 1981. 59.50x (ISBN 0-306-40484-2, Plenum Pr). Plenum Pub.

Flameless Atomic Absorption Analysis: An Update, STP 618. 1977. pap. 14.00 (ISBN 0-8031-0355-7, 04-618000-39). ASTM.

Frank, C. W., et al. Spectroscopy: NMR, Fluorescence, FT-IR. (Advances in Polymer Science Ser.: Vol. 54). (Illus.). 170p. 1984. 41.00 (ISBN 0-387-12591-4). Springer-Verlag.

Fuwa, K., et al, eds. Atomic Spectroscopy in Japan. (Journal Spectrochimica Acta Ser.: No. 36). 160p. 1981. pap. 17.50 (ISBN 0-08-028731-X). Pergamon.

Gaydon, A. G. The Spectroscopy of Flames. 2nd ed. 1974. 43.00x (ISBN 0-412-12870-5, 6120, Pub. by Chapman & Hall). Methuen Inc.

Gaydon, A. G. & Pearse, R. W. Identification of Molecular Spectra. 4th ed. 1976. 82.00 (ISBN 0-412-14350-X, NO. 6215, Pub. by Chapman & Hall). Methuen Inc.

Gettins, W. J. & Wyn-Jones, E., eds. Techniques & Applications of Fast Reactions in Solution. (Nato Advanced Study Institutes Series: Math & Physical Sciences: No. C50). 1979. lib. bdg. 58.00 (ISBN 90-277-1022-8, Pub. by Reidel Holland). Kluwer Academic.

Ghosh, P. K. Introduction to Photoelectron Spectroscopy. LC 82-17374. (Chemical Analysis: A Series of Monographs on Analytical Chemisty & Its Applications). 377p. 1983. 58.95x (ISBN 0-471-06427-0, Pub. by Wiley-Interscience). Wiley.

Gillespie, Allesia M. A Manual of Fluorometric & Spectrophotometric Experiments. 146p. 1985. pap. text ed. 25.00 (ISBN 2-88124-005-4). Gordon.

Gonser, U., ed. Moessbauer Spectroscopy II: The Exotic Side of the Methods. (Topics in Currents Physics Ser.: Vol. 25). (Illus.). 210p. 1981. 33.00 (ISBN 0-387-10519-0). Springer-Verlag.

Gorry. Basic Molecular Spectroscopy. (Illus.). 160p. 1985. pap. text ed. 15.95 (ISBN 0-408-01553-5). Butterworth.

Grell, E., ed. Membrane Spectroscopy. (Molecular Biology, Biochemistry, & Biophysics Ser.: Vol. 31). (Illus.). 512p. 1981. 89.50 (ISBN 0-387-10332-5). Springer-Verlag.

Grove, E. L., ed. Applied Atomic Spectroscopy. Incl. Vol. 1. 331p. 47.50x (ISBN 0-306-33905-6); Vol. 2. 364p. 55.00 (ISBN 0-306-33906-4). LC 77-17444. (Modern Analytical Chemistry Ser.). (Illus.). 1978. 2 vols. 80.00 (Plenum Pr). Plenum Pub.

Guenther, Harold. NMR Spectroscopy: An Introduction. LC 78-31736. 436p. 1980. 94.95x (ISBN 0-471-27580-8); pap. 32.95x (ISBN 0-471-27579-4). Wiley.

Hansma, Paul K., ed. Tunneling Spectroscopy: Capabilities, Applications, & New Techniques. LC 82-16161. 512p. 1982. 75.00x (ISBN 0-306-41070-2, Plenum Pr). Plenum Pub.

Harris, Daniel C. & Bertolucci, Michael D. Symmetry & Spectroscopy: An Introduction to Vibrational & Electronic Spectroscopy. (Illus.). 1978. 18.95x (ISBN 0-19-855152-5). Oxford U Pr.

Hawkins, Donald T. Auger Electron Spectroscopy: A Bibliography, 1925-1975. LC 76-55815. 312p. 1977. 95.00x (ISBN 0-306-65168-8, Plenum Pr). Plenum Pub.

Haykin, S., ed. Nonlinear Methods of Spectral Analysis. 2nd ed. (Topics in Applied Physics Ser.: Vol. 34). (Illus.). 280p. (Second Corrected & Updated Edition). 1983. pap. 28.00 (ISBN 0-387-12386-5). Springer-Verlag.

Henderson, S. T. Daylight & Its Spectrum. 2nd ed. LC 77-88254. 349p. 1978. 58.95x (ISBN 0-470-99328-6). Halsted Pr.

Herber, R. H., ed. Chemical Mossbauer Spectroscopy. 392p. 1984. 59.50x (ISBN 0-306-41885-1, Plenum Pr). Plenum Pub.

Hollas, J. Michael. High Resolution Spectroscopy. 1982. text ed. 130.00 (ISBN 0-408-10605-0). Butterworth.

Hummel, Dieter O. Polymer Spectroscopy. LC 73-90783. (Monographs in Modern Chemistry: Vol. 6). (Illus.). 401p. 1974. 96.90x (ISBN 3-527-25411-0). VCH Pubs.

International Conference on Atomic Spectroscopy. Recent Advances in Analytical Spectroscopy: Proceedings of the 9th International Conference on Atomic Spectroscopy & 22nd Colloquium Spectroscopicum Internationale, Tokyo, Japan, 4-8 September 1981. Fuwa, K., ed. (IUPAC Symposium Ser.). (Illus.). 336p. 1982. 83.00 (ISBN 0-08-026221-X). Pergamon.

Ionin, B. I. & Ershov, B. A. NMR Spectroscopy in Organic Chemistry. LC 66-18972. (Physical Methods in Organic Chemistry Ser.). 382p. 1970. 39.50x (ISBN 0-306-30424-4, Plenum Pr). Plenum Pub.

Jacobs, P. A., et al, eds. Structure & Reactivity of Modified Zeolites: Proceedings of an International Conference, Prague, July 9-13, 1984. (Studies in Surface Science & Catalysis: No. 18). 376p. 1984. 74.00 (ISBN 0-444-42351-6, I-234-84). Elsevier.

Jansson, Peter A. Deconvolution: With Applications in Spectroscopy. LC 83-15647. 1984. 69.00 (ISBN 0-12-380220-2). Acad Pr.

Jenkins, Gwilym M. & Watts, Donald G. Spectral Analysis & Its Applications. LC 67-13840. 1968. 48.00x (ISBN 0-8162-4464-2). Holden-Day.

Jones, D. W., ed. Introduction to the Spectroscopy of Biological Polymers. 1977. 59.50 (ISBN 0-12-389250-3). Acad Pr.

Jordan, Peter C. Chemical Kinetics & Transport. LC 78-20999. (Illus.). 1979. 29.50x (ISBN 0-306-40122-3, Plenum Pr). Plenum Pub.

Karasek, F. W., et al, eds. Mass Spectrometry in Environmental Sciences. 598p. 1985. 75.00x (ISBN 0-306-41552-6, Plenum Pr). Plenum Pub.

Karr, Clarence, ed. Infrared & Raman Spectroscopy of Lunar & Terrestrial Minerals. 1975. 78.00 (ISBN 0-12-399950-2). Acad Pr.

Kessler, M. F. & Phillips, J. P., eds. Galactic & Extragalactic Infrared Spectroscopy. 1984. lib. bdg. 58.00 (ISBN 90-277-1704-4, Pub. by Reidel Holland). Kluwer Academic.

Kevan, Larry & Kispert, Lowell D. Electron Spin Double Resonance Spectroscopy. LC 75-44418. pap. 108.50 (ISBN 0-317-09907-8, 2055603). Bks Demand UMI.

Kharkevich, A. A. Spectra & Analysis. LC 60-9256. 222p. 1960. 34.50x (ISBN 0-306-10638-8, Consultants). Plenum Pub.

Kliger, David S., ed. Ultrasensitive Laser Spectroscopy. LC 82-18417. (Quantum Electronics Ser.). 1983. 55.00 (ISBN 0-12-414980-4). Acad Pr.

Klopffer, W. Introduction to Polymer Spectroscopy. (Polymers-Properties & Application: Vol. 7). (Illus.). 210p. 1984. 40.00 (ISBN 0-387-12850-6). Springer-Verlag.

Knystautas, E. J. & Drouin, R., eds. Fast Ion-Beam Spectroscopy. 398p. 1982. 118.50. Elsevier.

Kortuem, G. Reflectance Spectroscopy: Principles, Methods, Applications. Lohr, J. E., tr. LC 79-86181. (Illus.). 1969. 54.00 (ISBN 0-387-04587-2). Springer-Verlag.

Laidlaw, W. G. Introduction to Quantum Concepts in Spectroscopy. LC 79-4513. 260p. 1980. Repr. of 1970 ed. lib. bdg. 19.50 (ISBN 0-88275-925-6). Krieger.

Lakowicz, Joseph R. Principles of Fluorescence Spectroscopy. 485p. 1983. 32.50x (ISBN 0-306-41285-3, Plenum Pr). Plenum Pub.

Laser Spectroscopy II: Proceedings of the Third International Conference,Jackson Lake Lodge, Wyoming, USA, July 4-8, 1977. (Springer Series in Optical Sciences: Vol. 7). (Illus.). 1977. 42.00 (ISBN 0-387-08543-2). Springer-Verlag.

Lever, A. B., ed. Inorganic Electronic Spectroscopy. 2nd ed. (Studies in Physical & Theoretical Chemistry: No. 33). 862p. 1984. 109.25 (ISBN 0-444-42389-3, I-314-84). Elsevier.

Levy, George C. Topics in Carbon-13 NMR Spectroscopy, Vol. 1. LC 72-1262. 292p. 1974. 43.50 (ISBN 0-471-53154-5, Pub. by Wiley-Interscience). Wiley.

Levy, George C., ed. NMR Spectroscopy: New Methods & Applications. LC 82-11458. (ACS Symosium Ser.: No. 191). 388p. 1982. lib. bdg. 54.95 (ISBN 0-8412-0723-2). Am Chemical.

Lim, S. H., ed. Advances in Multi-Photon Processes & Spectroscopy, Vol. 1. 511p. 1984. 60.00x (ISBN 9971-966-17-4, Pub. by World Sci Singapore). Taylor & Francis.

Lin, S. H. & Neusser, H. J., eds. Muliphoton Spectroscopy of Molecules: Quantum Electronics: Principles & Applications. LC 83-2584. 1984. 59.00 (ISBN 0-12-450520-1). Acad Pr.

Lindenbaum, S. J., ed. Experimental Meson Spectroscopy, 1983: Seventh International Conference, Brookhaven. LC 84-70910. (AIP Conference Proceedings: No. 113). 506p. 1984. lib. bdg. 46.00 (ISBN 0-88318-312-9). Am Inst Physics.

Long, Gary J., ed. Mossbauer Spectroscopy Applied to Inorganic Chemistry. (Modern Inorganic Chemistry Ser.). 686p. 1984. 92.50x (ISBN 0-306-41647-6, Plenum Pr). Plenum Pub.

Lumb, Michael, ed. Luminescence Spectroscopy. 1979. 77.00 (ISBN 0-12-459550-2). Acad Pr.

L'Vov, B. V. Atomic Absorption Spectrochemical Analysis. 1970. 62.50 (ISBN 0-9960017-2-7, Pub. by A Hilger England). Heyden.

Lyons, W. S., ed. Analytical Spectroscopy: Proceedings of the 26th Conference on Analytical Chemistry in Energy Technology, Knoxville, TN, Oct. 11-13, 1983. (Analytical Chemistry Symposium Ser.: No. 19). 394p. 1984. 75.00 (ISBN 0-444-42312-5, I-138-84). Elsevier.

McGucken, William. Nineteenth-Century Spectroscopy: Development of the Understanding of Spectra, 1802-1897. LC 74-94886. pap. 62.30 (ISBN 0-317-08471-2, 2011868). Bks Demand UMI.

McGuire, G. E. Auger Electron Spectroscopy Reference Manual: A Book of Standard Spectra for Indentification & Interpretation of Auger Spectroscopy Data. LC 79-24223. 1980p. 1979. spiral bdg. 49.50x (ISBN 0-306-40333-1, Plenum Pr). Plenum Pub.

McLennan, D. J. A Revised Transition State Spectrum for Concerted Bimolecular B - Eliminations. 1976. pap. text ed. 14.00 (ISBN 0-08-020472-4). Pergamon.

Macomber, James D. The Dynamics of Spectroscopic Transitions: Illustrated by Magnetic Resonance & Laser Effects. LC 75-25852. (Wiley-Interscience Monographs in Chemical Physics). (Illus.). pap. 89.50 (ISBN 0-317-09275-8, 2013078). Bks Demand UMI.

Mandelstam, S. L., ed. Spectrochemical Analysis in the U. S. S. R. 112p. 1983. pap. 17.50 (ISBN 0-08-028747-6). Pergamon.

Margolis, H. A. Spectra & the Steenrod Algebra. (Mathematical Library: Vol. 29). 500p. 1984. 65.00 (ISBN 0-444-86516-0, North-Holland). Elsevier.

Martin, G. J., et al. N-NMR Spectroscopy. (NMR-Basic Principles & Progress Ser.: Vol. 18). (Illus.). 390p. 1981. 89.50 (ISBN 0-387-10459-3). Springer-Verlag.

Martin, Maryvonne L., et al. Practical NMR Spectroscopy. pap. 123.00 (ISBN 0-317-26326-9, 2025202). Bks Demand UMI.

Mattson, James, ed. Laboratory Systems & Spectroscopy. (Computers in Chemistry & Instrumentation: Vol. 5). 1977. 69.75 (ISBN 0-8247-6207-X). Dekker.

Mavrodineanu, Radu. & Boiteux, Henri. Flame Spectroscopy. LC 64-20088. (Wiley Series in Pure & Applied Spectroscopy). pap. 160.00 (ISBN 0-317-08746-0, 2007476). Bks Demand UMI.

Mazing, M. A. Research on Spectroscopy & Luminescence, Part 2: On the Broadening & Shift of Spectral Lines in the Plasma of a Gaseous Discharge. LC 62-12860. (P. N. Lebedev Physics Institute Ser.: Vol. 15). 66p. 1962. 22.50x (ISBN 0-306-17042-6, Consultants). Plenum Pub.

Meloan, Clifton E. Instrumental Analysis Using Spectroscopy. LC 68-20179. (Medical Technology Ser.: No. 1). pap. 44.50 (ISBN 0-317-09062-3, 2050349). Bks Demand UMI.

Merritt & McEwen. Mass Spectronomy, Pt. B. (Practical Spectroscopy Ser.: Vol. 3). 416p. 1980. 75.00 (ISBN 0-8247-6947-3). Dekker.

Mid-America Spectroscopy Symposium. Developments in Applied Spectroscopy: Proceedings of the Thirteenth Annual Symposium on Spectroscopy Held in Chicago, Illinois, April 30-May 3, 1962, Vol. 2. Ferraro, J. R. & Ziomek, J. S., eds. LC 61-17720. pap. 112.00 (ISBN 0-317-28823-7, 2020721). Bks Demand UMI.

Mid-America Spectroscopy Symposium (14th; 1963; Chicago, IL) Developments in Applied Spectroscopy, Vol. 3: Proceedings of the Fourteenth Annual Mid-America Spectroscopy Symposium Held in Chicago, Illinois May 20-23, 1963. Forrette, J. E. & Lanterman, E., eds. LC 61-17720. (Illus.). pap. 105.80 (ISBN 0-317-07933-6, 2020722). Bks Demand UMI.

Mid-America Spectroscopy Symposium (15th; 1964; Chicago. IL) Developments in Applied Spectroscopy, Vol. 4: Proceedings of the Fifteenth Annual Mid-America Spectroscopy Symposium Held in Chicago, Illinois, June 2-5, 1964. Davis, Elwin N., ed. LC 61-17720. (Illus.). pap. 139.50 (ISBN 0-317-07928-X, 2020723). Bks Demand UMI.

Mid-America Spectroscopy Symposium (18th; 1967; Chicago. IL), et al. Developments in Applied Spectroscopy, Vol 6: Selected Papers from the Eighteenth Annual Mid-America Spectroscopy Symposium Held in Chicago, Illinois, May 15-18, 1967. Baer, William K. & Perkins, Alfred J., eds. LC 61-17720. (Illus.). pap. 103.30 (ISBN 0-317-07921-2, 2020724). Bks Demand UMI.

Mid-America Spectroscopy Symposium (19th; 1968, Chicago, IL) Developments in Applied Spectroscopy: Vol. 7-A: Selected Papers from the Seventh Annual Meeting of the Society for Applied Spectroscopy (Nineteenth Annual Mid-America Spectroscopy Symposium) held in Chicago, Illinois, May 13-17. 1968. Grove, E. L. & Perkins, Alfred J., eds. LC 61-17720. (Illus.). pap. 87.80 (ISBN 0-317-07908-5, 2020726). Bks Demand UMI.

Mid-America Spectroscopy Symposium (20th; 1969; Chicago, IL) Developments in Applied Spectroscopy Vol. 8: Selected Papers from the Twentieth Annual Mid-America Spectroscopy Symposium Held in Chicago, Illinois, May 12-15, 1969. Grove, E. L., ed. LC 61-17720. (Illus.). pap. 83.80 (ISBN 0-317-07916-6, 2020725). Bks Demand UMI.

Miller, F. A., ed. Topics in Vibrational Spectroscopy: Dedicated to the Memory of Sir Harold W. Thompson. 300p. 1985. pap. 69.00 (ISBN 0-08-032602-1). Pergamon.

Mills, K., et al, eds. Instrumental Data for Drug Analysis, Vol. 1. 648p. 1982. 102.50 (ISBN 0-444-00718-0). Elsevier.

Ministry of Education. Scientific Terms Spectroscopy: Japanese-English, English-Japanese. (Japanese & Eng.). 165p. 1974. leatherette 14.95 (ISBN 0-686-92512-2, M-9341). French & Eur.

Mladjenovic, M. Development of Magnetic B-Ray Spectroscopy. (Lecture Notes in Physics Ser.: Vol. 52). 1976. 17.00 (ISBN 0-387-07851-7). Springer-Verlag.

Moller, Karl & Rothchild, Walter G. Far-Infrared Spectroscopy. LC 70-118624. 818p. 1971. 74.95 (ISBN 0-471-61313-4). Krieger.

Mooney, E. F. Annual Reports on NMR Spectroscopy, 1982, Vol. 11B. 95.00 (ISBN 0-12-505349-5). Acad Pr.

Mooney, E. F., ed. Annual Reports on NMR Spectroscopy. Incl. Vol. 1. 1968. 69.00 (ISBN 0-12-505350-9); Vol. 5B. 1974. 80.00 (ISBN 0-12-505345-2); Vol. 6, 2 pts. 1976-78. Pt. B. 49.50 (ISBN 0-12-505346-0); Pt. C. 95.00 (ISBN 0-12-505347-9); Vol. 7. 1978. 60.00 (ISBN 0-12-505307-X); Vol. 8. 1978. 85.00 (ISBN 0-12-505308-8); Vol. 9. 1979. 75.00 (ISBN 0-12-505309-6). Acad Pr.

Mooney, E. F. & Webb, G. A., eds. Annual Reports on NMR Spectroscopy, 2 Vols. 1983. Vol. 13. 99.50 (ISBN 0-12-505313-4); Vol. 14. 90.00 (ISBN 0-12-505314-2). Acad Pr.

Mooney, E. F. & Webb, Graham, eds. Animal Reports in NMR Spectroscopy, Vol. 10A. 1980. 80.00 (ISBN 0-12-505310-X). Acad Pr.

--Annual Reports in NMR Spectroscopy, Vol. 10B. 1980. 92.50 (ISBN 0-12-505348-7). Acad Pr.

Moritz, H. & Torok, T. Technical Dictionary of Spectroscopy & Spectral Analysis: English, German, French, Russian. 1971. 72.00 (ISBN 0-08-015864-1). Pergamon.

Muller, Rudolf O. Spectrochemical Analysis by X-Ray Fluorescence. LC 70-107540. 350p. 1972. 49.50x (ISBN 0-306-30436-8, Plenum Pr). Plenum Pub.

Newland, D. E. An Introduction to Random Vibrations & Spectral Analysis. 2nd ed. LC 74-75025. (Illus.). pap. text ed. 25.95x (ISBN 0-582-30530-6). Longman.

Painter, Paul C., et al. The Theory of Vibrational Spectroscopy & Its Applications to Polymeric Materials. LC 81-12969. 530p. 1982. 74.95x (ISBN 0-471-09346-7, Pub. by Wiley-Interscience). Wiley.

Pao, Y. H., ed. Optoacoustic Spectroscopy & Detection. 1977. 45.00 (ISBN 0-12-544150-9). Acad Pr.

Parikh, V. M. Absorption Spectroscopy of Organic Molecules. LC 72-3460. 1974. pap. text ed. 24.95 (ISBN 0-201-05708-5). Addison-Wesley.

Parsons, M. L. & McElfresh, P. M. Flame Spectroscopy: Atlas of Spectral Lines. LC 76-165368. 96p. 1971. 39.50x (ISBN 0-306-65156-4, IFI Plenum). Plenum Pub.

Parsons, M. L., et al. Handbook of Flame Spectroscopy. LC 75-17865. 476p. 1975. 69.50x (ISBN 0-306-30856-8, Plenum Pr). Plenum Pub.

Pavia, Donald L., et al. Introduction to Spectroscopy: A Guide for Students of Organic Chemistry. LC 77-11348. 1979. text ed. 25.95 (ISBN 0-7216-7119-5). HR&W.

Payne, J. P., et al. The Medical & Biological Applications of Mass Spectroscopy. 1979. 39.00 (ISBN 0-12-547950-6). Acad Pr.

Pecora, Robert. Dynamic Light Scattering: Applications of Photon Correlation Spectroscopy. 416p. 1985. 59.50x (ISBN 0-306-41790-1, Plenum Pr). Plenum Pub.

Perlow, Gilbert J., ed. Workshop on New Directions in Mossbauer Spectroscopy, Argonne National Lab, June 1977. LC 77-90635. (AIP Conference Proceedings: No. 38). (Illus.). 1977. lib. bdg. 15.00 (ISBN 0-88318-137-1). Am Inst Physics.

Reddell, James R., ed. Studies on the Caves & Cave Fauna of the Yucatan Peninsula. (Association for Mexican Cave Studies: Bulletin 6). 296p. 1977. 13.00 (ISBN 0-686-70407-X). Speleo Pr.

Reddell, James R. & Mitchell, Robert W., eds. Studies on the Cavernicole Fauna of Mexico. (Association for Mexican Cave Studies: Bulletin 4). 239p. 1971. 13.00 (ISBN 0-686-70405-3). Speleo Pr.

Sloane, Bruce. Cavers, Caves, & Caving. 1977. 19.95 (ISBN 0-8135-0835-5). Rutgers U Pr.

Watson, Richard A., ed. The Cave Research Foundation: Origins & the First Twelve Years, 1957-1968. (Illus.). 495p. 1981. pap. 15.00 (ISBN 0-939748-02-9). Cave Bks MO.

SPENT REACTOR FUEL REPROCESSING

see Reactor Fuel Reprocessing

SPERMATOPHYTA

see Phanerogams

SPERMATOZOA

see also Flagella (Microbiology)

Andre, Jean, ed. The Sperm Cell. 1983. 71.75 (ISBN 90-247-2784-7, Pub. by Martinus Nijhoff Netherlands). Kluwer Academic.

Baccetti, Baccio, ed. Comparative Spermatology. 1971. 98.50 (ISBN 0-12-069950-8). Acad Pr.

Bacetti, B. & Afzelius, B. The Biology of the Sperm Cell. (Monographs in Developmental Biology: Vol. 10). (Illus.). 250p. 1976. 54.25 (ISBN 3-8055-2204-5). S Karger.

Duckett, J. G. & Racey, P. A., eds. The Biology of the Male Gamete: Linnean Society Supplement No. 1 to the Biological Journal, Vol. 7. 1975. 73.00 (ISBN 0-12-223050-7). Acad Pr.

Fawcett, Don W. & Bedford, Michael J., eds. Spermatozoon: Maturation, Motility, Surface Properties & Comparative Aspects. LC 79-9196. (Illus.). 464p. 1979. text ed. 60.00 (ISBN 0-8067-0601-5). Urban & S.

Hadek, Robert. Mammalian Fertilization: An Atlas of Ultrastructure. 1969. 55.00 (ISBN 0-12-312950-8). Acad Pr.

Inserm-International Symposium, Nouzilly, Nov. 4-7, 1973. The Biology of Spermatozoa: Proceedings. Hafez, E. S. & Thibault, C. G., eds. (Illus.). vii, 256p. 1975. 47.00 (ISBN 3-8055-2104-9). S Karger.

Mann, T. Spermatophores: Development, Structure, Biochemical Attributes & Role in the Transfer of Spermatozoa. (Zoophysiology Ser.: Vol. 15). (Illus.). 240p. 1984. 49.00 (ISBN 0-387-13583-9). Springer-Verlag.

Silvestrini, B. & Caputo, A., eds. Lonidamine: A New Pharmacolocial Approach to the Study & Control of Spermatogenesis & Tumors. (Chemotherapy Journal: Vol. 27, Suppl.). (Illus.). 120p. 1981. pap. 15.50 (ISBN 3-8055-3438-8). S Karger.

SPERRY, ELMER AMBROSE, 1860-1930

Hughes, Thomas Parke. Elmer Sperry: Inventor & Engineer. LC 71-110373. (Studies in the History of Technology). (Illus.). 448p. 1971. 37.00x (ISBN 0-8018-1133-3). Johns Hopkins.

SPHAERIALES

Cain, Roy L. Studies of Coprophilous Sphaeriales in Ontario. (Illus.). 1968. Repr. of 1934 ed. 14.00 (ISBN 3-7682-0531-2). Lubrecht & Cramer.

SPHAGNUM

Brown, Edmund R. & Very, Alice. How to Use Peat Moss. (Orig.). 1953. pap. 2.00 (ISBN 0-8283-1162-5). Branden Pub Co.

SPHECIDAE

Bohart, R. M. & Menke, A. S. Sphecid Wasps of the World: A Generic Revision. 1976. 90.00x (ISBN 0-520-02318-8). U of Cal Pr.

Evans, Howard. Comparative Ethology & Evolution of the Sand Wasps. LC 66-18245. 1966. 32.50x (ISBN 0-674-15201-8). Harvard U Pr.

SPHERE

see also Circle; Geometry, Modern; Trigonometry, Spherical

Coolidge, Julian L. Treatise on the Circle & the Sphere. LC 78-128872. 1971. text ed. 27.50 (ISBN 0-8284-0236-1). Chelsea Pub.

Heller, Wilfried, et al. Angular Scattering Functions for Spheroids. LC 77-156067. 144p. 1972. text ed. 12.00x (ISBN 0-8143-1454-6). Wayne St U Pr.

Schaffer, Juan J. Geometry of Spheres in Normed Spaces. (Lecture Notes in Pure & Applied Math Ser: Vol. 20). 1976. 45.00 (ISBN 0-8247-6554-0). Dekker.

Toth. Harmonic & Minimal Maps with Applications in Geometry & Physics. 1984. 70.00 (ISBN 0-470-20127-4). Wiley.

Wenninger, Magnus J. Spherical Models. LC 78-58806. 1979. 34.50 (ISBN 0-521-22279-6); pap. 13.95 (ISBN 0-521-29432-0). Cambridge U Pr.

SPHERICAL ASTRONOMY

see Astronomy, Spherical and Practical

SPHERICAL HARMONICS

see also Ausdehnungslehre; Harmonic Functions

Hobson, Ernest W. Spherical & Ellipsoidal Harmonics. LC 55-233. xi, 500p. 1955. 17.95 (ISBN 0-8284-0104-7). Chelsea Pub.

Mueller, C. Spherical Harmonics. (Lecture Notes in Mathematics: Vol. 17). 1966. pap. 10.70 (ISBN 0-387-03600-8). Springer-Verlag.

Silberger, A. J. PGL-2, Over the P-Adics: Its Representations, Spherical Functions, & Fourier Analysis. LC 70-139951. (Lecture Notes in Mathematics: Vol. 166). 1970. pap. 14.00 (ISBN 0-387-05193-7). Springer-Verlag.

SPHERICAL TRIGONOMETRY

see Trigonometry, Spherical

SPHEROIDAL FUNCTIONS

see Functions, Spheroidal

SPICES

Beaufort County Open Land Trust. Sea Island Seasons. 1980. 9.95 (ISBN 0-918544-40-8). Wimmer Bks.

Center for Self Sufficiency Learning Institute Staff. At Your Own Pace Bibliography on Herb & Spice Plant Growing. 35p. 1985. pap. text ed. 2.75 (ISBN 0-910811-68-7, Pub. by Center Self Suff). Prosperity & Profits.

Clair, Colin. Dictionnaire des Herbes et des Epices. (Fr.). 259p. 1963. pap. 6.95 (ISBN 0-686-56842-7, M-6621). French & Eur.

Coffee, Cocoa, Tea & Spices Industry. (UNIDO Guides to Information Sources: No. 28). pap. 4.00 (ISBN 0-686-93191-2, UN198, UN). Unipub.

Dictionary of Spice Technology. (Eng. & Chinese.). 172p. 1978. pap. 4.95 (ISBN 0-686-92609-9, M-9568). French & Eur.

Hayes, Elizabeth S. Spices & Herbs: Lore & Cookery. 13.00 (ISBN 0-8446-5772-7). Peter Smith.

Heinerman, John. Complete Book of Spices: Their Medical, Nutritional & Cooking Uses. LC 82-80700. 1983. 15.95 (ISBN 0-87983-347-5); pap. 12.95 (ISBN 0-87983-281-9). Keats.

Jank, Joseph K. Spices: Their Botanical Origin, Their Chemical Composition, Their Commercial Use Including Seeds, Herbs & Leaves. 1980. lib. bdg. 49.95 (ISBN 0-8490-3111-7). Gordon Pr.

Lowenfeld, Claire & Back, Philippa. The Complete Book of Herbs & Spices. (Illus.). 319p. 1980. 19.95 (ISBN 0-7153-7656-X). David & Charles.

Maclaren, W. A. Rubber, Tea & Cacao with Special Sections on Coffee, Spices & Tobacco. 1980. lib. bdg. 75.00 (ISBN 0-8490-3110-9). Gordon Pr.

Morton, Julia F. Herbs & Spices. (Golden Guide Ser.). (Illus.). 1977. pap. 2.95 (ISBN 0-307-24364-8, Golden Pr). Western Pub.

Muenscher, Walter C. & Rice, Myron A. Garden Spice & Wild Pot-Herbs: An American Herbal. LC 78-56899. (Illus.). 218p. 1978. pap. 12.95 (ISBN 0-8014-9174-6). Comstock.

Purseglove, et al. Spices, 2 vols. (Tropical Agriculture Ser.). (Illus.). 1981. Vol. 1. text ed. 45.00x (ISBN 0-582-46811-6); Vol. 2. text ed. 45.00x (ISBN 0-582-46342-4). Longman.

Rosengarten, Frederick. The Book of Spices. rev. ed. 1981. pap. 3.95 (ISBN 0-515-06490-4, Y3220). Jove Pubns.

SPIDERS

Brignoli, Paolo M. A Catalogue of the Araneae Described Between 1940 & 1981. LC 83-7937. 784p. 1983. 90.00 (ISBN 0-7190-0856-5, Pub. by Manchester Univ Pr). Longwood Pub Group.

Bristowe, W. S. The Comity of Spiders, 2 Vols. Repr. of 1941 ed. Set. 34.00 (ISBN 0-384-05895-7). Johnson Repr.

British Arachnological Society. 60.00x (Pub. by EW Classey Bk). State Mutual Bk.

Browning, John. Tarantulas. (Illus.). 96p. 1981. 4.95 (ISBN 0-87666-931-3, KW-075). TFH Pubns.

Fabre, J. Henri. The Life of the Spider. 1912. 30.00 (ISBN 0-8482-3989-X). Norwood Edns.

Foelix, Rainer F. Biology of Spiders. (Illus.). 320p. 1982. text ed. 30.00x (ISBN 0-674-07431-9). Harvard U Pr.

Helle, W. & Sabelis, M. Spider Mites: Their Biology & Control, Pt. A. (World Crop Pests Ser.: Vol. 1A). Date not set. write for info. (ISBN 0-444-42372-9). Elsevier.

--Spides Mites: Their Biology & Control, Pt. B. (World Crop Pests Ser.: Vol. 1B). Date not set. write for info. (ISBN 0-444-42374-5). Elsevier.

Jones, Dick. The Larousse Guide to Spiders. LC 83-81216. (Nature Guides Ser.). (Illus.). 320p. (Orig.). 1983. pap. 11.95 (ISBN 0-88332-324-9, 8076). Larousse.

Kaston, B. J. How to Know the Spiders. 3rd ed. (Pictured Key Nature Ser.). 288p. 1978. write for info. wire coil (ISBN 0-697-04898-5). Wm C Brown.

Locket, G. H., et al. British Spiders, 2 vols. combined Vols. 1 & 2. (Illus.). 1978. Repr. of 1951 ed. 36.00x (ISBN 0-565-00838-2, Pub. by Brit Mus Nat Hist). Sabbot-Natural Hist Bks.

Locket, G. M., et al. British Spiders, Vol. 3. (Illus.). 1974. 27.00x (ISBN 0-903874-02-4, Pub. by Brit Mus Nat Hist). Sabbot-Natural Hist Bks.

Lund, Dale. All about Tarantulas. (Illus.). 1977. 9.95 (ISBN 0-87666-909-7, PS-749). TFH Pubns.

Perrero, Laurie & Perrero, Louis. Tarantulas: In Nature & As Pets. (Illus.). 1979. pap. 1.95 (ISBN 0-89317-029-1). Windward Pub.

Petrunkevich, Alexander. A Study of Amber Spiders. 1942. pap. 75.00x (ISBN 0-686-51318-5). Elliots Bks.

Reed, John R. A Gallery of Spiders: Poems. LC 80-81894. (Ontario Review Press Poetry Ser.). 72p. 1980. 10.95 (ISBN 0-86538-005-8); pap. 6.95 (ISBN 0-86538-006-6). Ontario Rev NJ.

Roberts, M. J. British Spiders. write for info. (ISBN 0-12-589680-8). Acad Pr.

Witt, Peter N. & Rovner, Jerome S., eds. Spider Communication: Mechanisms & Ecological Significance. LC 81-47164. (Illus.). 304p. 1981. 35.00x (ISBN 0-691-08291-X). Princeton U Pr.

SPIDERS–AUSTRALIA

Child, John. Australian Spider. pap. 8.50x (ISBN 0-392-07647-0, SpS). Sportshelf.

Mascord, Ronald. Australian Spiders in Colour. LC 76-133867. (Illus.). 1970. 6.75 (ISBN 0-8048-0952-6). C E Tuttle.

SPIDERS–GREAT BRITAIN

Bristowe, W. S. The Comity of Spiders, 2 Vols. Repr. of 1941 ed. Set. 34.00 (ISBN 0-384-05895-7). Johnson Repr.

SPIDERS–NORTH AMERICA

Comstock, John H. Spider Book. rev ed. Gertsch, W. J., ed. (Illus.). 740p. 1948. 42.50x (ISBN 0-8014-0084-8). Comstock.

Emerton, James H. Common Spiders of the United States. 1902. pap. 4.50 (ISBN 0-486-20223-2). Dover.

--Common Spiders of the United States. 14.50 (ISBN 0-8446-2032-7). Peter Smith.

Gertsch, Willis J. American Spiders. 2nd ed. 320p. 1979. 36.50 (ISBN 0-442-22649-7). Van Nos Reinhold.

Oehler, Charles M. Jumping Spiders (Araneae: Salticidae) in the Cincinnati Region of Ohio Including Butler, Clermont, Hamilton, & Warren Counties. 1980. 5.00 (ISBN 0-86727-087-X). Ohio Bio Survey.

SPIN (DYNAMICS)

see Rotational Motion

SPIN-LATTICE RELAXATION

Wolf, Dieter. Spin Temperature & Nuclear Spin Relaxation in Matter: Basic Principles & Applications. (International Series of Monographs on Physics). (Illus.). 1979. text ed. 49.95x (ISBN 0-19-851295-3). Oxford U Pr.

SPIN, ISOBARIC

see Isobaric Spin

SPINES (INFORMATION RETRIEVAL SYSTEM)

Coblans, H., et al. Science & Technology Policies Information Exchange System (SPINES) Feasibility Study. (Science Policy Studies & Documents: No. 33). (Illus.). 115p. (Orig.). 1974. pap. 6.00 (ISBN 92-3-101185-5, U571, UNESCO). Unipub.

SPINNING

see also Cotton Spinning; Woolen and Worsted Manufacture; Yarn

Baines, Patricia. Spinning Wheels, Spinners & Spinning. 1980. pap. 10.95 (ISBN 0-686-27277-3). Robin & Russ.

--Spinning Wheels, Spinners & Spinning. new ed. pap. 10.95 (ISBN 0-686-37658-7). Robin & Russ.

Blake, W. A., et al, eds. Spinning. (Engineering Craftsmen: No. D4). (Illus.). 1968. spiral bdg. 37.50x (ISBN 0-85083-009-5). Intl Ideas.

Brown, Rachel. The Weaving, Spinning, & Dyeing Book. LC 77-1653. (Illus.). 1978. 25.00 (ISBN 0-394-49801-1). Knopf.

Burnham, Dorothy. The Comfortable Arts: Traditional Spinning & Weaving in Canada. (National Gallery of Canada Ser.). (Illus.). 256p. 1982. pap. 24.95 (ISBN 0-88884-474-3, 56315-4, Pub. by Natl Mus Canada). U of Chicago Pr.

Crowfoot, Grace M. & Roth, H. Ling. Handspinning & Wool Combing. (Illus.). Repr. 5.95 (ISBN 0-686-09824-2). Robin & Russ.

Endrei, Walter. L' Evolution Des Techniques Du Filage & Du Tissage Du Moyen Age a la Revolution Industrielle. (Industrie & Artisanat: No. 4). 1968. pap. 14.00x (ISBN 90-2796-135-2). Mouton.

Henshaw, D. E. Worsted Spinning. 1981. 50.00x (ISBN 0-686-87279-7, Pub. by Textile Inst). State Mutual Bk.

Hochberg, B. Handspinner's Handbook. rev. ed. LC 76-12949. (Illus.). 68p. 1980. pap. 5.95 (ISBN 0-9600990-5-0). B Hochberg.

Howar, V. Weaving, Spinning & Dyeing: A Beginner's Manual. 1976. 11.95 (ISBN 0-13-947812-4, Spec); pap. 5.95 (ISBN 0-13-947804-3). P-H.

Kroll, Carol. The Whole Craft of Spinning from the Raw Material to the Finished Yarn. 1981. pap. 2.50 (ISBN 0-486-23968-3). Dover.

Leadbeater, Eliza. Handspinning. 112p. 1976. 18.25 (ISBN 0-8231-5048-8). Branford.

--Spinning & Spinning Wheels. (Shire Album Ser.: No. 43). (Illus.). 32p. (Orig.). 1983. pap. 2.95 (ISBN 0-85263-469-2, Pub. by Shire Pubns England). Seven Hills Bks.

Lord, P. R., ed. Spinning in the Seventies. 296p. 1970. 40.00x (ISBN 0-900541-01-6, Pub. by Meadowfield Pr England). State Mutual Bk.

Manfre, G. Limit of the Spinning Process in Manufacturing Synthetic Fibers. (CISM - International Centre for Mechanical Sciences, Courses & Lectures: Vol. 255). (Illus.). 66p. 1976. pap. 9.20 (ISBN 0-387-81308-X). Springer-Verlag.

Mitchell, Lillias. Irish Spinning Dyeing & Weaving. (Illus.). 1978. 12.95 (ISBN 0-85221-101-5). Dufour.

Nield, R. Open-End Spinning. 56p. 1975. 30.00x (ISBN 0-686-63778-X). State Mutual Bk.

Robinson, J. S., ed. Spinning, Extruding & Processing of Fibers: Recent Advances. LC 80-13137. (Chemical Technology Review Ser.: No. 159). 436p. 1980. 48.00 (ISBN 0-8155-0801-8). Noyes.

Rohlena, V. Open-End Spinning. LC 75-1772. (Textile Science & Technology Ser.: Vol. 1). 380p. 1975. 74.50 (ISBN 0-444-99870-5). Elsevier.

Simmons, Paula. Spinning & Weaving with Wool. LC 77-76137. (Illus.). 224p. 1977. pap. 12.95 (ISBN 0-914718-23-1). Pacific Search.

Spinning. 50.00x (ISBN 0-85083-009-5, Pub. by Engineering Ind). State Mutual Bk.

Spinning: The Lodz Textile Seminars. (Training for Industry Ser.). pap. 2.00 (ISBN 0-686-93280-3, UN70/2B6V2, UN). Unipub.

Van Wagenen, Jared. The Golden Age of Homespun. (Illus.). 1963. pap. 2.25 (ISBN 0-917334-05-1). Fenimore Bk.

Ziabicki, A. & Kawai, Hiromichi. High Speed Fiber Spinning: Science & Engineering Aspects. 584p. 1985. 110.00 (ISBN 0-471-89792-2). Wiley.

SPINNING, METAL

see Metal-Spinning

SPINNING TOP

see Top

SPINOR ANALYSIS

see also Calculus of Tensors; Vector Analysis

Cartan, Elie. The Theory of Spinors. 160p. 1981. pap. 5.00 (ISBN 0-486-64070-1). Dover.

Corson, Edward M. Introduction to Tensors, Spinors, & Relativistic Wave Equations. 2nd ed. LC 80-85523. 222p. 1981. text ed. 15.95 (ISBN 0-8284-0315-5). Chelsea Pub.

Dirac, P. A. Spinors in Hilbert Space. LC 74-18371. 91p. 1974. 22.50x (ISBN 0-306-30798-7, Plenum Pr). Plenum Pub.

Hermann, Robert. Spinors, Clifford, & Cayley Algebras. (Interdisciplinary Mathematics Ser: Vol. 7). 276p. 1974. 25.00 (ISBN 0-915692-06-6, 991600215). Math Sci Pr.

Penrose, Roger & Rindler, Wolfgang. Spinors & Space Time, Vol. 1: Two-Spinor Calculus & Relativistic Fields. 480p. 1984. 89.50 (ISBN 0-521-24527-3). Cambridge U Pr.

--Spinors & Space Time, Vol. 2: Spinor & Twistor Methods in Space-Time Geometry. 400p. Date not set. price not set (ISBN 0-521-25267-9). Cambridge U Pr.

SPIRULINA

see also Oscillatoriceae

Spirulina Users Staff. The Whole Truth about Spirulina. pap. 5.95 (ISBN 0-9610380-0-4, Dist. by New Era Pr). Univ of Trees.

SPITFIRE (FIGHTER PLANES)

Aeronautical Staff. Supermarine Spitfire. LC 66-22653. (Aero Ser: Vol. 10). 1966. pap. 3.95 (ISBN 0-8168-0536-9). Aero.

Quill, Jeffrey. Spitfire: A Test Pilot's Story. (Illus.). 332p. 1984. 19.95 (ISBN 0-295-96152-X). U of Wash Pr.

Rice, Michael S. Pilot's Manual for Supermarine Spitfire. (Illus.). 56p. 1974. pap. 3.95 (ISBN 0-87994-028-X, Pub. by AvPubns). Aviation.

Sweetman, Bill. Spitfire, Bk. 5. (Crown's World War II Fighter Planes Ser.). 1981. 6.98 (ISBN 0-517-54261-7). Crown.

SPLICING

see Knots and Splices

SPLINE THEORY

Ahlberg, J. Harold, et al. Theory of Splines & Their Applications. (Mathematics in Science & Engineering Ser.: Vol. 38). 1967. 60.00 (ISBN 0-12-044750-9). Acad Pr.

Bohmer, K., et al, eds. Spline Functions. (Lectures in Mathematics: Vol. 501). 1976. pap. 23.00 (ISBN 0-387-07543-7). Springer-Verlag.

De Boor, C. A Practical Guide to Splines. (Applied Mathematical Sciences Ser.: Vol. 27). (Illus.). 1978. pap. 22.00 (ISBN 0-387-90356-9). Springer-Verlag.

DeVore, R. A. & Scherer, K., eds. Quantitative Approximation. LC 80-17554. 1980. 35.00 (ISBN 0-12-213650-0). Acad Pr.

Holland, A. B. & Shaney, B. N. General Problem of Approximation & Spline Functions. LC 77-24577. 352p. (Orig.). 1979. lib. bdg. 22.50 (ISBN 0-88275-598-6). Krieger.

Karlin, Samuel. Total Positivity: Vol. 1. 1968. 35.00x (ISBN 0-8047-0314-0). Stanford U Pr.

--Residues of Pesticides & Other Contaminants in the Total Environment. (Residue Reviews Ser.: Vol. 93). (Illus.). 255p. 1984. 29.50 (ISBN 0-387-96019-8). Springer-Verlag.
Halbert, Frederic & Halbert, Sandra. The Bitter Harvest: A Personal Story of PBB Contamination. LC 78-23531. Repr. of 1978 ed. 39.80 (ISBN 0-8357-9123-8, 2012732). Bks Demand UMI.
Huber, J. T. Upgrading Residues & By-Products for Animals. 144p. 1981. 54.00 (ISBN 0-8493-5445-5). CRC Pr.
IAEA. Origin & Fate of Chemical Residues in Food, Agriculture & Fisheries. (Panel Proceedings Ser.). (Illus.). 189p. 1976. pap. 20.00 (ISBN 92-0-111375-7, ISP399, IAEA). Unipub.
Impact Monitoring of Residues from the Use of Agricultural Pesticides in Developing Countries: Report. 1976. pap. 7.50 (ISBN 0-685-71574-4, F936, FAO). Unipub.
Jensen, A. A. Residues of Pesticides & Other Contaminants in the Total Environment. (Residue Reviews: Vol. 89). 155p. 1983. 31.00 (ISBN 0-387-90884-6). Springer-Verlag.
Kaemmerer, K. & Buntenkoetter, S. Residue Reviews: The Problems of Residues in Meat of Edibles, Vol. 46. Gunther, F. A., ed. LC 62-18595. 250p. 1973. 53.00 (ISBN 0-387-90060-8). Springer-Verlag.
Magallona, E. D., et al. Residue Reviews, Vol. 56. (Illus.). 160p. 1975. 25.00 (ISBN 0-387-90115-9). Springer-Verlag.
Moye, H. Anson. Analysis of Pesticide Residues. (Chemical Analysis Ser.). 467p. 1981. 78.50x (ISBN 0-471-05461-5, Pub by Wiley-Interscience). Wiley.
Nishizawa, Y., et al. Residue Reviews: Sumithion, Vol. 60. LC 62-18595. (Illus.). 208p. 1976. 33.00 (ISBN 0-387-90091-8). Springer-Verlag.
Peakall, D. B. Residue Reviews, Vol. 54. LC 62-18595. (Illus.). x, 190p. 1975. 39.00 (ISBN 0-387-90099-3). Springer-Verlag.
Pesticide Residues in Food Evaluations 1981: The Monographs. (Plant Production & Protection Papers: No. 42). 576p. 1982. pap. 41.00 (ISBN 92-5-101306-3, F2399, FAO). Unipub.
Pesticide Residues in Food: Report of the Joint Meeting, Rome, November 1970. (Agricultural Planning Studies: No. 87). 44p. 1971. pap. 4.50 (ISBN 92-5-101534-1, F310, FAO). Unipub.
Pesticide Residues in Food: Report of the 1974 Joint FAO-WHO Expert Meeting. (Agricultural Planning Studies: No. 97). pap. 6.25 (F314, FAO). Unipub.
Pesticides Residues in Food: Report of the Joint Meeting, Geneva, December 1968. (Agricultural Planning Studies: No. 78). 40p. 1969. pap. 6.00 (ISBN 92-5-101532-5, F309, FAO). Unipub.
Recommended International Maximum Limits for Pesticide Residues: Fourth Series. 1974. pap. 4.50 (ISBN 92-5-100230-4, F605, FAO). Unipub.
Recommended International Standard for Pesticide Residues: Second Series. 1970. pap. 4.50 (F639, FAO). Unipub.
Recommended International Tolerances for Pesticide Residues. 1972. pap. 0.00 write for info. (F585, FAO). Unipub.
Residue Reviews, Vol. 58. LC 62-18595. 180p. 1975. 32.00 (ISBN 0-387-90135-3). Springer-Verlag.
Residue Reviews, Vol. 59. LC 62-18595. (Illus.). 160p. 1975. 29.00 (ISBN 0-387-90145-0). Springer-Verlag.
Residue Reviews, Vol. 74. (Illus.). 150p. 1980. 35.50 (ISBN 0-387-90503-0). Springer-Verlag.
Residue Reviews, Vol. 94. (Illus.). 160p. 1985. 31.00 (ISBN 0-387-96130-5). Springer-Verlag.
Simms, R. C., et al. Residue of Pesticides & other Contaminants in the Total Environment. (Residue Reviews: Vol. 88). (Illus.). 164p. 1983. 25.00 (ISBN 0-387-90851-X). Springer-Verlag.
Soltes, Ed J. Wood & Agricultural Residues: Research on Use for Feed, Fuels, & Chemicals. 1983. 60.00 (ISBN 0-12-654560-X). Acad Pr.
Spindler, M., et al. Residues of Pesticides & Other Contaminants in the Total Environment. (Residue Reviews Ser.: Vol. 90). 145p. 1983. 24.00 (ISBN 0-387-90905-2). Springer-Verlag.
U. S. Dept. of Energy. Anaerobic Fermentation of Agricultural Residue: Potential for Improvement & Implementation. 430p. 1981. pap. 59.50x (ISBN 0-89934-099-7, B.021). Solar Energy Info.
Workshop on the Role of Earthworms in the Stabilization of Organic Residues, 2 vols. 1981. 70.00 set (ISBN 0-686-84201-4, TD-772-W6). Beech Leaf.

SPRINGER SPANIEL
see Dogs–Breeds–Springer Spaniels

SPRINGFIELD RIFLE
Brophy, William S. The Springfield Nineteen Hundred & Three Rifles: The Illustrated, Documented Story of the Design, Development, & Production of All the Models, Appendages, & Accessories. Schnell, Judith, ed. (Illus.). 608p. 1985. 49.95 (ISBN 0-8117-0872-1). Stackpole.
Campbell, Clark S. The O Three Springfields. LC 78-180733. (Illus.). 1978. 35.00 (ISBN 0-9603094-5-4). Ray Riling.
Frasca, Albert J. & Hill, Robert H. The Forty Five - Seventy Springfield. Suydam, Charles R., ed. LC 80-51230. (Illus.). 396p. 1980. deluxe ed. 49.50 (ISBN 0-937500-11-9); deluxe ed. 99.50x limited ed. (ISBN 0-937500-10-0). Springfield Pub Co.

SPRINGS
see also Divining-Rod; Water, Underground; Wells
Alpha Pyramis Research Division. Natural & Hot Springs: An International Directory. 75p. 1983. text ed. 4.75 (ISBN 0-913597-07-4, Pub. by Alpha Pyramis). Prosperity & Profits.
Brock, Thomas D. Thermophilic Microorganisms & Life at High Temperatures. LC 78-6110. (Springer Ser. in Microbiology). (Illus.). 1978. 39.00 (ISBN 0-387-90309-7). Springer-Verlag.
Brune, Gunnar. Springs of Texas, Vol. 1. LC 80-71016. (Illus.). 584p. 1981. 35.00 (ISBN 0-9604766-0-1). G Brune.
Pearl, Richard M. Springs of Colorado. 1975. pap. 2.75 (ISBN 0-940566-07-9). R M Pearl Bks.

SPRINGS (MECHANISM)
Carlson. Spring Designers Handbook. (Mechanical Engineering Ser.: Vol. 1). 1978. 59.75 (ISBN 0-8247-6623-7). Dekker.
--Springs: Troubleshooting & Failure Analysis. (Engineering Troubleshooting Ser.: Vol. 1). 216p. 1980. 39.75 (ISBN 0-8247-1003-7). Dekker.
Din Standards for Springs. 489.00 (ISBN 0-686-28177-2, 10380-5/29). Heyden.
Gross, E. T., et al, eds. Coil Spring Making. 2nd ed. (Engineering Craftsmen: No. H6). (Illus.). 1974. spiral bdg. 45.00x (ISBN 0-85083-172-5). Trans-Atlantic.
Hudson, D. Helical Spring Making. 1986. 30.00 (ISBN 0-08-025447-0); pap. 12.00 (ISBN 0-08-025448-9). Pergamon.
Spring Research Association, Sheffield, ed. Strip Spring Making & Forming. (Engineering Craftsmen: No. H7). (Illus.). 1977. spiral bdg. 39.95x (ISBN 0-85083-331-0). Intl Ideas.
Strip Spring Making & Forming. 50.00x (ISBN 0-85083-331-0, Pub. by Engineering Ind). State Mutual Bk.
Waller, R. A. Building on Springs. 1969. 20.00 (ISBN 0-08-006399-3). Pergamon.

SPRITE (AUTOMOBILE)
see Automobiles, Foreign–Types–Sprite

SPRUCE
Photosynthesis & Respiration in White Spruce & Balsam Fir, No. 85. 1961. 0.65 (ISBN 0-686-20697-5). SUNY Environ.
Pinchot, Gifford. Adirondack Spruce, A Study of the Forest in Ne-Ha-Sa-Ne Park. LC 77-125756. (American Environmental Studies). 1971. Repr. of 1907 ed. 14.00 (ISBN 0-405-02682-X). Ayer Co Pubs.

SPS (COMPUTER PROGRAM LANGUAGE)
see SIMSCRIPT (Computer Program Language)

SPSS (ELECTRONIC COMPUTER SYSTEM)
Barcikowski, Robert S., ed. Computer Packages & Research Design: Vol. 3-SPSS & SPSSX with Annotations of Input & Output from the BMDP, SAS, SPSS & SPSSX Statistical Packages. (Illus.). 620p. (Orig.). 1983. pap. text ed. 36.00 (ISBN 0-8191-3496-1). U Pr of Amer.
Hull, C. Hadlai & Nie, Norman. SPSS Update: New Procedures & Facilities for Releases 7-9. 2nd ed. 1981. text ed. 16.95 (ISBN 0-07-046542-8). McGraw.
Klecka, W., et al. SPSS Primer. 1975. text ed. 15.95 (ISBN 0-07-035023-X). McGraw.
Nie, N. H. & Hull, C. H. SPSS-Eleven: The SPSS Batch System for the DEC PDP-11. 2nd rev. ed. 1982. 16.95x (ISBN 0-07-046546-0). McGraw.
Nie, Norman H. & Hadlai, H. C. SPSS Pocket Guide: Release 9. (Data Analysis Ser.). 56p. 1981. pap. text ed. 3.95 (ISBN 0-07-046543-6). McGraw.
Norusis, M. J. SPSS Introductory Guide: Basic Statistics & Operations. 1982. 15.95x (ISBN 0-07-047528-8). McGraw.
SPSS Inc. SPSS-X Tables. 176p. 1985. 15.95 (ISBN 0-07-046558-4). McGraw.
SPSS Inc. Staff. SPSS Reference Handbook. 150p. cancelled (ISBN 0-07-046557-6). Mcgraw.
--SPSS-X Graphics. 320p. 1984. 37.95 (ISBN 0-07-046554-1). McGraw.
SPSS, Inc. Staff. SPSS-X User's Guide. 864p. 1983. 30.95 (ISBN 0-07-046550-9). McGraw.
SPSS Inc. Staff. SPSS-X User's Guide. 2nd ed. 1000p. 1984. write for info. (ISBN 0-07-046553-3). McGraw.

SPUN GLASS
see Glass Fibers

SPURRED RYE
see Ergot

SPUTTERING (PHYSICS)
see also Ion Bombardment
Behrisch, R., ed. Sputtering by Particle Bombardment II. (Topics in Applied Physics: Vol. 52). (Illus.). 385p. 1983. 47.00 (ISBN 0-387-12593-0). Springer Verlag.
--Sputtering by Particle Bombardment I: Physics & Applications. (Topics in Applied Physics Ser.: Vol. 47). (Illus.). 1981. 42.00 (ISBN 0-387-10521-2). Springer-Verlag.
Behrisch, R., et al, eds. Ion Surface Interaction, Sputtering & Related Phenomena. LC 73-85272. 334p. 1973. 80.95 (ISBN 0-677-15850-5). Gordon.

SQUABS
see Pigeons

SQUARE (INSTRUMENT)
see Carpenters' Square

SQUARES, LEAST
see Least Squares

SQUIDHOUND
see Striped Bass

SQUIDS
Arnold, J. M. Loligo Pealei. LC 74-77352. 1974. pap. 6.00x (ISBN 0-685-52859-6). Marine Bio.
Cousteau, Jacques-Yves & Diole, Philippe. Octopus & Squid: The Soft Intelligence. LC 72-76141. 304p. 1973. 12.95 (ISBN 0-385-06896-4). Doubleday.
FAO Fisheries Technology Service & Hamabe, Mototsugu, eds. Squid Jigging from Small Boats. 84p. 1982. 42.95x (ISBN 0-85238-122-0, Pub. by Fishing News England). State Mutual Bk.
Hamabe, Mototsugu, et al. Squid Jigging from Small Boats: An FAO Fishing Manual. 84p. 1982. pap. 19.00 (ISBN 0-85238-122-0, FN99, FNB). Unipub.
International Squid Symposium: Proceedings, August 9-12, 1981, Boston, Massachusetts. 390p. (Prepared by the New England Fisheries Development Foundation and the National Marine Fisheries Service). 1982. pap. 33.50 (ISBN 0-89059-026-5, UPB117, UPB). Unipub.
Moynihan, Martin & Rodaniche, A. F., eds. The Behaviour & Natural History of the Caribbean Reef Squid (Sepiotheuthis Sepioiodea) (Advances in Ethology Ser.: Vol. 25). (Illus.). 144p. (Orig.). 1982. pap. text ed. 21.60 (ISBN 0-686-37065-1). Parey Sci Pubs.

SQUIRRELS
see also Ground Squirrels
Alvarez, Ticul. A New Subspecies of Ground Squirrel (Spermophilus Spilosoma) from Tamaulipas, Mexico. (Museum Ser.: Vol. 14, No. 8). 4p. 1962. pap. 1.25 (ISBN 0-317-04910-0). U of KS Mus Nat Hist.
Gooch, Bob. Squirrels & Squirrel Hunting. LC 72-81371. (Illus.). 160p. 1972. 6.00 (ISBN 0-87033-172-8). Tidewater.
Horwich, R. H. The Ontogeny of Social Behavior in the Gray Squirrel (Sciurus carolinensis) (Advances in Ethology Ser.: Vol. 8). (Illus.). 103p. (Orig.). 1972. pap. text ed. 23.50 (ISBN 0-686-29206-5). Parey Sci Pubs.
Kelson, Keith R. The Subspecies of the Mexican Red-Bellied Squirrel: Sciurus Aureogaster. (Museum Ser.: Vol. 5, No. 17). 8p. 1952. pap. 1.25 (ISBN 0-317-04869-4). U of KS Mus Nat Hist.
Laidler, Keith. Squirrels in Britain. LC 80-66421. (Illus.). 176p. 1980. 19.95 (ISBN 0-7153-7825-2). David & Charles.
Wells-Gosling, Nancy. Flying Sqirrels: Gliders in the Dark. LC 84-600310. (Nature Books). (Illus.). 128p. 1985. 24.95 (ISBN 0-87474-952-2, WEFS); pap. 9.95 (ISBN 0-87474-951-4, WEFSP). Smithsonian.
Woods, Shirley E., Jr. The Squirrels of Canada. (Illus.). 208p. 1981. lib. bdg. 29.95 (ISBN 0-660-10344-3, 56511-4, Pub. by Natl Mus Canada). U of Chicago Pr.

STABILITY
see also Equilibrium; Liapunov Functions; Soil Stabilization; Structural Stability
Al'muhamedov, M. I., et al. Stability & Dynamic Systems. (Translations Series: No. 1, Vol. 5). 1962. 27.00 (ISBN 0-8218-1605-5, TRANS 1-5). Am Math.
Betchov, Robert & Criminale, William O., Jr. Stability of Parallel Flows. (Applied Mathematics & Mechanics Ser.: Vol. 10). 1967. 75.00 (ISBN 0-12-093750-6). Acad Pr.
Bhatia, N. P. & Szegoe, G. P. Dynamical Systems: Stability Theory & Applications. (Lecture Notes in Mathematics: Vol. 35). (Illus., Orig.). 1967. pap. 21.90 (ISBN 0-387-03906-6). Springer-Verlag.
Control Theory Centre Symposium, University of Warwick, 1972. Stability of Stochastic Dynamical Systems: Proceedings. Curtain, R. F., ed. LC 72-91895. (Lecture Notes in Mathematics: Vol. 294). (Illus.). 332p. 1972. pap. 13.00 (ISBN 0-387-06050-2). Springer-Verlag.
Drazin, P. G. & Reid, W. H. Hydrodynamic Stability. LC 80-40273. (Cambridge Monographs on Mechanics & Applied Mathematics). (Illus.). 600p. 1981. 95.00 (ISBN 0-521-22798-4). Cambridge U Pr.
Dym, C. L. Stability Theory & Its Applications to Structural Mechanics. (Mechanics of Elastic Stability Ser.: No. 3). 200p. 1974. 22.50x (ISBN 90-286-0094-9). Sijthoff & Noordhoff.
--Stability Theory & Its Application To Structural Mechanics. 1974. lib. bdg. 22.50 (ISBN 90-28600-94-9, Pub. by Martinus Nijhoff Netherlands). Kluwer Academic.
Eckhaus, Viktor. Studies in Non-Linear Stability Theory. (Springer Tracts in Natural Philosophy: Vol. 6). (Illus.). 1965. 19.00 (ISBN 0-387-03407-2). Springer-Verlag.
Graef, John R. Stability of Dynamical Systems: Theory & Application. (Lecture Notes in Pure & Applied Mathematics: Vol. 28). 1977. 55.00 (ISBN 0-8247-6410-2). Dekker.
Halanay, A. Differential Equations: Stability, Oscillations, Time Lags. (Mathematics in Science & Engineering Ser.: Vol. 23). 1966. 83.00 (ISBN 0-12-317950-5). Acad Pr.
Kimbark, Edward W. Power System Stability, 2 vols. Vol. 1., 355pg. 48.50x (ISBN 0-471-47586-6); Vol. 2., 280pg. 45.95x (ISBN 0-471-47619-6, Pub. by Wiley-Interscience). Wiley.
Krall, A. M. Stability Techniques for Continuous Linear Systems. (Notes on Mathematics & Its Applications Ser.). 160p. (Orig.). 1967. 33.75 (ISBN 0-677-01420-1). Gordon.
Krasovskii, Nikolai N. Stability of Motion: Applications of Lyapunov's Second Method to Differential Systems & Equations with Delay. Brenner, J. L., tr. 1963. 15.00x (ISBN 0-8047-0098-2). Stanford U Pr.
Kroupa, V. F. Frequency Stability Fundamentals & Measurements. LC 83-18336. 400p. 1983. 62.95 (ISBN 0-87942-171-1, PC01644). Inst Electrical.
LaSalle, J. P. The Stability of Dynamical Systems. (CBMS-NSF Regional Conference Ser.: No. 25). v, 76p. (Orig.). 1976. pap. text ed. 14.00 (ISBN 0-89871-022-7). Soc Indus-Appl Math.
Lefschetz, Solomon. Stability of Nonlinear Control Systems. (Mathematics in Science & Engineering Ser.: Vol. 13). 1965. 42.50 (ISBN 0-12-440350-6). Acad Pr.
Leipholz, H. Stability Theory. (Ger). 1970. 64.50 (ISBN 0-12-442550-X). Acad Pr.
Liapounoff, M. A. Probleme General de la Stabilite du Mouvement. (Annals of Math Studies). 1947. 21.00 (ISBN 0-527-02733-2). Kraus Repr.
Marschall, Charles W. & Maringer, Robert E. Dimensional Instability-an Introduction. 1977. 44.00 (ISBN 0-08-021305-7). Pergamon.
Martell, Arthur E. & Smith, Robert M. Critical Stability Constants, Vol. 5: First Supplement. 622p. 1982. 79.50x (ISBN 0-306-41005-2, Plenum Pr). Plenum Pub.
Martell, Arthur E. & Smith, Robert M., eds. Critical Stability Constants, Vols.1-4. Incl. Vol. 1. Amino Acids. 469p. 1974. 59.50x (ISBN 0-306-35211-7); Vol. 2. Amines. 415p. 1975. 59.50x (ISBN 0-306-35212-5); Vol. 3. Other Organic Ligands. 495p. 1977. 65.00x (ISBN 0-306-35213-3); Vol. 4. Inorganic Complexes. 257p. 1976. 49.50x (ISBN 0-306-35214-1). LC 74-10610. (Illus., Plenum Pr). Plenum Pub.
Narenda, Kumpati S. & Taylor, James H. Frequency Domain Criteria for Absolute Stability. (Electrical Science Ser.). 1973. 60.00 (ISBN 0-12-514050-9). Acad Pr.
Panovko, Ya. G. & Gubanova, I. I. Stability & Oscillations of Elastic Systems: Paradoxes, Fallacies, & New Concepts. LC 65-11341. 291p. 1965. 40.00x (ISBN 0-306-10735-X, Consultants). Plenum Pub.
Popov, Igor V. & Kotlov, F. V., eds. The Stability of Slopes. LC 62-12857. 83p. 1963. 25.00x (ISBN 0-306-10657-4, Consultants). Plenum Pub.
Popov, V. M. Hyperstability of Control Systems. Georgescu, R., tr. from Romanian. LC 73-83000. (Die Grundlehren der Mathematischen Wissenschaften: Vol. 204). 400p. 1973. 51.00 (ISBN 0-387-06373-0). Springer-Verlag.
Porter, Brian. Stability Criteria for Linear Dynamical Systems. 1968. 41.50 (ISBN 0-12-562050-0). Acad Pr.
Rocard, Yves. Dynamic Instability: Automobiles, Aircraft, Suspension Bridges. Meyer, M. L., tr. (Illus.). 1958. 12.00 (ISBN 0-8044-4833-7). Ungar.
Siljak, D. D. Large Scale Dynamic Systems: Stability & Structure. (Systems Science & Engineering Ser.: Vol. 2). 416p. 1978. 45.75 (ISBN 0-444-00246-4, North-Holland). Elsevier.
Stability Theory by Liapunov's Direct Method. LC 77-7285. (Applied Mathematical Sciences: Vol. 22). (Illus.). 1977. 25.00 (ISBN 0-387-90258-9). Springer-Verlag.
Symposium Herrenalb - Germany - September 8-12 1969. Instability of Continuous Systems. Leipholz, H., ed. LC 72-146050. (Illus.). 1971. 92.10 (ISBN 0-387-05163-5). Springer-Verlag.

Symposium in Applied Mathematics, New York, 1960. Hydrodynamic Instability: Proceedings. Bellman, R., et al, eds. LC 50-1183. (Vol. 13). 319p. 1962. pap. 25.00 (ISBN 0-8218-1313-7, PSAPM-13). Am Math.

Szebehely, Victor G., ed. Instabilities in Dynamical Systems. (NATO Advanced Study Institutes Ser.). 1979. lib. bdg. 39.50 (ISBN 90-277-0973-4, Pub. by Reidel Holland). Kluwer Academic.

Yoshizawa, T. Stability Theory & Existence of Periodic Solutions & Almost Periodic Solutions. LC 74-28140. (Applied Mathematical Sciences Ser.: Vol. 14). vii, 233p. 1975. pap. 19.50 (ISBN 0-387-90112-4). Springer-Verlag.

STABILITY OF AIRPLANES

see also Gyroscope

Babister, A. W. Aircraft Dynamic Stability & Response. (Illus.). 230p. 1980. pap. 19.50 (ISBN 0-08-024768-7). Pergamon.

Etkin, Bernard. Dynamics of Atmospheric Flight. LC 73-165946. (Illus.). 579p. 1972. text ed. 49.00x (ISBN 0-471-24620-4). Wiley.

Saczalski, Kenneth, et al, eds. Aircraft Crashworthiness. LC 75-26665. pap. 160.00 (2055727). Bks Demand UMI.

STABILITY OF SHIPS

see also Gyroscope

De Heere, R. F. Scheltema & Bakker, A. R. Buoyance & Stability of Ships. 222p. 1970. 80.00x (ISBN 0-85950-081-0, Pub. by Stam Pr England). State Mutual Bk.

Derrett, D. R. Ship Stability for Masters & Mates. 4th ed. (Illus.). 420p. 1984. text ed. 24.50x (ISBN 0-540-07388-1, Pub. by Stanford Maritime). Sheridan.

Hind, J. Anthony. Stability & Trim of Fishing Vessels. (Illus.). 120p. 23.75 (ISBN 0-686-70989-6, FN72, FNB). Unipub.

Pursey, H. J. Merchant Ship Stability. 6th, rev. ed. 201p. 1983. 24.50x (ISBN 0-85174-442-7). Sheridan.

Taylor, L. G. The Principles & Practice of Ship Stability. (Illus.). 198p. 1984. text ed. 24.50x (ISBN 0-85174-488-5, Pub. by Brown Son & Ferguson). Sheridan.

--Principles & Practices of Ship Practices. 155p. 1984. 24.50x (ISBN 0-85174-310-2). Sheridan.

Vossers, G. Behaviour of Ships in Waves. 272p. 1962. 100.00x (ISBN 0-85950-085-3, Pub. by Stam Pr England). State Mutual Bk.

STABILITY OF STRUCTURES

see Structural Stability

STABILIZATION OF SOILS

see Soil Stabilization

STABLES

see also Barns

Brann, Donald R. How to Build a Stable & a Red Barn Tool House. LC 72-88710. (Illus.). 1973. lib. bdg. 5.95 (ISBN 0-87733-079-4); pap. 7.95 (ISBN 0-87733-679-2). Easi-Bild.

Brown, Jeremy & Powell-Smith, Vincent. Horse & Stable Management. 256p. 1984. 19.50 (ISBN 0-246-11217-4, Pub. by Granada England). Sheridan.

Sadler, Julius T., Jr. & Sadler, Jacqueline D. American Stables: An Architectural Tour. 1981. 29.95 (ISBN 0-8212-1105-6, 036676). NYGS.

Smith, P. C. Design & Construction of Stables. 15.00x (ISBN 0-87556-320-1). Saifer.

STAFFORDSHIRE TERRIER

see Dogs–Breeds–Staffordshire Terrier

STAGE LIGHTING

Howard, John T., Jr. A Bibliography of Theatre Technology: Acoustics & Sound, Lighting, Properties, & Scenery. LC 81-7204. xii, 345p. 1982. lib. bdg. 37.50 (ISBN 0-313-22839-6, HTT/). Greenwood.

Lighting for Theatrical Presentations on Educational & Community Proscenium-Type Stages. 4.50 (ISBN 0-686-47875-4, CP-34). Illum Eng.

Millerson, Gerald. Technique of Lighting for Television & Motion Pictures. 2nd ed. LC 99-943709. (Library of Communication Techniques Ser.). 366p. 1982. 31.50 (ISBN 0-240-51128-X); pap. 20.95 (ISBN 0-240-51192-1). Focal Pr.

Stoddard, Richard, ed. Stage Scenery, Machinery & Lighting: A Guide to Information Sources. LC 76-13574. (Performing Arts Information Guide Ser.: Vol. 2). 1977. 60.00x (ISBN 0-8103-1374-X). Gale.

STAGGERS, GRASS

see Grass Tetany

STAGING (CONSTRUCTION)

see Scaffolding

STAINLESS STEEL

see Steel, Stainless

STAINS AND STAINING

see also Varnish and Varnishing; Wood Finishing

Grotz, George. Staining & Finishing Unfinished Furniture & Other Naked Woods. LC 68-25596. (Illus.). 1968. pap. 3.50 (ISBN 0-385-01906-8, Dolp). Doubleday.

Hayward, Charles H. Staining & Wood Polishing. (A Home Craftsman Bk.). (Illus.). 214p. 1980. pap. 6.95 (ISBN 0-8069-8684-0). Sterling.

STAINS AND STAINING (MICROSCOPY)

Clark, George & Clark, Margaret P. Primer in Neurological Staining Procedures. (Illus.). 84p. 1971. 12.75x (ISBN 0-398-02176-7). C C Thomas.

Clark, George & Kasten, Frederick H. History of Staining. 3rd ed. (Illus.). 301p. 1983. lib. bdg. 31.00 (ISBN 0-683-01705-5). Williams & Wilkins.

Gray, Peter. The Microtomists Formulary & Guide. LC 74-23818. 808p. 1975. Repr. of 1954 ed. 44.50 (ISBN 0-88275-247-2). Krieger.

Humason, Gretchen L. Animal Tissue Techniques. 4th ed. LC 78-17459. (Illus.). 661p. 1979. text ed. 33.95 (ISBN 0-7167-0299-1). W H Freeman.

Kater, S. B. & Nicholson, C., eds. Intracellular Staining in Neurobiology. LC 73-77837. (Illus.). 332p. 1973. 45.00 (ISBN 0-387-06261-0). Springer-Verlag.

STANDARDIZATION

see also Production Standards; Quality Control; Specifications; Testing; Tolerance (Engineering) also subdivision Standards, or Grading and Standardization under subjects

Bongers, C. Standardization: Mathematical Methods in Assortment Determination. 265p. 1980. lib. bdg. 24.00 (ISBN 0-89838-029-4, Pub. by Martinus Nijhoff Netherlands). Kluwer Academic.

Standardization on Industrialization of Developing Countries. (UNIDO Monographs on Industrialization of Developing Countries: Problems & Prospects). pap. 4.00 (ISBN 0-686-93279-X, UN69/2B39/VOL. 12, UN). Unipub.

Verman, Lal C. Standardization: A New Discipline. LC 72-8370. (Illus.). pap. 120.30 (ISBN 0-317-10688-0, 2015419). Bks Demand UMI.

STANDARDIZATION–BIBLIOGRAPHY

Struglia, Erasmus J., ed. Standards & Specifications Information Sources. LC 65-24659. (Management Information Guide Ser.: No. 6). 1965. 60.00x (ISBN 0-8103-0806-1). Gale.

STANDARDS

see subdivision Standards under subjects, e.g. Engineering Instruments

STANDARDS, ELECTRIC

see Electric Standards

STANDARDS, ENGINEERING

Yuen, Aubrey. Tolerances: Geometric & Position Reference & Workbook. 2nd ed. Coombs, Marian, ed. LC 85-50378. (Series One). (Illus.). 256p. 1985. price not set; pap. text ed. 27.95 (ISBN 0-9614079-2-1). TVR Pub Co.

STANNERIES

see Tin Mines and Mining

STAR CATALOGS

see Stars–Catalogs

STAR CLUSTERS

see Stars–Clusters

STARCH

Mishler, John M., IV. Pharmacology of Hydroxyehty Starch: Use in Therapy & Blood Banking. (Illus.). 1982. text ed. 45.00x (ISBN 0-19-261239-5). Oxford U Pr.

Radley, J. A., ed. Examination & Analysis of Starch & Starch Products. (Illus.). 268p. 1976. 63.00 (ISBN 0-85334-692-5, Pub. by Elsevier Applied Sci England). Elsevier.

--Industrial Uses of Starch & Its Derivatives. 268p. 1976. 63.00 (ISBN 0-85334-691-7, Pub. by Elsevier Applied Sci England). Elsevier.

Van Beynum & Roels. Starch Conversion Technology. 464p. 1985. 65.00 (ISBN 0-8247-7194-X). Dekker.

STARCH INDUSTRY

Radley, J. A., ed. Starch Production Technology. (Illus.). 287p. 1976. 118.50 (ISBN 0-85334-662-3, Pub. by Elsevier Applied Sci England). Elsevier.

STARFISHES

Clark, A. H. Ophiuroidea of the Hawaiian Islands. (BMB Ser.). Repr. of 1949 ed. 19.00 (ISBN 0-527-02303-5). Kraus Repr.

Ely, C. A. Shallow-Water Asteroidea & Ophiuroidea of Hawaii. (BMB Ser.). Repr. of 1942 ed. 12.00 (ISBN 0-527-02284-5). Kraus Repr.

Spencer, W. K. The Palaeozoic Asterozoa, Pts. I-X. Repr. of 1940 ed. Set. 120.00 (ISBN 0-384-57050-X). Johnson Repr.

Verrill, Addison E. Monography of the Shallow-Water Starfishes of the North Pacific Coast from the Arctic Ocean to California, 2 vols. Incl. Part One: Text (ISBN 0-527-38175-6); Part Two: Plates (ISBN 0-527-38176-4). (Harriman Alaska Expedition, 1899). (Illus.). 1914. lib. bdg. 37.00 ea. (ISBN 0-685-23304-9). Kraus Repr.

STARLINGS

see also Mynahs

Feare, Christopher. The Starling. (Illus.). 1984. 27.95x (ISBN 0-19-217705-2). Oxford U Pr.

STARS

see also Astronomy; Astrophysics; Black Holes (Astronomy); Constellations; Galaxies; Life on Other Planets; Magellanic Clouds; Mechanics, Celestial; Meteors; Milky Way; Nebulae; Planets; Solar System

also names of individual stars

Allen, Richard H. Star Names: Their Lore & Meaning. rev. ed. 1963. pap. 7.95 (ISBN 0-486-21079-0). Dover.

--Star Names: Their Lore & Meaning. Orig. Title: Star-Names & Their Meanings. 16.00 (ISBN 0-8446-1527-7). Peter Smith.

Aller, Lawrence H. Atoms, Stars, & Nebulae. Rev. ed. LC 76-134951. (The Harvard Books on Astronomy). (Illus.). pap. 90.80 (ISBN 0-317-09183-2, 2019508). Bks Demand UMI.

Aller, Lawrence H. & McLaughlin, Dean B., eds. Stellar Structures. Midway rep. ed. LC 63-16723. (Stars & Stellar Systems Ser.: Vol. 8). (Illus.). 1981. pap. 35.00x (ISBN 0-226-45969-1). U of Chicago Pr.

Alter, G., et al, eds. Catalogue of Star Clusters & Associations. 2nd ed. 80.00x (ISBN 0-685-27543-4). Adlers Foreign Bks.

Baliunas, S. L. & Hartmann, L., eds. Cool Stars, Stellar Systems, & the Sun: Proceedings of the Third Cambridge Workshop on Cool Stars, Stellar Systems, & the Sun, Held in Cambridge MA, October 5-7. (Lecture Notes in Physics Ser.: Vol. 193). vii, 364p. 1984. pap. 22.00 (ISBN 0-387-12907-3). Springer-Verlag.

Black, D. C. & Matthews, Mildred S., eds. Protostars & Planets II. LC 85-11223. 1985. 45.00 (ISBN 0-8165-0950-6). U of Ariz Pr.

Bonnet, R. & Dupree, A., eds. Solar Phenomena in Stars & Stellar Systems. 1981. 69.50 (ISBN 90-277-1275-1, Pub. by Reidel Holland). Kluwer Academic.

Breuer, Reinhard. Contact with the Stars: The Search for Extraterrestrial Life. LC 81-9908. (Illus.). 292p. 1982. text ed. 31.95 (ISBN 0-7167-1355-1). W H Freeman.

Byrne, Patrick B. & Rodono, Marcello, eds. Activity in Red-Dwarf Stars. 1983. lib. bdg. 85.00 (ISBN 90-277-1601-3, Pub. by Reidel Holland). Kluwer Academic.

Chiosi, C. & Stalio, R., eds. Effects of Mass Loss on Stellar Evolution. 375p. 1981. 73.50 (ISBN 90-277-1292-1, Pub. by Reidel Holland). Kluwer Academic.

Chiu, Hong-Yee & Muriel; Amador, eds. Stellar Evolution. 827p. 1972. 55.00x (ISBN 0-262-12058-5). MIT Pr.

Chiu Hone-Yee, et al. Stellar Astronomy, 2 Vols. 756p. 1969. Vol. 1,388. 119.25 (ISBN 0-677-13790-7); Vol. 2,368. 93.75 (ISBN 0-677-13800-8); Set. 183.75 (ISBN 0-677-12980-7). Gordon.

Clark, D. H. & Stephenson, F. R., eds. Historical Supernovae. LC 76-44364. 1977. text ed. 31.00 (ISBN 0-08-020914-9); pap. text ed. 13.00 (ISBN 0-08-021639-0). Pergamon.

Clark, David H. Superstars: How Stellar Explosions Shape the Destiny of Our Universes. (Illus.). 224p. 1984. 17.95. McGraw.

Cox, J. P., ed. Principle of Stellar Structure, 2 Vols. LC 68-26755. (Illus.). 1327p. 1968. Set. 350.25 (ISBN 0-677-01950-5). Gordon.

De Jager, C., ed. The Brightest Stars. (Geophysics & Astrophysics Monographs: No. 19). 472p. 1981. PLB 73.50 (ISBN 90-277-1109-7, Pub. by Reidel Holland); pap. 31.50 (ISBN 90-277-1109-7). Kluwer Academic.

De Jong, T. & Maeder, A., eds. Star Formation. (Symposium of the International Astronomical Union: No. 75). 1977. lib. bdg. 39.50 (ISBN 90-277-0796-0, Pub. by Reidel Holland); pap. 24.00 (ISBN 90-277-0797-9). Kluwer Academic.

De Lorre, C. & Willis, A., eds. Wolf-Rayet Stars: Observations, Physics, Evolution. 1982. 69.50 (ISBN 90-277-1469-X, Pub. by Reidel Holland); pap. 34.50 (ISBN 90-277-1470-3). Kluwer Academic.

Forbes, George. The Stars. 1928. 15.00 (ISBN 0-686-17423-2). Ridgeway Bks.

Gehrels, T., ed. Planets, Stars & Nebulae Studied With Photopolarimetry. LC 73-86446. 1133p. 1974. 27.50x (ISBN 0-8165-0428-8). U of Ariz Pr.

Giacconi & Ruffini, R. Physics & Astrophysics of Neutron Stars & Black Holes: Proceedings. (Enrico Fermi Summer School Ser.: Vol. 65). 876p. 1980. pap. 57.50 (ISBN 0-444-85446-0, North-Holland). Elsevier.

Goldberg, Howard S. & Scadron, Michael D. Physics of Stellar Evolution & Cosmology. 405p. 1982. 59.50 (ISBN 0-677-05540-4). Gordon.

Golden, Frederic. Quasars, Pulsars, & Black Holes: A Scientific Detective Story. LC 75-37646. (Illus.). 128p. 1976. 9.95 (ISBN 0-684-14501-4, ScribT). Scribner.

Gratton, Livio, ed. Star Evolution. (Italian Physical Society: Course 28). (Illus.). 1966. 77.50 (ISBN 0-12-368828-0). Acad Pr.

Grossinger, Richard. The Night Sky: The Science & Anthropology of the Stars & Planets. LC 81-5293. 544p. 1981. 16.95 (ISBN 0-87156-288-X). Sierra.

Hirshfeld, Alan & Sinnott, Roger, eds. Sky Catalogue 2000.0. LC 81-17975. 684p. Vol. 1, 1982. 52.50 (ISBN 0-521-24710-1); Vol. 2, 1985. 49.50 (ISBN 0-521-25818-9); Vol. 1, 1982. pap. 32.50 (ISBN 0-521-28913-0); Vol. 2, 1985. pap. 29.95 (ISBN 0-521-27721-3). Cambridge U Pr.

Hughes, James S., Jr. Star Particle Theory: An Introductory Survey. (Illus.). 16p. 1974. 15.00 (ISBN 0-915386-00-3). Arctinurus Co.

IAU Colloquium, Ohio State University, Columbus, 1969. Stellar Rotation: Proceedings. Slettebak, A., ed. LC 76-118131. 355p. 1970. lib. bdg. 45.00 (ISBN 90-277-0156-3, Pub. by Reidel Holland). Kluwer Academic.

I.A.U. Symposium, No. 46 Jodrell Bank, England, August 5-7, 1970. The Crab Nebula: Proceedings. Davies, R. D. & Smith, F. G., eds. LC 73-154735. (I.A.U. Symposia: No. 46). 470p. 1971. 50.00 (ISBN 90-277-0183-0, Pub. by Reidel Holland). Kluwer Academic.

IAU Symposium, No. 69, Besancon, France September 9-13 1974. Dynamics of Stellar Systems: Proceedings. Hayli, Auram, ed. LC 75-12976. (IAU Symposia: No. 69). 470p. 1975. 79.00 (ISBN 90-277-0589-5); pap. 58.00 (ISBN 90-277-0590-9, Pub. by Reidel Holland). Kluwer Academic.

I.A.U. Symposium, No.42, St. Andrews, Fife, Scotland, August 11-13, 1970. White Dwarf: Proceedings. Luythen, S. J., ed. LC 75-146966. (I.A.U. Symposia). 164p. 1971. lib. bdg. 21.00 (ISBN 90-277-0180-6, Pub. by Reidel Holland). Kluwer Academic.

International Astronomical Union Symposium, No. 54. Problems of Calibration of Absolute Magnitudes & Temperature of Stars: Proceedings. Hauck, B. & Westerlund, B., eds. LC 73-83562. 1973. lib. bdg. 47.50 (ISBN 90-277-0365-5, Pub. by Reidel Holland); pap. text ed. 36.00 (ISBN 90-277-0372-8, Pub. by Reidel Holland). Kluwer Academic.

Irvine, J. M. Neutron Stars. (Oxford Studies in Physics). (Illus.). text ed. 39.50x (ISBN 0-19-851460-3). Oxford U Pr.

Jascheck, Mercedes & Keenan, Philip C., eds. Cool Stars with Excesses of Heavy Elements. 1985. lib. bdg. 54.00 (ISBN 90-277-1957-8, Pub. by Reidel Holland). Kluwer Academic.

Jeans, James. The Stars in Their Courses. 173p. 1982. Repr. of 1931 ed. lib. bdg. 25.00 (ISBN 0-89760-414-8). Telegraph Bks.

Kaufmann, William J., III. Stars & Nebulas. LC 78-17544. (Illus.). 204p. 1978. pap. text ed. 10.95 (ISBN 0-7167-0085-9). W H Freeman.

Kippenhahn, Rudolf. One Hundred Billion Suns: The Birth, Life, & Death of the Stars. LC 82-72398. (Illus.). 256p. 1983. 25.00 (ISBN 0-465-05263-0). Basic.

Kitchin, C. R. & Meadows, A. J. Early Emission Line Stars. 1982. 35.00 (ISBN 0-9960023-3-2, Pub. by A Hilger England). Heyden.

Kumar, S. S., ed. Low Luminosity Stars. 560p. 1969. 149.25 (ISBN 0-677-13000-7). Gordon.

Kyselka, Will & Lanterman, Ray. North Star to Southern Cross. LC 75-37655. (Illus.). 160p. 1976. 10.00x (ISBN 0-8248-0411-2); pap. 4.95 (ISBN 0-8248-0419-8). UH Pr.

Lebovitz, Norman, et al, eds. Theoretical Principles in Astrophysics & Relativity. LC 76-25636. (Illus.). 1978. lib. bdg. 25.00x (ISBN 0-226-46989-1). U of Chicago Pr.

Lucas, R., et al, eds. Birth & Infancy of Stars: Proceedings of the Les Houches Summer School, Session XLI, 8 August-2 September 1983, Vol. 41. 846p. 1985. 159.25 (ISBN 0-444-86917-4, North-Holland). Elsevier.

McEwan, D. An Easy & Concise Guide to the Starry Heavens. 1910. 15.00 (ISBN 0-686-17429-1). Ridgeway Bks.

Martin, Martha E. The Friendly Stars. rev. ed. Menzel, Donald H., ed. (Illus.). 147p. 1964. pap. 3.50 (ISBN 0-486-21099-5). Dover.

--Friendly Stars. rev. ed. (Illus.). 13.25 (ISBN 0-8446-2538-8). Peter Smith.

Meadows, A. J. Stellar Evolution. 2nd ed. 1978. text ed. 28.00 (ISBN 0-08-021668-4); pap. text ed. 7.75 (ISBN 0-08-021669-2). Pergamon.

Novotny, Eva. Introduction to Stellar Atmospheres & Interiors. 1973. text ed. 34.95x (ISBN 0-19-501588-6). Oxford U Pr.

Ogorodnikov, K. F. Dynamics of Stellar Systems. 1965. 54.00 (ISBN 0-08-010163-1); pap. 28.00 (ISBN 0-08-013772-5). Pergamon.

O'Leary, Brian & Beatty, J. Kelly, eds. The New Solar System. 2nd ed. 240p. 1982. 24.95 (ISBN 0-933346-36-0); pap. 13.95 (ISBN 0-933346-37-9). Sky Pub.

Payne-Gaposchkin, Cecilia. Stars & Clusters. LC 79-4472. (Books on Astronomy). (Illus.). 1979. 22.50x (ISBN 0-674-83440-2). Harvard U Pr.

Philip, A. G. & Upgven, A. R., eds. The Nearby Stars & the Stellar Luminosity Function. 550p. 1983. 42.00 (ISBN 0-9607902-5-X); pap. 32.00 (ISBN 0-9607902-4-1). Davis Pr.

Pulsating Stars, Vols. 1 & 2. 1969-70. 25.00x ea. (Plenum Pr). Vol. 1 (ISBN 0-306-30401-5). Vol. 2 (ISBN 0-306-37092-1). Plenum Pub.

Reddish, V. C. Stellar Formation. 225p. 1978. text ed. 53.00 (ISBN 0-08-018062-0); 21.00 (ISBN 0-08-023053-9). Pergamon.

Reeves, Hubert. Evolution Stellaire et Nucleosynthese. (Cours & Documents de Mathematiques & de Physique Ser.). 114p. (Orig.). 1968. 30.25 (ISBN 0-677-50150-1). Gordon.

--Nuclear Reactions in Stellar Surfaces & Their Relations with Stellar Evolution. (Topics in Astrophysics & Space Physics Ser). (Illus.). 98p. 1971. 26.50x (ISBN 0-677-02960-8). Gordon.

--Stellar Evolution & Nucleosynthesis. (Documents on Modern Physics Ser.). 114p. (Orig.). 1968. 27.95 (ISBN 0-677-30150-2). Gordon.

Ridpath, Ian & Tirion, Wil. Universe Guide to Stars & Planets. LC 84-24133. (Illus.). 384p. 1985. 19.95 (ISBN 0-87663-366-1); pap. 10.95 (ISBN 0-87663-859-0). Universe.

Rigutti, Mario. A Hundred Billion Stars. Giacconi, Mirella, tr. from Italian. LC 83-906. (Illus.). 316p. 1984. 27.50x (ISBN 0-262-18111-8). MIT Pr.

Roger, R. S. & Dewdney, P. E., eds. Regions of Recent Star Formation. 1982. lib. bdg. 59.50 (ISBN 90-277-1383-9, Pub. by Reidel Holland). Kluwer Academic.

Sandage, Allan & Sandage, Mary, eds. Galaxies & the Universe, Vol. IX. LC 74-7559. (Stars & Stellar Systems Midway Reprint Ser.). (Illus.). 818p. 1983. pap. text ed. 40.00x (ISBN 0-226-45970-5). U of Chicago Pr.

Schwartzschild. Structure & Evolution of the Stars. 1962. pap. 6.00 (ISBN 0-486-61479-4). Dover.

Shapiro, Stuart L. & Teukolsky, Saul A. Black Holes, White Dwarfs, & Neutron Stars: The Physics of Compact Objects. LC 82-20112. 645p. 1983. 48.50 (ISBN 0-471-87317-9, Pub. by Wiley-Interscience); pap. 26.95 (ISBN 0-471-87316-0). Wiley.

Shklovskii, Iosif S. Stars: Their Birth, Life & Death. Rodman, Richard B., tr. LC 77-13889. (Illus.). 442p. 1978. text ed. 32.95x (ISBN 0-7167-0024-7). W H Freeman.

Slettebek, Arne, ed. Be A Shell Stars. (Symposia of the International Astronomical Union Ser.: No. 70). 1976. lib. bdg. 79.00 (ISBN 90-277-0699-9, Pub. by Reidel Holland); pap. 60.50 (ISBN 90-277-0700-6). Kluwer Academic.

Spiegel, E. A. & Zahn, J. P., eds. Problems of Stellar Convection: Proceedings of the Colloquium No. 38 of the International Astronomical Union Held in Nice, 16-20 August, 1976. (Lecture Notes in Physics Ser: Vol. 71). 1977. pap. 22.00 (ISBN 0-387-08532-7). Springer-Verlag.

Stein, R. F. & Cameron, A. G., eds. Stellar Evolution. LC 65-25285. 464p. 1966. 45.00x (ISBN 0-306-30221-7, Plenum Pr). Plenum Pub.

Strand, K. A., ed. Basic Astronomical Data. LC 63-11402. (Stars & Stellar Systems Ser.: Vol. III, Midway Reprint Ser.). 1980. pap. text ed. 23.00x (ISBN 0-226-45964-0). U of Chicago Pr.

Struve, Otto. Stellar Evolution. 1950. 31.00x (ISBN 0-691-08043-7). Princeton U Pr.

Sugimoto, D. & Schramm, D., eds. Fundamental Problems in the Theory of Stellar Evolution. 1981. 47.50 (ISBN 90-277-1273-5, Pub. by Reidel Holland); pap. 21.00 (ISBN 90-277-1274-3, Pub. by Reidel Holland). Kluwer Academic.

Sweeney, James S., Jr. Seasonal Star Charts. 24p. (Orig.). 1972. pap. text ed. 8.95 (ISBN 0-8331-1802-1). Hubbard Sci.

Symposium No. 49 of the International Astronomical Union, Buenos Aires, Argentina. Aug. 1971. Wolf-Rayet & High Temperature Stars: Proceedings. Bappu, M. K. & Sahade, J, eds. LC 72-87470. 263p. 1973. lib. bdg. 45.00 (ISBN 90-277-0246-2, Pub. by Reidel Holland); pap. text ed. 31.50 (ISBN 90-277-0361-2). Kluwer Academic.

Symposium of the International Astronomical Union, No. 59, Mount Stromlo, Canberra, Australia, Aug. 16-18, 1973. Stellar Instability & Evolution: Proceedings. Ledoux, P., et al, eds. LC 74-80520. 200p. 1974. lib. bdg. 37.00 (ISBN 90-277-0479-1, Pub. by Reidel Holland); pap. text ed. 26.00 (ISBN 90-277-0480-5). Kluwer Academic.

Tassoul, Jean-Louis. Theory of Rotating Stars. LC 78-51198. (Astrophysics Ser: No. 1). (Illus.). 1978. 62.50 (ISBN 0-691-08211-1); pap. 19.00 (ISBN 0-691-08214-6). Princeton U Pr.

Tayler, R. J. The Stars: Their Structure & Evolution. (Wykeham Science Ser.: No. 10). 220p. 1974. pap. cancelled (ISBN 0-85109-110-5). Taylor & Francis.

Tayler, R. J. & Everest, A. S. The Stars: Their Structure & Evolution. (Wykeham Science Ser.: No. 10). 220p. 1974. Repr. 11.75x (ISBN 0-8448-1112-2). Crane Russak Co.

Trieste Colloquim on Astrophysics, 2nd, September 12-17, 1969. Mass Loss from the Stars: Proceedings. Hack, M., ed. (Astrophysics & Space Science Library: No.13). 345p. 1969. lib. bdg. 42.00 (ISBN 90-277-0118-0, Pub. by Reidel Holland). Kluwer Academic.

Underhill, Anne B. The Early Type Stars. 296p. 1966. pap. text ed. 80.95 (ISBN 0-677-01240-3). Gordon.

--The Early Type Stars. (Astrophysics & Space Science Library: No. 6). 282p. 1966. 39.50 (ISBN 90-277-0141-5, Pub. by Reidel Holland). Kluwer Academic.

Unno, Wasaburo, et al, eds. Nonradial Oscillations of Stars. 323p. 1979. 34.50x (ISBN 0-86008-258-X, Pub. by U of Tokyo Japan). Columbia U Pr.

Voigt, H. H. & Schaifers, K., eds. Astronomy & Astrophysics: Stars & Star Clusters. (Landbolt Boernstein Ser.: Group VI, Vol. 2, Subvolume b). (Illus.). 480p. 1982. 346.80 (ISBN 0-387-10976-5). Springer-Verlag.

Westerlund, Bengt E., ed. Stars & Star Systems. (Astrophysics & Space Science Library: No. 75). 1979. lib. bdg. 34.00 (ISBN 90-277-0983-1, Pub. by Reidel Holland). Kluwer Academic.

STARS–ATLASES

Audouze, Jean & Israel, Guy, eds. The Cambridge Atlas of Astronomy. (Illus.). 432p. 1985. 75.00 (ISBN 0-521-26369-7). Cambridge U Pr.

Bok, Bart J. & Bok, Priscilla F. The Milky Way. 5th ed. LC 80-22544. (Harvard Books on Astronomy Ser.). (Illus.). 384p. 1981. text ed. 25.00 (ISBN 0-674-57503-2). Harvard U Pr.

Brown, Peter L. Star & Planet Spotting: A Field Guide to the Night Sky. rev. ed. (Illus.). 176p. 1981. 9.95 (ISBN 0-7137-0655-4, Pub. by Blandford Pr England); pap. 6.95 (ISBN 0-7137-1265-1). Sterling.

Hodge, Paul W. & Wright, Frances W. The Large Magellanic Cloud. LC 67-61082. (Illus.). 114p. 1967. 35.00x (ISBN 0-87474-041-X). Smithsonian.

Jackson, Joseph H. & Baumert, John H. Pictorial Guide to the Planets. 3rd ed. LC 80-7897. (Illus.). 256p. 1981. 22.50i (ISBN 0-06-014869-1, HarpT). Har-Row.

Levitt, I. M. & Marshall, Roy K. Star Maps for Beginners. (Illus.). 64p. 1983. 7.95 (ISBN 0-671-47258-5, Fireside). S&S.

Lynds, Beverly T., ed. Dark Nebulae, Globules, & Protostars. LC 73-152040. (Illus.). 150p. 1971. 12.50x (ISBN 0-8165-0300-1). U of Ariz Pr.

Papadopoulos, C. Photographic Star Atlas, 3 vols. Incl. Vol. 1. Southern Stars. text ed. 200.00 (ISBN 0-08-023435-6); Vol. 2. Equatorial Stars. text ed. 325.00 (ISBN 0-08-021623-4); Vol. 3. Northern Stars. text ed. 200.00 (ISBN 0-08-021626-9). 1979. Vols. 1 & 2. text ed. 590.00 set (ISBN 0-08-021622-6). Pergamon.

--True Visual Magnitude Photographic Star Atlas, 3 vols. LC 78-41254. 1979. Set. 590.00 (ISBN 0-08-021622-6); Vol. 1. 240.00 (ISBN 0-08-023435-6); Vol. 2. 350.00 (ISBN 0-08-021623-4); Vol. 3. 240.00 (ISBN 0-08-021626-9). Pergamon.

Sandage, Allan. The Hubble Atlas of Galaxies. LC 60-16568. (Illus.). 141p. 1961. pap. 26.00 (ISBN 0-87279-629-9, 618). Carnegie Inst.

Sandage, Allan & Tammann, G. A. A Revised Shapley-Ames Catalog of Bright Galaxies. 1981. 29.00 (ISBN 0-87279-646-9, 635). Carnegie Inst.

Tirion, Wil. Sky Atlas 2000.0 Color. 1981. spiral bound 34.95 (ISBN 0-933346-33-6, 46336). Sky Pub.

--Sky Atlas 2000.0 Desk: Black Stars on White Backround. (Illus.). 1981. 15.95 (ISBN 0-933346-31-X). Sky Pub.

--Sky Atlas 2000.0 Field: White Stars on Black Backround. (Illus.). 1981. 15.95 (ISBN 0-933346-32-8, 46328). Sky Pub.

Vehrenberg, Hans. Atlas of Deep Sky Splendors. 4th ed. Orig. Title: Mein Messier-Buch. Tr. of Mein Messier-Buch. (Illus.). 240p. 1983. 39.95 (ISBN 0-933346-03-4). Sky Pub.

--Atlas of Deep Sky Splendors. 4th ed. LC 83-7656. (Illus.). 242p. 1984. 44.50 (ISBN 0-521-25834-0). Cambridge U Pr.

--Atlas of the Deep-Sky Splendors. (4th). (Illus.). 248p. 1983. 39.95 (ISBN 0-686-46902-X). Sky Pub.

Warner, Deborah J. The Sky Explored: Celestial Cartography, 1500-1800. LC 78-24737. 312p. 1979. 70.00x (ISBN 0-8451-1700-9). A R Liss.

Whitney, Charles A. Whitney's Star Finder: Revised for 1982 Through 1985. LC 81-47523. 128p. 1981. pap. 10.95 (ISBN 0-394-74953-7). Knopf.

Yamashita, Yasumasa, et al. An Atlas of Representative Stellar Spectra. LC 78-535. 129p. 1978. 85.95x (ISBN 0-470-26315-6). Halsted Pr.

STARS–ATMOSPHERES

Baschek, B., et al, eds. Problems in Stellar Atmospheres & Envelopes. LC 74-32493. (Illus.). 390p. 1975. 34.00 (ISBN 0-387-07092-3). Springer-Verlag.

Gingerich, Owen, ed. Theory & Observations of Normal Stellar Atmospheres: Proceedings of the Third Harvard-Smithsonian Conference on Stellar Atmosphere. 1970. 40.00x (ISBN 0-262-07035-9). MIT Pr.

Gray, D. F., ed. Stellar Turbulence: Proceedings of Colloquium 51 of the International Astronomical Union, Held at the University of Western Ontario, London, Ontario, Canada, August 27-30, 1979. (Lecture Notes in Physics: Vol. 114). 308p. 1980. pap. 26.00 (ISBN 3-540-09737-6). Springer-Verlag.

Gray, David F. The Observation & Analysis of Stellar Photospheres. LC 75-19229. 471p. 1976. 49.95x (ISBN 0-471-32380-2, Pub. by Wiley-Interscience). Wiley.

Greenstein, Jesse L., ed. Stellar Atmospheres. LC 61-9045. (Stars & Stellar Systems Ser: Vol. 6). (Illus.). 1961. 50.00x (ISBN 0-226-45958-6). U of Chicago Pr.

International Astrological Union Symposium, No. 51, Parksville, B. C., Canada Sept. 6-12, 1972 & Batten, A. H. Extended Atmospheres & Circumstellar Matter in Spectroscopic Binary Systems: Proceedings. LC 72-97942. 291p. 1973. lib. bdg. 50.00 (ISBN 90-277-0351-5, Pub. by Reidel Holland); pap. 34.75 (ISBN 90-277-0362-0, Pub. by Reidel Holland). Kluwer Academic.

Mihalas, Dimitri. Stellar Atmospheres. 2nd ed. LC 77-13211. (Astronomy & Astrophysics Ser.). (Illus.). 632p. 1978. text ed. 42.95x (ISBN 0-7167-0359-9). W H Freeman.

Novotny, Eva. Introduction to Stellar Atmospheres & Interiors. 1973. text ed. 34.95x (ISBN 0-19-501588-6). Oxford U Pr.

Swihart, Thomas L. Radiation Transfer & Stellar Atmospheres. (Astronomy & Astrophysics Ser.: Vol. 12). 142p. 1981. 38.00 (ISBN 0-912918-18-7, 0018). Pachart Pub Hse.

STARS–CATALOGS

Beyer, Steven L. The Star Guide: A Unique System for Identifying the Brightest Stars in the Night Sky. (Illus.). 336p. 1984. 19.45i (ISBN 0-316-09267-3); pap. 9.70i (ISBN 0-316-09268-1). Little.

Carnegie Institution of Washington. Albany Catalogue of Twenty Thousand Eight Hundred Eleven Stars for the Epoch Nineteen Hundred Ten: Prepared at the Dudley Observatory, Albany, New York. LC 32-5590. (Carnegie Institution of Washington Publication Ser.: No. 419). pap. 121.00 (ISBN 0-317-07801-1, 2006084). Bks Demand UMI.

Carnegie Institution Of Washington - Dept. Of Meridian Astronomy. General Catalogue of Thirty Three Thousand Three Hundred Forty-Two Stars for the Epoch 1950, 5 vols. Boss, Benjamin, et al, eds. 1937. Set. 150.00 (ISBN 0-384-07706-4). Johnson Repr.

Corwin, Harold G., et al. Southern Galaxy Catalogue: A Catalogue of 5481 Galaxies South of Declination-17 Degress Found on 1.2m U. K. Schmidt IIIa-J Plates. LC 85-50556. (The Unversity of Texas Monographs in Astronomy: No. 4). 342p. (Orig.). 1985. pap. write for info. (ISBN 0-9603796-3-0). U of Tex Dept Astron.

Hirshfeld, Alan & Sinnott, Roger W. Sky Catalogue 2000. 604p. 1982. 49.95; pap. 29.95 (ISBN 0-933346-34-4). Sky Pub.

Hirshfeld, Alan, ed. Sky Catalogue Two Thousands, Vol. 2. 1983. 49.95 (ISBN 0-933346-39-5); pap. 29.95 (ISBN 0-933346-38-7). Sky Pub.

Hoffleit, Dorrit & Jaschek, Carlos. The Bright Star Catalogue. 4th, rev. ed. xv, 472p. (Orig.). 1982. pap. 35.00 (ISBN 0-914753-00-2). Yale U Observ.

Maeder, Andre & Renzini, Alvio, eds. Observational Tests of the Stellar Evolution Theory. 1984. lib. bdg. 66.00 (ISBN 90-277-1774-5, Pub. by Reidel Holland); pap. text ed. 29.95 (ISBN 90-277-1775-3, Pub. by Reidel Holland). Kluwer Academic.

Webb Society & Jones, Kenneth G., eds. Webb Society Deep-Sky Observer's Handbook: Galaxies, Vol. IV. LC 77-359099. 256p. 1981. pap. 16.95x (ISBN 0-89490-050-1). Enslow Pubs.

STARS–CLUSTERS

see also Nebulae

Alter, G. & Ruprecht, J. Catalogue of Star Clusters & Associations. 1970. 65.00 (ISBN 0-9960008-7-9, Pub. by Akademiai Kaido Hungary). Heyden.

--The System of Open Star Clusters & the Galaxy Atlas of Open Star Clusters. 1963. 66.00 (ISBN 0-12-054250-1). Acad Pr.

Eighty-Fifth Symposium of the International Astronomical Union, Victoria, B. C., Canada, August 27-30, 1979. Star Clusters: Proceedings. Hesser, James E., ed. (International Astronomical Union Symposium Ser.: No. 85). 540p. 1980. lib. bdg. 63.00 (ISBN 90-277-1087-2, Pub. by Reidel Holland); pap. 31.50 (ISBN 90-277-1088-0). Kluwer Academic.

Goodman, Jeremy & Hut, Piet, eds. Dynamics of Star Clusters. 1985. lib. bdg. 69.00 (ISBN 90-277-1963-2, Pub. by Reidel Holland); pap. text ed. 29.00 (ISBN 90-277-1965-9). Kluwer Academic.

International Astronomical Union Colloquium No. 21, University of Toronto, Aug. 29-31, 1972. Variable Stars in Globular Clusters & in Related Systems: Proceedings. Fernie, J. D., ed. LC 73-83560. (Astrophysics & Space Science Library). 1973. lib. bdg. 39.50 (ISBN 90-277-0341-8, Pub. by Reidel Holland). Kluwer Academic.

Kukulin, V. I. & Jackson, D. F. Clustering Phenomena in Nuclei, Vol. 3: Direct Cluster Reactions-Progress Towards a Unified Theory, Clusters as Subsystems in Light Nuclei. 1983. 55.50 (ISBN 0-9940019-5-9, Pub. by Vieweg & Sohn Germany). Heyden.

Mardirossian, F., et al, eds. Clusters & Groups of Galaxies. 704p. 1984. lib. bdg. 89.50 (ISBN 90-277-1772-9, Pub. by Reidel Holland). Kluwer Academic.

Ruprecht, J., et al, eds. Catalogue of Star Clusters & Associations Plus Supplement No. 1. 1981. 115.00 (ISBN 0-9960072-5-3, Pub. by Akademiai Kaido Hungary). Heyden.

Shapley, Harlow. Galaxies. rev. ed. LC 61-7393. (Illus.). 1967. pap. text ed. 2.45x (ISBN 0-689-70179-9, 100). Atheneum.

Vehrenberg, Hans. Atlas of Deep Sky Splendors. 4th ed. Orig. Title: Mein Messier-Buch. Tr. of Mein Messier-Buch. (Illus.). 240p. 1983. 39.95 (ISBN 0-933346-03-4). Sky Pub.

--Atlas of Deep Sky Splendors. 4th ed. LC 83-7656. (Illus.). 242p. 1984. 44.50 (ISBN 0-521-25834-0). Cambridge U Pr.

Voigt, H. H. & Schaifers, K., eds. Astronomy & Astrophysics: Stars & Star Clusters. (Landbolt Boernstein Ser.: Group VI, Vol. 2, Subvolume b). (Illus.). 480p. 1982. 346.80 (ISBN 0-387-10976-5). Springer-Verlag.

STARS–RADIATION

Sobolev, Victor V. Moving Envelopes of Stars. Gaposchkin, Sergei, tr. LC 59-9284. (Illus.). 1960. 8.95x (ISBN 0-674-58800-2). Harvard U Pr.

Wilson, Ralph E. General Catalogue of Stellar Radial Velocities. 2nd ed. 1963. 5.00 (ISBN 0-87279-612-4). Carnegie Inst.

STARS–SPECTRA

Beckman, John E. & Crivellari, Lucio, eds. Progress in Stellar Spectral Line Formation Theory. 1985. lib. bdg. 59.00 (ISBN 90-277-2007-X, Pub. by Reidel Netherlands). Kluwer Academic.

Cowley, Charles R. Theory of Stellar Spectra. (Topics in Astrophysics & Space Physics Ser.). 272p. 1970. 67.25 (ISBN 0-677-02400-2). Gordon.

IAU Symposium, No. 36, Lunteren, Netherlands, June 1969. Ultraviolet Stellar Spectra & Related Ground-Based Observations: Proceedings. Houziaux, K. & Butler, H. E., eds. 361p. 1970. lib. bdg. 37.00 (ISBN 90-277-0152-0, Pub by Reidel Holland). Kluwer Academic.

Keenan, Philip C. & McNeil, Raymond C. An Atlas of Spectra of the Cooler Stars: Types G, K, M, S, & C. LC 76-18877. (Illus., Orig.). 1976. pap. 10.00 (ISBN 0-8142-0269-1). Ohio St U Pr.

Sobolev, Victor V. Moving Envelopes of Stars. Gaposchkin, Sergei, tr. LC 59-9284. (Illus.). 1960. 8.95x (ISBN 0-674-58800-2). Harvard U Pr.

STARS, DOUBLE

Binnendijk, Leendert. Properties of Double Stars: A Survey of Parallaxes & Orbits. LC 58-8011. pap. 66.40 (ISBN 0-317-08370-8, 2055279). Bks Demand UMI.

Couteau, Paul. Observing Visual Double Stars. Batten, Alan, tr. from Fr. (Illus.). 272p. 1981. 25.00x (ISBN 0-262-03077-2); pap. 8.95x (ISBN 0-262-53046-5). MIT Pr.

--Observing Visual Double Stars. Batten, Alan, tr. 257p. 1981. pap. 8.95x (ISBN 0-262-53046-5). MIT Pr.

Eggleton, P., et al, eds. Structure & Evolution of Close Binary Systems. LC 76-21688. (Symposium of the International Astronomical Union Ser.: No. 73). 1976. lib. bdg. 55.00 (ISBN 90-277-0682-4, Pub. by Reidel Holland); pap. 45.00 (ISBN 90-277-0683-2). Kluwer Academic.

Ghedini, Silvano. Software for Photometric Astronomy. LC 82-8574. (Illus.). 224p. 1982. pap. text ed. 26.95 (ISBN 0-943396-00-X). Willmann-Bell.

Heintz, Wulff D. Double Stars. (Geophysics & Astrophysics Monographs: No. 15). 1978. lib. bdg. 34.00 (ISBN 90-277-0885-1); pap. 16.00 (ISBN 90-277-0886-X, Pub. by Reidel Holland). Kluwer Academic.

Baxter, R. J. Exactly Solved Models in Statistical Mechanics. LC 81-68965. (Theoretical Chemistry Ser.). 1982. 81.00 (ISBN 0-12-083180-5). Acad Pr.

Berne, Bruce J., ed. Statistical Mechanics, 2 pts. Incl. Pt. 1: Equilibrium Techniques. 242p. 49.50x (ISBN 0-306-33505-0); Pt. 2: Time-Dependent Processes. 362p. 55.00x (ISBN 0-306-33506-9). LC 76-46977. (Modern Theoretical Chemistry Ser.: Vols. 5 & 6). (Illus.). 1977 (Plenum Pr). Plenum Pub.

Bowler, Dr. M. G. Lectures in Statistical Mechanics. (International Series in Natural Philosophy). (Illus.). 208p. 1982. 22.00 (ISBN 0-08-026516-2); pap. 11.00 (ISBN 0-08-026515-4). Pergamon.

Brownlee, K. A. Statistical Theory & Methodology: In Science & Engineering. LC 84-3941. 608p. 1984. Repr. of 1965 ed. lib. bdg. 47.00 (ISBN 0-89874-748-1). Krieger.

Brush, S. G. The Kind of Motion We Call Heat: A History of the Kinetic Theory of Gases in the Nineteenth Century, 2 bks. (Studies in Statistical Mechanics: Vol. 6). 1976. Bk. 1. 53.25 (ISBN 0-7204-0370-7, North-Holland); Bk. 2. 93.75 (ISBN 0-7204-0482-7); Set. 121.25 (ISBN 0-686-67836-2). Elsevier.

Chretien, M., et al, eds. Brandeis University Summer Institute in Theoretical Physics: 1966 Lectures: Statistical Physics, Phase Transitions & Superfluidity, 2 vols. Incl. Vol. 1. 336p. 93.75 (ISBN 0-677-10820-6); Vol. 2. 490p. 88.00 (ISBN 0-677-10830-3). 1968. Gordon.

--Brandeis University Summer Institute in Theoretical Physics: 1968 Lectures: Astrophysics & General Relativity, 2 vols. Incl. Vol. 1. 310p. 67.25 (ISBN 0-677-13480-0); Vol. 2. 396p. 101.25 (ISBN 0-677-13490-8). 1969. Gordon.

Cohen, E. G. D., ed. Fundamental Problems in Statistical Mechanics: Proceedings of the 5th International Summer School, Eschede, Netherlands-1980, Vol.5. 388p. 1981. 72.50 (ISBN 0-444-86137-8, North-Holland). Elsevier.

Crosignani, Bruno & Di Porto, Paolo. Statistical Properties of Scattered Light. (Quantum Electronics Ser.). 1975. 59.50 (ISBN 0-12-199050-8). Acad Pr.

DeWitt, C. & Stora, R. Les Houches Lectures: 1970, Statistical Mechanics & Quantum Field Theory. 568p. 1971. 150.25 (ISBN 0-677-13330-8). Gordon.

Dobson, A. J. An Introduction to Statistical Modelling. LC 83-7495. (Illus.). 200p. 1983. 25.00 (ISBN 0-412-24850-6, NO. 6864); pap. 14.95 (ISBN 0-412-24860-3, NO. 6865). Methuen Inc.

Eggwertz, S. & Lind, N. C., eds. Probabilistic Methods in the Mechanics of Solids & Structures. (International Union of Theoretical & Applied Mechanics Ser.). (Illus.). xxiv, 610p. 1985. 51.00 (ISBN 0-387-15087-0). Springer-Verlag.

Eyring, Henry, et al. Statistical Mechanics & Dynamics. 2nd ed. LC 78-1073. 785p. 1982. 39.95 (ISBN 0-471-37042-8, Pub. by Wiley-Interscience). Wiley.

Feynman, R. P. Statistical Mechanics: A Set of Lectures. 1981. pap. 31.95 (ISBN 0-8053-2509-3). Benjamin-Cummings.

Feynman, Richard P. Statistical Mechanics. LC 72-1769. (Frontiers in Physics Ser.: No. 36). 354p. 1972. pap. text ed. 31.95 (ISBN 0-8053-2509-3). Benjamin-Cummings.

Flory, P. J. Statistical Mechanics of Chain Molecules. LC 68-21490. 1969. 51.50x (ISBN 0-470-26495-0, Pub. by Wiley-Interscience). Wiley.

Friedman, Harold L. A Course in Statistical Mechanics. (Illus.). 272p. 1985. text ed. 54.95 (ISBN 0-13-184565-9). P-H.

Gibbs, J. Willard. Elementary Principles in Statistical Mechanics. LC 80-84972. 224p. 1981. 22.00 (ISBN 0-918024-19-6); pap. text ed. 12.00 (ISBN 0-918024-20-X). Ox Bow.

--Scientific Papers, 2 vols. Set. 21.50 (ISBN 0-8446-2127-7). Peter Smith.

Grabert, H. Projection Operator Techniques in Nonequilibrium Statistical Mechanics. (Springer Tratcs in Modern physics Ser.: Vol. 95). (Illus.). 220p. 1982. 34.00 (ISBN 0-387-11635-4). Springer-Verlag.

Heer, C. V. Statistical Mechanics, Kinetic, Theory & Stochastic Process. 1972. 31.50 (ISBN 0-12-336550-3). Acad Pr.

Hobson, Arthur. Concepts in Statistical Mechanics. LC 70-136362. (Illus.). 184p. 1971. 57.75 (ISBN 0-677-03240-4). Gordon.

Hoff, John C. A Practical Guide to Box-Jenkins Forecasting. (Research Methods Ser.). (Illus.). 316p. 1983. 30.00 (ISBN 0-534-02719-9). Lifetime Learn.

Honerkamp, J. & Pohlmeyer, J., eds. Structural Elements in Particle Physics & Statistical Mechanics. (NATO ASI Series B, Physics: Vol. 82). 470p. 1983. 69.50x (ISBN 0-306-41038-9, Plenum Pr). Plenum Pub.

Huang, Kerson. Statistical Mechanics. LC 63-11437. 470p. 1963. 46.50 (ISBN 0-471-41760-2). Wiley.

Hurt, Norman & Hermann, R. Quantum Statistical Mechanics & Lie Group Harmonic Analysis, Pt. A. LC 80-13949. (Lie Groups; History, Frontiers & Applications: Vol. 10). 250p. 1980. text ed. 36.00 (ISBN 0-915692-30-9, 991600118). Math Sci Pr.

International Solvay Conference on Physics, XVII, et al. Order & Fluctuations in Equilibrium & Nonequilibrium Statistical Mechanics: Proceedings. LC 80-13215. 374p. 1981. 85.00 (ISBN 0-471-05927-7, Pub. by Wiley Interscience). Wiley.

Israel, Robert B. Convexity in the Theory of Lattice Gasses. LC 78-51171. (Physic Ser). 1979. 27.00 (ISBN 0-691-08209-X); pap. 13.50 (ISBN 0-691-08216-2). Princeton U Pr.

IUPAP Conference. Statistical Mechanics of Irreversible Change: Proceedings of the 6th IUPAP Conference on Statistical Mechanics, 1971. LC 55-8426. pap. 35.00 (ISBN 0-317-08501-8, 2010184). Bks Demand UMI.

Jancel, R. Foundations of Classical & Quantum Statistical Mechanics. 1969. 59.00 (ISBN 0-08-012823-8). Pergamon.

Katz, Amnon. Principles of Statistical Mechanics: The Information Theory Approach. LC 67-12181. pap. 48.80 (ISBN 0-317-08729-0, 2055549). Bks Demand UMI.

Kerner, Edward H. Gibbs Ensemble: Biological Ensemble, Vol. 12. LC 73-185038. (International Science Review Ser.). 180p. 1970. 64.95 (ISBN 0-677-14180-7). Gordon.

Khinchin, A. I. Analytical Foundations of Physical Statistics. (Russian Monographs & Texts on the Physical Sciences). 64p. 1961. 24.50 (ISBN 0-677-20140-0). Gordon.

Khinchin, Alexander I. Mathematical Foundations of Statistical Mechanics. Gamow, George, tr. 1949. pap. text ed. 4.95 (ISBN 0-486-60147-1). Dover.

Kirkwood, John G. Selected Topics in Statistical Mechanics. Zwanzig, R. W., ed. LC 68-6792. (Documents on Modern Physics Ser.). (Illus.). 288p. 1967. 65.95 (ISBN 0-677-00330-7). Gordon.

--Theory of Solutions. Salsburg, Z. W. & Poirier, J., eds. (Documents on Modern Physics Ser.). 316p. (Orig.). 1968. 62.50 (ISBN 0-677-01030-3). Gordon.

Kittel, Charles. Elementary Statistical Physics. LC 58-12495. (Illus.). 228p. 1958. 34.50x (ISBN 0-471-49005-9). Wiley.

Kubo, R. Statistical Mechanics. 426p. 1971. text ed. 53.25 (ISBN 0-7204-0090-2, North-Holland). Elsevier.

Kuramoto, Y., ed. Chaos & Statistical Methods: Proceedings of the Sixth Kyoto Summer Institute, Kyoto, Japan, September 12-15, 1983. (Springer Series in Synergetics: Vol. 24). (Illus.). 255p. 1984. 35.00 (ISBN 0-387-13156-6). Springer-Verlag.

Landman, Uzi, ed. Statistical Mechanics & Statistical Methods in Theory & Applications. LC 77-22526. 814p. 1977. 115.00x (ISBN 0-306-31077-5, Plenum Pr). Plenum Pub.

Landsberg, Peter T. Thermodynamics & Statistical Mechanics. (Illus.). 1979. 29.95x (ISBN 0-19-851142-6). Oxford U Pr.

Lebovitz, J. L. & Montroll, E. W., eds. Nonequilibrium Phenomena: The Boltzmann Equation, No. 1. (Studies in Statistical Mechanics: Vol. 10). 251p. 1983. 40.00 (ISBN 0-444-86519-5, North-Holland). Elsevier.

Lebowitz, J. L. & Montroll, E. W., eds. Nonequilibrium Phenomena II: From Stochastics to Hydrodynamics. (Studies in Statistical Mechanics: Vol. 11). 308p. 1984. 45.00 (ISBN 0-444-86806-2). Elsevier.

Lee, T. D. Statistical Mechanics. (Concepts in Contemporary Physics Ser.). Date not set. lib. bdg. write for info. (ISBN 3-7186-0052-8); pap. write for info. (ISBN 3-7186-0053-6). Harwood Academic.

Levy, M. & Mitter, P., eds. New Developments in Quantum Field Theory & Statistical Mechanics: Cargese 1976. LC 77-8847. (NATO ASI Series B, Physics: Vol. 26). 483p. 1977. 75.00x (ISBN 0-306-35726-7, Plenum Pr). Plenum Pub.

Levy, Maurice & Jancovici, B., eds. Cargese Lecture Notes 1964: Vol. 1, Statistical Mechanics. 244p. (Orig.). 1966. 69.50x (ISBN 0-677-10980-6). Gordon.

Liboff, Richard L. Introduction to the Theory of Kinetic Equations. corr. ed. LC 76-30383. (Illus.). 410p. 1979. Repr. of 1969 ed. lib. bdg. 24.00 (ISBN 0-88275-496-3). Krieger.

Ma, Shang-Keng. Statistical Mechanics. 500p. 1984. 67.00x (ISBN 9971-966-06-9, Pub. by World Sci Singapore); pap. 30.00x (ISBN 9971-966-07-7, Pub. by World Sci Singapore). Taylor & Francis.

McQuarrie, Donald A. Statistical Mechanics. (Chemistry Ser.). 640p. 1976. text ed. 55.50 scp (ISBN 0-06-044366-9, HarpC). Har-Row.

Martin-Loef, A. Statistical Mechanics & the Foundations of Thermodynamics. (Lecture Notes in Physics Ser.: Vol. 101). 1979. pap. 13.00 (ISBN 0-387-09255-2). Springer-Verlag.

Matusita, K., ed. Statistical Theory & Data Analysis: Proceedings of the Pacific Area Statistical Conference, 1985. 812p. 1985. 118.75 (ISBN 0-444-87665-0, North-Holland). Elsevier.

Mayer, D. H. The Ruelle-Araki Transfer Operator in Classical Statistical Mechanics. (Lecture Notes in Physics: Vol. 123). 154p. 1980. pap. 15.00 (ISBN 0-387-09990-5). Springer-Verlag.

Mayer, Joseph E. & Mayer, Maria G. Statistical Mechanics. 2nd ed. LC 76-20668. 491p. 1977. 51.50x (ISBN 0-471-57985-8, Pub. by Wiley-Interscience). Wiley.

Meijer, P. H., ed. Quantum Statistical Mechanics. (Documents on Modern Physics Ser.). 182p. (Orig.). 1966. 41.75x (ISBN 0-677-01310-8). Gordon.

Mohling. Statistical Mechanics Methods & Applications. 608p. 1982. text ed. 53.95x (ISBN 0-470-27340-2). Halsted Pr.

Moraal, H. Classical, Discrete Spin Models. (Lecture Notes in Physics Ser.: Vol. 214). vii, 251p. 1984. pap. 14.00 (ISBN 0-387-13896-X). Springer-Verlag.

Ollagnier, J. Moulin. Ergodic Theory & Statistical Mechanics. (Lecture Notes in Mathematics: Vol. 1115). vi, 147p. 1985. pap. 12.00 (ISBN 0-387-15192-3). Springer Verlag.

Pathria, R. K. Advanced Statistical Mechanics. 1972. 26.00 (ISBN 0-08-018994-6). Pergamon.

Poland, D. & Scheraga, H. A. Theory of Helix Coil Transitions in Biopolymers. (Molecular Biology). 1970. 75.00 (ISBN 0-12-559550-6). Acad Pr.

Rasetti, M. Modern Methods in Equilibrium Statistical Mechanics. (Statistical Mechanics Ser.: Vol. 1). 270p. 1984. pap. 19.00x (ISBN 0-9902005-3-1, Pub. by World Sci Singapore). Taylor & Francis.

Rice, Oscar K. Statistical Mechanics, Thermodynamics, & Kinetics. LC 66-16379. (Chemistry Ser.). (Illus.). 586p. 1967. 34.95x (ISBN 0-7167-0133-2). W H Freeman.

Rice, Stuart A. & Freed, Karl F., eds. Statistical Mechanics: New Concepts, New Problems, New Applications. LC 72-85434. pap. 108.50 (ISBN 0-317-08081-4, 2019965). Bks Demand UMI.

Risken, H. The Fokker-Planck Equation Methods of Solution & Applications. (Springer Series in Synergetics: Vol. 18). (Illus.). 495p. 1984. 52.00 (ISBN 0-387-13098-5). Springer-Verlag.

Ruelle, David. Encyclopedia of Mathematics & Its Applications: Thermodynamic Formalism: The Mathematical Structures of Classical Equilibrium Statistical Mechanics, Vol. 5. 1984. 32.50 (ISBN 0-521-30225-0). Cambridge U Pr.

Schober, Anton. Irreversibility & Nonpotentiality in Statistical Mechanics. (Illus.). 495p. (Orig.). 1984. pap. 60.00 (ISBN 0-911767-23-1). Hadronic Pr Inc.

Schroedinger. Collected Papers, 4 vols. Incl. Vol. 1. Contributions to Statistical Mechanics; Vol. 2. Contributions to Field Theory; Vol. 3. Contributions to Quantum Theory; Vol. 4. General Scientific & Popular Papers. 1984. Set. 175.00 (ISBN 0-9904001-7-4, Pub. by Vieweg & Sohn Germany). Heyden.

Singer, K. Statistical Mechanics, Vols. 1-2. LC 72-95106. Vol. 1 1973. 1972 literature 32.00 (ISBN 0-85186-750-2, Pub. by Royal Soc Chem London); Vol. 2 1975. 1974 literature 45.00 (ISBN 0-85186-760-X). Am Chemical.

Society for Industrial & Applied Mathematics - American Mathematical Society Symposia - New York - April, 1971. Mathematical Aspects of Statistical Mechanics: Proceedings. Pool, J. C., ed. LC 72-321. (S I A M - A M S Proceedings: Vol. 5). 1972. 22.00 (ISBN 0-8218-1324-2, SIAMS-5). Am Math.

Sonntag, Richard E. & Van Wylen, Gordon J. Fundamentals of Statistical Thermodynamics. LC 84-15472. 390p. 1985. Repr. of 1966 ed. lib. bdg. 42.00 (ISBN 0-89874-785-6). Krieger.

Statistical Services Directory. 2nd ed. 461p. 1984. 180.00x (ISBN 0-8103-0668-9). Gale.

Stowe, K. Introduction to Statistical Mechanics & Thermodynamics. 534p. 1984. 38.50 (ISBN 0-471-87058-7). Wiley.

Summer Institute in Theoretical Physics, Mexico City, 1973. Particles, Quantum Fields & Statistical Mechanics: Proceedings. Alexanian, M. & Zepeda, A., eds. LC 74-28357. (Lecture Notes in Physics Ser.: Vol. 32). (Illus.). 135p. 1975. pap. 13.00 (ISBN 0-387-07022-2). Springer-Verlag.

Ter-Haar, D. & Henin, F. Lectures on Selected Topics in Equilibrium & Non-Equilibrium Statistical Mechanics. LC 77-8300. 1977. text ed. 25.00 (ISBN 0-08-017937-1). Pergamon.

Thompson, Richard L. Equilibrium States on Thin Energy Shells. LC 74-14723. (Memoirs Ser.: No. 150). 110p. 1974. pap. 11.00 (ISBN 0-8218-1850-3, MEMO-150). Am Math.

Toda, M., et al. Statistical Physics 1: Equilibrium Statistical Mechanics. (Spinger Series in Solid-State Sciences: Vol. 30). (Illus.). 270p. 1983. 37.00 (ISBN 0-387-11460-2). Springer-Verlag.

Tolman, Richard C. The Principles of Statistical Mechanics. LC 79-52649. 1980. pap. text ed. 10.95 (ISBN 0-486-63896-0). Dover.

Uhlenbeck, George, et al. Lectures in Statistical Mechanics. LC 62-21480. (Lectures in Applied Mathematics Ser.: Vol. 1). 181p. 1982. Repr. of 1963 ed. 33.00 (ISBN 0-8218-1101-0, LAM-1). Am Math.

Van Hemmen, J. L. & Morgenstern, I., eds. Heidelberg Colloquium on Spin Glasses: Proceedings of a Colloquium Held at the University of Heidelberg, May 30-June 3 1983. (Lecture Notes in Physics: Vol. 192). vii, 356p. 1983. pap. 20.00 (ISBN 0-387-12872-7). Springer-Verlag.

Weiner, J. H. Statistical Mechanics of Elasticity. 439p. 1983. 58.95 (ISBN 0-471-09773-X, Pub. by Wiley-Interscience). Wiley.

Yvon, J. Correlations & Entropy in Classical Statistical Mechanics. 1969. 31.00 (ISBN 0-08-012755-X). Pergamon.

Zuber, J & Stora, R. Recent Advances in Field Theory & Statistical Mechanics: Les Houches, Vol. 39. 1984. 166.75 (ISBN 0-444-86675-2). Elsevier.

STATISTICAL PHYSICS

see also Phase Transformations (Statistical Physics)

Binder, K., ed. Applications of the Monte Carlo Method in Statistical Physics. (Topics in Current Physics: Vol. 36). (Illus.). 330p. 1984. 34.00 (ISBN 0-387-12764-X). Springer-Verlag.

Brandt, S. Statistical & Computational Methods in Data Analysis. 2nd, rev. ed. 416p. 1976. 51.00 (ISBN 0-7204-0334-0, North Holland); pap. 28.00 (ISBN 0-444-86615-9). Elsevier.

Bratteli, O. & Robinson, D. W. Operator Algebras & Quantum Statistical Mechanics: Vol. I: C & W-Algebras. Symmetry Groups. Decomposition of States. (Texts & Monographs in Physics). 1979. 47.50 (ISBN 0-387-09187-4). Springer-Verlag.

Careri, Giorgio. Order & Disorder on Matter. 1983. text ed. 38.95 (ISBN 0-8053-1700-7); pap. 19.95 (ISBN 0-8053-1725-2). Benjamin-Cummings.

Fritz, J., et al, eds. Statistical Physics & Dynamical Systems: Rigorous Results. (Progress in Physics Ser.: Vol. 10). 510p. 1985. text ed. write for info. (ISBN 0-8176-3300-6). Birkhauser.

Guettinger, W. & Eikemeier, H., eds. Structural Stability in Physics: Proceedings of Two International Symposia. (Springer Ser. in Synergetics). (Illus.). 1979. 43.00 (ISBN 0-387-09463-6). Springer-Verlag.

Halmos, P. R. Lectures on Boolean Algebras. 150p. 1974. pap. 11.00 (ISBN 0-387-90094-2). Springer-Verlag.

Horton, C. W., Jr. & Reichl, L. E., eds. Statistical Physics & Chaos in Fusion Plasmas. LC 83-19649. (Nonequilibrium Problems in the Physical Science & Biology Ser.: 1-479). 361p. 1984. 85.00 (ISBN 0-471-88310-7, Pub. by Wiley-Interscience). Wiley.

Hughes, B. D. & Ninham, B. W. The Mathematics & Physics of Disordered Media: Percolation, Random Walk, Modeling & Simulation. (Lecture Notes in Mathematics: Vol. 1035). vii, 431p. 1983. pap. 20.00 (ISBN 0-387-12707-0). Springer-Verlag.

Ichimaru, Setsuo. Plasma Physics. (Frontiers in Physics Ser: No. 41). (Illus.). 352p. 1984. pap. text ed. 33.95x (ISBN 0-8053-8753-6). Benjamin-Cummings.

Isihara, A. Statistical Physics. 1971. 40.00 (ISBN 0-12-374650-7). Acad Pr.

Krylov, Nikolai S. Works on the Foundations of Statistical Physics. Migdal, A. B., et al, trs. from Rus. LC 78-70611. (Princeton Series in Physics). 1979. pap. 11.50x (ISBN 0-691-08227-8). Princeton U Pr.

Kubo, R., et al. Statistical Physics 2. (Springer Series in Solid-State Sciences: Vol. 31). (Illus.). 295p. 1985. 29.50 (ISBN 0-387-11461-0). Springer-Verlag.

Kuramoto, Y., ed. Chaos & Statistical Methods: Proceedings of the Sixth Kyoto Summer Institute, Kyoto, Japan, September 12-15, 1983. (Springer Series in Synergetics: Vol. 24). (Illus.). 255p. 1984. 35.00 (ISBN 0-387-13156-6). Springer-Verlag.

Landau, L. D. & Lifshitz, E. M. Course on Theoretical Physics: Statistical Physics, Vol. 5, Pt. 1. 3rd ed. (Illus.). 1980. text ed. 81.00 (ISBN 0-08-023039-3); pap. text ed. 22.50 (ISBN 0-08-023038-5). Pergamon.

Lovesey, Stephen W. Theory of Neutron Scattering from Condensed Matter, Vol. 2. (International Series of Monographs on Physics). (Illus.). 1984. 59.00x (ISBN 0-19-852017-4). Oxford U Pr.

Mandl, F. Statistical Physics. (Manchester Physics Ser). 1971. 24.95x (ISBN 0-471-56658-6, Pub. by Wiley-Interscience). Wiley.

Clayton, J. Introduction to Statistics: A Linguistic Approach. 2nd ed. 1984. 6.25 (ISBN 0-931021-00-6). Hurd Comm.
Clayton, Keith. An Introduction to Statistics for Psychology & Education. (No. 309). 448p. 1984. 22.95 (ISBN 0-675-20154-3); Additional supplements may be obtained from publisher. student guide 9.95 (ISBN 0-675-20258-2). Merrill.
Clelland, Richard C., et al. Basic Statistics with Business Applications. LC 72-8057. (Probability & Mathematical Statistics: Applied Probability & Statistics Section). (Illus.). pap. 120.00 (ISBN 0-8357-9843-7, 2055099). Bks Demand UMI.
Cochran, William G. Contributions to Statistics. LC 81-13077. (Wiley Series in Probability & Mathematical Statistics: Probability & Mathematical Section). 1835p. 1982. 95.00x (ISBN 0-471-09786-1, Pub. by Wiley-Interscience). Wiley.
Cochran, William G. & Snedecor, George W. Statistical Methods. 7th ed. (Illus.). 508p. 1980. text ed. 23.50x (ISBN 0-8138-1560-6). Iowa St U Pr.
Computer Science & Statistics: Proceedings. Eddy, W., ed. (Illus.). 378p. 1981. pap. 29.50 (ISBN 0-387-90633-9). Springer-Verlag.
Conference of European Statisticians. (Statistical Standards & Studies: No. 32). pap. 22.00 (UN82/2E/10, UN). Unipub.
Conover, W. J. & Iman, Ronald L. Introduction to Modern Business Statistics. 525p. 1983. 32.50 (ISBN 0-471-09669-5). Wiley.
--Study Guide to Accompany Introduction to Modern Business Statistics. 204p. 1983. pap. 13.95 (ISBN 0-471-09664-4). Wiley.
Cooke, D., et al. BASIC Statistical Computing. 176p. 1982. pap. text ed. 14.95 (ISBN 0-7131-3441-0). E Arnold.
Counting Statistics. (Advanced Health Physics Training Ser.). (Illus.). 110p. 1981. lib. bdg. 1700.00x training materials package (ISBN 0-87683-182-X); pap. text ed. 45.00x looseleaf (ISBN 0-87683-183-8); lesson plans 1250.00x (ISBN 0-87683-184-6); transparencies 250.00x (ISBN 0-87683-185-4); question blank 625.00x (ISBN 0-87683-186-2). G P Courseware.
Cox, D. R. Applied Statistics: Principles & Examples. 1981. 34.00x (ISBN 0-412-16560-0, NO.6549, Pub. by Chapman & Hall); pap. 12.50x (ISBN 0-412-16570-8, NO.6548). Methuen Inc.
Cox, D. R. & Hinkley, D. V. Theoretical Statistics. 1979. 21.00x (ISBN 0-412-16160-5, 6069, Pub. by Chapman & Hall). Methuen Inc.
Cox, D. R. & Lewis, P. A. The Statistical Analysis of Series of Events. (Monographs on Statistics & Applied Probability). 1966. 18.95 (ISBN 0-412-21800-3, 6343, Pub. by Chapman & Hall). Methuen Inc.
Crow, Edwin L., et al. Statistics Manual. (Illus.). 1955. pap. 6.00 (ISBN 0-486-60599-X). Dover.
Crowhurst, Norman H. Statistics. 110p. (Orig.). 1981. pap. text ed. 10.45 (ISBN 0-89420-111-5, 413040); cassette recordings 103.95 (ISBN 0-89420-202-2, 413000). Natl Book.
Croxton, Frederick E. Elementary Statistics: With Applications in Medicine & the Biological Sciences. (Illus.). 1953. pap. 6.95 (ISBN 0-486-60506-X). Dover.
Cruise, et al. A Resource Guide for Introductory Statistics. 356p. 1984. pap. text ed. 24.95 (ISBN 0-8403-3361-7). Kendall-Hunt.
Cruz, Ruperto Vazquez. Estadistica Elemental: Primera Part. 7th ed. pap. 4.50 (ISBN 0-8477-2619-3). U of PR Pr.
Csorgo, M., et al, eds. Statistics & Related Topics: Proceedings Conference, Ottawa, Canada, May, 1980. 388p. 1981. 53.25 (ISBN 0-444-86293-5, North-Holland). Elsevier.
Curtis, Wayne C. Statistical Concepts for Attorneys: A Reference Guide. LC 82-24068. xviii, 230p. 1983. lib. bdg. 35.00 (ISBN 0-89930-033-2, CSA/, Quorum). Greenwood.
Czuber, Eman. Wahrscheinlichkeitsrechnung & 'ihre Anwendung Auf Fehlerausgleichung, Statistik & Lebensversicherung, 2 Vols. (Bibliotheca Mathematica Teubneriana Ser.: Nos. 23 & 24). (Ger). 1969. Repr. of 1938 ed. Set. 60.00 (ISBN 0-384-10585-8). Johnson Repr.
Dale, Alfred G. An Economic Survey Method for Small Areas. (Area Economic Studies: No. 1). 1955. pap. 4.00 (ISBN 0-87755-020-4). Bureau Busn UT.
Daniel, Wayne W. & Terrell, James C. Business Statistics: Basic Concepts & Methodology. 3rd ed. LC 82-83254. 832p. 1982. text ed. 29.95 (ISBN 0-395-32601-X); instr's. resource manual 3.50 (ISBN 0-395-32602-8); study guide 12.50 (ISBN 0-395-32603-6); solutions manual 2.00 (ISBN 0-395-32604-4). HM.
Dapkus, F. Statistics One: A Text for Beginners. 1979. pap. text ed. 13.95 (ISBN 0-89669-042-3). Collegium Bk Pubs.
Das, M. N. & Giri, N. C. Design & Analysis of Experiments. LC 79-19286. 1981. 15.95x (ISBN 0-470-26861-1). Halsted Pr.
David, F. N. A First Course in Statistics. 2nd ed. (Griffin Monograph: No. 31). (Illus.). 1971. Repr. of 1953 ed. 10.75x (ISBN 0-02-843740-3). Hafner.
David, F. N. & Barton, D. E. Combinatorial Chance. 356p. 1962. text ed. 18.50x (ISBN 0-85264-057-9). Lubrecht & Cramer.
David, H. A. Method of Paired Comparisons. (Griffin's Statistical Monographs & Courses: Vol. 12). 1963. 9.75x (ISBN 0-02-843730-6). Hafner.
David, H. A., ed. Contributions to Survey Sampling & Applied Statistics: Papers in Honor of H. O. Hartley. 1978. 72.00 (ISBN 0-12-204750-8). Acad Pr.
--Order Statistics. 2nd ed. LC 80-16928. (Probability & Mathematical Statistics Ser.). 360p. 1981. 50.95x (ISBN 0-471-02723-5, Pub. by Wiley-Interscience). Wiley.
David, Herbert A. & David, Herbert T., eds. Statistics: An Appraisal. 664p. 1984. text ed. 31.25x (ISBN 0-8138-1721-8). Iowa St U Pr.
Davis, Harold T. & Nelson, William F. Elements of Statistics with Application to Economic Data. rev. & enl. 2nd ed. LC 78-163681. Repr. of 1937 ed. 28.50 (ISBN 0-404-01994-3). AMS Pr.
De Oliveira, J. Tiago & Epstein, Benjamin, eds. Some Recent Advances in Statistics. 1982. 49.50 (ISBN 0-12-691580-6). Acad Pr.
Depriest, Launder. Reliability in the Acquisitions Process. (Statistics Lecture Notes). 296p. 1983. 35.00 (ISBN 0-8247-1792-9). Dekker.
DeSanto, et al. Statistics Through Problem Solving. 2nd ed. Avenoso, Frank & Cheifetz, Philip, eds. LC 73-77244. 1978. pap. text ed. 16.50X (ISBN 0-916060-04-7). Math Alternatives.
Dietrich, Frank H., II & Kearns, Thomas. Basic Statistics. 1983. text ed. 26.95 (ISBN 0-02-329540-6). Dellen Pub.
Directory of International Statistics. 20.00 (ISBN 0-686-84920-5, E.81.XVII.6). UN.
Dixon, Wilfred J. & Massey, Frank J. Introduction to Statistical Analysis. 4th ed. (Illus.). 624p. 1983. 34.95 (ISBN 0-07-017073-8). McGraw.
Dolby & Tukey. The Statistics CumIndex, Vol. 1. LC 72-86074. 1973. 43.00 (ISBN 0-88274-000-8). R & D Pr.
Douglas, J. B. Analysis with Standard Contagious Distributions. (Statistical Distributions in Scientific Work Ser.: Vol. 4). 530p. 1980. 35.00 (ISBN 0-89974-012-X). Intl Co-Op.
Dowdy, S. & Wearden, S. Statistics for Research. (Probability & Mathematical Statistics Ser.). 537p. 1983. 36.95 (ISBN 0-471-08602-9); solutions manual 6.95 (ISBN 0-471-88394-8). Wiley.
Downie, N. M. & Heath, Robert W. Basic Statistical Methods. 5th ed. 384p. 1983. text ed. 23.95 scp (ISBN 0-06-041728-5, HarpC); scp study guide 9.95 (ISBN 0-06-041723-4). Har-Row.
--Metodos Estadisticos Aplicados. (Sp.). 1971. pap. 12.80 (ISBN 0-06-310074-6, IntlDept). Har-Row.
Downing, Douglas & Clark, Jeff. Business Statistics. (Business Review Ser.). 288p. 1985. pap. 8.95 (ISBN 0-8120-3576-3). Barron.
Dudewicz, Edward J. Introduction to Statistics & Probability. LC 75-26827. (American Sciences Press Ser. in Mathematical & Management Sciences: Vol. 1). 1976. text ed. 29.95 (ISBN 0-03-086688-X). Am Sciences Pr.
--Solutions in Statistics & Probability. LC 80-68285. (The American Sciences Press Ser. in Mathematical & Management Sciences: Vol. 3). 1980. pap. text ed. 24.95 (ISBN 0-935950-00-1). Am Sciences Pr.
Duncan, J. W. Statistical Services in Ten Years' Time. 53.00 (ISBN 0-08-022416-4). Pergamon.
Duncan, Otis D., et al. Statistical Geography: Problems in Analyzing Areal Data. LC 77-7890. (Illus.). 1977. Repr. of 1961 ed. lib. bdg. 17.75x (ISBN 0-8371-9676-0, DUSG). Greenwood.
Durran, J. H. Statistics & Probability. LC 70-96086. (School Mathematics Project Handbks). 1970. text ed. 27.95 (ISBN 0-521-06933-5). Cambridge U Pr.
Economic & Social Commission for Asia & the Pacific. Quarterly Bulletin of Statistics for Asia & the Pacific, Vols. 2-13. Incl. Vol. 3, Nos. 3 & 4, 2 Pts. No. 3. pap. 5.00 (UN74/2F82); No. 4. pap. 6.00 (UN74/2F92); Vol. 4, Nos. 1-4. 1974, 4 Pts. No. 1, Mar. pap. 6.00 (ISBN 0-686-93535-7, UN75/2F9); No. 2, June. pap. 5.00 (ISBN 0-686-99124-9, UN75/2F10); No. 3. pap. 6.00 (ISBN 0-686-99125-7, UN75/2F11); No. 4, December. pap. 4.00 (ISBN 0-686-99126-5, UN75/2F12); Vol. 5, Nos. 1-4. 1975, 4 Pts. No. 1, March. pap. 6.00 (ISBN 0-686-93539-X, UN76/2F6); No. 2, June. pap. 6.00 (ISBN 0-686-99127-3, UN76/2F7); No. 3, Sept. pap. 6.00 (ISBN 0-686-99128-1, UN76/2F9); No. 4, Dec. pap. 5.00 (ISBN 0-686-99129-X, UN76/2F9); Vol. 6. 1976, 2 Pts. No. 1 & 2 Mar.-Jun. pap. 7.00 (ISBN 0-686-93543-8, UN77/2F5); No. 3: Sept. pap. 6.00 (ISBN 0-686-99130-3, UN77/2F7); Vol. 7. 1977, 4 Pts. Nos. 1 March 1977. pap. 7.00 (ISBN 0-686-93545-4, UN78/2F3); No. 2: June 1977. pap. 5.00 (ISBN 0-686-99131-1, UN78/2F4); No. 3 Sept. 1977. pap. 6.00 (ISBN 0-686-99132-X, UN78/2F5); No. 4 Dec. 1977. pap. 6.00 (ISBN 0-686-99133-8, UN78/2F6); Vol. 8. 1978, 4 Pts. No. 1: March 1976. pap. 6.00 (ISBN 0-686-93549-7, UN78/2F9); No. 2: June 1978. pap. 6.00 (ISBN 0-686-99134-6, UN79/2F5); No. 3. pap. 6.00 (ISBN 0-686-99135-4, UN79/2F6); No. 4. pap. 6.00 (ISBN 0-686-99136-2, UN79/2F7); Vol. 9. 1979, 4 Pts. No. 1: March 1979. pap. 7.00 (ISBN 0-686-93553-5, UN79/2F8); No. 2: June 1979. pap. 6.00 (ISBN 0-686-99137-0, UN79/2F14); No. 3: Sept. 1979. pap. 6.00 (ISBN 0-686-99138-9, UN80/2F5); No. 4: Dec 1979. pap. 6.00 (ISBN 0-686-99139-7, UN80/2F7); Vol. 10, 4 Pts. No. 1: March 1980. pap. 7.00 (UN80/2F14); No. 2: June 1980. pap. 8.00 (UN80/2F16); No. 3: Sept. 1980. pap. 7.00 (UN81/2F2); No. 4: Dec. 1980. pap. 7.00 (UN81/2F4); Vol. 11. 1981, 4 Pts. No. 1: March 1981. pap. 8.00 (UN81/2F9); No. 2: June 1981. pap. 8.00 (UN81/2F13); No. 3: Sept. 1981. pap. 9.00 (UN82/2F2); No. 4: Dec. 1981. pap. 8.00 (UN82/2F4); Vol. 12, Nos. 1-2, 2 Pts. 1982. No. 1. pap. 9.00 (UN84/2F11); No.2. pap. 11.00 (UN83/2F5); No. 3: Sept. 1982. pap. 11.00 (UN83/2F6); No. 4: Dec. 1982. pap. 11.00 (UN83/2F10); Vol. 13, No. 1. March, 1983. (Illus.). 93p. 1983. pap. 11.00 (UN83/2F11). (Asian Economy Ser., UN). Unipub.
Edgington, E., ed. Randomization Tests. (Statistics, Textbooks & Monographs: Vol. 31). 1980. 39.75 (ISBN 0-8247-6878-7). Dekker.
Edwards. Linear Regession & Correlation Introduction. 2nd ed. (Illus.). 208p. 1984. text ed. 19.95 (ISBN 0-7167-1593-7); pap. text ed. 11.95 (ISBN 0-7167-1594-5). W H Freeman.
Edwards, Barry. The Readable Maths & Statistics Book. (Illus.). 336p. (Orig.). 1980. text ed. 34.95x (ISBN 0-04-310007-4). Allen Unwin.
Egle, K. Entscheidungstheorie. (Interdisciplinary Systems Research Ser.: No. 5). (Ger.). 246p. 1975. pap. 27.95x (ISBN 0-8176-0776-5). Birkhauser.
Ehrenberg, A. S. Data Reduction: Analyzing & Interpreting Statistical Data. LC 74-3724. 391p. 1975. 64.95x (ISBN 0-471-23399-4, Pub. by Wiley-Interscience); pap. 24.95x (ISBN 0-471-23398-6). Wiley.
--A Primer in Data Reduction: An Introduction Statistics Textbook. 305p. 1982. 58.95 (ISBN 0-471-10134-6); pap. 21.95 (ISBN 0-471-10135-4). Wiley.
Elandt-Johnson, Regina C. & Johnson, Norman L. Survival Models & Data Analysis. LC 79-22836. (Wiley Series in Probability & Mathematical Statistics: Applied Probability & Statistics). 457p. 1980. 48.95x (ISBN 0-471-03174-7, Pub. by Wiley-Interscience). Wiley.
Elzey, Freeman F. A First Reader in Statistics. 2nd ed. LC 74-83225. 1974. pap. text ed. 6.50 pub net (ISBN 0-8185-0140-5). Brooks-Cole.
--An Introduction to Statistical Methods in the Behavioral Sciences. LC 76-9924. (Brooks-Cole Series in Statistics). 1976. pap. text ed. 11.25 pub net (ISBN 0-8185-0194-4). Brooks-Cole.
--Introductory Statistics: A Microcomputer Approach. LC 84-12722. (Statistics Ser.). 260p. 1984. pap. text ed. 24.00 pub net (ISBN 0-534-03280-X). Brooks-Cole.
Everett, B. S. An Introduction to Latent Variable Models. LC 84-12677. (Monographs on Statistics & Applied Probability). 150p. 1984. text ed. 20.00 (ISBN 0-412-25310-0, 9196, Pub. by Chapman & Hall England). Methuen Inc.
Everitt, B. S. The Analysis of Contingency Tables. 1977. 12.95 (ISBN 0-412-14970-2, NO.6105, Pub. by Chapman & Hall). Methuen Inc.
Eykhoff, P. System Identification Parameter & State Estimation. LC 73-2781. 555p. 1974. 124.95x (ISBN 0-471-24980-7, Pub. by Wiley-Interscience). Wiley.
Fairley, William B. & Mosteller, Frederick. Statistics & Public Policy. LC 76-10415. (Behavioral Science-Quantitative Methods Ser.). 1977. text ed. 30.95 (ISBN 0-201-02185-4, Sch Div). Addison-Wesley.
Fidell, Linda S. & Tabachnick, Barbara G. Using Multivariate Statistics. LC 82-11767. 509p. 1982. text ed. 27.50 scp (ISBN 0-06-042045-6, HarpC). Har-Row.
Finkelstein, Mark & McCarty, George. Calculate Basic Statistics. LC 82-82511. 350p. 1982. pap. 14.95 (ISBN 0-936356-01-4). EduCALC Pubns.
Fisher, Iosif Z. Statistical Theory of Liquids. Switz, Theodore M., tr. LC 64-22249. pap. 86.80 suppl. (ISBN 0-317-08823-8, 2020284). Bks Demand UMI.
Fisher, Ronald A. Statistical Methods for Research Workers. 14th ed. (Illus.). 1973. 19.95x (ISBN 0-02-844730-1). Hafner.
Fisher, Walter D. Statistics Economized: Basic Statistics for Economics & Business. LC 81-40114. (Illus.). 282p. (Orig.). 1981. pap. text ed. 12.75 (ISBN 0-8191-1745-5). U Pr of Amer.
Fitz-Gibbon, Carol T. & Morris, Lynn L. How to Calculate Statistics. LC 78-58659. (Program Evaluation Kit: Vol. 7). 142p. 1978. pap. 9.95 (ISBN 0-8039-1072-X). Sage.
Fogiel, Max, intro. by. The Statistics Problem Solver: A Supplement to Any Class Text. rev. ed. LC 78-64581. (Illus.). 1056p. 1984. pap. text ed. 19.85 (ISBN 0-87891-515-X). Res & Educ.
Folks, J. Leroy. Ideas of Statistics. LC 80-14723. 368p. 1981. text ed. 30.00 (ISBN 0-471-02099-0). study guide avail. (ISBN 0-471-07972-3); tchrs.' manual avail. (ISBN 0-471-07969-3). Wiley.
Franke, J., et al, eds. Robust & Nonlinear Time Series Analysis. 2nd ed. (Lecture Notes in Statistics Ser.: Vol. 26). ix, 286p. 1984. pap. 16.00 (ISBN 0-387-96102-X). Springer-Verlag.
Freedman, David & Love, David. Mathematical Methods in Statistics: A Workbook. 1981. 6.95x (ISBN 0-393-95223-1). Norton.
Freedman, David, et al. Statistics. (Illus.). 608p. 1978. text ed. 26.95x (ISBN 0-393-09076-0); instr's. manual 2.95 (ISBN 0-393-09041-8). Norton.
Freund, John E. Modern Elementary Statistics. 6th ed. (Illus.). 576p. 1984. 31.95 (ISBN 0-13-593525-3). P-H.
--Statistics: A First Course. 3rd ed. (Illus.). 448p. 1981. text ed. 29.95 (ISBN 0-13-845958-4). P-H.
--Statistics: A First Course. 4th ed. (Illus.). 496p. 1986. text ed. 24.95 (ISBN 0-13-845975-4). P-H.
Freund, John E. & Williams, Frank J. Elementary Business Statistics: The Modern Approach. 4th ed. (Illus.). 576p. 1982. text ed. 29.95 (ISBN 0-13-253120-8). P-H.
Fried, Robert. Introduction to Statistics. 1976. 23.95 (ISBN 0-89876-075-5). Gardner Pr.
Futcher, W. G. Descriptive Statistics for Introductory Measurement. (Andrews University Monographs, Studies in Education: Vol. 1). viii, 96p. 1976. text ed. 7.95 (ISBN 0-943872-50-2). Andrews Univ Pr.
Gacula, Maximo C., Jr. & Singh, Jagbir. Statistical Methods in Food & Consumer Research. (Food Science & Technology Ser.). 1984. 79.50 (ISBN 0-12-272050-4). Acad Pr.
Gani, J., et al, eds. Progress in Statistics, 2 vols. (Colloquia Mathematica Societatis Janos Bolyai: No. 9). 912p. 1975. Set. 76.75 (ISBN 0-444-10702-9, North-Holland). Elsevier.
Ganssler, P. & Revesz, P., eds. Empirical Distributions & Processes: Selected Papers from a Meeting at Oberwolfach, Mar. 28-Apr. 3, 1976. (Lecture Notes in Mathematics Ser.: Vol. 566). 1976. soft cover 13.00 (ISBN 0-387-08061-9). Springer-Verlag.
Garcia, Ramon J., et al. Principios y Metodos Estadisticos para Comercio y Economia (I) (Span.). 1980. text ed. 12.40 (ISBN 0-538-22810-5, V81). SW Pub.
--Principios y Metodos Estadisticos para Comercio y Economia (II) 1982. text ed. 12.40 (ISBN 0-538-22820-2, V82). SW Pub.
Gilbert, Norma. Statistics. 2nd ed. 1981. text ed. 32.95 (ISBN 0-03-058091-9, CBS C); instr's manual 9.95 (ISBN 0-03-058093-5). SCP.
Gilchrist, W. Statistical Modelling. 300p. 1985. 29.95 (ISBN 0-471-90380-9). Wiley.
Ginsberg, J. H. & Genin, J. Statistics. 432p. 1984. 37.50 (ISBN 0-471-06494-7). Wiley.
--Statistics & Dynamics. 2nd ed. 925p. 45.50 (ISBN 0-471-09745-4). Wiley.
Gitlow, Howard S. Stat City: Understanding Statistics through Realistic Applications. 1982. pap. 15.25x (ISBN 0-256-02654-8). Irwin.
Gleason, Walter. Statistics: A First Course. 416p. 1981. text ed. write for info. (ISBN 0-534-00909-3). Wadsworth Pub.

World Statistics in Brief. 6th. ed. 2.50 (ISBN 0-686-75226-0, 81.XVII.14). UN.
World Statistics in Brief: United Nations Statistical Pocketbook. annual Incl. 1981. 5th ed. 1981. pap. 2.50 (UN81/17/2, UN); 1983. 7th ed. 1983. pap. 3.00 (UN83/17/2, UN); (No. 8). 108p. (Orig.). 1984. pap. 3.00 (UN83/17/10, UN). (Statistical Paper Ser.). (Orig., UN). Unipub.
Yamane, Taro. Estadistica con Problemas. (Span.). 1979. pap. text ed. 18.50 (ISBN 0-06-319777-4, Pub. by HarLA Mexico). Har-Row.
Young, Robert K. & Veldman, Donald J. Introductory Statistics for the Behavioral Sciences. 4th ed. LC 80-26006. 1981. text ed. 32.95 (ISBN 0-03-043051-8, HoltC); instr's manual 25.00 (ISBN 0-03-043056-9). HR&W.
Zaremba, Joseph, ed. Statistics & Econometrics: A Guide to Information Sources. (Economics Information Guide Ser.: Vol. 15). 650p. 1980. 60.00x (ISBN 0-8103-1466-5). Gale.
Zeisel, Hans. Say It with Figures. rev., 5th ed. LC 67-22535. 1968. 13.41xi (ISBN 0-06-037201-X, HarpT). Har-Row.
Zelen, Marvin, ed. Statistical Theory of Reliability. LC 63-9061. (U. S. Army. Mathematical Research Center. Madison, Wis.: No. 9). pap. 46.00 (ISBN 0-317-09139-5, 2015375). Bks Demand UMI.
Zepke, Brent E. Business Statistics: An Introduction. Cone, Nancy, ed. LC 78-21440. (College Outline Ser.). 192p. (Orig.). pap. text ed. 4.95 (ISBN 0-06-460180-3, CO 180, COS). B&N NY.
Ziegler, W. J. Contributions to Applied Statistics. (Experienta Supplementa, EXS: No. 22). 262p. 1976. 75.95x (ISBN 0-8176-0721-8). Birkhauser.
Zimmerman, Steve. Statistical Quality Control. (Quality & Reliability Ser.). 120p. 1985. 165.00 (ISBN 0-8247-7430-2). Dekker.

STATISTICS–BIBLIOGRAPHY

Congressional Information Service, Inc. Staff. ASI Annual, 1980, 2 vols. LC 73-82599. 2262p. 1981. lib. bdg. 590.00 set (ISBN 0-912380-83-7). Index Vol (ISBN 0-912380-84-5). Abstract Vol (ISBN 0-912380-85-3). Cong Info.
Kendall, Maurice G. & Doig, Alison G. Bibliography of Statistical Literature. 1981. Repr. of 1968 ed. Set. lib. bdg. 75.00x (ISBN 0-405-13881-4); Vol. I, 1950 To 1958. Vol. II, 1940 To 1949. Vol. III, Pre-1940. Ayer Co Pubs.
Kotz, Samuel & Watson, G. S., eds. Encyclopedia of Statistical Sciences, 2 vols. LC 81-10353. (Encyclopedia of Statistical Sciences Ser.). 1982. Vol. 1, A to Circular Probable Error, 480p. 85.00 (ISBN 0-471-05546-8, Pub. by Wiley-Interscience); Vol. 2, Classification to Eye Estimate, 613p. 85.00 (ISBN 0-471-05547-6, Pub. by Wiley-Interscience). Wiley.
Lidl, R., ed. Papers in Algebra, Analysis & Statistics. LC 82-1826. (Contemporary Mathematics Ser.: Vol. 9). 400p. 1982. pap. 24.00 (ISBN 0-8218-5009-1, CONM-9). Am Math.
Mitchell, Robert & Prickel, Donald. Number Power Five: Graphs, Tables, Schedules & Maps. (Number Power Ser.). 176p. (Orig.). 1983. pap. 4.95 (ISBN 0-8092-5516-2). Contemp Bks.
Savage, I. Richard. Bibliography of Nonparametric Statistics. LC 62-11403. 1962. pap. 7.95x (ISBN 0-674-07101-8). Harvard U Pr.
Subrahmaniam, Kocherlakota & Subrahmaniam, Kathleen. Multivariate Analysis: A Selected & Abstracted Bibliography. LC 73-90690. (Statistics Textbooks & Mongraphs: Vol 4). pap. 69.00 (ISBN 0-317-08363-5, 2055052). Bks Demand UMI.

STATISTICS–CHARTS, TABLES, ETC.

see also Tabulating Machines

Andrews, D. F. & Herzberg, A. M. Data. (Statistics Ser.). (Illus.). 460p. 1985. 39.00 (ISBN 0-387-96125-9). Springer Verlag.
Carr-Hill, Roy A. & Pritchard, Colin W. The Development & Exploitation of Empirical Birthweight Standards. (Illus.). 208p. 1985. 80.00x (ISBN 0-943818-08-7). Stockton Pr.
David, F. N., et al. Symmetric Function & Allied Tables. 278p. 1966. lib. bdg. 22.95x (ISBN 0-521-04788-9). Lubrecht & Cramer.
Eilon, S. & Watson-Gandy. Distribution Management: Mathematical Modelling & Practical Analysis. (Illus.). 240p. 1982. pap. text ed. 29.95x (ISBN 0-85264-191-5). Lubrecht & Cramer.
Gokhale, D. V. & Kullback, S. The Information in Contingency Tables. (Statistics Ser.: Vol. 23). 1978. 55.00 (ISBN 0-8247-6698-9). Dekker.
Guttman, I. Statistical Tolerance Regions: Classical & Bayesian. (Griffin's Statistical Monographs: No. 26). 150p. 1970. pap. text ed. 10.95X (ISBN 0-686-39549-2). Lubrecht & Cramer.
Neave, Henry R. Elementary Statistics Tables. (Illus.). 56p. (Orig.). 1981. pap. 3.95x (ISBN 0-04-001002-3). Allen Unwin.
Odeh, Owen. Tables for Tests Confidence Limits & Plans Based on Proportions. (Statistics, Textbooks & Monographs). 400p. 1983. 69.75 (ISBN 0-8247-7136-2). Dekker.
Ottestad, P. Statistical Models & Their Experimental Applications. (Griffin's Statistical Monographs: No. 25). 88p. 1970. pap. text ed. 5.25x (ISBN 0-85264-166-4). Lubrecht & Cramer.
Owen. Handbook of Statistical Tables. 1962. 29.95 (ISBN 0-201-05550-3). Addison-Wesley.
Pearson, E. S. & Hartley, H. O., eds. Biometrika Tables for Statisticians, Vol. 1. 3rd ed. 270p. 1976. lib. bdg. 25.95x (ISBN 0-904653-10-2). Lubrecht & Cramer.
--Biometrika Tables for Statisticians: Reprint with Corrections, Vol. 2. 385p. 1976. Repr. lib. bdg. 31.00x (ISBN 0-904653-11-0). Lubrecht & Cramer.
Pearson, Karl. Tables of the Incomplete Beta Function. 205p. 1968. lib. bdg. 35.95x (ISBN 0-521-05922-4). Lubrecht & Cramer.
--Tables of the Incomplete Gamma Function. 164p. 1965. lib. bdg. 17.50x (ISBN 0-521-05924-0). Lubrecht & Cramer.
Rohlf, F. James & Sokal, Robert R. Statistical Tables. 2nd ed. LC 81-2576. (Illus.). 219p. 1981. text ed. 25.95x (ISBN 0-7167-1257-1); pap. text ed. 11.95 (ISBN 0-7167-1258-X). W H Freeman.
Selby, Peter H. Using Graphs & Tables. LC 78-25962. (Self-Teaching Guides Ser.). 150p. 1979. pap. text ed. 6.95 (ISBN 0-471-05413-5, Pub. by Wiley Pr). Wiley.
Standard Country or Area Codes for Statistical Use. (Statistical Papers Ser.: No. 49). pap. 4.00 (UN82/17/8, UN). Unipub.
Tufte, Edward R. The Visual Display of Quantitative Information. (Illus.). 34.00 (ISBN 0-318-02992-8). Graphics Pr.
White, John, et al. Tables for Statisticians. 61p. 1984. pap. text ed. 5.00x (ISBN 0-7022-1146-X). U of Queensland Pr.
Yule, George U. Selected Papers by G. U. Yule, 1871-1951. Stuart, A. & Kendall, M. G., eds. 447p. 1971. lib. bdg. 27.25x (ISBN 0-85264-201-6). Lubrecht & Cramer.

STATISTICS–DATA PROCESSING

Afifi, Abdelmonem & Clark, Virginia A. Computer-Aided Multivariate Analysis. 360p. 1984. 32.00 (ISBN 0-534-02786-5). Van Nos Reinhold.
Andrews, Frank M., et al. A Guide for Selecting Statistical Techniques for Analyzing Social Science Data. 2nd ed. LC 74-620117. 80p. 1981. pap. 8.00x (ISBN 0-87944-274-3). Inst Soc Res.
Anscombe, F. Computing in Statistical Science Through APL. (Springer Series in Statistics). 416p. 1981. 29.50 (ISBN 0-387-90549-9). Springer-Verlag.
Becker, Richard A. & Chambers, John M. Extending the S System, Vol. II. LC 84-29933. (Statistics Ser.). 164p. 1985. pap. text ed. 14.95 (ISBN 0-534-05016-6). Brooks-Cole.
Bohrnstedt, George W. & Knoke, David. Statistics for Social Data Analysis. LC 81-82889. 530p. 1982. text ed. 27.50 (ISBN 0-87581-275-9). Peacock Pubs.
Bowen, Bruce D. & Weisberg, Herbert F. An Introduction to Data Analysis. LC 79-27870. (Illus.). 213p. 1980. text ed. 20.95 (ISBN 0-7167-1173-7); pap. text ed. 11.95 (ISBN 0-7167-1174-5). W H Freeman.
Brandt, S. Statistical & Computational Methods in Data Analysis. 2nd, rev. ed. 416p. 1976. 51.00 (ISBN 0-7204-0334-0, North Holland); pap. 28.00 (ISBN 0-444-86615-9). Elsevier.
Brecher, Steven L. Beating the Races with a Computer. LC 80-11311. 105p. (Orig.). 1980. pap. 14.95 (ISBN 0-9603792-0-7). Software Supply.
Casley, D. J. & Lury, D. A. Data Collection in Developing Countries. (Illus.). 1981. 47.50x (ISBN 0-19-877123-1); pap. 13.95x (ISBN 0-19-877124-X). Oxford U Pr.
Corsten, I. C. & Hermans, J., eds. COMPSTAT 1978: Proceedings. 540p. 1978. pap. text ed. 31.00x (ISBN 3-7908-0196-8). Birkhauser.
Deming, William E. Statistical Adjustment of Data. 261p. 1984. pap. 6.95 (ISBN 0-486-64685-8). Dover.
Dixon, W. J. & Nicholson, W. L. Exploring Data Analysis: The Computer Revolution in Statistics. LC 73-85786. 1974. 34.50x (ISBN 0-520-02470-2). U of Cal Pr.
Elandt-Johnson, Regina C. & Johnson, Norman L. Survival Models & Data Analysis. LC 79-22836. (Wiley Series in Probability & Mathematical Statistics: Applied Probability & Statistics). 457p. 1980. 48.95x (ISBN 0-471-03174-7, Pub. by Wiley-Interscience). Wiley.
Elzey, Freeman F. Introductory Statistics: A Microcomputer Approach. LC 84-12722. (Statistics Ser.). 260p. 1984. pap. text ed. 24.00 pub net (ISBN 0-534-03280-X). Brooks-Cole.
--Statistics: A Microcomputer Approach with Utility Supporting Software. 256p. 1984. pap. write for info. Wadsworth Pub.
Everitt, B. S. & Dunn, G. Advanced Methods of Data Exploration & Modelling. LC 83-292. xix, 253p. 1983. text ed. 20.00x (ISBN 0-435-82294-2). Heinemann Ed.
Flast, Robert H. VisiCalc Models: Finance-Statistics-Mathematics. 240p. 1984. 15.95 (Osborne-Mcgraw). Mcgraw.
Forthofer, Ronald N. & Lehnen, Robert G. Public Program Analysis: A New Categorical Data Approach. (Illus.). 294p. 1981. 31.95 (ISBN 0-534-97955-6); solutions manual 4.95 (ISBN 0-534-01133-0). Lifetime Learn.
Francis, Ivor. Statistical Software: A Comparative Review. 542p. 1981. 75.00 (ISBN 0-444-00658-3, North-Holland). Elsevier.
Freiberger, Walter, et al, eds. Statistical Methods for the Evaluation of Computer Systems Performance. 1972. 68.00 (ISBN 0-12-266950-9). Acad Pr.
Groenvald. Introduction to Probability & Statistics Using BASIC. (Statistics; Textbooks & Monographs: Vol. 26). 1979. 35.00 (ISBN 0-8247-6543-5). Dekker.
Harnisch, Delwyn & Palmer, Carolyn. An Introduction to Computer Applications in Statistics. 185p. (Orig.). 1984. pap. text ed. 8.20x (ISBN 0-87563-248-3). Stipes.
Hartwig, Frederick & Dearing, Brian E. Exploratory Data Analysis. LC 79-67621. (Quantitative Applications in the Social Sciences: No. 16). (Illus.). 83p. 1979. pap. 5.00 (ISBN 0-8039-1370-2). Sage.
Hoaglin, David C. & Mosteller, F., eds. Understanding Robust & Exploratory Data Analysis. LC 82-8528. (Applied Probability & Math Statistics Ser.). 447p. 1982. 39.95x (ISBN 0-471-09777-2, Pub. by Wiley-Interscience). Wiley.
Kalbfleisch, J. D. & Prentice, R. L. The Statistical Analysis of Failure Time Data. LC 79-21889. (Wiley Ser. in Probability & Mathematical Statistics: Applied Section). 321p. 1980. 38.95x (ISBN 0-471-05519-0, Pub. by Wiley-Interscience). Wiley.
Kennedy, W. & Gentle, J., eds. Statistical Computing. (Statistics: Textbooks & Monographs: Vol. 33). 865p. 1980. 34.50 (ISBN 0-8247-6898-1). Dekker.
Kvanli, Alan H., et al. Introduction to Business Statistics: A Computer Integrated Approach. (Illus.). 1000p. 1986. text ed. 30.00 (ISBN 0-314-93192-9). West Pub.
Launer, Robert & Siegel, Andrew, eds. Modern Data Analysis. 1982. 24.50 (ISBN 0-12-438180-4). Acad Pr.
Lawless, J. F. Statistical Models & Methods for Lifetime Data. LC 81-11446. (Wiley Series in Probability & Mathematical Statistics). 580p. 1982. 41.95x (ISBN 0-471-08544-8, Pub. by Wiley-Interscience). Wiley.
Lewi, Paul J. Multivariate Data Analysis in Industrial Practice. LC 82-6906. (Chemometrics Research Studies Ser.). 244p. 1982. 37.95 (ISBN 0-471-10466-3, Pub. by Res Stud Pr). Wiley.
Lewis, P. A., et al. Advanced Simulation & Statistics Package. 80p. 1985. pap. 59.95 (ISBN 0-534-05304-1); double-sided disk incl. Wadsworth Pub.
Lewis, Theodore G. Distribution Sampling for Computer Simulation. LC 74-25058. 176p. 1975. 26.00x (ISBN 0-669-97139-1). Lexington Bks.
Lim, Pacifico A. A Guide to Structured COBOL with Efficiency Techniques & Special Algorithms. 286p. 1982. pap. 13.95 (ISBN 0-442-24589-0). Van Nos Reinhold.
Mendenhall, William & Sincich, Terry. Statistics for Engineering & Computer Science. 1984. 32.95 (ISBN 0-02-380450-5). Dellen Pub.
Milton, R. C. & Nelder, J. A., eds. Statistical Computation. 1969. 65.00 (ISBN 0-12-498150-X). Acad Pr.
Moore, Richard W. Introduction to the Use of Computer Packages for Statistical Analyses. (Illus.). 1978. pap. text ed. 12.95 (ISBN 0-13-480970-X). P-H.
Morris, Carl & Rolph, John. Introduction to Data Analysis & Statistical Inference. (Illus.). 416p. 1981. pap. text ed. 31.95 (ISBN 0-13-480582-8). P-H.
Mosteller, Frederick & Tukey, John W. Data Analysis & Regression: A Second Course in Statistics. LC 76-15465. (Behavioral Science Ser.: Quantitative Methods). 1977. text ed. 32.95 (ISBN 0-201-04854-X). Addison-Wesley.
O'Dell, Jerry W. BASIC Statistics: An Introduction to Problem Solving with Your Personal Computer. LC 84-8804. (Illus.). 462p. (Orig.). 1984. 21.95 (ISBN 0-8306-0759-5); pap. 15.95 (ISBN 0-8306-1759-0, 1759). TAB Bks.
SAS Institute, Inc. SAS User's Guide: Statistics, 1982 Edition. 584p. (Orig.). 1982. pap. 14.95 (ISBN 0-917382-37-4). SAS Inst.
Scalzo, Frank & Hughes, Rowland. Elementary Computer-Assisted Statistics. rev. ed. LC 83-161. 362p. 1983. Repr. of 1978 ed. 22.50 (ISBN 0-89874-618-3). Krieger.
Schwartz, Ron & Basso, David. Statistical Programs in BASIC. 1984. cancelled (ISBN 0-8359-7107-4); pap. text ed. 16.95 (ISBN 0-8359-7106-6). Reston.
Sharp, Vicki F. How to Solve Statistical Problems with Your Pocket Calculator. (Illus.). 266p. pap. 8.95 (ISBN 0-8306-1303-X, 1303). TAB Bks.
Sorin, Martin D. Data Entry Without Keypunching: Improved Preparation for Social-Data Analysis. LC 78-24637. 288p. 1982. 23.00x (ISBN 0-669-02803-7). Lexington Bks.
Spencer, B. P. Benefit-Cost Analysis of Data Used to Allocate Funds. (Lecture Notes in Statistics Ser.: Vol. 3). 296p. 1980. pap. 21.00 (ISBN 0-387-90511-1). Springer-Verlag.
SPSS Incorporated. SPSS-PCplus Tables. 224p. (Orig.). 1985. pap. 14.95x (ISBN 0-918469-16-3). SPSS Inc.
SPSS Incorporated & Norusis, Marija. SPSS-PCplus. 656p. (Orig.). 1985. pap. 24.95x (ISBN 0-918469-14-7). SPSS Inc.
--SPSS-PCplus Advanced Statistics. 320p. (Orig.). 1985. pap. 19.95x (ISBN 0-918469-15-5). SPSS Inc.
Trivedi, Kishar S. Probability & Statistics with Reliability, Queuing & Computer Science Applications. (Illus.). 672p. 1982. text ed. 41.95 (ISBN 0-13-711564-4). P-H.
Van Tassel, Dennie. Basic-Pack Statistics Programs. (Series in Personal Computing). (Illus.). 240p. 1981. pap. text ed. 25.95 (ISBN 0-13-066381-6). P-H.
Velleman & Hoaglin. Applications, Basics & Computing of Exploratory Data Analysis. 384p. 1981. pap. text ed. write for info. (ISBN 0-87150-409-X, Duxbury Pr). PWS Pubs.
Wegner, P. An Introduction to Symbolic Programming. (Griffin's Statistical Monographs: No. 1). 219p. 1966. pap. 8.95x (ISBN 0-85264-129-X). Lubrecht & Cramer.
Weinert, H. L., ed. Reproducing Kernel Hilbert Spaces: Applications in Statistical Signal Processing. LC 82-9332. (Benchmark Papers in Electrical Engineering & Computer Science: Vol. 25). 655p. 1982. 63.50 (ISBN 0-87933-434-7). Van Nos Reinhold.
Wolff, Diane D. & Parsons, Michael L. Pattern Recognition Approach to Data Interpretation. 220p. 1983. 29.50x (ISBN 0-306-41302-7, Plenum Pr). Plenum Pub.
Zehna, Peter & Barr, Don. Statistics by Calculator. 1983. 13.95 (ISBN 0-13-844811-6, Spec). P-H.

STATISTICS–DICTIONARIES

Billard, Lynne & Steila, Donald. Dictionary of Statistical Terminology. 400p. Date not set. text ed. 30.00x (ISBN 0-86598-131-0). Rowman & Allanheld.
Broster, E. J. Glossary of Applied Management & Financial Statistics. 243p. 1974. 29.50x (ISBN 0-8448-0608-0). Crane-Russak Co.
Dudewicz, Edward J. & Koo, Joo O. The Complete Categorized Guide to Statistical Selection & Ranking Procedures. LC 80-68288. (The American Sciences Press Series in Mathematical & Management Sciences: Vol. 6). 1982. text ed. 85.00 (ISBN 0-935950-03-6). Am Sciences Pr.
Kendall, M. G. & Buckland, W. R. A Dictionary of Statistical Terms. 4th ed. LC 81-11829. 208p. 1983. text ed. 28.95x (ISBN 0-582-47008-0). Longman.
Kotz, S., et al. Encyclopedia of Statistical Sciences, Vol. 6: Muirhead's Theorem to Pixel. 1985. 85.00 (ISBN 0-471-05553-0). Wiley.
Kotz, S., et al, eds. Encyclopedia of Statistical Sciences, Vol. 7. 1985. 85.00 (ISBN 0-471-05555-7). Wiley.
Kotz, Samuel & Johnson, Norman L., eds. Encyclopedia of Statistical Sciences: Vol. 3: Faa di Bruno's Formula to Hypothesis Testing. 704p. 1983. 85.00 (ISBN 0-471-05549-2); subscription 67.50. Wiley.
Kotz, Samuel & Waston, G S., eds. Encyclopedia of Statistical Sciences: Lindberg Conditions to Mean Time Failure, Vol. 5. 720p. 1985. 85.00x (ISBN 0-471-05552-2, Pub. by Wiley-Interscience). Wiley.
Kotz, Samuel, et al, eds. Encyclopedia of Statistical Science: Icing the Tails to Limit Theorems, Vol. 4. 672p. 1983. 85.00 (ISBN 0-471-05551-4); subscription 67.50. Wiley.
Mulhall, Michael G. Dictionary of Statistics. 75.00 (ISBN 0-8490-0046-7). Gordon Pr.
Sahai, Hardeo & Berrios, Jose. A Dictionary of Statistical, Scientific & Technical Terms: English-Spanish, Spanish-English. Smith, Richard A. & Heise, Jeanne, eds. (Spanish Ser.). (Eng. & Span.). 143p. 1981. write for info. (ISBN 8-4534-0004-0, Pub. by Wadsworth Internacional Iberoamerica). Wadsworth Pub.
Webb, Augustus D. New Dictionary of Statistics: A Complement to the Fourth Edition of Mulhall's Dictionary of Statistics. LC 68-18017. 1971. Repr. of 1911 ed. 75.00x (ISBN 0-8103-3988-9). Gale.

Steam Generator & Auxiliaries. (Principles of Steam Generation Ser.: Module 11). (Illus.). 175p. 1982. spiral bdg. 10.00x (ISBN 0-87683-261-3); instr's. manual 15.00x (ISBN 0-87683-282-6). G P Courseware.

Universal Pressure Supercritical Boiler Fundamentals: Babcock & Wilcox Design, 4 vols. (Illus.). 1979. Set. looseleaf 136.00x (ISBN 0-87683-214-1); Vol. 1, 250pp. looseleaf 37.00x (ISBN 0-87683-215-X); Vol. II, 200pp. looseleaf 37.00x (ISBN 0-87683-216-8); Vol. III, 220pp. looseleaf 37.00x (ISBN 0-87683-217-6); Vol. IV, 220pp. looseleaf 37.00x (ISBN 0-87683-218-4). G P Courseware.

Universal Pressure Supercritical Boiler Fundamentals: Combustion Engineering Design, 4 vols. (Illus.). 1979. looseleaf 136.00x (ISBN 0-87683-219-2); Vol. I, 250pp. looseleaf 37.00x (ISBN 0-87683-220-6); Vol. II, 190pp. looseleaf 37.00x (ISBN 0-87683-221-4); Vol. III, 180pp. looseleaf 37.00x (ISBN 0-87683-222-2); Vol. IV, 200pp. looseleaf 37.00x (ISBN 0-87683-223-0). G P Courseware.

STEAM-BOILERS–EXAMINATIONS, QUESTIONS, ETC.

Rudman, Jack. Boiler Inspector. (Career Examination Ser.: C-87). (Cloth bdg. avail. on request). pap. 12.00 (ISBN 0-8373-0087-8). Natl Learning.

--Inspector of Low Pressure Boilers. (Career Examination Ser.: C-367). (Cloth bdg. avail. on request). pap. 8.00 (ISBN 0-8373-0367-2). Natl Learning.

--Steam Fireman. (Career Examination Ser.: C-1035). (Cloth bdg. avail. on request). pap. 10.00 (ISBN 0-8373-1035-0). Natl Learning.

STEAM ENGINEERING

see also Horsepower (Mechanics); Locomotives; Mechanical Engineering; Power (Mechanics); Steam-Boilers; Steam-Engines; Steam-Navigation; Steam Power-Plants

American Society of Mechanical Engineers, Research Committee on High Temperature Steam Generation. Behavior of Superheater Alloys in High Temperature, High Pressure Steam. Lien, George E., ed. LC 66-19905. (Illus.). pap. 29.80 (ISBN 0-317-08449-6, 2016886). Bks Demand UMI.

Arco Editorial Board. Stationary Engineer & Fireman. 5th ed. LC 66-25664. (Orig.). 1967. pap. 9.00 (ISBN 0-668-00070-8). Arco.

Bloom, Alan. Two Hundred Fifty Years of Steam. 208p. 1981. 45.00x (Pub. by Worlds Work England). State Mutual Bk.

Cho, Chun H. Efficient Allocation of Steam. Gyftopoulos, Elias P. & Cohen, Karen C., eds. (Industrial Energy-Conservation Manuals: No. 16). (Illus.). 40p. 1982. loose-leaf 20.00x (ISBN 0-262-03085-3). MIT Pr.

Flow Diagrams. (Principles of Steam Generation Ser.: Module 10). (Illus.). 110p. 1982. pap. text ed. 10.00 spiral bdg. (ISBN 0-87683-260-5); instr's. manual 15.00x (ISBN 0-87683-281-8). G P Courseware.

Ganapathy, V. Nomograms for Steam Generation & Utilization. LC 84-4522. 175p. 1985. 32.00 (ISBN 0-88173-000-9). Fairmont Pr.

Heavyside, G. T. Steam Renaissance. (Illus.). 128p. 1984. 21.00 (ISBN 0-7153-8294-2). David & Charles.

MacNaughton, Edgar. Elementary Steam Power Engineering. 3rd ed. LC 48-7834. pap. 120.00 (ISBN 0-317-07925-5, 2055263). Bks Demand UMI.

Meyer, C. A. Thermodynamic & Transport Properties of Steam. LC 67-3043. pap. 90.80 (ISBN 0-317-11072-1, 2011011). Bks Demand UMI.

Mitchell, Richard M. The Steam Launch. LC 81-83863. (Illus.). 256p. 1982. 39.95 (ISBN 0-87742-117-X). Intl Marine.

Moore, M. J. & Sieverding, C. H. Two-Phase Steam Flow in Turbines & Separators: Theory, Instrumentation, Engineering. LC 76-9125. 1976. text ed. 48.00 (ISBN 0-07-042992-8). McGraw.

Spangler, et al. Elements of Steam Engineering. 1984. pap. 11.95 (ISBN 0-917914-14-7). Lindsay Pubns.

Steam Coal: Prospects to 2000. 1978. 12.00x (ISBN 92-64-11867-5). OECD.

Stevens, Benjamin H. & Coughlin, Robert E. An Outline for Economic Evaluation of Steam Valley Preservation. (Discussion Paper Ser.: No. 10). 1966. pap. 5.75 (ISBN 0-686-32179-0). Regional Sci Res Inst.

Theoretical Steam Rate Tables. LC 75-88047. 1969. pap. 15.00 (ISBN 0-685-06532-4, I00003). ASME.

Universal Pressure Supercritical Boiler Fundamentals: Babcock & Wilcox Design, 4 vols. (Illus.). 1979. Set. looseleaf 136.00x (ISBN 0-87683-214-1); Vol. 1, 250pp. looseleaf 37.00x (ISBN 0-87683-215-X); Vol. II, 200pp. looseleaf 37.00x (ISBN 0-87683-216-8); Vol. III, 220pp. looseleaf 37.00x (ISBN 0-87683-217-6); Vol. IV, 220pp. looseleaf 37.00x (ISBN 0-87683-218-4). G P Courseware.

Universal Pressure Supercritical Boiler Fundamentals: Combustion Engineering Design, 4 vols. (Illus.). 1979. looseleaf 136.00x (ISBN 0-87683-219-2); Vol. I, 250pp. looseleaf 37.00x (ISBN 0-87683-220-6); Vol. II, 190pp. looseleaf 37.00x (ISBN 0-87683-221-4); Vol. III, 180pp. looseleaf 37.00x (ISBN 0-87683-222-2); Vol. IV, 200pp. looseleaf 37.00x (ISBN 0-87683-223-0). G P Courseware.

STEAM ENGINEERING–EXAMINATIONS, QUESTIONS, ETC.

Rudman, Jack. Assistant Stationary Engineer. (Career Examination Ser.: C-2279). (Cloth bdg. avail. on request). 1977. pap. 12.00 (ISBN 0-8373-2279-0). Natl Learning.

--Chief Stationary Engineer. (Career Examination Sr.: C-1184). (Cloth bdg. avail. on request). pap. 14.00 (ISBN 0-8373-1184-5). Natl Learning.

--Stationary Engineer. (Career Examination Ser.: C-758). (Cloth bdg. avail. on request). pap. 10.00 (ISBN 0-8373-0758-9). Natl Learning.

--Stationary Fireman. (Career Examination Ser.: C-760). (Cloth bdg. avail. on request). pap. 10.00 (ISBN 0-8373-0760-0). Natl Learning.

--Steam Fireman - Stationary Fireman. (Career Examination Ser.: C-1902). (Cloth bdg. avail. on request). pap. 10.00 (ISBN 0-8373-1902-1). Natl Learning.

STEAM-ENGINES

see also Horsepower (Mechanics); Locomotives; Marine Engines; Steam-Boilers; Steam-Turbines; Traction Engines

Beaumont, Anthony. Steam at Work: Road & Farm Engines. LC 81-67002. (Illus.). 96p. 1981. 18.95 (ISBN 0-7153-8121-0). David & Charles.

Building a 'Real' Vertical Steam Engine. (Illus.). 32p. 1979. pap. 4.95 (ISBN 0-85242-524-4). Aztex.

Building the 'Victoria' A 19th Century Steam Engine. (Illus.). 64p. 1978. pap. 5.95 (ISBN 0-85242-773-5). Aztex.

Eatwell, David & Cooper-Smith, John H. Return to Steam: Steam Tours on British Rail from Nineteen Sixty-Nine. 1978. 17.95 (ISBN 0-7134-0864-2, Pub. by Batsford England). David & Charles.

Hass, Ed. The Dean of Steam Fire Engine Builders. (Illus.). Date not set. price not set. E Hass.

Hayes, Geoffrey. Stationary Steam Engines. (Shire Album Ser.: No. 42). (Illus.). 32p. 1983. pap. 2.95 (ISBN 0-85263-652-0, Pub. by Shire Pubns England). Seven Hills Bks.

Jenkins, R. & Dickinson, H. W. James Watt & the Steam Engine. 536p. 1981. 49.00x (ISBN 0-903485-92-3, Pub. by Moorland). State Mutual Bk.

Jennings, Dana C. Days of Steam & Glory. (Illus.). 1968. pap. 2.95 (ISBN 0-87970-102-1). North Plains.

Johnson, Brian. Steam Traction Engines: Wagons & Rollers in Color. 2nd ed. (Blandord Color Ser.). (Illus.). 180p. 1983. Repr. of 1976 ed. 11.95 (ISBN 0-7137-0766-6, Pub. by Blandford Pr UK). Diamond Farm Bk.

L.B.S.C.'s Virginia: Live Steam Locomotive Construction. (Illus.). 200p. 1977. pap. 9.95 (ISBN 0-85242-411-6). Aztex.

Levine, Gary. The Car Solution: The Steam Engine Comes of Age. 224p. 1974. 7.50 (ISBN 0-8180-1707-4). Horizon.

Norbeck, Jack. Encyclopedia of American Steam Traction Engines. Dammann, George H., ed. LC 76-5764. (Agricultural Ser.). (Illus.). 320p. 1976. 24.95 (ISBN 0-912612-09-6). Crestline.

Schlomann, A. Illustrierte Technische Woerterbucher: Dampfkessel, Dampfmaschinen, Dampfturbinen, Vol. 3. (Ger., Eng., Fr., Rus., Span. & It.). 1133p. (Illustrated dictionary of boilers, steam engines and steam turbines). 1908. pap. 9.95 (ISBN 0-686-56484-7, M-7471, Pub. by R. Oldenbourg). French & Eur.

Siviter, Roger. Steam Specials: British Rail's Return to Steam. LC 81-65960. (Illus.). 96p. 1981. 14.95 (ISBN 0-7153-8126-1). David & Charles.

Smith, Andrew. Building a Vertical Steam Engine from Castings. (Illus.). 64p. 1978. pap. 4.95 (ISBN 0-85242-723-9). Aztex.

Steam Engine Design. 1983. pap. 9.95 (ISBN 0-917914-10-4). Lindsay Pubns.

Walshaw, T. D. Building Simple Model Steam Engines. (Illus.). 112p. 1979. pap. 7.95 (ISBN 0-85242-717-4). Aztex.

Wright, Roy V., ed. Boilers: Part Three. (Train Shed Ser.: No. 82). (Illus.). 1979. pap. 4.95 (ISBN 0-87962-085-4). N K Gregg.

STEAM ENGINES–HISTORY

Cushing, George & Starsmore, Ian. Steam at Thursford. (Illus.). 200p. 1982. 19.95 (ISBN 0-7153-8154-7). David & Charles.

Lord, John. Capital & Steam Power: Seventeen Fifty to Eighteen Hundred. 2nd ed. 253p. 1966. 26.00x (ISBN 0-7146-1339-8, F Cass Co). Biblio Dist.

--Capital & Steam-Power, Seventeen Fifty to Eighteen Hundred. Repr. of 1923 ed. 25.00x (ISBN 0-678-05216-6). Kelley.

Payen, Jacques. Capital et Machine a Vapeur Au XVIIIe Siecle: Les Freres Perier et L'introduction En France De la Machine a Vapeur De Watt. (Histoire Des Sciences et Des Techniques: No. 1). (Illus.). 1969. pap. 21.60 (ISBN 90-2796-264-2). Mouton.

Robinson, Eric H. & Musson, James, eds. James Watt & the Steam Revolution, a Documentary History. LC 71-96795. (Illus.). 1969. lib. bdg. 29.50x (ISBN 0-678-07756-8). Kelley.

Roll, Eric L. Early Experiment in Industrial Organization. LC 68-56059. (Illus.). Repr. of 1930 ed. 30.00x (ISBN 0-678-05193-3). Kelley.

Southern Pacific Steam Locomotives. 13.95x (ISBN 0-685-83394-1). Chatham Pub CA.

Tann, Jennifer, ed. The Selected Papers of Boulton & Watt: Vol. I: the Engine Partnership, 1775-1825. (Illus.). 448p. 1981. 75.00x (ISBN 0-262-02167-6). MIT Pr.

Thurston, Robert H. History of the Growth of the Steam-Engine. LC 74-159986. (Illus.). 1971. Repr. of 1939 ed. 42.50x (ISBN 0-8046-1687-6, Pub. by Kennikat). Assoc Faculty Pr.

Tuplin, W. A. The Steam Locomotive. 1980. text ed. 21.25x (ISBN 0-239-00198-2). Humanities.

Tyler, Colin. Digging by Steam. 173p. 1985. 9.95 (ISBN 0-85242-522-8, Pub. by Argus). Aztex.

STEAM-ENGINES, MARINE

see Marine Engines

STEAM-FITTING

see Pipe-Fitting

STEAM GENERATORS

see Steam-Boilers

STEAM-NAVIGATION

see also Marine Engineering; Navigation; Steam-Turbines; Steamboats and Steamboat Lines

Boyd, Thomas. Poor John Fitch: Inventor of the Steamboat. facsimile ed. LC 75-150171. (Select Bibliographies Reprint Ser). 1972. Repr. of 1935 ed. 20.00 (ISBN 0-8369-5684-2). Ayer Co Pubs.

Brown, Alexander C. Steam Packets on the Chesapeake. LC 61-12580. (Illus.). 207p. 1961. 12.95 (ISBN 0-87033-111-6). Tidewater.

Couling, David. Steam Yachts. LC 80-81524. (Illus.). 120p. 1980. 16.95 (ISBN 0-87021-963-4). Naval Inst Pr.

Fitch, John. The Original Steam-Boat Supported: Or, Reply to Mr. James Rumsey's Pamphlet. facsimile ed. LC 73-165631. (Select Bibliographies Reprint Ser). Repr. of 1788 ed. 15.00 (ISBN 0-8369-5938-8). Ayer Co Pubs.

Hammer, Thomas R. Criteria for Measurement of Stream Channels As an Indicator of Peak Flow History. (Discussion Paper Ser.: No. 36). 1970. pap. 5.75 (ISBN 0-686-32205-3). Regional Sci Res Inst.

Lindsay, William S. History of Merchant Shipping & Ancient Commerce, 4 Vols. LC 5-41460. Repr. of 1876 ed. Set. 120.00 (ISBN 0-404-04030-6); 30.00 ea. Vol. 1 (ISBN 0-404-04031-4). Vol. 2 (ISBN 0-404-04032-2). Vol. 3 (ISBN 0-404-04033-0). Vol. 4 (ISBN 0-404-04034-9). AMS Pr.

Mackay, J. S. The Analysis of Marine Steam Indicator Diagrams. 130p. 1949. 27.50x (ISBN 0-85264-019-6, Pub. by Griffin England). State Mutual Bk.

MacMullen, Jerry. Paddle-Wheel Days in California. (Illus.). 1944. 6.95 (ISBN 0-8047-0382-5). Stanford U Pr.

Mills, Randall V. Stern-Wheelers Up Columbia: A Century of Steamboating in the Oregon Country. LC 77-7161. (Illus.). xii, 212p. 1977. 17.95x (ISBN 0-8032-0937-1, BB650, Bison); pap. 3.75 (ISBN 0-8032-5874-7). U of Nebr Pr.

Morrison, John H. History of American Steam Navigation, 2 vols. 1977. lib. bdg. 200.00 (ISBN 0-8490-1965-6). Gordon Pr.

--History of Steam Navigation. (Illus.). 1967. Repr. of 1903 ed. 20.00 (ISBN 0-87266-023-0). Argosy.

Santos, Nelly E. Espanol Comercial. (Illus.). 410p. 1981. text ed. 21.95 scp (ISBN 0-06-045725-2, HarpC); instr's. manual avail. (ISBN 0-06-365825-9). Har-Row.

STEAM POWER-PLANTS

see also Boiling Water Reactors

Browning, Frank. Steam Plant Errors. (Shorey Lost Arts Ser.). 90p. pap. 4.00 (ISBN 0-8466-6010-5, U10). Shorey.

Crape, James R. Steam & Diesel Power Plant Operators Examinations. 2nd ed. LC 82-2198. (Illus.). 252p. 1982. pap. 21.95x (ISBN 0-916367-00-2, CU47-SD2). J R C Pub.

Fenichel, Allen H. Quantitative Analysis of the Growth & Diffusion of Steam Power in Manufacturing in the U. S., 1919-1938. Bruchey, Stuart, ed. LC 78-22679. (Energy in the American Economy Ser.). (Illus.). 1979. lib. bdg. 19.00x (ISBN 0-405-11982-8). Ayer Co Pubs.

Ganapathy. Steam Plant Calculations Manual. LC 84-19855. 168p. 1984. 39.75 (ISBN 0-8247-7256-3). Dekker.

Graham, Frank D. & Buffington. Power Plant Engineers Guide. 3rd ed. LC 82-17779. (Audel Ser.). (Illus.). 960p. 1983. 16.95 (ISBN 0-672-23329-0). G K Hall.

International Conference on the Properties of Steam, 9th, Munich, West Germany, Sep. 10-14, 1979 & Straub. Water & Steam: Their Properties & Current Industrial Applications: Proceedings. (Illus.). 704p. 1980. 140.00 (ISBN 0-08-025431-4). Pergamon.

Introduction to Steam Power Plants. (Basic Academics Ser.: Module 2). (Illus.). 60p. 1982. pap. text ed. 10.00x spiral binding (ISBN 0-87683-226-5); instrs. manual 15.00x (ISBN 0-87683-237-0). G P Courseware.

Lyon, W. S. Trace Element Measurements at the Coal-Fired Steam Plant. LC 77-435. 146p. 1977. text ed. 44.50 (ISBN 0-8493-5118-9). Krieger.

Mendelsohn, Robert O. Towards Efficient Regulation of Air Pollution from Coal-Fired Power Plants. LC 78-75020. (Outstanding Dissertations in Economics Ser.). 1979. lib. bdg. 29.00 (ISBN 0-8240-4055-4). Garland Pub.

Nuclear Power Plant Steam & Mechanical Fundamentals, 12 vols. 2nd ed. (Illus.). 988p. 1981. Set. pap. text ed. 65.00x (ISBN 0-87683-300-8); lesson plans BWR set 2900.00x (ISBN 0-87683-313-X); lesson plans PWR set 2900.00x (ISBN 0-87683-314-8). G P Courseware.

Nuclear Power Plant Steam & Mechanical Fundamentals, Vol. 2. 2nd ed. (Illus.). 100p. 1981. pap. text ed. 6.00x (ISBN 0-87683-302-4). G P Courseware.

Nuclear Power Plant Steam & Mechanical Fundamentals, Vol. 3. 2nd ed. (Illus.). 62p. 1981. pap. text ed. 6.00x (ISBN 0-87683-303-2). G P Courseware.

Nuclear Power Plant Steam & Mechanical Fundamentals, Vol. 4. 2nd ed. (Illus.). 74p. 1981. pap. text ed. 6.00x (ISBN 0-87683-304-0). G P Courseware.

Nuclear Power Plant Steam & Mechanical Fundamentals, Vol. 5. 2nd ed. (Illus.). 98p. 1981. pap. text ed. 6.00x (ISBN 0-87683-305-9). G P Courseware.

Nuclear Power Plant Steam & Mechanical Fundamentals, Vol. 6. 2nd ed. (Illus.). 86p. 1981. pap. text ed. 6.00x (ISBN 0-87683-306-7). G P Courseware.

Nuclear Power Plant Steam & Mechanical Fundamentals, Vol. 8. 2nd ed. (Illus.). 86p. 1981. pap. text ed. 6.00x (ISBN 0-87683-308-3). G P Courseware.

Nuclear Power Plant Steam & Mechanical Fundamentals, Vol. 9. 2nd ed. (Illus.). 90p. 1981. pap. text ed. 6.00x (ISBN 0-87683-309-1). G P Courseware.

Nuclear Power Plant Steam & Mechanical Fundamentals, Vol. 10. 2nd ed. (Illus.). 78p. 1981. pap. text ed. 6.00x (ISBN 0-87683-310-5). G P Courseware.

Nuclear Power Plant Steam & Mechanical Fundamentals, Vol. 11. 2nd ed. (Illus.). 66p. 1981. pap. text ed. 6.00x (ISBN 0-87683-311-3). G P Courseware.

Nuclear Power Plant Steam & Mechanical Fundamentals, Vol. 12. 2nd ed. (Illus.). 78p. 1981. pap. text ed. 6.00x (ISBN 0-87683-312-1). G P Courseware.

Potter, Philip J. Power Plant Theory & Design. 2nd ed. (Illus.). 710p. 1959. 47.50 (ISBN 0-471-06689-3). Wiley.

Singer, Joseph G. Combustion: Fossil Power Systems. Orig. Title: Combustion Engineering. 140p. 1981. 47.50 (ISBN 0-9605974-0-9). Combustion Eng.

Stattmann, F. Dictionary of Power Plant Engineering: Conventional Steam Power Plants, Pt. I. (Ger. & Fr.). 252p. 1971. 13.50 (ISBN 3-521-06059-4, M-7103). French & Eur.

Universal Pressure Supercritical Boiler Fundamentals: Babcock & Wilcox Design, 4 vols. (Illus.). 1979. Set. looseleaf 136.00x (ISBN 0-87683-214-1); Vol. 1, 250pp. looseleaf 37.00x (ISBN 0-87683-215-X); Vol. II, 200pp. looseleaf 37.00x (ISBN 0-87683-216-8); Vol. III, 220pp. looseleaf 37.00x (ISBN 0-87683-217-6); Vol. IV, 220pp. looseleaf 37.00x (ISBN 0-87683-218-4). G P Courseware.

Universal Pressure Supercritical Boiler Fundamentals: Combustion Engineering Design, 4 vols. (Illus.). 1979. looseleaf 136.00x (ISBN 0-87683-219-2); Vol. I, 250pp. looseleaf 37.00x (ISBN 0-87683-220-6); Vol. II, 190pp. looseleaf 37.00x (ISBN 0-87683-221-4); Vol. III, 180pp. looseleaf 37.00x (ISBN 0-87683-222-2); Vol. IV, 200pp. looseleaf 37.00x (ISBN 0-87683-223-0). G P Courseware.

Woodruff, Everett B. & Lammers, Herbert B. Steam-Plant Operation. 5th ed. 1983. 36.50 (ISBN 0-07-071732-X). McGraw.

Wyatt, L. M. Materials of Construction for Steam Power Plant. (Illus.). 312p. 1976. 52.00 (ISBN 0-85334-661-5, Pub. by Elsevier Applied Sci England). Elsevier.

STEEL-FRACTURE

Fisher, John W. Fatigue & Fracture in Steel Bridges: Case Studies. LC 83-23495. 315p. 1984. 45.95x (ISBN 0-471-80469-X, Pub. by Wiley-Interscience). Wiley.

Fracture Toughness in Relation to Steel Castings Design & Application. 1978. 10.00 (ISBN 0-686-44988-6). Steel Founders.

Toughness of Ferritic Stainless Steels-STP 706. 348p. 1978. 32.50x (ISBN 0-8031-0592-4, 04-706000-02). ASTM.

STEEL-HEAT TREATMENT

see also Case Hardening; Steel-Heat Treatment; Tempering

American Society for Metals. Carburizing & Carbonitriding. LC 76-55702. pap. 58.30 (ISBN 0-317-20679-6, 2025145). Bks Demand UMI.

Brooks, Charlie R. Heat Treatment of Ferrous Alloys. LC 78-16513. (Illus.). 1979. text ed. 45.00x (ISBN 0-07-008076-3). McGraw.

Evaluations of the Elevated Temperature Tensile & Creep Rupture Properties of 12 to 27 Percent Chromium Steels, DS 59. 330p. 1980. soft cover 24.00x (ISBN 0-8031-0338-7, 05-059000-40). ASTM.

Groenegress, H. W. Flame Hardening. 1964. pap. 6.50 (ISBN 0-387-03137-5). Springer-Verlag.

Krauss, George. Principles of Heat Treatment of Steel. 1980. 71.00 (ISBN 0-87170-100-6). ASM.

Report on Elevated-Temperature Properties of Selected Superalloys, DS7-S1. 1968. pap. 11.00 (ISBN 0-8031-0814-1, 05-007001-40). ASTM.

Schaefer, A. O., ed. Current Evaluation of Two & a Quarter Chrome One Molybdenum Steel in Pressure Vessels & Piping. 119p. 1972. pap. text ed. 9.50 (ISBN 0-685-28682-7, G00025). ASME.

Thelning, Kark-Erik. Steel & Its Heat Treatment. 2nd ed. (Illus.). 680p. 1984. text ed. 99.95 (ISBN 0-408-01424-5). Butterworth.

Unterweiser, Paul M. & Boyer, Howard E., eds. Heat Treater's Guide. 1982. 106.00 (ISBN 0-87170-141-3). ASM.

STEEL-METALLURGY

see also Steel-Heat Treatment

American Society for Testing & Materials. Structure & Properties of Ultrahigh-Strength Steels. LC 65-19686. (American Society for Testing & Materials Ser.: Special Technical Publication, No. 370). pap. 56.80 (ISBN 0-317-11239-2, 2000741). Bks Demand UMI.

American Society for Testing & Materials, Committee A-1 on Steel. Temper Embrittlement of Alloy Steels: A Symposium Presented at the Seventy-Fourth Annual Meeting, American Society for Testing & Materials. LC 73-185535. (American Society for Testing & Materials Ser.: No. 499). pap. 35.30 (ISBN 0-317-10341-5, 2015504). Bks Demand UMI.

Castro, Rene & De Cadenet, J. J. Welding Metallurgy of Stainless & Heat-Resisting Steels. LC 74-676582. pap. 50.00 (ISBN 0-317-26032-4, 2024434). Bks Demand UMI.

Dahl, W. & Lange, K. W., eds. Kinetics of Metallurgical Processes in Steelmaking: Proceedings. (Illus.). x, 584p. 1975. 100.30 (ISBN 0-387-07366-3). Springer-Verlag.

Dennis, W. H. Foundations of Iron & Steel Metallurgy. (Illus.). 246p. 1967. 15.00 (ISBN 0-444-20006-1, Pub. by Elsevier Applied Sci England). Elsevier.

Edneral, F. P. Electrometallurgy of Steel & Ferro-Alloys, 2 vols. 526p. 1979. 11.00 (ISBN 0-8285-1518-2, Pub. by Mir Pubs USSR). Imported Pubns.

Elliott, John F., ed. Steelmaking: The Chipman Conference. 1965. 40.00x (ISBN 0-262-05003-X). MIT Pr.

Gray, J. M., ed. Processing & Properties of Low Carbon Steel. LC 73-172124. pap. 106.30 (ISBN 0-317-08694-4, 2012653). Bks Demand UMI.

Harvey, Phillip, ed. Engineering Properties of Steels. 1982. 77.00 (ISBN 0-87170-144-8). ASM.

Honeycombe, R. W. Steels: Microstructure & Properties. 256p. 1981. 60.00x (Pub. by E Arnold England). State Mutual Bk.

Introduction to Today's Ultrahigh-Strength Structural Steels - STP 498. 64p. 1971. pap. 12.00 (ISBN 0-8031-0076-0, 04 498000 02). ASTM.

Kiessling, R. & Lange, N. Non-Metallic Inclusions in Steel. 2nd ed. 444p. 1978. text ed. 30.00x (ISBN 0-904357-18-X, Metals Soc). Brookfield Pub Co.

Lynn, Leonard H. How Japan Innovates: A Comparison with the U. S. in the Case of Oxygen Steelmaking. (Replica Edition Ser.). (Illus.). 224p. 1982. softcover 23.00x (ISBN 0-86531-900-6). Westview.

Mechanical Working & Steel Processing Conference Proceedings, 24th. LC 75-17963. 570p. 60.00 (ISBN 0-89520-153-4). Iron & Steel.

Metllurgy & Application of Steel Castings: Proceedings of the 20th Annual Conference, 1974. 1976. 65.00x (ISBN 0-686-44704-2, Pub. by Steel Castings). State Mutual Bk.

Modern Steelmaking Methods. 121p. (Orig.). 1981. pap. text ed. 30.00x (ISBN 0-901462-06-3, Metals Soc). Brookfield Pub Co.

Newby, John R., ed. Source Book on Forming of Steel Sheet: A Discriminative Selection of Outstanding Articles from the Periodical & Reference Literature. LC 76-28176. (American Society for Metals. Engineering Bookshelf Ser.). (Illus.). pap. 99.80 (ISBN 0-317-11148-5, 2019498). Bks Demand UMI.

Plaster, H. J. & Corr, A. M. J. Blast Cleaning & Allied Processes. 826p. 1973. 100.00x (ISBN 0-901994-03-0, Pub. by Portcullio Pr). State Mutual Bk.

Prager, Martin, ed. Factors Influencing the Time-Dependent Properties of Carbon Steels for Elevated Temperature Pressure Vessels, Vol. 19. 102p. 1983. pap. text ed. 24.00 (ISBN 0-317-02616-X, H00265). ASME.

Sarkar, A. D. Mould & Core Material for the Steel Industry. 1967. o. p. 24.00 (ISBN 0-08-012486-0). Pergamon.

Secondary Steelmaking. 136p. 1978. text ed. 20.00x (ISBN 0-904357-14-7, Metals Soc). Brookfield Pub Co.

Secondary Steelmaking for Product Improvement. 256p. 1985. pap. text ed. 35.00x (ISBN 0-904357-73-2, Metals Soc). Brookfield Pub Co.

Smith, G. V., ed. Effects of Melting & Processing Variables on Mechanical Properties of Steels, Series MPC-6. 1977. pap. text ed. 35.00 (ISBN 0-685-86861-3, G00126). ASME.

Strassburger, J. H., ed. Blast Furnace: Theory & Practice, 2 Vols. 1062p. 1969. Set. 255.50x (ISBN 0-677-10420-0). Gordon.

Transactions of the Iron & Steel Society, Vol. II. LC 83-122618. 130p. 1983. 52.00 (ISBN 0-911277-01-3). ISS Found.

Uys, J. M. & Bishop, H. L., eds. Process Simulation & Control in Iron & Steelmaking. LC 65-27847. (Metallurgical Society Conferences Ser.: Vol. 32). pap. 87.50 (ISBN 0-317-10476-4, 2001520). Bks Demand UMI.

Verlag-Stahleisen, ed. Atlas of Precipitates in Steels. 1983. 68.00 (ISBN 0-9906000-0-9, Pub. by Verlag Stahleisen W Germany). Heyden.

--Faults in Hot Dip Galvanizing. 1983. 32.00 (ISBN 0-9906000-3-3, Pub. by Verlag Stahleisen W Germany). Heyden.

STEEL-METALLURGY-MATHEMATICAL MODELS

Mulcahy, E. W. Pickling of Steels. 95p. 1981. 50.00x (ISBN 0-901994-20-0, Pub. by Portcullio Pr). State Mutual Bk.

STEEL-TESTING

American Society for Testing & Materials. ASTM Specifications for Structural Steel. pap. 58.50 (ISBN 0-317-26541-5, 2023991). Bks Demand UMI.

--Determination of Nonmetallic Compounds in Steel: A Symposium. LC 66-12290. (American Society for Testing & Materials Special Technical Publication Ser.: No. 393). pap. 25.80 (ISBN 0-317-09781-4, 2000967). Bks Demand UMI.

Bearing Steels: The Rating of Nonmetallic Inclusion-STP 575. 228p. 1975. 22.25 (ISBN 0-8031-0289-5, 04-575000-02). ASTM.

Correlation of Destructive Testing of Steel Castings with Stress Analysis & Mechanical Properties: A Summary Report. 1962. 6.00 (ISBN 0-686-44994-0). Steel Founders.

The Evaluation of Discontinuites in Commercial Steel Castings by Dynamic Loading to Failure in Fatigue. 1967. 6.00 (ISBN 0-686-44997-5). Steel Founders.

Glodowski, R. J., ed. Through-Thickness Tension Testing of Steel- STP 794. LC 82-72887. 152p. 1983. text ed. 21.00 (ISBN 0-8031-0232-1, 04-794000-02). ASTM.

Lindsay, R. W., ed. Quality Requirements of Super-Duty Steels. LC 59-14904. (Metallurgical Society Conferences Ser.: Vol. 3). pap. 79.80 (ISBN 0-317-10903-0, 2000666). Bks Demand UMI.

Smith, G. V. Evaluation of the Elevated Temperature Tensile & Creep-Rupture Properties of Three to Nine Percent Cr-Mo Steels, DS 58. 148p. 1975. pap. 14.75 (ISBN 0-8031-0337-9, 05-058000-40). ASTM.

Surface Indicator Scale: Elecroformed Nickel - includes Standard. 50.00 (ISBN 0-686-44990-8). Steel Founders.

Surface Indicator Scale: Plastic Replica. 1.00 (ISBN 0-686-44992-4). Steel Founders.

Ultrasonic Testing of Steel Castings. 1976. 10.00 (ISBN 0-686-44985-1). Steel Founders.

STEEL-WELDING

Abbaschian, G. J. & David, S. A., eds. Grain Refinement in Castings & Welds: Proceedings, TMS Fall Meeting, St. Louis Missouri, 1982. LC 83-61027. (Illus.). 293p. 1983. 42.00 (ISBN 0-89520-457-6). Metal Soc.

American Society for Metals. Welding & Brazing of Carbon Steels. Davis, Charles A., ed. LC 76-44372. Book 3: Resistance Welding. pap. 37.80 (ISBN 0-317-26234-3, 2052147); Book 4: Gas Welding & Brazing. pap. 43.00 (ISBN 0-317-26235-1). Bks Demand UMI.

American Welding Society. Guide for Steel Hull Welding: D3.5. 22p. 1985. 16.00 (ISBN 0-87171-252-0); member 12.00. Am Welding.

--Specification for Consumables Used for Electroslag Welding of Carbon & High Strength Low Alloy Steel: A5.25. 20p. 1978. 10.00 (ISBN 0-87171-150-8); member 7.50. Am Welding.

--Specification for Consumables Used for Electrogas Welding of Carbon & High Strength Low Alloy Steel: A5.26. 20p. 1978. 10.00 (ISBN 0-87171-147-8); member 7.50. Am Welding.

AWWA Standard for Field Welding of Steel Water Pipe. 16p. 5.40 (ISBN 0-686-44878-2, C206-82). Am Water Wks Assn.

Castro, Rene & De Cadenet, J. J. Welding Metallurgy of Stainless & Heat-Resisting Steels. LC 74-676582. pap. 50.00 (ISBN 0-317-26032-4, 2024434). Bks Demand UMI.

Lamellar Tearing in Welded Steel Fabrication LTWF. (WI) 16p. 1972. 18.00 (ISBN 0-686-95616-8). Am Welding.

Recommended Practices for Welding of Chromium-Molybdenum Steel Piping & Tubing: D10.8. 1978. 10.00 (ISBN 0-87171-153-2); member 7.50. Am Welding.

A Review of Welding Cast Steels & Its Effects on Fatigue & Toughness Properties. 1979. 15.00 (ISBN 0-686-45002-7). Steel Founders.

Specification for Iron, Steel, & Oxyfuel Gas Welding Rods: A5.2. 8p. 1980. 10.00 (ISBN 0-87171-200-8); member 7.50. Am Welding.

Specification for Low-Alloy, Steel Electrodes & Fluxes for Submerged Arc Welding: A5.23. 20p. 1980. 10.00 (ISBN 0-87171-202-4); member 7.50. Am Welding.

Specification for Steel, Low-Alloy Flux Cored Arc Welding Electrodes: A5.29-80. 20p. 1980. 10.00 (ISBN 0-87171-208-3). Am Welding.

Standard for Welded Steel Elevated Tanks, Standpipes & Reservoirs for Water Storage: AWWA D100-79. 63p. 1979. 8.00 (ISBN 0-686-95674-5). Am Welding.

Stout, R. D. & Doty, W. D. Weldability of Steels. 3rd ed. Epstein, S. & Somers, R., eds. 430p. 1978. 25.00 (ISBN 0-686-95608-7). Am Welding.

Structural-Welding-Code-Steel: AWS D1.1. 314p. 1982. 43.00 (ISBN 0-686-95786-5). Am Welding.

Studies of the Design of Steel Castings & Steel Weldments as Related to Methods of Their Manufacture: Castings vs. Weldments. 1959. 6.00 (ISBN 0-686-44993-2). Steel Founders.

Welding of Open Web Steel Joists. (Technical Digest Ser.: No. 8). 10.00 (ISBN 0-318-01793-8). Steel Joist Inst.

STEEL, HEAT RESISTANT

Atkins, M. Atlas of Continuous Cooling Transformation Diagrams for Engineering Steels. 1980. 102.00 (ISBN 0-87170-093-X). ASM.

Atlas of Heat-Resistant Alloy Microstructures. 60.00 (ISBN 0-686-44989-4). Steel Founders.

Atlas of Isothermal Transformation & Cooling Transformation Diagrams. 1977. 66.00 (ISBN 0-87170-043-3). ASM.

Evaluation of the Elevated Temperature Tensile & Creep-Rupture Properties of C-Mo, Mn-Mo, & Mn-Mo-Ni Steels, DS 47. 98p. 1971. pap. 6.25 (ISBN 0-8031-0811-7, 05-047000-02). ASTM.

Khare, A. K., ed. Ferritic Steels for High Temperatue Applications. 1983. 63.00 (ISBN 0-87170-153-7). ASM.

Properties of Austenitic Stainless Steels & Their Weld Metals: Influence of Slight Chemistry Variations - STP 679. 153p. 1979. pap. 13.50x (ISBN 0-8031-0537-1, 04-679000-02). ASTM.

STEEL, STAINLESS

see also Chromium-Molybdenum Steel

American Society for Metals. The Metallurgical Evolution of Stainless Steels: A Discriminative Selection of Outstanding Articles & Papers from the Scientific Literature. Pickering, F. B., ed. LC 79-12994. pap. 121.80 (ISBN 0-317-27687-5, 2019495). Bks Demand UMI.

American Society for Testing & Materials. Cleaning Stainless Steel: A Symposium. LC 73-80188. (American Society for Testing & Materials Special Technical Publications Ser.: 538). (Illus.). pap. 59.50 (ISBN 0-317-10763-1, 2009068). Bks Demand UMI.

Behal & Melilli, eds. Stainless Steel Castings - STP 756. 454p. 1982. 45.00 (ISBN 0-8031-0740-4, 04-756000-01). ASTM.

Demo, J. J. Structure, Constitution, & General Characteristics of Wrought Ferritic Stainless Steels - STP 619. 72p. 1976. 7.50 (ISBN 0-8031-0793-5, 04-619000-02). ASTM.

Elevated Temperature Properties As Influenced by Nitrogen Additions to Types 304 & 316 Austenitic Stainless Steels, STP 522. 121p. 1973. pap. 10.50 (ISBN 0-8031-0112-0, 04 522000 40). ASTM.

An Evaluation of the Yield, Tensile, Creep, & Rupture Strengths of Wrought 304, 316, 321, & 347 Stainless Steels at Elevated Temperatures, DS5-52. 85p. 1969. pap. 6.00 (ISBN 0-8031-0554-1, 05-005002-40). ASTM.

Lula, R. A., ed. Duplex Stainless Steels. 1983. 74.00 (ISBN 0-87170-166-9). ASM.

Lundin, C. D. & Chou, C. P. D. Hot Cracking Susceptibility of Austenitic Stainless Steel Weld Metals. 1983. bulletin no. 289 18.00 (ISBN 0-318-01894-2). Welding Res Coun.

Marshall, P., ed. Austenitic Stainless Steels: Microstructure & Mechanical Properties. 444p. 1984. 60.00 (ISBN 0-85334-277-6, I-262-84, Pub. by Elsevier Applied Sci England). Elsevier.

Metallurgical Society of AIME. The Metal Science of Stainless Steel: Proceedings of a Symposium Held at the 107th AIME Annual Meeting, 1978. Collings, E. W. & King, H. W., eds. LC 79-84706. pap. 55.00 (ISBN 0-317-28271-9, 2025449). Bks Demand UMI.

Parr, James G. & Hanson, Albert. An Introduction to Stainless Steel. LC 65-27458. pap. 39.30 (ISBN 0-317-08561-1, 2050985). Bks Demand UMI.

Peckner, Donald & Bernstein, I. M. Handbook of Stainless Steels. (Handbook Ser.). (Illus.). 928p. 1977. 78.50 (ISBN 0-07-049147-X). McGraw.

Properties of Austenitic Stainless Steels & Their Weld Metals: Influence of Slight Chemistry Variations - STP 679. 153p. 1979. pap. 13.50x (ISBN 0-8031-0537-1, 04-679000-02). ASTM.

Report on the Elevated-Temperature Properties of Stainless Steels, DS5-S1. 214p. 1965. pap. 6.00 (ISBN 0-8031-0555-X, 05-005001-40). ASTM.

Sedriks, A. John. Corrosion of Stainless Steels. LC 79-11985. (Corrosion Monographs). 282p. 1979. 48.95x (ISBN 0-471-05011-3, Pub. by Wiley-Interscience). Wiley.

Stainless Steels '84. 587p. 1985. pap. text ed. 62.00x (ISBN 0-904357-68-6, Metals Soc). Brookfield Pub Co.

Toughness of Ferritic Stainless Steels-STP 706. 348p. 1978. 32.50x (ISBN 0-8031-0592-4, 04-706000-02). ASTM.

World Stainless Steel Statistics, 1980. 250p. 1980. 250.00x (ISBN 0-8002-2814-6). Intl Pubns Serv.

STEEL, STRUCTURAL

see also Building, Iron and Steel; Plates, Iron and Steel

Berger & Wint, eds. New Concepts for Coating Protection of Steel Structures - STP 841. 135p. 1984. 28.00 (ISBN 0-8031-0236-4, 04-841000-14). ASTM.

Bowles, Joseph E. Structural Steel Design. (Illus.). 1980. text ed. 44.00 (ISBN 0-07-006765-1). McGraw.

Colvin, Thomas. Practical Steel Boatbuilding, Vol. 2. (Illus.). 224p. 1985. 25.00 (ISBN 0-87742-203-6). Intl Marine.

Cooper, Sol E. & Chen, Andrew C. Designing Steel Structures: Methods & Cases. (Illus.). 832p. 1985. text ed. 37.95 (ISBN 0-13-201385-1). P-H.

Council on Tall Buildings & Urban Habitats of Fritz Engineering Lab., Lehigh Univ. Structural Design of Tall Steel Buildings. LC 79-63736. 1077p. 1979. 75.00x (ISBN 0-87262-228-2). Am Soc Civil Eng.

Daniels, Stuart R. Inelastic Steel Structure. LC 65-25460. pap. 51.30 (ISBN 0-317-10636-8, 2021774). Bks Demand UMI.

Design of Compression Chords for Open Web Steel Joists. (Technical Digest Ser.: No. 1). 2.00 (ISBN 0-318-04225-8). Steel Joist Inst.

Design of Fire-Resistive Assemblies with Steel Joists. (Technical Digest Ser.: No. 4). 5.00 (ISBN 0-318-04228-2). Steel Joist Inst.

Djubek, Jozef, et al. Limit State of the Plate Elements of Steel Structures. 216p. 1984. text ed. 34.95 (ISBN 0-8176-1478-8). Birkhauser.

E.C.C.S. European Conference for Construction Steelwork. European Recommendations for Steel Construction. (ECCS Steel Manuals Ser.). 360p. (Orig.). 1981. pap. text ed. 42.00x. Longman.

Fifty Steel Joist Year Digest: A Compilation of SJI Specifications & Load Tables from 1928-1978. (Technical Digest Ser.: No. 7). 32.00 (ISBN 0-318-04232-0). Steel Joist Inst.

Gaylord, Edwin H., Jr. & Gaylord, Charles N. Design of Steel Bins for Storage of Bulk Solids. (Illus.). 400p. 1984. professional 70.00 (ISBN 0-13-201368-1). P-H.

Group Technical Digest 1-6. Set. 25.00 (ISBN 0-318-04231-2). Steel Joist Inst.

Howlett, J. H. & Jenkins, W. M. Joints in Structural Steelwork: The Design & Performance of Semi-Rigid & Rigid Joints in Steel & Composite Structures & Their Influence on Structural Behavior. Stainsky, R., ed. 185p. 1981. 66.95x (ISBN 0-470-27163-9). Halsted Pr.

Johnson, Bruce G., et al. Basic Steel Design. 2nd ed. 1980. text ed. 37.00 (ISBN 0-13-069344-8). P-H.

Kent, Earl. Structural Steels. 1977. pap. text ed. 10.00 (ISBN 0-918782-02-3). E Kent.

--Welding Structural Steels. 1977. pap. text ed. 10.00 (ISBN 0-918782-01-5). E Kent.

Kloss, Hans. Application of Structural Steel Design. LC 77-18605. (Illus.). 1980. 16.00 (ISBN 0-8044-4554-0). Ungar.

Knowles, Peter. Design of Structural Steelwork. (Illus.). 1977. 43.50x (ISBN 0-903384-16-7). Intl Ideas.

Lothers, John E. Design in Structural Steel. 3rd ed. LC 71-160254. (Civil Engineering & Engineering Mechanics Ser). (Illus.). 1972. 38.95 (ISBN 0-13-201921-3). P-H.

McCormac, Jack C. Structural Steel Design. 3rd ed. (Illus.). 661p. 1981. text ed. 35.50 scp (ISBN 0-06-044344-8, HarpC); sol. manual avail. (ISBN 0-06-364115-1). Har-Row.

McGuire, William. Steel Structures. 1968. text ed. 45.00 (ISBN 0-13-846493-6). P-H.

Marcus, Samuel H. Basics of Structural Steel Design. 2nd ed. 480p. 1980. text ed. 28.95 (ISBN 0-8359-0419-9); solution manual avail. (ISBN 0-8359-0420-2). Reston.

Merritt, Frederick S., ed. Structural Steel Designer's Handbook. (Illus.). 1000p. 1972. 67.50 (ISBN 0-07-041507-2). McGraw.

Morris, L. J., ed. Instability & Plastic Collapse of Steel Structures: Proceedings of the Michael R. Horne Conference originated by the University of Manchester with Co-Sponsor the Institution of Structural Engineers. (Illus.). 637p. 1983. text ed. 75.00x (ISBN 0-246-12196-3, Pub. by Granada England). Sheridan.

Parker, Harry & Hauf, Harold D. Simplified Design of Structural Steel. 5th ed. LC 83-1180. 401p. 1983. 29.95x (ISBN 0-471-89766-3, Pub. by Wiley-Interscience). Wiley.

Rapp, William G. Construction of Structural Steel Building Frames. 2nd ed. LC 79-19146. (Wiley Ser. of Practical Construction Guides). 400p. 1980. 57.50 (ISBN 0-471-05603-0, Pub. by Wiley-Interscience). Wiley.

Resource Systems International. Blueprint Reading: Tanks & Vessels. 1982. pap. text ed. 15.00 (ISBN 0-8359-0512-8). Reston.

Rockey, K. C. & Hill, H. V., eds. Thin Walled Steel Structures. 608p. 1969. 159.25 (ISBN 0-677-61270-2). Gordon.

Rudman, Jack. Steel Construction Inspector. (Career Examination Ser.: C-765). (Cloth bdg. avail. on request). pap. 10.00 (ISBN 0-8373-0765-1). Natl Learning.

Salmon, Charles G. & Johnson, John E. Steel Structures: Design & Behavior. 2rd ed. (Illus.). 1007p. 1980. text ed. 35.50 scp (ISBN 0-06-045694-9, HarpC); solutions manual avail. (ISBN 0-06-365805-4). Har-Row.

Shermer, Carl L. Design in Structural Steel. LC 79-16465. 318p. 1979. Repr. of 1972 ed. lib. bdg. 18.50 (ISBN 0-89874-008-8). Krieger.

Spacing of Bridging for Open Web Steel Joists. (Technical Digest Ser.: No. 2). 2.00 (ISBN 0-318-04226-6). Steel Joist Inst.

Spiegel, Leonard & Limbrunner, George F. Applied Structural Steel Design. (Illus.). 464p. 1986. text ed. 34.95 (ISBN 0-13-041567-7). P-H.

Structural Design of Steel Joist Roofs to Resist Ponding Loads. (Technical Digest Ser.: No. 3). 7.50 (ISBN 0-318-04227-4). Steel Joist Inst.

Structural Design of Steel Joist Roofs to Resist Uplift Loads. (Technical Digest Ser.: No. 6). 5.00 (ISBN 0-318-04230-4). Steel Joist Inst.

Taylor, Colin. Limit State Design for Structural Steelwork. 224p. pap. cancelled (ISBN 0-246-11243-3, Pub. by Granada England). Sheridan.

Vibration of Steel Joist: Concrete Slab Floors. (Technical Digest Ser.: No. 5). 7.50 (ISBN 0-318-04229-0). Steel Joist Inst.

Yu, Wei-Wen. Cold-Formed Steel Structures. LC 78-20815. 478p. 1979. Repr. of 1973 ed. lib. bdg. 26.50 (ISBN 0-88275-845-4). Krieger.

STEEL ALLOYS

see also Steel, Heat Resistant; Steel, Stainless

American Society of Civil Engineers. Design & Construction of Steel Chimney Liners. LC 80-475728. pap. 56.50 (ISBN 0-317-29141-6, 2025017). Bks Demand UMI.

An Evaluation of the Elevated-Temperature Tensile & Creep-Rupture Properties of Wrought Carbon Steel, DS 11-S1. 100p. 1969. pap. 6.00 (ISBN 0-8031-0812-5, 05-011001-40). ASTM.

Fletcher, E. E. High-Strength, Low-Alloy Steels: Status, Selection, & Physical Metallurgy. (Metals & Ceramics Information Ctr. Ser. (MCIC)). (Illus.). 120p. 1979. 40.00 (ISBN 0-935470-02-6). Battelle.

Lampman & Peters, eds. Ferroalloys & Other Additives to Liquid Iron & Steel- STP 739. 216p. 1981. 24.75 (ISBN 0-8031-0744-7, 04-739000-01). ASTM.

Linnert, G. E. Metallurgy, Welding, Carbon & Alloy Steels- Fundamentals: WM1, Vol. 1. 3rd ed. 474p. 1965. 28.00 (ISBN 0-686-95602-8, WM1); member 21.00. Am Welding.

--Metallurgy, Welding, Carbon & Alloy Steels: Technology: WM2, Vol. 2. 3rd ed. 674p. 1967. 30.00 (ISBN 0-686-95605-2, WM2); member 22.50. Am Welding.

Touloukian, Y. S. & Ho, C. Y. Properties of Selected Ferrous Alloying Elements, Vol. III. (M-H-CINDAS Data Series on Material Properties). 288p. 1981. text ed. 56.00 (ISBN 0-07-065034-9). McGraw.

STEEL AND IRON BUILDING

see Building, Iron and Steel

STEEL AND IRON SHIPS

see Ships, Iron and Steel

STEEL CASTINGS

Behal & Melilli, eds. Stainless Steel Castings - STP 756. 454p. 1982. 45.00 (ISBN 0-8031-0740-4, 04-756000-01). ASTM.

British & Foreign Specifications for Steel Castings. 4th ed. 238p. 1980. 110.00x (ISBN 0-686-44674-7, Pub. by Steel Castings). State Mutual Bk.

Cast-to-Shape: A History of the Steel Castings Industry in the United States. 1977. 30.00 (ISBN 0-686-44986-X). Steel Founders.

Continuous Casting, Vol. I. LC 83-81654. 163p. 1983. 40.00 (ISBN 0-89520-157-7). Iron & Steel.

Continuous Casting: Fourth International Iron & Steel Congress, London 1982. 606p. 1984. text ed. 45.00x (ISBN 0-904357-47-3, Pub. by Metals Soc). Brookfield Pub Co.

Continuous Casting of Steel. 336p. 1977. text ed. 20.00x (ISBN 0-904357-08-2, Metals Soc). Brookfield Pub Co.

Correlation of Destructive Testing of Steel Castings with Stress Analysis & Mechanical Properties: A Summary Report. 1962. 6.00 (ISBN 0-686-44994-0). Steel Founders.

Developments in Processes & Techniques: Proceedings of the 24th Annual Conference, 1979. 1979. 70.00x (ISBN 0-686-44698-4, Pub. by Steel Castings). State Mutual Bk.

Fracture Toughness in Relation to Steel Castings Design & Application. 1978. 10.00 (ISBN 0-686-44988-6). Steel Founders.

Herrmann, E. & Hoffmann, D. Handbook on Continuous Casting. (Illus.). 758p. 1980. lib. bdg. 625.00 (ISBN 3-87017-134-0, Pub. by Aluminium Verlag, Publ.). IR Pubns.

Hot Tears in Steel Castings. 1968. 30.00 (ISBN 0-686-44983-5). Steel Founders.

Impact Properties of Cast Steel Sections with Surface Discontinuities. 1967. 6.00 (ISBN 0-686-44996-7). Steel Founders.

Metllurgy & Application of Steel Castings: Proceedings of the 20th Annual Conference, 1974. 1976. 65.00x (ISBN 0-686-44704-2, Pub. by Steel Castings). State Mutual Bk.

Quality Control & the Significance of Mechanical Properties: Proceedings of One-Day Conference, 1974. 1975. 40.00x (ISBN 0-686-44710-7, Pub. by Steel Castings). State Mutual Bk.

Standard for the Visual Inspection of Casting Surfaces. 3.00 (ISBN 0-686-44991-6). Steel Founders.

Steel Castings in the Nineteen Eighties: Proceedings of the 26th Annual Conference, 1981. 1982. 90.00x (ISBN 0-686-44713-1, Pub. by Steel Castings). State Mutual Bk.

Steel Castings Res. & Trade Association, 24th Annual Conference, 1979. Developments in Processes & Techniques: Proceedings. 1979. 80.00x (ISBN 0-686-79290-4, Pub. by Steel Castings). State Mutual Bk.

Steel Castings Res. & Trade Association, 20th Annual Conference, 1974. Metallurgy & Applications of Steel Castings: Proceedings. 1976. 80.00x (ISBN 0-686-79283-1, Pub. by Steel Castings). State Mutual Bk.

Steel Castings Res & Trade Association, 22nd Annual Conference, 1979. Steel Castings Production: Proceedings. 1978. 80.00x (ISBN 0-686-79281-5, Pub. by Steel Castings). State Mutual Bk.

Steel Castings Research & Trade Assocation, 23rd Annual Conference, 1978. The Environment in Steel Foundries: Proceedings. 1978. 80.00x (ISBN 0-686-79280-7, Pub. by Steel Castings). State Mutual Bk.

Steel Castings Research & Trade Association, 17th Annual Conference, 1971. Metallurgical Processes Affecting the Quality of Steel Castings: Proceedings, 2 vols. 1972. 50.00x (ISBN 0-686-79286-6, Pub. by Steel Castings). State Mutual Bk.

Steel Castings Research & Trade Association, ed. Steel Castings Production: Proceedings of the 22nd Annual Conference, 1977. 1978. 65.00x (ISBN 0-686-44715-8, Pub. by Steel Castings). State Mutual Bk.

Steelcastings Research & Trade Association, ed. British & Foreign Specifications for Steel Castings. 4th ed. 1980. 85.00x (ISBN 0-686-79288-2, Pub. by Steel Castings). State Mutual Bk.

Steelmaking Conference: Proceedings of the 68th Conference. 510p. 1985. 60.00 (ISBN 0-932897-02-9). Iron & Steel.

Studies of the Design of Steel Castings & Steel Weldments as Related to Methods of Their Manufacture: Castings vs. Weldments. 1959. 6.00 (ISBN 0-686-44993-2). Steel Founders.

Ultrasonic Testing of Steel Castings. 1976. 10.00 (ISBN 0-686-44985-1). Steel Founders.

Vonderembse, Mark A. Decision Making in Continuous Steel Casting. Dufey, Gunter, ed. LC 80-17297. (Research for Business Decisions: No. 23). 124p. 1980. 39.95 (ISBN 0-8357-1107-2). UMI Res Pr.

Wieser, Peter F., ed. Steel Castings Handbook. 5th ed. (Illus.). 536p. 1980. 35.00 (ISBN 0-9604674-0-8). Steel Founders.

Yu, Wei-Wen. Cold-Formed Steel Structures. 2nd ed. 576p. 1985. 48.50 (ISBN 0-471-88484-7). Wiley.

STEEL INDUSTRY AND TRADE

see also Iron Industry and Trade; Steelwork

AIP Conference Proceedings No. 84, APS-AISI, Leigh University, 1981. Physics in the Steel Industry: Proceedings. Schwerer, Fred C., ed. LC 82-72033. 409p. 1982. lib. bdg. 36.00 (ISBN 0-88318-183-5). Am Inst Physics.

Allen, James A. Studies in Innovation in the Steel & Chemical Industries. LC 68-583. 246p. 1967. lib. bdg. 27.50x (ISBN 0-678-06790-2). Kelley.

ASTM Specifications for Ferroalloys. 51p. 1980. pap. 5.25 (ISBN 0-8031-0834-6, 03-109080-01). ASTM.

Bain, E C. Pioneering in Steel Research. 1975. 7.00 (ISBN 0-686-95117-4). ASM.

Barba, J. The Use of Steel. (Works of J. Barba Ser.). ix, 110p. Date not set. Repr. of 1875 ed. lib. bdg. 29.00 (ISBN 0-932051-61-8). Am Repr Serv.

Barnett, Donald F. & Schorsch, Louis. Steel: Upheaval in a Basic Industry. LC 82-10012. 344p. 1983. prof. ref. 29.95x (ISBN 0-88410-397-8). Ballinger Pub.

Blackford, Mansel G. A Portrait Cast in Steel: Buckeye International & Columbus, Ohio, 1881-1980. LC 82-6114. (Contributions in Economics & Economic History Ser.: No. 49). (Illus.). xviii, 225p. 1982. lib. bdg. 35.00 (ISBN 0-313-23393-4, BPC/). Greenwood.

Blair, John S. The Profitable Way: Carbon Plate Steel Specifying & Purchasing Handbook. (Illus.). 194p. 1978. 39.95x (ISBN 0-931690-08-0). Genium Pub.

--The Profitable Way: Carbon Sheet Steel Specifying & Purchasing Handbook. (Illus.). 158p. 1978. 39.95x (ISBN 0-931690-04-8). Genium Pub.

--The Profitable Way: Carbon Strip Steel Specifying & Purchasing Handbook. (Illus.). 194p. 1978. 39.95x (ISBN 0-931690-05-6). Genium Pub.

Bridge, James H. The Inside History of the Carnegie Steel Company. LC 73-38274. (The Evolution of Capitalism Ser.). 390p. 1972. Repr. of 1903 ed. 34.50 (ISBN 0-405-04112-8). Ayer Co Pubs.

Broude, Henry W. Steel Decisions & the National Economy. LC 63-13958. (Yale Studies in Economics Ser.: No. 16). pap. 86.80 (ISBN 0-317-29591-8, 2021983). Bks Demand UMI.

Bugayev, K., et al. Iron & Steel Production. Savin, Ivan V., tr. from Rus. (Illus.). 246p. 1971. 12.00x (ISBN 0-8464-0533-4). Beekman Pubs.

Cannon, James S. & Armentrout, Frederick S. Environmental Steel Update: Pollution in the Iron & Steel Industry. Schwartz, Wendy C., ed. LC 77-86496. 1977. pap. 42.00 (ISBN 0-87871-006-X). CEP.

Casson, Herbert N. The Romance of Steel: Story of a Thousand Millionaires. facsimile ed. LC 72-179510. (Select Bibliographies Reprint Ser). Repr. of 1907 ed. 37.50 (ISBN 0-8369-6639-2). Ayer Co Pubs.

Commission of the European Communities. Conference on the Quality of the Environment & the Iron & Steel Industry: 24-26 Sept. 1974. 1977. Eng. Ed. 105.00 (ISBN 0-08-020915-7); Ger. Ed. 97.00 (ISBN 0-08-020917-3); Fr. Ed. 97.00 (ISBN 0-08-020916-5). Pergamon.

DeBarbadillo, John J. & Snape, Edwin, eds. Sulfide Inclusions in Steel: An International Symposium, 7-8 November, 1974, Port Chester, New York Proceedings. LC 75-19315. (Materials-Metalworking Technology Ser.: No. 6). (Illus.). pap. 127.00 (ISBN 0-317-09688-5, 2051903). Bks Demand UMI.

Desai, P. The Bokaro Steel Plant. 1972. pap. 15.00 (ISBN 0-444-10388-0, North-Holland). Elsevier.

Detailing for Steel Construction. 288p. 1983. 32.00 (ISBN 0-318-17776-5, M013). Am Inst Steel Construct.

Electric Furnace Steelmaking: Collective Work. 401p. 1985. 100.00 (ISBN 0-89520-165-8). Iron & Steel.

Energy-Conscious Iron & Steelmaking. 1981. 70.00x (ISBN 0-904357-32-5, Metals Soc). Brookfield Pub Co.

Engineering for Steel Construction. 370p. 1984. 52.00 (ISBN 0-318-17775-7, M103). Am Inst Steel Construct.

Environmental Aspects of Iron & Steel Industry: A Workshop. (Industry Overviews: Vol. 8). pap. 5.00 (UNEP011, UNEP). Unipub.

The Establishment of Iron & Steel Industries in Developing Countries & Its Impact on Training & the Development of Skills: Report II. ii, 48p. 1981. pap. 7.15 (ISBN 92-2-102687-6). Intl Labour Office.

European Convention of Constructional Steelwork. European Recommendations for the Fire Safety of Steel Structures. 106p. 1983. 70.25 (ISBN 0-444-42120-3). Elsevier.

Goldberg, Walter H., ed. Ailing Steel: The Transatlantic Quarrel. LC 83-40527. 400p. 1986. 37.50 (ISBN 0-312-01502-X). St Martin.

Harrison, T. S. Handbook of Analytical Control of Iron & Steel Production. LC 78-41222. (Ellis Horwood Series in Analytical Chemistry). 602p. 1979. 124.95 (ISBN 0-470-26538-8). Halsted Pr.

Hessen, Robert. Steel Titan: The Life of Charles M. Schwab. (Illus.). 1975. 29.95x (ISBN 0-19-501937-7). Oxford U Pr.

Hogan, William T. Steel in the United States: Restructuring to Compete. LC 83-49519. 176p. 1984. 23.00x (ISBN 0-669-08234-1). Lexington Bks.

The Increasing Use of Continuous Processes in the Iron & Steel Industry & Their Techno-Economic Aspects. pap. 13.00 (ISBN 0-686-94609-X, UN792E7, UN). Unipub.

International Iron & Steel Congress. International Iron & Steel Congress: Proceedings of the 3rd, 16-20 April, Chicago, Illinois. LC 79-4097. pap. 160.00 (ISBN 0-317-27693-X, 2019494). Bks Demand UMI.

International Labour Office, Iron & Steel Committee, 10th Session, Geneva, 1981. The Improvement of Working Conditions & Working Environments in the Iron & Steel Industry: Report III. v, 86p. (Orig.). 1981. pap. 8.55 (ISBN 92-2-102688-4). Intl Labour Office.

International Symposium on Statistical Process Control in the Steel Industry. 219p. 1985. 60.00 (ISBN 0-932897-03-7). Iron & Steel.

Iron & Steel Society of AIME Staff. Steelmaking Conference Proceedings, 65th, Pittsburgh Meeting, March 28-31, 1982, Sponsored by the Steelmaking Division, the Iron & Steel Society of Aime. pap. 97.00 (ISBN 0-317-26839-2, 2023494). Bks Demand UMI.

Low-Waste & Non-Waste Technology in the Iron & Steel Industry. 191p. 1981. pap. 15.00 (ISBN 0-686-78452-9, UN812E4, UN). Unipub.

McHugh, Jeanne. Alexander Holley & the Makers of Steel. LC 79-27414. (Johns Hopkins Studies in History of Science & Technology). 416p. 1980. text ed. 35.00x (ISBN 0-8018-2329-3). Johns Hopkins.

Marcus, Maeva. Truman & the Steel Seizure Case: The Limits of Presidential Power. LC 77-4095. (Contemporary American History Ser.). 390p. 1977. 32.00x (ISBN 0-231-04126-8); pap. 16.00x (ISBN 0-231-04127-6). Columbia U Pr.

Mixed Gas Blowing in Steelmaking. 133p. 1982. pap. text ed. 28.00 (ISBN 0-89520-152-6). Iron & Steel.

Occupational Safety & Health in the Iron & Steel Industry. 341p. 1983. pap. text ed. 12.85 (ISBN 92-2-103471-2, ILO273, ILO). Unipub.

Oiks, G. Converter & Open Hearth Steel Manufacture. 507p. 1977. 8.45 (ISBN 0-8285-1545-X, Pub. by Mir Pubs USSR). Imported Pubns.

Organization for Economic Cooperation & Development Staff. The Steel Market in Nineteen Eighty-Three & the Outlook for Nineteen Eighty-Four. 38p. (Orig.). 1984. pap. 9.00x (ISBN 92-64-12598-1). OECD.

Otto, W. & Schaning, K. International Comparison of Standards-Materials: Steel & Cast Iron. 2nd ed. 1982. 95.00 (ISBN 0-686-39805-X, 11131-X, Pub. by DIN Germany). Heyden.

Plockinger, Erwin & Etterich, Otto, eds. Electric Furnace Steel Production. Babler, E. B. & Babler, P. E., trs. 500p. 1985. text ed. 57.00 (ISBN 0-471-90254-3, Pub. by Wiley Heyden). Wiley.

Pounds, Norman J. Geography of Iron & Steel. 4th rev. ed. (Orig.). 1968. pap. text ed. 6.00x (ISBN 0-09-106261-6, Hutchinson U Lib). Humanities.

Practical Engineering Applications Software. Steel Assembly Weight Determination. 1984. IBM-PC Version. incl. disk 125.00 (ISBN 0-471-80293-X); Apple Version. incl. disk 125.00 (ISBN 0-471-88428-6). Wiley.

Proceedings: Fortieth Electric Furnace Conference. LC 46-22879. 450p. 1983. 60.00 (ISBN 0-89520-154-2). Iron & Steel.

Process Technology Division (PTD) Conference Proceedings, Vol. 5: Measurement & Control Instrumentation in the Steel & Iron Industry. 254p. 1985. 60.00 (ISBN 0-932897-05-3). Iron & Steel.

Report on the Steel Plate Sector. 144p. (Orig.). 1982. pap. 8.50x (ISBN 92-64-12261-3). OECD.

Russell, Clifford S. & Vaughan, William J. Steel Production: Processes, Products, & Residuals. LC 75-36945. (Resources for the Future Ser). 350p. 1976. 26.50x (ISBN 0-8018-1824-9). Johns Hopkins.

Schroeder, Gertrude G. The Growth of Major Steel Companies: 1900-1950. LC 78-64218. (Johns Hopkins University. Studies in the Social Sciences. Seventieth Ser. 1952: 2). Repr. of 1953 ed. 24.50 (ISBN 0-404-61322-5). AMS Pr.

Sixty-Seventh Steelmaking Proceedings. 381p. 1984. 60.00 (ISBN 0-89520-164-X). Iron & Steel.

Sketchley, Peter & Lappe, Frances M. Casting New Molds: First Steps Toward Worker Control in a Mozambique Steel Factory. LC 82-897. 60p. 1980. pap. 3.95 (ISBN 0-935028-08-0). Inst Food & Develop.

Specification for the Design, Fabrication & Erection of Steel Safety-Related Structures for Nuclear Facilities: AISC-ANSI N690. 288p. 1984. 10.00 (ISBN 0-318-17777-3, S327). Am Inst Steel Construct.

Stahlschlussel. La Cle des Aciers. (Ger., Fr. & Eng.). 400p. (A Key to the Steel Industry). 110.00 (ISBN 0-686-56740-4, M-6524). French & Eur.

Standard for Welded Steel Elevated Tanks, Standpipes & Reservoirs for Water Storage: AWWA D100-79. 63p. 1979. 8.00 (ISBN 0-686-95674-5). Am Welding.

Statistics of World Trade in Steel, 1982. 73p. 1983. pap. text ed. 9.50 (UN83/2E24, UN). Unipub.

Statistics of World Trade in Steel, 1983. 71p. 1985. 8.50 (ISBN 0-317-18369-9). UN.

Steel & Iron Dimensional Standards. 5th ed. (Din Handbook: No. 28). 1982. 59.00 (ISBN 0-686-39808-4, 11125-1, Pub. by DIN Germany). Heyden.

Steel & Iron-Quality Standards One. (Din Handbook: No. 4). 1982. 77.50 (ISBN 0-686-39806-8, 11441-1, Pub. by DIN Germany). Heyden.

Steel & Iron Quality Standards Two. (Din Handbook: No. 155). 1982. 77.50 (ISBN 0-686-39807-6, 11441-1, Pub. by DIN Germany). Heyden.

Steel Casting Handbook Supplements. Incl. Supplement 1. Design Rules & Data. 2.00 (ISBN 0-686-44966-5); Supplement 3. Tolerances. 2.00 (ISBN 0-686-44967-3); Supplement 4. Drafting Practices for Castings. 2.00 (ISBN 0-686-44968-1); Supplement 5. General Properties of Steel Castings. 2.00 (ISBN 0-686-44969-X); Supplement 6. Repair Welding & Fabrication Welding of Steel Castings. 5.00 (ISBN 0-686-44970-3); Supplement 7. Welding of High Alloy Castings. 5.00 (ISBN 0-686-44971-1); Supplement 8. High Alloy Data Sheets, Corrosion Series. 5.00 (ISBN 0-686-44972-X); Supplement 9. High Alloy Data Sheets, Heat Series. 5.00 (ISBN 0-686-44973-8); Supplement 10. A Glossary of Foundry Terms. 2.00 (ISBN 0-686-44974-6); Supplement 11. Hardenability & Heat Treatment. 2.00 (ISBN 0-686-44975-4). 20.00 (ISBN 0-686-44963-0); Set. 35.00 (ISBN 0-686-44964-9); 3-Ring Binder 4.00 (ISBN 0-686-44965-7). Steel Founders.

Steel Castings Res. & Trade Association, 19th Annual Conference, 1973. Plant Engineering in Steel Foundries: Proceedings. 1974. 75.00x (ISBN 0-686-79284-X, Pub. by Steel Castings). State Mutual Bk.

Steel Castings Res. & Trade Association, 21st Annual Conference, 1976. Quality Assurance in the Steel Founding Industry: Proceedings. 1976. 80.00x (ISBN 0-686-79282-3, Pub. by Steel Castings). State Mutual Bk.

Steel Castings Res. & Trade Association, 16th Annual Conference, 1970. Steel Foundry Practice: Proceedings, 2 vols. 1971. 50.00x set (ISBN 0-686-79289-0, Pub. by Steel Castings). State Mutual Bk.

The Steel Industry in the Eighties. 176p. 1980. text ed. 60.00x (ISBN 0-904357-31-7, Metals Soc). Brookfield Pub Co.

The Steel Market in 1974. pap. 8.50 (ISBN 0-686-92824-5, UN75/2E11, UN). Unipub.

The Steel Market in 1975. pap. 11.00 (ISBN 0-686-92823-7, UN76/2E13, UN). Unipub.

The Steel Market in 1976. pap. 11.00 (ISBN 0-686-92821-0, UN77/2E15, UN). Unipub.

The Steel Market in 1980. 107p. 1982. pap. 12.00 (ISBN 0-686-86997-4, UN81/2E17, UN). Unipub.

Steelmaking Conference: Proceedings of the 68th Conference. 510p. 1985. 60.00 (ISBN 0-932897-02-9). Iron & Steel.

Strategy for Energy Use in the Iron & Steel Industry. (Economic Commission for Europe Ser.: No. 41). (Illus.). 171p. 1985. pap. 21.00 (UN83/2E22, UN). Unipub.

Structural Change in the Iron & Steel Industry. pap. 16.00 (ISBN 0-686-94408-9, UN79/2E/6, UN). Unipub.

Symposium at the TMS-AIME Fall Meeting, Milwaukee, Wisconsin, Sept. 16-20, 1979. Boron in Steel. Morral, J. E. & Banerji, S. K., eds. (Proceedings). 215p. 26.00 (ISBN 0-89520-363-4, 185); members 16.00 (ISBN 0-317-37154-1); student members 9.00 (ISBN 0-317-37155-X). Metal Soc.

Tedesco, Paul H. Patriotism, Protection & Prosperity: James Moore Swank, the American Iron & Steel Association & the Tariff, 1873-1913. Bruchey, Stuart, ed. LC 84-48315. (American Economic History Ser.). 325p. 1985. lib. bdg. 40.00 (ISBN 0-8240-6663-4). Garland Pub.

Transactions of the Iron & Steel Society, Vol. I. LC 83-122618. 130p. 1982. 52.00 (ISBN 0-911277-00-5). ISS Found.

Transactions of the Iron & Steel Society, Vol. IV. 112p. 1984. 52.00 (ISBN 0-911277-03-X). ISS Found.

Verrill, Charles O., ed. The Future of the International Steel Industry. 1984. 30.00 (ISBN 0-318-03938-9). Intl Law Inst.

Walker, Charles R. Steeltown: An Industrial Case History of the Conflict Between Progress & Security. LC 78-81489. (Illus.). 1970. Repr. of 1950 ed. 12.00x (ISBN 0-8462-1398-2). Russell.

Walker, R. D., ed. Small-Scale Steelmaking. (Illus.). 179p. 1983. 40.75 (ISBN 0-85334-181-8, Pub. by Elsevier Applied Sci England). Elsevier.

Williams, R. V. Control & Analysis in Iron & Steel Making. (Monographs in Materials). 256p. 1983. text ed. 59.95 (ISBN 0-408-10713-8). Butterworth.

STEEL INDUSTRY AND TRADE–BIBLIOGRAPHY

Worldwide Guide to Equivalent Irons & Steels. 1979. 112.00 (ISBN 0-87170-088-3). ASM.

STEEL INDUSTRY AND TRADE–JAPAN

Japan's Iron & Steel Industry 1981. 30th ed. LC 55-33803. 227p. (Orig.). 1981. pap. 35.00 (ISBN 0-8002-3005-1). Intl Pubns Serv.

Kawahito, Kiyoshi. The Japanese Steel Industry: With an Analysis of the U.S. Steel Import Problem. LC 70-170470. (Special Studies in International Economics & Development). 1972. 39.50x (ISBN 0-275-28273-2). Irvington.

The Prewar Japanese Steel Industry & Iron Ore Resources in Southeast Asia: The Development of Malaysian Iron Ore By the Ishihara Sangyo Company. (Project on Technology Transfer, Transformation & Development: The Japanese Experience). 77p. 1981. pap. 5.00 (ISBN 92-808-0235-6, TUNU163, UNU). Unipub.

STEEL INDUSTRY AND TRADE–VOCATIONAL GUIDANCE

I.L.O. Training & Retraining of Men & Women Wokers in the Metal Trades, with Special Reference to Technological Changes: Report III, Metal Trades Committee, 11th Session, Geneva, 1983. 73p. 1983. pap. 7.15 (ISBN 92-2-103362-7). Intl Labour Office.

STEEL PIPE

see Pipe, Steel

STEEL-ROLLING

see Rolling (Metal-Work)

STEEL SQUARE

see Carpenters' Square

STEEL WORK

see Steelwork

STEELWORK

see also Steel Castings

Blair, John S. The Profitable Way: Carbon Plate Steel Specifying & Purchasing Handbook. (Illus.). 194p. 1978. 39.95x (ISBN 0-931690-08-0). Genium Pub.

--The Profitable Way: Carbon Sheet Steel Specifying & Purchasing Handbook. (Illus.). 158p. 1978. 39.95x (ISBN 0-931690-04-8). Genium Pub.

--The Profitable Way: Carbon Strip Steel Specifying & Purchasing Handbook. (Illus.). 194p. 1978. 39.95x (ISBN 0-931690-05-6). Genium Pub.

Iron & Steel Society of AIME. Mechanical Working & Steel Processing XIII: Proceedings of the 17th Mechanical Working & Steel Processing Conference, Holiday Inn-Airport, Pittsburgh, PA, January 22-23, 1975. pap. 95.50 (ISBN 0-317-28715-X, 2020643). Bks Demand UMI.

--Mechanical Working & Steel Processing XVIII: Proceedings of the 21st Mechanical Working & Steel Processing Conference, Marriott Inn, Cleveland, Ohio, October 24-25, 2979. pap. 98.00 (ISBN 0-317-28856-3, 2020642). Bks Demand UMI.

Jackson, W. J. & Hubbard, M. W. Steelmaking for Steel Founders. 335p. 1979. 70.00x (ISBN 0-686-79287-4, Pub. by Steel Castings). State Mutual Bk.

Johnston, Bruce G. & Lin, Fung-Jen. Basic Steel Design. (Illus.). 384p. 1986. text ed. 33.95 (ISBN 0-13-067737-X). P-H.

Knowles, Peter. Design of Structural Steelwork. (Illus.). 1977. 43.50x (ISBN 0-903384-16-7). Intl Ideas.

Mechanical Working & Steel Processing Conference Proceedings, 25th. LC 75-17963. 570p. 1984. 60.00 (ISBN 0-89520-158-5). Iron & Steel.

Mechanical Working & Steel Processing Conference Proceedings, 26th. 299p. 1985. 60.00 (ISBN 0-89520-166-6). Iron & Steel.

Sangdahl & Semchyshen, eds. Application of Two & One Quarter Cr-1Mo Steel for Thick-Wall Pressure Vessels-STP 755. 473p. 1982. 45.00 (ISBN 0-8031-0741-2, 04-755000-02). ASTM.

Steel Designer's Manual. 4th. Rev. ed. (Illus.). 1089p. (Orig.). 1983. pap. text ed. 35.00x (ISBN 0-246-12046-0, Pub. by Granada England). Sheridan.

Steelmaking Conference: Proceedings of the 68th Conference. 510p. 1985. 60.00 (ISBN 0-932897-02-9). Iron & Steel.

Trahair, N. S. The Behaviour & Design of Steel Structures. 1977. pap. 26.00x (ISBN 0-412-14900-1, 6292, Pub. by Chapman & Hall). Methuen Inc.

STEERS

see Beef Cattle

STEFANSSON, VILHJALMUR, 1879-1962

Diubaldo, Richard J. Stefansson & the Canadian Arctic. (Illus.). 1978. 21.95 (ISBN 0-7735-0324-2). McGill-Queens U Pr.

Vilhjalmar Stefanson. facs. ed. 56p. pap. 4.95 (ISBN 0-8466-0189-3, S189). Shorey.

STEGANOGRAPHY

see Cryptography

STEINMETZ, CHARLES PROTEUS, 1865-1923

Alger, P. L. Steinmetz: The Philosopher. 194p. 1965. 47.75 (ISBN 0-677-65170-8). Gordon.

STELLAR ATMOSPHERES

see Stars–Atmospheres

STELLAR STATISTICS

see Statistical Astronomy

STENOGRAPHY

see Shorthand

STEPHENSON, ROBERT, 1803-1859

Smith, D. J. Robert Stephenson. (Clarendon Biography Ser.). (Illus.). 1973. pap. 3.50 (ISBN 0-912728-77-9). Newbury Bks.

STEPPES

see also Deserts; Pampas; Prairies; Tundras

Zlotin, R. I. & Khodashova, K. S., eds. The Role of Animals in Biological Cycling of Forest-Steppe Ecosystems. Lewus, William & Grant, W. E., trs. from Russian. LC 80-12228. 240p. 1980. 26.50 (ISBN 0-87933-377-4). Van Nos Reinhold.

STEREOCHEMISTRY

see also Atoms; Chemistry, Organic; Chemistry, Physical and Theoretical; Isomerism; Molecular Rotation; Polarization (Light)

Allinger, N. L., et al. Topics in Stereochemistry, Vol. 14. 315p. 1983. 108.00 (ISBN 0-471-89858-9, Pub. by Wiley-Interscience). Wiley.

Allinger, Norman, et al. Topics in Stereochemistry, Vol. 13. LC 61-13943. 489p. 1982. 100.00 (ISBN 0-471-05680-4, Pub. by Wiley-Interscience). Wiley.

Ariens, E. J. & Soudjin, W. Stereochemistry & Biological Activity of Drugs. (Illus.). 204p. 1983. 37.00x (ISBN 0-632-01155-6). Blackwell Pubns.

Armarego, W. Stereochemistry of Heterocyclic Compounds: Part II-Oxygen; Sulfur; Mixed N, O, & S; & Phosphorus Heterocycles. LC 76-26023. 512p. 1977. 66.50 (ISBN 0-471-03322-7). Krieger.

Aylett, B. J. & Harris, M. M. Progress in Stereochemistry, Vol. 4. LC 54-12738. 389p. 1969. 35.00x (ISBN 0-306-30684-0, Plenum Pr). Plenum Pub.

Bartok, M., et al. Stereochemistry of Catalytic Reactions on Metals. LC 84-13085. 1985. 115.00 (ISBN 0-471-90553-4). Wiley.

Bentley, R. Molecular Asymmetry in Biology, Vols. 1 & 2. (Molecular Biology Ser). 1969-70. Vol. 1. 65.00 (ISBN 0-12-089201-4); Vol. 2. 82.50 (ISBN 0-12-089202-2). Acad Pr.

Bernal, Ivan, et al. Symmetry: A Stereoscopic Guide for Chemists. LC 75-178258. (Illus.). 180p. 1972. text ed. 35.95 (ISBN 0-7167-0168-5). W H Freeman.

Boschke, F., ed. Stereo- & Theoretical Chemistry. LC 51-5497. (Topics in Current Chemistry: Vol. 31). (Illus.). 160p. 1972. pap. 27.20 (ISBN 0-387-05841-9). Springer-Verlag.

--Stereochemistry One: In Memory of van't Hoff. LC 51-5497. (Topics in Current Chemistry: Vol. 47). (Illus.). 150p. 1974. 39.00 (ISBN 0-387-06648-9). Springer-Verlag.

--Stereochemistry Two: In Memory of van't Hoff. LC 51-5497. (Topics in Current Chemistry: Vol. 48). (Illus.). 160p. 1974. 33.00 (ISBN 0-387-06682-9). Springer-Verlag.

Brocas, J. & Gielen, M. Permutational Approach to Dynamic Stereochemistry. 720p. 1983. 87.95 (ISBN 0-07-007971-4). McGraw.

Burdett, Jeremy K. Molecular Shapes: Theoretical Models of Inorganic Stereochemistry. LC 80-15463. 287p. 1980. 42.95 (ISBN 0-471-07860-3, Pub. by Wiley-Interscience). Wiley.

Cohen, I. Bernard, ed. Theory of Solutions & Stereo-Chemistry. LC 80-2103. (Development of Science Ser.). (Illus.). 1981. lib. bdg. 35.00x (ISBN 0-405-13868-7). Ayer Co Pubs.

Crabbe, Pierre. ORD & CD in Chemistry & Biochemistry: An Introduction. 1972. 41.50 (ISBN 0-12-194650-9). Acad Pr.

Dale, Johannes. Stereochemistry & Conformational Analysis. (Illus.). 230p. 1978. pap. 20.60x (ISBN 0-89573-101-0). VCH Pubs.

Deslongchamps, P. Stereoelectronic Effects in Organic Chemistry. (Organic Chemistry Ser.: Vol. 1). (Illus.). 390p. 1983. 55.00 (ISBN 0-08-026184-1); pap. 27.50 (ISBN 0-08-029248-8). Pergamon.

Doyle, M. P. & West, C. T., eds. Stereoselective Reductions. (Benchmark Papers in Organic Chemistry: Vol. 6). 1976. 71.00 (ISBN 0-12-786368-0). Acad Pr.

Eliel, E. L. & Allinger, N. L., eds. Topics in Stereochemistry Ser, Vol. 5. 338p. 1970. 28.50 (ISBN 0-471-23750-7, Pub. by Wiley). Krieger.

Eliel, Ernest L. Elements of Stereochemistry. LC 68-57277. pap. 26.00 (ISBN 0-317-28035-X, 2055718). Bks Demand UMI.

Eliel, Ernest L. & Allinger, Norman L., eds. Topics in Stereochemistry. LC 67-13943. 1969. Vol. 4, 280p. 23.50 (ISBN 0-471-23748-5, Pub. by Wiley); Vol. 8, 448pp. 1974. 35.00 (ISBN 0-471-23755-8). Krieger.

--Topics in Stereochemistry, Vol. 10. LC 67-13943. pap. 91.30 (ISBN 0-317-30020-2, 2025020). Bks Demand UMI.

Eliel, Ernest L., et al. Topics in Stereochemistry, Vol. 15. (Topics in Stereo Chemistry Ser.: No. 2-297). 337p. 1984. 97.00 (ISBN 0-471-88564-9, Pub. by Wiley-Interscience). Wiley.

Eliel, Norman L., ed. Topics in Sterochemistry, Vol. 3. LC 67-13943. pap. 97.30 (ISBN 0-317-08878-5, 2055275). Bks Demand UMI.

Finar, I. L. Stereochemistry & the Chemistry of Natural Products. 2nd ed. (Organic Chemistry Ser.: Vol. 2). 834p. 1959. 26.95 (ISBN 0-471-25888-1). Halsted Pr.

Geoffroy, Gregory, ed. Topics in Inorganic & Organometallic Stereochemistry, Vol. 12. Elial, Ernest L. (Topics in Stereochemistry Ser.). 352p. 1981. 90.00 (ISBN 0-471-05292-2, Pub. by Wiley-Interscience). Wiley.

Gunstone, F. D. Guidebook to Stereochemistry. LC 75-12762. pap. 31.00 (ISBN 0-317-27819-3, 2025243). Bks Demand UMI.

Kagan, Henri. Organic Stereochemistry. Whiting, M. C. & Whiting, U. H., trs. LC 79-11500. 166p. 1979. pap. text ed. 24.95 (ISBN 0-470-26725-9). Wiley.

Kepert, David L. Inogenic Stereochemistry. (Inorganic Chemistry Concepts Ser.: Vol. 6). (Illus.). 227p. 1982. 70.00 (ISBN 0-387-10716-9). Springer-Verlag.

Ketley, A. D., ed. The Stereochemistry of Macromolecules, Vol 3. LC 67-19404. pap. 119.00 (ISBN 0-317-08344-9, 2055060). Bks Demand UMI.

Klyne & Buckingham, J. Atlas of Stereochemistry: Absolute Configurations of Organic Molecules, 2 vols. 2nd ed. (Illus.). 1978. 55.00x ea. Vol. I (ISBN 0-19-520058-6). Vol. II (ISBN 0-19-520059-4). Oxford U Pr.

McEwen, W. E. & Berlin, K. D., eds. Organophosphorous Stereochemistry, 2 pts. Incl. Pt. 1. Origins of P(3&4) Compounds. 387p. 1975. 77.00 (ISBN 0-12-787031-8); Pt. 2. P(5) Compounds. 1975. 70.00 (ISBN 0-12-787032-6). (Benchmark Papers on Organic Chemistry: Vols. 3 & 4). 1975. Acad Pr.

Marchand, Alan P. Stereochemical Applications of NMR Studies in Rigid Bicyclic Systems. LC 82-13648. (Methods in Stereochemical Analysis: Vol. 1). (Illus.). xiii, 231p. 1982. 92.50x (ISBN 0-89573-112-6). VCH Pubs.

Marshall, James L. Carbon-Carbon & Carbon-Proton NMR Couplings: Applications to Organic Stereochemistry & Conformational Analysis. LC 82-16117. (Methods in Sterochemical Analysis Ser.: Vol. 2). (Illus.). 241p. 1983. 49.95x (ISBN 0-89573-113-4). VCH Pubs.

Nakanishi, Koji & Harada, Nobuyuki. Excition Coupled Circular Dichroism-Application in Organic & Bioorganic Stereochemistry. LC 81-51270. (Illus.). 460p. 1983. text ed. 34.00x (ISBN 0-935702-09-1). Univ Sci Bks.

Nogradi, M. Stereochemistry: Basic Concepts & Applications. 250p. 1980. text ed. 59.00 (ISBN 0-08-021161-5). Pergamon.

Potapov, V. M. Stereochemistry. 678p. 1980. 13.50 (ISBN 0-8285-1538-7, Pub. by Mir Pubs USSR). Imported Pubns.
Ramsay, O. Bertrand. Sterochemistry. 1981. 34.95 (ISBN 0-471-26103-3, Wiley Heyden); pap. 23.95 (ISBN 0-471-26104-1). Wiley.
Retey, James & Robinson, John A. Stereospecificity in Organic Chemistry & Enzymology. (Monographs in Modern Chemistry: Vol. 13). (Illus.). 324p. 1982. 86.30x (ISBN 0-89573-038-3). VCH Pubs.
Tamm, C. Stereochemistry. (New Comprehensive Biochemistry Ser.: Vol. 3). 342p. 1982. 59.75 (ISBN 0-444-80389-0, Biomedical Pr). Elsevier.
Ugi, I., et al. Perspectives in Theoretical Stereochemistry. (Lecture Notes in Chemistry Ser.: Vol. 36). 265p. 1984. pap. 19.30 (ISBN 0-387-13391-7). Springer-Verlag.
Vogtle, F. & Weber, E., eds. Stereochemistry. (Topics in Current Chemistry Ser.: Vol. 125). (Illus.). 250p. 1984. 45.00 (ISBN 0-387-13569-3). Springer-Verlag.
Watson, William H., Jr., ed. Stereochemistry & Reactivity of Systems Containing PI Electrons. (Methods in Stereochemical Analysis Ser.: Vol. 3). (Illus.). 439p. 1984. 44.90x (ISBN 0-89573-117-7). VCH Pubs.

STEREOLOGY

Elias, H. & Hyde, D. M. A Guide to Practical Stereology. (Karger Continuing Education Ser.: Vol. 1). (Illus.). x, 306p. 1983. 42.00 (ISBN 3-8055-3466-3). S Karger.
International Congress for Stereology - 2nd - Chicago - 1967. Proceedings. Elias, H., ed. (Illus.). 1967. pap. 36.00 (ISBN 0-387-03987-2). Springer-Verlag.
Miles, R. E. & Serra, J., eds. Geometrical Probability & Biological Structures: Buffon's 200 Anniversary. (Lecture Notes in Biomathematics: Vol. 23). 1978. pap. 19.00 (ISBN 0-387-08856-3). Springer-Verlag.
Weibel, Ewald. Stereological Methods: Vol. 1, Practical Methods of Biological Morphometry. LC 78-75269. 1980. 66.50 (ISBN 0-12-742201-3). Acad Pr.
--Stereological Methods, Vol. 2: Theoretical Foundations. LC 78-75269. 1981. 62.50 (ISBN 0-12-742202-1). Acad Pr.

STEREOMETRY

see Mensuration

STEREOPHONIC SOUND SYSTEMS

Audio Equipment. rev. ed. (Illus.). pap. 1.95 (ISBN 0-89552-006-0). DMR Pubns.
Cameron. How to Buy & Install Your Hi-Fi Stereo System. (Illus.). 112p. 1980. pap. 10.95 (ISBN 0-8359-2921-3). Reston.
Corry, Davidson. Making the Connection. (Illus.). 1975. pap. 3.50 (ISBN 0-686-14616-6). Pacific Pipeline.
Fantel, Hans. Better Listening. 192p. 1983. pap. 6.95 (ISBN 0-684-17892-3, ScribT). Scribner.
Green, C. & Bourgue, R. Theory & Servicing of AM, FM & FM Stereo Receivers. 1980. 31.95 (ISBN 0-13-913590-1). P-H.
Johnson, Kenneth W. & Walker, Willard C. Hi-Fidelity: Concepts & Components for Consumers. (Illus.). 1979. pap. 9.95 (ISBN 0-8403-1992-4). Kendall-Hunt.
Mandl, Matthew. Repairing & Maintaining Your Own Stereo System. (Illus.). 176p. 1983. 24.95 (ISBN 0-13-773515-4). P-H.
Prentiss, Stan. AM Stereo & TV Stereo-New Sound Dimensions. (Illus.). 192p. (Orig.). 1985. 12.95 (ISBN 0-8306-0932-6, 1932); pap. 12.45 (ISBN 0-8306-1932-1). TAB Bks.
Robin, Christopher. How to Build Your Own Stereo Speakers: Construction, Applications, Circuits & Characteristics. (Illus.). 1978. ref. ed. 21.95 (ISBN 0-87909-374-9); pap. 12.95 (ISBN 0-8359-2936-1). Reston.
Rosenthal, Murray P. How to Select & Use Hi-Fi & Stereo Equipment. 1979. pap. 9.85 (ISBN 0-8104-0424-9). Hayden.
Sands, Leo G. Sound Systems Installers Handbook. 3rd ed. LC 73-79074. (Illus.). 1973. cancelled (ISBN 0-672-21803-8, 21803); pap. cancelled (ISBN 0-672-20980-2, 20980). Sams.
Tarumoto, David H., ed. High-Performance Review, Vol. 1: Audio Equipment & Recordings for the Perceptive Listener. (Illus.). 580p. 1981-82. pap. 26.00x (ISBN 0-88232-068-8, Pub. by High-Performance Review Pub). Delbridge Pub Co.
Wells, A. Building Stereo Speakers. (McGraw-Hill VTX Ser.). 208p. 1983. 9.95 (ISBN 0-07-069251-3). McGraw.

STEREOPHOTOGRAMMETRY

see Photogrammetry

STEREOSCOPE

Brewster, David. The Stereoscope, Its History, Theory & Construction. LC 77-167716. (Illus.). 235p. 1971. Repr. of 1856 ed. 14.95 (ISBN 0-87100-017-2, 2017). Morgan.
Darrah, William C. The World of Stereographs. LC 77-92123. 246p. 1977. 22.50 (ISBN 0-913116-04-1). W C Darrah.

STERIDES

see Steroids

STERILIZATION

see also Radiation Sterilization

Block, Seymor S., ed. Disinfection, Sterilization & Preservation. 3rd ed. LC 82-24002. (Illus.). 1053p. 1983. text ed. 87.50 (ISBN 0-8121-0863-9). Lea & Febiger.
Borick, Paul M., ed. Chemical Sterilization. LC 73-4967. (Benchmark Papers in Microbiology Ser.: Vol. 1). 352p. 1973. 49.95 (ISBN 0-87933-036-8). Van Nos Reinhold.
Perkins, John J. Principles & Methods of Sterilization in Health Sciences. 2nd ed. (Illus.). 584p. 1982. 28.50x (ISBN 0-398-01478-7). C C Thomas.
Popenoe, Paul. The Conservation of the Family. Rosenberg, Charles, ed. LC 83-48555. (The History of Hereditarian Thought Ser.). 266p. 1985. Repr. of 1926 ed. lib. bdg. 32.00 (ISBN 0-8240-5825-9). Garland Pub.

STERN, OTTO, 1888-

Estermann, Immanuel, ed. Recent Research in Molecular Beams: A Collection of Papers Dedicated to Otto Stern on the Occasion of His 70th Birthday. 1959. 44.00 (ISBN 0-12-243250-9). Acad Pr.

STEROID HORMONES

see also Hormones, Sex

Agarwal, M. K., ed. Principles of Recepterology. LC 83-15441. (Illus.). vii, 677p. 1983. 88.00x (ISBN 3-11-009558-0). De Gruyter.
Dorfman, Ralph & Ungar, F., eds. Metabolism of Steroid Hormones. 1965. 95.00 (ISBN 0-12-221150-2). Acad Pr.
Dorfman, Ralph I., et al, eds. Biogenesis & Action of Steroid Hormones: Report of a Symposium at Kaike Spa, Yonago, Japan, Aug. 16-17, 1967. LC 68-54863. (Illus.). 1968. text ed. 8.50x (ISBN 0-87672-000-9). Geron-X.
Fuxe, K., et al. Steroid Hormone Regulation of the Brain: Proceedings of an International Symposium, 27-28 October 1980, Wenner-Gren Center, Stockholm, Sweden. (Wenner-Gren Ser.: Vol. 34). (Illus.). 428p. 1981. 88.00 (ISBN 0-08-026864-1). Pergamon.
Gorog, S., ed. Advances in Steroid Analysis: Proceedings of a Symposium in Egar, Hungary, May 1981. (Analytical Chemistry Symposia Ser.: Vol. 10). 552p. 1982. 95.75 (ISBN 0-444-99711-3). Elsevier.
Gower, D. B. Steroid Hormones. 120p. 1980. 35.00x (ISBN 0-85664-838-8, Pub. by Croom Helm England). State Mutual Bk.
--Steroid Hormones. 1980. pap. 12.95 (ISBN 0-8151-3832-6). Year Bk Med.
Grant, J. K. & Beastall, G. H. Clinical Biochemistry of Steroid Hormones: Methods & Applications. 320p. 1984. 45.00 (ISBN 0-444-00849-7). Elsevier.
Gupta, Derek. Radioimmunoassay of Steroid Hormones. 2nd ed. (Illus.). 265p. 1980. 48.80x (ISBN 3-5272-5863-9). VCH Pubs.
Idler, David R., ed. Steroids in Nonmammalian Vertebrates. 1972. 78.00 (ISBN 0-12-370350-6). Acad Pr.
Kaye, A. M. & Kaye, Myra, eds. The Development of Responsiveness to Steroid Hormones: Bat-Sheva Seminar on the Development of Responsiveness to Steroid Hormones Weizmann Institute of Science, Israel 18-26 Oct., 1978. LC 79-42938. (Advances in the Biosciences Ser.: Vol. 25). (Illus.). 494p. 1980. 75.00 (ISBN 0-08-024940-X). Pergamon.
Leavitt, W. W. & Clark, J. H., eds. Steroid Hormone Receptor Systems. LC 79-13753. (Advances in Experimental Medicine & Biology Ser.: Vol. 117). 500p. 1979. 65.00x (ISBN 0-306-40182-7, Plenum Pr). Plenum Pub.
Makin, H. L. Biochemistry of Steroid Hormones. 2nd ed. 1983. 91.50 (B3090-8). Mosby.
Makin, H. L., ed. Biochemistry of Steroid Hormones. 2nd ed ed. (Illus.). 640p. 1984. text ed. 125.00x (ISBN 0-632-00986-1). Blackwell Pubns.
Moudgil, V. K., ed. Molecular Mechanism of Steroid Hormone Action: Recent Advances. (Illus.). xii, 824p. 1985. 116.00x (ISBN 3-11-010118-1). De Gruyter.
O'Malley. Chemistry of Steroid Hormones. Date not set. write for info. (ISBN 0-444-00864-0). Elsevier.
Pasqualini, J. R., ed. Recent Advances in Steroid Biochemistry, Vols. 2-3. LC 75-4332. Vol. 2, 312p., 1975. pap. text ed. 61.00 (ISBN 0-08-019709-4); Vol. 3, 1977. pap. text ed. 55.00 (ISBN 0-08-021307-3). Pergamon.
Pasqualini, Jorge. Receptors & Mechanism of Action of Steroid Hormones, Pt. 2. (Modern Pharmacology & Toxicology Ser.: Vol. 8). 1977. 75.00 (ISBN 0-8247-6440-4). Dekker.
Polvani, Filippo, et al, eds. Meeting on Gas Chromatographic Determination of Hormonal Steroids. LC 68-19262. (Illus.). 1968. 60.00 (ISBN 0-12-561240-0). Acad Pr.
Roy, A. K. & Clark, J. H., eds. Gene Regulation by Steroid Hormones. (Illus.). 400p. 1980. 55.00 (ISBN 0-387-90464-6). Springer-Verlag.
Salhanick, Hilton A., et al. Metabolic Effects of Gonadal Hormones & Contraceptive Steroids. LC 71-89792. 762p. 1969. 49.50x (ISBN 0-306-30422-8, Plenum Pr). Plenum Pub.
Scholler, R. & Jayle, M. F. Gas Chromatography of Hormonal Steroids. 574p. 1968. 151.50 (ISBN 0-677-13280-8). Gordon.
Sluyser, Mels. Interaction of Steroid Hormone Receptors with DNA. 200p. 1985. lib. bdg. 46.50 (ISBN 0-89573-366-8, Pub. by Ellis Horwood Ltd UK). VCH Pubs.
Wittliff, James L. & Dapunt, Otto. Steroid Receptors & Hormone Dependent Neoplasia. LC 80-80877. (Illus.). 320p. 1980. 57.00x (ISBN 0-89352-043-8). Masson Pub.
Witzmann, Rupert F. Steroids: The Keys to Life. 288p. 1981. 31.50 (ISBN 0-442-29590-1). Van Nos Reinhold.

STEROIDS

see also Lipids; Steroid Hormones

Akhrem, A. A. & Titov, Y. A. Total Steroid Synthesis. LC 69-12525. 362p. 1970. 45.00x (ISBN 0-306-30380-9, Plenum Pr). Plenum Pub.
Azarnoff, Daniel L. Steroid Therapy. LC 74-24511. pap. 88.00 (ISBN 0-317-29812-7, 2016651). Bks Demand UMI.
Bartos, J. & Pesez, M. Colormetric & Fluorimetric Analysis of Steroids. 1977. 55.00 (ISBN 0-12-080150-7). Acad Pr.
Beato, M., ed. Steroid Induced Utherine Proteins: Proceedings Symposium, Marburg, September 27-29, 1979. (Developments in Endocrinology Ser.: Vol. 8). 1980. 68.00 (ISBN 0-444-80203-7). Elsevier.
Bernstein, Seymour, et al. Physical Properties of Steroid Conjugates. LC 68-9218. 1968. 42.00 (ISBN 0-387-04060-9). Springer-Verlag.
Briggs, M. H. & Christie, G. A., eds. Advances in Steroid Biochemistry & Pharmacology, Vols. 1-7. Incl. Vol. 1. 1970. 89.50 (ISBN 0-12-037501-X); Vol. 2. 1971. 83.50 (ISBN 0-12-037502-8); Vol. 3. 1972. 60.00 (ISBN 0-12-037503-6); Vol. 4. 1974. 70.00 (ISBN 0-12-037504-4); Vol. 5. 1976. 75.00 (ISBN 0-12-037505-2); Vol. 6. 1978. 43.00 (ISBN 0-12-037506-0); Vol. 7. 1980. 37.00 (ISBN 0-12-037507-9). Acad Pr.
Charney, William & Herzog, Hershel. Microbiological Transformation of Steroids: A Handbook. 1968. 95.00 (ISBN 0-12-169950-1). Acad Pr.
Chinn, L. J., et al. Chemistry & Biochemistry of Steroids. (Illus.). 1969. text ed. 12.00x (ISBN 0-87672-003-3). Geron-X.
Clark, J. H. & Peck, E. J. Female Sex Steroids: Receptors & Function. (Monographs on Endocrinology: Vol. 14). (Illus.). 1979. 50.00 (ISBN 0-387-09375-3). Springer-Verlag.
Clark, T. J. Steroids in Asthma: A Reappraisal in the Light of Inhalation Therapy. (Illus.). 236p. 1983. 48.00 (ISBN 0-683-11204-X). Williams & Wilkins.
Colowick, Sidney P. & Kaplan, Nathan O., eds. Methods in Enzymology: Steroids & Isoprenoids, Vol. 110, Pt. A. 1985. 55.00 (ISBN 0-12-182010-6). Acad Pr.
--Methods in Enzymology: Steroids & Isoprenoids, Vol. 111, Pt. B. 1985. 66.50 (ISBN 0-12-182011-4). Acad Pr.
Dence, Joseph B. Steroids & Peptides: Selected Chemical Aspects for Biology, Biochemistry & Medicine. LC 79-21236. 418p. 1980. 74.95 (ISBN 0-471-04700-7, Pub. by Wiley-Interscience). Wiley.
Duax, William L. & Norton, Dorita A., eds. Atlas of Steroid Structure, Vol. 1. LC 75-22419. 586p. 1975. 85.00x (ISBN 0-306-66101-2, IFI Plenum). Plenum Pub.
Duax, William L., et al, eds. Atlas of Steroid Structure, Vol. 2. 765p. 1983. 140.00x (ISBN 0-306-66102-0, IFI Plenum). Plenum Pub.
Eik-Nes, K. B. & Horning, E. C. Gas Phase Chromatography of Steroids. LC 68-18620. (Monographs on Endocrinology: Vol. 2). (Illus.). 1968. 29.00 (ISBN 0-387-04277-6). Springer-Verlag.
Fried, John & Edwards, John A. Organic Reactions in Steroid Chemistry, Vol. 2. LC 76-153192. 480p. 1972. 26.50. Krieger.
Goldman, Bob, et al. Death in the Locker Room: Steroids & Sports. (Illus.). 456p. 1984. 19.95 (ISBN 0-89651-155-3). Icarus.
Gorog, S. Quantitative Analysis of Steroids. (Studies in Analytical Chemistry: No. 5). 440p. 1983. 86.75 (ISBN 0-444-99698-2). Elsevier.
Hanson, J. R., ed. Terpenoids & Steroids, Vols. 1-9. Incl. Vol. 1. 1969-70 Literature. 1971. 47.00 (ISBN 0-85186-256-X); Vol. 2. 1970-71 Literature. 1972. 41.00 (ISBN 0-85186-266-7); Vol. 3. 1971-72 Literature. 1973. 47.00 (ISBN 0-85186-276-4); Vol. 4. 1972-73 Literature. 1974. 54.00 (ISBN 0-85186-286-1); Vol. 5. 1973-74 Literature. 1975. 54.00 (ISBN 0-85186-296-9); Vol. 6. 1974-75 Literature. 1976. 54.00 (ISBN 0-85186-306-X); Vol. 7. 1975-76 Literature. 1977. 65.00 (ISBN 0-85186-316-7); Vol. 8. 1976-77 Literature. 1978. 59.00 (ISBN 0-85186-326-4); Vol. 9. 1979. 72.00 (ISBN 0-85186-650-6, Pub. by Royal Soc Chem London). LC 74-615720. Am Chemical.
Heftmann, E. Chromatography of Steroids. (Journal of Chromatography Library: Vol. 8). 204p. 1976. 42.75 (ISBN 0-444-41441-X). Elsevier.
--Steroid Biochemistry. 1969. 46.50 (ISBN 0-12-336650-X). Acad Pr.
Hobkirk, Ronald. Steroid Biochemistry, 2 vols. 1979. Vol. 1, 176 Pgs. 61.00 (ISBN 0-8493-5193-6); Vol. 2, 208 Pgs. 66.00 (ISBN 0-8493-5194-4). CRC Pr.
Idler, David R., ed. Steroids in Nonmammalian Vertebrates. 1972. 78.00 (ISBN 0-12-370350-6). Acad Pr.
Iizuka, H. & Naito, A. Microbial Conversion of Steroids & Alkaloids. 396p. 1981. 53.00 (ISBN 0-387-10794-0). Springer-Verlag.
International Congress of Endocrinology. Adrenal Steroid Antagonism: Proceedings Satellite Workshop of the VII International Congress of Endocrinology, July 7, 1984. Agarwal, M. K., ed. LC 84-19947. (Illus.). viii, 399p. 1984. 79.50X (ISBN 3-11-010090-8). De Gruyter.
Kautsky. Steroid Analysis by HPLC. (Chromatographic Science Ser.: Vol. 16). 424p. 1981. 65.00 (ISBN 0-8247-1324-9). Dekker.
Klopper, A., et al, eds. Research on Steroids. 1979. 48.50 (ISBN 0-12-416050-6). Acad Pr.
Lipsett, Mortimer, ed. Gas Chromatography of Steroids in Biological Fluids. LC 65-25243. 315p. 1965. 34.50x (ISBN 0-306-30204-7, Plenum Pr). Plenum Pub.
McKerns, Kenneth W., ed. The Sex Steroids: Molecular Mechanisms. LC 78-120858. 454p. 1971. 52.50x (ISBN 0-306-50053-1, Plenum Pr). Plenum Pub.
Margalith, Pinhas Z. Steroid Microbiology. (Illus.). 300p. 1986. price not set (ISBN 0-398-05187-9). C C Thomas.
Martini, L. & Pecile, A., eds. Hormonal Steroids, Biochemistry, Pharmacology, Therapeutics, 2 Vols. 1965. Vol. 1. 83.50 (ISBN 0-12-475301-9); Vol. 2. 83.50 (ISBN 0-12-475302-7). Acad Pr.
Mauvais-Jarvis, P., et al, eds. Percutaneous Absorption of Steroids. LC 80-40243. 1980. 47.00 (ISBN 0-12-480680-5). Acad Pr.
Menon, K. M. & Reel, Jerry R., eds. Steroid Hormone Action & Cancer. LC 76-25873. (Current Topics in Molecular Endocrinology Ser.: Vol. 4). 190p. 1976. 39.50x (ISBN 0-306-34004-6, Plenum Pr). Plenum Pub.
Pincus, Gregory & Vollmer, E., eds. Biological Activities of Steroids in Relation to Cancer: Proceedings. 1960. 80.00 (ISBN 0-12-557068-6). Acad Pr.
Schroeders, F. H. & De Voogt, H. J., eds. Steroid Receptors, Metabolism & Prostate Cancer. (International Congress Ser.: Vol. 494). 278p. 1980. 58.50 (ISBN 0-444-90119-1, Excerpta Medica). Elsevier.
Schuermann, K. & Reulen, H. J., eds. Steroids & Brain Edema. LC 72-91334. (Illus.). 350p. 1972. pap. 20.00 (ISBN 0-387-05958-X). Springer-Verlag.
Shoppee, Charles W. Chemistry of the Steroids. 2nd ed. 491p. 1964. 22.50x (ISBN 0-306-30667-0, Plenum Pr). Plenum Pub.
Strauss, Jerome F., III & Menon, K. M., eds. Lipoprotein & Cholesterol Metabolism in Steroidogenic Tissues. 350p. 1985. pap. text ed. 35.00 (ISBN 0-89313-069-9). G F Stickley Co.
Wittliff, James L. & Dapunt, Otto. Steroid Receptors & Hormone Dependent Neoplasia. LC 80-80877. (Illus.). 320p. 1980. 57.00x (ISBN 0-89352-043-8). Masson Pub.

STEVEDORING

see Cargo Handling

STIRRERS (MACHINERY)

see Mixing Machinery

STOATS

see Weasels

STOCHASTIC ANALYSIS

Arato, M., et al, eds. Stochastic Differential Systems: Proceedings. (Lecture Notes in Control & Information Sciences Ser.: Vol. 36). 230p. 1981. pap. 19.50 (ISBN 0-387-11038-0). Springer-Verlag.
Arkin, V. I. & Evstigneev, J. V. Stochastic Models of Control & Economic Dynamics. Date not set. 49.00 (ISBN 0-12-062080-4). ACad Pr.

Bensoussan, A. Stochastic Control by Functional Analysis Methods. (Studies in Mathematics & Its Applications: Vol. 11). 410p. 1982. 53.25 (ISBN 0-444-86329-X, North-Holland). Elsevier.

Bensoussan, A., et al, eds. Applied Stochastic Control in Econometrics & Management. (Contributions to Economic Analysis Ser.: Vol. 130). 304p. 1981. 64.00 (ISBN 0-444-85408-8, North-Holland). Elsevier.

Davenport, Wilbur B. & Root, William L. An Introduction to the Theory of Random Signals & Noise. LC 57-10220. pap. 98.30 (ISBN 0-317-28211-5, 2055968). Bks Demand UMI.

Davis, Mark H. & Vinter, Richard. Stochastic Modelling & Control. (Monographs on Statistics & Applied Probability). 350p. 1985. 39.95x (ISBN 0-317-17595-5, 6874, Pub. by Chapman & Hall England). Methuen Inc.

Elliot, R. J. Stochastic Calculus & Applications. (Applications of Mathematics Ser.: Vol. 18). 302p. 1982. 47.00 (ISBN 0-387-90763-7). Springer-Verlag.

Elworthy, K. D. Stochastic Differential Equations on Manifolds. LC 82-4426. (London Mathematical Society Lecture Note Ser.: No. 70). 326p. 1982. pap. 32.50 (ISBN 0-521-28767-7). Cambridge U Pr.

Friedman, Avner & Pinsky, Mark, eds. Stochastic Analysis. 1978. 45.00 (ISBN 0-12-268380-3). Acad Pr.

Grassman, W. K. Stochastic Systems for Management. 358p. 1981. 33.25 (ISBN 0-444-00449-1, North Holland). Elsevier.

Gurland, John. Stochastic Models in Medicine & Biology: Proceedings of a Symposium Conducted by the Mathematics Research Center, 1963. LC 64-14509. (U. S. Army Mathematics Research Center Ser.: No. 10). pap. 102.50 (ISBN 0-317-12991-0, 2021134). Bks Demand UMI.

Ito, K., ed. Stochastic Analysis: Proceedings of the Taniguchi International Symposium, Katata & Kyoto, 1982. (Mathematical Library: Vol. 32). 1984. 92.75 (ISBN 0-444-87588-3, North-Holland). Elsevier.

Jacobs, O. L. R., et al, eds. Analysis & Optimization of Stochastic Systems. (IMA Conference Ser.). 1980. 49.50 (ISBN 0-12-378680-0). Acad Pr.

Kallianpur, G. & Koelzow, D., eds. Measure Theory Applications to Stochastic Analysis: Proceedings, Oberwolfach Conference, Germany, July 3-9, 1977. (Lecture Notes in Mathematics Ser.: Vol. 695). 1978. pap. 19.00 (ISBN 0-387-09098-3). Springer-Verlag.

Keisler, H. Jerome. An Infinitesimal Approach to Stochastic Analysis. LC 83-26647. (Memoirs of the American Mathematical Society: No. 297). 186p. 1984. pap. 16.00 (ISBN 0-8218-2297-7, (MEMO-297)). Am Math.

Kendall, D. G. & Harding, E. F., eds. Stochastic Analysis: A Tribute to the Memory of Rollo Davidson. LC 72-8605. pap. 119.80 (ISBN 0-317-08894-7, 2013983). Bks Demand UMI.

Lee, S. M., et al. Network Analysis for Management Decisions. (International Series in Management Science-Operational Research). 1981. lib. bdg. 30.00 (ISBN 0-89838-077-4). Kluwer Academic.

Malliaris, T. G. Stochastic Methods in Economics & Finance. (Advanced Textbooks in Economics: Vol. 17). 304p. 1982. 37.50 (ISBN 0-444-86201-3, North-Holland). Elsevier.

Mohammed, S. E. Stochastic Functional Differential Equations. LC 83-24973. (Research Notes Ser.: No. 99). 208p. 1984. pap. text ed. 21.95 (ISBN 0-273-08593-X). Pitman Pub MA.

Pinsky. Stochastic Analysis Applications. (Advances in Probability & Related Topics Ser.). 368p. 1984. 59.75 (ISBN 0-8247-1906-9). Dekker.

Rao, M. M. Foundations of Stochastic Analysis. LC 81-10831. (Probability & Mathematical Statistics Ser.). 1981. 55.00 (ISBN 0-12-580850-X). Acad Pr.

Stoyan, Dietrich & Daley, Daryl J., eds. Comparison Methods for Queues & Other Stochastic Models. LC 81-16365. (Probability & Mathematical Statistics Applied Section Ser.). 217p. 1983. text ed. 39.95x (ISBN 0-471-10122-2, Pub. by Wiley-Interscience). Wiley.

Townsend, James T. & Ashby, F. Gregory. Stochastic Modeling of Elementary Psychological Processes. LC 82-9613. (Illus.). 560p. 1984. 69.50 (ISBN 0-521-24181-2); pap. 27.95 (ISBN 0-521-27433-8). Cambridge U Pr.

Truman, A. & Williams, D., eds. Stochastic Analysis & Applications. (Lecture Notes in Mathematics Ser.: Vol. 1095). v, 199p. 1984. pap. 13.50 (ISBN 0-387-13891-9). Springer-Verlag.

Whittle, P. Optimisation Over Time: Dynamic Programming & Stochastic Control, Vol. 1. (Probability & Mathematical Statistics-Applied Probability & Statistics Section Ser.). 317p. 1982. 54.95x (ISBN 0-471-10120-6, Pub. by Wiley-Interscience). Wiley.

STOCHASTIC COMMUNICATION THEORY
see Statistical Communication Theory

STOCHASTIC INTEGRALS
see Integrals, Stochastic

STOCHASTIC PROCESSES
see also Estimation Theory; Markov Processes; Martingales (Mathematics); Monte Carlo Method; Random Noise Theory; Random Walks (Mathematics); Stochastic Analysis

Adler, Robert J. The Geometry of Random Fields. LC 80-40842. (Probability & Mathematical Statistics Ser.). 280p. 1981. 61.95x (ISBN 0-471-27844-0, Pub. by Wiley-Interscience). Wiley.

Adomian, G., ed. Applied Stochastic Processes. LC 80-19890. 1980. 31.50 (ISBN 0-12-044380-5). Acad Pr.

Adomian, George, ed. Stochastic Systems: Monograph. (Mathematics in Science & Engineering Ser.). 345p. 1983. 49.50 (ISBN 0-12-044370-8). Acad Pr.

Agarwal, G. S. & Dattagupta, S., eds. Stochastic Processes Formalism & Applications. (Lecture Notes in Physics: Vol. 184). 324p. 1983. pap. 19.00 (ISBN 0-387-12326-1). Springer-Verlag.

Alberti, Peter M. & Uhlmann, Armin. Stochasticity & Partial Order. 1982. lib. bdg. 28.50 (ISBN 90-277-1350-2, Pub. by Reidel Holland). Kluwer Academic.

Albeverio, S., ed. Infinite-Dimensional Analysis: Stochastic Processes. (Research Notes in Mathematics Ser.: No. 124). 250p. 1985. pap. text ed. 21.95 (ISBN 0-273-08684-7). Pitman Pub MA.

Albeverio, S., et al, eds. Stochastic Processes in Quantum Theory & Statistical Physics: Proceedings, Marseille, France, 1981. (Lecture Notes in Physics Ser.: Vol. 173). 337p. 1982. pap. 19.00 (ISBN 0-387-11956-6). Springer-Verlag.

--Stochastic Aspects of Classical & Quantum Systems. (Lecture Notes in Mathematics Ser.: Vol. 1109). ix, 227p. 1985. pap. 14.40 (ISBN 0-387-13914-1). Springer-Verlag.

American Society of Mechanical Engineers. Stochastic Problems in Control. LC 68-8579. pap. 31.00 (ISBN 0-317-08716-9, 2016484). Bks Demand UMI.

American Society of Mechnical Engineers. Stochastic Processes in Dynamical Problems. LC 71-105935. pap. 30.30 (ISBN 0-317-27786-3, 2024180). Bks Demand UMI.

Aoki, Masanao. Optimization of Stochastic Systems. (Mathematics in Science & Engineering Ser: Vol. 32). 1967. 68.50 (ISBN 0-12-058850-1). Acad Pr.

Arato, M. Linear Stochastic Systems with Constant Coefficients: A Statistical Approach. (Lecture Notes in Control & Information Sciences: Vol. 45). 309p. 1982. pap. 17.50 (ISBN 0-387-12090-4). Springer-Verlag.

Archetti, F. & Cugiani, M. Numerical Techniques for Stochastic Systems. 406p. 1980. 85.00 (ISBN 0-444-86000-2). Elsevier.

Arnold, L. & Lefever, R., eds. Stochastic Nonlinear Systems in Physics, Chemistry, & Biology. (Springer Series in Synergetics: Vol. 8). (Illus.). viii, 237p. 1985. 33.00 (ISBN 0-387-10713-4). Springer-Verlag.

Arnold, Ludwig. Stochastic Differential Equations: Theory & Applications. LC 73-22256. 228p. 1974. 48.50x (ISBN 0-471-03359-6, Pub. by Wiley-Interscience). Wiley.

Assefi, Touraj. Stochastic Processes & Estimation Theory with Applications. LC 79-17872. 291p. 1979. 37.50x (ISBN 0-471-06454-8, Pub. by Wiley-Interscience). Wiley.

Astrom, K. J. Introduction to Stochastic Control Theory. (Mathematics in Science & Engineering Ser.: Vol. 70). 1970. 60.00 (ISBN 0-12-065650-7). Acad Pr.

Bailey, Norman T. Elements of Stochastic Processes with Applications to the Natural Sciences: Applied Probability & Statistics Section. LC 63-23220. (Probability & Mathematical Statistics Ser.). 249p. 1964. 45.95x (ISBN 0-471-04165-3, Pub. by Wiley-Interscience). Wiley.

Bartholomew, D. J. Stochastic Models for Social Processes. 3rd ed. (Wiley Ser. in Probability & Mathematical Statistics: Applied Probability & Statistics Section). 365p. 1982. 57.95x (ISBN 0-471-28040-2, Pub. by Wiley-Interscience). Wiley.

--Stochastic Models for Social Processes. 2nd ed. LC 73-2776. (Probability & Mathematical Statistics Ser.: Applied Probability & Statistic Section). 408p. 1974. 68.95 (ISBN 0-471-05451-8, Pub. by Wiley-Interscience). Wiley.

Bartlett, M. S. Introduction to Stochastic Processes. 3rd ed. LC 76-57094. (Illus.). 404p. 1981. pap. 22.95 (ISBN 0-521-28085-0). Cambridge U Pr.

--An Introduction to Stochastic Processes with Special Reference to Methods & Applications. 3rd ed. LC 76-57094. (Illus.). 1978. 59.50 (ISBN 0-521-21585-4). Cambridge U Pr.

--Stochastic Population Models in Ecology & Epidemiology. (Monographs in Applied Probability & Statistics). 1960. 10.95x (ISBN 0-416-52330-7, NO.6429). Methuen Inc.

Basawa, Ishwar & Rao, Prakasa, eds. Statistical Interference for Stochastic Processes. LC 79-50533. (Probability & Mathematical Statistics Ser.). 1980. 75.00 (ISBN 0-12-080250-3). Acad Pr.

Beard, E., et al. Risk Theory: The Stochastic Basis of Insurance. 2nd ed. (Monographs on Applied Probability & Statistics). 1977. 17.50x (ISBN 0-412-15100-6, NO.6031, Pub. by Chapman & Hall). Methuen Inc.

Becker, P. W. Recognition of Patterns Using the Frequencies of Occurence of Binary Words. 2nd & rev. ed. (Illus.). 1978. pap. 26.00 (ISBN 0-387-81506-6). Springer-Verlag.

Bendat, Julius S. & Piersol, Allan G. Random Data: Analysis & Measurement Procedures. LC 71-160211. (Illus.). 407p. 1971. 45.50x (ISBN 0-471-06470-X, Pub. by Wiley-Interscience). Wiley.

Bensoussan, A. & Lions, J. L. Applications of Variational Inequalities in Stochastic Control. (Studies in Mathematics & Its Applications: Vol. 12). Orig. Title: Applications des Inequations Variationnelles en Controle Stochastique. 564p. 1982. 74.50 (ISBN 0-444-86358-3, North-Holland). Elsevier.

Bertsekas, Dimitri P. Dynamic Programming & Stochastic Control. (Math in Science & Engineering Ser.). 1976. 45.00 (ISBN 0-12-093250-4). Acad Pr.

Bertsekas, Dimitri P. & Shreve, Steven E. Stochastic Optimal Control: The Discrete Time Case. (Mathematics in Science & Engineering Ser.). 1978. 70.00 (ISBN 0-12-093260-1). Acad Pr.

Bharucha-Reid, Albert T., ed. Probabilistic Analysis in Applied Mathematics, 4 vols. Vol. 1 1968. 68.50 (ISBN 0-12-095701-9); Vol. 2 1970. 59.50 (ISBN 0-12-095702-7); Vol. 3 1973. 77.00 (ISBN 0-12-095703-5). Acad Pr.

Bhat, U. Narayan. Elements of Applied Stochastic Processes. LC 70-178140. (Probability & Mathematical Statistics Ser.). 414p. 1972. 45.95x (ISBN 0-471-07199-4, Pub. by Wiley-Interscience). Wiley.

--Elements of Applied Stochastic Processes. 2nd ed. LC 84-7338. (Probability & Mathematical Statistics-Applied Probability & Statistics Section Ser.: 1-346). 685p. 1984. text ed. 44.95x (ISBN 0-471-87826-X, Pub. by Wiley-Interscience). Wiley.

Bichteler, K. Stochastic Integration & Stochastic Differential Equations. (North-Holland Mathematics Studies). 1984. write for info. (North-Holland). Elsevier.

Blanc-LaPierre, Andre & Fortet, R. Theory of Random Functions, 2 Vols. LC 65-16343. (Illus.). 810p. 1968. Set. 153.95 (ISBN 0-677-04250-7). Gordon.

Borovkov, A. A. Stochastic Processes in Queueing Theory. LC 75-43242. (Applications of Math Ser.: Vol. 4). (Illus.). 1976. pap. 46.00 (ISBN 0-387-90161-2). Springer-Verlag.

Bucy, R. S., et al. Stochastic Differential Equations. McKean, H. P. & Keller, J. B., eds. LC 72-13266. (SIAM-AMS Proceedings: No. 6). 1973. 39.00 (ISBN 0-8218-1325-0, SIAMS-6). Am Math.

Carmeli. Statistical Theory & Random Matrices. (Pure & Applied Mathematics Ser.). 184p. 1983. 45.00 (ISBN 0-8247-1779-1). Dekker.

Chen, H. Recursive Estimation & Control for Stochastic Systems. (Probability & Mathematical Statistics Ser.). 378p. 1985. 39.95 (ISBN 0-471-81566-7). Wiley.

Chiang, Chin L. Introduction to Stochastic Processes, & Their Applications. LC 74-14821. 544p. 1980. 39.50 (ISBN 0-88275-200-6). Krieger.

Chung, K. L. Elementary Probability Theory with Stochastic Processes. (Undergraduate Texts in Mathematics Ser.). (Illus.). 1979. 19.80 (ISBN 0-387-90362-3). Springer-Verlag.

Cinlar, E. Introduction to Stochastic Processes. (Illus.). 448p. 1975. ref. ed. 32.95 (ISBN 0-13-498089-1). P-H.

Cinlar, E., et al. Seminar on Stochastic Processes, 1982. (Progress in Probability & Statistics Ser.: Vol. 5). 310p. 1983. text ed. 24.95 (ISBN 0-8176-3131-3). Birkhauser.

Cinlar, E., et al, eds. Seminar on Stochastic Processes, 1981. (Progress in Probability & Statistics: Vol. 1). 248p. 1982. text ed. 17.50 (ISBN 0-8176-3072-4). Birkhauser.

CISM (International Center for Mechanical Sciences), Dept. for General Mechanics, Technical Univ. of Vienna, 1971. Approximate Analysis of Stochastic Processes in Mechanics. Zeman, J. L., ed. (CISM Pubns. Ser.: No. 95). (Illus.). iv, 157p. 1973. pap. 16.40 (ISBN 0-387-81131-1). Springer-Verlag.

Control Theory Centre Symposium, University of Warwick, 1972. Stability of Stochastic Dynamical Systems: Proceedings. Curtain, R. F., ed. LC 72-91895. (Lecture Notes in Mathematics: Vol. 294). (Illus.). 332p. 1972. pap. 13.00 (ISBN 0-387-06050-2). Springer-Verlag.

Cramer, Harald. Structural & Statistical Problems for a Class of Stochastic Processes. LC 74-160260. (S. S. Wilks Memorial Lecture Ser.). 1971. pap. 11.50x (ISBN 0-691-08099-2). Princeton U Pr.

Cramer, Harold. Random Variables & Probability Distribution. 3rd ed. (Cambridge Tracts in Mathematics & Mathematical Physics). 1970. 29.95 (ISBN 0-521-07685-4). Cambridge U Pr.

Crigelionis, B., ed. Stochastic Differential Systems; Filtering & Control: Proceedings. (Lecture Notes in Control & Information Sciences Ser.: Vol. 25). 362p. 1981. pap. 26.00 (ISBN 0-387-10498-4). Springer-Verlag.

Davenport, W. Probability & Random Processes: An Introduction for Applied Scientists & Engineers. 1970. 49.00 (ISBN 0-07-015440-6). McGraw.

Davis, M. H. Linear Estimation & Stochastic Control. LC 77-23389. 1977. pap. text ed. 16.95x (ISBN 0-412-15130-8). Halsted Pr.

--Linear Estimation & Stochastic Control. 1977. (Pub. by Chapman & Hall); pap. 16.95x (ISBN 0-412-15130-8, NO. 6563). Methuen Inc.

--Stochastic Control & Nonlinear Filtering. (Tata Institute Lectures on Mathematics Ser.). iv, 109p. 1984. pap. 7.10 (ISBN 0-387-13343-7). Springer-Verlag.

Dempster, M. A., ed. Stochastic Programming. LC 77-92826. (Institute of Mathematics & Its Applications Conference Ser.). 1980. 95.00 (ISBN 0-12-208250-8). Acad Pr.

Dempster, M. A. & Lenstra, J. K., eds. Deterministic & Stochastic Scheduling. 1982. 48.00 (ISBN 90-277-1397-9, Pub. by Reidel Holland). Kluwer Academic.

Dickman, Andreas & Mitter, Peter, eds. Stochastic Modelling of Social Processes. 1984. 30.00 (ISBN 0-12-215490-8). Acad Pr.

Doberkat, E. E. Stochastic Automata: Stability, Nondeterminism, & Prediction. (Lecture Notes in Computer Science Ser.: Vol. 113). 135p. 1981. pap. 12.00 (ISBN 0-387-10835-1). Springer-Verlag.

Dobryshin, R. L., et al, eds. Locally Interacting Systems & Their Application in Biology: Proceedings of the School - Seminar on Markov Interaction Processes in Biology, Held in Pushchino, Moscow Region, March, 1976. (Lecture Notes in Mathematics Ser.: Vol. 653). 1978. pap. 16.00 (ISBN 0-387-08450-9). Springer-Verlag.

Doob, Joseph L. Stochastic Processes. LC 52-11857. (Wiley Series in Probability & Mathematical Statistics). 654p. 1953. 52.50x (ISBN 0-471-21813-8, Pub. by Wiley-Interscience). Wiley.

Dudley, R. M., et al. Ecole d'Ete de Probabilities de Saint-Flour XII, 1982. (Lecture Notes in Mathematics Ser.: Vol. 1097). x, 396p. 1984. pap. 22.50 (ISBN 0-387-13897-8). Springer-Verlag.

Elliot, R. J. Stochastic Calculus & Applications. (Applications of Mathematics Ser.: Vol. 18). 302p. 1982. 47.00 (ISBN 0-387-90763-7). Springer-Verlag.

Ephremides, A., ed. Random Processes: Multiplicity & Canonical Decompositions, Pt. 1. LC 75-1287. (Benchmark Papers in Electrical Engineering & Computer Science: No. 11). 352p. 1973. 57.50 (ISBN 0-87933-022-8). Van Nos Reinhold.

Evans, M. W., et al, eds. Memory Function Approaches to Stochastic Problems in Condensed Matter. (Advances in Chemical Physics Ser.: Pt. 1). 640p. 1985. 85.00 (ISBN 0-471-80482-7). Wiley.

Fleming, W. H. & Gorostiza, L. G., eds. Advances in Filtering & Optimal Stochastic Control: Proceedings; Cocoyoc, Mexico 1982. (Lecture Notes in Control & Information Science: Vol. 42). 392p. 1982. pap. 19.50 (ISBN 0-387-11936-1). Springer-Verlag.

Florens, J. P., et al, eds. Specifying Statistical Models, From Parametric to Non-Parametric, Using Bayesian or Non-Bayesian Approaches: Proceedings, Louvain-la-Neuve, Belgium, 1981. (Lecture Notes in Statistics Ser.: Vol. 16). (Illus.). 204p. 1983. pap. 15.00 (ISBN 0-387-90809-9). Springer-Verlag.

Fox, D. R. Theory of Stochastic Processes. 1965. 20.00x (ISBN 0-412-15170-7, NO. 6430, Pub. by Chapman & Hall). Methuen Inc.

Frehland, E. Stochastic Transport Processes in Discrete Biological Systems. (Lecture Notes in Biomathematics Ser.: Vol. 47). 169p. 1982. pap. 13.00 (ISBN 0-387-11964-7). Springer-Verlag.

Friedman, Avner. Stochastic Differential Equations & Applications, 2 vols. (Probability & Mathematical Statistics Ser.). Vol. 1,1975. 49.50 (ISBN 0-12-268201-7); Vol. 2, 1976. 64.50 (ISBN 0-12-268202-5). Acad Pr.

Sagirow, P. Stochastic Methods in the Dynamics of Satellites. (CISM - International Centre for Mechanical Sciences, Courses & Lectures: Vol. 57). 132p. 1975. pap. 17.20 (ISBN 0-387-81092-7). Springer-Verlag.
Saleh, B. Photoelectronic Statistics: With Applications to Spectroscopy & Optical Communication. LC 77-9936. (Springer Ser. in Optical Sciences: Vol. 6). (Illus.). 1977. 46.00 (ISBN 0-387-08295-6). Springer-Verlag.
Sattinger, David H. Branching in the Presence of Symmetry. LC 82-61451. (CBMS-NSF Regional Conference Ser.: No. 40). vii, 73p. 1983. pap. text ed. 12.00 (ISBN 0-89871-182-7). Soc Indus-Appl Math.
Sengupta, J. K. Decision Models in Stochastic Programming. (Systems Science & Engineering Ser.: Vol. 7). 190p. 1982. 53.25 (ISBN 0-444-00667-2, North-Holland). Elsevier.
Shlesinger, M. F. & Weiss, G. H., eds. The Wonderful World of Stochastics: A Tribute to Elliott W. Montroll. (Studies in Statistical Mechanics: Vol. 12). 250p. 1985. 45.00 (ISBN 0-444-86937-9, North-Holland). Elsevier.
Shuler, K. E., ed. Advances in Chemical Physics, Vol. 15. LC 58-9935. 391p. 1969. 24.00 (ISBN 0-471-78967-4). Krieger.
Skorohod, A. V. Random Linear Operators. 1984. lib. bdg. 43.00 (ISBN 0-318-00431-3, Pub. by Reidel Holland). Kluwer Academic.
Skorokhod, A. V. Studies in the Theory of Random Processes. (Illus.). 199p. 1982. pap. 4.50 (ISBN 0-486-64240-2). Dover.
Skwirzynski, J. K., ed. Communication Systems & Random Process Theory, No. 12. (Nato Advanced Study Institute Ser.,Applied Science Ser.). 996p. 1978. 75.00x (ISBN 90-286-0568-1). Sijthoff & Noordhoff.
Smith, Tony E. The Cell-Court Theory of Stochastic Point Processes. (Discussion Paper Ser.: No. 52). 1972. pap. 4.50 (ISBN 0-686-32219-3). Regional Sci Res Inst.
Sobczyk, K. Stochastic Wave Propagation. (Fundamental Studies in Engineering: Vol. 6). 1985. 68.75 (ISBN 0-444-99614-1). Elsevier.
Sorenson. Parameter Estimation: Principles & Problems. (Control & Systems Theory Ser.: Vol. 9). 400p. 1980. 49.75 (ISBN 0-8247-6987-2). Dekker.
Srinivasan, S. K. Stochastic Point Processes & Their Applications. LC 73-84664. (Griffin Statistical Monograph Ser.: No. 34). (Orig.). 1973. pap. 15.25x (ISBN 0-02-852660-0). Hafner.
Srinivasan, S. K. & Sampath, G. Stochastic Models for Spike Trains of Single Neurons. (Lecture Notes in Biomathematics: Vol. 16). 1977. 14.00 (ISBN 0-387-08257-3). Springer-Verlag.
Stancu-Minasian, I. M. Stochastic Programming with Multiple Objective Functions. 1985. lib. bdg. 59.00 (ISBN 90-277-1714-1, Pub. by Reidel Holland). Kluwer Academic.
Stengel, Robert F. Stochastic Optimal Control. 40.00 (ISBN 0-471-86462-5). Wiley.
Stochastic Processes & the Wiener Integral. LC 72-91439. (Pure & Applied Mathematics Ser.: No. 13). pap. 139.80 (ISBN 0-317-07837-2, 2055026). Bks Demand UMI.
Stochastic Processes Applied to Physics & Other Related Topics: Proceeding of the Conferencein Cali, Colombia, June21-July 9, 1982. (ACIF Ser.: Vol. 1). xxvi, 782p. 1983. 75.00x (ISBN 9971-950-56-1, Pub. by World Sci Singapore). Taylor & Francis.
Stroock, D. W. An Introduction to the Theory of Large Deviations. (Universitext Ser.). 195p. 1984. pap. 18.00 (ISBN 0-387-96021-X). Springer-Verlag.
--Topics in Stochastic Differential Equations. (Tata Institute Lectures on Mathematics). 91p. 1982. pap. 9.00 (ISBN 0-387-11549-8). Springer-Verlag.
Sudakov, V. N., ed. Investigations in the Theory of Stochastic Processes. (Seminars in Mathematics Ser.: Vol. 12). 25.00x (ISBN 0-306-18812-0, Consultants). Plenum Pub.
Symposium in Applied Mathematics, - New York - 1963. Stochastic Processes in Mathematical Physics & Engineering: Proceedings. Bellman, R., ed. LC 64-18128. (Proceedings of Symposia in Applied Mathematics: Vol. 16). 318p. 1980. pap. 34.00 (ISBN 0-8218-1316-1, PSAPM-16). Am Math.
Syski. Random Processes: A First Look. (Statistics; Textbooks & Monographs Ser.: Vol. 29). 1979. 29.75 (ISBN 0-8247-6893-0). Dekker.
Takacs, L. Stochastic Process: Problems & Solutions. 1966. pap. 8.95x (ISBN 0-412-20340-5, 6284, Pub. by Chapman & Hall). Methuen Inc.
Takacs, Lajos. Combinatorial Methods in the Theory of Stochastic Processes. LC 76-55801. 276p. 1977. Repr. of 1967 ed. lib. bdg. 19.50 (ISBN 0-88275-491-2). Krieger.
Taylor, Howard & Karlin, Samuel. An Introduction to Stochastic Modeling. 1984. text ed. 28.00i (ISBN 0-12-684880-7). Acad Pr.
Thomas, John B. An Introduction to Applied Probability & Random Processes. LC 80-15349. (Illus.). 352p. 1981. Repr. of 1971 ed. lib. bdg. 26.50 (ISBN 0-89874-232-3). Krieger.
UNESCO Working Group on Systems Analysis, 4th, Flattnitz, Karnten, Austria June 6-10, 1983. Stochastic Phenomena & Chaotic Behavior im Complex Systems: Proceedings. Schuster, P., ed. (Synergetics Ser.: Vol. 21). (Illus.). 270p. 1984. 35.00 (ISBN 0-387-13194-9). Springer-Verlag.
Urkowitz, Harry. Signal Theory & Random Processes. LC 83-70360. (Radar Ser.). (Illus.). 750p. 1983. 72.00 (ISBN 0-89006-121-1). Artech Hse.
Van Doorn, E. A. Stochastic Monotonicity & Queuing Applications of Birth-Death Processes. (Lecture Notes in Statistics Ser.: Vol. 4). 118p. 1981. pap. 12.00 (ISBN 0-387-90547-2). Springer-Verlag.
Volta Memorial Conference, Como, Italy, 1977. Stochastic Behavior in Classical & Quantum Hamiltonian Systems: Proceedings. Casati, G. & Ford, J., eds. (Lecture Notes in Physics: Vol. 93). 1979. pap. 22.00 (ISBN 0-387-09120-3). Springer-Verlag.
Vom Scheidt, J. & Purkert, W. Random Eigenvalue Problems. (North-Holland Series in Probability & Applied Mathematics). 176p. 1984. 25.00 (ISBN 0-444-00769-5, North-Holland). Elsevier.
Watanabe, S. Lectures on Stochastic Differential Equations & Malliavin Calculus. (Tata Institute Lectures on Mathematics Ser.). viii, 118p. 1984. pap. 9.50 (ISBN 0-387-12897-2). Springer-Verlag.
Wax, Nelson, ed. Selected Papers on Noise & Stochastic Processes. 1954. pap. 7.00 (ISBN 0-486-60262-1). Dover.
Wentzell, A. Theorie Zufaelliger Prozesse. (Mathematische Reihe: No. 65). (Ger.). 264p. 1979. 50.95 (ISBN 0-8176-1021-9). Birkhauser.
Wets, R. J., ed. Stochastic Systems: Modeling, Indentification Optimization II. (Mathematical Programming Studies: Vol. 6). 1977. pap. 27.75 (ISBN 0-7204-0570-X, North-Holland). Elsevier.
Wets, Roger J., ed. Stochastic Systems: Modeling, Identification, & Optimization I. Benes, Vaclav E. LC 76-50621. (Mathematical Programming Studies: Vol. 5). 1977. pap. 20.50 (ISBN 0-7204-0569-6, North-Holland). Elsevier.
Wickens, Thomas D. Models for Behavior: Stochastic Processes in Psychology. LC 81-17349. (Illus.). 353p. 1982. text ed. 33.95x (ISBN 0-7167-1352-7); pap. text ed. 18.95 (ISBN 0-7167-1353-5). W H Freeman.
Williams, D., ed. Stochastic Process: Proceedings. (Lecture Notes in Mathematics Ser.: Vol. 851). 540p. 1981. pap. 29.00 (ISBN 0-387-10690-1). Springer-Verlag.
Witt, U. & Perske, J. SMS: A Program Package for Simulation & Gaming of Stochastic Market Processes & Learning Behavior. (Lecture Notes in Economics & Mathematical Systems Ser.: Vol. 202). (Illus.). 266p. 1982. pap. 21.00 (ISBN 0-387-11551-X). Springer-Verlag.
Wong, E. Introduction to Random Processes: A Dowden & Culver Book. (Springer Texts in Electrical Engineering). 175p. 1983. pap. 19.95 (ISBN 0-387-90757-2). Springer-Verlag.
Wong, E. & Hajek, B. Stochastic Processes in Engineering Systems. 2nd ed. (Texts in Electrical Engineering Ser.). 240p. 1985. 29.80 (ISBN 0-387-96061-9). Springer-Verlag.
Yavin, Y. Feedback Strategies for Partially Observable Stochastic Systems. (Lecture Notes in Control & Information Sciences: Vol. 48). 233p. 1983. pap. 14.50 (ISBN 0-387-12208-7). Springer-Verlag.
Ziemba, W. T. Stochastic Optimization Models in Finance. 1975. 65.00 (ISBN 0-12-780850-7). Acad Pr.

STOCHASTIC SAMPLING
see Monte Carlo Method

STOCK (ANIMALS)
see Livestock

STOCK-RANGES
see also Cattle Trade; Grazing; Range Research
Barnes, William C. Western Grazing Grounds & Forest Ranges. Bruchey, Stuart, ed. LC 78-56685. (Management of Public Lands in the U.S. Ser.). (Illus.). 1979. Repr. of 1913 ed. lib. bdg. 26.50x (ISBN 0-405-11317-X). Ayer Co Pubs.
Dobie, J. Frank. The Longhorns. (Illus.). 1941. 17.45i (ISBN 0-316-18796-8). Little.
Pratt, D. J. & Gwynne, M. D., eds. Rangeland Management & Ecology in East Africa. LC 77-70207. 320p. 1977. 23.50 (ISBN 0-88275-525-0). Krieger.
U. S. Senate. The Western Range. Bruchey, Stuart, ed. LC 78-53570. (Development of Public Land Law in the U. S. Ser.). (Illus.). 1979. Repr. of 1936 ed. lib. bdg. 43.00x (ISBN 0-405-11390-0). Ayer Co Pubs.

STOICHIOMETRY
see Chemistry–Problems, Exercises, etc.; Chemistry, Physical and Theoretical

STOL AIRCRAFT
see Short Take-Off and Landing Aircraft

STOMATA
Martin, E. S. & Donkin, M. E. Stomata. (Studies in Biology: No. 155). 1983. pap. text ed. 8.95 (ISBN 0-7131-2868-2). E Arnold.

STONE
see also Blasting; Masonry; Petrology; Quarries and Quarrying; Rocks; Stone-Cutting
Amoroso, G. G. & Passina, V. Stone Decay & Conservation: Atmospheric Pollution, Cleaning, Consolidation & Protection. (Materials Science Monographs: Vol. 11). 453p. 1983. 98.00 (ISBN 0-444-42146-7, I-269-83). Elsevier.
The Development Potential of Dimension Stone. pap. 8.50 (ISBN 0-686-94782-7, UN76/2A4, UN). Unipub.
McRaven, Charles. Building with Stone. (Illus.). 1980. 15.34i (ISBN 0-690-01879-7); pap. 9.95 (ISBN 0-690-01912-2). Har-Row.

STONE-CUTTING
Barnett, George E. Chapters on Machinery & Labor. LC 68-25563. (Masterworks in Industrial Relations Ser.). 191p. 1969. Repr. of 1926 ed. 6.95x (ISBN 0-8093-0397-3). S Ill U Pr.
Kindersley, David & Cardozo, Lida L. Letters Slate Cut. LC 80-54744. (Illus.). 96p. 1981. pap. 9.95 (ISBN 0-8008-4741-5, Pentalic). Taplinger.
Noel, P. Technologie de la Pierre de Taille. (Fr.). 376p. 1968. 49.95 (ISBN 0-686-56777-3, M-6429). French & Eur.

STONE-FLIES
Leiser, Eric & Boyle, Robert H. Stoneflies for the Angler. LC 81-47478. (Illus.). 192p. 1982. 18.50 (ISBN 0-394-50822-X). Knopf.
Surdick, Rebecca F. Nearctic Genera of Chloroperlinae: Plecoptera: Cloroperlidae. LC 84-16284. (Illinois Biological Monographs: No. 54). (Illus.). 156p. 1985. pap. 14.95x (ISBN 0-252-01163-5). U of Ill Pr.

STONE HOUSES
see also Trulli
Conservation of Historic Stone Buildings & Monuments. 1982. pap. 21.25 (ISBN 0-309-03275-X); 30.00 (ISBN 0-309-03288-1). Natl Acad Pr.
Nearing, Helen. Our Home Made of Stone. 1983. 15.00 (ISBN 0-89272-175-8). Soc Sci Inst.
Watson, Lewis & Watson, Sharon. How to Build a Low-Cost House of Stone. 5th ed. LC 78-54225. (Illus.). 1974. pap. 8.95 (ISBN 0-9603236-1-9). Stonehouse.

STONE IMPLEMENTS
Ericson, Jonathon E. & Purdy, Barbara A., eds. Prehistoric Quarries & Lithic Production. LC 83-18822. (New Directions in Archaeology Ser.). (Illus.). 170p. 1984. 39.50 (ISBN 0-521-25622-4). Cambridge U Pr.
Hellweg, Paul. Flintknapping: The Art of Making Stone Tools. LC 83-72653. (Illus.). 112p. (Orig.). 1984. pap. 5.95 (ISBN 0-942568-05-2). Canyon Pub Co.
Keeley, Lawrence H. Experimental Determination of Stone Tool Uses: A Microwear Analysis. LC 79-11838. (Prehistoric Archeology & Ecology). (Illus.). 1980. lib. bdg. 18.00x (ISBN 0-226-42888-5); pap. 7.00x o. s. i. (ISBN 0-226-42889-3). U of Chicago Pr.
Pitts, Michaels. Later Stone Implements. (Shire Archaeology Ser.: No. 14). (Illus.). 1983. pap. 5.95 (ISBN 0-85263-518-4, Pub. by Shire Pubns England). Seven Hills Bks.
Purdy, Barbara A. Florida's Prehistoric Stone Technology: A Study of the Flintworking Techniques of Early Florida Stone Implement Makers. LC 80-24726. (Illus.). xvi, 165p. 1981. 25.00 (ISBN 0-8130-0697-X). U Presses Fla.
Timms, Peter. Flint Implements of the Old Stone Age. (Shire Archaeology Ser.: No. 2). (Illus.). 56p. 1980. pap. 5.95 (ISBN 0-85263-517-6, Pub. by Shire Pubns England). Seven Hills Bks.
Woodbury, R. B. Prehistoric Stone Implements of Northeastern Arizona. (HU PMP). (Illus.). 1954. 29.00 (ISBN 0-527-01286-6). Kraus Repr.
Wright, R. V. Stone Tools As Cultural Markers: Change, Evolution & Complexity. (AIAS Prehistory & Material Culture: No. 12). 1977. text ed. 33.25x (ISBN 0-391-00835-8); pap. text ed. 24.25x (ISBN 0-391-00836-6). Humanities.

STONE INDUSTRY AND TRADE
see also Quarries and Quarrying
Miller, Richard. Noise Control Solutions for the Stone Industry. (Illus.). 90p. pap. text ed. 45.00 (ISBN 0-89671-028-9). SEAI Tech Pubns.

STONE-MASONS
Rudman, Jack. Maintenance Mason. (Career Examination Ser.: C-1355). (Cloth bdg. avail. on request). pap. 10.00 (ISBN 0-8373-1355-4). Natl Learning.
--Maintenance Mason Foreman. (Career Examination Ser.: C-1356). (Cloth bdg. avail. on request). pap. 12.00 (ISBN 0-8373-1356-2). Natl Learning.
--Mason. (Career Examination Ser.: C-473). (Cloth bdg. avail. on request). pap. 10.00 (ISBN 0-8373-0473-3). Natl Learning.
--Mason's Helper. (Career Examination Ser.: C-474). (Cloth bdg. avail. on request) (ISBN 0-8373-0474-1). pap. 10.00 (ISBN 0-686-66500-7). Natl Learning.
Sanders, Scott R. Stone Country. LC 84-43154. (Illus.). 256p. 1985. 24.95 (ISBN 0-253-18515-7). Ind U Pr.

STORAGE
see Cold Storage; Warehouses;
also names of stored products, e.g. Farm Produce, Coal, etc.

STORAGE AND MOVING TRADE
see also Transportation
Rack Storage of Materials. (Two Hundred Ser.). 84p. 1974. pap. 6.50 (ISBN 0-685-44136-9, 231C). Natl Fire Prot.

STORAGE BATTERIES
see also Electric Batteries
Aviation Maintenance Publishers. Aircraft Batteries: Lead Acid & Nickel Cadmium. Crane, Dale, ed. (Aviation Technician Training Ser.). 32p. 1975. pap. 3.95 (ISBN 0-89100-052-6, EA-AB-1). Aviation Maint.
Bagshaw, Norman E. Batteries on Ships. LC 82-10954. (Battery Applications Bk.Ser.). 203p. 1983. 59.95x (ISBN 0-471-90021-4, Res Stud Pr). Wiley.
Batterie, Varta. Sealed Nickel Cadmium Batteries. 1982. pap. 31.00 (ISBN 0-9961074-9-5, Pub. by VDI W Germany). Heyden.
Bechtel National, Inc. Photovoltaic Power Systems: Handbook for Battery Energy Storage. 127p. 1982. pap. 29.95x (ISBN 0-89934-164-0, P046). Solar Energy Info.
Falk, S. Uno & Salkind, Alvin J. Alkaline Storage Batteries. LC 77-82980. (Electrochemical Society Ser.). 1969. 91.95x (ISBN 0-471-25362-6, Pub. by Wiley-Interscience). Wiley.
Grevich, J. D. Testing Procedures for Automotive AC & DC Charging Systems. 1972. text ed. 26.90 (ISBN 0-07-024673-4). McGraw.
Hehner, Nels E. Storage Battery Manufacturing Manual. 2nd ed. 1976. 30.00 (ISBN 0-685-65141-X). IBMA Pubns.
Himy, Albert. Silver-Zinc Battery: Phenomena & Design Principles. 1985. 15.00 (ISBN 0-317-28947-0). Vantage.
Linden, D. Handbook of Batteries & Fuel Cells. 1088p. 1983. 78.50 (ISBN 0-07-037874-6). McGraw.
Mantell, Charles L. Batteries & Energy Systems. 2nd ed. (Illus.). 352p. 1983. 36.50 (ISBN 0-07-040031-8). McGraw.
Marsh, Ken, ed. Battery Book One: Lead Acid Traction Batteries. LC 81-65733. (Illus.). 72p. (Orig.). 1981. pap. 7.95 (ISBN 0-939488-00-0). Curtis Instruments.
Safety Recommendations for Lead-Acid Industrial Storage Batteries for Railway & Marine Starting Application. 1984. 5.50 (ISBN 0-318-18014-6, IB 11-1984). Natl Elec Mfrs.
Safety Recommendations for Lead-Acid Industrial Storage Batteries Used for Motive Power Service. 1984. 5.50 (ISBN 0-318-18013-8, IB 10-1984). Natl Elec Mfrs.
Sandia National Labs Staff. Design & Development of a Sealed 100-Ah Nickel-Hydrogen Battery. 77p. Date not set. pap. 9.95 (ISBN 0-317-20246-4, S-010). Solar Energy Info.
Tucker, Allen E., ed. Cylinders & Accumulators, Vol. G. rev. ed. (Fluid Power Standards 1984 Ser.). (Illus.). 368p. 1984. 81.50 (ISBN 0-942220-77-3); Set. write for info. Natl Fluid Power.
Vinal, George W. Storage Batteries: A General Treatise on the Physics & Chemistry of Secondary Batteries & Their Engineering Applications. 4th ed. LC 54-12826. 446p. 1955. 50.95x (ISBN 0-471-90816-9, Pub. by Wiley-Interscience). Wiley.
Waterford, Van. The Complete Battery Book. (Illus.). 352p. (Orig.). 1985. 24.95 (ISBN 0-8306-0757-9, 1757); pap. 16.95 (ISBN 0-8306-1757-4). TAB Bks.
Webster, Edna R. T. A. Willard: Wizard of the Storage Battery. 1976. 8.95 (ISBN 0-686-21901-5); pap. 5.00 (ISBN 0-686-21902-3). Wilmar Pubs.

STORAGE DEVICES, COMPUTER
see Computer Storage Devices

STORAGE ELEMENTS (CALCULATING-MACHINES)
see Magnetic Memory (Calculating-Machines)

STORAGE OF ENERGY
see Energy Storage

STORAGE TUBES
Stanley, William & Dougherty, James. Digital Signal Processing. 2nd ed. 1984. text ed. 32.95 (ISBN 0-8359-1321-X); solutions manual avail. Reston.

STORAGE WAREHOUSES
see Warehouses

BOOKS - SUBJECT INDEX STRAWBERRIES

STORMS
see also Dust Storms; Hail; Hurricanes; Meteorology; Rain and Rainfall; Snow; Thunderstorms; Tornadoes; Typhoons; Winds also names of specific cities or geographic locations, with or without the subdivision Storm
Committee on Atmospheric Sciences, ed. Severe Storms: Predicion, Detection & Warning. LC 77-77588. (Illus.). 1977. pap. text ed. 7.95 (ISBN 0-309-02613-X). Natl Acad Pr.
DeGroot, W., ed. Stormwater Detention Facilities. LC 82-73613. 439p. 1982. pap. 31.00x (ISBN 0-87262-348-3). Am Soc Civil Eng.
Nalivkin, D. V., ed. Hurricanes, Storms & Tornadoes: Geographic Characteristics & Geological Activity. Bhattacharya, B. B., tr. from Rus. 605p. 1983. lib. bdg. 26.50 (ISBN 90-6191-408-6, Pub. by Balkema RSA). IPS.
Present Techniques of Tropical Storm Surge Prediction. (Reports on Marine Science Affairs: No. 13). (Illus.). vii, 874p. 1978. pap. 20.00 (ISBN 92-63-10500-6, W384, WMO). Unipub.
Storm Data for the United States, 1970 to 1974: A Quinquennial Compilation of the U. S. Environmental Data Service's Official Monthly Reports of Storm Activity Logged by the U. S. Weather Bureau. 400p. 1982. 185.00x (ISBN 0-8103-1140-2). Gale.
Storm Data for the United States, 1975 to 1979: A Quinquennial Compilation of the U. S. Environmental Data Service's Official Monthly Reports of Storm Activity Logged by the U. S. Weather Bureau. 400p. 1982. 185.00x (ISBN 0-8103-1139-9). Gale.
Whipple, A. B. Storm. (Planet Earth Ser.). 1982. 14.95 (ISBN 0-8094-4312-0). Time-Life.
--Storm. LC 82-1766. (Planet Earth Ser.). 1982. lib. bdg. 19.94 (ISBN 0-8094-4313-9, Pub. by Time-Life). Silver.
Whipple, William & Randall, Clifford. Stormwater Management in Urbanizing Areas. (Illus.). 240p. 1983. 38.00 (ISBN 0-13-850214-5). P-H.
STORMS, MAGNETIC
see Magnetic Storms
STOVES
see also Heating; Stoves, Wood
Bacon, Richard M. The Forgotten Art of Building & Using a Brick Bake Oven. LC 77-74809. (Forgotten Arts Ser.). (Illus.). 64p. (Orig.). 1977. pap. 4.95 (ISBN 0-911658-76-9). Yankee Bks.
Groft, Tammis K. Cast with Style: Nineteenth Century Cast-Iron Stoves from the Albany Area. rev. ed. (Illus.). 120p. pap. text ed. 11.95 (ISBN 0-939072-03-3). Albany Hist & Art.
Harrington, Geri. Fireplace Stoves, Hearths, & Inserts. LC 80-7587. (Illus.). 192p. 1980. 20.00i (ISBN 0-06-011821-0, HarpT). Har-Row.
Kern, Barbara & Kern, Ken. Ken Kern's Masonry Stove. (Illus.). 1983. 17.95 (ISBN 0-684-17775-7, ScribT). Scribner.
Lyle. The Book of Masonry Stoves: Rediscovering an Old Way of Warming. 192p. 1984. text ed. 34.95 (ISBN 0-471-80867-9). Wiley.
Mercier, Jean. Lexique Anglais-Francais Du Programmateur De Cuisiniere: Fonctionnement et Pieces Composantes. (Eng. & Fr.). 29p. 1973. pap. 1.95 (ISBN 0-686-57045-6, M-6406). French & Eur.
Sabin, A. Ross, ed. Range Service (Gas, Electric, Microwave) (Illus.). 254p. 1980. 20.00 (ISBN 0-938336-06-1). Whirlpool.
Schneider, Jason. Complete Guide to Woodburning Stoves. (Orig.). 1979. pap. 6.95 (ISBN 0-346-12488-3). Cornerstone.
Sunset Editors. Wood Stoves. LC 79-88160. (Illus.). 96p. 1979. pap. 4.95 (ISBN 0-376-01882-8, Sunset Bks). Sunset-Lane.
Using Coal & Wood Stoves Safely. 1974. pap. 2.00 (ISBN 0-685-58194-2, HS-8). Natl Fire Prot.
Wik, Ole. How to Build an Oil Barrel Stove. LC 76-3768. (Illus.). 1976. pap. 1.95 (ISBN 0-88240-077-0). Alaska Northwest.
STOVES, WOOD
Sadler, John M. How to Heat Your Home Without Going Broke: Build Yourself an Amazing Stainless Steel Wood Stove. LC 77-14493. (Illus.). 1977. lib. bdg. 11.00 (ISBN 0-930250-00-1); pap. 5.95 (ISBN 0-930250-01-X); Do-it-yourself bdg. 3.50 (ISBN 0-930250-02-8). J M Sadler.
Self, Charles R. Wood Heating Handbook. 2nd ed. 1983. 16.95 (ISBN 0-8306-0096-5); pap. 9.95 (ISBN 0-8306-1472-9, 1472). TAB Bks.
Stewart, Gordon A. Wood Heat: Peril or Pleasure. LC 82-82869. (Illus.). 176p. 1983. 10.95 (ISBN 0-910937-08-7); pap. 5.95 (ISBN 0-910937-09-5). Laranmark.
Using Coal & Wood Stoves Safely. 1974. pap. 2.00 (ISBN 0-685-58194-2, HS-8). Natl Fire Prot.
Wik, Ole. Wood Stoves: How to Make & Use Them. LC 77-21710. 1977. pap. 5.95 (ISBN 0-88240-083-5). Alaska Northwest.
STOWAGE
see also Ships–Cargo; Trim (Of Ships)
Flere, W. A. Handy Guide to Stowage. 1970. 11.50 (ISBN 0-85288-005-7). Heinman.
Thomas, O. O. Stowage: The Properties & Stowage of Cargoes. rev. ed. (Illus.). 1983. 80.00 (ISBN 0-85174-450-8). Heinman.
Thomas, O. O., et al. Thomas' Stowage: The Properties & Stowage of Cargoes. (Illus.). 370p. 1983. text ed. 65.00x (ISBN 0-85174-450-8, Pub. by Brown Son & Ferguson). Sheridan.
Thomas, R. E. & Thomas, O. O. Stowage: The Properties & Stowage of Cargoes. 1981. 70.00x (ISBN 0-85174-000-6, Pub. by Nautical England). State Mutual Bk.
STRAIN GAGES
Dally, James W. & Riley, William F. Experimental Stress Analysis. 2d ed. LC 77-393. (Illus.). 1977. text ed. 43.00x (ISBN 0-07-015204-7). McGraw.
Hearn, E. J. & Mech, M. I. Strain Gauges. 80p. 1971. 39.00x (ISBN 0-900541-24-5, Pub. by Meadowfield Pr). State Mutual Bk.
Perry, C. C. & Lissner, H. R. Strain Gage Primer. 2nd ed. 1962. 55.95 (ISBN 0-07-049461-4). McGraw.
Window, A. L. & Holister, G. S. Strain Gauge Technology. (Illus.). x, 356p. 1982. 74.00 (ISBN 0-85334-118-4, Pub. by Elsevier Applied Sci England). Elsevier.
STRAINS AND STRESSES
see also Buckling (Mechanics); Deformations (Mechanics); Elasticity; Engineering Design; Girders, Continuous; Graphic Statics; Influence Lines; Materials–Fatigue; Photoelasticity; Plates (Engineering); Residual Stresses; Shells (Engineering); Shock (Mechanics); Sound Pressure; Strain Gages; Strength of Materials; Stress Corrosion; Stress Waves; Structural Design; Structural Dynamics; Thermal Stresses; Torsion
Amadei, B. Rock Anisotropy & the Theory of Stress Measurements. (Lecture Notes in Engineering Ser.: Vol. 2). 478p. 1983. pap. 29.00 (ISBN 0-387-12388-1). Springer-Verlag.
American Society for Testing & Materials. Stress Corrosion Cracking: The Slow Strain-Rate Technique - STP 665. 441p. 1979. 39.75x (ISBN 0-8031-0579-7, 04-665000-27). ASTM.
American Society of Civil Engineers & Yong, R. N., eds. Limit Equilibrium, Plasticity & Generalized Stress-Strain in Geotechnical Engineering. LC 81-69233. 875p. 1981. pap. 55.75x (ISBN 0-87262-282-7). Am Soc Civil Eng.
Argyris, J. H. & Kelsey, S. Energy Theorems & Structural Analysis. 85p. 1960. 22.50x (ISBN 0-306-30664-6, Plenum Pr). Plenum Pub.
Avram, C., et al. Concrete Strength & Strains. (Developments in Civil Engineering Ser.: Vol. 3). 558p. 1982. 100.00 (ISBN 0-444-99733-4). Elsevier.
Budynas, Richard G. Advanced Strength & Applied Stress Analysis. (Illus.). 1977. text ed. 45.00 (ISBN 0-07-008828-4). McGraw.
Collins, J. A. Failure of Materials in Mechanical Design: Analysis, Prediction, Prevention. LC 80-20674. 629p. 1981. 55.95x (ISBN 0-471-05024-5, Pub. by Wiley-Interscience). Wiley.
Conway, J. B. Stress-Rupture Parameters: Origin, Calculation, & Use. 318p. 1969. 80.95 (ISBN 0-677-01860-6). Gordon.
Dally, James W. & Riley, William F. Experimental Stress Analysis. 2d ed. LC 77-393. (Illus.). 1977. text ed. 43.00x (ISBN 0-07-015204-7). McGraw.
D'Isa, Frank A. Mechanics of Metals. 1968. 21.95 (ISBN 0-201-01550-1). Addison-Wesley.
Fenves, Steven J., et al. STRESS: User's Manual. 1964. pap. 16.00x (ISBN 0-262-06029-9). MIT Pr.
Finkel'shtein, B. N. Relaxation Phenomena in Metals & Alloys. LC 62-21590. 244p. 1963. 45.00x (ISBN 0-306-10664-7, Consultants). Plenum Pub.
Full-Scale Load Testing of Structures - STP 702. 214p. 1980. 24.75x (ISBN 0-8031-0368-9, 04-702000-10). ASTM.
Gibbs, H. G. & Richards, T. H., eds. Stress, Vibration & Noise Analysis in Vehicles. (Illus.). 485p. 1975. 68.50 (ISBN 0-85334-642-9, Pub. by Elsevier Applied Sci England). Elsevier.
Griffel, William. Handbook of Formulas for Stress & Strain. LC 66-17539. 1966. 30.00 (ISBN 0-8044-4332-7). Ungar.
Hansen, E. Strain Facies. LC 72-89551. (Minerals, Rocks & Inorganic Materials Ser.: Vol. 2). (Illus.). 1971. 33.00 (ISBN 0-387-05204-6). Springer-Verlag.
Hetenyi, Miklos. Beams on Elastic Foundation: Theory with Applications in the Fields of Civil & Mechanical Engineering. (Illus.). 1946. 20.00x (ISBN 0-472-08445-3). U of Mich Pr.
Heyman, Jacques. Elements of Stress Analysis. LC 81-15495. (Illus.). 140p. 1982. 37.50 (ISBN 0-521-24523-0). Cambridge U Pr.
Holister, G. S. Experimental Stress Analysis. (Cambridge Engineering Pubns.). 1967. 49.50 (ISBN 0-521-05312-9). Cambridge U Pr.
Holister, G. S., ed. Developments in Stress Analysis, Vol. 1. (Illus.). 197p. 1979. 39.00 (ISBN 0-85334-812-X, Pub. by Elsevier Applied Sci England). Elsevier.
International Symposium On Stress Waves In Anelastic Solids - Providence - 1963. Proceedings. Kolsky, H. & Prager, W., eds. (Illus.). 1964. 69.70 (ISBN 0-387-03221-5). Springer-Verlag.
James, P. J., ed. Isostatic Pressing Technology. (Illus.). 251p. 1983. 48.00 (ISBN 0-85334-192-3, I-124-83, Pub. by Elsevier Applied Sci England). Elsevier.
Jones, N. & Wierzbicki, T., eds. Structural Crashworthiness. (Illus.). 320p. 1983. text ed. 89.95 (ISBN 0-408-01308-7). Butterworth.
Kani, Gaspar. Analysis of Multistory Frames. Hyman, Charles J., tr. LC 57-6114. 1967. 8.50 (ISBN 0-8044-4486-2). Ungar.
Kannappan, Sam. Introduction to Pipe Stress Analysis. Date not set. 42.00 (ISBN 0-471-81589-6). Wiley.
Kleinlogel, Adolf. Rigid Frame Formulas. LC 58-6789. 1953. 40.00 (ISBN 0-8044-4551-6). Ungar.
Kleinlogel, Adolf & Haselbach, Arthur. Multibay Frames. LC 63-10863. 1963. 32.50 (ISBN 0-8044-4548-6). Ungar.
Krug, S. & Stein, P. Influence Surfaces of Orthogonal Anisotropic Plates. Juhl, H., tr. (Eng. & Ger., Illus.). 1961. 69.70 (ISBN 0-387-02711-4). Springer-Verlag.
Mathewson, C. H. Critical Shear Stress & Incongruent Shear in Plastic Deformation. (Connecticut Academy of Arts & Sciences Transaction: Vol. 38). 1951. pap. 10.50 (ISBN 0-208-01099-8, Archon). Shoe String.
Mechanical Properties at High Rates of Strain: Oxford 1974. (Institute of Physics Conference Ser.: No. 21). 1974. 65.00 (ISBN 0-9960030-0-2, Pub. by Inst Physics England). Heyden.
Mechanical Properties at High Rates of Strain 1979. (Reports on Progress in Physics Ser.: No. 47). 90.00 (ISBN 0-9960032-7-4, Pub. by Inst Physics England). Heyden.
Meyers, Marc A. & Murr, Lawrence E., eds. Shock Waves & High-Strain-Rate Phenomena in Metals: Concepts & Applications. LC 80-27395. 1116p. 1981. 130.00x (ISBN 0-306-40633-0, Plenum Pr). Plenum Pub.
Morgan, Kenneth S. Calculator Programs for Pipe Stress Engineering. 1985. 37.50 (ISBN 0-471-81982-4). Wiley.
Mura, T. Micromechanics of Defects in Solids. 1982. lib. bdg. 98.00 (ISBN 90-247-2560-7, Pub. by Martinus Nijhoff Netherlands). Kluwer Academic.
Myslivec, A. & Kysela, Z. Bearing Capacity of Building Foundations. (Developments in Geotechnical Engineering Ser.: Vol. 21). 1978. 59.75 (ISBN 0-444-99794-6). Elsevier.
National Symposium Fracture Mechanics. Stress Analysis & Growth of Cracks-STP 513. 307p. 1972. 27.50x (ISBN 0-8031-0362-X, 04-513000-30). ASTM.
Nichols, R. W., ed. Developments in Stress Analysis for Pressurized Components, Vol. 1. (Illus.). 210p. 1977. 52.00 (ISBN 0-85334-724-7, Pub. by Elsevier Applied Sci England). Elsevier.
Pugh, Anthony. Introduction to Tensegrity. LC 75-5951. 150p. 1976. 22.00x (ISBN 0-520-02996-8); pap. 4.95 (ISBN 0-520-03055-9, CAL 325). U of Cal Pr.
Ramsay, John G. Folding & Fracturing of Rocks. (International Ser. in Earth & Planetary Sciences). (Illus.). 1967. text ed. 66.95 (ISBN 0-07-051170-5). McGraw.
Richards, T. H. Energy Methods in Stress Analysis with an Introduction to Finite Element Techniques. LC 79-29647. (Engineering Science Ser.). 410p. 1977. pap. 42.95x (ISBN 0-470-27068-3). Halsted Pr.
Roark, Raymond J. & Young, Warren C. Formulas for Stress & Strain. 5th ed. (Illus.). 512p. 1976. 53.50 (ISBN 0-07-053031-9). McGraw.
Robinson, J. Lister. Mechanics of Materials. LC 68-55336. 345p. 1969. text ed. 19.95 (ISBN 0-471-72810-1, Pub. by Wiley). Krieger.
Sandor, Bela I. Fundamentals of Cyclic Stress & Strain. LC 70-176415. (Illus.). 184p. 1972. text ed. 22.50x (ISBN 0-299-06100-0). U of Wis Pr.
Schneider, R. W. & Rodabaugh, E. C., eds. Stress Indices & Stress Intensification Factors of Pressure Vessel & Piping Components. (PVP Ser.: Vol. 50). 1164p. 1981. 30.00 (ISBN 0-686-34508-8, H00186). ASME.
Sih, G. C., ed. Stress Analysis of Notch Problems. (Mechanics of Fracture Ser.: No. 5). 312p. 1978. 45.00x (ISBN 90-286-0166-X). Sijthoff & Noordhoff.
Stanley, P., ed. Computing Developments in Experimental & Numerical Stress Analysis. (Illus.). x, 239p. 1976. 33.50 (ISBN 0-85334-680-1, Pub. by Elsevier Applied Sci England). Elsevier.
Stress & Deflection Reduction in 2x4 Studs Spaced 24 Inches on Center Resulting from the Addition of Interior & Exterior Surfaces, Vol. 3. (Research Report Ser.). 45p. 1981. pap. 5.50 (ISBN 0-86718-117-6); pap. 4.00 members. Natl Assn Home.
Symposium, Chicago, Illinois, August, 3-6, 1981. Implementation of Computer Procedures & Stress-Strain Laws in Geotechnical Engineering: Proceedings, 2 vols. Desai, C. S. & Saxena, S. K., eds. LC 81-67486. 704p. (Orig.). 1981. pap. 55.00x (ISBN 0-89386-003-4). Acorn NC.
Theocaris, P. S. Moire Fringes in Strain Analysis. 1969. text ed. 37.00 (ISBN 0-08-012974-9); pap. text ed. 15.00 (ISBN 0-08-012973-0). Pergamon.
Thompson, Anthony W., ed. Work Hardening in Tension & Fatigue: Proceedings of a Symposium, Cincinnati, Ohio, Nov. 11, 1975. LC 77-76058. pap. 66.30 (ISBN 0-317-08184-5, 2015014). Bks Demand UMI.
Timoshenko, Stephen P. & Gere, J. Theory of Elastic Stability. 2nd ed. (Engineering Societies Monographs). (Illus.). 1961. text ed. 52.00 (ISBN 0-07-064749-6). McGraw.
Timoshenko, Stephen P. & Goodier, J. N. Theory of Elasticity. 3rd ed. LC 69-13617. (Engineering Societies Monographs Ser). (Illus.). 1969. text ed. 52.00 (ISBN 0-07-064720-8). McGraw.
Timoshenko, Stephen P. & Woinowsky-Krieger, S. Theory of Plates & Shells. 2nd ed. (Engineering Societies Monographs). (Illus.). 1959. text ed. 52.00 (ISBN 0-07-064779-8). McGraw.
Tuma, J. J. & Cheng, F. Y. Schaum's Outline of Dynamic Structural Analysis. (Schaum's Outline Ser.). 240p. 1982. text ed. 9.95 (ISBN 0-07-065437-9). McGraw.
Underwood, et al, eds. Chevron Notched Specimens: Testing & Stress Analysis - STP 855. 360p. 1984. 44.00 (ISBN 0-8031-0401-4, 04-855000-30). ASTM.
Yong, R. N. & Selig, E. T., eds. Application of Plasticity & Generalized Stress-Strain in Geotechnical Engineering. LC 81-71796. 359p. 1982. pap. 27.25x (ISBN 0-87262-294-0). Am Soc Civil Eng.
STRATIGRAPHIC GEOLOGY
see Geology, Stratigraphic
STRATIGRAPHIC PALEONTOLOGY
see Paleontology, Stratigraphic
STRATOSPHERE
Bower, Frank A. & Ward, Richard B., eds. Stratospheric Ozone & Man, Vol. I: Stratospheric Ozone. 232p. 1981. 74.50 (ISBN 0-8493-5753-5). CRC Pr.
--Stratospheric Ozone & Man, Vol. II: Man's Interactions & Concerns. 280p. 1981. 79.50 (ISBN 0-8493-5755-1). CRC Pr.
Chamberlain, Joseph, ed. Chemistry & Physics of the Stratosphere. 171p. 1976. pap. 3.00 (ISBN 0-87590-221-9). Am Geophysical.
Conkin, Barbara M. & Conkin, James E. Stratigraphy: Foundation & Concepts. 1984. 45.00 (ISBN 0-442-21747-1). Van Nos Reinhold.
Cumberland, John H., et al, eds. Economics of Managing Chlorofluorocarbons: Stratospheric Ozone & Climate Issues. LC 82-11279. (Resources for the Future Ser.). 536p. 1982. text ed. 28.00x (ISBN 0-8018-2963-1). Johns Hopkins.
Environmental Studies Board, National Research Council. Causes & Effects of Stratospheric Ozone Reduction: An Update. 339p. 1982. pap. text ed. 13.95 (ISBN 0-309-03248-2). Natl Acad Pr.
Panel on Atmospheric Chemistry, Committee on Impacts of Stratospheric Change, National Research Council. Halocarbons: Effects on Stratospheric Ozone. 352p. 1976. pap. 11.75 (ISBN 0-309-02532-X). Natl Acad Pr.
Papers Presented at the WMO Symposium on the Geophysical Aspects & Consequences of Changes in the Composition of the Stratosphere: Toronto, June 26-30, 1978. xii, 301p. 1977. pap. 30.00 (ISBN 92-63-10511-1, W397, WMO). Unipub.
Whitten, R. C., ed. The Stratospheric Aerosol Layer. (Topics in Current Physics Ser.: Vol. 28). (Illus.). 152p. 1982. 28.00 (ISBN 0-387-11229-4). Springer-Verlag.
STRAW
Jackson, M. G. Treating Straw for Animal Feeding: An Assessment of Its Technical & Economic Feasibility. (Animal Production & Health Papers: No. 10). (Eng., Fr. & Span.). 84p. 1978. pap. 7.50 (ISBN 92-5-100584-2, F1480, FAO). Unipub.
STRAWBERRIES
Maas, John L. Compendium of Strawberry Diseases. (Illus.). 138p. 1984. pap. text ed. 17.00 (ISBN 0-89054-054-3). Am Phytopathol Soc.
Montgomerie, J. G. Red Core Disease of Strawberry. 47p. 1977. 30.00x (ISBN 0-85198-375-8, Pub. by CAB Bks England). State Mutual Bk.

Plakides, Antonios G. Strawberry Diseases. LC 64-21596. (Louisiana State University Studies Biological Science Ser.: No. 5). pap. 51.80 (ISBN 0-317-29858-5, 2019566). Bks Demand UMI.
Ulrich, Albert, et al. Strawberry Deficiency Symptoms: A Visual & Plant Analysis Guide to Fertilization. LC 79-67379. (Illus.). 58p. 1980. pap. text ed. 8.00 (ISBN 0-931876-37-0, 4098). Ag & Nat Res.

STREAKED BASS
see Striped Bass

STREAM FLOW MEASUREMENTS
see Stream Measurements

STREAM GAUGING
see Stream Measurements

STREAM MEASUREMENTS
see also Flow Meters; Water-Power

Coughlin, Robert E., et al. Perception & Use of Streams in Suburban Areas: Effects of Water Quality & of Distance from Residence to Stream. (Discussion Paper Ser.: No. 53). 1972. pap. 4.50 (ISBN 0-686-32220-7). Regional Sci Res Inst.
Fiering, Myron B. Streamflow Synthesis. LC 67-29625. pap. 39.80 (ISBN 0-317-10931-6, 2001560). Bks Demand UMI.
Gabler, Ray. New England White Water River Guide. rev., 2nd ed. (Illus.). 376p. (Orig.). 1981. pap. 8.95 (ISBN 0-910146-33-0). Appalach Mtn.
Hammer, Thomas R. Impact of Urbanization on Peak Streamflow. (Discussion Paper Ser.). 1973. pap. 4.50 (ISBN 0-686-32503-6). Regional Sci Res Inst.
--Stream Channel Enlargement Due to Urbanization. (Discussion Paper Ser.: No. 55). 1972. pap. 4.50 (ISBN 0-686-32222-3). Regional Sci Res Inst.
Herschy, R. W. Streamflow Measurement. (Illus.). 568p. 1985. 97.50 (ISBN 0-85334-327-6, Pub. by Elsevier Applied Sci England). Elsevier.
Manual on Stream Gauging, 2 Vols. (Operational Hydrology Reports: No. 13). 1980. Set. pap. 52.00 (ISBN 92-63-10519-7, W483, WMO). Vol. 1 Fieldwork 308p. Vol. 2 Computation of Discharge, 258p. Unipub.
Parde, Maurice. Beziehungen Zwischen Niederschlag und Abfluss Bei Grossen Sommer Hochwassern. pap. 10.00 (ISBN 0-384-44780-5). Johnson Repr.
Use of Weirs & Flumes in Stream Gauging. (Technical Note Ser.). (Illus.). 57p. (Orig.). 1972. pap. 10.00 (ISBN 0-685-02935-2, W93, WMO). Unipub.

STREAM POLLUTION
see Water-Pollution

STREAM SELF-PURIFICATION
see also Water-Pollution

West, Elizabeth A. Equilibrium of Natural Streams. 205p. 1980. 14.95x (ISBN 0-86094-007-1, Pub. by GEO Abstracts England); pap. 12.30 (ISBN 0-86094-006-3, Pub. by GEO Abstracts England). State Mutual Bk.

STREAMFLOW DATA
see Stream Measurements

STREAMLINING
see Aerodynamics

STREET-CARS
see Electric Railroads-Cars

STREET CLEANING
see also Refuse and Refuse Disposal

APWA Research Foundation. Street Cleaning Practice. 3rd ed. (Illus.). 1978. text ed. 28.00x (ISBN 0-917084-27-6). Am Public Works.

STREET RAILWAY MOTORS
see Electric Railway Motors

STREETS
see also City Traffic; Pavements; Roads

American Society of Civil Engineers, et al. Residential Streets: Objective Principles & Design Considerations. LC 74-19958. 48p. 1974. pap. 6.00 (ISBN 0-87420-559-X, R06); pap. 4.50 members. Natl Assn Home.
Guide to Successful Street Paving. 12p. 1976. pap. 1.40 (ISBN 0-89312-159-2, PA048P). Portland Cement.
An Informational Guide for Roadway Lighting. rev. & updated ed. 1984. pap. 3.00 (ISBN 0-686-32361-0, GL-5). AASHTO.

STRENGTH OF MATERIALS
see also Elasticity; Fracture Mechanics; Graphic Statics; Materials-Creep; Materials-Fatigue; Materials at High Temperatures; Materials at Low Temperatures; Mechanical Wear; Photoelasticity; Residual Stresses; Strains and Stresses; Strengthening Mechanisms in Solids; Structural Design; Testing Machines

Accelerated Strength Testing. 1978. 36.25 (ISBN 0-686-71022-3, SP-56) (ISBN 0-686-71023-1). ACI.
Alexander, J. M. Strength of Materials: Fundamentals, Vol. 1. LC 80-42009. (Mechanical Engineering Ser.). 267p. 1981. 89.95x (ISBN 0-470-27119-1). Halsted Pr.
Black, P. Strength of Materials. 1966. 26.00 (ISBN 0-08-011555-1). Pergamon.
Breneman, John W. Strength of Materials. 3rd ed. 1965. 29.40 (ISBN 0-07-007536-0). McGraw.
Bruch, Charles D. Strength of Materials for Technology. LC 77-27629. 376p. 1978. text ed. 29.95x (ISBN 0-471-11372-7); solutions manual avail. (ISBN 0-471-04513-6). Wiley.
Buckley, D. H. Surface Effects in Adhesion, Friction, Wear & Lubrication. (Tribiology Ser.: Vol. 5). 632p. 1981. 106.50 (ISBN 0-444-41966-7). Elsevier.
Budynas, Richard G. Advanced Strength & Applied Stress Analysis. (Illus.). 1977. text ed. 45.00 (ISBN 0-07-008828-4). McGraw.
Byars, Edward F., et al. Engineering Mechanics of Deformable Bodies. 4th ed. 548p. 1983. text ed. 33.95 scp (ISBN 0-06-041109-0, HarpC); solution manual avail. (ISBN 0-06-361100-7). Har-Row.
Carlsson, J., ed. Mechanical Behaviour of Materials: Proceedings of the Fourth International Conference on Mechanical Behaviour of Materials, Stockholm, Sweden, August 15-19, 1983, 2 Vols, No. IV. (International Series on Strength & Fracture of Materials & Structures). (Illus.). 1175p. 1984. 225.00 (ISBN 0-08-029340-9). Pergamon.
Cernica, John N. Strength of Materials. 2nd ed. LC 76-57840. 1977. text ed. 34.95 (ISBN 0-03-077090-4, HoltC). HR&W.
Chang, Fa-Hwa. Applied Strength of Materials. 459p. 1986. text ed. price not set (ISBN 0-02-322320-0). Macmillan.
Den Hartog, Jacob P. Strength of Materials. 1949. pap. 6.00 (ISBN 0-486-60755-0). Dover.
Eby, Ronald K., ed. Durability of Macromolecular Materials. LC 78-31777. (Symposium Ser.: No. 95). 1979. 49.95 (ISBN 0-8412-0485-3). Am Chemical.
El-Dakhakhni, Wagih M. Strength of Materials. (Arabic.). 600p. 1983. pap. 19.50 (ISBN 0-471-08725-4). Wiley.
Felbeck, David K. & Atkins, Anthony C. Strength & Fracture of Engineering Solids. (Illus.). 608p. 1984. 41.95 (ISBN 0-13-851709-6). P-H.
Fridman, Ya. B., ed. Strength & Deformation in Nonuniform Temperature Fields. LC 63-17641. 169p. 1964. 30.00x (ISBN 0-306-10688-4, Consultants). Plenum Pub.
Gifkins, R. C., ed. Strength of Metals & Alloys (ICSMA 6) Proceedings of the 6th International Conference, Melbourne, Australia, August 16-20, 1982, 3 Vols. LC 82-9851. (International Series on the Strength & Fracture of Materials & Structures). 1200p. 1982. 240.00 (ISBN 0-08-029325-5). Pergamon.
Granet, Irving. Strength of Materials for Engineering Technology. 2nd ed. (Illus.). 448p. 1979. 26.95 (ISBN 0-8359-7074-4); solutions manual avail. (ISBN 0-8359-7075-2). Reston.
Halperin, D. A. Statics & Strength of Materials. 2nd ed. 287p. 1981. 31.95 (ISBN 0-471-05651-0). Wiley.
Halperin, Don A. Statics & Strength of Materials for Technology. 2nd ed. LC 79-26256. 287p. 1981. text ed. 28.95 (ISBN 0-471-06042-9); solutions manual avail. Wiley.
Harris, Charles O. Statics & Strength of Materials. 552p. 1982. 31.95 (ISBN 0-471-08293-7); tchr's ed. avail. (ISBN 0-471-86318-1). Wiley.
--Strength of Materials. 3rd. ed. LC 70-164361. (Illus.). pap. 58.80 (ISBN 0-317-11005-5, 2004580). Bks Demand UMI.
Hearn, E. J. Mechanics of Materials. 730p. 1977. text ed. 89.00 (ISBN 0-08-020618-2); Part 1. pap. text ed. 24.00 (ISBN 0-08-018749-8); Part 2. pap. text ed. 19.75 (ISBN 0-08-020617-4). Pergamon.
Higdon, Archie, et al. Mechanics of Materials: SI Version. 3rd ed. LC 77-7069. 752p. 1978. text ed. 42.95 (ISBN 0-471-02379-5); solutions manual o.p. 10.00 (ISBN 0-471-03683-8). Wiley.
--Mechanics of Materials. 4th ed. LC 84-7583. 744p. 1985. 37.95 (ISBN 0-471-89044-8). Wiley.
Holister, G. S., ed. Developments in Composite Materials, Vol. 2. (Developments Ser.). (Illus.). 207p. 1981. 52.00 (ISBN 0-85334-966-5, Pub. by Elsevier Applied Sci England). Elsevier.
Jackson, John J. & Wirtz, Harold G. Schaum's Outline of Statics & Strength of Materials. (Schaum's Outline Ser.). 416p. 1983. pap. text ed. 9.95 (ISBN 0-07-032121-3). McGraw.
Jensen, A. C. & Chenowith, H. Applied Strength of Materials. 4th ed. 384p. 1982. text ed. 30.40 (ISBN 0-07-032490-5). McGraw.
Jensen, Alfred E. & Chenoweth, Harry H. Statics & Strength of Materials. 3rd ed. LC 75-8820. (Illus.). 608p. 1975. text ed. 35.00 (ISBN 0-07-032472-7). McGraw.
Johnson, W. Impact Strength of Materials. 372p. 1972. text ed. 65.00 (ISBN 0-7131-3266-3). E Arnold.
Juvinall, Robert C. Engineering Considerations of Stress, Strain, & Strength. (Illus.). 1967. text ed. 45.00 (ISBN 0-07-033180-4). McGraw.
Kollbrunner, C. F. & Basler, K. Torsion in Structures: An Engineering Approach. Glauser, E. C., tr. 1969. 28.50 (ISBN 0-387-04582-1). Springer-Verlag.
Kraut, George. Statics & Strengths of Materials. 1984. text ed. 29.95 (ISBN 0-8359-7112-0); instr's manual avail. (ISBN 0-8359-7113-9). Reston.
Lawton, C. W. & Seeley, R. R., eds. Fatigue, Creep, & Pressure Vessels for Elevated Temperature Service. (MCP Ser.: Vol. 17). 206p. 1981. 40.00 (ISBN 0-686-34500-2, H00210). ASME.
Levinson, Irving J. Mechanics of Materials. 2nd ed. 1970. text ed. 29.95 (ISBN 0-13-571380-3). P-H.
--Statics & Strength of Materials. 1970. 29.95 (ISBN 0-13-844506-0). P-H.
Loo, F. T., ed. Failure Prevention & Reliability, 1981. 1981. 40.00 (ISBN 0-686-34485-5, I00142). ASME.
Marcinkowski, M. J. Unified Theory of the Mechanical Behavior of Matter. LC 78-27799. pap. 68.80 (ISBN 0-317-28028-7, 2055722). Bks Demand UMI.
Marschall, Charles W. & Maringer, Robert E. Dimensional Instability-an Introduction. 1977. 44.00 (ISBN 0-08-021305-7). Pergamon.
Martin, J. W. & Hull, R. A. Strong Materials. LC 72-189452. (Wykeham Science Ser.: No. 21). 124p. 1972. 9.95x (ISBN 0-8448-1123-8). Crane Russak Co.
Megson, T. Strength of Materials for Civil Engineers. 1980. 34.50 (ISBN 0-442-30755-1). Van Nos Reinhold.
Mirolyubov, I. N. An Aid to Solving Problems in Strength of Materials. 477p. 1974. 11.00 (ISBN 0-8285-2103-4, Pub. by Mir Pubs USSR). Imported Pubns.
Morrow, Harold W. Statics & Strengths of Materials. (Illus.). 512p. 1981. text ed. 29.95 (ISBN 0-13-844720-9). P-H.
Mott, Robert L. Applied Strength of Materials. (Illus.). 1978. ref. 29.95 (ISBN 0-13-043299-7). P-H.
Nash, William A. Strength of Materials. 2nd ed. (Schaum Outline Ser.). 1972. 9.95 (ISBN 0-07-045894-4). McGraw.
Neathery, Raymond F. Applied Strength of Materials. LC 81-14732. 419p. 1982. 29.95 (ISBN 0-471-07991-X); solutions manual avail. (ISBN 0-471-86323-8). Wiley.
Parker, Harry & Hauf, Harold D. Simplified Mechanics & Strength of Materials. 3rd ed. LC 76-56465. 325p. 1977. 34.95x (ISBN 0-471-66562-2, Pub. by Wiley-Interscience). Wiley.
Peterson, Aldor C. Applied Engineering Mechanics: Strength of Materials. 2nd ed. 300p. 1982. text ed. 40.93 (ISBN 0-205-07222-4, 327222); cancelled (ISBN 0-205-07223-2). Allyn.
Pincus, Alexis G. & Holmes, Thomas R. Annealing & Strengthening in the Glass Industry. LC 77-83834. (Processing in the Glass Industry Ser.). 332p. 1977. 34.95 (ISBN 0-911993-06-1). Ashlee Pub Co.
Polakowski, N. H. & Ripling, E. Strength & Structure of Engineering Materials. 1965. text ed. 37.95 (ISBN 0-13-851790-8). P-H.
Popov, Egor P. Introduction to Mechanics of Solids. 1968. ref. ed. 38.95 (ISBN 0-13-487769-1). P-H.
Popov, Howard P. Mechanics of Materials. 2nd ed. 1976. 38.95 (ISBN 0-13-571356-0). P-H.
Research & Education Association Staff. Problem Solver in Strength of Materials & Mechanics of Solids. rev. ed. LC 80-83305. (Illus.). 1152p. (Orig.). 1984. pap. text ed. 23.85x (ISBN 0-87891-522-2). Res & Educ.
Robinson, J. Lister. Mechanics of Materials. LC 68-55336. 345p. 1969. text ed. 19.95 (ISBN 0-471-72810-1, Pub. by Wiley). Krieger.
Rosenthal, Daniel. Resistance & Deformation of Solid Media. LC 72-10583. 372p. 1974. text ed. 28.00 (ISBN 0-08-017100-1). Pergamon.
Ruiz, C. & Koenigsburger, F. Design for Strength & Production. 280p. 1970. 75.25x (ISBN 0-677-62050-0). Gordon.
Sandor, Bela I. Strength of Materials. (Illus.). 1978. ref. ed. 38.95 (ISBN 0-13-852418-1). P-H.
Simon, Andrew L. & Ross, David A. Principles of Statics & Strength of Materials. 528p. 1983. text ed. write for info. (ISBN 0-697-08604-6); instr's. manual avail. (ISBN 0-697-08605-4). Wm C Brown.
Singh, Surendra. Strength of Materials. 2nd rev. ed. 710p. 1983. 20.00x (ISBN 0-7069-1516-X, Pub. by Vikas India). Advent NY.
Spath, Wilhelm. Impact Testing of Materials. rev. ed. Rosner, M. E., ed. (Illus.). 214p. 1962. 55.75x (ISBN 0-677-00910-0). Gordon.
Stepin, P. Strength of Materials. (Russian Monographs). 376p. 1963. 87.95 (ISBN 0-677-20380-2). Gordon.
Stevens, Karl K. Statics & Strength of Materials. (Illus.). 1979. ref. ed. 38.95 (ISBN 0-13-844688-1). P-H.
Taplin, D. M. Advances in Research on the Strength & Fracture of Materials, 6 Vols. Incl. Vol. 1. An Overview. 100.00 (ISBN 0-08-022136-X); Vol. 2a. Physical Metallurgy of Fracture. 100.00 (ISBN 0-08-022138-6); Vol. 2b. Fatigue. 100.00 (ISBN 0-08-022140-8); Vol. 3a. 100.00 (ISBN 0-08-022142-4); Vol. 3b. Applications & Non-Metals. incl. index 100.00 (ISBN 0-08-022144-0). 1978. 530.00 (ISBN 0-08-022130-0). Pergamon.
Thrower. Technical Statics & Strength of Materials. 2nd ed. 1986. text ed. write for info. Breton Pubs.
Thurlimann, Bruno & Furler, Rene. Strength of Brick Walls Under Enforced End Rotation. (IBA Ser.: No. 89). 14p. 1979. pap. text ed. 4.95x (ISBN 3-7643-1108-8). Birkhauser.
Timoshenko, S. Strength of Materials: Part 1, Elementary Theory & Problems. LC 76-11851. 456p. 1976. Repr. of 1955 ed. lib. bdg. 29.50 (ISBN 0-88275-420-3). Krieger.
--Strength of Materials: Part 2, Advanced Theory & Problems. LC 76-11851. 588p. 1976. Repr. of 1956 ed. lib. bdg. 34.00 (ISBN 0-88275-421-1); 58.00 set (ISBN 0-89874-621-3). Krieger.
Timoshenko, Stephen P. & Goodier, J. N. Theory of Elasticity. 3rd ed. LC 69-13617. (Engineering Societies Monographs Ser). (Illus.). 1969. text ed. 52.00 (ISBN 0-07-064720-8). McGraw.
Ugural, A. C. & Fenster, S. K. Advanced Strength & Applied Elasticity. LC 74-27388. 1975. text ed. 34.25 (ISBN 0-444-00160-3); instr's manual avail. Elsevier.
Volkov, Sergei D. Statistical Strength Theory. (Russian Monographs). (Illus.). 280p. 1962. 60.25x (ISBN 0-677-20350-0). Gordon.
Weiner, Jack. Wet Strength of Paper. 2nd ed. LC 52-26053. (Bibliographic Ser.: No. 168, Supp. 3). 1977. pap. 20.00 (ISBN 0-87010-052-1). Inst Paper Chem.
Willems, Nicholas, et al. Strength of Materials. (Illus.). 576p. 1981. text ed. 39.95 (ISBN 0-07-070297-7). McGraw.
Yamada, Hiroshi. Strength of Biological Materials. LC 75-110279. 308p. 1973. Repr. of 1970 ed. 18.00 (ISBN 0-88275-119-0). Krieger.
Zimmerli, Bruno & Thurlimann, Bruno. Strength Interaction Surfaces for Tall Buildings. (IBA Ser.: No 91). 12p. 1979. pap. text ed. 4.95x (ISBN 0-8176-1124-X). Birkhauser.

STRENGTH OF MATERIALS-TABLES, CALCULATIONS, ETC.

Griffel, William. Handbook of Formulas for Stress & Strain. LC 66-17539. 1966. 30.00 (ISBN 0-8044-4332-7). Ungar.
Roark, Raymond J. & Young, Warren C. Formulas for Stress & Strain. 5th ed. (Illus.). 512p. 1976. 53.50 (ISBN 0-07-053031-9). McGraw.

STRENGTHENING MECHANISMS IN SOLIDS
see also Precipitation Hardening

Ashby, M. F., et al, eds. Dislocation Modeling of Physical Systems: Proceedings of the International Conference, Gainesville, Florida USA, June 22-27, 1980. LC 80-41473. (Illus.). 640p. 1981. 83.00 (ISBN 0-08-026724-6). Pergamon.
Burke, John J., et al, eds. Strengthening Mechanisms: Metals & Ceramics. LC 66-22986. (Sagamore Army Materials Research Conference Ser.: Vol. 12). 630p. 1966. 35.00x (ISBN 0-306-34512-9, Plenum Pr). Plenum Pub.
Case, John & Chilver, A. H. Strength of Materials & Structures: An Introduction to the Mechanics of Solids & Structures. 2nd ed. (Illus.). 1971. pap. text ed. 32.50x (ISBN 0-7131-3244-2). Intl Ideas.
Nabarro, F. R. Dislocations in Solids: Applications & Recent Advances. (Dislocations in Solids Ser.: Vol. 6). 552p. 1984. 94.25 (ISBN 0-444-86490-3, I-004-84, North Holland). Elsevier.
Research & Education Association Staff. Problem Solver in Strength of Materials & Mechanics of Solids. rev. ed. LC 80-83305. (Illus.). 1152p. (Orig.). 1984. pap. text ed. 23.85x (ISBN 0-87891-522-2). Res & Educ.
Stephens, R. C. Strength of Materials: Theory & Examples. (Illus.). 1970. pap. text ed. 23.50x (ISBN 0-7131-3211-6). Intl Ideas.
Yokobori, T. Interdisciplinary Approach to Fractures & Strength of Solids. 328p. 1968. 87.95 (ISBN 0-677-61320-2). Gordon.

STRESS (COMPUTER PROGRAM LANGUAGE)

Microcomp, Ltd. Microcomputer Software for Civil, Structural & Design Engineers: FE-STATIC-CM Manual & Disk. 1984. ring binder, incl. disk 450.00x (ISBN 0-87201-533-5). Gulf Pub.
--Microcomputer Software for Civil, Structural & Design Engineers: STRESS-CM Manual & Disk. 1984. ring binder, incl. disk 1450.00x (ISBN 0-87201-531-9). Gulf Pub.

STRESS CORROSION
see also subdivision Corrosion under names of particular metals
American Society for Testing & Materials. Stress Corrosion Cracking: The Slow Strain-Rate Technique - STP 665. 441p. 1979. 39.75x (ISBN 0-8031-0579-7, 04-665000-27). ASTM.
American Society for Testing & Materials Staff. Stress Corrosion Testing. LC 67-20038. (American Society for Testing & Materials Ser.: Special Technical Publication, No. 425). pap. 97.00 (ISBN 0-317-11257-0, 2001144). Bks Demand UMI.
Arup, H. & Parkins, R. N. Stress Corrosion Research, No. 30. (NATO Advanced Study Institute Ser.). 279p. 1979. 30.00x (ISBN 90-286-0647-5). Sijthoff & Noordhoff.
Holister, G. S. Experimental Stress Analysis: Principles & Methods. LC 67-10159. (Cambridge Engineering Ser.). pap. 83.30 (ISBN 0-317-27993-9, 2025587). Bks Demand UMI.
Parkins, R. N., ed. Electrochemical Test Methods for Stress Corrosion Cracking: Selected Papers from the Conference on Electrochemical Test Methods for Stress Corrosion Cracking, Firminy, France, Sept. 1980. (Illus.). 160p. 1981. 18.75 (ISBN 0-08-026140-X). Pergamon.
Stanley, P. Non-Linear Problems in Stress Analysis. (Illus.). 472p. 1978. 100.00 (ISBN 0-85334-780-8, Pub. by Elsevier Applied Sci England). Elsevier.
Stress Corrosion - New Approaches, STP 610. 429p. 1976. 43.00 (ISBN 0-8031-0580-0, 04-610000-27). ASTM.
VDE, ed. International Conference on Experimental Stress Analysis VDI 313, 6th: Proceedings. 1978. 200.00 (ISBN 0-686-40552-8, 99610741XS, Pub. by VDI W Germany). Wiley.

STRESS RELAXATION
see also Materials–Creep
Day, D. E. Relaxation Processes in Glasses: Special Journal Issue. 1974. Repr. 57.50 (ISBN 0-444-10613-8, North-Holland). Elsevier.
Knibbe, D. E. Diffusion-Controlled Stress Relaxation of Swollen Rubber-Like Networks. 60p. 1968. 24.25 (ISBN 0-677-61185-4). Gordon.
Stress Relaxation Testing - STP 676. 224p. 1979. 23.75x (ISBN 0-8031-0581-9, 04-676000-23). ASTM.

STRESS WAVES
see also Shock Waves; Strains and Stresses
International Symposium On Stress Waves In Anelastic Solids - Providence - 1963. Proceedings. Kolsky, H. & Prager, W., eds. (Illus.). 1964. 69.70 (ISBN 0-387-03221-5). Springer-Verlag.
Kolsky, H. Stress Waves in Solids. 2nd ed. (Illus.). 1963. pap. text ed. 6.95 (ISBN 0-486-61098-5). Dover.
Nowacki, Wojoiech. Stress Waves in Non-Elastic Solids. 1978. text ed. 48.00 (ISBN 0-08-021294-8). Pergamon.
Wasley, Richard J. Stress Wave Propagation in Solids. (Monographs & Textbooks in Material Science: Vol. 7). 328p. 1973. 65.00 (ISBN 0-8247-6039-5). Dekker.

STRESSES
see Strains and Stresses

STRIDULATION
see Sound Production by Animals

STRIP CONDUCTORS
see Microwave Wiring

STRIP MINING
Board on Mineral & Energy Resources. Surface Mining of Non-Coal Minerals. LC 79-91887. xxiii, 339p. 1979. pap. 11.95 (ISBN 0-309-02942-2). Natl Acad Pr.
Brawner, C. O., ed. Stability in Surface Mining, Vol. 3. LC 81-70690. 872p. 1982. 39.00x (ISBN 0-89520-292-1). Soc Mining Eng.
Crawford, John T., III & Hustrulid, William A., eds. Open Pit Mine Planning & Design. LC 79-52269. (Illus.). 367p. 1979. text ed. 30.00x (ISBN 0-89520-253-0). Soc Mining Eng.
DeVore, R. William & Graves, Donald H. Nineteen Eighty-Five Symposium on Surface Mining, Hydrology, Sedimentology & Reclamation: Proceedings. LC 83-60966. (Illus.). 600p. (Orig.). 1985. text ed. 45.00 (ISBN 0-89779-064-2, UKY BU139). OES Pubns.
DeVore, R. William & Graves, Donald H., eds. Nineteen Eighty-Four Symposium on Surface Mining, Hydrology, Sedimentology & Reclamation: Proceedings. LC 83-60966. (Illus.). 492p. (Orig.). 1984. pap. 45.00 (ISBN 0-89779-062-6, UKY BU136). OES Pubns.
--Proceedings, Symposium on Surface Mining, Hydrology, Sedimentology, & Reclamation, 1982. LC 82-51182. (Illus.). 728p. (Orig.). 1982. pap. 45.00 (ISBN 0-89779-054-5, UKY BU129). OES Pubns.
De Vore, R. William & Graves, Donald H., eds. Proceedings, 1983 Symposium on Surface Mining, Hydrology, Sedimentology & Reclamation. LC 83-60966. (Illus.). 554p. (Orig.). 1983. pap. 45.00 (ISBN 0-89779-058-8, UKY BU 133). OES Pubns.
Geotechnical Practice for Stability in Open Pit Mining. LC 72-86923. 1971. 20.50x (ISBN 0-89520-013-9). Soc Mining Eng.
Hutnik, Russell & Davis, Grant, eds. Ecology & Reclamation of Devastated Land, 2 Vols. LC 76-122849. (Illus.). 1070p. 1973. Vol. 1, 552p. 98.25x (ISBN 0-677-15580-8); Vol. 2, 518p. 98.25x (ISBN 0-677-15590-5); Set. 175.75x (ISBN 0-677-15600-6). Gordon.
International Surface Mining Conference, 2d, Minneapolis, 1968. Case Studies of Surface Mining: Proceedings. Hartman, Howard L., ed. LC 70-89678. 1969. pap. 82.50 (ISBN 0-317-10744-5, 2004547). Bks Demand UMI.
Landy, Marc Karnis. The Politics of Environmental Reform: Controlling Kentucky Strip Mining. LC 76-15907. (Resources for the Future Working Papers Ser.). 416p. 1976. pap. 13.00x (ISBN 0-8018-1888-5). Johns Hopkins.
Martin, James W. & Martin, Thomas J. Surface Mining Equipment. LC 82-81951. (Illus.). 450p. 1982. 37.95 (ISBN 0-9609060-0-2). Martin Consult.
Munn, Robert F. Strip Mining: An Annotated Bibliography. LC 72-96636. 110p. 1973. 4.00 (ISBN 0-937058-09-2). West Va U Pr.
National Research Council Commission on Natural Resources. Surface Mining: Soil, Coal, & Society. 1981. pap. 11.50 (ISBN 0-309-03140-0). Natl Acad Pr.
Sendlein, L. V. & Yazicigil, H., eds. Surface Mining Environmental Monitoring & Reclamation Handbook. 750p. 1983. 89.75 (ISBN 0-444-00791-1, Excerpta Medica). Elsevier.
Stability in Open Pit Mining. LC 75-157732. 1971. 22.00x (ISBN 0-89520-009-0). Soc Mining Eng.
Strip-Mineable Coals Guidebook. LC 80-81269. 1980. 103.00 (ISBN 0-942218-08-6). Minobras.
Surface Mining. LC 68-24169. 1968. 30.00x (ISBN 0-89520-002-3). Soc Mining Eng.
Surface Mining & Quarrying. 449p. (Orig.). 1983. pap. text ed. 69.95x (ISBN 0-900488-66-2). Imm North Am.
Surface Mining of Non-Coal Minerals. Incl. Appendix I: Sand & Gravel Mining, & Quarrying & Blasting for Crushed Stone & Other Construction Minerals. 7.95 (ISBN 0-309-03020-X); Appendix II: Mining & Processing of Oil Shale & Tar Sands. 8.75 (ISBN 0-309-03037-4). 1980. Natl Acad Pr.
Thames, John, ed. Reclamation & Use of Disturbed Land in the Southwest. LC 76-17133. Repr. of 1977 ed. 71.50 (ISBN 0-8357-9623-X, 2055250). Bks Demand UMI.

STRIPED BASS
Boyle, Robert H. & Ciampi, Elgin. Bass. (Illus.). 144p. 1980. 27.50 (ISBN 0-393-01379-0). Norton.
Woolner, Frank & Lyman, Hal. Striped Bass Fishing. LC 82-20300. 192p. 1983. 18.95 (ISBN 0-8329-0279-9, Pub. by Winchester Pr); pap. 12.95 (ISBN 0-8329-0281-0). New Century.

STRONGLY INTERACTING PARTICLES
see Hadrons

STRONTIUM
Skoryna, Stanley C., ed. Handbook of Stable Strontium. LC 80-16090. 660p. 1981. 89.50x (ISBN 0-306-40417-6). Plenum Pub.

STRONTIUM–ISOTOPES
Faure, G. & Powell, J. L. Strontium Isotope Geology. LC 72-75720. (Minerals, Rocks & Inorganic Materials Ser.: Vol. 5). (Illus.). 200p. 1972. 22.00 (ISBN 0-387-05784-6). Springer-Verlag.

STRUCTURAL ALUMINUM
see Aluminum, Structural

STRUCTURAL ANALYSIS (MATHEMATICS)
see Lattice Theory

STRUCTURAL DESIGN
see also Building; Strains and Stresses; Strength of Materials; Structural Frames;
also names of specific structures, with or without the subdivision Design, or Design and Construction, e.g. Bridges; Factories–Design and Construction
Ambrose, James. Simplified Design of Building Structures. LC 79-413. 268p. 1979. 34.95 (ISBN 0-471-04721-X, Pub. by Wiley-Interscience). Wiley.
Atrek, E., et al. Optimum Structural Design: New Concepts & Software Systems. Gallagher, R. H. & Ragsdell, K. M., eds. (Numerical Methods in Engineering Ser.). 727p. 1984. text ed. 100.00x (ISBN 0-471-90291-8, 1405, Pub. by Wiley-Interscience). Wiley.
Beckett, Derrick & Marsh, Paul. Introduction to Structural Design: Timber. (Illus.). 1974. 42.50x (ISBN 0-903384-02-7). Intl Ideas.
Benjamin, B. S. Structural Design with Plastics. 2nd ed. 416p. 1981. 34.50 (ISBN 0-442-20167-2). Van Nos Reinhold.
Boswell, L. F., ed. Platform Superstructures: Design & Construction. (Illus.). 300p. 1984. text ed. 65.00x (ISBN 0-246-12524-1, Pub. by Granada England). Sheridan.
Brousse, P., ed. Structural Optimization. (CISM-International Center for Mechanical Sciences: Vol. 237). 1976. pap. 23.10 (ISBN 0-387-81376-4). Springer-Verlag.
Burke, J. J. & Weiss, V., eds. Application of Fracture Mechanics to Design. LC 78-14819. (Sagamore Army Materials Research Conference Proceedings Ser.: Vol. 22). 347p. 1978. 55.00x (ISBN 0-306-40040-5, Plenum Pr). Plenum Pub.
Cowan, Henry J. Structural System. (Illus.). 356p. 1981. pap. 16.95 (ISBN 0-442-21713-7). Van Nos Reinhold.
Currie, B. & Sharpe, R. A. Structural Detailing. (Illus.). 160p. pap. text ed. 18.50x (ISBN 0-7121-1985-X). Trans-Atlantic.
Davies, J. M. Manual of Stressed Skin Diaphram Design. 441p. 1982. 82.50 (ISBN 0-471-87485-X). Wiley.
Fraser, D. J. Conceptual Design & Preliminary Analysis of Structures. LC 81-760. 320p. 1981. text ed. 34.95 (ISBN 0-273-01645-8). Pitman Pub MA.
Gallagher, R. H. Optimum Structural Design: Theory & Applications. LC 72-8600. (Numerical Methods in Engineering Ser.). 358p. 1973. 69.95x (ISBN 0-471-29050-5, Pub. by Wiley-Interscience). Wiley.
Gaythwaite, John W. The Marine Environment & Structural Design. 236p. 1981. 26.50 (ISBN 0-442-24834-2). Van Nos Reinhold.
Hall, Arthur S. & Woodhead, Ronald W. Frame Analysis. 2nd ed. LC 78-27890. 384p. 1980. Repr. of 1967 ed. lib. bdg. 21.50 (ISBN 0-88275-858-6). Krieger.
Harris, Charles O. Elementary Structural Design. LC 51-649. (Illus.). pap. 42.80 (ISBN 0-317-10792-5, 2010570). Bks Demand UMI.
Hassoun, M. Nadim. Design of Reinforced Concrete Structures. 1985. text ed. write for info. (ISBN 0-534-03759-3, 21R2400, Pub. by PWS Engineering). PWS Pubs.
Haug, Edward J., et al. Design Sensitivity Analysis of Structural Systems. (Mathematics in Science & Engineering Ser.). Date not set. price not set (ISBN 0-12-332920-5). Acad Pr.
Jones, N., ed. Structural Crashworthiness: Proceedings of the Structural Crashworthiness Conference, Liverpool University, 14-16 September 1983. 100p. 1983. pap. 42.00 (ISBN 0-08-031136-9). Pergamon.
Kirsch, Uri. Optimum Structural Design. (Illus.). 448p. 1981. text ed. 45.00 (ISBN 0-07-034844-8). McGraw.
Kloss, Hans. Application of Structural Steel Design. LC 77-18605. (Illus.). 1980. 16.00 (ISBN 0-8044-4554-0). Ungar.
Lenoe, Edward M., et al, eds. Fibrous Composites in Structural Design. LC 79-28668. 888p. 1980. 110.00x (ISBN 0-306-40354-4, Plenum Pr). Plenum Pub.
Makowski, Z. S., ed. Analysis, Design & Construction of Braced Domes. (Illus.). 750p. 1984. 89.50 (ISBN 0-89397-191-X). Nichols Pub.
Maxwell-Cook, John C. Fundamental Structural Diagrams. (Viewpoint Publication Ser.). (Illus.). 1978. text ed. 26.50x (ISBN 0-7210-1073-3). Scholium Intl.
Melaragno, Michele. Simplified Truss Design. LC 84-23384. 416p. 1985. Repr. of 1981 ed. lib. bdg. write for info. (ISBN 0-89874-820-8). Krieger.
Morris, O. E. Handbook of Structural Design. LC 62-10728. 822p. 1963. 45.00 (ISBN 0-442-12104-0, Pub. by Van Nos Reinhold). Krieger.
Newmark, N. M. & Rosenblueth, E. Fundamentals of Earthquake Engineering. (Civil Engineering & Engineering Mechanics Ser.). (Illus.). 1972. ref. ed. 50.00 (ISBN 0-13-336206-X). P-H.
Page, J. K. Application of Building Climatology to the Problems of Housing & Building for Human Settlements. (Technical Note Ser.: No. 150). (Illus.). 64p. (Orig.). 1976. pap. 16.00 (ISBN 0-685-74378-0, W200, WMO). Unipub.
Parker, Harry & Hauf, Harold D. Simplified Design of Structural Wood. 3rd ed. LC 78-9888. 269p. 1979. 29.95x (ISBN 0-471-66630-0, Pub. by Wiley-Interscience). Wiley.
Polak, Peter. Designing for Strength. (Illus.). 315p. 1983. 49.50x (ISBN 0-333-32674-1); pap. 24.95x (ISBN 0-333-32676-8). Scholium Intl.
Rhodes & Walker, eds. Development of Thin-Walled Structures, Vol. 2. 1984. 55.50 (ISBN 0-85334-247-4, Pub. by Elsevier Applied Sci England). Elsevier.
Rice, Paul F. & Hoffman, Edward S. Structural Design Guide to AISC Specifications for Buildings. LC 75-40491. (Illus.). pap. 92.00 (ISBN 0-317-11089-6, 2007877). Bks Demand UMI.
Structural Design of Nuclear Plant Facilities, 3 vols. 2118p. 1975. pap. 73.00x (ISBN 0-87262-172-3). Am Soc Civil Eng.
Structural Design of Nuclear Plant Facilities, 3 vols. 1263p. 1973. pap. 52.00x (ISBN 0-87262-155-3). Am Soc Civil Eng.
Structural Response to Explosion-Induced Ground Motions. 148p. 1975. pap. text ed. 8.00 (ISBN 0-87262-150-2). Am Soc Civil Eng.
Study of Damage to a Residential Structure from Blast Vibrations. 71p. 1974. pap. 4.50x (ISBN 0-87262-074-3). Am Soc Civil Eng.
Survey of Current Structural Research. (Manual & Report on Engineering Practice Ser.: No. 51). 335p. 1970. pap. 29.75x (ISBN 0-87262-225-8). Am Soc Civil Eng.
Symposium Warsaw, Aug. 21-24, 1973. Optimization in Structural Design. Sawczuk, A. & Mroz, Z., eds. (International Union of Theoretical & Applied Mechanics). (Illus.). 600p. 1975. 115.70 (ISBN 0-387-07044-3). Springer-Verlag.

STRUCTURAL DRAWING
see also Engineering Drawings
Edwards, C. W. Overlay Drafting Systems. 192p. 34.95 (ISBN 0-07-019047-X). McGraw.
Goetsch, David L. Drafting & Drawing for Structural Systems. 368p. 1982. 21.95 (ISBN 0-442-22996-8); pap. 7.95 (ISBN 0-442-22996-8). Van Nos Reinhold.
Newman, Morton. Standard Structural Details for Building Construction. 1967. 55.50 (ISBN 0-07-046345-X). McGraw.
Weaver, Gerald L. Structural Detailing for Technicians. (Illus.). 256p. 1974. pap. 29.20 (ISBN 0-07-068712-9). McGraw.
Weaver, Rip. Structural Drafting. LC 76-15454. (Illus.). 200p. 1977. 16.95x (ISBN 0-87201-810-5); wkbk. 86p. 1980. 7.95X (ISBN 0-87201-389-8). Gulf Pub.

STRUCTURAL DYNAMICS
see also Earthquakes and Building; Wind Pressure
Au-Yang, M. K. & Moody, F. J., eds. Interactive-Fluid-Structural Dynamic Problems in Power Engineering. (PVP Ser.: vol. 46). 177p. 1981. 30.00 (ISBN 0-686-34516-9, H00182). ASME.
Beards, C. F. Structural Vibration Analysis: Modelling, Analysis & Damping of Vibrating Structures. LC 82-25482. 153p. 1983. 44.95x (ISBN 0-470-27422-0). Halsted Pr.
--Vibration Analysis & Control System Dynamic. LC 81-6646. (Ser. in Engineering Science: Civil Engineering). 169p. 1981. 54.95x (ISBN 0-470-27255-4). Halsted Pr.
Biggs, John M. Introduction to Structural Dynamics. 1964. text ed. 45.00 (ISBN 0-07-005255-7). McGraw.
Boswell, Laurence F. Dynamics of Structural Systems. 200p. 1984. 40.00x (ISBN 0-246-11269-7, Pub. by Granada England). Sheridan.
Chopra, Anil K. Dynamics of Structures: A Primer. 120p. 1982. 10.00 (ISBN 0-9605004-4-8). Earthquake Eng.
Clough, R. & Penzien, J. Dynamics of Structures. (Illus.). 672p. 1975. text ed. 48.00 (ISBN 0-07-011392-0). McGraw.
Craig, Roy R. Structural Dynamics: An Introduction to Computer Methods. LC 80-39798. 527p. 1981. text ed. 46.50 (ISBN 0-471-04499-7). Wiley.
DeCampoli, Giuseppe. The Statics of Structural Components: Understanding the Basics of Structural Design. LC 82-20122. 296p. 1983. 29.95 (ISBN 0-471-87169-9, Pub. by Wiley-Interscience). Wiley.
Donea, J. M. Advanced Structural Dynamics. (Illus.). 470p. 1980. 72.25 (ISBN 0-85334-859-6, Pub. by Elsevier Applied Sci England). Elsevier.
Eaton, K. J. & Eaton, K. J., eds. Proceedings of International Conference on Wind Effects on Buildings & Structures: Heathrow Nineteen Seventy-Five. LC 75-2730. 650p. 1976. 125.00 (ISBN 0-521-20801-7). Cambridge U Pr.
Garas, G. S. & Armer, F. K. Design for Dynamic Loading: The Use of Model Analysis. LC 82-7978. (Illus.). 382p. 1982. text ed. 57.00x (ISBN 0-86095-706-3). Longman.
Herrmann, G. & Perrone, N., eds. The Dynamic Response of Structures. 1973. 61.00 (ISBN 0-08-016850-7). Pergamon.
Heymann, M. Structure & Realization Problems in the Theory of Dynamical Systems. (International Centre for Mechanical Sciences: No. 204). 1976. soft cover 12.00 (ISBN 0-387-81348-9). Springer-Verlag.
Hurty, Walter C. & Rubinstein, M. F. Dynamics of Structures. (Illus.). 1964. 41.95 (ISBN 0-13-222075-X). P-H.
International Research Seminar on Wind Effects on Buildings & Structures. Wind Effects on Buildings & Structures: Proceedings of the International Research Seminar, Ottawa, Canada, 11-15, September, 1967, 2 vols. LC 76-358270. Vol. 1. pap. 160.00 (ISBN 0-317-10749-6, 2019449); Vol. 2. pap. 117.30 (ISBN 0-317-10750-X). Bks Demand UMI.

Kolousek, V., et al. Wind Effects on Civil Engineering Structures. (Studies in Wind Engineering & Industrial Aerodynamics: Vol. 2). 1984. 125.00 (ISBN 0-444-99636-2). Elsevier.
Lin, Y. K. Probabilistic Theory of Structural Dynamics. LC 75-42154. 380p. 1976. Repr. of 1967 ed. 24.00 (ISBN 0-88275-377-0). Krieger.
Meirovitch, Leonard. Computational Methods in Structural Dynamics. (Mechanics: Dynamical Systems Ser.: No. 4). 450p. 1980. 35.00x (ISBN 90-286-0580-0). Sijthoff & Noordhoff.
Newmark, N. M. & Rosenblueth, E. Fundamentals of Earthquake Engineering. (Civil Engineering & Engineering Mechanics Ser.). (Illus.). 1972. ref. ed. 50.00 (ISBN 0-13-336206-X). P-H.
Paz, Mario. Structural Dynamics. 2nd ed. 1984. 42.95 (ISBN 0-442-27535-8). Van Nos Reinhold.
Raczkowski, George. Principles of Machine Dynamics. LC 78-72995. 104p. (Orig.). 1979. pap. 14.95x (ISBN 0-87201-440-1). Gulf Pub.
Smith, George V., ed. Material-Environment Interactions in Structural & Pressure Containment Devices. (MPC: No. 15). 160p. 1980. 30.00 (ISBN 0-686-69854-1, G00188). ASME.
Srinivasan, A. V., ed. Structural Dynamic Aspects of Bladed Disk Assemblies: Presented at the Winter Annual Meeting of ASME, NY Dec. 5-10, 1976 (Sponsored by Structures & Materials Comm., Aerospace Div., Structures & Dynamics Comm., Gas Turbine Division) LC 76-28856. pap. 30.00 (ISBN 0-317-11231-7, 2016850). Bks Demand UMI.
Structures, Structural Dynamics & Materials Conference: Proceedings, 25th, Palm Springs CA, 1984, 2 vols. (Illus.). 1188p. 1984. 125.00 (ISBN 0-317-36862-1, CP844 & 845); members 100.00 (ISBN 0-317-36863-X). AIAA.
Twenty-Fifth Structures, Structural Dynamics & Materials, Parts I & II. 125.00 (ISBN 0-317-06648-X). AIAA.
Twenty-Fourth Structures, Structural Dynamics & Materials, Parts I & II. 125.00 (ISBN 0-317-06653-6). AIAA.
Twenty-Third Structures, Structural Dynamics & Materials, Parts I & II. 125.00 (ISBN 0-317-06662-5). AIAA.
Zukas, Jonas A., et al. Impact Dynamics. LC 81-11683. 452p. 1982. 57.95x (ISBN 0-471-08677-0, Pub. by Wiley-Interscience). Wiley.

STRUCTURAL ENGINEERING

see also Air-Supported Structures; Foundations; Hydraulic Engineering; Soil Mechanics; Structural Frames; Structures, Theory Of;
also specific kinds of structures, e.g. Bridges, Buildings; specific structural forms, e.g. Girders; specific systems of construction, e.g. Buildings, Iron and Steel

Adams, R. D. & Wake, W. C. Structural Adhesive Joints in Engineering. 320p. 1984. 52.50 (ISBN 0-85334-263-6, I-166-84, Pub. by Elsevier Applied Sci England). Elsevier.
Ambrose, James & Vergun, Dimitry. Simplified Building Design for Wind & Earthquake Forces. LC 79-26660. 142p. 1980. 37.50x (ISBN 0-471-05013-X, Pub. by Wiley-Interscience). Wiley.
American Society for Testing & Materials. Structural Fatigue in Aircraft. LC 66-28344. (American Society for Testing & Materials. Special Technical Publication Ser.: No. 404). pap. 51.80 (ISBN 0-317-09263-4, 2001130). Bks Demand UMI.
American Society of Civil Engineers, compiled By. Current Research on Tall Buildings. 140p. 1972. pap. 5.50 (ISBN 0-87262-039-5). Am Soc Civil Eng.
--The Current State of Knowledge of Lifeline Earthquake Engineering. 486p. 1977. pap. 23.00x (ISBN 0-87262-086-7). Am Soc Civil Eng.
--Design of Steel Transmission Pole Structures. 82p. 1978. pap. 6.00x (ISBN 0-87262-139-1). Am Soc Civil Eng.
--Design of Structures to Resist Nuclear Weapons Effects. (Manual & Report on Engineering Practice Ser.: No. 42). 172p. 1961. pap. 8.00x (ISBN 0-87262-218-5). Am Soc Civil Eng.
American Society of Civil Engineers & Steyert, Richard D., eds. The Economics of High-Rise Apartment Buildings of Alternate Design Configuration. 187p. 1972. pap. 6.00x (ISBN 0-87262-038-7). Am Soc Civil Eng.
American Society of Civil Engineers, compiled by. Guide to Investigation of Structural Failures. 84p. 1979. pap. 6.50x (ISBN 0-87262-184-7). Am Soc Civil Eng.
--International Seminar on Probabilistic & Extreme Load Design of Nuclear Plant Facilities. 454p. 1979. pap. 27.00x (ISBN 0-87262-146-4). Am Soc Civil Eng.
--Mathematical Model of Aggregate Plant Production. 115p. 1974. pap. 6.50x (ISBN 0-87262-071-9). Am Soc Civil Eng.
American Society of Civil Engineers & Shinozuka, M., eds. Probabilistic Methods in Structural Engineering. LC 81-69228. 415p. 1981. pap. 30.00x (ISBN 0-87262-286-X). Am Soc Civil Eng.
American Society of Civil Engineers, compiled by. Quality System in Construction. 210p. 1974. pap. 11.00x (ISBN 0-87262-073-5). Am Soc Civil Eng.
American Society of Civil Engineers. Structural Failures: Modes, Causes, Responsibilities. (Illus.). pap. 27.80 (ISBN 0-317-08323-6, 2019539). Bks Demand UMI.
Apfelbaum, H. Jack & Ottesen, Walter O. Basic Engineering Sciences & Structural Engineering for Engineer-in-Training Examinations. Hollander, Lawrence J., ed. (Professional Engineering Examinations Ser.). (Illus.). 1970. 23.95 (ISBN 0-8104-5712-1). Hayden.
Arya, Suresh C., et al. Design of Structures & Foundations for Vibrating Machines. LC 78-56171. 190p. 1979. 37.95x (ISBN 0-87201-294-8). Gulf Pub.
Augusti, G. & Barath, A. Probabilistic Methods in Structural Engineering. (Illus.). 636p. 1984. 90.00 (ISBN 0-412-22230-2, NO. 6823, Pub. by Chapman & Hall). Methuen Inc.
Axelrad, E. L. & Emmerling, F. A., eds. Flexible Shells: Theory & Applications. (Illus.). 290p. 1984. 23.00 (ISBN 0-387-13526-X). Springer-Verlag.
Bares, R. A., ed. Plastics in Material & Structural Engineering. (Illus.). 962p. 1982. 164.00 (ISBN 0-686-48179-8, 0706). T-C Pubns CA.
Biggs, John M. Introduction to Structural Engineering: Analysis & Design. (Illus.). 304p. 1986. text ed. 38.95 (ISBN 0-13-501008-X). P-H.
Billington, David. The Tower & the Bridge: The New Art of Structural Engineering. LC 83-70758. (Illus.). 306p. 1983. 24.95 (ISBN 0-465-08677-2). Basic.
Billington, David P. The Tower & the Bridge: The New Art of Structural Engineering. (Illus.). 328p. 1985. pap. 12.95 (ISBN 0-691-02393-X). Princeton U Pr.
Billout, Guy. Stone & Steel: A Look at Engineering. (Illus.). 1980. 8.95x (ISBN 0-13-846873-7). P-H.
Boswell, Laurence F. Dynamics of Structural Systems. 200p. 1984. 40.00x (ISBN 0-246-11269-7, Pub. by Granada England). Sheridan.
Brebbia, C. A., et al. Vibrations of Engineering Structures. (Lecture Notes in Engineering Ser.: Vol. 10). 300p. 1985. pap. 21.00 (ISBN 0-387-13959-1). Springer-Verlag.
Breyer, Donald E. & Ank, John A. Design of Wood Structures. (Illus.). 1980. 47.95 (ISBN 0-07-007671-5). McGraw.
Buchholdt, H. A. Introduction to Cable Structures. 250p. Date not set. price not set (ISBN 0-521-30263-3). Cambridge U Pr.
Buckle, Ian. W. Morgan's the Elements of Structures. 2nd ed. 252p. 1977. pap. text ed. 24.95 (ISBN 0-273-01079-4). Pitman Pub MA.
Celorio, Cesar A. Mathematics Applied to Structural Engineering: Part One, Design for Lateral Forces. 1978. pap. 6.50 (ISBN 0-918168-03-1). C A Celorio.
Charlton, T. M. A History of Theory of Structures in the Nineteenth Century. LC 81-15515. (Illus.). 240p. 1982. 47.50 (ISBN 0-521-23419-0). Cambridge U Pr.
Chen, W. F. & Han, D. J. Tubular Members in Offshore Structures. (Surveys in Structural Engineering & Structural Mechanics Ser.). 1985. text ed. 34.95 (ISBN 0-273-08581-6). Pitman Pub MA.
Civil-Structural Inspection, Course 29. (Illus.). 260p. 1979. spiral bdg. 41.00x (ISBN 0-87683-115-3). G P Courseware.
Cook, Robert D. Concepts & Applications of Finite Element Analysis. 2nd ed. LC 80-26255. 537p. 1981. text ed. 49.45 (ISBN 0-471-03050-3); 30.00 (ISBN 0-471-08200-7). Wiley.
Cowan, Henry J. Architectual Structures: An Introduction to Structural Mechanics. LC 79-13735. (Civil Engineering Ser.). 320p. 1980. text ed. 34.95 (ISBN 0-273-01054-9). Pitman Pub MA.
Croxton, P. C., et al. Structures & Materials: A Programmed Approach. (Illus.). 300p. 1974. text ed. 18.50x (ISBN 0-8464-0890-2). Beekman Pubs.
Davies, G. A., ed. Structural Impact & Crashworthiness, Vol. 1. 272p. 1984. 42.00 (ISBN 0-85334-288-1, I-258-84, Pub. by Elsevier Applied Sci England). Elsevier.
Davies, J. M. Manual of Stressed Skin Diaphram Design. 441p. 1982. 82.50 (ISBN 0-471-87485-X). Wiley.
Dent, Colin. Construction Measurement: Elementary Substructures & Superstructures. 364p. 1980. pap. 18.50x (ISBN 0-246-11256-5, Pub. by Granada England). Sheridan.
Design & Construction of Steel Chimney Liners. 226p. 1975. pap. 9.00x (ISBN 0-87262-111-1). Am Soc Civil Eng.
Dym, C. L. Stability Theory & Its Application To Structural Mechanics. 1974. lib. bdg. 22.50 (ISBN 90-28600-94-9, Pub. by Martinus Nijhoff Netherlands). Kluwer Academic.
Elrod, Ron E. Engineering Handbook for Advertising Structures. 750p. 1985. pap. write for info. (ISBN 0-911380-67-1). Signs of Times.
Feld, Jacob. Construction Failure. LC 68-30908. (Practical Construction Guides Ser.). 1968. 45.95x (ISBN 0-471-25700-1, Pub. by Wiley-Interscience). Wiley.
Fenves, Steven J., et al. Numerical & Computer Methods in Structural Mechanics: Proceedings. 1973. 86.50 (ISBN 0-12-253250-3). Acad Pr.
Ferguson, Phil M. Reinforced Concrete Fundamentals. 4th ed. LC 78-21555. 724p. 1979. text ed. 45.45x (ISBN 0-471-01459-1). Wiley.
--Reinforced Concrete Fundamentals: SI Version. 4th ed. LC 80-24409. 694p. 1981. text ed. 45.45x (ISBN 0-471-05897-1). Wiley.
Fertis, Demeter G. Dynamics & Vibration of Structures. LC 83-8416. 504p. 1983. Repr. of 1973 ed. 39.50 (ISBN 0-89874-635-3). Krieger.
Florin, Gustav. Theory & Design of Surface Structures Slabs & Plates. (Structural Engineering Ser.: Vol. 2). (Illus.). 222p. 1980. 38.00x (ISBN 0-87849-034-5); pap. 24.00 (ISBN 0-87849-035-3). Trans Tech.
Foster, Jack S. Structure & Fabric, 2 pts. LC 78-53853. (Mitchell's Building Construction Ser.). 1978. Pt. 1, 264p. pap. 17.95x (ISBN 0-470-26348-2). Halsted Pr.
Francis, A. J. Introducing Structures. (International Series in Structure & Solid Body Mechanics). 1980. 41.00 (ISBN 0-08-022701-5); pap. 12.00 (ISBN 0-08-022702-3). Pergamon.
Full-Scale Load Testing of Structures - STP 702. 214p. 1980. 24.75x (ISBN 0-8031-0368-9, 04-702000-10). ASTM.
Fumagalli, E. Statical & Geomechanical Models. (Illus.). xv, 182p. 1973. 62.00 (ISBN 0-387-81096-X). Springer-Verlag.
Gallagher, J. P. & Crooker, T. W., eds. Structural Integrity Technology. (Orig.). 1979. 30.00 (ISBN 0-685-96310-1, H00144). ASME.
Gaylord, E. H., Jr. & Gaylord, C. N. Structural Engineering Handbook. 2nd ed. 1979. 67.50 (ISBN 0-07-023123-0). McGraw.
Gibson, J. E. Computing in Structural Engineering. (Illus.). xv, 290p. 1975. 52.00 (ISBN 0-85334-614-3, Pub. by Elsevier Applied Sci England). Elsevier.
Gjelsvik, Atle. The Theory of Thin Walled Bars. LC 80-26501. 248p. 1981. 42.95x (ISBN 0-471-08594-4, Pub. by Wiley-Interscience). Wiley.
Gokhfeld, D. A. & Cherniavsky, O. F. Limit Analysis of Structures at Thermal Cycling. (Mechanics of Plastic Solids Ser.: No. 4). 576p. 1980. 110.00x (ISBN 90-286-0455-3). Sijthoff & Noordhoff.
Gordon, J. E. Structures: Or Why Things Don't Fall Down. LC 81-9755. (Quality Paperbacks Ser.). (Illus.). 395p. 1981. pap. 9.95 (ISBN 0-306-80151-5). Da Capo.
Guide for Design of Steel Transmission Towers. (Manual & Report on Engineering Practice Ser.: No. 52). 55p. 1971. pap. 5.00x (ISBN 0-87262-226-6). Am Soc Civil Eng.
Hall, W. H. & Gaus, M. P., eds. Behavior of Metal Structures. 240p. 1983. pap. 23.75x (ISBN 0-87262-364-5). Am Soc Civil Eng.
Hall, W. J. Structural & Geotechnical Mechanics: A Volume Honoring Nathan M. Newmark. LC 76-28735. (Illus.). 1977. ref. ed. 52.00 (ISBN 0-13-853804-2). P-H.
Hart, Gary C. Uncertainty Analysis Loads & Safety in Structural Engineering. (Illus.). 240p. 1982. 38.00 (ISBN 0-13-935619-3). P-H.
Heins, C. P., Jr. & Derucher, K. Structural Analysis & Design. (Civil Engineering Ser.: Vol. 2). 1980. 45.00 (ISBN 0-8247-6922-8). Dekker.
Hill, L. A., Jr. Compendium of Structural Aids. 1975. pap. text ed. 12.20 scp (ISBN 0-7002-2482-3, HarpC). Har-Row.
Hoffer, K. Permanent Fasteners for Light-Weight Structures. (Illus.). 220p. pap. 51.00 (ISBN 0-9911001-4-X, Pub. by Aluminium W Germany). Heyden.
Institute of Mechanical Engineers. Vehicle Structures. 1984. 63.00 (MEP200). Soc Auto Engineers.
Irvine, Carol L. & Jones, Rhonda A. Structural Engineering Practice Problem Manual. (Engineering Review Manual Ser.). (Illus.). 232p. 1985. pap. text ed. 24.95 (ISBN 0-932276-47-4). Prof Engine.
Irvine, H. M. Cable Structures. (Illus.). 304p. 1981. 47.50x (ISBN 0-262-09023-6). MIT Pr.
Irwin, Andrew & Sibbald, Walter. Falsework: A Handbook of Design & Practice. 192p. 1983. pap. 29.50x (ISBN 0-246-11809-1, Pub. by Granada England). Sheridan.
Johnson, Sidney M. Deterioration, Maintenance & Repair of Structures. LC 80-12763. 384p. 1981. Repr. of 1965 ed. lib. bdg. 29.95 (ISBN 0-89874-095-9). Krieger.
Ketter, Robert, et al. Structural Analysis & Design, Vol. 1. (Illus.). 1979. text ed. 44.00 (ISBN 0-07-034291-1). McGraw.
Kurtz, Max. Structural Engineering for Professional Engineer's Examination. 3rd ed. (Illus.). 1978. 29.50 (ISBN 0-07-035657-2); pap. 16.95 o. p. (ISBN 0-07-035674-2). McGraw.
Lateral Stresses in the Ground & Design of Earth Retaining Structures. 334p. 1970. pap. 14.00x (ISBN 0-87262-023-9). Am Soc Civil Eng.
Lauer, Kenneth R. Structural Engineering for Architects. (Illus.). 672p. 1981. text ed. 38.00 (ISBN 0-07-036622-5). McGraw.
Laursen, Harold I. Structural Analysis. 2nd ed. LC 77-21575. (Illus.). 1977. text ed. 42.00x (ISBN 0-07-036643-8). McGraw.
Leipholz, H. H., ed. Structural Control: Proceedings of the Iutam Symposium, Waterloo, Ont. Canada, June, 1979. 810p. 1980. 93.75 (ISBN 0-444-85485-1, North-Holland). Elsevier.
LePatner, B. & Johnson, S. Structural & Foundation Failures: A Casebook for Architects, Engineers & Lawyers. 1982. 41.50 (ISBN 0-07-032584-7). McGraw.
Leporati, Ezio. The Assessment of Structural Safety. (Structural Engineering Research Ser.). 133p. 1980. pap. 26.95 (ISBN 0-471-27886-6, Research Studies Pr). Wiley.
Lin Yen Tung & Stotesbury, Sidney D. Structural Concepts & Systems for Architects & Engineers. LC 79-23458. 588p. 1980. text ed. 46.00x (ISBN 0-471-05186-1). Wiley.
McGuire, William & Gallagher, Richard H. Matrix Structural Analysis. LC 78-8471. 460p. 1979. text ed. 51.75 (ISBN 0-471-03059-7); solutions manual avail. (ISBN 0-471-05535-2). Wiley.
McKaig, Thomas H. Applied Structural Design of Buildings. 3rd ed. LC 79-23743. 508p. 1980. Repr. of 1965 ed. 35.00 (ISBN 0-89874-070-3). Krieger.
Madsen, Henrik O. Methods of Structural Safety. (Illus.). 336p. 1986. text ed. 49.95 (ISBN 0-13-579475-7). P-H.
Makowski, Z. S. Analysis Design & Construction of Double Layer Grids. 414p. 1981. 97.00x (ISBN 0-470-27274-0). Halsted Pr.
Matheson, J. A., et al. Hyperstatic Structures: An Introduction to the Theory of Statically Indeterminate Structures. 2nd ed. (Illus.). 500p. 1971. 19.75 (ISBN 0-8088-7017-3). Davey.
Moan, T. & Shinozuka, M., eds. Structural Safety & Reliability: Proceedings of the International Conference, Trondheim, Norway, June '81. (Developments in Civil Engineering Ser.: Vol. 4). 820p. 1982. 117.00 (ISBN 0-444-41994-2). Elsevier.
Morgan, et al. Structural Mechanics. pap. 31.50x (ISBN 0-273-40116-5, SpS). Sportshelf.
Morgan, William. The Elements of Structure. 2nd ed. Buckle, I., ed. (Illus.). 1978. pap. text ed. 27.95x (ISBN 0-273-01079-4). Sportshelf.
Morton, J., ed. Structural Impact & Crashworthiness, Vol. 2. 556p. 1984. 57.00 (ISBN 0-85334-293-8, I-259-84, Pub. by Elsevier Applied Sci England). Elsevier.
Morton, N. Structural Engineering Design Programs: Software Project. 1984. write for info. (users manual & 4 diskettes) (ISBN 0-07-079572-X). McGraw.
Mosburg, Lewis G., Jr. Structuring Exploration Deals, Vol. 1. 345p. 1983. text ed. 40.00x (ISBN 0-910649-02-2). Energy Textbks.
Mosley, W. H. & Spencer, W. J. Microcomputer Applications in Structural Engineering. 250p. 1984. pap. 34.50 (ISBN 0-444-00919-1); diskette 25.00 (ISBN 0-444-00948-5). Elsevier.
National Structural Engineering Conference. Methods of Structural Analysis: Proceedings of the National Structural Engineering Conference, August 22-25, 1976, Madison, Wisconsin, 2 vols. Saul, William E. & Payrot, Alain H., eds. Vol. 1. pap. 131.80 (ISBN 0-317-10736-4, 2019541); Vol. 2. pap. 138.80 (ISBN 0-317-10737-2). Bks Demand UMI.
Noor, A. K. & Housner, J. M., eds. Advances & Trends in Structural & Solid Mechanics: Proceedings of the Symposium, Washington D.C., USA, 4-7 October 1982. 587p. 1983. 165.00 (ISBN 0-08-029990-3). Pergamon.
Nooshin. Formex Configuration Processing in Structural Engineering. 1984. 42.00 (ISBN 0-85334-315-2). Elsevier.
Oden, J. T., et al, eds. Recent Advances in Matrix Methods of Structural Analysis & Design. LC 78-135710. 904p. 1970. 39.75 (ISBN 0-8173-3505-6). U of Ala Pr.
Park, K. C. & Jones, R. F., Jr., eds. Computer Analysis of Large-Scale Structures. (AMD Ser.: Vol. 49). 102p. 1981. 24.00 (ISBN 0-686-34481-2, H00196). ASME.

Avestruz, Fred S. Risk & Technology Choice in Developing Countries: The Case of Philippine Sugar Factories. (Illus.). 192p. (Orig.). 1985. lib. bdg. 19.75 (ISBN 0-8191-4774-5); pap. text ed. 10.75 (ISBN 0-8191-4775-3). U Pr of Amer.
Baikow, V. E. Manufacture & Refining of Raw Cane Sugar. 2nd ed. (Sugar Ser.: Vol. 2). 588p. 1982. 159.75 (ISBN 0-444-41896-2). Elsevier.
Birch, G. G. & Parker, K. J., eds. Sugar: Science & Technology. (Illus.). 475p. 1979. 89.00 (ISBN 0-85334-805-7, Pub. by Elsevier Applied Sci England). Elsevier.
Delden, E. Standard Fabrication Practices for Cane Sugar Mills. (Sugar Ser.: Vol. 1). 254p. 1981. 59.75 (ISBN 0-444-41958-6). Elsevier.
Eichner, Alfred S. The Emergence of Oligopoly: Sugar Refining As a Case Study. LC 78-16472. (Illus.). 1978. Repr. of 1969 ed. lib. bdg. 28.75x (ISBN 0-313-20598-1, EIEO). Greenwood.
Hoynak, P. X. & Bollenback, G. N. This Is Liquid Sugar (Including Supplement) 1966. text ed. 14.50x (ISBN 0-934636-04-4). Key Bk Serv.
Hugot, E. Handbook of Cane Sugar Engineering. 2nd ed. 1079p. 1972. 234.00 (ISBN 0-444-40896-7). Elsevier.
Isaias, Issay. Small-Scale Cane Sugar Processing & Residue Utilization. (Agricultural Services Bulletins: No. 19). 61p. 1980. pap. 7.50 (ISBN 92-5-100935-X, F2069, FAO). Unipub.
Jenkins, G. H. Introduction to Cane Sugar Technology. 478p. 1966. 83.00 (ISBN 0-444-40319-1). Elsevier.
Kaplinsky, Raphael. Sugar-Processing: The Development of a Third-World Technology. (Illus.). 148p. (Orig.). 1983. pap. 9.75 (ISBN 0-903031-98-1, Pub. by Intermediate Tech England). Intermediate Tech.
Lof, George O. G. & Kneese, Allen V. The Economics of Water Utilization in the Beet Sugar Industry. LC 68-16166. (Resources for the Future Ser). (Illus.). Repr. of 1968 ed. 25.70 (ISBN 0-8357-9268-4, 2015741). Bks Demand UMI.
Matur, R. B. Handbook of Cane Sugar Technology. 498p. 1981. 50.00x (ISBN 0-686-76642-3, Pub. by Oxford & IBH India). State Mutual Bk.
Meade, George P. & Chen, James C. Cane Sugar Handbook: A Manual for Cane Sugar Maufacturers & Their Chemists. 10th ed. LC 76-51046. 947p. 1977. 105.00x (ISBN 0-471-58995-0, Pub. by Wiley-Interscience). Wiley.
Molasses Utilization. (Agricultural Services Bulletins: No. 25). (Illus.). 1975. pap. 7.50 (ISBN 92-5-100292-4, F714, FAO). Unipub.
Moynagh, Michael. Brown or White? A History of the Fiji Sugar Industry 1873-1973. (Pacific Research Monograph: No. 5). 306p. 1981. pap. text ed. 9.00 (ISBN 0-908160-87-9, 1121, Pub. by ANUP Australia). Australia N U P.
Paturau, J. M. By-Products of the Cane Sugar Industry: An Introduction to Their Industrial Utilization. 2nd, rev. ed. (Sugar Technology Ser.: Vol. 3). 366p. 1982. 74.50 (ISBN 0-444-42034-7). Elsevier.
Payne, J. H. Unit Operations in Cane Sugar Production. (Sugar Technology Ser.: Vol. 4). 204p. 1982. 51.00 (ISBN 0-444-42104-1). Elsevier.
Plews, R. W., ed. Analytical Methods Used in Sugar Refining. (Illus.). 234p. 1969. 42.75 (ISBN 0-444-20046-0, Pub. by Elsevier Applied Sci England). Elsevier.
Prevention of Dust Explosions, Pulverized Sugar & Cocoa. (Sixty Ser.). 1967. pap. 2.00 (ISBN 0-685-58076-8, 62). Natl Fire Prot.
Water Pollution Caused by Wastes from Sugar Refineries. (General Fisheries Council of the Mediterranean (GFCM): Studies & Reviews: No. 3). (Eng. & Fr.). 23p. 1958. pap. 7.50 (ISBN 92-5-101921-5, F1769, FAO). Unipub.

SUGAR BEET
see Beets and Beet Sugar

SUGAR-CANE
Alexander, A. G. Sugarcane Physiology. 1973. 138.25 (ISBN 0-444-41016-3). Elsevier.
Blackburn, F. Sugar-Cane. (Tropical Agriculture Ser.). (Illus.). 414p. 1984. text ed. 75.00 (ISBN 0-582-46028-X). Longman.
Clements, Harry F. Sugarcane Crop Logging & Crop Control: Principles & Practices. LC 79-9894. (Illus.). 540p. 1980. text ed. 40.00x (ISBN 0-8248-0508-9). UH Pr.
Humbert, Roger P. Growing of Sugar Cane. 2nd ed. 778p. 1968. 149.00 (ISBN 0-444-40310-8). Elsevier.
Isaias, Issay. Small-Scale Cane Sugar Processing & Residue Utilization. (Agricultural Services Bulletins: No. 19). 61p. 1980. pap. 7.50 (ISBN 92-5-100935-X, F2069, FAO). Unipub.
Payne, J. H., ed. Noel Deerr-Classic Papers of a Sugar Cane Technologist. (Sugar Ser.: Vol. 5). 646p. 1983. 138.50 (ISBN 0-444-42149-1, I-272-83). Elsevier.
Peng, S. Y. The Biology & Control of Weeds in Sugar Cane. (Developments in Crop Science Ser.: Vol. 4). 250p. 1984. 71.25 (ISBN 0-444-42133-5). Elsevier.
Sugarcane Production in Asia. 339p. 1980. pap. 14.75 (ISBN 0-686-97527-8, APO120, APO). Unipub.

SUGAR GROWING
see also Beets and Beet Sugar; Sugar–Manufacture and Refining; Sugar-Cane
Eisenberg, Peter L. The Sugar Industry in Pernambuco, 1840-1910: Modernization Without Change. LC 75-117340. 1974. 34.00x (ISBN 0-520-01731-5). U of Cal Pr.
Howell, R. B. Louisiana Sugar Plantations. 1969. 10.95 (ISBN 0-87511-060-6). Claitors.
Sitterson, J. Carlyle. Sugar Country. LC 73-10738. (Illus.). 414p. 1973. Repr. of 1953 ed. lib. bdg. 22.50x (ISBN 0-8371-7027-3, SISC). Greenwood.
Timoshenko, Vladimir P. & Swerling, Boris C. The World's Sugar: Progress & Policy. 1957. 30.00x (ISBN 0-8047-0501-1). Stanford U Pr.

SUGAR-REFINING
see Sugar–Manufacture and Refining

SUGAR SUBSTITUTES
Business Communications Staff. Sugar, Sweeteners & Substitutes. 1983. 1250.00 (ISBN 0-89336-091-0, C-005R). BCC.
Marshall, J. John, ed. Mechanisms of Saccharide Polymerization & Depolymerization. LC 80-16155. 1980. 44.00 (ISBN 0-12-474150-9). Acad Pr.

SUGARS
see also Polysaccharides
Cantor, Sidney M., ed. Use of Sugars & Other Carbohydrates in the Food Industry. LC 55-4135. (Advances in Chemistry Ser: No. 12). 1955. pap. 10.95 (ISBN 0-8412-0013-0). Am Chemical.
Chaballe, L. Y. Elsevier's Sugar Dictionary: In English, French, Spanish, Dutch & German. 1984. 79.75 (ISBN 0-444-42376-1, I-410-84). Elsevier.
Methods of Analysis for Sugars. 29p. 1970. pap. 4.50 (ISBN 92-5-101744-1, F656, FAO). Unipub.
Pancoast, Harry M. & Junk, W. Ray. Handbook of Sugars. 2nd ed. (Illus.). 1980. text ed. 59.50 (ISBN 0-87055-348-8). AVI.

SUILLUS
Smith, A. H. & Thiers, H. D. A Contribution Toward a Monograph of North American Species of Suillus. (Illus.). 1964. pap. 8.75 (ISBN 0-934454-26-4). Lubrecht & Cramer.

SULPHATE RESISTANT CONCRETE
Swenson, E. G., ed. Performance of Concrete: Resistance of Concrete to Sulphate & Other Environmental Conditions. LC 74-350285. 1968. 15.00x (ISBN 0-8020-3208-7). U of Toronto Pr.

SULPHIDES
Buchanan, D. L. & Jones, M. J., eds. Sulphide Deposits in Mafic & Ultramafic Rocks: Proceedings of Nickel Sulphide Field Conference III, Western Australia, 1982. (Orig.). 1984. pap. text ed. 78.00x (ISBN 0-900488-71-9). Imm North Am.
Dodgeson, K. S., et al, eds. Sulfates of Microbial Origin, Vols. 1 & 2. 1982. Vol. 1, 216p. 59.00 (ISBN 0-8493-6035-8); Vol. 2, 208p. 59.00 (ISBN 0-8493-6036-6). CRC Pr.
Fiechter, A., ed. New Substrates. LC 72-152360. (Advances in Biochemical Engineering: Vol. 6). (Illus.). 1977. 36.00 (ISBN 0-387-08363-4). Springer-Verlag.
Forssberg, K. S., ed. Flotation of Sulphide Minerals: Developments in Mineral Processing. (No. 8). 480p. 1985. 102.00 (ISBN 0-444-42494-6). Elsevier.
Jones, M. J., ed. Complex Sulphide Ores. 278p. (Orig.). 1980. pap. text ed. 161.00x (ISBN 0-900488-51-4). IMM North Am.
Mills, K. C. Thermodynamic Data for Inorganic Sulphides, Selenides & Tellurides. LC 74-173939. pap. 160.00 (ISBN 0-317-08901-3, 2051842). Bks Demand UMI.
Sohn, H. Y., et al, eds. Advances in Sulfide Smelting: Proceedings, TMS Fall Extractive Meeting, San Francisco, 1983. LC 83-62531. (Illus.). 1143p. 1983. 60.00 (ISBN 0-89520-463-0). Metal Soc.
Torchinskii, Yu M. Sulfhydyl & Disulfide Groups of Proteins. LC 73-83903. (Studies in Soviet Sciences - Life Sciences). (Illus.). 285p. 1974. 45.00x (ISBN 0-306-10888-7, Consultants). Plenum Pub.
Vaughan, David J. & Craig, James R. Mineral Chemistry of the Metal Sulfides. LC 76-62585. (Earth Science Ser.). (Illus.). 1978. 72.50 (ISBN 0-521-21489-0). Cambridge U Pr.

SULPHONAMIDES
Akiba, K. Bond Switch at Hypervalent Sulfur in Thiathiophtene Analogous Systems. (Sulfur Reports Ser.). Date not set. price not set flexicover (ISBN 3-7186-0037-4). Harwood Academic.
Kobayashi, M. & Kamigata, N. Azosulfones: Versatile Precursors for Aryl Radicals, Aryl Cations, Aryl Anions, Carbenes & Benzynes. (Sulfur Reports Ser.). 49p. 1982. 23.00 (ISBN 3-7186-0040-4). Harwood Academic.
Okazaki, R. The Chemistry of S (IV) Thiocumulenes. (Sulfur Reports Ser.). 68p. 1980. write for info. flexicover (ISBN 3-7186-0042-0). Harwood Academic.

SULPHONATION
Gilbert, Everett E. Sulfonation & Related Reactions. Olah, George A., ed. LC 76-52491. 542p. 1977. Repr. of 1965 ed. lib. bdg. 32.50 (ISBN 0-88275-528-5). Krieger.
Interlaboratory Cooperative Study of the Precision & Accuracy of the Measurement of Total Sulfation in the Atmosphere Using ASTM D 2914, DS 55-S2. 65p. 1974. pap. 5.00 (ISBN 0-8031-0383-2, 05-055020-17). ASTM.

SULPHUR
see also Organosulphur Compounds
Airborne Sulphur Pollution: Effects & Control: Report Prepared Within the Framework of the Convention on Long-Range Transboundary Air Pollution. (Illus.). 265p. 1985. pap. 19.00 (UN84/2E8, UN). Unipub.
Benesch, Reinhold, et al. Sulfur in Proteins. 1959. 81.00 (ISBN 0-12-088150-0). Acad Pr.
Blair, Graeme. Sulfur in the Tropics. (Technical Bulletin Ser.: T-12). (Illus.). 71p. (Orig.). 1979. pap. 4.00 (ISBN 0-88090-011-3). Intl Fertilizer.
Bothe, H. & Trebst, A., eds. Biology of Inorganic Nitrogen & Sulfur Metabolism. (Proceedings in Life Sciences Ser.). (Illus.). 370p. 1981. 52.00 (ISBN 0-387-10486-0). Springer-Verlag.
Bourne, Douglas J., ed. New Uses of Sulfur-II. LC 78-1004. (Advances in Chemistry Ser.: No. 165). 1978. 29.95 (ISBN 0-8412-0391-1). Am Chemical.
Cavallini, D., et al, eds. Natural Sulfur Compounds: Novel Biochemical & Structural Aspects. 565p. 1980. 69.50x (ISBN 0-306-40335-8, Plenum Pr). Plenum Pub.
Ciba Foundation. Sulphur in Biology. (Ciba Symposium Ser.: Vol. 72). 1980. 55.75 (ISBN 0-444-90108-6). Elsevier.
--Sulphur in Biology. LC 79-24939. (Ciba Foundation Symposium, New Ser.: 72). pap. 81.00 (ISBN 0-317-29756-2, 2022191). Bks Demand UMI.
De Wispelaere, C., ed. Air Pollution Modeling & Its Applications, No. IV. (NATO Challenges for Modern Society Ser.: Vol. 7). 806p. 1985. 110.00x (ISBN 0-306-41908-4, Plenum Pr). Plenum Pub.
Ellison, S. P., Jr. Sulfur in Texas. (Illus.). 48p. 1971. 2.00 (ISBN 0-686-29324-X, HB 2). Bur Econ Geology.
Foroulis, Z. A., ed. High Temperature Metallic Corrosion of Sulfur & Its Compounds. LC 71-120299. pap. 68.80 (ISBN 0-317-08511-5, 2051581). Bks Demand UMI.
Heal, Henry. The Inorganic Heterocyclic Chemistry of Sulphur, Nitrogen & Phosphorus. 1981. 86.00 (ISBN 0-12-335680-6). Acad Pr.
Hogg, D. R. Organic Compounds of Sulphur, Selenium & Tellurium, Vols. 1-5. Incl. Vol. 1. 1969-70 Literature. 1971. 47.00 (ISBN 0-85186-259-4); Vol. 2. 1970-1972 Literature. 1973. 52.00 (ISBN 0-85186-269-1); Vol. 3. 1972-74 Literature. 1975. 63.00 (ISBN 0-85186-279-9); Vol. 4. 1974-76 Literature. 1977. 88.00 (ISBN 0-85186-289-6); Vol. 5. 1979. 98.00 (ISBN 0-85186-620-4, Pub. by Royal Soc Chem London). LC 72-78527. Am Chemical.
Interlaboratory Cooperative Study in the Precision & Accuracy of the Determination of Sulfur Oxides in Gaseous Combustion Products, DS 55-S9. 90p. 1977. pap. 12.00 (ISBN 0-8031-0379-4, 05-055090-17). ASTM.
International Conference on the Control of Sulphur & Other Gaseous Emissions, 3rd, University of Salford, 1979. The Control of Sulphur & Other Gaseous Emissions: Proceedings, No. 57. 460p. 1981. 80.00x (ISBN 0-85295-117-5, Pub. by Inst Chem Eng England). State Mutual Bk.
International Symposium, Dubrovnik, Yugoslavia, 7-14 Sept. 1977. Sulphur in the Atmosphere: Proceedings. Husar, R. B., et al, eds. 1978. text ed. 83.00 (ISBN 0-08-022932-8). Pergamon.
Karchmer, J. H., ed. The Analytical Chemistry of Sulfur & Its Compounds, Part 2. LC 77-84969. (Chemical Analysis Ser.: Vol. 29). pap. 160.00 (ISBN 0-317-08929-3, 2006494). Bks Demand UMI.
Kharasch, N. Mechanisms of Reactions of Sulfur Compounds, 5 vols. 1971. Set, 1146p. 264.75 (ISBN 0-677-65300-X); Vol. 1 1967, 288p. 75.25 (ISBN 0-677-65310-7); Vol. 2. 1968, 288p. 75.25 (ISBN 0-677-65320-4); Vol. 3. 1969, 192p. 48.75 (ISBN 0-677-65330-1); Vol. 4 1970, 192p. 49.95 (ISBN 0-677-65340-9); Vol. 5 1971, 186p. 49.95 (ISBN 0-677-65350-6). Gordon.
Kuriyama, Kinya, et al. Sulfur Amino Acids: Biochemical & Clinical Aspects. LC 83-7982. (Progress in Clinical & Biological Research Ser.: Vol. 125). 510p. 1983. 86.00 (ISBN 0-8451-0125-0). A R Liss.
Long-Range Transport of Sulphur in the Atmosphere & Acid Rain: Lectures Presented at the Thirty-third Session of the WMO Executive Committee. 53p. 1983. pap. text ed. 8.00 (ISBN 92-63-10603-7, W560, WMO). Unipub.
McLachlan, K. D. An Atlas of Sulphur Deficiency in Commercial Plants. 18p. 1978. pap. 6.00 (ISBN 0-643-00210-3, C003, CSIRO). Unipub.
--Sulphur in Australasian Agriculture. (Illus.). 256p. 1975. 36.00x (ISBN 0-424-06850-8, Pub by Sydney U Pr). Intl Spec Bk.
McLachlan, K. D., ed. Handbook on Sulphur in Australian Agriculture. (Illus.). 1977. pap. 2.25x (ISBN 0-643-00087-9, Pub. by CSIRO). Intl Spec Bk.
Meyer, B. Sulfur, Energy, & Environment. 448p. 1977. 83.00 (ISBN 0-444-41595-5). Elsevier.
Nickless, Graham, ed. Inorganic Sulphur Chemistry. 770p. 1969. 121.50 (ISBN 0-444-40684-0). Elsevier.
Nriagu, Jerome O. Sulfur in the Environment: Ecological Impacts, Pt. 2. (Environmental Science & Technology Ser.). 482p. 1978. 90.95x (ISBN 0-471-04255-2, Pub. by Wiley-Interscience). Wiley.
Oae, S., ed. Organic Chemistry of Sulfur. LC 72-95072. 713p. 1977. 85.00x (ISBN 0-306-30740-5, Plenum Pr). Plenum Pub.
Pfeiffer, John B., ed. Sulfur Removal & Recovery from Industrial Processes. LC 75-11557. (Advances in Chemistry Ser.: No. 139). 1975. 24.95 (ISBN 0-8412-0217-6). Am Chemical.
Prevention of Sulfur Fires & Explosions. (Sixty Ser.). 1971. pap. 2.00 (ISBN 0-685-58071-7, 655). Natl Fire Prot.
Raymont, Michael E., ed. Sulfur: New Sources & Uses. LC 82-1645. (ACS Symposium Ser.: No. 183). 1982. 33.95 (ISBN 0-8412-0713-5). Am Chemical.
Roy, A. B. & Trudinger, P. Biochemistry of Inorganic Compounds of Sulphur. LC 78-79056. (Illus.). 1970. 67.50 (ISBN 0-521-07581-5). Cambridge U Pr.
Royal Society Discussion Meeting. Ecological Effects of Deposited Sulphur & Nitrogen Compounds: Proceedings of a Royal Society Discussion Meeting Held on September 5-7 1983. Beament, James, et al, eds. (Philosophical Transactions of the Royal Society, Series B: Vol. 305). (Illus.). 319p. 1984. lib. bdg. 99.00x (ISBN 0-85403-229-0, Pub. by Royal Soc London). Scholium Intl.
Sander, U., et al, eds. Sulphur, Sulphur Dioxide, Sulphuric Acid. More, A. I., tr. 428p. 1984. Repr. of 1982 ed. text ed. 35.00x (ISBN 0-902777-64-5). VCH Pubs.
Senning, Alexander. Sulfur in Organic & Inorganic Chemistry, Vol. 4. 416p. 1982. 99.75 (ISBN 0-8247-1350-8). Dekker.
Senning, Alexander, ed. Sulfur in Organic & Inorganic Chemistry, Vol. 1. 1971. 99.75 (ISBN 0-8247-1615-9). Dekker.
Stirling, C. J. & Patai. The Chemistry of the Sulphonium Group, Pt. 1. LC 80-40122. (Chemistry of Functional Groups Ser.). 385p. 1981. 113.95 (ISBN 0-471-27769-X, Pub. by Wiley-Interscience). Wiley.
Stirling, C. J., ed. The Chemistry of Sulphoniom Group, Part 2. LC 80-40122. (Chemistry of Functional Group Ser.). 462p. 1981. 128.95 (ISBN 0-471-27770-3, Pub. by Wiley-Interscience). Wiley.
Sulfur Bacteria. 129p. 1979. pap. 15.00x (ISBN 0-8031-0582-7, 04-650000-16). ASTM.
Sulphur & Lime Sulphur. (Specifications for Plant Protection Products: No. 24). pap. 7.50 (F2009, FAO). Unipub.
VDI Editors. Oxygen-Containing Sulphur Compounds VDI 314. 1978. 71.00 (ISBN 0-9961074-2-8, Pub. by VDI W Germany). Heyden.
Voronkov, Mikhail G., et al. Reactions of Sulphur with Organic Compounds. 421p. 1984. 69.50x (ISBN 0-306-10978-6, Consultants). Plenum Pub.

SULPHUR BONDING
Ivanov, M. V. & Freney, J. R., eds. The Global Biogeochemical Sulphur Cycle Scope 19. LC 82-8506. (Scientific Committee on Problems of the Environment Ser.: 1409). 472p. 1983. 84.95x (ISBN 0-471-10492-2, 1-409 SCOPE, Pub. by Wiley-Interscience). Wiley.

SULPHUR DIOXIDE
Interlaboratory Cooperative Study of the Precision & Accuracy of the Measurement of Sulfur Dioxide Content in the Atmosphere Using ASTM D 2914, DS 55-S1. 82p. 1974. pap. 5.00 (ISBN 0-8031-0382-4, 05-055010-17). ASTM.
Lee, Kaiman. Air Pollution: Its Effect on the Urban Man & His Adaptive Strategies. LC 74-182905. 52p. 1974. 12.00x (ISBN 0-915250-13-6). Environ Design.
Sander, U., et al, eds. Sulphur, Sulphur Dioxide, Sulphuric Acid. More, A. I., tr. 428p. 1984. Repr. of 1982 ed. text ed. 35.00x (ISBN 0-902777-64-5). VCH Pubs.

Miller, Richard K. Fifth Generation Computers: A Report on Major International Research Projects & Cooperatives. (Illus.). 200p. 1985. pap. text ed. 590.00 (ISBN 0-89671-061-0). SEAI Tech Pubns.

Paddon, D. J., ed. Supercomputers & Parallel Computations. (The Institute of Mathematics & Its Applications Conference Ser.). (Illus.). 1984. 39.00x (ISBN 0-19-853601-1). Oxford U Pr.

Sumner, F., ed. Supercomputer Systems Technology: Design & Application. (Computer State of the Art Report: Ser.10 No.6). (Illus.). 400p. 1982. 445.00 (ISBN 0-08-028569-4). Pergamon.

SUPERCONDUCTIVITY

see also Superconductors; Superfluidity

AIP Conference, Univ. of Rochester, 1971. Superconductivity in D- & F- Band Metals: AIP Conference Proceedings, No. 4. Douglass, D. H., ed. LC 74-188879. 375p. 1972. 14.00 (ISBN 0-88318-103-7). Am Inst Physics.

Basov, N. G., ed. Superconductivity. LC 77-17959. (P. N. Lebedev Physics Institute Ser: Vol. 86). (Illus.). 178p. 1977. 55.00x (ISBN 0-306-10939-5, Consultants). Plenum Pub.

Blatt, John M. Theory of Superconductivity. (Pure and Applied Physics Ser.: Vol. 17). 1964. 69.50 (ISBN 0-12-104950-7). Acad Pr.

Bogoliubov, N. N., ed. Theory of Superconductivity. (International Science Review Ser.). (Illus.). 370p. 1968. 56.75 (ISBN 0-677-00080-4). Gordon.

Business Communications Staff. The Superconductivity Industry. 1980. 750.00 (ISBN 0-89336-144-5, E-032R). BCC.

Chu, C. W. & Woolam, J. A., eds. High Pressure & Low-Temperature Physics. LC 78-7290. 614p. 1978. 89.50x (ISBN 0-306-40014-6, Plenum Pr). Plenum Pub.

Cohen, Morrel H., ed. Superconductivity in Science & Technology. LC 67-25534. pap. 42.80 (ISBN 0-317-08095-4, 2020047). Bks Demand UMI.

Deaver, B. & Ruvalds, John, eds. Advances in Superconductivity. (NATO ASI Series B, Physics: Vol. 100). 538p. 1983. 75.00x (ISBN 0-306-41388-4, Plenum Pr). Plenum Pub.

Deaver, B. S., Jr., et al, eds. Future Trends in Superconductive Electronics. LC 78-66638. (AIP Conference Proceedings: No. 44). (Illus.). 1979. lib. bdg. 22.00 (ISBN 0-88318-143-6). Am Inst Physics.

Douglass, D. H., ed. Superconductivity in D-& F-Band Metals. LC 76-46953. 648p. 1976. 95.00x (ISBN 0-306-30994-7, Plenum Pr). Plenum Pub.

Fischer, O. & Maple, M. B., eds. Superconductivity in Ternary Compounds I: Structural, Electronics & Lattices Properties. (Topics in Current Physics Ser.: Vol. 32). (Illus.). 320p. 1982. 37.00 (ISBN 0-387-11670-2). Springer-Verlag.

Foner, S. & Schwartz, B., eds. Superconducting Machines & Devices: Large Systems Applications. LC 74-624. (NATO ASI Series B, Physics: Vol. 1). 692p. 1974. 89.50x (ISBN 0-306-35701-1, Plenum Pr). Plenum Pub.

Ginzburg, V. L. & Kirzhnits, D. A., eds. High-Temperature Superconductivity. Agyei, A. K., tr. from Russian. LC 82-5295. 364p. 1982. 59.50x (ISBN 0-306-10970-0, AACR2, Consultants). Plenum Pub.

Goldman, Allen M. & Wolf, Stuart A., eds. Percolation, Localization, & Superconductivity. (NATO ASI Series B: Physics: Vol. 109). 472p. 1984. 79.50x (ISBN 0-306-41713-8, Plenum Pr). Plenum Pub.

Grassie, A. D. The Superconducting State. 40.00x (ISBN 0-686-97024-1, Pub. by Scottish Academic Pr Scotland). State Mutual Bk.

Gray, Kenneth E., ed. Nonequilibrium Superconductivity, Phonons, & Kapitza Boundaries. LC 81-1858. (NATO ASI Series B, Physics: Vol. 65). 710p. 1981. 95.00x (ISBN 0-306-40720-5, Plenum Pr). Plenum Pub.

Gregory, W. D., et al, eds. Science & Technology of Superconductivity, Vol. 1 & 2. LC 72-77226. 1973. Vol. 1, 476p. 65.00x (ISBN 0-306-37631-8, Plenum Pr); Vol. 2, 391p. 65.00x (ISBN 0-306-37632-6, Plenum Pr). Plenum Pub.

Lueders, G., et al. Method of Correlation Function in Superconductivity Theory. Hoehler, G., et al, eds. (Springer Tracts in Modern Physics Vol. 56). (Illus.). 1971. 56.70 (ISBN 0-387-05251-8). Springer-Verlag.

Maple, M. B. & Fischer, O., eds. Superconductivity in Ternary Compounds II: Superconductivity & Magnetism. (Topics in Current Physics: Vol. 34). (Illus.). 335p. 1982. 35.00 (ISBN 0-387-11814-4). Springer-Verlag.

Matsubara, T. & Kotani, A., eds. Superconductiving in Magnetic & Exotic Materials: Proceedings of the Sixth Taniguchi International Symposium, Kashikojima, Japan, Nov. 14-18, 1983. (Springer Series in Solid-State Sciences Ser.: Vol. 52). (Illus.). 225p. 1984. 25.00 (ISBN 0-387-13324-0). Springer-Verlag.

Narlikar, A. V. & Ekbote, S. N. Superconductivity & Superconducting Materials. LC 83-188223. (Solid Physics Ser.: No. 1). (Illus.). 306p. 1983. 39.00 (ISBN 0-9605004-9-9, Pub. by South Asian Pubs India). Eng Pubns.

New House, Vernon. Applied Superconductivity, 2 vols. 1975. Vol. 1. 82.50 (ISBN 0-12-517701-1); Vol. 2. 72.00 (ISBN 0-12-517702-X). Acad Pr.

Parks, R. D., ed. Superconductivity, Vol 1. LC 68-23775. pap. 160.00 (ISBN 0-317-08358-9, 2055056). Bks Demand UMI.

--Superconductivity, Vol. 2. LC 68-23775. (Illus.). pap. 160.00 (ISBN 0-317-07985-9, 2055076). Bks Demand UMI.

Rose-Innes, A. C. & Rhoderick, E. H. Introduction to Superconductivity. 2nd ed. 1977. pap. 24.00 (ISBN 0-08-021652-8). Pergamon.

Shoenberg, David. Superconductivity. 2nd ed. (Cambridge Monographs on Physics). pap. 67.50 (ISBN 0-317-09142-5, 2051478). Bks Demand UMI.

SQUID-Superconducting Quantum Interference Devices & Their Applications: International Conference, Oct. 4-8, 1976, Berlin. 1977. 70.00x (ISBN 3-11-006878-8). De Gruyter.

Suhl, Harry & Maple, M. Brian, eds. Superconductivity in D & F-Band Metals. LC 80-12907. 1980. 55.00 (ISBN 0-12-676150-7). Acad Pr.

Tanenbaum, M. & Wright, W. V., eds. Superconductors: Proceedings. LC 62-18707. pap. 40.30 (ISBN 0-317-08032-6, 2000686). Bks Demand UMI.

Taylor, A. W. & Noakes, G. R. Superconductivity. (Wykeham Science Ser.: No. 11). 110p. 1970. 9.95x (ISBN 0-8448-1113-0). Crane Russak Co.

Tinkham, M. Superconductivity. (Documents on Modern Physics Ser.). 142p. 1964. pap. 24.50 (ISBN 0-677-00065-0). Gordon.

Tinkham, Michael. Introduction to Superconductivity. Bayne, Bradford & Gardner, Michael, eds. LC 79-22625. 312p. 1980. Repr. of 1975 ed. lib. bdg. 22.50 (ISBN 0-89874-049-5). Krieger.

Vonsovsky, S. V., et al. Superconductivity of Transition Metals: Their Alloys & Compounds. (Springer Series in Solid-State Sciences: Vol. 27). (Illus.). 512p. 1982. 47.00 (ISBN 0-387-11382-7). Springer-Verlag.

Wallace, P. R., ed. Superconductivity: McGill Summer School Proceedings, 2 vols. 1969. Vol. 1, 544p. 122.25x (ISBN 0-677-13810-5); Vol. 2, 420p. 94.75x (ISBN 0-677-13820-2); Set. 195.95x (ISBN 0-677-13210-7). Gordon.

SUPERCONDUCTORS

Al'tov, V. A., et al, eds. Stabilization of Superconducting Magnetic Systems. LC 77-8618. (International Cryogenics Monographs Ser.). 338p. 1977. 52.50x (ISBN 0-306-30943-2, Plenum Pr). Plenum Pub.

Appleton, A. D. Superconducting D. C. Machines. 1984. write for info. Elsevier.

Basov, N. G., ed. Electronic Characteristics & Electron-Phonon Interaction in Superconducting Metals & Alloys. LC 77-16799. (P. N. Lebedev Physics Institute Ser.: Vol. 82). (Illus.). 104p. 1977. 55.00 (ISBN 0-306-10937-9, Consultants). Plenum Pub.

Carr, W. J., Jr. AC Loss & Macroscopic Theory of Superconductors. 170p. 1983. 57.50 (ISBN 0-677-05700-8). Gordon.

Collings, E. W. Design & Fabrication of Conventional & Unconventional Superconductors. LC 84-5923. (Illus.). 225p. 1984. 32.00 (ISBN 0-8155-0989-8). Noyes.

Foner, S. & Schwartz, B., eds. Superconducting Machines & Devices: Large Systems Applications. LC 74-624. (NATO ASI Series B, Physics: Vol. 1). 692p. 1974. 89.50x (ISBN 0-306-35701-1, Plenum Pr). Plenum Pub.

Foner, Simon & Schwartz, Brian B., eds. Superconductor Materials Science: Metallurgy, Fabrication, & Applications. LC 81-8669. (NATO ASI Series: Series B: Physics: Vol. 68). 1000p. 1981. 135.00x (ISBN 0-306-40750-7, Plenum Pr). Plenum Pub.

Gubser, D. U., et al, eds. Inhomogeneous Superconductors, 1979. LC 79-57620. (AIP Conference Proceedings: No. 58). (Illus.). 325p. lib. bdg. 20.50 (ISBN 0-88318-157-6). Am Inst Physics.

Huebener, R. P. Magnetic Flux Structures in Superconductors. (Springer Series in Solid State Sciences: Vol. 6). (Illus.). 1979. 38.00 (ISBN 0-387-09213-7). Springer-Verlag.

Kustom, R. L. Thyristor Networks for the Transfer of Energy Between Superconducting Coils. LC 79-5410. 144p. 1980. 30.00x (ISBN 0-299-08050-1). U of Wis Pr.

Mahan, G. D. & Roth, Walter, eds. Superionic Conductors. LC 76-28538. (Physics of Solids & Liquids Ser.). 438p. 1976. 62.50x (ISBN 0-306-30975-0, Plenum Pr). Plenum Pub.

Meyerhoff, Robert W., ed. Manufacture of Superconducting Materials: An International Conference, 8-10 November, 1976, Port Chester, New York, Proceedings. LC 77-11148. (Materials-Metalworking Technology Ser.). (Illus.). pap. 59.80 (ISBN 0-317-09703-2, 2019478). Bks Demand UMI.

Moon, F. C., ed. Mechanics of Superconducting Structures. (AMD: No. 41). 137p. 1980. 24.00 (ISBN 0-686-69856-8, G00174). ASME.

Savitskii, E. M. & Baron, V. V., eds. Physics & Metallurgy of Superconductors. LC 78-107529. 206p. 1970. 32.50x (ISBN 0-306-10842-9, Consultants). Plenum Pub.

Savitskii, E. M., et al. Superconducting Materials. LC 72-91517. (International Cryogenics Monographs). 459p. 1973. 75.00x (ISBN 0-306-30586-0, Plenum Pr). Plenum Pub.

Schwartz, Brian B. & Foner, Simon, eds. Superconductor Applications: SQUIDs & Machines. LC 76-51750. (NATO ASI Series B, Physics: Vol. 21). 737p. 1977. 105.00x (ISBN 0-306-35721-6, Plenum Pr). Plenum Pub.

Shenoy, G. K., ed. Ternary Superconductors. Dunlap, B. D., et al. 322p. 1981. 68.50 (ISBN 0-444-00626-5, North-Holland). Elsevier.

Suenaga, Masaki & Clark, Alan F., eds. Filamentary A-15 Superconductors. LC 80-24312. (Cryogenic Materials Ser.). 385p. 1980. 59.50x (ISBN 0-306-40622-5, Plenum Pr). Plenum Pub.

Ullmaier, H. Irreversible Properties of Type Two Superconductors. (Springer Tracts in Modern Physics Ser.: Vol. 76). (Illus.). 180p. 1975. 36.00 (ISBN 0-387-07424-4). Springer-Verlag.

Van Duzer, T. & Turner, O., eds. Principles of Superconductive Devices & Circuits. 370p. 1981. 41.50 (ISBN 0-444-00411-4). Elsevier.

Weber, Harald W., ed. Anisotropy Effects in Superconductors. LC 76-56737. 316p. 1977. 49.50x (ISBN 0-306-31006-6, Plenum Pr). Plenum Pub.

SUPERFLUIDITY

see also Superconductivity

Balian, R., et al, eds. Physics of Defects: Proceedings of the Les Houches Summer School Session, XXXV. (Les Houches Summer Session Ser.: Vol. 35). 884p. 1982. 170.25 (ISBN 0-444-86225-0). Elsevier.

Donnelly, Russell J. Experimental Superfluidity. LC 66-23686. (Illus., Orig.). 1967. pap. 7.00x (ISBN 0-226-15757-1). U of Chicago Pr.

Putterman, S. J. Superfluid Hydrodynamics. LC 74-75578. (Low Temperature Physics Ser.: Vol. 3). 443p. 1975. 66.00 (ISBN 0-444-10681-2, North-Holland); pap. 27.75 (ISBN 0-444-10713-4). Elsevier.

SUPERMARINE SPITFIRE

see Spitfire (Fighter Planes)

SUPERNOVAE

Bartel, N., ed. Supernovae As Distance Indicators. (Lecture Notes in Physics: Vol. 224). vi, 226p. 1985. pap. 13.70 (ISBN 0-387-15206-7). Springer-Verlag.

Brancazio, Peter J. & Cameron, A. G., eds. Supernovae & Their Remnants: Proceedings of a Conference Held at Goddard Space Center, 1967. (Illus.). 248p. 1969. 69.50 (ISBN 0-677-13290-5). Gordon.

Clark, D. H. & Stephenson, F. R., eds. Historical Supernovae. LC 76-44364. 1977. text ed. 31.00 (ISBN 0-08-020914-9); pap. text ed. 13.00 (ISBN 0-08-021639-0). Pergamon.

International Conference on Supernovae; May 7-11, 1973, Lecce, Italy. Supernovae & Supernova Remnants: Proceedings. Cosmovici, ed. LC 73-91428. (Astrophysics & Space Science Library: No. 45). 400p. 1974. lib. bdg. 55.00 (ISBN 90-277-0427-9, Pub. by Reidel Holland). Kluwer Academic.

Kafatos, M. & Henry, R. B., eds. The Crab Nebula & Related Supernova Remnants. (Illus.). 320p. Date not set. price not set (ISBN 0-521-30530-6). Cambridge U Pr.

Meyerhoff, Roland & Gillespie, George H., eds. Supernovae Spectra: La Jolla Institute, 1980. (AIP Conference Proceedings: No. 63). 173p. 1980. lib. bdg. 18.25 (ISBN 0-88318-162-2). Am Inst Physics.

Murdin, Paul & Murdin, Leslie. Supernovae. 260p. Date not set. price not set. (ISBN 0-521-30038-X). Cambridge U Pr.

Schramm, David, ed. Supernovae. (Astrophysics & Space Science Library: No. 66). 1977. lib. bdg. 29.00 (ISBN 90-277-0806-1, Pub. by Reidel Holland). Kluwer Academic.

Texas Workshop on Type I Supernovae, Austin, March 17-19, 1980. Type One Supernovae: Proceedings. Wheeler, J. C., ed. LC 80-52944. (Illus.). 1980. pap. 10.00 (ISBN 0-9603796-1-4). U of Tex Dept Astron.

SUPERPHOSPHATES

see Phosphates

SUPERSCRIPT (COMPUTER PROGRAM)

Lehman, Carol & Lehman, Mark. TRS-80 Word Processing Applications Using SuperScripsit. 1984. pap. text ed. 22.50 (ISBN 0-8359-7878-8); instr's manual avail. (ISBN 0-8359-7880-X). Reston.

SUPERSCRIPTSIT (COMPUTER PROGRAM)

Bieber-Moses, Jeanette J. SuperSCRIPSIT Word Processing for the TRS-80 Models III, 4, & 4P. 1985. pap. 17.95 (ISBN 0-673-18086-7). Scott F.

Elia, L. & Fall, J. Word Processimg with SUPERSCRIPSIT & the TRS-80. 1985. 15.64 (ISBN 0-87350-345-7) (ISBN 0-87350-346-5). exercise disk avail. Milady.

SUPERSONIC AERODYNAMICS

see Aerodynamics, Supersonic

SUPERSONIC AERONAUTICS

see High-Speed Aeronautics

SUPERSONIC PLANES

see also Sonic Boom

Horwitch, Mel. Clipped Wings: The American SST Conflict. (Illus.). 432p. 1982. 35.00x (ISBN 0-262-08115-6). MIT Pr.

SUPERSONIC TESTING

see Ultrasonic Testing

SUPERSONIC WAVES

see Ultrasonic Waves

SUPERSONICS

see Aerodynamics, Supersonic; Ultrasonics

SUPERTANKERS

see Tankers

SUPPLIES, MILITARY

see Military Supplies

SURF

see Ocean Waves

SURF-BOATS

see Life-Boats

SURFACE ACTIVE AGENTS

see also Detergents, Synthetic

Ash, M. & Ash, I. Encyclopedia of Surfactants, Vol. IV. 1985. 75.00 (ISBN 0-8206-0317-1). Chem Pub.

--Encyclopedia of Surfactants, Vol. 1, A-F. 1980. 75.00 (ISBN 0-8206-0249-3). Chem Pub.

--Encyclopedia of Surfactants, Vol. 2, G-O. 1981. 75.00 (ISBN 0-8206-0287-6). Chem Pub.

--Encyclopedia of Surfactants, Vol. 3, P-Z. 1981. 75.00 (ISBN 0-8206-0289-2). Chem Pub.

Asinger, F., et al. Chemistry, Physics & Application of Surface Active Substances, 3 vols. 3004p. 1967. Set. 708.25 (ISBN 0-677-10510-X). Gordon.

Attwood, D. & Florence, A. T. Surfactant Systems: Their Chemistry, Pharmacy & Biology. 1982. 99.00x (ISBN 0-412-14840-4, 6714, Pub. by Chapman & Hall). Methuen Inc.

Bluestein, Bernard R. & Hilton, Clifford L., eds. Amphoteric Surfactants. LC 82-12999. (Surfactant Science Ser.: Vol. 12). (Illus.). 352p. 1982. 55.00 (ISBN 0-8247-1277-3). Dekker.

Cross, J., ed. Anionic Surfactants: Chemical Analysis. (Surfactant Science Ser.: Vol. 8). 272p. 1977. softcover 55.00 (ISBN 0-8247-7131-1). Dekker.

Danielli, J. F., et al, eds. Recent Progress in Surface Science, 3 vols. Incl. Vol. 1. 1964. 73.50 (ISBN 0-12-571801-2); Vol. 2. 1964. 83.00 (ISBN 0-12-571802-0); Vol. 3. 1970. 80.50 (ISBN 0-12-571803-9). Acad Pr.

Datyner, Arved. Surfactants in Textile Processing. (Surfactant Science Ser.: No. 14). (Illus.). 232p. 1983. 49.50 (ISBN 0-8247-1812-7). Dekker.

DiStasio, J. I., ed. Surfactants, Detergents & Sequestrants: Developments since 1979. LC 81-38360. (Chem. Tech. Rev. 192). 353p. 1981. 48.00 (ISBN 0-8155-0856-5). Noyes.

The Infrared Spectra Atlas of Surfactants: Surface Active Agents. 295.00 (ISBN 0-8456-0086-9). Sadtler Res.

Kitahara & Watanabe. Electrical Phenomena at Interface. (Surfactant Science Ser.). 504p. 1984. 79.50 (ISBN 0-8247-7186-9). Dekker.

Linfield, Warner M., ed. Anionic Surfactants, Pt. 1. (Surfactants Science Ser.: Vol. 7). 328p. 1976. 79.50 (ISBN 0-8247-6158-8). Dekker.

--Anionic Surfactants, Pt. 2. (Surfactant Science Ser.: Vol. 7). 1976. 79.50 (ISBN 0-8247-6159-6). Dekker.

Lissant. Demulsification. (Surfactant Science Ser.). 176p. 1983. 37.50 (ISBN 0-8247-1802-X). Dekker.

Lucassen-Reynders, E. H. Anionic Surfactants. (Surfactants Science Ser.: Vol. 11). 1981. 75.00 (ISBN 0-8247-1017-7). Dekker.

Mittal, K. L., ed. Surfactants in Solution, 3 Vols. 712p. 1984. 255.00x set (Plenum Pr); Vol. 1, 712p. 95.00x (ISBN 0-306-41483-X); Vol. 2, 718p. 95.00x (ISBN 0-306-41484-8); Vol. 3, 740p. 95.00x (ISBN 0-306-41485-6). Plenum Pub.

SURFACE CHEMISTRY
see also Adsorption; Capillarity; Catalysis; Colloids; Surface Tension

SURFACE HARDENING
see also Case Hardening; Diffusion Coatings

SURFACE TENSION
see also Capillarity; Surface Active Agents; Surface Chemistry

SURFACES
see also Coordinates; Curvature; Geometry, Algebraic; Quaternions; Sphere

Agranovich, V. M. & Mills, D. L., eds. Surface Polaritons: Electromagnetic Waves of Surfaces & Interfaces. (Modern Problems in Condensed Matter Sciences Ser.: Vol. 1). 704p. 1982. 147.00 (ISBN 0-444-86165-3). Elsevier.

Auciello, O. & Kelly, R., eds. Ion Bombardment Modification of Surfaces: Fundamentals & Applications. (Beam Modification of Materials Ser.: No. 1). 468p. 1984. 94.50 (ISBN 0-444-42365-6, I-308-84). Elsevier.

Bauer, R. S., ed. Surfaces & Interfaces: Physics & Electronics. 650p. 1984. 77.00 (ISBN 0-444-86784-8, I-200-84, North Holland). Elsevier.

Berkeley, R. C., et al. Microbial Adhesion to Surfaces. LC 80-41358. 559p. 1981. 125.00x (ISBN 0-470-27083-7). Halsted Pr.

Binh, Vu T., ed. Surface Mobilities on Solid Materials: Fundamental Concepts & Applications. (NATO ASI Series B, Physics: Vol. 86). 598p. 1983. 89.50x (ISBN 0-306-41125-3, Plenum Press). Plenum Pub.

Brakke, Kenneth A. The Motion of a Surface by Its Mean Curvature. (Mathematical Notes Ser.: No. 20). 1978. 24.00 (ISBN 0-691-08204-9). Princeton U Pr.

Burago, Yu. D. Isoperimetric Inequalities in the Theory of Surfaces of Bounded External Curvature. LC 70-122625. (Seminars in Mathematics Ser.: Vol. 10). 99p. 1970. 20.00x (ISBN 0-306-18810-4, Consultants). Plenum Pub.

Burke, John J. & Weiss, Volker, eds. Surface Treatment for Improved Performance & Properties. (Sagamore Army Materials Research Conference Proceedings Ser.: Vol. 26). 225p. 1982. text ed. 42.50 (ISBN 0-306-40897-X, Plenum Pr). Plenum Pub.

Burke, John J., et al, eds. Surfaces & Interfaces I: Chemical & Physical Characteristics. LC 64-12568. (Sagamore Army Materials Research Conference Ser.: Vol. 13). 488p. 1967. 35.00x (ISBN 0-306-34513-7, Plenum Pr). Plenum Pub.

--Surfaces & Interfaces II: Physical & Mechanical Properties. (Sagamore Army Materials Research Conference Ser.: Vol. 14). 506p. 1968. 35.00x (ISBN 0-306-34514-5, Plenum Pr). Plenum Pub.

Cadenhead, D. A., ed. Progress in Surface & Membrane Science, Vol. 13. (Serial Publication). 1979. 70.00 (ISBN 0-12-571813-6). Acad Pr.

Cadenhead, D. A. & Danielli, James F., eds. Progress in Surface & Membrane Science, Vol. 12. 1979. 71.50 (ISBN 0-12-571812-8). Acad Pr.

Caudano, R., et al, eds. Vibrations at Surfaces. LC 81-15830. 596p. 1981. 89.50x (ISBN 0-306-40824-4, Plenum Pr). Plenum Pub.

Cesari, L. Surface Area. (Annals of Mathematics Studies: No. 35). 1956. 37.00 (ISBN 0-527-02752-9). Kraus Repr.

Darboux, Gaston. Theorie Generale Des Surfaces, 4 Vols. 2nd ed. LC 67-16997. (Fr). 1968. Set. 85.00 (ISBN 0-8284-0216-7). Chelsea Pub.

Davison, S. G., ed. Progress in Surface Science, Vols. 1-7. Incl. Vol. 1, 4 pts. Vol. 1, 1971 Complete. 81.00 (ISBN 0-08-016878-7); Pts 1-4. pap. 15.50 ea.; Pt. 1. pap. (ISBN 0-08-016549-4); Pt. 2, 1971. pap. (ISBN 0-08-016629-6); Pt. 3, 1972. pap. (ISBN 0-08-016815-9); Pt. 4. 1972. pap. (ISBN 0-08-016792-6); Vol. 2, 4 pts. 1972. Vol. 2, Complete. 81.00 (ISBN 0-08-017135-4); Pts. 1-4. pap. 15.50 ea.; Pt. 1. pap. (ISBN 0-08-016934-1); Pt. 2. pap. (ISBN 0-08-016879-5); Pt. 3. pap. (ISBN 0-08-016944-9); Pt. 4. pap. (ISBN 0-08-016952-X); Vol. 3, 4 pts. Vol. 3, Complete. 81.00 (ISBN 0-08-017150-8); Pts. 1-4. pap. 15.50 ea.; Pt. 1. pap. (ISBN 0-08-016981-3); Pt. 2, 1972. pap. (ISBN 0-08-017045-5); Pt. 3, 1972. pap. (ISBN 0-08-017046-3); Pt. 4, 1973. pap. (ISBN 0-08-017127-3); Vol. 4, 3 pts. 1974. Vol. 4, Complete. 81.00 (ISBN 0-08-017778-6); Pts. 1-3. pap. 15.50 ea.; Pt. 1-1973. pap. Pt. 2. pap. (ISBN 0-08-017790-5); Pt. 3. pap. (ISBN 0-08-017798-0); Vol. 5, 4 pts. 1974. Vol. 5, Complete. 81.00 (ISBN 0-08-017791-3); Pts. 1-4. pap. 15.50 ea.; Pt. 1-1974. pap. (ISBN 0-08-017904-5); Pt. 2-1974. pap. (ISBN 0-08-017792-1); Pt. 3-1974. pap. (ISBN 0-08-018051-5); Pt. 4-1975. pap. (ISBN 0-08-018150-3); Vol. 6, 3 pts. 1975. Pt. 1. pap. 8.00 (ISBN 0-08-018223-2); Pt. 2. pap. 22.00 (ISBN 0-08-018974-1); Pt. 3. pap. 12.50 (ISBN 0-08-018975-X); Vol. 6-7 Complete-1978. 77.00 (ISBN 0-08-019460-5); Vol. 7, 3 pts. 1976. Pt. 1. pap. 10.00 (ISBN 0-08-018977-6); Pt. 2. pap. 12.00 (ISBN 0-08-018978-4); Pt. 3. pap. 11.00 (ISBN 0-08-018979-2); Vol. 9 Complete. 273p. 1980. 81.00 (ISBN 0-08-026052-7). pap. write for info. Pergamon.

--Progress in Surface Science, Vol. 11. LC 77-141188. 378p. 1983. 106.00 (ISBN 0-08-030875-9, 17). Pergamon.

Ducan, James P. & Mair, Susan G. Sculptured Surfaces in Engineering & Medicine. LC 82-1116. (Illus.). 400p. 1983. 82.50 (ISBN 0-521-23450-6). Cambridge U Pr.

Eberlein, Patrick. Geodesics & Ends in Certain Surfaces Without Conjugate Points. LC 77-28627. (Memoirs Ser.: No. 199). 111p. 1982. pap. 14.00 (ISBN 0-8218-2199-7, MEMO-199). Am Math.

--Surfaces of Nonpositive Curvature. LC 79-15112. (Memoirs: No. 218). 90p. 1979. pap. 10.00 (ISBN 0-8218-2218-7, MEMO-218). Am Math.

Feuerbacher, B., et al. Photoemission & the Electronic Properties of Surfaces. 540p. 1978. 103.95x (ISBN 0-471-99555-X). Wiley.

Garcia-Moliner, F. & Flores, F. Introduction to the Theory of Solid Surfaces. LC 78-17617. (Cambridge Monographs on Physics). (Illus.). 1979. 89.50 (ISBN 0-521-22294-X). Cambridge U Pr.

Gauss, Karl F. General Investigations of Curved Surfaces. Hiltebeitel & Moorehead, trs. LC 65-6415. 1965. 14.00 (ISBN 0-911216-02-2). Raven.

Hayden, C., ed. Pavement Surface Characteristics & Materials - STP 763. 131p. 1982. pap. 17.00 (ISBN 0-8031-0785-4, 04-763000-47). ASTM.

Hoehler, G., ed. Structural Studies of Surfaces. (Springer Tracts in Modern Physics Ser.: Vol. 91). (Illus.). 190p. 1982. 33.00 (ISBN 0-387-10964-1). Springer-Verlag.

Kirschner, J. M. Polarized Electrons at Surfaces. (Tracts in Modern Physics Ser.: Vol. 106). (Illus.). 175p. 1985. 24.00 (ISBN 0-387-15003-X). Springer-Verlag.

Lalov, I. J., ed. Modern Problems of Surface Physics: Proceedings of the First International School on Condensed Matter Physics, Varna, Bulgaria, Sept. 29-Oct. 12, 1980. 924p. pap. 42.00x (ISBN 0-317-12932-5, Pub. by World Sci Singapore). Taylor & Francis.

Latanision, R. M. & Fischer, T. E. Advances in Mechanics & Physics of Surfaces, Vol. 1. 262p. 1981. 69.50 (ISBN 3-7186-0026-9). Harwood Academic.

Lowell, S. & Shields, J. E. Powder Surface Area & Porosity. 2nd ed. (Powder Technology Ser.). 230p. 1984. 50.00 (ISBN 0-412-25240-6, NO. 9012, Pub. by Chapman & Hall England). Methuen Inc.

Matijevic, E., ed. Surface & Colloid Science, Vol. 10. LC 67-29459. (Illus.). 360p. 1978. 49.50x (ISBN 0-306-38260-1, Plenum Pr). Plenum Pub.

Matijevic, Egon, ed. Surface & Colloid Science, Vol. 12. LC 67-29459. 484p. 1982. 65.00x (ISBN 0-306-40616-0, Plenum Pr). Plenum Pub.

Nizzoli, F, et al, eds. Dynamical Phenomena at Surfaces, Intersurfaces & Superlattices, Vol. 3. (Springer Series in Surface Sciences: Vol. 3). (Illus.). 350p. 1985. 29.50 (ISBN 0-387-15505-8). Springer-Verlag.

Pogorelov, A. V., ed. Topics in the Theory of Surfaces in Elliptic Space. (Russian Tracts on the Physical Sciences Ser.). (Illus.). 146p. 1962. 45.25x (ISBN 0-677-20400-0). Gordon.

Prutton, Martin. Surface Physics. 2nd ed. (Illus.). 1983. 15.95x (ISBN 0-19-851863-3). Oxford U Pr.

Pullman, Bernard, et al, eds. Dynamics on Surfaces. 1984. lib. bdg. 69.00 (ISBN 90-277-1830-X, Pub. by Reidel Holland). Kluwer Academic.

Rand, D. A. & Bond, A. M. Electrochemistry: The Interfacing Science. (Studies in Physical & Theoretical Chemistry: Vol. 34). 482p. 1984. 109.25 (ISBN 0-444-42304-4). Elsevier.

Rohde, S. M. & Cheng, H. S., eds. Surface Roughness Effects in Hydrodymanic & Mixed Lubrication. 218p. 1980. 30.00 (ISBN 0-686-69862-2, G00193). ASME.

Sorensen, Smith T., ed. Dynamics & Instability of Fluid Interfaces. (Lecture Notes in Physics: Vol. 105). 1979. pap. 20.00 (ISBN 0-387-09524-1). Springer-Verlag.

Svec, A. Global Differential Geometry of Surfaces. 1982. lib. bdg. 28.50 (ISBN 90-277-1295-6, Pub. by Reidel Holland). Kluwer Academic.

Thomas, R. R. Rough Surfaces. (Illus.). 310p. 1982. text ed. 55.00x (ISBN 0-582-46816-7). Longman.

Vanselow & England, eds. Chemistry & Physics of Solid Surfaces, Vol. III. 352p. 1982. 44.95 (ISBN 0-8493-0128-9). CRC Pr.

Zariski, O. Algebraic Surfaces. 2nd ed. LC 70-148144. (Ergebnisse der Mathematik & Ihrer Grenzgebiete: Vol. 61). 1971. 37.00 (ISBN 0-387-05335-2). Springer-Verlag.

Zieschang, H. Finite Groups of Mapping Classes of Surfaces. (Lecture Notes in Mathematics Ser.: Vol. 875). 340p. 1981. pap. 20.00 (ISBN 0-387-10857-2). Springer Verlag.

SURFACES (CHEMISTRY)
see Surface Chemistry

SURFACES (TECHNOLOGY)
see also Metallic Films; Thin Films

Belyaev, A. I., ed. Surface Phenomena in Metallurgical Processes. LC 65-11335. 288p. 1965. 37.50x (ISBN 0-306-10704-X, Consultants). Plenum Pub.

Bogenschutz, A. F. Surface Technology & Electroplating in the Electronics Industry. 392p. 1981. 70.00x (ISBN 0-901994-50-2, Pub. by Portcullio Pr). State Mutual Bk.

Briggs, D. & Seah, M. P. Practical Surface Analysis by Auger & Photo-Electron Spectoscopy. 533p. 1983. 83.95x (ISBN 0-471-26279-X, Pub. by Wiley-Interscience). Wiley.

Davison, S. G., ed. Progress in Surface Science, Vol. 12. 436p. 1983. 110.00 (ISBN 0-08-030876-7). Pergamon.

Dyachenko, P. E., et al. Actual Contact Area Between Touching Surfaces. LC 64-13145. 1964. 22.50x (ISBN 0-306-10678-7, Consultants). Plenum Pub.

Gibson, J. M. & Dawson, L. R., eds. Layered Structures Epitaxy & Interfaces, Vol. 37. LC 85-3077. 1985. text ed. 50.00 (ISBN 0-931837-02-2). Materials Res.

International Course, Trieste, Jan. 16-April 10, 1974. Surface Science: Proceedings, 2 Vols. (Illus.). 302p. 1976. Vol. 1. pap. 45.00 (ISBN 92-0-130375-0, ISP396-1, IAEA); Vol. 2. pap. 28.00 (ISBN 0-685-62848-5). Unipub.

Kane, Philip F. & Larrabee, Graydon B., eds. Characterization of Solid Surfaces. LC 73-84000. (Illus.). 670p. 1974. 59.50x (ISBN 0-306-30752-9, Plenum Pr). Plenum Pub.

Kingston, R. H., ed. Semiconductor Surface Physics. LC 60-14439. 1957. 20.00x (ISBN 0-8122-7113-0). U of Pa Pr.

Leyden, D. & Collins, W. Silyated Surfaces, Vol. 7. (Midland Macromolecular Monographs). 388p. 1980. 80.95 (ISBN 0-677-13370-7). Gordon.

Ling, Frederick F. Surface Mechanics. LC 72-10012. pap. 84.00 (ISBN 0-317-11062-4, 2006492). Bks Demand UMI.

Loomis, William R., ed. New Directions in Lubrication, Materials, Wear, & Surface Interactions: Tribology in the 80's. LC 84-22663. (Illus.). 841p. 1985. 69.00 (ISBN 0-8155-1013-6). Noyes.

Marchessault, R. H. & Skaar, Christen, eds. Surfaces & Coatings Related to Paper & Wood. LC 66-27617. 1967. 24.95x (ISBN 0-8156-5017-5). Syracuse U Pr.

Moore, D. F. Elastomer Friction Lubrication. 305p. 1972. text ed. 50.00 (ISBN 0-08-016749-7); pap. text ed. 27.00 (ISBN 0-08-019002-2). Pergamon.

Niku-Lari, A., ed. Advances in Surface Treatments: Technology, Applications, Effects, Vol. 1. (Illus.). 240p. 1984. 44.00 (ISBN 0-08-031126-1). Pergamon.

Quantitative Surface Analysis of Materials, STP 643. 217p. 1978. 21.50 (ISBN 0-8031-0543-6, 04-643000-39). ASTM.

Skobel'tsyn, D. V., ed. Surface Properties of Semiconductors & Dynamics of Ionic Crystals. LC 77-136983. (P. N. Lebedev Physics Institute Ser.: Vol. 48). 148p. 1971. 27.50x (ISBN 0-306-10854-2, Consultants). Plenum Pub.

Snogren, R. C. Handbook of Surface Preparation. 594p. 1974. 40.00 (ISBN 0-686-48221-2, 0502). T-C Pubns CA.

Surface Analysis Techniques for Metallurgical Applications, STP 596. 146p. 1976. pap. 15.00 (ISBN 0-8031-0584-3, 04-596000-28). ASTM.

Surface Noise & Vibration Conference Proceedings. 1985. 40.00 (P161). Soc Auto Engineers.

Swedlow, J. L., ed. The Surface Crach: Physical Problems & Computational Solutions. Presented at the Winter Annual Meeting of ASME, New York, N. Y., November 26-30, 1972. LC 72-88547. pap. 52.00 (ISBN 0-317-08113-6, 2016841). Bks Demand UMI.

Thomas, T. R. & King, M., eds. Surface Topography in Engineering. (BHRA Fluid Engineering Ser.: Vol. 3). 1977. pap. 40.00x (ISBN 0-900983-66-3, Dist. by Air Science Co.). BHRA Fluid.

Williams, R. H., et al, eds. Interdisciplinary Surface Science: Proceedings of the 5th Interdisciplinary Surface Science Conference, (ISSC), April 6-9, 1981, University of Liverpool, U. K. 260p. 1983. pap. 33.00 (ISBN 0-08-029318-2, A145, C125). Pergamon.

Wolfram, E., ed. International Conference on Colloid & Surface Science: Proceedings. 1975. 11.50 (ISBN 0-9960003-7-2, Pub. by Akademiai Kaido Hungary). Heyden.

Zimmerli, Bruno & Thurlimann, Bruno. Strength Interaction Surfaces for Tall Buildings. (IBA Ser.: No 91). 72p. 1979. pap. text ed. 4.95x (ISBN 0-8176-1124-X). Birkhauser.

SURFACES, ALGEBRAIC

Barth, W. & Peters, C. A. Compact Complex Surfaces. (A Series of Modern Surveys in Mathematics, Band 4: Vol. 4). 320p. 1984. 38.00 (ISBN 0-317-04553-9). Springer-Verlag.

Beauville, A. Complex Algebraic Surfaces. LC 82-9490. (London Mathematical Society Lecture Note Ser.: No. 68). 150p. 1983. pap. 22.95 (ISBN 0-521-28815-0). Cambridge U Pr.

Miyanishi, M. Non-Complete Algebraic Surfaces. (Lecture Notes in Mathematics Ser.: Vol. 857). 244p. 1981. pap. 19.00 (ISBN 0-387-10703-7). Springer-Verlag.

Moishezon, B. Complex Surfaces & Connected Sums of Complex Projective Planes. LC 77-22136. (Lecture Notes in Mathematics: Vol. 603). (Illus.). 1977. pap. text ed. 18.00 (ISBN 0-387-08355-3). Springer-Verlag.

Persson, U. On Degenerations of Algebraic Surfaces. LC 77-8972. (Memoirs Ser: No. 189). 144p. 1977. paper 14.00 (ISBN 0-8218-2189-X, MEMO-189). Am Math.

Steklov Institute of Mathematics, Academy of Sciences, U.S.S.R., No. 75. Algebraic Surfaces: Proceedings. Safarevic, I. R., ed. (Proceedings of the Steklov Institute of Mathematics). 1983. Repr. of 1967 ed. 60.00 (ISBN 0-8218-1875-9, STEKLO-75). Am Math.

Tu, Loring W. Hodge Theory & the Local Torelli Problem. LC 83-3781. (Memoirs of the American Mathematical Society Ser.: No. 279). 66p. 1983. pap. 10.00 (ISBN 0-8218-2279-9). Am Math.

White, A. T. Graphs, Groups & Surfaces. 2nd, rev. & enl. ed. (Mathematics Studies: Vol. 8). 314p. 1985. 30.00 (ISBN 0-444-87643-X, North-Holland). Elsevier.

Zariski, O. An Introduction to the Theory of Algebraic Surface. 2nd ed. LC 68-59477. (Lecture Notes in Mathematics: Vol. 83). vi, 100p. 1972. pap. 10.70 (ISBN 0-387-04602-X). Springer-Verlag.

SURFACES, CONFORMAL REPRESENTATION OF
see Surfaces, Representation Of

SURFACES, CUBIC

Manin, Yu I. Cubic Forms: Algebra, Geometry, Arithmetic. Hazewinkel, M., tr. from Rus. LC 72-88278. (Mathematical Library: Vol. 4). 304p. 1974. 53.25 (ISBN 0-444-10456-9, North-Holland). Elsevier.

SURFACES, CURVES ON
see Curves on Surfaces

SURFACES, FERMI
see Fermi Surfaces

SURFACES, MINIMAL

Guisti, E. Minimal Surfaces & Functions of Bounded Variation. (Monographs in Mathematics). 1984. text ed. 39.95 (ISBN 0-8176-3153-4). Birkhauser.

Hoffman, D. A. & Osserman, R. The Geometry of the Generalized Gauss Map. LC 80-23014. (Memoirs: No. 236). 105p. 1980. pap. 10.00 (ISBN 0-8218-2236-5). Am Math.

Osserman, Robert. A Survey of Minimal Surfaces. 192p. 1986. pap. 6.00 (ISBN 0-486-64998-9). Dover.

SURFACES, REPRESENTATION OF
see also Conformal Mapping; Map-Projection

Beem, J. K. & Woo, P. Y. Doubly Timelike Surfaces. LC 52-42839. (Memoirs: No. 92). 115p. 1969. pap. 9.00 (ISBN 0-8218-1292-0, MEMO-92). Am Math.

Ibach, H., et al, eds. Electron Spectroscopy for Surface Mapping. (Topics in Current Physics Ser.: Vol. 4). (Illus.). 1977. 42.00 (ISBN 0-387-08078-3). Springer-Verlag.

Youngs, J. W. Representation Problem for Frechet Surfaces. LC 52-42839. (Memoirs: No. 8). 143p. 1980. pap. 13.00 (ISBN 0-8218-1208-4, MEMO-8). Am Math.

SURFACES, RIEMANN
see Riemann Surfaces

SURFACTANTS
see Surface Active Agents

SURGE (ELECTRICITY)
see Transients (Electricity)

SURVEYING
see also Area Measurement; Building Sites; Cartography; Geodesy; Hydrographic Surveying; Mine Surveying; Railroads–Surveying; Roads–Surveying; Topographical Drawing; Topographical Surveying

Ali, Jamil. Determination of the Coordinates of Positions for the Correction of Distances Between Cities. 1967. 24.95x (ISBN 0-8156-6007-3, Am U Beirut). Syracuse U Pr.

Allen, A. L., et al. Practical Field Surveying & Computations. (Illus.). 688p. 1968. 37.00 (ISBN 0-434-90061-3, Pub. by W Heinemann Ltd). David & Charles.

American Society of Civil Engineers, compiled by. Guide to Right of Way Survey Practices. 13p. 1981. pap. 6.00x (ISBN 0-87262-279-7). Am Soc Civil Eng.

Anderson, J. & Mikhail, E. Introduction to Surveying. 720p. 1984. 32.95 (ISBN 0-07-001653-4). McGraw.

Aqua Group. Contract Administration for Architects & Quantity Surveyors. 5th ed. 87p. 1979. pap. text ed. 17.25x (ISBN 0-258-97139-8, Pub. by Granada England). Brookfield Pub Co.

Glicksman, Martin. Food Hydrocolloids, Vol. II. 208p. 1983. 72.00 (ISBN 0-8493-6042-0). CRC Pr.

SUZUKI MOTORCYCLE

Aspel, Geoff. Suzuki. LC 83-73616. (Illus.). 64p. (Orig.). 1984. 7.95 (ISBN 0-668-06164-2); pap. 3.95 (ISBN 0-668-06171-5). Arco.

Clew, Jeff. Suzuki 250 & 350 Twins '69 - '78. new ed. (Owners Workshop Manuals Ser.: No. 120). 1979. 10.50 (ISBN 0-85696-120-5, Pub. by J H Haynes England). Haynes Pubns.

Clymer Publications. Suzuki: 380-750cc Triples, 1972-1977 Service, Repair, Maintenance. (Illus.). 1977. pap. 13.95 (ISBN 0-89287-285-3, M368). Clymer Pubns.

Collett, George. Suzuki GT 380, 550 '72 - '77. new ed. (Owners Workshop Manuals Ser.: No. 216). 1979. 10.50 (ISBN 0-85696-216-3, Pub. by J H Haynes England). Haynes Pubns.

Darlington, Mansur. Suzuki GT750 (3-cyl) Models '71 - '77. new ed. (Owners Workshop Manuals Ser.: No. 302). 1979. 10.50 (ISBN 0-85696-302-X, Pub. by J H Haynes England). Haynes Pubns.

--Suzuki Trail Bikes 90 Thru 400cc's '71-'79. new ed. (Owners Workshop Manuals Ser.: No. 218). 1979. 10.50 (ISBN 0-85696-520-0, Pub. by J H Haynes England). Haynes Pubns.

Hoy, Ray. Suzuki Service-Repair Handbook 125-500cc Twins: 1964-1976. 3rd rev. ed. (Illus.). pap. 13.95 (ISBN 0-89287-132-6, M-366). Clymer Pubns.

Jorgensen, Eric. Suzuki DS80-250 Singles, 1978-1980: Service, Repair, Maintenance. (Illus., Orig.). pap. text ed. 13.95 (ISBN 0-89287-316-7, M363). Clymer Pubns.

Jorgensen, Eric, ed. Suzuki GS1000 Chain Drive Fours: 1978-1979 Service-Repair-Performance. (Illus., Orig.). pap. text ed. 13.95 (ISBN 0-89287-315-9, M375). Clymer Pubns.

--Suzuki GS750 Fours, 1977-1982: Service, Repair, Performance. (Illus.). pap. 13.95 (ISBN 0-89287-189-X, M370). Clymer Pubns.

--Suzuki GS850 & GS1000 Shaft Drive Fours 1979-1984: Service, Repair, Maintenance. (Illus., Orig.). pap. text ed. 13.95 (ISBN 0-89287-305-1, M376). Clymer Pubns.

--Suzuki 50-400cc Rm Series Singles, 1975-81: Service, Repair, Performance. (Illus.). pap. 13.95 (ISBN 0-89287-196-2, M371). Clymer Pubns.

Rabone, David. Suzuki Owners Workshop Manual: Five Hundred Twins '68 Thru '76. new ed. (Owners Workshop Manuals Ser.: No. 135). 1979. 10.50 (ISBN 0-85696-135-3, Pub. by J H Haynes England). Haynes Pubns.

Sales, David. Suzuki GS & GSX1100 Fours: 1980-1981 (Service, Repair, Performance) Wauson, Sydnie A., ed. (Illus., Orig.). 1981. pap. 13.95 (ISBN 0-89287-353-1, M378). Clymer Pubns.

Wilkins, Stewart. Suzuki B100 P, B120 Student '66 - '77. new ed. (Owners Workshop Manuals Ser.: No. 298). 1979. 10.50 (ISBN 0-85696-298-8, Pub. by J H Haynes England). Haynes Pubns.

--Suzuki Owners Workshop Manual: Gt 125, 185 Twins '73 Thru '77. new ed. (Owners Workshop Manuals Ser.: No. 301). 1979. 10.50 (ISBN 0-85696-301-1, Pub. by J H Haynes England). Haynes Pubns.

SW RADIO

see Radio, Short Wave

SWALLOWS

see also Purple Martin

Hodges, William J. & Swegle, Margaret A. Adventures of the Sea Swallows. LC 81-80930. (Illus., Orig.). 1981. pap. 5.00 (ISBN 0-9605992-0-7). Mountain Calif.

Whittemore, Margaret. Chimney Swifts & Their Relatives. 176p. 1981. pap. 6.95x (ISBN 0-912542-02-0). Nature Bks Pubs.

SWAMPS

see Fens; Marshes; Moors and Heaths

SWANS

see also Trumpeter Swan

Breucker, H. Seasonal Spermatogenesis in the Mute Swan (Cygnus Olor) (Advances in Anatomy, Embryology, & Cell Biology Ser.: Vol. 72). (Illus.). 104p. 1982. pap. 27.00 (ISBN 0-387-11326-6). Springer-Verlag.

Kortright, E. H. Ducks, Geese & Swans of North America. rev. ed. Bellrose, Frank C., rev. by. LC 75-33962. (Illus.). 568p. 1981. 29.95 (ISBN 0-8117-0535-8). Stackpole.

Wildlife Education Staff. Ducks, Geese & Swans: Waterfowl. (Illus., Orig.). 1984. pap. 1.95 (ISBN 0-937934-21-6). Wildlife Educ.

Wilmore, Sylvia B. Swans of the World. LC 74-3669. (Illus.). 224p. 1974. 14.95 (ISBN 0-8008-7524-9). Taplinger.

--Swans of the World. LC 74-3669. (Illus.). 1979. pap. 8.50 (ISBN 0-8008-7523-0). Taplinger.

SWEAT

see Perspiration

SWEAT BEES

see Bees

SWEET POTATOES

see also Yams

Yen, Douglas E. The Sweet Potato & Oceania: An Essay in Ethnobotany. LC 74-75842. (Bulletin Ser: No. 236). (Illus.). 389p. 1974. 18.00 (ISBN 0-910240-17-5). Bishop Mus.

SWELL

see Ocean Waves

SWIDDEN AGRICULTURE

see Shifting Cultivation

SWIDDEN FARMING

see Shifting Cultivation

SWINE

see also Pork Industry and Trade

Baker, J. K. & Juergenson, E. M. Approved Practices in Swine Production. 6th ed. LC 79-142330. 438p. 1979. 18.60 (ISBN 0-8134-2038-5, 2038); text ed. 13.95x. Interstate.

Board on Agriculture & Renewable Resources. Nutrient Requirements of Swine. 8th rev. ed. (Nutrient Requirements of Domestic Animals Ser.). (Illus.). 64p. 1979. pap. 7.50 (ISBN 0-309-02870-1). Natl Acad Pr.

Bundy, Clarence E., et al. Swine Production. 1976. text ed. 31.50 (ISBN 0-13-879783-8). P-H.

Cole & Foxcroft. Control of Pig Reproduction. 1982. text ed. 119.95 (ISBN 0-408-10768-5). Butterworth.

Cole, D. J., ed. Pig Production. LC 70-38754. (Illus.). 434p. 1972. 32.50x (ISBN 0-271-01114-9). Pa St U Pr.

Cole, D. J. & Haresign, W., eds. Recent Developments in Pig Nutrition. 336p. 1985. pap. text ed. 25.95 (ISBN 0-407-00339-8). Butterworth.

Cunha, ed. Swine Feeding & Nutrition. (Animal Feeding & Nutrition Ser). 1977. 33.00 (ISBN 0-12-196550-3). Acad Pr.

Fennel, William E. A Pig Watcher's Guide to Biology. 88p. 1982. pap. text ed. 8.95 (ISBN 0-8403-2797-8). Kendall-Hunt.

Hawkins, Hedley & Enderby, Nigel. Outdoor Pig Production. 256p. 1986. 20.00x (ISBN 0-246-12242-0, Pub. by Granada England). Sheridan.

Hulme, Susan. Pig Keeping. 80p. 1982. pap. 2.75 (ISBN 0-86230-023-1). Triplegate.

Krider, J. L., et al. Swine Production. 5th ed. (Agricultural Science Ser.). 688p. 1982. 43.95x (ISBN 0-07-035503-7). McGraw.

Marrable, A. W. Embryonic Pig: A Chronological Account. (Illus.). 130p. 1971. 15.95x (ISBN 0-8464-1091-5). Beekman Pubs.

Midwest Plan Service Engineers. Swine Housing & Equipment Handbook. 4th ed. Midwest Plan Service Staff, ed. LC 82-2292. (Illus.). 112p. 1983. pap. 6.00 (ISBN 0-89373-054-8, MWPS-8). Midwest Plan Serv.

Mitchelmore, Peter. The Pigkeeper's Guide. LC 80-68686. (Illus.). 136p. 1981. 12.95 (ISBN 0-7153-7995-X). David & Charles.

The Nutrient Requirement of Pigs: Technical Review by an Agricultural Research Council Working Party. 307p. 1981. cloth 135.00x (ISBN 0-85198-483-5, Pub. by CAB Bks England). State Mutual Bk.

Pig Breeding, Recording & Progeny Testing in European Countries. (Agricultural Planning Studies: No. 44). pap. 4.50 (F317, FAO). Unipub.

Pond, Wilson G. & Houpt, Katherine A. The Biology of the Pig. LC 77-90909. (Illus.). 352p. 1978. 34.95x (ISBN 0-8014-1137-8). Comstock.

Pond, Wilson G. & Maner, Jerome H. Swine Production & Nutrition. (Illus.). 733p. 1984. 59.00 (ISBN 0-87055-450-6). AVI.

--Swine Production in Temperate & Tropical Environments. LC 73-16068. (Illus.). 646p. 1974. text ed. 37.95x (ISBN 0-7167-0840-X). W H Freeman.

Swine Management Packet. 3.25 (ISBN 0-8134-0546-7); 3.25 (ISBN 0-8134-0547-5, 544-547). Interstate.

Sybesma, Watse, ed. The Welfare of Pigs: Current Topics in Veterinary Medicine & Animal Science, No. 11. x, 334p. 1981. 49.00 (ISBN 90-247-2521-6, Pub. by Martinus Nijhoff Netherlands). Kluwer Academic.

Van Loon, Dirk. Small-Scale Pig Raising. LC 78-12938. (Illus.). 272p. 1978. pap. 8.95 (ISBN 0-88266-136-1). Garden Way Pub.

Whittemore, Colin T. Pig Production: The Scientific & Practical Principles. LC 79-42758. (Longman Handbooks in Agriculture Ser.). (Illus.). 145p. (Orig.). 1980. pap. text ed. 13.50x (ISBN 0-582-45590-1). Longman.

SWINE–ANATOMY

Gilbert, Stephen G. Pictorial Anatomy of the Fetal Pig. 2nd, rev. ed. LC 63-10797. (Illus.). 96p. 1966. pap. 7.95x (ISBN 0-295-73877-4). U of Wash Pr.

Groves, C. Ancestors for the Pigs: Taxonomy & Phylogeny of the Genus SUS. (Department of Prehistory, Research School of Pacific Studies Technical Bulletin: No. 3). 96p. 1982. pap. text ed. 8.80 (ISBN 0-909596-75-1, Pub. by ANUP Australia). Australia N U P.

Hughes, Paul & Varley, Mike. Reproduction in the Pig. LC 80-40241. 254p. 1980. text ed. 23.95 (ISBN 0-408-70946-4); pap. text ed. 23.95 (ISBN 0-408-70921-9). Butterworth.

Leone, Charles & Ogilvie, P. W. Fetal Pig Manual. 2nd ed. LC 63-18095. 1963. spiral bdg. 5.95x (ISBN 0-8087-1210-1). Burgess.

Odlaug, Theron O. Laboratory Anatomy of the Fetal Pig. 7th ed. (Laboratory Anatomy Ser.). 112p. 1984. write for info. wire coil (ISBN 0-697-04928-0). Wm C Brown.

Sack, W. O. Essentials of Pig Anatomy & Horowitz-Kramer Atlas of the Musculoskeletal Anatomy of the Pig. LC 81-71150. (Illus.). x, 192p. 1982. text ed. 12.50x (ISBN 0-9601152-2-6). Veterinary Textbks.

Thorpe, Darwin R. Fetal Pig: A Dissection Guide in Color. (Illus.). 1970. pap. text ed. 6.95 (ISBN 0-87484-140-2). Mayfield Pub.

SWITCHES, ELECTRIC

see Electric Contactors; Electric Relays

SWITCHES, RAILROAD

see Railroads–Construction

SWITCHING THEORY

see also Telephone Switching Systems, Electronic; Threshold Logic

Biorci, Giuseppe, ed. Network & Switching Theory. (Electrical Science Ser). 1968. 85.00 (ISBN 0-12-099550-6). Acad Pr.

Biswas, Nripendra U. Introduction to Logic & Switching Theory. 368p. 1975. 67.25x (ISBN 0-677-02860-1). Gordon.

Boyce, Jefferson. Digital Logic: Operation & Analysis. 2nd ed. (Illus.). 464p. 1982. 32.95 (ISBN 0-13-214619-3). P-H.

Davio, Marc, et al. Discrete & Switching Functions. 1978. text ed. 127.95x (ISBN 0-07-015509-7). McGraw.

Din Standards for Electrical Engineering: Graphical Symbols & Wiring Diagrams. 325.00 (ISBN 0-01-006120-7, 10061-5/07). Heyden.

Friedman, Arthur & Menon, Premachandran R. Theory & Design of Switching Circuits. LC 75-15888. (Illus.). 581p. 1975. 36.95 (ISBN 0-914894-52-8). Computer Sci.

Friedman, Arthur D. Logical Design of Digital Systems. LC 74-82932. (Illus., Solutions manual avail. only to instructors for course adoptions). 1975. text ed. 26.95 (ISBN 0-914894-50-1). Computer Sci.

Gavrilov, M. A. & Zakrevsky, A. D., eds. LYAPAS: A Programming Language for Logic & Coding Algorithms. (ACM Monograph Ser). 1969. 90.00 (ISBN 0-12-277850-2). Acad Pr.

GRINSEC. Electronic Switching. (Studies in Telecommunication: Vol. 2). 680p. 1983. 89.00 (ISBN 0-444-86448-2, North Holland). Elsevier.

Hill, Frederick J. & Peterson, Gerald R. Introduction to Switching Theory & Logical Design. 3rd ed. LC 80-20333. 617p. 1981. text ed. 41.50 (ISBN 0-471-04273-0); solutions manual avail. (ISBN 0-471-09081-6). Wiley.

Kohavi, Zvi. Switching & Finite Automata Theory. 2nd ed. Feigenbaum & Hamming, eds. (McGraw-Hill Computer Science Ser.). (Illus.). 1978. text ed. 46.95 (ISBN 0-07-035310-7). McGraw.

Lee, Samuel C. Modern Switching Theory & Digital Design. 1978. ref. 36.95 (ISBN 0-13-598680-X). P-H.

Lyon-Caen, Robert. Diodes, Transistors, & Integrated Circuits for Switching Systems. (Electrical Science Ser.). 1968. 85.00 (ISBN 0-12-460550-8). Acad Pr.

McDonald, John C., ed. Fundamentals of Digital Switching. (Applications of Communications Theory Ser.). 432p. 1983. 55.00x (ISBN 0-306-41224-1, Plenum Press). Plenum Pub.

Mano, M. Morris. Computer Logic Design. (Automatic Computation Ser.). (Illus.). 464p. 1972. 38.95 (ISBN 0-13-165472-1). P-H.

Marcus, Mitchell P. Switching Circuits for Engineers. 3rd ed. (Illus.). 336p. 1975. ref. ed. 37.95 (ISBN 0-13-879908-3). P-H.

Millman, Jacob & Taub, H. Pulse, Digital & Switching Waveforms. 1965. text ed. 49.95 (ISBN 0-07-042386-5). McGraw.

Motil, John M. Digital System Fundamentals. Truxal, J. G. & Rohrer, R., eds. (Electronic Systems Ser.). (Illus.). 416p. 1972. 42.00 (ISBN 0-07-043515-4). McGraw.

Mukhopadhyay, Amar, ed. Recent Developments in Switching Theory. (Electrical Science Ser). 1971. 90.00 (ISBN 0-12-509850-2). Acad Pr.

Oberman, R. M. Digital Circuits for Binary Arithmetic. 340p. 1979. 59.95x (ISBN 0-470-26373-3). Halsted Pr.

Pearce, J. G. The World of Electronic Switching. (Illus.). 140p. 8.00 (ISBN 0-317-06294-8). Telephony.

Pearce, J. Gordon. Telecommunications Switching. LC 80-20586. (Applications of Communications Theory Ser.). 348p. 1981. 35.00x (ISBN 0-306-40584-9, Plenum Pr). Plenum Pub.

Perrin, J. P., et al. Switching Machines, 2 vols. Incl. Vol.2. Sequential Systems. lib. bdg. 53.00 (ISBN 90-277-0197-0). LC 70-118379. 1972 (Pub. by Reidel Holland). Kluwer Boston.

Rhyne, V. Thomas. Fundamentals of Digital Systems Design. LC 72-6903. (Illus.). 560p. 1973. 39.95 (ISBN 0-13-336156-X). P-H.

Rosner, Roy D. Distributed Telecommunications Networks via Satellites & Packet Switching. (Engineering Ser.). 235p. 1982. 31.50 (ISBN 0-534-97933-5). Lifetime Learn.

Sparkes, J. J. Transistor Switching & Sequential Circuits. 1969. pap. 10.75 (ISBN 0-08-012981-1). Pergamon.

Stapleton, Gerald. Beginner's Guide to Computer Logic. LC 70-155978. (Illus.). 1971. pap. 7.95 (ISBN 0-8306-0548-7, 548). TAB Bks.

Sum. Switch Mode Power Conversation. (Electrical Engineering & Electronics Ser.). 240p. 1984. 45.00 (ISBN 0-8247-7234-2). Dekker.

Symposium on the Application of Switching Theory in Space Technology (1962: Sunnyvale, CA) Switching Theory in Space Technology. Aiken, Howard & Main, William F., eds. LC 63-10730. (Illus.). pap. 91.80 (ISBN 0-317-09300-2, 2002905). Bks Demand UMI.

Thayse, A. Boolean Calculus of Differences. (Lecture Notes in Computer Science Ser.: Vol. 101). 144p. 1981. pap. 12.00 (ISBN 0-387-10286-8). Springer-Verlag.

Thelliez, S. Introduction to the Study of Ternary Switching Structures. (Information & Systems Theory Ser.). 198p. 1975. 40.50x (ISBN 0-677-30330-0). Gordon.

Tou, Julius T., ed. Applied Automata Theory. LC 68-26634. (Electrical Science Ser.). 1969. 80.00 (ISBN 0-12-696230-8). Acad Pr.

Unger, Stephen H. Asynchronous Sequential Switching Circuit. LC 82-18014. 304p. 1983. Repr. of 1969 ed. 21.50 (ISBN 0-89874-565-9). Krieger.

Veatch, H. C. Pulse & Switching Circuit Action. 1971. text ed. 31.00 (ISBN 0-07-067386-1). McGraw.

Wickes, William E. Logic Design with Integrated Circuits. LC 68-21185. pap. 65.50 (ISBN 0-317-28030-9, 2055721). Bks Demand UMI.

SWORDS

Draeger, Donn F. & Warner, Gordon. Japanese Swordsmanship: Technique & Practice. (Illus.). 224p. 1982. 29.95 (Pub. by John Weatherhill Inc Japan). C E Tuttle.

Gunsaulus, H. C. Japanese Sword-Mounts. (Field Museum of Natural History). (Illus.). 1923. 26.00 (ISBN 0-527-01876-7). Kraus Repr.

Japanese Swordsmiths. rev. ed. 1100p. 1980. vinyl bdg. 75.00 (ISBN 0-686-65147-2, 910704-60). Hawley.

Joly, Henri. Shosankenshu: Japanese Sword Mounts. 45.00 (ISBN 0-87556-133-0). Saifer.

Peterson, Harold L. The American Sword, Seventeen Seventy-Five to Nineteen Forty-Five. LC 65-25409. (Illus.). 1983. 35.00 (ISBN 0-9603094-1-1). Ray Riling.

Rankin, Robert H. Small Arms of the Sea Services: A History of the Firearms & Edged Weapons of the U. S. Navy, Marine Corps & Coast Guard from the Revolution to the Present. LC 72-186706. (Illus.). 260p. 1972. 14.50 (ISBN 0-910598-10-X). Flayderman.

Yumoto, John M. Samurai Sword: A Handbook. LC 58-7497. (Illus.). 1958. 11.00 (ISBN 0-8048-0509-1). C E Tuttle.

SYLVICULTURE

see Forests and Forestry

SYLVIDAE

Bent, Arthur C. Life Histories of North American Thrushes, Kinglets & Their Allies. (Illus.). 1949. pap. 7.95 (ISBN 0-486-21086-3). Dover.

--Life Histories of North American Thrushes, Kinglets & Their Allies. (Illus.). 14.50 (ISBN 0-8446-1643-5). Peter Smith.

SYMBIOSIS

Batra, Lekh R., ed. Insect Fungus Symbiosis: Nutrition, Mutualism & Commensalism. LC 78-20640. 288p. 1979. text ed. 27.50x (ISBN 0-470-26671-6). Allanheld.

--Insect-Fungus Symbiosis: Nutrition, Mutualism & Commensalism. LC 78-20640. (Illus.). 276p. 1979. text ed. 44.95x (ISBN 0-470-26671-6). Halsted Pr.

Cook, Clayton B., et al, eds. Cellular Interactions in Symbiosis & Parasitism. LC 79-23304. (Ohio State University Biosciences Colloquia: No. 5). (Illus.). 321p. 1980. 25.00x (ISBN 0-8142-0315-9). Ohio St U Pr.

Goff, Lynda J., ed. Algal Symbiosis: A Continuum of Interaction Strategies. LC 83-7275. (Illus.). 224p. 1984. 42.50 (ISBN 0-521-25541-4). Cambridge u Pr.

Harley, J. L. & Smith, S. E., eds. Mycorrhizal Symbiosis. 1984. 65.00 (ISBN 0-12-325560-0). Acad Pr.

Lyons, J. M., et al, eds. Genetic Engineering of Symbiotic Nitrogen Fixation & Conservation of Fixed Nitrogen. LC 81-4683. (Basic Life Sciences Ser.: Vol. 17). 712p. 1981. 79.50 (ISBN 0-306-40730-2, Plenum Pr). Plenum Pub.

Margulis, Lynn. Symbiosis in Cell Evolution: Life & Its Environment on the Early Earth. LC 80-26695. (Illus.). 419p. 1981. text ed. 30.95x (ISBN 0-7167-1255-5); pap. text ed. 18.95x (ISBN 0-7167-1256-3). W H Freeman.

Nutman, P. S., ed. Symbiotic Nitrogen Fixation in Plants. LC 75-2732. (International Biological Programme Ser.: No. 7). (Illus.). 652p. 1976. 130.00 (ISBN 0-521-20645-6). Cambridge U Pr.

Perry, Nicolette. Symbiosis: Close Encounter of the Natural Kind. (Illus.). 128p. 1983. 16.95 (ISBN 0-7137-1229-5, Pub. by Blandford Pr England). Sterling.

Steinhaus, Edward A. Insect Microbiology: An Account of the Microbes Associated with Insects & Ticks. (Illus.). 1967. Repr. of 1946 ed. 26.95x (ISBN 0-02-852920-0). Hafner.

SYMBOLIC AND MATHEMATICAL LOGIC

see Logic, Symbolic and Mathematical

SYMBOLIC LANGUAGE

see ALGOL (Computer Program Language)

SYMBOLS (IN SCIENCE TECHNOLOGY, ETC.)

see Technology–Abbreviations;

see subdivision Notation under names of sciences, e.g. Chemistry–Notation

SYMMETRIC FUNCTIONS

David, F. N., et al. Symmetric Function & Allied Tables. 278p. 1966. lib. bdg. 22.95x (ISBN 0-521-04788-9). Lubrecht & Cramer.

--Symmetric Function & Allied Tables. 278p. 1966. 27.00x (ISBN 0-85264-702-6, Pub. by Griffin England). State Mutual Bk.

MacDonald, I. G. Symmetric Functions & Hall Polynomials. (Oxford Mathematical Monographs). 1979. 45.00x (ISBN 0-19-853530-9). Oxford U Pr.

Robinson, Gilbert. Representation Theory of the Symmetric Group. LC 63-424. (Mathematical Expositions Ser.: No. 12). pap. 53.50 (ISBN 0-317-09069-0, 2014385). Bks Demand UMI.

Satake, Ichiro. Algebraic Structures of Symmetric Domains. LC 80-7551. (Publications of the Mathematical Society of Japan Ser.: No. 14). 315p. 1981. 48.00x (ISBN 0-691-08271-5). Princeton U Pr.

SYMMETRIC SPACES

see also Lie Groups

Bucy, R. S., et al. Stochastic Differential Equations. McKean, H. P. & Keller, J. B., eds. LC 72-13266. (SIAM-AMS Proceedings: No. 6). 1973. 39.00 (ISBN 0-8218-1325-0, SIAMS-6). Am Math.

Butler, Philip H. Point Group Symmetry Applications: Methods & Tables. LC 80-17947. 578p. 1981. 75.00 (ISBN 0-306-40523-7, Plenum Pr). Plenum Pub.

Drucker, Daniel. Exceptional Lie Algebras & the Structure of Hermitian Symmetric Spaces. LC 78-15619. (Memoirs: No. 208). 207p. 1982. pap. 18.00 (ISBN 0-8218-2208-X). Am Math.

Helgason, Sigurdur. Differential Geometry, Lie Groups & Symmetric Spaces. (Pure & Applied Mathematics Ser.). 1978. 29.50 (ISBN 0-12-338460-5). Acad Pr.

James, Gordon. Encyclopedia of Mathematics & Its Applications: The Representation Theory of the Symmetric Group, Vol. 16. 1984. 49.50 (ISBN 0-317-14393-X, 30236-6). Cambridge U Pr.

Kowalski, O. Generalized Symmetric Spaces. (Lecture Notes in Mathematics: Vol. 805). 187p. 1980. pap. 15.00 (ISBN 0-387-10002-4). Springer-Verlag.

Mostow, G. D. Strong Rigidity of Locally Symmetric Spaces. (Annals of Mathematics Studies: No. 78). 220p. 1974. 22.50x (ISBN 0-691-08136-0). Princeton U Pr.

Namikawa, Y. Toroidal Compactification of Siegel Spaces. (Lecture Notes in Mathematics: Vol. 812). 162p. 1980. pap. 15.00 (ISBN 0-387-10021-0). Springer-Verlag.

Terras, A. Harmonic Analysis on Symmetric Spaces & Applications I. (Illus.). 355p. 1985. pap. 39.00 (ISBN 0-387-96159-3). Springer-Verlag.

SYMMETRY (BIOLOGY)

Rosen, J. Symmetry Discovered. LC 75-6006. (Illus.). 150p. 1975. 24.95 (ISBN 0-521-20695-2). Cambridge U Pr.

Rosen, Joe. A Symmetry Primer for Scientists. LC 82-10876. 192p. 1983. 28.95 (ISBN 0-471-87672-0, Pub. by Wiley-Interscience). Wiley.

SYMMETRY (CHEMISTRY)

Flurry, Robert L., Jr. Symmetry Groups: Theory & Chemical Applications. (Illus.). 1980. text ed. 44.95 (ISBN 0-13-880013-8). P-H.

Jaffe, H. H. & Orchin, Milton M. Symmetry in Chemistry. LC 76-7534. 206p. 1977. pap. text ed. 7.50 (ISBN 0-88275-414-9). Krieger.

Rosen, Joe. A Symmetry Primer for Scientists. LC 82-10876. 192p. 1983. 28.95 (ISBN 0-471-87672-0, Pub. by Wiley-Interscience). Wiley.

SYMMETRY (PHYSICS)

Bars, Itzhak, et al, eds. Symmetries in Particle Physics. 320p. 1984. 47.50x (ISBN 0-306-41801-0, Plenum Pr). Plenum Pub.

Bernal, Ivan, et al. Symmetry: A Stereoscopic Guide for Chemists. LC 75-178258. (Illus.). 180p. 1972. text ed. 35.95 (ISBN 0-7167-0168-5). W H Freeman.

Chand, Ramesh, ed. Symmetries & Quark Models. 420p. 1970. 80.95 (ISBN 0-677-13880-6). Gordon.

Chretien, M. & Deser, S., eds. Brandeis University Summer Institute in Theoretical Physics: 1965 Lectures, 2 vols. Incl. Vol. 1. Axiomatic Field Theory. 526p. pap. 91.50 (ISBN 0-677-10705-6); Vol. 2. Particle Symmetries. 702p. pap. 106.50 (ISBN 0-677-10755-2). 1966. Gordon.

Elliot, J. P. & Dawber, P. G. Symmetry in Physics, Vols. 1 & 2. 1985. Vol. 1. pap. 15.95 ea. (ISBN 0-19-520455-7). Vol. 2 (ISBN 0-19-520456-5). Oxford U Pr.

Ezra, G. S. Symmetry Properties of Molecules. (Lecture Notes in Chemistry Ser.: Vol. 28). 202p. 1982. pap. 17.70 (ISBN 0-387-11184-0). Springer-Verlag.

Foata, D., ed. Combinatoire et Representation Du Groupe Symetrique. (Lecture Notes in Mathematics Ser: Vol. 579). 1977. pap. 20.40 (ISBN 0-387-08143-7). Springer-Verlag.

Fonda, L. & Ghirardi, G. C. Symmetry Principles in Quantum Physics. (Theoretical Physics Ser: Vol. 1). 1970. 45.00 (ISBN 0-8247-1213-7). Dekker.

Gatto, R., ed. Scale & Conformal Symmetry in Hadron Physics. LC 73-4324. pap. 60.00 (ISBN 0-317-09058-5, 2011957). Bks Demand UMI.

Gibson, W. M. & Pollard, B. R. Symmetry Principles in Elementary Particle Physics. LC 74-31796. (Cambridge Monographs on Physics). (Illus.). 395p. 1980. 85.00 (ISBN 0-521-20787-8); pap. 29.95 (ISBN 0-521-29964-0). Cambridge U Pr.

Gilchrist, T. L. & Storr, R. C. Organic Reactions & Orbital Symmetry. 2nd ed. LC 78-54578. (Cambridge Texts in Chemistry & Biochemistry Ser.). (Illus.). 1979. 75.00 (ISBN 0-521-22014-9); pap. 24.95 (ISBN 0-521-29336-7). Cambridge U Pr.

Gourdin, M. Formalisme Langrangien et Lois de Symetrie. (Cour & Documents de Mathematiques & de Physique Ser.). 108p. (Fr). 1967. 37.25 (ISBN 0-677-50070-X). Gordon.

Gruber, Bruno & Millman, Richard S., eds. Symmetries in Science. LC 80-18665. 505p. 1980. 65.00x (ISBN 0-306-40541-5, Plenum Pr). Plenum Pub.

Jacob, M., ed. Supersymmetry & Supergravity: Collected Articles from Physics Report. 600p. 1985. 67.00x (ISBN 0-317-27191-1, Pub by World Sci Singapore); pap. 30.00 (ISBN 0-317-27192-X). Taylor & Francis.

Kettle, S. A. Symmetry & Structure. 1985. 34.95 (ISBN 0-471-90501-1). Wiley.

Kramer, P. & Rieckers, A., eds. Group Theoretical Methods in Physics: Sixth International Colloquium, Tuebingen 1977. (Lecture Notes in Physics: Vol. 79). 1978. pap. 32.00 (ISBN 0-387-08848-2). Springer-Verlag.

Lichtenberg, D. B. Unitary Symmetry & Elementary Particles. 2nd ed. 1978. 39.50 (ISBN 0-12-448460-3). Acad Pr.

Loeb, Arthur L. Color & Symmetry. LC 78-13084. 196p. 1978. Repr. of 1971 ed. 26.50 (ISBN 0-88275-745-8). Krieger.

Lopes, L. J. Lectures on Symmetries. (Documents on Modern Physics Ser.). 182p. 1969. 57.75x (ISBN 0-677-02250-6). Gordon.

Low, F. Symmetries & Elementary Particles. (Documents on Modern Physics Ser.). 112p. (Orig.). 1967. 24.50x (ISBN 0-677-01750-2). Gordon.

Maruani, J. & Serre, J., eds. Symmetries & Properties of Non-Rigid Molecules: A Comprehensive Survey. (Studies in Physical & Theoretical Chemisty Ser.: Vol. 23). 520p. 1983. 117.00 (ISBN 0-444-42174-2). Elsevier.

Mead, C. A. Symmetry & Chirality. LC 51-5497. (Topics in Current Chemistry: Vol. 49). (Illus.). 90p. 1974. 22.00 (ISBN 0-387-06705-1). Springer-Verlag.

Morrison, James D., ed. Asymmetric Synthesis, Vol. 3: Stereodifferentiating Addition Reactions, Pt. B. LC 83-15830. 1984. 84.50 (ISBN 0-12-507703-3). Acad Pr.

Orchin, Milton & Jaffe, H. H. Symmetry, Orbitals, & Spectra. LC 76-136720. 396p. 1971. 54.50 (ISBN 0-471-65550-3, Pub. by Wiley-Interscience). Wiley.

Robertson, Stewart. Polytopes & Symmetry. LC 83-15171. (London Mathematical Society Lecture Notes Ser.: No. 90). 150p. 1984. pap. 14.95 (ISBN 0-521-27739-6). Cambridge U Pr.

Rosen, J. Symmetry Discovered. LC 75-6006. (Illus.). 150p. 1975. 24.95 (ISBN 0-521-20695-2). Cambridge U Pr.

Rosen, Joe. A Symmetry Primer for Scientists. LC 82-10876. 192p. 1983. 28.95 (ISBN 0-471-87672-0, Pub. by Wiley-Interscience). Wiley.

Rossman, M. G. The Molecular Replacement Method. (International Science Review). 276p. 1972. 72.75x (ISBN 0-677-13940-3). Gordon.

Ryder. Elementary Particles & Symmetries. (Documents on Modern Physics Ser.). 278p. 1975. 49.95 (ISBN 0-677-05130-1). Gordon.

Solvay Conference on Physics. Symmetry Properties of Nuclei. 372p. 1974. 108.75 (ISBN 0-677-14450-4). Gordon.

Weyl, Hermann. Symmetrie. 2nd ed. (Science & Society Ser.: No. 11). (Ger.). 158p. 1981. text ed. 15.95x (ISBN 0-8176-1280-7). Birkhauser.

Zichlichi, A., ed. Recent Developments in Particle Symmetries. 1966. 64.50 (ISBN 0-12-780562-1). Acad Pr.

SYMPHONY (COMPUTER PROGRAM)

Alves, Jeffrey R. & Curtin, Dennis P. Planning & Budgeting with Lotus Symphony. (Illus.). 144p. 1984. pap. 19.50 (ISBN 0-88703-010-6). Van Nos Reinhold.

Andersen, Dick. Symphony Encore: Program Notes. (Illus.). 281p. 1984. 21.95 (ISBN 0-89588-247-7). SYBEX.

Baras, Edward M. Symphony Book. 300p. (Orig.). 1985. pap. 19.95 (ISBN 0-07-881160-0, 160-0). Osborne-McGraw.

--Symphony Master: The Expert's Guide. 352p. (Orig.). 1985. pap. 19.95 (ISBN 0-07-881170-8, 170-8). Osborne McGraw.

Barton, Taylor J. The Illustrated Symphony Book. Berliner, Thomas H., ed. LC 84-29181. (Illus.). 240p. Date not set. pap. 17.95 (ISBN 0-915381-69-9). WordWare Pub.

Beil, Don. Symphony: First Introduction to Business Software. 1984. cancelled (ISBN 0-8359-7440-5). Reston.

Bolocan, David. Advanced Symphony Applications. Date not set. price not set. TAB Bks.

Cobb, Douglas. Mastering Symphony. (Illus.). 763p. Date not set. 24.95 (ISBN 0-89588-244-2). SYBEX.

Desautels, Edouard J. Symphony for the IBM Personal Computer & Compatible Computers. (Micropower Ser.). 200p. 1985. pap. 17.95 (ISBN 0-697-00600-X). Wm C Brown.

Estoppel. Symphony Applications: A Manager's Toolkit. 1985. pap. 19.95 (ISBN 0-471-82430-5). Wiley.

Ewing, David & LeBlond, Geoffrey. Using Symphony. LC 84-60645. (Symphony Ser.). 700p. 1984. pap. 19.95 (ISBN 0-88022-124-0, 141). Que Corp.

Feldman, Duane. Symphony: Advanced Topics. LC 83-60685. (Symphony Ser.). 350p. 1985. pap. 19.95 (ISBN 0-88022-145-3, 172). Que Corp.

--Symphony Tips, Tricks & Traps. LC 84-61398. 360p. 1985. 19.95 (ISBN 0-88022-098-8, 154). Que Corp.

Fenn, Darien. Using Symphony's Command Language. LC 84-62754. (Symphony Ser.). 350p. 1985. pap. 18.95 (ISBN 0-88022-146-1, 173); disk 39.95. Que Corp.

Graff, Lois & Cohen, Neil. Financial Analysis with Symphony. 384p. 1985. 19.95 (ISBN 0-89303-448-7); incl. disk 41.95 (ISBN 0-89303-450-9). Brady Comm.

Harris, Daniel H. Symphony Mastery. 432p. 1985. text ed. 38.95 (ISBN 0-13-880022-7). P-H.

Honig, Lawrence M. Programming Customs Applications with Symphony's Command Language. 288p. 1986. pap. 22.95 (ISBN 0-394-74119-6, RanC). Random.

The Lotus Guide to Learning Symphony. 400p. 1985. pap. 22.95 (ISBN 0-201-16686-0). Addison-Wesley.

Maffei, Nick. Money Management Worksheets for 1-2-3 Symphony. (Illus.). 192p. (Orig.). 1985. 21.95 (ISBN 0-8306-0968-7, 1968); pap. 14.95 (ISBN 0-8306-1968-2). TAB Bks.

Matthews, Carole B. & Matthews, Martin S. Symphony Business Solutions. LC 84-45893. 340p. (Orig.). 1985. pap. 19.95 (ISBN 0-8019-7615-4). Chilton.

Myers, Mary A. Presenting Symphony. (Illus.). 128p. 1984. pap. cancelled (ISBN 0-88056-359-1). Dilithium Pr.

Olson, David O., et al. Solving Cash Flow Problems Using 1-2-3 & Symphony. LC 84-45693. 300p. 1985. spiral incl. disk o.p. 39.95 (ISBN 0-8019-7605-7); pap. 19.95 (ISBN 0-8019-7604-9). Chilton.

Ross, Steven & Ball, David. Symphony Allegro. (Illus.). 352p. (Orig.). pap. cancelled (ISBN 0-317-14622-X, 88-7). Creative Comp.

Seybold, P. B. & Marshak, R. T. Integrated Desk-Top Environments: Symphony, Framework, Visi-On & DesQ. 208p. 1985. pap. 15.95 (ISBN 0-07-056324-1). McGraw.

Simpson, Alan. The Best Book of Symphony. 21.95 (ISBN 0-672-22420-8). Sams.

Symphony for Business. (Symphony Ser.). pap. cancelled (ISBN 0-88022-140-2). Que Corp.

Weber Systems Editors. Symphony User's Handbook. 1985. pap. 14.95 (ISBN 0-345-32376-9). Ballantine.

Weber Systems Inc. Staff, et al. Symphony Command Language Programmer's Guide. (Application Software Ser.). 250p. (Orig.). 1985. pap. 17.95 (ISBN 0-938862-39-1). Weber Systems.

Williams, Robert E. The Power of Symphony. (Illus.). 200p. 1984. 14.95 (ISBN 0-943518-23-7); 34.95, incl. diskette. Mgmt Info Inc.

Wright, Charles. Mass Communication. 3rd ed. 224p. Date not set. pap. text ed. 9.95 (ISBN 0-317-18771-6, RanC). Random.

SYNAPSES

see also Neurotransmitters

Bloom, F. E., ed. Dynamics of Synaptic Modulation. 100p. 1976. pap. text ed. 8.95x (ISBN 0-262-52037-0). MIT Pr.

Brzin, M., et al, eds. Synaptic Constituents in Health & Disease: Proceedings of the Third Meeting of the European Society for Neurochemistry, Bled, August 31st-Sept, 5th, 1980. (Illus.). 760p. 1980. 150.00 (ISBN 0-08-025921-9). Pergamon.

Cottrell, Glen A., et al, eds. Synapses. 1977. 58.00 (ISBN 0-12-192550-1). Acad Pr.

DeRobertis, E. Synaptic Receptors: Isoloation & Molecular Biology. (Modern Pharmacology-Toxicology Ser.: Vol. 4). 408p. 1975. 69.75 (ISBN 0-8247-6237-1). Dekker.

Eccles, John C. Physiology of Synapses. (Illus.). 1964. Repr. 34.00 (ISBN 0-387-03112-X). Springer-Verlag.

Gray, E. G. The Synapse. rev. ed. Head, J. J., ed. LC 76-53173. (Carolina Biology Readers Ser.). (Illus.). 16p. 1977. pap. 1.60 (ISBN 0-89278-235-8, 45-9635). Carolina Biological.

Hall, Zach W., et al. Chemistry of Synaptic Transmission: Essays & Sources. LC 73-92880. (Illus.). 620p. 1974. 30.00x (ISBN 0-913462-03-9); pap. 18.95x (ISBN 0-913462-06-3). Chiron Pr.

Hanin, Israel & Goldberg, Alan M., eds. Progress in Cholinergic Biology: Model Cholinergic Synapses. 382p. 1982. text ed. 90.00 (ISBN 0-89004-758-8). Raven.

International Society for Neurovegetative Research-Tinany-1972. Neurovegetative Transmission Mechanisms: Proceedings. Csillik, B. & Kappers, J. A., eds. (Journal of Neural Transmission: Suppl. 11). (Illus.). 350p. 1974. 91.50 (ISBN 0-387-81173-7). Springer Verlag.

Iversen, L. L., et al, eds. Handbook of Psychopharmacology: Vol. 5: Synaptic Modulators. LC 75-6851. 393p. 1975. 49.50x (ISBN 0-306-38925-8, Plenum Pr). Plenum Pub.

Jones, D. G. Some Current Concepts of Synaptic Organization. (Advances in Anatomy, Embryology & Cell Biology Ser.: Vol. 55, Pt. 4). (Illus.). 1978. pap. 21.00 (ISBN 0-387-09011-8). Springer-Verlag.

Jones, Gareth D. Current Topics in Research on Synapses, Vol. 1. 236p. 1984. 38.00 (ISBN 0-8451-3900-2). A R Liss.

--Current Topics in Research on Synapses, Vol. 2. 184p. 1984. 29.00 (ISBN 0-8451-3901-0). A R Liss.

Tapia, R. & Cotman, C. W., eds. Regulatory Mechanisms of Synaptic Transmission. 430p. 1981. 49.50x (ISBN 0-306-40740-X, Plenum Pr). Plenum Pub.

Usdin, Earl & Bunney, William, Jr., eds. Pre-Postsynaptic Receptors. (Modern Pharmacology-Toxicology Ser.: Vol.3). 360p. 1975. 65.00 (ISBN 0-8247-6312-2). Dekker.

Zakusov, V. V. Pharmacology of Central Synapses. (Illus.). 1980. 66.00 (ISBN 0-08-020549-6). Pergamon.

SYNCHRONOUS CONVERTERS

see Rotary Converters

SYNCHROS

see also Servomechanisms

Boyes, Geoffrey, ed. Synchro & Resolver Conversion. (Illus.). 196p. (Orig.). 1980. pap. 11.50 (ISBN 0-916550-06-0). Analog Devices.

SYNCHYTRIUM

Karling, J. S. Synchytrium. 1964. 76.50 (ISBN 0-12-399150-1). Acad Pr.

SYNOPTIC METEOROLOGY

Barry, R. G. & Perry, A. H. Synoptic Climatology: Methods & Applications. 500p. 1973. 56.00x (ISBN 0-416-08500-8, 2078). Methuen Inc.

SYNTHETIC CHEMISTRY

see Chemistry, Inorganic–Synthesis; Chemistry, Organic–Synthesis

SYNTHETIC COMPOUNDS

see Detergents, Synthetic

SYNTHETIC CONSCIOUSNESS

see Conscious Automata

SYNTHETIC FABRICS

see also Nonwoven Fabrics; Rayon; Textile Fibers, Synthetic

Bendure, Zelma & Pfeiffer, Gladys. America's Fabrics: Origin & History, Manufacture, Characteristics & Uses. LC 72-5260. (Technology & Society Ser.). (Illus.). 703p. 1972. Repr. of 1946 ed. 46.00 (ISBN 0-405-04685-5). Ayer Co Pubs.

Koerner, Robert M. & Welsh, Joseph P. Construction & Geotechnical Engineering Using Synthetic Fabrics. LC 79-21733. (Ser. on Practical Construction Guides). 267p. 1980. 42.50x (ISBN 0-471-04776-7, Pub. by Wiley-Interscience). Wiley.

New Developments & Requirements for Automotive Fabrics. 99p. 1983. 50.00 (ISBN 0-318-01531-5, 16024). Indus Fabrics.

Walczak, Z. Formation of Synthetic Fibers. 350p. 1977. 67.25x (ISBN 0-677-04490-9). Gordon.

SYNTHETIC FIBERS
see Textile Fibers, Synthetic

SYNTHETIC FUELS

Anderson, Larry L. & Tillman, David A. Synthetic Fuels from Coal: Overview & Assessment. LC 79-17786. (A Wiley-Interscience Publication). pap. 43.00 (ISBN 0-317-26175-4, 2025184). Bks Demand UMI.

Bach, W., et al, eds. Renewable Energy Prospects: Proceedings of the Conference on Non-Fossil Fuel & Non-Nuclear Fuel Energy Strategies, Honolulu, USS, January 1979. 340p. 1980. 26.00 (ISBN 0-08-024252-9). Pergamon.

Bartok, William, ed. Combustion of Synthetic Fuels. LC 83-2822. (ACS Symposium Ser.: No. 217). 246p. 1983. lib. bdg. 34.95x (ISBN 0-8412-0773-9). Am Chemical.

Battelle Columbus Laboratories. Preliminary Environmental Assessment of Biomass Conversion to Synthetic Fuels. 346p. 1980. pap. 49.95x (ISBN 0-89934-049-0, B049-PP). Solar Energy Info.

Brykowski, F. J., ed. Ammonia & Synthesis Gas: Recent & Energy-Saving Processes. LC 81-11033. (Chem. Tech. Rev. 193; Energy Tech. Rev. 68). (Illus.). 354p. 1982. 48.00 (ISBN 0-8155-0859-X). Noyes.

Business Communications Staff. Synfuels: Equipment, Technology, Supplies, Money, People. 1982. 975.00 (ISBN 0-89336-281-6, E-042). BCC.

California State Legislature. California Synthetic Fuels Program: Final Report. 176p. 1980. pap. 19.95x (ISBN 0-89934-058-X, B001). Solar Energy Info.

Chemical Engineering Magazine. Synfuels Engineering. (Illus.). 300p. 1982. 45.00 (ISBN 0-07-010698-3). McGraw.

Committee for Economic Development. Helping Insure Our Energy Future: A Program for Developing Synthetic Fuel Plants Now. 1979. lib. bdg. 6.00 (ISBN 0-87186-769-9); pap. 4.50 (ISBN 0-87186-069-4). Comm Econ Dev.

Cowser, K. E. & Richmond, C. R., eds. Synthetic Fossil Fuel Technologies. (Illus.). 632p. 1984. text ed. 85.00 (ISBN 0-250-40624-1). Butterworth.

Deutch, John M. Prospects for Synthetic Fuels in the United States. 1982. 2.50x (ISBN 0-317-06611-0). Colo Assoc.

Harlan, James K. Starting with Synfuels: Benefits, Costs & Program Design Assessments. 376p. 1982. prof ref 37.50 (ISBN 0-88410-869-4). Ballinger Pub.

Hill, Richard F. Synfuels Industry Development. LC 80-65895. (Illus.). 168p. 1980. pap. text ed. 25.00 (ISBN 0-86587-083-7). Gov Insts.

Hill, Richard F., et al, eds. Synfuels Industry Opportunities. Boardman, Elliot B. & Heavner, Martin L. LC 80-84730. 178p. 1981. text ed. 32.50 (ISBN 0-86587-088-8). Gov Insts.

Hoffman, E. J. Synfuels: The Problems & the Promise. LC 81-68123. 347p. 1982. 29.50x (ISBN 0-9601552-4-4). Energon Co.

Institute of Gas Technology. Nonpetroleum Vehicular Fuel: IV Symposium. 292p. 1984. 50.00 (ISBN 0-910091-51-X). Inst Gas Tech.

Meyers, Robert A. Handbook of Synfuels Technology. (Illus.). 928p. 1984. 89.50 (ISBN 0-07-041762-8). McGraw.

Moran, Robert T. & Harris, Philip R. Managing Cultural Synergy. LC 81-83310. (International Management Productivity Ser.: Vol. 2). 400p. 1982. 24.95x (ISBN 0-87201-827-X). Gulf Pub.

Nowacki, Perry, ed. Health Hazards & Pollution Control in Synthetic Liquid Fuel Conversion. LC 80-16694. (Pollution Tech. Review, No. 68; Environmental Health Review, No. 2; Chemical Tech. Review, No. 165; Energy Tech. Review: No. 57). 511p. (Orig.). 1980. 54.00 (ISBN 0-8155-0810-7). Noyes.

Pelofsky, Arnold H. Synthetic Fuels Processing. (Energy Library Ser: Vol. 1). 1977. 75.00 (ISBN 0-8247-6544-3). Dekker.

Petrakis, L. & Grandy, D. W. Free Radicals in Coals & Synthetic Fuels. (Coal Science & Technology Ser.: No. 5). 274p. 1983. 66.00 (ISBN 0-444-42237-4, I-306-83). Elsevier.

Probstein, R. F. & Hicks, R. E. Synthetic Fuels. (Chemical Engineering Ser.). 576p. 1982. 41.50x (ISBN 0-07-050908-5). McGraw.

Probstein, Ronald F. & Gold, Harris. Water in Synthetic Fuel Production: The Technology & Alternatives. 1978. pap. text ed. 16.50x (ISBN 0-262-66039-3). MIT Pr.

Satriana, M. J., ed. Synthetic Oils & Lubricant Additives: Advances since 1979. LC 82-2234. (Chemical Technical Review Ser.: No. 207). (Illus.). 356p. 1982. 48.00 (ISBN 0-8155-0899-9). Noyes.

Silber, Bettina, ed. Synfuels: Whether & Whither? (Americans for Energy Independence Energy Policy Ser.). 50p. (Orig.). 1983. pap. 6.00 (ISBN 0-934458-06-5, 83-72331). Americans Energy Ind.

Steele, Henry B. Economic Potentialities of Synthetic Liquid Fuels from Oil Shale. Bruchey, Stuart, ed. LC 78-22751. (Energy in the American Economy Ser.). (Illus.). 1979. lib. bdg. 40.00x (ISBN 0-405-12015-X). Ayer Co Pubs.

Synthetic Fuels from Oil Shale & Tar Sands (Symposium III) 707p. 1983. 75.00 (ISBN 0-910091-48-X). Inst Gas Tech.

Thumann, Albert, ed. The Emerging Synthetic Fuel Industry. 300p. 1981. text ed. 32.00 (ISBN 0-915586-41-X). Fairmont Pr.

VDI. Synthetic Crude from Oil Sands. (Progress Report of the VDI-Z, Series 3: No. 80). 108p. (Orig.). 1983. pap. 34.00 (ISBN 0-9907000-1-1, Pub. by VDI W Germany). Heyden.

--Synthetic Fuels from Coal. (Progress Report of the VDI-Z, Series 3: No. 79). 226p. (Orig.). 1983. pap. 62.00 (ISBN 0-9907000-0-3, Pub. by VDI W Germany). Heyden.

Washington Gasohol Commission Staff, ed. The Washington Gasohol Seminars, 1980. 45p. 1980. pap. 6.00 (ISBN 0-939864-01-0). Wash Gasohol.

SYNTHETIC PERFUMES
see Perfumes

SYNTHETIC PRODUCTS
see also Chemurgy; Perfumes; Plastics; Rubber, Artificial; Synthetic Fabrics; Synthetic Fuels; Textile Fibers, Synthetic

Bartmann, Wilhelm & Trost, Barry M., eds. Selectivity: A Goal for Synthetic Efficiency. 424p. 1983. text ed. 42.50x (ISBN 0-89573-205-X). VCH Pubs.

Boschke, F. L., ed. Syntheses of Natural Products. (Topics in Current Chemistry Ser.: Vol. 91). 118p. 1980. 45.00 (ISBN 0-387-09827-5). Springer-Verlag.

Bruins, Paul F. Unsaturated Polyester Technology. new ed. LC 74-12774. 448p. 1976. 69.50 (ISBN 0-677-21160-0). Gordon.

Flavin, Christopher. The Future of Synthetic Materials: The Petroleum Connection. LC 80-51137. (Worldwatch Papers Ser.). 1980. pap. 2.00 (ISBN 0-916468-35-6). Worldwatch Inst.

The Future of Synthetic Materials: Petroleum Connection. (Worldwatch Institute Papers: No. 36). 55p. 1980. pap. 2.95 (ISBN 0-916468-35-6, WW36, WW). Unipub.

Venkataraman, Krishnasami, ed. The Chemistry of Synthethic Dyes, 8 vols. Incl. Vol. 1. 1952. 98.50 (ISBN 0-12-717001-4); Vol. 2. 1952. 98.50 (ISBN 0-12-717002-2); Vol. 3. 1970. 98.50 (ISBN 0-12-717003-0); Vol. 4. 1971. 98.50 (ISBN 0-12-717004-9); Vol. 5. 1971. 99.00 (ISBN 0-12-717005-7); Vol. 6. 1972. 98.50 (ISBN 0-12-717006-5); Vol. 7. 1974. 98.50 (ISBN 0-12-717007-3); Vol. 8. 1978. 98.50 (ISBN 0-12-717008-1). (Organic & Biological Chemistry Ser.). Set. 649.50. Acad Pr.

SYNTHETIC RUBBER
see Rubber, Artificial

SYNTHETIC TEXTILE FIBERS
see Textile Fibers, Synthetic

SYRPHIDAE

Bezzi, Mario. Syrphidae of the Ethiopian Region. Repr. of 1915 ed. 16.00 (ISBN 0-384-04095-0). Johnson Repr.

Gilbert, Francis S. Hoverflies. (Naturalists Handbooks: No. 5). (Illus.). 96p. Date not set. price not set (ISBN 0-521-25766-2). Cambridge U Pr.

SYSTEM ANALYSIS
see also Bond Graphs; Control Theory; Discrete Time Systems; Electric Networks; Flow Charts; Flowgraphs; Mathematical Optimization; Nonlinear Theories; Switching Theory; Systems Engineering

Ackoff, Russell & Emery, Fred. On Purposeful Systems. (Systems Inquiry Ser.). 296p. 1982. pap. text ed. 14.95x (ISBN 0-914105-00-0). Intersystems Pubns.

Aggarwal, J. K. & Vidyasagar, M., eds. Nonlinear Systems: Stability Analysis. (Benchmark Papers in Electrical Engineering & Computer Science: Vol. 16). 1977. 70.50 (ISBN 0-12-786035-5). Acad Pr.

Aguilar, Rodolfo J. Systems Analysis & Design in Engineering, Architecture, Construction, & Planning. (Civil Engineering & Engineering Mechanics Ser). (Illus.). 448p. 1973. ref. ed. 33.95 (ISBN 0-13-881458-9). P-H.

Alexander, Milton J. Information Systems Analysis: Theory & Application. LC 73-89599. (Illus.). 432p. 1974. text ed. 28.95 (ISBN 0-574-19100-3, 13-2100); instr's guide avail. (ISBN 0-574-19101-1, 13-2101). SRA.

Allen, R. J. & Lientz, Bennett P. Systems in Action. LC 77-16546. 1978. text ed. 20.60 (ISBN 0-673-16149-8); pap. text ed. 16.85 (ISBN 0-673-16150-1). Scott F.

Allkin, Robert & Bisby, Frank. Databases in Systematics. (Systematics Association Special Ser.: Vol. 26). 1984. 49.50 (ISBN 0-12-053040-6). Acad Pr.

Analysis Instrumentation Symposium, 27th, St. Louis, 1981. Analysis Instrumentation, Vol. 19: Proceedings. 144p. pap. text ed. 24.00x (ISBN 0-87664-521-X). Instru Soc.

Anderson, B. D. & Arbib, M. A. Foundations of System Theory Finitary & Infinitary Conditions. (Lecture Notes in Economics & Math Systems: Vol. 115). 93p. 1976. pap. 13.00 (ISBN 0-387-07611-5). Springer-Verlag.

Aoki, Masanao & Marzollo, Angelo, eds. New Trends in Dynamic System Theory & Economics. LC 78-27701. 1979. 41.50 (ISBN 0-12-058860-9). Acad Pr.

Ardema, M. D., ed. Singular Perturbations in Systems & Control. (CISM, Courses & Lectures: No. 280). (Illus.). 337p. 1983. pap. 22.50 (ISBN 0-387-81751-4). Springer-Verlag.

Arens, Alvin A. & Ward, D. Dewey. Systems Understanding Aid for Auditing. Rev. ed. 128p. 1983. pap. text ed. 12.95x (ISBN 0-912503-00-9). Systems Pubns.

Aseltine, J. A. Transform Method in Linear System Analysis. (Electrical & Electronic Eng. Ser). 1958. 48.00 (ISBN 0-07-002389-1). McGraw.

Asmussen, E., ed. International Calibration Study of Traffic Conflict Techniques. (NATO ASI Series, Series F Computer & Systems Sciences: No. 5). 229p. 1984. 36.60 (ISBN 0-387-12716-X). Springer Verlag.

Athey, Thomas H. Systematic Systems Approach: An Integrated Method for Solving Systems Problems. (Illus.). 416p. 1982. text ed. 31.95 (ISBN 0-13-880914-3). P-H.

Atwood, Jerry W. The Systems Analyst: How to Design Computer-Based Systems. 1977. text ed. 14.50x (ISBN 0-8104-5102-6). Hayden.

Aubin, Jean-Pierre & Ekeland, Ivar. Applied Nonlinear Analysis. (Pure & Applied Mathematics Ser.: 1237). 518p. 1984. 47.50x (ISBN 0-471-05998-6, Pub. by Wiley-Interscience). Wiley.

Auslander, et al. Introduction to Dynamic Systems & Control. (Illus.). 400p. 1974. text ed. 47.00 (ISBN 0-07-002491-X). McGraw.

Awad, Elias M. Systems Analysis & Design. 1979. 29.95x (ISBN 0-256-02091-4). Irwin.

Bagchi, A. & Jongen, H. T., eds. Systems & Optimization. (Lecture Notes in Control & Information Sciences Ser.: Vol. 66). x, 206p. 1985. pap. 13.00 (ISBN 0-387-15004-8). Springer-Verlag.

Bailey, Norman T. Mathematics, Statistics & Systems for Health. LC 77-1307. (Wiley Series Probability & Mathematical Statistics: Applied Probability & Statistics). 222p. 1977. 48.95x (ISBN 0-471-99500-2, Pub. by Wiley-Interscience). Wiley.

Bailey, Robert W. Human Error in Computer Systems. (Illus.). 160p. 1983. 21.95 (ISBN 0-13-445056-6). P-H.

Balabanian, Norman & Bickart, Theodore. Linear Network Theory: Analysis, Properties, Design & Synthesis. (Illus.). 648p. 1981. 34.95 (ISBN 0-916460-10-X). Matrix Pub.

Balakrishnan, A. V. Elements of State Space Theory of Systems. (University Series in Modern Engineering). ix, 187p. 1983. pap. 26.00 (ISBN 0-387-90904-4). Springer-Verlag.

Batty, Michael & Hutchinson, Bruce, eds. Systems Analysis in Urban Policy-Making & Planning. (NATO Conference Series II, Systems Science: Vol. 12). 605p. 1983. 85.00x (ISBN 0-306-41118-0). Plenum Pub.

Bayraktar, B. A. & Muller-Merbach, H., eds. Education in Systems Science. (NATO Conference Ser.). 384p. 1978. 29.00x (ISBN 0-85066-182-X). Taylor & Francis.

Beachley, Norman H. & Harrison, Howard L. Introduction to Dynamic System Analysis. (Illus.). 1978. text ed. 31.95 scp (ISBN 0-06-040557-0, HarpC). Har-Row.

Bednarek, A. R. & Cesari, L., eds. Dynamical Systems: Symposium, II. 1982. 60.00 (ISBN 0-12-084720-5). Acad Pr.

Bedrosian, S. D. & Porter, W. A., eds. Recent Trends in Systems Theory. 1976. 36.00 (ISBN 0-08-020590-9). Pergamon.

Beer, Stafford. Platform for Change. LC 73-10741. 457p. 1975. 48.95x (ISBN 0-471-06189-1, Pub. by Wiley-Interscience). Wiley.

Beishon. Systems Behavior. 3rd ed. 320p. 1982. text ed. 31.50 (ISBN 0-06-318211-4, Pub. by Har-Row Ltd England); pap. text ed. 15.50 (ISBN 0-06-318212-2, Pub. by Har-Row Ltd England). Har-Row.

Bensoussan, A. & Lions, J. L., eds. Analysis & Optimization of Systems: Proceedings. (Lecture Notes in Control & Information Sciences Ser.: Vol. 28). 999p. 1980. pap. 66.00 (ISBN 0-387-10472-0). Springer-Verlag.

--Analysis & Optimization of Systems: Proceedings of the Sixth International Conference on Analysis & Optimization of Systems, Nice, June 19-22, 1983. (Lecture Notes in Control & Information Sciences,: Vol. 62, Pt. 1). (Illus.). xix, 591p. 1984. pap. 34.50 (ISBN 0-387-13551-0). Springer-Verlag.

--Analysis & Optimization of Systems, Versailles, France, 1982: Proceedings. (Lecture Notes in Control & Information Sciences Ser.: Vol. 44). (Illus.). 987p. 1983. pap. 51.00 (ISBN 0-387-12089-0). Springer-Verlag.

--International Symposium on Systems Optimization & Analysis. (Lecture Notes in Control & Information Sciences: Vol. 14). (Illus.). 1979. pap. 20.00 (ISBN 0-387-09447-4). Springer-Verlag.

Bensoussan, E. & Lions, J. L., eds. Analysis & Optimization of Systems: Proceedings of the Sixth International Conference on Analysis & Optimization of Systems. Nice, June 19-22, 1983. (Lecture Notes in Control & Information Sciences: Vol. 63, Pt. 2). (Illus.). xix, 700p. 1984. pap. 34.50 (ISBN 0-387-13552-9). Springer-Verlag.

Bernussou, J. & Titli, A. Interconnected Dynamical Systems: Stability, Decomposition & Decentralisation. (North-Holland Systems & Control Ser.: Vol. 5). 330p. 1982. 59.75 (ISBN 0-444-86504-7, North Holland). Elsevier.

Bingham, John E. & Davies, Garth W. A Handbook of Systems Analysis. 2nd ed. LC 77-28954. 229p. 1980. pap. 24.95x (ISBN 0-470-26997-9). Halsted Pr.

Blanchard, B. & Fabrycky, W. Systems Engineering & Analysis. 1981. 34.95 (ISBN 0-13-881631-X). P-H.

Blaquiere, Austin. Nonlinear System Analysis. (Electrical Science Ser.). 1966. 75.00 (ISBN 0-12-104350-9). Acad Pr.

Blauberg, I. V., et al. Systems Theory: Philosophical & Methodological Problems. 318p. 1977. 5.95 (ISBN 0-8285-0440-7, Pub. by Progress Pubs USSR). Imported Pubns.

Bogart, T. F. Basic Concepts in Linear Systems: Theory & Experiments. 136p. 1983. pap. 14.95 (ISBN 0-471-87513-9). Wiley.

Bogdanov, A. A. Bogdanov: Essays in Tektology. Gorelik, George, tr. from Rus. (Systems Inquiry Ser.). 280p. (Orig.). 1980. pap. text ed. 15.95x (ISBN 0-914105-06-X). Intersystems Pubns.

Boguslaw, Robert. Systems Analysis & Social Planning: Human Problems of Post-Industrial Society. 1982. text ed. 29.50x (ISBN 0-8290-0111-5). Irvington.

Bolton, Ralph. Systems Contracting. 1979. pap. 7.50 (ISBN 0-8144-2236-5). AMACOM.

Bose, N. K. Multidimensional Systems: Theory & Applications. (IEEE Reprint Ser.). 295p. 1979. 39.95x (ISBN 0-471-05214-0); (Pub. by Wiley-Interscience). Wiley.

Bose, Nirmal K. Applied Multidimensional System Theory. (Electrical-Computer Science & Engineering Ser.). 350p. 1982. 32.50 (ISBN 0-442-27214-6). Van Nos Reinhold.

Boulding, Kenneth E. The World as a Total System. 1985. 25.00 (ISBN 0-8039-2443-7). Sage.

Bowen & Behr. The Logical Design of Multiple Microprocessor Systems. (Illus.). 272p. 1980. text ed. 37.50 (ISBN 0-13-539908-4). P-H.

Bowler, T. D. General Systems Thinking: Its Scope & Applicability. (General Systems Research Ser.: Vol. 4). 234p. 1981. 39.25 (ISBN 0-444-00420-3, North-Holland). Elsevier.

Boyd, David R., et al. Systems Approach to Emergency Medical Care. 544p. 1983. 48.00 (ISBN 0-8385-8792-5). ACC.

Brethower, Dale M. Behavioral Analysis in Business & Industry: A Total Performance System. (Illus.). 130p. (Orig.). 1972. pap. 10.00 (ISBN 0-914474-06-5); instr's. manual avail. F Fournies.

Brown, D. Systems Analysis & Design for Safety. 399p. 1976. text ed. 31.95 (ISBN 0-13-881177-6). P-H.

Brown, David B. & Herbanek, Jeffrey A. Systems Analysis for Applications: Software Design. (Illus.). 466p. 1984. text ed. 37.95x (ISBN 0-8162-1160-4). Holden-Day.

Brown, R. F. Compartmental Systems Analysis. (Cybernetics & Systems Ser.). 1984. 58.00 (ISBN 0-9901003-8-3, Pub. by Abacus England). Heyden.

Buckley, Walter, ed. Modern Systems Research for the Behavioral Scientist: A Sourcebook. LC 66-19888. (Illus.). 1968. 45.00 (ISBN 0-202-30011-0). Aldine Pub.

Burr, Stefan A., ed. The Mathematics of Networks. LC 82-18469. (Proceedings of Symposia in Applied Mathematics: No. 26). 142p. 1984. pap. 17.00 (ISBN 0-8218-0031-0, PSAPM-26). Am Math.

Candullo, C. System Developments Standards. 544p. 1985. 49.95 (ISBN 0-07-009724-0). McGraw.

Cavallo, Roger. The Role of Systems Methodology in Social Science Research. (Frontiers in Systems Research Ser.: Vol. 1). 1979. lib. bdg. 22.00 (ISBN 0-89838-005-7, Pub. by Martinus Nijhoff Netherlands). Kluwer Academic.

Champine, G. Distributed Computer Systems: Impact on Management Design & Analysis. 380p. 1980. 44.75 (ISBN 0-444-86109-2, North-Holland). Elsevier.

Chandra, Jagdish, ed. Chaos in Nonlinear Dynamical Systems. LC 84-52603. viii, 191p. 1984. text ed. 25.00 (ISBN 0-89871-052-9). Soc Indus Appl Math.

Gross, Charles A. Power System Analysis. LC 78-8631. 478p. 1979. 40.95 (ISBN 0-471-01899-6). Wiley.
Gruver, W. A. & Sachs, E. Algorithmic Methods in Optimal Control. (Research Notes in Mathematics Ser.: No. 47). 256p. 1981. pap. text ed. 27.50 (ISBN 0-273-08473-9). Pitman Pub MA.
Gupta, S. C. Transform & State Variable Methods in Linear Systems. LC 66-17635. 444p. 1971. Repr. of 1966 ed. text ed. 26.50 (ISBN 0-88275-022-4). Krieger.
Gvishiani, J. M., ed. Systems Research: Methodological Problems. 380p. 1983. 67.50 (ISBN 0-08-030000-6). Pergamon.
Habermann, A. N. Introduction to Operating System Design. LC 75-34073. (Computer Science Ser.). (Illus.). 480p. 1976. text ed. 31.95 (ISBN 0-574-21075-X, 13-4075). SRA.
Halfon, Efraim, ed. Theoretical Systems Ecology: Advances & Case Studies. LC 78-27014. 1979. 65.00 (ISBN 0-12-318750-8). Acad Pr.
Happ, H. H., ed. Gabriel Kron & Systems Theory. LC 72-89636. 1973. 12.50x (ISBN 0-912756-02-0). Union Coll.
Harris, C. J. & Miles, J. F. Stability of Linear Systems: Some Aspects of Kinematic Similarity. (Mathematics in Science & Engineering Ser.). 1980. 33.00 (ISBN 0-12-328250-0). Acad Pr.
Hartnett, William E., ed. Systems: Approaches, Theories, Applications. (Epistome Ser.: No. 3). 1977. lib. bdg. 42.00 (ISBN 90-277-0822-3, Pub. by Reidel Holland). Kluwer Academic.
Haug, E. J., ed. Computer Aided Analysis & Optimization of Mechanical System Dynamics. (NATO ASI Ser., Series F - Computer & Systems Sciences: Vol. 9). xxii, 700p. 1984. 49.50 (ISBN 0-387-12887-5). Springer-Verlag.
Havin, V. P., et al. Linear & Complex Analysis Problem Book. (Lecture Notes in Mathematics: Vol. 1043). xviii, 721p. 1984. pap. 28.00 (ISBN 0-387-12869-7). Springer-Verlag.
Hedrick, J. K. & Paynter, H. M., eds. Nonlinear System Analysis & Synthesis, Vol. 1: Fundamental Principles, No. G00138. 146p. 1978. pap. 15.00 (ISBN 0-685-99209-8). ASME.
Henstock, Ralph. Linear Analysis. LC 79-1233. pap. 112.80 (ISBN 0-317-27872-X, 2055796). Bks Demand UMI.
Herman, Robert. Algebra-Geometric & Lie Theoretic Techniques in Systems Theory, Pt. A. (Interdisciplinary Mathematics Ser.: No. 13). 256p. 1977. 27.00 (ISBN 0-915692-17-1, 991600185). Math Sci Pr.
Hermann, R. Cartanian Geometry, Nonlinear Waves. (Interdisciplinary Mathematics Ser.: Vol. XXI). 585p. 1980. 60.00 (ISBN 0-915692-29-5, 991600282). Math Sci Pr.
--Cartanian Geometry, Nonlinear Waves & Control Theory, Pt. A. (Interdisciplinary Mathematics Ser.: Vol. XX). 501p. 1970. pap. 60.00 (ISBN 0-915692-27-9, 991600290). Math Sci Pr.
Hermann, Robert. Algebraic Topics in Systems Theory. (Interdisciplinary Mathematics Ser: No. 3). 177p. 1973. 18.00 (ISBN 0-915692-02-3). Math Sci Pr.
--Geometric Structure of Systems Control Theory & Physics: Part B. LC 74-30856. (Interdisciplinary Mathematics Ser.: No. 11). 484p. 1976. 49.00 (ISBN 0-915692-14-7, 991600185). Math Sci Pr.
--Linear Systems Theory & Introductory Algebraic Geometry. (Interdisciplinary Mathematics Ser.: No. 8). 282p. 1974. 30.00 (ISBN 0-915692-08-2, 991600207). Math Sci Pr.
Hernandez, Ernie, Jr. Police Handbook for Applying the Systems Approach & Computer Technology. LC 82-17662. (Illus.). 231p. 1982. 26.95 (ISBN 0-910657-00-9); pap. 19.95 (ISBN 0-910657-01-7). Frontline.
Hersey, Mayo D. Theory & Research in Lubrication: Foundations for Future Developments. LC 66-21058. 488p. 1966. text ed. 28.50 (ISBN 0-471-37346-X, Pub. by Wiley). Krieger.
Hice, G. F., et al. System Development Methodology. 2nd, rev. ed. 450p. 1978. 53.25 (ISBN 0-444-85143-7, North-Holland). Elsevier.
Hinrichsen, D. & Isidori, A., eds. Feedback Control of Linear & Nonlinear Systems, Bielefeld, FRG Germany, & Rome, Italy: Proceedings. (Lecture Notes in Control & Information Sciences Ser.: Vol. 39). 284p. 1982. pap. text ed. 16.00 (ISBN 0-387-11749-0). Springer-Verlag.
Hoare, C. A. & Perrott, R. H., eds. Operating Systems Techniques. (Automatic Programming Information Centre Studies in Data Processing: No. 9). 1973. 70.00 (ISBN 0-12-350650-6). Acad Pr.
Hoos, Ida R. Systems Analysis in Public Policy: A Critique. LC 79-170723. (Institute of Governmental Studies). 300p. 1972. 37.50x (ISBN 0-520-02105-3). U of Cal Pr.
--Systems Analysis in Public Policy: A Critique. rev. ed. LC 82-48766. 320p. 1983. text ed. 35.00 (ISBN 0-520-04953-5, CAL 622); pap. 7.95 (ISBN 0-520-04952-7). U of Cal Pr.
Hopeman, Richard. Systems Analysis & Operations Management. LC 69-19269. 1969. text ed. 19.95 (ISBN 0-675-09514-X). Merrill.
Hosier. Structured Analysis & Design, 2 vols. (Infotech Computer State of the Art Reports). 646p. 1978. Set. 125.00 (ISBN 0-08-028543-0). Pergamon.
Hsia, Tien C. System Identification: Least Squares Method. LC 75-3515. (Illus.). 192p. 1977. 33.00x (ISBN 0-669-99630-0). Lexington Bks.
Huggett, R. Earth Surface Systems. (Physical Environment Ser.: Vol. 1). (Illus.). 280p. 1985. 52.00 (ISBN 0-387-15421-3). Springer Verlag.
Huggett, Richard. Systems Analysis in Geography. (Contemporary Problems in Geography Ser.). (Illus.). 1980. text ed. 36.00x (ISBN 0-19-874081-6); pap. text ed. 13.95x (ISBN 0-19-874082-4). Oxford U Pr.
Hung, Y. S. & MacFarlane, A. G. Multivariable Feedback: A Quasi-Classical Approach. (Lecture Notes in Control & Information Sciences: Vol. 40). 182p. 1982. pap. 12.00 (ISBN 0-387-11902-7). Springer-Verlag.
Hurst, J. Willis & Walker, H. Kenneth. Problem-Oriented System. 302p. 1972. pap. 18.00 (ISBN 0-686-74092-0). Krieger.
Iberall, A. Bridges in Science, from Physics to Social Science. new ed. LC 74-21588. (Technical Monographs). (Illus.). 371p. (Orig.). 1974. pap. 6.00 (ISBN 0-914780-03-4). Gen Tech Serv.
Iberall, A. S. On Nature, Life, Mind & Society. LC 76-43594. (Technical Monographs). 1976. pap. 6.00 (ISBN 0-914780-04-2). Gen Tech Serv.
IFAC-IFORS-IIASA Workshop, Bielsko-Biala, Poland, June 1977. Systems Analysis Applications to Complex Programs: Proceedings. Cichocki, K. & Straszak, A., eds. 328p. 1978. 79.00 (ISBN 0-08-022029-0). Pergamon.
IFAC Symposium, 6th, Washington, DC, June 1982 & Bekey, G. A. Identification & System Parameter Estimation, 1982: Proceedings, 2 vols. (IFAC Proceedings Ser.). (Illus.). 1700p. 1983. Set. 425.00 (ISBN 0-08-029344-1). Pergamon.
IFIP Conference, 11th, Copenhagen, DK, July 25-29, 1983. System Modelling & Optimization: Proceedings. Thoft-Christian, P., ed. (Lectures Notes in Control & Information Sciences: Vol. 59). x, 892p. 1984. pap. 49.50 (ISBN 0-387-13185-X). Springer-Verlag.
Inmon, W. H. Information Systems Architecture: A System Developer's Primer. (Illus.). 288p. 1986. text ed. 35.95 (ISBN 0-13-464694-0). P-H.
International Commission on Irrigation & Drainage, New Delhi, India, ed. The Application of Systems Analysis Irrigation, Drainage & Flood Control: A Manual for Engineers & Water Technologists. (Water Development, Supply & Management Ser.: Vol. 11). (Illus.). 1980. text ed. 57.00 (ISBN 0-08-023425-9); pap. text ed. 21.00 (ISBN 0-08-023431-3). Pergamon.
International Seminar on Trends in Mathematical Modelling, Venice, Dec. 1971. Proceedings. Hawkes, N., ed. LC 72-96971. (Lecture Notes in Economics & Mathematical Systems: Vol. 80). 288p. 1973. pap. 18.00 (ISBN 0-387-06144-4). Springer-Verlag.
Iooss, G., et al, eds. Chaotic Behavior of Deterministic Systems. (Les Houches Summer School Proceedings Ser.: Vol. 36). 1984. 144.25 (ISBN 0-444-86542-X, I-440-83). Elsevier.
Jaczewski, J. Logical Systems for Industrial Applications. (Studies in Automation & Control: Vol. 1). 452p. 1978. 68.00 (ISBN 0-444-99804-7). Elsevier.
Jamieson, D. M., et al, eds. The General Theory of Systems Applied to Management & Organization: Theory, Vol. 1. (Systems Inquiry Ser.). 400p. 1980. pap. text ed. 14.75 (ISBN 0-914105-11-6). Intersystems Pubns.
Jamshidi, M. & Malek-Zavarei, M. Introduction to Linear Systems: Computer Aided Approach. 450p. 1984. 65.00 (ISBN 0-08-028701-8); pap. 20.00 (ISBN 0-08-028702-6). Pergamon.
Jantsch, Erich. Design for Evolution: Self-Organization & Planning in the Life of Human Systems. Laszlo, Ervin, ed. LC 74-77525. (International Library of Systems Theory & Philosophy Ser). 320p. 1975. 9.95 (ISBN 0-8076-0757-6). Braziller.
Jeffery, D. Ross & Lawrence, Micheal J. Systems Analysis & Design. (Illus.). 240p. 1984. pap. text ed. 24.95 (ISBN 0-13-880261-0). P-H.
Johannides, David F. Cost Containment Through Systems Engineering: A Guide for Hospitals. LC 79-15217. 326p. 1979. text ed. 39.75 (ISBN 0-89443-098-X). Aspen Systems.
Johnson, Johnny R. & Johnson, David E. Linear Systems Analysis. LC 81-3721. 594p. 1981. Repr. of 1975 ed. lib. bdg. 34.50 (ISBN 0-89874-352-4). Krieger.
Jong, M. T. Methods of Discrete Signal & System Analysis. 1982. 42.00 (ISBN 0-07-033025-5). McGraw.
Jury, Eliahu I. Inners & Stability of Dynamic Systems. 2nd ed. LC 81-8343. 340p. 1982. 29.50 (ISBN 0-89874-341-9). Krieger.
--Theory & Application of the Z-Transform Method. LC 64-17145. 344p. 1973. Repr. of 1964 ed. 20.50 (ISBN 0-88275-122-0). Krieger.
Kailath, Thomas. Linear Systems. (Information & Systems Sciences Ser.). (Illus.). 1980. text ed. 40.95 (ISBN 0-13-536961-4). P-H.
Karnopp, Dean C. & Rosenberg, Ronald C. System Dynamics: A Unified Approach. LC 74-22466. 402p. 1975. 45.95x (ISBN 0-471-45940-2, Pub. by Wiley-Interscience). Wiley.
Kauffman, Draper, Jr. Systems Two: Human Systems. Dewane, Michael L., ed. (The Future Systems Ser.). (Illus.). 57p. 1981. pap. text ed. 5.95 (ISBN 0-941506-01-0). Future Syst TLH.
Kennington, Jeff L. & Helgason, Richard V. Algorithms for Network Programming. LC 80-258. 291p. 1980. 40.95x (ISBN 0-471-06016-X, Pub. by Wiley Interscience). Wiley.
Kieso, Donald E., et al. Systems Understanding Aid for Financial Accounting. 128p. (Orig.). 1983. pap. text ed. 12.95x (ISBN 0-912503-01-7). Systems Pubns.
Kilgannon, Pete. Business Data Processing & Systems Analysts. 336p. 1980. pap. text ed. 19.95 (ISBN 0-7131-2755-4). E Arnold.
Klir, George J. Architecture of Systems Problem Solving. 556p. 1985. 75.00x (ISBN 0-306-41867-3, Plenum Pr). Plenum Pub.
Knops, R. J., ed. Nonlinear Analysis & Mechanics: Heriot-Watt Symposium, Vol. 1. (Research Notes in Mathematics Ser.: No. 17). (Orig.). 1977. pap. text ed. 23.00 (ISBN 0-273-01128-6). Pitman Pub MA.
Kohn, Robert E. A Linear Programming Model for Air Pollution Control. 1978. 40.00x (ISBN 0-262-11062-8). MIT Pr.
Kolman, Bernard & Beck, Robert. Elementary Linear Programming with Applications. (Computer Science & Applied Mathematics Ser.). 1980. text ed. 22.50i (ISBN 0-12-417860-X); instrs' manual 2.50i (ISBN 0-12-417862-6). Acad Pr.
Kreider, Donald L., et al. Introduction to Linear Analysis. 1966. 31.95 (ISBN 0-201-03949-4). Addison-Wesley.
Kuo, Franklin F. & Kaiser, J. F. System Analysis by Digital Computer. LC 66-25226. 438p. 1966. text ed. 28.00 (ISBN 0-471-51121-8, Pub. by Wiley). Krieger.
Kuong, Javier F., ed. Audit & Control of Advanced On-Line Systems, Manual. 1983. 195.00 (ISBN 0-940706-00-8, MAP-7). Management Advisory Pubns.
L.A. International. Systems Analysis. LC 82-90412. 31p. 1983. 5.95 (ISBN 0-533-05351-X). Vantage.
Lago, G. V. & Benningfield, L. M. Circuit & System Theory. LC 79-10878. 575p. 1979. text ed. 47.50x (ISBN 0-471-04927-1). Wiley.
Lampson, B. W., et al, eds. Distributed Systems: Architecture & Implementation, An Advanced Course. (Springer Study Edition). 510p. 1983. pap. 24.00 (ISBN 0-387-12116-1). Springer-Verlag.
Langefors, Borje & Samuelson, Kjell. Information & Data in Systems. 192p. 1976. 21.95 (ISBN 0-442-80349-4). Van Nos Reinhold.
Lapatra, Jack W. Applying the Systems Approach to Urban Development. LC 73-11942. (Community Development Ser.: Vol. 5). 296p. 1973. pap. 21.95 (ISBN 0-87933-298-0). Van Nos Reinhold.
Lasota, Andrzej & Mackey, Micheal C. Probabilistic Properties of Deterministic Systems. 400p. Date not set. price not set. (ISBN 0-521-30248-X). Cambridge U Pr.
Laszlo, E. Systems Science & World Order: Selected Studies. (Systems Science & World Order Library). 278p. 1982. 40.00 (ISBN 0-08-028924-X). Pergamon.
Laszlo, Ervin, ed. The Relevance of General Systems Theory. LC 72-81355. 192p. 1972. 8.95 (ISBN 0-8076-0659-6); pap. 3.45 (ISBN 0-8076-0658-8). Braziller.
--The World System: Models, Norms, Variations. (International Library of Systems Theory & Philosophy Ser). 224p. 1973. 7.95 (ISBN 0-8076-0695-2); pap. 5.95 (ISBN 0-8076-0696-0). Braziller.
Lathi, B. P. Signals, Systems & Controls. LC 73-464. 640p. 1974. text ed. 36.95 scp (ISBN 0-7002-2431-9, HarpC). Har-Row.
Lazarevic, B. & Lazarevic, B., eds. Global & Large Scale System Models: Proceedings. (Lecture Notes in Control & Information Sciences: Vol. 19). 1979. pap. 17.00 (ISBN 0-387-09637-X). Springer-Verlag.
Lazowska, Edward D., et al. Quantitative System Performance: Computer System Analysis Using Queueing Network Models. LC 83-13791. (Illus.). 417p. 1984. text ed. 41.95 (ISBN 0-13-746975-6). P-H.
Lee, B. Introducing Systems Analysis & Design, 2 vols. 400p. 1979. Vol. 1. pap. 26.25 (ISBN 0-471-89405-2); Vol. 2. pap. 40.45 (ISBN 0-471-89406-0). Wiley.
Lee, Barry. Introducing Systems Analysis & Design, Vol. I. LC 79-301329. (Illus.). 1978. pap. 30.00x (ISBN 0-85012-206-6). Intl Pubns Serv.
--Introducing Systems Analysis & Design, Vol. 2. (Illus., Orig.). 1979. pap. 42.00x (ISBN 0-85012-207-4). Intl Pubns Serv.
Leeson, Marjorie. Delta Products Case Study. 120p. 1981. pap. text ed. 9.95 (ISBN 0-574-21288-4, 13-4288); solutions manual avail. (ISBN 0-574-21289-2, 13-4289). SRA.
--Systems Analysis & Design. 464p. 1981. text ed. 19.95 (ISBN 0-574-21279-5, 13-4285); instr's. guide avail. (ISBN 0-574-21286-8, 13-4286). SRA.
Leslie, Robert E. Systems Analysis & Design: Method & Invention. (Illus.). 656p. 1986. text ed. 29.95 (ISBN 0-13-898164-7). P-H.
Levan, N. Systems & Signals. (University Series in Modern Engineering). 173p. 1983. pap. 18.00 (ISBN 0-387-90900-1). Springer Verlag.
Levy, Leon S. Discrete Structures of Computer Science. LC 79-11218. 310p. 1980. text ed. 33.95x (ISBN 0-471-03208-5). Wiley.
Lilienfeld, Robert. The Rise of Systems Theory: An Ideological Analysis. LC 77-12609. 1978. 42.50x (ISBN 0-471-53533-8, Pub. by Wiley-Interscience). Wiley.
Lions, J. L. Some Methods in Mathematical Analysis of Systems & Their Control. 572p. 1981. 93.50 (ISBN 0-677-60200-6). Gordon.
Liu, Chung L. & Liu, J. W. Linear Systems Analysis. (Illus.). 416p. 1975. text ed. 44.00 (ISBN 0-07-038120-8). McGraw.
Lohmuller, Keith. Introduction to Business Programming & Systems Analysis. (Illus.). 238p. (Orig.). 1983. 18.95 (ISBN 0-8306-0437-5, 1437); pap. 13.50 (ISBN 0-8306-1437-0). TAB Bks.
Lorin, Harold. Sorting & Sort Systems. (Illus.). 480p. 1975. 31.95 (ISBN 0-201-14453-0). Addison-Wesley.
Lovelace, Dennis J. A Universal Systems Model for Organization Design. 1982. 9.00 (ISBN 0-533-05339-0). Vantage.
Lucas, Henry C., Jr. Implementation: The Key to Successful Information Systems. LC 80-27009. 224p. 1981. 37.00x (ISBN 0-231-04434-8). Columbia U Pr.
Luchsinger, Vincent P. & Dock, V. Thomas. The Systems Approach: An Introduction. 1976. perfect bdg. 10.95 (ISBN 0-8403-2649-1). Kendall-Hunt.
Luenberger, David G. Introduction to Dynamic Systems: Theory, Models & Applications. LC 78-12366. 446p. 1979. 46.00 (ISBN 0-471-02594-1); solutions manual avail. (ISBN 0-471-06081-X). Wiley.
McCarthy, Thomas. The Critical Theory of Jurgen Habermas. 1978. 25.00x (ISBN 0-262-13138-2); pap. 13.50 (ISBN 0-262-63073-7). MIT Pr.
McClamroch, N. H. State Models of Dynamic Systems. (Illus.). 248p. 1980. 22.00 (ISBN 0-387-90490-5). Springer-Verlag.
MacDonald, D. Robert. Specifying Systems Specifications. (Orig.). 1985. pap. text ed. price not set (ISBN 0-917072-57-X). Yourdon.
McFarland, D. J., ed. Motivational Control Systems Analysis. 1975. 75.50 (ISBN 0-12-483860-X). Acad Pr.
McGillem, C. D. & Cooper, George R. Continuous & Discrete Signal & System Analysis. 2nd ed. LC 83-12845. 1984. text ed. 39.95 (ISBN 0-03-061703-0, HoltC). HR&W.
McMenamin, Stephen M. & Palmer, John F. Essential Systems Analysis. LC 84-11913. (Illus.). 408p. (Orig.). 1984. pap. text ed. 28.00 (ISBN 0-917072-30-8). Yourdon.
Mahmoud, M. S., et al. Discrete Systems: Analysis, Control & Optimization. (Communications & Control Engineering Ser.). (Illus.). 690p. 1984. 49.50 (ISBN 0-387-13645-2). Springer-Verlag.
Majone, Giandomenico & Quade, Edward S. Pitfalls of Analysis. LC 79-41700. (Wiley IIASA International Series on Applied Systems Analysis). 224p. 1980. 48.95x (ISBN 0-471-27746-0, Pub. by Wiley-Interscience). Wiley.
Marchesini, G. & Mitter, S. K., eds. Mathematical Systems Theory. (Lecture Notes in Economics & Mathematical Systems: Vol. 131). 1976. 23.00 (ISBN 0-387-07798-7). Springer-Verlag.
Marshall, George R. Systems Analysis in the Small Systems Environment. 1985. text ed. 27.95 (ISBN 0-8359-7445-6). Reston.

Sutherland. Societal Systems: Methodology, Modeling & Management. (System Science & Engineering Ser.: Vol. 3). 336p. 1978. 45.75 (ISBN 0-444-00239-1, North-Holland). Elsevier.

Sutherland, John W. A General Systems Philosophy for the Social & Behavioral Sciences. Laszlo, Ervin, ed. (International Library of Systems Theory & Philosophy Ser). 1973. 7.95 (ISBN 0-8076-0724-X). Braziller.

Swisher, George M. Introduction to Linear Systems Analysis. (Illus.). 744p. 1976. 34.95 (ISBN 0-916460-05-3). Matrix Pub.

Symposium on Recent Advances in Optimization Techniques 1965, Carnegie Institute of Technology. Recent Advances in Optimization Techniques: Proceedings. Lavi, Abrahim, et al, eds. LC 66-4421. pap. 160.00 (ISBN 0-317-08576-X, 2006349). Bks Demand UMI.

Teague, Lavette C., Jr. & Pidgeon, Christopher W. Structured Analysis Methods for Computer Information Systems. 400p. 1984. pap. text ed. 24.95 (ISBN 0-574-21495-X, 13-4495); instr's guide avail. (ISBN 0-574-21496-8, 13-3496). SRA.

Thierauf, Robert J. Systems Analysis & Design of Real-Time Management Information Systems. LC 74-28368. (Illus.). 624p. 1975. ref. ed. 33.95 (ISBN 0-13-881219-5). P-H.

Thierauf, Robert J. & Reynolds, George W. Systems Analysis & Design. 2nd ed. 512p. 1986. pap. text ed. 26.92 (ISBN 0-675-08172-6). Merrill.

--Systems Analysis & Design: A Case Study Approach. 1980. text ed. 23.95 (ISBN 0-675-08172-6). Additional supplements may be obtained from publisher. Merrill.

Thomas, Roland E. & Rosa, Albert J. Circuits & Signals: An Introduction to Linear & Interface Circuits. LC 83-21588. 758p. 1983. text ed. 38.50 (ISBN 0-471-89560-1); write for info. solutions (ISBN 0-471-89500-8). Wiley.

Townley, Helen M. Systems Analysis for Information Retrieval. 128p. 1978. 26.50x (ISBN 0-233-96920-9, 05826-2, Pub. by Gower Pub Co England). Lexington Bks.

Tsokos, C. P. & Padgett, W. J. Random Integral Equations with Applications to Stochastic Systems. (Lecture Notes in Mathematics: Vol. 233). 174p. 1971. pap. 10.00 (ISBN 0-387-05660-2). Springer-Verlag.

Tzafestas, Spyros G., ed. Walsh Functions in Signal & Systems Analysis & Design. (Illus.). 368p. 1985. 59.50 (ISBN 0-442-28298-2). Van Nos Reinhold.

U. S. - Italy Seminar on Variable Structure Systems, 2nd. Variable Structure Systems with Application to Economics & Biology: Proceedings. Mobler, R. R. & Ruberti, A., eds. (Lecture Notes in Economics & Mathematical Systems: Vol. 111). (Illus.). vi, 321p. 1975. pap. 20.00 (ISBN 0-387-07390-6). Springer-Verlag.

Vallee, Jacques, et al. Design & Use of the Forum System. (Group Communication Through Computers: Vol. 1). 139p. 1974. 10.50 (ISBN 0-318-14412-3, R32). Inst Future.

Van Dixhoorn, J. J. & Evans, F. J., eds. Physical Structure in Systems Theory: Network Approaches Engineering & Economics. 1975. 59.00 (ISBN 0-12-712450-0). Acad Pr.

Van Gigch, John P. Applied General Systems Theory. 2nd ed. 1978. text ed. 36.50 scp (ISBN 0-06-046776-2, HarpC). Har-Row.

Van Gigch, John P. & Hill, Richard E. Using Systems Analysis to Implement Cost-Effectiveness & Program Budgeting in Education. LC 71-153558. 64p. 1971. pap. 10.95 (ISBN 0-87778-007-2). Educ Tech Pubns.

Van Rootselaar, B., ed. Annals of Systems Research. Incl. (Vol. 2). 1972. pap. 20.50 (ISBN 90-207-0378-1); (Vol. 3). 1974. pap. 20.50 (ISBN 90-207-0458-3); (Vol. 4). 1975. pap. 23.00 (ISBN 90-207-0551-2); (Vol. 5). 1976. pap. 20.50 (ISBN 90-207-0657-8); (Vol. 6). 1977. pap. 20.00 (ISBN 0-686-28540-9). (Annals of Systems Research Ser). pap. (Pub. by Martinus Nijhoff Netherlands). Kluwer Academic.

--Annals of Systems Research 1978. (Annals of Systems Research Ser.: No. 7). 1980. lib. bdg. 21.50 (ISBN 90-207-0876-7, Pub. by Martinus Nijhoff Netherlands). Kluwer Academic.

Van Valkenburg, M. E. Network Analysis. 3rd ed. (Illus.). 699p. 1974. 40.95 (ISBN 0-13-611095-9). P-H.

Vichas, Robert P. New Encyclopedic Dictionary of Systems & Procedures. 700p. 1981. 39.95 (ISBN 0-13-612630-8). P-H.

Vidyasagar, M. Nonlinear Systems Analysis. LC 77-24379. (Illus.). 1978. ref ed. 43.95 (ISBN 0-13-623280-9). P-H.

Vinti, C., ed. Nonlinear Analysis & Optimization. (Lecture Notes in Mathematics Ser.: Vol. 1107). v, 214p. 1984. pap. 11.00 (ISBN 0-387-13903-6). Springer-Verlag.

Von Bertalanffy, Ludwig. General System Theory: Essays on Its Foundation & Development. rev. ed. LC 68-25176. 1969. pap. 7.95 (ISBN 0-8076-0453-4). Braziller.

--Perspectives on General System Theory. Taschdjian, Edgar & Von Bertalanffy, Maria, eds. LC 75-10993. 220p. 1976. 8.95 (ISBN 0-8076-0797-5). Braziller.

Von Foerster, Heinz. Observing Systems. (Systems Inquiry Ser.). 425p. (Orig.). 1982. pap. text ed. 14.95x (ISBN 0-914105-19-1). Intersystems Pubns.

Waddington, C. H. The Man-Made Future. LC 77-29043. 1978. 26.00 (ISBN 0-312-51045-4). St Martin.

Walter, E. Identifiability of State Space Models: With Applications to Transformation Systems. (Lecture Notes in Biomathematics: Vol. 46). 202p. 1982. pap. 16.00 (ISBN 0-387-11590-0). Springer-Verlag.

Ward, Paul T. Systems Development Without Pain: A User's Guide to Modeling Organizational Patterns. LC 83-27368. (Illus.). 288p. 1984. pap. 27.50 (ISBN 0-917072-40-5). Yourdon.

Waters, Kathleen & Murphy, Gretchen. Systems Analysis & Computer Applications in Health Information Management. LC 82-18468. 449p. 1982. 36.95 (ISBN 0-89443-838-7). Aspen Systems.

Waters, S. J. Systems Specifications. (Illus.). 113p. (Orig.). 1979. pap. 19.50x (ISBN 0-85012-188-4). Intl Pubns Serv.

Wedde, H., ed. Adequate Modeling of Systems. (Illus.). 336p. 1983. pap. 27.00 (ISBN 0-387-12567-1). Springer-Verlag.

Weinberg, Gerald M. An Introduction to General Systems Thinking. LC 74-26689. (Systems Engineering & Analysis Ser.). 279p. 1975. 39.95x (ISBN 0-471-92563-2, Pub. by Wiley-Interscience); member 32.75. Assn Inform & Image Mgmt.

--Rethinking Systems Analysis & Design. 193p. 1982. text ed. 25.00 (ISBN 0-316-92844-5). Little.

Weinberg, Victor. Structured Analysis. (Illus.). 1980. text ed. 37.50 (ISBN 0-13-854414-X). P-H.

Werley, Harriet, et al, eds. Health Research: The Systems Approach. LC 73-92207. (Illus.). 330p. 1976. text ed. 23.95 (ISBN 0-8261-1710-4). Springer Pub.

Wetherbe, James C. Cases in Structured Systems Design. 2nd ed. (Illus.). 230p. 1984. pap. text ed. 13.50 (ISBN 0-314-77860-8). West Pub.

--Cases in Systems Design. (Data Processing & Information Systems Ser.). 1979. pap. text ed. 11.95 (ISBN 0-8299-0229-5). West Pub.

--System Analysis & Design: Traditional, Structured & Advanced Concepts & Techniques (International Ed) 2nd ed. LC 80-27802. (Illus.). 400p. 1984. 17.00 (ISBN 0-314-77859-4). West Pub.

--Systems Analysis & Design: Traditional Structured & Advanced Concepts & Techniques. 2nd ed. (Illus.). 400p. 1984. text ed. 23.95 (ISBN 0-314-77858-6); write for info. instr's manual (ISBN 0-314-77861-6). West Pub.

--Systems Analysis for Computer-Based Informtion Systems. 1979. text ed. 19.95 (ISBN 0-8299-0228-7). West Pub.

Wets, Roger J., ed. Stochastic Systems: Modeling, Identification, & Optimization I. Benes, Vaclav E. LC 76-50621. (Mathematical Programming Studies: Vol. 5). 1977. pap. 20.50 (ISBN 0-7204-0569-6, North-Holland). Elsevier.

Whitehouse, Gary E. Systems Analysis & Design Using Network Techniques. (Industrial & Systems Engineering Ser). (Illus.). 464p. (Reference ed.). 1973. 34.95 (ISBN 0-13-881474-0). P-H.

Wiberg, Donald M. State Space & Linear Systems. (Schaum Outline Ser). 1971. pap. 9.95 (ISBN 0-07-070096-6). McGraw.

Willer & Anderson. Network Exchange & Coercion: The Elementary Theory & Its Applications. 29.95 (ISBN 0-444-99078-X, WNE/, Pub. by Elsevier). Greenwood.

Wilson, Brian. Systems, Concepts, Methodologies & Applications. 400p. 1984. 29.95 (ISBN 0-471-90443-0). Wiley.

Wong, K. K. Risk Analysis & Control: A Guide for DP Managers. 152p. (Orig.). 1977. pap. 27.50x (ISBN 0-85012-179-5). Intl Pubns Serv.

Woolf, E., et al, eds. Systems Analysis & Design. 350p. (Orig.). 1985. pap. text ed. 32.50x (ISBN 0-7121-0496-8). Trans-Atlantic.

Young, Thomas V. Linear Systems & Digital Signal Processing. (Illus.). 400p. 1985. text ed. 37.95 (ISBN 0-13-537366-2). P-H.

Zadeh, L. A. & Desoer, C. A. Linear System Theory. LC 78-26008. 650p. 1979. Repr. of 1963 ed. lib. bdg. 37.50 (ISBN 0-88275-809-8). Krieger.

Zarrop, M. B. Optimal Experiment Design for Dynamic System Identification. (Lecture Notes in Control & Information Sciences: Vol. 21). 197p. 1979. pap. 17.00 (ISBN 0-387-09841-0). Springer-Verlag.

Zeleny, M., ed. Autopoiesis: A Theory of Living Organization. (Series in General Systems Research: Vol. 3). 314p. 1981. 77.00 (ISBN 0-444-86178-5, North-Holland). Elsevier.

Zemanian, A. H. Realizability Theory for Continuous Linear Systems. (Mathematics in Science & Engineering Ser.: Vol. 97). 1972. 60.00 (ISBN 0-12-779550-2). Acad Pr.

SYSTEM SIMULATION

see Simulation Methods

SYSTEM THEORY

see System Analysis

SYSTEMATIC BOTANY

see Botany–Classification

SYSTEMATIC ZOOLOGY

see Zoology–Classification

SYSTEMS, THEORY OF

see System Analysis

SYSTEMS ANALYSIS

see System Analysis

SYSTEMS ENGINEERING

see also Bionics; Dynamic Programming; Maintainability (Engineering); Man-Machine Systems; Operations Research; Reliability (Engineering); Simulation Methods; Weapons Systems

Amaria, P. J, et al. Arctic Systems. LC 77-3871. (NATO Conference Series II, Systems Science: Vol. 2). 956p. 1977. 115.00x (ISBN 0-306-32842-9, Plenum Pr). Plenum Pub.

Andrews, Michael. Principles of Firmware Engineering in Microprogram Control. LC 80-19386. (Illus.). 347p. 1980. 36.95 (ISBN 0-914894-63-3). Computer Sci.

Andriole, Stephen J. Interactive Computer Based Systems Design & Development. 1983. 16.95 (ISBN 0-89433-191-4). Van Nos Reinhold.

Atherton, D. Nonlinear Control Engineering. 1982. pap. 26.95 (ISBN 0-442-30486-2). Van Nos Reinhold.

Banathy, Bela H., ed. Systems Education: Perspectives, Programs, & Methods. (Systems Inquiry Ser.). 177p. 1983. pap. 15.95x (ISBN 0-914105-02-7). Intersystems Pubns.

Barlow, Richard E., et al, eds. Reliability & Fault Tree Analysis: Theoretical & Applied Aspects of System Reliability & Safety Assessment. LC 75-22580. (Illus.). xxxix, 927p. 1975. text ed. 42.50 (ISBN 0-89871-033-2). Soc Indus-Appl Math.

Bignell, Victor & Fortune, Joyce. Understanding Systems Failures. LC 83-12016. 272p. 1984. pap. 6.50 (ISBN 0-7190-0973-1, Pub. by Manchester Univ Pr). Longwood Pub Group.

Billinton, R. & Allan, R. N. Reliability Evaluation of Engineering Systems. LC 82-18578. 359p. 1983. 42.50 (ISBN 0-306-41296-9, Plenum Press). Plenum Pub.

Blanchard, B. & Fabrycky, W. Systems Engineering & Analysis. 1981. 34.95 (ISBN 0-13-881631-X). P-H.

Bochmann, G. V. Concepts for Distributed System Design. (Illus.). 259p. 1983. pap. 21.00 (ISBN 0-387-12049-1). Springer-Verlag.

Booth, Grayce M. The Design of Complex Information Systems: Common Sense Methods for Success. (Illus.). 288p. 1983. 32.95 (ISBN 0-07-006506-3). McGraw.

Bose, Nirmal K., ed. Multidimensional Systems: Theory & Applications. LC 78-55096. 1979. 41.55 (ISBN 0-87942-109-6, PC01107). Inst Electrical.

Botterill, A. E. Systems Engineering for Materials Processing. 1986. cancelled (ISBN 0-08-029974-1); pap. price not set (ISBN 0-08-029973-3). Pergamon.

Brackett, Michael H. Developing Data Structured Information Systems. LC 82-62821. (Illus.). 184p. (Orig.). 1983. pap. 20.00 (ISBN 0-9605884-1-8). Orr & Assocs.

Breipohl, Arthur M. Probabilistic System Analysis: An Introduction to Probabilistic Models, Decisions & Applications of Random Processes. LC 77-94920. 352p. 1970. 43.50 (ISBN 0-471-10181-8). Wiley.

Brookes, Cyril H., et al. Information Systems Design. (Illus.). 477p. 1982. 28.00 (ISBN 0-7248-0641-5). P-H.

Buhr, Raymond. Systems Design with Ada. (Illus.). 288p. 1984. text ed. 33.00 (ISBN 0-13-881623-9). P-H.

Butheel, A. & Dewilde, P., eds. Rational Approximation in Systems Engineering. 244p. 1983. 29.95 (ISBN 0-8176-3159-3). Birkhauser.

Camp & Smay. Microprocessor Systems Engineering. (Illus.). 656p. 1979. 29.95 (ISBN 0-916460-26-6). Matrix Pub.

Campbell, Sally. Microcomputer Software Design: How to Develop Complex Application Programs. (Illus.). 232p. 1983. 21.95 (ISBN 0-13-580639-9); pap. 12.95 (ISBN 0-13-580621-6). P-H.

Cannon, Robert H. Dynamics of Physical Systems. 1967. text ed. 48.00 (ISBN 0-07-009754-2). McGraw.

Carlbom, Ingrid. High-Performance Graphics System Architecture: A Methodology for Design & Evaluation. Stone, Harold S., ed. LC 84-2673. (Computer Science: Systems Programming Ser.: No. 21). 182p. 1984. 39.95 (ISBN 0-8357-1595-7). UMI Res Pr.

Case Centennial Symposium on Large Scale Systems, Cleveland, O., July 1980. Large Scale Systems: Proceedings. Haimes, Yacov Y., ed. (Studies in Management Sciences & Systems: Vol. 7). 184p. 1982. 42.75 (ISBN 0-444-86367-2, I-112-82, North-Holland). Elsevier.

Chase, Wilton P. Management of System Engineering. LC 83-18746. 1984. Repr. of 1974 ed. lib. bdg. 26.50 (ISBN 0-89874-682-5). Krieger.

Chestnut, Harold. Systems Engineering Methods. LC 67-17336. (Wiley Ser. on Systems Engineering & Analysis). pap. 101.00 (ISBN 0-317-08335-X, 2051601). Bks Demand UMI.

--Systems Engineering Tools. LC 65-19484. (Wiley Series on Systems Engineering & Analysis). (Illus.). pap. 160.00 (ISBN 0-317-08334-1, 2055158). Bks Demand UMI.

Conference on Systems & Computer Science, 1965: University of Western Ontario. Systems & Computer Science. Hart, John F. & Takasu, Satoru, eds. LC 68-114245. pap. 65.30 (ISBN 0-317-10999-5, 2014240). Bks Demand UMI.

Dasgupta, Subrata. The Design & Description of Computer Architectures. LC 83-21826. 300p. 1984. 40.95x (ISBN 0-471-89616-0, Pub. by Wiley-Interscience). Wiley.

Davis, William S. Tools & Techniques for Structured Systems Analysis & Design. LC 83-4629. 208p. 1983. pap. 15.95 (ISBN 0-201-10274-9). Addison-Wesley.

DeNeufville, R. & Stafford, J. Systems Analysis for Engineers & Managers. 48.00 (ISBN 0-07-016370-7). McGraw.

Dhillion, B. Reliability Engineering in Systems Design & Operation. 336p. 1982. 39.95 (ISBN 0-442-27213-8). Van Nos Reinhold.

Doebelin, E. O. System Dynamics: Modeling & Response. LC 77-187802. 448p. 1972. 36.95 (ISBN 0-675-09120-9). Merrill.

English, J. M. Cost Effectiveness: Economic Evaluation of Engineered Systems. LC 68-28500. Repr. of 1968 ed. 59.90 (ISBN 0-8357-9868-2, 2013052). Bks Demand UMI.

ERA. The Engineering of Microprocessor Systems: Guidelines on System Development. LC 79-40952. 1979. 25.00 (ISBN 0-08-025435-7); pap. 8.00 (ISBN 0-08-025434-9). Pergamon.

Fitzgerald, Jerry. Designing Controls into Computerized Systems. LC 81-67870. (Illus.). 157p. 1981. pap. 16.95 (ISBN 0-932410-36-7). FitzGerald & Assocs.

Flavin, Matt. Fundamental Concepts of Information Modeling. (Illus.). 136p. (Orig.). 1981. pap. 17.50 (ISBN 0-917072-22-7). Yourdon.

Fluid Film Bearing Committee of the Lubrication Division. Topics in Fluid Film Bearing & Rotor Bearing Systems Design & Optimization: Presented at the Design Engineering Conference, Chicago, Ill., April 17-20, 1978. Rohde, S. M., et al, eds. LC 78-52526. pap. 70.00 (ISBN 0-317-11248-1, 2017648). Bks Demand UMI.

Forms Design & Management. 1979. 7.00 (ISBN 0-934356-19-X). Assn Syst Mgmt.

Franta, W. R. & Chlamtac, Imrich. Local Networks: Motivation, Technology & Performance. LC 80-7725. (Illus.). 512p. 1982. 44.50x (ISBN 0-669-03779-6). Lexington Bks.

Garner, K. C. Introduction to Control Systems Performance Measurements. 1968. 28.00 (ISBN 0-08-012499-2); pap. 11.25 (ISBN 0-08-012498-4). Pergamon.

Gheorghe, Adrian. Applied Systems Engineering. 342p. 1982. text ed. 48.95x (ISBN 0-471-09997-X, Pub.by Wiley-Interscience). Wiley.

Glasson, B. C. EDP System Development Guidelines. LC 83-72639. 268p. 1984. pap. 24.95 (ISBN 0-89435-072-2). QED Info Sci.

Gonzalez, Harvey J. & Fein, Lois. Datatran: A Comprehensive & Practical System for Developing & Maintaining Data Processing Systems. (Illus.). 432p. 1983. text ed. 41.95 (ISBN 0-13-196493-3). P-H.

Graupe, Daniel. Identification of Systems. 2nd ed. LC 75-31781. 288p. 1976. 19.50 (ISBN 0-88275-359-2). Krieger.

Hahn, H. & Herz, B. Higher Order Root-Locus Technique with Applications in Control System Design. 1981. 42.00 (ISBN 0-9940017-5-4, Pub. by Vieweg & Sohn Germany). Heyden.

Hammer, Preston, ed. Advances in Mathematical Systems Theory. LC 67-27111. (Illus.). 1967. 20.00x (ISBN 0-271-73132-X). Pa St U Pr.

Hammer, Willie. Handbook of System & Product Safety. LC 72-2683. (Illus.). 368p. 1972. ref. ed. 45.95 (ISBN 0-13-382226-5). P-H.

Handler, A. Benjamin. Systems Approach to Architecture. LC 79-100397. (Elsevier Architectural Science Ser.). pap. 48.00 (ISBN 0-317-10850-6, 2007768). Bks Demand UMI.

Rutherford, D. Tanker Cargo Handling: A Practical Handbook. (Illus.). 111p. 1980. text ed. 19.95x (ISBN 0-85264-256-3). Lubrecht & Cramer.

Vendrell, J. The Oil Rig Moorings Handbook. 1981. 20.00x (Pub. by Nautical England). State Mutual Bk.

Woolcott, T. W. Liquified Petroleum Gas Tanker Practice. 1981. 60.00x (ISBN 0-85174-295-5, Pub. by Brown, Son & Ferguson). State Mutual Bk.

--Liquified Petroleum Gas Tanker Practice. 125p. 1977. 32.00x (ISBN 0-85174-295-5). Sheridan.

TANKS

see also Pressure Vessels

American Society of Civil Engineers, compiled by. Design of Water Intake Stuctures for Fish Protection. LC 81-70988. 175p. 1982. pap. 18.50x (ISBN 0-87262-291-6). Am Soc Civil Eng.

AWWA Standard for Welded Steel Elevated Tanks, Standpipes & Reservoirs for Water Storage: D-100-79. rev. ed. (AWWA Standards Ser.). (Illus.). 72p. 1979. pap. text ed. 10.20 (ISBN 0-89867-160-4). Am Water Wks Assn.

Brownell, Lloyd E. & Young, Edwin H. Process Equipment Design: Vessel Design. LC 59-5882. 408p. 1959. 74.95 (ISBN 0-471-11319-0, Pub by Wiley-Interscience). Wiley.

Chamberlain, Peter & Ellis, Chris. Pictorial History of Tanks of the World, 1915-1945. (Illus.). 1981. 24.95 (Arms & Armour Pr). Sterling.

Ecology & Environment, Inc. Toxic Substance Storage Tank Containment. LC 84-22697. (Pollution Technology Review Ser.: No. 116). (Illus.). 274p. 1985. 36.00 (ISBN 0-8155-1018-7). Noyes.

Miscavich, Ron. Equipment Safety Program - Tanks. Boehler, Ted, ed. (Illus.). 1977. pap. text ed. 4.50 (ISBN 0-916974-27-8). NAUI.

Properties of Materials for Liquified Natural Gas Tankage - STP 579. 424p. 1975. 39.75 (ISBN 0-8031-0538-X, 04-579000-30). ASTM.

Resource Systems International. Tanks, Vessels & Other Components. 1982. pap. text ed. 15.00 (ISBN 0-8359-7538-X). Reston.

TANKS (MILITARY SCIENCE)

see also Antitank Guns; Armored Vehicles, Military

Ayliffe-Jones, Noel. World Tanks & Reconnaissance Vehicles since 1945. (Illus.). 144p. 1984. 19.95 (ISBN 0-88254-978-2). Hippocrene Bks.

Bonds, Ray, ed. An Illustrated Guide to World War II Tanks & Fighting Vehicles. LC 80-70975. (Illustrated Military Guides Ser.). (Illus.). 160p. 1981. 9.95 (ISBN 0-668-05232-5, 5232). Arco.

Chamberlain, Peter & Doyle, Hilary L. Encyclopedia of German Tanks of World War II. LC 77-29061. (Illus.). 1978. 14.95 (ISBN 0-668-04565-5, 4565). Arco.

Chamberlain, Peter & Ellis, Chris. British & American Tanks of World War II. LC 69-13591. (Illus.). 1977. pap. 8.95 (ISBN 0-668-04304-0). Arco.

Crow, Duncan, ed. Modern Battle Tanks. LC 78-4192. (Illus.). 1978. pap. 7.95 (ISBN 0-668-04650-3). Arco.

Feist, Uwe. German Panzers from Mk. I to Mk. V Panther. LC 66-25077. (Armor Ser.: Vol. 2). (Illus.). 1966. pap. 3.95 (ISBN 0-8168-2004-X). Aero.

Forty, George & Batchelor, John. United States Tanks of World War II in Action. (Illus.). 160p. 1983. 16.95 (ISBN 0-7137-1214-7, Pub. by Blandford Pr England). Sterling.

Foss, Christopher. Jane's Light Tanks & Armoured Cars. (Illus.). 192p. 1984. 18.95 (ISBN 0-7106-0322-3). Jane's Pub Inc.

Foss, Christopher F. The Illustrated Guide to Modern Tanks & Fighting Vehicles. LC 80-65165. (Illustrated Military Guides Ser.). (Illus.). 160p. 1980. 9.95 (ISBN 0-668-04965-0, 4965-0). Arco.

--Jane's Main Battle Tanks. (Illus.). 205p. 1984. 18.95 (ISBN 0-7106-0277-4). Jane's Pub Inc.

Guderian, Heinz. Panzer Leader. LC 79-19897. Repr. of 1952 ed. 19.95 (ISBN 0-89201-076-2). Zenger Pub.

Hoffschmidt, Edward J. & Tantum, William H. German Tank & Antitank. 260p. 1968. 12.50 (ISBN 0-87364-151-5). Paladin Pr.

Hunnicutt, R. P. Sherman: A History of the American Medium Tank. LC 78-67013. (Illus.). 576p. 1978. 45.00 (ISBN 0-89141-080-5, Pub by Taurus Enterprises). Presidio Pr.

Icks, Robert J. Tanks & Armored Vehicles 1900-1945. 272p. 1971. 12.95 (ISBN 0-87364-228-7). Paladin Pr.

Kays, William B. Construction of Linings for Reservoirs, Tanks, & Pollution Control Facilties. LC 77-3944. (Wiley Series of Practical Construction Guides). 379p. 1977. 59.95x (ISBN 0-471-02110-5, Pub. by Wiley-Interscience). Wiley.

Liddell-Hart, B. H. Tanks: The History of the Royal Tank Regiment & Its Predecessors, 1914-1915, 2 vols. Repr. of 1959 ed. Set. 49.95 (ISBN 0-89201-079-7). Zenger Pub.

Macksey, Kenneth. Tank Facts & Feats. (Guinness Superlatives Ser.). (Illus.). 256p. 1980. 17.95 (ISBN 0-85112-204-3, Pub. by Guinness Superlatives England). Sterling.

--The Tanks, Nineteen Forty-Five to Nineteen Seventy-Five. (Illus.). 336p. 1981. 23.95 (ISBN 0-85368-293-3). Stackpole.

Nowarra, Heinz J. German Tanks, Nineteen Fourteen to Nineteen Sixty-Eight. (Illus., Orig.). 1968. pap. 2.95 (ISBN 0-668-01753-8). Arco.

Paine, Sheperd. Modeling Tanks & Military Vehicles. Angle, Burr, ed. (Illus.). 76p. (Orig.). 1982. pap. 8.95 (ISBN 0-89024-045-0). Kalmbach.

Spielberger, Walter J. Gepard. (Ger., Illus.). 255p. 1982. 39.95 (ISBN 0-933852-30-4). Nautical & Aviation.

White, B. T. Tanks & Other A. F. V. 's of the Blitzkrieg Era, 1939-1941. (Illus.). 161p. 1982. 9.95 (ISBN 0-7137-0704-6, Pub. by Blandford Pr England). Sterling.

TANNING

see also Leather

Bienkiewicz, Krzysztof J. Physical Chemistry of Leather Making. LC 80-27191. 556p. 1983. 46.50 (ISBN 0-89874-304-4). Krieger.

Churchill, James E. The Complete Book of Tanning Skins & Furs. 224p. 1983. 14.95 (ISBN 0-8117-1719-4). Stackpole.

European Leather Guide & Tanners of the World. 1985. 175.00x (ISBN 0-685-79495-4). State Mutual Bk.

Farnham, Albert S. Home Tanning & Leather Making Guide. (Illus.). 176p. pap. 3.50 (ISBN 0-936622-11-3). A R Harding Pub.

Frey, et al. Home Tanning. facsimile ed. (Shorey Lost Arts Ser.). (Illus.). 30p. pap. 1.50 (ISBN 0-8466-6009-1, U9). Shorey.

Grantz, Gerald. Home Book of Taxidermy & Tanning. (Illus.). 160p. (Orig.). 1985. pap. 8.95 (ISBN 0-8117-2259-7). Stackpole.

Hawks, Catharine A., et al. The Care of Tanned Skins in Mammal Research Collections. (Museology Ser.: No. 6). (Illus.). 32p. 1984. pap. 4.00 (ISBN 0-89672-130-2). Tex Tech Pr.

Hobson, Phyllis. Tan Your Hide: Home Tanning Furs & Leathers. LC 77-2593. (Illus.). 144p. 1977. pap. 6.95 (ISBN 0-88266-101-9). Garden Way Pub.

International Labour Office & United Nations Industrial Development Organisation. Tanning of Hides & Skins. (Technology Series. Technical Memorandum: No. 1). xii, 225p. (Orig.). 1981. pap. 14.25 (ISBN 92-2-102904-2). Intl Labour Office.

Kellogg, Kathy. Home Tanning & Leathercraft Simplified. (Illus.). 192p. (Orig.). 1984. pap. 8.95 (ISBN 0-913589-04-7). Williamson Pub Co.

Mason, Otis. Aboriginal Skin-Dressing. (Shorey Indian Ser.). (Illus.). 100p. Shorey.

Rural Tanning Techniques. (Agricultural Development Papers: No. 68). 252p. 1960. pap. 11.25 (ISBN 0-686-92694-3, F417, FAO). Unipub.

Urwick Technology Management Ltd. Environmental Impacts & Policies for the EEC Tanning Industry. 86p. 1977. 24.00x (ISBN 0-86010-065-0, Pub. by Graham & Trotman England). State Mutual Bk.

TANTALUM

Tantalum: Physico-Chemical Properties of Its Compounds & Alloys. (Atomic Energy Review Ser.: No. 3). (Illus.). 133p. (Orig.). 1973. pap. 10.50 (ISBN 92-0-149072-0, IAER3, IAEA). Unipub.

TAPE-CONTROLLED MACHINE TOOLS

see Machine Tools–Numerical Control

TAPE RECORDERS

see Magnetic Recorders and Recording

TAPE RECORDINGS (DATA STORAGE)

see Data Tapes

TAPHRINA

Mix, A. J. A Monograph of the Genus Taphrina. (Bibliotheca Mycologica Ser.: Vol.18). 1969. Repr. of 1949 ed. 21.00 (ISBN 3-7682-0583-5). Lubrecht & Cramer.

TAPS AND DIES

Vezzani, A. A. & Salmonson, Donald. Reading & Detailing Assembly Drawings: Dies. LC 61-9841. 1972. 9.25x (ISBN 0-911168-10-9). Prakken.

TAR

see also Coal Tar

American Chemical Society, Division of Fuel Chemistry. Oil Shale, Tar Sands, & Related Materials: General Papers: Storch Award Symposium: Preprints of Papers Presented at San Francisco, California, August 24-29, 1980. (Preprints of Papers: Vol. 25, No. 3). pap. 74.50 (ISBN 0-317-28241-7, 2013279). Bks Demand UMI.

Butler, James N., et al. Pelagic Tar from Bermuda & the Sargasso Sea. LC 73-175455. (Bermuda Biological Station Special Pubn.: No. 10). (Illus.). vi, 346p. pap. 8.00 (ISBN 0-917642-10-4). Bermuda Bio.

Grissom, M. Catherine, ed. Oil Shales & Tar Sands: A Bibliography, Supplement 2. 588p. 1984. pap. 38.25 (ISBN 0-87079-526-0, DOE/TIC-3367); microfiche 4.50 (ISBN 0-87079-527-9, DOE/TIC-3367). DOE.

Jensen, Howard, et al, eds. Analytical Chemistry of Liquid Fuel Sources: Tar Sands, Oil Shale, Coal, & Petroleum. LC 78-10399. (Advances in Chemistry Ser.: No. 170). 1978. 34.95 (ISBN 0-8412-0395-4). Am Chemical.

Stauffer, H. C., ed. Oil Shale, Tar Sands, & Related Materials. LC 81-10948. (ACS Symposium Ser.: No. 163). 1981. 39.95 (ISBN 0-8412-0640-6). Am Chemical.

Teh Fu Yen, ed. Shale Oil, Tar Sands, & Related Fuel Sources: A Symposium Co-Sponsored by the Division of Fuel Chemistry & the Division of Petroleum Chemistry of the American Chemical Society. LC 76-16510. (Advances in Chemistry Ser.: No. 151). (Illus.). pap. 47.80 (ISBN 0-317-10922-7, 2051257). Bks Demand UMI.

TASTE

Bosma, James F. Oral Sensation & Perception: Second Symposium. (Illus.). 580p. 1970. photocopy ed. 54.50x (ISBN 0-398-00194-4). C C Thomas.

--Symposium on Oral Sensation & Perception. (Illus.). 376p. 1967. photocopy ed. 39.50x (ISBN 0-398-00193-6). C C Thomas.

Brillat-Savarin, Anselme. The Physiology of Taste. Orig. Title: La Physiologie du Gout. (Illus.). 350p. 1982. pap. 9.95 (ISBN 0-918172-11-X). Leetes Isl.

Cagan, Robert H. & Kare, Morley R., eds. Biochemistry of Taste & Olfaction. (Nutrition Foundation Ser.). 1981. 55.00 (ISBN 0-12-154450-8). Acad Pr.

Compilation of Odor & Taste Threshold Values Data-DS 48A. 508p. 1978. 27.50 (ISBN 0-8031-0306-9, 05-048010-36). ASTM.

Denton, Derek A. & Coghlan, John P., eds. Olfaction & Taste, Vol. 5. 1975. 55.50 (ISBN 0-12-209750-5). Acad Pr.

Kashara, Y., et al, eds. Proceedings of the Seventeenth Japanese Symposium on Taste & Smell. (Eng. & Japanese., Illus.). 209p. 1984. pap. 16.00 (ISBN 0-317-17341-3). IRL Pr.

Pfaff, Donald, ed. Taste, Olfaction & the Central Nervous System: A Festschrift in Honor of Carl Pfaffmann. LC 84-43054. 346p. 1985. cloth 29.95 (ISBN 0-87470-039-6). Rockefeller.

Reutter, K. Taste Organ in the Bullhead (Teleostei) (Advances in Anatomy, Embryology & Cell Biology: Vol. 55, Pt. 1). (Illus.). 1978. pap. 32.00 (ISBN 0-387-08880-6). Springer-Verlag.

Van der Starre, H, ed. Olfaction & Taste: Proceedings of the International Symposium on Olfaction & Taste, 7th, the Netherlands 1980. x, 512p. 1980. 60.00 (ISBN 0-904147-20-7). IRL Pr.

Yoshida, Masaaki, ed. Proceedings of the Sixteenth Symposium of the Japanese Association for the Study of Taste & Smell. (Eng. & Japanese., Illus.). 190p. 1982. pap. 16.00 (ISBN 0-317-17342-1). IRL Pr.

TAUBERIAN THEOREMS

Ganelius, T. H. Tauberian Reminder Theorems. (Lecture Notes in Mathematics: Vol. 232). 75p. 1971. pap. 9.00 (ISBN 0-387-05657-2). Springer-Verlag.

Postnikov, A. G., ed. Tauberian Theory & Its Applications. LC 80-23821. (Proceedings of the Steklov Institute of Mathematics: No. 144). 1980. 34.00 (ISBN 0-8218-3048-1). Am Math.

TAXIDERMY

see also Zoological Specimens–Collection and Preservation;

also subdivision Collection and Preservation under Zoological Specimens, and Birds, Fishes, Reptiles, and similar headings

Billard, Ruth S. Ralph Morrill's in Museum Quality Fish Taxidermy: A Guide to Molding with Plaster, Casting with Resin, Painting with an Airbrush. LC 84-70664. (Illus.). 275p. 1984. lib. bdg. 30.00x (ISBN 0-9611112-0-8). Bill Art.

Farnham, Albert B. Home Taxidermy for Pleasure & Profit. (Illus.). 246p. pap. 3.50 (ISBN 0-936622-12-1). A R Harding Pub.

Grantz, Gerald. Home Book of Taxidermy & Tanning. (Illus.). 160p. (Orig.). 1985. pap. 8.95 (ISBN 0-8117-2259-7). Stackpole.

Harrison, James M. Bird Taxidermy. LC 76-50731. (Illus.). 1977. 12.50 (ISBN 0-7153-7372-2). David & Charles.

Haynes, Michael D. Haynes on Air Brush Taxidermy. LC 78-13541. (Illus.). 1979. 12.50 (ISBN 0-668-04634-1, 4634). Arco.

McFall, Waddy F. Taxidermy Step by Step. LC 82-62602. (Illus.). 256p. 1975. 14.95 (ISBN 0-8329-2099-1, Pub. by Winchester Pr). New Century.

Metcalf, John C. Taxidermy: A Complete Manual. (Illus.). 166p. 1981. pap. 15.00x (ISBN 0-7156-1565-3, Pub. by Duckworth England). Biblio Dist.

Moyer, John W. Practical Taxidermy. 2nd ed. 146p. 1984. pap. 9.95 (ISBN 0-471-80356-1). Wiley.

O'Connor, P. A. Advanced Taxidermy. (Illus.). 204p. 1984. 35.00 (ISBN 0-86230-062-2). Triplegate.

Phillips, John E. How to Make Extra Profits in Taxidermy. LC 84-10409. (Illus.). 160p. (Orig.). 1984. pap. 11.95 (ISBN 0-8329-0345-0, Pub. by Winchester Pr). New Century.

Pray, Leon L. Taxidermy. (Illus.). 1943. 10.95 (ISBN 0-02-598790-9). Macmillan.

Schaefer, Gerald O. Taxidermy Color or the Dummy's Guide to Speedy Airbrush Coloring. (Illus.). 55p. 1985. wkbk. 8.95 (ISBN 0-9614928-0-5). Schaefer Studios.

Tinsley, Russell. Taxidermy Guide. 2nd ed. (Illus.). 224p. 1977. pap. 8.95 (ISBN 0-88317-032-9). Stoeger Pub Co.

TAXONOMY

see Botany–Classification

TCHEBYCHEFF APPROXIMATION

see Chebyshev Approximation

TCHEBYCHEFF'S POLYNOMIALS

see Chebyshev Polynomials

TEA

see also Caffeine

Ball, Samuel. An Account of the Cultivation & Manufacture of Tea in China. LC 78-74309. (The Modern Chinese Economy Ser.). 382p. 1980. lib. bdg. 51.00 (ISBN 0-8240-4250-6). Garland Pub.

Hudson, Charles M., ed. Black Drink: A Native American Tea. LC 78-18751. (Illus.). 184p. 1979. 14.00x (ISBN 0-8203-0462-X). U of Ga Pr.

Maclaren, W. A. Rubber, Tea & Cacao with Special Sections on Coffee, Spices & Tobacco. 1980. lib. bdg. 75.00 (ISBN 0-8490-3110-9). Gordon Pr.

Okakura, Kakuzo. Book of Tea. Bleiler, Everett F., ed. 19[illegible] pap. 2.25 (ISBN 0-486-20070-1). Dover.

Pratt, James N. The Tea Lover's Treasury. LC 82-3472. (Illus.). 240p. (Orig.). 1982. pap. 8.95 (ISBN 0-89286-191-6). One Hund One Prods.

Stewart, Hilary. Wild Teas, Coffees, & Cordials. (Illus.). 128p. 1981. pap. 8.95 (ISBN 0-295-95804-9). U of Wash Pr.

Tea. (Commodity Projections: 1985). 1979. pap. 7.50 (ISBN 0-686-59432-0, F1613, FAO). Unipub.

Wernkoven, J. Tea Processing. (Agricultural Services Bulletins: No. 26). (Illus.). 214p. 1974. pap. 22.00 (ISBN 92-5-100614-8, F715, FAO). Unipub.

TEA TRADE

Coffee, Cocoa, Tea & Spices Industry. (UNIDO Guides to Information Sources: No. 28). pap. 4.00 (ISBN 0-686-93191-2, UN198, UN). Unipub.

Report of the Third Session of the Intergovernmental Group on Tea to the Committee on Commodity Problems. 1976. pap. 7.50 (ISBN 92-5-100029-8, F1099, FAO). Unipub.

TECHNICAL ASSISTANCE

see also United Nations–Technical Assistance

Absorption & Diffusion of Imported Technology: Proceedings of a Workshop Held in Singapore, 26-30 Jan. 1981. 111p. 1982. pap. text ed. 12.00 (ISBN 0-88936-298-X, IDRC171, IDRC). Unipub.

The Application of Space Technology to Development. pap. 2.50 (ISBN 0-686-94707-X, UN72/2A/12, UN). Unipub.

Appropriate Technologies in Civil Engineering Works in Developing Countries. pap. 3.50 (ISBN 0-686-94717-7, UN76/2A2, UN). Unipub.

Barnett, A. & Bell, R. M. Rural Energy & the Third World: A Review of Social Science Research & Technology Policy Problems. LC 82-373. (Illus.). 302p. 1982. 40.00 (ISBN 0-08-028953-3); 18.00 (ISBN 0-08-028954-1). Pergamon.

Central America & the Caribbean: Development Assistance Abroad. pap. 14.50 (TAICH105, TAICH). Unipub.

Computer Technology for Development: 2nd Report. pap. 3.50 (ISBN 0-686-95000-3, UN73/2A/12, UN). Unipub.

The Development of Engineering Design Capabilities in Developing Countries. pap. 2.50 (ISBN 0-686-94786-X, UN72/2B2, UN). Unipub.

Fransman, Martin & King, Kenneth, eds. Technological Capability in the Third World. LC 83-13737. 256p. 1984. 30.00 (ISBN 0-312-78792-8). St Martin.

--Document Delivery for Sci-Tech Libraries. (Science & Technology Libraries: Vol. 2, No. 4). 127p. 1982. pap. text ed. 15.00 (ISBN 0-86656-200-1, B200). Haworth Pr.

--Fee-Based Services in Sci-Tech Libraries. LC 84-19186. (Science & Technology Libraries: Vol. 5, No. 2). 120p. 1985. text ed. 19.95 (ISBN 0-86656-326-1). Haworth Pr.

--Management of Sci-Tech Libraries. LC 84-6615. (Science & Technology Libraries: Vol. 4, Nos. 3-4). 169p. 1984. text ed. 24.95 (ISBN 0-86656-280-X, B280); pap. text ed. 9.95 (ISBN 0-86656-284-2, B284). Haworth Pr.

--Online vs. Manual Searching in Sci-Tech Libraries. (Science & Technology Libraries: Vol. 3, No. 1). 83p. 1982. pap. text ed. 15.00 (ISBN 0-86656-203-6, B203). Haworth Pr.

--Role of Maps in Sci-Tech Libraries. LC 84-27919. (Science & Technology Libraries: Vol. 5, No. 3). 136p. 1985. text ed. 17.95 (ISBN 0-86656-395-4). Haworth Pr.

--Role of Patents in Sci-Tech Libraries. LC 82-2885. (Science & Technology Libraries Ser.: Vol. 2, No. 2). 97p. 1982. 25.00 (ISBN 0-86656-114-5, B114). Haworth Pr.

--Sci-Tech Libraries in Museums & Aquariums. (Science & Technology Libraries: Vol. 6, Nos. 1-2). 200p. text ed. write for info. (ISBN 0-86656-484-5). Haworth Pr.

--Scientific & Technical Libraries in the Seventies: A Guide to Information Sources. (Books, Publishing & Libraries Information Guide Ser.: Vol. 4). 300p. 1980. 60.00x (ISBN 0-8103-1483-5). Gale.

--Serving End-Users in Sci-Tech Libraries. LC 84-10789. (Science & Technology Libraries: Vol. 5, No. 1). 122p. 1984. text ed. 19.95 (ISBN 0-86656-327-X, B327). Haworth Pr.

Reedijk, C., et al, eds. Large Libraries & New Technological Developments. 200p. 1985. lib. bdg. 20.00 (ISBN 3-598-10508-8). K G Saur.

Small Technical Libraries. 40p. (Orig.). 1980. Repr. of 1979 ed. 6.00 (ISBN 92-3-101088-3, U606, UNESCO). Unipub.

TECHNICAL LITERATURE

see also Patents; Technical Reports

Anthony, Ed. Information Sources in Engineering. 2nd ed. (Illus.). 560p. 1985. text ed. 75.95 (ISBN 0-408-11475-4). Butterworth.

Grogan, Denis. Science & Technology: An Introduction to the Literature. 4th ed. 400p. 1982. 27.50 (ISBN 0-85157-315-0, Pub. by Bingley England); pap. 18.50 (Pub. by Bingley England). Shoe String.

Klienman, Joseph M. List of Specifications & Standards Pertaining to Technical Publications. 1983. pap. 15.00x (ISBN 0-914548-24-7). Soc Tech Comm.

Library Association, London, ed. British Technology Index, 1980. LC 63-23735. 929p. 1981. 295.00x (ISBN 0-85365-504-9). Intl Pubns Serv.

Turley, Raymond. Understanding the Structure of Scientific & Technical Literature: A Case-Study Approach. 173p. 1983. 16.00 (ISBN 0-85157-368-1, Pub. by Bingley England). Shoe String.

TECHNICAL REPORTS

Here are entered works on the processing and use of technical and scientific reports. Guides to technical authorship are entered under the heading Technical Writing.

see also Technical Writing

American National Standard for Guidelines for Format & Production of Scientific & Technical Reports, Z39.18. 1974. 6.00 (ISBN 0-686-15226-3). ANSI.

American National Standard for Standard Technical Report Number, (STRN), Z39.23. 1983. 5.00 (ISBN 0-686-15231-X). ANSI.

Houp, Kenneth W. & Pearsall, Thomas E. Reporting Technical Information. 5th ed. 560p. 1984. pap. text ed. write for info. (ISBN 0-02-474920-6). Macmillan.

Jones, Paul W. & Keene, Michael L. Writing Scientific Papers-Reports. 8th ed. 365p. 1981. pap. text ed. write for info. (ISBN 0-697-03773-8). Wm C Brown.

Michaelson, Herbert B. How to Write & Publish Engineering Papers & Reports. (Professional Writing Ser.). (Illus.). 158p. 1982. 17.95 (ISBN 0-89495-016-9); pap. 11.95 (ISBN 0-89495-017-7). ISI Pr.

Morrisey, George L. Effective Business & Technical Presentations. 2nd ed. LC 74-24920. 224p. 1975. pap. text ed. 12.95 (ISBN 0-201-04828-0). Addison-Wesley.

Mount, Ellis, ed. Role of Technical Reports in Sci-Tech Libraries. LC 81-7231. (Science & Technology Libraries Ser.: Vol. 1, No. 4). 82p. 1982. pap. 15.00 (ISBN 0-917724-74-7, B74). Haworth Pr.

Ruthowski, Katherine, ed. NCTA Technical Papers, 1985. (NCTA Technical Papers). (Illus.). 330p. (Orig.). 1985. 35.00 (ISBN 0-940272-11-3). Natl Cable.

Swanson, Edward. A Manual of AACR 2 Examples for Technical Reports. 1984. pap. text ed. 10.00 (ISBN 0-936996-15-3). Soldier Creek.

Walter, John A. Technical Report Form. rev. ed. 35p. 1973. pap. 2.15x (ISBN 0-88408-000-5). Univ Co-Op Soc.

TECHNICAL REPORTS–ILLUSTRATION

see Technical Illustration

TECHNICAL RUSSIAN

see Russian Language–Technical Russian

TECHNICAL SCHOOLS

see Technical Education

TECHNICAL SOCIETIES

see also Learned Institutions and Societies

Brown, Mary, et al. Agricultural Education in a Technical Society: An Annotated Bibliography of Resources. LC 72-7501. pap. 60.00 (ISBN 0-317-26603-9, 2024189). Bks Demand UMI.

McMahon, A. Michal & Morris, Stephanie A. Technology in Industrial America: The Committee on Science & the Arts of the Franklin Institute. Guide to the Records of the Committee on Science & the Arts of the Franklin Institute, 1824-1900. LC 77-77872. 40.00 (ISBN 0-8420-2123-X). Scholarly Res Inc.

Sinclair, Angela, ed. A Guide to Appropriate Technology Institutions. 124p. (Orig.). 1984. pap. 9.75x (ISBN 0-946688-95-8, Pub. by Intermediate Tech England). Intermediate Tech.

Young, Margaret L., ed. Scientific & Technical Organizations & Agencies Directory. 1000p. 1985. 140.00x (ISBN 0-8103-2100-9). Gale.

TECHNICAL TERMS

see Technology–Dictionaries; Technology–Terminology

TECHNICAL VOCABULARY

see Technology–Language

TECHNICAL WRITING

Here are entered guides to authorship in engineering, science, and technology. Similar guides in other fields are entered under a corresponding term if in common usage, e.g. Medical Writing; otherwise under (subject)–authorship.

see also French Language–Technical French; Russian Language–Technical Russian; Science News; Technical Reports

Adamson, Thomas A. Inside Grant & Project Writing. Pavlina, Connie L., ed. LC 78-70335. 1979. ring binder 46.00x (ISBN 0-932724-00-0). PAM Pubs.

Alred, Gerald J., et al. Business & Technical Writing: An Annotated Bibliography of Books, 1880-1980. LC 80-29211. 249p. 1981. 15.00 (ISBN 0-8108-1397-1). Scarecrow.

Alvarez, Joseph A. The Elements of Technical Writing. 208p. 1980. pap. text ed. 11.95 (ISBN 0-15-522160-4, HC); instructor's manual avail. (ISBN 0-15-522161-2). HarBraceJ.

Andrews, Deborah C. & Blickle, Margaret D. Technical Writing: Principles & Forms. 2nd ed. 1982. text ed. write for info. (ISBN 0-02-303470-X). Macmillan.

Bacon, Terry R. & Freeman, Lawrence H. Shipley Associates Style Guide for Oil & Gas Professionals. Date not set. 24.95 (ISBN 0-933427-01-8). Shipley.

Balachandran, Sarojini. Technical Writing: A Bibliography. 1977. pap. 4.60 (ISBN 0-931874-07-6). Assn Busn Comm.

Barnett, Marva T. Writing for Technicians. Rev. ed. LC 80-69550. (Technical Communications Ser.). 358p. 1982. pap. text ed. 14.00 (ISBN 0-8273-1867-7); instr's. guide 4.20 (ISBN 0-8273-1868-5). Delmar.

Barrass, R. Scientists Must Write: A Guide to Better Writing for Scientists, Engineers & Students. 1978. pap. 9.95x (ISBN 0-412-15430-7, NO. 6385, Pub. by Chapman & Hall England). Methuen Inc.

Bell, P. Hightech Writing. 240p. 1985. pap. 19.95 (ISBN 0-471-81864-X). Wiley.

Bingham, Earl. Pocketbook for Technical & Professional Writers. 304p. 1981. pap. text ed. write for info. (ISBN 0-534-01004-0). Wadsworth Pub.

Bjelland, Harley. Technical Writing: The Easy Way. LC 81-90026. (Illus.). 116p. (Orig.). 1981. pap. 10.00 (ISBN 0-939648-00-8). Norway Bks.

Blicq, Ron S. Technically Write! Communicating in a Technological Era. 3rd ed. (Illus.). 416p. 1986. pap. text ed. 19.95 (ISBN 0-13-898750-5). P H.

Bly, Robert W. & Blake, Gary. Technical Writing: Structure, Standards & Style. LC 82-15223. 160p. 1982. 11.95 (ISBN 0-07-006174-2); pap. 6.95 (ISBN 0-07-006173-4). McGraw.

Booth, Vernon. Communicating in Science: Writing & Speaking. 80p. 1985. pap. 6.95 (ISBN 0-521-27771-X). Cambridge U Pr.

Bricq, Ron S. Technically Write! Communicating in a Technological Era. 2nd ed. (Illus.). 448p. 1981. pap. text ed. 20.95 (ISBN 0-13-898700-9). P-H.

Brock, Thomas D. The Successful Textbook Publishing: The Author's Guide. 1985. 28.50 (ISBN 0-910239-01-0). Sci Tech Inc.

Brogan, John A. Clear Technical Writing. 1973. 20.30 (ISBN 0-07-007974-9). McGraw.

Brown, John F. Engineering Report Writing. 2nd ed. 171p. 1985. 11.95 (ISBN 0-9612488-2-3). J F Brown.

Brunner, Ingrid & Mathes, J. C. The Technician As Writer: Preparing Technical Reports. 240p. 1980. pap. text ed. write for info. (ISBN 0-02-315950-2). Macmillan.

Brunner, Ingrid, et al. The Technician As Writer: Preparing Technical Reports. 1980. pap. 18.76 scp (ISBN 0-672-61523-1); scp tchrs manual 3.67 (ISBN 0-672-61524-X). Bobbs.

Brusaw, Charles T. & Alred, Gerald J. Handbook of Technical Writing. 2nd ed. LC 81-51836. 695p. 1982. pap. text ed. 13.95 (ISBN 0-312-35808-3). St Martin.

Clarke, Emerson. Guide to Technical Literature Production. 1960. pap. 10.00 (ISBN 0-686-00899-5). T W Pubs.

Clements, W. & Berlo, R. The Scientific Report: A Guide for Authors. Society for Technical Communication, ed. 52p. (Orig.). pap. text ed. 15.00x (ISBN 0-914548-39-5). Soc Tech Comm.

Clements, W. & Waite, R. G. Guide for Beginning Technical Editors. Society for Technical Communication, ed. 54p. 1983. pap. text ed. 15.00x (ISBN 0-914548-40-9). Soc Tech Comm.

Cochran, Wendell, et al, eds. Geowriting: A Guide to Writing, Editing, & Printing in Earth Science. 3rd ed. LC 79-50569. 1979. pap. 4.00 (ISBN 0-913312-13-4). Am Geol.

Collins, Sarah H. & Tuttle, Frederick B., Jr. Technical & Scientific Writing. 127p. 1979. pap. 6.95 (ISBN 0-8106-1718-8). NEA.

Couture, Barbara & Goldstein, Jone R. Cases for Technical & Professional Writing. 1984. pap. text ed. 13.95 (ISBN 0-316-15830-5); tchr's. manual avail. (ISBN 0-316-15831-3). Little.

D'Agenais & Carruthers. Creating Effective Manuals. 1986. text ed. price not set (ISBN 0-538-21200-4, U20). SW Pub.

Dagher, Joseph P. Technical Communication: A Practical Guide. (Illus.). 1978. pap. text ed. 19.95 (ISBN 0-13-898247-3). P-H.

Damerst, William A. Clear Technical Reports. 2nd ed. 325p. 1982. pap. text ed. 15.95 (ISBN 0-15-507692-2, HC). HarBraceJ.

Day, Robert A. How to Write & Publish a Scientific Paper. 2nd ed. (Professional Writing Ser.). (Illus.). 181p. 1983. 17.95 (ISBN 0-89495-021-5); pap. text ed. 11.95 (ISBN 0-89495-022-3). ISI Pr.

Delaware Technical & Community College, English Department. Writing Skills for Technical Students. 400p. 1982. pap. text ed. 15.95 (ISBN 0-13-970665-8). P-H.

Dodds, Robert H. Writing for Technical & Business Magazines. LC 80-23843. (Illus.). 208p. 1982. Repr. of 1969 ed. text ed. 14.95 (ISBN 0-89874-237-4). Krieger.

Drobnic, Karl, et al. Sci Tech: Reading & Writing the English of Science & Technology. 132p. (Orig.). 1981. pap. text ed. 4.95 (ISBN 0-89285-156-2). English Lang.

Duke, Judith S. The Technical, Scientific & Medical Publishing Market. LC 84-26163. (Communications Library). 218p. 1985. professional 29.95 (ISBN 0-86729-084-6, 424-BW). Knowledge Indus.

Estrin, Herman A. Technical & Professional Writing. 1976. pap. text ed. write for info. (ISBN 0-686-23137-6). Preston.

Ewer, J. R. & Latorre, G. A Course in Basic Scientific English. (English As a Second Language Bk.). 199p. 1969. pap. text ed. 6.95x (ISBN 0-582-52009-6); teacher's bk. 3.95x (ISBN 0-582-52059-2). Longman.

Ewing, David W. Writing for Results in Business, Government, the Sciences & the Professions. 2nd ed. LC 79-11756. 448p. 1979. 32.50 (ISBN 0-471-05036-9). Wiley.

--Writing for Results: In Business, Government, the Sciences & the Professions. 2nd ed. 464p. 1985. pap. 14.95 (ISBN 0-471-82590-5). Wiley.

Fabish, Susan. On-The-Job Technical Writing. (Illus.). 1984. 44.50 (ISBN 0-916780-25-2). CES.

Fear, David E. Technical Writing. 2nd ed. 1978. pap. text ed. 10.00 (ISBN 0-394-32100-6, RanC). Random.

Fearing, Bertie B. & Allen, Jo. Teaching Technical Writing in the Secondary School. (Theory & Research into Practice Ser.). 56p. (Orig.). 1984. pap. 6.00 (ISBN 0-8141-5295-3). NCTE.

Glendinning, Eric H. English in Mechanical Engineering. (English in Focus Ser). 1974. pap. text ed. 9.95x (ISBN 0-19-437512-9); tchr's ed. 12.00x (ISBN 0-19-437501-3). Oxford U Pr.

Gould, Jay R., ed. Directions in Technical Writing & Communication. LC 77-75832. (Technical Writing & Communications Ser.: Vol. 1). 1978. pap. 7.95x (ISBN 0-89503-006-3). Baywood Pub.

Gray, Dwight E. So You Have to Write a Technical Report: Elements of Technical Report Writing. LC 70-120541. ix, 117p. 1970. pap. 7.00 (ISBN 0-87815-002-1). Info Resources.

Grimm, Susan. How to Write Computer Manuals for Users. 211p. 1982. 21.00 (ISBN 0-534-97941-6). Van Nos Reinhold.

Harkins, C. & Plung, D. L., eds. A Guide to Writing Better Technical Papers. LC 81-20042. 1981. 25.95 (ISBN 0-87942-157-6, PC01529). Inst Electrical.

Harnad, Stevan, ed. Peer Commentary on Peer Review: A Case Study in Scientific Quality Control. LC 82-19860. 80p. 1983. pap. 13.95 (ISBN 0-521-27306-4). Cambridge U Pr.

Harty, Kevin J. Strategies for Business & Technical Writing. 2nd ed. 287p. 1985. pap. text ed. 11.95 (ISBN 0-15-583925-X, HC). HarBraceJ.

Harvill, Lawrence R. & Kraft, Thomas L. Technical Report Standards: How to Prepare & Write Effective Technical Reports. LC 77-70964. (Illus.). 1979. pap. 15.95 (ISBN 0-930206-01-0). M-A Pr.

Heebink, Denise M. Effective Written Communications & Technical Writing for the Allied Health Professional. 121p. 1985. pap. text ed. 20.00 (ISBN 0-933195-12-5). Cal College Pr.

Hoover, Hardy. Essentials for the Scientific & Technical Writer. 224p. 1981. pap. 4.50 (ISBN 0-486-24060-6). Dover.

--Essentials for the Scientific & Technical Writer. 12.00 (ISBN 0-8446-5775-1). Peter Smith.

Jordan, Michael P. Fundamentals of Technical Description. LC 83-17557. 128p. 1984. pap. 11.50 (ISBN 0-89874-681-7). Krieger.

--Fundamentals of Technical Prose. LC 85-4312. 124p. (Orig.). 1986. lib. bdg. price not set (ISBN 0-89874-771-6). Krieger.

Jordan, Stello, et al, eds. Handbook of Technical Writing Practices. LC 75-129051. (Wiley Series on Human Communication). (Illus.). Vol. 1. pap. 160.00 (ISBN 0-317-10865-4, 2055514); Vol. 2. pap. 160.00 (ISBN 0-317-10866-2). Bks Demand UMI.

Journet, Debra & Kling, Julie L. Readings for Technical Writers. 1984. pap. text ed. 14.10x (ISBN 0-673-15557-9). Scott F.

Katz, Michael J. Elements of the Scientific Paper. LC 85-40464. (Illus.). 1985. text ed. 20.00x (ISBN 0-300-03491-1); pap. 6.95x (ISBN 0-300-03532-2). Yale U Pr.

Katzin, Emanuel. How to Write a Really Good User's Manual. (Illus.). 256p. 1985. 29.95 (ISBN 0-442-24758-3). Van Nos Reinhold.

Kelly, R. A. Use of English for Technical Students. 2nd ed. 1970. pap. text ed. 17.95x (ISBN 0-245-50843-0). Intl Ideas.

King, Lester S. Why Not Say It Clearly: A Guide to Scientific Writing. 1978. pap. text ed. 10.95 (ISBN 0-316-49346-5, Little Med Div). Little.

Koenigsec. Technical Writing. Date not set. price not set. Macmillan.

Kolin, Philip & Kolin, Janeen. Models for Technical Writing. LC 83-61618. 500p. 1985. pap. text ed. 13.95 (ISBN 0-312-53587-2); instr's. manual avail. St Martin.

Lannon, John M. Technical Writing. 3rd ed. 1984. pap. text ed. 21.95 (ISBN 0-316-51448-9); tchr's. manual avail. (ISBN 0-316-51449-7). Little.

Leonard, David C. & McGuire, Peter J. Readings in Technical Writing. 304p. 1983. pap. text ed. write for info. (ISBN 0-02-369840-3). Macmillan.

Lieblich, Jerome H., ed. Instructions for the Preparation of Specifications, Standards & Technical Manuals, 2 vols. 788p. Set. loose-leaf 119.50 (ISBN 0-912702-12-5). Global Eng.

Losano, et al. Manual for Technical Writing & Busines Communication. 160p. 1983. pap. 10.95 (ISBN 0-8403-3127-4). Kendall-Hunt.

Lynch, Barbara S. & Chapman, Charles F. Writing for Communication in Science & Medicine, or Out of Your Mind with Comprehensive Assurance. 336p. 1980. 24.95 (ISBN 0-442-24959-4). Van Nos Reinhold.

McCartney, Eugene S. Recurrent Maladies in Scholarly Writing. LC 77-90361. 1969. Repr. of 1953 ed. text ed. 9.00x (ISBN 0-87752-068-2). Gordian.

McGehee, Brad M. The Complete Guide to Writing Software User Manuals. 300p. (Orig.). 1984. pap. 14.95 (ISBN 0-89879-138-3). Writers Digest.

MacKenzie, R. N., et al. Technical Writing: Forms & Formats. (Illus.). 176p. 1983. pap. text ed. 11.95 (ISBN 0-8403-3217-3, 40321701). Kendall-Hunt.

McQuaid, Robert W. The Craft of Writing Technical Manuals. LC 82-91154. (Illus.). 54p. 1983. 15.00 (ISBN 0-912259-00-0). R W McQuaid.

Maimon, Elaine P., et al. Writing in the Arts & Sciences. 1981. text ed. 15.95 (ISBN 0-316-54424-8); tchr's ed. avail. (ISBN 0-316-54425-6). Little.

Clauser, H., ed. Progress in Assessing Technological Innovation, Vol. 1. 103p. 1975. text ed. 7.95x (ISBN 0-87762-169-1). Technomic.
Cockburn, Cynthia. Brothers: Male Dominance & Technological Change. 254p. (Orig.). 1983. pap. 8.95 (ISBN 0-86104-384-7, Pub by Pluto Pr). Longwood Pub Group.
Computer Technology for Development: 2nd Report. pap. 3.50 (ISBN 0-686-95000-3, UN73/2A/12, UN). Unipub.
Cooper, C. A. & Clark, J. A., eds. Employment, Economics & Technology: The Impact of Technological Change on the Labor Market. LC 82-42543. 180p. 1982. 25.00x (ISBN 0-312-24459-2). St Martin.
Das, Ram. Appropriate Technology. 1981. 11.95 (ISBN 0-533-04744-7). Vantage.
Dauw, Dean C. Creativity & Innovation in Organizations. 4th ed. 380p. 1980. pap. text ed. 15.95x (ISBN 0-917974-42-5). Waveland Pr.
David, Paul A. Technical Choice Innovation & Economic Growth: Essays on American & British Experience in the Nineteenth Century. LC 74-76583. pap. 86.00 (ISBN 0-317-26014-6, 2024448). Bks Demand UMI.
De Camp, L. Sprague. The Fringe of the Unknown. LC 83-60205. 205p. 1983. 17.95 (ISBN 0-87975-204-1); pap. 9.95 (ISBN 0-87975-217-3). Prometheus Bks.
Development, Environment & Technology: Towards a Technology for Self-Reliance. 51p. 1978. pap. 6.00 (ISBN 0-686-68949-6, UN78/2D11, UN). Unipub.
Dizard, W. P. The Comming Information Age: An Overview of Technology, Economics, & Politics. 2nd ed. LC 84-12625. 224p. 1984. pap. text ed. 13.95x (ISBN 0-582-28522-4). Longman.
Dosi, Giovanni. Technical Change & Industrial Transformation. LC 83-16017. 338p. 1984. 29.95 (ISBN 0-312-78775-8). St Martin.
El-Hadidy, B. & Horne, E. E., eds. The Infrastructure of an Information Society: Proceedings of the 1st International Conference in Cairo, Egypt, 13-15 Dec. 1982. 644p. 1984. 69.00 (ISBN 0-444-87549-2, I-303-84, North Holland). Elsevier.
Elster, Jon. Explaining Technical Change: A Case Study in the Philosophy of Science. LC 82-9702. (Studies in Rationality & Social Change). (Illus.). 304p. 1983. 39.50 (ISBN 0-521-24920-1); pap. 12.95 (ISBN 0-521-27072-3). Cambridge U Pr.
Ericsson, T., ed. Computers in Materials Technology: Proceedings of the Conference Held in Linkoping, June 1980. 200p. 1981. 39.00 (ISBN 0-08-027570-2). Pergamon.
Etzioni, Amitai & Remp, Richard. Technological Shortcuts to Social Change. LC 72-83834. 236p. 1973. 10.95x (ISBN 0-87154-236-6). Russell Sage.
Ewing, David W., ed. Technological Change & Management. LC 78-125645. 1970. 10.00x (ISBN 0-674-87230-4, Pub. by Harvard Busn. School). Harvard U Pr.
Farzin, Yeganeh. The Effect of Discount Rate & Substitute Technology on Depletion of Exhaustible Resources. LC 82-8612. (World Bank Staff Working Papers: No. 516). (Orig.). 1982. pap. 5.00 (ISBN 0-8213-0004-0). World Bank.
Fassbender, A. G., et al. Energy Efficient Industrial Technology in Europe & Japan. LC 83-13065. (Energy Technology Review No. 85). (Illus.). 416p. 1984. 45.00 (ISBN 0-8155-0958-8). Noyes.
Foster, Richard. The S-Curve: Profiting from Technological Change. 384p. 1984. 19.95 (ISBN 0-671-50918-7). Summit Bks.
Freeman, Christopher. The Economics of Industrial Innovation. 2nd ed. 320p. 1983. 30.00x (ISBN 0-262-06083-3). MIT Pr.
From Idea to Application: Some Selected Nuclear Techniques in Research & Development. (Proceedings Ser.). (Illus.). 301p. 1978. pap. 35.00 (ISBN 92-0-131078-1, ISP476, IAEA). Unipub.
Gabor, Dennis. Innovations: Scientific, Technological & Social. 1970. pap. 3.95 (ISBN 0-19-519412-8). Oxford U Pr.
Game, Ann & Pringle, Rosemary. Gender at Work. 180p. 1983. pap. text ed. 9.95 (ISBN 0-86861-261-8). Allen Unwin.
Gannon, Colin A. Towards a Strategy for Conservation in a World of Technological Change. (Discussion Paper Ser.: No. 24). 1968. pap. 5.75 (ISBN 0-686-32193-6). Regional Sci Res Inst.
Gerstenfeld, Arthur. Technological Innovation: Government-Industry Cooperation. LC 78-14800. 277p. 1979. 42.50x (ISBN 0-471-03647-1, Pub. by Wiley-Interscience). Wiley.
Gold, Bela, et al, eds. Technological Progress & Industrial Leadership: The Growth of the U. S. Steel Industry, 1900-1965. LC 83-48756. 832p. 1984. 60.00x (ISBN 0-669-07535-3). Lexington Bks.
Graham, Robert W., ed. Primary Electrochemical Cell Technology: Advances Since 1977. LC 81-38329. (Energy Tech. Rev. 66; Chem. Tech. Rev. 191). 388p. 1981. 48.00 (ISBN 0-8155-0853-0). Noyes.
Grayson, Leslie, ed. Social & Economic Impact of New Technology. (IFI Data Base Library). 130p. 1984. 85.00x (ISBN 0-306-65209-9, Plenum Pr). Plenum Pub.
Gryskiewicz, Stanley S. & Shields, James, eds. Blueprint for Innovation: Proceedings. (Creativity Week Ser.: No. 6). 1984. 20.00 (ISBN 0-912879-80-7). Ctr Creat Leader.
Hall, Peter, ed. Technology, Innovation & Economic Policy. LC 85-40077. 224p. 1985. 29.95 (ISBN 0-312-78932-7). St Martin.
Halty-Carrere, Maximo. Technological Development Strategies for Developing Countries: A Review for Policy Makers. 155p. 1979. pap. text ed. 12.95x (ISBN 0-920380-24-7, Pub. by Inst Res Pub Canada). Brookfield Pub Co.
Hanreider, Wolfram, ed. Technology, Strategy & Arms Control. 215p. 1985. 28.00x (ISBN 0-8133-0177-7); pap. text ed. 13.95x (ISBN 0-8133-0178-5). Westview.
Hecht, Norman L. Design Principles. LC 82-46060. (Vol. 5). (Illus.). 120p. 1983. 29.95 (ISBN 0-250-40315-3). Butterworth.
Henwood, Felicity & Thomas, Graham, eds. Science, Technology & Innovation: A Research Bibliography. LC 83-40179. 264p. 1984. 23.95 (ISBN 0-312-70281-7). St Martin.
Hewlett, W. R. Inventions of Opportunity: Matching Technology with Market Needs. LC 83-81659. 364p. 1983. 27.50 (ISBN 0-9612030-0-5, HP 92233B). Hewlett-Packard.
Historical Background of Technology Transfer, Transportation, & Development in Japan. (Human & Social Development Programme - Research Papers). 39p. 1980. pap. 5.00 (ISBN 92-808-0048-5, TUNU031, UNU). Unipub.
Holloman, J. Herbert. Technical Change & American Enterprise. LC 74-19049. 52p. 1974. 1.50 (ISBN 0-89068-013-2). Natl Planning.
Iftikhar, Ahmed. Technological Change & Agrarian Structure: A Study of Bangladesh. (WEP Study Ser.). xiii, 136p. 1981. pap. 8.75 (ISBN 92-2-102543-8, ILO169, ILO). Unipub.
Innovations in Appropriate Technology: A Case Study. 72p. 1981. pap. 19.25 (ISBN 0-686-79203-3, APO110, APO). Unipub.
International Peace Academy Conference. Peacekeeping & Technology: Concepts for the Future. Hanning, Hugh, ed. (IPA Report Ser.: No. 17). 65p. 1983. pap. 7.00 (ISBN 0-937722-04-9). Intl Peace.
Inventive Activity in the Asian & the Pacific Region. 152p. 1981. pap. 8.25 (ISBN 92-805-0028-7, WIPO66, WIPO). Unipub.
Investigation of Scientific & Technological Potentialities in Tradition & Culture of Communities for the Satisfaction of Basic Needs (Egyptian Case) Progress Report. 6p. 1981. pap. 5.00 (ISBN 92-808-0316-6, TUNU140, UNU). Unipub.
Jones, Barry. Sleepers, Wake! Technology & the Future of Work. 2nd ed. (Illus.). 302p. 1985. pap. 9.95 (ISBN 0-19-554453-6). Oxford U Pr.
Jones, Barry O. Sleepers, Wake! Technology & the Future of Work. (Illus.). 1983. 24.95x (ISBN 0-19-554343-2). Oxford U Pr.
Kay, Neil M. The Innovating Firm: A Behavioral Theory of Corporate R & D. 1979. 32.50x (ISBN 0-312-41809-4). St Martin.
Kingston, William. Innovation. 1979. 11.95 (ISBN 0-7145-3540-0); pap. 4.95 (ISBN 0-7145-3611-3). Riverrun NY.
Konecci, Eugene B. & Kuhn, Robert L., eds. Technology Venturing: American Innovation & Risk-Taking. LC 85-12192. 272p. 1985. 35.95 (ISBN 0-03-005183-5). Praeger.
Kraus, H., ed. The Impact of New Technologies on Information Systems in Public Administration in the 80's. 420p. 1984. 57.50 (ISBN 0-444-86725-2, North-Holland). Elsevier.
Kuhn, Robert L., ed. Commercializing Defense Related Technology. LC 83-21379. 270p. 1982. 29.95x (ISBN 0-03-069717-4). Praeger.
Lancaster, F. W. Toward Paperless Information Systems. (Library & Information Science Ser.). (192). 1978. 33.00 (ISBN 0-12-436050-5). Acad Pr.
Lawrence, Colin & Shay, Robert. Technological Innovation, Regulation, & the Monetary Economy. 200p. 1986. prof. ref. 29.95 (ISBN 0-88730-078-2). Ballinger Pub.
Lynn, Leonard H. How Japan Innovates: A Comparison with the U. S. in the Case of Oxygen Steelmaking. (Replica Edition Ser.). (Illus.). 224p. 1982. softcover 23.00x (ISBN 0-86531-900-6). Westview.
Majumdar, Badiul A. Innovations, Product Developments & Technology Transfers: An Empirical Study of Dynamic Competitive Advantage, The Case of Electronic Calculators. LC 80-1451. (Illus.). 198p. (Orig.). 1982. pap. text ed. 11.75 (ISBN 0-8191-2066-9). U Pr of Amer.
Mansfield, Edwin, ed. Industrial Research & Technological Innovation. (Illus.). 1968. 12.95x (ISBN 0-393-09724-2, NortonC). Norton.
Martin. Managing Technological Innovation. 1984. text ed. 27.95 (ISBN 0-8359-4201-5). Reston.
Martin, J. C. Managing Technological Innovation & Entrepreneurship. 340p. 1984. 29.95 (ISBN 0-317-18033-9). Robot Inst Am.
Mensch, Gerhard. Stalemate in Technology: Innovations Overcome the Depression. 272p. 1983. pap. 14.95 (ISBN 0-88410-054-5). Ballinger Pub.
--Theory of Innovation. LC 73-11655. Date not set. price not set (ISBN 0-669-89474-5). Lexington Bks.
Morehouse, Ward. Separate, Unequal, but More Autonomous. (Working Papers in the World Order Models Project Ser.). 50p. (Orig.). 1981. pap. 2.00 (ISBN 0-911646-11-6). Transaction Bks.
Morishima, M. Why Has Japan Succeeded? Western Technology & the Japanese Ethos. LC 81-15544. 218p. 1982. 29.95 (ISBN 0-521-24494-3). Cambridge U Pr.
Morison, Elting E. Men, Machines, & Modern Times. 1966. 15.00x (ISBN 0-262-13025-4); pap. 6.95x (ISBN 0-262-63018-4). MIT Pr.
Morse, Dean & Warner, Aaron W., eds. Technological Innovation & Society. LC 66-18342. (Seminar on Technology & Social Change Ser.). 214p. 1966. 29.00x (ISBN 0-231-02927-6). Columbia U Pr.
Mueller, Eva, et al. Technological Advance in an Expanding Economy: Its Impact on a Cross-Section of the Labor Force. LC 71-627965. 254p. 1969. 12.00x (ISBN 0-87944-073-2). Inst Soc Res.
National Academy Of Engineering. Process of Technological Innovation. LC 72-601240. (Illus., Orig.). 1969. pap. 5.75 (ISBN 0-309-01726-2). Natl Acad Pr.
National Research Council. Diffusion of Biomass Energy Technologies in Developing Countries. 120p. 1984. pap. 9.25 (ISBN 0-309-03442-6). Natl Acad Pr.
--Outlook for Science & Technology: The Next Five Years. LC 81-9878. (Illus.). 788p. 1982. 27.95x (ISBN 0-7167-1345-4); pap. 17.95x (ISBN 0-7167-1346-2). W H Freeman.
Nelson, Richard R., ed. Government & Technical Progress: Cross-Industry Analysis. (The Technical Policy & Economic Growth Ser.). (Illus.). 512p. 1982. 45.00 (ISBN 0-08-028837-5, L110). Pergamon.
Oakey, Raymond. High Technology Small Firms: Innovation & Regional Development in Britain & the United States. LC 83-40705. 250p. 1984. 25.00 (ISBN 0-312-37239-6). St Martin.
Oboler, Eli M. To Free the Mind: Libraries, Technology, & Intellectual Freedom. 135p. 1983. 15.00 (ISBN 0-87287-325-0). Libs Unl.
An On-Line Materials Property Base. (MDC Ser.: Vol. 20). 1983. pap. text ed. 30.00 (ISBN 0-317-02638-0, H00284). ASME.
Panel on Advanced Technology Competition & the Industrialized Allies, National Academy of Sciences. International Competition in Advanced Technology: Decisions for America. 69p. 1983. pap. text ed. 9.50 (ISBN 0-309-03379-9). Natl Acad Pr.
Parker, C. Going for Growth: Technological Innovation in Manufacturing Industries. 1985. 24.95 (ISBN 0-471-90633-6). Wiley.
Parker, R. C. The Management of Innovation. LC 82-2737. 221p. 1982. 34.95x (ISBN 0-471-10421-3, Pub. by Wiley Interscience). Wiley.
Perkins, W. J., ed. High Technology Aids for the Disabled. 216p. 1983. text ed. 39.95 (ISBN 0-407-00256-1). Butterworth.
Policies for Informatics: Documents from the SPIN Working Group, Venice, Italy, Nov. 1979. 254p. 1981. pap. 45.00 (ISBN 0-89059-011-7, UPB104, UNESCO). Unipub.
Powell, James. Investing in High Tech Industries: Picking Tomorrow's Winners Today. 1985. 35.00 (ISBN 0-87094-596-3). Dow Jones-Irwin.
Rahman, Abdur. Intellectual Colonization: Science & Technology in East-West Relations. 160p. 1983. text ed. 22.50x (ISBN 0-7069-2336-7, Pub. by Vikas India). Advent NY.
Ramo, Simon. What's Wrong with Our Technological Society - & How to Fix It. LC 83-696. 320p. 1983. 21.50 (ISBN 0-07-051169-1). McGraw.
Rice, Rex. VLSI Support Technologies: Computer-Aided Design, Testing, & Packaging. (Tutorial Texts Ser.). 450p. 1982. 30.00 (ISBN 0-8186-0386-0, Q386). IEEE Comp Soc.
Ritterberger, Volker, ed. Science & Technology in a Changing International Order: The United Nations Conference on Science & Technology for Development. (Special Studies in Social, Political, & Economic Development). 200p. 1982. lib. bdg. 32.00x (ISBN 0-86531-146-3). Westview.
Rogers, E. & Shoemaker, F. Communication of Innovations. 2nd ed. LC 78-122276. 1971. text ed. 16.95 (ISBN 0-02-926680-7). Free Pr.
Rosenberg, Nathan. Perspectives on Technology. LC 75-14623. 336p. 1976. 52.50 (ISBN 0-521-20957-9). Cambridge U Pr.
Rosenbloom, Richard S., ed. Research on Technological Innovation, Management & Policy, Vol. 1. 1983. 40.00 (ISBN 0-89232-273-X). Jai Pr.
Rothwell, Roy & Zegveld, Walter. Innovation & the Small & Medium Sized Firm. 1982. lib. bdg. 30.00 (ISBN 0-89838-099-5). Kluwer Nijhoff.
Ruthven, Kenneth. Society & the New Technology. LC 83-7236. (Modern World Issues Ser.). (Illus.). 64p. 1984. pap. 4.50 (ISBN 0-521-27214-9). Cambridge U Pr.
Sahal, D. Patterns of Technological Innovation. 1981. 47.95 (ISBN 0-201-06630-0). Addison-Wesley.
Sahal, Devendra, ed. Research, Development, & Technological Innovation: Recent Perspectives on Management. LC 79-3095. 288p. 1980. 31.50x (ISBN 0-669-03377-4). Lexington Bks.
Sanders, Ralph. International Dynamics of Technology. LC 82-9220. (Contributions in Political Science Ser.: No. 87). xiii, 332p. 1983. lib. bdg. 35.00 (ISBN 0-313-23401-9, SAD/). Greenwood.
Scherer, F. M. Innovation & Growth: Schumpeterian Perspectives. (Illus.). 264p. 1984. text ed. 35.00x (ISBN 0-262-19222-5). MIT Pr.
Science and Technology for Development: Case Studies on Technical Change. (STPI Module Ser.: No. 12). 33p. 1981. pap. 5.00 (ISBN 0-88936-282-3, IDRCTS34, IDRC). Unipub.
Science & Technology for Development: Technical Changes in Industrial Branches. (STPI Module Ser.: No. 10). 45p. 1981. pap. 5.00 (ISBN 0-88936-275-0, IDRCTS31, IDRC). Unipub.
Skinner, Wickham & Chakraborty, Kishore. The Impact of New Technology: People & Organizations in Manufacturing & Allied Industries. (Work in America Institute Studies in Productivity: Vol. 18). (Orig.). 1982. pap. 35.00 (ISBN 0-08-029499-5). Pergamon.
--The Impact of New Technology: People & Organizations in Manufacturing & Allied Industries. (Studies in Productivity: Highlights of the Literature Ser.: Vol. 18). 66p. 1982. pap. 35.00 (ISBN 0-08-029499-5). Work in Amer.
--The Impact of New Technology: People & Organizations in the Service Industries. (Studies in Productivity: Highlights of the Literature Ser.: Vol. 19). 74p. 1982. pap. 35.00 (ISBN 0-08-029500-2). Work in Amer.
Skorov, G. E., ed. Science, Technology & Economic Growth in the Developing Countries. 1978. text ed. 32.00 (ISBN 0-08-022223-4). Pergamon.
Smith, Vincent K. Technical Change, Relative Prices, & Environmental Resource Evaluation. LC 74-6840. pap. 29.30 (ISBN 0-317-26482-6, 2023816). Bks Demand UMI.
Smith, W. Novis & Larson, C. F., eds. Innovation & U. S. Research: Problems & Recommendations. LC 80-16172. (ACS Symposium Ser.: No. 129). 1980. 34.95 (ISBN 0-8412-0561-2). Am Chemical.
The Social Effects of Technological Developments in the Food & Drink Industries, Including Those Arising from New Production Methods, & the Need for Training & Retraining: Food & Drink Industries Committee Report II. (Programme of Industrial Activities). 51p. 1985. pap. 7.15 (ISBN 92-2-103821-1, ILO369, ILO). Unipub.
Solo, Robert A. & Rogers, Everett M., eds. Inducing Technological Change for Economic Growth & Development. 238p. 1972. 8.50x (ISBN 0-87013-170-2). Mich St U Pr.
Stern, B. T., ed. Information & Innovation: Proceedings of a Seminar of ICSU-AB on the Role of Information in the Innovative Process, Amsterdam, The Netherlands, 1982. (Contemporary Topics in Information Transfer Ser.: Vol. 1). 192p. 1983. 38.50 (ISBN 0-444-86496-2, I-497-82, North Holland). Elsevier.
Stoneman, Paul. The Economic Analysis of Technological Change. (Illus.). 1983. 37.50x (ISBN 0-19-877194-0); pap. 15.95x (ISBN 0-19-877193-2). Oxford U Pr.
Sven B. Lundstedt, Ohio State University & E. William, JFK School of Government, Harvard University, eds. Managing Innovation: The Social Dimensions of Creativity, Invention & Technology. LC 82-293. (Pergamon Policy Studies on Business & Economics Ser.). (Illus.). 280p. 1982. 32.00 (ISBN 0-08-028815-4, L120). Pergamon.
Technology and Employment in Industry. pap. 21.50 (ISBN 92-2-101238-7, ILO21, ILO). Unipub.

Technology & Institutional Response: Papers Presented to a Joint Session of the American Military Institute at the Duquesne History Forum, Pittsburgh, Pennsylvania, 1 November 1972. 132p. 1975. pap. text ed. 13.50x (ISBN 0-89126-007-2). MA-AH Pub.

Technology Assessment for Development. 166p. 1980. pap. 13.00 (ISBN 0-686-68975-5, UN80 2A1, UN). Unipub.

Technology Behaviour of Industrial Enterprises. (Science & Technology for Development Ser.: STPI Module 11). 57p. 1981. pap. 5.00 (ISBN 0-88936-276-9, IDRC32, IDRC). Unipub.

Technology Committee. SMI Handbook of Spring Design. Williams, Patricia, ed. (Illus.). 43p. (Orig.). 1981. pap. 5.00 (ISBN 0-9604120-1-8). Spring Manufact.

Thakur, C. P. Technological Change & Industry. LC 72-924275. (Illus.). 348p. 1974. 15.00x (ISBN 0-89684-505-2). Orient Bk Dist.

Thompson, Jacqueline. Future Rich: The People, Companies & Industries Minting America's Next Fortunes. LC 84-20590. (Illus.). 288p. 1985. 18.95 (ISBN 0-688-04039-X). Morrow.

Thwaites, A. T. & Oakey, R. P. The Regional Economic Impact of Technological Change. LC 83-13851. 256p. 1985. 29.95 (ISBN 0-312-66906-2). St Martin.

Ting, Wenlee. Business & Technological Dynamics in Newly Industrializing Asia. LC 84-8387. (Illus.). xv, 199p. 1985. lib. bdg. 35.00 (ISBN 0-89930-073-1, TII/, Quorum). Greenwood.

Tushman, Michael L. & Moore, William L. Readings in the Management of Innovation. LC 81-12149. (Pitman Ser. in Business Management & Organizational Behavior). 672p. 1982. pap. text ed. 18.95 (ISBN 0-273-01786-1). Pitman Pub MA.

Twiss, Brian C. Managing Technological Innovation. 2nd ed. LC 79-42618. (Illus.). 235p. 1980. text ed. 25.00x (ISBN 0-582-49708-6). Longman.

Twiss, T. Two Lectures on Machinery. (The Development of Industrial Society Ser.). 76p. 1971. Repr. of 1844 ed. 15.00x (ISBN 0-7165-1778-7, BBA 02145, Pub. by Irish Academic Pr Ireland). Biblio Dist.

Tybout, Richard A., ed. Economics of Research & Development. LC 65-18734. (Illus.). 478p. 1965. 7.50 (ISBN 0-8142-0123-7). Ohio St U Pr.

Vedin, Bengt-Arne. Creativity Management in Media Industry Applied to Technology. 97p. (Orig.). 1980. pap. text ed. 9.95x (ISBN 0-86238-002-2, Pub. by Chartwell-Bratt England). Brookfield Pub Co.

--Innovation Organisation. 92p. (Orig.). 1980. pap. text ed. 9.95x (ISBN 0-86238-005-7, Pub. by Chartwell-Bratt England). Brookfield Pub Co.

Walcoff, Carol & Ouellette, Robert P. Techniques for Managing Technological Innovation: Overcoming Process Barriers. LC 82-72860. (Illus.). 151p. 1982. 29.95 (ISBN 0-250-40603-9). Butterworth.

Walsh, William D. The Diffusion of Technological Change in the Pennsylvania Pig Iron Industry: 1850-1870. LC 75-2601. (Dissertations in American Economic History). (Illus.). 1975. 27.50x (ISBN 0-405-07222-8). Ayer Co Pubs.

Weinstein, Jay. Sociology-Technology: The Foundations of Postacademic Social Science. LC 80-24637. 290p. 1982. 39.95 (ISBN 0-87855-404-1). Transaction Bks.

Whittaker, Allan G., et al, eds. Technology Advances in Engineering & Their Impact on Detection, Diagnosis & Prognosis Methods. LC 82-23664. 319p. 1983. 44.50 (ISBN 0-521-25606-2). Cambridge U Pr.

Wise, Kensall D., et al. Microcomputers: A Technology Forecast & Assessment to the Year 2000. LC 79-18186. (Systems Engineering & Analysis Ser.). 251p. 1980. 37.95 (ISBN 0-471-04780-5, Pub. by Wiley-Interscience). Wiley.

Wools, Blanche. The Use of Technology in the Administrative Function of School Library Media Programs. 1983. 15.00x (ISBN 0-931510-10-4). Hi Willow.

York, Neil L. Mechanical Metamorphosis: Technological Change in Revolutionary America. LC 84-11845. (Contributions in American Studies: No. 78). (Illus.). xviii, 240p. 1985. lib. bdg. 35.00 (ISBN 0-313-24475-8, YMM/). Greenwood.

TECHNOLOGICAL INNOVATIONS–AFRICA

Priorities for Science & Technology Research in Africa: Report of a Seminar Held at the University of Ife, Ile-Ife, Nigeria, 3-6 Dec. 1979. 32p. 1981. pap. 5.00 (ISBN 0-88936-279-3, IDRC162, IDRC). Unipub.

The Rural Access Road Program: Appropriate Technology in Kenya. (WEP Study Ser.). 167p. 1981. pap. 11.50 (ISBN 92-2-102204-8, ILO165, ILO). Unipub.

Woillet, M. J. C. Appropriate Technology: Scope for Cooperation among the Countries of the West African Economic Community. 104p. (2nd Impression). 1981. pap. 8.75 (ISBN 92-2-102359-1, ILO156, ILO). Unipub.

TECHNOLOGICAL INNOVATIONS–ASIA

Avestruz, Fred S. Risk & Technology Choice in Developing Countries: The Case of Philippine Sugar Factories. (Illus.). 192p. (Orig.). 1985. lib. bdg. 19.75 (ISBN 0-8191-4774-5); pap. text ed. 10.75 (ISBN 0-8191-4775-3). U Pr of Amer.

Fong, Chan O. Technological Leap: Malaysian Industry in Transition. (Illus.). 250p. 1985. pap. 16.95x (ISBN 0-19-582615-9). Oxford U Pr.

TECHNOLOGICAL INNOVATIONS–EUROPE

Bentley, Raymond. Technological Change in the German Democratic Republic. 340p. 1984. 25.00x (ISBN 0-86531-812-3). Westview.

International Resource Development Inc. Staff. European Local Area Network Markets. 180p. 1983. 1650.00x (ISBN 0-88694-583-6). Intl Res Dev.

Malerba, Franco. The Semiconductor Business: The Economics of Rapid Growth & Decline. LC 85-40372. (Economics of Technological Change Ser.). 272p. 1985. text ed. 27.50x (ISBN 0-299-10460-5). U of Wis Pr.

Nakamura, S. An Inter-Industry Translog Model of Prices & Technical Change for the West German Economy. (Lecture Notes in Economics & Mathematical Systems: Vol. 221). 290p. 1984. pap. 21.00 (ISBN 0-387-12709-7). Springer Verlag.

TECHNOLOGICAL INNOVATIONS–GREAT BRITAIN

David, Paul A. Technical Choice Innovation & Economic Growth: Essays on American & British Experience in the Nineteenth Century. LC 74-76583. pap. 86.00 (ISBN 0-317-26014-6, 2024448). Bks Demand UMI.

Davies, S. The Diffusion of Process Innovations. LC 78-15143. 1979. 42.50 (ISBN 0-521-22193-5). Cambridge U Pr.

Oakey, Raymond. High Technology Small Firms: Innovation & Regional Development in Britain & the United States. LC 83-40705. 250p. 1984. 25.00 (ISBN 0-312-37239-6). St Martin.

Wilkinson, Barry. The ShopFloor Politics of New Technology. viii, 120p. 1983. pap. text ed. 14.50x (ISBN 0-435-82951-3). Gower Pub Co.

TECHNOLOGICAL INNOVATIONS–SOVIET UNION

Parrott, Bruce. Politics & Technology in the Soviet Union. 440p. 1985. pap. text ed. 10.95x (ISBN 0-262-66054-7). MIT Pr.

TECHNOLOGICAL MUSEUMS

see Industrial Museums

TECHNOLOGICAL SOCIETIES

see Technical Societies

TECHNOLOGICAL TRANSFER

see Technology Transfer

TECHNOLOGISTS

see also Laboratory Technicians; Technicians in Industry

The American Key Personnel List; Advanced Composites Materials. 500.00 (ISBN 0-686-48251-4, 0601). T-C Pubns CA.

The European Key Personnel List; Advanced Composites. 500.00 (ISBN 0-686-48252-2, 0602). T-C Pubns CA.

Groeg, Otto J., ed. Who's Who in Technology: Austria, Germany, Switzerland, 2 vols. 1055p. 1979. Set. 195.00x (ISBN 3-921220-24-6). Intl Pubns Serv.

Jones, Donald H. & Ferrari, Lorraine D., eds. Who's Who in Technology Today: Chemical & Related Technologies, Vol. 3. 1981-82 ed. LC 80-644137. 1981. 65.00 (ISBN 0-933980-10-8). Tech Recog Corp.

Who's Who in Technology, 3 Vols. (International Red Ser.). 1984. Set. pap. 160.00 (WWIR102, WWIR). Unipub.

TECHNOLOGY

see also Building; Chemistry, Technical; Electric Engineering; Engineering; Factories; High Technology; Industrial Arts; Inventions; Machinery; Manufactures; Membranes (Technology); Mills and Mill-Work; Mineral Industries; Railroad Engineering; Technical Education; Technocracy; Technological Innovations

also names of specific industries, arts trades, etc., e.g. Clock and Watch Making, Printing, Tailoring

Abdel-Malek, Anouar & Blue, Gregory, eds. Science & Technology in the Transformation of the World. 497p. 1982. 36.25 (ISBN 92-808-0339-5, TUNU193, UNU). Unipub.

Academy of Engineering. Technology, Trade & the U. S. Economy. 1978. pap. 9.75 (ISBN 0-309-02761-6). Natl Acad Pr.

Advances in Technology Yield Profitability: Papers from the SPE Pacific Technical Conference, February 1983, Anaheim, California. (Illus.). 436p. 43.00 (ISBN 0-686-48228-X, 1510). T-C Pubns CA.

AICPA Technical Practice Aids: As of June 1, 1983. 1328p. pap. 15.50 (ISBN 0-317-04268-8). Commerce.

Alcorn, Paul A. Social Issues in Technology: A Format for Investigation. (Illus.). 240p. 1985. text ed. 22.95 (ISBN 0-13-815929-7). P-H.

Alford, Jonathan, ed. The Impact of New Military Technolgy. LC 80-67839. (Adelphi Library: Vol. 4). 140p. 1981. text ed. 33.50x (ISBN 0-916672-74-3). Allanheld.

Alston, Liviu L., ed. High-Voltage Technology. (United Kingdom Atomic Energy Authority, Harwell Post-Graduate Ser.). (Illus.). pap. 106.50 (ISBN 0-317-09403-3, 2051952). Bks Demand UMI.

Annals of Assurance Sciences: Vol. 8: Assurance Technologies in Action. 598p. 1969. 119.25 (ISBN 0-677-13690-0). Gordon.

Arendt, Hannah. Human Condition. LC 58-5535. 1970. pap. 11.95 (ISBN 0-226-02593-4, P361, Phoen). U of Chicago Pr.

Bame, E. Allen & Cummings, Paul. Exploring Technology. LC 79-53783. (Technology Series). (Illus.). 288p. 1980. text ed. 13.95 (ISBN 0-87192-112-X, 000-3); tchr's. guide 13.25 (ISBN 0-87192-114-6); activity manual 8.95 (ISBN 0-87192-113-8). Davis Mass.

Beddow, K. Particulate Science & Technology. 1984. text ed. 75.00 (ISBN 0-07-004267-5). McGraw.

Black, Bruce J. Manufacturing Technology for Level-2 Technicians. (Illus.). 183p. 1983. pap. text ed. 18.95x (ISBN 0-7131-3485-2). Intl Ideas.

Boar, Bernard H. Application Prototyping: A Requirements Definition Strategy for the '80's. LC 83-16934. 210p. 1984. 32.50x (ISBN 0-471-89317-X, Pub. by Wiley-Interscience). Wiley.

Boon, G. K. Technology & Sector Choice in Economic Development. 324p. 1978. 40.00x (ISBN 90-286-0068-X). Sijthoff & Noordhoff.

Boorstin, Daniel J., ed. Technology & Society, 53 bks. 1972. Repr. Set. 1502.50 (ISBN 0-405-04680-4). Ayer Co Pubs.

Boroush, M. A., et al, eds. Technology Assessment: Creative Futures. (Systems Science & Engineering Ser.: Vol. 5). 406p. 1980. 58.50 (ISBN 0-444-00328-2, North-Holland). Elsevier.

Botkin, James, et al. Global Stakes: The Future of High Technology in America. 240p. 1984. pap. 7.95 (ISBN 0-14-007039-7). Penguin.

Braden, Patricia L. Technological Entrepreneurship: The Allocation of Money & Effort in Technology-Based Firms. (Michigan Business Reports: No. 62). (Illus.). 1977. pap. 5.00 (ISBN 0-87712-187-7). U Mich Busn Div Res.

British Technology Index. 926p. 1980. 90.00x (ISBN 0-85365-504-9, Pub. by Lib Assn England). State Mutual Bk.

Bronwell, Arthur B. Science & Technology in the World of the Future. LC 74-114914. 1970. 22.50 (ISBN 0-471-10594-5, Pub. by Wiley). Krieger.

Brownstone, David M. Successful Selling Skills for Small Business. 120p. 1978. 8.00 (ISBN 0-686-48199-2, 0812). T-C Pubns CA.

Bush, George P. & Dreyfuss, Robert, eds. Technology & Copyright: Sources & Materials. 2nd, rev. ed. 552p. 1979. 22.50 (ISBN 0-912338-17-2); microfiche 15.50 (ISBN 0-912338-18-0). Lomond.

The Business & Technology Videolog. LC 78-74186. 1981. pap. 39.50 (ISBN 0-88432-070-7). Video-Forum.

Certon, M. J. & Davidson, H. F. Industrial Technology Transfer, No. 19. (NATO Advanced Study Applied Science Ser.). 480p. 1977. 45.50x (ISBN 90-286-0426-X). Sijthoff & Noordhoff.

Chapman, W. A. Workshop Technology, Pt. 2. 4th ed. (Illus.). 1972. 22.95x (ISBN 0-7131-3272-8). Intl Ideas.

--Workshop Technology, Part 3. 3rd. ed. (Illus.). 675p. 1975. pap. 29.95x (ISBN 0-7131-3351-1). Intl Ideas.

Chatfield, C. Statistics for Technology: A Course in Applied Statistics. 3rd ed. 1983. pap. 12.95 (ISBN 0-412-25340-2, NO. 6845, Pub. by Chapman & Hall). Methuen Inc.

Chemical Engineering Magazine. Process Technology & Flowsheets, Vol. 2. LC 83-12117. 360p. 1983. 36.95 (ISBN 0-07-024388-3). McGraw.

Clarke, Robin. Building for Self-Sufficiency. LC 76-5093. (Illus.). 302p. 1977. pap. 5.95 (ISBN 0-87663-945-7). Universe.

Clews, G. & Leonard, R. Technology & Production. (Industrial Studies). 192p. 1985. text ed. 25.25x (ISBN 0-86003-527-1, Pub. by Philip Alan). Humanities.

Codlin, Ellen M. ASLIB Directory, Vol. 1: Information Sources in Science, Technology & Commerce. 634p. 1977. 90.00x (Pub. by Aslib England). State Mutual Bk.

Cole, James S. Technological Innovations in the 80's. (American Assembly Ser.). 192p. 1984. 12.95 (ISBN 0-13-902123-X); pap. 6.95 (ISBN 0-13-902115-9). P-H.

Commercial Names & Sources: Desk-Top Data Bank. 434p. 55.00 (ISBN 0-686-48115-1, 0310). T-C Pubns CA.

Compton, W. Dale, ed. The Interaction of Science & Technology. LC 75-83548. 137p. 1969. 12.50x (ISBN 0-252-00024-2). U of Ill Pr.

Coppa, Frank & Harmond, Richard. Technology in the Twentieth Century. 272p. 1983. pap. text ed. 13.95 (ISBN 0-8403-3021-9). Kendall-Hunt.

Daggett, et al. Technology at Work: A Survey of Technology. 1986. text ed. price not set (ISBN 0-538-16300-3, P30). SW Pub.

Darrow, Ken & Pam, Rick. Appropriate Technology Sourcebook, Vol. 1. rev. ed. LC 76-29526. 1981. 10.50 (ISBN 0-917704-12-6); pap. 5.50 (ISBN 0-917704-08-8); vol. 1 & 2 pap set avail. (ISBN 0-917704-09-6); vol. 1 & 2 cloth set avail. (ISBN 0-917704-13-4). Appropriate Techn Proj.

--Appropriate Technology Sourcebook, Vol. 2. (Illus.). 1981. 11.50 (ISBN 0-917704-11-8); pap. 6.50 (ISBN 0-917704-06-1); vol. 1 & 2 pap set avail. (ISBN 0-917704-09-6); vol. 1 & 2 cloth set avail. (ISBN 0-917704-13-4). Appropriate Techn Proj.

DeGregori, Thomas R. A Theory of Technology: Continuity & Change in Human Development. 176p. (Orig.). 1985. pap. text ed. 13.50x (ISBN 0-8138-1778-1). Iowa St U Pr.

Dempsey, Michael W., ed. Illustrated Fact Book of Science. LC 82-16412. (Illus.). 236p. 1983. 9.95 (ISBN 0-668-05729-7, 5729). Arco.

De Veen, J. J. The Rural Access Roads Programme: Apropriate Technology in Kenya. International Labour Office, Geneva, ed. (Illus.). 175p. (Orig.). 1984. pap. 11.40 (ISBN 92-2-102204-8). Intl Labour Office.

DeVore, Paul W. Technology: An Introduction. LC 79-53782. (Technology Ser.). (Illus.). 397p. 1980. text ed. 18.95 (ISBN 0-87192-115-4, 000-5). Davis Mass.

Dickson, David. The Politics of Alternative Technology. LC 75-7919. 1977. pap. 4.50x (ISBN 0-87663-917-1). Universe.

Din Standards for Technology of Length Measurement. 728.00 (ISBN 0-686-28166-7, 10051-5/11). Heyden.

DOE Technical Information Center. Patents (DOE) Available for Licensing: A Bibliography for the Period 1966-1974. 60p. 1983. pap. 9.25 (ISBN 0-87079-512-0, DOE/TIC-3398 SUPPL. 1); microfiche 4.50 (ISBN 0-87079-513-9, DOE/TIC-3398 SUPPL. 1). DOE.

Domestic & Foreign Technology Licensing 1984. (Patents, Trademarks, & Literary Property Course Handbook Ser.: 1984-85). 1984. 35.00 (ISBN 0-317-15179-7). PLI.

Durbin, Paul T., ed. A Guide to the Culture of Science, Technology, & Medicine. 784p. 1984. 19.95x (ISBN 0-02-907890-3). Free pr.

--Research in Philosophy & Technology, Vol. 1. 350p. (Orig.). 1979. lib. bdg. 45.00 (ISBN 0-89232-022-2). Jai Pr.

--Research in Philosophy & Technology, Vol. 2. (Orig.). 1979. lib. bdg. 45.00 (ISBN 0-89232-101-6). Jai Pr.

Egziabher, Tewolde Berhan Gebre. Technology Generation & the Technological Space: Project on Research and Development Systems in Rural Settings. 31p. 1982. pap. 5.00 (ISBN 92-808-0390-5, TUNU196, UNU). Unipub.

Elsevier Science Publishing Company, ed. Engineering & Technology Catalog, 1984. Date not set. write for info. Elsevier.

Engineering Concepts Curriculum Project - State University of New York. Man & His Technology. (Illus.). 256p. 1973. text ed. 25.00 (ISBN 0-07-019510-2). McGraw.

Enrick, N. L. Manufacturing Analysis for Productivity & Quality-Cost Enhancement. 2nd ed. 158p. 1983. 23.00 (ISBN 0-686-48156-9, 1204). T-C Pubns CA.

Environmentally Appropriate Technology: Renewable Energy & Other Developing Technologies for a Conserver Society in Canada. 1978. pap. 9.00 (ISBN 0-660-01003-8, SSC91, SSC). Unipub.

European Sources of Science & Technology. 5th ed. 500p. 1981. 190.00x (ISBN 0-582-90108-1, Pub. by Longman). Gale.

Feibleman, James K. Understanding Human Nature: A Popular Guide to the Effects of Technology on Man & His Behavior. LC 77-77126. 1978. 8.95 (ISBN 0-8180-1322-2). Horizon.

Gardner, James H, ed. Technology & the Future of U. S. Industry in World Competition. (ITT Key Issues Lecture Ser.). 112p. 1985. pap. write for info. (ISBN 0-932431-03-8). White River.

Giarini, Orio & Louberge, Henri. The Diminishing Returns of Technology: An Essay on the Crisis in Economic Growth. 1978. pap. text ed. 8.50 (ISBN 0-08-023337-6). Pergamon.

Gibbons, Michael & Gummett, Philip, eds. Science, Technology & Society Today. LC 83-20639. 192p. 1984. 16.00 (ISBN 0-7190-1090-X, Pub. by Manchester Univ Pr); pap. 7.50 (ISBN 0-7190-0878-6). Longwood Pub Group.

Gold, Bela, ed. Technological Change: Economics, Management & Environment. LC 74-17112. 1975. 33.00 (ISBN 0-08-018012-4). Pergamon.
Gold, Bela, et al. Evaluating Technological Innovations: Methods, Expectations, & Findings. LC 79-4749. 384p. 1980. 35.50x (ISBN 0-669-03638-2). Lexington Bks.
Goldstein, Eleanor C., ed. Technology, Vol. 1(incl. 1981 & 1982 Supplements) (Social Issues Resources Ser.). 1983. 70.00 (ISBN 0-89777-028-5). Soc Issues.
Gov. Rockefeller Symposium Winrock, Arkansas, Oct. 1970. Technology Utilization Ideas for the 70's & Beyond. Forbes, Fred W. & Dergarabedian, Paul, eds. (Science & Technology Ser.: Vol. 26). 1971. lib. bdg. 30.00x (ISBN 0-87703-057-X, Pub. by Am Astronaut). Univelt Inc.
Granger, John V. Technology & International Relations. LC 78-15363. (Illus.). 202p. 1979. text ed. 23.95 (ISBN 0-7167-1004-8); pap. text ed. 12.95 (ISBN 0-7167-1003-X). W H Freeman.
Greenwald, Harry P. Sourceguide of Government Technology & Financial Assistance. LC 81-71407. 1982. 49.50 (ISBN 0-914470-14-0). Venture Econ Inc.
Grootings, Peter, ed. Technology & Work: East West Comparisons. 256p. 1985. 29.95 (ISBN 0-7099-3801-2, Pub. by Croom Helm Ltd). Longwood Pub Group.
Guide to American Scientific & Technical Directories. 2nd ed. 350p. 1975. 25.00 (ISBN 0-686-62442-4). B Klein Pubns.
Hafemeister, D. W. & Schroeer, D., eds. Physics, Technology & the Nuclear Arms Race (APS Baltimore, 1983) LC 83-72533. (Aip Conference Proceedings Ser.: No. 104). 384p. 1983. lib. bdg. 36.75 (ISBN 0-88318-203-3). Am Inst Physics.
Haggerty, Patrick E. The Productive Society. LC 74-77475. (Bejamin Fairless Memorial Lectures Ser.). 173p. 1974. 19.00x (ISBN 0-231-03864-X). Columbia U Pr.
Hall, Courtney R. History of American Industrial Science. LC 72-5052. (Technology & Society Ser.). (Illus.). 453p. 1972. Repr. of 1954 ed. 27.00 (ISBN 0-405-04704-5). Ayer Co Pubs.
Hanks, Joyce M. & Rolf, Asal. Research in Philosophy & Technology: Supplement 1 - Jacques Ellul. 47.50 (ISBN 0-89232-478-3). Jai Pr.
Hanle, Paul A., ed. High Technology on Earth: Studies in Using Aerospace Systems & Methods. LC 78-14329. (Smithsonian Studies in Air & Space: No. 3). pap. 20.00 (ISBN 0-317-09477-7, 2011429). Bks Demand UMI.
Harrison, James, ed. Science Now. LC 84-6437. (Illus.). 192p. 1984. 21.95 (ISBN 0-668-06209-6, 6209). Arco.
Heiner, Carol W. & Hendrix, Wayne R. People Create Technology. LC 79-53802. (Technology Series). (Illus.). 256p. 1980. text ed. 13.95 (ISBN 0-87192-109-X, 000-2); tchr's guide 11.95 (ISBN 0-87192-111-1); activity manual 5.95 (ISBN 0-87192-110-3). Davis Mass.
Heinman, S. A. Scientific & Technical Revolution: Economic Aspects. 342p. 1981. 8.00 (ISBN 0-8285-2074-7, Pub. by Progress Pubs USSR). Imported Pubns.
Hellinger, Stephen H. & Hellinger, Douglas A. Unemployment & the Multinationals: A Strategy for Technological Change in Latin America. 1976. 16.50x (ISBN 0-8046-9126-6, Pub by Kennikat). Assoc Faculty Pr.
Herman, Herbert. Treatise on Materials Science & Technology: Embrittlement of Engineering Alloys, Vol. 25. 1983. 89.00 (ISBN 0-12-341825-9). Acad Pr.
Herman, Stewart W., et al. Energy Futures: Industry & the New Technologies. LC 76-30324. 1977. pap. 11.95 (ISBN 0-88410-617-9). INFORM.
High Tech Ventures. 35.00 (ISBN 0-317-29524-1, #CO2232, Law & Business). HarBraceJ.
Hill, Christopher T. & Utterback, James M., eds. Technological Innovation for a Dynamic Economy. (Policy Studies). 1979. pap. 11.75 (ISBN 0-08-025103-X). Pergamon.
Hill, Stephen & Johnston, Ron, eds. Future Tense? Technology in Australia. LC 82-17429. (Illus.). 215p. 1983. text ed. 32.50x (ISBN 0-7022-1674-7). U of Queensland Pr.
Igor, Boy. And Yet it Moves: The Realization & Suppression of Science & Technology. (Illus.). 144p. (Orig.). 1985. pap. 4.00 (ISBN 0-934727-00-7). Zamisdat Pr.
Index to Technical Papers from the Annual & Fall Meetings of ACSM & ASP, 1975-1982. 1983. 11.00 (ISBN 0-937294-48-9). ASP & RS.
Infotech, ed. Technology Management. (Computer State of the Art Report, Series 10: No. 8). 400p. 1982. 445.00 (ISBN 0-08-028571-6). Pergamon.
Ingels, Margaret. Willis Haviland Carrier, Father of Air-Conditioning. LC 72-5056. (Technology & Society Ser.). (Illus.). 178p. 1972. Repr. of 1952 ed. 15.00 (ISBN 0-405-04708-8). Ayer Co Pubs.
International Association for the Advancement of Appropriate Technology for Developing Countries, 1979 Symposium. New Dimensions of Appropriate Technology: Selected Proceedings. Edwards, Alfred L. & Oyeka, I. C., eds. Wagner, Thomas, tr. xii, 251p. (Orig.). 1980. pap. 5.00 (ISBN 0-87712-208-3). U Mich Busn Div Res.
An Introduction to Policy Analysis in Science & Technology. (Science Policy Studies & Documents: No. 46). (Illus.). 93p. (2nd Printing 1982). 1979. pap. 5.00 (ISBN 92-3-101725-X, U955, UNESCO). Unipub.
Jefkins, Frank. Modern Marketing. (Illus.). 256p. 1983. pap. text ed. 14.95x (ISBN 0-7121-2802-6). Trans-Atlantic.
Jequier, Nicolas. Appropriate Technology: Problems & Promises, Part I (The Major Policy Issues) 1977. pap. text ed. 2.50x (ISBN 0-917704-04-5). Appropriate Techn Proj.
Jequier, Nicolas, ed. Appropriate Technology: Problems & Promises. 1976. 12.50x (ISBN 92-64-11492-0). OECD.
Johnson, Harry G. Technology & Economic Interdependence. LC 75-34703. 200p. 1976. 25.00 (ISBN 0-312-78855-X). St Martin.
Kates, Robert W. & Hohenemser, Christoph. Perilous Progress: Technology As Hazard. (Study in Science, Technology, & Public Policy). 460p. 1985. softcover 32.50x (ISBN 0-8133-7025-6). Westview.
Kazimi, Mujid & Makhoul, John. Perspectives on Technological Development in the Arab World. (Monograph: No. 8). 95p. (Orig.). pap. text ed. 4.95 (ISBN 0-937694-03-7). Assn Arab-Amer U Grads.
Kohanski, Alexander S. Philosophy & Technology. LC 77-75257. 1977. 8.50 (ISBN 0-8022-2202-1). Philos Lib.
Laboratory Testing, Field Trails, & Technological Development. (Rural Water Supply Handpumps Project Report: No. 1). 122p. 1982. pap. 5.00 (ISBN 0-686-39781-9, WS-8202). World Bank.
Lambert, Jill. Scientific & Technical Journals. 191p. 1985. lib. bdg. 19.00 (ISBN 0-85157-375-4, Pub. by Bingley England). Shoe String.
Lamberton, Don, et al. The Trouble with Technology. LC 83-10961. 200p. 1983. 25.00 (ISBN 0-312-81985-4). St Martin.
Landau, Ralph & Hannay, N. Bruce, eds. Taxation, Technology & the U. S. Economy. (Pergamon Policy Studies on Business & Economics). 200p. 1981. 39.00 (ISBN 0-08-027564-8). Pergamon.
Landau, Ralph & Jorgenson, Dale, eds. Technology & Economic Policy. 280p. 1986. prof. ref. 29.95x (ISBN 0-88730-068-5); pap. 16.95x (ISBN 0-88730-069-3). Ballinger Pub.
Laudan, Rachel, ed. The Nature of Technolological Knowledge: Are Models of Scientific Change Relevant? 1984. lib. bdg. 24.95 (ISBN 90-277-1716-8, Pub. by Reidel Holland). Kluwer Academic.
Leading Consultants in Technology, 2 vols. 2nd ed. Set. 195.00. Data Vol (ISBN 0-89235-086-5). Index Vol (ISBN 0-89235-098-9). Res Pubns CT.
Lebedev, N. N. Chemistry & Technology of Basic Organic & Petrochemical Synthesis, 2 vols. 638p. 1984. Set. 16.00 (ISBN 0-8285-2784-9, Pub. by Mir Pubs USSR). Imported Pubns.
Lesko, Matthew. Information High Tech. 720p. 1985. pap. 15.95 (ISBN 0-317-20718-0). Har-Row.
Lipscombe, Joan & Williams, Bill. Are Science & Technology Neutral? (Science in a Social Context Ser.). 1979. pap. 4.95 (ISBN 0-408-71312-7). Butterworth.
McGraw-Hill, ed. McGraw-Hill Yearbook of Science & Technology 1984. (Illus.). 520p. 1983. 46.00 (ISBN 0-07-045492-2). McGraw.
McGraw-Hill Editors. Yearbook of Science & Technology, 1985. 335p. 1984. 50.00 (ISBN 0-07-045366-7). McGraw.
--Yearbook of Science & Technology, 1986. 528p. 1985. write for info. (ISBN 0-07-046181-3). McGraw.
Maidens, Melinda, ed. American Technology: Are We Falling Behind? (Editorials on File Ser.). 192p. 1982. 19.95x (ISBN 0-87196-677-8). Facts on File.
Mancuso, Joseph. Managing-Marketing Technology Products, 2 vols. LC 74-82598. 1975. Vol.1. 9.00x (ISBN 0-89006-045-2); Vol. 2. 9.00 (ISBN 0-89006-046-0); Set. 18.00 (ISBN 0-89006-047-9). Artech Hse.
--Marketing Technology Products. 1975. Vol. 2. 9.00 (ISBN 0-89006-046-0). Artech Hse.
Mansfield, Edwin, et al. The Production & Application of New Industrial Technology. 1977. 15.95x (ISBN 0-393-09168-6). Norton.
Marshall, Ken. Package Deals: A Study of Technology Development & Transfer. (Illus.). 130p. 1983. 15.50x (ISBN 0-903031-85-X, Pub. by Intermediate Tech England); pap. 9.75x (ISBN 0-903031-86-8). Intermediate Tech.
Martin, Robert J. High-Tech Bits. 1984. 1.25 ea. (ISBN 0-8010-6170-9). Baker Bk.
Mazur, Allan. The Dynamics of Technical Controversy. LC 81-3257. (Illus.). 175p. (Orig.). 1981. casebound 11.95x (ISBN 0-89461-033-3); pap. text ed. 5.95x (ISBN 0-89461-034-1). Comm Pr Inc.
Mehta, S. S. Productivity, Production Function & Technical Change. 1980. text ed. 10.50x (ISBN 0-391-01830-2). Humanities.
Method for Priority Determination in Science & Technology. (Science Policy Studies & Documents: No. 40). 108p. 1977. pap. 5.00 (ISBN 92-3-101485-4, U841, UNESCO). Unipub.
Mitcham, Carl & Mackey, Robert, eds. Philosophy & Technology: Readings in the Philosiphical Problems of Technology. LC 82-19818. 416p. 1983. pap. text ed. 12.95 (ISBN 0-02-921430-0). Free Pr.
Morehead, John W. Finding & Licensing New Products & Technology from the U. S. A. LC 82-50568. 609p. 1982. 495.00 (ISBN 0-943420-00-8). Tech Search Intl.
Morgan, Robert P., et al. Science & Technology for Development: The Role of U. S. Universities. (Policy Studies). (Illus.). 1979. 56.00 (ISBN 0-08-025107-2). Pergamon.
Moritani, Masanori. Japanese Technology: Getting the Best for the Least. Simul International, tr. (Illus.). 230p. 1982. pap. 19.95x (ISBN 4-377-00554-5, Pub. by Simul Pr Japan). Intl Spec Bk.
Mtewa, Mekki, ed. Science, Technology & Development: Options & Policies. LC 82-42546. (Illus.). 254p. (Orig.). 1982. lib. bdg. 25.50 (ISBN 0-8191-2533-4); pap. text ed. 13.25 (ISBN 0-8191-2534-2). U Pr of Amer.
Muesing, Edith E. The Alternative to Technological Culture. 96p. 1982. pap. 6.50 (ISBN 0-89962-270-4). Todd & Honeywell.
Nader, Claire & Zahlan, A. B., eds. Science & Technology in Developing Countries. LC 69-16284. (Illus.). 1969. 67.50 (ISBN 0-521-07380-4). Cambridge U Pr.
Nanda, B. R., ed. Science & Technology in India. 1978. 9.00x (ISBN 0-8364-0170-0). South Asia Bks.
National Academy of Sciences. Frontiers in Science & Technology. LC 83-1574. (Illus.). 240p. 1983. text ed. 32.95 (ISBN 0-7167-1516-3); pap. text ed. 16.95 (ISBN 0-7167-1517-1). W H Freeman.
National Computing Centre. Information Technology Strategy. 45p. 1983. pap. 7.75x (ISBN 0-471-87897-9). Wiley.
Nelkin, Dorothy. Controversy: Politics of Technical Decisions. 2nd ed. LC 78-21339. (Focus Editions Ser.: Vol. 8). 256p. 1984. 28.00 (ISBN 0-8039-2250-7); pap. 14.00 (ISBN 0-8039-2251-5). Sage.
O'Brien, David M. & Marchand, Donald A. The Politics of Technology Assessment: Instructions, Processes, & Policy Disputes. LC 81-47763. (Illus.). 320p. 1982. 33.50x (ISBN 0-669-04837-2). Lexington Bks.
Olsen, Fred A., ed. Technology: A Reign of Benevolence & Destruction. LC 73-16385. 1974. 29.50x (ISBN 0-8422-5130-8); pap. text ed. 8.95x (ISBN 0-8422-0356-7). Irvington.
O'Neill, Gerard K. The Technology Edge: Opportunities for America in World Competition. 256p. 1984. 16.95 (ISBN 0-671-44766-1). S&S.
Organization for Economic Cooperation & Development Staff, et al. Appropriate Technology Directory, Vol. II. 394p. 1985. pap. 24.00x (ISBN 92-64-12643-0). OECD.
Pacey, Arnold. The Culture of Technology. (Illus.). 224p. 1985. 20.00x (ISBN 0-262-66056-3); pap. 7.95. MIT Pr.
Peacocke, A. R. The Sciences & Theology in the Twentiety Century. (Oxford International Symposia Ser.). 320p. 1981. 25.00x (ISBN 0-85362-188-8). Routledge & Kegan.
Peterson, Russell. Technology: Its Promise & Its Problems. (Illus.). 1979. pap. 2.50 (ISBN 0-87081-123-1). Colo Assoc.
Policy Instruments to Define the Pattern of Demand for Technology. (Science & Technology for Development Ser.: STPI Module 7). 88p. 1981. pap. 5.00 (ISBN 0-88936-265-3, IDRCTS27, IDRC). Unipub.
Powell, Russell H., ed. Handbooks & Tables in Science & Technology. 2nd ed. LC 82-19842. 384p. 1983. 55.00x (ISBN 0-89774-039-4). Oryx Pr.
Puu, Tonu & Wibe, Soren, eds. The Economics of Technological Progress. LC 79-24308. 400p. 1980. 37.50 (ISBN 0-312-23666-2). St Martin.
Raffaele, Joseph A. The Management of Technology: Change in a Society of Organized Advocacies. rev. ed. LC 79-63752. 1979. pap. text ed. 14.25 (ISBN 0-8191-0739-5). U Pr of Amer.
Ramo, Simon. America's Technology Slip. LC 80-21525. pap. 76.00 (ISBN 0-317-10720-8, 2021503). Bks Demand UMI.
Rangarao, B. V. & Chaubey, N. P., eds. Social Perspective of Development of Science & Technology in India. 1983. 22.00x (ISBN 0-8364-0931-0, Pub. by Heritage India). South Asia Bks.
Rheingold, Howard & Levine, Howard. Talking Tech: A Conversational Guide to Science & Technology. LC 82-21537. (Illus.). 324p. 1983. pap. 6.70 (ISBN 0-688-01603-0, Quill NY). Morrow.
Richards, J. W. Technical Development in the Small Plant. 1970. 28.50x (ISBN 0-249-44024-5). Intl Ideas.
Roman, D. D. & Puett, J. F. International Business & Technological Innovation. 498p. 1982. 37.00 (ISBN 0-444-00715-6, North-Holland). Elsevier.
Rosenberg, Nathan. Inside the Black Box: Technology & Economics. LC 82-4563. 304p. 1983. 29.95 (ISBN 0-521-24808-6); pap. 13.95 (ISBN 0-521-27367-6). Cambridge U Pr.
--Perspectives on Technology. LC 84-23495. 360p. 1984. pap. 14.95 (ISBN 0-87332-303-3). M E Sharpe.
--Technology & American Economic Growth. LC 76-52621. 214p. 1972. pap. 7.95 (ISBN 0-87332-104-9). M E Sharpe.
Rosenbloom, Richard S. & Wolek, Francis W. Technology & Information Transfer: A Survey of Practice in Industrial Organizations. LC 70-119550. pap. 47.50 (ISBN 0-317-10820-4, 2002225). Bks Demand UMI.
Rossini, Frederick D. Fundamental Measures & Constants for Science & Technology. LC 74-14759. 142p. 1974. text ed. 34.50 (ISBN 0-8493-5079-4). Krieger.
Rouse, W. B. Systems Engineering Models of Human Machine Interactions. (Systems Science & Engineering Ser.: Vol. 6). 152p. 1980. 39.25 (ISBN 0-444-00366-5, North-Holland). Elsevier.
Rudman, Jack. Mechanical Technology. (Occupational Competency Examination Ser.: OCE-25). (Cloth bdg. avail. on request). pap. 13.95 (ISBN 0-8373-5725-X). Natl Learning.
--Technical Support Aide. (Career Examination Ser.: C-2476). (Cloth bdg. avail. on request). pap. 10.00 (ISBN 0-8373-2476-9). Natl Learning.
Rumford, Benjamin T. Collected Works of Count Rumford, 5 vols. Brown, Sanborn C., ed. Incl. Vol. 1. Nature of Heat. (Illus.). xiv, 507p. 1968 (ISBN 0-674-13951-8); Vol. 2. Practical Applications of Heat. (Illus.). x, 533p. 1969 (ISBN 0-674-13952-6); Vol. 3. Devices & Techniques. (Illus.). x, 514p. 1969; Vol. 4. Light & Armament. (Illus.). viii, 511p. 1970 (ISBN 0-674-13954-2); Vol. 5. Public Institutions. (Illus.). xii, 524p. 1970 (ISBN 0-674-13955-0). LC 68-17633. 30.00x ea. (Belknap Pr). Harvard U Pr.
Rybak, B., ed. Advanced Technobiology. 712p. 1979. 56.00x (ISBN 90-286-0299-2). Sijthoff & Noordhoff.
Saettler, Paul. Instructional Technology & Programmed Instruction. 93p. 1969. pap. text ed. 6.95x (ISBN 0-8290-1112-9). Irvington.
Salam, Abdus. Pakistan-American Institute of Science & Technology (PAISTECH), University of Maryland, Proceedings. Zubairi, M. Yameen, ed. 1984. write for info. (ISBN 0-930895-03-7). Byron Daven Pubs.
Sanders, Ralph, ed. Science & Technology: Vital National Resources. LC 74-17562. 146p. 1975. 12.50 (ISBN 0-912338-11-3); microfiche 9.50 (ISBN 0-912338-12-1). Lomond.
Sardar, Ziauddin. Science, Technology & Development in the Muslim World. LC 77-12756. 1977. text ed. 28.00x (ISBN 0-391-00771-8). Humanities.
Schuurman & Egbert. Technology & the Future: A Philosophical Challenge. 1980. 19.95x (ISBN 0-88906-111-4). Radix Bks.
Science & Technology for Development, STPI Module 4: The Present Situation of Science & Technology in the STPI Countries. 65p. 1980. pap. 5.00 (ISBN 0-686-69634-4, IDRCTS22, IDRC). Unipub.
Science & Technology in Latin America. 1983. pap. text ed. 85.00x (ISBN 0-582-90057-3). Gale.
Science & Technology in the United Kingdom. 400p. 1982. 195.00x (ISBN 0-582-90051-4, Pub. by Longman). Gale.
Scientific Revolution & Inter-Paradigmatic Dialogues. 30p. 1979. pap. 5.00 (ISBN 92-808-0075-2, TUNU028, UNU). Unipub.
Shanahan, William F. Resumes for Technicians: A Complete Resume Preparation & Job-Getting Guide. LC 82-24444. 144p. 1983. lib. bdg. 12.95 (ISBN 0-668-05748-3); pap. 6.95 (ISBN 0-668-05751-3). Arco.

Sherman, P. M. Strategic Planning for Technology Industries. LC 81-1446. 1982. 24.95 (ISBN 0-201-06664-5). Addison-Wesley.
Sinclair, Angela, ed. A Guide to Appropriate Technology Institutions. 124p. (Orig.). 1984. pap. 9.75x (ISBN 0-946688-95-8, Pub. by Intermediate Tech England). Intermediate Tech.
Singer, Hans. Technologies for Basic Needs. 2nd ed. x, 161p. 1982. 11.40 (ISBN 92-2-103068-7); 17.10 (ISBN 92-2-103069-5). Intl Labour Office.
Skevington, David, ed. Guide to Science & Technology in the U. S.A. LC 73-81380. (Illus.). 383p. 1973. 155.00x (ISBN 0-85280-340-0). Intl Pubns Serv.
Slater, Phil, ed. Outlines of a Critique of Technology. Hoare, Quintin & Burgess, Peter, trs. (Ink Links Ser.). 1980. 11.95 (ISBN 0-906133-31-9, Pub by Pluto Pr). Longwood Pub Group.
Smolin, Ronald P., ed. Directory of Public High Technology Corporations. 3rd ed. 1100p. 1985. 195.00 (ISBN 0-89563-063-X). Trans-Atlantic.
--New Issues in High Technology: A Directory of New Hi-Tech Corporations 1983-84. 1983. pap. 75.00 (ISBN 0-89563-057-5). Intl Ideas.
Society of Manufacturing Engineers. Group Technology at Work. 1984. 35.00 (ISBN 0-87263-154-0). SME.
Soft Technologies, Hard Choices. (Worldwatch Institute Papers: No. 21). 48p. 1978. pap. 2.95 (ISBN 0-686-94925-0, WW21, WW). Unipub.
Steffens, Henry J. & Mueller, H. N., eds. Science, Technology, & Culture: AMS Studies in Modern Society, Political & Social Issues, No. 5. LC 74-580. 32.50 (ISBN 0-404-11275-7). AMS Pr.
Steinberg, Rolf. Dead Tech: A Guide to the Archaeology of Tomorrow. Stone, Michael, tr. from Ger. LC 83-392. (A Sierra Club Paperback Library Bk.). (Illus.). 132p. (Orig.). 1983. pap. 14.95 (ISBN 0-87156-347-9). Sierra.
Stotz, Jack, ed. Space Technology Transfer to Community & Industry. (Science & Technology Ser.: Vol. 29). 1972. 20.00x (ISBN 0-87703-062-6, Pub. by Am Astronaut). Univelt Inc.
Subramanyam: Scientific & Technical Information. 1981. 29.75 (ISBN 0-8247-1356-7). Dekker.
Susskind, Charles. Understanding Technology. LC 72-12344. pap. 43.80 (ISBN 0-317-20640-0, 2024131). Bks Demand UMI.
A Systems Approach to Science & Technology Policy-Making & Planning. (Studies on Scientific & Technological Development: No. 7). (Span.). 1972. pap. 1.00 (ISBN 0-8270-5935-3). OAS.
Szyliowicz, Joseph S. Technology & International Affairs. LC 81-13985. 302p. 1981. 39.95 (ISBN 0-03-053321-X). Praeger.
Technical Co-operation in Industry. (Monographs on Industrialization of Developing Countries: Problems & Prospects). pap. 4.00 (ISBN 0-686-93277-3, UN69/2B39/VOL. 21, UN). Unipub.
Technical Guide, 1978. Incl. Vol.1. Consumer Prices (ISBN 92-2-101866-0); Vol. 2. Employment, Unemployment, Hours of Work, Wages (ISBN 92-2-101867-9). 1978. 14.25 ea.; 22.80 set (ISBN 92-2-101868-7). Intl Labour Office.
Technological Change & Manpower in a Centrally Planned Economy: A Study Dealing with the Metal-Working Industry in the USSR. (Labour & Automation, Bulletin: No. 3). 1966. 2.30 (ISBN 92-2-100973-4). Intl Labour Office.
Technology for Development: First International Conference. 367p. (Orig.). 1980. pap. text ed. 60.00x (ISBN 0-85825-140-X, Pub. by Inst Engineering Australia). Brookfield Pub Co.
Teich, Albert H. & Thornton, Ray. Science, Technology, & the Issues of the Eighties: Policy Outlook. (WVSS in Science, Technology, & Public Policy). (Illus.). 315p. (Orig.). 1982. lib. bdg. 28.00x (ISBN 0-86531-360-1); pap. text ed. 13.50x (ISBN 0-86531-361-X). Westview.
Thomas, Sari, ed. Studies in Mass Communication & Technology. LC 83-25746. (Studies in Communication: Vol. 1). 272p. 1984. text ed. 35.00 (ISBN 0-89391-133-X). Ablex Pub.
Thorburn, Craig. Teknologi Kampungan: A Compendium of Indonesian Indigenous Technologies. Darrow, Ken & Stanley, Bill, eds. (Illus.). 154p. 1982. pap. 5.00 (ISBN 0-917704-16-9). Appropriate Techn Proj.
The Timetable of Technology. LC 82-11899. (Illus.). 240p. 1982. 30.00 (ISBN 0-87851-209-8). Hearst Bks.
Town, H. C. & Moore, H. Manufacturing Technology: Advanced Machines & Processes. (Illus.). 352p. 1980. 33.00 (ISBN 0-7134-1096-5, Pub. by Batsford England); pap. 15.50 (ISBN 0-7134-1097-3). David & Charles.
Traditional Technology, a Neglected Component of Appropriate Technology. 27p. 1981. pap. 5.00 (ISBN 92-808-0250-X, TUNU112, UNU). Unipub.
United Nations Environment Programme. Directory of Institutions & Individuals Active in Environmentally-Sound & Appropriate Technologies. 28.00 (ISBN 0-08-025658-9). Pergamon.
U. S. Technology & Export Controls. 1978. 10.00 (ISBN 0-686-27829-1). M & A Products.
Weitzsacker, E. U. von & Swaminathan, M. S., eds. New Frontiers in Technology Applications: Integration of Emerging & Traditional Technologies. (Science & Technology for Development Ser.: Vol. 2). (Illus.). 271p. 1983. 28.50 (ISBN 0-907567-66-5, TYP152, TYP); pap. 15.00 (ISBN 0-907567-67-3, TYP151). Unipub.
Wells, Louis T., Jr. Technology & Third World Mulinationals. International Labour Office, ed. (Working Papers Multinationals: No. 19). iii, 31p. (Orig.). 1982. pap. 8.55 (ISBN 92-2-103021-0). Intl Labour Office.
White, John A. Values & Scientists. 88p. (Orig.). 1984. lib. bdg. 19.00 (ISBN 0-8191-3584-4); pap. text ed. 7.50 (ISBN 0-8191-3585-2). U Pr of Amer.
White, Nelson & White, Anne. Collected Rituals from the T. O. T. & Other Sources. LC 82-50719. 100p. (Orig.). 1982. pap. 20.00 (ISBN 0-939856-28-X). Tech Group.
Who's Who in Frontier Science & Technology. 1st. ed. LC 82-82015. 846p. 1984. 84.50 (ISBN 0-8379-5701-X, 030290). Marquis.
Who's Who in Technology Today, 5 vols. 4th ed. Incl. Vol. 1. Electronics & Computer Science. 95.00 (ISBN 0-943692-09-1); Vol. 2. Physics & Optics. 95.00 (ISBN 0-943692-10-5); Vol. 3. Chemistry & Biotechnology. (ISBN 0-943692-11-3); Vol. 4. Mechanical, Civil, Energy, & Earth Science. 95.00 (ISBN 0-943692-12-1); Vol. 5. The Expertise Index to Who's Who in Technology Today. Set. 425.00 (ISBN 0-943692-13-X). Set. 450.00 (ISBN 0-943692-15-6). Res Pubns CT.
Williams, Charles F., et al. Technology for Tomorrow. 1985. 10.50 (ISBN 0-538-16250-3, P25). SW Pub.
Williams, W. Randy. Engineered Job Hunting: A Job Search Manual for the Technical Professions. (Illus.). 196p. 1984. 17.95 (ISBN 0-13-277905-6); pap. 7.95 (ISBN 0-13-277897-1). P-H.
World Summary of Statistics on Science & Technology. (Statistical Reports & Studies: No. 17). 66p. (Orig.). 1970. pap. 5.00 (ISBN 92-3-000792-7, U731, UNESCO). Unipub.
Young, Thomas. Course of Lectures on Natural Philosophy & the Mechanical Arts, 2 Vols. LC 7-31708. Repr. of 1807 ed. Set. 135.00 (ISBN 0-384-70408-5); Vol. 1. 75.00 (ISBN 0-384-70406-9); Vol. 2. 65.00 (ISBN 0-384-70407-7). Johnson Repr.

TECHNOLOGY–ABBREVIATIONS
see also Technology–Notation
Pugh, Eric, compiled by. Pugh's Dictionary of Acronyms & Abbreviations. 348p. 1981. lib. bdg. 87.50x (ISBN 0-89774-012-2). Oryx Pr.
Wennrich, Peter. Anglo-American & German Abbreviations in Science & Technology, 4 vols. 2900p. 1980. Set. lib. bdg. 125.00 (ISBN 3-7940-1014-0). K G Saur.
Wuster, ed. Technical & Scientific Abbreviations & Acronyms: English-German. 200p. 1968. 27.00 (ISBN 0-9913000-6-8, Pub. by O Brandstetter WG). Heyden.
Zalucki, H. Dictionary of Russian Technical & Scientific Abbreviations. (Eng., Rus. & Ger.). 387p. 1968. 70.25 (ISBN 0-444-40657-3). Elsevier.

TECHNOLOGY–ABSTRACTING AND INDEXING
Bearman, Toni C. & Kunberger, William. A Study of Coverage Overlap Among Major Science & Technology Abstracting & Indexing Services. 1977. 20.00 (ISBN 0-942308-12-3). NFAIS.
Maizell, Robert, et al. Abstracting Scientific & Technical Literature. LC 78-9756. 316p. 1979. Repr. of 1971 ed. 21.50 (ISBN 0-88275-703-2). Krieger.
Manual on Methods for Retrieving & Correlating Technical Data-STP 468-A. 74p. 1969. pap. 3.00 (ISBN 0-8031-0399-9, 04-468000-41). ASTM.
Owen, Dolores B. Abstracts & Indexes in Science & Technology: A Descriptive Guide. 2nd ed. LC 84-10902. 252p. 1984. 17.50 (ISBN 0-8108-1712-8). Scarecrow.

TECHNOLOGY–ADDRESSES, ESSAYS, LECTURES
Abelson, Philip H. & Kulstad, Ruth, eds. The Science Centennial Review. LC 80-69480. (Science Compendia Ser.: Vol. 9). (Illus.). 188p. 1980. text ed. 14.00x (ISBN 0-87168-305-9); pap. text ed. 6.00x (ISBN 0-87168-250-8). AAAS.
ACSM-ASP Fall Convention, Sept. 1982. Technical Papers. pap. 12.00 (ISBN 0-937294-39-X); pap. 7.00 members. ASP & RS.
Annual Science & Technology Report to the Congress 1981. 1981. 6.50 (ISBN 0-318-18086-3, NSF 82-9). NSF.
Baldwin, J. & Brand, Stewart, eds. Soft Tech. 1978. pap. 5.00 (ISBN 0-14-004806-5). Penguin.
Bigelow, Jacob. The Useful Arts. LC 72-5034. (Technology & Society ser.). (Illus.). 762p. 1972. Repr. of 1840 ed. 42.00 (ISBN 0-405-04687-1). Ayer Co Pubs.
Caribbean Seminar on Science & Technology Policy & Planning, 2nd. Proceedings. (Studies on Scientific & Technological Development: No. 28). 1977. pap. text ed. 4.00 (ISBN 0-8270-6000-9). OAS.
Carr, Marilyn, ed. The AT Reader: Theory & Practice of Appropriate Technology. (Illus.). 468p. (Orig.). 1985. pap. 19.50x (ISBN 0-942850-03-3, Pub. by Intermediate Tech England). Intermediate Tech.
EMI Shielding Conference Proceedings 1984. 1985. pap. 150.00 (ISBN 0-89336-445-2). BCC.
European Production Study Group Meeting, Loughborough Univ., 1981. Employment Consequences of Technological Change: Proceedings. Bosworth, Derek L., ed. 236p. 1984. text ed. 34.50x (ISBN 0-8419-5086-5). Holmes & Meier.
First International Seminar on Science & Technology in the Transformation of the World: A Report of Proceedings, Belgrade, Yugoslavia, Oct. 1979. 112p. 1980. pap. 10.00 (ISBN 92-808-0196-1, TUNU117, UNU). Unipub.
Florman, Samuel. Blaming Technology: The Retreat from Responsibility. LC 81-5818. 256p. 1981. 12.95 (ISBN 0-312-08362-9). St Martin.
Gaskell, P., et al, eds. The Structure of Non-Crystalline Materials: 1982. 610p. 1983. 62.00x (ISBN 0-8002-3077-9). Taylor & Francis.
The Gear-Box of Priorities: Positions. 15p. 1981. pap. 5.00 (ISBN 92-808-0168-6, TUNU126, UNU). Unipub.
Hall, Rupert & Smith, Norman, eds. History of Technology: Fifth Annual Volume, 1980. 168p. 1980. 40.00 (ISBN 0-7201-1585-X). Mansell.
Heidegger, Martin. The Question Concerning Technology & Other Essays. Lovitt, William, tr. from Ger. LC 77-87181. 1978. lib. bdg. 24.00x (ISBN 0-8240-2427-3). Garland Pub.
--The Question Concerning Technology & Other Essays. Lovitt, William, tr. (Orig.). 1977. pap. 6.95xi (ISBN 0-06-131969-4, TB 1969, Torch). Har-Row.
International Workshop on Appropriate Tech., Delft Univ. of Technology, Sept. 4-7, 1979. Fundamental Aspects of Appropriate Technology: Proceedings. Bemer, G. & De Schutter, J., eds. 220p. (Orig.). 1980. pap. 14.00x (ISBN 90-286-0640-8). Sijthoff & Noordhoff.
Jarrett, Henry, et al. Science & Resources: Prospects & Implications of Technological Advance. LC 77-23132. (Resources for the Future, Inc.). (Illus.). 1977. Repr. of 1959 ed. lib. bdg. 22.50x (ISBN 0-8371-9470-9, JASR). Greenwood.
Jenkins, S. H. Technical Papers from the 7th IAWPR Conference, Paris, 1974. 99.00 (ISBN 0-08-019839-2). Pergamon.
Johnston, R. & Gummett, P. Directory Technology. 240p. 1980. 30.00x (ISBN 0-85664-740-3, Pub. by Croom Helm England). State Mutual Bk.
Kuo, B. C., ed. Proceedings: Symposium on Incremental Motion Control Systems & Devices, 12th Annual. (Illus.). 320p. 1983. 50.00x (ISBN 0-931538-05-X). Incremental Motion.
Mambert, W. A. Presenting Technical Ideas: A Guide to Audience Communication. LC 67-28335. (Wiley Series on Human Communication). (Illus.). pap. 43.60 (ISBN 0-317-10710-0, 2055175). Bks Demand UMI.
Neyman, Jerzy, ed. The Heritage of Copernicus: Theories: "Pleasing to the Mind". 1974. pap. 14.95x (ISBN 0-262-64016-3). MIT Pr.
Plant Animal Biotechnology Conference: Proceedings. 1985. pap. 150.00 (ISBN 0-89336-446-0). BCC.
Russell, Edward J. Science & Modern Life. facsimile ed. LC 70-117833. (Essay Index Reprint Ser). Repr. of 1955 ed. 14.00 (ISBN 0-8369-2440-1). Ayer Co Pubs.
Technical Bulletins, 23 vols. Incl. Vol. 1. Field Methods of Water Hardness Determination. Douglas, I; Vol. 2. Techniques for Tracing Subterranean Drainage. Drew, D. P. & Smith, D. I.; Vol. 3. The Determination of the Infiltration Capacity of Field Soils Using the Cylinder Infiltrometer. Hills, R. C; Vol. 4. A Method for the Direct Measurement of Erosion on Rock Surfaces. High, C. & Hanna, F. C.; Vol. 5. Techniques of Till Fabric Analysis. Andrews, J. T; Vol. 6. Field Method of Hillslope Description. Leopold, L. B. & Dunne, T.; Vol. 7. The Measurement of Soil Frost-Heave in the Field. James, P. A; Vol. 8. A System for the Field Measurement of Soil Water Movement. Knapp, B. J; Vol. 9. An Instrument System for Shore Process Studies. Kirk, R. M; Vol. 10. Slope Profile Survey. Young, A; Vol. 11. Electrochemical & Fluorometric Tracer Techniques for Streamflow Measurements. Church, M; Vol. 12. The Measurement of Soil Moisture. Curtis, L. F. & Trudgill, S.; Vol. 13. Drainage Method Morphometry. Gardiner, V; Vol. 14. The Use of Electrode Instrumentation for Water Analysis. Edwards, A. M., et al.; Vol. 15. Instruments for Measuring Soil Creep. Anderson, E. W. & Finlayson, B.; Vol. 16, Pt. 1. Shorter Technical Methods: Survey of Slopes, Multiple Crest Stage Recorder, Erosional Loss of Rock Tablets, Organic Content of Suspended Sediments. Finlayson, B. & Osmaston, H. A.; Vol. 16, Pt. 2. Shorter Technical Methods: Soil Creep, Slope Profiles, Schmidt Test Hammer, Erosion Pins. Finlayson, B. & Osmaston, H. A.; Vol. 17. An Instrument System for Measuring Soil Movement. Finlayson, B. & Osmaston, H. A.; Vol. 18. WATSPEC: A Computer Program for Determining the Equilibrium Speciation of Aqueous Solutions. Wigley, T. M; Vol. 19. An Automatic Fluid-Scannning Switch Tensionmeter System. Burt, T. P; Vol. 20. Introduction to Pollen Analysis. Jones, R. L. & Cunpill, P. R.; Vol. 21. HYDRODAT: A System of FORTRAN Computer Programs for the Preparation & Analysis of Hydrological Data from Charts. Beven, K. J. & Callen, J. L.; Vol. 22. Shorter Technical Methods III. Grieve, I. C; Vol. 23. Soil Aggregate Stability Tests for the Geomorphologist. Grieve, A. C. 1980. Set. pap. text ed. 175.00 (ISBN 0-686-64926-5, Pub. by GEO Abstracts England); pap. text ed. 8.00 ea. State Mutual Bk.
Technical Conference 1984: Proceedings. 214p. 1985. 15.00 (ISBN 0-935030-08-5). Irrigation.
Thornton, Jesse E., compiled by. Science & Social Change. LC 72-357. (Essay Index Reprint Ser.). Repr. of 1939 ed. 29.00 (ISBN 0-8369-2830-X). Ayer Co Pubs.
Tushman, Michael L. & Moore, William L. Readings in the Management of Innovation. LC 81-12149. (Pitman Ser. in Business Management & Organizational Behavior). 672p. 1982. pap. text ed. 18.95 (ISBN 0-273-01786-1). Pitman Pub MA.
UNA-USA National Policy Panel. Science & Technology in an Era of Independence. LC 74-29459. (Illus.). 1975. pap. text ed. 2.00x (ISBN 0-934654-12-3). UNA-USA.
United Nations Conference on Science & Technology for Development. Technology, Employment & Basic Needs: ILO Overview Paper. 3rd ed. 27p. 1977. pap. 4.50 (ISBN 92-2-101928-4, ILO106, ILO). Unipub.
Velikhov, E. P., et al, eds. Science, Technology & the Future: Soviet Scientists Analysis of the Problems of & Prospects for the Development of Science & Technology & Their Role in Society. LC 79-40113. (Illus.). 480p. 1980. 43.00 (ISBN 0-08-024743-1). Pergamon.

TECHNOLOGY–AUTHORSHIP
see Technical Writing

TECHNOLOGY–BIBLIOGRAPHY
see also Industrial Arts–Bibliography
Agajanian, A. H. MOSFET Technologies: A Comprehensive Bibliography. LC 80-21773. 390p. 1980. 95.00x (ISBN 0-306-65193-9, IFI Plenum). Plenum Pub.
Alsmeyer, D. & Atkins, A. G., eds. Guide to Science & Technology in the Asia Pacific Area. 540p. 150.00x (ISBN 0-582-90100-6, Pub. by Longman). Gale.
Aluri, Rao & Robinson, Judith. A Guide to U. S. Government Scientific & Technical Resources. 259p. 1983. lib. bdg. 23.50 (ISBN 0-87287-377-3). Libs Unl.
Applied Science & Technology Index; 1958-1969. 100.00 (ISBN 0-685-22228-4); write for info. (01#1970-1980). Wilson.
Bibliographic Guide to Technology: 1976, 2 vols. 1977. Set. lib. bdg. 225.00 (ISBN 0-8161-6831-8, Biblio Guides). G K Hall.
Bibliographic Guide to Technology: 1978, 2 vols. 1979. lib. bdg. 225.00 (ISBN 0-8161-6861-X, Biblio Guides). G K Hall.
Bibliographic Guide to Technology: 1979, 2 vols. 1980. Set. lib. bdg. 195.00 (ISBN 0-8161-6878-4, Biblio Guides). G K Hall.

Bibliographic Guide to Technology: 1980, 2 vols. 1981. Set. lib. bdg. 225.00 (ISBN 0-8161-6895-4, Biblio Guides). G K Hall.

Bibliographic Guide to Technology: 1981, 2 vols. 1982. Set. lib. bdg. 225.00 (ISBN 0-8161-6965-9, Biblio Guides). G K Hall.

Bibliographic Guide to Technology: 1982, 2 vols. 1983. Set. lib. bdg. 250.00 (ISBN 0-8161-6981-0, Biblio Guides). G K Hall.

Black, George W., Jr. American Science & Technology: A Bicentennial Bibliography. LC 78-15820. 172p. 1979. 15.95x (ISBN 0-8093-0898-3). S Ill U Pr.

Bolton, Henry C. Catalogue of Scientific & Technical Periodicals. 1665-1895. 2nd ed. Repr. of 1897 ed. 72.00 (ISBN 0-384-04985-0). Johnson Repr.

Committee On Data For Science And Technology Of The International Council Of Scientific Unions. International Compendium of Numerical Data Projects. 1969. 38.00 (ISBN 0-387-04570-8). Springer-Verlag.

Cutcliffe, Stephen H., et al, eds. Technology & Values in American Civilization: A Guide to Information Sources. (American Information Guide Ser.: Vol. 9). 728p. 1980. 60.00x (ISBN 0-8103-1475-4). Gale.

Engineering Societies Library Staff. Classed Subject Catalog of the Engineering Societies Library, New York City, 1st Supplement. 1965. 110.00 (ISBN 0-8161-0700-9, Hall Library). G K Hall.

--Classed Subject Catalog of the Engineering Societies Library, New York City, 2nd Supplement. 1966. 110.00 (ISBN 0-8161-0752-1, Hall Library). G K Hall.

--Classed Subject Catalog of the Engineering Societies Library, New York City, 3rd Supplement. 1967. 110.00 (ISBN 0-8161-0756-4, Hall Library). G K Hall.

--Classed Subject Catalog of the Engineering Societies Library, New York City, 4th Supplement, 1968 & 5th Supplement, 1969. Fourth Suppl. 110.00 (ISBN 0-8161-0817-X, Hall Library); Fifth Suppl. 110.00 (ISBN 0-8161-0836-6). G K Hall.

--Classed Subject Catalog of the Engineering Societies Library, New York City, 6th Supplement. 1970. 110.00 (ISBN 0-8161-0883-8, Hall Library). G K Hall.

--Classed Subject Catalog of the Engineering Societies Library, New York City, 12 vols. 1185.00, incl. index (ISBN 0-8161-0653-3, Hall Library); index alone 100.00 (ISBN 0-8161-0237-6). G K Hall.

Fifty Year Index to ASTM Technical Papers & Reports. 216p. 1952. 6.00 (ISBN 0-8031-0770-6, 13-002500-00). ASTM.

Five-Year Index to ASTM Technical Papers & Reports, 1951-55. 96p. 1957. 3.50 (ISBN 0-8031-0774-9, 13-002550-00). ASTM.

Five-Year Index to ASTM Technical Papers & Reports, 1956-60. 152p. 1962. 3.50 (ISBN 0-8031-0773-0, 13-002600-00). ASTM.

Five-Year Index to ASTM Technical Papers & Reports, 1961-65. 152p. 1966. 6.50 (ISBN 0-8031-0772-2, 13-002650-00). ASTM.

Five-Year Index to ASTM Technical Papers & Reports, 1966-70. 180p. 1971. 9.50 (ISBN 0-8031-0771-4, 13-002700-00). ASTM.

Houghton, Bernard. Technical Information Sources: A Guide to Patent Specifications, Standards, & Technical Reports Literature. 2nd ed. (Guides to Subject Literature Ser.). 119p. 1972. 14.50 (ISBN 0-208-01074-2, Linnet). Shoe String.

Jones, E. G., ed. Guide to Science & Technology in Eastern Europe: A Reference Guide to Science & Technology in Eastern Europe. (Illus.). 320p. 150.00x (ISBN 0-582-90101-4, Pub. by Longman). Gale.

Keller, Alex & Hollister-Short, Graham. The History of Mechanical Technology: An Annotated Bibliography. LC 84-45401. 300p. 1985. lib. bdg. 40.00 (ISBN 0-8240-8949-9). Garland Pub.

Kren, Claudia. Medieval Science & Technology: A Selected, Annotated Bibliography. Multhauf, Robert & Wells, Ellen, eds. LC 84-48012. (Bibliographies on the History of Science & Technology Ser.). 400p. 1985. lib. bdg. 53.00 (ISBN 0-8240-8969-3). Garland Pub.

Library Association, ed. British Technology Index, 1977. LC 63-23735. 1978. 175.00x (ISBN 0-85365-561-8). Intl Pubns Serv.

Malinowsky, H. Robert & Richardson, Jeanne M. Science & Engineering Literature: A Guide to Reference Sources. 3rd ed. LC 80-21290. (Library Science Text). 342p. 1980. lib. bdg. 33.00x (ISBN 0-87287-230-0); pap. text ed. 21.00 (ISBN 0-87287-245-9). Libs Unl.

Northeastern University - Dodge Library, Boston. Selective Bibliography in Science & Engineering. 1964. 78.00 (ISBN 0-8161-0701-7, Hall Library). G K Hall.

Pure & Applied Science Books, 1876-1982, 6 vols. 7784p. 1982. Set. 300.00x (ISBN 0-8352-1437-0). Bowker.

Scientific & Technical Books & Serials in Print 1985, 3 vols. 1984. 120.00 (ISBN 0-8352-1860-0). Bowker.

Technology Book Guide: 1974. 1974. lib. bdg. 195.00 (ISBN 0-8161-6803-2, Biblio Guides). G K Hall.

TECHNOLOGY–DICTIONARIES

see also Technology–Terminology; also names of specific industries, with or without the subdivision Dictionaries

Abbreviated Russian-Persian Technical Dictionary. (Rus. & Persian.). 477p. 1974. 13.50 (ISBN 0-686-97386-0, M-9053). French & Eur.

Alzugaray, J. J. Voces Extranjeras en el Lengua Technologico. (Span. & Eng.). 1980. pap. 9.95 (ISBN 0-686-92477-0, S-33100). French & Eur.

Ansteinsson. English-Norse, Norse-English Technical Dictionary. 45.00 (ISBN 0-317-19060-1, N433). Vanous.

Ansteinsson, ed. English-Norsk Technical Dictionary, Vol. 1. rev. ed. (Eng. & Norwegian.). 542p. 1983. 45.00 (ISBN 0-317-18981-6, N433). Vanous.

--Norsk-English Technical Dictionary, Vol. II. (Norwegian & Eng.). 328p. 1980. 38.00 (ISBN 0-317-18984-0, N432). Vanous.

Ansteinsson, J. Norwegian Technical Dictionary: English-Norwegian Oil Supplement, Vol. 1. 3rd. ed. (Norwegian & Eng.). 1983. 45.00x (ISBN 8-2702-8007-0, N433). Vanous.

Ansteinsson, J. & Andreassen, A. T. Norwegian-English, English-Norwegian Technical Dictionary, 2 Vols. (Norwegian & Eng.). Set. 65.00 (ISBN 8-2702-8007-0). Heinman.

Ansteinsson, J., ed. Norwegian Technical Dictionary: Norwegian-English, Vol. 2. rev. 4th ed. (Norwegian & Eng.). 1980. 38.00x (ISBN 82-702-8006-2, N432). Vanous.

Appleby, B. L. Elsevier's Dictionary of Commercial Terms & Phrases: In English, German, Spanish, French & Swedish. 1984. 181.50 (ISBN 0-444-42270-6, I-251-84). Elsevier.

Applied Technical Dictionary: Acoustics. 50.00x (ISBN 0-569-08535-7, Pub. by Collets). State Mutual Bk.

Applied Technical Dictionary: Air Conditioning & Refrigeration. (Eng., Ger., Fr., Rus. & Slovak.). 69.00x (ISBN 0-569-08534-9, Pub. by Collets). State Mutual Bk.

Applied Technical Dictionary: Oil Processing & Petrochemistry. (Eng., Ger., Fr., Rus. & Slovak.). 1981. 50.00x (ISBN 0-569-08533-0, Pub. by Collets). State Mutual Bk.

Applied Technical Dictionary: Silicate Technology. (Eng., Ger., Fr & Slovak.). 50.00x (ISBN 0-569-08557-8, Pub. by Collets). State Mutual Bk.

Asimov, Isaac. Enciclopedia Biografica De Ciencia y Tecnologia. 2nd ed. (Espn.). 800p. 1974. 47.95 (ISBN 84-292-7004-3, S-50544). French & Eur.

Bajic, B., et al. Technical-Economical Dictionary for Business Purposes. (Eng., Fr., Ger. & Serbocroation.). 1700p. 1973. 95.00 (ISBN 0-686-92638-2, M-9689). French & Eur.

Bazzi, Maria. Enciclopedia De las Tecnicas Pictoricas. (Espn.). 342p. 1965. 12.25 (ISBN 84-279-4511-6, S-50549). French & Eur.

Belle Isle, J. Gerald. Dictionnaire Technique General: Anglais-Francais. 2nd ed. (Eng. & Fr.). 555p. 1977. 79.95 (ISBN 0-686-56913-X, M-6158). French & Eur.

Benacka, S. English-Slovak Technical Dictionary. (Eng. & Slovak.). 1358p. 1980. 79.00x (ISBN 0-569-08529-2, Pub. by Collet's). State Mutual Bk.

Bennett, H. Concise Chemical & Technical Dictionary. 4th ed. 1986. 95.00 (ISBN 0-8206-0310-4). Chem Pub.

Bilginer, Sadettin. Deutsch-Turkisches Worterbuch Fur Technische Berufe. 2nd ed. (Ger. & Turkish.). 448p. 1966. leatherette 55.00 (ISBN 3-7736-5270-4, M-7348, Pub. by Verlag W. Girardet). French & Eur.

Bordes, Gerard. La Grande Encyclopedie Alpha des Sciences et des Techniques, 20 vols. (Fr.). 1976. Set. 1225.00 (ISBN 0-686-57311-0, M-6290). French & Eur.

Burger, E., ed. Technical Reference Dictionary. 571p. 1979. 95.00 (ISBN 0-686-92324-3, M-9890). French & Eur.

Busto, M. Pequeno Diccionario Tecnologico: Farmacia, Quimica, Fisica, Medicina y Ciencias Naturales. (Span.). 226p. 1964. 13.50 (ISBN 0-686-57357-9, S-50248). French & Eur.

Callaham, Ludmilla I. Russian-English Chemical & Polytechnical Dictionary. 3rd ed. LC 75-5982. (Rus. & Eng.). 852p. 1975. 62.95x (ISBN 0-471-12998-4, Pub. by Wiley-Interscience). Wiley.

Camarao, P. C. & Serra, M. A. Great Technical Dictionary: Dicionario Tecnico English-Portuguese. (Eng. & Portuguese.). 462p. 1979. pap. 39.95 (ISBN 0-686-97435-2, M-9214). French & Eur.

Carcamo, L. Dictionnaire pour Ingenieurs et Techniciens: Francais-Espagnol, Espagnol-Francais. (Fr. & Span.). 1106p. 1981. 95.00 (ISBN 0-686-92423-1, M-7669). French & Eur.

Chernukhin, A. E. English-Russian Polytechnical Dictionary. (Eng. & Rus.). 97.00 (ISBN 0-08-021936-5). Pergamon.

Chernukhin, A. E., ed. English-Russian Polytechnical Dictionary. (Eng. & Rus.). 688p. 1979. 70.00x (ISBN 0-569-08580-2, Pub. by Collets). State Mutual Bk.

Chesnel De la Charbouclais, L. P. Dictionnaire de Technologie, 2 vols. Migne, J. P., ed. (Troisieme et Derniere Encyclopedie Theologique Ser.: Vols. 28-29). (Fr.). 1306p. Repr. of 1858 ed. lib. bdg. 166.50x (ISBN 0-89241-308-5). Caratzas.

Collazo, Javier L. English-Spanish Spanish-English Encyclopedic Dictionary of Technical Terms, 3 vols. LC 79-16074. (Eng. & Span.). 1980. Set, English Edition. 154.00 (ISBN 0-07-079172-4); Set, Spanish Edition. 154.00 (ISBN 0-07-079162-7). McGraw.

Collocott, T. C., et al, eds. Chambers Diccionario Cientifico y Tecnologico-Technical Dictionary with Reverse Indices: Spanish-English-French-German, 2 vols. 3rd ed. 1979. Set. 165.00x (ISBN 84-282-0531-0). Adlers Foreign Bks.

Comfort, Jeremy, et al. Basic Technical English. (Illus.). 1982. pap. 6.25x student's ed. (ISBN 0-19-457382-6); pap. 6.95x tchr.'s ed (ISBN 0-19-457383-4). Oxford U Pr.

Concise Polish-English Technical Dictionary. 1985. write for info. (P550). Vanous.

Concise Technical Dictionary: Polish-English. 1985. write for info. Vanous.

Crane, Dale, ed. Capstan Encyclopedic Dictionary of Technical Terms. LC 84-12177. (ABC (A Basic Course) Ser.). (Illus., Orig.). 1984. pap. 29.95 (ISBN 0-914565-02-8). Capstan Pubns.

Cusset, Francis. English-French & French-English Technical Dictionary. rev. ed. (Eng. & Fr.). 1967. 28.50 (ISBN 0-8206-0043-1). Chem Pub.

--Vocabulaire Technique Allemand-Francais, Francais-Allemand. 8th ed. (Fr. & Ger.). 474p. 1977. 29.95 (ISBN 0-686-56970-9, M-6097). French & Eur.

--Vocabulaire Technique Anglais-Francais, Francais-Anglais. 9th ed. (Fr. & Ger.). 434p. 1977. 47.50 (ISBN 0-686-56971-7, M-6098). French & Eur.

Czerni & Skrzynka. Polish-English Dictionary of Science & Technology. (Pol. & Eng.). 754p. 1976. 95.00x (ISBN 0-686-44737-9, Pub. by Collets). State Mutual Bk.

Czerni, et al. Science & Technical English & Polish Dictionary. 1982. 50.00 (ISBN 0-317-18987-5, P536). Vanous.

Czerni, S. & Skrzynska, M. Polish Concise Technology Dictionary: Polish-English. 5th ed. 846p. 1983. 50.00x (ISBN 0-89918-537-1). Vanous.

--Polish Science & Technology Dictionary: English-Polish. 6th ed. (Pol. & Eng.). 910p. 1982. 50.00x (ISBN 0-89918-536-3, P536). Vanous.

Czerni, Sergiusz & Skrzynska, Maria, eds. Polish-English Dictionary of Science & Technology. 3rd ed. (Pol. & Eng.). 1976. 30.00x (ISBN 0-686-19981-2). Intl Learn Syst.

--Polish-English, English-Polish Dictionary of Science & Technology, 2 Vols. rev. & enl. ed. 1755p. Set. 85.00 (ISBN 0-318-04724-1, Pub. by Wydawnictwa Poland). Heinman.

Dabac, Ulatko. Technisches Woerterbuch, 2 vols. (Serbocroation & Ger.). 1969. 112.00 (ISBN 3-7625-0550-0, M-7653, Pub. by Bauverlag). French & Eur.

De la Cierva, Patronato J. Diccionario Ruso-Espanol de la Ciencia y la Tecnica. 2nd ed. (Span.). 700p. 1972. 50.00 (ISBN 84-237-0407-6, S-50249). French & Eur.

Denti, Renzo. Dizionario Tecnico Italiano-Inglese, Inglese-Italiano. 10th rev. ed. (Eng. & Ital.). 1811p. 1981. 78.00x (ISBN 88-203-1052-X). S F Vanni.

DeVries, Louis. German-English Technical & Engineering Dictionary. 2nd ed. (Ger. & Eng.). 1966. 67.95 (ISBN 0-07-016631-5). McGraw.

Deweerdt, Jacques. Vocabulaire Fondamental de Technologie. (Fr.). 272p. 1974. pap. 19.95 (ISBN 0-686-57280-7, M-4654). French & Eur.

Diccionario Tecnico Frances-Espanol. (Fr. & Span.). 544p. 1973. leatherette 20.95 (ISBN 84-283-0334-7, S-31563). French & Eur.

Diccionario Tecnologico Ingles-Espanol. (Eng. & Span.). 454p. 1974. 41.95 (ISBN 84-205-0492-0, S-31501). French & Eur.

Dictionary of Science & Technology. (Eng. & Chinese.). 469p. 1973. 14.95 (ISBN 0-686-92348-0, M-9261). French & Eur.

Dictionary of Science & Technology. (Eng. & Chinese.). 1689p. 1978. 9.95 (ISBN 0-686-92375-8, M-9560). French & Eur.

Dictionary of Science & Technology: Eng. & Chinese. (Chinese.). 713p. 1979. pap. 5.95 (ISBN 0-686-92552-1, M-9587). French & Eur.

Dictionary of Technical Information. 182p. 1980. 20.00x (ISBN 0-569-08388-5, Pub. by Collet's). State Mutual Bk.

Dictionnaire Technique Generale Anglais-Francais. new ed. (Fr. & Eng.). 664p. 1979. 39.95 (ISBN 0-686-57117-7, M-6158). French & Eur.

Din Standards: Two-Thousand Six-Hundred Definitions of Technical Terms According to Din. 53.00 (ISBN 0-686-28197-7, 10804-1). Heyden.

Dorian, A. F. Dictionary of Science & Technology: English-German. 2nd., rev. ed. 1402p. 1978. 138.50 (ISBN 0-444-41649-8). Elsevier.

--Dictionary of Science & Technology: German-English. 2nd ed. 1120p. 1981. 121.50 (ISBN 0-444-41997-7). Elsevier.

Dorian, A. F., ed. Dictionary of Science & Technology, 2 Vols. 1979. Vol. I: Eng. & Fr. 138.50 (ISBN 0-444-41829-6); Vol. II: Fr. & Eng. 138.50 (ISBN 0-444-41911-X). Elsevier.

Editura Tehnica. Dictionar Tehnic Poliglot. 1233p. 1984. Repr. of 1967 ed. text ed. 98.50x (ISBN 0-8290-0987-6). Irvington.

Enciclopedia De la Ciencia y De la Tecnica, 6 vols. 3rd ed. (Espn.). 3055p. 1977. Set. leather 320.00 (ISBN 84-85185-10-2, S-50566). French & Eur.

Enciclopedia de la Ciencia y de la Tecnica, 8 vols. 5th ed. (Espn.). 3055p. 1977. Set. leather 320.00 (ISBN 84-7060-483-X, S-50567). French & Eur.

Enciclopedia De la Ciencia y De la Tecnica, 4 vols. (Espn.). 1344p. 1978. Set. 64.00 (ISBN 84-278-0549-7, S-50543). French & Eur.

Enciclopedia de la Tecnica y de la Mecanica, 8 vols. 5th ed. (Espn.). 2920p. 1975. Set. 360.00 (ISBN 84-278-0072-X, S-14237). French & Eur.

L' Encyclopedie Des Sciences Industrielles: Generalites, Electricite, Electronique, 2 vols. (Fr.). 1612p. 1973. Set. 175.00 (ISBN 0-686-57147-9, M-6204). French & Eur.

Encyclopedie Des Sciences Industrielles: Generalites, Mechanique, 2 vols. (Fr.). 1973. Set. 175.00 (ISBN 0-686-57146-0, M-6203). French & Eur.

Encyclopedie Internationale Des Sciences et Des Techniques, 11 vols. (Fr.). Set. 850.00 (ISBN 0-686-57161-4, M-6220). French & Eur.

Encyclopedie Scientifique et Technique, 5 vols. (Fr.). 2480p. 1975. Set. 495.00 (ISBN 0-686-57166-5, M-6233). French & Eur.

Encyclopedie Thematique Weber: Vol. 7, La Technique 1. (Fr.). 59.95 (ISBN 0-686-57173-8, M-6240). French & Eur.

Encyclopedie Thematique Weber: Vol. 8, La Technique 2. (Fr.). 59.95 (ISBN 0-686-57174-6, M-6241). French & Eur.

English-Chinese Dictionary of Scientific & Technology Abreviations. (Eng. & Chinese.). 587p. 1979. pap. 9.95 (ISBN 0-686-97363-1, M-9250). French & Eur.

An English-Chinese Dictionary of Technology. (Eng. & Chinese.). 1098p. 1978. leatherette 19.95 (ISBN 0-686-92474-6, M-9578). French & Eur.

English-Polish Dictionary of Science & Technology. 4th ed. (Eng. & Pol.). 892p. 90.00x (ISBN 0-569-08263-3, Pub. by Collets). State Mutual Bk.

Engstroem, E. Swedish-English, English-Swedish Technical Dictionary, 2 vols. rev. enl ed. (Swedish & Eng.). Set. 125.00 (ISBN 0-685-42614-9). Heinman.

Ernst, Richard. Dictionary of Engineering & Technology: English-German, Vol. II. 5th ed. 1000p. 1985. 69.00 (ISBN 0-19-520485-9). Oxford U Pr.

--Dictionary of Engineering & Technology: With Extensive Treatment of the Most Modern Techniques & Processes, Vol. 2, English-German. 4th, rev. & enl. ed. (Eng. & Ger.). 1975. text ed. 69.00x (ISBN 0-19-520109-4). Oxford U Pr.

Ernst, Richard, compiled by. Comprehensive Dictionary of Engineering & Technology, 2 vols. 1085p. 1985. Vol. 1, French & English. 100.00 (ISBN 0-521-30377-X); Vol. 2, English & French. 110.00 (ISBN 0-521-30378-8). Cambridge U Pr.

Ernst, Richard, ed. Dictionary of Engineering & Technology, Vol. 1. 4th ed. 1980. 69.00x (ISBN 0-19-520269-4). Oxford U Pr.

Feutry, Michel, et al, eds. Technological Dictionary: Mechanics, Metallurgy, Hydraulics & Related Industries. (In 4 languages). 1976. lib. bdg. 55.00x (ISBN 2-85608-000-6). Marlin.

Freeman, H. A Glossary of Technical Concepts Containing 4300 Din Definitions. 703p. 1983. pap. 87.00 (ISBN 0-686-40807-1, Pub. by DIN Germany). Heyden.

--Technisches Taschenwoerterbuch. 3rd ed. (Ger. & Eng.). 584p. (German-English Technical Dictionary). 1972. 12.50 (ISBN 3-19-006212-9, M-7648, Pub. by M. Hueber). French & Eur.

Freeman, Henry G. Technisches Englisch. 7th ed. (Ger. -Eng.). 1975. 48.00 (ISBN 3-7736-5011-6, M-7647, Pub. by Girardet). French & Eur.

Frigyes, A. Control & Measurement. 222p. 1980. 20.00x (ISBN 0-569-08044-4, Pub. by Collet's). State Mutual Bk.

Gerrish, Howard H. Technical Dictionary. rev. ed. LC 81-20005. 368p. 1982. text ed. 10.00 (ISBN 0-87006-400-2). Goodheart.

Gil, L. Suarez, ed. Diccionario Tecnico Maritimo: Ingles-Espanol, Espanol-Ingles. (Eng. & Span.). 708p. 1980. pap. 75.00 (ISBN 84-205-0772-5, S-32729). French & Eur.

Glossary on Educational Technology. 140p. 1973. pap. 7.95 (ISBN 0-686-56478-2, M-7429, Pub. by Vlg. Dokumentation). French & Eur.

Grunwald-Beyer, A. Technisches Taschenwoerterbuch. (Ger. & Fr.). 533p. 25.00 (ISBN 3-87749-013-1, M-7646, Pub. by Georg Siemens Verlagsbuchhandlung). French & Eur.

Guinle, R. L. English-Spanish Technical Dictionary. (Eng & Span.). 37.50 (ISBN 0-87559-188-4). Shalom.

--A Modern Spanish-English & English-Spanish Technical & Engineering Dictionary. (Span. & Eng.). 1969. Repr. of 1938 ed. 27.95 (ISBN 0-7100-1478-3). Routledge & Kegan.

Gullberg. Swedish-English Technical Dictionary. 200.00 (ISBN 0-317-19084-9, SW207). Vanous.

Gullberg, Ingvar E. Swedish-English Dictionary of Technical Terms Used in Business, Industry, Administration, Education & Research. 2nd rev. & enl. ed. (Swedish & Eng.). 150.00 (ISBN 91-1-775052-0). Heinman.

--Swedish-English Fact Ordbok (Technical Terms) 2nd ed. (Swedish & Eng.). 1977. 200.00x (ISBN 91-177-5052-0, SW-207). Vanous.

Hoyer-Kreuter. Technological Dictionary in Three Languages, 3 vols. Schlomann, Alfred, ed. Incl. Vol. 1. German-English-French; Vol. 2. English-German-French; Vol. 3. French-German-English. (Ger., Fr & Eng.). Set. 135.00 (ISBN 0-8044-0202-7). Ungar.

Ibeas, F. F. English-Spanish Technical Dictionary. 2nd ed. (Eng. & Span.). pap. 45.00 (ISBN 0-686-77977-0). Heinman.

Ibeas, F. Franco, ed. Diccionario technologico ingles-espanol. (Eng. & Span.). 1975. 60.95 (ISBN 84-205-0707-5, 21379). Larousse.

Japanese-Chinese Science & Technology Dictionary. (Japanese & Chinese.). 175p. 1976. 19.95 (ISBN 0-686-92480-0, M-9260). French & Eur.

Jehlicka, Schalitz. Diccionario Enciclopedico Tecnico Mecansimos Engranajes y Acoplamientos. (Span.). 289p. 1969. 39.95 (ISBN 0-686-92517-3, S-33735). French & Eur.

Kettridge, J. O. French-English & English-French Dictionary of Technical Terms & Phrases, 2 vols. Incl. Vol. 1. French-English. 40.00 (ISBN 0-7100-0144-4); Vol. 2. English-French. 40.00 (ISBN 0-7100-0166-5). (Fr. & Eng.). 1970. Repr. of 1959 ed. Set. 70.00 (ISBN 0-7100-0082-0). Routledge & Kegan.

Kettridge, Julius O. Dictionary of Technical Terms, 2 vols. (Fr. & Eng.). Set. 55.50 (ISBN 0-685-11207-1). French & Eur.

Khatib, Ahmed. English-Arabic Dictionary of Scientific & Technical Terms. (Illus.). 1983. 48.00x (ISBN 0-86685-075-9). Intl Bk Ctr.

Kirshner, Ulrich. Vox--Enciclopedia Cultural, Tomo 10: Tecnica. (Espn.). 210p. 1977. leatherette 29.95 (ISBN 84-7153-497-5, S-50499). French & Eur.

Kroeger-Jannetti, A. Technisches Taschenwoerterbuch. (Ger. & Span.). 804p. 32.00 (ISBN 3-87749-012-3, M-7645, Pub. by Georg Siemens Verlagsbuchhandlung). French & Eur.

Kucera, A. The Compact Dictionary of Exact Science & Technology: English-German. (Eng. & Ger.). 571p. 1980. 49.95 (ISBN 3-87097-088-X, M-9027). French & Eur.

Kucera, Antonin. Technisches Woerterbuch, Vol. 1. (Rus. & Ger.). 1966. 25.00 (ISBN 3-87097-025-1, M-7654, Pub. by Brandstetter). French & Eur.

--Technisches Woerterbuch, Vol. 2. (Rus. & Ger.). 1966. 32.00 (ISBN 3-87097-026-X, M-7655, Pub. by Brandstetter). French & Eur.

Kuznetsov, B., ed. Russian-English Polytechnical Dictionary. LC 80-41193. (Rus. & Eng.). 900p. 1981. 120.00 (ISBN 0-08-023609-X). Pergamon.

Lapedes, D. Dizionario Enciclopedico Scientifico e Tecnico: Inglese-Italiano, Italiano-Inglese. (Eng. & Ital.). 2122p. 1980. Leatherette 175.00 (ISBN 0-686-92540-8, M-9201). French & Eur.

Leskova, T. & Plisek, V. Czech-English Technical Textile Dictionary. (Czech. & Eng.). 468p. 1980. 60.00x (ISBN 0-686-72090-3, Pub. by Collet's). State Mutual Bk.

McGraw-Hill Editors. Dictionary of Science & Engineering. 960p. 1984. 36.00 (ISBN 0-07-045483-3). McGraw.

--McGraw-Hill Encyclopedia of Science & Technology, 15 vols. 5th ed. (Illus.). 12715p. 1982. Set. 1100.00 (ISBN 0-07-079280-1). McGraw.

McGraw-Hill Editors & Parker, Sybil, eds. McGraw-Hill Concise Encyclopedia of Science & Technology. LC 83-26794. (Illus.). 2065p. 1984. 95.00 (ISBN 0-07-045482-5). Mcgraw.

Malgorn, G. Dictionnaire Technique Anglais-Francais. (Eng. & Fr.). 495p. 1976. 37.50 (ISBN 0-686-57027-8, M-6385). French & Eur.

--Dictionnaire Technique Francais-Anglais. (Fr. & Eng.). 475p. 1956. 37.50 (ISBN 2-04-002947-8, M-6386). French & Eur.

Malgorn, Guy. Diccionario Tecnico Espanol-Frances. (Span. & Fr.). 1979. write for info. leatherette (S-50241). French & Eur.

--Diccionario Tecnico Espanol-Ingles. (Span. & Eng.). 594p. 1977. 26.95 (ISBN 84-283-0889-6, S-31442). French & Eur.

--Diccionario Tecnico Ingles-Espanol. (Eng. & Span.). 632p. 1978. pap. 26.95 (ISBN 84-283-0923-X, S-31490). French & Eur.

--Dictionaire Technique Francais-Espagnol. 2nd ed. (Fr.-Eng.). 544p. 1974. 42.50 (ISBN 0-686-57028-6, M-6387). French & Eur.

--Spanish-English, English-Spanish Technical Dictionary, 2 Vols. 2nd ed. Rodriguez, Maria R. & Armisen, Pedro, trs. from Fr. (Orig.). 1985. Set. pap. 35.00 (ISBN 0-318-04723-3, Pub. by Paraninfo Spain). Span.-Eng., xxiv-570p (ISBN 84-283-1354-7). Eng.-Span., xxiv-606p (ISBN 84-283-0923-X). Heinman.

Maliova, Libuse, ed. Czech-English, English-Czech Technical Dictionary, 2 vols. 1990p. Set. 70.00 (ISBN 0-318-03164-7, Pub. by SNTL Czechoslovakia). Heinman.

Marei, H. Basic Technical Dictionary: French-English-German-Arabic. (Fr., Eng., Ger. & Arabic.). 363p. 1973. lib. bdg. 45.00 (ISBN 0-686-92506-8, M-9752). French & Eur.

Marolli, G. Dizionario Tecnico Italiano-Inglese, Inglese-Italiano. (Ital. & Eng.). 2048p. 1978. write for info. (M-9197). French & Eur.

Mastropasqua, V. Dizionario Tecnico Nautico: Italiano-Inglese, Inglese-Italiano. (Ital. & Eng.). 879p. 1967. pap. 49.95 (ISBN 0-686-92533-5, M-9297). French & Eur.

Meadows, A. J., et al. Dictionary of New Information Technology. 256p. 1982. 29.00x (ISBN 0-7126-0019-1, Pub. by Century Pub Co). State Mutual Bk.

Mingot, Tomas De Galiana. Pequeno Larousse de ciencias y tecnicas. new ed. (Span.). 1056p. 1975. 26.95 (ISBN 0-685-55467-8, 21115). Larousse.

Mink, Auteur H. Dictionnaire Technique Francais-Espagnol. (Fr.). 1120p. 1979. 75.00 (ISBN 0-686-57049-9, M-6411). French & Eur.

Mink, H. Diccionario Tecnico: Suplemento, Vol. 2. (Span. & Ger.). 384p. 1981. Leatherette 49.50 (ISBN 0-686-92524-6, S-50270). French & Eur.

--Diccionario Tecnico, Tomo 1: Aleman-Espanol. 2nd ed. (Span.). 1376p. 1978. 60.00 (ISBN 84-254-0994-2, S-50190, French & Eur). French & Eur.

Moureau, Magdeleine & Rouge, Janine. Dictionnaire Technique des Termes Utilises Dans l'Industrie du Petrole, Anglais-Francais, Francais-Anglais. (Eng. & Fr.). 914p. (Dictionary of Technical Terms Used in the Oil Industry, English-French, French-English). 1977. 95.00 (ISBN 0-686-56757-9, M-6419). French & Eur.

Nagy, E. & Klar, J., eds. English-Hungarian Technical Dictionary. (Eng. & Hungarian.). 792p. 1980. 70.00x (ISBN 0-686-72096-2, Pub. by Collet's). State Mutual Bk.

Nagy, T. Hungarian-English Technical Dictionary. (Hungarian & Eng.). 752p. 1980. 70.00x (ISBN 0-569-00731-3, Pub. by Collet's). State Mutual Bk.

Naxerova, A. Technisches Woerterbuch, Vol. 1. (Czech. & Ger.). 1970. 40.00 (ISBN 3-87097-049-9, M-7649, Pub. by Brandstetter). French & Eur.

Novak, J. & Binder, R. A Concise English-Slovak & Slovak-English Technical Dictionary. (Eng. & Slovak.). 610p. 1980. 45.00x (ISBN 0-569-07469-X, Pub. by Collet's). State Mutual Bk.

--A Concise English-Slovak & Slovak-English Technical Dictionary. 3rd ed. (Eng. & Slovak.). 610p. 1971. 39.00x (ISBN 0-569-07469-X, Pub. by Collets). State Mutual Bk.

Piraux, Henry, ed. Dizionario Tecnico Ingles-Italiano: Elettronica, Elettrotecnica. (Ital.). 534p. 1981. 26.00x (ISBN 0-913298-73-5). S F Vanni.

Pollet, Ray J. Lexique de Termes Techniques: Un Lexique Anglais-Francais. (Eng. Fr.). 233p. 1976. pap. 25.00 (ISBN 0-686-57084-7, M-6460). French & Eur.

Popic, R., et al. Scientific Technological Dictionary. (Eng. & Serbocroatian.). 1140p. 1980. 95.00 (ISBN 0-686-97432-8, M-9688). French & Eur.

Pretz, Bernhard. Dictionary of Military & Technological Abbreviations & Acronyms. 450p. 1983. 45.00x (ISBN 0-7100-9274-1). Routledge & Kegan.

Pugh, Eric. Third Dictionary of Acronyms & Abbreviations: More Abbreviations in Management, Technology, & Information Science. 208p. 1977. 19.50 (ISBN 0-208-01535-3, Linnet). Shoe String.

Radde, Karl H. Woerterbuch der Technik, Vol. 1. (Span. & Ger.). 1977. 86.00 (ISBN 3-7736-5530-4, M-6949). French & Eur.

--Woerterbuch der Technik, Vol. 2. (Span. & Ger.). 1977. 86.00 (ISBN 3-7736-5531-2, M-6950). French & Eur.

Rapatz, F. & Roll, F. Diccionario Enciclopedico Tecnico: Materiales Siderurgicos. (Span.). 260p. 1968. 39.95 (ISBN 0-686-92516-5, S-33724). French & Eur.

Razso, Imre. English-Hungarian Technical Dictionary-Angol-Magyar Muszaki Szotar. (Eng. & Hungarian.). 37.50 (ISBN 0-87557-041-0, 041-0). Saphrograph.

Rechenbach, Charles W. & Garnett, Eugene R. A Bibliography of Scientific, Technical, & Specialized Dictionaries. LC 78-81497. 158p. 1969. pap. 16.95 (ISBN 0-8132-0251-5). Cath U Pr.

Sacklowski. Diccionario Enciclopedico Tecnico Magnitudes y Unidades Fisicas. (Span.). 224p. 1976. 39.95 (ISBN 0-686-92520-3, S-33726). French & Eur.

Schlegelmich, A. Worterbuch der Technik: Italienisch-Deutsch. (Ital. & Ger.). 630p. 1981. 95.00 (ISBN 3-7736-5110-4, M-122653). French & Eur.

Schlegelmilch, Alibert. Polytechnisches Woerterbuch, Vol. 1. 2nd ed. (Fr. & Ger.). 1976. 36.00 (ISBN 0-686-56638-6, M-7590, Pub. by Veb Verlag Technik). French & Eur.

--Polytechnisches Woerterbuch, Vol. 2. 2nd ed. (Fr. & Ger.). 1977. 36.00 (ISBN 0-686-56639-4, M-7591, Pub. by Veb Verlag Technik). French & Eur.

Schuurmans, G. Kluwer's Universeel Technisch Woordenboek: Duits-Nederlands. (Ger.). 433p. 1980. 75.00 (ISBN 90-201-0606-6, M-9471). French & Eur.

--Kluwer's Universeel Technisch Woordenboek, Nederlands-Engels. (Dutch & Eng.). 775p. 1977. 75.00 (ISBN 90-2010-605-8, M-9468). French & Eur.

--Kluwer's Universeel Technisch Woordenboek: Nederlands-Frans. (Dutch & Fr.). 643p. 1977. 75.00 (ISBN 90-201-0609-0, M-9472). French & Eur.

--Kluwer's Universeel Technish Woordenboek: Frans-Nederlands. (Fr. & Dutch.). 622p. 1975. 75.00 (ISBN 90-201-0608-2, M-9473). French & Eur.

--Kluwer's Universel Technisch Woordenboek: Nederlands-Duits. (Ger. & Dutch.). 428p. 1980. 75.00 (ISBN 90-201-0607-4, M-9470). French & Eur.

Schuurmans-Stekhoven, G. Dictionnaire Technique Universal Kluwer, Francais-Neerlandais. (Fr. & Dutch.). 636p. 1978. 75.00 (ISBN 0-686-56776-5, M-6506). French & Eur.

--Dictionnaire Technique Universal Kluwer Neerlandais-Francais. (Dutch & Fr.). 656p. 1978. 79.95 (ISBN 0-686-56775-7, M-6507). French & Eur.

Scientific & Technical Books & Serials in Print 1986, 3 vols. 4100p. 1985. 149.95 (ISBN 0-8352-2083-4). Bowker.

Shipp, James F. Russian-English Dictionary of Surnames: Important Names from Science & Technology. (Rus. & Eng.). xvi, 317p. (Orig.). 1981. pap. text ed. 18.50x (ISBN 0-917564-10-3). Wychwood Pr.

Shuurmans, G. Kluwer's Universeel Technisch Woordenboek: Engels-Nederlands. (Eng. & Dutch.). 571p. 1981. 75.00 (ISBN 90-2010-771-2). French & Eur.

Smolin, Ronald P., ed. High-Tech Glossary. 2nd ed. 1984. pap. 10.00x (ISBN 0-89563-061-3). Intl Ideas.

Strasak, Jaroslav. Technisches Deutschfuer Auslaender. (Ger., Technical German for Foreigners). 1969. 12.95 (ISBN 3-87097-041-3, M-7644). French & Eur.

Technical Dictionary English-Slovene. (Eng. & Slovene.). 1137p. 1975. 125.00 (ISBN 0-686-92318-9, M-9891). French & Eur.

Technical Dictionary of Crystallography. 132p. 1980. 40.00x (ISBN 0-686-72093-8, Pub. by Collet's). State Mutual Bk.

Technik-Worterbuch: Optik & Optischer Geratebau. 432p. 1980. vinyl 90.00x (ISBN 0-686-72097-0, Pub. by Collet's). State Mutual Bk.

Tver, David F., compiled by. Dictionary of Business & Science. 3rd ed. LC 74-7838. 632p. 1974. 27.50x (ISBN 0-87201-172-0). Gulf Pub.

Vox, ed. Diccionario Monografico de Technologia. (Span.). 1979. leatherette 17.50 (ISBN 84-7153-383-9, S-36146). French & Eur.

Walther, R., ed. Dictionary of Technology: English-German. 1200p. 1985. 129.75 (ISBN 0-444-99591-9). Elsevier.

--Dictionary of Technology: German-English. 1050p. 1985. 129.75 (ISBN 0-444-99590-0). Elsevier.

Walther, Rudolf. Polytechnic Dictionary: German-English, English-German, 2 vols. 4th ed. (Ger. & Eng.). 87.50x ea. (ISBN 3-7736-5100-7). Adlers Foreign Bks.

--Polytechnical Dictionary, 2 vols. Incl. Vol. 1. English-German. 1968. 110.00 (ISBN 0-08-012435-6); Vol. 2. German-English. 1968. 110.00 (ISBN 0-08-013223-5). 195.00 ea. Pergamon.

--Polytechnisches Woerterbuch, Vol. 1. 7th ed. (Eng. & Ger., Dictionary of Polytechnics). 1978. 40.00 (ISBN 0-686-56640-8, M-7592, Pub. by Veb Verlag Technik). French & Eur.

--Polytechnisches Woerterbuch, Vol. 2. 3rd ed. (Eng. & Ger., Dictionary of Polytechnics). 1977. 40.00 (ISBN 0-686-56641-6, M-7593, Pub. by Veb Verlag Technik). French & Eur.

--Woerterbuch der Technik. (Eng. & Ger., Dictionary of Technology). 1974. 88.00 (ISBN 3-7736-5100-7, M-6952). French & Eur.

Webel, A. A German-English Dictionary of Technical, Scientific & General Terms. 3rd ed. (Ger. & Eng.). 1969. Repr. of 1952 ed. 37.50 (ISBN 0-7100-2258-1). Routledge & Kegan.

Weroniecki, T., ed. Diccionario Tecnico Espanol-Polaco. (Span. & Pol.). 545p. 1981. 49.95 (ISBN 83-204-0287-5, S-37602). French & Eur.

Zamoyska, H. Multilingual Student's Dictionary of Basic Terms Used in Chemistry, Mathematics, Physics & Allied Fields. 1978. 49.00x (ISBN 0-686-44734-4, Pub. by Collets). State Mutual Bk.

Zhong Wai Publishing Company. An English-Chinese Dictionary of Engineering & Technology. (Eng. & Chinese.). 1036p. 1980. 84.95x (ISBN 0-471-09371-8). Wiley.

Zimmermann, Ralf. Dictionary of Lighting. 362p. 1980. 70.00x (ISBN 0-569-08526-8, Pub. by Collet's). State Mutual Bk.

TECHNOLOGY–DICTIONARIES–BIBLIOGRAPHY

Taylor, Betty W. Transfer of Technology: A Bibliography of Materials in the English Language. (A Collection of Bibliographic & Research Resources Ser.). 89p. (Orig.). 1985. Looseleaf 100.00; pap. text ed. 35.00 (ISBN 0-379-20902-0). Oceana.

Technical Guide, 1978. Incl. Vol.1. Consumer Prices (ISBN 92-2-101866-0); Vol. 2. Employment, Unemployment, Hours of Work, Wages (ISBN 92-2-101867-9). 1978. 14.25 ea.; 22.80 set (ISBN 92-2-101868-7). Intl Labour Office.

TECHNOLOGY–EXHIBITIONS

see Exhibitions

TECHNOLOGY–HISTORY

see also Industrial Arts–History

Alpert, Carl. Technion: The Story of Israel's Institute of Technology. LC 82-11556. (Illus.). 439p. 1983. 25.00x (ISBN 0-87203-102-0). Hermon.

Banu (Sons of) Musa Bin Shakir. The Book of Ingenious Devices. Hill, Donald R., tr. 1978. lib. bdg. 68.50 (ISBN 90-277-0833-9, Pub. by Reidel Holland). Kluwer Academic.

Bernhard, C. G. & Crawford, E., eds. Science, Technology & Society in the Time of Alfred Nobel: Proceedings of a Nobel Symposium held at Bjorkborn, Karlskoga, Sweden, August 17-22, 1981. LC 82-11254. (Illus.). 440p. 1982. 65.00 (ISBN 0-08-027939-2). Pergamon.

Black, George W., Jr. American Science & Technology: A Bicentennial Bibliography. LC 78-15820. 172p. 1979. 15.95x (ISBN 0-8093-0898-3). S Ill U Pr.

Bugliarello, George & Doner, Dean B., eds. History & Philosophy of Technology. LC 78-26846. 392p. 1979. 22.50 (ISBN 0-252-00462-0). U of Ill Pr.

Burke, James. Connections. LC 78-21662. 1979. 24.95 (ISBN 0-316-11681-5). Little.

Cardwell. Turning Points in Western Technology. 256p. 1972. pap. text ed. 8.95 (ISBN 0-88202-003-X, Sci Hist). Watson Pub Intl.

Chase, Stuart. The Most Probable World. LC 81-2037. xii, 239p. 1981. Repr. of 1968 ed. lib. bdg. 25.00x (ISBN 0-313-22971-6, CHMP). Greenwood.

Cordell, Arthur J. & Gilmour, James, eds. The Role & Function of Government Laboratories & the Transfer of Technology to the Manufacturing Sector. (Science Council of Canada Background Studies: No. 35). 1976. pap. 12.00 (ISBN 0-685-77314-0, SSC72, SSC). Unipub.

Daniels, George H., ed. Nineteenth-Century American Science: A Reappraisal. LC 79-186547. 292p. 1972. text ed. 17.95x (ISBN 0-8101-0381-8). Northwestern U Pr.

Daumas, Maurice, ed. The History of Technology & Invention, Vol. 3. (Illus.). 1978. 30.00 (ISBN 0-517-52037-0). Crown.

--History of Technology & Invention: Progress Through the Ages, 2 vols. Incl. Vol. 1. The Origins of Technological Civilization (ISBN 0-517-50727-7); Vol. 2. The First Stages of Mechanization (ISBN 0-517-50728-5). (Illus.). 1969. 30.00 ea. Crown.

--A History of Technology & Invention Progress Through the Ages, Vol. 1: The Origins of Technological Civilization to 1450. 520p. 1980. 60.00x (ISBN 0-7195-3730-4, Pub. by Murray Pubs England). State Mutual Bk.

--History of Technology & Invention Process Through the Ages, Vol. 2: The First Stages of Mechanization 1450-1725. 694p. 1980. 60.00x (ISBN 0-7195-3731-2, Pub. by Murray Pubs England). State Mutual Bk.

--A History of Technology & Invention Progress Through the Ages, Vol. 3: The Expansion of Mechanization 1725-1860. 700p. 1980. 60.00x (ISBN 0-7195-3732-0, Pub. by Murray Pubs England). State Mutual Bk.

Derry, Thomas K. & Williams, Trevor I. Short History of Technology from the Earliest Times to A. D. 1900. (Illus.). 1961. o. p. 29.95x (ISBN 0-19-500142-7); pap. 13.95x (ISBN 0-19-881231-0, OPB). Oxford U Pr.

Eastwood, Bruce. Directory of Audio-Visual Sources: History of Science, Medicine & Technology. 160p. 1979. 20.00 (ISBN 0-88202-185-0). Watson Pub Intl.

Ellicott, Andrew. The Journal of Andrew Ellicott. Cohen, I. Bernard, ed. LC 79-7960. (Three Centuries of Science in America Ser.). (Illus.). 1980. Repr. of 1803 ed. lib. bdg. 39.00x (ISBN 0-405-12541-0). Ayer Co Pubs.

Feldman, Anthony & Gunston, Bill. Technology at Work. (Horizons of Knowledge Ser.). (Illus.). 336p. 1980. 24.95 (ISBN 0-87196-413-9). Facts on File.

Ferrari, Guy. How to Profit from Future Technology: A Guide to Success in the Eighties & Beyond. Adams, Mary, ed. LC 82-73571. 300p. 1983. pap. 14.95 (ISBN 0-911321-01-2). Windsor Hse.

Fleming, Donald & Fish, Joseph. Science & Technology in Providence, 1760-1914: An Essay in the History of Brown University in the Metropolitan Community. LC 52-9555. (Illus.). 54p. 1952. pap. 4.00x (ISBN 0-87057-031-5). U Pr of New Eng.

Forbes, R. J. Studies in Ancient Technology, 9 vols. 2nd, rev. ed. Incl. Vols. 1-7. 1964-66. 40.00 ea.; Vols. 8-9. Metallurgy in Antiquity. (Illus.). 1971-72. Set. 95.00 (ISBN 90-04-03487-0). Heinman.

Fox, Robert & Weisz, George, eds. The Organisation of Science & Technology in France 1808-1914. LC 80-40227. (Illus.). 336p. 1980. 44.50 (ISBN 0-521-23234-1). Cambridge U Pr.

Habakkuk, H. J. American & British Technology in the Nineteenth Century. pap. 11.95 (ISBN 0-521-09447-X). Cambridge U Pr.

Hall, A. Rupert & Smith, Norman. History of Techology. 8th ed. 152p. 1983. 40.00 (ISBN 0-7201-5451-0). Mansell.

Hall, A. Rupert & Smith, Norman, eds. History of Technology: First Annual Volume, 1976. 192p. 1976. 35.00 (ISBN 0-7201-0546-3). Mansell.

--History of Technology: Fourth Annual Volume, 1979. 192p. 1979. 35.00 (ISBN 0-7201-0916-7). Mansell.

--History of Technology: Second Annual Volume, 1977. 270p. 1977. lib. bdg. 35.00 (ISBN 0-7201-0716-4). Mansell.

--History of Technology: Third Annual Volume, 1978. (Illus.). 196p. 1978. lib. bdg. 35.00 (ISBN 0-7201-0813-6). Mansell.

Hall, Rupert & Smith, Norman, eds. History of Technology: Fifth Annual Volume, 1980. 168p. 1980. 40.00 (ISBN 0-7201-1585-X). Mansell.

Headrick, Daniel R. The Tools of Empire: Technology & European Imperialism in the Nineteenth Century. 1981. pap. text ed. 7.95x (ISBN 0-19-502832-5). Oxford U Pr.

Hindle, Brooke. America's Wooden Age: Aspects of Its Early Technology. LC 74-7842. (Illus.). 224p. 1985. pap. 14.95 (ISBN 0-912882-60-3, 22235). Sleepy Hollow.

A History of Technology, 7 vols. Incl. Vol. 1. From Early Times to Fall of Ancient Empires. Singer, Charles, et al, eds. 1954. 98.00x (ISBN 0-19-858105-X); Vol. 2. The Mediterranean Civilizations & the Middle Ages, c. 700 B.C. to c. A.D. 1500. Singer, Charles, et al, eds. 1956. 98.00x (ISBN 0-19-858106-8); Vol. 3. From the Renaissance to the Industrial Revolution, c. 1500-c. 1750. Singer, Charles, et al, eds. 1957. 98.00x (ISBN 0-19-858107-6); Vol. 4. The Industrial Revolution, c. 1750 to c. 1850. Singer, Charles, et al, eds. 1958. 98.00x (ISBN 0-19-858108-4); Vol. 5. The Late Nineteenth Century, c. 1850 to c. 1900. Singer, Charles, et al, eds. 1958. 98.00x (ISBN 0-19-858109-2); Vol. 6. The Twentieth Century, C. 1900 to C. 1950, Part I. Williams, Trevor I., ed. (Illus.). 1978. 98.00x (ISBN 0-19-858151-3); Vol. 7. The Twentieth Century, C. 1900 to C. 1950, Part II. Williams, Trevor I., ed. (Illus.). 1978. 98.00x (ISBN 0-19-858155-6). Oxford U Pr.

Hodges, Henry. Technology in the Ancient World. (Illus.). 1970. 13.95 (ISBN 0-394-44808-1). Knopf.

Hoke, Donald, ed. The History & Sociology of Technology: Proceedings of the 24th Annual Meeting of the Society for the History of Technology. 355p. 8.95 (ISBN 0-89326-090-8). Milwaukee Pub Mus.

Jennings, Humphrey. Pandaemonium: The Coming of the Machine As Seen by Contemporary Observers, 1660-1886. 480p. 1985. 17.95 (ISBN 0-02-916470-2). Free Pr.

Jeon, Sang-Woon. Science & Technology in Korea: Traditional Instruments & Techniques. (East Asian Science Ser). 448p. 1974. 35.00x (ISBN 0-262-10014-2). MIT Pr.

Joel, A. E., Jr. Switching Technology 1925-1975: A History of Engineering & Science in the Bell System. Schindler, G. E., ed. (Illus.). 600p. 1982. 25.00 (ISBN 0-686-83987-0). Bell Telephone.

Jones, Barry O. Sleepers, Wake! Technology & the Future of Work. (Illus.). 1983. 24.95x (ISBN 0-19-554343-2). Oxford U Pr.

Kebabian, Paul B. & Lipke, William C., eds. Tools & Technologies: America's Wooden Age. (Illus.). 119p. (Orig.). 1979. pap. 12.50 (ISBN 0-87451-987-X). U Pr of New Eng.

Kern, Stephen. The Culture of the Time & Space, 1880-1918. (Illus.). 416p. 1983. text ed. 25.00x (ISBN 0-674-17972-2). Harvard U Pr.

McClary, Andrew. Biology & Society: The Evolution of Man & His Technology. (Illus.). 352p. 1975. pap. text ed. write for info. (ISBN 0-02-378510-1). Macmillan.

Mathias, Peter, ed. Science & Society, 1600-1900. (Illus.). 176p. 1972. 32.50 (ISBN 0-521-08375-3). Cambridge U Pr.

Mensch, Gerhard. Stalemate in Technology: Innovations Overcome the Depression. 272p. 1983. pap. 14.95 (ISBN 0-88410-054-5). Ballinger Pub.

OECD Staff. Assessing the Impacts of Technology on Society. 80p. (Orig.). 1983. pap. 9.00x (ISBN 92-64-12409-8). OECD.

Oliver, John W. History of American Technology. LC 56-6269. pap. 120.00 (ISBN 0-317-10652-X, 2012521). Bks Demand UMI.

Pacey, Arnold. The Maze of Ingenuity: Ideas & Idealism in the Development of Technology. LC 74-18380. 337p. 1975. text ed. 30.00x (ISBN 0-8419-0181-3). Holmes & Meier.

--The Maze of Ingenuity: Ideas & Idealism in the Development of Technology. 1976. pap. 8.95x (ISBN 0-262-66030-X). MIT Pr.

Pursell, Carroll W., Jr., ed. Technology in America: A History of Individuals & Ideas. (Illus.). 265p. 1981. pap. 9.95x (ISBN 0-262-66049-0). MIT Pr.

Raper, Richard, ed. A History of Technology: Consolidated Indexes, Vol. 8. 232p. 1984. text ed. 45.00x (ISBN 0-19-822905-4). Oxford U Pr.

Rupertaall, A. & Smith, Norman, eds. History of Technology Annual, Vol. 7. 152p. 1982. 43.00 (ISBN 0-7021-1633-5). Mansell.

Schmandt-Besserat, Denise, ed. Early Technologies. LC 78-59574. (Invited Lectures on the Middle East at the University of Texas at Austin Ser.: Vol. 3). (Illus.). iv, 105p. 1979. pap. 15.50 (ISBN 0-89003-032-4). Undena Pubns.

Science & Technology for Development, STPI Module 3: The Evolution of Science & Technology in STPI Countries. (STPI Module Ser.). 43p. 1981. pap. 5.00 (ISBN 0-88936-255-6, IDRCTS20, IDRC). Unipub.

Sil. Manuscripts of the Dibner Collection: Manuscripts in the History of Science & Technology in the Smithsonian Institution Libraries. LC 85-11576. (Illus.). 176p. 1985. 35.00x (ISBN 0-88135-025-7). Watson Pub Intl.

Singer, Charles, et al, eds. A History of Technology: Consolidated Indexes. (A History of Technology Ser.: Vol. VIII). 250p. 1985. 45.00x (ISBN 0-19-833905-4). Oxford U Pr.

Stimulating Technological Progress. (CED Statement on National Policy Ser.). lib. bdg. 6.50 (ISBN 0-87186-770-2); pap. 5.00 (ISBN 0-87186-070-8). Comm Econ Dev.

Technics & Praxis. (Boston Studies in the Philosophy of Science XXIV Synthesis Library: No. 130). 1978. lib. bdg. 24.00 (ISBN 9-0277-0953-X, Pub. by Reidel Holland); pap. 8.50 (ISBN 9-0277-0954-8). Kluwer Academic.

Traditional Technology - Obstacle or Resource? Bamboo-Cement Rain-Water Collectors & Cooking Stoves. 18p. 1981. pap. 5.00 (ISBN 92-808-0261-5, TUNU156, UNU). Unipub.

Uselding, Paul J. Studies in the Technological Development of the American Economy During the First Half of the Nineteenth Century. LC 75-2600. (Dissertations in American Economic History). (Illus.). 1975. 21.00x (ISBN 0-405-07221-X). Ayer Co Pubs.

White, K. D. Greek & Roman Technology. LC 82-74518. (Aspects of Greek & Roman Life Ser.). (Illus.). 272p. 1983. 39.50x (ISBN 0-8014-1439-3). Cornell U Pr.

White, Lynn, Jr. Medieval Religion & Technology: Collected Essays. LC 77-83113. (Center for Medieval & Renaissance Studies, UCLA: No. 13). 1978. 39.50x (ISBN 0-520-03566-6). U of Cal Pr.

Williams, Trevor I. A Short History of Twentieth-Century Technology, 1900-1950. (Illus.). 1982. 29.95 (ISBN 0-19-858159-9). Oxford U Pr.

Yarwood, Doreen. Five Hundred Years of Technology in the Home. (Illus.). 168p. 1983. 31.50 (ISBN 0-7134-3506-2, Pub. by Batsford England). David & Charles.

TECHNOLOGY–HISTORY–CHINA

Bennett, Adrian A. John Fryer: The Introduction of Western Science & Technology into Nineteenth-Century China. LC 68-4092. (East Asian Monograph Ser.: No. 24). 1967. pap. 11.00x (ISBN 0-674-47650-6). Harvard U Pr.

Guohao, Li, et al, eds. Exploration in the History of Science & Technology in China. 835p. 1985. text ed. 79.95 (ISBN 0-88738-064-6). Transaction Bks.

Institute of National Science & Chinese Academy of Science. Ancient China's Technology & Science. (China Knowledge Ser.). (Illus.). 632p. (Orig.). 1983. 16.95 (ISBN 0-8351-1235-7); pap. 9.95 (ISBN 0-8351-1001-X). China Bks.

Joseph Needham's Contribution to the History of Science & Technology in China. 30p. 1981. pap. 5.00 (ISBN 92-808-0187-2, TUNU139, UNU). Unipub.

Needham, Joseph & Tsuen-Hsuin, Tsien. Science & Civilization in China: Chemistry & Chemical Technology Part 1: Paper & Printing, Vol. 5. (Illus.). 485p. 1985. 89.50 (ISBN 0-521-08690-6). Cambridge U Pr.

World Sci Singapore, ed. Thirty Years' Review of China's Science & Technology, 1949-1979. viii, 314p. 1982. 60.00x (ISBN 9971-950-48-0, Pub. by World Sci Singapore). Taylor & Francis.

TECHNOLOGY–HISTORY–GREAT BRITAIN

Butt, John, et al. Industrial History in Pictures: Scotland. LC 68-23824. 1968. 17.95x (ISBN 0-678-05585-8). Kelley.

Hodgen, Margaret T. Change & History: A Study of the Dated Distributions of Technological Innovations in England. 1952. 25.00 (ISBN 0-384-23800-9). Johnson Repr.

Library Association, London, ed. British Technology Index, 1978. LC 63-23735. 828p. 1979. 285.00x (ISBN 0-85365-911-7). Intl Pubns Serv.

--British Technology Index, 1979. LC 63-23735. 960p. 1980. 295.00x (ISBN 0-85365-653-3). Intl Pubns Serv.

TECHNOLOGY–HISTORY–GREECE

Brumbaugh, Robert S. Ancient Greek Gadgets & Machines. LC 75-3983. (Illus.). 152p. 1975. Repr. of 1966 ed. lib. bdg. 18.75x (ISBN 0-8371-7427-9, BRGG). Greenwood.

Lloyd, G. E. Greek Science After Aristotle. LC 72-11959. (Ancient Culture & Society Ser.). (Illus.). 208p. 1973. pap. 5.95x (ISBN 0-393-00780-4). Norton.

Oleson, John P. The History of Greek & Roman Technology. 1985. lib. bdg. 40.00 (ISBN 0-8240-8978-2). Garland Pub.

White, K. D. Greek & Roman Technology. LC 82-74518. (Aspects of Greek & Roman Life Ser.). (Illus.). 272p. 1983. 39.50x (ISBN 0-8014-1439-3). Cornell U Pr.

TECHNOLOGY–HISTORY–INDIA

Bhardwaj, H. C. Aspects of Ancient Indian Technology. 1979. 16.95 (ISBN 0-89684-055-7, Pub. by Motilal Banarsidass India). Orient Bk Dist.

Gupta, S. P. Modern India & Progress in Science & Technology. 166p. 1979. 15.95x (ISBN 0-7069-0743-4, Pub by Vikas India). Advent NY.

Jaggi, O P. History of Science & Technology in India. 2500p. 1982. 675.00 (ISBN 0-317-14273-9, Pub. by Holdan Bk Ltd UK). State Mutual Bk.

Qaisar, Ahsan J. The Indian Response to European Technology & Culture, A. D. 1498-1707. (Illus.). 1982. 35.00x (ISBN 0-19-561313-9). Oxford U Pr.

Rangarao, B. V. & Chaubey, N. P., eds. Social Perspective of Development of Science & Technology in India. 1983. 22.00x (ISBN 0-8364-0931-0, Pub. by Heritage India). South Asia Bks.

Vyasulu, Vinod, ed. Technological Choice in the Indian Environment. 351p. 1980. 44.95x (ISBN 0-940500-59-0, Pub. by Sterling India). Asia Bk Corp.

Wakhlu, O. N. Society Technology & Development. 280p. 1984. text ed. 30.00x (ISBN 0-86590-375-1, Pub. by B R Pub Corp Delhi). Apt Bks.

TECHNOLOGY–HISTORY–JAPAN

Historical Background of Technology Transfer, Transportation, & Development in Japan. (Human & Social Development Programme - Research Papers). 39p. 1980. pap. 5.00 (ISBN 92-808-0048-5, TUNU031, UNU). Unipub.

Kasuga, Yutaka. Transfer & Development of Coal-Mine Technology in Hokkaido. (Project on Technology Transfer, Transformation, & Development: The Japanese Experience). 1982. pap. 5.00 (ISBN 92-808-0335-2, TUNU192, UNU). Unipub.

Project on Technology Transfer, Transformation, and Development: The Japanese Experience. Endogenous Technology & Society in Japan. 40p. 1982. pap. 5.00 (ISBN 92-808-0221-6, TUNU179, UNU). Unipub.

Science & Technology in Japanese History: University & Society. 10p. 1980. pap. 5.00 (ISBN 92-808-0174-0, TUNU125, UNU). Unipub.

Science & Technology in the History of Modern Japan: Imitation or Endogenous Creativity? 22p. 1981. pap. 5.00 (ISBN 92-808-0185-6, TUNU134, UNU). Unipub.

Technological Independence & Progress of Standardization in the Japanese Railways. 1981. pap. 5.00 (ISBN 92-808-0223-2, TUNU154, UNU). Unipub.

TECHNOLOGY–HISTORY–SOVIET UNION

Amann, R., et al, eds. The Technological Level of Soviet Industry. LC 77-76298. (Illus.). 1977. 62.00x (ISBN 0-300-02076-7). Yale U Pr.

Harvey, Mose L., et al. Science & Technology As An Instrument of Soviet Policy. new ed. LC 72-92184. (Monographs in International Affairs). (Illus.). 219p. 1972. text ed. 8.95 (ISBN 0-933074-14-X); pap. text ed. 5.95 (ISBN 0-933074-15-8). AISI.

TECHNOLOGY–INFORMATION SERVICES

Center for Business Information Staff, ed. Appropriate Technology Organizations: A Worldwide Directory. LC 83-43053. 149p. 1984. pap. 29.95x (ISBN 0-89950-098-6). McFarland & Co.

Chen, Ching-Chih, ed. Scientific & Technical Information Sources. 1977. 50.00x (ISBN 0-262-03062-4). MIT Pr.

Committee On Data For Science And Technology Of The International Council Of Scientific Unions. International Compendium of Numerical Data Projects. 1969. 38.00 (ISBN 0-387-04570-8). Springer-Verlag.

Eaton, J. & Smithers, j. This Is It: A Manager's Guide to Information Technology. 345p. 1982. text ed. 38.50x (ISBN 0-86003-514-X, Pub. by Philip Allan England); pap. text ed. 19.50x (ISBN 0-86003-614-6). Humanities.

Glaeser, P. S., ed. Data for Science & Technology: Proceedings of the 7th International CODATA Conference, Kyoto, Japan, 8-11 October 1980. (Illus.). 638p. 1981. 165.00 (ISBN 0-08-026201-5); pap. 46.00 (ISBN 0-08-026203-1). Pergamon.

Herner, Saul. A Brief Guide to Sources of Scientific & Technical Information. 2nd ed. LC 80-81087. (Illus.). xi, 160p. 1980. lexotone soft cover 15.00 (ISBN 0-87815-031-5). Info Resources.

Manual on Methods for Retrieving & Correlating Technical Data-STP 468-A. 74p. 1969. pap. 3.00 (ISBN 0-8031-0399-9, 04-468000-41). ASTM.

Rules of Law on Technical Data. 1971. 7.00 (ISBN 0-686-27831-3). M & A Products.

Sherlock. Guide to Technical Communication. 1985. 19.29 (ISBN 0-205-07790-0, 177790). Allyn.

TECHNOLOGY–LANGUAGE

see also French Language–Technical French; Russian Language–Technical Russian; Technical Writing

Block, J. & Labonville, J. English Skills for Technicians. 1971. 20.30 (ISBN 0-07-005910-1). McGraw.

Killer, W. K. Illustrated Technical German for Builders. 4th ed. (Eng. & Ger.). 183p. 1977. 15.95 (ISBN 3-7625-0898-4, M-7468, Pub. by Bauverlag). French & Eur.

TECHNOLOGY–MUSEUMS

see Industrial Museums

TECHNOLOGY–NOTATION

see also Technology–Abbreviations

Dyball, G. E. Mathematics for Technician Engineers: Levels 4 & 5. 384p. 1983. write for info. (ISBN 0-07-084664-2). McGraw.

TECHNOLOGY–PERIODICALS

Center for Research Libraries. Scientific & Technical Journals Listing, 1981. 142p. (Orig.). 1981. pap. text ed. 10.00 (ISBN 0-932486-24-X); members free. Ctr Res Lib.

Miller, Richard K. Directory of Technical Magazines & Directories. 1982. text ed. 45.00 (ISBN 0-915586-33-9). Fairmont Pr.

Provisional World List of Periodicals Dealing with Science & Technology Policies: 1973. (Science Policy Studies & Documents: No. 33). 112p. 1974. pap. 6.00 (ISBN 92-3-101189-8, U500, UNESCO). Unipub.

Williams, Martha E., ed. Annual Review of Information Science & Technology, 1981, Vol. 16. LC 66-25096. 422p. 1981. 45.00x (ISBN 0-914236-90-3, 303-BW). Knowledge Indus.

Yannarella, Philip A. & Aluri, Rao. U. S. Government Scientific & Technical Periodicals. LC 75-38740. 271p. 1976. 15.00 (ISBN 0-8108-0888-9). Scarecrow.

TECHNOLOGY–PHILOSOPHY

see also Machinery in Industry; Technology and Civilization

Agassi, Joseph. Technology: Philosophical & Social Aspects. 1986. lib. bdg. 39.50 (ISBN 90-277-2044-4, Pub. by Reidel Holland); pap. text ed. 19.95 (ISBN 90-277-2045-2). Kluwer Academic.

Bugliarello, George & Doner, Dean B., eds. History & Philosophy of Technology. LC 78-26846. 392p. 1979. 22.50 (ISBN 0-252-00462-0). U of Ill Pr.

Building the Future. (UNESCO & the Solidarity of Nations: No. 3). 258p. 1981. pap. 7.00 (ISBN 92-3-101968-6, U1153, UNESCO). Unipub.

Davis, Gregory H. Technology: Humanism or Nihilism: A Critical Analysis of the Philosophical Basis & Practice of Modern Technology. LC 81-40178. 304p. (Orig.). 1981. lib. bdg. 24.00 (ISBN 0-8191-1776-5); pap. text ed. 12.00 (ISBN 0-8191-1777-3). U Pr of Amer.

Durbin, Paul T., ed. Research in Philosophy & Technology, Vol. 4. 450p. 1981. 47.50 (ISBN 0-89232-181-4). Jai Pr.

Durbin, Paul T. & Rapp, Friedrich, eds. Philosophy & Technology. 1983. lib. bdg. 59.00 (ISBN 90-277-1576-9, Pub. by Reidel Holland). Kluwer Academic.

Ellul, Jacques. Technological Society. 1967. pap. 4.95 (ISBN 0-394-70390-1, V390, Vin). Random.

Feibleman, James. Technology & Reality. 250p. 1982. 25.00 (ISBN 90-247-2519-4, Pub. by Martinus Nijhoff Netherlands). Kluwer Academic.

Florman, Samuel. The Existential Pleasures of Engineering. LC 75-9480. 1977. pap. 4.95 (ISBN 0-312-27546-3). St Martin.

Fuller, R. Buckminster. Operating Manual for Spaceship Earth. 1970. pap. 7.95 (ISBN 0-671-20783-0, Touchstone Bks). S&S.

Giedion, Siegfried. Mechanization Takes Command. (Illus.). 1969. pap. 13.95 (ISBN 0-393-00489-9, Norton Lib). Norton.

Kursunoglu, Behram & Perlmutter, Arnold, eds. Impact of Basic Research on Technology. LC 73-82141. (Studies in the Natural Sciences: Vol. 1). 318p. 1973. 49.50x (ISBN 0-306-36901-X, Plenum Pr). Plenum Pub.

Mitcham, Carl & Mackey, Robert. Bibliography of the Philosophy of Technology. LC 74-168204. pap. 55.80 (ISBN 0-317-10819-0, 2007277). Bks Demand UMI.

Morison, Elting E. Men, Machines, & Modern Times. 1966. 15.00x (ISBN 0-262-13025-4); pap. 6.95x (ISBN 0-262-63018-4). MIT Pr.

Morison, George S. The New Epoch: As Developed by the Manufacture of Power. LC 72-5064. (Technology & Society Ser.). (Illus.). 148p. 1972. Repr. of 1903 ed. 12.00 (ISBN 0-405-04715-0). Ayer Co Pubs.

Philosophy (Concepts) of Scientific & Technological Development. 17p. 1980. pap. 5.00 (ISBN 92-808-0176-7, TUNU109, UNU). Unipub.

Rapp, Friedrich. Analytical Philosophy of Technology. xiv, 199p. 1981. 34.00 (ISBN 90-277-1221-2, Pub. by Reidel Holland). Kluwer Academic.

Rescher, Nicholas. Unpopular Essays on Technological Progress. LC 79-21648. (Illus.). 1980. 12.95 (ISBN 0-8229-3411-6). U of Pittsburgh Pr.

Schmookler, Jacob. Invention & Economic Growth. LC 66-14453. 1966. 20.00x (ISBN 0-674-46400-1). Harvard U Pr.

Winner, Langdon. Autonomous Technology: Technics-Out-of-Control As a Theme in Political Thought. LC 76-40100. 1977. pap. 8.95 (ISBN 0-262-73049-9). MIT Pr.

--The Whale & the Reactor: A Search for Limits in an Age of High Technology. LC 85-8718. 180p. 1986. lib. bdg. price not set (ISBN 0-226-90210-2). U of Chicago Pr.

TECHNOLOGY–SOCIAL ASPECTS

Here are entered works on the impact of technology on modern society. Works on the role of technology in the history and development of civilization are entered under Technology and Civilization.

Adkins, Bruce, ed. Man & Technology: The Social & Cultural Challenge of Modern Technology. 320p. 1984. pap. text ed. 28.00x (ISBN 0-905332-30-X). Westview.

Agassi, Joseph. Technology: Philosophical & Social Aspects. 1986. lib. bdg. 39.50 (ISBN 90-277-2044-4, Pub. by Reidel Holland); pap. text ed. 19.95 (ISBN 90-277-2045-2). Kluwer Academic.

Akashi, H. Appropriate Technolgy & Education & Economic Management: Biological, Medical & Environmental Systems. (Control Science & Technology Ser.: Vol. 7). 110.00 (ISBN 0-08-028719-0). Pergamon.

Akin, William E. Technocracy & the American Dream: The Technocrat Movement, 1900-1941. LC 75-22651. 1977. 32.00x (ISBN 0-520-03110-5). U of Cal Pr.

Amara, Roy. Toward Understanding the Social Impact of Computers. 136p. 1974. 10.50 (ISBN 0-318-14427-1, R29). Inst Future.

Anthony, Arthur B. Economic & Social Problems of the Machine Age. LC 30-24166. 40p. 1984. Repr. of 1930 ed. lib. bdg. 19.95x (ISBN 0-89370-860-7). Borgo Pr.

Ballard, Edward G. Man & Technology: Toward the Measurement of a Culture. 1978. text ed. 15.50x (ISBN 0-391-00751-3); pap. text ed. 9.45x (ISBN 0-391-01048-4). Duquesne.

Bannon, Liam & Barry, Ursala, eds. Information Technology: Impact on the Way of Life. (Information & Technology Development Ser.: Vol. 1). 381p. 1983. 55.00 (ISBN 0-907567-34-7, TYP114, TYP); pap. 30.00 (ISBN 0-907567-35-5, TYP112). Unipub.

Baranson, Jack. Technology & the Multinationals. LC 77-14699. 1978. 25.00x (ISBN 0-669-02021-4). Lexington Bks.

Basheer, S. & Ahmed, Alice P., eds. Technology, International Stability, & Growth. LC 83-3696. 180p. 1983. 19.50 (ISBN 0-8046-9314-5, Natl U). Assoc Faculty Pr.

Bereano, Philip L. Technology As a Social & Political Phenomenon. LC 76-18723. 544p. 1976. text ed. 46.50x cloth (ISBN 0-471-06875-6). Wiley.

Blackburn, Phil, et al. Technology, Economic Growth & the Labour Process. LC 84-22849. 272p. 1985. 29.95 (ISBN 0-312-79001-5). St Martin.

Boenau, A. Bruce & Niiro, Katsuyuki, eds. Post-Industrial Society. 508p. (Orig.). 1984. pap. text ed. 19.75 (ISBN 0-8191-3613-1). U Pr of Amer.

Borgman, Albert. Technology & the Character of Contemporary Life: A Philosophical Inquiry. LC 84-8639. 342p. 1985. lib. bdg. 25.00x (ISBN 0-226-06628-2). U of Chicago Pr.

Bowers, Robert. Econergy: The Concept of Plenty. LC 82-80466. 125p. 1982. 14.95 (ISBN 0-88247-655-6); pap. 8.95 (ISBN 0-88247-667-X). R & E Pubs.

Boyle, C., et al. People, Science & Technology: A Guide to Advanced Industrial Society. LC 83-24368. 278p. 1984. 26.50x (ISBN 0-389-20455-2, 08016). B&N Imports.

Braun, Ernst. Wayward Technology. LC 83-22586. (Contributions in Sociology Ser.: No. 48). xi, 224p. 1984. lib. bdg. 27.50 (ISBN 0-313-24398-0, BWT/). Greenwood.

Brod, Craig & St. John, Wes. Technostress: The Human Cost of the Computer Revolution. 288p. 16.95 (ISBN 0-201-11211-6). Addison-Wesley.

Brown, Richard D. Modernization: The Transformation of American Life, 1600-1865. (American Century Ser.). 229p. 1976. o. p. 10.00; pap. 6.95 (ISBN 0-8090-0125-X). Hill & Wang.

Bugliarello, George & Simon, H. A., eds. Technology, the University, & the Community. 1976. 50.00 (ISBN 0-08-017872-3). Pergamon.

Burlingame, Roger. Engines of Democracy: Inventions & Society in Mature America. LC 75-22804. (America in Two Centuries Ser). (Illus.). 1976. Repr. of 1940 ed. 48.50x (ISBN 0-405-07676-2). Ayer Co Pubs.

--March of the Iron Men: A Social History of Union Through Invention. LC 75-22805. (America in Two Centuries Ser). (Illus.). 1976. Repr. of 1938 ed. 42.00x (ISBN 0-405-07677-0). Ayer Co Pubs.

Cavalieri, Liebe F. The Double-Edged Helix: Science in the Real World. Anshen, Ruth N., ed. (Convergence Ser.: Vol. II). 207p. 1981. 20.00x (ISBN 0-231-05306-1). Columbia U Pr.

Chen, Kan, ed. Technology & Social Institutions. LC 74-77658. 1974. 20.75 (ISBN 0-87942-035-9, PC00315). Inst Electrical.

Clarke, Robin. Science & Technology in World Development. 208p. 1985. 19.95x (ISBN 0-19-219195-0); pap. 7.95x (ISBN 0-19-289176-6). Oxford U Pr.

Cole, Sam & Miles, Ian. Worlds Apart: Technology & North-South Relations in the Global Economy. 256p. 1984. 18.95x (ISBN 0-8476-7374-X). Rowman.

Collingridge, David. The Social Control of Technology. 1981. 27.50 (ISBN 0-312-73168-X). St Martin.

--The Social Control of Technology. 200p. 1981. pap. 16.00x (ISBN 0-335-10031-7, Pub. by Open Univ Pr). Taylor & Francis.

Conrad, J., ed. Society, Technology & Risk Assessment. LC 80-40533. 1980. 47.00 (ISBN 0-12-186450-2). Acad Pr.

Cooper, Charles & Clark, John. Employment, Economics & Technology: The Impact of Technical Change on the Labour Market. 1982. 60.00x (ISBN 0-7108-0157-2, Pub. by Harvester Pr England). State Mutual Bk.

Coppock, Rob. Social Constraints on Technological Progress. 291p. 1984. text ed. 32.95x (ISBN 0-566-00754-1). Gower Pub Co.

Dauber, Roslyn & Cain, Melinda, eds. Women & Technological Change in Developing Countries. LC 80-21653. (AAAS Selected Symposium Ser.: No. 53). 266p. 1980. pap. 28.50x (ISBN 0-89158-791-8). Westview.

De Moll, Lane & Coe, Gigi, eds. Stepping Stones: Appropriate Technology & Beyond. LC 78-54392. (Illus., Orig.). 1978. 14.50x (ISBN 0-8052-3694-5). Schocken.

Dierkes, Meinolf, et al, eds. Technological Risk: Its Perception & Handling in the European Community. LC 80-18899. 160p. 1980. text ed. 35.00 (ISBN 0-89946-059-3). Oelgeschlager.

Dorf, Richard C. & Hunter, Yvonne, eds. Appropriate Visions. LC 78-9045. 1978. 16.00x (ISBN 0-87835-072-1); pap. 12.50 (ISBN 0-87835-069-1). Boyd & Fraser.

Elliott, D. & Elliott, R. The Control of Technology. (Wykeham Science Ser.: No. 39). 260p. 1976. 8.70x (ISBN 0-8448-1166-1). Crane Russak Co.

Evans, Donald D. & Adler, Laurie N., eds. Appropriate Technology for Development: A Discussion with Case Histories. (Special Studies in Social, Political, & Economic Development). 1979. softcover 35.00x (ISBN 0-89158-567-2). Westview.

Florman, Samuel. Blaming Technology: The Irrational Search for Scapegoats. 224p. 1982. pap. 6.95 (ISBN 0-312-08363-7). St Martin.

Fools! How You May Destroy Yourself with Thought Control & Technological Slavery. (Analysis Ser.: No. 5). 1982. pap. 10.00 (ISBN 0-686-42840-4). Inst Analysis.

Fried, Jacob & Molnar, Paul. Technological & Social Change: A Transdisciplinary Model. 1979. text ed. 17.50 (ISBN 0-89433-074-8). Petrocelli.

Fuller, Buckminster & Dil, Anwar. Humans in Universe. (Illus.). 235p. 1983. 19.95 (ISBN 0-89925-001-7). Mouton.

Fuller, R. Buckminster. GRUNCH of Giants. 120p. 1983. 8.95 (ISBN 0-312-35193-3). St Martin.

Fusfeld, Herbert I. & Haklisch, Carmela S., eds. Science & Technology Policy: Perspectives for the Nineteen-Eighties. LC 79-28295. (Annals of the New York Academy of Sciences: Vol. 334). 285p. 1979. 52.00x (ISBN 0-89766-037-4); pap. 42.00x (ISBN 0-89766-036-6). NY Acad Sci.

Gehlen, Arnold. Man in the Age of Technology. Lipscomb, Pat, tr. LC 79-23963. (European Perspectives Ser.). (Ger.). 1980. 21.00x (ISBN 0-231-04852-1). Columbia U Pr.

Gendron, Bernard. Technology & the Human Condition. LC 76-28120. 1977. pap. text ed. 12.95 (ISBN 0-312-78925-4). St Martin.

George, F. H. Machine Takeover: The Growing Threat to Human Freedom in a Computer-Controlled Society. LC 76-27722. 208p. 1977. text ed. 24.00 (ISBN 0-08-021229-8). Pergamon.

Ghosh, Pradip K. & Morrison, Denton E., eds. Appropriate Technology in Third World Development. LC 83-26682. xiv, 494p. 1984. lib. bdg. 49.95 (ISBN 0-313-24150-3, GAT/). Greenwood.

Gill, Colin. Work, Unemployment & the New Technology. 220p. 1985. 24.95x (ISBN 0-7456-0022-0); pap. 9.95x (ISBN 0-7456-0023-9). Basil Blackwell.

Goody, Jack, ed. Technology, Tradition & the State in Africa. (Illus.). 88p. 1980. pap. 8.95x (ISBN 0-521-29892-X). Cambridge U Pr.

Grayson, Leslie, ed. Social & Economic Impact of New Technology. (IFI Data Base Library). 130p. 1984. 85.00x (ISBN 0-306-65209-9, Plenum Pr). Plenum Pub.

High Technology in the Work Place: Japan & the United States, A Seminar Report. 40p. 1984. 4.00 (ISBN 0-317-06766-4). Japan Soc.

Hoke, Donald, ed. The History & Sociology of Technology: Proceedings of the 24th Annual Meeting of the Society for the History of Technology. 355p. 8.95 (ISBN 0-89326-090-8). Milwaukee Pub Mus.

IFAC Symposium, Bari, Italy, May 1979. Criteria for Selecting Appropriate Technologies Under Different Cultural, Technical & Social Conditions: Proceedings. De Giorgio, A. & Roveda, C., eds. (IFAC Proceedings Ser.). (Illus.). 320p. 1980. 78.00 (ISBN 0-08-024455-6). Pergamon.

International Symposium on Science & Technology for Development, Singapore, 1979. Science, Technology & Global Problems: Issues of Development: Towards a New Role for Science & Technology. Goldsmith, Maurice & King, Alexander, eds. LC 79-40879. (Illus.). 200p. 1979. 57.00 (ISBN 0-08-024691-5). Pergamon.

International Symposium on Science & Technology for Development, Mexico City, 1979. Science, Technology & Global Problems: Science & Technology in Development Planning. Urquidi, Victor L., ed. LC 79-40912. 200p. 1979. 48.00 (ISBN 0-08-025227-3). Pergamon.

Kasson, John F. Civilizing the Machine: Technology & Republican Values in America 1776-1900. 1977. pap. 6.95 (ISBN 0-14-004415-9). Penguin.

Kidd, Charles V. Manpower Policies for the Use of Science & Technology in Development. (Policy Studies). 1980. 26.00 (ISBN 0-08-025124-2). Pergamon.

Kupperman, Robert H. Technological Advances & Consequent Dangers: Growing Threats to Civilization. LC 84-1815. (Significant Issues Ser.: Vol. 6, No. 1). 11p. 1984. 5.95 (ISBN 0-89206-053-0). CSI Studies.

Ladriere, Jean. The Challenge Presented to Cultures by Science & Technology. 165p. 1977. pap. 14.50 (ISBN 92-3-101418-8, U811, UNESCO). Unipub.

Lagadec, P. Le Risque Technologique Majeur. (Fr.). 1982. 68.00 (ISBN 0-08-027058-1). Pergamon.

Lapham, Lewis H., ed. High Technology & Human Freedom. LC 85-8341. (International Symposia Ser.). 176p. (Orig.). 1985. 19.95 (ISBN 0-87474-598-5, LAHT); pap. 9.95 (ISBN 0-87474-599-3, LAHTP). Smithsonian.

Lawless, Edward W. Technology & Social Shock. 1977. pap. 15.00x (ISBN 0-8135-0781-2). Rutgers U Pr.

Lewis, W. David & Griessman, B. Eugene, eds. The Southern Mystique: Technology & Human Values in a Changing Region. LC 76-55011. 177p. 1977. 11.95 (ISBN 0-8173-5317-8). U of Ala Pr.

Long, Franklin A. & Oleson, Sandy. Appropriate Technology & Social Values: A Critical Appraisal. LC 79-18528. (American Academy of Arts & Sciences Ser.). 304p. 1980. prof ref 29.95 (ISBN 0-88410-373-0). Ballinger Pub.

Maillat, Denis, ed. Technology: A Key Factor for Regional Development. 256p. (Orig.). 1982. pap. text ed. 17.95x (ISBN 0-317-05737-5, Pub. by Gorgi Switzerland). Brookfield Pub Co.

Marstrand, Pauline, ed. New Technology & the Future of Work & Skills. LC 84-43293. 260p. 1984. 25.00 (ISBN 0-86187-388-2). F Pinter Pubs.

Millionschikov, M., et al. Scientific & Technological Revolution: A Study of the Soviet Union, Capitalist, & Third World Countries. 279p. 1975. 17.50x (ISBN 0-8464-0818-X). Beekman Pubs.

Moore, L. K. & Plung, D. L., eds. Marketing Technical Ideas & Products Successfully. LC 84-22414. (Reprint Ser.). 1985. 48.95 (ISBN 0-87942-185-1, PC01792). Inst Electrical.

Morehouse, Ward & Chopra, Ravi. Chicken & Egg: Electronics & Social Change in India. (Illus.). 100p. (Orig.). 1983. pap. 8.00x. Learn Res Intl Stud.

Morehouse, Ward, ed. Science, Technology & the Social Order. LC 79-65035. (Illus.). 150p. 1979. pap. text ed. 4.95 (ISBN 0-87855-797-0). Transaction Bks.

Murrell, Hywel. Men & Machines. (Essential Psychology Ser.). 1976. pap. 4.50x (ISBN 0-416-82310-6, NO. 2331). Methuen Inc.

National Academy of Sciences. Science & Technology: A Five-Year Outlook. LC 79-15862. (Illus.). 544p. 1979. pap. 13.95x (ISBN 0-7167-1141-9). W H Freeman.

National Science & Technology Policies in Europe & North America: 1978. (Science Policy Studies & Documents: No. 43). (Eng. & Fr., Illus.). 458p. 1979. pap. 24.25 (ISBN 92-3-001584-9, U942, UNESCO). Unipub.

New Technologies: Their Impact on Employment & the Working Environment. 174p. 1983. pap. 11.40 (ISBN 92-2-102975-1, ILO211, ILO). Unipub.

Noble, David. America by Design: Science, Technology & the Rise of Corporate Capitalism. 1977. 17.95 (ISBN 0-394-49983-2). Knopf.

Noble, David F. America by Design: Science, Technology, & the Rise of Corporate Capitalism. (Galaxy Books). (Orig.). 1979. pap. 9.95 (ISBN 0-19-502618-7, GB 588, GB). Oxford U Pr.

Norman, Colin. Soft Technologies, Hard Choices. LC 78-60435. (Worldwatch Papers). 1978. pap. 2.00 (ISBN 0-916468-20-8). Worldwatch Inst.

North-South Technology Transfer: The Adjustment Ahead. (Analytical Studies). 222p. (Orig.). 1982. pap. text ed. 20.00x (ISBN 92-64-12265-6). OECD.

Office for Science & Technology. Science, Technology & Global Problems: The United Nations Advisory Committee on the Application of Science & Technology to Development. 62p. 1979. 19.00 (ISBN 0-08-025131-5). Pergamon.

Pacey, Arnold. The Maze of Ingenuity: Ideas & Idealism in the Development of Technology. LC 74-18380. 337p. 1975. text ed. 30.00x (ISBN 0-8419-0181-3). Holmes & Meier.

Palaith, D. E. What Prometheus Began: Challenge of Technology in the Third World. LC 75-14395. 1975. 4.00 (ISBN 0-686-11967-3). Bks Intl DH-TE.

Parkman, R. The Cybernetic Society. 402p. 1974. text ed. 32.00 (ISBN 0-08-016949-X). Pergamon.

Pasmore, William A. & Sherwood, John J., eds. Sociotechnical Systems: A Sourcebook. LC 77-20543. 365p. 1978. pap. 14.95 (ISBN 0-88390-142-0). Univ Assocs.

Perelman, Lewis J., et al, eds. Energy Transitions: Long-Term Perspectives. (AAAS Selected Symposium: No. 48). 250p. 1981. 24.50x (ISBN 0-89158-862-0). Westview.

Peterson, Russell. Technology: Its Promise & Its Problems. (Illus.). 1979. pap. 2.50 (ISBN 0-87081-123-1). Colo Assoc.

Piel, E. Joseph & Truxal, John G. Technology: Handle with Care. 304p. 1975. pap. text ed. 20.00 (ISBN 0-07-049923-3). McGraw.

Pool, Ithiel de Sola. Technologies of Freedom. (Illus.). 344p. 1983. 20.00 (ISBN 0-674-87232-0, Belknap Pr). Harvard U Pr.

Pope John Center Staff. Technological Powers & the Person: Nuclear Energy & Reproductive Technology. Lossing, Larry D. & Bayer, Edward J., eds. (Illus.). 370p. (Orig.). 1983. pap. 15.95 (ISBN 0-935372-12-1). Pope John Ctr.

President's Commission. Science & Technology, Promises & Dangers in the Eighties. (Illus.). 101p. 1981. 12.95 (ISBN 0-13-795518-9); pap. 4.95 (ISBN 0-13-795500-6). P-H.

Rabinowitch, V. & Rabinowitch, E., eds. Views on Science, Technology & Development. LC 74-32201. 300p. 1975. text ed. 44.00 (ISBN 0-08-018241-0). Pergamon.

Radhakrishna, S., ed. Science Technology & Global Problems-Views from the Developing World. (Illus.). 1980. 53.00 (ISBN 0-08-024489-0). Pergamon.

Rahman, A. Science, Technology & Economic Development. 1979. 26.00x (ISBN 0-8002-3466-9). Intl Pubns Serv.

Reddy, A. K. Technology, Development & the Environment: A Re-Appraisal. (Illus.). 60p. 1980. 7.00 (ISBN 0-08-025693-7). Pergamon.

Ritterbush, Philip C. & Green, Martin, eds. Technology As Institutionally Related to Human Values. LC 74-10037. 1974. 10.00 (ISBN 0-87491-511-2). Acropolis.

Roman, Daniel D. Science, Technology, & Innovation: A Systems Approach. LC 79-12737. 1980. text ed. 35.45 (ISBN 0-471-84195-1, Pub. by Grid). Wiley.

Rothschild, Joan, ed. Machina ex Dea: Feminist Perspectives on Technology. (Athene Ser.). 264p. 1983. 27.50 (ISBN 0-08-029404-9); pap. 10.95 (ISBN 0-08-029403-0). Pergamon.

Sage, Andrew P. Methodology for Large Scale Systems. (Illus.). 1977. text ed. 43.00 (ISBN 0-07-054438-7). McGraw.

Sharing the Traditional Technology: Project Meeting Report, Tokyo, Japan, September, 1977. (Human & Social Development Programme - Programme Documents). (Illus.). 56p. 1979. pap. 6.75 (ISBN 92-808-0009-4, TUNU009, UNU). Unipub.

Smith, Christopher A., ed. Discovery '84, Technology for the Disabled: The Conference Papers. (Illus.). 264p. (Orig.). 1985. pap. 18.00x (ISBN 0-916671-61-5). Material Dev.

The Social Effects of Technological Developments in the Food & Drink Industries, Including Those Arising from New Production Methods, & the Need for Training & Retraining: Food & Drink Industries Committee Report II. (Programme of Industrial Activities). 51p. 1985. pap. 7.15 (ISBN 92-2-103821-1, ILO369, ILO). Unipub.

Social Values & the Development of Technology. 17p. 1982. pap. 5.00 (ISBN 92-808-0304-2, TUNU186, UNU). Unipub.

Societal Utilization of Scientific & Technological Research. (Science Policy Studies & Documents: No. 47). 32p. 1981. pap. 5.00 (ISBN 92-3-101858-2, U1100, UNESCO). Unipub.

Soule, George. What Automation Does to Human Beings. Stein, Leon, ed. LC 77-70534. (Work Ser.). 1977. Repr. of 1956 ed. lib. bdg. 20.00x (ISBN 0-405-10202-X). Ayer Co Pubs.

Spiegel, Michael S. Reality in Transition. Edelen, Ellen A., ed. (Illus.). 128p. (Orig.). 1985. pap. 10.00 (ISBN 0-932163-00-9). Separate Real.

Spiegel-Rosing, Ina & Price, Derek De Solla, eds. Science, Technology & Society: A Cross-Disciplinary Perspective. LC 76-55928. (Illus.). 607p. 1977. 37.50 (ISBN 0-8039-9858-9). Sage.

Stanley, Manfred. The Technological Conscience: Survival & Dignity in an Age of Expertise. LC 78-428. 1978. 17.95 (ISBN 0-02-930610-8). Free Pr.

--The Technological Conscience: Survival & Dignity in an Age of Expertise. LC 81-8199. 1981. pap. 9.95X (ISBN 0-226-77096-6). U of Chicago Pr.

Summers, Gene F., ed. Technology & Social Change in Rural Areas. (Rural Studies Ser.). 400p. 1984. pap. 26.50x (ISBN 0-86531-600-7). Westview.

Taneja, V. R. Tryst with Education in the Technetronic Society. 98p. 1984. text ed. 10.95x (ISBN 0-86590-180-5, Pub. by Sterling India). Apt Bks.

Technology on Trial: Public Participation in Decision-Making Related to Science & Technology. 124p. 1979. 7.00x (ISBN 92-64-11936-1). OECD.

Teich, Albert H., ed. Technology & Man's Future. 3rd ed. 350p. 1981. pap. text ed. 12.95x (ISBN 0-312-78996-3). St Martin.

Thompson, George W., Jr. Technology & Human Fulfillment. LC 85-6039. (Orig.). 1985. lib. bdg. 22.50 (ISBN 0-8191-4678-1); pap. text ed. 10.75 (ISBN 0-8191-4679-X). U Pr of Amer.

Thought Control & Technological Slavery in America. (Analysis Ser.: No. 1). 1982. pap. 10.00 (ISBN 0-686-42834-X). Inst Analysis.

Thought Control & Technological Slavery in America: Illustration & Selected Correspondence. (Analysis Ser.). 75p. 1983. pap. 20.00 (ISBN 0-686-42852-8). Inst Analysis.

Thrall, Charles A. & Starr, Jerold M., eds. Technology, Power & Social Change. LC 74-4213. (Arcturus Books Paperbacks). 179p. 1974. pap. 2.45 (ISBN 0-8093-0688-3). S Ill U Pr.

Tirman, John, ed. The Militarization of High Tech. 264p. 1984. professional reference 28.00 (ISBN 0-88410-947-X). Ballinger Pub.

Toffler, Alvin. The Third Wave. 544p. 1980. 14.95 (ISBN 0-688-03076-X). Telecom Lib.

A UNESCO Symposium. 408p. 1981. pap. 30.00 (ISBN 92-3-101664-4, U1099, UNESCO). Unipub.

Vacca, Roberto. Modest Technologies for a Complicated World. 144p. 1980. 31.00 (ISBN 0-08-024067-4). Pergamon.

Vallee, Jacques, et al. A Study of Social Effects. (Group Communication Through Computers: Vol. 2). 160p. 1974. 10.50 (ISBN 0-318-14424-7, R33). Inst Future.

Watt, Kenneth E., et al. The Unsteady State: Environmental Problems, Growth, & Culture. LC 77-3879. 1977. text ed. 15.00x (ISBN 0-8248-0480-5, Eastwest Ctr). UH Pr.

Wilkinson, Barry. The ShopFloor Politics of New Technology. viii, 120p. 1983. pap. text ed. 14.50x (ISBN 0-435-82951-3). Gower Pub Co.

Winner, Langdon. Autonomous Technology: Technics-Out-of-Control As a Theme in Political Thought. LC 76-40100. 1977. pap. 8.95 (ISBN 0-262-73049-9). MIT Pr.

Wolff, Edward A., ed. Urban Alternatives: Proceedings of the USERC Environmental Resources & Urban Development Workshop. LC 76-16432. 1976. pap. text ed. 22.00 (ISBN 0-08-021171-2). Pergamon.

World Plan of Action for the Application of Science & Technology to Development. pap. 8.50 (ISBN 0-686-94381-3, UN71/2A/18, UN). Unipub.

TECHNOLOGY–STUDY AND TEACHING

see also Technical Education

Bradley-Payne. Humanities & Technologies: An Interdisciplinary Approach. 216p. 1983. pap. text ed. 14.95 (ISBN 0-8403-3083-9). Kendall-Hunt.

Engineering Manpower Commission. Engineering & Technology Degrees, 1983, 3 parts. (Illus.). 1984. pap. 200.00 (ISBN 0-87615-034-2, 201-83 (A, B, C)); pap. 75.00 part I: by Schools (ISBN 0-87615-044-X); pap. 100.00 part II: by Minorities (ISBN 0-87615-054-7); pap. 75.00 part III: by Curriculum (ISBN 0-87615-064-4). AAES.

--Engineering & Technology Enrollments, Fall 1983, 2 pts. 1984. pap. 101.00x part I: Engineering Enrollments (ISBN 0-87615-085-7, 207-84 (A,B)); pap. 101.00x part II: Technology Enrollments (ISBN 0-87615-095-4); pap. 202.00 (ISBN 0-87615-075-X). AAES.

Giachino, J. W. & Gallington, R. O. Course Construction in Industrial Arts, Vocational & Technical Education. 4th ed. 1977. text ed. 18.95 (ISBN 0-8269-4065-X). Am Technical.

Harbour, Jerry L. Introduction to Professional Technical Training. (Illus.). 281p. (Orig.). 1985. pap. write for info. (ISBN 0-88746-057-7). Intl Human Res.

Kailath, Thomas, ed. Modern Signal Processing: Proceedings of the Arab School on Science & Technology. LC 84-19289. (Illus.). 440p. 1985. text ed. 79.95 (ISBN 0-89116-386-7). Hemisphere Pub.

Kimeldorf, Martin. Special Needs in Technology Education. LC 83-71907. (Illus.). 279p. 1984. text ed. 11.95. Davis Mass.

Management Training of Scientific & Technical Personnel in the Public Services of Developing Countries: Report of an Expert Group Meeting: San Jose, Costa Rica. LC 84-46787. 35p. 1983. 5.00 (ISBN 0-317-16140-7). UN.

Shaw, K. E., ed. Aspects of Educational Technology, Vol. XVII: Staff Development & Career Updating. 300p. 1984. 35.00 (ISBN 0-89397-175-8). Nichols Pub.

Useem, Elizabeth. Low Tech Education in a High Tech World: Corporations & Classrooms in New Information Society. (AAAS Issues in Science & Technology Ser.). 256p. 1986. 19.18x (ISBN 0-02-933150-1). Free Pr.

Useem, Elizabeth L. Low Tech Education in a High Tech World: Corporations & Classrooms in the New Information Society. 256p. 19.95 (ISBN 0-02-933150-1). Free Pr.

TECHNOLOGY–TERMINOLOGY

Agnew, Irene, ed. Glossary of English & Russian Computer & Automated Control Systems Terminology. (Eng. & Rus.). 1978. soft covers 15.00 (ISBN 0-686-31723-8). Agnew Tech-Tran.

Appleby, B. L. Elsevier's Dictionary of Commercial Terms & Phrases: In English, German, Spanish, French & Swedish. 1984. 181.50 (ISBN 0-444-42270-6, I-251-84). Elsevier.

Buck, Frederick H. Glossary of Mongolian Technical Terms. LC 58-59834. (American Council of Learned Societies Publications). (Mongolian.). 79p. (Orig.). 1958. pap. 3.00x (ISBN 0-87950-257-6). Spoken Lang Serv.

Comfort, Jeremy, et al. Basic Technical English. (Illus.). 1982. pap. 6.25x student's ed. (ISBN 0-19-457382-6); pap. 6.95x tchr.'s ed (ISBN 0-19-457383-4). Oxford U Pr.

Crane, Dale, ed. Capstan Encyclopedic Dictionary of Technical Terms. LC 84-12177. (ABC (A Basic Course) Ser.). (Illus., Orig.). 1984. pap. 29.95 (ISBN 0-914565-02-8). Capstan Pubns.

Engineering Technicians: Some Problems of Nomenclature & Classification. (Studies in Engineering Education: No. 7). 144p. 1981. pap. 11.50 (ISBN 92-3-101831-0, U1095, UNESCO). Unipub.

Freeman, H. G. Two Thousand Six Hundred Definitions of Technical Terms According to Din: English-German, German-English. 1977. 53.00 (ISBN 0-686-39804-1, 10804-1, Pub. by DIN Germany). Heyden.

Gordon, Michael, et al, eds. Dictionary of New Information Technology Acronyms. 217p. 1983. 56.00x (ISBN 0-8103-4309-6, Pub. by Kogan Page UK). Gale.

Gullberg, Ingvar E. Swedish-English Fact Ordbok (Technical Terms) 2nd ed. (Swedish & Eng.). 1977. 200.00x (ISBN 91-177-5052-0, SW-207). Vanous.

Huckin, Thomas & Olsen, Leslie. English for Science & Technology: A Handbook for Non-Native Speakers. (Illus.). 576p. 1983. 24.95 (ISBN 0-07-030821-7). McGraw.

Interrante, C. G. & Heymann, F. J., eds. Standardization of Technical Terminology: Principles & Practices - STP 806. LC 82-73769. 146p. 1983. text ed. 24.00 (ISBN 0-8031-0247-X, 04-806000-42). ASTM.

Markov, A. S., et al. Dictionary of Scientific & Technical Terminology. 1984. lib. bdg. 34.50 (ISBN 0-318-01661-3, Pub. by Martinus Nijhoff Netherlands). Kluwer Academic.

Rheingold, Howard & Levine, Howard. Talking Tech: A Conversational Guide to Science & Technology. LC 81-14130. (Illus.). 320p. 1982. 13.50 (ISBN 0-688-00783-X). Morrow.

Sahai, Hardeo & Berrios, Jose. A Dictionary of Statistical, Scientific & Technical Terms: English-Spanish, Spanish-English. Smith, Richard A. & Heise, Jeanne, eds. (Spanish Ser.). (Eng. & Span.). 143p. 1981. write for info. (ISBN 8-4534-0004-0, Pub. by Wadsworth Internacional Iberoamerica). Wadsworth Pub.

Science & Technology for Development. 784p. 1979. pap. 26.00 (UN79115, UN). Unipub.

Seiden, Eric A. DARCED Technical Reference Manual. Dar Systems International Staff, ed. 25p. 1984. pap. 10.00 (ISBN 0-916163-31-8). Dar Syst.

Smolin, Ronald P., ed. High-Tech Glossary. 2nd ed. 1984. pap. 10.00x (ISBN 0-89563-061-3). Intl Ideas.

Swann, Harvey J. French Terminologies in the Making. LC 18-23121. (Columbia University. Studies in Romance Philology & Literature: No. 24). Repr. of 1918 ed. 22.00 (ISBN 0-404-50624-0). AMS Pr.

Technisch Wissenschaftliches Taschenwoerterbuch. (Ger.). 408p. (Technical Scientific Dictionary). 32.00 (ISBN 3-87749-014-X, M-7643, Pub. by Georg Siemens Verlagsbuchhandlung). French & Eur.

Terminology of Technical & Vocational Education. (IBEDATA Ser.). 88p. (3rd Printing 1981). 1978. pap. 5.00 (ISBN 92-3-001593-8, U884, UNESCO). Unipub.

Vervalin, Charles H., ed. Communication & the Technical Professional. LC 81-593. 140p. (Orig.). 1981. pap. 17.95x (ISBN 0-87201-133-X). Gulf Pub.

World Energy Conference, ed. Energy Terminology: A Multi-Lingual Glossary. 275p. 1983. 100.00 (ISBN 0-08-029314-X, B110); pap. 40.00 (ISBN 0-08-029315-8). Pergamon.

TECHNOLOGY–VOCATIONAL GUIDANCE

Casagrande, Diane O. & Casagrande, Roger D. Oral Communication: A Tool for Technical Success. 300p. 1985. pap. text ed. write for info. (ISBN 0-534-05532-X). Wadsworth Pub.

Engineering Manpower Commission Staff. Engineering & Technology Degrees, 1984, Pt. I. Sheridan, P. J., ed. 50p. (Orig.). 1985. pap. 75.00 (ISBN 0-87615-045-8). AAES.

--Engineering & Technology Degrees, 1984, Pt. II. Sheridan, Patrick J., ed. 144p. (Orig.). 1985. pap. 100.00 (ISBN 0-87615-055-5). AAES.

--Engineering & Technology Degrees 1984, Pt. III. Sheridan, Patrick J., ed. 86p. (Orig.). 1985. pap. 75.00 (ISBN 0-87615-065-2). AAES.

--Engineering & Technology Enrollments Fall 1984: Pt. I, Engineering Enrollments. Heydt, Carolyn, ed. 410p. 1984. pap. 100.00 (ISBN 0-87615-086-5). AAES.

--Engineering & Technology Enrollments, Fall 1984: Pt. II-Technology Enrollments. Heydt, Carolyn, ed. 300p. 1985. pap. 100.00 (ISBN 0-87615-096-2). AAES.

Gale, Barry & Gale, Linda. Discover Your High-Tech Talents. 1984. 16.95 (ISBN 0-671-49968-8); pap. 8.95 (ISBN 0-671-50740-0). S&S.

Goldberg, Joan R. High-Tech Career Strategies for Women. 224p. 15.95 (ISBN 0-02-544460-3, Collier); pap. 7.95 (ISBN 0-02-008280-0). Macmillan.

Marrs, T. W. High Technology Careers. 225p. 1985. pap. 9.95 (ISBN 0-87094-589-0). Dow Jones-Irwin.

O'Brien, Mark. High-Tech Jobs for Non-Tech Grads. (Illus.). 112p. 1986. pap. 8.95 (ISBN 0-13-387911-9). P-H.

Weinstein, Robert. One Hundred & Forty High-Tech Careers. 288p. 1985. pap. 7.95 (ISBN 0-02-079700-1, Collier). Macmillan.

TECHNOLOGY AND CIVILIZATION

Here are entered works on the role of technology in the history and development of civilization. Works on the impact of technology on modern society are entered under Technology–Social Aspects.

see also Machinery in Industry; Technocracy; Technology–Philosophy

Alvares, Claude A. Homo Faber: Technology & Culture in India, China & the West from 1500 to the Present Day. xvi, 275p. 1980. lib. bdg. 47.50 (ISBN 90-247-2283-7). Kluwer Academic.

Anderson, Robert M., et al. Divided Loyalties: Whistle-Blowing at Bart. LC 79-89588. (Science & Society: A Purdue University Series in Science, Technology, & Human Values: Vol. 4). (Illus.). 400p. 1980. pap. 4.95 (ISBN 0-931682-09-6). Purdue Univ.

Aristotelian Society for the Systematic Study of Philosophy. Men & Machines: Proceedings, Supplementary Vol. 26. 17.00 (ISBN 0-384-38120-0); pap. 12.00 (ISBN 0-384-38121-9). Johnson Repr.

Asimov, Isaac. The Roving Mind. 350p. 1985. 19.95 (ISBN 0-317-19994-3); pap. 10.95 (ISBN 0-87975-315-3). Prometheus Bks.

Attinger, E. O., ed. Global Systems Dynamics. 353p. 1970. 42.95 (ISBN 0-471-03640-4). Halsted Pr.

Ayres, C. E. Science-the False Messiah. Bd. with Holier Than Thou; The Way of the Righteous. LC 71-130660. Repr. of 1927 ed. 37.50x (ISBN 0-678-00774-8). Kelley.

Bernard, H. Russell & Pelto, Pertti J. Technology & Social Change. (Illus.). 352p. 1972. text ed. 24.95x (ISBN 0-02-309010-3, 30901). Macmillan.

TECHNOLOGY AND ETHICS

TECHNOLOGY AND LAW

TECHNOLOGY AND STATE

see also Research and Development Contracts; Science and State

Averch, Harvey A. A Strategic Analysis of Science & Technology Policy. LC 84-47961. 232p. 1985. text ed. 20.00x (ISBN 0-8018-2467-2). Johns Hopkins.

Behari, Bepin. Economic Growth & Technological Change in India. 1974. 12.00x (ISBN 0-686-20218-X). Intl Bk Dist.

China: Rural Processing Technology. (Agricultural Services Bulletins: No. 36). 63p. 1979. pap. 7.50 (ISBN 92-5-100728-4, F1553, FAO). Unipub.

Covello, Vincent & Abernathy, Mark. Technological Risk: A Bibliography. (Public Administration Ser.: P 1220). 83p. 1983. pap. 12.75 (ISBN 0-88066-550-5). Vance Biblios.

Danhof, Clarence H. Government Contracting & Technological Change. LC 79-28531. (Illus.). x, 472p. 1980. Repr. of 1968 ed. lib. bdg. 37.50x (ISBN 0-313-22297-5, DAGT). Greenwood.

Doctors, Samuel I. Technology Transfer by State & Local Government. LC 81-11194. 280p. 1981. text ed. 35.00 (ISBN 0-89946-050-X). Oelgeschlager.

Duller, H. J. Development Technology. (International Library of Anthropology). 192p. (Orig.). 1982. pap. 14.95x (ISBN 0-7100-0990-9). Routledge & Kegan.

Gilpin, Robert G., Jr. France in the Age of the Scientific State. LC 68-14442. (Center of International Studies Ser.). 1968. 46.00 (ISBN 0-691-05619-6). Princeton U Pr.

Golden, William T., et al, eds. Science Advice to the President. LC 79-28743. (Pergamon Policy Studies). 268p. 1980. 55.00 (ISBN 0-08-025963-4). Pergamon.

Goodman, Richard A. & Morote, Julian P., eds. Planning for National Technology Policy. LC 83-13790. 460p. 1984. 35.95 (ISBN 0-03-061343-4). Praeger.

Gryski, Gerard S. Bureaucratic Policy Making in a Technological Society. 320p. 1981. 18.95x (ISBN 0-87073-831-3); pap. text ed. 9.95x (ISBN 0-87073-829-1). Schenkman Bks Inc.

Gummett, Philip. Science & Technology Policy in the 1980's & Beyond. 275p. 1984. pap. text ed. 32.00 (ISBN 0-582-90200-2). Gale.

Harvey, Mose L., et al. Science & Technology As An Instrument of Soviet Policy. new ed. LC 72-92184. (Monographs in International Affairs). (Illus.). 219p. 1972. text ed. 8.95 (ISBN 0-933074-14-X); pap. text ed. 5.95 (ISBN 0-933074-15-8). AISI.

Herspring, Dale R. East German Civil-Military Relations: The Impact of Technology, 1949-1972. LC 73-11035. (Special Studies in International Politics & Government). 1973. 29.50x (ISBN 0-275-28753-X). Irvington.

Hough, Granville W. Technology Diffusion: Federal Programs & Procedures. LC 73-88035. 406p. 1975. 44.00 (ISBN 0-912338-05-9); microfiche 12.50 (ISBN 0-912338-06-7). Lomond.

James, Jeffrey & Watanabe, Susumu, eds. Technology, Institutions & Government Policies. LC 84-17955. 320p. 1985. 29.95 (ISBN 0-312-79006-6). St Martin.

Johnston, Ron & Gummett, Philip, eds. Directing Technology: Policies for Promotion & Control. LC 78-26073. 1979. 10.95 (ISBN 0-312-21218-6). St Martin.

Junta del Acuerdo de Cartagena. Andean Pact Technology Policies. 58p. 1976. pap. 5.00 (ISBN 0-88936-077-4, IDRC60, IDRC). Unipub.

Killian, James R., Jr. Sputnik, Scientists, & Eisenhower: A Memoir of the First Special Assistant to the President for Science & Technology. LC 77-21560. 1977. 30.00x (ISBN 0-262-11066-0); pap. 9.95 (1982) (ISBN 0-262-61035-3). MIT Pr.

Kistiakowsky, George B. A Scientist at the White House. 1976. 27.50x (ISBN 0-674-79496-6). Harvard U Pr.

Kuehn, Thomas J. & Porter, Alan L. Science, Technology & National Policy. (Illus.). 608p. 1980. 39.95x (ISBN 0-8014-1343-5); pap. 12.95x (ISBN 0-8014-9876-7). Cornell U Pr.

Levitt, Seymour H. & Tapley, Norah, eds. Technological Basis of Radiation Therapy: Practical Clinical Applications. LC 83-9889. (Illus.). 336p. 1984. text ed. 45.00 (ISBN 0-8121-0898-1). Lea & Febiger.

Mattelart, A. & Stourdze, Y. Technology, Culture & Communication: A Report to the French Minister of Research & Industry. (Information Research & Resource Reports Ser.: Vol. 6). 244p. 1985. 44.50 (ISBN 0-444-87606-5, North-Holland). Elsevier.

Mercer, James L. & Philips, Ronald J. Public Technology: Key to Improved Government Productivity. LC 80-69693. pap. 71.80 (ISBN 0-317-27065-6, 2023538). Bks Demand UMI.

Morehouse, Ward. Separate, Unequal, but More Autonomous: Technology, Equity & World Order in the Millennial Transition. 51p. 1981. pap. 2.00 (ISBN 0-911646-11-6). World Policy.

Nanyenya-Takirambudde, Peter. Technology Transfer & International Law. LC 79-23571. 190p. 1980. 34.95 (ISBN 0-03-047531-7). Praeger.

Nayar, B. R. India's Quest for Technological Independence, 2 Vols. 1110p. 1983. Set. text ed. 67.00x (ISBN 0-391-03080-9, Pub. by Lancers India). Vol. 1-Policy Foundations & Policy Change (ISBN 0-391-03081-7). Vol. 2-The Results of Policy (ISBN 0-391-03082-5). Humanities.

Nelson, Richard R., ed. Government & Technical Progress: Cross-Industry Analysis. (The Technical Policy & Economic Growth Ser.). (Illus.). 512p. 1982. 45.00 (ISBN 0-08-028837-5, L110). Pergamon.

Norman, Colin. The God That Limps: Science & Technology in the Eighties. 1981. 14.95 (ISBN 0-393-01504-1); pap. 6.95 (ISBN 0-393-30026-9). Norton.

OECD. Science & Technology Policy for the Eighties. 168p. (Orig.). 1981. pap. text ed. 13.75x (ISBN 92-64-12254-0). OECD.

Pearton, Maurice. The Knowledgeable State: Diplomacy, Technology & War Since 1830. 304p. 1982. 59.00x (ISBN 0-686-44690-9, Pub. by Hutchinson). State Mutual Bk.

Sanders, Ralph. International Dynamics of Technology. LC 82-9220. (Contributions in Political Science Ser.: No. 87). xiii, 332p. 1983. lib. bdg. 35.00 (ISBN 0-313-23401-9, SAD/). Greenwood.

Shapley, Deborah & Roy, Rustum. Lost at the Frontier: U. S. Science & Technology Policy Adrift. 223p. 1985. 19.95 (ISBN 0-89495-041-X); pap. 13.95 (ISBN 0-89495-042-8). ISI Pr.

Skolnikoff, Eugene B. The International Imperatives of Technology: Technological Development and the International Political System. LC 74-184628. (Research Ser.: No. 16). 1972. pap. 2.95x (ISBN 0-87725-116-9). U of Cal Intl St.

Smith, Gordon B., et al, eds. Soviet & East European Law & the Scientific-Technical Revolution. (Pergamon Policy Studies on International Politics). (Illus.). 330p. 1981. 37.00 (ISBN 0-08-027195-2). Pergamon.

Teague, Robert & Erickson, Clint, eds. Computers & Society: A Reader. LC 74-4279. 350p. 1974. pap. text ed. 13.95 (ISBN 0-8299-0021-7). West Pub.

Technocracy Inc., ed. Technocracy: Technological Social Design. (Illus.). 76p. (Orig.). 1975. pap. 2.00 (ISBN 0-686-28500-X). Technocracy.

The Technology of Repression & Repressive Technology: The Social Bearers & Cultural Consequences. 21p. 1980. pap. 5.00 (ISBN 92-808-0182-1, TUNU121, UNU). Unipub.

Teich, Albert H., ed. Technology & Man's Future. 3rd ed. 350p. 1981. pap. text ed. 12.95x (ISBN 0-312-78996-3). St Martin.

Tisdell, F. Science & Technology Policy: Priorities of Governments. LC 80-41228. 210p. 1981. 29.95x (ISBN 0-412-23320-7, NO. 6552, Pub. by Chapman & Hall). Methuen Inc.

Welkin, Dorothy. Technological Decisions & Democracy: European Experiments in Public Participation. LC 77-9133. pap. 28.00 (ISBN 0-317-10754-2, 2021937). Bks Demand UMI.

Wenk, Edward, Jr. Margins for Survival: Overcoming Political Limits in Steering Technology. LC 78-40932. (Illus.). 1979. pap. 13.25 (ISBN 0-08-023372-4). Pergamon.

Zeman, Zavis P. & Hoffman, David, eds. The Dynamics of the Technological Leadership of the World. 58p. 1980. pap. text ed. 3.00x (ISBN 0-920380-44-1, Inst Res Pub Canada). Brookfield Pub Co.

TECHNOLOGY ASSESSMENT

Cetron, Marvin J. & Bartocha, Bodo, eds. Technology Assessment in a Dynamic Environment. LC 72-75869. 1050p. 1973. 217.50 (ISBN 0-677-13150-X). Gordon.

Cetron, Marvin J., et al, eds. Methodology of Technology Assessment. 1969. pap. write for info. (ISBN 0-677-15315-5). Gordon.

Closing the Gap Between Technology & Application: Proceedings. 215p. 20.00 (ISBN 0-318-14008-X); members 10.00 (ISBN 0-318-14009-8). Educom.

Emmanuel, Arghiri. Appropriate of Underdeveloped Technology. (Wiley-IRM Series on Multinationals). 186p. 1982. 29.95x (ISBN 0-471-10467-1, Pub. by Wiley-Interscience). Wiley.

Gannon, Colin A. Towards a Strategy for Conservation in a World of Technological Change. (Discussion Paper Ser.: No. 24). 1968. pap. 5.75 (ISBN 0-686-32193-6). Regional Sci Res Inst.

Mc-Graw Hill Editors. McGraw-Hill Yearbook of Science & Technology, 1982-83: Annual Supplement. LC 62-12028. (Illus.). 500p. 1982. 42.00 (ISBN 0-07-045489-2). McGraw.

Morita-Lou, Hiroko, ed. Science & Technology Indicators for Development. 150p. Date not set. pap. 18.00 (ISBN 0-8133-0294-3). Westview.

Nakamura, Robert. Clinical Laboratory Assays: New Technology & Future Directions. 400p. 1983. 49.50 (ISBN 0-89352-212-0). Masson Pub.

Office of Technology Assessment, Congress of the United States. Technology & East West Trade. LC 80-26121. 312p. 1981. text ed. 30.00x (ISBN 0-86598-041-1). Allanheld.

Office of Technology Assessment, Congress of the U. S. Technology & Handicapped People. 224p. 1983. text ed. 29.50 (ISBN 0-8261-4510-8). Springer Pub.

O'Keefe, Lawrence P. Technology Assessment for State & Local Government: A Guide to Decision Making. LC 82-71314. pap. 55.50 (ISBN 0-317-26718-3, 2023520). Bks Demand UMI.

Piel, E. Joseph & Truxal, John G. Technology: Handle with Care. 304p. 1975. pap. text ed. 20.00 (ISBN 0-07-049923-3). McGraw.

Porter, A. R., et al. A Guidebook for Technology Assessment & Impact Analysis. LC 79-12699. (Systems Sciences & Engineering Ser.: Vol. 4). 544p. 1980. 33.75 (ISBN 0-444-00314-2, North Holland). Elsevier.

Srinivisan, Mangalam, ed. Technology Assessment & Development. LC 82-3795. 288p. 1982. 34.95 (ISBN 0-03-059543-6). Praeger.

United Nations Institute for Training and Research. Assessing the United Nations Sale of Assessments: Is It Fair? Is It Equitable? (UNITAR Policy & Efficacy Studies: No. 9). 59p. 1983. pap. 5.00 (ISBN 0-686-44046-3, UN82/15PE9, UNITAR). Unipub.

Waller, Ray A. & Covello, Vincent T., eds. Low-Probability-High-Consequence Risk Analysis: Issues, Methods & Case Studies. (Advances in Risk Analysis Ser.: Vol. 2). 582p. 1984. 75.00x (ISBN 0-306-41725-1, Plenum Pr). Plenum Pub.

TECHNOLOGY TRANSFER

see also Technological Forecasting

American Society of Photogrammetry. Proceedings: Second Technology Exchange Week in Panama. (Eng & Sp.). 724p. 1982. eng. ed. (10.00 member) 14.00 (ISBN 0-937294-53-5); sp. ed. (10.00 member) 14.00 (ISBN 0-937294-54-3). ASP & RS.

Appropriate Industrial Technology for Basic Industries, No. 13. 94p. 1983. pap. text ed. 4.00 (ISBN 0-317-01267-3, UNID232, UNIDO). Unipub.

Balasubramanyam, V. N. International Transfer of Technology to India. LC 73-163952. (Special Studies in International Economics & Development). 1973. 39.50x (ISBN 0-275-28245-7). Irvington.

Benson, Barbara, ed. Benjamin Henry Latrobe & Moncure Robinson: The Engineer As Agent of Technological Transfer. (Illus.). 72p. 1975. pap. 1.25 (ISBN 0-914650-07-6). Eleutherian Mills-Hagley.

Bereny, Justin A. Technology Transfer: Survey of an Emerging Service Industry, 1970. 130p. pap. 49.50x (ISBN 0-89934-231-0). Business Technology Bks.

Bertsch, Gary & McIntyre, John R., eds. National Security & Technology Transfer: The Strategic Dimensions of East-West Trade. LC 83-50026. (Illus.). 258p. 1983. pap. 17.95x (ISBN 0-86531-614-7). Westview.

Bhattasali, B. N. Transfer of Technology Among the Developing Countries. LC 70-186286. 94p. 1972. 10.50 (ISBN 92-833-1013-6, APO4, APO). Unipub.

Boczek, B. & Boleslaw, A. The Transfer of Marine Technology to Developing Nations in International Law. 79p. 1982. 7.50 (ISBN 0-911189-04-1). Law Sea Inst.

Boon, Gerard K. Technology Transfer in Fibres, Textile & Apparel. 600p. 1981. 166.25 (ISBN 90-286-0520-7). Sijthoff & Noordhoff.

Bradbury, F., ed. Technology Transfer Practice on International Firms. 324p. 1978. 37.50x (ISBN 9-0286-0377-8). Sijthoff & Noordhoff.

Bradbury, F. P. & Jervis, R., eds. Transfer Processes in Technical Change. 290p. 1978. 40.00x (ISBN 90-286-0347-6). Sijthoff & Noordhoff.

Carlson, Dennis G. African Fever: A Study of British Science, Technology, & Politics in West Africa, 1787-1864. LC 81-5621. 1984. 15.95 (ISBN 0-88202-196-6). Watson Pub Intl.

Carrick, R. J. East-West Technology Transfer in Perspective. LC 78-78134. (Policy Papers in International Affairs Ser.: No. 9). 1978. pap. 5.50x (ISBN 0-87725-509-1). U of Cal Intl St.

Conference on Technology Transfer: Meeting Held October 13-15, 1981, Mt. Pocono, Pennsylvania. (The National SAMPE Technical Conference Ser.: Vol. 13). 697p. 1983. 55.00 (ISBN 0-938994-19-0). Soc Adv Material.

Contractor, Farok J. International Technology Licensing: Compensation, Costs, & Negotiation. LC 80-8768. 208p. 1981. 29.50 (ISBN 0-669-04359-1). Lexington Bks.

--Licensing in International Strategy: A Guide for Planning & Negotiations. LC 84-22756. (Illus.). 288p. 1985. lib. bdg. 45.00 (ISBN 0-89930-024-3, CLI/, Quorum). Greenwood.

Control of Restrictive Practices in Transfer of Technology Transactions: Selected Principal Regulations, Policy Guidelines & Case Law at the National & Regional Levels. 55p. 1983. pap. 7.00 (ISBN 0-686-44445-0, UN82/2D8, UN). Unipub.

Cortes, Mariluz & Bocock, Peter. North-South Technology Transfer: A Case Study of Petrochemicals in Latin America. LC 83-49365. 184p. 1984. text ed. 25.00x (ISBN 0-8018-3259-4). Johns Hopkins.

Council for Mutual & Economic Assistance: Foreign Trade among Soviet Union & other Eastern European Countries, Transfer of Technology in the Socialist State, 3 Vols. 1979. Set. lib. bdg. 150.00set (ISBN 0-930342-90-9). W S Hein.

Doctors, Samuel I. Technology Transfer by State & Local Government. LC 81-11194. 280p. 1981. text ed. 35.00 (ISBN 0-89946-050-X). Oelgeschlager.

Encarnacao, J., et al, eds. CAD-CAM As a Basis for Development of Technology in Developing Nations: Proceedings of th IFIP WG 5.2 Working Conference, Sao Paulo, Brazil, October 1981. 437p. 1982. 76.75 (ISBN 0-444-86320-6). Elsevier.

Fallenbuchl, Z. East-West Technology Transfer: Study of Poland, 1971-1980. 199p. (Orig.). 1983. pap. text ed. 22.00x (ISBN 92-64-12484-5). OECD.

Fikentscher, Wolfgang. Draft International Code of Conduct on the Transfer of Technology. (IIC Studies: Vol. 4). 211p. (Orig.). 1980. pap. 30.00x (ISBN 0-89573-030-8). VCH Pubs.

Fordham Corporate Law Institute & Hawk, Barry E. Antitrust, Technology Transfers, & Joint Ventures in International Trade: Annual Proceedings of the Fordham Corporate Law Institute. New York, N.Y. & Fordham University. School of Law, eds. LC 83-189452. xi, 407p. Date not set. price not set. Bender.

Frame, J. Davidson. International Business & Global Technology. LC 82-48480. 224p. 1983. 25.00 (ISBN 0-669-06156-5); pap. 12.00x (ISBN 0-669-09814-0). Lexington Bks.

Fusfeld, Herbert I. Industrial Productivity & International Technical Cooperation. Haklisch, Carmela S., ed. (Illus.). 160p. 1982. 21.00 (ISBN 0-08-028810-3). Pergamon.

Gee, S., ed. Technology Transfer in Industrialized Countries. 464p. 1979. 35.00x (ISBN 90-286-0038-8). Sijthoff & Noordhoff.

Gee, Sherman. Technology Transfer, Innovation, & International Competitiveness. LC 80-22786. 248p. 1981. 34.50x (ISBN 0-471-08468-9, Pub. by Wiley-Interscience). Wiley.

Global Economic Challenge: Trade Policy, Energy & Jobs, & Technology Transfer, Vol. II. 1980. pap. 3.00 (ISBN 0-934654-23-9). UNA-USA.

Guidelines for Evaluation of Transfer of Technology Agreemets. (Development & Transfer of Technology: No. 12). 72p. 1982. pap. 10.50 (ISBN 0-686-96624-4, UPB109, UNIDO). Unipub.

Guidelines for the Acquisition of Foreign Technology in Developing Countries. pap. 4.00 (ISBN 0-686-94512-3, UN73/2B1, UN). Unipub.

Guidelines on Technology Issues in the Pharmaceutical Sector in the Developing Countries. 68p. 1983. pap. text ed. 8.50 (ISBN 0-686-46325-0, UN82/2D15, UN). Unipub.

Handbook on the Acquisition of Technology by Developing Countries. pap. 6.00 (ISBN 0-686-94558-1, UN78/2D15, UN). Unipub.

Hanson, Philip. Trade & Technology in Soviet-Western Relations. 300p. 1981. 36.00x (ISBN 0-231-05276-6). Columbia U Pr.

Hawk, Barry E., ed. Nineteen Eighty-Two Fordham Corporate Law Institute on Antitrust, Technology Transfers & Joint Ventures in International Trade. 1983. 60.00 (ISBN 0-317-09691-5, 558). Bender.

Heller, Peter B. Technology Transfer & Human Values: Concepts, Applications, Cases. (Illus.). 380p. (Orig.). 1985. lib. bdg. 27.00 (ISBN 0-8191-4548-3); pap. text ed. 15.25 (ISBN 0-8191-4549-1). U Pr of Amer.

Heston, Alan W. & Pack, Howard, eds. Technology Transfer: New Issues, New Analysis. (The Annals of the American Academy of Political & Social Science: Vol. 458). 322p. 1981. 15.00 (ISBN 0-8039-1707-4); pap. 7.95 (ISBN 0-8039-1706-6). Sage.

Hill, Malcolm R. East-West Trade, Industrial Co-operation & Technology Transfer. 235p. 1983. text ed. 37.00x (ISBN 0-566-00591-3). Gower Pub Co.

Howe, P. J. Transfer of Nuclear Technology. 1977. 39.00 (ISBN 0-08-022132-7). Pergamon.

TECTONICS, PLATE

see Plate Tectonics

TEEPEE BURNERS

see Incinerators

TEILHARD DE CHARDIN, PIERRE, 1881-1955

TELECOMMUNICATION

see also Artificial Satellites in Telecommunication; Astronautics–Communication Systems; Broadcasting; Cables, Submarine; Computer Networks; Data Transmission Systems; Electronic Publishing; Error-Correcting Codes (Information Theory); Interstellar Communication; Phase-Locked Loops; Pulse Techniques (Electronics); Radio; Signal Theory (Telecommunication); Speech Processing Systems; Statistical Communication Theory; Switching Theory; Telegraph; Telephone; Television

Advances in Communication Systems, 4 vols. Vol. 1 1965. 80.00 (ISBN 0-12-010901-8); Vol. 2 1966. 80.00 (ISBN 0-12-010902-6); Vol. 3 1968. 80.00 (ISBN 0-12-010903-4); Vol. 4 1975. 80.00 (ISBN 0-12-010904-2). Acad Pr.

Alisouskas, Vincent & Tomasi, Wayne. Digital & Data Communications. (Illus.). 320p. 1985. text ed. 32.95 (ISBN 0-13-212424-6). P-H.

Anderson, Kari J., compiled by. Pacific Telecommunications Conference '83: Directions. 124p. 1983. pap. text ed. 20.00x (ISBN 0-8248-0925-4, Pac Telecom). UH Pr.

Arredondo, Larry A. Getting Started in Telecommunications Management. 1980. softcover 30.00 (ISBN 0-936648-04-X). Telecom Lib.

--Telecommunications Management for Business & Government. Newton, Harry, ed. 280p. 1981. 30.00 (ISBN 0-936648-07-4). Telecom Lib.

Babe, R. E. Cable Television & Telecommunications in Canada: An Economic Analysis. LC 75-620061. 338p. 1975. pap. 7.50 (ISBN 0-87744-129-4). Mich St U Pr.

Bashshur, Rashid L., et al. Telemedicine: Explorations in the Use of Telecommunications in Health Care. (Illus.). 376p. 1975. write for info.; pap. 47.50x spiral bdg. (ISBN 0-398-03311-0). C C Thomas.

Baughcum, Allan & Faulhaber, Gerald. Telecommunications Access & Public Policy. Voigt, Melvin J., ed. LC 84-6233. (Telecommunications & Information Science Ser.). 300p. 1984. text ed. 35.00 (ISBN 0-89391-259-X). Ablex Pub.

Bell Laboratories. Human Factors in Telecommunications International Symposium, 9th. 1980. 75.00 (ISBN 0-686-37981-0). Info Gatekeepers.

Bendat, Julius S. Principles & Applications of Random Noise Theory. rev. ed. LC 77-7225. 456p. 1977. Repr. of 1958 ed. lib. bdg. 26.00 (ISBN 0-88275-556-0). Krieger.

Blackwell, Deborah J. Telecommunications & Education. 1974. pap. 4.00x (ISBN 0-89011-467-6, TEC-103). Abt Bks.

--Telecommunications & Health Services. 1974. pap. 3.50x (ISBN 0-89011-466-8, TEC-104). Abt Bks.

Bone, Jan. Opportunities in Telecommunications. 150p. 1984. 5.95 (ISBN 0-317-37009-X). ALA.

Bones, R. Concise Encyclopedia Dictionary of Telecommunications. Date not set. 15.00 (ISBN 0-444-99955-8). Elsevier.

Bonham, George W., et al. The Communications Revolution & the Education of Americans. LC 80-66849. 64p. (Orig.). 1980. pap. 6.95 (ISBN 0-915390-24-8, Pub. by Change Mag). Transaction Pubs.

Boss, Richard W., et al. Telecommunications - Making Sense out of New Technology & New Legislation: Proceedings of the 21st Annual Clinic on Library Applications of Data Processing. Divilbiss, J. L., ed. 1985. text ed. 15.00 (ISBN 0-87845-072-6). U of Ill Lib Info Sci.

Boutmy, E. J. & Danthine, A., eds. Teleinformatics Seventy-Nine: Proceedings of the International Cenference, Paris, June '79. 316p. 1979. 64.00 (ISBN 0-444-85349-9, North Holland). Elsevier.

Brey, Ron & Grigsby, Charles. Telecourse Student Survey, 1984. 60p. (Orig.). 1985. pap. 5.00 (ISBN 0-87117-153-8). Am Assn Comm Jr Coll.

Brock, Gerald W. The Telecommunications Industry: The Dynamics of Market Structure. LC 80-25299. (Harvard Economic Studies: No. 151). (Illus.). 384p. 1981. text ed. 25.00x (ISBN 0-674-87285-1). Harvard U Pr.

--The Telecommunications Industry: The Dynamics of Market Structure. 336p. 1981. 25.00 (ISBN 0-686-98080-8). Telecom Lib.

Brown, H. U. Telecommunications for Health Care. 112p. 1982. 42.50 (ISBN 0-8493-5588-5). CRC Pr.

Business Telecoms: The New Regime. 197p. 1981. text ed. 98.00x (ISBN 0-686-87214-2, Pub. by Online Conferences England). Brookfield Pub Co.

Bylanski, P. & Ingram, D. G. Digital Transmission Systems. rev. ed. (IEE Telecommunications Ser.). 430p. pap. 35.00 (ISBN 0-906048-37-0, TE004, Pub. by Peregrinus England). Inst Elect Eng.

Cantraine, G. & Destin, E. J., eds. New Systems & Services in Telecommunications II: Proceedings of the 2nd International Conference on New Systems & Services in Telecommunications, Liege, Belgium, Nov. 16-18, 1984. 470p. 1984. 55.75 (ISBN 0-444-87550-6, North-Holland). Elsevier.

Cantraine, G. & Destine, J., eds. New Systems & Services in Telecommunications. 368p. 1981. 64.00 (ISBN 0-444-86206-4, North Holland). Elsevier.

Carne, E. Bryan. Modern Telecommunications. (Applications of Communications Theory Ser.). 306p. 1984. 29.50x (ISBN 0-306-41841-X, Plenum Pr). Plenum Pub.

Carroll, David. Telecommunications for the IBM PCjr. 224p. 1984. pap. 15.95 (ISBN 0-13-902503-0). P-H.

Cattermole, Kenneth W. & O'Reilly, eds. Mathematical Topics in Telecommunications: Optimisation in Electronics & Communications, Vol. 1. 176p. 1984. text ed. 24.95x (ISBN 0-471-80765-6, Pub. by Wiley Interscience). Wiley.

Cattermole, Kenneth W. & O'Reilly, John J., eds. Mathematical Topics in Telecommunications: Problems of Randomness in Communication Engineering, Vol. 2. 352p. 1984. text ed. 32.50x (ISBN 0-471-80763-X, Pub. by Wiley Interscience). Wiley.

Cellular Communications: Proceedings of the Industry Conference, Chicago 1984. 294p. 1984. pap. text ed. 150.00x (ISBN 0-86353-015-X, Pub. by Online). Brookfield Pub Co.

Chin, Felix. Regulatory Reform of Telecommunications: A Selected Bibliography. (Public Administration Ser.: Bibliography P-521). 50p. 1980. pap. 5.50 (ISBN 0-88066-074-0). Vance Biblios.

Christie, Bruce. Human Factors of Information Technology in the Office. LC 84-20903. (Information Processing Ser.). 1985. 26.95 (ISBN 0-471-90631-X). Wiley.

Churchill College, Cambridge England. Human Factors in Telecommunications International Symposium, 8th. 1977. 75.00 (ISBN 0-686-37980-2). Info Gatekeepers.

Clark, D. & Unwin, K. Information Services in Rural Areas: Prospects for Telecommunications Access. 122p. 1980. 25.00x (ISBN 0-86094-058-6, Pub. by GEO Abstracts England). State Mutual Bk.

Clatanoff, Robert M., ed. Ad Valorem Assessment of Telecommunications Property: A Bibliography, Directory & Resource Guide. (CPL Bibliographies Ser: No. 83). 32p. 1982. 8.00 (ISBN 0-86602-083-7). Coun Plan Librarians.

Clatonoff, Robert M. Ad Valorem Assessment of Telecommunications Property. (Research & Information Ser.: No.2). 103p. 1981. 16.50 (ISBN 0-88329-049-9). Intl Assess.

Coates, R. F. Modern Communication Systems. 2nd ed. (Electronic & Electrical Engineering Ser.). (Illus.). 405p. 1984. text ed. 39.95x (ISBN 0-333-33344-6). Scholium Intl.

Codding, George A., Jr. The International Telecommunication Union: An Experiment in International Cooperation. LC 72-4663. (International Propaganda & Communications Ser.). 523p. 1972. Repr. of 1952 ed. 27.50 (ISBN 0-405-04744-4). Ayer Co Pubs.

Codding, George A., Jr. & Rutknowski, Anthony. The ITU in a Changing World. (Artech Telecommunications Library). 350p. 1982. 46.00 (ISBN 0-89006-113-0). Artech Hse.

Committee On Telecommunications. Reports on Selected Topics in Telecommunications. (Orig.). 1969. pap. 6.75 (ISBN 0-309-01751-3). Natl Acad Pr.

Compaine, Benjamin. Understanding New Media: Trends & Issues in Electronic Distribution of Information. 400p. 1984. professional reference 29.95x (ISBN 0-88410-977-1). Ballinger Pub.

Conference on Telecommunication Transmission (1975: London) Conference on Telecommunication Transmission, September 9-11, 1975. LC 76-371266. (Institution of Electrical Engineers Conference Publication Ser.: No. 131). pap. 51.50 (ISBN 0-317-10159-5, 2012128). Bks Demand UMI.

Connor, F. R. Modulation. 2nd ed. (Introductory Topics in Electronics & Telecommunication). 144p. 1982. pap. text ed. 9.95 (ISBN 0-7131-3457-7). E Arnold.

Conrath, David, et al. Evaluating Telecommunications Technology in Medicine. LC 83-71833. (Illus.). 250p. 1983. 50.00 (ISBN 0-89006-126-2). Artech Hse.

Cooper, Edward & Poda, Christopher L., eds. Broadband Network Technology: An Overview for the Data & Telecommunications Industries. LC 83-51319. (Illus.). 163p. (Orig.). 1984. pap. 19.95 (ISBN 0-9613248-0-5). Sytek Pr.

Courville, L., et al, eds. Economic Analysis of Telecommunications: Theory & Applications. 414p. 1983. 64.00 (ISBN 0-444-86674-4, I-180-83, North Holland). Elsevier.

The Data Comms Market in Western Europe 1981-87. (Online Seminar 1981). 179p. (Orig.). 1981. pap. text ed. 75.95 (ISBN 0-903796-72-4, Pub. by Online Conferences England). Brookfield Pub Co.

Demand for Telecommunications Services in the U.S. 1980-2000. 200.00 (ISBN 0-686-32972-4). Info Gatekeepers.

Design Curves for Optical Waveguide Digital Communications Systems. (User Manual & Handbook Ser.: Vol. III). 168p. 50.00 (ISBN 0-686-32957-0). Info Gatekeepers.

Diamond, Edwin, et al. Telecommunications in Crisis: The First Amendment, Technology, & Deregulation. 1983. pap. 6.00 (ISBN 0-932790-39-9). Cato Inst.

Digital Transmission & Its Potential. 50.00 (ISBN 0-686-32967-8). Info Gatekeepers.

Documents in American Telecommunications Policy. Kittross, John M., ed. LC 75-23904. (Historical Studies in Telecommunications Ser.). (Illus.). 1976. Repr. 86.00x (ISBN 0-405-07764-5). Ayer Co Pubs.

DOD Automated Telecommunications Market (I-SA AMPE) 434p. 1981. 1200.00 (ISBN 0-86621-002-4, A919). Frost & Sullivan.

Dordick, H. S. Understanding Modern Telecommunications. 336p. 1986. price not set (ISBN 0-07-017662-0). McGraw.

Dunlop, J. & Smith, D. G. Telecommunications Engineering. 1985. pap. 19.95 (ISBN 0-442-30586-9). Van Nos Reinhold.

Elton, C. J., et al, eds. Evaluating New Telecommunications Services. LC 78-4684. (NATO Conference Series II, Systems Science: Science Vol. 6). 798p. 1978. 105.00x (ISBN 0-306-40004-9, Plenum Pr). Plenum Pub.

Emerine, Richard, et al. A Planning Study for Investigation of Corporate Structures in the Telecommunications Common Carrier Industry. 1973. pap. 18.00x (ISBN 0-89011-462-5, TEC-101). Abt Bks.

Evans, Christopher. The Micro Millenium. 256p. 1980. 10.95 (ISBN 0-686-98078-6). Telecom Lib.

Evans, D. S., ed. Breaking up Bell: Essays on Industrial Organization & Regulation. 298p. 1983. 26.50 (ISBN 0-444-00734-2, North-Holland). Elsevier.

Eward, Ronald S. The Competition & Deregulation of International Telecommunications. 1985. text ed. 50.00 (ISBN 0-89006-158-0). Artech Hse.

Experimental Technology Incentives Program. Toward Competitive Provision of Public Record Message Services. 1981. 75.00 (ISBN 0-686-37963-2). Info Gatekeepers.

Feitz, Frank J. Bum Connection. 204p. 1980. 4.95 (ISBN 0-686-98047-6). Telecom Lib.

First European Fiber Optics & Communications Exposition: EFOC '80, Paris. 125.00 (ISBN 0-686-33024-2). Info Gatekeepers.

First Fiber Optics & Communications Exposition: FOC '78, Chicago, Ill. 125.00 (ISBN 0-686-33020-X). Info Gatekeepers.

Fixed Communications System Service Demand Assessment: 18 to 30 GHz. Exec. Summary. 20.00 (ISBN 0-686-33011-0); Final Report. 100.00 (ISBN 0-686-33012-9); Appendix. 100.00 (ISBN 0-686-33013-7). Info Gatekeepers.

Frankel, Theodore. Tables for Traffic Management & Design. 1977. 8.95 (ISBN 0-686-98071-9). Telecom Lib.

Fransecky, Roger B. Telecommunications & Community Services. 1974. pap. 3.00x (ISBN 0-89011-468-4, TEC-102). Abt Bks.

Fraser, W. Telecommunications. 2nd ed. 812p. 1969. 119.25 (ISBN 0-677-61240-0). Gordon.

Freeman, Roger. Telecommunication System Engineering: Analog & Digital Network Design. LC 79-26661. 480p. 1980. 45.95 (ISBN 0-471-02955-6, Pub. by Wiley-Interscience). Wiley.

Freeman, Roger L. Reference Manual for Telecommunications. LC 84-13207. 1500p. 1984. text ed. 75.00 (ISBN 0-471-86753-5, Pub. by Wiley-Interscience). Wiley.

--Telecommunications Transmission Handbook. 700p. 1980. 49.50 (ISBN 0-686-98109-X). Telecom Lib.

The Future of the Electronics & Telecommunications Industries in Australia. 93p. (Orig.). 1978. pap. text ed. 18.00x (ISBN 0-85825-099-3, Pub. by Inst Engineering Australia). Brookfield Pub Co.

Gallager, Robert G. Information Theory & Reliable Communication. LC 68-26850. 588p. 1968. 54.00x (ISBN 0-471-29048-3). Wiley.

Glossary of Fiber Optics Terms. (Eng., Fr, Span. & Ger.). 35.00 (ISBN 0-686-32959-7). Info Gatekeepers.

Godfrey, Dave & Parkhill, Douglas. Gutenberg Two: The New Electronics & Social Change. 2nd rev. ed. 224p. 1980. 10.95 (ISBN 0-686-98075-1). Telecom Lib.

Goeller, Lee & Goldstone, Gerald. The Business Communications Review Manual of PBXs. 2nd ed. 350p. 1982. 145.00 (ISBN 0-686-98056-5). Telecom Lib.

Grant, Sam. A Communication Manager's Guide to Telecommunications in Great Britain. new ed. 1979. 75.00 (ISBN 0-936648-00-7). Telecom Lib.

Grant, Steven C. A Management Guide to Automatic Call Distributors. 240p. 1981. 125.00 (ISBN 0-686-98043-3). Telecom Lib.

GRINSEC. Electronic Switching. (Studies in Telecommunication: Vol. 2). 680p. 1983. 89.00 (ISBN 0-444-86448-2, North Holland). Elsevier.

Gross, Lynne S. Telecommunications: An Introduction to Radio, Television & the Developing Media. 480p. 1983. pap. text ed. write for info. (ISBN 0-697-04359-2). Wm C Brown.

--Telecommunications: An Introduction to Radio, Television & the Developing Media. 2nd ed. 496p. 1986. pap. text ed. price not set (ISBN 0-697-00479-1); price not set instr's. manual (ISBN 0-697-00906-8). Wm C Brown.

Hamsher, Donald H., ed. Communications System Engineering Handbook. 1967. 89.50 (ISBN 0-07-025960-7). McGraw.

Haykin, Simon. Communication Systems. 2nd ed. (Management Ser.). 653p. 1983. 42.50 (ISBN 0-471-09691-1); solution manual avail. (ISBN 0-471-87155-9). Wiley.

Herring, James M. & Gross, Gerald C. Telecommunications: Economics & Regulations. LC 74-4686. (Telecommunications Ser.). 558p. 1974. Repr. of 1936 ed. 35.00x (ISBN 0-405-06050-5). Ayer Co Pubs.

Hoover, Stewart M. The Electronic Giant. 160p. (Orig.). 1981. pap. 6.95 (ISBN 0-87178-217-0). Brethren.

Horizon House, Inc. Intelcom '77; Telecommunications & Economec Development, 3 vols. 1772p. 1977. Set. pap. text ed. 25.00 (ISBN 0-89006-085-1). Artech Hse.

--Intelcom '79 Conference Proceedings: Change... The New Definition of International Communications. 602p. 1979. pap. text ed. 10.00 (ISBN 0-89006-086-X). Artech Hse.

House, William C. Electronic Communication Systems. 1980. 25.00 (ISBN 0-89433-098-5). Petrocelli.

How to Find Information on Telecommunications. 150.00 (ISBN 0-686-33029-3). Info Gatekeepers.

Hudson, J. E. Adaptive Array Principles. (IEE Electromagnetic Waves Ser.). 288p. 1981. casebound 84.50 (ISBN 0-906048-55-9, EW011, Pub. by Peregrinus England). Inst Elect Eng.

Inose, H. Telecommunication Technologies. 1984. 95.00 (ISBN 0-444-87565-4). Elsevier.

Interconnection Glossary. 25.00 (ISBN 0-686-32974-0). Info Gatekeepers.

International Conference London, 1983. Business Telecom: Proceedings of the International Conference London, 1983. 350p. (Orig.). 1983. pap. text ed. 123.50x (ISBN 0-903796-95-3, Pub. by Online Conferences England). Brookfield Pub Co.

The International Fiber Optics & Communications Exposition in Its Fourth Year: FOC '81 East, Cambridge, Mass. 125.00 (ISBN 0-686-33023-4). Info Gatekeepers.

International Resource Development Inc. U. K. Telecommunication Market Opportunities. 186p. 1983. 1650.00x (ISBN 0-88694-573-9). Intl Res Dev.

International Telecommunications Standards: Issues & Implications for the 1980's. 1983. 75.00 (ISBN 0-317-11967-2). Info Gatekeepers.

Jefferson, George. Communications Getting It All Together: The British Computer Society Lecture, No. 4. (British Computer Society). 14p. 1983. 11.95x (ISBN 0-471-26269-2, Wiley Heyden). Wiley.

Jewett, Jim & Shrago, Jackie. Designing Optimal Voice Networks. 240p. 40.00 (ISBN 0-317-06285-9). Telephony.

--Designing Optimal Voice Networks for Business, Government & Telephone Companies. 240p. 1980. 39.95 (ISBN 0-686-98044-1). Telecom Lib.

Jordan, Alan H. The Only Telemarketing Book You'll Ever Need. 191p. 1982. 99.00 (ISBN 0-940896-06-0). Add-Effect Assoc.

Kaufman, Robert J. Cost-Effective Telecommunications Management: Turning Telephone Costs Into Profits. 288p. 1983. 24.95 (ISBN 0-8436-1609-1). Van Nos Reinhold.

Kay, Peg & Powell, Patricia, eds. Future Information Technology: Nineteen Eighty-Four Telecommunications. 2nd ed. (National Bureau of Standards Special Publications 500-119. Computer Science & Technology Ser.). 347p. (Orig.). pap. 9.50 (ISBN 0-318-11722-3). Gov Printing Office.

Telecommunication Transmission. (IEE Conference Ser.: No. 246). 1985. 83.00 (ISBN 0-85296-307-6). Inst Electrical.
Telecommunications, 33 vols. (Illus.). 14902p. 1974. Set. 805.00 (ISBN 0-405-06030-0). Ayer Co Pubs.
Telecommunications Energy Conference-Intelec 81. (IEE Conference Publication Ser.: No. 196). 371p. 1981. 96.00 (ISBN 0-85296-236-3). Inst Elect Eng.
Telecommunications in China. 130.00 (ISBN 0-686-33028-5). Info Gatekeepers.
Telecommunications in Egypt: Short Term Plan for Cairo. 200.00 (ISBN 0-686-32971-6). Info Gatekeepers.
Telecommunications Market in Brazil 1978-1982. 500.00 (ISBN 0-686-33016-1). Info Gatekeepers.
Telecommunications Market Studies: Egypt. 75.00 (ISBN 0-686-32984-8). Info Gatekeepers.
Telecommunications Market Studies: Hong Kong. 75.00 (ISBN 0-686-32983-X). Info Gatekeepers.
Telecommunications Market Studies: India. 75.00 (ISBN 0-686-32985-6). Info Gatekeepers.
Telecommunications Market Studies: Mexico. 75.00 (ISBN 0-686-32986-4). Info Gatekeepers.
Telecommunications Market Studies: Taiwan. 50.00 (ISBN 0-686-32988-0). Info Gatekeepers.
Telecommunications Market Studies: Venezuela. 75.00 (ISBN 0-686-32987-2). Info Gatekeepers.
Telecommunications Markets in Nineteen Selected Countries. 200.00 (ISBN 0-686-32970-8). Info Gatekeepers.
Telecommunications Policy Research Conference, Annual 10th. Proceedings. Gandy, Oscar, et al, eds. LC 83-6408. 256p. 1983. text ed. 24.95 pers. ed. (ISBN 0-89391-195-X); text ed. 39.50 inst. ed. Ablex Pub.
Telecommunications Reports. yearly 188.00 (ISBN 0-686-98052-2). Telecom Lib.
Telecommunications User's Handbook. pap. 13.00 (ISBN 0-87102-096-3, 50-7843); pap. 9.00 members. Natl Ret Merch.
Teleconferencing, a New Communications Service for the 1980's. 225.00 (ISBN 0-686-33033-1). Info Gatekeepers.
Teleconferencing Bibliography. 35.00 (ISBN 0-686-33032-3). Info Gatekeepers.
Teleconferencing Guide. 90.00 (ISBN 0-686-33031-5). Info Gatekeepers.
Telehealth Handbook. 75.00 (ISBN 0-686-32979-1). Info Gatekeepers.
Telephone Terminal Equipment: Registration List. 50.00 (ISBN 0-686-32973-2). Info Gatekeepers.
Television As the Home Communications Terminal. (Reports Ser.: No. 176). 176p. 1981. 985.00x (ISBN 0-88694-176-8). Intl Res Dev.
Temes, Lloyd. Schaum's Outline of Electronic Communication. (Schaum Outline Ser.). (Illus.). 1979. pap. 8.95 (ISBN 0-07-063495-5). McGraw.
Third Fiber Optics & Communications Exposition: FOC '80, San Francisco. 125.00 (ISBN 0-686-33022-6). Info Gatekeepers.
Thirty-Twenty GHz Mixed User Architecture Development Study. Exec. Study. 20.00 (ISBN 0-686-33007-2); Final Report. 100.00 (ISBN 0-686-33008-0). Info Gatekeepers.
Thomas, Ronald R. Telecommunication for the Executive. 180p. 1984. 19.95 (ISBN 0-89433-233-3). Petrocelli.
--Telecommunications for the Executive. (Illus.). 180p. 1984. 19.95. Van Nos Reinhold.
Tischler, Morris. Experiments in Telecommunications. Haas, Mark, ed. (Linear Integrated Circuit Applications Ser.). (Illus.). 176p. 1980. pap. text ed. 16.00x (ISBN 0-07-064782-8). McGraw.
Transborder Data Flow Policies: Papers Presented at the IBI Conference on Transborder Data Flow Policies, Rome, Italy, 23-27 June 1980. 681p. 1981. pap. 62.50 (ISBN 0-89059-012-5, UPB105, UPB). Unipub.
Transmission Cost Comparison for Satellite, Fiber Optics & Microwave Radio Community. 225.00 (ISBN 0-686-32975-9). Info Gatekeepers.
Transport & Communications Bulletin for Asia & the Pacific, Nos. 50-53. No. 50. pap. 5.00 (ISBN 0-686-94303-1, UN76/2F16, UN); No. 51. pap. 3.50 (ISBN 0-686-99337-3, UN77/2F20); No. 52. pap. 5.00 (ISBN 0-686-99338-1, UN79/2F2); No. 53. pap. 7.00 (ISBN 0-686-99339-X, UN80/2F8). Unipub.
Trends & Recent Developments in Telecommunications Policy & Regulation in the United States. 100.00 (ISBN 0-686-32966-X). Info Gatekeepers.
Tsividis, Yannis & Antognetti, Paolo, eds. Design of MOS VLSI Circuits for Telecommunications. (Illus.). 640p. 1985. text ed. 34.95 (ISBN 0-13-200643-X). P-H.
A Twenty-Five Year Forecast for Commercial Communications Satellites. 225.00 (ISBN 0-686-33002-1). Info Gatekeepers.
User's Guide for Voice & Data Communications Security Equipment. 75.00 (ISBN 0-686-32978-3). Info Gatekeepers.
Veley. Semiconductors & Electronic Communications Made Easy. (Illus.). 322p. 1982. o.p 15.95 (ISBN 0-8306-0052-3); pap. 8.95 (ISBN 0-8306-1435-4). TAB Bks.
ViewText 'Eighty-One Conference. 50.00 (ISBN 0-686-33030-7). Info Gatekeepers.
Vilips, Vess V. Data Modem: Selection & Evaluation Guide. LC 77-189393. (Modern Frontiers in Applied Science Ser.). (Illus.). pap. 24.80 (ISBN 0-317-08738-X, 2010073). Bks Demand UMI.
Vocabulary for Fiber Optics & Lightwave Communications. 40.00 (ISBN 0-686-32964-3). Info Gatekeepers.
Wallenstein, Gerd. International Telecommunication Agreements. LC 77-72058. (International Telecommunications Agreements Ser.). 1979. Set. (3 bdgs.) 300.00 (ISBN 0-379-10045-2); Suppl. 1. 50.00. Oceana.
Walp, Robert M., ed. Telecommunication in Alaska. 141p. 1982. pap. text ed. 15.00x (ISBN 0-8248-0926-2, Pac Telecom). UH Pr.
Washington Group. Major Markets in Telecommunications. Rosenzweig, Benjamin Z., ed. (New Technologies Market Reviews). 250p. (Orig.). 1985. pap. text ed. 127.00 (ISBN 0-912257-05-9). Marketing Intl.
Wedemeyer, Dan J., ed. Pacific Telecommunications Conference '81: Proceedings. 693p. 1981. pap. text ed. 25.00x (ISBN 0-8248-0922-X, Pac Telecom). UH Pr.
--Pacific Telecommunications Conference '82: Proceedings. 297p. 1982. pap. text ed. 25.00x (ISBN 0-8248-0923-8, Pac Telecom). UH Pr.
--Pacific Telecommunications Conference '83: Proceedings. 257p. 1983. pap. text ed. 30.00x (ISBN 0-8248-0924-6, Pac Telecom). UH Pr.
--PTC '85: Proceedings. 438p. 1985. pap. text ed. 45.00x (ISBN 0-8248-1009-0, Pacific Telecomm). UH Pr.
West, A. & Janson, P., eds. Local Networks for Computer Communications. 470p. 1981. 66.00 (ISBN 0-444-86287-0). Elsevier.
Wicklein, John. Electronic Nightmare. 282p. 1981. 14.95 (ISBN 0-686-98118-9). Telecom Lib.
--Electronic Nightmare: The Home Communications Set & Your Freedom. LC 81-70490. 304p. 1982. pap. 11.95x (ISBN 0-8070-6165-4, BP634, Pub. by Ariadne Bks.). Beacon Pr.
Williams, Francis. Transmitting World News: A Study of Telecommunciations & the Press. LC 72-4686. (International Propaganda & Communications Ser.). (Illus.). 95p. 1972. Repr. of 1953 ed. 12.00 (ISBN 0-405-04770-3). Ayer Co Pubs.
Willis, Jerry & Schrock, Jay. Exploring the Outer Limits: Telecommunications & Personal Computers. 384p. 1985. pap. 17.95 (ISBN 0-88056-349-4). Dilithium Pr.
Wilson, John L. Business System Options. 1978. 7.95 (ISBN 0-686-98070-0). Telecom Lib.
Woolfe. Videotex: Television - Telephone Information Services. 184p. 1980. 34.95 (ISBN 0-471-26089-4, Wiley Heyden). Wiley.
World's Submarine Telephone Cable Systems, 1980. 100.00 (ISBN 0-686-32977-5). Info Gatekeepers.
Wozencraft, John M. & Jacobs, I. M. Principles of Communication Engineering. LC 65-16429. 720p. 1965. 58.00x (ISBN 0-471-96240-6). Wiley.
Zacharis, John. Exploring Careers in Communications & Telecommunications. 1985. 8.97 (ISBN 0-8239-0644-2). Rosen Group.
Zima, Joseph P. Interviewing: Key to Effective Management. 352p. 1983. pap. text ed. 17.95 (ISBN 0-574-22720-2, 13-5720); instr's guide avail. (ISBN 0-574-22721-0, 13-5721). SRA.

TELECOMMUNICATION–APPARATUS AND SUPPLIES

Coughlin, Vincent J. Telecommunication Equipment: Equipment Fundamentals & Network Structures. (Illus.). 144p. 1984. 24.50 (ISBN 0-442-21737-4). Van Nos Reinhold.
DeFrance, J. J. Communications Electronics Circuits. 2nd ed. LC 71-187116. 1972. text ed. 37.95 (ISBN 0-03-083139-3, HoltC). HR&W.
Gurrie, Michael & O'Connor, Patrick. Voice-Data Telecommunications Systems: An Introduction to Technology. (Illus.). 416p. 1986. text ed. 34.95 (ISBN 0-13-943283-3). P-H.
Institute for Telecommunication Sciences. A User's Manual for Optical Waveguide Communications. (User Manual & Handbook Ser.: Vol. I). 287p. 1978. 95.00. Info Gatekeepers.
Kuecken, John A. Talking Computers & Telecommunications. 256p. 1982. 28.95 (ISBN 0-442-24721-4). Van Nos Reinhold.
Lancaster, Kathleen L., ed. International Telecommunications: User Requirements & Supplier Strategies. LC 81-48462. (An Arthur D. Little Bk.). 208p. 1982. 27.50x (ISBN 0-669-05368-6). Lexington Bks.
Miller, Stewart E. & Chynoweth, Alan G., eds. Optical Fiber Telecommunications. LC 78-20046. 1979. 65.50 (ISBN 0-12-497350-7). Acad Pr.
Telecommunications Equipment Leasing. (Reports Ser.: No. 525). 256p. 1982. 1285.00x (ISBN 0-88694-525-9). Intl Res Dev.
Telecommunications Systems & Equipment in Oceania. 344p. 1983. 1700.00 (ISBN 0-86621-544-1). Frost & Sullivan.
Telecommunications Systems & Equipment Market in the Middle East Arab Countries. 399p. 1984. 1750.00 (ISBN 0-86621-620-0). Frost & Sullivan.
Teleconferencing. (Reports Ser.: No. 534). 115p. 1983. 985.00x (ISBN 0-88694-534-8). Intl Res Dev.
Texas Instruments Inc. Solid State Communications: Design of Communications Equipment Using Semiconductors. (Texas Instruments Electronics Ser.). 1966. 49.00 (ISBN 0-07-063739-3). McGraw.
Videotex Business Applications Market. (Reports Ser.: No. 195). 136p. 1982. 1285.00x (ISBN 0-88694-195-4). Intl Res Dev.
Welzenbach, Lanora F., ed. Contracting for Communications Services. 100p. (Orig.). 1984. pap. text ed. 15.00 (ISBN 0-915164-20-5). Natl Assn Coll.

TELECOMMUNICATION–DATA PROCESSING

Cambron, Jim. The First Primer of Microcomputer Telecommunications. (Illus.). 128p. (Orig.). 1984. 14.95 (ISBN 0-8306-0688-2, 1688); pap. 10.25 (ISBN 0-8306-1688-8). TAB Bks.
Chapuis, R. J. One Hundred Years of Telephone Switching (1878-1978) Part 1, Manual & Electromechanical Switching, 1878-1960s. (Studies in Telecommunications: Vol. 1). 464p. 1982. 95.00 (ISBN 0-444-86289-7, North Holland). Elsevier.
Computer-Based Conference Systems for Developing Countries: Report of a Workshop Held in Ottawa, Canada, 26-30 October 1981. 43p. 1982. pap. 7.00 (ISBN 0-88936-325-0, IDRC190, IDRC). Unipub.
Computer Telecommunications. Date not set. price not set (C101392). HarBraceJ.
Conference on Transnational Data Flow: TDF '79. 105.00 (ISBN 0-686-33025-0). Info Gatekeepers.
Couch, Leon W. Digital & Analog Communication Systems. 672p. 1983. text ed. write for info. (ISBN 0-02-325240-5). Macmillan.
Data Communications Standards Library. 330p. 1981. 85.00 (ISBN 0-686-98095-6). Telecom Lib.
Davidoff, Frank & Rossi, John, eds. Digital Video One. (Illus.). 114p. 1982. pap. text ed. 25.00 (ISBN 0-940690-02-0). Soc Motion Pic & TV Engrs.
Design Curves for Optical Waveguide Digital Communications Systems. (User Manual & Handbook Ser.: Vol. III). 168p. 50.00 (ISBN 0-686-32957-0). Info Gatekeepers.
Fishman, Katherine D. The Computer Establishment. 468p. 1981. 20.95 (ISBN 0-686-98079-4). Telecom Lib.
Freeman, Roger L. Telecommunication Transmission Handbook. 2nd ed. LC 81-7499. 706p. 1981. 61.95x (ISBN 0-471-08029-2, Pub. by Wiley-Interscience). Wiley.
Glasgal, Ralph. Techniques in Data Communications. 200p. 1983. text ed. 39.00 (ISBN 0-89006-122-X). Artech Hse.
Hills, Michael T. Telecommunications Switching Principles. (Illus.). 1979. text ed. 40.00x (ISBN 0-262-08092-3). MIT Pr.
Johansen, Robert & Ferguson, John. Teleconference on Integrated Data Bases in Postsecondary Education, a Transcript & Summary. 70p. 1975. 7.50 (ISBN 0-318-14425-5). Inst Future.
Johansen, Robert, et al. Effects on Working Patterns. (Group Communication Through Computers: Vol. 5). 199p. 1978. 12.00 (ISBN 0-318-14413-1, R41). Inst Future.
--Electronic Education: Using Teleconferencing in Postsecondary Organizations. 176p. 1978. 12.00 (ISBN 0-318-14414-X, R42). Inst Future.
Kearsley, Greg. Training for Tomorrow: Distributed Learning Through Computer & Communications Technology. 128p. 1985. 19.95 (ISBN 0-201-11652-9). Addison-Wesley.
Kellejian, Robert. Applied Electronic Communication: Circuits, Systems, Transmission. rev. ed. 608p. 1980. 29.95 (ISBN 0-574-21580-8, 13-4580); instr's. guide avail. SRA.
Kennedy, M. Carlos, intro. by. Digital Video Two. (Illus.). 162p. (Orig.). 1982. pap. text ed. 25.00 (ISBN 0-940690-03-9). Soc Motion Pic & TV Engrs.
Leemon, Sheldon & Levitan, Arlan. MacTalk: Telecomputing on the Macintosh. Compute!, ed. (Orig.). 1985. pap. 14.95 (ISBN 0-942386-85-X). Compute Pubns.
Lewis, Sash. Plugging In: The Microcomputerist's Guide to Telecommunications. LC 84-45165. 192p. (Orig.). 1985. pap. 11.95 (ISBN 0-8019-7450-X). Chilton.
Lucantoni, D. M. Algorithmic Analysis of a Communication Model with Retransmission of Fluid Messages. (Research Notes in Mathematics Ser. No. 81). 154p. 1983. pap. text ed. 20.95 (ISBN 0-273-08571-9). Pitman Pub MA.
Marcus, Richard, ed. Digital Video Three. Rev. ed. (Illus.). 230p. (Orig.). 1982. pap. text ed. 25.00 (ISBN 0-940690-04-7). Soc Motion Pic & TV Engrs.
Martin, James. Application Development Without Programmers. 345p. 1982. 32.50 (ISBN 0-686-98081-6). Telecom Lib.
--Computer Networks & Distributed Processing. 562p. 1981. 34.00 (ISBN 0-686-98085-9). Telecom Lib.
--Design Strategy for Distributed Processing. 624p. 1981. 37.50 (ISBN 0-686-98083-2). Telecom Lib.
--Telecommunications & the Computer. 670p. 1976. 37.50 (ISBN 0-686-98073-5). Telecom Lib.
Meyer, Bruce L. Data Communications Practice, Vol. XI. 1979. 13.00 (ISBN 0-686-98067-0). Telecom Lib.
National Computing Centre. Introducing Computerized Telephone Switchboards (PABXs) (Illus.). 92p. (Orig.). 1982. 15.00x (ISBN 0-85012-364-X). Intl Pubns Serv.
Nora, Simon & Minc, Alain. The Computerization of Society: A Report to the President of France. 1980. pap. 6.95 (ISBN 0-262-64020-1). MIT Pr.
Packet Data Communications 1978. 375.00 (ISBN 0-686-32976-7). Info Gatekeepers.
Packet Data Communications 1981. rev. ed. (Illus.). 361p. 1981. pap. 375.00x (ISBN 0-940520-20-6, Pub. by Future Syst Inc). Monegon Ltd.
Programming & Services Strategies for 2-way TV & Viewdata Systems. (Report Ser.: No. 177). 228p. 1981. 985.00x (ISBN 0-88694-177-6). Intl Res Dev.
Report Analyzes Telecommunications Brokering Business. 250p. write for info. C C M I.
Reynolds, George W. Introduction to Business Telecommunications. 320p. 1984. Additional supplements may be obtained from publisher. text ed. 27.95 (ISBN 0-675-20108-X). Merrill.
Richardson, Robert M. Synchronous Packet Radio Using the Software Approach: Vancouver Protocol, Vol. 1. Blevins, T. F., ed. 223p. 1983. 22.00x (ISBN 0-940972-07-7). Richcraft Eng.
Rosenberg, Jerry M. Dictionary of Computers, Data Processing, & Telecommunications. LC 83-12359. 614p. 1984. 32.50x (ISBN 0-471-87638-0); pap. 14.95 (ISBN 0-471-88582-7). Assn Inform & Image Mgmt.
Rosner, Roy D. Distributed Telecommunications Networks via Satellites & Packet Switching. (Engineering Ser.). 235p. 1982. 31.50 (ISBN 0-534-97933-5). Lifetime Learn.
Schwartz, Mischa. Information Transmission, Modulation & Noise: A Unified Approach. 3rd ed. (McGraw-Hill Electrical & Electronic Engineering Ser.). (Illus.). 672p. 1980. text ed. 46.00 (ISBN 0-07-055782-9). McGraw.
Shanmugam, K. Sam. Digital & Analog Communication Systems. LC 78-26191. 600p. 1979. text ed. 44.00 (ISBN 0-471-03090-2); tchr's manual avail. (ISBN 0-471-07832-8). Wiley.
--Digital & Analog Communication Systems. 600p. 1979. 32.95 (ISBN 0-686-98113-8). Telecom Lib.
Sherman, Kenneth. Data Communications: A User's Guide. 348p. 1981. 21.95 (ISBN 0-686-98096-4). Telecom Lib.
Software Engineering for Telecommunication Switching Systems. (IEE Conference Publication Series). 219p. pap. 74.00 (ISBN 0-85296-242-8, IC198). Inst Elect Eng.
Srinath, M. D. & Rajasekaran, P. K. An Introduction to Statistical Signal Processing with Applications. LC 78-15417. 499p. 1979. 49.95x (ISBN 0-471-04404-0, Pub. by Wiley-Interscience). Wiley.
Stafford, R. H. Digital Television: Bandwidth Reduction & Communication Aspects. LC 80-17542. 387p. 1980. 47.50 (ISBN 0-471-07857-3, Pub. by Wiley-Interscience). Wiley.
Takamura, S., et al. Software Design for Electronic Switching Systems. (Illus.). 256p. 1979. 48.00 (ISBN 0-906048-18-4). Inst Elect Eng.
Telecom Library Research Group. Telecom Library Guide to Key Systems & Mini-PBXs. 156p. 1981. 75.00 (ISBN 0-686-98036-0). Telecom Lib.
Utz, Peter. The Complete Home Video Book, 2 vols, Vol. I & II. LC 82-10129. (Illus.). 608p. 1983. 29.95 set (ISBN 0-13-161364-2); Vol. 1. pap. 16.95 (ISBN 0-13-161349-9); Vol. 2. pap. 9.95 (ISBN 0-13-161356-1). P-H.

Vallee, Jacques & Askevold, Gerald. Computer Conferencing in the Geo Sciences. 93p. 1977. 9.00 (ISBN 0-318-14411-5). Inst Future.
Vallee, Jacques, et al. Social, Managerial, & Economic Issues. (Group Communication Through Computers: Vol. 4). 222p. 1978. 15.00 (ISBN 0-318-14421-2, R40). Inst Future.
--A Study of Social Effects. (Group Communication Through Computers: Vol. 2). 160p. 1974. 10.50 (ISBN 0-318-14424-7, R33). Inst Future.
Wilson, John L. Business System Options. 1978. 7.95 (ISBN 0-686-98070-0). Telecom Lib.
Woolfe. Videotex: Television - Telephone Information Services. 184p. 1980. 34.95 (ISBN 0-471-26089-4, Wiley Heyden). Wiley.
Zorkoczy, Peter. Information Technology: An Introduction. LC 82-10115. (Communications Library). (Illus.). 137p. 1983. Professional 35.95 (ISBN 0-86729-037-4); members 31.00. Assn Inform & Image Mgmt.

TELECOMMUNICATION–DICTIONARIES

Aries, S. J. Dictionary of Telecommunications. 336p. 1981. 39.95 (ISBN 0-408-00328-6). Butterworth.
Bones, R. A., ed. Dictionary of Telecommunications. (Illus.). 1970. 15.00 (ISBN 0-8022-2309-5). Philos Lib.
Clason, W. E. Elsevier's Telecommunication Dictionary. 2nd rev. ed. (Eng., Fr., Ital., Span., Dutch & Ger.). 604p. 1976. 125.75 (ISBN 0-444-41394-4). Elsevier.
Dictionary of Telecommunications: English-Chinese. (Eng. & Chinese.). 721p. 1961. pap. 12.95 (ISBN 0-686-92554-8, M-9589). French & Eur.
Goedecke. Dictionary of Electrical Engineering, Telecommunications & Electronics: English-German-French, Vol. 3. 1967. 39.00 (ISBN 0-9913001-1-4, Pub. by O Brandstetter WG). Heyden.
--Dictionary of Electrical Engineering, Telecommunications & Electronics: French-English-German, Vol. 2. 1966. 34.00 (ISBN 0-9913001-0-6, Pub. by O Brandstetter WG). Heyden.
Goedecke, W. Woerterbuch der Elektrotechnik, Fernmeldetechnik und Elektonik, Vol. 1. (Ger., Eng. & Fr., Dictionary of Electrical Engineering, Telecommunication Engineering & Electronics). 1966-68. 56.00 (ISBN 3-87097-013-8, M-7018). French & Eur.
Graham, John. Facts on File Dictionary of Telecommunications. (Illus.). 224p. 1983. 15.95 (ISBN 0-87196-120-2). Facts on File.
--The Facts on File Dictionary of Telecommunications. 224p. 1984. pap. 6.95 (ISBN 0-87196-876-2). Facts on File.
Langenscheidts Fachwoerterbuch Fernmeldewesen. (Ger. & Span.). 769p. 32.00 (ISBN 0-686-56628-9, M-7537, Pub. by Langenscheidt). French & Eur.
Langley, Graham. Telephony's Dictionary. 35.00 (ISBN 0-317-06280-8). Telephony.
Proulx, G. J. Dictionnaire d'Electronique et Tele-Communication: Anglais-Francais. (Fr. & Eng.). 582p. 1979. 15.95 (ISBN 0-686-57089-8, M-6469). French & Eur.
Sippl, Charles. Data Communications Dictionary. 545p. 1984. pap. 12.95. Van Nos Reinhold.
Wernicke, H. Dictionary of Electronics, Communications & Electrical Engineering, 2 vols. 1300p. Vol. 1. 36.00x (ISBN 0-685-05199-4); Vol. 2. 36.00x (ISBN 0-685-05200-1). Adlers Foreign Bks.

TELECOMMUNICATION–ECONOMIC ASPECTS

George Washington University. Challenges in Telecommunications & Information Handling for the New Administration. 212p. 1981. pap. text ed. 25.00x (ISBN 0-914894-30-7). Computer Sci.
Nora, Simon & Minc, Alain. The Computerization of Society: A Report to the President of France. 1980. pap. 6.95 (ISBN 0-262-64020-1). MIT Pr.

TELECOMMUNICATION–EXAMINATIONS, QUESTIONS, ETC.

Rudman, Jack. Telecommunications Aide. (Career Examination Ser.: C-2877). (Cloth bdg. avail. on request). pap. 10.00 (ISBN 0-8373-2877-2). Natl Learning.

TELECOMMUNICATION–HISTORY

Communications Satellites Calendar, Nineteen Fifty-Eight to Nineteen Eighty-Two. 75.00 (ISBN 0-686-32991-0). Info Gatekeepers.
Kutsch, Arnulf. Rundfunkwissenschaft im Dritten Reich. (Rundfunkstudien Ser.: Vol. 2). (Ger.). 600p. 1985. lib. bdg. write for info. (ISBN 3-598-21572-X). K G Saur.
Sterling, Christopher H., ed. Historical Studies in Telecommunications, 5 bks in 6 vols. 1976. Set. 610.00x (ISBN 0-405-07756-4). Ayer Co Pubs.

TELECOMMUNICATION–LAW AND LEGISLATION

Cable Communication Policy Act of 1984. 35.00 (ISBN 0-317-29482-2, #CO3360, Law & Business). HarBraceJ.
Forrest, Herbert E. & Wiley, Richard E. Regulation & Deregulation after the AT & T Divestiture. LC 85-110902. (Patents, Copyrights, Trademarks, & Literary Property Course Handbook Ser.: No. 192). 1984. 40.00. PLI.
Irwin, David. Telecommunications Regulatory Monitor. LC 84-203579. write for info. Amer Bar Assn.
Negotiating Telecommunication Contracts. 35.00 (ISBN 0-317-29495-4, #CO3301, Law & Business). HarBraceJ.
Noll, Edward M. General Radiotelephone License Handbook. 7th ed. LC 82-50660. 608p. 1982. pap. 18.95 (ISBN 0-672-21930-1). Sams.
Special Commission on Election Law & Voter Participation. Changing Communications Technology & Future Federal Elections. 170p. 1984. 8.00 (ISBN 0-89707-143-3). Amer Bar Assn.
Telecommunications Law Reform: Legislative Analysis. 64p. 1980. 3.75 (ISBN 0-8447-0227-7). Am Enterprise.

TELECOMMUNICATION–TRAFFIC

Jewett, Jim & Shrago, Jackie. Traffic Engineering Tables. 480p. 125.00 (ISBN 0-317-06284-0). Telephony.
Lawson, Robert W. A Practical Guide to Teletraffic Engineering & Administration. 128p. 20.00 (ISBN 0-317-06282-4). Telephony.
Mina, Ramses. Introduction to Teletraffic Engineering. 11.00 (ISBN 0-317-06287-5). Telephony.
Newell, G. F. The M-M Service System with Ranked Servers in Heavy Traffic. (Lecture Notes in Economics & Mathematical Systems Ser.: Vol. 231). xi, 126p. 1984. 11.00 (ISBN 0-387-13377-1). Springer-Verlag.

TELECOMMUNICATION (COMPUTER PROGRAMS)

Enright, Thomas E., et al. Compute's Guide to Telecomputing on the Apple. Compute Editors, ed. (Orig.). 1985. pap. 9.95 (ISBN 0-942386-98-1). Compute Pubns.
Killen, Harold B. Telecommunication & Data Communication System Design with Troubleshooting. (Illus.). 336p. 1986. text ed. 32.95 (ISBN 0-13-902545-6). P-H.
Levitan, Arlan R. & Leemon, Sheldon. Compute's Telecomputing on the IBM. Compute Editors, ed. (Orig.). 1985. pap. 14.95 (ISBN 0-942386-96-5). Compute Pubns.

TELECOMMUNICATION LINES

see also Radio Lines

Clement, M. A. Transmission. 52p. 7.00 (ISBN 0-317-06288-3). Telephony.
Kieffer, Tom & Hansen, Terry. Get Connected: A Guide to Telecommunications. Pressler, Rich, ed. (Illus.). 400p. 1984. pap. 24.95 (ISBN 0-912677-28-7). Ashton-Tate Bks.
Kuecken, John A. Exploring Antennas & Transmission Lines by Personal Computer. (Illus.). 384p. 1985. 39.95 (ISBN 0-442-24714-1). Van Nos Reinhold.
Tokarz, Roger F. Solving Noise & Transmission Problems in Telephone Loop Plant. (Illus.). 84p. 10.00 (ISBN 0-317-06293-X). Telephony.

TELECOMMUNICATION SYSTEMS

see also Data Transmission Systems; Intercommunication Systems; Microwave Communication Systems; Mobile Communication Systems

Arlen, Gary H. & Adler, Richard, eds. Videotex-Teleservices Directory, Nineteen Eighty-Five. 272p. (Orig.). 1985. pap. text ed. 80.00 (ISBN 0-9609768-1-7). Arlen Comm Inc.
Bartee, Thomas, ed. Data Communications Network & Systems. LC 84-51868. 39.95 (ISBN 0-672-22235-3, 22235). Sams.
Business Communications Staff. Emerging Local Area Network Business. 1985. pap. 1500.00 (ISBN 0-89336-438-X, G-074R). BCC.
Carlson, A. B. Communications Systems. 3rd ed. (Electrical Engineering Ser.). 704p. 1985. price not set (ISBN 0-07-009960-X). McGraw.
Clement, M. A. Transmission. 52p. 7.00 (ISBN 0-317-06288-3). Telephony.
Conference on Software Engineering for Telecommunication Switching Systems(1973: University of Essex) Conference on Software Engineering for Telecommunication Switching Systems. (Institution of Electrical Engineers Conference Publications: No. 97). pap. 86.50 (ISBN 0-317-10093-9, 2012131). Bks Demand UMI.
Dewilde, P. & May, C. A., eds. Links for the Future-Science, Systems & Services for Communication: Proceedings of the International Conference on Communications-ICC, 1984, Amsterdam, the Netherlands, 14-17, 1984, 2 pts. 1550p. 1984. Set. 160.00 (ISBN 0-444-87524-7, I-266-84, North Holland). Elsevier.
Intel Staff. Telecommunications Product Handbook. 224p. 1985. pap. 12.00 (ISBN 0-917017-19-6, 230730-003). Intel Corp.
Kelleher, Kathleen & Cross, Thomas B. Teleconferencing: Linking People Together. (Illus.). 352p. 1985. text ed. 32.95 (ISBN 0-13-902370-4). P-H.
Pearce, J. G. Common Control of Telephone Systems. (Illus.). 40p. 5.00 (ISBN 0-317-06292-1). Telephony.
Telecoms Today: Tools, Tactics & Strategies. 259p. 1984. pap. text ed. 90.00x (ISBN 0-86353-006-0, Pub. by Online). Brookfield Pub Co.

TELECONFERENCING

see Telephone–Conference Calls

TELEGRAPH

see also Cables, Submarine; Morse Code

The Electric Telegraph: An Historical Anthology. LC 75-23897. (Historical Studies in Telecommunications Ser.). (Illus.). 1976. Repr. 43.00x (ISBN 0-405-07757-2). Ayer Co Pubs.
Famie, John J. A History of Electric Telegraphy to the Year 1837. LC 74-4678. (Telecommunications Ser.). (Illus.). 566p. 1974. Repr. of 1884 ed. 38.50x (ISBN 0-405-06044-0). Ayer Co Pubs.
Field, Henry M. The Story of the Atlantic Telegraph. LC 72-5049. (Technology & Society Ser.). (Illus.). 415p. 1972. Repr. of 1893 ed. 24.00 (ISBN 0-405-04701-0). Ayer Co Pubs.
Head, Francis B. Stokers & Pokers. LC 69-10757. Repr. of 1849 ed. 25.00x (ISBN 0-678-05601-3). Kelley.
Hubbard, Geoffrey. Cooke & Wheatstone & the Invention of the Electric Telegraph. LC 66-38233. (Illus.). 1965. 22.50x (ISBN 0-678-06529-2). Kelley.
Johnson, John J. Pioneer Telegraphy in Chile, 1852-1876. LC 68-54275. (Stanford University. Stanford Studies in History, Economics & Political Science: Vol. 6 No. 1). Repr. of 1948 ed. 19.50 (ISBN 0-404-50971-1). AMS Pr.
Lehnert, Joseph. Introduction to Telegraph Engineering. 155p. 1977. 36.95X (ISBN 0-471-25848-2, Wiley Heyden). Wiley.
Plum, William R. The Military Telegraph During the Civil War in the United States, 2 vols. LC 74-4690. (Telecommunications Ser). 1566p. 1974. Repr. of 1882 ed. 55.00x (ISBN 0-405-06053-X). Ayer Co Pubs.
Reid, James D. The Telegraph in America: Its Founders, Promoters & Noted Men. LC 74-7493. (Telecommunications Ser). (Illus.). 926p. 1974. Repr. of 1879 ed. 63.00 (ISBN 0-405-06056-4). Ayer Co Pubs.
Rudman, Jack. Radio & Telegraph Operator. (Career Examination Ser.: C-1443). (Cloth bdg. avail. on request). pap. 10.00 (ISBN 0-8373-1443-7). Natl Learning.
Sterling, Christopher M. An Original Anthology: Eyewitness to Early American Telegraphy. LC 74-4698. (Telecommunications Ser). (Illus.). 212p. 1974. 25.50x (ISBN 0-405-06043-2). Ayer Co Pubs.
Thompson, Robert L. Wiring a Continent: The History of the Telegraph Industry in the United States, 1832-1866. LC 72-5078. (Technology & Society Ser.). (Illus.). 590p. 1972. Repr. of 1947 ed. 34.00 (ISBN 0-405-04727-4). Ayer Co Pubs.
Wiesner. Telegraph & Data Transmission over Shortwave Radio Links: Fundamental Principles & Networks Paper. 199p. 1984. pap. 21.95 (ISBN 0-471-90599-2). Wiley.
Wilson, Geoffrey. The Old Telegraphs. (Illus.). 252p. 1976. 45.00x (ISBN 0-8476-1291-0). Rowman.

TELEGRAPH, SUBMARINE

see Cables, Submarine

TELEGRAPH, WIRELESS

see also Electric Waves; Radio

Blake, George C. History of Radio Telegraphy & Telephony. LC 74-4667. (Telecommunications Ser). (Illus.). 425p. 1974. Repr. of 1928 ed. 35.50x (ISBN 0-405-06034-3). Ayer Co Pubs.
Fahie, J. J. History of Wireless Telegraphy, 1838-99. LC 77-161144. (History of Broadcasting: Radio to Television Ser). 1971. Repr. of 1901 ed. 30.00 (ISBN 0-405-03565-9). Ayer Co Pubs.
Hawks, Ellison. Pioneers of Wireless. LC 74-4685. (Telecommunications Ser). (Illus.). 400p. 1974. Repr. of 1927 ed. 27.00x (ISBN 0-405-06049-1). Ayer Co Pubs.
Lodge, Oliver J. Signalling Through Space Without Wires: Being a Description of the Work of Hertz & His Successors. 3rd ed. LC 74-9688. (Telecommunications Ser.). (Illus.). 138p. 1974. 14.00x (ISBN 0-405-06051-3). Ayer Co Pubs.

TELEMETER

International Telemetering Conference. International Telemetering Conference, November 14, 15, 16, 1978. (International Telemetering Conference Ser.: Vol. 14). pap. 160.00 (ISBN 0-317-28951-9, 2051629). Bks Demand UMI.
International Telemetering Conference: Proceedings of the 19th International Telemetering Conference, Vol. XIX. LC 66-4573. 869p. 1983. text ed. 159.00x (ISBN 0-87664-791-3). Instru Soc.
International Telemetering Conference, Vol. XVIII: Proceedings. LC 66-4573. 937p. 1982. pap. text ed. 159.00x (ISBN 0-87664-703-4). Instru Soc.
ITC. International Telemetering Conference, Vol. XV: Proceedings. LC 66-4573. 568p. 1979. text ed. 95.00x (ISBN 0-87664-459-0). Instru Soc.
National Telemetering Conference, 1966. Proceedings. LC 57-20724. 413p. 1966. 17.00x (ISBN 0-306-38906-1, Plenum Pr). Plenum Pub.
Rudman, Jack. Telemetric Systems Specialist. (Career Examination Ser.: C-1940). (Cloth bdg. avail. on request). pap. 12.00 (ISBN 0-8373-1940-4). Natl Learning.
Telemetering Proceedings Index, 1956-1979: An Index of All Papers Published in the Proceedings of National Telemetering Conference (1956-1979) & International Telemetering Conference (1967-1979) LC 81-80534. 284p. 1981. pap. text ed. 35.00x (ISBN 0-87664-509-0). Instru Soc.

TELEMETER (PHYSIOLOGICAL APPARATUS)

Caceres, C. A., ed. Biomedical Telemetry. 1965. 76.50 (ISBN 0-12-153850-8). Acad Pr.

TELEMETRY, BIOLOGICAL

see Biotelemetry

TELENCEPHALON

Braak, H. Architectonics of the Human Telencephalic Cortex. (Studies of Brain Functions: Vol. 4). (Illus.). 147p. 1980. 31.00 (ISBN 0-387-10312-0). Springer-Verlag.
Ebbesson, Sven, ed. Comparative Neurology of the Telencephalon. LC 79-12145. (Illus.). 528p. 1980. 65.00x (ISBN 0-306-40237-8, Plenum Pr). Plenum Pub.

TELEPHONE

see also Radiotelephone

Applied Psychology Research Unit. Human Factors in Telephony. 1961. pap. 20.00 (ISBN 0-686-37971-3). Info Gatekeepers.
Bell, Alexander G. The Bell Telephone: The Deposition of Alexander Graham Bell in the Suit Brought by the United States to Annul the Bell Patents. LC 74-4665. (Telecommunications Ser.). (Illus.). 480p. 1974. Repr. of 1905 ed. 33.00 (ISBN 0-405-06032-7). Ayer Co Pubs.
Benes, V. E. Mathematical Theory of Connecting Networks & Telephone Traffic. (Mathematics in Science and Engineering, Ser.: Vol. 17). 1965. 65.00 (ISBN 0-12-087550-0). Acad Pr.
Bennett, A. R. The Telephone Systems of the Continent of Europe, 1895, 2 vols. in 1. LC 74-4666. (Telecommunications Ser). 395p. 1974. Repr. of 1895 ed. 36.50x (ISBN 0-405-06033-5). Ayer Co Pubs.
Brandon, Belinda B., ed. Effect of the Demographics of Individual Households on Their Telphone Usage. LC 80-27158. 432p. 1981. prof ref 45.00x (ISBN 0-88410-695-0). Ballinger Pub.
Business Communications Staff. The Dynamic Telephone Related Hardware Business. 172p. 1984. 1250.00 (ISBN 0-89336-338-3, G-071). BCC.
Caristi, Anthony J. Electronic Telephone Projects. LC 79-63868. 168p. 1979. pap. 8.95 (ISBN 0-672-21618-3, 21618). Sams.
Casson, H. History of the Telephone. 1977. lib. bdg. 59.95 (ISBN 0-8490-2007-7). Gordon Pr.
Casson, Herbert N. The History of the Telephone. facsimile ed. LC 76-175693. (Select Bibliographies Reprint Ser). Repr. of 1910 ed. 27.50 (ISBN 0-8369-6608-2). Ayer Co Pubs.
Chorafas, Dimitris N. Telephony: Today & Tomorrow. (Illus.). 272p. 1984. pap. text ed. 23.95 (ISBN 0-13-902700-9). P-H.
De Sola Pool, Ithiel, ed. The Social Impact of the Telephone. 512p. 1977. pap. 10.95x (ISBN 0-262-66048-2). MIT Pr.
Du Moncel, Theodore A. The Telephone, the Microphone, & the Phonograph. LC 74-4673. (Telecommunications Ser). (Illus.). 282p. 1974. Repr. of 1879 ed. 23.50x (ISBN 0-405-06039-4). Ayer Co Pubs.
Fike, J. L. & Friend, G. E. Understanding Telephone Electronics. 2nd ed. LC 84-50902. (Understanding Ser.). 277p. 1984. pap. text ed. 14.95 (ISBN 0-89512-159-X, LCB7141). Tex Instr Inc.
Harder, Warren J. Daniel Drawbaugh: The Edison of the Cumberland Valley. LC 59-9201. 1961. 15.00x (ISBN 0-8122-7225-0). U of Pa Pr.
Het PTT-BEDRIJF, The Netherlands. Human Factors in Telephone Communications International Symposium, 3rd. 1967. pap. 75.00 (ISBN 0-686-37973-X). Info-Gatekeepers.

Human Factors in Telecommunications International Symposium, 2nd. 1963. pap. 20.00 (ISBN 0-686-37972-1). Info Gatekeepers.

Jordan, Alan H. The Encyclopedia of Telephone Cost Reduction Techniques. 246p. 1981. pap. 99.00 (ISBN 0-940896-03-6). Add-Effect Assoc.

Lee, Frank E. Telephone Theory, Principles & Practice, Vol. I. 1976. 6.95 (ISBN 0-686-98057-3). Telecom Lib.

Prescott, George B. Bell's Electric Speaking Telephone: Its Invention, Construction, Application, Modification & History. LC 72-5069. (Technology & Society Ser.). (Illus.). 536p. 1972. Repr. of 1884 ed. 38.50 (ISBN 0-405-04718-5). Ayer Co Pubs.

Reilly, Eugene J. The Complete Guide to Telephone System Evaluation. 300p. 1980. 175.00 (ISBN 0-686-98041-7). Telecom Lib.

Rhodes, Frederick L. Beginnings of Telephony. LC 7-4694. (Telecommunications Ser). (Illus.). 286p. 1974. Repr. of 1929 ed. 25.50x (ISBN 0-405-06057-2). Ayer Co Pubs.

Rogers, Tom. You & Your Telephone. LC 80-52229. 96p. 1980. pap. 7.95 (ISBN 0-672-21744-9). Sams.

Rudman, Jack. PBX Equipment Installer & Repairer. (Career Examination Ser.: C-1385). (Cloth bdg. avail. on request). pap. 8.00 (ISBN 0-8373-1385-6). Natl Learning.

Singer, Benjamin D. Social Functions of the Telephone. LC 81-20525. 125p. 1981. perfect bound 9.95 (ISBN 0-88247-603-3). R & E Pubs.

Sterling, Christopher H. & Shiers, George, eds. The Telephone: An Historical Anthology. LC 75-23899. (Historical Studies in Telecommunications Ser.). (Illus.). 1976. Repr. 54.00x (ISBN 0-405-07758-0). Ayer Co Pubs.

Thompson, Silvanus P. Philipp Reis: Inventor of the Telephone. LC 74-4696. (Telecommunications Ser). (Illus.). 200p. 1974. Repr. of 1883 ed. 16.00x (ISBN 0-405-06060-2). Ayer Co Pubs.

VDE Berlin. Human Factors in Telecommunications International Symposium, 4th. 1968. 75.00 (ISBN 0-686-37974-8). Info Gatekeepers.

Ward, John T. Meetings by Telephone. 55p. 1980. 3.25 (ISBN 0-686-98119-7). Telecom Lib.

Wasserman, Neil. From Invention to Innovation: The Case of Long-Distance Telephone Transmission at the Turn of the Century. LC 84-62499. (AT&T Series in Telephone History). (Illus.). 176p. 1985. text ed. 17.50x (ISBN 0-8018-2715-9). Johns Hopkins.

Waterford, Van. All about Telephones. 190p. 1978. 5.95 (ISBN 0-686-98101-4). Telecom Lib.

--All about Telephones. (Illus.). 256p. (Orig.). 1983. 16.95 (ISBN 0-8306-0137-6); pap. 11.50 (ISBN 0-8306-1537-7, 1537). TAB Bks.

Welch, S. Signalling in Telecommunications Networks. (Illus.). 392p. 1979. pap. 38.00 (ISBN 0-906048-46-X). Inst Elect Eng.

TELEPHONE–APPARATUS AND SUPPLIES

Arnsdorff, Edward F. How to Install & Repair Your Telephone. 2nd ed. (Illus.). 47p. 1983. pap. 3.50 (ISBN 0-9612878-0-2). T A P.

Bellamy, John. Digital Telephony. LC 81-11633. 526p. 1982. 54.95x (ISBN 0-471-08089-6, Pub. by Wiley-Interscience). Wiley.

Clifford, Martin. Your Telephone: Operation, Selection & Installation. LC 83-50377. 336p. 1983. pap. 13.95 (ISBN 0-672-22065-2, 22065). Sams.

Cook, William J. & Ma, Christopher. The Telephone Survival Guide. 1985. pap. 5.95 (ISBN 0-671-55400-X, Wallaby). PB.

Cordless Telephones. (Reports Ser.: No. 536). 164p. 1983. 985.00 (ISBN 0-88694-536-4). Intl Res Dev.

De Sola Pool, Ithiel. Forecasting the Telephone. LC 82-22637. (Communications & Information Sciences Ser.). 192p. 1983. text ed. 27.50 (ISBN 0-89391-048-1). Ablex Pub.

Gilder, Jules. More Telephone Accessories You Can Build. 129p. 1981. 6.50 (ISBN 0-686-98104-9). Telecom Lib.

Gilder, Jules H. Telephone Accessories You Can Build. 84p. 1976. 7.25 (ISBN 0-686-98103-0). Telecom Lib.

Grant, Steven C. A Management Guide to Efficient Automatic Call Distributors. Brooks, Yvonne C., ed. 264p. 1981. pap. 125.00 (ISBN 0-936648-08-2). Telecom Lib.

Hobbs, Marivin. Modern Communications Switching Systems. 2nd ed. 1983. pap. 9.95 (ISBN 0-8306-1278-5, 1278). TAB Bks.

Jones, Michael P., ed. Laboratory Testing Data on Telephone Security Devices & Equipment. Abr. ed. (Illus.). 36p. 1984. pap. text ed. 6.00 (ISBN 0-89904-081-0). Crumb Elbow Pub.

LaCarrubba, Joseph & Zimmer, Louis. How to Buy, Install, & Maintain Your Own Telephone Equipment. rev., 4th ed. (Illus.). 52p. (Orig.). 1981. pap. 4.00 (ISBN 0-930256-09-3). Almar.

--How to Buy, Install & Maintain Your Own Telephone Equipment. 50p. 1978. 3.50 (ISBN 0-686-98105-7). Telecom Lib.

Sunier, John. The Handbook of Telephones & Accessories. 432p. 1978. 9.95 (ISBN 0-686-98102-2). Telecom Lib.

Talley, David. Basic Carrier Telephony. 3rd, rev. ed. 218p. 1977. 9.95 (ISBN 0-686-98107-3). Telecom Lib.

--Basic Electronic Switching for Telephone Systems. 240p. 1981. 8.35 (ISBN 0-686-98106-5). Telecom Lib.

TELEPHONE–CONFERENCE CALLS

Bohm, Ronald J. & Templeton, Lee. The Executive Guide to Video Teleconferencing. 150p. 1984. text ed. 40.00 (ISBN 0-89006-148-3). Artech Hse.

Gold, Elliot M. & Singletary, Shirley A. Definitive Buyer's Guide to Teleconferencing Products & Services. 157p. 1983. softcover 40.00 (ISBN 0-07-600004-4). McGraw.

Knowledge Industry Publication, Inc. The Teleconferencing Resources Directory 1985-1986: Audio & Video Conferencing Equipment, Facilities & Services. (Video Bookshelf Ser.). 148p. 1985. pap. 47.50 (ISBN 0-86729-150-8). Knowledge Indus.

Parker, L. A. & Olgren, C. H., eds. The Teleconferencing Resource Book: A Guide to Applications & Planning. 452p. 1984. 50.00 (ISBN 0-444-86887-9). Elsevier.

Parker, Lorne A. & Olgren, Christine H. Teleconferencing Technology & Applications. LC 83-70175. (Telecommunications Ser.). (Illus.). 300p. 1983. 50.00 (ISBN 0-89006-119-X). Artech Hse.

Rao, K. Ramamohan & Srinivasan, Ram. Teleconferencing. (Illus.). 272p. 1985. 46.95 (ISBN 0-442-27826-8). Van Nos Reinhold.

TELEPHONE–EXAMINATIONS, QUESTIONS, ETC.

Rudman, Jack. Foreman (Telephones) (Career Examination Ser.: C-1970). (Cloth bdg. avail. on request). pap. 10.00 (ISBN 0-8373-1970-6). Natl Learning.

--Senior Telephone Inspector. (Career Examination Ser.: C-2217). (Cloth bdg. avail. on request). 1977. pap. 12.00 (ISBN 0-8373-2217-0). Natl Learning.

--Senior Telephone Operator. (Career Examination Ser.: C-1027). (Cloth bdg. avail. on request). pap. 12.00 (ISBN 0-8373-1027-X). Natl Learning.

--Supervisor (Telephones) (Career Examination Ser.: C-426). (Cloth bdg. avail. on request). pap. 12.00 (ISBN 0-8373-0426-1). Natl Learning.

--Switchboard Operator. (Career Examination Ser.: C-883). (Cloth bdg. avail. on request). pap. 10.00 (ISBN 0-8373-0883-6). Natl Learning.

--Switchboard Supervisor. (Career Examination Ser.: C-884). (Cloth bdg. avail. on request). pap. 12.00 (ISBN 0-8373-0884-4). Natl Learning.

--Telephone Maintainer. (Career Examination Ser.: C-807). (Cloth bdg. avail. on request). pap. 8.00 (ISBN 0-8373-0807-0). Natl Learning.

--Telephone Operator. (Career Examination Ser.: C-806). (Cloth bdg. avail. on request). pap. 8.00 (ISBN 0-8373-0806-2). Natl Learning.

--Telephone Services Operator. (Career Examination Ser.: C-2586). (Cloth bdg. avail. on request). pap. 10.00 (ISBN 0-8373-2586-2). Natl Learning.

TELEPHONE, WIRELESS

see Radio

TELEPHONE CABLES

Pansini, Anthony J. Undergrounding Telephone Lines. 112p. 1978. 7.95 (ISBN 0-686-98123-5). Telecom Lib.

Rudman, Jack. Foreman Lineman. (Career Examination Ser.: C-2024). (Cloth bdg. avail. on request). pap. 10.00 (ISBN 0-8373-2024-0). Natl Learning.

--Telephone Cable Maintainer. (Career Examination Ser.: C-830). (Cloth bdg. avail. on request). pap. 8.00 (ISBN 0-8373-0830-5). Natl Learning.

World's Submarine Telephone Cable Systems, 1980. 100.00 (ISBN 0-686-32977-5). Info Gatekeepers.

Young, Peter. Power of Speech: A History of Standard Telephones & Cables 1883-1983. 224p. 1983. text ed. 18.95x (ISBN 0-04-382039-5). Allen Unwin.

TELEPHONE EXCHANGES

see Telephone Stations

TELEPHONE STATIONS

see also Telephone Switching Systems, Electronic

Beckmann, Petr. Elementary Queue Theory & Telephone Traffic. 1976. 7.75 (ISBN 0-686-98072-7). Telecom Lib.

Bouwman, Vern. Telephone Plant Records. 7.00 (ISBN 0-317-06286-7). Telephony.

Briley, Bruce E. Introduction to Telephone Switching. LC 83-8835. 251p. 1983. 26.95 (ISBN 0-201-11246-9). Addison-Wesley.

Chapuis, R. J. One Hundred Years of Telephone Switching (1878-1978) Part 1, Manual & Electromechanical Switching, 1878-1960s. (Studies in Telecommunications: Vol. 1). 464p. 1982. 95.00 (ISBN 0-444-86289-7, North Holland). Elsevier.

Clement, M. A. Transmission. 52p. 7.00 (ISBN 0-317-06288-3). Telephony.

The Digital Experience: The Awareness & Understanding of Digital Switching Grow. 64p. 20.00 (ISBN 0-317-06283-2). Telephony.

Fleming, Paul. Principles of Switching, Vol. X. 1979. 15.00 (ISBN 0-686-98066-2). Telecom Lib.

Goeller, L. F., Jr. Design Background for Telephone Switching, Vol. IX. 1978. 10.75 (ISBN 0-686-98065-4). Telecom Lib.

Hobbs, Marivin. Modern Communications Switching Systems. 2nd ed. 1983. pap. 9.95 (ISBN 0-8306-1278-5, 1278). TAB Bks.

Hobbs, Marvin. Modern Communications Switching Systems. 2nd ed. 308p. 1981. 9.95 (ISBN 0-686-98114-6). Telecom Lib.

Jewett, Jim & Shrago, Jackie. Designing Optimal Voice Networks. 240p. 40.00 (ISBN 0-317-06285-9). Telephony.

--Traffic Engineering Tables. 480p. 125.00 (ISBN 0-317-06284-0). Telephony.

--Traffic Engineering Tables: The Complete Practical Encyclopedia. 480p. 1980. 125.00 (ISBN 0-686-98045-X). Telecom Lib.

Joel, Amos E. Electronic Switching: Digital Central Office Systems of the World. LC 81-20041. 268p. 1982. 33.95x (ISBN 0-471-86884-1, Pub. by Wiley-Interscience); pap. 22.00x (ISBN 0-471-86883-3). Wiley.

Kingsbury, John E. The Telephone & Telephone Exchanges: Their Invention & Development. LC 72-5057. (Technology & Society Ser.). (Illus.). 580p. 1972. Repr. of 1915 ed. 40.00 (ISBN 0-405-04709-6). Ayer Co Pubs.

Kuehn, Dick & RAK Associates. Interconnect: Why & How. 75p. 1982. 15.00 (ISBN 0-686-98038-7). Telecom Lib.

Lawson, Robert W. A Practical Guide to Teletraffic Engineering & Administration. 128p. 20.00 (ISBN 0-317-06282-4). Telephony.

Lee, Frank E. Station Installation & Maintenance, Vol. II. 1976. 6.75 (ISBN 0-686-98058-1). Telecom Lib.

Local Measured Service: What Telephone Companies Should Know. 2nd ed. 12.00 (ISBN 0-317-06295-6). Telephony.

Mina, Ramses. Introduction to Teletraffic Engineering. 11.00 (ISBN 0-317-06287-5). Telephony.

National Computing Centre. Introducing Computerized Telephone Switchboards (PABXs) (Illus.). 92p. (Orig.). 1982. 15.00x (ISBN 0-85012-364-X). Intl Pubns Serv.

--Introducing Computerized Telephone Switchboards: PABXS. 1983. pap. 12.60 (ISBN 0-471-88705-6, DP00, Pub. by Wiley Interscience). Wiley.

Pearce, J. G. Common Control of Telephone Systems. (Illus.). 40p. 5.00 (ISBN 0-317-06292-1). Telephony.

--The World of Electronic Switching. (Illus.). 140p. 8.00 (ISBN 0-317-06294-8). Telephony.

Riley, Eugene W. & Acuna, Victor E. Understanding Transmission, Vol. VII. 1976. 7.95 (ISBN 0-686-98063-8). Telecom Lib.

Smidt, Ollie. Engineering Economics. 7.00 (ISBN 0-317-06289-1). Telephony.

Talley, David. Basic Electronic Switching for Telephone Systems. 240p. 1981. 8.35 (ISBN 0-686-98106-5). Telecom Lib.

--Basic Telephone Switching Systems. 2nd ed. 1979. pap. 10.50 (ISBN 0-8104-5687-7). Hayden.

Tally, David. Basic Electronic Switching for Telephone Systems. 1975. pap. 8.35 (ISBN 0-8104-5808-X); exam set 0.80 (ISBN 0-8104-0591-1); final exam 0.30 (ISBN 0-8104-0594-6). Hayden.

Tokarz, Roger F. Solving Noise & Transmission Problems in Telephone Loop Plant. (Illus.). 84p. 10.00 (ISBN 0-317-06293-X). Telephony.

Wilson, Kenneth C. Understanding Station Carrier, Vol. VI. 1975. 6.00 (ISBN 0-686-98062-X). Telecom Lib.

TELEPHONE SWITCHING

see Telephone Stations

TELEPHONE SWITCHING SYSTEMS, ELECTRONIC

The Digital Experience: The Awareness & Understanding of Digital Switching Grow. 64p. 20.00 (ISBN 0-317-06283-2). Telephony.

Meurling, John & Jeans, Richard. A Switch in Time: An Engineer's Tale. LC 84-51993. (Illus.). 181p. 1985. 20.00 (ISBN 0-917845-02-1). Telephony.

Pearce, J. G. The World of Electronic Switching. (Illus.). 140p. 8.00 (ISBN 0-317-06294-8). Telephony.

TELEPROCESSING NETWORKS

see Computer Networks

TELESCOPE

see also Radar Telescope

Asimov, Isaac. Eyes on the Universe: A History of the Telescope. LC 75-15830. 288p. 1975. 8.95 (ISBN 0-395-19427-X). HM.

Barlow, B. V. The Astronomical Telescope. (Wykeham Science Ser.: No. 31). 220p. 1975. pap. cancelled (ISBN 0-85109-440-6). Taylor & Francis.

Barlow, B. V. & Everest, A. S. The Astronomical Telescope. (Wykeham Science Ser.: No. 31). 220p. 1975. 9.95x (ISBN 0-8448-1158-0). Crane Russak Co.

Barr, L. D., et al, eds. Advanced Technology Optical Telescopes II, Vol. 444. 332p. 57.00 (ISBN 0-89252-479-0). Photo-Optical.

Basov, N. G., ed. Radio, Submillimeter, & X-Ray Telescopes. LC 76-48290. (P. N. Lebedev Physics Institute Ser.: Vol. 77). (Illus.). 221p. 1976. 59.50 (ISBN 0-306-10930-1, Consultants). Plenum Pub.

Bell, Louis. The Telescope. 287p. 1981. pap. 6.95 (ISBN 0-486-24151-3). Dover.

--The Telescope. (Illus.). 13.25 (ISBN 0-8446-5877-4). Peter Smith.

Berry, Richard. Build Your Own Telescope: Complete Plans for Five High-Quality Telescopes That Anyone Can Build. (Illus.). 240p. 1985. 25.00 (ISBN 0-317-19458-5). Scribner.

Brown, Sam. All about Telescopes. 3rd ed. LC 67-31540. (Illus.). 1976. 19.95x (ISBN 0-933346-20-4). Sky Pub.

Burbridge, G. & Hewitt, A., eds. Telescopes for the Nineteen Eighties. (Illus.). 275p. 1981. text ed. 27.00 (ISBN 0-8243-2902-3). Annual Reviews.

Capaccioli, Massimo, ed. Astronomy with Schmidt-Type Telescopes. 1984. lib. bdg. 84.00 (ISBN 90-277-1756-7, Pub. by Reidel Holland). Kluwer Academic.

Cohen, Martin. In Quest of Telescopes. (Illus.). 131p. 1980. 13.95 (ISBN 0-933346-25-5, 6255). Sky Pub.

--In Quest of Telescopes. 131p. 1982. 13.95 (ISBN 0-521-24989-9). Cambridge U Pr.

Cornell, James & Carr, John, eds. Infinite Vistas: How the Space Telescope & Other Advances Are Revolutionizing Our Knowledge of the Universe. 256p. 1985. 18.95 (ISBN 0-684-18287-4, ScribT). Scribner.

Eicher, David J., ed. Deep-Sky Observing with Small Telescopes. (Illus.). 320p. 1985. pap. 14.95 (ISBN 0-89490-075-7). Enslow Pubs.

Hasluck, Paul N. Telescope Making (1905) (Illus.). 160p. 1983. pap. 12.50 (ISBN 0-87556-498-4). Saifer.

King, Henry C. The History of the Telescope. LC 79-87811. (Illus.). 1979. pap. 9.95 (ISBN 0-486-23893-8). Dover.

--The History of the Telescope. (Illus.). 19.00 (ISBN 0-8446-5780-8). Peter Smith.

--The History of the Telescope. LC 79-87811. (Illus.). 480p. 1980. Repr. of 1979 ed. 16.50x (ISBN 0-938164-05-8). Vintage Bk Co.

Klushansev, P. All about the Telescope. 70p. 1981. 5.95 (ISBN 0-8285-1966-8, Pub. by Progress Pubs USSR). Imported Pubns.

Kuiper, Gerald P. & Middlehurst, Barbara, eds. Telescopes: Stars & Stellar Systems, Vol. I. LC 60-14356. (Midway Reprint Ser.). (Illus.). 1977. pap. text ed. 21.00x (ISBN 0-226-45962-4). U of Chicago Pr.

Levenson, Jordan. How to Buy & Understand Refracting Telescopes. LC 81-81885. (Illus., Orig.). 1981. pap. 18.95x (ISBN 0-914442-09-0). Levenson Pr.

Muirden, James. How to Use An Astronomical Telescope. 480p. 1985. 21.95 (ISBN 0-671-47744-7, Linden). S&S.

Texereau, Jean. How to Make a Telescope. 2nd ed. Strickler, Allen, tr. (Illus.). 440p. 1984. text ed. 19.95 (ISBN 0-943396-04-2). Willmann-Bell.

Thompson, Allyn J. Making Your Own Telescope. rev. ed. (Illus.). 1980. Repr. of 1947 ed. 9.95 (ISBN 0-933346-12-3). Sky Pub.

Traister, Robert J. & Harris, Susan E. Astronomy & Telescopes: A Beginner's Handbook. (Illus.). 192p. 1983. o.p 19.95 (ISBN 0-8306-0419-7, 1419); pap. 14.95 (ISBN 0-8306-1419-2). TAB Bks.

Trueblood, Mark & Genet, Russell M. Microcomputer Control of Telescopes. 1985. pap. 19.95x (ISBN 0-943396-05-0). Willmann Bell.

Van Schooneveld, Cornelis, ed. Image Formation from Coherence Functions in Astronomy. (Astrophysics & Space Science Library: No. 76). 1979. lib. bdg. 39.50 (ISBN 90-277-0987-4, Pub. by Reidel Holland). Kluwer Academic.

Willard, Berton C. Russell W. Porter, Arctic Explorer, Artist, Telescope Maker. LC 76-8090. (Illus.). 1976. 12.50 (ISBN 0-87027-168-7). Cumberland Pr.

Worvill, Roy. Stars & Telescopes for the Beginner. LC 79-14034. (Illus.). 1980. 7.95 (ISBN 0-8008-4464-5). Taplinger.

TELESCOPE, RADIO

see Radio Telescope

Oringel, Robert S. Audio Control Handbook: For Radio & Television Broadcasting. 5th rev. & enl. ed. (Communication Arts Bks.). (Illus.). 380p. 1983. pap. text ed. 14.95 (ISBN 0-8038-0550-0). Hastings.
Schreff, David J. How to Build a Career in Cable TV. 200p. (Orig.). 1983. pap. 9.95 (ISBN 0-911675-01-9). Skybridge Pub Inc.
Television Factbook, 2 vols, No. 50. rev. ed. LC 67-118025. 1981-82. Set. 165.00 (ISBN 0-911486-06-2). Services Vol (ISBN 0-911486-07-0). Stations Vol (ISBN 0-911486-08-9). TV Factbk.
Turow, Joseph. Media Industries: The Production of News & Entertainment. LC 83-17519. (Communication Ser.). 288p. 1984. text ed. 29.95 (ISBN 0-582-28359-0). Longman.

TELEVISION BROADCASTING–DATA PROCESSING

Knowledge Industry Publications Staff, ed. Microcomputers in TV Studios. 125p. 1985. pap. text ed. 29.95 (ISBN 0-86729-131-1, 532-BW). Knowledge Indus.

TELEVISION BROADCASTING–HISTORY

Barnouw, Erik. Tube of Plenty: The Evolution of American Television. rev. ed. (Illus.). 1982. pap. 9.95 (ISBN 0-19-503092-3, GB 481, GB). Oxford U Pr.
Katzman, Natan. Program Decisions in Public Television. 72p. 1976. pap. 3.50 (ISBN 0-686-77629-1, Pub Telecomm). NAEB.
Udelson, Joseph H. The Great Television Race: A History of the American Television Industry 1925-1941. LC 81-7562. (Illus.). 240p. 1982. 18.95 (ISBN 0-8173-0082-1). U of Ala Pr.

TELEVISION CAMERAS

Abramson, Albert. Electronic Motion Pictures: A History of the Television Camera. LC 74-4663. (Telecommunications Ser). (Illus.). 228p. 1974. Repr. of 1955 ed. 24.50 (ISBN 0-405-06031-9). Ayer Co Pubs.

TELEVISION FILM

see also Video Tapes

Dwight, John A. & Peel, William J. Video Reading Technics, Bk. 1. 1976. pap. text ed. 5.30 (ISBN 0-934902-00-3); tchr's ed. 10.00 (ISBN 0-934902-04-6). Learn Concepts OH.
Leaver, K. D., et al. Thin Films. (The Wykeham Science Ser.: No.17). 120p. 1971. pap. cancelled (ISBN 0-85109-230-6). Taylor & Francis.
Martin, Mick & Potter, Marsha. Video Movie Guide 1986. 256p. (Orig.). 1986. pap. 2.95 (ISBN 0-345-32766-7). Ballantine.
Wiegand, Ingrid. Professional Video Production. LC 84-21323. (Video Bookshelf Ser.). 200p. 1984. Professional 39.95 (ISBN 0-86729-067-6); pap. 24.95 students ed. (ISBN 0-86729-112-5, 522-BW). Knowledge Indus.

TELEVISION GAMES

see Video Games

TELEVISION IN SCIENCE

Gray, Suzanne K., et al, eds. NOVA: Science Adventures on Television. 1974. 2.50 (ISBN 0-89073-000-8). Boston Public Lib.
--NOVA: Science Adventures on Television II. 1975. 4.00 (ISBN 0-89073-006-7). Boston Public Lib.

TELEVISION INDUSTRY

see also Television Broadcasting

Fireman, Judy, ed. The TV Book. LC 77-5303. (Illus.). 1977. pap. 7.95 (ISBN 0-89480-002-7). Workman Pub.

TELEVISION PICTURE TUBES

Middleton, Herman A. Hayden's Complete Tube Caddy, Tube Substitution Guidebook. 24th ed. 1979. pap. 5.95 (ISBN 0-8104-0809-0). Hayden.

TELEVISION RELAY SYSTEMS

Crowe, Steve. Satellite Television & Your Backyard Dish. Krieger, Robin, ed. LC 81-90593. (Illus.). 200p. (Orig.). 1982. 20.00 (ISBN 0-910419-00-0); pap. 15.00 (ISBN 0-910419-01-9); trade special 15.00 (ISBN 0-910419-02-7). Satellite.
Efrein, Joel. Cablecasting Production Handbook. LC 74-33617. (Illus.). 210p. 1975. 12.95 (ISBN 0-8306-5768-1, 768). TAB Bks.
Harrington, Thomas P. & Cooper, Robert B., Jr. How to Tune the Hidden Signals on Satellite TV. (Illus.). 140p. (Orig.). 1984. pap. 14.95 (ISBN 0-916661-04-0). Universal Elect.
Telepay vs. Videodisc: The Exploding Pay-per-View Market. (Reports Ser.: No. 510). 281p. 1982. 985.00x (ISBN 0-88694-510-0). Intl Res Dev.
Thomassen, Cora E., ed. CATV & Its Implications for Libraries. LC 74-620101. (Allerton Park Institute: No. 19). 91p. 1974. 7.00x (ISBN 0-87845-040-8). U of Ill Lib Info Sci.

TELEVISION REPEATER STATIONS

see Television Relay Systems

TELEVISION STATIONS

see also Television Relay Systems

Bermingham, Alan. The Small TV Studio: Equipment & Facilities. (Media Manual Ser.). (Illus.). 160p. 1975. pap. 14.95 (ISBN 0-240-50869-6). Focal Pr.
Television Digest's Cable & Station Coverage Atlas. rev. ed. LC 67-118025. 1981-82. 115.50 (ISBN 0-911486-05-4). TV Factbk.

TELEVISION TRANSMISSION

see Television–Transmitters and Transmission

TELEX SERVICES

see Teletype

TELLURIUM

Gerlach, E., ed. The Physics of Selenium & Tellurium. (Springer Series in Solid State Sciences: Vol.13). (Illus.). 1979. 37.00 (ISBN 0-387-09692-2). Springer-Verlag.
Hogg, D. R. Organic Compounds of Sulphur, Selenium & Tellurium, Vols. 1-5. Incl. Vol. 1. 1969-70 Literature. 1971. 47.00 (ISBN 0-85186-259-4); Vol. 2. 1970-1972 Literature. 1973. 52.00 (ISBN 0-85186-269-1); Vol. 3. 1972-74 Literature. 1975. 63.00 (ISBN 0-85186-279-9); Vol. 4. 1974-76 Literature. 1977. 88.00 (ISBN 0-85186-289-6); Vol. 5. 1979. 98.00 (ISBN 0-85186-620-4, Pub. by Royal Soc Chem London). LC 72-78527. Am Chemical.
Irgolic, K. Organic Chemistry of Tellurium. LC 73-84669. 466p. 1974. 92.50 (ISBN 0-677-04110-1). Gordon.
Mills, K. C. Thermodynamic Data for Inorganic Sulphides, Selenides & Tellurides. LC 74-173939. pap. 160.00 (ISBN 0-317-08901-3, 2051842). Bks Demand UMI.
Patai, S. The Chemistry of Organic Selenium & Tellurium Compounds. 1000p. 1985. price not set (ISBN 0-471-90425-2). Wiley.
Wilcox. Lead Tin Telluride, Silver Halides & Czochralski Growth. (Preparation & Properties of Solid State Materials Ser.: Vol. 6). 344p. 1981. 65.00 (ISBN 0-8247-1367-2). Dekker.

TEMPERATURE

see also Atmospheric Temperature; Cold; Heat; Low Temperature Research; Melting Points; Ocean Temperature; Thermal Stresses; Thermistors; Thermostat

Alexandrov, V. Y. Cells, Macromolecules, & Temperature. (Ecological Studies Ser: Vol. 21). 1977. 51.00 (ISBN 0-387-08026-0). Springer-Verlag.
Benedict, Robert P. Fundamentals of Temperature, Pressure & Flow Measurements. 3rd ed. LC 83-23558. 532p. 1984. 54.50x (ISBN 0-471-89383-8, Pub. by Wiley-Interscience). Wiley.
Evolution of the International Practical Temperature Scale of Nineteen Sixty-Eight, STP 565. 102p. 1974. pap. 7.00 (ISBN 0-8031-0339-5, 04-565000-40). ASTM.
Frerking, Marvin E. Crystal Oscillator Design & Temperature Compensation. 1978. 24.95 (ISBN 0-442-22459-1). Van Nos Reinhold.
Hannequin, Arthur. Essai Critique sur L'hypothese Atomesdans La Sciene Contemporaine. Cohen, I. Bernard, ed. LC 80-2127. (Development of Science Ser.). (Illus.). 1981. lib. bdg. 40.00x (ISBN 0-405-13876-8). Ayer Co Pubs.
Hensel, H. Thermoregulation & Temperature Regulation. (Physiological Society Monographs Ser.). 1981. 59.50 (ISBN 0-12-341260-9). Acad Pr.
Koch, E., ed. Non-Isothermal Reaction Analysis. 1978. 99.50 (ISBN 0-12-417350-0). Acad Pr.
Kutz, Myer. Temperature Control. LC 74-32302. 230p. 1975. Repr. of 1968 ed. 13.50 (ISBN 0-88275-264-2). Krieger.
McGee, Thomas G. Handbook of Temperature Measurement. 400p. 1984. text ed. 42.50 (ISBN 0-02-948990-3). Macmillan.
Messer, J. Temperature Dependent Thomas-Fermi Theory, Vol. 147. (Lecture Notes in Physics Ser.). 131p. 1981. pap. 12.00 (ISBN 0-387-10875-0). Springer-Verlag.
Meyer, Kirstine B. Die Entwickelung De Temperaturbegriffs Im Laufe der Zeiten (the Discovery of Temperature in the Course of Time) Cohen, I. Bernard, ed. LC 80-2134. (Development of Science Ser.). (Illus.). 1981. Repr. of 1913 ed. lib. bdg. 15.00x (ISBN 0-405-13886-5). Ayer Co Pubs.
Olsen, H. N., et al. Temperature Measurements in Seeded Air & Nitrogen Plasmas. LC 79-131016. 133p. 1970. 19.00 (ISBN 0-403-04524-X). Scholarly.
Quinn, T. J. Temperature. (Monographs in Physical Measurement). 1983. 65.00 (ISBN 0-12-569680-9). Acad Pr.
Reck, Ruth A. & Hummel, John R., eds. Interpretation of Climate & Photochemical Models, Ozone & Temperature Measurements: AIP Conference Proceedings, No. 82, La Jolla Institute, March 9-11, 1981. LC 82-71345. 320p. 1982. 33.00 (ISBN 0-88318-181-9). Am Inst Physics.
Roller, Duane E. The Early Development of the Concepts of Temperature & Heat: The Rise & Decline of the Caloric Theory. LC 50-8653. (Harvard Case Histories in Experimental Science Ser.: Case 3). pap. 27.50 (ISBN 0-317-09176-X, 2011607). Bks Demand UMI.
Schooley, James F., ed. Temperature: Its Measurement & Control in Science & Industry, Proceedings of the Sixth International Symposium, Washington, DC, March 15, 1982. LC 62-19138. 1472p. 1982. 110.00 (ISBN 0-88318-403-6). Am Inst Physics.
Smorodinsky, Y. A. Temperature. 263p. 1985. 4.95 (ISBN 0-8285-2898-5, Pub by Mir Pubs USSR). Imported Pubns.
Symposium on Temperature, 1971. Temperature: Its Measurement & Control in Science & Industry, 3 pts, Vol. 4. Plumb, Harmon H., ed. Incl. Pt. 1. Basic Methods, Scales & Fixed Points, Radiation. Preston-Thomas, H., et al, eds.; Pt. 2. Resistance, Electronic & Magnetic Thermometry; Controls & Calibration; Bridges. Rubin, L. G., et al, eds.; Pt. 3. Thermocouples, Biology & Medicine, Geophysics & Space. Finch, D. I., et al, eds.. LC 62-19138. pap. 160.00 ea. (2052133). Bks Demand UMI.
Uhrbrock, Richard S. Analysis of the Downey Will-Temperament Tests. LC 72-177689. (Columbia University. Teachers College. Contributions to Education: No. 296). Repr. of 1928 ed. 17.50 (ISBN 0-404-55296-X). AMS Pr.
Voegtli, Otilia. How to Use Temperature Rhythm. 144p. 1966. 12.75x (ISBN 0-398-01989-4). C C Thomas.

TEMPERATURE–MEASUREMENT

see Thermometers and Thermometry

Symposium on Temperature, 1971. Temperature: Its Measurement & Control in Science & Industry, 3 pts, Vol. 4. Plumb, Harmon H., ed. Incl. Pt. 1. Basic Methods, Scales & Fixed Points, Radiation. Preston-Thomas, H., et al, eds.; Pt. 2. Resistance, Electronic & Magnetic Thermometry; Controls & Calibration; Bridges. Rubin, L. G., et al, eds.; Pt. 3. Thermocouples, Biology & Medicine, Geophysics & Space. Finch, D. I., et al, eds.. LC 62-19138. pap. 160.00 ea. (2052133). Bks Demand UMI.

TEMPERATURE–PHYSIOLOGICAL EFFECT

see also Cold–Physiological Effect; Thermobiology

Effect of Constant & Cycling Temperature on Ectotherms: Proceedings of Conference at Trinity College, Dublin, 1-2 July 1981. (Illus.). 248p. 1981. 35.00 (ISBN 0-08-028005-6, H145). Pergamon.
Precht, H., et al. Temperature & Life. LC 73-13495. (Illus.). 779p. 1973. 80.00 (ISBN 0-387-06441-9). Springer-Verlag.
Wieser, E., ed. Effects of Temperature on Ectothermic Organisms: Ecological Implications & Mechanisms of Compensation. LC 73-10671. (Illus.). 298p. 1974. 59.00 (ISBN 0-387-06420-6). Springer-Verlag.

TEMPERATURE, ANIMAL AND HUMAN

see Body Temperature

TEMPERATURES, LOW

see Low Temperatures

TEMPERING

American Society for Testing & Materials, Committee A-1 on Steel. Temper Embrittlement of Alloy Steels: A Symposium Presented at the Seventy-Fourth Annual Meeting, American Society for Testing & Materials. LC 73-185535. (American Society for Testing & Materials Ser.: No. 499). pap. 35.30 (ISBN 0-317-10341-5, 2015504). Bks Demand UMI.

TENSOR ANALYSIS

see Calculus of Tensors

TERATOLOGY

see Abnormalities (Animals)

TERMINALS, DATA (COMPUTERS)

see Computer Input-Output Equipment

TERMITES

Bentley, Robert S. The Termite Man. Date not set. 7.95 (ISBN 0-8062-2403-7). Carlton.
Brian, M. V., ed. Production Ecology of Ants & Termites. LC 76-54061. (International Biological Programme Ser.: No. 13). (Illus.). 1977. 95.00 (ISBN 0-521-21519-6). Cambridge U Pr.
Ernst, E., et al. A Bibliography of Termite Literature: 1966-1978. 1985. write for info. (ISBN 0-471-90466-X). Wiley.
Kofoid, Charles A., ed. Termites & Termite Control. 2nd rev. ed. (Illus.). Repr. of 1934 ed. 46.00 (ISBN 0-384-30050-2). Johnson Repr.
Krishna, Kumar & Weesner, Frances M., eds. Biology of Termites, 2 Vols. Vol. 1, 1969. 90.00 (ISBN 0-12-426301-1); Vol. 2, 1970. 90.00 (ISBN 0-12-426302-X). Acad Pr.
Maeterlinck, Maurice. La Vie des Termites. 210p. 1969. 10.95 (ISBN 0-686-56295-X). French & Eur.
Roonwal, M. L. Termite Life & Termite Control in Tropical South Asia. 177p. 1979. 39.00x (ISBN 0-686-45809-5, Pub. by United Bk Traders India). State Mutual Bk.
Termites & Soils. Wood, T. G. 1971. 45.00 (ISBN 0-12-440850-8). Acad Pr.
Usher, M. B. & Ocloo, J. K. The Natural Resistance of Eighty-Five West African Hardwood Timbers to Attack by Termites & Micro-Organisms. 1979. 35.00x (ISBN 0-85135-103-4, Pub. by Centre Overseas Research). State Mutual Bk.
Watson, J. A., ed. Caste Differentiation in Social Insects. (Current Themes in Tropical Science Ser.: Vol. 3). (Illus.). 400p. 1985. 110.00 (ISBN 0-08-030783-3). Pergamon.
Williams, R. M. Evaluation of Field & Laboratory Methods for Testing Termite Resistance of Timber & Building Materials in Ghana, with Relevant Biological Studies. 1973. 35.00x (ISBN 0-85135-065-8, Pub. by Centre Overseas Research). State Mutual Bk.

TERPENES

see also Essences and Essential Oils

Dev, Sukh & Misra, R., eds. Handbook of Terpenoids: Diterpenoids, Vol. II. 736p. 1985. 123.75 (ISBN 0-8493-3605-8). CRC Pr.
Dev, Sukh, et al. Handbook of Terpenoids, Vol. I & II. 1982. 2 vols. set 215.00 (ISBN 0-8493-3600-7). CRC Pr.
Glasby, John S. Encyclopedia of the Terpenoids. LC 81-19866. 2324p. 1982. 567.00 (ISBN 0-471-27986-2, Pub by Wiley-Interscience). Wiley.
Newman, A. A., ed. Chemistry of Terpenes & Terpenoids. 1972. 75.50 (ISBN 0-12-517950-2). Acad Pr.
Phytochemical Society of North American Symposium. Recent Advances in Phytochemistry: Structure, Biogenesis, Distribution. Runeckles, V. C. & Mabry, T. J., eds. 1974. Vol. 7. 51.00 (ISBN 0-12-612407-8); Vol. 8. 51.00 (ISBN 0-12-612408-6). Acad Pr.
Simonsen, John. The Terpenes, Vol. 3. 2nd ed. Barton, D. H., ed. pap. 147.80 (ISBN 0-317-20816-0, 2024537). Bks Demand UMI.
Taylor, William I., ed. Cyclopentanoid Terpene Derivatives. LC 74-85243. (Organic Substances of Natural Origin Ser.: Vol. 2). (Illus.). pap. 110.50 (ISBN 0-317-07880-1, 2055001). Bks Demand UMI.

TERRAIN SENSING, REMOTE

see Remote Sensing

TERRAIN VEHICLES

see All Terrain Vehicles

TERRAPINS

see Turtles

TERRESTRIAL MAGNETISM

see Magnetism, Terrestrial

TERRESTRIAL PHYSICS

see Geophysics

TERRIERS

see also Dogs–Breeds, subdivided to specific types of terriers, e.g. Dogs–Breeds–Scottish Terriers

Marvin, John T. Book of All Terriers. 2nd ed. LC 75-36864. (Complete Breed Book Ser.). (Illus.). 256p. 1983. 13.95 (ISBN 0-87605-316-9). Howell Bk.
Stone, Ben & Migliorini, Mario. Clipping & Grooming Your Terrier. LC 70-127113. 104p. 1982. pap. 7.95 (ISBN 0-668-05326-7, 5326). Arco.

TERTIARY PERIOD

see Geology, Stratigraphic–Tertiary

TEST-BORING

see Boring

TEST PROBES

see Probes (Electronic Instruments)

TESTACEA

see Mollusks

TESTICLE

see also Spermatozoa

Bollack, C. G. & Clavert, A., eds. Epididymis & Fertility: Biology & Pathology. (Progress in Reproductive Biology: Vol. 8). (Illus.). x, 174p. 1981. 50.75 (ISBN 3-8055-2157-X). S Karger.
De Kreter, D. M., et al, eds. The Pituitary & Testis: Clinical & Experimental Studies. (Monographs on Endocrinology: Vol. 25). (Illus.). 200p. 1983. 52.00 (ISBN 0-387-11874-8). Springer-Verlag.
Donohue, John P. Testis Tumors. (IPU: Vol. 7). (Illus.). 324p. 1983. lib. bdg. 46.50 (ISBN 0-683-02613-5). Williams & Wilkins.
Dufau, Maria & Means, Anthony, eds. Hormone Binding & Target Cell Activation in the Testis. LC 74-23709. (Current Topics in Molecular Endocrinology: Vol. 1). 380p. 1974. 47.50x (ISBN 0-306-34001-1, Plenum Pr). Plenum Pub.
Fasana, Fortunato, ed. Hydrocele in the Temperate & Tropical Countries, 2 Vols. 1983. Vol. I. 55.00 (ISBN 0-8493-6076-5); Vol. II. 55.00 (ISBN 0-8493-6077-3). CRC Pr.
Fonkalsrud, E. W. Undescended Testes. 1980. 41.95 (ISBN 0-8151-3257-3). Year Bk Med.
Hadziselimovic, F. Cryptorchidism: Management & Implications. (Illus.). 135p. 1983. 51.00 (ISBN 0-387-11881-0). Springer-Verlag.
International Symposium on Crytorchidism. Cryptorchidism: Proceedings. LC 79-40947. (Serono Symposia). 1980. 75.00 (ISBN 0-12-097450-9). Acad Pr.

Johnson, A. D., et al, eds. Testis. Vol. 1 1970. 90.00 (ISBN 0-12-386601-4); Vol. 2 1970. 90.00 (ISBN 0-12-386602-2); Vol. 3 1971. 90.00 (ISBN 0-12-386603-0); Vol. 4 1977. 86.00 (ISBN 0-12-386604-9); Set. o. p. 300.00. Acad Pr.

Kelami, A. & Pryor, J. P., eds. Maldescensus Testis. (Progress in Reproductive Biology & Medicine: Vol. 10). (Illus.). viii, 176p. 1984. 70.75 (ISBN 3-8055-3791-3). S Karger.

Pavone-Macaluso, M., et al, eds. Testicular Cancer & Other Tumors of the Genitourinary Tract. (Ettore Majorana International Sciences Ser.: Life Sciences-Vol. 18). 526p. 1985. 85.00 (ISBN 0-306-41906-8, Plenum Pr). PLenum Pub.

Rosemberg, Eugenia & Paulsen, C. Alvin, eds. The Human Testis. LC 70-129058. (Advances in Experimental Medicine & Biology Ser.: Vol. 10). 669p. 1970. 69.50x (ISBN 0-306-39010-8, Plenum Pr). Plenum Pub.

Setchell, Brian P. The Mammalian Testis. LC 77-79704. (Illus.). 459p. 1978. 55.00x (ISBN 0-8014-1140-8). Cornell U Pr.

Stalsberg, Helge, ed. An International Survey of Distributions of Histologic Types of Tumours of the Testis & Ovary. (UICC Technical Report Ser.: Vol. 75). (Illus.). 353p. (Orig.). 1983. pap. text ed. 27.25 (ISBN 92-9018-075-7, Pub. by Intl Union Against Cancer Switzerland). J K Burgess.

Wershub, Leonard P. The Human Testis: A Clinical Treatise. (Illus.). 276p. 1962. photocopy ed. 27.50x (ISBN 0-398-02044-2). C C Thomas.

TESTING

see also Environmental Engineering; Non-Destructive Testing; Standardization; Strength of Materials; Surfaces (Technology); Testing Machines; Ultrasonic Testing; X-Rays–Industrial Applications

also subdivision Testing under names of things tested, e.g. Automobiles–Testing

ASTM Standards on Precision & Accuracy for Various Applications. 1977. pap. 10.25 (ISBN 0-8031-0284-4, 03-511077-34). ASTM.

Boruch, Robert F., et al. Reanalyzing Program Evaluations: Policies & Practices for Secondary Analysis of Social & Educational Programs. LC 81-2841. (Social & Behavioral Science Ser.). 1981. text ed. 35.00x (ISBN 0-87589-495-X). Jossey-Bass.

Dynamic Geotechnical Testing, STP 654. 406p. 1978. 34.50 (ISBN 0-8031-0326-3, 04-654000-38). ASTM.

Meyers, William R. The Evaluation Enterprise: A Realistic Appraisal of Evaluation Careers, Methods & Applications. LC 81-81961. (Social & Behavioral Science Ser.). 1981. text ed. 23.95x (ISBN 0-87589-503-4). Jossey-Bass.

Peddie, Bill & White, Graham. Testing in Practice. (Orig.). 1978. pap. text ed. 3.25x (ISBN 0-86863-258-9, 00506). Heinemann Ed.

Recent Developments in Mechanical Testing, STP 608. 133p. 1976. pap. 14.50 (ISBN 0-8031-0547-9, 04-608000-23). ASTM.

Reproducibility & Accuracy of Mechanical Tests, STP- 626. 152p. 1977. pap. 15.00 (ISBN 0-8031-0556-8, 04-626000-23). ASTM.

Roid, Gale & Haladyna, Tom. A Technology for Test-Item Writing. (Educational Technology Ser.). 1981. 33.00 (ISBN 0-12-593250-2). Acad Pr.

Scriven, Michael. Theory & Practice of Evaluation. 160p. Date not set. pap. 12.50 (ISBN 0-918528-13-5). Edgepress.

Sharpe, R. S. Research Techniques in Non-Destructive Testing, Vol. 7. 1984. 80.00 (ISBN 0-12-639057-6). Acad Pr.

Testing & Quality Control: The Lodz Textile Seminars. (Training for Industry Ser.). pap. 2.00 (ISBN 0-686-93276-5, UN70/2B6/7, UN). Unipub.

Tucker, Allen E., ed. Testing, Vol. J. rev. ed. (Fluid Power Standards 1984 Ser.). (Illus.). 421p. 1984. 96.00 (ISBN 0-942220-79-X); Set. write for info. Natl Fluid Power.

TESTING MACHINES

American Society for Testing & Materials. Application of Advanced & Nuclear Physics to Testing Materials. LC 65-19687. (American Society for Testing & Materials Ser.: Special Technical Publication, No. 373). pap. 35.30 (ISBN 0-317-10989-8, 2000739). Bks Demand UMI.

Network Editors, ed. Advanced Techniques & Future Developments. 1982. 49.00x (ISBN 0-904999-22-X, Pub. by Network). State Mutual Bk.

--Analog & Hybrid Testing Quality Assurance & Product Testing. 1982. 110.00x (ISBN 0-686-87068-9, Pub. by Network). State Mutual Bk.

--Applications of ATE. 1982. 95.00x (ISBN 0-904999-37-8, Pub. by Network). State Mutual Bk.

--ATE for Equipment Production & Maintenance. 1982. 60.00x (ISBN 0-904999-61-0, Pub. by Network). State Mutual Bk.

Seventy-Three Magazine Editors. Ninety-Nine Test Equipment Projects You Can Build. (Illus.). 1979. pap. 12.95 (ISBN 0-8306-9748-9, 805). TAB Bks.

Spath, Wilhelm. Impact Testing of Materials. rev. ed. Rosner, M. E., ed. (Illus.). 214p. 1962. 55.75x (ISBN 0-677-00910-0). Gordon.

TETANY, GRASS

see Grass Tetany

TETHYS (PALEOGRAPHY)

see also Continental Drift

Sonnenfeld, Peter, ed. Tethys: The Ancestral Mediterranean. LC 80-13974. (Benchmark Papers in Geology Ser.: Vol. 53). 352p. 1981. 44.50 (ISBN 0-87933-355-3). Van Nos Reinhold.

TETRACYCLINE

Mitscher, L. A. The Chemistry of Tetracycline Antibiotics. (Medicinal Research Ser.: Vol. 9). 1978. 75.00 (ISBN 0-8247-6716-0). Dekker.

TETRANCHIDAE

Tuttle, Donald M. & Baker, Edward W. The Spider Mites of the Southwestern United States & a Revision of the Family Tetranychidae. LC 67-30668. (Illus.). 143p. 1968. 7.50x (ISBN 0-8165-0085-1). U of Ariz Pr.

TEXAS INSTRUMENTS COMPUTERS

see also Ti 99-4a (Computer); Ti Cc 40 (Computer); Ti Professional Computer; Ti Programmable 59 (Calculating Machine)

Abelson, Hal. TI LOGO. (Illus.). 1984. pap. 17.95 (ISBN 0-07-038459-2, BYTE Bks). McGraw.

Ahl, David H. The Texas Instruments Ideabook. (The Ideabook Ser.). 150p. 1983. pap. 8.95 (ISBN 0-916688-51-8, 3R). Creative Comp.

Aronofsky, Julius S., et al. Programmable Calculators: Business Applications. (Illus.). 1978. pap. text ed. 11.95 (ISBN 0-07-002317-4). McGraw.

Berk, Joseph & Berk, Susan. Financial Analysis on TI Computers. LC 84-45158. 220p. (Orig.). 1984. pap. 12.95 (ISBN 0-8019-7518-2). Chilton.

Capelia, M. E. & Wienstock, M. Games Ti's Plays. 14.95 (ISBN 0-317-05649-2). P-H.

Chiu, Y. & Mullish, H. Munchers: Twenty-Five Simple Games for the Texas Instruments 99-2 Basic Computer. (Illus.). 160p. 1984. pap. 9.95 (ISBN 0-07-010839-0, BYTE Bks). Mcgraw.

Compute! Magazine Staff. Compute's First Book of TI Games. Regena, C., ed. 211p. (Orig.). 1983. pap. 12.95 (ISBN 0-942386-17-5). Compute Pubns.

Compute! Magazine Staff, ed. Compute's TI Collection, Vol. 1. (Orig.). 1984. pap. 12.95 (ISBN 0-942386-71-X). Compute Pubns.

Consumer Guide Editors. The User's Guide to Texas Instruments. (Orig.). 1983. pap. 3.95 (ISBN 0-671-49504-6). PB.

Creative Programming Inc., Staff. Creative Programming: Texas Instruments Professional, Vol. I. 75p. (Orig.). 1983. wkbk. 9.95 (ISBN 0-912079-10-X, 501). Creat Prog Inc.

Desautels, Edouard J. Lotus 1-2-3 for the TI Professional Computer. 272p. 1984. 17.95 (ISBN 0-697-00377-9); incl. diskette o.p. 29.95 (ISBN 0-317-05722-7). Wm C Brown.

DeVault, Mary & Goldner, Paul. The Texas Instruments Software Digest. cancelled 12.95 (ISBN 0-89303-855-5). Brady Comm.

Drury, Donald W. Learning MS-BASIC on the TI Professional Computer. LC 84-8698. (Illus.). 240p. (Orig.). 1984. 21.95 (ISBN 0-8306-0815-X); pap. 15.95 (ISBN 0-8306-1815-5, 1815). TAB Bks.

Goldner, Paul, et al. The Texas Instruments Home Computer. cancelled 12.95 (ISBN 0-89303-888-1). Brady Comm.

Haskell, Richard & Haskell, Jeff. TI BASIC. (Illus.). 208p. 1984. pap. 14.95 (ISBN 0-13-921107-1). P-H.

Heidt, Meridee & Poirot, James. Microcomputer Workbook, Texas Instruments Edition. 100p. (Orig.). 1982. pap. text ed. 6.95 (ISBN 0-88408-159-1). Sterling Swift.

Inman, Don, et al. Beginner's BASIC. LC 79-65510. (Texas Instruments Home Computer User Software Ser.). 144p. 1979. pap. 9.95 (ISBN 0-89512-028-3). Tex Instr Inc.

Microcomputer Data Manuals. 1982. write for info. Tex Instr Inc.

Molesworth, Ralph. Introduction to Assembly Language for the TI Home Computer. Davis, Steve, ed. LC 83-90770. (Illus.). 144p. (Orig.). 1983. pap. 16.95 (ISBN 0-911061-01-0). S Davis Pub.

Peckham, Herbert D. Programming in BASIC with the TI Home Computer. 1979. pap. text ed. 23.95 (ISBN 0-07-049156-9, BYTE Bks). McGraw.

Radl, Shirley R. & Klemp, Marjorie. Quick & Easy Word Processing with Your TI Professional Computer. LC 84-91755. 200p. 1985. pap. 19.95 (ISBN 0-911061-07-X). S Davis Pub.

Schneider, Alvin D. & Nelson, Charles P. Professional's Guide to TI Professional Computers. LC 84-50066. 18.95 (ISBN 0-672-22255-8). Sams.

Speitel, Tom, et al. Science Computer Programs for Kids... & Other People: TI Version. (Illus.). 1984. pap. 12.95 (ISBN 0-8359-6902-9). Reston.

Stultz, Russell A. The Illustrated TI LOGO Book. 1984. pap. 15.95 (ISBN 0-13-450339-2). P-H.

Texas Instruments Engineering Staff. The Bipolar Microcomputer Components Data Book. 3rd, rev. ed. LC 81-51167. 560p. 1981. pap. 12.50 (ISBN 0-89512-110-7, LCC5831). Tex Instr Inc.

Texas Instruments Learning Center Staff & Texas Instruments Personal Computer Division Staff. User's Reference Guide. rev. ed. LC 81-51829. (Texas Instruments Home Computer User Software Ser.). 200p. 1981. pap. 9.95 loose leaf three hole punched (ISBN 0-89512-048-8). Tex Instr Inc.

TMS32010 User's Guide. 400p. 1984. 8.00 (SPRU001B). Tex Instr Inc.

TMS7000 Family Data Manual. 350p. 1983. write for info. Tex Instr Inc.

Turner, Len. Texas Instruments Home Computer Games Programs. 96p. 1983. 8.95 (ISBN 0-86668-032-2). ARCsoft.

--Texas Instruments Home Computer Graphics Programs. 112p. 1983. 9.95 (ISBN 0-86668-031-4). ARCsoft.

Watt, D. Learning with TI LOGO. (Illus.). 320p. 1983. pap. 16.95 (ISBN 0-07-068580-0, BYTE Bks). McGraw.

Wortman, Leon A. Business Solutions Using the Texas Instruments Professional Computer. LC 83-15899. 416p. 1983. pap. 22.95 (ISBN 0-89303-344-8); diskette 35.00 (ISBN 0-89303-345-6). Brady Comm.

TEXAS INSTRUMENTS PROFESSIONAL COMPUTER

see Ti Professional Computer

TEXT PROCESSING (COMPUTER SCIENCE)

Longacre, Robert E., ed. Theory & Application in Processing Texts in Non-IndoEuropean Languages. (Papers in Textlinguistics: Vol. 43). (Illus.). ix, 272p. (Orig.). 1984. pap. 24.00x (ISBN 3-87118-643-0, Pub. by Helmut Buske Verlag Hamburg). Benjamins North Am.

Sampath, G. An Introduction to Text Processing. (Illus.). xii, 273p. (Orig.). 1985. pap. 20.00 (ISBN 0-9615070-0-4). River Valley Pub.

Srihari, Sargur N., ed. Computer Text Recognition & Error Correction. LC 84-48518. (Tutorial Text Ser.). 353p. (Orig.). 1985. pap. text ed. 36.00 (ISBN 0-8186-0579-0, 579); microfiche 36.00 (ISBN 0-8186-4579-2). IEEE Comp Soc.

TEXTILE CHEMICALS

see also Fillers (In Paper, Paint, etc.); Textile Finishing

Bogle, Michael. Textile Dyes, Finishes & Auxiliaries. LC 76-25746. (Reference Library of Science & Technology Ser.: Vol. 8). (Illus.). 1977. lib. bdg. 24.00 (ISBN 0-8240-9902-8). Garland Pub.

Gutcho, M. H., ed. Household & Industrial Fabric Conditioners. LC 79-27919. (Chemical Technology Review Ser.: No. 152). (Illus.). 431p. 1980. 54.00 (ISBN 0-8155-0793-3). Noyes.

TEXTILE CHEMISTRY

Bird, C. L. & Boston, W. S. The Theory of Coloration of Textiles. 432p. 1975. 80.00x (ISBN 0-686-98192-8, Pub. by Soc Dyers & Colour). State Mutual Bk.

Carter, Mary E. Essential Fiber Chemistry. (Fiber Science Ser.: Vol. 2). 1971. 65.00 (ISBN 0-8247-1088-6). Dekker.

Chemicals for Waste Business. 1983. 1250.00 (ISBN 0-89336-309-X, C-038). BCC.

Coated Fabrics Technology: Major Papers from the Journal of Coated Fabrics, Vol. 2. LC 73-86380. 217p. 1979. pap. 19.95 (ISBN 0-87762-236-1). Technomic.

Farnfield, Carolyn A. & Perry, D. R. Identification of Textile Materials. 262p. 1975. 99.00x (ISBN 0-686-63769-0). State Mutual Bk.

Joseph, Marjory L. Introductory Textile Science. 4th ed. LC 80-20831. 406p. 1981. text ed. 29.95 (ISBN 0-03-056884-6, HoltC). HR&W.

McKelvey, J. B. Cotton Modification with Oxiranes (Epoxides) 58p. 1971. 39.00x (ISBN 0-900541-10-5, Pub. by Meadowfield Pr England). State Mutual Bk.

McPhee, J. R. & Phil, D. The Mothproofing of Wool. 58p. 1971. 39.00x (ISBN 0-686-97038-1, Pub. by Meadowfield Pr England). State Mutual Bk.

Makinson. Shrinkproofing of Wool. (Fiber Science Ser.: Vol. 8). 1979. 75.00 (ISBN 0-8247-6776-4). Dekker.

Metzger, Jacques. Thiazole & Its Derivatives, 3 pts. LC 78-17740. (Chemistry of Heterocyclic Compounds Ser.: Vol. 34). 1979. Pt. 1, 612p. 190.95 ea (ISBN 0-471-03993-4, Pub. by Wiley-Interscience). Pt. 2, 590p (ISBN 0-471-04126-2). Pt. 3, 406p (ISBN 0-471-04127-0). Wiley.

Nettles, John E. Handbook of Chemistry Specialties: Textile Fiber Processing, Preparation, & Bleaching. LC 83-5862. 496p. 1983. 65.00 (ISBN 0-471-89318-8, Pub. by Wiley-Interscience). Wiley.

Nunn, D. M. The Dyeing of Synthetic-Polymer & Acetate Fibres. 1979p. 1979. 100.00x (ISBN 0-686-98190-1, XPub. by Soc Dyers & Colour); pap. 55.00x (ISBN 0-686-98191-X). State Mutual Bk.

Peirce, F. T. & Womersley, J. R. Cloth Geometry. 80p. 1978. 40.00x (ISBN 0-900739-28-2, Pub. by Textile Inst England). State Mutual Bk.

Peters, Raymond H. Textile Chemistry, Vols. 2 & 3. Incl. Vol. 2: Impurities in Fibres. 374p. 1967. 70.25 (ISBN 0-444-40452-X); Vol. 3: The Physical Chemistry of Dyeing. 890p. 1975. 138.50 (ISBN 0-444-41120-8). Elsevier.

Sarkar, A. K. Fluorescent Whitening Agents. 116p. 1971. 39.00x (ISBN 0-900541-20-2, Pub. by Meadowfield Pr England). State Mutual Bk.

Segal, Leon. Decrystallized Cotton. 62p. 1971. 39.00x (ISBN 0-900541-02-4, Pub. by Meadowfield Pr England). State Mutual Bk.

Slater, K. The Thermal Behaviour of Textiles. 147p. 1976. 70.00x (ISBN 0-686-63807-7). State Mutual Bk.

Sodano, Charles S. Water & Soil Repellents for Fabrics. LC 79-13241. (Chemical Technology Review Ser.: No. 134). (Illus.). 395p. 1979. 39.00 (ISBN 0-8155-0761-5). Noyes.

Winkler, Werner. Fachworterbuch Chemiefasern. (Ger., Eng. & Fr.). 350p. (Technical Dictionary of Textile Chemistry). leatherette 47.50 (ISBN 0-686-56605-X, M-7387, Pub. by Deutscher Fachverlag). French & Eur.

TEXTILE FABRICS

see also Brocade; Crease-Resistant Fabrics; Nonwoven Fabrics; Silk; Synthetic Fabrics; Textile Fibers; Textile Industry; Yarn

Alderman, Sharon & Wertenberger, Kathryn. Handwoven, Tailormade: A Tandem Guide to Fabric Designing, Weaving, Sewing & Tailoring. LC 82-81683. (Illus.). 147p. 1982. 17.50 (ISBN 0-934026-08-4). Interweave.

ASTM Performance Standards for Textile Fabrics. 174p. 1983. 17.00 (ISBN 0-8031-0839-7, 03-413083-18). ASTM.

Barrett, Clotilde & Smith, Eunice. Double Two-Tie Unit Weaves. 88p. 1983. pap. 12.00 (ISBN 0-937452-06-8); 1.50. Colo Fiber.

Berg, Gerald, ed. Viral Pollution of the Environment. 248p. 1983. 76.00 (ISBN 0-8493-6245-8). CRC Pr.

Birrell, Verla. The Textile Arts: A Handbook of Weaving, Braiding, Printing, & Other Textile Techniques. LC 58-8363. (Illus.). 530p. 1973. pap. 8.95 (ISBN 0-8052-0390-7). Schocken.

Burnip, M. S. & Newton, A. Non-Woven Fabrics. 105p. 1970. 70.00x (ISBN 0-686-63777-1). State Mutual Bk.

Business Communications Staff. High Tech Textiles for Clothing, Insulation, Specialties. 1984. 1500.00 (ISBN 0-89336-358-8, GB-069). BCC.

Cohen, Allen C. Beyond Basic Textiles. (Illus.). 350p. 1982. loose-leaf 16.50 (ISBN 0-87005-407-4). Fairchild.

Collier, A. M. A Handbook of Textiles. 3rd ed. 7.80 (ISBN 0-08-024974-4); pap. 5.75 (ISBN 0-08-018057-4). Pergamon.

Collins, Herbert R. Threads of History: Americana Recorded on Cloth - 1775 to the Present. LC 79-16166. (Illus.). 566p. 1979. 60.00x (ISBN 0-87474-326-5). Smithsonian.

Constantine, M. Whole Cloth. 1986. cancelled. Van Nos Reinhold.

Corbman, B. Textiles: Fiber to Fabric. 6th ed. 608p. 1982. text ed. 29.00 (ISBN 0-07-013137-6). McGraw.

Crawshaw, G. H. & Ince, J. Textile Floorcoverings. 84p. 1977. 70.00x (ISBN 0-686-63800-X). State Mutual Bk.

Dantyagi, Susheela. Fundamentals of Textiles & Their Care. 4th ed. 1983. pap. 12.95x (ISBN 0-86131-431-X, Pub. by Orient Longman India). Apt Bks.

Dyson, E., et al. Yarn Production & Properties. 96p. 1974. 70.00x (ISBN 0-686-63811-5). State Mutual Bk.

Fabric Filtration Seminar '81. 66p. 1981. 60.00 (ISBN 0-318-01529-3, 16015). Indus Fabrics.

Fabric Filtration Seminar '82. 130p. 1982. 60.00 (ISBN 0-318-01528-5, 16010). Indus Fabrics.

Fabric Filtration Seminar '83. 82p. 1983. 60.00 (ISBN 0-318-01527-7, 16005). Indus Fabrics.

The Fabric Revolution. 1981. 50.00x (ISBN 0-900739-43-6, Pub. by Textile Inst). State Mutual Bk.

Fabrics for Clinical-Biological Warfare. 110p. 1982. 50.00 (ISBN 0-318-01476-9, 10030). Indus Fabrics.

Fabrics for Protective Clothing: Fire Entry to Disposables. 66p. 1981. 35.00 (ISBN 0-318-01530-7, 16020). Indus Fabrics.

Fourt, Lyman E. & Hollies, Norman R. Clothing: Comfort & Function. LC 70-134699. (Fiber Science Ser.). (Illus.). pap. 65.80 (ISBN 0-317-08345-7, 2017851). Bks Demand UMI.

Gioello, Debbie A. Understanding Fabrics: From Fiber to Finished Cloth. (Language of Fashion Ser.). (Illus.). 350p. 1982. text ed. 30.00 (ISBN 0-87005-377-9). Fairchild.
Greenwood, K. Weaving: Control of Fabric Structure. 72p. 1975. 39.00 (ISBN 0-900541-65-2, Pub. by Meadowfield Pr England). State Mutual Bk.
The Growth Role for Fabrics in Solid Waste Management. 96p. 1980. 50.00 (ISBN 0-318-01477-7, 10035). Indus Fabrics.
Happey, F., ed. Contemporary: Textile Engineering. 1983. 79.50 (ISBN 0-12-323750-5). Acad Pr.
Healer, Carol B. Programmed Instruction in Textiles. LC 70-632246. (Illus.). 84p. 1970. pap. 1.00x (ISBN 0-88215-015-4). Ohio St U Lib.
Hearle, J. W. & Miles, L. W., eds. The Setting of Fibers & Fabrics. 251p. 1971. 40.00x (ISBN 0-900541-49-0, Pub. by Meadowfield Pr England). State Mutual Bk.
Herbert, R. W. The Organization of a Seasonal Range of Knitted Fabrics. 1979. 60.00x (ISBN 0-686-63779-8). State Mutual Bk.
Landi, Sheila. The Textile Conservators Manual. 360p. 1985. text ed. 104.95 (ISBN 0-408-10624-7). Butterworth.
Lord, P. R. & Mech, M. I. Weaving: Conversion of Yarn to Fabric. 376p. 1976. 42.00x (ISBN 0-900541-78-4, Pub. by Meadowfield England). State Mutual Bk.
Lyle, Dorothy S. Modern Textiles. 2nd ed. LC 81-11574. 513p. 1982. text ed. 36.00 (ISBN 0-471-07805-0); instr's. manual 8.00 (ISBN 0-471-01839-2). Wiley.
--Performance of Textiles. LC 76-54110. 592p. 1977. 48.50x (ISBN 0-471-01418-4). Wiley.
McKnight Staff. Exploring Fabrics. LC 76-53072. 1977. text ed. 18.36 (ISBN 0-87345-613-0); tchr's ed. 42.67 (ISBN 0-87345-615-7). McKnight.
Marine Fabric & Hardware Directory. 20.00 (ISBN 0-318-01516-1, 12080). Indus Fabrics.
Martin, Rebecca. Textiles in Daily Life in the Middle Ages. LC 84-28492. (Illus.). 68p. 1985. pap. 7.95 (ISBN 0-910386-80-3). Ind U Pr.
Meredith, R. & Hearle, J. W., eds. Physical Methods of Investigating Textiles. LC 59-13795. (Illus.). pap. 110.30 (ISBN 0-317-10818-2, 2011955). Bks Demand UMI.
Miller, Edward. Textiles: Properties & Behavior. (Illus.). 192p. 1984. pap. 16.95 (ISBN 0-7134-2545-8, Pub. by Batsford England). David & Charles.
New Developments in Fiber & Fabric Technology. 60.00 (ISBN 0-318-01479-3). Indus Fabrics.
Newton, A. & Ford, J. E. The Production & Properties of Non-Woven Fabrics. 93p. 1973. 70.00x (ISBN 0-686-63785-2). State Mutual Bk.
Non-Conventional Methods of Fabric Production: The Lodz Textile Seminars. (Training for Industry Ser.). pap. 2.00 (ISBN 0-686-93208-0, UN73/2/6, UN). Unipub.
Nutter, W. Yarn Production & Properties. 110p. 1971. 70.00x (ISBN 0-686-63812-3). State Mutual Bk.
O'Shea, Mortimer. Interior Furnishings. 1981. 50.00x (ISBN 0-686-87276-2, Pub. by Textile Inst). State Mutual Bk.
Pettit, Florence H. America's Printed & Painted Fabrics, 1600-1900. 1970. 24.95 (ISBN 0-8038-0340-0). Hastings.
Rhodes, Tonya S. Color Related Decorating Textiles. LC 76-24006. (Shuttle Craft Guild Monograph: No. 14). (Illus.). 35p. 1965. pap. 7.45 (ISBN 0-916658-14-7). HTH Pubs.
Robinson, A. T. & Marks, R. Woven Cloth Construction. 178p. 1973. 37.50x (ISBN 0-686-63810-7). State Mutual Bk.
Schwartz, Peter, et al. Fabric Forming Systems. LC 82-7967. (Textile Ser.). (Illus.). 175p. 1983. 24.00 (ISBN 0-8155-0908-1). Noyes.
Siewert, Carol H., et al. Basic Textiles: A Learning Package. 228p. 1973. 19.95 (ISBN 0-395-14220-2). HM.
Smith, Betty & Block, Ira. Textiles in Perspective. (Illus.). 512p. 1982. text ed. 29.95 (ISBN 0-13-912808-5). P-H.
Smith, P. A. Yarn Production & Properties. 123p. 1969. 70.00x (ISBN 0-686-63813-1). State Mutual Bk.
Snowden, D. C. The Production of Woven Fabrics. 94p. 1972. 70.00x (ISBN 0-686-63794-1). State Mutual Bk.
Sommar, Helen G. A Brief Guide to Sources of Fiber & Textile Information. LC 72-89909. (Illus.). viii, 138p. 1973. text ed. 5.00 (ISBN 0-87815-009-9). Info Resources.
A Study on Cotton Textiles. (Fr.). 1966. pap. 3.00 (ISBN 0-686-93131-9, G112, GATT). Unipub.
Textile Technology Forum '81. 133p. 1981. 50.00 (ISBN 0-318-01537-4, 16035). Indus Fabrics.
Textile Technology Forum '82. 130p. 1982. 50.00 (ISBN 0-318-01536-6, 16030). Indus Fabrics.
Textile Technology Forum '83. 140p. 1983. 50.00 (ISBN 0-318-01538-2, 16036). Indus Fabrics.
Thomas, Michel. Textiles: History of an Art. LC 85-42942. (Illus.). 272p. 1985. 65.00 (ISBN 0-8478-0640-5). Rizzoli Intl.
Tortora, Phyllis G. Understanding Textiles. 2nd ed. 1982. text ed. write for info. (ISBN 0-02-420870-1). Macmillan.
Turner, J. P. The Production & Properties of Narrow Fabrics. 114p. 1976. 70.00x (ISBN 0-686-63784-4). State Mutual Bk.
Weaver, J. William, ed. Analytical Methods for a Textile Laboratory. 3rd ed. LC 84-70596. (Illus.). x, 403p. 1984. 50.00 (ISBN 0-9613350-0-9). Am Assn Text.
Williams, John C., ed. Preservation of Paper & Textiles of Historic & Artistic Value II. LC 81-46. (ACS Advances in Chemistry Ser.: No. 193). 1981. 49.95 (ISBN 0-8412-0553-1). Am Chemical.
Williamson, R. Fluoresent Brightening Agents. (Textile Science & Techology Ser.: Vol. 4). 154p. 1980. 40.50 (ISBN 0-444-41914-4). Elsevier.
Wilson, D. K. The Production of Textile Yarns by the False-Twist Technique. 66p. 1978. 70.00x (ISBN 0-686-63791-7). State Mutual Bk.
--The Production of Textured Yarns by Methods Other That the False-Twist Technique. 55p. 1977. 70.00x (ISBN 0-686-63792-5). State Mutual Bk.
Wingate, Isabel B. & Burkholder, Ralph. Laboratory Swatch Book, Textile Fabrics & Their Selection. 7th ed. 252p. 1976. write for info. wire coil (ISBN 0-697-08313-6). Wm C Brown.
Wright, Helena E. Merrimack Valley Textile Museum. LC 82-49169. 404p. 1983. lib. bdg. 43.00 (ISBN 0-8240-9172-8). Garland Pub.
Wyles, D. H. Developments in the Finishing of Cotton & Man-Made Fiber Fabrics. 81p. 1973. 70.00x (ISBN 0-686-63761-5). State Mutual Bk.

TEXTILE FABRICS–DICTIONARIES

American Fabrics Magazine, ed. Encyclopedia of Textiles. 3rd ed. (Illus.). 656p. 1980. 49.95 (ISBN 0-13-276576-4, Busn). P-H.
Burnham, Dorothy K. Warp & Weft: A Dictionary of Textile Terms. (Illus.). 240p. 1982. 35.00 (ISBN 0-684-17332-8, ScribT). Scribner.
English-Chinese Textile Dictionary. (Eng. & Chinese.). 532p. 1977. leatherette 29.95 (ISBN 0-686-92346-4, M-9269). French & Eur.
Grayson, Martin, ed. Encyclopedia of Textiles, Fibers & Non-Woven Fabrics. LC 84-13213. (Encyclopedia Reprint Ser.). 581p. 1984. 59.95x (ISBN 0-471-81461-X, 1-631). Wiley.
Hofer, Alfons. Illustriertes Textil und Mode - Lexikon. (Ger., Illus.). 342p. 19.95 (ISBN 3-87150-081-X, M-7476, Pub. by Deutscher Fachverlag). French & Eur.
Hohenadel, P. & Relton, J. A Modern Textile Dictionary: English-German. (Ger. & Eng.). 484p. 1977. 62.50 (ISBN 3-87097-077-4, M-9024). French & Eur.
Joseph, Marjory & Gieseking, Audrey. Illustrated Guide to Textiles. 3rd ed. (Illus.). 1981. pap. 12.95x (ISBN 0-8087-3435-0). Plycon Pr.
Klapper, Marvin. Textile Glossary. LC 72-88888. 120p. 1973. pap. 1.95 (ISBN 0-87005-116-4). Fairchild.
Leskova, T. & Plisek, V. Czech-English Technical Textile Dictionary. (Czech. & Eng.). 468p. 1980. 60.00x (ISBN 0-686-72090-3, Pub. by Collet's). State Mutual Bk.
Linton, George E. The Modern Textile & Apparel Dictionary. 4th, rev. enlarged ed. 149.00x (ISBN 0-686-97037-3, Pub. by Meadowfield Pr England). State Mutual Bk.
Michelson, Derrick O. Fachworterbuch Textil. (Ger. & Eng.). 136p. (Dictionary of Textiles). 13.50 (ISBN 3-87150-106-9, M-7404, Pub. by Deutscher Fachuerlag). French & Eur.
Rabinowitch, Z. E. & Lupandin, K. K. English-Russian Textile Dictionary. (Eng. & Rus.). 640p. 1961. Leatherette 14.95 (ISBN 0-686-92372-3, M-9111). French & Eur.
Rodriguez, Joaquin O. Diccionario textil panamericano: English-Spanish Dictionary of Textile Terms. 2nd ed. (Span.). 1971. 35.00 (ISBN 0-912476-04-4). W R C Smith.
Schaeffer, Albrecht. Enzyklopaedie der Gesamten Textilveredlung. (Ger.). 1966. 80.00 (ISBN 3-500-16110-3, M-7056). French & Eur.
Scheengluth, Carlos. Diccionario Ilustrado De Terminologia Textil Aleman-Espanol, Espanol-Aleman. (Ger. & Span.). 700p. 1975. 66.00 (ISBN 84-335-6220-7, S-50056). French & Eur.
Schock, Sarina & Gebert, Erika. Fachworterbuch Textil. (Ger. & Fr.). 136p. 9.95 (ISBN 3-87150-039-9, M-7405, Pub. by Deutscher Fachverlag). French & Eur.
Wingate, Isabel B., ed. Fairchild's Dictionary of Textiles. 6th ed. LC 78-73964. 1979. 40.00 (ISBN 0-87005-198-9). Fairchild.
ZTDI. Textile Dictionary. (Eng., Fr., Ger. & Span.). 536p. 1980. 115.00 (ISBN 0-444-41772-9). Elsevier.

TEXTILE FABRICS–MOISTURE

see Moisture in Textiles

TEXTILE FABRICS–TESTING

De Boos, A. G. Chemical Testing & Analysis. 51p. 1974. 70.00x (ISBN 0-686-63753-4). State Mutual Bk.
East, G. C. Chemical Testing & Analysis. 68p. 1971. 70.00x (ISBN 0-686-63752-6). State Mutual Bk.
Hunter, L. The Production & Properties of Staple-Fibre Yarns Made by Recently Developed Techniques. 168p. 1978. 70.00x (ISBN 0-686-27733-3). State Mutual Bk.
Jones, E. B. Chemical Testing & Analysis. 1978. 70.00x (ISBN 0-686-63754-2). State Mutual Bk.
Leon, N. H. Chemical Reactivity & Modification of Keratin Fibres. 81p. 1975. 70.00x (ISBN 0-686-63750-X). State Mutual Bk.
Lyle, Dorothy S. Performance of Textiles. LC 76-54110. 592p. 1977. 48.50x (ISBN 0-471-01418-4). Wiley.
Lyons, W. James. Impact Phenomena in Textiles. (Press Research Monographs: No. 19). 1963. 22.50x (ISBN 0-262-12008-9). MIT Pr.
Renbourn, E. T. Physiology & Hygiene of Materials & Clothing. 60p. 1971. 39.00x (ISBN 0-900541-12-1, Pub. by Meadowfield Pr England). State Mutual Bk.
Slater, K. Comfort Properties of Textiles. 91p. 50.00x (ISBN 0-686-63755-0). State Mutual Bk.
Straw, W. A. Chemical Testing & Analysis. 50p. 1969. 70.00x (ISBN 0-686-63751-8). State Mutual Bk.
Weston, H. Physical Testing & Quality Control. 150p. 1974. 70.00x (ISBN 0-686-63780-1). State Mutual Bk.

TEXTILE FABRICS–AFRICA

Reswick, Irmtraud. Traditional Textiles of Tunisia. (Illus.). 272p. 1985. pap. 24.95 (ISBN 0-295-96281-X). U of Wash Pr.

TEXTILE FABRICS–GREAT BRITAIN

Albrecht-Mathey, Elisabeth. The Printed Fabrics of Mulhouse & Alsace, 1750-1800. 1981. 40.00x (ISBN 0-85317-091-6, Pub. by Lewis Pubs). State Mutual Bk.
Fairclough, Oliver & Leary, Emmeline. Textiles by William Morris & Co. (Illus., Orig.). 1981. pap. 20.00 (ISBN 0-686-79147-9). Eastview.
Flanagan, James F. Spitalfields Silks of the Eighteenth & Nineteenth Centuries. 1981. 25.00x (ISBN 0-85317-360-5, Pub. by Lewis Pubs). State Mutual Bk.
Parry, Linda. William Morris Textiles. LC 82-70184. (Illus.). 192p. 1983. 46.95 (ISBN 0-670-77075-2, Studio); pap. 24.95 (ISBN 0-670-77074-4). Viking.
Sutton, Ann. The Textiles of Wales. (Illus.). 128p. 1985. 23.45. Dodd.
Tuchscherer, Jean-Michel. The Printed Fabrics of Mulhouse & Alsace, 1801-1850. 1981. 40.00x (ISBN 0-85317-017-7, Pub. by Lewis Pubs). State Mutual Bk.

TEXTILE FABRICS–GUATEMALA

O'Neale, Lila M. Textiles of Highland Guatemala. (Illus.). 1945. 37.00 (ISBN 0-384-43370-7). Johnson Repr.
Rowe, Ann P. A Century of Change in Guatemalan Textiles. LC 81-70077. (Illus.). 152p. 1982. pap. 18.95 (ISBN 0-295-95908-8, Pub. by Ctr for Inter-Amer Relations). U of Wash Pr.

TEXTILE FABRICS–INDIA

Calico Museum, Ahmedabad. Treasures of Indian Textiles. (Illus.). 148p. 1980. 49.95x (ISBN 0-940500-44-2). Asia Bk Corp.
Calico Museum-Ahmedabad, ed. Treasures of Indian Textiles. 146p. 1980. text ed. 52.50x (ISBN 0-391-02523-6, Pub. by UBS India). Humanities.
Gittinger, Mattiebelle. Master Dyers to the World: Technique & Trade in Early Indian Dyed Cotton Textiles. McEuen, Caroline K., ed. (Illus.). 208p. 1982. pap. 20.00 (ISBN 0-87405-020-0). Textile Mus.
Jayakar, Pupul & Irwin, John. Textiles & Ornaments of India. Wheeler, Monroe, ed. LC 75-169305. (Museum of Modern Art Publications in Reprint). (Illus.). 96p. 1972. Repr. of 1956 ed. 20.00 (ISBN 0-405-01564-X). Ayer Co Pubs.
Mehta, Rustam J. Masterpieces of Indian Textiles. 4th ed. (Illus.). 56p. 1981. Repr. of 1970 ed. text ed. 30.00x (ISBN 0-686-32160-X, Pub. by Taraporevala India). Apt Bks.
Treasures of Indian Textiles: Calico Museum of Shmedabad. 1981. 40.00x (ISBN 0-8364-0764-4, Pub. by Marg India). South Asia Bks.

TEXTILE FABRICS–INDONESIA

Warming, Wanda & Gaworski, Michael E. The World of Indonesian Textiles. LC 80-82526. (Illus.). 200p. 1981. 45.00 (ISBN 0-87011-432-8). Kodansha.

TEXTILE FABRICS–ITALY

Trilling, James. The Roman Heritage: Textiles from Egypt & the Eastern Mediterranean, 300-600 A.D. LC 82-50367. (Textile Museum Journal Ser.). (Illus.). 112p. (Orig.). 1982. pap. 17.50 (ISBN 0-87405-019-7). Textile Mus.

TEXTILE FABRICS–JAPAN

Blakemore, Frances. Japanese Design: Through Textile Patterns. LC 78-2430. (Illus.). 1978. 10.95 (ISBN 0-8348-0132-9). Weatherhill.
Japan Textile Color Design Center. Textile Designs of Japan, Vol. I: Free-Style Designs. LC 79-89347. (Textile Designs of Japan Ser.). (Illus.). 440p. 1980. 195.00 (ISBN 0-87011-396-8). Kodansha.
--Textile Designs of Japan, Vol. II: Geometric Designs. LC 79-89347. (Textile Designs of Japan Ser.). (Illus.). 416p. 1980. 195.00 (ISBN 0-87011-403-4). Kodansha.
Miss Jean Christie Design Centre Bookshop Staff, ed. Textile Designs of Japan: Free-Style Designs, Vol. I. 66p. 1981. 195.00x (ISBN 0-906026-05-9, Pub. by Christie England). State Mutual Bk.
--Textile Designs of Japan: Geometric Designs, Vol. II. 62p. 195.00x (ISBN 0-906026-06-7, Pub. by Christie England). State Mutual Bk.
Miss Jean Christie, Design Centre Bookshop, ed. Textile Designs of Japan: Ukinawan, Ainu, & Foreign Design, Vol. III. 62p. 195.00x (ISBN 0-906026-07-5, Pub. by Christie England). State Mutual Bk.

TEXTILE FABRICS–PERU

Tidball, Harriet. Peru: Textiles Unlimited. LC 76-24015. (Shuttle Craft Guild Monograph: Nos. 25-26). (Illus.). 82p. 1968. pap. 10.95 set (ISBN 0-916658-25-2). HTH Pubs.
--Peru: Textiles Unlimited, Part II. LC 76-24015. (Shuttle Craft Guild Monograph: No. 26). (Illus.). 46p. 1969. pap. 10.95 set (ISBN 0-916658-26-0). HTH Pubs.

TEXTILE FABRICS, ISLAMIC

Serjeant, R. B. Islamic Textiles. 1972. 35.00x (ISBN 0-86685-028-7). Intl Bk Ctr.
Spuhler, Friedrich. Islamic Carpets & Textiles. Wingfield Digby, George & Wingfield Digby, Cornelia, trs. from Xger. (Illus.). 251p. 1978. 75.00 (ISBN 0-571-09783-9). Faber & Faber.

TEXTILE FABRICS, MUSLIM

see Textile Fabrics, Islamic

TEXTILE FACTORIES

see also Textile Machinery

Stevens, E. C. Electricity in Textile Factories. 1979. 50.00x (ISBN 0-686-63763-1). State Mutual Bk.

TEXTILE FIBERS

see also Rayon; Textile Chemistry; Textile Fabrics;
also specific fibers, e.g. Cotton, Nylon

Carter, Mary E. Essential Fiber Chemistry. (Fiber Science Ser.: Vol. 2). 1971. 65.00 (ISBN 0-8247-1088-6). Dekker.
Cook, J. Gordon. Handbook of Polyolefin Fibers. 608p. 1967. 90.00x (ISBN 0-900541-50-4, Pub. by Meadowfield Pr England). State Mutual Bk.
--Handbook of Textile Fibers. 1160p. 1968. 125.00x (ISBN 0-900541-00-8, Pub. by Meadowfield Pr England). State Mutual Bk.
Food & Agriculture Organization of the United Nations. Per Capita Fibre Consumption 1967-1969: Cotton, Wool, Flax, Silk & Man-Made Fibres. Incl. Per Capita Fibre Consumption 1970-1972: Cotton, Wool, Flax, & Man-Made Fibres. Food & Agriculture Organization of the United Nations. pap. 15.50 (F1188); Per Capita Fibre Consumption 1971-1973: Cotton, Wool, Flax, Silk, & Man Made Fibre. 188p. 1975. pap. 16.25 (F1189); Per Capita Fibre Consumption 1973-1974: Cotton, Wool & Man-Made Fibres. 1977. pap. 8.25 (ISBN 92-5-000102-9, F1190). pap. 15.50 (F1187, FAO). Unipub.
Fry, M. Color & Fiber. 1986. cancelled (ISBN 0-442-20055-2). Van Nos Reinhold.
Gioello, Debbie A. Profiling Fabrics: Properties, Performance, & Construction Techniques. (Language of Fashion Ser.). (Illus.). 325p. 1981. text ed. 27.50 (ISBN 0-87005-259-4). Fairchild.
Grayson, Martin, ed. Encyclopedia of Textiles, Fibers & Non-Woven Fabrics. LC 84-13213. (Encyclopedia Reprint Ser.). 581p. 1984. 59.95x (ISBN 0-471-81461-X, 1-631). Wiley.
Harrison, P. W. New Ways of Produce Textiles. 274p. 1972. 55.00x (ISBN 0-686-63776-3). State Mutual Bk.
Hearle, J. W. & Greeg, R. Fibre Structure. 203p. 1970. 70.00x (ISBN 0-686-63764-X). State Mutual Bk.
Hearle, J. W. & Miles, L. W., eds. The Setting of Fibers & Fabrics. 251p. 1971. 40.00x (ISBN 0-900541-49-0, Pub. by Meadowfield Pr England). State Mutual Bk.
Hochberg, B. Fibre Facts. LC 81-83115. (Illus.). 68p. (Orig.). 1981. pap. 5.95 (ISBN 0-9600990-6-9). B Hochberg.
Jeffries, R. Bicomponent Fibres. 76p. 1971. 39.00x (ISBN 0-900541-48-2, Pub. by Meadowfield Pr England). State Mutual Bk.
Lyle, Dorothy S. Modern Textiles. 2nd ed. LC 81-11574. 513p. 1982. text ed. 36.00 (ISBN 0-471-07805-0); instr's. manual 8.00 (ISBN 0-471-01839-2). Wiley.

BOOKS - SUBJECT INDEX TEXTILE PRINTING

Meredith, R. The Structures & Properties of Fibres. 85p. 1975. 70.00x (ISBN 0-686-63798-4). State Mutual Bk.
Morton, W. E. Physical Properties of Textile Fibres. 660p. 1975. 110.00x (ISBN 0-686-63781-X). State Mutual Bk.
Mukherjee, R. R. & Radhakrishnan, T. Long Vegetable Fibres. 81p. 1972. 70.00x (ISBN 0-686-63771-2). State Mutual Bk.
Pizzuto, Joseph. Fabric Science. 4th ed. Price, Arthur & Cohen, Allen, eds. (Illus.). 1980. ring-binder, wkbk. 16.50 (ISBN 0-87005-265-9). Fairchild.
Robinson, J. S., ed. Spinning, Extruding & Processing of Fibers: Recent Advances. LC 80-13137. (Chemical Technology Review Ser.: No. 159). 436p. 1980. 48.00 (ISBN 0-8155-0801-8). Noyes.
Ryder, M. L. The Production & Properties of Wool & Other Animal Fibres. 63p. 1975. 70.00x (ISBN 0-686-63788-7). State Mutual Bk.
Schick, Martin, ed. Surface Characteristics of Fibers & Textiles, Pt. 2. (Fiber Science Ser.: Vol. 7). 1977. 75.00 (ISBN 0-8247-6531-1). Dekker.
Textile Fibres: The Lodz Textiles Seminars. (Training for Industry Ser.). pap. 2.00 (ISBN 0-686-93275-7, UN70/2B6/1, UN). Unipub.
Whewell, C. S. The Finishing of Textile Fabrics. 72p. 1970. 70.00x (ISBN 0-686-63765-8). State Mutual Bk.

TEXTILE FIBERS, SYNTHETIC

Battista, Orlando A., ed. Synthetic Fibers in Papermaking. LC 64-13211. 340p. 1964. text ed. 21.00 (ISBN 0-470-05894-3, Pub. by Wiley). Krieger.
Bauer, R. & Koslowski, H. J. Chemiefaser-Lexikon. (Ger.). 230p. 1977. 24.95 (ISBN 3-87150-093-3, M-7318, Pub. by Deutscher Fachverlag). French & Eur.
Chemicals for Waste Business. 1983. 1250.00 (ISBN 0-89336-309-X, C-038). BCC.
Datye, Deshav Vinayak & Vaidya, Ashok Amrut. Chemical Processing of Synthetic Fibers & Blends. LC 83-19809. 565p. 1984. 80.00x (ISBN 0-471-87654-2, Pub. by Wiley-Interscience). Wiley.
Dembeck, Adeline A. Guidebook to Man-Made Textile Fibers & Textured Yarns of the World: Film-To-Yarn Non-Wovens. 3rd ed. LC 68-28677. 1969. leatherette 11.00 (ISBN 0-911546-01-4). United Piece.
Hancox, N. L., ed. Fibre Composite Hybrid Materials. 290p. 1981. text ed. 43.50x (ISBN 0-02-949950-X). Macmillan.
Hicks, E. M., Jr., et al. The Production of Synthetic-Polymer Fibres. 127p. 1971. 70.00x (ISBN 0-686-63790-9). State Mutual Bk.
Hughes, A. J., et al. The Production of Man-Made Fibres. 177p. 1976. 70.00x (ISBN 0-686-63789-5). State Mutual Bk.
Manfre, G. Limit of the Spinning Process in Manufacturing Synthetic Fibers. (CISM - International Centre for Mechanical Sciences, Courses & Lectures: Vol. 255). (Illus.). 66p. 1976. pap. 9.20 (ISBN 0-387-81308-X). Springer-Verlag.
Pajgrt, O., et al, eds. Processing of Polyester Fibres. (Textile Science & Technology Ser.: Vol. 2). 550p. 1980. 95.75 (ISBN 0-444-99860-8). Elsevier.
Robinson, J. S., ed. Manufacture of Yarns & Fabrics from Synthetic Fibers. LC 80-15170. (Chemical Technology Review: No. 163). (Illus.). 394p. (Orig.). 1980. 48.00 (ISBN 0-8155-0807-7). Noyes.
Ziabicki, A. & Kawai, Hiromichi. High Speed Fiber Spinning: Science & Engineering Aspects. 584p. 1985. 110.00 (ISBN 0-471-89792-2). Wiley.

TEXTILE FINISHING

Fry, M. Color & Fiber. 1986. cancelled (ISBN 0-442-20055-2). Van Nos Reinhold.
Harrison, P. W. Textile Finishing. 326p. 1978. 75.00x (ISBN 0-686-63799-2). State Mutual Bk.
Shaw, T. & Lewis, J. The Finishing of Wool Fabrics. 89p. 1972. 70.00x (ISBN 0-686-63766-6). State Mutual Bk.
Textile Finishing: The Lodz Textiles Seminars. (Training for Industry Ser.). pap. 2.00 (ISBN 0-686-93272-2, UN70/2B6/6, UN). Unipub.
Wyles, D. H. Developments in the Finishing of Cotton & Man-Made Fiber Fabrics. 81p. 1973. 70.00x (ISBN 0-686-63761-5). State Mutual Bk.

TEXTILE INDUSTRY

see also Bleaching; Cotton Manufacture; Cotton Trade; Dyes and Dyeing; Knit Goods Industry; Lace and Lace Making; Rug and Carpet Industry; Silk Manufacture and Trade; Spinning; Textile Chemistry; Textile Factories; Textile Finishing; Textile Machinery; Textile Printing; Weaving; Wool Trade and Industry; Woolen and Worsted Manufacture

Amsalem, Michel A. Technology Choice in Developing Countries: The Textile & Pulp & Paper Industries. (Illus.). 224p. 1983. 30.00x (ISBN 0-262-01072-0). MIT Pr.
Arthur, Jett C, Jr., ed. Textile & Paper Chemistry & Technology. LC 77-7938. (ACS Symposium Ser.: No. 49). 1977. 27.95 (ISBN 0-8412-0377-6). Am Chemical.
Atkins, M. H. & Lowe, J. F. Case Studies in Pollution Control in the Textile Dyeing & Finishing Industries: A Study in Non-Technical Language of Essential Information on the Economics of Control, the Problems & Their Solutions. 1979. 53.00 (ISBN 0-08-022457-1). Pergamon.
Automating the Sewing Room. 1982. 40.00 (ISBN 0-318-01187-5, 13110). Indus Fabrics.
Bagnall, William R. Textile Industries of the United States: Vol. 1, 1639-1810. LC 68-22370. Repr. of 1893 ed. 45.00x (ISBN 0-678-00735-7). Kelley.
Bhatnagar, Vijay M., ed. Advances in Fire Retardant Textiles. LC 72-91704. (Progress in Fire Retardancy Ser.: Vol. 5). 500p. 1974. pap. 14.95 (ISBN 0-87762-143-8). Technomic.
Birrell, Verla. The Textile Arts: A Handbook of Weaving, Braiding, Printing, & Other Textile Techniques. LC 58-8363. (Illus.). 530p. 1973. pap. 8.95 (ISBN 0-8052-0390-7). Schocken.
Boon, Gerard K. Technology Transfer in Fibres, Textile & Apparel. 600p. 1981. 166.25 (ISBN 90-286-0520-7). Sijthoff & Noordhoff.
Booth, J. E. Textile Mathematics, Vol. 1. 162p. 1975. 40.00x (ISBN 0-686-63802-6). State Mutual Bk.
--Textile Mathematics, Vol. 3. 144p. 1977. 40.00x (ISBN 0-686-63804-2). State Mutual Bk.
Chin, Rockwood. Management, Industry & Trade in Cotton Textiles. 1965. 10.95x (ISBN 0-8084-0207-2). New Coll U Pr.
Collingwood, Peter. The Techniques of Sprang. LC 73-17319. (Illus.). 300p. 1974. 21.95 (ISBN 0-8230-5220-6). Watson-Guptill.
Cooper, S. G. The Textile Industry: Environmental Control & Energy Conservation. LC 78-53999. 385p. (Pollution technology review no. 42; energy technology review no. 28). 1978. 42.00 (ISBN 0-8155-0702-X). Noyes.
Destler, I. M., et al. The Textile Wrangle: Conflict in Japanese-American Relations, 1969-1971. LC 78-14429. 1979. 37.50x (ISBN 0-8014-1120-3). Cornell U Pr.
Enrick, Norbert L. Industrial Engineering Manual: For the Textile Industry. 2nd ed. LC 77-15461. 360p. 1978. lib. bdg. 23.65 (ISBN 0-88275-631-1). Krieger.
--Management Control Manual for the Textile Industry. 2nd rev. ed. LC 79-13534. 356p. 1980. lib. bdg. 23.65 (ISBN 0-88275-994-9). Krieger.
--Time Study Manual for the Textile Industry. 2nd ed. LC 81-17159. 1982. lib. bdg. 23.65 (ISBN 0-89874-044-4). Krieger.
The Fabric Revolution. 1981. 50.00x (ISBN 0-900739-43-6, Pub. by Textile Inst). State Mutual Bk.
Goy, R. S. & Jenkins, J. A. Industrial Applications of Textile. 65p. 1970. 70.00x (ISBN 0-686-63770-4). State Mutual Bk.
Grossbart, June, et al. An Introductory Textile Manual. LC 81-40721. (Illus.). 110p. (Orig.). 1982. pap. text ed. (ISBN 0-8191-1897-4). U Pr of Amer.
Guggenheim, Gus N. Protocol for Productivity. Guggenheim, Alan, ed. (Textile Industry Management Ser.: No. 1). 132p. 1982. 17.95x (ISBN 0-910377-03-0); pap. 13.95x (ISBN 0-910377-00-6). Guggenheim.
Habert, R., et al. Lexique de l'Industrie Textile: Francais-Anglais. (Fr. & Eng.). 240p. 1974. pap. 9.95 (ISBN 0-686-92180-1, M-9222). French & Eur.
Healer, Carol B. Programmed Instruction in Textiles. LC 70-632246. (Illus.). 84p. 1970. pap. 1.00x (ISBN 0-88215-015-4). Ohio St U Lib.
Huenlich, R. Textil-Fachwoerterbuch. 2nd ed. (Ger.). 144p. 1970. pap. 12.95 (ISBN 3-7949-0166-5, M-7665, Pub. by Fachverlag Schiele & Schoen). French & Eur.
Lord, P. R., ed. Spinning in the Seventies. 296p. 1970. 40.00x (ISBN 0-900541-01-6, Pub. by Meadowfield Pr England). State Mutual Bk.
Lourie, Janice. Textile Graphics: Computer Aided. new ed. LC 73-188789. (Illus.). 300p. 1973. 15.00 (ISBN 0-87005-108-3). Fairchild.
Lyle, Dorothy S. Modern Textiles. 2nd ed. LC 81-11574. 513p. 1982. text ed. 36.00 (ISBN 0-471-07805-0); instr's. manual 8.00 (ISBN 0-471-01839-2). Wiley.
Manual on Instrumentation & Quality Control in the Textile Industry. (Development & Transfer of Technology Ser.). 46p. 1982. pap. 8.50 (ISBN 0-686-96619-8, UPB106, UNIDO). Unipub.
Miller, Richard K. Noise Control Solutions for the Textile Industry. (Illus.). 90p. text ed. 45.00 (ISBN 0-89671-035-1). SEAI Tech Pubns.
Miller, Richard K., et al. Noise Control Solutions for the Textile Industry. 45.00 (ISBN 0-89671-004-1). Fairmont Pr.
New Techniques in Web-Processing of Textiles with Emphasis on Cotton. pap. 2.50 (ISBN 0-686-94694-4, UN76/2B1, UN). Unipub.
Non-Conventional Methods of Fabric Production, Vol. 5. pap. 2.00 (UN70/2B6, UN). Unipub.
Occupational Safety & Health in the Textiles Industry: Textiles Committee, Report III. 65p. 1985. pap. 7.15 (ISBN 92-2-103753-3, ILO356, ILO). Unipub.
OECD Staff. Emission Control Costs in the Textile Industry. 180p. (Orig.). 1981. pap. 10.50x (ISBN 92-64-12134-X). OECD.
--The Textile Industry in OECD Countries, 1981. (Eng. & Fr.). 1983. pap. 9.00x (ISBN 92-64-02491-3). OECD.
Olson, Edward S. Textile Wet Processes: Preparation of Fibers & Fabrics, Vol. 1. LC 83-2251. (Illus.). 205p. (Orig.). 1983. 28.00 (ISBN 0-8155-0939-1, Noyes Pubns). Noyes.
Review of Textile Progress: A Survey of World Literature, 1965-66, Vol. 17. LC 60-1460. pap. 152.80 (ISBN 0-317-09916-7, 2020708). Bks Demand UMI.
Schlomann, A. Illustrierte Technische Woerterbuecher: Faserrohstoffe, Vol. 14. (Ger., Eng., Fr., Rus., Span. & It., Illustrated dictionary of raw material of the textile industry). 1958. 46.50 (ISBN 0-686-56487-1, M-7474, Pub. by R. Oldenbourg). French & Eur.
Siewert, Carol H., et al. Basic Textiles: A Learning Package. 228p. 1973. 19.95 (ISBN 0-395-14220-2). HM.
Slater, K. Textile Mechanics, Vol. 1. 175p. 1981. 50.00x (ISBN 0-900739-27-4, Pub. by Textile Inst England). State Mutual Bk.
Sommar, Helen G. A Brief Guide to Sources of Fiber & Textile Information. LC 72-89909. (Illus.). viii, 138p. 1973. text ed. 5.00 (ISBN 0-87815-009-9). Info Resources.
Spinning: The Lodz Textile Seminars. (Training for Industry Ser.). pap. 2.00 (ISBN 0-686-93280-3, UN70/2B6V2, UN). Unipub.
Technical Dictionary: The Textile Industry. (Eng., Fr., Ger. & Arabic.). 1975. 30.00x (ISBN 0-686-44748-4, Pub. by Collets). State Mutual Bk.
Textile Fibres: The Lodz Textiles Seminars. (Training for Industry Ser.). pap. 2.00 (ISBN 0-686-93275-7, UN70/2B6/1, UN). Unipub.
Textile Industry. (Monographs on Industrialization of Developing Countries: Problems & Prospects). pap. 4.00 (ISBN 0-686-93274-9, UN69/2B/39V7, UN). Unipub.
Textile Terms & Definitions. 228p. 1981. 95.00x (ISBN 0-900739-17-7, Pub. by Textile Inst England). State Mutual Bk.
Textile Wastes & Their Reclamation: A Survey of Recent Literature, 1980. 1981. 60.00x (ISBN 0-686-97148-5, Pub. by W Spring England). State Mutual Bk.
Tupling, George H. The Economic History of Rossendale. Repr. of 1927 ed. 19.00 (ISBN 0-384-61970-3). Johnson Repr.
Velco, G. Textile Dictionary. (Eng., Fr., Ger., Rus. & Bulgarian.). 1977. 70.00x (ISBN 0-686-44749-2, Pub. by Collets). State Mutual Bk.
Vigo, Tyrone L. & Nowacki, Louis J., eds. Energy Conservation in Textile & Polymer Processing. LC 79-15523. (ACS Symposium Ser.: No. 107). 1979. 29.95 (ISBN 0-8412-0509-4). Am Chemical.
Vincent, J. J. Shuttleless Looms. 1979. 39.00x (ISBN 0-904095-32-0, Pub. by Meadowfield Pr England). State Mutual Bk.
Vries, Louis de. Woerterbuch der Textilindustrie, Vol. 2. (Eng & Ger., Dictionary of Textile Industry). pap. 25.00 (ISBN 0-686-56612-2, M-6948). French & Eur.
Wadsworth, Alfred P. & Mann, Julia. Cotton Trade & Industrial Lancashire 1600-1780. LC 68-6121. (Illus.). Repr. of 1931 ed. 37.50x (ISBN 0-678-06768-6). Kelley.
Weaver, J. William, ed. Analytical Methods for a Textile Laboratory. 3rd ed. LC 84-70596. (Illus.). x, 403p. 1984. 50.00 (ISBN 0-9613350-0-9). Am Assn Text.
Wingate, Isabel B. & Burkholder, Ralph. Laboratory Swatch Book, Textile Fabrics & Their Selection. 7th ed. 252p. 1976. write for info. wire coil (ISBN 0-697-08313-6). Wm C Brown.
Wira, ed. Quality Control of Cloth Dimensions & the Shrinkage of Yarns & Fabrics. 1977. 30.00x (ISBN 0-686-87172-3). State Mutual Bk.
Wittgen, Rudolf. Die Absatzwege der Baumwollindustrie in den 80er Jahren. (Schriften zur Textilindustrie: Vo. 28). (Ger.). xiv, 308p. 1982. 37.35 (ISBN 3-8204-5821-2). P Lang Pubs.

TEXTILE INDUSTRY–BIBLIOGRAPHY

Kopycinski, Joseph V., ed. Textile Industry Information Sources. LC 64-25644. (Management Information Guide Ser.: No. 4). 1964. 60.00x (ISBN 0-8103-0804-5). Gale.
Sommar, Helen G. A Brief Guide to Sources of Fiber & Textile Information. LC 72-89909. (Illus.). viii, 138p. 1973. text ed. 5.00 (ISBN 0-87815-009-9). Info Resources.

TEXTILE INDUSTRY–DIRECTORIES

Fairchild Book Research Division. Fairchild Textile & Apparel Directory. 210p. 1983. pap. 50.00 (ISBN 0-87005-442-2). Fairchild.
--Fairchild's Textile & Apparel Financial Directory, 1984. 11th ed. 190p. 1984. pap. 50.00 (ISBN 0-87005-470-8). Fairchild.
Fairchild Market Research Division. Home Textiles. (Fairchild Fact File Ser.). (Illus.). 51p. 1982. pap. text ed. 15.00 (ISBN 0-87005-425-2). Fairchild.
--The Textile-Apparel Industries. (Fairchild Fact Files Ser.). (Illus.). 64p. 1981. pap. text ed. 15.00 (ISBN 0-87005-395-7). Fairchild.
Farnfield, Carolyn A. A Guide to Sources of Information in the Textile Industry. 130p. 1974. 40.00x (ISBN 0-686-63767-4). State Mutual Bk.
Jones, C. E., et al. Cumulative Index to the Journal of the Textile Institute. 174p. 1971. 80.00x (ISBN 0-686-63758-5). State Mutual Bk.
Murphy, T., et al. Statistical Methods for Textile Technologists. 107p. 1979. 40.00x (ISBN 0-686-63797-6). State Mutual Bk.

TEXTILE INDUSTRY–HISTORY

Addy, John. The Textile Revolution. (Seminar Studies in History). (Illus.). 1976. pap. text ed. 6.25x (ISBN 0-582-35220-7). Longman.
Goody, Esther N., ed. From Craft to Industry: The Ethnography of Proto-Industrial Cloth Production. LC 82-4205. (Cambridge Papers in Social Anthropology: No. 10). 304p. 1983. 42.50 (ISBN 0-521-24614-8). Cambridge U Pr.
Harrison, P. W. & Cordelier, M. Contributions of Science to the Development of the Textile Industry: The Present Situation & Future Prospects. 199p. 1975. 40.00x (ISBN 0-686-63756-9). State Mutual Bk.
Homespun to Factory Made: Woolen Textiles in America 1776-1876: Illustrated Catalogue of the Permanent Exhibit at the Merrimack Valley Textile Museum. LC 77-81330. (Illus.). 1977. 6.95 (ISBN 0-937474-02-9). Museum America.
Katzenberg, Dena S. Blue Traditions: Indigo Dyed Textiles & Related Cobalt Glazed Ceramics from the 17th Through the 19th Century. LC 73-91962. (Illus.). 1973. pap. 15.00 (ISBN 0-912298-35-9). Baltimore Mus.
Lander, Ernest M., Jr. Textile Industry in Antebellum South Carolina. LC 69-12590. (Illus.). 1969. 13.95x (ISBN 0-8071-0311-X). La State U Pr.
Manchester & Bradford. Review of Textile Progress. 538p. 1972. 75.00x (ISBN 0-686-63796-8). State Mutual Bk.
Molloy, Peter M. The Lower Merrimack River Valley: An Inventory of Historic Engineering & Industrial Sites. 2nd ed. 1978. 3.50 (ISBN 0-937474-03-7). Museum America.
Power, E. G. A Textile Community in the Industrial Revolution. Reeves, Marjorie, ed. (Then & There Ser.). (Illus.). 108p. (Orig.). 1978. pap. text ed. 3.40 (ISBN 0-582-20420-8). Longman.
Thomas, Michel. Textiles: History of an Art. LC 85-42942. (Illus.). 272p. 1985. 65.00 (ISBN 0-8478-0640-5). Rizzoli Intl.
Trilling, James. The Roman Heritage: Textiles from Egypt & the Eastern Mediterranean, 300-600 A.D. LC 82-50367. (Textile Museum Journal Ser.). (Illus.). 112p. (Orig.). 1982. pap. 17.50 (ISBN 0-87405-019-7). Textile Mus.
Wild, J. P. Textile Manufacture in the Northern Roman Provinces. LC 74-77294. (Cambridge Classical Studies). (Illus.). 1970. 29.95 (ISBN 0-521-07491-6). Cambridge U Pr.
Wilson, Kax. A History of Textiles. (Illus.). 1979. lib. bdg. 34.00x (ISBN 0-89158-491-9); pap. 20.00x (ISBN 0-686-86882-X). Westview.

TEXTILE MACHINERY

see also Looms

Benson, Anna P. Textile Machines. (Shire Album Ser.: No. 103). (Illus.). 32p. (Orig.). 1983. pap. 2.95 (ISBN 0-85263-647-4, Pub. by Shire Pubns England). Seven Hills Bks.
Shaw, J. & Chisholm, A. A. Textile Machinery. 69p. 1969. 70.00x (ISBN 0-686-63801-8). State Mutual Bk.
Unwin, George. Samuel Oldknow & the Arkwrights. LC 68-5554. (Illus.). Repr. of 1924 ed. 27.50x (ISBN 0-678-06767-8). Kelley.

TEXTILE PLANTS

see Textile Fibers

TEXTILE PRINTING

Chapman, S. D. & Chassagne, S. European Textile Printers in the Eighteenth Century: A Study of Peel & Oberkampf. (Pasold Studies in Textile History). (Illus.). xiii, 257p. 1981. text ed. 45.00x (ISBN 0-435-32170-6). Gower Pub Co.
Dawson, T. L. Chapter Four - Carpet & Yarn Printing. 75.00x (ISBN 0-686-98203-7, Pub. by Soc Dyers & Colour); pap. 50.00x (ISBN 0-686-98204-5). State Mutual Bk.

Janz, George J. Thermodynamic Properties of Organic Compounds. rev. ed. (Physical Chemistry Ser.: Vol. 6). 1967. 65.00 (ISBN 0-12-380451-5). Acad Pr.

Jelinek, R., ed. Thermodynamics. (Computer Program for Chemical Engineering Education Ser.). 1972. pap. 15.95 (ISBN 0-88408-032-3). Sterling Swift.

Jennings, Burgess H. The Thermal Environment: Conditioning & Control. 1978. text ed. 33.95 scp (ISBN 0-06-043311-6, HarpC). Har-Row.

John, James E. & Haberman, William L. Engineering Thermodynamics. 1979. text ed. 37.69 (ISBN 0-205-06570-8, 326570); solutions man. avail. (ISBN 0-205-06571-6). Allyn.

Jones, James B. & Hawkins, George A. Engineering Thermodynamics: An Introductory Textbook. LC 60-10316. (Illus.). 724p. 1960. text ed. 47.50 (ISBN 0-471-44946-6). Wiley.

Jones, M. N., ed. Biochemical Thermodynamics. (Studies in Modern Thermodynamics: Vol. 1). 390p. 1979. 78.75 (ISBN 0-444-41761-3). Elsevier.

Karapetyants, M. Chemical Thermodynamics. 640p. 1978. 15.00 (ISBN 0-8285-0644-2, Pub. by Mir Pubs USSR). Imported Pubns.

Karlekar, B. V. Thermodynamics for Engineers. (Illus.). 544p. 1983. 37.95 (ISBN 0-13-914986-4). P-H.

Kern, Raymond & Weisbrod, Alain. Thermodynamics for Geologists. McKie, Duncan, tr. from Fr. LC 67-22353. 304p. 1967. pap. 12.95x (ISBN 0-87735-306-9). Freeman Cooper.

Kestin, Joseph, ed. The Second Law of Thermodynamics. (Benchmark Papers on Energy: Vol. 5). 1976. 68.00 (ISBN 0-12-786839-9). Acad Pr.

Kieffer, S. W. & Navrotsky, A. Microscopic to Macroscopic: Atomic Environments to Mineral Thermodynamics. Ribber, Paul H., ed. 428p. 1985. 13.00 (ISBN 0-318-17825-7). Mineralogical Soc.

Kirillin, V. A. Engineering Thermodynamics. 560p. 1981. 16.00 (ISBN 0-8285-2056-9, Pub. by Mir Pubs USSR). Imported Pubns.

Klotz, Irving M. & Rosenberg, R. M. Chemical Thermodynamics. 3rd ed. 1972. 36.95 (ISBN 0-8053-5506-5); pap. 15.95 (ISBN 0-8053-5507-3). Benjamin-Cummings.

Kreith, Frank & West, R. E. Economics of Solar Energy & Conservation Systems, 3 vols. 1980. 84.00 ea. Vol. 1, 320p (ISBN 0-8493-5229-0). Vol. 2. 320p (ISBN 0-8493-5230-4). Vol. 3, 288p (ISBN 0-8493-5231-2). CRC Pr.

Krichevski, I. R. & Petrianov, I. V. Termodinamica para Muchos. (Span.). 173p. 1980. pap. 3.25 (ISBN 0-8285-1863-7, Pub. by Mir Pubs USSR). Imported Pubns.

Krishnan, R. S., et al. Thermal Expansion of Crystals. LC 77-30620. (International Ser. in the Science of the Solid State: Vol. 12). 1980. 48.00 (ISBN 0-08-021405-3). Pergamon.

Kulshrestha, S. K. A Textbook of Applied Thermodynamics: Steam & Thermal Engineering. (Illus.). xi, 443p. 1983. text ed. 37.50x (ISBN 0-7069-2158-5, Pub. by Vikas India). Advent NY.

Kurata, Michio. Thermodynamics of Polymer Solutions. Fujita, Hiroshi, tr. from Jap. (MMI Press Polymer Monographs: Vol. 1). 306p. 1982. 94.00 (ISBN 3-7186-0023-4). Harwood Academic.

Kwang-Chu-Chao, ed. Applied Thermodynamics. LC 68-56051. 1968. 21.95 (ISBN 0-8412-0102-1). Am Chemical.

Kyle, B. G. Chemical & Process Thermodynamics. (Illus.). 512p. 1984. 39.95 (ISBN 0-13-128637-4). P-H.

Lacey, William N. & Sage, Bruce H. Thermodynamics of One-Component Systems. 1957. 68.50 (ISBN 0-12-432550-5). Acad Pr.

Lamprecht, I. & Zotin, A. I., eds. Thermodynamics & Regulation of Biological Processes. LC 84-23302. (Illus.). xiv, 573p. 1984. 123.00x (ISBN 3-11-009789-3). De Gruyter.

Landsberg, Peter T. Thermodynamics & Statistical Mechanics. (Illus.). 1979. 29.95x (ISBN 0-19-851142-6). Oxford U Pr.

Lavenda, B. H. Nonequilibrium Statistical Thermodynamics. 1985. write for info. (ISBN 0-471-90670-0). Wiley.

Lefax Pub. Co. Editors. Physical & Thermodynamic Data. (Lefax Data Bks.: No. 646). (Illus.). looseleaf bdg. 3.00 (ISBN 0-685-14162-4). Lefax.

Lehmann, T. The Constitutive Law in Thermoplasticity. (CISM International Centre for Mechanical Sciences Ser.: Courses & Lectures, No. 281). (Illus.). iv, 601p. 1984. pap. 31.30 (ISBN 0-387-81796-4). Springer-Verlag.

Lewis, Alexander D. Gas Power Dynamics. LC 77-15095. 544p. 1978. Repr. of 1962 ed. lib. bdg. 34.00 (ISBN 0-88275-629-X). Krieger.

Lindblad, Goran. Non-Equilbrium Entropy & Irreversibility. 1983. lib. bdg. 29.50 (ISBN 90-277-1640-4, Pub. by Reidel Holland). Kluwer Academic.

Look, Dwight C., Jr. & Sauer, Harry, Jr. Engineering Thermodynamics. 650p. 1985. text ed. write for info. (ISBN 0-534-05448-X, 26R2000, Pub. by PWS Engineering). PWS Pubs.

Lupis, Claude H. Chemical Thermodynamics of Materials. 608p. 1983. 80.00 (ISBN 0-444-00713-X, North Holland); pap. 41.50 (ISBN 0-444-00779-2, North Holland). Elsevier.

McChesney, Malcolm. Thermodynamics of Electrical Processes. LC 75-166417. pap. 71.50 (ISBN 0-317-10940-5, 2016147). Bks Demand UMI.

McGlashan, M. L. Chemical Thermodynamics. LC 79-40919. 1980. 47.50 (ISBN 0-12-482650-4). Acad Pr.

McKie, Douglas & De Heathcote, Niels. The Discovery of Specific & Latent Heats. LC 74-26274. (History, Philosophy & Sociology of Science Ser). 1975. Repr. 19.00x (ISBN 0-405-06602-3). Ayer Co Pubs.

Mahan, Bruce H. Elementary Chemical Thermodynamics. (Orig.). 1963. pap. text ed. 17.95 (ISBN 0-8053-6801-9). Benjamin-Cummings.

Manrique. Termodinamica. 2nd ed. (Span.). 352p. 1981. pap. text ed. write for info. (ISBN 0-06-315510-9, Pub. by HarLA Mexcio). Har-Row.

Marti, E. & Oswald, Wiedemann, eds. Angewandte Chemische Thermodynamik und Thermoanalytik: Vortrage D. Rapperswiler TA-Symposiums. (Experientia Supplementum: No. 37). 385p. 1980. 56.95x (ISBN 0-8176-1142-8). Birkhauser.

Martin, L. R. & Gokcen, N. A. Thermodynamics, Solutions Manual. (Illus.). 1978. pap. 6.95x (ISBN 0-918910-02-1). Techscience Inc.

Martin, Martin C. Elements of Thermodynamics. (Illus.). 224p. 1986. text ed. 32.95 (ISBN 0-13-273434-6). P-H.

Martin-Loef, A. Statistical Mechanics & the Foundations of Thermodynamics. (Lecture Notes in Physics Ser.: Vol. 101). 1979. pap. 13.00 (ISBN 0-387-09255-2). Springer-Verlag.

Meyer, C. A. Thermodynamic & Transport Properties of Steam. LC 67-3043. pap. 90.80 (ISBN 0-317-11072-1, 2011011). Bks Demand UMI.

Miller, Ingo. Thermodynamics. (Interaction of Mathematics & Mechanics Ser.). 496p. 1985. text ed. 69.50 (ISBN 0-273-08577-8). Pitman Pub MA.

Mills, K. C. Thermodynamic Data for Inorganic Sulphides, Selenides & Tellurides. LC 74-173939. pap. 160.00 (ISBN 0-317-08901-3, 2051842). Bks Demand UMI.

Milora, Stanley L. & Tester, Jefferson W. Geothermal Energy As a Source of Electric Power: Thermodynamics & Economic Design Criteria. LC 76-7008. 190p. 1976. text ed. 35.00x (ISBN 0-262-13123-4). MIT Pr.

Modell, Michael & Reid, Robert C. Thermodynamics & Its Applications. 2nd ed. (Illus.). 512p. 1983. text ed. 41.95 (ISBN 0-13-915017-X). P-H.

Mooney, David A. Introduction to Thermodynamics & Heat Transfer. 1955. text ed. 40.95 (ISBN 0-13-499681-X). P-H.

Moore, Desmond F. Thermodynamic Principles of Energy Degrading. (Illus.). 155p. 1981. text ed. 32.50x (ISBN 0-333-29506-4, Pub. by Macmillan England); pap. 19.50x (ISBN 0-333-29504-8, Pub. by Macmillan England). Scholium Intl.

Moran, Michael. Availability Analysis: A Guide to Efficient Energy Use. (Illus.). 304p. 1982. 55.00 (ISBN 0-13-054874-X). P-H.

Morse, Philip M. Thermal Physics. 2nd ed. 1969. 45.95 (ISBN 0-8053-7202-4). Benjamin-Cummings.

Morton, A. S. Basic Thermodynamics. 15.00 (ISBN 0-685-28342-9). Philos Lib.

Munster, Arnold. Classical Thermodynamics. Halberstadt, E. S., tr. LC 71-122348. pap. 100.30 (ISBN 0-317-12980-5, 2020834). Bks Demand UMI.

Nash, Leonard K. Elements of Statistical Thermodynamics. 2nd ed. 1974. 7.95 (ISBN 0-201-05229-6). Addison-Wesley.

Newman, Stephen A., ed. Chemical Engineering Thermodynamics. LC 82-70702. (Illus.). 544p. 1982. 49.95 (ISBN 0-250-40520-2). Butterworth.

--Thermodynamics of Aqueous Systems with Industrial Applications. LC 80-16044. (ACS Symposium Ser.: No. 133). 1980. 69.95 (ISBN 0-8412-0569-8); supplement 9.95 (ISBN 0-8412-0590-6). Am Chemical.

Noll, W. The Foundations of Mechanics & Thermodynamics: Selected Papers. LC 74-1651. 340p. 1974. 38.00 (ISBN 0-387-06646-2). Springer-Verlag.

Nordstrom, D. Kirk & Munoz, James L. Geochemical Thermodynamics. (Illus.). 475p. 1985. text ed. 41.95x (ISBN 0-8053-6816-7). Benjamin-Cummings.

Nowacki, W. & Sneddon, I. N., eds. Thermomechanics in Solids. (CISM-International Center for Mechanical Sciences: Vol. 223). 1977. pap. 15.40 (ISBN 0-387-81343-8). Springer-Verlag.

Obert, Edward F. & Young, Robert L. Elements of Thermodynamics & Heat Transfer. 2nd ed. LC 79-23780. 558p. 1980. Repr. of 1962 ed. lib. bdg. 33.00 (ISBN 0-89874-005-3). Krieger.

Oonk, H. A. Phase Theory: The Thermodynamics of Heterogeneous Equilibria. (Studies in Modern Thermodynamics: Vol. 3). 270p. 1981. 64.00 (ISBN 0-444-42019-3). Elsevier.

Osbourne, Alan & Neild, A. B., eds. Modern Marine Engineer's Manual, Vol. 1. 2nd ed. LC 65-18208. (Illus.). 1965. Vol. 1. 30.00x (ISBN 0-87033-063-2). Cornell Maritime.

Oster, G. F., et al, eds. Irreversible Thermodynamics & the Origin of Life. new ed. 82p. 1974. 37.25x (ISBN 0-677-14270-6). Gordon.

Owen, D. R. A First Course in the Mathematical Foundatioms of Thermodynamics. (Undergraduate Texts in Mathematics Ser.). (Illus.). 190p. 1984. 28.80 (ISBN 0-387-90897-8). Springer Verlag.

Pacault, A. & Vidal, C., eds. Synergetics - Far from Equilibrium: Proceedings of the Conference Far from Equilibrium, Instabilities & Structures, Bordeaux, France Sept. 27-29, 1978. (Illus.). 1979. 40.00 (ISBN 0-387-09304-4). Springer-Verlag.

Peusner, L. The Principles of Network Thermodynamics. Date not set. price not set. Entropy Ltd.

Pfund, P. A. & Yao, S. C., eds. Tube Bundle Thermal-Hydraulics. 73p. 1982. 20.00 (G00212). ASME.

Pimentel, George C. & Spratley, Richard D. Understanding Chemical Thermodynamics. LC 69-13419. (Illus.). 1969. pap. text ed. 20.00x (ISBN 0-8162-6791-X). Holden-Day.

Pippard, A. B. Elements of Classical Thermodynamics. 1966. pap. text ed. 12.95x (ISBN 0-521-09101-2). Cambridge U Pr.

Pitzer & Brewer. Thermodynamics. 2nd ed. (Advanced Chemistry Ser.). 1961. text ed. 53.95 (ISBN 0-07-037622-0). McGraw.

Prausnitz, J. M. Molecular Thermodynamics of Fluid-Phase Equilibria. LC 69-16866. 1969. ref. ed. 44.95 (ISBN 0-13-599639-2). P-H.

Prausnitz, John M., et al. Molecular Thermodynamics of Fluid-Phase Equilibria. 2nd ed. (Illus.). 720p. 1985. text ed. 44.95 (ISBN 0-13-599564-7). P-H.

Rastogi, R. P. & Misra, R. R. An Introduction to Chemical Thermodynamics. 4th rev. ed. 512p. 1983. 40.00x (ISBN 0-7069-2325-1, Pub. by Vikas India). Advent NY.

Raznjevic, Kuzman. Handbook of Thermodynamic Tables & Charts. 400p. 1976. 67.50 (ISBN 0-07-051270-1). McGraw.

Redlich, Otto. Thermodynamics: Fundamentals, Applications. 278p. 1976. 64.00 (ISBN 0-444-41487-8). Elsevier.

Research & Education Association Staff. Heat Transfer Problem Solver. LC 84-61813. (Illus.). 800p. 1984. pap. text ed. 23.85 (ISBN 0-87891-557-5). Res & Educ.

--Thermodynamics Problem Solver. LC 84-61810. (Illus.). 992p. 1984. pap. text ed. 23.85 (ISBN 0-87891-555-9). Res & Educ.

Reynolds, William C. & Perkins, Henry C. Engineering Thermodynamics. 2nd ed. 1977. text ed. 45.95 (ISBN 0-07-052046-1). McGraw.

Rice, Oscar K. Statistical Mechanics, Thermodynamics, & Kinetics. LC 66-16379. (Chemistry Ser.). (Illus.). 586p. 1967. 34.95x (ISBN 0-7167-0133-2). W H Freeman.

Rock, Peter A. Chemical Thermodynamics. McQuarrie, Donald A., ed. LC 82-51233. (Physical Chemistry Ser.). (Illus.). 553p. 1983. 32.00x (ISBN 0-935702-12-1). Univ Sci Bks.

Rolle, Kurt A. Introduction to Thermodynamics. 2nd ed. LC 79-90390. 1980. text ed. 29.95 (ISBN 0-675-08268-4). Additional supplements may be obtained from publisher. Merrill.

Ruelle, David. Encyclopedia of Mathematics & Its Applications: Thermodynamic Formalism: The Mathematical Structures of Classical Equilibrium Statistical Mechanics, Vol. 5. 1984. 32.50 (ISBN 0-521-30225-0). Cambridge U Pr.

Rumer, Y. B. & Ryvkin, M. S. Thermodynamics, Statistical Physics & Kinetics. 1980. 12.00 (ISBN 0-8285-1853-X, Pub. by Mir Pubs USSR). Imported Pubns.

Sandfort, John F. Heat Engines: Thermodynamics in Theory & Practice. LC 78-25847. (Illus.). Repr. of 1962 ed. lib. bdg. 27.50x (ISBN 0-313-20784-4, SAEN). Greenwood.

Sandler, Stanley I. Chemical & Engineering Thermodynamics. LC 77-1312. 587p. 1977. 50.45 (ISBN 0-471-01774-4); sol. manual avail. (ISBN 0-471-02736-7). Wiley.

Sawada, Hideo. Thermodynamics of Polymerization. 1976. 85.00 (ISBN 0-8247-6470-6). Dekker.

Schaetzle. Thermal Energy Storage in Aquifiers. (Design & Applications). 275p. 1980. text ed. 29.00 (ISBN 0-08-025977-4). Pergamon.

Schmidt, Frank W. & Henderson, Robert E. Introduction to Thermal Sciences: Thermodynamics Fluid Dynamics Heat Transfer. LC 83-21877. 445p. 1984. text ed. 35.50 (ISBN 0-471-87599-6). Wiley.

Schmidt, Frank W. & Willmott, A. John. Thermal Energy Storage & Regeneration. (Illus.). 352p. 1981. 54.50 (ISBN 0-07-055346-7). McGraw.

Sciene Press. Irreversible Thermodynamics. 1981. 37.50 (ISBN 0-442-20074-9). Van Nos Reinhold.

Seader, J. D. Thermodynamic Efficiency of Chemical Processes. Gyftopoulos, Elias P. & Cohen, Karen C., eds. (Industrial Energy-Conservation Manuals: No. 1). (Illus.). 80p. 1982. loose-leaf 20.00x (ISBN 0-262-19201-2). MIT Pr.

Sears, Francis W. & Salinger, Gerhard L. Thermodynamics, the Kinetic Theory of Gases & Statistical Mechanics. 3rd ed. 464p. 1975. text ed. 36.95 (ISBN 0-201-06894-X). Addison-Wesley.

Sedov, L., ed. Macroscopic Theories of Matter & Fields: A Thermodynamic Approach. Yankovsky, Eusene, tr. 263p. 1983. pap. 7.95 (ISBN 0-8285-2742-3, Pub. by Mir Pubs USSR). Imported Pubns.

Seely. Elements of Thermal Technology. (Engineering Technology Ser.: Vol. 3). 464p. 1981. 35.00 (ISBN 0-8247-1174-2). Dekker.

Silver, Howard & Nydahl, John. Introduction to Engineering Thermodynamics. LC 76-3601. (Illus.). 500p. 1977. text ed. 30.95 (ISBN 0-8299-0053-5); solutions manual avail. (ISBN 0-8299-0573-1). West Pub.

Skrotzki, Bernhardt G. Basic Thermodynamics: Elements of Energy Systems. 1963. text ed. 33.45 (ISBN 0-07-057945-8). McGraw.

Smith, E. Brian. Basic Chemical Thermodynamics. 3rd ed. (Illus.). 1983. 21.95x (ISBN 0-19-855521-0); pap. 9.95x (ISBN 0-19-855522-9). Oxford U Pr.

Smith, Norman O. Elementary Statistical Thermodynamics: A Problems Approach. 232p. 1982. 29.50x (ISBN 0-306-41205-5, Plenum Pr); pap. 14.95x (ISBN 0-306-41216-0). Plenum Pub.

Sneeden, J. B. & Kerr, S. V. Applied Heat for Engineers. (Illus.). 420p. 1976. pap. text ed. 35.00x (ISBN 0-216-87481-5). Intl Ideas.

Sonntag, Richard & University of Michigan, Ann Arbor. Fundamentals of Classical Thermodynamics: SI Version. (Series in Thermal & Transport Sciences). 864p. 1981. pap. 19.80x (ISBN 0-471-04505-5). Wiley.

Sonntag, Richard E. & Van Wylen, Gordon J. Introduction to Thermodynamics: Classical & Statistical. 2nd ed. LC 81-16062. 810p. 1982. text ed. 43.45 (ISBN 0-471-03134-8). Wiley.

Soumerai, Henri. A Unified Thermodynamic Treatment of Heat, Mass & Momentum Exchange. Date not set. 60.00 (ISBN 0-471-81854-2). Wiley.

Spence, Lawrence E. Finite Mathematics & Calculus: With Business Social & Behavioral Science Applications. 760p. 1982. text ed. 27.50 scp (ISBN 0-06-046368-6, HarpC); student sol. manual scp 11.50 (ISBN 0-06-041843-5); instr. manual avail. (ISBN 0-06-366386-4). Har-Row.

Starling, Kenneth E. Fluid Thermodynamic Properties for Light Petroleum Systems. LC 70-184683. 270p. 1973. 34.95x (ISBN 0-87201-293-X). Gulf Pub.

Stowe, K. Introduction to Statistical Mechanics & Thermodynamics. 534p. 1984. 38.50 (ISBN 0-471-87058-7). Wiley.

Stull, Daniel R., et al. The Chemical Thermodynamics of Organic Compounds. LC 83-19972. 884p. Repr. of 1984 ed. cancelled (ISBN 0-89874-706-6). Krieger.

Sushkov, V. V. Technical Thermodynamics. (Russian Monographs Ser). 392p. 1965. 94.95x (ISBN 0-677-20520-1). Gordon.

Sussman, M. V. Elementary General Thermodynamics. LC 74-133896. 1972. text ed. 31.95 (ISBN 0-201-07358-7). Addison-Wesley.

Sychev, V. V. Complex Thermodynamic Systems. LC 73-83896. (Studies in Soviet Science - Physical Sciences Ser.). (Illus.). 242p. 1973. 35.00x (ISBN 0-306-10886-0, Consultants). Plenum Pub.

--Complex Thermodynamic Systems. 240p. 1981. 8.00 (ISBN 0-8285-2279-0, Pub. by Mir Pubs USSR). Imported Pubns.

--Differential Equations of Thermodynamics. 240p. 1983. 7.95 (ISBN 0-8285-2593-5, Pub. by Mir Pubs USSR). Imported Pubns.

Symposium on Measurement in Unstaedy Flow, Worcester, Mass., 1962. Symposium on Measurement in Unsteady Flow: Presented at the ASME Hydraulic Division Conference, Worcester, Mass., May 21-23, 1962. LC 63-2546. pap. 29.50 (ISBN 0-317-11163-9, 2050440). Bks Demand UMI.

THERMOPHYSICAL PROPERTIES
see also Materials–Thermal Properties
American Society of Mechanical Engineers. Thermophysical Properties: Proceedings of the Fourth Symposium, University of Maryland, College Park, Maryland, 1968. Moszynski, J. R., ed. LC 59-1391. pap. 121.50 (ISBN 0-317-29841-0, 2051923). Bks Demand UMI.
Gerritsen, J. K., et al, eds. Thermophysical Properties Research Literature Retrieval Guide: Supplement II, 1971-1977, 6 vols. LC 79-16324. 1979. Set. 375.00 (ISBN 0-306-67210-3, IFI Plenum). Plenum Pub.
Hagen, A. W. Thermal Energy from the Sea. LC 75-24767. (Energy Technology Review No. 8: Ocean Technology Review No. 5). (Illus.). 150p. 1976. 24.00 (ISBN 0-8155-0597-3). Noyes.
Landshoff, R. K. & Magee, J. L. Thermal Radiation Phenomena, 2 vols. Incl. Vol. 1. Radiative Properties of Air. 648p. 55.00x (ISBN 0-306-68421-7); Vol. 2. Excitation & Non-Equilibrium Phenomena in Air. 288p. 55.00x (ISBN 0-306-68422-5). LC 69-17515. 1969 (IFI Plenum). Plenum Pub.
Purdue University, Thermophysical Properties Research Center. Thermophysical Properties of Matter: The TPRC Data Series, Vol 12: Thermal Expansion: Metallic Elements & Alloys. LC 73-129616. pap. 160.00 (ISBN 0-317-07898-4, 2022726). Bks Demand UMI.
--Thermophysical Properties Research Literature Retrieval Guide. 2nd ed. Touloukian, Y. S., et al, eds. LC 60-14226. Bk. 1. pap. 160.00 (ISBN 0-317-10668-6, 2022724); Bk. 2. pap. 158.00 (ISBN 0-317-10669-4); Bk. 3. pap. 160.00 (ISBN 0-317-10670-8). Bks Demand UMI.
Symposium on Thermophysical Properties (6th: 1973: Atlanta). Thermophysical Properties: Proceedings of the 6th Symposium. Sponsored by Standing Committee on Thermophysical Properties, Heat Transfer Division, ASME,...Atlanta, Georgia, Auguat 6-8, 1973. Liley, P. E., ed. LC 59-1391. pap. 103.80 (ISBN 0-317-08104-7, 2016833). Bks Demand UMI.
Thermophysical Properties: Proceedings of the Seventh Symposium. (Bk. No. G00133). 1978. 90.00 (ISBN 0-685-37587-0). ASME.
Touloukian, Y. S., et al. Thermophysical Properties of Matter, 15 vols. Incl. Vol. 1. Thermal Conductivity: Metallic Elements & Alloys. 1595p. 1970. 175.00 (ISBN 0-306-67021-6); Vol. 2. Thermal Conductivity: Nonmetallic Solids. 1302p. 1970. 150.00 (ISBN 0-306-67022-4); Vol. 3. Thermal Conductivity: Nonmetallic Liquids & Gases. 707p. 1970. 110.00x (ISBN 0-306-67023-2); Vol. 4. Specific Heat: Metallic Elements & Alloys. 830p. 1970. 120.00x (ISBN 0-306-67024-0); Vol. 5. Specific Heat: Nonmetallic Solids. 1737p. 1970. 190.00x (ISBN 0-686-66835-9) (ISBN 0-306-67025-9); Vol. 6. Specific Heat: Nonmetallic Liquids & Gases. 383p. 1970. 85.00x (ISBN 0-306-67026-7); Supplement, 157 p., 1976. 50.00; Vol. 7. Thermal Radiative Properties: Metallic Elements & Alloys. 1644p. 1970. 175.00 (ISBN 0-306-67027-5); Vol. 8. Thermal Radiative Properties: Nonmetallic Solids. 1890p. 1972. 215.00x (ISBN 0-306-67028-3); Vol. 9. Thermal Radiative Properties: Coatings. 1569p. 1972. 165.00 (ISBN 0-306-67030-5); Vol. 10. Thermal Diffusivity. 748p. 1973. 110.00 (ISBN 0-306-67030-5); Vol. 11. Viscosity. 804p. 1975. 120.00x (ISBN 0-306-67031-3); Vol. 12. Thermal Expansion: Metallic Elements & Alloys. 1442p. 1975. 170.00 (ISBN 0-306-67032-1); Vol. 13. Thermal Expansion: Nonmetallic Solids. 1800p. 1977. 195.00 (ISBN 0-306-67033-X); Master Index to Materials & Properties. LC 79-11021. 197p. 1979. 85.00x (ISBN 0-306-67092-5). LC 73-129616. (TPRC Data Ser.). 16805p. 1970. Set. 995.00 (ISBN 0-306-67020-8, IFI Plenum). Plenum Pub.
--Thermophysical Properties Research Literature Retrieval Guide: Supplement 1, (Covering the Years 1964-1970, 6 vols. Incl. Vol. 1. Elements & Inorganic Compounds. 736p. 90.00x (ISBN 0-306-67201-4); Vol. 2. Organic Compounds & Polymeric Materials. 264p. 45.00x (ISBN 0-306-67202-2); Vol. 3. Alloys, Intermetallic Compounds & Cermets. 390p. 50.00x (ISBN 0-306-67203-0); Vol. 4. Oxide Mixtures & Minerals. 242p. 45.00x (ISBN 0-306-67204-9); Vol. 5. Mixtures & Solutions. 298p. 45.00x (ISBN 0-306-67205-7); Vol. 6. Coatings, Systems, & Composites. 270p. 45.00x (ISBN 0-306-67206-5). LC 60-14226. 1973. Set. 375.00 (ISBN 0-306-67200-6, IFI Plenum). Plenum Pub.

THERMOPLASTICS
Bruins, Paul, ed. Basic Principles of Thermoforming. LC 75-188122. 294p. 1973. 56.75x (ISBN 0-677-14990-5). Gordon.
Business Communications Staff. Engineering Thermoplastics. 1983. 1500.00 (ISBN 0-89336-342-1, P-015). BCC.
--High Temperature Thermoplastics. 1983. 1500.00 (ISBN 0-89336-175-5, P-051R). BCC.
--Thermoplastics Elastomers: Rubber Substitutes, P-026N. 1985. 1750.00 (ISBN 0-89336-431-2). BCC.
Coloring & Additives, Surface Finishing & Assembly, Thermoplastics, Vol. II. 207p. 16.00 (ISBN 0-686-48229-8, 1504). T-C Pubns CA.
Foams: Molding Thermosetting & Thermoplastic Structural Foam. 137p. 1983. 78.00 (ISBN 0-317-12678-4, LS115). T-C Pubns CA.
Folkes, M. J. Short Fibre Reinforced Thermoplastics. (Polymer Engineering Research Studies Ser.). 176p. 1982. 39.95x (ISBN 0-471-10209-1, Pub. by Res Stud Pr). Wiley.
--Short Fibre Reinforced Thermoplastics. (Illus.). 186p. 1982. 40.00 (ISBN 0-686-48236-0, 0808). T-C Pubns CA.
Heat Treatment of Thermoplastics & Thermosets. 129p. 1982. 78.00 (ISBN 0-317-12679-2). T-C Pubns CA.
Learning Systems Ltd, ed. Elements of Injection Moulding of Thermoplastics. (Illus., Orig.). 1969. pap. text ed. 5.95 (ISBN 0-85334-043-9). Transatlantic.
MacDermott. Selecting Thermoplastics for Engineering Applications. (Plasitics Engineering Ser.). 184p. 1984. 39.75 (ISBN 0-8247-7099-4). Dekker.
Margolis, James M. Engineering Thermoplastics. (Plastics Engineering Ser.). 432p. 1985. 65.00 (ISBN 0-8247-7294-6). Dekker.
Mascia, L. Thermoplastics: Materials Engineering. (Illus.). xiii, 446p. 1983. 77.75 (ISBN 0-85334-146-X, I-432-82, Pub. by Elsevier Applied Sci England). Elsevier.
Metallizing Thermoplastics & Thermosets, 1973-Feb. 1983. 135p. 1983. 78.00 (ISBN 0-686-48310-3, LS127). T-C Pubns CA.
Ogorkiewicz, R. M., ed. Engineering Properties of Thermoplastics. LC 72-83219. pap. 82.50 (ISBN 0-8357-9885-2, 2051614). Bks Demand UMI.
Riew, C. Keith & Gillham, John K., eds. Rubber-Modified Thermoset Resins. LC 84-21566. (Advances in Chemistry Ser.: No. 208). 372p. 1984. lib. bdg. 89.95x (ISBN 0-8412-0828-X). Am Chemical.
Titow, W. V. & Lenham, B. J. Reinforced Thermoplastics. LC 75-16335. 295p. 1975. 53.95x (ISBN 0-470-87518-6). Halsted Pr.
VDI, ed. Recycling of Thermoplastic Wastes. 206p. 1979. 42.00 (ISBN 0-9961071-9-3, Pub. by VDI W Germany). Heyden.

THERMOSTAT
Society of Plastics Engineers. Thermosets by Design: Regional Technical Conference Sponsored by the Chicago Section & the Thermose Division of SPE, March 7-9, 1984, Ramada, the O'Hare Inn, Des Plaines, Ill. pap. 20.00 (ISBN 0-317-30375-9, 2024724). Bks Demand UMI.
Vacuumschmelze, G. Thermostat Metals. 144p. 1983. 18.95 (ISBN 0-471-26262-5). Wiley.

THEROPHYTES
see Annuals (Plants)

THETA FUNCTIONS
see Functions, Theta

THIN FILMS
see also Metallic Films; Plastic Films
Baglin, J. E., et al, eds. Thin Films & Interfaces II: Materials Research Society Symposia Proceedings, Nov., 1983, Boston, MA, Vol. 25. 690p. 1984. 85.00 (ISBN 0-444-00905-1, North-Holland). Elsevier.
Barlow, W. A. Langmuir-Blodgett Films. (Thin Films Science & Technology Ser.: Vol. 1). 288p. 1980. 70.25 (ISBN 0-444-41901-2). Elsevier.
Bunshah, Rointan F., et al. Deposition Technologies for Films & Coatings: Developments & Applications. LC 82-7862. (Illus.). 585p. 1983. 69.00 (ISBN 0-8155-0906-5). Noyes.
Chopra, Kasturi L. Thin Film Phenomena. LC 78-12782. 864p. 1979. Repr. of 1969 ed. 48.00 (ISBN 0-88275-746-6). Krieger.
Coutts, T. J., ed. Active & Passive Thin Film Devices. 1978. 140.00 (ISBN 0-12-193850-6). Acad Pr.
Dash, J. G. Films on Solid Surfaces. 1975. 59.50 (ISBN 0-12-203350-7). Acad Pr.
Dash, J. G. & Ruvalds, J., eds. Phase Transitions in Surface Films. LC 79-28484. (NATO ASI Series B, Physical Sciences: Vol. 51). 379p. 1980. 59.50 (ISBN 0-306-40348-X, Plenum Pr). Plenum Pub.
Daunt, John G. & Lerner, E., eds. Monolayer & Submonolayer Helium Films. LC 73-12930. 160p. 1973. 35.00x (ISBN 0-306-30757-X, Plenum Pr). Plenum Pub.
Degiorgio, V. & Corti, M., eds. Physics of Amphiphiles: Micelles, Vesicles & Microemulsions: Proceedings of the International School of Physics, Enrico Fermi Course XC, Varenna, Italy, 19-29 July, 1983. 900p. 1985. 148.25 (ISBN 0-444-86940-9, North-Holland). Elsevier.
Dupuy, C. H., ed. Physics of Nonmetallic Thin Films. LC 76-8385. (NATO ASI Series B, Physics: Vol. 14). 510p. 1976. 75.00 (ISBN 0-306-35714-3, Plenum Pr). Plenum Pub.
Eckertova, Ludmila. Physics of Thin Films. LC 76-12177. 254p. 1977. 32.50x (ISBN 0-306-30910-6, Plenum Pr). Plenum Pub.
Hass, Georg, ed. Physics of Thin Films, Vol. 12. 1982. 59.50 (ISBN 0-12-533012-X). Acad Pr.
Hass, Georg & Francombe, Maurice H., eds. Physics of Thin Films: Advances in Research & Development, Vol. 11. (Serial Publication Ser.). 1980. 69.50 (ISBN 0-12-533011-1). Acad Pr.
Hass, Georg, et al, eds. Physics of Thin Films: Advances in Research & Development. Incl. Vol. 1. Haas, Georg, ed. 1963. 82.50 (ISBN 0-12-533001-4); Vol. 2. Haas, Georg & Thun, R. E., eds. 1964. 82.50 (ISBN 0-12-533002-2); Vol. 3. 1966. 82.50 (ISBN 0-12-533003-0); Vol. 4. 1967. 82.50 (ISBN 0-12-533004-9); Vol. 5. 1969. 82.50 (ISBN 0-12-533005-7); Vol. 6. Francombe, Maurice H. & Hoffman, Richard W., eds. 1971. 82.50 (ISBN 0-12-533006-5); Vol. 7. 1974. 82.50 (ISBN 0-12-533007-3); Vol. 10. 1978. 74.50 (ISBN 0-12-533010-3); lib ed. 87.00 (ISBN 0-12-533078-2); microfiche 50.00 (ISBN 0-12-533079-0). Acad Pr.
Kazmerski, Lawrence L., ed. Polycrystalline & Amorphous Thin Films & Devices. LC 79-8860. (Materials Science & Technology Ser.). 1980. 47.50 (ISBN 0-12-403880-8). Acad Pr.
Klabunde, Kenneth J., ed. Thin Films from Free Atoms & Particles. Date not set. price not set (ISBN 0-12-410755-9). Acad Pr.
Kressel, H., ed. Characterization of Epitaxial Semiconductor Films. (Methods & Phenomena Ser.: Vol. 2). 216p. 1976. Repr. 57.50 (ISBN 0-444-41438-X). Elsevier.
Lam, H. Y. & Thompson, M. J., eds. Comparison of Thin Film Transistor & SOI Technologies: Proceedings of Materials Research Society Symposia, 33th, Held February 1984, Albuquerque, New Mexico, Vol. 33. 336p. 1985. 67.00 (ISBN 0-444-00899-3, North-Holland). Elsevier.
Leaver, K. D., et al. Thin Films. LC 75-153871. (Wykeham Science Ser.: No. 17). 120p. 1971. 9.95x (ISBN 0-8448-1119-X). Crane Russak Co.
--Thin Films. (The Wykeham Science Ser.: No.17). 120p. 1971. pap. cancelled (ISBN 0-85109-230-6). Taylor & Francis.
Lewis, B. & Anderson, J. C. Nucleation & Growth of Thin Films. 1979. 81.00 (ISBN 0-12-446680-X). Acad Pr.
Maissel, L. & Glang, R. Handbook of Thin Film Technology. (Classic Handbook Program). 1970. 79.50 (ISBN 0-07-039742-2). McGraw.
Meyer, Otto & Kappeler, Franz, eds. Ion Beam Surface Layer Analysis, 2 vols. Incl. Vol. 1. 494p. 75.00 (ISBN 0-306-35045-9); Vol. 2. 491p (ISBN 0-306-35046-7). 75.00. LC 76-2606. 1976. Set. 138.00x (Plenum Pr). Plenum Pub.
Oechsner, H., ed. Thin-Film & Depth-Profile Analysis. (Topics in Current Physics Ser.: Vol. 37). (Illus.). 225p. 1984. 29.00 (ISBN 0-387-13320-8). Springer-Verlag.
Poate, J. M., et al, eds. Thin Films: Interdiffusion & Reactions. LC 77-25348. (Electrochemical Society Ser.). 578p. 1978. 69.95x (ISBN 0-471-02238-1, Pub. by Wiley-Interscience). Wiley.
Rhodes, J. & Walker, A. C., eds. Developments in Thin-Walled Structures, No. 2. (Illus.). 244p. 1984. 55.50 (ISBN 0-85334-247-4, Pub. by Elsevier Applied Sci England). Elsevier.
Roberts, G. G. & Pitt, C. W., eds. Langmuir-Blodgett Films, 1982. (Thin Films Science & Technology Ser.: Vol. 3). 330p. 1983. 74.50 (ISBN 0-444-42173-4). Elsevier.
Schneider, H. G. & Ruth, V. Advances in Epitaxy & Endotaxy. (Illus.). 250p. 1973. 28.50x (ISBN 0-685-39169-8). Adlers Foreign Bks.
Schwartz, Bertram & Schwartz, Newton, eds. Measurement Techniques for Thin Films. 30.00 (ISBN 0-384-54361-8); pap. 24.00 (ISBN 0-384-54362-6). Johnson Repr.
SreeHarsha, K. S. & Aita, C. R., eds. Thin Films: The Relationship of Structure to Properties, Vol. 47. 1985. text ed. 35.00 (ISBN 0-931837-12-X). Materials Res.
Stuart, R. V. Vacuum Technology, Thin Films, & Sputtering: An Introduction. LC 82-13748. 1983. 23.00 (ISBN 0-12-674780-6). Acad Pr.
Symposium on Thin Film Phenomena-Interfaces & Interactions (1977: Atlanta) Thin Film Phenomena-Interfaces & Interactions: Proceedings of the Symposium. Baglin, John E. & Poate, John M., eds. LC 77-91607. (Electrochemical Society. Proceedings Ser.: Vol. 78-2). pap. 134.00 (ISBN 0-317-08747-9, 2051978). Bks Demand UMI.
Tellier. Size Effects in Thin Films. (Thin Films Science & Technology Ser.: Vol. 2). 310p. 1982. 68.00 (ISBN 0-444-42106-8). Elsevier.
Vossen, John L. & Kern, Wernwe, eds. Thin Film Processes. 1978. 57.50 (ISBN 0-12-728250-5). Acad Pr.
Yarwood, J., ed. Vacuum & Thin Film Technology. 1978. text ed. 30.00 (ISBN 0-08-022112-2). Pergamon.

THIN LAYER CHROMATOGRAPHY
Angele, H. Four-Language Technical Dictionary of Chromatography: English, German, French, Russian. LC 76-103000. (Eng., Ger., Fr. & Rus.). 1971. text ed. 50.00 (ISBN 0-08-015865-X). Pergamon.
Blau, Karl & King, Graham S., eds. Handbook of Derivatives for Chromatography. LC 78-310911. pap. 148.00 (ISBN 0-317-26142-8, 2025195). Bks Demand UMI.
Bruner, F., ed. The Science of Chromatography: Lectures Presented at the A. J. P. Martin Honorary Symposium Urbino, Italy May 27-31, 1985. (Journal of Chromatography Library: No. 32). 476p. 1985. 92.75 (ISBN 0-444-42443-1). Elsevier.
Chaiken, Irwin M., et al. Affinity Chromatography & Biological Recognition (Symposium) 1983. 47.00 (ISBN 0-12-166580-1). Acad Pr.
Fried & Sherma. Thin Layer Chromatography. (Chromatographic Science Ser.: Vol. 17). 520p. 1982. 49.50 (ISBN 0-8247-1288-9). Dekker.
Gasparic, Jiri. Laboratory Handbook of Paper & Thin-Layer Chromatography. Churacek, Jaroslov, ed. LC 77-14168. 1978. 83.95x (ISBN 0-470-99298-0). Halsted Pr.
Giddings. Advances in Chromatography, Vol. 19. 336p. 1981. 65.00 (ISBN 0-8247-1246-3). Dekker.
--Advances in Chromatography, Vol. 20. 304p. 1982. 65.00 (ISBN 0-8247-1868-2). Dekker.
Iliuc, I. Tribology of Thin Layers. (Tribology Ser.: Vol. 4). 226p. 1980. 55.50 (ISBN 0-444-99768-7). Elsevier.
Irwin. Analytic Pyrolysis. (Chromatographic Science Ser.: Vol. 22). 432p. 1982. 85.00 (ISBN 0-8247-1869-0). Dekker.
Kirchner, Justus G. & Weissberger. Techniques of Chemistry: Thin Layer Chromatography. 2nd ed. LC 78-9163. (Techniques of Chemistry Ser.: Vol. 14). 1137p. 1978. 139.95x (ISBN 0-471-93264-7, Pub. by Wiley-Interscience). Wiley.
Lederer, M. Advanced Thin-Layer Chromatography. 1971. 21.50 (ISBN 0-317-17781-8). Elsevier.
Macek, K., et al. Bibliography of Paper & Thin-Layer Chromatography, 1970-1973 & Survey of Applications. (Journal of Chromatography Supplement Ser.: Vol. 5). 744p. 1976. pap. 106.50 (ISBN 0-444-41299-9). Elsevier.
Mohr & Pomerening. Affinity Chromatography. (Chromatography Science Ser.). 312p. 1986. price not set (ISBN 0-8247-7468-X). Dekker.
Moody & Thomas. Chromatographic Separation with Foamed Plastics & Rubbers. (Chromatographic Science Ser.). 176p. 1982. 35.00 (ISBN 0-8247-1549-7). Dekker.
Stahl, E., ed. Thin-Layer Chromatography: A Laboratory Handbook. 2nd. ed. Ashworth, M. R., tr. LC 69-14538. (Illus.). 1969. 83.00 (ISBN 0-387-04736-0). Springer-Verlag.
Touchstone, J. C. & Rogers, Dexter, eds. Practice of Thin Layer Chromatography. 2nd ed. LC 82-13654. 405p. 1983. 47.00x (ISBN 0-471-09766-7, Pub. by Wiley-Interscience). Wiley.
Touchstone, Joseph C., ed. Advances in Thin Layer Chromatography: Clinical & Environmental Applications. LC 81-23146. 521p. 1982. text ed. 65.00x (ISBN 0-471-09936-8, Pub. by Wiley-Interscience). Wiley.
--Quantitative Thin-Layer Chromatography. LC 72-13689. (Illus.). pap. 86.00 (ISBN 0-317-09311-8, 2055519). Bks Demand UMI.
Touchstone, Joseph C. & Rogers, Dexter, eds. Thin Layer Chromatography: Quantitative Environmental & Clinical Applications. LC 80-36871. 561p. 1980. 73.95x (ISBN 0-471-07958-8, Pub. by Wiley-Interscience). Wiley.
Touchstone, Joseph C. & Sherma, Joseph, eds. Densitometry in Thin Layer Chromatography: Practice & Applications. LC 78-9900. 764p. 1979. 69.00 (ISBN 0-471-88041-8). Krieger.
--Techniques & Applications of Thin Layer Chromatography. LC 84-11924. 395p. 1985. text ed. 70.00x (ISBN 0-471-88017-5, Pub. by Wiley-Interscience). Wiley.
Wagner, H., et al. Plant Drug Analysis: A Thin Layer Chromatography Photo-Atlas. Scott, T. A., tr. (Ger., Illus.). 350p. 1984. 58.00 (ISBN 0-387-13195-7). Springer-Verlag.
Zlatkis, A. & Kaiser, R., eds. HPTLC: High Performance Thin-Layer Chromatography. (Journal of Chromatography Library: Vol. 9). 240p. 1976. 64.00 (ISBN 0-444-41525-4). Elsevier.

THIOKOL
see Rubber, Artificial

THIOPHENE
Gronowitz, Salo. Thiophene & Its Derivatives, Vol. 44. 2nd ed. (Chemistry of Heterocyclic Compounds Monographs). 784p. 1985. 205.00 (ISBN 0-471-38120-9). Wiley.

Hartough, Howard D. Thiophene & Its Derivatives. LC 51-13781. (The Chemistry of Heterocyclic Compounds). pap. 137.80 (ISBN 0-317-08757-6, 2007400). Bks Demand UMI.

Lukevics, E., et al. Thiophene Derivatives of Group IV B Elements. (Sulfur Reports Ser.: Vol. 2, No. 5). 38p. 1982. 24.50 (ISBN 3-7186-0133-8). Harwood Academic.

THORACICA

see Barnacles

THORIUM

see also Nuclear Fuels

Albert, Roy E. Thorium: Its Industrial Hygiene Aspects. (U. S. Atomic Energy Commission Monographs). 1966. 17.50 (ISBN 0-12-048656-3). Acad Pr.

Atomic Energy Review - Thorium: Physico-Chemical Properties of Its Compounds & Alloys. (Special Issue Ser.: No. 5). (Illus.). 241p. 1975. pap. 21.75 (ISBN 92-0-149075-5, IAER5, IAEA). Unipub.

Boyle, R. W. Geochemical Prospecting for Thorium & Uranium. (Developments in Economic Geology Ser.: Vol. 16). 498p. 1983. 85.00 (ISBN 0-444-42070-3). Elsevier.

Brazil's Uranium-Thorium Deposits: Geology Reserves Potential. 144p. 1980. pap. 95.00 (ISBN 0-686-61573-5, MF15, Miller Freeman). Unipub.

El Shazly, E. M., compiled by. Geology of Uranium & Thorium: 1961-1966, Vol. 2. Incl. Geology of Uranium & Thorium. Shazly, E. M. El, compiled by. (Bibliographical Ser.: No. 31). 134p. 1962. pap. write for info. (ISBN 92-0-044062-2, ISP21/4, IAEA). (Bibliographical Ser.: No. 31). 102p. 1968. pap. write for info. (ISBN 92-0-044168-8, ISP2131, IAEA). Unipub.

McNeil, Mary. Brazil's Uranium-Thorium Deposits, Geology, Reserves, Potential: A World Mining Report. LC 79-87816. (Illus.). 1979. pap. 95.00 (ISBN 0-87930-119-8). Miller Freeman.

Makarov, Evgeniis S. Crystal Chemistry of Simple Compounds of Uranium, Thorium, Plutonium, Neptunium. Uvarov, E. B., tr. from Rus. LC 59-14486. pap. 38.30 (ISBN 0-317-08925-0, 2003366). Bks Demand UMI.

Osmond, J. K. & Cowart, J. B. Natural Uranium & Thorium Series Disequilibrium: New Approaches to Geochemical Problems. (Nuclear Science Applications Ser.: Section B). 50p. 1982. 19.75 (ISBN 3-7186-0131-1). Harwood Academic.

Radiation Protection in Mining & Milling of Uranium and Thorium. (Occupational Safety & Health Ser.: No. 32). pap. 20.00 (ISBN 92-2-101504-1, ILO25, ILO). Unipub.

Roth, E., compiled by. Thorium Fuel Cycle. (Bibliographical Ser.: No. 39). 462p. 1972. pap. write for info. (ISBN 92-0-054070-8, IAEA). Unipub.

Utilization of Thorium in Power Reactors. (Technical Reports Ser.: No. 52). (Illus.). 376p. 1966. pap. 25.75 (ISBN 92-0-055066-5, IDC52, IAEA). Unipub.

Weissert & Schileo. Fabrication of Thorium Fuel Elements. LC 68-25126. 1968. 11.10 (ISBN 0-89448-007-3, 300001). Am Nuclear Soc.

Wymer, Ray G., ed. Thorium Fuel Cycle: Proceedings. LC 67-62083. (AEC Symposium Ser.). 847p. 1968. pap. 29.95 (ISBN 0-87079-228-8, CONF-660524); microfiche 4.50 (ISBN 0-87079-229-6, CONF-660524). DOE.

Yemel'yanov, V. S. & Yevstyukin, A. I. Metallurgy of Nuclear Fuels. 1969. 110.00 (ISBN 0-08-012073-3). Pergamon.

THOROUGHBRED HORSE

Blood-Horse Staff. Thoroughbred Stallion Records, 1981. 1300p. 1982. lib. bdg. 85.00 (ISBN 0-936032-46-4). Blood-Horse.

Bowen, Edward. Thoroughbreds of 1979. 1980. 36.25 (ISBN 0-936032-16-2). Blood-Horse.

An Introduction to the Thoroughbred Horse. Rev. ed. (Illus.). 17p. 1980. pap. 2.50 (ISBN 0-936032-66-9). Blood-Horse.

Loder, Eileen P. Bibliography of the History & Organisation of Horse Racing & Thoroughbred Breeding in Great Britain & Ireland. 352p. 1981. 100.00x (ISBN 0-85131-297-7, Pub. by Allen & Co). State Mutual Bk.

Napier, Miles. Blood Will Tell. pap. write for info (ISBN 0-85131-254-3, NL51, Dist. by Miller). J A Allen.

Thoroughbred Owners & Breeders Association. The Breeder's Guide for 1980. 1981. 57.50 (ISBN 0-936032-41-3). Blood-Horse.

Varola, Franco. Functional Development of the Thoroughbred. 340p. 1981. 67.00x (ISBN 0-85131-307-8, Pub. by Allen & Co). State Mutual Bk.

Welker, Carole E. Thoroughbred. LC 73-77061. (Breed Ser.). 64p. 1974. pap. 1.95 (ISBN 0-88376-002-9). Dreenan Pr.

THRASHERS

Bent, Arthur C. Life Histories of North American Nuthatches, Wrens, Thrashers & Their Allies. (Illus.). 1948. pap. 9.95 (ISBN 0-486-21088-X). Dover.

--Life Histories of North American Nuthatches, Wrens, Thrashers & Their Allies. (Illus.). 14.75 (ISBN 0-8446-1640-0). Peter Smith.

THREE BODIES, PROBLEM OF

see Problem of Three Bodies

THRESHING MACHINES

see also Separators (Machines)

Clymer, Floyd. Floyd Clymer's Album of Historical Steam Traction Engines & Threshing Equipment. (Illus.). 160p. pap. 9.95 (ISBN 0-317-11542-1). Diamond Farm Bk.

THRESHOLD LOGIC

see also Switching Theory

Dertouzos, Michael. Threshold Logic: A Synthesis Approach. (Press Research Monographs: No. 32). 1965. 27.50x (ISBN 0-262-04009-3). MIT Pr.

Threshold Analysis Handbook. pap. 8.50 (ISBN 0-686-94268-X, UN78/4/2, UN). Unipub.

THRIPS

Priesner, H. Die Thysanopteren Europas. 1963. Repr. of 1928 ed. 34.10 (ISBN 90-6123-121-3). Lubrecht & Cramer.

Wilson, T. H. A Monographic Revision of the Heliothripinae of the World - Thysanoptera. (Memoirs Ser: No. 23). (Illus.). 354p. 1974. 25.00 (ISBN 0-686-17150-0). Am Entom Inst.

THROMBOLYTIC AGENTS

see Fibrinolytic Agents

THUNDER-STORMS

see Thunderstorms

THUNDERBOLT (FIGHTER PLANES)

Aeronautical Staff of Aero Publishers. Republic P-47. LC 66-19665. (Aero Ser: Vol. 6). 1966. pap. 3.95 (ISBN 0-8168-0520-2). Aero.

Morgan, Len. The P-47 Thunderbolt. LC 63-22711. (Famous Aircraft Ser.). (Illus.). 1979. pap. 6.95 (ISBN 0-8168-5648-6). Aero.

THUNDERSTORMS

see also Lightning

Kessler, Edwin, ed. Thunderstorm Morphology & Dynamics. 2nd, rev. & enl. ed. LC 85-8450. (Thunderstorms: A Social, Scientific, & Technological Documentary Ser.: Vol. 2). (Illus.). 432p. 1985. text ed. 68.50x (ISBN 0-8061-1936-5). U of Okla Pr.

Magono, C. Thunderstorms. (Developments in Atmospheric Science Ser.: Vol. 12). 262p. 1980. 70.25 (ISBN 0-444-15179-6). Elsevier.

THYRISTORS

Blicher, A. Power Thyristor Physics. (Applied Physics & Engineering Ser.: Vol. 12). 1976. 52.50 (ISBN 0-387-90173-6). Springer-Verlag.

Dewan, Shashi & Straughen, Alan. Power Semiconductor Circuits. LC 75-8911. 523p. 1975. 45.50 (ISBN 0-471-21180-X, Pub. by Wiley-Interscience). Wiley.

Finney, David. The Power Thyristor & Its Applications. (Illus.). 320p. 1980. 34.95 (ISBN 0-07-084533-6). McGraw.

Sen, P. C. Thyristor DC Drives. LC 80-21226. 307p. 1981. 51.95x (ISBN 0-471-06070-4, Pub. by Wiley-Interscience). Wiley.

Sheperd, William. Thyristor Control of AC Circuits. (Illus.). 300p. 1975. text ed. 47.50x (ISBN 0-8464-0925-9). Beekman Pubs.

Sugandhi, Krishna K. & Sughandi, Rajendra K. Thyristors: Theory & Applications. 2nd ed. 315p. 1984. 29.95x (ISBN 0-470-20015-4). Halsted Pr.

THYROID HORMONES

see also Calcitonin

Cassano, C. & Andreoli, M., eds. Current Topics in Thyroid Research. 1966. 95.00 (ISBN 0-12-163750-6). Acad Pr.

Draper, M. W. & Nissenson, R. A., eds. Parathyroid Hormone. (Journal: Mineral & Electrolyte Metabolism: Vol. 8, No. 3-4). (Illus.). vi, 124p. 1982. pap. 33.25 (ISBN 3-8055-3550-3). S Karger.

Hamolsky, Milton W. Thyroid Testing. LC 77-152025. (Medical Technology Ser.). (Illus.). Repr. of 1971 ed. 27.30 (ISBN 0-8357-9423-7, 2014551). Bks Demand UMI.

Hershman, Jerome M. & Bray, George A., eds. The Thyroid: Physiology & Treatment of Disease. (International Encyclopedia of Pharmacology & Therapeutics: Vol. 101). (Illus.). 1979. 165.00 (ISBN 0-08-017685-2). Pergamon.

Oppenheimer, Jack & Samuels, Herbert, eds. Molecular Basis of Thyroid Hormone Action. 1983. 58.00 (ISBN 0-12-527560-9). Acad Pr.

Ramsden, David. Peripheral Metabolism & Action of Thyroid Hormones, Vol. 1. 1977. 19.20 (ISBN 0-904406-54-7). Eden Pr.

Ramsden, David B. Peripheral Metabolism & Action of Thyroid Hormones, Vol. 2. (Annual Research Reviews). 1978. 28.80 (ISBN 0-88831-029-3). Eden Pr.

Turakulov, Ya. Kh., et al. Thyroid Hormones: Biosynthesis, Physiological Effects, & Mechanisms of Action. LC 75-28119. (Studies in Soviet Science: Life Science Ser.). (Illus.). 329p. 1975. 49.50x (ISBN 0-306-10919-0, Consultants). Plenum Pub.

THYSANOPTERA

see Thrips

TI 99-4A (COMPUTER)

Apps, Vince. The Texas Program Book: TI 99-4A. 104p. 1984. pap. 12.95 (ISBN 0-946576-00-9, Pub. by Phoenix Pub). David & Charles.

Blackadar, Thomas. The Best of TI 99-4A Cartridges. LC 83-50716. (Illus.). 150p. (Orig.). 1984. pap. 9.95 (ISBN 0-89588-137-3). SYBEX.

Brewer, Bill & Willis, Jerry. How to Use the TI 99-4A. 124p. 1983. pap. 3.95 (ISBN 0-88056-135-1). Dilithium Pr.

Budin, Howard. Speed Walker: Fun to Program Your TI 99. 39p. (Orig.). 1984. pap. 2.95 (ISBN 0-523-42247-4). Pinnacle Bks.

Casciato & Horsfall. TI 99-4A: Twenty-Four BASIC Programs. LC 83-50831. 224p. 1983. pap. 12.95 (ISBN 0-672-22247-7, 22247); incl. tape 19.95 (ISBN 0-672-26172-3, 26172). Sams.

Casciato, Carol A. & Horsfall, Donald. TI-99 4A BASIC Reference Manual. LC 83-51181. 17.95 (ISBN 0-672-22246-9). Sams.

Casciato, Carol Ann & Horsfall, Donald J. The TI 99-4A User's Guide. LC 83-61067. 192p. 1983. pap. 11.95 (ISBN 0-672-22071-7, 22071). Sams.

Dertouzos, Michael. Threshold Logic: A Synthesis Approach. (Press Research Monographs: No. 32). 1965. 27.50x (ISBN 0-262-04009-3). MIT Pr.

Dusthimer, David & Buchholz, Ted. TI-99 4A. LC 83-51669. (Tool Kit Ser.). 8.95 (ISBN 0-672-22310-4). Sams.

Fabbri, Tony. Animation, Games & Sound for the TI 99-4A. (Prentice-Hall Personal Computing Ser.). (Illus.). 224p. 1985. pap. text ed. 17.95 (ISBN 0-13-037227-7). P-H.

Flynn, Brian. Thirty-Three Programs for the TI 99-4A. 199p. (Orig.). 1984. pap. 12.95 (ISBN 0-942386-42-6). Compute Pubns.

Garrison, Paul. The Last Whole TI 99-4A Book: Programs & Possibilities. LC 83-26046. 472p. 1984. pap. 12.95 (ISBN 0-471-87920-7). Wiley.

Golstein, Larry Joel & Weist, Edward. TI 99-4A: User's Guide. cancelled 10.95 (ISBN 0-89303-890-3). Brady Comm.

Grillo, John P. & Robertson, J. D. Data & File Management for the TI 99-4A. (Microcomputer Power Ser.). 196p. 1984. pap. 15.95 (ISBN 0-697-00245-4). Wm C Brown.

Grillo, John P., et al. Introduction to Graphics for the TI 99-4A. (Microcomputer Power Ser.). 130p. 1984. 14.95 (ISBN 0-697-00237-3). Wm C Brown.

Heller, Dave & Heller, Dorothy. Free Software for Your TI 99-4A. (Free Software Ser.). (Illus.). 208p. 1984. pap. 8.95 (ISBN 0-86582-124-0, EN79214). Enrich.

Herold, Raymond. Compute's Guide to TI-99-4A Sound & Graphics. 224p. (Orig.). 1984. pap. 12.95 (ISBN 0-942386-46-9). Compute Pubns.

Holtz, Frederick. TI 99-4A Game Programs. (Illus.). 240p. 1983. 17.95 (ISBN 0-8306-0730-7); pap. 11.50 (ISBN 0-8306-1630-6, 1630). TAB Bks.

--Using & Programming the TI 99-4A, Including Ready-to-Run Programs. (Illus.). 224p. 16.95 (ISBN 0-8306-0620-3, 1620); pap. 10.25 (ISBN 0-8306-1620-9). TAB Bks.

Hunter, James F. & Guntle, Gegory. TI-99 4A Trivia Database. LC 84-51277. 8.95 (ISBN 0-672-22395-3). Sams.

Inman, Don, et al. Introduction to TI BASIC. 300p. 1980. pap. 12.95 (ISBN 0-8104-5185-9). Hayden.

--Introduction to TI BASIC. 2nd ed. 352p. pap. 14.95 (6401). Hayden.

Jones, Aubrey B., Jr. I Speak BASIC to My TI 99-4A. pap. 9.75 student text (6173); tchr's manual 18.75 (6163); exam 15.00 (6183); Tchrs' Manual, 20 Student Texts, & Exam. classroom set 200.00 (6153). Hayden.

Knight, Timothy. TI-99 4A Graphics & Sounds. LC 84-50804. 9.95 (ISBN 0-672-22386-4). Sams.

Knight, Timothy & LaBatt, Darren. TI-99 4A BASIC Programs. LC 84-50803. 9.95 (ISBN 0-672-22385-6). Sams.

Kreutner, Donald C. TI 99-4A Favorite Programs Explained. 180p. 1983. pap. 12.95 (ISBN 0-88022-050-3, 46). Que Corp.

Loreto, Remo A. The TI 99-4A in Bits & Bytes. Wartman, Robert, ed. (Illus., Orig.). 1983. pap. 14.99 (ISBN 0-914209-01-9). R A Loreto.

McComic, Ira. Learning TI 99-4A Home Computer Assembly Language Programming. (Illus.). 224p. 1984. cancelled (ISBN 0-13-527870-8); pap. 16.95 (ISBN 0-13-527862-7). P-H.

--Learning TI-99-4A Home Computer Assembly Language Programming. Stultz, Russell A., ed. LC 83-23386. (Illus.). 240p. 1984. pap. 16.95 (ISBN 0-915381-56-7). WordWare Pub.

McEvoy, Seth. Creating Arcade Games on the TI 99-4A. 200p. 1984. pap. 12.95 (ISBN 0-942386-27-2). Compute Pubns.

Manning, William A. & Ingalsbe, Lon. Get Personal with Your TI 99. (Illus.). 198p. 1983. pap. 9.95 (ISBN 0-88056-098-3). Dilithium Pr.

Meck, H. R. Numerical Analysis with the TI 99-4A, Apple II, IIe & TRS 80 Model I-III. 256p. 1984. 19.95 (ISBN 0-13-626649-5); pap. 14.95 (ISBN 0-13-626631-2). P-H.

Morley, M. S. Fundamentals of TI 99-4A Assembly Language. (Illus.). 322p. (Orig.). 1984. 16.95 (ISBN 0-8306-0722-6, 1722); pap. 11.95 (ISBN 0-8306-1722-1). TAB Bks.

Mullish, Henry & Kruger, Dov. Zappers: Having Fun Programming & Playing Twenty-Three Games for the TI 99-4A. 128p. 1984. pap. 9.95 (ISBN 0-671-49862-2, Pub. by Computer Bks). S&S.

Nadler, Bob. The TI 99-4A Illustrated. 176p. pap. 10.95 (6408). Hayden.

Nanos, Shirley A., et al. The TI 99-4A Microcomputer. (Nanos Reference Cards Ser.). 20p. (Orig.). 1984. pap. 5.95 (ISBN 0-915069-21-0). Nanos Sys.

Ninety Niner Home Computer Magazine Editors. The Best of Ninety-Niner, Vol. I. (Illus.). 360p. (Orig.). 1984. pap. 19.95 (ISBN 0-933094-11-6). Emerald Pub.

Ohr, Stephan. Adventures with the TI 99-4A. 192p. pap. 12.95 (6400). Hayden.

Peckham, H. D. Hands-on BASIC for the TI 99-4A. 352p. 1984. 22.00 (ISBN 0-07-049155-0). McGraw.

Phillips, Gary & Reese, David. The Texas Instrument User's Encyclopedia: TI 99, 2, 4, 4a & 8. Mellin, Michael F. & Sandberg, Robert, eds. 300p. (Orig.). 1983. pap. 14.95 (ISBN 0-912003-15-4). Bk Co.

Prothro, Brian K. Cracking the 99-4A. (Illus.). 175p. (Orig.). Date not set. pap. 12.95 (ISBN 0-917915-00-3). Midnight Express.

Regena, C. Programmer's Reference Guide to TI 99-4A. 312p. 1983. 14.95 (ISBN 0-942386-12-4). Compute Pubns.

Ross, Peter. Introducing LOGO for the Texas Instruments 99-4A, Tandy Color Computer, & Apple II Computer. 160p. 1983. pap. 12.95 (ISBN 0-201-14652-5). Addison-Wesley.

Rugg, Tom & Feldman, Phil. Thirty-Two BASIC Programs for the TI 99-4A. (Illus.). 288p. 1983. pap. 19.95 (ISBN 0-88056-136-X); incl. cassette 39.95 (ISBN 0-88056-188-2); incl. disk 39.95 (ISBN 0-88056-203-X). Dilithium Pr.

Schechter, Gil M. TI 99-4A: Fifty-One Fun & Educational Programs. LC 83-50373. 96p. 1983. pap. 4.95 (ISBN 0-672-22192-6, 22192); incl. tape 11.95 (ISBN 0-672-26168-5, 26168). Sams.

Schmalhofer, Gregory. TI-99 4A Calc. LC 84-51273. 8.95 (ISBN 0-672-22414-3). Sams.

Schreiber, Linda M. The Last Word on the TI 99-4A. (Illus.). 224p. (Orig.). 1984. pap. 11.50 (ISBN 0-8306-1745-0, 1745). TAB Bks.

Searle, Bill. Introduction to BASIC with the TI 99-4A. cancelled 9.95 (ISBN 0-89303-571-8). Brady Comm.

Shaw, Stephen. Getting Started with the Texas TI 99-4A. 150p. 1984. pap. 12.95 (ISBN 0-946576-04-1, Pub. by Phoenix Pub). David & Charles.

Stedman, Robert & Cosgrove, Ron. Kids BASIC for the TI 99-4A. cancelled 9.95 (ISBN 0-89303-603-X). Brady Comm.

Thompson, Thomas, Jr. Games & Graphics for the TI 99-4A. 128p. pap. 8.95 (6407). Hayden.

Thornburg, David D. Computer Art & Animation: A User's Guide to TI 99-4A Color LOGO. (Illus.). 224p. 1983. pap. 12.95 (ISBN 0-201-07958-5). Addison-Wesley.

Turner, Len. One Hundred One Programming Tips & Tricks for the Texas Instruments TI 99-4A Home Computer. 128p. 1983. 8.95 (ISBN 0-86668-025-X). ARCsoft.

--Texas Instruments Computer Program Writing Workbook. 96p. 1983. 4.95 (ISBN 0-86668-812-9). ARCsoft.

--Thirty-Six Texas Instruments TI 99-4A Programs for Home, School & Office. 96p. 1983. 8.95 (ISBN 0-86668-024-1). Arcsoft.

Wang, Shih-Ho. Fifty Complete Programs for Texas Instruments TI 99-4A Computer. (Illus.). 112p. 1983. pap. 6.95 (ISBN 0-914729-00-4). Blue Mtn Com.

Weber Systems, Inc. Staff. TI 99-4A Users Handbook. LC 83-60591. (WSI's How to Use Your Personal Computer). 350p. 1984. pap. 14.95 (ISBN 0-938862-49-9). Weber Systems.

Willis, Jerry, et al. Things to Do with Your TI 99-4A Computer. pap. 3.95 (ISBN 0-451-12842-7, Sig). NAL.

Winter, M. J. Computer Playground for the TI 99-4A. (Computer Playground Ser.). (Illus.). 128p. 1983. pap. 9.95 (ISBN 0-88190-297-7, BO297). Datamost.

Wyatt, Allen. BASIC Tricks for the TI-99 4A. LC 84-50802. 9.95 (ISBN 0-672-22384-8). Sams.

--TI-99 4A Games. LC 84-51462. 8.95 (ISBN 0-672-22398-8). Sams.

Zaks, Rodnay. Your First TI 99-4A Program. LC 83-50962. (Illus.). 182p. (Orig.). 1983. pap. 12.95 (ISBN 0-89588-157-8). SYBEX.

TI CC 40 (COMPUTER)

Barnett, Nancy B. & Baker, John T. Texas Instruments Compact Computer Forty User's Guide. 336p. (Orig.). 1983. pap. 14.95 (ISBN 0-89512-057-7). Tex Instr Inc.

Thomas, D. Learn BASIC: A Guide to Programming the Texas Instruments Professional Compact Computer 40. (Illus.). 256p. pap. 9.95 (ISBN 0-07-064257-5, BYTE Bks). McGraw.

TI PROFESSIONAL COMPUTER

Dawson, J. B. Understanding the TI PC: A Programming Digest. 108p. (Orig.). 1985. pap. 9.95 (ISBN 0-9615084-0-X). Prosoft AZ.

TI PROGRAMMABLE 59 (CALCULATING MACHINE)

Ballantyne, E. J., Jr., et al, eds. Manual of Geophysical Hand-Calculator Programs TI & HP Volumes. 1981. TI Vol. looseleaf 50.00 (ISBN 0-931830-20-6); HP Vol. 50.00 (ISBN 0-931830-17-6); Set, TI & HP. 90.00 (ISBN 0-317-12576-1). Soc Exploration.

Fielding, Leslie. Handheld Calculator Programs for Rotating Equipment Design. LC 82-9962. (Illus.). 480p. 1983. 41.95 (ISBN 0-07-020695-3). McGraw.

Garrison, Paul. Programming the TI-59 & HP-41 Calculators. (Illus.). 300p. (Orig.). 1982. 18.95 (ISBN 0-8306-2442-2); pap. 13.50 (ISBN 0-8306-1442-7, 1442). TAB Bks.

Skillman, William. Radar Calculations Using the TI-59 Programmable Calculator. (Illus.). 350p. 1983. 53.00 (ISBN 0-89006-112-2). Artech Hse.

Zehna, Peter. Probability by Calculator: Solving Probability Problems with the Programmable Calculator. 181p. 1982. 17.95 (ISBN 0-13-711523-7); pap. 9.95 (ISBN 0-13-711515-6). P-H.

TICKS

East Coast Fever & Related Tick-Borne Diseases. (Animal Production & Health Papers: No. 19). 996p. (Selected Reprints of Papers UNDP-FAO Regional Project). 1980. pap. 71.50 (ISBN 92-5-100974-0, F2137, FAO). Unipub.

Evans, G. Owen, et al. The Terrestrial Acari of the British Isles-an Introduction to Their Morphology, Biology & Classification, Vol. 1: Introduction & Biology. (Illus.). 219p. 1961. Repr. of 1968 ed. 14.00x (ISBN 0-565-00696-7, Pub. by Brit Mus Nat Hist England). Sabbot-Natural Hist Bks.

Furman, Deane P. & Loomis, Edmond C. The Ticks of California (Acari Ixodida) LC 83-9265. (Bulletin of the California Insect Survey Ser.: Vol. 25). 240p. 1984. lib. bdg. 25.00x (ISBN 0-520-09685-1). U of Cal Pr.

McDaniel, Burruss. How to Know the Mites & Ticks. (Pictured Key Nature Ser.). 350p. 1979. write for info. wire coil (ISBN 0-697-04757-1); pap. text ed. o.p. avail. (ISBN 0-697-04756-3). Wm C Brown.

Obenchain, F. D. & Galun, R., eds. The Physiology of Ticks. (Current Themes in Tropical Science Ser.: Vol. 1). (Illus.). 450p. 1982. 140.00 (ISBN 0-08-024937-X). Pergamon.

Peterson, Paul C., et al. The Feather Mite Family Eustathiidae: (Acarina: Sarcoptiformes) (Monograph: No. 21). (Illus.). 143p. 1980. pap. 15.00 (ISBN 0-910006-29-6). Acad Nat Sci Phila.

Pomerantzev, B. I. Arachnida Ixodid Ticks (Ixodae) Elbl, A. & Anastos, G., trs. 1959. 10.00 (ISBN 0-934454-08-6). Lubrecht & Cramer.

Rodriguez, J. G., ed. Recent Advances in Acarology. LC 79-17386. 1979. Vol. 1. 51.00 (ISBN 0-12-592201-9); Vol. 2. 46.50 (ISBN 0-12-592202-7). Acad Pr.

Van Der Hammen, L. A Berlese, Acari Myriopoda et Scorpiones Eighteen Eighty-Two to Nineteen Three, 12 vols. 4616p. 1980. Set. 315.00 (ISBN 90-6193-603-9, Pub. by Junk Pubs Netherlands). Kluwer Academic.

Walker, J. B. The Ixodid Ticks of Kenya. 220p. 1974. 49.00x (ISBN 0-686-45849-4, Pub. by CAB Bks England). State Mutual Bk.

Weber, Walter J. Fleas, Ticks & Cockroaches-Disease Transmitters. 70p. 1984. pap. 10.00 (ISBN 0-913702-27-7). Thomson Pub CA.

Yeoman, G. H. & Walker, J. B. The Ixodid Ticks of Tanzania: A Study of the Zoogeography of the Ixodidae of an East African Country. 215p. 1967. 45.00x (ISBN 0-686-45850-8, Pub. by CAB Bks England). State Mutual Bk.

TIDAL CURRENTS

see Ocean Currents

TIDAL WAVES

see Tsunamis

TIDE MARSHES

see Marshes

TIDES

see also Earth Tides; Estuaries

Brosche, F. & Suendermann, J., eds. Tidal Friction & the Earth's Rotation, Bielefeld, FRG, 1981: Proceedings. (Illus.). 345p. 1983. pap. 30.00 (ISBN 0-387-12011-4). Springer-Verlag.

Bruun, P. & Mehta, A. J. Stability of Tidal Inlets: Theory & Engineering. (Developments in Geotechnical Engineering Ser.: Vol. 23). 510p. 1978. 76.75 (ISBN 0-444-41728-1). Elsevier.

Chapman, S. & Lindzen, R. S. Atmospheric Tides, Thermal & Gravitational. 210p. 1970. 57.75 (ISBN 0-677-61810-7). Gordon.

--Atmospheric Tides: Thermal & Gravitational. 200p. 1970. 23.70 (ISBN 90-277-0113-X, Pub. by Reidel Holland). Kluwer Academic.

Godin. The Analysis of Tides. 292p. 1982. 70.00x (ISBN 0-85323-441-8, Pub. by Liverpool Univ England). State Mutual Bk.

Gray, T. K. & Gashus, O. K., eds. Tidal Power. LC 70-179031. 630p. 1972. 85.00x (ISBN 0-306-30559-3, Plenum Pr). Plenum Pub.

Hopkins, F. N. Lights & Tides of the World, 2 vols. & 2 supplements. rev. ed. 1973. Set. 90.00 (ISBN 0-686-77975-4). Heinman.

Komar, Paul D. Beach Processes & Sedimentation. (Illus.). 464p. 1976. 43.95 (ISBN 0-13-072595-1). P-H.

Laplace, Pierre S. Celestial Mechanics, Vols. 1-4. LC 69-11316. Set. text ed. 195.00 (ISBN 0-8284-0194-2). Chelsea Pub.

--Celestial Mechanics, Vol. 5. LC 63-11316. (Mecanique Celeste, Tome V, Fr). 1969. Repr. of 1832 ed. text ed. 20.00 (ISBN 0-8284-0214-0). Chelsea Pub.

Marchuk, G. I. & Kagan, B. A. Ocean Tides: Mathematical Models & Numerical Experiments. Cartwright, D. E., tr. LC 82-18898. (Illus.). 240p. 1984. 72.00 (ISBN 0-08-026236-8). Pergamon.

Melchoir, P. The Tides of the Planet Earth. 2nd ed. LC 82-16567. (Illus.). 648p. 1983. 99.00 (ISBN 0-08-026248-1). Pergamon.

National Oceanographic & Atmospheric Administration. Current & Tide Tables (1985) for Puget Sound, Deception Pass, the San Juans, Gulf Islands & Strait of Juan de Fuca. abr. ed. Island Canoe Company, ed. (Illus.). 96p. 1985. pap. 4.50 (ISBN 0-918439-03-5). Island Canoe.

Russell, Robert C. Waves & Tides. LC 73-135252. (Illus.). 348p. Repr. of 1953 ed. lib. bdg. 22.50x (ISBN 0-8371-5171-6, RUWT). Greenwood.

Severn, R. T., et al, eds. Tidal Power & Estuary Management. (Colston Paper Ser.: No. 30). (Illus.). 296p. 1979. technical 65.00 (ISBN 0-85608-023-3). Transatlantic.

Silvester, R. Coastal Engineering, Vol. 2: Sedimentation, Estuaries, Tides, Effluents, Modelling. LC 72-97435. (Developments in Geotechnical Engineering Ser.: Vol. 4B). 338p. 1974. 68.00 (ISBN 0-444-41102-X). Elsevier.

Wave & Tidal Energy International Symposium, 1st. Proceedings, 2 vols. Stephens, H. S., ed. (Illus.). 1979. Set. pap. 69.00x (ISBN 0-906085-00-4, Dist. by Air Science Co.). BHRA Fluid.

TIGERS

Courtney, Nicholas. The Tiger: Symbol of Freedom. (Illus.). 128p. 1981. 25.00 (ISBN 0-7043-2245-5, Pub. by Quartet England). Charles River Bks.

Matjushkin, E. N. & Zhivotchenko, V. I. The Amur Tiger in the USSR. 50p. 1980. pap. 8.00 (ISBN 0-686-75150-7, IUCN97, IUCN). Unipub.

Rathmore, Fateh S., et al. With Tigers in the Wild: An Experience in an Indian Forest. (Illus.). 196p. 1983. text ed. 75.00x (ISBN 0-7069-1023-0, Pub. by Vikas India). Advent NY.

Schaller, George B. Deer & the Tiger: A Study of Wildlife in India. LC 66-23697. (Illus.). 1967. 14.00x (ISBN 0-226-73633-4). U of Chicago Pr.

TILAPIA MOSSAMBICA

Pullin, F. S. Summary Report of the ICLARM Conference on the Biology & Culture of Tilapias. 1984 ed. (ICLARM Conference Proceedings Ser.: No. 6). (Illus.). 13p. (Orig.). pap. 5.00x (ISBN 0-89955-423-7, Pub. by ICLARM Philippines). Intl Spec Bk.

Smith, E. R., et al, eds. Summary Report of the PCARRD-ICLARM Workshop on Philippine Tilapia Economics. (ICLARM Conference Proceedings Ser.: No. 10). (Illus.). 45p. (Orig.). 1984. pap. 5.00x (ISBN 0-317-17300-6, Pub. by ICLARM Philippines). Intl Spec Bk.

Wohlfarth, G. W. & Hulata, G. I. Applied Genetics of Tilapias. 26p. 1982. pap. text ed. 5.25 (ISBN 0-89955-375-3, Pub. by ICLARM Philippines). Intl Spec Bk.

TILLAGE

see also Shifting Cultivation

Boone, F. R., ed. Experiences with Three Tillage Systems on a Marine Loam Soil II: 1976-1979: A Joint Study of the Westmaas Research Group on New Tillage Systems, Carried Out on the Westmaas Experimental Husbandry Farm. (Agricultural Research Reports: No. 925). (Illus.). 263p. 1985. pap. 28.00 (ISBN 90-220-0855-X, PDC280, Pudoc). Unipub.

Di'Itri, F. M. Conservation Tillage. (Illus.). 345p. 1985. 39.95 (ISBN 0-87371-024-X). Lewis Pubs Inc.

Unger, P. W. & Van Doren, J. M., Jr., eds. Predicting Tillage Effects on Soil Physical Properties & Processes. (ASA Special Publication Ser.). 198p. 1982. pap. 10.00 (ISBN 0-89118-069-9). Am Soc Agron.

TILLICH, PAUL, 1886-1965

Adams, James L. Paul Tillich's Philosophy of Culture, Science & Religion. LC 81-43775. 320p. 1982. lib. bdg. 26.25 (ISBN 0-8191-2221-1); pap. text ed. 13.00 (ISBN 0-8191-2222-X). U Pr of Amer.

Carey, John J., ed. Theonomy & Autonomy: Studies in Paul Tillich's Engagement with Modern Culture. LC 83-25847. xxii, 287p. 1984. Repr. of 1978 ed. 21.95x (ISBN 0-86554-105-1, MUP/H99). Mercer Univ Pr.

TILT-UP CONCRETE CONSTRUCTION

see Precast Concrete Construction

TIMBER

see also Forests and Forestry; Lumber; Pulpwood; Trees; Wood;

also names of timber-trees, e.g. Oak, Pine

American Institute of Timber Construction (AITC) Timber Construction Manual. 704p. 1985. 34.95 (ISBN 0-471-82758-4). Wiley.

Baird, J. A. & Ozelton, E. C. Timber Designer's Manual. 2nd ed. (Illus.). 656p. 1984. text ed. 75.00x (ISBN 0-246-12375-3, Pub. by Granada England). Sheridan.

Benni, C. A. & Bolza, Eleanor. South American Timbers. 1982. 60.00x (ISBN 0-686-97897-8, Pub. by CSIRO Australia). State Mutual Bk.

Clutter, Jerome L. & Fortson, James C. Timber Management: A Quantitative Approach. LC 82-25611. 333p. 1983. 32.50 (ISBN 0-471-02961-0). Wiley.

Desch, H. E. Timber: Its Structure, Properties & Utilization. 6th ed. 416p. (Orig.). 1980. pap. text ed. 24.95x (ISBN 0-917304-62-4). Timber.

Duerr, William A., ed. Timber! Problems, Prospects, Policies. LC 72-1160. 260p. 1973. 10.95x (ISBN 0-8138-1700-5). Iowa St U Pr.

Findlay, W. P. Timber: Properties & Uses. 224p. 1975. pap. cancelled (ISBN 0-258-97113-4, Pub. by Granada England). Sheridan.

Forest Industries Commission on Timber Valuation & Taxation. Timber Tax Journal, Vol. 18. 335p. 1982. 30.00 (ISBN 0-686-43165-0, Pub. by FICTVT). Intl Spec Bk.

Fowler, Gene. Timber Line. 416p. 1974. pap. 2.75 (ISBN 0-89174-007-4). Comstock Edns.

Hyde, William F. Timber Supply, Land Allocation, & Economic Efficiency. LC 80-8021. (Resources for the Future Ser.). (Illus.). 243p. 1980. text ed. 21.00x (ISBN 0-8018-2489-3). Johns Hopkins.

Keating, W. G. & Bolza, Eleanor. Characteristics, Properties & Uses of Timbers: South-east Asia, Northern Australia & the Pacific, Vol. I. LC 82-45895. (Illus.). 392p. 1983. 39.50x (ISBN 0-89096-141-7). Tex A&M Univ Pr.

Keenan, F. J. & Tejada, Marcelo. Tropical Timber for Building Materials in the Andean Group Countries of South America. (Illus.). 151p. 1985. pap. 13.00 (ISBN 0-88936-423-0, IDRCTS49, IDRC). Unipub.

Ozelton, E. C. & Baird, J. A. Timber Designer's Manual. (Illus.). 1976. 29.95x (ISBN 0-8464-0927-5). Beekman Pubs.

Record, Samuel J. & Hess, Robert W. Timbers of the New World. LC 73-140611. (Use & Abuse of America's Natural Resources Ser). (Illus.). 718p. 1972. Repr. of 1943 ed. 57.50 (ISBN 0-405-02806-7). Ayer Co Pubs.

Timber Trends & Prospects in Africa. 90p. 1967. pap. 21.00 (ISBN 92-5-101735-2, F462, FAO). Unipub.

U. S. Dept. of Agriculture-Forest Service. Timber Resources for America's Future: Forest Resource Report No. 14. LC 72-2872. (Use & Abuse of America's Natural Resources Ser). 728p. 1972. Repr. of 1958 ed. 41.00 (ISBN 0-405-04538-7). Ayer Co Pubs.

Usher, M. B. & Ocloo, J. K. The Natural Resistance of Eighty-Five West African Hardwood Timbers to Attack by Termites & Micro-Organisms. 1979. 35.00x (ISBN 0-85135-103-4, Pub. by Centre Overseas Research). State Mutual Bk.

Van Name, Willard G. Vanishing Forest Reserves. Bruchey, Stuart, ed. LC 78-56688. (Management of Public Lands in the U. S. Ser.). 1979. Repr. of 1929 ed. lib. bdg. 17.00x (ISBN 0-405-11356-0). Ayer Co Pubs.

Zivnuska, John A. U. S. Timber Resources in a World Economy. LC 67-21585. (Resources for the Future Ser.). Repr. of 1967 ed. 34.30 (ISBN 0-8357-9290-0, 2016069). Bks Demand UMI.

TIMBER–MENSURATION

see Forests and Forestry–Mensuration

TIMBER–PRESERVATION

see Wood–Preservation

TIMBER–TESTING

see Wood–Testing

TIMBER CRUISING

see Forests and Forestry–Mensuration

TIME

see also Cycles; Chronology; Horology; Space and Time

Bartlett, M. S. Probability, Statistics & Time: A Collection of Essays. (Monographs on Applied Probability & Statistics). 1975. 17.95x (ISBN 0-412-14150-7, NO. 6029, Pub. by Chapman & Hall England); pap. 12.95x (ISBN 0-412-22260-4, NO. 2964). Methuen Inc.

Consumer Time-Sharing Services. (Reports Ser.: No. 155). 148p. 1980. 985.00x (ISBN 0-88694-155-5). Intl Res Dev.

Cunynghame, Henry H. Time & Clocks: A Description of Ancient & Modern Methods of Measuring Time. LC 77-78127. (Illus.). 208p. 1970. Repr. of 1906 ed. 35.00x (ISBN 0-8103-3576-X). Gale.

Denbigh, K. G. An Inventive Universe. LC 75-13561. 220p. 1975. 8.95 (ISBN 0-8076-0802-5). Braziller.

Denbigh, Kenneth G. Three Concepts of Time. 160p. 1981. pap. 22.00 (ISBN 0-387-10757-6). Springer-Verlag.

Doob, Leonard W. Patterning of Time. LC 72-97346. pap. 121.50 (ISBN 0-317-10352-0, 2017547). Bks Demand UMI.

Fraser, J. T. The Genesis & Evolution of Time: A Critique of Interpretation in Physics. LC 82-8622. (Illus.). 224p. 1982. lib. bdg. 20.00x (ISBN 0-87023-370-X). U of Mass Pr.

--Of Time, Passion & Knowledge: Reflections on the Strategy of Existence. LC 74-12783. 544p. 1975. 20.00 (ISBN 0-8076-0770-3). Braziller.

--Time As Conflict: A Scientific & Humanistic Study. (Science & Culture Ser.: No. 35). 356p. 1978. 26.95x (ISBN 0-8176-0950-4). Birkhauser.

Fraser, J. T., et al, eds. Study of Time II: 2nd Conference of the International Society for the Study of Time, Summer, 1973. (Illus.). ix, 487p. 1975. 39.50 (ISBN 0-387-07321-3). Springer-Verlag.

--Study of Time III: 3rd Conference of the International Society for the Study of Time. 1978. 37.00 (ISBN 0-387-90311-9). Springer-Verlag.

Freeman, Eugene & Sellars, Wilfrid, eds. Basic Issues in the Philosophy of Time. LC 73-128197. (The Monist Library of Philosophy Ser.). 241p. 1971. 19.95 (ISBN 0-87548-078-0). Open Court.

Friedman, William, ed. Developmental Psychology of Time. (Developmental Psychology Ser.). 1982. 36.50 (ISBN 0-12-268320-X). Acad Pr.

Gorman, B. S. & Wessman, A. E., eds. The Personal Experience of Time. LC 77-21964. (Emotions, Personality, & Psychotherapy Ser.). (Illus.). 310p. 1977. 32.50x (ISBN 0-306-31039-2, Plenum Pr). Plenum Pub.

Greenaway, Frank, ed. Time & the Sciences. (At the Crossroads of Culture Ser.). 182p. 1979. pap. 12.25 (ISBN 92-3-101657-1, U986, UNESCO). Unipub.

Gribbin, John. Timewarps. 1980. pap. 4.95 (ISBN 0-385-29078-0, Delta). Dell.

Hintikka, Jaakko. Time & Necessity: Studies in Aristotle's Theory of Modality. 1973. 37.50x (ISBN 0-19-824365-0). Oxford U Pr.

Howse, Derek. Greenwich Time & the Discovery of the Longitude. (Illus.). 1980. 25.00x (ISBN 0-19-215948-8). Oxford U Pr.

Jaspers, Karl. Die Geistige Situation der Zeit. (Sammlung Goeschen: No. 1000). 1979. 5.10x (ISBN 3-11007-878-3). De Gruyter.

Jesperson, James & Fitz-Randolph, Jane. From Sundials to Atomic Clocks: Understanding Time & Frequency. (Illus.). 192p. pap. 5.00 (ISBN 0-486-24265-X). Dover.

Jordan, Richard D. The Temple of Eternity: Thomas Traherne's Philosophy of Time. LC 70-189560. (National University Publications). 1972. 12.95 (ISBN 0-8046-9019-7, Pub by Kennikat). Assoc Faculty Pr.

Kingham, E. G., et al, eds. Real Time Data Handling & Process Control, II. 386p. 1984. 57.75 (ISBN 0-444-86846-1, North-Holland). Elsevier.

Koehler, Patricia & School, Beverly. Playing with Time. 144p. (Orig.). 1981. pap. 8.00 (ISBN 0-87879-262-7). Acad Therapy.

Krudy, E S, et al, eds. Time: A Bibliography. 218p. 1976. 24.00 (ISBN 0-904147-05-3). IRL Pr.

Landsberg, P. T., ed. The Enigma of Time. 1984. pap. 15.00 (ISBN 0-9903000-7-2, Pub. by A Hilger England). Heyden.

Lebhar, Godfrey M. Use of Time. 1958. 7.00 (ISBN 0-912016-00-0). Lebhar Friedman.

McCarthy, Dennis D. & Pilkington, John D., eds. Time & the Earth's Rotation. (International Astronomical Union Symposium: No. 82). 1979. lib. bdg. 42.00 (ISBN 90-277-0892-4, Pub. by Redel Holland); pap. 26.00 (ISBN 90-277-0893-2). Kluwer Academic.

Macey, Samuel L. Clocks & the Cosmos: Time in Western Life & Thought. (Illus.). 256p. 1980. 21.00 (ISBN 0-208-01773-9, Archon). Shoe String.

Medrich, Elliott A. & Roizen, Judith A. The Serious Business of Growing Up: A Study of Children's Lives Outside School. LC 81-7650. 412p. 1981. 28.50x (ISBN 0-520-04296-4); pap. 9.95 (ISBN 0-520-05071-1). U of Cal Pr.

Mellor, David H. Real Time. LC 81-3841. 210p. 1981. 34.50 (ISBN 0-521-24133-2). Cambridge U Pr.

Muller, H. J. Out of the Night: A Biologist's View of the Future. Rosenberg, Charles, ed. (The History of Hereditarian Thought Ser.). 22.00 (ISBN 0-8240-5821-6). Garland Pub.

Newton-Smith, W. H. The Structure of Time. (International Library of Philosophy & Scientific Method Ser.). (Illus.). 1980. 32.50x (ISBN 0-7100-0362-5). Routledge & Kegan.

O'Neil, W. M. Time & the Calendars. (Illus.). 224p. 1978. Repr. of 1975 ed. 23.00 (ISBN 0-424-00003-2, Pub by Sydney U Pr). Intl Spec Bk.

Park, David. The Image of Eternity: Roots of Time in the Physical World. LC 79-22984. 160p. 1980. lib. bdg. 14.50x (ISBN 0-87023-286-X). U of Mass Pr.

Patrides, C. A. Aspects of Time. 1976. 32.50x (ISBN 0-8020-2232-4). U of Toronto Pr.

Prior, Arthur N. Past, Present & Future. 1967. 39.95x (ISBN 0-19-824311-1). Oxford U Pr.

--Time & Modality. LC 78-26696. (Illus.). 1979. Repr. of 1957 ed. lib. bdg. 22.50x (ISBN 0-313-20911-1, PRTI). Greenwood.

Reitmeister, Louis A. A Philosophy of Time. LC 72-10699. 452p. 1974. Repr. of 1962 ed. lib. bdg. 25.00x (ISBN 0-8371-6618-7, REPT). Greenwood.

Rektorys, Karel. The Method of Discretization in Time. 1982. lib. bdg. 69.00 (ISBN 90-277-1342-1, Pub. by Reidel Holland). Kluwer Academic.

Rescher, N. & Urquhart, A. J. Temporal Logic. LC 74-141565. (Library of Exact Philosophy: Vol. 3). (Illus.). 1971. 39.00 (ISBN 0-387-80995-3). Springer-Verlag.

Schlesinger, George N. Aspects of Time. LC 79-66954. 180p. 1980. lib. bdg. 17.50 (ISBN 0-915144-69-7); pap. text ed. 4.95 (ISBN 0-915144-70-0). Hackett Pub.

Shallis, Michael. On Time: An Investigation into Scientific Knowledge & Human Experience. LC 82-10499. (Illus.). 208p. 1983. 14.95 (ISBN 0-8052-3853-0). Schocken.

Sims, Reginald W. & Price, James H., eds. Evolution, Time & Space. 1983. 59.00 (ISBN 0-12-644550-8). Acad Pr.

Steiner, Duane R. Stretching Time: An Easy to Read Practical Guide to Time Effectiveness. LC 82-90237. (Illus.). 156p. (Orig.). 1982. pap. 7.95 (ISBN 0-9608350-0-8). Deccom.

Tidcombe, Marianne. The Bookbindings of T. J. Cobden-Sanderson: A Study in His Work, 1884-1893, Based on His Time Book in the British Library. (Illus.). 420p. 1984. 90.00 (ISBN 0-7123-0027-9, Pub. by British Lib). Longwood Pub Group.

Toulmin. The Discovery of Time. LC 81-71398. pap. 9.95 (ISBN 0-226-80842-4). U Of Chicago Pr.

VanGool, W., et al, eds. Energy & Time in the Economic & Physical Sciences: Papers & Comments; Workshop Held June 1984 Wolfheze, the Netherlands. 386p. 1985. 59.25 (ISBN 0-444-87748-7, North Holland). Elsevier.

Whitrow, G. J. The Natural Philosophy of Time. 2nd ed. (Illus.). 1980. pap. 19.95x (ISBN 0-19-858215-3). Oxford U Pr.

Whysler, R. O. Get Going! Tips on Managing Your Time & Increasing Your Effectiveness. (Illus.). 75p. (Orig.). 1982. pap. 13.00x looseleaf (ISBN 0-935402-11-X); lib. bdg. 12.00x (ISBN 0-935402-12-8). Intl Comm Serv.

Wiley, Bertha M. Time & Telling Time. LC 66-28928. 1967. pap. 3.96 (ISBN 0-8224-6950-2); tchrs.' manual free (ISBN 0-8224-6952-9). Pitman Learning.

Wold, Astri H. Decoding Oral Language. (European Monographs in Social Psychology Ser.). 1978. 39.50 (ISBN 0-12-336250-4). Acad Pr.

Zelkind, Irving & Sprug, Joseph. Time Research: 1172 Studies. LC 74-14970. 253p. 1974. 17.50 (ISBN 0-8108-0768-8). Scarecrow.

TIME, GEOLOGICAL
see Geological Time

TIME AND MOTION STUDY

Barnes, Ralph M. Motion & Time Study: Design & Measurement of Work. 7th ed. LC 80-173. 689p. 1980. text ed. 44.50x (ISBN 0-471-05905-6). Wiley.

Gilbreth, Frank B. Motion Study. LC 72-89986. (Management History Ser.: No. 14). (Illus.). xxiii, 139p. 1972. Repr. of 1911 ed. 18.50 (ISBN 0-87960-016-0). Hive Pub.

Gilbreth, Frank B. & Gilbreth, Lillian M. Fatigue Study. LC 73-1155. (Management History Ser.: No. 29). (Illus.). viii, 167p. 1973. Repr. of 1916 ed. 17.50 (ISBN 0-87960-028-4). Hive Pub.

Gurvitch, G. The Spectrum of Social Time. Korenbaum, Myrtle, ed. Bosserman, Phillip, tr. from Fr. (Synthese Library). 152p. 1964. lib. bdg. 21.00 (ISBN 90-277-0006-0, Pub. by Reidel Holland). Kluwer Academic.

Knight, Frank B., ed. Essentials of Brownian Motion & Diffusion. LC 80-29504. (Mathematical Surveys Ser.: Vol. 18). 201p. 1981. 39.00 (ISBN 0-8218-1518-0, SURV 18). Am Math.

Kolstee, Hans M. Motion & Power. (Illus.). 256p. 1982. text ed. 25.95 (ISBN 0-13-602953-1). P-H.

Kreiss, H. & Oliger, J. Methods for the Approximate Solution of Time Dependent Problems. (GARP Publications Ser.: No. 10). (Illus.). 107p. 1973. pap. 14.00 (ISBN 0-685-34859-8, W299, WMO). Unipub.

McDowall, David, et al. Interrupted Time Series Analysis. LC 80-52761. (Quantitative Applications in the Social Sciences Ser.: No. 21). (Illus.). 96p. 1980. pap. 5.00 (ISBN 0-8039-1493-8). Sage.

Mundel, Marvin E. Motion & Time Study. 5th ed. (P-H Industrial Engineering Ser.). (Illus.). 1978. ref. 34.95 (ISBN 0-13-602987-6). P-H.

Niebel, Benjamin W. Motion & Time Study. 7th ed. 1982. 29.95x (ISBN 0-256-02527-4). Irwin.

Salmon, Wesley C. Space, Time, & Motion: A Philosophical Introduction. 2nd rev. ed. LC 80-18423. (Illus.). 160p. 1981. pap. 8.95x (ISBN 0-8166-1004-5). U of Minn Pr.

TIME AND SPACE
see Space and Time

TIME-DELAY NETWORKS
see Delay Lines

TIME MEASUREMENTS
see also Automatic Timers; Chronometer; Clocks and Watches; Horology; Sun-Dials

Andrewes, William & Atwood, Seth. The Time Museum: An Introduction. Chandler, Bruce, ed. (Illus.). 32p. (Orig.). 1983. pap. 4.95 (ISBN 0-912947-00-4). Time Museum.

Dascalu, D. Transit Time Effects in Unipolar Solid-State Devices. 1977. 33.00 (ISBN 0-9961003-6-9, Pub. by Abacus England). Heyden.

Hannan, E. J., et al, eds. Time Series in the Time Domain. (Handbook of Statistics Ser.: Vol. 5). 496p. 1985. 96.00 (ISBN 0-444-87629-4, North-Holland). Elsevier.

Kartaschoff, P. Frequency & Time. (Monographs in Physical Measurement). 1978. 47.50 (ISBN 0-12-400150-5). Acad Pr.

Maynard, Harold B. Methods-Time Measurement. LC 48-7173. (McGraw-Hill Industrial Organization & Management Ser.). (Illus.). pap. 75.50 (ISBN 0-317-10748-8, 2055405). Bks Demand UMI.

Osborne, E. F. Global Timing Systems of Nanosecond Accuracy Using Satellite References. LC 70-131393. 189p. 1969. 19.00 (ISBN 0-403-04526-6). Scholarly.

Poole, Reginald L. Medieval Reckonings of Time. 1977. lib. bdg. 59.95 (ISBN 0-8490-2220-7). Gordon Pr.

Schoenberg, Isaac J. Mathematical Time Exposures. LC 82-62766. 270p. 1983. 34.50 (ISBN 0-88385-438-4); pap. 18.00. Math Assn.

Turner, Anthony. Time Museum Catalogue of the Collection; Volume I: Time Measuring Instruments, Part 3: Water-Clocks, Sand-Glasses, Fire-Clocks. Chandler, Bruce, ed. (Illus.). 183p. 1984. 95.00 (ISBN 0-912947-01-2). Time Museum.

--Time Museum Catalogue of the Collection; Volume I: Time Measuring Instruments, Part 1: Astrolabes & Related Devices. Chandler, Bruce, ed. (Illus.). 220p. 1985. 95.00 (ISBN 0-912947-02-0). Time Museum.

TIME-OF-FLIGHT MASS SPECTROMETRY

Binks, Robert, et al. Tables for Use in High Resolution Mass Spectometry. Incl. Chemical Formulae from Mass Determinations. Henneberg, D. & Casper, K.. LC 75-130645. pap. 52.00 (ISBN 0-317-29340-0, 2024031). Bks Demand UMI.

Harvey, J. A., ed. Experimental Neutron Resonance Spectroscopy. 1970. 90.00 (ISBN 0-12-329850-4). Acad Pr.

Milne, George W., ed. Mass Spectrometry. LC 78-23298. 533p. 1980. Repr. of 1971 ed. 36.50 (ISBN 0-88275-789-X). Krieger.

Quayle, A., ed. Advances in Mass Spectrometry, Vol. 8. (Advances in Mass Spectrometry Ser.). 1200p. 1980. 490.95 (ISBN 0-471-25987-X, Pub. by Wiley Heyden). Wiley.

TIME PRODUCTION STANDARDS
see Production Standards

TIME-SERIES ANALYSIS
see also Harmonic Analysis

Anderson, D. D. Analyzing Time Series: Proceedings of the International Time Series Meeting, Guernsey, Oct. 1979. 1980. 76.75 (ISBN 0-444-85464-9). Elsevier.

Anderson, O. D. & Perryman, M. R. Applied Time Series Analysis. 1982. 68.00 (ISBN 0-444-86424-5, I-182-82A). Elsevier.

Anderson, O. D., ed. Time Series Analysis, Theory & Practice: Proceedings of the Conference, Nottingham, March 1983, Vol. 5. 1984. 59.25 (ISBN 0-444-87568-9, I-438-84, North-Holland). Elsevier.

--Time Series Analysis, Theory & Practice: Proceedings of the Conference, Toronto, Aug. 18-21, 1983, Vol. 7. 312p. 1985. 59.25 (ISBN 0-444-87684-7, North-Holland). Elsevier.

--Time Series Analysis: Theory & Practice, No. 4. 352p. 1983. 72.50 (ISBN 0-444-86731-7, I-253-83). Elsevier.

--Time Series: Proceedings of the International Conference, Held at Nottingham University, March, 1979. 1980. 85.00 (ISBN 0-444-85418-5). Elsevier.

Anderson, O. D. & Ord, J. K., eds. Time Series Analysis, Theory & Practice-Hydrological, Geophysical & Spatial Applications: Proceedings of the Conference, Toronto, Aug. 10-14, 1983, Vol. 6. 308p. 1985. 59.25 (ISBN 0-444-87683-9, North-Holland). Elsevier.

Anderson, O. D. & Perryman, M. R., eds. Time Series Analysis: Proceedings of the International Conference, Held in Houston, Texas, August, 1980. 1981. 83.00 (ISBN 0-444-86177-7). Elsevier.

Anderson, O. D., et al, eds. Time Series Analysis: Theory & Practice: Proceedings of International Conference, Valencia, Spain, June 22-26, 1981, No. 1. 756p. 1982. 85.00 (ISBN 0-444-86337-0). Elsevier.

Anderson, Theodore W. Statistical Analysis of Time Series. LC 70-126222. (Probability & Mathematical Statistics Ser.). 704p. 1971. 53.50x (ISBN 0-471-02900-9). Wiley.

Aoki, M. Notes on Economic Times Series Analysis: System Theoretic Perspectives. (Lecture Notes in Economics & Mathematical Systems Ser.: Vol. 220). 249p. 1983. pap. 19.00 (ISBN 0-387-12696-1). Springer-Verlag.

Blackman, R. B. & Tukey, J. W. Measurement of Power Spectra from the Point of View of Communications Engineering. 1958. pap. 5.00 (ISBN 0-486-60507-8). Dover.

Bloomfield, Peter. Fourier Analysis of Time Series: An Introduction. LC 75-34294. (Probability & Mathematical Statistics Ser.). 258p. 1976. 33.95x (ISBN 0-471-08256-2, Pub. by Wiley-Interscience). Wiley.

Bowerman, Bruce & O'Connell, Richard. Forecasting & Times Series: An Applied Approach. LC 78-20869. 1979. text ed. 19.95 (ISBN 0-87150-389-1, Duxbury Pr). PWS Pubs.

Box, George E. & Jenkins, Gwilym. Time Series Analysis, Forecasting & Control. rev. ed. LC 76-8713. 500p. 1976. text ed. 49.00x (ISBN 0-8162-1104-3). Holden-Day.

Brillinger, D. R. & Krishnaiah, P. R. Handbook of Statistics: Time Series in the Frequency Domain. (Handbook of Statistics: Vol. 3). 1984. 88.50 (I-461-83). Elsevier.

Brillinger, David R. Time Series: Data Analysis & Theory. enl. ed. LC 80-84117. (Illus.). 552p. 1980. text ed. 44.00x (ISBN 0-8162-1150-7). Holden-Day.

Bry, Gerhard & Boschan, Charlotte. Cyclical Anaylsis of Time Series: Selected Procedures & Computer Programs. (Technical Paper Ser.: No. 20). (Illus.). 230p. 1971. text ed. 14.00x (ISBN 0-87014-223-2, Dist. by Columbia U Pr). Natl Bur Econ Res.

Davis, Harold T. Analysis of Economic Time Series. (Cowles Commission Monograph Ser., No. 6). 1941. 8.50 (ISBN 0-911536-18-3). Trinity U Pr.

Ellis, Dennis & Nathan, Jay. An Executive's Guide to Time Series Forecasting. LC 84-81422. (Orig.). 1986. pap. text ed. write for info. (ISBN 0-932126-11-1). Graceway.

Family Service Association of America. Detailed Instructions for a Time Analysis, Vol. 3. (Time & Cost Analysis Ser.). 54p. 1968. pap. 8.50 (ISBN 0-87304-075-9). Family Serv.

Findley, David, ed. Applied Time Series Analysis, Vol. 2. 1981. 60.00 (ISBN 0-12-256420-0). Acad Pr.

Forehand, Garlie A., ed. Applications of Time Series Analysis to Evaluation. LC 81-48580. (Program Evaluation Ser.: No. 16). 1982. 8.95x (ISBN 0-87589-918-8). Jossey-Bass.

Franke, J., et al, eds. Robust & Nonlinear Time Series Analysis. 2nd ed. (Lecture Notes in Statistics Ser.: Vol. 26). ix, 286p. 1984. pap. 16.00 (ISBN 0-387-96102-X). Springer-Verlag.

Fuller, Wayne A. Introduction to Statistical Time Series. LC 76-6954. (Probability & Mathematical Statistics Ser.). 470p. 1976. 47.50x (ISBN 0-471-28715-6, Pub. by Wiley-Interscience). Wiley.

Goldstein, Harvey. The Design & Analysis of Longitudinal Studies: Their Role in the Measurment of Change. 1979. 35.00 (ISBN 0-12-289580-0). Acad Pr.

Graupe, Daniel. Time Series Analysis, Identification & Adaptive Filtering. LC 81-20738. 402p. (Orig.). 1984. 38.50 (ISBN 0-88275-713-X). Krieger.

Grenander, Ulf & Rosenblatt, Murray. Statistical Analysis of Stationary Time Series. 2nd ed. LC 83-62687. 308p. 1984. text ed. 17.95 (ISBN 0-8284-0320-1). Chelsea Pub.

Hannan, E. J. Time Series Analysis. 1967. pap. 10.95x (ISBN 0-412-20480-0, NO. 6141, Pub. by Chapman & Hall). Methuen Inc.

Hannan, Edward J. Multiple Time Series. LC 77-112847. (Wiley Series in Probability & Mathematical Statistics). 536p. 1970. 66.50x (ISBN 0-471-34805-8, Pub by Wiley-Interscience). Wiley.

Harvey, A. C. Time Series Models. 240p. 1981. text ed. 32.00x (ISBN 0-86003-032-6, Pub. by Philip Allan England). Humanities.

Holt, C. A. & Shore, R. W. Bayesian Analysis in Economic Theory & Time Series Analysis. (Studies in Bayesian Econometrics: Vol. 2). 180p. 1980. 36.25 (ISBN 0-444-85414-2, North-Holland). Elsevier.

Jenkins, Gwilym M. & Watts, Donald G. Spectral Analysis & Its Applications. LC 67-13840. 1968. 48.00x (ISBN 0-8162-4464-2). Holden-Day.

Koopmans, L. H. The Spectral Analysis of Time Series. 1974. 58.50 (ISBN 0-12-419250-5). Acad Pr.

Kreiss, H. & Oliger, J. Methods for the Approximate Solution of Time Dependent Problems. (GARP Publications Ser.: No. 10). (Illus.). 107p. 1973. pap. 14.00 (ISBN 0-685-34859-8, W299, WMO). Unipub.

McCleary, Richard, et al. Applied Time Series Analysis for the Social Sciences. LC 79-27873. (Illus.). 331p. 1980. 28.00 (ISBN 0-8039-1205-6); pap. 14.00 (ISBN 0-8039-1206-4). Sage.

Makridakis, S., et al. The Forecasting Accuracy of Major Time Series Methods. LC 83-17055. 301p. 1984. text ed. 39.95x (ISBN 0-471-90327-2, Pub. by Wiley-Interscience). Wiley.

Mehra, Raman K. & Lainiotis, Dmitri G., eds. System Identification: Advances & Case Studies. 1976. 58.50 (ISBN 0-12-487950-0). Acad Pr.

Mendel, Jerry M. Optimal Seismic Deconvolution: An Estimation Based Approach. LC 82-22739. (Monograph). 1983. 39.50 (ISBN 0-12-490780-6). Acad Pr.

Morrison, Donald F. Applied Linear Statistical Methods. 544p. 1983. 42.95 (ISBN 0-13-041020-9). P-H.

Nerlove, M., et al. Problems of Time Series Analysis. 104p. 1980. pap. text ed. 12.95x (ISBN 3-411-01587-X). Birkhauser.

Ostrom, Charles W., Jr. Time Series Analysis: Regression Techniques. LC 77-93283. (University Papers Ser.: Quantitative Applications in the Social Sciences, No. 9). 85p. 1978. pap. 5.00 (ISBN 0-8039-0942-X). Sage.

Pandit, S. M. & Wu, S. M. Time Series & System Analysis with Applications. 586p. 1983. 46.45 (ISBN 0-471-86886-8); write for info solutions avail (ISBN 0-471-87392-6). Wiley.

Pankratz, Alan. Forecasting with Univariate Box-Jenkins Models: Concepts & Cases. LC 83-1404. (Probability & Mathematical Statistics: Applied Probability & Statistics Section). 562p. 1983. 36.95x (ISBN 0-471-09023-9, 1-346, Pub. by Wiley-Interscience). Wiley.

Parzen, E. Time Series Analysis of Irregularly Observed Data: Proceedings of a Symposium Held at Texas A & M University, College Station, Texas, February 10-13, 1983. (Lecture Notes in Statistics Ser.: Vol. 25). (Illus.). 370p. 1984. pap. 22.00 (ISBN 0-387-96040-6). Springer-Verlag.

Priestley, M. B., ed. Spectral Analysis & the Time Series, 2 Vols. in 1, Vol. 1 & Vol.2. (Probability & Mathematical Statistics Ser.). 1983. 42.50 (ISBN 0-12-564922-3). Acad Pr.

Rao, T. S. & Gabr, M. M. An Introduction to Bispectral Analysis & Bilinear Time Series Models. (Lecture Notes in Statistics Ser.: Vol. 24). (Illus.). 280p. 1984. pap. 17.00 (ISBN 0-387-96039-2). Springer-Verlag.

Robinson, Enders A. Physical Applications of Stationary Time Series. 2nd. ed. (Illus.). 314p. 1980. 42.00 (ISBN 0-02-851050-X). Macmillan.

--Times Series Analysis & Applications. LC 81-81825. (Illus.). 628p. 1981. 25.00 (ISBN 0-910835-00-4). Goose Pond Pr.

Robinson, Enders A. & Silvia, Manual T. Digital Foundations of Time Series Analysis: Wave-Equation Space-Time Processing. 450p. 1981. Vol. I, 464. 1979. 46.00x (ISBN 0-8162-7270-0); Vol. II, 450. 1981. text ed. 46.00x (ISBN 0-8162-7271-9). Holden-Day.

Shugart, H. H., Jr., ed. Time Series & Ecological Processes. LC 78-5410. (SIAM-SIMS Conference Ser.: No. 5). (Illus.). xxi, 303p. (Orig.). 1978. pap. text ed. 26.00 (ISBN 0-89871-032-4). Soc Indus-Appl Math.

Tong, H. Threshold Models in Non-Linear Time Series Analysis. (Lecture Notes in Statistics: Vol. 21). (Illus.). 323p. 1983. pap. 24.00 (ISBN 0-387-90918-4). Springer-Verlag.

Vargin, V. V. Catalyzed Controlled Crystallization of Glasses in the Lithium Aluminosilicate System, Pt. 1. LC 65-25265. 74p. 1965. 25.00x (ISBN 0-306-10733-3, Consultants). Plenum Pub.

Webster, R. T. & Young, C. S., eds. Industrial Applications of Titanium & Zirconium; 3rd Conference. LC 83-72890. (Special Technical Publications: No. 830). 222p. 1984. text ed. 35.00 (ISBN 0-8031-0211-9, 04-830000-05). ASTM.

Williams, J. C. & Belov, A. F., eds. Titanium & Titanium Alloys: Scientific & Technological Aspects, 3 vols. LC 79-9156. 2499p. 1982. Set. 250.00x (ISBN 0-306-40191-6, Plenum Pr). Plenum Pub.

TITANIUM DIOXIDE CRYSTALS

R. H. Chandler Ltd., ed. Titanium Dioxide Production, Nineteen Sixty-Five to Nineteen Seventy-Five. 140p. 1976. 110.00x (ISBN 0-686-78921-0, Pub. by Chandler England). State Mutual Bk.

TITRATION

see Volumetric Analysis

TIZARD, HENRY THOMAS, SIR, 1885-1959

Snow, C. P. Appendix to Science & Government. LC 61-7396. 1962. pap. text ed. 1.25x (ISBN 0-674-79352-8). Harvard U Pr.

TOADS

see also Horned Toads

Bush, Don. Wart Toad. LC 82-60482. (Illus.). 40p. 1982. 4.50x (ISBN 0-943978-00-9). Rolling Hills Pr.

Wright, Albert H. & Wright, Anna A. Handbook of Frogs & Toads of the United States & Canada. 3rd ed. (HANH Ser.). (Illus.). 652p. 1949. 36.50x (ISBN 0-8014-0462-2). Comstock.

TOADSTOOLS

see Mushrooms

TOBACCO

see also Cigarettes; Nicotine

Analysis of Drugs & Metabolites by Gas Chromatography - Mass Spectometry: Natural, Pyrolytic & Metabolic Products of Tobacco & Marijuana, Vol. 7. 1980. 89.75 (ISBN 0-8247-6861-2). Dekker.

Cutting Tobacco's Toll. (Worldwatch Institute Papers: No. 18). 40p. 1978. pap. 2.95 (ISBN 0-686-94956-0, WW18, WW). Unipub.

Drake, Bill. The Cultivator's Handbook of Natural Tobacco. (Illus.). 1981. pap. 3.95 (ISBN 0-686-32843-4). Cultivators Res Serv.

Encyclopedie du Tabac et Des Fumeurs. (Fr.). 80p. 1976. 95.00 (ISBN 0-686-57153-3, M-6212). French & Eur.

Maclaren, W. A. Rubber, Tea & Cacao with Special Sections on Coffee, Spices & Tobacco. 1980. lib. bdg. 75.00 (ISBN 0-8490-3110-9). Gordon Pr.

Robert, Joseph C. The Tobacco Kingdom. 1938. 11.75 (ISBN 0-8446-1386-X). Peter Smith.

Sittig, Marshall. Tobacco Substitutes. LC 76-2318. (Chemical Technology Review: No. 67). (Illus.). 182p. 1976. 36.00 (ISBN 0-8155-0616-3). Noyes.

Tso, Tien C. Physiology & Biochemistry of Tobacco Plants. LC 79-178259. (Illus.). 393p. 1982. 61.00 (ISBN 0-87933-000-7). Van Nos Reinhold.

West, George A. Tobacco, Pipes & Smoking Customs of the American Indians. Repr. of 1934 ed. lib. bdg. 57.50x (ISBN 0-8371-4635-6, WETS). Greenwood.

TOBACCO–DISEASES AND PESTS

Interaction Between Long & Short Particles of Tobacco Rattle Virus. (Agricultural Research Reports: 784). 1972. pap. 11.25 (ISBN 90-220-0418-X, PDC46, PUDOC). Unipub.

TOBACCO–PHYSIOLOGICAL EFFECT

Abel, Ernest L. Smoking & Reproduction: A Comprehensive Bibliography. LC 82-15660. xviii, 163p. 1982. lib. bdg. 35.00 (ISBN 0-313-23663-1, ASR/). Greenwood.

Cumming, G. & Bonsignore, G., eds. Smoking & the Lung. (Ettore Majorana International Science Series, Life Sciences: Vol. 17). 520p. 1985. 82.50x (ISBN 0-306-41828-2, Plenum Pr). Plenum Pub.

Curtis, Lindsay R. Cigarrillo: Contaminante, No. 1. 48p. pap. 1.10 (ISBN 0-311-46073-9). Casa Bautista.

Eysenck, A J. & Eaves, L. J. The Causes & Effects of Smoking. 116p. 1980. 49.00x (ISBN 0-85117-186-9, Pub. by Smith England). State Mutual Bk.

Greenhalgh, R. M., ed. Smoking & Arterial Disease. 315p. 1981. text ed. 57.95x (ISBN 0-8464-1215-2). Beekman Pubs.

Homburger, F. Experimental Aspects of Cigarette Smoke Carcinogenesis. (Lectures in Toxicology Ser.: Vol. 9). 12p. 1982. 66.00 (ISBN 0-08-028013-7). Pergamon.

Schmeltz, I., ed. The Chemistry of Tobacco & Tobacco Smoke. LC 72-76934. 186p. 1972. 35.00x (ISBN 0-306-30597-6, Plenum Pr). Plenum Pub.

Shephard, Roy J. The Risks of Passive Smoking. (Illus.). 1982. text ed. 27.95x (ISBN 0-19-520393-3). Oxford U Pr.

TOLERANCE (ENGINEERING)

Foster, Lowell W. Geo-Metrics II: The Application of Geometric Tolerancing Techniques (Using Customary System) Rev. ed. LC 82-11655. (Illus.). 320p. 1983. pap. text ed. 19.95 (ISBN 0-201-11520-4); pap. 2.00. Addison-Wesley.

Instrument Fitting. 1982. 50.00x (ISBN 0-85083-069-9, Pub. by Engineering Ind). State Mutual Bk.

Lieblich, Jerome H., ed. Dimensioning & Tolerances (An Interpretation of ANSI y14.5) 96p. 1976. lib. bdg. 5.95x (ISBN 0-912702-19-2). Global Eng.

Liggett, John V. Fundamentals of Position Tolerance. (Manufacturing Data Ser.). (Illus.). 1970. pap. 11.75 (ISBN 0-87263-020-X). SME.

Madsen, David A. Geometric Dimensioning & Tolerancing. rev. ed. (Illus.). 128p. 1984. pap. text ed. 8.00 (ISBN 0-87006-461-4). Goodheart.

Tolerancing. (Metrology Ser.: Module 27-5). (Illus.). 60p. 1979. spiral bdg. 8.00x (ISBN 0-87683-084-X). G P Courseware.

TOMAHAWK (FIGHTER PLANES)

see P-Forty (Fighter Planes)

TOMATOES

Ballantyne, Janet. Garden Way's Red & Green Tomato Cookbook. LC 82-2884. (Illus.). 158p. 1982. pap. 5.95 (ISBN 0-88266-262-7). Garden Way Pub.

Doty, Walter & Sinnes, A. Cort. All about Tomatoes. Susan Lammers, ed. LC 76-29249. (Illus.). 96p. (Orig.). 1981. pap. 5.95 (ISBN 0-917102-97-5). Ortho.

Gould, Wilbur A. Tomato Production, Processing & Quality Evaluation. 2nd ed. (Illus.). 1983. text ed. 57.50 (ISBN 0-87055-426-3). AVI.

Mittleider, Jacob R. Let's Grow Tomatoes. LC 80-84563. (Illus.). 150p. 1981. pap. 7.95 (ISBN 0-88290-176-1, 4027). Horizon Utah.

Rast, A. T. Variability of Tobacco Mosaic Virus in Relation to Control of Tomato Mosaic in Glasshouse Tomato Crops by Resistance Breeding & Cross Protection. (Agricultural Research Reports: No. 834). (Illus.). 80p. 1975. pap. 14.00 (ISBN 9-0220-0559-3, PDC99, PUDOC). Unipub.

Recommended International Standard for Tomato Juice Preserved Exclusively by Physical Means. 3rd ed. (CAC-RS Ser.: No. 49-1971). 17p. 1974. pap. 4.50 (ISBN 92-5-101788-3, F590, FAO). Unipub.

Turkensteen, L. J. Partial Resistance of Tomatoes Against Phytophthora Infestans, the Late Blight Fungus. new ed. (Illus.). 88p. 1974. pap. 16.00 (ISBN 90-220-0497-X, PDC112, PUDOC). Unipub.

Villareal, Ruben L. Tomatoes in the Tropics. (IADS Development-Oriented Ser.). 200p. 1980. lib. bdg. 22.00x (ISBN 0-89158-989-9). Westview.

TOMOGRAPHY

Archer, Carol R. Atlas of Computed Tomography of the Larynx. (Illus.). 200p. 1985. 27.50 (ISBN 0-87527-240-1). Green.

Baert, A. L. Atlas of Computer Tomography: Volume Two, Abdominal Computer Tomography. (Illus.). 210p. 1980. 130.00 (ISBN 0-387-10093-8). Springer-Verlag.

Bradac, G. B. & Oberson, R. Angiography & Computed Tomography in Cerebroarterial Occlusive Diseases. (Illus.). 290p. 1983. 70.00 (ISBN 0-387-11453-X). Springer-Verlag.

Caille, J. M. & Salomon, G., eds. Computerized Tomography: Proceedings. (Illus.). 310p. 1980. pap. 54.00 (ISBN 0-387-09808-9). Springer Verlag.

Carter, Barbara L., ed. Computed Tomography of the Head & Neck. (Contemporary Issues in Computed Tomography Ser.: Vol. 5). (Illus.). 344p. 1985. text ed. 44.50 (ISBN 0-443-08380-0). Churchill.

Chynn, K. Y. & Finby, N. Manual of Cranial Computerized Tomography. (Illus.). vi, 106p. 1982. 84.25 (ISBN 3-8055-3432-9). S Karger.

Claussen, C. & Lochner, B. Dynamic Computed Tomography. Dougherty, F. C., tr. from Ger. (Illus.). 175p. 1985. 21.00 (ISBN 0-387-13435-2). Springer-Verlag.

De Groot, J. Correlative Neuroanatomy of Computed Tomography & Magnetic Resonance Imaging. LC 83-22175. (Illus.). 248p. 1984. text ed. 45.00 (ISBN 0-8121-0917-1). Lea & Febiger.

Ell, P. J. & Holman, B. L., eds. Computed Emission Tomography. (Illus.). 1982. 85.00x (ISBN 0-19-261347-2). Oxford U Pr.

Ell, Peter J., et al. Atlas of Computerized Emission Tomography. (Illus.). 288p. 1980. text ed. 115.00x (ISBN 0-443-02228-3). Churchill.

Esser, Peter D., ed. Emission Computed Tomography: Current Trends. LC 83-6853. (Illus.). 320p. (Orig.). 1983. pap. text ed. 29.50 (ISBN 0-932004-16-4). Soc Nuclear Med.

Felix, R. E., et al, eds. Contrast Media in Computed Tomography. (International Congress Ser.: No. 561). 330p. 1981. 55.50 (ISBN 0-444-90225-2, Excerpta Medica). Elsevier.

Gademann, G. NMR-Tomography of the Normal Brain. (Illus.). 110p. 1984. 36.50 (ISBN 0-387-13233-3). Springer-Verlag.

Glenn, William V., Jr., et al. Multiplanar CT Of The Spine. (Illus.). 544p. 1984. text ed. 125.00 (ISBN 0-8391-1910-0, 20230). Univ Park.

Godwin, David J., et al. Computed Tomography of the Chest. (Illus.). 492p. 1984. text ed. 65.00 (ISBN 0-397-50591-4, 65-07560, Lippincott Medical). Lippincott.

Gonzalez, Carlos F., et al. Computed Brain & Orbital Tomography: Technique & Interpretation. LC 76-28530. (Diagnostic & Therapeutic Radiology Ser.). 276p. 1976. 70.00x (ISBN 0-471-01692-6, Pub. by Wiley-Med). Wiley.

Haaga, John R. & Alfidi, Ralph J., eds. Computed Tomography of the Whole Body, 2 vols. LC 82-22868. (Illus.). 1069p. 1983. text ed. 125.00 (ISBN 0-8016-2047-3). Mosby.

Hanafee, William & Mancuso, Anthony. Introductory Workbook for CT of the Head & Neck. (Illus.). 217p. 1984. lib. bdg. 38.00 (ISBN 0-683-03873-7). Williams & Wilkins.

Haughton, Victor M., ed. Computed Tomography of the Spine. (Contemporary Issues in Computed Tomography Ser.: No. 2). (Illus.). 221p. 1983. text ed. 35.00 (ISBN 0-317-19657-X). Churchill.

Heiss, W. D. & Phelps, M. F., eds. Positron Emission Tomography of the Brain. (Illus.). 244p. 1983. 54.00 (ISBN 0-387-12130-7). Springer-Verlag.

Heiss, W. D., et al. Atlas der Positonen-Emissions-Tomographie de Gehirns- Atlas of Position Emission Tomography of the Brain. (Illus.). 145p. 1985. 52.00 (ISBN 0-387-15636-4). Springer Verlag.

Hendee, William R. The Physical Principles of Computed Tomography. 1983. 35.00 (ISBN 0-316-35594-1). Little.

Herman, G. T. & Natterer, F., eds. Mathematical Aspects of Computerized Tomography: Proceedings. (Lecture Notes in Medical Information Ser.: Vol. 8). 309p. 1981. pap. 28.50 (ISBN 0-387-10277-9). Springer-Verlag.

Higgins, Charles B. & Carlsson, Erik, eds. C.T. of the Heart & Great Vessels: Experimental Evaluation & Clinical Application. LC 82-71767. (Illus.). 416p. 1982. 68.00 (ISBN 0-87993-180-9). Futura Pub.

Jacobs, Lawrence, et al. Computerized Tomography of the Orbit & Sella Turcica. 376p. 1980. text ed. 108.00 (ISBN 0-685-95340-8). Raven.

Jeanmart, L., et al. Atlas of Pathological Computer Tomography: Computer Tomography of Neck, Chest, Spine, & Limbs, Vol. 3. (Illus.). 210p. 1983. 105.00 (ISBN 0-387-11439-4). Springer-Verlag.

Kak, A. C. & Slaney, M. Tomographic Imaging with Non-Diffracting & Diffracting Sources. 200p. 1985. avail. (ISBN 0-87942-198-3). IEEE.

--Tomographic Imaging with Non-Diffracting & Diffracting Sources. 200p. 1985. write for info. (ISBN 0-87942-198-3). Inst Electrical.

Katz, M. B. Questions of Uniqueness & Resolution in Reconstruction of 2-D & 3-D Objects from Their Projections. (Lecture Notes in Biomathematics: Vol. 26). 1978. pap. 15.00 (ISBN 0-387-09087-8). Springer-Verlag.

Knapp, W. & Vyska, K., eds. Current Topics in Tumor Cell Physiology & Diagnostic Implications for Positron Emission Tomography. (Illus.). 115p. 1984. pap. 23.00 (ISBN 0-387-13007-1). Springer-Verlag.

Kreel, L. Computer Tomography with the General Purpose Scanner. 2nd ed. 1977. incl. 240 slides 532.00 (ISBN 9-0219-3043-9, Excerpta Medica). Elsevier.

Kricun, Robert & Kricun, Morrie. Computerized Tomography of the Spine: Diagnostic Exercises. (Illus.). 1985. text ed. 35.00 (ISBN 0-8391-1986-0, 20869). Univ Park.

Kuhns. Atlas of Computed Tomography Variants. 1983. 69.95 (ISBN 0-8151-5210-8). Year Bk Med.

Lanksch, W., et al. Computed Tomography in Head Injuries. Dougherty, F. C., tr. from Ger. (Illus.). 1979. 51.00 (ISBN 0-387-09634-5). Springer-Verlag.

Lee, Joseph K. T., et al, eds. Computed Body Tomography. (Illus.). 608p. 1983. text ed. 89.50 (ISBN 0-89004-703-0). Raven.

Lee, Seungho H. & Rao, Krishna C. Cranial Computed Tomography. (Illus.). 704p. 1982. text ed. 95.00 (ISBN 0-07-037399-X). McGraw.

Littleton, Jesse T. & Durizch, Mary L., eds. Sectional Imaging Methods: A Comparison. (Illus.). 1983. text ed. 65.00 (ISBN 0-8391-1783-3, 18597). Univ Park.

Mancuso, Anthony & Hanafee, William. Computed Tomography & Magnetic Resonance Imaging of the Head & Neck. 2nd ed. 436p. 1985. 84.75 (ISBN 0-683-05476-7). Williams & Wilkins.

Marshall, Christopher. Physical Basis of Computerized Tomography. 171p. 1982. 37.50 (ISBN 0-87527-314-9). Green.

Morgan, Carlisle L. & Phil, M. Basic Principles of Computed Tomography. (Illus.). 356p. 1983. text ed. 59.50 (ISBN 0-8391-1705-1, 13331). Univ Park.

Moss, Albert & Goldberg, Henry, eds. Computed Tomography, Ultrasound & X-Ray: An Integrated Approach. LC 76-1666. 1980. 85.00 (ISBN 0-12-788525-0). Acad Pr.

Partain, Leon C., ed. Nuclear Magnetic Resonance & Correlative Imaging Modalities. 312p. (Orig.). 1984. text ed. 49.50 (ISBN 0-932004-17-2). Soc Nuclear Med.

Pfurtscheller, G., et al, eds. Brain Ischemia: Quantitative EEG & Imaging Techniques. (Progress in Brain Research Ser.: Vol. 62). 1985. 87.00 (ISBN 0-444-80582-6). Elsevier.

Post, M. J. Computed Tomography of the Spine. 967p. 1983. lib. bdg. 127.00 (ISBN 0-683-06951-9). Williams & Wilkins.

Price, Ronald R. & Croft, Barbara Y., eds. Single Photon Emission Computed Tomography & Other Selected Computer Topics. LC 80-52817. (Illus.). 252p. 1980. pap. 29.50 (ISBN 0-932004-06-7). Soc Nuclear Med.

Reivich, Martin. Positron Emission Tomography. LC 85-6798. 492p. 1985. 79.50 (ISBN 0-8451-0244-3). A R Liss.

Ritman, Erik L., et al. Imaging Physiological Functions: Experience with the Dynamic Spatial Reconstructor. LC 84-18242. 318p. 1985. 37.95 (ISBN 0-03-069352-7). Praeger.

Roth, K. NMR Tomography & Spectroscopy in Medicine: An Introduction. Telger, T. C., tr. from German. (Illus.). 130p. 1984. pap. 18.00 (ISBN 0-387-13442-5). Springer-Verlag.

Salamon, G. & Huang, Y. P. Computed Tomography of the Brain Atlas of Normal Anatomy. (Illus.). 160p. 1980. 129.00 (ISBN 0-387-08825-3). Springer-Verlag.

Schnitzlein, H. Norman, et al. Computed Tomography of the Head & Spine: A Photographic Atlas of CT, Gross & Microscopic Anatomy. LC 82-13515. (Illus.). 126p. 1982. text ed. 65.00 (ISBN 0-8067-1771-8). Urban & S.

Siegelman, Stanley S., ed. Computed Tomography of the Pancreas. (Contemporary Issues in Computed Tomography Ser.: No. 1). (Illus.). 257p. 1983. text ed. 39.00 (ISBN 0-443-08266-9). Churchill.

Siegelman, Stanley S., et al, eds. Computed Tomography of the Kidneys & Adrenals. (Contemporary Issues in Computed Tomography Ser.: Vol. 3). (Illus.). 287p. 1984. text ed. 39.50 (ISBN 0-443-08267-7). Churchill.

Sorgen, Richard A & Russo, Robert D., Jr. Abdominal C.T. For Resident & Clinician. 108p. 1982. 39.50 (ISBN 0-87527-289-4). Green.

Takahashi, S., ed. Illustrated Computer Tomography: A Practical Guide to CT Interpretations. (Illus.). 350p. 1983. 85.00 (ISBN 0-387-11432-7). Springer-Verlag.

Valk, J. Computed Tomography & Cerebral Infarctions. 190p. 1980. 42.50 (ISBN 0-89004-646-8). Raven.

Wackenheim, A., et al. Atlas of Pathological Computer Tomography, Vol. 1: Cranio-Cerebral Computed Tomography. (Illus.). 150p. 1980. Set. 130.00 (ISBN 0-387-09879-8). Springer-Verlag.

Walsh, James W., ed. Computed Tomography of the Pelvis. (Contemporary Issues in Computed Tomography Ser.: Vol. 6). (Illus.). 267p. 1985. text ed. 39.00 (ISBN 0-443-08386-X). Churchill.

Wegener, O. H. Whole Body Computerized Tomography. (Illus.). 396p. 1983. 35.00 (ISBN 3-8055-2773-X). S Karger.

Weissberg, Leon, et al. Cerebral Computed Tomography. 2nd ed. (Illus.). 368p. 1984. 49.00 (ISBN 0-7216-1077-3). Saunders.

TOOL AND DIE INDUSTRY

Arnett, Harold E. & Smith, Donald N. The Tool & Die Industry: Problems & Prospects. (Michigan Business Reports, New Ser.: No. 1). (Illus.). 109p. (Orig.). 1975. pap. 6.00 (ISBN 0-87712-173-7). U Mich Busn Div Res.

Davis, John E. An Introduction to Tool Marks, Firearms & the Striagraph. 302p. 1958. photocopy ed. 25.50x (ISBN 0-398-00402-1). C C Thomas.

Fields, Carl. Exploring Careers in Tool & Die Making. 1985. 8.97 (ISBN 0-8239-0633-7). Rosen Group.

International Labour Office Staff. Tool & Die Making: Equipment Planning Guide for Vocational & Technical Training & Education Programmes, No. 2. 2nd ed. 215p. (Orig.). 1984. pap. 22.80 (ISBN 92-2-101891-1). Intl Labour Office.

Antonelli, P. L., et al. Concordance-Homotopy Groups of Geometric Automorphism Groups. LC 73-171479. (Lecture Notes in Mathematics: Vol. 215). 1971. pap. 11.00 (ISBN 0-387-05560-6). Springer-Verlag.

Azencott, R. & Wilson, E. N. Homogenous Manifolds with Negative Curvature II. LC 76-44403. (Memoirs: No. 178). 102p. 1976. pap. 13.00 (ISBN 0-8218-2178-4, MEMO178). Am Math.

Berglund, J. F. & Hoffmann, K. H. Compact Semitopological Semigroups & Weakly Almost Periodic Functions. (Lecture Notes in Mathematics: Vol. 42). (Orig.). 1967. pap. 10.70 (ISBN 0-387-03913-9). Springer-Verlag.

Berglund, J. F., et al. A Compact Right Topological Semigroups & Generalizations of Almost Periodicity. (Lecture Notes in Mathematics: Vol. 663). (Illus.). 1978. pap. 17.00 (ISBN 0-387-08919-5). Springer-Verlag.

Boas, R. P. Collected Works of Hidehiko Yamabe. (Notes on Mathematics & Its Applications Ser.). 154p. 1967. 38.50 (ISBN 0-677-00610-1). Gordon.

Burckel, R. B. Weakly Almost Periodic Functions on Semi-Groups. (Notes on Mathematics & Its Applications Ser.). 128p. 1970. 44.25 (ISBN 0-677-02170-4). Gordon.

Carruth & Hildebrandt. The Theory of Topological Semigroups. (Monographs & Textbooks in Pure & Applied Mathematics). 408p. 1983. 45.00 (ISBN 0-8247-1795-3). Dekker.

Dunkl, C. F. & Ramirez, D. E. Representations of Communicative Semitopological Semigroups. (Lecture Notes in Mathematics Ser.: Vol. 435). vi, 181p. 1975. pap. 14.00 (ISBN 0-387-07132-6). Springer-Verlag.

Higgins, P. J. An Introduction to Topological Groups. LC 74-82222. (London Mathematical Society Lecture Note Ser.: No. 15). 100p. 1974. 15.95 (ISBN 0-521-20527-1). Cambridge U Pr.

Hofmann, Karl H. & Mostert, Paul S. Splitting in Topological Groups. LC 52-42839. (Memoirs: No. 43). 82p. 1972. pap. 12.00 (ISBN 0-8218-1243-2, MEMO-43). Am Math.

Hsiang, W. Y. Cohomology Theory of Topological Transformation Groups. (Ergebnisse der Mathematik und Ihrer Grenzgebiete Ser.: Vol. 85). 190p. 1975. 36.00 (ISBN 0-387-07100-8). Springer-Verlag.

Husain, Taqdir. Introduction to Topological Groups. LC 80-23942. 232p. 1981. Repr. of 1966 ed. lib. bdg. 14.50 (ISBN 0-89874-193-9). Krieger.

Johnson, B. E. Cohomology in Banach Algebras. LC 72-4561. (Memoirs Ser.: No. 127). 96p. 1972. pap. 10.00 (ISBN 0-8218-1827-9, MEMO-127). Am Math.

Montgomery, Deane & Zippin, Leo. Topological Transformation Groups. LC 74-265. 302p. 1974. Repr. of 1955 ed. 18.00 (ISBN 0-88275-169-7). Krieger.

Mukherjea, A. & Tserpes, N. A. Measures on Topological Semi-Groups: Convolution Products & Random Walks. (Lecture Notes in Mathematics: Vol. 547). 1976. 17.00 (ISBN 0-387-07987-4). Springer-Verlag.

Pontryagin, Lev S. Topological Groups. 2nd ed. (Russian Monographs). 560p. 1966. 112.25 (ISBN 0-677-20390-X). Gordon.

Shershin, Anthony C. Introduction to Topological Semigroups. LC 79-23432. pap. 40.80 (ISBN 0-317-08690-1, 2022609). Bks Demand UMI.

TOPOLOGICAL IMBEDDINGS

Besov, Oleg V., et al. Integral Representations of Functions & Imbedding Theorems, 2 vols. (Scripta Series in Mathematics). 1979. Vol. 1, 345p. 19.95x ea. (ISBN 0-470-26540-X). Vol. 2, 311p (ISBN 0-470-26593-0). Halsted Pr.

Glauert, A. Fixation, Dehydration & Embedding of Biological Specimens. (Practical Methods in Electron Microscopy Ser.: Vol. 3, No. 1). 1975. pap. 18.00 (ISBN 0-444-10666-9, Biomedical Pr). Elsevier.

Nadler, Sam B., Jr. & Quinn, J. Embeddability & Structure Properties of Real Curves. LC 72-4343. (Memoirs: No. 125). 74p. 1972. pap. 10.00 (ISBN 0-8218-1825-2, MEMO-125). Am Math.

Rushing, T. Benny. Topological Embeddings. (Pure & Applied Mathematics Ser., Vol. 52). 1973. 75.00 (ISBN 0-12-603550-4). Acad Pr.

Steklov Institute of Mathematics, Academy of Sciences, U S S R. Topological Imbeddings in Euclidean Space: Proceedings. Keldys, L. V., ed. (Proceedings of the Steklov Institute of Mathematics: No. 81). 1968. 58.00 (ISBN 0-8218-1881-3, STEKLO-81). Am Math.

Wells, J. H. & Williams, L. R. Embeddings & Extensions in Analysis. LC 74-31234. (Ergebnisse der Mathematik und Ihrer Grenzgebiete Ser.: Vol. 84). 125p. 1975. text ed. 23.00 (ISBN 0-387-07067-2). Springer-Verlag.

Whallon, Robert & Brown, James A., eds. Essays on Archaeological Typology. LC 82-4213. (Kampsville Seminars in Archeology Ser.). (Illus.). 216p. 1982. 15.00 (ISBN 0-942118-14-6, CC72.7.K35); pap. 9.00 (ISBN 0-942118-15-4). Ctr Amer Arche.

TOPOLOGICAL VECTOR SPACES

see Linear Topological Spaces

TOPOLOGY

see also Algebraic Topology; Algebras, Linear; Banach Spaces; Categories (Mathematics); Cluster Set Theory; Combinatorial Topology; Differential Topology; Distance Geometry; Games of Strategy (Mathematics); Geometry, Algebraic; Graph Theory; Homotopy Theory; Knot Theory; Lattice Theory; Linear Topological Spaces; Metric Spaces; Moment Spaces; Polytopes; Topological Dynamics; Transformation Groups; Uniform Spaces

Abdel-Nour, Jabbour. Arabe-Francais Dictionnaire. 1983. 40.00 (ISBN 0-86685-334-0). Intl Bk Ctr.

Abramov, L. M., et al. Fifteen Papers on Topology & Logic. LC 51-5559. (Translations Ser.: No. 2, Vol. 39). 1964. 25.00 (ISBN 0-8218-1739-6, TRANS 2-39). Am Math.

--Fourteen Papers on Logic, Algebra, Complex Variables & Topology. LC 51-5559. (Translations Ser.: No. 2, Vol. 48). 1965. 32.00 (ISBN 0-8218-1748-5, TRANS 2-48). Am Math.

Aleksandrov, A. D., et al. Eleven Papers on Topology, Function Theory, & Differential Equations. LC 51-5559. (Translations Ser.: No. 2, Vol. 1). 1955. 26.00 (ISBN 0-8218-1701-9, TRANS 2-1). Am Math.

--Nine Papers on Topology, Lie Groups, & Differential Equations. LC 51-5559. (Translations Ser.: No. 2, Vol. 21). 1962. 33.00 (ISBN 0-8218-1721-3, TRANS 2-21). Am Math.

Aleksandrov, P. S., et al. Ten Papers on Topology. LC 51-5559. (Translatons Ser.: No. 2, Vol. 30). 1963. 30.00 (ISBN 0-8218-1730-2, TRANS 2-30). Am Math.

Aleksandrov, Pavel S. Combinatorial Topology, 3 vols. Incl. Vol. 1. Introduction, Complexes, Coverings, Dimension. 1956 (ISBN 0-910670-01-3); Vol. 2. The Betti Groups. 1957 (ISBN 0-910670-02-1); Vol. 3. Homological Manifolds, Duality, Classification & Fixed Point Theorems. 1960 (ISBN 0-910670-03-X). LC 56-13930. (Illus.). 15.00x ea. Graylock.

Alexandroff, Paul. Elementary Concepts of Topology. Farley, Alan E., tr. 1961. pap. 2.50 (ISBN 0-486-60747-X). Dover.

Alexandroff, Paul S. & Hopf, H. Topologie. LC 65-21833. (Ger.). 17.50 (ISBN 0-8284-0197-7). Chelsea Pub.

Alo, R. A. & Shapiro, H. L. Normal Topological Spaces. LC 73-79304. (Tracts in Mathematics Ser.: No. 65). (Illus.). 250p. 1974. 49.50 (ISBN 0-521-20271-X). Cambridge U Pr.

Alo, R. A., et al, eds. TOPO 72: General Topology & Its Applications. LC 74-390. (Lecture Notes in Mathematics: Vol. 378). xiv, 651p. 1974. pap. 31.00 (ISBN 0-387-06741-8). Springer-Verlag.

Ancikov, A. M., et al. Seventeen Papers on Topology & Differential Geometry. LC 51-5559. (Translations Ser.: No. 2, Vol. 92). 1970. 35.00 (ISBN 0-8218-1792-2, TRANS 2-92). Am Math.

Anderson, G. A. Surgery with Coefficients. (Lecture Notes in Mathematics: Vol. 591). 1977. 13.00 (ISBN 3-540-08250-6). Springer-Verlag.

Anderson, R. D., ed. Symposium on Infinite Dimensional Topology. LC 69-17445. (Annals of Mathematic Studies, 69). 230p. 1972. text ed. 29.00x (ISBN 0-691-08087-9). Princeton U Pr.

Andrunakievic, V. A., et al. Twelve Papers on Topology, Algebra & Number Theory. LC 51-5559. (Translations Ser.: No. 2, Vol. 52). 1966. 36.00 (ISBN 0-8218-1752-3, TRANS 2-52). Am Math.

Antonovskii, M. Ja, et al. Topological Semifields & Their Applications to General Topology. LC 77-11046. (Translation Ser. No 2: Vol. 106). 142p. 1979. pap. 23.00 (ISBN 0-8218-3056-2, TRAN 2/106). Am Math.

Arazy, J. & Friedman, Y. Contractive Projections in C Sub 1 & C to Infinity. LC 77-28610. (Memoirs Ser: No. 200). 165p. 1978. pap. 14.00 (ISBN 0-8218-2200-4, MEMO-200). Am Math.

Arhangelsky, A. V., et al. Eleven Papers on Topology. LC 51-5559. (Translations Ser.: No. 2, Vol. 78). 1968. 33.00 (ISBN 0-8218-1778-7, TRANS 2-78). Am Math.

Arkangeliskii, A. V. & Ponomarev, V. I. Fundamentals of General Topology. 1984. lib. bdg. 69.00 (ISBN 90-277-1355-3, Pub. by Reidel Holland). Kluwer Academic.

Armstrong, M. A. Basic Topology. Rev. ed. (Undergraduate Texts in Mathematics). (Illus.). 250p. 1983. Repr. of 1983 ed. 22.00 (ISBN 0-387-90839-0). Springer-Verlag.

Aubin, Jean-Pierre. Applied Abstract Analysis. LC 77-2382. (Pure & Applied Mathematics Ser.). 263p. 1977. 47.50x (ISBN 0-471-02146-6, Pub. by Wiley-Interscience). Wiley.

Auslander, Louis & Markus, Lawrence. Flat Lorentz Three Manifolds. LC 52-42839. (Memoirs: No. 30). 60p. 1959. pap. 11.00 (ISBN 0-8218-1230-0, MEMO-30). Am Math.

Ball, Joseph. Factorization & Model Theory for Contraction Operators with Unitary Part. LC 77-25161. (Memoirs Ser.: No. 198). 68p. 1978. pap. 12.00 (ISBN 0-8218-2198-9, MEMO-198). Am Math.

Banaschewski, B., ed. Categorical Aspects of Topology & Analysis, Ottawa 1981: Proceedings. (Lecture Notes in Mathematics Ser.: Vol. 915). 385p. 1982. pap. 22.00 (ISBN 0-387-11211-1). Springer-Verlag.

Baranovic, T. M., et al. Eleven Papers on Topology & Algebra. LC 51-5559. (Translations Ser.: No. 2, Vol. 55). 1966. 37.00 (ISBN 0-8218-1755-8, TRANS 2-55). Am Math.

Bierberbach, L. Theorie der Geometrishen Konstruktionen. (Mathematische Rehihe Ser.: No. 13). (Ger., Illus.). 162p. 1952. 23.95x (ISBN 0-8176-0030-2). Birkhauser.

Bing, R. H. The Geometric Topology of Three Manifolds. LC 83-14962. (Colloquium Publications Ser.: Vol. 40). 240p. 1983. 54.00 (ISBN 0-8218-1040-5). Am Math.

Bing, R. H., et al, eds. Continua, Decompositions, Manifolds. (Illus.). 279p. 1983. text ed. 35.00x (ISBN 0-292-78061-3). U of Tex Pr.

Blackett, D. W. Elementary Topology: A Combinatorial & Algebraic Approach. 1982. 22.00 (ISBN 0-12-103060-1). Acad Pr.

Blaschke, W. Einfuehrung in die Goemetrie der Waben. (Elemente der Mathematik Vom Hoeheren Standpunkt Aus: Vol. 4). (Ger.). 108p. 1955. pap. 16.95x (ISBN 0-8176-0033-7). Birkhauser.

--Projektive Geometrie. 3rd ed. (Mathematische Reihe Ser.: No. 17). (Illus.). 197p. 1954. 23.95x (ISBN 0-8176-0032-9). Birkhauser.

Bokstein, M. F., et al. Four Papers on Topology. LC 51-5559. (Translations Ser.: No. 2, Vol. 11). 1964. Repr. of 1959 ed. 32.00 (ISBN 0-8218-1711-6, TRANS 2-11). Am Math.

Boltyanskii, V. G., et al. Topology & Topological Algebra. (Translations Ser.: No. 1, Vol. 8). 1962. 24.00 (ISBN 0-8218-1608-X, TRANS 1-8). Am Math.

Bonnesen, T. & Fenchel, W. Theorie der Konvexen Koerper. LC 49-29452. (Ger). 6.95 (ISBN 0-8284-0054-7). Chelsea Pub.

Booss, B. & Bleecker, D. D. Topology & Analysis. Mader, A., tr. from Ger. (Universitext Ser.). (Illus.). xvi, 451p. 1985. 34.00 (ISBN 0-387-96112-7). Springer-Verlag.

Bronstein, I. U., et al. Eleven Papers on Logic, Algebra, Analysis & Topology. LC 51-5559. (Translations, Ser.: No. 2, Vol. 97). 1970. 33.00 (ISBN 0-8218-1797-3, TRANS 2-97). Am Math.

Brouwer, L. E. & Freudenthal, H. L. E. J. Brouwer, Collected Works, Vol. 2: Geometry, Analysis, Topology & Mechanics. 706p. 1976. 127.75 (ISBN 0-7204-2805-X, North-Holland). Elsevier.

Brown, R. & Thickstun, T. L., eds. Low-Dimensional Topology: Proceedings of the Conference on Topology in Low Dimension, Bangor, 1979. LC 81-2664. (London Mathematical Society Lecture Notes Ser.: No. 48). 300p. 1982. pap. 32.50 (ISBN 0-521-28146-6). Cambridge U Pr.

Burckhardt, J. J. Die Bewegungsgruppen der Kristallographie. rev. 2nd ed. (Mineralogisch-Geotechnische Reihe Ser.: No. 2). (Ger.). 209p. 1966. 44.95x (ISBN 0-8176-0058-2). Birkhauser.

Butzer, P. L., et al, eds. Linear Operators & Approximation, 2 vols. (International Series of Numerical Mathematics: Nos. 20 & 25). 1973. Vol. 1, 506p. 71.95x (ISBN 0-8176-0590-8); Vol. 2, 608p.,1975. 69.95x (ISBN 0-8176-0760-9). Birkhauser.

Cairns, Stewart S. Introductory Topology. LC 68-8995. (Illus.). Repr. of 1968 ed. 48.70 (ISBN 0-8357-9917-4, 2012450). Bks Demand UMI.

Calenko, M. S., et al. Twelve Papers on Algebra, Number Theory & Topology. LC 80-20715. (Translations Ser.: No. 2, Vol. 58). 1966. 34.00 (ISBN 0-8218-1758-2, TRANS 2-58). Am Math.

Cantrell, James C. Geometric Topology. LC 78-31631. 1979. 67.50 (ISBN 0-12-158860-2). Acad Pr.

Carin, V. S., et al. Nine Papers on Foundations, Algebra, Topology, Functions of a Complex Variable. (Translations Ser.: No. 2, Vol. 15). 1960. 29.00 (ISBN 0-8218-1715-9, TRANS 2-15). Am Math.

Carruth. The Theory of Topological Semigroups. (Pure & Applied Mathematics Ser.). 183p. 1986. price not set (ISBN 0-8247-7320-9). Dekker.

Cartan, H. & Eilenberg, S. Homological Algebra. (Mathematical Ser.: Vol. 19). 1956. 46.00 (ISBN 0-691-07977-3). Princeton U Pr.

Cech, E. Point Sets. 1969. 65.00 (ISBN 0-12-164850-8). Acad Pr.

Ceitin, G. S., et al. Fourteen Papers on Logic, Geometry, Topology, & Algebra. LC 72-2350. (Translations Ser.: No. 2, Vol. 100). 1972. 48.00 (ISBN 0-8218-3050-3, TRANS 2-100). Am Math.

Cernikov, S. N., et al. Twelve Papers on Algebra, Algebraic Geometry & Topology. LC 51-5559. (Translations Ser.: No. 2, Vol. 84). 1969. 36.00 (ISBN 0-8218-1784-1, TRANS 2-84). Am Math.

Chapman, Thomas A. Approximation Results in Topological Manifolds. LC 81-12791. (Memoirs of the American Mathematical Society: No. 251). 65p. 1981. pap. 9.00 (ISBN 0-8218-2251-9). Am Math.

Chinn, W. G. & Steenrod, N. E. First Concepts of Topology. LC 66-20367. (New Mathematical Library: No. 18). 160p. 1975. pap. 10.00 (ISBN 0-88385-618-2). Math Assn.

Choquet, Gustav. Topology. (Pure & Applied Mathematics Ser.: Vol. 19). 1966. 65.00 (ISBN 0-12-173450-1). Acad Pr.

Christensen, J. P. Topology & Borel Structure. (Mathematical Studies: Vol. 10). 133p. 1974. pap. 42.75 (ISBN 0-444-10608-1, North-Holland). Elsevier.

Christenson, Charles & Voxman, William. Aspects of Topology. (Textbooks & Monographs in Pure & Applied Maths: Vol.39). 1977. 29.75 (ISBN 0-8247-6331-9). Dekker.

Conner, P. E. Notes on the Witt Classification of Hermitian Innerproduct Spaces over a Ring of Algebraic Integers. 157p. 1979. text ed. 20.00x (ISBN 0-292-75516-3). U of Tex Pr.

Coxeter, H. S. Unvergangliche Geometrie. (Science & Civilization Ser.: No. 17). (Ger., Illus.). 552p. 1963. 53.35x (ISBN 0-8176-0071-X). Birkhauser.

Cronin, Jane. Fixed Points & Topological Degree in Nonlinear Analysis. LC 63-21550. (Mathematical Surveys Ser.: Vol. 11). 198p. 1982. pap. 30.00 (ISBN 0-8218-1511-3, SURV-11). Am Math.

Csaszar, A. General Topology. Cohn, P. M., ed. 1978. 60.00 (ISBN 0-9960018-2-4, Pub. by A Hilger England). Heyden.

--Topology, 2 vols. (Colloquia Mathematica Societatis Janos Bolyai: Vol. 23). 1260p. 1980. Set. 149.00 (ISBN 0-444-85406-1, North-Holland). Elsevier.

Davis, M. Multiaxial Actions on Manifolds. LC 78-3765. (Lecture Notes in Mathematics: Vol. 643). 1978. pap. 14.00 (ISBN 0-387-08667-6). Springer-Verlag.

Dixmier, J. General Topology. Berberian, S. K., tr. from Fr. (Undergraduate Texts in Mathematics Ser.). 125p. 1984. 19.80 (ISBN 0-387-90972-9). Springer Verlag.

Dugundji, James. Topology. 1966. text ed. 45.72 (ISBN 0-205-00271-4, 5602718). Allyn.

Dynkin, E. B., et al. Eleven Papers on Analysis, Probability & Topology. LC 51-5559. (Translations, Ser.: No. 2, Vol. 12). 1966. Repr. of 1959 ed. 27.00 (ISBN 0-8218-1712-4, TRANS 2-12). Am Math.

Ehrenpreis, Leon. Theory of Distributions for Locally Compact Spaces. LC 52-42839. (Memoirs: No. 21). 80p. 1982. pap. 14.00 (ISBN 0-8218-1221-1, MEMO-21). Am Math.

Ehrhart, E. Polynomes Arithmetiques et Methode des Polyedres en Combinatoire. (International Series of Numerical Mathematics: No. 35). (Ger.). 169p. 1977. pap. 27.95x (ISBN 0-8176-0872-9). Birkhauser.

Engelking, R. Dimension Theory. (Mathematical Library Ser.: Vol. 19). 314p. 1979. 64.00 (ISBN 0-444-85176-3, North Holland). Elsevier.

Faddeev, L. D. & Mal'Cev, A. A., eds. Topology: General & Algebraic Topology & Applications, Proceedings of the International Topological Conference Held in Leningrad, August 23-27, 1982. (Lecture Notes in Mathematics Ser.: Vol. 1060). vi, 389p. 1984. 21.00 (ISBN 0-387-13337-2). Springer-Verlag.

Fenn, Roger, ed. Low-Dimensional Topology. (London Mathematical Society Lecture Note Ser.: No. 95). 350p. 1985. pap. 27.95 (ISBN 0-521-26982-2). Cambridge U Pr.

Fenn, Roger A. Techniques of Geometric Topology. LC 81-18189. (London Mathematical Society Lecture Note Ser.: No. 57). 208p. 1983. pap. 27.95 (ISBN 0-521-28472-4). Cambridge U Pr.

Firby, P. A. & Gardiner, C. F. Surface Topology. (Mathematics & its Applications Harwood Ser.). 216p. 1982. 54.95X (ISBN 0-470-27528-6). Halsted Pr.

Flachsmeyer, J., et al, eds. Contributions to Extension Theory of Topological Structures: Proceedings. 1969. 68.00 (ISBN 0-12-258050-8). Acad Pr.

Flegg, H. Graham. From Geometry to Topology. LC 74-78155. 150p. 1974. 19.50x (ISBN 0-8448-0364-2). Crane-Russak Co.

Sutherland, Wilson A. Introduction to Metric & Topological Spaces. (Illus.). 1975. 24.95x (ISBN 0-19-853155-9); pap. 16.95x (ISBN 0-19-853161-3). Oxford U Pr.
Symposium in Pure Mathematics, - Tempe, Ariz., - 1960. Differential Geometry: Proceedings. Allendoerfer, C. B., ed. LC 50-1183. (Proceedings of Symposia in Pure Mathematics: Vol. 3). 1961. 27.00 (ISBN 0-8218-1403-6, PSPUM-3). Am Math.
Symposium on General Topology & Its Relations to Modern Analysis & Algebra - 2nd - Prague - 1967. Proceedings. Novak, J., ed. 1967. 76.00 (ISBN 0-12-522556-3). Acad Pr.
Thomeier, S., ed. Topology & Its Applications. (Lecture Notes in Pure & Applied Mathematics Ser.: Vol. 12). 504p. 1975. 45.00 (ISBN 0-8247-6212-6). Dekker.
Tukey, J. W. Convergence & Uniformity in Topology. (Annals of Math Studies). 1940. 11.00 (ISBN 0-527-02718-9). Kraus Repr.
Verona, A. Stratified Mappings: Structure & Triangulability. (Lecture Notes in Mathematics Ser.: Vol. 1102). ix, 160p. 1984. pap. 12.00 (ISBN 0-387-13898-6). Springer-Verlag.
Virginia Polytechnic Institute & State University, March 22-24, 1973. Topology Conference: Proceedings. Dickman, R. F. & Fletcher, P., eds. (Lecture Notes in Mathematics: Vol. 375). x, 283p. 1974. pap. 17.00 (ISBN 0-387-06684-5). Springer-Verlag.
Von Neumann, John. Continuous Geometry. (Mathematical Ser.: Vol. 25). 1960. 33.00x (ISBN 0-691-07928-5). Princeton U Pr.
White, A., ed. Anomalies, Geometry & Topology: Proceedings of the Symposium on Anomalies, Geometry & Topology. 540p. 1985. 65.00x (ISBN 0-317-27182-2, Pub. by World Sci Singapore). Taylor & Francis.
Whyburn, Gordon T. Analytic Topology. LC 63-21794. (Colloquium Pbns. Ser.: Vol. 28). 280p. 1980. pap. 34.00 (ISBN 0-8218-1028-6, COLL-28). Am Math.
--Topological Analysis. LC 64-12193. (Princeton Mathematical Ser.: Vol. 23). Repr. of 1964 ed. 34.30 (ISBN 0-8357-9515-2, 2015485). Bks Demand UMI.
Wilansky, Albert. Topology for Analysis. LC 81-1616. 1983. Repr. of 1970 ed. 28.50 (ISBN 0-89874-343-5). Krieger.
Wilder, Raymond L. Topology of Manifolds. rev. ed. LC 49-6722. (Colloquium Pbns. Ser.: Vol. 32). 403p. 1979. pap. 45.00 (ISBN 0-8218-1032-4, COLL-32). Am Math.
Wong, Y. C. The Topology of Uniform Convergence on Order-Bounded Sets. (Lecture Notes in Mathematics: Vol. 531). 1976. pap. 13.00 (ISBN 0-387-07800-2). Springer-Verlag.
Young, L. C. On Generalized Surfaces of Finite Topological Types. LC 52-42839. (Memoirs: No. 17). 63p. 1955. pap. 9.00 (ISBN 0-8218-1217-3, MEMO-17). Am Math.
Zaslavsky, Thomas. Facing up to Arrangements: Face-Count Formulas for Partitions of Space by Hyperplanes. (Memoirs: No. 154). 102p. 1975. pap. 11.00 (ISBN 0-8218-1854-6, MEMO-154). Am Math.

TOPS
see Top

TORBUTS
see Flatfishes

TORNADOES
see also Storms

Corliss, William R. Tornadoes, Dark Days, Anomalous Precipitation & Related Weather Phenomena. LC 82-63156. (Catalog of Geophysical Anomalies Ser.). (Illus.). 196p. 1983. 11.95 (ISBN 0-915554-10-0). Sourcebook.
Flight Deck Uses for the HP-41C Series: Vol. 4, Tornado Block Forecasting (Via NWS Facsimile Charts) 50p. 1984. 15.00 (ISBN 0-938880-03-9); 2 magnetic cards incl. MNP Star.
Nalivkin, D. V., ed. Hurricanes, Storms & Tornadoes: Geographic Characteristics & Geological Activity. Bhattacharya, B. B., tr. from Rus. 605p. 1983. lib. bdg. 26.50 (ISBN 90-6191-408-6, Pub. by Balkema RSA). IPS.
Stanford, John. Tornado! Accounts of Tornadoes in Iowa. (Illus.). 1977. pap. 5.95 (ISBN 0-8138-0365-9). Iowa St U Pr.

TORQUE

Bear, W. Forrest & Hoerner, Thomas A. Torque & Torque Wrenches. (Illus.). 24p. 1971. pap. text ed. 2.65x (ISBN 0-913163-05-8, 171). Hobar Pubns.
CES Industries, Inc. Ed-Lab Experiment Manual: CES 307 Torque Synchros. (Illus.). 1981. write for info. (ISBN 0-86711-011-2). CES Industries.
Singer, S. Fred, ed. Torques & Attitude Sensing in Earth Satellites. (Applied Mathematics & Mechanics Ser.: Vol. 7). 1964. 65.00 (ISBN 0-12-646850-8). Acad Pr.

TORREY, JOHN 1796-1873

New York Botanical Garden Library. Catalog of the Manuscript & Archival Collections & Index to the Correspondence of John Torrey. 1973. 68.00 (ISBN 0-8161-1018-2, Hall Library). G K Hall.

TORSION

Analysis of Structural Systems for Torsion. 438p. 1973. pap. 36.25 (ISBN 0-685-85112-5, SP-35) (ISBN 0-685-85113-3). ACI.
Connor, Pierre E. & Floyd, E. E. Torsion in SU-bordism. LC 52-42839. (Memoirs: No. 60). 74p. 1969. pap. 10.00 (ISBN 0-8218-1260-2, MEMO-60). Am Math.
Design Proposals for Shear & Torsion. (PCI Journal Reprints Ser.). 72p. pap. 12.00 (ISBN 0-686-40133-6, JR228). Prestressed Concrete.
Gugenheim, V. K. & May, J. Peter. On the Theory & Applications of Differential Torsion Products. Gugenheim, A. M., tr. LC 74-2164. (Memoirs: No. 142). 73p. 1974. pap. 10.00 (ISBN 0-8218-1842-2, MEMO-142). Am Math.
Kollbrunner, C. F. & Basler, K. Torsion in Structures: An Engineering Approach. Glauser, E. C., tr. 1969. 28.50 (ISBN 0-387-04582-1). Springer-Verlag.
Lambeck, J. Torsion Theories, Additive Semantics & Rings of Quotients. LC 70-148538. (Lecture Notes in Mathematics: Vol. 177). 1971. pap. 11.00 (ISBN 0-387-05340-9). Springer-Verlag.
Nestorides, E. J., ed. Handbook on Torsional Vibration. 1958. 125.00 (ISBN 0-521-04326-3). Cambridge U Pr.

TORTICOLLIS

Jones, Peter G. Torticollis in Infancy & Childhood: Sternomastoid Fibrosis & the Sternomastoid Tumour. (Illus.). 156p. 1968. photocopy ed. 15.50x (ISBN 0-398-00946-5). C C Thomas.

TORTOISES
see Turtles

TOWBOATS
see Tugboats

TOXIC SUBSTANCES
see Poisons

TOXICOLOGY
see also Industrial Toxicology

Aquatic Toxicology & Hazard Assessment (Fourth Conference)- STP 737. 466p. 1981. 43.00 (ISBN 0-8031-0799-4, 04-737000-16). ASTM.
Aquatic Toxicology-STP 667: 2nd Conference. 403p. 1979. 37.75x (ISBN 0-8031-0279-8, 667, 04-667000-16). ASTM.
Aquatic Toxicology-STP 707: 3rd Conference. 417p. 1980. 39.50x (ISBN 0-8031-0280-1, 707, 04-707000-16). ASTM.
Ayres, John C. & Kirschman, John C., eds. Impact of Toxiology on Food Processing. (Institute of Food Technologists Basic Symposia Ser.). (Illus.). 1981. lib. bdg. 55.00 (ISBN 0-87055-387-9). AVI.
Bababunmi, E. A. & Smith, R. L. Toxicology in the Tropics. 280p. 1980. 37.50 (ISBN 0-85066-194-3, Pub. by Taylor & Francis England). J K Burgess.
Balazs, Tibor. Cardiac Toxicology, Vol. I. 240p. 1981. 79.50 (ISBN 0-8493-5555-9). CRC Pr.
--Cardiac Toxicology, Vol. II. 240p. 1981. 79.50 (ISBN 0-8493-5556-7). CRC Pr.
--Cardiac Toxicology, Vol. III. 232p. 1981. 79.50 (ISBN 0-8493-5558-3). CRC Pr.
Bandal, S. Kris, et al, eds. The Pesticide Chemist & Modern Toxicology. LC 81-10790. (ACS Symposium Ser.: No. 160). 1981. 49.95 (ISBN 0-8412-0636-8). Am Chemical.
Barlow, S. M. & Sullivan, F. M., eds. Reproductive Hazards of Industrial Chemicals. 610p. 1982. 75.00 (ISBN 0-12-078960-4). Acad Pr.
Bartosek, Ivan, et al, eds. Animals in Toxicological Research. (Monographs of the Mario Negri Institute for Pharmacological Research). 224p. 1982. text ed. 38.50 (ISBN 0-89004-811-8). Raven.
Baselt, Randall C. Disposition of Toxic Drugs & Chemicals in Man. 2nd ed. LC 81-66543. (Illus.). 800p. 1982. text ed. 49.50 (ISBN 0-931890-08-X). Biomed Pubns.
Bayer, Marc J. Toxicologic Emergencies. LC 83-15758. (Illus.). 352p. 1983. pap. text ed. 19.95 (ISBN 0-89303-188-7). Brady Comm.
Bioassays & Toxicity Testing. 1979. pap. 16.25 (ISBN 0-685-96671-2, F1576, FAO). Unipub.
Brown, S. S. & Davies, D. S. Organ-Directed Toxicity: Symposium on Chemical Indices & Mechanisms of Organ-Directed Toxicity, Barcelona, Spain, 4-7 March 1981. (IUPAC Symposium Ser.). (Illus.). 400p. 1981. 99.00 (ISBN 0-08-026197-3). Pergamon.
Brown, Stanley S. & Sunderman, F. William, Jr., eds. Nickel Toxicology. 1981. 40.00 (ISBN 0-12-137680-X). Acad Pr.
Brusick, David. Principles of Genetic Toxicology. LC 80-16514. 300p. 1980. 29.50x (ISBN 0-306-40414-1, Plenum Pr). Plenum Pub.
Budden, R., et al, eds. The Rat Electrocardiogram in Acute & Chronic Pharmacology & Toxicology: Proceedings of an International Workshop Held in Hanover, July 1980. (Illus.). 208p. 1981. 66.00 (ISBN 0-08-026867-6). Pergamon.
Buikema, Jr. & Cairns, Jr., eds. Aquatic Invertebrate Bioassays- STP 715. 218p. 1980. 24.00 (ISBN 0-8031-0802-8, 04-715000-16). ASTM.
Cairns, John, Jr., ed. Multispecies Toxicity Testing. (Illus.). 288p. 1985. 37.50 (ISBN 0-08-031936-X). Pergamon.
Caldwell, John & Jakoby, William B., eds. Biological Basis of Detoxification. LC 82-18933. (Biochemical Pharmacology & Toxicology). 1983. 59.50 (ISBN 0-12-155060-5). Acad Pr.
Chambers, P. L. & Klinger, W., eds. Further Studies in the Assessment of Toxic Actions: Proceedings. (Archives of Toxicology Supplementum Ser.: No. 4). (Illus.). 507p. 1981. pap. 64.00 (ISBN 0-387-10191-8). Springer-Verlag.
Chambers, P. L., et al, eds. Toxicology in the Use, Misuse, & Abuse of Food, Drugs & Chemicals. (Archives of Toxicology: Suppl. 6). (Illus.). 380p. 1983. pap. 55.00 (ISBN 0-387-12392-X). Springer-Verlag.
Clayton, G. D. & Clayton, F. E. Pattys Industrial Hygiene & Toxicology, 4 vols. 3rd ed. 937p. 1981. 85.00 (ISBN 0-471-08431-X). Wiley.
Cravey, Robert H. & Baselt, Randall C., eds. Introduction to Forensic Toxicology. LC 79-56929. (Illus.). 300p. 1981. text ed. 48.00 (ISBN 0-931890-06-3). Biomed Pubns.
Curry, A. S., ed. & intro. by. Analytical Methods in Human Toxicology, Part 1. (Illus.). 319p. 1985. 59.00 (ISBN 0-89573-416-8). VCH Pubs.
Dean, Jack H., et al, eds. Immunotoxicology & Pharmacology. (Target Organ Toxicology Ser.). 520p. 1985. text ed. 98.00 (ISBN 0-89004-838-X). Raven.
Deichmann, W. B., ed. Toxicology & Occupational Medicine. (Developments in Toxicology & Environmental Science Ser.: Vol. 4). 480p. 1979. 86.00 (ISBN 0-444-00288-X, Biomedical Pr). Elsevier.
De Serres, F. J. & Pero, Ronald W., eds. Individual Susceptibility to Genotoxic Agents in the Human Population. LC 84-11467. (Environmental Science Research Ser.: Vol. 30). 528p. 1984. 69.50x (ISBN 0-306-41679-4, Plenum Pr). Plenum Pub.
Devries, A. & Kochva, E., eds. Toxins of Animal & Plant Origin, 3 vols. LC 71-130967. (Illus.). 1142p. 1973. Set. 212.50 (ISBN 0-677-14710-4); Vol. 1-1971,512. 106.50 (ISBN 0-677-12430-9); Vol. 2-1972,338. 72.75x (ISBN 0-677-12440-6); Vol. 3-1973,292. 68.25x (ISBN 0-677-12450-3). Gordon.
Dinnar, Uri. Cardiovascular Fluid Dynamics. 264p. 1981. 79.00 (ISBN 0-8493-5573-7). CRC Pr.
Dixon, Robert L., ed. Reproductive Toxicology. (Target Organ Toxicology Ser.). 368p. 1985. text ed. 69.50 (ISBN 0-89004-474-0). Raven.
Dortland, R. J. Toxicological Evaluation of Parathion & Azinphosmethyl in Freshwater Model Ecosystems. (Agricultural Research Reports: No. 898). 120p. 1980. pap. 20.75 (ISBN 90-220-0732-4, PDC210, PUDOC). Unipub.
The Dose Makes the Poison: A Plain-Language Guide to Toxicology. LC 83-51229. (Illus.). 224p. (Orig.). 1984. 15.95x (ISBN 0-915241-01-3); pap. 9.95x (ISBN 0-915241-00-5). Vincente Bks.
Dreosti, Ivor E. & Smith, Richard M., eds. Neurobiology of the Trace Elements: Neurotoxicology & Neuropharmacology, Vol. 2. LC 83-8413. (Contemporary Neuroscience Ser.). 320p. 1983. 49.50 (ISBN 0-89603-047-4). Humana.
Drill, Victor A. & Lazar, Paul, eds. Cutaneous Toxicity. (Target Organ Toxicology Ser.). 288p. 1984. text ed. 58.50 (ISBN 0-89004-933-5). Raven.
Duncan, W., ed. Experimental Model Systems in Toxicology & Their Significance in Man. (International Congress Ser.). (Proceedings). 1974. pap. 77.75 (ISBN 0-444-15106-0). Elsevier.
Elliott, H. W., et al, eds. Annual Review of Pharmacology & Toxicology, Vol. 16. LC 61-5649. (Illus.). 1976. text ed. 20.00 (ISBN 0-8243-0416-0). Annual Reviews.
Fawcett, Don W. & Newburne, James W. Workshop on Cellular & Molecular Toxicology. LC 79-26853. 300p. Repr. of 1980 ed. 22.00 (ISBN 0-683-06996-9). Krieger.
Filov, V. A., et al. Quantitative Toxicology: Selected Topics. LC 78-12530. (Environmental Science & Technology Ser.). 462p. 1979. 98.50 (ISBN 0-471-02109-1, Pub. by Wiley-Interscience). Wiley.
Fiserova-Bergerova, Vera, ed. Modeling of Inhalation Exposure to Vapors: Uptake, Distribution. & Elimination, 2 Vols. 1983. Vol. I, 184pp. 54.00 (ISBN 0-8493-6315-2); Vol. II, 208pp. 58.00 (ISBN 0-8493-6316-0). CRC Pr.
Flouride: The Cause of the Poisoning of America. 2.00 (ISBN 0-318-04608-3). Top-Ecol Pr.
Garrod, J. W., ed. Testing for Toxicity. 366p. 1981. 40.00x (ISBN 0-85066-218-4). Taylor & Francis.
George, R. & Okun, R., eds. Annual Review of Pharmacology & Toxicology, Vol. 18. LC 61-5649. (Illus.). 1978. text ed. 20.00 (ISBN 0-8243-0418-7). Annual Reviews.
--Annual Review of Pharmacology & Toxicology, Vol. 19. LC 61-5649. (Illus.). 1979. text ed. 20.00 (ISBN 0-8243-0419-5). Annual Reviews.
--Annual Review of Pharmacology & Toxicology, Vol. 20. LC 61-5649. (Illus.). 1980. text ed. 20.00 (ISBN 0-8243-0420-9). Annual Reviews.
--Annual Review of Pharmacology & Toxicology, Vol. 21. LC 61-5649. (Illus.). 1981. text ed. 20.00 (ISBN 0-8243-0421-7). Annual Reviews.
--Annual Review of Pharmacology & Toxicology, Vol. 22. LC 61-5649. (Illus.). 1982. text ed. 22.00 (ISBN 0-8243-0422-5). Annual Reviews.
--Annual Review of Pharmacology & Toxicology, Vol. 23. LC 61-5649. (Illus.). 1983. text ed. 27.00 (ISBN 0-8243-0423-3). Annual Reviews.
George, R., et al, eds. Annual Review of Pharmacology & Toxicology, Vol. 24. LC 61-5649. (Illus.). 1984. text ed. 27.00 (ISBN 0-8243-0424-1). Annual Reviews.
Golberg, Leon, ed. Structure Activity Correlation as a Predictive Tool in Toxicology: Fundamentals, Methods, & Applications. LC 82-3007. (Chemical Industry Institute of Toxicology Ser.). (Illus.). 330p. 1983. text ed. 59.50 (ISBN 0-89116-276-3). Hemisphere Pub.
Goldberg, Alan M., ed. Acute Toxicity Testing. (Alternative Methods in Toxicology Ser.). 304p. 1984. text ed. 45.00 (ISBN 0-913113-03-4). M Liebert.
--In Vitro Toxicology. (Alternative Methods in Toxicology Ser.). 500p. 1985. text ed. 67.00 (ISBN 0-913113-05-0). M Liebert.
--Product Safety Evaluation. (Alternative Methods in Toxicology Ser.). 376p. 1983. text ed. 49.50 (ISBN 0-913113-00-X). M Liebert.
Goldfrank, Lewis & Kirstein, Robert. Toxologic Emergencies. 2nd ed. 224p. 1981. pap. 18.50 (ISBN 0-8385-8965-0). ACC.
Goldfrank, Lewis R. & Kirstein, Robert, eds. Toxicologic Emergencies: A Comprehensive Handbook in Problem Solving. 2nd ed. (Illus.). 447p. 1982. 45.00 (ISBN 0-8385-8965-0). ACC.
Gossel, Thomas A. & Bricker, J. Douglas. Principles of Clinical Toxicology. (Illus.). 368p. 1984. text ed. 39.50 (ISBN 0-89004-951-3). Raven.
Gralla, E. J. Scientific Consideration in Monitoring & Evaluating Toxicological Research. 1981. 29.50 (ISBN 0-07-024047-7). McGraw.
Grant, W. Morton. Toxicology of the Eye: Drugs, Chemicals, Plants, Venoms, 2 vols. 2nd ed. (Illus.). 1216p. 1974. 74.50x (ISBN 0-398-02299-2). C C Thomas.
Grice, H. C., ed. The Selection of Doses in Chronic Toxicity-Carcinogenicity Studies. (Current Issues in Toxicology Ser.). (Illus.). 130p. 1984. pap. 17.00 (ISBN 0-387-12845-X). Springer-Verlag.
Gross, Paul & Braun, Daniel C. Toxic & Biomedical Effects of Fibers: Asbestos, Talc, Inorganic Fibers, Man-Made Vitreous Fibers & Organic Fibers. LC 83-23612. (Illus.). 257p. 1984. 36.00 (ISBN 0-8155-0971-5). Noyes.
Guthrie, F. E. & Perry, J. J., eds. Introduction to Environmental Toxicology. 484p. 1980. 39.50 (ISBN 0-444-00359-2, Biomedical Pr). Elsevier.
Hathcock, John, ed. Nutritional Toxicology, Vol. 1. LC 82-4036. (Nutrition: Basic & Applied Science Ser.). 1982. 65.00 (ISBN 0-12-332601-X). Acad Pr.
Hayes, A. W., et al, eds. Developments in the Science & Practice of Toxicology: Proceedings of the Third International Congress of Toxicology, San Diego, CA, August 28 - September 3, 1983. (Developments in Toxicology & Environmental Science Ser.: Vol. 11). 614p. 1984. 121.25 (ISBN 0-444-80547-8). Elsevier.
Hayes, A. Wallace, ed. Principles & Methods of Toxicology. (Illus.). 764p. 1984. student ed. 46.50 (ISBN 0-88167-002-2). Raven.
--Toxicology of the Eye, Ear, & Other Special Senses. (Target Organ Toxicology Ser.). 268p. 1985. text ed. 56.50 (ISBN 0-89004-840-1). Raven.
Hodgson, E. Reviews in Environmental Toxicology, Vol. 1. 1984. 81.00 (ISBN 0-444-80562-1, I-252-84). Elsevier.
Hodgson, E. & Guthrie, F. E. Introduction to Biochemical Toxicology. 438p. 1980. 34.50 (ISBN 0-444-00347-9, Biomedical Pr). Elsevier.

Witschi, Hanspeter & Nettesheim, Paul. Mechanisms in Respiratory Toxicology, 2 Vols. 288p. 1981. Vol. I, 240p. 86.00 (ISBN 0-8493-5689-X); Vol. II 240p. 81.00 (ISBN 0-8493-5690-3). CRC Pr.

Wong. Therapeutic Drug Monitoring & Toxicology. (Chromatographic Science Ser.). 544p. 1985. 89.75 (ISBN 0-8247-7246-6). Dekker.

Woodhead, A. D., et al, eds. Assessment of Risk from Low-Level Exposure to Radiation & Chemicals: A Critical Overview. (Basic Life Sciences Ser.: Vol. 33). 542p. 1985. 65.00x (ISBN 0-306-42003-1, Plenum Pr). Plenum Pub.

Yoshida, H., et al, eds. Advances in Pharmacology & Therapeutics: Proceedings of the Eighth International Congress of Pharmacology, Tokyo, Japan, July 19-24, 1981, Series No. 2, Vol. 5. (Illus.). 380p. 1982. 77.00 (ISBN 0-08-028025-0). Pergamon.

Zakim, D. & Vessey, D. A. Biomedical Pharmacology & Toxicology, Vol. 1. 384p. 1985. 35.00 (ISBN 0-471-86793-4). Wiley.

Zbinden, G. Progress in Toxicology, Vol. 1. LC 73-12957. 1973. pap. 19.00 (ISBN 0-387-06495-8). Springer-Verlag.

Zbinden, Gerhard, et al, eds. Application of Behavioral Pharmacology in Toxicology. 410p. 1983. text ed. 52.00 (ISBN 0-89004-902-5). Raven.

TOXINS AND ANTITOXINS

see also Antidotes; Mycotoxins

Ajl, S. J., et al, eds. Microbial Toxins: A Comprehensive Treatise. Incl. Vol. 1. Bacterial Protein Toxins. 1970. 85.50 (ISBN 0-12-046501-9); Vol. 2A. Bacterial Protein Toxins. 1971. 71.50 (ISBN 0-12-046502-7); Vol. 3. Bacterial Protein Toxins. 1970. 85.50 (ISBN 0-12-046503-5); Vol. 4. Bacterial Endotoxins. 1971. 74.50 (ISBN 0-12-046504-3); Vol. 5. Bacterial Endotoxins. 1971. 82.50 (ISBN 0-12-046505-1); Vol. 6. Fundal Toxins. 1971. 85.50 (ISBN 0-12-046506-X); Vol. 7. Algal & Fungal Toxins. 1971. 71.50 (ISBN 0-12-046507-8); Vol. 8. Fungal Toxins. 1972. 71.50 (ISBN 0-12-046508-6). Acad Pr.

Albert, Adrian. Selective Toxicity: The Physico-Chemical Basis of Therapy. 7th Ed ed. 792p. 1985. text ed. 69.95 (ISBN 0-412-26010-7, NO. 9126, Pub. by Chapman & Hall England); pap. text ed. 34.95 (ISBN 0-412-26020-4, NO. 9127). Methuen Inc.

Alouf, J. E., et al, eds. Bacterial Protein Toxins. (Fems Symposia Ser.). 1984. 26.00 (ISBN 0-12-053080-5). Acad Pr.

Bergin, Edward J. & Grandon, Ronald E. The American Survival Guide: How to Survive in Your Toxic Environment. (Illus.). 512p. 1984. pap. 11.95 (ISBN 0-380-87460-1, 87460-1). Avon.

Berlin, A., ed. Assessment of Toxic Agents at the Workplace. 660p. 1984. text ed. 98.50 (ISBN 0-89838-613-6, Pub. by Martinus Nijhoff Netherlands). Kluwer Academic.

Betina, V., ed. Mycotoxins: Production, Isolation, Separation & Purification, Vol. 8. (Developments in Food Science Ser.). 500p. 1984. 113.50 (ISBN 0-444-42289-7, I-051-84). Elsevier.

Bragg, Paul. Toxicless Diet - Purification. 1.75x (ISBN 0-686-29873-X). Cancer Control Soc.

Cohen, P. & Van Heyningen, S., eds. Molecular Actions of Toxins & Viruses. (Molecular Aspects of Cellular Regulation Ser.: Vol. 2). 370p. 1982. 79.25 (ISBN 0-444-80400-5, I-143-82, Biomedical Pr). Elsevier.

Colowick, Sidney & Jakoby, William, eds. Methods in Enzymology: Detoxication & Drug Metabolism: Conjugation & Related Systems, Vol. 77. (Methods in Enzymology Ser.). 1981. 55.00 (ISBN 0-12-181977-9). Acad Pr.

De Spain, June. Little Cyanide Cookbook: B-17 Recipes. 5.95 (ISBN 0-912986-00-X). Cancer Control Soc.

Detoxification Diet. 0.50 (ISBN 0-686-29908-6). Cancer Control Soc.

Eagers, R. Y. Toxic Properties of Inorganic Fluorine Compounds. 152p. 1969. 22.25 (ISBN 0-444-20044-4, Pub. by Elsevier Applied Sci England). Elsevier.

Garrod, J. W., ed. Testing for Toxicity. 365p. 1981. text ed. 37.00 (ISBN 0-85066-218-4, Pub. by Taylor & Frances England). J K Burgess.

Giannini, A. James & Slaby, Andrew E. Handbook of Overdose & Detoxification Emergencies. 1982. pap. text ed. 16.95 (ISBN 0-87488-182-X). Med Exam.

Hodgson, E. & Bend, J. R., eds. Reviews in Biochemical Toxicology, Vol. 2. 300p. 1980. 52.25 (ISBN 0-444-00386-X, Biomedical Pr). Elsevier.

Homburger, F. Experimental Aspects of Cigarette Smoke Carcinogenesis. (Lectures in Toxicology Ser.: Vol. 9). 12p. 1982. 66.00 (ISBN 0-08-028013-7). Pergamon.

The Infrared Spectra Handbook of Priority Pollutants & Toxic Chemicals. 1982. 265.00 (ISBN 0-8456-0077-X). Sadtler Res.

Keeler, Tu. Handbook of Natural Toxins. 848p. 1983. 145.00 (ISBN 0-8247-1893-3). Dekker.

Kurata, H. & Veno, Y., eds. Toxigenic Fungi: Proceedings of the Mycotoxin Symp. held in the Third Internat. Mycological Congress, Tokyo, Aug. 30-Sept. 3, 1983. (Developments in Food Science Ser.: Vol. 7). 400p. 1984. 86.75 (ISBN 0-444-99630-3, I-141-84). Elsevier.

Middlebrook, John H. & Kohn, Leonard D., eds. Receptor-Mediated Binding & Internalization of Toxins & Hormones. 1981. 44.00 (ISBN 0-12-494850-2). Acad Pr.

Mycotoxins: Report of the Joint FAO-WHO-UNEP Conference 1977. (Food & Nutrition Papers: No. 2). (Eng., Fr. & Span.). 115p. 1978. pap. 8.00 (ISBN 92-5-100489-7, F1335, FAO). Unipub.

O'Donoghue, John L., ed. Neurotoxicity of Industrial & Commercial Chemicals, Vol. I. 240p. 1985. 72.00 (ISBN 0-8493-6454-X). CRC Pr.

Ohsaka, Akira, et al, eds. Animal, Plant, & Microbial Toxins. Incl. Vol. 1, Biochemistry. 581p (ISBN 0-306-37065-4); Vol. 2, Chemistry, Pharmacology & Immunology. 587p (ISBN 0-306-37066-2). LC 76-8171. (Illus.). 1976. 75.00x ea. (Plenum Pr). Plenum Pub.

Plaa, G. L. & Hewitt, W. R., eds. Toxicology of the Liver. (Target Organ Toxicology Ser.). 350p. 1982. text ed. 59.00 (ISBN 0-89004-584-4). Raven.

Rechcigl, Miloslav, Jr., ed. CRC Handbook of Naturally Occurring Food Toxicants. 360p. 1983. 67.00 (ISBN 0-8493-3965-0). CRC Pr.

Rosenberg, Philip, ed. Toxins: Animal, Plant & Microbial. 1978. text ed. 170.00 (ISBN 0-08-022640-X). Pergamon.

Seventh International Symposium on Animal, Plant, & Microbial Toxins, Brisbane, Australia, 11-16 July, 1982 & Endean, R. Seventh World Congress on Animal, Plant & Microbial Toxins: Proceedings. (Illus.). 544p. 1983. pap. 100.00 (ISBN 0-08-029803-6). Pergamon.

Singhal, Radhey L. & Thomas, John A., eds. Lead Toxicity. LC 79-16784. (Illus.). 524p. 1980. text ed. 45.00 (ISBN 0-8067-1801-3). Urban & S.

Tice, Raymond R., et al, eds. Genotoxic Effects of Airborne Agents. LC 81-23497. (Environmental Science Research Ser.: Vol. 25). 672p. 1982. 75.00x (ISBN 0-306-40983-6, Plenum Pr). Plenum Pub.

Tilden, J. H. Toxemia Explained. 2.95x (ISBN 0-87983-253-3). Cancer Control Soc.

--Toxemia Explained. rev. ed. LC 81-81290. 200p. 1981. pap. 2.95 (ISBN 0-87983-253-3). Keats.

Tu, Anthony T. Handbook of Natural Toxins: Insect Poisons, Allergens, & Other Invertebrates Venoms, Vol. 2. LC 84-17471. 704p. 135.00 (ISBN 0-8247-7207-5). Dekker.

Yacobi, Avraham & Barry, Herbert, III, eds. Experimental & Clinical Toxicokinetics. LC 84-71408. 208p. 1984. 39.00 (ISBN 0-917330-51-X). Am Pharm Assn.

TRACE ELEMENTS

see also names of specific elements, e.g. Boron

Ahuja, Sut, et al, eds. Chemical Analysis of the Environment & Other Techniques. LC 73-82575. 384p. 1973. 49.50x (ISBN 0-306-39305-0, Plenum Pr). Plenum Pub.

American Society for Testing & Materials. Symposium on Spectrochemical Analysis for Trace Elements. LC 58-3176. (American Society for Testing & Materials Special Technical Publications Ser: No. 221). pap. 21.30 (ISBN 0-317-09810-1, 2000112). Bks Demand UMI.

Aubert, H. & Pinta, M. Trace Elements in Soils. (Developments in Soil Science: Vol. 7). 396p. 1977. 89.50 (ISBN 0-444-41511-4). Elsevier.

Braetter, Peter & Schramel, Peter, eds. Trace Element Analytical Chemistry in Medicine & Biology, Vol. 2. 1189p. 1983. 112.00 (ISBN 3-11-008681-6). De Gruyter.

Chalmers, R. A., ed. Gains & Losses: Errors in Trace Analysis. 90p. 1983. pap. 27.50 (ISBN 0-08-030239-4). Pergamon.

Das, M. S., ed. Trace Analysis & Technological Development. LC 83-12788. 407p. 1983. 42.95x (ISBN 0-470-27462-X). Halsted Pr.

Di Ferrante, R. K. Trace Metals: Exposure & Health Effects. 1979. 48.00 (ISBN 0-08-022446-6). Pergamon.

Dreosti, Ivor E. & Smith, Richard M., eds. Neurobiology of the Trace Elements: Vol. 1, Trace Element Neurobiology & Deficiencies. LC 83-8412. (Contemporary Neuroscience Ser.). 384p. 1983. 49.50 (ISBN 0-89603-046-6). Humana.

Heydorn, K. Neutron Activation Analysis for Clinical Trace Element Research, Vol. II. 224p. 1984. 60.00 (ISBN 0-8493-5774-8). CRC Pr.

Hofstader, Robert A., et al, eds. Analysis of Petroleum for Trace Metals. LC 76-46297. (Advances in Chemistry Ser.: No. 156). 1976. 34.95 (ISBN 0-8412-0349-0). Am Chemical.

Javier-Son, A., ed. New Analytical Techniques for Trace Constituents of Metallic & Metal-Bearing Ores - STP 747. 135p. 1981. 15.00 (ISBN 0-8031-0743-9, 04-747000-01). ASTM.

Kharasch, Norman, ed. Trace Metals in Health & Disease. 330p. 1979. 46.00 (ISBN 0-89004-389-2). Raven.

Kothny, Evaldo L., ed. Trace Elements in the Environment. LC 73-87347. (Advances in Chemistry Ser: No. 123). 1973. 29.95 (ISBN 0-8412-0185-4). Am Chemical.

Lawrence, James F. Trace Analysis, Vol. 4. 1985. 65.00 (ISBN 0-12-682104-6). Acad Pr.

Lepp, N. W., ed. Effect of Heavy Metal Pollution on Plants: Vol. 1, Effects of Trace Metals on Plant Function. (Pollution Monitoring Ser.). (Illus.). 352p. 1981. 55.50 (ISBN 0-85334-959-2, Pub. by Elsevier Applied Sci England). Elsevier.

--Effect of Heavy Metal Pollution on Plants: Vol. 2, Metals in the Environment. (Pollution Monitoring Ser.). (Illus.). 257p. 1981. 46.25 (ISBN 0-85334-923-1, Pub. by Elsevier Applied Sci England). Elsevier.

Leppard, Gary C., ed. Trace Element Speciation in Surface Waters: Its Ecological Implications. (NATO Conference Series I, Ecology: Vol. 6). 320p. 1983. 45.00x (ISBN 0-306-41269-1, Plenum Press). Plenum Pub.

Newberne. Trace Substances & Health, Pt. II. 224p. 1982. 39.75 (ISBN 0-8247-1850-X). Dekker.

Oikawa, Kikuo. Trace Analysis of Atmospheric Samples. LC 77-3458. 158p. 1977. 39.95 (ISBN 0-470-99013-9). Halsted Pr.

Onishi, H. Photometric Determination of Trace Metals: Individual Metals, Aluminum to Lithium, Vol. 1, Pt. 2a. 4th ed. 1985. 100.00 (ISBN 0-471-86139-1). Wiley.

Pleban. Analysis of Trace Metals in Biological Materials. 1981. write for info. (ISBN 0-85501-624-8). Wiley.

Prasad, Ananda S., ed. Clinical, Biochemical, & Nutritional Aspects of Trace Elements. (Current Tropics in Nutrition & Disease Ser.: Vol. 6). 608p. 1982. 96.00 (ISBN 0-8451-1605-3). A R Liss.

Reeves, R. D. & Brooks, R. R. Trace Element Analysis of Geological Materials: Vol. 51. LC 78-8064. (Chemical Analysis: Monographs on Analytical Chemistry & Its Applications). 421p. 1979. 69.00 (ISBN 0-471-71338-4, Pub. by Wiley-Interscience). Wiley.

Reid, E., ed. Trace-Organic Sample Handling. LC 80-49715. (Methodological Surveys Analysis: Vol. 10). 383p. 1981. 117.95x (ISBN 0-470-27071-3). Halsted Pr.

Report of the Consultation on the Establishment of the European Research Network on Trace Elements. 1978. pap. 7.50 (ISBN 92-5-100342-4, F1234, FAO). Unipub.

Sandell, E. B. & Onishi, Hiroshi. Photometric Determination of Traces of Metals: General Aspects, Vol. 3. 4th ed. LC 77-18937. (Chemical Analysis Ser.). 1085p. 1978. 122.00 (ISBN 0-471-03094-5, Pub. by Wiley-Interscience). Wiley.

Sauchelli, Vincent. Trace Elements in Agriculture. LC 74-81358. 228p. 1969. 16.50 (ISBN 0-442-15633-2, Pub. by Van Nos Reinhold). Krieger.

Schramel, P., ed. Trace Elements: Analytical Chemistry in Medicine & Biology. 1000p. 1980. text ed. 72.00x (ISBN 3-11-008357-4). De Gruyter.

Schrauzer, G. N., ed. Inorganic & Nutritional Aspects of Cancer. LC 77-13974. (Advances in Experimental Medicine & Biology Ser.: Vol. 91). 362p. 1977. 49.50x (ISBN 0-306-32691-4, Plenum Pr). Plenum Pub.

Schroeder, Henry A. The Trace Elements & Man. LC 72-85731. (Illus.). 192p. 1973. pap. 6.95 (ISBN 0-8159-6907-4). Devin.

Schuller, Pieter L. & Egan, Harold. Cadmium, Lead, Mercury & Methylmercury Compounds: A Review. 1977. pap. 7.50 (ISBN 92-5-100094-8, F730, FAO). Unipub.

Schwartz, Stephen E. Trace Atmospheric Constituents: Properties, Transformations & Fates. LC 82-16095. (Advances in Environmental Science & Technology Ser.). 547p. 1983. 69.95 (ISBN 0-471-87640-2, Pub. by Wiley-Interscience). Wiley.

Shkolnik, M. Y. Trace Elements in Plants. (Developments in Crop Science Ser.: Vol. 6). 464p. 1984. 82.75 (ISBN 0-444-42320-6, I-136-84). Elsevier.

Svehla & Wilson. Photometric Methods in Inorganic Trace Analysis. (Wilson & Wilson's Comprehensive Analytical Chemistry Ser.: Vol. 20). 1985. 100.00 (ISBN 0-444-99588-9). Elsevier.

Valkovic, Vlado. Trace Elements in Petroleum. 269p. 1978. 41.95x (ISBN 0-87814-084-0). Pennwell Bks.

Winefordner, J. D., ed. Trace Analysis: Spectroscopic Methods for Elements. LC 75-41460. (Chemical Analysis Ser.: Vol. 46). 484p. 1976. 67.00x (ISBN 0-471-95401-2, Pub. by Wiley-Interscience). Wiley.

Wong, C. S. & Boyle, Edward, eds. Trace Metals in Sea Water. (NATO Conference Series IV, Marine Sciences: Vol. 9). 934p. 1983. 115.00 (ISBN 0-306-41165-2, Plenum Press). Plenum Pub.

Zief, Morris & Mitchell, James W. Contamination Control in Trace Element Analysis. LC 76-16837. (Chemical Analysis Ser.: Vol. 47). 262p. 1976. 62.00x (ISBN 0-471-61169-7, Pub. by Wiley-Interscience). Wiley.

TRACE ELEMENTS IN THE BODY

Fowden, L., et al, eds. Trace Element Deficiency: Metabolic & Physiological Consequences. (Royal Society of London Ser.). (Illus.). 213p. 1982. lib. bdg. 65.50x (ISBN 0-85403-171-5, Pub. by Royal Soc London). Scholium Intl.

Lawrence, James F., ed. Trace Analysis, Vol. 3. (Serial Publication). 1984. 49.50 (ISBN 0-12-682103-8). Acad Pr.

Newberne, P. M., ed. Trace Substances & Health: A Handbook, Part 1. 1976. 75.00 (ISBN 0-8247-6341-6). Dekker.

Prasad, Ananda S.. Trace Elements & Iron in Human Metabolism. LC 78-13446. (Topics in Hematology Ser.). (Illus.). 408p. 1978. 45.00x (ISBN 0-306-31142-9, Plenum Med Bk). Plenum Pub.

Rennert, Owen M. & Chan, Waiyee, eds. Metabolism of Trace Metals in Man, Vol. II. 176p. 1984. 57.00 (ISBN 0-8493-5799-3). CRC Pr.

Rennert, Owen M. & Chan, Wayiee, eds. Metabolism of Trace Metals in Man, Vol. I. 192p. 1984. 57.00 (ISBN 0-8493-5798-5). CRC Pr.

Tsalev, D. L. Atomic Absorption Spectrometry in Occupational & Environmental Health Practice, Vol. II. 312p. 1984. 78.00 (ISBN 0-8493-5604-0). CRC Pr.

TRACERS (BIOLOGY)

Boulton, A. A., et al, eds. Neurobiology of the Trace Amines. LC 84-626. (Experimental & Clinical Neuroscience Ser.). (Illus.). 624p. 59.50 (ISBN 0-89603-063-6). Humana.

Cold Spring Harbor Symposia on Quantitative Biology: Biological Application of Tracer Elements, Vol.13. LC 34-8174. (Illus.). 233p. 1949. 38.00x (ISBN 0-87969-012-7). Cold Spring Harbor.

Feinendegen, L. E. Tritium Labeled Molecules in Biology & Medicine. (Atomic Energy Commision Monographs). 1967. 29.50 (ISBN 0-12-251550-1). Acad Pr.

Kamen, Martin D. Isotopic Tracers in Biology: An Introduction to Tracer Methodology. 3rd ed. (Organic & Biological Chemistry, Vol. 1). 1957. 66.50 (ISBN 0-12-394862-2). Acad Pr.

Polak, J. M. & Varndel, I. M. Immunolabelling for Electron Microscopy. 1984. 49.50 (ISBN 0-444-80563-X, I-431-84). Elsevier.

Tracer Studies on Non-Protein Nitrogen for Ruminants, 3: Proceedings (Egypt) (Panel Proceedings Ser.). (Illus.). 160p. pap. 20.00 (ISBN 92-0-111376-5, ISP455-3, IAEA). Unipub.

Tracer Techniques in Tropical Animal Production. (Panel Proceedings Ser.). (Illus.). 209p. (Orig.). 1974. pap. 17.75 (ISBN 92-0-111074-X, ISP360, IAEA). Unipub.

Welch, Teresa J., et al. Fundamentals of the Tracer Method. LC 71-180190. (Illus.). Repr. of 1972 ed. 49.30 (ISBN 0-8357-9547-0, 2013579). Bks Demand UMI.

TRACERS (CHEMISTRY)

Benes, P. & Majer, V. Trace Chemistry of Aqueous Solutions: General Chemistry & Radiochemistry. (Topics In Inorganic & General Chemistry Ser.: Vol. 18). 252p. 1980. 55.50 (ISBN 0-444-99798-9). Elsevier.

Lawrence, James. Trace Analysis, Vol. 2. (Serial Publication Ser.). 38.50 (ISBN 0-12-682102-X). Acad Pr.

Nesmeyanov, A. N. Guide to Practical Radio Chemistry, Vol. 2. 446p. 1984. 9.00 (ISBN 0-8285-2888-8, Pub. by Mir Pubs USSR). Imported Pubns.

Polak, J. M. & Varndel, I. M. Immunolabelling for Electron Microscopy. 1984. 49.50 (ISBN 0-444-80563-X, I-431-84). Elsevier.

Tracer Studies on Non-Protein Nitrogen for Ruminants, 3: Proceedings (Egypt) (Panel Proceedings Ser.). (Illus.). 160p. pap. 20.00 (ISBN 92-0-111376-5, ISP455-3, IAEA). Unipub.

Wolfe, Robert R. Tracers in Metabolic Research: Radioisotope & Stable Isotope-Mass Spectrometry Methods. LC 83-19601. (Laboratory & Research Methods in Biology & Medicine Ser.: Vol. 9). 300p. 1984. 56.00 (ISBN 0-8451-1658-4). A R Liss.

TRACERS, RADIOACTIVE

see Radioactive Tracers

TRACHYSPHYRUS

Porter, Charles. A Revision of the South American Species of Trachysphyrus - (Hymenoptera, Ichneumonidae) (Memoirs Ser: No. 10). (Illus.). 387p. 1967. 25.00x (ISBN 0-686-17146-2). Am Entom Inst.

TRACK-TYPE VEHICLES

see Tracklaying Vehicles

Rudman, Jack. Director of Traffic Control. (Career Examination Ser.: C-1877). (Cloth bdg. avail. on request). pap. 14.00 (ISBN 0-8373-1877-7). Natl Learning.
--Traffic Engineer 1. (Career Examination Ser.: C-803). (Cloth bdg. avail. on request). pap. 10.00 (ISBN 0-8373-1886-6). Natl Learning.
Shinar, David. Psychology on the Road: The Human Factor in Traffic Safety. LC 78-18219. 212p. 1978. 40.00 (ISBN 0-471-03997-7). Wiley.
Somers, Ronald, ed. Road User Protection: Selected Papers from the 8th International Conference on Accident & Traffic Medicine, Aarhus, Denmark, 10-13 June 1980. 70p. 1981. pap. 32.00 (ISBN 0-08-028099-4). Pergamon.
Zaruba, Robert J. Questions & Answers on the Rules of the Road. 4th ed. LC 82-72002. (Illus.). 128p. 1982. pap. text ed. 10.00 (ISBN 0-87033-290-2). Cornell Maritime.

TRAFFIC VOLUME
see Traffic Flow

TRAILERS
see also Mobile Homes
Brobst, William A. Pulling Your Tail: A Primer on the Art of Motorcycle Trailering. LC 82-90072. (Illus.). 64p. 1982. pap. 5.65 (ISBN 0-9608112-0-6). Transport Env.
Thompson, John. Trailer Life's Secrets of Successful RVing: Detailed Tips & Hints for Successful RV Trips. (Illus.). 400p. (Orig.). 1981. pap. 12.95 (ISBN 0-934798-03-6). TL Enterprises.
Wright, Don & Trailer Life Editors. Trailer Life's Guide to Fulltime RVing: Everything You Need to Know to Enjoy the Total Freedom & Adventure of Life on the Road. (Illus.). 352p. 1981. 12.95 (ISBN 0-934798-05-2). TL Enterprises.

TRAINS, RAILROAD
see Railroads–Trains

TRAJECTORIES, SPACE
see Space Trajectories

TRANSACTIONAL ANALYSIS
Ernst, Franklin H., Jr. Transactional Analysis in Psychobiology: From Prince to Frog to Principle. 1981. pap. 9.50 (ISBN 0-916944-36-0). Addresso'set.
Pitman, Liz. Transactional Analysis for Social Workers & Counsellors: An Introduction. (Library of Social Work). 172p. (Orig.). 1984. pap. 11.95x (ISBN 0-7100-9581-3). Routledge & Kegan.

TRANSCENDENTAL FUNCTIONS
see Functions, Transcendental

TRANSCENDENTAL NUMBERS
see Numbers, Transcendental

TRANSDUCERS
see also Loud-Speakers; Magnetic Amplifiers; Microphone; Wave Guides
Anan'eva, A. A., et al. Ceramic Acoustic Detectors. LC 65-11334. 122p. 1965. 35.00x (ISBN 0-306-10702-3, Consultants). Plenum Pub.
CES Industries, Inc. Staff. Ed-Lab Experiment Manual: CES 311 Transducers. (Illus.). 1982. write for info. (ISBN 0-86711-050-3). CES Industries.
Harvey, G. F., ed. ISA Transducer Compendium. Incl. Pt. 3. Three Thousand Transducers Variable of Temperature, Heat Flux, Magnetic Qualities, Humidity & Moisture, Electromagnetic & Nuclear Radiation. 71.80 (2050193). LC 68-57392. Repr. of 1972 ed. Bks Demand UMI.
Lenk, John D. Handbook of Controls & Instrumentation. (Illus.). 1980. text ed. 27.95 (ISBN 0-13-377069-9). P-H.
Mattiat, Oskar E., ed. Ultrasonic Transducer Materials. LC 71-131885. 185p. 1971. 39.50x (ISBN 0-306-30501-1, Plenum Pr). Plenum Pub.
Neubert, Hermann K. Instrument Transducers: An Introduction to Their Performance & Design. 2nd ed. (Illus.). 1975. 76.00x (ISBN 0-19-856320-5). Oxford U Pr.
Seippel, Robert. Transducers: Sensors & Detectors. 1983. text ed. 26.95 (ISBN 0-8359-7797-8). Reston.
Sheingold, Daniel H., ed. Transducer Interfacing Handbook: A Guide to Analog Signal Conditioning. LC 80-65520. (Illus.). 266p. 1980. 14.50 (ISBN 0-916550-05-2). Analog Devices.
Smolyakov, A. V. & Tkachenko, V. M. The Measurement of Turbulent Fluctuations: An Introduction to Hot-Wire Anemometry & Related Transducers. Chomet, S., tr. from Rus. (Illus.). 298p. 1983. 39.50 (ISBN 0-387-12144-7). Springer-Verlag.
Sydenham, Peter H. Transduce in Measurement & Control. 3rd ed. 132p. 1984. pap. 19.00 (ISBN 0-85274-777-2, Pub. by A Hilger England). Heyden.
--Transducers in Measurement & Control. rev ed. LC 80-141947. 128p. 1980. pap. text ed. 21.85x (ISBN 0-87664-460-4). Instru Soc.
Transducer Market in West Europe. 1982. 1700.00 (ISBN 0-86621-033-4, E617). Frost & Sullivan.
Woolvet, G. A. Transducers in Digital Systems. rev. ed. (IEE Control Engineering Ser.: No. 3). (Illus.). 201p. 1979. pap. 26.00 (ISBN 0-906048-13-3, CE003). Inst Elect Eng.

TRANSFER, RADIATIVE
see Radiative Transfer

TRANSFER MACHINES
see Machine-Tools

TRANSFER OF TECHNOLOGY
see Technology Transfer

TRANSFINITE NUMBERS
see Numbers, Transfinite

TRANSFORMATION, CONFORMAL
see Conformal Mapping

TRANSFORMATION, LAPLACE
see Laplace Transformation

TRANSFORMATION GROUPS
Bredon, Glen E. Introduction to Compact Transformation Groups. (Pure & Applied Mathematics Ser). 1972. 77.00 (ISBN 0-12-128850-1). Acad Pr.
Bronstein, I. U. Extensions of Minimal Transformation Groups. 327p. 1979. 47.50x (ISBN 90-286-0368-9). Sijthoff & Noordhoff.
Conference on Compact Transformation Groups, 2nd. Proceedings, Pt. 1. LC 72-95314. (Lecture Notes in Mathematics: Vol. 298). xii, 453p. 1972. pap. 19.00 (ISBN 0-387-06077-4). Springer-Verlag.
--Proceedings, Pt. 2. LC 72-95314. (Lecture Notes in Mathematics: Vol. 299). xi, 327p. 1972. pap. 16.00 (ISBN 0-387-06078-2). Springer-Verlag.
Conference on Transformation Groups - New Orleans - 1967. Proceedings. Mostert, P. S., ed. LC 68-27313. (Illus.). 1968. 47.50 (ISBN 0-387-04299-7). Springer-Verlag.
Conner, Pierre E. Lectures on the Action of a Finite Group. LC 68-57940. (Lecture Notes in Mathematics: Vol. 73). 1968. pap. 10.70 (ISBN 0-387-04243-1). Springer-Verlag.
Davis, M. Multiaxial Actions on Manifolds. LC 78-3765. (Lecture Notes in Mathematics: Vol. 643). 1978. pap. 14.00 (ISBN 0-387-08667-6). Springer-Verlag.
De Medrano, Lopez. Involutions on Manifolds. LC 74-139952. (Ergebnisse der Mathematik und Ihrer Grenzgebiete: Vol. 59). (Illus.). 1971. 28.00 (ISBN 0-387-05092-2). Springer-Verlag.
Evans, Bruce D. C-Bundles & Compact Transformation Groups. LC 82-11544. (Memoirs of the American Mathematical Society Ser.: No. 269). 63p. 1982. pap. 9.00 (ISBN 0-8218-2269-1, MEMO/269). Am Math.
Hajek, O., et al, eds. Global Differentiable Dynamics, Proceedings. (Lecture Notes in Mathematics.: Vol. 235). (Illus.). x, 140p. 1971. pap. 9.00 (ISBN 0-387-05674-2). Springer-Verlag.
Kosniowski, Czes, ed. Transformation Groups. LC 76-40837. (London Mathematical Society Lecture Notes Ser.: No. 26). 1977. limp bdg. 21.95 (ISBN 0-521-21509-9). Cambridge U Pr.
Palais, Richard S. Global Formulation of the Lie Theory of Transformation Groups. LC 52-42839. (Memoirs: No. 22). 123p. 1971. pap. 10.00 (ISBN 0-8218-1222-X, MEMO-22). Am Math.
Seshadri, R & Na, T. Y. Group Invariance in Engineering Boundary Value Problems. (Illus.). 225p. 1985. 29.50 (ISBN 0-387-96128-3). Springer-Verlag.
Tondeur, Philippe. Introduction to Lie Groups & Transformation Groups. 2nd ed. LC 78-99012. (Lecture Notes in Mathematics: Vol. 7). 1969. pap. 10.70 (ISBN 0-387-04599-6). Springer-Verlag.

TRANSFORMATIONS (MATHEMATICS)
see also Complexes; Conformal Mapping; Ergodic Theory; Fourier Transformations; Functor Theory; Geometry, Algebraic; Homotopy Theory; Integral Transforms; Laplace Transformation; Lattice Theory; Spectral Theory (Mathematics); Transformation Groups; Linear Programming
Anderson, R. L. & Ibragimov, N. H. Lie-Backlund Transformations in Applications. LC 78-78207. (SIAM Studies in Applied Mathematics: No. 1). x, 124p. 1979. text ed. 17.50 (ISBN 0-89871-151-7). Soc Indus-Appl Math.
Aseltine, J. A. Transform Method in Linear System Analysis. (Electrical & Electronic Eng. Ser). 1958. 48.00 (ISBN 0-07-002389-1). McGraw.
Baer, Reinhold. Linear Algebra & Projective Geometry. (Pure and Applied Mathematics Ser.: Vol. 2). 1952. 59.50 (ISBN 0-12-072250-X). Acad Pr.
Banach, Stefan. Theorie Des Operations Lineaires. 2nd ed. LC 63-21849. (Fr). 10.95 (ISBN 0-8284-0110-1). Chelsea Pub.
Berndt, Bruce C., et al. Chapter Nine of Ramanujan's Second Notebook: Infinite Series Identities, Transformations, & Evaluations, Vol. 23. LC 83-11803. (Contemporary Mathematics Ser.: No. 23). 84p. 1983. pap. 17.00 (ISBN 0-8218-5024-5). Am Math.
Bracewell, R. The Fourier Transform & Its Applications. 2nd ed. (Electrical Engineering Ser.). (Illus.). 1978. text ed. 48.00 (ISBN 0-07-007013-X). McGraw.
Brown, Scott S. Bounds on Transfer Principles for Algebraically Closed & Complete Discretely Valued Fields. LC 78-9121. 92p. 1978. pap. 12.00 (ISBN 0-8218-2204-7, MEMO-204). Am Math.
Campbell, S. L. & Meyer, C. D. Generalized Inverses of Linear Transformations. (Surveys & References Ser.: No. 4). 284p. 1979. text ed. 54.50 (ISBN 0-273-08422-4). Pitman Pub MA.
Clebsch, Rudolph F., tr. Vorlesungen Ueber Geometrie Mit Besonderer Benutzung der Vortrage Von Clebsch, 2 Vols. in 3 Pts. (Bibliotheca Mathematica Teubneriana Ser. 43-44). (Ger). 1969. Repr. Set. 140.00 (ISBN 0-384-09295-0). Johnson Repr.
Coolidge, Julian L. Treatise on the Circle & the Sphere. LC 78-128872. 1971. text ed. 27.50 (ISBN 0-8284-0236-1). Chelsea Pub.
Eckhaus, W. & Van Harten, A. The Inverse Scattering Transformation & the Theory of Solitons: An Introduction. (North Holland Mathematics Studies: Vol. 50). 222p. 1981. 40.50 (ISBN 0-444-86166-1, North-Holland). Elsevier.
Effros, E. G. & Hahn, Frank. Locally Compact Transformation Groups & C-Algebras. LC 52-42839. (Memoirs: No. 75). 93p. 1967. pap. 9.00 (ISBN 0-8218-1275-0, MEMO-75). Am Math.
Elliott, Douglas F. & Rao, K. Ramamohan. Fast Transforms: Algorithms, Analyses, Applications. LC 79-8852. (Computer Science & Applied Mathematical Ser.). 1983. 75.00 (ISBN 0-12-237080-5). Acad Pr.
Giffin, Walter C. Transform Techniques for Probability Modeling. (Operation Research Industrial Engineering Ser.). 1975. 59.50 (ISBN 0-12-282750-3). Acad Pr.
Gilkey, Peter B. Invariance Theory, the Heat Equation, & the Atiyah-Singer Index Theorem. LC 84-61166. (Mathematics Lecture Ser.: No. 11). viii, 349p. 1985. text ed. 40.00 (ISBN 0-914098-20-9). Publish or Perish.
Gupta, S. C. Transform & State Variable Methods in Linear Systems. LC 66-17635. 444p. 1971. Repr. of 1966 ed. text ed. 26.50 (ISBN 0-88275-022-4). Krieger.
Halmos, P. R., ed. Finite-Dimension Vector Spaces. 2nd ed. (Undergraduate Texts in Mathematics Ser.). 200p. 1974. Repr. of 1958 ed. 21.00 (ISBN 0-387-90093-4). Springer-Verlag.
Hermann, Robert. Geometric Theory of Non-Linear Differential Equations: Backlund Transformations, Solitons, Pt. A. LC 76-17201. (Interdisiplinary Mathematics Ser.: No. 12). 313p. 1976. 38.00 (ISBN 0-915692-16-3, 991600355). Math Sci Pr.
Hirchman, I. I. & Widder, D. V. The Convolution Transform. LC 54-6080. pap. 69.50 (ISBN 0-317-08684-7, 2001140). Bks Demand UMI.
Jury, Eliahu I. Theory & Application of the Z-Transform Method. LC 64-17145. 344p. 1973. Repr. of 1964 ed. 20.50 (ISBN 0-88275-122-0). Krieger.
Karlin, Samuel. Total Positivity: Vol. 1. 1968. 35.00x (ISBN 0-8047-0314-0). Stanford U Pr.
Lie, Sophus. Geometrie der Beruehrungstransformationen. LC 72-113134. (Ger.). 1976. 29.50 (ISBN 0-8284-0291-4). Chelsea Pub.
--Transformationsgruppen, 3 Vols. 2nd ed. LC 76-113135. (Ger). 1970. 99.50 set (ISBN 0-8284-0232-9). Chelsea Pub.
Logan, John D., ed. Invariant Variational Principles. 1977. 49.50 (ISBN 0-12-454750-8). Acad Pr.
Martin, G. E. Transformation Geometry: An Introduction to Symmetry. (Undergraduate Texts in Mathematics Ser.). (Illus.). 240p. 1982. 29.95 (ISBN 0-387-90636-3). Springer-Verlag.
Matsuno, Yoshimasa. Bilinear Transformation Method: Monograph. (Mathematics in Science & Engineering Ser.). 1984. 50.00 (ISBN 0-12-480480-2). Acad Pr.
Moon, P. & Spencer, D. E. Field Theory Handbook: Including Coordinate Systems, Differential Equations & Their Solutions. 2nd ed. LC 77-178288. (Illus.). viii, 236p. 1971. 57.90 (ISBN 0-387-02732-7). Springer-Verlag.
Murray, Francis J. Introduction to Linear Transformations in Hilbert Space. (Annals of Math Studies). 1941. 11.00 (ISBN 0-527-02720-0). Kraus Repr.
Pettofrezzo, Anthony J. Matrices & Transformations. 1978. pap. text ed. 3.50 (ISBN 0-486-63634-8). Dover.
Rogers, C. & Shadwick, W. F. Backlund Transformations & Their Applications. LC 81-22783. (Mathematics in Science & Engineering Ser.). 1982. 49.50 (ISBN 0-12-592850-5). Acad Pr.
Segre, Beniamino. Some Properties of Differentiable Varieties & Transformations: With Special Reference to the Analytic & Algebraic Cases. 2nd ed. LC 72-137498. (Ergebnisse der Mathematik und Ihrer Grenzgebiete: Vol. 13). 1971. pap. 34.00 (ISBN 0-387-05085-X). Springer-Verlag.
Walter, E. Identifiability of State Space Models: With Applications to Transformation Systems. (Lecture Notes in Biomathematics: Vol. 46). 202p. 1982. pap. 16.00 (ISBN 0-387-11590-0). Springer-Verlag.
Widder, D. V. Transform Theory. (Pure & Applied Mathematics Ser.: Vol. 42). 1971. 63.50 (ISBN 0-12-748550-3). Acad Pr.
Yaglom, I. M. Geometric Transformations. Shields, Allen, tr. LC 62-18330. (New Mathematical Library: No. 8). 133p. 1975. pap. 8.75 (ISBN 0-88385-608-5). Math Assn.
--Geometric Transformations III. Shenitzer, Abe, tr. LC 72-5702. (New Mathematical Library: No. 24). 237p. 1975. pap. 10.00 (ISBN 0-88385-624-7). Math Assn.

TRANSFORMATIONS, FOURIER
see Fourier Transformations

TRANSFORMATIONS, INFINITESIMAL
Lie, Sophus. Differentialgleichungen. LC 66-12880. (Ger). 25.00 (ISBN 0-8284-0206-X). Chelsea Pub.

TRANSFORMERS, ELECTRIC
see Electric Transformers

TRANSFORMS, INTEGRAL
see Integral Transforms

TRANSIENT PHENOMENA
see Transients (Dynamics)

TRANSIENTS (DYNAMICS)
see also Water Hammer
Woosley, Stanford E., ed. High Energy Transients in Astrophysics: Conference Proceedings, Santa Cruz, California, 1983. LC 84-71205. (AIP Conference Proceedings: No. 115). 714p. 1984. lib. bdg. 51.25 (ISBN 0-88318-314-5). Am Inst Physics.

TRANSIENTS (ELECTRICITY)
Aidala, Joseph B. & Katz, Leon. Transients in Electric Circuits. (Illus.). 1980. text ed. 29.95 (ISBN 0-13-929943-2). P-H.
Felsen, L. B., contrib. by. Transient Electromagnetic Fields. (Tropics in Applied Physics Ser.: Vol. 10). (Illus.). 340p. 1976. 59.00 (ISBN 0-387-07553-4). Springer-Verlag.
Greenwood, Allan. Electrical Transients in Power Systems. 544p. 1971. 58.95 (ISBN 0-471-32650-X). Wiley.
International Conference on Pressure Surges, 3rd. Proceedings, 2 vols. Hansan, J. A. & Stephens, H. S., eds. 600p. (Orig.). 1980. PLB 87.00x (ISBN 0-906085-24-1, Dist. by Air Science Co.). BHRA Fluid.
Ragaller, Klaus, ed. Surges in High-Voltage Networks. LC 80-16117. (Brown Boveri Symposia Ser.). 448p. 1980. 65.00x (ISBN 0-306-40457-5, Plenum Pr). Plenum Pub.
Rudenberg, Reinhold. Electrical Shock Waves in Power Systems: Traveling Waves in Lumped & Distributed Circuit Elements. LC 68-14272. (Illus.). 1968. 20.00x (ISBN 0-674-24350-1). Harvard U Pr.

TRANSISTOR AMPLIFIERS
Carson, Ralph S. High-Frequency Amplifiers. 2nd ed. LC 75-8780. 291p. 1975. 34.95x (ISBN 0-471-86832-9, Pub. by Wiley-Interscience); 29.95. Wiley.
Lenk, John D. Handbook of Modern Solid State Amplifiers. (Illus.). 400p. 1974. ref. ed 26.95 (ISBN 0-13-380394-5); pap. 7.95 (ISBN 0-13-380386-4). P-H.

TRANSISTOR CIRCUITS
Cattermole, Kenneth W. Transistor Circuits. 2nd ed. 488p. 1964. 106.50 (ISBN 0-677-00990-9). Gordon.
Coughlin, Robert. Principles & Applications of Semiconductors & Circuits. LC 78-149974. (Electronic Technology Ser). (Illus.). 1971. 32.95 (ISBN 0-13-700971-2). P-H.
Cowles, Lawrence G. Transistor Circuit Design. (Illus.). 432p. 1972. 34.95 (ISBN 0-13-930032-5). P-H.
Driscoll, Fred & Coughlin, Robert F. Solid State Devices & Applications. (Illus.). 384p. 1975. 31.95 (ISBN 0-13-822106-5). P-H.
Gerrish, H. H. & Dugger, W. E., Jr. Transistor Electronics. LC 81-6740. 368p. 1981. 16.00 (ISBN 0-87006-394-4); wkbk. 6.00 (ISBN 0-87006-318-9). Goodheart.
Gray, Paul E. & Searle, Campbell L. Electronic Principles: Physics, Models & Circuits. LC 78-107884. 1969. text ed. 51.00 (ISBN 0-471-32398-5). Wiley.
Hayward, W. H. Introduction to Radio Frequency Design. (Illus.). 384p. 1982. 34.95 (ISBN 0-13-494021-0). P-H.

Babuel-Peyrissac, Jean-Paul. Equations Cinetiques des Fluides & des Plasmas. (Cours & Documents de Mathematiques & de Physique Ser.). 306p. 1975. 129.50 (ISBN 0-677-50630-9). Gordon.

Bass, J. & Fischer, K. H. Metals: Electronic Transport Phenomena. (Landolt Boernstein Ser.: Group III, Vol. 15, Subvol. A). (Illus.). 400p. 1982. 263.60 (ISBN 0-387-11082-8). Springer-Verlag.

Bear, Jacob & Corapcioglu, M. Yavuz, eds. Fundamentals of Transport Phenomena in Porous Media. (NATO Advanced Science Institute Series E: Applied Science: Vol. 82). 1013p. 1984. 132.50 (ISBN 90-247-2982-3, Pub. by Martinus Nifhoff Netherlands). Kluwer Academic.

Beek, W. J. & Muttzall, K. M. Transport Phenomena. LC 74-4651. 332p. 1975. (Pub. by Wiley-Interscience); pap. text ed. 29.95x (ISBN 0-471-06174-3, Pub. by Wiley-Interscience). Wiley.

Bellman, Richard E. Invariant Imbedding & Time-Dependent Transport Processes. LC 64-9242. (Modern Analytic & Computational Methods in Science & Mathematics Ser.: Vol. 2). pap. 68.80 (ISBN 0-317-08610-3, 2007641). Bks Demand UMI.

Brenner, H. Transport Processes in Porous Media. 1986. write for info. (ISBN 0-07-007645-6). McGraw.

Brutsaert, Wilfried & Jirka, Gerhard H., eds. Gas Transfer at Water Surfaces. 1984. lib. bdg. 78.00 (ISBN 0-318-00439-9, Pub. by Reidel Holland). Kluwer Academic.

Burgers, J. M. Flow Equations for Composite Gases. (Applied Mathematics & Mechanics Ser.: Vol. 11). 1969. 85.00 (ISBN 0-12-143250-5). Acad Pr.

Cercignani, C., ed. Kinetic Theories & the Boltzmann Equation: Lectures Given at the 1st Session of the Centro Interrrazionale Matematico Estivo (C. I. M. E.) Held at Montecatini, Italy, June 10-18, 1981. (Lecture Notes in Mathematics: Vol. 1048). vii, 248p. 1984. pap. 15.50 (ISBN 0-387-12899-9). Springer-Verlag.

Chen, J. C. & Bankoff, S. G., eds. Nonequilibrium Interfacial Transport Processes. 1979. 18.00 (ISBN 0-686-59664-1, I00124). ASME.

Duderstadt, James J. & Martin, William R. Transport Theory. LC 78-13672. 1979. 59.95x (ISBN 0-471-04492-X, Pub. by Wiley-Interscience). Wiley.

Dullien, F. A. Transport Phenomena in Porous Media & Pore Structure. LC 79-52794. 1979. 55.00 (ISBN 0-12-223650-5). Acad Pr.

Fahien, Ray. Fundamentals of Transport Phenomena. (Chemical Engineering Ser.). (Illus.). 640p. 1983. 42.00 (ISBN 0-07-019891-8). McGraw.

Ganapol, B. D., ed. New Frontiers in Transport Theory: Selected Papers from the 6th Conference at U. of Ariz, Tuscon, April 1979. 122p. 1980. pap. 41.00 (ISBN 0-08-026698-3). Pergamon.

Geankoplis. Transport Processes & Unit Operations. 2nd ed. 1983. text ed. 48.97 (ISBN 0-205-07788-9, 3277887). Allyn.

Geankoplis, Christie J. Mass Transport Phenomena. LC 79-154348. 1984. Repr. of 1972 ed. 34.95 (ISBN 0-9603070-0-1). Geankoplis.

--Transport Processes: Momentum, Heat & Mass. 350p. 1983. scp 39.21 (ISBN 0-205-07787-0, 327787). Allyn.

Geiger, G. H. & Poirier, D. R. Transport Phenomena in Metallurgy. LC 75-164648. 1973. text ed. 34.95 (ISBN 0-201-02352-0). Addison-Wesley.

Gordon, R. J. Momentum Transport & Fluid Flow. LC 80-24473. (AIChEMI Modular Instruction C. Ser.: Vol. 1). 62p. 1980. pap. 30.00 (ISBN 0-8169-0172-4); pap. 15.00 members (ISBN 0-317-03840-0). Am Inst Chem Eng.

Gordon, R. J., ed. Momentum Transport, Viscoelasticity & Turbulence. LC 80-24473. (AIChEMI Modular Instruction C. Ser.: Vol. 2). 50p. 1981. pap. 30.00 (ISBN 0-8169-0178-3); pap. 15.00 members (ISBN 0-317-03841-9). Am Inst Chem Eng.

Hershey, Daniel, ed. Transport Analysis. LC 70-183564. (Illus.). 350p. 1973. 49.50x (ISBN 0-306-30555-0, Plenum Pr); pap. 12.95x (ISBN 0-306-20006-6). Plenum Pub.

International School of Statistical Mechanics, June 1974, Sitges Barcelona. Transport Phenomena: Proceedings. Kirczenow, G. & Marro, J., eds. (Lecture Notes in Physics Ser.: Vol. 31). (Illus.). xiv, 517p. 1974. pap. 25.00 (ISBN 0-387-06955-0). Springer-Verlag.

Jackson, R. Transport in Porous Catalysts. (Chemical Engineering Monographs: Vol. 4). 198p. 1977. 51.00 (ISBN 0-444-41593-9). Elsevier.

Kaper, H. G. & Lekkerkerker, C. J., eds. Spectral Methods in Linear Transport Theory. (Operator Theory, Advances & Applications Ser.: Vol. 5). 360p. 1982. text ed. 31.95 (ISBN 0-8176-1372-2). Birkhauser.

Kondratyav, K. Ya. Radiation in the Atmosphere. (International Geophysics Ser.: Vol. 12). 1969. 99.00 (ISBN 0-12-419050-2). Acad Pr.

Kourganoff, Vladimir. Introduction a la Theorie Generale Du Transfer les Particules. (Cours & Documents de Mathematiques & de Physique Ser.). 216p. (Orig.). 1967. 57.75 (ISBN 0-677-50050-5). Gordon.

--Introduction to the General Theory of Particle Transfer. (Documents on Modern Physics Ser.). 230p. 1969. 44.25 (ISBN 0-677-30050-6). Gordon.

Kramer, B., et al, eds. Localization, Interaction & Transport Phenomena. (Springer Series in Solid-State Sciences: Vol. 61). (Illus.). ix, 264p. 1985. 29.00 (ISBN 0-387-15451-5). Springer-Verlag.

Lakshminarayanaiah, N. Transport Phenomena in Membranes. 1969. 82.00 (ISBN 0-12-434250-7). Acad Pr.

Lebovitz, J. L. & Montroll, E. W., eds. Nonequilibrium Phenomena: The Boltzmann Equation, No. 1. (Studies in Statistical Mechanics: Vol. 10). 251p. 1983. 40.00 (ISBN 0-444-86519-5, North-Holland). Elsevier.

Lih, M. Transport Phenomena in Medicine & Biology. LC 74-6059. 531p. 1975. 35.00 (ISBN 0-471-53532-X, Pub. by Wiley). Krieger.

Mujumdar, A. S. & Mashelkar, R. A. Advances in Transport Processes, Vol. 2. 432p. 1982. 48.95x (ISBN 0-470-27320-8). Halsted Pr.

Nunge, Richard J. Flow Through Porous Media. LC 78-146798. 248p. 1970. 15.95 (ISBN 0-8412-0111-0). Am Chemical.

OECD Staff & ECMT Staff. Transport & Energy. (ECMT Round Table: No. 52). 129p. (Orig.). 1981. pap. text ed. 9.00x (ISBN 92-821-1068-0). OECD.

Oppenheim, Irwin, et al. Stochastic Processes in Chemical Physics: The Master Equation. LC 76-27843. 1977. text ed. 40.00x (ISBN 0-262-15017-4). MIT Pr.

Reggiani, L., ed. Hot-Electron Transport in Semiconductors. (Topics in Applied Physics Ser.: Vol. 58). (Illus.). 305p. 1985. 43.50 (ISBN 0-387-13321-6). Springer-Verlag.

Research & Education Association Staff. Transport Phenomena Problem Solver. LC 84-61816. (Illus.). 864p. 1984. pap. text ed. 23.85 (ISBN 0-87891-562-1). Res & Educ.

Sjodin, R. A. Transport in Skeletal Muscle. (Membrane Transport in the Life Sciences Ser.). 157p. 1982. text ed. 40.50x (ISBN 0-471-05265-5, Pub. by Wiley-Interscience). Wiley.

Society for Industrial & Applied Mathematics-American Mathematical Society Symposia, New York, April, 1967. Transport Theory: Proceedings. Abu-Shumays, I. K., et al, eds. LC 68-23112. (SIAM-AMS Proceedings: Vol. 1). 1969. 30.00 (ISBN 0-8218-1320-X, SIAMS-1). Am Math.

Steenbrink, P. A. Optimization of Transport Networks. LC 73-2793. 325p. 1974. 63.95 (ISBN 0-471-82098-9, Pub. by Wiley-Interscience). Wiley.

Steklov Institute of Mathematics, Academy of Sciences, U S S R, No. 97. Milne Problem with Anisotropic Scattering: Proceedings. Maslennikov, M. Y., ed. (Proceedings of the Steklov Institute of Mathematics: No. 97). 1969. 43.00 (ISBN 0-8218-1897-X, STEKLO-97). Am Math.

Stewart-David, David. Theory & Practice of Transport. 1980. pap. 11.50 (ISBN 0-434-91864-4, Pub. by W Heinemann Ltd). David & Charles.

Symposium on the Boltzmann Equation, Vienna, 1972. The Boltzmann Equation (Theory & Applications) Proceedings. Cohen, E. G. & Thirring, W., eds. LC 73-76978. (Acta Physica Austriaca: Suppl. 10). (Illus.). xii, 642p. 1973. 87.40 (ISBN 0-387-81137-0). Springer-Verlag.

Tellier. Size Effects in Thin Films. (Thin Films Science & Technology Ser.: Vol. 2). 310p. 1982. 68.00 (ISBN 0-444-42106-8). Elsevier.

Transport ATPases, Vol. 402. 120.00x (ISBN 0-89766-196-6); pap. 120.00x (ISBN 0-89766-197-4). NY Acad Sci.

Wing, Milton G. Milton an Introduction to Transport Theory. LC 62-18985. 169p. 1962. 10.25 (ISBN 0-471-95418-7). Krieger.

TRANSPORTATION

see also Aeronautics, Commercial; Automobiles; Bridges; Canals; Carriages and Carts; Coastwise Navigation; Coastwise Shipping; Ferries; Harbors; Inland Navigation; Inland Water Transportation; Local Transit; Pipe Lines; Pneumatic-Tube Transportation; Railroads; Roads; Shipping; Steam-Navigation; Steamboats and Steamboat Lines; Streets; Traffic Engineering; Urban Transportation; Vehicles

also subdivision Transportation under special subjects, e.g. Farm Produce–Transportation

Adams, John. Transport Planning: Vision & Practice. 288p. (Orig.). 1981. pap. 17.50x (ISBN 0-7100-0844-9). Routledge & Kegan.

Adler, Hans A. Sector & Project Planning in Transportation. LC 67-28574. (World Bank Staff Occasional Papers Ser: No. 4). 96p. 1967. pap. 5.00x (ISBN 0-8018-0009-9). Johns Hopkins.

Altschiller, Donald. Transportation in America. (The Reference Shelf Ser.: Vol. 54, No. 3). 204p. 1982. text ed. 8.00 (ISBN 0-8242-0667-3). Wilson.

American Society of Civil Engineers, compiled by. Broadening Horizons: Transportation & Development Around the Pacific. LC 80-66122. 432p. 1980. pap. 32.00x (ISBN 0-87262-244-4). Am Soc Civil Eng.

American Society of Civil Engineers & Klohn, Charles H., eds. Joint Usage of Utility & Transportation Corridors. LC 81-68750. 127p. 1981. pap. 15.50x (ISBN 0-87262-277-0). Am Soc Civil Eng.

American Society of Civil Engineers, compiled by. Modes of Transportation. 156p. 1968. pap. 8.75x (ISBN 0-87262-021-2). Am Soc Civil Eng.

--Transportation & Energy. 456p. 1978. pap. 15.00x (ISBN 0-87262-135-9). Am Soc Civil Eng.

The Application of Modern Transport Technology to Mineral Development in Developing Countries. pap. 12.00 (ISBN 0-686-94705-3, UN76/8/1, UN). Unipub.

The Arabian Transport Directory 1985. 1985. 175.00x (ISBN 0-686-69889-4, Pub. by Parrish-Rogers England). State Mutual Bk.

Areskoug, S., et al, eds. Off-Road Transportation & Soil-Working: Means to Promote Development & Operations. 120p. 1985. pap. 30.00 (ISBN 0-08-031652-2). Pergamon.

Banister, David. Transport Mobility & Deprivation in Inter-Urban Areas. 212p. 1980. text ed. 37.95x (ISBN 0-566-00307-4). Gower Pub Co.

Barr, Robert C. Transportation Bleves: Causes - Effects - Guidelines. Lyons, Paul R., ed. LC 78-720334. 1979. pap. 49.50 incl. slides & tape (ISBN 0-87765-139-6, SL-36). Natl Fire Prot.

Blonk, W. A. Transport & Regional Development. 352p. 1979. text ed. 47.50x (ISBN 0-566-00285-X). Gower Pub Co.

Borrup, Roger & Smith, Carl L. Hyde Park Division. (Transportation Bulletin Ser.: No. 82). (Illus.). 1977. 7.50 (ISBN 0-910506-18-3). De Vito.

Bowersox, Donald J., et al. Introduction to Transportation. 1981. text ed. write for info. (ISBN 0-02-313030-X). Macmillan.

Carter, Everett & Homburger, Wolfgang S. Introduction to Transportation Engineering: Highways & Transit. (Illus.). 1978. text. ref. ed. 26.95 (ISBN 0-87909-388-9). Reston.

Clark, Colin. Regional & Urban Location. LC 81-21510. 1982. 32.50x (ISBN 0-312-66903-8). St Martin.

Cohn, Louis F. & McVoy, Gary R. Environmental Analysis of Transportation Systems. LC 81-14637. 374p. 1982. 53.50x (ISBN 0-471-08098-5, Pub. by Wiley-Interscience). Wiley.

Committee on Transportation, Assembly of Engineering, Natl. Research Council. A Review of Short Haul Passenger Transportation. 1976. pap. 7.75 (ISBN 0-309-02445-5). Natl Acad Pr.

Computer Control of Transport. 61p. (Orig.). 1981. pap. text ed. 24.00x (ISBN 0-85825-149-3, Pub. by Inst Engineering Australia). Brookfield Pub Co.

Convention on International Trade in Endangered Species of Wild Fauna & Flora. Guidelines for the Transport & Preparation of Shipment of Live Wild Animals & Plants. 109p. 1981. pap. 13.00 (ISBN 0-686-93565-9, UPB100, UNEP); pap. 13.00 Fr. ed. (ISBN 0-686-99140-0, UPB102); pap. 13.00 Span. ed. (ISBN 0-686-99141-9, UPB101). Unipub.

Coyle, John J. & Bardi, Edward J. Transportation. (Illus.). 542p. 1982. text ed. 28.95 (ISBN 0-314-63158-5). West Pub.

Daggett, Stuart. Principles of Inland Transportation. LC 78-31183. (Illus.). 1979. Repr. of 1955 ed. lib. bdg. 47.50x (ISBN 0-313-20956-1, DAPI). Greenwood.

Dearing, Charles L. & Owen, Wilfred. National Transportation Policy. LC 79-28670. (Illus.). xiv, 459p. 1980. Repr. of 1949 ed. lib. bdg. 37.50x (ISBN 0-313-22301-7, DENT). Greenwood.

A Design Guide for Wildlife Protection & Conservation for Transportation Facilities. 1976. pap. 3.00 (ISBN 0-686-20957-5, GWP-1). AASHTO.

Du Jonchay, Yvan. Handbook of World Transport. 221p. 1980. 20.00 (ISBN 0-87196-393-0). Facts on File.

Dwyer, M. J., ed. The Performance of Off-Road Vehicles & Machines: Proceedings of the 8th International ISTVS Conference, Cambridge, August 1984. 120p. 1984. pap. 30.00 (ISBN 0-08-031655-7). Pergamon.

Energy Storage Systems, E-017 R. 1982. 950.00 (ISBN 0-89336-326-X). BCC.

European Conference of Ministers of Transport. Infrastructural Capacity Problems Raised by International Transit. (ECMT Roundtables Ser.). (Illus.). 135p. (Orig.). 1980. pap. text ed. 4.50x (ISBN 92-821-1059-1, 7580021). OECD.

Florian, Michael & Gaudry, Marc, eds. Transportation Supply Models. 225p. 1981. 31.00 (ISBN 0-08-026075-6). Pergamon.

Foster, Mark S. From Streetcar to Superhighway: American City Planners & Urban Transportation, 1900-1940. LC 80-27202. (Technology & Urban Growth Ser.). (Illus.). 263p. 1981. 34.95 (ISBN 0-87722-210-X). Temple U Pr.

Fraser, Gordon. Modern Transportation & Internatonal Crime. (Illus.). 120p. 1970. photocopy ed. 14.50x (ISBN 0-398-00604-0). C C Thomas.

Geil, J. Energy & Transportation: Power. 1976. pap. text ed. 8.84 (ISBN 0-13-277475-5). P-H.

Gilbert, Gorman & Samuels, Robert E. The Taxicab: An Urban Transportation Survivor. LC 82-2726. (Illus.). xiv, 200p. 1982. 19.95x (ISBN 0-8078-1528-4). U of NC Pr.

Glaister, Stephen. Fundamentals of Transport Economics. 1981. 27.50x (ISBN 0-312-31152-4). St Martin.

Goldstein, Eleanor C., ed. Transportation, Vol. 1 (incl. 1978-1979 Supplements) (Social Issues Resources Ser.). 1980. 70.00 (ISBN 0-89777-018-8). Soc Issues.

--Transportation, Vol. 2 (incl. 1980-1984 Supplements) (Social Issues Resources Ser.). 1984. 70.00 (ISBN 0-89777-050-1). Soc Issues.

Guidelines on Citizen Participation in Transportation Planning. 1978. 97p. pap. 7.00 (ISBN 0-686-32374-2, GCP-1). AASHTO.

Handler, Gabriel Y. & Mirchandani, Pitu. Location on Networks: Theory & Algorithms. (Illus.). 1979. text ed. 40.00x (ISBN 0-262-08090-7). MIT Pr.

Harper, Donald V. Transportation in America: Users, Carriers, Government. 2nd ed. (Illus.). 624p. 1982. text ed. 31.95 (ISBN 0-13-930297-2). P-H.

Hay, William W. An Introduction to Transportation Engineering. 2nd ed. LC 77-9293. 652p. 1977. text ed. 49.75x (ISBN 0-471-36433-9); tchr's manual avail. (ISBN 0-471-04712-0). Wiley.

Heavyside, G T. Tribute to the Deltics. (Illus.). 192p. 1982. 10.95 (ISBN 0-7153-8281-0). David & Charles.

Height, Frank, ed. Design for Passenger Transport. new ed. (Illus.). 1979. text ed. 37.00 (ISBN 0-08-023735-5). Pergamon.

Holder, Jack J., Jr. & Spychalski, John C., eds. Transport & Logistics Challenges, 1974-1980. 1974. pap. 5.00 (ISBN 0-8134-1685-X, 1685). Interstate.

Hurdle, H. V. & Hauer, E., eds. Transportation & Traffic Theory Eighth International Symposium. 736p. 1983. 40.00x (ISBN 0-8020-2461-0). U of Toronto Pr.

Hutchins, G. B. Transportation & the Environment. 106p. 1977. 9.95x (ISBN 0-8464-1146-6). Beekman Pubs.

IAVSD-Symposium Held at the Technical University Berlin, 6th, September 1979. The Dynamics of Vehicles on Roads & on Tracks: Proceedings. Willumeit, H. P., ed. 522p. 1980. pap. text ed. 46.00 (ISBN 90-265-0327-X, Pub. by Swets Pub Serv Holland). Swets North Am.

IFAC-IFIP-IFORS International Conference, 4th, Baden-Baden, BRD, April 1983. Control in Transportation Systems: Proceedings. Lauber, R. & Klamt, D., eds. (IFAC Proceedings Ser.). 450p. 1984. 115.00 (ISBN 0-08-029365-4). Pergamon.

Institute of Transportation Engineers. Transportation & Traffic Engineering Handbook. 2nd. ed. (Illus.). 992p. 1982. 75.00 (ISBN 0-13-930362-6). P-H.

International Technical Conference on Slurry Transportation, 3rd: Proceedings. LC 78-52717. (Illus.). 224p. 1978. pap. 50.00 (ISBN 0-932066-03-8). Slurry Tech.

Jaiswal, N. K., ed. Scientific Management of Transport Systems: Proceedings International Conference, New Delhi, Nov. 26-28, 1980. 378p. 1981. 55.50 (ISBN 0-444-86205-6, North-Holland). Elsevier.

James, George W., ed. Airline Economics. (Illus.). 352p. 1981. 38.50x (ISBN 0-669-04909-3). Lexington Bks.

Jansson, Jan Owen. Transport System Optimization & Pricing. LC 83-10566. 280p. 1984. 54.95x (ISBN 0-471-10264-4, Pub. by Wiley-Interscience). Wiley.

TRANSPORTATION, AUTOMOTIVE
see also Automobiles; Motor Buses; Motor-Trucks; Motor Vehicles; Traffic Safety
Boyle, David H. How to Succeed in Big Time Trucking. LC 77-70986. (Orig.). 1977. pap. 6.95 (ISBN 0-913668-97-4). Ten Speed Pr.
Bruce-Briggs, B. The War Against the Automobile. LC 77-3909. 1977. 10.95 (ISBN 0-525-23008-4). Dutton.
Denham, H. W. Road Transport Records. 12.50x (ISBN 0-392-04425-0, SpS). Sportshelf.
Guide for Motorist Aid System. 1974. 1.00 (ISBN 0-686-29468-8). AASHTO.
J. J. Keller & Associates, Inc, ed. Driver's Pocket Guide to Hazardous Materials. 5th ed. LC 77-90372. (ORS-2). (Orig.). 1984. pap. 2.25 (ISBN 0-934674-26-4). J J Keller.
J. J. Keller & Associates, Inc., ed. Fleet Reports & Records Encyclopedia. LC 81-86193. (21M). 400p. 1984. 3-ring binder 45.00 (ISBN 0-934674-43-4). J J Keller.
Markets for Small Scale Electrical Generation Systems: E-043. 1981. 875.00 (ISBN 0-89336-284-0). BCC.
Rudman, Jack. Highway Transportation Specialist. (Career Examination Ser.: C-2248). (Cloth bdg. avail. on request). pap. 10.00 (ISBN 0-8373-2248-0). Natl Learning.
--Supervisor of Motor Transport. (Career Examination Ser.: C-1509). (Cloth bdg. avail. on request). pap. 10.00 (ISBN 0-8373-1509-3). Natl Learning.
Walters, Alan A. The Economics of Road User Charges. LC 68-8702. (Occasional Papers Ser: No. 5). (Illus.). 243p. (Orig.). 1969. pap. 7.50x (ISBN 0-8018-0653-4). Johns Hopkins.
Wyckoff, D. Daryl & Maister, David H. Owner-Operators: Independent Trucker. LC 74-23978. (Illus.). 192p. 1975. 20.50x (ISBN 0-669-96800-5). Lexington Bks.

TRANSPORTATION, MILITARY
see also Vehicles, Military
Marshall, S. L. The Soldiers Load. 120p. Date not set. Repr. 1.50 (ISBN 0-686-31001-2). MCA.
Rose, Joseph R. American Wartime Transportation. LC 53-7856. (Illus.). 1953. text ed. 5.00x (ISBN 0-911090-19-3). Pacific Bk Supply.
Whitehurst, Clinton H., Jr. Defense Transportation System. 1976. pap. 6.25 (ISBN 0-8447-3221-4). Am Enterprise.

TRANSURANIUM ELEMENTS
DOE Technical Information Center. Radioactive Waste Management: Transuranic Wastes: A Bibliography. 146p. 1982. pap. 14.50 (ISBN 0-87079-481-7, DOE/TIC-3390); microfiche 4.50 (ISBN 0-87079-482-5, DOE/TIC-3390). DOE.
Gel'man, Anna D., et al. Complex Compounds of Transuranium Elements. LC 62-12851. 195p. 1962. 35.00x (ISBN 0-306-10516-0, Consultants). Plenum Pub.
Gol'danskii, V. I. & Polikanov, S. M. The Transuranium Elements. LC 73-83895. (Illus.). 161p. 1973. 35.00x (ISBN 0-306-10901-8, Consultants). Plenum Pub.
Hanson, Wayne C., ed. Transuranic Elements in the Environment: A Summary of Environmental Research on Transuranium Radionuclides Funded by the U. S. Department of Energy Through Calendar Year 1979. DOE Technical Information Center. LC 80-607069. 746p. 1980. hardbound 26.75 (ISBN 0-87079-119-2, DOE/TIC-22800); microfiche 4.50 (ISBN 0-87079-331-4, DOE/TIC-22800). DOE.
Max Planck Society for the Advancement of Science, Gmelin Institute for Inorganic Chemistry. Transurane-Transuranium Elements. (Gmelin Handbuch der Anorganischen Chemie, 8th Ed., New Suppl.: Vol. 20d, Pt. 2). (Illus.). 278p. 1975. 188.20 (ISBN 0-387-93288-7). Springer-Verlag.
Seaborg, G. T., ed. Transuranium Elements: Products of Modern Alchemy. LC 78-7803. (Benchmark Papers in Physical Chemistry & Chemical Physics: Vol. 1). 488p. 1978. 56.00 (ISBN 0-87933-326-X). Van Nos Reinhold.
Treatment of Incorporated Transuranium Elements. (Technical Reports Ser.: No. 184). (Illus.). 170p. 1978. pap. 19.75 (ISBN 92-0-125278-1, IDC184, IAEA). Unipub.

TRAPPING
see also Fur-Bearing Animals; Fur Trade; Game and Game-Birds
Bateman, J. E. Trapping: A Practical Guide. LC 78-15117. (Illus.). 190p. 1979. 14.95 (ISBN 0-8117-1743-7). Stackpole.
Bateman, James A. Animal Traps & Trapping. LC 70-144110. (Illus.). 228p. 1971. 12.95 (ISBN 0-8117-0103-4). Stackpole.
Dearborn, Ned. Trapping on the Farm. 38p. pap. 3.95 (ISBN 0-8466-6028-8, U28). Shorey.
Errington, Paul L. Muskrats & Marsh Management. LC 77-14177. (Illus.). x, 183p. 1978. pap. 4.50 (ISBN 0-8032-5892-5, BB 664, Bison). U of Nebr Pr.
Get Set to Trap. (Illus.). 1982. Student Ed. 1.95 (ISBN 0-916682-36-6); Instr. Ed. 2.95 (ISBN 0-916682-35-8). Outdoor Empire.
Harding, A. R. Deadfalls & Snares. (Illus.). 218p. pap. 3.50 (ISBN 0-936622-03-2). A R Harding Pub.
Ingram, Arthur. Trapping & Poaching. (Shire Album Ser.: No. 34). 32p. 1984. pap. 2.95 (ISBN 0-85263-432-3, 3, Pub. by Shire Pubns England). Seven Hills Bks.
McCracken, Harold & Van Cleve, Harry. Trapping. (Illus.). 1974. 8.95 (ISBN 0-498-08272-5). A S Barnes.
Mason, Otis T. Traps of the American Indians. facs. ed. (Illus.). 18p. pap. 2.95 (ISBN 0-8466-4007-4, I7). Shorey.
Musgrove, Bill & Blair, Gerry. Fur Trapping. (Illus.). 1979. pap. write for info. (Pub. by Winchester Pr). New Century.
Smith, Guy N. Ferreting & Trapping for Amateur Gamekeepers. 2nd ed. (Illus.). 160p. 1979. 13.50 (ISBN 0-904558-73-8). Saiga.
Walters, Keith. The Book of the Free Trapper. 1981. 7.95 (ISBN 0-913150-46-0). Pioneer Pr.

TRASH
see Refuse and Refuse Disposal

TRAWLS AND TRAWLING
see also Fisheries
Amos, D. Single Vessel Midwater Trawling. (Marine Bulletin Ser.: No. 43). 30p. 1980. 2.00 (ISBN 0-938412-26-4, P872). URI MAS.
Brabans, J. & Nedelec, C. Bottom Trawls for Small-Scale Fishing. (Fisheries Technical Papers: No. 189). (Eng., Fr. & Span.). 44p. 1979. pap. 9.00 (ISBN 92-5-100727-6, F1899, FAO). Unipub.
Brabant, J. C. & Nedelec, C. Bottom Trawls for Small-Scale Fishing: Adaptation for Pair Trawling. (Fisheries Technical Papers: No. 189). (Eng. & Fr., Illus.). 27p. 1983. pap. text ed. 7.50 (ISBN 92-5-101235-0, F2420, FAO). Unipub.
Garner, John. Modern Deep Sea Trawling Gear. 1978. 40.00 (ISBN 0-685-63436-1). State Mutual Bk.
--Pelagic & Semi-Pelagic Trawling Gear. (Illus.). 60p. 1979. 33.75 (ISBN 0-85238-088-7, FN74, FNB). Unipub.
--Pelagic & Semi Pelagic Trawling Gear. 1978. 50.00x (ISBN 0-685-63446-9). State Mutual Bk.
Hjul, Peter. The Stern Trawler. 1978. 50.00 (ISBN 0-685-63457-4). State Mutual Bk.
Hjul, Peter, ed. The Stern Trawler. (Illus.). 228p. 21.75 (ISBN 0-85238-025-9, FN21, FNB). Unipub.
Merluza Trawlers for Peru: A Techno-Economic Evaluation. (Fisheries Technical Papers: No. 132). 57p. 1974. pap. 7.50 (ISBN 0-686-92756-7, F1750, FAO). Unipub.
Motte, G. A. & Iitaka, Y. Evaluation of Trawl Performance by Statistical Inference of the Catch. (Marine Technical Report Ser.: No. 36). 1975. pap. 2.00 (ISBN 0-938412-08-6). URI MAS.
Pair Trawling with Small Boats. (Training Ser.: No. 1). 77p. 1981. pap. 8.25 (ISBN 92-5-100627-X, F2095, FAO). Unipub.
Report on Selective Shrimp Trawls: Expert Consultation Held at the Netherlands, 1973. (Fisheries Reports: No. 139). 71p. 1973. pap. 7.50 (ISBN 0-686-93970-0, F784, FAO). Unipub.
Scharfe, J. S. A New Method for "Aimed" One-Boat Trawling in Midwater & on the Bottom. (General Fisheries Council of the Mediterranean: (GFCM) Studies & Reviews: No. 13). (Eng., Fr. & Span.). 60p. 1960. pap. 6.00 (ISBN 92-5-101931-2, F1777, FAO). Unipub.
Thomson, David. Pair Trawling & Pair Seining: The Technology of Two-Boat Fishing. (Illus.). 168p. 1978. 35.00 (ISBN 0-85238-087-9, FN73, FNB). Unipub.

TREE BREEDING
Burley, J. & Nikles, D. C. Selection & Breeding to Improve Some Tropical Conifers, 2 Vols, Vol. 1. 1972. Vol. 1. 90.00x (ISBN 0-85074-026-6, Pub. by For Lib Comm England); Vol. 2. 95.00x (ISBN 0-85074-027-4). State Mutual Bk.
Burley, J. & Nikles, G. Tropical Provenance & Progeny Research & International Cooperation. 1973. 100.00x (ISBN 0-85074-022-3, Pub. by For Lib Comm England). State Mutual Bk.
Burley, J. & Wood, P. J. A Manual on Species & Provenance Research with Particular Reference to the Tropics. 1976. 50.00x (ISBN 0-85074-016-9, Pub. by For Lib Comm England). State Mutual Bk.
--A Manual on Species & Provenance Research with Particular Reference to the Tropics. 1977. 30.00x (ISBN 0-85074-024-X, Pub. by For Lib Comm England). State Mutual Bk.
--Manual Sobre Investigaciones de Especies y Procedencias con Referencia Especial a Los Tropicos. 1979. 50.00x (ISBN 0-85074-058-4, Pub. by For Lib Comm England). State Mutual Bk.
Burley, J. & Styles, B. T., eds. Tropical Trees: Variation Breeding & Conservation. 1976. 49.50 (ISBN 0-12-145150-X). Acad Pr.
Cannell, M. G. & Last, F. T., eds. Tree Physiology & Yield Improvement. 1977. 80.50 (ISBN 0-12-158750-9). Acad Pr.
Chapman, Arthur G. & Wray, Robert D. Christmas Trees for Pleasure & Profit. 3rd ed. (Illus.). 1979. 12.95 (ISBN 0-8135-0872-X). Rutgers U Pr.
Gerhold, H. D., et al, eds. The Breeding of Pest Resistant Trees. 1966. 76.00 (ISBN 0-08-011764-3). Pergamon.
James, N. D. The Arboriculturalist's Companion. 1972. 19.95x (ISBN 0-631-14110-3). Basil Blackwell.
Longman, K. A. Vegetative Propagation of Trees in the 1980s. 1980. 30.00x (ISBN 0-85074-055-X, Pub. by For Lib Comm England). State Mutual Bk.
Miksche, J. P., ed. Modern Methods in Forest Genetics. LC 76-8828. (Illus.). 1976. 36.00 (ISBN 0-387-07708-1). Springer-Verlag.
Namkoong, G., et al. A Philosophy of Strategy for Breeding Tropical Forest Trees. 1980. 30.00x (ISBN 0-85074-034-7, Pub. by For Lib Comm England). State Mutual Bk.
Nikles, D. G., et al. Progress & Problems of Genetic Improvement of Tropical Forest Trees, 2 Vols. 1978. 165.00x (ISBN 0-85074-020-7, Pub. by For Lib Comm England). State Mutual Bk.
Sprague, James W. The Tree That Made a Million Dollars. 105p. 1985. 5.95 (ISBN 0-917802-18-7). Theoscience Found.
Wilde, S. S., et al. Soil & Plant Analysis for Tree Culture. 172p. 1981. 45.00 (ISBN 0-686-76665-2, Pub. by Oxford & IBH India). State Mutual Bk.

TREE PLANTING
Burley, J. & Wood, P. J. Manual Sobre Investigaciones de Especies y Procedencias con Referencia Especial a Los Tropicos. 1979. 50.00x (ISBN 0-85074-058-4, Pub. by For Lib Comm England). State Mutual Bk.
Tree Planting Practices in Temperate Asia: Burma, India and Pakistan. (Forestry Development Papers: No. 14). pap. 4.50 (F482, FAO). Unipub.
Webb, D. B., et al. A Guide to Species Selection for Tropical & Sub-Tropical Plantations. 1980. 60.00x (ISBN 0-85074-033-9, Pub. by For Lib Comm England). State Mutual Bk.

TREE RINGS
see also Dendrochronology
Agerter, Sharlene R. & Glock, Waldo S. An Annotated Bibliography of Tree Growth & Growth Rings, 1950-1962. LC 64-17274. pap. 47.00 (ISBN 0-317-10270-2, 2055332). Bks Demand UMI.
Baillie, M. G. Tree-Ring Dating & Archeology. LC 81-16079. (Illus.). 1982. lib. bdg. 28.00 (ISBN 0-226-03630-8). U of Chicago Pr.
Bowers, Nathan A. Cone-Bearing Trees of the Pacific Coast. rev. ed. (Illus.). 1985. pap. 6.95 (ISBN 0-87015-203-3). Pacific Bks.
Fritts, H. C. Tree Rings & Climate. 1977. 88.50 (ISBN 0-12-268450-8). Acad Pr.

TREE SEEDS
see also Tree Breeding
Forest Tree Seed Directory: 1956. pap. 18.00 (F195, FAO). Unipub.
Forest Tree Seed Directory: 1961. pap. 4.75 (F196, FAO). Unipub.
Greaves, A. Descriptions of Seed Sources & Collections for Provenances of Pinus Caribaea. 1978. 30.00x (ISBN 0-85074-035-5, Pub. by For Lib Comm England). State Mutual Bk.

TREES
see also Dwarf Fruit Trees; Flowering Trees; Forests and Forestry; Fruit-Culture; Grafting; Leaves; Lumbering; Nurseries (Horticulture); Nuts; Ornamental Trees; Pruning; Shrubs; Timber; Tree Rings; Wood
also classes, orders, species, etc. of trees, e.g. Elm, Pine, Spruce
Barefoot, A. C. & Hankins, Frank W. Identification of Modern Tertiary Woods. (Illus.). 1982. 98.00x (ISBN 0-19-854378-6). Oxford U Pr.
Bernatzky, A. Tree Ecology & Preservation. (Developments in Agricultural & Managed-Forest Ecology Ser.: Vol. 2). 358p. 1978. 72.50 (ISBN 0-444-41606-4). Elsevier.
Bowen, Glyn D. & Nambiar, E. K. Nutrition in Forest Trees in Plantations. 1985. 75.00 (ISBN 0-12-120980-6). Acad Pr.
Bowers, Nathan A. Cone-Bearing Trees of the Pacific Coast. rev. ed. (Illus.). 1985. pap. 6.95 (ISBN 0-87015-203-3). Pacific Bks.
Bridgeman, Peter. Trees for Town & Country. LC 79-52380. (Illus.). 1979. 18.95 (ISBN 0-7153-7841-4). David & Charles.
Brown, F. B. Cornaceae & Allies in the Marquesas & Neighboring Islands. (BMB). pap. 8.00 (ISBN 0-527-02158-X). Kraus Repr.
Clouston, Brian & Stansfield, Kathy, eds. After the Elm. (Illus.). 186p. 1980. text ed. 24.50x (ISBN 0-8419-6107-7). Holmes & Meier.
--Trees in Towns: Maintenance & Management. (Illus.). 182p. 1981. 28.50 (ISBN 0-85139-658-5). Nichols Pub.
Collingwood, G. & Brush, W. Knowing Your Trees. 9.50 (ISBN 0-686-26731-1, 23). Am Forestry.
Copeland, E. B. Pteridophytes of the Society Islands. (BMB Ser.). Repr. of 1932 ed. 12.00 (ISBN 0-527-02199-7). Kraus Repr.
Dicks, W. Groups, Trees & Projective Modules. (Lecture Notes in Mathematics: Vol. 790). 127p. 1980. pap. 13.00 (ISBN 0-387-09974-3). Springer-Verlag.
Downing, Andrew J. Rural Essays. Curtis, George W., ed. LC 69-13713. (Architecture & Decorative Art Ser.). 640p. 1975. Repr. of 1854 ed. lib. bdg. 55.00 (ISBN 0-306-71035-8). Da Capo.
Dyson, S. L. The Stories of the Trees. LC 78-175735. (Illus.). 272p. 1974. Repr. of 1890 ed. 40.00x (ISBN 0-8103-3033-4). Gale.
Elias, Thomas S., et al. Trees & the Community. 1973. pap. 4.00x (ISBN 0-89327-051-2). NY Botanical.
Environmental Design Press. Trees of the West. 20.50 (ISBN 0-442-22207-6). Van Nos Reinhold.
Forest Tree Seed Directory, 1975. 283p. 1975. pap. 24.00 (ISBN 92-5-001587-9, F197, FAO). Unipub.
Friedrich, Paul. Proto-Indo-European Trees. LC 70-104332. 1970. 16.00x (ISBN 0-226-26480-7). U of Chicago Pr.
Fundter, J. M. Names for Dipterocarp Timbers & Trees from Asia. 252p. 1982. 42.25 (ISBN 90-220-0795-2, PDC255, Pudoc). Unipub.
Grace, Julie, ed. Trees & Shrubs. (Know Your Garden Ser.). (Illus.). 179p. 1983. Repr. of 1973 ed. 24.95 (ISBN 0-917304-84-5). Timber.
Guia de Arboles. Leatherette 44.95 (ISBN 0-686-97407-7, S-36343). French & Eur.
Habit, Mario, et al. Prosopis Tamarugo: Fodder Tree for Arid Zones. (Plant Production & Protection Papers: No. 25). (Eng., Fr. & Span.). 119p. 1981. pap. 8.75 (ISBN 92-5-101055-2, F2229, FAO). Unipub.
Haller, John M. Tree Care. LC 76-50995. (Illus.). 1977. pap. 8.95 (ISBN 0-672-23280-4). Audel.
Hammett, K. R. Plant Training, Pruning & Tree Surgery. (Illus.). 68p. 1983. 10.50 (ISBN 0-7153-6409-X). David & Charles.
Harlow, William M. Fruit Key & Twig Key to Trees & Shrubs. (Illus.). 12.00 (ISBN 0-8446-0678-2). Peter Smith.
--Textbook of Dendrology. 6th ed. (Illus.). 1979. text ed. 37.95 (ISBN 0-07-026570-4). McGraw.
Harvey, Nigel. Trees, Woods & Forests. (Shire Album Ser.: No. 74). (Illus.). 32p. 1981. pap. 2.95 (ISBN 0-85263-572-9, Pub. by Shire Pubns England). Seven Hills Bks.
Heatwole, Harold. A Coral Island: The Story of One Tree Reef. (Illus.). 200p. 1982. 24.95x (ISBN 0-00-216442-6, Pub. by W Collins Australia). Intl Spec Bk.
Helliwell, Rodney. Garden Trees: A Guide to the Siting, Selection & Maintenance of Trees in Small & Medium Sized Gardens. (Forestry Research Studies). 95p. 1983. pap. 23.95 (ISBN 0-471-10382-9, Pub. by Res Stud Pr). Wiley.
Hora, Bayard, ed. Oxford Encyclopedia of Trees of the World. LC 80-40560. (Illus.). 1981. 27.50 (ISBN 0-19-217712-5). Oxford U Pr.
Horn, Henry S. Adaptive Geometry of Trees. LC 70-140279. (Monographs in Population Biology: No. 3). 1971. 26.00x (ISBN 0-691-08089-5). Princeton U Pr.
Horticultural Committee of the Garden Club of America. Plants That Merit Attention: Trees, Vol. 1. (Illus.). 360p. 1984. 44.95 (ISBN 0-917304-75-6). Timber.
Hudak, Joseph. Trees for Every Purpose. (Illus.). 1980. 34.95 (ISBN 0-07-030841-1). McGraw.
Kondo, Riki H. Trees. (Instant Nature Guides). (Illus.). 1979. pap. 2.95 (ISBN 0-448-12674-5, G&D). Putnam Pub Group.
Kozlowski, T. T. Growth & Development of Trees, 2 Vols. LC 70-127688. (Physiological Ecology Ser). 1971. Vol. 1. 70.00 (ISBN 0-12-424201-4); Vol. 2. 80.50 (ISBN 0-12-424202-2). Acad Pr.
Kozlowski, Theodore T. Tree Growth & Environmental Stresses. LC 78-10815. (Geo. S. Long Publication Ser.). (Illus.). 184p. 1979. 15.00x (ISBN 0-295-95636-4). U of Wash Pr.
Kramer, Paul J. & Kozlowski, T. T. Physiology of Trees. (Botanical Sciences Ser.). 1960. text ed. 54.95 (ISBN 0-07-035351-4). McGraw.
Krussmann, Gerd. Manual of Cultivated Broad-leaved Trees & Shrubs, Vol. 1. Epp, Michael, tr. from Ger. Tr. of Handbuch der Laubgeholze. 498p. 1984. 65.00 (ISBN 0-917304-78-0). Timber.
Kunkel, Gunther. Flowering Trees in Subtropical Gardens. (Illus.). 1978. 37.00 (ISBN 9-06193-592-X, Pub. by Junk Pubs. Netherlands). Kluwer Academic.
Leenhouts, P. W. Genus Canarium in the Pacific. (BMB Ser.). pap. 10.00 (ISBN 0-527-02324-8). Kraus Repr.

Li Hui-Lin. The Origin & Cultivation of Shade & Ornamental Trees. LC 62-11271. (Illus.). 288p. 1974. pap. 9.95 (ISBN 0-8122-1070-0, Pa Paperbks). U of Pa Pr.
Line, Les & Sutton, Ann. The Audubon Society Book of Trees. (Audubon Society Ser.). (Illus.). 264p. 1981. 50.00 (ISBN 0-8109-0673-2). Abrams.
Maino, Evelyn & Howard, Frances. Ornamental Trees: An Illustrated Guide to Their Selection & Care. (Illus.). 1955. pap. 9.95 (ISBN 0-520-00795-6). U of Cal Pr.
Meiggs, Russell. Trees & Timber in the Ancient Mediterranean World. (Illus.). 1982. 79.00x (ISBN 0-19-814840-2). Oxford U Pr.
Miller, Howard A. How to Know the Trees. 3rd ed. (Pictured Key Nature Ser.). 288p. 1978. write for info. wire coil (ISBN 0-697-04896-9). Wm C Brown.
Mitchell, Alan. The Gardener's Book of Trees. (Illus.). 228p. 1981. 25.00x (ISBN 0-460-04403-6, Pub. by J M Dent England). Biblio Dist.
Mitchell, Alan & Ruggerio, Michael. Trees of North America. LC 79-738. (Spotter's Guides). (Illus.). 1979. 3.95 (ISBN 0-8317-8818-6, Mayflower Bks); pap. 1.95 (ISBN 0-8317-8819-4). Smith Pubs.
Nadel, Ira B. & Oberlander, Cornelia H. Trees in the City. LC 77-1713. 1978. text ed. 16.25 (ISBN 0-08-021489-4); pap. text ed. 7.75 (ISBN 0-08-021488-6). Pergamon.
Nooteboom, H. P. Revision of the Symplocaceae of the Old World. (Leiden Botanical Ser: No. 1). 1975. lib. bdg. 53.00 (ISBN 90-6021-242-8, Pub. by Leiden Univ Holland). Kluwer Academic.
One Hundred Finest Trees & Shrubs. 2.25 (ISBN 0-686-21127-8). Bklyn Botanic.
Opeke, Lawrence K. Tropical Tree Crops. 1982. 49.95x (ISBN 0-471-10060-9, Pub. by Wiley-Interscience); pap. 19.95x (ISBN 0-471-10066-8). Wiley.
Peterson, Russell. The Pine Tree Book. (Illus.). 1980. 14.95 (ISBN 0-89616-005-X); pap. 7.95 (ISBN 0-89616-006-8). Brandywine.
Petrides, George A. Field Guide to Trees & Shrubs. 1973. 15.95 (ISBN 0-395-13651-2); pap. 10.95 (ISBN 0-395-17579-8). HM.
Polunin, Oleg. Trees & Bushes of Europe. (Illus.). 1976. 18.95x (ISBN 0-19-217631-5). Oxford U Pr.
Ponce, John, compiled by. Trees of the San Jacinto Mountains. (Illus.). 32p. 1976. pap. 1.75 (ISBN 0-913612-02-2). Strawberry Valley.
Poplars & Willows. (Forestry Ser.: No. 10). 360p. 1980. 40.00 (ISBN 92-5-100500-1, F2046, FAO). Unipub.
Pruning Shade Trees & Practicing Tree Surgery. facs. ed. (Shorey Lost Arts Ser.). 52p. pap. 2.95 (ISBN 0-8466-6041-5, U41). Shorey.
RHS Enterprises Ltd., ed. Trees for Small Gardens. 1982. 15.00x (ISBN 0-900629-99-1, Pub. by RHS Ent England). State Mutual Bk.
Rudman, Jack. Tree Trimmer Foreman. (Career Examination Ser.: C-2574). (Cloth bdg. avail. on request). pap. 12.00 (ISBN 0-8373-2574-9). Natl Learning.
Rushforth, Keith. Pocket Guide to Trees. 1981. 7.95 (ISBN 0-686-73804-7). S&S.
Sapody, C & Toth, I., eds. A Colour Atlas of Flowering Trees & Shrubs. 312p. 1982. 51.00 (Pub. by Akademiai Kiado Hungary). Heyden.
Schuler, Stanley, ed. Simon & Schuster's Guide to Trees. (Illus.). 1978. 19.95 (ISBN 0-671-24124-9); pap. 9.95 (ISBN 0-671-24125-7). S&S.
Serre, J. P. Trees. 140p. 1980. 31.00 (ISBN 0-387-10103-9). Springer-Verlag.
Smith, J. Russell. Tree Crops: A Permanent Agriculture. rev. ed. (Illus.). 408p. 1985. pap. 12.95 (ISBN 0-8159-6908-2). Devin.
Standley, P. Trees & Shrubs of Mexico, 5 vols. 1976. Set. lib. bdg. 600.00 (ISBN 0-8490-2766-7). Gordon Pr.
Symonds, George W. The Tree Identification Book. LC 58-5359. 272p. 1973. 19.95 (ISBN 0-688-00039-8); pap. 10.95 (ISBN 0-688-05039-5). Morrow.
Thomas, Graham S. Trees in the Landscape. (A National Trust Book Ser.). (Illus.). 208p. 1984. 22.95 (ISBN 0-224-02051-X, Pub. by Jonathan Cape). Merrimack Pub Cir.
Thompson, A. Robert. Rope Knots & Tree Climbing Safety for Tree Workers. facs. ed. (Shorey Lost Arts Ser.). 66p. pap. 2.95 (ISBN 0-8466-6046-6, U46). Shorey.
Tranquillini, W. Physiological Ecology of the Alpine Timberline. (Ecological Studies: Vol. 31). (Illus.). 1979. 37.00 (ISBN 0-387-09065-7). Springer-Verlag.
Tree & Shrub Forms-Their Landscape Use. 2.25 (ISBN 0-686-21157-X). Bklyn Botanic.
Trees for the Yard, Orchard & Woodlot. 1978. pap. 6.95 (ISBN 0-87857-229-5). Rodale Pr Inc.
Walden, Fred. Dictionary of Trees. LC 63-2400. (Orig.). pap. 3.95 (ISBN 0-8200-0401-4). Great Outdoors.
Walker, Laurence C. Trees: An Introduction to Trees & Forest Ecology for the Amateur Naturalist. (Illus.). 288p. 1984. 23.95 (ISBN 0-13-930157-7); pap. 10.95 (ISBN 0-13-930140-2). P-H.
Watts, Tom. Pacific Coast Tree Finder: A Manual for Identifying Pacific Coast Trees. 1973. pap. 1.50 (ISBN 0-912550-06-6). Nature Study.
--Rocky Mountain Tree Finder: A Manual for Identifying Rocky Mountain Trees. 58p. 1972. pap. 1.50 (ISBN 0-912550-05-8). Nature Study.
Wilson, Ernest H. Aristocrats of the Trees. (Illus.). 279p. 1974. Repr. of 1930 ed. 6.95 (ISBN 0-486-20038-8). Dover.
--Aristocrats of the Trees. (Illus.). 9.00 (ISBN 0-8446-5100-1). Peter Smith.
Youngman, W. & Randall, C. Growing Your Trees. 4.50 (ISBN 0-686-26730-3, 37). Am Forestry.
Zimmermann, M. H. & Brown, C. L. Trees: Structure & Function - with a Chapter on Irreversible Thermodynamics of Transport Phenomena by M. T. Tyree. LC 70-163210. (Illus.). xiii, 336p. 1975. pap. 23.00 (ISBN 0-387-07063-X). Springer-Verlag.

TREES–BIBLIOGRAPHY

Agerter, Sharlene R. & Glock, Waldo S. An Annotated Bibliography of Tree Growth & Growth Rings, 1950-1962. LC 64-17274. pap. 47.00 (ISBN 0-317-10270-2, 2055332). Bks Demand UMI.
Ortho Books Staff. All about Trees. Ferguson, Barbara J., ed. LC 82-82155. (Illus.). 112p. 1982. pap. 5.95 (ISBN 0-89721-007-7). Ortho.

TREES–BREEDING

see Tree Breeding

TREES–CHEMISTRY

see Wood–Chemistry

TREES–DISEASES AND PESTS

see also Fruit–Diseases and Pests; Fungicides; Insecticides; Insects, Injurious and Beneficial; Parasitic Plants; Plant Diseases;
also names of particular trees, e.g. Elm; names of diseases and pests

Ash Dieback, No. 88. 1966. 1.00 (ISBN 0-686-20700-9). SUNY Environ.
Baxter, Dow V. Disease in Forest Plantations. LC 67-18144. (Bulletin Ser.: No. 51). (Illus.). 251p. 1967. text ed. 4.25x (ISBN 0-87737-028-1). Cranbrook.
Blanchard, Robert & Tattar, Terry. Field & Laboratory Guide to Tree Pathology. 1981. 25.50 (ISBN 0-12-103980-3). Acad Pr.
Boethal, D. J. & Eikenbary, R. D., eds. Pest Management Programs for Deciduous Tree Fruits & Nuts. LC 79-12616. 267p. 1979. 39.50x (ISBN 0-306-40178-9, Plenum Pr). Plenum Pub.
Browne, Frances G. Pests & Diseases of Forest Plantation Trees: An Annotated List of the Principle Species Occurring in the British Commonwealth. 1968. 98.00x (ISBN 0-19-854367-0). Oxford U Pr.
Campana, R. J. & Stipes, R. J. Compendium of Elm Diseases. LC 81-67058. (Illus.). 96p. 1981. saddle stitched 17.00 (ISBN 0-89054-042-X). Am Phytopathol Soc.
Gerhold, H. D., et al, eds. The Breeding of Pest Resistant Trees. 1966. 76.00 (ISBN 0-08-011764-3). Pergamon.
Ghani, M. A. & Cheema, M. A., eds. Biology, Ecology & Behaviour of Principal Natural Enemies of Major Insect Pests of Forest Trees in Pakistan. 100p. 1973. 49.00x (ISBN 0-85198-283-2, Pub. by CAB Bks England). State Mutual Bk.
Gibson, J. A. Diseases of Forest Trees Widely Planted as Exotics in the Tropics & Southern Hemisphere, Part 1. 1975. 30.00x (ISBN 0-85074-036-3, Pub. by for Lib Comm England). State Mutual Bk.
--Diseases of Forest Trees Widely Planted as Exotics in the Tropics & Southern Hemisphere, Part 2. 1978. 30.00x (ISBN 0-85074-028-2, Pub. by For Lib Comm England). State Mutual Bk.
Heybroek, H. M., et al, eds. Resistance to Diseases & Pests in Forest Trees: Proceedings of the Third International Workshop on the Genetics of Host-Parasite Interactions in Forestry, Wageningen, The Netherlands, 14-21 Sept. 1980. 514p. (59 papers, index). 1982. 66.75 (ISBN 90-220-0794-4, PDC248, Pudoc). Unipub.
Manion, Paul D. Tree Disease Concepts in Relation to Forest & Urban Tree Management Practice. (Illus.). 400p. 1981. text ed. 29.95 (ISBN 0-13-930701-X). P-H.
Maramorosch, Karl & Raychaudhuri, S. P., eds. Mycoplasma Diseases of Trees & Shrubs. LC 81-3534. 1981. 38.50 (ISBN 0-12-470220-1). Acad Pr.
Novak, Vladimir, et al, eds. Atlas of Insects Harmful to Forest Trees. (Illus.). 126p. 1977. 85.00 (ISBN 0-444-99874-8). Elsevier.
Powell, Conway L. & Bagaraj, D. Joseph. VA Mycorrhiza. 288p. 1984. 75.00 (ISBN 0-8493-5694-6). CRC Pr.
Roberts, H. Forest Insects in Nigeria. 1969. 30.00x (ISBN 0-85074-006-1, Pub. by For Lib Comm England). State Mutual Bk.
White, M. G. The Problem of the Phytolyma Gall Bug in the Establishment of Chlorophora. 1966. 30.00x (ISBN 0-686-45545-2, Pub. by For Lib Comm England). State Mutual Bk.

TREES–PLANTING

see Tree Planting

TREES–AFRICA

Hargreaves, Dorothy & Hargreaves, Bob. African Trees. LC 72-85426. (Illus.). 64p. 1972. pap. 3.00 (ISBN 0-910690-07-3). Hargreaves.
Palmer. A Field Guide to the Trees of Southern Africa. 29.95 (ISBN 0-00-219339-6, Collins Pub England). Greene.
Voorhoeve, A. G. Liberian High Forest Trees. 428p. (2nd printing, 32 full page photos, 72 full page drawings). 1979. 80.00 (ISBN 90-220-0701-4, PDC119, PUDOC). Unipub.

TREES–CARIBBEAN AREA

Little, Elbert L., Jr., et al. Arboles Comunes de Puerto Rico y las Islas Virgenes, Vol. 1. University of Puerto Rico Press, tr. from Span. Tr. of Common Trees of Puerto Rico & the Virgin Islands. (Illus.). xxxix, 731p. 1978. 20.00 (ISBN 0-8477-2313-5). U of PR Pr.

TREES–EUROPE

Fairhurst, Alan & Aoothill, Eric. The Blandford Guide to Trees of the British Countryside. (Illus.). 144p. 1981. 24.95 (ISBN 0-7137-0938-3, Pub. by Blandford Pr England). Sterling.
Hadfield, Miles. Discovering England's Trees. (Discovering Ser.: No. 86). (Illus.). 96p. (Orig.). 1980. pap. 3.50 (ISBN 0-85263-490-0, Pub. by Shire Pubns England). Seven Hills Bks.
Hart, Cyril & Raymond, Charles. British Trees in Colour. (Illus.). 152p. 1985. pap. 13.95 (ISBN 0-7181-2545-2, Pub. by Michael Joseph). Merrimack Pub Cir.
Harz, Kurt. Trees & Shrubs. (Illus.). 150p. 1981. pap. 5.95 (ISBN 0-7011-2542-X, Pub. by Chatto & Windus). Merrimack Pub Cir.
Mitchell. A Field Guide to the Trees of Britain & Northern Europe. 24.95 (ISBN 0-00-219213-6, Collins Pub England). Greene.
Mitchell & Wilkinson. The Trees of Britain & Northern Europe. pap. 14.95 (ISBN 0-00-219035-4, Collins Pub England). Greene.
Richens, R. H. Elm. LC 82-17690. (Illus.). 325p. 1983. 72.50 (ISBN 0-521-24916-3). Cambridge U Pr.

TREES–HAWAII

Belknap, Jodi P. Majesty: The Exceptional Trees of Hawaii. Cazimero, Momi, ed. LC 82-60598. 72p. 1982. 12.95 (ISBN 0-686-38728-7). Outdoor Circle.
Hargreaves, Dorothy & Hargreaves, Bob. Tropical Trees of Hawaii. LC 64-23259. (Illus.). 1964. pap. 3.00 (ISBN 0-910690-02-2). Hargreaves.
Kuck, Loraine E. & Tongg, Richard C. Guide to Tropical & Semi-Tropical Flora. LC 58-7494. (Illus.). pap. 13.50 (ISBN 0-8048-0227-0). C E Tuttle.
--Hawaiian Flowers & Flowering Trees LC 58-7494. (Illus.). 1958. boxed 19.50 (ISBN 0-8048-0237-8). C E Tuttle.
Lamb, Samuel H. Native Trees & Shrubs of the Hawaiian Islands. LC 80-19715. 160p. 1981. pap. 14.95 (ISBN 0-913270-91-1). Sunstone Pr.

TREES–LATIN AMERICA

Hargreaves, Dorothy & Hargreaves, Bob. Tropical Trees: Found in the Carribbean, South American, Central America, Mexico. LC 65-19767. (Illus.). 1965. pap. 3.00 (ISBN 0-910690-05-7). Hargreaves.
Herwitz, Stanley R. The Regeneration of Selected Tropical Tree Species in Corcovado National Park, Costa Rica. (U.C. Publications in Geography: Vol. 24). 1981. pap. 15.00x (ISBN 0-520-09631-2). U of Cal Pr.
McMinn, Howard E. & Maino, Evelyn. An Illustrated Manual of Pacific Coast Trees. 2nd ed. 1937. 12.95 (ISBN 0-520-00846-4); pap. 6.95 (ISBN 0-520-04364-2). U of Cal Pr.

TREES–NEW ZEALAND

Eagle, Audrey. Eagle's Trees & Shrubs of New Zealand in Colour. (Illus.). 311p. 1983. Repr. of 1975 ed. 95.00x (ISBN 0-686-84831-4, Pub. by W Collins New Zealand). Intl Spec Bk.

TREES–NORTH AMERICA

Harlow, William M. Fruit Key & Twig Key. (Illus., Orig.). 1946. pap. 2.25 (ISBN 0-486-20511-8). Dover.
--Trees of Eastern & Central United States & Canada. (Illus.). 11.50 (ISBN 0-8446-0679-0). Peter Smith.
--Trees of the Eastern & Central United States & Canada. (Illus.). 1942. pap. 3.50 (ISBN 0-486-20395-6). Dover.
--Trees of the Eastern & Central United States & Canada. LC 57-4601. 1957. lib. bdg. 10.50x (ISBN 0-88307-554-7). Gannon.
Harrar, Ellwood S. & Hough, Romeyn B. Hough's Encyclopedia of American Woods, 16 vols. 1972. 75.00 ea. (ISBN 0-8315-0075-1). Speller.
Hyland, Fay & Steinmetz, Ferdinand H. Trees & Other Woody Plants of Maine. 72p. pap. 3.50 (ISBN 0-89621-018-9). U Maine Orono.
Jaynes, Richard A., ed. Nut Tree Culture in North America. LC 78-71628. (Illus.). 1979. 17.50 (ISBN 0-9602248-0-7). N Nut Growers.
Ketchledge, E. H. Trees of the Adirondack High Peak Region. 2nd ed. LC 67-28444. (Illus.). pap. 2.95 (ISBN 0-935272-07-0). ADK Mtn Club.
Knobel, Edward. Identify Trees & Shrubs by Their Leaves: A Guide to Trees & Shrubs Native to the Northeast. (Illus.). 12.00 (ISBN 0-8446-4629-6). Peter Smith.
Lanner, Ronald M. Trees of the Great Basin: A Natural History. (Max C. Fleischmann Series in Great Basin Natural History). (Illus.). 256p. 1984. 19.50 (ISBN 0-87417-081-8); pap. 12.50 (ISBN 0-87417-082-6). U of Nev Pr.
Li Hui-Lin. Trees of Pennsylvania, the Atlantic States, & the Lake States. LC 72-80377. (Illus.). 1972. 27.50x (ISBN 0-8122-7665-5); pap. 10.95 (ISBN 0-8122-1064-6, Pa Paperbks). U of Pa Pr.
Patterson, Jack & Stevenson, George B. Native Trees of the Bahamas. (Illus.). pap. 5.95 (ISBN 0-916224-42-2). Banyan Bks.
Peattie, Donald C. A Natural History of Western Trees. LC 80-12263. (Illus.). xvi, 751p. 1980. pap. 14.95 (ISBN 0-8032-8701-1, BB 741, Bison). U of Nebr Pr.
Preston, Richard J., Jr. North American Trees. 3rd ed. 1976. text ed. 10.50x (ISBN 0-8138-1170-8). Iowa St U Pr.
Sargent, Charles S. Manual of the Trees of North America, 2 Vols. 2nd ed. (Illus.). 1922. pap. text ed. 7.95 ea.; Vol. 1. pap. text ed. (ISBN 0-486-20277-1); Vol. 2. pap. text ed. (ISBN 0-486-20278-X). Dover.
--Manual of the Trees of North America, 2 Vols. (Illus.). 1962. Set. 28.00 (ISBN 0-8446-2864-6). Peter Smith.
The Spotter's Handbook to Wildflowers, Trees & Birds or North America. LC 79-10397. (Spotter's Guides). (Illus.). 1980. 5.95 (ISBN 0-8317-7953-5, Mayflower Bks); pap. 3.95 (ISBN 0-8317-7954-3). Smith Pubs.
Sudworth, George B. Forest Trees of the Pacific Slope. (Illus.). 1967. pap. 7.95 (ISBN 0-486-21752-3). Dover.
--Forest Trees of the Pacific Slope. (Illus.). 16.75 (ISBN 0-8446-3031-4). Peter Smith.
Your Native Shade Trees. 1972. 0.15 (ISBN 0-686-20734-3). SUNY Environ.

TREES–UNITED STATES

Allison, R. Bruce & Durbin, Elizabeth. Wisconsin's Famous & Historic Trees. (Illus.). 120p. pap. 14.95 (ISBN 0-913370-14-2). Wisconsin Bks.
Arno, Stephen F. Discovering Sierra Trees. (Discovering Sierra Ser.). 89p. (Orig.). 1973. pap. 2.95 (ISBN 0-939666-04-9). Yosemite Natl Hist.
--Northwest Trees. LC 77-82369. (Illus.). 1977. pap. 8.95 (ISBN 0-916890-50-3). Mountaineers.
Audubon Society & Little, Elbert L., Jr. Audubon Field Guide to North American Trees. Western ed. 1980. 13.50 (ISBN 0-394-50761-4). Knopf.
Barnes, Burton V. & Wagner, Warren H., Jr. Michigan Trees: A Guide to the Trees of Michigan & the Great Lakes. (Biological Science). (Illus.). 384p. 1981. text ed. 15.00x (ISBN 0-472-08017-2); pap. text ed. 8.95x (ISBN 0-472-08018-0). U of Mich Pr.
Basten, Fred E. An Illustrated Guide to the Legendary Trees of Santa Monica Bay. LC 80-83609. (Illus.). 128p. (Orig.). 1980. pap. 6.95 (ISBN 0-937536-01-6). Graphics Calif.
Brown, Clair. Louisiana Trees & Shrubs. 1965. 7.50 (ISBN 0-87511-012-6). Claitors.
Burns, G. P. & Otis, C. H. The Handbook of Vermont Trees. LC 78-68710. pap. 5.25 (ISBN 0-8048-1315-9). C E Tuttle.
Dame, Lorin L. & Brooks, Henry. Handbook of the Trees of New England with Ranges Throughout the United States & Canada. (Illus., With a new Table of Changes in Nomenclature). 11.25 (ISBN 0-8446-4533-8). Peter Smith.
Duncan, Wilbur H. Guide to Georgia Trees. LC 41-11394. 64p. 1941. pap. 3.50x (ISBN 0-8203-0214-7). U of Ga Pr.
Elias, Thomas. The Complete Trees of North America Field Guide & Natural History. (Outdoor Life-Nature Book). 864p. 1980. 22.95 (ISBN 0-442-23862-2). Van Nos Reinhold.
Gupton, Oscar W. & Swope, Fred C. Trees & Shrubs of Virginia. LC 80-21585. (Illus.). 205p. 1981. 10.95 (ISBN 0-8139-0886-8). U Pr of Va.
Harrar, Elwood S. & Harrar, George J. Guide to Southern Trees. (Illus.). 1962. pap. 6.95 (ISBN 0-486-20945-8). Dover.
Harrar, Elwood S. & Harrar, J. George. Guide to Southern Trees. (Illus.). 13.25 (ISBN 0-8446-2210-9). Peter Smith.

Hutchings, J. M. The Mammoth Trees of Calaveras: Scene of Wonder & Curiosity in California, 1872. Jones, William R., ed. (Illus.). 32p. 1978. pap. 1.00 (ISBN 0-89646-050-9). Outbooks.

Knobel, Edward. Identify Trees & Shrubs by Their Leaves. (Illus.). 1972. pap. 2.75 (ISBN 0-486-22896-7). Dover.

Kurz, Herman & Godfrey, Robert K. Trees of Northern Florida. LC 62-17479. (Illus.). xxxiv, 311p. 1962. pap. 15.00 (ISBN 0-8130-0666-X). U Presses Fla.

Lakela, Olga & Wonderlin, Richard P. Trees of Central Florida. (Illus.). 1980. 14.95 (ISBN 0-916224-51-1). Banyan Bks.

Li Hui-Lin. Trees of Pennsylvania, the Atlantic States, & the Lake States. LC 72-80377. (Illus.). 1972. 27.50x (ISBN 0-8122-7665-5); pap. 10.95 (ISBN 0-8122-1064-6, Pa Paperbks). U of Pa Pr.

Metcalf, Woodbridge. Introduced Trees of Central California. (California Natural History Guides: No. 27). (Illus.). 1969. pap. 2.25 (ISBN 0-520-01548-7). U of Cal Pr.

--Native Trees of the San Francisco Bay Region. (California Natural History Guides Ser.: No. 4). (Orig.). 1959. pap. 4.95 (ISBN 0-520-00853-7). U of Cal Pr.

Muenscher, Walter C. Keys to Woody Plants. 6th, rev. ed. (Illus.). 108p. 1950. 11.95x (ISBN 0-8014-0307-3). Comstock.

Muller, Katherine K., et al. Trees of Santa Barbara. (Illus.). 1974. 10.00 (ISBN 0-916436-00-4). Santa Barb Botanic.

Perry, Robert C. Trees & Shrubs for Dry California Landscapes. LC 81-81013. (Illus.). 184p. 1981. 32.50 (ISBN 0-9605988-0-4); text ed. 32.50 (ISBN 0-9605988-1-2). Land Design.

Peterson, Victor P. Native Trees of Southern California. (California Natural History Guides Ser.: No. 14). (Illus.). 1966. pap. 5.95 (ISBN 0-520-01004-3). U of Cal Pr.

Peterson, Victor P. & Peterson, Victor P., Jr. Native Trees of the Sierra Nevada. (Natural History Guides Ser.: No. 36). 1974. pap. 3.95 (ISBN 0-520-02666-7). U of Cal Pr.

Phillips, Roger. Trees of North America & Europe. 1978. 25.00 (ISBN 0-394-50259-0); pap. 12.95 (ISBN 0-394-73541-2). Random.

Preston, Richard J., Jr. North American Trees. 3rd ed. (Illus.). 1977. pap. 5.95x (ISBN 0-262-66031-8). MIT Pr.

--Rocky Mountain Trees. 2nd rev. ed. LC 68-20408. (Illus.). 1968. pap. 5.95 (ISBN 0-486-21898-8). Dover.

--Rocky Mountain Trees: A Handbook of the Native Species, with Plates & Distribution Maps. 3rd rev. ed. (Illus.). 13.50 (ISBN 0-8446-2758-5). Peter Smith.

Randall, Warren R. Manual of Oregon Trees & Shrubs. 1981. pap. text ed. 6.95x (ISBN 0-88246-092-7). Oreg St U Bkstrs.

Record, Samuel J. & Hess, Robert W. Timbers of the New World. LC 73-140611. (Use & Abuse of America's Natural Resources Ser). (Illus.). 718p. 1972. Repr. of 1943 ed. 57.50 (ISBN 0-405-02806-7). Ayer Co Pubs.

Rosendahl, Carl O. Trees & Shrubs of the Upper Midwest. LC 55-8489. 1955. 17.50x (ISBN 0-8166-0118-6). U of Minn Pr.

Shanks, Royal E. & Sharp, Aaron J. Summer Key to Trees of Tennessee & the Great Smokies. (Illus.). 24p. 1963. pap. 1.75x (ISBN 0-87049-040-0). U of Tenn Pr.

Sponsler, Olenus L. Trees. 1939. 2.00x (ISBN 0-685-21809-0). Wahr.

Stevenson, George B. Palms of South Florida. (Illus.). 1974. pap. 7.95 (ISBN 0-916224-41-4). Banyan Bks.

--Trees of Everglades National Park. (Illus.). pap. 1.95 (ISBN 0-916224-38-4). Banyan Bks.

Symonds, George W. The Tree Identification Book. LC 58-5359. 272p. 1973. 19.95 (ISBN 0-688-00039-8); pap. 10.95 (ISBN 0-688-05039-5). Morrow.

Trelease, W. The American Oaks. (Plant Monograph Ser.). (Illus.). 1969. 52.50 (ISBN 3-7682-0600-9). Lubrecht & Cramer.

Vines, Robert A. Trees of East Texas. (Illus.). 556p. 1977. pap. 10.95 (ISBN 0-292-78017-6). U of Tex Pr.

--Trees of North Texas. (Elma Dill Russell Spencer Foundation Ser.: No. 14). (Illus.). 486p. 1982. text ed. 24.95x (ISBN 0-292-78018-4); pap. 10.95 (ISBN 0-292-78019-2). U of Tex Pr.

Watts, May T. Master Tree Finder: A Manual for Identifying Trees by Their Leaves East of Rockies. 1963. pap. 1.50 (ISBN 0-912550-01-5). Nature Study.

Watts, May T. & Watts, Tom. Desert Tree Finder: A Manual for Identifying Desert Trees of Ariz., Calif., N. Mex. 1974. pap. 1.50 (ISBN 0-912550-07-4). Nature Study.

--Winter Tree Finder: A Manual for Identifying Deciduous Trees in Winter East of Rockies. 1970. pap. 1.50 (ISBN 0-912550-03-1). Nature Study.

Wharton, Mary E. & Barbour, Roger W. Trees & Shrubs of Kentucky. LC 73-77257. (Illus.). 592p. 1973. 19.00 (ISBN 0-8131-1294-X). U Pr of Ky.

Wigginton, Brooks E. Trees & Shrubs for the Southeast. LC 63-22479. 304p. 1963. 15.00 (ISBN 0-8203-0189-2). U of Ga Pr.

TREES, CARE OF

see also Pruning

Bernatzky, A. Tree Ecology & Preservation. (Developments in Agricultural & Managed-Forest Ecology Ser.: Vol. 2). 358p. 1978. 72.50 (ISBN 0-444-41606-4). Elsevier.

Bridgman, Peter. Tree Surgery: The Complete Guide. LC 75-31320. (Illus.). 160p. 1976. 18.95 (ISBN 0-7153-7050-2). David & Charles.

Clouston, Brian & Stansfield, Kathy, eds. Trees in Towns: Maintenance & Management. (Illus.). 182p. 1981. 28.50 (ISBN 0-85139-658-5). Nichols Pub.

TREMATODA

Cort, William W. Some North American Larval Trematodes. (Illus.). 1915. pap. 8.00 (ISBN 0-384-09870-3). Johnson Repr.

Dawes, Benjamin. Trematoda. 1946. 87.50 (ISBN 0-521-07219-0). Cambridge U Pr.

Faust, Ernest C. Life History Studies on Montana Trematodes. (Illus.). 1918. 12.00 (ISBN 0-384-15190-6). Johnson Repr.

Harrah, Ezra C. North American Monostomes Primarily from Fresh Water Hosts. (Illinois Biological Monographs: Vol. 7). 1922. pap. 8.00 (ISBN 0-384-21430-4). Johnson Repr.

Manter, Harold W. Some North American Fish Trematodes. (Illinois Biological Monographs: Vol. 10, No. 2). Repr. of 1926 ed. 12.00 (ISBN 0-384-35200-6). Johnson Repr.

Miller, Harry M. Comparative Studies on Furcocercous Cercariae. (Illinois Biological Monographs: Vol. 10, No. 3). (Illus.). Repr. of 1926 ed. 12.00 (ISBN 0-384-38972-4). Johnson Repr.

Pratt, Ivan & McCauley, James E. Trematodes of the Pacific Northwest. LC 61-63803. (Studies in Zoology Ser: No. 11). 128p. (Orig.). 1961. pap. 7.95x (ISBN 0-87071-111-3). Oreg St U Pr.

Schell, Stewart. Trematodes of North America North of Mexico. (Illus.). 260p. (Orig.). 1985. pap. 25.95 (ISBN 0-317-26191-6). U Pr of Idaho.

Schell, Stewart C. Trematodes of North America. LC 83-51527. (GEM Bks.). (Illus.). 384p. (Orig.). 1985. pap. 25.95 (ISBN 0-89301-095-2). U Pr of Idaho.

Smyth, J. D. & Halton, D. W. The Physiology of Trematodes. 2nd ed. LC 82-12961. (Illus.). 450p. 1984. 59.50 (ISBN 0-521-22283-4); pap. 24.95 (ISBN 0-521-29434-7). Cambridge U Pr.

Yamaguti, Satyu. Monogenetic Trematodes of Hawaiian Fishes. (Illus.). 287p. 1968. text ed. 20.00x (ISBN 0-87022-891-9). UH Pr.

TREMELLALES

Martin, G. W. Revision of the North Central Tremellales. 1969. Repr. of 1952 ed. 14.00 (ISBN 3-7682-0636-X). Lubrecht & Cramer.

TRIANGLE

Triangles & Quadrangles: Level Four Texts. rev. ed. (Math Components Ser.). 56p. 1983. 2.75 (ISBN 0-88336-841-2). New Readers.

TRIANGLES (INSTRUMENTS)

see Rulers (Instruments)

TRIANGULATION

see Errors, Theory of; Least Squares

TRIASSIC PERIOD

see Geology, Stratigraphic–Triassic

TRIAZINES

Temple, Caroll & Montgomery, John A. Triazoles One, Two, Four, Vol. 37. LC 80-15637. (Chemistry of Heterocyclic Compounds, a Series of Monographs). 791p. 1981. 317.50 (ISBN 0-471-04656-6, Pub. by Wiley-Interscience). Wiley.

TRIBOLIUM

Sokoloff, A. The Biology of Tribolium: With Special Emphasis on Genetic Aspects, Vol. 3. 1977. 125.00x (ISBN 0-19-857512-2). Oxford U Pr.

--The Biology of Tribolium with Special Emphasis on Genetic Effects, Vol. 1. (Illus.). 1972. 68.00x (ISBN 0-19-857353-7). Oxford U Pr.

Sokoloff, Alexander. The Biology of Tribolium with Special Emphasis on Genetic Aspects, Vol. 2. (Illus.). 1974. 98.00x (ISBN 0-19-857381-2). Oxford U Pr.

TRIBOLOGY

Barwell, F. T. Bearing Systems: Principles & Practice. (Illus.). 1979. 78.00x (ISBN 0-19-856319-1). Oxford U Pr.

Bowden, Frank P. & Tabor, David. Friction: An Introduction to Tribology. LC 82-110. 192p. 1982. Repr. of 1973 ed. lib. bdg. 12.50 (ISBN 0-89874-474-1). Krieger.

Buckley, D. H. Surface Effects in Adhesion, Friction, Wear & Lubrication. (Tribiology Ser.: Vol. 5). 632p. 1981. 106.50 (ISBN 0-444-41966-7). Elsevier.

Czichos. Tribology: A Systems Approach to the Science & Technology of Friction, Lubrication & Wear. (Tribology Ser.: Vol. 1). 400p. 1978. 76.50 (ISBN 0-444-41676-5). Elsevier.

Dorinson, A. & Ludema, K. C. Mechanics & Chemistry in Lubrication. (Tribology Ser.: No. 9). 650p. 1985. 120.50 (ISBN 0-444-42492-X). Elsevier.

Dowson, Duncan. A History of Tribology. (Illus.). 1979. text ed. 90.00x (ISBN 0-582-44766-6). Longman.

Dumbleton, J. H. The Tribology of Natural & Artificial Joints. (Tribology Ser.: Vol. 3). 460p. 1981. 74.50 (ISBN 0-444-41898-9). Elsevier.

Halling, J. Introduction to Tribology. (Wykeham Science Ser.: No. 5). 168p. 1975. pap. cancelled (ISBN 0-85109-061-3). Taylor & Francis.

Halling, J. & Smith, W. E. Introduction to Tribology. LC 75-19385. (Wykeham Technology Ser.: No. 5). 168p. 1975. 6.50x (ISBN 0-8448-1126-2). Crane-Russak Co.

Halling, J., ed. Principles of Tribology. (Illus.). 1978. pap. text ed. 27.50x (ISBN 0-333-24686-1). Scholium Intl.

Hebda, M. & Kajdas, C., eds. Eurotrib, '81: Proceedings of the Third International Tribology Congress, Warsaw, 8 Vols. Incl. Vol. 1. Tribological Processes in Solid Body Contact Areas; Vol. 2. Tribological Processes in Contact Areas of Lubricated Solid Bodies; Vol. 3. Lubricants & Their Applications; Vol. 4. Other Tribological Problems. 2778p. 1982. 404.25 set (ISBN 0-444-99655-9). Elsevier.

Kragelsky, I. V. & Alisin, V. V., eds. Friction, Wear & Lubrication: A Complete Handbook of Tribology, 3 Vols. (Illus.). 800p. 130.00 (ISBN 0-08-027591-5, A115); firm 60.00 (ISBN 0-686-97493-X). Pergamon.

Moore, D. F. Elastomer Friction Lubrication. 305p. 1972. text ed. 50.00 (ISBN 0-08-016749-7); pap. text ed. 27.00 (ISBN 0-08-019002-2). Pergamon.

Schey, John A. Tribology in Metalworking. 1983. 96.00 (ISBN 0-87170-155-3). ASM.

Suh, Nam P. & Saka, Nannaji, eds. Fundamentals of Tribology. (Illus.). 1206p. 1980. 100.00x (ISBN 0-262-19183-0). MIT Pr.

Szeri. Tribology: Friction, Lubrication & Wear. 1980. 52.00 (ISBN 0-07-062663-4). McGraw.

TRICHOPTERA

see Caddis-Flies

TRICYCLES

see Bicycles and Tricycles

TRIGLYCERIDES

Litchfield, Carter. Analysis of Triglycerides. 1972. 67.00 (ISBN 0-12-451950-4). Acad Pr.

Senior, John R., ed. Medium Chain Triglycerides. LC 68-13318. (Orig.). 1968. 15.00x (ISBN 0-8122-7564-0). U of Pa Pr.

TRIGONOMETRIC SERIES

see Fourier Series

TRIGONOMETRICAL FUNCTIONS

Ives, Howard C. Natural Trigonometric Functions to Seven Decimal Places for Every Ten Seconds of Arc Together with Miscellaneous Tables. 2nd ed. LC 42-22096. pap. 94.00 (ISBN 0-317-08531-X, 2016480). Bks Demand UMI.

Mergener, Robert J. Functions: An Approach to Algebra & Trigonometry. 2nd ed. 1982. pap. text ed. 19.95 (ISBN 0-8403-3249-1, 40324902). Kendall-Hunt.

Rice, William & Dorsett, Joseph L. Circular & Trigonometric Functions. 1977. pap. text ed. 14.95 (ISBN 0-8403-1704-2). Kendall-Hunt.

Seven Place Natural Trigonometrical Functions: Together with Many Miscellaneous Tables. rev. ed. LC 39-17191. pap. 57.50 (ISBN 0-317-09161-1, 2016481). Bks Demand UMI.

Steklov Institute of Mathematics. Multiple Trigonometric Sums. Karacuba, A. A., et al, eds. Cubarikov, V. N. & Arhipov, G. I. LC 82-18403. (Proceedings of the Steklov Institute of Mathematics Ser.: Vol. 151). 48.00 (ISBN 0-8218-3067-8, STEKLO/151). Am Math.

Trig, Log, Antilog, & Log of Trig. Functions, 6 Place Tables. pap. 2.30 (ISBN 0-686-00487-6). Dennison.

TRIGONOMETRY

Abbott, P. Trigonometry. (Teach Yourself Ser.). 1975. pap. 5.95 (ISBN 0-679-10409-7). McKay.

Arya, J. C. & Lardner, R. W. Algebra & Trigonometry with Applications. (Illus.). 272p. 1983. text ed. 29.95 (ISBN 0-13-021675-5). P-H.

Ayres, Frank, Jr. Trigonometry. (Schaum's Outline Ser). (Orig.). 1954. pap. 8.95 (ISBN 0-07-002651-3). McGraw.

Barnett, R. A. College Algebra, Trigonometry & Analytic Geometry. 608p. 1984. 31.95 (ISBN 0-07-003881-3). McGraw.

Barros-Neto, Jose. Algebra & Trigonometry for College Students. (Illus.). 550p. 1985. text ed. 28.95 (ISBN 0-314-85218-2). West Pub.

Beckenbach, et al. Modern College Algebra & Trigonometry. 5th ed. 1985. text ed. write for info. Wadsworth Pub.

Boyle, Patrick J. Trigonometry with Applications. 372p. 1983. text ed. 23.50 scp (ISBN 0-06-040898-7, HarpC); instr's. manual avail. (ISBN 0-06-360869-3). Har-Row.

Britton, Jack R. & Bello, Ignacio. Contemporary College Algebra & Trigonometry. 581p. 1982. text ed. 23.50 scp (ISBN 0-06-040989-4, HarpC); instr. manual avail. (ISBN 0-06-360922-3); chapter test avail. (ISBN 0-06-360923-1). Har-Row.

Cable, John, et al. Algebra & Trigonometry. 1984. text ed. 32.14 (ISBN 0-205-08208-4, 568208); study guide avail. (568210). Allyn.

Campbell, Howard E. Concepts of Trigonometry. LC 80-22168. 249p. 1981. text ed. write for info. (ISBN 0-87150-299-2, 2351, Prindle). PWS Pubs.

Carico, Charles C. College Algebra & Trigonometry. LC 82-11055. 500p. 1983. text ed. 29.50x (ISBN 0-471-07700-3); student ed. 13.45 (ISBN 0-471-09269-X). Wiley.

Churchill, Ruel V. & Brown, James W. Complex Variables & Applications. 4th ed. (Illus.). 416p. 1984. text ed. 40.95 (ISBN 0-07-010873-0). McGraw.

Denney, Frank C. Trigonometry. 1976. text ed. 23.50 scp (ISBN 0-06-382560-0, HarpC). Har-Row.

Dorsett, Joseph L. Integrated Algebra & Trigonometry. 2nd ed. 1977. pap. text ed. 16.95 (ISBN 0-8403-1699-2). Kendall-Hunt.

Douthitt, C. B. & McMillan, J. A. Trigonometry. 1977. text ed. 22.95 (ISBN 0-07-017670-1). McGraw.

Downing. Trigonometry the Easy Way. (Easy Way Ser.). 225p. 1984. pap. 7.95 (ISBN 0-8120-2717-5). Barron.

Drooyan, et al. Essentials of Trigonometry. 4th ed. 385p. 1986. text ed. 26.95 (ISBN 0-02-330570-3). Macmillan.

Drooyan, Irving, et al. Essentials of Trigonometry. 3rd ed. 1981. text ed. 20.95x (ISBN 0-02-330270-4); pap. text ed. write for info. (ISBN 0-02-330280-1). Macmillan.

--Trigonometry: An Analytic Approach. 4th ed. 370p. 1982. text ed. write for info. (ISBN 0-02-330350-6). Macmillan.

Dubisch, Roy. Trigonometry. LC 55-6084. pap. 102.50 (ISBN 0-317-08418-6, 2012451). Bks Demand UMI.

Durbin, John. College Algebra & Trigonometry. LC 83-16829. (Recreational Computing Ser.: 1-704). 688p. 1984. text ed. 27.95 (ISBN 0-471-03367-7); solutions manual avail. (ISBN 0-471-88351-4); test manual avail. (ISBN 0-471-81066-5). Wiley.

Elich, Joseph, et al. Trigonometry: A Modern Approach. 2nd ed. LC 84-9287. 1985. text ed. 26.95 (ISBN 0-201-10523-3). Addison-Wesley.

Ellis, Robert & Gulick, Denny. Fundamentals of College Algebra & Trigonometry. 448p. 1984. text ed. 24.95 (ISBN 0-15-529350-8, HC). HarBraceJ.

Engelsohn, Harold S. Trigonometry: A Complete & Concrete Approach. (Illus.). 1981. text ed. 28.95 (ISBN 0-07-019419-X). McGraw.

Ewen, Dale & Akers, Lynn R. Trigonometry with Applications. (Illus.). 384p. 1984. 24.95 (ISBN 0-201-11312-0); instr's manual 2.00 (ISBN 0-201-11314-7). Addison-Wesley.

Farley, Reuben W., et al. Trigonometry: A Unitized Approach. (Illus.). 1975. pap. text ed. 28.95 (ISBN 0-13-930909-8). P-H.

Feldman, Bernard. Trigonometry. 1974. write for info. (ISBN 0-534-00354-0). Wadsworth Pub.

Fisher, Robert C. & Ziebur, Allen D. Integrated Algebra, Trigonometry & Analytic Geometry. 4th ed. (Illus.). 560p. 1982. 29.95 (ISBN 0-13-468967-4). P-H.

Flanders, Harley & Price, Justin J. Algebra & Trigonometry. 2nd ed. 1981. text ed. 29.95 (ISBN 0-03-057779-9, CBS C); instr's manual 12.95 (ISBN 0-03-058249-0); study guide 11.95 (ISBN 0-03-058252-0). SCP.

--Trigonometry. 2nd ed. 1982. text ed. 27.95 (ISBN 0-03-057802-7, CBS C). SCP.

Fleming, Walter & Varberg, Dale. Algebra & Trigonometry. 2nd ed. (Illus.). 576p. 1984. text ed. 29.95 (ISBN 0-13-021535-X). P-H.

Fuller, Gordon. Algebra & Trigonometry. 1971. text ed. 28.95 (ISBN 0-07-022605-9). McGraw.

Gaughan, Edward D. & Hall, Carl E. College Algebra & Trigonometry. LC 83-15470. (Mathematics Ser.). 550p. 1983. text ed. 22.75 pub net (ISBN 0-534-02777-6). Brooks-Cole.

Gehrmann & Lester. Trigonometry. (College Outline Ser.). 1984. pap. text ed. 8.95 (ISBN 0-15-601693-1, BFP). HarBraceJ.

Gilbert & Gilbert. Algebra & Trigonometry. 1986. text ed. write for info (ISBN 0-534-06120-6). Wadsworth Pub.

--College Trigonometry. 1985. write for info (ISBN 0-534-03647-3). Wadsworth Pub.

Gilligan, Lawrence & Nenno, Robert B. College Algebra. 1981. text ed. 25.55x (ISBN 0-673-16229-X). Scott F.

--College Algebra & Trigonometry: Precalculus Math. 1981. text ed. 25.55 (ISBN 0-673-16230-3). Scott F.

Plettinger, H. Anne. Table of the Sin Function & Sin Squared Function for Values from 2 Degrees to 87 Degrees. 46p. 1965. 32.50 (ISBN 0-677-01100-8). Gordon.

Von Vega, Baron. Von Vega's Seven-Place Logarithmic Tables of Numbers & Trigonometrical Functions. Fischer, W. L. F., tr. 575p. 1981. write for info. (ISBN 0-86670-000-5). Moffat Pub.

TRIGONOMETRY, PLANE

Barnett, Raymond A. Analytic Trigonometry with Applications. 3rd ed. 320p. write for info. (ISBN 0-534-02858-6). Wadsworth Pub.

Dickson, Leonard E. Plane Trigonometry with Practical Applications. LC 70-114597. (Illus.). 1970. Repr. of 1922 ed. text ed. 9.95 (ISBN 0-8284-0230-2). Chelsea Pub.

Fleming, Walter & Varberg, Dale E. Plane Trigonometry. 1980. text ed. 28.95 (ISBN 0-13-679043-7). P-H.

Fuller, Gordon. Plane Trigonometry with Tables. 5th ed. LC 77-22329. (Illus.). 1978. text ed. 29.95 (ISBN 0-07-022612-1). McGraw.

Granville, William A. Plane Trigonometry & Four-Place Tables. LC 52-3178. pap. 69.00 (ISBN 0-317-08698-7, 2000160). Bks Demand UMI.

Groza, Vivian S. & Sellers, Gene. Plane Trigonometry. (Illus.). 1979. pap. text ed. 27.95 (ISBN 0-7216-4325-6). HR&W.

Gustafson, David R. Plane Trigonometry. 2nd ed. LC 84-9446. 1984. text ed. 21.00 pub net (ISBN 0-534-03606-6). Brooks-Cole.

Heineman, E. Richard. Plane Trigonometry. 5th ed. (Illus.). 1980. text ed. 29.95 (ISBN 0-07-027932-2). McGraw.

Johnston, Carol. Plane Trigonometry: A New Approach. 2nd ed. LC 77-16841. 1978. text ed. 28.95 (ISBN 0-13-677666-3). P-H.

Mazet, P. Analytic Sets in Locally Convex Spaces. (Mathematics Studies: Vol. 89). 1984. 38.50 (ISBN 0-444-86867-4, I-088-84, North-Holland). Elsevier.

Niles, Nathan O. Plane Trigonometry. 3rd ed. LC 75-28337. 394p. 1976. text ed. 32.50 (ISBN 0-471-64025-5); solutions manual avail. (ISBN 0-471-01716-7). Wiley.

Rees, Charles, et al. Plane Trigonometry with Tables. 7th ed. (Illus.). 1977. text ed. 23.95. P-H.

Rice, Bernard J. & Strange, Jerry D. Plane Trigonometry. 3rd ed. LC 80-26108. 322p. 1981. text ed. write for info. (ISBN 0-87150-297-6, 2381, Prindle). PWS Pubs.

Robison, J. Vincent. Modern Algebra & Trigonometry. 2nd ed. (Illus.). 448p. 1972. text ed. 33.95 (ISBN 0-07-053330-X). McGraw.

Sparks, Fred W., et al. Plane Trigonometry. 8th ed. (Illus.). 352p. 1984. text ed. 28.95 (ISBN 0-13-679225-1). P-H.

Washington, Allyn J. & Edmond, Carolyn E. Plane Trigonometry. LC 76-7883. 1977. 27.95 (ISBN 0-8465-8622-3); instr's. guide 10.95 (ISBN 0-8465-8623-1). Benjamin-Cummings.

TRIGONOMETRY, SPHERICAL

see also Sphere

Clough-Smith, J. H. An Introduction to Spherical Trigonometry. 1981. 50.00x (ISBN 0-85174-320-X, Pub. by Nautical England). State Mutual Bk.

TRILOBITES

Bergstrom, Jan. Organization, Life & Systematics of Trilobites. (Fossils & Strata Ser: No. 2). 1973. 12.00x (ISBN 8-200-09330-1, Dist. by Columbia U Pr). Universitet.

Lake, P. The Cambrian Trilobites, 14 vols., pts. 1-14. Repr. of 1946 ed. Set. 120.00 (ISBN 0-685-13363-X). Johnson Repr.

Morris, S. F. & Fortey, R. A. Catalogue of the Type & Figured Specimens of Trilobites in the British Museum (Natural History) 176p. 1984. 50.00x (ISBN 0-565-00882-X, Pub. by Brit Mus Nat Hist England). Sabbot-Natural Hist Bks.

Reed, F. Cowper. The Lower Palaeozoic Trilobites of Girvan, 6 vols. 1935. Set. 53.00 (ISBN 0-384-50090-0). Johnson Repr.

Thomas, A. T., et al. Trilobites in British Stratigraphy. (Illus.). 80p. 1984. pap. text ed. 17.00x (ISBN 0-632-01201-3). Blackwell Pubns.

Whittard, W. F. The Ordovician Trilobites of the Shelve Inlier, West Shropshire, Pts. 1-2. 12.00 (ISBN 0-384-68200-6). Johnson Repr.

TRIM (OF SHIPS)

Ball, John E. Exterior & Interior Trim. LC 75-6060. 192p. 1975. pap. 13.00 (ISBN 0-8273-1120-6); instr.'s guide 2.25 (ISBN 0-8273-1121-4). Delmar.

TRIPLE INTEGRALS

see Integrals, Multiple

TRIPLET STATE

see also Atomic Spectra

Devaquet, A., et al. Triplet States One. (Topics in Current Chemistry Ser.: Vol. 54). (Illus.). iv, 164p. 1975. 42.00 (ISBN 0-387-07107-5). Springer-Verlag.

Wagner, P. J., et al. Triplet States: No. 3. (Topics in Current Chemistry: Vol 66). 1976. 40.00 (ISBN 0-387-07655-7). Springer-Verlag.

Wild, U. P., et al. Triplet States Two. LC 75-1466. (Topics in Current Chemistry Ser: Vol. 55). (Illus.). 150p. 1975. 36.00 (ISBN 0-387-07197-0). Springer-Verlag.

Zahlan, A. B., et al. Triplet State. (Illus.). 1967. 52.50 (ISBN 0-521-06892-4). Cambridge U Pr.

TRITIUM

Anthony, Evans E. Handbook of Tritium NMR Spectroscopy & Applications. LC 84-15273. 1985. 39.95 (ISBN 0-471-90583-6). Wiley.

Behaviour of Tritium in the Environment. (Proceedings Ser.). (Illus.). 711p. 1979. pap. 62.50 (ISBN 92-0-020079-6, ISP498, IAEA). Unipub.

Buncel, E. Tritium in Organic Chemistry. (Isotopes in Organic Chemistry Ser.: Vol. 4). 300p. 1978. 70.25 (ISBN 0-444-41741-9). Elsevier.

Evans, E. A. Tritium & Its Compounds. 441p. 1966. 26.00 (ISBN 0-442-02339-1, Pub. by Van Nos Reinhold). Krieger.

Feinendegen, L. E. Tritium Labeled Molecules in Biology & Medicine. (Atomic Energy Commision Monographs). 1967. 29.50 (ISBN 0-12-251550-1). Acad Pr.

Handling of Tritium-Bearing Wastes. (Technical Reports Ser.: No. 203). (Illus.). 137p. 1981. pap. 21.25 (ISBN 92-0-125081-9, IDC203, IAEA). Unipub.

Jacobs, D. G. Sources of Tritium & Its Behavior upon Release to the Environment. LC 68-67209. (AEC Critical Review Ser.). 90p. 1968. 10.25 (ISBN 0-87079-345-4, TID-24635); microfiche 4.50 (ISBN 0-87079-346-2, TID-24635). DOE.

Management of Tritium at Nuclear Facilities. (Technical Reports Ser.: No. 234). 62p. (Orig.). 1984. pap. 13.00 (ISBN 92-0-125084-3, IDC234, IAEA). Unipub.

Muentzing, Arne. Triticale: Results & Problems. (Advances in Plant Breeding Ser.: Vol. 10). (Illus.). 103p. (Orig.). 1979. pap. text ed. 35.00 (ISBN 3-489-76210-X). Parey Sci Pubs.

Rothchild, S., ed. Advances in Tracer Methodology. Incl. Vol. 1. 332p. 1963. 40.00x (ISBN 0-306-38201-6); Vol. 3. 333p. 1966. 42.50x (ISBN 0-306-38203-2); Vol. 4. 293p. 1968. 42.50x (ISBN 0-306-38204-0). LC 62-13475 (Plenum Pr). Plenum Pub.

Tritium & Other Environmental Isotopes in the Hydrological Cycle. (Technical Reports Ser.: No. 73). (Illus.). 83p. 1967. pap. 7.75 (ISBN 92-0-145067-2, IDC73, IAEA). Unipub.

Tritium & Other Radionuclide Labled Organic Compounds Incorporated in Genetic Material. LC 79-84486. (NCRP Reports Ser.: No. 63). 1979. 10.00 (ISBN 0-913392-47-2). NCRP Pubns.

Tritium in Some Typical Ecosystems. (Technical Reports Ser.: No. 207). (Illus.). 118p. 1981. pap. 17.25 (ISBN 92-0-125181-5, IDC207, IAEA). Unipub.

Tritium in the Environment. LC 79-63514. (NCRP Reports Ser.: No. 62). 1979. 9.00 (ISBN 0-913392-46-4). NCRP Pubns.

Tritium Measurement Techniques. LC 76-16301. (NCRP Reports Ser.: No. 47). 1976. 9.00 (ISBN 0-913392-29-4). NCRP Pubns.

TRIUMPH (AUTOMOBILE)

see Automobiles, Foreign–Types–Triumph

TRIUMPH MOTORCYCLE

Brotherwood, Clive. Triumph 350 & 500 Unit Twins '57 - '73. new ed. (Owners Workshop Manuals Ser.: No. 137). 1979. 10.50 (ISBN 0-85696-137-X, Pub. by J H Haynes England). Haynes Pubns.

Clew, Jeff. Triumph Pre-Unit Twins '47 - '60. (Owners Workshop Manuals Ser.: No. 251). 1979. 10.50 (ISBN 0-85696-251-1, Pub. by J H Haynes England). Haynes Pubns.

Clew, Jeff & Rogers, Chris. Triumph 650 & 750 4-valve Twins '63 - '83. (Owners Workshop Manuals Ser.: No. 122). 1981. 10.50 (ISBN 0-85696-579-0, Pub. by J H Haynes England). Haynes Pubns.

Meek, Frank. Triumph Trident & BSA Rocket 3 '60 - 72. (Owners Workshop Manuals Ser.: No. 136). 1979. 10.50 (ISBN 0-85696-136-1, Pub. by J H Haynes England). Haynes Pubns.

TROMBICULINAE

see Chiggers (Mites)

TROPICAL AGRICULTURE

see Tropical Crops

TROPICAL CROPS

see also special crops, e.g. Coffee

Beets, Willem C. Multiple Cropping & Tropical Farming Systems. 250p. 1982. 33.50x (ISBN 0-86531-518-3). Westview.

Benson, Jacqueline M. Weeds in Tropical Crops: Review of Abstracts on Constraints in Production Caused by Weeds in Maize, Rice, Sorghum-Millet, Groundnuts, and Cassava, 1952-1980. (Plant Production & Protection Papers: No. 32, Suppl. 1). 68p. 1982. pap. 7.50 (ISBN 92-5-101206-7, F2333, FAO). Unipub.

Blackburn, F. Sugar-Cane. (Tropical Agriculture Ser.). (Illus.). 414p. 1984. text ed. 75.00 (ISBN 0-582-46028-X). Longman.

Burt, Robert, et al, eds. The Role of Centrosema, Desmodium & Stylosanthes in Improved Tropical Pastures. (Tropical Agriculture Ser.). (Illus.). 315p. 1982. 29.00x (ISBN 0-86531-401-2). Westview.

Cobley, L. S. An Introduction to the Botany of Tropical Crops. 2nd ed. LC 76-7447. (Longman Text Ser.). (Illus.). 1977. pap. text ed. 18.95x (ISBN 0-582-44153-6). Longman.

Cook, A. A. Diseases of Tropical Fruits & Nuts. LC 75-18737. 1975. 35.00x (ISBN 0-02-843070-0). Hafner.

Crowder, L. V. & Chheda, H. R. Tropical Grassland Husbandry. Wrigley, G., ed. (Tropical Agriculture Ser.). (Illus.). 562p. 1983. text ed. 60.00x (ISBN 0-582-46677-6). Longman.

De T. Alvim, Paulo, ed. Ecophysiology of Tropical Crops. 1977. 62.50 (ISBN 0-12-055650-2). Acad Pr.

Goerling, T. James. Tropical Root Crops & Rural Development. (Working Paper: No. 324). 85p. 1979. 5.00 (ISBN 0-686-36081-8, WP-0324). World Bank.

Goldsworthy, Peter R. & Fisher, N. M., eds. The Physiology of Tropical Field Crops. 664p. 1984. 74.95 (ISBN 0-471-10267-9). Wiley.

Gomez, A. A. & Gomez, K. A. Multiple Cropping in the Humid Tropics of Asia. 248p. 1983. pap. text ed. 15.00 (ISBN 0-88936-304-8, IDRC176, IDRC). Unipub.

Hill, D. S. & Waller, J. M. Pests & Diseases of Tropical Crops: Principles & Methods, Vol. 1. LC 81-18561. (Illus.). 192p. (Orig.). 1982. pap. text ed. 7.95x (ISBN 0-582-60614-4). Longman.

Holliday, Paul. Fungus Diseases of Tropical Crops. LC 79-41602. (Illus.). 500p. 1980. 150.00 (ISBN 0-521-22529-9). Cambridge U Pr.

Inglett, G. E. & Charalambous, George, eds. Tropical Foods: Chemistry & Nutrition, Vol. 1. 1979. 39.50 (ISBN 0-12-370901-6). Acad Pr.

Jarrett, H. R. Tropical Geography. (Aspects Geographies Ser.). (Illus.). 222p. 1983. pap. text ed. 21.00x (ISBN 0-7121-2018-1). Intl Ideas.

Kaddar, T., et al. The Vital Role of Potassium Fertilizers in Tropical Agriculture: The Present Position, Future Potential & Constraints to Progress. Roth, E. N. & Frederick, E. D., eds. (Technical Bulletin Ser.: T-29). (Illus.). 15p. (Orig.). 1984. pap. text ed. 4.00 (ISBN 0-88090-051-2). Intl Fertilizer.

Kahn, T. N. Winged Bean Production in the Tropics. (Plant Production & Protection Papers: No. 38). 223p. 1982. pap. 16.00 (ISBN 92-5-101230-X, F2366, FAO). Unipub.

Knapp, Ruediger. Gegenseitige Beeinflussung und Temperatur-Wirkung bei tropischen und subtropischen Pflanzen: Bericht ueber neue experimentelle Untersuchungen an Nutzpflanzen und Arten der spontanen Vegetation. (Illus.). 1967. pap. 6.00 (ISBN 3-7682-0576-2). Lubrecht & Cramer.

Kranz, J., et al, eds. Diseases, Pests & Weeds in Tropical Crops. LC 78-6212. 666p. 1977. 110.95 (ISBN 0-471-99667-X, Pub. by Wiley-Interscience). Wiley.

Martin, Franklin W., ed. CRC Handbook of Tropical Food Crops. 304p. 1984. 74.50 (ISBN 0-8493-0536-5). CRC Pr.

Mohlenbrock. Growing Tropical Fruit Trees. (Illus.). 1979. pap. 3.95 (ISBN 0-8200-0409-X). Great Outdoors.

Norman, M. J., et al. The Ecology of Tropical Food Crops. (Illus.). 320p. 1984. 59.50 (ISBN 0-521-24082-4); pap. 24.95 (ISBN 0-521-28428-7). Cambridge U Pr.

Norman, M. J. T. Annual Cropping Systems in the Tropics: An Introduction. LC 79-10625. (Illus.). x, 276p. 1979. text ed. 20.00 (ISBN 0-8130-0632-5). U Presses Fla.

On-Farm Maize Drying & Storage in the Humid Tropics. (Agricultural Services Bulletins: No. 40). 69p. 1980. pap. 7.50 (ISBN 92-5-100944-9, F2077, FAO). Unipub.

Onwueme, I. C. The Tropical Tuber Crops: Yam, Cassava, Sweet Potato, Cocoyams. LC 77-20932. Repr. of 1978 ed. 47.20 (ISBN 0-8357-9996-4, 2051823). Bks Demand UMI.

Plucknett, Donald L. Small-Scale Processing & Storage of Tropical Root Crops. (Tropical Agriculture Ser.). 1979. lib. bdg. 39.00x (ISBN 0-89158-471-4). Westview.

Pushkarnath. Potato in Sub-Tropics. 306p. 1981. 30.00x (ISBN 0-86125-203-9, Pub. by Orient Longman India). State Mutual Bk.

Robinson, J. B. Annotated Bibliography of Colour Illustrated Mineral Deficiency Symptoms in Tropical Crops. 84p. 1974. 49.00x (ISBN 0-85198-304-9, Pub. by CAB Bks England). State Mutual Bk.

Sinha. Field Crop Production in Tropical Africa. Date not set. price not set (ISBN 0-471-90102-4). Wiley.

Skerman, P. J. Tropical Forage Legumes. (Plant Production & Protection Papers: No. 2). 609p. 1977. 40.25 (ISBN 92-5-100163-4, F1401, FAO). Unipub.

Terry, E. R. & Oduro, K. A., eds. Tropical Root Crops - Research Strategies for the 1980's: Proceedings of the First Triennial Root Crops Symposium of the International Society of Root Crops, Africa Branch, 8-12 September 1980, Ibadan, Nigeria. (Eng. & Fr.). 280p. 1981. pap. 18.00 (ISBN 0-88936-285-8, IDRC163, IDRC). Unipub.

Tropical Agriculture Research Center, Yatabe, Japan. International Symposium on Distribution, Characteristics & Utilization of Problem Soils: Proceedings of a Symposium on Tropical Agricultural Research, Tsukuba, October 19-26, 1981. (Tropical Agriculture Research Ser.: No. 15). (Illus.). 418p. (Orig.). 1982. pap. text ed. 35.00x (Pub. by Japan Sci Soc Pr Japan). Intl Spec Bk.

Tropical Products Institute, ed. Proceedings of a Symposium on Sorghum & Millets for Human Food. 138p. 1977. 60.00x (ISBN 0-686-45810-9, Pub. by Trop Prods Inst England). State Mutual Bk.

--Proceedings of the Confeence of Handling Processing & Marketing of Tropical Fish. 511p. 1977. 75.00x (ISBN 0-686-45811-7, Pub. by Trop Prods Inst England). State Mutual Bk.

--Proceedings of the Conference on Animal Feeds of Tropical & Subtropical Origin. 1975. 75.00x (ISBN 0-686-45813-3, Pub. by Trop Prods Inst England). State Mutual Bk.

--Proceedings of the Conference on Spices. 261p. 1973. 60.00x (ISBN 0-686-45814-1, Pub. by Trop Prods Inst England). State Mutual Bk.

--Proceedings of the Conference on the Development of Feed Resources & Improvement of Animal Feeding Methods in the Cento Region Countries. 218p. 1972. 50.00x (ISBN 0-686-45815-X, Pub. by Trop Prods Inst England). State Mutual Bk.

--Proceedings of the Conference on Tropical & Subtropical Fruits. 307p. 1970. 55.00x (ISBN 0-686-45816-8, Pub. by Trop Prods Inst England). State Mutual Bk.

--Rodent Damage to Growing Crops & to Farm & Village Storage in Tropical & Subtropical Regions: Postal Survey, 1972-1973. 1976. 52.00x (ISBN 0-686-45817-6, Pub. by Trop Prods Inst England). State Mutual Bk.

Uritani, Ikuzo & Reyes, Edilberto D., eds. Tropical Root Crops: Postharvest Physiology & Processing. (Illus.). 328p. (Orig.). 1984. pap. 26.00x (ISBN 4-7622-6358-3, Pub. by Japan Sci Soc Japan). Intl Spec Bk.

Van Atta, Marian. Living off the Land: Subtropic Handbook. 3rd ed. LC 74-15408. (Illus.). 64p. 1983. pap. 2.50 (ISBN 0-938524-00-3). Geraventure.

Williams, C. N. The Agronomy of the Major Tropical Crops. (Illus.). 1975. text ed. 24.00x (ISBN 0-19-580296-9). Oxford U Pr.

Williams, C. N. & Joseph, K. T. Climate, Soil & Crop Production in the Humid Tropics. (Illus.). 1970. pap. 18.95x (ISBN 0-19-638138-X). Oxford U Pr.

Yeo, Peter. An Initial Course in Tropical Agriculture for the Staff of Co-operatives. 2nd ed. 54p. (Orig.). 1978. pap. 4.00x (ISBN 0-903031-39-6, Pub. by Intermediate Tech England). Intermediate Tech.

TROPICAL FISH

see also Aquariums

Axelrod, H., et al. Exotic Tropical Fishes. rev. ed. (Illus.). 1302p. 1980. 39.95 (ISBN 0-87666-543-1, H-1028); looseleaf 49.95 (ISBN 0-87666-537-7, H-1028L). TFH Pubns.

Axelrod, Herbert R. The T.F.H. Book of Tropical Aquariums. (Illus.). 96p. 1982. 6.95 (ISBN 0-87666-800-7, HP 005). TFH Pubns.

--Tropical Fish for Beginners. (Illus.). 1972. 7.95 (ISBN 0-87666-752-3, PS-304). TFH Pubns.

Axelrod, Herbert R. & Burgess, Warren. Pacific Marine Fishes, 7 bks. Incl. Book 1. (Illus.). 1972 (ISBN 0-87666-123-1, PS-697); Book 2. (Illus.). 1973 (ISBN 0-87666-124-X, PS-699). 29.95 ea. TFH Pubns.

Axelrod, Herbert R. & Schultz, Leonard P. Handbook of Tropical Aquarium Fishes. rev. ed. 736p. 1983. 8.95 (ISBN 0-87666-491-5, PS-663). TFH Pubns.

Axelrod, Herbert R. & Vorderwinkler, W. Encyclopedia of Tropical Fish. new ed. 1975. 14.95 (ISBN 0-87666-158-4, H-905). TFH Pubns.

Axelrod, Herbert R., et al. Exotic Tropical Fishes. 19.95 (ISBN 0-87666-051-0, H-907); looseleaf 29.95 (ISBN 0-87666-052-9, H-907L). TFH Pubns.

Boardman, Edward T. Guide to Higher Aquarium Animals. (Bulletin Ser.: No. 21). (Illus.). 107p. 1944. 2.00x (ISBN 0-87737-006-0). Cranbrook.

Colin, Patrick. Neon Gobies. (Illus.). 304p. 1976. 19.95 (ISBN 0-87666-450-8, H-957). TFH Pubns.

Conroy, D. A. Evaluation of the Present State of World Trade in Ornamental Fish. (Fisheries Technical Papers: No. 146). 133p. (2nd Printing 1976). 1975. pap. 9.00 (ISBN 92-5-101911-8, F877, FAO). Unipub.

Dulin, Mark. Fish Diseases. 1979. 4.95 (ISBN 0-87666-524-5, KW-066). TFH Pubns.

Dulin, Mark P. Diseases of Marine Aquarium Fishes. (Illus.). 1976. pap. 7.95 (ISBN 0-87666-099-5, PS-731). TFH Pubns.

Favre, Henri. Larousse des poissons d'aquarium. Rousselet-Blanc, Pierre, ed. (Larousse des animaux familiers). (Fr., Illus.). 120p. 1975. 19.25x (ISBN 2-03-014854-7). Larousse.

Goldstein, R. J. Introduction to Cichlids. 1970. pap. 9.95 (ISBN 0-87666-788-4, PS-662). TFH Pubns.

Greenberg, Jerry. Fishwatcher's Field Guide. plastic card 3.95 (ISBN 0-916224-78-3). Banyan Bks.

Greenberg, Jerry & Greenberg, Idaz. Guide to Corals & Fishes of Florida, the Bahamas, the Caribbean. (Illus.). 64p. pap. 5.95 (ISBN 0-913008-08-7). Banyan Bks.

--Waterproof Guide to Corals & Fishes of Florida, the Bahamas, & the Caribbean. (Illus.). 64p. pap. 8.95 special (ISBN 0-913008-07-9). Banyan Bks.

Hermansson, Birgir. Training Fishermen at Sea: An FAO Fishing Manual. (Illus.). 96p. 1979. pap. 13.25 (ISBN 0-85238-094-1, FN77, FNB). Unipub.

Innes, William T. Innes Exotic Aquarium Fish. 6.95 (ISBN 0-87666-090-1, PS642). TFH Pubns.

The Living Reef with Special Fishwatcher's Supplement. LC 70-187354. (Illus.). 126p. 1979. pap. 8.95 (ISBN 0-913008-01-X). Banyan Bks.

Maurus, Walt. All about Bettas. (Orig.). 1976. 8.95 (ISBN 0-87666-783-3, PS-654). TFH Pubns.

Mills, Dick. Aquarium Fishes. LC 80-80742. (Arco Fact Guides in Color Ser.). (Illus.). 128p. 1980. 7.95 (ISBN 0-668-04944-8, 4944-8). Arco.

--A Fishkeeper's Guide to the Tropical Aquarium. (Fishkeeper's Guide Ser.). (Illus.). 120p. 1985. 7.95 (ISBN 0-668-06347-5). Arco.

Randall, John E. Caribbean Reef Fishes. 2nd, rev. ed. (Illus.). 352p. 1983. 29.95 (ISBN 0-87666-498-2, H-932). TFH Pubns.

Roberts, Mervin. Tropical Fish. (Illus.). pap. 6.95 (ISBN 0-87666-780-9, H-915). TFH Pubns.

Rousselet-Blanc, Pierre, ed. Larousse Des Poissons D'Aquarium. (Fr.). 120p. 1975. 27.50 (ISBN 0-686-56996-2, M-6336). French & Eur.

Scheel, Joegen. Rivulins of the Old World. 19.95 (ISBN 0-87666-137-1, PS-660). TFH Pubns.

Schmitz, Siegfried. Aquarium Fishes. LC 78-32633. (Nature Guides Ser.). (Illus.). 144p. 1979. pap. 4.95 (ISBN 0-7011-2356-7, Pub. by Chatto & Windus). Merrimack Pub Cir.

Schofield, Diane. Beginning with Tropicals. pap. 2.95 (ISBN 0-87666-165-7, M-523). TFH Pubns.

Simon & Schuster's Guide to Freshwater & Marine Aquarium Fish. LC 76-56863. 1977. pap. 9.95 (ISBN 0-671-22809-9). S&S.

Start Right with Tropical Fish. (Illus.). pap. 2.95 (ISBN 0-87666-160-6, M-510). TFH Pubns.

Takeshita, Glen. Koi for Home & Garden. 1969. 4.95 (ISBN 0-87666-754-X, PS-659). TFH Pubns.

Van Atta, Marian. Living off the Land: Subtropic Handbook. 3rd ed. LC 74-15408. (Illus.). 64p. 1983. pap. 2.50 (ISBN 0-938524-00-3). Geraventure.

Walker, Braz. All about Cichlids. (Illus., Orig.). 1978. 7.95 (ISBN 0-86622-038-0, PS-751). TFH Pubns.

--Angelfish. (Illus.). 1974. 7.95 (ISBN 0-87666-755-8, PS-711). TFH Pubns.

--Tropical Fish Identifier. LC 76-126851. (Illus.). 256p. 1981. pap. 6.95 (ISBN 0-8069-8968-8). Sterling.

Whitern, Wilfred L. Livebearers. (Illus.). 93p. 1979. 4.95 (ISBN 0-87666-518-0, KW-049). TFH Pubns.

TROPICAL FISH BREEDING

Axelrod, Herbert & Shaw, Susan. Breeding Aquarium Fishes, Bk. 1. 1968. 16.95 (ISBN 0-87666-006-5, H-930). TFH Pubns.

Axelrod, Herbert R. Koi of the World. (Illus.). 239p. 1973. 39.95 (ISBN 0-87666-092-8, H-947). TFH Pubns.

--Tropical Fish. (Illus.). 1979. 4.95 (ISBN 0-87666-510-5, KW-020). TFH Pubns.

Pauly, Daniel. Fish Population Dynamics in Tropical Waters: A Manual for Use with Programmable Calculators. (ICLARM Studies & Reviews: 8). (Illus.). 325p. 1984. 29.50x (ISBN 971-1022-03-6, Pub. by ICLARM Philippines); pap. 25.00 (ISBN 971-1022-04-4). Intl Spec Bk.

Quayle, D. B. Tropical Oyster Culture: A Selected Bibliography. 40p. 1975. pap. 5.00 (ISBN 0-88936-066-9, IDRC52, IDRC). Unipub.

Schroder, Johannes H. Genetics for Aquarists. (Illus.). 1976. pap. 9.95 (ISBN 0-87666-461-3, PS-656). TFH Pubns.

Whitern, Wilfred L. Livebearers. (Illus.). 93p. 1979. 4.95 (ISBN 0-87666-518-0, KW-049). TFH Pubns.

TROPICAL PLANTS

Bogden, A. V. Tropical Pasture & Fodder Plants: Grasses & Legumes. LC 76-14977. (Tropical Agriculture Ser.). pap. 122.30 (ISBN 0-317-29850-X, 2019606). Bks Demand UMI.

Buritica, P. & Hennen, J. F. Pucciniosireae: Uredinales, Pucciniaceae. LC 79-27151. (Flora Neotropica Monograph: No. 24). (Illus.). 50p. 1980. pap. 7.75x (ISBN 0-89327-219-1). NY Botanical.

Burkill, H. M. The Useful Plants of West Tropical Africa, Vol. 1. 900p. 1985. 100.00x (ISBN 0-947643-01-X, Pub. by Prospect England). U Pr of Va.

Chadha, K. L. & Randhawa, G. S., eds. International Symposium on Tropical & Sub-Tropical Horticulture, 3rd: Vol. 2, Use of Growth Regulators in Horticultural, Plantation & Medicinal Crops. (Illus.). 266p. 1978. 20.00 (ISBN 0-88065-238-1, Pub. by Messers Today & Tomorrow Printers & Publishers). Scholarly Pubns.

Clements, R. J. & Cameron, D. G. Collecting & Testing Tropical Forage Plants. 162p. 1980. pap. 12.75 (ISBN 0-643-00389-4, C061, CSIRO). Unipub.

Clements, R. J. & Cameron, D. G., eds. Collecting & Testing Tropical Forage Plants. 154p. 1981. 35.00x (ISBN 0-643-00389-4, Pub. by CSIRO Australia). State Mutual Bk.

--Collecting & Testing Tropical Forage Plants. 154p. 1981. 20.00x (ISBN 0-686-78035-3, Pub. by CSIRO Australia). State Mutual Bk.

--Collecting & Testing Tropical Forage Plants. 1982. pap. 10.00x (ISBN 0-643-00389-4, Pub. by CSIRO). Intl Spec Bk.

Coghlan, Richard. Landscape Gardening in the Tropics. (Illus.). 1975. 30.00x (ISBN 0-8464-0545-8). Beekman Pubs.

Cook, Allyn A. Diseases of Tropical & Subtropical Field, Fiber & Oil Plants. (Illus.). 545p. 1981. text ed. 45.00x (ISBN 0-02-949300-5). Macmillan.

Croat, Thomas B. Flora of Barro Colorado Island. LC 76-23371. (Illus.). 953p. 1978. 60.00x (ISBN 0-8047-0950-5). Stanford U Pr.

Crowder, L. V. & Chheda, H. R. Tropical Grassland Husbandry. Wrigley, G., ed. (Tropical Agriculture Ser.). (Illus.). 562p. 1983. text ed. 60.00x (ISBN 0-582-46677-6). Longman.

De Thabrew. Popular Tropical Aquarium Plants. 1981. 30.00x (ISBN 0-686-98215-0, Pub. by Thornhill Pr England). State Mutual Bk.

Engler, A. Hochgebirgsflora Des Tropischen Afrikas. (Akad. D. Wissenschaften, Berlin Ser.). (Ger.). 461p. 1975. pap. text ed. 70.40x (ISBN 3-87429-088-3). Lubrecht & Cramer.

Etherington, Dan M. Multi-Period Budgeting & the Economic Assessment of Perennial Corporation Intercropping Systems. (Development Studies Centre - Occasional Paper: No. 26). 47p. (Orig.). 1982. pap. text ed. 2.00 (ISBN 0-909150-51-6, 1106, Pub. by ANUP Australia). Australia N U P.

Gentry, Alwyn H. Bignoniaceae: Crescentieae & Tourretieae, Pt. 1. LC 80-10846. (Flora Neotropica Monograph: No. 25). (Illus.). 132p. 1980. pap. 15.75x (ISBN 0-89327-222-1). NY Botanical.

Graf, Alfred B. Tropica: Color Cyclopedia of Exotic Plants. 2nd ed. 1981. 115.00 (ISBN 0-684-16771-9, ScribT). Scribner.

--Tropica: Color Encyclopedia of Exotic Plants. 2nd ed. LC 77-82461. (Illus.). 1981. 115.00x (ISBN 0-911266-16-X). Roehrs.

Halle, F., et al. Tropical Trees & Forests: An Architectural Analysis. 1978. 82.00 (ISBN 0-387-08494-0). Springer-Verlag.

Hargreaves, Dorothy & Hargreaves, Bob. Tropical Blossoms of the Pacific. LC 72-113701. (Illus.). 1970. pap. 3.00 (ISBN 0-910690-08-1). Hargreaves.

--Tropical Trees: Found in the Carribbean, South American, Central America, Mexico. LC 65-19767. (Illus.). 1965. pap. 3.00 (ISBN 0-910690-05-7). Hargreaves.

--Tropical Trees of Hawaii. LC 64-23259. (Illus.). 1964. pap. 3.00 (ISBN 0-910690-02-2). Hargreaves.

--Tropical Trees of the Pacific. LC 72-113702. (Illus.). 1970. pap. 3.00 (ISBN 0-910690-09-X). Hargreaves.

Jamieson, B. G. & Reynolds, J. F. Tropical Plant Types. 1967. pap. 18.75 (ISBN 0-08-012120-9). Pergamon.

Opeke, Lawrence K. Tropical Tree Crops. 1982. 49.95x (ISBN 0-471-10060-9, Pub. by Wiley-Interscience); pap. 19.95x (ISBN 0-471-10066-8). Wiley.

Roth, Ingrid. Structural Patterns of Tropical Barks. (Encyclopedia of Plant Anatomy: Special Part Ser.: Vol. 9, Pt. 3). (Illus.). 609p. 1981. 112.35x (ISBN 3-443-14012-2). Lubrecht & Cramer.

Van Atta, Marian. Living off the Land: Subtropic Handbook. 3rd ed. LC 74-15408. (Illus.). 64p. 1983. pap. 2.50 (ISBN 0-938524-00-3). Geraventure.

TROPICAL RAIN FORESTS

see Rain Forests

TROPICS–CLIMATE

Ayoade, J. O. Introduction to Climatology for the Tropics. LC 82-2648. 258p. 1983. 34.95x (ISBN 0-471-10349-7, Pub. by Wiley-Interscience); pap. 15.95 (ISBN 0-471-10407-8, Pub. by Wiley-Interscience). Wiley.

Experiment Design Proposal for the GARP Atlantic Tropical Experiment. (GATE Report Ser.: No. 1). 1972. pap. 20.00 (W278, WMO). Unipub.

The GARP Atlantic Tropical Experiment (GATE) Monograph. (GARP Publications Ser.: No. 25). 477p. 1982. pap. 40.00 (ISBN 0-686-81848-2, W537, WMO). Unipub.

GARP Tropical Experiment Board, 1st Session. Report of the GARP Experiment Board 1st Session. (GARP Special Reports: No. 4). pap. 8.00 (ISBN 0-686-93934-4, W325, WMO). Unipub.

Kalk, M., et al, eds. Lake Chilwa. (Monographiase Bilogicae: No. 35). 1979. lib. bdg. 79.00 (ISBN 90-6193-087-1, Pub. by Junk Pubs Netherlands). Kluwer Academic.

Lauer, W., et al. Studien Zur Klima- und Vegetations Kunde der Tropen. 1952. 20.00 (ISBN 0-384-58675-9). Johnson Repr.

Longman, K. A. & Jenik, I. J. Tropical Forest & Its Environment. LC 73-85681. (Illus.). 160p. (Orig.). 1974. pap. text ed. 10.95x (ISBN 0-582-44045-9). Longman.

Regional Seminar on Synoptic Analysis & Forecasting in the Tropics of Asia & the South-West Pacific: Proceedings, Singapore, 1970. (Publications Ser.: No. 321). 552p. 1972. pap. 55.00 (ISBN 0-686-93906-9, WMO). Unipub.

Report of a Workshop on Atmospheric Carbon Dioxide: Scientific Workshop, Washington, D.C., 1976. pap. 10.00 (ISBN 0-686-93941-7, W218, WMO). Unipub.

Report of Second Session of Tropical Experiment Council. (GARP Special Reports: No. 7). vi, 14p. 1972. pap. 5.00 (W322, WMO). Unipub.

Report of the 1st Session of the GARP Tropical Experiment Council. (GARP Special Reports: No. 3). pap. 3.00 (ISBN 0-686-93933-6, W326, WMO). Unipub.

Report on the GARP Tropical Experiment in the Atlantic: Interim Planning. (GARP Special Reports: No. 2). pap. 2.00 (ISBN 0-686-93929-8, W327, WMO). Unipub.

TROUT

Bergman, Ray & Janes, Edward C. Trout. 1976. 25.00 (ISBN 0-394-49957-3); pap. 15.95 (ISBN 0-394-73144-1). Knopf.

Childerhose, R. J. & Trim, Marj. Pacific Salmon & Steelhead Trout. LC 78-65830. (Illus.). 166p. 1979. pap. 16.95 (ISBN 0-295-95866-9). U of Wash Pr.

Edwards, David J. Salmon & Trout Farming in Norway. 1978. 50.00x (ISBN 0-685-63450-7). State Mutual Bk.

Hines, Neal O. Fish of Rare Breeding: Salmon & Trout of the Donaldson Strains. LC 76-608113. (Illus.). 167p. 1976. 17.50x (ISBN 0-87474-163-7). Smithsonian.

Jordan, David S. Trout & Salmon of Pacific Coast. facs. ed. 16p. pap. 1.95 (ISBN 0-8466-0071-4, S71). Shorey.

Punola, John A. Guide to Pennsylvania Trout. (Illus.). 104p. (Orig.). 1981. pap. 4.95 (ISBN 0-939888-00-9). Path Pubns NJ.

Roberts, Ronald J. & Shepherd, C. Jonathan. Handbook of Trout & Salmon Diseases. (Illus.). 172p. 26.00 (ISBN 0-85238-066-6, FN51, FNB). Unipub.

Salmon & Trout Feeds & Feeding. (European Inland Fisheries Advisory Commision (EIFAC): Technical Papers: No. 12). (Eng. & Fr.). 33p. 1971. pap. 7.50 (ISBN 92-5-100823-X, F1862, FAO). Unipub.

Stevenson, John P. Trout Farming Manual. 1980. 60.75x (ISBN 0-686-64739-4, Pub. by Fishing News England). State Mutual Bk.

Willers, William B. Trout Biology: An Angler's Guide. LC 81-50829. 224p. 1981. 21.50 (ISBN 0-299-08720-4). U of Wis Pr.

TRS-80 COMPUTERS

see also Tandy 2000 (Computer); Trs-80 Color Computer; Trs-80 Model I (Computer); Trs-80 Model Ii (Computer); Trs-80 Model Iii (Computer); Trs-80 Model 4 (Computer); Trs-80 Model 12 (Computer); Trs-80 Model 16 (Computer); Trs-80 Model 100 (Computer); Trs-80 Pc-1 (Computer)

Adams, John D. Introduction to TRS-80 Data Files. 102p. (Orig.). 1984. spiral binding 24.95 (ISBN 0-88006-066-2, CC7398). Green Pub Inc.

Ahl, David H., ed. More BASIC Computer Games: TRS-80. LC 78-50028. (Illus.). 196p. (Orig.). 1980. pap. 7.95 (ISBN 0-916688-19-4, 6C4). Creative Comp.

Albrecht, Bob, et al. My TRS-80 Likes Me. 1980. pap. 2.50 (ISBN 0-318-01183-2). Radio Shack.

--Number Patterns. 1980. pap. 2.50 (ISBN 0-318-01184-0). Radio Shack.

--TRS-80 BASIC: A Self Teaching Guide. LC 80-10268. (Self Teaching Guides Ser.: No. 1581). 351p. 1980. pap. 12.95 (ISBN 0-471-06466-1, Pub. by Wiley Pr). Wiley.

Allen, Brandt R. VisiCalc: TRS-80. 1984. pap. text ed. 10.95 (ISBN 0-8359-8409-5). Reston.

Andree, Richard V. & Andree, Josephine P. Explore Computing with the TRS-80 & with Programming in BASIC. (Illus.). 256p. 1982. pap. text ed. 12.95 (ISBN 0-13-296137-7). P-H.

Baird, Chuck, et al. Encyclopedia for the TRS-80, Vol. 7. Putnam, Katherine & Comiskey, Kate, eds. 265p. 1982. 19.95 (ISBN 0-88006-042-5, EN8107); pap. 10.95 (ISBN 0-88006-043-3, EN8087). Green Pub Inc.

Barden, William, Jr. How to Do It on the TRS-80. 352p. 1983. 29.95 (ISBN 0-936200-08-1). Blue Cat.

--TRS-80 Assembly Language Subroutines. (Illus.). 282p. 1982. pap. 18.95 (ISBN 0-13-931188-2). P-H.

BASIC Conversions Handbook for TRS-80, Apple & PET Users. 96p. 5.95 (ISBN 0-317-05253-5, 62-2088). Radio Shack.

Behrendt, Bill. Pocket Magic: Twenty-Five Intriguing, Animated Games for the TRS-80 PC & the Sharp PC-1211. 96p. 1982. 17.95 (ISBN 0-13-683847-2); pap. 9.95 (ISBN 0-13-683839-1). P-H.

Berenbon, Howard. Mostly BASIC: Applications for Your TRS-80, Bk. 1. LC 80-53269. 168p. 1980. pap. 12.95 (ISBN 0-672-21788-0, 21788). Sams.

--Mostly BASIC Applications for Your TRS-80, Bk.2. 224p. 1981. pap. 12.95 (ISBN 0-672-21865-8, 21865). Sams.

Blattner, John W., et al. Encyclopedia for the TRS-80, Vol. 5. Putnam, Katherine & Comiskey, Kate, eds. 239p. (Orig.). 1982. 19.95 (ISBN 0-88006-035-2, EN8105); pap. 10.95 (ISBN 0-88006-036-0, EN8085). Green Pub Inc.

Blechman, Fred. Programs for Beginners on the TRS-80. (Illus.). 150p. 1981. pap. 10.95 (ISBN 0-8104-5182-4). Hayden.

Blechman, Fred, et al. Encyclopedia for the TRS-80, Vol. 6. Putnam, Katherine & Comiskey, Kate, eds. (Illus.). 303p. 1982. 19.95 (ISBN 0-88006-040-9, EN8106); pap. 10.95 (ISBN 0-88006-041-7, EN8086). Green Pub Inc.

Brain Bank. The BASIC Conversions Handbook for Apple, Commodore, TRS-80, & Atari Users. write for info. Hayden.

Brain, David, et al. The BASIC Conversions Handbook for Apple, TRS-80 & PET Users. 80p. (Orig.). 1982. pap. 9.95 (ISBN 0-8104-5534-X). Hayden.

Budin, Howard. Speed Walker: Fun to Program Your TRS-80. 89p. (Orig.). 1984. pap. 2.95 (ISBN 0-523-42244-X). Pinnacle Bks.

Burke, Ronald & Kramer, Arthur. Microcomputer Courseware for Technical Mathematics (Apple II & TRS-80) User's Manual. 1983. 11.70 (ISBN 0-07-009050-5). McGraw.

Burns, Edward. TRS-80 Teaching Aid: Ready-to-Run Programs for the Classroom & Home. (Illus.). 1984. pap. 15.95 (ISBN 0-8359-7875-3). Reston.

Busch, David. Teach Your TRS-80 to Program Itself. 2nd ed. (Illus.). 238p. 1984. 16.95 (ISBN 0-8306-0798-6); pap. 11.50 (ISBN 0-8306-1798-1, 1798). TAB Bks.

--TRS-80 Model 100 Sub-Routine Cookbook. cancelled 12.95 (ISBN 0-317-05651-4). Brady Comm.

Busch, David D. TRS-80 Portable Computer Subroutine Cookbook. (Illus.). 192p. 1984. pap. 12.95 (ISBN 0-89303-904-7). Brady Comm.

Carroll, Charles J. Eighty Practical Time-Saving Programs for the TRS-80. (Illus.). 252p. o.p 15.95 (ISBN 0-8306-0010-8, 1293); pap. 11.50 (ISBN 0-8306-1293-9, 1293). TAB Bks.

Chance, David. Thirty-Three Challenging Computer Games for the TRS-80, Apple & PET. (Illus.). 252p. 15.95 (ISBN 0-8306-9703-9, 1275); pap. 9.25 (ISBN 0-8306-1275-0). TAB Bks.

Chance, David W. Thirty-Three Adult Computer Games in BASIC for the IBM PC, Apple II, IIe & TRS-80. (Illus.). 378p. 1983. 18.95 (ISBN 0-8306-0627-0, 1627); pap. 13.50 (ISBN 0-8306-1627-6). TAB Bks.

Chien, Chao. TRS-80 Assembly Language. 1984. 17.95 (ISBN 0-03-070441-3). HR&W.

Cole, Jim. Murder in the Mansion & Other Computer Adventures. 2nd ed. (Illus.). 96p. (Pocket BASIC for the TRS-80). 1981. pap. 6.95 (ISBN 0-86668-501-4). ARCsoft.

--Pocket Computer Program Writing Workbook. 96p. 1983. 4.95 (ISBN 0-86668-817-X). ARCsoft.

Creative Programming Inc., Staff. Creative Programming: TRS-80, Vol. IV. rev. ed. 1983. spiral 9.95 (ISBN 0-912079-12-6, 104). Creat Prog Inc.

--Creative Programming: TRS-80, Teacher's Resource Book. 130p. 1983. 19.95 (ISBN 0-912079-08-8, 199). Creat Prog Inc.

DaCosta, Frank. Writing BASIC Adventure Programs for the TRS-80. LC 82-5945. (Illus.). 228p. 1982. 14.95 (ISBN 0-8306-2422-8, 1422); pap. 10.25 (ISBN 0-8306-1422-2, 1422). TAB Bks.

Dasenbrock, David. Battlestar BASIC for the TRS-80. LC 83-61060. 12.95 (ISBN 0-672-22006-7). Sams.

Decker, Jack. TRS-80 ROM Routines Documented. 126p. 1983. pap. text ed. 19.95 (ISBN 0-915363-01-1). Alter Source.

Dempsey, Tom. The TRS-80 Beginner's Guide to Games & Graphics. 1984. 16.95 (ISBN 0-317-06048-1); pap. 16.95 (ISBN 0-936200-10-3). Blue Cat.

Derfler, Frank. TRS-80 Data Communications. (Illus.). 159p. 1982. 18.95 (ISBN 0-13-931238-2); pap. 12.95 (ISBN 0-13-931220-X). P-H.

Directories from InfoSource, Inc. Business Software for the TRS-80: An Applications Directory. LC 83-45381. 168p. (Orig.). 1984. pap. 12.95 (ISBN 0-8019-7433-X). Chilton.

Domuret, Allan J., et al. Encyclopedia for the TRS-80, Vol. 3. Putnam, Katherine & Comiskey, Kate, eds. (Illus.). 265p. 1981. text ed. 19.95 (ISBN 0-88006-031-X, EN8103); pap. text ed. 10.95 (ISBN 0-88006-032-8, EN8083). Green Pub Inc.

Dwyer, Thomas A. & Critchfield, Margot. Structured Program Design with the TRS-80 BASIC. (Illus.). 352p. 1983. pap. 17.95 (ISBN 0-07-018493-3, BYTE Bks). McGraw.

Elia, L. & Fall, J. Word Processing with SUPERSCRIPSIT & the TRS-80. 1985. 15.64 (ISBN 0-87350-345-7) (ISBN 0-87350-346-5). exercise disk avail. Milady.

Farvour, James. Microsoft BASIC Decoded & Other Mysteries. (TRS-80 Information Ser.: Vol. II). (Illus.). 312p. (Orig.). 1981. pap. 29.95 (ISBN 0-936200-01-4). Blue Cat.

Fassnacht, Philip R., et al. The TRS-80 & TDP-100 Color BASIC & Extended System. rev. ed. (Nanos Reference Cards Ser.). (Illus.). 16p. 1982. 4.95 (ISBN 0-915069-08-3). Nanos Sys.

Faulk, Ed. How to Write a TRS-80 Program. (How to Write Ser.). (Illus.). 224p. 1982. pap. 14.95 (ISBN 0-88190-033-8, BO033). Datamost.

Finkel, LeRoy & Brown, Jerald R. TRS-80 Data File Programming. (Self-Teaching Guides: No. 1-581). 320p. 1983. pap. text ed. 14.95 (ISBN 0-471-88486-3, Pub. by Wiley Press). Wiley.

Fiske, Thomas S. Low Cost Costing: Product Costing with Your Microcomputer. (Illus.). 94p. (Orig.). 1984. pap. 24.95 spiral bound (ISBN 0-88006-084-0); Apple II, II Plus, IIe. spiral bound incl. disk 24.95 (ISBN 0-88006-067-0, CC7399); IBM-PC. spiral bound incl. disk 24.95 (ISBN 0-88006-071-9, CC7402); TRS-80 Model I, Model III. spiral bound incl. disk 24.95 (ISBN 0-88006-072-7, CC7403); spiral bound incl. disk 24.95 (ISBN 0-88006-092-1, CC7421). Green Pub Inc.

Genet, Russell M. Real-Time Control with the TRS-80. LC 82-50020. 166p. 1982. pap. 14.95 (ISBN 0-672-21831-3, 21831). Sams.

Getting Started with TRS-80 BASIC. 6.95 (ISBN 0-317-05267-5, 26-2107). Radio Shack.

Goodwin, Mark D. Level II ROMs. (Illus.). 532p. 1983. 24.95 (ISBN 0-8306-0275-5, 1575); pap. 17.50 (ISBN 0-8306-0175-9). TAB Bks.

Grauer, Robert T. TRS-80 COBOL. (Illus.). 352p. 1983. text ed. 31.95 (ISBN 0-13-931212-9); pap. text ed. 21.95 (ISBN 0-13-931204-8). P-H.

Grauer, Robert T., et al. BASIC Is Child's Play: TRS-80 Edition. (Illus.). 112p. 1984. pap. text ed. 18.95 (ISBN 0-13-058801-6). P-H.

Green, Wayne. Encyclopedia for the TRS-80, Vol. 2. McCarthy, Nan, et al, eds. (Encyclopedia for the TRS-80 Ser.). (Illus.). 283p. 1981. text ed. 19.95 (ISBN 0-88006-029-8, EN8102); pap. text ed. 10.95 (ISBN 0-88006-030-1, EN8082). Green Pub Inc.

Haigh, Roger W. & Radford, Loren E. BASIC for Microcomputers: Apple, TRS-80, PET. 337p. 1983. 21.95 (ISBN 0-442-27843-8). Van Nos Reinhold.

Hallgren, Richard. Interface Projects for the TRS-80. (Illus.). 152p. 1982. 18.95 (ISBN 0-13-469437-6); pap. 12.95 (ISBN 0-13-469429-5). P-H.

Hanson, R. N. & Rigby, S. D. Gregg Personal Keyboarding: TRS-80 Version. 96p. 1982. 36.95 (ISBN 0-07-079993-8). McGraw.

Hare, Robert R. An Introduction to Personal Computing: BASIC Programming on the TRS-80. 300p. 1983. pap. write for info. Wadsworth Pub.

--Personal Computing: BASIC Programming on the TRS-80. LC 83-7502. (Computer Science Ser.). 500p. 1983. pap. text ed. 18.00 pub net (ISBN 0-534-02768-7). Brooks-Cole.

Haskell, Richard. TRS-80 Extended Color BASIC. (Illus.). 170p. 1983. 19.95 (ISBN 0-13-931253-6); pap. 12.95 (ISBN 0-13-931246-3). P-H.

Heiserman, David. Computer Art & Animation for the TRS-80. (Illus.). 288p. 1983. text ed. 20.95 (ISBN 0-13-164749-0); pap. text ed. 15.95 (ISBN 0-13-164731-8). P-H.

Heiserman, David L. One Hundred One Programming Surprises & Tricks for Your TRS-80 Computer. (Illus.). 206p. (Orig.). 1984. pap. 11.50 (ISBN 0-8306-1741-8, 1741). TAB Bks.

Inman, Don & Conlan, Jim. Problem-Solving on the TRS-80 Pocket Computer. LC 81-10358. (Self-Teaching Guide Ser.). 255p. 1982. pap. text ed. 9.95 (ISBN 0-471-09270-3, Pub. by Wiley Pr). Wiley.

Inman, Don, et al. More TRS-80 BASIC. LC 81-150. (Self-Teaching Guide Ser.: No. 1581). 280p. 1981. pap. text ed. 12.95 (ISBN 0-471-08010-1, Pub. by Wiley Pr). Wiley.

Introduction to TRS-80 Graphics. 134p. 7.95 (ISBN 0-317-05259-4, 62-2073). Radio Shack.

Jones, Aubrey B., Jr. I Speak BASIC to My TRS-80. (I Speak BASIC Ser.). 224p. (Orig.). 1982. pap. text ed. 9.75 (ISBN 0-8104-6174-9); tchr's. manual 18.75 (ISBN 0-8104-6166-8); exam set 15.00 (ISBN 0-8104-6186-2); classroom set (tchr's. manual, 20 student texts & exam set) 200.00 (ISBN 0-8104-6156-0). Hayden.

K-Eight Math Cross Reference. 1981. pap. 4.95 (ISBN 0-318-01171-9). Radio Shack.

Kater, D. TRS-80 Word Processing with Scripsit. 176p. 1982. 19.95 (ISBN 0-07-033360-2, BYTE Bks). McGraw.

Kater, David & Thomas, Susan. TRS-80 Graphics. (Illus.). 256p. 1982. pap. 14.95 (ISBN 0-07-033303-3, BYTE Bks). McGraw.

Kellogg, Orson. The Radio Shack Notebook Computer. LC 83-50719. (Illus.). 121p. 1984. pap. 8.95 (ISBN 0-89588-150-0). SYBEX.

Kitsz, Dennis B. The Custom TRS-80 & Other Mysteries. (TRS-80 Information Ser.). (Illus.). 336p. (Orig.). 1982. pap. 29.95 (ISBN 0-936200-02-2). Blue Cat.

Klein, Jack. Mod-4. 218p. (Orig.). 1984. pap. text ed. 9.95 (ISBN 0-930615-00-X). Crest Sftware.

Kohl, Rachel, et al. The Genie in the Computer: Easy BASIC Through Graphics TRS-80. LC 82-13663. 169p. 1982. pap. text ed. 12.95 (ISBN 0-471-87049-8, Pub. by Wiley Pr). Wiley.

Lehman, Carol & Lehman, Mark. TRS-80 Word Processing Applications Using SuperScripsit. 1984. pap. text ed. 22.50 (ISBN 0-8359-7878-8); instr's manual avail. (ISBN 0-8359-7880-X). Reston.

Lewis, P. Enterprise Sandwich Shops: A Market Simulation TRS-80 Version. 1984. 199.00 (ISBN 0-07-079181-3). McGraw.

Lewis, Ted G. The TRS-80 Means Business. LC 81-11384. 194p. 1982. pap. 14.95 (ISBN 0-471-08239-2); incl. disk 34.90 (ISBN 0-471-87565-1). Wiley.

Librach, Hank. Pocket Computer Primer. LC 82-80270. 96p. (Orig.). 1982. pap. 9.95 (ISBN 0-942412-00-1); pre-recorded cassette 8.95 (ISBN 0-686-87024-7). Micro Text Pubns.

Lien, David A. & Kater, David. Learning TRS-80 Disk BASIC. LC 82-71959. (CompuSoft Learning Ser.). (Illus.). 400p. pap. cancelled (ISBN 0-932760-02-3). CompuSoft.

Lindley, Craig A. TRS-80 Z80 Assembly Language Library. (Illus.). 355p. (Orig.). 1983. looseleaf binder 34.97 (ISBN 0-88006-060-3, BK7395). Green Pub Inc.

Lord, Kenniston W., Jr. Using the Radio Shack TRS-80 in Your Home. 512p. 1983. 23.50 (ISBN 0-442-25707-4); pap. 14.95 (ISBN 0-442-26079-2). Van Nos Reinhold.

McCaul, Earles. TRS-80 Assembly Language Made Simple. LC 81-84281. 192p. 1981. pap. 12.95 (ISBN 0-672-21851-8, 21851). Sams.

McCunn, Donald H. Computer Programming for the Complete Idiot. LC 79-53299. 128p. (Orig.). 1979. pap. 6.95 (ISBN 0-932538-04-5). Design Ent SF.

McNitt, Lawrence. Invitation to COBOL for the TRS-80. (Illus.). 240p. 1983. pap. text ed. 15.00 (ISBN 0-89433-209-0). Petrocelli.

--Invitation to FORTRAN for the TRS-80. (Illus.). 240p. 1983. pap. 15.00 (ISBN 0-89433-210-4). Petrocelli.

--Invitation to Pascal for the TRS-80. 1985. 16.95 (ISBN 0-89433-253-8). Petrocelli.

Mazur, Ken, ed. The Creative TRS-80. (The Creative Ser.). (Illus.). 408p. 1983. pap. 15.95 (ISBN 0-916688-36-4, 18Y). Creative Comp.

Melton, Henry. Clean Slate Word Processing for the TRS-80. LC 82-51039. 384p. 1983. 17.95 (ISBN 0-672-22005-9, 22005); incl. disk 79.95. Sams.

--Clean Slate Word Processing for the TRS-80. 1983. write for info. Bobbs.

Model I TRS-DOS Manual. 5.95 (ISBN 0-317-05274-8, 26-104). Radio Shack.

More TRS-80 Assembly Language Programming. 430p. 5.95 (ISBN 0-317-05258-6, 62-2075). Radio Shack.

Muscat, E. & Lorton, P. Microcomputer Applications for the Data Processing Work Kit TRS-80 Diskette. (Microcomputer Software Ser.). 1982. 99.00 (ISBN 0-07-044107-3); Apple II Plus Version. 99.00 (ISBN 0-07-044108-1); user's guide 4.80 (ISBN 0-07-044109-X). McGraw.

Nahigian, J. Victor & Hodges, William S. Computer Games for the TRS-80. 151p. (Orig.). 1981. pap. text ed. 10.95 (ISBN 0-316-59691-4). Little.

Nickles, Herbert & Culp, George. Instructional Computing with the TRS-80. 300p. 1984. pap. write for info. Wadsworth Pub.

Nickles, Herbert & Culp, George H. Instructional Computing with the TRS-80. LC 83-10160. 288p. 1983. pap. text ed. 14.00 pub net (ISBN 0-534-02966-3). Brooks-Cole.

Noonan, Larry. Basic BASIC-English Dictionary for the Apple, PET & TRS-80. (Illus.). 154p. 1983. 17.95 (ISBN 0-8306-1521-0, 1521). TAB Bks.

O'Dell, Jerry W. TRS-80 As a Controller. (Illus.). 209p. (Orig.). 1984. spiral binding 12.95 (ISBN 0-88006-061-1, BK7394). Green Pub Inc.

Pellier, P. Programming Real Time Games on the TRS-80. Martres, Laurent, tr. from Fr. 112p. Date not set. price not set. Blue Cat.

Pennington, H. C., et al. Getting Started on the Sharp 1500 & Radio Shack PC-2. 280p. 16.95 (ISBN 0-936200-11-1). Blue Cat.

Pennington, Harvard C. TRS-80 Disk & Other Mysteries. (TRS-80 Information Ser.: Vol. I). (Illus.). 128p. (Orig.). 1979. pap. 22.50 (ISBN 0-936200-00-6). Blue Cat.

Poe, Elmer. Using the Z80 in the TRS-80. LC 82-50651. 256p. 1982. pap. 13.95 (ISBN 0-672-21839-9, 21839). Sams.

Poirot, James L. & Retzlaff, Don. Microcomputer Workbook: TRS-80. 124p. 1979. pap. 6.95 wkbk. (ISBN 0-88408-121-4); pap. 6.95 tchr's. ed. (ISBN 0-88408-146-X). Sterling Swift.

The Power of the TRS-80 Computer. (Illus.). 175p. 1984. pap. 14.95 (ISBN 0-916752-62-3). Dorison Hse.

Presley, Bruce. A Guide to Programming the Radio Shack TRS-80. 2nd ed. 352p. 1985. pap. 19.95 (ISBN 0-931717-14-0); drilled for a 3 ring binder tchr's guide 19.95 (ISBN 0-931717-15-9). Lawrenceville Pr.

Putnam, Katherine & Comiskey, Kate, eds. Encyclopedia for the TRS-80, Vol. 4. (Illus.). 253p. (Orig.). 1981. 19.95 (ISBN 0-88006-033-6, EN8104); pap. 10.95 (ISBN 0-88006-034-4, EN8084). Green Pub Inc.

--Encyclopedia for the TRS-80, Vol. 8. 219p. (Orig.). 1982. 19.95 (ISBN 0-88006-044-1, EN8108); pap. 10.95 (ISBN 0-88006-045-X, EN8088). Green Pub Inc.

--Encyclopedia for the TRS-80, Vol. 9. (Illus.). 253p. (Orig.). 1982. 19.95 (ISBN 0-88006-046-8, EN8109); pap. 10.95 (ISBN 0-88006-047-6, EN8089). Green Pub Inc.

--Encyclopedia for the TRS-80, Vol. 10. (Illus.). 177p. (Orig.). 1982. 19.95 (ISBN 0-88006-048-4, EN8110); pap. 10.95 (ISBN 0-88006-049-2, EN8090). Green Pub Inc.

Radio Shack TRS-80 Educational Software Sourcebook. 6.95 (ISBN 0-317-11010-1). Radio Shack.

Richardson, Robert M. Disassembled Handbook for TRS-80, Vol. 3. Abear, Gerald J., ed. 236p. 1981. 20.00x (ISBN 0-940972-03-4). Richcraft Eng.

--Morse Code, Baudot & ASCIL Radio Teletype Programming for the TRS-80 & Model III Microcomputers: Disassembled Handbook for the TRS-80, Vol. 4. Abear, Gerald J., ed. 285p. 1981. 18.00 (ISBN 0-940972-04-2). Richcraft Eng.

Rigsby, Mike. Verbal Control with Microcomputers. (Illus.). 312p. (Orig.). 1982. pap. 11.95 (ISBN 0-8306-1468-0, 1468). TAB Bks.

Rosenfelder, Lewis. BASIC Faster & Better & Other Mysteries. (TRS-80 Information Ser.: Vol. 4). (Illus.). 290p. (Orig.). 1981. pap. text ed. 29.95 (ISBN 0-936200-03-0). Blue Cat.

Rugg, Tom & Feldman, Phil. Thirty-Two BASIC Programs for the TRS-80 (Level II) Computer. LC 79-56399. 270p. 1983. pap. 19.95 (ISBN 0-918398-27-4); incl. disk 39.95; incl. cassette 39.95. Dilithium Pr.

Sawusch, Mark R. & Summers, Tan A. One Thousand One Things to Do with Your TRS-80. (Illus.). 256p. (Orig.). 1984. 15.95 (ISBN 0-8306-0806-0, 1806); pap. 9.95 (ISBN 0-8306-1806-6). TAB Bks.

Shaffer & Shaffer Applied Research & Development. VisiCalc Programming: No Experience Necessary for the TRS-80 Personal Computer. 256p. 1983. pap. 59.95 incl. disk & manual in slipcase (ISBN 0-316-78238-6). Little.

Spencer, Donald D. Programming the TRS-80 Pocket Computer. (Illus.). 176p. 1982. pap. text ed. 8.95 (ISBN 0-13-730531-1). P-H.

Tanner, Dennis F. The TRS-80 Graphics Handbook. 248p. 1984. 24.95 (ISBN 0-442-28300-8); pap. 15.95 (ISBN 0-442-28299-0). Van Nos Reinhold.

Titus, C., et al. TRS-80 Interfacing, Bk. 2. LC 79-65749. 256p. 1980. pap. 11.95 (ISBN 0-672-21739-2, 21739); Set. 20.95 (ISBN 0-672-21765-1, 21765). Sams.

Titus, Jonathan A. TRS-80 Interfacing, Bk. 1. LC 79-65749. 192p. 1979. pap. 10.95 (ISBN 0-672-21633-7, 21633). Sams.

TRS-80 Agricultural Software Sourcebook. 2.95 (ISBN 0-317-05278-0, 26-2774). Radio Shack.

TRS-80 Educational Software Sourcebook. 1983. pap. 6.95 (ISBN 0-318-01175-1). Radio Shack.

TRS-80 Microcomputer Information Handbook for Educators. 1981. pap. 2.50 (ISBN 0-318-01174-3). Radio Shack.

TRS-80 Microcomputer Newsletter Reprints. January-December 1981. 9.95 (ISBN 0-317-05282-9, 26-2240); January-December 1982. 12.95 (ISBN 0-317-05283-7, 26-2241). Radio Shack.

TRS-80 Microcomputer Newsletter Reprints, Vol. 1. 122p. 4.95 (ISBN 0-317-05281-0, 26-2115). Radio Shack.

TRS-80 Pocket Reference Handbook. 228p. 6.95 (ISBN 0-317-05260-8, 62-2084). Radio Shack.

TRS-80 Z80 Assembly Language Library. incl. disks 29.97 (ISBN 0-317-06047-3). Green Pub Inc.

Uffenbeck, John E. Hardware Interfacing with the TRS-80. (Illus.). 240p. 1983. text ed. 24.95 (ISBN 0-13-383877-3); pap. 14.95 (ISBN 0-13-383869-2). P-H.

Vick, Bill, et al. Encyclopedia for the TRS-80, Vol. 1. McCarthy, Nan & Crocker, Chris, eds. (Illus.). 269p. (Orig.). 1981. 19.95 (ISBN 0-88006-025-5, EN8101); pap. text ed. 10.95 (ISBN 0-88006-026-3, EN8081). Green Pub Inc.

Vickers, Ralph. Beyond Beginning BASIC. 220p. 1983. pap. 14.95 (ISBN 0-88056-126-2). Dilithium Pr.

Wagner, Michael J. Machine Language Disk I-O & Other Mysteries. (TRS-80 Information Ser.: Vol. 5). (Illus.). 288p. (Orig.). 1982. pap. 29.95 (ISBN 0-936200-06-5). Blue Cat.

Wayne Green Books Editors. Encyclopedia for the TRS-80, No. 10. (Illus.). 250p. (Orig.). 1981-82. 19.50 (ISBN 0-88006-056-5, EN8100); pap. 10.50 (ISBN 0-88006-057-3, EN8080). Green Pub Inc.

Weber Systems, Inc. Staff. BASIC Accounting System for TRS-80 Computers. cancelled (ISBN 0-317-05716-2). Weber Systems.

Weber Systems Staff. BASIC Business Package for TRS-80 Computers. LC 82-70599. (Applications Software Ser.). 210p. (Orig.). 1984. pap. 14.95 (ISBN 0-938862-27-8). Weber Systems.

Witham, Joan, ed. The Softside Sampler: TRS-80 Entertainment Programs. 128p. 1983. pap. 10.95 (ISBN 0-317-00366-6). Hayden.

Wu, Nesa L. BASIC: The Time-Sharing Language. 2nd ed. 340p. 1980. pap. text ed. write for info. (ISBN 0-697-08138-9); solutions manual avail. (ISBN 0-697-08139-7). Wm C Brown.

Zabinski, Michael P. Introduction to TRS-80 Level II BASIC. 1980. 9.95 (ISBN 0-318-01180-8). Radio Shack.

--TRS-80 for Kids from Eight to Eighty, 2 vols. LC 82-61990. 136p. 1982. pap. 10.95 ea. (22046). Vol. 1 (ISBN 0-672-22046-6). Vol. 2 (ISBN 0-672-22070-9). Sams.

Zabinski, P. Introduction to TRS-80 Level II BASIC & Computer Programming. (Illus.). 256p. 1980. text ed. 17.95 (ISBN 0-13-499970-3); pap. text ed. 12.95 (ISBN 0-13-499962-2). P-H.

TRS-80 COLOR COMPUTER

Adams, Tony, et al. Learning LOGO on the TRS-80 Color Computer. (Illus.). 174p. 1984. pap. 12.95 (ISBN 0-13-527961-5). P-H.

Albrecht, Robert L. & Inman, Don. BASIC for Your TRS-80 Super. LC 81-16286. (Self-Teaching Guides Ser.: No. 1-581). 374p. 1982. pap. text ed. 10.95 (ISBN 0-471-09644-X, Pub. by Wiley Pr). Wiley.

Anbarlian, Harry. Spreadsheeting on the TRS-80 Color Computer. (Personal Computing Ser.). 320p. 1983. 22.95 (ISBN 0-07-001595-3, BYTE Bks); incl. cassettes 39.95 (ISBN 0-07-079110-4). McGraw.

Barden, William, Jr. TRS-80 Model I, III, & Color Computer Interfacing Projects. LC 82-60876. 276p. 1983. pap. 14.95 (ISBN 0-672-22009-1, 22009). Sams.

Brewer, Bill & Willis, Jerry. How to Use the TRS-80 Color Computer. (How to Use Ser.). (Illus.). 128p. 1984. pap. 5.95 (ISBN 0-88056-342-7). Dilithium Pr.

Clark, Ron. One Hundred One Color Computer Programming Tips & Tricks. 128p. (Orig.). 1982. pap. 7.95 (ISBN 0-86668-007-1). ARCsoft.

TRS-80 PC-1 (COMPUTER)

Loop, Jeffrey P., et al. The TRS-80 Pocket (PC-1) Basic System. (Nanos Reference Cards Ser.). 10p. (Orig.). 1982. pap. 2.95 (ISBN 0-915069-09-1). Nanos Sys.

TRS-80 POCKET COMPUTER

Berenbon, Howard. TRS-80 Sharp Pocket Computer Programs. LC 83-50938. 224p. 1984. pap. 15.95 (ISBN 0-672-22078-4, 22078). Sams.

Cole, Jim. Practical PC-2-PC-1500 Pocket Computer Programs. 96p. 1983. 7.95 (ISBN 0-86668-028-4). Arcsoft.

Craig, John C. One Hundred Nineteen Practical Programs for the TRS-80 Pocket Computer. (Illus.). 308p. 1982. 15.95 (ISBN 0-8306-0061-2); pap. 10.25 (ISBN 0-8306-1350-1, 1350). TAB Bks.

TRS-80 Pocket Computer Programs. 80p. 1.95 (ISBN 0-317-05254-3, 62-2086). Radio Shack.

Wadsworth, Nat. Pocket Computer Programs. 176p. pap. 12.95 (6283). Hayden.

TRUCK FARMING

see also Vegetable Gardening

Fordam, R. & Biggs, A. G. Principles of Vegetable Crop Production. 250p. (Orig.). 1985. pap. text ed. 22.50x (ISBN 0-00-383014-4, Pub. by Collins England). Sheridan.

Market Gardening. Rev. ed. (Better Farming Ser.: No. 19). 56p. 1977. pap. 7.50 (ISBN 92-5-100620-2, F77, FAO). Unipub.

Utzinger, James D. Fundamentals of Vegetable Crop Science. 1984. text ed. 28.95 (ISBN 0-8359-2204-9). Reston.

TRUCKS, AUTOMOBILE

see Motor-Trucks

TRUFFLES

Gray, William D. The Use of Fungi As Food & in Food Processing, Pt. 1. (Monotopic Reprint Ser.). 1971. 11.95 (ISBN 0-87819-104-6). CRC Pr.

TRULLI

Allen, Edward. Stone Shelters. (Illus.). 1969. pap. 9.95 (ISBN 0-262-51010-3). MIT Pr.

TRUMPETER SWAN

Banko, Winston E. The Trumpeter Swan: Its History, Habits, & Population in the United States. LC 80-12533. (Illus.). x, 214p. 1980. pap. 5.95 (ISBN 0-8032-6057-1, BB 731, Bison). U of Nebr Pr.

TRUSSES

see also Bridges; Influence Lines; Roofs

Alcock, N. W. Cruck Construction: An Introduction & Catalogue. (CBA Research Reports Ser.: No. 42). 180p. 1981. pap. text ed. 24.50x (ISBN 0-906780-11-X, Pub. by Coun Brit Archaeology). Humanities.

Melaragno, Michele. Simplified Truss Design. LC 84-23384. 416p. 1985. Repr. of 1981 ed. lib. bdg. write for info. (ISBN 0-89874-820-8). Krieger.

Midwest Plan Service Engineers. Designs for Glued Trusses. 4th ed. Midwest Plan Service Staff, ed. LC 80-39547. (Illus.). 84p. 1981. pap. 5.00 (ISBN 0-89373-051-3, MWPS-9). Midwest Plan Serv.

Parker, Harry & Ambrose, James. Simplified Design of Roof Trusses Architects & Builders. 3rd ed. LC 81-19800. 301p. 1982. 32.50x (ISBN 0-471-07722-4, Pub. by Wiley-Interscience). Wiley.

TSETSE-FLIES

Austen, Ernest E. Handbook of the Tsetse-Flies. 16.00 (ISBN 0-384-02585-4). Johnson Repr.

--Monograph of the Tsetse-Flies. 35.00 (ISBN 0-384-02595-1). Johnson Repr.

Harriss, E. G. & Williams, N. G. Mixtures of Insecticides for Tsetse Fly Control: Potentiation Between a-Endosulfan & Deltalmethrin Applied to Glossina Austeni Newst. 1981. 35.00x (ISBN 0-85135-122-0, Pub. by Centre Overseas Research). State Mutual Bk.

Insecticides & Application Equipment for Tsetse Control: Prepared by the Centre for Overseas Pest Research, London, with the Support of the United Nations Development Programme. (Animal Production & Health Papers: No. 3). (Eng. & Fr.). 80p. 1977. pap. 9.00 (ISBN 92-5-100183-9, F723, FAO). Unipub.

Koeman, J. H. & Balk, F. The Environmental Impact of Tsetse Control Operations. (Animal Production & Health Papers: No. 7). (Eng. & Fr.). 74p. 1980. pap. 7.50 (ISBN 92-5-101001-3, F2160, FAO). Unipub.

Laird, M., ed. Tsetse: The Future for Biological Methods in Integrated Control. (Illus.). 220p. 1977. pap. 10.00 (ISBN 0-88936-109-6, IDRC77, IDRC). Unipub.

McKelvey, John H., Jr. Man Against Tsetse: Struggle for Africa. LC 72-12409. (Illus.). 324p. 1973. 24.50x (ISBN 0-8014-0768-0). Cornell U Pr.

TSUNAMIS

see also Earthquakes; Ocean Waves

Adams, William M., ed. Tsunamis in the Pacific Ocean. 1970. 30.00x (ISBN 0-8248-0095-8, Eastwest Ctr). UH Pr.

Iwasaki, T. & Iida, K., eds. Tsunamis: Their Science & Engineering. 1983. lib. bdg. 113.00 (ISBN 0-686-39790-8, Pub. by Reidel Holland). Kluwer Academic.

Myles, Douglas. The Great Waves. (Illus.). 224p. 1985. 16.95 (ISBN 0-07-044237-1). McGraw.

Pollard, Michael. North Sea Surge. (Illus.). 1979. 30.00 (ISBN 0-900963-82-4, Pub. by Terence Dalton England). State Mutual Bk.

Seismic Sea Waves. 1978. pap. 18.50 (ISBN 0-660-00565-4, SSC105, SSC). Unipub.

Toksoz, M. N. & Johnston, D. H., eds. Seismic Wave Attenuation. (Geophysics Reprint Ser.: No. 2). (Illus.). 465p. 1981. 15.00 (ISBN 0-931830-16-8). Soc Exploration.

Tsunami Research Symposium, 1974: Proceedings of an International Symposium of Tsunami Research. (Illus.). 258p. 1976. pap. 22.75 (ISBN 92-3-101330-0, U771, UNESCO). Unipub.

TUATARA

Robb, J. The Tuatara. 70p. 1977. 39.00x (ISBN 0-904095-26-6, Pub. by Meadowfield Pr England). State Mutual Bk.

TUBES

see also Pipe

Local Heat Treatment of Welds in Piping & Tubing: D10.10. 32p. 1975. 10.00 (ISBN 0-87171-123-0); 7.50. Am Welding.

Pipe & Tube Fabrication. 50.00x (ISBN 0-85083-017-6, Pub. by Engineering Ind). State Mutual Bk.

TUFF

see Volcanic Ash, Tuff, etc.

TUGBOATS

Brady, Edward M. Tugs, Towboats & Towing. LC 67-17537. (Illus.). 242p. 1967. 15.00x (ISBN 0-87033-127-2). Cornell Maritime.

Drushka, Ken. Against Wind & Weather: The History of Towboating in British Columbia. LC 82-670019. (Illus.). 264p. 1982. 24.95 (ISBN 0-295-95905-3, Pub. by Douglas & McIntyre Canada). U of Wash Pr.

Lang, Steven & Spectre, Peter. On the Hawser: A Tugboat Album. LC 79-67416. (Illus.). 522p. 1980. 35.00 (ISBN 0-89272-071-9, PIC436). Down East.

TUNA FISHERIES

Nakamura, Hiroshi. Tuna: Distribution & Migration. (Illus.). 84p. 9.75 (ISBN 0-85238-002-X, FN14, FNB). Unipub.

Report of the Fifth Joint Meeting of the Indo-Pacific Fishery Commission: Special Committee on Management of Indo-Pacific Tuna, Fifth Session; & the Indian Ocean Fishery Commission Committee on Management of Indian Ocean Tuna, Sixth Session, Manila, Philippines, 3-4 March 1978. (Fisheries Reports: No. 217). (Eng. & Fr.). 17p. 1979. pap. 7.50 (ISBN 92-5-100765-9, F1630, FAO). Unipub.

Saila, Saul B. & Norton, Virgil J. Tuna: Status, Trends, & Alternative Management Arrangements. LC 73-20846. (Resources for the Future, Program of International Studies of Fishery Arrangements, Paper: No. 6). pap. 20.00 (ISBN 0-317-26479-6, 2023814). Bks Demand UMI.

World Scientific Meeting on the Biology of Tunas & Related Species: Proceedings. (Fisheries Reports: No. 6, Vol. 4). 426p. 1964. pap. 25.50 (ISBN 0-686-93000-2, F1650, FAO). Unipub.

TUNAMIS

see Tsunamis

TUNDRAS

Bliss, L. C., et al, eds. Tundra Ecosystems. LC 79-50913. (International Biological Programme Ser.: No. 25). (Illus.). 1000p. 1981. 140.00 (ISBN 0-521-22776-3). Cambridge U Pr.

Brown, J., et al, eds. An Arctic Ecosystem: The Coastal Tundra at Barrow, Alaska. LC 78-22901. (US-IBP Synthesis Ser.: Vol. 12). 571p. 1981. 38.50 (ISBN 0-87933-370-7). Van Nos Reinhold.

Hobbie, J. E., ed. Limnology of Tundra Ponds: Barrow, Alaska. LC 80-26373. (US-IBP Synthesis Ser.: Vol. 13). 514p. 1980. 38.50 (ISBN 0-87933-386-3). Van Nos Reinhold.

Sverdrup, Harald U. Among the Tundra People. Sargent, Marston C., et al, eds. Sverdrup, Molly, tr. LC 78-60483. (Illus.). 10.75 (ISBN 0-89626-004-6); pap. 5.95x (ISBN 0-686-50011-3). Scripps Inst Ocean.

Tieszen, L L., ed. Vegetation & Production Ecology of an Alaskan Arctic Tundra. LC 78-14039. (Ecological Studies: Vol. 29). (Illus.). 1979. 49.00 (ISBN 0-387-90325-9). Springer-Verlag.

Wielgolaski, F. E., et al, eds. Fennoscandian Tundra Ecosystems, Pt. 1: Plants & Microorganisms. LC 75-4809. (Ecological Studies: Vol. 16). (Illus.). 500p. 1975. text ed. 77.00 (ISBN 0-387-07218-7). Springer-Verlag.

--Fennoscandian Tundra Ecosystems, Pt. 2: Animals & Systems Analysis. (Ecological Studies: Vol. 17). (Illus.). 370p. 1976. 77.00 (ISBN 0-387-07551-8). Springer-Verlag.

TUNGSTEN

Geology of Canadian Tungsten Occurences. 122p. 1984. pap. text ed. 10.00x (ISBN 0-660-11486-0, Pub. by Canadian Pub Ctr). Brookfield Pub Co.

Harris, P. M. & Humphreys, D. S. C. Tungsten: A Review, Paper #2. (Occasional Papers of the Institution of Mining & Metallurgy Ser.). 42p. (Orig.). 1984. pap. text ed. 14.00x (ISBN 0-900488-65-4). IMM North Am.

Mining Journal Books Ltd. Tungsten. 190p. 1980. 40.00x (ISBN 0-900117-21-4, Pub. by Mining Journal England). State Mutual Bk.

Specification for Tungsten Arc-Welding Electrodes: A5.12. 7p. 1980. 10.00 (ISBN 0-87171-197-4); member 7.50. Am Welding.

Tungsten Inert Gas (TIG), Metal Inert Gas (MIG) & Submerged Arc Welding. (Welding Inspection Ser.: Module 28-3). (Illus.). 58p. 1979. spiral bdg. 8.00x (ISBN 0-87683-107-2). G P Courseware.

Yih, W. H. & Wang, C. T. Tungsten: Sources, Metallurgy, Properties, & Applications. LC 78-10773. (Illus.). 516p. 1979. 69.50x (ISBN 0-306-31144-5, Plenum Pr). Plenum Pub.

TUNICATA

Berrill, J. N. Tunicata. 1950. 28.00 (ISBN 0-384-04065-9). Johnson Repr.

Fraser, J. H. British Pelagic Tunicates. LC 80-42174. (Synopses of the British Fauna Ser.: No. 20). 65p. 1982. pap. 14.95 (ISBN 0-521-28367-1). Cambridge U Pr.

Kolisko, E. & Kolisko, L. Zoology No. 6 Tunicatal Molluscs. 1981. 15.00x (ISBN 0-906492-42-4, Pub. by Kolisko Archive). State Mutual Bk.

Kolisko, Eugen. Zoology for Everybody: Tunicates & Molluscs, Vol. 6. (Illus.). 1983. pap. 4.50 (ISBN 0-317-07217-X, Pub. by Kolisko Archives). St George Bk Serv.

Thompson, H. Pelagic Tunicates of Australia. 1982. 30.00x (ISBN 0-686-97903-6, Pub. by CSIRO Australia). State Mutual Bk.

TUNNEL DIODES

see also Junction Transistors

Chow, Woo F. Principles of Tunnel Diode Circuits. LC 64-20080. 387p. 1964. text ed. 24.50 (ISBN 0-471-15615-9, Pub. by Wiley). Krieger.

TUNNELING (PHYSICS)

DeVault, Don. Quantum Mechanical Tunnelling in Biological Systems. 2nd ed. LC 83-15445. (Illus.). 200p. 1984. 44.50 (ISBN 0-521-24904-X). Cambridge U Pr.

Duke, C. B. Tunneling in Solids. (Solid State Physics, Suppl. 10). 1969. 76.00 (ISBN 0-12-607770-3). Acad Pr.

Jones, M. J., ed. Tunnelling '76. 455p. 1977. text ed. 95.00x (ISBN 0-900488-34-4). IMM North Am.

TUNNELS AND TUNNELING

see also Blasting; Boring; Excavation; Subways; also names of individual tunnels

Aerodynamics & Ventilation of Vehicle Tunnels, 2nd International Symposium. Proceedings. 1977. text ed. 60.00x (ISBN 0-900983-51-5, Dist. by Air Science Co.). BHRA Fluid.

Beaver, Patrick. A History of Tunnels. (Illus.). 180p. 1973. 7.95 (ISBN 0-8065-0369-6). Citadel Pr.

--A History of Tunnels. (Illus.). 155p. 1976. pap. 4.95 (ISBN 0-8065-0527-3). Citadel Pr.

Bickel, John O. & Kuesel, T. R., eds. Tunnel Engineering Handbook. 640p. 1982. 57.50 (ISBN 0-442-28127-7). Van Nos Reinhold.

Girnau, G. & Haack, A. Tunnelling Research. pap. 22.00 (ISBN 0-08-029952-0). Pergamon.

Helmers, Dow. Historic Alpine Tunnel. (Illus.). 208p. 1978. write for info.; pap. 14.95 (ISBN 0-937080-02-0). Century One.

Institution of Civil Engineers Staff, ed. Computer Methods in Tunnel Design. 200p. 1978. 30.25x (ISBN 0-7277-0056-1). Am Soc Civil Eng.

--Hazards in Tunnelling & on Falsework. 128p. 1975. 39.50x (ISBN 0-7277-0013-8). Am Soc Civil Eng.

International Symposium on the Aerodynamics & Ventilation of Vehicle Tunnels, 1st. Proceedings. 1973. text ed. 47.00x (ISBN 0-900983-28-0, Dist. by Air Science Co.). BHRA Fluid.

International Tunnelling Association. Advances in Tunnelling & Subsurface Technology & Use. pap. 37.00 (ISBN 0-08-025446-2). Pergamon.

Jones, M. H. & Woodcock, J. T. Ultraviolet Spectometry of Flotation Reagents With Special Reference to the Determination of Xanthate in Flotation Liquors. 28p. 1973. 11.50 (ISBN 0-900488-20-4). IMM North Am.

Jones, M. J., ed. Tunnelling '79. 408p. 1979. text ed. 100.00x (ISBN 0-900488-47-6). IMM North Am.

--Tunnelling '82. 301p. (Orig.). 1982. pap. text ed. 110.00x (ISBN 0-900488-62-X). IMM North Am.

Jones, Michael J. Eurotunnel '80. 156p. (Orig.). 1980. pap. text ed. 77.75x (ISBN 0-900488-50-6). IMM North Am.

Lane, Kenneth S. Field Test Sections Save Cost in Tunnel Support: Report from Underground Construction Research Council. LC 76-378194. pap. 20.00 (ISBN 0-317-08502-6, 2014477). Bks Demand UMI.

Mann, C. David & Kelley, Martin N., eds. RETC Proceedings, 1985. LC 85-70960. (Rapid Excavation & Tunneling Ser.). (Illus.). 1278p. 1985. 75.00x (ISBN 0-89520-441-X, 441-X). Soc Mining Eng.

Megaw, T. M. & Bartlett, John. Tunnels Planning Design & Construction, Vol. I. LC 81-4111. (Engineering Science Ser.). 284p. 1981. 84.95x (ISBN 0-470-27151-5). Halsted Pr.

--Tunnels Planning Design Construction, 2 vols. LC 81-4111. (Engineering Science Ser.). 605p. 1982. 84.95x (ISBN 0-470-27209-0); 169.95x set (ISBN 0-470-27217-1). Halsted Pr.

Morgan-Grampian Books, ed. Tunnelling Directory, 1985. 300p. 1985. 125.00x (ISBN 0-686-75515-4, Pub. by Morgan-Grampian Bk). State Mutual Bk.

Penoi, Jon R. Tunnels: Journey into a Dark Universe. LC 83-62371. (Illus.). 65p. 1983. pap. 3.50 (ISBN 0-942316-04-5). Pueblo Pub Pr.

Phillps, G. A. Thames Crossings: Bridges, Tunnels & Ferries. LC 81-65954. (Illus.). 288p. 1981. 37.50 (ISBN 0-7153-8202-0). David & Charles.

Pursall, B. R. & King, A. L., eds. Aerodynamics & Ventilation of Vehicle Tunnels Review & Bibliography. (BHRA Fluid Engineering Ser.: Vol. 2). 1977. pap. 47.00x (ISBN 0-900983-62-0, Dist. by Air Science Co.). BHRA Fluid.

Rapid Excavation & Tunneling Conference, 1979. R E T C Proceedings, 2 vols. Hustrulid, William A. & Maevis, Alfred C., eds. LC 79-52280. (Illus.). 1819p. 1979. 60.00x (ISBN 0-89520-266-2). Soc Mining Eng.

Society of Mining Engineers of AIME-RETC Proceedings. LC 76-21404. 1976. 40.00x (ISBN 0-89520-037-6). Soc Mining Eng.

Stack, Barbara. Handbook of Mining & Tunnelling Machinery. LC 80-4159. 742p. 1982. 107.95x (ISBN 0-471-27937-4, Pub. by Wiley-Interscience). Wiley.

Stephens, H. S. & Wood, P., eds. Proceedings: Third International Symposium on the Aerodynamics & Ventilation of Vehicle Tunnels, 2 vols. (Illus.). 1979. Set. lib. bdg. 98.00x (ISBN 0-906085-28-4, Dist. by Air Science Co.). BHRA Fluid.

Sutcliffe, Harry & Wilson, John W., eds. Rapid Excavation & Tunneling Conference Proceedings, 1983, 2 vols. LC 83-70933. (Illus.). 1258p. 1983. Set. 70.00x (ISBN 0-89520-411-8, 411-8). Soc Mining Eng.

Szechy, K. Art of Tunnelling. Szechy, D., et al, trs. 95.00 (ISBN 0-8044-4919-8). Ungar.

Tunnel & Shaft Conference, Minneapolis, 1968. Rapid Excavation: Problems & Progress Proceedings. Yardley, Donald H., ed. LC 78-98023. (Illus.). pap. 105.00 (ISBN 0-317-10974-X, 2002907). Bks Demand UMI.

TUNNELS AND TUNNELING–EXAMINATIONS, QUESTIONS, ETC.

Rudman, Jack. Assistant Bridge & Tunnel Maintainer. (Career Examination Ser.: C-27). (Cloth bdg. avail. on request). pap. 10.00 (ISBN 0-8373-0027-4). Natl Learning.

--Bridge & Tunnel Lieutenant. (Career Examination Ser.: C-111). (Cloth bdg. avail. on request). pap. 12.00 (ISBN 0-8373-0111-4). Natl Learning.

--Bridge & Tunnel Maintainer. (Career Examination Ser.: C-94). (Cloth bdg. avail. on request). pap. 10.00 (ISBN 0-8373-0094-0). Natl Learning.

--Bridge & Tunnel Supervisor. (Career Examination Ser.: C-2222). (Cloth bdg. avail. on request). pap. 12.00 (ISBN 0-8373-2222-7). Natl Learning.

--Senior Bridge & Tunnel Maintainer. (Career Examination Ser.: C-1472). (Cloth bdg. avail. on request). pap. 12.00 (ISBN 0-8373-1472-0). Natl Learning.

--Sergeant-Bridge & Tunnel Authority. (Career Examination Ser.: C-732). (Cloth bdg. avail. on request). pap. 12.00 (ISBN 0-8373-0732-5). Natl Learning.

--Tunnel Maintainer. (Career Examination Ser.: C-824). (Cloth bdg. avail. on request). pap. 10.00 (ISBN 0-8373-0824-0). Natl Learning.

TURBELLARIA

Betchaku, Teiichi, et al. Biology of Turbellaria: Experimental Advances, II. LC 72-13502. 1973. 29.50x (ISBN 0-8422-7112-0). Irvington.

Higley, Ruth. Morphology & Biology of Some Turbellaria from the Mississippi Basin. (Illus.). 1918. pap. 8.00 (ISBN 0-384-23090-3). Johnson Repr.

Schockaert, Ernest R. & Ball, Ian R., eds. The Biology of Turbellaria. 316p. 1981. 69.50 (ISBN 90-6193-757-4, Pub. by Junk Pubs Netherlands). Kluwer Academic.

Shapira, Jacob, et al. Biology of Turbellaria. (Illus.). 220p. 1973. text ed. 39.50x (ISBN 0-8422-7085-X). Irvington.

TURBIDITES
Mutti, E. Turbidites of the Northern Apennines: Introduction to Facies Analysis. Ricci Lucchi, F., ed. (AGI Reprint Ser.: No. 3). 1978. 5.00 (ISBN 0-913312-18-5). Am Geol.
TURBINE CARS
see Automobiles, Gas-Turbine
TURBINE-POWERED TRANSPORTS
see Jet Transports
TURBINES
see also Air-Turbines; Gas-Turbines; Steam-Turbines; Turbogenerators; Turbomachines
Balje, O. E. Turbomechanics: A Guide to Design, Selection & Theory. LC 80-21524. 513p. 1981. 64.95 (ISBN 0-471-06036-4, Pub. by Wiley-Interscience). Wiley.
Cooper, Paul, ed. Polyphase Flow in Turbomachinery. 1978. 40.00 (ISBN 0-685-66809-6, H00123). ASME.
Cruse, T. A., ed. Fatigue Life Technology, Bk No. H00096. Gallagher, J. P. pap. text ed. 18.00 (ISBN 0-685-79860-7). ASME.
Hawthorne, W. R., ed. Aerodynamics of Turbines & Compressors. (High Speed Aerodynamics & Jet Propulsion Ser.: Vol. 10). 1964. 63.00 (ISBN 0-691-07904-8). Princeton U Pr.
McBirnie, S. C. & Fox, W. J. Marine Steam Engines & Turbines. 4th ed. (Illus.). 672p. 1980. text ed. 57.50 (ISBN 0-408-00387-1). Butterworth.
Venediktov, V. C. Turbines & Jet Nozzles with Two-Phase Flows. LC 70-130509. 253p. 1969. 22.00 (ISBN 0-403-04543-6). Scholarly.
Wilson, R. F. & Lissaman, P. B. Aerodynamics of Wind Turbines. (Industrial Aerodynamics Ser.: Vol. 1). Date not set. price not set. Elsevier.
TURBOGENERATORS
Curless, Todd. Turbochargers: Theory, Installation, Maintenance & Repair. LC 84-16425. (Illus.). 176p. (Orig.). 1984. pap. 11.95 (ISBN 0-8306-0211-9, 2111). TAB Bks.
Garrison, Paul. Aircraft Turbocharging. (Illus.). 144p. 1982. pap. 5.95 (ISBN 0-8306-2306-X, 2306). TAB Bks.
Heller, Samuel. Direct Current Motors & Generators: Repairing, Rewinding & Redesigning. LC 82-72814. (Illus.). 1660p. (Orig.). 1982. Set. pap. 148.00 (ISBN 0-911740-09-0). Datarule.
TURBOJET PLANE ENGINES
see Airplanes–Turbojet Engines
TURBOJET TRANSPORTS
see Jet Transports
TURBOMACHINES
see also Compressors; Pumping Machinery; Turbines
American Society of Mechanical Engineers. Turbomachinery Developments in Steam & Gas Turbines: Presented at the Winter Annual Meeting of the American Society of Mechanical Engineers, Atlanta, Georgia, November 27-December 2, 1977. Steltz, W. G., ed. LC 77-88002. (Illus.). pap. 26.00 (ISBN 0-317-11146-9, 2013321). Bks Demand UMI.
Danenshyar, M. One-Dimensional Compressible Flow. 1977. text ed. 35.00 (ISBN 0-08-020414-7); pap. text ed. 11.75 (ISBN 0-08-020413-9). Pergamon.
Dixon, S. L. Fluid Mechanics & Thermodynamics of Turbomachinery: In SI-Metric Units. 3rd ed. 44.00 (ISBN 0-08-022721-X); pap. 15.00 (ISBN 0-08-022722-8). Pergamon.
--Worked Examples in Turbomachinery: Fluid Mechanics & Thermodynamics. LC 75-9757. 116p. 1975. text ed. 22.00 (ISBN 0-08-019797-3); pap. text ed. 10.00 (ISBN 0-08-019700-0). Pergamon.
Japikse, David. Turbomachinery Diffuser Design Technology. LC 85-90311. (Design Technology Ser.: DTS 1). (Illus.). 400p. 1984. text ed. 1450.00 (ISBN 0-933283-00-8). Concepts ETI.
Joint Fluids Engineering Gas Turbine Conference & Products Show (1980: New Orleans, LA) Measurement Methods in Rotating Components of Turbomachinery. Lakshiminarayana, B. & Runstadler, P., eds. LC 79-57425. pap. 87.30 (ISBN 0-317-19855-6, 2023149). Bks Demand UMI.
Logan. Turbomachinery. 160p. 1981. 24.50 (ISBN 0-8247-1509-8). Dekker.
Proceedings of the First Turbomachinery Maintenance Congress. (Illus.). 360p. (Orig.). 1985. pap. 52.50 (ISBN 0-9615256-0-6). Turbomachinery.
Project Squid Workshop on Transonic Flow Problems in Turbomachinery, Feb. 1976. Transonic Flow Problems in Turbomachinery: Proceedings. Adamson, T. C. & Platzer, M. F., eds. LC 77-22185. (Illus.). 660p. 1977. text ed. 79.50 (ISBN 0-89116-069-8). Hemisphere Pub.
Project Squid Workshop on Turbulence in Internal Flows: Turbomachinery & Other Applications, Airlie House, Warrenton, Va., June 14-15, 1976. Turbulence in Internal Flows: Turbomachinery & Other Engineering Applications, Proceedings. Murthy, S. N., ed. LC 77-15615. (Illus.). 573p. 1977. 84.50 (ISBN 0-89116-073-6). Hemisphere Pub.
Sawyer, John W. & Hallberg, Kurt, eds. Sawyer's Turbomachinery Maintenance Handbook, 3 vols. LC 80-53539. (Illus.). 1060p. 1981. Set. 180.00x (ISBN 0-937506-03-6). Turbo Intl Pubn.
--Sawyer's Turbomachinery Maintenance Handbook: Gas Turbines - Turbocompressors. (Illus.). 375p. 1980. 60.00x (ISBN 0-937506-01-X). Turbo Intl Pubn.
--Sawyer's Turbomachinery Maintenance Handbook: Steam Turbines - Power Recovery Turbines. (Illus.). 350p. 1981. 60.00x (ISBN 0-937506-00-1). Turbo Intl Pubn.
--Sawyer's Turbomachinery Maintenance Handbook, Vol. III: Support Services & Equipment. (Illus.). 340p. 1981. 60.00x (ISBN 0-937506-02-8). Turbo Intl Pubn.
Shepherd, Dennis G. Principles of Turbomachinery. (Illus.). 1956. text ed. write for info. (ISBN 0-02-409660-1). Macmillan.
Tabakoff, W., ed. Particular Laden Flows in Tubomachinery. 150p. 1982. 30.00 (G00210). ASME.
Thompson, W. E., ed. Fluid-Structure Interactions in Turbomachinery. 78p. 1981. 20.00 (ISBN 0-686-34488-X, H00202). ASME.
Turbomachinery International Handbook. 45.00 (ISBN 0-686-31377-1). Busn Journals.
Turbomachinery Maintenance Handbooks, 3 vols. Ea. 60.00 (ISBN 0-686-31375-5). Busn Journals.
Vavra, Michael H. Aero-Thermodynamics & Flow in Turbomachines. LC 74-9545. 626p. 1974. Repr. of 1960 ed. 38.50 (ISBN 0-88275-189-1). Krieger.
Wilson, David G. The Design of High-Efficiency Turbomachinery & Gas Turbines. (Illus.). 592p. 1983. 38.50x (ISBN 0-262-23114-X). MIT Pr.
TURBULENCE
see also Atmospheric Turbulence
Adams, Roy N. & Denman, Eugene D. Wave Propagation & Turbulent Media. LC 66-30179. (Modern Analytic & Computational Methods in Science & Mathematics Ser.). pap. 33.50 (ISBN 0-317-08452-6, 2007766). Bks Demand UMI.
Barenblatt, G. I. & Iooss, G., eds. Nonlinear Dynamics & Turbulence. 360p. 1983. text ed. 59.95 (ISBN 0-273-08560-3). Pitman Pub MA.
Bradbury, J. S., et al, eds. Turbulent Shear Flows, Two. (Illus.). 480p. 1980. 78.00 (ISBN 0-387-10067-9). Springer-Verlag.
Bradbury, L. J. & Durst, F., eds. Turbulent Shear Flows Four. (Illus.). 370p. 1985. 58.00 (ISBN 0-387-13744-0). Springer-Verlag.
Bradbury, L. J., et al. Turbulent Shear Flow 3rd: University of California, Selected Papers, 1981. (Illus.). 321p. 1982. 69.00 (ISBN 0-387-11817-9). Springer-Verlag.
Bradshaw, P. Engineering Calculation Methods for Turbulent Flow. 1981. 49.50 (ISBN 0-12-124550-0). Acad Pr.
--An Introduction to Turbulance & Its Measurements. Woods, W. A., ed. 218p. 1971. pap. text ed. 19.25 (ISBN 0-08-016621-0). Pergamon.
Bradshaw, P., ed. Turbulence. 2nd. rev ed. (Topics in Applied Physics Ser.: Vol. 12). (Illus.). 1978. pap. 27.00 (ISBN 0-387-08864-4). Springer-Verlag.
Centre National de la Recherche Scientifique. Mechanics of Turbulence. (Illus.). 490p. 1964. 129.50 (ISBN 0-677-10050-7). Gordon.
Chorin, Alexandre J. Lectures on Turbulence Theory. LC 75-11033. (Mathematics Lecture Ser., No. 5). 160p. 1975. pap. text ed. 12.00 (ISBN 0-914098-14-4). Publish or Perish.
Davies, J. T. Turbulence Phenomena: An Introduction to the Eddy Transfer of Momentum, Mass & Heat, Particularly at Interfaces. 1972. 75.00 (ISBN 0-12-206070-9). Acad Pr.
Dumas, R. & Fulachier, L., eds. Structure of Complex Turbulent Shear Flow: Marseille, France, 1982, Proceedings. (IUTLM Symposium). (Illus.). 444p. 1983. 42.00 (ISBN 0-387-12156-0). Springer-Verlag.
Eppler, R., ed. Laminar Turbulent Transitions. (International Union of Theoretical & Applied Mechanics). (Illus.). 432p. 1980. 43.70 (ISBN 0-387-10142-X). Springer-Verlag.
Favre, A. & Hasselmann, K., eds. Turbulent Fluxes Through the Sea Surface, Wave Dynamics, & Prediction, Vol. 1. (NATO Conference Series V, Air-Sea Interactions: Vol. 1). 691p. 1978. 89.50x (ISBN 0-306-40005-7, Plenum Pr). Plenum Pub.
Fiedler, H. Structure & Mechanisms of Turbulence I: Proceedings of the Symposium on Turbulence Held at the Technische Hochschule Berlin, August 1-5, 1977. (Lecture Notes in Physics: Vol. 75). (Illus.). 1978. pap. 19.00 (ISBN 0-387-08765-6). Springer-Verlag.
Fiedler, H., ed. Structure & Mechanisms of Turbulence II: Proceedings of the Symposium on Turbulence Held at the Technische Hochschule Berlin, August 1-5, 1977. (Lecture Notes in Physics: Vol. 76). (Illus.). 1978. pap. 23.00 (ISBN 0-387-08767-2). Springer-Verlag.
Frost, Walter & Moulden, T. H., eds. Handbook of Turbulence: Fundamentals & Applications, Vol. 1. LC 77-23781. (Illus.). 498p. 1977. 75.00x (ISBN 0-306-31004-X, Plenum Pr). Plenum Pub.
Hinze, J. O. Turbulence. 2nd ed. 1975. 54.00 (ISBN 0-07-029037-7). McGraw.
Jimenez, J., ed. Role of Coherent Structures in Modelling Turbulence & Mixing: Proceedings. (Lecture Notes in Physics Ser.: Vol. 136). 393p. 1981. pap. 30.00 (ISBN 0-387-10289-2). Springer-Verlag.
Kline, S. J., et al, eds. AFOSR-HTTM-Stanford Conference on Complex Turbulent Flows: 1980-81 Comparison of Computation & Experiment, 3 Vols. 632p. 125.00 set (ISBN 0-9607348-3-X); Vol. I. Objectives, Evaluation of Data, Specification of Test Cases 50.00, 632 p., 03/1981, 81-0908 (ISBN 0-9607348-0-5); Vol. II. Taxonomies, Reporters' Summaries, Evaluation, & Conclusions 50.00, 416 p., 03/1982, 81-84184 (ISBN 0-9607348-1-3); Vol. III. Comparison of Computation with Experiment, & Computors' Summary Reports 50.00, 514 p., 03/1982, 81-84184 (ISBN 0-9607348-2-1). Dept Mech E CA.
Kollman, W. Prediction Methods for Turbulent Flows. 1980. text ed. 47.50 (ISBN 0-07-035259-3). McGraw.
Kollmann, Wolfgang, ed. Prediction Methods for Turbulent Flows. LC 79-16852. (Von Karman Inst. Bk.). (Illus.). 480p. 1980. text ed. 72.50 (ISBN 0-89116-178-3). Hemisphere Pub.
Kozlov, V. V., ed. Laminar-Turbulent Transition. (International Union of Theoretical & Applied Mechanics). (Illus.). xxxviii, 757p. 1985. 85.00 (ISBN 0-387-15250-4). Springer-Verlag.
Kuramoto, Y. Chemical Oscillations, Waves, & Turbulence. (Springer Series in Synergetics: Vol. 19). (Illus.). 170p. 1984. 32.00 (ISBN 0-387-13322-4). Springer-Verlag.
Leslie, D. C. Developments in the Theory of Turbulence. (Illus.). 368p. 1983. pap. 24.95x (ISBN 0-19-856161-X). Oxford u Pr.
Libby, P. A. & Williams, F., eds. Turbulent Reacting Flows. (Topics in Applied Physics Ser.: Vol. 44). (Illus.). 260p. 1980. 56.00 (ISBN 0-387-10192-6). Springer Verlag.
Lin, Chia-Ch'iao. Statistical Theories of Turbulence. (Princeton Aeronautical Paperbacks Ser: No. 10). pap. 20.00 (ISBN 0-317-09284-7, 2001133). Bks Demand UMI.
Lumley, John L. Stochastic Tools in Turbulence. (Applied Mathematics & Mechanics Ser.,: Vol. 12). 1970. 59.50 (ISBN 0-12-460050-6). Acad Pr.
Noye, J. & Fletcher, C., eds. Computational Techniques & Applications CTAC-83: Proceedings of International Conference, University of Sidney, Australia, 1983. 982p. 1984. 92.75 (ISBN 0-444-87527-1, I-188-84, North Holland). Elsevier.
Olsen, John H., et al, eds. Aircraft Wake Turbulence & Its Detection. LC 70-159027. Tr. of Et Al. 602p. 1971. 75.00x (ISBN 0-306-30541-0, Plenum Pr). Plenum Pub.
Pao, Yih-Ho & Goldburg, Arnold. Clear Air Turbulence & Its Detection. LC 73-76507. 542p. 1969. 49.50x (ISBN 0-306-30397-3, Plenum Pr). Plenum Pub.
Patterson, G. K., et al, eds. Turbulence: Fifth Biennial Symposium. new ed. LC 79-2082. (Illus.). 1979. lib. bdg. 45.00 (ISBN 0-89500-019-9). Sci Pr.
Phillips, O. M. The Dynamics of the Upper Ocean. 2nd ed. LC 76-26371. (Cambridge Monographs on Mechanics & Applied Mathematics Ser.). (Illus.). 1977. 69.50 (ISBN 0-521-21421-1). Cambridge U Pr.
Rajaratnam, N. Turbulent Jets. (Developments in Water Science: Vol. 5). 304p. 1976. 74.50 (ISBN 0-444-41372-3). Elsevier.
Reynolds, A. J. Turbulent Flows in Engineering. LC 73-8464. (Illus.). pap. 90.90 (ISBN 0-317-11132-9, 2051617). Bks Demand UMI.
Rodi, W., ed. Turbulent Buoyant Jets & Plumes, Vol. 6. (HMT Ser.). 192p. 1982. 39.00 (ISBN 0-08-026492-1). Pergamon.
Sagdeev, R. Z. Nonlinear & Turbulent Processes in Physics, 3 vols. 1748p. 1984. text ed. 235.00 (ISBN 3-7186-0212-1). Harwood Academic.
--Nonlinear & Turbulent Processes in Physics, Vol. 1. 670p. 1984. text ed. 115.00 (ISBN 3-7186-0216-4). Harwood Academic.
--Nonlinear & Turbulent Processes in Physics, Vol. 2. 494p. 1984. text ed. 93.00 (ISBN 3-7186-0217-2). Harwood Academic.
--Nonlinear & Turbulent Processes in Physics, Vol. 3. 564p. 1984. text ed. 105.00 (ISBN 3-7186-0218-0). Harwood Academic.
Smith, J. R. Turbulence in Lakes & Rivers. 1975. 11.00x (ISBN 0-900386-21-5, Pub. by Freshwater Bio). State Mutual Bk.
Smolyakov, A. V. & Tkachenko, V. M. The Measurement of Turbulent Fluctuations: An Introduction to Hot-Wire Anemometry & Related Transducers. Chomet, S., tr. from Rus. (Illus.). 298p. 1983. 39.50 (ISBN 0-387-12144-7). Springer-Verlag.
Spalding, D. Brian & Afgan, N., eds. Heat Transfer & Turbulent Buoyant Convection: Studies & Applications for Natural Environment, Buildings, Engineering Systems, Vol. 2. LC 77-1868. (Thermal & Fluids Engineering Ser.). (Illus.). Repr. of 1977 ed. 82.90 (ISBN 0-8357-9188-2, 2016696). Bks Demand UMI.
Stanisic, M. M. The Mathematical Theory of Turbulence. (Universitext Ser.). (Illus.). xvi, 429p. 1985. 29.00 (ISBN 0-387-96107-0). Springer-Verlag.
Swinney, H. L. & Gollub, J. P., eds. Hydrodynamic Instabilities & the Transition to Turbulence. 2nd ed. (Topics in Applied Physics: Vol. 45). (Illus.). 325p. 1985. pap. 19.50 (ISBN 0-387-13319-4). Springer-Verlag.
Symposium at Pittsburgh, Penn., June, 1974. Turbulence in Mixing Operations: Theory & Application to Mixing & Reaction. Brodkey, Robert S., ed. 1975. 57.50 (ISBN 0-12-134450-9). Acad Pr.
Symposium in Applied Mathematics, New York, 1960. Hydrodynamic Instability: Proceedings. Bellman, R., et al, eds. LC 50-1183. (Vol. 13). 319p. 1962. pap. 25.00 (ISBN 0-8218-1313-7, PSAPM-13). Am Math.
Tennekes, Hendrik & Lumley, John L. First Course in Turbulence. 1972. 27.50x (ISBN 0-262-20019-8). MIT Pr.
Turbulence: Induced Vibrations & Noise of Structures. 144p. 1983. pap. text ed. 30.00 (ISBN 0-317-02659-3, H00285). ASME.
Zakin, J. L. & Patterson, C. K., eds. Turbulence in Liquids: Proceedings of the Fourth Biennial Symposium on Turbulence in Liquids. LC 76-52537. 1977. lib. bdg. 35.00 (ISBN 0-89500-000-8). Sci Pr.
TURDIDAE
Bent, Arthur C. Life Histories of North American Thrushes, Kinglets & Their Allies. (Illus.). 1949. pap. 7.95 (ISBN 0-486-21086-3). Dover.
--Life Histories of North American Thrushes, Kinglets & Their Allies. (Illus.). 14.50 (ISBN 0-8446-1643-5). Peter Smith.
TURF MANAGEMENT
Beard, J. Turfgrass: Science & Culture. (Illus.). 1972. ref. ed. 30.95 (ISBN 0-13-933002-X). P-H.
Beard, James B. Turf Management for Golf Courses. (Orig.). 1982. 45.00x (ISBN 0-8087-2872-5). Burgess.
Beard, James B., et al, eds. Turfgrass Bibliography from 1672-1972. 730p. 1977. 35.00x (ISBN 0-87013-195-8). Mich St U Pr.
Madison, John H. Principles of Turfgrass Culture. LC 80-39763. 440p. 1982. Repr. of 1971 ed. lib. bdg. 27.50 (ISBN 0-89874-197-1). Krieger.
Rorison, I. H. & Hunt, Roderick. Amenity Grassland: An Ecological Perspective. LC 79-40823. 261p. 1980. 79.95 (ISBN 0-471-27666-9, Pub. by Wiley-Interscience). Wiley.
Turgeon, A. J. & Giles, Floyd. Turfgrass Management. (Illus.). 1980. text ed. 25.95 (ISBN 0-8359-7885-0); instrs' manual avail. (ISBN 0-8359-7886-9). Reston.
Vargas, J. M., Jr. Management of Turfgrass Disease. (Orig.). 1981. text ed. 24.95x (ISBN 0-8087-2214-X). Burgess.
TURING MACHINES
Hume, J. N. & Holt, R. C. Introduction to Computer Science Using the Turing Programming Language. 1984. text ed. 24.95 (ISBN 0-8359-3168-4); pap. text ed. 19.95 (ISBN 0-8359-3167-6). Reston.
Jones, Neil D. Computability Theory. (ACM Monograph Ser). 1973. 45.00 (ISBN 0-12-390050-6). Acad Pr.
TURKEYS
Borghese, Anita. The Great Year-Round Turkey Cookbook. LC 79-13605. (Illus.). 1979. 12.95 (ISBN 0-8128-2673-6). Stein & Day.
Latham, Roger M. The Complete Book of the Wild Turkey. rev. ed. LC 76-7079. (Illus.). 224p. 1976. 12.95 (ISBN 0-8117-0414-9). Stackpole.
Mercia, Leonard. Raising Your Own Turkeys. LC 81-6353. (Illus.). 160p. (Orig.). 1981. pap. 5.95 (ISBN 0-88266-253-8). Garden Way Pub.
Podoll, David. Small Scale Turkey Growing for the Beginner. (Shorey Lost Arts Ser.). 26p. 1975. pap. 2.95 (ISBN 0-8466-6044-X, U44). Shorey.
Sanderson, Glen C. & Schultz, Helen C., eds. Wild Turkey Management: Current Problems & Programs. LC 72-87838. (Illus.). 366p. 1973. text ed. 22.00x (ISBN 0-8262-0133-4). U of Mo Pr.
Walters, John & Parker, Michael. Keeping Ducks, Geese, & Turkeys. (The Garden Farming Ser.). (Illus.). 125p. 1983. pap. 5.95 (ISBN 0-7207-1437-0, Pub. by Michael Joseph). Merrimack Pub Cir.
Williams, Lovett E., Jr. The Book of the Wild Turkey. LC 81-5078. 204p. 1981. 21.95 (ISBN 0-8329-3370-8, Pub. by Winchester Pr). New Century.
TURNING
see also Lathes; Woodwork

Annis, L., et al, eds. Turning, Vol. 1. 2nd ed. (Engineering Craftsmen: No. H2). (Illus.). 1977. spiral bdg. 37.50x (ISBN 0-85083-403-1). Intl Ideas.
The Art of Wood Turning. (Illus.). 48p. 1983. 7.50 (ISBN 0-686-47658-1); 6.00. Am Craft.
Automatic Turning Machines. 1982. 50.00x (ISBN 0-85083-217-9, Pub. by Engineering Ind). State Mutual Bk.
Boulter, Bruce. Woodturning in Pictures. (Illus.). 144p. (Orig.). 1983. pap. 12.95 (ISBN 0-8069-7742-6). Sterling.
Coggins, Frank W. The Woodturner's Handbook. (Illus.). 224p. 21.95 (ISBN 0-8306-0769-2, 1769); pap. 12.95 (ISBN 0-8306-1769-8). TAB Bks.
Fletcher, S. G., et al, eds. Turning, Vol. 2. (Engineering Craftsmen: No. H23). 1969. spiral bdg. 37.50x (ISBN 0-85083-038-9). Intl Ideas.
Holtzapffel, John J. Hand or Simple Turning: Principles & Practice. (Illus.). 1976. Repr. of 1881 ed. 16.50 (ISBN 0-486-23365-0). Dover.
--The Principles & Practice of Ornamental & Complex Turning. (Illus.). 656p. 1973. Repr. of 1894 ed. 19.95 (ISBN 0-486-22965-3). Dover.
Krar, S. F. & Oswald, J. W. Turning Technology: Engine & Turret Lathes. LC 78-153723. 1971. pap. text ed. 14.80 (ISBN 0-8273-0206-1); instructor's guide o.p. 3.60 (ISBN 0-8273-0207-X). Delmar.
Matthews, J. E., et al, eds. Automatic Turning Machines. 2nd ed. (Engineering Craftsmen Ser.: No. H30/3). (Illus.). 1978. spiral bdg 43.50x (ISBN 0-85083-405-8). Trans-Atlantic.
Nish, Dale L. Creative Woodturning. LC 75-6952. (Illus.). 280p. 1975. text ed. 15.95 (ISBN 0-8425-0469-9); pap. text ed. 12.95 (ISBN 0-8425-1557-7). Brigham.
Pain, F. Practical Wood Turner. rev. ed. LC 74-6436. (Home Craftsman Bk.). (Illus.). 1979. pap. 6.95 (ISBN 0-8069-8580-1). Sterling.
Raffan, Richard. Turning Wood with Richard Raffan. LC 84-52130. (Illus.). 176p. 1985. pap. 17.95 (ISBN 0-918804-24-8, Dist. by W W Norton). Taunton.
Rebhorn, Eldon. Woodturning. 1970. text ed. 16.64 (ISBN 0-87345-047-7). McKnight.
Ruley, M. J. Projects in General Metalwork. 1969. text ed. 15.28 (ISBN 0-87345-135-X). McKnight.
Seale, Roland. Practical Designs for Wood Turning. LC 79-65084. (Home Craftsman Bk.). (Illus.). 152p. 1979. pap. 6.95 (ISBN 0-8069-8874-6). Sterling.
Society of Manufacturing Engineers. Turning & Boring. 1985. 35.00 (ISBN 0-87263-169-9). SME.
Stokes, Gordon. Modern Wood Turning. LC 76-16365. (Home Craftsman Bk.). (Illus.). 128p. 1979. pap. 6.95 (ISBN 0-8069-8518-6). Sterling.
Thorlin, Anders. Ideas for Woodturning. (Creative Handcrafts Ser.). (Illus.). 128p. 1980. 13.95 (ISBN 0-13-450361-9, Spec); pap. 5.95 (ISBN 0-13-450353-8). P-H.
Turning One. 50.00x (ISBN 0-85083-010-9, Pub. by Engineering Ind). State Mutual Bk.
Turning Two. 1982. 50.00x (ISBN 0-85083-038-9, Pub. by Engineering Ind). State Mutual Bk.

TURNOUTS, RAILROAD
see Railroads–Construction

TURNPIKES (MODERN)
see Express Highways

TURTLES
see also Sea Turtles
Ashley, Laurence M. Laboratory Anatomy of the Turtle. (Laboratory Anatomy Ser.). 50p. 1982. write for info. wire coil (ISBN 0-697-04601-X). Wm C Brown.
Boulenger, G. A. Catalogue of the Chelonians, Rhynchocephalians, & Crocodiles in the British Museum. new ed. (Illus.). 1966. 26.60 (ISBN 3-7682-0443-X). Lubrecht & Cramer.
Brown, Laura E. & Moll, Don. The Status of the Nearly Extinct Illinois Mud Turtle (Kinosternon Flavescens Spooneri Smith 1951) with Recommendations for its Conservation. 49p. 1979. 2.25 (ISBN 0-89326-042-8). Milwaukee Pub Mus.
Carr, Archie. Handbook of Turtles: The Turtles of the United States, Canada, & Baja California. (HANH Ser.). (Illus.). 557p. 1952. 45.00x (ISBN 0-8014-0064-3). Comstock.
Freiberg, Marcos A. Turtles of South America. (Illus.). 128p. 1981. 14.95 (ISBN 0-87666-913-5, PS-757). TFH Pubns.
Galbreath, Edwin C. A New Extinct Emydid Turtle from the Lower Pliocene of Oklahoma. (Museum Ser.: Vol. 1, No. 16). 16p. 1948. 1.25 (ISBN 0-317-04796-5). U of Ks Mus Nat Hist.
Harless, Marion & Morlock, Henry. Turtles: Perspectives & Research. LC 78-16177. 695p. 1979. 80.50x (ISBN 0-471-35204-7, Pub. by Wiley-Interscience). Wiley.
Hirth, H. F. Synopsis of Biological Data on the Green Turtle: Chylonia Mydas (Linnaeus, 1758) (Fisheries Synopses: No. 85). 71p. 1971. pap. 7.50 (ISBN 92-5-101901-0, F1180, FAO). Unipub.
Jocher, Willy. Turtles for Home & Garden. (Illus.). 1973. 6.95 (ISBN 0-87666-777-9, PS-307). TFH Pubns.
Legler, John M. A New Subspecies of Slider Turtle (Pseudemys Scripta) from Coahuila, Mexico. (Museum Ser.: Vol. 13, No. 3). 12p. 1960. pap. 1.25 (ISBN 0-686-80365-5). U of KS Mus Nat Hist.
Nicholls, Richard E. Book of Turtles. LC 77-4413. (Illus., Orig.). 1977. lib. bdg. 12.90 (ISBN 0-914294-85-7); pap. 5.95 (ISBN 0-914294-86-5). Running Pr.
Plummer, Michael V. & Shirer, Hampton W. Movement Patterns in a River Population of the Softshell Turtle, Trionyx Muticus. (Occasional Papers: No. 43). 26p. 1975. pap. 1.50 (ISBN 0-686-80377-9). U of KS Mus Nat Hist.
Pritchard, Peter C. Encyclopedia of Turtles. (Illus.). 1979. 49.95 (ISBN 0-87666-918-6, H-1011). TFH Pubns.
Roberts, Mervin F. Turtles. (Illus.). 96p. 1980. 4.95 (ISBN 0-87666-928-3, KW-051). TFH Pubns.
Rudloe, Jack. Time of the Turtle. 1980. pap. 4.95 (ISBN 0-14-005590-8). Penguin.
Smith, Malcolm. The Fauna of British India, Including Ceylon & Burma: Reptilia & Amphibia, 2 vols. Incl. Vol. 1. Loricata, Testudines. 189p. Repr. of 1931 ed. Vol. 1. 15.00 (ISBN 0-88359-005-0); Vol. 2. Sauria. Repr. of 1935 ed. Vol. 2. 22.50 (ISBN 0-88359-006-9). (Illus.). 1973. Set. 35.00 (ISBN 0-88359-007-7). R Curtis Bks.
Turtle Lore. (Illus.). pap. 1.50 (ISBN 0-685-57147-5). E A Seemann.
Turtles. Wilkie, H. (Pet Care Ser.). 1983. pap. 3.95 (ISBN 0-8120-2631-4). Barron.
Ward, Joseph P. Relationships of Chrysemyd Turtles of North America: Testudines: Emydidae. (Special Publications of the Museum Ser.: No. 21). (Illus.). 50p. 1984. pap. 9.00 (ISBN 0-89672-121-3). Tex Tech Pr.
Webb, Robert G., ed. Description of a New Softshell Turtle from the Southeastern United States. (Museum Ser.: Vol. 11, No. 9). 9p. 1959. pap. 1.25 (ISBN 0-317-04579-2). U of KS Mus Nat Hist.

TURTLES, FOSSIL
Packard, Earl L. New Turtle from the Marine Miocene of Oregon. (Studies in Geology Ser: No. 2). 32p. 1940. pap. 3.95x (ISBN 0-87071-062-1). Oreg St U Pr.

TWILIGHT
Rozenberg, Georgii V. Twilight: A Study in Atmospheric Optics. LC 65-11345. 368p. 1966. 34.50x (ISBN 0-306-30220-9, Plenum Pr). Plenum Pub.
United States. Nautical Almanac Office & Gale Research Company. Sunrise & Sunset Tables for Key Cities & Weather Stations in the United States. LC 76-24796. 1977. 70.00x (ISBN 0-8103-0464-3). Gale.

TWO-PHASE FLOW
see also Cavitation
Azbel, David. Two Phase Flows in Chemical Engineering. LC 80-20936. (Illus.). 400p. 1981. 95.00 (ISBN 0-521-23772-6). Cambridge U Pr.
Bergles, A. E. & Ishigai, S. Two Phase Flow Dynamics & Reactor Safety. 1981. 110.00 (ISBN 0-07-004904-1). McGraw.
Bergles, A. E., et al. Two-Phase Flow & Heat Transfer in the Power & Process Industries. (Illus.). 695p. 1981. 69.50 (ISBN 0-07-004902-5). McGraw.
Bergles, Arthur E., et al. Two-Phase Flow & Heat Transfer in the Power & Process Industries. LC 80-22025. (Illus.). 707p. 1980. text ed. 69.50 (ISBN 0-89116-197-X). Hemisphere Pub.
Chia-Shun Yih. Stratified Flows. LC 79-24817. 1980. 39.50 (ISBN 0-12-771050-7). Acad Pr.
Delhaye, J. M. & Cognet, G., eds. Measuring Techniques in Gas-Liquid Two-Phase Flows: Symposium, Nancy, France, July 5-8, 1984. (International Union of Theoretical & Applied Mechanics (IUTAM)). 760p. 1984. 59.00 (ISBN 0-387-12736-4). Springer-Verlag.
Delhaye, J. M., et al. Thermohydraulics of Two-Phase Systems for Industrial Design & Nuclear Engineering. LC 80-14312. (Hemisphere Series in Thermal & Fluids Engineering). (Illus.). 544p. 1980. text ed. 59.95 (ISBN 0-07-016268-9). McGraw.
Hetsroni, G., ed. Basic Two Phase Flow Modeling in Reactor Safety & Performance: EPRI Workshop Held at Tampa, Fla. 27 Feb.--2 March 1979. 170p. 1980. pap. 50.00 (ISBN 0-08-026160-4). Pergamon.
Hewitt, G. F. Measurement of Two Phase Flow Parameters. 1979. 44.00 (ISBN 0-12-346260-6). Acad Pr.
Hsu, Yih-Yun & Graham, Robert W. Transport Processes in Boiling & Two-Phase Systems, Including Near-Critical Fluids. LC 75-38662. (Series in Thermal & Fluids Engineering). pap. 139.50 (ISBN 0-317-08866-1, 2055327). Bks Demand UMI.
Lahey, Richard T., Jr. & Wallis, Graham B., eds. Non-Equilibrium Two-Phase Flows: Papers Presented at the Winter Annual Meeting of ASME, Houston, TX, November 30-December 5, 1975. LC 75-25192. pap. 20.00 (ISBN 0-317-08087-3, 2016830). Bks Demand UMI.
NATO Advanced Study Institute on Two-Phase Flows & Heat Transfer, Istanbul, Aug. 1976. Two-Phase Flows & Heat Transfer: Proceedings, 3 vols. Kakac, S., et al, eds. LC 77-8801. 1469p. 1977. Set. text ed. 265.00 (ISBN 0-89116-167-8). Hemisphere Pub.
Pai, Shih-I. Two-Phase Flows. (Vieweg Tracts in Pure & Applied Physics Ser.: Vol. 3). 1977. 49.50 (ISBN 0-9940011-4-2, Pub. by Vieweg & Sohn Germany). Heyden.
Round, Gilbert F., ed. Solid-Liquid Flow Abstracts, 3 Vols. 1064p. 1969. Set. 283.00x (ISBN 0-677-40120-5); Vol. 1, 448p. 127.25x (ISBN 0-677-40080-2); Vol. 2, 460p. 130.75 (ISBN 0-677-40090-X); Vol. 3, 156p. 62.50x (ISBN 0-677-40100-0). Gordon.
Saha, P., ed. Scaling in Two-Phase Flow. (HTD: Vol. 14). 53p. 1980. 12.00 (ISBN 0-686-69860-6, G00187). ASME.
Specialists Meeting on Transient Two-Phase Flow, Toronto, Canada, Aug. 3-4, 1976. Transient Two-Phase Flow: Proceedings, 2 vols. Banerjee, S. & Weaver, K., eds. (Illus.). 1978. Set. pap. text ed. 139.00 (ISBN 0-89116-153-8). Hemisphere Pub.
Stanley, Marland L. Two-Phase Flow Measurement: Principles, Designs & Applications. LC 82-227454. (Technical Report of an International Colloquim on Two-Phase Flow Instrumentation Ser.). 568p. 1982. pap. text ed. 44.95x (ISBN 0-87664-699-2). Instru Soc.
Symposium on Basic Mechanisms in Two-phase Flow & Heat Transfer, 1980, Chicago. Basic Mechanisms in Two-phase Flow & Heat Transfer. Rothe, P. H. & Lahey, R. T., eds. LC 80-69186. pap. 33.80 (ISBN 0-317-27790-1, 2024181). Bks Demand UMI.
Two-Phase Flow & Heat Transfer Workshop, Ft. Lauderdale, Oct. 1976. Two-Phase Transport & Reactor Safety: Proceedings, 4 vols. Veziroglu, T. N. & Kakac, S., eds. LC 77-14094. 1416p. 1978. Set. text ed. 385.00 (ISBN 0-89116-168-6). Hemisphere Pub.
Wallis, Graham. One-Dimensional Two-Phase Flow: The First Complete Account of John Paul Jones' Greatest Battle. (Illus.). 1969. 54.00 (ISBN 0-07-067942-8). McGraw.
Xuejun Chen & Veziroglu, T. Nejat, eds. Two-Phase Flow & Heat Transfer: China-U. S. Progress. LC 84-27908. (Illus.). 1000p. 1985. 175.00 (ISBN 0-89116-432-4). Hemisphere Pub.

TWO-PHASE MATERIALS
see Composite Materials

TYPE AND TYPE-FOUNDING
see also Linotype; Printing–Specimens; Type-Setting
Blades, William. Books in Chains & Other Bibliographical Papers. LC 68-30610. 1968. Repr. of 1892 ed. 35.00x (ISBN 0-8103-3298-1). Gale.
Burns, Aaron, ed. The ITC Typeface Collection. (Illus.). 572p. 1982. 49.95 (ISBN 0-9608034-0-8). Intl Typeface.
Duff, E. Gordon. Early English Printing: A Series of Facsimilies of All the Types Used in England During the 15th Century. 1969. Repr. of 1896 ed. 23.50 (ISBN 0-8337-0947-X). B Franklin.
Fournier, Pierre S. & Carter, Harry. Fournier on Typefounding. new ed. LC 78-150161. (Illus.). 412p. 1973. lib. bdg. 25.50 (ISBN 0-8337-1224-1). B Franklin.
Gates, David. Type. 208p. 1973. 18.50 (ISBN 0-8230-5522-1). Watson-Guptill.
Goudy, Frederic W. Alphabet & Elements of Lettering. rev. ed. 13.00 (ISBN 0-8446-2145-5). Peter Smith.
Goudy, Frederick W. Alphabet & Elements of Lettering. (Illus.). 1922. pap. 4.95 (ISBN 0-486-20792-7). Dover.
Grafton, Carol B., ed. Pictorial Archive of Printer's Ornaments from the Renaissance to the 20th Century. (Pictorial Archive Ser.). (Illus., Orig.). 1980. pap. 5.00 (ISBN 0-486-23944-6). Dover.
Jaspert, W. Pincus, et al. Encyclopaedia of Type Faces. 5th, rev. ed. 432p. 1984. 45.00 (ISBN 0-7137-1347-X, Pub. by Blandford Pr England). Sterling.
Kelly, Rob R. American Wood Type: Eighteen Twenty-Eight to Nineteen Hundred. (Quality Paperbacks Ser.). 1977. pap. 8.95 (ISBN 0-306-80059-4). Da Capo.
Menten, Theodore, ed. Art Nouveau & Early Art Deco Type & Design. (Dover Pictorial Archives Ser). (Illus.). 96p. (Orig.). 1972. pap. 4.50 (ISBN 0-486-22825-8). Dover.
Morison, Stanley. John Fell, the University Press & the Fell Types. LC 78-74401. (Nineteenth-Century Book Arts & Printing History Ser.: Vol. 14). 315p. 1980. lib. bdg. 100.00 (ISBN 0-8240-3888-6). Garland Pub.
Sabin, Tracy. Getting the Type You Want. (Illus.). 1980. pap. 7.95 (ISBN 0-930904-01-X). Graphic Dimens.
Silver, Rollo G. Typefounding in America, 1787-1825. LC 65-19396. pap. 50.00 (ISBN 0-317-10827-1, 2007195). Bks Demand UMI.
Sutton, James & Bartram, Alan. An Atlas of Typeforms. 116p. 1980. 60.00x (ISBN 0-85331-011-4, Pub. by Lund Humphries England). State Mutual Bk.
Swann, Cal. Techniques of Typography. (Illus.). 96p. 1982. pap. 12.00 (ISBN 0-913720-40-2). Beil.
Swanson, Ellen. Mathematics into Type. rev. ed. LC 72-170708. 98p. 1982. pap. 14.00 (ISBN 0-8218-0053-1, MIT). Am Math.
Updike, Daniel B. Printing Types: Their History, Forms & Use, 2 vols. 1980. pap. 9.95 ea. Vol. 1 (ISBN 0-486-23928-4). Vol. 2 (ISBN 0-486-23929-2). Dover.

TYPE AND TYPE-FOUNDING–BIBLIOGRAPHY
Blades, William. Books in Chains & Other Bibliographical Papers. LC 68-30610. 1968. Repr. of 1892 ed. 35.00x (ISBN 0-8103-3298-1). Gale.

TYPE-SETTING
see also Computerized Type-Setting; Printing–Layout and Typography; Printing–Style Manuals; Type and Type-Founding
Buhl, Tom. How to Start, Operate & Enjoy a Successful Typesetting Business. 2nd ed. (Illus.). 136p. 1981. pap. 15.95 (ISBN 0-939374-00-5). Homefront Graphics.
Chirich, Nancy. The Graphics Connection. (Illus.). 272p. (Orig.). 1985. pap. 11.95 (ISBN 0-912761-04-0). Ed-it Prods.
Craig, James. Phototypesetting: A Design Manual. Malmstrom, Margit, ed. (Illus.). 1978. 22.50 (ISBN 0-8230-4011-9). Watson-Guptill.
Hughes, Tom. Handbook of Operating Cost & Specifications for Phototypesetting Equipment. LC 74-25457. 1977. 34.50 (ISBN 0-912920-38-6). North Am Pub Co.
Jacobs, Marvin. How to Establish a Cold Typesetting Department & Train Operating Personnel. LC 74-15718. 1974. 21.00 (ISBN 0-912920-35-1). North Am Pub Co.
Kleper, Michael L. How to Build a Basic Typesetting System. LC 79-53427. (Illus.). 1979. pap. 10.00 (ISBN 0-930904-00-1). Graphic Dimensions.
--Telecommunicating Typesetters. (Illus.). 1982. pap. 10.00 (ISBN 0-930904-02-8). Graphic Dimensions.
--Typesetting by Microcomputer. (Illus.). 1982. pap. 10.00 (ISBN 0-930904-04-4). Graphic Dimensions.
Labuz, Ronald A. How to Typeset from a Wordprocessor: An Interfacing Guide. 218p. 1984. pap. 29.95 (ISBN 0-8352-1899-6). Bowker.
Labuz, Ronald A. & Altimonte, Paul. The Interface Data Book for Word Processing Typesetting. 195p. 1984. pap. 29.95 (ISBN 0-8352-1908-9). Bowker.
Larken, H. W. Compositors Work in Printing. 3rd ed. 382p. 1969. 30.00x (ISBN 0-905418-08-5, Pub. by Gresham Bks). State Mutual Bk.
Morton, A. Mechanical Composition, 3 pts. Incl. Pt. 1. Line Composition. 78p (ISBN 0-08-013964-7); Pt. 2. The Monotype Keyboard. 52p (ISBN 0-08-013965-5); Pt. 3. Caster Metallurgy. 100p (ISBN 0-08-013966-3). 1969. pap. 3.50 ea. Pergamon.
Rice, Stanley. Type-Caster: Universal Copyfitting. 96p. 1980. 14.95 (ISBN 0-442-22565-2). Van Nos Reinhold.
Schemel, George J. & Borbely, James A. Facing Your Type. (Illus., Orig.). 1982. pap. 2.25 (ISBN 0-943316-00-6). Typrofile Pr.
Seybold, John W. Fundamentals of Modern Photocomposition. (Illus.). 1979. text ed. 27.50 (ISBN 0-918514-03-7). Seybold.
Thompson, John S. History of Composing Machines: A Complete Record of the Art of Composing Type by Machinery. LC 72-5077. (Technology & Society Ser.). (Illus.). 590p. 1972. Repr. of 1904 ed. 18.00 (ISBN 0-405-04726-6). Ayer Co Pubs.

TYPE-SETTING MACHINES
see also Linotype
Huss, Richard E. The Development of Printers' Mechanical Typesetting Methods, 1822-1925. LC 77-190498. (Illus.). 400p. 1973. 25.00x (ISBN 0-8139-0336-X, Bibliographical Society, University of Virginia). U Pr of Va.
Kleper, Michael L. How to Build a Basic Typesetting System. LC 79-53427. 90p. (Orig.). 1979. pap. 10.00 (ISBN 0-89938-002-6). Tech & Ed Ctr Graph Arts RIT.

Morton, A. Mechanical Composition, 3 pts. Incl. Pt. 1. Line Composition. 78p (ISBN 0-08-013964-7); Pt. 2. The Monotype Keyboard. 52p (ISBN 0-08-013965-5); Pt. 3. Caster Metallurgy. 100p (ISBN 0-08-013966-3). 1969. pap. 3.50 ea. Pergamon.

Seybold, John W. World of Digital Typesetting. (Illus.). 1984. pap. 29.95x (ISBN 0-918514-08-8). Seybold.

Seybold Publications. Comparison Guide to Phototypesetting Systems. 2nd, rev. ed. 83p. 1983. 30.00 (ISBN 0-935220-08-9). Assn Info Sys.

TYPEWRITERS

see also Teletype

Boyce, B. Mercury Systems Inc. Practice Set in Word-Information Processing for Conventional & Text-Editing Typewriters. 1981. 8.24 (ISBN 0-07-006901-8). McGraw.

Marshak, Ronni T. A Seybold Study: Electronic Typewriters - Getting Started for Less than 2000.00. 1983. pap. 100.00 (ISBN 0-918514-04-5). Seybold.

Ortega, Wenceslao & Sampere, Alberto. Mecanografia Cien: Practicas Secretariales. (Span.). 180p. 1973. pap. text ed. 7.00 (ISBN 0-06-316641-0, IntlDept). Har-Row.

Post, Dan R., ed. Collector's Guide to Antique Typewriters. LC 81-82642. (Illus.). 128p. 1981. 12.95 (ISBN 0-911160-86-8). Post-Era.

Rudman, Jack. Typewriter Repairman (Electric) (Career Examination Ser.: C-1646). (Cloth bdg. avail. on request). pap. 12.00 (ISBN 0-8373-1646-4). Natl Learning.

--Typewriter Repairman (Manual) (Career Examination Ser.: C-1645). (Cloth bdg. avail. on request). 1977. pap. 12.00 (ISBN 0-8373-1645-6). Natl Learning.

Young, George. Selectric Interface. McCarthy, Nan, ed. (Illus.). 124p. 1982. pap. 12.97 (ISBN 0-88006-051-4, BK 7388). Green Pub Inc.

TYPEWRITING

see also Tabulation Typewriting

Altholz, et al. Type Right! A Complete Program for Business Typewriting. LC 78-73160. 1980. text ed. 17.20 (ISBN 0-8224-2128-3); tchrs' manual o.p. 7.96 (ISBN 0-8224-2129-1); stationary supplies 7.80 (ISBN 0-8224-2131-3); classroom mgmt manual (3 ring binder) 1981 30.00 (ISBN 0-8224-2132-1). Glencoe.

Bates, Billy P. Typewriting Identification (I.S.Q.T.) Identification System for Questioned Typewriting. (Illus.). 112p. 1971. 10.00x (ISBN 0-398-00110-3). C C Thomas.

Beaumont, Lee R., et al. Keyboarding Speed-Control Builders. 1985. text ed. 5.45 (ISBN 0-538-20080-4, T08). SW Pub.

Ben'Ary, Ruth. Touch Typing in Ten Lessons. rev. ed. (Illus., Orig.). 1982. pap. 4.95 (ISBN 0-399-50809-0, G&D). Putnam Pub Group.

Buchanan, Laurie. Pages To Go!! How to Start & Maintain a Successful Freelance Typing Service. 80p. (Orig.). 1982. pap. 14.95 (ISBN 0-943102-00-6). Pages to Go.

--Pages to Go!!! How to Start & Maintain a Successful Freelance Typing Service. write for info. (ISBN 0-943102-00-6). Buchanan L.

Crawford, T. James, et al. Basic Information Keyboarding Skills. 1982. text ed. 7.10 (ISBN 0-538-26010-6, Z01). SW Pub.

Curchak, Norma, et al. Legal Typewriting. 2nd ed. (Illus.). 1980. pap. text ed. 13.15 (ISBN 0-07-014940-2). McGraw.

Flanders, Robert G. Learn to Type. 2nd ed. LC 78-54788. (Illus.). 1978. pap. 6.95 (ISBN 0-89709-036-5). Liberty Pub.

Gades, Robert & Holder, Birdie H. Typewriting: A Comprehensive Program. 1979. pap. text ed. 18.95 (ISBN 0-8403-3023-5, 40302301). Kendall-Hunt.

--Typewriting: A Comprehensive Program, Working Papers. 1979. pap. text ed. 11.95 (ISBN 0-8403-2047-7). Kendall-Hunt.

Grossman, Jeremy. Quick Typing: A Self-Teaching Guide. LC 79-26243. (Self-Teaching Guides Ser.). 157p. 1980. pap. text ed. 6.95 (ISBN 0-471-05287-6). Wiley.

Grubbs, Robert L. & White, James L. Sustained Timed Writings. 4th ed. 96p. 1982. pap. 7.72 (ISBN 0-07-025063-4). McGraw.

Hale, Jordan. A Typing Sourcebook. LC 77-25064. 1978. pap. 10.83 scp (ISBN 0-672-97324-3); scp tchr's kit 7.33 (ISBN 0-672-97184-4). Bobbs.

Heller, Jack. Typing for Individual Achievement. Rubin, Audrey, ed. LC 80-26244. (Illus.). 192p. 1981. text ed. 19.44 (ISBN 0-07-027921-7). McGraw.

Hewitt, Shirley. Individualized Typing Series: Pt. I, Beginning. 2nd ed. 1972. student guide 6.95 (ISBN 0-89420-227-8, 117100); cassette recordings 235.50 (ISBN 0-89420-150-6, 117000). Natl Book.

--Individualized Typing Series: Pt. III, Advanced. 1972. student guide 8.25 (ISBN 0-89420-088-7, 119100); cassette recordings 242.45 (ISBN 0-89420-152-2, 119000). Natl Book.

Hutchinson, Betty & Hutchinson, Warner. Computer Typing Made Simple. LC 84-8143. (Made Simple Ser.). 112p. 1985. pap. 4.95 (ISBN 0-385-19429-3). Doubleday.

Levine, Nathan. Typing Made Simple. (Made Simple Ser.). 1958. pap. 4.95 (ISBN 0-385-01224-1). Doubleday.

Lieberman & Schimmel. Typing the Easy Way. (The Easy Way Ser.). 1982. pap. 8.95 (ISBN 0-8120-2284-X). Barron.

Lloyd, Alan C. & Krevolin, R. You Learn to Type. 1966. 18.20 (ISBN 0-07-038160-7). McGraw.

Lloyd, Alan C., et al. Typing Two: Advanced Course Gregg Typing. LC 81-15629. (Gregg Typing, Ser. 7). (Illus.). 288p. 1982. text ed. 16.12 (ISBN 0-07-038282-4). McGraw.

Mitchell, William, et al. College Typewriting, a Mastery Approach: Comprehensive. 416p. 1982. 19.95 (ISBN 0-574-20650-7, 13-3650); Instructor's Guide Avail. (ISBN 0-574-20651-5, 13-3651); Working Papers Avail. 9.95 (ISBN 0-574-20652-3, 13-3652); Model Answer Key 3.25 (ISBN 0-574-20653-1, 13-3653); Keyboard Tapes 175.00 (ISBN 0-574-20510-1, 13-3510); Transparency Masters Available 30.00 (13-3556); Lesson Planning Guides Available (ISBN 0-574-20556-X). SRA.

Montaperto, Nicki. How to Start a Profitable Typing Service at Home. LC 81-47080. 240p. (Orig.). 1981. pap. 5.05i (ISBN 0-06-463540-6, EH 540, EH). B&N NY.

Owen, Betty. Typing for Beginners. 1976. pap. 3.95 (ISBN 0-399-50820-1, G&D). Putnam Pub Group.

Pate, Ellen & Spengler, Barbara. Handbook for Typists: Operation of the Selectric Typewriter, Technical Information, Format Illustrations & Procedures. 96p. (Orig.). 1983. pap. text ed. 8.95 (ISBN 0-8403-2967-9, 40296702). Kendall-Hunt.

--Inroduction to Typewriting (Self-Paced) Keyboarding, Formatting Techniques, Personal & Career-Support Typing. 224p. 1980. pap. text ed. 9.95 (ISBN 0-8403-2195-3). Kendall-Hunt.

Reiff. Integrated Keyboarding - Communication Skills. 1984. text ed. 3.25 wkbk. (ISBN 0-538-23630-2, W63). SW Pub.

Wachs, Rosalind. It's Easy to Type. pap. 1.00 (ISBN 0-87497-064-4). Assoc Bk.

Winger, Fred E., et al. Gregg Typing: Refresher-Advanced Course. (Illus.). 1979. 18.20 (ISBN 0-07-071006-6). McGraw.

Yacht, Carol. Clear & Simple Guide to Touch Typing. (Clear & Simple Guides Ser.). (Illus.). 96p. (Orig.). 1981. pap. 5.95 (ISBN 0-671-42223-5). Monarch Pr.

Zimmer, Kenneth. High School Typewriting. LC 74-9198. 320p. 1977. text ed. 15.36 (ISBN 0-02-479730-8); tchr's manual 14.00 (ISBN 0-02-479780-4); text ed. 15.36 vocational course (ISBN 0-02-479740-5); Set 1. working papers 5.60 (ISBN 0-686-61289-2); Set 2. working papers 5.60 (ISBN 0-686-61289-2); Set 3. working papers 4.20 (ISBN 0-686-61290-6). Glencoe.

TYPEWRITING–COPYING PROCESSES

see Copying Processes

TYPEWRITING–EXAMINATIONS, QUESTIONS, ETC.

Hammer, Hy, ed. Test Preparation for Stenographer-Typist. LC 82-11429. 208p. (Orig.). 1982. pap. 8.00 (ISBN 0-668-05535-9, 5535). Arco.

Koch, Harry W. Typist & Stenographer Examinations. 2nd ed. 1976. 6.00 (ISBN 0-913164-63-1). Ken-Bks.

TYPEWRITING–PROGRAMMED INSTRUCTION

Grayson, Fred N. Learn to Type on Your Home Computer. LC 83-23728. (Illus.). 1984. pap. 5.95 (ISBN 0-399-50991-7, G&D). Putnam Pub Group.

Layman, N. Kathryn & Renner, Adrienne G. Word Processing Exercises for Word Processors, Microcomputers, & Electronic Typewriters. (Working Papers). 224p. 1984. 10.95wkbk. (ISBN 0-13-967514-0). P-H.

Lloyd, A., et al. Series Seven Typing Complete Course, Gregg Typing. 496p. 1982. 21.36 (ISBN 0-07-038280-8). McGraw.

Moon, Harry R. Typing from Rough Drafts. 1984. 12.70 (ISBN 0-87350-335-X); tchr's manual 10.30 (ISBN 0-87350-343-0); work papers packet 4.90 (ISBN 0-87350-306-6). Milady.

Pack, Alice C. & Joy, Robert O. Learning to Type in English As a Second Language. 1976. pap. text ed. 11.75 (ISBN 0-8191-0025-0). U Pr of Amer.

Stanwell, S. T., et al. Typewell Typewriting Course: Advanced Display, Vol. 4. 1977. wire bound 19.95x (ISBN 0-7131-1842-3). Intl Ideas.

TYPEWRITING–STUDY AND TEACHING

Hughes, Barbara, ed. Typing Manual. 4rd ed. 38p. 1981. pap. text ed. 10.00 (ISBN 0-935012-00-1). Edit Experts.

Levine, Nathan. Teach Yourself Typing. LC 82-6812. (Illus.). 96p. 1982. pap. 3.95 (ISBN 0-668-05455-7, 5455). Arco.

Lloyd, Alan C., et al. Typing One: General Course Gregg Typing. LC 81-15629. (Gregg Typing, Ser. 7). (Illus.). 288p. 1982. text ed. 15.56 (ISBN 0-07-038281-6). McGraw.

Ortega, Wenceslao & Sampere, Alberto. Mecanografia Cien, Libro 1. (Span.). 1971. pap. text ed. 7.00 (ISBN 0-06-316640-2, IntlDept). Har-Row.

TYPHOONS

see also Hurricanes; Storms

Typhoon Modification. (Illus.). 141p. 1975. pap. 25.00 (ISBN 92-63-10408-5, W176, WMO). Unipub.

Typhoon Operational Experiment. (World Weather Watch Tropical Cyclone Programme, Topex Reports: No. 3). 25p. 1981. pap. 7.00 (ISBN 92-63-10573-1, W491, WMO). Unipub.

Visher, S. S. Tropical Cyclones of the Pacific. (BMB). Repr. of 1925 ed. 21.00 (ISBN 0-527-02123-7). Kraus Repr.

TYPOGRAPHY

see Printing–Layout and Typography

U

UCSD-P (COMPUTER SYSTEM)

Bowles, K. L., et al. Problem Solving Using UCSD Pascal. 2nd ed. (Illus.). 350p. 1984. pap. 17.95 (ISBN 0-387-90822-6). Springer Verlag.

Bowyer, Kevin & Tomboulian, Sherryl. Pascal Programming for the IBM PC: IBM DOS, Pascal & UCSD P-System Pascal. LC 83-3921. (Illus.). 352p. 1983. pap. 19.95 (ISBN 0-89303-280-8); bk. & diskette 49.95 (ISBN 0-89303-761-3); disk 30.00 (ISBN 0-89303-762-1). Brady Comm.

Clark, Randy & Koehler, Stephen. The UCSD Pascal Handbook. (Software Ser.). (Illus.). 384p. 1982. text ed. 24.95 (ISBN 0-13-935544-8); pap. text ed. 18.95 (ISBN 0-13-935536-7). P-H.

Grant, Charles W. & Butah, Jon. Introduction to the UCSD p-System. LC 81-50655. (Illus.). 300p. 1982. pap. 15.95 (ISBN 0-89588-061-X, P370). SYBEX.

Haigh, Roger & Radford, Loren. UCSD Pascal: Featuring the Apple IIe & II Plus. 461p. 1983. text ed. write for info (ISBN 0-87150-457-X, 8090). PWS Pubs.

Hergert, Richard & Hergert, Douglas. Doing Business with Pascal. LC 82-62361. (Illus.). 371p. 1983. pap. text ed. 17.95 (ISBN 0-89588-091-1). SYBEX.

Moffat, David V. UCSD Pascal Examples & Exercises. (Illus.). 224p. 1986. pap. text ed. 14.95 (ISBN 0-13-935396-8). P H.

Overgaard, Mark & Stringfellow, Stan. Personal Computing with the UCSD-P System. 2nd ed. 320p. 1986. pap. text ed. 18.95 (ISBN 0-13-658030-0). P-H.

--Personal Computing with the USCD P-System. (Illus.). 464p. 1983. pap. text ed. 16.95 (ISBN 0-13-658070-X). P-H.

--Personal Computing with UCSD-P System. (Illus.). 400p. 1983. 23.95 (ISBN 0-13-658096-3); pap. text ed. 16.95 (ISBN 0-13-658070-X). P-H.

Pollack, Seymour V. Programming the IBM Personal Computer: UCSD Pascal. LC 82-21249. 400p. 1983. pap. 40.45 with diskette (ISBN 0-03-063669-8); pap. 20.95 (ISBN 0-03-062637-4). HR&W.

UDDER

Schalm, O. W., et al. Bovine Mastitis. LC 78-123423. (Illus.). 360p. 1971. text ed. 16.50 (ISBN 0-8121-0332-7). Lea & Febiger.

UFO

see Flying Saucers

UHF RADIO

see Radio, Short Wave

UHF TELEVISION

see Television–Ultrahigh Frequency Apparatus and Supplies

ULTIMATE STRENGTH ANALYSIS

see Plastic Analysis (Theory of Structures)

ULTRACENTRIFUGES

see Centrifuges

ULTRAFILTRATION

Ambard, L. & Trautmann, S. Ultrafiltration. Monnier, A., tr. (Illus.). 80p. 1960. 9.75x (ISBN 0-398-04189-X). C C Thomas.

Cooper, Anthony R., ed. Ultrafiltration Membranes & Applications. LC 80-18685. (Polymer Science & Technology Ser.: Vol. 13). 724p. 1981. 95.00x (ISBN 0-306-40548-2, Plenum Pr). Plenum Pub.

Nemeth, K. Application of Electro-Ultrafiltration (EUF) in Agricultural Production. 1982. pap. text ed. 22.00 (ISBN 90-247-2641-7, Pub. by Martinus Nijhoff Netherlands). Kluwer Academic.

Torrey, S., ed. Membrane & Ultrafiltration Technology: Developments since 1981. LC 83-22009. (Chemical Technology Review Ser.: No. 226). (Illus.). 463p. 1984. 64.00 (ISBN 0-8155-0977-4). Noyes.

ULTRAHIGH FREQUENCY RADIO

see Radio, Short Wave

ULTRAHIGH FREQUENCY TELEVISION

see Television–Ultrahigh Frequency Apparatus and Supplies

ULTRAHIGH TEMPERATURES

see High Temperatures

ULTRALIGHT AIRCRAFT

Christy, Joe. Ultralight Flying for the Private Pilot. (Illus.). 192p. 1985. pap. 12.95 (ISBN 0-8306-2382-5, 2382). TAB Bks.

Lambie, Jack. The Ultralight Kit Book. LC 84-8884. (Illus.). 252p. (Orig.). 1984. pap. 12.95 (ISBN 0-8306-2369-8, 2369). TAB Bks.

Lennon, Andy. Canard: A Revolution in Flight. LC 84-71364. (AV Bk.: No. 8). (Illus.). 200p. 1984. pap. 17.95 (ISBN 0-938716-18-2). Ultralight Pubns.

ULTRAMINIATURE CAMERAS

see Miniature Cameras

ULTRASONIC METAL-CUTTING

Rozenberg, L. D., et al. Ultrasonic Cutting. LC 64-7762. 154p. 1964. 35.00x (ISBN 0-306-10690-6, Consultants). Plenum Pub.

Thomas, Ralph H. Ultrasonics in Packaging & Plastics Fabrication. 192p. 1974. 22.95 (ISBN 0-8436-1102-2). Van Nos Reinhold.

ULTRASONIC TESTING

American Welding Society. Terms for Ultrasonic Testing in 11 Languages UTL. 102p. 1967. 20.00 (ISBN 0-686-43363-7). Am Welding.

Fitting, Dale & Adler, Laszlo. Ultrasonic Spectral Analysis for Nondestructive Evaluation. LC 80-14991. 364p. 1981. 59.50x (ISBN 0-306-40484-2, Plenum Pr). Plenum Pub.

Fundamentals of Ultrasonic Testing, Module 32-1. (Nondestructive Examination Techniques II Ser.). 84p. 1979. spiral bdg. 9.00x (ISBN 0-87683-098-X). G P Courseware.

Kornilovich, Yu. E. & Belokhovstikova, V. I. Ultrasound in the Production & Inspection of Concrete: Pt. 1, Production Applications. 1965. 29.50x (ISBN 0-306-17035-3, Consultants). Plenum Pub.

Operation of Ultrasonic Test Equipment, Module 32-2. (Nondestructive Examination Techniques II Ser.). (Illus.). 48p. 1979. spiral bdg. 7.00x (ISBN 0-87683-099-8). G P Courseware.

Silk. Ultrasonic Transducers for Nondestructive Testing. 1984. 39.00 (ISBN 0-9903003-0-7, Pub. by A Hilger England). Heyden.

Szilard, J, ed. Ultrasonic Testing: Non-Conventional Testing Techniques. LC 80-41592. 648p. 1982. 96.95x (ISBN 0-471-27938-2, Pub. by Wiley-Interscience). Wiley.

Tret'yakov, A. K. & Filonidov, A. M. Ultrasound in the Production & Inspection of Concrete: Pt. 2, Inspection of Hydraulic Construction. 1965. 29.50x (ISBN 0-306-17036-1, Consultants). Plenum Pub.

Viktorov, I. A. Rayleigh & Lamb Waves: Physical Theory & Applications. LC 67-10537. 154p. 1967. 39.50 (ISBN 0-306-30286-1, Plenum Pr). Plenum Pub.

ULTRASONIC WAVES

see also Ultrasonic Testing

Bartrum, Royal J., Jr. & Crow, Harte C. Case Studies in Ultrasound. (Illus.). 1979. text ed. 28.95 (ISBN 0-7216-1553-8). Saunders.

Courant, R. & Friedrichs, K. O. Supersonic Flow & Shock Waves. (Applied Mathematical Sciences: Vol. 21.). 1948. 42.00 (ISBN 0-387-90232-5). Springer-Verlag.

Goldberg, Barry & Wells, Peter N. Ultrasonics in Clinical Diagnosis. 3rd ed. (Illus.). 1983. pap. 35.00 (ISBN 0-443-02141-4). Churchill.

Kapustin, Alexander P. Effects of Ultrasound on the Kinetics of Crystallization. LC 63-17640. 65p. 1963. 20.00x (ISBN 0-306-10661-2, Consultants). Plenum Pub.

NCRP. Biological Effects of Ultrasound: Mechanisms & Clinical Implications. LC 83-61833. (NCRP Report Ser.: No. 74). 266p. 1983. pap. text ed. 15.00 (ISBN 0-913392-64-2). Natl Coun Radiation.

Nozdrev, V. F. Application of Ultrasonics to Molecular Physics. (Russian Monographs). (Illus.). 542p. 1963. 132.95 (ISBN 0-677-20360-8). Gordon.

Oliner, A. A. Acoustic Surface Waves. LC 77-17957. (Topics in Applied Physics Ser.: Vol. 24). (Illus.). 1978. 64.00 (ISBN 0-387-08575-0). Springer-Verlag.

Rozenberg, L. D., ed. High-Intensity Ultrasonic Fields. LC 78-128509. 429p. 1971. 59.50x (ISBN 0-306-30497-X, Plenum Pr). Plenum Pub.

Viktorov, I. A. Rayleigh & Lamb Waves: Physical Theory & Applications. LC 67-10537. 154p. 1967. 39.50 (ISBN 0-306-30286-1, Plenum Pr). Plenum Pub.

ULTRASONIC WAVES–INDUSTRIAL APPLICATIONS

see also Ultrasonic Metal-Cutting

Kochergin, Sergei M. & Vyaseleva, Galina Y. Electrodeposition of Metals in Ultrasonic Fields. LC 65-26633. 69p. 1966. 25.00x (ISBN 0-306-10751-1, Consultants). Plenum Pub.

Severdenko, V. P., et al, eds. Ultrasonic Rolling & Drawing of Metals. LC 73-188920. 206p. 1972. 35.00x (ISBN 0-306-10872-0, Consultants). Plenum Pub.

ULTRASONICS

see also Sound Pressure; Ultrasonic Waves

American Welding Society. Handbook on the Ultrasonic Examination of Welds: VEW.(IIW) 44p. 1977. 32.00 (ISBN 0-686-43357-2); 24.00. Am Welding.

Beyer, R. T. & Letcher, S. V. Physical Ultrasonics. (Pure & Applied Physics Ser.: Vol. 32). 1969. 76.00 (ISBN 0-12-095050-2). Acad Pr.

Cracknell, A. P. Ultrasonics. (The Wykeman Science Ser.: No. 55). 200p. 1980. pap. cancelled (ISBN 0-85109-770-7). Taylor & Francis.

Cracknell, A. P. & Clark, J. L. Ultrasonics. LC 79-26250. (Wykeham Science Ser.: No. 55). 200p. 1980. pap. 15.95x (ISBN 0-8448-1330-3). Crane-Russak Co.

El piner, Isaak E Imovich. Ultrasound: Physical, Chemical, & Biological Effects (Authorized Translation From the Russian) by F. L. Sinclair. LC 64-7760. pap. 95.30 (ISBN 0-317-08454-2, 2003361). Bks Demand UMI.

Ensminger, Dale. Ultrasonics: The Low & High-Intensity Applications. LC 72-90963. (Illus.). pap. 146.80 (ISBN 0-317-07982-4, 2055005). Bks Demand UMI.

Grossman, Charles C., ed. Diagnostic Ultrasound: Proceedings of the First International Conference, University of Pittsburgh, 1965. LC 65-27810. pap. 133.00 (ISBN 0-317-27899-1, 2055788). Bks Demand UMI.

Hykes, David L., et al. Ultrasound Physics & Instrumentation. (Illus.). 247p. 1985. text ed. 36.00 (ISBN 0-443-08407-6). Churchill.

Lutz, H. & Meudt, R. Manual of Ultrasound. (Illus.). 160p. 1984. pap. 26.00 (ISBN 0-387-12377-6). Springer-Verlag.

Mason, Warren P., ed. Physical Acoustics: Principles & Methods. Incl. Vol. 1A. Methods & Devices. 1964. 80.50 (ISBN 0-12-477901-8); Vol. 1B. Methods & Devices. 1964. 76.50 (ISBN 0-12-477941-7); Vol. 2A. Properties of Gases, Liquids & Solutions. 1965. 80.50 (ISBN 0-12-477902-6); Vol. 2B. Properties of Polymers & Nonlinear Acoustics. 1965. 76.50 (ISBN 0-12-477942-5); Vol. 3A. Applications to the Study of Imperfections & Lattice Dynamics. 1966. 80.50 (ISBN 0-12-477903-4); Vol. 3B. Applications to the Study of Imperfections & Lattice Dynamics. 1965. 73.50 (ISBN 0-12-477943-3); Vol. 4A. Applications to Quantum & Solid State Physics. 1966. 76.50 (ISBN 0-12-477904-2); Vol. 4B. Applications to Quantum & Solid State Physics. 1968. 80.50 (ISBN 0-12-477944-1); Vol. 5. 1969. 76.50 (ISBN 0-12-477905-0); Vol. 6. Thurston, R., ed. 1970. 77.50 (ISBN 0-12-477906-9); Vol. 7. 1970. 77.50 (ISBN 0-12-477907-7); Vol. 8. 1971. 77.50 (ISBN 0-12-477908-5); Vol. 9. 1972. 76.50 (ISBN 0-12-477909-3); Vol. 10. 1973. 82.50 (ISBN 0-12-477910-7); Vol. 13. Thurston, R. N., ed. 1977. 75.00 (ISBN 0-12-477913-1); Vol. 14. Thurston, R. N., ed. 1979. 77.50 (ISBN 0-12-477914-X). Acad Pr.

Meire, Hylton B., et al. Ultrasound Teaching Cases, Vol. 1. (Illus.). 176p. 1983. text ed. 59.95 (ISBN 0-318-00042-3). Butterworth.

Menter, Sir James, et al. Ultrasound & X-Rays in Engineering & Medicine. (Royal Society of London). (Illus.). 171p. text ed. 50.00x (ISBN 0-85403-116-2, Pub by Royal Soc London). Scholium Intl.

Moss, Albert & Goldberg, Henry, eds. Computed Tomography, Ultrasound & X-Ray: An Integrated Approach. LC 76-1666. 1980. 85.00 (ISBN 0-12-788525-0). Acad Pr.

Nosov, Vladimir A. Ultrasonics in the Chemical Industry. LC 64-23248. (Soviet Progress in Applied Ultrasonics Ser.: Vol. 2). pap. 42.80 (ISBN 0-317-10629-5, 2020692). Bks Demand UMI.

Puskar, A. The Use of High-Intensity Ultrasonics. (Materials Science Monographs: Vol. 13). 304p. 1983. 70.25 (ISBN 0-444-99690-7). Elsevier.

Rozenberg, L. D., ed. Physical Principles of Ultrasonic Technology, Vol. 1. Wood, James S., tr. LC 72-90337. (Ultrasonic Technology Ser.). 515p. 1973. 75.00 (ISBN 0-306-35041-6, Plenum Pr). Plenum Pub.

Sanders, Roger C., ed. Ultrasound Annual, 1982. (Illus.). 364p. 1982. text ed. 63.00 (ISBN 0-89004-861-4). Raven.

Thijsen, J. M. & Nicholas, D., eds. Ultrasonic Tissue Characterization. 1983. 34.50 (ISBN 90-247-2757-X, Pub. by Martinus Nijhoff Netherlands). Kluwer Academic.

Ultrasonics International 1983. 680p. (Orig.). 1983. pap. text ed. 99.95 (ISBN 0-408-22163-1). Butterworth.

Ultrasound Imaging Equipment Markets in the EEC. 250p. 1983. 1400.00 (ISBN 0-86621-506-9). Frost & Sullivan.

Ultrasound in Industrial Processing & Control. LC 63-17637. (Soviet Progress in Applied Ultrasonics Ser.: Vol. 1). pap. 52.50 (ISBN 0-317-08430-5, 2020691). Bks Demand UMI.

Wagai & Omoto, eds. Ultrasound in Medicine & Biology. (International Congress Ser.: Vol. 505). 282p. 1980. 69.00 (ISBN 0-444-90138-8, Excerpta Medica). Elsevier.

Williams, A. R. Ultrasound: Biological Effects & Potential Hazards. (Medical Physics Ser.). 1983. 49.50 (ISBN 0-12-756960-X). Acad Pr.

ULTRASONICS IN MEDICINE

Alvisi, C. Investigative Ultrasonology: Technical Advances, No. 1. 250p. 1979. 50.00x (ISBN 0-686-91723-5, Pub. by Pitman Bks England). State Mutual Bk.

--Investigative Ultrasonology Two: Clinical Advances. 344p. 1981. 70.00x (ISBN 0-272-79576-3, Pub. by Pitman Bks England). State Mutual Bk.

Alvisi, C. & Hill, C. R. Investigative Ultrasonlogy Two: Clinical Advances. 256p. text ed. cancelled (ISBN 0-272-79576-3). Pitman Pub MA.

Alvisi, C. & Hill, C. R., eds. Investigative Ultrasonology. 200p. 1981. text ed. 48.00x (ISBN 0-8464-1221-7). Beekman Pubs.

Anderhub, Beth. Manual of Abdominal Sonography. (Illus.). 256p. 1983. text ed. 37.50 (ISBN 0-8391-1804-X, 18589). Univ Park.

Athey, Patricia A. & McClendon, Linda. Diagnostic Ultrasound for Radiographers. LC 83-13203. (Illus.). 121p. (Orig.). 1983. pap. 12.95x (ISBN 0-940122-09-X). Multi Media CO.

Atkinson, Peter & Woodcock, John. Doppler Ultrasound & Its Use in Clinical Measurement. (Medical Physics Ser.: Vol. 5). 1982. 55.00 (ISBN 0-12-066260-4). Acad Pr.

Barnes, Broda O. & Barnes, Charlotte W. Heart Attack Rareness in Thyroid-Treated Patients. 104p. 1972. 12.75x (ISBN 0-398-02519-3). C C Thomas.

Bartrum, Royal J., Jr. & Crow, Harte C. Real Time Ultrasound: A Manual for Physician & Technical Personnel. 2nd ed. LC 77-72802. (Illus.). 1983. text ed. 26.00 (ISBN 0-7216-1552-X). Saunders.

Brascho, Donn J. & Shawker, Thomas H. Abdominal Ultrasound in the Cancer Patient. LC 80-15838. (Diagnostic & Therapeutic Radiology Ser.). 414p. 1980. 65.00 (ISBN 0-471-01742-6, Pub. by Wiley Med). Wiley.

Brown, Ross E. Ultrasonography: Basic Principles & Clinical Applications. LC 72-13842. (Illus.). 320p. 1975. 28.50 (ISBN 0-87527-095-6). Green.

Cadkin, Alan V. & Motew, Martin N. Clinical Atlas of Gray Scale Ultrasonography in Obstetrics. (Illus.). 384p. 1979. photocopy ed. 78.50x (ISBN 0-398-03842-2). C C Thomas.

Callen, Peter W. Ultrasonography in Obstetrics & Gynecology. (Illus.). 368p. 1983. 47.95 (ISBN 0-7216-2331-X). Saunders.

Canty, Timothy G., et al. Ultrasonography of Pediatric Surgical Disorders. 288p. 1981. 61.00 (ISBN 0-8089-1395-6, 790783). Grune.

Christie, A. D. Ultrasound & Infertility. 179p. (Orig.). 1981. pap. text ed. 29.95x (ISBN 0-86238-017-0, Pub. by Chartwell-Bratt England). Brookfield Pub Co.

DeMaria, Anthony N. Two-Dimensional Echocardiography. LC 81-50609. (Illus.). 1985. text ed. write for info. (ISBN 0-914316-25-7). Yorke Med.

Etter, Lewis E. Glossary of Words & Phrases Used in Radiology, Nuclear Medicine & Ultrasound. 2nd ed. 384p. 1970. 33.50x (ISBN 0-398-00526-5). C C Thomas.

Ewen, Sol J. & Glickstein, Cyrus. Ultrasonic Therapy in Periodontics. (Illus.). 144p. 1968. photocopy ed. 15.50x (ISBN 0-398-00535-4). C C Thomas.

Fleischer, Arthur C. & James, A. Everette. Real-Time Sonography. 431p. 1983. 57.50 (ISBN 0-8385-8270-2). ACC.

Fry, F. J., ed. Ultrasound: Its Applications in Biology & Medicine, 2 vols. (Methods & Phenomena Ser.: Vol. 3). 760p. 1978. Set. 117.00 (ISBN 0-444-41641-2). Elsevier.

Ghadially, Feroze N. Diagnostic Ultrastructural Pathology. (Illus.). 120p. (Orig.). 1984. pap. text ed. 19.95 (ISBN 0-407-00356-8). Butterworth.

Gill, R. W. & Dadd, M. J., eds. Proceedings of the Fourth Meeting of the World Federation for Ultrasound in Medicine & Biology. (Illus.). 500p. 1985. 100.00 (ISBN 0-08-032792-3, Pub. by P P A). Pergamon.

Gilsbach, J. M. Intraoperative Doppler Sonography in Neurosurgery. (Illus.). 120p. 1983. pap. 16.50 (ISBN 0-387-81768-9). Springer-Verlag.

Goldberg, Barry B. Abdominal Ultrasonography. 2nd ed. LC 84-2257. 528p. 1984. 55.00x (ISBN 0-471-08569-3, Pub. by Wiley Med). Wiley.

Gosink, Barbara B. & Squire, Lucy F. Diagnostic Radiology. 2nd ed. (Series of Exercises in Diagnostic Radiology: Vol. 8). (Illus.). 220p. 1981. text ed. 17.95 (ISBN 0-7216-4175-X). Saunders.

Hagen-Ansert, Sandra L. Textbook of Diagnostic Ultrasonography. 2nd ed. LC 82-8190. 683p. 1983. text ed. 55.95 (ISBN 0-8016-2016-3). Mosby.

Hanrath, P. Cardiovascular Diagnosis by Ultrasound. 1982. 39.50 (ISBN 90-247-2692-1, Pub. by Martinus Nijhoff Netherlands). Kluwer Academic.

Harper, A. Patricia, ed. Ultrasound Mammography. (Illus.). 224p. 1984. text ed. 39.50 (ISBN 0-8391-1807-4, 18090). Univ Park.

Harrigan, Pamela. Principles of Interpretation in Echocardiography. LC 84-13198. 1985. 65.00 (ISBN 0-471-87952-5, Pub. by Wiley Med). Wiley.

Hill, C. R. & Alvisi, C., eds. Investigative Ultrasonology One: Technical Advances. 170p. text ed. cancelled (ISBN 0-272-79575-5, Pub. by Pitman Bks Ltd UK). Pitman Pub MA.

Holman, B. Leonard, ed. Diagnostic Ultrasound: Collected Papers. (Medical Instrumentation Ser.: No. 106). (Illus.). 46p. 1983. pap. text ed. 17.00 (ISBN 0-910275-26-2); tchr's ed. 15.00 (ISBN 0-686-46129-0). Assn Adv Med instrs.

Hussey, M. Basic Physics & Technology of Medical Diagnostic Ultrasound. 240p. 1985. pap. 24.00 (ISBN 0-444-00945-0). Elsevier.

Hykes, David L., et al. Ultrasound Physics & Instrumentation. (Illus.). 247p. 1985. text ed. 36.00 (ISBN 0-443-08407-6). Churchill.

Jeanty, P. & Romero, R. Obstetrical Ultrasound. 304p. 1983. 45.00 (ISBN 0-07-032319-4). McGraw.

Jellins, Jack & Kobayashi, J., eds. Ultrasonic Examination of the Breast. 397p. 1983. 35.00 (ISBN 0-471-90324-8, Pub. by Wiley Med). Wiley.

Kelly, Elizabeth, ed. Ultrasonic Energy: Biological Investigations & Medical Applications. LC 65-10078. (Illus.). Repr. of 1965 ed. 99.00 (ISBN 0-8357-9701-5, 2019048). Bks Demand UMI.

Kraus, Robert, ed. The Practice of Echocardiography. 352p. 1985. text ed. 37.50 (ISBN 0-471-08261-9, Pub. by Wiley Med.). Wiley.

Kremkau, Frederick W. Diagnostic Ultrasound: Principles, Instrumentation, & Exercises. 2nd ed. 304p. 1984. 29.50 (ISBN 0-8089-1643-2, 792386). Grune.

Kurjak, A., ed. Progress in Medical Ultrasound: Reviews & Comments, Vol. 1: 1980. 336p. 1980. 61.75 (ISBN 0-444-90144-2, Excerpta Medica). Elsevier.

--Progress in Medical Ultrasound, Vol. 3: Reviews & Comments. 376p. 1982. 61.75 (ISBN 0-444-90242-2, Excerpta Medica). Elsevier.

--Recent Advances in Ultrasound Diagnosis, Vol. 2. (International Congress Ser.: Vol. 498). 560p. 1980. 105.75 (ISBN 0-444-90125-6, Excerpta Medica). Elsevier.

Latin, V., ed. Ultrasonics in Medicine: Proceedings at Dubrovnik, May, 1981. (International Congress Ser.: Vol. 547). 146p. 1981. pap. 24.00 (ISBN 0-444-90200-7, Excerpta Medica). Elsevier.

Lerski, R. A. & Morley, P., eds. Ultrasound '82: Proceedings of the Third Meeting of the World Federation for Ultrasound in Medicine & Biology, Brighton, England, July 1982 (Fifth World Congress of Ultrasound in Medicine & Biology) (Illus.). 524p. 1983. 100.00 (ISBN 0-08-029805-2). Pergamon.

Levi, S., ed. Ultrasound & Cancer: Invited Papers & Selected Free Communications Presented at the First International Symposium, Brussels, Belgium, July 23-24, 1982. (International Congress Ser.: No. 587). 384p. 1982. 81.00 (ISBN 0-444-90270-8, I-281-82, Excerpta Medica). Elsevier.

Linhart, Joseph W. & Joyner, Claude R. Diagnostic Echocardiography. LC 81-14075. (Illus.). 373p. 1982. text ed. 54.50 (ISBN 0-8016-3042-8). Mosby.

Lunt, R. M. Handbook of Ultrasonic B-Scanning in Medicine. LC 77-22257. (Techniques of Measurement in Medicine Ser.: No. 1). (Illus.). 1978. 37.50 (ISBN 0-521-21753-9); pap. 12.95x (ISBN 0-521-29264-6). Cambridge U Pr.

Meire, H. B. & Farrant, P. Basic Clinical Ultrasound. 1982. 25.00x (ISBN 0-686-92011-2, Pub. by Brit Inst Radiology England). State Mutual Bk.

Meire, Hylton B., et al. Ultrasound Teaching Cases, Vol. 1. (Illus.). 176p. 1983. text ed. 59.95 (ISBN 0-318-00042-3). Butterworth.

Meudt, R. & Hinselmann, M. Ultrasonoscopic (Real Time) Differential Diagnosis in Obstetrics & Gynecology. 2nd ed. LC 78-9759. (Illus.). 1978. 63.00 (ISBN 0-387-08839-3). Springer-Verlag.

Millner, R., et al, eds. Ultrasound Interaction in Biology & Medicine. 215p. 1983. 37.50x (ISBN 0-306-41367-1, Plenum Pr). Plenum Pub.

Miskovits, Christine & Peters, Bruce E. Diagnostic Medical Ultrasound Examination Review. 1983. pap. text ed. 23.00 (ISBN 0-87488-410-1). Med Exam.

Nanda, Navin C. & Gramiak, Raymond. Clinical Echocardiography. LC 78-4116. 452p. 1978. text ed. 49.50 (ISBN 0-8016-3622-1). Mosby.

Nudelman, Sol & Patton, Dennis D., eds. Imaging for Medicine: Nuclear Medicine, Ultrasonics, & Thermography, Vol. 1. LC 79-25680. (Illus.). 512p. 1980. 59.50x (ISBN 0-306-40384-6, Plenum Pr). Plenum Pub.

Omoto, Ryozo & Kobayashi, Mitsunao. Atlas of Essential Ultrasound Imaging. LC 81-83231. (Illus.). 334p. 1981. text ed. 35.00 (ISBN 0-89640-061-1). Igaku-Shoin.

Partain, Leon C., ed. Nuclear Magnetic Resonance & Correlative Imaging Modalities. 312p. (Orig.). 1984. text ed. 49.50 (ISBN 0-932004-17-2). Soc Nuclear Med.

Phillips, Betty J. Manual of Echocardiographic Techniques. LC 79-3921. (Illus.). 276p. 1980. text ed. 24.95 (ISBN 0-7216-7219-1). Saunders.

Powis, Raymond L. & Powis, Wendy J. A Thinker's Guide to Ultrasonic Imaging. (Illus.). 430p. 1984. 47.50 (ISBN 0-8067-1581-2). Urban & S.

Raviv, J., et al, eds. Computer Aided Tomography & Ultrasonics in Medicine. 320p. 1979. 47.00 (ISBN 0-444-85299-9, North Holland). Elsevier.

Raymond, Howard W. Fundamentals of Abdominal Sonography: A Teaching Approach. 208p. 1979. 45.50 (ISBN 0-8089-1144-9, 793526). Grune.

Repacholi, Michael H. & Benwell, Deirdre A., eds. Essentials of Medical Ultrasound. LC 80-85522. (Medical Methods Ser.). (Illus.). 352p. 1982. 49.50 (ISBN 0-89603-028-8). Humana.

Sanders, Roger C. & Hill, Michael C., eds. Ultrasound Annual, 1983. (Ultrasound Annual Ser.). (Illus.). 336p. 1983. text ed. 47.50 (ISBN 0-89004-954-8). Raven.

--Ultrasound Annual, 1984. (Illus.). 302p. 1984. text ed. 48.50 (ISBN 0-89004-579-8). Raven.

Shirley. A User's Guide to Diagnostic Ultrasound. 352p. 1978. text ed. 25.00 (ISBN 0-8391-1307-2). Univ Park.

Sigel, Bernard. Operative Ultrasonography. LC 81-18599. (Illus.). 186p. 1982. text ed. 20.00 (ISBN 0-8121-0837-X). Lea & Febiger.

Silverman, Norman & Snider, Arlene. Two Dimensional Echocardiography in Congenital Heart Disease. (Illus.). 296p. 1982. 45.00 (ISBN 0-8385-9058-6). ACC.

Skolnick, M. Leon. Real-Time Ultrasound Imaging in the Abdomen. (Illus.). xi, 241p. 1981. 41.50 (ISBN 0-387-90570-7). Springer-Verlag.

Spencer, Merrill P. & Reid, John M. Cerebrovascular Evaluation with Dopler Ultrasound. 1982. lib. bdg. 44.50 (ISBN 90-247-2384-1, Pub. by Martinus Nijhoff Netherlands). Kluwer Academic.

Stroke, George W., et al, eds. Ultrasonic Imaging & Holography: Medical, Sonar, & Optical Applications. LC 74-1371. 642p. 1974. 89.50x (ISBN 0-306-30762-6, Plenum Pr). Plenum Pub.

Taylor, K. J. Manual of Ultrasonography. 1980. text ed. 22.50 (ISBN 0-443-08053-4). Churchill.

Taylor, Kenneth J. W., ed. Diagnostic Ultrasound in Gastrointestinal Disease. (Clinics in Diagnostic Ultrasound: Vol. 1). (Illus.). 1979. text ed. 24.00 (ISBN 0-443-08046-1). Churchill.

Van Mill, G. J., et al. Atlas of Two-Dimensional Echocardiography in Congenital Defects. 1983. lib. bdg. 56.00 (ISBN 0-89838-560-1, Pub. by Martinus Nijhoff Netherlands). Kluwer Academic.

Wagai & Omoto, eds. Ultrasound in Medicine & Biology. (International Congress Ser.: Vol. 505). 282p. 1980. 69.00 (ISBN 0-444-90138-8, Excerpta Medica). Elsevier.

Weill, F. S. & Le Mouel, A. Exercises in Diagnostic Ultrasonography of the Abdomen. (Illus.). 125p. 1983. pap. 19.00 (ISBN 0-387-12228-1). Springer-Verlag.

Wells, P. N. T. & Ziskin, Marvin, eds. New Techniques & Instrumentation in Ultrasound. (Clinics in Diagnostic Ultrasound Ser.). (Illus.). 224p. 1980. text ed. 26.00 (ISBN 0-443-08075-5). Churchill.

Wells, P. T. Biomedical Ultrasonics. 1977. 99.50 (ISBN 0-12-742940-9). Acad Pr.

White, D. N., ed. Recent Advances in Ultrasound in Biomedicine, Vol.1. (Ultrasound in Biomedicine Ser.). 270p. 1980. pap. 74.95 (ISBN 0-471-27892-0, Pub. by Res Stud Pr). Wiley.

White, Denis, et al, eds. Ultrasound in Medicine, Vols. 1-4. Incl. Vol. 1. 613p. 1975. 75.00x (ISBN 0-306-34201-4); Vol. 2. White, Denis & Barnes, Ralph, eds. 568p. 1976. 65.00x (ISBN 0-306-34202-2); Vol. 3A: Clinical Aspects. White, Denis & Brown, Russ, eds. 1225p. 1977. 115.00x (ISBN 0-306-34203-0); Vol. 3B: Engineering Aspects. White, Denis & Brown, Russ, eds. 1054p. 1977. 115.00x (ISBN 0-306-34204-9); Vol. 4. 692p. 1978. 79.50x (ISBN 0-306-34205-7). LC 74-23484 (Plenum Pr). Plenum Pub.

--Ultrasound in Biomedicine: Cumulative Bibliography of the World Literature to 1978. (Illus.). 712p. 1981. 110.00 (ISBN 0-08-027374-2). Pergamon.

Wicks, J. D. Fundamentals of Ultrasonographic Techniques. 1983. 24.50 (ISBN 0-8151-9277-0). Year Bk Med.

Winsberg, Fred. Clinical Ultrasound Review, Vol. 1. LC 80-19595. (Annual Review of Ultrasound). 348p. 1981. 60.00 (ISBN 0-471-05738-X, Pub. by Wiley Med). Wiley.

--Clinical Ultrasound Review, Vol. 2. 2nd ed. (Clinical Ultrasound Review Ser.). 474p. 1982. 70.00 (ISBN 0-471-08262-7, Pub. by Wiley Med). Wiley.

Winsberg, Fred & Stewart, James, eds. Clinical Ultrasound Reviews, Vol. 3. 388p. 1983. 80.00x (ISBN 0-471-09826-4). Wiley.

Woodcock. Ultrasonics. (Medical Physics Handbook: Vol. 1). 1979. 29.50 (ISBN 0-9960018-9-1, Pub. by A Hilger England). Heyden.

Yiu-Chiu, Victoria S. & Chiu, Lee C. Atlas of Obstetrical Ultrasonography. (Illus.). 312p. 1982. text ed. 50.00 (ISBN 0-8391-1765-5). Univ Park.

ULTRASTRUCTURE (BIOLOGY)

Biology Colloquium, 30th, Oregon State University, 1969. Biological Ultrastructure: The Origin of Cell Organelles: Proceedings. Harris, Patricia J., ed. LC 52-19235. (Illus.). 1971. 9.95x (ISBN 0-87071-169-5). Oreg St U Pr.

Bogolepov, N. N. Ultrastructure of the Brain in Hypoxia. Burov, Michael, tr. 208p. 1983. 8.95 (ISBN 0-8285-2573-0, Pub. by Mir Pubs USSR). Imported Pubns.

Damjanov, Ivan. Ultrastructural Pathology of Human Tumors, Vol. 2. Horrobin, D. F., ed. (Annual Research Reviews). 144p. 1980. 24.00 (ISBN 0-88831-082-X). Eden Pr.

Fawcett, Don. The Cell. 2nd ed. (Illus.). 928p. 1981. text ed. 40.00 (ISBN 0-7216-3584-9). Saunders.

Fuller, R., ed. Microbial Ultrastructure. 1977. 65.00 (ISBN 0-12-269450-3). Acad Pr.

Hadek, Robert. Mammalian Fertilization: An Atlas of Ultrastructure. 1969. 55.00 (ISBN 0-12-312950-8). Acad Pr.

King, Robert C. & Akai, Hiromu, eds. Insect Ultrastructure, Vol. 2. 604p. 1984. 85.00x (ISBN 0-306-41545-3, Plenum Pr). Plenum Pub.

Ludwig, H. & Metzger, H. The Human Female Reproductive Tract: A Scanning Electron Microscopic Atlas. (Illus.). 1976. 89.00 (ISBN 0-387-07675-1). Springer-Verlag.

Threadgold, L. T. The Ultrastructure of the Animal Cell. 2nd ed. Kerkut, G. A., ed. 472p. 1976. text ed. 65.00 (ISBN 0-08-018958-X); pap. text ed. 28.00 (ISBN 0-08-018957-1). Pergamon.

Tixier-Vidal, A. & Farquhar, Marilyn G., eds. The Anterior Pituitary. 1975. 73.00 (ISBN 0-12-692050-8). Acad Pr.

ULTRA-VIOLET RAYS

see also Spectrum, Ultra-Violet

Calkins, John, ed. The Role of Solar Ultraviolet Radiation in Marine Ecosystems. LC 82-3792. (NATO Conference Series IV, Marine Sciences: Vol. 7). 740p. 1982. 89.50x (ISBN 0-306-40909-7, Plenum Pr). Plenum Pub.

Green, Alex E., ed. The Middle Ultraviolet: Its Science & Technology. LC 66-22839. (Wiley Series in Pure & Applied Optics). pap. 101.50 (ISBN 0-317-09204-9, 2007393). Bks Demand UMI.

Harm, Walter. Biological Effects of Ultraviolet Radiation. LC 77-88677. (IUPAB Biophysics Ser.: No. 1). (Illus.). 1980. 44.50 (ISBN 0-521-22121-8); pap. 15.95 (ISBN 0-521-29362-6). Cambridge U Pr.

Harris, S. E., et al, eds. Laser Techniques in the Extreme Ultraviolet (OSA, Boulder, Colorado, 1984) AIP Conference Proceedings No. 119. LC 84-72128. (Optical Science & Engineering Ser.: No. 5). 527p. 1984. lib. bdg. 46.25 (ISBN 0-88318-318-8). Am Inst Physics.

Lang, L., ed. Absorption Spectra in the Ultraviolet & Visible Region, Vol. 22. 420p. 1978. lib. bdg. 46.50 (ISBN 0-88275-872-1). Krieger.

Madey, J. M., et al, eds. Free Electron Generation of Extreme Ultraviolet Coherent Radiation (Brookhaven-OSA, 1983) AIP Conference Proceedings No. 118. LC 84-71539. (Optical Science & Engineering Ser.: No. 4). 319p. 1984. lib. bdg. 40.50 (ISBN 0-88318-317-X). Am Inst Physics.

Parrish, John, et al. UV-A: Biological Effects of Ultraviolet Radiation. LC 78-14968. (Illus.). 272p. 1978. 32.50x (ISBN 0-306-31121-6, Plenum Pr). Plenum Pub.

Parrish, John A., et al. UV-A: Biological Effects of Ultraviolet Radiation with Emphasis on Human Responses to Longwave Ultraviolet. LC 78-14968. pap. 68.00 (ISBN 0-317-26187-8, 2052076). Bks Demand UMI.

Pestemer, M. Correlation Tables for the Structural Determination of Organic Compounds by Ultraviolet Light Absorptiometry. 163p. 1975. 57.70x (ISBN 3-527-25531-1). VCH Pubs.

Phillips, Roger. Sources & Applications of Ultra-Violet Radiation. 1983. 60.00 (ISBN 0-12-553880-4). Acad Pr.

White, Robert G. Handbook of Ultraviolet Methods. LC 64-23240. 373p. 1965. 35.00x (ISBN 0-306-30202-0, Plenum Pr). Plenum Pub.

UMBELLIFERAE

Heywood, V. H., ed. The Biology & Chemistry of the Umbelliferae. (Botanical Journal of the Linnean Society: Vol. 64, Suppl. 1). 1972. 76.00 (ISBN 0-12-346940-6). Acad Pr.

Schlessman, Mark A. Systematics of Tuberous Lomatiums (Umbelliferae) Anderson, Christiane, ed. LC 84-6399. (Systematic Botany Monographs). (Illus.). 55p. (Orig.). 1984. pap. 8.50 (ISBN 0-912861-04-5). Am Soc Plant.

UNCERTAINTY (COMMUNICATION THEORY)

David, Martin & Smeeding, Timothy, eds. Horizontal Equity, Uncertainty & Economic Well-Being. LC 85-5879. 496p. 1985. 48.00 (ISBN 0-226-13726-0). U of Chicago Pr.

Fiddle, Seymour, ed. Uncertainty: Behavioral & Social Dimensions. LC 80-82073. 410p. 1980. 41.95 (ISBN 0-03-057022-0). Praeger.

Kirzner, Israel M. Discovery & the Capitalist Process. LC 85-5799. 192p. 1985. lib. bdg. 22.50x (ISBN 0-226-43777-9). U of Chicago Pr.

UNCOOKED FOOD

see Food, Raw

UNDERGROUND CONSTRUCTION

see also Foundations; Subways; Tunnels and Tunneling

American Society of Civil Engineers, compiled by. Need for National Policy for the Use of Underground Space. 238p. 1973. pap. 14.50x (ISBN 0-87262-102-2). Am Soc Civil Eng.

Austrian Society for Geomechanics, 18th Colloquium. Stability of Rock Slopes & Underground Excavations. Mueller, L., ed. (Illus.). 1970. 33.70 (ISBN 0-387-80958-9). Springer-Verlag.

AWS Conference, 1980. Underwater Welding of Offshore Platforms & Pipelines, OPP: Proceedings. 189p. 1981. 25.00 (ISBN 0-87171-215-6). Am Welding.

Barker, Michael B. Building Underground for People. (Illus.). 1978. pap. 3.00 (ISBN 0-913962-27-9); pap. 2.50 members. Am Inst Arch.

Baum, Gregory, et al. The Earth Shelter Handbook. (Illus.). 252p. (Orig.). 1980. pap. 12.95 (ISBN 0-937816-05-1). Tech Data.

Bulson, P. S. Buried Structures: Static & Dynamic Strength. (Illus.). 320p. 1985. 42.50 (ISBN 0-412-21560-8, 6665, Pub. by Chapman & Hall). Methuen Inc.

Campbell, Stu. The Underground House Book. LC 80-14992. (Illus.). 208p. (Orig.). 1980. pap. 10.95 (ISBN 0-88266-166-3). Garden Way Pub.

Carter, David. Build It Underground: A Guide for the Self-Builder & Building Professional. LC 81-85021. (Illus.). 224p. 1982. pap. 7.95 (ISBN 0-8069-7582-2). Sterling.

Engineering Foundation Conference on Use of Shotcrete for Underground Structural Support. Use of Shotcrete for Underground Structural Support: Proceedings of the Engineering Foundation Conference, Berwick Academy, South Berwick, Maine, July 16-20, 1973 - with the Cooperation of ASCE & ACI. (American Concrete Institute Ser.: SP-45). (Illus.). pap. 118.80 (ISBN 0-317-10278-8, 2019550). Bks Demand UMI.

Fletcher, Gordon A. & Smoots, Vernon A. Construction Guide for Soils & Foundations. LC 73-21789. (Practical Construction Guides Ser). 420p. 1974. 49.95x (ISBN 0-471-26400-8, Pub. by Wiley-Interscience). Wiley.

Golany, Gideon. Earth-Sheltered Habitat: History, Architecture & Urban Design. 192p. 1982. 21.95 (ISBN 0-442-22992-5); 14.95 (ISBN 0-442-22993-3). Van Nos Reinhold.

Holthusen, T. Lance, ed. The Potential of Earth-Shelter & Underground Space: Today's Resource for Tomorrow's Space & Energy Viability: Proceedings of the Underground Space Conference & Exposition, Kansas City, MO, June 8-10, 1981. (Illus.). 501p. 1981. 66.00 (ISBN 0-08-028050-1). Pergamon.

Kern, Barbara & Kern, Ken. The Earth Sheltered: Owner-Built Home. LC 82-99912. (Illus.). 272p. (Orig.). 1982. pap. 9.95 (ISBN 0-910225-00-1). Owner-Builder.

Oehler, Mike. The Fifty Dollar & up Underground House Book. 4th ed. 1986. cancelled (ISBN 0-442-27312-6). Van Nos Reinhold.

Reynoldson, George. Let's Reach for the Sun: Thirty Original Solar & Earth Sheltered Home Designs. rev. ed. (Illus.). 144p. 1981. pap. 12.95 (ISBN 0-9603570-1-7). Space-Time.

Roy, Robert L. Underground Houses: How to Build a Low-Cost Home. (Illus.). 128p. 1983. pap. 6.95 (ISBN 0-8069-8856-8). Sterling.

Scott. Underground Homes: An Alternative Lifestyle. 400p. 1981. pap. 10.95 (ISBN 0-8306-1372-2, 1372). TAB Bks.

Scott, Ray G. How to Build Your Own Underground Home. 2nd ed. LC 84-16417. (Illus.). 256p. 1985. 19.95 (ISBN 0-8306-0792-7); pap. 11.95 (ISBN 0-8306-1792-2, 1792). TAB Bks.

Society of Mining Engineers of AIME-RETC Proceedings. LC 76-21404. 1976. 40.00x (ISBN 0-89520-037-6). Soc Mining Eng.

Stephansson, Ove, ed. Rock Bolting-Theory & Application in Mining & Underground Construction: Proceedings of the International Conference, Abisko, Sweden, 28 August 2 September 1983. 560p. 1983. lib. bdg. 45.00 (ISBN 90-6191-514-7, Pub. by Balkema RSA). IPS.

Storr, Eric D., ed. State of the Art in Underground Development & Construction. 250p. 1984. pap. text ed. 30.00x (ISBN 0-85825-202-3, Pub. by Inst Engineers Australia). Brookfield Pub Co.

Underground Rock Chambers. 608p. 1972. text ed. 29.50 (ISBN 0-87262-033-6). Am Soc Civil Eng.

Underground Space Center. Earth Sheltered Residential Design Manual. 256p. 1982. 24.95 (ISBN 0-442-28678-3); pap. 16.95 (ISBN 0-442-28679-1). Van Nos Reinhold.

Underground Space Center, et al. Underground Building Design: Commercial & Institutional Structures. 1983. 24.95 (ISBN 0-442-28687-2); pap. 16.95 (ISBN 0-442-28686-4). Van Nos Reinhold.

Underground Space Center Staff. Earth Sheltered Homes: Plans & Designs Underground Space Center. 1981. pap. 14.95 (ISBN 0-442-28676-7). Van Nos Reinhold.

--Earth Sheltered Housing: Code, Zoning, & Financing Issues. 144p. 1982. 14.95 (ISBN 0-442-28689-9); pap. 10.95 (ISBN 0-442-28688-0). Van Nos Reinhold.

The Use of Underground Space to Achieve National Goals. 353p. 1972. pap. 22.00x (ISBN 0-87262-045-X). Am Soc Civil Eng.

Vance, Mary. Underground Construction: A Bibliography. (Architecture Ser.: Bibliography A 1353). 1985. pap. 2.25 (ISBN 0-89028-323-0). Vance Biblios.

Wade, Herb. Building Underground: The Design & Construction Handbook for Earth-Sheltered Houses. Balitas, Maggie, ed. LC 82-18553. (Illus.). 304p. (Orig.). 1983. 19.95 (ISBN 0-87857-421-2, 04-000-0); pap. 14.95 (ISBN 0-87857-422-0, 04-000-1). Rodale Pr Inc.

Wampler, Louis. Underground Homes. rev. ed. LC 80-18701. (Illus.). 121p. 1980. pap. 5.95 (ISBN 0-88289-273-8). Pelican.

UNDERGROUND CORROSION

see Soil Corrosion

UNDERGROUND NUCLEAR EXPLOSIONS

see also Elastic Waves; Shock Waves

Bolt, Bruce A. Nuclear Explosions & Earthquakes: The Parted Veil. LC 75-28295. (Illus.). 309p. 1976. text ed. 26.95 (ISBN 0-7167-0276-2). W H Freeman.

Glasstone, Samuel & AEC Technical Information Center. Public Safety & Underground Nuclear Detonations. 276p. 1971. 23.50 (ISBN 0-87079-315-2, TID-25708). DOE.

Peaceful Nuclear Explosions - 2: Their Practical Application. Incl. Peaceful Nuclear Explosions - 3: Applications, Characteristics & Effects. (Panel Proceedings Ser.). (Eng., Fr., Rus., Span., Illus.). 488p. 1974. pap. 43.00 (ISBN 92-0-061074-9, ISP367); Peaceful Nuclear Explosions - 4. Technical Committee, Vienna, Jan. 20-24, 1975. (Panel Proceedings Ser.). (Illus.). 479p. 1975. pap. 49.25 (ISBN 92-0-061075-7, ISP414); Peaceful Nuclear Explosions - 5. (Panel Proceedings Ser.). (Illus.). 216p. 1978. pap. 24.25 (ISBN 92-0-061078-1, ISP473); Peaceful Nuclear Explosions - 1: Phenomenology & Status Report, 1970. (Panel Proceedings Ser.). (Illus.). 454p. (Orig.). 1970. pap. 32.00 (ISBN 92-0-061070-6, ISP273). (Panel Proceedings Ser.). (Illus.). 355p. (Orig.). 1972. pap. 28.75 (ISBN 92-0-061071-4, ISP298, IAEA). Unipub.

Performance of Nuclear Power Reactor Components. (Proceedings Ser.). (Illus.). 678p. (Orig.). 1970. pap. 52.00 (ISBN 92-0-050170-2, ISP240, IAEA). Unipub.

UNDERGROUND RAILROADS

see Subways

UNDERGROUND STRUCTURES

see Underground Construction

UNDERGROUND WATER

see Water, Underground

UNDERGROUND WEAPONS TESTING

see Underground Nuclear Explosions

UNDERSEA RESEARCH STATIONS, MANNED

see Manned Undersea Research Stations

UNDERWATER ACOUSTICS

see also Sonar

Albers, V. Underwater Sound. 1982. 52.95 (ISBN 0-87933-006-6). Van Nos Reinhold.

Albers, V. M., ed. Underwater Acoustics, Vol. 2. LC 62-8011. 429p. 1967. 69.50x (ISBN 0-306-37562-1, Plenum Pr). Plenum Pub.

Albers, Vernon M. Underwater Acoustics Handbook. 2nd ed. LC 64-15069. (Illus.). 1965. 29.75x (ISBN 0-271-73106-0). Pa St U Pr.

--Underwater Acoustics Instrumentation. LC 76-84217. pap. 24.80 (ISBN 0-317-08626-X, 2051122). Bks Demand UMI.

Andersen, Neil R. & Zahuranec, Bernard J., eds. Oceanic Sound Scattering Prediction. LC 77-3445. (Marine Science Ser.: Vol. 5). 859p. 1977. 110.00x (ISBN 0-306-35505-1, Plenum Pr). Plenum Pub.

Barkhatov, A. N. Modeling of Sound Propagation in the Sea. LC 74-136985. 91p. 1971. 25.00x (ISBN 0-306-10855-0, Consultants). Plenum Pub.

Bjorno, L., ed. Underwater Acoustics & Signal Processing. 1981. 87.00 (ISBN 90-277-1255-7, Pub. by Reidel Holland). Kluwer Academic.

Brekhovskich, L. M. & Lysanov, Y. P. Fundamentals of Oceanic Acoustics. (Springer Series in Electrophysics: Vol. 8). (Illus.). 250p. 1982. 49.00 (ISBN 0-387-11305-3). Springer-Verlag.

Burdic, William S. Underwater Acoustic System Analysis. (Illus.). 480p. 1984. 50.95 (ISBN 0-13-936716-0). P-H.

Caruthers, J. W. Fundamentals of Marine Acoustics. (Elsevier Oceanography Ser.: Vol. 18). 154p. 1977. 49.00 (ISBN 0-444-41552-1). Elsevier.

Clay, Clarence S. & Medwin, Herman. Acoustical Oceanography: Principles & Applications. LC 77-1133. (Ocean Engineering Ser.). 544p. 1977. text ed. 59.95x (ISBN 0-471-16041-5, Pub. by Wiley-Interscience). Wiley.

Cox, Albert W. Sonar & Underwater Sound. LC 74-15547. (Illus.). 1975. 24.00x (ISBN 0-669-95935-9). Lexington Bks.

DeSanto, J. A., ed. Ocean Acoustics. (Topics in Current Physics: Vol. 8). (Illus.). 1979. 46.00 (ISBN 0-387-09148-3). Springer-Verlag.

Flatte, S. M., ed. Sound Transmission Through a Fluctuating Ocean. LC 77-88676. (Cambridge Monographs on Mechanics & Applied Mathematics). (Illus.). 1979. 54.50 (ISBN 0-521-21940-X). Cambridge U Pr.

Keller, J. & Papadakis, J., eds. Wave Propagation & Underwater Acoustics. (Lecture Notes in Physics Ser: Vol. 70). 1977. pap. 18.00 (ISBN 0-387-08527-0). Springer-Verlag.

Kinsler, Lawrence E., et al. Fundamentals of Acoustics. 3rd ed. LC 81-7463. 480p. 1982. text ed. 41.50x (ISBN 0-471-02933-5); answers avail. (ISBN 0-471-09743-8). Wiley.

Kuperman, William A. & Jensen, Finn B., eds. Bottom-Interacting Ocean Acoustics. LC 80-24616. (NATO Conference Series IV-Marine Sciences: Vol. 5). 730p. 1981. 95.00x (ISBN 0-306-40624-1, Plenum Pr). Plenum Pub.

Lauterborn, W., ed. Cavitation & Inhomogeneities in Underwater Acoustics: Proceedings. (Springer Ser. in Electrophysics: Vol. 4). (Illus.). 319p. 1980. 42.00 (ISBN 0-387-09939-5). Springer-Verlag.

Milne, P. H. Underwater Acoustic Positioning Systems. LC 83-80348. 288p. 1983. 49.95x (ISBN 0-87201-012-0). Gulf Pub.

Officer, Charles B. Introduction to the Theory of Sound Transmission, with the Application to the Ocean. LC 58-6693. (McGraw-Hill Series in the Geological Sciences Ser.). pap. 73.00 (ISBN 0-317-08768-1, 2051899). Bks Demand UMI.

Report of the Meeting for Consultations on Underwater Noise: Rome, 1968. (Fisheries Reports: No. 76). 35p. 1970. pap. 7.50 (ISBN 0-686-93032-0, F1682, FAO). Unipub.

Tacconi, Giorgio, ed. Aspects of Signal Processing, 2 vols. LC 77-3238. (NATO Advanced Study Institute: C. Math & Phys. Science 33). 1977. lib. bdg. 87.00 set (ISBN 90-277-0798-7, Pub. by Reidel Holland). Kluwer Academic.

Urick, Robert J. Principles of Underwater Sound. 3rd, rev. ed. (Illus.). 448p. 1983. 41.95 (ISBN 0-07-066087-5). McGraw.

Ziomek, Lawerence J. Underwater Acoustics: A Linear Theory Approch. Date not set. 45.00 (ISBN 0-12-781720-4). Acad Pr.

UNDERWATER ARCHAEOLOGY

Arnold, J. Barto & Weddle, Robert. The Nautical Archeology of Padre Island: The Spanish Shipwrecks of 1554. (Studies in Archeology Ser.). 1978. 68.00 (ISBN 0-12-063650-6). Acad Pr.

Fowler, H. W. Archaeological Fishbones Collected by E. W. Gifford in Fiji. (BMB). pap. 10.00 (ISBN 0-527-02322-1). Kraus Repr.

Keith, Donald H., ed. Underwater Archaelogy: The Proceedings of the Thirteenth Conference on Underwater Archaeology. (Illus.). 450p. 1984. pap. text ed. 18.00x (ISBN 0-910651-04-3). Fathom Eight.

Masters, P. M. Quarternary Coastlines & Marine Archaeology: Towards the Prehistory of Land Bridges & Continental Shelves. Fleming, N. C., ed. LC 82-45021. 1983. 42.00 (ISBN 0-12-479250-2). Acad Pr.

Muckelroy, K. Maritime Archaeology. LC 78-5693. (New Studies in Archaeology). 1979. o.p 59.50 (ISBN 0-521-22079-3); pap. 17.95x (ISBN 0-521-29348-0). Cambridge U Pr.

Negris, P. Ancient Underwater Ruins. 30p. pap. 4.00 (ISBN 0-89005-338-3). Ares.

Throckmorton, P., et al. Surveying in Archaeology Underwater. (Colt Archaeological Institute Monograph: Vol. 5). 94p. 1969. pap. text ed. 13.50x (ISBN 0-85668-063-X, Pub. by Aris & Phillips England). Humanities.

Underwater Archaeology: A Nascent Discipline. LC 72-76249. (Museums & Monuments Ser.: No. 13). (Illus.). 306p. 1972. 22.50 (ISBN 92-3-101011-5, U690, UNESCO). Unipub.

UNDERWATER DRILLING

American Geological Institute. Deep Sea Drilling Project, Legs 26-44. (AGI Reprint Ser.: No. 2). 1976. 10.00 (ISBN 0-913312-17-7). Am Geol.

--Deep Sea Drilling Project, Legs 45-62. LC 78-74943. (AGI Reprint Ser.: No. 4). 1979. pap. 10.00 (ISBN 0-913312-12-6). Am Geol.

Atteraas, L., et al, eds. Underwater Technology-Offshore Petroleum: Proceedings of the International Conference, Bergen, Norway, April 14-16 1980. LC 80-40414. 450p. 1980. 78.00 (ISBN 0-08-026141-8). Pergamon.

Buffler, Richard T. Ocean Margin Drilling Program Atlases, Vol. 6. (Regional Atlas Ser.). 1985. write for info. spiral bdg (ISBN 0-86720-256-4, Marine Sci Intl). Jones & Bartlett.

Carmona-Agosto, Vivian, et al, eds. Wind, Waves, & Weather. Rossman, Marcela, tr. from Eng. (Rotary Drilling Series, Unit V: Lesson 1). (Span., Illus.). 44p. 1982. pap. text ed. 4.50 (ISBN 0-88698-046-1, 2.50112). PETEX.

Collip, Bruce G. Buoyancy, Stability & Trim. (Rotary Drilling Ser.: Unit V, Lesson 3). (Illus.). 30p. (Orig.). 1976. pap. text ed. 4.50 (ISBN 0-88698-071-2, 2.50310). PETEX.

ETA Offshore Seminars, Inc. Technology of Offshore Drilling, Completion & Production. LC 75-21903. 426p. 1976. 51.95x (ISBN 0-87814-066-2). Pennwell Bks.

Gerding, Mildred, ed. Helicopter Safety. rev. ed. (Rotary Drilling Ser.: Unit 5, Lesson 7). (Illus.). 37p. (Orig.). 1980. pap. text ed. 4.50 (ISBN 0-88698-075-5, 2.50710). PETEX.

Haggard, Rusty. Diving & Equipment. 2nd, rev. ed. Janicek, Nancy, ed. (Rotary Drilling Ser.: Unit V, Lesson 5). (Illus.). 45p. (Orig.). 1982. pap. text ed. 4.50 (ISBN 0-88698-073-9, 2.50520). PETEX.

Hayes, Dennis E. & Rabinowitz, Philip D., eds. Ocean Margin Drilling Program Atlases, Vol. 12. (Regional Atlas Ser.). 1985. write for info. spiral bdg (ISBN 0-86720-262-9, Marine Sci Intl). Jones & Bartlett.

Henderson, Celina, ed. Spread Mooring Systems. Rossman, Marcela, tr. from Eng. (Rotary Drilling Ser.: Unit V, Lesson 2). (Span., Illus.). 53p. (Orig.). 1982. pap. text ed. 4.50 (ISBN 0-88698-045-3, 2.50212). PETEX.

Hussong, Donald M., ed. Ocean Margin Drilling Program Atlases, Vol. 9. (Regional Atlas Ser.). 1985. write for info. spiral bdg (ISBN 0-86720-259-9, Marine Sci Intl). Jones & Bartlett.

Jones, Michael E. The Logistic Support of a Manned Underwater Production Complex. 1982. 79.00x (ISBN 0-86010-398-6, Pub. by Order Dept Graham Trotman England). State Mutual Bk.

Kruse, Curtis. Jacking Systems & Rig Moving Procedures. (Rotary Drilling Ser.: Unit V, Lesson 4). (Illus.). 52p. (Orig.). 1976. pap. text ed. 4.50 (ISBN 0-88698-072-0, 2.50410). PETEX.

Kulm, Laverne D. Ocean Margin Drilling Program Atlases, Vol. 1. (Regional Atlas Ser.). 1985. write for info. spiral (ISBN 0-86720-251-3, Marine Sci Intl). Jones & Bartlett.

Ladd, John W. & Buffler, Richard T. Ocean Margin Drilling Program Atlases, Vol. 7. (Regional Atlas Ser.). 1985. write for info. spiral bdg (ISBN 0-86720-257-2, Marine Sci Intl). Jones & Bartlett.

Leecraft, Jodie. Diesel Engines & Electric Power. (Rotary Drilling Ser.: Unit I, Lesson 11). (Illus.). 90p. (Orig.). 1982. pap. text ed. 5.00 (ISBN 0-88698-027-5, 2.11121). PETEX.

Life Offshore. (Rotary Drilling Ser.: Unit V, Lesson 9). (Illus.). 28p. (Orig.). 1978. pap. text ed. 4.50 (ISBN 0-88698-076-3, 2.50910). PETEX.

Rabinowitz, Philip D. & Schouten, Hans. Ocean Margin Drilling Program Atlases, Vol. 11. (Regional Atlas Ser.). 1985. write for info. spiral bdg (ISBN 0-86720-261-0, Marine Sci Intl). Jones & Bartlett.

Society for Underwater Technology, et al. Offshore Site Investigation. 650p. 1980. 55.00x (ISBN 0-86010-160-6, Pub. by Graham & Trotman England). State Mutual Bk.

Speed, Robert C. Ocean Margin Drilling Program Atlases, Vol. 10. (Regional Atlas Ser.). 1985. write for info. spiral bdg (ISBN 0-86720-260-2, Marine Sci Intl). Jones & Bartlett.

Spread Mooring Systems. (Rotary Drilling Ser.: Unit V, Lesson 2). (Illus.). 1976. pap. text ed. 4.50 (ISBN 0-88698-070-4, 2.50210). PETEX.

Subsea Blowout Preventers & Marine Riser Systems. (Rotary Drilling Ser.: Unit III, Lesson 4). (Illus.). 58p. (Orig.). 1976. pap. text ed. 5.00 (ISBN 0-88698-052-6, 2.30410). PETEX.

Talwani, Manik, et al, eds. Deep Drilling Results in the Atlantic Ocean: Ocean Crust. LC 79-88753. (Maurice Ewing Series Two). (Illus.). 431p. 1979. 23.00 (ISBN 0-87590-401-7, ME0200). Am Geophysical.

--Deep Drilling Results in the Atlantic Ocean: Continental Margins & Paleoenvironment, Vol. 3. LC 79-88754. (Maurice Ewing Ser.). (Illus.). 437p. 1979. 23.00 (ISBN 0-87590-402-5, ME0300). Am Geophysical.

Vessel Inspection & Maintenance. (Rotary Drilling Ser., Unit V,: Lesson 6). (Illus.). 37p. 1977. pap. text ed. 4.50 (ISBN 0-88698-074-7). PETEX.

Von Der Borch, C. C., ed. Synthesis of Deep Sea Drilling Results in the Indian Ocean. (Oceanography Ser.: Vol. 21). 176p. 1978. 64.00 (ISBN 0-444-41675-7). Elsevier.

Wind, Waves, & Weather. (Rotary Drilling Ser., Unit V: Lesson 1). (Illus.). 49p. 1977. pap. text ed. 4.50 (ISBN 0-88698-069-0, 2.50110). PETEX.

UNDERWATER EXPLORATION

see also Marine Biology; Oceanographic Research; Photography, Submarine; Underwater Archaeology

Anderson, Frank J. Submarines, Diving, & the Underwater World: A Bibliography. ix, 238p. 1975. 25.00 (ISBN 0-208-01508-6, Archon). Shoe String.

Burgess, Robert F. The Cave Divers. LC 75-22130. (Illus.). 1982. 9.95 (ISBN 0-396-07204-6). Florida Classics.

Cousteau, Jacques & Sivirine, Alexis. Jacques Cousteau's Calypso. LC 83-3751. (Illus.). 192p. 1983. 37.50 (ISBN 0-8109-0788-7). Abrams.

Dillon, Lawrence S. Ultrastructure, Macromolecules, & Evolution. LC 80-20550. 716p. 1981. 69.50x (ISBN 0-306-40528-8, Plenum Pr). Plenum Pub.

Ekelof, Gunnar. Guide to the Underworld. Lesser, Rika, tr. from Swedish. LC 80-13181. 112p. 1980. 10.00x (ISBN 0-87023-306-8). U of Mass Pr.

Ellsberg, Edward. Men under the Sea. LC 81-6869. (Illus.). xii, 365p. 1981. Repr. of 1939 ed. lib. bdg. 42.50x (ISBN 0-313-23030-7, ELMU). Greenwood.

Geyer, R. A. Submersibles & Their Use in Oceanography & Ocean Engineering. (Elsevier Oceanography Ser.: Vol. 17). 384p. 1977. 78.75 (ISBN 0-444-41545-9). Elsevier.

Hackman, Donald J. & Caudy, Don W. Underwater Tools. (Illus.). 152p. 1981. 32.95 (ISBN 0-935470-08-5). Battelle.

International Conference on Underwater Education, 9th, Miami Beach, Fla., Sep. 29 - Oct. 2, 1977. Proceedings. Fead, Lou, ed. 1977. pap. 15.00 (ISBN 0-916974-22-7); addendum free (ISBN 0-916974-23-5). NAUI.

International Listing of Chambers: 1976 Edition. 43p. 1976. 2.95 (ISBN 0-916974-09-X). NAUI.

Jones, Michael E. Deepwater Oil Production & Manned Underwater Structures. (Illus.). 245p. 1981. 55.00x (ISBN 0-8448-1401-6). Crane-Russak Co.

Lewis, Thomas R. Organization, Training, Search & Recovery Procedures for the Underwater Unit. 2nd ed. LC 79-83668. (Illus.). 1979. 6.95 (ISBN 0-918616-04-2). Northern Mich.

Protection of the Underwater Heritage: Protection of the Cultural Heritage. (Promotion of the Cultural Heritage: Technical Handbooks for Museums & Monuments: No. 4). (Illus.). 200p. 1981. pap. 22.50 (ISBN 92-3-101863-9, U1155, UNESCO). Unipub.

Society of Photo-Optical Instrumentation Engineers, Seminar. Underwater Photo-Optical Instrumentation Applications, 1968: Proceedings, Vol. 12. 28.00 (ISBN 0-89252-015-9). Photo-Optical.

U. S. National Oceanic & Atmospheric Administration. The Complete Underwater Diving Manual. (Nautical Ser.). (Illus.). 1971. pap. 12.50 (ISBN 0-679-50826-0). McKay.

Wilson, Earl J. The Mexican Caribbean: Twenty Years of Underwater Exploration. (Illus.). 176p. 1982. 10.00 (ISBN 0-686-78411-1). Exposition Pr FL.

UNDERWATER PHOTOGRAPHY

see Photography, Submarine

UNDULATED PARAKEET

see Budgerigars

UNDULATORY THEORY

see Wave-Motion, Theory Of

UNGULATA

see also names of ungulate animals, e.g. Deer Horses

Ecology & Management of Wild Grazing Animals in Temperate Zones. (Illus.). 1960. pap. 20.00 (ISBN 2-88032-016-X, IUCN34, IUCN). Unipub.

Fraser, Andrew F. Reproductive Behaviour in Ungulates. 1968. 39.00 (ISBN 0-12-266450-7). Acad Pr.

Jones, Robert L. & Hanson, Harold C. Mineral Licks, Geophagy, & Biogeochemistry of North American Ungulates. (Illus.). 302p. 1985. text ed. 21.50x (ISBN 0-8138-1151-1). Iowa St U Pr.

Leuthold, W. African Ungulates: A Comparative Review of Their Ethology & Behavioral Ecology. Farner, D. S., ed. LC 76-44535. (Zoophysiology & Ecology Ser.: Vol. 8). (Illus.). 1977. 46.00 (ISBN 0-387-07951-3). Springer-Verlag.

Lydekker, Richard. Catalogue of the Ungulate Mammals in the British Museum, 5 Vols. (Illus.). Repr. of 1916 ed. Set. 150.00 (ISBN 0-384-34486-0); 30.00 ea. Johnson Repr.

UNIDENTIFIED FLYING OBJECTS

see Flying Saucers

UNIFIED FIELD THEORIES

Debever, Robert, ed. Elie Cartan & Albert Einstein: Letters on Absolute Parallelism. LC 78-73832. 1979. 32.00 (ISBN 0-691-08229-4). Princeton U Pr.

De Sabbata, V. & Schmutzer, E., eds. Unified Field Theories of More Than Four Dimensions Including Exact Solutions: Proceedings of the 8th Course of the International School Cosmology & Gravitation Erice, Trapani, Siciliy, May 20-June 1, 1982. viii, 458p. 1983. 53.00x (ISBN 9971-950-50-2, Pub. by World Sci Singapore). Taylor & Francis.

Hadlock, Charles. Field Theory & Its Classical Problems. LC 78-71937. (Carus Mathematical Monograph: No. 19). 339p. 1979. 24.00 (ISBN 0-88385-020-6). Math Assn.

Hall, George M. Farewell to Darwin Unfied Field Theory of Physics: The Genetic Process & Psychology. (Illus.). 480p. 27.50 (ISBN 0-87527-166-9). Green.

Klotz, Alexander H. Macrophysics & Geometry: From Einstein's Unified Field Theory to Cosmology. LC 81-3849. 160p. 1982. 44.50 (ISBN 0-521-23938-9). Cambridge U Pr.

Leveille, J. P., et al, eds. The Second Workshop on Grand Unification: University of Michigan, Ann Arbor, April 24-26,1981. 350p. 1981. text ed. 27.50x (ISBN 0-8176-3055-4). Birkhauser.

Sokolow, Leonid. A Dual Ether Universe: Introducing a New Unified Field Theory. LC 76-56036. 1977. 12.50 (ISBN 0-682-48721-X, University). Exposition Pr FL.

Tonnelat, Marie A. Einstein's Theory of Unified Fields. 198p. 1966. 63.00x (ISBN 0-677-00810-4). Gordon.

Weldon, H. A., et al, eds. Fourth Workshop on Grand Unification. (Progress in Physics Ser.: Vol. 9). 430p. 1983. text ed. 29.95 (ISBN 0-8176-3169-0). Birkhauser.

UNIFORM SPACES

Harris, Douglas. Structures in Topology. LC 52-42839. (Memoirs Ser.: No. 115). 96p. 1971. pap. 9.00 (ISBN 0-8218-1815-5, MEMO-115). Am Math.

UNIFORMITY OF NATURE

see also Knowledge, Theory of; Logic; Philosophy of Nature

Mandelbrot, Benoit B. The Fractal Geometry of Nature. LC 81-15085. (Illus.). 460p. 1982. text ed. 34.95 (ISBN 0-7167-1186-9). W H Freeman.

UNIPOLAR TRANSISTORS

see Field Effect Transistors

UNIT CONSTRUCTION

Hua, L. K. Starting with the Unit Circle: Background to Higher Analysis. (Illus.). 192p. 1981. 39.00 (ISBN 0-387-90589-8). Springer-Verlag.

Jones, Arthur J., et al. Principles of Unit Construction. 232p. 1980. Repr. of 1939 ed. lib. bdg. 20.00 (ISBN 0-89987-426-6). Darby Bks.

--Principles of Unit Construction. (Educational Ser.). 1939. Repr. 20.00 (ISBN 0-8482-4667-5). Norwood Edns.

Meyerowitz, Patricia. Making Jewelry & Sculpture Through Unit Construction. 11.25 (ISBN 0-8446-5794-8). Peter Smith.

UNITED NATIONS–TECHNICAL ASSISTANCE

International Labour Organisation Staff & United Nations Development Programme. Bangladesh: Project Findings & Recommendations: Report. LC 81-197847. (Illus.). ii, 68p. 1980. write for info. (ISBN 9-221-02576-4). UN.

UNESCO Science & Technology Activities in Asia & the Pacific. (Science Policy Studies & Documents: No. 51). 37p. 1983. pap. 5.00 et (ISBN 92-3-102066-8, U1325, UNESCO). Unipub.

UNITED NATIONS EDUCATIONAL, SCIENTIFIC AND CULTURAL ORGANIZATION

Jacoby, E. G. Methods of School Enrollment Projection (UNESCO) (Education Studies & Documents: No. 32). pap. 16.00 (ISBN 0-317-16602-6). Kraus Repr.

MBow, Amandou-Mahtar. UNESCO, 1984-1985: Introduction to the Draft Programme & Budget. 120p. 1983. pap. text ed. 7.50 (ISBN 92-3-102149-4, U1306, UNESCO). Unipub.

Records of the General Conference: Twenty-First Session, Belgrade, Sept. 23-Oct. 28, 1980, 3 Vols. Incl. Vol. 1. Resolutions. 1980. pap. 13.25 (ISBN 92-3-101916-3, U1086, UNESCO); Vol. 2. Reports. 295p. 1982. pap. 15.00 (ISBN 92-3-101960-0, U1222); Proceedings. 1982. pap. 46.50 (ISBN 92-3-002010-9, U1235). pap. write for info. (UNESCO). Unipub.

Statistical Digest, 1981. 323p. 1981. pap. 11.50 (ISBN 92-3-101994-5, U1192, UNESCO). Unipub.

UNESCO List of Documents & Publications: 1979. 174p. 1980. pap. 12.25 (ISBN 92-3-101607-5, U1114, UNESCO). Unipub.

UNITED STATES–ARMY–ORDNANCE AND ORDNANCE STORES

Fuller, Claud E. Breech-Loader in the Service 1816-1917. LC 65-27415. (Illus.). 1965. 14.50 (ISBN 0-910598-03-7). Flayderman.

Hickox, Ron G. U. S. Military Edged Weapons of the Second Seminole War: 1835-1842. LC 84-80577. (Illus.). 102p. (Orig.). 1984. pap. text ed. 15.95 (ISBN 0-9613064-1-6). R G Hickox.

Hicks, James E. Notes on U. S. Ordnance. 8.00 (ISBN 0-685-02574-8). Modern Bks.

--U. S. Military Firearms. 18.95 (ISBN 0-87505-109-X). Borden.

Mesko, Jim. U. S. Infantry: Vietnam. (Weapons in Action Ser.: No. 3006). (Illus.). 50p. 1983. pap. 4.95 (ISBN 0-89747-151-2). Squad Sig Pubns.

UNITED STATES–ATOMIC ENERGY COMMISSION

Ford, Daniel. The Cult of the Atom: The Secret Papers of the Atomic Energy Commission. 1984. pap. 6.95 (ISBN 0-671-25302-6). S&S.

History of the U.S. Atomic Energy Commission: AEC Technical Information Center, 2 vols. Incl. Vol. 1. New World, 1939 Through 1946. Hewlett, R. G. & Anderson, O. E. LC 62-14633. 766p. 1962. pap. 27.50 (ISBN 0-87079-471-X, WASH-1214); microfiche 4.50 (ISBN 0-87079-472-8, WASH-1214); Vol. 2. Atomic Shield, 1947 Through 1952. Hewlett, R. G. & Duncan, F. 718p. 1969. pap. 26.50 (ISBN 0-87079-473-6, WASH-1215); microfiche 4.50 (ISBN 0-87079-474-4, WASH-1215). LC 62-14633. pap. DOE.

Lilienthal, David E. Change, Hope & the Bomb. 1963. 22.00 (ISBN 0-691-06903-4); pap. 7.95x (ISBN 0-691-01850-2). Princeton U Pr.

UNITED STATES–CLIMATE

Bomar, George W. Texas Weather. (Illus.). 277p. 1983. 22.50 (ISBN 0-292-78052-4); pap. 9.95 (ISBN 0-292-78053-2). U of Tex Pr.

Carter, E. A. & Seaquist, V. G. Extreme Weather History & Climate Atlas from Alabama. 350p. (Orig.). 1984. 15.95 (ISBN 0-317-04384-6); pap. 10.95. Strode.

Climate Normals of the U. S. Base, 1951-1980. LC 77-3859. 728p. 1983. Repr. 160.00x (ISBN 0-8103-1025-2). Gale.

Eichenlaub, Val. Weather & Climate of the Great Lakes Region. LC 78-51526. (Illus.). 1979. text ed. 21.95x (ISBN 0-268-01929-0); pap. text ed. 8.95 (ISBN 0-268-01930-4). U of Notre Dame Pr.

Ludlum, David M. The American Weather Book. dual ed. (Illus.). 352p. 1982. 14.95 (ISBN 0-395-32049-6); pap. 8.95 (ISBN 0-395-32122-0). HM.

--The New Jersey Weather Book. 250p. 1983. 25.00 (ISBN 0-8135-0915-7); pap. 14.95 (ISBN 0-8135-0940-8). Rutgers U Pr.

Pennsylvania University Bicentennial Conference. Conservation of Renewable Natural Resources. Zon, Raphael & Cooper, William, eds. LC 68-26200. Repr. of 1941 ed. 19.50x (ISBN 0-8046-0356-1, Pub. by Kennikat). Assoc Faculty Pr.

Rose, Martin R., et al. The Past Climate of Arroyo Hondo, New Mexico, Reconstructed from Tree Rings. LC 80-21834. (Arroyo Hondo Archaeological Ser.: Vol. 4). (Illus.). 138p. (Orig.). 1981. pap. 8.00 (ISBN 0-933452-05-5). Schol Am Res.

Ruffner, James A. & Bair, Frank E., eds. Weather of the United States Cities, 2 vols. LC 80-22694. (Illus.). 1100p. 1981. Set. 160.00x (ISBN 0-8103-1034-1). Gale.

UNITED STATES–ENVIRONMENTAL PROTECTION AGENCY

Durant, Robert F. When Government Regulates Itself: EPA, TVA & Pollution Control in the 1970's. LC 84-22058. 224p. 1985. text ed. 18.95x (ISBN 0-87049-458-9). U of Tenn Pr.

Haskell, Elizabeth H. The Politics of Clean Air: EPA Standards for Coal Burning Power Plants. LC 81-13863. 224p. 1982. 29.95 (ISBN 0-03-059701-3). Praeger.

TFP Sullivan, ed. U. S. Environmental Protection Agency Guidebook, 1984-1985. 280p. 1984. pap. 38.00 (ISBN 0-86587-070-5). Gov Insts.

U. S. Environmental Protection Agency. Legislative History of Environmental Protection Agency: Legal Compilation, Forty Vols. & Index, January 1974. 1978. Repr. Set. lib. bdg. 1645.00 (ISBN 0-89941-282-3). W S Hein.

U. S. Environmental Protection Agency Staff. Multi-Media Compliance Inspection Manual. (Illus.). 195p. 1984. pap. 35.00 (ISBN 0-86587-030-6). Gov Insts.

UNITED STATES–EXPLORING EXPEDITIONS

Cassin, John. United States Exploring Expedition During the Years 1838, 1839, 1840, 1841, 1842 Under the Command Charles Wilkes, U.S.N, 2 vols, Vol. 8. Sterling, Keir B., ed. LC 77-81079. (Biologists & Their World Ser.). (Illus.). 1978. Repr. of 1858 ed. lib. bdg. 48.00x (ISBN 0-405-10656-4). Ayer Co Pubs.

Girard, Charles. United States Exploring Expedition During the Years 1838, 1839, 1840, 1841, 1842 Under the Command of Charles Wilkes, U.S.N. Herpetology, 2 vols, Vol. 20. Srling, Keir B., ed. LC 77-81095. (Biologists & Their World Ser.). (Illus.). 1978. Repr. of 1858 ed. lib. bdg. 50.00x (ISBN 0-405-10678-5). Ayer Co Pubs.

Hutchings, James M. Seeking the Elephant, Eighteen Forty-Nine: James Mason Hutchings' Journal of His Overland Trek to California. Sargent, Shirley, ed. LC 80-67777. (American Trail Ser.: No. XII). (Illus.). 210p. 1981. 30.00 (ISBN 0-87062-136-X). A H Clark.

Jacobsen, Johann A. Alaskan Voyage, Eighteen Eighty-One to Eighteen Eighty-Three: An Expedition to the Northwest Coast of America. Gunther, Erna, tr. (Illus.). xiv, 266p. 1977. pap. 12.50 (ISBN 0-226-39033-0). U of Chicago Pr.

Lindestrom, Peter. Geographia Americae with an Account of the Delaware Indians. Scott, Franklyn D., ed. LC 78-15195. (Scandinavians in America Ser.). (Illus.). 1979. Repr. of 1925 ed. lib. bdg. 37.00x (ISBN 0-405-11648-9). Ayer Co Pubs.

Platt, Rutherford. Wilderness, the Discovery of a Continent of Wonder. LC 72-9919. (Illus.). 310p. 1973. Repr. of 1961 ed. lib. bdg. 17.75x (ISBN 0-8371-6608-X, PLWI). Greenwood.

Powell, John W. & Jones, William R. The Canons of the Colorado. (Illus.). 1980. pap. 2.95 (ISBN 0-89646-059-2). Outbooks.

Stanton, William. The Great United States Exploring Expedition of 1838-1842. LC 73-84390. (Illus.). 1975. 30.00 (ISBN 0-520-02557-1). U of Cal Pr.

Townsend, John K. Narrative of a Journey across the Rocky Mountains to the Columbia River. LC 78-17422. (Illus.). xviii, 259p. 1978. 19.95x (ISBN 0-8032-4402-9); pap. 5.50 (ISBN 0-8032-9401-8, BB 671, Bison). U of Nebr Pr.

Wilkes, Charles. Narrative of the United States Exploring Expedition During the Years Eighteen Thirty-Eight, Eighteen Thirty-Nine, Eighteen Fourty, Eighteen Fourty-Two, 5vols. (Illus.). 2445p. 1970. Repr. of 1845 ed. Set. 125.00 (ISBN 0-8398-2169-7). Parnassus Imprints.

UNITED STATES–NATIONAL SCIENCE FOUNDATION

Cole, Jonathan, et al. Peer Review in the National Science Foundation: Phase One of a Study. 1978. pap. text ed. 11.75 (ISBN 0-309-02788-8). Natl Acad Pr.

UNITED STATES–STATISTICS, MEDICAL

Cassedy, James H. American Medicine & Statistical Thinking, 1800-1860. LC 83-12831. (Illus.). 306p. 1984. text ed. 22.50x (ISBN 0-674-02560-1). Harvard U Pr.

Hospital Statistics, 1984. 262p. (Orig.). 1984. 49.50 (ISBN 0-87258-424-0, 082084). Am Hospital.

Kuzma, Jan. Basic Statistics for the Health Sciences. (Illus.). 260p. 1984. text ed. 22.95 (ISBN 0-87484-587-4, 587). Mayfield Pub.

Levy, Paul S., et al. Serum Uric Acid Values of Youth 12 to 17 Years, U.S. Stevenson, Taloria, ed. LC 75-619039. (Data from the Health Examination Survey Ser. 11: No. 152). 50p. 1975. pap. 1.50 (ISBN 0-8406-0041-0). Natl Ctr Health Stats.

Roberts, Jean & Ahuja, Elizabeth M. Hearing Sensitivity & Related Medical Findings among Youths Twelve to Seventeen Years: U.S. Stevenson, Taloria, ed. LC 75-619079. (Data from the Health Examination Survey Series 11: No. 154). 51p. 1975. pap. text ed. 1.50 (ISBN 0-8406-0043-7). Natl Ctr Health Stats.

Wilder, Charles S. Health Characteristics by Geographic Region, Large Metropolitan Areas, & Other Places of Residence in the United States: 1980-1981. Olmstead, Mary, ed. (Series 10-146). 60p. 1984. pap. text ed. 1.95 (ISBN 0-8406-0288-X). Natl Ctr Health Stats.

UNITS

see also Metric System; Weights and Measures

American Association for the Advancement of Science, Section on Engineering Staff. Systems of Units, National & International Aspects: A Symposium Organized by Section M on Engineering. Kayan, Carl F., ed. LC 59-15335. (American Association for the Advancement of Science Ser.: No. 57). pap. 76.80 (ISBN 0-317-27548-8, 2015170). Bks Demand UMI.

UNIVAC COMPUTER

Kelly, Jennifer A. Computer Operations for 1100 Systems. (Orig.). Date not set. pap. price not set. Datametrics Syst.

Stern, Nancy. From ENIAC to UNIVAC: An Appraisal of the Eckert-Mauchy Computers. (Illus.). 280p. 1981. 25.00 (ISBN 0-932376-14-2, EY-AX013-DP). Digital Pr.

UNIVERSAL AUTOMATION COMPUTER

see Univac Computer

UNIVERSE

see Cosmogony; Cosmology

UNIX (COMPUTER OPERATING SYSTEM)

AT&T Technologies Staff. The UNIX System V Software Catalog. 1985. 19.95 (ISBN 0-8359-8068-5). Reston.

Banahan, Mark & Rutter, Andy. The UNIX Book. LC 82-21853. 218p. 1983. pap. 16.95 (ISBN 0-471-89676-4, Pub. by Wiley Pr). Wiley.

Bell Labs Staff. UNIX, 2 vols. 1983. Vol. 1, 208 p. pap. 37.45 (ISBN 0-03-061742-1); Vol. II, 320 p. pap. 37.45 (ISBN 0-03-061743-X). HR&W.

Blackburn, Laurie & Taylor, Marcus. Pocket Guide: UNIX. (Pitman Programming Pocket Guides Ser.). 64p. 1984. pap. 6.95 (ISBN 0-273-02106-0). Pitman Pub MA.

Brown, Constance C., et al. Preparing Documents with UNIX. (Illus.). 240p. 1986. text ed. 21.95 (ISBN 0-13-699976-X). P-H.

Brown, Patrick & Muster, John. UNIX for People. 1984. text ed. 24.95 (ISBN 0-13-937459-0); pap. text ed. 21.95 (ISBN 0-13-937442-6). P-H.

Byers, Robert A. Introduction to UNIX System V. 350p. 1985. pap. 17.95 (ISBN 0-912677-29-5). Ashton-Tate Bks.

Christian, Kaare. The UNIX Operating System. LC 82-24811. 318p. 1983. text ed. 28.95 (ISBN 0-471-87542-2); pap. 21.95 (ISBN 0-471-89052-9). Wiley.

Clukey, Lee P. UNIX & XENIX Demystified. LC 85-2658. (Illus.). 250p. 1985. 21.95 (ISBN 0-8306-0874-5, 1874); pap. 16.95 (ISBN 0-8306-1874-0). TAB Bks.

Cscapes. C Library Reference for UNIX. rev. ed. 16p. 1983. 4.00 (ISBN 0-916151-00-X). Specialized Sys.

Farkas, Daniel J. Micro UNIX: A Guide to UNIX in the Microcomputer Environment. (Illus.). 320p. (Orig.). pap. cancelled (ISBN 0-916688-81-X, 81-X). Creative Comp.

Franzosa, Bill, ed. The UNIX System Encyclopedia. 2nd ed. (Illus.). 1985. pap. 44.95 (ISBN 0-917195-01-9). Yates Vent.

Gauthier, Richard. Using the Unix System. 1981. text ed. 23.95 (ISBN 0-8359-8164-9); pap. 19.95 (ISBN 0-8359-8162-2). Reston.

Halamka, John D. Real World UNIX. LC 84-50358. 200p. (Orig.). 1984. pap. 16.95 (ISBN 0-89588-093-8). SYBEX.

Hume, J. N. & Holt, R. C. Pascal under UNIX. 1983. text ed. 22.95 (ISBN 0-8359-5446-3); pap. text ed. 16.95 (ISBN 0-8359-5445-5). Reston.

Kernighan, Brian W. & Pike, Robert. The UNIX Programming Environment. LC 83-62851. (P-H Software Ser.). 368p. 1984. text ed. 26.95 (ISBN 0-13-937699-2); pap. text ed. 19.95 (ISBN 0-13-937681-X). P-H.

Krieger, Morris. Word Processing on the UNIX System. (A BYTE Book). (Illus.). 1984. pap. 18.95 (ISBN 0-07-035498-7). McGraw.

Lomuto, Ann N. & Lomuto, Nico. A UNIX Primer. (P-H Software Ser.). (Illus.). 256p. 1983. pap. text ed. 22.50 (ISBN 0-13-937731-X). P-H.

McGilton, Henry & Morgan, Rachel. Introducing the UNIX System. (Illus.). 480p. 1983. pap. 19.95 (ISBN 0-07-045001-3, BYTE Bks). McGraw.

Moore, F. Richard. Programming in C with a Bit of UNIX. (Illus.). 208p. 1985. pap. text ed. 19.95 (ISBN 0-13-730094-8). P-H.

Pinchot, Roy. UNIX Encyclopedia. 1985. pap. cancelled (ISBN 0-912677-44-9). Ashton-Tate Bks.

Rochkind, Marc J. Advanced UNIX Programming. 192p. 1985. text ed. 32.95 (ISBN 0-13-011818-4); pap. text ed. 24.95 (ISBN 0-13-011800-1). P-H.

Schreiner, Axel T. & Friedman, H. George, Jr. Introduction to Compiler Construction with UNIX. 224p. 1985. text ed. 25.00 (ISBN 0-13-474396-2). P-H.

Shirota, Y. & Kunii, T. L. First Book on UNIX for Executives. xii, 156p. 1984. pap. 16.00 (ISBN 0-387-70003-X). Springer-Verlag.

Silvester. UNIX: An Introduction for Computer Users. 200p. Date not set. price not set (ISBN 0-471-90205-5). Wiley.

Silvester, P. P. The UNIX System Book. (Springer Books on Professional Computing). (Illus.). 230p. 1984. pap. 16.50 (ISBN 0-387-90906-0). Springer Verlag.

Sobell, Mark G. A Practical Guide to the UNIX System. 1984. 24.95 (ISBN 0-8053-8910-5, 38910). Benjamin-Cummings.

--A Practical Guide to the UNIX System V. 1985. 20.95 (ISBN 0-8053-8915-6). Benjamin Cummings.

Specialized Systems Consultants. UNIX Command Summary (BSD 4.2) 32p. (Orig.). 1984. pap. 6.00 (ISBN 0-916151-05-0). Specialized Sys.

--UNIX Command Summary System III. Rev. ed. 32p. 1983. pap. 6.00 (ISBN 0-916151-01-8). Specialized Sys.

--UNIX Command Summary (System V) 48p. (Orig.). 1984. pap. 6.00 (ISBN 0-916151-06-9). Specialized Sys.

Strong, B. & Hosler, J. UNIX for Beginners: Basic Word Processing Skills with ED. 1985. pap. 24.95 (ISBN 0-471-80664-1). Wiley.

--UNIX for Beginners: Basic Word Processing Skills with VI. 400p. 1985. pap. 24.95 (ISBN 0-471-80666-8). Wiley.

Thomas, Rebecca & Yates, Jean. The Programmer's Guide to the UNIX System. 496p. 1983. write for info. (ISBN 0-201-08849-5). Addison-Wesley.

--User Guide to the UNIX System: Includes Berkeley & Bell System V. 2nd ed. 520p. 1984. 18.95 (ISBN 0-07-881109-0, 109-0). Osborne-McGraw.

Topham, D. W. & Trong, H. UNIX & XENIX: A Step by Step Approach for Micros. (Illus.). 528p. 1985. pap. 21.95 (ISBN 0-89303-918-7). Brady Comm.

Twitty, William B. & Microtrend Inc. UNIX on the IBM PC. (Microtrend Ser.). (Illus.). 224p. 1984. pap. 14.95 (ISBN 0-13-939075-8). P-H.

UNIX System Guidebook: A Guide for Serious Users. 1984. 16.50 (ISBN 0-387-90906-0). Springer-Verlag.

UNIX Training Market. 1985. write for info. (ISBN 0-86621-348-1, A1432). Frost & Sullivan.

Waite Group. UNIX Primer Plus. LC 83-60162. 416p. 1983. pap. 19.95 (ISBN 0-672-22028-8, 22028). Sams.

Waite, Mitchell, et al. UNIX System V Primer. LC 84-51098. 432p. 1984. pap. 19.95 (ISBN 0-672-22404-6). Sams.

Walker, Andy. The UNIX Environment. LC 84-13046. 151p. 1984. pap. 15.95 (ISBN 0-471-90564-X). Wiley.

Weber Systems, Inc. UNIX User's Handbook. 400p. 1985. pap. 16.95 (ISBN 0-345-32000-X). Ballantine.

Weinberg, Paul N. & Groff, James R. Understanding UNIX: A Conceptual Guide. 238p. 1983. pap. 19.95 (ISBN 0-88022-064-3, 120). Que Corp.

Wetzel, William. UNIX Quick Reference Guide. 1983. 12.95 (ISBN 0-13-937771-9, Spec). P-H.

UPHOLSTERY

Brumbaugh, James. Upholstering. 2nd ed. LC 82-17781. (Illus.). 394p. 1983. 12.95 (ISBN 0-672-23372-X). Audel.

Cox, Dorothy. Modern Upholstery. (Illus.). 152p. 1980. pap. 13.50x (ISBN 0-7135-1599-6, LTB). Sportshelf.

Davis, Kenneth & Henvey, Thom. Restoring & Reupholstering Furniture. Stoner, Carol, ed. (Illus.). 176p. 1982. 21.95 (ISBN 0-87857-429-8, 14-123-0). Rodale Pr Inc.

Edwards, Margaret. Upholstery & Canework. (Illus.). 128p. 1983. 10.95 (ISBN 0-7207-1418-4, Pub. by Michael Joseph). Merrimack Pub Cir.

Howes, C. Practical Upholstery. rev. ed. LC 77-18394. (Home Craftsman Bk.). (Illus.). 128p. 1980. pap. 6.95 (ISBN 0-8069-8578-X). Sterling.

Locke, Lee J., ed. Essentials of Upholstery & Trim, for Vintage & Classic. (Illus.). 176p. 1970. 15.00 (ISBN 0-911160-48-5). Post-Era.

MacDonald, Robert J. Basic Upholstery Repair & Restoration. (Illus.). 144p. 1984. 19.95 (ISBN 0-7134-1820-6, Pub. by Batsford England). David & Charles.

Marshall, Mel. How to Repair, Reupholster & Refinish Furniture. LC 79-4706. (Popular Science Bk.). (Illus.). 1979. 13.95i (ISBN 0-06-013035-0, HarpT). Har-Row.

Palmer, Frederick. Practical Upholstering: And the Cutting of Slip Covers. LC 80-51766. (Illus.). 288p. 1982. 19.95 (ISBN 0-8128-2753-8); pap. 11.95 (ISBN 0-8128-6170-1). Stein & Day.

Parker, Page & Fornia, Alice. Upholstering for Everyone. (Illus.). 688p. 1976. text ed. 29.95 (ISBN 0-87909-857-0). Reston.

Sheraton, Thomas. The Cabinet-Maker & Upholsterer's Drawing Book. (Illus.). 18.00 (ISBN 0-8446-4637-7). Peter Smith.

Sunset Editors. Furniture Upholstery. 2nd ed. LC 80-80858. (Illus.). 112p. 1980. pap. 4.95 (ISBN 0-376-01183-1, Sunset Bks.). Sunset-Lane.

Tierney, William F. Modern Upholstering Methods. 1965. text ed. 18.64 (ISBN 0-87345-482-0). McKnight.

Zimmernman, Fred W. Upholstering Methods. LC 80-25308. (Illus.). 196p. 1981. text ed. 14.00 (ISBN 0-87006-313-8). Goodheart.

URANINITE

see also Radium; Uranium

Krass, A. S., et al. Uranium Enrichment & Nuclear Weapon Proliferation. LC 83-8486. 270p. 1983. 33.00x (ISBN 0-8002-3079-5). Taylor & Francis.

Parent, Joseph D. A Survey of United States & Total World Production, Proved Reserves, & Remaining Recoverable Resources of Fossil Fuels & Uranium, as of December 31, 1982. xviii, 250p. 1984. 30.00 (ISBN 0-910091-52-8). Inst Gas Tech.

URANIUM

see also Nuclear Fuels; Transuranium Elements

AIF Uranium Seminar: Set of Papers. (Technical & Economic Reports: Uranium). 1983. 100.00 (ISBN 0-318-02245-1). Atomic Indus Forum.

Annual Uranium Seminar: Proceedings, No. 5. LC 81-71601. (Illus.). 187p. 1982. text ed. 20.00x (ISBN 0-89520-291-3). Soc Mining Eng.

Annual Uranium Seminar, 3rd: Proceedings. LC 79-48044. (Illus.). 177p. 1980. pap. 20.00x (ISBN 0-89520-260-3). Soc Mining Eng.

Bargmann, Eve. Uranium; the Real Facts: A Medical Response to the Marline Corporation's Uranium Fact Book. 1982. pap. 2.00 (ISBN 0-937188-23-9). Pub Citizen Inc.

Bickel, Lennard. The Deadly Element: The Story of Uranium. LC 78-66243. (Illus.). 320p. 1980. pap. 7.95 (ISBN 0-8128-6089-6). Stein & Day.

Board on Mineral Resources. Concepts of Uranium Resources & Producibility. 1978. pap. 8.50 (ISBN 0-309-02864-7). Natl Acad Pr.

Boyle, R. W. Geochemical Prospecting for Thorium & Uranium. (Developments in Economic Geology Ser.: Vol. 16). 498p. 1983. 85.00 (ISBN 0-444-42070-3). Elsevier.

Brawner, Carroll O., ed. First International Conference on Uranium Mine Waste Disposal. LC 80-69552. (Illus.). 626p. 1980. 25.00x (ISBN 0-89520-279-4). Soc Mining Eng.

British Nuclear Energy Society, ed. Uranium Isotope Separation. 260p. 1975. 70.00x (ISBN 0-7277-0022-7, Pub. by Brit Nuclear England). State Mutual Bk.

Cameron, A. E., ed. Determination of the Isotopic Composition of Uranium. AEC Technical Information Center. (National Nuclear Energy Ser.: Div. I, Vol. 13). 173p. 1950. pap. 16.00 (ISBN 0-87079-177-X, TID-5213); microfilm 10.00 (ISBN 0-87079-452-3, TID-5213). DOE.

Capaldi, G., et al, eds. Uranium Geochemistry, Mineralogy, Geology, Exploration & Resources. 201p. 1984. pap. text ed. 78.00X (ISBN 0-900488-70-0). Imm North Am.

Committee on Mineral Resources & Environment, National Research Council. Reserves & Resources of Uranium in the United States: Mineral Resources & the Environment Supplementary Report. ix, 236p. 1975. pap. 8.50 (ISBN 0-309-02423-4). Natl Acad Pr.

Committee on Nuclear & Alternative Energy Systems. Problems of U. S. Uranium Resources & Supply to the Year 2010. 1978. pap. 7.50 (ISBN 0-309-02782-9). Natl Acad Pr.

Current Practices & Options for Confinement of Uranium Mill Tailings. (Technical Reports Ser.: No. 209). (Illus.). 102p. 1981. pap. 18.00 (ISBN 92-0-125281-1, IDC209, IAEA). Unipub.

The Determination of Low Concentrations of Uranium in Ores & Solid Mill Products by X-Ray Fluorescence Spectrometry. (Scientific Bulletin Ser.: CM 75-4). 1979. pap. 1.00 (ISBN 0-685-96907-X, SSC126, SSC). Unipub.

Discussions of the Uranium Geology Working Groups: IGC, Sydney. (Technical Reports Ser.: No. 183). (Illus.). 90p. 1978. pap. 13.75 (ISBN 92-0-145078-8, IDC183, IAEA). Unipub.

El Shazly, E. M., compiled by. Geology of Uranium & Thorium: 1961-1966, Vol. 2. Incl. Geology of Uranium & Thorium. Shazly, E. M. El, compiled by. (Bibliographical Ser.: No. 31). 134p. 1962. pap. write for info. (ISBN 92-0-044062-2, ISP21/4, IAEA). (Bibliographical Ser.: No. 31). 102p. 1968. pap. write for info. (ISBN 92-0-044168-8, ISP2131, IAEA). Unipub.

Erickson, David M. Uranium Development in Less Developed Countries: A Handbook of Concerns. (Lincoln Institute Monograph: No. 81-4). 83p. 1981. pap. text ed. 14.00 (ISBN 0-686-30624-4). Lincoln Inst Land.

Evaluation of Uranium Resources. (Panel Proceedings Ser.). (Illus.). 344p. 1979. pap. 48.50 (ISBN 92-0-141079-4, ISP507, IAEA). Unipub.

Extraction of Uranium from Aqueous Solutions by Coals of Different Rank & Petrographic Composition. pap. 5.55 (SSC39, SSC). Unipub.

Fuerstenau, Maurice C. & Palmer, R. B., eds. Gold, Silver, Uranium & Coal - Geology, Mining, Extraction, & Environment. LC 82-73914. (Illus.). 526p. 1983. pap. text ed. 40.00x (ISBN 0-89520-406-1, 406-1). Soc Mining Eng.

Galloway, W. E., et al. Depositional Framework, Hydrostratigraphy & Uranium Mineralization of the Oakville Sandstone (Miocene), Texas Coastal Plain. (Report of Investigations Ser.: RI 113). (Illus.). 51p. 1982. 2.50 (ISBN 0-318-03245-7). Bur Econ Geology.

Geology & Metallogenesis of Uranium Deposits of South America: Proceedings of a Working Group Meeting, San Luis, Argentina, Sept. 21-23, 1981. 275p. (Orig.). 1984. pap. 44.00 (ISBN 92-0-041084-7, ISP641, IAEA). Unipub.

The Geology of Uranium. 134p. 1958. 29.50x (ISBN 0-306-10538-1, Consultants). Plenum Pub.

Harrington, Charles D. Uranium Production Technology. LC 59-13493. 584p. 1959. 33.00 (ISBN 0-442-03154-8, Pub. by Van Nos Reinhold). Krieger.

Harris, Stuart, ed. Social & Environmental Choice: The Impact of Uranium Mining in the Northern Territory. (Centre for Resources & Environmental Studies Mongraph: No. 3). 178p. 1981. pap. text ed. 6.95 (ISBN 0-86740-169-9, 0039, Pub. by ANUP Australia). Australia N U P.

Hodge, H. C., et al, eds. Uranium, Plutonium & the Transplutonic Elements. (Handbook of Experimental Pharmacology: Vol. 36). (Illus.). xxiii, 995p. 1973. 220.00 (ISBN 0-387-06168-1). Springer-Verlag.

Hutchison, Clyde A. & AEC Technical Information Center. Chemical Separation of the Uranium Isotopes. (National Nuclear Energy Ser.: Div. III, Vol. 3). 178p. 1952. pap. 17.50 (ISBN 0-87079-159-1, TID-5224); microfilm 10.00 (ISBN 0-87079-160-5, TID-5224). DOE.

Joint Steering Group on Uranium Resources of the OECD Nuclear Energy Agency & the International Atomic Energy Agency. World Uranium Geology & Resource Potential. LC 80-81724. (Illus.). 524p. 1980. pap. 50.00 (ISBN 0-87930-085-X). Miller Freeman.

Katzin, Leonard I., ed. Production & Separation of U-233: Collected Papers. AEC Technical Information Center. (National Nuclear Energy Ser.: Div. IV, Vol. 17b). 743p. 1952. pap. 50.50 (ISBN 0-87079-383-7, TID-5223); microfilm 18.75 (ISBN 0-87079-341-1, TID-5223). DOE.

Makarov, Evgeniis S. Crystal Chemistry of Simple Compounds of Uranium, Thorium, Plutonium, Neptunium. Uvarov, E. B., tr. from Rus. LC 59-14486. pap. 38.30 (ISBN 0-317-08925-0, 2003366). Bks Demand UMI.

Management of Uranium Mill Tailings, Low Level Waste & Hazardous Waste: Proceedings of the Seventh Symposium, 2 vols. (Orig.). 1985. pap. text ed. 38.00 (ISBN 0-910069-08-5). Geotech Engineer Prog.

Management of Uranium Mill Tailings, Low-Level Waste & Hazardous Waste: Proceedings of the Sixth Symposium, 1984. 670p. 1984. 35.00 (ISBN 0-910069-07-7). Geotech Engineer Prog.

Management of Uranium Mill Tailings, Low-Level Waste & Hazardous Waste: Proceedings of the Seventh Symposium, 1985, 2 vols. Set. write for info. (ISBN 0-910069-08-5); write for info. (ISBN 0-910069-09-3); write for info. (ISBN 0-910069-10-7). Geotech Engineer Prog.

Manual on the Projection of Uranium Production Capability: General Guidelines. (Technical Reports Ser.: No. 238). 37p. 1985. pap. 9.75 (ISBN 92-0-145084-2, IDC238, IAEA). Unipub.

Max Planck Society for the Advancement of Science, Gmelin Institute for Inorganic Chemistry. Uranium, Pt. C, Section 3. (Illus.). 360p. 1975. 242.40 (ISBN 0-387-93290-9). Springer-Verlag.

Merriman, J. R. & Benedict, M., eds. Recent Developments in Uranium Enrichment. LC 82-25312. (AIChE Symposium: Vol. 78). 1982. pap. 25.00 (ISBN 0-8169-0245-3, S-221); pap. 12.50 (ISBN 0-686-47553-4). Am Inst Chem Eng.

Mining Journal Books Ltd. Uranium & Nuclear Energy. 326p. 1980. 45.00x (ISBN 0-900117-20-6, Pub. by Mining Journal England). State Mutual Bk.

--Uranium: Balance of Supply & Demand Nineteen Seventy Eight to Nineteen Ninety. 60p. 1980. 45.00x1311 (ISBN 0-900117-19-2, Pub. by Mining Journal England). State Mutual Bk.

Mining Journal Books Ltd., ed. The Uranium Equation. 1982. 69.00x (ISBN 0-900117-27-3, Pub. by Mining Journal England). State Mutual Bk.

Moss, Norman. The Politics of Uranium. LC 81-21888. 252p. 1982. 15.00x (ISBN 0-87663-390-4). Universe.

--The Politics of Uranium. LC 81-12888. 252p. 1984. pap. 8.95 (ISBN 0-87663-851-5). Universe.

Neff, Thomas L. The International Uranium Market. LC 84-9255. 360p. 1984. prof ref 32.50x (ISBN 0-88410-850-3). Ballinger Pub.

OECD Staff & NEA Staff. Uranium Extraction Technology. 270p. (Orig.). 1983. pap. 20.00 (ISBN 92-64-12397-0). OECD.

--Uranium Mill Tailings. (Eng. & Fr.). 238p. (Orig.). 1982. pap. text ed. 16.00x (ISBN 92-64-02288-0). OECD.

OECD's Nuclear Energy Agency & the International Atomic Energy Agency. Uranium, Resource Production & Demand. 350p. 1984. pap. 32.00x (ISBN 92-64-12550-7). OECD.

Organisation for Economic Co-Operation & Development. Long-Term Radiological Aspects of Management of Wastes from Uranium Mining & Milling. 116p. (Orig.). 1985. pap. 24.00x (ISBN 92-64-12651-1). OECD.

Osmond, J. K. & Cowart, J. B. Natural Uranium & Thorium Series Disequilibrium: New Approaches to Geochemical Problems. (Nuclear Science Applications Ser.: Section B). 50p. 1982. 19.75 (ISBN 3-7186-0131-1). Harwood Academic.

Practical Hydromet 'Eighty-Four: Proceedings of the Seventh Annual Symposium on Uranium & Precious Metals. (Illus.). 126p. 1984. pap. 28.00x (ISBN 0-89520-423-1). Soc Mining Eng.

Production of Yellow Cake & Uranium Fluorides. (Panel Proceedings Ser.). (Illus.). 355p. 1981. pap. 50.25 (ISBN 92-0-041080-4, ISP553, IAEA). Unipub.

Radetzki, Marian. Uranium: Economic & Political Instability in a Strategic Commodity Market. 1981. 35.00 (ISBN 0-312-83424-1). St Martin.

Radiation Protection in Mining & Milling of Uranium and Thorium. (Occupational Safety & Health Ser.: No. 32). pap. 20.00 (ISBN 92-2-101504-1, ILO25, ILO). Unipub.

Radiological Safety in Uranium & Thorium Mines & Mills. (Safety Ser.: No. 43). 1976. pap. 11.75 (ISBN 92-0-123176-8, ISP449, IAEA). Unipub.

Recognition & Evaluation of Uraniferous Areas. (Panel Proceedings Ser.). (Illus.). 295p. 1977. pap. 35.00 (ISBN 92-0-041077-4, ISP450, IAEA). Unipub.

Recommended Instrumentation for Uranium & Thorium Exploration. (Technical Reports Ser.). 104p. (Orig.). 1974. pap. 12.50 (ISBN 92-0-145074-5, IDC158, IAEA). Unipub.

The Recovery of Uranium. (Illus., Orig.). 1971. pap. 33.75 (ISBN 92-0-040071-X, ISP262, IAEA). Unipub.

Royal Society of London, et al. Theoretical & Practical Aspects of Uranium Geology. Bowie, S. H. & Fyfe, W. S., eds. (Illus.). 1979. lib. bdg. 46.00x (ISBN 0-85403-106-5, Pub. by Royal Soc London). Scholium Intl.

Schlitt, W. J. & Shock, D. A., eds. In Situ Uranium Leaching & Ground Water Restoration. LC 79-52217. (Illus.). 137p. 1979. pap. 20.00x (ISBN 0-89520-267-0). Soc Mining Eng.

Seaborg, Glenn & Katzin, Leonard I., eds. Production & Separation of U-233: Survey. AEC Technical Information Center. (National Nuclear Energy Ser.: Division IV, Vol. 17A). 236p. 1951. pap. 20.50 (ISBN 0-87079-384-5, TID-5222); microfilm 10.00 (ISBN 0-87079-342-X, TID-5222). DOE.

Smith, Robert B. & Harden, Kim, eds. Sixth Annual Uranium Seminar. (Uranium Seminar Ser.). (Illus.). 147p. 1983. pap. text ed. 30.00x (ISBN 0-89520-408-8, 408-8). Soc Mining Eng.

Sorantin, H. Determination of Uranium & Plutonium in Nuclear Fuels. (Topical Presentations in Nuclear Chemistry Ser.: Vol. 5). (Illus.). 285p. 1975. 81.20x (ISBN 3-527-25475-7). VCH Pubs.

South Texas Uranium Seminar. LC 78-73975. (Illus.). 1979. pap. text ed. 20.00x (ISBN 0-89520-256-5). Soc Mining Eng.

Tatsch, J. H. Uranium Deposits: Origin, Evolution, & Present Characteristics. LC 75-9304. (Illus.). 303p. 1976. 96.00 (ISBN 0-912890-11-8). Tatsch.

Thermal Conductivity of Uranium Dioxide. (Technical Reports Ser.: No. 59). 1966. pap. 7.50 (ISBN 92-0-145166-0, IDC59, IAEA). Unipub.

Thermodynamic & Transport Properties of Uranium Dioxide & Related Phases. (Technical Reports Ser.: No. 39). 1965. pap. 9.00 (ISBN 92-0-145065-6, IDC39, IAEA). Unipub.

Uranium & Nuclear Energy, 1980. 370p. 1981. cloth 75.00x (ISBN 0-86103-041-9, Pub. by Westbury House). State Mutual Bk.

Uranium & Nuclear Issues. 156p. 1983. 25.00 (ISBN 0-919307-28-0). Can Nuclear Assn.

The Uranium-Carbon & Plutonium-Carbon Systems: A Thermochemical Assessment. (Technical Reports Ser.: No. 14). (Illus.). 44p. 1963. pap. 6.25 (ISBN 92-0-145063-X, IDC14, IAEA). Unipub.

Uranium Evaluation & Mining Techniques: Proceedings of an International Seminar Organized by the IAEA with the cooperation of the OECD Nuclear Energy Agency & held in Beunos Aires, 1-4 October 1979. 550p. 1981. pap. 77.00 (ISBN 92-0-040280-1, ISP524, IAEA). Unipub.

Uranium Exploration Case Histories: Proceedings of an Advisory Group Meeting, Vienna, 26-29 November 1979, Jointly Organized by IAEA and NEA (OCED) 407p. 1982. pap. 56.50 (ISBN 92-0-141081-6, ISP584, IAEA). Unipub.

Uranium Exploration Geology. (Panel Proceedings Ser.). (Illus., Orig.). 1971. pap. 25.75 (ISBN 92-0-041070-7, ISP277, IAEA). Unipub.

Uranium Exploration Methods. (Illus.). 320p. (Orig.). 1974. pap. 32.00 (ISBN 92-0-041073-1, ISP334, IAEA). Unipub.

Uranium Exploration Methods. (Eng. & Fr.). 980p. (Orig.). 1982. pap. 48.00x (ISBN 92-64-02350-X). OECD.

Uranium Exploration: 1975. pap. 6.50 (SSC82, SSC). Unipub.

Uranium in the Pine Creek Geosyncline: Proceedings. (Proceedings Ser.). (Illus.). 762p. 1980. pap. 103.75 (ISBN 92-0-140080-2, ISP555, IAEA). Unipub.

Uranium Mill Tailings Management: Proceedings of the First Symposium, 1978, 2 vols. Set. 17.00 (ISBN 0-910069-11-5); Vol. 1; 172 pgs. write for info. (ISBN 0-910069-00-X); Vol. 2; 141 pgs. write for info. (ISBN 0-910069-01-8). Geotech Engineer Prog.

Uranium Mill Tailings Management: Proceedings of the Fourth Symposium, 1981. 729p. 1981. 28.00 (ISBN 0-910069-04-2). Geotech Engineer Prog.

Uranium Mill Tailings Management: Proceedings of the Fifth Symposium, 1982. 557p. 1982. 30.00 (ISBN 0-910069-06-9). Geotech Engineer Prog.

Uranium Mill Tailings Management: Proceedings of the Second Symposium, 1979. 331p. 1979. 20.00 (ISBN 0-910069-02-6). Geotech Engineer Prog.

Uranium Mill Tailings Management: Proceedings of the Third Symposium, 1980. 573p. 1980. 25.00 (ISBN 0-910069-03-4). Geotech Engineer Prog.

Vance, J. E. & Warner, J. C. Uranium Technology. (National Nuclear Energy Ser.: Div. VII, Vol. 2A). 231p. 1951. pap. 20.50 (ISBN 0-87079-227-X, TID-5231); microfilm 10.00 (ISBN 0-87079-463-9, TID-5231). DOE.

Vein-Type & Similar Uranium Deposits in Rocks Younger than Proterozoic: Proceedings of a Technical Committee Meeting Organized by the International Atomic Energy Agency & Held in Lisbon, Sept. 24-28, 1979. (Panel Proceedings Ser.). 395p. 1982. pap. 50.25 (ISBN 0-686-91858-4, ISP600, IAEA). Unipub.

Warnecke, Steven J. Uranium, Nonproliferation & Energy Security. (The Atlantic Papers: No. 37). 121p. 1980. 6.50x (ISBN 0-916672-77-8, Pub. by Atlantic Inst France). Allanheld.

Warner, J. C., et al, eds. Metallurgy of Uranium & Its Alloys. AEC Technical Information Center. (National Nuclear Energy Ser.: Div. IV, Vol. 12). 208p. 1953. pap. 19.00 (ISBN 0-87079-273-3, NNES-IV-12A); microfilm 10.00 (ISBN 0-87079-453-1, NNES-IV-12A). DOE.

Williams, Roy E. A Guide to the Prevention of Ground Water Contamination by Uranium Mill Wastes. 173p. 1982. text ed. 38.00 (ISBN 0-910069-05-0). Geotech Engineer Prog.

World Uraniam Potential: An International Evaluation. 1979. 16.00 (ISBN 92-64-11883-7). OECD.

Yemel'yanov, V. S. & Yevstyukin, A. I. Metallurgy of Nuclear Fuels. 1969. 110.00 (ISBN 0-08-012073-3). Pergamon.

URANIUM–BIBLIOGRAPHY

Maximov, V., compiled by. Uranium Carbides, Nitrides & Silicides. (Bibliographical Ser.: No. 33). 110p. 1968. pap. write for info. (ISBN 92-0-044368-0, STI/PUB/21/33, IAEA). Unipub.

--Uranium Carbides, Nitrides & Silicides. (Bibliographical Ser.: No. 14). 175p. 1964. pap. write for info. (ISBN 92-0-044064-9, STI/PUB/21/14, IAEA). Unipub.

URANIUM ORES

see also Prospecting

Borehole Logging for Uranium Exploration: A Manual. (Technical Reports Ser.: No. 212). (Illus.). 279p. 1982. pap. 33.50 (ISBN 92-0-145082-6, IDC212, IAEA). Unipub.

Bowie, S. H., et al, eds. Uranium Prospecting Handbook. 346p. 1977. pap. text ed. 49.00x (ISBN 0-900488-15-8). IMM North Am.

Brazil's Uranium-Thorium Deposits: Geology Reserves Potential. 144p. 1980. pap. 95.00 (ISBN 0-686-61573-5, MF15, Miller Freeman). Unipub.

Cameron, Eion M. Uranium Exploration in Athabaska Basin. 320p. 1983. pap. text ed. 49.95x (ISBN 0-660-11508-5, Pub. by Minister Supplies Canada). Brookfield Pub Co.

Consultants Bureau Staff. The Geology of Uranium. LC 59-24987. (Soviet Journal of Atomic Energy, Supplement: 1957; No. 6). Repr. of 1958 ed. 33.50 (ISBN 0-317-27110-5, 2024705). Bks Demand UMI.

Exploration for Uranium Ore Deposits. (Proceedings Ser.). (Illus.). 808p. 1977. pap. 87.75 (ISBN 92-0-040076-0, ISP434, IAEA). Unipub.

Formation of Uranium Ore Deposits. (Proceedings Ser.). (Illus.). 750p. 1975. pap. 75.00 (ISBN 92-0-040274-7, ISP374, IAEA). Unipub.

Galloway, W. E., et al. Depositional & Ground-Water Flow Systems in the Exploration for Uranium: Syllabus for Research Colloquium Held in Austin, 1978. (Illus.). 267p. 1979. 6.00 (ISBN 0-318-03374-7). Bur Econ Geology.

Joint Steering Group on Uranium Resources of the OECD Nuclear Energy Agency & the International Atomic Energy Agency. World Uranium Geology & Resource Potential. LC 80-81724. (Illus.). 524p. 1980. pap. 50.00 (ISBN 0-87930-085-X). Miller Freeman.

McNeil, Mary. Brazil's Uranium-Thorium Deposits, Geology, Reserves, Potential: A World Mining Report. LC 79-87816. (Illus.). 1979. pap. 95.00 (ISBN 0-87930-119-8). Miller Freeman.

OECD Staff. Economics of Uranium Ore Processing Operations. 250p. (Orig.). 1983. pap. 18.00x (ISBN 92-64-02493-X). OECD.

Processing of Low-Grade Uranium Ores. (Panel Proceedings Ser.). (Illus.). 247p. 1967. pap. 16.25 (ISBN 92-0-041067-7, ISP146, IAEA). Unipub.

Rich, R. A., et al. Hydrothermal Uranium Deposits. (Developments in Economic Geology Ser.: Vol. 6). 264p. 1977. 51.00 (ISBN 0-444-41551-3). Elsevier.

Significance of Mineralogy in the Development of Flow Sheets for Processing Uranium Ores. (Technical Reports Ser.: No. 196). (Illus.). 276p. 1980. pap. 41.25 (ISBN 92-0-145080-X, IDC196, IAEA). Unipub.

Uranium Deposits in Africa: Geology & Exploration. (Panel Proceedings Ser.). (Illus.). 262p. 1980. pap. 37.00 (ISBN 92-0-041079-0, ISP509, IAEA). Unipub.

Uranium Deposits in Latin America: Geology & Exploration. (Panel Proceedings Ser.). (Illus.). 625p. 1981. pap. 86.00 (ISBN 92-0-041081-2, ISP505, IAEA). Unipub.

Uranium Deposits in Metamorphic Environments. 1979. 78.70 (ISBN 0-942218-09-4). Minobras.

V

VACUUM MICROBALANCE

Conference on Vacuum Microbalance Techniques (9th: 1970: Berlin, Germany) Progress in Vacuum Microbalance Techniques: Proceedings of the Ninth Conference on Vacuum Microbalance Techniques, Technical University, Berlin, Germany, June, 1970, Vol. 1. Gast, Th. & Robens, E., eds. LC 72-82129. pap. 104.80 (ISBN 0-317-29331-1, 2024022). Bks Demand UMI.

Conference on Vacuum Microbalance Techniques (10th: 1972: Uxbridge, England. Progress in Vacuum Microbalance Techniques: Proceedings of the 10th Conference on Vacuum Microbalance Techniques, Brunal University, Uxbridge, England, June 1972, Vol. 2. Bevan, S. C. & Gregg, S. J., eds. LC 72-82129. pap. 66.50 (ISBN 0-317-29333-8, 2024023). Bks Demand UMI.

Vacuum Microbalance Techniques, 8 vols. Incl. Vol. 1. Katz, Max J. 152p. 1961. 29.50x (ISBN 0-306-38401-9); Vol. 2. Walker, Raymond F. 179p. 1962. 29.50x (ISBN 0-306-38402-7); Vol. 3. Behrndt, Klaus H. 215p. 1973. 35.00x (ISBN 0-306-38403-5); Vol. 4. Waters, Paul M. 288p. 1965. 34.50x (ISBN 0-306-38404-3); Vol. 5. Behrndt, Klaus H. 264p. 1966. 35.00x (ISBN 0-306-38405-1); Vol. 6. Czanderna, A. W. 178p. 1967. 32.50x (ISBN 0-306-38406-X); Vol. 7. Massen, C. H. & Van Beckum, H. T. 238p. 1971. 32.50x (ISBN 0-306-38407-8); Vol. 8. Czanderna, A. W. 251p. 1971. 35.00x (ISBN 0-306-38408-6). LC 61-8595 (Plenum Pr). Plenum Pub.

VACUUM-PUMPS

Dushman, Saul & Lafferty, J. M., eds. Scientific Foundations of Vacuum Technique. 2nd ed. LC 61-17361. 1962. 78.95x (ISBN 0-471-22803-6, Pub. by Wiley-Interscience). Wiley.

VACUUM TECHNOLOGY

see also Vacuum Metallurgy; Vacuum-Pumps; Vacuum-Tubes; Vapor-Plating

American Vacuum Society Education Comm., ed. Experimental Vacuum Science & Technology. 288p. 1973. 65.00 (ISBN 0-8247-6068-9). Dekker.

Bhatia, Mahesh V. & Cheremisinoff, Paul N., eds. Air Movement & Vacuum Devices. LC 79-63114. (Process Equipment Ser.: Vol. 3). 323p. 1981. 35.00 (ISBN 0-87762-291-4). Technomic.

Carpenter, L. G., ed. Vacuum Technology. 2nd ed. 1983. 25.00 (ISBN 0-9960026-8-5, Pub. by A Hilger England). Heyden.

Colligon, J. S., ed. Directory of Manufacturers of Vacuum Plant, Components & Associated Equipment in the UK, 1982. 56p. 1982. pap. 13.25 (ISBN 0-08-029323-9, C145, A145). Pergamon.

Guthrie, Andrew. Vacuum Technology. LC 63-20631. 532p. 1963. 50.50x (ISBN 0-471-33722-6, Pub. by Wiley-Interscience). Wiley.

Halliday, B., ed. International Directory of Vacuum Equipment, Manufacturers & Suppliers. 48p. 1983. pap. 17.00 (ISBN 0-08-031117-2, 11, 17, 16). Pergamon.

Hurrle, Karl, et al. Technical Dictionary of Vacuum Physics & Vacuum Technology (English, French, German, Rusian) 1973. text ed. 44.00 (ISBN 0-08-016957-0). Pergamon.

Israeli Vacuum Congress, Fifth, Israel, April 1978. Advances in Vacuum Science & Technology: Proceedings. Yarwood, J. & Margoninski, Y., eds. 1979. pap. 14.25 (ISBN 0-08-024238-3). Pergamon.

Latham, R. V. High Voltage Vacuum Insulation: The Physical Basis. LC 80-41602. 1981. 47.00 (ISBN 0-12-437180-9). Acad Pr.

Normand, C. E., et al. Vacuum Problems & Techniques. (National Nuclear Energy Ser.: Division I, Vol. 11). 289p. 1950. 23.50 (ISBN 0-87079-356-X, TID-5210); microfilm 10.00 (ISBN 0-87079-357-8, TID-5210). DOE.

Stuart, R. V. Vacuum Technology, Thin Films, & Sputtering: An Introduction. LC 82-13748. 1983. 23.00 (ISBN 0-12-674780-6). Acad Pr.

Vacuum Metallurgy Conference: Proceedings. 209p. 1985. 60.00 (ISBN 0-89520-167-4). Iron & Steel.

Weber, Fritz W. Elsevier's Dictionary of High Vacuum Science & Technology. (Eng., Ger., Fr., Ital., Span. & Rus.). 539p. 1968. 113.00 (ISBN 0-444-40625-5). Elsevier.

Weston, G. F. Ultrahigh Vacuum Practice. (Illus.). 304p. 1985. text ed. 84.95 (ISBN 0-408-01485-7). Butterworth.

Williams, B., ed. Film Preparation & Etching Using Vacuum or Plasma Technology: Proceedings of the SIRA International Seminar, Brighton, U. K., 22-24 March 1983. 100p. 1984. 27.50 (ISBN 0-08-031150-4). Pergamon.

Yarwood, J. Vacuum Devices: Proceedings of the Conference, University of Cambridge, 25-27 March 1980. 144p. 1981. pap. 24.00 (ISBN 0-08-027330-0). Pergamon.

Yarwood, J., ed. Vacuum & Thin Film Technology. 1978. text ed. 30.00 (ISBN 0-08-022112-2). Pergamon.

--Vacuum Seventy-Eight: Selected Proceedings of the Conference on Medium High & Ultra-High Vacuum Technology, Oxford, England, 1978. Grossart, G. S. (Illus.). 1979. pap. 29.00 (ISBN 0-08-024229-4). Pergamon.

VACUUM-TUBES

see also Cathode Ray Tubes; Diodes; Electric Discharges through Gases; Electron Tubes; Electronics; Klystrons; Storage Tubes; X-Rays

Howard W. Sams Engineering Staff. Tube Substitution Handbook. 21st ed. LC 80-13842. 128p. 1980. pap. 4.95 (ISBN 0-672-21746-5). Sams.

RCA Commercial Engineering Staff. Rca Receiving Tube Manual Rc-30. (Illus.). 752p. 1975. pap. 3.95 (ISBN 0-913970-17-4). RCA Dist Spec Prods.

Ryans, J. & Roper, D. Process Vacuum Systems Design & Operation. 384p. 1986. price not set (ISBN 0-07-054355-0). McGraw.

VALENCE (THEORETICAL CHEMISTRY)

see also Atomic Orbitals; Chemical Bonds; Macromolecules; Molecular Orbitals

Brown, David B., ed. Mixed-Valence Compounds: Theory & Applications in Chemistry, Physics, Geology & Biology. (NATO Advanced Study Institute, C. Mathematical & Physical Sciences Ser.: No. 58). 525p. 1980. lib. bdg. 60.50 (ISBN 90-277-1152-6, Pub. by Reidel Holland). Kluwer Academic.

Cartmell & Fowles. Valency & Molecular Structure. 4th ed. 1977. 19.95 (ISBN 0-408-70809-3). Butterworth.

Coulson, Charles A. Coulson's Valence. 3rd ed. McWeeny, Roy, ed. (Illus.). 1979. 59.00x (ISBN 0-19-855144-4); pap. 25.95x (ISBN 0-19-855145-2). Oxford U Pr.

Epictis, N. B., et al. Unified Valence Bond Theory of Electronic Structure. (Lecture Notes in Chemistry: Vol. 29). 303p. 1982. pap. 23.40 (ISBN 0-387-11491-2). Springer-Verlag.

Epiotis, N. D. Unified Valence Bond Theory of Electronic Structure-Applications. (Lecture Notes in Chemistry: Vol. 34). 585p. 1983. pap. 41.40 (ISBN 0-387-12000-9). Springer-Verlag.

Jorgensen, C. K. Oxidation Numbers & Oxidation States. LC 68-56944. 1969. 42.00 (ISBN 0-387-04658-5). Springer-Verlag.

Kuznetsov, V. I., ed. Theory of Valency in Progress. 262p. 1980. 8.95 (ISBN 0-8285-1707-X, Pub. by Mir Pubs USSR). Imported Pubns.

O'Dwyer, M. F., et al. Valency. LC 77-8366. (Illus.). 1978. pap. 19.50 (ISBN 0-387-90268-6). Springer-Verlag.

--Valency. 2nd. ed. (Heidelberg Science Library). (Illus.). xii, 252p. 1985. pap. 19.50 (ISBN 0-387-90268-6). Springer-Verlag.

Parks, R. D., ed. Valence Instabilities & Related Narrow-Band Phenomena. LC 77-3155. (Illus.). 562p. 1977. 85.00x (ISBN 0-306-31047-3, Plenum Pr). Plenum Pub.

Pickering, H. S. The Covalent Bond. LC 78-50008. (Wykeham Science Ser.: No. 47). 101p. 1978. 19.50x (ISBN 0-8448-1310-9). Crane-Russak Co.

Stranges, Anthony N. Electrons & Valence: Development of the Theory, 1900-1925. LC 81-48378. (Illus.). 304p. 1982. 28.50x (ISBN 0-89096-124-7). Tex A&M Univ Pr.

Wachter, P. & Boppart, H., eds. Valence Instabilities: Proceedings of the International Conference on Valence Instabilities, Zurich, Switzerland, April, 1982. 598p. 1982. 66.00 (North Holland). Elsevier.

VALUE DISTRIBUTION THEORY

Kujala, Robert O. & Vitter, Albert L., III, eds. Value Distribution Theory: Deficit & Bezout Estimates, Pt. B. (Pure & Applied Mathematics Ser.: Vol. 25). 288p. 1973. 45.00 (ISBN 0-8247-6125-1). Dekker.

Kujala, Robert O. & Vitter, Albert L., 3rd, eds. Value Distribution Theory, Pt. A. (Pure & Applied Mathematics Ser.: Vol. 25). 288p. 1974. 45.00 (ISBN 0-8247-6124-3). Dekker.

Laine, I. & Rickman, S., eds. Value Distribution: Proceedings, Joensuu, Finland, 1981. (Lecture Notes in Mathematics: Vol. 981). 245p. 1983. pap. 17.00 (ISBN 0-387-12003-3). Springer-Verlag.

The Problem of Distribution of Benefits & Costs & Selective Corrective Measures. (Current Problems of Economic Integration Ser.). pap. 7.00 (ISBN 0-686-93040-1, UN75/2D/10, UN). Unipub.

Wu, Hung-Hsi. Equidistribution Theory of Holomorphic Curves. LC 78-100997. (Annals of Mathematics Studies: No. 64). 1970. 23.00 (ISBN 0-691-08073-9). Princeton U Pr.

Yang, Chung-Chun, ed. Value Distribution Theory & Its Applications. LC 83-21465. (Contemporary Mathematics Ser.: Vol. 25). 253p. 1984. pap. text ed. 28.00 (ISBN 0-8218-5025-3). Am Math.

VALVES

Control Valve Terminology: ISA Standard S75.05. 48p. 1983. pap. text ed. 20.00x (ISBN 0-87664-753-0). Instru Soc.

Driskell, L. R. Control Valve Sizing. 192p. 1982. pap. text ed. 29.95x (ISBN 0-87664-620-8); pap. text ed. 10.00x instr's guide (ISBN 0-87664-621-6). Instru Soc.

--Introduction to Control Valves. LC 81-80513. 142p. 1982. Instr's Guide: 40. pap. text ed. 10.00x (ISBN 0-87664-617-8); Student Text: 142. pap. text ed. 24.95x (ISBN 0-87664-616-X). Instru Soc.

Driskoll, L. R. Selection of Control Valves. 1982. Instr's Guide: 56p. pap. text ed. 10.00x (ISBN 0-87664-619-4); Student Text: 142p. pap. text ed. 24.95x (ISBN 0-87664-618-6). Instru Soc.

Equivalent Valves Reference Manual. 18th ed. 220p. (Orig.). 1980. pap. 59.95x (ISBN 0-87201-257-3). Gulf Pub.

Fong, J. T. & Tashjian, B. J., eds. Inservice Data Reporting & Analysis, PVP-PB-32. (Pressure Vessel & Piping Division Ser.). 1978. 30.00 (ISBN 0-685-66802-9, H00137). ASME.

Greene, R. W. The Chemical Engineering Guide to Valves. 250p. 1984. 37.50 (ISBN 0-07-024313-1). McGraw.

ISA Handbook of Control Values. 2nd ed. LC 73-368254. 544p. 1976. text ed. 44.95 (ISBN 0-87664-234-2). Instru Soc.

Lyons, Jerry L. Lyon's Valve Designers Handbook. 960p. 1981. 64.50 (ISBN 0-442-24963-2). Van Nos Reinhold.

Piper, Charles. Handbook 10: Valves. LC 83-161604. (Mud Equipment Manual Ser.). (Illus.). 56p. (Orig.). 1985. pap. 19.95x (ISBN 0-87201-622-6). Gulf Pub.

Schweitzer, Philip A. Handbook of Valves. LC 81-19373. 190p. 1982. Repr. of 1972 ed. lib. bdg. 24.50 (ISBN 0-89874-467-9). Krieger.

Supervision of Water Supply Valves. (Twenty Ser). 1958. pap. 2.00 (ISBN 0-685-58116-0, 26). Natl Fire Prot.

Valve & Pipe Fittings. (Industrial Equipment & Supplies Ser.). 1980. 350.00 (ISBN 0-686-31541-3). Busn Trend.

Valve Inspection. (Mechanical Inspection Ser.: Module 30-3). (Illus.). 66p. 1979. spiral bdg. 8.00x (ISBN 0-87683-125-0). G P Courseware.

Valves & Actuators Market. 311p. 1984. 1450.00 (ISBN 0-86621-555-7). Frost & Sullivan.

VALVES, ELECTRIC

see Electron Tubes

VANADIUM

Clark, R. Chemistry of Titanium & Vanadium. 1968. 70.29 (ISBN 0-444-40679-4). Elsevier.

EA Engineering, Science & Technology. Inc. Staff. Vanadium: Environmental & Community Health Impact. LC 85-70627. (Orig.). 1985. pap. 10.00 (ISBN 0-89364-052-2, 847-86450). Am Petroleum.

VAN ALLEN RADIATION BELTS

Roederer, J. G. Dynamics of Geomagnetically Trapped Radiation. LC 73-109668. (Physics & Chemistry in Space: Vol. 2). (Illus.). 1970. 24.00 (ISBN 0-387-04987-8). Springer-Verlag.

VANGUARD (SATELLITE)

see Project Vanguard

VANISHING ANIMALS

see Rare Animals

VANISHING BIRDS

see Rare Birds

VANS

see also Campers and Coaches, Truck

Chilton Staff. Chilton's Repair & Tune-up Guide: Dodge-Plymouth Vans 1967-86. LC 85-47986. 336p. (Orig.). 1986. pap. 12.50 (ISBN 0-8019-7686-3). Chilton.

--Chilton's Repair & Tune-up Guide: Ford Vans 1961-86. LC 85-47964. 356p. (Orig.). 1986. pap. 12.50 (ISBN 0-8019-7663-4). Chilton.

Chilton's Automotive Editorial Staff. Chevrolet-GMC Vans, 1967-1982. 1982. pap. 11.95 (ISBN 0-8019-7169-1). Chilton.

--Chilton's Light Truck & Van Wiring Diagram Manual 1980-98: Moter-Age Professional Mechanic's Edition. LC 85-47806. 1200p. 1985. pap. 49.00 (ISBN 0-8019-7634-0). Chilton.

--Chilton's Truck & Van Repair Manual 1977-84. LC 77-16756. 1464p. 1984. sw 20.75 (ISBN 0-8019-7357-0); hw o.p. 21.75. Chilton.

--Chilton's Truck & Van Service Manual 1978-84. LC 82-71518. (Motor Age Professional Mechanics Edition). 1632p. 1984. text ed. 37.50 (ISBN 0-8019-7358-9). Chilton.

--Dodge - Plymouth Vans 1967-84: RTUG. LC 83-45307. 264p. 1984. pap. 11.95 (ISBN 0-8019-7465-8). Chilton.

--Dodge-Plymouth Vans, Nineteen Sixty-Seven to Nineteen Eighty-Two. 1982. pap. 11.95 (ISBN 0-8019-7168-3). Chilton.

--Ford Vans, Nineteen Sixty-One to Nineteen Eighty-Two. 1982. pap. 11.95 (ISBN 0-8019-7171-3). Chilton.

--Ford Vans 1961-84. LC 83-45301. 308p. 1984. pap. 11.95 (ISBN 0-8019-7458-5). Chilton.

--Truck & Van Repair Manual 1977-84. LC 77-16756. 1468p. 1984. pap. 20.95 (ISBN 0-8019-7357-0). Chilton.

Edmund's Vans, Pickups, Off Road. (Orig.). 1985. pap. 2.95 (ISBN 0-440-02296-7). Dell.

Girdler, Allan. Customizing Your Van. 2nd, rev. ed. Caiati, Carl, rev. by. (Illus.). 256p. 1983. 16.95 (ISBN 0-8306-0212-7); pap. 10.95 (ISBN 0-8306-0112-0, 212). TAB Bks.

Hoy, Ray. Ford Vans: 1969-1983 Shop Manual. (Illus.). pap. text ed. 12.95 (ISBN 0-89287-302-7, A249). Clymer Pubns.

Jorgensen, Eric, ed. Dodge & Plymouth Vans, 1971-1983: Shop Manual. (Illus.). pap. text ed. 12.95 (ISBN 0-89287-314-0, A244). Clymer Pubns.

Martinez, Alberto & Nory, J. L. Vans. LC 81-66414. (Illus.). 192p. 1981. 24.95 (ISBN 0-86710-006-0). Edns Vilo.

Self, Charles. Do-It-Yourselfer's Guide to Auto Body Repair & Painting. (Illus.). 1978. pap. 9.95 (ISBN 0-8306-6949-3, 949). TAB Bks.

Woodall's RV Owner's Handbook, Vol. 1. pap. 6.95 (ISBN 0-671-24614-3). Woodall.

Woodall's RV Owner's Handbook, Vol. 2. pap. 4.95 (ISBN 0-671-25163-5). Woodall.

VAPOR DEPOSITION

see Vapor-Plating

VAPOR-LIQUID EQUILIBRIUM

Fredenslund, et al. Vapor-Liquid Equilibria Using UNIFAC: A Group Contribution Method. 380p. 1977. 89.50 (ISBN 0-444-41621-8). Elsevier.

Gmehling, J. & Onken, U. Vapor-Liquid Equilibrium Data Collection: Aqueous Organic Systems, Vol. I, Pt. I. rev. ed. Behrens, D. & Eckermann, R., eds. (Dechema Chemistry Data Ser.). 698p. 1981. text ed. 120.00x (ISBN 3-921567-01-7, Pub. by Dechema Germany). Scholium Intl.

--Vapor-Liquid Equilibrium Data Collection Part 2d, Organic Hydroxy Compounds: Alcohols & Phenols (Supplement 2) (Dechema Chemistry Data Ser.: Vol. I). (Illus.). 800p. 1982. 117.50x (ISBN 0-686-43226-6, Pub. by Dechema Germany). Scholium Intl.

--Vapor-Liquid Equilibrium Data Collection Part 5 Carboxylic Acids, Anhydrides, Esters. (Vol. I). (Illus.). 715p. 1982. 122.00x (ISBN 0-686-43231-2, Pub. by Dechema Germany). Scholium Intl.

--Vapor-Liquid Equilibrium Data Collection: Volume I, Part 1A - Supplement 1 to Aqueous Organic Systems. 1981. lib. bdg. 127.50x (ISBN 3-921-56733-5, Pub. by Dechema Germany). Scholium Intl.

--Vapor-Liquid Equilibrium Data Collection: Volume I, Part 2C-Organic Hydroxy Compounds: Alcohols (Supplement 1) (Dechema Chemistry Data Ser.). (Illus.). 698p. 1982. lib. bdg. 105.00x (ISBN 3-921-56729-7). Scholium Intl.

Hirata, M., et al. Computer Aided Data Book of Vapor-Liquid Equilibria. 960p. 1975. 125.75 (ISBN 0-444-99855-1). Elsevier.

Knapp, H. & Doring, R. Vapor-Liquid Equilibra for Mixtures of Low Boiling Substances. Berhens, D. & Eckermann, R., eds. (Dechema Chemistry Data Ser.). (Illus.). 910p. 1982. 138.50x (ISBN 0-686-43225-8, Pub. by Dechema Germany). Scholium Intl.

Kojima, K. & Tochigi, K. Prediction of Vapor-Liquid Equilibria by the ASOG Method. (Physical Science Data Ser.: Vol. 3). 264p. 1980. 66.00 (ISBN 0-444-99773-3). Elsevier.

Wichterle, I., et al, eds. Vapor-Liquid Equilibrium Data Bibliography: Supplement 1. 334p. 1976. 95.75 (ISBN 0-444-41464-9). Elsevier.

--Vapor-Liquid Equilibrium Data Bibliography: Supplement II, 1979. LC 79-109407. 286p. 1979. 100.00 (ISBN 0-444-41822-9). Elsevier.

VAPOR-PHASE CHROMATOGRAPHY

see Gas Chromatography

VAPOR-PLATING

American Society for Testing & Materials. Handbook of Vapor Degreasing. LC 76-1382. (ASTM Special Technical Publication: No. 310A). pap. 20.00 (ISBN 0-317-26535-0, 2023986). Bks Demand UMI.

Flaud, J. M. & Camy-Peyret, C. Water Vapour Line Parameters from Microwave to Medium Infrared: An Atlas of H2 to the Sixteenth, O; H2 to the Seventeenth, O; H2 to the Eighteenth, O; Line Positions & Intensities Between O & 4350 Cm to the -1. (International Tables of Constants Ser.: Vol. 19). xvi, 259p. 1981. 83.00 (ISBN 0-08-026181-7). Pergamon.

Hawkins, Donald T., ed. Chemical Vapor Deposition, 1960-1980: A Bibliography. LC 81-15344. (IFI Data Base Library). 750p. 1981. text ed. 125.00x (ISBN 0-306-65201-3, IFI Plenum). Plenum Pub.

Powell, Carroll F., et al, eds. Vapor Deposition. LC 66-13515. (The Electrochemical Society Ser.). (Illus.). pap. 160.00 (ISBN 0-317-11088-8, 2051258). Bks Demand UMI.

VAPOR PRESSURE

Gupte, Parag A., et al, eds. Documentation of the Basis for Selection of the Contents of Chapter 3 Vapor Pressure in Manual for Predicting Chemical Process Design Data. 130p. 1984. pap. 90.00 spiral (ISBN 0-8169-0313-1). Am Inst Chem Eng.

Habermehl, G. Venomous Animals & Their Toxins. (Illus.). 210p. 1981. pap. 17.50 (ISBN 0-387-10780-0). Springer-Verlag.
Minton, S. A. Venom Diseases. (Illus.). 256p. 1974. 16.75x (ISBN 0-398-03051-0). C C Thomas.
Schmidt, Justin O. Insect Venoms. 200p. Date not set. 18.50 (ISBN 0-03-055446-2). Praeger.
Shankland, D. L., et al, eds. Pesticide & Venom Neurotoxicity. LC 77-25006. 293p. 1978. 45.00 (ISBN 0-306-31123-2, Plenum Pr). Plenum Pub.
Tu, Anthony T. Venoms: Chemistry & Molecular Biology. LC 76-30751. 560p. 1977. 83.95x (ISBN 0-471-89229-7, Pub. by Wiley-Interscience). Wiley.

VENOMOUS SNAKES
see Poisonous Snakes

VENTILATION
see also Air Conditioning; Dampness in Buildings; Dust–Removal; Fans (Machinery); Heating; Mine Ventilation;
also subdivision Heating and Ventilation or Ventilation under special subjects

Air Conditioning & Ventilating Systems. (Eighty-Ninety Ser.). 1974. pap. 2.50 (ISBN 0-685-58161-6, 90A). Natl Fire Prot.
Alden, John L. & Kane, John M. Design of Industrial Ventilation Systems. 5th ed. (Illus.). 260p. 1982. 29.95 (ISBN 0-8311-1138-0). Indus Pr.
Blower & Exhaust Systems, Dust, Stock & Vapor Removal or Conveying. (Eighty-Ninety Ser). 1973. pap. 2.00 (ISBN 0-685-58176-4, 91). Natl Fire Prot.
Brumbaugh, James. Heating, Ventilating, & Air Conditioning Library, 3 vols. 2nd ed. LC 83-7064. (Illus.). 1983. 14.95 ea. Vol. 1 (ISBN 0-672-23389-4, 23248). Vol. 2 (ISBN 0-672-23390-8, 23249). Vol. 3 (ISBN 0-672-23391-6, 23250). 41.95, set of 3 vols. (ISBN 0-672-23227-8). Audel.
Brumbaugh, James E. Heating, Ventilating & Air Conditions Library. (Audel). (Illus.). Set. 41.95 (ISBN 0-672-23388-6); Vol. 1. 14.95 (ISBN 0-672-23389-4); Vol. 2. 14.95 (ISBN 0-672-23390-8); Vol. 3. 14.95 (ISBN 0-672-23391-6); 41.95. G K Hall.
Clark, Deborah B. & Bradford, Debra. Pressure Cycled Ventilators. (Illus.). 208p. 1984. text ed. 24.95 (ISBN 0-13-699090-8); pap. text ed. 19.95 (ISBN 0-13-699082-7). P-H.
Clifford, George. Heating, Ventilating & Air Conditioning. 1984. text ed. 39.95 (ISBN 0-8359-2812-8); sol. manual avail. (ISBN 0-8359-2813-6). Reston.
Croome, D. J. & Roberts, B. M. Air Conditioning & Ventilation of Buildings, Vol. 1. 2nd ed. LC 79-40965. (International Ser. in Heating, Ventilation & Refrigeration: Vol. 14). (Illus.). 575p. 1981. text ed. 66.00 (ISBN 0-08-024779-2). Pergamon.
Davies, Donald G. & Barnes, Charles D., eds. Regulation of Ventilation & Gas Exchange. (Research Topics in Physiology). 1978. 49.50 (ISBN 0-12-204650-1). Acad Pr.
Din Standards for Central-Heating & Ventilation Plants. 248.00 (ISBN 0-01-005732-3, 10057-5/23). Heyden.
Doring, G. & Rudolphi. Tiefkuhl Lexikon. (Ger.). 239p. 10.95 (ISBN 3-87150-020-8, M-7666, Pub. by Deutscher Fachverlag). French & Eur.
European Heating & Ventilating Associations, ed. The International Dictionary of Heating, Ventilating, & Air Conditioning. LC 79-41714. 416p. 1982. 79.95x (ISBN 0-419-11650-8, NO. 6553, E&FN Spon England). Methuen Inc.
Griscom, John H. Uses & Abuses of Air: Showing Its Influence in Sustaining Life & Producing Disease. LC 79-125743. (American Environmental Studies). 1970. Repr. of 1854 ed. 17.00 (ISBN 0-405-02668-4). Ayer Co Pubs.
Hartman, Howard L., et al. Mine Ventilation & Air Conditioning. 2nd ed. Mutmansky, Jan M. & Wang, Y. J., eds. LC 81-19662. 791p. 1982. 57.50x (ISBN 0-471-05690-1, Pub. by Wiley-Interscience). Wiley.
Havrella, Raymond. Heating, Ventilating & Air Conditioning Fundamentals. LC 80-17155. (Contemporary Construction Ser.). (Illus.). 288p. 1981. text ed. 23.72 (ISBN 0-07-027281-6). McGraw.
Hedden, Jay. Heating, Cooling & Ventilation: Solar & Conventional Solutions. Kummings, Gail S., ed. LC 81-67294. (Illus.). 144p. 1981. 19.95 (ISBN 0-932944-39-6); pap. 7.95 (ISBN 0-932944-40-X). Creative Homeowner.
International Symposium on the Aerodynamics & Ventilation of Vehicle Tunnels, 1st. Proceedings. 1973. text ed. 47.00x (ISBN 0-900983-28-0, Dist. by Air Science Co.). BHRA Fluid.
Kelsey, Neal. Ventilator Concepts. 2nd ed. 200p. 1985. pap. text ed. price not set (ISBN 0-933195-15-X). Cal College Pr.
Leeds, Lewis W. Lectures on Ventilation. (Library of Victorian Culture). (Illus.). 1976. pap. text ed. 5.00 (ISBN 0-89257-015-6). Am Life Foun.
Lindeke, Wolfgang. Dictionary of Ventilation & Health. 186p. 1980. 25.00x (ISBN 0-569-08522-5, Pub. by Collet's). State Mutual Bk.
McDermott, Henry J. Handbook of Ventilation for Contaminant Control. 2nd ed. (Illus.). 256p. 1985. pap. text ed. 35.00 (ISBN 0-250-40641-1). Butterworth.
--Handbook of Ventilation for Contaminant Control (Including Osha Requirements) LC 76-22253. 1976. 39.95 (ISBN 0-250-40139-8). Butterworth.
McDonald, W. F. Notes on the Problems of Cargo Ventilation. (Technical Note Ser.: No. 17). 38p. 1957. pap. 7.00 (ISBN 0-685-22329-9, W11, WMO). Unipub.
McQuiston, F. C. & Parker, J. D. Heating, Ventilating, & Air Conditioning: Analysis & Design. 2nd ed. 666p. 1982. 42.50 (ISBN 0-471-08259-7); write for info. solutions (ISBN 0-471-86657-1). Wiley.
Martz, Kathren V. & Joiner, Jerry. Management of the Patient-Ventilator System: A Team Approach. 2nd ed. (Illus.). 272p. 1983. pap. text ed. 16.95 (ISBN 0-8016-3180-7). Mosby.
Payne, J. P. & Bushman, J. A., eds. Artificial Ventilation: Technical, Biological & Clinical Aspects. LC 80-40391. 1980. 41.50 (ISBN 0-12-547960-3). Acad Pr.
Rattenborg, C. C. Clinical Use of Mechanical Ventilation. (Illus.). 320p. 1981. pap. 24.95 (ISBN 0-8151-7072-6). Year Bk Med.
Rudman, Jack. Foreman (Ventilation & Drainage) (Career Examination Ser.: C-278). (Cloth bdg. avail. on request). pap. 10.00 (ISBN 0-8373-0278-1). Natl Learning.
--Senior Heating & Ventilating Engineer. (Career Examination Ser.: C-1918). (Cloth bdg. avail. on request). pap. 12.00 (ISBN 0-8373-1918-8). Natl Learning.
--Superintendent of Heating & Ventilation. (Career Examination Ser.: C-2380). (Cloth bdg. avail. on request). pap. 12.00 (ISBN 0-8373-2380-0). Natl Learning.
--Supervisor (Ventillation & Drainage) (Career Examination Ser.: C-1506). (Cloth bdg. avail. on request). pap. 10.00 (ISBN 0-8373-1506-9). Natl Learning.
--Ventilation & Drainage Maintainer. (Career Examination Ser.: C-1528). (Cloth bdg. avail. on request). pap. 10.00 (ISBN 0-8373-1528-X). Natl Learning.
Scheck, P. A., et al, eds. Perspectives in High Frequency Ventilation. 1983. lib. bdg. 54.50 (ISBN 0-89838-571-7, Pub. by Martinus Nijhoff Netherlands). Kluwer Academic.
Stamper, Eugene & Koral, Richard L., eds. Handbook of Air Conditioning, Heating & Ventilating. 3rd ed. LC 78-71559. (Illus.). 1420p. 1979. 70.00 (ISBN 0-8311-1124-0). Indus Pr.
Standards for Ventilation Systems. (DIN Standards Ser.). 536.00 (ISBN 0-686-31840-4, 11351-3/85). Heyden.
Symposium on Artificial Ventilation, Paris, 1969. Proceedings. Minkowski, A., et al, eds. (Biology of the Neonate: Vol. 16, No. 1-3). 1970. pap. 25.75 (ISBN 3-8055-0755-0). S Karger.

VENTRICULOCISTERNOSTOMY

Hanrath, P. Evaluation of Left Ventricular Function by Ultrasound. 1982. 39.50 (ISBN 0-686-38401-6, Pub. by Martinus Nijhoff Netherlands). Kluwer Academic.

VENUS (PLANET)

Brandt, J. C. & McElroy, M. E. Atmosphere of Venus & Mars. 296p. (Orig.). 1968. 80.95 (ISBN 0-677-11590-3). Gordon.
Burgess, Eric. Venus: An Errant Twin. LC 85-384. (Illus.). 176p. 1985. 29.95 (ISBN 0-231-05856-X). Columbia U Pr.
Hunt, Garry & Moore, Patrick. The Planet Venus. LC 82-5045. (Illus.). 240p. 1983. 22.00 (ISBN 0-571-09050-8). Faber & Faber.
Hunten, Donald M., et al, eds. Venus. LC 83-1064. 1143p. 1983. 49.95x (ISBN 0-8165-0788-0). U of Ariz Pr.
Jastrow, R. & Rasool, S. I., eds. Venus Atmosphere. 616p. 1969. 129.50 (ISBN 0-677-13260-3). Gordon.
Nunis, Doyce B., Jr. The Seventeen Sixty-Nine Transit of Venus: The Baja California Observations of Jean-Baptiste Chappe d'Auteroche, Vicente de Doz, & Joaquin Velazquez Cardenas de Leon. Donahue, James, et al, trs. from Fr. & Span. LC 82-3548. (Baja California Travels Ser.: No. 46). (Illus.). 185p. 1982. 60.00 (ISBN 0-938644-18-1). Nat Hist Mus.

VERMES
see Worms

VERMIN
see Household Pests; Pests

VERRUCIDAE

Darwin, Charles. The Fossil Balanidae & Verrucidae. 1854. pap. 6.00 (ISBN 0-384-10850-4). Johnson Repr.

VERTEBRATES
see also Amphibians; Birds; Fishes; Mammals; Reptiles

Andrews, Christopher, et al. Viruses of Vertebrates. 4th ed. 1978. text ed. 37.50 (ISBN 0-02-857150-9). Macmillan.
Aspey, Wayne P. & Lustick, Sheldon I., eds. Behavioral Energetics: The Cost of Survival in Vertebrates. LC 82-12512. (Ohio State Univ. Biosciences Colloquia: No. 7). 312p. 1983. 27.50x (ISBN 0-8142-0332-9). Ohio St U Pr.
Banks, Edwin M., ed. Vertebrate Social Organization. LC 76-26571. (Benchmark Papers in Animal Behavior: Vol. 8). 1977. 67.00 (ISBN 0-12-786130-0). Acad Pr.
Bellairs, Ruth. Developmental Processes in Higher Vertebrates. LC 70-80928. (Illus.). 1971. 19.95x (ISBN 0-87024-204-0). U of Miami Pr.
Blackwelder, Richard E. Guide to the Taxonomic Literature of Vertebrates. 256p. 1972. 9.50x (ISBN 0-8138-1630-0). Iowa St U Pr.
Carter, G. S. Structure & Habit in Vertebrate Evolution. LC 67-25160. (Biology Ser.). (Illus.). 544p. 1967. 20.00x (ISBN 0-295-95121-4). U of Wash Pr.
Cheeseman, C. L. & Mitson, R. B., eds. Telemetric Studies of Vertebrates. (Symposia of the Zoological Society of London Ser.: No. 49). 1982. 59.00 (ISBN 0-12-613349-2). Acad Pr.
Colbert, Edwin H. Evolution of the Vertebrates: A History of the Backboned Animals Through Time. 3rd ed. LC 79-27621. 510p. 1980. 39.50x (ISBN 0-471-04966-2, Pub. by Wiley Interscience). Wiley.
Cope, Edward D. The Vertebrata of the Tertiary Formations of the West, 1 vol. in two, Vol. 3. Sterling, Keir B., ed. LC 77-81093. (Biologists & Their World Ser.). (Illus.). 1978. Repr. of 1883 ed. Set. lib. bdg. 108.00x (ISBN 0-405-10672-6); Vol. 1. lib. bdg. 41.00x (ISBN 0-405-10673-4); Vol. 2. 45.50x (ISBN 0-405-10674-2). Ayer Co Pubs.
Crispens, Charles G., Jr. The Vertebrates: Their Forms & Functions. (Illus.). 224p. 1978. 23.50x (ISBN 0-398-03721-3). C C Thomas.
Csuti, Blair. Type Specimens of Recent Mammals in the Museum of Vertebrate Zoology, University of California, Berkeley. (U. C. Publications in Zoology Ser.: Vol. 114). 80p. 1981. 13.50x (ISBN 0-520-09622-3). U of Cal Pr.
Davis, David E., ed. CRC Handbook of Census Methods for Terrestrial Vertebrates. 424p. 1982. 125.00 (ISBN 0-8493-2970-1). CRC Pr.
Eisenberg, John F., ed. Vertebrate Ecology in the Northern Neotropics. LC 79-9436. (Symposia of the National Zoologigal Park Ser.: No. 4). (Illus.). 271p. 1980. text ed. 25.00x (ISBN 0-87474-410-5); pap. text ed. 12.50x (ISBN 0-87474-409-1). Smithsonian.
Ewert, Jorg-Peter, et al, eds. Advances in Vertebrate Neuroethology. (NATO ASI Series No. A, Life Sciences: Vol. 56). 1256p. 1983. 150.00x (ISBN 0-306-41197-0, Plenum Pr). Plenum Pub.
Gans, Carl, et al. Vertebrates: A Laboratory Text. 2nd, rev. ed. Wessells, Norman K. & Center, Elizabeth M., eds. LC 81-17228. (Illus.). 288p. 1981. lab manual 14.95x (ISBN 0-86576-015-2). W Kaufmann.
Goodman, Joel M., et al. Phylogenetic Development of Vertebrate Immunity, No. 2. new ed. (Illus.). 220p. 1972. text ed. 28.50x (ISBN 0-8422-7057-4). Irvington.
Hardisty, M. W. Biology of the Cyclostomes. LC 79-40803. 350p. 1979. 65.00x (ISBN 0-412-14120-5, NO.6142, Pub. by Chapman & Hall England). Methuen Inc.
Hecht, Peter C., et al, eds. Major Patterns in Vertebrate Evolution. LC 77-6440. (NATO ASI Series A, Life Sciences: Vol. 14). 917p. 1977. 89.50x (ISBN 0-306-35614-7, Plenum Pr). Plenum Pub.
Hildebrand, Milton. Analysis of Vertebrate Structure. 3rd ed. 1985. price not set (ISBN 0-471-82568-9). Wiley.
Horton, J. Development & Differentiation of Vertebrate Lymphocytes. (Developments in Immunology Ser.: Vol. 8). 1980. 55.50 (ISBN 0-444-80195-2). Elsevier.
Hughes, A. The Visual System in Evolution in Vertebrates. LC 77-4371. (Handbook of Sensory Physiology: Vol. 7, Pt. 5). 1977. 201.00 (ISBN 0-387-07908-4). Springer-Verlag.
Hughes, G. M. The Vertebrate Lung. rev. ed. Head, J. J., ed. LC 77-75590. (Carolina Biology Readers Ser.). (Illus.). 16p. 1979. pap. 1.60 (ISBN 0-89278-259-5, 45-9659). Carolina Biological.
Hughes, G. M., ed. Respiration of Amphibious Vertebrates. 1976. 63.50 (ISBN 0-12-360750-7). Acad Pr.
Idler, David R., ed. Steroids in Nonmammalian Vertebrates. 1972. 78.00 (ISBN 0-12-370350-6). Acad Pr.
Jacobs, George J. Dictionary of Vertebrate Zoology, Russian-English: English-Russian. LC 78-16321. 1978. pap. text ed. 4.25x (ISBN 0-87474-551-9). Smithsonian.
Jacobs, Louis, ed. Aspects of Vertebrate History. 1980. pap. 9.95 (ISBN 0-89734-053-1). Mus Northern Ariz.
Jameson, E. W., Jr. Patterns of Vertebrate Biology. (Illus.). 480p. 1981. 29.80 (ISBN 0-387-90520-0). Springer-Verlag.
Lowe, Charles H., Jr., ed. The Vertebrates of Arizona: With Major Section on Arizona Habitats. LC 63-11981. 270p. 1964. pap. 8.95x (ISBN 0-8165-0348-6). U of Ariz Pr.
McFarland, William N., et al. Vertebrate Life. 1979. text ed. write for info. (ISBN 0-02-378870-4). Macmillan.
--Vertebrate Life. 2nd ed. 624p. 1985. text ed. write for info. (ISBN 0-02-378860-7). Macmillan.
MacPhail, Euan. Brain & Intelligence in Vertebrates. (Illus.). 1982. 32.50x (ISBN 0-19-854550-9); pap. 15.95x (ISBN 0-19-854551-7). Oxford U Pr.
Marshall, Patricia T. & Hughes, George M. Physiology of Mammals & Other Vertebrates. 2nd ed. LC 78-73810. (Illus.). 1981. 49.50 (ISBN 0-521-22633-3); pap. 21.95 (ISBN 0-521-29586-6). Cambridge U Pr.
Moltz, Howard. Ontogeny of Vertebrate Behavior. 1971. 77.50 (ISBN 0-12-504350-3). Acad Pr.
Muller-Schwarze, Dietland & Mozell, M., eds. Chemical Signals in Vertebrates 1. LC 77-2565. 619p. 1977. 65.00x (ISBN 0-306-31032-5, Plenum Pr). Plenum Pub.
Neidermeier, William, et al. Phylogenetic Development of Vertebrate Immunity, No. 1. (Illus.). 206p. 1973. text ed. 28.50x (ISBN 0-8422-7056-6). Irvington.
Nixon, Marion. The Oxford Book of Vertebrates. (Illus.). 1972. 27.50x (ISBN 0-19-910009-8). Oxford U Pr.
Norris, David O. Vertebrate Endocrinology. 2nd ed. LC 84-19425. (Illus.). 505p. 1985. text ed. 39.75 (ISBN 0-8121-0967-8). Lea & Febiger.
Organ, James A. A Manual for the Biology of the Vertebrates. (Illus.). 1977. lab manual 8.95 (ISBN 0-89529-009-X). Avery Pub.
Panchen, A. L., ed. The Terrestrial Environment & the Origin of Land Vertebrates. LC 80-40225. 1981. 96.00 (ISBN 0-12-544780-9). Acad Pr.
Pearson, Ronald & Ball, John N. Lecture Notes on Vertebrate Zoology. LC 80-29672. 225p. 1981. pap. 28.95x (ISBN 0-470-27143-4). Halsted Pr.
Randall, D. J., et al. The Evolution of Air Breathing in Vertebrates. LC 80-462. (Illus.). 176p. 1981. 34.50 (ISBN 0-521-22259-1). Cambridge U Pr.
Reichenbach-Klinke, H. & Elkan, E. Principal Diseases of Lower Vertebrates. Incl. Book 1. Diseases of Fishes. (Illus.). pap. 19.95 (ISBN 0-87666-042-1, PS-205); Book 2. Diseases of Amphibians. pap. 19.95 (ISBN 0-87666-044-8, PS-206); Book 3. Diseases of Reptiles. o. p. 19.95 (ISBN 0-87666-045-6, PS-207). 1972. pap. TFH Pubns.
Romer, Alfred S. & Parsons, Thomas S. The Vertebrate Body. 6th ed. (Illus.). 1986. text ed. 38.95 (ISBN 0-03-058446-9, CBS C). SCP.
--The Vertebrate Body: Shorter Version. 5th ed. LC 77-11353. (Illus.). 1978. text ed. 34.95 (ISBN 0-7216-7682-0, CBS C). SCP.
Rugh, Roberts. A Guide to Vertebrate Development. 7th ed. 1977. pap. 15.95x spiral bdg. (ISBN 0-8087-1849-5). Burgess.
Sandri, C., et al, eds. Membrane Morphology of the Vertebrate Nervous System: A Study with Freeze-Etch Technique. 2nd, rev. ed. (Progress in Brain Research Ser.: Vol. 46). 1982. 83.00 (ISBN 0-444-80393-9, Biomedical Pr). Elsevier.
Saunders, Jeffrey J. Late Pleistocene Vertebrates of the Western Ozark Highland, Missouri. (Reports of Investigations Ser.: No. 33). (Illus.). 118p. 1977. pap. 3.50 (ISBN 0-89792-066-X). Ill St Museum.
Schafer, Jr. & Walker, eds. Vertebrate Pest Control & Management Materials: Third Conference - STP 752. 206p. 1981. 23.00 (ISBN 0-8031-0760-9, 04-752000-48). ASTM.
Schmalhausen, Ivan I. Origin of Terrestrial Vertebrates. Kelso, Leon, tr. 1968. 66.00 (ISBN 0-12-625750-7). Acad Pr.
Seigel, Richard A., et al, eds. Vertebrate Ecology & Systematics: A Tribute to Henry S. Fitch. (Special Publications Ser.: No. 10). (Illus.). 278p. (Orig.). 1984. pap. 30.00 (ISBN 0-89338-019-9). U of KS Mus Nat Hist.
Selander, Robert K., et al. Vertebrates from the Barrier Islands of Tamaulipas, Mexico. (Museum Ser.: Vol. 12, No. 7). 37p. 1962. pap. 2.00 (ISBN 0-686-79809-0). U of KS Mus Nat Hist.
Selley, L. J. & Beamish, F. W. H., eds. The Cyclostomata: An Annotated Bibliography. 1977. lib. bdg. 131.50 (ISBN 90-6193-562-8, Pub. by Junk Pubs Netherlands). Kluwer Academic.

DED Vibrations Conference 1975, Washington, D. C. Vibration Testing--Instrumentation & Data Analysis: Presented at ASME/DED Vibrations Conference, Washington, D. C. Magrab, Edward B. & Shinaishin, Osman A., eds. LC 75-8349. (American Society of Mechanical Engineers Series - Applied Mechanics Division: Vol. 12). (Illus.). pap. 37.00 (ISBN 0-317-09976-0, 2015395). Bks Demand UMI.

Dimarogonas, Andrew D. Vibration Engineering. LC 75-38518. (Illus.). 565p. 1976. text ed. 37.95 (ISBN 0-8299-0035-7). West Pub.

Dinca, F. & Teodosiu, C. Nonlinear & Random Vibrations. (Eng.). 1974. 76.50 (ISBN 0-12-216750-3). Acad Pr.

Durig, J. R., ed. Vibrational Spectra & Structure: A Series of Advances, Vol. 11. 362p. 1982. 117.00 (ISBN 0-444-42103-3, I-262-82). Elsevier.

Evan-Wanowski, R. Resonance Oscillations in Mechanical Systems. 1976. 68.00 (ISBN 0-444-41474-6). Elsevier.

Ferraro, John. Vibrational Spectroscopy at High External Pressures: The Diamond Anvil Cell (Monograph) LC 83-22355. 1984. 59.00 (ISBN 0-12-254160-X). Acad Pr.

French, A. P. Vibrations & Waves. (M.I.T. Introductory Physics Ser). (Illus.). 1971. pap. text ed. 9.95x (ISBN 0-393-09936-9). Norton.

Gibbs, H. G. & Richards, T. H., eds. Stress, Vibration & Noise Analysis in Vehicles. (Illus.). 485p. 1975. 68.50 (ISBN 0-85334-642-9, Pub. by Elsevier Applied Sci England). Elsevier.

Gough, W. & Richards, J. P. Vibrations & Waves. 278p. 1983. 64.95 (ISBN 0-470-27446-8). Halsted Pr.

Gould, Sydney H. Variational Methods for Eigenvalue Problems: An Introduction to the Weinstein Method of Intermediate Problems. 2nd ed. LC 66-76289. (Mathematical Expositions Ser.). 1966. 27.50x (ISBN 0-8020-1404-6). U of Toronto Pr.

Gumenskii, B. M. & Komarov, N. S. Soil Drilling by Vibration. LC 61-12724. 80p. 1961. 29.50x (ISBN 0-306-10604-3, Consultants). Plenum Pub.

Gutman, I. Industrial Uses of Mechanical Vibrations. (Illus.). 332p. 1968. 20.00x (ISBN 0-8464-1110-5). Beekman Pubs.

Haberman, R. Mathematical Models: Mechanical Vibrations, Population, Dynamics & Traffic Flow, An Introduction to Applied Mathematics. 1977. 39.95 (ISBN 0-13-561738-3). P-H.

Harker, Ralph J. Generalized Methods of Vibration Analysis. LC 82-17440. 435p. 1983. 52.50 (ISBN 0-471-86735-7, Pub. by Wiley Interscience). Wiley.

Harris, Cyril M. & Crede, Charles E. Shock & Vibration Control Handbook. 2nd ed. 1976. 63.00 (ISBN 0-07-026799-5). McGraw.

Hartog, Den J., ed. Mechanical Vibrations. (Civil, Mechanical & Other Engineering Ser.). 436p. 1985. pap. 8.95 (ISBN 0-486-64785-4). Dover.

Hohenemser, Kurt. Elastokinetik. LC 50-2567. (Ger). 9.95 (ISBN 0-8284-0055-5). Chelsea Pub.

Hussey, Martin. Fundamentals of Mechanical Vibration. 296p. 1984. pap. text ed. 14.95 (ISBN 0-02-949100-2). Macmillan.

Hutton, David V. Applied Mechanical Vibrations. (Mechanical Engineering Ser.). (Illus.). 416p. 1980. text ed. 40.00x (ISBN 0-07-031549-3). McGraw.

Iremonger, M. J. & Smith, P. D., eds. Basic Mechanical Vibrations. (Illus.). 128p. 1985. pap. text ed. 15.95 (ISBN 0-408-01554-3). Butterworth.

IUTAM-IAHR Symposium Karlsruhe, Germany, Aug 14-16, 1972. Flow-Induced Structural Vibrations: Proceedings. Naudascher, E., ed. (Illus.). 700p. 1974. 111.00 (ISBN 0-387-06317-X). Springer-Verlag.

Jackson, Charles. The Practical Vibration Primer. LC 79-50249. (Illus.). 120p. 1979. 29.95x (ISBN 0-87201-891-1). Gulf Pub.

Jones, R. S. Noise & Vibration Control in Buildings. 448p. 1984. 44.95 (ISBN 0-07-006431-8). McGraw.

Kushul', Mikhail Y. Self-Induced Oscillations of Rotors. LC 64-19440. 124p. 1964. 32.50x (ISBN 0-306-10693-0, Consultants); 32.50 (ISBN 0-686-66517-1). Plenum Pub.

Lalanne, Michael, et al. Mechanical Vibrations for Engineers. 266p. 1983. 17.95x (ISBN 0-471-90197-0, Pub. by Wiley-Interscience). Wiley.

Leet, Lewis D. Vibrations from Blasting Rock. LC 60-10037. Repr. of 1960 ed. 37.50 (ISBN 0-8357-9183-1, 2017747). Bks Demand UMI.

McCallion, H. Vibration of Linear Mechanical Systems. LC 73-181235. pap. 79.00 (ISBN 0-317-11053-5, 2006380). Bks Demand UMI.

Mac Duff, J. N. & Malone, William F. Vibration Control. 2nd ed. 1984. cancelled (ISBN 0-89874-030-4). Krieger.

Makhult, Mihaly. Machine Support Design Based on Vibration Calculus. Meszner, Seebestyen, tr. from Ger. & Hungarian. (Illus.). 136p. 1977. text ed. 39.50x (ISBN 0-569-08228-5, Pub. by Collets England). Scholium Intl.

Marguerre, K. Mechanics of Vibrations. Wolfel, H., ed. (Mechanics of Structural Systems Ser.: No. 2). 282p. 1979. 30.00x (ISBN 90-286-0086-8). Sijthoff & Noordhoff.

Meirovitch, L. Elements of Vibration Analysis. 2nd ed. 624p. 1986. text ed. price not set (ISBN 0-07-041342-8). McGraw.

Meirovitch, Leonard. Analytical Methods in Vibrations. 1967. write for info. (ISBN 0-02-380140-9). Macmillan.

--Elements of Vibration Analysis. (Illus.). 480p. 1975. text ed. 45.00 (ISBN 0-07-041340-1). McGraw.

Merchant, H. C. & Geers, T. L., eds. Productive Applications of Mechanical Vibrations. (AMD Ser.: Vol. 52). 1982. 30.00 (H00238). ASME.

Morrow, Charles T. Shock & Vibration Engineering. LC 63-7556. pap. 101.00 (ISBN 0-317-08532-8, 2011956). Bks Demand UMI.

Mueller, P. C. & Schiehlen, W. O. Forced Linear Vibrations. (CISM-International Center for Mechanical Sciences Courses & Lectures Ser.: Vol. 172). (Illus.). 1977. pap. 21.30 (ISBN 0-387-81487-6). Springer-Verlag.

Nashif, Ahid & Jones, David I G. Vibration Damping. LC 84-17247. 416p. 1985. 51.50x (ISBN 0-471-86772-1, Pub. by Wiley-Interscience). Wiley.

National Congress on Pressure Vessel & Piping (3rd: 1979: San Francisco) Flow Induced Vibrations: Presented at the Third National Congress on Pressure Vessel & Piping Technology, San Francisco, CA, June 25-29, 1979. Chen, Shoei-Sheng & Bernstein, Martin D., eds. LC 79-50128. pap. 39.50 (ISBN 0-317-08572-7, 2021116). Bks Demand UMI.

Natke, H. G., ed. Identification of Vibrating Structures. (CISM - International Centre for Mechanical Sciences Courses & Lectures Ser.: Vol. 272). (Illus.). 510p. 1982. pap. 36.90 (ISBN 0-387-81651-8). Springer-Verlag.

Nigam, N. C. Introduction to Random Vibrations, Vol. I. Irvine, ed. (Structural Mechanics Ser.). (Illus.). 360p. 1983. text ed. 37.50x (ISBN 0-262-14035-7). MIT Pr.

Noise & Vibration Data. 120p. 1982. 55.00x (ISBN 0-85461-058-8, Pub. by Trade & Tech). State Mutual Bk.

Norkin, S. B. Differential Equations of the Second Order with Retarded Argument: Some Problems of the Theory of Vibrations of Systems with Retardation. LC 70-37627. (Translations of Mathematical Monographs,: Vol. 31). 1972. 39.00 (ISBN 0-8218-1581-4, MMONO-31). Am Math.

Pain, H. J. Physics of Vibrations & Waves. 3rd ed. LC 83-5880. 350p. 1983. 44.95x (ISBN 0-471-90181-4, Pub. by Wiley-Interscience); pap. 18.95x (ISBN 0-471-90182-2). Wiley.

Pippard, Brian. The Physics of Vibration, Vol. 1. LC 77-85685. (Illus.). 1978. 95.00 (ISBN 0-521-21899-3). Cambridge U Pr.

--The Physics of Vibration: The Simple Vibrator in Quantum Mechanics, Vol. 2. LC 77-85685. (Illus.). 200p. 1983. 42.50 (ISBN 0-521-24623-7). Cambridge U Pr.

Rebane, K. K. Impurity Spectra of Solids: Elementary Theory of Vibrational Structure. LC 69-12540. 253p. 1970. 35.00x (ISBN 0-306-30416-3, Plenum Pr). Plenum Pub.

Richart, F. E., Jr., et al. Vibrations of Soils & Foundations. (Civil Engineering Ser). 1970. ref. ed. 39.95 (ISBN 0-13-941716-8). P-H.

Roach, G. F. Vibration Theory. 250p. 1982. 60.00x (ISBN 0-906812-12-7, Pub. by Shiva Pub England); pap. 40.00x (ISBN 0-906812-11-9). State Mutual Bk.

Rocard, Y. General Dynamics of Vibrations. 1960. 27.50 (ISBN 0-8044-4838-8). Ungar.

San Diego State University Staff & Rao, S. S. Mechanical Vibrations. 1985. text ed. write for info. (ISBN 0-201-06550-9). Addison Wesley.

Sanchez-Palencia, E. Non-Homogeneous Media & Vibration Theory. (Lecture Notes in Physics Ser.: Vol. 127). 398p. 1980. pap. 28.00 (ISBN 0-387-10000-8). Springer-Verlag.

Schmidt, Gunter & Tondl, Ales. Non-Linear Vibrations. 400p. Date not set. price not set (ISBN 0-521-26698-X). Cambridge U Pr.

Seto, William W. Mechanical Vibrations. (Orig.). 1964. pap. 8.95 (ISBN 0-07-056327-6). McGraw.

Skudrzyk, Eugen. Simple & Complex Vibratory Systems. LC 66-18222. (Illus.). 1968. 36.75x (ISBN 0-271-73127-3). Pa St U Pr.

Steidel, Robert F. An Introduction to Mechanical Vibrations. 2nd rev. ed. 400p. 1980. 42.45 (ISBN 0-471-08483-2). Wiley.

Szymkowiak, Edward. Optimized Vibration Testing & Analysis. LC 62-38584. 107p. 1983. pap. text ed. 25.00 (ISBN 0-915414-70-8). Inst Environ Sci.

Szymkowiak, Edward A., ed. Tutorial: Mil-Std-810D Dynamic Environments - Guidelines to Implementation. 160p. 1985. 30.00 (ISBN 0-915414-80-5). Inst Environ Sci.

Taylor, W. & Pelmear, P. L., eds. Vibration White Finger in Industry. 1975. 36.00 (ISBN 0-12-684550-6). Acad Pr.

Tempest, W., ed. Infrasound & Low Frequency Vibration. 1977. 66.00 (ISBN 0-12-685450-5). Acad Pr.

Thomson, William. Theory of Vibrations with Applications. 2nd ed. (Illus.). 608p. 1981. text ed. 39.95 (ISBN 0-13-914523-0). P-H.

Tiersten, H. F. Linear Piezoelectric Plate Vibrations: Elements of the Linear Theory of Piezoelectricity & the Vibrations of Piezoelectric Plates. LC 69-14562. (Illus.). 212p. 1969. 39.50x (ISBN 0-306-30376-0, Plenum Pr). Plenum Pub.

Timoshenko, S., et al. Vibration Problems in Engineering. 4th ed. LC 74-6191. 521p. 1974. text ed. 47.00x (ISBN 0-471-87315-2). Wiley.

Trade & Technical Press Editors. Handbook of Noise & Vibration Control. 4th ed. 850p. 1982. Repr. of 1979 ed. 110.00 (ISBN 0-85461-073-1, Pub by Trade & Tech England). Brookfield Pub Co.

--Noise & Vibration Data. 120p. 1976. 19.00x (ISBN 0-85461-058-8, Pub by Trade & Tech England). Brookfield Pub Co.

Tse, Francis S., et al. Mechanical Vibrations: Theory & Applications. 2nd ed. 1978. text ed. 42.89 (ISBN 0-205-05940-6, 3259404); sol. man. free avail. (ISBN 0-205-05941-4, 3259412). Allyn.

Tustin, Wayne. Aerospace Vibration Testing, Measurement, Analysis & Calibration. Date not set. price not set. Tustin Inst.

--Calibration of Vibration Transducers. 1965. text ed. write for info. Tustin Inst.

--Industrial Vibration, Measurement, Analysis & Testing. Date not set. price not set. Tustin Inst.

Vehicle Noise & Vibration. 1984. 56.00 (MEP198). Soc Auto Engineers.

Vernon, J. B. Linear Vibration & Control System Theory with Computer Applications. LC 67-13530. 281p. 1967. text ed. 19.50 (ISBN 0-471-90651-4, Pub. by Wiley). Krieger.

--Linear Vibration Theory: Generalized Properties & Numerical Methods, Vol. 1. LC 66-26760. 365p. 1967. text ed. 26.00 (ISBN 0-471-90660-3, Pub. by Wiley). Krieger.

Vernon, James B. Linear Vibration Theory: Generalized Properties & Numerical Methods. pap. 95.30 (ISBN 0-317-09206-5, 2007405). Bks Demand UMI.

Vierck, Robert K. Vibration Analysis. 2nd ed. 1979. text ed. 36.50 scp (ISBN 0-7002-2525-0, HarpC). Har-Row.

Wallace, R. H. Understanding & Measuring Vibrations. LC 78-135386. (Wykeham Technology Ser.: No. 4). 148p. 1970. 9.95x (ISBN 0-8448-1125-4). Crane Russak Co.

--Understanding & Measuring Vibrations. (Wykeham Science Ser.: No. 4). 148p. 1970. pap. cancelled (ISBN 0-85109-180-6). Taylor & Francis.

Walshaw, A. C. Mechanical Vibrations with Applications. (Mechanical Engineering Ser.). 197p. 1984. 34.95 (ISBN 0-470-20115-0). Halsted Pr.

White, R. G., et al. Noise & Vibration. 866p. 1983. 124.95x (ISBN 0-470-27553-7). Halsted Pr.

Wilson, W. Ker. Vibration Engineering. 292p. 1959. 65.00x (ISBN 0-85264-023-4, Pub. by Griffin England). State Mutual Bk.

VIBRATION–PHYSIOLOGICAL EFFECT

Bianchi, G., et al, eds. Man under Vibration: Suffering & Protection. (Studies in Environmental Science: Vol. 13). 438p. 1982. 83.00 (ISBN 0-444-99743-1). Elsevier.

Taylor, W., ed. The Vibration Syndrome. 1974. 45.00 (ISBN 0-12-684760-6). Acad Pr.

VIBRATION (AERONAUTICS)

Surface Noise & Vibration Conference Proceedings. 1985. 40.00 (P161). Soc Auto Engineers.

VIBRATIONAL SPECTRA

see also Molecular Spectra

Atkinson, George H., ed. Time-Resolved Vibrational Spectroscopy (Symposium) LC 83-9928. 1983. pap. 47.50 (ISBN 0-12-066280-9). Acad Pr.

Bratos, S. & Pick, R. M., eds. Vibrational Spectroscopy of Molecular Liquids & Solids. LC 80-12174. (NATO ASI Series B, Physics: Vol. 56). 475p. 1980. 69.50x (ISBN 0-306-40445-1, Plenum Pr). Plenum Pub.

Durig, J. R., ed. Vibrational Spectra & Structure: A Series of Advances, Vol. 9. 520p. 1981. 130.00 (ISBN 0-444-41943-8). Elsevier.

--Vibrational Spectra & Structure: A Series of Advances, Vol. 10. 498p. 1981. 129.75 (ISBN 0-686-80642-5). Elsevier.

--Vibrational Spectra & Structure: A Series of Advances, Vol. 11. 362p. 1982. 117.00 (ISBN 0-444-42103-3, I-262-82). Elsevier.

--Vibrational Spectra & Structure: A Series of Advances, Vol. 13. 460p. 1984. 115.00 (ISBN 0-444-42394-X). Elsevier.

Durig, James R., ed. Vibrational Spectra & Structure, Vol. 1. pap. 52.00 (ISBN 0-317-08365-1, 2055083). Bks Demand UMI.

--Vibrational Spectra & Structure: A Series of Advances, Vol. 2. 300p. 1975. 85.00 (ISBN 0-8247-6193-6). Dekker.

--Vibrational Spectra & Structure: A Series of Advances, Vol. 3. 344p. 1975. 85.00 (ISBN 0-8247-6220-7). Dekker.

--Vibrational Spectra & Structure: A Series of Advances, Vols. 4-7. 1981. Vol. 4. 81.00 (ISBN 0-444-41437-1); Vol. 5. 81.00 (ISBN 0-444-41437-1); Vol. 7. 93.75 (ISBN 0-444-41707-9). Elsevier.

Hallam, H. E., ed. Vibrational Spectroscopy of Trapped Species: Infrared & Raman Studies of Matrix-Isolated Molecules, Radicals & Ions. LC 72-8601. 430p. 1973. 114.95x (ISBN 0-471-34330-7, Pub. by Wiley-Interscience). Wiley.

Hallam, Harry E., ed. Vibrational Spectroscopy of Trapped Species: Infrared & Raman Studies of Matrix-Isolated Molecules, Radicals & Ions. LC 72-8601. pap. 110.50 (ISBN 0-317-26652-7, 2024035). Bks Demand UMI.

Harris, Daniel C. & Bertolucci, Michael D. Symmetry & Spectroscopy: An Introduction to Vibrational & Electronic Spectroscopy. (Illus.). 1978. 18.95x (ISBN 0-19-855152-5). Oxford U Pr.

Jones, L. H. Inorganic Vibrational Spectroscopy, Vol. 1. LC 72-146803. pap. 58.00 (ISBN 0-8357-9083-5, 2055078). Bks Demand UMI.

Lazarev, A. N. Vibrational Spectra & Structure of Silicates. LC 70-136984. 239p. 1972. 42.50x (ISBN 0-306-10856-9, Consultants). Plenum Pub.

Maslowsky, Edward. Vibrational Spectra of Organometallic Compounds. LC 76-18694. (Illus.). pap. 103.00 (ISBN 0-317-09212-X, 2013117). Bks Demand UMI.

Person. Vibrational Intensities in Infrared & Raman Spectroscopy. (Studies in Physical & Theoretical Chemistry: Vol. 20). 466p. 1982. 95.75 (ISBN 0-444-42115-7). Elsevier.

Schutte, C. J. The Theory of Molecular Spectroscopy - Vol. 1: The Quantum Mechanics & Group Theory of Vibrating & Rotating Molecules. 512p. 1976. 106.50 (ISBN 0-7204-0291-3, North-Holland). Elsevier.

Turrell, G. Infrared & Raman Spectra of Crystals. 1972. 66.00 (ISBN 0-12-705050-7). Acad Pr.

Woodward, L. A. Introduction to the Theory of Molecular Vibrations & Vibrational Spectroscopy. (Illus.). 1972. 59.00x (ISBN 0-19-855352-8). Oxford U Pr.

VIBRATORS

Skudrzyk, Eugen. Simple & Complex Vibratory Systems. LC 66-18222. (Illus.). 1968. 36.75x (ISBN 0-271-73127-3). Pa St U Pr.

VIBRATORY COMPACTING

Hausner, Henry H., et al, eds. Vibratory Compacting: Principles & Methods. LC 65-24898. (Perspectives in Powder Metallurgy Series: Fundamentals, Methods & Applications: Vol. 2). (Illus.). pap. 78.00 (ISBN 0-317-08350-3, 2019458). Bks Demand UMI.

Pilkey, W. D. & Cohen, R., eds. System Identification of Vibrating Structures: Mathematical Models from Test Data Presented at 1972 Winter Annual Meeting of the American Society of Mechanical Engineers. LC 72-92594. (Illus.). pap. 51.50 (ISBN 0-317-08340-6, 2019473). Bks Demand UMI.

VIC-20 (COMPUTER)

Adler, Howard. Commodore 64 & VIC-20 Computer Programs for Beginners. 96p. 1983. 8.95 (ISBN 0-86668-033-0). ARCsoft.

--One Hundred One Programming Tips & Tricks for the VIC-20 & Commodore 64. 128p. 1983. 8.95 (ISBN 0-86668-030-6). ARCsoft.

--Thirty-Four VIC-20 Computer Programs for Home, School & Office. 96p. 1983. 8.95 (ISBN 0-86668-029-2). Arcsoft.

--VIC-20 & Commodore 64 Computer Program Writing Workbook. 96p. 1983. 4.95 (ISBN 0-86668-811-0). ARCsoft.

Banse, Timothy P. Home Applications & Games for the VIC-20 Personal Computer. (Microcomputer Bookshelf Ser.). 170p. (Orig.). 1984. pap. 9.95 (ISBN 0-316-08046-2). Little.

Barrett, Terry P. & Jones, Antonia J. Winning Games on the VIC-20. (Recreational Computing Ser.: No. 1-704). 143p. (Orig.). 1983. pap. 12.95 (ISBN 0-471-80601-3, 1-704, Pub. by Wiley Pr). Wiley.

Blackadar, Thomas. The Best of VIC-20 Software. LC 83-51188. (Illus.). 173p. (Orig.). 1984. pap. 7.95 (ISBN 0-89588-139-X). SYBEX.

Brannon, Charles. SpeedScript: The Word Processor for the Commodore 64 & VIC-20. Compute Editors, ed. 160p. (Orig.). 1985. pap. 9.95 (ISBN 0-942386-94-9). Compute Pubns.

Burns. VIC-20: Fifty Easy-to-Run Computer Games. 1984. write for info. (ISBN 0-672-22288-4). Sams.

Burns, Edward. VIC-20: Fifty Easy-to-Run Computer Games. LC 83-50375. 128p. 1983. pap. 5.95 (ISBN 0-672-22188-8, 22188); incl. tape 12.95 (ISBN 0-672-26170-7, 26170). Sams.

Busch, David. BASIC Games for Your VIC-20 Computer. 9.95 (ISBN 0-89303-910-1). Brady Comm.

--VIC-20 Games, Graphics, & Applications. LC 83-50374. 136p. 1983. pap. text ed. 8.95 (ISBN 0-672-22189-6, 22189); incl. tape 15.95 (ISBN 0-672-26167-7, 26167). Sams.

--VIC-20 Subroutine Cookbook. (Illus.). 208p. pap. cancelled (ISBN 0-89303-931-4). Brady Comm.

Camp, Robert. Creating Arcade Games on the VIC. 185p. 1984. pap. 12.95 (ISBN 0-942386-25-6). Compute Pubns.

Carter, L. R. & Huzan, E. Learn Computer Programming with the Commodore VIC-20. 1983. pap. 5.95 (ISBN 0-679-10537-9). Mckay.

Church, Norm & Schneider, Bruce. KeepTrack Reporter. 100p. 1984. Commodore 64 or VIC 20. pap. 9.95 (ISBN 0-88056-142-4); Commodore 64 or VIC 20. incl. cassette 39.95 (ISBN 0-88056-197-1); incl. disk 39.95 (ISBN 0-88056-196-3). Dilithium Pr.

Coffron, James W. The VIC-20 Connection. LC 83-50227. (Illus.). 273p. 1983. pap. 9.95 (ISBN 0-89588-128-4). SYBEX.

Commodore Computer. VIC-20 Programming Reference Guide. 304p. 1982. 16.95 (ISBN 0-672-21948-4, 21948). Sams.

Compute! Magazine Staff. Compute's First Book of VIC. (Illus.). 212p. (Orig.). 1982. pap. 12.95 (ISBN 0-942386-07-8). Compute Pubns.

--Compute's First Book of VIC Games. 201p. 1983. 12.95 (ISBN 0-942386-13-2). Compute Pubns.

--Compute's Third Book of VIC. 244p. (Orig.). 1984. pap. 12.95 (ISBN 0-942386-43-4). Compute Pubns.

Compute! Magazine Staff, ed. Compute's Second Book of VIC Games. 2nd ed. (Orig.). 1984. pap. 12.95 (ISBN 0-942386-57-4). Compute Pubns.

Compute Publications Staff, ed. Compute's VIC-20 Collection. (Orig.). 1985. pap. 12.95 (ISBN 0-87455-007-6). Compute Pubns.

Consumer Guide Editors. The User's Guide to Commodore 64 & VIC-20 Computers, Software & Peripherals. 80p. pap. 4.98 (ISBN 0-318-02641-4). Pubns Intl Ltd.

Davies, G. Russ. Mapping the VIC. 386p. (Orig.). 1984. pap. 14.95 (ISBN 0-942386-24-8). Compute Pubns.

Downey, James, et al. Easy Interfacing Projects for the VIC-20. 160p. 1984. 19.95 (ISBN 0-13-223439-4); pap. 12.95 (ISBN 0-13-223421-1). P-H.

Dusthimer, David & Buehholz, Ted. VIC-20. LC 83-51669. (Tool Kit Ser.). 8.95 (ISBN 0-672-22310-4). Sams.

Fabbri, Tony. Animation, Games, & Sound for the VIC-20. (Personal Computing Ser.). (Illus.). 224p. 1984. pap. 15.95 (ISBN 0-13-037342-7); incl. disk 29.95 (ISBN 0-13-037334-6). P-H.

Fichter, Harold. VIC-20: Easy Guide to Home Applications. LC 83-51182. 208p. 1984. pap. 8.95 (ISBN 0-672-22224-8, 22224). Sams.

Fulgham, Barbara. Fifty Simple Ready-to-Run VIC-20 Programs. (Illus.). 176p. (Orig.). 1984. 12.95 (ISBN 0-8306-0754-4); pap. 6.95 (ISBN 0-8306-1754-X, 1754). TAB Bks.

Gardner, David A. & Gardner, Marianne L. VIC-20 BASIC Made Easy. (Illus.). 256p. 1984. text ed. 19.95 (ISBN 0-13-941980-2); pap. text ed. 14.95 (ISBN 0-13-941972-1). P-H.

Geere, Ron. Learning to Use the VIC-20 Computer. (Learning to Use Computer Series, A Gower Read-Out Publication). 86p. (Orig.). 1982. pap. text ed. 12.00x (ISBN 0-566-03453-0). Gower Pub Co.

Georgiou, V. J. VIC-20 Interfacing Blue Book. (Illus.). 104p. 1983. pap. 14.95 (ISBN 0-912911-00-X). Microsignal.

Glazer, Amihai. Managing Money with Your VIC-20. LC 84-18233. (P-H Personal Computing Ser.). (Illus.). 180p. 1985. pap. text ed. 13.95 (ISBN 0-13-550682-4). P-H.

Hampshire, Nick. VIC Games. 1983. 192 pp 12.95 (ISBN 0-317-02349-7, 1060); 1 cassette & documentation 192 pp 29.95 (7501). Hayden.

--VIC Graphics. pap. 13.95 187 pp (ISBN 0-317-01210-X, 1057); 1 cassette & documentation 256 pp 29.95 (7500). Hayden.

--VIC Revealed. 1983. pap. 14.95 (ISBN 0-317-00360-7). Hayden.

Hartnell, Tim. Getting Acquainted with Your VIC-20. 132p. 1981. pap. 9.95 (ISBN 0-916688-28-3, 15R). Creative Comp.

Hartnell, Tim & Ramshaw, Mark. Zap! Pow! Boom! Arcade Games for the VIC-20. 1983. text ed. 17.95 (ISBN 0-8359-9539-9); pap. text ed. 12.95 (ISBN 0-8359-9538-0). Reston.

Haskell, Richard & Windeknecht, Thomas. Commodore 64 & VIC-20 BASIC. (Illus.). 200p. 1984. pap. 14.95 (ISBN 0-13-152281-7). P-H.

Haviland, Robert P. Computer Companion for the VIC-20. 128p. 1983. pap. 10.25 (ISBN 0-8306-0613-0, 1613). TAB Bks.

Heeb, Dan. Compute'S VIC-20 & Commodore 64 Tool Kit: Kernal. Compute Editors, ed. (Orig.). 1985. 16.95 (ISBN 0-942386-33-7). Compute Pubns.

--Compute's VIC-20 & Commodore 64 Tool Kit: BASIC. 16.95 (ISBN 0-942386-32-9). Compute Pubns.

Heil, John A. & Martin, Jack. VIC-20: The Affordable Learning Tool for the Mature Adult. (Illus.). 208p. 1983. pap. 14.95 (ISBN 0-88693-001-4). Banbury Bks.

Heilborn, John & Talbott, Ran. VIC-20 User Guide. 388p. (Orig.). 1983. pap. 15.95 (ISBN 0-07-047854-6, 54-6). Osborne-McGraw.

Held, Gilbert. VIC-20 BASIC: Quick Reference Guide. 1983. pap. 2.95 (ISBN 0-471-88238-0); pap. 29.50 prepack of 10 (ISBN 0-471-88248-8). Wiley.

Hergert, Douglas. The Commodore 64-VIC-20 BASIC Handbook. LC 83-50718. (Illus.). 185p. 1983. pap. 14.95 (ISBN 0-89588-116-0). SYBEX.

Herriott, John. Mastering the VIC-20. 224p. 1983. pap. 10.25 (ISBN 0-8306-1612-8, 1612). TAB Bks.

--Using & Programming the VIC-20, Including Ready-to-Run Programs. 192p. (Orig.). 1984. 15.95 (ISBN 0-8306-0702-1, 1702); pap. 10.25 (ISBN 0-8306-1702-7). TAB Bks.

Jones, Antonia J. & Coley, Elizabeth A. Mastering the VIC-20. LC 82-24724. 200p. 1983. 19.95 (ISBN 0-471-88893-1, Pub by Wiley Pr); pap. 14.95 (ISBN 0-471-88892-3); cassette o.p. 19.95 (ISBN 0-471-88852-4); cassette set 34.90 (ISBN 0-471-88853-2); disk 19.95 (ISBN 0-471-88909-1); disk set 34.95 (ISBN 0-471-88851-6). Wiley.

Kahn, Donald, Jr. & Scrimshaw, Nevin B. Discover Your VIC-20: A Beginner's Guide to Real Programming. 120p. 1984. pap. 10.95 (ISBN 0-8176-3160-7); incl. cassette 29.95 (ISBN 0-8176-3177-1). Birkhauser.

Librach, Hank. Getting the Most from Your VIC-20. 136p. 1984. pap. 9.95 (ISBN 0-13-354357-9). P-H.

Ludinski, G. Brainteasers for the VIC-20. 144p. 1984. pap. 12.95 (ISBN 0-946576-12-2, Pub. by Phoenix Pub). David & Charles.

McEvoy, Seth. Create-a-Game for Your VIC-20. (Orig.). pap. cancelled (ISBN 0-440-51624-2, Dell Trade Pbks). Dell.

Maurer, W. Douglas. Commodore Vic-20 Assembly Language. (Illus.). 400p. 1985. pap. text ed. 19.95 (ISBN 0-88175-003-4). Computer Sci.

Micro Staff. Mastering Your VIC-20. 192p. 1983. 19.95 (ISBN 0-88731-001-X). Computerist.

Nadler, Bob. The VIC-20 Illustrated. 176p. pap. 10.95 (6303). Hayden.

Nanos, Shirley A., et al. The VIC-20 Microcomputer. (Nanos Reference Cards Ser.). (Illus.). 18p. (Orig.). 1983. pap. 5.95 (ISBN 0-915069-15-6). Nanos Sys.

Noble, Tony. The VIC-20 for Kids of All Ages. LC 83-14567. (Illus.). 152p. 1983. pap. text ed. 10.95 (ISBN 0-471-88233-X, Pub by Wiley Pr). Wiley.

Phillips, Gary & Tierce, Roger. The Commodore VIC-20 User's Encyclopedia. Mellin, Michael F. & Ritz, Roberta, eds. 216p. (Orig.). 1983. pap. 14.95 (ISBN 0-912003-09-X). Bk Co.

Ramshaw, Clifford. VIC Innovative Computing. (Illus.). 148p. (Orig.). 14.95 (ISBN 0-86161-108-X). Melbourne Hse.

Renko, Hal & Edwards, Sam. Cosmic Games for the Commodore VIC-20. (Illus.). 192p. 1983. pap. 5.95 (ISBN 0-201-16476-0). Addison-Wesley.

Reyden, John V., ed. Vic 20 Exposed. (Illus.). 168p. (Orig.). 1983. pap. 14.95 (ISBN 0-318-03943-5). Melbourne Hse.

Roberts, Sam. Tricks for VIC's. 115p. 9.95 (ISBN 0-317-06036-8). Elcomp.

--Tricks for VICs. 1984. 9.95 (ISBN 3-88963-176-2). Blue Cat.

Rugg, Tom, et al. More Than Thirty-Two BASIC Programs for the VIC-20 Computer. LC 83-5198. (Illus.). 270p. 1983. pap. 19.95 (ISBN 0-88056-181-5); incl. cassette 39.95 (ISBN 0-88056-059-2). Dilithium Pr.

Sanders, William B. The Elementary VIC. (Elementary Ser.). (Illus.). 200p. (Orig.). 1983. pap. text ed. 14.95 (ISBN 0-88190-116-4, BO116). Datamost.

Savage, Earl R. VIC-20 Programmer's Notebook. LC 83-50494. 256p. 1983. pap. text ed. 14.95 (ISBN 0-672-22089-X, 22089). Sams.

Schnapp, Russell L. & Stafford, Irvin G. VIC-20 Computer Graphics Toolbox. (Prentice-Hall Personal Computing Ser.). (Illus.). 176p. 1984. pap. text ed. 14.95 (ISBN 0-13-941998-5); incl. cassette 29.95 (ISBN 0-13-942012-6); cassette 14.95 (ISBN 0-13-942004-5). P-H.

Second Book of VIC. 270p. 1983. 12.95 (ISBN 0-942386-16-7). Compute Pubns.

Skier, K. Top-Down Assembly Language Programming for Your VIC-20 & Commodore-64. 434p. 1983. pap. 19.95 (ISBN 0-07-057863-X, BYTE Bks). McGraw.

Smith, Alan M., ed. PCDex: Magazine Resource Guide for Commodore 64, VIC-20 & PET-CBM Personal Computers. 216p. (Orig.). 1984. pap. 14.95 (ISBN 0-918391-00-8). Altacom.

Titus, C. A. & Titus, J. A. VIC-20 Starter Book. LC 83-51224. 352p. 1984. pap. 15.95 (ISBN 0-672-22258-2, 22258). Sams.

Traister, Robert S. How to Write Picture Programs for the Commodore VIC-20. 96p. 1984. pap. 11.95 (ISBN 0-13-441536-1). P-H.

VIC-20 Exposed. 14.95 (ISBN 0-318-00658-8). Melbourne Hse.

Weber Systems, Inc. Staff. VIC-20 User's Handbook. 280p. 1984. pap. 9.95 (ISBN 0-345-31591-X). Ballantine.

Weinstock, Mike & Capella, Mark. Games VIC's Play. 1984. cancelled (ISBN 0-317-07020-7). Datamost.

West, Raeto. Programming the VIC-20. 1984. pap. 24.95 (ISBN 0-942386-52-3). Compute Pubns.

Willis, Jerry & Willis, Deborrah. How to Use the Commodore VIC-20. (Illus.). 124p. 1983. pap. 5.95 (ISBN 0-88056-134-3). Dilithium Pr.

Willis, Jerry, et al. Things to Do with Your Commodore VIC-20 Computer. pap. 3.95 (ISBN 0-451-12844-3, Sig). NAL.

WSI Staff. User's Handbook to the VIC-20. LC 83-60590. (WSI's How to Use Your Personal Computer). 280p. 1983. pap. cancelled (ISBN 0-938862-48-0). Weber Systems.

Zaks, Rodnay. Your First VIC-20 Program. LC 83-50670. (Illus.). 182p. 1983. pap. 12.95 (ISBN 0-89588-129-2). SYBEX.

VIDEO CASSETTE RECORDERS

Mandl, Matthew. Maintenance & Repair of Video Cassette Recorders. (Illus.). 304p. 1986. text ed. 24.95 (ISBN 0-13-545526-X). P-H.

Schorn, J. L. Video Magazine's Guide to Choosing & Using Your VCR. (Illus.). 208p. 1985. 9.95 (ISBN 0-07-051599-9). McGraw.

VIDEO DISCS

International Resource Development Inc. Videocassette & Videodisc Hardware & Software Markets. 167p. 1983. 1285.00x (ISBN 0-88694-579-8). Intl Res Dev.

Lenk, John D. Complete Guide to Laser-Videodisc Player Troubleshooting & Repair. rev. ed. (Illus.). 272p. 1985. text ed. 29.95 (ISBN 0-13-160813-4). P-H.

National Video Clearinghouse, Inc. The Kodak Videotape & Disc Guide to Home Entertainment. (Illus.). 725p. (Orig.). 1985. pap. 13.95 (ISBN 0-935478-27-2). Natl Video.

Schwartz, Ed. The Educators Handbook to Interactive Videodisc. 104p. (Orig.). 1985. pap. 14.95 (ISBN 0-89240-049-8); members 11.95. Assn Ed Comm Tech.

Telepay vs. Videodisc: The Exploding Pay-per-View Market. (Reports Ser.: No. 510). 281p. 1982. 985.00x (ISBN 0-88694-510-0). Intl Res Dev.

Videodisc Hardware & Software Market. 1983. 1375.00 (ISBN 0-86621-158-6). Frost & Sullivan.

Videodiscs: Markets, Technologies, Competition, Status: G-064. 1981. 900.00 (ISBN 0-89336-301-4). BCC.

VIDEO DISPLAY TERMINALS

Bishop, J. Home Video Production: Getting the Most from Your Video Equipment. (VTX Ser.). 224p. 1985. price not set (ISBN 0-07-005472-X). McGraw.

Bohm, Ronald J. & Templeton, Lee. The Executive Guide to Video Teleconferencing. 150p. 1984. text ed. 40.00 (ISBN 0-89006-148-3). Artech Hse.

Dworaczek, Marian. Health & Safety Aspects of Visual Display Terminals: A Bibliography. 2nd ed. (Public Administration Series - Bibliography: P-1421). 66p. 1984. pap. 9.75 (ISBN 0-88066-921-7). Vance Biblios.

Panel on Impact of Video Viewing on Vision of Workers, National Research Council. Video Displays, Work, & Vision. 288p. 1983. pap. 14.50 (ISBN 0-309-03388-8). Natl Acad Pr.

Pinsky, Mark, et al. Video Display Terminals: Health & Safety Update, 1983. (Excerpts from Microwave News). 29p. 1984. pap. 10.00 (ISBN 0-9610580-1-3). Microwave.

Slesin, Louis & Zybko, Martha. Video Display Terminals: Safety & Health (Excerpts from Microwave News) 84p. (Orig.). 1983. pap. 8.50 (ISBN 0-9610580-0-5). Microwave.

Stephens, David. A Programmer's Guide to Video Display Terminals. 335p. (Orig.). 1985. pap. 30.00 (ISBN 0-936158-01-8). Atlan Pub Corp.

Umbers, I. G. CRT-TV Displays in the Control of Process Plant: A Review of Applications & Human Factors Design Criteria, 1976. 1981. 30.00x (ISBN 0-686-97052-7, Pub. by W Spring England). State Mutual Bk.

VIDEO DIRECTION

see Video Recordings–Production and Direction

VIDEO GAMES

Baughman, Susan S. & Clagett, Patricia D., eds. Video Games & Human Development: A Research Agenda for the '80s. 72p. 1983. pap. 20.00 (ISBN 0-943484-01-4). Gutman Lib.

Chiu, Y. & Mullish, H. Crunchers: Twenty-One Games for the Timex-Sinclair 1000 (2k) (McGraw-Hill VTX Ser.). 144p. 1983. pap. 8.95 (ISBN 0-07-010831-5, BYTE Bks). McGraw.

Consumer Guide Editors. How to Win at Atari Computer Games. (Illus.). 64p. 1983. pap. 8.95 spiral bound cancelled (ISBN 0-671-49558-5, Fireside). S&S.

--How to Win at Donkey Kong. 32p. (Orig.). 1982. pap. 1.95 (ISBN 0-671-45840-X). PB.

--How to Win at E.T. the Video Game. 32p. 1983. pap. 2.50 (ISBN 0-440-13767-5). Dell.

--How to Win at Video Games. 1984. spiral bdg. 1.98 (ISBN 0-517-42470-3). Outlet Bk Co.

--How to Win Video Games. 96p. (Orig.). 1982. pap. 2.95 (ISBN 0-671-45841-8). PB.

Crawford, Chris. The Art of Computer Game Design: Reflections of a Master Game Designer. 120p. (Orig.). 1984. pap. 14.95 (ISBN 0-07-881117-1, 117-1). Osborne-McGraw.

David, Ed. The Intelligent Idiot's Guide to Getting the Most Out of Your Home Video Equipment. rev. ed. LC 82-13292. (Illus.). 224p. (Orig.). 1982. lib. bdg. 19.90 (ISBN 0-89471-178-4); pap. 9.95 (ISBN 0-89471-177-6). Running Pr.

DeNure, Dennis. How to Play a ValGame. (Illus.). 110p. 1984. write for info (ISBN 0-915659-02-6). Video Athlete.

--The Joystick of Thought. (Illus.). 125p. (Orig.). 1985. Repr. 9.95 (ISBN 0-915659-03-4). Video Athlete.

--The New Peace Sign. (Illus.). 125p. (Orig.). 1985. 4.95 (ISBN 0-915659-04-2). Video Athlete.

--Star Scorers of AVAA. (Illus.). 125p. 1984. 19.95 (ISBN 0-915659-01-8). Video Athlete.

Goodman, Danny. The Simon & Schuster Guide to the TRS-80 Model 100. 128p. 1984. pap. 9.95 (ISBN 0-671-49254-3, Pub. by Computer Bks). S&S.

Graham, Ian. Computers & Video Games. write for info. EDC.

Greenfield, Patricia. Mind & Media: The Effects of Television, Video Games, & Computers. (The Developing Child Ser.). (Illus.). 223p. 1984. text ed. 12.50x (ISBN 0-674-57620-9); pap. 4.95 (ISBN 0-674-57621-7). Harvard U Pr.

International Resource Development Inc. Videogames & Electronic Toys. 185p. 1983. 1285.00x (ISBN 0-88694-550-X). Intl Res Dev.

Jennings, Gordon. Repairing Your Home Video Game. (Orig.). 1983. pap. 9.95 (ISBN 0-88190-277-2, BO277). Datamost.

Kordestani, Paul. Gamester's Guide to Arcade Video Games. (Illus.). 384p. (Orig.). 1984. pap. 16.50 (ISBN 0-8306-0181-3, 1581). TAB Bks.

Loftus, Geoffrey R. & Loftus, Elizabeth F. Mind at Play: The Psychology of Video Games. LC 83-70761. (Illus.). 191p. 1983. text ed. 14.95 (ISBN 0-465-04609-6). Basic.

Prager, Emily. The Official I-Hate-Video Games Book. (Illus., Orig.). 1982. pap. 2.95 (ISBN 0-671-45804-3). PB.

Robertin, Hector & Bratton, Joseph C. Computers, Video Games & Your Child's Development. LC 83-62878. (Illus.). 120p. 1984. pap. 9.95 (ISBN 0-912921-02-1). Pau Hana Pr.

Rovin, Jeff. The Complete Guide to Conquering Video Games: How to Win Every Game in the Galaxy. Du Bay, Bill, tr. (Illus.). 407p. (Orig.). 1982. pap. 5.95 (ISBN 0-02-029970-2, Collier). Macmillan.

--The Complete Guide to Conquering Video Games: How to Win Every Game in the Galaxy. 1983. 13.25 (ISBN 0-8446-6032-9). Peter Smith.

Schwarz, Haller. More Pac-Mania. 96p. (Orig.). 1983. pap. 1.95 (ISBN 0-523-41993-7). Pinnacle Bks.

Scott, Michael D. Electronic Game Pirates: The Scramble for Viable Protection. 23p. (Orig.). 1981. pap. text ed. 10.00 (ISBN 0-910215-00-6). Law & Tech Pr.

Uston, Ken. Score! Beating the Top Sixteen Video Games. Date not set. pap. 2.50 (ISBN 0-451-11813-8, AE1813, Sig). NAL.

Video Game Books, Inc. Playing Donkey Kong to Win. 32p. 1982. pap. 2.50 (ISBN 0-346-12584-7). Cornerstone.

Zavisca, Ernest & Beltowski, Gary. Be a Home Videogame Superstar. (Illus.). 256p. pap. 1.95 (ISBN 0-8326-2262-1, 7070). Delair.

--Break a Million! at Pac-Man. (Illus.). 64p. pap. 1.00 (ISBN 0-8326-2257-5, 7066). Delair.

VIDEO PRODUCTION

see Video Recordings–Production and Direction

VIDEO RECORDINGS–DIRECTION
see Video Recordings–Production and Direction
Floyd, Steve & Floyd, Beth, eds. Handbook of Interactive Video. LC 82-12690. (Video Bookshelf Ser.). 168p. 1982. professional 34.95 (ISBN 0-86729-019-6, 505-BW). Knowledge Indus.

VIDEO RECORDINGS–PRODUCTION AND DIRECTION
Hurn, Bruce. Computer Graphics & Animation for Video. 175p. 1985. 34.95 (ISBN 0-86729-133-8, 531-BW). Knowledge Indus.

VIDEO TAPE RECORDERS AND RECORDING
Atienza, Loretta J. VTR Workshop: Small Format Video. (Monographs on Communication Technology & Utilization: No. 4). (Illus.). 114p. (2nd Printing 1979). 1977. pap. text ed. 5.00 (ISBN 92-3-101467-6, U748, UNESCO). Unipub.
Bensinger, Charles. The Video Guide. 3rd ed. LC 82-50488. 254p. 1982. 18.95 (ISBN 0-672-22051-2). Sams.
Bunyan, John A. More Practical Video. (Video Bookshelf Ser.). (Illus.). 200p. 1985. pap. 24.95 professional (ISBN 0-86729-079-X, 525-BW). Knowledge Indus.
Bunyan, John A., et al. Practical Video: The Manager's Guide to Applications. LC 78-23533. 203p. 1978. pap. 17.95 professional (ISBN 0-914236-20-2, 509-BW). Knowledge Indus.
Cartwright, Steve R. Training with Video. (Video Bookshelf Ser.). 165p. 1985. 34.50 (ISBN 0-86729-132-X). Knowledge Indus.
Clason, W. Elsevier's Dictionary of Television & Video Recording. LC 74-77577. (Eng., Ger., Fr., Span., Ital. & Dutch.). 608p. 1975. 125.75 (ISBN 0-444-41224-7). Elsevier.
Clifford, Martin. The Complete Guide to Video. LC 83-60165. 342p. 1983. pap. text ed. 15.95 (ISBN 0-672-21912-3). Sams.
Cohen, Henry B. The Home Video Book: How to Understand & Use Home Video, Home Computers & Electronic Games. (Illus.). 192p. 1983. pap. 9.95 (ISBN 0-8174-3993-5, Amphoto). Watson-Guptill.
Costello, Marjorie & Heiss, Michael. How to Select & Use Home Video Equipment. 144p. 1984. pap. 9.95 (ISBN 0-89586-209-3). H P Bks.
Cristol, A. Solid State Video Cameras. (EPO Applied Technology Ser.: Vol. 7). 250p. 1986. 62.50 (ISBN 0-08-030579-2). Pergamon.
Davidoff, Frank & Rossi, John, eds. Digital Video One. (Illus.). 114p. 1982. pap. text ed. 25.00 (ISBN 0-940690-02-0). Soc Motion Pic & TV Engrs.
Dranov, Paula, et al. Video in the 80s: Emerging Uses for Television in Business, Education, Medicine & Government. LC 80-15745. 186p. 1980. pap. 19.95 professional (ISBN 0-86729-065-X, 516-BW). Knowledge Indus.
Duton, Mark & Owen, David. The Complete Home Video Handbook. LC 82-5410. (Illus.). 1982. 19.95 (ISBN 0-394-52761-5). Random.
Efrein, Joel. Video Tape Production & Communication Techniques. LC 70-114712. (Illus.). 1970. 12.95 (ISBN 0-8306-0541-X, 541). TAB Bks.
Foss, Hannen. The Home Video Book: How to Make Your Own Home Video Programmes. 128p. 30.00x (ISBN 0-241-10572-2, Pub. by Hamish Hamilton England). State Mutual Bk.
--How to Make Your Own Video Programmes: For Family, Educational & Business Use. (Illus.). 128p. 1982. 19.95 (ISBN 0-241-10572-2, Pub. by Hamish Hamilton England). David & Charles.
Friedburg, Ardy. The Complete Video Cassette Recorder Book. 96p. (Orig.). 1984. pap. 3.95 (ISBN 0-523-42326-8). Pinnacle Bks.
Goodman, Robert L. Maintaining & Repairing Videocassette Recorders. (Illus.). 416p. 1983. 22.95 (ISBN 0-8306-0103-1); pap. 15.95 (ISBN 0-8306-1503-2, 1503). TAB Bks.
Harwood, Don. Everything You Always Wanted to Know about Portable Videotape Recording. 4th ed. LC 78-56480. (Illus.). 1983. pap. 9.95 (ISBN 0-915146-05-3, V101). VTR Pub.
--Video As a Second Language: How to Make a Video Documentary. rev. ed. LC 79-63869. (Illus.). 1979. pap. 5.50 (ISBN 0-915146-06-1, V102). VTR Pub.
Hirschman, Robert & Procter, Richard. How to Shoot to Better Video. (VideoWare Ser.). (Illus.). 128p. 1985. pap. 7.95 (Pub. by H Leonard Bks). H Leonard Pub Corp.
Holland, Daniel W., et al. Using Nonbroadcast Video in the Church. 128p. 1980. pap. 5.95 (ISBN 0-8170-0895-0). Judson.
Home Entertainment in the 1980s. (Reports Ser.: No. 511). 206p. 1982. 985.00x (ISBN 0-88694-511-9). Intl Res Dev.
Iuppa, Nicholas V. A Practical Guide to Interactive Video Design. LC 84-7872. (Video Bookshelf Ser.). 135p. 1984. professional 34.95 (ISBN 0-86729-041-2, 508-BW). Knowledge Indus.
Jolly, Brad. Videotaping Local History. LC 82-8730. (Illus.). 140p. 1982. pap. 12.95 (ISBN 0-910050-57-0). AASLH Pr.
Kennedy, M. Carlos, intro. by. Digital Video Two. (Illus.). 162p. (Orig.). 1982. pap. text ed. 25.00 (ISBN 0-940690-03-9). Soc Motion Pic & TV Engrs.
Knittel, Patricia, ed. Selected Bibliography: Videotex, Vol. I. 1983. pap. 15.00 (ISBN 0-89938-016-6). Tech & Ed Ctr Graph Arts RIT.
Knowledge Industry Publications. The Home Video Yearbook, 1982-1983. 268p. 1982. 95.00x (ISBN 0-87196-704-9). Facts on File.
Kortman, Peter J. Handbook of Video Cassette Recording. 1986. cancelled (ISBN 0-442-24855-5). Van Nos Reinhold.
Kybett, Harry. The Complete Handbook of Videocassette Recorders. 2nd ed. (Illus.). 322p. 1983. pap. 12.95 (ISBN 0-8306-1211-4, 1211). TAB Bks.
--Video Tape Recorders. 2nd ed. LC 78-51582. (Illus.). 400p. 1978. pap. 12.95 (ISBN 0-672-21521-7). Sams.
Lachenbruch, David. Video Cassette Recorders: The Complete Home Guide. LC 78-72182. (Illus.). 1979. pap. 6.95 (ISBN 0-89696-016-1, An Everest House Book). Dodd.
Lancaster, Don. Son of Cheap Video. LC 80-51714. 224p. 1980. pap. 10.95 (ISBN 0-672-21723-6, 21723); Set. 15.95 (21766). Sams.
Langman, Larry. The Video Encyclopedia. LC 83-47602. 250p. 1983. lib. bdg. 21.00 (ISBN 0-8240-9108-6). Garland Pub.
Langman, Larry & Spinelli, Paul. The Complete Video Book. 1984. pap. 3.95 (ISBN 0-8217-1332-9). Zebra.
Lanzendorf, Peter. The Video Taping Handbook: The Newest Systems, Cameras, & Techniques. LC 82-19291. (Illus.). 240p. 1983. 16.95 (ISBN 0-517-54952-2, Harmony); pap. 7.95 (ISBN 0-517-54953-0). Crown.
Lenk, John D. Complete Guide to Modern VCR Troubleshooting & Repair. (Illus.). 288p. 1985. text ed. 27.95 (ISBN 0-13-160359-0). P-H.
--Complete Guide to Videocassette Recorder Operation & Service. (Illus.). 464p. 1983. 29.95 (ISBN 0-13-160820-7). P-H.
--Complete Guide to Videocassettte Recorder Operation & Servicing. 384p. 1985. pap. 15.95 (ISBN 0-13-160854-1). P-H.
Levine, Pamela, et al. The Complete Guide to Home Video Programming. 1984. pap. 10.95 (ISBN 0-03-071082-0, Owl Bks). HR&W.
McGinty, Gerald P. Videocassette Recorders: Theory & Servicing. (Illus.). 1979. pap. text ed. 14.75 (ISBN 0-07-044988-0). McGraw.
Marcus, Richard, ed. Digital Video Three. Rev. ed. (Illus.). 230p. (Orig.). 1982. pap. text ed. 25.00 (ISBN 0-940690-04-7). Soc Motion Pic & TV Engrs.
Medoff, Norman J. & Tanquary, Tom. Portable Video: ENG & EFP. (Video Bookshelf Ser.). 175p. 1985. 34.95 (ISBN 0-86729-147-8); pap. 24.95 (ISBN 0-86729-148-6). Knowledge Indus.
Millerson, Gerald. Video Camera Techniques. (Media Manual Ser.). (Illus.). 160p. (Orig.). 1983. pap. 14.95 (ISBN 0-240-51225-1). Focal Pr.
Moss, Robin. Video: The Educational Challenge. 160p. 1983. 25.25 (ISBN 0-7099-1747-3, Pub. by Croom Helm Ltd). Longwood Pub Group.
National Video Clearinghouse, Inc. The Kodak Videotape & Disc Guide to Home Entertainment. (Illus.). 725p. (Orig.). 1985. pap. 13.95 (ISBN 0-935478-27-2). Natl Video.
Ogden, Andrew & Spence, Steve. Jungle Video: A Practical Guide to Production. (Illus.). 56p. 1979. pap. 4.95 (ISBN 0-9602756-0-6). Jungle Video.
Pasternak, Bill. Video Cassette Recorders: Buying, Using & Maintaining. (Illus.). 156p. (Orig.). 1983. 14.95 (ISBN 0-8306-0490-1); pap. 8.95 (ISBN 0-8306-1490-7, 1490). TAB Bks.
Quick, John & Wolff, Herbert. Small-Studio Video Tape Production. 2nd ed. LC 75-28730. (Illus.). 217p. 1976. text ed. 10.95 (ISBN 0-201-06291-7). Addison-Wesley.
Roberts, R. S. Dictionary of Audio, Radio & Video. 256p. 1981. 39.95 (ISBN 0-408-00339-1). Butterworth.
Robinson, J. F. & Lowe, Stephen. Videotape Recording. 3rd ed. LC 80-41244. 1981. 35.95 (ISBN 0-240-51083-6). Focal Pr.
Robinson, Joseph F. Using Videotape. 2nd ed. Beards, P. H., ed. (Media Manual Ser.). (Illus.). 195p. 1981. pap. 14.95 (ISBN 0-240-51107-7). Focal Pr.
Rosen, Frederic W. Shooting Video. 1983. pap. 10.95 (ISBN 0-240-51709-1). Focal Pr.
Sigel, Efrem, ed. Videotext: The Coming Revolution in Home-Office Information Retrieval. LC 79-18935. (Communications Library). 154p. 1980. professional 27.95 (ISBN 0-914236-41-5, 422-BW). Knowledge Indus.
Smith, Welby. Video Fundamentals. 186p. 1983. 19.95 (ISBN 0-13-941948-9); pap. 12.95 (ISBN 0-13-941930-6). P-H.
Society of Photo-Optical Instrumentation Engineers, Seminar. Military Airborne Video Recording: Requirements, Utilization, & Techniques, Proceedings, Vol. 36. Rostocki, Stanley J., ed. 238p. 1973. 9.00 (ISBN 0-89252-047-7). Photo-Optical.
Utz, Peter. The Complete Home Video Book, 2 vols, Vol. I & II. LC 82-10129. (Illus.). 608p. 1983. 29.95 set (ISBN 0-13-161364-2); Vol. 1. pap. 16.95 (ISBN 0-13-161349-9); Vol. 2. pap. 9.95 (ISBN 0-13-161356-1). P-H.
--Video User's Handbook. 2nd ed. (Illus.). 1982. text ed. 24.95 (ISBN 0-13-941880-6, Spec); pap. 14.95 (ISBN 0-13-941872-5). P-H.
Van Deusen, Richard E. Practical AV-Video Budgeting. LC 84-17079. (Video Bookshelf Ser.). (Illus.). 168p. 1984. professional 34.95 (ISBN 0-86729-100-1). Knowledge Indus.
Video. 1978. 5.00 (ISBN 0-87104-633-4, Branch Lib). NY Pub Lib.
Video Yearbook 1985. 633p. 1984. 140.00x (ISBN 0-686-97115-9, Pub. by Link House Mag England). State Mutual Bk.

VIDEO TAPES
see also Television Film
Bension, Shmuel. New York Production Manual 1979-80: The "Producer's Masterguide" for Motion Picture, Television, Commercials & Videotape Industries. LC 79-644582. 1979. pap. 35.00 (ISBN 0-935744-00-2). NY Prod Manual.
Bension, Shmuel, ed. New York Production Manual, 1981: The Producer's Masterguide for Motion Picture. Television, Commercials & Videotape Industries. 1100p. pap. 58.00 (ISBN 0-935744-01-0). NY Prod Manual.
Botein, Michael & Pearce, Alan. Videotex & Electronic Publishing: A Legal, Regulatory & Economic Analysis. 56p. (Orig.). 1982. pap. text ed. write for info. Comm Media.
Chicorel, Marietta, ed. Chicorel Index to Video Tapes & Cassettes, Vol. 27. 1978. 125.00x (ISBN 0-934598-66-5). Am Lib Pub Co.
Fuller, Barry, et al. Single-Camera Video Production Handbook: Techniques, Equipment, & Resources for Producing Quality Video Programs. (Illus.). 252p. 1982. 26.95 (ISBN 0-13-810762-9); pap. 16.95 (ISBN 0-13-810754-8). P-H.
Geddes, Marion & Sturtridge, Gill, eds. Video in the Language Classroom. (Practical Language Teaching Ser.: No. 7). (Illus.). 192p. (Orig.). 1982. pap. text ed. 9.00x (ISBN 0-435-28971-3). Heinemann Ed.
Gordon, George N. & Falk, Irving A. Videocassette Technology in American Education. LC 72-81494. 176p. 1972. 21.95 (ISBN 0-87778-035-8). Educ Tech Pubns.
Himmelstein, Harold. On the Small Screen. 224p. 1981. 13.95 (ISBN 0-03-058343-8). Praeger.
International Resource Development Inc. Videocassette & Videodisc Hardware & Software Markets. 167p. 1983. 1285.00x (ISBN 0-88694-579-8). Intl Res Dev.
Lebaron, John. Making Television: A Video Production Guide for Teachers. LC 81-703. (Orig.). 1981. pap. text ed. 18.95x (ISBN 0-8077-2636-2). Tchrs Coll.
McInnes, James. Video in Education & Training. (Illus.). 192p. 1980. 24.95 (ISBN 0-240-51071-2). Focal Pr.
McQuillin, Lon. The Video Production Guide. Bensinger, Charles, ed. (Illus.). 382p. 1983. pap. 28.95 (ISBN 0-672-22053-9). Sams.
Martin, Mick & Potter, Marsha. Video Movie Guide 1986. 256p. (Orig.). 1986. pap. 2.95 (ISBN 0-345-32766-7). Ballantine.
Panel on Impact of Video Viewing on Vision of Workers, National Research Council. Video Displays, Work, & Vision. 288p. 1983. pap. 14.50 (ISBN 0-309-03388-8). Natl Acad Pr.
Quilliam, Patti, ed. The Video Source Book--UK. 2nd ed. LC 81-642038. 500p. (Orig.). 1982. pap. 28.00 (ISBN 0-935478-12-4). Natl Video.
Rohrlick, Paula. Exploring the Arts: Films & Videotapes for Young Viewers. LC 82-9588. (Illus.). 181p. 1982. 29.95 (ISBN 0-8352-1515-6). Bowker.
Sherr, Sol. Video & Electronic Displays: A User's Guide. LC 81-21915. 352p. 1982. 37.50x (ISBN 0-471-09037-9, Pub. by Wiley-Interscience). Wiley.
The Video Age: Television Technology & Applications in the 1980s. LC 82-15177. (Video Bookshelf). 264p. 1982. professional 29.95 (ISBN 0-86729-033-1, 511-BW). Knowledge Indus.
Video Reference Guide, 1983. 128p. 35.00 (ISBN 0-318-01045-3). Orion Res.
Video Technology: Its Use & Application in Law. (Litigation & Administrative Practice Course Handbook Ser.: Vol. 252). 250p. 1984. 35.00 (ISBN 0-317-11469-7, H4-4936). PLI.

VIDEOTEX (DATA TRANSMISSION SYSTEM)
Alber, A. Videotex-Teletext: Principle & Practices. 416p. 1985. 32.95 (ISBN 0-07-000957-0). McGraw.
Aldrich, Michael. Videotex: Key to the Wired City. 144p. 1982. 29.00x (ISBN 0-907621-12-0, Pub. by Quiller Pr England). State Mutual Bk.
Arlen, Gary H. & Adler, Richard, eds. Videotex-Teleservices Directory, Nineteen Eighty-Five. 272p. (Orig.). 1985. pap. text ed. 80.00 (ISBN 0-9609768-1-7). Arlen Comm Inc.
Botein, Michael & Pearce, Alan. Videotex & Electronic Publishing: A Legal, Regulatory & Economic Analysis. 56p. (Orig.). 1982. pap. text ed. write for info. Comm Media.
Chorafas, Dimitris. Interactive Videotex. (Illus.). 300p. 1981. text ed. 21.95 (ISBN 0-89433-127-2). Petrocelli.
Collier, Harry, et al, eds. Electronic Publishing Review: The International Journal of the Transfer of Published Information via Videotex & Online Media. 1984. per year 66.00 (ISBN 0-317-00229-5). Learned Info.
Gecsei, Jan. Architecture of Videotex Systems. (Illus.). 320p. 1983. 36.95 (ISBN 0-13-044776-5). P H.
Hurly, Paul, et al. The Videotex & Teletext Handbook: Home & Office Communications Using Microcomputers & Terminals. LC 85-737. 400p. 1985. pap. text ed. 24.95 scp (ISBN 0-06-042992-5, HarpC). Har-Row.
International Resource Development Inc. Videotex vs. Audiotex: The Competition for Home Information & Transactional Services. 204p. 1983. 1285.00x (ISBN 0-88694-560-7). Intl Res Dev.
Tydeman, John & Lipinski, Hubert. Teletext & Videotex in the United States: Market Potential, Technology, & Public Policy Issues. (Illus.). 314p. 1982. 36.95 (ISBN 0-07-000427-7). McGraw.
Videotex Business Applications Market. (Reports Ser.: No. 195). 136p. 1982. 1285.00x (ISBN 0-88694-195-4). Intl Res Dev.
Videotex 'Eighty-Four U. S. A. 442p. 1984. pap. text ed. 120.00x (ISBN 0-86353-009-5, Pub. by Online). Brookfield Pub Co.
Videotex Eighty-One. 470p. 1981. 95.00x (ISBN 0-903796-91-0, Pub. by Online). Taylor & Francis.
Videotex International. 418p. 1984. pap. text ed. 140.00x (ISBN 0-86353-020-6, Pub. by Online). Brookfield Pub Co.
Weaver, David H. Videotex Journalism: Teletext, Viewdata, & the News. 160p. 1983. text ed. 18.00x (ISBN 0-89859-263-1). L Erlbaum Assocs.
Woolfe. Videotex: Television - Telephone Information Services. 184p. 1980. 34.95 (ISBN 0-471-26089-4, Wiley Heyden). Wiley.
The World Videotex Report. 950p. (Orig.). 1984. pap. text ed. 169.95x (Online Pubns Ltd). Brookfield Pub Co.

VIEW CAMERAS
Shaman, Harvey. The View Camera: Operations & Techniques. LC 75-42770. (Illus.). 128p. 1977. pap. 9.95 (ISBN 0-8174-0598-4, Amphoto). Watson-Guptill.
Stroebel, Leslie. View Camera Technique. 4th ed. (Illus.). 312p. 1980. 25.95 (ISBN 0-240-51086-0). Focal Pr.

VIEWDATA
Fedida, Sam & Malik, Rex. The Viewdata Revolution. 186p. 1979. 44.95 (ISBN 0-470-26879-4). Halsted Pr.
Firth, R. J. Managing Viewdata Systems. 150p. 1984. pap. text ed. 21.55 (ISBN 0-471-81043-6). Wiley.
--Viewdata Systems: A Practical Evaluation Guide. 100p. 1982. pap. 14.20 (ISBN 0-471-89431-1). Wiley.
Programming & Services Strategies for 2-way TV & Viewdata Systems. (Report Ser.: No. 177). 228p. 1981. 985.00x (ISBN 0-88694-177-6). Intl Res Dev.
Viewdata. (Online Conference Papers, London, October 1982). 500p. (Orig.). 1982. pap. text ed. 130.00x (ISBN 0-903796-90-2, Pub. by Online Conferences England). Brookfield Pub Co.
Viewdata-DP Integration. 42p. 1980. 23.00x (ISBN 0-903796-71-6, Pub. by Online). Taylor & Francis.
Weaver, David H. Videotex Journalism: Teletext, Viewdata, & the News. 160p. 1983. text ed. 18.00x (ISBN 0-89859-263-1). L Erlbaum Assocs.

VINEGAR
Hanssen, Maurice. Cider Vinegar: A Comprehensive Guide to Its Uses & Properties. LC 74-27432. (Illus.). 128p. 1975. pap. 1.50 (ISBN 0-668-03751-2). Arco.
Scott, Cyril. Cider Vinegar. 1982. pap. 2.95 (ISBN 0-87904-011-4). Lust.

VINES
see Climbing Plants

VINEYARDS
see Grapes; Viticulture

VINICULTURE
see Viticulture

Tinsley, T. W. & Harrap, K. A. Moving Frontiers in Invertebrate Virology. Melnick, J. L., ed. (Monographs in Virology: Vol. 6). (Illus.). 1972. 16.75 (ISBN 3-8055-1464-6). S Karger.

The Use of Viruses for the Control on Insect Pests & Disease Vectors. (Agricultural Planning Studies: No. 91). 48p. (Orig.). 1974. pap. 4.50 (ISBN 0-685-40246-0, F490, FAO). Unipub.

Wakely, D. G. Applied Plant Virology. 288p. 1985. 22.95 (ISBN 0-471-82727-4). Wiley.

Waterson, A. P. & Wilkinson, L. An Introduction to the History of Virology. LC 77-17892. (Illus.). 1978. 49.50 (ISBN 0-521-21917-5). Cambridge U Pr.

Waterson, A. P., ed. Recent Advances in Clinical Virology, No. 2. (Illus.). 178p. 1980. text ed. 40.00 (ISBN 0-443-02094-9). Churchill.

--Recent Advances in Clinical Virology, No. 3. LC 80-49993. (Illus.). 278p. 1983. text ed. 55.00 (ISBN 0-443-02646-7). Churchill.

Willis, D. B., ed. Iridoviridae. (Current Topics in Microbiology & Immunology Ser.: Vol. 116). (Illus.). 190p. 1985. 45.00 (ISBN 0-387-15172-9). Springer-Verlag.

Wilson, Graham S. Topley & Wilson's Principles of Bacteriology, Virology & Immunity, Vol. I. 7th ed. (Illus.). 552p. 1983. lib. bdg. 90.00 (ISBN 0-683-09064-X). Williams & Wilkins.

Zoon, K. C., et al, eds. Interferon: Proceedings of the International Workshop, Sept. 28-30, 1983, Bethesda, MD. 286p. 1984. 49.00 (ISBN 0-444-00937-X). Elsevier.

VIRUS DISEASES OF PLANTS

see also Insects As Carriers of Disease

Beale, Helen P., ed. Bibliography of Plant Viruses & Index to Research. LC 73-3200. 1495p. 1976. 130.00x (ISBN 0-231-03763-5). Columbia U Pr.

Esau, Katherine. Viruses in Plant Hosts: Form, Distribution & Pathologic Effects. LC 68-9831. (John Charles Walker Lecture Ser.: 1968). pap. 58.80 (ISBN 0-317-09037-2, 2015359). Bks Demand UMI.

Gibbs, A. J. & Harrison, B. D. Plant Virology: The Principles. LC 76-1924. 292p. 1979. 37.95x (ISBN 0-470-26637-6). Halsted Pr.

International Organization of Citrus Virologists - 3rd Conference. Proceedings. Price, W. C., ed. LC 61-64183. 1965. 11.50 (ISBN 0-8130-0190-0). U Presses Fla.

International Organization of Citrus Virologists - 4th Conference. Proceedings. Childs, J. F., ed. LC 59-63553. 1968. 11.50 (ISBN 0-8130-0046-7). U Presses Fla.

International Organization of Citrus Virologists - 5th Conference. Proceedings. Price, W. C., ed. LC 59-63553. 1972. 11.50 (ISBN 0-8130-0327-X). U Presses Fla.

Lamberti, F., et al, eds. Nematode Vectors of Plant Viruses. (NATO ASI Series A, Life Sciences: Vol. 2). 460p. 1975. 59.50x (ISBN 0-306-35602-3, Plenum Pr). Plenum Pub.

Maramorosch, Karl, ed. Insect & Plant Viruses: An Atlas. 1978. 65.00 (ISBN 0-12-470275-9). Acad Pr.

Rayechaudhuri, S. P. & Nariani, T. K. Virus & Mycoplasm Diseases of Plants in India. 102p. 1977. 50.00x (ISBN 0-686-84449-1, Pub by Oxford & I B H India). State Mutual Bk.

Smith, K. M. Textbook of Plant Virus Diseases. 3rd ed. 1973. 57.50 (ISBN 0-12-651350-3). Acad Pr.

VIRUS RESEARCH

Goddard, M. & Butler, M., eds. Viruses & Wastewater Treatment: Proceedings of International Symposium Held at the University of Surrey, Guilford, 15-17 September 1980. (Illus.). 316p. 1981. 66.00 (ISBN 0-08-026401-8). Pergamon.

Harnden, Michael R. Approaches to Anti-Viral Agent. 350p. 1985. lib. bdg. 52.50 (ISBN 0-317-30654-5, Pub. by Macmillan Pr UK). VCH Pubs.

Kurstak, E. & Kurstak, C., eds. Comparative Diagnosis of Viral Diseases, Vol. 3: Vertebrate Animal & Related Viruses, DNA Viruses, Vol. 3 Part A. LC 81-7951. 1981. 66.00 (ISBN 0-12-429703-X) (ISBN 0-686-85518-3). Acad Pr.

--Comparative Diagnosis of Viral Diseases, Vol. 4: Vertebrate Animal & Related Viruses, Part B-BNA Viruses, Vol. 4, Part B. LC 81-7951. 1981. 87.00 (ISBN 0-12-429704-8). Acad Pr.

Lauffer, M. A., ed. Advances in Virus Research, Vol. 27. (Serial Publication Ser.). 334p. 1982. 60.00 (ISBN 0-12-039827-3). Acad Pr.

Lauffer, Max A. & Maramorosch, Karl, eds. Advances in Virus Research, Vol. 28. (Serial Publication Ser.). 1983. 65.00 (ISBN 0-12-039828-1). Acad Pr.

Mayo, Michael A. & Harrap, K. A., eds. Vectors in Virus Biology. (Special Publications Society General Microbiology Ser.: No. 12). 1984. 37.00 (ISBN 0-12-481480-8). Acad Pr.

Pollard, Morris. Virus Directed Host Response. (Perspectives in Virology: Vol. 5). 1967. 56.00 (ISBN 0-12-560550-1). Acad Pr.

Smith, Kenneth M. & Lauffer, Max A., eds. Advances in Virus Research, Vol. 18. 1974. 70.00 (ISBN 0-12-039818-4). Acad Pr.

Smith, Kenneth M., et al, eds. Advances in Virus Research. Incl. Vol. 1. 1953. 66.00 (ISBN 0-12-039801-X); Vol. 2. 1954. 66.00 (ISBN 0-12-039802-8); Vol. 3. 1955. 70.00 (ISBN 0-12-039803-6); Vol. 4. 1957. 70.00 (ISBN 0-12-039804-4); Vol. 5. 1958. 70.00 (ISBN 0-12-039805-2); Vol. 6. 1959. 70.00 (ISBN 0-12-039806-0); Vol. 7. 1961. 70.00 (ISBN 0-12-039807-9); Vol. 8. 1962. 71.00 (ISBN 0-12-039808-7); Vol. 9. 1963. 70.00 (ISBN 0-12-039809-5); Vol. 10. 1964. 67.50 (ISBN 0-12-039810-9); Vol. 11. 1965. 75.00 (ISBN 0-12-039811-7); Vol. 12. 1967. 75.00 (ISBN 0-12-039812-5); Vol. 13. 1968. 70.00 (ISBN 0-12-039813-3); Vol. 14. 1969. 70.00 (ISBN 0-12-039814-1); Vol. 15. 1969. 77.00 (ISBN 0-12-039815-X); Vol. 16. 1970. 78.00 (ISBN 0-12-039816-8); Vol. 17. 1972. 70.00 (ISBN 0-12-039817-6); Vol. 21. 1977. 70.00 (ISBN 0-12-039821-4); Vol. 22. 1978. 70.00 (ISBN 0-12-039822-2); Vol. 23. 1979. 70.00 (ISBN 0-12-039823-0); Vol. 24. 1979. 70.00 (ISBN 0-12-039824-9). Acad Pr.

VIRUSES

see also Bacteriophage; Host-Virus Relationships; Interferons; Virus Diseases of Plants; Virus Research

Andrewes, Sir Christopher. Natural History of Viruses. (World Naturalist Series). (Illus.). 1967. 10.00x (ISBN 0-393-06277-5). Norton.

Atherton, J. G. & Holmes, I. R. ICTV Code for the Description of Virus Characters. (Monographs in Virology: Vol. 14). vi, 154p. 1983. 41.75 (ISBN 3-8055-3769-7). S Karger.

Balaban, M., ed. Nucleic Acids & Nucleic Acid Complexes Viruses. (Structural Aspects of Recognition & Assembly of Biological Macromolecules Ser.: Vol. 2). 484p. 1981. 69.00 (ISBN 0-86689-003-3, 992200113). Balaban Intl Sci Serv.

Becker, Yechiel. Antiviral Drugs & Interferon: The Molecular Basis of Their Activity. (Developments in Molecular Virology). 464p. 1984. 65.00 (ISBN 0-89838-643-8, Pub. by Martinus Nijhoff Netherlands). Kluwer Academic.

Berns, Kenneth I., ed. The Parvoviruses. (Viruses Ser.). 424p. 1984. 59.50x (ISBN 0-306-41412-0, Plenum Pr). Plenum Pub.

Bishop, D. H. & Compans, R. W., eds. The Replication of Negative Strand Viruses. (Developments in Cell Biology Ser.: Vol. 7). 990p. 1981. 205.00 (ISBN 0-444-00606-0, Biomedical Pr). Elsevier.

Bishop, David H. Rhabdoviruses, Vol. I. LC 79-20575. 208p. 1979. 59.00 (ISBN 0-8493-5913-9). CRC Pr.

--Rhabdoviruses, 2 vols. 1980. Vol. II, 256 Pgs. 64.00 (ISBN 0-8493-5914-7); Vol. III, 272 Pgs. 69.50 (ISBN 0-8493-5915-5). CRC Pr.

Bishop, David H. & Compans, Richard W., eds. Nonsegmented Negative Strand Viruses: Paramyxonviruses & Rhabodoviruses (Symposium) 1984. 59.00 (ISBN 0-12-102480-6). Acad Pr.

Blasecki. Mechanisms of Immunity to Virus-Induced Tumors. (Immunology Ser.: Vol. 12). 376p. 1981. 57.50 (ISBN 0-8247-1162-9). Dekker.

Burnet, F. M. & Stanley, W. M., eds. The Viruses: Biochemical, Biological & Biophysical Properties. Incl. Vol. 1. General Virology. 1959; Vol. 2. Plant & Bacterial Viruses. 1959. 66.00 (ISBN 0-12-145602-1); Vol. 3. Animal Viruses. 1959. Acad Pr.

Carter, W. A., ed. Selective Inhibitors of Viral Functions. LC 73-81479. (Uniscience Ser). 377p. 1973. 64.00 (ISBN 0-87819-027-9). CRC Pr.

Cohen, P. & Van Heyningen, S., eds. Molecular Actions of Toxins & Viruses. (Molecular Aspects of Cellular Regulation Ser.: Vol. 2). 370p. 1982. 79.25 (ISBN 0-444-80400-5, I-143-82, Biomedical Pr). Elsevier.

Cold Spring Harbor Symposia on Quantitative Biology: Viruses, Vol. 18. LC 34-8174. 1954. 38.00x (ISBN 0-87969-017-8). Cold Spring Harbor.

Collier, L. H. & Oxford, J., eds. Developments in Antiviral Therapy. LC 80-41168. 1981. 55.00 (ISBN 0-12-181150-6). Acad Pr.

Colter, John S. & Paranchych, William. Molecular Biology of Viruses. 1967. 90.00 (ISBN 0-12-182250-8). Acad Pr.

Compans, Richard W. & Bishop, David H., eds. Segmented Negative Strand Viruses: Arenaviruses, Bunyaviruses & Orthomyxoviruses, Vol. 1. 1984. 49.00 (ISBN 0-12-183501-4). Acad Pr.

Cooper, J. I. & MacCallum, F. O. Viruses & the Environment. (Illus.). 190p. 1984. 32.00x (ISBN 0-412-22870-X, NO. 6437); pap. 15.95x (ISBN 0-412-22880-7, NO. 6869). Methuen Inc.

Dales, S. & Pogo, Beatriz G. Biology of Poxviruses. (Virology Monographs: Vol. 18). (Illus.). 140p. 1981. 35.00 (ISBN 0-387-81643-7). Springer-Verlag.

Dalton, A. J. & Haguenau, F., eds. Ultrastructure of Tumors Induced by Viruses: Charles Oberling Memorial Volume. (Ultrastructure in Biological Systems). 1962. 49.50 (ISBN 0-12-200950-9). Acad Pr.

Dalton, Albert J. & Hagoenau, Francoise. Ultrastructure of Animal Viruses & Bacteriophages: An Atlas. (Ultrastructure in Biological Systems Ser.). 1973. 83.00 (ISBN 0-12-200960-6). Acad Pr.

Doerffler, W., ed. The Molecular Biology of Adenoviruses 1. (Current Topics in Microbiology & Immunity Ser.: Vol. 109). (Illus.). 240p. 1983. 42.50 (ISBN 0-387-13034-9). Springer-Verlag.

Dubois-Dalco, M., et al. Assembly of Enveloped RNA Viruses. Kingsbury, D. W., ed. (Illus.). 250p. 1984. 49.50 (ISBN 0-387-81802-2). Springer-Verlag.

Evans, Alfred S., ed. Viral Infections of Humans. LC 76-9650. 616p. 1976. 39.50x (ISBN 0-306-30880-0, Plenum Pr); pap. 15.00x (ISBN 0-306-31137-2). Plenum Pub.

--Viral Infections of Humans: Epidemiology & Control. 2nd ed. LC 82-3684. 775p. 1982. 49.50 (ISBN 0-306-40676-4, Plenum Med Bk). Plenum Pub.

Fareed, George C., et al. Molecular Biology of Polyomaviruses & Herpesviruses. LC 82-23750. 247p. 1983. 52.95 (ISBN 0-471-05058-X, Pub. by Wiley Interscience). Wiley.

Fenner, F., et al. The Biology of Animal Viruses. 2nd ed. 1974. 83.00 (ISBN 0-12-253040-3). Acad Pr.

Fox, John P. & Hall, Carrie E. Viruses in Families. LC 75-12023. (Illus.). 462p. 1980. 44.00 (ISBN 0-88416-042-4). PSG Pub Co.

Fraenkel-Conrat, H. & Wagner, R. R., eds. Comprehensive Virology, Vol. 14: Newly Characterized Vertebrate Viruses. LC 79-810. (Illus.). 562p. 1979. 55.00x (ISBN 0-306-40231-9, Plenum Pr). Plenum Pub.

--Comprehensive Virology, Vol. 2: Reproduction of Small & Intermediate RNA Viruses. LC 74-13471. (Illus.). 354p. 1974. 39.50x (ISBN 0-306-35142-0, Plenum Pr). Plenum Pub.

--Comprehensive Virology, Vol. 3: Reproduction of DNA Animal Viruses. LC 74-17457. (Illus.). 502p. 1974. 49.50x (ISBN 0-306-35143-9, Plenum Pr). Plenum Pub.

--Comprehensive Virology, Vol. 4: Reproduction of Large RNA Viruses. LC 74-20501. (Illus.). 359p. 1975. 39.50x (ISBN 0-306-35144-7, Plenum Pr). Plenum Pub.

--Comprehensive Virology, Vol. 5: Structure & Assembly of Virions, Pseudovirions, & Intraviral Nucleic Acids. LC 74-5494. (Illus.). 236p. 1975. 35.00x (ISBN 0-306-35145-5, Plenum Pr). Plenum Pub.

--Comprehensive Virology, Vol. 6: Reproduction of Small RNA Viruses. LC 75-46506. (Illus.). 236p. 1976. 35.00x (ISBN 0-306-35146-3, Plenum Pr). Plenum Pub.

--Comprehensive Virology, Vol. 7: Reproduction of Bacterial DNA Viruses. (Illus.). 312p. 1977. 35.00x (ISBN 0-306-35147-1, Plenum Pr). Plenum Pub.

Fraenkel-Conrat, Heinz. Design & Function at the Threshold of Life: The Viruses. (Orig.). 1962. pap. 21.50 (ISBN 0-12-265168-5). Acad Pr.

Herrmann, Ernest C., Jr., ed. Conference on Antiviral Substances, Third, Vol. 284. (Annals of the New York Academy of Sciences). 720p. 1977. 58.00x (ISBN 0-89072-030-4). NY Acad Sci.

Hirsch, Martin S., et al. Investigation of Oncogenic Viruses, Vol. 2. 272p. 1974. text ed. 32.50x (ISBN 0-8422-7235-6). Irvington.

Horne. The Structure & Function of Viruses. (Studies in Biology: No. 95). 1978. pap. text ed. 8.95 (ISBN 0-7131-2706-6). Univ Park.

Horzinck, Marian C., ed. Non-Arthropod Borne Togaviruses. 216p. 1981. 44.00 (ISBN 0-12-356550-2). Acad Pr.

Hoyle, L. Influenza Viruses. (Virology Monographs: Vol. 4). (Illus.). 1968. 61.00 (ISBN 0-387-80892-2). Springer-Verlag.

Hsiung, Gueh-Djen & Green, Robert H. Virology & Rickettsiology, 2 pts, Vol. 1. (Illus.). 1979. Pt. 1, 448p. 19.95 (ISBN 0-8493-7061-2); Pt. 2, 448p. 19.95 (ISBN 0-8493-7062-0). CRC Pr.

Hughes, Sally S. The Virus: A History of the Concept. LC 77-5120. (Illus.). 1977. 12.00 (ISBN 0-88202-168-0, Sci Hist). Watson Pub Intl.

Incidence, Monitoring & Treatment of Viruses in Water Supply Systems. 91p. 1983. pap. 13.00x (ISBN 0-87262-376-9). Am Soc Civil Eng.

International Committee on Taxonomy of Viruses, 1st Report. Classification & Nomenclature of Viruses: Proceedings. Wildy, P., ed. (Monographs in Virology: Vol. 5). 1971. 11.50 (ISBN 3-8055-1196-5). S Karger.

International Congress on Microbiology, 12th, Munich, 1978. Fungal Viruses: Proceedings. Molitoris, H. P., ed. (Proceedings in Life Sciences Ser.). (Illus.). 1979. 36.00 (ISBN 0-387-09477-6). Springer-Verlag.

Jurnak, Frances & McPherson, Alexander, eds. Biological Macromolecules & Assemblies: Virus Structures, Vol. 1. LC 83-21732. 397p. 1984. 69.95 (ISBN 0-471-87077-3, Pub. by Wiley-Interscience). Wiley.

Kirsten, W. H., ed. Malignant Transformation by Viruses. (Recent Results in Cancer Research Ser.: Vol. 6). (Illus.). 1966. 28.00 (ISBN 0-387-03645-8). Springer-Verlag.

Knight, C. A. Chemistry of Viruses. 2nd ed. LC 74-11220. (Illus.). x, 336p. 1975. pap. 33.50 (ISBN 0-387-06772-8). Springer-Verlag.

Koch, Gebhard & Richter, Dietmar. Biosynthesis, Modification & Processing of Cellular & Viral Polyproteins. 1980. 43.50 (ISBN 0-12-417560-0). Acad Pr.

Koch, William. Survival Factor in Neoplastic & Viral Diseases. 15.00x (ISBN 0-686-29776-8). Cancer Control Soc.

Krech, U., et al. Cytomegalovirus Infections of Man. (Illus.). 124p. 1971. 13.75 (ISBN 3-8055-1261-9). S Karger.

Kurstak, Edouard & Maramorosch, Karl. Viruses & Environment. 1979. 57.00 (ISBN 0-12-429766-8). Acad Pr.

Kurstak, Edouard, ed. Arctic & Tropical Arboviruses. 1979. 35.00 (ISBN 0-12-429765-X). Acad Pr.

Lauffer, M. A., ed. Advances in Virus Research, Vol. 20. (Serial Publication Ser.). 1976. 70.00 (ISBN 0-12-039820-6). Acad Pr.

Lauffer, M. A., et al, eds. Advances in Virus Research, Vol. 19. (Serial Publication). 1974. 70.00 (ISBN 0-12-039819-2). Acad Pr.

Lauffer, Max, et al, eds. Advances in Virus Research, Vol. 25. LC 53-11559. (Serial Publication). 1979. 75.50 (ISBN 0-12-039825-7). Acad Pr.

Lehmann-Grube, F., ed. Lymphocytic Choriomeningitis Virus & Other Arenaviruses. LC 73-10673. xiii, 339p. 1973. pap. 39.00 (ISBN 0-387-06403-6). Springer-Verlag.

Libikova, H., ed. Biology of Viruses of the Tick-Borne Encephalitis Complex: Proceedings. (Symposia of the Czechoslovak Academy of Sciences: Vol. 3). 1962. 55.00 (ISBN 0-12-448050-0). Acad Pr.

Mahy, B. W. & Barry, R. D., eds. Negative Strand Viruses & the Host Cell. 1978. 99.00 (ISBN 0-12-465350-2). Acad Pr.

Majer, M. & Plotkin, S. A., eds. Strains of Human Viruses. 160p. 1972. 41.75 (ISBN 3-8055-1401-8). S Karger.

Martin, S. J. The Biochemistry of Viruses. LC 77-8231. (Texts in Chemistry & Biochemistry Ser.). (Illus.). 1978. 44.50 (ISBN 0-521-21678-8); pap. 15.95 (ISBN 0-521-29229-8). Cambridge U Pr.

Matthews, R. E., ed. Classification & Nomenclature of Viruses. (Journal: Intervirology: Vol. 17, No. 1-3, 1982). (Illus.). 200p. 1982. 15.50 (ISBN 3-8055-3557-0). S Karger.

--Classification & Nomenclature of Viruses: Report of the International Committee on Taxonomy of Viruses, 3rd. (Intervirology: Vol. 12, Nos. 3-5, 1979). 1980. pap. 4.25 (ISBN 3-8055-0523-X). S Karger.

Meulen, V. Ter & Katz, M., eds. Slow Virus Infections of the Central Nervous System. LC 77-1570. 1977. 44.00 (ISBN 0-387-90188-4). Springer-Verlag.

Nayak, Debi, ed. The Molecular Biology of Animal Virus, Vol. 1. 1977. 75.00 (ISBN 0-8247-6533-8). Dekker.

--The Molecular Biology of Animal Viruses, Vol. 2. 1977. 75.00 (ISBN 0-8247-6534-6). Dekker.

New York Academy of Sciences, Nov. 28-30, 1979. Genetic Variation of Viruses, Vol. 354. Palese, Peter & Roizman, Bernard, eds. LC 80-25770. (Annals of the New York Academy of Sciences). 507p. 1980. 99.00x (ISBN 0-89766-097-8); pap. 99.00x (ISBN 0-89766-098-6). NY Acad Sci.

Notkins, Abner L., ed. Viral Immunology & Immunopathology. 1975. 55.00 (ISBN 0-12-522050-2). Acad Pr.

Olson. Virus Infections: Modern Concepts & Status. (Microbiology Ser.: Vol. 6). 304p. 1982. 45.00 (ISBN 0-8247-1859-3). Dekker.

The Parvoviruses. (Virology Monographs: Vol. 15). 1976. 35.00 (ISBN 0-387-81355-1). Springer-Verlag.

Perez-Bercoff, R., ed. The Molecular Biology of the Picornaviruses. LC 79-13845. (NATO ASI Ser. A, Life Sciences: Vol. 23). 387p. 1979. 49.50x (ISBN 0-306-40192-4, Plenum Pr). Plenum Pub.

Philipson, L. & Pettersson, U. Molecular Biology of Adenoviruses. LC 75-6658. (Virology Monographs: Vol. 14). (Illus.). iv, 115p. 1975. 35.00 (ISBN 0-387-81284-9). Springer-Verlag.

Roizman, Bernard, ed. The Herpesviruses, Vol. 2. (The Viruses Ser.). 380p. 1983. 42.50x (ISBN 0-306-41083-4, Plenum Press). Plenum Pub.

Wolverton, Van. Visi-On Calc Worksheets for Business. (Illus.). 225p. 1984. 18.95 (ISBN 0-912213-08-6). Paladin.

VISION

see also Binocular Vision; Color Vision; Eye; Optics, Physiological

Abrahamson, Edwin & Ostroy, Sanford E., eds. Molecular Processes in Vision. LC 80-29543. (Benchmark Papers in Biochemistry: Vol. 3). 448p. 1981. 57.95 (ISBN 0-87933-372-3). Van Nos Reinhold.

Ali, M. A., ed. Photoreception & Vision in Invertebrates. (NATO ASI Ser. A: Life Sciences: Vol. 74). 868p. 1984. 115.00 (ISBN 0-306-41626-3, Plenum Pr). Plenum Pub.

Autrum, H., ed. Comparative Physiology & Evolution of Vision in Invertebrates: A: Invertebrate Photoreceptors. LC 78-21470. (Handbook of Sensory Physiology: Vol. 7, Pt. 6A). (Illus.). 1979. 187.00 (ISBN 0-387-08837-7). Springer-Verlag.

Brock, ed. Robot Vision & Sensory Control: Proceedings of the Second International Conference, Stuttgart, BRD, Nov. 1982. iv, 388p. 1983. 85.00 (ISBN 0-444-86548-9, North-Holland). Elsevier.

Cline, David, et al. Dictionary of Visual Science. 3rd ed. LC 78-14640. 736p. 1980. 40.00 (ISBN 0-8019-6778-3). Chilton.

Cool, J. & Smith, E. L., eds. Frontiers in Visual Science: Proceedings of the University of Houston College of Optometry Dedication Symposium, Houston Texas, March, 1977. LC 78-24191. (Springer Series in Optical Sciences: Vol. 8). (Illus.). 1978. 54.00 (ISBN 0-387-09185-8). Springer-Verlag.

Evans, John M. An Introduction to Clinical Scotometry. 1938. 75.00x (ISBN 0-685-89759-1). Elliots Bks.

Fein, Alan & Levine, Joseph S. Visual System: Proceedings of a Symposium in Honor of Edward F. MacNichol, Jr., Held in Woods Hole, MA, Dec. 2-3, 1983, Vol. 5. LC 84-27828. (MBL Lectures in Biology). 208p. 1985. 44.00 (ISBN 0-8451-2204-5). A R Liss.

Freeman, R. D., ed. Developmental Neurobiology of Vision. LC 79-19389. (NATO ASI Series A, Life Sciences: Vol. 27). 460p. 1979. 59.50x (ISBN 0-306-40306-4, Plenum Pr). Plenum Pub.

Freese, Arthur J. The Miracle of Vision. LC 76-26226. 1977. 12.45i (ISBN 0-06-011371-5, HarpT). Har-Row.

Frisby, John. Seeing: Illusion, Brain & Mind. (Illus.). 1980. 22.50 (ISBN 0-19-217672-2). Oxford U Pr.

Getz, Donald J. & McGraw, Lora. Vision Training for Better Learning. 1981. spiral bound 15.95 (ISBN 0-87804-430-2). Mafex.

Griffin, John R. Binocular Anomalies: Procedures for Vision Therapy. LC 75-18293. (Illus.). 1976. 50.00 (ISBN 0-87873-020-6). Prof Press.

How We See. 1977. 8.00 (ISBN 0-87453-175-6). Denoyer.

Hughes, A. The Visual System in Evolution in Vertebrates. LC 77-4371. (Handbook of Sensory Physiology: Vol. 7, Pt. 5). 1977. 201.00 (ISBN 0-387-07908-4). Springer-Verlag.

Hurvich, Leo M. Color Vision. LC 80-19077. (Illus.). 280p. 1981. pap. text ed. 35.00x (ISBN 0-87893-337-9). Sinauer Assoc.

Huxley, Aldous. The Art of Seeing. 3rd ed. LC 82-70423. (Illus.). 170p. 1982. pap. 6.95 (ISBN 0-916870-48-0). Creative Arts Bk.

Ingle, D. & Schneider, G. E., eds. Subcortical Visual Systems. (Brain, Behavior & Evolution: Vol. 3, No. 1-4). 1970. pap. 55.25 (ISBN 3-8055-1149-3). S Karger.

Jacobs, Lawrence, et al. Computerized Tomography of the Orbit & Sella Turcica. 376p. 1980. text ed. 108.00 (ISBN 0-685-95340-8). Raven.

Kirban, Salem. The Medical Approach Versus the Nutritional Approach to Eyesight. 1982. 5.00 (ISBN 0-912582-51-0). Kirban.

Kirk, Edith. Vision Pathology in Education. (Illus.). 240p. 1981. 24.50x (ISBN 0-398-04504-6). C C Thomas.

Lythgoe, J. N. The Ecology & Vision. (Illus.). 1979. 55.00x (ISBN 0-19-854529-0). Oxford U Pr.

Marr, David C. Vision. LC 81-15076. (Illus.). 397p. 1982. text ed. 23.95 (ISBN 0-7167-1284-9). W H Freeman.

Mazohkin-Porshnyakov, G. A. Insect Vision. LC 67-10310. 300p. 1969. 37.50x (ISBN 0-306-30268-3, Plenum Pr). Plenum Pub.

Motokawa, K. Physiology of Color & Pattern Vision. (Illus.). 1970. 45.00 (ISBN 0-387-04977-0). Springer-Verlag.

Niemeyer, G. & Huber, Charles. Techniques in Clinical Electrophysiology of Vision. 1982. lib. bdg. 99.00 (ISBN 90-6193-727-2, Pub. by Junk Pubs Netherlands). Kluwer Academic.

Panel on Impact of Video Viewing on Vision of Workers, National Research Council. Video Displays, Work, & Vision. 288p. 1983. pap. 14.50 (ISBN 0-309-03388-8). Natl Acad Pr.

Polyak, Stephen. Vertebrate Visual System. Kluver, Heinrich, ed. LC 55-5153. (Illus.). 1957. 100.00x (ISBN 0-226-67494-0). U of Chicago Pr.

Priestley, Joseph. History & Present State of Discoveries Relating to Vision, Light, & Colours. Cohen, I. Bernard, ed. LC 80-2142. (Development of Science Ser.). (Illus.). 1981. lib. bdg. 70.00x (ISBN 0-405-13897-0). Ayer Co Pubs.

Proenza, Luis M., et al. Clinical Applications of Visual Psychophysics. LC 81-2237. (Illus.). 352p. 1981. 44.50 (ISBN 0-521-24056-5). Cambridge U Pr.

Reichardt, W., ed. Processing of Optical Data by Organisms & by Machines. (Italian Physical Society: Course No. 43). 1970. 95.00 (ISBN 0-12-368843-4). Acad Pr.

Revien, Leon & Gabor, Mark. Sports-Vision: Dr. Revien's Eye Exercise Program for Athletes. LC 80-54623. (Illus.). 128p. 1981. pap. 4.95 (ISBN 0-89480-152-X, 457). Workman Pub.

Rose, Albert, ed. Vision: Human & Electronic. LC 73-97422. (Optical Physics & Engineering Ser.). (Illus.). 200p. 1974. 27.50x (ISBN 0-306-30732-4, Plenum Pr). Plenum Pub.

Rosenbloom, Alfred A. & Morgan, Meredith. Vision & Aging: General & Clinical Perspectives. 1985. 60.00 (ISBN 0-87873-045-1). Prof Press.

Royal Society Discussion, March 7 & 8, 1979. The Psychology of Vision. Longuet-Higgins, H. C. & Sutherland, N. S., eds. (Illus.). 218p. 1980. text ed. 61.00x (ISBN 0-85403-141-3, Pub. by Royal Soc London). Scholium Intl.

Shichi, Hitoshi. Biochemistry of Vision. (Monograph). 1983. 45.00 (ISBN 0-12-640020-2). Acad Pr.

Smythe, R. H. Vision in the Animal World. LC 75-13590. (Illus.). 175p. 1975. 27.50 (ISBN 0-312-84980-X). St Martin.

Stiles, W. S. Mechanisms of Color Vision. 1978. 59.00 (ISBN 0-12-671350-2). Acad Pr.

Stone, Jonathan. Parallel Processing in the Visual Systems: The Classification of Retinal Ganglion Cells & Its Impact on the Neurobiology of Vision. (Perspectives in Vision Research Ser.). 430p. 1983. 55.00x (ISBN 0-306-41220-9, Plenum Pr). Plenum Pub.

Wasserman, Gerald S. Color Vision: An Historical Introduction. LC 78-5346. (Behavior Ser.). 224p. 1978. 42.95x (ISBN 0-471-92128-9, Pub. by Wiley-Interscience). Wiley.

Weale, R. A. Focus on Vision. (Illus.). 208p. 1983. pap. text ed. 15.00x (ISBN 0-674-30701-1). Harvard U Pr.

Yarbus, A. L. Eye Movements & Vision. LC 66-19932. 236p. 1967. 25.00x (ISBN 0-306-30298-5, Plenum Pr). Plenum Pub.

VISIWORD (COMPUTER PROGRAM)

Myers, Dave. VisiWord: Word Processing for You & Your Business. (Illus.). 260p. (Orig.). 1983. pap. 18.95 (ISBN 0-912213-01-9). Paladin.

Myers, David. VisiWord: Word Processing for You & Your Business. 1984. pap. 18.95 (ISBN 0-912213-01-9). Random.

VISTRA

see Rayon

VISUAL-AURAL RANGE

see Omnirange System

VISUAL DATA PROCESSING

see Optical Data Processing

VITAMINS

see also Cyanocobalamine

Adams, Ruth. The Complete Home Guide to All the Vitamins. 432p. 1972. pap. 3.95 (ISBN 0-915962-05-5). Larchmont Bks.

Adams, Ruth & Murray, Frank. The Vitamin B-Six Book. 176p. (Orig.). 1980. pap. 2.95 (ISBN 0-915962-30-6). Larchmont Bks.

--Vitamin B-Twelve & Folic Acid. 176p. (Orig.). 1981. pap. 2.95 (ISBN 0-915962-31-4). Larchmont Bks.

--Vitamin C, the Powerhouse Vitamin. 192p. 1975. pap. 1.50 (ISBN 0-532-12187-2). Woodhill.

--Vitamin E, Wonder Worker of the 70's? 128p. 1972. pap. 1.50 (ISBN 0-532-12142-2). Woodhill.

Alderton, Peggy. The Vitamin, Mineral Connection. 30p. 1985. pap. 2.95 (ISBN 0-317-14757-9). Books World.

Babior, Bernard M., ed. Cobalamin: Biochemistry & Pathophysiology. LC 74-32499. pap. 122.30 (ISBN 0-317-07781-3, 2017398). Bks Demand UMI.

Baker, Herman & Frank, Oscar. Clinical Vitaminology: Methods & Interpretation. LC 68-24678. pap. 62.50 (ISBN 0-317-28628-5, 2051326). Bks Demand UMI.

Barker, B. M. Vitamins in Medicine, Vol. 1. 1980. 83.95 (ISBN 0-8151-0422-7). Year Bk Med.

Basu, T. K. & Schorah, C. J. Vitamin C in Health & Disease. (Illus., Orig.). 1982. lib. bdg. 21.50 (ISBN 0-87055-406-9). AVI.

Bauerfeind, Jack C., ed. Carotenoid As Colorants & Vitamin A Precursors: Technological & Nutritional Applications. LC 80-984. (Food Science & Technology Ser.). 1981. 90.00 (ISBN 0-12-082850-2). Acad Pr.

Benowicz, Robert J. Vitamins & You. 352p. 1984. pap. 3.95 (ISBN 0-425-07482-X). Berkley Pub.

Bicknell, F. & Prescott, F. Vitamins in Medicine. 47.50 (ISBN 0-911238-63-8). B Of A.

Biokinesiology Institute & Barton, John. Which Vitamin - Which Herb Do You Need? 2nd ed. (Illus.). 64p. 1981. pap. 2.00 (ISBN 0-937216-16-X). Biokinesiology.

Bland, Jeffrey. Choline, Lecithin, Inositol. Passwater, Richard, ed. (Good Health Guide Ser.). 1983. pap. 1.45 (ISBN 0-87983-277-0). Keats.

Blate, Michael. The G-Jo Institute Manual of Vitamins & Minerals. (The G-Jo Institute Self-Health Ser.). 96p. (Orig.). 1983. pap. 6.95 (ISBN 0-916878-18-X). Falkynor Bks.

Borsook, Henry. Vitamins: What They Are. (Orig.). pap. 2.50 (ISBN 0-515-05834-3). Jove Pubns.

Bosco, Dominick. The People's Guide to Vitamins & Minerals: From A to Zinc. 336p. 1980. pap. 8.95 (ISBN 0-8092-7139-7). Contemp Bks.

Bourne, G. H. & Cama, H. R., eds. Vitamin & Carrier Functions of Polyprenoids. (World Review of Nutrition & Dietetrics: Vol. 31). (Illus.). 1978. 58.75 (ISBN 3-8055-2801-9). S Karger.

Briggs, M. H. Vitamins in Human Biology & Medicine. 272p. 1981. 86.50 (ISBN 0-8493-5673-3). CRC Pr.

Brubacher, D., et al, eds. Methods for the Determination of Vitamins in Foods. 152p. 1985. 30.00 (ISBN 0-85334-339-X, Pub. by Elsevier Applied Sci England). Elsevier.

Burk, Dean. Vitamin B17, B15, Brief Foods-Vitamins. 1.50 (ISBN 0-686-29881-0). Cancer Control Soc.

Business Communications Staff. Bulk Vitamins & Their Major Markets. 1980. 975.00 (ISBN 0-89336-235-2, GA-036R). BCC.

--Vitamins & Food Supplements. 1980. 975.00 (ISBN 0-89336-090-2, GA-036R). BCC.

Center for Self Sufficiency Research Division. International Directory of Herb, Health, Vitamin & Natural Food Catalogs. 200p. 1985. pap. text ed. 3.50 (ISBN 0-910811-36-9, Pub. by Center Self Suff). Prosperity & Profits.

Challem, Jack J. Vitamin C Updated. Passwater, Richard A. & Mindell, Earl, eds. (Good Health Guide Ser.). 36p. 1983. pap. text ed. 1.45 (ISBN 0-87983-285-1). Keats.

Chinoy, N. J., ed. The Role of Ascorbic Acid in Growth, Differentiation & Metabolism of Plants. (Advances in Agricultural Biotechnology Ser.). 1984. lib. bdg. 46.50 (ISBN 90-247-2908-4, Pub. by Martinus Nijhoff Netherlands). Kluwer-Academic.

Colgan, Michael. Your Personal Vitamin Profile: A Medical Scientist Shows You How to Chart Your Individual Vitamin & Mineral Formala. 1982. 14.95 (ISBN 0-688-01505-0); pap. 8.95 (ISBN 0-688-01506-9). Morrow.

Colowick, Sidney, et al, eds. Methods in Enzymology: Vitamins & Coenzymes, Vol. 67, Pt F. 1980. 70.00 (ISBN 0-12-181967-1). Acad Pr.

Consumer Guide. The Vitamin Book. 1979. (Fireside); pap. 5.95 (ISBN 0-671-24819-7). S&S.

Cowgill, George R. The Vitamin B: Requirements of Man. 1934. 49.50x (ISBN 0-686-50034-2). Elliots Bks.

DeLuca, H. F. Vitamin D: Metabolism & Function. (Monographs on Endocrinology: Vol. 13). (Illus.). 1979. 20.00 (ISBN 0-387-09182-3). Springer-Verlag.

DeLuca, H. F. & Suttie, J. W., eds. Fat-Soluble Vitamins. 550p. 1970. 50.00x (ISBN 0-299-05600-7). U of Wis Pr.

DeMoss, Virginia. Runner's World Vitamin Book. 204p. 1982. spiral bdg. 11.95 (ISBN 0-89037-146-6). Anderson World.

Dolphin, David. B-12, 2 vols. LC 81-10300. 1176p. 1982. Set of Vols. 1 & 2. 154.95x (ISBN 0-471-03655-2, Pub. by Wiley-Interscience). Wiley.

--BTwelve, Vols. 1 & 2. Chemistry, Vol. 1, 671p. 85.95 (ISBN 0-471-80846-6); Biochemistry & Medicine, Vol. 2, 505p. 85.95 (ISBN 0-471-80844-X); Two vol. set, 1176p. 165.95 (ISBN 0-471-03655-2). Wiley.

European Symposium, 3rd, Zurich. Vitamin B-Twelve: Proceedings. Zayalak, B. J. & Friedrich, W., eds. 1979. 88.00x (ISBN 3-11-007668-3). De Gruyter.

Flodin, N. W. Vitamin-Trace Mineral-Protein Interactions, Vol. 1. Horrobin, D. F., ed. (Annual Research Reviews). 1979. 26.40 (ISBN 0-88831-042-0). Eden Pr.

--Vitamin-Trace Mineral-Protein Interactions, Vol. 2. Horrobin, D. F., ed. (Annual Research Reviews). 1980. 30.00 (ISBN 0-88831-062-5, Dist. by Pergamon). Eden Pr.

Flodin, Nestor W. Vitamin-Trace Mineral-Protein Interactions. (Annual Research Reviews Ser.: Vol. 4). 386p. 1981. 38.00 (ISBN 0-88831-114-1). Eden Pr.

--Vitamin-Trace Mineral-Protein Interactions, Vol. 3. Horribin, David F., ed. (Annual Research Reviews). 362p. 1980. 38.00 (ISBN 0-88831-085-4). Eden Pr.

Food & Nutrition Board. Human Vitamin B-Six Requirements. 1978. pap. 14.75 (ISBN 0-309-02642-3). Natl Acad Pr.

Herbert, Victor & Barrett, Stephen. Vitamins & "Health" Foods: The Great American Hustle. 200p. 1981. 11.95 (ISBN 0-89313-054-0). G F Stickley.

Hoffer, Abram. Vitamin B3 (Niacin) Passwater, Richard A. & Mindell, Earl R., eds. (Good Health Guide Ser.). 32p. 1982. pap. 1.45 (ISBN 0-87983-266-5). Keats.

Holmes, Marjorie. God & Vitamins. 368p. 1982. pap. 3.50 (ISBN 0-380-56994-9, 68536-1). Avon.

Koser, Stewart A. Vitamin Requirements of Bacteria & Yeasts. (Illus.). 672p. 1968. 59.75x (ISBN 0-398-01041-2). C C Thomas.

Lawson, D. E., ed. Vitamin D. 1978. 84.50 (ISBN 0-12-439850-2). Acad Pr.

Leibovitz, Brian. Carnitine: The Vitamin B Phenomenon. 224p. (Orig.). 1984. pap. 2.95 (ISBN 0-440-11061-0). Dell.

Lesser, Michael. Nutrition & Vitamin Therapy. LC 79-52100. 1980. pap. 7.95 (ISBN 0-394-17600-6, E748, Ever). Grove.

Lindlahr, Victor H. The Lindlahr Vitamin Cookbook. LC 80-19202. 319p. 1980. Repr. of 1972 ed. lib. bdg. 13.95x (ISBN 0-89370-611-6). Borgo Pr.

Lines, Anni A. Vitamins & Minerals: The Health Connection. 1985. pap. 6.95 (ISBN 0-932090-14-1). Health Plus.

Marshall, Charles W. Vitamins & Minerals: Help or Harm? (Illus.). 256p. 1983. 14.95 (ISBN 0-89313-061-3). G F Stickley.

Mervyn, Len. Vitamin E Updated. Passwater, Richard A. & Mindell, Earl R., eds. (Good Health Guide Ser.). 32p. (Orig.). 1983. pap. 1.45 (ISBN 0-87983-274-6). Keats.

Mervyn, Leonard. The B Vitamins: Their Major Role in Maintaining Your Health. 96p. (Orig.). 1983. pap. 1.95 (ISBN 0-7225-0667-8). Thorsons Pubs.

Mindell, Earl. Earl Mindell's Vitamin Bible for Kids. 1981. 6.95x (ISBN 0-89256-198-X). Cancer Control Soc.

--Earl Mindell's Vitamin Bible for Your Kids. 1981. 3.95 (ISBN 0-89256-183-1); pap. 2.95 (ISBN 0-89256-198-X). Rawson Assocs.

--Earl Mindell's Vitamin Bible for your Kids. 256p. 1982. pap. 3.95 (ISBN 0-553-22660-6). Bantam.

--Vitamin Bible. 7.95x (ISBN 0-89256-114-9); pap. 3.95x (ISBN 0-446-93613-8). Cancer Control Soc.

Munson, P. L., et al, eds. Vitamins & Hormones, Vol. 38. (Serial Publication Ser.). 1981. 61.50 (ISBN 0-12-709838-0). Acad Pr.

Munson, Paul L., et al, eds. Vitamins & Hormones: Advances in Research & Applications, Vol. 37. LC 43-10535. 1980. 60.00 (ISBN 0-12-709837-2). Acad Pr.

New York Academy of Sciences Annals, Nov. 11-13, 1981. Vitamin E: Biochemical, Hematological, Clinical Aspects, Vol. 393. Lubin, Bertram & Machlin, Lawrence J., eds. 506p. 1982. 95.00x (ISBN 0-89766-176-1). NY Acad Sci.

Newbold, H. L. Vitamin C Against Cancer. 1979. 8.95 (ISBN 0-345-28099-7). Ballantine.

Nobile, Sylvia & Woodhill, Joan M. Vitamin C-The Mysterious Redox-System: A Trigger of Life? (Illus.). 185p. 1981. text ed. 29.00 (ISBN 0-85200-419-2, Pub. by MTP Pr England). Kluwer Academic.

Norman. Vitamin D: Molecular Biology & Clinical Nutrition. (Basic & Clinical Nutrition Ser.: Vol. 2). 760p. 1980. 99.75 (ISBN 0-8247-6891-4). Dekker.

Norman, A. W., et al. Vitamin D Fourth Workshop: Basic Research & Its Clinical Applications. 1979. 88.00x (ISBN 3-11-007712-4). De Gruyter.

Norman, A. W., et al, eds. Vitamin D & Problems Related to Uremic Bone Diseases: Proceedings of the Workshop on Vitamin D, 2nd, Wiesbaden, West Germany, Oct. 1974. xvi, 799p. 1975. 82.00x (ISBN 3-11-005775-1). De Gruyter.

Norman, Anthony W. Vitamin D: The Calcium Homeostatic Hormone. (Basic & Applied Science of Nutrition Ser.). 1979. 70.00 (ISBN 0-12-521050-7). Acad Pr.

Oliver, Martha H. Cooking with Vitamins: How to Get the Most Out of Food You Cook. LC 80-84432. 200p. 1982. 8.95 (ISBN 0-87983-157-X). Keats.

Painter, Paul C., et al. The Theory of Vibrational Spectroscopy & Its Applications to Polymeric Materials. LC 81-12969. 530p. 1982. 74.95x (ISBN 0-471-09346-7, Pub. by Wiley-Interscience). Wiley.

Pauling, Linus. Vitamin C, the Common Cold, & the Flu. LC 76-28516. (Illus). 230p. 1976. pap. 10.95x (ISBN 0-7167-0361-0). W H Freeman.

Pratt, J. M. Inorganic Chemistry of Vitamin B1120. 1972. 60.00 (ISBN 0-12-564050-1). Acad Pr.

Prince, Francine. Francine Prince's Vitamin Diet for Quick & Easy Weight Loss. 1982. 6.95 (ISBN 0-686-97447-6); pap. 7.95 (ISBN 0-346-12521-9). Cornerstone.

Requirements of Vitamin A, Thiamine, Riboflavin & Niacin: Report of a Joint FAO-WHO Expert Group. (Nutrition Meetings Reports: No. 41). 86p. (3rd Printing 1978). 1967. pap. 5.25 (ISBN 92-5-100453-6, F1467, FAO). Unipub.

Rivlin, Richard, ed. Riboflavin. LC 74-31027. (Illus). 446p. 1975. 49.50x (ISBN 0-306-30814-2, Plenum Pr). Plenum Pub.

Sebrell, W. H., Jr. & Harris, Robert S., eds. Chemistry, Physiology, Pathology, Methods. Incl. Vol. 1. 2nd ed. 1967. 81.00 (ISBN 0-12-633761-6); Vol. 2. 1968. 78.00 (ISBN 0-12-633762-4); Vol. 3. 1971. 86.00 (ISBN 0-12-633763-2); Vol. 5. 1972. 71.50 (ISBN 0-12-633765-9); Vols. 6-7. Gyorgy, Paul & Pearson, W. N., eds. 1968. Vol. 6. 59.50 (ISBN 0-12-633706-3); Vol. 7. 56.00 (ISBN 0-12-633707-1). Acad Pr.

Seib, Paul A., ed. Ascorbic Acid: Chemistry, Metabolism, & Uses. Tolbert, Bert M. LC 82-13795. (ACS Advances in Chemistry Ser.: No. 200). 1982. 84.95 (ISBN 0-8412-0632-5). Am Chemical.

Shute, Evan V. Common Questions on Vitamin E & Their Answers. LC 79-87677. 1979. pap. 2.25 (ISBN 0-87983-191-X). Keats.

Sodano, C. S. Vitamins-Synthesis, Production & Use: Advances Since 1970. LC 78-61894. (Chemical Technology Review Ser.: No. 119). (Illus). 305p. 1979. 42.00 (ISBN 0-8155-0728-3). Noyes.

Strohecker, Rolf & Henning, Heinz M. Vitamin Assay: Tested Methods. 2nd ed. LC 65-22514. (Illus). 360p. 1972. 33.60x (ISBN 3-527-25280-0). VCH Pubs.

Szekely, Edmond B. The Book of Vitamins. (Illus). 40p. 1978. pap. 2.95 (ISBN 0-89564-045-7). IBS Intl.

Vitamin C, the Common Cold & the Flu. rev. ed. 224p. 1983. pap. 2.95 (ISBN 0-425-06455-7). Berkley Pub.

Vitamin D: Biochemical, Chemical & Clinical Aspects Related to Calcium Metabolism: Proceedings of the Third Workshop on Vitamin D, Pacific Grove California, USA, January 1977. 1977. 70.00x (ISBN 3-11-006918-0). De Gruyter.

Vitamins & Hormones, Vol. 39. 1982. 65.00 (ISBN 0-12-709839-9). Acad Pr.

Wade. Miracle of Organic Vitamins for Better Health. pap. 4.95. P-H.

WHO-FAO Joint Expert Group, Geneva, 1969. Requirements of Ascorbic Acid, Vitamin D, Vitamin B12, Folate & Iron. (Technical Report Ser: No. 452). 75p. 1970. pap. 2.00 (ISBN 92-4-120452-4, 669). World Health.

Zechmeister, Laszlo. CIS-Trans Isomeric Carotenoids, Vitamins A & Arylpolyenes. 1962. 41.50 (ISBN 0-12-777850-0). Acad Pr.

VITICULTURE

see also Grapes; Wine and Wine Making

Brunel, Gaston. A Guide to the Vineyards of the Cotes du Rhone. (Illus). 254p. 30.00 (ISBN 0-312-92274-4). St Martin.

Christensen, L. P., et al. Grapevine Nutrition & Fertilization in the San Joaquin Valley. 1978. pap. 5.00 (ISBN 0-931876-25-7, 4087). Ag & Nat Res.

Frederick, Kenneth D. Water Management & Agricultural Development: A Case Study of the Cuyo Region of Argentina. LC 74-24402. (Resources for the Future Research Ser). (Illus). 208p. 1975. 16.50x (ISBN 0-8018-1701-3). Johns Hopkins.

Kasimatis, A. N., et al. Wine Grape Varieties in the North Coast Counties of California. 1977. pap. 3.00 (ISBN 0-931876-22-2, 4069). Ag & Nat Res.

--Wine Grape Varieties in the San Joaquin Valley. 1972. pap. 5.00 (ISBN 0-931876-23-0, 4009). Ag & Nat Res.

Nelson, Klayton E. Harvesting & Handling California Table Grapes for Market. LC 79-51948. (Illus). 1979. pap. 12.00 (ISBN 0-931876-33-8, 1913). Ag & Nat Res.

Pearkes, Gillian. Vinegrowing in Britain. (Illus). 336p. 1985. 19.95 (ISBN 0-460-04393-5, BKX 05269, Pub. by J M Dent England). Biblio Dist.

Pongracz, D. P. Practical Viticulture. (Illus). 240p. 1978. 16.00x (ISBN 0-8476-2387-4). Rowman.

Scheer, Arnold H. & Juergenson, E. M. Approved Practices in Fruit & Vine Production. 2nd ed. (Illus). 590p. 1976. 19.95 (ISBN 0-8134-1704-X, 1704); text ed. 14.95x. Interstate.

Wagner, Philip M. Wine-Grower's Guide. rev ed. (Illus). 1965. 14.95 (ISBN 0-394-40183-2). Knopf.

Weaver, Robert J. Grape Growing. LC 76-22753. 371p. 1976. 32.50x (ISBN 0-471-92324-9, Pub. by Wiley-Interscience). Wiley.

Winkler, A. J., et al. General Viticulture. rev. ed. LC 73-87507. (Illus). 1975. 27.50 (ISBN 0-520-02591-1). U of Cal Pr.

VITICULTURE-PORTUGAL

Stanislawski, Dan. Landscapes of Bacchus: The Vine in Portugal. (Illus). 224p. 1970. 14.50x (ISBN 0-292-70010-5). U of Tex Pr.

VIZSLA (DOG)

see Dogs-Breeds-Vizsla

VLSI

see Integrated Circuits-Very Large Scale Integration

VOICE

see also Automatic Speech Recognition; Respiration

Aldwell, Edward & Schachter, Carl. Harmony & Voice Leading, Vol. 2. 276p. 1979. text ed. 17.95 (ISBN 0-15-531517-X, HC); wkbk. 7.95 (ISBN 0-15-531518-8). HarBraceJ.

Appelman, D. Ralph. Science of Vocal Pedagogy: Theory & Application. LC 67-10107. (Illus). 448p. 1967. 27.50x (ISBN 0-253-35110-3); companion cassettes of 3 tapes 17.50 (ISBN 0-253-35115-4); Tape 1. 6.95 (ISBN 0-253-35112-X); Tape 2. 6.95 (ISBN 0-253-35113-8); Tape 3. 6.95 (ISBN 0-253-35114-6). Ind U Pr.

Barnett, B. Aspects of Vocal Multiphonics. Date not set. 7.25 (ISBN 0-939044-19-6). Lingua Pr.

Boone, Daniel R. The Voice & Voice Therapy. 3rd ed. (Illus). 320p. 1983. 27.95 (ISBN 0-13-943118-7). P-H.

Business Communications Staff. Voice Compression Technology. 1985. pap. 1750.00 (ISBN 0-89336-430-4, G-092). BCC.

Butenschon, Sine & Borchgrevink, Hans. Voice & Song. LC 81-38464. 80p. 1982. pap. 22.95 (ISBN 0-521-28011-7). Cambridge U Pr.

Committee on Evaluation of Sound Spectrograms, National Research Council. On the Theory & Practice of Voice Identification. 1979. pap. text ed. 7.50 (ISBN 0-309-02873-6). Natl Acad Pr.

Damste, P. H. & Lerman, J. W. An Introduction to Voice Pathology: Functional & Organic. (Illus). 120p. 1975. 15.75x (ISBN 0-398-03289-0). C C Thomas.

Fairbanks, Grant. Voice & Articulation Drillbook. 2nd ed. 1960. text ed. 17.50 scp (ISBN 0-06-041990-3, HarpC). Har-Row.

Fracht, J. A. & Robinson, E. Singer's & Speaker's Handbook. 1978. text ed. 15.00 (ISBN 0-8206-0238-8). Chem Pub.

Heath Company. Voice Synthesis. (Illus). 376p. 1983. 129.95 (ISBN 0-87119-091-5, EE-3403A). Heathkit-Zenith Ed.

Hirano, M. Clinical Examination of Voice. (Disorders of Human Communications Ser.: Vol. 5). (Illus). 100p. 1982. 19.80 (ISBN 0-387-81659-3). Springer-Verlag.

Large, John, ed. Contributions of Voice Research to Singing. LC 79-57539. (Illus). 432p. 1980. pap. text ed. 30.00 (ISBN 0-933014-53-8). College-Hill.

Laver, J. The Phonetic Description of Voice Quality. LC 77-82501. (Cambridge Studies in Linguistics: No. 31). (Illus). 225p. 1980. 44.50 (ISBN 0-521-23176-0). Cambridge U Pr.

Laver, John. Voice Quality: A Classified Research Bibliography. (Library & Information Sources in Linguistics Ser.). viii, 225p. 1979. 28.00x (ISBN 90-272-0996-0, 5). Benjamins North Am.

Mayer, Lyle V. Fundamentals of Voice & Diction. 6th ed. 288p. 1982. pap. text ed. write for info. (ISBN 0-697-04195-6). Wm C Brown.

Morse, Ph. A., ed. The Perception of Species-Specific Vocalizations. (Brain, Behavior & Evolution Journal: Vol. 16, No. 5-6). (Illus). iv, 144p. 1980. pap. 13.25 (ISBN 3-8055-0733-X). S Karger.

Moses, Paul J. Voice of Neurosis. LC 54-8213. (Illus). 140p. 1954. 42.00 (ISBN 0-8089-0334-9, 792985). Grune.

VOLATILE OILS

see Essences and Essential Oils

VOLCANIC ASH, TUFF, ETC.

Cook, Earl F., ed. Tufflavas & Ignimbrites. 1966. 23.95 (ISBN 0-444-00008-9, North Holland). Elsevier.

Fisher, R. V. & Schmincke, H. U. Pyroclastic Rocks. (Illus). 350p. 1984. 49.50 (ISBN 0-387-12756-9). Springer-Verlag.

Tan, Kim H. Andosols. 1984. 59.50 (ISBN 0-442-28282-6). Van Nos Reinhold.

VOLCANISM

see also Rocks, Igneous; Volcanoes

Aramaki, S. & Kushiro, I., eds. Arc Volcanism: Selected Papers from the International Symposium on "Arc Volcanism" Held in Tokyo & Hakone & Sponsored by the Volcanological Society of Japan & the International Association of Volcanology & Chemistry of the Earth's Interior, Aug. 31-Sept. 5, 1981. (Developments in Volcanology Ser.: Vol. 2). 634p. 1984. Repr. 88.50 (ISBN 0-444-42234-X, I-307-83). Elsevier.

Axelrod, Daniel I. Role of Volcanism in Climate & Evolution. LC 81-80345. (Special Paper: No. 185). (Illus). 1981. pap. 7.00 (ISBN 0-8137-2185-7). Geol Soc.

Explosive Volcanism, Geophysics Research Board, National Research Council. Explosive Volcanism: Inception, Evolution, & Hazards. 1983. text ed. 24.50 (ISBN 0-309-03393-4). Natl Acad Pr.

Gass, I. G., ed. Volcanic Processes in Ore Genesis. 188p. (Orig). 1980. pap. text ed. 46.00x (ISBN 0-900488-33-6). IMM North Am.

Gorshkov, G. S. Volcanism & the Upper Mantle: Investigations in the Kurile Island Arc. LC 69-12530. (Monographs in Geoscience Ser). 385p. 1970. 39.50x (ISBN 0-306-30407-4, Plenum Pr). Plenum Pub.

Harris, A. L., ed. Nature & Timing of Orogenic Activity in the Caledonian & Hercynian Rocks of the British Isles. (Illus). 64p. 1984. pap. text ed. 25.00x (ISBN 0-632-01298-6). Blackwell Pubns.

Hooke, Robert. Lectures & Discourses of Earthquakes & Subterraneous Eruptions. Albritton, Claude C., Jr., ed. LC 77-6521. (History of Geology Ser). 1978. Repr. of 1705 ed. lib. bdg. 21.00x (ISBN 0-405-10443-X). Ayer Co Pubs.

Iddings, Joseph P. Problem of Volcanism. 1914. 75.00x (ISBN 0-686-50031-8). Elliots Bks.

Le Bas, M. J. Carbonatite-Nephelinite Volcanism: An African Case History. 347p. 1977. 114.95x (ISBN 0-471-99422-7, Pub. by Wiley-Interscience). Wiley.

Lunar & Planetary Institute, Houston, Texas. Basaltic Volcanism on Terrestrial Planets. (Illus). 1200p. 1982. 66.00 (ISBN 0-08-028086-2); student ed. 45.00 (ISBN 0-08-028807-3). Pergamon.

Olson, Gunder E. Story of The Volcano House. (Illus). 1974. pap. 4.95 (ISBN 0-912180-22-6). Petroglyph.

Scrope, George P. The Geology & Extinct Volcanos of the Central France. 2nd rev. ed. Albritton, Claude C., Jr., ed. LC 77-6540. (History of Geology Ser). (Illus). 1978. Repr. of 1858 ed. lib. bdg. 27.00 (ISBN 0-405-10459-6). Ayer Co Pubs.

Sheets, Payson D. & Grayson, Donald K., eds. Volcanic Activity & Human Ecology. LC 79-51701. 1979. 57.50 (ISBN 0-12-639120-3). Acad Pr.

Sheridan, M. F. & Barberi, F., eds. Explosive Volcanism. (Developments in Vulcanology: Vol. 3). 482p. 1983. 84.75 (ISBN 0-444-42251-X, I-389-83). Elsevier.

Simkin, Tom, et al. Volcanoes of the World: A Regional Gazetteer & Chronology of Volcanism During the Last 10,000 Years. LC 81-6594. 240p. 1981. 28.95 (ISBN 0-87933-408-8). Van Nos Reinhold.

Williams, Howel & McBirney, Alexander R. Volcanology. LC 79-50180. (Illus). 1982. Repr. of 1979 ed. text ed. 35.00x (ISBN 0-87735-321-2). Freeman Cooper.

Williams, Howell & Curtis, G. H. The Sutter Buttes of California: A Study of Plio-Pleistocene Volcanism. (Library Reprint Ser.: No. 97). 1979. Repr. of 1977 ed. 16.50x (ISBN 0-520-03808-8). U of Cal Pr.

VOLCANOES

see also Rocks, Igneous; also names of volcanoes, e.g. Hekla, Vesuvius

Bolt, Bruce A., intro. by. Earthquakes & Volcanoes: Readings from Scientific American. LC 79-21684. (Illus). 154p. 1980. text ed. 20.95 (ISBN 0-7167-1163-X); pap. text ed. 10.95 (ISBN 0-7167-1164-8). W H Freeman.

Bullard, Fred M. Volcanoes of the Earth. rev. ed. LC 76-2560. (Illus). 613p. 1976. pap. 19.95 (ISBN 0-292-78705-7). U of Tex Pr.

--Volcanoes of the Earth. 2nd rev. ed. (Illus). 655p. 1984. 35.00 (ISBN 0-292-78706-5). U of Tex Pr.

Civetta, L., et al. Physical Volcanology. (Developments in Solid Earth Geophysics Ser.: Vol. 6). 333p. 1974. 87.25 (ISBN 0-444-41141-0). Elsevier.

Decker, Robert & Decker, Barbara. Volcanoes. LC 80-20126. (Geology Ser). (Illus). 244p. 1981. pap. text ed. 11.95 (ISBN 0-7167-1242-3). W H Freeman.

Francis, Peter. Volcanoes. 1976. pap. 7.95 (ISBN 0-14-021897-1, Pelican). Penguin.

Gangemi, Kenneth. The Volcanoes from Puebla. 192p. 1979. 11.95 (ISBN 0-7145-2577-4, Dist by Scribner). M Boyars.

Harnly, Caroline D. & Tyckoson, David A. Mount St. Helens: An Annotated Bibliography. LC 83-20170. 261p. 1984. 17.50 (ISBN 0-8108-1668-7). Scarecrow.

Johnson, R. W., ed. Volcanism in Australasia. 406p. 1976. 64.00 (ISBN 0-444-41462-2). Elsevier.

Kaye, Glen. Hawaii Volcanoes: The Story Behind the Scenery. LC 76-23359. (Illus). 1976. 8.95 (ISBN 0-916122-41-7); pap. 3.75 (ISBN 0-916122-18-2). KC Pubns.

McBride, L. R. About Hawaii's Volcanoes. (Illus). 1977. pap. 3.75 (ISBN 0-912180-00-5). Petroglyph.

Macdonald, Gordon A. Volcanoes. 1972. 42.95 (ISBN 0-13-942219-6). P-H.

Macdonald, Gordon A., et al. Volcanoes in the Sea: The Geology of Hawaii. 2nd ed. LC 82-23685. (Illus). 527p. 1983. 29.95 (ISBN 0-8248-0832-0). UH Pr.

Mulford, John W. Volcano Watcher's Guide to the Caribbean. LC 75-79949. (Bulletin Ser.: No. 54). (Illus., Orig). 1969. pap. 0.75x (ISBN 0-87737-031-1). Cranbrook.

Pease, Robert W. Modoc County: A Geographic Time Continuum on the California Volcanic Tableland. LC 66-63867. (University of California Publications in Geography Ser.: Vol. 17). pap. 80.00 (ISBN 0-317-29508-X, 2021274). Bks Demand UMI.

Powers of Nature. LC 76-57002. (Special Publication Ser.: No. XII). (Illus). 1978. 6.95 (ISBN 0-87044-234-1); lib. bdg. 8.50 (ISBN 0-87044-239-2). Natl Geog.

Ream, Lenny R. Northwest Volcanoes: A Roadside Geologic Guide. (Illus). 123p. (Orig). 1983. pap. 6.95 (ISBN 0-918499-05-4). Jackson Mtn.

Rinehart, C. Dean & Smith, Ward C. Earthquakes & Young Volcanoes Along the Eastern Sierra Nevada: At Mammoth Lakes 1980, Lone Pine 1872, & Inyo & Mono Craters. Smith, Genny, ed. LC 81-51293. (Illus). 64p. (Orig). 1982. pap. 5.95 (ISBN 0-931378-02-8, Dist. by W. Kaufmann Inc.). Genny Smith Bks.

Rosenfeld, Charles & Cooks, Robert. Earthfire: The Eruption of Mount St. Helens. (Illus). 250p. 1984. pap. 9.95 (ISBN 0-262-68044-0). MIT Pr.

Scientific American. Volcanoes & the Earth's Interior: Readings from Scientific American. LC 81-15092. (Illus). 141p. 1982. text ed. 21.95 (ISBN 0-7167-1383-7); pap. text ed. 10.95 (ISBN 0-7167-1384-5). W H Freeman.

Secor, R. J. Mexico's Volcanoes: A Climbing Guide. (Illus). 120p. (Orig). 1981. pap. text ed. 8.95 (ISBN 0-89886-016-4). Mountaineers.

Simkin, Tom & Fiske, Richard, eds. Krakatau 1883: The Volcanic Eruption & Its Effects. (Illus). 400p. 1983. text ed. 25.00x (ISBN 0-87474-842-9); pap. 19.95x (ISBN 0-87474-841-0). Smithsonian.

Steinbrugge, Karl V. Earthquakes, Volcanoes, & Tsunamis: An Anatomy of Hazards. (Illus). 1982. 35.00 (ISBN 0-9609050-0-6). Skandia.

Tazieff, H. & Sabroux, J. C., eds. Forecasting Volcanic Events. (Developments in Volcanology Ser.: Vol. 1). 1984. 71.25 (ISBN 0-444-42241-2). Elsevier.

Tazieff, Haroun. Nyiragongo: The Forbidden Volcano. Bernard, Jack, tr. from Fr. (Illus). 1979. 16.95 (ISBN 0-8120-5296-X). Barron.

Time-Life Books, ed. Volcano. LC 81-18539. (Planet Earth Ser.: No. 2). (Illus). 1982. 14.95 (ISBN 0-8094-4304-X). Time-Life.

Time-Life Books Editors. Volcano. LC 81-18539. (Planet Earth Ser.). lib. bdg. 19.94 (ISBN 0-8094-4305-8, Pub. by Time-Life). Silver.

Vasilevsky, M. M. Born of Fire. 101p. 1979. pap. 4.45 (ISBN 0-8285-1524-7, Pub. by Mir Pubs USSR). Imported Pubns.

Westervelt, William D., ed. Hawaiian Legends of Volcanoes. LC 63-22542. (Illus). 1963. 7.25 (ISBN 0-8048-0240-8). C E Tuttle.

VOLKSWAGEN (AUTOMOBILE)

see Automobiles, Foreign-Types-Volkswagen

VOLTAGE REGULATORS

Humpage, W. Derek. Z-Transform Electromagnetic Transient Analysis in High-Voltage Networks. (IEE Power Engineering Ser.: No. 3). 264p. 1982. pap. 65.00 (ISBN 0-906048-79-6, P0003, Pub. by Peregrinus England). Inst Elect Eng.

Pressman, Abraham I. Switching & Linear Power Supply, Power Converter Design. (Illus). 1977. text ed. 25.95 (ISBN 0-8104-5847-0); net solutions manual 1.95 (ISBN 0-8104-5827-6). Hayden.

Rieger, Heinz. Alternating Voltage & Current. (Siemens Programmed Instruction Ser.: No. 12). pap. 20.00 (ISBN 0-317-27756-1, 2052089). Bks Demand UMI.

Spencer, John D. & Pippenger, Dale E. The Voltage Regulator Handbook for Design Engineers. LC 77-87869. 1977. pap. 5.65 (ISBN 0-89512-101-8, LCC4350). Tex Instr Inc.

Texas Instruments Engineering Staff. The Voltage Regulator Data Book, 1983. 226p. (Orig.). 1983. pap. text ed. 5.65 (ISBN 0-89512-116-6, SLVD001). Tex Instr Inc.

Vaughn, Martin. IC Voltage Regulator Sourcebook, with Experiments. (Illus.). 196p. (Orig.). 1983. 14.95 (ISBN 0-8306-0157-0); pap. 11.50 (ISBN 0-8306-0557-6, 1557). TAB Bks.

VOLTAIC ARC
see Electric Arc

VOLTAIC CELL
see Electric Batteries

VOLTERRA EQUATIONS

Linz, Peter. Analytical & Numerical Methods for Volterra Equations. LC 84-51968. (Studies in Applied Mathematics: No. 7). xiii, 227p. 1985. text ed. 32.50 (ISBN 0-89871-198-3). Soc Indus-Appl Math.

VOLUME (MATHEMATICS)
see also Gaging; Volumetric Analysis

Circles & Volume: Level Four Texts. rev. ed. (Math Components Ser.). 32p. 1983. 2.00 (ISBN 0-88336-842-0). New Readers.

VOLUME FEEDING
see Food Service

VOLUMETRIC ANALYSIS

Fernando, Quintus & Ryan, Michael D. Calculations in Analytical Chemistry. 241p. 1982. pap. text ed. 12.95 (ISBN 0-15-505710-3, HC). HarbraceJ.

Gyenes, I. Titration in Non-Aqueous Media. 474p. 1968. 24.00 (ISBN 0-442-32925-3, Pub. by Van Nos Reinhold). Krieger.

Huber, Walter. Titrations in Nonaqueous Solvents. 1967. 55.50 (ISBN 0-12-358750-6). Acad Pr.

Humphries, J. W. The Calibration & Verification of Volumetric Measures. 1980. 20.00x (ISBN 0-643-00350-9, Pub. by CSJRO Australia). State Mutual Bk.

Jackson, D. S. Titrimetric Methods. LC 61-17728. 185p. 1961. 25.00x (ISBN 0-306-30155-5, Plenum Pr). Plenum Pub.

Lambert, J., et al. The Essentials of Volumetric Analysis. 2nd ed. 1971. pap. text ed. 4.50x (ISBN 0-435-65534-5). Heinemann Ed.

Phillips, John P. Automatic Titrators. 1959. 53.00 (ISBN 0-12-553456-6). Acad Pr.

Scholz, E. Karl Fischer Titration. Lee, D., tr. from Ger. (Illus.). 150p. 1984. 34.50 (ISBN 0-387-13734-3). Springer-Verlag.

Serjeant, E. P. Potentiometry & Potentiometric Titrations. LC 83-21903. (Chemical Analysis: A Series of Monographs on Analytical Chemistry & it Applications). 725p. 1984. 75.00x (ISBN 0-471-07745-3, 1-075, Pub. by Wiley-Interscience). Wiley.

Stock, John T. Amperometric Titrations. LC 74-32274. 742p. 1975. Repr. of 1965 ed. 44.50 (ISBN 0-88275-268-5). Krieger.

VOLVO (AUTOMOBILE)
see Automobiles, Foreign–Types–Volvo

VON KARMAN, THEODOR, 1881-1963

Theodore von Karman - in Memoriam. 178p. 1965. text ed. 13.00 ltd. ed (ISBN 0-89871-158-4). Soc Indus-Appl Math.

VON NEUMANN ALGEBRAS
see also Hilbert Algebras

Berberian, S. K. Baer-Rings. LC 72-189105. (Die Grundlehren der Mathematischen Wissenschaften Ser.: Vol. 195). 315p. 1972. 37.00 (ISBN 0-387-05751-X). Springer-Verlag.

Dixmier, J. Von Neumann Algebras. (Mathematical Library: Vol. 27). 438p. 1981. 57.50 (ISBN 0-444-86308-7, North-Holland). Elsevier.

Goodearl, K. R. Von Neumann Regular Rings. (Monographs & Studies: Vol. 4). 388p. 1979. text ed. 59.95 (ISBN 0-686-91967-X). Pitman Pub MA.

Greiner, P. C. & Stein, E. M. Estimates of the Neumann Problem. (Mathematical Notes Ser.: No. 19). 1977. 20.00 (ISBN 0-691-08013-5). Princeton U Pr.

Guichardet, A. Lecons Sur Certaines Algebres Topologiques. (Cours & Documents de Mathematiques & de Physique Ser.). (Fr.). 194p. 1967. 57.75x (ISBN 0-677-50010-6). Gordon.

--Special Topics in Topological Algebras. (Notes on Mathematics & Its Applications Ser.). 202p. (Orig.). 1968. 65.95 (ISBN 0-677-30010-7). Gordon.

Heims, Steve J. John Von Neumann & Norbert Wiener: From Mathematics to the Technologies of Life & Death. 546p. 1980. pap. 11.95 (ISBN 0-262-58056-X). MIT Pr.

Nakagami, Y. & Takesaki, M. Duality for Crossed Products of Von Neumann Algebras. (Lecture Notes in Mathematics: Vol. 731). 1979. pap. 13.00 (ISBN 0-387-09522-5). Springer-Verlag.

Olsen, Catherine. Index Theory in Von Neumann Algebras. LC 83-22519. (Memoirs Ser.: No. 294). 72p. 1984. pap. 8.00 (ISBN 0-8218-2295-0). Am Math.

Schwartz, Jacob T. W Algebras. (Notes on Mathematics & Its Applications Ser.). 266p. 1967. 60.25x (ISBN 0-677-00670-5). Gordon.

Stratila, S. & Axido, L. Lectures on Von Neumann Algebras. 1979. 69.00 (ISBN 0-9961001-5-6, Pub. by Abacus England). Heyden.

Van Daele, A. Continuous Crossed Products & Type 111 von Neumann Algebras. LC 77-91096. (London Mathematical Society Lecture Note Ser.: No. 31). 1978. 15.95 (ISBN 0-521-21975-2). Cambridge U Pr.

VOR
see Omnirange System

VORTEX-MOTION
see also Wakes (Fluid Dynamics)

Bengtsson, L. & Lighthill, J., eds. Intense Atmospheric Vortices, Reading UK 1981 Proceedings. (Topics in Atmospheric & Oceanographic Sciences Ser.). (Illus.). 360p. 1982. pap. 29.00 (ISBN 0-387-11657-5). Springer-Verlag.

Lugt, Hans J. Vortex Flow in Nature & Technology. LC 82-23903. 297p. 1983. 53.50x (ISBN 0-471-86925-2, Pub. by Wiley-Interscience). Wiley.

Marchioro, C., et al. Vortex Methods in Two-Dimensional Fluid Dynamics. (Lecture Notes in Physics Ser.: Vol. 203). iii, 137p. 1984. pap. 10.00 (ISBN 0-387-13352-6). Springer-Verlag.

Swift, Walter L., et al, eds. Vortex Flows. 171p. 1980. 28.00 (ISBN 0-686-69866-5, G00181). ASME.

VOYAGES, SCIENTIFIC
see Scientific Expeditions

VULCANISM
see Volcanism

VULCANITE
see Rubber

VULTURES

Rich, P. V. New World Vultures with Old World Affinities. (Contributions to Vertebrate Evolution: Vol. 5). (Illus.). 1979. pap. 16.75 (ISBN 3-8055-0280-X). S Karger.

Wilbur, Sandford R. & Jackson, Jerome A., eds. Vulture Biology & Management. LC 82-45912. (Illus.). 554p. 1983. text ed. 35.00 (ISBN 0-520-04755-9). U of Cal Pr.

W

W ALGEBRAS
see C Algebras; Von Neumann Algebras

WAGON MAKING
see Carriage and Wagon Making

WAGONS
see also Carriages and Carts

Spivey, Towana. A Historical Guide to Wagon Hardware & Blacksmith Supplies. (Contributions of the Museum of the Great Plains Ser.: No. 9). (Illus.). 1979. pap. 13.95 (ISBN 0-685-96446-9). Mus Great Plains.

WAGONS, ARMY
see Vehicles, Military

WAGTAILS

Bent, Arthur C. Life Histories of North American Wagtails, Shrikes, Vireos & Their Allies. (Illus.). 1950. pap. 8.95 (ISBN 0-486-21085-5). Dover.

--Life Histories of North American Wagtails, Shrikes, Vireos & Their Allies. (Illus.). 14.00 (ISBN 0-8446-1644-3). Peter Smith.

WAKES (FLUID DYNAMICS)
see also Cavitation

Fenech, Henri, ed. Heat Transfer & Fluid Flow in Nuclear Systems. LC 81-8670. 300p. 1981. 61.00 (ISBN 0-08-027181-2). Pergamon.

WALKING, ANIMAL
see Animal Locomotion

WALL BOARD
see also Paperboard; Particle Board

Application of Gypsum Board As a Roofing Substrate. write for info. (GA-275). Gypsum Assn.

Gypsum Board Products Glossary of Terminology. write for info. (GA-505-85). Gypsum Assn.

Gypsum Wallboard Winter Related Job Problems. write for info. (GA-220-79). Gypsum Assn.

Kozloski, Arnold. Do Your Own Drywall: An Illustrated Guide. (Illus.). 160p. (Orig.). 1985. 17.95 (ISBN 0-8306-0838-9, 1838); pap. 10.95 (ISBN 0-8306-1838-4). TAB Bks.

Repair of Gypsum Board Joint Ridging. write for info. (GA-221). Gypsum Assn.

Repairing Nails Pops in Gypsum Board Surfaces. write for info. (GA-222). Gypsum Assn.

WALL-PAPER

Hand, Jackson. How to Do Your Own Painting & Wall Papering. (Popular Science Skill Bk.). (Illus.). 1976. (HarpT); pap. 3.95i 2nd ed. 1976 (ISBN 0-06-011793-1, TD-283, HarpT). Har-Row.

How to Wallpaper. (Home Care Guides Ser.). (Illus.). 1981. pap. 2.50 (ISBN 0-686-71126-2). S&S.

Jablonski, Ramona. Victorian Wallpaper Designs. (International Design Library). (Illus.). 48p. 1981. pap. 3.50 (ISBN 0-916144-89-5). Stemmer Hse.

Lennander, Jean. Fifty-Eight Wallpaper Crafts. LC 81-52552. 48p. (Orig.). 1982. pap. 2.95 (ISBN 0-87239-506-5, 2102). Standard Pub.

Oman, Charles C. & Hamilton, Jean. Wallpapers: An International History & Illustrated Survey from the Victoria & Albert Museum. (Illus.). 464p. 1982. 85.00 (ISBN 0-8109-1778-5). Abrams.

Sunset Editors. Wallcoverings. LC 82-81370. (Illus.). 96p. (Orig.). 1982. pap. 5.95 (ISBN 0-376-01719-8, Sunset Bks). Sunset-Lane.

WALLACE, ALFRED RUSSEL, 1823-1913

Fichman, Martin. Alfred Russel Wallace. (English Authors Ser.). 1981. lib. bdg. 14.50 (ISBN 0-8057-6797-5, Twayne). G K Hall.

McKinney, H. Lewis. Wallace & Natural Selection. LC 72-75203. (Studies in the History of Science & Medicine Ser.: No. 8). (Illus.). Repr. of 1972 ed. 29.00 (ISBN 0-8357-9597-7, 2013373). Bks Demand UMI.

Marchant, James. Alfred Russel Wallace: Letters & Reminiscences. LC 74-26273. (History, Philosophy & Sociology of Science Ser). 1975. Repr. 35.00x (ISBN 0-405-06601-5). Ayer Co Pubs.

Wallace, Alfred R. My Life, 2 Vols. LC 72-1668. (Illus.). Repr. of 1905 ed. 84.50 (ISBN 0-404-08184-3). AMS Pr.

WALLS
see also Foundations; Masonry; Sea-Walls

Better Homes & Gardens Editors. Better Homes & Gardens All About Your House: Your Walls & Ceilings. LC 81-70036. (All About Your House Ser.). (Illus.). 160p. 1983. 9.95 (ISBN 0-696-02163-3). BH&G.

Concrete Craftsman Series: Cast-in-Place Walls. 74p. 1984. 1-9 copies 7.95 ea.; 10-49 copies 6.35 ea.; 50 or more copies 4.00 ea.; member bulk prices avail. ALA.

Fields, Curtis P. The Forgotten Art of Building a Stone Wall. LC 78-169930. (Forgotten Arts Ser.). (Illus.). 64p. (Orig.). 1971. pap. 4.95 (ISBN 0-911658-52-1). Yankee Bks.

Gatz, Konrad, et al, eds. Curtain Wall Construction. Stern, David & Winkler, Felix, trs. from Ger. LC 67-29398. (Illus.). 1965. 64.50x (ISBN 0-89197-718-X). Irvington.

Harris, W. R. Drywall: Installation & Design. (Illus.). 168p. 1979. 11.95 (ISBN 0-8269-0703-2). Am Technical.

Kozloski, Arnold. Do Your Own Drywall: An Illustrated Guide. (Illus.). 160p. (Orig.). 1985. 17.95 (ISBN 0-8306-0838-9, 1838); pap. 10.95 (ISBN 0-8306-1838-4). TAB Bks.

Kramer, Jack. Fences, Hedges & Walls. LC 74-11055. (Illus.). 128p. 1975. 8.95 (ISBN 0-684-13891-3, ScribT). Scribner.

Russell, James E. Walks, Walls & Fences. Auer, Marilyn M., ed. LC 81-65752. (Illus., Orig.). 1981. 17.95 (ISBN 0-932944-35-3); pap. 6.95 (ISBN 0-932944-36-1). Creative Homeowner.

Schuler, Stanley. The Wall Book. LC 73-87709. (Illus.). 176p. 1974. 8.95 (ISBN 0-87131-143-7); pap. 4.95 (ISBN 0-87131-150-X). M Evans.

Sunset Editors. Wall Systems & Shelving. LC 81-81381. (Illus.). 96p. (Orig.). 1981. pap. 4.95 (ISBN 0-376-01711-2, Sunset Bks.). Sunset-Lane.

Vivian, John. Building Stone Walls. rev. ed. LC 75-20773. (Illus.). 122p. 1979. pap. 5.95 (ISBN 0-88266-074-8). Garden Way Pub.

West, H. W., et al. The Resistance to Lateral Loads of Walls Built of Calcium Silicate Bricks. 1979. 20.00x (ISBN 0-900910-33-X, Pub. by Brit Ceramic Soc England). State Mutual Bk.

Wilby, C. W. Design Graphs for Brick-Block Double Skin Panel Walls. LC 81-6257. 132p. 1981. 26.95x (ISBN 0-470-27193-0). Halsted Pr.

Window & Wall Testing - STP 552. 75p. 1974. pap. 6.25 (ISBN 0-8031-0600-9, 04-552000-10). ASTM.

WALTON, IZAAK, 1593-1683

Marston, E. Thomas Ken & Izaak Walton: A Sketch of Their Lives & Family Connection. 1908. Repr. 35.00 (ISBN 0-8274-3613-0). R West.

Marston, R. B. Walton & Some Earlier Writers on Fish & Fishing. 1894. Repr. 30.00 (ISBN 0-8274-3691-2). R West.

WANG WORD PROCESSORS

Chaban, Jane. Wang Word Processing Training Program. (Illus.). 272p. 1986. pap. text ed. 22.95 (ISBN 0-13-944729-6). P-H.

Dumpe, Bert. Using the Wang for Business: The Technician's Perspective. 346p. 1984. pap. text ed. 28.70 scp (ISBN 0-06-041801-X, HarpC); instr's. manual avail. (ISBN 0-06-361782-X). Har-Row.

WAR-SHIPS
see Warships

WARBLERS
see Wood Warblers

WARBLING PARAKEET
see Budgerigars

WAREHOUSES
see also Pallets (Shipping, Storage, etc.)

Apple, James M. Material Handling Systems Design. (Illus.). 656p. 1972. 51.50 (ISBN 0-471-06652-4, Pub. by Wiley-Interscience). Wiley.

Automation in Warehousing: Proceedings of the Fifth International Conference, Atlanta, GA, U. S. A., December 1983. 80.00 (ISBN 0-903608-52-9, IFSPUBS). Scholium Intl.

Automation in Warehousing: Proceedings of the Third International Conference, Chicago, 1979 & Stratford-upon-Avon, 1980, 2 Vols. 456p. 1980. Set. pap. 76.00 set (ISBN 0-317-05233-0, Pub. by IFSPUBS). Scholium Intl.

Burton, J. A. Effective Warehousing. 3rd ed. (Illus.). 352p. 1981. pap. text ed. 22.50x (ISBN 0-7121-0591-3). Trans-Atlantic.

Frey, Stephen L. Warehouse Operations. 224p. 1983. 39.95 (ISBN 0-930206-14-2). M-A Pr.

International Conference on Automation in Warehousing, 1st, Univ. of Nottingham, Eng., April 1975. Proceedings. 380p. 1977. pap. 39.00x (ISBN 0-685-89048-1). Scholium Intl.

International Conference on Automation in Warehousing, 2nd, Keele, Eng., Mar. 1977. Proceedings. 300p. 1977. softbound 70.00x (ISBN 0-685-89050-3). Scholium Intl.

Itoh, Teiji. Kura: Design & Tradition of the Japanese Storehouse. abr. ed. Terry, Charles S., tr. from Japanese. LC 80-21087. (Illus.). 192p. 1980. pap. 17.50 (ISBN 0-914842-53-6). Madrona Pubs.

Management's Guide to Efficient Money-Saving Warehousing. 1982. 91.50 (ISBN 0-85013-138-3). Dartnell Corp.

Nelson, Raymond A. Computerizing Warehouse Operations. 250p. 1985. 29.95 (ISBN 0-13-163924-2, Busn). P-H.

Powell, Victor G. Warehousing: Analysis for Effective Operations. 240p. 1976. text ed. 36.75x (ISBN 0-220-66301-7, Pub. by Busn Bks England). Brookfield Pub Co.

Rudman, Jack. Warehouse Examiner. (Career Examination Ser.: C-895). (Cloth bdg. avail. on request). pap. 12.00 (ISBN 0-8373-0895-X). Natl Learning.

--Warehouseman. (Career Examination Ser.: C-890). (Cloth bdg. avail. on request). pap. 10.00 (ISBN 0-8373-0890-9). Natl Learning.

Siegel, Robert L. & Associates for James Knuppe. Development of Miniwarehouses. (Illus.). 55p. 1981. pap. 17.50 (ISBN 0-86718-023-4); pap. 13.00 members. Natl Assn Home.

White, J. A., ed. Automation in Warehousing: Proceedings of the 5th International Conference, Atlanta, GA, Dec. 4-7, 1983. 280p. 1984. 67.50 (ISBN 0-444-86886-0, I-130-84). Elsevier.

WARFARE, MECHANIZED
see Mechanization, Military

WARHAWK (FIGHTER PLANES)
see P-Forty (Fighter Planes)

WARING'S PROBLEM
see Partitions (Mathematics)

WARPING
see Weaving

WARSHIPS
see also Aircraft Carriers; Damage Control (Warships); Submarines
also navies of the various countries, e.g. Great Britain–Navy; also names of ships

Baxter, James P. Introduction of the Ironclad Warship. (Illus.). x, 398p. 1968. Repr. of 1933 ed. 27.50 (ISBN 0-208-00621-4, Archon). Shoe String.

Breyer, Siegfried. Battleships of the World. (Illus.). 570p. 1980. 50.00 (ISBN 0-686-65674-1, Mayflower Bks). Smith Pubs.

Buxton, Ian. Big Gun Monitors: The History of the Design, Construction & Operation of the Royal Navy's Monitors. LC 80-81901. (Illus.). 215p. 1980. 21.95 (ISBN 0-87021-104-8). Naval Inst Pr.

Conway Maritime Editors. Conway's All the World's Fighting Ships Eighteen Sixty to Nineteen Hundred & Five. LC 79-11466. (Illus.). 1979. 35.00 (ISBN 0-8317-0302-4, Mayflower Bks). Smith Pubs.

Conway Maritime Press, ed. All the World's Fighting Ships, 1922-1946. (Illus.). 448p. 1980. 65.00 (ISBN 0-8317-0303-2, Mayflower Bks). Smith Pubs.

Conway Maritime Press Ltd., ed. Conway's All the World's Fighting Ships 1947-1982. 480p. 125.00x (ISBN 0-85177-225-0, Pub. by Conway Maritime England). State Mutual Bk.

Dulin, Robert O., Jr. & Garzke, William H., Jr. Battleships: Allied Battleships of World War Two. LC 79-90551. (Battleships Ser.: Vol. 2). (Illus.). 352p. 1980. 39.95 (ISBN 0-87021-100-5). Naval Inst Pr.

Fletcher, R. A. Warships & Their Story. 1977. lib. bdg. 69.95 (ISBN 0-8490-2808-6). Gordon Pr.

Friedman, Norman. Battleship Design & Development, 1905-1945. LC 78-24525. (Illus.). 1979. 14.95 (ISBN 0-8317-0700-3, Mayflower Bks). Smith Pubs.

--Modern Warship Design & Development. (Illus.). 192p. 1980. 22.50 (ISBN 0-686-65676-8, Mayflower Bks). Smith Pubs.

--The U. S. Destroyers: An Illustrated Design History. (Illus.). 544p. 1982. 46.95 (ISBN 0-87021-733-X). Naval Inst Pr.

Hodges, Peter. The Big Gun: Battleship Main Armament, 1860-1945. LC 80-84051. (Illus.). 160p. 1981. 22.95 (ISBN 0-87021-917-0). Naval Inst Pr.

Hodges, Peter & Friedman, Norman. Destroyer Weapons of World War Two. LC 79-84585. (Illus.). 192p. 1979. 19.95 (ISBN 0-87021-929-4). Naval Inst Pr.

Hovgaard, William. Modern History of Warships. 516p. 1980. 44.50x (ISBN 0-85177-040-1, Pub. by Cornell England). State Mutual Bk.

Howard, Frank. Sailing Ships of War, Fourteen Hundred to Eighteen Sixty. (Illus.). 1980. 29.95 (ISBN 0-8317-7656-0). Smith Pubs.

Howarth, David. The Dreadnoughts. Time-Life Books Editors, ed. (Seafarers Ser.). (Illus.). 1980. 13.95 (ISBN 0-8094-2711-7). Time-Life.

Howarth, David P. The Dreadnoughts. LC 78-27881. (The Seafarers Ser.). (Illus.). 1979. lib. bdg. 21.27 (ISBN 0-8094-2712-5, Pub. by Time-Life); 22.60 (ISBN 0-8094-2713-3). Silver.

Jane's Fighting Ships, 1977-1978. 79.50 (ISBN 0-531-03277-9). Key Bk Serv.

Kent, Earl. Unsafe on Any Sea-L.H.A. Ships of the U.S. Navy. 1976. pap. text ed. 25.00 (ISBN 0-918782-00-7). E Kent.

Lyon, Hugh. An Illustrated Guide to Modern Warships. LC 80-65166. (Illustrated Military Guides Ser.). (Illus.). 160p. 1980. 9.95 (ISBN 0-668-04966-9, 4966-9). Arco.

McKee, Alexander. King Henry VIII's Mary Rose: Its Fate & Future: the Story of One of the Most Exciting Projects in Marine Archaeology. 1978. (Pub. by Souvenir Pr). Intl Spec Bk.

McMahon, William E. Dreadnought Battleships & Battle Cruisers. LC 78-50769. (Illus.). 1978. lib. bdg. 14.75 (ISBN 0-8191-0465-5). U Pr of Amer.

Manning, T. D. The British Destroyer. 1981. 40.00x (ISBN 0-906223-13-X). State Mutual Bk.

Moore, John, ed. Jane's Fighting Ships 1984-85. (Jane's Yearbooks). (Illus.). 1984. 125.00 (ISBN 0-7106-0795-4). Jane's Pub Inc.

Moore, John E. Warships of the Royal Navy. LC 79-84202. (Illus.). 136p. 1979. 12.95 (ISBN 0-87021-978-2). Naval Inst Pr.

--Warships of the Soviet Navy. (Illus.). 224p. 19.50 (ISBN 0-86720-567-9). Jane's Pub Inc.

Moore, John E., ed. Jane's Fighting Ships 1975-76. LC 75-15172. 1975. 79.50 (ISBN 0-531-03251-5). Key Bk Serv.

Morrison, Samuel L. & Rowe, John S. Warships of the U. S. Navy. 1983. 19.95 (ISBN 0-86720-667-5). Jane's Pub Inc.

Overshiner, Elwyn E. Course Zero-Nine-Five to Eternity: The Saga of Destroyer Squadron Eleven. LC 80-82005. (Illus.). 224p. (Orig.). 1980. pap. 4.95 (ISBN 0-937480-00-2). Overshiner.

Pater, Alan F., ed. United States Battleships: The History of America's Greatest Fighting Fleet. LC 68-17423. 1968. 19.95 (ISBN 0-917734-07-6). Monitor.

Pears, Randolph. British Battleships Eighteen Ninety-Two to Nineteen Fifty-Seven. 1981. 40.00x (ISBN 0-906223-14-8). State Mutual Bk.

Preston, Anthony, ed. Warship, Vol. 1. LC 78-55455. (Illus.). 135p. 1978. 23.95 (ISBN 0-87021-975-8). Naval Inst Pr.

Preston, Antony. The Destroyers. LC 77-82132. (Illus.). 1977. 14.95 (ISBN 0-13-202127-7). P-H.

Raven, Alan & Roberts, John. British Battleships of World War Two. LC 76-22915. (Illus.). 436p. 1976. 44.95 (ISBN 0-87021-817-4). Naval Inst Pr.

Reilly, John C. & Scheina, Robert L. American Battleships, Eighteen Eighty-Six to Nineteen Twenty-Three: Predreadnought Design & Construction. LC 79-91326. 236p. 1980. 31.95 (ISBN 0-87021-524-8). Naval Inst Pr.

Reilly, John C., Jr. United States Navy Destroyers of World War II in Action. (Illus.). 160p. 1983. 16.95 (ISBN 0-7137-1026-8, Pub. by Blandford Pr England). Sterling.

Roberts, John. The Battlecruiser Hood. 128p. 1982. 50.00x (ISBN 0-85177-250-1, Pub. by Conway Maritime England). State Mutual Bk.

--The Battlecruiser Hood: Anatomy of the Ship Ser. LC 81-85587. (Illus.). 96p. 1982. 21.95 (ISBN 0-87021-078-5). Naval Inst Pr.

--Warship, Vol. 5. LC 78-55455. (Illus.). 288p. 1982. 23.95 (ISBN 0-87021-980-4). Naval Inst Pr.

Roberts, John, ed. Warship, Vol. IV. LC 78-55455. (Illus.). 292p. 1981. 23.95 (ISBN 0-87021-979-0). Naval Inst Pr.

--Warship, Vol. III. LC 78-55455. (Illus.). 300p. 1981. 23.95 (ISBN 0-87021-977-4). Naval Inst Pr.

Roberts, Walter A. U. S. Navy Fights. facs. ed. (Essay Index Reprint Ser). 1942. 21.00 (ISBN 0-8369-2068-6). Ayer Co Pubs.

Scott, Douglas. The Burning of the Ships. 344p. 1982. pap. 2.75 (ISBN 0-345-29549-8). Ballantine.

Smith, Myron, Jr. Mountaineer Battlewagon: U.S.S. West Virginia (BB-18) 48p. (Orig.). 1982. pap. 5.95 (ISBN 0-933126-16-6). Pictorial Hist.

Taylor, Theodore. H. M. S. Hood vs. Bismarck: The Battleship Battle. (World War II Ser.: Bk. 2). 144p. 1982. pap. 2.25 (ISBN 0-380-81174-X, 81174-X, Flare). Avon.

Toland, John. No Man's Land. 512p. 1982. pap. 3.95 (ISBN 0-345-29865-9). Ballantine.

Trotter, W. P. & Burt, R. A. Battleships of the Grand Fleet. LC 81-86414. (Illus.). 96p. 1982. 19.95 (ISBN 0-87021-916-2). Naval Inst Pr.

U. S. Battleships in Action. 1980. pap. 4.95 (ISBN 0-89747-107-5). Squad Sig Pubns.

U. S. Navy Department. Allied Landing Craft & Ships. (Illus.). 200p. 1985. 11.95 (ISBN 0-87021-064-5). Naval Inst Pr.

Wilson, Herbert W. Battleships in Action, 2 Vols. 1968. Repr. of 1926 ed. Set. 59.00x (ISBN 0-403-00046-7). Scholarly.

Woodward, David. Sunk! How the Great Battleships Were Lost. (Illus.). 176p. 1982. 17.95 (ISBN 0-04-359009-8). Allen Unwin.

WARSHIPS–DAMAGE CONTROL

see Damage Control (Warships)

WASHING

see Laundry and Laundry Industry

WASPS

Coville, Rollin E. Wasps of the Genus Trypoxylon Subgenus Trypargilum in North America: Hymenoptera: Sphecidae. (Publications in Entomology Ser.: Vol. 97). 1982. pap. 17.00x (ISBN 0-520-09651-7). U of Cal Pr.

Evans & Matthews. Systematics & Nesting Behavior of Australian Bembix Sand Wasps - (Hymenoptera, Sphecidae) (Memoirs Ser: No. 20). (Illus.). 1973. 35.00x (ISBN 0-686-17148-9). Am Entom Inst.

Evans, Howard E. Wasp Farm. LC 77-90903. (Illus.). 208p. (Orig.). 1985. pap. text ed. 9.95x (ISBN 0-8014-9315-3). Cornell U Pr.

Evans, Howard E. & Eberhard, Mary J. The Wasps. LC 71-124448. (Ann Arbor Science Library Ser.). 272p. 1970. 7.95 (ISBN 0-472-00118-3). U of Mich Pr.

Fabre, J. Henri. The Hunting Wasps. 1930. 20.00 (ISBN 0-8482-3987-3). Norwood Edns.

Krombein, Karl V. Biosystematic Studies of Ceylonese Wasps, XIV: A Revision of Carinostigmus Tauneki. LC 84-600058. (Smithsonian Contributions to Zoology: No. 396). pap. 20.00 (ISBN 0-317-26750-7, 2024352). Bks Demand UMI.

Porter, Charles. A Revision of the South American Species of Trachysphyrus - (Hymenoptera, Ichneumonidae) (Memoirs Ser: No. 10). (Illus.). 387p. 1967. 25.00x (ISBN 0-686-17146-2). Am Entom Inst.

Richards, O. W. The Australian Social Wasps: (Hymenoptera: Vespidae) (Illus.). 132p. 1978. pap. text ed. 7.50x (ISBN 0-686-30717-8, Pub. by Brit Mus Nat Hist England). Sabbot-Natural Hist Bks.

--The Social Wasps of the Americas Excluding the Vespinae. (Illus.). 1978. 88.00x (ISBN 0-565-00785-8, Pub. by Brit Mus Nat Hist). Sabbot-Natural Hist Bks.

Spoczynska, Joy D. The World of the Wasp. LC 74-13621. 188p. 1975. 18.50x (ISBN 0-8448-0560-2). Crane-Russak Co.

Spradbery, J. Philip. Wasps: An Account of the Biology & Natural History of Social & Solitary Wasps. LC 73-7872. (Biology Ser). (Illus.). 424p. 1973. 35.00x (ISBN 0-295-95287-3). U of Wash Pr.

Wasbauer, Marius S. & Kimsey, Lynn S. Spider Wasps of the Subfamily Pompilinae (Hymenoptern: Pompilidae) LC 85-1060. 1985. 18.00x (ISBN 0-520-09957-5). U of Cal Pr.

WASTE, DISPOSAL OF

see Factory and Trade Waste; Refuse and Refuse Disposal; Sewage Disposal

WASTE AS FUEL

see Refuse As Fuel

WASTE HEAT

Bhumralker, Williams. Atmospheric Effects of Waste Heat Discharges: Energy, Power & Environment, Vol. 13. 203p. 1982. pap. 35.00 (ISBN 0-8247-1653-1). Dekker.

Conference on Waste Heat Management & Utilization, Miami Beach, May 9-11, 1977. Waste Heat Management & Utilization: Proceedings, 3 vols. new ed. Lee, S. S. & Sengupta, S., eds. LC 78-13267. (Illus.). 2541p. 1979. Set. text ed. 340.00 (ISBN 0-89116-158-9). Hemisphere Pub.

Eisenbud, M. & Gleason, G. Electric Power & Thermal Discharges: Thermal Considerations in the Production of Electric Power. 454p. 1969. 85.75 (ISBN 0-677-03290-0). Gordon.

Godfriaux, Bruce L., ed. Power Plant Waste Heat Utilization in Aquaculture. LC 78-73590. 288p. 1979. text ed. 38.00 (ISBN 0-916672-24-7). Allanheld.

Goss, L. Barry, ed. Factors Affecting Power Plant Waste Heat Utilization: Proceedings of a Workshop Held in Atlanta, Georgia, 28 Nov. - 1 Dec., 1978. LC 79-29656. (Illus.). 230p. 1980. 24.00 (ISBN 0-08-025548-5). Pergamon.

International Advanced Course & Workshop on Thermal Effluent Disposal from Power Generation, Aug. 23-28, 1976, Dubrovnik, Yugoslavia. Thermal Effluent Disposal from Power Generation: Proceedings. Zaric, Z., ed. LC 77-28808. (Thermal & Fluids Engineering, International Centre for Heat & Mass Transfer Ser.). (Illus.). 375p. 1978. text ed. 74.50 (ISBN 0-89116-093-0). Hemisphere Pub.

Kenney, W. F. Recovering Waste Heat. Gyftopoulos, Elias P. & Cohen, Karen C., eds. (Industrial Energy-Conservation Manuals: No. 8). (Illus.). 88p. 1982. loose-leaf 20.00x (ISBN 0-262-11081-4). MIT Pr.

Rimberg, David. Utilization of Waste Heat from Power Plants. LC 74-82359. (Pollution Technology Review No. 14; Energy Technology Review No. 3). (Illus.). 175p. 1975. 18.00 (ISBN 0-8155-0555-8). Noyes.

Sengupta, Subrata & Lee, Samuel S., eds. Waste Heat: Utilization & Management. LC 82-6095. (Illus.). 1010p. 1983. text ed. 125.00 (ISBN 0-89116-256-9). Hemisphere Pub.

Thumann, Albert. The Waste Heat Recovery Handbook. 250p. 1983. text ed. 36.00 (ISBN 0-915586-64-9). Fairmont Pr.

Use of Organic Fluids for Waste Heat Recovery in Ships & Industry. 1981. 125.00x (ISBN 0-686-97129-9, Pub. by Marine Mgmt England). State Mutual Bk.

WASTE LANDS

see also Drainage; Fens; Irrigation; Marshes; Moors and Heaths; Reclamation of Land; Sand Dunes

Young, Arthur. General Report on Enclosures, Drawn up by Order of the Board of Agriculture. LC 72-120417. 1970. Repr. of 1808 ed. 37.50x (ISBN 0-678-00702-0). Kelley.

WASTE MANAGEMENT

see Salvage (Waste, etc.)

WASTE OIL

see Petroleum Waste

WASTE PAPER

Plaut, Thomas. An Econometric Analysis of Regional Wastepaper Markets. (Discussion Paper Ser.: No. 104). 1978. pap. 3.25 (ISBN 0-686-32270-3). Regional Sci Res Inst.

Plaut, Thomas & Steiker, Gene. Characteristics of Wastepaper Markets & Trends in Scrap Paper Recycling, Prices, Demand & Availability: A National & Regional Overview. (Discussion Paper Ser.: No. 103). 1978. pap. 3.25 (ISBN 0-686-32269-X). Regional Sci Res Inst.

Waste Paper Data: 1975-1976. pap. 7.50 (F1270, FAO). Unipub.

WASTE PRODUCTS

see also Factory and Trade Waste; Reactor Fuel Reprocessing; Recycling (Waste, etc.); Refuse and Refuse Disposal

Anderson, L. L. & Tillman, D. A., eds. Fuels from Waste. 1977. 55.00 (ISBN 0-12-056450-5). Acad Pr.

Arthur. New Concepts & Practices in Activated Sludge Process Control. LC 81-69767. (Activated Sludge Process Control Ser.). 125p. 1982. 34.95 (ISBN 0-250-40528-8). Butterworth.

Bell. Purdue Thirty-Sixth Industrial Waste Conference Proceedings. LC 77-84415. 997p. 1982. 75.00 (ISBN 0-250-40493-1). Butterworth.

Bewick, Michael W., ed. Handbook of Organic Waste Conversion. (Van Nostrand Reinhold Environmental Engineering Ser.). 432p. 1980. 29.95 (ISBN 0-442-20679-8). Van Nos Reinhold.

Cargo, Douglas B. Solid Wastes: Factors Influencing Generation Rates. LC 78-16823. (Research Papers Ser.: No. 174). (Illus.). 1978. pap. 10.00 (ISBN 0-89065-081-0). U Chicago Dept Geog.

Cherry. Plating Waste Treatment. LC 81-68033. 324p. 1982. 59.95 (ISBN 0-250-40417-6). Butterworth.

Conference on Disposal of Solid Waste Materials (1977, University of Michigan) Geotechnical Practice for Disposal of Solid Waste Material: Proceedings of the Conference on June 13-15, 1977, University of Michigan, Ann Arbor, Michigan. LC 77-152066. (Illus.). pap. 160.00 (ISBN 0-317-10625-2, 2019547). Bks Demand UMI.

Exner, Jurgen H., ed. Detoxication of Hazardous Waste. LC 82-70696. (Illus.). 362p. 1982. 39.95 (ISBN 0-250-40521-0). Butterworth.

Ferrero, G. L., et al, eds. Anaerobic Digestion & Carbohydrate Hydrolysis of Waste: Proceedings of an EEC Seminar Held 8-10 May 1984, Luxembourg. 536p. 1984. 72.00 (ISBN 0-85334-324-1, Pub. by Elsevier Applied Sci England). Elsevier.

Gloyna, E. F. Waste Stabilization Ponds. (Monographs Ser: No. 60). 175p. 1971. pap. 8.00 (ISBN 92-4-140060-9, 1444). World Health.

Joy, C. & Hickson, W. Liquid Waste Management. (Botany Bay Project Working Paper Ser.: No. 2). 1978. pap. 7.95 (ISBN 0-7081-1343-5, Pub by ANUP Australia). Australia N U P.

Jurgensen, Barbara. How to Live Better on Less: A Guide for Waste Watchers. 3.95 (ISBN 0-686-95848-9). Alternatives.

Leidner. Plastics Waste. (Plastics Engineering Ser.: Vol. 1). 328p. 1981. 44.00 (ISBN 0-8247-1381-8). Dekker.

Long, F. A. & Schweitzer, Glenn E., eds. Risk Assessment at Hazardous Waste Sites. LC 82-16376. (Symposium Ser.: No. 204). 128p. 1982. lib. bdg. 29.95 (ISBN 0-8412-0747-X). Am Chemical.

Lowrance, William W., ed. Assessment of Health Effects at Chemical Waste Disposal Sites. LC 81-15397. (Illus.). 172p. (Orig.). 1982. pap. text ed. 12.50 (ISBN 0-86576-025-X). W Kaufmann.

Mallow, Alex. Hazardous Waste Regulations: An Interpretive Guide. 640p. 1981. 44.00 (ISBN 0-442-21935-0). Van Nos Reinhold.

Malushitsky, Yuri N. Centrifugal Model Testing of Waste-Heap Embankments. Schofield, A. N., ed. LC 78-67431. (Illus.). 1981. 84.50 (ISBN 0-521-22423-3). Cambridge U Pr.

Neal, A. W. Formation & Use of Industrial by-Products: A Guide. 1975. 19.95x (ISBN 0-8464-0420-6). Beekman Pubs.

Parker, Homer. Wastewater Systems Engineering. (Illus.). 464p. 1975. 41.95 (ISBN 0-13-945758-5). P-H.

Stafford, D. A., et al. Methane Production from Waste Organic Matter. LC 78-31274. 304p. 1980. 86.50 (ISBN 0-8493-5223-1). CRC Pr.

Sundstrom, Donald W. & Klei, Herbert E. Wastewater Treatment. LC 78-13058. (Illus.). 1979. 41.95 (ISBN 0-13-945832-8). P-H.

Taiganides, E. P., ed. Animal Wastes. (Illus.). 429p. 1977. 77.75 (ISBN 0-85334-721-2, Pub. by Elsevier Applied Sci England). Elsevier.

Tolley, George S. & Havlicek, Joseph, Jr., eds. Environmental Policy Series Vol. IV: Solid Waste. 312p. 1985. prof. ref. 39.95 ea. (ISBN 0-88410-627-6). Ballinger Pub.

Volume Reduction of Low-Activity Solid Wastes. (Technical Reports Ser.: No. 106). (Illus., Orig.). 1970. pap. 7.25 (ISBN 92-0-125170-X, IDC106, IAEA). Unipub.

Waste Recovery by Micro-Organisms. 1978. pap. 13.25 (ISBN 0-685-65236-X, UM36, UNESCO). Unipub.

WASTE RECYCLING

see Recycling (Waste, etc.)

WASTE REUSE

see Recycling (Waste, etc.)

WASTE WATERS

see Sewage

WASTES, AGRICULTURAL

see Agricultural Wastes

WASTES, NUCLEAR

see Radioactive Wastes

WASTES, RADIOACTIVE

see Radioactive Wastes

WATCH MAKERS

see Clock and Watch Makers

WATCH MAKING

see Clock and Watch Making

WATCH REPAIRING

see Clocks and Watches–Repairing and Adjusting

WATCHES

see Clocks and Watches

WATFIV (COMPUTER PROGRAM LANGUAGE)

Basso, Daivd T. & Schwartz, Ronald D. Programming with FORTRAN-WATFOR-WATFIV. (Orig.). 1981. pap. text ed. 15.95 (ISBN 0-316-08315-1); tchr's ed. avail. (ISBN 0-316-08317-8). Little.

Bauer, C. R. & Peluso, A. P. Basic FORTRAN IV with WATFOR & WATFIV. 1974. 21.95 (ISBN 0-201-00411-9). Addison-Wesley.

Boillot, Michel H. & Shingles, Carol R. Understanding WATFIV. (Illus.). 1980. pap. text ed. 22.95 (ISBN 0-8299-0232-5). West Pub.

Carnahan, Brice & Wilkes, James O. Digital Computing & Numerical Methods with FORTRAN IV WATFOR & WATFIV Programming. LC 72-13010. 477p. 1973. text ed. 45.45 (ISBN 0-471-13500-3). Wiley.

Chattergy, Rahul & Pooch, Udo W. Top-Down, Modular Programming in FORTRAN with WATFIV. 217p. (Orig.). 1980. pap. 16.95 (ISBN 0-316-13826-6). Little.

Conway, Richard & Archer, James. Programming for Poets: A Gentle Introduction Using FORTRAN with WATFIV. (Orig.). 1978. pap. text ed. 16.95 (ISBN 0-316-15421-0). Little.

Cress, P., et al. FORTRAN IV with WATFOR & WATFIV. 1970. ref. ed. 22.95 (ISBN 0-13-329433-1). P-H.

--Structured FORTRAN with WATFIV-S. 1980. pap. 22.95 (ISBN 0-13-854752-1). P-H.

Forsythe, Alexandra I., et al. Computer Science: Programming in FORTRAN IV with WATFOR-WATFIV. LC 74-96044. 210p. 1975. pap. 14.00x (ISBN 0-471-26685-X). Wiley.

Holt, R. C. & Hume, J. N. Fundamentals of Structured Programming Using FORTRAN with SF-K & WATFIV-S. 2nd ed. (Illus.). 1977. pap. text ed. 18.95 (ISBN 0-87909-302-1). Reston.

McKeown, Patrick G. Structured Programming Using WATFIV. 405p. 1985. pap. text ed. 19.95 (ISBN 0-15-584414-8, HC). HarBraceJ.

Stuart, Frederic. WATFOR WATFIV FORTRAN Programming. LC 78-162424. 239p. 1971. pap. 30.50 (ISBN 0-471-83471-8). Wiley.

Tremblay, Jean P. & Bunt, Richard B. Structured FORTRAN WATFIV-S Programming. 1979. pap. text ed. 24.95 (ISBN 0-07-065171-X). McGraw.

Wei, Yin-Min & Post, Richard. Elements of Computers & Programming with WAFTIV. 175p. 1985. pap. text ed. 15.95x (ISBN 0-89787-405-6). Gorsuch Scarisbrick.

WATER

see also Erosion; Feed-Water; Floods; Glaciers; Hail; Hydraulic Engineering; Ice; Lakes; Moisture; Ocean; Oceanography; Rain and Rainfall; Rivers; Sea-Water; Snow; Springs; Steam; Wells

also headings beginning with the word Water

American Society of Civil Engineers & American Water Works Association, eds. Glossary: Water & Wastewater Control Engineering. LC 80-70933. 398p. 1969. 25.00x (ISBN 0-87262-262-2). Am Soc Civil Eng.

Annual Conferences Proceedings, 1982. 1282p. 68.60 (ISBN 0-686-44871-5). Am Water Wks Assn.

ASCE Hydraulics Division, Univ. of Minnesota, June, 1980. Surface Water Impoundments, 2 vols. Stefan, H., ed. LC 81-67445. 1724p. 1981. Set. pap. 115.00x (ISBN 0-87262-271-1). Am Soc Civil Eng.

Ben-Naim, Arieh. Water & Aqueous Solutions: Introduction to a Molecular Theory. LC 74-7325. (Illus.). 474p. 1974. 65.00x (ISBN 0-306-30774-X, Plenum Pr). Plenum Pub.

Bennett, Gary F., ed. Water: Nineteen Eighty. LC 81-93783. (AIChE Symposium Ser.: Vol. 77). 344p. 1981. pap. 38.00 (ISBN 0-8169-0217-8, S-209); pap. 20.00 members. Am Inst Chem Eng.

Bjorseth, A. & Angeletti, G., eds. Analysis of Organic Micropollutants in Water. 1982. 49.50 (ISBN 90-277-1398-7, Pub. by Reidel Holland). Kluwer Academic.

Bowen, Robert. Surface Water. 290p. 1982. 60.95x (ISBN 0-471-87418-3, Pub. by Wiley-Interscience). Wiley.

Bragg, Paul C. & Bragg, Patricia. Shocking Truth About Water. 24th ed. LC 77-101348. pap. 4.95 (ISBN 0-87790-000-0). Health Sci.

Brown, William E. & Sacks, Richard S. Review Manual for Operators. LC 81-68888. (Illus.). 182p. 1981. pap. text ed. 19.95 (ISBN 0-250-40501-6). Butterworth.

Cairns, John, Jr., et al. Biological Monitoring of Water & Effluent Quality-STP 607. 242p. 1977. 24.25 (ISBN 0-8031-0190-2, 04-607000-16). ASTM.

Carmichael, W. W., ed. The Water Environment: Algal Toxins & Health. (Environmental Science Research Ser.: Vol. 20). 504p. 1981. 69.50 (ISBN 0-306-40756-6, Plenum Pr). Plenum Pub.

Catalan Lafuente, Jose. Diccionario Tecnico Del Agua. (Span.). 301p. 1977. pap. 29.95 (ISBN 84-400-2913-6, S-50098). French & Eur.

Chorley, Richard J., ed. Water, Earth & Man. 1969. 58.00x (ISBN 0-416-12030-X, NO. 2138). Methuen Inc.

Chow Ven Te, ed. Advances in Hydroscience, 12 vols. Incl. Vol. 1. 1964. 87.50 (ISBN 0-12-021801-1); Vol. 2. 1966. 87.50 (ISBN 0-12-021802-X); Vol. 3. 1967. 87.50 (ISBN 0-12-021803-8); Vol. 4. 1968. 87.50 (ISBN 0-12-021804-6); Vol. 5. 1969. 87.50 (ISBN 0-12-021805-4); Vol. 6. 1970. 87.50 (ISBN 0-12-021806-2); Vol. 7. 1971. 87.50 (ISBN 0-12-021807-0); Vol. 8. 1972. 87.50 (ISBN 0-12-021808-9); Vol. 9. 1973. 87.50 (ISBN 0-12-021809-7); Vol. 10. 1975. 90.00 (ISBN 0-12-021810-0); Vol. 11. 1978. 90.00 (ISBN 0-12-021811-9); lib. bdg. 120.00 o.p (ISBN 0-12-021876-3); Vol. 12. 1981. 80.00 (ISBN 0-12-021812-7). Acad Pr.

Cocannouer, Joseph. Water & the Cycle of Life. 10.95 (ISBN 0-8159-7202-4). Devin.

Cooper, P. F. & Atkinson, B., eds. Biological Fluidised Bed Treatment of Water & Wastewater. LC 80-41740. 411p. 1981. 106.95 (ISBN 0-470-27112-4). Halsted Pr.

Degremont Company. Water Treatment Handbook. 5th ed. LC 79-87503. 1186p. 1979. 89.95x (ISBN 0-470-26749-6). Halsted Pr.

Deming, H. G. Water: The Fountain of Opportunity. Gillam, W. S. & McCoy, W. S., eds. (Illus.). 1975. 25.00x (ISBN 0-19-501841-9). Oxford U Pr.

Dictionnaire Technique de L'Eau. (Fr.). pap. 19.95 (ISBN 0-686-57115-0, M-6156). French & Eur.

The Environment, Water, & the Coast, 1977-1982. LC 83-26398. 108p. (Orig.). 1984. pap. 4.00 (ISBN 0-87772-296-X). Inst Gov Stud Berk.

Fischer, Hugo B. & List, E. John. Mixing in Inland & Coastal Waters. 1979. 50.00 (ISBN 0-12-258150-4). Acad Pr.

Franks, Felix & Mathias, S. F. Biophysics of Water: Proceedings of a Working Conference Held at Girton College Cambridge, June 29 - July 3, 1981. 400p. 1982. 69.95x (ISBN 0-471-10229-6, Pub. by Wiley-Interscience). Wiley.

Geraghty, Miller, Van der Leeden, & Troise. Water Atlas of the U. S. 3rd ed. LC 73-76649. 1973. 45.00 (ISBN 0-912394-03-X). Water Info.

Glysson, E. A., et al, eds. Innovations in the Water & Wastewater Fields. (Illus.). 240p. 1984. text ed. 34.95 (ISBN 0-250-40645-4). Butterworth.

Greacen, E. L. Soil Water Assessment by the Neutron Method. 148p. 1982. pap. 21.75 (ISBN 0-643-00414-9, C063, CSIRO). Unipub.

Halldin, S. Comparison of Forest Water & Energy Exchange Models: Proceeding Workshop Held in Sweden, September 1978. (Developments in Agriculture & Managed-Forest Ecology Ser.: Vol. 9). 258p. 1980. 68.00 (ISBN 0-444-41844-X). Elsevier.

Hammer, Mark J. Water & Waste-Water Technology, SI Version. LC 77-9243. 504p. 1977. 35.95 (ISBN 0-471-03787-7); solutions manual 6.50 (ISBN 0-471-03819-9). Wiley.

Harper, D. M. & Bullock, J. A., eds. Rutland Water: A Decade of Change. 1982. lib. bdg. 54.50 (ISBN 90-6193-759-0, Pub. by Junk Pubs Netherlands). Kluwer Academic.

Hawkins, Donald T. Physical & Chemical Properties of Water: A Bibliography, 1957-1974. LC 76-4552. 570p. 1976. 110.00x (ISBN 0-306-65164-5, IFI Plenum). Plenum Pub.

Hepple, P., ed. Joint Problems of the Oil & Water Industries. (Illus.). 195p. 1967. 29.75 (ISBN 0-444-39953-4, Pub. by Elsevier Applied Sci England). Elsevier.

Hunt, Cynthia A. & Garrels, Robert M. Water: The Web of Life. LC 78-152663. (Illus.). 1972. text ed. 9.95 (ISBN 0-393-06386-0); pap. 3.95x (ISBN 0-393-09407-3). Norton.

Ilmavirta, V. & Jones, R. I. Lakes & Water Management. 1982. 54.50 (ISBN 90-6193-758-2, Pub. by Junk Pubs Netherlands). Kluwer Academic.

Ives, Richard. Notes from the Water Journals. 1980. pap. 4.00 (ISBN 0-917652-20-7). Confluence Pr.

Jenkins, S. H. Workshop Progress in Water, Vol. 7, bks. 5-6. 7th ed. 99.00 (ISBN 0-08-019841-4). Pergamon.

Kilpatrick, F. & Matchett, D., eds. Water & Energy: Technical & Policy Issues. LC 82-71351. 668p. 1982. pap. 52.00x (ISBN 0-87262-308-4). Am Soc Civil Eng.

Kottegoda, N. T. Stochastic Water Resources Technology. LC 79-23032. 384p. 1980. 74.95x (ISBN 0-470-98975-0). Halsted Pr.

Lamont, I. M. Water Research Topics, Vol. 1. (Series in Water Research Topics). 263p. 1981. 74.95x (ISBN 0-470-27212-0). Halsted Pr.

Langworthy, ed. Water Treatment Plant Operation, 4 vols. 1981. Set. 69.95 (ISBN 0-250-40500-8). Butterworth.

Leopold, Luna B. Water: A Primer. LC 73-19844. (Geology Ser.). (Illus.). 172p. 1974. text ed. 22.95 (ISBN 0-7167-0264-9); pap. text ed. 12.95 (ISBN 0-7167-0263-0). W H Freeman.

Luck, Werner A. Structure of Water & Aqueous Solutions. (Illus.). 590p. 1974. 67.50x (ISBN 3-527-25588-5). VCH Pubs.

Manual on Water, STP 442A. 4th ed. 471p. 1978. pap. 28.50 (ISBN 0-8031-0503-7, 04-442010-16); Supplement to Manual on Water-STP 442A-S1 1983. pap. 12.00 (ISBN 0-8031-0504-5, 04 442011 6). ASTM.

Marston, Edwin H. The Dynamic Environment: Water, Transportation, & Energy. LC 74-82346. pap. 108.00 (ISBN 0-317-10809-3, 2012461). Bks Demand UMI.

Miller, David H., ed. Water at the Surface of the Earth: Student Edition. LC 82-13769. (International Geophysics Ser.). 1982. 26.50 (ISBN 0-12-496752-3). Acad Pr.

Molyneux, P. Water-Soluble Synthetic Polymers: Properties & Behavior, Vol. I. 240p. 1984. 75.00 (ISBN 0-8493-6135-4). CRC Pr.

--Water-Soluble Synthetic Polymers: Properties & Behavior, Vol. II. 280p. 1984. 83.00 (ISBN 0-8493-6136-2). CRC Pr.

Powers of Nature. LC 76-57002. (Special Publication Ser.: No. XII). (Illus.). 1978. 6.95 (ISBN 0-87044-234-1); lib. bdg. 8.50 (ISBN 0-87044-239-2). Natl Geog.

Powledge, Fred. Water: The Nature, Uses & Future of Our Most Precious & Abused Resource. 1983. pap. 8.95 (ISBN 0-374-51798-3). FS&G.

Pushkarev, V. V., et al. Treatment of Oil-Containing Wastewater. LC 83-70667. viii, 214p. 1983. 42.50 (ISBN 0-89864-004-0). Allerton Pr.

Roger, Dominque, photos by. Precious Water. (Eng., Fr. & Span.). 72p. 1981. 17.00 (ISBN 92-3-001963-1, U1199, UNESCO). Unipub.

Roth. Collins Guide to the Weather. 29.95 (ISBN 0-00-219010-9, Collins Pub England). Greene.

United Nations Economic Commission for Europe, Committee on Water Problems. Selected Water Problems in Islands & Coastal Waters: Proceedings, Malta, 1978. (ECE Seminars & Symposia). (Illus.). 110.00 (ISBN 0-08-024447-5). Pergamon.

Vuks, M. F. & Sidorova, A. I., eds. Water in Biological Systems, Vol. 3. LC 69-12513. 82p. 1971. 25.00x (ISBN 0-306-19003-6, Consultants). Plenum Pub.

Water Practice Manuals: Recreation, Water & Land. 336p. 1981. 55.00x (ISBN 0-901427-11-X, Pub. by Inst Water Eng). State Mutual Bk.

Water: Where Water Comes From. (Better Farming Ser.: No. 28). 31p. 1981. pap. 7.50 (ISBN 92-5-101086-2, F2265, FAO). Unipub.

Wolman, Abel. Water, Health, & Society: Selected Papers. White, Gilbert F., ed. LC 69-16005. pap. 103.00 (ISBN 0-317-11256-2, 2055237). Bks Demand UMI.

World Meteorological Organization. Weather & Water. 1966. pap. 2.00 (ISBN 0-685-22348-5, W51, WMO). Unipub.

Young, Virgil E. Sprinkler Irrigation System. rev. 3rd ed. (Illus.). 200p. (Orig.). 1976. pap. text ed. 4.98 (ISBN 0-916970-01-9). Mist'er Rain.

WATER–ANALYSIS

see also Water–Composition

Albone, D. J. & Payne, K. W. The Determination of Microgram Quantities of Sulphur & Other Elements in Rainwater by X-Ray Fluorescence Spectrometry, 1978. 1981. 40.00x (ISBN 0-686-97056-X, Pub. by W Spring England). State Mutual Bk.

American Water Works Association. Simplified Procedures for Water Examination, Including Supplement on Instrumental Methods - M12. (AWWA Manuals). (Illus.). 190p. 1978. pap. text ed. 20.40 (ISBN 0-89867-070-5). Am Water Wks Assn.

--Standard Methods for the Examination of Water & Wastewater. 15th ed. (General References Ser.). (Illus.). 1200p. 1980. text ed. 50.00 (ISBN 0-89867-262-7). Am Water Wks Assn.

Analyzing Organics in Drinking Water. (AWWA Handbooks Ser.). (Illus.). 120p. 1981. pap. text ed. 17.10 (ISBN 0-89867-256-2). Am Water Wks Assn.

ASTM Power Plant Water Analysis Manual. 232p. 1984. pap. text ed. 39.00 (ISBN 0-8031-0200-3, 0341918416); Lab Manual. 44.00 (ISBN 0-8031-0201-1, 0341908416). ASTM.

Boyd, Claude E. Water Quality in Warmwater Fish Ponds. (Illus.). 359p. 1979. pap. 9.95 (ISBN 0-8173-0055-4, Pub. by Ag Experiment). U of Ala Pr.

Camp, Thomas & Meserve, Robert L. Water & Its Impurities. 2nd ed. LC 74-7012. (Illus.). 384p. 1974. 48.50 (ISBN 0-87933-112-7). Van Nos Reinhold.

Cardwell, Rick D., et al, eds. Aquatic Toxicology & Hazard Assessment-STP 854: Seventh Symposium. LC 84-70338. (Illus.). 590p. 1985. text ed. 60.00 (ISBN 0-8031-0410-3, 04-854000-16). ASTM.

Cheremisinoff, Paul N., et al. Groundwater-Leachate - Modeling-Monitoring-Sampling. LC 84-51875. 146p. 1984. pap. 24.50 (ISBN 0-87762-376-7). Technomic.

Ciaccio, Leoanrd L., ed. Water & Water Pollution Handbook, Vol. 3. 1972. 95.00 (ISBN 0-8247-1117-3). Dekker.

Ciaccio, Leonard L., ed. Water & Water Pollution Handbook, Vol. 1. 1971. 95.00 (ISBN 0-8247-1104-1). Dekker.

--Water & Water Pollution Handbook, Vol. 2. 400p. 1971. 95.00 (ISBN 0-8247-1116-5). Dekker.

Cottrell, A. H. The Mechanical Properties of Matter. LC 80-12439. 340p. 1981. Repr. of 1964 ed. lib. bdg. 23.50 (ISBN 0-89874-168-8). Krieger.

Crompton, T. R. Determination of Organic Substances in Water, 2 vols. 1985. Vol. 1. 85.00 (ISBN 0-471-90468-6); Vol. 2. write for info. (ISBN 0-471-90469-4). Wiley.

Dorsey, Noah E. Properties of Ordinary Water-Substances in All Its Phases: Water-Vapor, Water, & All the Ices. LC 68-19563. (American Chemical Society Monograph Ser.: No. 81). pap. 160.00 (ISBN 0-317-09001-1, 2015237). Bks Demand UMI.

Ferronsky, V. I. & Polyakov, V. A. Environmental Isotopes in the Hydrosphere. 466p. 1982. 79.95x (ISBN 0-471-10114-1, Pub. by Wiley-Interscience). Wiley.

Flaud, J. M. & Camy-Peyret, C. Water Vapour Line Parameters from Microwave to Medium Infrared: An Atlas of H2 to the Sixteenth, O; H2 to the Seventeenth, O; H2 to the Eighteenth, O; Line Positions & Intensities Between O & 4350 Cm to the -1. (International Tables of Constants Ser.: Vol. 19). xvi, 259p. 1981. 83.00 (ISBN 0-08-026181-7). Pergamon.

Franks, Felix. Polywater. 224p. 1981. pap. 5.95 (ISBN 0-262-56029-1). MIT Pr.

Franks, Felix, ed. Water: A Comprehensive Treatise, 6 vols. Incl. Vol. 1. The Physics & Physical Chemistry of Water. LC 78-165694. 596p. 1972. 75.00x (ISBN 0-306-37181-2); Vol. 2. Water in Crystalline Hydrates. LC 78-165694. 681p. 1973. 75.00x (ISBN 0-306-37182-0); Vol. 3. Aqueous Solutions of Simple Electrolytes. LC 78-165694. 472p. 1973. 75.00x (ISBN 0-306-37183-9); Vol. 4. Aqueous Solutions of Amphiphiles & Macromolecules. LC 74-17244. 839p. 1975. 85.00x (ISBN 0-306-37184-7); Vol. 5. Water in Disperse Systems. LC 74-17190. 366p. 1975. 59.50x (ISBN 0-306-37185-5); Vol. 6. Recent Advances. LC 78-165694. 465p. 1979. 69.50x (ISBN 0-306-40139-8); Vol. 7. Water & Aqueous Solutions at Subzero Temperatures. 400p. 1982. 69.50 (ISBN 0-306-40710-8). (Illus., Plenum Pr). Plenum Pub.

Frei, R. W. & Brinkman, U. A. Analysis & Chemistry of Water Pollutants. LC 83-5556. (Current Topics in Enviromental & Toxicological Chemistry Ser.: Vol. 6). (Illus.). 304p. 1983. 49.50 (ISBN 0-677-06150-1). Gordon.

Greenberg, Arnold, et al, eds. Standard Methods for the Examination of Water & Wastewater. 16th ed. 1268p. 1985. 90.00x (ISBN 0-87553-131-8). Am Pub Health.

Greeson, Phillip E., ed. River-Quality Assessments: Proceedings of a Symposium Held in Tucson, Arizona, November 2-3, 1977. LC 79-87721. pap. 49.80 (ISBN 0-317-11245-7, 2017814). Bks Demand UMI.

Henry, C. D., et al. Geochemistry of Ground Water in the Miocene Oakville Sandstone: A Major Aquifer & Uranium Host of the Texas Coastal Plain. (Report of Investigations Ser.: RI 118). (Illus.). 63p. 1982. 2.50 (ISBN 0-318-03256-2). Bur Econ Geology.

Hoell, Karl, et al. Water: Examination, Assessment, Conditioning, Chemistry, Bacteriology, Biology. 1972. 30.40 (ISBN 3-11-003728-9). De Gruyter.

Interdisciplinary Analysis of Water Resource Systems. 411p. 1975. pap. 21.00x (ISBN 0-87262-115-4). Am Soc Civil Eng.

Introduction to Water Quality Analysis, Vol. 4. (Illus.). 168p. (AWWA Handbooks) 11.00 (ISBN 0-686-44869-3). Am Water Wks Assn.

Jackson & Wright, eds. Analysis of Waters Associated with Alternative Fuel Production - STP 720. 205p. 1981. 23.00 (ISBN 0-8031-0763-3, 04-720000-16). ASTM.

Kavanaugh, Michael & Leckie, James O., eds. Particulates in Water: Characterization, Fate, Effects, & Removal. LC 80-19663. (Advances in Chemistry Ser.: No. 189). 1980. 64.95 (ISBN 0-8412-0499-3). Am Chemical.

Koniecko, Edward S. Handbook for Water Analysis. rev. ed. (Quality Control Bk.). 144p. (Orig.). 1982. pap. 20.00x (ISBN 0-89529-139-8). Avery Pub.

Leppard, Gary C., ed. Trace Element Speciation in Surface Waters: Its Ecological Implications. (NATO Conference Series I, Ecology: Vol. 6). 320p. 1983. 45.00x (ISBN 0-306-41269-1, Plenum Press). Plenum Pub.

McCoy, James W. Chemical Analysis of Industrial Water. (Illus.). 1969. 30.00 (ISBN 0-8206-0017-2). Chem Pub.

Mackereth, F. J., et al. Water Analysis: Some Revised Methods for Limnologists. 1978. 25.00x (ISBN 0-900386-31-2, Pub. by Freshwater Bio). State Mutual Bk.

Methods & Measurements of Periphyton Communities, STP 690: A Review. 183p. 1979. 24.00 (ISBN 0-8031-0512-6, 04-690000-16). ASTM.

Methods for Water Balance Computations. (Studies & Reports in Hydrology: No. 17). (Illus.). 127p. (Orig.). 1975. pap. 15.00 (ISBN 92-3-100664-9, U385, UNESCO). Unipub.

Midgley, Derek & Torrance, Kenneth. Potentiometric Water Analysis. LC 77-7213. 1978. 101.95x (ISBN 0-471-99532-0, Pub. by Wiley-Interscience). Wiley.

Minear, Keith. Water Analysis, Vol. 2. LC 82-1755. 1984. 65.00 (ISBN 0-12-498302-2). Acad Pr.

--Water Analysis, Vol. 3. LC 82-1755. 1984. 69.00 (ISBN 0-12-498303-0). Acad Pr.

Minear, Roger & Keith, L. H., eds. Water Analysis: Solution Control Parameters & Analysis Techniques of Inorganic Species, Vol. I. 1982. 44.00 (ISBN 0-12-498301-4). Acad Pr.

--Pollution Control Technology for Industrial Wastewater. LC 81-38394. (Pollution Technology Review 80). (Illus.). 712p. 1981. 48.00 (ISBN 0-8155-0855-7). Noyes.

The Determination of Polychlorinated Biphenyls in Open Ocean Waters. (Intergovernmental Oceanographic Commission Technical Ser.: No. 26). (Illus.). 48p. 1985. pap. 7.50 (ISBN 92-3-102262-8, U1412, UNESCO). Unipub.

Devik, O., ed. Harvesting Polluted Waters: Waste Heat & Nutrient-Loaded Effluents in the Aquaculture. LC 75-40281. (Environmental Science Research Ser.: Vol. 8). (Illus.). 335p. 1976. 42.50x (ISBN 0-306-36308-9, Plenum Pr). Plenum Pub.

Disposal of Oil & Debris Resulting from a Spill Cleanup Operation, STP 703. 158p. 1980. soft cover 15.75x (ISBN 0-8031-0324-7, 04-703000-16). ASTM.

Duedall, I. W., et al. Wastes in the Ocean: Industrial & Sewage Wastes in the Ocean, Vol. 1. (Environmental Science & Technology Ser.). 431p. 1983. 69.95 (ISBN 0-471-09772-1); Set. 180.00 (ISBN 0-471-82054-7). Wiley.

Dugan, Patrick. Biochemical Ecology of Water Pollution. LC 74-26780. 170p. 1975. pap. text ed. 12.95x (ISBN 0-306-20012-0, Rosetta). Plenum Pub.

Dugan, Patrick R. Biochemical Ecology of Water Pollution. LC 72-167676. 170p. 1972. 29.50x (ISBN 0-306-30540-2, Plenum Pr). Plenum Pub.

Eckenfelder, W. W. & Ford, D. Water Pollution Control. (Illus.). 17.50 (ISBN 0-8363-0099-8). Jenkins.

Estimating the Hazard of Chemical Substances to Aquatic Life, STP 657. 283p. 1978. pap. 19.50 (ISBN 0-8031-0336-0, 04-657000-16). ASTM.

Fallows, James M. The Water Lords: The Report on Industry & Environmental Crisis in Savannah, Georgia. LC 70-149318. (Ralph Nader Study Group Reports Ser.). 1971. 12.95 (ISBN 0-670-75160-X, Grossman). Viking.

Feder & Burrell. Impact of Seafood Cannery Waste on the Benthic Biota & Adjacent Waters at Dutch Harbor Alaska. (IMS Report Ser.: No. R82-1). 225p. 21.00. U of AK Inst Marine.

Foerstner, U. & Wittmann, G. T. Metal Pollution in the Aquatic Environment. rev., 2nd ed. (Illus.). 486p. 1981. 56.00 (ISBN 0-387-10724-X). Springer-Verlag.

A Framework for the Implementation of the Comprehensive Plan for the Global Investigation of Pollution in the Marine Environment. (Intergovernmental Oceanographic Commission Technical Ser.: No. 25). 28p. 1985. pap. 7.50 (ISBN 92-3-102256-3, U1411, UNESCO). Unipub.

Fried, J. J. Groundwater Pollution. LC 74-29680. (Developments in Water Science: Vol. 4). 330p. 1976. 76.75 (ISBN 0-444-41316-2). Elsevier.

Goldberg, E. G. A Guide to Marine Pollution. 178p. 1972. 48.75 (ISBN 0-677-12500-3). Gordon.

Grava, Sigurd. Urban Planning Aspects of Water Pollution Control. LC 72-87147. (Illus.). 223p. 1969. 30.00x (ISBN 0-231-03280-3). Columbia U Pr.

Groundwater Pollution: Prepared by the Institute of Geology & Mines of Spain in Cooperation with the Massachusetts Institute of Technology, Cambridge, Mass., U.S.A. within the Framework of the FAO-UNDP-Govt. of Spain Project on Groundwater Pollution in Spain. (Irrigation & Drainage Papers: No. 31). (Eng. & Span.). 149p. 1979. pap. 10.75 (ISBN 92-5-100699-7, F1847, FAO). Unipub.

Guswa, J. H., et al. Groundwater Contamination & Emergency Response Guide. LC 84-14842. (Pollution Technology Review Ser.: No. 111). (Illus.). 490p. 1985. 48.00 (ISBN 0-8155-0999-5). Noyes.

Halasi-Kun, ed. Pollution & Water Resources, Vol. 13, Pt. 1. (Columbia University Seminar Ser.). 1981. 28.00 (ISBN 0-08-025988-X). Pergamon.

Halasi-Kun, G. J. Pollution & Water: Selected Reports, Vol. 13, No. 3. 28.00 (ISBN 0-08-027511-7). Pergamon.

Halasi-Kun, George J., ed. Pollution & Water Resources: Hydrogeology & Other Selected Reports. (Columbia University Seminar Ser.: Vol. XIV-1, 1981). (Illus.). 195p. 39.00 (ISBN 0-08-028792-1). Pergamon.

--Pollution & Water Resources: Pollution & Hydrology of Surface & Ground Water - Selected Reports. (Columbia University Seminar Ser.: Vol. XIII-2, 1980). (Illus.). 187p. 1981. 28.00 (ISBN 0-08-027215-0). Pergamon.

--Pollution & Water Resources: Pollution, Coastal Biology & Water Resources-Selected Reports. (Columbia University Seminar Ser.: Vol. XIV-2, 1981). (Illus.). 200p. 1982. 39.00 (ISBN 0-08-028793-X). Pergamon.

--Pollution & Water Resources: Toxic Pollution, Microstructures in Meteorites & Water Resources Management. (Columbia University Seminar Ser.: Vol. XVI). (Illus.). 250p. 1984. 49.95 (ISBN 0-08-031624-7). Pergamon.

Halsi-Kun, George J., ed. Pollution & Water Resources: The Climatography of New Jersey, 1825-1980. (Columbia University Seminar Ser.: Vol. XIV, No. 3). (Illus.). 288p. 1982. 53.00 (ISBN 0-08-028794-8). Pergamon.

Hatem, Mary B., ed. Marine Polymetallic Sulfides: A National Overview & Future Needs. pap. 1.50 (ISBN 0-943676-21-5). MD Sea Grant Col.

Hendricks, Charles W., et al. Fresh Water Pollution I: Bacteriologial & Chemical Pollution of Fresh Water. new ed. LC 72-13708. (Illus.). 220p. 1973. text ed. 29.00x (ISBN 0-8422-7076-0). Irvington.

Henze, M., ed. Anaerobic Treatment of Wastewater in Fixed Film Reactors: Proceedings of the IAWPRC Specialised Seminar on Anaerobic. Treatment of Wastewater, Copenhagen, Denmark, June 16-18, 1982. (Water Science & Technology: Vol. 15, No. 8-9). (Illus.). 390p. 1983. pap. 80.00 (ISBN 0-08-031018-4). Pergamon.

Hester, F. J. Economic Aspects of the Effects of Pollution on the Marine & Anadromous Fisheries of the Western United States of America. (Fisheries Technical Papers: No. 162). (Illus.). 41p. 1976. pap. 7.50 (ISBN 92-5-100116-2, F894, FAO). Unipub.

Houck, Daniel C., et al. Contaminant Removal from Public Water Systems. LC 84-22748. (Pollution Technology Review Ser.: No. 120). (Illus.). 524p. 1985. 52.00 (ISBN 0-8155-1022-5). Noyes.

Hudson, James F., et al. Pollution-Pricing: Industrial Response to Wastewater Charges. LC 80-8363. 240p. 1981. 29.50x (ISBN 0-669-04033-9). Lexington Bks.

IAWPR International Conference on Water Pollution Research, 10th, Toronto, June 1980. Water Pollution Research & Development. Jenkins, S. H., ed. (Water Science & Technology Ser.). (Illus.). 1388p. 1981. 215.00 (ISBN 0-08-026025-X). Pergamon.

Impact of Nuclear Releases into the Aquatic Environment. (Proceedings Ser.). (Illus.). 521p. 1976. pap. 48.00 (ISBN 92-0-020375-2, ISP406, IAEA). Unipub.

International Conference on Pumped Storage Development & Its Environmental Effects, University of Wisconsin, Milwaukee, 1971) International Conference on Pumped Storage Development & Its Environmental Effects, University of Wisconsin, Milwaukee, 1971: Proceedings. Karedi, Gabor M., et al, eds. LC 73-123983. (Proceedings of American Water Resources Association Ser.: No. 15). (Illus.). pap. 147.00 (ISBN 0-317-09815-2, 2003127). Bks Demand UMI.

Jaag, O., et al, eds. Water Pollution Research: Proceedings of the Second International Conference. 2nd ed. 1966. Set. 245.00 (ISBN 0-08-011438-5). Pergamon.

James, A., ed. Mathematical Models in Water Pollution Control. LC 77-7214. 420p. 1978. 79.95x (ISBN 0-471-99471-5, Pub. by Wiley-Interscience). Wiley.

--Mathematical Models in Water Pollution Control. LC 77-7214. (A Wiley-Interscience Publication). pap. 109.00 (ISBN 0-317-26332-3, 2025200). Bks Demand UMI.

Jenkins, S. H. Mediterranean Pollution: Proceedings of a Conference Held in Palma, Mallorca, Sept. 1979. (Progress in Water Technology Ser.: Vol. 12, Nos. 1 & 4). 850p. 1980. 110.00 (ISBN 0-08-026058-6). Pergamon.

--Ninth International Conference on Water Pollution Research. 140.00x (ISBN 0-08-022939-5). Pergamon.

--Nitrogen As a Water Pollutant. flexi-cover 99.00x (ISBN 0-08-020900-9). Pergamon.

--Water Quality: Management & Pollution Control Problems. 45.00x (ISBN 0-08-017006-4). Pergamon.

Jenkins, S. H., ed. Water Pollution Research & Control: Proceedings of the Eleventh Biennial Conference of the International Association on Water Pollution Research, Capetown, March 29-April 2, 1982, Vol. 14, No. 11. (Illus.). 1500p. 1983. 195.00 (ISBN 0-08-029689-0). Pergamon.

Jenkins, S. H. & Hansen, P. Schjodtz, eds. Airborne Pollutants from Coal Fired Power Plants: Water Pollution: Part of an IAWPRC International Conference on Coal Fired Power Plants & the Aquatic Environment, 16-18 August 1982, Copenhagen, Vol. 15-12. LC 83-19445. (Illus.). 144p. 1983. pap. 40.00 (ISBN 0-08-031024-9). Pergamon.

--Cooling Water Discharges from Coal Fired Power Plants: Water Pollution Problems: Part of an IAWPRC International Conference on Coal Fired Power Plants & the Aquatic Environment, 16-18 August 1982, Copenhagen, Vol. 15-10. LC 83-19445. (Illus.). 276p. 1983. pap. 40.00 (ISBN 0-08-031025-7). Pergamon.

--Solid Wastes from Coal Fired Power Plants: Water Pollution Problems: Part of an IAWPRC International Conference on Coal Fired Power Plants & the Aquatic Environment, 16-18 August 1982, Copenhagen, Vol. 15/11. LC 83-19445. (Illus.). 258p. 1983. pap. 40.00 (ISBN 0-08-031026-5). Pergamon.

Johnson, A. A. Water Pollution in the Greater New York Area. 232p. 1970. 42.95 (ISBN 0-677-14470-9). Gordon.

Keith, Lawrence H. Advances in the Identification & Analysis of Organic Pollutants in Water, 2 vols. LC 81-68031. 1214p. 1981. text ed. 59.95 ea. Vol. 1 (ISBN 0-250-40397-8). Vol. 2 (ISBN 0-250-40398-6). Set. text ed. 99.95 (ISBN 0-250-40472-9). Butterworth.

--Identification & Analysis of Organic Pollutants in Water. LC 76-1730. (Illus.). 1976. 49.95 (ISBN 0-250-40131-2). Butterworth.

Kester, D. R., et al. Wastes in the Ocean: Deep-Sea Waste Disposal, Vol. 5. (Environmental Science & Technology Ser.). 432p. 1984. 26.50 (ISBN 0-471-89331-5). Wiley.

Kester, Dana R., et al. Wastes in the Ocean: Dredged Material Disposal in the Ocean, Vol. 2. (Environmental Science & Technology Ser.). 299p. 1983. 49.95x (ISBN 0-471-09771-3, Pub. by Wiley-Interscience). Wiley.

Ketchum, Bostwick H., et al, eds. Ocean Dumping of Industrial Wastes. (Marine Science Ser.: Vol. 12). 536p. 1981. 79.50x (ISBN 0-306-40653-5, Plenum Pr). Plenum Pub.

Kirkwood, James P. Special Report on the Pollution of River Waters. LC 75-125750. (American Environmental Studies). (Illus.). 1970. Repr. of 1876 ed. 24.00 (ISBN 0-405-02676-5). Ayer Co Pubs.

Kneese, Allen V. Water Pollution: Economic Aspects & Research Needs. (Resources for the Future Ser). 120p. 1962. pap. 5.00x (ISBN 0-8018-0343-8). Johns Hopkins.

Knight, Allen W. & Simmons, Mary Ann, eds. Water Pollution: A Guide to Information Sources. LC 73-17537. (Man & the Environment Information Guide Ser.: Vol. 9). 1980. 60.00x (ISBN 0-8103-1346-4). Gale.

Knowles, Forrest E., et al. Fresh Water Pollution II: Radioactive Pollutants. new ed. (Illus.). 220p. 1973. text ed. 29.00x (ISBN 0-8422-7090-6). Irvington.

Kraybill, H. F., et al, eds. Aquatic Pollutants & Biologic Effects with Emphasis on Neoplasia, Vol. 298. (Annals of the New York Academy of Sciences). 604p. 1977. 54.00x (ISBN 0-89072-044-4). NY Acad Sci.

Kumpf, H. E. Economic Impact of the Effects of Pollution on the Coastal Fisheries of the Atlantic & Gulf of Mexico Regions of the United States of America. (Fisheries Technical Papers: No. 172). (Illus.). 86p. 1977. pap. 7.50 (ISBN 92-5-100380-7, F1238, FAO). Unipub.

Laboratory Management. (Manual of Pratice System Management Ser.: No. 1). (Illus.). 56p. 1981. 8.00 (ISBN 0-686-36998-X). Water Pollution.

Lam, D. C., et al. Effluent Transport & Diffusion Models for the Coastal Zone. (Lecture Notes on Coastal & Estuarine Studies: Vol. 5). (Illus.). 170p. 1984. pap. 19.00 (ISBN 0-387-90928-1). Springer-Verlag.

Larkin, Peter A. Freshwater Pollution, Canadian Style. (Environmental Damage & Control in Canada Ser.: Vol. 3). (Illus.). 168p. 1974. pap. 4.95 (ISBN 0-7735-0208-4). McGill-Queens U Pr.

Laws, Edward A. Aquatic Pollution: An Introductory Text. LC 80-23311. (Environmental Science & Technology Ser.). 482p. 1981. 46.50x (ISBN 0-471-05797-5, Pub. by Wiley-Interscience). Wiley.

Lectures Presented at the Fifth FAO-SIDA Workshop on Aquatic Pollution in Relation to Protection of Living Resources: Scientific & Administrative Bases for Management Measures. 1979. pap. 27.50 (ISBN 92-5-100601-6, F1509, FAO). Unipub.

Louden, Louise. Toxicity of Chemicals & Pulping Wastes to Fish. LC 79-64742. (Bibliographic Ser.: No. 265, Suppl. I). 1979. pap. 60.00 (ISBN 0-87010-058-0). Inst Paper Chem.

Mandel, S. & Shiftan, Z. Groundwater Resources: Investigation & Development. LC 80-990. (Water Pollution Ser.). 1981. 41.50 (ISBN 0-12-468040-2). Acad Pr.

Mason, C F. Biology of Freshwater Pollution. LC 80-41551. (Illus.). 240p. (Orig.). 1982. pap. 12.95x (ISBN 0-582-45596-0). Longman.

Measurement of Organic Pollutants in Water & Wastewater- STP 686. 356p. 1979. 36.50x (ISBN 0-8031-0508-8, 04-686000-16). ASTM.

Miller, E. Willard & Miller, Ruby M. Environmental Hazards-Water Pollution: A Bibliography. (Public Administration Ser.: Bibliography P-1612). 49p. 1985. pap. 7.50 (ISBN 0-89028-262-5). Vance Biblios.

Mitchell, Ralph, ed. Water Pollution Microbiology. LC 73-168641. 1972. (Pub. by Wiley-Interscience); Vol. 2 1978, 442p. 54.95x (ISBN 0-471-01902-X). Wiley.

--Water Pollution Microbiology. LC 73-168641. pap. 106.50 (ISBN 0-317-26263-7, 2055711). Bks Demand UMI.

Moore, Ralph L. Neutralization of Waste Water by pH Control. LC 77-94491. 160p. 1978. text ed. 29.95x (ISBN 0-87664-383-7). Instru Soc.

National Research Council. Oil in the Sea: Inputs, Fates, & Effects. 601p. 1985. text ed. 39.50 (ISBN 0-309-03479-5). Natl Acad Pr.

Nemerow, Nelson L. Industrial Water Pollution: Origins, Characteristics & Treatment. LC 76-46612. 1978. text ed. 36.95 (ISBN 0-201-05246-6). Addison-Wesley.

Nriagu, Jerome O. Aquatic Toxicology. (Advances in Environmental Science & Technology Ser.: No. 2-010). 525p. 1983. 96.50 (ISBN 0-471-88901-6, Pub. by wiley-Interscience). Wiley.

Nrigau, Jerome O. & Simmons, Milagros S. Toxic Contaminants in the Great Lakes. LC 83-16689. (Advances in Environmental Science & Technology Ser.: 2-010). 527p. 1984. 97.95 (ISBN 0-471-89087-1, Pub. by Wiley-Interscience). Wiley.

Nuclear Techniques in Groundwater Pollution Research. (Panel Proceedings Ser.). (Illus.). 286p. 1981. pap. 40.50 (ISBN 92-0-141080-8, ISP518, IAEA). Unipub.

Nutrient Control. (Manual of Practice, Facilities Development: 7). (Illus.). 216p. (Orig.). 1983. pap. text ed. 22.30 (ISBN 0-943244-44-7). Water Pollution.

Ocean Affairs Board, Natl. Research Council. Disposal in the Marine Environment: An Oceanographic Assessment. LC 76-1319. 1976. pap. 6.50 (ISBN 0-309-02446-3). Natl Acad Pr.

Ocean Science Board. Tropospheric Transport of Pollutants & Natural Substances to the Ocean. 1978. pap. 13.25 (ISBN 0-309-02735-7). Natl Acad Pr.

OECD Staff. Control Policies for Specific Water Pollutants. 246p. (Orig.). 1983. pap. 17.00x (ISBN 92-64-12386-5). OECD.

Oglesby, Ray. River Ecology & Man. (Environmental Science: An Interdisciplinary Monograph Ser.). 1972. 60.00 (ISBN 0-12-524450-9). Acad Pr.

Okidi, C. O. Regional Control of Ocean Pollution: Legal & Institutional Problems & Prospects. 292p. 1978. 34.00x (ISBN 90-286-0367-0). Sijthoff & Noordhoff.

Ouano, E. A., et al. Water Pollution Control in Developing Countries. 1978. 175.00 (ISBN 0-08-023567-0). Pergamon.

Overton, D. E. & Meadows, M. E. Stormwater Modeling. 1976. 49.50 (ISBN 0-12-531550-3). Acad Pr.

Page, G. William. Municipal Characteristics Associated with Toxic Contaminants in Groundwater. ii, 28p. 1985. write for info. (ISBN 0-938744-35-6). U of Wis Ctr Arch-Urban.

Palmer, C. Mervin. Algae & Water Pollution. (Illus.). 123p. 1980. text ed. 33.00 (ISBN 0-7194-0052-X, Pub. by Castle Hse England). J K Burgess.

Pearson, E. A. & De Fraga Frangipane, E. Marine Pollution & Marine Waste Disposal. 140.00x (ISBN 0-08-019730-2). Pergamon.

Peskin, Henry M. & Seskin, Eugene P. Cost-Benefit Analysis & Water Pollution Policy. 1975. 14.95x (ISBN 0-87766-119-7, 75000); pap. 9.95x (ISBN 0-87766-120-0, 77000). Urban Inst.

Pollution Control on the Passaic River. 85p. 1982. 14.00 (ISBN 0-686-81772-9). Ctr Analysis Public Issues.

Pretreatment of Industrial Waste. (Manual of Practice Facilities Development Ser.: No. 3). (Illus.). 157p. 1981. 14.00 (ISBN 0-686-36999-8). Water Pollution.

Principles for Developing Coastal Water Quality Criteria. (GESAMP Reports & Studies: No. 5). (Illus.). 23p. 1976. pap. 7.50 (ISBN 92-5-100078-6, F1072, FAO). Unipub.

Pye, Veronica I., et al. Groundwater Contamination in the United States. LC 83-6695. 352p. (Orig.). 1983. 35.00x (ISBN 0-8122-7896-8); pap. 14.95x (ISBN 0-8122-1152-9). U of Pa Pr.

Ravera, O., ed. Biological Aspects of Freshwater Pollution: Proceedings of the Course Held at the Joint Research Centre, Ispra, Italy, 5-9 June 1978. (Illus.). 1979. 43.00 (ISBN 0-08-023442-9). Pergamon.

Report of the Fifth Session of the Indo-Pacific Fishery Commission Working Party on Aquaculture & Environment. (Fisheries Technical Papers). 16p. 1981. pap. 11.50 (ISBN 92-5-100962-7, FAO). Unipub.

WATER–PURIFICATION

see also Saline Water Conversion; Water-Supply Engineering

WATER–QUALITY OF
see Water Quality

WATER–SEEPAGE
see Seepage

WATER–WASTE
see also Water-Conservation

Houck, Daniel C., et al. Contaminant Removal from Public Water Systems. LC 84-22748. (Pollution Technology Review Ser.: No. 120). (Illus.). 524p. 1985. 52.00 (ISBN 0-8155-1022-5). Noyes.
Morley, D. A. Mathematical Modelling in Water & Wastewater Treatment. (Illus.). 366p. 1979. 66.75 (ISBN 0-85334-842-1, Pub. by Elsevier Applied Sci England). Elsevier.
Pure & Wholesome. LC 81-70989. 181p. 1982. pap. 18.50x (ISBN 0-87262-290-8). Am Soc Civil Eng.
Water Treatment Waste Disposal. (AWWA Handbooks-Proceedings Ser.). (Illus.). 136p. 1978. pap. text ed. 10.20 (ISBN 0-89867-058-6). Am Water Wks Assn.

WATER, UNDERGROUND
see also Hydrogeology; Divining-Rod; Seepage; Soil Moisture; Springs; Wells
American Society of Civil Engineers, compiled By. Ground Water Management. (Manual & Report on Engineering Practice Ser.: No. 40). 230p. 1972. pap. 16.00x (ISBN 0-87262-216-9). Am Soc Civil Eng.
Back, W. & Letolle, R., eds. Geochemistry of Groundwater: Proceedings of the 26th International Geological Congress, Paris, France-July 1980. (Developments in Water Science Ser.: Vol. 16). 370p. 1982. 64.00 (ISBN 0-444-42036-3). Elsevier.
Bear, Jacob. Hydraulics of Ground Water. (Water Resources & Environmental Engineering Ser.). (Illus.). 1979. text ed. 75.00 (ISBN 0-07-004170-9). McGraw.
Bitton, Gabriel & Gerba, Charles, eds. Groundwater Pollution Microbiology. LC 83-1475. (Environmental Science & Technology Ser.: No. 1-121). 377p. 1984. 49.95 (ISBN 0-471-09656-3, Pub by Wiley Interscience). Wiley.
Bouwer, Herman. Groundwater Hydrology. (Environment Water & Resources Ser). (Illus.). 1978. text ed. 45.00x (ISBN 0-07-006715-5). McGraw.
Brown, R. H., et al, eds. Ground Water Studies: An International Guide for Research, Suppl. 4. pap. price not set (ISBN 92-3-101471-4, U271, UNESCO). Unipub.
Canter, L. W. Ground Water Quality Management. (Illus.). 450p. 1985. 49.95 (ISBN 0-87371-018-5). Lewis Pubs Inc.
Canter, Larry W. & Knox, R. C. Effect of Septic Tank Systems on Ground Water Quality. LC 84-23280. (Illus.). 336p. 1985. 29.95 (ISBN 0-87371-012-6). Lewis Pubs Inc.
--Ground Water Pollution Control. (Illus.). 529p. 1985. 49.95 (ISBN 0-87371-014-2). Lewis Pubs Inc.
Cheremisinoff, Paul N., et al. Groundwater-Leachate - Modeling-Monitoring-Sampling. LC 84-51875. 146p. 1984. pap. 24.50 (ISBN 0-87762-376-7). Technomic.
Dasgupta, Partha. The Control of Resources. (Illus.). 240p. 1983. text ed. 18.50x (ISBN 0-674-16980-8). Harvard U Pr.
Davis, Stanley N. & De Wiest, Roger J. M. Hydrogeology. 463p. 1966. 40.50 (ISBN 0-471-19900-1). Wiley.
Everett, Lorne G. Groundwater Monitoring. LC 80-82885. (Illus.). 480p. 1980. 150.00x (ISBN 0-931690-14-5). Genium Pub.
Fogg, G. E., et al. Three-Dimensional Ground-Water Modeling in Depositional Systems, Wilcox Group, Oakwood Salt Dome Area, East Texas. (Report of Investigations Ser.: RI 133). (Illus.). 55p. 1983. 3.25 (ISBN 0-318-03289-9). Bur Econ Geology.
Fried, J. J. Groundwater Pollution. LC 74-29680. (Developments in Water Science: Vol. 4). 330p. 1976. 76.75 (ISBN 0-444-41316-2). Elsevier.
Glover, Robert E. Transient Ground Water Hydraulics. 1978. 21.00 (ISBN 0-918334-24-1). WRP.
Green, Donald E. Land of the Underground Rain: Irrigation on the Texas High Plains, 1910-1970. LC 72-7589. (Illus.). 328p. 1973. pap. 8.95 (ISBN 0-292-74629-6). U of Tex Pr.
Ground Water - M21. (AWWA Manuals). (Illus.). 142p. 1973. pap. text ed. 17.10 (ISBN 0-89867-079-9). Am Water Wks Assn.
Ground Water in the Pacific Region. 289p. 1983. pap. text ed. 38.00 (ISBN 0-317-01252-5, UN83/2A12, UN). Unipub.
Ground Water in the Western Hemisphere. (Natural Resources-Water Ser.: No. 4). pap. 20.00 (ISBN 0-686-94825-4, UN76/2A5, UN). Unipub.
Ground-Water Models: Concepts, Problems & Methods of Analysis with Examples of Their Application, Vol. 1. (Studies & Reports in Hydrology: No. 34). (Illus.). 235p. 1982. pap. 26.25 (ISBN 92-3-102006-4, U1224, UNESCO). Unipub.
Ground Water Storage & Artificial Recharge. (Natural Resources-Water Ser.: No. 2). pap. 17.00 (ISBN 0-686-94824-6, UN74/2A11, UN). Unipub.
Ground Water Studies: An International Guide for Research & Practice, Suppl. 3, Chaps. 6, 7, 8, Sec 8.5. (Studies & Reports in Hydrology: No. 7). 1977. pap. 18.00 (ISBN 92-3-101471-4, U833, UNESCO). Unipub.
Groundwater Legislation in Europe. (Legislative Studies: No. 5). (Orig.). 1964. pap. 9.25 (ISBN 0-685-09386-7, F213, FAO). Unipub.
Groundwater Pollution: Prepared by the Institute of Geology & Mines of Spain in Cooperation with the Massachusetts Institute of Technology, Cambridge, Mass., U.S.A. within the Framework of the FAO-UNDP-Govt. of Spain Project on Groundwater Pollution in Spain. (Irrigation & Drainage Papers: No. 31). (Eng. & Span.). 149p. 1979. pap. 10.75 (ISBN 92-5-100699-7, F1847, FAO). Unipub.
Guswa, J. H., et al. Groundwater Contamination & Emergency Response Guide. LC 84-14842. (Pollution Technology Review Ser.: No. 111). (Illus.). 490p. 1985. 48.00 (ISBN 0-8155-0999-5). Noyes.
Halek, V. & Svek, J. Groundwater Hydraulics. (Development in Water Science: Vol. 7). 620p. 1979. 115.00 (ISBN 0-444-99820-9). Elsevier.
Harr, Milton E. Groundwater & Seepage. 1962. 46.50 (ISBN 0-07-026740-5). McGraw.
Hunt, Bruce. Mathematical Analysis of Groundwater Resources. (Illus.). 288p. 1983. text ed. 49.95 (ISBN 0-408-01399-0). Butterworth.
Husmann, Siegfried, ed. Proceedings of the International Symposium on Groundwater Ecology, 1st, Schlitz, September 1975. 232p. 1976. pap. text ed. 29.95 (ISBN 90-265-0240-0, Pub. by Swets Pub Serv Holland). Swets North Am.
Johnson, et al, eds. Water for Subsurface Injection - STP 735. 150p. 1981. 14.00 (ISBN 0-8031-0800-1, 04-735000-16). ASTM.
Kovacs, G., et al. Subterranean Hydrology. LC 80-54120. 1981. 49.00 (ISBN 0-918334-35-7). WRP.
Lane, Paul H. & Rossman, Antonio. Owens Valley Groundwater Conflict. Smith, Genny, ed. 28p. 1978. pap. 2.50 (ISBN 0-931378-03-6, Dist. by W. Kaufmann Inc.). Genny Smith Bks.
Lloyd, J. W. Case-Studies in Groundwater Resources Evaluation. (Illus.). 1981. 74.00x (ISBN 0-19-854530-4). Oxford U Pr.
Matthess, Georg. The Properties of Groundwater. Harvey, John C., tr. LC 81-7481. 406p. 1982. 58.95x (ISBN 0-471-08513-8, Pub. by Wiley-Interscience). Wiley.
Miller, David W. Waste Disposal Effects on Ground Water: A Comprehensive Survey of the Occurrence & Control of Ground-Water Contamination Resulting from Waste Disposal Practices. LC 78-65680. (Illus.). 512p. 1980. pap. 18.00 (ISBN 0-912722-01-0). Prem Press.
Morrison, Robert D. Ground Water Monitoring: Procedures, Equipment & Applications. (Illus.). 132p. 1983. text ed. 33.00 (ISBN 0-9611060-0-X, 83-070805). Timco Mfg.
National Research Council Commission on Natural Resources. Coal Mining & Ground-Water Resources in the United States. 1981. pap. text ed. 11.00 (ISBN 0-309-03186-9). Natl Acad Pr.
Nuclear Techniques in Groundwater Pollution Research. (Panel Proceedings Ser.). (Illus.). 286p. 1981. pap. 40.50 (ISBN 92-0-141080-8, ISP518, IAEA). Unipub.
Nyer, Evan K. Groundwater Treatment Technology. (Illus.). 224p. 1985. 32.50 (ISBN 0-442-26706-1). Van Nos Reinhold.
O'Hare, M., et al. Artificial Recharge. (Illus.). 523p. 1985. 49.95 (ISBN 0-87371-050-9). Lewis Pubs Inc.
Plummer, F. B. & Sargent, E. C. Underground Waters & Subsurface Temperatures of the Woodbine Sand in Northeast Texas. (Bull 3138 Ser.). (Illus.). 178p. 1931. 1.00 (ISBN 0-686-29351-7). Bur Econ Geology.
Polubarinova-Kochina, P. Theory of Ground Water Movement. De Wiest, R., tr. 1962. 62.50x (ISBN 0-691-08048-8). Princeton U Pr.
Price, Michael. Introducing Groundwater. (Special Topics in Geology Ser: No. 2). (Illus.). 176p. 1985. text ed. 25.00x (ISBN 0-04-553005-X); pap. text ed. 11.95x (ISBN 0-04-553006-8). Allen Unwin.
Pye, Veronica I., et al. Groundwater Contamination in the United States. LC 83-6695. 352p. (Orig.). 1983. 35.00x (ISBN 0-8122-7896-8); pap. 14.95x (ISBN 0-8122-1152-9). U of Pa Pr.
Reichert, W. H. Annotated Guide to Sources of Information on the Geology, Minerals, & Ground-Water Resources of the Puget Sound Region: Washington, King County Section. (Information Circular Ser.: No. 61). (Illus.). 63p. 1978. 1.50 (ISBN 0-686-34734-X). Geologic Pubns.
Remson, Irwin, et al. Numerical Methods in Subsurface Hydrology. LC 75-142139. 389p. 1971. 64.50 (ISBN 0-471-71650-2, Pub. by Wiley-Interscience). Wiley.
A Review of the United Nations Ground-Water Exploration & Development Programme in the Developing Countries, 1962-1977. (Natural Resources-Water Ser.: No. 7). pap. 7.00 (ISBN 0-686-92881-4, UN79/2A4, UN). Unipub.
Royer, Denise W. Summary of Groundwater Resources of Perry County, Pennsylvania. (Water Resource Report: No. 59). (Illus.). 70p. 1984. pap. 15.35 (ISBN 0-8182-0059-6). Commonweal PA.
Rushton, K. R. & Redshaw, S. C. Seepage & Groundwater Flow: Numerical Analysis by Analog & Digital Methods. LC 78-23359. (Series in Geotechnical Engineering). 339p. 1979. 79.95 (ISBN 0-471-99754-4, Pub. by Wiley-Interscience). Wiley.
Saleem, Zubair A., ed. Advances in Groundwater Hydrology. LC 77-92093. pap. 85.30 (ISBN 0-317-28827-X, 2017812). Bks Demand UMI.
Schlitt, W. J. & Shock, D. A., eds. In Situ Uranium Leaching & Ground Water Restoration. LC 79-52217. (Illus.). 137p. 1979. pap. 20.00x (ISBN 0-89520-267-0). Soc Mining Eng.
Smith, M. A. Contaminated Land: Reclamation & Treatment. (NATO-Challenges of Modern Society Ser.). 456p. 1985. 65.00x (ISBN 0-306-41928-9, Plenum Pr). Plenum Pub.
Taylor, Larry E. Groundwater Resources of the Upper Susquehanna River Basin, Pennsylvania. (Water Resource Report: No. 58). (Illus.). 136p. 1984. pap. 14.00 (ISBN 0-8182-0058-8). Commonweal PA.
Taylor, Larry E. & Werkheiser, William H. Groundwater Resources of the Lower Susquehanna River Basin, Pennsylvania. (Water Resource Report: No. 57). (Illus.). 130p. 1984. pap. 15.75 (ISBN 0-8182-0057-X). Commonweal PA.
Thomas, Harold E. Conservation of Ground Water: A Survey of the Present Ground-Water Situation in the United States. Repr. of 1951 ed. lib. bdg. 19.50x (ISBN 0-8371-3431-5, THGW). Greenwood.
Todd, David K., ed. Ground-Water Resources of the United States: An Illustrated Compendium of the Nation's Underground Water Resources Compiled from Publications of the United States Geological Survey. LC 80-80553. (Illus.). 749p. 1983. 39.00 (ISBN 0-912722-02-9). Prem Press.
Travis, Curtis C. & Etnier, Elizabeth L., eds. Groundwater Pollution: Environmental & Legal Problems. (AAAS Selected Symposium: No. 95). 160p. 1984. 23.00x (ISBN 0-8133-0001-0). Westview.
USDI. Ground Water Manual. (Selected Government Publications a Wiley Reprint Ser.: 1-698). 480p. 1983. 35.95x (ISBN 0-471-80008-2, Pub. by Wiley-Interscience). Wiley.
Van Der Leeden, Frits. Geraghty & Miller's Groundwater Bibliography. 3rd ed. LC 83-50806. 400p. 1983. 22.00 (ISBN 0-912394-19-6). Water Info.
Van Duijvenbooden, W., et al, eds. Quality of Groundwater. (Studies in Environment Science: Vol. 17). 1128p. 1981. 159.75 (ISBN 0-444-42022-3). Elsevier.
Verruijt, A. Grounderwater Flow. 2nd ed. (Illus.). 145p. 1982. text ed. 35.00x (ISBN 0-333-32958-9); pap. text ed. 20.00x (ISBN 0-333-32959-7). Scholium Intl.
--Theory of Groundwater Flow. 200p. 1970. 55.75x (ISBN 0-677-61660-0). Gordon.
Wang, Herbert F. & Anderson, Mary P. Introduction to Groundwater Modeling: Finite Difference & Finite Element Methods. LC 81-2665. (Illus.). 237p. 1981. text ed. 35.95x (ISBN 0-7167-1303-9). W H Freeman.
Ward, C. H., et al. Ground Water Quality. (Environmental Science & Technology Ser.). 560p. 1985. 45.00 (ISBN 0-471-81597-7). Wiley.
Williams, Roy E. A Guide to the Prevention of Ground Water Contamination by Uranium Mill Wastes. 173p. 1982. text ed. 38.00 (ISBN 0-910069-05-0). Geotech Engineer Prog.
Wood, Eric F. & Princeton Water Resorces Group. Groundwater Contamination from Hazardous Wastes. (Illus.). 192p. 1984. 30.95 (ISBN 0-13-366286-1). P-H.
Zimmie & Riggs, eds. Permeability & Groundwater Contaminant Transport - STP 746. 245p. 1981. 28.00 (ISBN 0-8031-0797-8, 04-746000-38). ASTM.

WATER-ANALYSIS
see Water–Analysis

WATER AND PLANTS
see Plant-Water Relationships

WATER-BEETLES
Arnett, Ross H., Jr. Checklist of the Beetles of North & Central America & the West Indies: Ground Beetles, Water Beetles, & Related Groups, Vol. 1. 135p. 1983. 15.00x (ISBN 0-916846-12-1). Flora & Fauna.
Balfour-Browne, F. Water Beetles & Other Things (Half a Century's Work) 226p. 1962. 37.00x (ISBN 0-317-07182-3, Pub. by FW Classey UK). State Mutual Bk.

WATER-BIRDS
see also Sea Birds; Shore Birds; Waterfowl; also families and names of water-birds, e.g. Anatidae; Gulls, Murres, Terns
Baird, S. F., et al. Water Birds of North America, 2 vols. in one. (Natural Sciences in America Ser). (Illus.). 1974. 74.00 (ISBN 0-405-05716-4). Ayer Co Pubs.
Burton, P. J. Feeding & the Feeding Apparatus in Waders. (Illus.). 1974. text ed. 21.00x (ISBN 0-565-00719-X, Pub. by Brit Mus Nat Hist). Sabbot-Natural Hist Bks.
Cogswell, Howard L. Water Birds of California. (Natural History Guides Ser.). 1977. 12.95 (ISBN 0-520-02994-1); pap. 5.75 (ISBN 0-520-02699-3). U of Cal Pr.
Romashko, Sandra. Birds of the Water, Sea & Shore. LC 77-81169. (Illus.). 1985. pap. 3.95x (ISBN 0-89317-016-X). Windward Pub.
Scott, P. A Coloured Key to the Wildfowl of the World. rev. ed. (Illus.). 1972. 15.00 (ISBN 0-685-12001-5). Heinman.

WATER-BIRDS, PROTECTION OF
see Birds, Protection of

WATER CHEMISTRY
see also Limnology
Bidwell, Joseph P. & Spotte, Stephen. Artificial Seawaters: Formulas & Methods. 360p. 1985. write for info. (ISBN 0-86720-057-X). Jones & Bartlett.
British Nuclear Energy Society, ed. Water Chemistry of Nuclear Reactor Systems. 534p. 1978. 125.00x (ISBN 0-7277-0053-7, Pub. by Brit Nuclear England). State Mutual Bk.
--Water Chemistry of Nuclear Reactor Systems, No. 2. 430p. 1981. 135.00x (ISBN 0-7277-0126-6, Pub. by Brit Nuclear England). State Mutual Bk.
Camp, Thomas & Meserve, Robert L. Water & Its Impurities. 2nd ed. LC 74-7012. (Illus.). 384p. 1974. 48.50 (ISBN 0-87933-112-7). Van Nos Reinhold.
Committee on Water Treatment Chemicals, National Research Council. Water Chemicals Codex. 1982. pap. text ed. 7.25 (ISBN 0-309-03338-1). Natl Acad Pr.
Dickson, Kenneth L. & Maki, Alan W., eds. Modeling the Fate of Chemicals in the Aquatic Environment. LC 82-71527. (Illus.). 413p. 1982. 45.00 (ISBN 0-250-40552-0). Butterworth.
Drever, James I. The Geochemistry of Natural Waters. (Illus.). 400p. 1982. 37.95 (ISBN 0-13-351403-X). P-H.
Ecological Analysts. The Sources, Chemistry, Fate & Effects of Chromium in Aquatic Environments. LC 82-71261. (Orig.). 1982. pap. 8.10 (ISBN 0-89364-046-8, 847-89600). Am Petroleum.
Golterman, H. Methods for Chemical Analysis of Fresh Waters. 2nd ed. (Blackwell Scientific Pubns.: IBP Handbk. No. 8). (Illus.). 1978. pap. 17.50 (ISBN 0-632-00459-2, B 1888-6). Mosby.
Head, P. C., ed. Practical Estuarine Chemistry: A Handbook. (Estuarine & Brackish-Water Sciences Association Handbook). 350p. 1985. 54.50 (ISBN 0-521-30165-3). Cambridge U Pr.
Kay, Robert L., ed. The Physical Chemistry of Aqueous Systems: A Symposium in Honor of Henry S. Frank on His Seventieth Birthday. LC 74-1384. 258p. 1974. 42.50 (ISBN 0-306-30782-0, Plenum Pr). Plenum Pub.
Kitano, Yasushi, ed. Geochemistry of Water. LC 74-23330. (Benchmark Papers in Geology Ser: No. 16). 455p. 1975. 67.50 (ISBN 0-12-786856-9). Acad Pr.
Loewenthal, R. E. & Marais, G. V. Carbonate Chemistry of Aquatic Systems: High Salinity Waters, Vol. 2. 600p. 1984. 39.95 (ISBN 0-250-40150-9). Butterworth.
McCoy, James W. Chemical Treatment of Cooling Water. 2nd ed. (Illus.). 1983. 40.00 (ISBN 0-8206-0298-1). Chem Pub.
Moore, J. W. & Ramamoorthy, S. Organic Chemicals in Natural Water: Applied Monitoring & Impact Assessment. (Springer Series on Environmental Management). (Illus.). 290p. 1984. 39.80 (ISBN 0-387-96034-1). Springer-Verlag.
Morel, Francois M. Principles of Aquatic Chemistry. 446p. 1983. 49.95x (ISBN 0-471-08683-5, Pub. by Wiley-Interscience). Wiley.
Pagenkopf, G. K. Introduction to Natural Water Chemistry. (Environmental Science Ser.: Vol. 3). 1978. 32.50 (ISBN 0-8247-6706-3). Dekker.
Parker, Gerald C. Facts About Swimming Pools: A Guide to Their Operation & Maintenance. (Illus.). 53p. (Orig.). 1981. pap. 4.95x (ISBN 0-9609588-0-0). Pool Pubns.
Salomons, W. & Foerstner, U. Metals in the Hydrocycle. (Illus.). 340p. 1984. 35.00 (ISBN 0-387-12755-0). Springer-Verlag.
Snoeyink, Vernon L. & Jenkins, David. Water Chemistry. LC 79-21331. (SPE Monographs). 183p. 1980. 20.45x (ISBN 0-471-05196-9); 20.45 (ISBN 0-471-06272-3). Wiley.

Garzon, Camilo E. Water Quality in Hydroelectric Projects: Considerations for Planning in Tropical Forest Regions. 48p. Date not set. 5.00 (ISBN 0-318-02923-5, BK0363). World Bank.

Gessford, John E. The Use of Reservoir Water for Hydroelectric Power Generation. Bruchey, Stuart, ed. LC 78-22684. (Energy in the American Economy Ser.). (Illus.). 1979. lib. bdg. 12.00x (ISBN 0-405-11987-9). Ayer Co Pubs.

Goodman, Louis J. & Love, Ralph N., eds. Small Hydroelectric Projects for Rural Development: Planning & Management. (Pergamon Policy Studies). 250p. 1981. 22.00 (ISBN 0-08-025966-9). Pergamon.

McGuigan, Dermot. Harnessing Water Power for Home Energy. LC 77-27404. (Illus.). 1978. pap. 6.95 (ISBN 0-88266-115-9). Garden Way Pub.

Marier, Donald & Stoiaken, Larry, eds. Alternative Sources of Energy: Hydropower, No. 68, Sept.-Oct. 84.. ed. 72p. 1984. pap. 4.25 (ISBN 0-917328-58-2). ASEI.

Monition, L., et al. Micro Hydro-Electric Power Stations. 185p. 1984. text ed. 29.95x (ISBN 0-471-90255-1, Pub by Wiley-Interscience). Wiley.

Smallwood, Kenneth L. Water: A Source of Energy for Today & Tomorrow. Ide, Arthur F., ed. & illus. LC 82-6059. (E Equals MC Squared Ser.: Vol. 3). (Illus.). 60p. (Orig.). 1982. 12.95 (ISBN 0-86663-802-4). Ide Hse.

United Nations Economic Commission for Europe, Geneva, Switzerland. Hydroelectricity Prospects in the New Energy Situation: Proceedings of a Symposium of the Committee on Electric Power of the United Nations Commission for Europe, Athens, Greece, 5-9 Nov. 1979. LC 80-40819. 530p. 1981. 125.00 (ISBN 0-08-025702-X). Pergamon.

WATER PURIFICATION

see Water–Purification

WATER QUALITY

Amavis, R. & Smeets, J., eds. Principles & Methods for Determining Ecological Criteria on Hydrobiocenoses. LC 76-14624. 1976. pap. text ed. 89.00 (ISBN 0-08-021233-6). Pergamon.

American Society for Testing & Materials. Water Quality Criteria. LC 67-14533. (American Society for Testing & Materials. Special Technical Publication Ser.: 416). pap. 31.80 (ISBN 0-317-10923-5, 2000707). Bks Demand UMI.

American Society of Civil Engineers, compiled by. Is Water Quality Enhancement Feasible? 137p. 1970. pap. 11.75x (ISBN 0-87262-025-5). Am Soc Civil Eng.

American Water Works Association. Taste & Odor Control Experiences Handbook. (AWWA Handbooks-General Ser.). (Illus.). 118p. 1976. pap. text ed. 8.00 (ISBN 0-89867-011-X). Am Water Wks Assn.

--Upgrading Water Treatment Plants to Improve Water Quality. (Handbooks-Proceedings). (Illus.). 132p. 1980. pap. text ed. 12.00 (ISBN 0-89867-245-7). Am Water Wks Assn.

Aquatic Environmental Quality: Problems & Proposals. (Fisheries Research Board of Canada Reports). (Illus.). 37p. 1978. pap. 5.50 (ISBN 0-660-00878-5, SSC89, SSC). Unipub.

Aquifer Contamination & Protection. (Studies & Reports in Hydrology: No. 30). 442p. 1980. pap. 46.50 (ISBN 92-3-101886-8, U1102, UNESCO). Unipub.

Barnes, D. & Wilson, F. Chemistry & Unit Operations in Water Treatment. (Illus.). 325p. 1983. 61.00 (ISBN 0-85334-169-9, I-463-82, Pub. by Elsevier Applied Sci England). Elsevier.

Beck, M. B. Water Quality Management: A Review of the Development & Application of Mathematical Models. (Lecture Notes in Engineering Ser.: Vol. 11). viii, 107p. 1985. pap. 10.50 (ISBN 0-387-13986-9). Springer-Verlag.

Beck, M. B. & Van Straten, G., eds. Uncertainty & Forecasting of Water Quality. (Illus.). 386p. 1983. 36.00 (ISBN 0-387-12419-5). Springer-Verlag.

Beck, Robert E. & Goplerud, C. Peter, III. Waters & Water Rights, Vol. 3: Water Pollution & Water Quality Legal Controls. 2nd ed. 1984. text ed. 45.00x (ISBN 0-87473-177-1); 1985 suppl. incl. A Smith Co.

Beltrami, Edward. The High Cost of Clean Water: Models for Water Quality Management Ser. (The UMAP Expository Monograph). 53p. 1982. pap. text ed. 8.95 (ISBN 0-8176-3098-8). Birkhauser.

Biswas, Asit K. Models for Water Quality Management. (M-H Series in Water Resources & Environmental Engineering). (Illus.). 392p. 1981. text ed. 60.00 (ISBN 0-07-005481-9). McGraw.

Bower, Blair T., et al. Incentives in Water Quality Management: France & the Ruhr Area. LC 81-4732. (Resources for the Future Research Paper: R-24). (Illus.). 320p. 1981. pap. text ed. 14.00x (ISBN 0-8018-2661-6). Johns Hopkins.

Boyd, C. E. Water Quality Management for Pond Fish Culture. (Developments in Aquaculture & Fisheries Science Ser.: Vol. 9). 318p. 1982. 64.00 (ISBN 0-444-42054-1). Elsevier.

Boyle, Terence P., ed. Validation & Predictability of Laboratory Methods for Assessing the Fate & Effects of Contaminants in Aquatic Ecosystems - STP 865. LC 85-5985. (Illus.). 242p. 1985. text ed. 34.00 (ISBN 0-8031-0433-2, 04-865000-16). ASTM.

Brown, G. W. Forestry & Water Quality. 1983. pap. text ed. 8.65x (ISBN 0-88246-007-2). Oreg St U Bkstrs.

Cairns, John, Jr. & Dickson, K. L., eds. Biological Methods for the Assessment of Water Quality, STP 528. 262p. 1972. 16.25 (ISBN 0-8031-0114-7, 04 528000 16). ASTM.

Camp, Thomas & Meserve, Robert L. Water & Its Impurities. 2nd ed. LC 74-7012. (Illus.). 384p. 1974. 48.50 (ISBN 0-87933-112-7). Van Nos Reinhold.

Canter, L. W. Ground Water Quality Management. (Illus.). 450p. 1985. 49.95 (ISBN 0-87371-018-5). Lewis Pubs Inc.

--River Water Quality Monitoring. (Illus.). 230p. 1985. 28.00 (ISBN 0-87371-011-8). Lewis Pubs Inc.

Cardwell, Rick D., et al, eds. Aquatic Toxicology & Hazard Assessment-STP 854: Seventh Symposium. LC 84-70338. (Illus.). 590p. 1985. text ed. 60.00 (ISBN 0-8031-0410-3, 04-854000-16). ASTM.

Cleary, Edward. The ORANSCO Story: Water Quality Management in the Ohio Valley under an Interstate Compact. LC 67-16036. pap. 87.80 (ISBN 0-317-19885-8, 2023087). Bks Demand UMI.

Committee on Drinking Water, National Research Council. Drinking Water & Health. Incl. Vol. I. 1977. 26.50 (ISBN 0-309-02619-9); Vol. II. 1980. 15.50 (ISBN 0-309-02931-7); Vol. III. 1980. 17.00 (ISBN 0-309-02932-5). Natl Acad Pr.

Coughlin, Robert E. The Perception & Valuation of Water Quality: A Review of Research Method & Findings. (Discussion Paper Ser.: No. 80). 1975. pap. 4.50 (ISBN 0-686-32246-0). Regional Sci Res Inst.

Coulston, Frederick & Mrak, E., eds. Water Quality: Proceedings of an International Symposium. (Ecotoxicology & Environmental Quality Ser.). 1977. 45.00 (ISBN 0-12-193150-1). Acad Pr.

Disinfection. (AWWA Handbooks - Proceedings). (Illus.). 224p. 1977. pap. text ed. 12.00 (ISBN 0-89867-053-5). Am Water Wks Assn.

Dorfman, Robert, et al, eds. Models for Managing Regional Water Quality. LC 72-87770. (Illus.). 512p. 1973. 27.50x (ISBN 0-674-57825-2). Harvard U Pr.

Eckenfelder, Walter W. Principles of Water Quality Management. LC 79-20509. (Illus.). 704p. 1980. 34.95 (ISBN 0-8436-0338-0). Van Nos Reinhold.

Effects of Urbanization & Industrialization on the Hydrological Regime & on Water Quality. (Studies & Reports in Hydrology: No. 24). 1979. pap. 50.50 (ISBN 92-3-001537-7, U864, UNESCO). Unipub.

EIFAC. Report on Copper & Freshwater Fish: EIFAC Working Paper on Water Quality Criteria for European Freshwater Fish. (European Inland Fisheries Advisory Commission (EIFAC): Technical Papers: No. 27). 1976. pap. 7.50 (ISBN 0-685-74522-8, F2029, FAO). Unipub.

Friedman, Norman J., ed. Prevention of Micro-Organism Growth in Water Supplies. LC 79-5244. (Illus.). 1979. lib. bdg. 46.00 (ISBN 0-89500-024-5). Sci Pr.

Garzon, Camilo E. Water Quality in Hydroelectric Projects: Considerations for Planning in Tropical Forest Regions. 48p. Date not set. 5.00 (ISBN 0-318-02923-5, BK0363). World Bank.

Goddard, M. & Butler, M., eds. Viruses & Wastewater Treatment: Proceedings of the International Symposium Held at the University of Surrey, Guilford, 15-17 September 1980. (Illus.). 316p. 1981. 66.00 (ISBN 0-08-026401-8). Pergamon.

Golterman, H. L., ed. Interactions Between Sediments & Fresh Water. (Illus.). 1977. pap. 52.00 (ISBN 90-220-0632-8, PDC47, PUDOC). Unipub.

Gomella, C & Mounier, J. P., eds. Eutrophication & Water Supply: Proceedings of the Specialised Conference of the IWSA held in Vienna, Austria, Oct. 7-9, 1981. (Illus.). 284p. 1983. pap. 66.00 (ISBN 0-08-030419-2). Pergamon.

Gower, A M. Water Quality in Catchment Ecosystems. LC 79-42907. (Institution of Environmental Sciences Ser.). 335p. 1980. 69.95x (ISBN 0-471-27692-8, Pub. by Wiley-Interscience). Wiley.

Hammer, Thomas B. Water Quality Deterioration in a Suburbanizing Basin: Brandywine Creek, Pennsylvania. (Discussion Paper Ser.: No. 78). 1974. pap. 4.50 (ISBN 0-686-32244-4). Regional Sci Res Inst.

Howard, William T. & Hammer, Thomas R. Water-Quality Impacts of Unsewered Housing. (Discussion Paper Ser.: No. 66). 1973. pap. 4.50 (ISBN 0-686-32232-0). Regional Sci Res Inst.

Introduction to Water Quality Analysis, Vol. 4. (Illus.). 168p. (AWWA Handbooks) 11.00 (ISBN 0-686-44869-3). Am Water Wks Assn.

James, A., ed. Mathematical Models in Water Pollution Control. LC 77-7214. 420p. 1978. 79.95x (ISBN 0-471-99471-5, Pub. by Wiley-Interscience). Wiley.

James, A. & Evison, Lilian, eds. Biological Indicators of Water Quality. LC 79-557. 628p. 1979. 74.95x (ISBN 0-471-27590-5, Pub. by Wiley-Interscience). Wiley.

Jenkins, S. H. The Agricultural Industry & its Effects on Water Quality Programme. flexi-cover 89.00x (ISBN 0-08-024889-6). Pergamon.

--Water Quality: Management & Pollution Control Problems. 45.00x (ISBN 0-08-017006-4). Pergamon.

Johnson, Merike. Natural Water Quality. (Botany Bay Project-Working Paper: No. 4). (Illus.). 1979. pap. 5.95 (ISBN 0-7081-0340-5, 0512, Pub. by ANUP Australia). Australia N U P.

Kneese, Allen V. & Bower, Blair T. Managing Water Quality: Economics, Technology & Institutions. (Illus.). pap. 84.50 (ISBN 0-317-10637-6, 2019813). Bks Demand UMI.

Krenkel, Peter A. & Novotny, Vladimir. Water Quality Management. LC 80-516. 1980. 70.00 (ISBN 0-12-426150-7). Acad Pr.

McGauhey, P. H. Engineering Management of Water Quality. LC 67-28085. 1968. text ed. 45.00 (ISBN 0-07-044975-9). McGraw.

Mark & Mattson. Water Quality Measurement. (Pollution Engineering & Technology Ser.: Vol. 18). 496p. 1981. 66.75 (ISBN 0-8247-1334-6). Dekker.

Metallurgical Society of AIME. Water Quality Management for the Metals & Minerals Industries, a Short Course (In Conjunction with the 104th AIME Annual Meeting, New York, 1975) pap. 36.80 (ISBN 0-317-10692-9, 2004307). Bks Demand UMI.

O'Kane, J. P. Estuarine Water-Quality Management with Moving Element Models & Optimization Techniques. LC 79-19405. (Water Resources Engineering Ser.). 155p. 1980. text ed. 63.50 (ISBN 0-273-08443-7). Pitman Pub MA.

Olive, John H. & Smith, Kenneth R. Benthic Macroinvertebrates As Indexes of Water Quality in the Scioto River Basin, Ohio. 1975. 8.00 (ISBN 0-86727-077-2). Ohio Bio Survey.

Orlob, Gerald T., ed. Mathematical Modeling of Water Quality: Streams, Lakes & Reservoirs. (IIASA International Series on Applied Systems Analysis). 518p. 1983. 112.95x (ISBN 0-471-10031-5, Pub. by Wiley-Interscience). Wiley.

Pavoni, Joseph, ed. Handbook of Water Quality Management Planning. LC 77-21601. 440p. 1977. 31.50 (ISBN 0-442-23282-9). Krieger.

Polyelectrolytes: Aids to Better Water Quality. (AWWA Handbooks-Proceedings). (Illus.). 128p. 1972. pap. text ed. 6.00 (ISBN 0-89867-037-3). Am Water Wks Assn.

Power Plant Instrumentation for Measurement of High-Purity Water Quality - STP 742. 235p. 1981. 26.50 (ISBN 0-8031-0798-6, 04-742000-16). ASTM.

Reeves, H. Clyde, et al, eds. Funding Clean Water. LC 83-22202. (Lincoln Institute of Land Policy Ser.). 226p. 1984. 36.00x (ISBN 0-669-07409-8). Lexington Bks.

Rinaldi, Sergio, et al. Modeling & Control of River Quality. LC 77-30475. (Illus.). 1978. text ed. 90.00 (ISBN 0-07-052925-6). McGraw.

River Water Quality Assessment. (AWWA Handbooks - Proceedings). (Illus.). 112p. 1976. pap. text ed. 7.20 (ISBN 0-89867-048-9). Am Water Wks Assn.

Sanders, Thomas, et al. Design of Networks for Monitoring Water Quality. LC 83-61028. 336p. 30.00 (ISBN 0-918334-51-9). WRP.

Schaller, Frank W. & Bailey, George W., eds. Agricultural Management & Water Quality. (Illus.). 472p. 1983. text ed. 39.95 (ISBN 0-8138-0082-X). Iowa St U Pr.

Schmidtke, Norbert W. & Smith, Daniel W., eds. Scale-up of Water & Wastewater Treatment Processes. 512p. 1983. text ed. 39.95 (ISBN 0-250-40638-1). Butterworth.

Sittig, Marshall, ed. Priority Toxic Pollutants: Health Impacts & Allowable Limits. LC 80-311. (Environmental Health Review Ser.: No. 1). 370p. 1980. 54.00 (ISBN 0-8155-0797-6). Noyes.

Smethurst, George. Basic Water Treatment for Application Worldwide. 224p. 1979. 19.75x (ISBN 0-7277-0071-5). Am Soc Civil Eng.

State Water Quality Planning Issues. 64p. (Orig.). 1982. pap. 8.00 (ISBN 0-87292-031-3, RM 719). Coun State Govts.

Tchobanoglous, George & Schroeder, Edward D. Water Quality Management: An Introduction. (Illus.). 1985. 35.95 (ISBN 0-201-05433-7); solutions manual avail. Addison-Wesley.

Tebbutt, T. H. Principles of Water Quality Control. (Illus.). 248p. 1983. 40.00 (ISBN 0-08-028705-0); pap. 15.00 (ISBN 0-08-028704-2). Pergamon.

Thomas, William A., ed. Indicators of Environmental Quality. LC 72-86142. (Environmental Science Research Ser.: Vol. 1). 285p. 1972. 45.00x (ISBN 0-306-36301-1, Plenum Pr); pap. 9.95 (ISBN 0-306-20011-2). Plenum Pub.

Tolley, George S., et al, eds. Environmental Policy Series Volume III: Water Quality. 232p. 1983. prof ref 28.00 (ISBN 0-88410-632-2). Ballinger Pub.

Train, Russel E. Quality Criteria for Water. (Illus.). 256p. 1979. text ed. 32.00 (ISBN 0-7194-0023-6, Pub. by Castle Hse England). J K Burgess.

The Value & Limitations of Various Approaches to the Monitoring of Water Quality for Freshwater Fish. (European Inland Fisheries Advisory Commission (EIFAC): Technical Papers: No. 32). (Eng. & Fr.). 31p. 1978. pap. 7.50 (ISBN 92-5-100664-4, F1542, FAO). Unipub.

Ward, C. H., et al. Ground Water Quality. (Environmental Science & Technology Ser.). 560p. 1985. 45.00 (ISBN 0-471-81597-7). Wiley.

Water Quality & Treatment: A Handbook of Public Water Supplies. 3rd ed. (General References Ser.). (Illus.). 654p. 1971. text ed. 42.60 (ISBN 0-89867-005-5). Am Water Wks Assn.

Water Quality Criteria for European Freshwater Fish: Report on Cadmium & Freshwater Fish. (European Inland Fisheries Advisory Commission (EIFAC): Technical Papers: No. 30). (Eng. & Fr.). 32p. 1977. pap. 7.50 (ISBN 92-5-002056-2, F771, FAO). Unipub.

Water Quality Criteria for European Freshwater Fish: Report on Water Temperature & Inland Fisheries Based Mainly on Slavonic Literature. (European Inland Fisheries Advisory Commission (EIFAC): Technical Papers: No. 6). (Eng. & Fr.). 32p. 1968. pap. 7.50 (ISBN 92-5-002056-2, F1719, FAO). Unipub.

Water Quality Criteria for European Freshwater Fish: Report on Chromium & Freshwater Fish. (European Inland Fisheries Advisory Commission (EIFAC): Technical Papers: No. 43). (Eng. & Fr.). 37p. 1983. pap. text ed. 7.50 (ISBN 92-5-101350-0, F2458, FAO). Unipub.

Water Quality Investigations in the Mackenzie Basin with Special Reference to the Potential for Impairment of Water Quality by Pipeline or Road Construction. 1979. pap. 4.75 (ISBN 0-686-59491-6, SSC128, SSC). Unipub.

Water Quality Parameters, STP 573. 590p. 1975. 29.50 (ISBN 0-8031-0598-3, 04-573000-16). ASTM.

Water Quality Surveys: A Guide for the Collection & Interpretation of Water Quality Data. (Studies & Reports in Hydrology: No. 23). 1978. pap. 29.75 (ISBN 92-3-101473-0, U851, UNESCO). Unipub.

Water Quality Technology Conference, 1981: Advances in Laboratory Techniques for Quality Control. (AWWA Handbooks-Proceedings Ser.). (Illus.). 1982. pap. text ed. 18.60 (ISBN 0-89867-267-8). Am Water Wks Assn.

Water Quality Technology Conference, 1980: Advances in Laboratory Techniques for Quality Control. (AWWA Handbooks-Proceedings Ser.). (Illus.). 1981. pap. text ed. 18.00 (ISBN 0-89867-251-1). Am Water Wks Assn.

Water Quality Technology Conference: 1975-Laboratory Tools for Safe Water. (AWWA Handbooks-Proceedings Ser.). (Illus.). 1976. pap. text ed. 12.00 (ISBN 0-89867-045-4). Am Water Wks Assn.

Water Quality Technology Conference: 1976, the Water Laboratory - Key to Process & Quality Control. (AWWA Handbooks-Proceedings Ser.). (Illus.). 342p. 1977. pap. text ed. 12.00 (ISBN 0-89867-051-9). Am Water Wks Assn.

Water Quality Technology Conference: 1973-Water Quality. (AWWA Handbooks-Proceedings Ser.). (Illus.). 272p. 1974. pap. text ed. 12.00 (ISBN 0-89867-041-1). Am Water Wks Assn.

Water Quality Technology Conference: 1974-Water Quality. (AWWA Handbooks-Proceedings Ser.). (Illus.). 248p. 1975. pap. text ed. 12.00 (ISBN 0-89867-043-8). Am Water Wks Assn.

Weber, Lavern J., ed. Aquatic Toxicology, Vol. 2. 240p. 1984. text ed. 51.50 (ISBN 0-89004-927-0). Raven.

Weber, Walter J., Jr. Physicochemical Processes for Water Quality Control. LC 77-37026. (Environmental Science & Technology Ser.). 640p. 1972. 57.95x (ISBN 0-471-92435-0, Pub. by Wiley-Interscience). Wiley.

Williams, W. D., ed. An Ecological Basis for Water Resource Management. LC 78-74750. (Illus.). 417p. 1980. text ed. 39.50 (ISBN 0-7081-0836-9, 0546, Pub. by ANUP Australia). Australia N U P.

Zoeteman, B. C. Sensory Assessment of Water Quality. (Pergamon Series on Environmental Science: Vol. 2). (Illus.). 160p. 1980. 39.00 (ISBN 0-08-023848-3). Pergamon.

WATER REQUIREMENTS OF PLANTS

see Plants–Water Requirements

WATER RESOURCES DEVELOPMENT

see also Flood Control; Inland Navigation; Irrigation; Water-Power; Water-Supply

Ackerman, Edward A., et al. Technology in American Water Development. LC 77-86377. (Resources for the Future, Inc. Publications). Repr. of 1959 ed. 47.50 (ISBN 0-404-60326-2). AMS Pr.

American Society of Civil Engineers. Water Systems Seventy-Nine: Proceedings of the ASCE Water Resources Planning & Management Division Specialty Conference, University of Houston, Hilton Hotel Center, February 25-28, 1979. LC 79-105513. pap. 59.30 (ISBN 0-317-10837-9, 2019548). Bks Demand UMI.

American Water Resources Association. Proceedings of the Fourth American Water Resources Conference Held November 18-22, 1968, Commodore Hotel, New York, New York. Cohen, Philip & Francisco, Martha N., eds. (American Water Resources Association Proceedings Ser.: No. 6). pap. 160.00 (ISBN 0-317-28825-3, 2017811). Bks Demand UMI.

Andrijanov, V. G. Meteorological & Hydrological Data Required in Planning the Development of Water Resources. (Operational Hydrology Reports: No. 5). 42p. 1975. pap. 10.00 (ISBN 92-63-10419-0, W261, WMO). Unipub.

Askew, A. J., et al, eds. Logistics & Benefits of Using Mathematical Models of Hydrologic & Water Resource Systems: Selected Papers from an International Symposium, IIASA Laxenburg, Austria. 270p. 1981. 55.00 (ISBN 0-08-025662-7). Pergamon.

AWWA Research Foundation. Future of Water Reuse: Proceedings, Vols. 1, 2, 3. (Illus.). 1810p. (Orig.). 1985. pap. 50.00 (ISBN 0-915295-02-4, 90506). AWWA Res Found.

Baumann, Duane & Dworkin, Daniel. Water Resources for Our Cities. Natoli, Salvatore J., ed. LC 78-59100. (Resource Papers for College Geography Ser.). (Illus.). 1978. pap. text ed. 4.00 (ISBN 0-89291-130-1). Assn Am Geographers.

Beard, Leo R. & Maxwell, W. H., eds. Water Resources Management in Industrial Areas. (Water Resources Ser.: Vol. 1). 463p. 1982. 71.25 (ISBN 0-907567-30-4, TYP129, TYP); pap. 48.75 (ISBN 0-907567-31-2, TYP128). Unipub.

Berkman, Richard L. & Viscusi, W. Kip. Damming the West: The Report on the Bureau of Reclamation. LC 72-77707. (Ralph Nader Study Group Reports). 286p. 1973. 12.95 (ISBN 0-670-25460-6, Grossman). Viking.

Biswas, Asit K. Models for Water Quality Management. (M-H Series in Water Resources & Environmental Engineering). (Illus.). 392p. 1981. text ed. 60.00 (ISBN 0-07-005481-9). McGraw.

Biswas, Asit K., ed. Systems Approach to Water Management. (Illus.). 1976. text ed. 48.00 (ISBN 0-07-005480-0). McGraw.

Biswas, Asu K. & Dakang, Zuo, eds. Long Distance Water Transfer: A Chinese Case Study & International Experience. (Water Resources Ser.: Vol. 3). 416p. 1983. 48.75 (ISBN 0-907567-52-5, TYP144, TYP); pap. 28.25 (ISBN 0-907567-53-3, TYP143). Unipub.

Black, Peter E. Conservation of Water & Related Land Resources. LC 81-21103. 234p. 1982. 29.95x (ISBN 0-03-060419-2). Praeger.

Bourne, Peter G., ed. Water Resource Development: Economic & Sociological Perspectives. 1984. 45.00 (ISBN 0-12-119580-5). Acad Pr.

Bredehoeft, John & Bachmat, Y. Groundwater Management: The Use of Numerical Models. (Water Resources Monograph: Vol. 5). (Illus.). 127p. 1980. pap. 10.00 (ISBN 0-87590-306-1, WR0500). Am Geophysical.

Canter, L. W. Environmental Impact of Water Resources Projects. (Illus.). 400p. 1985. 39.95 (ISBN 0-87371-015-0). Lewis Pubs Inc.

Challenges in Water Utility Management. (AWWA Handbooks Ser.). (Illus.). 90p. 1980. pap. text ed. 12.00 (ISBN 0-89867-239-2). Am Water Wks Assn.

Crawford, A. Berry & Peterson, Dean F. Environmental Management in the Colorado River Basin. LC 74-121364. 313p. 1974. pap. 8.00 (ISBN 0-87421-068-2). Utah St U Pr.

Crosson, Pierre R., et al, eds. Selected Water Management Issues in Latin American Agriculture. LC 77-10193. (Resources for the Future Ser.). (Illus.). 1978. text ed. 16.50x (ISBN 0-8018-2047-2). Johns Hopkins.

Cunha, Luis V., et al. Management & Law for Water Resources. LC 77-7611. 1977. 32.00 (ISBN 0-918334-20-9). WRP.

Dean, Robert & Lund, Ebba. Water Reuse: Problems & Solutions. LC 81-67892. 1982. 47.50 (ISBN 0-12-208080-7). Acad Pr.

Degremont Company Editors. Water Treatment Handbook. LC 72-96505. (Illus.). 1116p. 1973. 40.00 (ISBN 0-686-02503-2). Taylor-Carlisle.

DeGroot, W., ed. Stormwater Detention Facilities. LC 82-73613. 439p. 1982. pap. 31.00x (ISBN 0-87262-348-3). Am Soc Civil Eng.

De Vore, R. William & Haan, Charles T., eds. International Symposium on Urban Storm Water Management: Proceedings 1978. 348p. 1978. pap. text ed. 33.50 (ISBN 0-89779-002-2, UKY BU116). OES Pubns.

Downey, Lawrence L. Water Resources Policy & the Nineteen Seventy-Seven South Dakota Legislature. 1977. write for info. U of SD Gov Res Bur.

Downing, J. A. & Rigler, F. H., eds. A Manual on Methods for the Assessment of Secondary Productivity in Fresh Waters. 2nd ed. (Illus.). 500p. 1984. text ed. 55.00x (ISBN 0-632-00616-1). Blackwell Pubns.

Effects of Urbanization & Industrialization on the Hydrological Regime & on Water Quality. (Studies & Reports in Hydrology: No. 24). 1979. pap. 50.50 (ISBN 92-3-001537-7, U864, UNESCO). Unipub.

An Evaluation of Climate & Water Resources for Development of Agriculture in the Sudano-Sahelian Zone of West Africa. Abr. ed. 45p. 1978. pap. 6.75 (ISBN 0-686-93557-8, UNEP024, UNEP). Unipub.

Experimental Facilities in Water Resources Education. (Technical Papers in Hydrology: No. 24). 83p. 1983. pap. text ed. 9.25 (ISBN 92-3-102107-9, U1311, UNESCO). Unipub.

Expert Group Meetings on Water Pricing: Proceedings. (Water Resources Development Ser.: No. 55). 83p. 1981. pap. 8.00 (ISBN 0-686-96521-3, UN81/2F11, UN). Unipub.

Expert Working Group Meeting on Water: Proceedings. (Water Resources Development Ser.: No. 53). pap. 12.00 (UN81/2F3, UN). Unipub.

Feachem, Richard, et al. Water, Health & Development: An Interdisciplinary Evaluation. 286p. 1981. 35.00x (ISBN 0-905402-06-5, Pub. by Tri-Med England). State Mutual Bk.

Fitzsimmons, Stephen J. & Salama, Ovadia A. Man & Water: A Social Report. 1973. pap. 20.00x (ISBN 0-89011-485-4, ECR-102). Abt Bks.

Fleming, Lizanne, ed. California Water Resources Directory: A Guide to Organizations & Information Resources. LC 82-70810. (California Information Guides Ser.). (Illus., Orig.). 1984. pap. 20.00x (ISBN 0-912102-60-8). Cal Inst Public.

Frederick, Kenneth D. Water Management & Agricultural Development: A Case Study of the Cuyo Region of Argentina. LC 74-24402. (Resources for the Future Research Ser). (Illus.). 208p. 1975. 16.50x (ISBN 0-8018-1701-3). Johns Hopkins.

Garstka, Walter U. Water Resources & the National Welfare. LC 77-74260. 1978. 32.00 (ISBN 0-918334-19-5). WRP.

Gates, Paul W., et al. Four Persistent Issues: Essays on California's Land Ownership Concentration, Water Deficits, Sub-State Regionalism, & Congressional Leadership. LC 78-17964. 1978. pap. 5.75x (ISBN 0-87772-257-9). Inst Gov Stud Berk.

Geophysics Study Committee, National Research Council. Scientific Basis of Water-Resource Management. 1982. pap. text ed. 12.25 (ISBN 0-309-03244-X). Natl Acad Pr.

Glysson, E. A., et al, eds. Innovations in the Water & Wastewater Fields. (Illus.). 240p. 1984. text ed. 34.95 (ISBN 0-250-40645-4). Butterworth.

Goldman, Charles R., et al, eds. Environmental Quality & Water Development. LC 72-83739. (Illus.). 510p. 1973. 46.95 (ISBN 0-7167-0256-8). W H Freeman.

Goodman, Alvin S. Principles of Water Resources Planning. (Illus.). 576p. 1984. 38.95 (ISBN 0-13-710616-5). P-H.

Gottschalk, Lars, et al, eds. Stochastic Processes in Water Resources Engineering. LC 77-78942. 1977. 18.00 (ISBN 0-918334-21-7). WRP.

Green, P. V. The Need for Long Term Lagoons: A Literature Survey, 1980. 1981. 69.00x (ISBN 0-686-97125-6, Pub. by W Spring England). State Mutual Bk.

Ground Water Storage & Artificial Recharge. (Natural Resources-Water Ser.: No. 2). pap. 17.00 (ISBN 0-686-94824-6, UN74/2A11, UN). Unipub.

Guidelines for the Drafting of Water Codes. (Water Resources Development Ser.: No. 43). pap. 6.00 (ISBN 0-686-94823-8, UN74/2F2, UN). Unipub.

Haimes, Yacov Y. Hierarchical Analyses of Water Resources Systems: Modeling & Optimization of Large-Scale Systems. (Illus.). 1977. text ed. 46.95x (ISBN 0-07-025507-5). McGraw.

Haimes, Yacov Y., ed. Risk-Benefit Analysis in Water Resources Planning & Management. LC 81-17824. 304p. 1981. text ed. 49.50x (ISBN 0-306-40884-8, Plenum Pr). Plenum Pub.

Halasi-Kun, George J. Pollution & Water Resources: Water Quality, Plant Fertilization & Other Topics. (Columbia University Seminar Ser.: Vol. 15-1). (Illus.). 252p. 1983. 50.00 (ISBN 0-08-029400-6). Pergamon.

Halsi-Kun, George J., ed. Pollution & Water Resources: The Climatography of New Jersey, 1825-1980. (Columbia University Seminar Ser.: Vol. XIV, No. 3). (Illus.). 288p. 1982. 53.00 (ISBN 0-08-028794-8). Pergamon.

Hammer, Mark J. & Mackichan, Kenneth A. Hydrology & Quality of Water Resources. LC 80-209. 486p. 1981. 31.95 (ISBN 0-471-02681-6); solutions manual avail. (ISBN 0-471-08573-1); problem papers avail. Wiley.

Haveman, Robert. Water Resource Investment & the Public Interest: An Analysis of Federal Expenditures in Ten Southern States. LC 65-18545. 1965. 11.95x (ISBN 0-8265-1077-9). Vanderbilt U Pr.

Helweg, Davis. Water Resource Planning. 416p. Date not set. 22.95 (ISBN 0-471-04770-8). Wiley.

Howe, Charles W., ed. Benefit-Cost Analysis for Water System Planning. LC 72-182565. (Water Resources Monograph: Vol. 2). (Illus.). 114p. 1971. pap. 10.00 (ISBN 0-87590-302-9). Am Geophysical.

Hromadka, T. V., II & Clements, J. Computer Methods in Urban Watershed Hydraulics. Hromadka, Laura, ed. LC 83-82787. (Illus.). 296p. (Orig.). 1984. pap. text ed. 38.50 (ISBN 0-914055-02-X). Lighthouse Pubns.

Hromadka, T. V., II & Durban, T. J. Computer Methods in Water Resources. Hromadka, Laura, ed. LC 83-82824. (Illus.). 318p. (Orig.). 1984. pap. text ed. 37.50 (ISBN 0-914055-01-1). Lighthouse Pubns.

Hydrology & Water Resources Symposium 83. 341p. (Orig.). 1984. pap. text ed. 28.00x (ISBN 0-85825-213-9, Pub. by Inst. Engineering Australia). Brookfield Pub Co.

Hyman, Eric, et al. The Theory & Practice of Environmental Quality Analysis: Water Resources Management, Land Suitability Analysis, Economics & Aesthetics, No. 27. 103p. 1980. 15.00 (ISBN 0-86602-027-6). CPL Biblios.

IFAC Symposium, Cleveland, O., May 1980. Water & Related Land Resource Systems: Proceedings. Haimes, Y. & Kindler, J., eds. LC 80-41690. (IFAC Proceedings Ser.). (Illus.). 550p. 1981. 130.00 (ISBN 0-08-027307-6). Pergamon.

Institution of Civil Engineers Staff, ed. Management of National & Regional Water Resources. 104p. 1973. 30.25x (ISBN 0-901948-65-9). Am Soc Civil Eng.

Interdisciplinary Analysis of Water Resource Systems. 411p. 1975. pap. 21.00x (ISBN 0-87262-115-4). Am Soc Civil Eng.

International Conference on Transfer of Water Resources Knowledge. 1st, Colorado State Univ., Sep. 14-16, 1972. Transfer of Water Resources Knowledge: Proceedings. Vlachos, Evan, ed. LC 73-80678. 1973. 18.00 (ISBN 0-918334-05-5). WRP.

Ivanov, K. E. Water Movement in Mirelands. 296p. 1981. 59.50 (ISBN 0-12-376460-2). Acad Pr.

James, L. Douglas, ed. Man & Water: The Social Sciences in Management of Water Resources. LC 73-77253. (Illus.). 266p. 1974. 22.00x (ISBN 0-8131-1292-3). U Pr of Ky.

Kelso, Maurice M., et al. Water Supplies & Economic Growth in an Arid Environment: An Arizona Case Study. LC 72-92106. 327p. 1973. pap. 8.50x (ISBN 0-8165-0368-0). U of Ariz Pr.

Kneese, Allen V. & Smith, Stephen C., eds. Water Research. LC 66-26687. (Resources for the Future Ser). 533p. 1967. 30.00x (ISBN 0-8018-0344-6). Johns Hopkins.

Knetsch, Jack L., ed. Outdoor Recreation & Water Resources Planning. LC 73-92765. (Water Resources Monograph Ser.: Vol. 3). (Illus.). 121p. 1974. pap. 10.00 (ISBN 0-87590-304-5). Am Geophysical.

Koch, Stuart G. Water Resources Planning in New England. LC 79-66453. (Illus.). 197p. 1980. 18.00x (ISBN 0-87451-176-3). U Pr of New Eng.

Krutilla, John V. The Columbia River Treaty: The Economics of an International River Basin Development. LC 67-16037. (Resources for the Future Ser.). 248p. 1967. 17.00x (ISBN 0-8018-0350-0). Johns Hopkins.

Krutilla, John V. & Eckstein, Otto. Multiple Purpose River Development: Studies in Applied Economic Analysis. (Resources for the Future Ser). 316p. 1969. pap. 10.00x (ISBN 0-8018-1091-4). Johns Hopkins.

Kuelen, Van H. Simulation of Water Use & Herbage Growth in Arid Regions. 180p. 1981. 105.00x (ISBN 0-686-76664-4, Pub. by Oxford & IBH India). State Mutual Bk.

Kundell, James E., ed. Georgia Water Resources: Issues & Options. 114p. 1980. pap. 10.00x (ISBN 0-89854-066-6). U of GA Inst Govt.

Kuntze, H. Iron Clogging in Soils & Pipes. (Water Resources Engineering Ser.). 140p. 1982. pap. text ed. 35.95 (ISBN 0-273-08561-1). Pitman Pub MA.

LaConte, P. & Haines, Y. Y. Water Resources & Land-Use Planning: A Systems Approach. 1982. lib. bdg. 57.50 (ISBN 90-247-2726-X, Pub. by Martinus Nijhoff Netherlands). Kluwer Academic.

Laible, J., et al, eds. Finite Elements in Water Resources: Proceedings of the 5th International Conference, Burlington, Vermont, June 1984. 800p. 1984. 95.00 (ISBN 0-387-13468-9). Springer-Verlag.

Lundqvist, Jan & Lohm, Ulrik, eds. Strategies for River Basin Management: Environmental Integration of Land & Water in a River Basin. 1985. lib. bdg. 56.00 (ISBN 90-277-2111-4, Pub. by Reidel Holland). Kluwer Academic.

L'Vovich, M. I. World Water Resources & Their Future. LC 79-67029. (Illus.). 416p. 1979. 34.00 (ISBN 0-87590-224-3). Am Geophysical.

McBean, Edward A., et al, eds. Reliability in Water Resources Management. LC 79-64191. 1979. 18.00 (ISBN 0-918334-30-6). WRP.

McKean, Roland N. Efficiency in Government Through Systems Analysis. LC 58-7902. Repr. of 1958 ed. 86.50 (ISBN 0-8357-9878-X, 2012597). Bks Demand UMI.

McPherson, Murray B. Regional Earth Science Information in Local Water Management. 185p. 1975. pap. 12.75x (ISBN 0-87262-151-0). Am Soc Civil Eng.

Major, David C. Multiobjective Water Resources Planning. LC 77-899. (Water Resources Monograph: Vol. 4). (Illus.). 81p. 1977. pap. 10.00 (ISBN 0-87590-305-3). Am Geophysical.

Major, David C. & Lenton, Roberto L. Applied Water Resource Systems Planning. (Environmental Sciences Ser.). (Illus.). 1979. text ed. 37.95 (ISBN 0-13-043364-0). P-H.

Manual for the Compilation of Balances of Water Resources & Needs. pap. 5.00 (ISBN 0-686-94730-4, UN74/2E/2, UN). Unipub.

Marino, M. A. & Luthin. Seepage & Groundwater. (Developments in Water Science Ser.: Vol. 13). 490p. 1982. 106.50 (ISBN 0-444-41975-6). Elsevier.

Martin, Roscoe C. Water for New York: A Study in State Administration of Water Resources. LC 60-9946. 1960. 9.95x (ISBN 0-8156-2028-4). Syracuse U Pr.

Mather, John R. Water Resources: Distribution Use & Management. LC 83-21795. (Environmental Science & Technology Series, Texts & Monographs: 1-121). 464p. 1983. 40.00x (ISBN 0-471-89401-X, Pub. by Wiley-Interscience). Wiley.

Mendel, Donald J. The Oahe Sub-District: A Case Study in Water Resources Administration. 1963. write for info. U of SD Gov Res Bur.

Meta Systems, Inc. Systems Analysis in Water Resources Planning. LC 75-290. (Illus.). 393p. 1975. text ed. 30.00 (ISBN 0-912394-13-7). Water Info.

Methods & Problems of Flood Control in Asia & the Far East. (Water Resources Development Ser.: No. 2). pap. 2.00 (ISBN 0-686-94780-0, UN51/2F5, UN). Unipub.

Moreell, Ben. Our Nation's Water Resources: Policies & Politics. LC 72-2857. (Use & Abuse of America's Natural Resources Ser). 290p. 1972. Repr. of 1956 ed. 21.00 (ISBN 0-405-04521-2). Ayer Co Pubs.

National Systems of Water Administration. pap. 9.50 (ISBN 0-686-94682-0, UN74/2A/10, UN). Unipub.

O'Laoghaire, D. T. Optimal Expansion of a Water Resources System. 1974. 60.00 (ISBN 0-12-525450-4). Acad Pr.

Pansini, Anthony J. The Northeast Be Dammed! rev. ed. LC 77-140933. 1971. softbd. 50.00 (ISBN 0-911876-01-4). Greenvale.

Parker, Dennis J. & Penning-Rowsell, Edmund C. Water Planning in Britain. (Resource Management Ser.: No. 1). (Illus.). 288p. (Orig.). 1980. text ed. 40.00x (ISBN 0-04-711006-6). Allen Unwin.

Pereira, H. C. Land Use & Water Resources. LC 72-85437. (Illus.). 180p. (Orig.). 1973. pap. 15.95x (ISBN 0-521-09750-9). Cambridge U Pr.

Planning of Water Resources Projects. (Water Resources Development Ser.: No. 41). pap. 6.00 (ISBN 0-686-94758-4, UN73/2F7, UN). Unipub.

Post, Roy G. & Seale, Robert L., eds. Water Production Using Nuclear Energy. LC 66-24303. (Illus.). pap. 98.00 (ISBN 0-317-10713-5, 2055358). Bks Demand UMI.

Postel, Sandra. Water: Rethinking Management in an Age of Scarcity. (Worldwatch Papers). 1984. pap. 4.00 (ISBN 0-916468-62-3). Worldwatch Inst.

Prospects for Metropolitan Water Management. 240p. 1970. pap. 5.25x (ISBN 0-87262-026-3). Am Soc Civil Eng.

Rain & Stormwater Harvesting in Rural Areas: A Report of the United Nations Environment Programme. (Water Resources Ser.: No. 5). (Illus.). 235p. 1983. 37.50 (ISBN 0-907567-38-X, TYP149, TYP); pap. 18.75 (ISBN 0-907567-39-8, TYP148). Unipub.

Reckhow, Kenneth H. & Chapra, Steven. Engineering Approaches for Lake Management, 2 vols. LC 79-56115. 200p. 1983. Vol. 1: Data Analysis & Empirical Modeling. text ed. 39.95 (ISBN 0-250-40344-7); Vol. 2: Mechanistic Modeling. text ed. 49.95 (ISBN 0-250-40392-7); Set. text ed. 85.00 (ISBN 0-250-40516-4). Butterworth.

Regional Conference on Water Resources Development in Asia & the Far East: Proceedings, 9th Session. (Water Resources Development Ser.: No. 40). pap. 6.00 (ISBN 0-686-92926-8, UN72/2F/21, UN). Unipub.

Regional Conference on Water Resources Development in Asia & the Far East: Proceedings, 10th Session. (Water Resources Development Ser.: No. 44). pap. 8.50 (ISBN 0-686-92936-5, UN74/2F10, UN). Unipub.

Regional Symposium on the Development of Deltaic Areas, 3rd. Third Regional Symposium on the Development of Deltaic Areas: Proceedings. (Water Resources Development Ser.: No. 50). pap. 17.00 (ISBN 0-686-92995-0, UN78 2F10, UN). Unipub.

Regional Technical Conference on Flood Control in Asia & the Far East: Proceedings, 1951. (Water Resources Development Ser.: No. 3). pap. 5.00 (ISBN 0-686-92923-3, UN53/2F1, UN). Unipub.

Report of the Expert Consultation on the Development of Quicker Methods of Resource Appraisal of Inland Waters, Ghana, 1975. (Fisheries Reports: No. 179). 1976. pap. 7.50 (ISBN 0-685-74521-X, F827, FAO). Unipub.

Report of the FAO-Danida Regional Seminar on Small-Scale Water Resources Development in Africa (West) 29p. 1978. pap. 7.50 (ISBN 92-5-100449-8, F1320, FAO). Unipub.

Report of the Sixth Session of the European Commission of Agriculture, Working Party of Water Resources & Irrigation. 25p. 1978. pap. 7.50 (ISBN 92-5-100345-9, F1231, FAO). Unipub.

Report of the United Nations Water Conference. pap. 8.50 (ISBN 0-686-94398-8, UN77/2A12, UN). Unipub.

Rural Water Supply in Developing Countries: Proceedings of A Workshop in Training Held in Zomba, Malawi, 5-12 Aug. 1980. 144p. 1981. pap. 12.00 (ISBN 0-88936-292-0, IDRC167, IDRC). Unipub.

Seminar on Community Preparedness & Disaster Prevention: Proceedings. (Water Resources Development Ser.: No. 49). pap. 10.00 (ISBN 0-686-92999-3, UN78/2F13, UN). Unipub.

Seventh Session of the Committee on Natural Resources: Proceedings. (Water Resources Development Ser.: No. 54). 146p. 1981. pap. 12.00 (ISBN 0-686-82549-7, UN81/2F10, UN). Unipub.

Skogerboe, G. V. Water & Energy Development in an Arid Environment: The Colorado River Basin. flexi-cover 57.00 (ISBN 0-08-028752-2). Pergamon.

Smallwood, J. B., Jr., ed. Water in the West. (Illus.). 86p. 1983. pap. text ed. 9.95x (ISBN 0-89745-024-8). Sunflower U Pr.

Smith, Courtland. The Salt River Project: A Case Study in Cultural Adaptation to an Urbanizing Community. LC 76-187826. 151p. 1972. pap. 3.75x (ISBN 0-8165-0336-2). U of Ariz Pr.

Smith, D. W. & Hrudey, S. E., eds. Design of Water & Wastewater Services for Cold Climate Communities: Seminar in Edmonton in June 1980 of the 10th IAWPR Conference. (Illus.). 190p. 1981. 39.00 (ISBN 0-08-029079-5, E140). Pergamon.

Stevens, Georgiana G. Jordan River Partition. LC 65-19768. (Studies: No. 6). 1965. pap. 3.00x (ISBN 0-8179-3062-0). Hoover Inst Pr.

Stockton, Charles W. Long-Term Streamflow Records Reconstructed from Tree Rings. LC 74-21007. (Papers of the Laboratory of Tree-Ring Research: No. 5). 111p. 1975. pap. 7.95x (ISBN 0-8165-0376-1). U of Ariz Pr.

Strong, Ann L. Private Property & the Public Interest: The Brandywine Experience. LC 74-24390. (Illus.). 232p. 1975. 22.50x (ISBN 0-8018-1662-9). Johns Hopkins.

Symposium on Karst Hydrology & Water Resources, Dubrovnik, Yugo., Jun 2-7, 1975. Karst Hydrology & Water Resources, 2 vols. Yevjevich, V., ed. LC 76-12972. 1976. Set. 25.00 (ISBN 0-686-67935-0); Vol. 1. (ISBN 0-918334-15-2); Vol. 2. (ISBN 0-918334-16-0). WRP.

Teaching the Systems Approach to Water Resources Development. (Technical Papers in Hydrology: No. 25). 20p. 1983. pap. text ed. 6.00 (ISBN 92-3-102108-7, U1307, UNESCO). Unipub.

Thomson, Keith P., et al, eds. Remote Sensing & Water Resources Management. (American Water Resources Association Proceedings: No. 17). pap. 111.30 (ISBN 0-317-11249-X, 2017815). Bks Demand UMI.

Tourbier, J. Toby & Westmacott, Richard. Water Resources Protection Technology. LC 80-54911. (Illus.). 184p. 1981. pap. 28.00 (ISBN 0-87420-595-6, W08); pap. 21.00 members. Urban Land.

Triennial Report on Water Resources Development: 1968-1970. pap. 5.00 (ISBN 0-686-94302-3, UN71/2A/15, UN). Unipub.

United Nations. Water Development & Management, 4 vols. Incl. Part 1. 97.00 (ISBN 0-08-023402-X); Part 2. 145.00 (ISBN 0-08-023404-6); Part 3. 175.00 (ISBN 0-08-023406-2); Part 4. 225.00 (ISBN 0-08-023408-9). 660.00 set (ISBN 0-08-021987-X). Pergamon.

University Of California - Berkeley. Dictionary Catalog of the Water Resources Center Archives, 5 vols. 1970. lib. bdg. 495.00 (ISBN 0-8161-0884-6, Hall Library); first suppl. (1971) 115.00 (ISBN 0-8161-0895-1); second suppl. (1972 115.00 (ISBN 0-8161-0983-4). G K Hall.

University of California, Berkeley. Dictionary Catalog of the Water Resources Center Archives, Fourth Suppl. 942p. 1975. lib. bdg. 115.00 (ISBN 0-8161-0002-0, Hall Library). G K Hall.

University of California, Berkeley, Water Resources Center. Dictionary Catalog of the Water Resources Center Archives: Sixth Supplement, 2 vols. 1978. Set. lib. bdg. 260.00 (ISBN 0-8161-0244-9, Hall Library). G K Hall.

Vansteenkiste, G. C. System Simulation in Water Resources: Proceedings of the IFIP Working Conference Bruges Belgium, 1975. 418p. 1976. 85.00 (ISBN 0-444-11093-3, North-Holland). Elsevier.

Water & Metropolitan Man. 94p. 1969. pap. 7.75x (ISBN 0-87262-011-5). Am Soc Civil Eng.

Water & Society, Conflicts in Development: Water Conflicts & Research Priorities, Part 2. (Water Development, Supply & Management Ser.: Vol. 8). (Illus.). 260p. 1980. 40.00 (ISBN 0-08-023422-4). Pergamon.

Water for the Southwest: Historical Survey & Guide to Historic Sites. 219p. 1973. pap. text ed. 13.00 (ISBN 0-87262-056-5). Am Soc Civil Eng.

Water Policy Initiatives: Positions of the National Water Policy Committee of ASCE on the President's June 1978 Statements. 280p. 1979. pap. 19.50x (ISBN 0-87262-193-6). Am Soc Civil Eng.

Water Problems of Urbanizing Areas. 358p. 1979. pap. 20.00x (ISBN 0-87262-145-6). Am Soc Civil Eng.

Water Resources: Planning & Management: A Select Bibliography. (Eng. & Fr.). pap. 7.00 (ISBN 0-686-94860-2, UN77/1/4, UN). Unipub.

Water Science & Technology, Vol. 14, Nos. 1-2. flexi-cover 72.50x (ISBN 0-08-029095-7). Pergamon.

Weather & Water. (Eng., Fr. & Span., Illus.). 24p. 1977. pap. 5.00 (ISBN 92-63-10463-8, W213, WMO). Unipub.

White, Gilbert F., et al. Drawers of Water: Domestic Water Use in East Africa. LC 74-172172. (Illus.). 328p. 1972. 25.00x (ISBN 0-226-89490-8). U of Chicago Pr.

Wood, E. F. & Szollosi-Nagy, A., eds. Real-Time Forecasting Control of Water Resource Systems: Proceedings of a IIASA Workshop, October, 1979. (IIASA Proceedings Ser: Vol. 8). 1980. 68.00 (ISBN 0-08-024486-6). Pergamon.

Workshop on Efficient Use & Maintenance of Irrigation Systems at the Farm Level in China: Proceedings. (Water Resources Development Ser.: No. 51). 108p. 1980. pap. 9.00 (ISBN 0-686-72367-8, UN792F16, UN). Unipub.

World Water Balance & Water Resources of the Earth: Prepared by the Chief Administration of the Hydrometeorological Service under the Council of Ministers of the USSR & USSR Committee for the International Hydrological Decade. (Studies & Reports in Hydrology: No. 25). (Illus.). 663p. (Includes Atlas of World Water Balance (37x26.5 cm.) containing 65 maps & explanatory text). 1978. 111.50 (ISBN 92-3-101497-8, U872, UNESCO). Unipub.

Yang-ch'eng Shih. American Water Resources, 2 vols. 732p. Set. text ed. 48.00x (ISBN 0-8290-0390-8); Irvington.

Yaron, D. & Tapiero, C., eds. Operations Research in Agriculture & Water Resources. 586p. 1980. 85.00 (ISBN 0-444-86044-4, North-Holland). Elsevier.

Zaman, Munir & Biswas, Asit K., eds. River Basin Development: Proceedings of the National Symposium on River Basin Development, Dacca, Bangladesh, 4-10 Dec. 1981. (Water Resources Ser.: No. 4). (Illus.). 239p. 1983. 41.25 (ISBN 0-907567-56-8, TYP146, TYP); pap. 20.75 (ISBN 0-907567-57-6, TYP145). Unipub.

Zuidema, Floris C. Impact of Urbanization & Industrialization on Water Resources Planning & Management: A Contribution to the International Hydrological Programme Report of the UNESCO-IHP Workshop on Impact of Urbanization & Industrialization on Regional & National Water Planning & Management, Sandvoort, the Netherlands, 10-14 Oct. 1977. (Studies & Reports in Hydrology: No. 26). (Illus.). 111p. 1979. pap. 11.50 (ISBN 92-3-101624-5, U974, UNESCO). Unipub.

WATER RESOURCES DEVELOPMENT–DATA PROCESSING

Michalson, Edgar L., et al, eds. Multiple Objectives: Planning Water Resources. 1975-76. 5.00 set (ISBN 0-686-15776-1); Vol. 1. 3.00 (ISBN 0-89301-019-7); Vol. 2. 3.00 (ISBN 0-89301-027-8). U Pr of Idaho.

Morlock-Rahn, G. Wassim-Countersimulation Von Wasserversorgung Ung Abwasserentsorgung in Verdichtungsraeumen. (Interdisciplinary Systems Research Ser.: No. 71). (Ger.). 259p. 1979. pap. 34.95x (ISBN 0-8176-1113-4). Birkhauser.

WATER STORAGE

see also Dams; Irrigation; Reservoirs; Runoff; Water-Supply

International Conference on Pumped Storage Development & Its Environmental Effects, University of Wisconsin, Milwaukee, 1971) International Conference on Pumped Storage Development & Its Environmental Effects, University of Wisconsin, Milwaukee, 1971: Proceedings. Karedi, Gabor M., et al, eds. LC 73-123983. (Proceedings of American Water Resources Association Ser.: No. 15). (Illus.). pap. 147.00 (ISBN 0-317-09815-2, 2003127). Bks Demand UMI.

Standard for Welded Steel Elevated Tanks, Standpipes & Reservoirs for Water Storage: AWWA D100-79. 63p. 1979. 8.00 (ISBN 0-686-95674-5). Am Welding.

Watt, Simon B. Ferrocement Water Tanks & Their Construction. (Illus.). 118p. (Orig.). 1978. pap. 7.75x (ISBN 0-903031-51-5, Pub. by Intermediate Tech England). Intermediate Tech.

WATER-SUPPLY

see also Aqueducts; Arid Regions; Dams; Droughts; Forests and Forestry; Irrigation; Reservoirs; Runoff; Stream Measurements; Water–Pollution; Water–Purification; Water-Conservation; Water Quality; Wells

American Society of Civil Engineers, compiled By. Consumptive Use of Water & Irrigation Water Requirements. 227p. 1974. pap. 10.75x (ISBN 0-87262-068-9). Am Soc Civil Eng.

American Water Works Association. Computer-Based Automation in Water Systems. (AWWA Handbooks-General Ser.). (Illus.). 104p. 1980. pap. text ed. 12.00 (ISBN 0-89867-230-9). Am Water Wks Assn.

--Reference Handbook: Basic Science Concepts & Applications. (General References Ser.). (Illus.). 756p. 1980. text ed. 24.00 (ISBN 0-89867-202-3). Am Water Wks Assn.

AQTST-Aquifer Test Analysis with a Hand-Held Calculator. 18.75 (ISBN 0-318-02531-0). Natl Water Well.

AWWA Research Foundation. Future of Water Reuse: Proceedings, Vols. 1, 2, 3. (Illus.). 1810p. (Orig.). 1985. pap. 50.00 (ISBN 0-915295-02-4, 90506). AWWA Res Found.

Bardach, Eugene & Angelides, Sotirios. Water Banking: How to Stop Wasting Agricultural Water. LC 78-50766. 56p. 1978. pap. 2.00 (ISBN 0-917616-26-X). ICS Pr.

Bartlett, R. E. Pumping Stations for Water & Sewage. (Illus.). 150p. 1974. 26.00 (ISBN 0-85334-577-5, Pub. by Elsevier Applied Sci England). Elsevier.

Belan, F. Water Treatment: Calculations, Examples, Problems. 293p. 1984. pap. 6.95 (ISBN 0-317-07272-2, Pub. by Mir Pubs USSR). Imported Pubns.

Biswas, Asit K., ed. United Nations Water Conference: Summary & Main Documents. new ed. LC 77-30461. 1978. text ed. 50.00 (ISBN 0-08-022392-3). Pergamon.

Bittinger, Morton N. & Green, Elizabeth B. You Never Miss the Water till... The Ogallalla Story. LC 80-50167. 1981. 7.00 (ISBN 0-918334-33-0). WRP.

Cairncross, Sandy, et al. Evaluation for Village Water Supply Planning. 179p. 1980. 34.95 (ISBN 0-471-27662-6, Pub. by Wiley-Interscience). Wiley.

Campbell, Stu. Home Water Supply: How to Find, Filter, Store & Conserve It. Griffith, Roger, ed. LC 83-1635. (Illus.). 280p. (Orig.). 1983. pap. 12.95 (ISBN 0-88266-324-0). Garden Way Pub.

Chaudhry, M. H. & Yevjevich, V. Closed-Conduit Flow. LC 81-51337. 1981. 35.00 (ISBN 0-918334-41-1). WRP.

Crosson, Pierre R., et al, eds. Selected Water Management Issues in Latin American Agriculture. LC 77-10193. (Resources for the Future Ser.). (Illus.). 1978. text ed. 16.50x (ISBN 0-8018-2047-2). Johns Hopkins.

Darr, P., et al. The Demand for Urban Water. (Studies in Applied Regional Science: No. 6). 1976. pap. 15.50 (ISBN 90-207-0647-0, Pub. by Martinus Nijhoff Netherlands). Kluwer Academic.

The Development of Waterworks in Japan. (Project on Technology Transfer, Transformation & Development: The Japanese Experience). 38p. 1981. pap. 5.00 (ISBN 92-808-0240-2, TUNU166, UNU). Unipub.

De Wayne, M. L., ed. Water, Human Values & the Eighties. 100p. 1981. pap. 15.25 (ISBN 0-08-028098-6). Pergamon.

Dictionnaire Technique de L'Eau. (Fr.). pap. 19.95 (ISBN 0-686-57115-0, M-6156). French & Eur.

Distribution Systems: Actions & Innovations. (General Handbooks). (Illus.). 256p. 1980. pap. text ed. 24.00 (ISBN 0-89867-246-5). Am Water Wks Assn.

Dyhr-Nielsen, M. Long-Range Water-Supply Forecasting. (Operational Hydrology Reports: No. 20). 20p. 1982. pap. 6.00 (ISBN 92-63-10587-1, W519, WMO). Unipub.

Elmendorf, Mary & Buckles, Patricia. Appropriate Technology for Water Supply & Sanitation: Sociocultural Aspects of Water Supply & Excreta Disposal, Vol. 5. 67p. 1980. pap. 3.00 (ISBN 0-686-39786-X, WS-8006). World Bank.

Environmental Impact Analysis Research Council at the Chicago National Convention, Oct. 1978. Appropriate Technology in Water Supply & Waste Disposal. American Society of Civil Engineers, ed. 280p. 1979. pap. 17.00x (ISBN 0-87262-148-0). Am Soc Civil Eng.

Fahm, Lattee A. The Waste of Nations: The Economic Utilization of Human Waste in Agriculture. LC 79-88260. (LandMark Studies). (Illus.). 188p. 1980. text ed. 28.50x (ISBN 0-916672-28-X). Allanheld.

Falkenmark, Malin, ed. Rural Water Supply & Health: The Need for a New Strategy. (Scandinavian Institute of African Studies). (Illus.). 118p. 1983. text ed. 17.50x (ISBN 0-8419-9763-2, Africana). Holmes & Meier.

Farm-Level Water Management in Selected Asian Countries. 159p. 1980. pap. 13.25 (ISBN 92-833-1461-1, APO88, APO). Unipub.

Feachem, Richard G. & Bradley, David J. Appropriate Technology for Water Supply & Sanitation: Health Aspects of Excreta & Sullage Management - A State-of-the-Art Review, Vol. 3. 303p. 1980. pap. 15.00 (ISBN 0-686-39785-1, WS-8005). World Bank.

Fleming, George. Computer Simulation Techniques in Hydrology. (Environmental Science Ser.). 352p. 1975. 42.50 (ISBN 0-444-00157-3). Elsevier.

Frederick, Kenneth D. Water for Western Agriculture. LC 82-47985. (A Resources for the Future Research Paper Ser.). (Illus.). 256p. (Orig.). 1982. pap. text ed. 15.00x (ISBN 0-8018-2832-5). Johns Hopkins.

--Water Management & Agricultural Development: A Case Study of the Cuyo Region of Argentina. LC 74-24402. (Resources for the Future Research Ser). (Illus.). 208p. 1975. 16.50x (ISBN 0-8018-1701-3). Johns Hopkins.

Frontinus, Sextus J. Stratagems & Aqueducts. (Loeb Classical Library: No. 174). 12.50x (ISBN 0-674-99192-3). Harvard U Pr.

Futoma, David J., et al. Analysis of Polycyclic Aromatic Hydrocarbons in Water Systems. 200p. 1981. 66.00 (ISBN 0-8493-6255-5). CRC Pr.

Geophysics Research Board. Climate, Climatic Change & Water Supply. 1977. pap. 9.25 (ISBN 0-309-02625-3). Natl Acad Pr.

Gibson, Ulric P. & Singer, Rexford D. Water Well Manual: A Practical Guide for Locating & Constructing Wells for Individual & Small Community Water Supplies. LC 71-153696. (Illus.). 156p. 1971. pap. 13.00 (ISBN 0-912722-00-2). Prem Press.

Giefer, Gerald J. Sources of Information in Water Resources. LC 75-20953. 312p. 1976. 30.00 (ISBN 0-912394-15-3). Water Info.

Giefer, Gerald J. & Todd, David K., eds. Water Publications of State Agencies - First Supplement. LC 72-75672. 1976. 28.00 (ISBN 0-912394-17-X). Water Info.

A Guide to Water Well Casing & Screen Selection. 76p. (Published by Roscoe Moss). 12.50 (ISBN 0-318-02527-2). Natl Water Well.

A Guide to Water Well Casing & Screen Selection. (Span.). pap. 6.25 (ISBN 0-318-02528-0). Natl Water Well.

Hackleman, Michael. Waterworks: An Owner-Builder Guide to Rural Water Systems. LC 82-45289. (Illus.). 1983. pap. 14.95 (ISBN 0-385-17559-0, Dolp). Doubleday.

Hamilton, Lawrence S., ed. Forest & Watershed Development & Conservation in Asia & the Pacific. (Special Studies in Natural Resources & Energy Management). 650p. 1982. softcover 28.50x (ISBN 0-86531-534-5). Westview.

Hofkes, E. H. Small Community Water Supplies: Technology of Small Water Supply Systems in Developing Countries. 488p. 1981. 32.95x (ISBN 0-471-90289-6, Pub. by Wiley-Interscience). Wiley.

Horner, Jack K. Natural Radioactivity in Water Supplies. (Westview Studies in Water Policy & Management). 325p. 1985. pap. 27.50x (ISBN 0-8133-0050-9). Westview.

Incidence, Monitoring & Treatment of Viruses in Water Supply Systems. 91p. 1983. pap. 13.00x (ISBN 0-87262-376-9). Am Soc Civil Eng.

International Commission on Irrigation & Drainage, New Delhi, India, ed. The Application of Systems Analysis Irrigation, Drainage & Flood Control: A Manual for Engineers & Water Technologists. (Water Development, Supply & Management Ser.: Vol. 11). (Illus.). 1980. text ed. 57.00 (ISBN 0-08-023425-9); pap. text ed. 21.00 (ISBN 0-08-023431-3). Pergamon.

Kabermatten, John M. & Julius, DeAnne S. Appropriate Technology for Water Supply & Sanitation: A Planner's Guide, Vol. 2. 194p. 1980. pap. 5.00 (ISBN 0-686-39784-3, WS-8004). World Bank.

Kalbermatten, John M. & Julius, DeAnne S. Appropriate Technology for Water Supply & Sanitation: A Summary of Technical & Economic Options, Vol. 1a. 38p. 1980. pap. 3.00 (ISBN 0-686-39782-7, WS-8003). World Bank.

--Appropriate Technology for Water Supply & Sanitation: Technical & Economic Options, Vol. 1. 122p. 1980. write for info. (WS-8002). World Bank.

Kasperson, Roger E. & Kasperson, Jeanne X., eds. Water Re-Use & the Cities. LC 75-44888. (Illus.). 252p. 1977. 25.00x (ISBN 0-87451-125-9). U Pr of New Eng.

Kneese, Allen V. & Smith, Stephen C., eds. Water Research. LC 66-26687. (Resources for the Future Ser). 533p. 1967. 30.00x (ISBN 0-8018-0344-6). Johns Hopkins.

Korten, Frances F. Building National Capacity to Develop Water Users' Associations: Experience From the Philippines, No. 528. v, 69p. 1982. pap. 3.00 (ISBN 0-8213-0051-2). World Bank.

LaConte, P. & Haines, Y. Y. Water Resources & Land-Use Planning: A Systems Approach. 1982. lib. bdg. 57.50 (ISBN 90-247-2726-X, Pub. by Martinus Nijhoff Netherlands). Kluwer Academic.

Lamson-Scribner, Frank H., Jr. & Huang, John, eds. Municipal Water Supply Project Analysis: Case Studies. ix, 520p. 1977. pap. 8.50 (ISBN 0-686-36158-X). World Bank.

LeGrand, Harry. A Standardized System for Evaluating Waste Disposal Sites. 42p. non-members 15.00, (ISBN 0-318-02530-2); members 12.00, (ISBN 0-318-03618-5). Natl Water Well.

Little, A. H. Water Supplies & the Treatment & Disposal of Effluents. 71p. 1975. 50.00x (ISBN 0-686-63808-5). State Mutual Bk.

Long-Term Perspectives For Water Use & Supply in the ECE Region: Report on Recent Experience and Prospects for Time Horizons 1990 and 2000. 33p. 1981. pap. 7.00 (ISBN 0-686-97582-0, UN81/2E22, UN). Unipub.

Long-Term Planning of Water Management, 3 Vols. Vol. 1. pap. 8.50 (ISBN 0-686-94486-0, UN76/2E27, UN); Vol. 2. pap. 13.00 (ISBN 0-686-99373-X, UN76/2E28); Vol. 3. pap. price not set (UN76/2E29). Unipub.

McBean, Edward A., et al, eds. Inputs for Risk Analysis in Water Systems. LC 79-64192. 1979. 16.00 (ISBN 0-918334-29-2). WRP.

McPherson, Murray B. Regional Earth Science Information in Local Water Management. 185p. 1975. pap. 12.75x (ISBN 0-87262-151-0). Am Soc Civil Eng.

Makkink, G. F. & Van Heemst, H. D. Simulation of the Water Balance of Arable Land & Pastures. (Illus.). 85p. 1975. pap. 12.00 (ISBN 90-220-0566-6, PDC87, PUDOC). Unipub.

Manual for the Compilation of Balances of Water Resources & Needs. pap. 5.00 (ISBN 0-686-94730-4, UN74/2E/2, UN). Unipub.

Mara, D. Duncan. Appropriate Technology for Water Supply & Sanitation: Sanitation Alternative for Low-Income Communities - Brief Introduction, Vol. 1b. 48p. 1982. pap. 3.00 (ISBN 0-686-39783-5, WS-8201). World Bank.

Mather, John R. The Climatic Water Budget in Environmental Analysis. LC 77-17726. (Illus.). 1978. 29.00x (ISBN 0-669-02087-7). Lexington Bks.

Matson, Tim. Earth Ponds: The Country Pond Maker's Guide. (Illus.). 104p. 1982. pap. 10.95 (ISBN 0-914378-86-4). Countryman.

Michigan Department of Health. Ground Water Heat Pump Installations in Michigan. 23p. pap. 3.75 (ISBN 0-318-02533-7). Natl Water Well.

Midwest Plan Service Personnel. Private Water Systems Handbook. 4th ed. LC 79-19040. (Illus.). 72p. 1979. pap. 5.00 (ISBN 0-89373-045-9, MWPS-14). Midwest Plan Serv.

Morley, D. A. Mathematical Modelling in Water & Wastewater Treatment. (Illus.). 366p. 1979. 66.75 (ISBN 0-85334-842-1, Pub. by Elsevier Applied Sci England). Elsevier.

Narayana, Dhruva, et al. Analog Computer Simulation of the Runoff Characteristics of an Urban Watershed. LC 77-141023. 88p. 1969. 19.00 (ISBN 0-403-04522-3). Scholarly.

National Systems of Water Administration. pap. 9.50 (ISBN 0-686-94682-0, UN74/2A/10, UN). Unipub.

Newell, Frederick H. Water Resources: Present & Future Uses. LC 72-2859. (Use & Abuse of America's Natural Resources Ser). (Illus.). 350p. 1972. Repr. of 1920 ed. 21.00 (ISBN 0-405-04523-9). Ayer Co Pubs.

Ozone Treatment of Water for Cooling Applications. 38.00 (ISBN 0-317-07455-5). Intl Ozone.

Pacey, Arnold, ed. Water for the Thousand Millions, Vol. 4. LC 77-23127. 1977. pap. text ed. 7.25 (ISBN 0-08-021805-9). Pergamon.

Pineo, C. S. & Subrahmanyan, D. V. Community Water Supply & Excreta Disposal Situation in the Developing Countries. (Offset Publication Ser.: No. 15). (Also avail. in French). 1975. pap. 4.80 (ISBN 92-4-170015-7). World Health.

Principles & Methods for the Provision of Economic Incentives in Water Supply & Waste Water Disposal Systems, Including the Fixing of Charges. pap. 2.50 (ISBN 0-686-94451-8, UN76/2E25, UN). Unipub.

Rudman, Jack. Assistant Superintendent of Water Works. (Career Examination Ser.: C-2003). (Cloth bdg. avail. on request). pap. 12.00 (ISBN 0-8373-2003-8). Natl Learning.

--Assistant Water Maintenance Foreman. (Career Examination Ser.: C-2919). (Cloth bdg. avail. on request). pap. 12.00 (ISBN 0-8373-2919-1). Natl Learning.

--District Foreman (Water Supply) (Career Examination Ser.: C-2037). (Cloth bdg. avail. on request). pap. 12.00 (ISBN 0-8373-2037-2). Natl Learning.

--District Foreman (Watershed Maintenance) (Career Examination Ser.: C-428). (Cloth bdg. avail. on request). pap. 12.00 (ISBN 0-8373-0428-8). Natl Learning.

--Foreman (Water Supply) (Career Examination Ser.: C-279). (Cloth bdg. avail. on request). pap. 10.00 (ISBN 0-8373-0279-X). Natl Learning.

--Foreman (Watershed Maintenance) (Career Examination Ser.: C-280). (Cloth bdg. avail. on request). pap. 10.00 (ISBN 0-8373-0280-3). Natl Learning.

--Supervising Water Use Inspector. (Career Examination Ser.: C-1051). (Cloth bdg. avail. on request). pap. 10.00 (ISBN 0-8373-1051-2). Natl Learning.

--Water Plant Operator. (Career Examination Ser.: C-897). (Cloth bdg. avail. on request). pap. 12.00 (ISBN 0-8373-0897-6). Natl Learning.

--Water Use Inspector. (Career Examination Ser.: C-898). (Cloth bdg. avail. on request). pap. 12.00 (ISBN 0-8373-1533-6). Natl Learning.

Rybczynski, Witold & Polprasert, Chongrak. Appropriate Technology for Water Supply & Sanitation: Low-Cost Technology Options for Sanitation - a State-of-the-Art Review & Annotated Bibliography, Vol. 4. 1978. pap. write for info. (Co. Pub with International Development Research Centre Pub.). World Bank.

Saunders, Robert J. & Warford, Jeremy J. Village Water Supply: Economics & Policy in the Developing World. LC 76-11758. (A World Bank Research Publication Ser). 296p. 1976. 22.50x (ISBN 0-8018-1876-1). Johns Hopkins.

Schiller, E. J. & Droste, R. L., eds. Water Supply & Sanitation in Developing Countries. LC 81-86538. (Illus.). 368p. 1982. 45.00 (ISBN 0-250-40490-7). Butterworth.

Scientific Framework of World Water Balance. 1971. pap. 5.00 (ISBN 92-3-100804-8, U586, UNESCO). Unipub.

Shuval, Hillel I. & Gunnerson, Charles G. Appropriate Technology for Water Supply & Sanitation: Night-Soil Composting, Vol. 10. 81p. 1981. pap. 3.00 (ISBN 0-686-39787-8, WS-8101). World Bank.

Skinner, Brian J. Earth Resources. 3rd ed. (Illus.). 208p. 1986. text ed. 17.95 (ISBN 0-13-223108-5); pap. text ed. 14.95 (ISBN 0-13-223090-9). P-H.

Small Water System Solutions Seminar Proceedings. 80p. 10.20 (ISBN 0-686-44873-1). Am Water Wks Assn.

Steel, E. W. & McGhee, Terence. Water Supply & Sewerage. 5th ed. (Illus.). 1979. text ed. 42.00 (ISBN 0-07-060929-2). McGraw.

Tarlock, A. Dan. Water Resource Management: 2nd ed. 1983 Supplement. (University Casebook Ser.). 223p. 1982. pap. text ed. 7.50 (ISBN 0-88277-103-5). Foundation Pr.

Thirsty Third World. 42p. 1982. 25.00x (ISBN 0-901090-08-5, Pub. by Natl Water England). State Mutual Bk.

Van der Leeden, Frits. Water Resources of the World. LC 75-20952. (Illus.). 1975. 60.00 (ISBN 0-912394-14-5). Water Info.

Van Keulen, H. Simulation of Water Use & Herbage Growth in Arid Regions. (Illus.). 150p. 1975. pap. 22.00 (ISBN 90-220-0557-7, PDC88, PUDOC). Unipub.

Van Lelyveld, H. & Zoeteman, B. C. Water Supply & Health: Proceedings of the International Symposium at the Netherlands, 1980. (Studies in Environmental Science: Vol. 12). 398p. 1981. 81.00 (ISBN 0-444-41960-8). Elsevier.

Vermeer, E. B. Water Conservance & Irrigation in China. 1977. lib. bdg. 45.00 (ISBN 90-6021-410-2, Pub. by Leiden Univ Holland). Kluwer Academic.

Village Water Supply. (World Bank Paper). 98p. 1976. 5.00 (ISBN 0-686-36161-X, PP-7602). World Bank.

Wagner, E. G. & Lanoix, J. N. Water Supply for Rural Areas & Small Communities. (Monograph Ser: No. 42). (Eng, Fr, & Span., Illus.). 337p. 1959. 17.60 (ISBN 92-4-140042-0). World Health.

Waste & Water Management Systems. 52p. 1976. 35.00 (ISBN 0-318-01547-1, 22030). Indus Fabrics.

Water Management in Industrialized River Basins. (Documents Ser.). 164p. 1980. 10.00x (ISBN 92-64-12063-7). OECD.

Water Supply & Waste Disposal. 46p. 1980. pap. 3.00 (ISBN 0-686-39678-2). World Bank.

Water Treatment. (Illus.). 410p. 1984. looseleaf 75.00x (ISBN 0-87683-368-7). G P Courseware.

Water Treatment. (Principles of Steam Generation Ser.: Module 2). (Illus.). 80p. 1982. spiral bdg. 10.00x (ISBN 0-87683-252-4); instr's. manual 15.00x (ISBN 0-87683-273-7). G P Courseware.

Water Utility Accounting. 2nd ed. (General References Ser.). (Illus.). 288p. 1980. text ed. 33.60 (ISBN 0-89867-237-6). Am Water Wks Assn.

WHO Expert Committee. Geneva, 1968. Community Water Supply: Report. (Technical Report Ser.: No. 420). (Also avail. in French & Spanish). 1969. pap. 1.20 (ISBN 92-4-120420-6). World Health.

WHO Scientific Group. Geneva, 1971. Techniques for the Collection & Reporting of Data on Community Water Supply: Report. (Technical Report Ser.: No. 490). (Also avail. in French & Spanish). 1972. pap. 1.20 (ISBN 92-4-120490-7). World Health.

Widstrand, C. G., et al. Water & Society: The Social & Ecological Effects of Water Exploitation in Developing Countries, Part 1. flexi-cover 22.00 (ISBN 0-08-028751-4). Pergamon.

Wisler, Chester O. & Brater, E. F. Hydrology. 2nd ed. LC 59-14981. 408p. 1959. 39.50x (ISBN 0-471-95634-1). Wiley.

Wood, E. F. & Szollosi-Nagy, A., eds. Real-Time Forecasting Control of Water Resource Systems: Proceedings of a IIASA Workshop, October, 1979. (IIASA Proceedings Ser: Vol. 8). 1980. 68.00 (ISBN 0-08-024486-6). Pergamon.

Woolley. Silver Chloride & Water Systems. 1986. 100.00x (ISBN 0-08-023923-4). Pergamon.

WATER-SUPPLY–AFRICA

Balek, Jaroslav. Hydrology & Water Resources in Tropical Africa. (Developments in Water Science Ser.: Vol. 8). 208p. 1977. 70.25 (ISBN 0-444-99814-4). Elsevier.

Caponera, Dante A. Water Law in Selected African Countries: Benin, Burundi, Ethopia, Gabon, Kenya, Mauritius, Sierra Leone, Swaziland, Upper Volta, Zambia. (Legislative Studies: No. 17). (Eng., Fr. & Span.). 273p. 1979. pap. 19.75 (ISBN 92-5-100748-9, F1620, FAO). Unipub.

Fortmann, Louise & Roe, Emery. Water Use in Rural Botswana. 150p. (Orig.). 1982. pap. text ed. 5.50 (ISBN 0-86731-059-6). RDC Ctr Intl Stud.

Nissen-Petersen, Erik. Rain Catchment & Water Supply in Rural Africa. 1982. 29.00x (ISBN 0-340-28429-3, Pub. by Hodder & Stoughton England). State Mutual Bk.

White, Gilbert F., et al. Drawers of Water: Domestic Water Use in East Africa. LC 74-172172. (Illus.). 328p. 1972. 25.00x (ISBN 0-226-89490-8). U of Chicago Pr.

WATER SUPPLY–AUSTRALIA

When Should I Water. (Discovering Soils Ser.: No. 8). 76p. 1979. pap. text ed. 6.00 (ISBN 0-643-02522-7, C044, CSIRO). Unipub.

WATER-SUPPLY–CANADA

Canada Water Yearbook 1977-1978. 120p. 1980. pap. 6.50 (ISBN 0-660-10142-4, SSC141, SSC). Unipub.

Hydrological Atlas of Canada. 1978. pap. 65.00 (ISBN 0-660-01591-9, SSC122, SSC). Unipub.

MacIver, Ian. Urban Water Supply Alternatives: Perception & Choice in the Grand Basin, Ontario. LC 70-115926. (Research Papers Ser.: No. 126). 1970. pap. 10.00 (ISBN 0-89065-033-0). U Chicago Dept Geog.

WATER-SUPPLY–CHINA

Biswas, Asu K. & Dakang, Zuo, eds. Long Distance Water Transfer: A Chinese Case Study & International Experience. (Water Resources Ser.: Vol. 3). 416p. 1983. 48.75 (ISBN 0-907567-52-5, TYP144, TYP); pap. 28.25 (ISBN 0-907567-53-3, TYP143). Unipub.

Nickum, James E., ed. Water Management Organization in China. LC 80-5458. 288p. 1981. 30.00 (ISBN 0-87332-140-5). M E Sharpe.

Rural Water Supply in China. 92p. 1981. pap. 9.00 (ISBN 0-88936-261-0, IDRCTS25, IDRC). Unipub.

WATER-SUPPLY–GERMANY

Weimann, Reinhold. Fragen des Wasserhaushalts Mittelrheingebeit. 20.00 (ISBN 0-384-66530-6). Johnson Repr.

WATER-SUPPLY–GREAT BRITAIN

Okun, Daniel A. Regionalization of Water Management: A Revolution in England & Wales. (Illus.). 377p. 1977. 42.75 (ISBN 0-85334-738-7, Pub. by Elsevier Applied Sci England). Elsevier.

Porter, Elizabeth. Water Management in England & Wales. LC 77-83998. (Cambridge Geographical Studies: No. 10). (Illus.). 1979. 49.50 (ISBN 0-521-21865-9). Cambridge U Pr.

Royal United Services Institute, ed. Will the Wells Run Dry? 18.00x (ISBN 0-686-75611-8, Pub. by Royal United England). State Mutual Bk.

Water Practice Manuals: The Structure & Management of the British Water Industry, Bk. 1. 255p. 1981. 40.00x (ISBN 0-901427-07-1, Pub. by Inst Water Eng). State Mutual Bk.

WATER-SUPPLY–GREECE

Lang, Mabel. Waterworks in the Athenian Agora. LC 69-22670. (Excavations of the Athenian Agora Picture Bks.: No. 11). (Illus.). 1968. pap. 1.50x (ISBN 0-87661-611-2). Am Sch Athens.

WATER-SUPPLY–INDIA

Rao, K. L. India's Water Wealth: Its Assessment, Uses & Projections. 284p. 1981. 30.00x (ISBN 0-86131-197-3, Pub. by Orient Longman India). State Mutual Bk.

Roa, K. L. India's Water Wealth. rev. ed. cancelled (ISBN 0-8364-0580-3, Pub. by Orient Longman). South Asia Bks.

WATER-SUPPLY–ISRAEL

Shuval, Hillel I., ed. Water Quality Management Under Conditions of Scarcity: Israel As a Case Study. LC 79-8848. (Water Pollution Ser.). 1980. 49.50 (ISBN 0-12-641280-4). Acad Pr.

WATER SUPPLY–NEAR EAST

The Development of Waterworks in Japan. (Project on Technology Transfer, Transformation & Development: The Japanese Experience). 38p. 1981. pap. 5.00 (ISBN 92-808-0240-2, TUNU166, UNU). Unipub.

Report of the Fifth Session of the Regional Commission on Land & Water Use in the Near East: Islamabad, Pakistan, 20-22 Oct. 1976. (Land & Water Development Documents: No. 13). 32p. 1976. pap. 7.50 (ISBN 92-5-100238-X, F2090, FAO). Unipub.

WATER-SUPPLY–UNITED STATES

Ackerman, Edward A., et al. Technology in American Water Development. LC 77-86377. (Resources for the Future, Inc. Publications). Repr. of 1959 ed. 47.50 (ISBN 0-404-60326-2). AMS Pr.

American Water Works Association. Controlling Organics in Drinking Water: Proceedings. (AWWA Handbooks-Proceedings). (Illus.). 136p. 1979. pap. text ed. 10.20 (ISBN 0-89867-223-6). Am Water Wks Assn.

--Energy & Water Use Forecasting. (AWWA Handbooks-General Ser.). (Illus.). 104p. 1980. pap. text ed. 12.00 (ISBN 0-89867-236-8). Am Water Wks Assn.

--Safe Water: A Factbook on the SDWA for Noncommunity Water Systems. (Illus.). 52p. 1980. pap. 1.80 (ISBN 0-89867-224-4). Am Water Wks Assn.

--Water Customer Information. (AWWA Handbooks Proceedings Ser.). (Illus.). 56p. 1979. pap. text ed. 7.20 (ISBN 0-89867-222-8). Am Water Wks Assn.

AWWA Distribution System Symposium Nineteen Eighty: Proceedings: 1980. (AWWA Handbooks Proceedings Ser.). (Illus.). 179p. 1980. pap. text ed. 11.40 (ISBN 0-89867-235-X). Am Water Wks Assn.

Blake, Nelson M. Land into Water-Water into Land: A History of Water Management in Florida. LC 79-21836. (Illus.). viii, 344p. 1980. 19.95 (ISBN 0-8130-0642-2). U Presses Fla.

--Water for the Cities: A History of the Urban Water Supply Problem in the United States. (Illus.). 1956. 14.95x (ISBN 0-8156-2017-9). Syracuse U Pr.

Cain, Louis P. Sanitation Strategy for a Lakefront Metropolis: The Case of Chicago. LC 76-14711. 173p. 1978. 15.00 (ISBN 0-87580-064-5). N Ill U Pr.

Carr, Donald E. Death of the Sweet Waters. (Illus.). 1966. 6.95 (ISBN 0-393-06354-2). Norton.

Franko, David A. & Wetzel, Robert G. To Quench Our Thirst. (Illus.). 176p. 1983. text ed. 20.00x (ISBN 0-472-10032-7); pap. text ed. 8.50x (ISBN 0-472-08037-7). U of Mich Pr.

Geraghty, Miller, Van der Leeden, & Troise. Water Atlas of the U. S. 3rd ed. LC 73-76649. 1973. 45.00 (ISBN 0-912394-03-X). Water Info.

Halasi-Kun, George J., ed. Pollution & Water Resources: Toxic Pollution, Microstructures in Meteorites & Water Resources Management. (Columbia University Seminar Ser.: Vol. XVI). (Illus.). 250p. 1984. 49.95 (ISBN 0-08-031624-7). Pergamon.

Hoffman, Abraham. Vision or Villainy: Origins of the Owens Valley-Los Angeles Water Controversy. LC 80-6111. (Environmental History Ser.: No.3). (Illus.). 328p. 1981. 22.50x (ISBN 0-89096-112-3). Tex A&M Univ Pr.

Holtz, David & Sebastian, Scott, eds. Municipal Water Systems: The Challenge for Urban Resource Management. LC 77-74425. (Illus.). 320p. 1978. 17.50x (ISBN 0-253-33938-3). Ind U Pr.

Kahrl, William L. Water & Power: The Conflict over Los Angeles' Water Supply in the Owens Valley. (Illus.). 595p. 1983. pap. 10.95 (ISBN 0-520-05068-1, CAL 651). U of Cal Pr.

Kundell, James E., ed. Georgia Water Resources: Issues & Options. 114p. 1980. pap. 10.00x (ISBN 0-89854-066-6). U of GA Inst Govt.

Managing Water Rates & Finances. (AWWA Handbooks-General Ser.). (Illus.). 208p. 1980. pap. text ed. 19.20 (ISBN 0-89867-228-7). Am Water Wks Assn.

Martin, William E., et al. Saving Water in a Desert City. LC 83-43263. 122p. 1984. pap. text ed. 10.00x (ISBN 0-915707-04-7). Johns Hopkins.

Napier, Ted L. & Scott, Donald, eds. Water Resources Research: Problems & Potentials for Agriculture & Rural Communities. LC 83-4821. 247p. 1983. 6.00 (ISBN 0-935734-10-4). Soil Conservation.

Newell, Frederick H. Water Resources: Present & Future Uses. LC 72-2859. (Use & Abuse of America's Natural Resources Ser). (Illus.). 350p. 1972. Repr. of 1920 ed. 21.00 (ISBN 0-405-04523-9). Ayer Co Pubs.

Operator Certification Study Guide. (AWWA Handbooks Ser.: General). (Illus.). 104p. 1979. pap. 12.00 (ISBN 0-89867-227-9). Am Water Wks Assn.

Potter, Loren D. & Gosz, James R. Water Resources in the Southern Rockies & High Plains: Forest Recreation Use & Aquatic Interactions. LC 83-16833. (Illus.). 331p. 1984. 29.95x (ISBN 0-8263-0692-6). U of NM Pr.

Seckler, David, ed. California Water: A Study in Resource Management. LC 76-139773. 1971. 48.50x (ISBN 0-520-01884-2). U of Cal Pr.

Sheaffer, John R. & Stevens, Leonard A. Future Water: An Exciting Solution to America's Resource Crisis. LC 83-61855. (Illus.). 288p. 1983. FPT 14.95 (ISBN 0-688-01575-1). Morrow.

Thomas, Harold E. Conservation of Ground Water: A Survey of the Present Ground-Water Situation in the United States. Repr. of 1951 ed. lib. bdg. 19.50x (ISBN 0-8371-3431-5, THGW). Greenwood.

Todd, David K., ed. Ground-Water Resources of the United States: An Illustrated Compendium of the Nation's Underground Water Resources Compiled from Publications of the United States Geological Survey. LC 80-80553. (Illus.). 749p. 1983. 39.00 (ISBN 0-912722-02-9). Prem Press.

Water Quality Technology Conference - 1979: Advances in Laboratory Techniques for Quality Control. (AWWA Handbooks Proceedings Ser.). (Illus.). 350p. 1980. pap. text ed. 14.40 (ISBN 0-89867-231-7). Am Water Wks Assn.

Wollman, Nathaniel & Bonem, Gilbert W. The Outlook for Water: Quality, Quantity & National Growth. LC 75-149243. (Resources for the Future Ser). (Illus.). 352p. 1971. 24.00x (ISBN 0-8018-1260-7). Johns Hopkins.

Wurm, Ted G. Hetch Hetchy & Its Dam Railroad. LC 73-87231. (Illus.). 300p. 1973. 25.00 (ISBN 0-8310-7102-8). Howell-North.

Yang-ch'eng Shih. American Water Resources, 2 vols. 732p. Set. text ed. 48.00x (ISBN 0-8290-0390-8); Irvington.

WATER-SUPPLY, AGRICULTURAL

Alberda, Th. Production & Water Use of Several Food & Fodder Crops Under Irrigation in the Desert Area of Southwestern Peru. (Agricultural Research Reports: No. 928). (Illus.). 50p. 1985. pap. 7.50 (ISBN 90-220-0869-X, PDC291, Pudoc). Unipub.

Napier, Ted L. & Scott, Donald, eds. Water Resources Research: Problems & Potentials for Agriculture & Rural Communities. LC 83-4821. 247p. 1983. 6.00 (ISBN 0-935734-10-4). Soil Conservation.

WATER-SUPPLY, INDUSTRIAL

see also Water–Pollution; Water–Purification

Brandvold, D. C. Water Treatment: Industrial-Commercial-Municipal. 2nd ed. (Illus.). 1982. pap. 5.00 (ISBN 0-9610178-0-5). Branchemco.

Collie, M. J., ed. Industrial Water Treatment Chemicals & Processes: Developments Since 1978. LC 83-2411. (Chem. Tech. Rev. 217; Pollution Tech. Rev. 98). (Illus.). 319p. (Orig.). 1983. 42.00 (ISBN 0-8155-0936-7). Noyes.

Industrial Water Economy. (Symposium Ser.: No. 67). 216p. 1981. 75.00x (ISBN 0-85295-142-6, Pub. by IChemE). State Mutual Bk.

Institution of Chemical Engineers. Industrial Water Economy. 52.50 (ISBN 0-08-028765-4). Pergamon.

Jenkins, S. H. Industrial Effluents. 1977. flexi-cover 99.00 (ISBN 0-08-019845-7). Pergamon.

--Instrumentation & Control for Water & Wastewater Treatment & Transport Systems. flexi-cover 99.00x (ISBN 0-08-022098-3). Pergamon.

McCoy, James W. Chemical Analysis of Industrial Water. (Illus.). 1969. 30.00 (ISBN 0-8206-0017-2). Chem Pub.

Wong, Shue-Tuck. Perception of Choice & Factors Affecting Industrial Water Supply Decisions in Northeastern Illinois. LC 68-56934. (Research Papers Ser.: No. 117). 96p. 1968. pap. 10.00 (ISBN 0-89065-024-1). U Chicago Dept Geog.

WATER-SUPPLY, RURAL

see also Water-Supply, Agricultural

Glennie, Colin. Village Water Supply in the Decade: Lessons From Field Experience. LC 82-23749. 152p. 1983. 31.95x (ISBN 0-471-10525-2, Pub. by Wiley-Interscience). Wiley.

Mann, H. T. & Williamson, D. Water Treatment & Sanitation: Simple Methods for Rural Areas. 2nd ed. (Illus.). 92p. (Orig.). 1979. pap. 7.75x (ISBN 0-903031-23-X, Pub. by Intermediate Tech England). Intermediate Tech.

Miller, Duncan. Self-Help & Popular Participation in Rural Water Systems. (Development Center Studies). (Illus.). 150p. (Orig.). 1980. pap. text ed. 9.00x (ISBN 92-64-12027-0, 4180011). OECD.

Orem, Howard & Snyder, Suzen. Country Land & Its Uses. LC 74-22154. (Illus.). 310p. 1975. 13.95 (ISBN 0-87961-031-X); pap. 7.95 (ISBN 0-87961-030-1). Naturegraph.

Rain & Storm Water Harvesting: Additional Water Supply. 25p. 1982. pap. 7.50 (ISBN 0-686-95409-2, UNEP064, UNEP). Unipub.

Rain & Stormwater Harvesting in Rural Areas: A Report of the United Nations Environment Programme. (Water Resources Ser.: No. 5). (Illus.). 235p. 1983. 37.50 (ISBN 0-907567-38-X, TYP149, TYP); pap. 18.75 (ISBN 0-907567-39-8, TYP148). Unipub.

Water Supply Systems for Rual Fire Protection. (Twenty Ser.). 1969. pap. 2.00 (ISBN 0-685-58117-9, 25). Natl Fire Prot.

Water: Where Water Comes From. (Better Farming Ser.: No. 28). 31p. 1981. pap. 7.50 (ISBN 92-5-101086-2, F2265, FAO). Unipub.

Wright, Forrest B. Rural Water Supply & Sanitation. 3rd ed. LC 75-14110. 320p. 1977. 22.00 (ISBN 0-88275-334-7). Krieger.

WATER-SUPPLY ENGINEERING

see also Boring; Hydraulic Engineering; Water-Supply, Industrial

Ackerman, Edward A., et al. Technology in American Water Development. LC 77-86377. (Resources for the Future, Inc. Publications). Repr. of 1959 ed. 47.50 (ISBN 0-404-60326-2). AMS Pr.

American Water Works Association. Annual Conference: Proceedings: 1975. Incl. Annual Conference: Proceedings. 1976, 2 Vols. (AWWA Handbooks Ser.). (Illus.). 1976. Vol. I. pap. text ed. 22.80, 592P. (ISBN 0-89867-046-2); Vol. II. pap. text ed. 22.80, 700P. (ISBN 0-89867-047-0); Annual Conference: Proceedings. 1977. 2 Pts. (AWWA Handbooks Ser.). (Illus.). 1400p. 1977. pap. text ed. 39.00 (ISBN 0-89867-052-7); Annual Conference: Proceedings. 1978. 2 Pts. (AWWA Handbooks Ser.). (Illus.). 1400p. 1978. pap. text ed. 48.00 (ISBN 0-89867-056-X); Annual Conference: Proceedings. 1979. (AWWA Handbooks Ser.). (Illus.). 1200p. 1979. pap. text ed. 57.60 (ISBN 0-89867-229-5); Annual Conference: Proceedings. 1980. (AWWA Handbooks Ser.). (Illus.). 1452p. 1980. pap. text ed. 57.60 (ISBN 0-89867-238-4); Annual Conference: Proceedings. 1981. 2 Pts. (AWWA Handbooks Ser.). (Illus.). 1310p. 1981. pap. text ed. 62.40 set (ISBN 0-89867-260-0); Annual Conference: Proceedings. 1982. 2 Pts. (AWWA Handbooks Ser.). (Illus.). 1310p. 1982. pap. 68.60 set (ISBN 0-89867-281-3). (AWWA Handbooks - Proceedings). (Illus.). 1120p. 1975. pap. text ed. 26.40 (ISBN 0-89867-044-6). Am Water Wks Assn.

--Basic Management Principles for Small Water Systems. (AWWA Handbooks-General Ser.). (Illus.). 132p. 1982. pap. 18.20 (ISBN 0-89867-280-5). Am Water Wks Assn.

--Controlling Corrosion Within Water Systems. (AWWA Handbooks - Proceedings). (Illus.). 120p. 1978. pap. text ed. 9.60 (ISBN 0-89867-057-8). Am Water Wks Assn.

--Corrosion Control. (AWWA Handbooks-Proceedings Ser.). (Illus.). 70p. 1982. pap. 10.20 (ISBN 0-89867-283-X). Am Water Wks Assn.

--Corrosion Control by Deposition of CaCO3 Films Handbook. (AWWA Handbooks - General). (Illus.). 68p. 1978. pap. text ed. 9.60 (ISBN 0-89867-020-9). Am Water Wks Assn.

--Cross-Connections & Backflow Prevention Handbook. 2nd ed. (AWWA Handbooks - General). (Illus.). 64p. 1974. pap. text ed. 8.40 (ISBN 0-89867-250-3). Am Water Wks Assn.

--Design of Pilot Plant Studies. (AWWA Handbooks-Proceedings Ser.). (Illus.). 108p. 1982. pap. 11.40 (ISBN 0-89867-285-6). Am Water Wks Assn.

--Dual Distribution Systems. (AWWA Handbooks - Proceedings). (Illus.). 112p. 1976. pap. text ed. 7.20 (ISBN 0-89867-050-0). Am Water Wks Assn.

--Financial Planning & the Use of Financial Information for General Management Personnel. (AWWA Handbooks-Proceedings Ser.). (Illus.). 80p. 1982. pap. 10.20 (ISBN 0-89867-277-5). Am Water Wks Assn.

--Guidelines for Selection of Instruments for the Small Laboratory - M15. (AWWA Manuals). (Illus.). 90p. 1978. pap. text ed. 13.80 (ISBN 0-89867-073-X). Am Water Wks Assn.

--Index to Journal AWWA: 1956-1965. (Journal Indexes Ser.). 133p. 1967. text ed. 12.00 (ISBN 0-89867-000-4). Am Water Wks Assn.

--Index to Journal AWWA: 1966-1975. (Journal Indexes Ser.). 200p. 1977. text ed. 19.20 (ISBN 0-89867-006-3). Am Water Wks Assn.

--Safety Practice for Water Utilities - M3. (AWWA Manuals). (Illus.). 128p. 1977. pap. text ed. 16.20 (ISBN 0-89867-061-6). Am Water Wks Assn.

--Upgrading Existing Water Treatment Plants. (AWWA Handbooks - Proceedings). (Illus.). 272p. 1974. pap. text ed. 12.60 (ISBN 0-89867-042-X). Am Water Wks Assn.

American Water Works Association-AWWA RF Merged Index, 1973-1980. (American Water Works Association Handbooks). 264p. 1982. pap. text ed. 22.40 (ISBN 0-89867-276-7). Am Water Wks Assn.

Automation & Instrumentation: M2. (AWWA Manuals Ser.). (Illus.). 160p. 1977. pap. text ed. 19.20 (ISBN 0-89867-060-8). Am Water Wks Assn.

Civil Engineering Specification for the Water Industry. 80p. 1982. 30.00x (ISBN 0-904561-37-2, Pub. by Natl Water England). State Mutual Bk.

Cox, C. R. Operation & Control of Water Treatment Processes. (Monograph Ser: No. 49). (Eng, Fr, Rus, & Span., Illus.). 390p. 1964. 20.80 (ISBN 92-4-140049-8). World Health.

Disinfection. (AWWA Handbooks - Proceedings). (Illus.). 224p. 1977. pap. text ed. 12.00 (ISBN 0-89867-053-5). Am Water Wks Assn.

Emergency Planning for Water Utility Management, M19. (AWWA Manuals). (Illus.). 102p. 1973. pap. text ed. 16.20 (ISBN 0-89867-077-2). Am Water Wks Assn.

Fair, Gordon M., et al. Water & Wastewater Engineering: Water Supply & Wastewater Removal, Vol. 1. LC 66-16139. 489p. 1966. 53.45x (ISBN 0-471-25130-5). Wiley.

Faust, Aly. Chemistry of Natural Waters. LC 80-70322. 400p. 1981. text ed. 49.95 (ISBN 0-250-40387-0). Butterworth.

Fiering, Myron B. & Jackson, Barbara B., eds. Synthetic Streamflows. LC 77-172418. (Water Resources Monograph: Vol. 1). (Illus.). 99p. 1971. pap. 10.00 (ISBN 0-87590-300-2). Am Geophysical.

Garb, Forrest A. Waterflood Manual for Hewlett Packard Calculators. LC 81-20274. (Illus.). 94p. (Orig.). 1982. 21.95x (ISBN 0-87201-895-4). Gulf Pub.

Glossary: Water & Wastewater Control Engineering. 2nd ed. (General References Ser.). (Illus.). 456p. 1981. text ed. 25.00 (ISBN 0-89867-263-5). Am Water Wks Assn.

Graf, Walter H. Water Resources & Environmental Engineering. LC 79-128788. 1984. 45.00 (ISBN 0-918334-56-X). WRP.

Hammer, Mark J. Water & Waste-Water Technology. LC 75-2000. 502p. 1975. 34.95x (ISBN 0-471-34726-4); solutions manual avail. (ISBN 0-471-03819-9); tchr's. Manual avail. (ISBN 0-471-34727-2). Wiley.

--Water & Waste-Water Technology. 2nd ed. 1986. price not set (ISBN 0-471-82961-7). Wiley.

Hartman, Loyal M. & Seastone, Don. Water Transfers: Economic Efficiency & Alternative Institutions. LC 70-108382. pap. 36.00 (ISBN 0-317-28863-6, 2020963). Bks Demand UMI.

Haszpra, Otto. Modelling Hydroelastic Vibrations. (Water Resources Engineering Ser.). 136p. 1979. text ed. 29.95x (ISBN 0-273-08441-0). Pitman Pub MA.

Hetch Hetchy & Its Dam Railroad. 25.00 (ISBN 0-685-83341-0). Chatham Pub CA.

Huisman, L. & Olsthorn, T. N. Artificial Groundwater Recharge. (Water Resources Engineering Ser.). 336p. 1983. text ed. 65.95 (ISBN 0-273-08544-1). Pitman Pub MA.

Jenkins, S. H., ed. Progress in Water Technology, Vols. 1-7. Incl. Vol. 1. Application of New Concepts of Physical-Chemical Waste Water Treatment. Eckenfelder & Cecil. 1976. 45.00 (ISBN 0-08-017243-1); Vol. 2. Phosphorus in Fresh Water & the Marine Environment. 1973. 45.00 (ISBN 0-08-017697-6); Vol. 3. Water Quality: Management & Pollution Control Problems. 1973; Vol. 4. Marine, Municipal & Industrial Waste Water Disposal: Proceedings, Sorrento, Italy. 1975. 42.00 (ISBN 0-08-018070-1); Vol. 5. Design-Operation Interaction at Large Treatment Plants. 1976. flexi-cover 50.00 (ISBN 0-08-018293-3); Vol. 6. Instrumentation, Control & Automation for Waste Water Treatment Systems. 1974. 45.00 (ISBN 0-08-017976-2); Vol. 7. Atlanta Conference Proceedings. 1975. Pts. 2-4, 1976. pap. text ed. 110.00 (ISBN 0-08-019839-2); Pts. 5-6, 1976. pap. text ed. 90.00 (ISBN 0-08-019841-4); Pts. 2-6, 2 Vols. pap. text ed. write for info. (ISBN 0-08-020225-X). LC 73-1162. write for info. Pergamon.

Jordan, Thomas D. A Handbook of Gravity-Flow Water Systems for Small Communities. (Illus.). 240p. (Orig.). 1984. pap. 9.75 (ISBN 0-946688-50-8, Pub. by Intermediate Tech England). Intermediate Tech.

Leakage: Control, Policy & Practice. 150p. 1982. 35.00x (ISBN 0-904561-95-X, Pub. by Natl Water England). State Mutual Bk.

Lehr, Jay H., et al. Domestic Water Treatment. (Illus.). 1979. 26.95 (ISBN 0-07-037068-0). McGraw.

Lloyd, J. W. Case-Studies in Groundwater Resources Evaluation. (Illus.). 1981. 74.00x (ISBN 0-19-854530-4). Oxford U Pr.

Loucks, Daniel P., et al. Water Resources Systems Planning & Analysis. (Illus.). 560p. 1981. text ed. 38.95 (ISBN 0-13-945923-5). P-H.

A Manager's Guide to the Priciples of Planned Inspection & Maintenance in the Water Industry. 16p. 1981. 30.00x (ISBN 0-901090-10-7, Pub. by Natl Water England). State Mutual Bk.

Master Planning Airport Water Supply Systems for Fire Protection. (Four Hundred Ser). 1969. pap. 2.00 (ISBN 0-685-58218-3, 419). Natl Fire Prot.

BOOKS - SUBJECT INDEX

WATERSHEDS

Meinck, F. & Mohle, K. Dictionary of Water & Sewage Engineering. 2nd rev. ed. (Ger., Eng., Fr., & Ital.). 738p. 1977. 138.50 (ISBN 0-444-99811-X). Elsevier.
Miller, Duncan. Self-Help & Popular Participation in Rural Water Systems. (Development Center Studies). (Illus.). 150p. (Orig.). 1980. pap. text ed. 9.00x (ISBN 92-64-12027-0, 4180011). OECD.
Minimizing & Recycling Water Plant Sludge. (AWWA Handbooks - Proceedings). (Illus.). 124p. 1973. pap. text ed. 7.20 (ISBN 0-89867-039-X). Am Water Wks Assn.
A Monograph on the Church & Dry Creek Valley Ditches. 130p. 1985. write for info. Walther.
Rudman, Jack. Assistant Water Service Foreman. (Career Examination Ser.: C-2924). (Cloth bdg. avail. on request). pap. 12.00 (ISBN 0-8373-2924-8). Natl Learning.
--Senior Water Plant Operator. (Career Examination Ser.: C-1638). (Cloth bdg. avail. on request). pap. 12.00 (ISBN 0-8373-1638-3). Natl Learning.
--Senior Water Use Inspector. (Career Examination Ser.: C-1639). (Cloth bdg. avail. on request). pap. 12.00 (ISBN 0-8373-1639-1). Natl Learning.
--Supervisor (Water & Sewer Systems) (Career Examination Ser.: C-2907). (Cloth bdg. avail. on request). pap. 10.00 (ISBN 0-8373-2907-8). Natl Learning.
--Water District Supervisor. (Career Examination Ser.: C-2625). (Cloth bdg. avail. on request). pap. 12.00 (ISBN 0-8373-2625-7). Natl Learning.
--Water Maintainance Foreman. (Career Examination Ser.: C-2925). (Cloth bdg. avail. on request). pap. 12.00 (ISBN 0-8373-2925-6). Natl Learning.
--Water Maintainance Man. (Career Examination Ser.: C-2657). (Cloth bdg. avail. on request). pap. 10.00 (ISBN 0-8373-2657-5). Natl Learning.
--Water Plant Operator Trainee. (Career Examination Ser.: C-886). (Cloth bdg. avail. on request). pap. 10.00 (ISBN 0-8373-0886-0). Natl Learning.
--Water Plant Supervisor. (Career Examination Ser.: C-2445). (Cloth bdg. avail. on request). pap. 12.00 (ISBN 0-8373-2445-9). Natl Learning.
Sanks, Robert L., ed. Water Treatment Plant Design for the Practicing Engineer. LC 77-76914. 1978. 49.95 (ISBN 0-250-40183-5). Butterworth.
Schuab. Elementary Soil & Water Engineering. 3rd ed. 1985. write for info. (ISBN 0-471-82587-5). Wiley.
Shaw, T. L., ed. Mechanics of Wave-Induced Forces on Cylinders. (Water Resources Engineering Ser.). (Illus.). 752p. 1979. text ed. 64.95 (ISBN 0-273-08433-X). Pitman Pub MA.
Sizing Water Services Lines & Meters - M22. (AWWA Manuals). (Illus.). 112p. 1975. pap. text ed. 16.20 (ISBN 0-89867-080-2). Am Water Wks Assn.
Skelly, J. D. Water Treatment, Vol. 2, Pt. 14. (Marine Engineering Practice Ser.). 1977. pap. 11.50x (ISBN 0-900976-66-7, Pub. by Inst Marine Eng). Intl Spec Bk.
Small Water System Problems. (AWWA Handbooks-Proceedings Ser.). (Illus.). 117p. 1981. pap. text ed. 12.00 (ISBN 0-89867-266-X). Am Water Wks Assn.
Small Water System Solutions. (AWWA Handbooks-Proceedings Ser.). (Illus.). 80p. 1982. pap. text ed. 10.20 (ISBN 0-89867-282-1). Am Water Wks Assn.
Spanish Translations of Selected 1976 Journal Articles. (AWWA Handbooks - General). (Illus.). 88p. 1977. pap. text ed. 12.00 (ISBN 0-89867-018-7). Am Water Wks Assn.
Steel, E. W. & McGhee, Terence. Water Supply & Sewerage. 5th ed. (Illus.). 1979. text ed. 42.00 (ISBN 0-07-060929-2). McGraw.
Supervision of Water Supply Valves. (Twenty Ser). 1958. pap. 2.00 (ISBN 0-685-58116-0, 26). Natl Fire Prot.
Tebbutt, T. H. Principles of Water Quality Control. (Illus.). 248p. 1983. 40.00 (ISBN 0-08-028705-0); pap. 15.00 (ISBN 0-08-028704-2). Pergamon.
Technical Association of the Pulp & Paper Industry. Water Supply & Treatment: State-of-the-Art. LC 79-120640. pap. 23.50 (ISBN 0-317-29320-6, 2022337). Bks Demand UMI.
Thirsty Third World. 42p. 1982. 25.00x (ISBN 0-901090-08-5, Pub. by Natl Water England). State Mutual Bk.
Topics in Light Water Reactor Physics: Final Report of the NORA Project. (Technical Reports Ser.: No. 113). (Illus., Orig.). 1970. pap. 11.50 (ISBN 92-0-135170-4, IDC113, IAEA). Unipub.
A Training Course in Water Distribution - M8. (AWWA Manuals). (Illus.). 168p. 1962. pap. text ed. 10.20 (ISBN 0-89867-066-7). Am Water Wks Assn.
Treatment Techniques for Controlling Trihalomethanes in Drinking Water. (AWWA Handbooks-General Ser.). (Illus.). 312p. 1982. pap. text ed. 16.80 (ISBN 0-89867-279-1). Am Water Wks Assn.
Unny, T. E. & McBean, Edward A., eds. Experience in Operation of Hydrosystems: Forecasting & Operation. LC 82-50383. 612p. 1982. 33.00 (ISBN 0-918334-49-7). WRP.
Vlachos, Evan & Hendricks, David W. Technology Assessment for Water Supplies. LC 76-19871. 1977. 21.00 (ISBN 0-918334-13-6). WRP.
Walker, R. Water Supply Treatment & Distribution. (Illus.). 1978. 37.95 (ISBN 0-13-946004-7). P-H.
Walski, Thomas M. Analysis of Water Distribution Systems. 400p. 1984. 42.50 (ISBN 0-442-29192-2). Van Nos Reinhold.
Water Distribution Operator Training Handbook. (AWWA Handbooks - General Ser.). (Illus.). 232p. 1976. pap. text ed. 14.40 (ISBN 0-89867-013-6). Am Water Wks Assn.
Water Forum '81, 2 vols. LC 81-67746. 1404p. 1981. Set. pap. 95.00x (ISBN 0-87262-275-4). Am Soc Civil Eng.
Water Plant Instrumentation & Automation. (AWWA Handbooks-Proceedings Ser.). (Illus.). 304p. 1976. pap. text ed. 14.40 (ISBN 0-89867-049-7). Am Water Wks Assn.
Water Pollution Control Federation. Water Reuse. (Manual of Practice, System Mgmnt. Ser.: 3). (Illus.). 128p. (Orig.). 1983. pap. text ed. 20.00 (ISBN 0-943244-45-5). Water Pollution.
Water Pollution Control Federation Staff, ed. Prime Movers: Engines, Turbines, Pumps, Blowers & Generators. (Manual of Practice Ser.: No. OM-5). (Illus.). 181p. 1984. pap. 40.00 (ISBN 0-943244-56-0). Water Pollution.
Water Quality Technology Conference, 1981: Advances in Laboratory Techniques for Quality Control. (AWWA Handbooks-Proceedings Ser.). (Illus.). 1982. pap. text ed. 18.60 (ISBN 0-89867-267-8). Am Water Wks Assn.
Water Quality Technology Conference, 1980: Advances in Laboratory Techniques for Quality Control. (AWWA Handbooks-Proceedings Ser.). (Illus.). 1981. pap. text ed. 18.00 (ISBN 0-89867-251-1). Am Water Wks Assn.
Water Quality Technology Conference: 1975-Laboratory Tools for Safe Water. (AWWA Handbooks-Proceedings Ser.). (Illus.). 1976. pap. text ed. 12.00 (ISBN 0-89867-045-4). Am Water Wks Assn.
Water Quality Technology Conference: 1976, the Water Laboratory - Key to Process & Quality Control. (AWWA Handbooks-Proceedings Ser.). (Illus.). 342p. 1977. pap. text ed. 12.00 (ISBN 0-89867-051-9). Am Water Wks Assn.
Water Quality Technology Conference: 1973-Water Quality. (AWWA Handbooks-Proceedings Ser.). (Illus.). 272p. 1974. pap. text ed. 12.00 (ISBN 0-89867-041-1). Am Water Wks Assn.
Water Quality Technology Conference: 1974-Water Quality. (AWWA Handbooks-Proceedings Ser.). (Illus.). 248p. 1975. pap. text ed. 12.00 (ISBN 0-89867-043-8). Am Water Wks Assn.
Water Quality Technology Conference: 1977-Water Quality in the Distribution System. (AWWA Handbooks-Proceedings Ser.). (Illus.). 320p. 1978. pap. text ed. 12.00 (ISBN 0-89867-055-1). Am Water Wks Assn.
Water Treatment Plant Design. 364p. 1969. 15.00x (ISBN 0-87262-012-3). Am Soc Civil Eng.
Water Treatment Plant Design. (General References Ser.). (Illus.). 362p. 1969. text ed. 18.00 (ISBN 0-89867-004-7). Am Water Wks Assn.
Water Utility Management Practices - M5. (AWWA Manuals Ser.). (Illus.). 1980. pap. text ed. 16.80 (ISBN 0-89867-063-2). Am Water Wks Assn.
Water Utility Operating Data, 1981. (AWWA Handbooks - General). (Illus.). 1981. pap. text ed. 30.00 (ISBN 0-89867-255-4). Am Water Wks Assn.
Yevjevich, V., ed. Karst Water Research Needs. LC 81-51338. 1981. 18.00 (ISBN 0-918334-40-3). WRP.
Yevjevich, Vujica, ed. Coping with Droughts. Da Cunha, L. V., et al. LC 83-50242. 450p. 1984. 39.00 (ISBN 0-918334-52-7). WRP.

WATER TANKS
see Tanks

WATER TRANSPORTATION
see Coastwise Shipping; Inland Water Transportation; Shipping

WATER WAVES
see also Ocean Waves

Barber, N. F. & Ghey, G. Water Waves. (Wykeham Science Ser.: No. 5). 152p. 1969. 5.75x (ISBN 0-8448-1107-6). Crane Russak Co.
Crapper. Introduction to Waterwaves. (Mathematics & Its Applications Ser.). 224p. 1984. 54.95 (ISBN 0-470-20122-3). Wiley.
Dean, Robert G. & Dalrymple, Robert A. Water Wave Mechanics for Engineers & Scientists. (Illus.). 384p. 1984. text ed. 41.95 (ISBN 0-13-946038-1). P-H.
Le Mehante, B. An Introduction to Hydrodynamics & Water Waves. LC 75-18631. (Illus.). 512p. 1976. text ed. 44.00 (ISBN 0-387-07232-2). Springer-Verlag.

WATER-WHEELS
see also Turbines

Aston, Norman. Leicestershire Watermills. 1982. 40.00x (ISBN 0-905837-02-9, Pub. by Sycamore Pr England). State Mutual Bk.

WATERFALLS

Barton, R. M. Waterfalls of the World. 1981. 30.00x (ISBN 0-686-97153-1, Pub. by D B Barton England). State Mutual Bk.
Plumb, Gregory A. Waterfalls of the Pacific Northwest. (Illus.). 192p. 1983. pap. 9.95 (ISBN 0-916076-60-1). Writing.

WATERFOWL
see also names of families of water fowl, e.g. Anatidae

Burk, Bruce. Waterfowl Studies. LC 82-62596. 1976. 21.95 (ISBN 0-8329-1807-5, Pub. by Winchester Pr). New Century.
Frith, H. J. Waterfowl in Australia. (Illus.). 349p. 1967. 17.50 (ISBN 0-8248-0063-X, Eastwest Ctr). UH Pr.
Goodman, Donald C. & Fisher, Harvey I. Functional Apparatus in Waterfowl: (Aus: Anatidae) LC 62-9267. (Illus.). 206p. 1962. 6.50x (ISBN 0-8093-0066-4). S Ill U Pr.
Hammack, Judd & Brown, Gardner M., Jr. Waterfowl & Wetlands: Toward Bioeconomic Analysis. LC 74-6815. (Resources for the Future Research Report Ser). (Illus.). 108p. 1974. 10.00x (ISBN 0-8018-1625-4). Johns Hopkins.
Hochbaum, H. Albert. Travels & Traditions of Waterfowl. (Illus.). 1967. pap. 2.95 (ISBN 0-8166-0448-7, MP8). U of Minn Pr.
Johnsgard, Paul A. A Guide to North American Waterfowl. LC 78-20612. (Midland Bks: No. 291). (Illus.). 288p. 1979. 15.95x (ISBN 0-253-12789-0); pap. 7.95x (ISBN 0-253-20291-4). Ind U Pr.
--Waterfowl of North America. LC 74-30900. (Illus.). 624p. 1975. 35.00x (ISBN 0-253-36360-8). Ind U Pr.
--Waterfowl: Their Biology & Natural History. LC 68-11563. (Illus.). xx, 218p. 1968. 12.95 (ISBN 0-8032-0087-0). U of Nebr Pr.
Johnson, A. A. & Payn, W. H. Ornamental Waterfowl. 4th ed. (Illus.). 134p. 1979. 13.50 (ISBN 0-904558-71-1). Saiga.
Maass, David & Hill, Gene. A Gallery of Waterfowl & Upland Birds. LC 78-61769. (Illus.). 1978. text ed. 39.95 (ISBN 0-8227-8019-4). Petersen Pub.
Meanley, Brooke. Waterfowl of the Chesapeake Bay Country. LC 81-18361. (Illus.). 224p. 1982. 19.95 (ISBN 0-87033-281-3). Tidewater.
Ogilvie, M. A. Wildfowl of Britain & Europe. 1982. 16.50x (ISBN 0-19-217723-0). Oxford U Pr.
Ratti, John T., et al, eds. Waterfowl Ecology & Management: Selected Readings. LC 82-70782. (Illus.). xvi, 1328p. (Orig.). 1982. pap. 23.00 10 or more orders (ISBN 0-933564-09-0). Wildlife Soc.
Sowls, Lyle K. Prairie Ducks: A Study of Their Behavior, Ecology & Management. LC 77-14153. (Illus.). xiv, 194p. 1978. pap. 3.50 (ISBN 0-8032-5895-X, BB 665, Bison). U of Nebr Pr.
Todd, Frank S. Waterfowl: Ducks, Geese & Swans of the World. LC 79-63521. (Illus.). 1979. 45.00 (ISBN 0-15-004036-9). HarBraceJ.
Weller, Milton W. The Island Waterfowl. new ed. (Illus.). 122p. 1980. text ed. 11.95x (ISBN 0-8138-1310-7). Iowa St U Pr.
Wobeser, Gary A. Diseases of Wild Waterfowl. LC 81-19256. 312p. 1981. text ed. 45.00x (ISBN 0-306-40764-7, Plenum Pr). Plenum Pub.
Wylie, Stephen & Furlong, Stewart. Key to North American Waterfowl. LC 72-6951. (Illus.). 1972. plastic bdg. 4.95 (ISBN 0-915180-17-0). Harrowood Bks.
Wylie, Stephen R. & Furlong, Stewart S. Key to North American Waterfowl. Livingston, Robert A., ed. (Illus.). 32p. 1972. 4.95 (ISBN 0-87098-047-5). Livingston.
--Key to North American Waterfowl. rev ed. (Permaguide Ser.). (Illus.). 1978. Repr. of 1972 ed. 4.95 (ISBN 0-931766-00-1). Schroeder Prints.

WATERPROOFING
see also Corrosion and Anti-Corrosives; Dampness in Buildings

Perkins, Philip H. Concrete Structures: Repair, Waterproofing & Protection. LC 77-23140. 302p. 1977. 96.95x (ISBN 0-470-99087-2). Halsted Pr.
Waterproofing of Floor, Draining & Installation of Scuppers. (Eighty-Ninety Ser.). 1972. pap. 2.00 (ISBN 0-685-58177-2, 92M). Natl Fire Prot.

WATERSHEDS

ASCE Conference, Irrigation & Drainage Division, 1980. Watershed Management 1980: Proceedings of the ASCE Conference, 2 vols. LC 80-66952. 1122p. 1980. Set. pap. 68.00x (ISBN 0-87262-250-9). Am Soc Civil Eng.
Bosch, Vanden, et al. Urban Watershed Management: Flooding & Water Quality. Bedient, Philip B. & Rowe, Peter G., eds. (Rice University Studies: Vol. 65, No. 1). 205p. 1979. pap. 10.00x (ISBN 0-89263-240-2). Rice Univ.
Casebook of Methods of Computation of Quantitative Changes in the Hydrological Regime of River Basins Due to Human Activities. (Studies & Reports in Hydrology: No. 28). (Illus.). 330p. 1980. pap. 24.25 (ISBN 92-3-101798-5, U1037, UNESCO). Unipub.
Experiences in the Development & Management of International River & Lake Basins. (Natural Resources-Water Ser.: No. 10). 424p. 1983. pap. text ed. 38.00 (ISBN 0-686-46322-6, UN82/2A17, UN). Unipub.
Gangstad, Edward O., ed. Weed Control Methods for River Basin Management. 232p. 1978. 66.00 (ISBN 0-8493-5328-9). CRC Pr.
Gregory, K. J. & Walling, D. E., eds. Fluvial Processes in Instrumented Watersheds: Studies of Small Watershed in the British Isles. (The Special Publication of the Institute of British Geographers: No. 6). 1980. 25.00 (ISBN 0-12-301150-7). Acad Pr.
Guidelines for Watershed Management. (Conservation Guides: No. 1). (Eng. & Fr., Illus.). 306p. (3rd Printing 1983). 1977. pap. 22.00 (ISBN 92-5-100242-8, F741, FAO). Unipub.
Hamilton, Lawrence S. & King, Peter N. Tropical Forested Watershed: Hydrologic & Soil Response to Various Uses & Conversions. (Replica Edition Ser.). 160p. 1983. pap. 17.50x (ISBN 0-86531-994-4). Westview.
Hammer, Thomas R. A New Approach to the Estimation of Low Frequency Floods for Small Watersheds: Eastern Slope, Pennsylvania. (Discussion Paper Ser.: No. 79). 1975. pap. 4.50 (ISBN 0-686-32245-2). Regional Sci Res Inst.
Integrated River Basin Development. 1980. pap. 8.00 (ISBN 0-686-94504-2, UN70/2A/4, UN). Unipub.
Jenkins, S. H. River Basin Management. flexi-cover 99.00x (ISBN 0-08-022938-7). Pergamon.
Jenkins, S. J., ed. New Developments in River Basin Management. (Illus.). 320p. 1981. 52.00 (ISBN 0-08-028391-8). Pergamon.
Kapetsky, J. M., ed. Seminar on River Basin Management & Development: Blantyre, Malawi, December 8-10, 1980. (Commission for Inland Fisheries of Africa (CIFA): Technical Papers: No. 8). (Eng. & Fr.). 313p. 1981. pap. 22.50 (ISBN 92-5-001159-8, F2295, FAO). Unipub.
Kudrna, Frank L. Watershed Planning: A Selected Research Bibliography, No. 1014. 1976. 5.50 (ISBN 0-686-20391-7). CPL Biblios.
Lal, R. & Russell, E. W., eds. Tropical Agricultural Hydrology: Watershed Management & Land Use. LC 80-41590. 482p. 1981. 74.95x (ISBN 0-471-27931-5, Pub. by Wiley-Interscience). Wiley.
Lundqvist, Jan & Lohm, Ulrik, eds. Strategies for River Basin Management: Environmental Integration of Land & Water in a River Basin. 1985. lib. bdg. 56.00 (ISBN 90-277-2111-4, Pub. by Reidel Holland). Kluwer Academic.
Ongley, Edwin D. Introduction to the Physical Landscape: Watersheds & Fluvial Systems. (CISE Learning Package Ser.: No. 21). (Illus.). 52p. (Orig.). 1976. pap. text ed. 3.00x (ISBN 0-936876-33-6). Learn Res Intl Stud.
River Basin Development Policies & Planning, Vols. 1 & 2. (Natural Resources-Water Ser.: No. 6). pap. 24.00 (ISBN 0-686-92887-3, UN77/2A4, UN). Unipub.
Saha, Suranjit K. & Barrow, Christopher J. River Basin Planning: Theory & Practice. 380p. 1981. 58.95 (ISBN 0-471-09977-5, Pub. by Wiley-Interscience). Wiley.
Satterlund, Donald R. Wildland Watershed Management. LC 70-190212. 400p. 1972. 36.00x (ISBN 0-471-06840-3). Wiley.
Schumm, Stanley A. The Fluvial System. LC 77-9333. 338p. 1977. 45.50 (ISBN 0-471-01901-1, Pub by Wiley-Interscience). Wiley.
Smith, D. I. & Stopp, P. The River Basin. LC 77-85688. (Topics in Geography Ser.). (Illus.). 1979. 22.95 (ISBN 0-521-21900-0); pap. 10.95x (ISBN 0-521-29307-3). Cambridge U Pr.

Toebes, C. & Ouryvaer, V., eds. Representative & Experimental Basins: An International Guide for Research & Practice. (Studies & Reports in Hydrology: No. 4). (Illus.). 348p. (Orig.). 1970. 24.25 (ISBN 92-3-100808-0, U551, UNESCO). Unipub.

Waters, Thomas F. The Streams & Rivers of Minnesota. LC 77-84166. (Illus.). 1977. 12.95 (ISBN 0-8166-0821-0). U of Minn Pr.

Watershed Development, With Special Reference to Soil & Water Conservation. (Soils Bulletins: No. 44). (Illus.). 266p. 1979. pap. 19.00 (ISBN 92-5-100859-0, F1966, FAO). Unipub.

Williams, Julia & Hamilton, Lawrence S. Watershed Forest Influences in the Tropics & Subtropics: A Selected, Annotated Bibliography. xiii, 217p. (Orig.). 1982. pap. text ed. 3.00 (ISBN 0-86638-036-1). E W Center HI.

WATERWORKS

see Water-Supply

WATT, JAMES, 1736-1819

Arago, M. Historical Eloge of James Watt. LC 74-26247. (History, Philosophy & Sociology of Science Ser.). 1975. Repr. of 1839 ed. 21.00x (ISBN 0-405-06577-9). Ayer Co Pubs.

Jenkins, R. & Dickinson, H. W. James Watt & the Steam Engine. 536p. 1981. 49.00x (ISBN 0-903485-92-3, Pub. by Moorland). State Mutual Bk.

Lord, John. Capital & Steam Power: Seventeen Fifty to Eighteen Hundred. 2nd ed. 253p. 1966. 26.00x (ISBN 0-7146-1339-8, F Cass Co). Biblio Dist.

--Capital & Steam-Power, Seventeen Fifty to Eighteen Hundred. Repr. of 1923 ed. 25.00x (ISBN 0-678-05216-6). Kelley.

Robinson, Eric H. & Musson, James, eds. James Watt & the Steam Revolution, a Documentary History. LC 71-96795. (Illus.). 1969. lib. bdg. 29.50x (ISBN 0-678-07756-8). Kelley.

Watt, James & Black, Joseph. Partners in Science: Letters of James Watt & Joseph Black. Robinson, Eric & McKie, Douglas, eds. 518p. 1969. text ed. 30.00x (ISBN 0-674-65480-3). Harvard U Pr.

WAVE FILTERS, ELECTRIC

see Electric Filters

WAVE GUIDES

Brown, R. G., et al. Lines, Waves & Antennas: The Transmission of Electric Energy. 2nd ed. (Illus.). 471p. 1973. text ed. 41.50 (ISBN 0-471-06677-X). Wiley.

Harmuth, H. F. Advances in Electronics & Electron Physics: Antennas & Waveguides for Nonsinusoidal Waves. Marton, L., ed. (Serial Publication Ser.: Supplement 15). 1984. 60.00 (ISBN 0-12-014577-4). Acad Pr.

Schwinger, Julian & Saxon, D. Discontinuities in Wave Guides. (Documents on Modern Physics Ser.). 178p. 1968. 46.25x (ISBN 0-677-01840-1). Gordon.

Shevchenko, Viktor V. Continuous Transitions in Open Waveguides. Beckmann, Petr, tr. from Rus. LC 72-145593. (Electromagnetics Ser.: Vol. 5). (Illus.). 1971. 25.00x (ISBN 0-911762-08-6). Golem.

Waldron, R. A. Theory of Waveguides & Cavities. 134p. 1969. 37.25x (ISBN 0-677-61480-2). Gordon.

WAVE-LENGTH TABLES

see Spectrum Analysis–Tables, etc.

WAVE MECHANICS

see also Atomic Orbitals; Coulomb Functions; Energy-Band Theory of Solids; Matrix Mechanics; Molecular Orbitals; Quantum Statistics; Tunneling (Physics); Spinor Analysis; Tunneling (Physics); Weber Functions

AIP Conference Proceeding No. 86, Adelaide, Australia, 1982. Momentum Wave Functions: Proceedings. Weigold, Erich, ed. LC 82-72375. 345p. 1982. lib. bdg. 34.00 (ISBN 0-88318-185-1). Am Inst Physics.

Andrade, E. N. An Approach to Modern Physics. 11.25 (ISBN 0-8446-0456-9). Peter Smith.

Bhartia, P. & Bahl, I. J. Millimeter Wave Engineering & Applications. LC 83-12404. 736p. 1984. 69.95x (ISBN 0-471-87083-8, Pub. by Wiley-Interscience). Wiley.

Bleistein, Norman. Mathematical Methods for Wave Phenomena: Monograph. (Computer Science & Applied Mathematics Ser.). 1984. 55.00 (ISBN 0-12-105650-3). Acad Pr.

Bramson, Maury. Convergence of Solutions of the Kolmogorov Equation to Travelling Waves. LC 83-6437. (Memoirs of the American Mathematical Society: No. 285). pap. 16.00 (ISBN 0-8218-2285-3). Am Math.

Brekhovskikh, L. & Goncharov, V. Mechanics of Continua & Wave Dynamics. (Springer Series on Wave Phenomena: Vol. 1). (Illus.). 360p. 1985. 49.00 (ISBN 0-387-13765-3). Springer-Verlag.

Brillouin, Leon. Wave Propagation & Group Velocity. (Pure & Applied Physics Ser.: Vol. 8). 1960. 33.50 (ISBN 0-12-134968-3). Acad Pr.

Bube, Richard H. Electronic Properties of Crystalline Solids: An Introduction to Fundamentals. 1974. 59.00 (ISBN 0-12-138550-7). Acad Pr.

Button, Kenneth J. Infrared & Millimeter Waves: Vol. 9: Millimeter Components & Techniques, Pt. 1. LC 79-6949. 1983. 61.00 (ISBN 0-12-147709-6). Acad Pr.

Button, Kenneth J., ed. Infrared & Millimeter Waves, Vol. 10: Millimeter Components & Techniques, Pt. II. 1984. 65.00 (ISBN 0-12-147710-X). Acad Pr.

CISM (International Center for Mechanical Sciences), Dept for Mechanics of Rigid Bodies. Thermodynamic Effects in Wave Propogation. Chen, P., ed. (CISM Pubns. Ser.: No. 72). 33p. 1973. pap. 7.70 (ISBN 0-387-81176-1). Springer-Verlag.

Gombas, P. & Kisdi, D. Wave Mechanics & Its Applications. LC 73-5789. 250p. 1974. text ed. 28.00 (ISBN 0-08-016979-1). Pergamon.

Heitler, Walter. Elementary Wave Mechanics: With Applications to Quantum Chemistry. 2nd ed. 1956. pap. 11.95x (ISBN 0-19-851115-9). Oxford U Pr.

Holden, Alan. Stationary States. (Illus., Orig.). 1971. pap. text ed. 4.95x (ISBN 0-19-501497-9). Oxford U Pr.

Hughes, James S. Wave Functions: An Explanatory Hypothesis. (Illus.). 1976. 50.00 (ISBN 0-915386-02-X). Arctinurus Co.

International Symposium on Recent Developments in Classical Wave Scattering, Ohio State Univ., Columbus, 1979. Recent Developments in Classical Wave Scattering: Focus on the T-Matrix Approach. Varadan, V. V. & Varadan, V. K., eds. (Illus.). 670p. 1980. 83.00 (ISBN 0-08-025096-3). Pergamon.

Kollberg, E., ed. Microwave & Millimeter: Wave Mixers. LC 84-10887. 1984. 59.95 (ISBN 0-87942-179-7, PC01735). Inst Electrical.

Lipson, S. G. & Lipson, H. Optical Physics. 2nd ed. LC 79-8963. (Illus.). 496p. 1981. 64.50 (ISBN 0-521-22630-9); pap. 24.95 (ISBN 0-521-29584-X). Cambridge U Pr.

Lucken, E. A. Nuclear Quadrupole Coupling Constants. 1969. 57.50 (ISBN 0-12-458450-0). Acad Pr.

Ludwig, G. Wave Mechanics. 1968. pap. 10.75 (ISBN 0-08-012303-1). Pergamon.

Mainardi, F., ed. Wave Propagation with Viscoelastic Media. (Research Notes in Mathematics Ser.: No. 52). 280p. (Orig.). 1982. text ed. 26.00 (ISBN 0-273-08511-5). Pitman Pub MA.

Mandel, J. & Brun, L., eds. Mechanical Waves in Solids. (CISM-International Center for Mechanical Sciences Courses & Lectures Ser.: Vol. 222). (Illus.). 1975. pap. 29.00 (ISBN 0-387-81398-5). Springer-Verlag.

Miklowitz, Julius, ed. Wave Propagation in Solids. LC 72-101230. pap. 47.30 (ISBN 0-317-08536-0, 2010125). Bks Demand UMI.

Petersen, R. David & Myers, Grant G. Waveform Analysis in Medicine: An Introduction. (Illus.). 308p. 1976. 31.25x (ISBN 0-398-03004-9). C C Thomas.

Pilanti. Elastic Theory of Waves. 2nd ed. Date not set. write for info. (ISBN 0-444-00837-3). Elsevier.

Provis, D. G., ed. Waves on Water of Variable Depth. (Lecture Notes in Physics: Vol. 64). 1977. 18.00 (ISBN 0-387-08253-0). Springer-Verlag.

Richards, W. G., et al. Bibliography of ab initio Molecular Wave Functions: Supplement for 1970-1973. 1974. pap. 49.50x (ISBN 0-19-855356-0). Oxford U Pr.

Ross, D. Energy from the Waves. 2nd rev. ed. LC 80-41076. (Illus.). 160p. 1981. 24.00 (ISBN 0-08-026715-7); pap. 10.00 (ISBN 0-08-026716-5). Pergamon.

Sarpkaya, Turgut & Isaacson, Michael. Mechanics of Wave Forces on Offshore Structures. 624p. 1981. 39.50 (ISBN 0-442-25402-4). Van Nos Reinhold.

Schroedinger, Erwin. Collected Papers on Wave Mechanics. 3rd ed. LC 78-11493. 1978. text ed. 14.95 (ISBN 0-8284-1302-9). Chelsea Pub.

Shaw, Ronald. Wave Energy: A Design Challenge. LC 82-11780. (Ellis Horwood Series in Energy & Fuel Science). 202p. 1982. 54.95x (ISBN 0-470-27539-1). Halsted Pr.

Shebalov, A. N. Theory of Ship Wave Resistance for Unsteady Motion in Still Water. (University of Michigan Dept. of Naval Architecture & Marine Engineering Report Ser.: No. 67). pap. 20.00 (ISBN 0-317-28264-6, 2022628). Bks Demand UMI.

Skjelbreia, Lars. Gravity Waves: Stokes Third Order Approximation, Table of Functions. 341p. 1959. pap. 3.00x (ISBN 0-87262-333-5). Am Soc Civil Eng.

Sobczyk, K. Stochastic Wave Propagation. (Fundamental Studies in Engineering: Vol. 6). 1985. 68.75 (ISBN 0-444-99614-1). Elsevier.

Steiner, Erich. Determination & Interpretation of Molecular Wave Functions. LC 75-78120. (Monographs in Physical Chemistry: No. 3). 250p. 1976. 52.50 (ISBN 0-521-21037-2). Cambridge U Pr.

Waves, Tides, Currents & Beaches. 24p. 1963. pap. 3.00x (ISBN 0-87262-334-3). Am Soc Civil Eng.

Wiegel, R. L., ed. Directional Wave Spectra Applications. LC 82-70873. 501p. 1982. pap. 36.00x (ISBN 0-87262-303-3). Am Soc Civil Eng.

Wiegel, Robert L. Gravity Waves: Tables of Functions. 32p. 1967. pap. 3.00x (ISBN 0-87262-331-9). Am Soc Civil Eng.

Workshop-Seminar on Momentum Wave Function Determination in Atomic, Molecular & Nuclear Systems, Indiana Univ., Bloomington, May 31-June 4, 1976. Momentum Wave Functions: Proceedings-1976. Devins, D. W., ed. LC 77-82145. (AIP Conference Proceedings: No. 36). (Illus.). 1977. lib. bdg. 17.50 (ISBN 0-88318-135-5). Am Inst Physics.

WAVE-MOTION, THEORY OF

see also Interference (Light); Light, Wave Theory Of; Polarization (Light); Sound; Spectrum Analysis

Achenbach, J. D. Wave Propagation in Elastic Solids. (Applied Mathematics & Mechanics Ser.: Vol. 16). 400p. 1973-75. 85.00 (ISBN 0-444-10465-8, North-Holland); pap. 36.25 (ISBN 0-444-10840-8). Elsevier.

Alonso, Marcelo & Finn, Edward J. Fundamental University Physics, 2 vols. 2nd ed. Incl. Vol. 1. Mechanics. 1979. text ed. 17.95 (ISBN 0-201-00076-8); Vol. 2. Fields & Waves. 1983. text ed. 19.95 (ISBN 0-201-00077-6). 1980. Addison-Wesley.

Babich, V. M., ed. Mathematical Problems in Wave Propagation Theory, Pt. II. LC 69-12506. (Seminars in Mathematics Ser.: Vol. 15). 119p. 1971. 27.50x (ISBN 0-306-18815-5, Plenum Pr). Plenum Pub.

--Mathematical Problems in Wave Propagation Theory, Pt. III. LC 79-13851. (Seminars in Mathematics Ser.: Vol. 17). 139p. 1972. 27.50x (ISBN 0-306-18817-1, Plenum Pr). Plenum Pub.

--Mathematical Problems in Wave Propagation Theory, Pt. 1. LC 77-103945. (Seminars in Mathematics Ser.: Vol. 9). 107p. 1970. 27.50x (ISBN 0-306-18809-0, Consultants). Plenum Pub.

Baldock, G. R. & Bridgeman, T. The Mathematical Theory of Wave Motion. (Mathematics & Its Applications Ser.). 261p. 1983. pap. 32.95 (ISBN 0-470-27464-6). Halsted Pr.

Barber, N. F. & Ghey, G. Water Waves. (Wykeham Science Ser.: No. 5). 152p. 1969. 5.75x (ISBN 0-8448-1107-6). Crane Russak Co.

Birman, M. S., ed. Topics in Mathematical Physics, 5 vols. Incl. Vol. 1. Spectral Theory & Wave Processes. LC 67-16365. 114p. 1967 (ISBN 0-306-18401-X); Vol. 2. Spectral Theory & Problems in Diffraction. LC 68-28089. 134p. 1968 (ISBN 0-306-18402-8); Vol. 3. Spectral Theory. LC 78-93768. 93p. 1969 (ISBN 0-306-18403-6); Vol. 4. Spectral Theory & Wave Processes. LC 68-28089. 121p. 1971 (ISBN 0-306-18404-4); Vol. 5. Spectral Theory. LC 68-28089. 112p. 1972 (ISBN 0-306-18405-2). 25.00x ea. (Consultants). Plenum Pub.

Brillouin, Leon. Wave Propagation & Group Velocity. (Pure & Applied Physics Ser.: Vol. 8). 1960. 33.50 (ISBN 0-12-134968-3). Acad Pr.

Chapple, M. A Level Physics: Wave Motion-Sound & Light, Vol. 2. 2nd ed. (Illus.). 240p. (Orig.). 1979. pap. text ed. 14.95x (ISBN 0-7121-0155-1, Pub. by Macdonald & Evans England). Trans-Atlantic.

Debnath, Lokenath, ed. Nonlinear Waves. LC 83-15102. 350p. 1983. 42.50 (ISBN 0-521-25468-X). Cambridge U Pr.

Elliott, Ralph N. The Elliott Wave Theory as Outlined in Nature's Law & the Secret of the Universe. (Illus.). 131p. 1983. 187.50 (ISBN 0-89901-114-4). Found Class Reprints.

Elmore, William C. & Heald, Mark A. Physics of Waves. LC 68-58209. xiii, 477p. 1983. pap. text ed. 20.00 (ISBN 0-9613127-0-X). Heald Pubns.

--Physics of Waves. 477p. 1985. pap. 9.95 (ISBN 0-486-64926-1). Dover.

Flumiani, C. M. The Strange Elliott Wave Theory Flow of Speculative Matter into the Active Cylinder Theory Stream Resulting in the Dominion of the Averages. (Illus.). 181p. 1983. 115.50x (ISBN 0-86654-083-0). Inst Econ Finan.

Jeffrey, A. & Kawahara, T. Asymptotic Methods in Nonlinear Wave Theory. LC 81-10569. (Applicable Mathematics Ser.). 256p. (Orig.). 1982. pap. text ed. 46.95 (ISBN 0-273-08509-3). Pitman Pub MA.

Karpman, V. I. Non-Linear Waves in Dispersive Media. Cap, Ferdinand, tr. 1975. text ed. 35.00 (ISBN 0-08-017720-4). Pergamon.

Lax, Peter D. & Phillips, Ralph S. Scattering Theory. (Pure & Applied Mathematics Ser.,: Vol. 26). 1967. 66.00 (ISBN 0-12-440050-7). Acad Pr.

Levine, H. Unidirectional Wave Motion. (Applied Mathematics & Mechanics Ser.: Vol. 23). 502p. 1978. 89.50 (ISBN 0-444-85043-0, North-Holland). Elsevier.

Merrill, Arthur A. Filtered Waves, Basic Theory. LC 77-77420. (Illus.). 1977. 15.00 (ISBN 0-911894-36-5). Analysis.

Nonlinear Wave Motion. Benjamin, T. B. & Benney, D. J. LC 73-19504. (Lectures in Applied Mathematics Ser.: Vol. 15). 229p. 1974. 50.00 (ISBN 0-8218-1115-0, LAM-15). Am Math.

Rogers, C. & Moodie, T. B. Wave Phenomena: Modern Theory & Applications. (Mathematical Studies: Vol. 97). 1984. 60.00 (ISBN 0-444-87586-7, North-Holland). Elsevier.

Roseau, M. Asymptotic Wave Theory. LC 74-26167. (Applied Mathematics & Mechanics Ser.: Vol. 20). 349p. 1976. 74.50 (ISBN 0-444-10798-3, North-Holland). Elsevier.

Symposium in Applied Mathematics, Carnegie Institute of Technology, 1952. Wave Motion & Vibration Theory: Proceedings. Heins, A. E., ed. LC 50-1183. (Vol. 5). 169p. 1954. 24.00 (ISBN 0-8218-1305-6, PSAPM-5). Am Math.

Uscinski, Barry J. The Elements of Wave Propagation in Random Media. (Illus.). 1977. text ed. 48.95x (ISBN 0-07-066650-4). McGraw.

Whitham, G. B. Linear & Nonlinear Waves. LC 74-2070. (Pure & Applied Mathematics Ser.). 636p. 1974. 48.50x (ISBN 0-471-94090-9, Pub. by Wiley-Interscience). Wiley.

WAVEFRONT RECONSTRUCTION IMAGING

see Holography

WAVES

see also Damping (Mechanics); Delay Lines; Doppler Effect; Elastic Waves; Electric Waves; Ether (Of Space); Light; Radiation; Shock Waves; Sound-Waves; Turbulence; Wave Mechanics

Adams, Roy N. & Denman, Eugene D. Wave Propagation & Turbulent Media. LC 66-30179. (Modern Analytic & Computational Methods in Science & Mathematics Ser.). pap. 33.50 (ISBN 0-317-08452-6, 2007766). Bks Demand UMI.

Al'pert, Y. L. Waves & Satellites in the Near-Earth Plasma. LC 74-19475. (Studies in Soviet Science: Physical Sciences). (Illus.). 196p. 1974. 45.00 (ISBN 0-306-10910-7, Consultants). Plenum Pub.

Beckman, J. E. & Phillips, J. P. Submillimetre Wave Astronomy. LC 82-4487. (Illus.). 370p. 1982. 52.50 (ISBN 0-521-24733-0). Cambridge U Pr.

Behrens, Heinrich. Electron Radial Wave Functions & Nuclear Beta-Decay. (International Series of Monographs in Physics). (Illus.). 1982. 79.00x (ISBN 0-19-851297-X). Oxford U Pr.

Brekhovskikh, L. M. Waves in Layered Media. 2nd ed. LC 79-51695. (Applied Mathematics & Mechanics Ser.). 1976. 66.50 (ISBN 0-12-130560-0). Acad Pr.

Buckley, R. Oscillations & Waves. (Student Monographs in Physics). 64p. 1985. pap. write for info. (Pub. by Adam Hilger Techo Hse UK). Heyden.

Burt, Philip B. Quantum Mechanics & Nonlinear Waves: Physics. (Monographs & Tracts Ser.). 331p. 1981. 82.50 (ISBN 3-7186-0072-2). Harwood Academic Pubs.

Button, Kenneth, ed. Infrared & Millimeter Waves: Systems & Components, Vol. 6. 1982. 67.50 (ISBN 0-12-147706-1). Acad Pr.

Button, Kenneth J., ed. Infrared & Millimeter Waves: Coherent Sources & Applications Pt. II, Vol. 7. 416p. 1983. 85.00 (ISBN 0-12-147707-X). Acad Pr.

--Infrared & Millimeter Waves: Instrumentation, Vol. II. LC 79-6949. 1979. 67.50 (ISBN 0-12-147702-9). Acad Pr.

--Infrared & Millimeter Waves: Sources of Radiation, Vol. 1. LC 79-6949. 1979. 65.00 (ISBN 0-12-147701-0). Acad Pr.

--Infrared & Millimeter Waves: Submillimeter Techniques, Vol. 3. 1980. 65.00 (ISBN 0-12-147703-7). Acad Pr.

--Infrared & Millimeter Waves, Vol. 13: Millimeter Components & Techniques, Pt. IV. Date not set. 85.00 (ISBN 0-12-147713-4). Acad Pr.

Buttton, Kenneth J., et al, eds. Reviews of Infrared & Millimeter Waves: Vol. 2. Optically Pumped Far-Infrared Lasers. 492p. 1984. 69.50x (ISBN 0-306-41487-2, Plenum Pr). Plenum Pub.

Chow, P. L., et al, eds. Multiple Scattering & Waves in Random Media. 286p. 1981. 42.75 (ISBN 0-444-86280-3, North-Holland). Elsevier.

Collins, J. H. & Masotti, L. Computer-Aided Design of Surface Acoustic Wave Devices, Vol. 2. 308p. 1976. 68.00 (ISBN 0-444-41476-2). Elsevier.
Connor, F. R. Wave Transmission. (Introductory Topics in Electronics & Telecommunications Ser.). (Illus.). 1972. pap. text ed. 17.95x (ISBN 0-7131-3278-7). Intl Ideas.
Dodd, et al. Solitions & Nonlinear Wave Equations. 1984. 25.00 (ISBN 0-317-12003-4). Academie Pr.
Elliott, Ralph N. & Flumiani, C. M. The Elliott Wave Theory in Projection Charts. enl. ed. (Illus.). 129p. 1982. 187.50x (ISBN 0-86654-022-9). Inst Econ Finan.
Elmore, William C. & Heald, Mark A. Physics of Waves. 477p. 1985. pap. 9.95 (ISBN 0-486-64926-1). Dover.
Favre, A. & Hasselmann, K., eds. Turbulent Fluxes Through the Sea Surface, Wave Dynamics, & Prediction, Vol. 1. (NATO Conference Series V, Air-Sea Interactions: Vol. 1). 691p. 1978. 89.50x (ISBN 0-306-40005-7, Plenum Pr). Plenum Pub.
Felsen, L. B. Hybrid Formulation of Wave Propagation & Scattering. 1984. lib. bdg. 52.00 (ISBN 90-247-3094-5, Pub. by Martinus Nijhoff Netherlands). Kluwer Academic.
French, A. P. Vibrations & Waves. (M.I.T. Introductory Physics Ser). (Illus.). 1971. pap. text ed. 9.95x (ISBN 0-393-09936-9). Norton.
Froissart, Marcel, ed. Hyperbolic Equations & Waves: Battelle Seattle 1968 Recontres. LC 76-86498. (Illus.). 1970. 40.80 (ISBN 0-387-04883-9). Springer-Verlag.
Goldin, Edwin. Waves & Photons: An Introduction to Quantum Optics. LC 82-10991. (Pure & Applied Optics Ser.). 211p. 1982. 29.95x (ISBN 0-471-08592-8, Pub. by Wiley-Interscience). Wiley.
Gossard, E. E. Waves in the Atmosphere. LC 73-89155. (Developments in Atmospheric Science Ser.: Vol. 2). 456p. 1975. 121.50 (ISBN 0-444-41196-8). Elsevier.
Gough, W. & Richards, J. P. Vibrations & Waves. 278p. 1983. 64.95 (ISBN 0-470-27446-8). Halsted Pr.
Hirose, Akira & Lonngren, Karl E. Introduction to Wave Phenomena. 425p. 1985. 45.95x (ISBN 0-471-81440-7, Pub. by Wiley-Interscience). Wiley.
Hlawiczka, Paul. Gyrotropic Waveguides. 1982. 34.00 (ISBN 0-12-349940-2). Acad Pr.
Infrared & Millimeter Waves, Vol. 12: Electromagnetic Waves in Matter, Pt. II. LC 79-6949. 304p. 1984. 69.00 (ISBN 0-12-147712-6). Acad Pr.
International School of Mathematical Physics, Erice, Italy, June 27-July 9, 1977. Invariant Wave Equations: Proceedings. Velo, G. & Wightman, A. S., eds. (Lecture Notes in Physics Ser.: Vol. 73). 1978. pap. 25.00 (ISBN 0-387-08655-2). Springer-Verlag.
International Symposium on Recent Developments in Classical Wave Scattering, Ohio State Univ., Columbus, 1979. Recent Developments in Classical Wave Scattering: Focus on the T-Matrix Approach. Varadan, V. V. & Varadan, V. K., eds. (Illus.). 670p. 1980. 83.00 (ISBN 0-08-025096-3). Pergamon.
International Symposium on Unsteady Flow in Open Channels. Proceedings. 1977. text ed. 60.00x (ISBN 0-900983-54-X, Dist. by Air Science Co.). BHRA Fluid.
Ishimaru, A. Single Scattering & Transport Theory. (Wave Propagation & Scattering in Random Media: Vol. 1). 1978. 41.50 (ISBN 0-12-374701-5). Acad Pr.
--Wave Propagation & Scattering in Random Media: Multiple Scattering Turbulence, Rough Surfaces & Remote Sensing, Vol. 2. 1978. 57.50 (ISBN 0-12-374702-3). Acad Pr.
Jayant, N. S., ed. Waveform Quantization & Coding. LC 75-44651. 1976. 49.85 (ISBN 0-87942-073-1, PC00687). Inst Electrical.
Jenny, Hans. Cymatics, 2 vols. Incl. Vol. 1. The Structure & Dynamics of Waves & Vibrations. LC 75-10800. (Eng. & Ger.); Vol. 2. Wave Phenomena, Vibrational Effects, Harmonic Oscillations with Their Structure, Kinetics & Dynamics. LC 75-10801. (ISBN 0-8052-3600-7). (Illus.). 186p. 1975. Repr. 45.00x ea. Schocken.
Keller, J. & Papadakis, J., eds. Wave Propagation & Underwater Acoustics. (Lecture Notes in Physics Ser: Vol. 70). 1977. pap. 18.00 (ISBN 0-387-08527-0). Springer-Verlag.
Kuramoto, Y. Chemical Oscillations, Waves, & Turbulence. (Springer Series in Synergetics: Vol. 19). (Illus.). 170p. 1984. 32.00 (ISBN 0-387-13322-4). Springer-Verlag.
Lighthill, James. Waves in Fluids. LC 77-8174. (Illus.). 1978. 67.50 (ISBN 0-521-21689-3); pap. 29.95x (ISBN 0-521-29233-6). Cambridge U Pr.
Livsic, M. S. Operators, Oscillations, Waves. LC 72-11580. (Translations of Mathematical Monographs: Vol. 34). 280p. (Orig.). 1973. 47.00 (ISBN 0-8218-1584-9, MMONO-34). Am Math.
Melcher, James R. Field-Coupled Surface Waves: A Comparative Study of Surface-Coupled EHD & MHD Systems. 1963. 22.50x (ISBN 0-262-13015-7). MIT Pr.
Minikin, R. R. Winds, Waves, & Maritime Structures. 295p. 1963. 75.00x (ISBN 0-85264-091-9, Pub. by Griffin England). State Mutual Bk.
Morawetz, C. S. Lectures on Nonlinear Waves & Shocks. (Tata Institute Lectures on Mathematics Ser.). 137p. 1982. pap. 10.00 (ISBN 0-387-10830-0). Springer-Verlag.
Nelkon, M. Optics, Waves & Sound. 6th ed. 1973. pap. text ed. 14.50x (ISBN 0-435-68662-3). Heinemann Ed.
Pain, H. J. Physics of Vibrations & Waves. 3rd ed. LC 83-5880. 350p. 1983. 44.95x (ISBN 0-471-90181-4, Pub. by Wiley-Interscience); pap. 18.95x (ISBN 0-471-90182-2). Wiley.
Pierce, John R. Almost All about Waves. 1974. pap. 5.95x (ISBN 0-262-66027-X). MIT Pr.
Roberts, Jo. Internal Gravity Waves in the Ocean. (Marine Science Ser.: Vol.2). 288p. 1975. 65.00 (ISBN 0-8247-6226-6). Dekker.
Santosa, Fadil, et al, eds. Inverse Problems of Acoustic & Elastic Waves. LC 84-52372. (Illus.). ix, 365p. 1984. text ed. 38.50 (ISBN 0-89871-050-2). Soc Indus Appl Math.
The Scattering & Diffraction of Waves. LC 59-11511. (Harvard Monographs in Applied Science: No. 7). (Illus.). pap. 59.00 (ISBN 0-317-09160-3, 2002784). Bks Demand UMI.
Silvester, R. Coastal Engineering, Vol. 1: Generation, Propagation & Influence of Waves. LC 72-97435. (Developments in Geotechnical Engineering Ser.: Vol. 4A). 450p. 1974. 68.00 (ISBN 0-444-41101-1). Elsevier.
Stoker, James J. Water Waves. LC 56-8228. (Pure & Applied Mathematics Ser.). (Illus.). 595p. 1957. 61.95x (ISBN 0-470-82863-3, Pub. by Wiley-Interscience). Wiley.
Turner, G. Alan. Heat & Concentration Waves: Analysis & Applications. 1972. 57.50 (ISBN 0-12-704050-1). Acad Pr.
Wave & Tidal Energy International Symposium, 1st. Proceedings, 2 vols. Stephens, H. S., ed. (Illus.). 1979. Set. pap. 69.00x (ISBN 0-906085-00-4, Dist. by Air Science Co.). BHRA Fluid.
West, Bruce J., ed. Nonlinear Properties of Internal Waves: La Jolla Institute, 1981. (AIP Conference Proceedings: No. 76). 351p. 1981. lib. bdg. 32.00 (ISBN 0-88318-175-4). Am Inst Physics.
Whitham, G. B. Linear & Nonlinear Waves. LC 74-2070. (Pure & Applied Mathematics Ser.). 636p. 1974. 48.50x (ISBN 0-471-94090-9, Pub. by Wiley-Interscience). Wiley.
Wiegel, Robert L. Oceanographical Engineering. 1964. ref. ed. O.P. 43.95 (ISBN 0-13-629600-9). P-H.
Woolf, Virginia. Waves: The Two Holograph Drafts. Graham, J. W., ed. LC 71-185714. 1976. 50.00x (ISBN 0-8020-1628-6). U of Toronto Pr.
Young, Hugh D. Fundamentals of Waves, Optics & Modern Physics. 2nd ed. 1975. 42.95 (ISBN 0-07-072521-7). McGraw.

WAVES, ELECTROMAGNETIC
see Electromagnetic Waves

WAVES, SEISMIC
see Seismic Waves

WAVES, ULTRASONIC
see Ultrasonic Waves

WAX MODELING
Feinberg, Wilbert. Lost-Wax Casting: A Practitioner's Manual. Byrne, Jim, ed. (Illus.). 96p. 1983. pap. 11.50x (ISBN 0-903031-88-4, Pub. by Intermediate Tech England). Intermediate Tech.

WAXES
Bennett, H. Industrial Waxes, 2 vols. Incl. Vol. 1. Natural Waxes; Synthetic Waxes (ISBN 0-8206-0224-8); Vol. 2. Compounded Waxes; Technology (ISBN 0-8206-0225-6). 1975. 30.00 ea. Chem Pub.
Halpern, M. G., ed. Polishing & Waxing Compositions: Recent Developments. LC 82-7691. (Chemical Technology Rev. 213). (Illus.). 301p. 1983. 36.00 (ISBN 0-8155-0916-2). Noyes.
Kolattukudy, P. E., ed. Chemistry & Biochemistry of Natural Waxes. 460p. 1976. 95.75 (ISBN 0-444-41470-3). Elsevier.

WEAK INTERACTIONS (NUCLEAR PHYSICS)
Barger, Vernon & Cline, David. Neutrino Mass & Gauge Structure of Weak Interactions (Telemark, 1982) AIP Conference Proceedings 99, Particles & Fields Subseries 30. LC 83-71072. 283p. 1983. lib. bdg. 34.50 (ISBN 0-88318-198-3). Am Inst Physics.
Behrens, Heinrich. Electron Radial Wave Functions & Nuclear Beta-Decay. (International Series of Monographs in Physics). (Illus.). 1982. 79.00x (ISBN 0-19-851297-X). Oxford U Pr.
Chang, N. P., ed. Five Decades of Weak Interactions, Vol. 294. (Annals of the New York Academy of Sciences Ser.). 102p. 1977. 12.00x (ISBN 0-89072-040-1). NY Acad Sci.
Collins, G. B., et al, eds. Weak Interactions as Probes of Unification: Virginia Polytechnic Institute 1980. (AIP Conference Proceedings Ser.: No. 72). 689p. 1981. lib. bdg. 39.50 (ISBN 0-88318-171-1). Am Inst Physics.
Georgi, Howard. Weak Interactions & Modern Particle Theory. 1984. text ed. 29.95 (ISBN 0-8053-3163-8). Benjamin-Cummings.
Lee, T. D., ed. Weak Interactions & High Energy Neutrino Physics. (Italian Physical Society Ser.: Course 32). 1966. 75.00 (ISBN 0-12-368832-9). Acad Pr.
Morales, A., ed. Weak Interactions & Neutrinos: Proceedings of the International Workshop, 8th Javea, Spain, Sept. 5-11, 1982. 340p. 1983. 79.00x (ISBN 9971-950-89-8, Pub. by World Sci Singapore). Taylor & Francis.
Zichichi, A., ed. Strong & Weak Interactions. 1967. 97.50 (ISBN 0-12-780545-1). Acad Pr.

WEAPONS
see Arms and Armor; Firearms

WEAPONS SYSTEMS
The AR-7 Exotic Weapons System. (Illus.). 72p. 1981. pap. 12.00 (ISBN 0-87364-242-2). Paladin Pr.
Arcangelis, Mario de. Electronic Warfare. (Illus.). 312p. 1985. 19.95 (ISBN 0-7137-1501-4, Pub. by Blandford Pr England). Sterling.
Bearden, T E. Solutions to Tesla's Secrets & the Soviet Tesla Weapons with Reference Articles for Solutions to Tesla's Secrets, 2 pts. LC 81-85737. (Illus.). 188p. (Orig.). 1982. Set. pap. 14.00 (ISBN 0-9603536-3-1). Tesla Bk Co.
Beckett, Brian. Weapons of Tomorrow. 160p. 1983. (full discount avail.) 14.95 (ISBN 0-306-41383-3, Plenum Pr). Plenum Pub.
Chant, Chris. Armed Forces of the United Kingdom. LC 80-66428. (Illus.). 80p. 1980. 14.95 (ISBN 0-7153-8024-9). David & Charles.
Constant, James N. Fundamentals of Strategic Weapons, 2 Vols. 1982. lib. bdg. 195.00 (ISBN 90-247-2545-3, Pub. by Martinus Nijhoff Netherlands). Kluwer Academic.
Cornell, Alexander H. International Collaboration in Weapons & Equipment Development & Production by the NATO Allies. (Atlantic Ser.: No. 2). 248p. lib. bdg. 54.50 (ISBN 90-247-2564-X, Pub. by Martinus Nijhoff Netherlands). Kluwer Academic.
Fessler, Edward A. Directed-Energy Weapons: A Juridical Analysis. LC 79-65950. 204p. 1980. 37.95x (ISBN 0-03-053511-5). Praeger.
Friedman, Richard S., et al. Advanced Technology Warfare. (Illus.). 1985. 22.95 (ISBN 0-517-55850-5, Harmony); pap. 12.95 (ISBN 0-517-55851-3, Harmony). Crown.
Garnell, P. Guided Weapon Control Systems. 2nd ed. (Illus.). 248p. 1985. 44.00 (ISBN 0-08-025468-3). Pergamon.
Goad, K. J. & Halsey, D. H. Ammunition, Grenades & Mines. LC 81-23411. (Brassey's Battlefield Weapons Systems & Technology: Vol. 3). 160p. 1982. 35.00 (ISBN 0-08-028326-8, T120); pap. 17.50 (ISBN 0-08-028327-6). Pergamon.
Gutteridge, William & Taylor, Trevor, eds. The Dangers of New Weapons Systems. LC 82-23066. 200p. 1983. 27.50 (ISBN 0-312-18217-1). St Martin.
Hecht, Jeff. Beam Weapons: The Next Arms Race. LC 83-24713. (Illus.). 363p. 1984. (full discount avail.) 17.95 (ISBN 0-306-41546-1, Plenum Pr). Plenum Pub.
Jane's Weapon System, 1978. 79.50x (ISBN 0-686-73474-2). Key Bk Serv.
Kaldor, Mary. The Baroque Arsenal. (American Century Ser.). 294p. 1981. 14.95 (ISBN 0-8090-2812-3); pap. 7.25 (ISBN 0-8090-1501-3). Hill & Wang.
Lee, et al. Guided Weapons. (Brassey's Battlefield Weapons Systems & Technology: Vol. 8). 160p. 1983. 27.00 (ISBN 0-08-028336-5); pap. 12.50 (ISBN 0-08-028337-3). Pergamon.
Lee, R. G. An Introduction to Battlefield Weapons Systems & Technology. (Illus.). 160p. 1981. 29.50 (ISBN 0-08-027043-3); pap. 15.00 (ISBN 0-08-027044-1). Pergamon.
Paladin Press. Mini-14 Exotic Weapons System. (Exotic Weapons Systems Ser.). 80p. 1982. pap. 12.00 (ISBN 0-87364-250-3). Paladin Pr.
Royal United Services Institute. Rusi & Brassey's Defence Yearbook 1982. 92nd ed. 365p. 1981. 40.00 (ISBN 0-08-027039-5); pap. 25.00 (ISBN 0-08-027040-9). Pergamon.
The Ruger 1022 Exotic Weapons System. (Illus.). 96p. 1983. pap. 12.00 (ISBN 0-87364-274-0). Paladin Pr.
Ryan, J. W. Guns, Mortars & Rockets. (Brassey's Battlefield Weapons Systems & Technology: Vol. 2). (Illus.). 236p. 1982. 26.00 (ISBN 0-08-028324-1, P110); pap. 13.00 (ISBN 0-08-028325-X). Pergamon.
Stine, G. Harry. Confrontation in Space. (Illus.). 209p. 1981. 13.95 (ISBN 0-13-167437-4); pap. 6.95 (ISBN 0-13-167429-3). P-H.
Surveillance & Target Acquisition. (Brassey's Battlefield Weapons Systems & Technology Ser.: Vol. 7). 160p. 1982. 40.00 (ISBN 0-08-028334-9); pap. 16.00 (ISBN 0-08-028335-7). Pergamon.
Union of Concerned Scientists Staff. The Fallacy of Star Wars: Why Space Weapons Can't Protect Us. Tirman, John, ed. LC 84-13129. 1984. pap. 4.95 (ISBN 0-394-72894-7, Vin). Random.
Weapon Systems, Nineteen Eighty-FIve. (Illus.). 153p. 1985. pap. 8.00 (ISBN 0-318-11842-4). Gov Printing Office.
Weapon Systems, Nineteen Eighty-Four. 137p. 1984. pap. 8.00 (ISBN 0-318-11841-6). Gov Printing Office.

WEAR, MECHANICAL
see Mechanical Wear

WEARING PROPERTIES
see Mechanical Wear

WEASELS
Powell, Roger A. The Fisher: Life History, Ecology, & Behavior. LC 81-14775. (Illus.). 196p. 1982. 19.50x (ISBN 0-8166-1053-3). U of Minn Pr.

WEATHER
see also Atmospheric Electricity; Atmospheric Pressure; Atmospheric Temperature; Climatology; Evaporation; Humidity; Meteorology; Rain and Rainfall; Snow; Storms; Weather Control; Weather Forecasting; Winds;
also names of countries, cities, etc., with or without the subdivision Climate
Andrews, Billy. Outstanding Weather Phenomena in the Ark-La-Tex. Hughes, Jeff, ed. LC 84-2938. (Illus.). 216p. (Orig.). 1984. pap. text ed. 10.50 (ISBN 0-910653-11-9, 8101-E). Archival Servs.
Anthes, Richard A. Weather Around Us. (Physical Science Ser.). 1976. pap. text ed. 9.95 (ISBN 0-675-08635-3); Set of 4. cassettes & filmstrips o.p. 135.00 (ISBN 0-675-08634-5). Merrill.
Bair, Frank E. & Ruffner, James, eds. The Weather Almanac. 1979. pap. 7.95 (ISBN 0-380-43000-2, 52654-9). Avon.
Battan, Louis J. Weather. 2nd ed. (Illus.). 160p. 1985. text ed. 18.95 (ISBN 0-13-947698-9); pap. text ed. 15.95 (ISBN 0-13-947680-6). P-H.
--Weather in Your Life. (Illus.). 308p. 1985. pap. 12.95 (ISBN 0-7167-1437-X). W H Freeman.
Berger, Andre L., ed. Climatic Variations & Variability: Facts & Theories. xxvi, 771p. 1981. 87.50 (ISBN 90-277-1300-6, Pub. by Reidel Holland). Kluwer Academic.
Brown, Cecil. Days Without Weather. 250p. 1982. 12.95 (ISBN 0-374-13530-4). FS&G.
Brown, Seyom, et al. Regimes for the Ocean, Outer Space, & Weather. 1977. 22.95 (ISBN 0-8157-1156-5); pap. 8.95 (ISBN 0-8157-1155-7). Brookings.
Consolidated Report on the Voluntary Assistance Programme, Including Projects Approved for Circulation in 1977. (Eng. & Fr.). 323p. 1978. pap. 15.00 (ISBN 92-63-10501-4, W391, WMO). Unipub.
Conway, H. McKinley, Jr. & Liston, Linda L., eds. The Weather Handbook. rev. ed. LC 79-54253. (Illus.). 1974. 12.95 (ISBN 0-910436-00-2). Conway Data.
Corliss, William R. Tornadoes, Dark Days, Anomalous Precipitation & Related Weather Phenomena. LC 82-63156. (Catalog of Geophysical Anomalies Ser.). (Illus.). 196p. 1983. 11.95 (ISBN 0-915554-10-0). Sourcebook.
Crawford, William P. Mariner's Weather. (Illus.). 1979. 22.95 (ISBN 0-393-03221-3). Norton.
Dickson, H. Climate & Weather. 1976. lib. bdg. 59.95 (ISBN 0-8490-1638-X). Gordon Pr.
Eagleman, Joe R. Severe & Unusual Weather. 250p. 1982. 34.95 (ISBN 0-442-26195-0). Van Nos Reinhold.
--Severe & Unusual Weather Discussion Guide. 96p. 1982. pap. text ed. 7.95 (ISBN 0-8403-2777-3). Kendall-Hunt.
Ecodyne Corporation. Weather Data Handbook. 320p. 1980. 42.50 (ISBN 0-07-018960-9). McGraw.
Forrester, Frank H. One Thousand & One Questions Answered about the Weather. (Illus.). 15.50 (ISBN 0-8446-5886-3). Peter Smith.
--One Thousand One Questions Answered about the Weather. (Illus.). 448p. 1982. pap. 5.95 (ISBN 0-486-24218-8). Dover.
From, Lester D. & Staver, Allen E. Fundamentals of Weather: A Workbook Approach. 1979. 16.50 (ISBN 0-8403-2023-X). Kendall-Hunt.
Gregory, Michael. Hunger Weather Nineteen Fifty-Nine to Nineteen Seventy-Five, Vol. 2. 216p. (Orig.). 1982. pap. 8.95x (ISBN 0-934600-03-1). Mother Duck Pr.
Guide on the Global Data Processing System. 154p. 1983. pap. 21.00 (ISBN 92-63-12305-5, W546, WMO). Unipub.

Hanzawa, M. & Fournier, T. H. System for the Collection of Ships' Weather Reports, 2 Pts. (World Weather Watch Planning Reports: No. 25). (Eng. & Fr.). 1968. pap. 12.00 (ISBN 0-685-22344-2, W237, WMO). Unipub.

Hardy, Ralph, et al. The Weather Book. LC 81-84683. (Illus.). 224p. 1982. 24.95 (ISBN 0-316-34623-3). Little.

Hein, W. Lexikon der Schulphysik: Waerme und Wetter, Vol. 2. (Ger.). 37.00 (ISBN 3-7614-0108-6, M-7223). French & Eur.

Herman, John R. & Goldberg, Richard A. Sun, Weather, & Climate. LC 79-22363. (Illus.). 1980. Repr. of 1978 ed. 50.00x (ISBN 0-8103-1018-X). Gale.

--Sun, Weather, & Climate. (Earth Science Ser.). 360p. 1985. pap. 7.95 (ISBN 0-486-64796-X). Dover.

Hidore, John J. Weather & Climate: Text-Exercises-Weather Maps. LC 84-61956. 238p. 1984. pap. 15.95 (ISBN 0-941226-05-0). Park Pr Co.

Humphreys, William J. Rain Making & Other Weather Vagaries. LC 77-10228. Repr. of 1926 ed. 16.50 (ISBN 0-404-16208-8). AMS Pr.

Kondratyev, K. Y. & Hunt, G. E. Weather & Climate on Planets. (Illus.). 750p. 1981. 105.00 (ISBN 0-08-026493-X). Pergamon.

Kotsch, William J. Weather for the Mariner. 3rd. ed. LC 83-13084. 1983. 16.95 (ISBN 0-87021-756-9). Naval Inst Pr.

Lutgens, Frederick K. & Tarbuck, Edward J. The Atmosphere: An Introduction to Meteorology. 3rd ed. (Illus.). 576p. 1986. 30.95 (ISBN 0-13-049917-X). P H.

McAdie, Alexander G. Making the Weather. LC 77-10233. Repr. of 1923 ed. 13.50 (ISBN 0-404-16213-4). AMS Pr.

McCormac, Billy M. & Seliga, Thomas A., eds. Solar-Terrestrial Influences on Weather & Climate. 1979. lib. bdg. 24.00 (ISBN 90-277-0978-5, Pub. by Reidel Holland). Kluwer Academic.

McKenzie, Alexander A. World Record Wind: Measuring Gusts of 231 Miles an Hour. (Illus.). 36p. (Orig.). 1984. pap. 2.00 (ISBN 0-9613227-0-5). A A McKenzie.

Malone, Thomas F., intro. by. Weather & Climate Modification: Problems & Progress. LC 79-22479. 1980. Repr. of 1973 ed. 50.00x (ISBN 0-8103-1017-1). Gale.

Marriott, Paul J. Red Sky at Night Shepard's Delight? 1981. 30.00x (ISBN 0-9505730-5-1, Pub. by Sheba Bks). State Mutual Bk.

Ninth Status Report on Implementation. (World Weather Watch Planning Reports: No. 484). 1978. pap. 25.00 (ISBN 92-63-10484-0, W364, WMO). Unipub.

Padial, Antonio & Roderman, Winifred H. Weather. (Science in Action Ser.). (Illus.). 48p. 1982. pap. text ed. 2.85 (ISBN 0-915510-79-0). Janus Bks.

Pearce, E. A. & Smith, Gordon. The Times Books World Weather Guide. LC 84-40112. (Illus.). 480p. 1984. 22.50 (ISBN 0-8129-1123-7). Times Bks.

Petersen, William F. Man, Weather, Sun. (Illus.). 496p. 1948. 49.75x (ISBN 0-398-04392-2). C C Thomas.

Report of the Third Session of the Inter-Governmental Panel Meeting on ALPEX. (GARP Special Reports: No. 40). 122p. 1982. pap. 15.00 (ISBN 0-686-44828-6, W548, WMO). Unipub.

The Results of the Global Weather Experiment: Lectures Presented at the Thirty-fourth Session of the WMO Executive Committee. 134p. 1983. pap. text ed. 13.00 (ISBN 92-63-10610-X, W561, WMO). Unipub.

Riley, Denis & Spolton, Lewis. World Weather & Climate. 2nd ed. LC 81-3853. (Illus.). 128p. 1982. pap. 10.95 (ISBN 0-521-28442-2). Cambridge U Pr.

Rubin, Louis D., Sr. & Duncan, Jim. The Weather Wizard's Cloud Book. (Illus.). 70p. 1984. pap. 12.95 (ISBN 0-912697-10-5). Algonquin Bks.

Sanders, Ti. The Weather Is Front Page News. (Illus.). 224p. 1984. 17.95 (ISBN 0-89651-902-3); pap. 9.95 (ISBN 0-89651-903-1). Icarus.

Schwoegler, Bruce & McClintock, Michael. Weather & Energy. 224p. 1982. 26.50 (ISBN 0-07-055746-2). McGraw.

Singer, Oscar. Singer's Lock: The Revolution in the Understanding of Weather, Pt. 1. LC 83-90086. (Illus.). 351p. 1983. 19.95x (ISBN 0-9610922-0-3); computer print-out & plastic transparent tool 10.00x (ISBN 0-9610922-1-1). Singer Pr.

Sloane, Eric. Eric Sloane's Weather Book. (Illus.). 1977. pap. 7.95 (ISBN 0-8015-2365-6, 0772-230, Hawthorn). Dutton.

Smith, L. P. Weather & Food. (No. 1). (Fr., Illus.). 80p. 1962. pap. 2.00 (ISBN 0-685-22347-7, W17, WMO). Unipub.

Tenth Anniversary of the World Weather Watch: Lectures Presented at the 24th Session of the WMO Executive Committee. 44p. 1973. pap. 15.00 (ISBN 0-685-39019-5, W226, WMO). Unipub.

Weather. LC 79-798. (Spotter's Guide). (Illus.). 1979. 3.95 (ISBN 0-8317-9393-7, Mayflower Bks); pap. 1.95 (ISBN 0-8317-9394-5). Smith Pubs.

World Meteorological Organization. Weather & Water. 1966. pap. 2.00 (ISBN 0-685-22348-5, W51, WMO). Unipub.

World Meteorological Organization Executive Committee. Abridged Report with Resolutions of the 29th Session of the WMO Executive Committee: 1977. (Illus.). 1978. pap. 25.00 (ISBN 92-63-10483-2, W361, WMO). Unipub.

Youldon, G. Weather. 1982. 5.90 (ISBN 0-531-02467-9); 1.95 (ISBN 0-531-05167-6). Watts.

WEATHER CONTROL

see also Meteorology in Aeronautics; Rain-Making; Water-Supply

Breuer, Georg. Weather Modification, Prospect & Problems. Morth, H. T., tr. from Ger. LC 79-73236. (Illus.). 1980. 34.50 (ISBN 0-521-22453-5); pap. 12.95 (ISBN 0-521-29577-7). Cambridge U Pr.

Committee on Atmospheric Sciences. Weather & Climate Modification. (Illus.). 256p. 1973. pap. 10.25 (ISBN 0-309-02121-9). Natl Acad Pr.

Fleagle, Robert G., ed. Weather Modification: Science & Public Policy. LC 68-8511. (Public Policy Issues in Resource Management Ser.: Vol. 3). (Illus.). 158p. 1968. 20.00x (ISBN 0-295-78551-9). U of Wash Pr.

Fleagle, Robert G., et al. Weather Modification in the Public Interest. LC 74-590. (Illus.). 98p. 1974. 17.50x (ISBN 0-295-95321-7). U of Wash Pr.

McAdie, Alexander G. Making the Weather. LC 77-10233. Repr. of 1923 ed. 13.50 (ISBN 0-404-16213-4). AMS Pr.

Mason, Basil J. Clouds, Rain, & Rainmaking. 2nd ed. LC 74-16991. pap. 49.30 (ISBN 0-317-20591-9, 2024497). Bks Demand UMI.

Neiburger, Morris. Artificial Modification of Clouds & Precipitation. (Technical Note Ser.: No. 105). 33p. (Orig.). 1969. pap. 8.00 (ISBN 0-685-04905-1, W75, WMO). Unipub.

Papers Presented at the Second WMO Scientific Conference on Weather Modification: Boulder, Colorado, 2-6 Aug. 1976. xvii, 592p. 1976. pap. 50.00 (ISBN 92-63-10443-3, W201, WMO). Unipub.

Scientific Conference on Weather Modification: WMO-IAMAP. (Publications Ser.: No. 399). pap. 50.00 (W169, WMO). Unipub.

Sewell, W. Derrick, et al. Human Dimensions of Weather Modification. LC 66-18571. (Research Papers Ser.: No. 105). 423p. 1966. pap. 10.00 (ISBN 0-89065-014-4). U Chicago Dept Geog.

Taubenfeld, Howard J., ed. Weather Modification & the Law. LC 68-24047. 228p. 1968. 12.00 (ISBN 0-379-00363-5). Oceana.

Thomas, William A. Legal & Scientific Uncertainties of Weather Modification. LC 77-82058. 1977. 12.75 (ISBN 0-8223-0393-0). Duke.

Vieira, Anthony G. An Outline of Weather Control. 64p. 1984. 5.50 (ISBN 0-682-40196-X). Exposition Pr FL.

Weather Modification Papers: Second WMO Scientific Conference on Weather Modification; Boulder, 1976. (Illus.). 1977. pap. 50.00 (ISBN 92-63-10443-3, WMO). Unipub.

Wegman & DePrist. Statistical Analysis of Weather Modification Experiments. (Lecture Notes in Statistics Ser.: Vol. 3). 184p. 1980. 29.75 (ISBN 0-8247-1177-7). Dekker.

WMO-IAMAP Scientific Conference on Weather Modification: Proceedings. (Illus.). 538p. 1975. pap. 50.00 (ISBN 92-63-10399-2, WMO). Unipub.

World Weather Watch: Consolidated Report on the Voluntary Assistance Program Including Projects Approved for Circulation in 1976. (Publications Ser.: 465). 1977. pap. 15.00 (ISBN 92-63-10465-4, W225, WMO). Unipub.

WEATHER FORECASTING

see also Astronautics in Meteorology; Meteorology As a Profession; Meteorology in Aeronautics; Numerical Weather Forecasting

Bair, Frank E. & Ruffner, James, eds. The Weather Almanac. 1979. pap. 7.95 (ISBN 0-380-43000-2, 52654-9). Avon.

Baird, Michael. Weather Forecasting For Astronomy. LC 82-50215. (Illus.). 120p. (Orig.). 1982. pap. 12.95 (ISBN 0-9608278-0-3). Winmark Pr.

Committee on Atmospheric Sciences, ed. Severe Storms: Predicion, Detection & Warning. LC 77-77588. (Illus.). 1977. pap. text ed. 7.95 (ISBN 0-309-02613-X). Natl Acad Pr.

Eleventh Status Report on Implementation: World Weather Watch. 98p. 1983. pap. 25.00 (ISBN 92-63-10601-0, W545, WMO). Unipub.

Federal Aviation Administration. Aviation Weather Services: Ac 00-45b. (Illus.). 1980. pap. 6.00 (ISBN 0-86677-001-1). Aviation.

Federal Aviation Administration & National Oceanic & Atmospheric Administration. Aviation Weather Services. rev. ed. 123p. 1979. pap. text ed. 5.50 (ISBN 0-939158-02-7). Flightshops.

First Planning Meeting for TOPEX. (World Weather Watch Tropical Cyclone Programme, Topex Reports: No. 1). 81p. 1980. pap. 10.00 (ISBN 92-63-10565-0, W479, WMO). Unipub.

Forecasting of Heavy Rains & Floods: Proceedings of the Joint RA 2 & RA 5 Training Seminar, Kuala Lumpur, Malaysia, Nov. 1968. (Illus.). 293p. (Orig.). 1970. pap. 20.00 (ISBN 0-685-04908-6, W340, WMO). Unipub.

Guide to Hydrological Practices: Analysis, Forecasting & Other Applications, Vol. II. (WMO Ser.: No. 168). 150p. 1983. pap. text ed. 40.00 (ISBN 92-63-14168-1, W578, WMO). Unipub.

Helmer, Olaf. Looking Forward: A Guide to Futures Research. LC 83-4520. (Illus.). 376p. 1983. 29.95 (ISBN 0-8039-2017-2). Sage.

High-Level Forecasting for Turbine-Engined Aircraft Operations over Africa & the Middle East. pap. 25.00 (ISBN 0-686-93870-4, W31, WMO). Unipub.

Holford, Ingrid. Interpreting the Weather: A Practical Guide for Householders, Gardeners, Motorist and Sportsmen. (Illus.). 1973. 14.95 (ISBN 0-7153-5800-6). David & Charles.

Johnson, David S. Twentieth Anniversary of the World Weather Watch: Opportunities & Outlook for an Improved WWW. 29p. 1983. pap. text ed. 11.00 (ISBN 92-63-10608-8, W553, WMO). Unipub.

Lectures on Forecasting of Tropical Weather, Including Tropical Cyclones, with Particular Relevance to Africa: Proceedings of WMO Seminar, Dakar, Nov. 1976. (Illus.). xvii, 331p. 1977. pap. 42.00 (ISBN 92-63-10492-1, W371, WMO). Unipub.

Lectures on Numerical Short-Range Weather Prediction: Proceedings of the WMO Regional Training Seminar, Moscow, 1965. 706p. 1969. pap. 50.00 (ISBN 0-685-02480-6, W102, WMO). Unipub.

Marchuk, G. I. Numerical Methods in Weather Prediction. rev. ed. 1974. 54.00 (ISBN 0-12-470650-9). Acad Pr.

Methods of Forecasting the State of Sea on the Basis of Meteorological Data. (Technical Note Ser.: No. 46). 35p. 1962. pap. 12.00 (ISBN 0-685-36786-X, W21, WMO). Unipub.

Mitchell-Christie, Frank. Practical Weather Forecasting. LC 77-84142. 1978. 10.95 (ISBN 0-8120-5210-2). Barron.

Ninth Status Report on Implementation. (World Weather Watch Planning Reports: No. 484). 1978. pap. 25.00 (ISBN 92-63-10484-0, W364, WMO). Unipub.

Papers Presented at the WMO Symposium on the Interpretation of Broad-Scale NWP Products for Local Forecasting Purposes: Warsaw, 11-16 Oct. 1976. xiii, 250p. 1976. pap. 30.00 (ISBN 92-63-10450-6, W206, WMO). Unipub.

Present Situation with Regard to the Application of Numerical Methods for Routine Weather Prediction & Prospects for the Future. (Technical Note Ser.: No. 67). (Illus.). 64p. 1965. pap. 6.00 (ISBN 0-685-36788-6, W34, WMO). Unipub.

Present Techniques of Tropical Storm Surge Prediction. (Reports on Marine Science Affairs: No. 13). (Illus.). vii, 874p. 1978. pap. 20.00 (ISBN 92-63-10500-6, W384, WMO). Unipub.

Ramsey, Dan. How to Forecast Weather. (Illus.). 224p. (Orig.). 1983. pap. 11.50 (ISBN 0-8306-0168-6, 1568). TAB Bks.

Regional Seminar on Synoptic Analysis & Forecasting in the Tropics of Asia & the South-West Pacific: Proceedings, Singapore, 1970. (Publications Ser.: No. 321). 552p. 1972. pap. 55.00 (ISBN 0-686-93906-9, WMO). Unipub.

Sloane, Eric. Sloan's Almanac & Weather Forecaster. 1977. pap. 5.95 (ISBN 0-8015-6877-3, 0578-170, Hawthorn). Dutton.

Synoptic Analysis & Forecasting in the Tropics of Asia & the Southwest Pacific: Proceedings of the Regional Seminar, Singapore, Dec. 1970. 552p. 1972. pap. 55.00 (ISBN 0-685-36789-4, W118, WMO). Unipub.

Taylor, James A., ed. Weather Forecasting for Agriculture & Industry: A Symposium. LC 72-6550. (Illus.). 250p. 1973. 24.50 (ISBN 0-8386-1260-1). Fairleigh Dickinson.

Watts, Alan. Instant Weather Forecasting. LC 68-9173. (Illus.). 1968. 7.95 (ISBN 0-396-05845-0). Dodd.

Weather Predicting: Course XV, Lessons 190-96. pap. 6.50 (ISBN 0-87887-361-9). Church of Light.

Weather Reporting. Incl. Basic Volume A - Observing Stations; Basic Volume B - Data Processing. 70.00 (ISBN 0-685-55834-7); Basic Volume C - Transmissions. 125.00 (ISBN 0-685-55836-3); 80.00 (ISBN 0-685-55837-1); Basic Volume D - Information for Shipping. 150.00 (ISBN 0-685-55838-X); 50.00 (ISBN 0-685-55839-8). (Two editions per year, by subscription; Supplements by Subscription, WMO). Unipub.

Whitnah, Donald R. A History of the United States Weather Bureau. LC 60-8345. pap. 54.60 (ISBN 0-317-09031-3, 2019039). Bks Demand UMI.

Wilson, Francis. The Larousse Guide to Weather Forecasting. LC 82-81529. (Nature Guides Ser.). (Illus.). 1982. 17.95 (8219); pap. 8.95 (ISBN 0-88332-280-3, 8218). Larousse.

WMO-IUGG Symposium on Numerical Weather Prediction: Proceedings, Tokyo, 1968. pap. 52.00 (ISBN 0-686-93903-4, W342, WMO). Unipub.

WMO-IUGG Synposium on Research & Development Aspects of Long-Range Forecasting: Boulder, Colorado, 1964. (Technical Note Ser.: No. 66). (Illus.). 64p. 1965. pap. 40.00 (ISBN 0-685-38488-8, W33, WMO). Unipub.

World Weather Watch: Consolidated Report on the Voluntary Assistance Program Including Projects Approved for Circulation in 1976. (Publications Ser.: 465). 1977. pap. 15.00 (ISBN 92-63-10465-4, W225, WMO). Unipub.

WEATHER MODIFICATION

see Weather Control

WEATHER SATELLITES

see Meteorological Satellites

WEATHER STATIONS

see Meteorological Stations

WEATHERING

see also Corrosion and Anti-Corrosives; Erosion; Materials–Deterioration; Soil Formation

Carroll, Dorothy. Rock Weathering. LC 77-107534. 203p. 1970. 35.00x (ISBN 0-306-30434-1, Plenum Pr). Plenum Pub.

Drever, James I., ed. The Chemistry of Weathering. 1985. lib. bdg. 44.00 (ISBN 90-277-1962-4, Pub. by Reidel Holland). Kluwer Academic.

Ollier, C. D. Weathering. rev. ed. LC 75-320198. (Geomorphology Text). (Illus.). 304p. 1975. pap. text ed. 22.95x (ISBN 0-582-30103-3). Longman.

Pinner, S. H., ed. Weathering & Degradation of Plastics. 144p. 1968. 34.75x (ISBN 0-677-11830-9). Gordon.

Small, John & Clark, Michael. Slopes & Weathering. LC 81-18025. (Cambridge Topics in Geography Second Ser.). 112p. 1982. 14.95 (ISBN 0-521-23340-2); pap. 8.95 (ISBN 0-521-29926-8). Cambridge U Pr.

Wilson, R. C. Residual Deposits: Surface Related Weathering Processes & Materials. (Illus.). 262p. 1983. text ed. 50.00x (ISBN 0-632-01072-X). Blackwell Pubns.

WEAVING

see also Lace and Lace Making; Looms; Silk Manufacture and Trade; Textile Fibers; Textile Fabrics; Woolen and Worsted Manufacture
also woven articles, e.g. Blankets, Carpets, Rugs

Atwater, Mary M. Guatemala Visited. LC 47-24720. (Shuttle Craft Guild Monograph: No. 15). (Illus.). 46p. 1965. pap. 7.45 (ISBN 0-916658-15-5). HTH Pubs.

Barrett, Clotilde. Boundweave. 100p. (Orig.). 1982. text ed. 9.95 (ISBN 0-937452-04-1). Colo Fiber.

--Summer & Winter & Beyond. Rev. ed. 50p. 1982. pap. 5.00 (ISBN 0-937452-05-X). Colo Fiber.

Barrett, Clotilde & Smith, Eunice. Double Two-Tie Unit Weaves. 88p. 1983. pap. 12.00 (ISBN 0-937452-06-8); 1.50. Colo Fiber.

Bradley, Lavinia. Inkle Weaving: A Comprehensive Manual. (Illus.). 90p. 1983. pap. 7.95 (ISBN 0-7100-9086-2). Routledge & Kegan.

Bronson, J. & Bronson, R. Early American Weaving & Dyeing: The Domestic Manufacturer's Assistant, & Family Directory in the Arts of Weaving & Dyeing. (Illus.). 224p. 1977. pap. 4.50 (ISBN 0-486-23440-1). Dover.

Brostoff, Laya. Double Weave: Theory & Practice. LC 79-91202. (Illus.). 45p. 1979. 5.00 (ISBN 0-934026-01-7). Interweave.

--Weaving a Tapestry. LC 82-82243. (Illus.). 162p. 1982. pap. text ed. 17.50 (ISBN 0-934026-10-6). Interweave.

Brown, Rachel. The Weaving, Spinning, & Dyeing Book. LC 77-1653. (Illus.). 1978. 25.00 (ISBN 0-394-49801-1). Knopf.

Burnham, Dorothy. The Comfortable Arts: Traditional Spinning & Weaving in Canada. (National Gallery of Canada Ser.). (Illus.). 256p. 1982. pap. 24.95 (ISBN 0-88884-474-3, 56315-4, Pub. by Natl Mus Canada). U of Chicago Pr.

Collingwood, Peter. The Techniques of Tablet Weaving. (Illus.). 416p. 1982. 35.00 (ISBN 0-8230-5255-9). Watson-Guptill.
Contemporary Satins. LC 76-23999. (Shuttle Craft Guild Monograph: No. 7). (Illus.). 33p. 1962. pap. 6.95 (ISBN 0-916658-07-4). HTH Pubs.
Endrei, Walter. L' Evolution Des Techniques Du Filage & Du Tissage Du Moyen Age a la Revolution Industrielle. (Industrie & Artisanat: No. 4). 1968. pap. 14.00x (ISBN 90-2796-135-2). Mouton.
Goodale, Ernest. Wearing & the Warners Eighteen Seventy to Nineteen Seventy. 1981. 30.00x (ISBN 0-85317-004-5, Pub. by Lewis Pubs). State Mutual Bk.
--Weaving & the Warners, Eighteen Seventy to Nineteen Seventy. (Illus.). 1971. text ed. 25.50x (ISBN 0-85317-004-5, Pub. by A & C Black England). Humanities.
Goodloe, William H. Coconut Palm Frond Weaving. LC 72-79018. (Illus.). 1972. pap. 3.95 (ISBN 0-8048-1061-3). C E Tuttle.
Gray, Herbi. On-loom Cardweaving: A Modern Extension of an Ancient Craft. (Illus.). 60p. (Orig.). 1982. pap. 8.95 (ISBN 0-9608406-0-5). H Gray.
Greenwood, K. Weaving: Control of Fabric Structure. 72p. 1975. 39.00 (ISBN 0-900541-65-2, Pub. by Meadowfield Pr England). State Mutual Bk.
Hargrove, John, compiled by. The Weavers Draft Book & Clothiers Assistant. 1979. pap. 4.95 (ISBN 0-912296-17-8, Dist. by U Pr of Va). Am Antiquarian.
Kurtz, Carol S. Designing for Weaving: A Study Guide for Weavers. (Illus.). 96p. 1981. 18.95 (ISBN 0-8038-1579-4). Hastings.
Lamb, Venice & Lamb, Alastair. West African Narrow Strip Weaving. Fiske, Patricia, ed. (Illus.). 48p. 1975. pap. 6.00 (ISBN 0-685-56285-9). Textile Mus.
Lord, P. R. & Mech, M. I. Weaving: Conversion of Yarn to Fabric. 376p. 1976. 42.00x (ISBN 0-900541-78-4, Pub. by Meadowfield England). State Mutual Bk.
Mary Meigs Atwater Recipe Book for Weavers. 16.50 (ISBN 0-937512-01-X). Wheelwright UT.
Maxson, Mary Lou & Bliss, Anne. Japanese Country Weaving. (Illus.). 1978. pap. 1.50x (ISBN 0-931870-02-X). Juniper Hse.
Mayer, Anita L. Clothing from the Hands That Weave. LC 84-81051. (Illus.). 168p. 1984. wire spiral 18.00 (ISBN 0-934026-14-9). Interweave.
Mitchell, Lillias. Irish Spinning Dyeing & Weaving. (Illus.). 1978. 12.95 (ISBN 0-85221-101-5). Dufour.
Morrison, Phylis. Spiders' Games: A Book for Beginning Weavers. LC 78-21754. (Illus.). 128p. 1979. 20.00 (ISBN 0-295-95620-8). U of Wash Pr.
Nass, Ulla. Weaves of the Incas. (Illus.). 108p. 1980. soft cover 16.95 (ISBN 0-9606468-1-7). Nass.
O'Connor, Paul R. A Twill of Your Choice. LC 81-81875. (Illus.). 173p. (Orig.). 1981. pap. 7.00 (ISBN 0-934026-06-8). Interweave.
Oelsner, G. H. Handbook of Weaves. Dale, Samuel S., ed. 1915. pap. 7.95 (ISBN 0-486-23169-0). Dover.
Ormerod, Allan. Modern Preparation & Weaving Machinery. 296p. text ed. 59.95 (ISBN 0-408-01212-9). Butterworth.
Plath, Iona. The Handweaver's Pattern Book: Over One Hundred-Twenty Upholster, Curtains, Place Mats, Etc. Orig. Title: The Craft of Handweaving. (Illus.). 128p. 1981. pap. 4.95 (ISBN 0-486-24166-1). Dover.
--The Handweaver's Pattern Book: Over 120 Designs for Upholstery, Curtains, Place Mats, Etc. (Illus.). 16.50 (ISBN 0-8446-5909-6). Peter Smith.
Radcliffe, William. Origin of the New System of Manufacture Commonly Called Power Loom Weaving. LC 68-30541. Repr. of 1828 ed. 25.00x (ISBN 0-678-00877-9). Kelley.
Regensteiner, Else. Weaving Sourcebook: Ideas & Techniques. 1983. 26.95 (ISBN 0-442-27507-2). Van Nos Reinhold.
Sarff, Laura & Harem, Jan. Symmography: Linear Thread Design. LC 78-72190. (Illus.). 1979. 12.95 (ISBN 0-87192-104-9). Davis Mass.
Saunders, Virginia & Cronk, Elsie. Reweave It Yourself. 4th ed. LC 58-13832. 118p. 1981. Repr. of 1958 ed. 11.95 (ISBN 0-686-34357-3). Cronk.
Simmons, Paula. Spinning & Weaving with Wool. LC 77-76137. (Illus.). 224p. 1977. pap. 12.95 (ISBN 0-914718-23-1). Pacific Search.
Stevenson, George B. Weaving with Coconut Palm. (Illus.). 1970. pap. 1.95 (ISBN 0-916224-40-6). Banyan Bks.
Sutton, Ann, et al. The Craft of the Weaver. LC 82-24942. (Illus.). 152p. (Orig.). 1982. 18.50 (ISBN 0-937274-09-7); pap. 12.95 (ISBN 0-937274-10-0). Lark Bks.
Tidball, Harriet. The Double Weave, Plain & Patterned. LC 61-669. (Shuttle Craft Guild Monograph: No. 1). (Illus.). 34p. 1960. pap. 6.95 (ISBN 0-916658-01-5). HTH Pubs.
--Handwoven Specialties. LC 76-24003. (Shuttle Craft Guild Monograph: No. 11). (Illus.). 38p. 1964. pap. 6.95 (ISBN 0-916658-11-2). HTH Pubs.
--Peru: Textiles Unlimited. LC 76-24015. (Shuttle Craft Guild Monograph: Nos. 25-26). (Illus.). 82p. 1968. pap. 10.95 set (ISBN 0-916658-25-2). HTH Pubs.
--Peru: Textiles Unlimited, Part II. LC 76-24015. (Shuttle Craft Guild Monograph: No. 26). (Illus.). 46p. 1969. pap. 10.95 set (ISBN 0-916658-26-0). HTH Pubs.
--Summer & Winter. LC 76-24010. (Shuttle Craft Guild Monograph: No. 19). (Illus.). 58p. 1966. pap. 8.45 (ISBN 0-916658-19-8). HTH Pubs.
--Surface Interest: Textiles of Today. LC 61-2332. (Shuttle Craft Guild Monograph: No. 2). (Illus.). 22p. 1961. pap. 6.45 (ISBN 0-916658-02-3). HTH Pubs.
--Textile Structure & Analysis. LC 76-24008. (Shuttle Craft Guild Monograph: No. 18). (Illus.). 31p. 1966. pap. 6.95 (ISBN 0-916658-18-X). HTH Pubs.
--Two-Harness Textiles: The Loom-Controlled Weaves. LC 76-24011. (Shuttle Craft Guild Monograph: No. 20). (Illus.). 30p. 1967. pap. 7.45 (ISBN 0-916658-20-1). HTH Pubs.
--Two-Harness Textiles: The Open-Work Weaves. LC 76-24012. (Shuttle Craft Guild Monographs: No. 21). (Illus.). 34p. 1967. pap. 7.45 (ISBN 0-916658-21-X). HTH Pubs.
--Undulating Weft Effects. LC 76-24001. (Shuttle Craft Guild Monographs: No. 9). (Illus.). 25p. 1963. pap. 6.95 (ISBN 0-916658-09-0). HTH Pubs.
--Weaving Inkle Bands. LC 76-24016. (Shuttle Craft Guild Monograph: No. 27). (Illus.). 40p. 1969. pap. 8.45 (ISBN 0-916658-27-9). HTH Pubs.
Tomita, Jun & Tomita, Noriko. Japanese Ikat Weaving: The Techniques of Kasuri. 128p. 1982. pap. 8.50 (ISBN 0-7100-9043-9). Routledge & Kegan.
Twiss, T. Two Lectures on Machinery. (The Development of Industrial Society Ser.). 76p. 1971. Repr. of 1844 ed. 15.00x (ISBN 0-7165-1778-7, BBA 02145, Pub. by Irish Academic Pr Ireland). Biblio Dist.
Van Gelder, Lydia. Ikat. (Illus.). 1980. 19.50 (ISBN 0-8230-2530-6). Watson-Guptill.
Walker, Sandra R. Country Cloth to Coverlets: Textile Traditions in Nineteenth Century Central Pennsylvania. LC 81-39246. (Illus.). 64p. (Orig.). 1981. pap. 8.95 (ISBN 0-271-00290-5). Pa St U Pr.
Waller, Irene. Fine-Art Weaving. (Illus.). 144p. 1980. 26.50 (ISBN 0-7134-0412-4, Pub. by Batsford England). David & Charles.
Weaving & Associated Processes: The Lodz Textile Seminars. (Training for Industry Ser.). pap. 2.00 (ISBN 0-686-93270-6, UN70/2B6/4, UN). Unipub.
White, Bjorg K. Weaving Guide Lesotho. International Labour Office, ed. 124p. (Orig.). 1981. pap. 8.55 (ISBN 92-2-102488-1). Intl Labour Office.
Wilson, Jean. Jean Wilson's Soumak Workbook. LC 82-82244. (Illus.). 49p. 1982. 5.00 (ISBN 0-934026-09-2). Interweave.
Windeknecht, Margaret. Creative Overshot. enl. ed. (Shuttlecraft Guild Monograph: Vol. 31). (Illus.). 64p. 1978. pap. 9.45 (ISBN 0-916658-34-1). HTH Pubs.
Worst, Edward F. Weaving with Foot-Power Looms. LC 74-75270. (Illus.). 275p. 1974. pap. 6.95 (ISBN 0-486-23064-3). Dover.

WEBER FUNCTIONS

Ivanov. Quasilinear Degenerate & Nonuniformly Elliptic & Parabolic Equations of Second Order. (Proceedings of the Steklov Institute of Mathematics). 1983. write for info (ISBN 0-8218-3080-5). Am Math.

WEDGWOOD, JOSIAH, 1730-1795

Graham, John M., II & Wedgwood, Hensleigh C. Wedgwood. LC 71-128384. (Brooklyn Museum Publications in Reprint Ser.). (Illus.). 122p. Repr. of 1948 ed. 17.00 (ISBN 0-405-00878-3). Ayer Co Pubs.
Smiles, Samuel. Josiah Wedgewood. LC 71-141603. 1971. Repr. of 1894 ed. 43.00x (ISBN 0-8103-3617-0). Gale.
Tames, R. Josiah Wedgwood. (Clarendon Biography Ser.). 1973. pap. 3.50 (ISBN 0-912728-80-9). Newbury Bks.
Tames, Richard. An Illustrated Life of Josiah Wedgwood. (Illus.). 1972. pap. 3.50 (ISBN 0-685-53295-X). ARS Ceramica.
Wedgwood, Barbara & Wedgwood, Hensleigh. The Wedgwood Circle: 1730-1897; Four Generations of Wedgwoods & Their Friends. LC 80-65213. (Illus.). 408p. 1980. 22.50 (ISBN 0-89860-038-3). Eastview.

WEED CONTROL

see also Herbicides

Aldrich, R. J. Weed-Crop Ecology: Principles in Weed Management. text ed. write for info. (ISBN 0-534-02833-0). Wadsworth Pub.
Anderson, Wood P. Weed Science: Principles. 2nd ed. (Illus.). 650p. 1983. text ed. 37.95 (ISBN 0-314-69632-6). West Pub.
Beste, C. E. & Humburg, N. E. Herbicide Handbook of the Weed Science Society of America. rev., 5th ed. 664p. pap. 10.00 (ISBN 0-686-39882-3). Weed Sci Soc.
British Crop Protection Conference: Weeds, 1982, 3 Vols. 1064p. (Orig.). 1983. pap. 68.00 (ISBN 0-901436-73-9, Pub. by BCPC England). Intl Spec Bk.
British Weed Control Conference, Tenth, Vols. 1-3. 1970. 95.00x (ISBN 0-901436-18-6, Pub. by BCPC Pubns England). State Mutual Bk.
CAB Books, ed. British Crop Protection Conference: Weeds, 3 vols. 1976. Set. 125.00x (ISBN 0-901436-40-2, Pub. by CAB Bks England). State Mutual Bk.
California Weed Conference Staff. Principles of Weed Control in California. (Illus.). 500p. text ed. 29.95 (ISBN 0-913702-32-3). Thomson Pub Ca.
Canada Department of Agriculture Staff Belleville, Ontario. Biological Control Programmes Against Insects & Weeds in Canada, 1959-1968. 266p. 1971. 35.00x (ISBN 0-85198-018-X, Pub. by CAB Bks England). State Mutual Bk.
Chancellor, R. J. Garden Weeds & Their Control. 93p. 1981. 24.00x (ISBN 0-909605-21-1, Pub. by Richmond Pub England). State Mutual Bk.
Charudattan, R. & Walker, H. Lynn. Biological Control of Weeds with Plant Pathogens. LC 82-1879. 293p. 1982. 45.50x (ISBN 0-471-08598-7, Pub. by Wiley-Interscience). Wiley.
Crafts, Alden S. Modern Weed Control. LC 74-76383. (Illus.). 1975. 33.00x (ISBN 0-520-02733-7). U of Cal Pr.
Crop Loss Assessment Methods: FAO Manual on the Evaluation & Prevention of Losses by Pests, Diseases, & Weeds. (Illus.). 1976. looseleaf bdg. 16.80 (ISBN 0-685-67374-X, FAO); suppl. 1 4.80 (ISBN 0-685-67375-8). Unipub.
Del Fosse, E. S. Proceedings of the Fifth International Symposium on Biological Control of Weeds. 647p. 1981. pap. 90.00x (ISBN 0-643-02837-4, Pub. by CAB Bks England). State Mutual Bk.
Del Fosse, E. S., ed. Biological Control of Weeds. 648p. 1982. 60.00x (ISBN 0-643-02837-4, Pub. by CSIRO Australia). State Mutual Bk.
--Biological Control of Weeds, Fifth International Symposium. (Illus.). 649p. 1982. pap. 35.00 (ISBN 0-643-02837-4, Pub. by CSIRO). Intl Spec Bk.
Dunn, P. H. Proceedings of the Second International Symposium on Biological Control of Weeds. 220p. 1973. 40.00x (ISBN 0-85198-299-9, Pub. by CAB Bks England). State Mutual Bk.
Eleventh British Weed Control Conference, 3 vols. 1972. Set. 90.00x (ISBN 0-686-45818-4, Pub. by CAB Bks England). State Mutual Bk.
Eleventh British Weed Control Conference: Vol. 1, 2 & 3. 1972. Set. 95.00x (ISBN 0-901436-26-7, Pub. by BCPC Pubns England). State Mutual Bk.
Fryer. Weed Control Handbook, Vol. II. (Illus.). 1978. Vol. 2. 36.50 (ISBN 0-632-00219-0, B 1716-2, Blackwell). Mosby.
Fryer, J. D. & Matsunaka, Shoichi. Integrated Control of Weeds. 262p. 1977. (Pub. by Japan Sci Soc Japan). Intl Spec Bk.
Gangstad, E. O. Weed Control Methods for Recreation Facility Management. 312p. 1982. 84.50 (ISBN 0-8493-5330-0). CRC Pr.
Gupta, O. P. Aquatic Weeds: Their Menace & Control. (Illus.). 272p. 1979. 20.00 (ISBN 0-88065-096-6, Pub. by Messers Today & Tomorrows Printers & Publishers India). Scholarly Pubns.
Julien, M. H., ed. Biological Control of Weeds: A World Catalogue of Agents & Their Target Weeds. 108p. 1982. 50.00x (ISBN 0-85198-494-0, Pub. by CAB Bks England). State Mutual Bk.
Peng, S. Y. The Biology & Control of Weeds in Sugar Cane. (Developments in Crop Science Ser.: Vol. 4). 250p. 1984. 71.25 (ISBN 0-444-42133-5). Elsevier.
Radosevich, Steven R. & Holt, Jodie S. Weed Ecology: Implications for Vegetation Management. LC 83-23249. 265p. 1984. 39.95x (ISBN 0-471-87674-7, Pub. by Wiley-Interscience). Wiley.
Ridout, J. Water Weed Problems: Potential Utilisation & Control. 1980. 40.00x (ISBN 0-85135-112-3, Pub. by Centre Overseas Research). State Mutual Bk.
Roberts, H. Weed Control Handbook: Vol. 1, Principles, Nineteen Eighty-Two. 7th ed. 1983. 110.00x (ISBN 0-686-45049-3, Pub. by BCPC Pubns England). State Mutual Bk.
Rosenthal, Sara S., et al. Biological Methods of Weed Control. 80p. (Orig.). 1984. pap. 10.00 (ISBN 0-913702-26-9). Thomson Pub CA.
Simmonds, F. T., ed. Proceedings of the First International Symposium on Biological Control of Weeds, 1969. 110p. 1970. 40.00x (ISBN 0-85198-134-8, Pub. by CAB Bks England). State Mutual Bk.
Swarbrick, J. T. The Australian Weed Control Handbook. 342p. 1981. pap. 11.95x (ISBN 0-89955-364-8, Pub. by Ento Pr Australia). Intl Spec Bk.
Tenth British Weed Control Conference, 3 vols. 1970. Set. 90.00x (ISBN 0-901436-18-6, Pub. by CAB Bks England). State Mutual Bk.
Wapshere, A. J. Proceedings of the Third International Symposium on Biological Control of Weeds. 140p. 1974. 45.00x (ISBN 0-85198-307-3, Pub. by CAB Bks England). State Mutual Bk.
Weed Control. 2.25 (ISBN 0-686-21165-0). Bklyn Botanic.
Wilson, F. A Review of the Biological Control of Insects & Weeds in Australia & Australian New Guinea. 104p. 1960. cloth 30.00x (ISBN 0-85198-065-1, Pub. by CAB Bks England). State Mutual Bk.

WEEDS

see also Weed Control;
also names of weeds

Bare, Janet E. Wildflowers & Weeds of Kansas. LC 78-16862. (Illus.). 1979. 29.95 (ISBN 0-7006-0176-7). U Pr of KS.
Barkley, T. M. Field Guide to the Common Weeds of Kansas. LC 82-21914. (Illus.). 160p. 1983. 17.95x (ISBN 0-7006-0233-X); pap. 7.95 (ISBN 0-7006-0224-0). U Pr of KS.
BCPC Weeds, 1980, 3 vols. 997p. 1982. pap. text ed. 68.00x (ISBN 0-901436-63-1, Pub. by B C P C England); Set. pap. text ed. 68.00 (ISBN 0-901436-65-8). Intl Spec Bk.
Benson, Jacqueline M. Weeds in Tropical Crops: Review of Abstracts on Constraints in Production Caused by Weeds in Maize, Rice, Sorghum-Millet, Groundnuts, and Cassava, 1952-1980. (Plant Production & Protection Papers: No. 32, Suppl. 1). 68p. 1982. pap. 7.50 (ISBN 92-5-101206-7, F2333, FAO). Unipub.
British Crop Protection Conference: Weeds, 1978. 1089p. 1982. pap. text ed. 55.00x (ISBN 0-901436-53-4, Pub. by B C P C England). Intl Spec Bk.
Cocannouer, Joseph. Weeds: Guardians of the Soil. (Illus.). pap. 7.95 (ISBN 0-8159-7205-9). Devin.
De Bray, Lys. The Wild Garden. (Illus.). 1978. 19.95 (ISBN 0-8317-9430-5, Mayflower Bks). Smith Pubs.
Duke, Stephen O., ed. Weed Physiology, Vols. I & II. 480p. 1985. 57.00 (ISBN 0-8493-6313-6); 86.00 (ISBN 0-8493-6314-4). CRC Pr.
Embertson, Jane. Pods: Wildflowers & Weeds in Their Final Beauty. (Illus.). 1979. pap. 14.95 (ISBN 0-684-15543-5, ScribT). Scribner.
Fischer, Bill, et al. Growers Weed Identification Handbook. (Illus.). 199p. 1978. 55.00x (ISBN 0-931876-43-5, 4030). Ag & Nat Res.
Gangstad, Edward O., ed. Weed Control Methods for River Basin Management. 232p. 1978. 66.00 (ISBN 0-8493-5328-9). CRC Pr.
Gupta, O. P. & Lamba, P. S. Modern Weed Science. (Illus.). 325p. 1977. 25.00 (ISBN 0-88065-095-8, Pub. by Messers Today & Tomorrows Printers & Publishers India). Scholarly Pubns.
Harris, Ben C. Eat the Weeds. LC 73-83951. 176p. 1973. pap. 1.50 (ISBN 0-87983-066-2). Keats.
Haselwood, E. L. & Motter, G. G., eds. Handbook of Hawaiian Weeds. 2nd ed. LC 83-5911. (Illus.). 501p. 1983. pap. text ed. 17.50x (ISBN 0-8248-0885-1). UH Pr.
Holm, Leroy, et al. A Geographical Atlas of World Weeds. LC 78-24280. 394p. 1979. 53.50 (ISBN 0-471-04393-1, Pub. by Wiley-Interscience). Wiley.
Holzner, W. & Numata, M. Biology & Ecology of Weeds. 1982. 99.50 (ISBN 90-6193-682-9, Pub. by Junk Pubs Netherlands). Kluwer Academic.
Hunter, Peter J. Peter Hunter's Guide to Grasses, Clovers, & Weeds. (Illus.). 80p. pap. 7.50 (ISBN 0-938670-02-6). By Hand & Foot.
Julien, M. H., ed. Biological Control of Weeds: A World Catalogue of Agents & Their Target Weeds. 108p. 1982. 50.00x (ISBN 0-85198-494-0, Pub. by CAB Bks England). State Mutual Bk.
Klingman, Glenn C. & Ashton, Floyd M. Weed Science: Principles & Practices. 2nd ed. LC 82-2750. 449p. 1982. text ed. 26.50x (ISBN 0-471-08487-5, Pub. by Wiley-Interscience). Wiley.
Muenscher, Walter C. Weeds. 2nd ed. LC 79-48017. (Illus.). 560p. 1980. 39.95x (ISBN 0-8014-1266-8). Comstock.
Parker, Kittie F. An Illustrated Guide to Arizona Weeds. LC 72-75471. 338p. 1972. pap. 12.50 (ISBN 0-8165-0288-9). U of Ariz Pr.
Prentice, T. Merrill & Sargent, Elizabeth O. Weeds & Wildflowers of Eastern North America. 1973. 25.00 (ISBN 0-87577-063-0). Peabody Mus Salem.

Radosevich, Steven R. & Holt, Jodie S. Weed Ecology: Implications for Vegetation Management. LC 83-23249. 265p. 1984. 39.95x (ISBN 0-471-87674-7, Pub. by Wiley-Interscience). Wiley.

Riemer, Donald N. Introduction to Freshwater Vegetation. (Illus.). 1984. lib. bdg. 35.00 (ISBN 0-87055-448-4). AVI.

Ross, Merrill & Lembi, Carole. Applied Weed Science. (Illus.). 432p. 1985. text ed. write for info. (ISBN 0-8087-2958-6). Burgess.

Saunders. Edible & Useful Wild Plants of the United States & Canada. LC 75-46193. (Illus.). 320p. 1976. pap. 4.50 (ISBN 0-486-23310-3). Dover.

Smith, William. Wonders in Weeds. 187p. 1977. 13.00x (ISBN 0-8464-1062-1). Beekman Pubs.

Spencer, Edwin R. All about Weeds. LC 73-91485. (Illus.). 352p. 1974. pap. 5.95 (ISBN 0-486-23051-1). Dover.

U. S. Department of Agriculture, Agricultural Research Service. Common Weeds of the United States. (Illus.). 16.50 (ISBN 0-8446-0066-0). Peter Smith.

Williams, G. H. Elsevier's Dictionary of Weeds of Western Europe: Their Common Names & Importance. 320p. (In 13 Languages). 1982. 74.50 (ISBN 0-444-41978-0). Elsevier.

WEEVILS

see Beetles

WEIGHING MACHINES

see also Weights and Measures

Griffiths, E. H. Weighing Machines: Application of Electricity & Electronics to Weighting Machines, Vol. 3. 248p. 1970. 49.75x (ISBN 0-85264-160-5, Pub. by Griffin England). State Mutual Bk.

Metcalfe, T. J. Weighing Machines: Non-Self-Indicating Mechanisms, Vol. 1. 192p. 1969. 42.50x (ISBN 0-85264-095-1, Pub. by Griffin England). State Mutual Bk.

--Weighing Machines: Semi-Self-Indicating & Self-Indicating Mechanisms, Vol. 2. 178p. 1969. 44.95x (ISBN 0-686-68843-0, Pub. by Griffin England). State Mutual Bk.

Norden, K. Elis. Electronic Weighing in Industrial Processes. (Illus.). 290p. 1984. text ed. 55.00x (ISBN 0-246-12168-8, Pub. by Granada England). Sheridan.

WEIGHTLESSNESS

Benedikt, E. T., ed. Weightlessness: Physical Phenomena & Biological Effects. special vol ed. 1960. 20.00x (ISBN 0-87703-000-6, Pub. by Am Astronaut). Univelt Inc.

Gordon, Solon A. & Cohen, Melvin J., eds. Gravity & the Organism. LC 70-156302. pap. 121.00 (ISBN 0-317-20702-4, 2024116). Bks Demand UMI.

McCally, Michael, et al, eds. Hypodynamics & Hypogravics: The Physiology of Inactivity & Weightlessness. LC 68-18675. (Illus.). 1968. 63.00 (ISBN 0-12-482050-6). Acad Pr.

Moscovitz, Toni. In Pursuit of Purple: Porphyria. (Illus.). 1978. 20.00 (ISBN 0-916750-28-0). Dayton Labs.

Second Zero Gravity Symposium-Los Angeles-1963. Physical & Biological Phenomena in a Weightless State. (Advances in the Astronautical Sciences Ser.: Vol. 14). 1963. 30.00x (ISBN 0-87703-015-4, Pub. by Am Astronaut). Univelt Inc.

WEIGHTS AND MEASURES

see also Decimal System; Electric Measurements; Electric Standards; Gages; Gravity; Measuring Instruments; Mensuration; Metric System; Specific Gravity; Weighing Machines

also units of weight or measure

Adams, John Quincy. Report to Congress on Weights & Measures. LC 79-53271. Repr. of 1821 ed. 12.50x (ISBN 0-87081-084-7). Colo Assoc.

American Metric Journal Editors. Metric in a Nutshell. 2nd ed. Hopkins, Robert A., ed. LC 76-19477. 1977. 8.95 (ISBN 0-917240-06-5). Am Metric.

Arbuthnot, John. Tables of Ancient Coins, Weights & Measures: 1754 Edition. 1981. write for info. (ISBN 0-08-027640-7, HE 085); microfiche 35.00 (ISBN 0-686-79357-9). Pergamon.

Fulwood, Robinson, et al. Height & Weight of Adults Ages Eighteen to Seventy-Four Years by Socioeconomic & Geographic Variables: United States, 1971-74. (Ser. II: No. 224). 60p. 1981. pap. text ed. 1.95 (ISBN 0-8406-0221-9). Natl Ctr Health Stats.

Gerolde, Steven. Universal Conversion Factors. LC 71-164900. 276p. 1971. 19.95x (ISBN 0-87814-005-0). Pennwell Bks.

Huntar, Alexander. A Treatise of Weights, Mets & Measures of Scotland. LC 74-80191. (English Experience Ser.: No. 671). 58p. 1974. Repr. of 1624 ed. 8.00 (ISBN 90-221-0671-3). Walter J Johnson.

Kempf, Albert F. & Richards, Thomas J. The Metric System Made Simple. LC 75-36631. (Made Simple Ser.). 144p. 1977. 4.95 (ISBN 0-385-11032-4). Doubleday.

Kula, Witold. Measures & Men. Szreter, R., tr. 336p. 1985. text ed. 26.50 (ISBN 0-691-05446-0). Princeton U Pr.

Langer, Rudolph Ernest, ed. Frontiers of Numerical Mathematics: A Symposium Conducted by the Mathematics Research Center, United States Army & the National Bureau of Standards at the University of Wisconsin, Madison, Wisconsin, October 30 & 31, 1959. LC 60-60026. (U.S. Army Mathematical Research Center Publication Ser.: No. 4). pap. 36.00 (ISBN 0-317-08424-0, 2004656). Bks Demand UMI.

Managing Metrication in Business & Industry. 203p. 1976. 37.00 (ISBN 0-8247-6469-2); subscribers 31.00. Am Natl.

Metric Measure. (Tops Cards Ser.: No.6). 1978. pap. 8.80 (ISBN 0-941008-06-1). Tops Learning.

Metric Practice Guide - E380-84. 42p. 1984. pap. 5.00 (ISBN 0-8031-0750-1, 03-503809-41). ASTM.

Metrication: The Australian Experience. 210p. 1975. 4.00 (ISBN 0-686-70962-4); subscribers 3.00. Am Natl.

Rudman, Jack. Inspector of Markets, Weights, & Measures. (Career Examination Ser.: C-368). (Cloth bdg. avail. on request). pap. 10.00 (ISBN 0-8373-0368-0). Natl Learning.

--Senior Inspector of Markets, Weights & Measures. (Career Examination Ser.: C-2716). (Cloth bdg. avail. on request). pap. 12.00 (ISBN 0-8373-2716-4). Natl Learning.

--Supervising Inspector of Markets, Weights & Measures. (Career Examination Ser.: C-1047). (Cloth bdg. avail. on request). pap. 10.00 (ISBN 0-8373-1047-4). Natl Learning.

Sheppard, T. & Musham, J. F. Money Scales & Weights. 1977. 25.00 (ISBN 0-685-51562-1, Pub by Spink & Son England). S J Durst.

Sohns, Marvin L. & Buffington, Audrey V. The Measurement Book. (Illus.). 1977. pap. 9.95 (ISBN 0-933358-00-8). Enrich.

Think Metric. 1975. text ed. 3.15 wkbk. (ISBN 0-538-13110-1, M11). SW Pub.

Weighing. (Tops Cards Ser.: No. 5). 1978. pap. 8.30 (ISBN 0-941008-05-3). Tops Learning.

Young, James M. Measures. 16p. 1983. pap. text ed. 4.00 (ISBN 0-941150-11-9). Barth.

Zupko, Ronald E. Italian Weights & Measures from the Middle Ages to the Nineteenth Century. LC 80-70299. (Memoirs Ser.: Vol. 145). 1981. 12.00 (ISBN 0-87169-145-0). Am Philos.

WEIGHTS AND MEASURES–DICTIONARIES

Zupko, Ronald E. A Dictionary of English Weights & Measures: From Anglo-Saxon Times to the Nineteenth Century. LC 68-14038. pap. 60.00 (ISBN 0-317-08979-X, 2015376). Bks Demand UMI.

WEIGHTS AND MEASURES–HISTORY

Adams, John Q. Report of the Secretary of State Upon Weights & Measures: Prepared in Obedience to a Resolution of the House of Representatives of the Fourteenth of December, 1819. Cohen, I. Bernard, ed. LC 79-7945. (Three Centuries of Science in America Ser.). 1980. Repr. of 1821 ed. lib. bdg. 23.00x (ISBN 0-405-12526-7). Ayer Co Pubs.

Berriman, Algernon E. Historical Metrology. LC 70-91753. Repr. of 1953 ed. lib. bdg. 19.75x (ISBN 0-8371-2424-7, BEHM). Greenwood.

Jewell, Brian. Veteran Scales & Balances. 96p. 1981. 40.00x (ISBN 0-85936-081-4, Pub. by Midas Bks England). State Mutual Bk.

McClean, J. R. The Origin of Weight. (Illus.). 1979. pap. 5.00 (ISBN 0-916710-46-7). Obol Intl.

O'Brien, D. Theories of Weight in the Ancient World, Vol. I: Democritus Weight & Size. 419p. 1981. pap. text ed. 55.75x (ISBN 90-04-06132-0, Pub. by E J Brill Holland). Humanities.

Zupko, Ronald E. French Weights & Measures before the Revolution: A Dictionary of Provincial & Local Units. LC 78-3249. 256p. 1979. 25.00x (ISBN 0-253-32480-7). Ind U Pr.

WEIGHTS AND MEASURES–GREAT BRITAIN–HISTORY

Zupko, Ronald E. British Weights & Measures: A History from Antiquity to the Seventeenth Century. (Illus.). 266p. 1977. 30.00x (ISBN 0-299-07340-8, 734). U of Wis Pr.

WEIMARANERS (DOGS)

see Dogs–Breeds–Weimaraners

WEIRS

see also Dams

Ackers, P., et al. Weirs & Fumes for Flow Measurement. LC 78-317. 327p. 1978. cloth 91.95x (ISBN 0-471-99637-8, Pub. by Wiley-Interscience). Wiley.

WELDING

see also Electric Welding; Oxyacetylene Welding and Cutting; Solder and Soldering

also specific materials or objects, with or without the subdivision Welding

Acceptance Inspection, Module 28-7. (Welding Inspection Ser.). (Illus.). 40p. 1979. spiral bdg. 7.00x (ISBN 0-87683-111-0). G P Courseware.

Advances in Welding Processes (WI) AWP. 414p. 1978. 120.00 (ISBN 0-686-95639-7). Am Welding.

American Society for Metals Staff. Welding of HSLA Structural Steels: Proceedings of an International Conference. Rothwell, A. B. & Gray, Malcolm J., eds. LC 78-18220. (Materials Metalworking Technology Ser.). pap. 160.00 (ISBN 0-317-27699-9, 2019490). Bks Demand UMI.

American Welding Society. Certification Manual for Welding Inspectors: CM. 2nd ed. 329p. 1980. 35.00 (ISBN 0-87171-190-7); 26.25. Am Welding.

--Current Welding Processes: CWP-T. text ed. 16.00 (ISBN 0-685-65944-5, CWP-T); text ed. 12.00 members (ISBN 0-685-65945-3, CWP-M); CWP-M. members 4.00 (ISBN 0-685-65946-1, CWP-P); 159 slides 140.00; CWP-P. 105.00. Am Welding.

--Guide for the Nondestructive Inspection of Welds: B1.0. 22p. 1977. 10.00 (ISBN 0-686-43386-6); member 7.50. Am Welding.

--Handbook on the Ultrasonic Examination of Welds: VEW.(IIW) 44p. 1977. 32.00 (ISBN 0-686-43357-2); 24.00. Am Welding.

--Introductory Welding Metallurgy: IWM-T. 144p. 1968. text ed. 16.00 (ISBN 0-685-65950-X); instr's manual 4.00 (ISBN 0-685-65951-8, IWM-M); slides 140.00 (ISBN 0-685-65952-6, IWM-P); member 12.00. Am Welding.

--Metric Practice Guide for the Welding Industry: A1.1. 30p. 1980. 12.00 (ISBN 0-87171-194-X); member 9.00. Am Welding.

--Specification for Welding Rods & Covered Electrodes for Welding Cast Iron: A5.15. 10p. 1982. 10.00 (ISBN 0-87171-220-2); member 7.50. Am Welding.

--Standard Methods for Mechanical Testing of Welds: B4.0-77. 1977. 12.00 (ISBN 0-87171-117-6). Am Welding.

Aronson, Charles N. Positioneering. (Illus.). 347p. 1969. 20.00 (ISBN 0-915736-01-2). C N Aronson.

Autoweld, 11 papers. 1983. 38.50 (ISBN 0-317-07145-9, 794). SME.

AWS A2 Committee on Definitions & Symbols. Symbols for Welding & Nondestructive Testing: AWS A2.4-79. new ed. LC 78-74600. 80p. pap. text ed. 22.00 (ISBN 0-87171-170-2). Am Welding.

AWS Conference on Welding for the Aerospace Industry, October 1980. Welding Technology for the Aerospace Industry: Proceedings. (Welding Technology Ser.). 176p. 1981. 25.00 (ISBN 0-686-95643-5). Am Welding.

AWS Conference, 1979. Maintenance Welding in Nuclear Power Plants: Proceedings. 176p. 1980. 25.00 (ISBN 0-87171-191-5); member 18.75. Am Welding.

AWS Conference, 1980. Underwater Welding of Offshore Platforms & Pipelines, OPP: Proceedings. 189p. 1981. 25.00 (ISBN 0-87171-215-6). Am Welding.

AWS Pipeline Conference, 1980. Pipeline Welding & Inspection, PWI: Proceedings. 108p. 1980. 25.00 (ISBN 0-87171-199-0); member 18.75. Am Welding.

AWS Structural Welding Committee. Structural Welding Code-Reinforcing Steel: AWS D1-1. (Illus.). 1979. 15.00 (ISBN 0-87171-125-7). Am Welding.

Baird, Ronald J. Oxyacetylene Welding. LC 79-6555. (Illus.). 1980. pap. text ed. 7.00 (ISBN 0-87006-501-7). Goodheart.

Bakish, Robert & White, S. S. Handbook of Electron Beam Welding. LC 64-7538. (Wiley Series on the Science & Technology of Materials). pap. 69.80 (ISBN 0-317-08643-X, 2007398). Bks Demand UMI.

Bazergui, A. & Marchand, L. PVRC Milestone Gasket Tests: First Results. 1984. bulletin no. 292 14.00 (ISBN 0-318-01897-7). Welding Res Coun.

Bell, J., et al, eds. Welding Practices, 6 vols. Incl. Vol. 1. General Welding & Cutting; Vol. 2. Advanced Pipe & Tube Welding; Vol. 3. Tungsten Arc Gas Shielded Welding; Vol. 4. Metal Arc Gas Shielded Welding; Vol. 5. Manual Metal Arc Welding; Vol. 6. Oxy-Acetlene Welding. 1977. Set. 200.00x (ISBN 0-89563-037-0). Intl Ideas.

Bell, T. Surface Heat Treatment of Steel. (Pergamon Materials Engineering Practice Ser.). 250p. 1986. 30.01 (ISBN 0-08-026700-9); pap. 12.51 (ISBN 0-08-026699-1). Pergamon.

Bennett & Siy. Blueprint Reading for Welders. LC 76-29579. (Illus.). 180p. 1978. instructor's guide o.p. 5.00 (ISBN 0-8273-1060-9); charts 11.40wall (ISBN 0-8273-1063-3); transparencies 160.00 (ISBN 0-8273-1889-8). Delmar.

Bennett, A. E. & Siy, L. Blueprint Reading for Welders. 4th ed. LC 82-46005. 304p. 1983. text ed. 14.40 (ISBN 0-8273-2144-9); instructors guide 5.10 (ISBN 0-8273-2145-7). Delmar.

Bennett, A. E. & Sly, Louis J. Blueprint Reading for Welders. 3rd ed. 1983. 22.95 (ISBN 0-442-21358-1). Van Nos Reinhold.

Blazynski, T. Z., ed. Explosive Welding, Forming & Compaction. LC 82-22627. (Illus.). 402p. 1983. 72.25 (ISBN 0-85334-166-4, I-461-82, Pub. by Elsevier Applied Sci England). Elsevier.

Bongio, Enrico P. Principles of Industrial Welding. 1978. text ed. 6.50 (ISBN 0-686-24289-0); text ed. 5.85 (ISBN 0-686-26120-8). Lincoln Arc Weld.

Brainbridge, C. G. Teach Yourself Welding. (Teach Yourself Ser.). 192p. 1981. pap. 4.95 (ISBN 0-679-10495-X). McKay.

British Nuclear Energy Society, ed. Welding & Fabrication in the Nuclear Industry. 416p. 1979. 125.00x (ISBN 0-7277-0083-9, Pub. by Brit Nuclear England). State Mutual Bk.

Brumbaugh, James. Welders Guide. 3rd ed. LC 82-17797. 940p. 1983. 19.95 (ISBN 0-672-23374-6). Audel.

Carr, Richard & O'Con, Robert. Welding Practices & Procedures. (Illus.). 416p. 1983. text ed. 23.95 (ISBN 0-13-948059-5). P-H.

Cary, Howard B. Modern Welding Technology. LC 78-2966. (Illus.). 1979. 32.95 (ISBN 0-13-599290-7). P-H.

Chrysler Learning, Inc. Weldtech Series in Welding: Basic Gas Metal-Arc Welding. (Illus.). 128p. 1983. pap. text ed. 10.95 (ISBN 0-13-948075-7). P-H.

--Weldtech Series in Welding: Basic Shielded Metal-Arc Welding. 128p. 1983. pap. 10.95 (ISBN 0-13-948083-8). P-H.

--Weldtech Series in Welding: Oxyacetylene Welding, Cutting, & Brazing. (Illus.). 80p. 1983. pap. 10.95 (ISBN 0-13-948091-9). P-H.

Classification & Application of Welded Joints for Machinery & Equipment: D14.4. 74p. 1977. 22.00 (ISBN 0-87171-118-4); members 16.50. Am Welding.

Control of Distortion in Welded Fabrications (WI): DWF. 73p. 1976. 26.00 (ISBN 0-686-95600-1, DWF). Am Welding.

Crossland, Bernard. Explosive Welding of Metals & Its Applications. (Series on Advanced Manufacturing). (Illus.). 1982. 48.00x (ISBN 0-19-859119-5). Oxford U Pr.

David, S. A., ed. Trends in Welding Research. 1982. 67.00 (ISBN 0-87170-150-2). ASM.

Davies, A. C. The Science & Practice of Welding: Practice of Welding, Vol. 2. 8th ed. (Illus.). 350p. 1985. 49.50 (ISBN 0-521-26114-7); pap. 17.95 (ISBN 0-521-27840-6). Cambridge U Pr.

--The Science & Practice of Welding: Welding Science & Technology, Vol. 1. 8th ed. (Illus.). 320p. 1984. 39.50 (ISBN 0-521-26113-9); pap. 12.95 (ISBN 0-521-27839-2). Cambridge U Pr.

Davis, Charles A., ed. Welding & Brazing of Carbon Steels, 2 bks. LC 76-44372. (Metalworking & Manufacturing Processes Ser.). (Illus.). Bk. 1-Arc Welding. pap. 43.00 (ISBN 0-317-09871-3, 2019480); Bk. 2-High-Deposition-Rate & Special-Application Welding. pap. 34.80 (ISBN 0-317-09872-1). Bks Demand UMI.

Developments in Mechanized, Automated & Robotic Welding: Proceedings. 320p. 1981. 62.00 (ISBN 0-317-05231-4, Pub. by IFSPUBS). Scholium Intl.

Devletian, J. H. & Wood, W. E. Factors Affecting Porosity in Aluminum Welds: A Review. 1983. bulletin no. 290 12.00 (ISBN 0-318-01895-0). Welding Res Coun.

Dictionary of Welding. 762p. 1980. 60.00x (ISBN 0-569-08525-X, Pub. by Collet's). State Mutual Bk.

Din, tr. from Ger. Din Handbook: Welding I-Standards on Filler Metals, Manufacture, Quality & Testing, No. 8. 420p. 1983. pap. 76.00 (ISBN 3-41011-584-6, Pub. by DIN Germany). Heyden.

Din Standards for Welding Practice One: Standards for Filler Metals: Manufacture, Quality, Testing. 549.00 (ISBN 0-686-28164-0, 10047-7/08). Heyden.

Din Standards for Welding Practice Two: Standards for Equipment & Accessories for Autogenous Processes, Soldering, Thermal Cutting, Thermal Spraying & Safety at Work. 311.00 (ISBN 0-686-28193-4, 10828-7/65). Heyden.

Duckworth, Walter E. & Hoyle, G. Electro-Slag Refining. 1969. 30.00 (ISBN 0-412-09670-6, NO.6091, Pub. by Chapman & Hall). Methuen Inc.

Easterling, Ken. Introduction to the Physical Metallurgy of Welding. 208p. 1983. text ed. 59.95 (ISBN 0-408-01351-6); pap. text ed. 29.95 (ISBN 0-408-01352-4). Butterworth.

Edgin, Charles A. General Welding. LC 81-1882. 325p. 1982. pap. 18.95 (ISBN 0-471-08001-2); tchrs. manual avail. (ISBN 0-471-09188-X). Wiley.

Vance, F. R., et al. Wildflowers of the Northern Great Plains. rev. ed. Orig. Title: Wildflowers Across the Prairie. (Illus.). 336p. 1984. 29.50x (ISBN 0-8166-1350-8); pap. 14.95 (ISBN 0-8166-1351-6). U of Minn Pr.

Vincett, B. A. Wild Flowers of Central Saudi Arabia. 114p. 1977. 60.00x (ISBN 0-317-07184-X, Pub. by FW Classey UK). State Mutual Bk.

Voss, John & Eifert, Virginia S. Illinois Wild Flowers. 2nd ed. (Popular Science Ser.: Vol. III). (Illus.). 256p. 1978. pap. 5.00 (ISBN 0-89792-070-8). Ill St Museum.

WILD FLOWERS–AFRICA, SOUTH

Jackson, W. P. Wild Flowers of Table Mountain. 120p. 1981. 37.50x (ISBN 0-86978-146-4, Pub. by Timmins Africa). Intl Spec Bk.

Pearse, R. O. Mountain Splendour. (Illus.). 239p. 1981. 37.50x (ISBN 0-86978-156-1, Pub. by Timmins Africa). Intl Spec Bk.

Schuyler, Arlene A. Wildflowers South Florida Natives: Indentification & Habitat of Indigenous Tropical Flora. Hall, Charlotte & Oppenheimer, Richard, eds. LC 82-90756. (Illus.). 112p. (Orig.). 1982. pap. 5.95 (ISBN 0-910991-00-6). Facts FL.

WILD FLOWERS–AUSTRALIA

Blackall, W. E. & Grieve, B. J. How to Know Western Australian Wildflowers, Pt. IIIB: Epacridaceae-Lamiaceae. (Illus.). 45p. 1982. 39.00x (ISBN 0-85564-161-4, Pub. BY U of W Austral Pr). Intl Spec Bk.

Galbraith, Jean. Collins Field Guide to the Wild Flowers of South-East Australia. (Illus.). 450p. 1982. 13.95x (ISBN 0-00-219246-2, Pub. by W Collins Australia). Intl Spec Bk.

Grieve, B. J. & Blackall, W. E. How to Know Western Australian Wildflowers, Pt. 4. 1977. 37.95x (ISBN 0-85564-078-2, Pub. by U of W Austral Pr). Intl Spec Bk.

Grieve, B. J. & Blackall, W. E., eds. How to Know Western Australian Wildflowers: A Key to the Flore of the Flora of the Extratropical Regions of Western Australia, Pt. IIIA. 350p. 1980. 39.00x (ISBN 0-85564-160-6, Pub. by U of West Australia Pr Australia). Intl Spec Bk.

WILD FLOWERS–CANADA

Porsild, A. E. Rocky Mountain Wild Flowers. (Illus.). 1974. pap. 6.95 (ISBN 0-660-00073-3, 56495-9, Pub. by Natl Gallery Canada). U of Chicago Pr.

Soper, James H. & Szczawinski, Adam F. Mount Revelstoke National Park Wild Flowers. (Illus.). 1976. pap. 2.95x (ISBN 0-660-00003-2, 56429-0, Pub. by Natl Mus Canada). Nat Gal Can.

WILD FLOWERS–EUROPE

Blamey & Fitter. The Wild Flowers of Britain & Europe. pap. 13.95 (ISBN 0-00-219550-X, Pub. by Collins Pub England). Greene.

Fitter & Blamey. The Wild Flowers of Britain & Northern Europe. pap. 14.95 (ISBN 0-00-219069-9, Collins Pub England). Greene.

Polunin, Oleg. Flowers of Europe: A Field Guide. 1969. 55.00x (ISBN 0-19-217621-8). Oxford U Pr.

Schauer & Caspari. A Field Guide to the Wild Flowers of Britain & Europe. pap. 15.95 (ISBN 0-00-219257-8, Collins Pub England). Greene.

Strid, Arne. Wild Flowers of Mount Olympus. 1981. 135.00x (ISBN 0-686-97063-2, Pub. by Goulandris Greece). State Mutual Bk.

Underhill, J. E. Sagebrush Wildflowers. (Wildflower Ser.). 64p. Date not set. 4.95 (ISBN 0-88839-171-4). Hancock House.

WILD FLOWERS–GREAT BRITAIN

Blamey & Fitter. The Wild Flowers of Britain & Europe. pap. 13.95 (ISBN 0-00-219550-X, Pub. by Collins Pub England). Greene.

Fitter & Blamey. The Wild Flowers of Britain & Northern Europe. pap. 14.95 (ISBN 0-00-219069-9, Collins Pub England). Greene.

Galbraith. A Field Guide to the Wild Flowers of South-East Australia. 39.95 (ISBN 0-00-219246-2, Collins Pub England). Greene.

Hutchinson, John. British Wild Flowers, 2 vols. LC 72-6576. (Illus.). 947p. 1973. Set. 50.00 (ISBN 0-8386-1267-9); Vol. 2. PLB 25.00 (ISBN 0-8386-1268-7); 25.00 (ISBN 0-686-85946-4). Fairleigh Dickinson.

Schauer & Caspari. A Field Guide to the Wild Flowers of Britain & Europe. pap. 15.95 (ISBN 0-00-219257-8, Collins Pub England). Greene.

WILD FLOWERS–HAWAIIAN ISLANDS

Kuck, Loraine E. & Tongg, Richard C. Guide to Tropical & Semi-Tropical Flora. LC 58-7494. (Illus.). pap. 13.50 (ISBN 0-8048-0227-0). C E Tuttle.

--Hawaiian Flowers & Flowering Trees. LC 58-7494. (Illus.). 1958. boxed 19.50 (ISBN 0-8048-0237-8). C E Tuttle.

WILD FLOWERS–MEDITERRANEAN REGION

Polunin, Oleg & Huxley, Anthony. Flowers of the Mediterranean. LC 79-670242. (Illus.). 260p. 1979. 15.95 (ISBN 0-7011-1029-5, Pub. by Chatto & Windus); pap. 9.95 (ISBN 0-7011-2284-6). Merrimack Pub Cir.

WILD FLOWERS–NORTH AMERICA

Albertson, Alice O. Nantucket Wild Flowers. LC 73-80640. (Illus.). 1973. Repr. of 1921 ed. 10.00 (ISBN 0-913728-02-0). Theophrastus.

Arnberger, Leslie P. Flowers of the Southwest Mountains. 6th ed. Jackson, Earl, ed. LC 74-84444. (Popular Ser.: No. 7). 1974. pap. 7.50 (ISBN 0-911408-00-2). SW Pks Mnmts.

Audubon Society. The Audubon Society Field Guide to North American Wildflowers. Incl. Eastern Region. LC 78-20383. 13.50 (ISBN 0-394-50432-1); Western. LC 78-20384. 13.50 (ISBN 0-394-50431-3). (Illus.). 1979. Knopf.

Bare, Janet E. Wildflowers & Weeds of Kansas. LC 78-16862. (Illus.). 1979. 29.95 (ISBN 0-7006-0176-7). U Pr of KS.

Batson, Wade T. Wild Flowers in South Carolina. LC 64-23760. (Illus.). 146p. 1980. pap. 6.95 (ISBN 0-87249-257-5). U of SC Pr.

Brown, Clair A. Wildflowers of Louisiana & Its Adjoining States. LC 72-79327. (Illus.). xi, 248p. 1972. 20.00 (ISBN 0-8071-0232-6); pap. 8.95 (ISBN 0-8071-0780-8). La State U Pr.

Campbell, Carlos C., et al. Great Smoky Mountains Wildflowers. 4th ed. LC 77-126938. (Illus.). 112p. 1977. spiral bdg. 4.95 (ISBN 0-87049-124-5). U of Tenn Pr.

Clark, Lewis J. Wild Flowers of the Pacific Northwest: From Alaska to Northern California. Trelawny, John G., ed. (Illus.). 1976. 55.95 (ISBN 0-686-67594-0). Superior Pub.

Clements, F. E. & Clements, E. S. Rocky Mountain Flowers: An Illustrated Guide for Plant-Lovers & Plant-Users. 3rd ed. (Illus.). 1963. 17.95x (ISBN 0-02-842970-2). Hafner.

Common Wildflowers of the Grand Canyon. (Nature & Scenic Bks.). pap. 3.50 (ISBN 0-937512-00-1). Wheelwright UT.

Craighead, John J., et al. A Field Guide to Rocky Mountain Wildflowers. LC 63-7093. (Peterson Field Guide Ser.). 1974. 15.95 (ISBN 0-395-07578-5); pap. 10.95 (ISBN 0-395-18324-3). HM.

Dannen, Kent & Dannen, Donna. Rocky Mountain Wildflowers. LC 81-7439. (Illus.). 64p. (Orig.). 1981. pap. 2.95 (ISBN 0-9606768-0-5). Tundra Pubns.

De Bray, Lys. The Wild Garden. (Illus.). 1978. 19.95 (ISBN 0-8317-9430-5, Mayflower Bks). Smith Pubs.

Dormon, Caroline. Flowers Native to the Deep South. 1958. 15.00 (ISBN 0-87511-025-8). Claitors.

Duncan, Wilbur H. & Foote, Leonard E. Wildflowers of the Southeastern United States. LC 74-75940. (Illus.). 304p. 1975. 16.50 (ISBN 0-8203-0347-X). U of Ga Pr.

Dunes of Dare Garden Club. Wildflowers of the Outer Banks: Kitty Hawk to Hatteras. LC 79-18927. (Illus.). xvii, 165p. 1980. pap. 6.95 (ISBN 0-8078-4061-0). U of NC Pr.

Dwelley. Spring Wildflowers of New England. (Illus.). 1973. 10.95 (ISBN 0-89272-008-5). Down East.

--Summer & Fall Wildflowers of New England. (Illus.). 1975. 10.95 (ISBN 0-89272-020-4). Down East.

Ferris, Roxana S. Flowers of the Point Reyes National Seashore. (Illus.). 1970. pap. 4.95 (ISBN 0-520-01694-7). U of Cal Pr.

Fleming, Glenn, et al. Wild Flowers of Florida. LC 76-43050. (Illus.). 1976. pap. 6.95 (ISBN 0-916224-08-2). Banyan Bks.

Greene, Wilhelmina F. & Blomquist, Hugo L. Flowers of the South: Native & Exotic. xiv, 208p. 1953. 9.95 (ISBN 0-8078-0635-8). U of NC Pr.

Gupton, Oscar W. & Swope, Fred C. Wildflowers of the Shenandoah Valley & Blue Ridge Mountains. LC 78-21296. (Illus.). 1979. 10.95 (ISBN 0-8139-0814-0). U Pr of Va.

Harris, Stuart K., et al. AMC Field Guide to Mountain Flowers of New England. LC 64-54301. (Illus.). 188p. 1977. pap. 5.95 (ISBN 0-910146-12-8). Appalach Mtn.

Haskins, Leslie L. Wild Flowers of the Pacific Coast. (Illus.). 405p. 1977. pap. 6.95 (ISBN 0-486-23469-X). Dover.

Horn, Elizabeth L. Wildflowers Three, the Sierra Nevada. (Illus.). 1976. pap. 10.95 (ISBN 0-911518-40-1). Touchstone Pr Ore.

Jaeger, Edmund C. Desert Wild Flowers. rev. ed. LC 41-22485. (Illus.). 1941. 11.95 (ISBN 0-8047-0364-7); pap. 6.95 (ISBN 0-8047-0365-5, SP81). Stanford U Pr.

Justice, William S. & Bell, C. Ritchie. Wild Flowers of North Carolina. LC 68-18051. xxviii, 217p. 1968. 14.95 (ISBN 0-8078-1064-9). U of NC Pr.

Keator, Glenn. Sierra Flower Finder: A Guide to Sierra Nevada Wildflowers. (Illus.). 1980. pap. 3.00 (ISBN 0-912550-09-0). Nature Study.

Larrison, Earl J., et al. Washington Wildflowers. LC 73-94499. (Trailside Ser.). (Illus.). 1977. pap. 9.95 (ISBN 0-914516-02-7). Seattle Audubon Soc.

Laurence, Jeanne. An Album of Alaskan Wildflowers. LC 74-75662. (Illus.). 225p. 1974. 50.00 (ISBN 0-87564-011-7). Superior Pub.

Lommasson, Robert C. Nebraska Wild Flowers. LC 70-188343. (Illus.). x, 229p. 1973. 16.50x (ISBN 0-8032-0816-2); pap. 10.50 (ISBN 0-8032-5768-6, BB 559, Bison). U of Nebr Pr.

McGrath, Anne. Wildflowers of the Adirondacks. 1981. softcover 9.95 (ISBN 0-932052-27-4). North Country.

McHoul, Lilian. Wild Flowers of Marin: A Layman's Handbook. LC 79-51455. (Illus.). 1979. pap. 4.95 (ISBN 0-912908-08-4). Tamal Land.

Mackenzie, Katherine. Wild Flowers of the Midwest. LC 75-44840. (Illus.). 1976. pap. 2.95 (ISBN 0-912766-33-6). Tundra Bks.

--Wild Flowers of the Northeast. LC 75-44841. (Illus.). 1976. pap. 2.95 (ISBN 0-912766-32-8). Tundra Bks.

--Wild Flowers of the South. (Illus.). 1977. pap. 2.95 (ISBN 0-912766-56-5). Tundra Bks.

Monserud, Wilma & Ownbey, Gerald B. Common Wild Flowers of Minnesota. LC 72-161439. (Illus.). 1971. 12.95 (ISBN 0-8166-0609-9). U of Minn Pr.

Moyle, John B. & Moyle, Evelyn W. Northland Wild Flowers. LC 76-55173. (Illus.). 1977. 19.50x (ISBN 0-8166-0806-7). U of Minn Pr.

--Northland Wild Flowers: A Guide for the Minnesota Region. (Illus.). x, 236p. 1984. pap. 12.95 (ISBN 0-8166-1355-9). U of Minn Pr.

Munz, Philip A. California Desert Wildflowers. (Illus., Orig.). 1962. pap. 5.95 (ISBN 0-520-00899-5). U of Cal Pr.

--California Mountain Wildflowers. (Orig.). 1963. pap. 4.95 (ISBN 0-520-00901-0). U of Cal Pr.

--California Spring Wildflowers: From the Base of the Sierra Nevada & Southern Mountains to the Sea. (Orig.). 1961. pap. 4.95 (ISBN 0-520-00896-0). U of Cal Pr.

--Shore Wildflowers of California, Oregon, & Washington. (Illus., Orig.). 1965. pap. 5.95 (ISBN 0-520-00903-7). U of Cal Pr.

Newcomb, Lawrence. Newcomb's Wildflower Guide: An Ingenious New Key System for Quick Positive Field Identification of the Wildflowers, Flowering Shrubs & Vines of Northeastern & North-Central North America. (Illus.). 1977. 18.45i (ISBN 0-316-60441-0). Little.

Niehaus, Theodore F. A Field Guide to Pacific States Wildflowers. (Peterson Field Guide Ser.). (Illus.). 432p. 1976. 16.95 (ISBN 0-395-21624-9). HM.

--Sierra Wildflowers: Mt. Lassen to Kern Canyon. (California Natural History Guides). (Illus., Orig.). 1974. 14.95x (ISBN 0-520-02742-6); pap. 6.95 (ISBN 0-520-02506-7). U of Cal Pr.

North American Wildflowers. (National Audubon Society Collection Nature Ser.). 96p. 1984. 5.98 (ISBN 0-517-44740-1, Bonanza). Outlet Bk Co.

Owensby, Clenton E. Kansas Prairie Wildflowers. (Illus.). 1980. text ed. 15.00 (ISBN 0-8138-0850-2); pap. text ed. 8.50 (ISBN 0-8138-1160-0). Iowa St U Pr.

Parker, Lucile. Mississippi Wildflowers. LC 80-20433. (Illus.). 144p. 1981. 29.95 (ISBN 0-88289-165-0). Pelican.

Parker, Richard. Wildflowers. LC 81-51068. (Illus.). 128p. (Orig.). 1985. pap. 5.95 (ISBN 0-89317-034-8). Windward Pub.

Parsons, Mary E. The Wild Flowers of California. (Illus.). 423p. Repr. of 1897 ed. 10.00 (ISBN 0-940228-06-8). Calif Acad Sci.

--Wild Flowers of California. Ferris, Roxana S., ed. 1966. pap. 6.95 (ISBN 0-486-21678-0). Dover.

--Wild Flowers of California. (Illus.). 14.50 (ISBN 0-8446-2708-9). Peter Smith.

Prentice, T. Merrill & Sargent, Elizabeth O. Weeds & Wildflowers of Eastern North America. 1973. 25.00 (ISBN 0-87577-063-0). Peabody Mus Salem.

Rickett, Theresa C. Wild Flowers of Missouri. 2nd ed. LC 54-62702. 1954. pap. 4.00x (ISBN 0-8262-0587-9). U of Mo Pr.

Sharples, Ada W. Alaska Wild Flowers. (Illus.). 1938. 6.95 (ISBN 0-8047-0358-2). Stanford U Pr.

Sharsmith, Helen K. Spring Wildflowers of the San Francisco Bay Region. (California Natural History Guides: No. 11). (Illus.). 1965. 14.95x (ISBN 0-520-03098-2); pap. 5.95 (ISBN 0-520-01168-6). U of Cal Pr.

Smith, Arlo I. A Guide to Wildflowers of the Mid-South: West Tennessee into Central Arkansas & South Through Alabama & into East Texas. LC 79-89883. (Illus.). 1980. 19.95 (ISBN 0-87870-076-5). Memphis St Univ.

Smith, Helen V. Michigan Wildflowers. LC 66-19039. (Bulletin Ser.: No. 42). 1966. 15.00x (ISBN 0-87737-019-2). Cranbrook.

The Spotter's Handbook to Wildflowers, Trees & Birds or North America. LC 79-10397. (Spotter's Guides). (Illus.). 1980. 5.95 (ISBN 0-8317-7953-5, Mayflower Bks); pap. 3.95 (ISBN 0-8317-7954-3). Smith Pubs.

Taylor & Douglas. Mountain Wild Flowers of the Pacific Northwest. LC 73-89237. (Illus.). 1975. 12.50 (ISBN 0-8323-0230-9). Binford.

Taylor, Ronald & Valum, Rolf. Wildflowers Two: Sagebrush Country. (Illus.). pap. 12.95 (ISBN 0-911518-26-6). Touchstone Pr Ore.

Taylor, Ronald J. Rocky Mountain Wildflowers. (Illus.). 104p. 1982. pap. 8.95 (ISBN 0-89886-066-0). Mountaineers.

Watts, May T. Flower Finder: A Manual for Identifying Spring Wildflowers & Flower Families East of Rockies. 1955. pap. 1.50 (ISBN 0-912550-00-7). Nature Study.

Wharton, Mary E. & Barbour, Roger W. A Guide to the Wildflowers & Ferns of Kentucky. LC 79-132833. (Illus.). 352p. 1971. 16.00 (ISBN 0-8131-1234-6). U Pr of Ky.

Wildflowers of the Monterey Area of California. (Nature & Scenic Bks.). pap. 3.50 (ISBN 0-937512-03-6). Wheelwright UT.

Wildflowers of the Wasatch & Uinta Mountains: Utah. (Nature & Scenic Bks.). pap. 3.95 (ISBN 0-937512-04-4). Wheelwright UT.

Wildflowers of Yellowstone & Grand Teton National Parks. (Nature & Scenic Bks.). pap. 3.95 (ISBN 0-937512-05-2). Wheelwright UT.

Wiley, Leonard. Rare Wild Flowers of North America. rev. 2nd ed. LC 73-80863. 1969. 15.00 (ISBN 0-911742-02-6); limited ed. 15.00 (ISBN 0-911742-00-X). L Wiley.

Young, Dorothy K. Wildflowers of the Redwood Empire. 3rd rev ed. LC 76-12996. Orig. Title: Redwood Empire, Wildflower Jewels. (Illus.). 108p. (Orig.). 1976. o.p 9.95 (ISBN 0-87961-053-0); pap. 4.95 (ISBN 0-87961-052-2). Naturegraph.

WILD-FOWL

see Game and Game-Birds; Water-Birds

WILD LIFE CONSERVATION

see Wildlife Conservation

WILD LIFE REFUGES

see Wildlife Refuges

WILD TURKEY

see Turkeys

WILDFLOWERS

see Wild Flowers

WILDLIFE CONSERVATION

see also Birds, Protection Of; Wildlife Management

Bailey, James A., et al, eds. Readings in Wildlife Conservation. LC 74-28405. (Illus.). 722p. (Orig.). 1974. pap. 10.00 (ISBN 0-933564-02-3). Wildlife Soc.

Barker, Elliott S. Smokey Bear & the Great Wilderness. LC 82-19373. (Illus.). 150p. (Orig.). 1982. pap. 12.95 (ISBN 0-86534-017-X). Sunstone Pr.

Benneward, Patrice, ed. From Outrage to Action: The Story of the National Audubon Society. (Illus., Orig.). 1982. pap. avail. (ISBN 0-930698-15-0). Natl Audubon.

Blouch, Ralph I. & Blouch, Ralph I., eds. International Association of Fish & Wildlife Agencies 69th Convention: Proceedings. (Orig.). 1980. 11.00 (ISBN 0-932108-04-0). IAFWA.

Bryant, Alan. Second Chance: The Story of the New Quay Hospital. (Illus.). 208p. 1982. 11.95 (ISBN 0-312-70828-9). St Martin.

Bryant, Jeannette, ed. Conservation Directory 1980. 25th rev. ed. LC 70-10646. 290p. 1980. 4.00 (ISBN 0-912186-34-8). Natl Wildlife.

Burton, Robert. Wildlife in Danger. LC 83-50393. (Silver Burdett Color Library). 48p. 1983. 14.00 (ISBN 0-382-06730-4). Silver.

Carson, Rachel. Silent Spring. (Illus.). 1962. 16.95 (ISBN 0-395-07506-8). HM.

Case, Marshall T. Look What I Found: The Young Conservationist's Guide to the Care & Feeding of Small Wildlife. 95p. 1983. pap. 9.95 (ISBN 0-8159-6119-7). Devin.

Connery, Robert H. Governmental Problems in Wild Life Conservation. LC 68-58560. (Columbia University Studies in the Social Sciences: No. 411). Repr. of 1935 ed. 20.00 (ISBN 0-404-51411-1). AMS Pr.

Convention on International Trade in Endangered Species of Wild Fauna & Flora, Geneva, 1977. Special Working Session of the Conference Parties (CITES) Proceedings. 271p. 1978. pap. 22.50 (ISBN 0-686-74017-3, CIT001, IUCN). Unipub.

Craighead, John J. & Craighead, Frank C., Jr. Hawks, Owls, & Wildlife. (Illus.). 16.00 (ISBN 0-8446-0562-X). Peter Smith.

A Design Guide for Wildlife Protection & Conservation for Transportation Facilities. 1976. pap. 3.00 (ISBN 0-686-20957-5, GWP-1). AASHTO.

Ecology & Management of Wild Grazing Animals in Temperate Zones. (Illus.). 1960. pap. 20.00 (ISBN 2-88032-016-X, IUCN34, IUCN). Unipub.

De Renzo, D. J., ed. Wind Power: Recent Developments. LC 79-14069. (Energy Technology Review Ser.: No. 46). (Illus.). 347p. 1979. 36.00 (ISBN 0-8155-0759-3). Noyes.

Development Planning & Research Associates, Inc., for U. S. Dept. of Agri., Manhattan, Kansas. Wind Energy Applications in Agriculture. 204p. 1982. pap. 29.50x (ISBN 0-89934-172-1, W064). Solar Energy Info.

Finlayson, A. N. International Wind Energy Symposium. 1982. 60.00 (I00153). ASME.

Flavin, Christopher. Wind Energy: A Turning Point. LC 81-52516. (Worldwatch Papers). 1981. pap. 2.00 (ISBN 0-916468-44-5). Worldwatch Inst.

Gipe, Paul. Wind Energy: How to Use It. 416p. 1983. pap. 16.95 (ISBN 0-8117-2273-2). Stackpole.

Golding, E. W. The Generation of Electricity by Wind Power. Rev. ed. 1976. 25.00x (ISBN 0-419-11070-4, NO. 6127, Pub. by E & FN Spon). Methuen Inc.

Griffith, S. K., et al. Wind Energy Systems: Export Market Potential. LC 83-51687. 308p. (Orig.). 1984. pap. 125.00 (ISBN 0-88016-011-X). Windbks.

Hiester, T. R. & Pennell, W. T. Siting Handbook for Large Wind Energy Systems. Orig. Title: Meteorological Aspects of Siting Large Wind Turbines. (Illus.). 510p. (Orig.). 1983. pap. 59.50 (ISBN 0-88016-004-7). Windbks.

Hinrichsen, E. N. Control of Large Wind Turbine Generators Connected to Utility Networks. 96p. 1984. pap. 22.00 (ISBN 0-88016-033-0). Windbks.

Holmes, J. D., et al, eds. Wind Engineering 1983: Proceedings of the 6th International Conference on Wind Engineering, Gold Coast, Australia, March 21-25 & Auckland, New Zealand, April 6-7, 1983, 3 vols. (Studies in Wind Engineering & Industrial Aerodynamics: Vol. 3). 1400p. 1984. Repr. Set. 296.50 (ISBN 0-444-42344-3, I-246-84). Elsevier.

Inglis, David R. Wind Power & Other Energy Options. LC 78-9102. (Illus.). 1978. 16.00 (ISBN 0-472-09303-7); pap. 9.95 (ISBN 0-472-06303-0). U of Mich Pr.

J. E. Minardi & M.O. Lawson of University of Dayton Research Institute for SERI, Operated by U. S. Department of Energy. Research on an Electrofluid Dynamic Wind Energy System. 60p. 1985. pap. 10.95 (ISBN 0-317-18860-7, W-069). Solar Energy Info.

Jarass, L., et al. Wind Energy. (Illus.). 209p. 1981. 48.00 (ISBN 0-387-10362-7). Springer-Verlag.

JBF Scientific Corporation. Small Wind Energy Systems Market Analysis. 375p. 1984. pap. 65.00 (ISBN 0-88016-013-6). Windbks.

Johnson, Gary L. Wind Energy Systems. (Illus.). 400p. 1985. text ed. 34.95 (ISBN 0-13-957754-8). P-H.

Justus, C. G. Winds & Wind System Performance. LC 77-18602. (Solar Ser.). (Illus.). 1978. pap. 4.50 (ISBN 0-89168-006-3). L Erlbaum Assocs.

Katzman, Martin T. Solar & Wind Energy: An Economic Evaluation of Current & Future Technologies. LC 83-23044. 212p. 1984. 38.50x (ISBN 0-86598-152-3). Rowman & Allanheld.

Koeppl, Gerald W. Putnam's Power from the Wind. 2nd ed. 400p. 1981. 27.50 (ISBN 0-442-23299-3). Van Nos Reinhold.

Le Gourieres, D. Wind Power Plants: Theory & Design. 300p. 1982. 55.00 (ISBN 0-08-029966-0); pap. 28.00 (ISBN 0-08-029967-9). Pergamon.

Linscott, Bradford S. Large, Horizontal-Axis Wind Turbines. 68p. 1984. pap. 7.95X (W067). Solar Energy Info.

Lornell, R. & Schaller, D. A. Wind Energy & Small Power Production. (Small Power Production & Wind Energy Ser.). 65p. 1984. pap. 25.00 (ISBN 0-88016-032-2). Windbks.

McGuigan, Dermot. Harnessing the Wind for Home Energy. LC 77-17916. (Illus.). 1978. lib. bdg. 9.95 o. p. (ISBN 0-88266-118-3); pap. 6.95 (ISBN 0-88266-117-5). Garden Way Pub.

March, Frederick, et al. Wind Power for the Electric-Utility Industry: Policy Incentives for Fuel Conservation. LC 81-48267. (An Arthur D. Little Bk.). 176p. 1982. 23.00x (ISBN 0-669-05321-X). Lexington Bks.

Marier, Donald & Stoiaken, Larry. Alternative Sources of Energy: Coming On Line, 12th Anniversary Issue - Hydropower, No. 62, July-Aug. 83. Incl. Alternative Sources of Energy: Community Energy Strategies 1981, No. 49, May - June 81. ASEI Magazine Staff. 60p. (Orig.). 1981. pap. 3.50 (ISBN 0-917328-39-6); Alternative Sources of Energy: Creative Cooling, No. 56, July - Aug. 83. Chandra, Subrato & Hay, Harold. 52p. (Orig.). 1982. pap. 3.50 (ISBN 0-917328-46-9); Alternative Sources of Energy: Energy Conserving Housing Techniques, No. 51, Sept. - Oct. 81. Campbell, et al. Marier, Donald & Stoiaken, Larry, eds. 54p. 1981. pap. 3.50 (ISBN 0-917328-43-4); Alternative Sources of Energy: Greenhouses, 1982, No. 54, Mar - Apr. 82. Marier, Donald. 56p. (Orig.). pap. 3.50 (ISBN 0-917328-44-2). 54p. (Orig.). 1983. pap. 3.50 (ISBN 0-917328-52-3). ASEI.

--Alternative Sources of Energy: Photovoltaics-A Technology Whose Time Has Come, No. 60, Mar.-Apr. 83. 44p. (Orig.). 1983. pap. 3.50 (ISBN 0-917328-50-7). ASEI.

Marier, Donald & Wallace, Dan. Wind Power for the Homeowner: A Guide to Selecting, Siting, & Installing an Electricity-Generating Wind Power System. (Illus.). 384p. 1981. 16.95 (ISBN 0-87857-334-8); pap. 12.95 (ISBN 0-87857-350-X). Rodale Pr Inc.

Marier, Donald & Stoiaken, Larry, eds. Alternative Sources of Energy: Windpower, No. 69. 64p. 1984. pap. 4.25 (ISBN 0-917328-59-0). ASEI.

Melaragno, Michele G. Wind in Architectural & Environmental Design. 512p. 1981. 38.50 (ISBN 0-442-25130-0). Van Nos Reinhold.

Meteorological Aspects of the Utilization of Wind as an Energy Source. (Technical Note Ser.: No. 175). (Illus.). 180p. 1981. pap. 36.00 (ISBN 92-63-10575-8, W504, WMO). Unipub.

Moment, Roger L. Wind Energy Systems Performance & Size Estimating. (Illus.). 63p. 1984. pap. 19.00 (ISBN 0-88016-044-6). Windbks.

Musgrove, Peter J., ed. Wind Energy Conversion 1983: Proceedings of the Fifth BWEA Wind Energy Conference. LC 83-20878. 384p. 1984. 62.50 (ISBN 0-521-26250-X). Cambridge U Pr.

--Wind Energy Conversion, 1984. (Illus.). 460p. 1985. 59.50 (ISBN 0-521-26899-0). Cambridge U Pr.

Naar, John. The New Wind Power. LC 81-15894. (Illus.). 1982. pap. 12.95 (ISBN 0-14-005985-7). Penguin.

National Rural Electric Cooperative Association, ed. Wind Energy in Rural United States. 320p. 1984. pap. 40.00 (ISBN 0-88016-030-6). Windbks.

Pacific Northwest Laboratory. Siting Guide for Large Wind Turbines. 508p. 1982. pap. 49.50x (ISBN 0-89934-161-6). Solar Energy Info.

--Wind Energy Resource Atlas, 12 vols. 1982. Set. pap. 260.00x (ISBN 0-89934-152-7, W-058). Solar Energy Info.

--Wind Energy Resource Atlas: Alaska, Vol. 10. 182p. 1981. pap. 29.95x (ISBN 0-89934-138-1, W052). Solar Energy Info.

--Wind Energy Resource Atlas: Hawaii & U. S. Pacific Trust Territories, Vol. 11. 112p. 1981. pap. 19.95x (ISBN 0-89934-139-X, W053). Solar Energy Info.

--Wind Energy Resource Atlas: Puerto Rico & U. S. Virgin Islands, Vol. 12. 83p. 19.95x (ISBN 0-89934-140-3, W054). Solar Energy Info.

--Wind Energy Resource Atlas: The Great Lakes Region (Illinois, Indiana, Michigan, Ohio, & Wisconsin, Vol. 3. 186p. 1981. pap. 29.95x (ISBN 0-89934-131-4, W045). Solar Energy Info.

--Wind Energy Resource Atlas: The North Central Region (Iowa, Minnesota, Nebraska, North Dakota, South Dakota, Vol. 2. 188p. 1981. pap. 29.95x (ISBN 0-89934-130-6, W044). Solar Energy Info.

--Wind Energy Resource Atlas: The Northeast Region (Connecticut, Maine, Massachusetts, New Hampshire, New Jersey, New York, Pennsylvania, Rhode Island, Vermont, Vol. 4. 215p. 1981. pap. 34.95x (ISBN 0-89934-132-2, W046). Solar Energy Info.

--Wind Energy Resource Atlas: The Northwest Region (Idaho, Montana, Oregon, Washington, Wyoming, Vol. 1. 193p. 1981. pap. 29.95x (ISBN 0-89934-129-2, W043). Solar Energy Info.

--Wind Energy Resource Atlas: The South Central Region (Arkansas, Kansas, Louisiana, Missouri, Oklahoma, & Texas, Vol. 7. 222p. 1981. pap. 34.50x (ISBN 0-89934-135-7, W049). Solar Energy Info.

--Wind Energy Resource Atlas: The Southeast Region (Alabama, Florida, Georgia, Mississippi, South Carolina, Vol. 6. 183p. 1981. pap. 29.95x (ISBN 0-89934-134-9, W048). Solar Energy Info.

--Wind Energy Resource Atlas: The Southwest Region (California & Nevada, Vol. 9. 132p. 1981. pap. 19.95x (ISBN 0-89934-137-3, W051). Solar Energy Info.

--Wind Energy Resource Atlas: The Southern Rocky Mountain Region (Arizona, Colorado, New Mexico, Utah, Vol. 8. 180p. 1981. pap. 29.95x (ISBN 0-89934-136-5, W050). Solar Energy Info.

Park, Gerald L., et al. Planning Manual for Utility Application of Large Wind Energy Conversion Systems. 243p. (Orig.). 1983. pap. 49.50 (ISBN 0-88016-005-5). Windbks.

Park, Jack. The Wind Power Book. LC 81-128. (Illus.). 1981. 21.95 (ISBN 0-917352-05-X); pap. 14.95 (ISBN 0-917352-06-8). Cheshire.

Program of Policy Studies in Science & Technology, for National Science Foun. Legal-Institutional Implications of Wind Energy Conversion Systems (WECS) 320p. 1982. pap. 34.50x (ISBN 0-89934-170-5, W061). Solar Energy Info.

Ramsdell, J. V. & Wetzel, J. S. Wind Measurement Systems & Wind Tunnel Evaluation of Selected Instruments. 70p. 1983. pap. 12.00 (ISBN 0-88016-006-3). Windbks.

Randall, P., ed. Wind Power Bibliography. 1980. 36.00 (ISBN 0-85296-463-3). Inst Elect Eng.

Raytheon Service Co. for U. S. Department of Energy. Wind Energy Systems Program Summary Nineteen Eighty. 230p. 1981. pap. 24.50x (ISBN 0-89934-108-X, W-040). Solar Energy Info.

Rocky Flats Wind Energy Research Center Staff, ed. Small Wind Turbines Systems Conference, 1981. 439p. 1984. pap. 85.00 (ISBN 0-88016-048-9). Windbks.

Sandia National Laboratory. Field Test Report of the Department of Energy's 100KW Vertical Axis Wind Turbine. 60p. 1985. pap. 14.95 (ISBN 0-317-18861-5, W-070). Solar Energy Info.

Schlueter, R. A., et al. Wind Turbine Arrays & Power Systems Operation. 1984. pap. 49.50 (ISBN 0-88016-020-9). Windbks.

Seiler, Farrell, ed. Wind Energy Systems: North America, Vol. 1 (of 4 vol. set) (Illus.). 516p. 1986. pap. 125.00 (ISBN 0-88016-022-5). Windbks.

Seiler, Farrell S. Wind Energy Abstracts, 1983, Pt. I. LC 84-51152. (Wind Energy Abstract Ser.: one of four vol. set). 100p. 1984. pap. 72.50 (ISBN 0-88016-016-0). Windbks.

--Wind Energy Systems: Europe, Asia, Africa, Latin America & Australia, Vol. 2 (of 4 vol. set) (Illus.). 516p. 1986. 125.00 (ISBN 0-88016-023-3). Windbks.

Seiler, Farrell S., ed. Megawatt Wind Turbines. LC 84-51179. (Wind Energy Systems Ser.: Vol. 4 (of 4 vol. set). (Illus.). 300p. 1986. pap. 125.00 (ISBN 0-88016-025-X). Windbks.

--Wind Energy Abstracts, 1983, Pt. II. LC 84-51152. (Wind Energy Abstract Ser.: one of four vol. set). 100p. 1984. pap. 72.50 (ISBN 0-88016-017-9). Windbks.

--Wind Energy Abstracts, 1984, Pt. I. LC 84-51152. (Wind Energy Abstracts Ser.: one of four vol. set). 100p. 1984. pap. 72.50 (ISBN 0-88016-027-6). Windbks.

--Wind Energy Systems, 4 Vols. (Illus.). 1732p. 1984. Set. pap. 380.00 (ISBN 0-88016-021-7). Windbks.

--Windmills & Windpumps. LC 84-51179. (Wind Energy Systems Ser.: Vol. 3 (of 4 vol. set)). (Illus.). 400p. 1986. pap. 125.00 (ISBN 0-88016-024-1). Windbks.

Sherman, J. M., et al. Wind Systems Life Cycle Cost Analysis: A Description & Users Manual. 88p. (Orig.). 1984. pap. 19.95 (ISBN 0-88016-019-5). Windbks.

Sites for Wind-Power Installations. (Technical Note Ser.: No. 63). 1964. pap. 5.00 (ISBN 0-685-22340-X, W30, WMO). Unipub.

The Spec Guide: Energy Products Specifications for Conservation, Solar Wind & Photovoltaics. 7th ed. (Illus.). 1985. 49.00 (ISBN 0-317-17142-9). SolarVision.

Spera, David, ed. Wind Turbine Technology: Horizontal Axis Megawatt Wind Energy Systems. (Illus.). 450p. 1984. pap. 85.00 (ISBN 0-88016-043-8). Windbks.

State of Florida, Govornor's Energy Office. Renewable Energy: Energy from the Wind. 1985. pap. 3.95 (W-071). Solar Energy Info.

Stephens, H. S. & Stapleton, C. A., eds. Papers Presented at the Third International Symposium on Wind Energy Systems. (Illus.). 579p. 1980. pap. 87.00x (ISBN 0-906085-47-0). BHRA Fluid.

Stoiaken, Larry & Marier, Don. Alternative Sources of Energy-Wind Power, No.66. 60p. (Orig.). 1984. pap. 4.25 (ISBN 0-917328-56-6). ASEI.

Stoiaken, Larry & Marier, Donald, eds. Alternative Sources of Energy-Wind Power, No. 72, Mar.-Apr. 85. 76p. (Orig.). pap. 4.25 (ISBN 0-917328-62-0). ASEI.

Sullivan, George. Wind Power for Your Home. 1978. 4.95 (ISBN 0-346-12316-X). Cornerstone.

Survey Research Laboratory Univ. of Illinois for National Science Foundation & U. S. Dept. of Energy. Public Reactions to Wind Energy Devices. 203p. 1982. pap. 29.50x (ISBN 0-89934-169-1, W062). Solar Energy Info.

Symposium on Wind Energy, 1st. Proceedings. 1977. 58.00x (ISBN 0-686-71055-X). BHRA Fluid.

Symposium on Wind Energy, 3rd. Proceedings. 1980. pap. 87.00x (ISBN 0-906085-47-0). BHRA Fluid.

Torrey, Volta. Wind-Catchers: American Windmills of Yesterday & Tomorrow. LC 76-13816. (Illus.). 240p. (Orig.). 1981. pap. 9.95 (ISBN 0-8289-0438-3). Greene.

Twidell, John, ed. Guidebook for Small Wind-Energy Conversion Systems. 200p. Date not set. price not set (ISBN 0-521-26898-2). Cambridge U Pr.

Uhran, Mark. Wind Energy for the Northeast. (Illus.). 208p. (Orig.). 1982. pap. 7.95 (ISBN 0-933614-14-4). Peregrine Pr.

U. S. Department of Energy. Applications Study for Wind Energy Systems at Federal Facilities, Final Report. 91p. Date not set. pap. 12.95 (ISBN 0-317-20241-3, W-072). Solar Energy Info.

--Federal Market for Wind Energy Systems. 110p. pap. 35.00 (ISBN 0-88016-015-2). Windbks.

U. S. Dept. of Energy. Home Wind Power. rev. ed. LC 81-2799. (Illus.). 208p. 1981. pap. 10.95 (ISBN 0-88266-252-X). Garden Way Pub.

Vance, Mary. Windmills & Wind Power: A Bibliography. (Architecture Ser.: Bibliography A-518). 59p. 1981. pap. 9.00 (ISBN 0-88066-105-4). Vance Biblios.

Vosburgh, Paul N. Commercial Applications of Wind Power. 272p. 1983. 24.95 (ISBN 0-442-29036-5). Van Nos Reinhold.

Wade, J. E. & Hewson, E. W. Wind Power Prospecting: A Guide to Biological Indicators. 110p. 1984. pap. 21.50 (ISBN 0-88016-018-7). Windbks.

Wade, J. E., et al. Wind Power Potential: A Prospector's Handbook of Remote Sensing Techniques. 329p. (Orig.). 1984. pap. text ed. 65.00 (ISBN 0-88016-034-9). Windbks.

Wegley, Harry L., et al. Siting Handbook for Small Wind Energy Conversion Systems. rev. ed. (Illus.). 100p. 1982. pap. 8.95 (ISBN 0-88016-003-9). Windbks.

Wind Energy. LC 78-4314. (Solar Ser.). (Illus.). 1978. pap. text ed. 3.00 (ISBN 0-89168-004-7). L Erlbaum Assocs.

Wind Energy Source Book. cancelled (ISBN 0-442-23357-4). Van Nos Reinhold.

Wind Energy Systems, 2nd International Symposium. Proceedings, 2 vols. Stephens, H. S. & Fantom, I., eds. (Illus.). 1979. Set. pap. text ed. 69.00x (ISBN 0-906085-03-9, Dist. by Air Science Co.). BHRA Fluid.

Wind Energy Technology Division. Federal Wind Energy Program Five Year Research Plan, 1985-1990 (Draft Version) 65p. 1984. pap. 14.95 (W068). Solar Energy Info.

Wind Power. LC 81-86271. (Fun with Science Ser.). 12.68 (ISBN 0-382-06628-6). Silver.

Wind Power: A Turning Point. (Worldwatch Institute Papers: No. 45). 55p. 1981. pap. 2.95 (ISBN 0-916468-44-5, WW45, WW). Unipub.

Wind Turbine Technology: Vertical Axis Wind Energy Systems. (Illus.). 1984. pap. 65.00 (ISBN 0-88016-007-1). Windbks.

Wind Workshop V: Biennial Wind Energy Conference & Workshop, 1981, 3 Vols. (Illus.). 1500p. 1984. Set. pap. 155.00 (ISBN 0-88016-036-5). Windbks.

Wind Workshop V: Biennial Wind Energy Conference & Workshop, 1981, Vol. 1. (Illus.). 550p. 1984. pap. 55.00 (ISBN 0-88016-037-3). Windbks.

Wind Workshop V: Biennial Wind Energy Conference & Workshop, 1981, Vol. 2. (Illus.). 730p. 1984. pap. 73.00 (ISBN 0-88016-038-1). Windbks.

Wind Workshop V: Biennial Wind Energy Conference & Workshop, 1981, Vol. 3. (Illus.). 330p. 1984. pap. 33.00 (ISBN 0-88016-039-X). Windbks.

Wind Workshop VI: Biennial Wind Energy Conference & Workshop, 1983, 1 Vol. (Illus.). 900p. 1984. Set. pap. 155.00p.n.s. (ISBN 0-88016-040-3). Windbks.

Wind Workshop VII: Biennial Wind Energy Conferences & Workshop, 1985. 1986. pap. 85.00 (ISBN 0-88016-041-1). Windbks.

WIND PRESSURE

Eaton, K. J. & Eaton, K. J., eds. Proceedings of International Conference on Wind Effects on Buildings & Structures: Heathrow Nineteen Seventy-Five. LC 75-2730. 650p. 1976. 125.00 (ISBN 0-521-20801-7). Cambridge U Pr.

International Research Seminar on Wind Effects on Buildings & Structures. Wind Effects on Buildings & Structures: Proceedings of the International Research Seminar, Ottawa, Canada, 11-15, September, 1967, 2 vols. LC 76-358270. Vol. 1. pap. 160.00 (ISBN 0-317-10749-6, 2019449); Vol. 2. pap. 117.30 (ISBN 0-317-10750-X). Bks Demand UMI.

Kinsman, Blair. Wind Waves. LC 83-20616. (Earth Sciences Ser.). 676p. 1984. pap. 13.50 (ISBN 0-486-64652-1). Dover.

Macdonald, Argus J. Wind Loading on Buildings. LC 75-11988. 219p. 1975. 39.95x (ISBN 0-470-55976-4). Halsted Pr.

McKenzie, Alexander A. World Record Wind: Measuring Gusts of 231 Miles an Hour. (Illus.). 36p. (Orig.). 1984. pap. 2.00 (ISBN 0-9613227-0-5). A A McKenzie.

Sachs, P. Wind Forces in Engineering. 2nd ed. 1978. 67.00 (ISBN 0-08-021299-9). Pergamon.

WIND TUNNELS

see also Aerodynamics

Pope, Alan & Goin, Kenneth L. High-Speed Wind Tunnel Testing. LC 78-15823. 486p. 1978. Repr. of 1965 ed. lib. bdg. 29.50 (ISBN 0-88275-727-X). Krieger.

Pope, Alan & Pope, Alan, Jr. Low-Speed Wind Tunnel Testing. 2nd ed. LC 84-3700. 1750p. 1984. text ed. 52.95x (ISBN 0-471-87402-7, Pub. by Wiley Interscience). Wiley.

Reinhold, Timothy A., ed. Wind Tunnel Modeling for Civil Engineering Applications. LC 82-14594. (Illus.). 704p. 1982. 65.00 (ISBN 0-521-25278-4). Cambridge U Pr.

WINDMILLS

see also Air-Turbines; Wind Power

Brangwyn, Frank & Preston, Hayter. Windmills. LC 70-176821. (Illus.). 126p. 1975. Repr. of 1923 ed. 43.00x (ISBN 0-8103-4077-1). Gale.

Brunnarius, Martin. The Windmills of Sussex. 1979. 39.00x (ISBN 0-85033-345-8, Pub. by Phillimore England). State Mutual Bk.

Fraenkel, Peter. Food from Windmills. (Illus.). 75p. (Orig.). 1975. pap. 4.50x (ISBN 0-903031-25-6, Pub. by Intermediate Tech England). Intermediate Tech.

Hays, Dick & Allen, Bill. Windmills & Pumps of the Southwest. (Illus.). 120p. 1983. pap. 7.95 (ISBN 0-89015-394-9). Eakin Pubns.

Mann, R. D. How to Build a "Cretan Sail" Windpump. (Illus.). 79p. (Orig.). 1983. pap. 9.75x (ISBN 0-903031-66-3, Pub. by Intermediate Tech England). Intermediate Tech.

Moon, Nigel. The Windmills of Leicestershire & Rutland. 1982. 90.00x (ISBN 0-905837-09-6, Pub. by Sycamore Pr England). State Mutual Bk.

Powell, F. E. Windmills & Wind Motors. 1985. pap. 4.95 (ISBN 0-917914-27-9). Lindsay Pubns.

Seiler, Farrell S., ed. Windmills & Windpumps. LC 84-51179. (Wind Energy Systems Ser.: Vol. 3 (of 4 vol. set)). (Illus.). 400p. 1986. pap. 125.00 (ISBN 0-88016-024-1). Windbks.

Shillingford, A. E. England's Vanishing Windmills. 1981. 40.00x (ISBN 0-906223-15-6). State Mutual Bk.

Wailes, Rex. Windmills & Watermills. 112p. 1981. 40.00x (ISBN 0-7063-6093-1, Pub. by Ward Lock Ed England). State Mutual Bk.

Wind Power Publishing & Cohen, Paul. The Investor's Guide for Purchasing a Windmill: The Paul Cohen Windmill Study. Hunker, Tracy, ed. 206p. 1984. 85.00 (W-066). Solar Energy Info.

WINDOWS

see also Glass

Doolin, James H. Window Units. 39p. 1982. pap. 15.00 (ISBN 0-914626-08-6). Doolco Inc.

Doors & Windows. LC 78-1384. (Home Repair & Improvement Ser.). (Illus.). 1978. lib. bdg. 15.94 (ISBN 0-8094-2407-X). Time-Life.

Gottlieb, Carla. The Window As a Symbol in Western Painting: From Divinity to Doubt. LC 80-53355. (Illus.). 550p. 1985. 100.00 (ISBN 0-9604420-1-4); pap. 75.00 (ISBN 0-9604420-2-2). Boian Bks.

Jensen, Tom. Skylights: The Definitive Guide to Planning, Installing & Maintaining Skylights & Natural Light Systems. LC 83-3089. (Illus.). 112p. (Orig.). 1983. lib. bdg. 19.80 (ISBN 0-89471-195-4); pap. 9.95 (ISBN 0-89471-194-6). Running Pr.

Sunset Editors. Windows & Skylights. LC 81-82871. (Illus.). 112p. (Orig.). 1982. pap. 5.95 (ISBN 0-376-01751-1, Sunset Bks). Sunset-Lane.

Talbot, Antony, ed. Handbook of Doormaking, Windowmaking & Staircasing. LC 79-91389. (A Home Craftsman Bk.). (Illus.). 256p. 1980. pap. 8.95 (ISBN 0-8069-8896-7). Sterling.

Time-Life Books. Doors & Windows. (Home Repair & Improvement). (Illus.). 1978. 11.95 (ISBN 0-8094-2406-1). Time-Life.

Turner, D. P. Window Glass Design Guide. (Illus.). 1977. 16.00 (ISBN 0-89397-028-X). Nichols Pub.

Wild, Suzanne W. & Wild, Rolf H. Windows You Can Build: To Save Energy & Money. LC 83-50933. (Illus.). 103p. (Orig.). 1983. pap. 5.95 (ISBN 0-914291-01-7). Thurau Pr.

Williams, T. Jeff. How to Install & Replace Doors & Windows. Smith, Sally W., ed. LC 83-62650. (Illus.). 96p. (Orig.). 1984. pap. 5.95 (ISBN 0-89721-023-9). Ortho.

Window & Wall Testing - STP 552. 75p. 1974. pap. 6.25 (ISBN 0-8031-0600-9, 04-552000-10). ASTM.

WINDS

see also Hurricanes; Jet Stream; Monsoons; Solar Wind; Storms; Tornadoes; Typhoons; Wind Pressure

Beaufort Scale of Wind Force: Technical & Operational Aspects. (Reports on Marine Science Affairs: No. 3). (Eng. & Fr.). 22p. 1970. pap. 5.00 (ISBN 0-685-02469-5, W269, WMO). Unipub.

Cermak, Jack E. Applications of Fluid Mechanics to Wind Engineering: Presented at the Winter Annual Meeting of ASME, New York, N. Y. November 17-21, 1974. pap. 20.00 (ISBN 0-317-08137-3, 2016871). Bks Demand UMI.

Effects of Winds & of Barometric Pressures on the Great Lakes. LC 22-19. (Carnegie Institution of Washington. Publication No.317). pap. 39.00 (ISBN 0-317-08556-5, 2007879). Bks Demand UMI.

Houghton, E. L. & Carruthers, N. B. Wind Forces on Buildings & Structures: An Introduction. 243p. 1976. 34.95x (ISBN 0-470-15147-1). Halsted Pr.

Ishizaki, Hatsuo & Chiu, Arthur, eds. Wind Effects on Structures. LC 76-45584. 320p. 1976. text ed. 40.00x (ISBN 0-8248-0523-2). UH Pr.

Lahey, James F., et al. Atlas of Five Hundred Mb Wind Characteristics for the Northern Hemisphere. 96p. 1958. wired bdg. 50.00x (ISBN 0-299-01703-6). U of Wis Pr.

--Atlas of Three Hundred Mb Wind Characteristics for the Northern Hemisphere. 128p. 1960. wired bdg. 50.00x (ISBN 0-299-01963-2). U of Wis Pr.

Lawson, T. V. Wind Effects on Buildings: Vol. 1, Design Applicatons. (Illus.). xii, 344p. 1980. 55.00x (ISBN 0-85334-887-1). Burgess-Intl Ideas.

--Wind Effects on Buildings: Vol. 2, Statistics & Meteorology. (Illus.). xii, 160p. 1980. 30.00x (ISBN 0-85334-893-6). Burgess-Intl Ideas.

Marier, Donald & DeWinkle, Carl. Alternative Sources of Energy: Wind-Photovoltaics, No. 58. 48p. (Orig.). 1982. pap. 3.50 (ISBN 0-917328-48-5). ASEI.

Michigan University Greenland Expeditions 1926-1933. Reports of the Greenland Expeditions of the University of Michigan, 2 vols. LC 68-55203. (Illus.). 1968. Repr. of 1941 ed. Set. lib. bdg. 55.00x (ISBN 0-8371-3850-7, MUGE). Greenwood.

Minikin, R. R. Winds, Waves, & Maritime Structures. 295p. 1963. 75.00x (ISBN 0-85264-091-9, Pub. by Griffin England). State Mutual Bk.

Palz, W. & Schnell, W. Wind Energy. 1983. lib. bdg. 32.50 (ISBN 90-2771-603-X, Pub. by Reidel Holland). Kluwer Academic.

Proctor, Lan. Sailing Strategy: Wind & Current. 3rd ed. (Illus.). 188p. 1977. 17.95x (ISBN 0-8464-1271-3). Beekman Pubs.

Rowlandson, L. G. & Schwarz, J. S. Radio Refractivity & Meteorological Data Plots from Radiosonde Launches Trade Winds: March 1969. LC 77-135079. 242p. 1970. 29.00 (ISBN 0-403-04534-7). Scholarly.

Schwarz, Jerald. Description of Computer Programs for the Analysis & Presentation of Trade Winds Data. LC 76-135092. 152p. 1969. 19.00 (ISBN 0-403-04537-1). Scholarly.

Simiu, Emil & Scanlan, Robert H. Wind Effects on Structures: An Introduction to Wind Engineering. LC 77-21192. 458p. 1978. 48.50x (ISBN 0-471-02175-X, Pub. by Wiley-Interscience). Wiley.

WINE AND WINE MAKING

see also Burgundy (Wine); Champagne (Wine); Claret; Fermentation; Port Wine; Sherry; Viticulture

Abel, Dominick. Guide to the Wines of the United States. 1979. 3.95 (ISBN 0-346-12427-1). Cornerstone.

Amerine, M. A. & Ough, C. S. Methods for Analysis of Musts & Wines. LC 79-17791. 341p. 1980. 56.00x (ISBN 0-471-05077-6, Pub. by Wiley-Interscience). Wiley.

Amerine, M. A., et al. Technology of Wine Making. 4th ed. (Illus.). 1980. text ed. 52.50 (ISBN 0-87055-333-X). AVI.

Amerine, Maynard A. & Joslyn, M. A. Table Wines: The Technology of Their Production. 2nd ed. LC 69-12471. (Illus.). 1970. 35.00 (ISBN 0-520-01657-2). U of Cal Pr.

Amerine, Maynard A., ed. Wine Production Technology in the United States. LC 80-28041. (Symposium Ser.: No. 145). 1981. 34.95 (ISBN 0-8412-0596-5); pap. 19.95 (ISBN 0-8412-0602-3). Am Chemical.

Anderson, Stanley F. & Hull, Raymond. Art of Making Wine. 1971. pap. 4.50 (ISBN 0-8015-0390-6, 0437-130, Hawthorn). Dutton.

Asher, Gerald. On Wine. 1982. 15.95 (ISBN 0-394-52737-2). Random.

Beer & Wine Industry. (UNIDO Guides to Information Sources: No. 25). pap. 4.00 (ISBN 0-686-93201-3, UN190, UN). Unipub.

Benson, Jeffrey & MacKenzie, Alastair. Sauternes: A Study of the Great Sweet Wines of Bordeaux. (Illus.). 172p. 1979. 26.00 (ISBN 0-85667-062-6, Pub. by Sotheby Pubns England). Biblio Dist.

Bernstein, Leonard S. The Official Guide to Wine Snobbery. LC 81-18707. 180p. 1982. 10.95 (ISBN 0-688-00807-0). Morrow.

Bone, Arther. How to Book of Choosing & Enjoying Wine. (How to Bks.). (Illus.). 96p. (Orig.). 1981. pap. text ed. 3.95 (ISBN 0-8069-9688-9, Pub. by Blandford Pr England). Sterling.

Braunig, M. Wine Service Procedures. 1974. 19.95 (ISBN 0-911202-20-X). Radio City.

Brennan, John M., ed. Buying Guide to California Wines. 3rd ed. (Illus.). 1985. 30.00 (ISBN 0-916040-53-4). Wine Consul Calif.

Broadbent, Michael. Michael Broadbent's Pocket Guide to Wine Tasting. (Illus.). 1982. 6.95 (ISBN 0-671-45235-5). S&S.

California Wine List Panel. A Consumer's Guide to One Hundred Sixty-One Jug Wines. Holzgang, David, ed. (California Wine List Ser.). 60p. (Orig.). 1981. pap. 4.95 (ISBN 0-932664-18-0). Wine Appreciation.

--Guide to One Hundred Twenty Chardonnays. Holzgang, David, ed. (California Wine List Ser.). 60p. 1981. pap. 4.95 (ISBN 0-932664-15-6). Wine Appreciation.

--Guide to One Hundred Twenty-Five Zinfandels. Holzgang, David, ed. (California Wine List Ser.). 60p. 1980. pap. 4.95 (ISBN 0-932664-16-4). Wine Appreciation.

Carosso, Vincent P. The California Wine Industry: A Study of the Formative Years, 1830-1895. (California Library Reprint Ser.). 1976. 32.00x (ISBN 0-520-03178-4). U of Cal Pr.

Church, Ruth E. Wines of the Midwest. LC 77-83753. (Illus.). vii, 248p. 1982. cloth 21.95 (ISBN 0-8040-0779-9, 82-75828, Pub by Swallow); pap. 9.95 (ISBN 0-8040-0426-9, 82-75836, Pub by Swallow). Ohio U Pr.

Cooper, Rosalind. The Wine Book. (Illus.). 1981. pap. 7.95 (ISBN 0-89586-131-3). H P Bks.

Dekovic, Gene. This Blessed Land. LC 80-84495. (Illus.). 112p. 1982. 12.95 (ISBN 0-937088-00-5). Illum Pr.

Fegan, Patrick W. Vineyards & Wineries of America: A Traveler's Guide. LC 82-15806. 1982. pap. 9.95 (ISBN 0-8289-0489-8). Greene.

Fingerhut, Bruce M. & Haskin, Steve. Read That Label: How to Tell What's Inside a Wine Bottle from What's on the Outside. (Illus.). 128p. (Orig.). 1983. pap. 4.95 (ISBN 0-89651-652-0). Icarus.

Foster, Charles. Home Winemaking. (Illus.). 128p. 1975. pap. 7.95x (ISBN 0-8464-0488-5). Beekman Pubs.

Gohdes, Clarence. Scuppernong: North Carolina's Grape & Its Wines. LC 81-9873. (Illus.). 125p. 1982. 14.95 (ISBN 0-8223-0460-0). Duke.

Grace, Virginia R. Amphoras & the Ancient Wine Trade. (Excavations of the Athenian Agora Picture Bks.: No. 6). (Illus.). 1979. pap. 1.50x (ISBN 0-87661-619-8). Am Sch Athens.

Guide to One Hundred Twenty-Five Cabernet Sauvignons: California Wine List Ser. 60p. pap. 4.95 (ISBN 0-932664-23-7). Wine Appreciation.

Haimo, Oscar. Cocktail & Wine Digest: The Barmen's Bible. 39th, new ed. (Illus.). 1979. Eng. & Span. eds. 6.00x (ISBN 0-686-17283-3); deluxe ed. 9.50x Eng. only (ISBN 0-686-17284-1). Haimo.

Hall, James J. & Bunton, John. Wines. 7.50x (ISBN 0-392-06157-0, LTB). Sportshelf.

Halliday, James. Wines & Wineries of New South Wales. 165p. 1981. text ed. 10.95x (ISBN 0-7022-1570-8). U of Queensland Pr.

Hardwick, Homer. Winemaking at Home. rev. ed. LC 68-13032. (Funk & W Bk.). (Illus.). 1970. 12.45i (ISBN 0-308-70206-9). T Y Crowell.

Haszonics, J. J. & Barratt, S. Wine Merchandising. (Illus.). 19.95 (ISBN 0-911202-19-6). Radio City.

Heckmann, Manfred. Corkscrews: An Introduction to Their Appreciation. Sullivan, Maurice, ed. (Illus.). 124p. 1981. 12.95 (ISBN 0-686-69566-6). Wine Appreciation.

Hill, Kenneth. Wine & Beermaking at Home. LC 75-40968. (Illus.). 116p. 1976. 9.95 (ISBN 0-87523-185-3). Emerson.

Hobson, Phyllis. Making Your Own Wine, Beer, & Soft Drinks. (Country Skills Library). (Illus.). 60p. 1975. pap. 2.95 (ISBN 0-88266-063-2). Garden Way Pub.

Howard & Gibat. Making Wine, Beer & Merry. Rev. ed. 178p. 1978. pap. 3.00 (ISBN 0-686-35948-8). Rutan Pub.

Hunderfund, Richard. Wines, Spirits & Fermentations. (Illus.). 192p. (Orig.). 1983. pap. 10.95. Star Pub CA.

Jagendorf, Moritz. Folk Wines, Cordials & Brandies: How to Make Them, along with the Pleasures of Their Lore. LC 63-21854. (Illus.). 1963. 17.50 (ISBN 0-8149-0125-5). Vanguard.

Johanns, Barbara B. Country Winemaking. (Illus.). 1982. pap. 6.95 (ISBN 0-914598-07-4). Padre Prods.

Johnson, Hugh. Hugh Johnson's Modern Encyclopedia of Wine. LC 82-3203. (Illus.). 544p. 1983. 29.95 (ISBN 0-671-45134-0). S&S.

--World Atlas of Wine. 1981. 59.00x (ISBN 0-686-78792-7, Pub. by RHS Ent England). State Mutual Bk.

Kafka, Barbara. American Food & California Wine. Topkis, Gladys, ed. LC 81-68837. (Great American Cooking Schools Ser.). (Illus.). 84p. 1981. pap. 5.95 (ISBN 0-941034-00-3). I Chalmers.

Kaufman, William I. California Wine Drinks. Sullivan, M. T., ed. 128p. pap. 4.95 (ISBN 0-932664-19-9). Wine Appreciation.

--Pocket Encyclopedia of California Wine. 158p. 1982. pap. 4.95 (ISBN 0-932664-22-9). Wine Appreciation.

Leverett, Brian. Basic Winemaking. 1982. 17.00x (ISBN 0-905868-10-2, Pub. by Gavin Pr). State Mutual Bk.

McCall, Peter. Diabetic Brewing & Winemaking. 84p. Date not set. pap. 3.95 (ISBN 0-900841-60-5, Pub. by Aztex Corp). Argus Bks.

McIllnay, Annabelle. Making Wine at Home. (Illus.). 160p. 1974. 6.95 (ISBN 0-8065-0442-0). Citadel Pr.

Mackey, Muriel H. Country Winemaking & Wine Cookery. (Illus.). 144p. 1982. 14.95 (ISBN 0-7153-8368-X). David & Charles.

Michaels, Marjorie. Stay Healthy with Wine: Natural Cures & Beauty Secrets from the Vineyards. 256p. 1981. 11.95 (ISBN 0-385-27168-9, Dial). Doubleday.

Morse, Roger A. Making Mead (Honey Wine) History, Recipes, Methods. (Illus.). 128p. 9.95 (ISBN 0-684-17330-1, ScribT). Scribner.

Nury, F. S. & Fugelsang, K. C. The Winemaker's Guide: Essential Information for Winemaking from Grapes or Other Fruits. 2nd ed. LC 78-65264. (Illus.). 1982. pap. 5.95 (ISBN 0-934136-27-0, Valley Calif). Western Tanager.

Olken, Charles, et al. The Connoisseurs' Handbook of California Wines. 2nd, rev. ed. LC 81-48103. (Illus.). 1982. pap. 5.95 (ISBN 0-394-71005-3). Knopf.

Paterson, John. Choosing Your Wine. (Illus.). 128p. 1981. 7.95 (ISBN 0-600-33217-9, 8180). Larousse.

Peynaud, Emile. Knowing & Making Wine. LC 84-11936. 400p. 1984. text ed. 34.95x (ISBN 0-471-88149-X, Pub. by Wiley-Interscience). Wiley.

Pocket Guide to Wine. 128p. 1981. 4.95 (ISBN 0-7064-1524-8, Rutledge Pr). Smith Pubs.

Pratt, James N. The Wine Bibber's Bible. rev., 2nd ed. LC 80-24680. (Illus.). 192p. 1981. pap. 6.95 (ISBN 0-89286-182-7). One Hund One Prods.

Ramey, Bern C. The Great Wine Grapes & the Wines They Make. (Illus.). 49.95 (ISBN 0-8436-2257-1). Great Wine Grapes.

--The Great Wine Grapes & the Wines They Make. 1978. 49.95 (ISBN 0-8436-2257-1). Van Nos Reinhold.

Ramos, Adam & Ramos, Joseph. Mixed Wine Drinks: Seven Hundred Recipes for Punches, Hot Drinks, Coolers & Cocktails. 2nd ed. LC 74-25080. (Illus.). 1982. pap. 9.95 (ISBN 0-914598-60-0). Padre Prods.

Roate, Mettja C. How to Make Wine in Your Own Kitchen. 12th ed. (Orig.). 1979. pap. 1.75 (ISBN 0-532-17241-8). Woodhill.

Robards, Terry. California Wine Label Album. LC 81-40502. 176p. 1981. looseleaf 16.95 (ISBN 0-89480-183-X). Workman Pub.

--The New York Times Book of Wine. 480p. 1977. pap. 7.95 (ISBN 0-380-01720-2, 60467-1). Avon.

Robinson, Janice. The Great Wine Book: The Finest Wines from the Most Renowned Vineyards of France, the United States, Germany, Italy, Spain, & Australia. LC 82-6427. (Illus.). 240p. 1982. 29.95 (ISBN 0-688-00727-9). Morrow.

Saintsbury, George. Notes on a Cellar Book. rev. ed. 1978. Repr. of 1920 ed. 12.50 (ISBN 0-8317-6450-3, Mayflower Bks). Smith Pubs.

Seldon, Philip. Vintage Magazine's Consumer's Guide to Wine. LC 79-8504. (Illus.). 416p. (Orig.). 1983. pap. 12.95 (ISBN 0-385-14961-1). Doubleday.

Shanken, Marvin R. The Impact American Wine Market Review & Forecast: 1982 Edition. 8th ed. (Illus.). 72p. 1982. pap. 150.00 (ISBN 0-918076-17-X). M Shanken Comm.

--The Impact American Wine Market Review & Forecast. 7th ed. (Illus.). 55p. 1981. pap. 100.00 (ISBN 0-918076-13-7). M Shanken Comm.

--The Impact American Wine Market Review & Forecast. 5th ed. (Illus.). 1979. pap. 75.00 (ISBN 0-918076-03-X). M Shanken Comm.
--The Imported Wine Market in America, 1960-1990. (Illus.). 107p. 1982. pap. 750.00 (ISBN 0-918076-16-1). M Shanken Comm.
Sharp, William J. & Martin, Joseph. Wine: How to Develop Your Taste & Get Your Money's Worth. (Illus.). 192p. 1976. (Spec); pap. 3.95 (ISBN 0-13-957738-6). P-H.
Stein, Clem, Jr. The Joy of Home Winemaking. LC 72-6901. (Illus.). 96p. 1973. 7.95 (ISBN 0-87396-073-4). Stravon.
Steinlage, Gerald F. Wines Brewing Distillation. LC 72-189987. 91p. 1972. pap. 3.95 (ISBN 0-914754-01-7). Steinlage.
Stockley, Tom. Great Wine Values. 150p. (Orig.). 1982. pap. 4.95 (ISBN 0-89716-107-6). Peanut Butter.
Sutcliffe, Serena. Andre Simon's Wines of the World. 2nd ed. (Illus.). 1981. 35.00 (ISBN 0-07-057423-5). McGraw.
Teiser, Ruth & Harroun, Catherine. Winemaking in California. 1982. 24.95 (ISBN 0-07-063401-7). McGraw.
Tritton, S. M. Guide to Better Wine & Beer Making for Beginners. 157p. 1969. pap. 2.95 (ISBN 0-486-22528-3). Dover.
--Tritton's Guide to Better Wine & Beer Making for Beginners. (Illus.). 160p. (Orig.). 1969. pap. 4.50 (ISBN 0-571-09171-7). Faber & Faber.
Turner, Ben. Winemaking & Brewing. (Illus.). 134p. 1976. 12.95 (ISBN 0-7207-0924-5, Pub. by Michael Joseph). Merrimack Pub Cir.
Turner, William. Book of Wines. LC 41-26942. 1980. Repr. of 1568 ed. 35.00x (ISBN 0-8201-1200-3). Schol Facsimiles.
Vine, Richard P. Commercial Winemaking: Processing & Controls. (Illus.). 1981. text ed. 32.50 (ISBN 0-87055-376-3). AVI.
Watkins, Derek. Wine & Beer Making. (Leisure & Travel Ser.). 1978. 7.95 (ISBN 0-7153-7503-2). David & Charles.
Weaver, Robert J. Grape Growing. LC 76-22753. 371p. 1976. 32.50x (ISBN 0-471-92324-9, Pub. by Wiley-Interscience). Wiley.
Webb, A. Dinsmore, ed. Chemistry of Winemaking. LC 74-19186. (Advances in Chemistry Ser: No. 137). 1974. 29.95 (ISBN 0-8412-0208-7); pap. 14.95 (ISBN 0-8412-0435-7). Am Chemical.
Whittow, Marion. Great Fermentations. (Illus.). 133p. Date not set. pap. 4.95 (ISBN 0-900841-69-9, Pub. by Aztex Corp). Argus Bks.
Williamson, Darcy. Wild Wines. 96p. (Orig.). 1980. pap. 4.95 (ISBN 0-89288-034-1). Maverick.
The Wine Album. (Illus.). 160p. 1982. gift boxed 15.95 (ISBN 0-698-11206-7, Coward). Putnam Pub Group.
World Wine & Wine Products Economy: A Study of Trends & Problems. (Commodity Bulletins: No. 43). 50p. 1969. pap. 7.25 (ISBN 92-5-101711-5, F528, FAO). Unipub.
Yoxall, H. W. The Wines of Burgundy: The International Wine & Food Society's Guide. LC 78-57582. (Illus.). 192p. 1980. pap. 8.95 (ISBN 0-8128-6091-8). Stein & Day.

WINE AND WINE MAKING–BIBLIOGRAPHY

Simon, Andre. Bibliotheca Vinaria, a Bibliography of Books & Pamphlets Dealing with Viticulture, Wine Making, Distillation, the Management, Sale Taxation, Use & Abuse of Wines & Spirits. vii, 340p. 1979. Repr. of 1913 ed. 130.00 (ISBN 0-900470-96-8). Oak Knoll.
Simon, Andre L. Bibliotheca Bacchica, Bibliographie Raisonee Des Ouvrages Imprimes Avant 1600 et Illustrant la Soif Humaine, 2 vols. in 1. (Fr., Illus.). xxvi, 473p. 1972. Repr. of 1927 ed. 130.00 (ISBN 0-900470-61-5). Oak Knoll.

WINE AND WINE-MAKING–DICTIONARIES

Debuigne, Gerard. Dictionnaire Vins. (Fr., Illus.). pap. 8.50 (ISBN 0-03-075459-3, 3742). Larousse.
--Larousse des vins. (Fr., Illus.). 271p. 1970. 47.50x (ISBN 2-03-019010-1). Larousse.
Dovaz, Michel. Encyclopedia of the Great Wines of Bordeaux. Julliard, ed. 254p. 1981. 75.00 (ISBN 2-260-00279-X, M-11718). French & Eur.
Hamlyn Pocket Dictionary of Wines. 1980. pap. 3.95 (ISBN 0-600-39498-0, 8056). Larousse.
Johnson, Frank E. The Professional Wine Reference. (Illus.). 354p. 1983. leather gold-gilded cover 35.00 (ISBN 0-9602566-1-X); pap. 9.95 (ISBN 0-9602566-0-1). Beverage Media.
Lichine, A. Encyclopedie des Vins & des Alcools de tous les Pays. (Fr.). 945p. 1980. pap. 23.95 (ISBN 2-221-50195-0, M-12633). French & Eur.
Lichine, Alexis. Alexis Lichine's New Encyclopedia of Wines & Spirits. 3rd ed. LC 80-22385. (Illus.). 734p. 1981. 40.00 (ISBN 0-394-51781-4). Knopf.
Price, Pamela V. Dictionary of Wines & Spirits. 408p. 1981. 40.00x (ISBN 0-7198-2744-2, Pub. by Northwood Bks). State Mutual Bk.
Renouil, Yves & Traversay, Yves de. Dictionnaire du Vin. (Fr.). 1962. 39.95 (ISBN 0-686-56731-5, M-6482). French & Eur.

WINE AND WINE-MAKING–AFRICA

Lesko, Leonard H. King Tut's Wine Cellar. LC 77-85654. (Illus.). 1977. pap. 3.95 (ISBN 0-930548-00-0). B C Scribe.
Simon, Andre L. All about South Africa. (All About Wines: Vol. 8). 7.50 (ISBN 0-87559-184-1). Shalom.

WINE AND WINE-MAKING–AUSTRALIA

Antcliff, A. J. Major Wine Grape Varieties of Australia. 62p. 1979. pap. 6.50 (ISBN 0-643-02517-0, C012, CSIRO). Unipub.
--Some Wine Grape Varieties for Australia. 50p. 1976. pap. 6.00 (ISBN 0-643-00180-8, C009, CSIRO). Unipub.
Halliday, James. Wines & Wineries of South Australia. (Illus.). 144p. 1981. text ed. 10.95 boards (ISBN 0-7022-1571-6). U of Queensland Pr.
--Wines & Wineries of Victoria. (Illus.). 152p. 1982. bds. 12.50 (ISBN 0-7022-1740-9). U of Queensland Pr.

WINE AND WINE-MAKING–EUROPE

Blum, Howard L. The Wines & Vines of Europe. LC 72-97409. (Orig.). pap. 1.95 (ISBN 0-87502-027-5). Benjamin Co.
Casas, Penelope. Foods & Wines of Spain. LC 82-47830. (Illus.). 1982. 18.95 (ISBN 0-394-51348-7). Knopf.
Loubere, Leo. The Red & the White: History of Wine in France & Italy in the 19th Century. LC 78-2304. (Illus.). 1978. 39.50x (ISBN 0-87395-370-3). State U NY Pr.
Stanislawski, Dan. Landscapes of Bacchus: The Vine in Portugal. (Illus.). 224p. 1970. 14.50x (ISBN 0-292-70010-5). U of Tex Pr.

WINE AND WINE-MAKING–ROME

Hoerle, Joseph. Catos Hausbuecher: Analyse Seiner Schrift de Agricultura. 1929. 22.00 (ISBN 0-384-23880-7). Johnson Repr.

WINGS (AIRPLANES)

see Airplanes–Wings

WINTER GARDENING

J. M. Dent & Sons Ltd., ed. Colour in the Winter Garden. 231p. 1981. 25.00x (ISBN 0-460-07798-8, Pub. by J M Dent England). State Mutual Bk.

WIRE

see also Exploding Wire Phenomena

Atmospheric Corrosion Investigation of Aluminum-Coated, Zinc-Coated & Copper-Bearing Steel Wire & Wire Products- STP 585. 90p. 1975. pap. 5.50 (ISBN 0-8031-0285-2, 04-585000-02). ASTM.
Ferrous Wire Drawing. 15.00 (ISBN 0-318-03187-6, 7516). Wire Assn Intl.
Magnum Publications Ltd., ed. Wire Industry Yearbook, Wire Industry Machinery Guide & Encyclopaedia of Wire. 1984. 125.00x (ISBN 0-686-96971-5, Pub. by Magnum England). State Mutual Bk.
Skirving, R. Scot. Wire Splicing. 2nd ed. 49p. 1980. pap. 6.50x (ISBN 0-85174-154-1). Sheridan.
Wire Association International: Proceedings, 54th Annual Conference. 50.00 (ISBN 0-318-04236-3). Wire Assn Intl.

WIRE EXPLOSIONS, ELECTRIC

see Exploding Wire Phenomena

WIRE-TAPPING

see also Eavesdropping

Carr, James G. The Law of Electronic Surveillance. LC 76-56748. 1977. 65.00 (ISBN 0-87632-108-2). Boardman.
Cederbaums, Juris. Wiretapping & Electronic Eavesdropping, the Law & Its Implications: A Comparative Study. (New York University Criminal Law Education & Research Center Monograph: No. 2). 77p. (Orig.). 1969. pap. text ed. 8.50x (ISBN 0-8377-0402-2). Rothman.
Dash, Samuel, et al. Eavesdroppers. LC 71-136498. (Civil Liberties in American History Ser). (Illus.). 1971. Repr. of 1959 ed. lib. bdg. 35.00 (ISBN 0-306-70074-3). Da Capo.
Fishman, Clifford. Wiretapping & Eavesdropping, Vol. 1. LC 78-18629. 1978. 74.50 (ISBN 0-686-29234-0); Suppl. 1984. 20.00; Suppl. 1983. 17.00. Lawyers Co-Op.
Fogelson, Robert M., ed. Wiretapping in New York City. LC 74-3843. (Criminal Justice in America Ser.). 1974. Repr. 12.00x (ISBN 0-405-06180-3). Ayer Co Pubs.
Greenman, Frederick P. Wire-Tapping: Its Relation to Civil Liberties. 1938. ltd. ed. 49.50x (ISBN 0-686-51326-6). Elliots Bks.
Moran, William B., ed. Covert Surveillance & Electronic Penetration. (Illus.). 1983. pap. 9.95 (ISBN 0-317-03311-5). Loompanics.
Paulsen, Monrad G. The Problems of Electric Eavesdropping. 136p. 1977. pap. 10.00 (ISBN 0-317-30880-7, B175). Am Law Inst.
Pollock, David A. Methods of Electronic Audio Surveillance. (Illus.). 406p. 1979. 28.00x (ISBN 0-398-02382-4). C C Thomas.

WIRELESS OPERATORS

see Radio Operators

WIRING, ELECTRIC

see Electric Wiring

WOLFRAMIUM

see Tungsten

WOLVES

see also Coyotes

Brown, David E., ed. The Wolf in the Southwest: The Making of an Endangered Species. LC 82-17399. 195p. 1983. pap. 9.95 (ISBN 0-8165-0796-1). U of Ariz Pr.
Fox, Michael W. Behavior of Wolves, Dogs & Related Canids. LC 83-18706. 220p. 1984. Repr. of 1971 ed. lib. bdg. 15.75 (ISBN 0-89874-686-8). Krieger.
Klinghammer, Erich. The Behavior & Ecology of Wolves. new ed. LC 77-89306. (Illus.). 1980. lib. bdg. 69.00 (ISBN 0-8240-7019-4, Garland STPM Pr). Garland Pub.
Mech, L. David. The Wolf. LC 73-100043. 1970. 17.95 (ISBN 0-385-08660-1). Natural Hist.
--The Wolf: The Ecology & Behavior of an Endangered Species. LC 80-27364. (Illus.). 385p. 1981. pap. 10.95 (ISBN 0-8166-1026-6). U of Minn Pr.
Mowat, Farley. Never Cry Wolf. 176p. 1984. pap. 2.95 (ISBN 0-553-23624-5). Bantam.
--Never Cry Wolf. 1963. 12.95 (ISBN 0-316-58639-0, Pub. by Atlantic Monthly Pr). Little.
Pimlott, Douglas H., ed. Wolves. (Illus.). 144p. 1975. pap. 10.00 (ISBN 2-88032-019-4, IUCN53, IUCN). Unipub.

WOMEN ENGINEERS

Haas, Violet B. & Perrucci, Carolyn C., eds. Professional Women in Science & Engineering. (Illus.). 272p. 1984. text ed. 24.00x (ISBN 0-472-10049-1); pap. text ed. 12.50x (ISBN 0-472-08042-3). U of Mich Pr.

WOMEN IN AERONAUTICS

see also Air Pilots

Earhart, Amelia. The Fun of It: Random Records of My Own Flying & of Women in Aviation. LC 71-159945. 1975. Repr. of 1932 ed. 40.00x (ISBN 0-8103-4078-X). Gale.
Mock, Jerrie. First Woman to Fly Solo Around the World: To Finish What Amelia Began. rev. ed. (Illus.). 300p. 1985. pap. write for info. (ISBN 0-931515-04-1). Triumph Pr.
Mondey, David. Women of the Air. LC 81-86277. (In Profile Ser.). 1982. PLB 12.68 (ISBN 0-382-06634-0). Silver.
Moolman, Valerie & Time-Life Books Editors. Women Aloft. (The Epic of Flight Ser.). (Illus.). 176p. 1981. 14.95 (ISBN 0-8094-3287-0). Time-Life.

WOMEN SCIENTISTS

Arnold, Lois B. Four Lives in Science: Women's Education in the Nineteenth Century. LC 83-42716. (Illus.). 192p. 1983. 14.95 (ISBN 0-8052-3865-4). Schocken.
Bleier, Ruth, ed. Feminist Approaches to Science. (Athene Ser.). (Illus.). 224p. 1986. 25.00 (ISBN 0-08-032787-7, Pub. by P P I); pap. 11.50 (ISBN 0-08-032786-9). Pergamon.
Brighton Women & Science Group. Alice Through the Microscope: The Power of Science Over Women's Lives. 310p. 19.95 (ISBN 0-86068-078-9, Virago Pr); pap. 9.95 (ISBN 0-86068-079-7). Merrimack Pub Cir.
Briscoe, Anne & Pfafflin, Sheila M., eds. Expanding the Role of Women in the Sciences. (Annals of the New York Academy of Sciences Ser.: Vol. 323). 344p. (Orig.). 1979. 47.00x (ISBN 0-89766-014-5); pap. 47.00x. NY Acad Sci.
Cesara, Manda. No Hiding Place: Reflections of a Woman Anthropologists. (Studies in Anthropology Ser.). 1982. 27.50 (ISBN 0-12-164880-X). Acad Pr.
Chipman, Susan F., et al, eds. Women & Mathematics: Balancing the Equation. 400p. 1985. text ed. 39.95 (ISBN 0-89859-369-7). L Erlbaum Assocs.
Cole, Jonathon R. Fair Science: Women in the Scientific Community. LC 79-7341. (Illus.). 1979. 24.95 (ISBN 0-02-906360-4). Free Pr.
Committee on the Education & Employment of Women in Science & Engineering. Climbing the Ladder II: An Update on the Status of Doctoral Women Scientists & Engineers. Office of Scientific & Engineering Personnel, National Research Council, ed. 112p. 1983. pap. text ed. 8.95 (ISBN 0-309-03341-1). Natl Acad Pr.
--Women Scientists in Industry & Government: How Much Progress in the 1970's. LC 80-80079. vii, 56p. 1980. pap. text ed. 5.50 (ISBN 0-309-03023-4). Natl Acad Pr.
Fins, Alice. Women in Science. (Illus.). 160p. 1983. 7.95 (ISBN 0-8442-6647-7, 6647-7, Passport Bks.); pap. 5.95 (ISBN 0-8442-6648-5). Natl Textbk.
Gornick, Vivian. Women in Science: Portraits from a World in Transition. 177p. 1983. 15.95 (ISBN 0-671-41738-X). S&S.
--Women in Science: Portraits from a World in Transition. 176p. 1985. pap. 10.95 (ISBN 0-671-41739-8, Touchstone Bks). S&S.
Haas, Violet B. & Perrucci, Carolyn C., eds. Professional Women in Science & Engineering. (Illus.). 272p. 1984. text ed. 24.00x (ISBN 0-472-10049-1); pap. text ed. 12.50x (ISBN 0-472-08042-3). U of Mich Pr.
Herzenberg, Caroline L. Women Scientists from Antiquity to the Present: An Index. 1985. lib. bdg. write for info. (ISBN 0-933951-01-9). Locust Hill Pr.
Humphreys, Sheila M., ed. Women & Minorities in Science: Strategies for Increasing Participation. (Selected Symposium: No. 66). 225p. 1982. lib. bdg. 26.00x. Westview.
Jacobs, Judith E., ed. Perspectives on Women & Mathematics. 166p. 1978. pap. 6.75 (ISBN 0-686-79358-7). NCTM.
Jaques Cattell Press, ed. American Men & Women of Science: Physical & Biological Sciences, 7 vols. 15th ed. 7010p. 1982. Set. 495.00 (ISBN 0-8352-1413-3); 85.00 ea. Bowker.
Kahle, Jane B., ed. Women in Science: A Report from the Field. 200p. 1985. 30.00 (ISBN 1-85000-019-0); pap. 18.00 (ISBN 1-85000-020-4). Taylor & Francis.
Keller, Evelyn F. Reflections on Gender & Science. LC 84-17327. 176p. 1985. 17.95x (ISBN 0-300-03291-9). Yale U Pr.
Keller, Evelyn F. & Freeman, W. H. A Feeling for the Organism: The Life & Work of Barbara McClintock. LC 82-21066. (Illus.). 235p. 1983. text ed. 17.95 (ISBN 0-7167-1433-7); pap. 8.95 (ISBN 0-7167-1504-X). W H Freeman.
Koblitz, Ann H. A Convergence of Lives. 304p. 1983. 19.95 (ISBN 0-8176-3162-3). Birkhauser.
Lantz, Alma E., et al. Re-Entry Programs for Female Scientists. LC 79-25364. 220p. 1980. 33.95 (ISBN 0-03-055771-2). Praeger.
Northeastern Women's Geoscientists Conference, First. Women in Geology: Proceedings. Halsey, S. D., et al, eds. LC 76-21580. (Illus.). 1976. pap. 2.00 (ISBN 0-915492-02-4). Ash Lad Pr.
Posner, Alice. Women in Engineering. 1981. 7.95 (ISBN 0-8442-6396-6, 6396-6); pap. 5.95 (ISBN 0-8442-6397-4, 6397-4). Natl Textbk.
Rosser, Sue V. Teaching Health & Science from a Feminist Perspective: A Practical Guide. (Athene Ser.). (Illus.). 200p. 1986. 16.95 (ISBN 0-08-033135-1, Pub. by P P I). Pergamon.
Rossiter, Margaret W. Women Scientists in America: Struggles & Strategies to 1940. 1984. pap. 10.95 (ISBN 0-8018-2509-1). Johns Hopkins.
Siegel, Patricia J. & Finley, Kay T. Women in the Scientific Search: An American Bio-bibliography, 1724-1979. LC 84-20290. 417p. 1984. 32.50 (ISBN 0-8108-1755-1). Scarecrow.
Smith, Walter S. & Stroup, Kala M. Science Career Exploration for Women. 1978. pap. 5.00 (ISBN 0-87355-010-2). Natl Sci Tchrs.
Weiss, Iris R. & Place, Carol, eds. Women Scientists Roster. (Orig.). 1979. pap. 5.00 (ISBN 0-87355-015-3). Natl Sci Tchrs.
Zimmerman, Jan, ed. The Technological Woman: Interfacing with Tomorrow. LC 82-14033. 304p. 1983. 26.95 (ISBN 0-03-062829-6). Praeger.

WOOD

see also Forests and Forestry; Hardwoods; Lumber; Plywood; Pulpwood; Wood-Using Industries; Woodwork; Woody Plants; also kinds of woods, e.g. Mahogany, Walnut

Aughanbaugh, John. An Ecological Study of Crall Woods. 1964. 2.00 (ISBN 0-686-86535-9). Ohio Bio Survey.
Baas, P. New Perspectives in Wood Anatomy. 1982. 54.00 (ISBN 90-247-2526-7, Pub. by Martinus Nijhoff Netherlands). Kluwer Academic.
Barefoot, A. C. & Hankins, Frank W. Identification of Modern Tertiary Woods. (Illus.). 1982. 98.00x (ISBN 0-19-854378-6). Oxford U Pr.
Bodig, Jozsef & Jayne, Benjamin A. Mechanics of Wood & Wood Composites. 736p. 1982. 44.50 (ISBN 0-442-00822-8). Van Nos Reinhold.
Boerhave Beekman, W., ed. Elsevier's Wood Dictionary, 3 Vols. (Eng., Fr., Span., Ital., Swedish, Dutch & Ger.). 1964-75. Set. 259.75 (ISBN 0-686-43878-7); Vol. 1. 89.50 (ISBN 0-444-40063-X); Vol. 2. 89.50 (ISBN 0-444-40053-2); Vol. 3. 89.50 (ISBN 0-444-40713-8). Elsevier.
Bosshard, B. Holzkunde: Mikroskopie und Makroskopie des Holzes, Vol. 1. 225p. 28.95x (ISBN 0-8176-1328-5). Birkhauser.
Breyer, Donald E. & Ank, John A. Design of Wood Structures. (Illus.). 1980. 47.95 (ISBN 0-07-007671-5). McGraw.
Brodatz, Phil. Wood & Wood Grains: A Photographic Album for Artists & Designers. 1972. 6.95 (ISBN 0-486-22424-4). Dover.
--Wood & Wood Grains: A Photographic Album for Artists & Designers. (Illus.). 15.50 (ISBN 0-8446-0040-7). Peter Smith.

Bucksch, Herbert. Holz Woerterbuch, Vol. 1. (Ger. & Eng., Dictionary of wood & woodworking practice). 1966. 59.95 (ISBN 3-7625-1168-3, M-7465, Pub. by Bauverlag). French & Eur.

--Holz Woerterbuch, Vol. 2. (Ger. & Eng., Dictionary of wood & woodworking practice). 1966. 67.50 (ISBN 3-7625-1170-5, M-7466, Pub. by Bauverlag). French & Eur.

Cheek, G. Manufacturing Processes: Woods. 1975. 7.20 (ISBN 0-13-555656-2); pap. text ed. 8.84 (ISBN 0-13-555649-X). P-H.

Constantine & Hobbs. Know Your Woods. 1975. text ed. 17.95 (ISBN 0-02-664790-7). Bennett IL.

Core, Harold, et al. Wood Structure & Identification. 2nd ed. 1979. pap. 12.95x (ISBN 0-8156-5043-4). Syracuse U Pr.

Corkhill, Thomas. The Complete Dictionary of Wood. LC 79-10183. (Illus.). 664p. 1980. 19.95 (ISBN 0-8128-2708-2). Stein & Day.

Cote, Wilfred A., Jr. Wood Ultrastructure: An Atlas of Electron Micrographs. LC 67-21204. (Illus.). 64p. 1967. pap. 20.00x (ISBN 0-295-97868-6). U of Wash Pr.

Cutter, Bruce, ed. Wood & Fiber Science. (Orig.). pap. text ed. 55.00 (ISBN 0-686-40829-2). Soc Wood.

De Montalembert, M. R. & Clement, J. Fuelwood Supplies in the Developing Countries. (Forestry Papers: No. 42). (Eng., Fr. & Span.). 134p. 1983. pap. text ed. 9.75 (ISBN 92-5-101252-0, F2429, FAO). Unipub.

Dictionnaire Technique du Bois en 4 Langues. (Ger., Rus., Eng. & Fr.). 640p. 37.50 (ISBN 0-686-57116-9, M-6157). French & Eur.

Edlin, Herbert L. What Wood Is That? A Manual of Wood Identification. (Illus.). 1969. 24.95 (ISBN 0-670-75907-4, Studio). Viking.

Gillespie, Robert H., ed. Adhesives for Wood: Research, Applications, & Needs. LC 84-14780. 250p. 1985. 36.00 (ISBN 0-8155-0997-9). Noyes.

Gurfinkel, German. Wood Engineering. 560p. text ed. 18.95 (ISBN 0-8403-2476-6). Kendall-Hunt.

Harlow, W. Inside Wood. 7.50 (ISBN 0-686-26732-X, NO. 27). Am Forestry.

Harrar, Ellwood S. & Hough, Romeyn B. Hough's Encyclopedia of American Woods, 16 vols. 1972. 75.00 ea. (ISBN 0-8315-0075-1). Speller.

Hausen, Bjorn M. Woods Injurious to Human Health. (Illus.). 189p. 1981. 31.50x (ISBN 3-11-008485-6). De Gruyter.

Higuchi, Takayoshi, ed. Biosynthesis & Biodegradation of Wood Components. 1985. 99.00 (ISBN 0-12-347880-4). Acad Pr.

Hoadley, R. Bruce. Understanding Wood: A Craftsman's Guide to Wood Technology. LC 78-65177. (Illus.). 272p. 1980. 19.95 (ISBN 0-918804-05-1, Dist. by W W Norton). Taunton.

Hoyle, Robert J., Jr. Wood Technology in the Design of Structures. 4th ed. LC 77-26026. (Illus.). 390p. 1978. pap. text ed. 18.50 (ISBN 0-87842-059-2). Mountain Pr.

Industrial Energy from Wood: New Technologies & Case Histories. 292p. 1981. 22.00 (ISBN 0-935018-14-X). Forest Prod.

Industrial Wood Energy Forum '82, 2 vols. 1983. Vol. I, 226 pp. 22.00 (ISBN 0-8403-2994-6); Vol. II, 236 pp. 22.00 (ISBN 0-8403-2995-4). Forest Prod.

Jekyll, Gertrude. Wood & Garden. (Illus.). 380p. 1981. 29.50 (ISBN 0-907462-11-1). Antique Collect.

Kollmann, F. F. & Cote, W. A. Principles of Wood Science & Technology, Vol. 1: Solid Wood. LC 67-29614. (Illus.). xii, 592p. 1968. 69.00 (ISBN 0-387-04297-0). Springer-Verlag.

Kollmann, F. F., et al. Principles of Wood Science & Technology, Vol. 2: Wood Base Materials Manufacture & Properties. LC 67-29614. (Illus.). 700p. 1975. 79.00 (ISBN 0-387-06467-2). Springer-Verlag.

Lazenby, William. Qualities & Uses of the Woods of Ohio. 1916. 1.00 (ISBN 0-86727-005-5). Ohio Bio Survey.

Maloney, Thomas M. Modern Particleboard & Dry-Process Fiberboard Manufacturing. LC 76-47094. (A Forest Industries Book). (Illus.). 1977. 50.00 (ISBN 0-87930-063-9). Miller Freeman.

Metclfe, C. R. & Chalk, L. Anatomy of the Dicotyledons: Wood Structure & Conclusion of the General Introduction, Vol. 2. 2nd ed. (Illus.). 1983. 75.00x (ISBN 0-19-854559-2). Oxford U Pr.

Meyer, Robert W. & Kellogg, Robert M., eds. Structural Use of Wood in Adverse Environments. 1982. 44.50 (ISBN 0-442-28744-5). Van Nos Reinhold.

Meylan, B. A. & Butterfield, B. G. Three-Dimensional Structure of Wood: A Scanning Electron Microscope Study. (Illus.). 80p. 1972. pap. text ed. 11.95x (ISBN 0-8156-5030-2). Syracuse U Pr.

Millett, R. & Storey, E. W. Design & Technology Wood. 1982. 25.00x (ISBN 0-08-017183-4, Pub. by A Wheaton). State Mutual Bk.

Murphey, Wayne K. & Jorgensen, Richard. Wood As an Industrial Arts Material. 1974. text ed. 25.00 (ISBN 0-08-017906-1); pap. text ed. 14.00 (ISBN 0-08-017907-X). Pergamon.

Ramachandran, V. S., ed. Concrete Admixtures Handbook: Properties, Science, & Technology. LC 84-4125. (Illus.). 626p. 1985. 72.00 (ISBN 0-8155-0981-2). Noyes.

Research & Education Association. Handbook of Wood Technology & House Construction. LC 81-50949. (Illus.). 864p. 1981. 26.75x (ISBN 0-87891-529-X). Res & Educ.

Richardson, Barry A. Wood Preservation. (Illus.). 1978. text ed. 37.00x (ISBN 0-904406-75-X, Construction Pr). Longman.

Shay, Frank. Drawn from the Wood. 12.50 (ISBN 0-87523-064-4). Emerson.

Skaar, Christen. Water in Wood. LC 70-39754. (Syracuse Wood Science Ser.: No. 4). pap. 44.10 (ISBN 0-317-08521-2, 2051340). Bks Demand UMI.

Smith, Nigel. Wood: An Ancient Fuel with a New Future. LC 80-54881. (Worldwatch Papers). 1981. pap. 2.00 (ISBN 0-916468-41-0). Worldwatch Inst.

Summitt, Robert & Sliker, Alan. Wood. (CRC Handbook of Materials Science: Vol. IV). 472p. 1980. 69.95 (ISBN 0-8493-0234-X). CRC Pr.

Talbot, Mike & Boyt, David, eds. Alternative Sources of Energy: Wood Energy, No. 57. 52p. 1982. pap. 3.50 (ISBN 0-917328-47-7). ASEI.

Taylor, Maisie. Wood in Archaeology. (Shire Archaeology Ser.: No. 17). (Illus.). 56p. 1981. pap. 5.95 (ISBN 0-85263-537-0, Pub. by Shire Pubns England). Seven Hills Bks.

U. S. Dept. of Forestry. Encyclopedia of Wood. LC 77-7728. (Illus.). 384p. 1980. pap. 13.95 (ISBN 0-8069-8890-8). Sterling.

Wallnig, G. & Evered, H. Dictionnaire Technique du Bois, en Quatre Langues. (Ger., Fr., Eng. & Rus.). 640p. 1973. 65.00 (ISBN 0-686-57254-8, M-6563). French & Eur.

Weiner, Jack, et al. Changes in the Value & Utility of Pulpwood, Sawlogs, & Veneer Bolts During Harvesting, Transport, & Storage. (Bibliographic Ser.: No. S60). 1974. 25.00 (ISBN 0-87010-028-9). Inst Paper Chem.

White, Marshall S. Wood Identification Handbook. (Illus.). 80p. 1982. 9.95 (ISBN 0-684-17349-2, ScribT). Scribner.

Wood Adhesives: Present & Future. pap. price not set (ISBN 0-471-81334-6). Wiley.

Wood as Packaging Material in Developing Countries. pap. 3.00 (ISBN 0-686-94363-5, UN72/2/B12, UN). Unipub.

Wood: World Trends & Prospects. (Freedom from Hunger Campaign Basic Studies: No. 16). (Orig.). 1967. pap. 9.25 (ISBN 0-685-09414-6, F493, FAO). Unipub.

World Production Capacities for Plywood, Particle Board & Fiberboard. 1978. pap. 11.00 (ISBN 0-685-65228-9, F1319, FAO). Unipub.

Youngquist, Wally G. & Fleischer, Herbert O. Wood in American Life 1776-2076. LC 77-85427. 192p. 1977. 11.00 (ISBN 0-935018-00-X); members 9.00. Forest Prod.

WOOD–CHEMISTRY

see also Cellulose

Browning, B. L., ed. The Chemistry of Wood. LC 74-23593. 700p. 1975. Repr. of 1963 ed. 46.50 (ISBN 0-88275-245-6). Krieger.

Fengel, Dietrich & Wegener, Gert. Wood: Chemistry, Ultrastructure, Reactions. (Illus.). xii, 600p. 1983. 112.00x (ISBN 3-11-008481-3). De Gruyter.

Goldstein, Irving S., ed. Wood Technology: Chemical Aspects. LC 77-2368. (ACS Symposium Ser.: No. 43). 1977. 34.95 (ISBN 0-8412-0373-3). Am Chemical.

Jayne, Benjamin A., ed. Theory & Design of Wood & Fiber Composite Materials. LC 72-1998. (Wood Science Ser.: No. 3). (Illus.). 464p. 1972. text ed. 25.00x (ISBN 0-8156-5031-0). Syracuse U Pr.

Loewus, F. A. & Runeckles, V. C., eds. The Structure, Biosyntheses, & Degradation of Wood. LC 77-8275. (Recent Advances in Phytochemistry Ser.: Vol. 11). 539p. 1977. 65.00x (ISBN 0-306-34711-3, Plenum Pr). Plenum Pub.

National Academy of Sciences. Potential of Lignocellulosic Materials for the Production of Chemicals, Fuels, & Energy. 91p. 1979. pap. 19.95x (ISBN 0-930978-92-7, B-037). Solar Energy Info.

Oliver, John F., ed. Adhesion in Cellulosic & Wood-Based Composites. LC 81-11983. (NATO Conference Series VI--Material Science: Vol. 3). 268p. 1981. 49.50x (ISBN 0-306-40812-0, Plenum Pr). Plenum Pub.

Rowell, Roger, ed. The Chemistry of Solid Wood. LC 83-22451. (Advances in Chemistry Ser.: No. 207). 614p. 1984. lib. bdg. 79.95x (ISBN 0-8412-0796-8). Am Chemical.

Sjostrom, Eero. Wood Chemistry: Fundamentals & Applications. LC 81-3614. 1981. 29.50 (ISBN 0-12-647480-X). Acad Pr.

Wenzl, Herman J. Chemical Technology of Wood. 1970. 90.00 (ISBN 0-12-743450-X). Acad Pr.

WOOD–DETERIORATION

see also Marine Borers

Edmondson, C. H. Resistance of Woods to Marine Borers in Hawaiian Waters. (BMB Ser.). Repr. of 1955 ed. 11.00 (ISBN 0-527-02325-6). Kraus Repr.

Nicholas, Darrel D. Wood Deterioration & Its Prevention by Preservative Treatments. Incl. Vol. 1. Degradation & Protection of Wood. 416p. 1982. pap. text ed. 35.00x (ISBN 0-8156-2285-6); Vol. 2. Preservatives & Preservative Systems. 448p. 1984. text ed. 37.00x o. p. (ISBN 0-8156-5038-8). LC 73-4640. (Wood Science Ser.: No. 5). (Illus.). 1973. pap. text ed. 37.00x (ISBN 0-8156-2303-8). Syracuse U Pr.

Partridge, Arthur D. & Miller, Daniel L. Major Wood Decays in the Inland Northwest. 125p. 1974. text ed. 4.50 (ISBN 0-89301-014-6). U Pr of Idaho.

WOOD–PRESERVATION

see also Marine Borers

Becker, G. & Theden, G., eds. Annual Report on Wood Protection, 1953-1954. Tr. of Jahresberichte Ueber Holzschutz. vi, 219p. 1955. 28.40 (ISBN 0-387-01928-6). Springer-Verlag.

--Annual Report on Wood Protection, 1955. Tr. of Jahresberichte Ueber Holzschutz. viii, 170p. 1956. 26.60 (ISBN 0-387-02057-8). Springer-Verlag.

--Annual Report on Wood Protection, 1959-1960. Tr. of Jahresberichte Ueber Holzschutz. v, 481p. 1969. 67.90 (ISBN 0-387-04576-7). Springer-Verlag.

--Annual Report on Wood Protection, 1961-62. 1972. 57.90 (ISBN 0-387-05827-3). Springer-Verlag.

Charles, F. W. B. The Conservation of Timber Buildings. LC 84-12984. (Illus.). 256p. 1984. 72.50 (ISBN 0-09-145090-X, Pub. by Hutchinson Educ). Longwood Pub Group.

Impregnated Fibrous Materials. (Panel Proceedings Ser.). (Illus.). 376p. (Orig.). 1968. pap. 24.00 (ISBN 92-0-161168-4, ISP209, IAEA). Unipub.

WOOD–STAINING

see Stains and Staining

WOOD–TESTING

Division of Building Research, ed. Testing Timber for Moisture Content. (Illus.). 31p. 1977. pap. 1.50x (ISBN 0-643-01073-4, Pub. by CSIRO). Intl Spec Bk.

Testing Timber for Moisture Content. 31p. 1974. pap. 6.00 (ISBN 0-643-01073-4, C035, CSIRO). Unipub.

Williams, R. M. Evaluation of Field & Laboratory Methods for Testing Termite Resistance of Timber & Building Materials in Ghana, with Relevant Biological Studies. 1973. 35.00x (ISBN 0-85135-065-8, Pub. by Centre Overseas Research). State Mutual Bk.

WOOD AS FUEL

see also Stoves, Wood

Emerging Energy & Chemical Applications of Methanol: Opportunities for Developing Countries. viii, 73p. 1982. pap. 5.00 (ISBN 0-8213-0018-0). World Bank.

Energy Generation & Cogeneration from Wood. 182p. 1980. 18.00 (ISBN 0-935018-13-1). Forest Prod.

Fichter, Harold O. Wood Heat Is Yours for the Axing. (Illus.). 1980. pap. 4.00 (ISBN 0-918424-02-X). Menaid.

Fuelwood & Rural Energy Production & Supply in Humid Tropics: Report for the UNU with Special Reference to Tropical Africa & South East Asia, Vol. 4. (Natural Resources & the Environment Ser.). (Illus.). 224p. 1982. 19.50 (ISBN 0-907567-08-8, TYP104, TYP). Unipub.

Georgia Technical Research Institute & Drucker, S. The Industrial Wood Energy Handbook. 272p. 1984. 37.50 (ISBN 0-442-22085-5). Van Nos Reinhold.

Hardware for Energy Generation in the Forest Products Industry. 155p. 1979. 18.00 (ISBN 0-935018-12-3). Forest Prod.

Harris, Michael. Heating with Wood. 1980. 12.00 (ISBN 0-8065-0718-7); pap. 7.95 (ISBN 0-8065-0686-5). Citadel Pr.

--Heating with Wood. 1980. pap. 7.95 (ISBN 0-8065-5068-6). Citadel Pr.

Kubler, Hans. Wood As Building & Hobby Material: How to Use Lumber & Wood-Base Panels & Round Wood Wisely in Construction, for Furniture, & As Fuel. LC 80-13380. 256p. 1980. 31.50x (ISBN 0-471-05390-2, Pub. by Wiley-Interscience); pap. 15.95x (ISBN 0-471-09848-5). Wiley.

National Academy of Sciences. Potential of Lignocellulosic Materials for the Production of Chemicals, Fuels, & Energy. 91p. 1979. pap. 19.95x (ISBN 0-930978-92-7, B-037). Solar Energy Info.

Nygards, Nils. Wood Gas Generator For Vehicles. 18p. 1979. pamphlet 3.00 (ISBN 0-686-35951-8). Rutan Pub.

Organic & Fuel Uses for Bark & Wood Residues. 45p. 1980. 7.00 (ISBN 0-935018-17-4); members 5.00 (ISBN 0-317-17407-X). Forest Prod.

Practical Application of Solar Energy to Wood Processing. 85p. 1977. 7.00 (ISBN 0-935018-15-8). Forest Prod.

Proceedings of the ESCAP-FAO-UNEP Expert Group on Fuelwood & Charcoal. (Energy Resources Development Ser.: No. 24). 120p. 11.00 (ISBN 0-317-18752-X, E.82.II.F.10). UN.

Stewart, Gordon A. Wood Heat: Peril or Pleasure. LC 82-82869. (Illus.). 176p. 1983. 10.95 (ISBN 0-910937-08-7); pap. 5.95 (ISBN 0-910937-09-5). Laranmark.

Talbot, James J. & Swanson, Winfield, eds. Woodpower -- New Perspectives on Forest Usage. (Illus.). 239p. 1981. 35.00 (ISBN 0-08-027562-1). Pergamon.

Tillman, David A. Wood As an Energy Resource. 1978. 22.50 (ISBN 0-12-691260-2). Acad Pr.

Truss Fabricators in the United States. Factors Affecting the Use of Lumber. 80p. 1979. 12.00 (ISBN 0-935018-20-4); members 9.00 (ISBN 0-317-17412-6). Forest Prod.

Wood: An Ancient Fuel with a New Future. (Worldwatch Institute Papers: No. 42). 48p. 1981. pap. 2.95 (ISBN 0-916468-41-0, WW42, WW). Unipub.

Wood, Energy & Households, Vol. 6: Perspectives on Rural Kenya. 272p. Date not set. 27.50 (ISBN 0-8419-9774-8, Africana). Holmes & Meier.

Wood Residue as an Energy Source. 118p. 1975. 18.00 (ISBN 0-935018-10-7); members 14.00 (ISBN 0-317-17424-X). Forest Prod.

WOOD FINISHING

see also Lacquer and Lacquering; Stains and Staining; Varnish and Varnishing

Frank, George. Eighty-Eight Rue de Charonne: Adventures in Wood Finishing. LC 80-54431. (Illus.). 128p. 1981. 9.95 (ISBN 0-918804-06-X, Dist. by W W Norton). Taunton.

Grotz, George. Staining & Finishing Unfinished Furniture & Other Naked Woods. LC 68-25596. (Illus.). 1968. pap. 3.50 (ISBN 0-385-01906-8, Dolp). Doubleday.

Hall, Alan & Heard, James. Wood Finishing & Refinishing. LC 81-4708. (Illus.). 216p. 1982. 16.95 (ISBN 0-03-018856-3, Owl Bks); pap. 9.95 (ISBN 0-03-018861-X). HR&W.

Hand, Jackson. How to Do Your Own Wood Finishing. 2nd ed. (Popular Science Skill Bk.). 1976. pap. 3.95i (ISBN 0-06-011792-3, TD-284, HarpT). Har-Row.

Hayward, Charles H. Staining & Wood Polishing. (A Home Craftsman Bk.). (Illus.). 214p. 1980. pap. 6.95 (ISBN 0-8069-8684-0). Sterling.

Jeffrey, Harry R. Wood Finishing. 1957. pap. text ed. 11.00 (ISBN 0-02-666200-0). Bennett IL.

Lincoln, W. A. The Complete Manual of Wood Veneering. (Illus.). 400p. 1985. 30.00 (ISBN 0-684-18189-4, ScribT). Scribner.

Newell, D. Wood Finishing. 1986. cancelled (ISBN 0-442-26835-1). Van Nos Reinhold.

Oughton, Frederick. The Complete Manual of Wood Finishing. LC 82-19195. (Illus.). 288p. 1983. 18.95 (ISBN 0-8128-2890-9); pap. 9.95 (ISBN 0-8128-6236-8). Stein & Day.

Philbin, Tom. Wood Finishing & Refinishing. Auer, Marilyn M., ed. LC 81-69641. (Illus.). 144p. (Orig.). 1982. 19.95 (ISBN 0-932944-53-1); pap. 7.95 (ISBN 0-932944-54-X). Creative Homeowner.

Scharff, Robert. Complete Book of Wood Finishing. 2nd ed. (Illus.). 384p. 1974. 37.95 (ISBN 0-07-055166-9). McGraw.

--Practical Wood Finishing Methods. 1981. 9.95 (ISBN 0-8359-5575-3). Reston.

Vanderwalker, F. N. Wood Finishing. rev. ed. LC 76-21190. (Illus.). 408p. 1980. pap. 8.95 (ISBN 0-8069-8798-7). Sterling.

--Wood Finishing-Plain & Decorative. LC 76-21190. (A Home Craftsman Bk.). (Illus.). 1970. pap. 7.95 (ISBN 0-8069-8798-7). Sterling.

WOOD PRESERVATIVES

see also Fungicides; Insecticides

Fungi of Pulp & Paper in New York, No. 87. 1965. 1.75 (ISBN 0-686-20699-1). SUNY Environ.

Richardson, Barry A. Wood Preservation. (Illus.). 1978. text ed. 37.00x (ISBN 0-904406-75-X, Construction Pr). Longman.

WOOD-PULP

Louden, Louise & Boye, Fred. Beating & Refining. LC 82-80231. (Bibliography Ser.: No. 291). 1982. pap. 58.00 (ISBN 0-87010-064-5). Inst Paper Chem.

Miller Freeman Publications, Inc., Staff. Pulping Processes: Mill Operations, Techology, & Practices. Smith, Kenneth E., ed. LC 81-81386. (A Pulp & Paper Focus Bk). (Illus.). 216p. 1981. pap. 35.00 (ISBN 0-87930-126-0). Miller Freeman.

Parham, Russell A. & Gray, Richard L. The Practical Identification of Wood Pulp Fibers. LC 82-50114. pap. 55.00 (ISBN 0-317-20555-2, 2022820). Bks Demand UMI.

Pulping & Papermaking Properties of Fast-Growing Plantation Wood Species. 1976. pap. 28.00 (ISBN 0-685-71579-5, F1177, FAO). Unipub.

Technical Association of the Pulp & Paper Industry. Non-Wood Plant Fiber Pulping: Progress Report No. 15. pap. 33.00 (ISBN 0-317-26883-X, 2025297). Bks Demand UMI.

Weiner, Jack & Pollock, Vera. Analytical Methods: Cellulose & Pulp, Vol. 3. 1st supplement ed. LC 60-51407. (Bibliographic Ser.: No. 194). 1968. pap. 8.00 (ISBN 0-87010-002-5); supplement 2, 1973 10.00 (ISBN 0-87010-003-3). Inst Paper Chem.

--Quality Control in the Pulp & Paper Industry, 3 Vols. (Bibliographic Ser.: No. 189, Supplement 1 & 2). 1973. 10.00 (ISBN 0-87010-007-6); Supp. 2, 81P. 1973. 8.00; 73P. 1959 8.00,. Inst Paper Chem.

WOOD PULP–BIBLIOGRAPHY

Louden, Louise. Pulping of Bagasse & Other Papermaking Fibers. LC 76-29080. (Bibliographic Ser.: No. 270). 1976. pap. 20.00 (ISBN 0-87010-045-9). Inst Paper Chem.

WOOD PULP INDUSTRY

see also Paper Making and Trade

Clark, James d'A. Pulp Technology & Treatment for Paper. LC 78-59149. (A Pulp & Paper Book). (Illus.). 752p. 1978. 75.00 (ISBN 0-87930-066-3). Miller Freeman.

Clawson, Marion. Decision Making in Timber Production, Harvest, & Marketing. LC 77-84930. (Resources for the Future Research Papers Ser.: No. R-4). pap. 32.30 (ISBN 0-317-29715-5, 2019816). Bks Demand UMI.

Edde, Howard. Environmental Control for Pulp & Paper Mills. LC 83-22011. (Pollution Technology Review Ser.: No. 108). (Illus.). 179p. 1984. 32.00 (ISBN 0-8155-0979-0). Noyes.

Future Technological Needs of the U. S. Pulp & Paper Industries: Proceedings. 1973. 5.00 (ISBN 0-686-20722-X). SUNY Environ.

Guide for Planning Pulp & Paper Enterprises. (Forestry Ser.: No. 1). (Illus.). 379p. (Orig., 2nd Printing 1977). 1973. 30.50 (ISBN 92-5-100058-1, F217, FAO). Unipub.

International Symposium on Transport & Handling in the Pulp & Paper Industry, Third, Vancouver, B. C. Sept. 1978. Transport & Handling in the Pulp & Paper Industry, Vol. 3: Proceedings. Kalish, John, ed. LC 74-20162. (A Pulp & Paper Book). (Illus.). 240p. 1979. 37.50 (ISBN 0-87930-109-0). Miller Freeman.

International Symposium on Transport & Handling in the Pulp & Paper Industry, 4th, London, England, Nov. 1980. Transport & Handling in the Pulp & Paper Industry, Vol. 4: Proceedings. Kalish, John E., ed. LC 74-20162. (A Pulp & Paper Bk). (Illus.). 208p. 1981. 59.50 (ISBN 0-87930-127-9). Miller Freeman.

Lavigne, John R. Instrumentation Applications for the Pulp & Paper Industry. LC 77-93837. (A Pulp & Paper Book). (Illus.). 1979. 35.00 (ISBN 0-87930-074-4). Miller Freeman.

Louden, Louise. Pulping of Bagasse & Other Papermaking Fibers. LC 76-29080. (Bibliographic Ser.: No. 270). 1976. pap. 20.00 (ISBN 0-87010-045-9). Inst Paper Chem.

Miller Freeman Publications, Inc., Staff. Energy Management & Conservation in Pulp & Paper Mills. Coleman, Matthew, ed. LC 81-81000. (A Pulp & Paper Focus Bk.). (Illus.). 206p. 1981. pap. 32.50 (ISBN 0-87930-099-X). Miller Freeman.

Miller, Richard K., et al. Noise Control Solutions for the Wood Products Industry. 45.00 (ISBN 0-89671-002-5). Fairmont Pr.

Nader, Ralph. The Paper Plantation. LC 73-1907. (Ralph Nader Study Group Reports). 288p. 1974. 11.95 (ISBN 0-670-53807-8, Grossman). Viking.

Parham, Russell A. & Gray, Richard L. The Practical Identification of Wood Pulp Fibers. 212p. 1982. 34.95 (ISBN 0-89852-400-8, 01 01R0100). TAPPI.

Pulp & Paper Industry Division Index to Technical Papers, 1960-1983. 80p. 1984. pap. text ed. 12.00x (ISBN 0-87664-804-9). Instru Soc.

Report of the Third Session of the Committee on Forestry. 1977. pap. 7.50 (ISBN 92-5-100298-3, F1101, FAO). Unipub.

Sittig, M. Pulp & Paper Manufacture: Energy Conservation & Pollution Prevention. LC 77-89631. (Pollution Technology Review Ser. No. 36: Energy Technology Review Ser. No. 17). (Illus.). 1978. 39.00 (ISBN 0-8155-0675-9). Noyes.

Symposium on New Pulps for the Paper Industry, Brussels, Belgium, May 1979. New Pulps for the Paper Industry: Proceedings. Haas, Leonard E., ed. LC 79-53919. (A PPI Bk.). (Illus.). 160p. 1979. pap. 40.00 (ISBN 0-87930-121-X). Miller Freeman.

Technical Association of the Pulp & Paper Industry. International Dissolving & Specialty Pulps Conference, 1983: Proceedings of the Technical Association of the Pulp & Paper Industry, Hyatt Regency Cambridge, Boston, MA, April 5-8, 1983. pap. 61.00 (ISBN 0-317-28917-9, 2020288). Bks Demand UMI.

--International Mechanical Pulping Conference, 1983: Proceedings of the Technical Association of the Pulp & Paper Industry, Capital Hilton, Washington, DC, June 13-17. pap. 81.00 (ISBN 0-317-28923-3, 2020289). Bks Demand UMI.

--Power Piping Data. Tenore, Frank M., ed. pap. 20.00 (ISBN 0-317-26877-5, 2025295). Bks Demand UMI.

--Practical Aspects of Pressing & Drying Seminar, 1985: Notes of TAPPI, the Waverly, Atlanta, GA March 18-22. pap. 58.50 (ISBN 0-317-26843-0, 2025284). Bks Demand UMI.

--Process Control Symposium, 1985: Notes of TAPPI, Marriott. pap. 32.80 (ISBN 0-317-26841-4, 2025283). Bks Demand UMI.

--Relative Humidity: Thermodynamic Charts. pap. 20.00 (ISBN 0-317-26870-8, 2025293). Bks Demand UMI.

Third International Pulp & Paper Process Control Symposium: Proceedings. LC 83-169761. 212p. 1983. pap. text ed. 25.00x (ISBN 0-87664-777-8). Instru Soc.

Weiner, Jack & Roth, Lillian. Air Pollution in the Pulp & Paper Industry. LC 73-82482. (Bibliographic Ser.: No. 237). supplement 1, 1970 8.00 (ISBN 0-87010-000-9); supplement 2, 1973 12.00 (ISBN 0-87010-001-7). Inst Paper Chem.

WOOD-RATS

Alvarez, Ticul. A New Subspecies of Wood Rat (Neotoma) from Northeastern Mexico. (Museum Ser.: Vol. 14, No. 11). 5p. 1962. pap. 1.25 (ISBN 0-317-04911-9). U of KS Mus Nat Hist.

Birney, Elmer C. Systematics of Three Species of Woodrats (Genus Neotome) in Central North America. (Miscellaneous Publications Ser.: No. 58). 173p. 1973. 9.00 (ISBN 0-317-04956-9). U of KS Mus Nat Hist.

Finley, Robert B., Jr. A New Subspecies of Wood Rat (Neotama Mexicana) from Colorado. (Museum Ser.: Vol. 5, No. 30). 8p. 1953. pap. 1.25 (ISBN 0-317-05012-5). U of KS Mus Nat Hist.

--The Wood Rats of Colorado: Distribution & Ecology. (Museum Ser.: Vol. 10, No. 6). 340p. 1958. 17.00 (ISBN 0-686-80280-2). U of KS Mus Nat Hist.

Kelson, Keith R. Comments on the Taxonomy & Geographic Distribution of Some North American Woodrats: Genus Neotoma. (Museum Ser.: Vol. 5, No. 16). 10p. 1952. pap. 1.25 (ISBN 0-317-04865-1). U of KS Mus Nat Hist.

Rainey, Dennis G. Eastern Woodrat, Neotoma Floridana: Life History & Ecology. (Museum Ser.: Vol. 8, No. 10). 12p. 1956. 5.75 (ISBN 0-317-04903-8). U of KS Mus Nat Hist.

Rainey, Dennis G. & Baker, Rollin H. The Pigmy Woodrat, Neotoma Goldmani: Its Distribution & Systematic Position. (Museum Ser.: Vol. 7, No. 15). 6p. 1955. pap. 1.25 (ISBN 0-317-04901-1). U of KS Mus Nat Hist.

WOOD-TURNING

see Turning

WOOD-USING INDUSTRIES

see also Woodworking Industries; also names of specific industries, e.g. Furniture industry and trade

Goldstein, Irving S., ed. Wood Technology: Chemical Aspects. LC 77-2368. (ACS Symposium Ser.: No. 43). 1977. 34.95 (ISBN 0-8412-0373-3). Am Chemical.

Kubler, Hans. Wood As Building & Hobby Material: How to Use Lumber & Wood-Base Panels & Round Wood Wisely in Construction, for Furniture, & As Fuel. LC 80-13380. 256p. 1980. 31.50x (ISBN 0-471-05390-2, Pub. by Wiley-Interscience); pap. 15.95x (ISBN 0-471-09848-5). Wiley.

MacKay, Donald. Empire of Wood: The MacMillian Bloedel Story. LC 82-51134. (Illus.). 448p. 1983. 27.50x (ISBN 0-295-95984-3). U of Wash Pr.

Mater, Jean. Citizens Involved: Handle with Care! A Forest Industry Guide to Working with the Public. 166p. 1977. pap. 7.95 (ISBN 0-917304-04-7); Public acceptance assessment checklist 2.95. Timber.

Miller, Richard K. Noise Control Solutions for the Wood Products Industry. 80p. text ed. 45.00 (ISBN 0-89671-032-7). SEAI Tech Pubns.

Talbot, James J. & Swanson, Winfield, eds. Woodpower -- New Perspectives on Forest Usage. (Illus.). 239p. 1981. 35.00 (ISBN 0-08-027562-1). Pergamon.

Third Tripartite Technical Meeting for the Timber Industry, Geneva, 1-10 December 1981: Note on the Proceedings. iii, 78p. 1982. 7.15 (ISBN 92-2-102767-8). Intl Labour Office.

United Nations Economic Commission for Europe, Geneva, Switzerland, ed. Energy Aspects of the Forest Industries: Proceedings of a Seminar Organized by the Timber Committee of the United Nations Economic Commission for Europe, Udine, Italy 13-17 Nov. 1978. LC 79-42869. (Illus.). 428p. 1979. 75.00 (ISBN 0-08-025661-9). Pergamon.

Wood Chips: Production, Handling, Transport. 2nd, Updated ed. (Forestry Papers: No. 9). (Eng. & Span., Illus.). 141p. 1976. pap. 10.00 (ISBN 92-5-100207-X, F1219, FAO). Unipub.

Wood, Virginia S. Live Oaking: Southern Timber for Tall Ships. LC 81-14152. (Illus.). 218p. 1981. text ed. 23.95x (ISBN 0-930350-20-0). NE U Pr.

Wood: World Trends & Prospects. (Freedom from Hunger Campaign Basic Studies: No. 16). (Orig.). 1967. pap. 9.25 (ISBN 0-685-09414-6, F493, FAO). Unipub.

WOOD WARBLERS

Bent, Arthur C. Life Histories of North American Wood Warblers, 2 Vols. (Illus.). Vol. 1. pap. 6.95 (ISBN 0-486-21153-3); Vol. 2. pap. 6.95 (ISBN 0-486-21154-1). Dover.

--Life Histories of North American Wood Warblers, 2 Vols. (Illus.). 12.00 ea. (ISBN 0-8446-1646-X). Peter Smith.

Chapman, Frank M. The Warblers of North America. (Illus.). 13.25 (ISBN 0-8446-1838-1). Peter Smith.

WOOD WASTE

see also Particle Board

Cheremisinoff, P. H., et al. Woodwastes Utilization & Disposal. LC 76-16931. (Illus.). 1976. pap. 9.95x (ISBN 0-87762-211-6). Technomic.

Data Notes Publishing Staff. Wood Recycling: Data Notes. LC 83-90734. 30p. 1983. pap. text ed. 4.95 (ISBN 0-911569-47-2, Pub. by Data Notes). Prosperity & Profits.

Pollock, Vera. Tall Oil. 3rd ed. LC 59-3433. (Bibliographic Ser.: No. 133-135, Supplement 3). 1976. pap. 22.00 (ISBN 0-87010-044-0). Inst Paper Chem.

WOODCHUCKS

see Marmots

WOODCOCK

Sheldon, William G. The Book of the American Woodcock. LC 67-11243. (Illus.). 250p. 1967. 15.00 (ISBN 0-87023-021-2). U of Mass Pr.

Sisley, Nick. Grouse & Woodcock: An Upland Hunter's Book. LC 79-15388. (Illus.). 192p. 1980. 13.95 (ISBN 0-8117-0717-2). Stackpole.

WOODCOCK, AMERICAN

see Woodcock

WOODEN BRIDGES

see Bridges, Wooden

WOODLAND PLANTS

see Forest Flora

WOODPECKERS

Bent, Arthur C. Life Histories of North American Woodpeckers. (Illus.). 1939. pap. 7.95 (ISBN 0-486-21083-9). Dover.

--Life Histories of North American Woodpeckers. (Illus.). 15.25 (ISBN 0-8446-1647-8). Peter Smith.

Kilham, Lawrence. Life History Studies of Woodpeckers of Eastern North America, No. 20. (Illus.). 240p. 1984. 19.00 (ISBN 0-318-01573-0). Nuttall Ornith.

Short, Lester L. Woodpeckers of the World. Weidner, James H., ed. LC 79-53793. (Delaware Museum of Natural History Monograph: No. 4). (Illus.). 694p. 1982. 99.95 (ISBN 0-913176-05-2). Foris Pubns.

WOODWORK

see also Cabinet-Work; Carpentry; Furniture Making; Joinery; Paneling; Plywood; Veneers and Veneering; Wood Finishing

Advanced Woodworking. LC 81-1310. (Home Repair & Improvement Ser.). lib. bdg. 15.94 (ISBN 0-8094-3478-4, Pub. by Time-Life). Silver.

Advanced Woodworking. Time Life Bks Editors, ed. (Home Repair & Improvement Ser.). (Illus.). 128p. 1981. 11.95 (ISBN 0-8094-3478-4). Time-Life.

Albers, Vernon M. How to Use Woodworking Tools Effectively & Safely. (Illus.). 190p. 1974. 8.95 (ISBN 0-498-01851-2). A S Barnes.

Anderson, Eric A. & Earle, George, eds. Design & Aesthetics in Wood. LC 75-171186. 1972. 34.50x (ISBN 0-87395-216-2). State U NY Pr.

The Art of Wood Turning. (Illus.). 48p. 1983. 7.50 (ISBN 0-686-47658-1); 6.00. Am Craft.

Bairstow, John E. Practical & Decorative Woodworking Joints. LC 84-51838. (Illus.). 128p. 1985. 17.95 (ISBN 0-8069-5544-9); pap. 11.95 (ISBN 0-8069-7948-8). Sterling.

Banister, Manly. Making Picture Frames in Wood. LC 81-50985. (Home Craftsman Bk.). (Illus.). 128p. 1981. pap. text ed. 6.95 (ISBN 0-8069-7542-3). Sterling.

Bealer, Alex W. Old Ways of Working Wood. rev. ed. (Illus.). 1980. 12.50 (ISBN 0-517-54047-9, C N Potter Bks). Crown.

Beazer, Cyril H. Random Reflections of a West Country Master Craftsman. 168p. 1981. 35.00x (ISBN 0-9507709-0-6, Pub. by Beazer England). State Mutual Bk.

Blandford, Percy W. The Illustrated Handbook of Woodworking Joints. (Illus.). 352p. 1984. 19.95o.p (ISBN 0-8306-0274-7); pap. 15.95 (ISBN 0-8306-0174-0, 1574). TAB Bks.

Boulter, Bruce. Woodturning in Pictures. (Illus.). 144p. (Orig.). 1983. pap. 12.95 (ISBN 0-8069-7742-6). Sterling.

Brimer, John B. The Homeowner's Complete Outdoor Building Book (Wood & Masonry Construction) (Popular Science Ser.). (Illus.). 512p. 1985. 29.95 (ISBN 0-943822-47-5). Rodale Pr Inc.

Brown, Emmett E. & Brown, Cyril. Polychromatic Assembly for Woodturning. rev. ed. Sorsky, R., ed. LC 82-80340. (Illus.). 120p. 1982. pap. 15.95 spiral bound (ISBN 0-941936-00-7). Linden Pub Fresno.

Bucksch, Herbert. Holz Woerterbuch, Vol. 1. (Ger. & Eng., Dictionary of wood & woodworking practice). 1966. 59.95 (ISBN 3-7625-1168-3, M-7465, Pub. by Bauverlag). French & Eur.

--Holz Woerterbuch, Vol. 2. (Ger. & Eng., Dictionary of wood & woodworking practice). 1966. 67.50 (ISBN 3-7625-1170-5, M-7466, Pub. by Bauverlag). French & Eur.

Capotosto, Rosario. Capotosto's Woodworking Techniques & Projects. 1982. pap. 25.95 (ISBN 0-442-21671-8). Van Nos Reinhold.

--Capotosto's Woodworking Wisdom: Five Hundred Original Jigs, Shop Aids & Tool Techniques for the Home Craftsman. 1983. 29.95 (ISBN 0-442-21696-3). Van Nos Reinhold.

--The Complete Book of Woodworking. LC 74-27319. (A Popular Science Ser). (Illus.). 448p. 1975. 18.22i (ISBN 0-06-010613-1, HarpT). Har-Row.

Cliffe, R. Woodworking Principles & Practices. (Illus.). 1981. 20.95 (ISBN 0-8269-4820-0). Am Technical.

Clifford, Jerrold R. Basic Woodworking & Carpentry...with Projects. (Illus.). 252p. 1980. pap. 6.95 (ISBN 0-8306-1058-8, 1058). TAB Bks.

Coggins, Frank W. The Woodturner's Handbook. (Illus.). 224p. 21.95 (ISBN 0-8306-0769-2, 1769); pap. 12.95 (ISBN 0-8306-1769-8). TAB Bks.

Cohen, M. Lost Art of Hand Woodworking. 1986. cancelled (ISBN 0-442-24656-0). Van Nos Reinhold.

Colorado Springs Fine Arts Center. Woodworking in the Rockies. LC 82-71534. (Illus.). 1982. 6.00 (ISBN 0-686-37084-8). Taylor Museum.

--Woodworking in the Rockies. LC 82-71534. (Illus.). 52p. (Orig.). 1982. pap. 6.00 (ISBN 0-686-35850-3). CO Springs Fine Arts.

Coppa & Avery Consultants. An Architectural Guide to Wood Construction, Preservation, Conservation, Restoration & Framing. (Architecture Series: Bibliography: A-1312). 11p. 1985. pap. 2.00 (ISBN 0-89028-242-0). Vance Biblios.

Corkhill, Thomas. The Complete Dictionary of Wood. LC 79-10183. (Illus.). 672p. 1982. pap. 14.95 (ISBN 0-8128-6142-6). Stein & Day.

DeChristoforo, R. J. Woodworking Techniques: Joints & Their Applications. (Illus.). 1979. ref.ed. 23.95 (ISBN 0-8359-8785-X). Reston.

DeCristoforo, R. J. Power Tool Woodworking for Everyone. rev. ed. LC 83-22995. (Illus.). 360p. 1983. 31.95 (ISBN 0-8359-5567-2). Shopsmith.

Douglass, J. H., et al. Units in Woodworking. LC 79-8737. (Industrial Arts Ser.). 320p. 1981. text ed. 18.20 (ISBN 0-8273-1332-2); pap. text ed. 14.40 (ISBN 0-8273-1333-0); comprehensive tests 2.80 (ISBN 0-8273-1335-7); instr's guide 2.85 (ISBN 0-8273-1334-9). Delmar.

Dunbar, Michael. Antique Woodworking Tools: A Guide to the Purchase, Restoration & Use of Old Tools for Today's Shop. (Illus.). 1977. 12.50 (ISBN 0-8038-5821-3). Hastings.

Endacott, G. W. Woodworking & Furniture Making. (Drake Home Craftman Ser.). (Illus.). 1976. pap. 5.95 (ISBN 0-8069-8804-5). Sterling.

Ensinger, Earl W. Problems in Artistic Woodturning. LC 78-60054. (Illus.). 1978. pap. 8.95 (ISBN 0-918036-07-0). Woodcraft Supply.

Eyers, A. S. Practical Woodwork for Laboratory Technicians. LC 79-117463. 1970. 14.50 (ISBN 0-08-015962-1). Pergamon.

Family Handyman Editors. Sixty-Six Family Handyman Wood Projects: PB. Newton, Richard, ed. (Illus.). 208p. 1985. 21.95 (ISBN 0-8306-0464-2, 2632); pap. 14.95 (ISBN 0-8306-1164-9). TAB Bks.

Feirer. Beginning Woodwork. 1984. text ed. 13.32 (ISBN 0-02-662640-3). Bennett IL.

--Industrial Arts Woodworking. rev. ed. 1982. text ed. 17.92 (ISBN 0-02-664670-6). Bennett IL.

Feirer. Woodworking for Industry. 1979. text ed. 23.72 (ISBN 0-02-666350-3); student guide 7.96 (ISBN 0-02-666360-0); tchr's. ed. 3.96 (ISBN 0-02-666380-5). Bennett IL.

Hindle, Brooke. America's Wooden Age: Aspects of Its Early Technology. LC 74-7842. (Illus.). 224p. 1985. pap. 14.95 (ISBN 0-912882-60-3, 22235). Sleepy Hollow.

Prevention of Dust Explosions in Woodworking & Wood Flour Manufacturing Plants. (Sixty Ser.). 1971. pap. 2.00 (ISBN 0-685-58069-5, 664). Natl Fire Prot.

Roberts, Kenneth D., ed. Alex Mathieson & Sons Ltd. Woodworking & Cooper Tools, 1899. 2nd, enl. ed. 1979. 7.50 (ISBN 0-913602-32-9). K Roberts.

Scott, Ernest. Working in Wood: An Illustrated Encyclopedia. (Illus.). 272p. 1980. 25.00 (ISBN 0-399-12550-7, Putnam). Putnam Pub Group.

Stone, Michael. Contemporary American Wooworkers. (Illus.). 208p. 1985. 29.95 (ISBN 0-87905-098-5). Gibbs M Smith.

WOODWORKING MACHINERY
see also Sawmills;
also kinds of machines, e.g. Lathes, Planing Machines

Albers, Vernon M. How to Use Woodworking Tools Effectively & Safely. (Illus.). 190p. 1974. 8.95 (ISBN 0-498-01851-2). A S Barnes.

Bradley, Ian. Shaping Machine & Lathe Tools. (Illus.). 80p. 1985. pap. 4.40 (ISBN 0-85242-485-X, Pub. by Argus). Aztex.

Chinn, Gary. The Garrett Wade Book of Woodworking Tools. LC 79-7082. (Illus.). 1980. 19.18i (ISBN 0-690-01840-1). T Y Crowell.

Cunningham, Beryl M. & Holtrop, Wm. Woodshop Tool Maintenance. rev. ed. (Illus.). 296p. 1974. pap. text ed. 23.48 (ISBN 0-02-666280-9). Bennett IL.

Fine Woodworking Magazine Editors. Fine Woodworking on Woodworking Machines. LC 84-52102. (Illus.). 112p. (Orig.). 1985. pap. 6.95 (ISBN 0-918804-31-0, Dist. by W W Norton). Taunton.

Griffiths, L. & Spence, P. Woodworking: Tools, Materials, Processes. (Illus.). 634p. 1981. 20.95 (ISBN 0-8269-4833-2). Am Technical.

Kebabian, Paul B. & Witney, Dudley. American Woodworking Tools. LC 78-7066. 1978. 31.50 (ISBN 0-8212-0731-8, 036870). NYGS.

Roberts, Kenneth D. Buck Brothers Chisels, Trade Catalogue 1890. 1976. 9.25 (ISBN 0-913602-19-1); pap. 6.50 (ISBN 0-685-67907-1). K Roberts.

--Leonard Bailey's Co. Bench Planes, 1883. 1975. 2.50. K Roberts.

--Some Nineteenth Century English Woodworking Tools. (Illus.). 496p. 1980. text ed. 40.00x (ISBN 0-913602-40-X). K Roberts.

Self, Charles R. The Complete Handbook of Woodworking Tools & Hardware. (Illus.). 400p. 1983. 21.95 (ISBN 0-8306-0484-7, 1484); pap. 14.95 (ISBN 0-8306-1484-2). TAB Bks.

Stefford, John & McMurdo, Guy. Woodwork Technology. (Illus.). 128p. 1978. 22.00x (ISBN 0-7217-4008-1, Pub. by Schofield & Sims UK). State Mutual Bk.

Walker, Philip. Woodworking Tools. (Shire Album Ser.: No. 50). (Illus.). 32p. (Orig.). 1983. pap. 2.95 (ISBN 0-85263-501-X, Pub. by Shire Pubns England). Seven Hills Bks.

Woodworking Industry Machinery. (UNIDO Guides to Information Sources: No. 31). pap. 4.00 (ISBN 0-686-93269-2, UNID214, UN). Unipub.

WOODY PLANTS
see also Climbing Plants; Forest Ecology; Forest Flora; Shrubs; Trees

Blackwell, Will H., Jr. Guide to the Woody Plants of the Tri-State Area. (Illus.). 1976. pap. text ed. 7.95 (ISBN 0-8403-1581-3). Kendall-Hunt.

Braun, E. L. The Woody Plants of Ohio. 1969. 39.95x (ISBN 0-02-841890-5). Hafner.

Browse, Philip M. Hardy Woody Plants from Seed. 165p. 1981. 30.00x (ISBN 0-686-75417-4, Pub. by Grower Bks). State Mutual Bk.

Burgess, Robert L. Woody Plants of Icelandic Park. LC 68-65253. (Illus.). 64p. 1968. pap. 1.00 (ISBN 0-911042-15-6). N Dak Inst.

Clark, G. Thomas. Winter Twigs of Arkansas: A Field Guide to Deciduous Woody Plants. LC 81-50399. (Illus.). 93p. (Orig.). 1981. pap. 9.95 (ISBN 0-914546-35-X). Rose Pub.

Duncan, Wilbur H. Woody Vines of the Southeastern United States. LC 74-13511. 84p. 1975. pap. 6.95x (ISBN 0-8203-0348-8). U of Ga Pr.

Herlocker, Dennis. Woody Vegetation of the Serengeti National Park. (Kleberg Studies in Natural Resources). (Illus.). 1975. pap. 5.95 (ISBN 0-89096-195-6). Tex A&M Univ Pr.

Hoag, Donald G. Trees & Shrubs for Northern Plains. LC 65-65406. (Illus.). 376p. 1965. pap. 12.50 (ISBN 0-911042-10-5). N Dak Inst.

Hyland, Fay & Campbell, Christopher S. Winter Keys to Woody Plants of Maine. 1977. pap. 4.95 (ISBN 0-89101-034-3). U Maine Orono.

Hyland, Fay & Hoisington, Barbara. The Woody Plants of Sphagnous Bogs of Northern New England & Adjacent Canada. (Illus.). 110p. pap. 3.95 (ISBN 0-89101-045-9). U Maine Orono.

Hyland, Fay & Steinmetz, Ferdinand H. Trees & Other Woody Plants of Maine. 72p. pap. 3.50 (ISBN 0-89621-018-9). U Maine Orono.

Kozlowski, T. T. Water Deficits & Plant Growth: Woody Plant Communities, Vol. 6. LC 68-14658. 1981. 75.00 (ISBN 0-12-424156-5). Acad Pr.

Kramer, Paul J. & Kozlowski, Theodore T. Physiology of Woody Plants. LC 78-27356. 1979. 35.00 (ISBN 0-12-425050-5). Acad Pr.

Lamb, Samuel H. Woody Plants of the Southwest. LC 76-357696. (Illus.). 1977. pap. 12.95 (ISBN 0-913270-50-4). Sunstone Pr.

Li, Hui-Lin. Woody Flora of Taiwan. (Illus.). 1963. 25.00 (ISBN 0-87098-019-X). Livingston.

Lynch, Daniel. Native & Naturalized Woody Plants of Austin & the Hill Country. Mosely, Jane, ed. LC 80-53737. (Illus.). 180p. (Orig.). 1981. pap. 7.95 (ISBN 0-938472-00-3). St Edwards Univ.

Rehder, A. The Bradley Bibliography: A Guide to the Literature of the Woody Plants of the World, Published Before the Beginning of the 20th Century, 5 vols. Sargent, C. S., ed. 3895p. 1976. Repr. Set. lib. bdg. 483.00x. Vols. I & II (ISBN 3-87429-107-3). Vol. III (ISBN 3-87429-108-1). Vol. IV (ISBN 3-87429-109-X). Vol. V (ISBN 3-87429-110-3). Lubrecht & Cramer.

Stephens, Homer A. Trees, Shrubs, & Woody Vines in Kansas. LC 69-10357. (Illus.). 1969. pap. 9.95 (ISBN 0-7006-0057-4). U Pr of KS.

--Woody Plants of the North Central Plains. LC 72-97834. (Illus.). 560p. 1973. 29.95x (ISBN 0-7006-0107-4). U Pr of KS.

Stupka, Arthur. Trees, Shrubs, & Woody Vines of Great Smoky Mountains National Park. LC 64-25370. (Illus.). 1964. pap. 5.95 (ISBN 0-87049-053-2); pap. text ed. 11.95 cloth (ISBN 0-87049-478-3). U of Tenn Pr.

Trelease, William. Winter Botany: An Identification Guide to Native & Cultivated Trees & Shrubs. (Illus.). pap. 6.95 (ISBN 0-486-21800-7). Dover.

Viertel, Arthur T. Trees, Shrubs, & Vines: A Pictorial Guide to the Ornamental Woody Plants of the Northern United States, Exclusive of Conifers. (Illus.). 1970. pap. 7.95x (ISBN 0-8156-0068-2). Syracuse U Pr.

Vines, Robert A. Trees, Shrubs, & Woody Vines of the Southwest. (Illus.). 1116p. 1960. 47.50 (ISBN 0-292-73414-X). U of Tex Pr.

WOOL
see also Wool Trade and Industry; Woolen and Worsted Manufacture; Yarn

Bird, C. L. The Theory & Practice of Wool Dyeing. 4th ed. 249p. 1972. 39.00x (ISBN 0-686-91778-2, Pub. by Soc Dyers & Colour). State Mutual Bk.

Ryder, Michael L. & Stephenson, Stuart K. Wool Growth. LC 66-16694. (Illus.). 1968. 97.50 (ISBN 0-12-605150-X). Acad Pr.

Smith, John. Chronicon Rusticum - Commerciale, 2 Vols. LC 68-18602. Repr. of 1747 ed. Set. 87.50x (ISBN 0-678-00483-8). Kelley.

Von Bergen, Werner, ed. Wool Handbook. 3rd ed. LC 63-11600. (Illus.). 1963-70. Vol. 2, Pt. 2. 115.00x (Pub. by Wiley-Interscience). Wiley.

WOOL CARDING

Crowfoot, Grace M. & Roth, H. Ling. Handspinning & Wool Combing. (Illus.). Repr. 5.95 (ISBN 0-686-09824-2). Robin & Russ.

WOOL TRADE AND INDUSTRY
see also Woolen and Worsted Manufacture

Brearley, Alan & Treadle, John. The Worsted Industry. 198p. 1982. 59.00x (ISBN 0-686-87182-0). State Mutual Bk.

Brearley, Alan & Tredale, John A. The Woolen Industry. 154p. 1982. 40.00x (ISBN 0-686-87180-4). State Mutual Bk.

Crockett, Norman L. The Woolen Industry of the Midwest. LC 75-111505. (Illus.). 176p. 1970. 16.00x (ISBN 0-8131-1195-1). U Pr of Ky.

Ensminger, M. Eugene. Sheep & Wool Science. 4th ed. LC 73-79612. 1970. text ed. 27.35 (ISBN 0-8134-1113-0); text ed. 20.50x. Interstate.

Freudenberger, Herman. The Waldstein Woolen Mill. (Kress Library Publications: No. 18). (Illus.). 1963. pap. 8.95x (ISBN 0-678-09912-X, Baker Lib). Kelley.

Lemon, H. How to Find Out About the Wool Textile Industry. 1969. pap. 14.00 (ISBN 0-08-012983-8). Pergamon.

Lipson, E. History of the Woolen & Worsted Industries. 273p. 1965. Repr. of 1921 ed. 35.00x (ISBN 0-7146-2339-3, F Cass Co). Biblio Dist.

Toomy, Barry J. Handling, Grading & Disposal of Wool. (Agricultural Services Bulletin: No. 55). 99p. (Orig.). 1984. pap. 8.00 (ISBN 92-5-101368-3, F2560, FAO). Unipub.

Von Bergen, Werner, ed. Wool Handbook. 3rd ed. LC 63-11600. (Illus.). 1963-70. Vol. 2, Pt. 2. 115.00x (Pub. by Wiley-Interscience). Wiley.

WOOLEN AND WORSTED MANUFACTURE
see also Weaving; Wool Carding

Brearley, Alan & Treadle, John. The Worsted Industry. 198p. 1982. 59.00x (ISBN 0-686-87182-0). State Mutual Bk.

Brown, T. D., ed. Wool in Double Jersey. 122p. 1973. 45.00x (ISBN 0-900541-79-2, Pub. by Meadowfield Pr England). State Mutual Bk.

Burnley, James. History of Wool & Wool-Combing. LC 68-55497. (Illus.). Repr. of 1889 ed. 37.50x (ISBN 0-678-00519-2). Kelley.

Farnworth, A. J. & Delmenico, J. Permanent Setting of Wool. 52p. 1971. 39.00x (ISBN 0-900541-18-0, Pub. by Meadowfield Pr England). State Mutual Bk.

James, John. History of the Worsted Manufacture in England. (Illus.). 640p. 1968. 35.00x (ISBN 0-7146-1399-1, F Cass Co). Biblio Dist.

Lipson, E. History of the Woolen & Worsted Industries. 273p. 1965. Repr. of 1921 ed. 35.00x (ISBN 0-7146-2339-3, F Cass Co). Biblio Dist.

McPhee, J. R. & Phil, D. The Mothproofing of Wool. 58p. 1971. 39.00x (ISBN 0-686-97038-1, Pub. by Meadowfield Pr England). State Mutual Bk.

Makinson. Shrinkproofing of Wool. (Fiber Science Ser.: Vol. 8). 1979. 75.00 (ISBN 0-8247-6776-4). Dekker.

Ramsay, George D. Wiltshire Woollen Industry in the Sixteenth & Seventeenth Centuries. LC 66-6103. Repr. of 1943 ed. 25.00x (ISBN 0-678-05192-5). Kelley.

Tidball, Harriet. Woolens & Tweeds. LC 62-698. (Shuttle Craft Guild Monograph: No. 4). (Illus.). 46p. 1961. pap. 6.95 (ISBN 0-916658-04-X). HTH Pubs.

WORD MAGIC (COMPUTER PROGRAM)

Scriven, Michael. Word Magic: Evaluating & Selecting Word Processing. (Data Processing Ser.). (Illus.). 282p. 1983. text ed. 25.00 (ISBN 0-534-97922-X); pap. 18.95 (ISBN 0-534-02854-3). Lifetime Learn.

--Word Magic: Evaluating & Selecting Word Processing. 1985. text ed. 25.00 (ISBN 0-317-03932-6); pap. 5.00. Edgepress.

WORD PROCESSING

Adams, Steve. The Quick & Easy Guide to Word Processing on the Apple. 128p. 1984. 4.95 (ISBN 0-912003-29-4). Bk Co.

Alden, Carole. Word Processing with Your Coleco Adam. LC 84-51243. 127p. 1984. pap. 5.95 (ISBN 0-89588-182-9). SYBEX.

All about Seventy Microcomputer Word Processing Packages. 51p. 25.00 (ISBN 0-318-03648-7). Datapro Res.

Anderson, Thomas J. & Trotter, W. Word Processing. LC 73-94097. (Illus.). 192p. 1974. 23.95 (ISBN 0-8144-5356-2); user's manual 9.95. AMACOM.

Anderson, Thomas J. & Trotter, William R. Word Processing Users' Manual. LC 73-94097. 1976. pap. 12.95 (ISBN 0-8144-5424-0). AMACOM.

Arnston, L. Joyce. Word-Information Processing: Concepts & Procedures. LC 82-18020. write for info. (ISBN 0-534-01346-5). Kent Pub Co.

Arntson, L. Joyce. Word-Information Processing: Applications, Skills & Procedures. LC 82-18009. write for info. (ISBN 0-534-01345-7). Kent Pub Co.

Aschner, Katherine. The Word Processing Handbook: A Step-by-Step Guide to Automating the Office. 200p. 1983. pap. 19.95 (ISBN 0-442-21076-0). Van Nos Reinhold.

--The Word Processing Handbook: A Step-by-Step Guide to Automating Your Office. LC 82-3. (Information & Comunications Management Guides Ser.). (Illus.). 193p. 1982. 32.95 (ISBN 0-86729-017-X, 705-BW); pap. 22.95 (ISBN 0-86729-018-8). Knowledge Indus.

--Word Processing Handbook: A Step-by-Step Guide to Automating Your Office. 2nd ed. 1983. pap. 8.95 (ISBN 0-88908-913-2). Self Counsel Pr.

Baber, Lina G. Word-Information Processing: Concepts & Applications. (Illus.). 352p. 1984. Additional supplements may be obtained from publisher. text ed. 23.95 (ISBN 0-675-20095-4). Merrill.

Baumann, Mary A. & Bahntge, Mary A. Legal Terminology & Transcription: Word Processing. 1985. pap. text ed. write for info.; tchrs' ed. avail. (ISBN 0-471-82042-3). Wiley.

Beil, D. The Bank Street Writer Book: The Rosetta Stone of Word Processing. 256p. 1984. 19.95 (ISBN 0-8359-0361-3). Reston.

Belkin, Gary S. How to Start & Run Your Own Word Processing Business. LC 83-21691. (Small Business Ser.: 1-382). 206p. 1984. pap. 9.95 (ISBN 0-471-88396-4, Pub. by Wiley Pr). Wiley.

Bergerud, Marly & Gonzalez, Jean. Word Information Processing: Concepts of Office Automation. 2nd ed. LC 83-19815. (Word Processing Ser.: 1-388). 528p. 1984. text ed. 26.95. Wiley.

Bergerud, Mary & Gonzalez, Jean. Word Information Processing Concepts. 387p. 1981. 16.95 (ISBN 0-686-98088-3). Telecom Lib.

Berner, Jeff. The Foolproof Guide to Scripsit Word Processing. LC 83-60044. (Illus.). 179p. pap. cancelled (ISBN 0-89588-098-9). SYBEX.

Berst, Jessie. The Computhink Guide to Word Processing. LC 83-50169. 192p. 1983. pap. 12.95 (ISBN 0-672-22069-5, 22069). Sams.

Bieber-Moses, Jeanette J. SuperSCRIPSIT Word Processing for the TRS-80 Models III, 4, & 4P. 1985. pap. 17.95 (ISBN 0-673-18086-7). Scott F.

Bolocan, David. The WORD Book. LC 85-2528. (Illus.). 240p. (Orig.). 1985. 24.95 (ISBN 0-8306-0958-X, 1958); pap. 16.95 (ISBN 0-8306-1958-5). TAB Bks.

Boudrot, Thomas E. Byte-Sized Activities: The Generic Word Processing Book. 1985. pap. 5.95 (ISBN 0-673-18175-8). Scott F.

Boulmetis, John & Purnell, Richard. An Introduction & Guide to Word Processing. 196p. 1983. pap. 11.20x (ISBN 0-89702-043-X). PAR Inc.

Boyce, B. Mercury Systems Inc. Practice Set in Word-Information Processing for Conventional & Text-Editing Typewriters. 1981. 8.24 (ISBN 0-07-006901-8). McGraw.

Boyce, B. & Popyk, M. K. The Electronic Office & You: Word Processing Concepts. 192p. 1984. 8.44 (ISBN 0-07-006921-2). McGraw.

Branson, John J., III. Home Word Processing Start-Up Guide: How to Start Your Own Business. (Illus.). 160p. 1985. pap. 11.95 (ISBN 0-13-392986-8). P H.

Brooks, Lloyd D. Consultamation, Inc. Word Processing Practice & Applications. 192p. 1982. 13.15 (ISBN 0-07-008081-X). McGraw.

Brown, Eric. Throw Away Your Pencil: Writing More Effectively with a Word Processor. 1984. pap. 14.95 (ISBN 0-8359-7689-0). Reston.

Brown, Eric D. Writing with a Word Processor: Communication in the Computer Age. 1984. pap. text ed. 15.95 (ISBN 0-8359-8857-0). Reston.

Burton, Philip E. A Dictionary of Word Processing. 256p. 1984. pap. 15.95 (ISBN 0-8240-7289-8). Garland Pub.

--A Dictionary of Word Processing & Printers. LC 84-10348. 264p. 1985. 22.95 (ISBN 0-8240-7289-8); pap. 15.95 (ISBN 0-8240-7291-X). Garland Pub.

Carter, Shirley G. Word Processing & Other Automated Publication Systems, Vol. 6. Zabielski, Robert J., ed. (Anthology). 250p. 1981. pap. 25.00x (ISBN 0-686-73138-7, Pub. by Soc Tech Comm). Univelt Inc.

Casady, Mona. Word Information Processing Concepts. 1984. text ed. 5.30 wkbk. (ISBN 0-538-23610-8, W61). SW Pub.

Cecela, Agnes. Word Processing Skills & Applications Using the Wang Systems. 2nd ed. 1985. pap. text ed. 21.95 (ISBN 0-8359-8824-4); instr's manual avail. (ISBN 0-8359-8825-2). Reston.

Cecil, P. B. Word Processing in the Modern Office. 2nd ed. 1980. pap. 21.95 (ISBN 0-8053-1758-9); instrs manual 4.95 (ISBN 0-8053-1760-0); student wkbk 7.95 (ISBN 0-8053-1761-9). Benjamin-Cummings.

Cecil, Paula B. Management of Word Processing Operations. 1980. 32.95 (ISBN 0-8053-1759-7); instr's guide 4.95 (ISBN 0-8053-1762-7). Benjamin-Cummings.

Chambers, Harry. Making the Most of Word Processing. 192p. 1982. 55.00x (ISBN 0-686-44697-6, Pub. by Hutchinson). State Mutual Bk.

Chambers, Harry T. Making the Most of Word Processing. 189p. 1982. text ed. 31.75 (ISBN 0-09-147420-5, Busn Bks England). Brookfield Pub Co.

Chirich, Nancy. The Graphics Connection. (Illus.). 272p. (Orig.). 1985. pap. 11.95 (ISBN 0-912761-04-0). Ed-it Prods.

Clippinger, Dorinda. Word Processing Input. 1983. pap. text ed. 15.95 (ISBN 0-8359-8802-3). Reston.

Cole, B. C. Beyond Word Processing: How to Use Your Personal Computer As a Processor. 1985. 12.95 (ISBN 0-07-011698-9). McGraw.

Coleman, Joseph. Word Processing Simplified & Self-Taught. LC 82-24501. (Simplified & Self-Taught Ser.). (Illus.). 128p. 1983. lib. bdg. 11.95 (ISBN 0-668-05599-5); pap. 4.95 (ISBN 0-668-05601-0). Arco.

Conlin, Jean M. & Conlin, Robert G. Word Processing Training on the Wang. 400p. 1985. pap. 26.95 (ISBN 0-13-963406-1). P-H.

Corchado, Veronica & McHugh, Kathleen. Selecting the Right Word Processing Software for the IBM PC. LC 84-50991. 96p. 1984. pap. 11.95 (ISBN 0-89588-177-2). SYBEX.

Cornelius, Hal & Lewis, William. A Career Blazer Guide to Word Processing. (Career Blazers Guides Ser.). 192p. 1983. pap. 7.95 (ISBN 0-671-45869-8). Monarch Pr.

Riley, John T. & Hurtz, Judie L. Teaching Word Processing in the Elementary School. 37p. 1983. pap. 7.95 (ISBN 0-912007-03-6). Computer Direct.
Rinearson, Peter. Word Processing Power with Microsoft Word: Professional Writing on Your IBM PC. 304p. 1985. pap. 16.95 (ISBN 0-914845-05-5). Microsoft.
--Word Processing with Style & Microsoft Word. 192p. Date not set. pap. 18.95 (ISBN 0-914845-28-4). Microsoft.
Rosen, Arnold & Fielden, Rosemary. Word Processing. 2nd ed. 430p. 1981. 18.95 (ISBN 0-686-98087-5). Telecom Lib.
Rosen, Arnold & Freiden, Rosemary. Word Processing. 2nd ed. 1982. 23.95 (ISBN 0-13-963488-6). P-H.
Rosen, Arnold & Hubbard, William. Word Processing Keyboarding Applications & Exercises. 291p. 1981. pap. text ed. 23.95 (ISBN 0-471-08700-9); Working Papers 188p. 7.95 (ISBN 0-471-09790-X); write for info. tchr's. manual (ISBN 0-471-07734-8). Wiley.
--Word Processing Keyboarding Applications & Exercises. 2nd ed. 352p. 1985. pap. 23.95 (ISBN 0-471-80855-5). Wiley.
Saffer, Sally M. Word Processing & the Changing Office Environment. 1985. text ed. 4.95 wkbk. (ISBN 0-538-23800-3, W80). SW Pub.
Sanderson, M. & Rawlinson, M. K. Word Processing Manual. 200p. 1982. pap. text ed. 19.95x (ISBN 0-7121-2323-7). Trans-Atlantic.
Sandler, Corey. Word Processing on the IBM PCjr: A Writer's Guide to the Hardware & Software. 240p. (Orig.). pap. cancelled (ISBN 0-916688-74-7, 74-7). Creative Comp.
Schamp, Kathleen L. PC Word Processing with DisplayWrite. (Illus.). 71p. 1985. pap. text ed. 8.95 (ISBN 0-942728-21-1). Custom Pub Co.
Schmeltz, L. R. Word Processing with Your Microcomputer. (Illus.). 256p. (Orig.). 1982. pap. 13.95 (ISBN 0-8306-1478-8, 1478). TAB Bks.
Segal. Business Writing Using Word Processing: Apple Writer. 1985. pap. write for info. (ISBN 0-471-81720-1). Wiley.
--Business Writing Using Word Processing: IBM Easywriter. 1985. pap. write for info. (ISBN 0-471-81721-X). Wiley.
--Business Writing Using Word Processing: IBM Wordstar. 1985. pap. write for info. (ISBN 0-471-81719-8). Wiley.
--Business Writing Using Word Processing. 1986. pap. price not set (ISBN 0-471-82404-6). Wiley.
Seybold, P. B. & Marshak, R. T. Word Processing Software for the IBM PC. (Illus.). 201p. 1984. pap. 15.95 (ISBN 0-07-056322-5, Byte Bks). McGraw.
Sikonowiz, Walter. Complete Book of Word Processing & Business Graphics. 256p. (Orig.). 1982. pap. 14.95 (ISBN 0-942412-03-6). Micro Text Pubs.
--The Complete Book of Word Processing & Business Graphics. 212p. 1983. 21.95 (ISBN 0-13-158667-X); pap. 14.95 (ISBN 0-13-158659-9). P-H.
Simons, G. L. Introducing Word Processing. 180p. 1981. pap. 22.50x (ISBN 0-85012-320-8). Intl Pubns Serv.
--Introducing Word Processing. 180p. 1981. pap. 20.75 (ISBN 0-471-89407-9). Wiley.
Simons, Gary F. Powerful Ideas for Text Processing. LC 83-51795. 200p. (Orig.). 1984. pap. 7.00 (ISBN 0-88312-930-2); program disk 8.95. microfiche (3) 3.80 (ISBN 0-88312-984-1). Summer Inst Ling.
Simpson, Alan, ed. Planning for the Word Processing. (Office of the Future Ser.: Vol. 3). 160p. 1982. pap. text ed. 23.50x (ISBN 0-566-03414-X). Gower Pub Co.
Smith, Brian R. & Austin, Daniel J. Word Processing: A Guide for Small Business. LC 82-24914. (Illus.). pap. 9.95 (ISBN 0-86616-021-3). Greene.
Software Digest. The Ratings Book: IBM-PC Word Processing Programs. 1984. pap. 14.95 (ISBN 0-916543-00-5). Software Inc.
Solomon, Owen. Teaching Writing with Computers: The Power Process. (Illus.). 176p. 1986. text ed. 21.95 (ISBN 0-13-896366-5); pap. text ed. 14.95 (ISBN 0-13-896358-4). P-H.
Sommer, Elyse. Word Processing for Better Business. LC 83-43295. 192p. 1984. pap. 14.95 (ISBN 0-8019-7429-1). Chilton.
Spear, Barbara. Word Processing with Your Adam. (Illus.). 160p. (Orig.). 1984. 15.95 (ISBN 0-8306-0766-8); pap. 9.25 (ISBN 0-8306-1766-3, 1766). TAB Bks.
Spear, Barbara & Mullowney, Terese. Word Processing with Your IBM PCjr. LC 84-8542. (Illus.). 160p. (Orig.). 1984. cancelled (ISBN 0-8306-0786-2, 1786). TAB Bks.
Spring, Marietta, et al. Excursions International: A Word Processing Simulation. 1983. 14.95 (ISBN 0-538-23450-4, W45). SW Pub.
Stephens, Jessie G. New Profits in Word Processing. 124p. (Orig.). 1983. pap. 19.95 (ISBN 0-914811-00-2). J N Goode.
Stern, Fred. Word Processing & Beyond: The Introductory Computer Book. LC 83-62394. (Illus.). 221p. 1983. pap. 9.95 (ISBN 0-912528-32-X). John Muir.
Stratton, John & Stratton, Dorothy. Magic Writing: A Writer's Guide to Word Processing. 1985. 12.95 (ISBN 0-452-25563-5, Plume). NAL.
Strong, Kline D. Word Processing Equipment. 80p. 1979. pap. 20.00 (ISBN 0-89707-061-5). Amer Bar Assn.
--Word Processing Equipment. 80p. pap. 20.00 (ISBN 0-89707-061-5). Chicago Review.
Stuart, Glenn. Word Processing Cookbook. 39.95 (ISBN 0-13-963398-7); pap. 19.95 (ISBN 0-13-963380-4); 25.95 (ISBN 0-13-963421-5). P-H.
Stultz, Russell A. The Illustrated Word Processing Dictionary. (Illus.). 176p. 1983. 23.95 (ISBN 0-13-450726-6); pap. 14.95 (ISBN 0-13-450718-5). P-H.
--The Word Processing Handbook. 237p. 1981. 17.95 (ISBN 0-13-963454-1); pap. 8.95 (ISBN 0-13-963447-9). P-H.
Taylor, Helen W., et al. Word Processing Applications. 1985. pap. text ed. 19.95 (ISBN 0-8359-8832-5). Reston.
Townsend, Carl. Exploring Word Processors: CP-M Edition. 200p. 1984. pap. 14.95 (ISBN 0-88056-104-1). Dilithium Pr.
Townsend, Kevin & Taphouse, Kate. Word Processing for Solicitors. 186p. 1983. text ed. 30.00x (ISBN 0-566-03450-6). Gower Pub Co.
Universal Training Systems Staff. Basic Word Processing Concepts-Operations. 1986. price not set incl. sound filmstrips (ISBN 0-538-23300-1, W30). SW Pub.
VanDiver, Gerald. The IBM PC & XT Word Processing Software Guide. 187p. 1984. 9.95 (ISBN 0-912603-11-9). Micro Info.
Van Uchelen, Rod. Word Processing: A Guide to Typography, Taste, & In-House Graphics. 128p. 1980. pap. 9.95 (ISBN 0-442-28646-5). Van Nos Reinhold.
Varner, Jane T. Word Processing Operations: Document Preparation. 352p. 1982. pap. text ed. 20.95 (ISBN 0-574-20630-2, 13-3630); working papers 7.95 (ISBN 0-574-20632-9, 13-3632); Legal & Medical - Technical Applications 7.95 (ISBN 0-574-20670-1, 13-3670); write for info. set instr's. guide (ISBN 0-574-20631-0, 13-3631). SRA.
Voelpel, Jack. Word Retrieval Handbook. 82p. (Orig.). 1983. pap. 4.95 (ISBN 0-940534-02-9). Beekman Hill.
Waite, Mitch & Arca, Julie. Word Processing Primer. 188p. 1982. pap. 16.95 (ISBN 0-07-067761-1, BYTE Bks). McGraw.
Walls, Betsy & Flynn, Mary A. Word & Information Processing. 1983. pap. text ed. 19.95 (ISBN 0-8359-8786-8). Reston.
Walls, Elizabeth & Flynn, Mary A. Word Processing Skills & Applications. 1984. pap. text ed. 12.95 (ISBN 0-8359-8812-0). Reston.
Waterhouse, Shirley. Word Processing Fundamentals. (Illus.). 1979. pap. text ed. 13.50 scp (ISBN 0-06-453722-6, HarpC); 3.50, scp inst. manual (ISBN 0-06-453912-1). Har-Row.
Waterhouse, Shirley A. Office Automation & Word Processing Fundamentals. 356p. 1983. pap. text ed. 14.50 scp (ISBN 0-06-046955-2, HarpC); instr's. manual avail. (ISBN 0-06-367007-0). Har-Row.
Webster, Tony. Office Automation & Word Processing Buyer's Guide. LC 83-18694. (Illus.). 328p. 1983. pap. 19.95 (ISBN 0-07-068962-8, BYTE Bks). Mcgraw.
Wheeler, C. A. & Dalton, M. Word Information Processing Simulations for Text Editors, Information Processors & Personal Computers. 267p. 1983. pap. 15.95 (ISBN 0-471-08159-0). Wiley.
Wheeler, Carol A. & Dalton, Marie. Word Processing Simulations for Electronic Typewriters & Text Editors. LC 81-11630. (Word Processing Ser.). 224p. 1982. pap. 15.95 (ISBN 0-471-08158-2). Wiley.
Will, Mimi & Dake, Donette. Concepts in Word Processing: The Challenge of Change. 275p. 1981. text ed. 21.81 (ISBN 0-205-07654-8, 1776541); pap. tchr's ed. free (ISBN 0-205-07655-6, 177655X). Allyn.
Will, Mimi & Weber, Nancy. How to Create a Successful Word Processing Business. 1984. 19.95 (ISBN 0-914475-00-2). TPW Pub Co.
Williamson, John McKim. Software Sayings of Jack Mack: Wit & Humor with Word Processing. LC 82-60964. (Jack Mack Paperbacks). 134p. 1982. pap. 8.95 (ISBN 0-910391-00-9). Jack Mack.
Williford, Jacklyn M. Word Processing Handbook: IBM DisplayWriter. LC 83-26092. 144p. 1984. pap. 14.95 (ISBN 0-471-88256-9, Pub. by Wiley Pr). Wiley.
--Word Processing Handbook: Wang OIS 142 System. LC 83-16683. 116p. 1984. pap. 14.95 (ISBN 0-471-88258-5, 1-999, Pub. by Wiley Pr). Wiley.
--Word Processing Handbooks: Xerox 860. LC 83-16713. 102p. 1984. pap. 14.95 (ISBN 0-471-88257-7, 1-999, Pub. by Wiley Pr). Wiley.
Wood, Michael. Word Processing on the BBC Micro: Wordwise & Epson. 100p. 1982. pap. text ed. 9.05 (ISBN 0-471-81046-0). Wiley.
Word Processing Curriculum Guide. 128p. 1980. 7.50 (ISBN 0-318-15257-6). Natl Busn Ed Assoc.
Word Processing Software Guide. 221p. 1984. 19.95 (ISBN 0-317-04407-9). Micro Info.
Word Processing: The Corresponding Secretary. 1981. pap. 5.70 (ISBN 0-87350-321-X); pap. 15.90 tchr's. manual (ISBN 0-87350-327-9); forms wkbk. 8.95 (ISBN 0-87350-326-0). Milady.
Word Processor Comparison Tables. 1985. 39.95 (ISBN 0-910085-10-2). Info Res MI.
WordSystems, Inc. Wang Word Processing Companion. (Illus.). 256p. 1984. 18.95 (ISBN 0-89303-945-4). Brady Comm.
Wormald, Karen E. Mastering English Skills for Word Processing. LC 83-9959. 128p. (Orig.). 1983. pap. 5.95 (ISBN 0-668-05828-5, 5828-5). Arco.
Zarrella, John. Word Processing & Text Editing. LC 80-114189. (Microprocessor Software Engineering Concepts Ser.). (Illus.). 156p. 1980. pap. 11.95 (ISBN 0-935230-01-7). Microcomputer Appns.
Zinsser, William. Writing with a Word Processor. LC 82-48140. (Illus.). 128p. 1983. 12.45i (ISBN 0-06-015055-6, HarpT); pap. 5.72i (ISBN 0-06-091060-7). Har-Row.

WORD PROCESSORS

see also Wang Word Processors

Alfred Computer Handy Guides: 12 Pocket Guides on Buying a Word Processor. pap. 3.50 ea. Alfred Pub.
Baumann, M. A. & Bahntge, M. A. Legal Keyboarding: Typewriters, Electric Typewriters, Word Processors. 286p. 1985. pap. 14.95 (ISBN 0-471-88590-8). Wiley.
Biagi, Shirley. A Writer's Guide to Word Processors. (Illus.). 160p. 1984. 13.95 (ISBN 0-13-971721-8); pap. 6.95 (ISBN 0-13-971713-7). P-H.
Boyce, B. Mercury Systems Inc. Practice Set in Word-Information Processing for Conventional & Text-Editing Typewriters. 1981. 8.24 (ISBN 0-07-006901-8). McGraw.
Brown, Eric D. Writing with a Word Processor: Communication in the Computer Age. 1984. pap. text ed. 15.95 (ISBN 0-8359-8857-0). Reston.
Collins, James L. & Sommers, Elizabeth A., eds. Writing-on-Line: Using Computers in the Teaching of Writing. 176p. 1985. pap. text ed. 9.75x (ISBN 0-317-19861-0). Boynton Cook Pubs.
Diernisse, Villy. Word Processors & Typewriters Worldwide: Opportunities & Pitfalls. (Illus.). 270p. 1984. 1500.00x (ISBN 0-910211-01-9). Laal Co.
Donohue, Brian. How to Buy an Office Computer or Word Processor. (Illus.). 232p. 1983. 17.95 (ISBN 0-13-403113-X); pap. 8.95 (ISBN 0-13-403105-9). P-H.
Flewitt, Peter. Pocket Guide: The Philips P5020 Word Processor. (Pitman Word Processing Pocket Guides Ser.). 64p. (Orig.). 1984. pap. 6.95 (ISBN 0-273-02074-9). Pitman Pub MA.
Gadney, Alan. Busy Person's Guide to Selecting the Right Word Processor: A Visual Shortcut to Understanding & Buying, Complete with Checklists & Product Guide. LC 84-6076. (Busy Person's Computer Buying Guides Ser.). (Illus.). 304p. 1984. 24.95 (ISBN 0-930828-05-4); pap. 14.95 (ISBN 0-930828-04-6). Festival Pubns.
Good, Phillip. Choosing a Word Processor. 1983. text ed. 21.95 (ISBN 0-8359-0761-9); pap. text ed. 15.95 (ISBN 0-8359-0760-0). Reston.
Good, Phillip I. Choosing a Word Processor. 1984. 10.95 (ISBN 0-910085-00-5); word porcessor, comparison tables 6.95, (ISBN 0-910085-01-3). Info Res MI.
Hallam, Teresa A. Microcomputer Use: Word Processor, Spreadsheets, & Databases with Accompanying Concept 3 Software; Instructor's Manual. 1985. text ed. 5.00 (ISBN 0-12-319629-9). Acad Pr.
Harris, Helen & Chauhan, Ela. So You Want to Buy a Word Processor? 147p. (Orig.). 1982. pap. text ed. 24.90x (ISBN 0-09-150351-5, Pub. by Busn Bks England). Brookfield Pub Co.
Hime, Robert. QuickWrite: IBMPC & PCjr. 128p. 1984. cancelled (ISBN 0-88056-219-6). Dilithium Pr.
Hurwood, Bernhardt. Successful Authors Tell You How to Write on a Word Processor. 256p. 1985. 18.95 (ISBN 0-312-92790-8); pap. 8.95 (ISBN 0-312-92791-6). Congdon & Weed.
International Resource Development Inc. PCs vs. CWPs in the Clerical Workstation of the Future. 257p. 1983. 1650.00x (ISBN 0-88694-566-6). Intl Res Dev.
Knapp, Linda R. The Word Processor & the Writing Teacher. 1985. pap. text ed. 17.95 (ISBN 0-8359-8831-7). Reston.
Labinger, Maddie. Pocket Guide: The Wang System 5. (Pitman Word Processing Pocket Guides Ser.). 64p. (Orig.). 1984. pap. 6.95 (ISBN 0-273-01962-7). Pitman Pub MA.
Labuz, Ronald A. How to Typeset from a Wordprocessor: An Interfacing Guide. 218p. 1984. pap. 29.95 (ISBN 0-8352-1899-6). Bowker.
Labuz, Ronald A. & Altimonte, Paul. The Interface Data Book for Word Processing Typesetting. 195p. 1984. pap. 29.95 (ISBN 0-8352-1908-9). Bowker.
Layman, N. Kathryn & Renner, Adrienne G. Word Processing Exercises for Word Processors, Microcomputers, & Electronic Typewriters. (Working Papers). 224p. 1984. 10.95wkbk. (ISBN 0-13-967514-0). P-H.
--Word Processors: A Programmed Training Guide with Practical Applications. (Illus.). 352p. 1981. text ed. 26.95 (ISBN 0-13-963520-3). P-H.
Low-End Word Processor Market. 318p. 1984. 1550.00 (ISBN 0-86621-078-4). Frost & Sullivan.
Manus, Steven & Scriven, Michael. How to Buy a Word Processor. LC 82-18458. (An Alfred Handy Guide). 64p. 1983. pap. 3.50 (ISBN 0-88284-222-6). Alfred Pub.
Nancarrow, Paula R., et al, eds. Word Processors & the Writing Process: An Annotated Bibliography. LC 83-22749. xi, 146p. 1984. lib. bdg. 29.95 (ISBN 0-313-23995-9, NAW/). Greenwood.
Oakeshott, Priscilla & Meadows, Jack. The Current Use of Word Processors by British Publishers. 1981. 25.00x (ISBN 0-906083-15-X, Pub. by Primary Com England). State Mutual Bk.
Poynter, Dan. Word Processors & Information Processing. 172p. 1983. 16.95 (ISBN 0-13-963553-X); pap. 11.95 (ISBN 0-13-963546-7). P-H.
--Word Processors & Information Processing: What They Are & How to Buy. 2nd ed. LC 81-11128. (Illus.). 172p. (Orig.). 1982. 11.95 (ISBN 0-915516-31-4). Para Pub.
Riordon, Tim. Practical Ways to Use Your Word Processor. (Illus.). 224p. 1985. pap. cancelled (ISBN 0-88056-147-5). Dilithium Pr.
Roberts, Ralph. The Word Processor Buyer's Survival Manual. (Illus.). 320p. (Orig.). 1984. 18.95 (ISBN 0-8306-0642-4); pap. 10.95 (ISBN 0-8306-1642-X, 1642). TAB Bks.
Rosen, Arnold. Getting the Most Out of Your Word Processor. (Illus.). 207p. 1983. 18.95 (ISBN 0-13-354555-5); pap. 9.95 (ISBN 0-13-354548-2). P-H.
Schulze, Joyce E. The Wang Self-Teaching Program. 125p. 1982. looseleaf bound 295.00 (ISBN 0-935506-06-3); 9 cassette lessons incl. Carnegie Pr.
Scriven, Michael. Word Magic: A Guide to Understanding & Evaluating Word Processing Equipment. 200p. 1983. 25.00 (ISBN 0-317-31316-9). Van Nos Reinhold.
Seiden, Eric A. DARAD Plus. rev. ed. Dar Systems Staff, ed. 75p. 1984. incl. Program Disk, Tech Ref. Manual & Self-Teaching Manual 79.95 (ISBN 0-916163-45-8). Dar Syst.
--DARAD Plus: A Self Teaching Manual. rev. ed. 50p. 1984. 3-ring binder 21.95 (ISBN 0-916163-44-X). Dar Syst.
--DARAD Technical Manual. 25p. 1984. 3-Ring binder 10.00 (ISBN 0-916163-29-6). Dar Syst.
--DARTED Technical Manual. 25p. 1983. pap. 10.00 3-ring binder (ISBN 0-916163-30-X). Dar Syst.
Strong, Kline D. Word Processing Equipment. 80p. 1979. pap. 20.00 (ISBN 0-89707-061-5). Amer Bar Assn.
Townsend, Kevin & Townsend, Kate. Choosing & Using a Word Processor. 282p. 1982. text ed. 33.00 (ISBN 0-566-03408-5). Gower Pub Co.
Zinsser, William. Writing with a Word Processor. LC 82-48140. (Illus.). 128p. 1983. 12.45i (ISBN 0-06-015055-6, HarpT); pap. 5.72i (ISBN 0-06-091060-7). Har-Row.

WORDPERFECT (COMPUTER PROGRAM)

Beacham, Walton & Beacham, Deborah. Using WordPerfect. LC 84-62131. 320p. 1985. 16.95 (ISBN 0-88022-132-1, 162). Que Corp.
Wingrove, S. Getting the Most from Wordperfect. 1984. 12.95 (ISBN 0-07-071018-X). McGraw.

WORDPRO (COMPUTER PROGRAM)

Westgate, Walsh. Introduction to Wordpro Four Plus. 276p. 1982. 33.95x (ISBN 0-7715-0460-8). Forkner.

WORDSTAR (COMPUTER PROGRAM)

Alferi, Vincent. The Practical Guide to WordStar & MailMerge. 350p. pap. 18.95 (6305). Hayden.
Arca, Julie A. Practical WordStar Uses. LC 83-72250. (Illus.). 303p. 1983. pap. 17.95 (ISBN 0-89588-107-1). SYBEX.

Elmes, James. Memoirs of Sir Christopher Wren. LC 77-94576. 1979. Repr. of 1823 ed. lib. bdg. 60.00 (ISBN 0-89341-241-4). Longwood Pub Group.
Furst, Viktor. The Architecture of Sir Christopher Wren. LC 56-36662. 244p. 1956. Repr. 49.00 (ISBN 0-686-01441-3). Somerset Pub.

WRENS

Australian Museum Trust. The Wrens & Warblers of Australia. 376p. 1982. 125.00x (ISBN 0-207-14480-X, Pub. by Angus & Robertson). State Mutual Bk.
Bent, Arthur C. Life Histories of North American Nuthatches, Wrens, Thrashers & Their Allies. (Illus.). 1948. pap. 9.95 (ISBN 0-486-21088-X). Dover.
--Life Histories of North American Nuthatches, Wrens, Thrashers & Their Allies. (Illus.). 14.75 (ISBN 0-8446-1640-0). Peter Smith.

WRIGHT BROTHERS

Hallion, Richard P., ed. The Wright Brothers: Heirs of Prometheus. LC 78-606141. (Illus.). 146p. 1979. 19.95 (ISBN 0-87474-504-7); pap. 8.95 (ISBN 0-87474-503-9). Smithsonian.
Wright, Orville & Wright, Wilbur. Wright Brothers' Aeroplane. Jones, William R., ed. (Illus.). 1981. pap. 2.00 (ISBN 0-89646-065-7). Outbooks.

WROUGHT-IRON

Arthur, Eric & Ritchie, Thomas. Iron: Cast & Wrought Iron in Canada from the Seventeenth Century to the Present. (Illus.). 256p. 1982. 27.50 (ISBN 0-8020-2429-7). U of Toronto Pr.
Christian, Marcus B. Negro Ironworkers in Louisiana. LC 72-85953. (Illus.). 64p. (Orig.). 1972. pap. 4.95 (ISBN 0-911116-74-5). Pelican.
D'Allemagne, Henry R. Decorative Antique Ironwork: A Pictorial Treasury. Ostoia, Vera K., tr. LC 67-20193. (Illus.). 1968. pap. 11.95 (ISBN 0-486-22082-6). Dover.
Gale, W. K. Ironworking. (Shire Album Ser.: No. 64). (Illus.). 32p. 1981. pap. 3.50 (ISBN 0-85263-546-X, Pub. by Shire Pubns England). Seven Hills Bks.
Geerlings, Gerald K. Wrought Iron in Architecture: An Illustrated Survey. (Antiques Ser.). 202p. 1984. pap. 9.95 (ISBN 0-486-24535-7). Dover.
Wrought Iron Work. (Illus.). 109p. 1960. pap. 6.00 (ISBN 0-89192-340-3, Pub. by Wepf & Co). Interbk Inc.

WRYNECK

see Torticollis

X

X CHROMOSOME

see Sex Chromosomes

X-FIFTEEN (ROCKET AIRCRAFT)

Crossfield, A. Scott & Blair, Clay, Jr. Always Another Dawn: The Story of a Rocket Test Pilot. LC 73-169413. (Literature & History of Aviation Ser). 1972. Repr. of 1960 ed. 31.00 (ISBN 0-405-03758-9). Ayer Co Pubs.

X-RAY CRYSTALLOGRAPHY

Amoros, Jose L., et al. The Laue Method. 1975. 78.00 (ISBN 0-12-057450-0). Acad Pr.
Arndt, U. W. & Wonacott, A. J. The Rotation Method in Crystallography. 276p. 1977. 70.25 (ISBN 0-7204-0594-7, Biomedical Pr). Elsevier.
Bragg, Lawrence. The Development of X-Ray Analysis. Phillips, David, ed. (Illus.). 1975. 21.95x (ISBN 0-02-841880-8). Hafner.
Brumberger, H., ed. Small-Angle X-Ray Scattering. 518p. 1967. 116.95 (ISBN 0-677-11190-8). Gordon.
Buerger, Martin J. X-Ray Crystallography. LC 80-12459. 554p. 1980. Repr. of 1942 ed. lib. bdg. 34.00 (ISBN 0-89874-176-9). Krieger.
Dunitz, Jack D. X-Ray Analysis & the Structure of Organic Molecules. LC 78-15588. (George Fisher Baker Non-Resident Lectureship Ser.). 528p. 1979. 79.50x (ISBN 0-8014-1115-7). Cornell U Pr.
Glusker, Jenny P. & Trueblood, Kenneth N. Crystal Structure Analysis: A Primer. 2nd ed. (Illus.). 320p. 1985. text ed. 37.50x (ISBN 0-19-503531-3); pap. 18.95x (ISBN 0-19-503543-7). Oxford U Pr.
Glusker, Jenny P., ed. Structural Crystallography in Chemistry & Biology. LC 80-13858. (Benchmark Papers in Physical Chemistry & Chemical Physics: Vol. 4). 421p. 1981. 50.00 (ISBN 0-87933-368-5). Van Nos Reinhold.
Hauptman, H. Crystal Structure Determination: The Role of Cosine Semivariants. LC 72-80574. 407p. 1972. 55.00x (ISBN 0-306-30703-0, Plenum Pr). Plenum Pub.
Horn, A. S. & De Ranter, C. J. X-Ray Crystallography & Drug Action. (Illus.). 1984. 59.00x (ISBN 0-19-855185-1). Oxford U Pr.
Jeffrey, J. W. Methods in X-Ray Crystallography. 1972. 92.00 (ISBN 0-12-382250-5). Acad Pr.
Kasper, John S. & Lonsdale, Kathleen, eds. International Tables for X-Ray Crystallography. 2nd ed. (Mathematical Tables Ser.: Vol. II). 1985. lib. bdg. 48.50 (ISBN 90-277-1956-X, Pub. by Reidel Holland). Kluwer Academic.
Ladd, M. F. & Palmer, R. A. Structure Determination by X-Ray Crystallography, 2nd ed. 526p. 1985. 39.50x (ISBN 0-306-41878-9, Plenum Pr). Plenum Pub.
Ladd, M. F. & Palmer, R. A., eds. Structure Determination by X-Ray Crystallography. LC 76-40229. (Illus.). 393p. 1977. 42.50x (ISBN 0-306-30844-4, Plenum Pr); pap. 17.50 (ISBN 0-306-40032-4). Plenum Pub.
Lipson, H. & Lee, R. M. Crystals & X-Rays. (Wykeham Science Ser.: No. 13). 198p. 1970. 9.95x (ISBN 0-8448-1115-7). Crane Russak Co.
Luger, Peter. Modern X-Ray Analysis on Single Crystals. 312p. 1980. 44.00 (ISBN 3-11-006830-3). De Gruyter.
Mirkin, Lev. I. Handbook of X-Ray Analysis of Polycrystalline Materials. LC 64-23250. 731p. 1964. 75.00x (ISBN 0-306-65109-2, IFI Plenum). Plenum Pub.
Rudman, Reuben. Low-Temperature X-Ray Diffraction: Apparatus & Techniques. LC 76-23259. (Illus.). 344p. 1976. 49.50x (ISBN 0-306-30923-8, Plenum Pr). Plenum Pub.
Srinivasan, B. & Parthasarathy, S. Some Statistical Applications in X-Ray Crystallography. LC 75-9676. 1976. text ed. 50.00 (ISBN 0-08-018046-9). Pergamon.
Stout, George H. & Jensen, Lyle H. X-Ray Structure Determination: A Practical Guide. (Illus.). 1968. write for info. (ISBN 0-02-417660-5). Macmillan.
Tanner, Brian K. & Bowen, D. Keith, eds. Characterization of Crystal Growth Defects by X-Ray Methods. LC 80-26509. (NATO ASI Series B, Physics: Vol. 63). 615p. 1981. 89.50x (ISBN 0-306-40628-4, Plenum Pr). Plenum Pub.
Van Olphen, H. & Parrish, W., eds. X-Ray & Electron Methods of Analysis. LC 68-13392. 164p. 1968. 39.50x (ISBN 0-306-39301-8, Plenum Pr). Plenum Pub.

X-RAY MICROSCOPE

Morgan, A. John. X-Ray Microanalysis in Electron Microscopy for Biologists. (Royal Microscopical Society Microscopy Handbooks Ser.). (Illus.). 72p. 1985. pap. 8.95 (ISBN 0-19-856409-0). Oxford U Pr.
Parsons, Donald F., ed. Ultrasoft X-Ray Microscopy: Its Application to Biological & Physical Sciences. (Annals of the New York Academy of Sciences: Vol. 342). 402p. 1980. 72.00x (ISBN 0-89766-066-8); pap. 72.00x (ISBN 0-89766-067-6). NY Acad Sci.

X-RAY PHOTOGRAMMETRY

Hallert, Bertil. X-Ray Photogrammetry. 1970. 34.00 (ISBN 0-444-40805-3). Elsevier.

X-RAY SCATTERING

see X-Rays–Scattering

X-RAY SPECTROSCOPY

Adler, Isidore. X-Ray Emission Spectrography in Geology. (Methods in Geochemistry & Geophysics: Vol. 4). xii, 258p. 1966. 68.00 (ISBN 0-444-40004-4). Elsevier.
Agarwal, B. K. X-Ray Spectroscopy. (Springer Series in Optical Sciences: Vol. 15). (Illus.). 1979. 48.00 (ISBN 0-387-09268-4). Springer-Verlag.
Bertin, Eugene P. Introduction to X-Ray Spectrometric Analysis. LC 77-27244. (Illus.). 499p. 1978. 42.50x (ISBN 0-306-31091-0, Plenum Pr). Plenum Pub.
--Principles & Practice of X-Ray Spectrometric Analysis. 2nd ed. LC 74-28043. (Illus.). 1079p. 1975. 95.00x (ISBN 0-306-30809-6, Plenum Pr). Plenum Pub.
Bruce, W. R. & Johns, H. E. The Spectra of X Rays Scattered in Low Atomic Number Materials. 1980. 10.00x (ISBN 0-686-69958-0, Pub. by Brit Inst Radiology). State Mutual Bk.
Fabian, Derek J., ed. Soft X-Ray Band Spectra & the Electronic Structures of Metals & Materials. 1969. 65.00 (ISBN 0-12-247450-3). Acad Pr.
Heinrich, Kurt F. Electron Beam X-Ray Microanalysis. 608p. 1980. 44.50 (ISBN 0-442-23286-1). Van Nos Reinhold.
Herglotz, H. K. & Birk, L. S., eds. X-Ray Spectrometry. (Practical Spectrometry Ser.: Vol. 2). 1978. soft cover 85.00 (ISBN 0-8247-7036-6). Dekker.
Hodgson, K. O., et al, eds. EXAFS & Near Edge Structure III. (Proceedings in Physics: Vol. 2). (Illus.). xv, 533p. 1984. 34.50 (ISBN 0-387-15013-7). Springer-Verlag.
I.A.U. Symposium, No. 37, Rome, Italy, May 8-18, 1969. Non-Solar X-Gamma-Ray Astronomy: Proceedings. Gratton, L., ed. LC 73-83561. (I.A.U. Symposia). 425p. 1970. lib. bdg. 45.00 (ISBN 90-277-0160-1, Puub. by Reidel Holland). Kluwer Academic.
Jenkins, R. & De Vries, J. L. Practical X-Ray Spectrometry. 2nd rev. ed. LC 72-113623. (Illus.). 1975. 18.00 (ISBN 0-387-91029-8). Springer-Verlag.
Russ, John C. Fundamentals of Energy Dispersive X-Ray Analysis. (Monographs in Materials). (Illus.). 336p. 1984. text ed. 79.95 (ISBN 0-408-11031-7). Butterworth.
Stern, Edward A., ed. Laboratory EXAFS Facilities, 1980: University of Washington Workshop. (AIP Conference Proceedings: No. 64). 165p. lib. bdg. 18.25 (ISBN 0-88318-163-0). Am Inst Physics.
Teo, B. K. & Joy, D. C., eds. EXAFS Spectroscopy: Techniques & Applications. LC 81-199. 284p. 1981. 45.00x (ISBN 0-306-40654-3, Plenum Pr). Plenum Pub.
Van Olphen, H. & Parrish, W., eds. X-Ray & Electron Methods of Analysis. LC 68-13392. 164p. 1968. 39.50x (ISBN 0-306-39301-8, Plenum Pr). Plenum Pub.

X-RAYS

see also Auger Effect; Electron Spectroscopy; Electron Spectroscopy; Gamma Rays; Plants, Effect of Radiation On; Radiography; Radiotherapy; Vacuum-Tubes; X-Ray Crystallography; X-Ray Microscope; X-Ray Spectroscopy

Abrahams, S. C., ed. Accuracy in X-Ray Intensity Measurements. (Transactions of the American Crystallographic Association Ser.: Vol. 1). 112p. 1965. pap. 15.00 (ISBN 0-686-60372-9). Polycrystal Bk Serv.
Barrett, C. S., et al, eds. Advances in X-Ray Analysis. Incl. Vol. 1. 494p. 1960; Vol. 2. o.p. (ISBN 0-306-38102-8); Vol. 3; Vol. 4. 568p. 1961; Vol. 5. o.p. (ISBN 0-306-38105-2); Vol. 6. 480p. 1963; Vol. 7. 662p. 1964; Vol. 10. 558p. 1967; Vol. 11. 495p. 1968. 65.00x (ISBN 0-306-38111-7); Vol. 12. 652p. 1969. 65.00x (ISBN 0-306-38112-5). LC 58-35928 (Plenum Pr). Plenum Pub.
Barrett, Charles S., et al, eds. Advances in X-Ray Analysis, Vol. 14. LC 58-35928. 500p. 1971. 65.00x (ISBN 0-306-38114-1, Plenum Pr). Plenum Pub.
--Advances in X-Ray Analysis, Vol. 21. LC 58-35928. 341p. 1978. 52.50x (ISBN 0-306-38421-3, Plenum Pr). Plenum Pub.
--Advances in X-Ray Analysis, Vol. 28. 410p. 1985. 52.50x (ISBN 0-306-41939-4, Plenum Pr). Plenum Pub.
Beaman, Donald R., et al, eds. Proceedings of the International Congress on X-Ray Optics & Microanalysis, 8th. LC 77-18656. 665p. 65.00 (ISBN 0-87812-180-3). Pendell Pub.
Birks, L. S. X-Ray Spectrochemical Analysis, Vol. 2. 2nd ed. LC 71-79144. (Illus.). 143p. 1969. text ed. 11.25 (ISBN 0-471-07525-6, Pub. by Wiley). Krieger.
Bloom, William L., Jr., et al. Medical Radiographic Technic. 3rd ed. (Illus.). 368p. 1979. photocopy ed. 37.75x (ISBN 0-398-00171-5). C C Thomas.
Bonnelle, C. & Mande, C., eds. Advances in X-Ray Spectroscopy: A Reference Text in Honour of Professor Y. Cauchois. LC 82-12300. (Illus.). 400p. 1982. 88.00 (ISBN 0-08-025266-4). Pergamon.
Bowen, D. K., et al. Application of Synchrotron Radiation X-Rays in Materials Science. 1984. write for info. Elsevier.
Brown, A. G. X-Rays & Their Applications. LC 75-34146. 258p. 1975. pap. 8.95x (ISBN 0-306-20021-X, Rosetta). Plenum Pub.
Brown, Percy. American Martyrs to Science Through the Roentgen Rays. (Illus.). 276p. 1936. photocopy ed. 27.50x (ISBN 0-398-04223-3). C C Thomas.
Cahoon, John B. Formulating X-Ray Techniques. 9th ed. Thompson, Thomas T., ed. LC 73-81713. 381p. 1974. 20.50 (ISBN 0-8223-0431-7). Duke.
Cauchois, Y., et al, eds. Wavelengths of X-Ray Emission Lines & Absorption Edges. LC 78-40419. 1978. 175.00 (ISBN 0-08-022448-2); pap. text ed. 80.00. Pergamon.
Cohen, I. Bernard, ed. Gravitation, Heat & X-Rays. LC 80-2104. (Development of Science Ser.). (Illus.). 1981. lib. bdg. 35.00x (ISBN 0-405-13869-5). Ayer Co Pubs.
Cullinan, John E. & Cullinan, Angeline M. Illustrated Guide to X-Ray Technics. 2nd ed. (Illus.). 179p. 1980. text ed. 36.50 (ISBN 0-397-50425-X, 65-05705, Lippincott Medical). Lippincott.
Dyson, Norman Allen. X-rays in Atomic & Nuclear Physics. LC 73-85203. pap. 98.50 (ISBN 0-317-08542-5, 2010051). Bks Demand UMI.
Earle, K. M. & Tousimis, A. J., eds. X-Ray & Electron Probe Analysis in Biomedical Research. LC 68-13392. 103p. 1969. 29.50x (ISBN 0-306-39303-4, Plenum Pr). Plenum Pub.
Felson, Benjamin, ed. Roentgen Techniques in Laboratory Animals: Radiography of the Dog & Other Experimental Animals. LC 68-23680. pap. 66.00 (ISBN 0-317-29361-3, 2055940). Bks Demand UMI.
Ginzburg, Vitaly L. Elementary Processes for Cosmic Ray Astrophysics. (Topics in Astrophysics & Space Physics Ser.). 140p. 1969. 45.25 (ISBN 0-677-01980-7). Gordon.
Gofman, John W. & O'Connor, Egan. X-Rays: Health Effects of Common Exams. LC 84-23527. (Illus.). 456p. 1985. 25.00 (ISBN 0-87156-838-1). Sierra.
Goldman, M. A Guide to the X-Ray Department. 100p. 1978. pap. 10.50 (ISBN 0-7236-0493-2). PSG Pub Co.
Goldstein, Joseph I., et al. Scanning Electron Microscopy & X-Ray Microanalysis: A Text for Biologists, Materials Scientists & Geologists. 688p. 1981. 32.50x (ISBN 0-306-40768-X, Plenum Pr). Plenum Pub.
Graham, D. & Eddie, T. X-Ray Techniques in Art Galleries & Museums. 136p. 1985. 22.00 (ISBN 0-9903003-3-1, Pub. by A Hilger England). Heyden.
Graham, Daniel & Thomson, John. Grenz Rays: An Illustrated Guide to the Theory & Practical Applications of Soft X-Rays. LC 79-42745. (Illus.). 164p. 1980. 26.00 (ISBN 0-08-025525-6). Pergamon.
Grant, C. L., et al, eds. Advances in X-Ray Analysis, Vol. 17. LC 58-35928. 600p. 1974. 65.00x (ISBN 0-306-38117-6, Plenum Pr). Plenum Pub.
Hayat, M. A. X-Ray Micro-Analysis in Biology. (Illus.). 496p. 1980. text ed. 51.00 (ISBN 0-8391-1511-3). Univ Park.
Heinrich, K. F., et al, eds. Advances in X-Ray Analysis, Vol. 15. LC 58-35928. 573p. 65.00x (ISBN 0-306-38115-X, Plenum Pr). Plenum Pub.
Hunt, Diana. The Doctor's Guide for Buying X-Ray Equipment & Accessories. (Illus.). 200p. 1981. text ed. write for info. Springtime.
International Commission on Radiological Protection. Protection of the Patient in X-Ray Diagnosis. (ICRP Publication Ser.: No. 16). 1971. pap. 25.00. Pergamon.
International Symposium on X-Ray Optics & X-Ray Microanalysis - 3rd - Stanford - California - 1962. Proceedings. Pattee, Howard H., Jr., et al, eds. 1964. 88.00 (ISBN 0-12-547050-9). Acad Pr.
James, R. W. The Optical Principles of the Diffraction of X-Rays. LC 82-80706. 1982. Repr. of 1948 ed. 42.00 (ISBN 0-918024-23-4). Ox Bow.
Lewin, Walter H. & Van den Heuvel, E. P., eds. Accretion-Driven Stellar X-Ray Sources. LC 83-1858. 380p. 1984. 79.50 (ISBN 0-521-24521-4). Cambridge U Pr.
Lipson, H. Crystals & X-rays. (The Wykeham Science Ser.: No. 13). 198p. 1970. pap. cancelled (ISBN 0-85109-150-4). Taylor & Francis.
McCarthy, Gregory J., et al, eds. Advances in X-Ray Analysis, Vol. 22. 510p. 1979. 69.50x (ISBN 0-306-40163-0, Plenum Pr). Plenum Pub.
Menter, Sir James, et al. Ultrasound & X-Rays in Engineering & Medicine. (Royal Society of London). (Illus.). 171p. text ed. 50.00x (ISBN 0-85403-116-2, Pub by Royal Soc London). Scholium Intl.
Merrill, Vinita. Atlas of Roentgenographic Positions & Standard Radiologic Procedures, 3 vols. 4th ed. LC 75-1144. 1975. Set. text ed. 99.50 (ISBN 0-8016-3412-1); Vol. 1. text ed. 49.75 (ISBN 0-8016-3404-0); Vol. 2. text ed. 49.75 (ISBN 0-8016-3405-9); Vol. 3. text ed. 49.75 (ISBN 0-8016-3406-7). Mosby.
Meschan, Isadore. Roentgen Signs in Diagnostic Imaging: Abdomen, Vol. 1. 2nd ed. (Illus.). 992p. 1984. 85.00 (ISBN 0-7216-6302-8). Saunders.
Moss, Albert & Goldberg, Henry, eds. Computed Tomography, Ultrasound & X-Ray: An Integrated Approach. LC 76-1666. 1980. 85.00 (ISBN 0-12-788525-0). Acad Pr.
Nitske, W. Robert. The Life of Wilhelm Conrad Rontgen: Discoverer of the X-Ray. LC 79-125167. pap. 91.50 (ISBN 0-317-28634-X, 2055371). Bks Demand UMI.
Noakes, G. R., et al, eds. Sources of Physics Teaching: Electrolysis, X-Ray Analysis. Electron Diffraction, Vol. 3. 1969. pap. 17.50x (ISBN 0-85066-031-9). Intl Ideas.
Ogilvie, Robert, et al, eds. X-Ray Optics & Microanalysis: Eighth International Congress. LC 77-18656. (Illus.). 1979. lib. bdg. 75.00 (ISBN 0-89500-012-1). Sci Pr.
Philip, A. Davis, ed. X-Ray Symposium 1981. 76p. 1981. pap. 12.00 (ISBN 0-9607902-0-9). Davis Pr.
Pickles, W. L., et al, eds. Advances in X-Ray Analysis, Vol. 18. LC 58-35928. 642p. 1975. 75.00x (ISBN 0-306-38118-4, Plenum Pr). Plenum Pub.
Queisser, H. J., ed. X-Ray Optics: Applications to Solids. (Topics in Applied Physics: Vol. 22). (Illus.). 1977. 51.00 (ISBN 0-387-08462-2). Springer-Verlag.

Y

--Ocean Yacht Navigator. 196p. 1982. 39.00x (ISBN 0-333-32077-8, Pub. by Nautical England). State Mutual Bk.
--Practical Yacht Navigator. 208p. 1982. 35.00x (ISBN 0-333-32081-6, Pub. by Nautical England). State Mutual Bk.
The World of Yachting, No. 5. (The World of Yachting Ser.). 224p. 1981. 37.50 (ISBN 2-86409-006-6). Edns Vilo.
Wright, Derek. Yacht Log. 120p. 1979. 14.95 (ISBN 0-88826-081-4). Superior Pub.

YALE UNIVERSITY–SHEFFIELD SCIENTIFIC SCHOOL

Baitsell, George A., ed. The Centennial of the Sheffield Scientific School (Yale University) 1950. 19.50x (ISBN 0-686-51350-9). Elliots Bks.
Chittenden, Russel H. History of the Sheffield Scientific School of Yale, 2 vols. 1928. 150.00x (ISBN 0-685-69797-5). Elliots Bks.
Kirby, Richard S., ed. Inventors & Engineers of Old New Haven. facs. ed. LC 78-86765. (Essay Index Reprint Ser). 1939. 15.00 (ISBN 0-8369-1144-X). Ayer Co Pubs.
Lawrence, Ernest O. Centennial of the Sheffield Scientific School. facsimile ed. Baitsell, George A., ed. LC 70-107681. (Essay Index Reprint Ser.). 1959. 21.50 (ISBN 0-8369-1544-5). Ayer Co Pubs.

YAMA-MAI

see Silkworms

YAMAHA MOTORCYCLE

Chilton's Automotive Editorial Staff. Yamaha XS360-400 1976-1980. (Illus.). 1981. pap. 10.95 (ISBN 0-8019-6969-7). Chilton.
--Yamaha 650, 1970-79. (Chilton's Repair & Tune-Up Guides). (Illus.). 1979. pap. 10.95 (ISBN 0-8019-6895-X, 6895). Chilton.
Clew, Jeff. Yamaha 250 & 350 Twins '70 - '79. (Owners Workshop Manuals Ser.: No. 040). 1980. 10.50 (ISBN 0-85696-505-7, Pub. by J H Haynes England). Haynes Pubns.
--Yamaha 500 Twin '73 - '79. new ed. (Owners Workshop Manuals Ser.: No. 308). 1980. 10.50 (ISBN 0-85696-308-9, Pub. by J H Haynes England). Haynes Pubns.
Clymer Publications. Yamaha Service Repair Handbook: 80-175cc Piston Port Singles, 1968-1976. (Illus.). pap. text ed. 13.95 (ISBN 0-89287-235-7, M410). Clymer Pubns.
--Yamaha: 250-400cc, 2-Stroke Twins 1965-1979, Service, Repair, Performance. 3rd ed. Jorgensen, Eric, ed. (Illus.). pap. 13.95 (ISBN 0-89287-283-7, M401). Clymer Pubns.
Darlington, Mansur. Yamaha RD400 Twin '76 - '79. (Owners Workshop Manuals Ser.: No. 333). 1977. 10.50 (ISBN 0-85696-548-0, Pub. by J H Haynes England). Haynes Pubns.
--Yamaha Trail Bikes 250, 360 & 400 '68 - '79. new ed. (Owners Workshop Manuals Ser.: No. 263). 1980. 10.50 (ISBN 0-85696-519-7, Pub. by J H Haynes England). Haynes Pubns.
--Yamaha Trail Bikes '72 - '79. (Owners Workshop Manuals Ser.: No. 210). 1981. 10.50 (ISBN 0-85696-661-4, Pub. by J H Haynes England). Haynes Pubns.
--Yamaha XS750 (3-cyl) Models '76 - '81. (Owners Workshop Manuals Ser.: No. 340). 1978. 10.50 (ISBN 0-85696-712-2, Pub. by J H Haynes England). Haynes Pubns.
Jorgensen, Eric, ed. Yamaha SR500 Singles: 1977-1980 Service-Repair-Performance. (Illus.). 191p. (Orig.). pap. 13.95 (ISBN 0-89287-212-8, M407). Clymer Pubns.
Reynolds, Mark & Shoemark, P. Yamaha 200 Twins '71 - '79. (Owners Workshop Manuals Ser.: No. 156). 1974. 10.50 (ISBN 0-85696-156-6, Pub. by J H Haynes England). Haynes Pubns.
Scott, Ed. Yamaha IT125-490 Singles 1976-1983: Service Repair Performance. Jorgensen, Eric, ed. (Illus., Orig.). pap. text ed. 13.95 (ISBN 0-89287-330-2, M414). Clymer Pubns.
--Yamaha XS1100 Fours: 1978-1981 Service-Repair-Performance. (Illus., Orig.). pap. text ed. 13.95 (ISBN 0-89287-309-4, M411). Clymer Pubns.
--Yamaha YZ50-80 Monoshock Serigles, 1978-1982: Service Repair Performance. Jorgensen, Eric, ed. (Illus., Orig.). pap. text ed. 13.95 (ISBN 0-89287-340-X, M393). Clymer Pubns.
Shoemark, P. Yamaha RD125 Twins '73 - '79. (Owners Workshop Manuals Ser.: No. 327). 1980. 10.50 (ISBN 0-85696-327-5, Pub. by J H Haynes England). Haynes Pubns.
Wauson, Sidnie A., ed. Yamaha DT & MX Series Singles 1977-1983. (Illus., Orig.). pap. text ed. 13.95 (ISBN 0-89287-331-0, M412). Clymer Pubns.
Woollett, Mick. Yamaha. LC 83-73617. (Illus.). 64p. (Orig.). 1984. 7.95 (ISBN 0-668-06165-0); pap. 3.95 (ISBN 0-668-06172-3). Arco.
Wright, Ron. Yamaha XJ550 Maxim-Seca, 1981 to 1983: Service, Repair, Performance. Wauson, Sydnie A., ed. (Illus.). 260p. 1984. 13.95 (ISBN 0-89287-372-8, M387). Clymer Pubns.
Yamaha XS 750 & 850 Triples 1976-1981 Service, Repair, Performance. (Illus.). pap. 13.95 (ISBN 0-89287-243-8, M404). Clymer Pubns.

YAMS

Miege, J. & Lyonga, S. N. Yams. (Illus.). 1982. 59.00x (ISBN 0-19-854557-6). Oxford U Pr.

YARN

see also Wool

Davenport, Elsie G. Your Yarn Dyeing. (Illus.). 1981. pap. 5.50 (ISBN 0-910458-02-2). Select Bks.
Dyson, E., et al. Yarn Production & Properties. 96p. 1974. 70.00x (ISBN 0-686-63811-5). State Mutual Bk.
Goswami, B. C., et al. Textile Yarns: Technology, Structure & Applications. LC 77-398. 482p. 1977. 56.50x (ISBN 0-471-31900-7, Pub. by Wiley-Interscience). Wiley.
Harrison, P. W. The Yarn Revolution. 162p. 1976. 60.00x (ISBN 0-686-63814-X). State Mutual Bk.
Henshaw, D. E. Self-Twist Yarn. 166p. 1971. 40.00x (ISBN 0-900541-38-5, Pub. by Meadowfield Pr England). State Mutual Bk.
Hossack, D. C. Tape Yarns. 64p. 1971. 39.00x (ISBN 0-900541-45-8, Pub. by Meadowfield Pr England). State Mutual Bk.
Hunter, L. The Production & Properties of Staple-Fibre Yarns Made by Recently Developed Techniques. 168p. 1978. 70.00x (ISBN 0-686-27733-3). State Mutual Bk.
Nutter, W. Yarn Production & Properties. 110p. 1971. 70.00x (ISBN 0-686-63812-3). State Mutual Bk.
Park, J. A Practical Introduction to Yarn Dyeing. 120p. 1981. 59.00x (ISBN 0-901956-28-7, Pub. by Soc Dyers & Colour). State Mutual Bk.
Smith, P. A. Yarn Production & Properties. 123p. 1969. 70.00x (ISBN 0-686-63813-1). State Mutual Bk.
Van Wagenen, Jared. The Golden Age of Homespun. (Illus.). 1963. pap. 2.25 (ISBN 0-917334-05-1). Fenimore Bk.
Wilson, D. K. The Production of Textile Yarns by the False-Twist Technique. 66p. 1978. 70.00x (ISBN 0-686-63791-7). State Mutual Bk.
--The Production of Textured Yarns by Methods Other That the False-Twist Technique. 55p. 1977. 70.00x (ISBN 0-686-63792-5). State Mutual Bk.

YASHICA CAMERA

see Cameras–Types–Yashica

YEAST

Arnold, Wilfred N., ed. Yeast Cell Envelopes: Biochemistry, Biophysics, & Ultrastructure, Vols. I & II. 1981. Vol. I, 144p. 56.00 (ISBN 0-8493-5965-1); Vol. Ii, 192p. 71.50 (ISBN 0-8493-5966-X). CRC Pr.
Bacila, Metry, et al, eds. Biochemistry & Genetics of Yeasts: Pure & Applied Aspects. LC 78-21898. 1978. 60.00 (ISBN 0-12-071250-4). Acad Pr.
Barnett, J. A., et al. A Guide to Identifying & Classifying Yeasts. LC 79-11136. (Illus.). 1979. 99.00 (ISBN 0-521-22762-3). Cambridge U Pr.
--Yeasts: Characteristics & Identification. LC 83-8390. 811p. 1984. 150.00 (ISBN 0-521-25296-2). Cambridge U Pr.
Barnett, Pankhurst. A New Key to the Yeasts. LC 73-86076. 273p. 1974. 98.75 (ISBN 0-444-10580-8, Biomedical Pr). Elsevier.
Berry, David R. Biology of Yeast. (Studies in Biology: No. 140). 64p. 1982. pap. text ed. 8.95 (ISBN 0-7131-2838-0). E Arnold.
Iwata, Kazuo, ed. Yeasts & Yeast-like Microorganisms in Medical Science: Proceedings of the Second International Specialized Symposium on Yeasts. 346p. 1976. 35.00 (ISBN 0-86008-294-6, Pub. by U of Tokyo Japan). Columbia U Pr.
Koser, Stewart A. Vitamin Requirements of Bacteria & Yeasts. (Illus.). 672p. 1968. 59.75x (ISBN 0-398-01041-2). C C Thomas.
Lodder, J. Yeasts: A Taxonomic Study. 138p. 1984. 181.25 (ISBN 0-7204-4054-8, Biomedical Pr). Elsevier.
Neumann, I. Biotaxonomische Untersuchungen an Einigen Hefen der Gattung Saccharomyces. 1972. 14.00 (ISBN 3-7682-5440-2). Lubrecht & Cramer.
Phaff, H. J., et al. The Life of Yeasts. rev. & enl. ed. (Illus.). 1978. 20.00x (ISBN 0-674-53325-9). Harvard U Pr.
Skinner, F. A., et al, eds. Biology & Activities of Yeasts. LC 80-41362. (Society for Applied Bacteriology Symposia Ser.: No. 9). 1981. 46.50 (ISBN 0-12-648080-X). Acad Pr.
Spencer, J. F., et al, eds. Yeast Genetics: Fundamental & Applied Aspects. (Springer Series in Molecular Biology). (Illus.). 533p. 1983. 59.00 (ISBN 0-387-90793-9). Springer-Verlag.
Strathern, Jeffery N., et al, eds. The Molecular Biology of the Yeast Saccharomyces: Metabolism & Gene Expression. LC 81-68203. (Cold Spring Harbor Monograph: Vol. 11B). 692p. 1982. 94.50x. Cold Spring Harbor.
Strathern, Jeffrey N., et al, eds. Molecular Biology of the Yeast Saccharomyces: Life Cycle & Inheritance. LC 81-68895. (Monograph Ser.: No. 11A). 1985. Repr. of 1981 ed. text ed. 40.00 (ISBN 0-87969-179-4). Cold Spring Harbor.
Von Wettstein, D., et al, eds. Molecular Genetics in Yeast: Proceedings of the Alfred Benzon Symposium 16, Copenhagen 15-19, June 1980. 441p. 79.00x (ISBN 0-686-44536-8, Pub. by Munksgaard Denmark). State Mutual Bk.

YIELD-LINE ANALYSIS

Hall, E. O. Yield Point Phenomena in Metals & Alloys. LC 75-120336. 288p. 1970. 45.00x (ISBN 0-306-30490-2, Plenum Pr). Plenum Pub.

YLIDES

Johnson, A. William. Ylide Chemistry. (Organic Chemistry Ser.: Vol. 7). 1966. 75.00 (ISBN 0-12-386450-X). Acad Pr.
Trost, Barry M. & Melvin, Lawrence S., Jr. Sulfer Ylides: Emerging Synthetic Intermediates. (Organic Chemistry Ser.). 1975. 75.00 (ISBN 0-12-701060-2). Acad Pr.

YORKSHIRE TERRIER DOGS

see Dogs–Breeds–Yorkshire Terrier

YOUNG, THOMAS, 1773-1829

Wood, Alexander. Thomas Young: Natural Philosopher. Oldham, Frank, ed. 1978. Repr. of 1954 ed. lib. bdg. 40.00 (ISBN 0-8492-2956-1). R West.

YOUNG'S MODULUS

see Elasticity

Z

ZEBRA PARAKEET

see Budgerigars

ZENITH Z-100 (COMPUTER)

Glatzer, Hal. How to Use Zenith Heath Computers. 1984. 19.95 (ISBN 0-318-01742-3). S-A Design Bks.
Goldstein, Larry Joel & Nunnally, Charles. Zenith-Heath Personal Computer: An Introduction to the Operating System, BASIC Programming & Applications. cancelled 15.95 (ISBN 0-318-01430-0). Brady Comm.
Kelley, Edward N. Cost, Rent, & Profit Computer: Rental Apartments. 233p. 1978. 47.00 (ISBN 0-686-46427-3). Inst Real Estate.
Kenner, Hugh. Heath-Zenith Z100 User's Guide. (Illus.). 208p. 1984. pap. 15.95 (ISBN 0-89303-516-5). Brady Comm.
--Zenith 100 User's Guide. cancelled 14.95 (ISBN 0-89303-991-8). Brady Comm.
Wilson, Steven C., et al. The Heath-Zenith HDOS 2.0 Microcomputer System. (Nanos Reference Cards Ser.). (Illus.). 22p. (Orig.). 1983. pap. 5.95 (ISBN 0-915069-14-8). Nanos Sys.

ZENO, OF ELEA

Zeuthen, H. G. & Hasse, eds. Zeno & the Discovery of Incommensurables in Greek Mathematics. LC 75-13270. (History of Ideas in Ancient Greece Ser.). (Ger. & Fr.). 1976. 11.00x (ISBN 0-405-07311-9). Ayer Co Pubs.

ZEOLITES

Barrer, R. M. Hydrothermal Chemistry of Zeolites: Synthesis, Isomorphous Replacements & Transformations. 1982. 60.00 (ISBN 0-12-079360-1). Acad Pr.
Boreshkov. Application of Zeolites in Catalysis. 1981. 17.00 (ISBN 0-9960014-9-2, Pub. by Akademiai Kaido Hungary). Heyden.
Flanigen, E. M. & Sand, Leonard B., eds. Molecular Sieve Zeolites I & II, 2 pts. LC 77-156974. (Advances in Chemistry Ser.: Nos. 101-102). 1971. Set. 64.95 (ISBN 0-8412-0617-1); Pt. 1. 39.95 (ISBN 0-8412-0114-5); Pt. 2. 36.95 (ISBN 0-8412-0115-3). Am Chemical.
Flank, William H., ed. Adsorption & Ion Exchange with Synthetic Zeolites. LC 80-18916. (ACS Symposium Ser.: No. 135). 1980. 34.95 (ISBN 0-8412-0582-5). Am Chemical.
Gottardi, G. & Galli, E. Natural Zeolites. (Minerals & Rocks Ser.: Vol. 18). (Illus.). 390p. 1985. 59.00 (ISBN 0-387-13939-7). Springer-Verlag.
Imelik, B., et al, eds. Catalysis by Zeolites: Proceedings. (Studies in Surface Science & Catalysis: Vol. 5). 352p. 1980. 76.75 (ISBN 0-444-41916-0). Elsevier.
Jacobs, P. A., et al, eds. Structure & Reactivity of Modified Zeolites: Proceedings of an International Conference, Prague, July 9-13, 1984. (Studies in Surface Science & Catalysis: No. 18). 376p. 1984. 74.00 (ISBN 0-444-42351-6, I-234-84). Elsevier.
Jacobs, Peter A., ed. Carboniogenic Activity of Zeolites. LC 77-1788. 254p. 1977. 64.00 (ISBN 0-444-41556-4). Elsevier.
Katzer, James R., ed. Molecular Sieves II. LC 77-720. (ACS Symposium Ser.: No. 40). 1977. 49.95 (ISBN 0-8412-0362-8). Am Chemical.
NATO Advanced Study Institute on Zeolites, Portugal, 1983 & Ribeiro, F. Ramoa. Zeolites: Proceedings: Science & Technology. 1984. lib. bdg. 85.00 (ISBN 90-2472-935-1, Pub. by Martinus Nijhoff Netherlands). Kluwer Academic.
Pond, Wilson G. & Mumpton, Frederick A., eds. Zeo-Agriculture: The Use of Natural Zeolites in Agriculture & Aquaculture. 450p. 1983. lib. bdg. 52.50x (ISBN 0-86531-602-3). Westview.
Rabo, Jule A., ed. Zeolite Chemistry & Catalysis. LC 76-17864. (ACS Monograph: No. 171). 1976. 79.95 (ISBN 0-8412-0276-1). Am Chemical.
Rees, L., ed. Proceedings of Fifth International Conference on Zeolites. 902p. 1980. 114.95 (ISBN 0-471-25989-6, Wiley Heyden). Wiley.
Sand, L. B. & Mumpton, F. A., eds. Natural Zeolites: Occurrence, Properties, Use. LC 77-30439. 1978. text ed. 140.00 (ISBN 0-08-021922-5). Pergamon.
Scott, Jeanette, ed. Zeolite Technology & Applications: Recent Advances. LC 80-19308. (Chemical Tech. Rev. 170). (Illus.). 381p. 1981. 64.00 (ISBN 0-8155-0817-4). Noyes.
Stucky, Galen D. & Dwyer, Francis G., eds. Intrazeolite Chemistry. LC 83-3818. (ACS Symposium Ser.: No. 218). 480p. 1983. lib. bdg. 54.95x (ISBN 0-8412-0774-7). Am Chemical.
Venuto & Habib. Fluid Catalytic Cracking with Zeolite Catalysts. LC 79-11529. (Chemical Industries Ser.: Vol. 1). 1979. 39.75 (ISBN 0-8247-6870-1). Dekker.

ZEPHYR AUTOMOBILE

see Automobiles, Foreign–Types–Zephyr

ZEPPELINS

see Air-Ships

ZERO-GRAVITY STATE–PHYSIOLOGICAL EFFECT

see Weightlessness

ZETA FUNCTIONS

see Functions, Zeta

ZILOG MODEL Z-80 (MICROPROCESSOR)

Barden, William, Jr. Z80 Microcomputer Design Projects. LC 80-50046. 208p. 1980. pap. 14.95 (ISBN 0-672-21682-5, 21682). Sams.
--Z80 Microcomputer Handbook. LC 77-93166. 304p. 1978. pap. 13.95 (ISBN 0-672-21500-4, 21500). Sams.
Carr, Joseph. Z80 User's Manual. (Illus.). 352p. 1980. text ed. 21.95 O.P. (ISBN 0-8359-9517-8); pap. text ed. 16.95 (ISBN 0-8359-9516-X). Reston.
Ciarcia, Steve. Build Your Own Z80 Computer. 473p. 1980. (BYTE Bks); pap. 19.95 (ISBN 0-07-010962-1). McGraw.
Coffron, James W. Getting Started with 8080, 8085, Z80, & 6800 Microprocessor Systems. (Illus.). 352p. 1984. pap. 14.95 (ISBN 0-13-354663-2). P-H.
--Practical Hardware Details for 8080, 8085, Z80, & 6800 Microprocessor Systems. (Illus.). 352p. 1981. text ed. 29.95 (ISBN 0-13-691089-0). P-H.
--Z80 Applications. LC 83-60950. (Illus.). 295p. 1983. pap. 15.95 (ISBN 0-89588-094-6). SYBEX.
Khambata, Adi J. Introduction to the Z80 Microcomputer. 336p. 1982. pap. 15.95 (ISBN 0-471-86167-7). Wiley.
Levanthal, Lance A., et al. Assembly Language Programming: Z-80. 640p. (Orig.). 1979. pap. text ed. 18.95 (ISBN 0-07-931021-4, 21-4). Osborne-McGraw.
Leventhal, Lance A. & Saville, Winthrop. Z80 Assembly Language Subroutines. 550p. (Orig.). 1983. pap. 17.95 (ISBN 0-07-931091-5, 91-5). Osborne-McGraw.
Lindley, Craig A. TRS-80 Z80 Assembly Language Library. (Illus.). 355p. (Orig.). 1983. looseleaf binder 34.97 (ISBN 0-88006-060-3, BK7395). Green Pub Inc.
Miller, Alan R. Eighty-Eighty & 280 Assembly Language: Techniques for Improved Programming. LC 80-21492. 318p. 1981. pap. text ed. 12.95 (ISBN 0-471-08124-8). Wiley.
Nanos, Shirley A. & Nanos, Paul P. The Z80 Microprocessor. rev. ed. (Nanos Reference Cards Ser.). 16p. 1982. 4.95 (ISBN 0-915069-12-1). Nanos Sys.
Nichols, Joseph, et al. Data Communications for Microcomputers: Practical Experiments for Z80 Based Microcomputers. (Illus.). 352p. 1983. pap. 17.95 (ISBN 0-07-046480-4, BYTE Bks). McGraw.
Nichols, Joseph C., et al. Z-Eighty Microprocessor Programming & Interfacing, 2 bks. LC 79-63822. 1979. Bk. 1, 304p. pap. 12.95 (ISBN 0-672-21609-4, 21609). Sams.
Poe, Elmer. Using the Z80 in the TRS-80. LC 82-50651. 256p. 1982. pap. 13.95 (ISBN 0-672-21839-9, 21839). Sams.
Robinson, Phillip R. The Programmer's Guide to the Z80 Chip. (Illus.). 364p. (Orig.). 1984. 18.95 (ISBN 0-8306-0656-4); pap. 13.50 (ISBN 0-8306-1656-X, 1656). TAB Bks.

also subdivision Collection and Preservation under Fishes, Insects and similar headings
Ashworth, J. H. Catalogue of the Chaetopoda in the British Museum (Natural History) A. Polychaeta: Part I Arenicolidae. (Illus.). xii, 175p. 1912. 17.50x (ISBN 0-565-00102-7, Pub. by British Mus Nat Hist England). Sabbot-Natural Hist Bks.
Clark, Hubert L. Catalogue of the Recent Sea-Urchins (Echinoidea) in the Collection of the British Museum (Natural History) (Illus.). xxviii, 250p. 1925. 25.00x (ISBN 0-565-00165-5, Pub. by British Mus Nat Hist England). Sabbot-Natural Hist Bks.
Gunther, Albert. Catalogue of Colubrine Snakes in the Collection of the British Museum. xvi, 281p. 1971. Repr. of 1858 ed. 9.00x (ISBN 0-565-00709-2, Pub. by British Mus Nat Hist England). Sabbot-Natural Hist Bks.
Hawks, Catharine A., et al. The Care of Tanned Skins in Mammal Research Collections. (Museology Ser.: No. 6). (Illus.). 32p. 1984. pap. 4.00 (ISBN 0-89672-130-2). Tex Tech Pr.
Preparation of Synopses on the Biology of Species of Living Aquatic Organisms. (Fisheries Synopses: No. 1, Rev. 1). 83p. 1965. pap. 7.50 (ISBN 0-686-92884-9, F1753, FAO). Unipub.
Taylor, Joan W. African Zoo in the Family: The Story of a Game Ranger's Wife & Her Wild Orphan Pets. (Illus.). 1965. 7.95 (ISBN 0-87523-156-X). Emerson.
Theodor, Oskar. An Illustrated Catalogue of the Rothschild Collection of Nycteribiidae (Diptera) in the British Museum (Natural History) (Illus.). viii, 506p. 1967. 76.00x (ISBN 0-565-00655-X, Pub. by British Mus Nat Hist England). Sabbot-Natural Hist Bks.

ZOOLOGISTS

see also Naturalists; Ornithologists
Allen, Garland. Thomas Hunt Morgan: A Scientific Biography. LC 77-85526. (Illus.). 1978. text ed. 46.00x (ISBN 0-691-08200-6). Princeton U Pr.
Goldschmidt, Richard B. Golden Age of Zoology. LC 56-7347. Orig. Title: Portraits from Memory: Recollections of a Zoologist. (Illus.). 191p. 1966. pap. 6.95x (ISBN 0-295-74043-4, WP19). U of Wash Pr.
Townsend, John K. Narrative of a Journey across the Rocky Mountains to the Columbia River. LC 78-17422. (Illus.). xviii, 259p. 1978. 19.95x (ISBN 0-8032-4402-9); pap. 5.50 (ISBN 0-8032-9401-8, BB 671, Bison). U of Nebr Pr.
Twitty, Victor C. Of Scientists & Salmanders. LC 66-24954. (Biology Ser.). (Illus.). 178p. 1966. text ed. 12.95x (ISBN 0-7167-0652-0). W H Freeman.
Visser, R. P. The Zoological Work of Petrus Camper (1722-1789) (Nieuwe Nederlandse Bijdragen tot de Geschiedenis der Geneeskunde en der Natuurwetenschappen: No. 12). 207p. 1985. pap. 21.25x (ISBN 90-6203-976-6, Pub. by Rodopi Holland). Humanities.

ZOOLOGY

see also Alpine Fauna; Anatomy, Comparative; Animals; Animals, Habits and Behavior of; Aquatic Animals; Cave Fauna; Color of Animals; Desert Fauna; Domestic Animals; Embryology; Entomology; Evolution; Extinct Animals; Forest Fauna; Fresh-Water Biology; Fresh-Water Fauna; Fur-Bearing Animals; Game and Game-Birds; Hibernation; Laboratory Animals; Marine Fauna; Morphology (Animals); Ornithology; Paleontology; Physiology, Comparative; Poisonous Animals; Protozoology; Soil Fauna; Variation (Biology); Zoogeography; Zoological Specimens–Collection and Preservation; Zoology, Experimental
also divisions, classes, orders, etc. of the animal kingdom, e.g. Invertebrates, Vertebrates; Birds, Insects, Mammals; Crustacea, and particular animals, e.g. Bears, Rabbits
Abramoff, Peter & Thomson, Robert G. Laboratory Outlines in Zoology. (Illus.). 398p. 1978. lab manual 14.95 (ISBN 0-7167-0017-4); individual experiments 0.95 (ISBN 0-686-68019-7); instr's handbk avail. (ISBN 0-685-93659-7). W H Freeman.
Agassiz, Louis & Gould, Augustus. Principles of Zoology, Touching the Structure, Development, Distribution, & Natural Arrangement of the Races of Animals Living & Extinct. LC 76-125729. (American Environmental Studies). (Illus.). 1970. Repr. of 1848 ed. 17.00 (ISBN 0-405-02654-4). Ayer Co Pubs.
Attenborough, David. The Zoo Quest Expeditions. 1983. pap. 4.95 (ISBN 0-14-005765-X). Penguin.
Barnes, R. S., ed. Estuarine Environment. Green, J. (Illus.). 133p. 1972. 26.00 (ISBN 0-85334-539-2, Pub. by Elsevier Applied Sci England). Elsevier.
Barnes, Robert D. Invertebrate Zoology. 4th ed. 1980. text ed. 39.95 (ISBN 0-03-056747-5, CBS C). SCP.
Beebe, William. Jungle Days. 1923. 27.50 (ISBN 0-8482-7390-7). Norwood Edns.
Bhattacharya, S. S. Zoology Practicals. 160p. 1981. 30.00x (ISBN 0-86125-643-3, Pub. by Orient Longman India). State Mutual Bk.
Boolootian, Richard A. Zoology: An Introduction to the Study of Animals. (Illus.). 1979. text ed. 23.95 (ISBN 0-02-312030-4); student study guide avail.; instrs'. manual avail.; lab. manual avail. Macmillan.
Boolootian, Richard A. & Stiles, Karl A. College Zoology. 10th ed. (Illus.). 768p. 1981. text ed. write for info. (ISBN 0-02-311990-X). Macmillan.
Burns, John M. Evolutionary Differentiation: Differentiating Gold-Banded Skippers-Autochton Cellus & More (Lepidoptera: Hesperiidae: Pyrginae. LC 84-600229. (Smithsonian Contributions to Zoology Ser.: No. 405). pap. 20.00 (ISBN 0-317-30477-1, 2024818). Bks Demand UMI.
Burns, Robert D. & Stiles, Karl A. Laboratory Explorations in General Zoology. 6th ed. 1977. write for info. (ISBN 0-02-317160-X, 31716). Macmillan.
Carus, Julius V. Geschichte der Zoologie Bis Auf Johann Mueller und Charles Darwin. Repr. of 1872 ed. 50.00 (ISBN 0-384-07825-7). Johnson Repr.
Colinvaux, Paul. Why Big Fierce Animals Are Rare: An Ecologist's Perspective. LC 77-71977. 1978. lib. bdg. 25.00x (ISBN 0-691-08194-8); pap. 7.95x (ISBN 0-691-02364-6). Princeton U Pr.
Crosby, Nina E. & Marten, Elizabeth H. Don't Teach Let Me Learn About Arachnids, Frogs, & Toads, the Animal Kingdom, Fish & Undersea Life. (Illus.). 88p. 1981. pap. 5.95 tchr's enrichment manual (ISBN 0-914634-97-6). DOK Pubs.
Cuvier, Georges B. Animal Kingdom, Arranged After Its Organization: Forming a Natural History of Animals, & an Introduction to Comparative Anatomy. LC 6-14947. (Illus.). 1969. Repr. of 1863 ed. 63.00 (ISBN 0-527-20900-7). Kraus Repr.
Ditmars, Raymond L. Confessions of a Scientist. facs. ed. LC 75-121463. (Essay Index Reprint Ser). 1934. 20.00 (ISBN 0-8369-1800-2). Ayer Co Pubs.
Dixon, Dougal. After Man: A Zoology of the Future. (Illus.). 128p. 1983. pap. 9.95 (ISBN 0-312-01162-8). St Martin.
Edwardss, Marcia & McDonnell, Unity, eds. Symposium Zoological Society London, No. 50. (Serial Publication). 336p. 1982. 49.00 (ISBN 0-12-613350-6). Acad Pr.
Elson, Lawrence M. The Zoology Coloring Book. (Illus.). 240p. 1982. pap. 8.61i (ISBN 0-06-460301-6, CO301). B&N NY.
Escherich, Peter. Social Biology of the Bushy-Tailed Woodrat, Neotoma Cinerea. (U.C. Publications in Zoology Ser.: Vol. 110). 1981. pap. 14.00x (ISBN 0-520-09595-2). U of Cal Pr.
Felts, William J. & Harrison, Richard J., eds. International Review of General & Experimental Zoology, 4 vols. Vol. 1, 1964. 70.00 (ISBN 0-12-368101-4); Vol. 3, 1968. 70.00 (ISBN 0-12-368103-0); Vol. 4, 1970. 70.00 (ISBN 0-12-368104-9); Set. o. p. 178.50. Acad Pr.
Florkin, Marcel & Sheer, Bradley T., eds. Chemical Zoology, 11 vols. Incl. Vol. 1. 1967. 90.00 (ISBN 0-12-261031-8); Vol. 2. 1968. 86.00 (ISBN 0-12-261032-6); Vol. 3. 1969. 94.50 (ISBN 0-12-261033-4); Vol. 4. 1969. 80.50 (ISBN 0-12-261034-2); Vol. 5. 1970. 70.00 (ISBN 0-12-261035-0); Vol. 6. 1971. 75.00 (ISBN 0-12-261036-9); Vol. 7. 1972. 78.00 (ISBN 0-12-261037-7); Vol. 8. 1974. 92.00 (ISBN 0-12-261038-5); Vol. 9. 1974. 85.00 (ISBN 0-12-261039-3); Vol. 10. 1978. 72.00 (ISBN 0-12-261040-7); Vol. 11. Mammalia. 1979. 60.50 (ISBN 0-12-261041-5). LC 67-23158. Set. 750.00. Acad Pr.
Folsch, D. W. & Nabholz, A., eds. Ethologische Aussagen zur Artgerechten Nutztierhaltung. (Animal Management Ser.: Vol. 13). 184p. 1982. pap. 16.95 (ISBN 0-8176-1338-2). Birkhauser.
Grant, Susan T. Beauty & the Beast: The Coevolution of Plants & Animals. 224p. 1984. 14.95 (ISBN 0-684-18186-X, ScribT). Scribner.
Grasse, Pierre P. & Tetry, Andree. Zoologie: Generalites, Protozoaires, Metazoaires I, Vol. 1. (Methodique Ser.). 1268p. 41.50 (ISBN 0-686-56434-0). French & Eur.
Griffiths, D. A. & Bowman, C. E. Acarology Six, 2 Vols. 1984. Vol. 1, 645p. 119.95 (ISBN 0-470-27410-7); Vol. 2, 700p. 100.00 (ISBN 0-470-27411-5); Set. 219.95 (ISBN 0-470-27412-3). Halsted Pr.
Hall, Thomas S. Source Book in Animal Biology. LC 74-120317. (Source Books in the History of the Sciences Ser). 1971. 45.00x (ISBN 0-674-82141-6). Harvard U Pr.
Hayami, Itaru. Natural History & Evolution of Cryptopecten. 170p. 1984. 34.50x (ISBN 0-86008-359-4, Pub. by U of Tokyo Japan). Columbia U Pr.
Hickman, Cleveland P., et al. Integrated Principles of Zoology. 6th ed. LC 78-27064. (Illus.). 1086p. 1979. text ed. 29.95 (ISBN 0-8016-2172-0). Mosby.
Hickman, Frances M. Laboratory Studies in Integrated Zoology. 5th ed. (Illus.). 508p. 1979. pap. text ed. 13.95 (ISBN 0-8016-2177-1). Mosby.
Hopkins, P. M. Intro to Zoology: A Laboratory Manual. 1984. 11.95x (ISBN 0-317-11641-X). Morton Pub.
--Introduction to Zoology: A Laboratory Manual. (Illus.). 224p. 1984. 10.95x (ISBN 0-88136-023-6). Jostens.
International Commission on Zoological Nomenclature: International Code of Zoological Nomenclature. 3rd ed. LC 84-40785. 1985. 20.00x (ISBN 0-520-05546-2). U of Cal Pr.
Johnson, Willis H., et al. Principles of Zoology. 2nd ed. LC 76-50607. 747p. 1977. text ed. 34.95 (ISBN 0-03-012046-2, HoltC); instr's manual 12.95 (ISBN 0-03-020781-9). HR&W.
Jordan, David S., et al. Animal Studies. 1907. 20.00 (ISBN 0-8482-4653-5). Norwood Edns.
Kaestner, Alfred. Invertebrate Zoology: Vol. 1, Porifera, Cnidaria, Platyhelminthes, Aschelminthes, Mollusca, Annelida & Related Phyla. LC 67-13947. 597p. 1967. 32.50 (ISBN 0-470-45415-6). Krieger.
Kershaw, Diana R. Animal Diversity. (Illus.). 442p. (Orig.). 1983. pap. text ed. 26.50x (ISBN 0-7231-0847-1, Pub. by U Tutor Pr England). Sheridan.
Kolisko, Eugen. Zoology for Everybody: Coelentrates & Echinoderms, Vol. 5. (Illus.). 1982. pap. 4.50 (ISBN 0-906492-42-4, Pub. by Kolisko Archives). St George Bk Serv.
--Zoology for Everybody: Tunicates & Molluscs, Vol. 6. (Illus.). 1983. pap. 4.50 (ISBN 0-317-07217-X, Pub. by Kolisko Archives). St George Bk Serv.
--Zoology for Everybody, Vol. 1: A General Survey. 2nd ed. (Illus.). 1977. pap. 3.95 (ISBN 0-906492-05-X, Pub. by Kolisko Archives). St George Bk Serv.
--Zoology for Everybody, Vol. 3: Mammals. (Illus.). 1979. pap. 4.50 (ISBN 0-906492-15-7, Pub. by Kolisko Archives). St George Bk Serv.
--Zoology for Everybody, Vol. 4: Protozoa. (Illus.). 1980. pap. 4.25 (ISBN 0-906492-24-6, Pub. by Kolisko Archives). St George Bk Serv.
Kolisko, Eugen, ed. Zoology for Everybody, Vol. 2: Birds. 2nd ed. (Illus.). 1978. pap. 3.95 (ISBN 0-906492-08-4, Pub. by Kolisko Archives). St George Bk Serv.
Krantz, Gerald W. Manual of Acarology. 2nd ed. 1978. text ed. 27.95x (ISBN 0-88246-064-1). Oreg St U Bkstrs.
Lamarck, J. B. Philosophie Zoologique, 2 vols. in 1. 1960. Repr. of 1809 ed. 42.00 (ISBN 3-7682-0028-0). Lubrecht & Cramer.
--Zoological Philosophy: An Exposition with Regard to the Natural History of Animals. Elliot, Hugh, tr. 500p. 1984. 30.00x (ISBN 0-226-46809-7); pap. 15.00 (ISBN 0-226-46810-0). U of Chicago Pr.
Lambkin, Lionel. Ceratodus, the Australian Lungfish. 1985. 11.95 (ISBN 0-533-06477-5). Vantage.
Lawrence, R. D. The Zoo That Never Was. LC 80-18956. (Illus.). 304p. 1981. 13.95 (ISBN 0-03-056811-0). HR&W.
Lehman, H. Eugene. Laboratory Studies in General Zoology. 6th Ed. ed. (Illus.). 1981. 12.95 (ISBN 0-89459-140-1). Hunter Textbks.
Linnaeus, Carl. Caroli Linnaei, Systema Naturae: A Photographic Facsimile of the First Volume of the Tenth Edition (1758) Regnum Animale. 824p. 1978. Repr. of 1956 ed. 33.75x (ISBN 0-565-00103-5, Pub. by Brit Mus Nat Hist England). Sabbot-Natural Hist Bks.
Lopez, Arcadia. Los Animales Del Parque. (Illus.). 1973. pap. 2.00 (ISBN 0-913632-06-6). Am Univ Artforms.
Makino, Sajiro. Atlas of the Chromosome Numbers in Animals. facsimile ed. 290p. 1951. pap. 11.95x (ISBN 0-8138-2220-3). Iowa St U Pr.
Milne-Edwards, Henri. Introduction a la Zoologie General (Introduction to General Zoology) Cohen, I. Bernard, ed. LC 80-2137. (Development of Science Ser.). 1981. Repr. of 1853 ed. lib. bdg. 16.00 (ISBN 0-405-13892-X). Ayer Co Pubs.
Needham, A. E. The Significance of Zoochromes. (Zoophysiology & Ecology Ser.: Vol. 3). (Illus.). 300p. 1974. 42.00 (ISBN 0-387-06331-5). Springer-Verlag.
Olson, Virgil J. & Olson, Helen. Capitol Reef: The Story Behind the Scenery. LC 75-184671. (Illus.). 1972. 8.95 (ISBN 0-916122-36-0); pap. 3.75 (ISBN 0-916122-11-5). KC Pubns.
Orr, Robert T. Vertebrate Biology. 5th ed. 1982. text ed. 36.95 (ISBN 0-03-057959-7, CBS C). SCP.
Perry, Richard. Life at the Sea's Frontiers. LC 73-3969. (The Many Worlds of Wildlife Ser.). (Illus.). 320p. 1974. 7.95 (ISBN 0-8008-4795-4). Taplinger.
Roberts, Tyson R. An Ichthyological Survey of the Fly River in Papua New Guinea: With Descriptions of New Species. LC 78-606184. (Smithsonian Contributions to Zoology Ser.: No. 281). pap. 20.00 (ISBN 0-317-30002-4, 2051859). Bks Demand UMI.
Savory, T. H. Zoological Systematics. 1979. 39.00x (ISBN 0-904095-31-2, Pub. by Meadowfield Pr England). State Mutual Bk.
Sellers, Larry G., et al. Explorations in Zoology. 203p. 1984. pap. 13.95 (ISBN 0-88725-020-3). Hunter Textbks.
--Explorations in Zoology. 203p. (Orig.). 1980. pap. 12.95 lab manual (ISBN 0-89459-122-3). Hunter Textbks.
Seton, Ernest T. Lives of the Hunted. 1901. 30.00 (ISBN 0-8482-6228-X). Norwood Edns.
Seton, Ernst T. Animal Heroes: Being the Histories of a Cat, a Dog, a Pigeon, a Lynx, Two Wolves & a Reindeer, & Elucidation of the Same. 40.00 (ISBN 0-8482-6307-3). Norwood Edns.
Smith, Frank. The Calciferous Glands of Lumbricidae & Diplocardia. 1923. pap. 8.00 (ISBN 0-384-56130-6). Johnson Repr.
Soule, Dorothy F. Zoology Made Simple. LC 67-15392. (Made Simple Ser.). 1967. pap. 3.95 (ISBN 0-385-08870-1). Doubleday.
Storer, Tracy I., et al. General Zoology. 6th ed. 1979. text ed. 39.95 (ISBN 0-07-061780-5). McGraw.
Symposium on Biochemistry & Physiology of Visual Pigments, Bochum Univ., Germany, 1972. Proceedings. Langer, H., ed. (Illus.). xiv, 366p. 1973. 38.00 (ISBN 0-387-06204-1). Springer-Verlag.
Van Der Hammen, L., ed. A. Berlese: Complete Acarological Works, 5 vols. (Illus.). 1977. lib. bdg. 263.00 set (ISBN 90-6193-582-2, Pub. by Junk Pub Netherlands). Kluwer Academic.
Vari, Richard P. Systematics of the Neotropical Characiform Genus Potamorhina. LC 84-1398. (Smithsonian Contributions to Zoology Ser.: No. 400). pap. 20.00 (ISBN 0-317-26576-8, 2023958). Bks Demand UMI.
Villa, Jaime. Biology of a Neotropical Glass Frog, Centrolenella Fleischmanni (Boettger), with Special Reference to its Frogfly Associates. (Illus.). 60p. 1984. 8.50 (ISBN 0-89326-098-3). Milwaukee Pub Mus.
Villee, Claude A. & Walker, Warren F., Jr. Introduction to Animal Biology. 1979. text ed. 35.95 (ISBN 0-7216-9026-2, CBS C). SCP.
Villee, Claude A., et al. General Zoology. 6th ed. LC 83-20253. (Illus.). 1984. text ed. 36.95 (ISBN 0-03-062451-7, CBS C). SCP.
Weisz, Paul B. Science of Zoology. 2nd ed. LC 72-4172. (Illus.). 1972. text ed. 37.95 (ISBN 0-07-069135-5). McGraw.
Whittow, G. Causey & Rahn, Herman, eds. Seabird Energetics. 340p. 1984. 55.00x (ISBN 0-306-41819-3, Plenum Pr). Plenum Pub.
Zoological Society of London Publications Staff. The Zoological Society of London 1826-1976 & Beyond: Symposia, No. 40. Zuckerman, Lord, ed. 1977. 49.50 (ISBN 0-12-613340-9). Acad Pr.
Zoological Society Of London - 24th Symposium. Diseases in Free Living Wild Animals. McDiarmid, ed. 1969. 52.50 (ISBN 0-12-613324-7). Acad Pr.

ZOOLOGY–ADDRESSES, ESSAYS, LECTURES

Gastang, Walter. Larval Forms & Other Zoological Verses. LC 85-14114. (Illus.). 106p. 1985. pap. 5.95 (ISBN 0-226-28423-9). U of Chicago Pr.
Herriot, James, et al. Animal Stories: Tame & Wild. LC 85-12575. (Illus.). 224p. 1985. 9.98 (ISBN 0-8069-4722-5). Sterling.
Mackal, Roy P. Searching for Hidden Animals. LC 79-6599. (Illus.). 320p. 1980. 12.95 (ISBN 0-385-14897-6). Doubleday.
Naumann, C. M., et al. Spezifitaet und Variabilitaet im Zygaenapurpuralis-Komples (Lepidoptera Zyganenidae) (Theses Zoologicae: No. 2). (Illus.). 264p. 1983. text ed. 35.00x (ISBN 3-7682-1339-0). Lubrecht & Cramer.
Van Der Spoel, S., et al, eds. Pathways in Malacology. 1979. lib. bdg. 53.00 (ISBN 90-313-0319-4, Pub. by Junk Pubs Netherlands). Kluwer Academic.

ZOOLOGY–BIBLIOGRAPHY

Aggasiz, Jean L. Bibliographia Zoologiae Et Geologiae, 4 Vols. (Sources of Science Ser.: No. 20). Set. 275.00 (ISBN 0-384-00404-0). Johnson Repr.
Day, M. H., ed. Vertebrate Locomotion. (Symposia of the Zoological Society of London Ser.: No. 48). 1981. 89.50 (ISBN 0-12-613348-4). Acad Pr.
Gerrick, David J. A Contribution Toward a Bibliography of Ohio Zoology. 1968. 5.00 (ISBN 0-86727-055-1). Ohio Bio Survey.
Harvard University Museum of Comparative Zoology. Catalogue of the Library of the Museum of Comparative Zoology, 8 Vols. 1967. 790.00 (ISBN 0-8161-0767-X, Hall Library). G K Hall.

--A New Species of Pocket Gopher (Genus Pappogeomys) from Jalisco, Mexico. (Museum Ser.: Vol. 9, No. 11). 5p. 1957. pap. 1.25 (ISBN 0-317-04925-9). U of KS Mus Nat Hist.
--Revisions of Pocket Gophers of the Genus Pappogeomys. (Museum Ser.: Vol. 16, No. 7). 196p. 1968. 10.00 (ISBN 0-317-04931-3). U of KS Mus Nat Hist.
Schwaner, Terry D. & Mount, Robert H. Systematic & Ecological Relationships of the Water Snakes Natrix Sipedon & N. Fasciata in Alabama & the Florida Panhandle. (Occasional Papers: No. 45). 44p. 1976. 2.50 (ISBN 0-317-04885-6). U of KS Mus Nat Hist.
Setzer, Henry W. Subspeciation in the Kangaroo Rat: Dipodomys Ordii. (Museum Ser.: Vol. 1, No. 23). 101p. 1949. 5.25 (ISBN 0-317-04932-1). U of KS Mus Nat Hist.
Sherborn, C. D. Index Animalium Sive Index Nominum Quae ab A.D. MDCCLVIII Generibus et Speciebus Animalium Inposita Sunt: Sectio Secunda, (1801-1850), Pts. 1-33. 1922. text ed. 410.00x (ISBN 0-565-00801-3, Pub. by Brit Mus Nat Hist). Sabbot-Natural Hist Bks.
Simpson, George G. Principles of Animal Taxonomy. LC 60-13939. (Columbia Biological Ser.: No. 20). (Illus.). 1961. 35.00x (ISBN 0-231-02427-4). Columbia U Pr.
Smith, James D. Systematics of the Chiropteran Family Mormoopidae. (Miscellaneous Publications Ser.: No. 56). 132p. 1972. 6.75 (ISBN 0-317-04934-8). U of KS Mus Nat Hist.
Stains, Howard J. A New Bat (Genus Leptonycteris) from Coahuila. (Museum Ser.: Vol. 9, No. 10). 4p. 1957. pap. 1.25 (ISBN 0-317-04943-7). U of KS Mus Nat Hist.
Sterling, Keir B., ed. Contributions to American Systematics. LC 73-17807. (Natural Sciences in America Ser.). (Illus.). 962p. 1974. Repr. 73.00x (ISBN 0-405-05724-5). Ayer Co Pubs.
Taxonomia y la Revolucion En las Ciencias Biologicas. rev. ed. (Serie De Biologia: No. 3). (Span.). 1980. pap. 3.50 (ISBN 0-8270-6050-5). OAS.
Taxonomy & Classification of the Subfamily Lamiinae: Tribes Parmenini Through Acanthoderini, Part vii, No.1. 1985. 21.00x (ISBN 0-317-27272-1). U of Cal Pr.
Taylor, Edward H. New Hylid Frogs from Eastern Mexico. (Museum Ser.: Vol. 1, No. 15). 8p. 1948. 1.50 (ISBN 0-317-04891-0). U of KS Mus Nat Hist.
Vaughan, Terry A. A New Subspecies of Bat (Myotis Velifer) from Southeastern California & Arizona. (Museum Ser.: Vol. 7, No. 8). 6p. 1954. pap. 1.25 (ISBN 0-317-04958-5). U of KS Mus Nat Hist.
Villa-R, Bernardo & Hall, E. Raymond. Subspeciation in Pocket Gophers of Kansas. (Museum Ser.: Vol. 1, No. 11). 20p. 1947. pap. 1.25 (ISBN 0-317-04959-3). U of KS Mus Nat Hist.
White, John A. Genera & Subgenera of Chipmunks. (Museum Ser.: Vol. 5, No. 32). 19p. 1953. pap. 1.25 (ISBN 0-317-04969-0). U of KS Mus Nat Hist.
--Geographic Distribution & Taxonomy of the Chipmunks of Wyoming. (Museum Ser.: Vol. 5, No. 34). 28p. 1953. pap. 1.50 (ISBN 0-317-04971-2). U of KS Mus Nat Hist.
--A New Chipmunk (Genus Eutamias) from the Black Hills. (Museum Ser.: Vol. 5, No. 19). 4p. 1952. pap. 1.25 (ISBN 0-317-04968-2). U of KS Mus Nat Hist.
--Taxonomy of the Chipmunks: Eutamias Quadrivittatus & Eutamias Umbrinus. (Museum Ser.: Vol. 5, No. 33). 20p. 1953. pap. 1.25 (ISBN 0-317-04970-4). U of KS Mus Nat Hist.
Williams, James D. & Etnier, David A. Subgenus Xenisma & a Diagnosis of the Telostei Cyprinodontidae: Description of a New Species, Fundulus Julsia, with Redescription of Fuldulus Albolineatus. (Occasional Papers: No. 102). (Illus.). 20p. 1982. 4.25 (ISBN 0-317-04836-8). U of KS Mus Nat Hist.
Wright, C. A., ed. Biochemical & Immunological Taxonomy of Animals. 1975. 76.00 (ISBN 0-12-765350-3). Acad Pr.

ZOOLOGY–DICTIONARIES

Audubon Society. Encyclopedia of Animal Life. Farrand, John, Jr., ed. (Illus.). 1982. 45.00 (ISBN 0-517-54657-4, C N Potter Bks). Crown.
Bastian, Hartmut. Ullstein Lexikon der Tierwelt. (Ger.). 1967. 27.50 (ISBN 3-550-06014-9, M-7676, Pub. by Ullstein Verlag/VVA). French & Eur.
Diccionario Riodeuro: Zoologia. (Span.). 432p. 1979. 17.95 (ISBN 0-686-57364-1, S-50171). French & Eur.
Dictionary of Zoology: English-Chinese. (Eng. & Chinese.). 52p. 1975. pap. 1.95 (ISBN 0-686-92583-1, M-9571). French & Eur.
Jacobs, George J. Dictionary of Vertebrate Zoology, Russian-English: English-Russian. LC 78-16321. 1978. pap. text ed. 4.25x (ISBN 0-87474-551-9). Smithsonian.
Jaeger, Edmund C. A Dictionary of Greek & Latin Combining Forms Used in Zoological Names. 2nd ed. (Gr., Lat. & Eng.). 176p. 1930. 18.50x (ISBN 0-398-04294-2). C C Thomas.
Jehan, L. F. Dictionnaire de Zoologie, 3 vols. Migne, J. P., ed. (Nouvelle Encyclopedie Theologique Ser.: Vols. 14-16). (Fr.). 2666p. Repr. of 1853 ed. lib. bdg. 336.50x (ISBN 0-89241-263-1). Caratzas.
Klemm, Michael. Zoologisches Woerterbuch Palaearktische Tiere. (Lat., Ger. & Rus.). 1973. 220.00 (ISBN 0-686-56474-X, M-7692, Pub. by Parey Berlin). French & Eur.
Parenti, Umberto. Diccionario De Zoologia. (Span.). 255p. 1973. leatherette 11.50 (ISBN 84-307-8256-7, S-50257). French & Eur.
Pennak, Robert W. Collegiate Dictionary of Zoology. 583p. 1964. 32.50x (ISBN 0-471-06790-3, Pub. by Wiley-Interscience). Wiley.
Smolik, H. Tierlexikon, 5 vols. (Ger.). 1968. pap. 32.00 (ISBN 3-499-16059-5, M-7667, Pub. by Rowohlt). French & Eur.

ZOOLOGY–EARLY WORKS

see Zoology–Pre-Linnean Works

ZOOLOGY–ECOLOGY

see Animal Ecology

ZOOLOGY–GEOGRAPHICAL DISTRIBUTION

see Zoogeography

ZOOLOGY–HISTORY

Jennison, George. Noah's Cargo: Some Curious Chapters of Natural History. LC 70-174390. (Illus.). Repr. of 1928 ed. 22.00 (ISBN 0-405-08670-9, Blom Pubns). Ayer Co Pubs.
Visser, R. P. The Zoological Work of Petrus Camper (1722-1789) (Nieuwe Nederlandse Bijdragen tot de Geschiedenis der Geneeskunde en der Natuurwetenschappen: No. 12). 207p. 1985. pap. 21.25x (ISBN 90-6203-976-6, Pub. by Rodopi Holland). Humanities.

ZOOLOGY–LABORATORY MANUALS

see also Anatomy, Comparative–Laboratory Manuals; Dissection

Boolootian, Richard A. & Heyneman, Donald. An Illustrated Laboratory Text in Zoology. brief ed. LC 76-30722. 253p. 1977. pap. text ed. 19.95x (ISBN 0-03-019021-5, HoltC). HR&W.
--An Illustrated Laboratory Text in Zoology. 4th ed. 1980. pap. text ed. 22.95 (ISBN 0-03-051176-3, CBS C). SCP.
Davis, William K., et al. Laboratory Exercises for General Zoology. 3rd ed. (Illus.). 131p. 1980. pap. text ed. 5.95x (ISBN 0-89641-030-7). American Pr.
Elliott, Alfred M. & Sloat, Barbara F. Laboratory Guide for Zoology. 6th ed. 1979. pap. text ed. 15.95x (ISBN 0-8087-0522-9). Burgess.
Gault, Jan, et al. Laboratory Investigations in Zoology. 176p. 1980. pap. 9.95 (ISBN 0-8403-2261-5). Kendall-Hunt.
Hartman, Margaret & Russell, Mercer P. Laboratory Manual for Biology of Animals. 1980. coil binding 9.95. Paladin Hse.
Hay, Jane. Zoology Laboratory Manual. 192p. 1981. pap. text ed. 11.95 (ISBN 0-8403-2512-6). Kendall-Hunt.
Hickman, Frances M. Laboratory Studies in Integrated Zoology. 5th ed. (Illus.). 508p. 1979. pap. text ed. 13.95 (ISBN 0-8016-2177-1). Mosby.
Keeney, Clifford. An Illustrated Guide to Cat Dissection. (Illus.). 256p. 1982. lab manual 12.95x (ISBN 0-89582-080-3). Morton Pub.
Kilgen, Ronald, et al. Laboratory Manual for Introductory Zoology. 1981. wire coil bdg. 6.95 (ISBN 0-88252-086-5). Paladin Hse.
Kilgen, Ronald H., et al. Laboratory Manual for Introductory Zoology. (Illus.). 160p. 1983. 10.95x (ISBN 0-88136-018-X). Jostens.
Lytle, Charles F. & Wodsedalek, J. E. General Zoology Laboratory Guide: Complete Version. 9th ed. 336p. 1984. write for info. wire coil bdg. (ISBN 0-697-04923-X). Wm C Brown.
--General Zoology Laboratory Guide: Short Version. 9th ed. 272p. 1984. write for info. wire coil (ISBN 0-697-04796-2). Wm C Brown.
Miller, Grover C. & Jones, Melissa. Laboratory Manual in General Zoology. 2nd ed. (Illus.). 108p. 1983. lab manual 10.95x (ISBN 0-89459-204-1). Hunter Textbks.
Nez, Martha & Haburay, J. Keitz. Laboratory Manual for General Zoology. 1978. pap. text ed. 8.50 (ISBN 0-8403-2673-4, 40267301). Kendall-Hunt.
Payne, James F. & Kennedy, Michael L. Laboratory Studies in Zoology. 2nd ed. (Illus.). 165p. 1981. lab manual 8.95 (ISBN 0-88725-007-6). Hunter Textbks.
Stamps, Judy A., et al. A Zoology Lab Manual. 280p. 1981. pap. text ed. 14.95 (ISBN 0-8403-2506-1). Kendall-Hunt.
Taylor, Walter K. Laboratory Instructions for General Zoology. (Illus.). 1979. pap. text ed. write for info. (ISBN 0-02-419790-4). Macmillan.
Thornton, John W. Animal Biology Laboratory Exercises. 120p. 1984. pap. 8.95 (ISBN 0-8403-3442-7). Kendall Hunt.
Underhill, James C. & Olson, Magnus. General Zoology Laboratory Guide. 3rd ed. 1978. spiral bdg. 10.95x (ISBN 0-8087-2108-9). Burgess.
Wingerd, Bruce D. Rabbit Dissection Manual. LC 84-15761. 80p. 1985. 9.95x (ISBN 0-8018-2470-2). Johns Hopkins.

ZOOLOGY–MORPHOLOGY

see Anatomy, Comparative; Morphology (Animals)

ZOOLOGY–NOMENCLATURE

International Trust for Zoological Nomenclature, ed. International Code of Zoological Nomenclature. 3rd ed. 320p. 1985. 26.50x (ISBN 0-565-00967-2, Pub. by Brit Mus Nat Hist England). Sabbot Natural Hist Bks.
Mayr, Ernst. Principles of Systematic Zoology. LC 68-54937. (Illus.). 1969. text ed. 54.95 (ISBN 0-07-041143-3). McGraw.
Rafinesque, S. C. Precis de Descouvertes Somiologiques. 11.25 (ISBN 0-8446-1371-1). Peter Smith.

ZOOLOGY–OUTLINES, SYLLABI, ETC.

Alexander, Gordon. General Zoology. 5th ed. (Illus., Orig.). 1964. pap. 5.95 (ISBN 0-06-460032-7, CO 32, COS). B&N NY.
Farmer, John N. Lecture Outline & Guide for Introductory Zoology. 128p. 1984. pap. text ed. 9.95 (ISBN 0-8403-3440-0). Kendall-Hunt.

ZOOLOGY–PICTORIAL WORKS

Here are entered scientific works of which the plates form the most important feature. Works on the art of animal painting and illustration are entered under the heading Animal Painting and Illustration The heading Animal Pictures is used for popular works containing chiefly pictures and photographs of animals.

Cherry, Marlin O. Zoology Laboratory Workbook. 4th ed. 152p. 1982. pap. text ed. 6.95x (ISBN 0-89641-108-7). American Pr.
Cramp, Stanley, ed. Handbook of the Birds of Europe, the Middle East, & North Africa: The Birds of the Western Paleartic, Vol. 3: Waders to Gulls. (Illus.). 1983. 98.00x (ISBN 0-19-857506-8). Oxford U Pr.
Farr, Gerald G. Zoology Illustrated. (Illus.). 65p. 1979. pap. text ed. 3.95x (ISBN 0-89641-056-0). American Pr.

ZOOLOGY–PRE-LINNEAN WORKS

see also Natural History–Pre-Linnean Works

Aristotle. Generation of Animals. (Loeb Classical Library: No. 366). 1943. 12.50x (ISBN 0-674-99403-5). Harvard U Pr.
Boreman, Thomas, ed. A Description of Three Hundred Animals. (Illus.). Repr. of 1786 ed. 18.00 (ISBN 0-384-05125-1). Johnson Repr.
Topsell, Edward. The Historie of Foure-Footed Beastes, Collected Out of All Volumes of C. Gesner, & All Other Writers to This Present Day. LC 72-6034. (English Experience Ser.: No. 561). 816p. 1973. Repr. of 1607 ed. 104.00 (ISBN 90-221-0561-X). Walter J Johnson.
--The Historie of Serpents; or, the Second Book of Living Creatures. LC 72-6035. (English Experience Ser.: No. 562). 336p. 1973. Repr. of 1608 ed. 58.00 (ISBN 90-221-0562-8). Walter J Johnson.
--History of Four-Footed Beasts, & Serpents & Insects, 3 Vols. 2nd ed. LC 65-23391. 1967. Repr. of 1658 ed. Set. lib. bdg. 150.00 (ISBN 0-306-70923-6). Da Capo.

ZOOLOGY–STUDY AND TEACHING

Kontio, A. Loren. Zoocollage. LC 71-173451. 1974. pap. 5.000 (ISBN 0-87812-035-1). Pendell Pub.

ZOOLOGY–AFRICA

Barrett, Samuel A., et al, eds. Cudahy-Massee-Milwaukee Museum African Expedition 1928-29. LC 71-11397. Repr. of 1930 ed. lib. bdg. 37.50x (ISBN 0-8371-4625-9, BAAE). Greenwood.
Cowles, Raymond B. Zulu Journal: Field Notes of a Naturalist in South Africa. LC 59-8760. 1959. pap. 1.95 (ISBN 0-520-00276-8, CAL73). U of Cal Pr.
Duellman, William E. The Biology of an Equatorial Herpetofauna in Amazonian Ecuador. (Miscellaneous Publications Ser.: No. 65). 352p. 1978. pap. 15.00 (ISBN 0-686-80352-3). U of KS Mus Nat Hist.
Owens, Mark & Owens, Delia. Cry of the Kalahari. 1984. 19.95 (ISBN 0-395-32214-6). HM.
Sale, J. B. The Importance & Values of Wild Plants & Animals in Africa. (Illus.). 44p. 1983. pap. text ed. 10.00 (ISBN 2-88032-502-1, IUCN122, IUCN). Unipub.
Taylor, Joan W. African Zoo in the Family: The Story of a Game Ranger's Wife & Her Wild Orphan Pets. (Illus.). 1965. 7.95 (ISBN 0-87523-156-X). Emerson.
Van Lawick-Goodall, Jane & Van Lawick-Goodall, Hugo. Innocent Killers. 1971. 12.95 (ISBN 0-395-12109-4). HM.

ZOOLOGY–AMERICA

Collins, Henry H., Jr. & Ransom, Jay E., eds. Harper & Row's Complete Field Guide to North American Wildlife: Eastern Edition. LC 80-8198. (Illus.). 810p. 1981. 17.50i (ISBN 0-690-01977-7, HarpT); flexible vinyl cover 12.95i (ISBN 0-690-01969-6); western edition 17.50i (ISBN 0-690-01979-3). Har-Row.
Flint, Oliver S. The Genus Brachycentrus in North America, with a Proposed Phylogeny of the Genera of Brachycentridae (Trichoptera) LC 84-600157. (Smithsonian Contributions to Zoology Ser.: No. 398). pap. 20.00 (ISBN 0-317-26339-0, 2024229). Bks Demand UMI.
Houbrick, Richard S. Genus Clypeomorus Jousseaume: Cerithiidae: Prosobranchia. LC 84-600025. (Smithsonian Contributions to Zoology: No. 403). pap. 33.80 (ISBN 0-317-26681-0, 2025111). Bks Demand UMI.
Osborn, Henry F. Elephants & Mastodons Arrive in America. (Shorey Historical Ser.). (Illus.). 26p. pap. 2.95 (ISBN 0-8466-6021-0, U21). Shorey.
Writers Program, New York. American Wild Life. LC 73-3644. (American Guide Ser.). (Illus.). 1940. Repr. 57.50 (ISBN 0-404-57943-4). AMS Pr.

ZOOLOGY–ANTARCTIC REGIONS

Scott, Robert F. Voyage of the Discovery, 2 Vols. LC 68-55218. (Illus.). 1969. Repr. of 1905 ed. Set. lib. bdg. 57.00x (ISBN 0-8371-1334-2, SCDI). Greenwood.
Scott, Robert S. Voyage of the 'Discovery' (Illus.). 1951. 18.00 (ISBN 0-685-20649-1). Transatlantic.

ZOOLOGY–ARCTIC REGIONS

Hosking, Eric, photos by. Antarctic Wildlife. Sage, Bryan. LC 82-1382. (Illus.). 160p. 1983. 22.95 (ISBN 0-87196-679-4). Facts on File.
Pennant, Thomas. Arctic Zoology, 2 vols. in one. LC 73-17835. (Natural Sciences in America Ser.). (Illus.). 1012p. 1974. Repr. 69.50x (ISBN 0-405-05758-X). Ayer Co Pubs.
Zoology II. Incl. Birds. Horring, Richard; Fishes. Pfaff, Johannes P; Insects. Henriksen, Kai L; Crustacea. Stephensen, Knud. LC 76-19379. (Thule Expedition, 5th, 1921-1924: Vol. 2, Nos. 6-9). (Illus.). Repr. of 1937 ed. 47.50 (ISBN 0-404-58310-5). AMS Pr.

ZOOLOGY–ARGENTINE REPUBLIC

Hudson, William H. Naturalist in La Plata. Repr. of 1923 ed. 35.00 (ISBN 0-404-03393-8). AMS Pr.

ZOOLOGY–ASIA

Brodsky, K. A. Mountain Torrent of the Tien Shan: An Ecology-Faunistic Essay. (Monographiae Biologicae: No. 39). (Illus.). 311p. 1980. lib. bdg. 79.00 (ISBN 90-6193-091-X, Pub. by Junk Pubs Netherlands). Kluwer Academic.
Howes, G. J. Anatomy & Phylogeny of the Chinese Major Carps, Ctenopharyngodon Steind, 1866, & Hypophthalmichthys Birkr, 1860. 49.00x (ISBN 0-686-78651-3, Pub. by Brit Mus Pubns England). State Mutual Bk.
Jones, J. Knox, Jr. & Johnson, David H. Review of the Insectivores of Korea. (Museum Ser.: Vol. 9, No. 22). 30p. 1960. pap. 1.75 (ISBN 0-686-80298-5). U of KS Mus Nat Hist.
Mathis, Wayne N. & Ghorpade, Kumar D. Studies of Parydrinae (Diptera: Ephydridae) A Review of the Genus Brachydeutere Loew from the Oriental, Australian, & Oceanian Regions, Part 1. LC 84-600345. (Smithsonian Contributions to Zoology Ser.: No. 406). pap. 20.00 (ISBN 0-317-30040-7, 2025043). Bks Demand UMI.

ZOOLOGY–AUSTRALIA

Australian Society of Animal Production 14th Biennial Conference, Brisbane, Queensland, May 1982. Animal Production in Australia: Proceeding. (Illus.). 708p. 1982. 59.50 (ISBN 0-08-024836-5); pap. 40.00 (ISBN 0-08-024837-3). Pergamon.
Groves, R. H. & Ride, W. D., eds. Species at Risk: Research in Australia. 250p. 1982. 40.00 (ISBN 0-387-11416-5). Springer-Verlag.
Mathis, Wayne N. & Ghorpade, Kumar D. Studies of Parydrinae (Diptera: Ephydridae) A Review of the Genus Brachydeutere Loew from the Oriental, Australian, & Oceanian Regions, Part 1. LC 84-600345. (Smithsonian Contributions to Zoology Ser.: No. 406). pap. 20.00 (ISBN 0-317-30040-7, 2025043). Bks Demand UMI.
Specht, R. L. & Mountford, C. P. Records of the American Australian Scientific Expedition to Arnhem Land, Vol. 4. 1964. 30.00x (ISBN 0-522-83685-2, Pub by Melbourne Pr). Intl Spec Bk.

ZOOLOGY–BRITISH GUIANA

Beebe, William. Edge of the Jungle. 1921. 27.50 (ISBN 0-8482-7358-3). Norwood Edns.

ZOOLOGY–CANADA

Cook, Francis R. Introduction to Canadian Amphibians & Reptiles. (National Museum of Science Ser.). 200p. 1984. pap. text ed. 12.95x (ISBN 0-317-03314-X, 56396-0, Pub. by Natl Mus Canada). U of Chicago Pr.

Zoology II. Incl. Birds. Horring, Richard; Fishes. Pfaff, Johannes P; Insects. Henriksen, Kai L; Crustacea. Stephensen, Knud. LC 76-19379. (Thule Expedition, 5th, 1921-1924: Vol. 2, Nos. 6-9). (Illus.). Repr. of 1937 ed. 47.50 (ISBN 0-404-58310-5). AMS Pr.

ZOOLOGY–CENTRAL AMERICA

Anderson, Sydney & Jones, J. Knox, Jr. Records of Harvest Mice, Reithrodontomys, from Central America, with Description of a New Subspecies from Nicaragua. (Museum Ser.: Vol. 9, No. 19). 11p. 1960. pap. 1.25 (ISBN 0-317-04926-7). U of KS Mus Nat Hist.

Brocchi, Paul. Mission Scientifique Au Mexique et Dans L'amerique Centrale....Recherches Zoologiques: Etude Des Batraciens De l' Amerque Centrale. Sterling, Keir B., ed. LC 77-81099. (Biologists & Their World Ser.). (Illus.). 1978. Repr. of 1882 ed. lib. bdg. 17.00x (ISBN 0-405-10681-5). Ayer Co Pubs.

Dumeril, Auguste H., et al. Mission Scientifique Au Mexique et Dans L'Amerique Centrale,....Recherches Zoologiques: Etude Sur les Reptiles, Avec Atlas, 2 vols. Sterling, Keir B., ed. LC 77-81098. (Biologists & Their World Ser.). (Fr., Illus.). 1978. Repr. of 1909 ed. lib. bdg. 110.00x (ISBN 0-405-10680-7). Ayer Co Pubs.

Jones, J. Knox, Jr. Bats from Guatemala. (Museum Ser.: Vol. 16, No. 5). 34p. 1966. pap. 2.00 (ISBN 0-317-04858-9). U of KS Mus Nat Hist.

Jones, J. Knox, Jr., et al. Noteworthy Records of Bats from Nicaragua, with a Checklist of the Chiropteran Fauna of the Country. (Occasional Papers: No. 2). 35p. 1971. pap. 2.00. U of KS Mus Nat Hist.

McCranie, James R. & Wilson, Larry D. A New Hylid Frog of the Genus Plectrohyla from a Cloud Forest in Honduras. (Occasional Papers: No. 92). 7p. 1981. 1.25 (ISBN 0-317-04882-1). U of KS Mus Nat Hist.

Sajdak, R. A., et al. Notes on the Movements of Basiliscus Plumifrons (Sauria: Iguanidae) in Costa Rica. 8p. 1980. 1.00 (ISBN 0-89326-062-2). Milwaukee Pub Mus.

Villa, Jaime. Venomous Snakes of Nicaragua. 48p. 1984. 6.95 (ISBN 0-89326-103-3). Milwaukee Pub Mus.

ZOOLOGY–EGYPT

Anderson, John. Reptilia & Batrachia. (Zoology of Egypt Ser.: No. 1). (Illus.). 1965. Repr. of 1898 ed. 105.00 (ISBN 3-7682-0240-2). Lubrecht & Cramer.

ZOOLOGY–GALAPAGOS ISLANDS

Froeschner, Richard C. Synopsis of the Heteropters or True Bugs of the Galapagos Islands. LC 84-600217. (Smithsonian Contributions to Zoology Ser.: No. 407). pap. 22.00 (ISBN 0-317-30173-X, 2025355). Bks Demand UMI.

ZOOLOGY–GREAT BRITAIN

Burton, John A. The National Trust Book of British Wild Animals. (Illus.). 194p. 1985. 17.95 (ISBN 0-224-02104-4, Pub. by Jonathan Cape). Merrimack Pub Cir.

Hawksworth, D. L., ed. The Changing Flora & Fauna of Britain. 1974. 75.50 (ISBN 0-12-333450-0). Acad Pr.

Roof, Nina J. & Johnson, Brylan R. The Proceedings of the Zoological Society of London: An Index to Illustrators. 300p. 1985. lib. bdg. 40.00 (ISBN 0-8240-8721-6). Garland pub.

Stout, Adam. The Old Gloucester: The Story of a Cattle Breed. 96p. 1980. text ed. 11.75x (ISBN 0-904387-42-9, Pub. by Sutton England). Humanities.

ZOOLOGY–GREECE

Gejvall, Nils-Gustaf. The Fauna. LC 66-36503. (Lerna Ser: Vol. 1). (Illus.). 1969. 15.00x (ISBN 0-87661-301-6). Am Sch Athens.

ZOOLOGY–INDIA

Andrews, H. E. Coleoptera: Carabidae-Carabinae. (Fauna of British India Ser.: Vol. 1). (Illus.). xxvii, 433p. 30.00 (ISBN 0-88065-006-0, Pub. by Messers Today & Tomorrows Printers & Publishers India). Scholarly Pubns.

Andrews, H. E., ed. Coleoptera: Carabidae-Harpalinae 1. (Fauna of British India Ser.: Vol. 2). (Illus.). xvi, 340p. 1977. Repr. of 1935 ed. 25.00 (ISBN 0-88065-009-5, Pub. by Messers Today & Tomorrows Printers & Publishers India). Scholarly Pubns.

Arrow, G. J. Coleoptera: Clavicornia, Erotylidae, Languriidae & Endomychidae. (Fauna of British India Ser.). (Illus.). xvi, 416p. 1976. Repr. of 1910 ed. 25.00 (ISBN 0-88065-016-8, Pub. by Messers Today & Tomorrows Printers & Publishers India). Scholarly Pubns.

--Coleoptera: Lamellicornia, Cetoniinae, & Dynastinae. (Fauna of British India Ser.). (Illus.). xiv, 328p. 1976. Repr. of 1925 ed. 25.00 (ISBN 0-88065-017-6, Pub. by Messers Today & Tomorrows Printers & Publishers India). Scholarly Pubns.

--Coleoptera: Lamellicornia, Coprinae, Pt. III. (Fauna of British India Ser.). (Illus.). xii, 452p. 1977. Repr. of 1931 ed. 25.00 (ISBN 0-88065-019-2, Pub. by Messers Today & Tomorrows Printers & Publishers India). Scholarly Pubns.

--Coleoptera: Lamellicornia, Rutelinae, Desmonoycinae & Euchirinae. (Fauna of British India Ser.). (Illus.). xiv, 400p. 1974. Repr. of 1917 ed. 15.00 (ISBN 0-88065-018-4, Pub. by Messers Today & Tomorrows Printers & Publishers India). Scholarly Pubns.

Baylis, H. A. Nematoda: Ascaroidea & Strongyloidea. (Fauna of British India Ser.). xxxvi, 416p. 1978. Repr. of 1936 ed. 30.00 (ISBN 0-88065-051-6, Pub. by Messers Today & Tomorrows Printers & PublishersIndia). Scholarly Pubns.

--Nematoda: Filaricidea, Dictophymoidea & Trichinelloidea, Vol. 2. (Fauna of British India Ser.). xxviii, 280p. 1978. Repr. of 1939 ed. 30.00 (ISBN 0-88065-052-4, Pub. by Messers Today & Tomorrows Printers & Publishers India). Scholarly Pubns.

Bhatia, B. L. Protozoa: Ciliophora. (Fauna of British India Ser.). (Illus.). xxii, 522p. 1979. Repr. 30.00 (ISBN 0-88065-058-3, Pub. by Messers Today & Tomorrows Printers & Publishers India). Scholarly Pubns.

--Protozoa: Sporozoa. (Fauna of British India Ser.). (Illus.). xx, 508p. 1979. Repr. 30.00 (ISBN 0-88065-103-2, Pub. by Messers Today & Tomorrows Printers & Publishers India). Scholarly Pubns.

Blandford, W. T. & Godwin-Austen, H. N. Mollusca: Testacelldae & Zonitidae, Vol. 1. (Fauna of British India Ser.). xxxii, 332p. 1978. Repr. of 1908 ed. 30.00 (Pub. by Messers Today & Tomorrows Printers & Publishers India). Scholarly Pubns.

Cameron, M. Coleoptera - Staphylinidae: Staphylinidae, Vol. II. (Fauna of British India Ser.). (Illus.). vii, 260p. 1978. Repr. of 1931 ed. 30.00 (ISBN 0-88065-027-3, Pub. by Messers Today & Tomorrows Printers & Publishers India). Scholarly Pubns.

--Coleoptera - Staphylinidae: Staphylinidae, Vol. 1. (Fauna of British India Ser.). (Illus.). xviii, 478p. 1978. Repr. of 1930 ed. 30.00 (ISBN 0-88065-026-5, Pub. by Messers Today & Tommorrows Printers & Publishers India). Scholarly Pubns.

--Coleoptera - Staphylinoidea: Staphylinidae, Vol. 4, Pt. 2. (Fauna of British India Ser.). (Illus.). 691p. 1977. Repr. of 1939 ed. 40.00 (ISBN 0-88065-030-3, Pub. by Messers Today & Tomorrows Printers & Publishers India). Scholarly Pubns.

--Coleoptera-Staphylinoidea: Staphylinodea, Vol. 4, Pt. 1. (Fauna of British India Ser.). (Illus.). Repr. of 1939 ed. 30.00 (ISBN 0-88065-029-X, Pub. by Messers Today & Tomorrows Printers & Publishers India). Scholarly Pubns.

Distant, W. L. Rhynchota: Heteroptera, Vol. 1. (Fauna of British India Ser,). xxxviii, 438p. 1977. Repr. of 1902 ed. 25.00 (ISBN 0-88065-048-6, Pub. by Messers Today & Tomorrows Printers & Publishers India). Scholarly Pubns.

--Rhynchota: Heteroptera, Vol. 2. (Fauna of British India Ser.). xviii, 504p. 1977. Repr. of 1902 ed. 25.00 (ISBN 0-88065-049-4, Pub. by Messers Today & Tomorrows Printers & Publishers India). Scholarly Pubns.

--Rhynchota: Heteroptera - Appendix, Vol. 5. (Fauna of British India Ser.). xii, 362p. 1977. Repr. of 1910 ed. 20.00 (ISBN 0-88065-077-X, Pub. by Messers Today & Tomorrows Printers & Publishers India). Scholarly Pubns.

--Rhynchota: Heteroptera-Homoptera, Vol. 3. (Fauna of British India Ser.). iiv, 504p. 1977. Repr. of 1906 ed. 25.00 (ISBN 0-88065-075-3, Pub. by Messers Today & Tomorrows Printers & Publishers India). Scholarly Pubns.

--Rhynchota: Homoptera - Appendix, Vol. 4. (Fauna of British India Ser.). xiv, 502p. 1977. Repr. of 1908 ed. 25.00 (ISBN 0-88065-076-1, Pub. by Messers Today & Tomorrows Printers & Publishers India). Scholarly Pubns.

--Rhynchota: Homoptera - Appendix, Vol. 6. (Fauna of British India Ser.). viii, 250p. 1977. Repr. of 1916 ed. 15.00 (ISBN 0-88065-078-8, Pub. by Messers Today & Tomorrows Printers & Publishers India). Scholarly Pubns.

--Rhynchota: Homoptera - Appendix, Heteroptera - Addenda, Vol. 7. (Fauna of British India Ser.). viii, 212p. 1977. Repr. of 1918 ed. 15.00 (ISBN 0-88065-079-6, Pub. by Messers Today & Tomorrows Printers & Publishers India). Scholarly Pubns.

Fowler, W. W. Coleoptera: General Introduction & Cicindelidae & Paussidae. (Fauna of British India Ser.). xx, 530p. 1973. Repr. of 1912 ed. 20.00 (ISBN 0-88065-085-0, Pub. by Messers Today & Tomorrows Printers & Publishers India). Scholarly Pubns.

Fraser, Thomas H. & Lachner, Ernest A. A Revision of the Cardinalfish Subgenera Pristiapogon & Zoramia (Genus Apogon) of the Indo-Pacific Region (Teleostei: Apogonidae) LC 84-600287. (Smithsonian Contributions to Zoology Ser.: No. 412). pap. 20.00 (ISBN 0-317-30175-6, 2025357). Bks Demand UMI.

Gahan, C. J. Coleoptera - Phytophaga - Cerambycidae. (Fauna of British India Ser.). xviii, 330p. 1974. Repr. of 1906 ed. 11.00 (ISBN 0-88065-090-7, Pub. by Messers Today & Tomorrows Printers & Publishers India). Scholarly Pubns.

Gude, G. K. Mollusca: Trochomorphidae & Janellidae, Vol. 2. xii, 522p. 1978. Repr. of 1914 ed. 30.00 (ISBN 0-88065-091-5, Pub. by Messers Today & Tomorrows Printers & Publishers India). Scholarly Pubns.

Land Operculates: Cyclophoridae, Truncatellidae, Assimineidae, Helicinidae, Vol. 3. (Fauna of British India Ser.). xiv, 386p. 30.00 (ISBN 0-88065-092-3, Pub. by Messers Today & Tomorrows Printers & Publishers India). Scholarly Pubns.

Marshall, G. A. Coleoptera - Rhynchophora - Curculionidae. (Fauna of British India Ser.). xvi, 370p. 1977. Repr. of 1916 ed. 30.00 (ISBN 0-88065-154-7, Pub. by Messers Today & Tomorrows Printers & Publishers India). Scholarly Pubns.

Maulik, S. Coleoptera - Phytophaga - Chrysomelidae: Chrysomelinae & Halticinae. (Illus.). xiv, 442p. 1977. Repr. of 1926 ed. 30.00 (ISBN 0-88065-156-3, Pub. by Messers Today & Tomorrows Printers & Publishers India). Scholarly Pubns.

--Coleoptera - Phytophaga - Chrysomelidae: Galerucinae. (Illus.). xiv, 658p. 1979. Repr. of 1936 ed. 30.00 (ISBN 0-88065-157-1, Pub. by Messers Today & Tomorrows Printers & Publishers India). Scholarly Pubns.

--Coleoptera - Phytophaga - Chrysomelidae: Hispinae & Cossidinae. (Fauna of British India Ser.). xii, 442p. 1973. Repr. of 1919 ed. 16.00 (ISBN 0-88065-155-5, Pub. by Messers Today & Tomorrows Printers & Publishers India). Scholarly Pubns.

Preston, H. B. Mollusca: Vol. 4: Freshwater Gastropoda & Pelycypoda. (Fauna of British India Ser.). xx, 246p. 1978. Repr. of 1915 ed. 30.00 (ISBN 0-88065-177-6, Pub. by Messers Today & Tomorrows Printers & Publishers India). Scholarly Pubns.

Smith, Malcolm A. Reptilia & Amphibia: Loricata, Te Studines, Vol. 1. 2nd ed. Shipley, A. B., ed. (Fauna of British India Ser.). (Illus.). xxviii, 185p. 1981. Repr. of 1933 ed. 20.00 (ISBN 0-88065-216-0, Pub. by Messers Today & Tomorrows Printers & Publishers India). Scholarly Pubns.

--Reptilia & Amphibia: Serpentes, Vol. 3. 2nd ed. Shipley, A. B., ed. (Fauna of British India Ser.). (Illus.). xii, 583p. 1981. Repr. of 1953 ed. 50.00 (ISBN 0-88065-218-7, Pub. by Messers Today &Tomorrows Printers & Publishers India). Scholarly Pubns.

--Reptillia & Amphibia: Sauria, Vol. 2. 2nd ed. Shipley, A. B., ed. (Fauna of British India Ser.). (Illus.). ix, 440p. 1981. Repr. of 1935 ed. 35.00 (ISBN 0-88065-217-9, Pub. by Messers Today & Tomorrows Printers & Publsihers India). Scholarly Pubns.

Srininvasan, M. S. Schwager's Car Nicobar Foraminifera in the Reports of the Novara Expedition. rev. ed. (Illus.). 91p. 1980. 12.00 (ISBN 0-88065-195-4, Pub. by Messers Today & Tomorrows Printers & Publishers India). Scholarly Pubns.

Stebbing, E. P. A Manual of Elementary Forest Zoology for India. 1978. Repr. of 1908 ed. 62.50x (ISBN 0-89955-291-9, Pub. by Intl Bk Dist). Intl Spec Bk.

Stuart-Baker, E. C. Aves, Vol. I. 2nd ed. (Fauna of British India Ser.). (Illus.). xxiv, 484p. 1974. Repr. of 1922 ed. 16.00 (ISBN 0-88065-198-9, Pub. by Messers Today & Tomorrows Printers & Publishers India). Scholarly Pubns.

ZOOLOGY–MADAGASCAR

Durrell, Gerald. Ark on the Move. 1983. 14.95 (ISBN 0-698-11211-3, Coward). Putnam Pub Group.

Jolly, A., et al, eds. Madagascar. LC 83-17394. (Key Environments Ser.). (Illus.). 250p. 1984. 19.50 (ISBN 0-08-028002-1). Pergamon.

ZOOLOGY–MEXICO

Alvarez, Ticul. Taxonomic Status of Some Mice of the Peromyscus Boylii Group in Eastern Mexico, with Description of a New Subspecies. (Museum Ser.: Vol. 14, No. 7). 10p. 1961. pap. 1.25 (ISBN 0-317-04908-9). U of KS Mus Nat Hist.

Anderson, Sydney. Neotropical Bats from Western Mexico. (Museum Ser.: Vol. 14, No. 1). 8p. 1960. pap. 1.25 (ISBN 0-317-04936-4). U of KS Mus Nat Hist.

Baker, Rollin H. A New Bat (Genus Pipistrellus) from Northeastern Mexico. (Museum Ser.: Vol. 7, No. 10). 4p. 1954. pap. 1.25 (ISBN 0-317-04950-X). U of KS Mus Nat Hist.

--A New Cottontail (Sylvilagus Floridanus) from Northeastern Mexico. (Museum Ser.: Vol. 7, No. 13). 4p. 1955. pap. 1.25 (ISBN 0-317-04952-6). U of KS Mus Nat Hist.

Baker, Rollin H. & Stains, Howard J. A New Long-Eared Myotis (Myotis Evotis) from Northeastern Mexico. (Museum Ser.: Vol. 9, No. 3). 4p. 1955. pap. 1.25 (ISBN 0-317-04954-2). U of KS Mus Nat Hist.

Brocchi, Paul. Mission Scientifique Au Mexique et Dans L'amerique Centrale....Recherches Zoologiques: Etude Des Batraciens De l' Amerque Centrale. Sterling, Keir B., ed. LC 77-81099. (Biologists & Their World Ser.). (Illus.). 1978. Repr. of 1882 ed. lib. bdg. 17.00x (ISBN 0-405-10681-5). Ayer Co Pubs.

Cressey, Roger F. Parasitic Copepods from the Gulf of Mexico & Caribbean Sea. LC 81-9055. (Smithsonian Contributions to Zoology: No. 389). pap. 20.00 (ISBN 0-317-29739-2, 2022199). Bks Demand UMI.

Dalquest, Walter W. & Hall, E. Raymond. A New Bat (Genus Myotis) from Mexico. (Museum Ser.: Vol. 1, No. 12). 8p. 1947. pap. 1.25 (ISBN 0-317-04976-3). U of KS Mus Nat Hist.

--Tadarida Femirisacca (Merriam) in Tamaulipas, Mexico. (Museum Ser.: Vol. 1, No. 13). 4p. 1947. pap. 1.25 (ISBN 0-317-04978-X). U of KS Mus Nat Hist.

Dumeril, Auguste H., et al. Mission Scientifique Au Mexique et Dans L'Amerique Centrale,....Recherches Zoologiques: Etude Sur les Reptiles, Avec Atlas, 2 vols. Sterling, Keir B., ed. LC 77-81098. (Biologists & Their World Ser.). (Fr., Illus.). 1978. Repr. of 1909 ed. lib. bdg. 110.00x (ISBN 0-405-10680-7). Ayer Co Pubs.

Finley, Robert B., Jr. A New Pinon Mouse (Peromyscus Truei) from Durango, Mexico. (Museum Ser.: Vol. 5, No. 20). 5p. 1952. pap. 1.25 (ISBN 0-317-05010-9). U of KS Mus Nat Hist.

Fitch, Henry S. Two New Anoles (Reptilla: Iguanidae) From Oaxaca with Comments on Other Mexican Species. 15p. 1978. 1.00 (ISBN 0-89326-034-7). Milwaukee Pub Mus.

Hall, E. Raymond. A New Bat (Myotis) from Mexico. (Museum Ser.: Vol. 14, No. 13). 4p. 1962. pap. 1.25 (ISBN 0-317-04812-0). U of KS Mus Nat Hist.

--A New Name for the Mexican Red Bat. (Museum Ser.: Vol. 5, No. 14). 4p. 1951. pap. 1.25 (ISBN 0-317-04795-7). U of KS Mus Nat Hist.

--Small Carnivores from San Josecito Cave (Pleistocene), Nuevo Leon, Mexico. (Museum Ser.: Vol. 9, No. 20). 8p. 1960. 1.25 (ISBN 0-317-04802-3). U of KS Mus Nat Hist.

Hall, E. Raymond & Villa-R, Bernardo. A New Pocket Gopher (Thomomys) & a New Spiny Pocket Mouse (Liomys) from Michoacan, Mexico. (Museum Ser.: Vol. 1, No. 14). 8p. 1948. pap. 1.25 (ISBN 0-317-05018-4). U of KS Mus Nat Hist.

Jaeger, Edmund C. Desert Wildlife. (Illus.). 1961. 11.95 (ISBN 0-8047-0123-7); pap. 6.95 (ISBN 0-8047-0124-5, SP68). Stanford U Pr.

Lee, Julian C. An Ecogeographic Analysis of the Herpetofauna of the Yucatan Peninsula. (Miscellaneous Publications: No. 67). 75p. 1980. 4.00 (ISBN 0-317-04867-8). U of KS Mus Nat Hist.

Leopold, A. Starker. Wildlife of Mexico: The Game Birds & Mammals. LC 59-6865. (Illus.). 568p. 1959. 42.00 (ISBN 0-520-00724-7). U of Cal Pr.

Page, Lawrence M. Redescription of Etheostoma Australe & a Key for the Identification of Mexican Etheostoma Percidae. (Occasional Papers: No. 89). 10p. 1981. 1.25 (ISBN 0-317-04828-7). U of KS Mus Nat Hist.

Rickart, Eric A. Reproduction Growth & Development in Two Species of Cloud Forest Peromycus from Southern Mexico. (Occasional Papers: No. 67). 22p. 1977. pap. 1.25 (ISBN 0-317-04907-0). U of Ks Mus Nat Hist.

Russell, Robert J. Four New Pocket Gophers of the Genus Cratogeomys from Jalisco, Mexico. (Museum ser.: Vol. 5, No. 31). 8p. 1953. pap. 1.25 (ISBN 0-317-04915-1). U of KS Mus Nat Hist.

Taylor, Edward H. New Hylid Frogs from Eastern Mexico. (Museum Ser.: Vol. 1, No. 15). 8p. 1948. 1.50 (ISBN 0-317-04891-0). U of KS Mus Nat Hist.

ZOOLOGY–NORTH AMERICA

Barton, Benjamin S. Notes on the Animals of North America, 1793. Sterling, Keir B., ed. & intro. by. LC 73-17801. (Natural Sciences in America Ser.). 150p. 1974. 12.00 (ISBN 0-405-05719-9). Ayer Co Pubs.

Early Nineteenth-Century Studies & Surveys. LC 73-17817. (Natural Sciences in America Ser.). 590p. 1974. Repr. 30.00x (ISBN 0-405-05733-4). Ayer Co Pubs.

Hennings, Darwen & Hoffmann, Robert S. A Review of the Taxonomy of the Sorex Vagrans Species Complex from Western North America. (Occasional Papers: No. 68). 35p. 1977. pap. 2.00 (ISBN 0-686-80294-2). U of KS Mus Nat Hist.

Krombein, Karl V. Revision of North American Lirirs Fabricius (Hymenoptera) Sphecoides, Larridae. LC 84-600998. (Smithsonian Contributions to Zoology: No. 404). pap. 25.00 (ISBN 0-317-30394-5, 2024751). Bks Demand UMI.

North American Wildlife. 12.95 (ISBN 0-933692-38-2). A R Collings.

Selected Works of Joel Asaph Allen. LC 73-17843. (Natural Sciences in America Ser.). (Illus.). 976p. 1974. Repr. 49.00x (ISBN 0-405-05765-2). Ayer Co Pubs.

Smith, Hobart M. & Brodie, Edmund. Reptiles of North America. (Golden Field Guide Ser.). (Illus.). 240p. (Orig.). 1982. pap. 7.95 (ISBN 0-307-13666-3, Golden Pr). Western Pub.

Sterling, Keir B., ed. American Natural History Studies: The Bairdian Period. LC 73-17793. (Natural Sciences in America Ser.). (Illus.). 912p. 1974. Repr. 64.00x (ISBN 0-405-05703-3). Ayer Co Pubs.

ZOOLOGY-OCEANIA

Adamson, A. M. Review of the Fauna of the Marquesas Islands & Discussion of Its Origin. (BMB Ser.: No. 159). Repr. of 1939 ed. 12.00 (ISBN 0-527-02267-5). Kraus Repr.

ZOOLOGY-SOUTH AMERICA

Cutright, Paul R. Great Naturalists Explore South America. facs. ed. LC 68-8454. (Essay Index Reprint Ser.) 1940. 26.50 (ISBN 0-8369-0357-9). Ayer Co Pubs.

De Azara, Don Felix. Apuntamientos para la Historia Natural de los Quadrupedos del Paraguay y Rio de la Plata, 2 vols. in one. Sterling, Keir B., ed. LC 77-81077. (Biologists & Their World Ser.). (Span.). 1978. Repr. of 1802 ed. lib. bdg. 52.00x (ISBN 0-405-10645-9). Ayer Co Pubs.

Duellman, William E. & Pyles, Rebecca A. A New Marsupial Frog (Hylidae: Gastrotheca) from the Andes of Ecuador. (Occasional Papers: No. 84). 13p. 1980. 1.25 (ISBN 0-317-04854-6). U of KS Mus Nat Hist.

Henderson, R. W., et al. Resource Partitioning in Amazonian Snake Communities. 12p. 1979. 1.00 (ISBN 0-89326-039-8). Milwaukee Pub Mus.

Lynch, John O. New Species of Frogs (Leptodactylidae Eleutherodactylus) from Amazonian Lowlands of Ecuador. (Occasional Papers: No. 31). 22p. 1974. pap. 1.25 (ISBN 0-686-32528-1). U of KS Mus Nat Hist.

Montanucci, Richard R. Systematics & Evolution of the Andean Lizard Genus Pholidobolus (Suaria Teiidae) (Miscellaneous Publications Ser.: No. 59). (Illus.). 52p. 1973. pap. 3.75 (ISBN 0-686-80376-0). U of KS Mus Nat Hist.

Noonan, Gerald R. South American Species of the Subgenus Anistosarsus Chaudoir (Genus Notiobia Party: Carabidae: Coleoptera) Part II: Evolution & Biogeography. 118p. 1981. 6.25 (ISBN 0-89326-072-X). Milwaukee Pub Mus.

ZOOLOGY-UNITED STATES

California Wildlife. 8.95 (ISBN 0-933692-37-4). A R Collings.

Eddy, Samuel, et al. Taxonomic Keys to the Common Animals of the North Central States. 4th. ed. 1982. spiral bdg. 12.95x (ISBN 0-8087-2210-7). Burgess.

Fletcher, Leslie. Florida's Fantastic Fauna & Flora. 320p. 1977. pap. 3.50 (ISBN 0-911980-09-1). Beau Lac.

Flowers, Seville, et al. Ecological Studies of the Flora & Fauna of Flaming Gorge Reservoir Basin, Utah & Wyoming. (Upper Colorado Ser: No. 3). 42.00 (ISBN 0-404-60648-2). AMS Pr.

Jaeger, Edmund C. Desert Wildlife. (Illus.). 1961. 11.95 (ISBN 0-8047-0123-7); pap. 6.95 (ISBN 0-8047-0124-5, SP68). Stanford U Pr.

Jaeger, Edmund C. Tracks & Trailcraft. (Illus.). 1948. 12.95 (ISBN 0-02-558830-3). Macmillan.

Martin, Alexander C., et al. American Wildlife & Plants: A Guide to Wildlife Food Habits. 1951. pap. 7.50 (ISBN 0-486-20793-5). Dover.

--American Wildlife & Plants: A Guide to Wildlife Food Habits. 15.75 (ISBN 0-8446-2536-1). Peter Smith.

Miller, Alden H. & Stebbins, Robert C. The Lives of Desert Animals in Joshua Tree National Monument. 1964. 32.50 (ISBN 0-520-00866-

9). U of Cal Pr.

Richardson, John. Fauna Boreali-Americana, Pt. I. LC 73-17836. (Natural Sciences in American Ser.). (Illus.). 1974. 26.50x (ISBN 0-405-05759-8). Ayer Co Pubs.

Stevenson, Henry M. Vertebrates of Florida: Identification & Distribution. LC 75-37723. 1976. 35.00 (ISBN 0-8130-0437-3). U Presses Fla.

Thorndike Press, ed. Maine Fish. LC 78-17234. (Maine Nature Ser.). (Illus.). 1978. pap. 3.95x (ISBN 0-89621-014-6). Thorndike Pr.

Weese, Asa O. Animal Ecology of an Illinois Elm-Maple Forest. pap. 8.00 (ISBN 0-384-66400-8). Johnson Repr.

Woodbury, Angus, et al. Ecological Studies of the Flora & Fauna of Navajo Reservoir Basin, Colorado & New Mexico. (Upper Colorado Ser: No. 5). Repr. of 1961 ed. 34.50 (ISBN 0-404-60655-5). AMS Pr.

Woodbury, Angus M., et al. Ecological Studies of Flora & Fauna in Glen Canyon. (Glen Canyon Ser: No. 7). Repr. of 1959 ed. 42.00 (ISBN 0-404-60640-7). AMS Pr.

--Ecological Studies of the Flora & Fauna of the Curecanti Reservoir Basins, Western Colorado. (Upper Colorado Ser.: No. 8). Repr. of 1962 ed. 42.50 (ISBN 0-404-60659-8). AMS Pr.

ZOOLOGY, ECONOMIC

see also Agricultural Pests; Animal Introduction; Birds, Injurious and Beneficial; Domestic Animals; Fur-Bearing Animals; Insects, Injurious and Beneficial; Pest Control; Pests; Predatory Animals; Wildlife Conservation

Graham, C. F. & Wareing, P. F. Developmental Control in Plants & Animals. 2nd ed. (Illus.). 400p. 1983. pap. text ed. 24.00 (ISBN 0-632-00758-3, B1935-1). Mosby.

International Congress of Animal Production, 9th. Proceedings. Mason, I., ed. 1967. 14.70 (ISBN 0-934454-70-1). Lubrecht & Cramer.

ZOOLOGY, EXPERIMENTAL

Felts, William J. & Harrison, Richard J., eds. International Review of General & Experimental Zoology, 4 vols. Vol. 1, 1964. 70.00 (ISBN 0-12-368101-4); Vol. 3, 1968. 70.00 (ISBN 0-12-368103-0); Vol. 4, 1970. 70.00 (ISBN 0-12-368104-9); Set. o. p. 178.50.

Acad Pr.

Gill, John L. Design & Analysis of Experiments in the Animal & Medical Sciences, Vol. 3. (Illus.). 1978. pap. text ed. 9.95x (ISBN 0-8138-0110-9). Iowa St U Pr.

Robertson, A. Selection Experiments in Laboratory & Domestic Animals: The Proceedings of a Symposium. 245p. 1980. pap. 75.00x (ISBN 0-85198-461-4, Pub. by CAB Bks England). State Mutual Bk.

Sperlinger, David. Animals in Research: New Perspectives in Animal Experimentation. LC 80-49974. 373p. 1981. 59.95 (ISBN 0-471-27843-2, Pub. by Wiley-Interscience). Wiley.

Symposia of the Zoological Society of London, 43rd. Artificial Breeding of Non-Domestic Animals. Watson, P. F., ed. 1979. 55.00 (ISBN 0-12-613343-3). Acad Pr.

ZOOLOGY, MEDICAL

see also Animals As Carriers of Disease; Zoology, Economic

Fricke, Ronald. Revision of the Genus Synchiropus (Teleostei: Callionymidae) (Theses Zoologicae: Vol. 1). (Illus.). 194p. 1981. text ed. 17.50x (ISBN 3-7682-1306-4). Lubrecht & Cramer.

Haine, Duane E. & Stevens, James L. An Atlas & Sourcebook of the Lesser Bushbaby, Galago Senegalensis. 320p. 1982. 89.50 (ISBN 0-8493-6320-9). CRC Pr.

Kilias, H. Revision Gesteinsbewohnender Sippen der Flechtengattung Catillaria Mass in Europa(Lecanorales, Lecideaceae) (Ger., Illus.). 240p. 1981. pap. 10.50 (ISBN 3-7682-1318-8). Lubrecht & Cramer.

Skadauge, E. Osmoregulation in Birds. (Zoophysiology Ser.: Vol. 12). (Illus.). 250p. 1981. 56.00 (ISBN 0-387-10546-8). Springer-Verlag.

ZOOPHYTA

see Coelenterata; Echinodermata; Polyzoa; Sponges

ZOOTOMY

see Anatomy, Comparative

ZYGNEMACEAE

Gauthier-Lievre, L. Zygnemacees Africaines. 1965. 35.00 (ISBN 3-7682-5420-8). Lubrecht & Cramer.